RELIGIOUS & INSPIRATIONAL BOOKS & SERIALS IN PRINT 1987

This edition of RELIGIOUS AND INSPIRATIONAL BOOKS AND SERIALS IN PRINT
was prepared by the R.R. Bowker
Company's Database Publishing Group in collaboration
with the Publication Systems Department

Staff of the Database Publishing Group includes:
Peter Simon, Vice President, Database Publishing Group
Ernest Lee, Director
Andrew Grabois, Managing Editor
Michael Johnson, Editor
Helen Murray, Lead Editor
James Cason, Michael Edmund, and Melissa Kapustey,
Assistant Editors;
William Garbe and Kenneth Goodman, Contributing Editors.

Senior Staff of the Bowker International Serials Database includes:
Leigh Carol Yuster, Executive Editor
Richard H. Oosterom, Editor
Jacqueline Mullikin, Editor
Edvika Popilskis, Data Sources Editor
Amine Babaali, Associate Editor

Senior Staff of Names and Numbers Department includes:
Brenda Sutton-McElroy, Managing Editor
Keith Schiffman, Senior Editor

Michael Gold, Director, Systems Development
Jack Murphy, Manager, Computer Operations

RELIGIOUS & INSPIRATIONAL BOOKS & SERIALS IN PRINT 1987

BOOKS

SUBJECT INDEX
AUTHOR INDEX
TITLE INDEX

SERIALS

SUBJECT INDEX
TITLE INDEX

R. R. BOWKER COMPANY
New York & London

Published by the R.R. Bowker, Division of Reed Publishing (USA) Inc.

International Standard Book Number 0-8352-2320-5
International Standard Serial Number 0000-0868
Library of Congress Catalog Card Number 78-63633

Printed and Bound in the United States of America

Contents

PREFACE vii
HOW TO USE RELIGIOUS AND INSPIRATIONAL
BOOKS AND SERIALS IN PRINT 1987 ix
BOOK INDEXES ix
SERIAL INDEXES x
KEYS TO ABBREVIATIONS xii
GENERAL xii
COUNTRY OF PUBLICATION CODES xiv
MONEY SYMBOLS xvi
MICROPUBLISHERS xvii
ABSTRACTING AND INDEXING SERVICES xix
SUBJECT AREA DIRECTORY xxi
BOOKS—SUBJECT INDEX 1
BOOKS—AUTHOR INDEX 647
BOOKS—TITLE INDEX 1163
SERIALS—SUBJECT INDEX 1681
SERIALS—TITLE INDEX 1759
KEY TO PUBLISHERS' AND DISTRIBUTORS'
ABBREVIATIONS 1777

ISBN
INTERNATIONAL STANDARD BOOK NUMBER

The 1987 RELIGIOUS AND INSPIRATIONAL BOOKS AND SERIALS IN PRINT lists each title or edition of a title in the book indexes with an ISBN. All publishers were notified and requested to submit a valid ISBN for their titles.

During the past decade, the majority of the publishers complied with the requirements of the standard and implemented the ISBN. At present, approximately 97% of all new titles and all new editions are submitted for listing with a valid ISBN.

To fulfill the responsibility of accomplishing total book numbering, the ISBN Agency allocated the ISBN prefixes 0-317, 0-318, 0-685 and 0-686 to number the titles in the BOOKS IN PRINT database without an ISBN. Titles not having an ISBN at the closing date of this publication are assigned an ISBN with one of these prefixes by the International Standard Book Numbering Agency.

Titles numbered within the prefixes 0-317, 0-318, 0-685 and 0-686 are:
—Publishers who did not assign ISBN to their titles.
—Distributors with titles published and imported from countries not in the ISBN system, or not receiving the ISBN from the originating publisher.
—Errors from transportation and transcription which occurred in transmitting the ISBN to the BOOKS IN PRINT database.

All the ISBN listed in this edition are validated by using the check digit control, and only valid ISBN are listed in the database.

All publishers participating in the ISBN system having titles numbered within the prefixes 0-317, 0-318, 0-685 and 0-686 will receive a computer printout, requesting them to submit the correct ISBN.

Publishers not participating in the ISBN system may request from the ISBN Agency the assignment of an ISBN Publisher Prefix, and start numbering their titles.

The Book Industry System Advisory Committee (BISAC) developed a standard format for data transmission, and many companies are already accepting orders transmitted on magnetic tape using the ISBN. Another standard format by BISAC for title updating is under development.

The ISBN Agency and the Data Services Division of the Bowker Company wish to express their appreciation to all publishers who collaborated in making the ISBN system the standard of the publishing industry.

For the additional information related to the ISBN total numbering, please refer to the ISBN/SAN Agency at the R.R. Bowker Company.

Preface

Many religious titles, especially those with a conservative-evangelical message, are now best sellers. The public demand for Christian devotional and self-help books and, in fact, for books of all religious faiths and persuasions has created a greater need by librarians and booksellers for organized bibliographic information.

This fifth edition of *Religious and Inspirational Books and Serials in Print* is published to continue to serve that need. It is a subject oriented bibliography covering all the world's religions from Anglicanism to Zen.

Our goal was to make this bibliography as complete as possible, covering the world's religions and a range of such allied subjects as the religious implications of abortion, homosexuality, business ethics, ecology, or any human experience. This listing includes books about the general topic of religion, as well as books about particular religions, both traditional and non-traditional. The full scope is covered in the Subject Area Directory. The topics range from Christianity, Buddhism and Confucianism to anthroposophy, metaphysics, visions and witchcraft.

ACQUISITION OF DATA

This edition of *Religious and Inspirational Books and Serials in Print* was produced from records stored on magnetic tape, edited by computer programs and set in type by computer-controlled photocomposition.

In order to produce the subject, author and title indexes to books, we have examined the databases used to produce *Books in Print, Books in Print Supplement, Forthcoming Books,* and *Subjects Guide to Books in Print*.

For the first edition, a marked effort was made to reach publishers of religious books which had not previously been represented in the *Books in Print* database. Publisher members of the Christian Booksellers Association were reached by mail and, in some cases, by telephone, as were publishers specializing in Judaica and Eastern religions and the official publishing outlets of religious organizations. General publishers as well as those specializing in religious books and related subjects were added to the data base in order to provide complete up to date information regarding the available literature in this area.

Complete entries appear in each of the three indexes. The author and title indexes include 61,204 entries for titles available from some 3,000 publishers. The subject index to books follows the headings assigned by the Library of Congress. Some books were assigned a single heading and others were assigned two or more headings; some books, therefore, appear more than once. In all, the 61,204 titles appear about 73,101 times under nearly 6,146 subject headings with some 5,282 cross references. Descriptions of the subject, author and title indexes can be found in the "How to Use" section.

UNIQUE FEATURE

Religious and Inspirational Books and Serials in Print 1987 has a unique feature designed to make its information more usable. This is the Subject Area Directory. This Directory gives a broad overview of the 6,146 subjects covered in the Book Indexes of *Religious and Inspirational Books and Serials in Print 1987.* The Library of Congress classification scheme was used to assign the various subjects to the topical areas with which they are associated. Since many subject headings contain listings for books concerning different aspects of the subject, these headings may appear under more than one area.

The Directory may be used by those wishing to know the range of information available regarding a specific topic. When looking at a particular area one is given a thorough guide to the subject headings containing books which pertain to that area. Additionally, the Directory serves as a guide to the broad areas with which a specific subject is concerned. Looking for the subject heading within the various areas will give an indication of the broader topics which encompass that subject.

Two areas which are necessarily broad, due to the use of the Library of Congress Classification scheme, are Practical Theology and Religion. The area of Practical Theology includes the subject headings containing works on the following topics: Worship, including liturgy, hymns and hymnbooks, and church music; Evangelism and Revivals; Pastoral Theology, including training of the clergy, sermons and other pastoral offices; Practical Religion and the Christian Life, including moral theology, inspirational literature, conversion literature and works on asceticism and mysticism; and Missionaries, including the lives of missionaries. Works concerning people whose lives are connected with the foregoing topics are also listed under Practical Theology, the name being given as the subject heading.

The area of Religion includes subject headings concerning the subject of religion. Included in the area are works about: Primitive Religions; the Psychology of Religion; Religion and Science; Comparative Mythology, including the classification of religions and religions in relation to one another;

General Religious Doctrines; Cults; and Mythology, including Classical, Germanic, Norse, Oriental, African and Oceanic mythology. Subject headings containing books concerning people connected with any of the foregoing topics and books about characters from any Religion, the name of the person or character being given as the subject heading.

There are two areas covering philosophy. We have attempted to limit these to subjects containing works with a religious viewpoint. Works about such subjects as Ethics and Logic have been included in Religious Philosophy. Works of a speculative nature, relating to such subjects as Consciousness and Metaphysics, are listed under Speculative Philosophy.

Prayerbooks, concordances and commentaries on the Bible or other sacred works are entered under specific subject headings in the Subject Index—Books section.

Entries for the Serials section were selected from the Bowker International Serials Database and provide the latest information included in and received since the publication of *Ulrich's International Periodicals Directory,* 25th edition, *Irregular Serials and Annuals,* 12th edition, and the Bowker International Serials Database Update, Vol. 2, no. 2. The arrangement of the indexes and entries follows the format of those publications; the subject index contains entries with complete information listed under the primary subject of the serial, cross-references to that entry appear under secondary subjects and in the title index. Actually, some 3,606 titles appear 4,675 times under some 162 subject headings. Subject headings for serials have been selected from the Bowker International Serials Database and have been revised to provide more direct access to the wide range of religious publications, and to fit the general scope of serial publications.

It is hoped that this edition will serve as a valuable reference tool for everyone interested in any aspect of religious and related topics. The participation of our users in offering suggestions for future editions of *Religious and Inspirational Books And Serials In Print,* and in the identification of any errors or omissions, will be welcomed and appreciated.

Ernest Lee
Director, Bibliographies
Database Publishing Group

Andrew Grabois
Managing Editor
Books In Print Database

Leigh C. Yuster
Executive Editor
Bowker International Series
Database

How to Use Religious and Inspirational Books and Serials in Print

BOOK INDEXES

GENERAL EDITORIAL POLICIES

In order to insure that the essential information in these listings is uniform, complete, and easy to find, the following editorial policies have been maintained:

If more than two authors are responsible for a certain publication , only the name of the first is given followed by *et al.*

Every effort is made by most contributing publishers to prepare their material with consideration for its accuracy throughout the life of this edition of *Religious And Inspirational Books And Serials In Print*. Most publishers anticipate price changes when they revise their material, list forthcoming books even if publication dates and prices are not set, and for the most part, try not to list books that may shortly become unavailable. In spite of these efforts, a number of changes in price will occur and a number of titles in this edition will become unavailable before the new edition is published. All prices are subject to change without notice.

Most prices are list prices. Lack of uniformity in publishers' data prohibits indicating trade discounts. A lower case "a" follows some of the trade edition prices and indicates that a specially priced library edition is available: "t" indicates a tenative price: "g" a guaranteed binding on a juvenile title: and "x" a short discount—20%, or less. Short discount (20% or less) information is generally supplied by publishers to Bowker for each publication. However, all publishers do not uniformly supply this information and Bowker can only make its best efforts to transmit this information when it is provided. PLB indicates a publishers' library binding. YA indicates that a title may be used for young adults. An "i" following the price indicates an invoice price. Specific policies for such titles should be obtained from the individual publishers.

Publishers' and distributors' names are abbreviated. A key to these abbreviations will be found in the *Key to Publishers' & Distributors' Abbreviations*. Entries in this "Key" are arranged alphabetically by the abbreviations used in the bibliographic entries. The full name, ISBN prefix, editorial address, telephone number, ordering address (if different from the editorial address), and imprints follow the abbreviation. SAN (Standard Address Number) is a unique identification code for each address of each organization in or served by the book industry.

For example:

Bowker, *(Bowker, R.R. Co; 0-8352).*
Div. of Reed Publishing USA, 245 W. 17th St.,
New York, NY 10011 Tel 212-645-9700
(SAN 214-1191); Orders to: P.O. Box 1807, Ann
Arbor, MI 48106 (SAN 214-1205).

If an entry contains a "Pub by" note after the price, the title should be ordered from the company whose abbreviation appears at the end of the entry. For example, an entry for a book published by Melbourne University Press but distributed by International Scholarly Book Services, Inc., will convey this information in the form "Pub by Melbourne U Pr" after the price with "Intl Schol Bk Serv" at the end of the entry.

ALPHABETICAL ARRANGEMENT OF ENTRIES IN AUTHOR AND TITLE INDEXES

Each entry is filed alphabetically by word, with the following exceptions:

M', Mc and *Mac* are filed as if they were spelled *Mac* and are interfiled with other names beginning with *Mac:* for example, Macan McAnnally, Macardle, McAree, McArthur,

Macarthur, Macartney, M'Aulay, Macaulay. Within a specific name group *Mc* and *Mac* are interfiled according to the given name of the author: for example, Macdonald, Agnes; McDonald, Alexander; MacDonald, Annie L.; McDonald, Austin F.; MacDonald, Betty. In the *Books—Author Index,* compound names are listed under the first part of the name and cross-references appear under the last part of the name.

Entries beginning with initial letters (whether authors' given names or titles of entries) are filed first: Smith, H. C. comes before Smith, Harold A.; *J. B. Priestly: The Man and His Ideas* comes before *Jade.*

Numerals, including year dates, are written out in most cases and are filed alphabetically:

SEVEN YEARS
SEVENTEEN
SEVENTEEN FAMOUS INVENTIONS
SEVENTEEN-FIFTEEN TO THE PRESENT
SEVENTEEN PAST YEARS
SEVENTEEN READER
SEVENTEENTH CENTURY

INFORMATION INCLUDED IN ENTRIES

Entries include the following bibliographic information, when available: author, co-author, editor, co-editor, translator, co-translator, title, number of volumes, edition, Library of Congress number, series, whether or not illustrated, year of publication, price with type of binding if other than cloth over boards, publisher's order number, International Standard Book Number, and publisher's name. (Information on the International Standard Book Numbering System in the United States and other English-speaking countries is available from the R. R. Bowker Co.)

BOOKS—SUBJECT INDEX

Entries are arranged alphabetically by author within subject. If no author is given, the entry is filed alphabetically by title within the author arrangement.

Headings and cross-references were updated to conform to the tenth edition of *Library of Congress Subject Headings* and its supplements.

Whenever official LC classification was unavailable, headings were assigned provisionally. Among these fall most of the titles now in preparation or to be published sometime in 1987. As LC headings for such books become available, the provisional headings will be verified or changed in future editions of *Religious And Inspirational Books And Serials In Print.*

ALPHABETICAL ARRANGEMENT OF SUBJECT HEADINGS

Subject headings are arranged alphabetically:

ABBEYS
ABSTINENCE
ADAGES
ADVENT

Many of the main headings are broken down still further:

BAPTISTS
BAPTISTS-CLERGY
BAPTISTS-EDUCATION
BAPTISTS-HISTORY

There are also many cross-references:

BARREN FIG TREE (PARABLE)
see JESUS CHRIST-PARABLES
CHURCHES
see also BAPTISTERIES; CATHEDRALS: CAVE CHURCHES; CHAPELS

Headings, patterned after those used in the card catalog in the Library of Congress, are explicit rather than general. Thus books on Bible philosophy are under BIBLE PHILOSOPHY, not under PHILOSOPHY.

In looking for books on missions, search past the main entry to the various subheadings:

MISSIONS
MISSIONS-HISTORY
MISSIONS-SERMONS
MISSIONS-THEORY
MISSIONS-AFRICA
MISSIONS-ALASKA
MISSIONS-FOREIGN
MISSIONS-HOME
MISSIONS-MEDICAL
MISSIONS-TO LEPERS

Note the sequence of the above cited headings and subheadings. The editors of this book took as a guideline the *Filing rules for the Dictionary Catalogs of the Library of Congress,* as prepared by the Processing Department of the Library of Congress.

Other typical examples of the sequence used are:

CLERGY-SALARIES
CLERGY, TRAINING OF
CLERGY IN LITERATURE

HYMNS
HYMNS-BIBLIOGRAPHY
HYMNS-CONCORDANCES
HYMNS-HISTORY AND CRITICISM
HYMNS, GERMAN
HYMNS, LATIN
HYMNS, SANSCRIT
HYMNS,YIDDISH

Although a constant effort is made to maintain consistency and to avoid splitting entries on a given subject among several headings, a certain amount is inevitable. The Library of Congress updates its subject headings constantly but cannot make such updating retroactive to cards and catalogs previously issued. If previously published titles which appeared under the older, more general headings did not indicate by their titles that they should have been moved to newer, specific headings they may have been left under the old headings.

SERIAL INDEXES

SERIALS—SUBJECT INDEX

Entries with bibliographic and buying information for selected current serials which are published periodically or irregularly are arranged alphabetically by title within subject category. The complete entry is listed under one subject heading. If a serial covers more than one subject, cross-references direct the user from related subjects to the subject under which the complete entry is listed.

SERIALS—TITLE INDEX

Title Index entries include the following: title, ISSN and country code, name of issuing body if main entry title contains only the initials of the issuing body. Cross-references for variant titles, parallel language titles, and former titles are included. The page number where the complete entry appears is printed in italic type; page numbers in roman type indicates pages of related subject listings.

INFORMATION INCLUDED IN MAIN ENTRIES

Basic Information. The following items are mandatory for listing: title, frequency of publication, publisher name and address, country of publication code, Dewey Decimal Classification number.

Title Information. Main entry title; ISSN; subtitle; key title (entered only if different from main entry title); parallel language title, variant title, title variation note, former title and ISSN; original title or translation and ISSN; translated edition title and ISSN; and "issued with" title and ISSN (ISSN given only when available).

Buying and Ordering Information. Publisher name and address and, when applicable, subscription address and/or distributor name and address; subscription price in currency of country of publication and U.S. rates for foreign publications when supplied by the publisher; price per issue if subscription rate is not applicable; the designation ‡ for a title not available from a subscription agency (printed after price information); the micropublisher if not the same as publisher (following notation on microform edition).

Abstracting and Indexing Information. Services which index the listed title on a regular basis are given in abbreviated form.

Author and Editor Information. Name of corporate author if corporate author is not also the publisher, name of editor or the abbreviation Ed. Bd. which indicates editorship by three or more persons (usually advanced degrees and titles have been omitted with the exception of medical, military, and clerical titles; absence of a title does not mean that the editor has none).

Bibliographic Notes. Year first published or year of first known issue; frequency of publication; year and number of latest issue if frequency is irregular; language notation if text is in language other than official language of country of publication; special features contained in the serial (such as book reviews, illustrations, charts, statistics); availability of cumulative indexes; availability of microform and other alternative formats; subject annotation; additional bibliographic notations, such as title of main series in cases of subseries entry, or irregularities in volume numbering.

RULES FOR MAIN ENTRY

Whenever possible, main entry cataloging is done from a sample page of the most recent issue, according to the following rules:

Serials with distinctive titles are usually entered under title. For Example:

Christian Librarian

If the title consists only of the name of the issuing body and a generic term, or if the name of the issuing body clarifies the content of the publication, entry is under the name of the issuing body. For example:

Directory of the Association of Theological Schools in the United States and Canada
is entered as
Association of Theological Schools in the United States and Canada. Directory.

A title is considered nondistinctive if it consists of a subject modified generic term and the name of the issuing body and is entered under the name of the issuing body. For example:

Workshop Proceedings of the School of Education of the University of Dayton
is entered as
University of Dayton. School of Education. Workshop Proceedings

Government publications with nondistinctive titles are usually entered under the name of the government jurisdiction of the issuing body: distinctive titles if government issuing bodies are entered under title. For example:

Great Britain. Royal Army Chaplains' Department. Journal
but
Israel Book News

Multilingual titles are entered under the first title given on the title page (or first title as reported by publisher if title page is not available). Titles in other languages are entered directly after the main entry title.

Titles which began with the initials of the issuing body are entered under the initials of the issuing body. Cross-references from full name of issuing body to initials in main entry are given in the *Serials—Title Index.*

FILING RULES

Articles at the beginning of titles have been omitted; articles and prepositions within titles are alphabetized as words:

Studies in Religion and Society
precedes
Studies in the History of Christian Thought

Hyphenated words are treated as separate words:

In-Touch
precedes
Indian Witness

Titles entered under corporate author of government jurisdiction are sequenced before distinctive titles which begin with the same words:

Church of England. Yearbook
precedes
Church of England Historical Society (Diocese of Sydney). Journal

Acronyms and initials are treated as such and are listed at the beginning of each letter of the alphabet with the exception of abbreviations U.N. (United Nations), U.S. (United States), Gt. Britain (Great Britain), and St. (Saint) which are filed as words.

S S C Booknews
Sabbath Sentinel
St. Luke's Journal of Theology
Scottish Baptist Magazine

Keys to Abbreviations

GENERAL

a	after price, specially priced library edition available
a	annual
abr.	abridged
abstr.	abstracts
adpt.	adapted
adv.	advertising
Amer.	American
annot.	annotation(s), annotated
ans.	answer(s)
app.	appendix
approx.	approximately
assn.	association
auth.	author
Ave.	Avenue
bd.	bound
bdg.	binding
bds.	boards
bi-m.	every two months
bib(s).	bibliography (ies)
bk(s).	book, books
bk. rev.	book reviews
bklet(s)	booklets
Blvd.	Boulevard
Bro.	Brother
c/o	care of
charts	charts (diagrams, graphs, tables)
circ.	circulation
coll.	college
comm.	commission, committee
co.	company
comp(s)	compiler(s)
cond.	condensed
contr.	controlled
corp.	corporation
cum. ind.	cumulative index
Cy.	county
d.	daily
dept.	department
diag(s).	diagram(s)
dir.	director
dist.	distributor
Div.	Division
doz.	dozen
Dr.	Drive
ea.	each
ed.	editor, edited, edition
Ed. Bd.	Editorial Board
ed., eds.	editions, editors, editor
educ.	education
elem.	elementary
ency.	encyclopedia
Eng.	English
enl.	enlarged
exp.	expurgated
fac.	facsimile
fasc.	fascicle
fict.	fiction
fig(s).	figures(s)
film rev.	film reviews
for.	foreign
fortn.	fortnightly
Fr.	French
frwd.	foreword
g	after price, guaranteed juvenile binding
gen.	general
Ger.	German
Gr.	greek
gr.	grade, grades
hdbk.	handbook
Heb.	Hebrew
i.	invoice price
i.t.a.	initial teaching alphabet
Illus	Illustrated, Illustration(s), illustrator(s)
in prep.	in preparation
incl.	includes, including
inst.	institute
intro.	introduction
ISSN	International Standard Serial Number
irreg.	irregular
It.	Italian
Jr.	Junior
Jt. auth.	joint author
jt. ed.	joint editor
k	kindergarten audience level
l.p.	long playing
ltd. ed.	limited edition
lab.	laboratory
lang(s).	language(s)
Lat.	Latin
lea.	leather
lib.	library
lit.	literature, literary
m.	monthly
math.	mathematics
mkt.	market prices
mod.	modern
mor.	morocco
MS, MSS	manuscript, manuscripts
music rev.	music reviews
N.S.	New Series
natl.	national
no., nos.	number, numbers
o.p.	out of print
orig.	original text, not a reprint
pap.	paper
pat.	patents
photos	photographs, photographer
play rev.	play reviews (theatre reviews)
PLB	publisher's library binding
P.O.	Post Office
Pol.	Polish
pop. ed.	popular edition
Port.	Portuguese
prep.	preparation
probs.	problems
Prof.	Professor
prog. bk.	programmed book
ps	preschool audience level
pseud.	pseudonym
pt(s).	part, parts
pub.	published, publisher, publishing
pubn.	publication
Pubns	Publications
q.	quarterly
record rev.	record reviews
ref(s).	reference(s)
repr.	reprint
reprod(s)	reproduction(s)
rev.	revised

rpm.	revolution per minute (photo records)
Rus.	Russian
s-a.	twice annually
s-m.	twice monthly
s-w.	twice weekly
s.p.	school price
sec.	section
sel.	selected
ser.	series
s & l	signed & limited
sep	single copy, direct to the consumer price
Soc.	Society
sols.	solutions
Span.	Spanish
Sr. (after given name)	Senior
Sr. (before given name)	Sister
St.	Saint, Street
stat.	statistics
subs.	subsidiary
subscr.	subscription
suppl.	supplement
t	after price, tentative price
tech.	technical
tele. rev.	television reviews
text ed.	text edition
3/m	3 times a month
3/yr.	3 times a year
tr.	translator, translated translation
tr. lit.	trade literature (manufacturers' catalogues, etc.)
tr. mk.	trade marks
univ.	university
vol(s).	volume, volumes
w.	weekly
wkbk.	workbook
x	after price, short discount (20% or less)
YA	young adult audience level
yrbk.	yearbook
‡	not available from a subscription agency
x	short discount
*	not updated

Country of Publication Codes

This list of countries and their codes has been taken from the list used by the Library of Congress in the MARC II format, 1972. The list used here is not the complete list of the MARC II format and is limited to presently existing national entities. The states of the United States, provinces and territories of Canada, divisions of the United Kingdom, and republics of the USSR are not listed separately.

The codes are mnemonic in most cases. The first letter of the two-letter code is the same as the first letter of the place name. Special codes not in the MARC format are used for publications of two international organizations: EI for European Communities and UN for United Nations and related organizations.

COUNTRY CODE SEQUENCE

AA	-ALBANIA
AE	-ALGERIA
AF	-AFGHANISTAN
AG	-ARGENTINA
AN	-ANDORRA
AO	-ANGOLA
AQ	-ANTIGUA
AS	-AMERICAN SAMOA
AT	-AUSTRALIA
AU	-AUSTRIA
AY	-ANTARCTICA
BA	-BAHRAIN
BB	-BARBADOS
BD	-BURUNDI
BE	-BELGIUM
BF	-BAHAMAS
BG	-BANGLADESH
BH	-BELIZE
BL	-BRAZIL
BM	-BERMUDA
BO	-BOLIVIA
BP	-BRITISH SOLOMON ISLANDS
BR	-BURMA
BS	-BOTSWANA
BT	-BHUTAN
BU	-BULGARIA
BX	-BRUNEI DARUSSALAM
CB	-CAMBODIA
CC	-CHINA, MAINLAND
CD	-CHAD
CE	-SRI LANKA
CF	-CONGO (BRAZZAVILLE)
CH	-CHINA, REPUBLIC OF
CJ	-CAYMAN ISLANDS
CK	-COLOMBIA
CL	-CHILE
CM	-CAMEROON
CN	-CANADA
CR	-COSTA RICA
CS	-CZECHOSLOVAKIA
CU	-CUBA
CV	-CAPE VERDE
CX	-CENTRAL AFRICAN REPUBLIC
CY	-CYPRUS
CZ	-CANAL ZONE
DK	-DENMARK
DM	-BENIN
DQ	-DOMINICA
DR	-DOMINICAN REPUBLIC
EC	-ECUADOR
EG	-EQUATORIAL GUINEA
EI	-EUROPEAN COMMUNITIES
ES	-EL SALVADOR
ET	-ETHIOPIA
FA	-FAEROE ISLANDS
FG	-FRENCH GUIANA
FI	-FINLAND
FJ	-FIJI
FK	-FALKLAND ISLANDS
FP	-FRENCH POLYNESIA
FR	-FRANCE
FT	-DJIBOUTI
GD	-GRENADA
GE	-GERMANY, EAST (DDR)
GH	-GHANA
GI	-GIBRALTAR
GL	-GREENLAND
GM	-GAMBIA
GO	-GABON
GP	-GUADELOUPE
GR	-GREECE
GT	-GUATEMALA
GU	-GUAM
GV	-GUINEA
GW	-GERMANY, WEST (BRD)
GY	-GUYANA (BRITISH GUIANA)
HK	-HONG KONG
HO	-HONDURAS
HT	-HAITI
HU	-HUNGARY
IC	-ICELAND
IE	-IRELAND
II	-INDIA
IO	-INDONESIA
IQ	-IRAQ
IR	-IRAN
IS	-ISRAEL
IT	-ITALY
IV	-IVORY COAST
JA	-JAPAN
JM	-JAMAICA
JO	-JORDAN
KE	-KENYA
KN	-KOREA, NORTH
KO	-KOREA, SOUTH
KU	-KUWAIT
LB	-LIBERIA
LE	-LEBANON
LH	-LIECHTENSTEIN
LO	-LESOTHO
LS	-LAOS
LU	-LUXEMBOURG
LY	-LIBYA
MC	-MONACO
MF	-MAURITIUS
MG	-MALAGASY REPUBLIC (MADAGASCAR)
MH	-MACAO
MJ	-MONTSERRAT
MK	-SULTANATE OF OMAN
ML	-MALI
MM	-MALTA
MP	-MONGOLIA
MQ	-MARTINIQUE
MR	-MOROCCO
MU	-MAURITANIA
MW	-MALAWI
MX	-MEXICO
MY	-MALAYSIA
MZ	-MOZAMBIQUE
NA	-NETHERLANDS ANTILLES
NE	-NETHERLANDS
NG	-NIGER
NL	-NEW CALEDONIA
NN	-VANUATU (NEW HEBRIDES)
NO	-NORWAY
NP	-NEPAL
NQ	-NICARAGUA
NR	-NIGERIA
NU	-NAURU
NZ	-NEW ZEALAND
PE	-PERU
PG	-GUINEA-BISSAU
PH	-PHILIPPINES
PK	-PAKISTAN
PL	-POLAND
PN	-PANAMA
PO	-PORTUGAL
PP	-PAPUA NEW GUINEA
PR	-PUERTO RICO
PY	-PARAGUAY
QA	-QATAR
RE	-REUNION
RH	-ZIMBABWE
RM	-RUMANIA
RW	-RWANDA
RY	-RYUKYU ISLANDS, SOUTHERN
SA	-SOUTH AFRICA
SE	-SEYCHELLES
SF	-SAO TOME E PRINCIPE
SG	-SENEGAL
SI	-SINGAPORE
SJ	-SUDAN
SK	-SIKKIM
SL	-SIERRA LEONE
SM	-SAN MARINO
SO	-SOMALIA
SP	-SPAIN
SQ	-SWAZILAND
SR	-SURINAM
SU	-SAUDI ARABIA
SW	-SWEDEN
SX	-NAMIBIA (SOUTH-WEST AFRICA)
SY	-SYRIA
SZ	-SWITZERLAND
TG	-TOGO
TH	-THAILAND
TI	-TUNISIA
TO	-TONGA
TR	-TRINIDAD & TOBAGO
TS	-UNITED ARAB EMIRATES
TT	-TRUST TERRITORY, PACIFIC ISLDS
TU	-TURKEY
TZ	-TANZANIA
UA	-EGYPT (ARAB REPUBLIC OF EGYPT)
UG	-UGANDA
UI	-UNITED KINGDOM MISC. ISLANDS
UK	-UNITED KINGDOM
UN	-UNITED NATIONS
UR	-U S S R
US	-UNITED NATIONS
UV	-BURKINA FASO
UY	-URUGUAY
VB	-VIRGIN ISLANDS (BRITISH)
VC	-VATICAN CITY
VE	-VENEZUELA
VI	-VIRGIN ISLANDS (U.S.)
VN	-VIETNAM
WS	-WESTERN SAMOA
XC	-MALDIVE ISLANDS
XI	-ST. KITTS-NEVIS
XK	-SAINT LUCIA
XM	-SAINT VINCENT
YE	-YEMEN
YS	-YEMEN, SOUTHERN
YU	-YUGOSLAVIA
ZA	-ZAMBIA
ZR	-ZAIRE

COUNTRY SEQUENCE

AFGHANISTAN - AF
ALBANIA - AA
ALGERIA - AE
AMERICAN SAMOA - AS
ANDORRA - AN
ANGOLA - AO
ANTARCTICA - AY
ANTIGUA - AQ
ARGENTINA - AG
AUSTRALIA - AT
AUSTRIA - AU
BAHAMAS - BF
BAHRAIN - BA
BANGLADESH - BG
BARBADOS - BB
BELGIUM - BE
BELIZE - BH
BENIN - DM
BERMUDA - BM
BHUTAN - BT
BOLIVIA - BO
BOTSWANA - BS
BRAZIL - BL
BRITISH SOLOMON ISLANDS - BP
BRUNEI DARUSSALAM - BX
BULGARIA - BU
BURKINA FASO - UV
BURMA - BR
BURUNDI - BD
CAMBODIA - CB
CAMEROON - CM
CANADA - CN
CANAL ZONE - CZ
CAPE VERDE - CV
CAYMAN ISLANDS - CJ
CENTRAL AFRICAN REPUBLIC - CX
CHAD - CD
CHILE - CL
CHINA, MAINLAND - CC
CHINA, REPUBLIC OF - CH
COLOMBIA - CK
CONGO (BRAZZAVILLE) - CF
COSTA RICA - CR
CUBA - CU
CYPRUS - CY
CZECHOSLOVAKIA - CS
DENMARK - DK
DJIBOUTI - FT
DOMINICA - DQ
DOMINICAN REPUBLIC - DR
ECUADOR - EC
EGYPT (ARAB REPUBLIC OF EGYPT) - UA
EL SALVADOR - ES
EQUATORIAL GUINEA - EG
ETHIOPIA - ET
EUROPEAN COMMUNITIES - EI
FAEROE ISLANDS - FA
FALKLAND ISLANDS - FK
FIJI - FJ
FINLAND - FI
FRANCE - FR
FRENCH GUIANA - FG
FRENCH POLYNESIA - FP
GABON - GO
GAMBIA - GM
GERMANY, EAST (DDR) - GE
GERMANY, WEST (BRD) - GW
GHANA - GH
GIBRALTAR - GI
GREECE - GR
GREENLAND - GL
GRENADA - GD
GUADELOUPE - GP
GUAM - GU
GUATEMALA - GT
GUINEA - GV
GUINEA-BISSAU - PG
GUYANA (BRITISH GUIANA) - GY
HAITI - HT
HONDURAS - HO
HONG KONG - HK
HUNGARY - HU
ICELAND - IC
INDIA - II
INDONESIA - IO
IRAN - IR
IRAQ - IQ
IRELAND - IE
ISRAEL - IS
ITALY - IT
IVORY COAST - IV
JAMAICA - JM
JAPAN - JA
JORDAN - JO
KENYA - KE
KOREA, NORTH - KN
KOREA, SOUTH - KO
KUWAIT - KU
LAOS - LS
LEBANON - LE
LESOTHO - LO
LIBERIA - LB
LIBYA - LY
LIECHTENSTEIN - LH
LUXEMBOURG - LU
MACAO - MH
MALAGASY REPUBLIC
(MADAGASCAR) - MG
MALAWI - MW
MALAYSIA - MY
MALDIVE ISLANDS - XC
MALI - ML
MALTA - MM
MARTINIQUE - MQ
MAURITANIA - MU
MAURITIUS - MF
MEXICO - MX
MONACO - MC
MONGOLIA - MP
MONTSERRAT - MJ
MOROCCO - MR
MOZAMBIQUE - MZ
NAMIBIA (SOUTH-WEST AFRICA) - SX
NAURU - NU
NEPAL - NP
NETHERLANDS - NE
NETHERLANDS ANTILLES - NA
NEW CALEDONIA - NL
NEW ZEALAND - NZ
NICARAGUA - NQ
NIGER - NG
NIGERIA - NR
NORWAY - NO
PAKISTAN - PK
PANAMA - PN
PAPUA NEW GUINEA - PP
PARAGUAY - PY
PERU - PE
PHILIPPINES - PH
POLAND - PL
PORTUGAL - PO
PUERTO RICO - PR
QATAR - QA
REUNION - RE
RUMANIA - RM
RWANDA - RW
RYUKYU ISLANDS, SOUTHERN - RY
SAINT KITTS-NEVIS-XI
SAINT LUCIA - XK
SAINT VINCENT - XM
SAN MARINO - SM
SAO TOME E PRINCIPE - SF
SAUDI ARABIA - SU
SENEGAL - SG
SEYCHELLES - SE
SIERRA LEONE - SL
SIKKIM - SK
SINGAPORE - SI
SOMALIA - SO
SOUTH AFRICA - SA
SPAIN - SP
SRI LANKA - CE
SUDAN - SJ
SULTANATE OF OMAN - MK
SURINAM - SR
SWAZILAND - SQ
SWEDEN - SW
SWITZERLAND - SZ
SYRIA - SY
TANZANIA - TZ
THAILAND - TH
TOGO - TG
TONGA - TO
TRINIDAD & TOBAGO - TR
TRUST TERRITORY, PACIFIC ISLDS - TT
TUNISIA - TI
TURKEY - TU
UGANDA - UG
UNITED ARAB EMIRATES - TS
UNITED KINGDOM - UK
UNITED KINGDOM MISC. ISLANDS - UI
UNITED NATIONS - UN
UNITED STATES - US
URUGUAY - UY
U S S R - UR
VANUATU (NEW HEBRIDES) - NN
VATICAN CITY - VC
VENEZUELA - VE
VIETNAM - VN
VIRGIN ISLANDS (BRITISH) - VB
VIRGIN ISLANDS (U.S.) - VI
WESTERN SAMOA - WS
YEMEN - YE
YEMEN, SOUTHERN - YS
YUGOSLAVIA - YU
ZAIRE - ZR
ZAMBIA - ZA
ZIMBABWE - RH

Money Symbols

SYMBOL	UNIT	COUNTRY
Arg.$	peso	Argentina
Aus.$	dollar	Australia
B.	baht	Thailand
B.$	dollar	Brunei Darussalam, Belize
Bl.	balboa	Panama
Bol.$	peso	Bolivia
Br.	birr	Ethiopia
Bs.	bolivar	Venezuela
C.$	cordoba; dollar	Nicaragua, Cayman Islands
Can.$	dollar	Canada
CFPF	franc	New Caledonia
Col.	colon	Costa Rica, El Salvador
Col.$	peso	Colombia
Cr.$	cruzeiro	Brazil
D.	dalasi	Gambia
DH., Dh.	dirham	Morocco, United Arab Emirates
DM.	mark	West Germany
din.	dinar	Algeria, Jordan, Kuwait, Libya, Tunisia, Yugoslavia
$	dollar; peso	various
Dr.	drachma	Greece
E.	emalangeni	Swaziland
EAs.	shilling	East Africa, Somalia, Tanzania, Uganda
EC$.	dollar	Dominica, St. Lucia
Esc.	escudo	Angola, Portugal, Mozambique
F.	franc	Djibouti, France, Guadeloupe, Mali, Martinique, Monaco, Rwanda
F$	dollar	Fiji
fl.	guilder; florin	Netherlands, Netherlands Antilles Surinam
FMG.	franc	Malagasy Republic
Fmk.	mark; markka	Finland
Fr.	franc	Belgium, Liechtenstein Luxembourg, Switzerland
Fr.CFA	franc	African Financial Community, Benin, Burkina Faso, Burundi, Cameroon, Central African Republic, Chad, Congo, Gabon, Ivory Coast, Niger, Reunion, Senegal, Togo
Ft.	forint	Hungary
g.	guarani	Paraguay
Gde.	gourde	Haiti
G.$	dollar	Guyana
HK$	dollar	Hong Kong
I.D.	dinar	Iran, Iraq
IS	shekel	Israel
Jam.$	dollar	Jamaica
K.	kina; kwacha	Malawi, Papua New Guinea, Zambia
Kcs.	koruny	Czechoslovakia
Kr.	krona; krone	Scandinavian countries
KShs.	shilling	Kenya
L.	lempira; lira	Honduras, Italy
Le.	leone	Sierra Leone
lei	lei	Rumania
lv.	lev	Bulgaria
M.	mark	East Germany
M.$	dollar; ringgit	Malaysia
Mex.$	peso	Mexico
$m.n.	moneda nacional	various
NC.	cedi	Ghana
NT.$	dollar	Republic of China (Taiwan)
N.Z.$	dollar	New Zealand
P.	pula; peso	Botswana, Philippines, various
£	pound	Ireland, Gt. Britain, Malta
£C	pound	Cyprus
£E	pound	Egypt
£L	pound; dinar	Lebanon
£N	pound; naira	Nigeria
£S	pound	Syria
ptas.	peseta	Spain
Q.	quetzal	Guatemala
R.	rand	South Africa, Lesotho, Namibia
RD.$	peso	Dominican Republic
Rps.	rupiah	Indonesia
Rs.	riel; rial; rupee	Cambodia, India, Iran, Mauritius, Nepal, Pakistan, Seychelles, Sri Lanka
Rub.	ruble	U.S.S.R.
S/	sucre; sole	Ecuador, Peru
S.	schilling	Austria
S.$	dollar	Singapore
SRl.	riyal	Saudia Arabia
SL.	pound	Sudan
TK.	taka	Bangladesh
TL.	pound; lira	Turkey
T.T.$	dollar	Trinidad and Tobago
UM	ouguiya	Mauritania
Urg.$	peso	Uruguay
VN.$	dollar	Vietnam
Won	won (hwan)	Korea
Y	yuan	Peoples Republic of China
Yen	yen	Japan
YRl.	rial	Yemen
Z	zaire	Zaire
Z.$	dollar	Zimbabwe
Zl.	zloty	Poland

Micropublishers

AMS	AMS Press, Inc. 56 E. 13th St. New York, NY 10003 212-777-4600
BLH	Bell & Howell Micro Photo Division Old Mansfield Rd. Wooster, OH 44691 216-264-6666
BLI	Balch Institute 18 S. 7th St. Philadelphia, PA 19106
CLA	Canadian Library Association Microfilm Project 151 Sparks St. Ottawa, Ont. K1P SE3, Canada
EDR	Eric Document Reproduction Service Box 190 Arlington, VA 22210 703-823-0500; 800-227-3742
FCM	Fairchild Microfilms Fairchild Publications, Inc. 7 E. 12th St. New York, NY 10003 212-741-4000
GMC	General Microfilm Co. 70 Coolidge Hill Rd. Watertown, MA 02172 617-926-5557
HPL	Harvester Press Microfilm Publications Ltd. 16 Ship St. Brighton, Sussex BN1 1AD England
IDC	Inter Documentation Co., AG. Poststrasse 14 6300 Zurich Switzerland
ISI	Institute for Scientific Information 3501 Market St. Philadelphia, PA 19104 215-386-0100
JAI	JAI Press, Inc. 36 Sherwood Pl. P.O. Box 1678 Greenwich, CT 06836 203-661-7602
JOH	Johnson Reprint Microeditions 111 Fifth Ave. New York, NY 10003 212-614-3200
JSC	J. S. Canner & Co. 49-65 Lansdowne St. Boston, MA 02115
KTO	Kraus Reprints & Periodicals Division of Kraus-Thomson Organization, Ltd. Route 100 Millwood, NY 10546 914-762-2200
LCP	The Library of Congress Photoduplication Service 20 First St., S.E. Washington, DC 20540 202-287-5650
LIB	Library Microfilms 737 Loma Verde Ave. Palo Alto, CA 94303 415-494-1812
MCA	Microfilming Corporation of America 130 Fifth Ave. New York NY 10011 212-645-3000
MCE	Professional Data Services (formerly Microcard Editions) c/o Congressional Information Services 4520 East-West Hwy, Ste. 800 Bethesda, MD 20814
MIM	Microforms International Marketing Co. (Subsidiary of Pergamon Press, Inc.) Maxwell House Fairview Park Elmsford, NY 10523 914-592-7700
MML	Micromedia Limited 158 Pearl St. Toronto, Ontario M5H 1L3 Canada
MMP	McLaren Micropublishing P.O. Box 972, Station F Toronto, Ontario M4Y 2N9 Canada
NBI	Newsbank, Inc. 58 Pine St. New Canaan, CT 06840 203-966-1100; 800-243-7694
NTI	National Technical Information Service 5285 Port Royal Rd. Springfield, VA 22161 703-487-4600

NYT	New York Times Information Bank 229 W. 43rd St. New York, NY 10036 212-556-1234	
OMP	Oxford Microform Publications Ltd. (Subsidiary of Pergamon Press, Ltd.) Headington Hill Hall Oxford 0X3 OBW, England	
PMC	Princeton Microfilm Corp. P.O. Box 2073 Princeton, NJ 08543 609-452-2066; 800-257-9502	
RRI	Fred B. Rothman & Co. 10368 W. Centennial Rd. Littleton, CO 80127 303-979-5657	
TMI	Tennessee Microfilms P.O. Box 1096 Nashville, TN 37202	
UMI	University Microfilms International 300 N. Zeeb Rd. Ann Arbor, MI 48106 313-761-4700	
UNM	University of Michigan Library Interlibrary Lending Circulation Department Harlan Hatcher Graduate Library Ann Arbor, MI 48104	
UNW	University of Wisconsin Library Interlibrary Loan Department 728 State St. Madison, WI 53706	
WDS	Dawson Microfiche Cannon House Parkfarm Road Folkestone, Kent CT30 1RR England	
WMP	World Microfilm Publications Ltd. 62 Queen's Grove London NW8 6ER England	
WSH	William S. Hein & Co., Inc. 1285 Main St. Buffalo, NY 14209 716-882-2600; 800-828-7581	

Abstracting and Indexing Services

Abstr. Anthropol.	Abstracts in Anthropology
Abstr.Bk.Rev. Curr.Leg.Per.	Abstracts of Book Reviews in Current Legal Periodicals
Abstr.Engl.Stud.	Abstracts of English Studies
Abstr.Musl.Rel.	Abstracts: European Muslims and Christian-Muslim Relations
Abstrax	Abstrax
Access	Access: the Supplementary Index to Periodicals
Adol.Ment. Health Abstr.	Adolescent Mental Health Abstracts
Air Un.Lib.Ind.	Air University Library Index to Military Periodicals
Alt.Press Ind.	Alternative Press Index
Amer.Bibl. Slavic & E. Eur.Stud.	American Bibliography of Slavic and East European Studies
Amer.Hist.& Life	America: History & Life (Parts A,B,C)
Amer.Hum.Ind.	American Humanities Index
Apic.Abstr.	Apicultural Abstracts
Art & Archaeol. Tech.Abstr.	Art and Archaeology Technical Abstracts
Art Ind.	Art Index
Arts & Hum. Cit.Ind.	Arts & Humanities Citation Index
Aus.Educ.Ind.	Australian Education Index
Aus.P.A.I.S.	Australian Public Affairs Information Service (Now: APAIS: Australian Public Affairs Information Service)
Bibl.Cart.	Bibliographia Cartographica
Bibl.Engl.Lang. & Lit.	Bibliography of English Language and Literature (Now: Annual Bibliography of English Language and Literature
Bibl.Ind.	Bibliographic Index
Biog.Ind.	Biography Index
Biol.Abstr.	Biological Abstracts
Biol.Dig.	Biology Digest
Bk.Rev.Dig.	Book Review Digest
Bk.Rev.Ind.	Book Review Index
Bk.Rev.Mo.	Book Reviews of the Month
Br.Archaeol. Abstr.	British Archaeological Abstracts
Br.Educ.Ind.	British Education Index
Br.Hum.Ind.	British Humanities Index
Bull.Signal.	Bulletin Signaletique (Now: P A S C A L Explore, P A S C A L Folio, P A S C A L Thema) (Programme Applique a la Selection et la Compilation Automatique de la Literature)
CERDIC	Bulletin du CERDIC (Centre des Recherches et de Documentation des Institutions Chretiennes) (Ceased)
C.I.J.E.	Current Index to Journals in Education
CINAHL (also C.I.N.L.)	Cumulative Index to Nursing and Allied Health Literature
C.I.S.Abstr.	C I A Abstracts (Centre International d'Information de Securite et Hygiene du Travail)
C.L.I.	Current Law Index
Can.Ind.	Canadian Periodical Index
Canon Law Abstr.	Canon Law Abstracts
Cath.Ind.	Catholic Periodical & Literature Index (Formerly: Catholic Periodical Index)
Chem.Abstr.	Chemical Abstracts
Child.Bk.Rev. Ind.	Children's Book Review Index
Chr.Per.Ind.	Christian Periodical Index
Commun.Abstr.	Communication Abstracts
Comput.Lit.Ind.	Computer Literature Index (Formerly: Quarterly Bibliography of Computers and Data Processing)
Curr.Bk.Rev. Cit.	Current Book Review Citations (Ceased)
Curr.Cont.	Current Contents
Curr.Cont. Africa	Current Contents Africa (Ceased)
Curr.Dig.Sov. Press	Current Digest of Soviet Press
Curr.Lit.Fam. Plan.	Current Literature in Family Planning
ERIC	Eric Clearinghouse (See: C.I.J.E.)
Educ.Admin. Abstr.	Educational Administration Abstracts
Educ.Ind.	Education Index
Eng.Ind.	Engineering Index (Now: Engineering Index Monthly and Author Index)
Excerp.Med.	Excerpta Medica
Film Lit.Ind.	Film Literature Index
Fuel & Energy Abstr.	Fuel & Energy Abstracts
G.Indian Per. Lit.	Guide to Indian Periodical Literature
G.Soc.Sci.& Rel.Per.Lit.	Guide to Social Science and Religion in Periodical Literature
Gdlns.	Guidelines
Geneal.Per.Ind.	Genealogical Periodical Annual Index
Geo.Abstr.	Geographical Abstracts
High.Educ. Abstr.	Higher Education Abstracts
High.Educ. Curr.Aware. Bull.	Higher Education Current Awareness Bulletin
Hisp.Amer.Per. Ind.	Hispanic American Periodicals Index
Hist.Abstr.	Historical Abstracts
Hum.Ind.	Humanities Index

I.C.U.I.S.Abstr.	I C U I S Abstracts Service (Institute on the Church in Urban Industrial Society) (Now: I C U I S Justice Ministries
Ind.Amer.Per. Verse	Index of American Periodical Verse
Ind.Artic.Jew. Stud.	Index of Articles on Jewish Studies
Ind.Heb.Per.	Index to Hebrew Periodicals
Ind.India	Index India
Ind.Islam.	Index Islamicus
Ind.Jew.Per.	Index to Jewish Periodicals
Ind.Med.	Index Medicus
Ind.Per.Lit.	Indian Periodical Literature
Ind.S.A.Per.	Index to South African Periodicals
Ind.Sel.Per.	Index to Selected Periodicals (Now: Index to Periodical Articles by & about Blacks)
Ind.U.S.Gov. Per.	Index to U.S. Government Periodicals
Int.Nurs.Ind.	International Nursing Index
Int.Z.Bibelwiss.	Internationale Zeitschriften fuer Bibelwissenschaft und Grenzgebiete
Jap.Per.Ind.	Japanese Periodicals Index
Key to Econ. Sci.	Key to Economic Science
LCR	Literary Criticism Register
LISA	Library & Information Science Abstracts
L.R.I.	Legal Resource Index
Leg.Per.	Index to Legal Periodicals
M.L.A.	Modern Language Abstracts in Scholarly Journals (Ceased)
Mag.Ind.	Magazine Index
Media Rev.Dig.	Media Review Digest
Met.Abstr.	Metallurgical Abstracts (Now: Metals Abstracts) see also: Cleaning/Finishing/Coating Digest Corrosion Prevention/Inhibition Digest Heat Processing Digest
Meth.Per.Ind.	Methodist Periodical Index
Music Artic. Guide	Music Article Guide
Music Ind.	Music Index
New Per.Ind.	New Periodicals Index (Ceased)
New Test.Abstr.	New Testament Abstracts
Numis.Lit.	Numismatic Literature
Old Test.Abstr.	Old Testament Abstracts
P.A.I.S.	P A I S Bulletin (Public Affairs Information Service)
PMR	Popular Magazine Review

Past.Care & Couns.Abstr.	Pastoral Care & Counseling Abstracts (Now: Abstracts of Research in Pastoral Care and Counseling)
Peace Res. Abstr.	Peace Research Abstracts Journal
Perf.Arts Biog. Master Ind.	Performing Arts Biography Master Index
Phil.Ind.	Philosopher's Index
Psychol.Abstr.	Psychological Abstracts
Psychol.R.G.	Psychopharmacology Reader's Guide (Ceased)
Pt.de Rep.	Point de Repers (Formed by the merger of: Periodex and RADAR)
R.G.	Reader's Guide to Periodical Literature
RILA	R I L A (International Repertory of the Literature of Art)
RILM	R I L M Abstracts of Music Literature (International Repertory of Music Literature)
Ref.Sour.	Reference Sources
Rehabil.Lit.	Rehabilitation Literature
Rel.& Theol. Abstr.	Religious & Theological Abstracts
Rel.Ind.One	Religion Index One: Periodicals
Rel.Ind.Two	Religion Index Two: Multi-Author Works
Rel.Per.	Index to Religious Periodical Literature (Now: Religion Index One: Periodicals; Religion Index Two: Multi-Author Works)
Rural Recreat. Tour.Abstr.	Rural Recreation and Tourism Abstracts (Now: Leisure, Recreation and Tourism Abstracts)
SSCI	Social Science Citation Index
Sage Fam.Stud. Abstr.	Sage Family Studies Abstracts
Sci.Abstr.	Science Abstracts. A. Physics Abstracts B. Electrical Engineering Abstracts C. Computer & Control Abstracts
Soc.Sci.Ind.	Social Sciences Index
Sociol.Abstr.	Sociological Abstracts
South.Bap.Per. Ind.	Southern Baptist Periodical Index (Ceased)
Sportsearch	Sportsearch
Theol.& Rel. Ind.	Theological & Religious Index (Now: Theological & Religious Bibliographies)
Vert.File Ind.	Vertical File Index
World Agri. Econ.& Rural Sociol.Abstr.	World Agricultural Economics & Rural Sociology Abstracts
World Alum. Abstr.	World Aluminum Abstracts

Subject Area Directory

The *Subject Area Directory* provides a topical outline to the Library of Congress subject categories listed in *Religious and Inspirational Books and Serials in Print 1987*. The *Subject Area Directory* is designed to provide general access to all major religions and religious topics found in *Religious and Inspirational Books and Serials in Print 1987*. The subjects were classified under the 48 major areas or topics derived from the Library of Congress Classification scheme. For instance, all subjects within *Religious and Inspirational Books and Serials in Print 1987* which deal with the topic of *Protestantism* or *Judaism* would be alphabetically arranged under their respective topic. This index is intended to provide the user with an overall view of the general topic with specific Library of Congress subjects used in *Religious and Inspirational Books and Serials in Print 1987* that relate to the area listed. Therefore, a user wishing to approach a topic, e.g., *Protestantism*, can scan this topic and isolate specific subjects for review of the bibliographic records within the main index.

ANGLICAN COMMUNION

ANDREWES, LANCELOT, BP. OF WINCHESTER, 1555-1626
ANGLICAN COMMUNION
BRAY, THOMAS, 1656-1730
CHRISTIAN LIFE-ANGLICAN AUTHORS
CLAPHAM SECT
HEBER, REGMALD, 1783-1826
KINGSLEY, CHARLES, 1819-1875
LORD'S SUPPER-ANGLICAN COMMUNION
MONASTICISM AND RELIGIOUS ORDERS, ANGLICAN
STRACHAN, JOHN, BP., 1778-1867
WARD, WILLIAM GEORGE, 1812-1882

ANTHROPOSOPHY

ANTHROPOSOPHY
STEINER, RUDOLF, 1861-1925

BAHAISM

BABISM
BAHA ULIAH, 1817-1892
BAHAISM
BAHAISM-JUVENILE LITERATURE
MARRIAGE-RELIGIOUS ASPECTS-BAHAI FAITH
MYSTICISM-BAHAISM

BAPTISTS

AFRO-AMERICAN BAPTISTS
AMERICAN BAPTIST CONVENTION
ANABAPTISTS
ANABAPTISTS-HISTORY
BACKUS, ISAAC, 1724-1806
BAPTISTS
BAPTISTS-ADDRESSES, ESSAYS, LECTURES
BAPTISTS-CATECHISMS AND CREEDS
BAPTISTS-CLERGY
BAPTISTS-DOCTRINAL AND CONTROVERSIAL WORKS
BAPTISTS-EDUCATION
BAPTISTS-GOVERNMENT
BAPTISTS-HISTORY
BAPTISTS-HYMNS
BAPTISTS-MISSIONS
BAPTISTS-RELATIONS-CATHOLIC CHURCH
BAPTISTS-SERMONS
BAPTISTS IN RUSSIA
CAREY, WILLIAM, 1761-1834
CHRISTIAN LIFE-BAPTIST AUTHORS
CLIFFORD, JOHN, 1836-1923
COMBER, THOMAS J., 1852-1887
FOSDICK, HARRY EMERSON, 1878-1964
JASPER, JOHN, 1812-1901
JUDSON, ADONIRAM, 1788-1850
KING, CORETTA SCOTT, 1927-
KING, MARTIN LUTHER, 1929-1968
ROBERTSON, PAT
SEVENTH-DAY BAPTISTS-MISSIONS
SOUTHERN BAPTIST CONVENTION
SOUTHERN METHODIST UNIVERSITY
SPURGEON, CHARLES HADDON, 1834-1892

BIBLE (SEE ALSO SACRED WORKS INDEX)

AARON, BIBLICAL CHARACTER
ABOTH-COMMENTARIES
ABRAHAM, THE PATRIARCH
ABRAHAM, THE PATRIARCH-FICTION
ABRAHAM, THE PATRIARCH-JUVENILE LITERATURE
ABRAHAM, THE PATRIARCH-POETRY
ADAM (BIBLICAL CHARACTER)
AMOS, THE PROPHET
APOCALYPTIC LITERATURE
APOSTLES
APOSTLES-JUVENILE LITERATURE
APOSTLES-LEGENDS
APOSTLES' CREED
BALAAM (BIBLICAL CHARACTER)
BARABBAS-FICTION
BEATITUDES
BEATITUDES-MEDITATIONS
BEGINNING
BENJAMIN, BIBLICAL CHARACTER
BETHLEHEM
BIBLE-ADDRESSES, ESSAYS, LECTURES
BIBLE-ANTIQUITIES
BIBLE-APPRECIATION
BIBLE-BIBLIOGRAPHY
BIBLE-BIOGRAPHY
BIBLE-BIOGRAPHY-N. T.
BIBLE-BIOGRAPHY-O. T.
BIBLE-CANON
BIBLE-CATECHISMS, QUESTION-BOOKS, ETC.
BIBLE-CHRONOLOGY
BIBLE-COMMENTARIES
BIBLE-COMMENTARIES-N. T.
BIBLE-COMMENTARIES-N. T. ACTS
BIBLE-COMMENTARIES-N. T. CATHOLIC EPISTLES
BIBLE-COMMENTARIES-N. T. COLOSSIANS
BIBLE-COMMENTARIES-N. T. CORINTHIANS
BIBLE-COMMENTARIES-N. T. EPHESIANS
BIBLE-COMMENTARIES-N. T. EPISTLES OF PAUL
BIBLE-COMMENTARIES-N. T. GALATIANS
BIBLE-COMMENTARIES-N. T. GOSPELS
BIBLE-COMMENTARIES-N. T. HEBREWS
BIBLE-COMMENTARIES-N. T. PASTORAL EPISTLES
BIBLE-COMMENTARIES-N. T. PHILEMON
BIBLE-COMMENTARIES-N. T. PHILIPPIANS
BIBLE-COMMENTARIES-N. T. REVELATION
BIBLE-COMMENTARIES-N. T. ROMANS
BIBLE-COMMENTARIES-N. T. THESSALONIANS
BIBLE-COMMENTARIES-O. T.
BIBLE-COMMENTARIES-O. T. APOCRYPHA
BIBLE-COMMENTARIES-O. T. FIVE SCROLLS
BIBLE-COMMENTARIES-O. T. HISTORICAL BOOKS
BIBLE-COMMENTARIES-O. T. MINOR PROPHETS
BIBLE-COMMENTARIES-O. T. PENTATEUCH
BIBLE-COMMENTARIES-O. T. POETICAL BOOKS
BIBLE-COMMENTARIES-O. T. PROPHETS
BIBLE-COMMENTARIES-O.T. WISDOM LITERATURE
BIBLE-CONCORDANCES
BIBLE-CONCORDANCES-DATA PROCESSING
BIBLE-CRITICISM, FORM
BIBLE-CRITICISM, INTERPRETATION, ETC.
BIBLE-CRITICISM, INTERPRETATION, ETC.-HISTORY
BIBLE-CRITICISM, INTERPRETATION, ETC.-N. T.
BIBLE-CRITICISM, INTERPRETATION, ETC.-N. T. ACTS
BIBLE-CRITICISM, INTERPRETATION, ETC.-N. T. APOCRYPHA
BIBLE-CRITICISM, INTERPRETATION, ETC.-N. T. EPISTLES
BIBLE-CRITICISM, INTERPRETATION, ETC.-N. T. GOSPELS
BIBLE-CRITICISM, INTERPRETATION, ETC.-N. T. REVELATION
BIBLE-CRITICISM, INTERPRETATION, ETC.-O. T
BIBLE-CRITICISM, INTERPRETATION, ETC.-O. T. APOCRYPHAL BOOKS
BIBLE-CRITICISM, INTERPRETATION, ETC.-O. T. HISTORICAL BOOKS
BIBLE-CRITICISM, INTERPRETATION, ETC.-O. T. MINOR PROPHETS
BIBLE-CRITICISM, INTERPRETATION, ETC.-O. T. PENTATEUCH
BIBLE-CRITICISM, INTERPRETATION, ETC.-O. T. POETICAL BOOKS
BIBLE-CRITICISM, INTERPRETATION, ETC.-O. T. PROPHETS
BIBLE-CRITICISM, INTERPRETATION, ETC.-O. T. WISDOM LITERATURE
BIBLE-CRITICISM, TEXTUAL
BIBLE-CRITICISM, TEXTUAL-N. T.
BIBLE-CRITICISM, TEXTUAL-O. T.
BIBLE-DICTIONARIES
BIBLE-ECONOMICS
BIBLE-ETHICS
BIBLE-ETHNOLOGY
BIBLE-EVIDENCES, AUTHORITY, ETC.
BIBLE-EVIDENCES, AUTHORITY, ETC.-N. T.
BIBLE-EVIDENCES, AUTHORITY, ETC.-O. T.
BIBLE-GENEALOGY
BIBLE-GEOGRAPHY
BIBLE-GEOGRAPHY-MAPS
BIBLE-HANDBOOKS, MANUALS, ETC.
BIBLE-HARMONIES
BIBLE-HERMENEUTICS
BIBLE-HISTORIOGRAPHY
BIBLE-HISTORY
BIBLE-HISTORY OF BIBLICAL EVENTS
BIBLE-HISTORY OF BIBLICAL EVENTS-FICTION
BIBLE-HISTORY OF BIBLICAL EVENTS-N. T.
BIBLE-HISTORY OF BIBLICAL EVENTS-O. T.
BIBLE-HISTORY OF CONTEMPORARY EVENTS, ETC.
BIBLE-HISTORY OF CONTEMPORARY EVENTS-N. T.
BIBLE-HISTORY OF CONTEMPORARY EVENTS-O. T.
BIBLE-HOMILETICAL USE
BIBLE-INDEXES, TOPICAL
BIBLE-INFLUENCE
BIBLE-INSPIRATION
BIBLE-INTERLINEAR TRANSLATIONS
BIBLE-INTRODUCTIONS
BIBLE-INTRODUCTIONS-APOCRYPHA AND APOCRYPHAL BOOKS
BIBLE-INTRODUCTIONS-N. T.
BIBLE-INTRODUCTIONS-N. T. GOSPELS
BIBLE-INTRODUCTIONS-O. T.
BIBLE-JUVENILE LITERATURE
BIBLE-LANGUAGE, STYLE
BIBLE-LITURGICAL USE
BIBLE-MANUSCRIPTS
BIBLE-MEDICINE, HYGIENE, ETC.
BIBLE-MEDITATIONS
BIBLE-MEDITATIONS-N. T.
BIBLE-MEDITATIONS-O. T.
BIBLE-MISCELLANEA
BIBLE-MUSIC
BIBLE-NAMES
BIBLE-NATURAL HISTORY
BIBLE-NATURAL HISTORY-JUVENILE LITERATURE

BIBLE–NUMISMATICS
BIBLE–PARABLES
BIBLE–PARAPHRASES
BIBLE–PERIODICALS
BIBLE–PHILOSOPHY
BIBLE–PICTURES, ILLUSTRATIONS, ETC.
BIBLE–POLITICAL SCIENCE
BIBLE–PRAYERS
BIBLE–PRINTING
BIBLE–PROPHECIES
BIBLE–PSYCHOLOGY
BIBLE–PUBLICATION AND DISTRIBUTION
BIBLE–QUOTATIONS, EARLY
BIBLE–READING
BIBLE–RELATION OF N. T. TO O. T.
BIBLE–SERMONS
BIBLE–SERMONS–N. T.
BIBLE–SERMONS–O. T.
BIBLE–STUDY
BIBLE–STUDY–BIBLIOGRAPHY
BIBLE–STUDY–OUTLINES, SYLLABI, ETC.
BIBLE–STUDY–N. T.
BIBLE–STUDY–O. T.
BIBLE–STUDY–TEXT-BOOKS
BIBLE–THEOLOGY
BIBLE–THEOLOGY–N. T.
BIBLE–THEOLOGY–O. T.
BIBLE–TRANSLATING
BIBLE–USE
BIBLE–VERSIONS
BIBLE–VERSIONS, ENGLISH
BIBLE AND FEMINISM
BIBLE AND LAW
BIBLE AND SCIENCE
BIBLE AND SPIRITUALISM
BIBLE AND THEOSOPHY
BIBLE AS LITERATURE
BIBLE GAMES AND PUZZLES
BIBLE IN LITERATURE
BIBLE IN LITERATURE–BIBLIOGRAPHY
BIBLE PLAYS
BIBLE STORIES
BIBLE STORIES–N. T.
BIBLE STORIES–O. T.
CAIN
CABALA
CHILDREN IN THE BIBLE
CHURCH–BIBLICAL TEACHING
COMMANDMENTS, TEN
CONCORDANCES
COSMOGONY
COSMOLOGY
COSMOLOGY–CURIOSA AND MISCELLANEA
DANIEL, THE PROPHET
DANIEL, THE PROPHET–DRAMA
DANIEL, THE PROPHET–JUVENILE LITERATURE
DAVID, KING OF ISRAEL
DAVID, KING OF ISRAEL–JUVENILE LITERATURE
DEMONIAC POSSESSION
DEMYTHOLOGIZATION
DEVIL
DIVES AND LAZARUS
DIVORCE–BIBLICAL TEACHING
ELIJAH, THE PROPHET
ELIJAH, THE PROPHET–JUVENILE LITERATURE
ELISHA THE PROPHET
ENOCH
ESCHATOLOGY–BIBLICAL TEACHING
ESTHER, QUEEN OF PERSIA
ESTHER, QUEEN OF PERSIA–DRAMA
ESTHER, QUEEN OF PERSIA–JUVENILE LITERATURE
EUTHALIUS, BP. OF SULCA
EVE (BIBLICAL CHARACTER)
EXODUS, THE
EZEKIEL, THE PROPHET
EZRA, THE PROPHET
FAMILY–BIBLICAL TEACHING
GILGAMESH
GOD–BIBLICAL TEACHING
GOG AND MAGOG
GREEK LANGUAGE, BIBLICAL
GREEK LANGUAGE, BIBLICAL–DICTIONARIES
GREEK LANGUAGE, BIBLICAL–GLOSSARIES, VOCABULARIES, ETC.
GREEK LANGUAGE, BIBLICAL–GRAMMAR
GREEK LANGUAGE, BIBLICAL–READERS
GREEK LANGUAGE, BIBLICAL–SEMANTICS
GREEK LANGUAGE, BIBLICAL–SYNTAX
HEALING IN THE BIBLE
HERMENEUTICS
HESED (THE WORD)
HOPE–BIBLICAL TEACHING
HOSEA, THE PROPHET
ISAAC, THE PATRIARCH
ISAIAH, THE PROPHET
JACOB, THE PATRIARCH
JEREMIAH THE PROPHET
JEREMIAH THE PROPHET–FICTION
JESUS CHRIST–PARABLES
JESUS CHRIST–PARABLES–JUVENILE LITERATURE
JESUS CHRIST–PARABLES–SERMONS
JESUS CHRIST–TEACHINGS
JEZEBEL, WIFE OF AHAB, KING OF ISRAEL–FICTION
JOB, THE PATRIARCH
JOHN THE BAPTIST, SAINT, ca. 5 B.C.-ca. 30 A.D.
JOHN THE BAPTIST,–ART
JONAH, THE PROPHET
JONAH, THE PROPHET–JUVENILE LITERATURE
JOSEPH, THE PATRIARCH
JOSEPH, THE PATRIARCH–DRAMA
JOSEPH, THE PATRIARCH–FICTION
JOSEPH, THE PATRIARCH–JUVENILE LITERATURE
JOSHUA, SON OF NUN
JOSHUA, SON OF NUN–JUVENILE LITERATURE
KINGDOM OF GOD–BIBLICAL TEACHING
LAST SUPPER
LORD'S SUPPER–BIBLICAL TEACHING
MACCABEES
MACCABEES–COMMENTARIES
MAN (THEOLOGY)–BIBLICAL TEACHING
MARRIAGE–BIBLICAL TEACHING
MARY OF THE APOSTLES, MOTHER
MATTHEW, SAINT, APOSTLE
METAPHOR
MOSES
MOSES–FICTION
MOSES–JUVENILE LITERATURE
NAAMAN (BIBLICAL CHARACTER)
NEHEMIAH
NEW TESTAMENT GREEK
NOAH
NOAH'S ARK
NUMBERS IN THE BIBLE
PARABLES
PATRIARCHS (BIBLE)
PAUL, SAINT, APOSTLE
PEACE
PIETY
PILATE, PONTIUS, 1ST CENTURY
PRAYER–BIBLICAL TEACHING
PROPHETS
PSALTERS
READERS–BIBLE
REDEMPTION
REINCARNATION
REWARD (THEOLOGY)
RUTH (BIBLICAL CHARACTER)
RUTH (BIBLICAL CHARACTER)–JUVENILE LITERATURE
SAMSON, JUDGE OF ISRAEL
SAMSON, JUDGE OF ISRAEL–JUVENILE LITERATURE
SAMSON, JUDGE OF ISRAEL–POETRY
SAMUEL, THE PROPHET
SAUL, KING OF ISRAEL
SCHOLIA
SERVANT OF JEHOVAH
SETH (BIBLICAL CHARACTER)
SHEBA, QUEEN OF–LEGEND
SIMEON (BIBLICAL CHARACTER)
SOCIOLOGY, BIBLICAL
SOLOMON, KING OF ISRAEL
SPIRITUAL LIFE–BIBLICAL TEACHING
SYMBOLISM IN THE BIBLE
THOMAS, SAINT, APOSTLE–POETRY
TIMOTHY (BIBLICAL CHARACTER)–FICTION
TOWER OF BABEL
TYPOLOGY (THEOLOGY)
WOMEN IN THE BIBLE
ZACCHAEUS (BIBLICAL CHARACTER)–JUVENILE LITERATURE

BUDDHISM

ASOKA, KING OF MAGADHA, fl. 259 B.C.
AVATARS
BHUTAN
BUDDHISM
BUDDHISM–HISTORY
BUDDHISM–POETRY
BUDDHISM–RELATIONS–CHRISTIANITY
BUDDHISM–RELATIONS–SHINTO
BUDDHISM–SACRED BOOKS
BUDDHISM–BURMA
BUDDHISM–CHINA
BUDDHISM–EAST (FAR EAST)
BUDDHISM–GREAT BRITAIN
BUDDHISM–INDIA
BUDDHISM–JAPAN
BUDDHISM–KOREA
BUDDHISM–NEPAL
BUDDHISM–SRI LANKA
BUDDHISM–THAILAND
BUDDHISM–TIBET
BUDDHISM AND STATE
BUDDHIST CONVERTS FROM CHRISTIANITY
BUDDHIST DOCTRINES
BUDDHIST ETHICS
BUDDHIST LITERATURE
BUDDHIST LOGIC
BUDDHIST SECTS
CATHOLIC CHURCH–RELATIONS–BUDDHISM
CHANTS (BUDDHIST)
CHRISTIANITY AND OTHER RELIGIONS–BUDDHISM
CHUANG-TZU
DHARMA
FRANCK, FREDERICH, 1909-
GAUTAMA BUDDHA
HSUAN-TSANG, 596?-664
KARMA
KHOTANESE LANGUAGE
KNOAN
LAMAISM
LAMAISM–RELATIONS–CHRISTIANITY
LEGENDS, BUDDHIST
MAHAYANA BUDDHISM
MARRIAGE–RELIGIOUS ASPECTS–BUDDHISM
MEDICINE AND BUDDHISM
MEDITATION (BUDDHISM)
MI-LA RAS-PA, 1038-1122
MONASTICISM AND RELIGIOUS ORDERS, BUDDHIST
MYSTICISM–BUDDHISM
MYTHOLOGY, BUDDHIST
NADAPADA
NAGARJUNA–SIDDHA
NICHIREN, 1222-1282
NIRVANA
PALI LITERATURE
PHILOSOPHY, BUDDHIST
PHILOSOPHY, INDIC
PRAYER
PRIESTS, BUDDHIST
SANSKRIT LITERATURE
SANSKRIT POETRY–HISTORY AND CRITICISM
SANSKRIT POETRY–TRANSLATIONS INTO ENGLISH
SENGAI, GIBBON
SESSHU, 1420-1506
SHINRAN, 1173-1263
SONGS, INDIC
SUTRAS
TAIWAN–RELIGION
TALES, BUDDHIST
TANTRAS
TANTRIC BUDDHISM
TANTRISM
ZEN BUDDHISM
ZEN LITERATURE

CATHEDRALS AND ABBEYS

ABBEYS
ATHOS (MONASTERIES)
BATTLE ABBEY
BEC-HEL-LOUIN, FRANCE (BENEDICTINE ABBEY)
BET EL-WALI (TEMPLE)
BOURGES, SAINT-ETIENNE (CATHEDRAL)
BURY ST. EDMUNDS ABBEY
CANTERBURY CATHEDRAL
CATHEDRALS
CHARTRES, FRANCE–NOTRE-DAME (CATHEDRAL)
CHURCHES–ITALY
CIUDAD RODRIGO, SPAIN–CATHEDRAL
CLUNY, FRANCE (BENEDICTINE ABBEY)
CROWLAND ABBEY
DRYBURGH ABBEY
GLASTONBURY ABBEY
IBURG, GERMANY–BENEDICTINE ABBEY
KINLOSS ABBEY
LETHORONET, FRANCE (CISTERCIAN ABBEY)
LINDISFARNE ABBEY
MONT SAINT MICHEL, FRANCE
NOYON, FRANCE–NOTRE-DAME (CATHEDRAL)
PARIS–NOTRE-DAME
PETERBOROUGH CATHEDRAL
QUARR ABBEY
SAINT-DENIS, FRANCE (BENEDICTINE ABBEY)
TAVISTOCK ABBEY

CHRISTIAN SCIENCE

BOSTON–FIRST CHURCH OF CHRIST, SCIENTIST
CHRISTIAN SCIENCE
CHRISTIAN SCIENCE–HISTORY
EDDY, MARY (BAKER),
FAITH-CURE

CHRISTIANITY

ABORTION–RELIGIOUS ASPECTS–CHRISTIANITY
AELFRIC (CALLED GRAMMATICUS), 955-10201
AELRED, SAINT, 1109-1166
AGAPE
ALBIGENSES
ALCUIN, 735-804
ALEXANDRIAN SCHOOL, CHRISTIAN
ALEXIUS, SAINT
ANTONIUS, SAINT, THE GREAT, ca. 250-350
APOSTLES' CREED–SERMONS
APOSTOLIC FATHERS
ARATOR, SUBDEACON IN ROME. fl. 513-544
ASCETICISM
AVERROES, 1126-1198
BETHLEHEM
BOETHIUS, d. 524
BUDDHISM–RELATIONS–CHRISTIANITY
BUDDHIST CONVERTS FROM CHRISTIANITY
BUTTON, THOMAS DE, BP. OF EXETER, d. 1307
CAYCE, EDGAR, 1877-1945
CELTIC CHURCH
CHRISTIAN ANTIQUITIES
CHRISTIAN ART AND SYMBOLISM
CHRISTIAN ART AND SYMBOLISM–JUVENILE LITERATURE
CHRISTIAN BIOGRAPHY
CHRISTIAN BIOGRAPHY–JUVENILE LITERATURE
CHRISTIAN DEMOCRACY
CHRISTIAN ETHICS
CHRISTIAN ETHICS–ANGLICAN AUTHORS
CHRISTIAN ETHICS–CATHOLIC AUTHORS
CHRISTIAN ETHICS–DICTIONARIES
CHRISTIAN ETHICS–ORTHODOX EASTERN AUTHORS
CHRISTIAN LEADERSHIP
CHRISTIAN LIFE–BIBLIOGRAPHY
CHRISTIAN LITERATURE
CHRISTIAN LITERATURE, EARLY
CHRISTIAN LITERATURE, EARLY (COLLECTIONS)
CHRISTIAN LITERATURE, EARLY–BIBLIOGRAPHY
CHRISTIAN LITERATURE, EARLY–HISTORY AND CRITICISM
CHRISTIAN LITERATURE, EARLY–SOURCES
CHRISTIAN LITERATURE FOR CHILDREN
CHRISTIAN PATRON SAINTS
CHRISTIAN POETRY
CHRISTIAN REFORMED CHURCH
CHRISTIAN SOCIALIST, LONDON
CHRISTIAN UNION
CHRISTIAN UNION–CATHOLIC CHURCH
CHRISTIAN UNION–HISTORY
CHRISTIAN UNION–ORTHODOX EASTERN CHURCH
CHRISTIANITY
CHRISTIANITY–ADDRESSES, ESSAYS, LECTURES
CHRISTIANITY–BIBLIOGRAPHY
CHRISTIANITY–CONTROVERSIAL LITERATURE
CHRISTIANITY–ESSENCE, GENIUS, NATURE
CHRISTIANITY–MISCELLANEA
CHRISTIANITY–ORIGIN
CHRISTIANITY–PHILOSOPHY
CHRISTIANITY–PSYCHOLOGY
CHRISTIANITY–EARLY CHURCH, ca. 30-600
CHRISTIANITY–MIDDLE AGES, 600-1500
CHRISTIANITY–16TH CENTURY
CHRISTIANITY–17TH CENTURY
CHRISTIANITY–19TH CENTURY
CHRISTIANITY–20TH CENTURY
CHRISTIANITY–20TH CENTURY–ADDRESSES, ESSAYS, LECTURES
CHRISTIANITY AND ANTISEMITISM
CHRISTIANITY AND ATHEISM
CHRISTIANITY AND CULTURE
CHRISTIANITY AND DEMOCRACY
CHRISTIANITY AND ECONOMICS
CHRISTIANITY AND INTERNATIONAL AFFAIRS
CHRISTIANITY AND LITERATURE
CHRISTIANITY AND OTHER RELIGIONS
CHRISTIANITY AND OTHER RELIGIONS–BUDDHISM
CHRISTIANITY AND OTHER RELIGIONS–DRUIDISM

CHRISTIANITY AND OTHER RELIGIONS–GREEK
CHRISTIANITY AND OTHER RELIGIONS–HINDUISM
CHRISTIANITY AND OTHER RELIGIONS–ISLAM
CHRISTIANITY AND OTHER RELIGIONS–JUDAISM
CHRISTIANITY AND OTHER RELIGIONS–LAMAISM
CHRISTIANITY AND POLITICS
CHRISTIANITY AND PROGRESS
CHRISTIANITY AND PSYCHICAL RESEARCH
CHRISTIANITY IN LITERATURE
CHRISTIANS IN AFRICA
CHRISTIANS IN ASIA
CHRISTIANS IN BELIZE
CHRISTIANS IN CHINA
CHRISTIANS IN EASTERN EUROPE
CHRISTIANS IN INDIA
CHRISTIANS IN JAPAN
CHRISTIANS IN LATIN AMERICA
CHRISTIANS IN RUSSIA
CHRISTIANS IN THE NEAR EAST
CHRISTIANS IN TURKEY
CIVILIZATION, CHRISTIAN
CLEMENS, TITUS FLAVIUS, ALEXANDRINUS
CLOTILDA, SAINT, 747-545
COMMUNISM AND CHRISTIANITY
COMPANY FOR THE PROPAGATION OF THE GOSPEL IN NEW ENGLAND AND PARTS ADJACENT, LONDON
CONSTANTINE 1ST, THE GREAT, EMPEROR OF ROME, d. 337
CONSTANTINE 1ST, THE GREAT, EMPEROR OF ROME, d. 337–FICTION
CORPUS CHRISTI FESTIVAL
COUNTER-REFORMATION
CRUSADES
CRUSADES–BIBLIOGRAPHY
CRUSADES–JUVENILE LITERATURE
CRUSADES–POETRY
CRUSADES–FIRST, 1096-1099
CRUSADES–FIRST, 1096-1099–FICTION
CRUSADES–SECOND, 1147-1149
CRUSADES–THIRD, 1189-1192
CRUSADES–FOURTH, 1202-1204
CRUSADES–LATER, 13TH, 14TH, AND 15TH CENTURIES
CUTHBERT, SAINT
CYNEWULF
DIDACHE
DIONYSIUS AREOPAGITA, PSEUDO.
DIVORCE–RELIGIOUS ASPECTS–CHRISTIANITY
DOLET, ETIENNE, 1508-1546
DONATION OF CONSTANTINE
ECUMENICAL MOVEMENT
EDICT OF NANTES
EDMUND, SAINT, KING OF EAST ANGLIA, 841-870
EDWARD, THE CONFESSOR, KING OF ENGLAND, SAINT, d. 1066
ENTHUSIASM
EVANGELICAL REVIVAL
EVANGELICAL UNITED BRETHREN CHURCH
EVANGELICALISM
GEORGE, SAINT, d. 303
GILL, ERIC, 1882-1940
HILDEGARD, SAINT, 1098?-1178
INNER LIGHT
ISLAM–RELATIONS–CHRISTIANITY
JAMES, SAINT, APOSTLE
JESUS CHRIST
JESUS CHRIST–APPEARANCES
JESUS CHRIST–DEVOTIONAL LITERATURE
JESUS CHRIST–JUVENILE LITERATURE
JESUS CHRIST–TRANSFIGURATION
JESUS CHRIST IN FICTION, DRAMA, POETRY, ETC.
JOHN, SAINT, APOSTLE
JOSEPH, SAINT
JOSEPH OF ARIMATHEA
JOSEPH OF ARIMATHEA–LEGENDS
JUDAS ISCARIOT
LAMAISM–RELATIONS–CHRISTIANITY
LAZARUS, SAINT
LE MANS–CHURCH HISTORY–SOURCES–HISTORY AND CRITICISM
LIGUORI, ALFONSO MARIA DE, SAINT, 1696-1787
LUKE, SAINT
LUKE, SAINT–FICTION
MARK, SAINT
MARRIAGE–RELIGIOUS ASPECTS–CHRISTIANITY
MARY, VIRGIN
MARY, VIRGIN–APPARITIONS AND MIRACLES
MARY, VIRGIN–ART
MARY, VIRGIN–ASSUMPTION
MARY, VIRGIN–BIOGRAPHY
MARY, VIRGIN–CULTUS
MARY, VIRGIN–FEASTS
MARY, VIRGIN–JUVENILE LITERATURE
MARY, VIRGIN–LEGENDS
MARY, VIRGIN–MEDITATION
MARY, VIRGIN–MEDITATIONS
MARY, VIRGIN–POETRY
MARY, VIRGIN–PRAYER-BOOKS AND DEVOTIONS
MARY, VIRGIN–SERMONS
MARY, VIRGIN–THEOLOGY
MARY, VIRGIN, IN LITERATURE
MARY MAGDALENE, SAINT
MARY MAGDALENE, SAINT–ART
MARY MAGDALENE, SAINT–FICTION
MICHAEL, ARCHANGEL
MODESTUS, d. 634 or 635
MOODY BIBLE INSTITUTE OF CHICAGO
MOOR'S INDIAN CHARITY SCHOOL, LEBANON, CONNECTICUT
NICAEA, COUNCIL OF, 325
OLDHEIM, SAINT, BP. OF SHERBORNE, 640-709
ORIGEN
PAGEANTS
PALESTINE
PALESTINE–ANTIQUITIES
PALESTINE–DESCRIPTION AND TRAVEL
PALESTINE–HISTORICAL GEOGRAPHY
PALESTINE–HISTORICAL GEOGRAPHY–MAPS
PALESTINE–HISTORY
PALESTINE–JUVENILE LITERATURE
PALESTINE–RELIGION
PALESTINE–SOCIAL LIFE AND CUSTOMS
PASCHAL MYSTERY
PATRONAGE, ECCLESIASTICAL
PAUL, SAINT, APOSTLE–FICTION
PAUL, SAINT, APOSTLE–JUVENILE LITERATURE
PELAGIUS
PERSECUTION
PETER, SAINT, APOSTLE
PETER, SAINT, APOSTLE–FICTION
PETER, SAINT, APOSTLE–JUVENILE LITERATURE
PHILOSOPHY, CHRISTIAN
PIETISM
PRAYER
PROPHECY (CHRISTIANITY)
PRUDENTIUS CLEMENS, AURELIUS
RESTORATION MOVEMENT (CHRISTIANITY)
RICHARD 1ST, KING OF ENGLAND, 1157-1199
SAINTS
SAINTS IN ART
SAINTS–CALENDAR
SAINTS–CORRESPONDENCE, REMINISCENCES, ETC.
SAINTS–CULTUS
SAINTS–JUVENILE LITERATURE
SAINTS–LEGENDS
SAINTS, ENGLISH
SAINTS, WOMEN
SEVERINUS, SAINT, d. 482
SOCIALISM, CHRISTIAN
SOCIOLOGY, CHRISTIAN
SOCIOLOGY, CHRISTIAN–HISTORY
STEPHEN, SAINT, MARTYR
SUBLIME, THE
TAIPING REBELLION, 1850-1864
THOMAS, SAINT, APOSTLE
TRINITY UNIVERSITY, SAN ANTONIO, TEXAS–HISTORY
WILLIAM, SAINT, 1133-1144
WORLD CONFERENCE ON CHURCH, COMMUNITY AND STATE, OXFORD, 1937
WORLD COUNCIL OF CHURCHES

CHURCH OF ENGLAND

ABBOT, GEORGE, ABP. OF CANTERBURY, 1562-1633
ANGLICAN CHURCH OF CANADA
ANGLICAN ORDERS
BANCROFT, RICHARD, ABP. OF CANTERBURY, 1544-1610
BAXTER, RICHARD, 1615-1691
BELL, GEORGE KENNEDY ALLEN, BP. OF CHICHESTER, 1883-1958
BERKELEY, GEORGE, BP. OF CLOYNE, 1685-1753
BOIS, JOHN, 1560-1644
BUTLER, JOSEPH, BP. OF DURHAM, 1692-1752
CHURCH AND SOCIAL PROBLEMS–CHURCH OF ENGLAND
CHURCH OF ENGLAND
CHURCH OF ENGLAND–BIOGRAPHY
CHURCH OF ENGLAND–BISHOPS
CHURCH OF ENGLAND–BOOK OF COMMON PRAYER
CHURCH OF ENGLAND–BOOK OF COMMON PRAYER–PSALTER
CHURCH OF ENGLAND–CATECHISMS AND CREEDS
CHURCH OF ENGLAND–CLERGY
CHURCH OF ENGLAND–CLERGY–CORRESPONDENCE, REMINISCENSES, ETC.
CHURCH OF ENGLAND–DOCTRINAL AND CONTROVERSIAL WORKS
CHURCH OF ENGLAND–GOVERNMENT
CHURCH OF ENGLAND–HISTORY
CHURCH OF ENGLAND–LITURGY AND RITUAL
CHURCH OF ENGLAND–MISSIONS
CHURCH OF ENGLAND–PRAYER BOOKS AND DEVOTIONS
CHURCH OF ENGLAND–RELATIONS
CHURCH OF ENGLAND IN AMERICA
CHURCH OF IRELAND
CHURCH OF SOUTH INDIA
CRANMER, THOMAS, ABP. OF CANTERBURY, 1489-1556
CREIGHTON, MANDELL, BP. OF LONDON, 1843-1901
CREWE, NATHANIEL CREWE, 3RD BARON, BP. OF DURHAM, 1633-1721
DONNE, JOHN, 1573-1631
DONNE, JOHN, 1573-1631–BIBLIOGRAPHY
FINCH, ROBERT, 1783-1830
FITZRALPH, RICHARD ABP. OF ARMAGH, d. 1360
GOODMAN, GODFREY, BP. OF GLOUCESTER, 1583-1656
HENRY 8TH, KING OF ENGLAND, 1491-1547
INGLIS, CHARLES, BP. OF NOVA SCOTIA, 1734-1816
JAMES 1ST, KING OF GREAT BRITAIN 1566-1625
JEWEL, JOHN BP. OF SALISBURY, 1522-1571
JOHNSON, SAMUEL, 1696-1772
KEBLE, JOHN, 1792-1866
KEN, THOMAS, BP. OF BATH AND WELLS, 1637-1711
KENNETT, WHITE, BP. OF PETERBOROUGH, 1660-1728
LATIMER, HUGH, BP, OF WORCHESTER, 1485-1555
LAUD, WILLIAM ABP. OF CANTERBURY, 1573-1645
LAW, WILLIAM, 1686-1761
LEE, JAMES PRINCE, BP. OF MANCHESTER, 1804-1869
MANNING, HENRY EDWARD, CARDINAL, 1808-1892
MAURICE, FREDERICK DENISON, 1805-1872
NEWTON, JOHN, 1725-1807
OXFORD MOVEMENT
OXFORD UNIVERSITY
PARKER, MATTHEW, ABP. OF CANTERBURY, 1505-1575
PENANCE
PENANCE–HISTORY
PSALTERS
SANDERSON, ROBERT, BP. OF LINCOLN, 1587-1663
SHARP, JOHN, ABP. OF YORK, 1654-1714
SHERLOCK, THOMAS, BP. OF LONDON, 1678-1761
SMITH, SYDNEY, 1771-1845
SOCIETY FOR PROMOTING THE CHRISTIAN KNOWLEDGE
SOCIETY FOR PROMOTING CHRISTIAN KNOWLEDGE, LONDON
STUBBS, WILLIAM, BP. OF OXFORD, 1825-1901
SWIFT, JONATHAN, 1667-1745
TAYLOR, JEREMY, BP. OF DOWN AND CONNOR, 1613-1667
TAYLOR, JEREMY, BP. OF DOWN AND CONNOR, 1613-1667–BIBLIOGRAPHY
TEMPLE, WILLIAM, ABP. OF CANTERBURY, 1881-1944
TENISON, THOMAS, ABP. OF CANTERBURY, 1636-1715
THOMSON, WILLIAM, ABP. OF YORK, 1819-1890
TILLOTSON, JOHN, ARCHBISHOP OF CANTERBURY, 1630-1694
TRAHERNE, THOMAS, d. 1674
TYNDALE, WILLIAM, d. 1536
VICARS APOSTOLIC
WEEMS, MASON LOCKE, 1759-1825
WILBERFORCE, SAMUEL, BP. OF WINCHESTER, 1805-1873
WILKINS, JOHN, BP. OF CHESTER, 1614-1672

CONFUCIANISM

CONFUCIANISM
CONFUCIUS AND CONFUCIANISM
NEO-CONFUCIANISM
OU-YANG, HSIU, 1007-1072

CONGREGATIONALISM

ABBOTT, LYMAN, 1835-1922
ASHMUN, JEHUDI, 1794-1828
BEECHER, LYMAN, 1775-1863
BROWNISTS
BYLES, MATHER, 1707-1788
COLMAN, BENJAMIN, 1673-1747
CONGREGATIONAL CHRISTIAN CHURCHES
CONGREGATIONAL CHURCHES
CONGREGATIONAL CHURCHES–SERMONS
CONGREGATIONALISM
DODD, CHARLES HAROLD, 1884-
FINNEY, CHARLES GRANDISON, 1792-1875
FLINT, TIMOTHY, 1780-1840
FORSYTH, PETER TAYLOR, 1848-1921
GLADDEN, WASHINGTON, 1836-1918
HAYNES, LEMUEL, 1753-1833
HOOKER, THOMAS, 1586-1647
HOPKINS, SAMUEL, 1721-1803
LAW, ANDREW, 1749-1821
MATHER, COTTON 1663-1728
MATHER, INCREASE, 1639-1723
MORSE, JEDIDIAH, 1761-1826
STILES, EZRA, 1727-1795
TUCKER, WILLIAM JEWETT, 1839-1926
TWICHELL, JOSEPH HOPKINS, 1838-1918
WHEELOCK, ELEAZAR, 1711-1779
WORCESTER, NOAH, 1758-1837

DOCTRINAL THEOLOGY

ABELARD, PETER, 1079-1142
ABELARD, PETER, 1079-1142–FICTION
ABORTION
ABSOLUTE, THE
ANTICHRIST
ANTINOMIANISM
APOLOGETICS
APOLOGETICS–HISTORY
APOLOGETICS–EARLY CHURCH, ca. 30-600
APOLOGETICS–16TH CENTURY
APOLOGETICS–17TH CENTURY
APOLOGETICS–18TH CENTURY
APOLOGETICS–19TH CENTURY
APOLOGETICS–20TH CENTURY
APOLOGETICS, MISSIONARY
APOSTASY
APPARITIONS
ASSURANCE (THEOLOGY)
ATHANASIAN CREED
ATONEMENT
ATONEMENT–BIBLICAL TEACHING
ATONEMENT–HISTORY OF DOCTRINE
AUGUSTINIANS
BELIEF AND DOUBT
BLASPHEMY
BULTMANN, RUDOLF KARL, 1884-
BURIAL
CASUISTRY
CATHOLIC CHURCH–DOCTRINAL AND CONTROVERSIAL WORKS–DEBATES, ETC.
CEMETERIES
CHRONOLOGY, ECCLESIASTICAL
CLOUD OF UNKNOWING
COMMUNION OF SAINTS
COVENANTS
COVENANTS (THEOLOGY)
CREEDS
CREEDS–HISTORY AND CRITICISM
CREMATION
CROSSES
DEATH
DEATH–BIBLIOGRAPHY
DEATH–JUVENILE LITERATURE
DEATH–MEDITATIONS
DEATH OF GOD THEOLOGY
DEVIL
DIALETIC
DIALECTICAL THEOLOGY
DISPENSATIONALISM
DIVES AND LAZARUS
DIVORCE
DOGMA
DOGMA, DEVELOPMENT OF
DONATISTS
DREAMS
ECKHART, JOHANNES, 1260-1327
ELECTION (THEOLOGY)
EMPIRICAL THEOLOGY
EMPIRICISM
END OF THE WORLD
EPIPHANY
ESCHATOLOGY
ESCHATOLOGY–BIBLICAL TEACHING
ESCHATOLOGY, EGYPTIAN
ETERNITY
EXISTENTIALISM
FAITH
FAITH-CURE
FALL OF MAN
FATHERS OF THE CHURCH
FATHERS OF THE CHURCH–BIOBLIOGRAPHY
FATHERS OF THE CHURCH–BIBLIOGRAPHY

FATHERS OF THE CHURCH–DICTIONARIES
FEAR OF GOD
FEMINITY OF GOD
FORGIVENESS OF SIN
FREEDOM (THEOLOGY)
FUNDAMENTALISM
FUTURE LIFE
FUTURE LIFE–BIBLIOGRAPHY
FUTURE PUNISHMENT
GIFTS, SPIRITUAL
GLORY OF GOD
GNOSTICISM
GOD
GOD–ATTRIBUTES
GOD–COMPARATIVE STUDIES
GOD–HISTORY OF DOCTRINES
GOD–JUVENILE LITERATURE
GOD–KNOWABLENESS
GOD–LOVE
GOD–NAME
GOD–OMNIPOTENCE
GOD–PROMISES
GOD–PROOF
GOD–PROOF, EMPIRICAL
GOD–WILL
GOD–WISDOM
GOD–WORSHIP AND LOVE
GOD–WRATH
GOD IN LITERATURE
GRACE (THEOLOGY)
GUILT
HEAVEN
HELL
HOLINESS
HOLY, THE
HOLY CROSS
HOLY SHROUD
HOLY SPIRIT
HOLY WEEK
HUSBAND AND WIFE
HYPOSTATIC UNION
IMMACULATE CONCEPTION
IMAGE OF GOD
IMMANENCE OF GOD
INDIFFERENTISM (RELIGION)
INSPIRATION
INSTALLATION SERVICE (CHURCH OFFICERS)
JESUS CHRIST–ASCENSION
JESUS CHRIST–BIOGRAPHY
JESUS CHRIST–BIOGRAPHY–APOCRYPHAL AND LEGENDARY LITERATURE
JESUS CHRIST–BIOGRAPHY–HISTORY AND CRITICISM
JESUS CHRIST–BIOGRAPHY–JUVENILE LITERATURE
JESUS CHRIST–BIOGRAPHY–SERMONS
JESUS CHRIST–BIOGRAPHY–SOURCES
JESUS CHRIST–BIOGRAPHY–SOURCES, BIBLICAL
JESUS CHRIST–BIOGRAPHY–STUDY
JESUS CHRIST–CHARACTER
JESUS CHRIST–CHILDHOOD
JESUS CHRIST–CHRONOLOGY
JESUS CHRIST–CRUCIFIXION
JESUS CHRIST–DESCENT INTO HELL
JESUS CHRIST–DIVINITY
JESUS CHRIST–DRAMA
JESUS CHRIST–EXALTATION
JESUS CHRIST–EXAMPLE
JESUS CHRIST–FICTION
JESUS CHRIST–FICTION, JUVENILE
JESUS CHRIST–FRIENDS AND ASSOCIATES
JESUS CHRIST–HISTORICITY
JESUS CHRIST–HISTORY OF DOCTRINES
JESUS CHRIST–HUMANITY
JESUS CHRIST–INFLUENCE
JESUS CHRIST–KINGDOM
JESUS CHRIST–MESSIAHSHIP
JESUS CHRIST–MIRACLES
JESUS CHRIST–MIRACLES–JUVENILE LITERATURE
JESUS CHRIST–MISCELLANEA
JESUS CHRIST–NAME
JESUS CHRIST–NATIVITY
JESUS CHRIST–NATIVITY–JUVENILE LITERATURE
JESUS CHRIST–NATURES
JESUS CHRIST–NEW THOUGHT INTERPRETATIONS
JESUS CHRIST–PASSION
JESUS CHRIST–PASSION–DEVOTIONAL LITERATURE
JESUS CHRIST–PASSION–SERMONS
JESUS CHRIST–POETRY
JESUS CHRIST–PRIMACY
JESUS CHRIST–PROPHECIES
JESUS CHRIST–PROPHETIC OFFICE
JESUS CHRIST–RELICS OF THE PASSION
JESUS CHRIST–RESURRECTION
JESUS CHRIST–RESURRECTION–JUVENILE LITERATURE
JESUS CHRIST–RESURRECTION–SERMONS
JESUS CHRIST–SEVEN LAST WORDS
JESUS CHRIST–SIGNIFICANCE
JESUS CHRIST–SPIRITUALISTIC INTERPRETATION
JESUS CHRIST–TEACHING METHODS
JESUS CHRIST–TEMPTATION
JESUS CHRIST–TRIAL
JUSTICE
JUSTIFICATION
JUSTIFICATION–HISTORY OF DOCTRINES
KERYGMA
KINGDOM OF GOD
LAW (THEOLOGY)
LAW AND GOSPEL
LESSING, GOTTHOLD EPHRAIM, 1729-1781
LIFE
LIFE–ORIGIN
LOGOS
LOVE (THEOLOGY)
LOVE (THEOLOGY)–MEDITATIONS
LOVE (THEOLOGY)–SERMONS
MAGI
MAGI–FICTION
MAN–ORIGIN
MAN (THEOLOGY)
MARRIAGE
MARRIAGE–ANNULMENT
MARRIAGE, MIXED
MENTAL HEALING
MESSIAH
MESSIAH–PROPHECIES
METHODIST CHURCH–DOCTRINAL AND CONTROVERSIAL WORKS
MILLENNIUM
MIND AND BODY
MIRACLES
MISSION OF THE CHURCH
MODERNISM
MODERNIST-FUNDAMENTALIST CONTROVERSY
MOEHLER, JOHANN ADAM, 1796-1838
MONARCHIANISM
MONOTHEISM
MORAL EDUCATION
MYSTICAL UNION
NICENE CREED
NIEBUHR, HELMUT RICHARD, 1894-
NOMINALISM
ORIGEN
PACIFISM
PANNENBERG, WOLFHART, 1928-
PARADISE
PARADISE IN LITERATURE AND ART
PAULICIANS
PEACE (THEOLOGY)
PELAGIANISM
PENTECOST
PERFECTION
PERFECTION (PHILOSOPHY)
PERSEVERANCE (THEOLOGY)
PERSONALISM
POWER (THEOLOGY)
PREDESTINATION
PROCESS THEOLOGY
PROMISE (CHRISTIAN THEOLOGY)
PROVIDENCE AND GOVERNMENT OF GOD
PROVIDENCE AND GOVERNMENT OF GOD–SERMONS
PURGATORY
RAHNER, KARL, 1904-
RAPTURE (CHRISTIAN ESCHATOLOGY)
RECONCILIATION
REDEMPTION
REGENERATION (IN RELIGION, FOLK-LORE, ETC.)
REGENERATION (THEOLOGY)
RELIGIOUS THOUGHT
RELIGIOUS THOUGHT–HISTORY
RELIGIOUS THOUGHT–CHINA
RELIGIOUS THOUGHT–FRANCE
RELIGIOUS THOUGHT–GREAT BRITAIN
RELIGIOUS THOUGHT–GREECE
RELIGIOUS THOUGHT–INDIA
RELIGIOUS THOUGHT–RUSSIA
RELIGIOUS THOUGHT–UNITED STATES
REMARRIAGE
REPENTANCE
RESURRECTION
REVELATION
REVELATION–HISTORY OF DOCTRINES
REWARD (THEOLOGY)
RIGHT AND WRONG
SACRAMENTS–HISTORY OF DOCTRINES
SACRED MEALS
SALVATION
SALVATION–HISTORY OF DOCTRINES
SALVATION OUTSIDE THE CATHOLIC CHURCH
SANCTIFICATION
SCHAFF, PHILIP, 1819-1893
SCHISM
SCHUTZ, ROGER
SECOND ADVENT
SELF-LOVE (THEOLOGY)
SELF-REALIZATION
SERMON ON THE MOUNT
SERVETUS, MICHAEL, 1509-1553
SEX (THEOLOGY)
SIMPLICITY
SIN
SIN, MORTAL
SIN, ORIGINAL
SINS
SOCINIANISM
SON OF MAN
SOUL
SPIRITUAL LIFE–HISTORY OF DOCTRINES
SPRENGER, JACOB, 1436-1495
STRAUSS, DAVID FRIEDRICH, 1808-1874
SUICIDE
SUPERNATURAL (THEOLOGY)
TEILHARD DE CHARDIN, PIERRE, 1881-1955
TEMPTATION
THEISM
THEOLOGIANS
THEOLOGICAL LIBRARIES
THEOLOGY
THEOLOGY–BIBLIOGRAPHY
THEOLOGY–BIO-BIBLIOGRAPHY
THEOLOGY–COLLECTED WORKS
THEOLOGY–COLLECTED WORKS–EARLY CHURCH, ca. 30-600
THEOLOGY–COLLECTED WORKS–MIDDLE AGES, 600-1500
THEOLOGY–COLLECTED WORKS–16TH CENTURY
THEOLOGY–COLLECTED WORKS–17TH CENTURY
THEOLOGY–COLLECTED WORKS–18TH CENTURY
THEOLOGY–COLLECTED WORKS–19TH CENTURY
THEOLOGY–COLLECTED WORKS–20TH CENTURY
THEOLOGY–COLLECTIONS
THEOLOGY–DICTIONARIES
THEOLOGY–METHODOLOGY
THEOLOGY–MISCELLANEA
THEOLOGY–STUDY AND TEACHING
THEOLOGY–TERMINOLOGY
THEOLOGY–EARLY CHURCH, ca. 30-600
THEOLOGY–MIDDLE AGES, 600-1500
THEOLOGY–16TH CENTURY
THEOLOGY–17TH CENTURY
THEOLOGY–18TH CENTURY
THEOLOGY–19TH CENTURY
THEOLOGY–20TH CENTURY
THEOLOGY, DOCTRINAL
THEOLOGY, DOCTRINAL–ADDRESSES, ESSAYS, LECTURES
THEOLOGY, DOCTRINAL–HISTORY
THEOLOGY, DOCTRINAL–HISTORY–EARLY CHURCH, ca. 30-600
THEOLOGY, DOCTRINAL–HISTORY–MIDDLE AGES, 600-1500
THEOLOGY, DOCTRINAL–HISTORY–MODERN PERIOD, 1500-
THEOLOGY, DOCTRINAL–HISTORY–16TH CENTURY
THEOLOGY, DOCTRINAL–HISTORY–17TH CENTURY
THEOLOGY, DOCTRINAL–HISTORY–18TH CENTURY
THEOLOGY, DOCTRINAL–HISTORY–19TH CENTURY
THEOLOGY, DOCTRINAL–HISTORY–20TH CENTURY
THEOLOGY, DOCTRINAL–HISTORY–GERMANY
THEOLOGY, DOCTRINAL–HISTORY–GREAT BRITAIN
THEOLOGY, DOCTRINAL–HISTORY–UNITED STATES
THEOLOGY, DOCTRINAL–OUTLINES, SYLLABI, ETC.
THEOLOGY, DOCTRINAL–POPULAR WORKS
THEOLOGY, PURITAN
THOMAS AQUINAS, SAINT, 1225?-1274
THOMISTS
TRADITION (THEOLOGY)
TRANSCENDENCE OF GOD
TRINITY
TRUTH
TYPOLOGY (THEOLOGY)
VIRGIN BIRTH
VISIONS
WILL

EASTERN CHURCHES–ARMENIAN, COPTIC, ORTHODOX EASTERN CHURCH, ETC.

APHRAATES, THE PERSIAN SAGE, fl. 337-345
ARMENIAN CHURCH
BASIL, SAINT, 329-379
CATHOLIC CHURCH–RELATIONS–ORTHODOX EASTERN CHURCH
CHRISTIAN LIFE–ORTHODOX EASTERN AUTHORS
CHRISTIAN UNION–ORTHODOX EASTERN CHURCH
CHRISTIANITY AND OTHER RELIGIONS–GREEK
CHURCH MUSIC–ORTHODOX EASTERN CHURCH
COPTIC CHURCH
COPTIC LITERATURE–TRANSLATIONS
COPTIC PHILOLOGY
COPTS
DEMOTIC INSCRIPTIONS
EASTERN CHURCHES
EASTERN CHURCHES–LITURGY AND RITUAL
ETHIOPIC CHURCH
GREGORY, SAINT, BP. OF NYSSA, 322-398
GREGORY OF NAZIANZENUS, PATRIARCH OF CONSTANTINOPLE
JACOBITE CHURCH
LORD'S SUPPER–ORTHODOX EASTERN CHURCH
LOUKARKIS, KYRILLOS, PATRIARCH OF CONSTANTINOPLE, 1572-1638
MACARIUS 3RD, PATRIARCH OF ANTIOCH, fl. 1636-1666
MARRIAGE–ORTHODOX EASTERN CHURCH
METHODIUS, SAINT, ABP. OF MORAVIA, d. 885
MONASTICISM AND RELIGIOUS ORDERS, ORTHODOX EASTERN
MYSTICISM–ORTHODOX EASTERN CHURCH
NESTORIAN CHURCH
NESTORIAN TABLET OF SIAN-FA
NESTORIANS
NESTORIUS, PATRIARCH OF CONSTANTINOPLE, fl. 428
NEUMANN, JOHN NEPOMUCENE, BP. 1811-1860
NICEPHORUS, SAINT, PATRIARCH OF CONSTANTINOPLE
NICHOLAS, SAINT, BP. OF MYRA
ORTHODOX EASTERN CHURCH
ORTHODOX EASTERN CHURCH–HISTORY
ORTHODOX EASTERN CHURCH–HYMNS
ORTHODOX EASTERN CHURCH–LITURGY AND RITUAL
ORTHODOX EASTERN CHURCH–MISSIONS
ORTHODOX EASTERN CHURCH–PRAYER-BOOKS AND DEVOTIONS
ORTHODOX EASTERN CHURCH–RELATIONS–ANGLICAN COMMUNION
ORTHODOX EASTERN CHURCH–RELATIONS–CATHOLIC CHURCH
ORTHODOX EASTERN CHURCH–RELATIONS–PROTESTANT CHURCHES
ORTHODOX EASTERN CHURCH–SERMONS
ORTHODOX EASTERN CHURCH, GREEK
ORTHODOX EASTERN CHURCH, RUSSIAN
ORTHODOX EASTERN CHURCH, RUSSIAN–HISTORY
ORTHODOX EASTERN CHURCH, SERBIAN
PALAMAS, GREGORIUS, ABP. OF THESSALONICA, 1296-1359
PHILOSOPHY, BYZANTINE
PHOTIUS, d. 892
RASKOLNIKS
RASPUTIN, GRIGORII EFIMOVICH, 1871-1916
SCHISM–EASTERN AND WESTERN CHURCH
SINAI, SAINT CATHARINE (BASILIAN MONASTERY)
SPIRITUAL LIFE–ORTHODOX EASTERN AUTHORS
THEODORUS STUDITA, SAINT, 759-826
YABHALAHA 3RD, PATRIARCH OF THE NESTORIANS, 1244-1317

ECCLESIASTICAL THEOLOGY

ABSOLUTION
ANTI-CLERICALISM
APOSTOLIC SUCCESSION
BATH AND WELLS (DIOCESE)
BISHOPS
CATECHETICAL SERMONS
CATECHETICS
CATECHISMS
CATECHISMS–BIBLIOGRAPHY
CHANTRIES
CHURCH
CHURCH–ADDRESSES, ESSAYS, LECTURES
CHURCH–AUTHORITY
CHURCH–BIBLICAL TEACHING
CHURCH–FOUNDATION

CHURCH–HISTORY OF DOCTRINES
CHURCH–INFALLIBILITY
CHURCH–JUVENILE LITERATURE
CHURCH–PUBLIC OPINION
CHURCH–STUDY AND TEACHING
CHURCH–TEACHING OFFICE
CHURCH–UNITY
CHURCH AND COLLEGE
CHURCH AND EDUCATION
CHURCH AND EDUCATION IN GREAT BRITAIN
CHURCH AND INTERNATIONAL ORGANIZATION
CHURCH AND LABOR
CHURCH AND RACE RELATIONS
CHURCH AND SOCIAL PROBLEMS
CHURCH AND SOCIAL PROBLEMS–BAPTISTS
CHURCH AND SOCIAL PROBLEMS–CATHOLIC CHURCH
CHURCH AND SOCIAL PROBLEMS–CHURCH OF ENGLAND
CHURCH AND SOCIAL PROBLEMS–LUTHERAN CHURCH
CHURCH AND SOCIAL PROBLEMS–MENNONITES
CHURCH AND SOCIAL PROBLEMS–METHODIST CHURCH
CHURCH AND SOCIAL PROBLEMS–STUDY AND TEACHING
CHURCH AND SOCIAL PROBLEMS–GERMANY
CHURCH AND SOCIAL PROBLEMS–GREAT BRITAIN
CHURCH AND SOCIAL PROBLEMS–LATIN AMERICA
CHURCH AND SOCIAL PROBLEMS–UNITED STATES
CHURCH AND STATE
CHIRCH AND STATE–BIBLIOGRAPHY
CHURCH AND STATE–CATHOLIC CHURCH
CHURCH AND STATE–HISTORY
CHURCH AND STATE IN AFRICA
CHURCH AND STATE IN AUSTRALIA
CHURCH AND STATE IN BAVARIA
CHURCH AND STATE IN CANADA
CHURCH AND STATE IN EUROPE
CHURCH AND STATE IN FRANCE
CHURCH AND STATE IN GERMANY
CHURCH AND STATE IN GREAT BRITAIN
CHURCH AND STATE IN GREECE
CHURCH AND STATE IN GRENADA
CHURCH AND STATE IN GUATEMALA
CHURCH AND STATE IN IRELAND
CHURCH AND STATE IN ITALY
CHURCH AND STATE IN LATIN AMERICA
CHURCH AND STATE IN MALTA
CHURCH AND STATE IN MEXICO
CHURCH AND STATE IN NICARAGUA
CHURCH AND STATE IN NORWAY
CHURCH AND STATE IN ROME
CHURCH AND STATE IN RUSSIA
CHURCH AND STATE IN SWITZERLAND
CHURCH AND STATE IN THE HOLY ROMAN EMPIRE
CHURCH AND STATE IN THE UNITED STATES
CHURCH AND THE WORLD
CHURCH ANNIVERSARIES
CHURCH ATTENDANCE
CHURCH BULLETINS
CHURCH CALENDAR
CHURCH CAMPS
CHURCH CHARITIES
CHURCH COLLEGES
CHURCH COMMITTEES
CHURCH CORRESPONDENCE
CHURCH DECORATION AND ORNAMENT
CHURCH DISCIPLINE
CHURCH ENTERTAINMENTS
CHURCH FINANCE
CHURCH FINANCE–EARLY CHURCH, ca. 30-600
CHURCH FURNITURE
CHURCH GROUP WORK
CHURCH GROWTH
CHURCH LANDS
CHURCH MANAGEMENT
CHURCH MEETINGS
CHURCH MEMBERSHIP
CHURCH OFFICERS
CHURCH ORDERS, ANCIENT
CHURCH PLATE
CHURCH POLITY
CHURCH PROPERTY
CHURCH PROPERTY–MAINTENANCE AND REPAIR
CHURCH PROPERTY–TAXATION
CHURCH RENEWAL
CHURCH RENEWAL–CATHOLIC CHURCH
CHURCH SCHOOLS
CHURCH SECRETARIES
CHURCH SLAVIC LANGUAGE
CHURCH STATISTICS
CHURCH USHERS
CHURCH VESTMENTS
CHURCH WORK WITH DIVORCED PEOPLE
CITY CHURCHES
CITY CLERGY
CLERGY
CLERGY–LEGAL STATUS, LAWS, ETC.
CLERGY–MALPRACTICE
CLERGY–GREAT BRITAIN
CLERGY–IRAN
CLERGY–RUSSIA
CONFESSION
CONFESSION–JUVENILE LITERATURE
DEACONESSES
DEACONS
EX-NUNS
DIDACHE
FIRST COMMUNION
FLOWER ARRANGEMENT IN CHURCHES
GAMES
GOSPEL MUSIC
IMPEDIMENTS TO MARRIAGE (CANON LAW)
INFANT BAPTISM
INTERNATIONAL SUNDAY-SCHOOL LESSONS
JESUS CHRIST–MYSTICAL BODY
JOURNALISM, RELIGIOUS
LAY READER
LECTIONAIRIES
LIBERATION THEOLOGY
LIBERTY OF CONSCIENCE
LIBERTY OF SPEECH IN THE CHURCH
LITANIES
LORD'S SUPPER
LORD'S SUPPER–FIRST COMMUNION
LORD'S SUPPER–MEDITATIONS
MARRIAGE–ANNULMENT (CANON LAW)
MARRIAGE (CANON LAW)
MAXIMUS, SAINT, BP. OF TURIN, D. ca. 420
METHODIST CHURCH–CLERGY–CORRESPONDENCE, REMISCENCES, ETC.
MINISTERIAL RESPONSIBILITY
MONASTICISM AND RELIGIOUS ORDERS–DICTIONARIES
MONASTICISM AND RELIGIOUS ORDERS–PALESTINE
NEWSPAPERS
OATHS
OBEDIENCE
ORDINATION
ORDINATION OF WOMEN
PENANCE
PENANCE–HISTORY
PENITENTIALS
PRIVILEGES AND IMMUNITIES, ECCLESIASTICAL
PUBLIC RELATIONS–CHURCHES
RELIGION AND POLITICS
RUPERT OF DEUTZ, 1070-1135
SEMINARIANS
SERMON ON THE MOUNT–SERMONS
SERMONS
SERMONS–ILLUSTRATIONS
SERMONS–OUTLINES
SERMONS–TRANSLATIONS FROM FOREIGN LANGUAGES
SERMONS, AMERICAN
SERMONS, AMERICAN (SELECTIONS: EXTRACTS, ETC.)
SERMONS, ANGLO-SAXON
SERMONS, ENGLISH
SERMONS, ENGLISH–HISTORY AND CRITICISM
SERMONS, FRENCH
SERMONS, GERMAN
SERMONS, GREEK
SERMONS, JEWISH
SERMONS, LATIN
SINGLE PEOPLE
SINGLE WOMEN
SISTERHOODS
STEWARDSHIP, CHRISTIAN
STEWARDSHIP, CHRISTIAN–SERMONS
SUBURBAN CHURCHES
SUNDAY-SCHOOL SUPERINTENDENTS
SUNDAY-SCHOOLS
SUNDAY-SCHOOLS–EXERCISES, RECITATIONS, ETC.
SUNDAY-SCHOOLS–HISTORY
SUNDAY-SCHOOLS–HYMNS
SUNDAY-SCHOOLS–QUESTION-BOOKS
TAXATION, EXEMPTION FROM
TELEVISION IN RELIGION
UNCTION
UNMARRIED MOTHERS
VISITATIONS (CHURCH WORK)
VISITATIONS, ECCLESIASTICAL
WAR AND MORALS
WEEK-DAY CHURCH SCHOOLS
WEEK-DAY CHURCH SCHOOLS–TEXT-BOOKS
WOMEN
WOMEN–BIOGRAPHY
WOMEN–PRAYER-BOOKS AND DEVOTIONS
WOMEN–RELIGIOUS LIFE
WOMEN (IN RELIGION, FOLKLORE, ETC.)
WOMEN AND RELIGION
WOMEN CLERGY
WOMEN IN CHRISTIANITY
WOMEN IN CHURCH WORK
WOMEN IN RELIGION
WULFSTAN 2ND, ABP., OF YORK d. 1203
YOUNG MEN'S CHRISTIAN ASSOCIATIONS
YOUNG WOMEN'S CHRISTIAN ASSOCIATIONS

FRIENDS–SOCIETY OF FRIENDS–QUAKERS

COLLINS, ISAAC
EVANS, WILLIAM BACON
FOX, GEORGE, 1624-1691
FRIENDS, SOCIETY OF
FRIENDS, SOCIETY OF–AMERICAN FRIENDS SERVICE COMMITTEE
FRIENDS, SOCIETY OF–BIBLIOGRAPHY
FRIENDS, SOCIETY OF–BIOGRAPHY
FRIENDS, SOCIETY OF–DOCTRINAL AND CONTROVERSIAL WORKS
FRIENDS, SOCIETY OF–EDUCATION
FRIENDS, SOCIETY OF–FICTION, JUVENILE
FRIENDS, SOCIETY OF–HISTORY
FRIENDS, SOCIETY OF–SERMONS
FRIENDS, SOCIETY OF–GREAT BRITAIN
HICKS, EDWARD, 1780-1849
JONES, RUFUS MATTHEW, 1863-1948
JONES, THOMAS ELSA, 1888-
LILBURNE, JOHN, 1614?-1657
MARRIAGE–RELIGIOUS ASPECTS–SOCIETY OF FRIENDS
PENN, WILLIAM, 1644-1718
STEPHEN, CAROLINE EMELIA, 1834-1909
STORY, THOMAS, 1662-1742
WILKINSON, THOMAS, 1751-1836
WOOLMAN, JOHN, 1720-1772

HINDUISM–BRAHMANISM

ADVAITA
AGNI (HINDU DIETY)
AJIVIKAS
ART, HINDU
ASTRONOMY, HINDU
AVATARS
BHAGAVADGITA
BHAGAVATAS
BHAKTI
BRAHMANANDA, SWAMI, 1863-1922
BRAHMANAS
BRAHMANISM
CHANTS (HINDU)
CHRISTIANITY AND OTHER RELIGIONS–HINDUISM
CIVILIZATION, HINDU
COOKERY, YOGA
CULTUS, HINDU
DHARMA
GOD (HINDUISM)
GOVINDA SIMBA, 10TH GURU OF THE SIKHS, 1666-1708
HARE KRISHNA SECT
HINDI POETRY
HINDU ETHICS
HINDU HYMNS
HINDU LAW
HINDU LITERATURE
HINDU SECTS
HINDUISM
HINDUISM–ADDRESSES, ESSAYS, AND LECTURES
HINDUISM–DICTIONARIES
HINDUISM–RELATIONS–CHRISTIANITY
HINDUISM–RELATIONS–ISLAM
HINDUISM–SACRED BOOKS (SELECTIONS: EXTRACTS, ETC.)
HINDUS
HUSAIN, MAGVOOL FIDA
KARMA
KRISHNA
KRISHNA IN ART, LITERATURE, ETC.
MAHABHARATA
MAHABHARATA, BHAGAVADGITA
MAHARSHI, SRI RAMANA
MAHASHAY, NAG
MANDALA
MANU
MEDICINE, AYURVEDIC
MEDICINE, HINDU
MEHER BABA, 1894-1969
MYSTICISM–HINDUISM
MYTHOLOGY, HINDU
NANAK, 1ST GURU OF THE SIKHS, 1469-1538
NIRVANA
NIVEDITA, SISTER
PARAMANANDA, SWAMI, 1883-1940
PHILOSOPHY, HINDU
PHILOSOPHY, INDIC
PRAJNAPARAMITAS
PRAYER
PREMANANDA, SWAMI
PURANAS
PUSHAN (HINDU DIETY)
RADHAKRISHNAN, SARVEPALI, SIR, 1888-
RAMAKRISHNA, 1836-1886
RAMAKRISHNANDA, SWAMI
RAMANUJA
RAMAYANA
SAMADHI
SANKARACARYA
SANSKRIT LITERATURE
SANSKRIT POETRY–HISTORY AND CRITICISM
SANSKRIT POETRY–TRANSLATIONS INTO ENGLISH
SARADA DEVI, 1853-1920
SARASWATI, RAMABAI, PANDITA
SHAKTISM
SIKH HYMNS
SIKH WARS
SIKHISM
SIKHS
SINGH, KIRPAL
SIVA
SIVAISM
SOCIOLOGY, HINDU
SOMA
SONGS, INDIC
SUTRAS
SYRIAN CHURCH
TANTRAS
TURIYANADA, SWAMI, 1863-1922
UPANISHADS
VAISHNAVISM
VEDANTA
VEDAS
VEDAS RIGVEDA
VEDIC LITERATURE
VEGETARIANISM–RELIGIOUS ASPECTS
VIMALAKIRTINIRDESA–SUTRA
VISHNU
VIVEKANANDA, SWAMI, 1863-1902
WOMEN IN HINDUISM
YOGA
YOGA, HATHA
YOGA, RAJA
YOGANANDA, PARAMAHANSA, 1893-1952
YOGIS

ISLAM

ARABS IN FOREIGN COUNTRIES
ART, ISLAMIC
ASSASSINS (ISMAILITES)
AVERROES, 1126-1198
BLACK MUSLIMS
CALENDAR, ISLAMIC
CALIPHATE
CHRISTIANITY AND OTHER RELIGIONS–ISLAM
CIVILIZATION, ISLAMIC
DRUSES
GOD (ISLAM)
HADITH
HINDUISM–RELATIONS–ISLAM
IBN AL-ARABI, 1165-1240
INSCRIPTIONS, ISLAMIC
INTERNATIONAL LAW (ISLAMIC LAW)
ISLAM
ISLAM–BIBLIOGRAPHY
ISLAM–HISTORIOGRAPHY
ISLAM–HISTORY
ISLAM–JUVENILE LITERATURE
ISLAM–RELATIONS
ISLAM–RELATIONS–CHRISTIANITY
ISLAM–RELATIONS–JUDAISM
ISLAM–AFRICA
ISLAM–ASIA
ISLAM–EGYPT
ISLAM–INDIA
ISLAM–INDONESIA
ISLAM–IRAN
ISLAM–PAKISTAN
ISLAM–SAUDI ARABIA
ISLAM–SYRIA
ISLAM–TURKEY
ISLAM AND ECONOMICS
ISLAM AND SCIENCE
ISLAM AND STATE
ISLAMIC COUNTRIES
ISLAMIC COUNTRIES–POLITICS
ISLAMIC EMPIRE–HISTORY
ISLAMIC ETHICS
ISLAMIC LAW
ISLAMIC LAW–AFRICA
ISLAMIC LEARNING AND SCHOLARSHIP
ISLAMIC LITERATURE–HISTORY AND CRITICISM
ISLAMIC SECTS

ISLAMIC SECTS–MISSIONS
ISLAMIC THEOLOGY
ISMAILITES
JAMAL AL-DIN, AL-HUSAINI, AL-AFGHANI, HEY, 1839-1897
JESUS CHRIST–ISLAMIC INTERPRETATIONS
JIHAD
KAIRWAN MOSQUE OF SIDI OKBA
KORAN
MAHDI
MARRIAGE–ISLAM
MARRIAGE (ISLAMIC LAW)
MECCA
MISSIONS TO MUSLIMS
MOHAMMED, THE PROPHET, 570-632
MORISCOS
MOSQUES
MOTAZILITES
MUDEJARES
MUHAMMAD 'ABDUH, 1848-1905
MUHAMMAD RASHID RIDA
MUSLIMS
MUSLIMS IN AFRICA
MUSLIMS IN ASIA
MUSLIMS IN CHINA
MUSLIMS IN INDIA
MUSLIMS IN SOUTH ASIA
MUSLIMS IN THE UNITED STATES
MYSTICISM–ISLAM
PALESTINE
PALESTINE–ANTIQUITIES
PALESTINE–DESCRIPTION AND TRAVEL
PALESTINE–HISTORICAL GEOGRAPHY
PALESTINE–HISTORICAL GEOGRAPHY–MAPS
PALESTINE–HISTORY
PALESTINE–JUVENILE LITERATURE
PALESTINE–RELIGION
PALESTINE–SOCIAL LIFE AND CUSTOMS
PANISLAMISM
PARADISE
PARADISE IN LITERATURE AND ART
PERSIAN LITERATURE–TRANSLATIONS INTO ENGLISH
PHILOSOPHY, ISLAMIC
PRAYER
RELIGIOUS LIFE (ISLAM)
SAUDI ARABIA
SHIITES
SOCIOLOGY, ISLAMIC
SUFISM
WOMEN, MUSLIM

JUDAISM

ABOTH–COMMENTARIES
ABRAHAM BEN DAVID, OF POSQUIERES, 1125-1198
ADRET, SOLOMON BEN ABRAHAM
AGGADA
AKIBA BEN JOSEPH, 50-132
AMERICAN JEWISH JOINT DISTRIBUTION COMMITTEE
AMERICAN LITERATURE–JEWISH AUTHORS
AMORAIM
ANGELS (JUDAISM)
ANGLO-ISRAELISM
ANTISEMITISM
ARK OF THE COVENANT
ATONEMENT (JUDAISM)
BAR MITZVAH
BARRIOS, MIGUEL dE, 1635-1701
BENDERLEY, SAMSON
BEN-YEHUDA, ELIEZER, 1858-1922
CABALA
CAIRO GENIZAH
CALENDAR, JEWISH
CATHOLIC CHURCH–RELATIONS–JUDAISM
CENTRAL JEWISH INSTITUTE, NEW YORK
CHANTS (JEWISH)
CHRISTIANITY AND ANTISEMITISM
CHRISTIANITY AND OTHER RELIGIONS–JUDAISM
CHRONOLOGY, JEWISH
CIVILIZATION, MODERN–JEWISH INFLUENCE
COLLECTIVE SETTLEMENTS–ISRAEL
COLONIA BARON DE HIRSCH, ARGENTINE REPUBLIC
COMMANDMENTS (JUDAISM)
CONSERVATIVE JUDAISM
CONVERTS FROM JUDAISM
COOKERY, JEWISH
CULTUS, JEWISH
CULTUS, SEMITIC
DANCING–JEWS
DEAD SEA SCROLLS
DIVORCE (JEWISH LAW)
DREYFUS, ALFRED, 1859-1935
DURAN, SIMON BEN ZEMAH, 1361-1444
ELECTION (THEOLOGY)
ELISHA BEN ABUYAH, 2ND CENTURY–FICTION
ESCHATOLOGY, JEWISH
ESSENES
ETHICS, JEWISH
ETHICS, JEWISH–JUVENILE LITERATURE
FALASHAS
FASTS AND FEASTS–JUDAISM
FASTS AND FEASTS–JUDAISM–JUVENILE LITERATURE
FOLK-LORE, JEWISH
GENIZAH
GIDEON, JUDGE OF ISRAEL
GOD (JUDAISM)
HANUKKAH (FEAST OF LIGHTS)
HANUKKAH (FEAST OF LIGHTS)–JUVENILE LITERATURE
HASIDISM
HEBREW IMPRINTS
HEBREW LANGUAGE
HEBREW LANGUAGE–COMPOSITION AND EXERCISES
HEBREW LANGUAGE–DICTIONARIES
HEBREW LANGUAGE–DICTIONARIES–ENGLISH
HEBREW LANGUAGE–GRAMMAR
HEBREW LANGUAGE–PROGRAMMED INSTRUCTION
HEBREW LANGUAGE–READERS
HEBREW LANGUAGE–SELF-INSTRUCTION
HEBREW LANGUAGE–SYNTAX
HEBREW LANGUAGE–TEXTBOOKS FOR CHILDREN
HEBREW LITERATURE
HEBREW LITERATURE–BIBLIOGRAPHY
HEBREW LITERATURE–HISTORY AND CRITICISM
HEBREW LITERATURE–TRANSLATIONS INTO ENGLISH
HEBREW LITERATURE, MODERN–BIBLIOGRAPHY
HEBREW PHILOLOGY
HEBREW POETRY
HEBREW POETRY (COLLECTIONS)
HEBREW POETRY–HISTORY AND CRITICISM
HEBREW POETRY–TRANSLATIONS INTO ENGLISH
HERMENEUTICS
HEROD 1ST, THE GREAT, KING OF JUDEA, d. 4 B.C.–DRAMA
HIGH HOLY DAYS
HILLEL, THE ELDER, d. ca. 10
HIRSCH, EMIL GUSTAV, 1851-1923
HOLOCAUST, JEWISH (1939-1945)
HOLOCAUST, JEWISH (1939-1945)–ERRORS, INVENTIONS, ETC.
HOLOCAUST, JEWISH (1939-1945)–PERSONAL NARRATIVES
HOLOCAUST SURVIVORS
HONI HA-MEAGGEL, 1ST CENTURY B.C.
HYMNS, HEBREW
HYMNS, YIDDISH
ISLAM–RELATIONS–JUDAISM
ISRAEL
ISRAEL–DESCRIPTION AND TRAVEL
ISRAEL–HISTORY
ISRAEL–JUVENILE LITERATURE
ISRAEL–RELIGION
ISRAEL AND THE DIASPORA
JERUSALEM–DESCRIPTION–GUIDEBOOKS
JESUS CHRIST–JEWISH INTERPRETATIONS
JEWISH-ARAB RELATIONS
JEWISH CHILDREN
JEWISH CHRISTIANS
JEWISH DEVOTIONAL LITERATURE
JEWISH LAW
JEWISH LEARNING AND SCHOLARSHIP
JEWISH LEARNING AND SCHOLARSHIP–JUVENILE LITERATURE
JEWISH LITERATURE (COLLECTIONS)
JEWISH LITERATURE–BIBLIOGRAPHY
JEWISH LITERATURE–HISTORY AND CRITICISM
JEWISH POETRY
JEWISH QUESTION
JEWISH RELIGIOUS EDUCATION
JEWISH SECTS
JEWISH THEOLOGY
JEWISH WAY OF LIFE
JEWISH WIT AND HUMOR
JEWS
JEWS–ADDRESSES, ESSAYS, LECTURES
JEWS–ANTIQUITIES
JEWS–BIBLIOGRAPHY
JEWS–BIOGRAPHY
JEWS–CHARITIES
JEWS–CIVILIZATION
JEWS–DIASPORA
JEWS–DICTIONARIES AND ENCYCLOPEDIAS
JEWS–DIETARY LAWS
JEWS–EDUCATION
JEWS–ELECTION, DOCTRINE OF
JEWS–HISTORY
JEWS–HISTORY–CHRONOLOGY
JEWS–HISTORY–JUVENILE LITERATURE
JEWS–HISTORY–PHILOSOPHY
JEWS–HISTORY–TO 586 B.C.
JEWS–HISTORY–TO 70 A.D.
JEWS–HISTORY–586 B.C.-70 A.D.
JEWS–HISTORY–70-1789
JEWS–HISTORY–1789
JEWS–INTELLECTUAL LIFE
JEWS–LITURGY AND RITUAL
JEWS–MIGRATIONS
JEWS–MISCELLANEA
JEWS–PERSECUTIONS
JEWS–POLITICAL AND SOCIAL CONDITIONS
JEWS–PRAYER-BOOKS AND DEVOTIONS
JEWS–RESTORATION
JEWS–RITES AND CEREMONIES
JEWS–SOCIAL LIFE AND CUSTOMS
JEWS, YEMENITE
JEWS IN AFRICA
JEWS IN ARABIA
JEWS IN AUSTRIA
JEWS IN BABYLONIA
JEWS IN CANADA
JEWS IN CHINA
JEWS IN COMMUNIST COUNTRIES
JEWS IN EGYPT
JEWS IN EUROPE
JEWS IN FRANCE
JEWS IN GERMANY
JEWS IN GREAT BRITAIN
JEWS IN HUNGARY
JEWS IN IRAQ
JEWS IN ITALY
JEWS IN LATIN AMERICA
JEWS IN LITERATURE
JEWS IN LITHUANIA
JEWS IN PALESTINE
JEWS IN POLAND
JEWS IN RUMANIA
JEWS IN RUSSIA
JEWS IN SPAIN
JEWS IN THE ISLAMIC EMPIRE
JEWS IN THE LEVANT
JEWS IN THE NETHERLANDS
JEWS IN SCANDINAVIA
JEWS IN THE UNITED STATES
JEWS IN THE UNITED STATES - BIBLIOGRAPHY
JEWS IN THE UNITED STATES–BIOGRAPHY
JEWS IN THE UNITED STATES–FICTION
JEWS IN THE UNITED STATES–HISTORY
JEWS IN THE UNITED STATES–HISTORY–SOURCES
JEWS IN THE UNITED STATES–JUVENILE LITERATURE
JEWS IN THE UNITED STATES–SOCIAL LIFE AND CUSTOMS
JOSEPHUS FLAVIUS
JUDAH, HA-LEVI, 12TH CENTURY
JUDAISM
JUDAISM–ADDRESSES, ESSAYS, LECTURES
JUDAISM–APOLOGETIC WORKS
JUDAISM–BIBLIOGRAPHY
JUDAISM–COLLECTIONS
JUDAISM–DICTIONARIES
JUDAISM–HISTORY
JUDAISM–HISTORY–SOURCES
JUDAISM–JUVENILE LITERATURE
JUDAISM–QUOTATIONS, MAXIMS, ETC.
JUDAISM–RELATIONS
JUDAISM–RELATIONS–CHRISTIANITY
JUDAISM–RELATIONS–ISLAM
JUDAISM–WORKS TO 1900
JUDAISM AND SOCIAL PROBLEMS
JUDAS MACCABEUS, d. 160 B.C.
KAHANE, MEIR, 1932-
KARAITES
LEGENDS, JEWISH
MARRIAGE–JEWS
MARRIAGE–RELIGIOUS ASPECTS–JUDAISM
MASORAH
MEIR OF ROTHENBURG, RABBI
MENDELSSOHN, MOSES, 1729-1786
MENORAH
MERIT (JEWISH THEOLOGY)
MESSIAH
MESSIAH–PROPHECIES
MIDRASH
MIDRASH–TRANSLATIONS INTO ENGLISH
MISHNAH
MISSIONS TO JEWS
MOSES BEN MAIMON, 1135-1204
MOSKOWITZ, IRA
MUSIC, JEWISH
MYSTICISM–JUDAISM
MYTHOLOGY, JEWISH
MYTHOLOGY, SEMITIC
NATIONALISM–JEWS
NEGRO JEWISH RELATIONS
ORTHODOX JUDAISM
PALESTINE
PALESTINE–ANTIQUITIES
PALESTINE–DESCRIPTION AND TRAVEL
PALESTINE–HISTORICAL GEOGRAPHY
PALESTINE–HISTORICAL GEOGRAPHY–MAPS
PALESTINE–HISTORY
PALESTINE–JUVENILE LITERATURE
PALESTINE–RELIGION
PALESTINE–SOCIAL LIFE AND CUSTOMS
PASSOVER
PERSECUTION
PHARISEES
PHILO JUDAEUS
PHILOSOPHY, JEWISH
PIETY
PRAYER
PRAYER (JUDAISM)
PRIESTS, JEWISH
PRIESTS, JEWISH–VESTMENTS
PROSELYTES AND PROSELYTING, JEWISH
PURIM (FEAST OF ESTHER)
QUMRAN COMMUNITY
RABBINICAL LITERATURE
RABBINICAL LITERATURE–HISTORY AND CRITICISM
RABBIS
RABINOWITZ, SHALOM, 1859-1916
RECONSTRUCTIONIST JUDAISM
REDEMPTION
REFORM JUDAISM
REFUGEES, JEWISH
RESPONSA
REVEL, BERNARD, 1885-1940
ROSH HA-SHANAH
SEPHARDIM
SHAMASH
SHAVU'OTH (FEAST OF WEEKS)
SIMHAT TORAH
SOCIOLOGY, JEWISH
SOLOMON BEN ISAAC, CALLED RASHI, 1040-1105
SONGS, HASIDIC
SONGS, JEWISH
SUKKOTH
SYNAGOGUE ARCHITECTURE
SYNAGOGUE MUSIC
SYNAGOGUE MUSIC–HISTORY AND CRITICISM
SYNAGOGUES
TABERNACLE
TALES, HEBREW
TALES, JEWISH
TALMUD
TANNAIM
TORAH SCROLLS
TRADITION (JUDAISM)
WIESEL, ELIE, 1928-
WISE, ISAAC MAYER, 1819-1900
WOMEN, JEWISH
WORLD WAR, 1939-1945–JEWS
YESHIVA
YIDDISH LITERATURE
YIDDISH LITERATURE–HISTORY AND CRITICISM
YOM KIPPUR
YOUTH, JEWISH
ZEALOTS (JEWISH PARTY)
ZIONISM
ZIONISTS
ZOHAR

LUTHERAN CHURCHES

AUGSBURG CONFESSION
BOEHME, JAKOB, 1575-1624
CHRISTIAN LIFE–LUTHERAN AUTHORS
CHURCH AND SOCIAL PROBLEMS–LUTHERAN CHURCH
CHURCH MUSIC–LUTHERAN CHURCH
CONFIRMATION–LUTHERAN CHURCH
EVANGELICAL LUTHERAN CHURCH
EVANGELICAL LUTHERAN SYNOD OF MISSOURI, OHIO, AND OTHER STATES
HAUGE, HANS NIELSEN, 1771-1824
LUTHER, MARTIN, 1483-1546
LUTHER, MARTIN, 1483-1546–DRAMA
LUTHER, MARTIN, 1483-1546–JUVENILE LITERATURE
LUTHERAN CHURCH
LUTHERAN CHURCH–CATECHISMS AND CREEDS
LUTHERAN CHURCH–CLERGY
LUTHERAN CHURCH–DOCTRINAL AND CONTROVERSIAL WORKS
LUTHERAN CHURCH–EDUCATION
LUTHERAN CHURCH–HISTORY
LUTHERAN CHURCH–HYMNS
LUTHERAN CHURCH–LITURGY AND RITUAL
LUTHERAN CHURCH–MEMBERSHIP
LUTHERAN CHURCH–PRAYER-BOOKS AND DEVOTIONS

LUTHERAN CHURCH–RELATIONS–CATHOLIC CHURCH
LUTHERAN CHURCH–SERMONS
LUTHERAN CHURCH–YEARBOOKS
LUTHERAN CHURCH IN SCANDINAVIA
LUTHERAN CHURCH IN THE UNITED STATES
LUTHERANS IN NORTH AMERICA
MARRIAGE–RELIGIOUS ASPECTS–LUTHERAN CHURCH
MELANCHTHON, PHILIPP, 1497-1560
PSALTERS
SCHEFFLER, JOHANN, 1624-1677
STAUPITZ, JOHANN VON, 1524
UNITED LUTHERAN CHURCH IN AMERICA
WALTHER, CARL FERDINAND WILHELM, 1811-1887

MENNONITES

AMISH
ARNOLD, EBERHARD, 1883-1935
BRUDERHOF COMMUNITIES
CHRISTIAN LIFE–MENNONITE AUTHORS
CHURCH AND SOCIAL PROBLEMS–MENNONITES
COFFMAN, JOHN SAMUEL, 1848-1899
COOKERY, MENNONITE
HUTTERITE BRETHREN
MARRIAGE–BRUDERHOF COMMUNITIES
MARRIAGE–RELIGIOUS ASPECTS–MENNONITES
MENNO SIMONS, 1496-1561
MENNONITES
MENNONITES–BIBLIOGRAPHY
MENNONITES–CATECHISM AND CREEDS
MENNONITES–DOCTRINAL AND CONTROVERSIAL WORKS
MENNONITES–HISTORY
MENNONITES–HYMNS
MENNONITES–JUVENILE LITERATURE
MENNONITES–MISSIONS
MENNONITES–SERMONS
MENNONITES–SOCIAL LIFE AND CUSTOMS
MENNONITES IN RUSSIA
YODER, ROSANNA (MCGONEGAL)

METHODISM

AFRICAN METHODIST EPISCOPAL CHURCH
ALLEN, RICHARD, BP., 1760-1831
ASBURY, FRANCIS, 1745-1816
BROWNLOW, WILLIAM GANNAWAY, 1805-1877
CHRISTIAN LIFE–METHODIST AUTHORS
CHURCH AND SOCIAL PROBLEMS–METHODIST CHURCH
COKE, THOMAS, BP., 1747-1814
COLET, JOHN 1467?-1519
FREE METHODIST CHURCH
HAVEN, GILBERT, 1821-1880
HENSON, JOSIAH, 1789-1883
LEE, JASON, 1803-1845
LEE, JESSE, 1758-1816
METHODISM
METHODISM–HISTORY
METHODIST CHURCH
METHODIST CHURCH–BIOGRAPHY
METHODIST CHURCH–CLERGY
METHODIST CHURCH–CLERGY–CORRESPONDENCE, REMISCENCES, ETC.
METHODIST CHURCH–DOCTRINAL AND CONTROVERSIAL WORKS
METHODIST CHURCH–EDUCATION
METHODIST CHURCH–MISSIONS
METHODIST CHURCH–SERMONS
METHODIST EPISCOPAL CHURCH
METHODIST EPISCOPAL CHURCH–MISSIONS
METHODIST EPISCOPAL CHURCH, SOUTH–HISTORY
METHODIST PUBLISHING HOUSE, NASHVILLE
MOORE, ARTHUR JAMES, BP. 1888-
NORTH, FRANK MASON, 1850-1935
RALL, HARRIS FRANKLIN, 1870-1964
VINCENT, JOHN HEYL, BP., 1832-1920
WESLEY, CHARLES, 1707-1788
WESLEY, JOHN, 1703-1791
WESLEY, SUSANNA (ANNESLEY) 1670-1742
WESLEY FAMILY
WESLEYAN METHODIST CHURCH–MISSIONS
WESLEYAN METHODIST CHURCH OF AMERICA
WHITEFIELD, GEORGE, 1714-1770

MISSIONS

AMERICAN BOARD OF COMMISSIONERS FOR FOREIGN MISSIONS
AMERICAN MISSIONARY ASSOCIATION
APOLOGETICS, MISSIONARY
BRAND, PAUL WILSON, 1914-
CATHOLIC CHURCH–MISSIONS
CATHOLIC FOREIGN MISSION SOCIETY OF AMERICA
CHURCH MISSIONARY SOCIETY
CITY MISSIONS
FRANCISCANS–MISSIONS
FRANSON, FREDRIK
IFUGAOS
INDIANS OF MEXICO–MISSIONS
INDIANS OF NORTH AMERICA–MISSIONS
ISLAMIC SECTS–MISSIONS
JESUITS–MISSIONS
LEE, JASON, 1803-1845
LIVINGSTONE, DAVID, 1813-1873
MENNONITES–MISSIONS
METHODIST CHURCH–MISSIONS
METHODIST EPISCOPAL CHURCH–MISSIONS
MISSIONARIES
MISSIONARIES–APPOINTMENT, CALL, AND ELECTION
MISSIONARIES–CORRESPONDENCE, REMINISCENCES, ETC.
MISSIONARIES–JUVENILE LITERATURE
MISSIONARIES, ANGLO-SAXON
MISSIONARIES, BRITISH
MISSIONARIES, IRISH
MISSIONARY STORIES
MISSIONS
MISSIONS–BIBLICAL TEACHING
MISSIONS–BIBLIOGRAPHY
MISSIONS–EDUCATIONAL WORK
MISSIONS–HISTORY
MISSIONS–JUVENILE LITERATURE
MISSIONS–SERMONS
MISSIONS–STUDY AND TEACHING
MISSIONS–THEORY
MISSIONS–AFRICA
MISSIONS–AFRICA, CENTRAL
MISSIONS–AFRICA, EAST
MISSIONS–AFRICA, SOUTH
MISSIONS–AFRICA, WEST
MISSIONS–ALASKA
MISSIONS–ASIA
MISSIONS–AUSTRALIA
MISSIONS–BAHAMAS
MISSIONS–BOLIVIA
MISSIONS–BOTSWANA
MISSIONS–BRAZIL
MISSIONS–BRITISH COLUMBIA
MISSIONS–BURMA
MISSIONS–CAMEROONS
MISSIONS–CANADA
MISSIONS–CHINA
MISSIONS–CONGO
MISSIONS–EAST (FAR EAST)
MISSIONS–ESKIMOS
MISSIONS–ETHIOPIA
MISSIONS–EUROPE
MISSIONS–FIJI ISLANDS
MISSIONS–FINLAND
MISSIONS–FORMOSA
MISSIONS–GABON
MISSIONS–INDIA
MISSIONS–INDO-CHINA
MISSIONS–INDONESIA
MISSIONS–IRAN
MISSIONS–ISLANDS OF THE PACIFIC
MISSIONS–ISRAEL
MISSIONS–JAMAICA
MISSIONS–JAPAN
MISSIONS–KAFFRARIA
MISSIONS–KOREA
MISSIONS–LAOS
MISSIONS–LATIN AMERICA
MISSIONS–LIBERIA
MISSIONS–MADAGASCAR
MISSIONS–MALAWI
MISSIONS–MEXICO
MISSIONS–NEAR EAST
MISSIONS–NEW GUINEA
MISSIONS–NIGERIA
MISSIONS–NORTH AMERICA
MISSIONS–OCEANICA
MISSIONS–PERU
MISSIONS–PHILIPPINE ISLANDS
MISSIONS–RHODESIA
MISSIONS–RUSSIA
MISSIONS–SOLOMON ISLANDS
MISSIONS–SOUTH AMERICA
MISSIONS–SUDAN
MISSIONS–SWEDEN
MISSIONS–TAHITI
MISSIONS–TANGANYIKA
MISSIONS–TONGA ISLANDS
MISSIONS–UNITED STATES
MISSIONS–VIETNAM
MISSIONS–WEST INDIES
MISSIONS–ZAMBIA
MISSIONS, FOREIGN
MISSIONS, HOME
MISSIONS, MEDICAL
MISSIONS TO ITALIANS
MISSIONS TO JEWS
MISSIONS TO LEPERS
MISSIONS TO MORMONS
MISSIONS TO MUSLIMS
ORTHODOX EASTERN CHURCH–MISSIONS
PARISH MISSIONS
RADIO IN MISSIONARY WORK
SAN JOSE DE AQUAYO MISSION
SAN LUIS OBISPO MISSION
SAN SABA MISSION
SCHWEITZER, ALBERT, 1875-1965–JUVENILE LITERATURE
SEVENTH-DAY ADVENTISTS–MISSIONS
SEVENTH-DAY BAPTISTS–MISSIONS
SPANISH MISSIONS OF CALIFORNIA
SPANISH MISSIONS OF NEW MEXICO
SPANISH MISSIONS OF THE SOUTHWEST
SUDAN INTERIOR MISSION
WESLEYAN METHODIST CHURCH–MISSIONS
WHITE FATHERS
WOMEN IN MISSIONARY WORK
WOMEN MISSIONARIES

MORAVIAN CHURCH–UNITED BRETHREN

BOHEMIAN BRETHREN
CHURCH MUSIC–MORAVIAN CHURCH
MORAVIANS

MORMONS–CHURCH OF JESUS CHRIST OF LATTER-DAY SAINTS

BOOK OF MORMON
BRIGHAM YOUNG UNIVERSITY
CHRISTIAN LIFE–MORMON AUTHORS
CHURCH OF CHRIST OF LATTER-DAY SAINTS
CHURCH OF JESUS CHRIST OF LATTER-DAY SAINTS
IOWA INFANTRY–MORMON BATTALION, 1846-1847
MACK FAMILY
MISSIONS TO MORMONS
MORMON TRAIL
MORMONS AND MORMONISM
MORMONS AND MORMONISM–FICTION
MORMONS AND MORMONISM–HISTORY
MORMONS AND MORMONISM–HISTORY–SOURCES
MORMONS AND MORMONISM–MISSIONS
MORMONS AND MORMONISM–SERMONS
MORMONS AND MORMONISM–SONGS AND MUSIC
MORMONS AND MORMONISM IN MEXICO
POLYGAMY
RELIGIOUS EDUCATION–TEXTBOOKS–MORMON
REORGANIZED CHURCH OF JESUS CHRIST OF LATTER-DAY SAINTS
SALT LAKE CITY
SMITH, JOSEPH, 1805-1844
SMITH FAMILY
YOUNG, BRIGHAM, 1801-1877

NEW JERUSALEM CHURCH–NEW CHURCH–SWEDENBORGIANISM

NEW JERUSALEM CHURCH
NEW JERUSALEM CHURCH–DOCTRINAL AND CONTROVERSIAL WORKS
SWEDENBORG, EMANUEL, 1688-1772
RUNES
SUPERNATURAL
WHITE, ELLEN GOULD (HARMON), 1827-1915

OTHER BELIEFS AND MOVEMENTS–JEHOVAH'S WITNESSES, MOON, SUN MYUNG, ONEIDA COMMUNITY, ETC.

ARIANISM
AUROBINDO, SRI, 1872-1950
AVATARS
AVESTA
BAKER, GEORGE, SELF-NAMED FATHER DIVINE
BEGHARDS AND BEGUINES
BLACK MUSLIMS
BROTHERS OF THE COMMON LIFE
CAMBRIDGE PLATONISTS
CHILDREN OF GOD
CHRISTWARD MINISTRY
CONVERTS, SEVENTH-DAY ADVENTIST
CULTS
DIANETICS
DISCIPLES OF CHRIST
DISCIPLES OF CHRIST–HISTORY
DISCIPLES OF CHRIST–HYMNS
DISCIPLES OF CHRIST–SERMONS
DIVINE SCIENCE CHURCH–DOCTRINAL AND CONTROVERSIAL WORKS
DRUIDS AND DRUIDISM
ELLSKWATAWA, SHAWNEE PROPHET, 1775-1834
EPHRATA COMMUNITY
ETHICAL CULTURE MOVEMENT
FATHER DIVINE
FATIMITES
FISH MOVEMENT (CHRISTIANITY)
FOCOLARE MOVEMENT
FRIENDS OF GOD (GOTTESFREUNDE)
GHOSE, AUROBINDO, 1872-1950
GIPSIES
HAILE SELASSIE 1ST EMPEROR OF ETHIOPIA, 1891-1975
HUSSITES
INDIAN POETRY
INDIAN SHAKERS
INTERNATIONALER BUND FREIER EVANGELISCHER GEMEINDEN
JEHOVAH'S WITNESSES
JESUS PEOPLE
KAFIRS (AFRICAN PEOPLE)
KESWICK MOVEMENT
KRISHNAMURTI, JIDDU, 1895-
LANGO (AFRICAN TRIBE)
LOLLARDS
LYNN, JAMES JESSE, 1892-1955
MAHESH YOGI, MAHARISHI
MITHRAISM
MONTANISM
MOON, SUN MYUNG
MORTMAIN
NABATAEANS
NOYES, JOHN HUMPHREY, 1811-1886
ONEIDA COMMUNITY
PARSEES
PEOPLE'S TEMPLE
RAS TAFARI MOVEMENT
ROBERTSON, PAT
ROSICRUCIANS
SEEKERS (SECT)
SPIRITUALISM
T'AI CHI CH'UAN
TEMPLE OF GOD
TRANSCENDENTAL MEDITATION
TRANSCENDENTALISM (NEW ENGLAND)
UNITY SCHOOL OF CHRISTIANITY
VOODOOISM
WATCH TOWER BIBLE AND TRACT SOCIETY
WILKINSON, JEMIMA, 1752-1819
ZOROASTRIANISM
ZULUS

OTHER PROTESTANT DENOMINATIONS–ADVENTISTS, ARMINIANISM, CHURCH OF CHRIST, ETC.

ADVENTISTS
ANABAPTISTS
ANABAPTISTS–HISTORY
ARMINIANISM
ARMSTRONG, HERBERT W.
ASSEMBLIES OF GOD, GENERAL COUNCIL
BAPTISTS–ADDRESSES, ESSAYS, LECTURES
BEISSEL, JOHANN CONRAD, 1690-1768
BENDER, HAROLD STAUFFER, 1897-1962
CHAMBERS, OSWALD, 1874-1917
CHRISTIAN LIFE–SEVENTH DAY ADVENTIST
CHURCH OF CHRIST
CHURCH OF THE BRETHREN
CHURCHES OF CHRIST
COMENIUS, JOHANN AMOS, 1592-1670
EVANGELICAL AND REFORMED CHURCH
EVANGELICAL COVENANT CHURCH OF AMERICA
EVANGELICAL COVENANT CHURCH OF AMERICA–SERMONS
EVANGELICAL FREE CHURCH OF AMERICA
GLOSSOLALIA
HOPKINSON, FRANCIS, 1737-1791
HUBMAIER, BALTHASAR, d. 1528
MILLER, WILLIAM, 1795-1861

OTTERBEIN, PHILIP WILLIAM, 1726-1813
PENTECOSTAL CHURCHES
PENTECOSTAL CHURCHES–GREAT BRITAIN
PENTECOSTALISM
SALVATION ARMY
SEVENTEENTH CENTURY
SEVENTH-DAY ADVENTISTS
UNITED CHURCH OF CHRIST
UNITED CHURCH OF CHRIST–CATECHISMS AND CREEDS
UNITED CHURCH OF CHRIST–HYMNS–HISTORY AND CRITICISM
WALDENSES

PRACTICAL THEOLOGY–CHRISTIAN LIFE, EVANGELISM, PASTORAL THEOLOGY, PRACTICAL RELIGION, REVIVALS, WORSHIP, ETC.

ABORTION–MORAL AND ETHICAL ASPECTS
ABORTION–PUBLIC OPINION
ABORTION–RELIGIOUS ASPECTS
ABORTION–RELIGIOUS ASPECTS–CATHOLIC CHURCH
ABORTION–RELIGIOUS ASPECTS–CHRISTIANITY
ACTORS AND ACTRESSES–CORRESPONDENCE, REMINISCENCES, ETC.
ADOLESCENCE
ADOPTION
ADOPTION–JUVENILE LITERATURE
ADOPTION–PERSONAL NARRATIVES
ADVENT
ADVENT SERMONS
ADVERTISING–CHURCHES
AFRO-AMERICAN CHURCHES
AFRO-AMERICAN CLERGY
AGED
AGED–PRAYER-BOOKS AND DEVOTIONS
AGED–RELIGIOUS LIFE
AGING
ALCOHOL
ALCOHOLICS
ALCOHOLISM
ALCOHOLISM–TREATMENT
ALCOHOLISM AND RELIGION
ALLEGORY
ALLEGORY IN LITERATURE
ALTAR BOYS
ALTAR GILDS
ALTARPIECES
ALTARS
AMERICAN POETRY (COLLECTIONS)
AMERICAN POETRY (COLLECTIONS)–20TH CENTURY
AMERICAN WIT AND HUMOR–CHURCH AND CLERGY
AMUSEMENTS–MORAL AND RELIGIOUS ASPECTS
ANDOVER THEOLOGICAL SEMINARY
ANECDOTES
ANGLO-SAXON POETRY
ANTHEMS
ANXIETY
APHORISMS AND APOTHEGMS
ARMED FORCES–PRAYER-BOOKS AND DEVOTIONS
ARNOLD, MATTHEW, 1822-1888
ARNOLD, THOMAS, 1795-1842
ARS MORIENDI–BIBLIOGRAPHY
ATHLETES
AYLWARD, GLADYS
AUDIO-VISUAL MATERIALS
BACH, JOHANN SEBASTIAN, 1685-1750
BACH, JOHANN SEBASTIAN, 1685-1750–JUVENILE LITERATURE
BAPTISM
BAPTISM–BIBLICAL TEACHING
BASHFULNESS
BAY PSALM BOOK
BEATITUDES
BEATITUDES–MEDITATIONS
BEATITUDES–SERMONS
BEAUTY, PERSONAL
BELLOC, HILAIRE, 1870-1953
BELLS
BENEFICES, ECCLESIASTICAL
BEREAVEMENT
BETHENCOURT, JEAN DE, BARON DE SAINT-MARTIN-LE-GAILLARD, 1360-1425
BETHUNE, MARY JANE (MCCLEOD), 1875-1955
BETROTHAL
BIGAMY
BILLINGS, WILLIAM, 1746-1800
BIRTH CONTROL
BIRTH CONTROL–RELIGIOUS ASPECTS
BOY SCOUTS–PRAYER-BOOKS AND DEVOTIONS
BOYS–PRAYER-BOOKS AND DEVOTIONS
BOYS–RELIGIOUS LIFE
BRADSHAW, TERRY
BREDESEN, HARALD
BROTHERHOODS
BROTHERLINESS
BRYANT, ANITA
BULL, GEORGE STRINGER, 1799-1865
BULLETIN BOARDS IN RELIGIOUS EDUCATION
BUSINESS ETHICS
CALENDAR
CALENDAR REFORM
CAMERON, JAMES, 1800-1875
CAMP-MEETINGS
CANCER–PSYCHOLOGICAL ASPECTS
CANCER PATIENTS–PERSONAL NARRATIVES
CANDLES AND LIGHTS
CANON LAW
CANTATA
CANTICLES
CARDIJN, LEON JOSEPH MARIE, 1882-
CAROLS
CAROLS–HISTORY AND CRITICISM
CARROLL FAMILY
CARTER, JIMMY, PRES. U. S., 1924-
CASH, JOHNNY
CATACOMBS
CATHOLIC SCHOOLS–GREAT BRITAIN
CATHOLIC SCHOOLS–UNITED STATES
CATHOLIC WORKER MOVEMENT
CELIBACY
CEREBRAL PALSY–PERSONAL NARRATIVES
CHALICES
CHALK-TALKS
CHANTS (PLAIN, GEORGIAN, ETC.)
CHAPLAINS
CHARITABLE BEQUESTS
CHARITIES
CHARITIES–UNITED STATES
CHARITY
CHARITY ORGANIZATIONS
CHASTITY
CHESTERTON, GILBERT KEITH, 1874-1936
CHILDREN–DEATH AND FUTURE STATE
CHILDREN–MANAGEMENT
CHILDREN–PRAYER-BOOKS AND DEVOTIONS
CHILDREN AND DEATH
CHILDREN'S HYMNS
CHILDREN'S SERMONS
CHILDREN'S SONGS
CHILDREN'S STORIES
CHOIRS (MUSIC)
CHORAL MUSIC
CHORAL SPEAKING
CHORAL SINGING
CHORALE
CHORUSES, SACRED
CHRISTIAN AND MISSIONARY ALLIANCE–MISSIONS
CHRISTIAN EDUCATION
CHRISTIAN LIFE
CHRISTIAN LIFE–ANGLICAN AUTHORS
CHRISTIAN LIFE–BAPTIST AUTHORS
CHRISTIAN LIFE–BIBLIOGRAPHY
CHRISTIAN LIFE–CATHOLIC AUTHORS
CHRISTIAN LIFE–EARLY CHURCH, ca. 30-600
CHRISTIAN LIFE–LUTHERAN AUTHORS
CHRISTIAN LIFE–MENNONITE AUTHORS
CHRISTIAN LIFE–METHODIST AUTHORS
CHRISTIAN LIFE–MIDDLE AGES, 600-1500
CHRISTIAN LIFE–MORMON AUTHORS
CHRISTIAN LIFE–ORTHODOX EASTERN AUTHORS
CHRISTIAN LIFE–PICTURES, ILLUSTRATIONS, ETC.
CHRISTIAN LIFE–PRESBYTERIAN AUTHORS
CHRISTIAN LIFE–SEVENTH DAY ADVENTIST
CHRISTIAN LIFE–STORIES
CHRISTIAN LIFE–STUDY AND TEACHING
CHRISTMAS
CHRISTMAS–BIBLIOGRAPHY
CHRISTMAS–JUVENILE LITERATURE
CHRISTMAS–MEDITATIONS
CHRISTMAS–POETRY
CHRISTMAS CARDS
CHRISTMAS COOKERY
CHRISTMAS DECORATIONS
CHRISTMAS MUSIC
CHRISTMAS PLAYS
CHRISTMAS SERMONS
CHRISTMAS STORIES
CHRISTMAS TREES
CHRISTMAS TREES–JUVENILE LITERATURE
CHRONIC DISEASES
CHURCH COMMITTEES
CHURCH MUSIC
CHURCH MUSIC–BIBLIOGRAPHY
CHURCH MUSIC–CATHOLIC CHURCH
CHURCH MUSIC–CHURCH OF ENGLAND
CHURCH MUSIC–CHURCH OF JESUS CHRIST OF LATTER-DAY SAINTS
CHURCH MUSIC–DISCOGRAPHY
CHURCH MUSIC–HISTORY AND CRITICISM
CHURCH MUSIC–LUTHERAN CHURCH
CHURCH MUSIC–MORAVIAN CHURCH
CHURCH MUSIC–ORTHODOX EASTERN CHURCH
CHURCH MUSIC–PROTESTANT CHURCHES
CHURCH SOCIETIES
CHURCH WORK
CHURCH WORK–DATA PROCESSING
CHURCH WORK–FORMS, BLANKS, ETC.
CHURCH WORK–STATIONERY, ETC.
CHURCH WORK AS A PROFESSION
CHURCH WORK WITH ALCOHOLICS
CHURCH WORK WITH CHILDREN
CHURCH WORK WITH CRIMINALS
CHURCH WORK WITH DIVORCED PEOPLE
CHURCH WORK WITH FAMILIES
CHURCH WORK WITH JUVENILE DELINQUENTS
CHURCH WORK WITH MILITARY PERSONNEL
CHURCH WORK WITH MINORITIES
CHURCH WORK WITH NARCOTIC ADDICTS
CHURCH WORK WITH REFUGEES
CHURCH WORK WITH SINGLE PEOPLE
CHURCH WORK WITH STUDENTS
CHURCH WORK WITH THE AGED
CHURCH WORK WITH THE BEREAVED
CHURCH WORK WITH THE HANDICAPPED
CHURCH WORK WITH THE MENTALLY HANDICAPPED
CHURCH WORK WITH THE MENTALLY ILL
CHURCH WORK WITH THE SICK
CHURCH WORK WITH YOUNG ADULTS
CHURCH WORK WITH YOUTH
CHURCH YEAR
CHURCH YEAR–MEDITATIONS
CHURCH YEAR SERMONS
CHURCHWARDENS' ACCOUNTS
CIVIL RIGHTS
CLAPHAM SECT
CLAY, JOHN, 1796-1856
CLERGY–APPOINTMENT, CALL AND ELECTION
CLERGY–CORRESPONDENCE, REMINISCENCES, ETC.
CLERGY–MALPRACTICE
CLERGY–OFFICE
CLERGY–RELIGIOUS LIFE
CLERGY–SALARIES, PENSIONS, ETC.
CLERGY–GERMANY
CLERGY–GREAT BRITAIN
CLERGY–IRAN
CLERGY–RUSSIA
CLERGY–SCOTLAND
CLERGY (CANON LAW)
CLERGY, TRAINING OF
CLERGY IN LITERATURE
CLERGYMEN'S FAMILIES
CLERGYMEN'S WIVES
COLEGIO DE SAN PABLO
COMMANDMENTS, TEN
COMMANDMENTS, TEN–JUVENILE LITERATURE
COMMANDMENTS, TEN–SERMONS
COMMITMENT
COMMUNICATION (THEOLOGY)
COMMUNION SERMONS
COMMUNITY CHURCHES
CONCILIAR THEORY
CONCORDIA THEOLOGICAL SEMINARY, ST. LOUIS
CONDUCT OF LIFE
CONDUCT OF LIFE–EARLY WORKS TO 1900
CONDUCTING, CHORAL
CONFIRMATION
CONFIRMATION–INSTRUCTION AND STUDY
CONSCIENCE
CONSOLATION
CONTEMPLATION
CONVERTS
COOKERY
CORPORAL WORKS OF MERCY
CORTES, HERNANDO, 1485-1547
CORTES, HERNANDO, 1485-1547–BIBLIOGRAPHY
CORTES, HERNANDO, 1485-1547–JUVENILE LITERATURE
COUNCILS AND SYNODS
COUNCILS AND SYNODS, ECUMENICAL
COUNSELING
COVENANTS (CHURCH POLITY)
CREATIVE ACTIVITIES AND SEATWORK
DARRELL, JOHN
DATING (SOCIAL CUSTOMS)
DAY, DOROTHY, 1897-
DEADLY SINS
DEATH–SOCIAL ASPECTS
DECISION-MAKING
DEDICATION SERVICES
DEPRESSION, MENTAL
DESPAIR
DEVOTION
DEVOTIONAL CALENDARS
DEVOTIONAL EXERCISES
DEVOTIONAL LITERATURE
DEVOTIONAL LITERATURE (SELECTIONS: EXTRACTS, ETC.)
DEVOTIONAL LITERATURE–HISTORY AND CRITICISM
DIALOGUE SERMONS
DIDACHE
DIOCESES
DIRECTORS OF RELIGIOUS EDUCATION
DISCUSSION IN RELIGIOUS EDUCATION
DISSENTERS, RELIGIOUS
DISSENTERS, RELIGIOUS–ENGLAND
DIVORCE–RELIGIOUS ASPECTS–CHRISTIANITY
DRAPER, JOHN WILLIAM
DRUG ABUSE
DRUGS AND YOUTH
DRYDEN, JOHN, 1631-1700
EASTER
EASTER–ART
EASTER–DRAMA
EASTER–PRAYER-BOOKS AND DEVOTIONS
EASTER–SERMONS
EASTER EGGS
EASTER MUSIC
EASTER STORIES
ECCLESIASTICAL COURTS
ECCLESIASTICAL GEOGRAPHY
ECCLESIASTICAL LAW
ECONOMICS–MORAL AND RELIGIOUS ASPECTS
ECSTASY
ELDERS (CHURCH OFFICERS)
ELECTION SERMONS–MASSACHUSETTS
ELIOT, JOHN, 1604-1690
EMBLEMS
EMOTIONS
EMPATHY
ENCOURAGEMENT
ENVY
EPISCOPACY
EQUALITY
ERIKSON, ERIK HOMBURGER, 1902-
ETHNIC GROUPS
EVANGELISTIC SERMONS
EVANGELISTIC WORK
EVANGELISTS
EVIL, NON-RESISTANCE TO
EXEMPLA
EXPERIENCE (RELIGION)
EXPRESSION
FANTASY
FASTING
FASTS AND FEASTS
FATHER AND CHILD
FEAR
FINANCE, PERSONAL
FOOTBALL
FOOTBALL–BIOGRAPHY
FORGIVENESS
FRIENDSHIP
FUNERAL MUSIC
FUNERAL RITES AND CEREMONIES
FUNERAL SERMONS
FUNERAL SERVICE
GAY LIBERATION MOVEMENT
GIBRAN, KAHLIL, 1883-1931
GIDE, ANDRE PAUL GUILLAUME, 1869-1951
GIFT-BOOKS (ANNUALS, ETC.)
GIFTS
GOD–MISCELLANEA
GOOD FRIDAY
GRACE AT MEALS
GRAHAM, WILLIAM FRANKLIN, 1918-
GRANDPARENTS
GRELLET, STEPHEN, 1773-1855
GRIEF
GURDJIEFF, GEORGE IVANOVITCH, 1872-1949
HAENDEL, GEORG FRIEDRICH, 1685-1759
HANDBOOKS, VADE-MECUMS, ETC.
HANDICAPPED
HANDICRAFT
HANDICRAFT–JUVENILE LITERATURE
HANNINGTON, JAMES, BP., 1847-1885
HAPPINESS
HAUGE, HANS NIELSEN, 1771-1824
HEARD, GERALD, 1889-
HERALDRY, SACRED
HERALDS
HODGKIN'S DISEASE–PERSONAL NARRATIVES
HODGSON, FRANCIS, 1781-1852
HOLIDAY DECORATIONS

HOLIDAYS
HOLIDAYS–DRAMA
HOLIDAYS–JUVENILE LITERATURE
HOLY-WEEK SERMONS
HOMILETICAL ILLUSTRATIONS
HOMOSEXUALITY
HOMOSEXUALITY AND CHRISTIANITY
HOPE
HUMILITY
HUNGER
HYMN FESTIVALS
HYMN TUNES
HYMN WRITERS
HYMNS
HYMNS–ACCOMPANIMENT
HYMNS–BIBLIOGRAPHY
HYMNS–CONCORDANCES
HYMNS–DICTIONARIES, INDEXES, ETC.
HYMNS–HISTORY AND CRITICISM
HYMNS–JUVENILE LITERATURE
HYMNS, ASSYRO-BABYLONIAN
HYMNS, ASSYRO-BABYLONIAN–HISTORY AND CRITICISM
HYMNS, GERMAN
HYMNS, GREEK
HYMNS, LATIN
HYMNS, LATIN–HISTORY AND CRITICISM
HYMNS, SANSKRIT
HYMNS, SPANISH
HYMNS, SUMERIAN
HYMNS, SUMERIAN–HISTORY AND CRITICISM
HYPNOTISM–MORAL AND RELIGIOUS ASPECTS
INCEST
IDENTITY
INDIGENOUS CHURCH ADMINISTRATION
INFANTS
INTERCOMMUNION
INTERPERSONAL RELATIONS
JACKSON, MAHALIA, 1911-1972
JEALOUSY
JESUS CHRIST–PERSON AND OFFICES
JESUS CHRIST–PRAYERS
JESUS CHRIST–PRIESTHOOD
JOB SATISFACTION
JOGGING
JOY AND SORROW
JUDGMENT DAY
JUDSON, ADONIRAM, 1788-1850
JUDSON, ANN (HASSELTINE) MRS., 1789-1826
KAGAWA, TOYOHIKO, 1888-1960
KEMPE, MARGERY (BURNHAM), b. 1373
KINDNESS
KING, CORETTA SCOTT, 1927-
KING, MARTIN LUTHER, 1929-1968
KUHLMAN, KATHERINE
KUHN, ISOBEL
LAITY
LEARNING DISABILITIES
LEISURE
LENT
LENT–PRAYER BOOKS AND DEVOTIONS
LENTEN SERMONS
LESBIAN NUNS
LETTERS
LEWIS, CLIVE STAPLES, 1898-1963
LINCOLN, ABRAHAM, PRE. U. S., 1809-1865
LIQUOR PROBLEM
LITERATURE AND MORALS
LITURGICAL DRAMA
LITURGICAL DRAMAS
LITURGICS
LITURGIES
LITURGIES–BIBLIOGRAPHY
LITURGIES, EARLY CHRISTIAN
LITURGY AND DRAMA
LITURGY AND LITERATURE
LONLINESS
LORD'S PRAYER
LORD'S PRAYER–EARLY WORKS TO 1800
LORD'S PRAYER–JUVENILE LITERATURE
LORD'S PRAYER–MEDITATIONS
LORD'S PRAYER–SERMONS
LORD'S SUPPER–PRAYER BOOKS AND DEVOTIONS
LORD'S SUPPER–SERMONS
LORD'S SUPPER (LITURGY)
LOVE
LUST
LYMAN BEECHER LECTURES
MCAULEY, JEREMIAH, 1839-1884
MACKENZIE, JOHN
MAGNIFICAT
MAGNIFICAT (MUSIC)
MARRIAGE–RELIGIOUS ASPECTS
MARRIAGE–RELIGIOUS ASPECTS–BAHAI FAITH
MARRIAGE–RELIGIOUS ASPECTS–BUDDHISM
MARRIAGE–RELIGIOUS ASPECTS–CHRISTIANITY
MARRIAGE–RELIGIOUS ASPECTS–JUDAISM
MARRIAGE–RELIGIOUS ASPECTS–LUTHERAN CHURCH
MARRIAGE–RELIGIOUS ASPECTS–MENNONITES
MARRIAGE–RELIGIOUS ASPECTS–SOCIETY OF FRIENDS
MARRIAGE COUNSELING
MARRIAGE CUSTOMS AND RITES
MARRIAGE SERVICE
MARRIED PEOPLE–PRAYER-BOOKS AND DEVOTIONS
MEDITATION
MEDITATIONS
MEMORIAL SERVICE
MEMORIALS
MEN–PRAYER-BOOKS AND DEVOTIONS
MENTALLY HANDICAPPED CHILDREN–PERSONAL NARRATIVES
MENTALLY ILL–RELIGIOUS LIFE
MINORITIES
MISSALS
MONASTIC AND RELIGIOUS LIFE OF WOMEN
MONGOLISM–PERSONAL NARRATIVES
MOODY, DWIGHT LYMAN, 1837-1899
MOODY BIBLE INSTITUTE OF CHICAGO
MOTHER AND CHILD
MOTHERS
MOTHERS–RELIGIOUS LIFE
MOURNING CUSTOMS
MUELLER, GEORGE, 1805-1898
MUSIC–ANALYSIS, APPRECIATION
MUSIC, AMERICAN
MUSIC, BYZANTINE
MUSIC, HAWAIIAN
MUSIC, INDIC
MUSIC, MEXICAN
MUSIC IN CHURCHES
MUSICIANS–CORRESPONDENCE, REMINISCENCES, ETC.
MUSICOLOGY
MYASTHENIA GRAVIS
NEGRO CHURCHES
NEWMAN, HENRY, 1670-1743
NIGERIA–RELIGION
NONVIOLENCE
NOVITIATE
NUTRITION
OBEDIENCE
OBESITY
OBJECT-TEACHING
OCCASIONAL SERMONS
OCCASIONAL SERVICES
OCEANIA–RELIGION
OLD AGE
OLIPHANT, LAURENCE, 1829-1888
ORGAN–INSTRUCTION AND STUDY
ORGAN MUSIC
ORATORIO
PACIFISM
PACKARD, FREDERICK ADOLPHUS, 1794-1867
PAIN
PAPER WORK- JUVENILE LITERATURE
PARAPLEGIA
PARENT AND CHILD
PARENT EDUCATION
PARISH COUNCILS
PARISH HOUSES
PARISHES
PARISHES–CANADA
PARISHES–GREAT BRITAIN
PART-SONGS
PASCUA PASSION-PLAY
PASSION-MUSIC
PASSION-PLAYS
PASTORAL COUNSELING
PASTORAL COUNSELING (JUDAISM)
PASTORAL MEDICINE
PASTORAL PRAYERS
PASTORAL PSYCHOLOGY
PASTORAL THEOLOGY
PASTORAL THEOLOGY–ANGLICAN COMMUNION
PASTORAL THEOLOGY–CATHOLIC CHURCH
PASTORAL THEOLOGY–HANDBOOKS, MANUALS, ETC.
PATRIOTISM
PATTESON, JOHN COLERIDGE, BP., 1827-1871
PEACE OF MIND
PEACE SOCIETIES
PEALE, NORMAN VINCENT, 1898-
PENITENTIAL PSALMS (MUSIC)
PENTECOST
PENTECOST FESTIVAL
PERSONALITY
PHYSICIANS–BIOGRAPHY
PIETY
PILGRIMS AND PILGRIMAGES
PLYMOUTH BRETHREN
POETRY–COLLECTIONS
POLITICAL ETHICS
POLITICAL SCIENCE–EARLY WORKS TO 1700
POLYGAMY
PORNOGRAPHY
PORNOGRAPHY–RELIGIOUS ASPECTS
POSTURE IN WORSHIP
POVERTY
POVERTY (VIRTUE)
PRAISE
PRAYER
PRAYER–JUVENILE LITERATURE
PRAYER–SERMONS
PRAYER-BOOKS
PRAYER GROUPS
PRAYER-MEETINGS
PRAYERS
PRAYERS FOR THE DEAD
PREACHING
PREACHING–HISTORY
PREJUDICES AND ANTIPATHIES
PRIDE AND VANITY
PRIESTHOOD
PRIESTHOOD, UNIVERSAL
PRIESTS
PRISONERS–PERSONAL NARRATIVES
PRISONERS' WRITINGS
PRO-CHOICE MOVEMENT
PROSTITUTION
PSALMODY
PSALMS (MUSIC)
PSYCHOANALYSIS AND RELIGION
PSYCHOLOGY, RELIGIOUS
PUBLIC RELATIONS–CHURCHES
PUBLIC WORSHIP
RACE
RACE RELATIONS
RADIO IN RELIGION
RECITATIONS
RECREATION LEADERSHIP
REED, STANLEY FORMAN, 1884-
REFUGEES
REFUGEES–HONDURAS
REFUGEES–SALVADOR
REGISTERS OF BIRTHS, DEATHS, MARRIAGES, ETC.
REHABILITATION
RELIGION AND ASTRONAUTICS
RELIGIOUS AND ECCLESIASTICAL INSTITUTIONS
RELIGIOUS ARTICLES
RELIGIOUS DANCE, MODERN
RELIGIOUS DRAMA
RELIGIOUS DRAMA–BIBLIOGRAPHY
RELIGIOUS DRAMA–HISTORY AND CRITICISM
RELIGIOUS EDUCATION–AUDIO-VISUAL AIDS
RELIGIOUS EDUCATION–BIBLIOGRAPHY
RELIGIOUS EDUCATION–DATA PROCESSING
RELIGIOUS EDUCATION–HISTORY
RELIGIOUS EDUCATION–HOME TRAINING
RELIGIOUS EDUCATION–PSYCHOLOGY
RELIGIOUS EDUCATION–TEACHER TRAINING
RELIGIOUS EDUCATION–TEACHING METHODS
RELIGIOUS EDUCATION–TEXT-BOOKS
RELIGIOUS EDUCATION–TEXT-BOOKS FOR CHILDREN
RELIGIOUS EDUCATION–TEXT-BOOKS FOR YOUNG PEOPLE
RELIGIOUS EDUCATION–FRANCE
RELIGIOUS EDUCATION–GERMANY
RELIGIOUS EDUCATION–GREAT BRITAIN
RELIGIOUS EDUCATION AS A PROFESSION
RELIGIOUS EDUCATION OF ADOLESCENTS
RELIGIOUS EDUCATION OF ADULTS
RELIGIOUS EDUCATION OF CHILDREN
RELIGIOUS EDUCATION OF MENTALLY HANDICAPPED CHILDREN
RELIGIOUS EDUCATION OF PRE-SCHOOL CHILDREN
RELIGIOUS EDUCATION OF SOCIALLY HANDICAPPED CHILDREN
RELIGIOUS EDUCATION OF YOUNG PEOPLE
RELIGIOUS LIBERTY
RELIGIOUS LIBERTY–FRANCE
RELIGIOUS LIBERTY–GREAT BRITAIN
RELIGIOUS LIBERTY–SOVIET UNION
REMARRIAGE
RESPONSIVE WORSHIP
RETREATS
REVIVALS
ROBERTS, DAVID CORRELL
ROGERS, DALE EVANS
ROGERS, ROBIN ELIZABETH, 1950-1952
ROLLE, RICHARD, OF HAMPOLE, 1290-1349
RUNNING
RURAL CHURCHES
SABBATH
SABBATH–JUVENILE LITERATURE
SABBATH LEGISLATION
SACRAMENTALS
SACRAMENTS
SACRAMENTS–EARLY WORKS TO 1800
SACRAMENTS (CANON LAW)
SACRAMENTS (LITURGY)
SACRAMENTS AND CHRISTIAN UNION
SACRED VOCAL MUSIC
SAINT VALENTINE'S DAY
SALVATION IN LITERATURE
SANFORD, AGNES MARY (WHITE)
SANKEY, IRA DAVID, 1840-1908
SCHOOLS–EXERCISES AND RECREATIONS
SCHWEITZER, ALBERT, 1875-1965
SECRET SOCIETIES
SECURITY (PSYCHOLOGY)
SEGREGATION
SELF-ACCEPTANCE
SELF-ACTUALIZATION (PSYCHOLOGY)
SELF CONTROL
SELF-DECEPTION
SEQUENCES (LITURGY)
SERVICE (THEOLOGY)
SERVICE BOOKS (MUSIC)
SEX
SEX AND LAW
SEX AND RELIGION
SEX IN MARRIAGE
SEX IN MOVING-PICTURES
SEX INSTRUCTION
SEX INSTRUCTION FOR CHILDREN AND YOUTH
SEX ROLE
SEXUAL DEVIATION
SEXUAL ETHICS
SICK–PRAYER-BOOKS AND DEVOTIONS
SIGNS AND SYMBOLS
SIMPSON, ALBERT BENJAMIN, 1844-1919
SINGLE-PARENT FAMILY
SINGLE PEOPLE–RELIGIOUS LIFE
SKITS, STUNTS, ETC.
SLAVERY
SLAVERY–JUSTIFICATION
SLAVERY AND THE CHURCH
SLAVERY IN BRITISH GUIANA
SLAVERY IN THE UNITED STATES–ANTI-SLAVERY MOVEMENTS
SLAVERY IN THE UNITED STATES–CONTROVERSIAL LITERATURE
SLESSOR, MARY MITCHELL, 1848-1945
SMALL GROUPS
SMET, PIERRE JEAN DE, 1801-1873
SMITH, JOHN, 1790-1824
SOCIAL ACTION
SOCIAL CHANGE
SOCIAL CONFLICT
SOCIAL ETHICS
SOCIAL GOSPEL
SOCIAL PROBLEMS
SOCIAL PSYCHIATRY
SOCIAL REFORMERS–GREAT BRITAIN
SOCIAL SURVEYS
SOLZHENITSYN, ALEKSANDR ISAEVICH, 1918-
SONGS
SORIANO, FRANCESCO
SOUTH AMERICA RELIGION
SPIRIT
SPIRITUAL DIRECTION
SPIRITUAL DIRECTORS
SPIRITUAL EXERCISES
SPIRITUAL LIFE
SPIRITUALITY
SPIRITUALS (SONGS)
SPIRITUALS (SONGS)–HISTORY AND CRITICISM
STATE, THE
STEVENSON, WILLIAM, 1768-1857
STUDD, CHARLES THOMAS, 1860-1931
STUDENTS
STUDENTS–RELIGIOUS LIFE
STUDENTS–CHINA, 1949-
STURGES, A. A.
STURGES, SUSAN THOMPSON, 1820-1893
SUBURBAN LIFE
SUCCESS
SUFFERING
SUNDAY, WILLIAM ASHLEY, 1862-1935
SUNDAY
SUNDAY LEGISLATION
SUPERIORS, RELIGIOUS
SUSS, HEINRICH, 1300-1366
SYNANON FOUNDATION
TAKAHASHI, REIJI, 1930-
TAPPAN, LEWIS, 1788-1873
TAXATION
TAYLOR, JAMES HUDSON, 1832-1905
TAYLOR, MARIA (DYER)
TEACHERS–DEVOTION LITERATURE
TEACHING
TECHNOLOGY AND ETHICS
TELEPHONE IN CHURCH WORK
TEMPERANCE
TEMPERANCE AND RELIGION
TEMPERAMENT
TERMINAL CARE
THANKSGIVING DAY
THEATER–MORAL AND RELIGIOUS ASPECTS
THEOLOGICAL SEMINARIES
THEOLOGY, PRACTICAL
THOREAU, HENRY DAVID, 1817-1862

TITHES
TOLERATION
TORREY, CHARLES TURNER, 1813-1846
TORTURE
TRANCE
TRANSACTIONAL ANALYSIS
TRAPPISTS
TRUEBLOOD, DAVID ELTON, 1900-
TRUST IN GOD
TUNE-BOOKS
UNIVERSITIES AND COLLEGES–RELIGION
VACATION SCHOOLS, RELIGIOUS
VACATION SCHOOLS, RELIGIOUS–TEACHERS MANUALS
VACATION SCHOOLS, RELIGIOUS–TEXT-BOOKS
VALUES
VIOLENCE IN TELEVISION
VIRGINITY
VIRTUE AND VIRTUES
VOCATION
VOCATION (IN RELIGIOUS ORDERS, CONGREGATIONS, ETC.)
VOLUNTARISM
VOCATION, ECCLESIASTICAL
WATERS, ETHEL, 1900-1977
WEDDING ETIQUETTE
WEDDING SERMONS
WEDDINGS
WHITTIER, JOHN GREENLEAF, 1807-1892
WIDOWS
WILBERFORCE, WILLIAM, 1759-1833
WILDERNESS (THEOLOGY)
WINTHROP, JOHN, 1588-1649
WITNESS BEARING (CHRISTIANITY)
WIVES
WOMAN (THEOLOGY)
WOMEN
WOMEN–BIOGRAPHY
WOMEN–PRAYER-BOOKS AND DEVOTIONS
WOMEN–RELIGIOUS LIFE
WOMEN (IN RELIGION, FOLKLORE, ETC.)
WOMEN AND RELIGION
WOMEN CLERGY
WOMEN IN CHRISTIANITY
WOMEN IN CHURCH WORK
WOMEN IN RELIGION
WORK
WORK (THEOLOGY)
WORRY
WORSHIP
WORSHIP–EARLY CHURCH
WORSHIP–HISTORY
WORSHIP (RELIGIOUS EDUCATION)
WORSHIP PROGRAMS
YALE UNIVERSITY
YALE UNIVERSITY–DIVINITY SCHOOL
YOUNG ADULTS
YOUNG GERMANY
YOUNG MENS CHRISTIAN ASSOCIATIONS–FINANCE
YOUNG PEOPLE'S MEETINGS (CHURCH WORK)
YOUNG WOMEN–RELIGIOUS LIFE
YOUTH
YOUTH–CONDUCT OF LIFE
YOUTH–PRAYER-BOOKS AND DEVOTIONS
YOUTH–RECREATION
YOUTH–RELIGIOUS LIFE
YOUTH–SEXUAL BEHAVIOR

PRESBYTERIANISM

BARNES, ALBERT, 1798-1879
BOYD, ROBERT, 1578-1627
CHRISTIAN LIFE–PRESBYTERIAN AUTHORS
CHURCH OF SCOTLAND
CHURCH OF SCOTLAND–SERMONS
CUMBERLAND PRESBYTERIAN CHURCH IN TEXAS
FINLEY, ROBERT, 1772-1817
FINNEY, CHARLES GRANDISON, 1792-1875
HODGE, CHARLES, 1797-1878
LOVEJOY, ELIJAH PARISH, 1802-1837
LYON, JAMES
MARSHALL, PETER, 1902-1949
PRESBYTERIAN CHURCH
PRESBYTERIAN CHURCH–CATECHISMS AND CREEDS
PRESBYTERIAN CHURCH–CLERGY–CORRESPONDENCE, REMINISCENCES, ETC.
PRESBYTERIAN CHURCH–DOCTRINAL AND CONTROVERSIAL WORKS
PRESBYTERIAN CHURCH–HISTORY
PRESBYTERIAN CHURCH–HYMNS
PRESBYTERIAN CHURCH–LITURGY AND RITUAL
PRESBYTERIAN CHURCH–MEMBERSHIP
PRESBYTERIAN CHURCH–SERMONS
PRESBYTERIAN CHURCH IN THE U. S.
PRESBYTERIAN CHURCH IN THE U. S. A.
PRESBYTERIAN CHURCH IN THE U. S. A.–EDUCATION
PRESBYTERIAN CHURCH IN THE U. S. A.–HISTORY
PRESBYTERIANISM
UNITED PRESBYTERIAN CHURCH IN THE U. S. A.
WESTMINSTER ASSEMBLY OF DIVINES. CONFESSION OF FAITH
WESTMINSTER ASSEMBLY OF DIVINES. SHORTER CATECHISM
WITHERSPOON, JOHN, 1723-1794

PROTESTANT EPISCOPAL CHURCH IN THE UNITED STATES

BOOK OF COMMON PRAYER
BOSTON–TRINITY CHURCH
EPISCOPALIANS
PARISH MISSIONS
PIKE, JAMES ALBERT, BP., 1913-1969
PROTESTANT EPISCOPAL CHURCH IN THE U. S. A.
PROTESTANT EPISCOPAL CHURCH IN THE U. S. A.–BOOK OF COMMON PRAYER
PROTESTANT EPISCOPAL CHURCH IN THE U. S. A.–CLERGY
PROTESTANT EPISCOPAL CHURCH IN THE U. S. A.–DOCTRINAL AND CONTROVERSIAL WORKS
PROTESTANT EPISCOPAL CHURCH IN THE U. S. A.–HISTORY
PROTESTANT EPISCOPAL CHURCH IN THE U. S. A.–LITURGY AND RITUAL
PROTESTANT EPISCOPAL CHURCH IN THE U. S. A.–MISSIONS
PROTESTANT EPISCOPAL CHURCH IN THE U. S. A.–PRAYERBOOKS AND DEVOTIONS
PROTESTANT EPISCOPAL CHURCH IN THE U. S. A.–SERMONS
PSALTERS
SEABURY, SAMUEL, BP., 1729-1796
STATIONS OF THE CROSS

PROTESTANTISM

ARMAGH, IRELAND (ECCLESIASTICAL PROVINCE)
ASKEW, ANNE, 1521-1546
BALE, JOHN, BP. OF OSSORY, 1495-1563
BEDELL, WILLIAM, BP., 1571-1642
BRONTE, PATRICK, 1777-1861
BRUNNER, HEINRICH EMIL, 1889-
BUCER, MARTIN, 1491-1551
CATHOLIC CHURCH–DOCTRINAL AND CONTROVERSIAL WORKS–PROTESTANT AUTHORS
CATHOLIC CHURCH–RELATIONS–PROTESTANT CHURCHES
FOXE, JOHN, 1516-1587
FREEMASONS
FREEMASONS–HISTORY
FREEMASONS–KNIGHTS TEMPLARS
FREEMASONS–RITUALS
FREEMASONS–SYMBOLISM
FULLER, THOMAS, 1608-1661
MONASTICISM AND RELIGIOUS ORDERS, PROTESTANT
NEW ENGLAND–BIOGRAPHY
OBERLIN COLLEGE
OLDCASTLE, SIR JOHN, called LORD COBHAM, d. 1417
ORDER OF THE EASTERN STAR–RITUAL
PEASANTS' WAR, 1524-1525
PERCY, THOMAS, BP. OF DROMORE, 1729-1811
PERSECUTION
PROTESTANT CHURCHES
PROTESTANT CHURCHES–RELATIONS–CATHOLIC CHURCH
PROTESTANTISM
PROTESTANTISM–HISTORY
PROTESTANTS IN ENGLAND
PROTESTANTS IN FRANCE
PROTESTANTS IN IRELAND
PROTESTANTS IN LATIN AMERICA
PROTESTANTS IN RUSSIA
PROTESTANTS IN SPAIN
PROTESTANTS IN TAIWAN
PROTESTANTS IN THE UNITED STATES
PROTESTANTS IN THE WEST INDIES
PRYNNE, WILLIAM, 1600-1669
REFORMATION
REFORMATION–BIBLIOGRAPHY
REFORMATION–BIOGRAPHY
REFORMATION–EARLY MOVEMENTS
REFORMATION–SOURCES
REFORMATION–CZECHOSLOVAK REPUBLIC
REFORMATION–ENGLAND
REFORMATION–FRANCE
REFORMATION–GERMANY
REFORMATION–ITALY
REFORMATION–POLAND
REFORMATION–SCOTLAND
REFORMATION–SPAIN
REFORMATION–SWITZERLAND
ROBINSON, JOHN, 1575-1625
ST. BARTHOLOMEW'S DAY, MASSACRE OF, 1572
SMITH, JOSEPH H.
TEMPLARS
THORPE, WILLIAM d. 1407
WYCLIFFE, JOHN, d. 1384
ZIZKA, JAN, 1360-1424

PURITANISM

BRADFORD, WILLIAM, 1588-1657
BREWSTER, WILLIAM, 1566?-1644
BUNYAN, JOHN, 1628-1688
BUNYAN, JOHN, 1628-1688–FICTION
BUNYAN, JOHN, 1628-1688–STUDY
CARTWRIGHT, THOMAS, 1535-1603
CLAP, THOMAS, 1703-1767
COTTON, JOHN, 1584-1652
CROMWELL, OLIVER, 1599-1658
EDWARDS, JONATHAN, 1703-1758
LILBURNE, JOHN, 1614?-1657
MILTON, JOHN, 1608-1674
MILTON, JOHN, 1608-1674–CONCORDANCES
MILTON, JOHN, 1608-1674–KNOWLEDGE AND LEARNING
MILTON, JOHN, 1608-1674–PARADISE LOST
MILTON, JOHN, 1608-1674–PARADISE REGAINED
MILTON, JOHN, 1608-1674–RELIGION AND ETHICS
MILTON, JOHN, 1608-1674–SAMSON AGONISTES
MILTON, JOHN, 1608-1674–SOURCES
PILGRIMS (NEW PLYMOUTH COLONY)
PILGRIMS (NEW PLYMOUTH COLONY)–JUVENILE LITERATURE
PRESTON, JOHN, 1587-1628
PURITANS
STERRY, PETER, 1613-1672
THEOLOGY, PURITAN
VERMIGLI, PIETRO MARTIRE, 1500-1562
WIGGLESWORTH, MICHAEL, 1631-1705
WILLIAMS, ROGER, 1604?-1683
WINTHROP FAMILY
WITHERS, GEORGE, 1588-1667

RATIONALISM

AGNOSTICISM
ATHEISM
CHRISTIANITY AND ATHEISM
FREE THOUGHT
SECULARISM
SECULARIZATION
SECULARIZATION (THEOLOGY)
SKEPTICISM
SKEPTICISM–CONTROVERSIAL LITERATURE
SYMBOLISM (PSYCHOLOGY)
VOLTAIRE, FRANCOIS MARIE AROUET DE, 1694-1778

REFORMED OR CALVINISTIC CHURCHES

BEZE, THEODORE DE, 1519-1605
CALVIN, JEAN, 1509-1564
CALVINISM
DORT, SYNOD OF, 1618-1619
HEIDELBERG CATECHISM
HENRI 4TH, KING OF FRANCE, 1553-1610–FICTION
HUGUENOTS
HUGUENOTS IN FOREIGN COUNTRIES
HUGUENOTS IN FRANCE
KNOX, JOHN, 1505-1572
MERCERSBURG THEOLOGY
REFORMED CHURCH
REFORMED CHURCH–CATECHISMS AND CREEDS
REFORMED CHURCH–DOCTRINAL AND CONTROVERSIAL WORKS
REFORMED CHURCH–SERMONS
REFORMED CHURCH IN AMERICA
REFORMED CHURCH IN THE UNITED STATES
WALLOONS
ZWINGLI, ULRICH, 1484-1531

RELIGION–NATURAL THEOLOGY, MYTHOLOGY

AESCULAPIUS
AFRICA–RELIGION
AFRICA, EAST–RELIGION
AFRICA, NORTH–RELIGION
AFRICA, SUB-SAHARAN–RELIGIOUS LIFE AND CUSTOMS
AFRICA, WEST–RELIGION
AFRO-AMERICANS–RELIGION
AKANS (AFRICAN PEOPLE)
ALLEGORIES
AMAZONS
AMENHETEP 4TH, KING OF EGYPT, 1388-1358 B.C.
ANALOGY (RELIGION)
ANCESTOR WORSHIP
ANGELS
ANIMAL-WORSHIP
ANIMISM
ANTHROPOMORPHISM
APOTHEOSIS
ARABS IN SPAIN
ARABS IN THE UNITED STATES
ASSOCIATIONS, INSTITUTIONS, ETC.
ASSYRO-BABYLONIAN RELIGION
ASTROLOGY, EARLY
ASTRONOMY, HINDU
ATHLETES–RELIGIOUS LIFE
ATLANTIS
ATOMIC ENERGY–MORAL AND RELIGIOUS ASPECTS
ATOMIC WARFARE–MORAL AND RELIGIOUS ASPECTS
AUTHORITY (RELIGION)
AVATARS
AZTECS
AZTECS–ART
BAAL (DEITY)
BABYLONIA
BABYLONIA–ANTIQUITIES
BALI (ISLAND)–RELIGION
BAR KOKBA, fl. 130-JUVENILE LITERATURE
BEADS (IN RELIGION, FOLK-LORE, ETC.)
BEATIFIC VISION
BEKTASHI
BIOGRAPHY
BIOLOGY
BIOLOGY–JUVENILE LITERATURE
BIOLOGY–STUDY AND TEACHING
BIRTH (IN RELIGION, FOLK-LORE, ETC.)
BLACKS–RELIGION
BLESSING AND CURSING
BLOOD (IN RELIGION, FOLK-LORE, ETC.)
BODY, HUMAN (IN RELIGION, FOLK-LORE, ETC.)
BON (TIBETAN RELIGION)
BOOK OF THE DEAD
BOOK OF THE DEAD–DICTIONARIES, INDEXES, ETC.
BOYS–RELIGIOUS LIFE
BRAZIL–RELIGION
BREATH AND BREATHING (IN RELIGION, FOLK-LORE, ETC.)
BURMA–RELIGION
BUSHIDO
BUSINESSMEN–RELIGIOUS LIFE
BYZANTINE ANTIQUITIES
BYZANTINE EMPIRE–HISTORY
CAMPBELL, BEATRICE STELLA (TANNER), 1865-1940
CANADA–CHURCH HISTORY
CATS (IN RELIGION, FOLK-LORE, ETC.)
CAYCE, EDGAR, 1877-1945
CELTS
CENSORSHIP
CHANTS (BYZANTINE)
CHANTS (PLAIN, GREGORIAN, ETC.)
CHANTS (PLAIN, GREGORIAN, ETC.)–HISTORY AND CRITICISM
CHAPELS
CHAPELS (MUSIC)
CHEWA (AFRICAN TRIBE)
CHILDREN–RELIGIOUS LIFE
CHINA–RELIGION
CH'ONDOGYO
CHRISTIAN ANTIQUITIES
CHRISTIAN ART AND SYMBOLISM
CHRISTIAN ART AND SYMBOLISM–JUVENILE LITERATURE
CHRISTIANITY AND OTHER RELIGIONS–DRUIDISM
CHRISTIANITY AND OTHER RELIGIONS–LAMAISM
CITIES AND TOWNS–RELIGIOUS LIFE
CIVILIZATION–PHILOSOPHY
CIVILIZATION, ANCIENT
CIVILIZATION, MEDIEVAL
CIVILIZATION, SEMITIC
CLASSICAL ANTIQUITIES
CLASSIFICATION–BOOKS–RELIGION
COLLEGE STUDENTS–RELIGIOUS LIFE
COLLIER, JOHN, 1708-1786
COMIC BOOKS, STRIPS, ETC.
COMIC BOOKS, STRIPS, ETC.–MORAL AND RELIGIOUS ASPECTS
COMMUNISM AND RELIGION
CONNECTICUT–CHURCH HISTORY

CONVERSION
CONVERTS
CORINTH, GREECE–ANTIQUITIES
CORONADO ISLANDS
CORPORATIONS, RELIGIOUS
COSMOLOGY
COSMOLOGY–CURIOSA AND MISCELLANEA
COSMOLOGY–JUVENILE LITERATURE
CREATION
CREATION–EARLY WORKS TO 1800
CREATION–JUVENILE LITERATURE
CREATION IN ART
CREVECOEUR, MICHEL GUILLAUME JEAN DE, CALLED ST. JOHN DE CREVECOEUR, 1735-1813
CRIB IN CHRISTIAN ART AND TRADITION
CROMWELL, THOMAS, EARL OF ESSEX, 1485?-1540
CROSSWORD PUZZLES
CULT
CULTUS
CULTUS, AFRICAN
CULTUS, EGYPTIAN
CULTUS, GREEK
CULTUS, ROMAN
DAHOMEYANS
DANCE OF DEATH
DANCING (IN RELIGION, FOLK-LORE, ETC.)
DANTE ALIGHIERI, 1265-1321
DAYS
DEAD (IN RELIGION, FOLK-LORE, ETC.)
DEISM
DELPHIAN ORACLE
DELUGE
DEMONIAC POSSESSION
DEMONOLOGY
DEMONOLOGY–BIBLIOGRAPHY
DES MARQUETS, ANN
DEVIL
DEVIL IN LITERATURE
DINKA (NILOTIC TRIBE)
DIONYSIUS
DISSENTERS, RELIGIOUS
DISSENTERS, RELIGIOUS–ENGLAND
DIVINE RIGHT OF KINGS
DOGONS (AFRICAN PEOPLE)
DOGS (IN RELIGION, FOLK-LORE, ETC.)
DOLPHIN (IN RELIGION, FOLK-LORE, ETC.)
DOSTOEVSKII, FEDOR MIKHAILOVICH, 1821-1881
DRAMA, MEDIEVAL
DRUIDS AND DRUIDISM
DRUSES
DUALISM
EBNER VON ESCHENBACH, MARIE, FREIFRAU, 1830-1916
ECSTASY
EDDAS
EDWARD 2ND, KING OF ENGLAND, 1284-1327
EGYPT–CIVILIZATION
EGYPT–RELIGION
EGYPTIAN LANGUAGE–INSCRIPTIONS
EGYPTIAN LANGUAGE–PAPYRI
EGYPTOLOGY
ELEUSINIAN MYSTERIES
ELEUSIS
EMPEROR WORSHIP
ENDOGAMY AND EXOGAMY
ENGLISH DRAMA (COLLECTIONS)–TO 1500
ENGLISH DRAMA–HISTORY AND CRITICISM–TO 1500
ENGLISH LITERATURE–TRANSLATIONS FROM ORIENTAL LITERATURE
ENGLISH POETRY (COLLECTIONS)
ENGLISH POETRY (COLLECTIONS)–20TH CENTURY
ENGLISH POETRY–TRANSLATIONS FROM ANGLO-SAXON
ENTHUSIASM
ESCHATOLOGY
EUROPE–RELIGION
EUROPE, EASTERN–RELIGION
EUROPEAN WAR, 1914-1918–RELIGIOUS ASPECTS
EVIL IN LITERATURE
EVOLUTION
EVOLUTION–ADDRESSES, ESSAYS, LECTURES
EVOLUTION–HISTORY
EXCAVATIONS (ARCHAEOLOGY)
EXORCISM
EXPERIENCE (RELIGION)
FABLES
FAMILY
FAMILY–PRAYER-BOOKS AND DEVOTIONS
FAMILY–RELIGIOUS LIFE
FAMILY LIFE EDUCATION
FANATICISM
FATHER AND CHILD
FATHERS
FETISHISM
FIRE (IN RELIGION, FOLK-LORE, ETC.)
FISH (IN RELIGION, FOLK-LORE, ETC.)
FLOWERS (IN RELIGION, FOLK-LORE, ETC.)
FOLK LITERATURE
FOLK LITERATURE–THEMES, MOTIVES
FOLK-LORE
FOLK-LORE–CLASSIFICATION
FOLK-LORE–DICTIONARIES
FOLK-LORE, AFRICAN
FOLK-LORE, CHINESE
FOLK-LORE, GREEK
FOLK-LORE, HAITIAN
FOLK-LORE, HAWAIIAN
FOLK-LORE, INDIAN
FOLK-LORE, INDIC
FOLK-LORE, IRISH
FOLK-LORE, JAPANESE
FOLK-LORE, LATIN AMERICAN
FOLK-LORE, MALAYAN
FOLK-LORE, NORWEGIAN
FOLK-LORE, PALESTINE
FOLK-LORE OF THE SKY
FOLK-LORE OF TREES
FOLK MEDICINE
FOOD
FOOD–HISTORY
FORTUNA, GODDESS
FRANKL, VIKTOR EMIL
FULGENTIUS, FABIUS PLANCIADES
GALILEO (GALILEO GALILEI), 1564-1642
GASPE, DISTRICT, QUEBEC–DESCRIPTION AND TRAVEL
GAYAL
GEMS (IN RELIGION, FOLK-LORE, ETC.)
GENESIS (MIDDLE HIGH GERMAN POEM)
GERMANIC TRIBES–RELIGION
GERMANY–RELIGION
GHANA–RELIGION
GHOST DANCE
GIRLS–RELIGIOUS LIFE
GLOSSOLALIA
GOD–COMPARATIVE STUDIES
GOD (GREEK RELIGION)
GODESSES
GODESSES, HINDU
GODS
GOVERNORS–UNITED STATES
GREAT BRITAIN–ANTIQUITIES
GREAT BRITAIN–RELIGION
GREEK LITERATURE (COLLECTIONS)
GRUBER, FRANZ XAVIER, 1787-1863
GRUBER, FRANZ XAVIER, 1787-1863–JUVENILE LITERATURE
GUILDFORD, RICHARD, SIR, 1455-1506
HALLUCINOGENIC DRUGS AND RELIGIOUS EXPERIENCE
HARDENBERG, FRIEDRICH LEOPOLD, FREIHERR VON, 1772-1801
HARMONY OF THE SPHERES
HEALERS
HEALING (IN RELIGION, FOLK-LORE, ETC.)
HEALING IN THE BIBLE
HEINRICH VON DEM TURLIN, fl. 1220
HERBERT, GEORGE, 1593-1633
HEROES
HEROES–JUVENILE LITERATURE
HEWLETT, MAURICE HENRI, 1861-1923
HIPPOLYTUS
HOLY ALLIANCE
HOLY LANCE
HOLY WELLS
HOME ECONOMICS
HOMER
HOPKINS, GERARD MANLEY, 1844-1889
HORNS (IN RELIGION, FOLK-LORE, ETC.)
HORSES (IN RELIGION, FOLK-LORE, ETC.)
HUMAN ECOLOGY–MORAL AND RELIGIOUS ASPECTS
I CHING
ICELANDIC AND OLD NORSE LITERATURE
IDENTIFICATION (RELIGION)
IDOLS AND IMAGES
IFA
IFUGAOS
IMMORTALISM
IMMORTALITY
INCANTATIONS
INCARNATION
INDIA–RELIGION
INDIANS–RELIGION AND MYTHOLOGY
INDIANS OF CENTRAL AMERICA–RELIGION AND MYTHOLOGY
INDIANS OF MEXICO–RELIGION AND MYTHOLOGY
INDIANS OF NORTH AMERICA–DANCES
INDIANS OF NORTH AMERICA–FICTION, JUVENILE
INDIANS OF NORTH AMERICA–LEGENDS
INDIANS OF NORTH AMERICA–LEGENDS–JUVENILE LITERATURE
INDIANS OF NORTH AMERICA–MAGIC
INDIANS OF NORTH AMERICA–MEDICINE
INDIANS OF NORTH AMERICA–MUSIC
INDIANS OF NORTH AMERICA–RELIGION AND MYTHOLOGY
INDIANS OF NORTH AMERICA–RITES AND CEREMONIES
INDIANS OF SOUTH AMERICA–LEGENDS
INDIANS OF SOUTH AMERICA–MISSIONS
INDIANS OF SOUTH AMERICA–RELIGION AND MYTHOLOGY
INITIATIONS (IN RELIGION, FOLK-LORE, ETC.)
INSTITUTIONALISM (RELIGION)
INTERNATIONAL RELATIONS–MORAL AND RELIGIOUS ASPECTS
ISIS
JACKSON, CALIFORNIA
JAINISM
JAINS
JALAL AL-DIN RUMI, MAWLANA, 1207-1273
JAMES, WILLIAM, 1842-1910
JEANNERET-GRIS, CHARLES EDOUARD, 1887-1965
JEFFERSON, THOMAS, PRES. U. S., 1743-1826
JOHNSON, SAMUEL, 1709-1784
JUBILEE SINGERS
KENNEDY, JOHN FITZGERALD, PRES. U. S., 1917-1963–POETRY
KOREA–RELIGION
LANGLAND, WILLIAM, 1330-1400
LANGUAGES–RELIGIOUS ASPECTS
LARGE TYPE BOOKS
LEGENDS, JAPANESE
LIBERALISM (RELIGION)
LIBRARIES, CHURCH
LIBRARY CATALOGS
LINCOLN, ABRAHAM, PRES. U. S., 1809-1865
LONDON–RELIGION
LUO (NILOTIC TRIBE)
MCCULLOUGH, JOHN, 1832-1885
MACDONALD, GEORGE, 1824-1905
MALTA
MALTHUS, THOMAS ROBERT, 1766-1834
MANDAEAN LANGUAGE
MANDARI (AFRICAN PEOPLE)
MANN, HORACE, 1796-1859
MANUS TRIBE
MARVELL, ANDREW, 1621-1678
MASEFIELD, JOHN, 1878-1967
MASS MEDIA–MORAL AND RELIGIOUS ASPECTS
MASS MEDIA IN RELIGION
MAYAS–RELIGION AND MYTHOLOGY
MEDICINE, AYURVEDIC
MEDICINE, HINDU
MEDICINE, PRIMITIVE
MELANESIA
MELVILLE, HERMAN, 1819-1891
MESSALLINA, VALERIE–FICTION
METAMORPHOSIS (IN RELIGION, FOLK-LORE, ETC.)
MEXICAN AMERICANS
MEXICAN DRAMA
MEXICO–SOCIAL LIFE AND CUSTOMS
MILITARY RELIGIOUS ORDERS
MOJICA, JOSE, 1895-
MOLOKAI
MONASTERIES
MONASTIC AND RELIGIOUS LIFE
MOON (IN RELIGION, FOLK-LORE, ETC.)
MORALITIES
MOROCCO
MOTHER-GODDESSES
MOUNIER, JEAN JOSEPH, 1758-1806
MOVING-PICTURES–MORAL AND RELIGIOUS ASPECTS
MYSTERIES, RELIGIOUS
MYSTERIES AND MIRACLE-PLAYS
MYSTERIES AND MIRACLE-PLAYS–BIBLIOGRAPHY
MYSTERIES AND MIRACLE-PLAYS–HISTORY AND CRITICISM
MYSTERIES AND MIRACLE-PLAYS, ENGLISH
MYSTICISM
MYSTICISM–GERMANY
MYSTICISM–GREAT BRITAIN
MYSTICISM–INDIA
MYSTICISM–SPAIN
MYSTICISM IN LITERATURE
MYTH
MYTHOLOGY
MYTHOLOGY–BIBLIOGRAPHY
MYTHOLOGY–DICTIONARIES
MYTHOLOGY–JUVENILE LITERATURE
MYTHOLOGY, AFRICAN
MYTHOLOGY, ARMENIAN
MYTHOLOGY, ASSYRO-BABYLONIAN
MYTHOLOGY, AUSTRALIAN
MYTHOLOGY, AUSTRALIAN (ABORIGINAL)
MYTHOLOGY, BRITISH
MYTHOLOGY, CANAANITE
MYTHOLOGY, CELTIC
MYTHOLOGY, CHINESE
MYTHOLOGY, CLASSICAL
MYTHOLOGY, CLASSICAL–JUVENILE LITERATURE
MYTHOLOGY, EGYPTIAN
MYTHOLOGY, ESKIMO
MYTHOLOGY, FINNO-UGRIAN
MYTHOLOGY, GERMANIC
MYTHOLOGY, GREEK
MYTHOLOGY, GREEK–JUVENILE LITERATURE
MYTHOLOGY, HAWAIIAN
MYTHOLOGY, HITTITE
MYTHOLOGY, INDIC
MYTHOLOGY, INDO-EUROPEAN
MYTHOLOGY, IRISH
MYTHOLOGY, JAPANESE
MYTHOLOGY, NORSE
MYTHOLOGY, NORSE–JUVENILE LITERATURE
MYTHOLOGY, ORIENTAL
MYTHOLOGY, POLYNESIAN
MYTHOLOGY, ROMAN
MYTHOLOGY, SIBERIAN
MYTHOLOGY, SLAVIC
MYTHOLOGY, SUMERIAN
MYTHOLOGY, WELSH
MYTHOLOGY IN LITERATURE
NATIONALISM AND RELIGION
NATURAL THEOLOGY
NATURE–RELIGIOUS INTERPRETATIONS
NATURE (IN RELIGION, FOLK-LORE, ETC.)
NATURE WORSHIP
NDEMBU (AFRICAN TRIBE)
NEAR EAST–RELIGION
NEMEA, GREECE
NEW ENGLAND–CHURCH HISTORY
NEW ENGLAND–HISTORY–COLONIAL PERIOD, ca. 1600-1775
NEW ENGLAND–INTELLECTUAL LIFE
NEW ENGLAND–SOCIAL LIFE AND CUSTOMS
NEW ENGLAND THEOLOGY
NEW FRANCE–DISCOVERY AND EXPLORATION
NEW SOUTH WALES–RELIGION
NEW YORK (CITY)–CHURCHES
NEW YORK (CITY)–FIVE POINTS MISSION
NEW YORK (STATE)–CHURCH HISTORY
NEW YORK (STATE)–HISTORY–COLONIAL PERIOD, ca. 1600-1775
NGONDE (AFRICAN TRIBE)
NORMANDY–HISTORY–MEDIEVAL PERIOD
NORMANS
NORTH, JOHN WESLEY
NORTH CAROLINA–SOCIAL CONDITIONS
NORWAY–CHURCH HISTORY
NORWEGIANS IN THE UNITED STATES
NUER (AFRICAN TRIBE)
OEDIPUS
OEDOGONIACEAE
OKINAWA ISLAND
OLMECS
OLYMPIC GAMES
OMENS
ONONDAGA LANGUAGE
ORACLES
ORDINALIA
ORIENTAL STUDIES
ORPHEUS
OSIRIS
OSTIA, ITALY–ANTIQUITIES
OSTWALD, WILHELM, 1853-1932
OVIMBUNDU
OXFORD UNIVERSITY
OXFORD UNIVERSITY CHRIST CHURCH–HISTORY
PACCIOLI, LUCA, d. ca. 1514
PAGANISM
PAN (DEITY) IN LITERATURE
PANTHEISM
PARADISE
PARADISE IN LITERATURE AND ART
PARDO BAZAN, EMILIA, CONDESA DE, 1852-1921
PAULUS DIACONUS, 720-797
PECOS, NEW MEXICO
PELE (GODDESS)
PENNSYLVANIA–BOUNDARIES–VIRGINIA
PENNSYLVANIA–DESCRIPTION AND TRAVEL
PERSEPOLIS
PERU–HISTORY
PETER 1ST, THE GREAT, EMPEROR OF RUSSIA, 1672-1725
PEYOTISM
PHALLICISM
PHILIPPINE ISLANDS–CHURCH HISTORY
PINCKNEY, THOMAS, 1750-1828
PLACE, FRANCIS, 1771-1854
PLURALITY OF WORLDS
PNEUMA (WORD)
POLARITY (IN RELIGION, FOLK-LORE, ETC.)

POLYNESIA
POLYNESIA–SOCIAL LIFE AND CUSTOMS
POPULATION
POSTEL, GUILLAUME, 1510-1581
PRAYER
PRESTON, JENNET, d. 1612
PRIESTS, ASSYRO-BABYLONIAN
PRINCETON THEOLOGICAL SEMINARY–BIOGRAPHY
PROMETHEUS
PROPHETS
PROVERBS
PROVIDENCE AND GOVERNMENT OF GOD
PROVIDENCE AND GOVERNMENT OF GOD–SERMONS
PSYCHE (GODDESS)–FICTION
PSYCHE (GODDESS) LITERATURE
PSYCHIATRY AND RELIGION
PSYCHOLOGY
PSYCHOLOGY, APPLIED
PUPPETS AND PUPPET-PLAYS
PURITY, RITUAL
PUZZLES–JUVENILE LITERATURE
PYRAMIDS
PYRAMIDS–CURIOSA AND MISCELLANEA
QUEBEC (PROVINCE)–SOCIAL CONDITIONS
QUOTATIONS
RA (EGYPTIAN DIETY)
RAJASUYA
RAMESES 2ND, KING OF EGYPT
RAMESES 6TH, KING OF EGYPT
REDUCING
REED, STANLEY FORMAN, 1884-
REFERENCE BOOKS
REINCARNATION
RELIGION
RELIGION–ADDRESSES, ESSAYS, LECTURES
RELIGION–BIBLIOGRAPHY
RELIGION–DICTIONARIES
RELIGION–HISTORIOGRAPHY
RELIGION–HISTORY
RELIGION–PHILOSOPHY
RELIGION–QUOTATIONS, MAXIMS, ETC.
RELIGION–STUDY AND TEACHING
RELIGION, PRIMITIVE
RELIGION AND CULTURE
RELIGION AND ETHICS
RELIGION AND GEOGRAPHY
RELIGION AND HUMOR
RELIGION AND LABOR
RELIGION AND LANGUAGE
RELIGION AND LAW
RELIGION AND LITERATURE
RELIGION AND MUSIC
RELIGION AND SCIENCE
RELIGION AND SCIENCE–HISTORY OF CONTROVERSY
RELIGION AND SOCIOLOGY
RELIGION AND SPORTS
RELIGION AND STATE
RELIGION IN LITERATURE
RELIGION IN POETRY
RELIGION IN THE PUBLIC SCHOOLS
RELIGIONS
RELIGIONS–BIBLIOGRAPHY
RELIGIONS–BIOGRAPHY
RELIGIONS–DICTIONARIES
RELIGIONS–HISTORY
RELIGIONS–JUVENILE LITERATURE
RELIGIONS–PICTURES, ILLUSTRATIONS, ETC.
RELIGIONS (PROPOSED, UNIVERSAL, ETC.)
RELIGIOUS BIOGRAPHY
RELIGIOUS LITERATURE
RELIGIOUS LITERATURE (SELECTIONS: EXTRACTS, ETC.)
RELIGIOUS LITERATURE–AUTHORSHIP
RELIGIOUS LITERATURE–BIBLIOGRAPHY
RELIGIOUS LITERATURE–HISTORY AND CRITICISM
RELIGIOUS LITERATURE–PUBLICATION AND DISTRIBUTION
RELIGIOUS NEWSPAPERS AND PERIODICALS
RELIGIOUS NEWSPAPERS AND PERIODICALS–BIBLIOGRAPHY
RELIGIOUS POETRY
RELIGIOUS POETRY (LATIN)
RELIGIOUS POETRY–HISTORY AND CRITICISM
RELIGIOUS POETRY, AMERICAN
RELIGIOUS POETRY, ANGLO-SAXON
RELIGIOUS POETRY, ENGLISH
RELIGIOUS POETRY, ENGLISH–BIBLIOGRAPHY
RELIGIOUS POETRY, JAPANESE
RESTIF, NICHOLAS EDME, 1734-1806
RITES AND CEREMONIES
RITUAL
ROBERTS, EDWIN, b. 1831
ROSEGGER, PETER, 1843-1918
RUSKIN, JOHN, 1819-1900
RUSSIA–MORAL CONDITIONS
RUSSIA–RELIGION
SACRED BOOKS
SACRED BOOKS (SELECTIONS, EXTRACTS, ETC.
SACRIFICE
SAFWA (BANTU TRIBE)
WITCHCRAFT
SAHAJIYA
SAINT-SIMON, CLAUDE HENRI, COMTE DE, 1760-1825
SAMARITANS
SAMSON, ABBOT OF BURY ST. EDMUNDS, 1135-1211
SANTA CLAUS
SARCOPHAGI
SATANISM
SATTLER, MICHAEL–FICTION
SCANDINAVIAN MYTHOLOGY
SCHULZ, CHARLES M.
SCHWENK FELDERS
SEASONS
SEASONS–JUVENILE LITERATURE
SECTS
SECTS–AFRICA
SECTS–CANADA
SECTS–RUSSIA
SECTS–UNITED STATES
SECTS, MEDIEVAL
SEMITES
SEPULCHRAL MONUMENTS
SERPENTS (IN RELIGION, FOLK-LORE, ETC.)
SEVEN GODS OF FORTUNE
SEWALL, SAMUEL, 1652-1730
SHAKESPEARE, WILLIAM, 1564-1616
SHAKESPEARE, WILLIAM, 1564-1616–CRITICISM, TEXTUAL
SHAKESPEARE, WILLIAM, 1564-1616–KNOWLEDGE AND LEARNING
SHAKESPEARE, WILLIAM, 1564-1616–SUPERNATURAL ELEMENT
SHAMANISM
SHAW, GEORGE BERNARD, 1856-1950
SHERPAS
SHINTO
SHRINES
SIBYLS
SIDGWICK, HENRY, 1838-1900
SILENCE
SOCIALISM AND RELIGION
SOCIOLOGY
SPENSER, EDMUND, 1552?-1599
SPIRITS
STAR OF BETHLEHEM
STARS (IN RELIGION, FOLK-LORE, ETC.)
STONEHENGE
STOWE, HARRIET ELIZABETH (BEECHER), 1811-1896
SUMERIANS–RELIGION
SUN (IN RELIGION, FOLK-LORE, ETC.)
SUN-WORSHIP
SUPERMAN
SUPERNATURAL
SUPERSTITION
SYMBOLISM
SYMBOLISM IN LITERATURE
TABOO
TALANSI (AFRICAN TRIBE)
TALES, BUDDHIST
TALES, BURMESE
TALES, CHINESE
TALES, HASSIDIC
TALES, HAWAIIAN
TALES, HEBREW
TALES, JEWISH
TALES, POLYNESIAN
TALES, SUFI
TALES, THAI
TALES, YORUBAN
TALISMANS
TELLOH (MOUND)
TEMPLES
TEXAS CHRISTIAN UNIVERSITY
THEISM
THEOPHAINES
THONGA TRIBE
TIECK, JOHANN LUDWIG, 1773-1853
TIKOPIANS
TIVI (AFRICAN PEOPLE)
TOMBS
TOTEMISM
TOTEMS
TRANCE
TRIALS (WITCHCRAFT)
TRINITIES
TRUTH, SOJOURNER, d. 1883
TUATHA DE DANANN
TUTENKHAMUN, KING OF EGYPT
UMBANDA (CULTUS)
UNDSET, SIGRID, 1882-
UPJOHN, RICHARD, 1802-1878
VAIKHANASAS
VAUGHAN, HENRY, 1622-1695
VAULTS
VEGETARIANISM–RELIGIOUS ASPECTS
VISIONS
VOGUL MYTHOLOGY
VOTIVE OFFERINGS
VOWS
WANDERING JEW
WASHINGTON, GEORGE, PRES. U. S., 1732-1799
WATER (IN RELIGION, FOLK-LORE, ETC.
WAYFARING LIFE
WISDOM
WISDOM LITERATURE
WITCHCRAFT–JUVENILE LITERATURE
WITCHCRAFT–AFRICA
WITCHCRAFT–CHINA
WITCHCRAFT–EUROPE
WITCHCRAFT–GREAT BRITAIN
WITCHCRAFT–HAWAII
WITCHCRAFT–INDIA
WITCHCRAFT–IRELAND
WITCHCRAFT–MEXICO
WITCHCRAFT–NEW ENGLAND
WITCHCRAFT–PENNSYLVANIA
WITCHCRAFT–TANZANIA
YEZIDIS
YORUBAS
ZEUS
ZULUS

RELIGIOUS ART

ANGELS–ART
ARCHITECTURE–CHINA
ARCHITECTURE–EGYPT
ARCHITECTURE–GREAT BRITAIN
ARCHITECTURE–ITALY
ARCHITECTURE–TURKEY
ARCHITECTURE, ANCIENT
ARCHITECTURE, BAROQUE
ARCHITECTURE, BUDDHIST
ARCHITECTURE, BYZANTINE
ARCHITECTURE, CISTERCIAN
ARCHITECTURE, GOTHIC
ARCHITECTURE, GREEK
ARCHITECTURE, HINDU
ARCHITECTURE, ISLAMIC
ARCHITECTURE, MEDIEVAL
ART–PHILOSOPHY
ART, BUDDHIST
ART, BYZANTINE
ART, CISTERCIAN
ART, GOTHIC
ART, HINDU
ART, ISLAMIC
ART, JEWISH
ART, MEDIEVAL
ART, MEXICAN
ART AND MYTHOLOGY
ART AND RELIGION
BERNINI, GIOVANNI LORENZO, 1598-1680
BLAKE, WILLIAM, 1757-1827
CHAGALL, MARC, 1887-
CHRISTIAN ART AND SYMBOLISM
CHRISTIAN ART AND SYMBOLISM–JUVENILE LITERATURE
CHURCH ARCHITECTURE
CHURCH ARCHITECTURE–DESIGNS AND PLANS
CHURCH ARCHITECTURE–DETAILS
CHURCH ARCHITECTURE–HISTORY
CHURCH ARCHITECTURE–EUROPE
CHURCH ARCHITECTURE–FRANCE
CHURCH ARCHITECTURE–GREAT BRITAIN
CHURCH ARCHITECTURE–ITALY
CHURCH ARCHITECTURE–MEXICO
CHURCH ARCHITECTURE–PALESTINE
CHURCH ARCHITECTURE–SPAIN
CHURCH ARCHITECTURE–UNITED STATES
CHURCH MUSIC–PROTESTANT CHURCHES
EYCK, HUBERT VAN, 1366-1426
EYCK, JAN VAN, 1386-1440
FRANCESCO D'ASSISI, SAINT, 1182-1226–ART
GIOTTO DI BONDONE, 1266?-1337
GLASS PAINTING AND STAINING
GOD–ART
GODS IN ART
GRAIL
GROTESQUE
ICONS
ILLUMINATION OF BOOKS AND MANUSCRIPTS
ILLUMINATION OF BOOKS AND MANUSCRIPTS–CATALOGS
ILLUMINATION OF BOOKS AND MANUSCRIPTS–HISTORY
ILLUMINATION OF BOOKS AND MANUSCRIPTS–SPECIMENS, REPRODUCTIONS, ETC.
INDIANS OF MEXICO–SCULPTURE
JADE
JESUS CHRIST–ART
JESUS CHRIST–WORDS
JESUS CHRIST IN ART
JEWISH ART AND SYMBOLISM
KRISHNA IN ART, LITERATURE, ETC.
MAYAS–ART
MICHELANGELO (BUONARROTI, MICHELANGELO), 1475-1564
MOSAICS
MURAL PAINTING AND DECORATION
PAINTING–HISTORY
PAINTING, EUROPEAN
PAINTING, FLEMISH
PAINTING, INDIC
PAINTING, ISLAMIC
PAINTING, ITALIAN
PAINTING, MEDIEVAL
PAINTING, RENAISSANCE
PAINTING, RUSSIAN
PAINTINGS, ASIAN
PAINTINGS, DUTCH
PAINTINGS, MAORI
PICTURE-WRITING
PICTURE-WRITING, INDIAN
RAPHAEL (RAFFAELO SANZIO D'URBINO), 1483-1520
REMBRANDT, HARMENSZOON VAN RIJN, 1606-1669
ROBBIA, LUCA DELLA, 1400-1482
ROMANTICISM IN ART
ROME (CITY)–DESCRIPTION–GUIDEBOOKS
ROUAULT, GEORGES, 1871-1958
RUBENS, PETER PAUL, SIR, 1577-1640
SCULPTURE–CHINA
SCULPTURE–EGYPT
SCULPTURE–FRANCE
SCULPTURE–GREAT BRITAIN
SCULPTURE–IRELAND
SCULPTURE–JAPAN
SCULPTURE–NEAR EAST
SCULPTURE–OCEANICA
SCULPTURE–UNITED STATES
SCULPTURE, ANCIENT
SCULPTURE, GREEK
SCULPTURE, MEDIEVAL
SCULPTURE, RENAISSANCE
SCULPTURE, ROMAN
SCULPTURE, ROMANESQUE
SISTINE CHAPEL
SMITH, JOSEPH LINDON, 1863-1950
STOVE-PLATES
SYMBOLISM IN ART
SYNAGOGUE ARCHITECTURE
TERRA-COTTA SCULPTURE

RELIGIOUS HISTORY

ABYDOS, EGYPT
AMERICA–CHURCH HISTORY
ARABIA–ANTIQUITIES
ARABIA–DESCRIPTION AND TRAVEL
ARARAT, MOUNT
ASIA–RELIGION
ASIA, SOUTHEASTERN–RELIGION
ATHENS–ANTIQUITIES
AUSTRALIA–CHURCH HISTORY
AUSTRALIA–RELIGION
AUSTRIA–CHURCH HISTORY
BABYLON
BARONIUS, CESARE, 1538-1607
BREUIL, HENRI, 1877-1961
CAHAN, ABRAHAM, 1886-1951
CANADA–RELIGION
CAVE CHURCHES
CAVE TEMPLES
CHINA–ANTIQUITIES
CHINA–CHURCH HISTORY
CHRISTIAN ANTIQUITIES
CHURCH HISTORY
CHURCH HISTORY–BIBLIOGRAPHY
CHURCH HISTORY–DICTIONARIES
CHURCH HISTORY–HISTORIOGRAPHY
CHURCH HISTORY–JUVENILE LITERATURE
CHURCH HISTORY–PHILOSOPHY
CHURCH HISTORY–PRIMITIVE AND EARLY CHURCH, ca. 30-600
CHURCH HISTORY–PRIMITIVE AND EARLY CHURCH, ca. 30-600–FICTION
CHURCH HISTORY–MIDDLE AGES, 600-1500
CHURCH HISTORY–MIDDLE AGES, 600-1500–HISTORIOGRAPHY
CHURCH HISTORY–SOURCES
CHURCH HISTORY–MODERN PERIOD, 1500-
CHURCH HISTORY–18TH CENTURY
CHURCH HISTORY–19TH CENTURY
CHURCH HISTORY–20TH CENTURY
CHURCHES
CHURCHES–AFRICA
CHURCHES–ASIA
CHURCHES–CANADA
CHURCHES–DENMARK
CHURCHES–EGYPT
CHURCHES–EUROPE
CHURCHES–FRANCE
CHURCHES–GREAT BRITAIN
CHURCHES–MEXICO
CHURCHES–PALESTINE
CHURCHES–PORTUGAL
CHURCHES–ROMANIA
CHURCHES–UNITED STATES

CLASSICAL PHILOLOGY
CRUSADES
CRUSADES–BIBLIOGRAPHY
CRUSADES–JUVENILE LITERATURE
CRUSADES–FIRST, 1096-1099
CRUSADES–FIRST, 1096-1099–FICTION
CRUSADES–SECOND, 1147-1149
CRUSADES–THIRD, 1189-1192
CRUSADES–FOURTH, 1202-1204
CRUSADES–LATER, 13TH, 14TH, AND 15TH CENTURIES
CUBA–RELIGION
CUTHBERT, SAINT
DECCAN, INDIA–HISTORY
DIONYSIUS 1ST, OF TELL-MAHRE, PATRIARCH OF THE JACOBITES, d. 845
EGYPT–ANTIQUITIES
EGYPT–HISTORY–TO 640
EGYPT–HISTORY–640-1882
ENDOWMENTS
ENGLAND–ANTIQUITIES
ENLIGHTENMENT
EPITAPHS
EUROPE–HISTORY–476-1492
EUROPE–HISTORY–1492-1648
EUROPE–HISTORY–1918-1945
EVOLUTION–HISTORY
EYB, ALBRECHT VON, 1420-1475
FATIMA, PORTUGAL (SHRINE)
FERRARA–HISTORY
FIFTH MONARCHY MEN
FLORENCE–CHURCHES
FRANCE–CHURCH HISTORY
FRANKS
FULAH EMPIRE
GALILEE
GANGES RIVER
GAUL–HISTORY
GERMANY–CHURCH HISTORY
GOD–HISTORY OF DOCTRINES
GORDON RIOTS, 1780
GREAT AWAKENING
GREAT BRITAIN–CHURCH HISTORY
GREAT BRITAIN–CHURCH HISTORY–SOURCES
GREAT BRITAIN–CHURCH HISTORY–TO 843
GREAT BRITAIN–CHURCH HISTORY–ANGLO-SAXON PERIOD, 449-1066
GREAT BRITAIN–CHURCH HISTORY–MEDIEVAL PERIOD, 1066-1485
GREAT BRITAIN–CHURCH HISTORY–16TH CENTURY
GREAT BRITAIN–CHURCH HISTORY–17TH CENTURY
GREAT BRITAIN–CHURCH HISTORY–MODERN PERIOD, 1485-
GREAT BRITAIN–CHURCH HISTORY–18TH CENTURY
GREAT BRITAIN–CHURCH HISTORY–19TH CENTURY
GREAT BRITAIN–HISTORY–MEDIEVAL PERIOD, 1066-1485
GREAT BRITAIN–HISTORY–PURITAN REVOLUTION, 1642-1660
GREAT BRITAIN–HISTORY–RESTORATION, 1660-1688
GREAT BRITAIN–RELATIONS (GENERAL) WITH THE CATHOLIC CHURCH
GREECE–ANTIQUITIES
GREECE–RELIGION
GREEK LITERATURE–HISTORY AND CRITICISM
HAGIOGRAPHY
HAITI
HAITI–SOCIAL LIFE AND CUSTOMS
HAWAII–RELIGION
HELLENISM
HERESIES AND HERETICS
HERESIES AND HERETICS–EARLY CHURCH, ca. 30-600
HERESIES AND HERETICS–MIDDLE AGES, 600-1500
HERESIES AND HERETICS–MODERN PERIOD, 1500-
HERESY
HEROES
HEROES–JUVENILE LITERATURE
HERRNHUT, GERMANY–HISTORY
HILDEGARD, SAINT, 1098?-1178
HISTORY–METHODOLOGY
HISTORY–PHILOSOPHY
HISTORY (THEOLOGY)
HISTORY, ANCIENT
HISTORY, MODERN–16TH CENTURY
HITTITES
HOLY LANCE
HOLY LEAGUE, 1576-1593
HOLY ROMAN EMPIRE
HOLY ROMAN EMPIRE–HISTORY–843-1273
HUGUENOTS
HUGUENOTS IN FOREIGN COUNTRIES
HUGUENOTS IN FRANCE
HUMANISM
HUMANISM, RELIGIOUS
IBADAN, NIGERIA
ILLINOIS
IMPOSTORS AND IMPOSTURE
INDIA
INDIA–ANTIQUITIES
INDIA–BIOGRAPHY
INDIA–CHURCH HISTORY
INDIA–CIVILIZATION
INDIA–HISTORY–EARLY TO 1000 A.D
INDIA–INTELLECTUAL LIFE
INDIANS–ANTIQUITIES
INDIANS OF CENTRAL AMERICA
INDIANS OF MEXICO–ANTIQUITIES
INDIANS OF NORTH AMERICA–BIBLIOGRAPHY
INDIANS OF NORTH AMERICA–CULTURE
INDONESIA–RELIGION
INQUISITION
INSCRIPTIONS, ARAMAIC
INSCRIPTIONS, ISLAMIC
INSCRIPTIONS, LATIN
INSCRIPTIONS, SAFAITIC
IOWA INFANTRY–MORMON BATTALION, 1846-1847
IRAN–RELIGION
IRELAND–CHURCH HISTORY
ISTANBUL–ANTIQUITIES
ISTANBUL–CHURCH OF THE HOLY APOSTLES
ISTANBUL–HISTORY
ISTANBUL (PATRIARCHATE)–HISTORY
ITALIANS IN THE UNITED STATES
ITALY–CHURCH HISTORY
JAPAN–CHURCH HISTORY
JAPAN–CIVILIZATION
JAPAN–RELIGION
JERUSALEM
JERUSALEM–ANTIQUITIES
JERUSALEM–CHURCHES
JERUSALEM–DESCRIPTION
JERUSALEM–HISTORY
JERUSALEM–HISTORY–LATIN KINGDOM, 1099-1244
JERUSALEM–TEMPLE
JIB, AL, JORDAN
JORDAN–ANTIQUITIES
JORDAN–HISTORY
KARNAK, EGYPT
KENYON COLLEGE, GAMBIER, OHIO
KERALA, INDIA (STATE)
KINGS AND RULERS (IN RELIGION, FOLK-LORE, ETC.)
KNIGHTS OF MALTA
KNIGHTS OF SAINT CRISPIN
KONARAK, INDIA–TEMPLE
LAMBETH CONFERENCE
LATIN AMERICA–RELIGION
LEGENDS
LEGENDS–HISTORY AND CRITICISM
LEGENDS, CHINESE
LEGENDS, CHRISTIAN
LEGENDS, EGYPTIAN
LIGUORI, ALFONSO MARIA DE, SAINT, 1696-1787
LILBURNE, JOHN, 1614?-1657
LITURGICAL MOVEMENT
LONDON–CHURCHES
LORD'S SUPPER–HISTORY
LORD'S SUPPER IN LITERATURE
LOST TRIBES OF ISRAEL
MAI-CHI SHAN CAVES
MALAWI
MANDAEANS
MANICHAEISM
MANORS
MANUSCRIPTS
MANUSCRIPTS–BIBLIOGRAPHY
MANUSCRIPTS–CATALOGS
MANUSCRIPTS–FACSIMILES
MANUSCRIPTS (PAPYRI)
MAORIS
MARCION, OF SINOPE, 2ND CENTURY
MARTYRDOM
MARTYROLOGIES
MARTYRS
MARYLAND–HISTORY
MARYLAND–POLITICS AND GOVERNMENT
MASHONA
MASSACHUSETTS–CHURCH HISTORY
MASSACHUSETTS–HISTORY
MASSACHUSETTS–HISTORY–COLONIAL PERIOD, ca. 1600-1775
MASSACHUSETTS–HISTORY–COLONIAL PERIOD, ca. 1600-1775–SOURCES
MASSACHUSETTS–HISTORY, JUVENILE
MASSACHUSETTS–JUVENILE LITERATURE
MASSACHUSETTS–POLITICS AND GOVERNMENT–COLONIAL PERIOD, ca. 1600-1775
MAXIMUS, SAINT, BP. OF TURIN, D. ca. 420
MAXIMUS CONFESSOR, SAINT, ca. 580-662
MAYAS
MEDICINE AND RELIGION
MEDICINE-MAN
MESSIANISM, AMERICAN
MEXICO–HISTORY–CONQUEST, 1519-1540
MEXICO–RELIGION
MIDDLE AGE
MIDDLE AGES
MIDDLE AGES–HISTORY
MIDDLE AGES–JUVENILE LITERATURE
MIDDLEHAM, YORK, ENGLAND–COLLEGIATE CHURCH
MIGRATIONS OF NATIONS
MISSIONS–HISTORY
MOLOKANS
MONASTICISM AND RELIGIOUS ORDERS
MONASTICISM AND RELIGIOUS ORDERS–BIBLIOGRAPHY
MONASTICISM AND RELIGIOUS ORDERS–COMMON LIFE
MONASTICISM AND RELIGIOUS ORDERS–EARLY CHURCH, ca. 30-600
MONASTICISM AND RELIGIOUS ORDERS–EAST
MONASTICISM AND RELIGIOUS ORDERS–JUVENILE LITERATURE
MONASTICISM AND RELIGIOUS ORDERS–MIDDLE AGES, 600-1500
MONASTICISM AND RELIGIOUS ORDERS–RULES
MONASTICISM AND RELIGIOUS ORDERS–EGYPT
MONASTICISM AND RELIGIOUS ORDERS–FRANCE
MONASTICISM AND RELIGIOUS ORDERS–GERMANY
MONASTICISM AND RELIGIOUS ORDERS–GREAT BRITAIN
MONASTICISM AND RELIGIOUS ORDERS–IRELAND
MONASTICISM AND RELIGIOUS ORDERS–NEAR EAST
MONASTICISM AND RELIGIOUS ORDERS, ANGLICAN
MONASTICISM AND RELIGIOUS ORDERS, PROTESTANT
MONASTICISM AND RELIGIOUS ORDERS FOR WOMEN
MONASTICISM AND RELIGIOUS ORDERS FOR WOMEN–BIOGRAPHY
MONTENEGRO–CIVILIZATION
MONUMENTS
MORALITIES–HISTORY AND CRITICISM
MORGANTOWN, WEST VIRGINIA–FIRST CHRISTIAN CHURCH
MORMONS AND MORMONISM–HISTORY
MOUNTAIN MEADOWS MASSACRE, 1857
MYSTICISM–HISTORY
MYSTICISM–MIDDLE AGES, 600-1500
NATIVE AMERICAN CHURCH OF NORTH AMERICA
NATIVISTIC MOVEMENTS
NEAR EAST–ANTIQUITIES
NEAR EAST–CIVILIZATION
NEAR EAST–DESCRIPTION AND TRAVEL
NICARAGUA–CHURCH HISTORY
NIPPUR
NORTHERN IRELAND–RELIGION
ONTOLOGY
OSTRAKA
PARAGUAY–HISTORY
PARISH-IN-ELMET, ENGLAND
PASTORAL LITERATURE–HISTORY AND CRITICISM
PATARINES
PEASANTS' WAR, 1524-1525
PENNSYLVANIA–HISTORY
PENNSYLVANIA–POLITICS AND GOVERNMENT
PENNSYLVANIA GERMANS
PERU–RELIGION
PETAR 2ND, PRINCE BISHOP OF MONTENEGRO, 1813-1851
PETRA, ARABIA
PHILO BYBLIUS, FL. ca. 100A.D.
PIERRE DE DREUX, DUKE OF BRITTANY, 13TH CENTURY
PILGRIMS (NEW PLYMOUTH COLONY)
PILGRIMS (NEW PLYMOUTH COLONY)–JUVENILE LITERATURE
PLYMOUTH, MASSACHUSETTS–HISTORY
POLAND–HISTORY
POLITICAL SCIENCE–HISTORY–ISLAMIC COUNTRIES
POPISH PLOT, 1678
PREMONSTRATENSIANS
PROGRESS
PROSPER OF AQUITAINE
RABELAIS, FRANCOIS, ca. 1490-1553
REFORMERS
REFUGEES, RELIGIOUS
RELIGIONS–RELATIONS
RELIGION HISTORIANS
RELIGIOUS LIBERTY–GERMANY
RELICS AND RELIQUARIES
RENAISSANCE
RENAISSANCE–ENGLAND
RENAISSANCE–GERMANY
RENAISSANCE–ITALY
REVOLUTIONS
RHODE ISLAND–HISTORY
RIPON, TREATY OF, 1640
ROLFE, FREDERICK WILLIAM, 1860-1913
ROLLE, RICHARD, OF HAMPOLE, 1290-1349
ROMAN EMPERORS
ROME–CIVILIZATION
ROME–HISTORY–EMPIRE, 30 B.C.-476 A.D.
ROME–RELIGION
ROME (CITY)–ANTIQUITIES
ROME (CITY)–CHURCHES
RUSSIA–CHURCH HISTORY
ST. BARTHOLOMEW'S DAY, MASSACRE OF, 1572
SALEM, MASSACHUSETTS
SALEM, MASSACHUSETTS–HISTORY
SALT LAKE CITY
SAN FRANCISCO–HISTORY
SAUDI ARABIA
SAVANNAH–FIRST BRYAN BAPTIST CHURCH
SAXONS
SCANDINAVIA–RELIGION
SCIENCE–EARLY WORKS TO 1800
SCIENCE, MEDIEVAL
SCIENCE AND CIVILIZATION
SCIENTISTS
SCOTLAND–ANTIQUITIES
SCOTLAND–BIOGRAPHY
SCOTLAND–CHURCH HISTORY
SCOTLAND–CHURCH HISTORY–SOURCES
SCOTLAND–HISTORY
SCOTLAND–RELIGION
SCROLLS
SENEGAL
SEVENTEENTH CENTURY
SHIRAZ–HISTORY
SINKIANG
SLAVS–HISTORY
SOCIALISM IN GREAT BRITAIN
SONOMA, CALIFORNIA–HISTORY
SOUTH AFRICA–BIOGRAPHY
SOUTH AFRICA–CHURCH HISTORY
SOUTH AFRICA–DESCRIPTION AND TRAVEL
SOUTH AFRICA–RACE QUESTION
SOUTH AFRICA–RELIGION
SOUTH AFRICA–SOCIAL LIFE AND CUSTOMS
SOUTHERN STATES–CHURCH HISTORY
SOUTHERN STATES–CIVILIZATION
SOUTHERN STATES–SOCIAL LIFE AND CUSTOMS
SPAIN–BIOGRAPHY
SPAIN–CHURCH HISTORY
SPAIN–CIVILIZATION
SPAIN–FOREIGN RELATIONS
SPAIN–HISTORY
SPAIN–SOCIAL CONDITIONS
STRATFORD-UPON-AVON
SUDAN, EGYPTIAN–ANTIQUITIES
SWEDEN–CHURCH HISTORY
SWEDES IN FOREIGN COUNTRIES
SYRIA
SYRIAC LITERATURE
TAIZE (RELIGIOUS COMMUNITY)
TEOTIHUACAN, MEXICO
THAILAND–HISTORY
THAILAND–RELIGION
THEATER–GREAT BRITAIN–HISTORY
THEBES, EGYPT
THOMPSON, ERNEST TRICE, 1894-
TIBET
TIBET–CIVILIZATION
TIBET–DESCRIPTION AND TRAVEL
TIBET–HISTORY
TIBET–RELIGION
TRACY, WILLIAM, fl. 1530
TUAMOTU ISLANDS
TUNSTALL, ENGLAND (PARISH)
TURKEY
TURKEY–RELIGION
TURKEY–SOCIAL CONDITIONS
UGANDA
UGANDA–RELIGION
UNDERDEVELOPED AREAS–RELIGION
UNITED STATES–CHURCH HISTORY
UNITED STATES–CHURCH HISTORY–SOURCES
UNITED STATES–CHURCH HISTORY–20TH CENTURY
UNITED STATES–CIVILIZATION
UNITED STATES–HISTORY–SOURCES
UNITED STATES–HISTORY–REVOLUTION, 1775-1783
UNITED STATES–HISTORY–1783-1865
UNITED STATES–HISTORY–WAR OF 1812
UNITED STATES–HISTORY–WAR WITH MEXICO, 1845-1848
UNITED STATES–HISTORY–CIVIL WAR, 1861-1865–ADDRESSES, SERMONS, ETC.
UNITED STATES–HISTORY–CIVIL WAR, 1861-1865–JEWS
UNITED STATES–HISTORY–CIVIL WAR, 1861-1865–RELIGIOUS ASPECTS
UNITED STATES–INTELLECTUAL LIFE

UNITED STATES–MORAL CONDITIONS
UNITED STATES–POPULATION
UNITED STATES–RELIGION
UNITED STATES–RELIGION–20TH CENTURY
UKRAINE–CHURCH HISTORY
UTAH–DESCRIPTION AND TRAVEL
UTAH–HISTORY
UTAH EXPEDITION, 1857-1858
VALENCIA–HISTORY
VENEZUELA–CHURCH HISTORY
VILLEINAGE
VIRGINIA–GENEALOGY
VIRGINIA–HISTORY–COLONIAL PERIOD, ca. 1600-1775
VIRGINIA–RELIGION
WALES–CHURCH HISTORY
WALES–RELIGION
WALLOONS
WARREN COUNTY, NEW YORK–SOCIAL LIFE AND CUSTOMS
WARSAW–HISTORY–UPRISING OF 1943
WASHINGTON, D. C.–CHURCH OF THE SAVIOR
WASHINGTON, D. C. ST. JOHN'S CHURCH, LAFAYETTE SQUARE
WEBSTER, JOHN, 1580?-1625?
WEST INDIES–DESCRIPTION AND TRAVEL
WEST TOWN, CHINA
WESTMINSTER, ENGLAND
WILTSHIRE, ENGLAND
WORCESTER, ENGLAND
WORLD HISTORY
WORLD HISTORY–JUVENILE LITERATURE
WORLD WAR, 1939-1945–ADDRESSES, SERMONS, ETC.
WORLD WAR, 1939-1945–RELIGIOUS ASPECTS
WULFSTAN 2ND, ABP., OF YORK d. 1203
YORK, ENGLAND (DIOCESE)
ZAMBIA–RELIGION

RELIGIOUS PHILOSOPHY–ETHICS, LOGIC

ABELARD, PETER, 1079-1142
ABELARD, PETER, 1079-1142–FICTION
ABORTION–MORAL AND ETHICAL ASPECTS
ALTRUISM
BARTH, KARL, 1886-1968
BAUR, FERDINAND CHRISTIAN, 1792-1860
BERDIAEV, NIKOLAI ALEKSANDROVICH, 1874-1948
BIBLE–ETHICS
BIBLE–PHILOSOPHY
BOEHME, JAKOB, 1575-1624
BONHOEFFER, DIETRICH, 1906-1945
BUBER, MARTIN, 1878-1965
BUDDHIST ETHICS
BUDDHIST LOGIC
CENSORSHIP
CHRISTIAN ETHICS
CHRISTIANITY–PHILOSOPHY
DEATH
DEATH–BIBLIOGRAPHY
DEATH–JUVENILE LITERATURE
DEATH–MEDITATIONS
DEATH–RELIGIOUS AND MORAL ASPECTS
DECISION-MAKING (ETHICS)
DESCARTES, RENE, 1596-1650
DRUIDS AND DRUIDISM
DURKHEIM, EMILE, 1858-1917
EAST AND WEST
ETERNITY
ETHICS
ETHICS–ADDRESSES, ESSAYS, LECTURES
ETHICS–DICTIONARIES
ETHICS–HISTORY
ETHICS–JUVENILE LITERTURE
ETHICS, CHINESE
ETHICS, JAPANESE
ETHICS, JEWISH
ETHICS, JEWISH–JUVENILE LITERATURE
ETHICS, MODERN–20TH CENTURY
ETHICS, PRIMITIVE
EUCKEN, RUDOLF CHRISTOF, 1846-1926
EUTHANASIA
EXISTENTIALISM
EXISTENTIALISM IN LITERATURE
FAITH
FAITH AND REASON
FATE AND FATALISM
FLETCHER, JOSEPH FRANCIS, 1905-
FREE WILL AND DETERMINISM
GAY LIBERATION MOVEMENT
GENTILE, GIOVANNI, 1875-1944
GOOD AND EVIL
GUILLAUME DE CHAMPEAUX, BP., 1070?-1121
GURDJIEFF, GEORGE IVANOVITCH, 1872-1949
HAECKEL, ERNST HEINRICH PHILIPP AUGUST, 1834-1919
HEDONISM
HERMENEUTICS
HOLISM
HONESTY
HOPE
HOPE–SERMONS
HUMANISM, RELIGIOUS
HUMANISTIC ETHICS
IDEALISM
IDEOLOGY
JESUS CHRIST–ETHICS
JUNG, CARL GUSTAV, 1875-1961
KIERKEGAARD, SOREN AABYE, 1813-1855
KNOWLEDGE, THEORY OF (RELIGION)
LAW AND ETHICS
LIBERALISM (RELIGION)
LOCKE, JOHN, 1632-1704
LOGIC–EARLY WORKS TO 1800
MAITLAND, FREDERIC WILLIAM, 1850-1906
MARITAIN, JACQUES, 1882-1973
MARTYRDOM
MARX, KARL, 1818-1883
MEDICAL ETHICS
METAPHYSICS
METHODOLOGY
MISSION OF THE CHURCH
MO TI, fl. 400 B.C.
MOLINA, LUIS DE, 1535-1600
MONISM
MONTESQUIEU, CHARLES LOUIS DE SECONDAT, BARON DE LA BREDE ET DE, 1689-1755
MORRIS, GEORGE SYLVESTER
NATIVE RACES
NATIVISM
NATURAL LAW
NEBULAR HYPOTHESIS
NEOPLATONISM
NEO-SCHOLASTICISM
NEW THOUGHT
NIEBUHR, REINHOLD, 1892-1971
NIETZSCHE, FRIEDRICH WILHELM, 1844-1900
NOTHING (PHILOSOPHY)
OCKHAM, WILLIAM, d. ca. 1349
OEKUMENISCHE MARIENSCHWESTERNSCHAFT
OUSPENSKY, PETER DEMIANOVICH, 1878-1947
PEACE
PHILOSOPHERS
PHILOSOPHERS–SCOTLAND
PHILOSOPHICAL ANTHROPOLOGY
PHILOSOPHY
PHILOSOPHY–ADDRESSES, ESSAYS, LECTURES
PHILOSOPHY–BIBLIOGRAPHY
PHILOSOPHY–COLLECTED WORKS
PHILOSOPHY–HISTORY
PHILOSOPHY–INTRODUCTIONS
PHILOSOPHY–STUDY AND TEACHING
PHILOSOPHY, AMERICAN
PHILOSOPHY, ANCIENT
PHILOSOPHY, ARAB
PHILOSOPHY, BRITISH
PHILOSOPHY, CHINESE
PHILOSOPHY, COMPARATIVE
PHILOSOPHY, CHRISTIAN
PHILOSOPHY, FRENCH
PHILOSOPHY, GERMAN
PHILOSOPHY, JAPANESE
PHILOSOPHY, MEDIEVAL
PHILOSOPHY, MODERN
PHILOSOPHY, MODERN–18TH CENTURY
PHILOSOPHY, MODERN–20TH CENTURY
PHILOSOPHY, ORIENTAL
PHILOSOPHY, RENAISSANCE
PHILOSOPHY, RUSSIAN
PHILOSOPHY AND RELIGION
PHILOSOPHY IN LITERATURE
PHILOSOPHY OF NATURE
PHOTIUS, d. 892
PLATONISTS
POLITICAL SCIENCE–HISTORY–INDIA
POLITICAL SCIENCE–HISTORY–UNITED STATES
POSITIVISM
RADHAKRISHNAN, SARVEPALI, SIR, 1888-
RAMSY, PAUL
RATIONALISM
REASON
RELIGIOUS ETHICS
RELIGIOUS THOUGHT
RELIGIOUS THOUGHT–HISTORY
RELIGIOUS THOUGHT–AFRICA
RELIGIOUS THOUGHT–CHINA
RELIGIOUS THOUGHT–FRANCE
RELIGIOUS THOUGHT–GREAT BRITAIN
RELIGIOUS THOUGHT–GREECE
RELIGIOUS THOUGHT–INDIA
RELIGIOUS THOUGHT–RUSSIA
RELIGIOUS THOUGHT–UNITED STATES
RENAN, JOSEPH ERNEST, 1823-1890
REVOLUTION (THEOLOGY)
RIGHT TO DIE
RIPLEY, GEORGE, 1802-1880
ROMANTICISM
ROUSSEAU, JEAN JACQUES, 1712-1778
SANKHYA
SCHLEIERMACHER, FRIEDRICH ERNST DANIEL, 1768-1834
SCHOLASTICISM
SCIENCE–PHILOSOPHY
SELF-PERCEPTION
SELF-RELIANCE
SELF-RESPECT
SHAKESPEARE, WILLIAM, 1564-1616–PHILOSOPHY
SHAKESPEARE, WILLIAM, 1564-1616–RELIGION AND ETHICS
SOLOVYEV, VLADIMIR SERGEEVICH, 1853-1900
SPINOZA, BENEDICTUS DE, 1632-1677
STRAUSS, DAVID FRIEDRICH, 1808-1874
SYNCRETISM (RELIGION)
TEILHARD DE CHARDIN, PIERRE, 1881-1955
TELEVISION–MORAL AND RELIGIOUS ASPECTS
THEISM
THEODICY
THOMAS AQUINAS, SAINT, 1225?-1274
THOMAS AQUINAS, SAINT, 1225?-1274–FICTION
TILLICH, PAUL, 1886-1965
TIME (THEOLOGY)
TRANSCENDENTALISM
TRANSPLANTATION OF ORGANS, TISSUES, ETC.
TROELTSCH, ERNST, 1865-1923
TRUTH
TYSSOT DE PATOT, SIMON, b. 1655
VIOLENCE–MORAL AND RELIGIOUS ASPECTS
VIVEKANANDA, SWAMI, 1863-1902
WACH, JOACHIM, 1898-1955
WAR AND RELIGION
WAR AND RELIGION–BIBLIOGRAPHY
WEALTH, ETHICS OF
WHEWELL, WILLIAM, 1794-1866
WHITE, WILLIAM HALE, 1831-1913
WHITEHEAD, ALFRED NORTH, 1861-1947
WIEMAN, HENRY NELSON, 1884-1913
WORK ETHIC

ROMAN CATHOLIC CHURCH

ABBOTS
ABELARD, PETER, 1079-1142
ABELARD, PETER, 1079-1142–FICTION
ABORTION–RELIGIOUS ASPECTS
ABRAHAM A SANCTA CLARA, FATHER, 1644-1709
ACTON, JOHN EMERICH EDWARD DALBERG ACTON, 1ST BARON, 1834-1902
ADALARD, SAINT, ABBOT OF CORBIE, d. 826
ALACOQUE, MARGUERITE MARIE, SAINT, 1647-1690
ALBERTUS MAGNUS, SAINT, BP. OF RATISBONE, 1193-1280
ALEXANDER 3RD, POPE, d. 1181
ALEXANDER 7TH, POPE, 1594-1667
ALEXANDER DE HALES, d. 1245
AMAT, THADDEUS, BP., 1811-1878
AMBROSIUS, SAINT, BP. OF MILAN
AMERICAN LITERATURE–CATHOLIC AUTHORS
AMERICANISM (CATHOLIC CONTROVERSY)
ANDREWS, CHARLES FREER, 1871-1940
ANGLO-CATHOLICISM
ANSELM, SAINT, ARCHBISHOP OF CANTERBURY, 1033-1109
ANTHONY OF PADUA, SAINT, 1195-1231
ANTI-CATHOLICISM
ARMAGH, IRELAND (ECCLESIASTICAL PROVINCE)
AUGUSTANA COLLEGE
AUGUSTINE, SAINT, ABP. OF CANTERBURY, d. 604
AUGUSTINUS, AURELIUS, SAINT, BP. OF HIPPO, 354-430
AUGUSTINUS, AURELIUS, SAINT, BP. OF HIPPO, 354-430–BIBLIOGRAPHY
AURIA, SAINT, d. 1100
BALTIMORE CATECHISM
BASEL, COUNCIL OF, 1431-1449
BEATIFICATION
BEDE, THE VENERABLE, 673-735
BELLARMINO, ROBERTO FRANCESCO ROMOLO, SAINT, 1542-1621
BENEDICTINES
BENEDICTUS, SAINT, ABBOT OF MONTE CASSINO
BENNO 2ND, BP. OF OSNABRUCK, 1020-1088
BERNADETTE, SAINT (BERNADETTE SOUBIROUS), 1844-1879
BERNANOS, GEORGE, 1888-1948
BERNARD DE CLARIVAUX, SAINT, 1091?-1153
BERNARDINO DA SIENA, SAINT, 1380-1444
BERNWARD, SAINT, BP. OF HILDESHEIM, 993-1022
BERRIGAN, DANIEL
BERRIGAN, PHILIP
BERTHOLD VON REGENSBURG, d. 1272
BETRONE, CONSOLATA, SISTER, 1903-1946
BLOY, LEON, 1846-1917
BONAVENTURA, SAINT, CARDINAL, 1221-1274
BONIFACE, ORIGINALLY WINFRED, SAINT, BP. OF MAINZ, 680-755
BONIFACE 8TH, POPE, d. 1303
BOSCO, GIOVANNI, SAINT, 1815-1888
BOSSUET, JACQUES BENIGNE, BP. OF MEAUX, 1627-1704
BRENDAN, SAINT–LEGEND
BROWNSON, ORESTES AUGUSTUS, 1803-1876
BULLS, PAPAL
CABRINI, FRANCES XAVIER, SAINT, 1850-1917
CANISIUS, PETER, SAINT, 1524-1597
CANONIZATION
CAPUCHINS
CARDINALS
CARMELITE NUNS–FICTION
CARMELITES
CARMELITES–DRAMA
CARTHUSIANS
CASAS, BARTOLOME DE LAS, BP. OF CHIAPA, 1474-1566
CASILDA, SAINT, fl. 1050–JUVENILE LITERATURE
CATECHETICS–CATHOLIC CHURCH
CATHARINA, SAINT, OF ALEXANDRIA
CATHERINE OF GENOA, SAINT, 1447-1510
CATHERINE OF SIENA, SAINT, 1347-1380
CATHOLIC ACTION
CATHOLIC AUTHORS
CATHOLIC CHURCH
CATHOLIC CHURCH–ADDRESSES, ESSAYS, LECTURES
CATHOLIC CHURCH–APOLOGETIC WORKS
CATHOLIC CHURCH–BIBLIOGRAPHY
CATHOLIC CHURCH–BIOGRAPHY
CATHOLIC CHURCH–CATECHISMS AND CREEDS
CATHOLIC CHURCH–CEREMONIES AND PRACTICES
CATHOLIC CHURCH–CHARITIES
CATHOLIC CHURCH–CLERGY
CATHOLIC CHURCH–CLERGY–APPOINTMENT, CALL AND ELECTION
CATHOLIC CHURCH–CLERGY–CORRESPONDENCE, REMINISCENCES, ETC.
CATHOLIC CHURCH–COLLECTED WORKS
CATHOLIC CHURCH–DICTIONARIES
CATHOLIC CHURCH–DISCIPLINE
CATHOLIC CHURCH–DOCTRINAL AND CONTROVERSIAL WORKS
CATHOLIC CHURCH–DOCTRINAL AND CONTROVERSIAL WORKS–MISCELLANEOUS AUTHORS
CATHOLIC CHURCH–DOCTRINAL AND CONTROVERSIAL WORKS–PROTESTANT AUTHORS
CATHOLIC CHURCH–DOCTRINAL AND CONTROVERSIAL WORKS, POPULAR
CATHOLIC CHURCH–EDUCATION
CATHOLIC CHURCH–FINANCE
CATHOLIC CHURCH–GOVERNMENT
CATHOLIC CHURCH–HISTORY
CATHOLIC CHURCH–HISTORY–SOURCES
CATHOLIC CHURCH–HISTORY–MIDDLE AGES, 600-1500
CATHOLIC CHURCH–HISTORY–MODERN PERIOD, 1500-
CATHOLIC CHURCH–HYMNS
CATHOLIC CHURCH–INFALLIBILITY
CATHOLIC CHURCH–LITURGY AND RITUAL
CATHOLIC CHURCH–LITURGY AND RITUAL–BIBLIOGRAPHY
CATHOLIC CHURCH–LITURGY AND RITUAL–BREVIARY
CATHOLIC CHURCH–LITURGY AND RITUAL–HISTORY
CATHOLIC CHURCH–LITURGY AND RITUAL–HOURS
CATHOLIC CHURCH–LITURGY AND RITUAL–HYMNARY
CATHOLIC CHURCH–LITURGY AND RITUAL–MISSAL
CATHOLIC CHURCH–LITURGY AND RITUAL–MOZARABIC RITES
CATHOLIC CHURCH–LITURGY AND

RITUAL–OFFICE OF THE BLESSED VIRGIN MARY
CATHOLIC CHURCH–LITURGY AND RITUAL–PSALTER
CATHOLIC CHURCH–LITURGY AND RITUAL–STUDY AND TEACHING
CATHOLIG CHURCH–LITURGY AND RITUAL–TROPER
CATHOLIC CHURCH–MISSIONS
CATHOLIC CHURCH–PERIODICALS
CATHOLIC CHURCH–PERIODICALS–HISTORY
CATHOLIC CHURCH–PRAYER-BOOKS AND DEVOTIONS
CATHOLIC CHURCH–RELATIONS
CATHOLIC CHURCH–RELATIONS–BUDDHISM
CATHOLIC CHURCH–RELATIONS–JUDAISM
CATHOLIC CHURCH–RELATIONS–ORTHODOX EASTERN CHURCH
CATHOLIC CHURCH–RELATIONS–PROTESTANT CHURCHES
CATHOLIC CHURCH–RELATIONS (DIPLOMATIC)
CATHOLIC CHURCH–SERMONS
CATHOLIC CHURCH–SOCIETIES, ETC.
CATHOLIC CHURCH IN AFRICA
CATHOLIC CHURCH IN AMERICA
CATHOLIC CHURCH IN AUSTRALIA
CATHOLIC CHURCH IN CANADA
CATHOLIC CHURCH IN EUROPE
CATHOLIC CHURCH IN FRANCE
CATHOLIC CHURCH IN GERMANY
CATHOLIC CHURCH IN GREAT BRITAIN
CATHOLIC CHURCH IN GREAT BRITAIN–BIBLIOGRAPHY
CATHOLIC CHURCH IN INDIA
CATHOLIC CHURCH IN IRELAND
CATHOLIC CHURCH IN ITALY
CATHOLIC CHURCH IN JAPAN
CATHOLIC CHURCH IN LATIN AMERICA
CATHOLIC CHURCH IN MEXICO
CATHOLIC CHURCH IN POLAND
CATHOLIC CHURCH IN RUSSIA
CATHOLIC CHURCH IN SCOTLAND
CATHOLIC CHURCH IN SPAIN
CATHOLIC CHURCH IN THE NETHERLANDS
CATHOLIC CHURCH IN THE PHILIPPINE ISLANDS
CATHOLIC CHURCH IN THE UNITED STATES
CATHOLIC CHURCH IN THE UNITED STATES–BIBLIOGRAPHY
CATHOLIC CHURCH IN THE UNITED STATES–EDUCATION
CATHOLIC CHURCH IN THE UNITED STATES–HISTORY
CATHOLIC CHURCH IN THE UNITED STATES–HISTORY–SOURCES
CATHOLIC CHURCH IN VENEZUELA
CATHOLIC EMANCIPATION
CATHOLIC FOREIGN MISSION SOCIETY OF AMERICA
CATHOLIC LEARNING AND SCHOLARSHIPS
CATHOLIC LITERATURE
CATHOLIC LITERATURE (COLLECTIONS)
CATHOLIC LITERATURE–BIBLIOGRAPHY
CATHOLIC LITERATURE–HISTORY AND CRITICISM
CATHOLIC SCHOOLS
CATHOLIC SCHOOLS–GREAT BRITAIN
CATHOLIC SCHOOLS–UNITED STATES
CATHOLIC UNIVERSITIES AND COLLEGES
CATHOLIC UNIVERSITY OF AMERICA
CATHOLIC WORKER MOVEMENT
CATHOLICITY
CATHOLICS
CATHOLICS IN AUSTRIA
CATHOLICS IN CANADA
CATHOLICS IN ENGLAND
CATHOLICS IN FRANCE
CATHOLICS IN GERMANY
CATHOLICS IN IRELAND
CATHOLICS IN ITALY
CATHOLICS IN LITERATURE
CATHOLICS IN THE UNITED STATES
CECILIA, SAINT
CHAPTERS, CATHEDRAL, COLLEGIATE, ETC.
CHARLESTOWN, MASSACHUSETTS URSULINE CONVENT
CHESTER (DIOCESE)
CHESTER PLAYS
CHICHELE, HENRY, ABP. OF CANTERBURY, 1362-1443
CHRISTIAN ETHICS–CATHOLIC AUTHORS
CHRISTIAN LIFE–CATHOLIC AUTHORS
CHRISTIAN UNION–CATHOLIC CHURCH
CHURCH AND SOCIAL PROBLEMS–CATHOLIC CHURCH
CHURCH AND STATE–CATHOLIC CHURCH
CHURCH AND STATE IN NICARAGUA
CISTERCIANS
CISTERCIANS–HISTORY
CLARA OF ASSISI, SAINT, d. 1253
CLAUDEL, PAUL, 1868-1955
CLUNIACS
COLUMBA, SAINT, 521-597
COLUMBAN, SAINT, 543-615
COMBONI, DANIELE, BP., 1831-1881
CONFESSION–JUVENILE LITERATURE
CONFIRMATION–CATHOLIC CHURCH
CONSTANCE, COUNCIL OF, 1414-1418
CONVENTS AND NUNNERIES
CONVERTS, CATHOLIC
COSMAS, SAINT
COUGHLIN, CHARLES EDWARD, 1891-
COURTENAY, WILLIAM, ABP. OF CANTERBURY, 1342-1396
CRASHAW, RICHARD, 1613?-1649
CUTHBERT, SAINT
CYPRIANUS, SAINT, BP. OF CARTHAGE
CYRILLUS, SAINT, OF THESSALONICA, 827-869
DAMIEN DE VEUSTER, JOSEPH (FATHER DAMIEN), 1840-1889
DAUGHTERS OF SAINT PAUL
DAY, DOROTHY, 1897-
DIVINE OFFICE
DIVORCE (CANON LAW)
DOMINGO DE GUZMAN, SAINT, 1170-1221
DOMINICANS
DUNS, JOANNES, SCOTUS, 1265?-1308?
DUNSTAN, SAINT, ABP. OF CANTERBURY, d. 988
EADMER, d. 1124
ECKHART, JOHANNES, 1260-1327
ELPHINSTONE, WILLIAM, BP. OF ABERDEEN, 1431-1514
ENCYCLICALS, PAPAL
ENGLAND, JOHN, BP., 1786-1842
ENGLISH LITERATURE–CATHOLIC AUTHORS
ENGLISH LITERATURE–CATHOLIC AUTHORS–HISTORY AND CRITICISM
ERASMUS, DESIDERIUS, d. 1536
ERKEWALD, SAINT–LEGEND
EUSEBIUS PAMPHILI, BISHOP OF CAESAREA
EVANGELICAL COUNSELS
EXTREME UNCTION
FABRI, FELIX, 1441-1502
FASTS AND FEASTS–CATHOLIC CHURCH
FATIMA, NOSSA SENHORA DA
FENELON, FRANCOIS DE SALIGNAC DE LA MOTHE, ABP., 1651-1715
FERNANDO 5TH, EL CATOLICO, KING OF SPAIN, 1452-1516
FLAGET, BENEDICT JOSEPH, BP., 1763-1850
FLANAGAN, EDWARD JOSEPH, 1886-1948
FLEURY, ANDRE HERCULE DE, CARDINAL, 1653-1743
FRA ANGELICO (GIOVANNI DA FIESOLE), 1387-1455
FRANCESCO D'ASSISI, SAINT, 1182-1226
FRANCESCO D'ASSISI, SAINT, 1182-1226–BIBLIOGRAPHY
FRANCESCO D'ASSISI, SAINT, 1182-1226–FICTION
FRANCESCO D'ASSISI, SAINT, 1882-1226–JUVENILE LITERATURE
FRANCISCAN SISTERS
FRANCISCANS
FRANCISCANS–BIBLIOGRAPHY
FRANCISCANS–PRAYER-BOOKS AND DEVOTIONS
FRANCISCANS- THIRD ORDER
FRANCISCANS IN AMERICA
FRANCISCANS IN BOHEMIA
FRANCISCANS IN CHINA
FRANCISCANS IN ENGLAND
FRANCISCANS IN FRANCE
FRANCISCANS IN IRELAND
FRANCISCANS IN THE UNITED STATES
FRANCISCO XAVIER, SAINT, 1506-1552
FRANCO BAHAMONDE, FRANCISCO, 1892-1975
FRANCOIS DE SALES, SAINT, BISHOP OF GENEVA, 1567-1622
FREEMASONS AND CATHOLIC CHURCH
FRIARS
FULGENTIUS, SAINT, BP. OF RUSPA, 468-533
GABRIEL RICHARD, FATHER
GERMAINE COUSIN, SAINT, 1579-1601
GORDON, JOHN CLEMENT, 1643-1726
GRAVESEND, RICHARD, BP. OF LONDON, d. 1303
GREAT BRITAIN–FOREIGN RELATIONS–CATHOLIC CHURCH
GREGOIRE, HENRI, ABBE, 1750-1831
GREGORIUS 1ST, THE GREAT, SAINT, POPE, 540-604
GREGORIUS 7TH, SAINT, POPE, 1015-1085
GROSSETESTE, ROBERT, BP. OF LINCOLN, 1175-1253
GUILLAUME D'AUVERGNE, BP. OF PARIS, d. 1249
GUILLAUME DE DEQ'UILLEVILLE, 14TH CENTURY
GUYON, JEANNE MARIE (BOUVIER DE LA MOTTE), 1648-1717
HAGIOGRAPHY
HEALY, JAMES AUGUSTINE, BISHOP, 1830-1900
HECKER, ISAAC THOMAS, 1819-1888
HELENA, SAINT, ca. 246-326
HELOISE, 1101-1164–FICTION
HENRI 4TH, KING OF FRANCE, 1553-1610–FICTION
HENRY 2ND, KING OF ENGLAND, 1133-1189
HERMITS
HILDEGARD, SAINT, 1098?-1178
HOSPITALERS
HOURS, BOOKS OF
HUS, JOHN, 1369-1415
IGNATIUS, SAINT, BP. OF ANTIOCH, 1ST CENTURY
INDULGENCES
INNOCENTIUS 3RD, POPE, 1160 or 61-1216
INVESTITURE
ISIDORIUS, SAINT, BP. OF SEVILLE, d. 636
JAGERSTATTER, FRANZ, 1907-1943
JAIME DE PORTUGAL, CARDINAL, 1434-1459
JANSENISTS
JEANNE D'ARC, SAINT, 1412-1431
JEANNE D'ARC, SAINT, 1412-1431–DRAMA
JEANNE D'ARC, SAINT, 1412-1431–JUVENILE LITERATURE
JEROME, SAINT (HIERONYMUS, SAINT)
JESUITS
JESUITS–EDUCATION
JESUITS IN CANADA
JESUITS IN CHINA
JESUITS IN ENGLAND
JESUITS IN LATIN-AMERICA
JESUITS IN MEXICO
JESUITS IN NORTH AMERICA
JESUITS IN POLAND
JESUITS IN THE UNITED STATES
JOACHIM, ABBOT OF FIORE, 1132-1202
JOAN, MYTHICAL FEMALE POPE
JOHN 23RD, POPE, 1881-1963
JOHN 23RD, POPE, 1881-1963–JUVENILE LITERATURE
JOHN OF SALISBURY, BP. OF CHARTRES, d. 1180
JOHN OF THE CROSS, SAINT, 1542-1591
JOHN PAUL 2ND, POPE
JULIUS 2ND, POPE, 1443-1513
JOHN PAUL II, POPE, 1920-- ASSASSINATION ATTEMPT, 1981
JUNIPERUS, OF ASISSI, BROTHER, 13TH CENTURY
KENNEDY, JOHN FITZGERALD, PRES. U. S., 1917-1963–POETRY
KINO, EUSBIUS FRANCISCO, 1644-1711
KOLBE, MAXIMILLAN
LANGLEY, THOMAS, BP. OF DURHAM, d. 1437
LANGUAGE QUESTION IN THE CHURCH
LAS CASAS, BARTOLOME DE, 1474-1566
LATIN LANGUAGE–CHURCH LATIN
LAVIGERIE, CHARLES MARTIAL ALLEMAND, CARDINAL, 1825-1892
LEGION OF MARY
LEO 10TH, POPE, 1475-1521
LEO 13TH, POPE, 1810-1903
LEYVA, MARIANNA DE, KNOWN AS SIGNORA DI MONZA, 1575-1650
LIBERAL CATHOLIC CHURCH
LIBRARIES, CATHOLIC
LIGUORI, ALFONSO MARIA DE, SAINT, 1696-1787
LIPPI, FRA FILIPPO, 1412-1469
LITURGICAL MOVEMENT–CATHOLIC CHURCH
LITURGICS–CATHOLIC CHURCH
LORD'S SUPPER–CATHOLIC CHURCH
LOUIS, 9TH, SAINT, KING OF FRANCE, 1214-1270
LOURDES
LOURDES, NOTRE-DAME DE
LOYOLA, IGNACIO DE, SAINT, 1491-1556
LUIS DE GRANADA, 1504-1588
LUPUS, SERVATUS, ABBOT OF FERRIERES, 19TH CENTURY
LUTHERAN CHURCH–RELATIONS–CATHOLIC CHURCH
LYNDWOOD, WILLIAM, BP. OF ST. DAVID'S, 1375-1446
MCGLYNN, EDWARD, 1837-1900
MANNING, HENRY EDWARD, CARDINAL, 1808-1892
MARIA DE JESUS DE AGREDA, MOTHER, 1602-1665
MARIE DE L'INCARNATION, MOTHER, 1599-1672
MARIIA, MOTHER, 1891-1945
MARRIAGE–CATHOLIC CHURCH
MARTIALL, JOHN, 1534-1597
MARTIN, GREGORY, d. 1582
MARTIN, SAINT, BISHOP OF TOURS, 4TH CENT.
MARTIN DE PORRES, SAINT, 1579-1639
MARY MAGDALENE, SAINT
MARYKNOLL SISTERS OF ST. DOMINIC
MASS
MASS–CELEBRATION
MASS–JUVENILE LITERATURE
MASSES
MAUNOIR, JULIEN, 1606-1683
MAURIAC, FRANCOIS, 1885-1970
MAZARIN, JULES, CARDINAL, 1602-1661
MERLO, THECLA, 1894-1964
MERTON, THOMAS
MIGNE, JACQUES PAUL, 1800-1875
MINDSZENTY, JOZSEF, CARDINAL, 1892-
MODERNISM–CATHOLIC CHURCH
MOEHLER, JOHANN ADAM, 1796-1838
MONICA SAINT, d. 387–FICTION
MORE, THOMAS, SIR, SAINT, 1478-1535
MORE, THOMAS, SIR, SAINT, 1478-1535–DRAMA
MORELOS Y PAVON, JOSE MARIA TECLO, 1765-1815
MYSTICISM–CATHOLIC CHURCH
NEWMAN, JOHN HENRY, CARDINAL, 1801-1890
NICOLAUS CASANUS, CARDINAL, 1401-1464
NOVENAS
NUNS
O'CONNOR, FLANNERY
O'HARA, JOHN FRANCIS, 1888-1960
OLD CATHOLIC CHURCH
ORDER OF SAINT PATRICK
OTFRID VON WEISSENBURG, 9TH CENTURY
PADUA–MADONNA DELL'ARNE (CHAPEL)
PALESTRINA, GIOVANNI PIERLUIGI DA, 1525-1594
PALLOTTI, VINCENZO, SAINT, 1795-1850
PALMA, MAJORCA–CATHEDRAL
PAPACY
PAPACY–HISTORY
PAPACY–HISTORY–SOURCES
PAPAL DOCUMENTS
PAPAL STATES
PARIS–COLLEGE DE L'AVE MARIA
PARIS–NOTRE-DAME
PARIS–SAINTE-CHAPELLE
PARISH MISSIONS
PASCAL, BLAISE, 1623-1662
PATRICK, SAINT, 373?-463?
PATRONAGE, ECCLESIASTICAL
PAUL 2ND, POPE, 1443-1513
PAUL 6TH, POPE, 1897-
PENANCE
PENANCE–HISTORY
PERFECTION (CATHOLIC)
PERPETUA, SAINT
PERSECUTION
PETIT, ADOLPHE, 1822-1914
PETRUS LOMBARDUS, BP. OF PARIS, 12TH CENTURY
PETRUS THOMASIUS, SAINT, 1305-1366
PIERLEONI FAMILY
PIERRE LE VENERABLE, 1092-1156
PIO DA PIETRELCINA, FATHER
PIUS 5TH, POPE, 1504-1572
PIUS 6TH, POPE, 1717-1799
PIUS 7TH, POPE, 1742-1823
PIUS 9TH, POPE, 1792-1878
PIUS 10TH, SAINT, POPE, 1835-1914
PIUS 11TH, POPE, 1857-1939
PIUS 12TH, POPE, 1876-1958
PIUS 12TH, POPE, 1876-1958–DRAMA
POLE, REGINALD, 1500-1558
POOR CLARES
POPES
POPES–ELECTION
POPES–INFALLIBILITY
POPES–PRIMACY
POPES–TEMPORAL POWER
PORT ROYAL
PRESS, CATHOLIC
PRIORIES
PROTESTANT CHURCHES–RELATIONS–CATHOLIC CHURCH
PSALTERS
QUINDECIM SIGNA ANTI INDICIUM
RECOLLETS (FRANCISCAN)
REIMS–NOTRE DAME (CATHEDRAL)
RICHELIEU, ARMAND JEAN DU PLESSIS, CARDINAL, DUC DE, 1585-1642
RITA DE CASCIA, SAINT, 1381-1457
ROMAN QUESTION
ROSA OF LIMA, SAINT, 1586-1617
ROSARY
ROSATI, JOSEPH, BP., 1789-1843

SACRAMENTS–CATHOLIC CHURCH
SACRED HEART, DEVOTION TO
SAINT CECILIA'S DAY–SONGS AND MUSIC
ST. PATRICK'S DAY
SALESIANS
SALVATION OUTSIDE THE CATHOLIC CHURCH
SANCHEZ DE AREVALO RODRIGO, BISHOP, 1404-1470
SANTIAGO DE COMPOSTELA
SAVONAROLA, GIROLAMO MARIA FRANCESCO MATTEO, 1452-1498
SCHEFFER, JOHANN, 1624-1677
SCHISM–EASTERN AND WESTERN CHURCH
SCHISM, THE GREAT WESTERN, 1378-1417
SEIPEL, IGNAZ, 1876-1932
SERRA, JUNIPERO, FATHER, 1713-1784
SERAPHIM, SAINT, 1759-1833
SERVETUS, MICHAEL, 1509-1553
SETON, ELIZABETH ANN, MOTHER, 1774-1821
SHEEN, FULTON J., 1895-1979
SISTERS OF CHARITY OF ST. VINCENT DE PAUL
SISTERS OF MERCY
SOCIALISM AND CATHOLIC CHURCH
SOCIETY FOR THE PROPAGATION OF THE FAITH
SOCIETY FOR THE PROPAGATION OF THE GOSPEL IN FOREIGN PARTS, LONDON
SOCIETY OF THE SACRED HEART
SORROWS OF THE BLESSED VIRGIN MARY, DEVOTION TO
SOUTHWELL, ROBERT, 1561?-1595
SOUTHWELL FAMILY
SPALDING, MARTIN JOHN, ABP., 1810-1872
SPELLMAN, FRANCIS JOSEPH, CARDINAL, 1889-1967
SPIRITUAL LIFE–CATHOLIC AUTHORS
STAPLETON, THOMAS, 1535-1598
STATIONS OF THE CROSS
STAUPITZ, JOHANN VON, 1524
SWINFIELD, RICHARD DE BP. OF HEREFORD, d. 1317
SWITHUN, SAINT, BP. OF WINCHESTER, d. 862
TALLEYRAND-PERIGORD, CHARLES MAURICE DE, PRINCE DE BENEVENT, 1754-1838
TALLEYRAND-PERIGORD, ELIE DE, CARDINAL, 1301-1364
TAULER, JOHANN, 1300-1361
TEILHARD DE CHARDIN, PIERRE, 1881-1955
TERESA, SAINT, 1515-1582
THEOBALD, ABP. OF CANTERBURY, d. 1161
THERESE DE LISIEUX, SAINT, 1873-1897
THIRLBY, THOMAS, BP. 1506-1570
THOMAS A BECKET, SAINT, ABP. OF CANTERBURY, 1118?-1170
THOMAS A BECKET, SAINT, ABP. OF CANTERBURY, 1118?-1170–DRAMA
THOMAS A KEMPIS, 1380-1471
THOMAS AQUINAS, SAINT, 1225?-1274
TORRES, CAMILO
TRANSUBSTANTIATION
TRENT, COUNCIL OF 1545-1563
TRINITARIANS
URSULINES
VATICAN
VATICAN–JUVENILE LITERATURE
VATICAN COUNCIL, 1869-1870
VATICAN COUNCIL, 2ND, 1962-1965
VIANNEY, JEAN BAPTISTE MARIE, SAINT, 1786-1859
VICELINUS, SAINT, BP. OF OLDENBURG, d. 1154
VIDA, MARCO GIROLAMO, BP. OF ALBA, d. 1566
VINCENT DE PAUL, SAINT, 1581-1660
VOWS
WALA, SAINT, ABBOT OF CORBIE, d. 836
WALTER, HUBERT
WAYNFLETE, WILLIAM OF, 1395-1486
WERBURGA, SAINT
WILFRED, SAINT, BP. OF YORK, 634-709
WOLSEY, THOMAS, CARDINAL 1475?-1530
ZUMMARRAGA, JUAN DE, ABP., 1468-1548

SHAKERS

SHAKERS

SPECULATIVE PHILOSOPHY

CAMUS, ALBERT, 1913-1960
CONSCIOUSNESS
DESPAIR
DIVORCE–JUVENILE LITERATURE
DIVORCEES
HEGEL, GEORG WILHELM FRIEDRICH, 1770-1831
HEIDEGGER, MARTIN, 1889-
JASPERS, KARL, 1883-1969
KANT, IMMANUEL, 1724-1804
MARCEL, GABRIEL, 1887-
METAPHYSICS
MOORE, GEORGE EDWARD, 1873-1958–ETHICS
PHENOMENOLOGY
PHILOSOPHICAL THEOLOGY
PLATO, 427?-347 B.C.
PLOTINUS, d. 270 A.D.
REALITY
SARTRE, JEAN PAUL, 1905-
SCHILLER, FERDINAND CANNING SCOTT, 1864-1937
SCIENCE AND ETHICS
SELF
SELF (PHILOSOPHY)
SELF-KNOWLEDGE, THEORY OF
SEMANTICS (PHILOSOPHY)
SITUATION ETHICS
SOCRATES
STOICS
SUBSTANCE (PHILOSOPHY)
SUICIDE
TIME
WHITEHEAD, ALFRED NORTH, 1861-1947
WHOLE AND PARTS (PHILOSOPHY)
WITTGENSTEIN, LUDWIG, 1889-1951

TAOISM

LAO-TZU
TAO TE CHING
TAOISM

THEOSOPHY

BIBLE AND THEOSOPHY
BLAVATSKY, HELENE PETROVNA (HAHN-HAHN), 1831-1891
CHAKRAS (THEOSOPHY)
FUTURE LIFE–CASE STUDIES
GOOD WORKS (THEOLOGY)
JESUS CHRIST–THEOSOPHICAL INTERPRETATIONS
KRISHNAMURTI, JIDDU, 1895-
KUNG, HANS, 1928-
PHILOSOPHICAL THEOLOGY
REINCARNATION
SCHELLING, FRIEDRICH WILHELM JOSEPH VON, 1775-1854
THEOSOPHICAL SOCIETY
THEOSOPHY

UNITARIANISM

BROWNSON, ORESTES AUGUSTUS, 1803-1876
CHANNING, WILLIAM ELLERY, 1780-1842
EMERSON, RALPH WALDO, 1803-1882
EMERSON, RALPH WALDO, 1803-1882–BIBLIOGRAPHY
EMERSON, RALPH WALDO, 1803-1882–JUVENILE LITERATURE
MARTINEAU, HARRIET, 1802-1876
PARKER, THEODORE, 1810-1860
UNITARIAN CHURCHES
UNITARIAN CHURCHES–SERMONS
UNITARIAN UNIVERSALIST ASSOCIATION
UNITARIANISM

UNIVERSALISM–UNIVERSALISTS

UNIVERSALISM
UNIVERSALIST CHURCH

Books Subject Index

A

AARON, BIBLICAL CHARACTER

Paamoni, Zev. Aaron, the High Priest. (Biblical Ser.). (Illus.). 1970. 4.00 (ISBN 0-914080-27-X). Shulsinger Sales.

ABAILARD, PIERRE

see Abelard, Peter, 1079-1142

ABBEYS

see also Cathedrals; Convents and Nunneries; Monasteries;

also names of specific abbeys, e.g. Lindisfarne Abbey

Baumstein, Paschal M. My Lord of Belmont: A Biography of Leo Haid. (Illus.). xxii, 396p. 1985. 20.00 (ISBN 0-9614976-0-2). Archives Belmont.

Beckford, William. Recollections of an Excursion. 1983. 60.00x (ISBN 0-900000-78-3, Pub. by Centaur Bks). State Mutual Bk.

Bonney, T. G., et al. Abbeys & Churches of England & Wales. LC 77-23529. 1977. Repr. of 1890 ed. lib. bdg. 40.00 (ISBN 0-89341-203-1). Longwood Pub Group.

Brown, Philippa, ed. Sibton Abbey Cartularies & Charters: II. (Suffolk Charters VIII). 192p. 1986. 28.95 (ISBN 0-85115-443-3, Pub. by Boydell & Brewer). Longwood Pub Group.

Chibnall, Marjorie, ed. Charters & Custumals of the Abbey of Holy Trinity, Caen. (Records of Social & Economic History Ser.). (Illus.). 1982. 37.50x (ISBN 0-19-726009-8). Oxford U Pr.

Coulton, G. G. Scottish Abbeys & Social Life. 1977. lib. bdg. 59.95 (ISBN 0-8490-2573-7). Gordon Pr.

Crosby, Sumner M. The Royal Abbey of Saint-Denis from Its Beginnings to the Death of Suger 475-1151. LC 85-26464. 570p. 1987. text ed. 55.00 (ISBN 0-300-03143-2). Yale U Pr.

Crosby, Sumner M., et al. The Royal Abbey of Saint-Denis in the Time of Abbot Suger (1122-1151) Shultz, Ellen, ed. LC 80-28849. (Illus.). 128p. 1981. pap. 12.95 (ISBN 0-87099-261-9). Metro Mus Art.

Crossley, Frederick H. The English Abbey: Its Life & Work in the Middle Ages. LC 82-25127. (Illus.). xiv, 114p. 1983. Repr. of 1935 ed. lib. bdg. 45.00x (ISBN 0-313-23849-9, CRFE). Greenwood.

De Montrond, M. Dictionnaire des Abbayes et Monasteres ou Histoire Des Establissements Religieux. Migne, J. P., ed. (Troisieme et Derniere Encyclopedie Theologique Ser.: Vol. 16). (Fr.). 614p. Repr. of 1856 ed. lib. bdg. 81.00x (ISBN 0-89241-299-2). Caratzas.

McClendon, Charles B. The Imperial Abbey of Farfa. LC 86-3466. 336p. 1987. text ed. 35.00 (ISBN 0-300-03333-8). Yale U Pr.

Platt, Colin. The Abbeys & Priories of Medieval England. LC 84-80387. (Illus.). xvii, 270p. 1984. 32.50 (ISBN 0-8232-1117-7); pap. 19.95 (ISBN 0-8232-1118-5). Fordham.

Rees, U., ed. The Cartulary of Haughmond Abbey. 304p. 1985. text ed. 39.95x (ISBN 0-7083-0907-0, Pub. by U of Wales). Humanities.

Spence, Keith & McVeigh, Shaun. Cathedrals & Abbeys of England & Wales. (Blue Guides Ser.). (Illus.). 1984. 29.95 (ISBN 0-393-01664-1); pap. 16.95 (ISBN 0-393-30071-4). Norton.

Thorold, Henry. Collins Guide to Cathedrals, Abbeys & Priories of England & Wales. (Illus.). 332p. 1987. 24.95 (ISBN 0-00-217241-0). Salem Hse Pubs.

Turner, G. J. & Salter, H. E., eds. The Register of St. Augustine's Abbey, Canterbury: Commonly Called the Black Book, 2 pts. (British Academy, London, Record of the Social & Economic History of England & Wales Ser.: Vol. 2). Pt. 1, Reprint of 1915 Edition. pap. 45.00 (ISBN 0-8115-1242-8); Pt. 2, Reprint of 1924 Ed. pap. 36.00 (ISBN 0-8115-1243-6). Kraus Repr.

Wright, Geoffrey N. Discovering Abbeys & Priories. (Discovery Ser.: No. 57). (Illus.). 1985. pap. 4.50 (ISBN 0-85263-454-4, Pub. by Shire Pubns England). Seven Hills Bks.

ABBOT, GEORGE, ABP. OF CANTERBURY, 1562-1633

Christophers, Richard A. George Abbot, Archbishop of Canterbury, 1562-1633: A Bibliography. LC 65-27845. pap. 59.00 (ISBN 0-317-10344-X, 2016440). Bks Demand UMI.

ABBOTS

Salmon, Pierre. The Abbot in Monastic Tradition. Lavoie, Claire, tr. from Fr. LC 78-158955. (Cistercian Studies: No. 14). Tr. of L Abbe' dans la Tradition Monastique. 148p. 1972. 9.95 (ISBN 0-87907-814-6). Cistercian Pubns.

ABELARD, PETER, 1079-1142

Abailard, P. Sic et Non: A Critical Edition, 7 fascicles. Boyer, Blanche & McKeon, Richard, eds. Incl. Fascicle 1. (ISBN 0-226-00058-3);;; Fascicle 4. (ISBN 0-226-00061-3); Fascicle 5. (ISBN 0-226-00062-1); (ISBN 0-226-00064-8);. LC 74-7567. 1978. pap. text ed. 16.00x ea. O. P.; fascicles 1-7 complete in one clothbound vol. 130.00x (ISBN 0-226-00066-4). U of Chicago Pr.

Abelard, Peter. The Cruel Tragedy of My Life: The Autobiography of Peter Abelard. (Illus.). 131p. 1985. 97.45 (ISBN 0-89901-198-5). Found Class Reprints.

Beonio-Brocchieri Fumagalli, M. T. The Logic of Abelard. Pleasance, Simon, tr. from It. (Synthese Library: No. 1). 101p. 1969. lib. bdg. 18.50 (ISBN 90-277-0068-0, Pub. by Reidel Holland). Kluwer Academic.

Compayre, Gabriel. Abelard & the Origin & Early History of the Universities. LC 75-90094. (BCL Ser.: II). 1969. Repr. of 1893 ed. 11.50 (ISBN 0-404-01639-1). AMS Pr.

--Abelard & the Origin & Early History of the Universities. 1893. 10.00x (ISBN 0-403-00009-2). Scholarly.

Landgraf, Arthur. Commentarius Cantabrigiensis in Epistolas Pauli e Schola Petri Abaelardi, 3 vols. Incl. Vol. 1. In Epistolam Ad Romanos. 223p. 1937. 17.95 (ISBN 0-268-00133-2); Vol. 2. In Epistolam Ad Corinthios Iam et Iiam, Ad Galatas et Ad Ephesios. 1223p. 1960. 17.95 (ISBN 0-268-00134-0); Vol. 3. In Epistolam ad Philippenses, ad Colossenses, ad Thessalonicenses Primam et Secundam, ed Timotheam Priman et Secundam, ad Titum et Philemonem. 447p. 1944. 17.95 (ISBN 0-268-00132-4). (Mediaeval Studies Ser.: No. 2). U of Notre Dame Pr.

McCabe, Joseph. Peter Abelard. facsimile ed. LC 74-148889. (Select Bibliographies Reprint Ser). Repr. of 1901 ed. 22.00 (ISBN 0-8369-5655-9). Ayer Co Pubs.

--Peter Abelard (1079-1142) LC 72-85102. ix, 402p. 1972. Repr. of 1901 ed. lib. bdg. 23.50 (ISBN 0-8337-4244-2). B Franklin.

Meadows, Denis. A Saint & a Half. 1963. 5.00 (ISBN 0-8159-6803-5). Devin.

Smits, Edme R. Peter Abelard, Letters IX-XIV. xii, 315p. (Orig.). 1983. pap. 18.00x (ISBN 90-6088-085-4, Pub. by Boumas Boekhuis Netherlands). Benjamins North AM.

ABORIGINES

see Native Races

ABORTION

Baker, Don. Beyond Choice: The Abortion Story No One Is Telling. LC 85-15295. 1985. 8.95 (ISBN 0-88070-127-7). Multnomah.

Banks, Bill & Banks, Sue. Ministering to Abortion's Aftermath. 144p. (Orig.). 1982. pap. 3.95 (ISBN 0-89228-057-3). Impact Bks MO.

Batchelor, Edward, Jr., ed. Abortion: The Moral Issues. LC 82-7505. 256p. 1982. pap. 8.95 (ISBN 0-8298-0612-1). Pilgrim NY.

Benjamin, Dick. Abortion Is Murder. 1980. pap. 1.75 (ISBN 0-911739-04-1). Abbott Loop.

Burtchaell, James T. Rachel Weeping: The Case Against Abortion. LC 83-48986. 400p. 1984. pap. 10.95 (ISBN 0-06-061251-7, RD 517, HarpR). Har-Row.

Castelli, Jim, et al. The Abortion Issue in the Political Process: A Briefing for Catholic Legislators. Jackman, Paul, ed. 19p. pap. 3.00 (ISBN 0-915365-08-1). Cath Free Choice.

Ellingston, Jenefer. We Are the Mainstream. McKenna, Constance, ed. (Illus.). 16p. 1981. pap. 1.00 (ISBN 0-915365-02-2). Cath Free Choice.

Erdahl, Lowell O. Pro-Life, Pro-Peace: Life Affirming Alternatives to Abortion, War, Mercy Killing, & the Death Penalty. LC 86-3552. 160p. (Orig.). 1986. pap. 8.95 (ISBN 0-8066-2209-1, 10-5240). Augsburg.

Ervin, Paula. Women Exploited: The Other Victims of Abortion. 200p. (Orig.). 1985. pap. 6.95 (ISBN 0-87973-847-2, 847). Our Sunday Visitor.

Grady, John L. Abortion: Yes or No? LC 79-53228. 32p. 1968. pap. 1.00 (ISBN 0-89555-117-9). TAN Bks Pubs.

Gregory, Hamilton, ed. The Religious Case for Abortion. LC 82-61786. 96p. (Orig.). 1983. pap. 9.95 (ISBN 0-910915-00-8). Madison Polk.

Hardin, Garrett. Mandatory Motherhood: The True Meaning of "Right to Live". LC 74-4880. 136p. 1974. 6.95 (ISBN 0-8070-2176-8). Beacon Pr.

Harrison, Beverly W. Our Right to Choose: Toward a New Ethic of Abortion. LC 81-70488. 256p. 1983. 18.95x (ISBN 0-8070-1508-3). Beacon Pr.

--Our Right to Choose: Toward a New Ethic of Abortion. LC 81-70488. 356p. 1984. pap. 10.95 (ISBN 0-8070-1509-1, BP673). Beacon Pr.

Hurst, Jane. The History of Abortion in the Catholic Church. McKenna, Constance, ed. (Illus.). 31p. 1983. pap. 1.00 (ISBN 0-915365-04-9). Cath Free Choice.

Hynes, Kathleen. Un Cuestionamiento Etico. Peterson, Jan & Isasi-Diaz, Ada M., eds. Toro, Olga L., tr. from Eng. Tr. of An Ethical Inquiry. (Span.). 16p. 1984. pap. 1.00 (ISBN 0-915365-01-4). Cath Free Choice.

--An Ethical Inquiry. McKenna, Constance & Johnson, Karen, eds. 16p. 1981. pap. 1.00 (ISBN 0-915365-07-3). Cath Free Choice.

Justus, Adalu. Dear Mommy, Please Don't Kill Me. 14p. 1986. pap. 2.50 (ISBN 0-937109-01-0). Silo Pubs.

Koerbel, Pam. Abortion's Second Victim. 204p. 1986. pap. 6.95 (ISBN 0-89693-177-3). Victor Bks.

Koop, C. Everett & Schaeffer, Francis A. Whatever Happened to the Human Race? LC 83-70955. 168p. 1983. pap. 7.95 (ISBN 0-89107-291-8, Crossway Bks). Good News.

Lucas, J. R. Weeping in Ramah. LC 85-70477. 250p. (Orig.). 1985. pap. 7.95 (ISBN 0-89107-357-4, Crossway Bks). Good News.

Luker, Kristin. Abortion & the Politics of Motherhood. LC 83-47849. (California Series on Social Choice & Political Economy). 350p. 1984. 25.00x (ISBN 0-520-04314-6); pap. 7.95 (ISBN 0-520-05597-7, CAL759). U of Cal Pr.

McCarthy, John F. In Defense of Human Life. 71p. 1970. pap. 1.50 (ISBN 0-912414-02-2). Lumen Christi.

McKenna, Constance, ed. I Support You But I Can't Sign My Name. 20p. 1982. pap. 1.00 (ISBN 0-915365-06-5). Cath Free Choice.

McKenna, Constance, et al, eds. My Conscience Speaks. (Illus.). 48p. 1981. pap. 1.00 (ISBN 0-915365-05-7). Cath Free Choice.

Maguire, Daniel C. Reflections of a Catholic Theologian on Visiting an Abortion Clinic. 11p. pap. 1.50 (ISBN 0-915365-10-3). Cath Free Choice.

Maguire, Marjorie R. & Maguire, Daniel C. Abortion: A Guide to Making Ethical Choices. Jackman, Paul & Mooney, Anne S., eds. 44p. 1983. pap. 3.00 (ISBN 0-915365-00-6). Cath Free Choice.

Miles, Judith. Journal from an Obscure Place. LC 78-60279. 144p. 1978. pap. 3.95 (ISBN 0-87123-273-1, 200273). Bethany Hse.

Odell, Catherine & Odell, William. The First Human Right: A Pro-Life Primer. LC 82-61466. 1983. pap. 4.95 (ISBN 0-87973-620-8, 620). Our Sunday Visitor.

Scheidler, Joseph M. Closed: Ninety-Nine Ways to Stop Abortion. LC 85-42646. 350p. (Orig.). 1985. pap. 9.95 (ISBN 0-89107-346-9, Crossway Bks). Good News.

--Closed: Ninety-Nine Ways to Stop Abortion. LC 85-61055. 350p. (Orig.). 1985. pap. 9.95 (ISBN 0-89870-075-2). Ignatius Pr.

Shoemaker, Donald. Abortion, the Bible, & the Christian. (Direction Bks). 1977. pap. text ed. 1.25 (ISBN 0-8010-8109-2). Baker Bk.

Summerhill, Louise. The Story of Birthright: The Alternative to Abortion. LC 72-96117. 1973. pap. 3.50 (ISBN 0-913382-06-X, 101-4). Prow Bks-Franciscan.

Wennberg, Robert. Life in the Balance: Exploring the Abortion Controversy. 192p. (Orig.). 1985. pap. 7.95 (ISBN 0-8028-0061-0). Eerdmans.

ABORTION–MORAL AND ETHICAL ASPECTS

Baker, Don. Beyond Choice: The Abortion Story No One Is Telling. LC 85-15295. 1985. 8.95 (ISBN 0-88070-127-7). Multnomah.

Batchelor, Edward, Jr., ed. Abortion: The Moral Issues. LC 82-7505. 256p. 1982. pap. 8.95 (ISBN 0-8298-0612-1). Pilgrim NY.

Benjamin, Dick. Abortion Is Murder. 1980. pap. 1.75 (ISBN 0-911739-04-1). Abbott Loop.

Channer, J. H., ed. Abortion & the Sanctity of Human Life. 160p. 1986. pap. 7.50 (ISBN 0-85364-417-9, Pub. by Paternoster UK). Attic Pr.

De Danois, Vivian. Abortion & the Moral Degeneration of the American Medical Profession. (A Science of Man Library Bk). 92p. 1975. 81.50 (ISBN 0-913314-56-0). Am Classical Coll Pr.

Hardin, Garrett. Mandatory Motherhood: The True Meaning of "Right to Live". LC 74-4880. 136p. 1974. 6.95 (ISBN 0-8070-2176-8). Beacon Pr.

Harrison, Beverly W. Our Right to Choose: Toward a New Ethic of Abortion. LC 81-70488. 256p. 1983. 18.95x (ISBN 0-8070-1508-3). Beacon Pr.

--Our Right to Choose: Toward a New Ethic of Abortion. LC 81-70488. 356p. 1984. pap. 10.95 (ISBN 0-8070-1509-1, BP673). Beacon Pr.

Hynes, Kathleen. Un Cuestionamiento Etico. Peterson, Jan & Isasi-Diaz, Ada M., eds. Toro, Olga L., tr. from Eng. Tr. of An Ethical Inquiry. (Span.). 16p. 1984. pap. 1.00 (ISBN 0-915365-01-4). Cath Free Choice.

--An Ethical Inquiry. McKenna, Constance & Johnson, Karen, eds. 16p. 1981. pap. 1.00 (ISBN 0-915365-07-3). Cath Free Choice.

Justus, Adalu. Dear Mommy, Please Don't Kill Me. 14p. 1986. pap. 2.50 (ISBN 0-937109-01-0). Silo Pubs.

Kelly, Kent. Abortion-the American Holocaust. LC 81-65240. (Illus.). 149p. (Orig.). 1981. pap. 2.95 (ISBN 0-9604138-1-2). Calvary Pr.

McCartney, James J. Unborn Persons: Pope John Paul II & the Abortion Debate. (American University Studies VII-Theology & Religion: Vol. 21). 176p. 1987. text ed. 16.75 (ISBN 0-8204-0349-0). P Lang Pubs.

Maguire, Marjorie R. & Maguire, Daniel C. Abortion: A Guide to Making Ethical Choices. Jackman, Paul & Mooney, Anne S., eds. 44p. 1983. pap. 3.00 (ISBN 0-915365-00-6). Cath Free Choice.

Noonan, John T., Jr., intro. by. The Morality of Abortion: Legal & Historical Perspectives. LC 70-129118. 276p. 1970. pap. text ed. 6.95x (ISBN 0-674-58727-8). Harvard U Pr.

Odell, Catherine & Odell, William. The First Human Right: A Pro-Life Primer. LC 82-61466. 1983. pap. 4.95 (ISBN 0-87973-620-8, 620). Our Sunday Visitor.

Rodman, Hyman, et al. The Abortion Question. 250p. 1987. 25.00 (ISBN 0-231-05332-0). Columbia U Pr.

ABORTION–PUBLIC OPINION

Hekman, Randall. Justice for the Unborn: Why We Have Legal Abortion & How We Can Stop It. 200p. (Orig.). 1984. pap. 5.95 (ISBN 0-89283-194-4). Servant.

Maestri, William. Choose Life & Not Death: A Primer on Abortion, Euthanasia, & Suicide. LC 85-28687. 9.95 (ISBN 0-8189-0490-9). Alba.

National Council of Jewish Women. Abortion: Challenges Ahead. (Illus.). 25p. (Orig.). 1985. pap. text ed. 5.00 (ISBN 0-941840-19-0). NCJW.

ABORTION–RELIGIOUS ASPECTS

Adams, Walter E. Abortion: A Spiritual Holocast. 60p. (Orig.). 1986. pap. 3.95 (ISBN 0-937408-38-7). GMI Pubns Inc.

Bajema, Clifford E. Abortion & the Meaning of Personhood. (Direction Bks). 1974. pap. 1.25 (ISBN 0-8010-0672-4). Baker Bk.

Burtchaell, James T. Rachel Weeping: The Case Against Abortion. LC 83-48986. 400p. 1984. pap. 10.95 (ISBN 0-06-061251-7, RD 517, HarpR). Har-Row.

De Danois, Vivian. God & Abortion. (A Science of Man Library Bk). 1979. 51.50 (ISBN 0-89266-160-7). Am Classical Coll Pr.

Evangelicals for Social Action Staff & Sider, Ronald J. Completely Pro-Life. 160p. (Orig.). 1987. pap. 5.95 (ISBN 0-87784-496-8). Inter-Varsity.

Fowler, Paul. Abortion: Toward an Evangelical Consensus. (Critical Concern Ser.). 1987. 11.95 (ISBN 0-88070-173-0). Multnomah.

Hensley, Jeffrey, ed. The Zero People. 310p. 1983. pap. 7.95 (ISBN 0-89283-126-X). Servant.

Kowalczyk, John. An Orthodox View on Abortion. pap. 1.95 (ISBN 0-686-27070-3). Light&Life Pub Co MN.

McCarthy, John F. In Defense of Human Life. 71p. 1970. pap. 1.50 (ISBN 0-912414-02-2). Lumen Christi.

Miles, Judith. Journal from an Obscure Place. LC 78-60279. 144p. 1978. pap. 3.95 (ISBN 0-87123-273-1, 200273). Bethany Hse.

Stanford, Susan. Will I Cry Tomorrow? 1987. 9.95 (ISBN 0-8007-1512-8). Revell.

Swyhart, Barbara A. Bioethical Decision-making: Releasing Religion from the Spiritual. LC 75-13040. pap. 35.00 (2026973). Bks Demand UMI.

Whitehead, John W. Arresting Abortion: Practical Ways to Save Unborn Children. LC 84-71422. 128p. 1984. pap. 5.95 (ISBN 0-89107-314-0, Crossway Bks). Good News.

ABORTION–RELIGIOUS ASPECTS–CATHOLIC CHURCH

Abortion: An Eastern Orthodox Statement. pap. 0.25 (ISBN 0-686-01293-3). Eastern Orthodox.

Burtchaell, James T. Rachel Weeping: The Case Against Abortion. LC 83-48986. 400p. 1984. pap. 10.95 (ISBN 0-06-061251-7, RD 517, HarpR). Har-Row.

Castelli, Jim, et al. The Abortion Issue in the Political Process: A Briefing for Catholic Legislators. Jackman, Paul, ed. 19p. pap. 3.00 (ISBN 0-915365-08-1). Cath Free Choice.

Collins, Mary J., ed. A Church Divided: Catholics' Attitudes about Family Planning, Abortion, & Teenage Sexuality. (The Bishops Watch Ser.). (Orig.). 1986. pap. 5.00 (ISBN 0-915365-12-X). Cath Free Choice.

Connery, John. Abortion: The Development of the Roman Catholic Perspective. LC 76-51217. 1977. 12.95 (ISBN 0-8294-0257-8). Loyola.

Ellingston, Jenefer. We Are the Mainstream. McKenna, Constance, ed. (Illus.). 16p. 1981. pap. 1.00 (ISBN 0-915365-02-2). Cath Free Choice.

Hurst, Jane. La Historia de las Ideas sobre el Aborto en la Iglesia Catolica: Una Relacion Desconocida. Boyd, Susan J. & Peterson, Jan, eds. Inda, Caridad, tr. from Eng. (Aborto de Buena Fe Ser.). (Span., Illus.). 31p. 1985. pap. 1.00 (ISBN 0-915365-11-1). Cath Free Choice.

--The History of Abortion in the Catholic Church. McKenna, Constance, ed. (Illus.). 31p. 1983. pap. 1.00 (ISBN 0-915365-04-9). Cath Free Choice.

Hynes, Kathleen. An Ethical Inquiry. McKenna, Constance & Johnson, Karen, eds. 16p. 1981. pap. 1.00 (ISBN 0-915365-07-3). Cath Free Choice.

Katenkamp, Jane B. Respecting Life: An Activity Guide. (Illus.). 144p. (Orig.). 1985. pap. 14.95 (ISBN 1-55586-964-5). US Catholic.

Lotstra, H. Abortion: The Catholic Debate in America. 340p. 1985. 39.50x (ISBN 0-8290-0728-8). Irvington.

McKenna, Constance, ed. I Support You But I Can't Sign My Name. 20p. 1982. pap. 1.00 (ISBN 0-915365-06-5). Cath Free Choice.

McKenna, Constance, et al, eds. My Conscience Speaks. (Illus.). 48p. 1981. pap. 1.00 (ISBN 0-915365-05-7). Cath Free Choice.

Maguire, Daniel C. Reflections of a Catholic Theologian on Visiting an Abortion Clinic. 11p. pap. 1.50 (ISBN 0-915365-10-3). Cath Free Choice.

Reed, Evelyn & Moriarty, Claire. Abortion & the Catholic Church: Two Feminists Defend Women's Rights. 1973. pap. 0.35 (ISBN 0-87348-288-3). Path Pr NY.

A Reflection Guide on Human Sexuality & the Ordained Priesthood. 72p. 1983. pap. 2.95 (ISBN 1-55586-865-7). US Catholic.

ABORTION–RELIGIOUS ASPECTS–CHRISTIANITY

Brown, Harold O. J. The Bible on Abortion. 1977. 0.50 (ISBN 0-911802-43-6). Free Church Pubns.

Davis, John J. Abortion & the Christian. 128p. 1984. pap. 4.95 (ISBN 0-87552-221-1). Presby & Reformed.

Gorman, Michael J. Abortion & the Early Church: Christian, Jewish, & Pagan Attitudes in the Greco-Roman World. 4.95 (ISBN 0-8091-2511-0). Paulist Pr.

Klotz, J. A Christian View of Abortion. (Contemporary Theology Ser.). 1973. 3.95 (ISBN 0-570-06721-9, 12RT2560). Concordia.

Koop, C. Everett & Schaeffer, Francis A. Whatever Happened to the Human Race? LC 83-70955. 168p. 1983. pap. 7.95 (ISBN 0-89107-291-8, Crossway Bks). Good News.

Shoemaker, Donald. Abortion, the Bible, & the Christian. (Direction Bks). 1977. pap. text ed. 1.25 (ISBN 0-8010-8109-2). Baker Bk.

Shoemaker, Donald P. Abortion, the Bible & the Christian. 1976. 4.00 (ISBN 0-910728-15-1); pap. 1.25 (ISBN 0-910728-08-9). Hayes.

Singh, Tara. How to Raise a Child of God. 2nd ed. LC 86-82911. (Orig.). 1987. 19.95 (ISBN 1-55531-008-7); pap. 14.95 (ISBN 1-55531-009-5). Life Action Pr.

Summerhill, Louise. The Story of Birthright: The Alternative to Abortion. LC 72-96117. 1973. pap. 3.50 (ISBN 0-913382-06-X, 101-4). Prow Bks-Franciscan.

Young, Curt. The Least of These: What Everyone Should Know About Abortion. 1984. 7.95 (ISBN 0-8024-0355-7). Moody.

ABOTH–COMMENTARIES

Maimonides, Moses. Commentary to Mishnah Aboth. David, Arthur, tr. LC 68-27871. 1968. 9.95x (ISBN 0-8197-0154-8). Bloch.

Taylor, Charles. Sayings of the Jewish Fathers, 2 Vols. in 1. rev. ed. (Library of Jewish Classics). 1969. 25.00x (ISBN 0-87068-114-1). Ktav.

ABRAHAM, THE PATRIARCH

Abraham. 1979. 0.75 (ISBN 0-8198-0564-5). Dghtrs St Paul.

Anderson, Don. Abraham: Delay Is Not Denial. (Kingfisher Ser.). 200p. 1987. pap. 6.95 (ISBN 0-87213-000-2). Loizeaux.

Arieti, Silvano. Abraham & the Contemporary Mind. LC 80-68187. 187p. 1981. 14.95 (ISBN 0-465-00005-3). Basic.

Chambers, Oswald. Not Knowing Whither. 1957. pap. 2.95 (ISBN 0-87508-118-5). Chr Lit.

Getz, Gene A. When You're Confused & Uncertain. rev. ed. LC 86-477. (Biblical Renewal Ser.). 160p. 1986. pap. 5.95 (ISBN 0-8307-1122-8, 5418749). Regal.

Heap, Norman L. Abraham, Isaac, & Jacob, Servants & Prophets of God. 1987. 12.50 (ISBN 0-533-07272-7). Vantage.

Lindsay, Gordon. Abraham, Friend of God. (Old Testament Ser.). 1.25 (ISBN 0-89985-126-6). Christ Nations.

Madison, Leslie. Abraham's Test of Faith. 158p. (Orig.). 1982. pap. 3.50 (ISBN 0-89323-031-6). Bible Memory.

Meyer, F. B. Abraham. 1968. pap. 4.50 (ISBN 0-87508-340-4). Chr Lit.

Nee, Watchman. Changed into His Likeness. 1969. 4.95 (ISBN 0-87508-411-7); pap. 3.95 (ISBN 0-87508-410-9). Chr Lit.

Small, Dwight H. No Rival Love. 201p. (Orig.). 1985. pap. 4.95 (ISBN 0-87508-495-8). Chr Lit.

Stone, Michael E. The Testament of Abraham. LC 72-88770. (Society of Biblical Literature. Texts & Translation-Psuedepigrapha Ser.). 1972. pap. 8.95 (ISBN 0-89130-170-4, 060202). Scholars Pr GA.

Vermes, Geza. Scripture & Tradition in Judaism. 2nd rev. ed. (Studia Post Biblica: No. 4). 1973. text ed. 9.95x (ISBN 90-040-3626-1). Humanities.

Watchman, Nee. Changed into His Likeness. 1978. pap. 3.95 (ISBN 0-8423-0228-X). Tyndale.

ABRAHAM, THE PATRIARCH–FICTION

Traylor, Ellen G. Song of Abraham. 1981. pap. 4.50 (ISBN 0-8423-6071-9). Tyndale.

ABRAHAM, THE PATRIARCH–JUVENILE LITERATURE

Barrett, Ethel. Abraham: God's Faithful Pilgrim. LC 82-12330. (Bible Biography Ser.). 128p. (Orig.). 1982. pap. 2.50 (ISBN 0-8307-0769-7, 5810906). Regal.

Caffrey, Stephanie & Kenslea, Timothy. The Family That Wanted a Home. (Rainbow Books (Bible Story Books for Children)). (Orig.). 1978. pap. 1.00 (ISBN 0-8192-1235-0). Morehouse.

Rives, Elsie. Abraham: Man of Faith. (BibLearn Ser.). (Illus.). 1976. 5.95 (ISBN 0-8054-4223-5, 4242-23). Broadman.

Shimoni, S. Legends of Abraham the Patriarch. (Biblical Ser.). (Illus.). 1975. 3.00 (ISBN 0-914080-07-5). Shulsinger Sales.

ABRAHAM A SANCTA CLARA, FATHER, 1644-1709

Kann, Robert A. A Study in Austrian Intellectual History from Late Baroque to Romanticism. LC 73-16356. 367p. 1973. Repr. lib. bdg. 27.50x (ISBN 0-374-94504-7, Octagon). Hippocrene Bks.

ABRAHAM BEN DAVID, OF POSQUIERES, 1125-1198

Twersky, Isadore. Rabad of Posquieres: A Twelfth-Century Talmudist. LC 62-7192. (Semitic Ser: No. 18). 1962. 22.50x (ISBN 0-674-74550-7). Harvard U Pr.

ABSENT TREATMENT

see Mental Healing

ABSOLUTE, THE

Bhattacharrya, K. C. Search for the Absolute in Neo-Vedanta. Burch, George B., ed. LC 75-17740. 202p. 1976. text ed. 14.00x (ISBN 0-8248-0296-9). UH Pr.

Burch, George B. Alternative Goals in Religion: Love, Freedom, Truth. 1973. pap. 3.95 (ISBN 0-7735-0163-0). McGill-Queens U Pr.

Loer, Barbara. Das Absolute & Die Wirklichkeit in Schellings Philosophie: Mit der Erstedition einer Handschrift aus dem Berliner Schelling-Nachlass. LC 73-93164. (Quellen & Studien zur Philosophie, Vol. 7). (Illus.). viii, 288p. 1974. 53.20x (ISBN 3-11-004329-7). De Gruyter.

Orest. ONE. LC 76-47223. (Orig.). 1977. pap. 4.95 (ISBN 0-89407-002-9). Strawberry Hill.

Tillich, Paul. My Search for Absolutes: A Credo Perspective. Anshen, Ruth N., ed. (Illus.). 1984. pap. 6.95 (ISBN 0-671-50585-8, Touchstone Bks). S&S.

ABSOLUTE RIGHTS

see Natural Law

ABSOLUTION

see also Confession; Forgiveness of Sin; Indulgences; Penance

Lea, Henry C. History of Auricular Confession & Indulgences in the Latin Church, 3 Vols. LC 68-19287. 1968. Repr. of 1896 ed. lib. bdg. 67.25x (ISBN 0-8371-0140-9, LEHC). Greenwood.

ABSTINENCE

see Fasting; Temperance

ABYDOS, EGYPT

David, A. R. A Guide to Religious Ritual at Abydos. 182p. 1981. pap. text ed. 40.00x (ISBN 0-85668-060-5, Pub. by Aris & Phillips UK). Humanities.

Simpson, William K. The Terrace of the Great God at Abydos: The Offering Chapels of Dynasties 12 & 13, Vol. 5. LC 73-88231. 1974. 25.00 (ISBN 0-686-05519-5). Penn-Yale Expedit.

ACOLYTES

see Altar Boys

ACTION, CATHOLIC

see Catholic Action

ACTON, JOHN EMERICH EDWARD DALBERG ACTON, 1ST BARON, 1834-1902

Shaw, William A. Bibliography of the Historical Works of Dr. Creighton, Dr. Stubbs, Dr. S. R. Gardiner, & the Late Lord Acton. 1969. 17.50 (ISBN 0-8337-3242-0). B Franklin.

ACTORS–CORRESPONDENCE, REMINISCENCES, ETC.

There & Back: Memories & Thoughts of a Jewish Actor - Moreuski. LC 67-27245. 256p. 1967. 6.95 (ISBN 0-87527-057-3). Green.

Waters, Ethel & Michel, Charles. His Eye Is on the Sparrow. 1972. pap. 2.95 (ISBN 0-515-06738-5). Jove Pubns.

ADAGES

see Proverbs

ADALARD, SAINT, ABBOT OF CORBIE, d. 826

Cabaniss, Allen, ed. Charlemagne's Cousins: Contemporary Lives of Adalard & Wala. LC 67-26919. 1967. 14.95x (ISBN 0-8156-2115-9). Syracuse U Pr.

ADAM (BIBLICAL CHARACTER)

Hitchcock, Donald R. The Appeal of Adam to Lazarus in Hell. (Slavistic Printings & Reprintings Ser.: No. 302). 1979. text ed. 80.00x (ISBN 0-686-27016-9). Mouton.

Loredano, Giovanni. Life of Adam. LC 67-26617. 1967. Repr. of 1659 ed. 25.00x (ISBN 0-8201-1031-0). Schol Facsimiles.

Pagels, Elaine. Adam, Eve & the Serpent. 1987. 17.95 (ISBN 0-394-52140-4). Random.

Pitman, Michael. Adam & Evolution. 269p. 1986. pap. 12.95 (ISBN 0-8010-7092-9). Baker Bk.

Quinn, Esther C. The Penitence of Adam: (A Study of the Andrius MS., No. 36. Dufau, Micheline, tr. LC 79-19056. 192p. 1980. 21.00x (ISBN 84-499-3367-6). Romance.

Reed, Gwendolyn. Adam & Eve. LC 68-27712. (Illus.). 1968. PLB 11.88 (ISBN 0-688-51256-9). Lothrop.

Roberts, Douglas. To Adam with Love. pap. write for info (ISBN 0-515-09536-2). Jove Pubns.

Robinson, Stephen E. The Testament of Adam: An Examination of the Syriac & Greek Traditions. LC 80-12209. (Society of Biblical Literature Dissertation Ser.: No. 52). pap. 13.50 (ISBN 0-89130-399-5, 06-01-52). Scholars Pr GA.
Versteeg, J. P. Is Adam a "Teaching Model" in the New Testament? pap. 1.75 (ISBN 0-8010-9276-0). Baker Bk.
--Is Adam a Teaching Model in the New Testament? 1978. pap. 1.75 (ISBN 0-87552-500-8). Presby & Reformed.

ADOLESCENCE
see also Youth
Arledge, Byron W. Laugh with Your Teenager. 128p. 1985. pap. 4.95 (ISBN 0-8423-2102-0). Tyndale.
Bier, W. C., ed. Adolescent, His Search for Understanding. LC 62-17450. (Pastoral Psychology Ser.: No. 3). x, 246p. 1963. 17.50 (ISBN 0-8232-0480-4). Fordham.
Blair, Maury & Brendel, Doug. Maury, Hijo Del Dolor. Araujo, Juan S., tr. from Eng. Tr. of Maury, Wednesday's Child. (Span.). 144p. 1986. pap. 3.75 (ISBN 0-88113-204-7). Edit Betania.
Campbell, Ross. Si Amas a Tu Adolescente. Araujo, Juan S., tr. from Eng. Tr. of How To Really Love Your Teenager. (Span.). 144p. 1986. pap. 3.95 (ISBN 0-88113-030-3). Edit Betania.
Daughters of St. Paul. Teenagers Today. 1981. 4.00 (ISBN 0-8198-7303-9); pap. 3.00 (ISBN 0-8198-7304-7). Dghtrs St Paul.
Dobson, James. Preparing for Adolescence. LC 78-57673. 192p. 1980. 5.95 (ISBN 0-88449-111-0, A424717); pap. 2.95 (ISBN 0-88449-045-9, A324551). Vision Hse.
Hall, Stanley G. Adolescence-Its Psychology & Its Relation to Physiology, Anthropology, Sociology, Sex, Crime, Religion & Education, 2 vols. LC 79-89183. (American Education: Its Men, Institutions & Ideas Ser). 1970. Repr. of 1905 ed. Set. 65.00 (ISBN 0-405-01421-X); Vol. 1. 38.50 (ISBN 0-405-01422-8); Vol. 2. 35.00 (ISBN 0-405-01423-6). Ayer Co Pubs.
Kesler, Jay, ed. Parents & Teenagers. 696p. 1984. pap. 16.95 (ISBN 0-88207-817-8). Victor Bks.
Witte, Kaaren. Angels in Faded Jeans. LC 79-84795. 160p. 1979. pap. 3.95 (ISBN 0-87123-014-3, 210014). Bethany Hse.

ADOPTION
Dellinger, Annetta E. Adopted & Loved Forever. (Illus.). 1987. 3.95 (ISBN 0-570-04167-8). Concordia.
Macmanus, Sheila. The Adoption Book. (Orig.). 1984. pap. 4.95 (ISBN 0-8091-2578-1). Paulist Pr.
Miles, Judith. Journal from an Obscure Place. LC 78-60279. 144p. 1978. pap. 3.95 (ISBN 0-87123-273-1, 200273). Bethany Hse.
Strom, Kay M. Chosen Families. 240p. 1985. 10.95 (ISBN 0-310-33590-6, 11715). Zondervan.
Zimmerman, Martha. Should I Keep My Baby? 112p. (Orig.). 1983. pap. 3.95 (ISBN 0-87123-578-1, 210578). Bethany Hse.

ADOPTION–JUVENILE LITERATURE
Hess, Edith & Blass, Jacqueline. Peter & Susie Find a Family. Tr. of Peter & Susi Finden eine Familie. (Illus.). 28p. 1985. Repr. of 1981 ed. 10.95 (ISBN 0-687-30848-8). Abingdon.

ADOPTION–PERSONAL NARRATIVES
De Hartog, Jan. Adopted Children. rev. ed. 268p. 1987. pap. 13.95 (ISBN 0-915361-65-5, Dist. by Watts). Adama Pubs Inc.

ADVAITA
Adhvarindra, Dharmaraja. Vedanta-Paribhasa. Madhavananda, Swami, tr. (English & Sanskrit). pap. 8.95 (ISBN 0-87481-072-8). Vedanta Pr.
Chari, S. M. Advaita & Visistadvaita. 2nd ed. 1976. 11.95 (ISBN 0-8426-0886-9). Orient Bk Dist.
Cohen, S. S. Advaitic Sadhana. 1976. 8.95 (ISBN 0-8426-0989-X). Orient Bk Dist.
Deutsch, Eliot. Advaita Vedanta: A Philosophical Reconstruction. LC 69-19282. 1969. pap. text ed. 5.95x (ISBN 0-8248-0271-3, Eastwest Ctr). UH Pr.
Deutsch, Eliot & Van Buitenen, J. A. A Source Book of Advaita Vedeanta. LC 75-148944. pap. 65.60 (ISBN 0-317-12996-1, 2017216). Bks Demand UMI.
Indich, William M. Consciousness in Advaita Vedanta. 1980. 14.00x (ISBN 0-8364-0607-9). South Asia Bks.
Jones, Richard H. Science & Mysticism: A Comparative Study of Western Natural Science, Theravada Buddhism, & Advaita Vedanta. LC 84-46098. 272p. 1986. 35.00x (ISBN 0-8387-5093-1, Pub. by Bucknell U Pr). Assoc Univ Prs.
Satprakashananda, Swami. Methods of Knowledge According to Advaita Vedanta. 366p. 1975. Repr. of 1965 ed. 10.00 (ISBN 0-87481-154-6). Vedanta Pr.
Shankara. Laghu-Vakya-Vritti. (Sanskrit & English). pap. 1.50 (ISBN 0-87481-067-1). Vedanta Pr.
--Panchikaranam. (Sanskrit & English). pap. 2.00 (ISBN 0-87481-068-X). Vedanta Pr.
Vidyaranya, Swami. Pancadasi. Swahananda, Swami, tr. (Sanskrit & Eng). 10.00 (ISBN 0-87481-429-4). Vedanta Pr.

ADVENT
see also Second Advent
Alessi, Vincie, ed. Programs for Advent & Christmas. 1978. pap. 4.95 (ISBN 0-8170-0808-X). Judson.
Arnold, Eberhard, et al. When the Time Was Fulfilled: Talks & Writings on Advent & Christmas. LC 65-17599. 1965. 7.00 (ISBN 0-87486-104-7). Plough.
Bastin, Marcel, et al. God Day by Day, Vol. 4: Advent & Christmas. 184p. (Orig.). 1985. pap. 8.95 (ISBN 0-8091-2699-0). Paulist Pr.
Behm, Douglas R. An Advent Covenant Wreath. 16p. 1981. pap. text ed. 2.65 (ISBN 0-89536-482-4, 0102). CSS of Ohio.
Brokhoff, John. Advent & Event. 88p. (Orig.). 1980. pap. text ed. 3.25 (ISBN 0-89536-453-0, 0147). CSS of Ohio.
Carney, Mary L. Advent: A Calendar of Devotions, 1987. 48p. pap. 30.00 (ISBN 0-687-00887-5). Abingdon.
Carney, Mary Lou. Advent: A Calendar of Devotions, Nineteen Eighty-Six. 48p. (Orig.). 1986. pap. 30.00 (ISBN 0-687-00886-7). Abingdon.
Davidson, Robert, ed. Creative Ideas for Advent. 114p. (Orig.). 1980. pap. 9.95 (ISBN 0-940754-06-1). Ed Ministries.
Davidson, Robert G. Creative Ideas for Advent, Vol. 2. 100p. (Orig.). 1986. pap. 9.95 (ISBN 0-940754-35-5). Ed Ministries.
Dessem, Ralph. Celebrating Advent in the Sanctuary. 1983. pap. 2.50 (ISBN 0-89536-635-5, 0384). CSS of Ohio.
Evans, Jean. Make Ready the Way: An Advent-Christmas Journal Book. LC 81-52596. 64p. (Orig.). 1981. pap. text ed. 4.95 (ISBN 0-89390-030-3). Resource Pubns.
Fuller, Reginald H. Advent-Christmas. Achtemeier, Elizabeth, et al, eds. LC 79-7377. (Proclamation 2: Aids for Interpreting the Lessons of the Church Year, Ser. C). 64p. 1979. pap. 3.75 (ISBN 0-8006-4079-9, 1-4079). Fortress.
Griggs, Donald & Griggs, Patricia. Teaching & Celebrating Advent. rev. ed. (Griggs Educational Resources Ser.). (Illus.). 1980. pap. 6.95 (ISBN 0-687-41080-0). Abingdon.
Groh, Dennis E. In Between Advents: Biblical & Spiritual Arrivals. LC 86-45199. (The Bible for Christian Life Ser.). 64p. 1986. pap. 3.95 (ISBN 0-8006-2025-9). Fortress.
Hammond, Heather. Preparing for God's Gift: Devotions for Families Using the Advent Wreath. 40p. (Orig.). 1986. pap. 2.50 (ISBN 0-8066-2260-1, 23-1809). Augsburg.
Harupa, Gisela & Nold, Liselotte. Advent Day by Day in the Home. Kaste, Omar, tr. LC 62-17507. 1962. pap. 2.95 (ISBN 0-8066-0209-0, 10-0160). Augsburg.
Heisberger, Jean M., ed. Arise Jerusalem: Parish Advent Program, Advent Family Handbook. LC 78-70425. 1978. pap. text ed. 1.25 (ISBN 0-8091-9179-2). Paulist Pr.
Hopko, Thomas. Winter Pascha. LC 84-27622. 1983. pap. text ed. 6.95 (ISBN 0-88141-025-X). St Vladimirs.
Irwin, Kevin W. Advent Christmas: A Guide to the Eucharist & Hours. (Liturgical Seasons Ser.). 300p. (Orig.). 1986. pap. 12.95 (ISBN 0-916134-80-6). Pueblo Pub Co.
Kurtz, Muriel T. Prepare Our Hearts: Advent & Christmas Traditions for Families. 144p. (Orig.). 1986. pap. 6.95 spiral bdg. (ISBN 0-8358-0544-1). Upper Room.
Lawrence, Emeric. Jesus Present & Coming: Daily Meditations on the Advent & Christmas Masses. LC 82-20380. 128p. 1982. pap. 7.95 (ISBN 0-8146-1284-9). Liturgical Pr.
Living & Celebrating Advent Season. 3.50 (ISBN 0-8198-4418-7); 2.50 (ISBN 0-8198-4419-5). Dghtrs St Paul.
Montgomery, Mary & Montgomery, Herb. Christmas Is Coming. 40p. (Orig.). 1983. pap. text ed. 1.50 (ISBN 0-89622-197-0). Twenty-Third.
Nilsen, Mary Y. Our Family Shares Advent: Scripture, Prayer, & Activities for Families. (Illus.). 64p. (Orig.). 1980. pap. 7.95 (ISBN 0-86683-637-3, 8129, HarpR). Har-Row.
Olsen, V. Norskov, et al, eds. The Advent Hope in Scripture & History. 272p. (Orig.). 1987. 22.95 (ISBN 0-8280-0311-4). Review & Herald.
Reilly, Mary V., et al. Wait in Joyful Hope! (Illus., Orig.). 1980. pap. 4.95 (ISBN 0-8192-1275-X). Morehouse.
Sasser, Nancy L. Around the Advent Wreath: Devotions for Families Using the Advent Wreath. 40p. (Orig.). 1984. pap. 2.95 (ISBN 0-8066-2074-9, 23-1064). Augsburg.
Schmalenberger, Jerry. Advent & Christmas Saints. 1984. 3.75 (ISBN 0-89536-685-1, 4861). CSS of Ohio.
Schneider, Terrance L. Advent: Twenty-Eight Ways to Celebrate the Holy in the Holiday Rush. (Illus.). 37p. 1982. pap. text ed. 1.95 (ISBN 0-86716-017-9). St Anthony Mess Pr.
Schroeder, L. Celebrate-While We Wait. (Illus.). 1977. pap. 4.95 (ISBN 0-570-03052-8, 6-1177). Concordia.
Skelly, Herbert & Skelly, Margaret. An Advent Event. (Illus.). 32p. (Orig.). 1973. pap. 3.25 (ISBN 0-8192-1148-6); kit 13.95 (ISBN 0-8192-1283-0). Morehouse.
Sloyan, Gerard S. Advent-Christmas. LC 84-18756. (Proclamation 3 C Ser.). 64p. 1985. pap. 3.75 (ISBN 0-8006-4125-6). Fortress.
Smith, Delia. A Feast for Advent. 2nd ed. 96p. 1985. pap. 4.95 (ISBN 0-89622-219-5). Twenty-Third.
Stuhlmueller, Carroll. Biblical Meditations for Advent & the Christmas Season. LC 80-82083. (Biblical Meditations Ser.: Vol. 3). 288p. (Orig.). 1980. pap. 4.95 (ISBN 0-8091-2318-5). Paulist Pr.
Vawter, Bruce. Advent-Christmas. LC 84-18756. (Proclamation 3A Ser.). 64p. 1986. pap. 3.75 (ISBN 0-8006-4117-5, 1-4117). Fortress.
Warren, Mary P. On Our Way to Christmas: A Family Activity Book for Advent. 32p. (Orig.). 1980. pap. 4.95 (ISBN 0-8066-1784-5, 10-4768). Augsburg.
Williams, Doris & Griggs, Patricia. Preparing for the Messiah. (Griggs Educational Resources Ser.). 1979. pap. 5.95 (ISBN 0-687-33920-0). Abingdon.

ADVENT SERMONS
Achtemeier, Paul J. & Mebust, J. Leland. Advent-Christmas. Achtemeier, Elizabeth, et al, eds. LC 79-7377. (Proclamation 2: Aids for Interpreting the Lessons of the Church Year, Ser. B). 64p. (Orig.). 1981. pap. 3.75 (ISBN 0-8006-4060-8, 1-4060). Fortress.
Bass, George. The Cradle, the Cross & the Crown. Sherer, Michael L., ed. (Orig.). 1986. pap. 7.25 (ISBN 0-89536-817-X, 6866). CSS of Ohio.
Bringman, Dale. A Star Is Born. (Orig.). 1987. pap. price not set (ISBN 0-89536-881-1, 7867). CSS of Ohio.
Cole, Joan. Our Hearts Wait: Daily Prayer for Advent. 48p. 1984. pap. 1.50 (ISBN 0-89243-215-2). Liguori Pubns.
Eslinger, Richard. Prepare in the Wilderness. 1984. 5.25 (ISBN 0-89536-680-0, 4856). CSS of Ohio.
Liptak, David Q. Biblical Advent Homilies. 68p. (Orig.). 1986. pap. 8.95 (ISBN 0-941850-15-3). Sunday Pubns.
Long, Thomas. Shepherds & Bathrobes. (Orig.). 1987. pap. price not set (ISBN 0-89536-869-2, 7855). CSS of Ohio.
Lowery, Daniel L. Day by Day Through Advent: Reflections, Prayers, Practices. 80p. 1984. pap. 1.95 (ISBN 0-89243-216-0). Liguori Pubns.
Morgan, Robert. Advent Recollections: Five Dramatic Monologs. 1985. 3.50 (ISBN 0-89536-764-5, 5871). CSS of Ohio.
Mueller, Daniel. Just Follow the Signs. 1984. 5.00 (ISBN 0-89536-676-2, 4851). CSS of Ohio.
Peterson, Thomas. The Gospel Shines Through. (Orig.). 1987. pap. price not set (ISBN 0-89536-874-9, 7860). CSS of Ohio.
Rest, Friedrich. Our Christian Worship: Advent-Christmas. 1985. 4.75 (ISBN 0-89536-761-0, 5868). CSS of Ohio.
Ridenhour, Thomas E., Sr. Promise of Peace, Call for Justice. Sherer, Michael L., ed. (Orig.). 1986. pap. 6.75 (ISBN 0-89536-822-6, 6831). CSS of Ohio.
A Service for the Hanging of the Greens. 1984. 2.25 (ISBN 0-89536-709-2, 4890). CSS of Ohio.
Siewert, Alan E. An Unlikely Cast: Dramatic Monologues for Advent. 1976. pap. 3.50 (ISBN 0-89536-245-7, 2107). CSS of Ohio.

ADVENTISTS
see also Seventh-Day Adventists
Barton, Freeman, ed. Advent Christians & the Bible. 2nd, rev. ed. LC 84-80020. 96p. pap. 4.00 (ISBN 0-913439-03-7). Henceforth.
--Putting the Pieces Together: Advent Christians Interpret Prophecy. 80p. (Orig.). 1983. pap. 3.00 (ISBN 0-913439-02-9). Henceforth.
--Sovereignty & Freedom: A Struggle for Balance. 92p. (Orig.). 1978. pap. 2.50 (ISBN 0-913439-00-2). Henceforth.
Brunt, John C. Promise & Present: Adventist Eschatology & Ethics. Coffen, Richard W., ed. 96p. 1987. pap. 5.95 (ISBN 0-8280-0386-6). Review & Herald.
Emmerson, Walter L. Reformation & the Advent Movement. 224p. pap. 9.95 (ISBN 0-8280-0168-5). Review & Herald.
Jewett, Richard M. Orientation for New Adventists. (Waymark Ser.). 1978. pap. 2.95 (ISBN 0-8127-0184-4). Review & Herald.
Kistler, Robert. Adventists & Labor Unions in the U. S. Wheeler, Gerald, ed. LC 83-13664. (Illus.). 127p. (Orig.). 1984. pap. 9.95 (ISBN 0-8280-0221-5). Review & Herald.
Knight, George R., ed. Early Adventist Educators. LC 83-71043. (Illus.). xvi, 250p. 1983. 12.95 (ISBN 0-943872-60-X). Andrews Univ Pr.
Land, Gary, ed. Adventism in America. 304p. (Orig.). 1986. pap. 14.95 (ISBN 0-8028-0237-0). Eerdmans.
Loughborough, J. N. The Great Second Advent Movement: Its Rise & Progress. LC 71-38453. (Religion in America, Ser. 2). 502p. 1972. Repr. of 1905 ed. 32.00 (ISBN 0-405-04073-3). Ayer Co Pubs.
Numbers, Ronald L. & Butler, Jonathan M., eds. The Disappointed: Millerism & Millenarianism in the Nineteenth Century. (Religion in North America Ser.). 1987. 29.95 (ISBN 0-253-34299-6). Ind U Pr.
Savoy, Gene. The Millennium Edition of the Essaei Document: Secrets of an Eternal Race. Revised ed. LC 83-83221. Orig. Title: The Essaei Document. (Illus.). xii, 140p. 1983. text ed. 39.50 (ISBN 0-936202-07-6). Intl Comm Christ.

ADVERTISING–CHURCHES
see also Church Bulletins; Journalism, Religious; Public Relations–Churches
Kirban, Salem. Church Promotion Handbook. 1963. 10.00 (ISBN 0-912582-38-3). Kirban.

AELFRIC (CALLED GRAMMATICUS), 955-1020
Waterhouse, Ruth, ed. The Triangular Clause Relationship in Aelfric's Lives of Saints & in Other Works. LC 83-5399. (American Universtiy Studies IV: English Language & Literature: Vol. 1). 119p. (Orig.). 1983. pap. text ed. 12.10 (ISBN 0-8204-0007-6). P Lang Pubs.

AESCULAPIUS
Edelstein, Emma J. & Edelstein, Ludwig. Asclepius: A Collection & Interpretation of the Testimonies, 2 vols. in 1. facsimile ed. LC 75-10635. (Ancient Religion & Mythology Ser.). (Eng. & Gr.). 1976. Repr. of 1945 ed. 57.50x (ISBN 0-405-07009-8). Ayer Co Pubs.
Kerenyi, Carl. Archetypal Images in Greek Religion, 5 vols. Manheim, R., tr. Incl. Vol. 1. Prometheus: Archetypal Image of Human Existence. 1963; Vol. 2. Dionysos: Archetypal Image of Industructible Life. 1975; Vol. 3. Asklepios: Archetypal Image of the Physician's Existence. 1959. 37.00x (ISBN 0-691-09703-8); Vol. 4. Eleusis: Archetypal Image of Mother & Daughter. 1967; Vol. 5. Zeus & Hera-Archetypal Image of Father, Husband & Wife. Holme, tr. 1975. (Bollingen Ser.: Vol. 65). Princeton U Pr.
Walton, A. Asklepios: The Cult of the Greek God of Medicine. 136p. 1979. 15.00 (ISBN 0-89005-277-8). Ares.
Walton, Alice. The Cult of Asklepios. Repr. of 1894 ed. 15.00 (ISBN 0-384-65660-9). Johnson Repr.

AFFLICTION
see Suffering

AFRICA–RELIGION
Africa: A Season for Hope. 1985. write for info. (ISBN 0-912552-46-8). World Vision Intl.
Alexander, E. Curtis. African Foundations of Judaism & Christianity. LC 84-48679. (Alkebu-lan Historical Research Society Monograph: No. 3). 84p. (Orig.). 1985. pap. 5.95 (ISBN 0-938818-08-2). ECA Assoc.
--African Historical Religions: A Conceptual & Ethical Foundation for Western Religions. LC 83-83096. (Alkelbulan Historical Research Society Monograph Ser.: No. 2). (Illus.). 70p. 1984. pap. 4.95 (ISBN 0-938818-05-8). ECA Assoc.
Appiah-Kubi, Kofi & Torres, Sergio, eds. African Theology En Route: Papers from the Pan-African Conference of Third World Theologians, December 17-23, 1977, Accra, Ghana. LC 78-10604. 224p. (Orig.). 1978. pap. 10.95 (ISBN 0-88344-010-5). Orbis Bks.
Barnes, Sandra T. Ogun: An Old God for a New Age. LC 79-26577. (ISHI Occasional Papers in Social Change: No. 3). 72p. 1980. pap. text ed. 5.95x (ISBN 0-89727-011-8). ISHI PA.
Booth, Newell S. African Religions: A Symposium. LC 73-88062. 390p. 1977. text ed. 21.50x (ISBN 0-88357-012-2). Nok Pubs.
Buis, Robert. Religious Beliefs & White Prejudice. 71p. 1975. pap. text ed. 7.95x (ISBN 0-86975-044-5, Pub. by Ravan Pr). Ohio U Pr.
DeGruchy, John W. Bonhoeffer & South Africa: Theology in Dialogue. 128p. (Orig.). 1984. pap. 9.95 (ISBN 0-8028-0042-4). Eerdmans.
De Gruchy, John W. Cry Justice! Prayers, Meditations & Readings from South African Christians in a Time of Crisis. LC 86-667. (Illus.). 264p. (Orig.). 1986. pap. 6.95 (ISBN 0-88344-223-X). Orbis Bks.
Dickson, Kwesi A. Theology in Africa. LC 84-5154. 240p. (Orig.). 1984. pap. 9.95 (ISBN 0-88344-508-5). Orbis Bks.
Donders, Joseph G. Non-Bourgeois Theology: An African Experience of Jesus. LC 84-16677. 224p. (Orig.). 1985. pap. 10.95 (ISBN 0-88344-352-X). Orbis Bks.

El-Zein, Abdul H. The Sacred Meadows: A Structural Analysis of Religious Symbolism in an East African Town. LC 73-91310. (Studies in African Religion). 1974. text ed. 19.95x (ISBN 0-8101-0443-1). Northwestern U Pr.
Fernandez, James W. Bwiti: An Ethnography of the Religious Imagination in Africa. LC 81-47125. (Illus.). 708p. 1982. 97.50x (ISBN 0-691-09390-3); pap. 28.00x LPE (ISBN 0-691-10122-1). Princeton U Pr.
Harris, Grace G. Casting Out Anger: Religion among the Taita of Kenya. (Illus.). 193p. 1986. pap. text ed. 7.95x (ISBN 0-88133-233-X). Waveland Pr.
International African Seminar - 3rd - Salisburg - Southern Rhodesia. African Systems of Thought. Fortes, Meyer & Dieterlen, Germaine, eds. 1965. 42.00x (ISBN 0-19-724158-1). Oxford U Pr.
Johnson, William A. Africa's Mountain Valley; or, the Church in Regent's Town, West Africa. LC 72-3995. (Black Heritage Library Collection Ser.). Repr. of 1856 ed. 18.75 (ISBN 0-8369-9098-6). Ayer Co Pubs.
Jules-Rosette, Bennetta, ed. The New Religions of Africa. LC 78-16925. (Modern Sociology Ser.). (Illus.). 1979. 34.50x (ISBN 0-89391-014-7). Ablex Pub.
The Kairos Document: Challenge to the Churches. 80p. (Orig.). 1986. pap. 4.95 (ISBN 0-8028-0189-7). Eerdmans.
Kendrick, V. Ben. Buried Alive for Christ & Other Missionary Stories. LC 78-14984. 1978. pap. 3.95 (ISBN 0-87227-061-0). Reg Baptist.
King, Noel Q. African Cosmos: An Introduction to Religion in Africa. 1985. pap. text ed. write for info (ISBN 0-534-05334-3). Wadsworth Pub.
Koch, Kurt E. God among the Zulus. 336p. 1981. pap. 4.95 (ISBN 0-8254-3046-1). Kregel.
Lawson, Thomas E. Religions of Africa. LC 84-47729. (Religious Traditions of the World Ser.). (Illus.). 128p. (Orig.). 1984. pap. 6.95 (ISBN 0-06-065211-X, HarpR). Har-Row.
MacGaffey, Wyatt. Modern Kongo Prophets: Religion in a Plural Society. LC 82-48554. (African Systems of Thought: Midland Bks: No. 307). (Illus.). 304p. 1983. 22.50x (ISBN 0-253-33865-4); pap. 15.00X (ISBN 0-253-20307-4, MB 307). Ind U Pr.
McVeigh, Malcolm. God in Africa. 1982. 20.00 (ISBN 0-686-96557-4). Branden Pub Co.
Martin, Marie-Louise. Kimbangu: An African Prophet & His Church. Moore, D. M., tr. LC 75-45371. pap. 55.50 (ISBN 0-317-08451-8, 2012735). Bks Demand UMI.
Mbiti, John S. African Religions & Philosophy. xiv, 290p. (Orig.). 1969. pap. text ed. 13.50x (ISBN 0-435-89589-3). Heinemann Ed.
--Afrikanische Religion und Weltanschauung. Feuser, W. F., tr. from Eng. (Ger.). xvi, 375p. 1974. 19.20 (ISBN 3-11-002498-5). De Gruyter.
--Introduction to African Religion. (Orig.). 1975. pap. text ed. 10.00x (ISBN 0-435-94001-5). Heinemann Ed.
Middleton, John. Lugbara Religion: Ritual & Authority among an East African People. LC 60-51074. pap. 71.00 (ISBN 0-317-28622-6, 2055387). Bks Demand UMI.
Muzorewa, Gwinyai H. The Origins & Development of African Theology. LC 84-14769. 160p. (Orig.). 1985. pap. 9.95 (ISBN 0-88344-351-1). Orbis Bks.
Oduyoye, Mercy A. Hearing & Knowing: Theological Reflections on Christianity in Africa. LC 85-29873. 176p. (Orig.). 1986. pap. 9.95 (ISBN 0-88344-258-2). Orbis Bks.
Omoyajowo, J. A. Cherubim & Seraphim: The History of an African Independent Church. LC 78-64624. 256p. (Orig.). 1982. 21.50x (ISBN 0-88357-068-8); pap. 8.95 (ISBN 0-88357-069-6). NOK Pubs.
Onyioha, K. O. African Godianism: A Revolutionary Religion for Mankind Through Direct Communication with God. 1980. 15.00 (ISBN 0-914970-31-3). Conch Mag.
Parrinder, Geoffrey. African Traditional Religion. 3rd ed. LC 76-22490. (Illus.). 156p. 1976. Repr. of 1976 ed. lib. bdg. 25.00x (ISBN 0-8371-3401-3, PAF&, Pub. by Negro U Pr). Greenwood.
Pauw, Berthold A. Religion in a Tswana Chiefdom. LC 85-21881. (Illus.). xii, 274p. 1985. Repr. of 1960 ed. lib. bdg. 75.00x (ISBN 0-313-24974-1, PRTC). Greenwood.
Ray, Benjamin C. African Religions: Symbol, Ritual & Community. 1976. pap. write for info. (ISBN 0-13-018622-8). P-H.
Seligman, Charles G. Egypt & Negro Africa: Study in Divine Kingship. LC 74-15088. (Frazer Lecture: 1933). (Illus.). Repr. of 1934 ed. 21.50 (ISBN 0-404-12138-1). AMS Pr.
Shelton, Austin J. Igbo-Igala Borderland: Religion & Social Control in Indigenous African Colonialism. LC 70-141493. 1971. 44.50 (ISBN 0-87395-082-8). State U NY Pr.
Shorter, Aylward. African Christian Theology: Adaptation or Incarnation? LC 77-23325. 180p. (Orig.). 1977. 7.95 (ISBN 0-88344-002-4); pap. 4.95 (ISBN 0-88344-003-2). Orbis Bks.
--Prayer in the Religious Traditions of Africa. 1975. pap. 7.95 (ISBN 0-19-519848-4). Oxford U Pr.
Stakeman, Randolph. The Cultural Politics of Religious Change: A Study of the Sanoyea Kpelle in Liberia. (African Studies: Vol. 3). 264p. text ed. 49.95x (ISBN 0-88946-177-5). E Mellen.
Taber, Charles R., ed. The Church in Africa: Nineteen Seventy Seven. LC 78-14923. 1978. pap. 6.95 (ISBN 0-87808-161-5). William Carey Lib.
Tanner, Ralph E. Transition in African Beliefs: Traditional Religion & Christian Change: A Study in Sukumaland, Tanzania, East Africa. LC 67-21411. pap. 67.50 (ISBN 0-317-26638-1, 2025117). Bks Demand UMI.
Turner, Harold W. Religious Innovation in Africa: Collected Essays on New Religious Movements. 1979. lib. bdg. 32.50 (ISBN 0-8161-8303-1, Hall Reference). G K Hall.
Van Binsbergen, Wim M. J. Religious Change in Zambia: Exploratory Studies. (Monographs from the African Studies Centre, Leiden). (Illus.). 416p. 1981. 50.00x (ISBN 0-7103-0000-X). Methuen Inc.
Van Binsbergen, Wim M. J. & Schoffeleers, J. Matthew, eds. Theoretical Explorations in African Religion. 330p. 1984. 49.95x (ISBN 0-7103-0049-2). Methuen Inc.
Westerlund, David. African Religion in African Scholarship: A Preliminary Study of the Religious and Political Background. 104p. (Orig.). 1985. pap. 20.00x (ISBN 91-7146-344-5). Coronet Bks.
Westermann, Diedrich. Africa & Christianity. LC 74-15102. (Duff Lectures, 1935). Repr. of 1937 ed. 24.50 (ISBN 0-404-12151-9). AMS Pr.
Williams, Ethel L. & Brown, Clifton F. Howard University Bibliography of African & Afro-American Religious Studies: With Locations in American Libraries. LC 76-5604. 1977. 50.00 (ISBN 0-8420-2080-2). Scholarly Res Inc.
Wilson, Monica H. Religion & the Transformation of Society: A Study in Social Change in Africa. LC 73-134622. (The Scott Holland Memorial Lectures: 15; 1969). pap. 43.30 (ISBN 0-317-27081-8, 2024562). Bks Demand UMI.
Zahan, Dominique. The Religion, Spirituality, & Thought of Traditional Africa. Martin, Kate E. & Martin, Lawrence M., trs. from Fr. LC 78-23525. 1979. Repr. of 1970 ed. lib. bdg. 17.00x (ISBN 0-226-97777-3). U of Chicago Pr.
--The Religion, Spirituality, & Thought of Traditional Africa. Ezra, Kate & Martin, Lawrence M., trs. vi, 180p. 1979. pap. 6.50x (ISBN 0-226-97778-1). U of Chicago Pr.
Zuesse, Evan. Ritual Cosmos: The Sanctification of Life in African Religions. LC 79-13454. 256p. 1985. pap. 12.95x (ISBN 0-8214-0814-3). Ohio U Pr.
Zuesse, Evan M. Ritual Cosmos: The Sanctification of Life in African Religions. LC 79-13454. x, 256p. 1980. 21.95x (ISBN 0-8214-0398-2). Ohio U Pr.

AFRICA, EAST–RELIGION

Healey, Joseph G. A Fifth Gospel: The Experience of Black Christian Values. LC 80-25033. (Illus.). 220p. (Orig.). 1981. pap. 3.98 (ISBN 0-88344-013-X). Orbis Bks.
Trimingham, John S. Islam in East Africa. LC 79-52567. (Islam Ser.). 1980. Repr. of 1964 ed. lib. bdg. 18.00x (ISBN 0-8369-9270-9). Ayer Co Pubs.

AFRICA, NORTH–RELIGION

Abun-Nasr, Jamil M. A History of the Maghrib in the Islamic Period. (Illus.). 512p. Date not set. price not set (ISBN 0-521-33184-6); pap. price not set (ISBN 0-521-33767-4). Cambridge U Pr.
Holme, Leonard R. Extinction of the Christian Churches in North Africa. 1969. 20.50 (ISBN 0-8337-1724-3). B Franklin.

AFRICA, SUB-SAHARAN–RELIGIOUS LIFE AND CUSTOMS

Jules-Rosette, Bennetta. African Apostles: Ritual & Conversion in the Church of John Maranke. LC 75-8437. (Symbol, Myth & Ritual Ser.). (Illus.). 352p. 1975. 34.50x (ISBN 0-8014-0846-6). Cornell U Pr.
Mendelsohn, Jack. God, Allah & Ju Ju: Religion in Africa Today. LC 78-5872. 1978. Repr. of 1962 ed. lib. bdg. cancelled (ISBN 0-313-20483-7, MEGA). Greenwood.

AFRICA, WEST–RELIGION

Clarke, Peter B. West Africa & Christianity. 280p. 1986. pap. text ed. 17.95 (ISBN 0-7131-8263-6). E Arnold.
Janzen, John M. Lemba, Sixteen Fifty to Nineteen Thirty: A Drum of Affliction in Africa & the New World. 1982. lib. bdg. 91.00 (ISBN 0-8240-9306-2). Garland Pub.
Jenkins, Ulysses D. Ancient African Religion & the African American Church. LC 78-65794. (Illus.). 1978. 12.95 (ISBN 0-933184-00-X); pap. 6.95 (ISBN 0-933184-01-8). Flame Intl.
Sanneh, Lamin. West African Christianity: The Religious Impact. 304p. (Orig.). 1983. pap. 11.95 (ISBN 0-88344-703-7). Orbis Bks.

AFRICAN METHODIST EPISCOPAL CHURCH

Gaines, Wesley J. African Methodism in the South: Or Twenty-Five Years of Freedom. LC 71-99379. 1969. Repr. of 1890 ed. lib. bdg. 16.00 (ISBN 0-8411-0050-0). Metro Bks.
Heard, William H. From Slavery to the Bishopric in the A. M. E. Church: An Autobiography. LC 69-18564. (American Negro: His History & Literature, Ser. No. 2). 1969. Repr. of 1924 ed. 10.00 (ISBN 0-405-01867-3). Ayer Co Pubs.
Johnson, Walton J. Worship & Freedom: A Black American Church in Zambia. LC 77-22388. 190p. 1978. text ed. 34.50x (ISBN 0-8419-0315-8, Africana). Holmes & Meier.
Payne, Daniel A. History of the African Methodist Episcopal Church. LC 69-18573. (American Negro: His History & Literature Ser., No. 2). 1969. Repr. of 1891 ed. 19.00 (ISBN 0-405-01885-1). Ayer Co Pubs.
--Recollections of Seventy Years. LC 68-29015. (American Negro: His History & Literature Ser., No. 1). (Illus.). 1968. Repr. of 1888 ed. 14.00 (ISBN 0-405-01834-7). Ayer Co Pubs.
--The Semi-Centenary & the Retrospection of the African Methodist Episcopal Church. facsimile ed. LC 76-37598. (Black Heritage Library Collection). Repr. of 1866 ed. 16.50 (ISBN 0-8369-8974-0). Ayer Co Pubs.
Smith, Charles S. History of the African Methodist Episcopal Church, 1856-1922. 1922. 27.00 (ISBN 0-384-45261-2). Johnson Repr.
Turner, Henry M. The Genius & Theory of Methodist Polity, or the Machinery of Methodism. LC 75-99416. xii, 318p. 1972. Repr. of 1885 ed. lib. bdg. 16.50 (ISBN 0-8411-0089-6). Metro Bks.

AFRICAN TALES

see Tales, African

AFRO-AMERICAN BAPTISTS

Bacote, Samuel W. Who's Who among the Colored Baptists of the United States. Gaustad, Edwin S., ed. LC 79-52588. (The Baptist Tradition Ser.). (Illus.). 1980. Repr. of 1913 ed. lib. bdg. 28.50x (ISBN 0-405-12455-4). Ayer Co Pubs.
Brawley, Edward M., ed. Negro Baptist Pulpit. facs. ed. LC 74-154072. (Black Heritage Library Collection Ser.). 1890. 19.25 (ISBN 0-8369-8783-7). Ayer Co Pubs.
Carter, E. R. Biographical Sketches of Our Pulpit. LC 72-99355. 1969. Repr. of 1888 ed. lib. bdg. 14.00 (ISBN 0-8411-0026-8). Metro Bks.
Freeman, Edward A. The Epoch of Negro Baptists & the Foreign Mission Board. Gaustad, Edwin S., ed. LC 79-52593. (The Baptist Tradition Ser.). 1980. Repr. of 1953 ed. lib. bdg. 26.50x (ISBN 0-405-12460-0). Ayer Co Pubs.
Jordan, Lewis G. Up the Ladder in Foreign Missions. Gausted, Edwin S., ed. LC 79-52596. (The Baptist Tradition Ser.). (Illus.). 1980. Repr. of 1901 ed. lib. bdg. 27.50x (ISBN 0-405-12463-5). Ayer Co Pubs.
Lewis, James K. Religious Life of Fugitive Slaves & Rise of the Coloured Baptist Churches, 1820-1865, in What Is Now Ontario. Gaustad, Edwin S., ed. LC 79-52574. (The Baptist Tradition Ser.). 1980. lib. bdg. 21.00x (ISBN 0-405-12442-2). Ayer Co Pubs.
Martin, Dan. Human Touch. Rutledge, Don, tr. (Illus.). 1979. 6.95 (ISBN 0-937170-03-8). Home Mission.
Massey, Floyd, Jr. & McKinney, Samuel B. Church Administration in the Black Perspective. LC 76-9804. 176p. 1976. pap. 7.95 (ISBN 0-8170-0710-5). Judson.
Meshack, B. A. Is the Baptist Church Relevant to the Black Community. LC 75-38304. 1976. perfect bdg. softcover 9.95 (ISBN 0-88247-385-9). R & E Pubs.
Powell, Adam C., Sr. Against the Tide: An Autobiography. Gaustad, Edwin S., ed. LC 79-52603. (The Baptist Tradition Ser.). 1980. Repr. of 1938 ed. 27.50x (ISBN 0-405-12468-6). Ayer Co Pubs.

AFRO-AMERICAN CHURCHES

Cone, James H. For My People: Black Theology & the Black Church. LC 84-5195. (Bishop Henry McNeal Turner Studies in North America Black Religion: Vol. 1). 288p. (Orig.). 1984. pap. 9.95 (ISBN 0-88344-106-3). Orbis Bks.
Harris, James H. Black Ministers & Laity in the Urban Church: An Analysis of Political & Social Expectations. LC 86-28151. (Illus.). 146p. 1987. lib. bdg. 23.50 (ISBN 0-8191-5823-2); pap. text ed. 9.75 (ISBN 0-8191-5824-0). U Pr of Amer.
Labbe, Dolores E. Jim Crow Comes to Church: The Establishment of Segregated Catholic Parishes in South Louisiana. 14.00 (ISBN 0-405-10838-9, 11845). Ayer Co Pubs.
McCall, Emmanuel L. Black Church Life-Styles. LC 86-17591. 1986. pap. 5.95 (ISBN 0-8054-5665-1). Broadman.
Massey, Floyd, Jr. & McKinney, Samuel B. Church Administration in the Black Perspective. LC 76-9804. 176p. 1976. pap. 7.95 (ISBN 0-8170-0710-5). Judson.
Mukenge, Ida R. The Black Church in Urban America: A Case Study in Political Economy. LC 83-14593. 256p. 1984. lib. bdg. 27.50 (ISBN 0-8191-3431-7); pap. text ed. 13.50 (ISBN 0-8191-3432-5). U Pr of Amer.
Smith, Sidney. Ten Super Sunday Schools in the Black Community. LC 86-926. 1986. pap. 5.95 (ISBN 0-8054-6252-X). Broadman.

AFRO-AMERICAN CLERGY

Burkett, Randall K. Garveyism As a Religious Movement: The Institutionalization of a Black Civil Religion. LC 78-15728. (ATLA Monograph Ser.: No. 13). 242p. 1978. 19.00 (ISBN 0-8108-1163-4). Scarecrow.
Burkett, Randall K. & Newman, Richard. Black Apostles: Afro-American Clergy Confront the Twentieth Century. 1978. lib. bdg. 28.50 (ISBN 0-8161-8137-3, Hall Reference). G K Hall.
Bush, Lester E. & Mauss, Armand L., eds. Neither White nor Black: Mormon Scholars Confront the Race Issue in a Universal Church. 250p. 1984. pap. 11.95 (ISBN 0-941214-22-2). Signature Bks.
Dean, David M. Defender of the Race: James Theodore Holly, Black Nationalist Bishop. 150p. 1979. 16.95x (ISBN 0-931186-02-1). Lambeth Pr.
Harris, James H. Black Ministers & Laity in the Urban Church: An Analysis of Political & Social Expectations. LC 86-28151. (Illus.). 146p. 1987. lib. bdg. 23.50 (ISBN 0-8191-5823-2); pap. text ed. 9.75 (ISBN 0-8191-5824-0). U Pr of Amer.
Mitchell, Henry H. Black Preaching. LC 78-19508. 1979. pap. 8.95xi (ISBN 0-06-065761-8, RD297, HarpR). Har-Row.
Morrison-Reed, Mark. Black Pioneers in a White Denomination. LC 83-70747. 216p. 1983. pap. text ed. 9.95 (ISBN 0-8070-1601-2, BP 662). Beacon Pr.
Smith, Forrest M. Orange Morgan's 38, 325 Mornings. 1978. 7.00 (ISBN 0-918626-10-2); pap. 4.00 (ISBN 0-918626-07-2). Word Serv.
Wheeler, Edward L. Uplifting the Race: The Black Minister in the New South 1865-1902. 198p. (Orig.). 1986. lib. bdg. 24.75 (ISBN 0-8191-5161-0); pap. text ed. 11.75 (ISBN 0-8191-5162-9). U Pr of Amer.

AFRO-AMERICANS–RELIGION

see also Afro-American Baptists; Afro-American Churches; Afro-American Clergy; Black Muslims

Andrews, William L., ed. Sisters of the Spirit: Three Black Women's Autobiographies of the Nineteenth Century. LC 85-42544. (Religion in North America Ser.). 256p. 1986. 29.50x (ISBN 0-253-35260-6); pap. 8.95x (ISBN 0-253-28704-9). Ind U Pr.
Baer, Hans A. The Black Spiritual Movement: A Religious Response to Racism. LC 83-14559. 232p. 1984. text ed. 22.95x (ISBN 0-87049-413-9); pap. 8.95x (ISBN 0-87049-515-1). U of Tenn Pr.
Bechler, Leroy. The Black Mennonite Church in North America 1886-1986. LC 86-25691. 192p. 1986. 17.95x (ISBN 0-8361-1287-3). Herald Pr.
Bowman, Thea, Sr., ed. Families: Black & Catholic, Catholic & Black, Readings, Resources & Family Activities. 160p. 1985. pap. 14.95 (ISBN 1-55586-890-8). US Catholic.
Bowyer, O. R., et al. Prayer in the Black Tradition. 112p. 1986. pap. 5.95 (ISBN 0-8358-0538-7, ICN 609100, Dist. by Abingdon Press). Upper Room.
Bringhurst, Newell G. Saints, Slaves, & Blacks: The Changing Place of Black People Within Mormonism. LC 81-1093. (Contributions to the Study of Religion Ser.: No. 4). (Illus.). 256p. 1981. lib. bdg. 29.95 (ISBN 0-313-22752-7, BSB/). Greenwood.
Brown, Isaac V. Biography of the Reverend Robert Finley. LC 73-82178. (Anti-Slavery Crusade in America Ser). 1969. Repr. of 1857 ed. 18.00 (ISBN 0-405-00617-9). Ayer Co Pubs.
Burkett, Randall K. Garveyism As a Religious Movement: The Institutionalization of a Black Civil Religion. LC 78-15728. (ATLA Monograph Ser.: No. 13). 242p. 1978. 19.00 (ISBN 0-8108-1163-4). Scarecrow.
Catto, William T. Semi-Centenary Discourse. facs. ed. LC 78-154073. (Black Heritage Library Collection). 1857. 14.25 (ISBN 0-8369-8784-5). Ayer Co Pubs.
Cone, James. God of the Oppressed. 1978. pap. 6.95 (ISBN 0-8164-2607-4, HarpR). Har-Row.

Cone, James H. Black Theology & Black Power. LC 70-76462. (Orig.). 1969. pap. 5.95 (ISBN 0-8164-2003-3, SP59, HarpR). Har-Row.

Congress of Colored Catholics of the United States. Three Catholic Afro-American Congresses. 14.00 (ISBN 0-405-10863-X, 11829). Ayer Co Pubs.

Cullamar, Evelyn T. Babaylanism in Negros: 1896-1907. (Illus.). 133p. (Orig.). 1986. pap. 8.50x (ISBN 971-10-0293-0, Pub. by New Day Philippines). Cellar.

Fauset, Arthur H. Black Gods of the Metropolis, Negro Religious Cults of the Urban North. LC 73-120251. 1970. Repr. lib. bdg. 16.00x (ISBN 0-374-92714-6, Octagon). Hippocrene Bks.

--Black Gods of the Metropolis: Negro Religious Cults of the Urban North. LC 75-133446. 1971. pap. 9.95x (ISBN 0-8122-1001-8, Pa Paperbks). U of Pa Pr.

Frazier, E. Franklin & Lincoln, C. Eric. The Negro Church in America. Bd. with The Black Church Since Frazier. LC 72-96201. (Sourcebooks in Negro History Ser.). 1973. pap. 4.95 (ISBN 0-8052-0387-7). Schocken.

Gardiner, James J. & Roberts, J. Deotis, eds. Quest for a Black Theology. LC 76-151250. 128p. 1971. 6.95 (ISBN 0-8298-0196-0). Pilgrim NY.

Gillard, John T. The Catholic Church & the Negro. (Basic Afro-American Reprint Library). 1969. Repr. of 1929 ed. 19.00 (ISBN 0-384-18550-9). Johnson Repr.

Harris, James H. Black Ministers & Laity in the Urban Church: An Analysis of Political & Social Expectations. LC 86-28151. (Illus.). 146p. 1987. lib. bdg. 23.50 (ISBN 0-8191-5823-2); pap. text ed. 9.75 (ISBN 0-8191-5824-0). U Pr of Amer.

Harrison, William P. Gospel Among the Slaves. LC 70-168249. Repr. of 1893 ed. 27.50 (ISBN 0-404-00263-3). AMS Pr.

Jacobs, Sylvia M., ed. Black Americans & the Missionary Movement in Africa. LC 81-13230. (Contributions in Afro-American & African Studies: No. 66). (Illus.). xii, 255p. 1982. lib. bdg. 29.95 (ISBN 0-313-23280-6, JAA/). Greenwood.

Jones, Amos, Jr. Paul's Message of Freedom: What Does It Mean to the Black Church? 256p. 1984. 12.95 (ISBN 0-8170-0840-3). Judson.

Jones, C. C. Religious Instruction of the Negroes in the United States. 1842. 23.00 (ISBN 0-527-46700-6). Kraus Repr.

Jones, Charles C. Religious Instruction of the Negroes in the United States. LC 73-82466. Repr. of 1842 ed. 22.50x (ISBN 0-8371-1645-7, JOI&). Greenwood.

Jones, Major J. The Color of God: The Concept of God in Afro-American Religious Thought. 160p. 1987. 24.95 (ISBN 0-86554-274-0, H237); pap. 14.95 (ISBN 0-86554-276-7). Mercer Univ Pr.

Labbe, Dolores E. Jim Crow Comes to Church: The Establishment of Segregated Catholic Parishes in South Louisiana. 14.00 (ISBN 0-405-10838-9, 11845). Ayer Co Pubs.

McClain, William B. Black People in the Methodist Church: Whither Thou Goest? 160p. (Orig.). 1986. pap. 8.95 (ISBN 0-687-03588-0). Abingdon.

McCray, Walter A. Black Folks & Christian Liberty: Black, Christian, & Free to Be Cultural & Social. LC 78-71258. (Black Light Fellowship Ser.). 1978. pap. 9.95 (ISBN 0-933176-01-5). Black Light Fellow.

--Black Spirituality. 150p. (Orig.). pap. write for info. (ISBN 0-933176-04-X). Black Light Fellow.

--Discipling the Children of Black America: A Discussion of Christian Black Education for Black Youth. 50p. (Orig.). pap. write for info. (ISBN 0-933176-02-3). Black Light Fellow.

McKinney, Richard I. Religion in Higher Education among Negroes. LC 75-38785. (Religion in America, Ser. 2). 186p. 1972. Repr. of 1945 ed. 15.00 (ISBN 0-405-04075-X). Ayer Co Pubs.

Mapson, J. Wendell, Jr. The Ministry of Music in the Black Church. 1984. pap. 5.95 (ISBN 0-8170-1057-2). Judson.

Marable, Manning. Blackwater: Essays on Black & Southern History. 1978. 12.00 (ISBN 0-89421-028-9). Challenge Pr.

Mays, Benjamin E. Negro's God As Reflected in His Literature. LC 69-16578. (Illus.). Repr. of 1938 ed. 24.75x (ISBN 0-8371-1139-0, MAG&, Pub. by Negro U Pr). Greenwood.

Mays, Benjamin E. & Nicholson, Joseph W. Negro's Church. LC 70-83430. (Religion in America, Ser. 1). 1969. Repr. of 1933 ed. 25.50 (ISBN 0-405-00255-6). Ayer Co Pubs.

Miller, Harriet P. Pioneer Colored Christians. facsimile ed. LC 73-37313. (Black Heritage Library Collection). Repr. of 1911 ed. 13.50 (ISBN 0-8369-8950-3). Ayer Co Pubs.

Mitchell, Henry, et al. This Far by Faith: American Black Worship & Its African Roots. Hovda, Robert, ed. LC 77-89744. 1977. pap. 7.95 (ISBN 0-918208-05-X). Liturgical Conf.

Moses, Wilson J. Black Messiahs & Uncle Toms: Social & Literary Manipulations of a Religious Myth. LC 81-9645. 304p. 1982. 24.95x (ISBN 0-271-00294-8). Pa St U Pr.

Negro Pew. facs. ed. LC 76-149873. (Black Heritage Library Collection Ser). 1837. 10.00 (ISBN 0-8369-8753-5). Ayer Co Pubs.

Newman, Richard. Black Power & Black Religion: Essays & Reviews. LC 86-20906. 1986. lib. bdg. 25.00 (ISBN 0-933951-03-5). Locust Hill Pr.

Oglesby, Enoch H. Ethics & Theology from the Other Side: Sounds of Moral Struggle. LC 79-62897. 1979. pap. text ed. 11.50 (ISBN 0-8191-0706-9). U Pr of Amer.

Paris, Arthur E. Black Pentecostalism: Southern Religion in an Urban World. LC 81-16169. 192p. 1982. lib. bdg. 17.50x (ISBN 0-87023-353-X). U of Mass Pr.

Pipes, William H. Say Amen Brother, Old-Time Negro Preaching: A Study in American Frustration. LC 73-111585. Repr. of 1951 ed. 22.50x (ISBN 0-8371-4611-9, PSA&, Pub. by Negro U Pr). Greenwood.

Proctor, Samuel D. & Watley, William D. Sermons from the Black Pulpit. 128p. 1984. pap. 7.95 (ISBN 0-8170-1034-3). Judson.

Richardson, Marilyn. Black Women & Religion. 1980. 17.50 (ISBN 0-8161-8087-3, Hall Reference). G K Hall.

Salley, Christopher & Behm, Ronald. What Color Is Your God? Black Consciousness & the Christian Faith. LC 81-6758. 132p. (Orig.). 1981. pap. 4.50 (ISBN 0-87784-791-6). Inter-Varsity.

Sernett, Milton C., ed. Afro-American Religious History: A Documentary Witness. LC 84-24686. xii, 506p. 1985. text ed. 46.50 (ISBN 0-8223-0591-7); pap. text ed. 16.95 (ISBN 0-8223-0594-1). Duke.

Smith, Sidney. Ten Super Sunday Schools in the Black Community. LC 86-926. 1986. pap. 5.95 (ISBN 0-8054-6252-X). Broadman.

Sobel, Mechal. Trabelin' On: The Slave Journey to an Afro-Baptist Faith. LC 77-84775. (Contributions in Afro-American & African Studies: No. 36). 1978. lib. bdg. 35.00 (ISBN 0-8371-9887-9, STO/). Greenwood.

Thomas, Latta R. Biblical Faith & the Black American. 160p. 1976. pap. 4.95 (ISBN 0-8170-0718-0). Judson.

Tristano, Richard. Black Religion in the Evangelical South. 96p. 1986. pap. 4.00x (ISBN 0-317-43431-4). Glenmary Res Ctr.

Turner, Morrie. All God's Chillun Got Soul. 64p. 1980. pap. 3.95 (ISBN 0-8170-0892-6). Judson.

Washington, Joseph R., Jr. Black Religion: The Negro & Christianity in the United States. LC 84-5659. 328p. 1984. pap. text ed. 12.75 (ISBN 0-8191-3907-6). U Pr of Amer.

--Black Sects & Cults. 190p. 1984. pap. text ed. 10.50 (ISBN 0-8191-3906-8). U Pr of Amer.

Webb, Lillian A. About My Father's Business: The Life of Elder Michaux. LC 80-24595. (Contributions in Afro-American & African Studies: No. 61). (Illus.). 232p. 1981. lib. bdg. 29.95 (ISBN 0-313-22261-4, WFB/). Greenwood.

West, Cornel. Prophesy Deliverance! An Afro-American Revolutionary Christianity. LC 82-13483. 186p. 1982. pap. 11.95 (ISBN 0-664-24447-5). Westminster.

Williams, Ethel L. & Brown, Clifton F. Howard University Bibliography of African & Afro-American Religious Studies: With Locations in American Libraries. LC 76-5604. 1977. 50.00 (ISBN 0-8420-2080-2). Scholarly Res Inc.

Wills, David W. & Newman, Richard, eds. Black Apostles at Home & Abroad: Afro-Americans & the Christian Mission from the Revolution to Reconstruction. 420p. 1982. lib. bdg. 42.00 (ISBN 0-8161-8482-8, Hall Reference). G K Hall.

Wilmore, Gayraud S. Black & Presbyterian: The Heritage & the Hope. LC 82-23907. 142p. (Orig.). 1983. pap. 5.95 (ISBN 0-664-24440-8, Pub. by Geneva Press). Westminster.

--Black Religion & Black Radicalism: An Interpretation of the Religious History of Afro-American People. 2nd rev. & enl. ed. LC 83-8077. 320p. (Orig.). 1983. pap. 9.95 (ISBN 0-88344-032-6). Orbis Bks.

Wilmore, Gayraud S. & Cone, James H., eds. Black Theology: A Documentary History, 1966-1979. LC 79-12747. 672p. 1979. pap. 14.95 (ISBN 0-88344-042-3). Orbis Bks.

Wimberly, Edward P. Pastoral Counseling & Spiritual Values: A Black Point of View. LC 81-10918. 176p. (Orig.). 1982. pap. 7.75 (ISBN 0-687-30336-2). Abingdon.

Wimberly, Edward P. & Streaty, Anne. Liberation & Human Wholeness: The Conversion Experiences of Black People in Slavery & Freedom. 144p. (Orig.). 1986. pap. 10.95 (ISBN 0-687-21698-2). Abingdon.

AGAPE

Butler, Roy F. The Meaning of Agapao & Phileo in the Greek New Testament. 1977. 6.50x (ISBN 0-87291-089-X). Coronado Pr.

Cole, Richard L. Love-Feasts: A History of the Christian Agape. 59.95 (ISBN 0-8490-0563-9). Gordon Pr.

Evans, Colleen T. Love Is an Everyday Thing. rev. ed. 128p. 1984. pap. 4.95 (ISBN 0-8007-5157-4, Power Bks). Revell.

Manning, Joseph F. The Miracle of Agape Love. 160p. 1977. pap. 2.95 (ISBN 0-88368-079-3). Whitaker Hse.

Outka, Gene. Agape: An Ethical Analysis. LC 78-88070. (Publications in Religion Ser.: No. 17). 336p. 1972. 33.00x (ISBN 0-300-01384-1); pap. 8.95x (ISBN 0-300-02122-4). Yale U Pr.

AGED

see also Aging; Old Age

Biegert. So We're Growing Older. (Looking Up Ser.). 1982. pap. 1.25 booklet (ISBN 0-8298-0436-6). Pilgrim NY.

Groseclose, Kel. Three-Speed Dad in a Ten-Speed World. LC 83-2765. 176p. (Orig.). 1983. pap. 4.95 (ISBN 0-87123-585-4, 210585). Bethany Hse.

Hendrickson, Michael C., ed. The Role of the Church in Aging: Implications for Policy & Action. LC 85-17564. (Journal of Religion & Aging: Vol. 2, Nos. 1-2). 178p. 1986. text ed. 29.95 (ISBN 0-86656-482-9, B482); pap. text ed. 19.95 (ISBN 0-86656-483-7, B483). Haworth Pr.

Lester, Andrew D. & Lester, Judith L. Understanding Aging Parents. LC 80-17832. (Christian Care Bks.: Vol. 8). 120p. 1980. pap. 7.95 (ISBN 0-664-24329-0). Westminster.

Lochner, Dorthy M. America's Aged. 0.50 (ISBN 0-911802-52-5). Free Church Pubns.

National Council of Jewish Women. Self Help for Seniors. 30p. (Orig.). 1983. pap. text ed. 4.00 (ISBN 0-941840-14-X). NCJW.

Smith, Bert K. Aging in America. LC 72-6232. 256p. 1973. pap. 5.95 (ISBN 0-8070-2769-3, BP502). Beacon Pr.

AGED–PRAYER-BOOKS AND DEVOTIONS

Brandt, Catharine. You're Only Old Once: Devotions in Large Print. large type ed. LC 76-27085. 1977. pap. 6.95 (ISBN 0-8066-1570-2, 10-7495). Augsburg.

Janss, Edmund W. Making the Second Half the Best Half. LC 83-15779. 192p. (Orig.). 1984. pap. 4.95 (ISBN 0-87123-404-1, 210404). Bethany Hse.

Kunath, Anne & Riegert, Lillian. Prayers & Inspiration for Senior Children of God. 1979. pap. 1.75. De Vorss.

Lockerbie, Jeanette. The Quiet Moment: Devotions for the Golden Years. LC 82-7344. (Illus.). 96p. (Orig.). 1982. pap. 4.95 (ISBN 0-87239-606-1, 3009). Standard Pub.

Mooney, Patrick. A Gift of Love: Remembering the Old Anew. (Greeting Book Line Ser.). 48p. (Orig.). 1983. pap. 1.50 (ISBN 0-89622-168-7). Twenty-Third.

AGED–RELIGIOUS LIFE

see also Church Work with the Aged

Becker, Arthur H. Ministry with Older Persons: A Guide for Clergy & Congregations. LC 86-1101. 228p. (Orig.). 1986. pap. 12.95 (ISBN 0-8066-2196-6, 10-4444). Augsburg.

Boyle, Sarah-Patton. The Desert Blooms: A Personal Adventure in Growing Old Creatively. 208p. (Orig.). 1983. pap. 7.95 (ISBN 0-687-10484-X). Abingdon.

Brown, J. Paul. Counseling with Senior Citizens. LC 64-15217. (Successful Pastoral Counseling Ser.). pap. 36.00 (2027174). Bks Demand UMI.

Coupland, Susan. Beginning to Pray in Old Age. LC 85-17075. (Parish Life Sourcebks.: Vol. II). xiv, 80p. 1985. pap. 6.95 (ISBN 0-936384-29-8). Cowley Pubns.

Deekken, Alfons S. J. Growing Old & How to Cope with it. LC 86-80786. 192p. 1986. pap. 7.95 (ISBN 0-89870-104-X). Ignatius Pr.

Doughty, Stephen V. Ministry of Love: A Handbook for Visiting the Aged. LC 84-71674. 96p. (Orig.). 1984. pap. 3.95 (ISBN 0-87793-324-3). Ave Maria.

Dye, Harold. The Touch of Friendship. LC 79-51138. 1979. pap. 4.25 large type (ISBN 0-8054-5422-5). Broadman.

Fahey, Charles J. & Wakin, Edward. The Catholic Guide to the Mature Years. LC 84-60747. 144p. 1984. pap. 6.95 (ISBN 0-87973-603-8, 603). Our Sunday Visitor.

Fecher, Vincent J. Religion & Aging: An Annotated Bibliography. LC 82-81019. 119p. 1982. 16.00 (ISBN 0-911536-96-5); pap. 9.00 (ISBN 0-911536-97-3). Trinity U Pr.

Fischer, Kathleen R. Winter Grace, Spirituality for the Later Years. LC 84-61975. 1985. pap. 7.95 (ISBN 0-8091-2675-3). Paulist Pr.

Gager, Dorthy. It's My Move: Older Adults Choose How to Live. 80p. (Orig.). 1987. pap. 7.95 (ISBN 0-88177-045-0, DR045B). Discipleship Res.

Hendricks, William L. A Theology for Aging. 1986. 10.95 (ISBN 0-8054-1712-5). Broadman.

Hiltner, Seward, ed. Toward a Theology of Aging. LC 74-19593. (Special Issue of Pastoral Psychology). 83p. 1975. 16.95 (ISBN 0-87705-278-6); pap. 9.95 (ISBN 0-87705-287-5). Human Sci Pr.

Howell, John C. Senior Adult Family Life. LC 79-51139. 1979. pap. 4.95 large type (ISBN 0-8054-5423-3). Broadman.

Laurello, Bartholomew J. Ministering to the Aging. LC 79-90992. (Paths of Life Ser.). 96p. (Orig.). 1979. pap. 2.95 (ISBN 0-8091-2268-5). Paulist Pr.

LeFevre, Carol & LeFevre, Perry, eds. Aging & the Human Spirit: A Reader in Religion & Gerontology. 2nd ed. LC 84-72932. 367p. 1985. text ed. 24.95x (ISBN 0-913552-27-5); pap. text ed. 12.95x (ISBN 0-913552-28-3). Exploration Pr.

Lesnoff-Caravaglia, Gari, ed. Values, Ethics & Aging, Vol. 4. (Frontiers in Aging Ser.). 196p. 1985. 29.95 (ISBN 0-89885-162-9). Human Sci Pr.

Lyon, K. Brynolf. Toward a Practical Theology of Aging. LC 85-47720. (Theology & Pastoral Care Ser.). 128p. 1986. pap. 7.95 (ISBN 0-8006-1735-5). Fortress.

Maves, Paul B. Faith for the Older Years: Making the Most of Life's Second Half. LC 85-13466. 192p. (Orig.). 1986. pap. 9.95 (ISBN 0-8066-2195-8, 10-2181). Augsburg.

Otte, Elmer. Engaging the Aging in Ministry. 1981. pap. 7.95 (ISBN 0-9602938-5-X). Retirement Res.

Reynolds, Lillian R. No Retirement: Devotions on Christian Discipleship for Older People. LC 83-48916. 96p. 1984. pap. 4.50 (ISBN 0-8006-1779-7, 1-1779). Fortress.

Scarborough, Peggy. The Treasures of Age. (International Correspondence Program Ser.). (Orig.). 1985. pap. text ed. 6.95 (ISBN 0-87148-856-6). Pathway Pr.

Tournier, Paul. Learn to Grow Old. LC 72-78078. 256p. 1983. pap. 7.95 (ISBN 0-06-068361-9, RD-475, HarpR). Har-Row.

AGGADA

see also Legends, Jewish

Marmorstein, Arthur. Studies in Jewish Theology: The Arthur Marmorstein Memorial Volume. Rabbinowitz, Joseph & Lew, Meyer S., eds. LC 76-39174. (Essay Index Reprint Ser.). Repr. of 1950 ed. 21.00 (ISBN 0-8369-2702-8). Ayer Co Pubs.

Montefiore, C. G. & Loewe, H., eds. A Rabbinic Anthology. LC 73-91340. 1970. pap. 16.95 (ISBN 0-8052-0442-3). Schocken.

Nadich, Judah. Jewish Legends of the Second Commonwealth. 508p. 1983. 25.00 (ISBN 0-8276-0212-X, 490). Jewish Pubns.

Saperstein, Marc. Decoding the Rabbis: A Thirteenth-Century Commentary on the Aggadah. LC 80-13166. (Judaic Monographs: No. 3). 298p. 1980. text ed. 20.00x (ISBN 0-674-19445-4). Harvard U Pr.

AGING

see also Immortalism

Bianchi, Eugene C. On Growing Older. 176p. 1985. pap. 9.95 (ISBN 0-8245-0700-2). Crossroad NY.

Boskey, James B. & Hughes, Susan C. Teaching about Aging: Religious & Advocacy Perspectives. LC 82-17589. 184p. (Orig.). 1983. lib. bdg. 26.00 (ISBN 0-8191-2802-3); pap. text ed. 11.50 (ISBN 0-8191-2803-1). U Pr of Amer.

Davis, Richard H., ed. Religion & Aging: The Behavioral & Social Sciences Look at Religion & Aging. 84p. 1967. pap. 3.00 (ISBN 0-88474-009-9). U of S Cal Pr.

Fecher, Vincent J. Religion & Aging: An Annotated Bibliography. LC 82-81019. 119p. 1982. 16.00 (ISBN 0-911536-96-5); pap. 9.00 (ISBN 0-911536-97-3). Trinity U Pr.

Fries, James F. & Crapo, Lawrence M. Vitality & Aging: Implications of the Rectangular Curve. LC 81-4566. (Illus.). 172p. 1981. text ed. 23.95 (ISBN 0-7167-1308-X); pap. text ed. 13.95 (ISBN 0-7167-1309-8). W H Freeman.

Hulme, William E. Vintage Years: Growing Older with Meaning & Hope. LC 85-26399. 120p. (Orig.). 1986. pap. 8.95 (ISBN 0-664-24684-2). Westminster.

Jacob, Norma. Growing Old: A View from Within. LC 81-83072. 29p. 1981. 2.50x (ISBN 0-87574-239-4). Pendle Hill.

Johnson, Wingate M. The Years after Fifty. 14.00 (ISBN 0-405-18502-2). Ayer Co Pubs.

Kuhn, Margaret E. Maggie Kuhn on Aging. Hessel, Dieter, ed. LC 77-24294. 140p. 1977. pap. 3.95 (ISBN 0-664-24146-8). Westminster.

Lancaster, Helen. Aging. 1980. pap. 4.50 (ISBN 0-8309-0290-2). Herald Hse.

Maitland, David J. Aging: A Time for New Learning. LC 86-46038. 192p. (Orig.). 1987. pap. 9.95 (ISBN 0-8042-1107-8). John Knox.

Minirth, Frank B., et al. Beating the Clock: A Guide to Maturing Successfully. (Life Enrichment Ser.). 1986. pap. 3.95 (ISBN 0-8010-6205-5). Baker Bk.

Otte, Elmer & Bergmann, Mark. Engaging the Aging in Ministry. LC 12-2798. 1981. pap. 6.95 (ISBN 0-570-03833-2). Concordia.

Stagg, Frank. The Bible Speaks on Aging. LC 81-66092. 1981. softcover 6.50 (ISBN 0-8054-5292-3). Broadman.

Tengbom, Mildred. September Morning: A Practical Guide for the Middle Years. Eller, David, ed. 1985. pap. 9.95 (ISBN 0-87178-776-8). Brethren.

AGNI (HINDU DEITY)

Saraydarian, Torkom. Talks on Agni. LC 86-722414. 1987. pap. price not set (ISBN 0-911794-56-5). Aqua Educ.

AGNOSTICISM

see also Atheism; Belief and Doubt; Positivism; Rationalism; Skepticism

Armstrong, Richard A. Agnosticism & Theism in the Nineteenth Century. 1977. lib. bdg. 59.95 (ISBN 0-8490-1406-9). Gordon Pr.

Arnheim, Michael. Is Christianity True? LC 84-42861. (The Skeptic's Bookshelf Ser.). 198p. 1984. 20.95 (ISBN 0-87975-262-9). Prometheus Bks.

Lightman, Bernard. The Origins of Agnosticism: Victorian Unbelief & the Limits of Knowledge. LC 86-46288. 272p. 1987. text ed. 29.50x (ISBN 0-8018-3375-2). Johns Hopkins.

Mills, David. Overcoming Religion. 1980. pap. 3.95 (ISBN 0-8065-0742-X). Citadel Pr.

Russell, Bertrand. Am I an Atheist or an Agnostic. 32p. pap. cancelled (ISBN 0-911826-96-3). Am Atheist.

Samuel, L. The Impossibility of Agnosticism. pap. 0.75 (ISBN 0-87784-125-X). Inter-Varsity.

Strem, George G. Agnosticism Is Also Faith. LC 85-90970. 1986. 15.00 (ISBN 0-87212-194-1). Libra.

Ward, J. Naturalism & Agnosticism: The Gifford Lectures Delivered Before the University of Aberdeen in 1896-1898, 2 Vols. in 1. 4th ed. Repr. of 1899 ed. 36.00 (ISBN 0-527-94500-5). Kraus Repr.

AKHENATEN, KING OF EGYPT

see Amenhetep 4th, King of Egypt, 1388-1358 B.C.

AKIBA BEN JOSEPH, 50-132

Finkelstein, Louis. Akiba: Scholar, Saint & Martyr. LC 62-12354. (Temple Bks). 1970. pap. text ed. 6.95x (ISBN 0-689-70230-2, T11). Atheneum.

ALACOQUE, MARGUERITE MARIE, SAINT, 1647-1690

Cristiani, Leon. St. Margaret Mary Alacoque. 1976. 5.00 (ISBN 0-8198-0456-8). Dghtrs St Paul.

Hebert, Clarence, tr. Jesus Reveals His Heart: Letters of St. Margaret Mary. 1980. 4.75 (ISBN 0-8198-3905-1); pap. 3.50 (ISBN 0-8198-3906-X). Dghtrs St Paul.

ALBERTUS MAGNUS, SAINT, BP. OF RATISBONE, 1193-1280

Kovach, Francis J. & Shahan, Robert W., eds. Albert the Great: Commemorative Essays. LC 79-6713. 250p. 1980. 16.95x (ISBN 0-8061-1666-8). U of Okla Pr.

Madden, D. H. Chapter of Mediaeval History. LC 74-91048. 1969. Repr. of 1924 ed. 26.50x (ISBN 0-8046-0658-7, Pub. by Kennikat). Assoc Faculty Pr.

ALBIGENSES

see also Waldenses

Doellinger, Johann J. Beitrage Zur Sektengenchichte des Mittelalter, 2 vols in 1. LC 91-26634. (Social Science Ser). (Ger). 1970. Repr. of 1890 ed. Set. lib. bdg. 57.50 (ISBN 0-8337-0880-5). B Franklin.

ALCOHOL

see also Alcoholism; Temperance

Charles, Howard H. Alcohol & the Bible. LC 66-10970. 40p. 1981. pap. 1.50 (ISBN 0-8361-1941-X). Herald Pr.

Snyder, Charles R. Alcohol & the Jews: A Cultural Study of Drinking & Sobriety. LC 77-24885. (Arcturus Books Paperbacks). 240p. 1978. pap. 6.95x (ISBN 0-8093-0846-0). S Ill U Pr.

ALCOHOL AND YOUTH

Tirabassi, Becky & Lewis, Gregg. Just One Victory. (Campus Life Bks.). (Orig.). 1987. pap. 5.95 (ISBN 0-8423-1998-0). Tyndale.

ALCOHOL INTOXICATION

see Alcoholism

ALCOHOLICS

see also Church Work with Alcoholics

Clinebell, Howard J., Jr. Understanding & Counseling the Alcoholic. rev. ed. LC 56-10143. 1968. 13.95 (ISBN 0-687-42803-3). Abingdon.

Curlee-Salisbury, Joan. When the Woman You Love Is an Alcoholic. LC 78-73017. (When Bk). (Illus.). 1978. pap. 2.45 (ISBN 0-87029-143-2, 20229-1). Abbey.

Hill, Harold, et al. The Impossible Takes a Little Longer. 224p. 1985. pap. 6.95 (ISBN 0-8007-5192-2). Revell.

Osgood, Judy, ed. Mediations for Those Who Live with Alcoholism. 72p. 1987. pap. 5.95 (ISBN 0-916895-04-1). Gilgal Pubns.

ALCOHOLISM

see also Alcohol and Youth; Alcoholics

Badri, M. C. Islam & Alcoholism. LC 76-42173. 1976. pap. 2.75 (ISBN 0-89259-005-X). Am Trust Pubns.

Bergendoff, Conrad L. Pastoral Care for Alcoholism: An Introduction. 36p. 1981. pap. 1.95 (ISBN 0-89486-123-9). Hazelden.

Burkholder, J. Lawrence. To Drink or Not to Drink. 24p. (Orig.). 1981. pap. text ed. 0.75 (ISBN 0-8361-1967-3). Herald Pr.

Clinebell, Howard J., Jr. Understanding & Counseling the Alcoholic. rev. ed. LC 56-10143. 1968. 13.95 (ISBN 0-687-42803-3). Abingdon.

Dunn, Jerry G. & Palmer, Bernard. God Is for the Alcoholic. rev. ed. pap. 6.95 (ISBN 0-8024-3284-0). Moody.

Frank, P. El Alcohol y la Familia. 1981. pap. 1.50 (ISBN 0-89243-139-3). Liguori Pubns.

Hill, Harold, et al. The Impossible Takes a Little Longer. 224p. 1985. pap. 6.95 (ISBN 0-8007-5192-2). Revell.

Keller, John E. Drinking Problem. Hulme, William E., ed. LC 75-133036. (Pocket Counsel Bks.). 56p. 1971. pap. 2.50 (ISBN 0-8006-0155-6, 1-155). Fortress.

Kellermann, Joseph L. Reconciliation with God & Family. 16p. 1981. pap. 0.95 (ISBN 0-89486-146-8). Hazelden.

Klewin, Jean & Klewin, Thomas. When the Man You Love Is an Alcoholic. LC 79-51276. (When Bks). (Illus.). 1979. pap. 2.45 (ISBN 0-87029-149-1, 20232-5). Abbey.

Manning, William O. & Vinton, Jean, eds. Harmfully Involved: Updated for the Eighties. 168p. (Orig.). 1978. pap. 10.95 (ISBN 0-89486-056-9). Hazelden.

Mehl, Duane. You & the Alcoholic in Your Home. LC 78-66947. 1979. pap. 6.95 (ISBN 0-8066-1697-0, 10-7408). Augsburg.

Ohlemacher, Janet. Beloved Alcoholic: What to Do When a Family Member Drinks. 128p. 1984. pap. 4.95 (ISBN 0-310-45531-6, 12480P). Zondervan.

Porterfield, Kay M. Keeping Promises: The Challenge of the Sober Parent. 172p. (Orig.). 1984. pap. 4.95 (ISBN 0-89486-245-6). Hazelden.

Rehrer, Ronald. Now What Do I Do? 1982. pap. 4.95 (ISBN 0-570-03854-5, 12-2809). Concordia.

Spickard, Anderson & Thompson, Barbara R. Dying for a Drink: What You Should Know about Alcoholism. 192p. 1985. 11.95 (ISBN 0-8499-0467-6, 0467-6). Word Bks.

Steinglass, Peter, et al. The Alcoholic Family. LC 86-47741. 320p. 1987. 22.95x (ISBN 0-465-00097-5). Basic.

Twerski, Abraham J. Self-Discovery in Recovery. 128p. (Orig.). 1984. pap. 3.95 (ISBN 0-89486-238-3). Hazelden.

Tygstrup, Niels & Olsson, Rolf, eds. Alcohol & Disease. (Illus.). 290p. 1985. text ed. 62.50x (ISBN 91-22-00786-5, Pub. by Almqvist & Wiksell). Coronet Bks.

Van Impe, Jack. Alcohol: The Beloved Enemy. 190p. 1980. pap. 4.95 (ISBN 0-934803-07-2). J Van Impe.

W, Carolyn. Detaching with Love. 24p. (Orig.). 1984. pap. 0.95 (ISBN 0-89486-232-4). Hazelden.

ALCOHOLISM–TREATMENT

Porterfield, Kay M. Keeping Promises: The Challenge of the Sober Parent. 172p. (Orig.). 1984. pap. 4.95 (ISBN 0-89486-245-6). Hazelden.

Prasch, Billy. Alcoholism Recovery. 60p. 1984. pap. 2.00 (ISBN 0-8198-0725-7). Dghtrs St Paul.

Spickard, Anderson & Thompson, Barbara R. Dying for a Drink: What You Should Know about Alcoholism. 192p. 1985. 11.95 (ISBN 0-8499-0467-6, 0467-6). Word Bks.

Twerski, Abraham J. Self-Discovery in Recovery. 128p. (Orig.). 1984. pap. 3.95 (ISBN 0-89486-238-3). Hazelden.

W, Carolyn. Detaching with Love. 24p. (Orig.). 1984. pap. 0.95 (ISBN 0-89486-232-4). Hazelden.

ALCOHOLISM AND RELIGION

Addington, Gordon L. The Christian & Social Drinking. 1984. 1.75 (ISBN 0-911802-63-0). Free Church Pubns.

Gentry, Kenneth L., Jr. The Christian & Alcoholic Beverages: A Biblical Perspective. 1986. pap. 4.95 (ISBN 0-8010-3807-3). Baker Bk.

Jack, S. Spiritual Reflections for the Recovering Alcoholic. LC 84-18590. (Illus.). 90p. 1985. pap. 5.95 (ISBN 0-8189-0477-1). Alba.

Prasch, Billy. Alcoholism Recovery. 60p. 1984. pap. 2.00 (ISBN 0-8198-0725-7). Dghtrs St Paul.

ALCORAN

see Koran

ALCUIN, 735-804

Ellard, Gerald. Master Alcuin, Liturgist. LC 56-8943. (Jesuit Studies). 1956. 2.95 (ISBN 0-8294-0027-3). Loyola.

Wallach, Luitpold. Alcuin & Charlemagne: Studies in Carolingian History & Literature. Repr. of 1959 ed. 23.00 (ISBN 0-384-65585-8). Johnson Repr.

West, Andrew F. Alcuin & the Rise of the Christian Schools. LC 73-149674. Repr. of 1892 ed. 10.00 (ISBN 0-404-06908-8). AMS Pr.

--Alcuin & the Rise of the Christian Schools. 1892. Repr. 9.00x (ISBN 0-403-00031-9). Scholarly.

ALEXANDER 3RD, POPE, d. 1181

Somerville, Robert. Pope Alexander III & the Council of Tours (1163) A Study of Ecclesiastical Politics & Institutions in the Twelfth Century. (Center for Medieval & Renaissance Studies, UCLA: Publications No. 12). 1978. 24.50x (ISBN 0-520-03184-9). U of Cal Pr.

ALEXANDER 7TH, POPE, 1594-1667

Bargrave, John. Pope Alexander the Seventh & the College of Cardinals. Robertson, James C., ed. LC 78-160001. (Camden Society, London. Publications, First Ser.: No. 92). Repr. of 1867 ed. 19.00 (ISBN 0-404-50192-3). AMS Pr.

--Pope Alexander the Seventh & the College of Cardinals. 19.00 (ISBN 0-384-03435-7). Johnson Repr.

Krautheimer, Richard. The Rome of Alexander VII, 1655-1667. LC 84-26553. (Illus.). 214p. 1987. 34.50 (ISBN 0-691-04032-X); pap. 12.95 (ISBN 0-691-00277-0). Princeton U Pr.

ALEXANDER DE HALES, d. 1245

Wass, Meldon. Infinite God. pap. 2.25 (ISBN 0-8199-0052-4, L38345). Franciscan Herald.

ALEXANDRIAN SCHOOL, CHRISTIAN

Armstrong, A. H. An Introduction to Ancient Philosophy. 3rd ed. LC 81-3731. (Quality Paperback Ser.: No. 418). 260p. 1981. pap. 7.45 (ISBN 0-8226-0418-3). Littlefield.

ALEXIUS, SAINT

Rosler, Margarete. Die Fassungen der Alexius-Legende. Repr. of 1905 ed. 25.00 (ISBN 0-384-51670-X). Johnson Repr.

ALKORAN

see Koran

ALLAH

see God (Islam)

ALLEGORIES

see also Fables; Parables

Bunyan, John. Pilgrim's Progress. Helms, Hal M., ed. LC 81-85770. (Living Library Ser.). (Illus.). 270p. 1982. 6.95 (ISBN 0-941478-02-5). Paraclete Pr.

--The Pilgrim's Progress. Helms, Hal M., ed. (Illus.). 268p. pap. 6.95 (ISBN 0-941478-02-5, Pub. by Paraclete Pr). Upper Room.

--Pilgrims Progress, Sixteen Seventy-Eight. 288p. 1984. 30.00x (ISBN 0-905418-29-8, Pub. by Gresham England). State Mutual Bk.

ALLEGORY

see also Apocalyptic Literature; Symbolism in Literature

Betty, Stafford. Sing Like a Whippoorwill. (Illus., Orig.). 1987. pap. 6.95 (ISBN 0-89622-324-8). Twenty-Third.

Bloomfield, Morton W., ed. Allegory, Myth, & Symbol. (Harvard English Studies: 9). 440p. 1982. text ed. 32.50x (ISBN 0-674-01640-8); pap. text ed. 10.95x (ISBN 0-674-01641-6). Harvard U Pr.

DeRocco, Jovan. Legend of the Truant Tree. (Illus.). 112p. 1982. 6.50 (ISBN 0-682-49804-1). Exposition Pr FL.

Lamberton, Robert. Homer the Theologian: Neoplatonist Allegorical Rading & the Growth of the Epic Tradition. LC 85-1184. (Transformation of the Classical Heritage Ser.: No. 9). 375p. 1986. text ed. 40.00x (ISBN 0-520-05437-7). U of Cal Pr.

MacKenzie, W. Roy. English Moralities from the Point of View of Allegory. LC 68-54172. (Studies in Drama, No. 39). 1969. Repr. of 1914 ed. lib. bdg. 49.95x (ISBN 0-8383-0592-X). Haskell.

Mackenzie, William R. English Moralities from the Point of View of Allegory. LC 66-29466. 278p. 1966. Repr. of 1914 ed. 25.00x (ISBN 0-87752-066-6). Gordian.

Williams, David. Cain & Beowulf: A Study in Secular Allegory. LC 81-94507. 114p. 1981. 25.00x (ISBN 0-8020-5519-2). U of Toronto Pr.

ALLEGORY (ART)

see Allegories; Symbolism in Art

ALLIANCE, HOLY

see Holy Alliance

ALMS AND ALMS-GIVING

see Charities; Charity

ALTAR BOYS

Michno, Dennis G. A Manual for Acolytes: The Duties of the Server at Liturgigal Celebrations. LC 80-81096. (Illus., Orig.). 1981. pap. 4.95 (ISBN 0-8192-1272-5). Morehouse.

Peace, Philip C. More Than Candlelighting: A Guide for Training Acolytes. LC 82-18973. (Illus.). 64p. (Orig.). 1983. pap. 4.95 (ISBN 0-8298-0642-3). Pilgrim NY.

Womack, Edwin B. Come Follow Me: A Study Book for Acolytes. 1982. pap. 6.45 (ISBN 0-89536-536-7, 0348). CSS of Ohio.

You Are an Acolyte: A Manual for Acolytes. (Illus.). 1977. pap. 2.95 (ISBN 0-8066-1552-4, 10-7409). Augsburg.

ALTAR GILDS

Bockelman, A. E. Practical Guide for Altar Guilds. LC 62-16936. (Illus., Orig.). 1962. pap. 4.95 (ISBN 0-8066-0223-6, 10-5050). Augsburg.

Diggs, Dorothy C. Working Manual for Altar Guilds. rev. ed. (Orig.). 1957. pap. 3.95 (ISBN 0-8192-1028-5). Morehouse.

Gebauer, Victor. Manual for Altar Guilds. 72p. (Orig.). 1986. pap. 9.50 (ISBN 0-8066-2203-2, 10-4267). Augsburg.

Gent, Barbara & Sturges, Betty. The Altar Guild Book. LC 82-80469. (Illus.). 104p. (Orig.). 1982. pap. 5.95 (ISBN 0-8192-1305-5, 82-80469). Morehouse.

Hickman, Hoyt L. United Methodist Altars: A Guide for the Local Church. 96p. 1984. pap. 6.95 (ISBN 0-687-42985-4). Abingdon.

Lang, Paul H. What an Altar Guild Should Know. 1964. ring bdg. 5.95 (ISBN 0-570-03501-5, 14-1528). Concordia.

LeCroy, Anne K. & Hatchett, Marion J. The Altar Guild Handbook. 108p. (Orig.). 1986. pap. 4.95 (ISBN 0-86683-784-1, HarpR). Har-Row.

Perry, Edith W. Altar Guild Manual. (Orig.). 1945. pap. 2.95 (ISBN 0-8192-1067-6). Morehouse.

Stauffer, S. Anita. The Altar Guild: A Guide for the Ministry of Liturgical Preparations. 64p. 1978. pap. 2.95 (ISBN 0-8006-1321-X, 1-1321). Fortress.

ALTAR GUILDS

see Altar Gilds

ALTARPIECES

Philip, Lotte B. The Ghent Altarpiece & the Art of Jan Van Eyck. LC 73-113007. (Illus.). 380p. 1981. pap. 16.50 (ISBN 0-691-00316-5). Princeton U Pr.

Van Os, Henk. Sienese Altarpieces 1215-1460 Form, Content, Function: Vol. I 1215-1344. Van Der Ploeg, Kees, contrib. by. (Mediaevalia Groningana IV: Bk. IV). (Illus.). 163p. 1984. 28.00x (ISBN 90-6088-083-8, Pub. by Boumas Boekhuis Netherlands). Benjamins North AM.

ALTARS

Barbet, Jean. Architecture of Altars & Chimneys, 2 vols. (Printed Sources of Western Art Ser.). (Fr., Illus.). 1981. pap. 35.00 slipcase (ISBN 0-915346-59-1). A Wofsy Fine Arts.

Pocknee, Cyril E. Christian Altar in History & Today. LC 64-1983. 1962. text ed. 10.00x (ISBN 0-8401-1871-6). A R Allenson.

ALTRUISM

Sorokin, P. A. Forms & Techniques of Altruistic & Spiritual Growth: A Symposium. Repr. of 1954 ed. 28.00 (ISBN 0-527-84810-7). Kraus Repr.

AMAT, THADDEUS, BP., 1811-1878

Weber, Francis J. California's Reluctant Prelate: The Life & Times of Thaddeus Amat. (Illus.). 1964. 6.75 (ISBN 0-87093-061-3). Dawsons.

AMAZONS

Anderson, Florence M. Religious Cults Associated with the Amazons. LC 73-158253. Repr. of 1912 ed. 16.00 (ISBN 0-404-00749-X). AMS Pr.

AMBROSIUS, SAINT, BP. OF MILAN

Paredi, Angela. Saint Ambrose: His Life & Times. LC 63-19325. pap. 123.80 (ISBN 0-317-26143-6, 2024372). Bks Demand UMI.

AMENHETEP 4TH, KING OF EGYPT, 1388-1358 B.C.

Velikovsky, Immanuel. Oedipus & Akhnaton: Myth & History. LC 60-7886. 1960. 11.95 (ISBN 0-385-00529-6). Doubleday.

AMERICA–CHURCH HISTORY

Lovejoy, David S. Religious Enthusiasm in the New World: Heresy to Revolution. 336p. 1985. text ed. 25.00x (ISBN 0-674-75864-1). Harvard U Pr.

Singer, Gregg. A Theological Interpretation of American History. kivar 7.95 (ISBN 0-934532-23-0). Presby & Ref.

Wentz, Richard E. The Saga of the American Soul. LC 80-5598. 163p. 1980. pap. text ed. 9.50 (ISBN 0-8191-1150-3). U Pr of Amer.

AMERICAN BOARD OF COMMISSIONERS FOR FOREIGN MISSIONS

Strong, William E. Story of the American Board: An Account of the First Hundred Years of the American Board for Foreign Missions. LC 79-83443. (Religion in America Ser). 1969. Repr. of 1910 ed. 26.50 (ISBN 0-405-00277-7). Ayer Co Pubs.

AMERICAN JEWISH JOINT DISTRIBUTION COMMITTEE

Hoofien, Sigfried. Report of Mr. S. Hoofien to the Joint Distribution Committee of the American Funds for Jewish War Sufferers,New York. Davis, Moshe, ed. LC 77-70702. (America & the Holy Land Ser.). (Illus.). 1977. Repr. of 1918 ed. lib. bdg. 17.00x (ISBN 0-405-10254-2). Ayer Co Pubs.

AMERICAN LITERATURE–CATHOLIC AUTHORS

Finotti, Joseph. Bibliographia Catholica Americana: A List of Works by Catholic Authors & Published in the United States. LC 74-149232. (Bibliography & Reference Ser.: No. 401). 1971. Repr. of 1872 ed. lib. bdg. 23.50 (ISBN 0-8337-1128-8). B Franklin.

Gross, Raphael H., ed. Century of the Catholic Essay. facs. ed. LC 76-134087. (Essay Index Reprint Ser). 1946. 19.00 (ISBN 0-8369-2190-9). Ayer Co Pubs.

Mary Louise, Sr., ed. Over the Bent World. LC 73-105031. (Essay Index Reprint Ser). 1939. 40.00 (ISBN 0-8369-1676-X). Ayer Co Pubs.

AMERICAN LITERATURE–JEWISH AUTHORS

Baumgarten, Murray. City Scriptures: Modern Jewish Writing. LC 81-6879. 240p. 1982. text ed. 17.50x (ISBN 0-674-13278-5). Harvard U Pr.

Berger, Alan L. Crisis & Covenant: The Holocaust in American Jewish Fiction. (Series in Modern Jewish Literature & Culture). 234p. 1985. 39.50 (ISBN 0-88706-085-4); pap. 14.95 (ISBN 0-88706-086-2). State U NY Pr.

Chametzky, Jules. Our Decentralized Literature: Cultural Mediations in Selected Jewish & Southern Writers. LC 86-1259. 168p. 1986. lib. bdg. 25.00x (ISBN 0-87023-527-3); pap. text ed. 9.95 (ISBN 0-87023-540-0). U of Mass Pr.

Chapman, Abraham, ed. Jewish-American Literature: An Anthology. 727p. pap. 2.25 (ISBN 0-686-95132-8). ADL.

Gitenstein, R. Barbara. Apocalyptic Messianism & Contemporary Jewish-American Poetry. (Modern Jewish Literature & Culture Ser.). 128p. (Orig.). 1986. 39.50x (ISBN 0-88706-154-0); pap. 12.95x (ISBN 0-88706-155-9). State U NY Pr.

Gross, Theodore L. Literature of American Jews. LC 72-93311. 1973. 14.95 (ISBN 0-02-913190-1). Free Pr.

Harap, Louis. Creative Awakening: The Jewish Presence in Twentieth-Century American Literature, 1900-1940s-Published in Cooperation with the American Jewish Archives. LC 86-14986. (Contributions in Ethnic Studies: No. 17). 216p. 1987. lib. bdg. 29.95 (ISBN 0-313-25386-2, HFI). Greenwood.

--The Image of the Jew in American Literature. LC 74-12887. 608p. 1975. 10.00 (ISBN 0-8276-0054-2, 357). Jewish Pubns.

Mazow, Julia W., ed. The Woman Who Lost Her Names: Selected Writings by American Jewish Women. LC 79-2986. 240p. 1981. pap. text ed. 10.00 (ISBN 0-06-250567-X, CN 4017, HarpR). Har-Row.

Walden, Daniel, ed. Studies in American Jewish Literature: Isaac Bashevis Singer, 3 Vols. Incl. Vol. 1. A Mosaic of Jewish Writers; Vol. 3. Jewish Women Writers & Women in Jewish Literature; Vol. 2. From Marginality to Mainstream: A Mosaic of Jewish Writers; Vol. 4. The World of Chaim Potok. 1982. 12.95 ea. (ISBN 0-686-97287-2). State U NY Pr.

AMERICAN MISSIONARY ASSOCIATION

Beard, A. F. Crusade of Brotherhood, a History of the American Missionary Association. 1909. 24.00 (ISBN 0-527-06300-2). Kraus Repr.

Beard, Augustus F. Crusade of Brotherhood, a History of the American Missionary Association. LC 76-161728. Repr. of 1909 ed. 26.50 (ISBN 0-404-00004-5). AMS Pr.

Richardson, Joe M. Christian Reconstruction: The American Missionary Association & Southern Blacks, 1861-1890. LC 85-13946. (Illus.). 352p. 1986. 30.00x (ISBN 0-8203-0816-1). U of GA Pr.

AMERICAN PHILOSOPHY

see Philosophy, American

AMERICAN POETRY (COLLECTIONS)

Emerson, Ralph Waldo, ed. Parnassus. facsimile ed. LC 73-116400. (Granger Index Reprint Ser). 1874. 25.50 (ISBN 0-8369-6141-2). Ayer Co Pubs.

Hunter, Irene, ed. American Mystical Verse. LC 79-116407. (Granger Index Reprint Ser). 1925. 19.00 (ISBN 0-8369-6148-X). Ayer Co Pubs.

Reeves, Una G. Writing Verse As a Hobby. 1962. 6.95 (ISBN 0-8158-0172-6). Chris Mass.

Stevenson, Burton, ed. American History in Verse. Abridged ed. 494p. 1975. pap. 7.00 (ISBN 0-89084-024-5). Bob Jones Univ Pr.

AMERICAN POETRY (COLLECTIONS)–20TH CENTURY

Mirikitani, Janice, et al, eds. Time to Greez! Incantations from the Third World. LC 75-355. (Illus.). 224p. (Orig.). 1975. pap. 4.95 (ISBN 0-912078-44-8). Volcano Pr.

AMERICAN WIT AND HUMOR–CHURCH AND CLERGY

Adams, Doug. Humor in the American Pulpit from George Whitefield Through Henry Ward Beecher. rev. ed. 1981. 6.95 (ISBN 0-941500-10-1). Sharing Co.

Albran, Kehlog. The Profit. 108p. (Orig.). 1973. pap. 2.95 (ISBN 0-8431-0260-8). Price Stern.

Armbruster, Wally. A Bag of Noodles. (Illus.). (YA) 1973. pap. 3.95 (ISBN 0-570-03158-3, 12-2543). Concordia.

Armstrong, Wm. Clerical Cartoons. 2nd ed. (Armstrong Cartoon Ser.). (Illus.). 48p. (Orig.). 1971. pap. 1.00 (ISBN 0-913452-02-5). Jesuit Bks.

--Ecclesiastical Cartoons. 2nd ed. (Armstrong Cartoon Ser.). (Illus.). 48p. (Orig.). 1972. pap. 1.00 (ISBN 0-913452-08-4). Jesuit Bks.

Arnold, Oren. Junior Saints: The Rich Rare Humor of Kids in Church. LC 75-12108. (Illus.). 128p. 1976. pap. 4.95 (ISBN 0-8254-2117-9). Kregel.

--Snappy Steeple Stories. LC 79-128150. (Church Humor Series). 80p. 1970. pap. 1.95 (ISBN 0-8254-2107-1). Kregel.

Arnold, Oren, ed. More Steeple Stories. LC 77-76437. (Church Humor Series). 1969. pap. 1.95 (ISBN 0-8254-2105-5). Kregel.

Bonham, Tal D. The Treasury of Clean Church Jokes. LC 85-26837. 1986. pap. 3.50 (ISBN 0-8054-5719-4). Broadman.

Harrison, Hank. The Holy Grail. (The Grail Trilogy). (Illus.). 325p. (Orig.). 1987. 24.95 (ISBN 0-918501-18-0). Archives Pr.

Knight, George W., compiled by. Instant Cartoons for Church Newsletters, No. 3. 1986. pap. 4.95 (ISBN 0-8010-5473-7). Baker Bk.

Lofgren, Mikal. Wheat: Humor & Wisdom of J. Golden Kimball. LC 80-81556. 95p. 1980. 6.50 (ISBN 0-936718-04-8). Moth Hse.

Paris, Howard. Clip-Art Panel Cartoons for Churches 2. 96p. 1987. pap. 4.95 (ISBN 0-8010-7098-8). Baker Bk.

AMERICANISM (CATHOLIC CONTROVERSY)

see also Modernism–Catholic Church

America & Americanism. 1986. pap. 6.95 (ISBN 0-916786-82-X). St George Bk Serv.

Cross, Robert A. Emergence of Liberal Catholicism in America. LC 58-5593. 1958. 25.00x (ISBN 0-674-24800-7). Harvard U Pr.

AMISH

Denlinger, Martha. Real People. rev. ed. LC 74-16966. (Illus.). 96p. 1975. pap. 3.95 (ISBN 0-8361-1960-6). Herald Pr.

Fisher, Sara E. & Stahl, Rachel K. The Amish School. LC 84-81142. (People's Place Booklet: No. 6). (Illus.). 96p. (Orig.). 1985. pap. 4.50 (ISBN 0-934672-17-2). Good Bks PA.

Gingerich, Orland. The Amish of Canada. LC 72-94800. 248p. 1978. pap. 4.95 (ISBN 0-8361-1856-1). Herald Pr.

Good, Merle. Who Are the Amish? LC 85-70283. (Illus.). 128p. (Orig.). 1985. 24.95 (ISBN 0-934672-28-8); pap. 15.95 (ISBN 0-934672-26-1). Good Bks PA.

Hall, Barbara Y. Born Amish. (Illus.). 100p. (Orig.). 1980. pap. 6.95 (ISBN 0-9606154-0-7). Jacbar Pubns.

Hosteter, John A. The Amish. (Illus.). 40p. 1982. pap. 1.95 (ISBN 0-8361-3317-X). Herald Pr.

Hostetler, John A. Amish Life. 2nd ed. LC 82-83964. (Illus.). 48p. (Orig.). 1983. pap. 4.95 (ISBN 0-8361-3326-9). Herald Pr.

--Amish Society. rev., 3rd ed. LC 79-23823. 432p. 1980. pap. 9.95 (ISBN 0-8018-2334-X). Johns Hopkins.

Israel, Fred L., ed. Amish. LC 85-17516. (Let's Meet the Peoples of North America Ser.). (Illus.). 112p. 1986. lib. bdg. 15.95 (ISBN 0-87754-853-6). Chelsea Hse.

Lapp, Hannah B. To Belize with Love. LC 86-70999. 380p. (Orig.). (YA) 1986. pap. 14.95 (ISBN 0-931494-94-X). Brunswick Pub.

Miller, Betty. The Amish in Switzerland & Other European Countries. 1978. pap. 1.50 (ISBN 0-685-46025-8). O R Miller.

Miller, Levi. Our People: The Amish & Mennonites of Ohio. LC 82-84405. (Illus.). 56p. (Orig.). 1983. pap. 2.50 (ISBN 0-8361-3331-5). Herald Pr.

Naylor, Phyllis R. An Amish Family. 12.95 (ISBN 0-8488-0109-1, Pub. by Amereon Hse). Amereon Ltd.

Perkins, James A. & Oestreich, Nelson. The Amish: Two Perceptions Two. (Illus.). 24p. (Orig.). 1981. pap. 4.00 (ISBN 0-936014-10-5). Dawn Valley.

Renno, John R. Circumstances That Caused Me to Leave the Amish Church. 54p. 1987. pap. 3.00 (ISBN 1-55618-021-7). Brunswick Pub.

Ruth, John L. A Quiet & Peaceable Life. rev. ed. LC 85-70284. (People's Place Booklet: No. 2). (Illus.). 96p. (Orig.). 1985. pap. 4.50 (ISBN 0-934672-25-3). Good Bks PA.

Schrieber, William I. Our Amish Neighbors. LC 62-17137. (Illus.). 1978. pap. 5.95 (ISBN 0-226-74035-8). U of Chicago Pr.

Schwieder, Elmer & Schwieder, Dorothy. A Peculiar People: Iowa's Old Order Amish. facs. ed. (Illus.). 188p. 1975. 9.95x (ISBN 0-8138-0105-2). Iowa St U Pr.

Yoder, Joseph W. Rosanna of the Amish. rev. ed. 256p. 1973. pap. 3.95 (ISBN 0-8361-1714-X). Herald Pr.

Yoder, Paton. Eine Wurzel: Tennessee John Stolzfus. LC 79-26507. (Illus.). 192p. 1979. 10.50 (ISBN 0-915010-27-5). Sutter House.

AMOS, THE PROPHET

Barton, J. Amos' Oracles Against the Nations. LC 78-67630. (Society for Old Testament Study Ser.). 1980. 22.95 (ISBN 0-521-22501-9). Cambridge U Pr.

AMUSEMENTS–MORAL AND RELIGIOUS ASPECTS

Campbell, Viola D. Juguemos. (Illus.). 199p. 1983. pap. 3.50 (ISBN 0-311-11006-1). Casa Bautista.

Northbrooke, John. Treatise Against Dicing, Dancing, Plays & Interludes. LC 77-149667. Repr. of 1843 ed. 19.00 (ISBN 0-404-04793-9). AMS Pr.

Schultz, Thom, ed. The Best of Try This One. (Illus.). 80p. (Orig.). 1977. pap. 5.95 (ISBN 0-936664-01-0). Group Bks.

--More...Try This One. LC 80-80947. (Illus.). 80p. (Orig.). 1980. pap. 5.95 (ISBN 0-936664-00-2). Group Bks.

ANA

see Aphorisms and Apothegms; Proverbs; Quotations

ANABAPTISTS

see also Baptists; Mennonites; Peasants' War, 1524-1525

Arnold, Eberhard. The Early Anabaptists. 2nd, rev. ed. Brethren, Hutterian, ed. LC 84-14259. Tr. of History of the Baptizers Movement. (Ger.). 64p. 1984. pap. 4.00 (ISBN 0-87486-192-6). Plough.

Augsburger, Myron S. Broken Chalice. LC 70-160721. (Illus.). 1971. 7.95 (ISBN 0-8361-1651-8). Herald Pr.

Balke, William. Calvin & the Anabaptist Radicals. Heynen, William, tr. LC 81-12438. pap. 87.50 (ISBN 0-317-30132-2, 2025315). Bks Demand UMI.

Bender, Harold S. Anabaptist Vision. 1944. pap. 1.45 (ISBN 0-8361-1305-5). Herald Pr.

--Conrad Grebel, c. 1498-1526: The Founder of the Swiss Brethren Sometimes Called Anabaptists. (Studies in Anabaptist & Mennonite History Ser.: No. 6). pap. 85.80 (ISBN 0-317-28810-5, 2020335). Bks Demand UMI.

Brown, Hubert L. Black & Mennonite. LC 76-44043. 112p. 1976. pap. 3.95 (ISBN 0-8361-1801-4). Herald Pr.

Bullinger, Heinrich. An Holsom Antidotus or Counter-Poysen Agaynst the Pestylent Heresye & Secte of the Anabaptistes. Veron, J., tr. LC 73-6106. (English Experience Ser.: No. 574). 232p. 1973. Repr. of 1548 ed. 13.00 (ISBN 90-221-0574-1). Walter J Johnson.

Calvin, John. John Calvin's Treatises Against the Anabaptists & Against the Libertines. Farley, Benjamin W., tr. 360p. (Orig.). 1982. pap. 16.95 (ISBN 0-8010-2476-5). Baker Bk.

Davis, Kenneth R. Anabaptism & Asceticism. LC 73-19593. 384p. 1974. 19.95x (ISBN 0-8361-1195-8). Herald Pr.

Deppermann, Klaus. Melchior Hoffman: Social Unrest & Apocalyptic Visions in the Age of Reformation. Wren, Malcolm, tr. 450p. 1986. 38.95 (ISBN 0-567-09338-7, Pub. by T & T Clark Ltd UK). Fortress.

Friedmann, Robert. Glaubenszeugnisse Oberdeutscher Taufgesinnter, Band Zwei. (Tauferakten Kommission Ser., Vol. 12). 318p. (Ger). 9.50x (ISBN 0-8361-1186-9). Herald Pr.

--The Theology of Anabaptism. LC 73-7886. (Studies in Anabaptist & Mennonite History, No. 15). 176p. 1973. 12.95x (ISBN 0-8361-1194-X). Herald Pr.

Furcha, E. J., ed. & tr. Selected Writings of Hans Denck. LC 76-7057. (Pittsburgh Original Texts & Translations Ser.: No. 1). 1976. 5.50 (ISBN 0-915138-15-8). Pickwick.

Harder, Helmut. Guide to Faith. LC 79-50682. 1979. pap. 3.95 (ISBN 0-87303-022-2). Faith & Life.

Harder, Leland, ed. The Sources of Swiss Anabaptism. LC 85-5520. (Classics of the Radical Reformation: No. 4). 816p. 1985. 69.00x (ISBN 0-8361-1251-2). Herald Pr.

Hershberger, Guy F., ed. The Recovery of the Anabaptist Vision: A Sixtieth Anniversary Tribute to Harold S. Bender. LC 57-10214. pap. 92.00 (ISBN 0-317-26605-5, 2025419). Bks Demand UMI.

Kauffman, J. H. & Harder, Leland. Anabaptists: Four Centuries Later. LC 74-30347. 400p. 1975. 14.95x (ISBN 0-8361-1136-2); pap. 6.95 o. p. (ISBN 0-8361-1137-0). Herald Pr.

Kautsky, Karl. Communism in Central Europe in the Time of the Reformation. Mulliken, J. L. & Mulliken, E. G., trs. LC 66-22631. 1966. Repr. of 1897 ed. 29.50x (ISBN 0-678-00193-6). Kelley.

Klaassen, Walter. Anabaptism in Outline: Selected Primary Sources. 424p. 1981. pap. 12.95 (ISBN 0-8361-1241-5). Herald Pr.

--Selecciones Teologias Anabautista. Snyder, C. Arnoldo, tr. from Eng. LC 85-81079. (Span.). 280p. (Orig.). 1985. pap. 4.50 (ISBN 0-8361-1281-4). Herald Pr.

Krebs, Manfred & Rott, H. G., eds. Elsass Eins, Stadt Strassburg: 1522-32. (Tauferakten Kommission Ser., Vol. 7). 599p. (Ger). 1959. 35.00x (ISBN 0-8361-1167-2). Herald Pr.

--Elsass Zwei, Stadt Strassburg: 1533-35. (Tauferakten Kommission Ser., Vol. 8). 555p. (Ger). 1959. 35.00x (ISBN 0-8361-1168-0). Herald Pr.

McGrath, William. The Anabaptists: Neither Catholics nor Protestants. pap. 1.25 (ISBN 0-686-32317-3). Rod & Staff.

Mecenseffy, Grete. Osterreichische Tauferakten One. (Tauferakten Kommision Ser., Vol. 11). 402p. (Ger). 1964. 15.00x (ISBN 0-8361-1171-0). Herald Pr.

Ormerod, Oliver. The Picture of a Puritane: Or, a Relation of the Opinions - of the Anabaptists in Germanie, & of the Puritanes in England. LC 74-28879. (English Experience Ser.: No. 757). 1975. Repr. of 1605 ed. 9.50 (ISBN 90-221-0757-4). Walter J Johnson.

Roehrich, Gustave G. Essay on the Life, the Writings, & the Doctrine of the Anabaptist, Hans Denk. Foster, Claude R., et al, trs. from Fr. & Ger. LC 83-10295. 54p. (Orig.). 1983. pap. text ed. 5.50 (ISBN 0-8191-3347-7). U Pr of Amer.

Schornbaum, Karl. Quellen zur Geschichte der Wiedertaufer. 34.00 (ISBN 0-384-54249-2); pap. 28.00 (ISBN 0-384-54248-4). Johnson Repr.

Seguy, J. Les Assemblees Anabaptistes-Mennonites de France. 1977. 64.00x (ISBN 90-279-7524-8). Mouton.

Shenk, Wilbert. Anabaptism & Mission. LC 84-12863. (Missionary Study: No. 10). 264p. (Orig.). 1984. pap. 12.95 (ISBN 0-8361-3367-6). Herald Pr.

Snyder, C. Arnold. The Life & Thought of Michael Sattler. LC 83-22835. (Studies in Anabaptist & Mennonite History: No. 27). 264p. 1984. 19.95x (ISBN 0-8361-1264-4). Herald Pr.

Stayer, James M. Anabaptists & the Sword. 2nd rev. ed. 1976. 15.00 (ISBN 0-87291-081-4). Coronado Pr.

Stayer, James M. & Packull, Werner O. The Anabaptists & Thomas Muntzer. 176p. 1980. pap. text ed. 13.95 (ISBN 0-8403-2235-6). Kendall-Hunt.

Strege, Merle D., ed. Baptism & Church: A Believers' Church Vision. LC 85-43567. 224p. (Orig.). 1986. pap. 12.50 (ISBN 0-937021-00-8). Sagamore Bks MI.

Turner, William. A Preservative, or Triacle, Agaynst the Poyson of Pelagius. LC 78-171795. (English Experience Ser.: No. 418). 208p. 1971. Repr. of 1551 ed. 20.00 (ISBN 90-221-0418-4). Walter J Johnson.

Vedder, Henry C. Baltahsar Hubmaier: The Leader of the Anabaptists. LC 79-149670. Repr. of 1905 ed. 24.50 (ISBN 0-404-06755-7). AMS Pr.

Verheyden, A. L. Anabaptism in Flanders 1530-1650. LC 61-13872. (Studies in Anabaptist & Mennonite History, No. 9). 126p. 1961. 12.95x (ISBN 0-8361-1102-8). Herald Pr.

Weaver, J. Denny. Becoming Anabaptist. LC 86-33650. 176p. (Orig.). 1987. pap. 14.95 (ISBN 0-8361-3434-6). Herald Pr.

Weis, Frederick L. The Life & Teaching of Ludwig Hesser: Leader & Martyr of the Anabaptists, 1500-1529. LC 83-45633. Date not set. Repr. of 1930 ed. 31.50 (ISBN 0-404-19875-9). AMS Pr.

Westin, G. & Bergsten, T., eds. Balthasar Hubmaier. (Tauferakten Kommission Ser., Vol. 9). 507p. 1962. 30.00x (ISBN 0-8361-1169-9). Herald Pr.

Williams, George H. Radical Reformation. LC 62-7066. (Illus.). 960p. 1962. 24.95 (ISBN 0-664-20372-8). Westminster.

Yoder, John H., ed. The Legacy of Michael Sattler. LC 72-6333. (Classics of the Radical Reformation Ser., No. 1). 208p. 1973. 12.95 (ISBN 0-8361-1187-7). Herald Pr.

ANABAPTISTS–HISTORY

Bax, E. Belfort. Rise & Fall of the Anabaptists. 59.95 (ISBN 0-8490-0958-8). Gordon Pr.

Belk, Fred R. The Great Trek of the Russian Mennonites to Central Asia. LC 75-28340. (Studies in Anabaptist & Mennonite History: No. 18). pap. 63.00 (ISBN 0-317-26601-2, 2025418). Bks Demand UMI.

Blanke, Fritz. Brothers in Christ: The History of the Oldest Anabaptist. Nordenhaug, Joseph, tr. LC 61-6723. pap. 20.00 (2029246). Bks Demand UMI.
Dosker, Henry E., ed. The Dutch Anabaptists: Stone Lectures Delivered at Princeton Theological Seminary, 1918-1919. LC 83-45610. Date not set. Repr. of 1921 ed. 36.50 (ISBN 0-404-19828-7). AMS Pr.
Estep, William R. The Anabaptist Story. 1975. pap. 7.95 (ISBN 0-8028-1594-4). Eerdmans.
Heath, Richard. Anabaptism, from Its Rise at Zwickau to Its Fall at Munster. LC 83-45615. Date not set. Repr. of 1895 ed. 28.00 (ISBN 0-404-19833-3). AMS Pr.
Lienhard, M. The Origins & Characteristics of Anabaptism. (International Archives of the History of Ideas Ser: No. 87). 1977. lib. bdg. 53.00 (ISBN 90-247-1896-1, Pub. by Martinus Nijhoff Netherlands). Kluwer Academic.
Packull, Werner O. Mysticism & the Early South German-Austrian Anabaptist 1525-1531. LC 76-46557. (Studies in the Anabaptist & Mennonite History: No. 19). 296p. 1977. 19.95x (ISBN 0-8361-1130-3). Herald Pr.
Peachey, Paul, ed. Die Soziale Herkunft Der Schweizer Taufer in Der Feformationszeit. (Ger.). 157p. (Orig.). 1954. pap. 4.50x (ISBN 0-8361-1160-5). Herald Pr.
Yoder, John H., ed. Textos Encogidoes de la Reforma Radical. (Span.). 500p. (Orig.). 1984. pap. 25.00 (ISBN 0-8361-1237-7). Herald Pr.
Yoder, John H., tr. The Schleitheim Confession. 32p. 1977. pap. 1.95 (ISBN 0-8361-1831-6). Herald Pr.

ANALOGY (RELIGION)
see also Anthropomorphism
Edwards, Jonathan. Images or Shadows of Divine Things. Miller, Perry, ed. LC 73-8157. 1977. Repr. of 1948 ed. lib. bdg. 29.75x (ISBN 0-8371-6952-6, EDIS). Greenwood.
Phelan, Gerald B. Saint Thomas & Analogy. (Aquinas Lecture). 1941. 7.95 (ISBN 0-87462-105-4). Marquette.
Zeitz, James V. Spirituality & Analogia Entis According to Erich Przywara, S. J. Metaphysics & Religious Experience, the Ignation Exercises, the Balance in 'Similarity' & 'Greater Dissimilarity' According to Lateran IV. LC 82-17588. 358p. (Orig.). 1983. lib. bdg. 33.00 (ISBN 0-8191-2783-3); pap. text ed. 15.75 (ISBN 0-8191-2784-1). U Pr of Amer.

ANCESTOR WORSHIP
Ahern, Emily M. Cult of the Dead in a Chinese Village. LC 72-97202. (Illus.). 296p. 1973. 22.50x (ISBN 0-8047-0835-5). Stanford U Pr.
Smith, Robert J. Ancestor Worship in Contemporary Japan. LC 74-82780. (Illus.). xxii, 266p. 1974. 29.50x (ISBN 0-8047-0873-8). Stanford U Pr.
Willoughby, William C. Soul of the Bantu: A Sympathetic Study of the Magico-Religious Practices & Beliefs of the Bantu Tribes of Africa. LC 77-107526. Repr. of 1928 ed. cancelled (ISBN 0-8371-3773-X, WBA&, Pub. by Negro U Pr). Greenwood.

ANCHORITES
see Hermits

ANCIENT HISTORY
see History, Ancient

ANDOVER THEOLOGICAL SEMINARY
Williams, Daniel D. Andover Liberals: A Study in American Theology. LC 79-111636. 1970. Repr. of 1941 ed. lib. bdg. 17.50x (ISBN 0-374-98584-7, Octagon). Hippocrene Bks.

ANDREWS, CHARLES FREER, 1871-1940
Attwater, Donald, ed. Modern Christian Revolutionaries. facsimile ed. LC 76-156608. (Essay Index Reprint Ser). Repr. of 1947 ed. 23.00 (ISBN 0-8369-2304-9). Ayer Co Pubs.

ANGELA MERICI, SAINT, 1474-1540
Moran, Mary Y. Angela Gods Magnet. (Illus.). 48p. 1987. 5.95 (ISBN 0-89962-583-5). Todd & Honeywell.

ANGELS
see also Ark of the Covenant
Adler, Mortimer J. The Angels & Us. 205p. 1982. 11.95 (ISBN 0-02-500550-2). Macmillan.
Alexander, Dorsey & Alexander, Joyce. A Flurry of Angels: Angels in Literature. (Illus.). 1986. pap. 5.00. Turtles Quill.
Blazer, Howard A. Angels, Their Origin, Nature, Mission & Destiny. 64p. 1974. pap. 2.50x (ISBN 0-88428-034-9). Parchment Pr.
Boros, Ladislaus. Angels & Men. 1976. 6.95 (ISBN 0-8245-0201-9). Crossroad NY.
Capps, Charles. Angels. 224p. (Orig.). 1984. pap. 3.95 (ISBN 0-89274-308-5, HH-308). Harrison Hse.
D'Angelo, Dorie. Living with Angels. 5th ed. 1980. pap. 10.00 (ISBN 0-912216-22-0). Angel Pr.
Dellinger, Annetta E. Angels Are My Friends. LC 85-7858. 32p. 1985. 4.95 (ISBN 0-570-04120-1, 56-1531). Concordia.
Dimitry of Rostov, St. Angels & the Other Heavenly Bodiless Powers. pap. 0.25 (ISBN 0-686-05638-8). Eastern Orthodox.
Ellsworth, Irene B. I Met Angels in the Tangles of Life. LC 84-52166. 118p. (Orig.). 1985. pap. 4.95 (ISBN 0-9614165-0-5). Terhell Bks.
Fox, Robert J. Opus Sanctorum Angelorum: Work of the Holy Angels. 1.50 (ISBN 0-911988-49-1). AMI Pr.
French, Joel & French, Jane. War Beyond the Stars. LC 79-90267. (Illus.). 128p. 1979. pap. 4.95 (ISBN 0-89221-067-2). New Leaf.
Gaebelein, A. C. What the Bible Says About Angels. (Direction Bks). 120p. 1975. pap. 4.95 (ISBN 0-8010-3810-3). Baker Bk.
--What the Bible Says about Angels. 116p. 1987. pap. 4.95 (ISBN 0-8010-3810-3). Baker Bk.
Gilmore, G. Don. Angels, Angels, Everywhere. LC 81-8525. 180p. 1981. 11.95 (ISBN 0-8298-0477-3); pap. 6.95 (ISBN 0-8298-0479-X). Pilgrim NY.
Graham, Billy. Los Angeles: Agentes Secretos de Dios. Rojas, Juan, tr. from Eng. LC 76-20259. Tr. of Angels: God's Secret Agents. (Span.). 168p. 1976. pap. 4.95 (ISBN 0-89922-069-X). Edit Caribe.
--Angels. 1984. pap. 3.50 (ISBN 0-671-54147-1). PB.
--Angels: God's Secret Agents. 176p. 1986. 9.95 (ISBN 0-8499-0542-7, 0542-7); pap. 7.95 (ISBN 0-8499-3049-9). Word Bks.
Hakes, Thomas L. Where Have All the Little Angels Gone? (Illus.). 10p. 1985. pap. 2.00x (ISBN 0-915020-58-0). Bardic.
Knowles, Victor. What the Bible Says about Angels & Demons. LC 86-71104. (What the Bible Says Ser.). 405p. 1986. 13.95 (ISBN 0-89900-252-8). College Pr Pub.
Landersdorfer, Simon K., ed. Der Bael Tatpauopoos und Die Kerube Des Ezechiel. pap. 8.00 (ISBN 0-384-31200-4). Johnson Repr.
Leavell, Landrum P. Angels, Angels, Angels. LC 73-75627. 96p. 1973. pap. 5.95 (ISBN 0-8054-2222-6). Broadman.
Lindsay, Gordon. Ministry of Angels. 1.25 (ISBN 0-89985-018-9). Christ Nations.
Long, Valentine. Angels in Religion & Art. LC 77-117712. 1971. pap. 2.95 (ISBN 0-8199-0430-9). Franciscan Herald.
Lovasik, Lawrence G. The Angels: God's Messengers & Our Helpers. (Saint Joseph Picture Bks.). (Illus.). flexible bdg. 0.95 (ISBN 0-89942-281-0, 281). Catholic Bk Pub.
MacDonald, Hope. When Angels Appear. 128p. (Orig.). 1982. pap. 4.95 (ISBN 0-310-28531-3, 10047P). Zondervan.
MacGregor, Geddes. Angels: Ministers of Grace. (Illus.). 256p. 1987. 18.95 (ISBN 0-913729-42-6). Paragon Hse.
Miller, C. Leslie. All about Angels. LC 73-82096. 144p. (Orig.). 1973. pap. 3.50 (ISBN 0-8307-0467-1, 5010500). Regal.
Newhouse, Flower A. Rediscovering the Angels & Natives of Eternity. 7th ed. (Illus.). 11.00 (ISBN 0-910378-02-9). Christward.
Nystrom, Carolyn. Angels & Me. (Children's Bible Basics Ser.). (Illus.). 1984. 4.95 (ISBN 0-8024-6017-8). Moody.
Omoyajowo, Akin. Diversity in Unity: The Development & Expansion of the Cherubim & Seraphim Church in Nigeria. LC 83-21706. 126p. (Orig.). 1984. lib. bdg. 22.00 (ISBN 0-8191-3655-7). U Pr of Amer.
Parente, Pascal P. Beyond Space. 1977. pap. 4.50 (ISBN 0-89555-053-9). TAN Bks Pubs.
Richards, H. M., Jr. Angels: Secret Agents of God & Satan. LC 80-22223. (Flame Ser.). 64p. 1980. pap. 0.99 (ISBN 0-8127-0313-8). Review & Herald.
St. Thomas Aquinas. Saint Thomas Aquinas: On Spiritual Creatures. Fitzpatrick, Mary C., tr. (Medieval Philosophical Texts in Translation: No. 5). 1949. pap. 7.95 (ISBN 0-87462-205-0). Marquette.
Schneweis, Emil. Angels & Demons According to Lactantius. LC 79-8121. (Satanism Ser.). 192p. Repr. of 1944 ed. 26.00 (ISBN 0-404-18433-2). AMS Pr.

ANGELS–ART
Crockett, Silvia. Angels in Traditional Design. (International Design Library). (Illus.). 48p. (Orig.). 1987. pap. 3.95 (ISBN 0-88045-086-X). Stemmer Hse.
Nutting, George L. & Nutting, Ruth S. The Angel World. 115p. (Orig.). 1985. pap. 2.95 (ISBN 0-9612266-1-7). Numard Bks.

ANGELS (JUDAISM)
Newsom, Carol. The Songs of the Sabbath Sacrifice: Edition, Translation, & Commentary. (Harvard Semitic Museum Ser.). 1985. 34.95 (ISBN 0-89130-837-7, 04-04-27). Scholars Pr GA.

ANGER OF GOD
see God–Wrath

ANGLICAN CHURCH
see Church of England

ANGLICAN COMMUNION
Istavridis, Vasil T. Orthodoxy & Anglicanism. LC 67-79982. 1966. 15.00x (ISBN 0-8401-1183-5). A R Allenson.
Long, Charles H., ed. Anglican Cycle of Prayer, Nineteen Eighty-Seven. (Partners in Prayer Ser.). (Illus.). 128p. (Orig.). 1986. pap. 1.75 (ISBN 0-88028-053-0). Forward Movement.
Mullin, Robert B. Episcopal Vision-American Reality: High Church Theology & Social Thought in Evangelical America. 1986. 20.00 (ISBN 0-300-03487-3). Yale U Pr.
Rich, George. God Pursues a Priest. 60p. (Orig.). 1986. pap. 2.95 (ISBN 0-87227-109-9). Reg Baptist.
Welsby, Paul A. The History of the Church of England, 1945-80. 1984. 29.95x (ISBN 0-19-213231-8). Oxford U Pr.

ANGLICAN ORDERS
Anglican Orders (English) The Bull of His Holiness Leo XIII, September 13, 1896, & the Answer to the Archbishops of England March 29, 1897. (Church Historical Society, London, Ser.: No. 12). pap. 16.00 (ISBN 0-317-16454-6). Kraus Repr.
Anglican Orders (Latin) The Bull of His Holiness Leo XIII, September 13, 1896, & the Answer to the Archbishops of England March 29, 1897. (Church Historical Society, London, Ser.: No. 13). Repr. of 1932 ed. 40.00 (ISBN 0-8115-3136-8). Kraus Repr.
Ashmole, Elias. Institution, Laws & Ceremonies of the Most Noble Order of the Garter. LC 78-147882. (Illus.). 720p. 1971. Repr. of 1672 ed. 50.00 (ISBN 0-8063-0467-7). Genealog Pub.
Wolf, William J., ed. Anglican Spirituality. LC 81-84717. 176p. (Orig.). 1982. pap. 9.95 (ISBN 0-8192-1297-0). Morehouse.

ANGLO-CATHOLICISM
see also Catholicity
Copeland, W. J., et al, eds. Library of Anglo-Catholic Theology, 18 titles in 81 vols. Repr. of 1841 ed. Set. 2627.50 (ISBN 0-404-52010-3); write for info. AMS Pr.
Garrett, Leroy. The Stone-Campbell Movement. LC 80-65965. 739p. 1981. 21.95 (ISBN 0-89900-059-2). College Pr Pub.
Huelin, Gordon, ed. Old Catholics & Anglicans: 1931-81. (Illus.). 1983. text ed. 27.50x (ISBN 0-19-920129-3). Oxford U Pr.
Knox, Wilfred L. The Catholic Movement in the Church of England. 1925. 15.00 (ISBN 0-8414-5599-6). Folcroft.
L'Estrange, Hamon. Alliance of Divine Offices. LC 71-172316. (Library of Anglo-Catholic Theology: No. 12). Repr. of 1846 ed. 27.50 (ISBN 0-404-52104-5). AMS Pr.
Morse-Boycott, Desmond L. Lead, Kindly Light. LC 70-107728. (Essay Index Reprint Ser). 1933. 16.00 (ISBN 0-8369-1529-1). Ayer Co Pubs.
Norman, Edward. Roman Catholicism in England from the Elizabethan Settlement to the Second Vatican Council. (OPUS). 160p. 1985. 18.95x (ISBN 0-19-219181-0); pap. 9.95 (ISBN 0-19-281935-6). Oxford U Pr.

ANGLO-ISRAELISM
see also Lost Tribes of Israel
Allen, John H. Judah's Sceptre & Joseph's Birthright. 1946. 8.00 (ISBN 0-685-08809-X). Destiny.
Dickey, C. R. One Man's Destiny. 1942. 8.00 (ISBN 0-685-08811-1). Destiny.
Rand, Howard B. Behold, He Cometh. 1955. 5.00 (ISBN 0-685-08798-0). Destiny.
--Study in Hosea. 1955. 8.00 (ISBN 0-685-08815-4). Destiny.

ANGLO-SAXON POETRY
Barnouw, Adriaan J. Anglo-Saxon Christian Poetry. LC 74-20776. 1974. Repr. of 1914 ed. lib. bdg. 12.50 (ISBN 0-8414-3291-0). Folcroft.
Kennedy, Charles W., tr. Early English Christian Poetry. 1963. pap. 5.95 (ISBN 0-19-500246-6). Oxford U Pr.
Krapp, George P., ed. The Paris Psalter & Meters of Boethius. LC 33-2302. 239p. 1932. 30.00 (ISBN 0-231-08769-1). Columbia U Pr.
--The Vercelli Book. LC 32-10861. 152p. 1932. 27.50 (ISBN 0-231-08766-7). Columbia U Pr.

ANIMAL-WORSHIP
see also Totemism
Malyala, Panduranga R. Why Cow Protection? Date not set. 1.99 (ISBN 0-938924-01-X). Sri Shirdi Sai.
Micah Publications Editors, et al. Haggadah for the Liberated Lamb. LC 84-43165. (Illus.). 96p. (Orig.). 1985. pap. 8.95 (ISBN 0-916288-19-6). Micah Pubns.
Wilcox, Tamara. Bats, Cats, & Sacred Cows. LC 77-10834. (Myth, Magic & Superstition). (Illus.). 1977. PLB 14.65 (ISBN 0-8172-1026-1). Raintree Pubs.
Wood, J. G. Animals in the Bible: A Description of Their Meaning, Importance, Uses, Symbolical Value, 3 vols. (Illus.). 670p. 1986. Repr. Set. 337.45 (ISBN 0-89901-278-7). Found Class Reprints.

ANIMALS (IN RELIGION, FOLK-LORE, ETC.)
see Animal-Worship

ANIMISM
see also Bon (Tibetan Religion); Fetishism; Idealism; Idols and Images; Soul
Roth, Walter E. An Inquiry into the Animism & Folklore of the Guiana Indians. LC 16-9897. (Landmarks in Anthropology Ser). Repr. of 1915 ed. 23.00 (ISBN 0-384-52130-4). Johnson Repr.

ANNUALS
see Gift-Books (Annuals, etc.)

ANNULMENT OF MARRIAGE
see Marriage–Annulment

ANOINTINGS
see Unction

ANSELM, SAINT, ARCHBISHOP OF CANTERBURY, 1033-1109
Anselm Of Canterbury. Anselm of Canterbury: Vol. I, Monologion, Proslogion, Debate with Gaunilo, & a Meditation on Human Redemption. Hopkins, Jasper & Richardson, Herbert, trs. LC 74-19840. 161p. 1974. 39.95x (ISBN 0-88946-000-0). E Mellen.
--Anselm of Canterbury: Vol. II, Philosophical Fragments; De Grammatico; on Truth; Freedom of Choice; the Fall of the Devil; the Harmony of the Foreknowledge, the Predestination, & the Grace of God with Free Choice. Hopkins, Jasper & Richardson, Herbert, trs. LC 74-19840. 237p. 1976. 49.95x (ISBN 0-88946-250-X). E Mellen.
--Anselm of Canterbury: Vol. III, Two Letters Concerning Roscelin; the Incarnation of the Word; Why God Became a Man; the Virgin Conception & Original Sin; the Procession of the Holy Spirit; Three Letters on the Sacraments. Hopkins, Jasper & Richardson, Herbert, trs. LC 74-19840. 265p. 1976. 39.95x (ISBN 0-88946-350-6). E Mellen.
Barth, Karl. Anselm: Fides Quaerens Intellectum. Robertson, Ian W., tr. from Ger. LC 76-10795. (Pittsburgh Reprint Ser.: No. 2). 1985. text ed. 15.00 (ISBN 0-915138-75-1). Pickwick.
Charlesworth, M. J., tr. St. Anselm's Proslogion. LC 78-63300. 1979. text ed. 17.95x (ISBN 0-268-01696-8); pap. text ed. 6.95x (ISBN 0-268-01697-6). U of Notre Dame Pr.
Chibnall, Marjorie, et al, eds. Anselm Studies: An Occasional Journal. 273p. (Orig.). 1983. lib. bdg. 35.00x (ISBN 0-527-03662-5). Kraus Intl.
Eadmer. The Life of St. Anselm, Archbishop of Canterbury. Southern, R. W., ed. & tr. from Latin. (Oxford Medieval Texts Ser.). 1972. 49.00x (ISBN 0-19-822225-4). Oxford U Pr.
Evans, G. Rosemary. Anselm & a New Generation. 1980. 32.50x (ISBN 0-19-826651-0). Oxford U Pr.
Evans, Gillian, ed. St. Anselm, Archbishop of Canterbury: A Concordance to the Works of St. Anselm, 4 vols. LC 82-48973. (Orig.). 1985. Set. lib. bdg. 400.00 (ISBN 0-527-03661-7). Kraus Intl.
Hartshorne, Charles. Anselm's Discovery: A Re-Examination of the Ontological Proof for God's Existence. LC 65-20278. 349p. 1973. 23.95 (ISBN 0-87548-216-3); pap. 11.95 (ISBN 0-87548-217-1). Open Court.
Henry, D. P. Commentary on 'De Grammatico' The Historical-Logical Dimensions of a Dialogue of St. Anselm's. LC 73-86092. (Synthese Historical Library: No. 8). 200p. 1973. lib. bdg. 66.00 (ISBN 90-277-0382-5, Pub. by Reidel Holland). Kluwer Academic.
Hopkins, Jasper. Anselm of Canterbury: Vol. IV, Hermeneutical & Textual Problems in the Complete Treatises of St. Anselm. LC 74-19840. 202p. 1976. 49.95x (ISBN 0-88946-551-7). E Mellen.
--A Companion to the Study of St. Anselm. LC 72-79097. 278p. 1972. 13.95x (ISBN 0-8166-0657-9). U of Minn Pr.
--A New Interpretive Translation of St. Anselm's Monologion & Proslogion. LC 86-70086. xiv, 188p. Date not set. text ed. 25.00x (ISBN 0-938060-33-3); pap. text ed. 10.00x (ISBN 0-938060-34-1). Banning Pr.
Hopkins, Jasper, ed. Anselm of Canterbury, 4 vols. Richardson, Herbert, tr. from Lat. LC 74-19840. 1919. Set. 149.95x (ISBN 0-88946-977-6). E Mellen.
Schufreider, Gregory. An Introduction to Anselm's Argument. 131p. 1978. 29.95 (ISBN 0-87722-133-2); pap. 14.95 (ISBN 0-87722-129-4). Temple U Pr.
Southern, R. W. & Schmitt, F. S., eds. Memorials of Saint Anselm, Vol. I. (Auctores Britannici Medii Aevi). 370p. 1969. 22.50 (ISBN 0-85672-693-1, Pub. by British Acad). Longwood Pub Group.
Welch, A. C. Anselm & His Work. 1979. Repr. of 1901 ed. lib. bdg. 30.00 (ISBN 0-8492-2965-0). R West.

ANTHEMS
Here are entered works composed in the form of the anthem.
see also Sacred Vocal Music
Jackson, Francis, ed. Anthems for Choirs One: Fifty Anthems for Mixed Voices. 1973. pap. 8.75 (ISBN 0-19-353214-X). Oxford U Pr.

Ledger, Philip, ed. Anthems for Choirs Three: Twenty-Four Anthems for Sopranos & Altos, Three or More Parts. 1973. pap. text ed. 8.75x (ISBN 0-19-353242-5). Oxford U Pr.

--Anthems for Choirs Two: Twenty-Four Anthems for Sopranos & Altos, Unison & Two-Part. 1973. pap. text ed. 8.75x (ISBN 0-19-353240-9). Oxford U Pr.

Morris, Christopher, ed. Anthems for Choirs Four. 1976. pap. 8.75x (ISBN 0-19-353018-X). Oxford U Pr.

ANTHONY OF PADUA, SAINT, 1195-1231

O'Brien, Isidore. St. Anthony of Padua. 1976. 5.00 (ISBN 0-8198-0472-X). Dghtrs St Paul.

Stoddard, Charles W. St. Anthony, the Wonder-Worker of Padua. 2nd ed. 1971. pap. 2.50 (ISBN 0-89555-039-3). TAN Bks Pubs.

ANTHROPOLOGY, BIBLICAL

see Man (Theology)

ANTHROPOLOGY, PHILOSOPHICAL

see Philosophical Anthropology

ANTHROPOLOGY, THEOLOGICAL

see Man (Theology)

ANTHROPOMORPHISM

Nunn, T. Percy. Anthropomorphism & Physics. 1977. lib. bdg. 59.95 (ISBN 0-8490-1438-7). Gordon Pr.

ANTHROPOSOPHY

see also Karma; Reincarnation; Theosophy

Adams, George. Physical & Ethereal Spaces. (Illus.). 71p. 1978. pap. 5.00 (ISBN 0-85440-328-0, Pub. by Steinerbooks). Anthroposophic.

Belyi, Andre I. Anthroposophy & Russia. 1983. pap. 5.00 (ISBN 0-916786-69-2). St George Bk Serv.

Beredene, Jocelyn. What Difference Did the Deed of Christ Make? 1979. pap. 1.50 (ISBN 0-88010-103-2). Anthroposophic.

Blattman, George. The Sun. Tr. of Die Sonne. 240p. (Orig.). 1985. pap. text ed. 16.95 (ISBN 0-88010-148-2). Anthroposophic.

Bockemuhl, Jochen, et al. Toward a Phenomenology of the Etheric World: Investigations into the Life of Nature & Man. Gardner, Malcolm, et al, eds. Meeks, John, tr. from Ger. (Illus.). 200p. (Orig.). 1985. pap. 16.95 (ISBN 0-88010-115-6). Anthroposophic.

Bott, Victor. Anthroposophical Medicine: Spiritual Science & the Art of Healing. 208p. (Orig.). 1984. pap. 8.95 (ISBN 0-7225-0958-8). Thorsons Pubs.

Cusick, Lois. Waldorf Parenting Handbook: Useful Information on Child Development & Education from Anthroposophical Sources. 2nd, rev. ed. 1985. pap. 9.95 (ISBN 0-916786-75-7). St George Bk Serv.

Easton, Stewart. The Way of Anthroposophy: Answers to Modern Questions. 102p. (Orig.). 1986. pap. 7.00 (ISBN 0-85440-464-3, Pub. by Steinerbooks). Anthroposophic.

Easton, Stewart C. Man & World in the Light of Anthroposophy. Rev. ed. 536p. 1982. pap. 11.95 (ISBN 0-88010-006-0). Anthroposophic.

--Man & World in the Light of Anthroposophy. 2nd ed. 543p. 1982. pap. 21.00 (ISBN 0-88010-077-X). Anthroposophic.

Eccles, Sir John. The Human Mystery. LC 78-12095. (Illus.). 1978. 25.00 (ISBN 0-387-09016-9). Springer-Verlag.

Edmunds, L. Francis. Anthroposophy as a Healing Force. 14p. pap. 2.25 (ISBN 0-88010-037-0, Pub.by Rudolf Steiner Pr). Anthroposophic.

Education of the Child. 2nd ed. Tr. of Die Erziehung des Kindes vom Gesichtspunkee. 50p. 1985. pap. 5.95 (ISBN 0-88010-133-4). Anthroposophic.

Ege, Arvia M. The Experience of the Christmas Foundation Meeting, 1923. 14p. 1981. pap. 2.50 (ISBN 0-932776-03-5). Adonis Pr.

Emmichoven, F. W. The Anthroposophical Understanding of the Soul. Schwarzkopf, Friedemann, tr. from Ger. 170p. (Orig.). 1983. pap. 8.95 (ISBN 0-88010-019-2). Anthroposophic.

Frankl-Lundborg, Otto. What Is Anthroposophy? Wetzl, Joseph, tr. 1977. pap. 2.95 (ISBN 0-916786-14-5). St George Bk Serv.

Grosse, Rudolf. The Christmas Foundation Meeting: Beginning of a New Cosmic Age. Collis, Johanna, tr. from Ger. Tr. of Die Weihnachtstagung als Zeitenwende. 158p. (Orig.). 1984. pap. 14.00 (ISBN 0-919924-23-9, Steiner Bk Ctr). Anthroposophic.

Harwood, A. C. Recovery of Man in Childhood. 2nd ed. (Illus.). 212p. 1981. pap. 8.95 (ISBN 0-88010-001-X). Anthroposophic.

Husemann, Friedrich, et al. The Anthroposophical Approach to Medicine, Vol. 1. (Illus.). 411p. 1983. 30.00 (ISBN 0-88010-031-1). Anthroposophic.

Jocelyn, John & Jocelyn, Beredene. Beneficent Rule of Destiny. 1983. pap. 1.50 (ISBN 0-916786-73-0). St George Bk Serv.

Jones, D. Faulkner. The English Spirit. 2nd ed. 235p. 1982. 13.95 (ISBN 0-85440-388-4, Pub. by Steinerbooks); pap. 9.95 (ISBN 0-85440-389-2). Anthroposophic.

Konig, Karl. Brothers & Sisters. 96p. 1984. pap. 7.95 (ISBN 0-88010-112-1). Anthroposophic.

Kranich, Ernst M. Planetary Influences Upon Plants: Cosmological Botany. 184p. (Orig.). pap. 12.50 (ISBN 0-938250-20-5). Anthroposophic.

Mees, L. F. Blessed by Illness. 248p. (Orig.). 1983. pap. 10.95 (ISBN 0-88010-054-0). Anthroposophic.

Richter, Gottfried. Art & Human Consciousness. Frohlich, Margaret & Channer, Burley, trs. from Ger. (Illus.). 300p. (Orig.). 1985. 30.00 (ISBN 0-88010-108-3). Anthroposophic.

Roboz, Steven, ed. The Holy Grail: From the Works of Rudolf Steiner. 2nd ed. 1984. pap. 4.75 (ISBN 0-919924-24-7, Steiner Bk Ctr). Anthroposophic.

Sherrard, Philip. The Eclipse of Man & Nature: Spiritual Anthroposophy. 160p. (Orig.). Date not set. pap. 8.95 (Lindisfarne Pr). Inner Tradit.

Social Understanding Through Spiritual Scientific Knowledge. Steiner, Rudolf. 20p. 1982. pap. 2.00 (ISBN 0-88010-075-3). Anthroposophic.

Spirit in Matter: A Scientist's Answer to the Bishop Quevies. 1948. 10.00 (ISBN 0-906492-16-5, Pub. by Kolisko Archives). St George Bk Serv.

Spock, Marjorie. Reflections on Community Building. 1984. pap. 3.25 (ISBN 0-916786-67-6). St George Bk Serv.

--To Look on Earth with More Than Mortal Eyes. 1985. pap. 5.95 (ISBN 0-916786-79-X). St George Bk Serv.

Steiner, Rudolf. Ahrimanic Deception. 20p. (Orig.). 1985. pap. 2.95 (ISBN 0-88010-146-6). Anthroposophic.

--Anthroposophy: An Introduction. Burnett, V. Compton, tr. from Ger. 130p. 1983. pap. 7.00 (ISBN 0-85440-387-6, Pub by Steinerbooks). Anthroposophic.

--Anthroposophy & Christianity. Tr. of Christus und die menschliche Seele, Ueber den sinn deslebens, Theosophische Moral, Anthroposophie und Christentum, German. 26p. (Orig.). 1985. pap. 2.95 (ISBN 0-88010-149-0). Anthroposophic.

--Apocalypse of St. John. 2nd ed. Tr. of Die Apokalypse des Johannes. 227p. 1985. pap. 12.95 (ISBN 0-88010-131-8). Anthroposophic.

--The Arts & Their Mission. Monges & Moore, trs. from German. 125p. 1986. pap. 8.95 (ISBN 0-88010-154-7). Anthroposophic.

--At the Gates of Spiritual Science. Tr. of Vor dem Tore der Theosophie. 160p. 1986. 20.00 (ISBN 0-88010-224-1); pap. 8.95 (ISBN 0-88010-135-0). Anthroposophic.

--Awakening to Community. Spock, Marjorie, tr. from Ger. LC 74-81153. 178p. 1975. 14.00 (ISBN 0-910142-61-0). Anthroposophic.

--Balance in World & Man: Lucifer & Ahriman. pap. 2.75 (ISBN 0-919924-05-0). Anthroposophic.

--The Being of Man & His Future Evolution. Wehrle, Pauline, tr. from Ger. 148p. 1981. 18.00 (ISBN 0-85440-402-3, Pub. by Steinerbooks); pap. 11.95 (ISBN 0-85440-405-8). Anthroposophic.

--The Boundaries of Natural Science. Amrine, Frederick, tr. from Ger. LC 83-9943. 144p. 1983. 14.95 (ISBN 0-88010-018-4). Anthroposophic.

--Building Stones for an Understanding of the Mystery of Golgotha. 240p. 1972. 10.95 (ISBN 0-85440-263-2). Anthroposophic.

--Christ & the Human Soul. 4th ed. 81p. 1984. pap. 6.50 (ISBN 0-85440-013-3, Pub. by Steinerbooks). Anthroposophic.

--Christianity in Human Evolution. 1979. pap. 2.00 (ISBN 0-88010-095-8). Anthroposophic.

--The Christmas Foundation Meeting of the Anthroposophical Society. Seddon, R. G., ed. 37p. (Orig.). 1980. pap. 3.00 (ISBN 0-88010-094-X, Pub. by Steinerbooks). Anthroposophic.

--The Constitution of the School of Spiritual Science. 2nd ed. Adams, George & Rudel, Joan, trs. from Ger. 78p. 1980. pap. 5.00x (ISBN 0-88010-039-7, Pub. by Anthroposophical Society London). Anthroposophic.

--Curative Eurythmy. 132p. 1984. pap. 9.95 (ISBN 0-85440-398-1, Pub. by Steinerbooks). Anthroposophic.

--The Dead Are with Us. Osmond, D. S., tr. from Ger. 32p. 1973. pap. 2.95 (ISBN 0-85440-274-8, Pub. by Steinerbooks). Anthroposophic.

--The Deed of Christ & the Opposing Spiritual Powers Lucifer, Ahriman, Mephistopheles, Asuras. 2.75 (ISBN 0-919924-02-6, Pub by Steiner Book Centre Canada). Anthroposophic.

--Deeper Secrets in Human History in the Light of the Gospel of St. Matthew. 2nd ed. Tr. of Die tieferen Geheimmnisse des Menschheitswerdens im Lichte der Evangelien. 60p. 1985. pap. 6.95 (ISBN 0-88010-132-6). Anthroposophic.

--Discussions with Teachers. Fox, Helen, tr. from Ger. 166p. 1983. pap. 11.00 (ISBN 0-85440-404-X, Pub by Steinerbooks). Anthroposophic.

--Esoteric Christianity & the Mission of Christian Rosenkreutz. 2nd ed. Wehrle, Pauline, tr. from Ger. 200p. 1984. pap. 9.95 (ISBN 0-88440-413-7, Pub. by Steinerbooks). Anthroposophic.

--The Etherisation of the Blood: The Entry of the Etheric Christ into the Evolution of the Earth. 4th ed. Freeman, Arnold & Osmond, D. S., trs. from Ger. 42p. 1985. pap. 3.95 (ISBN 0-85440-248-9, Pub. by Steinerbooks). Anthroposophic.

--Exoteric & Esoteric Christianity. 17p. 1983. pap. 3.00 (ISBN 0-919924-20-4). Anthroposophic.

--Facing Karma. 1977. 2.00 (ISBN 0-910142-64-5). Anthroposophic.

--The Festival & Their Meaning. 399p. 1981. 21.00 (ISBN 0-85440-370-1, Pub. by Steinerbooks); pap. 15.00 (ISBN 0-85440-380-9). Anthroposophic.

--The Fifth Gospel. Davy, C. & Osmond, D. S., trs. from Ger. Tr. of Aus der Akkasha Forschung: Das Fuenfte Evangelium. 168p. 1985. pap. 9.95 (ISBN 0-85440-520-8, Pub. by Steinerbooks). Anthroposophic.

--The Foundation Stone. 72p. 1979. pap. 5.50x (ISBN 0-85440-346-9, Pub. by Steinerbooks). Anthroposophic.

--The Four Mystery Plays. Bittleston, Adam, tr. from Ger. 512p. (Orig.). 1982. pap. text ed. 16.00 (ISBN 0-85440-403-1). Anthroposophic.

--From Buddha to Christ. Church, Gilbert, ed. Tr. of Das Esoterische Christentum & die geistige Fuehrung der Menschheit. 103p. 1987. pap. 5.95 (ISBN 0-88010-178-4). Anthroposophic.

--Fruits of Anthroposophy. Meuss, Anna R., tr. from Ger. Tr. of Anthroposophie, ihre Erkenntniswurzeln und Lebensfruechete. 76p. 1986. 20.00 (ISBN 0-88010-203-9); pap. 7.95 (ISBN 0-88010-202-0). Anthroposophic.

--Fundamentals of Therapy: An Extension of the Art of Healing Through Spiritual Knowledge. 4th ed. Frommer, Eva A. & Josephson, J. M., trs. from Ger. Tr. of Grundlegendes fur eine Erweiterung der Heilkunst nach geisteswissenschaftlichen Erkenntnissen. 128p. 1983. pap. 7.95 (ISBN 0-85440-423-6, Pub. by Steinerbooks). Anthroposophic.

--Gospel of St. Luke. 1964. 14.95 (ISBN 0-85440-042-7). Anthroposophic.

--Gospel of St. Matthew. 2nd ed. Tr. of Matthaeus-Evangelium. 230p. 1985. pap. 10.95 (ISBN 0-88010-134-2). Anthroposophic.

--Health & Illness, Vol. 1. St. Goar, Maria, tr. from German. (Illus.). 155p. (Orig.). 14.00 (ISBN 0-88010-028-1); pap. 8.95 (ISBN 0-88010-000-1). Anthroposophic.

--How Can Mankind Find the Christ Again? 2nd ed. Hahn, Galdys, ed. Dawson, Frances E. & Hahn, Gladys, trs. from Ger. 1984. 15.00 (ISBN 0-88010-078-8); pap. 8.95 (ISBN 0-88010-079-6). Anthroposophic.

--The Human Soul in Relation to World Evolution. Stebbing, Rita, tr. from Ger. LC 84-21703. 180p. (Orig.). 1985. 16.00 (ISBN 0-88010-114-8); pap. 9.95 (ISBN 0-88010-113-X). Anthroposophic.

--Inner Impulses of Human Evolution: The Mexican Mysteries & the Knights Templar. Church, Gilbert, et al, eds. 180p. (Orig.). 1984. 16.00 (ISBN 0-88010-119-9); pap. 9.95 (ISBN 0-88010-118-0). Anthroposophic.

--Jesus & Christ. 1976. pap. 2.00 (ISBN 0-910142-74-2). Anthroposophic.

--Knowledge of the Higher Worlds & Its Attainment. 3rd ed. Monges, Henry B., tr. 1969. pap. 6.95 (ISBN 0-910142-20-3). Anthroposophic.

--The Life, Nature & Cultivation of Anthroposophy. Adams, George, tr. from Ger. 68p. 1976. pap. 5.95 (ISBN 0-85440-061-3, Pub. by Steinerbooks). Anthroposophic.

--Macrocosm & Microcosm. Tr. of Makrokosmos und Mikosmos. Seelenfragen, Lebensfragen, Geistesfragen. 205p. 1986. 20.00 (ISBN 0-88010-201-2); pap. 10.95 (ISBN 0-88010-200-4). Anthroposophic.

--Manifestations of Karma. 3rd ed. 262p. 1984. pap. 10.95 (ISBN 0-317-18543-8, Pub. by Steinerbooks). Anthroposophic.

--Man's Being, His Destiny & World Evolution. 3rd ed. McArthur, Erna & Riggins, William, trs. from Ger. 123p. (Orig.). 1984. pap. 7.95 (ISBN 0-88010-090-7). Anthroposophic.

--Metamorphoses of the Soul: Path of Experience, 2 vols. 2nd ed. Davy, Charles & Von Arnim, Christian, trs. from Ger. 1983. Set. pap. 12.00 ea. (ISBN 0-317-13485-X). Vol. 1: 171 pgs (ISBN 0-85440-414-7, Pub. by Steinerbooks). Vol. 2: 150 pgs (ISBN 0-85440-415-5, Pub. by Steinerbooks). Anthroposophic.

--The Michael Mystery: Letters to the Members of the Anthroposophical Society with Their Accompanying Guidelines. Spock, Marjorie, tr. 1985. 15.95 (ISBN 0-916786-77-3); pap. 9.95 (ISBN 0-317-30085-7). St George Bk Serv.

--On the Life of the Soul. O'Neil, Gisela & Howard, Alan, eds. Borton, Samuel L., tr. 18p. (Orig.). 1985. pap. 3.50 (ISBN 0-88010-076-1). Anthroposophic.

--Origins of Natural Science. Tr. of Der Entstehungsoment der Naturwissenschaft in der Weltgeschichte und ihre seitherige Entwickelung. 159p. (Orig.). 1985. 20.00 (ISBN 0-317-38883-5); pap. 9.95 (ISBN 0-88010-140-7). Anthroposophic.

--Philosophy, Cosmology & Religion: Ten Lectures. Easton, Stewart C., et al, eds. 180p. (Orig.). 1984. 16.00 (ISBN 0-88010-109-1); pap. 9.95 (ISBN 0-88010-110-5). Anthroposophic.

--Philosophy of Freedom. Wilson, Michael, tr. from Ger. 226p. 1973. pap. 7.95 (ISBN 0-910142-52-1). Anthroposophic.

--Prayer. 1966. pap. 2.00 (ISBN 0-910142-30-0). Anthroposophic.

--Prayers for Mothers & Children. 3rd. ed. Hersey, Eileen V. & Von Arnim, Christian, trs. from Ger. 76p. 1983. pap. 5.00 (ISBN 0-85440-195-4, Pub. by Steinerbooks). Anthroposophic.

--Preparing for the Sixth Epoch. Orig. Title: How Anthroposophic Groups Prepare for the Sixth Epoch. 1976. pap. 2.00 (ISBN 0-910142-72-6). Anthroposophic.

--The Principle of Spiritual Economy. Mollenhauer, Peter, tr. Tr. of Das Prinzip der Spirituellen Okonomie im Zusammenhang mit Wiederverkorperungsfragen. 220p. 1986. 20.00 (ISBN 0-88010-163-6); pap. 9.95 (ISBN 0-88010-162-8). Anthroposophic.

--The Significance of Spiritual Research for Moral Action. Cottrell, Alan P., tr. from Ger. 17p. 1981. pap. 2.00 (ISBN 0-88010-101-6). Anthroposophic.

--The Social Future. new rev. ed. Monges, Henry B., tr. from Ger. LC 72-87742. 151p. 1972. pap. text ed. 7.95 (ISBN 0-910142-34-3). Anthroposophic.

--Spiritual Science As a Foundation for Social Forms. Howard, Alan, ed. St. Goar, Maria, tr. from Ger. Tr. of Geisteswissenschaft als Erkenntnis der Grundimpulse sozialer Gestaltung. 300p. 1986. 30.00 (ISBN 0-88010-153-9); pap. 20.00 (ISBN 0-88010-152-0). Anthroposophic.

--The Stages of Higher Knowledge. 64p. 1974. pap. 4.50 (ISBN 0-910142-37-8). Anthroposophic.

--Temple Legend. Wood, John, tr. from German. 1986. 28.00 (ISBN 0-85440-780-4, Pub by Steinerbooks). Anthroposophic.

--Three Lectures on the Mystery Dramas. Pusch, Ruth, tr. from Ger. 101p. (Orig.). 1983. pap. 7.95 (ISBN 0-88010-060-5). Anthroposophic.

--True & False Paths in Spiritual Investigation. Parker, A. H., tr. from Ger. Tr. of Das Initiaten-Bewusstsein. Die wahren und die falschen Wege der geistigen Forschung. 222p. 1986. pap. 10.95 (ISBN 0-88010-135-0). Anthroposophic.

--Truth, Beauty & Goodness. 1986. pap. 1.50 (ISBN 0-916786-86-2). St George Bk Serv.

--Wonders of the World, Ordeals of the Soul, Revelations of the Spirit. Lenn, Dorothy, et al, trs. from Ger. 190p. 1983. pap. 11.00 (ISBN 0-85440-363-9, Pub by Steinerbooks). Anthroposophic.

--World History in the Light of Anthroposophy: And As a Foundation for Knowledge of the Human Spirit. new ed. Adams, George & Adams, Mary, trs. from Ger. 159p. 1977. 12.50 (ISBN 0-85440-315-9); pap. 9.00 (ISBN 0-85440-316-7). Anthroposophic.

--The Year Participated. Barfield, Owen, tr. from Ger. Tr. of Anthroposophischer Seelenkalender. 52p. 1986. pap. 7.95 (ISBN 0-85440-790-1, Pub. by Steinerbooks). Anthroposophic.

Unger, Carl. Life Forces from Anthroposophy. 1982. pap. 1.95 (ISBN 0-916786-63-3). St George Bk Serv.

Witzenmann, Herbert. Beppe Assenza. (Illus.). 160p. 1979. 29.95 (ISBN 0-85440-340-X, Pub. by Steinerbooks). Anthroposophic.

Wolff, Otto, ed. The Anthroposophical Approach to Medicine, Vol. 2. Karnow, G., tr. from Ger. Tr. of Das Bild des Menschen als Grundlage der Heilkunst. 1987. 40.00 (ISBN 0-88010-174-1). Anthroposophic.

Zeylmans-Van-Emmichoven, F. W. The Foundation Stone. 118p. 1983. pap. 5.95 (ISBN 0-85440-399-X). Anthroposophic.

ANTI-CATHOLICISM

see also Catholic Church–Doctrinal and Controversial Works; Nativism

Hughes, John & Breckinridge, John. A Discussion: Is the Roman Catholic Religion Inimical to Civil or Religious Liberty? Is the Presbyterian Religion Inimical to Civil or Religious Liberty? LC 76-122167. (Civil Liberties in American History Ser). 1970. Repr. of 1836 ed. lib. bdg. 75.00 (ISBN 0-306-71979-7). Da Capo.

Paz, D. G. The Priesthoods & Apostasies of Pierce Connally: A Study of Victorian Conversion & Anticatholicism. (Studies in American Religion: Vol. 18). 418p. 1986. lib. bdg. 69.95x (ISBN 0-88946-662-9). E Mellen.

Sanchez, Jose M. Anticlericalism: A Brief History. LC 72-3504. 256p. 1973. text ed. 14.95 (ISBN 0-268-00471-4). U of Notre Dame Pr.

Schwartz, Michael. The Persistent Prejudice: Anti-Catholicism in America. LC 84-60746. 240p. 1984. pap. 6.95 (ISBN 0-87973-715-8, 715). Our Sunday Visitor.

ANTI-CLERICALISM

Partin, Malcolm O. Waldeck-Rousseau, Combes, & the Church: The Politics of Anticlericalism, 1899-1905. LC 74-76167. pap. 77.80 (ISBN 0-317-20441-6, 2023432). Bks Demand UMI.

Sanchez, Jose M. Anticlericalism: A Brief History. LC 72-3504. 256p. 1973. text ed. 14.95 (ISBN 0-268-00471-4). U of Notre Dame Pr.

Ullman, Joan C. Tragic Week: A Study of Anticlericalism in Spain, 1875-1912. LC 67-27082. 1968. 27.50x (ISBN 0-674-90240-8). Harvard U Pr.

ANTI-REFORMATION

see Counter-Reformation

ANTICHRIST

Apostasy & the Antichrist. 46p. (Orig.). 1978. pap. 2.00 (ISBN 0-317-30297-3). Holy Trinity.

Archpriest Boris Molchanov. Antikhrist. Tr. of The Antichrist. 24p. 1976. pap. 1.00 (ISBN 0-317-29128-9). Holy Trinity.

Benson, John L. Who Is the Antichrist? LC 78-2426. 1978. pap. 2.50 (ISBN 0-87227-058-0). Reg Baptist.

Bloomfield, Arthur E. How to Recognize the Antichrist. LC 75-29424. 160p. 1975. pap. 3.95 (ISBN 0-87123-225-1, 210225). Bethany Hse.

Bousset, Wilhelm. The Antichrist Legend: A Chapter in Christian & Jewish Folklore. LC 79-8095. (Satanism Ser.). 344p. Repr. of 1896 ed. 37.50 (ISBN 0-404-18406-5). AMS Pr.

Bunyan, John. Ruin of Antichrist. pap. 1.95 (ISBN 0-685-19842-1). Reiner.

Burr, William H. Revelations of Antichrist: Concerning Christ & Christianity. LC 79-161340. (Atheist Viewpoint Ser). 448p. 1972. Repr. of 1879 ed. 29.00 (ISBN 0-405-03801-1). Ayer Co Pubs.

Burris, W. H. Revelations of Antichrist. 59.95 (ISBN 0-8490-0950-2). Gordon Pr.

Culleton, R. Gerald. The Reign of AntiChrist. 1974. pap. 6.00 (ISBN 0-89555-047-4). TAN Bks Pubs.

Dilsaver, Paul. Encounters with the Antichrist. 4.00 (ISBN 0-317-52034-2). Jelm Mtn.

Emmerson, Richard K. Antichrist in the Middle Ages: A Study of Medieval Apocalypticism, Art, & Literature. LC 79-3874. (Illus.). 320p. 1981. 35.00x (ISBN 0-295-95716-6). U of Wash Pr.

Gordon, Gregory S. Impeach the Anti-Christ. 96p. (Orig.). 1986. pap. 4.95 (ISBN 0-9616971-5-6). Dynamic Reflections.

Hippolytus, Saint. Antichrist. 1979. pap. 2.95 (ISBN 0-686-26145-3). Eastern Orthodox.

Huchede, P. History of Antichrist. 1976. pap. 2.00 (ISBN 0-89555-100-4). TAN Bks Pubs.

Lindsay, Gordon. America, Russia, & the Antichrist, Vol. 4. (Daniel Ser.). 0.95 (ISBN 0-89985-051-0). Christ Nations.

--The Antichrist & His Forerunner. (End of the Age Ser.: Vol. 2). 1.25 (ISBN 0-89985-068-5). Christ Nations.

--The Antichrist's Rise to Power. (End of the Age Ser.: Vol. 3). 1.25 (ISBN 0-89985-069-3). Christ Nations.

--The Rise of the Antichrist. (Revelation Ser.). 1.25 (ISBN 0-89985-042-1). Christ Nations.

--Signs of the Coming of the Antichrist. (End of the Age Ser.: Vol. 1). 1.25 (ISBN 0-89985-067-7). Christ Nations.

--Will the Antichrist Come Out of Russia? (Prophecy Ser.). 1.25 (ISBN 0-89985-066-9). Christ Nations.

Mains, David R. The Rise of the Religion of Anti-Christism. Markham, Judith, ed. 1985. 9.95 (ISBN 0-310-34830-7, Pub. by Zondervan Bks). Zondervan.

--The Truth about the Lie. 128p. 1987. pap. 4.95 (ISBN 0-310-34831-5). Zondervan.

Miceli, Vincent. The Antichrist. 14.95 (ISBN 0-8158-0395-8). Chris Mass.

Miceli, Vincent P. Women Priests & Other Fantasies. LC 80-66294. 1985. 19.95 (ISBN 0-8158-0423-7). Chris Mass.

Pink, Arthur W. The Antichrist. 1980. pap. 12.00 (ISBN 0-86524-000-0, 9802). Klock & Klock.

Price, Walter K. The Coming Antichrist. 240p. 1985. pap. 6.95 (ISBN 0-87213-695-7). Loizeaux.

White, John W. The Coming World Dictator. LC 80-71003. 119p. (Orig.). 1981. pap. 2.95 (ISBN 0-87123-042-9, 200042). Bethany Hse.

ANTINOMIANISM

see also Law and Gospel

Adams, Charles F. The Antinomian Controversy. LC 74-164507. 1976. Repr. of 1892 ed. lib. bdg. 25.00 (ISBN 0-306-70290-8). Da Capo.

Adams, Charles F., ed. Antionomianism in the Colony of Massachusetts Bay, 1636-38, Including the Short Story & Documents. 1966. 26.00 (ISBN 0-8337-0010-3). B Franklin.

Steele, Daniel. A Substitute for Holiness, Or Antinomianism Revived. (The Higher Christian Life Ser.). 370p. 1985. lib. bdg. 45.00 (ISBN 0-8240-6445-3). Garland Pub.

Stoever, William K. A Faire & Easie Way to Heaven: Covenant Theology & Antinomianism in Early Massachusetts. LC 77-14851. 251p. 1978. 22.00x (ISBN 0-8195-5024-8). Wesleyan U Pr.

Wheelwright, John. John Wheelwright: His Writings, Including His Fast-Day Sermon, 1637. 1966. 24.00 (ISBN 0-8337-3763-5). B Franklin.

--John Wheelwright's Writings, Including His Fast-Day Sermon, 1637, & His Mercurius Americanus, 1645. facs. ed. LC 70-128897. (Select Bibliographies Reprint Ser). 1876. 18.00 (ISBN 0-8369-5517-X). Ayer Co Pubs.

ANTIPATHIES

see Prejudices and Antipathies

ANTIQUITIES, CHRISTIAN

see Christian Antiquities

ANTIQUITIES, CLASSICAL

see Classical Antiquities

ANTIQUITIES, ECCLESIASTICAL

see Christian Antiquities

ANTIQUITIES, GRECIAN

see Classical Antiquities; Greece–Antiquities

ANTIQUITIES, ROMAN

see Classical Antiquities; Rome (City)–Antiquities

ANTISEMITISM

see also Jews–Persecutions

Abel, Ernest L. The Roots of Anti-Semitism. LC 73-8286. 264p. 1975. 25.00 (ISBN 0-8386-1406-X). Fairleigh Dickinson.

Anti-Semitism in the Soviet Union: Its Roots & Consequences. 664p. 1984. 35.00 (ISBN 0-88464-051-5); pap. 16.95 (ISBN 0-88464-052-3). ADL.

Arendt, Hannah. Antisemitism. LC 66-22273. Orig. Title: Origins of Totalitarianism, Pt. 1. 136p. 1968. pap. 3.95 (ISBN 0-15-607810-4, HB131, Harv). HarBraceJ.

Arnold, Caroline & Silverstein, Herma. Anti-Semitism: A Modern Perspective. LC 84-16351. (Illus.). 224p. 1985. 10.79 (ISBN 0-671-49850-9). Messner.

Belth, Nathan C. A Promise to Keep: A Narrative of the American Encounter with Anti-Semitism. LC 81-40403. (Illus.). 1981. pap. 7.95 (ISBN 0-8052-0682-5). Schocken.

--A Promise to Keep: The American Encounter with Anti-Semitism. 305p. Repr. 6.95 (ISBN 0-686-95111-5). ADL.

Berger, David, ed. History & Hate: The Dimensions of Anti-Semitism. 160p. 1986. 14.95 (ISBN 0-8276-0267-7). Jewish Pubns.

Berger, Rabbi E., et al. Judaism, Zionism, & Anti-Semitism. 72p. (Orig.). 1985. pap. 2.50 (ISBN 0-935177-01-9). Palestine Focus.

Bolitho, Hector. Beside Galilee. 206p. 1981. Repr. of 1933 ed. lib. bdg. 25.00 (ISBN 0-89987-076-7). Darby Bks.

Brin, Herb. ICH Bin Ein Jude. LC 81-15256. 146p. 1983. 9.95 (ISBN 0-8246-0275-7). Jonathan David.

Broun, Heywood & Britt, George. Christians Only: A Study in Prejudice. LC 73-19688. (Civil Liberties in American History Ser). 333p. 1974. Repr. of 1931 ed. lib. bdg. 39.50 (ISBN 0-306-70599-0). Da Capo.

Busi, Frederick. The Pope of AntiSemitism: The Career & Legacy of Edouard-Adolphe Drumont. 242p. (Orig.). 1986. text ed. 26.50 (ISBN 0-8191-5594-2); pap. text ed. 12.50 (ISBN 0-8191-5595-0). U Pr of Amer.

Coudenhove-Kalergi, H. Anti-Semitism Through the Ages. 59.95 (ISBN 0-87968-649-9). Gordon Pr.

Curtis, Michael, ed. Antisemitism in the Contemporary World. LC 85-13919. 200p. 1985. 32.50x (ISBN 0-8133-0157-2). Westview.

Curtiss, John S. An Appraisal of the Protocols of Zion. LC 78-63661. (Studies in Fascism: Ideology & Practice). Repr. of 1942 ed. 12.50 (ISBN 0-404-16924-4). AMS Pr.

Cutler, Allan H. & Cutler, Helen E. The Jew As Ally of the Muslim: Medieval Roots of Anti-Semitism. LC 84-40295. 594p. 1986. text ed. 50.00 (ISBN 0-268-01190-7, 85-11909). U of Notre Dame Pr.

Dinnerstein, Leonard. Uneasy at Home: Antisemitism & the American Jewish Experience. LC 87-521. 272p. 1987. 25.00 (ISBN 0-231-06252-4). Columbia U Pr.

Dolan, Edward F., Jr. Anti-Semitism. LC 85-8820. (Illus.). 135p. 1985. PLB 11.90 (ISBN 0-531-10068-5). Watts.

Epstein, Simon. Cry of Cassandra: The Resurgence of European Anti-Semitism. Posel, Norman S., tr. from Fr. Tr. of Antisemitism Francais. 256p. 1986. 15.95 (ISBN 0-915765-13-6, Pub. by Zenith Edit); pap. 7.95 (ISBN 0-915765-14-4, Pub. by Zenith Edit). Natl Pr Inc.

Flannery, Edward. The Anguish of the Jews: Twenty-Three Centuries of Antisemitism. rev. ed. LC 85-60298. 384p. 1985. pap. 12.95 (ISBN 0-8091-2702-4). Paulist Pr.

Gade, Richard E. Historical Survey of Anti-Semitism. pap. 5.95 (ISBN 0-8010-3747-6). Baker Bk.

Gerber, David A., ed. Anti-Semitism in American History. 440p. 1986. 29.95 (ISBN 0-252-01214-3). U of Ill Pr.

Givet, Jacques. The Anti-Zionist Complex. Abel, Evelyn, tr. from Fr. LC 81-16693. Tr. of Israel et le Genocide Inacheve. 192p. 1982. 11.95 (ISBN 0-89961-019-6). SBS Pub.

Glassman, Bernard. Anti-Semitic Stereotypes Without Jews: Images of the Jews in England, 1290-1700. LC 75-16391. 218p. 1975. 22.50x (ISBN 0-8143-1545-3). Wayne St U Pr.

Glassman, Samuel. Epic of Survival: The Story of Anti-Semitism. LC 80-69018. 400p. 20.00x (ISBN 0-8197-0481-4). Bloch.

Graeber, Isacque & Britt, Steuart H. Jews in a Gentile World: The Problem of Anti-Semitism. LC 78-26329. (Illus.). 1979. Repr. of 1942 ed. lib. bdg. 32.50x (ISBN 0-313-20878-6, GRJE). Greenwood.

Grosser, Paul E. & Halpern, Edwin G. Anti-Semitism: Causes & Effects of a Prejudice. 1979. pap. 5.95 (ISBN 0-8065-0703-9). Citadel Pr.

Heller, Celia. On the Edge of Destruction: Jews in Poland Between the Two World Wars. LC 76-22646. (Illus.). 1977. 36.00x (ISBN 0-231-03819-4). Columbia U Pr.

Hentoff, Nat, ed. Black Anti-Semitism & Jewish Racism. LC 70-89955. 1970. pap. 3.75 (ISBN 0-8052-0280-3). Schocken.

Holmes, Colin. Anti-Semitism in British Society Eighteen Seventy-Six to Nineteen Thirty-Nine. LC 78-21023. 328p. 1979. text ed. 49.50x (ISBN 0-8419-0459-6). Holmes & Meier.

Israeli, Raphuel. Peace Is in the Eye of the Beholder. xxiv, 389p. 1985. text ed. 62.00 (ISBN 0-89925-077-7). Mouton.

Katz, Jacob. From Prejudice to Destruction: Anti-Semitism, 1700-1933. LC 80-14404. 398p. 1980. 27.50x (ISBN 0-674-32505-2). Harvard U Pr.

--From Prejudice to Destruction: Anti-Semitism, 1700-1933. 400p. 1982. pap. 7.95 (ISBN 0-674-32507-9). Harvard U Pr.

Lazare, Bernard. Anti-Semitism: Its History & Causes. 1982. lib. bdg. 59.95 (ISBN 0-87700-426-9). Revisionist Pr.

Lebzelter, Gisela C. Political Anti-Semitism in England 1918-1939. LC 78-16795. 222p. 1979. text ed. 49.50x (ISBN 0-8419-0426-X). Holmes & Meier.

Leo Baeck Institute Yearbook: The Jewish Questions & Antisemitism II, Vol. 21. (Leo Baeck Institute Yearbooks Ser.). (Illus.). 388p. 1976. 28.00 (ISBN 0-317-24492-2, Pub. by Secker & Warburg UK). David & Charles.

Leroy-Beaulieu, Anatole. Israel among the Nations: A Study of the Jews & Antisemitism. facsimile ed. Hellman, Frances, tr. from Fr. LC 74-27996. (Modern Jewish Experience Ser.). (Eng.). 1975. Repr. of 1904 ed. 32.00x (ISBN 0-405-06723-2). Ayer Co Pubs.

Leschnitzer, Adolf. The Magic Background of Modern Anti-Semitism. LC 55-6501. x, 236p. (Orig.). pap. text ed. 12.95 (ISBN 0-8236-8134-3). Intl Univs Pr.

Low, Alfred D. Jews in the Eyes of the Germans: From the Enlightenment to Imperial Germany. LC 79-334. (Illus.). 528p. 1979. 19.95 (ISBN 0-915980-86-X). ISHI PA.

McWilliams, Carey. A Mask for Privilege: Anti-Semitism in America. LC 78-26197. 1979. Repr. of 1948 ed. lib. bdg. 24.75x (ISBN 0-313-20880-8, MCMP). Greenwood.

Maritain, Jacques. Le Mystere d'Israel. 260p. 1965. 9.95 (ISBN 0-686-56358-1). French & Eur.

Oberman, Heiko A. The Roots of Anti-Semitism: In the Age of Renaissance & Reformation. Porter, James I., tr. from Ger. LC 83-5695. 163p. 1983. 13.95 (ISBN 0-8006-0709-0, 1-709). Fortress.

Parkes, James W. Emergence of the Jewish Problem, 1878-1939. Repr. of 1946 ed. lib. bdg. 22.50x (ISBN 0-8371-2794-7, PJPR). Greenwood.

Patterson, Charles. Anti-Semitism: The Road to the Holocaust & Beyond. 160p. 1982. 11.95 (ISBN 0-8027-6470-3). Walker & Co.

Poliakov, Leon. History of Anti-Semitism, Vol. 1: From the Time of Christ to the Court Jews. LC 65-10228. 340p. 1964. 19.50 (ISBN 0-8149-0186-7). Vanguard.

--The History of Anti-Semitism, Vol. 2: From Mohammed to the Marranos. Gerardi, Natalie, tr. from Fr. LC 65-10228. Tr. of Histoire De l'antisemitisme: De Mahomet Aux Marranes. . 399p. 1974. 19.50 (ISBN 0-8149-0701-6). Vanguard.

Potter, Irving. The Cause of Anti-Jewism in the United States. 1982. lib. bdg. 59.95 (ISBN 0-87700-394-7). Revisionist Pr.

Prager, Dennis & Telushkin, Joseph. Why the Jews? The Reason for Anti-Semitism. 224p. 1983. 14.95 (ISBN 0-671-45270-3). S&S.

The Protocols of the Learned Elders of Zion. 299p. 1986. pap. 7.00 (ISBN 0-317-53280-4). Noontide.

Quinley, Harold E. & Glock, Charles Y. Anti-Semitism in America. LC 78-20649. 1979. 11.95 (ISBN 0-02-925640-2). Free Pr.

Rappaport, Ernest A. Anti-Judaism: A Psychohistory. LC 75-36297. 312p. 1976. 12.50 (ISBN 0-9603382-0-9). Perspective Chicago.

Reinharz, Jehuda, ed. Living with Antisemitism: Modern Jewish Responses. (Tauber Institute Ser.: No. 6). 1987. 45.00 (ISBN 0-87451-388-X). U Pr of New Eng.

Runes, Dagobert D. Jew & the Cross. 1966. pap. 0.95 (ISBN 0-8065-0111-1, 216). Citadel Pr.

--Let My People Live. LC 74-75083. 84p. 1975. 6.00 (ISBN 0-8022-2141-6). Philos Lib.

Salomon, George & Feitelson, Rose. The Many Faces of Anti-Semitism. 44p. 1978. 1.50 (ISBN 0-87495-045-7). Am Jewish Comm.

Sartre, Jean-Paul. Reflexions Sur la Question Juive. 1962. pap. 3.95 (ISBN 0-685-11523-2). French & Eur.

Selznick, Gertude J. & Steinberg, Stephen. The Tenacity of Prejudice: Anti-Semitism in Contemporary America. LC 78-31365. (Univ of California Five-Year Study of Anti-Semitism). (Illus.). 1979. Repr. of 1969 ed. lib. bdg. 24.75x (ISBN 0-313-20965-0, SETP). Greenwood.

Singerman, Robert. Antisemitic Propaganda: An Annotated Bibliography & Research. LC 81-43363. (History, Political Science, International Affairs, Area Studies). 220p. 1982. lib. bdg. 73.00 (ISBN 0-8240-9270-8, SS112). Garland Pub.

Slavin, Stephen L. & Pradt, Mary A. The Einstein Syndrome: Corporate Anti-Semitism in America Today. LC 81-43767. (Illus., Orig.). 1982. lib. bdg. 26.25 (ISBN 0-8191-2370-6); pap. text ed. 11.25 (ISBN 0-8191-2371-4). U Pr of Amer.

Steinberg, Milton. A Partisan Guide to the Jewish Problem. LC 86-1509. (Brown Classics in Judaica). 312p. 1986. pap. text ed. 13.50 (ISBN 0-8191-4493-2). U Pr of Amer.

Strong, Donald S. Organized Anti-Semitism in America: The Rise of Group Prejudice During the Decade 1930-1940. LC 78-26198. 1979. Repr. of 1941 ed. lib. bdg. 22.50x (ISBN 0-313-20883-2, STOA). Greenwood.

Szajkowski, Z. An Illustrated Sourcebook of Russian Antisemitism 1881-1977, 2 vols. Vol. 1, The Nineteenth Century. 50.00x (ISBN 0-87068-347-0); Vol. 2, The Twentieth Century. 45.00x (ISBN 0-87068-348-9). Ktav.

Trachtenberg, Joshua. The Devil & the Jews: The Medieval Conception of the Jew & Its Relation to Modern Anti - Semitism. 288p. 1983. pap. 6.95 (ISBN 0-8276-0227-8, 610). Jewish Pubns.

Valentin, Hugo. Antisemitism: Historically & Critically Examined. facsimile ed. Chater, A. G., tr. LC 79-164630. (Select Bibliographies Reprint Ser.). Repr. of 1936 ed. 22.00 (ISBN 0-8369-5914-0). Ayer Co Pubs.

Weinberg, Meyer. Because They Were Jews: A History of Antisemitism. LC 86-15013. (Contributions to the Study of World History Ser.: No. 4). 300p. 1986. lib. bdg. 35.95 (ISBN 0-313-25606-3, WBJ). Greenwood.

Westreich, Budd. The Stow Affair: Anti-Semitism in the California Legislature. (Illus.). 84p. 1981. 10.00 (ISBN 0-936300-02-7). Pr Arden Park.

Wilson, Nelly. Bernard-Lazare. LC 77-82524. 1979. 47.50 (ISBN 0-521-21802-0). Cambridge U Pr.

Wilson, Stephen. Ideology & Experience: Anti-Semitism in France at the Time of the Dreyfus Affair. (Littman Library of Jewish Civilization). (Illus.). 832p. 1982. 37.50x (ISBN 0-19-710052-X). Oxford U Pr.

--Ideology & Experience: Antisemitism in France at the Time of the Dreyfus Affair. LC 81-65467. (Illus.). 832p. 1982. 60.00 (ISBN 0-8386-3037-5). Fairleigh Dickinson.

Wistrich, Robert. Hitler's Apocalypse: Jews & the Nazi Legacy. 352p. 1986. 17.95 (ISBN 0-312-38819-5). St Martin.

Yaseen, Leonard C. The Jewish Connection: To Triumph over Anti-Semitism. (Illus.). 1985. pap. 9.95 (ISBN 0-317-39020-1). Crossroad NY.

Yinger, J. Milton. Anti-Semitism: A Case Study in Prejudice & Discrimination. 80p. pap. 2.50 (ISBN 0-88464-046-9). ADL.

Zimmerman, Moshe. Wilhelm Marr: The Patriarch of Anti-Semitism. (Studies in Jewish History). 192p. 1986. 19.95x (ISBN 0-19-504005-8). Oxford U Pr.

ANTISEMITISM AND CHRISTIANITY
see Christianity and Antisemitism

ANTITHESIS (IN RELIGION, FOLK-LORE, ETC.)
see Polarity (In Religion, Folk-Lore, etc.)

ANTONIUS, SAINT, THE GREAT, ca. 250-350

Budge, A. E., tr. from Syriac. The Paradise of the Fathers, 2 vols. (Illus.). 1984. Set. pap. 25.00 (ISBN 0-913026-56-5). Vol. 1, 386 pp. Vol. 2, 352 pp. St Nectarios.

Clausen, Sophronius. St. Anthony: Doctor of the Gospel. Brady, Ignatius, tr. from Ger. LC 61-11200. Orig. Title: Antonius. 140p. pap. 2.50 (ISBN 0-8199-0458-9). Franciscan Herald.

ANXIETY
see also Fear; Peace of Mind; Worry

Coe, David K. Angst & the Abyss: The Hermeneutics of Nothingness. (Academic Ser.). 1985. 17.95 (ISBN 0-89130-862-8, 01-01-49); pap. 11.95 (ISBN 0-89130-863-6). Scholars Pr GA.

Collins, Gary. Overcoming Anxiety. 1975. pap. 2.25 (ISBN 0-88449-017-3, A324101). Vision Hse.

Jeremiah, James T. God's Answers to Our Anxieties. (Direction Bks.). 1979. pap. 1.95 (ISBN 0-8010-5083-9). Baker Bk.

Little, Gilbert. Como Vencer Tension Nerviosa. Orig. Title: Nervous Christians. 128p. (Span). 1987. pap. 3.25 (ISBN 0-8254-1443-1). Kregel.

Little, L. Gilbert. Nervous Christians. 1956. pap. 3.95 (ISBN 0-8024-5878-5). Moody.

Weatherhead, Leslie D. Prescription for Anxiety: How You Can Overcome Fear & Despair. LC 57-5284. (Festival Bks.). 1979. pap. 1.95 (ISBN 0-687-33987-1). Abingdon.

APHORISMS AND APOTHEGMS
see also Proverbs; Quotations

Gibran, Kahlil. Sand & Foam. (Illus.). 1926. 9.95 (ISBN 0-394-44369-1). Knopf.

Hall, Clement. Collection of Many Christian Experiences, Sentences, & Several Places of Scripture Improved. xxv, 51p. 1961. Repr. of 1753 ed. 5.00 (ISBN 0-86526-019-2). NC Archives.

Khan, Inayat. Sacred Readings: The Gathas. (Sufi Message of Hazrat Inayat Khan Ser.: Vol. 13). 304p. 1982. 14.95 (ISBN 90-6325-021-5, Pub. by Servire BV Netherlands). Hunter Hse.

Vaughan, Henry H. Welsh Proverbs with English Translations. LC 68-17945. (Eng. & Welsh.). 1969. Repr. of 1889 ed. 43.00x (ISBN 0-8103-3205-1). Gale.

Whiting, B. J. Proverbs in the Earlier English Drama. LC 70-86290. 1969. Repr. of 1938 ed. lib. bdg. 34.50x (ISBN 0-374-98513-8, Octagon). Hippocrene Bks.

Williams, James G. Those Who Ponder Proverbs: Aphoristic Thinking & Biblical Literature. (Bible & Literature Ser.: No. 2). 1981. text ed. 19.95x (ISBN 0-907459-02-1, Pub. by Almond Pr England); pap. text ed. 9.95x (ISBN 0-907459-03-X, Pub. by Almond Pr England). Eisenbrauns.

APHRAATES, THE PERSIAN SAGE, fl. 337-345

Gavin, Frank S. Aphraates & the Jews. LC 77-168102. (Columbia University. Contributions to Oriental History & Philology: No. 9). Repr. of 1923 ed. 12.50 (ISBN 0-404-50539-2). AMS Pr.

Haefeli, Leo. Stilmittel Bei Afrath, Dem Perischen Weisen. (Ger). 1932. 19.00 (ISBN 0-384-20710-3). Johnson Repr.

APOCALYPTIC LITERATURE

Alexander, Paul J. The Byzantine Apocalyptic Tradition. Abrahamse, Dorothy, ed. LC 82-23816. 248p. 1985. 32.50x (ISBN 0-520-04998-5). U of Cal pr.

Le Apocalypse En Francais Au XIIIE, 2 Vols. Repr. of 1900 ed. Set. 116.00 (ISBN 0-384-04215-5). Johnson Repr.

Beale, G. K. The Use of Daniel in Jewish Apocalyptic Literature & in the Relevation of St. John. 364p. (Orig.). 1985. lib. bdg. 26.00 (ISBN 0-8191-4290-5); pap. text ed. 15.25 (ISBN 0-8191-4291-3). U Pr of Amer.

Beskow, Per. Strange Tales About Jesus: A Survey of Unfamiliar Gospels. LC 82-16001. 144p. 1983. pap. 9.95 (ISBN 0-8006-1686-3, 1-1686). Fortress.

Bloomfield, Arthur. Before the Last Battle-Armageddon. 192p. 1976. pap. 3.95 (ISBN 0-87123-035-6). Bethany Hse.

Bullinger, Ethelbert W. Commentary on Revelation. LC 83-24917. 768p. 1984. 22.95 (ISBN 0-8254-2239-6). Kregel.

Burkitt, F. C. Jewish & Christian Apocalypses. (British Academy, London, Schweich Lectures on Biblical Archaeology Series, 1914). pap. 19.00 (ISBN 0-8115-1255-X). Kraus Repr.

Charles, R. H., ed. The Book of the Secrets of Enoch. 100p. pap. 11.95 (ISBN 0-88697-010-5). Life Science.

Charles, R. H., intro. by. The Apoclypse of Baruch. 1976. Repr. of 1896 ed. 39.00x (ISBN 0-685-71069-6, Regency). Scholarly.

Collins, John. Apocalyptic Imagination. 288p. 1984. 24.50x (ISBN 0-8245-0623-5). Crossroad NY.

Collins, John J. Daniel: With an Introduction to Apocalyptic Literature. Knierim, Rolf, et al, eds. (The Forms of the Old Testament Literature Ser.: Vol. XX). 160p. (Orig.). 1984. pap. 12.95 (ISBN 0-8028-0020-3). Eerdmans.

Comstock, Susan T., et al, eds. The Apocalypse of Elijah. LC 79-24788. (Society of Biblical Literature Texts & Translations). 126p. 1981. pap. 14.25 (ISBN 0-89130-372-3, 06 02 19). Scholars Pr GA.

Cox, Clyde C. Apocalyptic Commentary. 1970. 6.95 (ISBN 0-87148-011-5). Pathway Pr.

Emmerson, Richard K. Antichrist in the Middle Ages: A Study of Medieval Apocalypticism, Art, & Literature. LC 79-3874. (Illus.). 320p. 1981. 35.00x (ISBN 0-295-95716-6). U of Wash Pr.

Fiorenza, Elizabeth S. The Apocalypse. (Read & Pray Ser.). 64p. 1976. pap. 1.25 (ISBN 0-8199-0726-X). Franciscan Herald.

Gitenstein, R. Barbara. Apocalyptic Messianism & Contemporary Jewish-American Poetry. (Modern Jewish Literature & Culture Ser.). 128p. (Orig.). 1986. 39.50x (ISBN 0-88706-154-0); pap. 12.95x (ISBN 0-88706-155-9). State U NY Pr.

Glatstein, Jacob, et al. Anthology of Holocaust Literature. LC 68-19609. (Temple Bks). 1972. pap. text ed. 6.95x (ISBN 0-689-70343-0, T23). Atheneum.

Graham, Billy. Approaching Hoofbeats: The Four Horsemen of the Apocalypse. 288p. 1985. pap. 3.95 (ISBN 0-380-69921-4). Avon.

Haffert, John M. Who Is the Woman of the Apocalypse? 104p. 1982. pap. 1.95 (ISBN 0-911988-47-5). AMI Pr.

Hanson, Paul D. The Dawn of Apocalyptic: The Historical & Sociological Roots of Jewish Apocalyptic Eschatology. rev. ed. LC 79-17099. 464p. 1979. 16.95 (ISBN 0-8006-0285-4, 1-285); pap. 12.95 (ISBN 0-8006-1809-2). Fortress.

Hanson, Paul D., ed. Visionaries & Their Apocalypses. LC 83-5488. (Issues in Religion & Theology Ser.). 176p. 1983. pap. 7.95 (ISBN 0-8006-1765-7). Fortress.

Hatchell, L. F. Apocalypse: World War III, Vol. I. (Illus.). 160p. 1980. pap. 3.95x (ISBN 0-940532-02-6). AOG.

Hicks, Robert & Bewes, Richard. The Last Things. (Understanding Bible Truth Ser.). (Orig.). 1981. pap. 1.50 (ISBN 0-89840-020-1). Heres Life.

Himmelfarb, Martha. Tours of Hell: An Apocalyptic Form in Jewish & Christian Literature. LC 83-23789. 256p. 1983. 23.00x (ISBN 0-8122-7882-8). U of Pa Pr.

--Tours of Hell: An Apocalyptic Form in Jewish & Christian Literature. LC 84-48729. 208p. 1985. pap. 12.95 (ISBN 0-8006-1845-9, 1-1845). Fortress.

Kallas, James. Revelation: God & Satan in the Apocalypse. LC 73-78268. 128p. 1973. pap. 6.95 (ISBN 0-8066-1332-7, 10-5490). Augsburg.

Kik, J. M. Eschatology of Victory. 1971. pap. 8.95 (ISBN 0-87552-313-7). Presby & Reformed.

Leemhuis, F., et al. The Arabic Text of the Apocalypse of Baruch: Editied & Translated With a Parallel Translation of the Syriac Text. viii, 154p. 1986. 32.25 (ISBN 90-04-07608-5, Pub. by E J Brill). Heinman.

McGinn, Bernard. Visions of the End: Apocalyptic Traditions in the Middle Ages. LC 79-4303. (Records of Civilization XCVI). 1979. 38.00 (ISBN 0-231-04594-8). Columbia U Pr.

McGinn, Bernard, tr. Apocalyptic Spirituality. LC 79-90834. (Classics of Western Spirituality Ser.). 352p. 1979. 13.95 (ISBN 0-8091-0305-2); pap. 7.95 (ISBN 0-8091-2242-1). Paulist Pr.

Morris, Leon. Apocalyptic. 88p. 1977. pap. 4.95 (ISBN 0-8028-1455-7). Eerdmans.

Nickelsburg, George W. Jewish Literature Between the Bible & the Mishnah: A Historical & Literary Introduction. LC 80-16176. 352p. 1981. 19.95 (ISBN 0-8006-0649-3, 1-649). Fortress.

Patrides, C. A. & Wittreich, Joseph A., Jr., eds. The Apocalypse in English Renaissance Thought & Literature. LC 84-71281. 452p. (Orig.). 1985. 52.00x (ISBN 0-8014-1648-5); pap. 19.95x (ISBN 0-8014-9893-7). Cornell U Pr.

Patte, Daniel. Early Jewish Hermeneutic in Palestine. LC 75-22225. (Society of Biblical Literature. Dissertation Ser.: No. 22). Repr. of 1975 ed. 89.50 (ISBN 0-8357-9570-5, 2017666). Bks Demand UMI.

Pick, Bernhard. The Apocryphal Acts of Paul, Peter, John, Andrew, & Thomas. 376p. 1909. 19.95 (ISBN 0-912050-60-8). Open Court.

Pryse, James M. The Apocalypse Unsealed. LC 76-41124. (Illus.). 1977. pap. 4.95 (ISBN 0-685-59031-3). Sym & Sign.

Rowland, Christopher. The Open Heaven: The Study of Apocalyptic in Judaism & Early Christianity. LC 82-7409. 540p. 1982. 29.50x (ISBN 0-8245-0455-0). Crossroad NY.

Rowley, H. H. The Relevance of Apocalyptic. 3rd, rev. ed. LC 64-12221. 240p. 1980. pap. text ed. 7.95 (ISBN 0-87921-061-3). Attic Pr.

Russell, D. S. Apocalyptic: Ancient & Modern. LC 78-54561. 96p. 1978. pap. 4.25 (ISBN 0-8006-1342-2, 1-1342). Fortress.

--Between the Testaments. LC 77-74742. 176p. 1960. pap. 5.95 (ISBN 0-8006-1856-4, 1-1856). Fortress.

--Method & Message of Jewish Apocalyptic. LC 64-18683. (Old Testament Library). 464p. 1964. 19.95 (ISBN 0-664-20543-7). Westminster.

Stone, Michael E., ed. The Armenian Version of IV Ezra. LC 78-17084. 1979. 15.00 (ISBN 0-89130-287-5); pap. 10.50 (ISBN 0-89130-255-7, 210201). Scholars Pr GA.

Swedenborg, Emanuel. Apocalypse Revealed, 2 vols. LC 78-5623. 1974. Vol. 1. Vol. 2. student ed. set 11.00 (ISBN 0-87785-017-8); student ed. 12.00 ea. Vol. 1 (ISBN 0-87785-015-1). Vol. 2 (ISBN 0-87785-016-X). pap. 7.00 (ISBN 0-87785-014-3). Swedenborg.

Tickle, John. The Book of Revelation: A Catholic Interpretation of the Apocalypse. 144p. 1983. pap. 3.95 (ISBN 0-89243-195-4). Liguori Pubns.

Torrance, Thomas F. Apocalypse Today. 192p. 1960. 10.95 (ISBN 0-227-67405-7). Attic Pr.

VanderKam, James C. Enoch & the Growth of an Apocalyptic Tradition. LC 83-10134. (Catholic Biblical Quarterly Monographs: No. 16). 217p. 1984. pap. 6.50 (ISBN 0-915170-15-9). Catholic Bibl Assn.

Wicks, Henry J. The Doctrine of God in the Jewish Apocryphal & Apocalyptic Literature. Repr. of 1915 ed. 29.00x (ISBN 0-87068-149-4). Ktav.

APOLOGETICS
see also Analogy (Religion); Bible–Evidences, Authority, etc.; Catholic Church–Apologetic Works; Faith and Reason; Natural Theology; Religion and Science; Theodicy; Witness Bearing (Christianity);
also subdivision Doctrinal and Controversial works under names of particuliar denominations, and also subdivision Apologetic Works under religious denominations, e.g. Catholic Church–Apologetic Works

Agassi, Joseph. The Gentle Art of Philosophical Polemics. 304p. 1986. 28.95 (ISBN 0-912050-63-2); pap. 13.95 (ISBN 0-8126-9036-2). Open Court.

Andreyev, I. M. Pravoslavno-Khristijanskaja Apologetika. Tr. of Orthodox-Christian Apologetics. 92p. 1965. pap. text ed. 5.00 (ISBN 0-317-30249-3). Holy Trinity.

Blanchard, John. What in the World Is a Christian? 1987. pap. 6.95 (ISBN 0-310-20101-2). Zondervan.

Bush, L. Russ, ed. Classical Readings in Christian Apologetics: A. D. 100-1800. 1986. pap. 11.95 (ISBN 0-310-45641-X, 11622P). Zondervan.

Cheve, C. F. Dictionnaire des Apologistes Involontaires, 2 vols. Migne, J. P., ed. (Nouvelle Encyclopedie Theologique Ser.: Vols. 38-39). (Fr.). 1494p. Repr. of 1853 ed. lib. bdg. 189.50x (ISBN 0-89241-279-8). Caratzas.

Craig, William L. Apologetics: An Introduction. 1984. 13.95 (ISBN 0-8024-0405-7). Moody.

Dyrness, William A. Christian Apologetics in a World Community. LC 82-21383. 180p. 1983. pap. 6.95 (ISBN 0-87784-399-6). Inter-Varsity.

Geffre, Claude & Jossua, Jean-pierre, eds. True & False Universality of Christianity. (Concilium Ser.: Vol. 135). 128p. (Orig.). 1980. pap. 5.95 (ISBN 0-8164-2277-X, HarpR). Har-Row.

Geisler, Norman L. Christian Apologetics. LC 76-24706. 464p. 1976. 15.95 (ISBN 0-8010-3704-2). Baker Bk.

Green, Michael. Choose Freedom. 1987. pap. 5.95 (ISBN 0-310-46361-0). Zondervan.

Halkin, Hillel. Letters to an American Jewish Friend: A Zionist's Polemic. LC 76-58650. 246p. 1977. pap. 6.95 (ISBN 0-8276-0207-3, 402). Jewish Pubns.

Ham, Ken. The Lie: Evolution. 188p. 1987. 10.95 (ISBN 0-89051-117-9). Master Bks.

Harkness, Georgia E. The Modern Rival of Christian Faith: An Analysis of Secularism. LC 77-27000. 1978. Repr. of 1952 ed. lib. bdg. 20.50x (ISBN 0-313-20174-9, HAMR). Greenwood.

Hirshaw, Cecil F. Apology for Perfection. LC 64-22766. (Orig.). 1964. pap. 2.50x (ISBN 0-87574-138-X). Pendle Hill.

Howe, Frederic R. Challenge & Response. 176p. 1985. pap. text ed. 7.95 (ISBN 0-310-45071-3, 12375P). Zondervan.

Jackson, Wayne. Fortify Your Faith. 74p. (Orig.). 1974. pap. text ed. 2.50 (ISBN 0-932859-09-7). Apologetic Pr.

--The Mythology of Modern Geology: A Refutation of Evolution's Most Influential Argument. 45p. (Orig.). 1980. pap. 1.95 (ISBN 0-932859-13-5). Apologetic Pr.

Keith, Alexander. Christian Evidences: Fulfilled Bible Prophecy. 456p. 1984. Repr. smythe sewn 20.00 (ISBN 0-86524-181-3, 9807). Klock & Klock.

Latourelle, Rene & O'Collins, Gerald, eds. Problems & Perspectives of Fundamental Theology. 416p. 1982. pap. 12.95 (ISBN 0-8091-2466-1). Paulist Pr.

Lewis, C. S. The Pilgrim's Regress: An Allegorical Apology for Christianity, Reason, & Romanticism. LC 82-101595. pap. 55.30 (ISBN 0-317-30149-7, 2025332). Bks Demand UMI.

MacDonald, William. Cual Es la Diferencia? Orig. Title: What Is the Difference? (Span.). 112p. 1981. pap. 2.75 (ISBN 0-8254-1450-4). Kregel.

McDowell, Josh. Evidence That Demands a Verdict. rev. ed. LC 78-75041. 1979. pap. 7.95 (ISBN 0-918956-46-3). Campus Crusade.

McDowell, Josh & Bellis, Dale. Evidence Growth Guide, Vol. 1: Explaining Misconceptions about Christianity. (Truth Alive Ser.). 80p. (Orig.). 1981. 4.95 (ISBN 0-86605-018-3). Campus Crusade.

--Evidence Growth Guide, Vol. 2: Uniqueness of the Bible. 80p. (Orig.). 1981. 4.95 (ISBN 0-86605-019-1). Campus Crusade.

Mornay, Philippe de. A Work Concerning the Trewnesse of the Christian Religion. Sidney, Philip, tr. from Fr. LC 75-45384. 680p. 1976. Repr. of 1587 ed. lib. bdg. 90.00x (ISBN 0-8201-1166-X). Schol Facsimiles.

Nash, Ronald. Christianity & the Hellenistic World. (CFUC Ser.). 1986. pap. 9.95 (ISBN 0-310-45210-4, 12383P). Zondervan.

Peukert, Helmut. Science, Action, & Fundamental Theology: Toward a Theology of Communicative Action. Bohman, James, tr. from Ger. (German Social Thought Ser.). 364p. 1984. text ed. 37.50x (ISBN 0-262-16095-1). MIT Pr.

Pittenger, William N. Christian Faith & the Question of History. LC 73-79353. pap. 39.00 (2026910). Bks Demand UMI.

Ramm, Bernard. Varieties of Christian Apologetics. (Twin Brooks Ser.). pap. 5.95 (ISBN 0-8010-7610-2). Baker Bk.

Sproul, R. C., et al. Classical Apologetics: A Rational Defense of the Christian Faith & a Critique of Presuppositional Apologetics. LC 83-12372. 432p. (Orig.). 1984. pap. 12.95 (ISBN 0-310-44951-0, 12372P). Zondervan.

Tertullian. Apological Works. (Father of the Church Ser.: Vol. 10). 430p. 1950. 34.95x (ISBN 0-8132-0010-5). Cath U Pr.

Thomas, J. D. Facts & Faith: The Bible & Faith, Vol. 2. 153p. 1980. 11.95 (ISBN 0-89112-012-2, Bibl Res Pr). Abilene Christ U.

Thompson, Bert. The Global, Universal, Worldwide Flood of Noah. (That You May Believe Ser.). 45p. (Orig.). 1986. pap. 1.50 (ISBN 0-932859-02-X). Apologetic Pr.

--The History of Evolutionary Thought. 192p. (Orig.). 1981. pap. 3.50 (ISBN 0-932859-10-0). Apologetic Pr.

--The Scientific Case for Creation. (That You May Believe Ser.). 47p. (Orig.). 1985. pap. 1.50 (ISBN 0-932859-03-8). Apologetic Pr.

--Theistic Evolution. 235p. (Orig.). 1977. pap. 5.50 (ISBN 0-932859-08-9). Apologetic Pr.

Thompson, Bert & Jackson, Wayne. Essays in Apologetics, Vol. 1. 183p. 1984. pap. 4.50. Apologetic Pr.

--Essays in Apologetics, Vol. 2. 255p. 1986. pap. 4.95 (ISBN 0-932859-06-2). Apologetic Pr.

--The Revelation of God in Nature. (That You May Believe Ser.). 22p. (Orig.). 1985. pap. 1.50 (ISBN 0-932859-04-6). Apologetic Pr.

Van Til, Cornelius. Christian Apologetics. 1976. pap. 3.95 syllabus (ISBN 0-87552-477-X). Presby & Reformed.

--Defense of the Faith. 1967. pap. 6.95 (ISBN 0-87552-483-4). Presby & Reformed.

Williams, A. Lukyn. Adversus Judaeos: A Bird's-Eye View of Christian Apologiae until the Renaissance. LC 36-11257. pap. 111.50 (ISBN 0-317-29839-9, 2051943). Bks Demand UMI.

APOLOGETICS–HISTORY

Vallee, Gerard. A Study in Anti-Gnostic Polemics: Irenaeus, Hippolytus & Epiphanius. 128p. 1981. pap. text ed. 8.95x (ISBN 0-919812-14-7, Pub. by Wilfrid Laurier Canada). Humanities.

APOLOGETICS–EARLY CHURCH, ca. 30-600
see also Alexandrian School, Christian

Arnobius, Afer. Adversvs Nationes Libri Seven, Bk. 7. (Corpus Scriptorum Ecclesiasticorum Latinorum, Vol. 4). 31.00. Johnson Repr.

Athenagoras. Legatio & De Resurrectione. Schoedel, William R., ed. (Oxford Early Christian Texts Ser). 1972. 34.95x (ISBN 0-19-826808-4). Oxford U Pr.

Augustine, Saint City of God, 2 Vols. Tasker, R. V., ed. Healey, John, tr. 1973. Repr. of 1945 ed. 12.95x ea. (ISBN 0-686-66408-6, Evman). Vol. 1 (ISBN 0-460-00982-6). Vol. 2 (ISBN 0-460-00983-4). Biblio Dist.
--City of God Against the Pagans, 7 vols. (Loeb Classical Library: No. 411-417). 13.95x ea. Harvard U Pr.
Bruce, F. F. The Defence of the Gospel in the New Testament. rev. ed. LC 77-2282. 1977. pap. 4.95 (ISBN 0-8028-1024-1). Eerdmans.
Burghardt, W. J., et al, eds. Athenagoras, Embassy for the Christians, the Resurrection of the Dead. LC 56-11421. (Ancient Christian Writers Ser.: No. 23). 193p. 1956. 10.95 (ISBN 0-8091-0036-3). Paulist Pr.
--Firmicus Maternus, the Error of the Pagan Religions. (Ancient Christian Writers Ser.: No. 37). 1970. 11.95 (ISBN 0-8091-0039-8). Paulist Pr.
Dennison, William D. Paul's Two-Age Construction & Apologetics. LC 85-20272. 144p. (Orig.). 1986. lib. bdg. 19.50 (ISBN 0-8191-5011-8); pap. text ed. 8.75 (ISBN 0-8191-5012-6). U Pr of Amer.
Minucius Felix, M. Octavius. pap. 31.00 (ISBN 0-384-39070-6). Johnson Repr.
St. Augustine. City of God, Bks. 1-7. LC 63-19613. (Fathers of the Church Ser.: Vol. 8). 401p. 1950. 29.95x (ISBN 0-8132-0008-3). Cath U Pr.

APOLOGETICS–16TH CENTURY

Becon, Thomas. The Physyke of the Soule. LC 74-28831. (English Experience Ser.: No. 713). 1975. Repr. of 1549 ed. 3.50 (ISBN 90-221-0713-2). Walter J Johnson.
Taft, A. I., ed. The Apologye of Syr Thomas More. (EETS, OS: No. 180). Repr. of 1929 ed. 67.00 (ISBN 0-527-00177-5). Kraus Repr.
Wilkinson, William. A Confutation of Certaine Articles Delivered by H. Niklaes, Unto the Familye of Love. LC 72-238. (English Experience Ser.: No. 279). 200p. 1970. Repr. of 1579 ed. 22.00 (ISBN 90-221-0279-3). Walter J Johnson.

APOLOGETICS–17TH CENTURY

Birch, David. Early Reformation English Polemics. Hogg, James, ed. (Elizabethan & Renaissance Studies). 181p. (Orig.). 1983. pap. 15.00 (ISBN 0-317-40131-9, Pub by Salzburg Studies). Longwood Pub Group.
Casaubon, Meric. A Letter of Meric Casaubon to Peter du Moulin Concerning Natural Experimental Philosophie. LC 76-47045. 1976. Repr. of 1669 ed. 90.00x (ISBN 0-8201-1284-4). Schol Facsimiles.
Grotius, Hugo. True Religion Explained & Defended. Coventry, F., tr. LC 72-201. (English Experience Ser.: No. 318). 350p. 1971. Repr. of 1632 ed. 28.00 (ISBN 90-221-0318-8). Walter J Johnson.
Hooker, Thomas. The Soules Exaltation. LC 78-298. (American Puritan Writings Ser.: No. 18). Repr. of 1638 ed. 67.50 (ISBN 0-404-60818-3). AMS Pr.
--The Soules Humiliation. LC 78-293. (American Puritan Writings Ser.: No. 16). 232p. Repr. of 1640 ed. 67.50 (ISBN 0-404-60816-7). AMS Pr.
--The Soules Implantation. LC 78-297. (American Puritan Writings Ser.: No. 17). 328p. Repr. of 1640 ed. 57.50 (ISBN 0-404-60817-5). AMS Pr.
Hubert, Marie L. Pascal's Unfinished Apology. LC 70-153272. 165p. 1973. Repr. of 1952 ed. 21.50 (ISBN 0-8046-1699-X, Pub. by Kennikat). Assoc Faculty Pr.
Melnick, Ralph. From Polemics to Apologetics: Jewish-Christian Rapprochment in 17th Century Amsterdam. 104p. 1981. pap. text ed. 8.75 (ISBN 90-232-1792-6, Pub. by Van Gorcum Holland). Longwood Pub Group.
Pascal, Blaise. Pensees. Desgranges, ed. 1962. pap. 9.95 (ISBN 0-685-11485-6). French & Eur.
--Pensees. Krailsheimer, A. J., tr. (Classics Ser.). (Orig.). 1966. pap. 3.95 (ISBN 0-14-044171-9). Penguin.
--The Thoughts of Blaise Pascal. LC 78-12814. 1978. Repr. of 1961 ed. lib. bdg. 24.25 (ISBN 0-313-20530-2, PATH). Greenwood.
Taylor, Thomas. Christ Revealed. LC 79-10885. 1979. Repr. of 1635 ed. 60.00x (ISBN 0-8201-1334-4). Schol Facsimiles.

APOLOGETICS–18TH CENTURY

Priestley, Joseph. An Examination of Dr. Reid's Inquiry into the Human Mind. Wellek, Rene, ed. LC 75-11249. (British Philosophers & Theologians of the 17th & 18th Centuries Ser.). 1978. Repr. of 1774 ed. lib. bdg. 51.00 (ISBN 0-8240-1800-1). Garland Pub.
Watson, Richard. An Apology for Christianity in a Series of Letters Addressed to Edward Gibbon. Wellek, Rene, ed. Bd. with An Apology for the Bible Addressed to Thomas Paine. LC 75-25132. (British Philosophers & Theologians of the 17th & 18th Centuries Ser.). 452p. 1978. lib. bdg. 51.00 (ISBN 0-8240-1765-X). Garland Pub.

APOLOGETICS–19TH CENTURY

Alexander, Archibald. Evidences of the Authenticity, Inspiration, & Canonical Authority of the Holy Scriptures. LC 70-38431. (Religion in America, Ser. 2). 314p. 1972. Repr. of 1836 ed. 23.50 (ISBN 0-405-04052-0). Ayer Co Pubs.
Bushnell, Horace. Nature & the Supernatural As Together Constituting the One System of God. LC 70-39569. Repr. of 1858 ed. 29.50 (ISBN 0-404-01246-9). AMS Pr.
Kierkegaard, Soren. Concluding Unscientific Postscript. Swenson, D. F. & Lowrie, W., trs. (American-Scandinavian Foundation). 1941. pap. 10.50x (ISBN 0-691-01960-6). Princeton U Pr.
Norton, Andrews. Discourse on the Latest Form of Infidelity. LC 71-122660. 1971. Repr. of 1839 ed. 18.00x (ISBN 0-8046-1309-5, Pub. by Kennikat). Assoc Faculty Pr.

APOLOGETICS–20TH CENTURY

Baxter, Batsell B. I Believe Because. 1971. pap. 8.95 (ISBN 0-8010-0548-5). Baker Bk.
Bell, Bernard I., ed. Affirmations, by a Group of American Anglo-Catholics, Clerical & Lay. facs. ed. LC 68-16906. (Essay Index Reprint Ser). 1938. 15.00 (ISBN 0-8369-0185-1). Ayer Co Pubs.
Blanch, Stuart Y. The Burning Bush. 1979. pap. 5.95 (ISBN 0-8192-1260-1). Morehouse.
Brunner, Emil. Scandal of Christianity: The Gospel as Stumbling Block to Modern Man. LC 65-12729. 1965. pap. 5.95 (ISBN 0-8042-0708-9). John Knox.
Cavanaugh, Joseph H. Evidence for Our Faith. 3rd ed. 1959. 8.00x (ISBN 0-268-00092-1). U. of Notre Dame Pr.
Chesterton, Gilbert K. Orthodoxy. 297p. 1980. Repr. lib. bdg. 39.50 (ISBN 0-89987-125-9). Darby Bks.
Guest, John. In Search of Certainty. LC 83-19273. (In Search of...Ser.). 1984. 9.95 (ISBN 0-8307-0919-3, 5111001). Regal.
Hopp, Kenneth H. Christianity Makes Sense. (Lifline Ser.). 80p. 1983. pap. 5.95 (ISBN 0-8163-0522-6). Pacific Pr Pub Assn.
Horvath, Tibor. Faith under Scrutiny. LC 75-1179. 343p. 1975. pap. text ed. 5.95 (ISBN 0-8190-0073-6). Loyola.
Jersild, Paul T. Invitation to Faith: Christian Belief Today. LC 77-84097. 1978. pap. 9.95 (ISBN 0-8066-1623-7, 10-3395). Augsburg.
Kreeft, Peter. Yes or No? Straight Answers to Tough Questions about Christianity. 168p. (Orig.). 1984. 5.95 (ISBN 0-89283-217-7). Servant.
Little, Paul E. Know Why You Believe. rev. ed. LC 68-8267. 1968. pap. 5.95 (ISBN 0-87784-529-8). Inter-Varsity.
Montgomery, John W., ed. & intro. by. Christianity for the Tough-Minded. LC 73-4842. 304p. 1973. kivar 9.95 (ISBN 0-87123-076-3, 210079). Bethany Hse.
Niebuhr, Reinhold. Faith & History: A Comparison of Christian & Modern Views of History. (Lib. Rep. Ed.). 1949. 25.00 (ISBN 0-684-15318-1, ScribT). Scribner.
Ratzinger, Joseph. Introduction to Christianity. 1970. 8.95 (ISBN 0-8245-0319-8). Crossroad NY.
Robinson, John A. Honest to God. LC 63-13819. 144p. 1963. pap. 7.95 (ISBN 0-664-24465-3). Westminster.
Ross, John E. Truths to Live by. facsimile ed. LC 72-37834. (Essay Index Reprint Ser). Repr. of 1929 ed. 19.00 (ISBN 0-8369-2622-6). Ayer Co Pubs.
Rupp, George. Beyond Existentialism & Zen: Religion in a Pluralistic World. 1979. 14.95x (ISBN 0-19-502462-1). Oxford U Pr.
Schaeffer, Francis A. God Who Is There. LC 68-29304. 1968. pap. 7.95 (ISBN 0-87784-711-8). Inter-Varsity.
Sheen, Fulton J. Peace of Soul. 1954. pap. 4.95 (ISBN 0-385-02871-7, D8, Im). Doubleday.
Spann, J. Richard, ed. Christian Faith & Secularism. LC 70-86062. (Essay & General Literature Index Reprint Ser). 1969. Repr. of 1948 ed. 28.50x (ISBN 0-8046-0589-0, Pub. by Kennikat). Assoc Faculty Pr.
Tozer, Aiden W. Born after Midnight. pap. 4.45 (ISBN 0-87509-258-6); pap. 3.45 mass market (ISBN 0-87509-167-9). Chr Pubns.
Tyrrell, Francis M. Man: Believer & Unbeliever. LC 73-20055. 475p. (Orig.). 1974. pap. 7.95 (ISBN 0-8189-0283-3). Alba.
Van Til, Cornelius. Christian Theory of Knowledge. 1969. pap. 10.95 (ISBN 0-87552-480-X). Presby & Reformed.
Walton, Alfred G. This I Can Believe. facs. ed. LC 79-142708. (Essay Index Reprint Ser). 1935. 18.00 (ISBN 0-8369-2207-7). Ayer Co Pubs.

APOLOGETICS, JEWISH

see Judaism

APOSTASY

see also Dogma; Heresy; Schism; Sects

Apostasy & the Antichrist. 46p. (Orig.). 1978. pap. 2.00 (ISBN 0-317-30297-3). Holy Trinity.
Archpriest Boris Molchanov. Epokha Apostasii. Tr. of The Epoch of Apostasy. 24p. 1976. pap. 1.00 (ISBN 0-317-29125-4). Holy Trinity.
Rahman, S. A. Punishment of Apostasy in Islam. pap. 7.50 (ISBN 0-686-18551-X). Kazi Pubns.

APOSTLES

see also Evangelists (Bible)

Alexander, Joseph. Commentary on the Acts of the Apostles. 1979. 27.50 (ISBN 0-86524-025-6, 4401). Klock & Klock.
Apostle to the Nations. 15.00 (ISBN 0-8198-0710-9); 14.00 (ISBN 0-8198-0711-7). Dghtrs St Paul.
Brown, Raymond E. The Churches the Apostles Left Behind. 160p. (Orig.). 1984. pap. 5.95 (ISBN 0-8091-2611-7). Paulist Pr.
Bruce, Alexander B. Training of the Twelve. LC 73-129738. 566p. 1979. 13.95 (ISBN 0-8254-2212-4); pap. 9.95 (ISBN 0-8254-2236-1). Kregel.
Cross, L. S. Paul's Letters Made Easy for Devotions. 120p. (Orig.). 1982. pap. 4.95 (ISBN 0-89221-090-7, Pub by SonLife). New Leaf.
Crowther, Duane S. Atlas & Outline of the Acts of the Apostles. LC 83-80528. 114p. 1983. pap. 6.95 (ISBN 0-88290-219-9). Horizon-Utah.
Finegan, Jack. The Archaeology of the New Testament: The Mediterranean World of the Early Christian Apostles. (Illus.). 400p. 1981. 40.00x (ISBN 0-86531-064-5). Westview.
Frodsham, Stanley H. Smith Wigglesworth: Apostle of Faith. 160p. 1948. pap. 2.50 (ISBN 0-88243-586-8, 02-0586). Gospel Pub.
Gloag, Paton J. A Critical & Exegetical Commentary on the Acts of the Apostles, 2 vols. 1979. 29.95 (ISBN 0-86524-006-X, 4402). Klock & Klock.
Gruss, Edmond C. Apostles of Denial. 1970. pap. 8.95 (ISBN 0-87552-305-6). Presby & Reformed.
Harris, Clarence. Without Controversy Great Is the Mystery of Godliness. rev. ed. Haris, Althea, ed. (Illus.). 185p. 1982. pap. 4.95 (ISBN 0-686-39817-3). Gospel Place.
Homan, Helen. By Post to the Apostles. facs. ed. LC 74-148219. (Biography Index Reprint Ser.). 1952. 20.00 (ISBN 0-8369-8066-2). Ayer Co Pubs.
Huold, Harry N. Twelve Who Followed: The Story of Jesus & His First Disciples. 128p. (Orig.). (YA) 1986. pap. 6.95 (ISBN 0-8066-2242-3, 10-6722). Augsburg.
Jones, John D. The Apostles of Christ. 268p. 1982. lib. bdg. 10.00 Smythe Sewn (ISBN 0-86524-139-2, 8403). Klock & Klock.
Kelsey, Morton T. Resurrection: Release from Oppression. LC 84-62150. 201p. 1985. pap. 8.95 (ISBN 0-8091-2673-7). Paulist Pr.
Lattimore, Richmond, tr. from Greek. Acts & Letters of the Apostles. 287p. 1982. 16.50 (ISBN 0-374-10082-9). FS&G.
LaVerdiere, Eugene. Acts of the Apostles. LC 79-1395. (The Read & Pray Ser.). 98p. 1979. 1.75 (ISBN 0-8199-0632-8). Franciscan Herald.
Lindsay, Gordon. Apostles, Prophets & Governments. 1.50 (ISBN 0-89985-121-5). Christ Nations.
--Did Politics Influence Jesus? 86p. (Orig.). 1982. pap. 2.50 (ISBN 0-89985-113-4, 1002). Christ Nations.
--Miracles of the Apostles, Vol. 4. (Miracles in the Bible Ser.). 0.95 (ISBN 0-89985-181-9). Christ Nations.
Livadeas, Themistocles & Charitos, Minas. The Real Truth Concerning Apostolos Makrakis. Orthodox Christian Educational Society, ed. Cummings, Denver, tr. from Hellenic. 230p. (Orig.). 1952. pap. 4.50x (ISBN 0-938366-30-0). Orthodox Chr.
McIntyre, William. Christ's Cabinet. rev. ed. 143p. 1982. Repr. of 1937 ed. 3.95 (ISBN 0-86544-017-4). Salv Army Suppl South.
Millard, Amos D. Learning from the Apostles. 128p. 1971. pap. 1.25 (ISBN 0-88243-537-X, 02-0537). Gospel Pub.
Rainbow Bridge: Two Disciples. 1981. casebound 10.00 (ISBN 0-87613-069-4); pap. 8.50 (ISBN 0-87613-068-6); pap. text ed. Write for info. (ISBN 0-87613-078-3). New Age.
Raya, Joseph & Vinck, Jose D. Apostolos: Byzantine Epistles Lectionary. 550p. 1981. 87.50x (ISBN 0-911726-37-3); folded sheets 67.50x (ISBN 0-911726-38-1). Alleluia Pr.
Ruffin, C. Bernard. The Twelve: The Lives of the Apostles After Calvary. LC 83-63168. 194p. (Orig.). 1984. pap. 7.95 (ISBN 0-87973-609-7, 609). Our Sunday Visitor.
Schmidt, Elisabeth. Do We Hear the Song of This Joy? Meditations on the Acts of the Apostles. Hackett, Allen, tr. from Fr. 120p. (Orig.). 1983. pap. 6.95 (ISBN 0-8298-0680-6). Pilgrim NY.
Schutz, J. H. Paul & the Anatomy of Apostolic Authority. LC 74-76573. (Society for New Testament Studies, Monographs: No. 26). 1975. 59.50 (ISBN 0-521-20464-X). Cambridge U Pr.
Stier, Rudolf E. Words of the Apostles. 1982. lib. bdg. 18.75 (ISBN 0-86524-087-6, 4403). Klock & Klock.
Thomas, W. Griffith. Outline Studies in Luke. LC 84-784. 408p. 1984. pap. text ed. 11.95 (ISBN 0-8254-3821-7). Kregel.
Thomas, W. H. The Apostle John: His Life & Writings. LC 84-785. 376p. 1984. pap. 10.95 (ISBN 0-8254-3822-5). Kregel.
--The Apostle Peter: His Life & Writings. LC 84-1493. 304p. 1984. pap. 9.95 (ISBN 0-8254-3823-3). Kregel.
Ulmer, Louise. Jesus' Twelve Disciples: Arch Bks. 1982. pap. 0.99 (ISBN 0-570-06160-1, 59-1307). Concordia.
Underwood, Walter L. The Contemporary Twelve: The Power of Character in Today's World. 112p. (Orig.). 1984. pap. 9.50 (ISBN 0-687-09520-4). Abingdon.
Vale, Eugene. The Thirteenth Apostle. 352p. 1983. pap. 7.95 (ISBN 0-9609674-0-0). Jubilee Pr.
Vaporis, Nomikos M., ed. The Apostolos: The Acts & Letters of the Holy Apostles Read in the Orthodox Church Throughout the Year. 420p. 1980. 55.00 (ISBN 0-916586-39-1). Holy Cross Orthodox.
White, Ellen G. The Acts of the Apostles. 633p. 1911. deluxe ed. 9.95 (ISBN 0-8163-0033-X, 01092-6). Pacific Pr Pub Assn.

APOSTLES–JUVENILE LITERATURE

Rowell, Edmon L., Jr. Apostles: Jesus' Special Helpers. (BibLearn Ser.). (Illus.). 1979. 5.95 (ISBN 0-8054-4246-4, 4242-46). Broadman.

APOSTLES–LEGENDS

Dvornik, Francis. The Idea of Apostolicity in Byzantium & the Legend of the Apostle Andrew. (Dumbarton Oaks Studies: Vol. 4). 342p. (LC A58-8640). 1958. 25.00x (ISBN 0-88402-004-5). Dumbarton Oaks.
Shank, Robert. Sources of Power of the Apostolic Witness. 125p. 1982. pap. 3.95 (ISBN 0-911620-05-2). Westcott.

APOSTLES' CREED

see also Communion of Saints

Barth, Karl. Dogmatics in Outline. pap. 5.95x (ISBN 0-06-130056-X, TB56, Torch). Har-Row.
Claudel, Paul. Je Crois en Dieu. 432p. 1961. 8.95 (ISBN 0-686-54394-7). French & Eur.
Friedman, Lionel J. Text & Iconography of Joinville's Credo. LC 58-7918. 1958. 12.00x (ISBN 0-910956-42-1). Medieval Acad.
Hayes, Edward J., et al. Catholicism & Reason. (Catholicism Catechism Ser.). 256p. (YA) 1981. pap. 5.95 (ISBN 0-913382-23-X, 103-14); tchr's manual 3.00 (ISBN 0-913382-25-6, 103-15). Prow Bks-Franciscan.
Lochman, Jan M. The Faith We Confess: An Ecumenical Dogmatics. Lewis, David, tr. LC 83-48908. 288p. 1984. 19.95 (ISBN 0-8006-0723-6, 1-723). Fortress.
Packer, J. I. The Apostle's Creed. 1983. pap. 3.95 (ISBN 0-8423-0051-1); Leader's Guide 2.95 (ISBN 0-8423-0052-X). Tyndale.
Perkins, Pheme. What We Believe: A Biblical Catechism of the Apostles Creed. 144p. (Orig.). 1986. pap. 3.95 (ISBN 0-8091-2764-4). Paulist Pr.
Ratzinger, Joseph. Introduction to Christianity. 1970. 8.95 (ISBN 0-8245-0319-8). Crossroad NY.
Swete, H. B. The Apostles' Creed, Its Relation to Primitive Christianity. 112p. 1981. Repr. of 1905 ed. lib. bdg. 50.00 (ISBN 0-89984-447-2). Century Bookbindery.

APOSTLES' CREED–SERMONS

Burghardt, W. J., et al, eds. Rufinus: A Commentary of the Apostles' Creed. LC 78-62468. (ACW Ser.: No. 20). 167p. 1955. 10.95 (ISBN 0-8091-0257-9). Paulist Pr.

APOSTOLATE, LAY

see Catholic Action

APOSTOLATE, LITURGICAL

see Liturgical Movement–Catholic Church

APOSTOLIC FATHERS

The Apostolic Fathers. LC 47-31345. (Fathers of the Church Ser.: Vol. 1). 412p. 1947. 21.95x (ISBN 0-8132-0001-6). Cath U Pr.
Goodspeed, Edgar J. Index Patristicus, Sive Clavis Patrum Apostolicorum Operum. LC 60-52358. 1960. 18.00x (ISBN 0-8401-0863-X). A R Allenson.
Lightfoot, J. B., ed. The Apostolic Fathers. (Twin Brooks Ser.). 584p. 1984. pap. 15.95 (ISBN 0-8010-5627-6). Baker Bk.
Parham, Charles F. & Parham, Sarah E. The Life of Charles F. Parham, Founder of the Apostolic Faith Movement. (The Higher Christian Life Ser.). 468p. 1985. lib. bdg. 60.00 (ISBN 0-8240-6436-4). Garland Pub.
Staniforth, Maxwell, tr. Early Christian Writings: The Apostolic Fathers. (Classics Ser.). 240p. 1968. pap. 5.95 (ISBN 0-14-044197-2). Penguin.

APOSTOLIC SUCCESSION

see also Anglican Orders; Bishops; Catholic Church–Clergy; Church of England–Clergy; Episcopacy; Popes

Chapman, H. John. Studies on the Early Papacy. LC 76-118517. 1971. Repr. of 1928 ed. 23.00x (ISBN 0-8046-1139-4, Pub. by Kennikat). Assoc Faculty Pr.

Dix, Gregory, ed. Apostoliki Paradosis: The Treatise on the Apostolic Tradition of St. Hippolytus of Rome, Bishop & Martyr, Vol. 1. (Church Historical Society, London, New Ser.: No. 24). Repr. of 1937 ed. 40.00 (ISBN 0-8115-3148-1). Kraus Repr.

Gay, Jules. Papes Du Onzieme Siecle et la Chretiente. 2nd ed. 1970. 21.00 (ISBN 0-8337-1302-7). B Franklin.

Kung, Hans, ed. Apostolic Succession. LC 68-25948. (Concilium Ser.: Vol. 34). 196p. 1968. 7.95 (ISBN 0-8091-0003-7). Paulist Pr.

APOTHEGMS

see Aphorisms and Apothegms

APPARITIONS

see also Demonology; Mary, Virgin–Apparitions and Miracles; Miracles; Theophanies; Visions

Christian, William A., Jr. Apparitions in Late Medieval & Renaissance Spain. LC 80-8541. (Illus.). 304p. 1981. 34.00x (ISBN 0-691-05326-X). Princeton U Pr.

Glanvill, Joseph. Saducismus Triumphatus: Or, Full & Plain Evidence Concerning Witches & Apparitions. LC 66-60009. 1966. Repr. of 1689 ed. 75.00x (ISBN 0-8201-1021-3). Schol Facsimiles.

Thompson, C. J. The Mystery & Lore of Apparitions, with Some Account of Ghosts, Spectres, Phantoms & Boggarts in Early Times. LC 70-167225. (Illus.). 331p. 1975. Repr. of 1930 ed. 40.00x (ISBN 0-8103-3981-1). Gale.

APPLIED PSYCHOLOGY

see Psychology, Applied

APPROPRIATION AND IMPROPRIATION

see Secularization

ARAB ARCHITECTURE

see Architecture, Islamic

ARABIA–ANTIQUITIES

Cleveland, Ray L. An Ancient South Arabian Necropolis: Objects from the Second Campaign 1951 in the Timna Cemetery. (American Foundation for the Study of Man: Vol. 4). (Illus.). 202p. 1965. 40.00x (ISBN 0-8018-0129-X). Johns Hopkins.

Grimme, Hubert. Texte und Untersuchungen Zur Safatenisch - Arabischen Religion. 1929. pap. 15.00 (ISBN 0-384-20070-2). Johnson Repr.

ARABIA–DESCRIPTION AND TRAVEL

Burton, Richard F. Personal Narrative of a Pilgrimage to Al-Madinah & Meccah, 2 Vols. (Illus.). 1893. Vol. 1. pap. 8.95 (ISBN 0-486-21217-3). Vol. 2. pap. 8.95 (ISBN 0-486-21218-1). Dover.

--Personal Narrative of a Pilgrimage to Al-Madinah & Meccah, 2 Vols. Burton, Isabel, ed. Set. 28.50 (ISBN 0-8446-1781-4). Peter Smith.

Montgomery, James A. Arabia & the Bible. rev. ed. (Library of Biblical Studies). 1969. 25.00x (ISBN 0-87068-090-0). Ktav.

Musil, Alois. Northern Arabia, According to the Original Investigations of Alois Musil. LC 77-87092. (American Geographical Society. Oriental Explorations & Studies: Map Vol.). Repr. of 1928 ed. 30.00 (ISBN 0-404-60237-1). AMS Pr.

Philby, Harry S. Arabia of the Wahhabis. LC 73-6297. (The Middle East Ser.). Repr. of 1928 ed. 33.00 (ISBN 0-405-05355-X). Ayer Co Pubs.

Rutter, Eldon. The Holy Cities of Arabia, 2 vols. LC 78-63477. Repr. of 1928 ed. Set. 49.50 (ISBN 0-404-16543-5). AMS Pr.

Stark, Freya. The Valleys of the Assassins. rev. ed. (Illus.). 1972. 28.50 (ISBN 0-7195-2429-6). Transatl Arts.

ARABIC PHILOSOPHY

see Philosophy, Arab; Philosophy, Islamic

ARABS IN ISRAEL

Sinai, Anne & Sinai, Robert I., eds. Israel & the Arabs: Prelude to the Jewish State. LC 78-161364. (A Facts on File Publication). pap. 64.00 (2025158). Bks Demand UMI.

ARABS IN SPAIN

see also Moriscos

Al-Maqqari, Ahmed, ed. History of the Mohammedan Dynasties in Spain, 2 Vols. De Gayangos, P., tr. 1969. Repr. of 1840 ed. Set. 175.00 (ISBN 0-384-35253-7). Johnson Repr.

Chejne, Anwar G. Muslim Spain: Its History & Culture. LC 73-87254. (Illus.). 616p. 1974. 32.50 (ISBN 0-8166-0688-9). U of Minn Pr.

Conde, Jose A. History of the Dominion of the Arabs in Spain, 3 Vols. Foster, Mrs. Jonathan, tr. Repr. of 1855 ed. Set. 55.00 (ISBN 0-404-09270-5); 18.50 ea. Vol. 1 (ISBN 0-404-09271-3). Vol. 2 (ISBN 0-404-09272-1). Vol. 3 (ISBN 0-404-09273-X). AMS Pr.

Dozy, Reinhart. Spanish Islam: History of the Moslems in Spain. 770p. 1972. Repr. of 1913 ed. 45.00x (ISBN 0-7146-2128-5, F Cass Co). Biblio Dist.

ARABS IN THE UNITED STATES

Elkholy, Abdo A. The Arab Moslems in the United States. 1966. 12.95x (ISBN 0-8084-0052-5); pap. 8.95x (ISBN 0-8084-0053-3). New Coll U Pr.

ARARAT, MOUNT

Irwin, James B. & Unger, Monte. More Than an Ark on Ararat. LC 85-4157. 1985. 6.95 (ISBN 0-8054-5018-1). Broadman.

Montgomery, John W. Quest for Noah's Ark. LC 74-21993. (Illus.). 384p. 1972. pap. 4.95 (ISBN 0-87123-477-7, 200477). Bethany Hse.

Parrot, Friedrich. Journey to Ararat. LC 73-115576. (Russia Observed, Series I). 1970. Repr. of 1846 ed. 20.00 (ISBN 0-405-03057-6). Ayer Co Pubs.

ARATOR, SUBDEACON IN ROME. fl. 513-544

McKinlay, A. P., ed. Arator: The Codices. 1942. 8.00x (ISBN 0-910956-18-9). Medieval Acad.

ARCHAEOLOGY, CHRISTIAN

see Christian Antiquities

ARCHAEOLOGY, CLASSICAL

see Classical Antiquities

ARCHBISHOPS

see Bishops

ARCHITECTURE–EGYPT

Briggs, Martin S. Muhammadan Architecture in Egypt & Palestine. LC 74-1287. (Architecture & Decorative Arts Ser.). (Illus.). 255p. 1974. Repr. of 1924 ed. lib. bdg. 39.50 (ISBN 0-306-70590-7). Da Capo.

Carrott, Richard G. The Egyptian Revival: Its Sources, Monuments, & Meaning (1808-1858) LC 76-24579. (Illus.). 1978. 44.50x (ISBN 0-520-03324-8). U of Cal Pr.

Curl, James S. The Egyptian Revival. (Illus.). 256p. 1982. 50.00 (ISBN 0-04-724001-6). Allen Unwin.

Kessler, Christel. The Carved Masonry Domes of Mediaeval Cairo. 1976. pap. 15.00x (ISBN 0-686-19945-6). Intl Learn Syst.

Spencer, Patricia. The Egyptian Temple: A Lexicographical Study. 300p. 1984. 50.00x (ISBN 0-7103-0065-4, Kegan Paul). Methuen Inc.

ARCHITECTURE–GREAT BRITAIN

Eastlake, Charles. History of the Gothic Revival. LC 71-96937. (Library of Victorian Culture). 1975. pap. text ed. 12.00 (ISBN 0-89257-035-0). Am Life Foun.

Lovell, Percy & Marcham, William, eds. Parish of St. Pancras, Pt. 2. LC 70-37855. (London County Council. Survey of London: No. 19). Repr. of 1938 ed. 74.50 (ISBN 0-404-51669-6). AMS Pr.

Smith, T. Roger & Slater, John. Architecture, Classic & Early Christian. 1980. Repr. of 1893 ed. lib. bdg. 35.00 (ISBN 0-89341-364-X). Longwood Pub Group.

Watson, P. Building the Medieval Cathedrals. LC 74-19525. (Introduction to the History of Mankind). 48p. 1976. pap. 4.95 limp bdg. (ISBN 0-521-08711-2). Cambridge U Pr.

ARCHITECTURE–ITALY

see also Architecture, Roman

Luchs, Allison. Cestello: A Cistercian Church of the Florentine Renaissance. LC 76-23642. (Outstanding Dissertations in the Fine Arts - 2nd Series - 15th Century). (Illus.). 1977. Repr. lib. bdg. 76.00 (ISBN 0-8240-2706-X). Garland Pub.

Sale, J. Russell. Filipino Lippi's Strozzi Chapel in Santa Maria Novella. Freedberg, Sydney J., ed. LC 78-74376. (Outstanding Dissertations in the Fine Arts Ser.). (Illus.). 1979. lib. bdg. 57.00 (ISBN 0-8240-3963-7). Garland Pub.

Shearman, J. The Vatican Stanze: Functions & Decoration. (Italian Lectures). 1971. pap. 2.50 (ISBN 0-85672-062-3, Pub. by British Acad). Longwood Pub Group.

Smith, Christine. The Baptistery of Pisa. LC 77-94715. (Outstanding Dissertations in the Fine Arts Ser.). (Illus.). 432p. 1978. lib. bdg. 53.00 (ISBN 0-8240-3249-7). Garland Pub.

Smith, Graham. The Casino of Pius IV. LC 76-3017. (Illus.). 1976. 44.50x (ISBN 0-691-03915-1). Princeton U Pr.

Weil, Mark. The History & Decoration of the Ponte S. Angelo. LC 72-163216. (Illus.). 232p. 1974. 32.50x (ISBN 0-271-01101-7). Pa St U Pr.

ARCHITECTURE–TURKEY

Kuran, Aptullah. Mosque in Early Ottoman Architecture. LC 68-16701. (Publications of the Center for Middle Eastern Studies Ser). (Illus.). 1968. 25.00x (ISBN 0-226-46293-5). U of Chicago Pr.

ARCHITECTURE, ANCIENT

see also Pyramids; Temples

see also Architecture–Egypt; Architecture, Greek and similar headings

Bowder, Diana. The Age of Constantine & Julian. (Illus.). 230p. 1978. text ed. 32.50x (ISBN 0-06-490601-9, 06359). B&N Imports.

Carrott, Richard G. The Egyptian Revival: Its Sources, Monuments, & Meaning (1808-1858) LC 76-24579. (Illus.). 1978. 44.50x (ISBN 0-520-03324-8). U of Cal Pr.

Krauss, Friedrich. Die Tempel von Paestum, 2 pts. (Denkmaeler Antiker Architektur, Vol. 9, Pt. 1, Fascicule 1). (Ger., Illus.). 97p. 1978. Repr. of 1959 ed. 70.0000169042x (ISBN 3-110022-37-0). De Gruyter.

Krauss, Friedrich & Herbig, Reinhard. Der Korinthisch-dorische Tempel am Forum von Paestum. (Denkmaeler antiker Architektur, Vol. 7). (Ger., Illus.). xii, 82p. 1978. Repr. of 1939 ed. 79.20x (ISBN 3-11-004991-0). De Gruyter.

Krencker, Daniel & Zschietzschmann, Willy. Roemische Tempel in Syrien: Nach Aufnahmen und Untersuchungen von Mitgliedern der Deutschen Baalbekexpedition, 1901-1904, 2 pts. (Denkmaeler antiker Architektur, Vol. 5). (Ger., Illus.). 298p. 1978. Repr. of 1938 ed. Pt. 1. 132.00x (ISBN 3-11-004989-9); Pt. 2. 84.00 (ISBN 3-11-004990-2). De Gruyter.

Lowrie, Harold. The Salient Characteristics of Ancient Christian Architecture. (Illus.). 142p. 1982. Repr. of 1880 ed. 84.55 (ISBN 0-89901-053-9). Found Class Reprints.

Meyer-Plath & Schneider, A. M. Die Landmauer von Konstantinopel, Part 2: Aufnahme, Beschreibung und Geschichte. (Denkmaeler antiker Architektur, Vol. 8). (Ger., Illus.). x, 170p. 1978. Repr. of 1943 ed. 120.00 (ISBN 3-11-004992-9). De Gruyter.

ARCHITECTURE, ARAB

see Architecture, Islamic

ARCHITECTURE, BAROQUE

Lewis, Douglas. The Late Baroque Churches of Venice. LC 78-94704. (Outstanding Dissertations in the Fine Arts Ser.). 1979. lib. bdg. 63.00 (ISBN 0-8240-3236-5). Garland Pub.

ARCHITECTURE, BUDDHIST

Basnayake, H. T. Sri Lankan Monastic Architecture. (Studies on Sri Lanka Ser.: No. 2). (Illus.). 186p. 1986. 85.00x (ISBN 81-7030-009-6, Pub. by SRI SATGURU Pubns India). Orient Bk Dist.

Coburn, Alexander. The Heian Period in the Evolution of Buddhist Architecture in Japan. (Illus.). 176p. 1985. Repr. of 1930 ed. 187.50 (ISBN 0-86650-167-3). Gloucester Art.

Dehejia, Vidya. Early Buddhist Rock Temples. LC 75-158835. (Studies in Ancient Art & Archaeology Ser.). (Illus.). 193p. 1972. 42.50x (ISBN 0-8014-0651-X). Cornell U Pr.

Govinda, Lama A. Psycho-Cosmic Symbolism of the Buddhist Stupa. LC 76-797. (Illus.). 144p. 1976. pap. 6.95 (ISBN 0-913546-36-4). Dharma Pub.

Rhie, Marylin M. Fo-Kuang Ssu: Literary Evidences & Buddhist Images. LC 76-23690. (Outstanding Dissertations in the Fine Arts - Far Eastern). (Illus.). 1977. Repr. of 1970 ed. lib. bdg. 55.00 (ISBN 0-8240-2721-3). Garland Pub.

Sarkar, H. Studies in Early Buddhist Architecture of India. (Illus.). 1966. 16.00x. Coronet Bks.

Soekmono, Dr. Chandi Borobudur: A Monument of Mankind. (Illus.). 53p. (Co-published with Van Gorcum, Amsterdam). 1976. pap. 8.25 (ISBN 92-3-101292-4, U69, UNESCO). Bernan-Unipub.

Soper, Alexander C. The Evolution of Buddhist Architecture in Japan. LC 76-26054. (Illus.). 1978. Repr. of 1942 ed. lib. bdg. 75.00 (ISBN 0-87817-196-7). Hacker.

Soper, Charlton W. The Important Muromachi, Momoyama & Edo Periods in the Growth of Buddhist Architecture in Japan. (Illus.). 101p. 1987. 127.50 (ISBN 0-86650-218-1). Gloucester Art.

--The Kamakura Period in the Evolution of Buddhist Architecture in Japan. (Illus.). 143p. 1987. 147.75 (ISBN 0-86650-217-3). Gloucester Art.

ARCHITECTURE, BYZANTINE

Beyer, Hermann W. Der Syrische Kirchenbau. (Studien Zur Spaetantiken Kunstgeschichte Ser.: Vol. 1). (Illus.). viii, 183p. 1978. Repr. of 1925 ed. 60.00x (ISBN 3-11-005705-0). De Gruyter.

Curcic, Slobodan. Gracanica: King Milutin's Church & Its Place in Late Byzantine Architecture. LC 79-11984. (Illus.). 1980. 34.95x (ISBN 0-271-00218-2). Pa St U Pr.

Macdonald, William. Early Christian & Byzantine Architecture. LC 62-7531. (Great Ages of World Architecture Ser). 128p. 1963. 7.95 (ISBN 0-8076-0176-4); pap. 7.95 (ISBN 0-8076-0338-4). Braziller.

Mathews, Thomas F. The Byzantine Churches of Istanbul: A Photographic Survey. LC 75-27173. (Illus.). 425p. 1976. 60.00x (ISBN 0-271-01210-2). Pa St U Pr.

ARCHITECTURE, CHURCH

see Church Architecture

ARCHITECTURE, CISTERCIAN

Lillich, Meredith P., ed. Studies in Cistercian Art & Architecture, III. (Cistercian Studies: No. 89). (Orig.). 1987. pap. write for info. (ISBN 0-87907-889-8). Cistercian Pubns.

Panagopoulos, Beata K. Cistercian & Mendicant Monasteries in Medieval Greece. LC 78-10769. (Illus.). 1979. lib. bdg. 24.00x (ISBN 0-226-64544-4). U of Chicago Pr.

ARCHITECTURE, ECCLESIASTICAL

see Church Architecture

ARCHITECTURE, GOTHIC

see also Architecture, Cistercian; Cathedrals; Church Architecture

Addison, Agnes. Romanticism & the Gothic Revival. 204p. 1967. Repr. of 1938 ed. 17.50x (ISBN 0-87752-000-3). Gordian.

Bruzelius, Caroline A. The Thirteenth-Century Church at St. Denis. LC 85-3354. 256p. 1986. 30.00 (ISBN 0-300-03190-4). Yale U Pr.

Coulton, George G. Art & the Reformation. LC 69-15789. (Illus.). xxii, 662p. 1969. Repr. of 1928 ed. 45.00 (ISBN 0-208-00738-5, Archon). Shoe String.

Dunlop, Ian. The Cathedrals' Crusade. LC 81-14431. (Illus.). 256p. 1982. 20.00 (ISBN 0-8008-1316-2). Taplinger.

Eastlake, Charles. History of the Gothic Revival. LC 71-96937. (Library of Victorian Culture). 1975. pap. text ed. 12.00 (ISBN 0-89257-035-0). Am Life Foun.

Fitchen, John. The Construction of Gothic Cathedrals: A Study of Medieval Vault Erection. LC 80-26291. (Illus.). 1977. pap. 12.95 (ISBN 0-226-25203-5, Phoen). U of Chicago Pr.

Jantzen, Hans. High Gothic. LC 83-43099. (Illus.). 196p. 1984. 25.00x (ISBN 0-691-04026-5); pap. 7.95x (ISBN 0-691-00372-6). Princeton U Pr.

Maines, Clark. The Western Portal of Saint-Loup-De-Naud. LC 78-74373. (Fine Arts Dissertations, Fourth Ser.). (Illus.). 511p. 1979. lib. bdg. 53.00 (ISBN 0-8240-3960-2). Garland Pub.

Murray, Stephen. Building Troyes Cathedral: The Late Gothic Campaigns. LC 85-45744. (Illus.). 272p. 1986. 47.50x (ISBN 0-253-31277-9). Ind U Pr.

Panofsky, Erwin. Gothic Architecture & Scholasticism. (Illus.). pap. 7.95 (ISBN 0-452-00834-4, Mer). NAL.

Parkhurst, Helen H. Cathedral: A Gothic Pilgrimage. 304p. 1980. Repr. of 1936 ed. lib. bdg. 40.00 (ISBN 0-8492-2174-9). R West.

Polk, Thomas E., II. Saint-Denis, Noyon & the Early Gothic Choir: Methodological Considerations for the History of Early Gothic Architecture, Vol. 4. (Sanctuaries of the Gallic-Frankish Church Ser.). (Illus.). 220p. 1982. pap. 32.10 (ISBN 3-8204-6177-9). P Lang Pubs.

Seymour, Charles, Jr. Notre-Dame of Noyon in the Twelfth Century: A Study in the Early Development of Gothic Architecture. (Illus.). 1968. pap. 3.95x (ISBN 0-393-00464-3, Norton Lib). Norton.

Street, George E. Gothic Architecture in Spain, 2 Vols. King, Georgiana G., ed. LC 68-56490. (Illus.). 1968. Repr. of 1914 ed. Set. 55.00 (ISBN 0-405-09008-0); 27.50 ea. Vol. 1 (ISBN 0-405-09009-9). Vol. 2 (ISBN 0-405-09010-2). Ayer Co Pubs.

Von Simson, Otto. The Gothic Cathedral: Origins of Gothic Architecture & the Medieval Concept of Order. LC 72-11946. (Bollingen Ser.: No. 48). (Illus.). 300p. 1973. 31.00 (ISBN 0-691-09741-0); pap. 9.50 (ISBN 0-691-01789-1). Princeton U Pr.

ARCHITECTURE, GREEK

see also Temples

also subdivision antiquities under names of cities, e.g. Athens–Antiquities

Panagopoulos, Beata K. Cistercian & Mendicant Monasteries in Medieval Greece. LC 78-10769. (Illus.). 1979. lib. bdg. 24.00x (ISBN 0-226-64544-4). U of Chicago Pr.

Scully. The Earth, the Temple, & the Gods. LC 79-12717. 1979. pap. 16.95x (ISBN 0-300-02397-9, Y-346). Yale U Pr.

ARCHITECTURE, HINDU

Acharya, P. K. Dictionary of Hindu Architecture. 1981. text ed. 58.50x. Coronet Bks.

--Encyclopedia of Hindu Architecture. (Illus.). 1979. text ed. 38.50x. Coronet Bks.

Chandra, Pramod. Studies in Indian Temple Architecture. LC 75-904089. 1975. 40.00x (ISBN 0-88386-649-8). South Asia Bks.

Ghosh, S. P. Hindu Religious Art & Architecture. (Illus.). 148p. 1983. text ed. 30.00x (ISBN 0-86590-124-4). Apt Bks.

Harle, J. C. Temple Gateways of South India: The Architecture & Iconography of the Cidammaram Gopuras. (Illus.). 179p. 1963. 65.00x (ISBN 0-317-39167-4, Pub. by Luzac & Co Ltd). State Mutual Bk.

Kramrisch, Stella. The Hindu Temple, 2 vols. 1980. Repr. Set. 65.00x (ISBN 0-8364-0411-4). South Asia Bks.

Krishna Murthy, C. Saiva Art & Architecture in South India. 1985. 48.00x (ISBN 0-8364-1417-9, Pub. by Sundeep). South Asia Bks.

Meister, Michael W. & Dhaky, M. A., eds. Encyclopedia of Indian Temple Architecture, Vol. 1, Part II: South India: Upper Dravidadesa. (Illus.). 736p. 1982. Set. text ed. 84.00x. U of Pa Pr.

Nath, R. History of Decorative Art in Mughal Architecture. 1986. Repr. of 1977 ed. 16.50 (ISBN 81-208-0077-X, Pub. by Motilal Banarsidass India). Orient Bk Dist.

Rajan, K. V. Indian Temple Styles: The Personality of Hindu Architecture. (Illus.). 194p. 1972. 22.50x (ISBN 0-89684-420-X). Orient Bk Dist.
Splendours of the Vijayanagara. 1981. 30.00x (ISBN 0-8364-0792-X, Pub. by Marg India). South Asia Bks.

ARCHITECTURE, ISLAMIC
see also Mosques
Briggs, Martin S. Muhammadan Architecture in Egypt & Palestine. LC 74-1287. (Architecture & Decorative Arts Ser.). (Illus.). 255p. 1974. Repr. of 1924 ed. lib. bdg. 39.50 (ISBN 0-306-70590-7). Da Capo.
Cousens, H. The Architectural Antiquities of Western India. (Illus.). 1983. text ed. 34.00x. Coronet Bks.
Creswell, K. Short Account of Early Muslim Architecture. 1968. 18.00x (ISBN 0-86685-010-4). Intl Bk Ctr.
Creswell, K. A. A Bibliography of the Architecture, Arts & Crafts of Islam. 2nd ed. 120.00 (ISBN 0-89410-306-7, Pub. by FP Van Eck Liechtenstein). Three Continents.
--Early Muslim Architecture: Umayyads, Early 'Abbasids, & Tulunids, 2 vols. in 3 pts. LC 75-11057. 1978. Repr. of 1932 ed. lib. bdg. 375.00 (ISBN 0-87817-176-2). Hacker.
--Muslim Architecture of Egypt, 2 vols. LC 75-11056. (Illus.). 1978. Repr. of 1952 ed. lib. bdg. 350.00 (ISBN 0-87817-175-4). Hacker.
Dodd, Erica C. & Khairallah, Shereen. The Image of the Word: A Study of Quranic Verses in Islamic Architecture, 2 vols. (Illus.). 434p. 1982. 95.00x (ISBN 0-8156-6061-8, Am U Beirut). Syracuse U Pr.
Grabar, Oleg, ed. Muqarnas: An Annual on Islamic Art & Architecture: The Art of the Mamluks, Vol. II. LC 83-643765. (Illus.). 240p. 1984. 35.00x (ISBN 0-300-03137-8). Yale U Pr.
Grover, Satish. The Architecture of India: Islamic. (Illus.). 280p. 1981. text ed. 45.00x (ISBN 0-7069-1130-X, Pub. by Vikas India). Advent NY.
Hillenbrand, Robert. Islamic Architecture: Style, Function, & Form. (Illus.). 200p. 1986. 22.50x (ISBN 0-85224-391-X, Pub. by Edinburgh U Pr Scotland). Columbia U Pr.
Hoag, John D. Islamic Architecture. LC 76-41805. (Masters of Art Ser.). (Illus.). 1977. 50.00 (ISBN 0-8109-1010-1). Abrams.
Islamic Art & Architecture. LC 76-14076. (Garland Library of the History of Art: XIII). 1977. lib. bdg. 61.00 (ISBN 0-8240-2423-0). Garland Pub.
The K. A. C. Cresswell Library of Islamic Art & Architecture. 1986. 39.50 (ISBN 977-424-101-0, Pub. by Am Univ Cairo Pr). Columbia U Pr.
Michell, George, ed. Architecture of the Islamic World: Its History & Social Meaning. LC 84-50341. (Illus.). 1984. 40.00f (ISBN 0-500-34076-5). Thames Hudson.
Nath, R. Islamic Architecture & Culture in India. (Illus.). 228p. 1983. text ed. 40.00x (ISBN 0-86590-135-X). Apt Bks.
Paccard, Andre. Traditional Islamic Craft in Moroccan Architecture, 2 vols. 1980. 495.00x (ISBN 0-686-69970-X, Pub. by Editions Atelier England). State Mutual Bk.
Parker, Richard B. & Sabin, Robin. The Islamic Monuments of Cairo: A Practical Guide. 3rd ed. Williams, Caroline, ed. 1986. pap. 12.50x (ISBN 977-424-036-7, Pub. by Am Univ Cairo Pr). Columbia U Pr.
Wilber, Donald N. Architecture of Islamic Iran: The Il Khanid Period. Repr. of 1955 ed. lib. bdg. 36.75x (ISBN 0-8371-2504-9, WIII). Greenwood.

ARCHITECTURE, MEDIEVAL
see also Cathedrals
Coulton, George G. Art & the Reformation. LC 69-15789. (Illus.). xxii, 662p. 1969. Repr. of 1928 ed. 45.00 (ISBN 0-208-00738-5, Archon). Shoe String.
Hardy, Paul E. & Bishop of Exeter. A Guide to the Preservation of Medieval Cathedrals & Churches. LC 82-14257. (Illus.). 160p. 1983. pap. text ed. 16.95 (ISBN 0-582-30514-4, Construction Press). Longman.
Knowles, David & Hadcock, R. Neville. Medieval Religious Houses, England & Wales. LC 72-181783. pap. 147.00 (ISBN 0-317-08419-4, 2016312). Bks Demand UMI.
Macdonald, William. Early Christian & Byzantine Architecture. LC 62-7531. (Great Ages of World Architecture Ser). 128p. 1963. 7.95 (ISBN 0-8076-0176-4); pap. 7.95 (ISBN 0-8076-0338-4). Braziller.
Moore, Charles H. The Mediaeval Church Architecture of England. facsimile ed. LC 74-37900. (Select Bibliographies Reprint Ser). Repr. of 1912 ed. 29.00 (ISBN 0-8369-6738-0). Ayer Co Pubs.
Norton, Charles E. Historical Studies of Church-Building in the Middle Ages. LC 78-95072. (Select Bibliographies Reprint Ser.). 1902. 32.00 (ISBN 0-8369-5072-0). Ayer Co Pubs.
Panagopoulos, Beata K. Cistercian & Mendicant Monasteries in Medieval Greece. LC 78-10769. (Illus.). 1979. lib. bdg. 24.00x (ISBN 0-226-64544-4). U of Chicago Pr.
Stoddard, Whitney S. Monastery & Cathedral in France: Medieval Architecture, Sculpture, Stained Glass, Manuscripts, the Art of the Church Treasuries. LC 66-23923. 412p. 1966. 35.00x (ISBN 0-8195-3071-9). Wesleyan U Pr.

ARCHITECTURE, MOORISH
see Architecture, Islamic

ARCHITECTURE, MUSLIM
see Architecture, Islamic

ARCHITECTURE, ROCOCO
Harries, Karsten. The Bavarian Rococo Church: Between Faith & Aestheticism. LC 82-1116. (Illus.). 304p. 1983. text ed. 42.00x (ISBN 0-300-02720-6). Yale U Pr.

ARCHITECTURE, ROMAN
see also Architecture–Italy; Temples
Anderson, William J. & Spiers, Richard P. The Architecture of Ancient Rome: An Account of Its Historic Development. LC 27-24681. 202p. 1927. Repr. 49.00x (ISBN 0-403-08618-3). Somerset Pub.

ARCHITECTURE, SARACENIC
see Architecture, Islamic

ARIANISM
see also Jesus Christ–Divinity; Unitarianism
Athanasius, St. Select Treatises of St. Athanasius in Controversy with the Arians, 2 vols. 5th ed. Newman, John H., tr. LC 77-84694. (Heresies of the Early Christian & Medieval Era Ser.). Repr. of 1890 ed. 72.00 set (ISBN 0-404-16100-6). AMS Pr.
Gregg, Robert C. & Groh, Dennis E. Early Arianism: A View of Salvation. LC 79-7379. 224p. 1981. 5.00 (ISBN 0-8006-0576-4, 1-576). Fortress.
Gregg, Robert C., ed. & intro. by. Arianism: Historical & Theological Reassessments. LC 85-81654. (Patristic Monograph Ser.: No. 11). viii, 380p. 1985. pap. 12.00 (ISBN 0-915646-10-2). Phila Patristic.
Gwatkin, Henry M. The Arian Controversy. new ed. LC 77-84702. Repr. of 1903 ed. 27.50 (ISBN 0-404-16109-X). AMS Pr.
--Studies of Arianism: Chiefly Referring to the Character & Chronology of the Reaction Which Followed the Council of Nicaea. 2nd ed. LC 77-84703. Repr. of 1900 ed. 38.00 (ISBN 0-404-16110-3). AMS Pr.
Kopecek, Thomas A. A History of Neo-Arianism. LC 79-89557. (Patristic Monograph: No. 8). 1979. pap. 14.00 (ISBN 0-915646-07-2). Phila Patristic.

ARK, NOAH'S
see Noah's Ark

ARK OF THE COVENANT
Miller, Patrick D., Jr. & Roberts, J. J. The Hand of the Lord: A Reassessment of the "Ark Narrative" of 1 Samuel. LC 76-48737. (Near Eastern Studies). 128p. 1977. 12.50x (ISBN 0-8018-1920-2). Johns Hopkins.
Sandifer, Kevin W. The Importance of the Ark of Covenant in Christianity. Sibley, J. Ashley, Jr., ed. 112p. (Orig.). 1986. pap. 6.25 (ISBN 0-910653-13-5, 8101M). Archival Servs.
Wead, Doug. Where Is the Lost Ark? LC 82-71755. 122p. (Orig.). 1982. pap. 2.95 (ISBN 0-87123-628-1, 200628). Bethany Hse.

ARMENIAN CHURCH
Arpee, Leon. The Armenian Awakening. (Works of Leon Arpee Ser.). xi, 234p. 1985. Repr. of 1909 ed. 34.00 (ISBN 0-932051-67-7, Pub. by Am Repr Serv). Am Biog Serv.
Dowling, Theodore E. Armenian Church. LC 71-131511. Repr. of 1910 ed. 16.00 (ISBN 0-404-02167-0). AMS Pr.
Fortescue, Edward F. Armenian Church: Founded by Saint Gregory the Illuminator. 1970. Repr. of 1872 ed. 21.50 (ISBN 0-404-02518-8). AMS Pr.
Garsoian, Nina & Mathews, Thomas, eds. East of Byzantium: Syria & Armenia in the Formative Period. LC 82-9665. (Dumbarton Oaks Symposium). (Illus.). 266p. 1982. 35.00x (ISBN 0-88402-104-1). Dumbarton Oaks.
Gregory. Teaching of Saint Gregory: An Early Armenian Catechism. Thomson, Robert W., et al, trs. from Arm. LC 78-115482. (Armenian Texts & Studies: No. 3). 1971. 14.00x (ISBN 0-674-87038-7). Harvard U Pr.
Gulleserian, Papken. Armenian Church. Poladian, Vartapet T., tr. LC 70-131508. Repr. of 1939 ed. 11.50 (ISBN 0-404-02949-3). AMS Pr.
Koghbatsi, Yeznik. Refutation of the Sects. Samuelian, Thomas J., ed. (Armenian Church Classics Ser.). (Illus.). 1986. pap. write for info (ISBN 0-934728-13-5). D O A C.
Rycaut, Paul. Present State of the Greek & Armenian Churches. LC 75-13321. Repr. of 1679 ed. 32.50 (ISBN 0-404-05476-5). AMS Pr.

ARMENIAN MYTHOLOGY
see Mythology, Armenian

ARMINIANISM
see also Calvinism; Methodism
Pierre du Moulin, the Elder. The Anatomy of Arminianisme. LC 76-57380. (English Experience Ser.: No. 797). 1977. Repr. of 1620 ed. lib. bdg. 46.00 (ISBN 90-221-0797-3). Walter J Johnson.

ARMSTRONG, HERBERT W.
Benware, Paul N. Ambassadors of Armstrongism. 182p. (Orig.). 1984. pap. 5.95 (ISBN 0-87508-046-4). Chr Lit.
Bowden, John. Herbert Armstrong & His Worldwide Church of God: An Exposure & an Indictment. 64p. 1982. saddle stitched 3.00 (ISBN 0-911826-24-6). Am Atheist.
Martin, Walter. Herbert W. Armstrong. 32p. 1969. pap. 2.95 (ISBN 0-87123-213-8, 210213). Bethany Hse.

ARNOLD, EBERHARD
Arnold, Eberhard. God's Revolution: The Witness of Eberhard Arnold. Hutterian Society of Brothers & Yoder, John H., eds. pap. 8.95 (ISBN 0-8091-2609-5). Paulist Pr.

ARNOLD, MATTHEW, 1822-1888
Aikat, Amulyachandra. On the Poetry of Matthew Arnold, Robert Browning & Rabindranath Tagore. 1978. lib. bdg. 37.00 (ISBN 0-8495-0053-2). Arden Lib.
--On the Poetry of Matthew Arnold, Robert Browning & Rabindranath Tagore. LC 72-13660. 1972. Repr. of 1921 ed. lib. bdg. 20.00 (ISBN 0-8414-1237-5). Folcroft.
Allott, Kenneth, ed. Writers & Their Background: Matthew Arnold. LC 75-15339. (Writers & Their Background Ser.). xxvi, 353p. 1976. 20.00x (ISBN 0-8214-0197-1); pap. 10.00x (ISBN 0-8214-0198-X). Ohio U Pr.
Arnold, Matthew. God & the Bible: A Review of Objections to "Literature & Dogma". LC 75-129382. Repr. of 1875 ed. 15.00 (ISBN 0-404-00386-9). AMS Pr.
--Works of Matthew Arnold, 15 Vols. LC 70-107157. 1970. Repr. of 1903 ed. Set. 395.00x (ISBN 0-403-00201-X); 40.00 ea. Scholarly.
Buckler, William E. On the Poetry of Matthew Arnold: Essays in Critical Reconstruction. (The Gotham Library). 228p. 1982. 35.00x (ISBN 0-8147-1039-5). NYU Pr.
Carroll, Joseph. The Cultural Theory of Matthew Arnold. LC 81-23996. 296p. 1982. 25.95x (ISBN 0-520-04616-1). U of Cal Pr.
Connell, William F. Educational Thought & Influence of Matthew Arnold. LC 74-109305. 1971. Repr. of 1950 ed. lib. bdg. 22.50x (ISBN 0-8371-3580-X, COMA). Greenwood.
Coulling, Sidney. Matthew Arnold & His Critics: A Study of Arnold's Controversies. LC 74-82498. xiv, 351p. 1974. 20.00x (ISBN 0-8214-0161-0). Ohio U Pr.
Dawson, Carl & Pfordresher, John, eds. Matthew Arnold: Prose Writings. (The Critical Heritage Ser.). 1979. 34.00x (ISBN 0-7100-0244-0). Methuen Inc.
Day, Paul W. Matthew Arnold & the Philosophy of Vico. 1964. 10.00 (ISBN 0-8274-2691-7). R West.
Eells, John S. Touchstones of Matthew Arnold. LC 76-136388. Repr. of 1955 ed. 22.50 (ISBN 0-404-02263-4). AMS Pr.
Groom, Bernard. On the Diction of Tennyson, Browning & Arnold. LC 79-138975. 57p. 1970. Repr. of 1939 ed. 14.50 (ISBN 0-208-01027-0, Archon). Shoe String.
Harding, Frank J. Matthew Arnold, the Critic & France. LC 76-50106. 1977. Repr. of 1964 ed. lib. bdg. 25.00 (ISBN 0-8414-4721-7). Folcroft.
Harvey, Charles H. Matthew Arnold: A Critic of the Victorian Period. LC 69-18273. 256p. 1969. Repr. of 1931 ed. 27.50 (ISBN 0-208-00732-6, Archon). Shoe String.
Honan, Park. Matthew Arnold: A Life. LC 80-26131. (Illus.). 544p. 1981. 19.95 (ISBN 0-07-029697-9). McGraw.
Jump, John D. Matthew Arnold. LC 76-7983. 1955. lib. bdg. 20.00 (ISBN 0-8414-5348-9). Folcroft.
Kelman, John. Prophets of Yesterday & Their Message for Today. facs. ed. LC 74-152181. (Essay Index Reprint Ser). 1924. 17.00 (ISBN 0-8369-2193-3). Ayer Co Pubs.
Kelso, Alexander. Matthew Arnold. 1978. lib. bdg. 10.00 (ISBN 0-8492-1444-0). R West.
Kingsmill, Hugh. Matthew Arnold. 1973. Repr. of 1928 ed. 40.00 (ISBN 0-8274-0720-3). R West.
Livingston, James C. Matthew Arnold & Christianity: His Religious Prose Writings. 250p. 1986. text ed. 17.95x (ISBN 0-87249-462-4). U of SC Pr.
Lund, T. W. Matthew Arnold: The Message & Meaning of a Life. LC 76-28474. 1888. lib. bdg. 8.50 (ISBN 0-8414-5807-3). Folcroft.
Moore, Charles L. Incense & Iconoclasm. 343p. 1980. Repr. of 1915 ed. lib. bdg. 30.00 (ISBN 0-89987-573-4). Century Bookbindery.
Sherman, Stuart P. Matthew Arnold: How to Know Him. 1973. lib. bdg. 20.00 (ISBN 0-8414-8083-4). Folcroft.
--Matthew Arnold, How to Know Him. 326p. 1968. Repr. of 1917 ed. 29.50 (ISBN 0-208-00453-X, Archon). Shoe String.
Smart, Thomas B. Bibliography of Matthew Arnold, Eighteen Ninety-Two. 1974. lib. bdg. 18.50 (ISBN 0-8414-7634-9). Folcroft.
Stanley, Carlton W. Matthew Arnold. 1978. Repr. of 1938 ed. 20.00 (ISBN 0-8492-2595-7). R West.
Strachey, Lytton. Eminent Victorians. 354p. 1969. pap. 6.95 (ISBN 0-15-628697-1, Harv). HarBraceJ.
Tillotson, Kathleen. Matthew Arnold & Carlyle. LC 73-16394. 1956. lib. bdg. 12.50 (ISBN 0-8414-8560-7). Folcroft.
Tollers, Vincent L., ed. Bibliography of Matthew Arnold, 1932-1970. 1974. 24.95x (ISBN 0-271-01113-0). Pa St U Pr.
Wilson, John D. Leslie Stephen & Matthew Arnold As Critics of Wordsworth. LC 72-2060. (English Biography Ser., No. 31). 1972. Repr. of 1939 ed. lib. bdg. 40.95x (ISBN 0-8383-1455-4). Haskell.
Woodfield, Malcom, ed. R. H. Hutton, Critic & Theologian: The Writings of R. H. Hutton on Newman, Arnold, Tennyson, Wordsworth & George Eliot. 240p. 42.00 (ISBN 0-19-818564-2). Oxford U Pr.

ARNOLD, THOMAS, 1795-1842
Stanley, Arthur P. Life & Correspondence of Thomas Arnold D. D, 2 vols. LC 75-29624. Repr. of 1845 ed. Set. 72.50 (ISBN 0-404-13980-9). AMS Pr.

ARS MORIENDI–BIBLIOGRAPHY
O'Connor, Sr. M. Catharine. Art of Dying Well. Repr. of 1942 ed. 15.00 (ISBN 0-404-04811-0). AMS Pr.

ART–PHILOSOPHY
Constable, Benjamin. Art, the Metaphysics of Love & Its Universal Mystical Symbols. (Illus.). 1977. 47.25 (ISBN 0-89266-046-5). Am Classical Coll Pr.
Coomaraswamy, Ananda K. Christian & Oriental Philosophy of Art. 1957. pap. 3.95 (ISBN 0-486-20378-6). Dover.
Dixon, John W., Jr. Art & Theological Imagination. (Illus.). 1978. 12.95 (ISBN 0-8164-0397-X, HarpR). Har-Row.
Malraux, Andre. Metamorphose des Dieux: L'Intemporel. (Illus.). 424p. 1976. 125.00 (ISBN 0-686-56329-8). French & Eur.
Maritain, Jacques. Art & Scholasticism & the Frontiers of Poetry. Evans, Joseph W., tr. from Fr. LC 74-13601. 240p. 1974. pap. 6.95x (ISBN 0-268-00557-5). U of Notre Dame Pr.
Mitchell, W. J. Iconology: Image, Text, Ideology. LC 85-1177. x, 226p. 1986. 20.00 (ISBN 0-226-53228-3). U of Chicago Pr.
Palmer, Michael. Paul Tillich's Philosophy of Art. LC 83-15056. (Theologische Bibliothek Toepelmann Ser.: Vol. 41). xxii, 217p. 1983. 49.50x (ISBN 3-11-009681-1). De Gruyter.
Tanahashi, Kazuaki. Penetrating Laughter: Hakuin's Zen & Art. LC 83-43155. (Illus.). 144p. 1984. 16.95 (ISBN 0-87951-952-5); pap. 8.95 (ISBN 0-87951-280-6). Overlook Pr.

ART, BUDDHIST
Art Institute of Chicago. The Great Eastern Temple: Treasures of Japanese Buddhist Art from Todai-ji. Mino, Yutaka, ed. LC 86-45044. (Midland Bks.: No. 390). (Illus.). 180p. 1986. 45.00x (ISBN 0-253-32634-6); pap. 20.00x (ISBN 0-253-20390-2). Ind U Pr.
Baskett, Mary. Footprints of the Buddha. LC 80-80133. (Illus.). 125p. (Orig.). 1980. pap. 8.95 (ISBN 0-87633-034-0). Phila Mus Art.
Burgess, Jas. Buddhist Art in India. 240p. 27.00X (ISBN 0-317-52134-9, Pub. by S Chand India). State Mutual Bk.
Coomaraswamy, Ananda K. Elements of Buddhist Iconography. (Illus.). 1979. text ed. 23.00x. Coronet Bks.
Fontein, J. Pilgrimage of Sudhana. 1967. text ed. 35.60x (ISBN 90-2796-387-8). Mouton.
Foucher, A. The Beginnings of Buddhist Art. 1972. 20.00 (ISBN 0-89684-370-X). Orient Bk Dist.
Genoud, C. & Inoue, T. Buddhist Wall-Painting of Ladakh. (Illus.). 116p. 1981. text ed. 75.00x (ISBN 2-88086-001-6, Pub. by Editions Olizane Holland). Humanities.
Ghosh, Mallar. Development of Buddhist Iconography in Eastern India. (Illus.). 1980. text ed. 44.00x. Coronet Bks.
Grunwedel, Albert. Buddhist Art in India. Gibson, Agnes C., tr. (Ger., Illus.). 236p. Repr. of 1901 ed. text ed. 37.50x. Coronet Bks.
Gupte, R. S. Iconography of the Hindus, Buddhists & Jains. 2nd ed. (Illus.). xviii, 201p. 1981. text ed. 45.00x (ISBN 0-86590-028-0, Pub. by Taraporevala India). Apt Bks.
Ishida, Hisatoyo. Esoteric Buddhist Painting: Japanese Arts Library, Vol. 15. LC 86-40437. (Japanese Arts Library). (Illus.). 210p. 1987. 29.95 (ISBN 0-87011-767-X). Kodansha.
Marshall, John. The Buddhist Art of Gandhara. (Illus.). 1981. Repr. of 1960 ed. text ed. 30.00x. Coronet Bks.
Mitra. Buddhist Monuments. 1971. 42.50 (ISBN 0-89684-490-0). Orient Bk Dist.

Pal, Pratapaditya. Light of Asia: Buddha Sakyamuni in Asian Art. LC 84-788. (Illus.). 344p. 1984. 35.00 (ISBN 0-295-96123-6, Pub. by LA County Museum of Art). U of Wash Pr.

Pal, Pratapaditya, et al. Light of Asia: Buddha Sakyamuni in Asian Art. (Illus.). 332p. 1984. 35.00 (ISBN 0-87587-116-X, Dist. by U of Wash Pr); pap. 16.95 (ISBN 0-87587-116-X). LA Co Art Mus.

Randall, Doanda, compiled by. Buddhist & Hindu Art in the Collection of John H. Mann. (Illus.). 285p. (Orig.). 1981. 65.00x (ISBN 0-940492-01-6). Asian Conserv Lab.

Rhie, Marylin M. Fo-Kuang Ssu: Literary Evidences & Buddhist Images. LC 76-23690. (Outstanding Dissertations in the Fine Arts - Far Eastern). (Illus.). 1977. Repr. of 1970 ed. lib. bdg. 55.00 (ISBN 0-8240-2721-3). Garland Pub.

Rosenfield, John M. & Ten Grotenhuis, Elizabeth. Journey of the Three Jewels: Japanese Buddhist Paintings from Western Collections. LC 79-15072. (Illus.). 1979. 19.95 (ISBN 0-87848-054-4). Asia Soc.

Saunders, E. Dale. Mudra: A Study of Symbolic Gestures in Japanese Buddhist Sculpture. (Bollingen Ser.: Vol. 58). (Illus.). 1960. 37.00x (ISBN 0-691-09796-8). Princeton U Pr.

Stein, Aurel. The Thousand Buddhas. LC 77-94623. 1979. Repr. of 1921 ed. lib. bdg. 10.00 (ISBN 0-89341-249-X). Longwood Pub Group.

Sugiyama, Jiro. Classic Buddhist Sculpture. LC 82-80738. (Japanese Arts Library: Vol. 11). (Illus.). 200p. 1982. 25.00 (ISBN 0-87011-529-4). Kodansha.

Sullivan, Michael. The Cave Temples of Maichishan. LC 69-15829. (Illus.). 1969. 70.00x (ISBN 0-520-01448-0). U of Cal Pr.

Vogel, J. P. Buddhist Art in India, Ceylon, & Java. (Illus.). 187p. 1977. Repr. of 1936 ed. text ed. 19.00x. Coronet Bks.

ART, BYZANTINE

Beckwith, John. Early Christian & Byzantine Art. (Pelican History of Art Ser.). 1980. pap. 18.95 (ISBN 0-14-056133-1, Pelican). Penguin.

Buchtal, Hugo. The Miniatures of the Paris Psalter: A Study in Middle Byzantine Painting. (Warburg Institute Studies: Vol. 2). Repr. of 1938 ed. 88.00 (ISBN 0-8115-1379-3). Kraus Repr.

Demus, Otto. Byzantine Mosaic Decoration: Aspects of Monumental Art in Byzantium. (Illus.). 162p. 1976. 25.00 (ISBN 0-89241-018-3). Caratzas.

Dionysius Of Fourna. Manuel d'iconographie Chretienne, Grecque et Latine. Durand, Paul, tr. 1963. Repr. of 1845 ed. 32.00 (ISBN 0-8337-0868-6). B Franklin.

Kontoglou, Photios. Byzantine Sacred Art. 2nd, rev. & enl. ed. Cavarnos, Constantine, compiled by. & tr. from Gr. LC 83-81152. (Illus.). 171p. 1985. 10.50 (ISBN 0-914744-60-7); pap. 7.95 (ISBN 0-914744-61-5). Inst Byzantine.

Vaboulis, Peter. Byzantine Decorative Art. (Illus.). 202p. 125.00 (ISBN 0-89241-035-3). Caratzas.

Vikan, Gary. Byzantine Pilgrimage Art. (Byzantine Collection Publications Ser.: No. 5). (Illus.). 52p. 1982. pap. 4.50x (ISBN 0-88402-113-0). Dumbarton Oaks.

Weitzmann, Kurt. Greek Mythology in Byzantine Art. LC 84-4849. (Illus.). 380p. 1984. text ed. 95.00 (ISBN 0-691-03574-1). Princeton U Pr.

ART, CHRISTIAN

see Christian Art and Symbolism

ART, CISTERCIAN

Lillich, Meredith P., ed. Studies in Cistercian Art & Architecture, II. (Cistercian Studies: No. 69). (Illus.). pap. 14.95 (ISBN 0-87907-869-3). Cistercian Pubns.

--Studies in Cistercian Art & Architecture, III. (Cistercian Studies: No. 89). (Orig.). 1987. pap. write for info. (ISBN 0-87907-889-8). Cistercian Pubns.

ART, ECCLESIASTICAL

see Christian Art and Symbolism

ART, GOTHIC

Bayard, Tania. Bourges Cathedral: The West Portals. LC 75-23780. (Outstanding Dissertations in the Fine Arts Ser. - Medieval). (Illus.). 1976. lib. bdg. 55.00 (ISBN 0-8240-1977-6). Garland Pub.

Dyorak, Max. Idealism & Naturalism in Gothic Art. Klawiter, Randolph J., tr. LC 67-22143. (Illus.). pap. 70.50 (ISBN 0-317-10425-X, 2022072). Bks Demand UMI.

Jantzen, Hans. High Gothic. LC 83-43099. (Illus.). 196p. 1984. 25.00x (ISBN 0-691-04026-5); pap. 7.95x (ISBN 0-691-00372-6). Princeton U Pr.

Male, Emile. The Gothic Image: Religious Art in France of the Thirteenth Century. Nussey, Dora, tr. from Fr. (Icon Editions). (Illus.). 440p. 1973. pap. 10.95 (ISBN 0-06-430032-3, IN-32, HarpT). Har-Row.

ART, HINDU

Banerjee, J. N. Development of Hindu Iconography. 3rd ed. (Illus.). 1974. text ed. 36.00x. Coronet Bks.

Boner, Alice. Vastusutra Upanisad: The Essence of Form in Sacred Art. xii, 192p. 1986. 32.00 (Pub. by Motilal Banarsidass). South Asia Bks.

Dubash, P. N. Hindoo Art in Its Social Setting. (Illus.). 278p. 1986. Repr. 30.00X (ISBN 0-8364-1752-6, Pub. by Usha). South Asia Bks.

Ghosh, S. P. Hindu Religious Art & Architecture. (Illus.). 148p. 1983. text ed. 30.00x (ISBN 0-86590-124-4). Apt Bks.

Gupte, R. S. Iconography of the Hindus, Buddhists & Jains. 2nd ed. (Illus.). xviii, 201p. 1981. text ed. 45.00x (ISBN 0-86590-028-0, Pub. by Taraporevala India). Apt Bks.

Krishna Murthy, C. Saiva Art & Architecture in South India. 1985. 48.00x (ISBN 0-8364-1417-9, Pub. by Sundeep). South Asia Bks.

Randall, Doanda, compiled by. Buddhist & Hindu Art in the Collection of John H. Mann. (Illus.). 285p. (Orig.). 1981. 65.00x (ISBN 0-940492-01-6). Asian Conserv Lab.

Sharma, B. N. Iconography of Sadasiva. LC 76-902916. 1976. 12.50 (ISBN 0-88386-823-7). South Asia Bks.

Splendours of the Vijayanagara. 1981. 30.00x (ISBN 0-8364-0792-X, Pub. by Marg India). South Asia Bks.

Stutley, Margaret. The Illustrated Dictionary of Hindu Iconography. (Illus.). 200p. 1985. 36.95 (ISBN 0-317-17180-1). Methuen Inc.

ART, ISLAMIC

Arnold, T. W. The Old & New Testaments in Muslim Religious Art. (British Academy, London, Schweidr Lectures in Biblical Archaeology Series, 1928). pap. 19.00 (ISBN 0-8115-1270-3). Kraus Repr.

Creswell, K. A. A Bibliography of the Architecture, Arts & Crafts of Islam. 2nd ed. 120.00 (ISBN 0-89410-306-7, Pub. by FP Van Eck Liechtenstein). Three Continents.

Grabar, Oleg, ed. Muqarnas: An Annual on Islamic Art & Architecture: The Art of the Mamluks, Vol. II. LC 83-643765. (Illus.). 240p. 1984. 35.00x (ISBN 0-300-03137-8). Yale U Pr.

Islamic Art & Architecture. LC 76-14076. (Garland Library of the History of Art: XIII). 1977. lib. bdg. 61.00 (ISBN 0-8240-2423-0). Garland Pub.

The K. A. C. Cresswell Library of Islamic Art & Architecture. 1986. 39.50 (ISBN 977-424-101-0, Pub. by Am Univ Cairo Pr). Columbia U Pr.

Kalus, Ludvik. Catalogue of Islamic Seals & Talismans in the Ashmolean Museum. 1985. 45.00x (Pub. by Ashmolean Museum). State Mutual Bk.

North, Anthony. Islamic Arms. (The Victoria & Albert Introductions to Decorative Arts Ser.). (Illus.). 48p. 1986. 9.95 (ISBN 0-88045-078-9). Stemmer Hse.

ART, JEWISH

see also Jewish Art and Symbolism

Altschuler, David, ed. The Precious Legacy: Judaic Treasures from the Czechoslavak State Collection. (Illus.). 256p. (Orig.). 1983. 40.00 (ISBN 0-671-49448-1); pap. 17.50 (ISBN 0-671-49498-8). Summit Bks.

Costanza, Mary S. The Living Witness: Art in the Concentration Camps & Ghettos. 1982. 19.95 (ISBN 0-02-906660-3). Free Pr.

Craig, Jonathan. Concepts in Jewish Art. LC 84-263. (Judaic Studies). (Illus.). 165p. 1986. 24.00x (ISBN 0-8046-9355-2, 9355, Pub. by Natl U). Assoc Faculty Pr.

Goldman, Bernard. The Sacred Portal: A Primary Symbol in Ancient Judaic Art. LC 86-10983. (Brown Classics in Judaica Ser.). (Illus.). 260p. 1986. pap. text ed. 15.75 (ISBN 0-8191-5269-2). U Pr of Amer.

Goldstein, David. The Ashkenazi Haggadah. (Illus.). 140p. 1985. 75.00 (ISBN 0-8109-1819-6). Abrams.

Kanof, Abram, intro. by. Ceremonial Art in the Judaic Tradition. LC 75-126321. (Illus.). 92p. 1975. pap. 3.00 (ISBN 0-88259-078-2). NCMA.

Mann, Vivian B. & Kleeblatt, Norman. Treasures of the Jewish Museum. LC 85-28913. (Illus.). 216p. 1986. text ed. 35.00x (ISBN 0-87663-493-5); pap. 19.95 (ISBN 0-87663-890-6). Universe.

Mann, Vivian B. & Tucker, Gordon, eds. The Seminar on Jewish Art: Proceedings. 37p. (Orig.). 1985. pap. 6.00 (ISBN 0-87334-029-9). Jewish Sem.

Moore, Clare, ed. The Visual Dimension: Aspects of Jewish Art. (Publications of the Oxford Centre for Postgraduate Hebrew Study Ser.: Vol. 5). (Illus.). 320p. 1987. text ed. 40.00x (ISBN 0-86598-081-0, Rowman & Littlefield). Rowman.

Ungerleider-Mayerson, Joy. Jewish Folk Art: From Biblical Days to Modern Times. 272p. 1986. 50.00 (ISBN 0-671-63007-5). Summit Bks.

Union of American Hebrew Congregations. Spiritual Resistance: Art from the Concentration Camps 1940-1945. LC 78-1169. (Illus.). 354p. 1981. 35.00 (ISBN 0-8276-0109-3, 421). Jewish Pubns.

Weinstein, Jay. A Collectors' Guide to Judaica. (Illus.). 1985. 29.95 (ISBN 0-500-23440-X). Thames Hudson.

ART, MEDIEVAL

see also Art, Byzantine; Art, Cistercian; Art, Gothic; Illumination of Books and Manuscripts

Brown University Dept. of Art Staff. The Survival of the Gods: Classical Mythology in Medieval Art. LC 86-72762. (Illus., Orig.). 1986. pap. text ed. 14.00 (ISBN 0-933519-10-9). D W Bell Gallery.

Coulton, George G. Art & the Reformation. LC 69-15789. (Illus.). xxii, 662p. 1969. Repr. of 1928 ed. 45.00 (ISBN 0-208-00738-5, Archon). Shoe String.

Crump, C. G. & Jacob, E. F., eds. Legacy of the Middle Ages. (Legacy Ser.). (Illus.). 1926. 32.50x (ISBN 0-19-821907-5). Oxford U Pr.

Gregoire, Reginald, et al. The Monastic Realm. LC 85-43046. (Illus.). 288p. 1985. 75.00 (ISBN 0-8478-0664-2). Rizzoli Intl.

Lethaby, William R. Mediaeval Art: From the Peace of the Church to the Eve of the Renaissance, 312-1350. facsimile ed. LC 70-157345. (Select Bibliographies Reprint Ser). Repr. of 1904 ed. 33.00 (ISBN 0-8369-5806-3). Ayer Co Pubs.

Mellinkoff, Ruth. The Horned Moses in Medieval Art & Thought. LC 77-85450. (California Studies in the History of Art: No. XIV). (Illus.). 1970. 40.00x (ISBN 0-520-01705-6). U of Cal Pr.

Nordenfalk, Carl, ed. Medieval & Renaissance Miniatures from the National Gallery of Art. LC 74-28397. (Illus.). pap. 8.95 (ISBN 0-89468-017-X). Natl Gallery Art.

Parker, Elizabeth C. The Descent from the Cross: Its Relation to the Extra-Liturgical Depositio Drama. LC 77-94713. (Outstanding Dissertations in the Fine Arts Ser.). 1978. lib. bdg. 41.00 (ISBN 0-8240-3245-4). Garland Pub.

Schapiro, Meyer. Late Antique, Early Christian & Mediaeval Art: Selected Papers, Vol. III. (Illus.). 422p. 1979. 25.00 (ISBN 0-8076-0927-7). Braziller.

Stoddard, Whitney S. Art & Architecture in Medieval France. (Icon Editions Ser.). Orig. Title: Monastery & Cathedral in Medieval France. (Illus.). 436p. 1972. pap. 14.95xi (ISBN 0-06-430022-6, IN-22, HarpT). Har-Row.

Zarnecki, George. Art of the Medieval World: Architecture, Sculpture, Painting, the Sacred Arts. 1976. 34.95 (ISBN 0-13-047514-9). P-H.

ART, MEXICAN

Bahm, Linda, et al. Fiestas of San Juan Nuevo: Ceremonial Art from Michoacan, Mexico. LC 83-42809. (Illus.). 70p. 1983. pap. 12.50 (ISBN 0-912535-00-8). Max Mus.

Brenner, Anita. Idols Behind Altars. LC 67-19527. (Illus.). 1929. 18.00 (ISBN 0-8196-0190-X). Biblo.

Stern, Jean, ed. The Cross & the Sword. LC 76-9415. Tr. of La Cruz y la Espada. (Eng. & Span., Illus.). 144p. 1982. pap. 10.00 (ISBN 0-295-95916-9, Pub. by San Diego Museum Art). U of Wash Pr.

ART AND MYTHOLOGY

Anzul, Dario. The Paintings of Mysticism & Violence in Full Colours of Dario Anzul. (Illus.). 97p. 1983. 225.75x (ISBN 0-86650-073-1). Gloucester Art.

Bernen, Satia & Bernen, Robert. A Guide to Myth & Religion in European Painting 1270-1700. LC 72-96070. 288p. 1973. 8.95 (ISBN 0-8076-0683-9). Braziller.

Brown University Dept. of Art Staff. The Survival of the Gods: Classical Mythology in Medieval Art. LC 86-72762. (Illus., Orig.). 1986. pap. text ed. 14.00 (ISBN 0-933519-10-9). D W Bell Gallery.

Clement, Clara. A Handbook of Legendary & Mythological Art. 59.95 (ISBN 0-8490-0279-6). Gordon Pr.

Clement, Clara E. Handbook of Legendary & Mythological Art. LC 68-26616. (Illus.). 1969. Repr. of 1881 ed. 45.00x (ISBN 0-8103-3175-6). Gale.

Jacobs, Michael. Mythological Painting. LC 78-25563. (Mayflower Gallery Ser.). (Illus.). 1979. 12.50 (ISBN 0-8317-6282-9, Mayflower Bks); pap. 6.95 (ISBN 0-8317-6283-7). Smith Pubs.

Knight, Richard P. Ancient Art & Mythology. (The Most Meaningful Classics in World Culture Ser.). 1979. Repr. of 1876 ed. 69.75 (ISBN 0-89266-189-5). Am Classical Coll Pr.

Matthews, Caitlin. Goddess. (Art & Imagination Ser.). (Illus.). 1983. pap. cancelled (ISBN 0-500-81031-1). Thames-Hudson.

Steiner, Rudolf. Art as Seen in the Light of Mystery Wisdom. 2nd ed. Tr. of Kunst im Lichte der Mysterienweisheit. 182p. 1984. pap. 9.95 (ISBN 0-85440-416-3, Pub. by Steinerbooks). Anthroposophic.

Waters, Clara E. A Handbook of Legendary & Mythological Art. LC 76-27524. (Illus.). 1976. Repr. of 1876 ed. lib. bdg. 50.00 (ISBN 0-89341-037-3). Longwood Pub Group.

Welles, Marcia L. Arachne's Tapestry: The Transformation of Myth in Seventeenth-Century Spain. (Illus.). 220p. 1986. text ed. 22.50 (ISBN 0-939980-11-8). Trinity U Pr.

Williamson, John. The Oak King, the Holly King, & the Unicorn: The Myths & Symbolism of the Unicorn Tapestries. LC 85-45242. (Illus.). 280p. 1987. pap. 12.95 (ISBN 0-06-096032-9, PL 6032, PL). Har-Row.

ART AND RELIGION

see also Art and Mythology; Christian Art and Symbolism; Gods in Art; Idols and Images

Adams, Dour & Apostolos-Cappadona, Diane. Art as Religious Studies. (Illus.). 272p. (Orig.). 1987. pap. 17.95 (ISBN 0-8245-0809-2). Crossroad NY.

Apostolos-Cappadona, Diane, ed. Art, Creativity & the Sacred: An Anthology in Religion & Art. (Illus.). 352p. 1983. pap. 16.95 (ISBN 0-8245-0609-X). Crossroad NY.

Bennett, Curtis. God As Form: Essays in Greek Theology with Special Reference to Christianity & the Contemporary Theological Predicament. LC 75-43851. 1976. 39.50 (ISBN 0-87395-325-8). State U NY Pr.

Blom, Dorothea. The Prophetic Element in Modern Art. 1983. pap. 2.50x (ISBN 0-87574-148-7, 148). Pendle Hill.

Burgess, James & Fergusson, James. The Cave Temples of India. (Illus.). 1969. text ed. 57.50x. Coronet Bks.

Chantre, Jean-Claude. Les Considerations Religieuses et Esthetiques D'un "Sturmer und Dranger". (European University Studies: No.1, Vol. 507). (Fr.). 650p. 1982. 62.10 (ISBN 3-261-04989-8). P Lang Pubs.

Coulton, George G. Art & the Reformation. LC 69-15789. (Illus.). xxii, 662p. 1969. Repr. of 1928 ed. 45.00 (ISBN 0-208-00738-5, Archon). Shoe String.

Cram, Ralph A. The Catholic Church & Art. 59.95 (ISBN 0-87968-817-3). Gordon Pr.

Detweiler, Robert, ed. Art, Literature, Religion: Life on the Borders. LC 82-3319. (AAR Thermatic Studies). 208p. 1983. 22.50 (ISBN 0-89130-578-5, 01 24 92). Scholars Pr GA.

Dillenberger, John. A Theology of Artistic Sensibilities: The Visual Arts & the Church. 280p. 1986. 22.50 (ISBN 0-8245-0783-5). Crossroad NY.

--The Visual Arts & Christianity in America: The Colonial Period Through the Nineteenth Century. LC 84-3897. (Scholars Press Studies in the Humanities). 1984. 29.25 (ISBN 0-89130-734-6, 00 01 05); pap. 19.50 (ISBN 0-89130-761-3). Scholars Pr GA.

Downes, David A. Ruskin's Landscape of Beatitude. LC 83-48767. (American University Studies IV (English Language & Literature): Vol. 4). 247p. 1984. pap. text ed. 24.75 (ISBN 0-8204-0049-1). P Lang Pubs.

Egenter, Richard. Desecration of Christ. 1967. 4.50 (ISBN 0-8199-0018-4, L38133). Franciscan Herald.

Eichenberg, Fritz. Art & Faith. (Illus., Orig.). 1952. pap. 2.50x (ISBN 0-87574-068-5). Pendle Hill.

Environment & Art in Catholic Worship. 100p. 1978. pap. 7.95 (ISBN 1-55586-563-1, V563). US Catholic.

Eustace, C. J. Infinity of Questions: Studies in the Art of Religion & the Religion of Art in the Lives of Helen Foley, Katherine Mansfield, et al. 170p. 1946. 10.00 (ISBN 0-87556-595-6). Saifer.

Fleming, John V. From Bonaventure to Bellini: An Essay in Franciscan Exegesis. LC 82-47593. (Princeton Essays on the Arts Ser.: No. 14). (Illus.). 192p. 1982. 28.00x (ISBN 0-691-07270-1); pap. 14.50 L.P.E. (ISBN 0-691-10143-4). Princeton U Pr.

Forsyth, Peter T. Religion in Recent Art. 3rd ed. LC 73-148780. Repr. of 1905 ed. 24.50 (ISBN 0-404-02515-3). AMS Pr.

Gregoire, Reginald, et al. The Monastic Realm. LC 85-43046. (Illus.). 288p. 1985. 75.00 (ISBN 0-8478-0664-2). Rizzoli Intl.

Jameson, Anna B. The History of Our Lord As Exemplified in Works of Art; with That of His Type; St. John the Baptist; & Other Persons of the Old & New Testament, 2 vols. LC 92-167006. (Illus.). 1976. Repr. of 1890 ed. Set. 70.00x (ISBN 0-8103-4304-5). Gale.

Klem, Herbert V. Oral Communication of the Scripture: Insights from African Oral Art. LC 81-10052. (Applied Cultural Anthropology Ser.). (Illus.). 280p. (Orig.). 1982. pap. text ed. 9.95x (ISBN 0-87808-332-4). William Carey Lib.

Labarge, Margaret W. Court, Church & Castle. (Illus.). 112p. 1972. pap. 3.25 (ISBN 0-88884-431-X, 56310-3, Pub. by Natl Mus Canada). U of Chicago Pr.

Lerner, Carol. A Biblical Garden. (Illus.). 1982. 13.50 (ISBN 0-688-01071-7). Morrow.

Leveen, J. The Hebrew Bible in Art. (British Academy, London, Schweich Lectures on Biblical Archaeology Series, 1939). pap. 28.00 (ISBN 0-8115-1281-9). Kraus Repr.

Malraux, Andre. Metamorphose des Dieux: L'Intemporel. (Illus.). 424p. 1976. 125.00 (ISBN 0-686-56329-8). French & Eur.

Martland, T. R. Religion As Art. LC 80-27104. (Series in Philosophy). 265p. 1981. 49.50x (ISBN 0-87395-520-X); pap. 16.95 (ISBN 0-87395-521-8). State U NY Pr.

Meister, Michael W. Discourses on Siva. LC 83-12529. (Illus.). 568p. 1985. 75.00 (ISBN 0-8122-7909-3). U of Pa Pr.

Miller, Barbara S., ed. Exploring India's Sacred Art: Selected Writings of Stella Kramrisch. LC 82-60302. (Illus., Orig.). 1983. 57.95x (ISBN 0-8122-7856-9); pap. 21.00x (ISBN 0-8122-1134-0). U of Pa Pr.

Omer, Mordechai. Turner & the Bible. (Illus.). 48p. (Orig.). 1981. pap. 7.75 (ISBN 0-900090-90-1, Pub. by Ashmolean Mus). Longwood Pub Group.

Paulson, Ronald. Book & Painting: Shakespeare, Milton, & the Bible. LC 82-2769. (Hodges Lectures Ser.). (Illus.). 248p. 1982. text ed. 23.50x (ISBN 0-87049-358-2). U of Tenn Pr.

Pepper, Stephen. Bob Jones University Collection of Religious Art: Italian Paintings. (Illus.). 336p. (Orig.). 1984. pap. 55.00 (ISBN 0-89084-263-9). Bob Jones Univ Pr.

Pfeiffer, John E. The Creative Explosion: An Inquiry into the Origins of Art & Religion. LC 84-72675. (Illus.). 270p. (Orig.). 1985. pap. text ed. 12.95x (ISBN 0-8014-9308-0). Cornell U Pr.

Physick, John. Victorian Church Art. (Illus.). 212p. (Orig.). 1984. pap. 12.95 (ISBN 0-901486-36-1, Pub. by Victoria & Albert Mus UK). Faber & Faber.

Rajan, K. V. India's Religious Art: Ideas & Ideals. (Illus.). 1982. text ed. 45.00x (ISBN 0-391-02916-9). Humanities.

Richter, Gottfried. Art & Human Consciousness. Frohlich, Margaret & Channer, Burley, trs. from Ger. (Illus.). 300p. (Orig.). 1985. 30.00 (ISBN 0-88010-108-3). Anthroposophic.

Rubin, William S. Modern Sacred Art & the Church of Assy. LC 61-15469. (Illus.). pap. 61.30 (ISBN 0-317-10614-7, 2051858). Bks Demand UMI.

Schaeffer, Francis A. Art & the Bible. LC 73-75891. 64p. 1973. pap. 2.95 (ISBN 0-87784-443-7). Inter-Varsity.

Scharper, Philip & Sharper, Sally, eds. The Gospel in Art by the Peasants of Solentiname. Walsh, Donaldly, tr. from Span. (Illus.). 70p. 1984. 10.95 (ISBN 0-88344-382-1). Orbis Bks.

Shalom of Safed. Images From The Bible: The Paintings of Shalom of Safed, the Words of Elie Wiesel. LC 79-51032. (Illus.). 112p. 1980. 40.00 (ISBN 0-87951-107-9); limited, signed 400.00 (ISBN 0-87951-108-7). Overlook Pr.

Shariati, Ali. Art Awaiting the Saviour. Fardjadi, Homa, tr. from Persian. 23p. 1980. pap. 1.00x (ISBN 0-941722-16-3). Book Dist Ctr.

Steiner, Rudolf. Art as Seen in the Light of Mystery Wisdom. 2nd ed. Tr. of Kunst im Lichte der Mysterienweisheit. 182p. 1984. pap. 9.95 (ISBN 0-85440-416-3, Pub. by Steinerbooks). Anthroposophic.

--The Arts & Their Mission. Monges & Moore, trs. from German. 125p. 1986. pap. 8.95 (ISBN 0-88010-154-7). Anthroposophic.

Stoddard, Whitney S. Monastery & Cathedral in France: Medieval Architecture, Sculpture, Stained Glass, Manuscripts, the Art of the Church Treasuries. LC 66-23923. 412p. 1966. 35.00x (ISBN 0-8195-3071-9). Wesleyan U Pr.

Stucki, Margaret E. War on Light: The Destruction of the Image of God in Man Through Modern Art. 5.95 (ISBN 0-686-18059-3). Freedom Univ-FSP.

Tillich, Paul. On Art & Architecture. Dillenberger, John & Dillenberger, Jane, eds. (Illus.). 272p. 1987. 14.50 (ISBN 0-8245-0829-7). Crossroad NY.

Weiss, Paul. Religion & Art. (Aquinas Lecture). 1963. 7.95 (ISBN 0-87462-128-3). Marquette.

ARYAMEN (HINDU DEITY)

Thieme, Paul. Mitra & Aryaman. (Connecticut Academy of Arts & Sciences Transaction: Vol. 41). 1967. 18.00 (ISBN 0-208-01104-8). Shoe String.

ASBURY, FRANCIS, 1745-1816

Ludwig, Charles. Francis Asbury. 1984. pap. 6.95 (ISBN 0-88062-024-2). Mott Media.

Wilson Story, Bettie. Gospel Trailblazer: The Exciting Story of Francis Asbury. 128p. 1984. pap. 6.95 (ISBN 0-687-15652-1). Abingdon.

ASCENSION OF CHRIST

see Jesus Christ–Ascension

ASCETICISM

see also Christian Life; Fasting; Hedonism; Martyrdom; Meditation; Monastic and Religious Life; Monastic and Religious Life of Women; Monasticism and Religious Orders; Mysticism; Perfection; Prayer; Retreats; Spiritual Direction; Spiritual Life; Vows; Wilderness (Theology)

Bhagat, M. G. Ancient Indian Asceticism. LC 76-104001. 1976. 20.00 (ISBN 0-89684-476-5). Orient Bk Dist.

--Ancient Indian Asceticism. LC 76-904001. 1976. 18.50x (ISBN 0-88386-865-2). South Asia Bks.

Brianchianinov, Ignatius. Asketitcheskije Opiti, Tom 2. Tr. of Ascetic Experiences. 332p. 20.00 (ISBN 0-317-28949-7); pap. 15.00 (ISBN 0-317-28950-0). Holy Trinity.

--Asketitcheskije Opiti, tom 3, Tom 3. Tr. of Ascetic Experiences. 315p. 20.00 (ISBN 0-317-28957-8); pap. 15.00 (ISBN 0-317-28958-6). Holy Trinity.

Budge, A. E., tr. from Syriac. The Paradise of the Fathers, 2 vols. (Illus.). 1984. Set. pap. 25.00 (ISBN 0-913026-56-5). Vol. 1, 386 pp. Vol. 2, 352 pp. St Nectarios.

Carthach, St. The Monastic Rule of St. Carthach: St. Mochuda the Younger. pap. 1.50 (ISBN 0-686-05656-6). Eastern Orthodox.

Chadwick, Owen, ed. Western Asceticism. LC 58-8713. (Library of Christian Classics). 364p. 1979. softcover 8.95 (ISBN 0-664-24161-1). Westminster.

Clark, Elizabeth A. Ascetic Piety & Women's Faith: Essays on Late Ancient Christianity. LC 86-21828. (Studies in Women & Religion: Volume 20). 448p. 1986. lib. bdg. 69.95 (ISBN 0-88946-529-0). E Mellen.

Constable, Giles. Attitudes Toward Self-Inflicted Suffering in the Middle Ages. (Stephen J. Brademas Lectures Ser.). 28p. (Orig.). pap. text ed. 2.50 (ISBN 0-916586-87-1). Hellenic Coll Pr.

Davis, Kenneth R. Anabaptism & Asceticism. LC 73-19593. 384p. 1974. 19.95x (ISBN 0-8361-1195-8). Herald Pr.

Dobrotoljubije tom Five, Vol. 5. Tr. of Philokalia. 343p. 20.00 (ISBN 0-317-28890-3); pap. 15.00 (ISBN 0-317-28891-1). Holy Trinity.

Dobrotoljubije Tom Four. Tr. of Philokalia. 451p. 25.00 (ISBN 0-317-28889-X); pap. 20.00 (ISBN 0-317-37275-0). Holy Trinity.

Dorotheus Of Gaza. Dorotheos of Gaza: Discourses & Sayings. LC 77-4295. (Cistercian Studies Ser: No. 33). 1977. 7.00 (ISBN 0-87907-933-9). Cistercian Pubns.

Gainet, J. C. Dictionnaire d'Ascetisme, 2 vols. Migne, J. P., ed. (Nouvelle Encyclopedie Theologique Ser.: Vols. 45-46). (Fr.). 1520p. Repr. of 1854 ed. lib. bdg. 192.50x (ISBN 0-89241-284-4). Caratzas.

Jouhanneaud, P. Dictionnaire Dogmatique, Historique, Ascetique et Pratique, des Indulgences des Confreries et Associations Catholiques. Migne, J. P., ed. (Nouvelle Encyclopedie Theologique Ser.: Vol. 27). (Fr.). 686p. Repr. of 1852 ed. lib. bdg. 87.50x (ISBN 0-89241-270-4). Caratzas.

Lubheid, Colm. John Climacus, The Ladder of Divine Ascent. (The Classics of Western Spirituality). 224p. pap. 12.95 (ISBN 0-8091-0312-5); pap. 9.95 (ISBN 0-8091-2330-4). Paulist Pr.

McNamara, Jo Ann. A New Song: Celibate Women in the First Three Christian Centuries. LC 83-10852. (Women & History Ser.: Nos. 6 & 7). 154p. 1983. text ed. 29.95 (ISBN 0-86656-249-4, B249). Haworth Pr.

Nouwen, Henri J. The Way of the Heart: Desert Spirituality & Contemporary Ministry. 96p. 1981. 8.95 (ISBN 0-86683-913-5, AY7443, HarpR). Har-Row.

Oman, J. C. The Mystics, Ascetics & Saints of India: A Study of Sadhmaism with an Account of the Yogis, Sanyasis, Bairagis, & other Strange Hindu Sectarians. 308p. 1984. text ed. 38.50x (ISBN 0-89563-650-6). Coronet Bks.

Rousseau, Phillip. Ascetics, Authority, & the Church in the Age of Jerome & Cassian. (Historical Monographs). 1978. 39.95x (ISBN 0-19-821870-2). Oxford U Pr.

Sheils, W. J., ed. Monks, Hermits & the Ascetic Tradition. (Studies in Church History: Vol. 22). 500p. 1985. 45.00x (ISBN 0-631-14351-3). Basil Blackwell.

Yuacharya Shri Mahaprajna. Ramblings of an Ascetic. xvi, 127p. 1979. 9.00 (ISBN 0-88065-212-8, Pub. by Messers Today & Tomorrows Printers & Publishers India). Scholarly Pubns.

ASHMUN, JEHUDI, 1794-1828

Bacon, Leonard. A Discourse Preached in the Center Church. facsimile ed. LC 78-168507. (Black Heritage Library Collection). Repr. of 1828 ed. 11.50 (ISBN 0-8369-8861-2). Ayer Co Pubs.

Gurley, Ralph R. Life of Jehudi Ashmun. facs. ed. LC 73-149867. (Black Heritage Library Collection Ser). 1835. 22.50 (ISBN 0-8369-8749-7). Ayer Co Pubs.

ASIA–RELIGION

Baird, Robert D. & Bloom, Alfred. Religion & Man: Indian & Far Eastern Religious Traditions. (Religion & Man: An Introduction, Pts. 2 & 3). 1972. pap. text ed. 14.95 scp (ISBN 0-06-040448-5, HarpC). Har-Row.

Browne, Lawrence E. The Eclipse of Christianity in Asia. 1967. Repr. 27.50x (ISBN 0-86527-049-X). Fertig.

Buhlmann, Walbert. The Search for God: An Encounter with the Peoples & Religions of Asia. Krokosz, B. & Dolan, A. P., trs. from Ger. LC 80-15732. Orig. Title: Alle haben denselben Gott. 221p. (Orig.). 1980. pap. 3.98 (ISBN 0-88344-450-X). Orbis Bks.

Caldarola, Carlo, ed. Religion & Societies: Asia & the Middle East. (Religion & Society: No. 22). 688p. 1982. text ed. 73.75 (ISBN 90-279-3259-X); Pub. 1984. pap. 29.50 (ISBN 3-11-010021-5). Mouton.

Canfield, Robert L. Faction & Conversion in a Plural Society: Religious Alignments in the Hindu Kush. (Anthropological Papers: No. 50). 1973. 3.00x (ISBN 0-932206-48-4). U Mich Mus Anthro.

Chan, Wing T. & Alfaruqi, Ismael R. Great Asian Religions. 1969. pap. write for info. (ISBN 0-02-320640-3, 32064). Macmillan.

Cox, Harvey. Turning East: The Promise & Peril of the New Orientalism. 1979. pap. 7.95 (ISBN 0-671-24405-1, Touchstone Bks). S&S.

England, John C., ed. Living Theology in Asia. LC 82-2288. 256p. (Orig.). 1982. pap. 9.95 (ISBN 0-88344-298-1). Orbis Bks.

Frazier, Allie M., ed. Readings in Eastern Religious Thought, 3 vols. Incl. Vol. 1. Hinduism; Vol. 2. Buddhism; Vol. 3. Chinese & Japanese Religions. (ISBN 0-664-24848-9). LC 69-14197. 1969. Westminster.

Fry, George C., et al. Great Asian Religions. 228p. 1984. pap. 9.95 (ISBN 0-8010-3511-2). Baker Bk.

Gorospe, Vitaliano R. The Four Faces of Asia: A Summary Report on the Asian Bishops' Meeting, Manila 1971. 1971. wrps. 3.00x (ISBN 0-686-09496-4). Cellar.

Hardon, John A. Religions of the Orient: A Christian View. LC 71-108377. pap. 55.30 (ISBN 0-317-30169-1, 2025351). Bks Demand UMI.

Heissig, Walther. The Religions of Mongolia. Samuel, Geoffrey, tr. from Ger. LC 80-146381. 1980. 31.00x (ISBN 0-520-03857-6). U of Cal Pr.

Hemer, C. J. The Letters to the Seven Churches of Asia in Their Local Setting. (JSoT Supplement Ser.: No. 11). 375p. 1986. text ed. 32.50x (ISBN 0-905774-95-7, Pub. by JSOT Pr England); pap. text ed. 14.95x (ISBN 0-905774-96-5). Eisenbrauns.

Jettmar, Karl. The Religions of the Hindukush, Vol. 1: The Religion of the Kafirs: The Pre-Islamic Heritage of Afghan Nuristan. Nayyar, Adam, tr. from Ger. (Illus.). 184p. 1986. text ed. 35.00 (ISBN 0-85668-163-6, Pub. by Aris & Phillips UK). Humanities.

--The Religions of the Hindukush Volume III: The Religions of the Chitralis. Nayyar, Adam, tr. from Ger. (Central Asian Studies). 1989. pap. text ed. 45.00 (ISBN 0-85668-368-X, Pub. by Aris & Phillips UK). Humanities.

--The Religions of the Hindukush Volume II: The Religion of the Dards. Nayyar, Adam, tr. from Ger. (Central Asian Studies). 200p. 1987. text ed. 45.00 (ISBN 0-85668-291-8, Pub. by Aris & Phillips UK). Humanities.

Johnson, David L. A Reasoned Look at Asian Religions. 150p. 1985. pap. 5.95 (ISBN 0-87123-798-9, 210798). Bethany Hse.

Kitagawa, Joseph M. Religions of the East. enl. ed. LC 60-7742. 352p. 1968. pap. 7.95 (ISBN 0-664-24837-3). Westminster.

Lyall, Alfred C. Asiatic Studies: Religious & Social, 2 vols. 826p. Repr. of 1882 ed. Set. text ed. 57.50x. Coronet Bks.

Miller, Robert J., ed. Religious Ferment in Asia. LC 73-11401. xii, 196p. 1974. 22.50x (ISBN 0-7006-0111-2). U Pr of KS.

Nacpil, Emerito, ed. The Human & the Holy: Asian Perspectives in Christian Theology. Elwood, Douglas J. 1978. pap. text ed. 10.00x (ISBN 0-686-23912-1, Pub. by New Day Pub). Cellar.

Nielsen, Niels, et al, eds. Religions of Asia. LC 82-60477. 384p. 1983. pap. text ed. 17.95 (ISBN 0-312-67096-6). St Martin.

Parpola, Asko & Hansen, Bent S., eds. South Asian Religion & Society. (Studies on Asian Topics (Scandinavian Institute of Asian Studies): No. 11). 262p. (Orig.). 1986. pap. 18.00 (ISBN 0-913215-16-3). Riverdale Co.

Parrinder, Geoffrey. Introduction to Asian Religions. 1976. pap. 7.95 (ISBN 0-19-519858-1). Oxford U Pr.

Siriwardena, R., ed. Equality & the Religious Traditions of Asia. 300p. 1987. 29.95 (ISBN 0-312-00401-X). St Martin.

Song, Choan-Seng. Third-Eye Theology: Theology in Formation in Asian Settings. LC 79-4208. pap. 72.00 (ISBN 0-317-26666-7, 2025121). Bks Demand UMI.

Spalding, Baird T. Life & Teaching of the Masters of the Far East, 5 vols. pap. 4.00 ea. Vol. 1 (ISBN 0-87516-363-7). Vol. 2 (ISBN 0-87516-364-5). Vol.3 (ISBN 0-87516-365-3). Vol. 4 (ISBN 0-87516-366-1). Vol. 5 (ISBN 0-87516-367-X). 20.00 set (ISBN 0-87516-538-9). De Vorss.

Young, Young Oon. World Religions. 1976. pap. 10.00 (ISBN 0-686-13408-7). Unification Church.

ASIA, SOUTHEASTERN–RELIGION

Hooker, M. B., ed. Islam in South East Asia. 272p. 1983. text ed. 39.95x (ISBN 0-686-46644-6, Pub. by EJ Brill Holland). Humanities.

Kirsch, A. Thomas. Feasting & Social Oscillation: A Working Paper on Religion & Society in Upland Southeast Asia. 57p. 1973. 5.00 (ISBN 0-87727-092-9, DP 92). Cornell SE Asia.

--Feasting & Social Oscillation: A Working Paper on Religion & Society in Upland Southeast Asia. LC 74-168308. (Cornell University, Southeast Asia Program, Data Paper: No. 92). pap. 20.00 (ISBN 0-317-29889-5, 2021843). Bks Demand UMI.

Kirsch, Thomas. Feasting & Social Oscillation: A Working Paper on Religion & Society in Upland Southeast Asia, No. 92. 67p. 1984. 5.00 (ISBN 0-317-11683-5). Cornell SE Asia.

Peletz, Michael G. Social History & Evolution in the Interrelationship of Adat & Islam in Rembau, Negeri Sembilan. 59p. (Orig.). 1981. pap. text ed. 9.50x (ISBN 9971-902-28-1, Pub. by Inst Southeast Asian Stud). Gower Pub Co.

Von Der Mehden, Fred. Religion & Modernization in Southeast Asia. 232p. 1986. text ed. 29.95x (ISBN 0-8156-2360-7); pap. text ed. 14.95x (ISBN 0-8156-2361-5). Syracuse U Pr.

Von der Mehden, Fred R. Religion & Nationalism in Southeast Asia: Burma, Indonesia, & the Philippines. (Illus.). 272p. 1963. pap. 7.95 (ISBN 0-299-02944-1). U of Wis Pr.

Wales, H. G. Divination in Thailand: The Hope & Fears of a Southeast Asian People. 200p. 1981. 25.00x (ISBN 0-7007-0147-8, Pub. by Curzon England). State Mutual Bk.

ASIAN STUDIES

see Oriental Studies

ASKEW, ANNE, 1521-1546

Bale, John. Select Works of John Bale, Bishop of Ossory. 51.00 (ISBN 0-384-03135-8). Johnson Repr.

ASMONEANS

see Maccabees

ASOKA, KING OF MAGADHA, fl. 259 B.C.

Gokhale, Balkrishna G. Buddhism & Asoka. LC 78-72443. Repr. of 1948 ed. 41.50 (ISBN 0-404-17298-9). AMS Pr.

Strong, John S. The Legend of King Asoka: A Study & Translation of the Asokavadana. LC 83-42579. (Princeton Library of Asian Translations). 336p. 1984. 30.00x (ISBN 0-691-06575-6). Princeton U Pr.

ASSASSINS (ISMAILITES)

Hodgson, Marshall G. The Order of Assassins. LC 78-63343. (The Crusades & Military Orders: Second Ser.). Repr. of 1955 ed. 46.50 (ISBN 0-404-17018-8). AMS Pr.

Lewis, Bernard. The Assassins: A Radical Sect in Islam. 1987. pap. 8.95 (ISBN 0-19-520550-2). Oxford U Pr.

Ridley, F. A. The Assassins: A Study of the Cult of the Assassins in Persia and Islam. (Islam Ser.). 1980. lib. bdg. 59.95 (ISBN 0-8490-3077-3). Gordon Pr.

Von Hammer-Purgstall, Joseph. History of the Assassins, Derived from Oriental Sources. Wood, Oswald C., tr. Repr. of 1835 ed. 22.50 (ISBN 0-8337-1562-3). B Franklin.

ASSEMBLIES OF GOD, GENERAL COUNCIL

Blumhofer, Edith W. The Assemblies of God: A Popular History. LC 85-70552. 160p. (Orig.). 1985. pap. 2.95 (ISBN 0-88243-469-1, 02-0469). Gospel Pub.

Brumback, Carl. Like a River. LC 76-58782. (Illus.). 176p. 1977. pap. 2.95 (ISBN 0-88243-564-7, 02-0564). Gospel Pub.

Carlson, G. Raymond. Our Faith & Fellowship. LC 77-75023. (Radiant Life Ser.). 128p. 1977. pap. 2.50 (ISBN 0-88243-908-1, 02-0908); teacher's ed. 3.95 (ISBN 0-88243-178-1, 32-0178). Gospel Pub.

Menzies, William W. Anointed to Serve: The Story of the Assemblies of God. LC 77-146707. (Illus.). 440p. 1971. 12.95 (ISBN 0-88243-465-9, 02-0465). Gospel Pub.

Steidl, G. Basics of Assembly Life. pap. 3.75 (ISBN 0-88172-126-3). Believers Bkshelf.

Williams, Ernest S. Systematic Theology, 3 vols. Incl. Vol. 1. pap. 6.95 (ISBN 0-88243-643-0, 02-0643); Vol. 2. pap. 6.95 (ISBN 0-88243-644-9, 02-0644); Vol. 3. pap. 6.95 (ISBN 0-88243-645-7, 02-0645). 1953. pap. 18.00 Set 3 vol (ISBN 0-88243-650-3, 02-0650). Gospel Pub.

ASSEMBLY, SCHOOL

see Schools–Exercises and Recreations

ASSISI–SAN FRANCESCO (CHURCH)

Tintori, Leonetto & Meiss, Millard. The Painting of the Life of St. Francis in Assisi, with Notes on the Arena Chapel. LC 62-10308. pap. 55.50 (ISBN 0-317-10175-7, 2050842). Bks Demand UMI.

ASSOCIATIONS, INSTITUTIONS, ETC.
DeBoer, John C. Let's Plan: A Guide to the Planning Process for Voluntary Organizations. LC 72-124329. (Illus., Orig.). 1970. pap. 3.95 (ISBN 0-8298-0177-4). Pilgrim NY.
Funchion, Michael F., ed. Irish American Voluntary Organizations. LC 83-6712. (Ethnic American Voluntary Organizations Ser.). xviii, 323p. 1983. lib. bdg. 45.00 (ISBN 0-313-22948-1, FIA/). Greenwood.
Gaudefroy-Demombynes, Maurice. Muslim Institutions. LC 84-12953. 216p. 1984. Repr. of 1950 ed. lib. bdg. 35.00x (ISBN 0-313-24287-9, GAMU). Greenwood.
Greenleaf, Robert K. Servant Leadership: A Journey into the Nature of Legitimate Power & Greatness. LC 76-45678. 348p. 1977. 9.95 (ISBN 0-8091-2527-7). Paulist Pr.
Rosen, Oded, ed. The Encyclopedia of Jewish Institutions: United States & Canada. 512p. 1983. 55.00 (ISBN 0-913185-00-0). Mosadot Pubns.

ASSURANCE (THEOLOGY)
see also Antinomianism; Inner Light; Perseverance (Theology)
Borchert, Gerald L. Assurance & Warning. (Orig.). 1987. pap. 5.95 (ISBN 0-8054-1011-2). Broadman.
Davis, Thomas G. Saved & Certain. (Orig.). 1955. pap. 3.95 (ISBN 0-8054-1611-0). Broadman.
Ironside, Harry A. Full Assurance. 1937. pap. 3.95 (ISBN 0-8024-2896-7). Moody.
Spray, Russell E. Blessed Assurance Sermon Outlines. (Pulpit Library). 80p. 1985. pap. 3.95 (ISBN 0-8010-8255-2). Baker Bk.

ASSYRO-BABYLONIAN HYMNS
see Hymns, Assyro-Babylonian

ASSYRO-BABYLONIAN PRIESTS
see Priests, Assyro-Babylonian

ASSYRO-BABYLONIAN RELIGION
Aude, Sapere, ed. The Chaldean Oracles. LC 78-58111. 1978. 10.00 (ISBN 0-935214-02-X). Heptangle.
Dougherty, Raymond P. The Shirkutu of Babylonian Deities. LC 78-63548. (Yale Oriental Ser. Researches: 5, Pt. 2). Repr. of 1923 ed. 25.00 (ISBN 0-404-60295-9). AMS Pr.
Frankfort, Henri. Kingship & the Gods: A Study of Ancient Near Eastern Religion As the Integration of Society & Nature. LC 48-5158. 1978. pap. 12.95 (ISBN 0-226-26011-9, P766, Phoen). U of Chicago Pr.
Gray, Clifton D., ed. The Samas Religious Texts Classified in the British Museum Catalogue As Hymns, Prayers, & Incantations. LC 78-72728. (Ancient Mesopotamian Texts & Studies). Repr. of 1901 ed. 17.50 (ISBN 0-404-18176-7). AMS Pr.
Hackman, George G., ed. Temple Documents of the Third Dynasty of Ur from Umma. LC 78-63524. (Babylonian Inscriptions in the Collection of James B. Nies: No. 5). Repr. of 1937 ed. 28.50 (ISBN 0-404-60135-9). AMS Pr.
Jastrow, Morris. Aspects of Religious Belief & Practice in Babylonia & Assyria. LC 68-56503. Repr. of 1911 ed. 25.00 (ISBN 0-405-08667-9, Blom Pubns). Ayer Co Pubs.
Keiser, Clarence E. Selected Temple Documents of the Ur Dynasty. LC 78-63533. (Yale Oriental Series: Babylonian Texts: No. 4). (Illus.). 240p. Repr. of 1919 ed. 42.50 (ISBN 0-404-60254-1). AMS Pr.
King, Leonard W. Babylonian Religion & Mythology. LC 73-18854. (Illus.). Repr. of 1899 ed. 18.45 (ISBN 0-404-11352-4). AMS Pr.
Langdon, Stephen H. Tammuz & Ishtar. LC 78-72750. (Ancient Mesopotamian Texts & Studies). Repr. of 1914 ed. 34.50 (ISBN 0-404-18193-7). AMS Pr.
Nikel, Johannes S. Ein Never Ninkarrak-Text. pap. 7.00 (ISBN 0-384-41600-4). Johnson Repr.
Sayce, Archibald H. The Religions of Ancient Egypt & Babylonia. LC 77-27223. (Gifford Lectures: 1902). Repr. of 1903 ed. 46.50 (ISBN 0-404-60457-9). AMS Pr.
Steinmetzer, Franz X. Die Babylonischen Kudurru Als Urkundenform. Repr. of 1922 ed. 22.00 (ISBN 0-384-57850-0). Johnson Repr.
Woodrow, Ralph. Babylon Mystery Religion: Ancient & Modern. (Illus.). 1981. 4.95 (ISBN 0-916938-00-X). R Woodrow.

ASTROLOGY–DATA PROCESSING
Cratch, Stephen C. & Johansson, Anders B. The Hindu Vedic Master Operations Guide: Astrological Software for the IBM PC. Johansson, Lilian M., ed. (Illus.). 200p. (Orig.). 1985. 30.00 (ISBN 0-914725-12-2); pap. 18.00 (ISBN 0-914725-10-6); spiral 24.00 (ISBN 0-914725-11-4). Astro Dynasty Pub Hse.

ASTROLOGY, EARLY
Chamber, John. A Treatise Against Iudicial Astrologie, 2 pts. LC 77-6872. (English Experience Ser.: No. 860). 1977. Repr. of 1601 ed. lib. bdg. 20.00 (ISBN 90-221-0860-0). Walter J Johnson.
Cumont, Franz. Astrology & Religion among the Greeks & Romans. 1912. pap. 3.50 (ISBN 0-486-20581-9). Dover.
Heydon, Christopher. A Defence of Iudiciall Astrologie: In Answer to a Treatise Lately Published by M. John Chamber. LC 77-7407. (English Experience Ser.: No. 873). 1977. Repr. of 1603 ed. lib. bdg. 58.00 (ISBN 90-221-0873-2). Walter J Johnson.
Lambe, John. A Briefe Description of the Notorious Life of J. Lambe. LC 76-57394. (English Experience Ser.: No. 811). 1977. Repr. of 1628 ed. lib. bdg. 3.50 (ISBN 90-221-0811-2). Walter J Johnson.
Levy, Raphael. The Astrological Works of Abraham Ibn Ezra: A Literary & Linguistic Study. (Johns Hopkins University Studies in Romance Literatures & Languages: Vol. 8). 172p. Repr. of 1927 ed. 16.00 (ISBN 0-384-32427-4). Johnson Repr.
Pingree, David, tr. The Yavanajataka of Sphujidhvaja, 2 vols. (Harvard Oriental Ser: No. 48). 1978. Set. 80.00x (ISBN 0-674-96373-3). Harvard U Pr.
Reiner, Erica & Pingree, D. Babylonian Planetary Omens, Enuma Anu Enlil, Tablet 50-51. LC 79-67168. (Bibliotheca Mesopotamica Ser.: Vol. 2, Pt. 2). 100p. (Orig.). 1980. pap. 15.00x (ISBN 0-89003-049-9). Undena Pubns.
Thierens, A. E. Astrology in Mesopotamian Culture. 1977. lib. bdg. 59.95 (ISBN 0-8490-1461-1). Gordon Pr.
Zoller, Robert. The Lost Key to Prediction: The Arabic Parts in Astrology. 350p. 1980. pap. 8.95 (ISBN 0-89281-013-0). Inner Tradit.

ASTROLOGY AND THE BIBLE
see Bible and Astrology

ASTRONOMY, HINDU
Kaye, G. R. Hindu Astronomy: Ancient Science of the Hindus. 134p. 1981. text ed. 42.00x. Coronet Bks.

ATHANASIAN CREED
Athanasius, St. Select Treatises of St. Athanasius in Controversy with the Arians, 2 vols. 5th ed. Newman, John H., tr. LC 77-84694. (Heresies of the Early Christian & Medieval Era Ser.). Repr. of 1890 ed. 72.00 set (ISBN 0-404-16100-6). AMS Pr.
Burn, A. E. The Athanasian Creed & Its Early Commentaries. (Texts & Studies Ser.: No. 1, Vol. 4, Pt. 1). pap. 19.00 (ISBN 0-8115-1691-1). Kraus Repr.

ATHEISM
see also Agnosticism; Deism; Rationalism; Skepticism; Theism
Bakunin, Michael. God & the State. facsimile ed. LC 78-148871. (Select Bibliographies Reprint Ser.). Repr. of 1916 ed. 12.00 (ISBN 0-8369-5643-5). Ayer Co Pubs.
Bard, Martin L. The Peril of Faith. 155p. (Orig.). 1982. pap. 5.00 (ISBN 0-910309-05-1). Am Atheist.
Bentley, Richard. Eight Boyle Lectures on Atheism. Wellek, Rene, ed. LC 75-11196. (British Philosophers & Theologians of the 17th & 18th Centuries Ser.: Vol. 3). 1976. Repr. of 1692 ed. lib. bdg. 51.00 (ISBN 0-8240-1752-8). Garland Pub.
Cudworth, Ralph. The True Intellectual System of the Universe, 2 vols. Wellek, Rene, ed. LC 75-11213. (British Philosophers & Theologians of the 17th & 18th Centuries Ser.: Vol. 16). 1978. Repr. of 1678 ed. Set. lib. bdg. 101.00 (ISBN 0-8240-1767-6). Garland Pub.
De Bona, Maurice, Jr. God Rejected: A Summary of Atheistic Thought. LC 75-46088. 1976. 4.95 (ISBN 0-916698-00-9); pap. 2.95 (ISBN 0-916698-01-7). Desserco Pub.
DeYoung, Mary. Call to Reason: An Introduction to Atheism. 3rd ed. 1979. pap. 7.50 (ISBN 0-936128-01-1). De Young Pr.
Diehl, Helmut. Atheismus Im Religionsunterricht. (European University Studies Thirty-Three: Vol. 6). (Ger.). 622p. 1982. 46.30 (ISBN 3-8204-6280-5). P Lang Pubs.
Drachman, A. Atheism In Pagan Antiquity. 178p. 1977. 12.50 (ISBN 0-89005-201-8). Ares.
Drachmann, A. B. Atheism in Pagan Antiquity. 69.95 (ISBN 0-87968-675-8). Gordon Pr.
Edwards, John. Some Thoughts Concerning the Several Causes & Occasions of Atheism, Especially in the Present Age. LC 80-48568. (The Philosophy of John Locke Ser.). 268p. 1984. lib. bdg. 35.00 (ISBN 0-8240-5603-5). Garland Pub.
Ellis, Albert. The Case Against Religion: A Psychotherapist's View & the Case Against Religiousity. 57p. 1985. saddle stiched 4.00 (ISBN 0-910309-18-3). Am Atheist.
Fabro, Cornelio. God in Exile: Modern Atheism. Gibson, Arthur, tr. LC 68-20846. 1272p. 1968. slipcase 35.00 (ISBN 0-8091-0053-3). Paulist Pr.
Foote, G. W. & Ball, W. P. The Bible Handbook. 372p. 1983. pap. 7.00 (ISBN 0-910309-26-4). Am Atheist.
Haldeman-Julius, E. What Can a Free Man Believe. 55p. pap. cancelled (ISBN 0-911826-99-8). Am Atheist.
Ingersoll, Robert. Some Reasons Why I Am a Freethinker. 38p. 1983. pap. 3.00 (ISBN 0-911826-67-X). Am Atheist.
Ingersoll, Robert G. Atheist Truth vs. Religion's Ghosts. 57p. 1980. pap. 3.25 (ISBN 0-911826-03-3). Am Atheist.
--The Trial of C. B. Reynolds. 44p. (Orig.). 1986. pap. 3.00 (ISBN 0-910309-25-6). Am Atheist.
Johnson, B. C. The Atheist Debater's Handbook. LC 81-80487. (Skeptics Bookshelf Ser.). 134p. 1981. 14.95 (ISBN 0-87975-152-5); pap. 8.95 (ISBN 0-87975-210-6). Prometheus Bks.
Knowlton, Charles. Fruits of Philosophy. 58p. 1980. pap. 4.00 (ISBN 0-911826-16-5). Am Atheist.
Lewis, Joseph. American Atheist Heritage. O'Hair, Madalyn M., ed. (Illus.). 55p. 1981. pap. 4.00 (ISBN 0-911826-28-9). Am Atheist.
Luijpen, William A. & Koren, H. J. Religion & Atheism. 200p. 1982. pap. 10.95 (ISBN 0-391-02801-4). Humanities.
McCabe, Joseph. Is the Position of Atheism Growing Stronger. 30p. pap. cancelled (ISBN 0-911826-85-8). Am Atheist.
--The Logic & Virtue of Atheism. 58p. 1980. saddle stitched 3.00 (ISBN 0-911826-13-0). Am Atheist.
MacIntyre, Alasdair & Ricoeur, Paul. The Religious Significance of Atheism. LC 68-28398. (Bampton Lectures in America Ser.: No. 18). 98p. 1969. 20.00 (ISBN 0-231-03139-4). Columbia U Pr.
Miller, J. Hillis. The Disappearance of God: Five Nineteenth Century Writers. 392p. 1976. text ed. 22.50x (ISBN 0-674-21101-4, Belknap Pr). Harvard U Pr.
Mills, David. Overcoming Religion. 1980. pap. 3.95 (ISBN 0-8065-0742-X). Citadel Pr.
Molnar, Thomas. Theist & Atheist: A Typology of Non-Belief. 1979. text ed. 30.00x (ISBN 90-279-7788-7). Mouton.
Murray, Jon & O'Hair, Madalyn. All the Questions You Ever Wanted to Ask American Atheists with All the Answers. 2nd ed. 248p. (Orig.). 1986. pap. 7.00 (ISBN 0-910309-24-8). Am Atheist.
Murray, Jon G. Essays on American Atheism, Vol. I. 350p. (Orig.). 1986. pap. 8.00 (ISBN 0-910309-28-0). Am Atheist.
--Essays on American Atheism, Vol. II. 300p. (Orig.). 1986. pap. 8.00 (ISBN 0-910309-29-9). Am Atheist.
Murray, Jon G., ed. Essays of an Atheist Activist. 67p. (Orig.). 1981. pap. 3.25 (ISBN 0-911826-02-5). Am Atheist.
Murray, William J. My Life Without God. LC 83-14269. 252p. 1984. pap. 5.95 (ISBN 0-8407-5884-7). Nelson.
Neusch, Marcel. The Sources of Modern Atheism: One Hundred Years of Debate over God. LC 82-60596. 1983. pap. 9.95 (ISBN 0-8091-2488-2). Paulist Pr.
Nielsen, Kai. The Philosophy & Atheism. (The Skeptic's Bookshelf Ser.). 231p. 1985. 20.95 (ISBN 0-87975-289-0). Prometheus Bks.
O'Hair, Madalyn. An Atheist Speaks. (American Atheist Radio Series Reprints). 321p. (Orig.). 1986. pap. 6.00 (ISBN 0-910309-27-2). Am Atheist.
--O'Hair on Prayer. 12p. (Orig.). 1980. saddle stiched 1.00 (ISBN 0-910309-30-2). Am Atheist.
--Why I Am An Atheist. rev. ed. 39p. 1980. Repr. of 1966 ed. 3.25 (ISBN 0-911826-12-2). Am Atheist.
O'Hair, Madalyn M. Atheist Magazines: A Sampling, 1927-1970. LC 72-171441. (Atheist Viewpoint Ser). 554p. 1972. Repr. of 1971 ed. 28.00 (ISBN 0-405-03812-7). Ayer Co Pubs.
--Freedom under Siege. 282p. cancelled (ISBN 0-911826-25-4). Am Atheist.
--Nobody Has a Prayer. 105p. (Orig.). 1982. pap. 3.00 (ISBN 0-910309-07-8). Am Atheist.
--What on Earth Is an Atheist? LC 71-88701. (Fifty-Two Programs from the American Atheist Radio Ser.). 282p. 1969. pap. 6.00 (ISBN 0-911826-00-9). Am Atheist.
--What on Earth Is an Atheist. LC 74-161339. (Atheist Viewpoint Ser). 288p. 1972. Repr. of 1969 ed. 18.00 (ISBN 0-405-03802-X). Ayer Co Pubs.
--Women & Atheism: The Ultimate Liberation. 23p. 1979. 2.50 (ISBN 0-911826-17-3). Am Atheist.
O'Hair, Madalyn M., ed. The Atheist Viewpoint, 25 bks. 1972. Set. 498.00 (ISBN 0-405-03620-5). Ayer Co Pubs.
--The Atheist Viewpoint. Date not set. cancelled (ISBN 0-405-03791-0, 395). Ayer Co Pubs.
Rahner, Karl S. Pastoral Approach to Atheism. LC 67-21347. (Concilium Ser.: Vol. 23). 189p. 7.95 (ISBN 0-8091-0107-6). Paulist Pr.
Russell, Bertrand. Am I an Atheist or an Agnostic. 32p. pap. cancelled (ISBN 0-911826-96-3). Am Atheist.
--Atheism: Collected Essays, 1943-1949. LC 71-169217. (Atheist Viewpoint Ser). 232p. 1972. Repr. of 1971 ed. 15.00 (ISBN 0-405-03808-9). Ayer Co Pubs.
Ruth, Eddie. The Right to Be Here. (Illus.). 28p. (Orig.). 1981. pap. 2.00 (ISBN 0-911826-27-0). Am Atheist.
Shapiro, Carl. Freethought Versus Religion: The Atheist Challenge. 50p. 1977. 8.00x (ISBN 0-914937-06-5). Ind Pubns.
--Why I Am an Atheist. 14p. (Orig.). 1979. write for info. (ISBN 0-914937-02-2); incl. cassette 10.00 (ISBN 0-317-18464-4). Ind Pubns.
Shelley, Percy Bysshe. Selected Essays on Atheism. LC 72-161341. (Atheist Viewpoint Ser). 100p. 1972. Repr. 13.00 (ISBN 0-405-03794-5). Ayer Co Pubs.
Smith, George H. Atheism: The Case Against God. LC 79-2726. (Skeptic's Bookshelf Ser.). 355p. 1979. pap. 10.95 (ISBN 0-87975-124-X). Prometheus Bks.
Stein, Gordon, ed. An Anthology of Atheism & Rationalism. LC 80-81326. (The Skeptic's Bookshelf Ser.). 354p. 1984. pap. 15.95 (ISBN 0-87975-267-X). Prometheus Bks.
Teller, Woolsey. The Atheism of Astronomy: A Refutation of the Theory That the Universe Is Governed by Intelligence. LC 79-169219. (Atheist Viewpoint Ser). 126p. 1972. Repr. of 1938 ed. 13.00 (ISBN 0-405-03806-2). Ayer Co Pubs.
Thrower, James. Marxist-Leninist 'Scientific Atheism' & the Study of Religion & Atheism in the U. S. S. R. (Ger.). 500p. 1983. 78.00 (ISBN 90-279-3060-0). Mouton.
Turner, James. Without God, Without Creed: The Origins of Unbelief in America. LC 84-15397. (New Studies in American Intellectual & Cultural History). 336p. 1986. pap. text ed. 12.95x (ISBN 0-8018-3407-4). Johns Hopkins.
Warren, Thomas B. Have Atheists Proved There Is No God? 1974. 8.00 (ISBN 0-934916-33-0). Natl Christian Pr.

ATHEISM, CHRISTIAN
see Death of God Theology

ATHEISM AND CHRISTIANITY
see Christianity and Atheism

ATHENS–ANTIQUITIES
Camp, John M. Gods & Heroes in the Athenian Agora. (Excavations of the Athenian Agora Picture Bks.: No. 19). (Illus.). 1980. pap. 3.00x (ISBN 0-87661-623-6). Am Sch Athens.
Immerwahr, Sara A. Early Burials from the Agora Cemeteries. (Excavations of the Athenian Agora Picture Bks.: No. 13). (Illus.). 1973. pap. 3.00x (ISBN 0-87661-613-9). Am Sch Athens.
Weinberg, Saul S. The Southeast Building, the Twin Basilicas, the Mosaic House. LC 75-25699. (Corinth Ser: Vol. 1, Pt. 5). (Illus.). 1971. Repr. of 1960 ed. 25.00x (ISBN 0-87661-015-7). Am Sch Athens.

ATHLETES–RELIGIOUS LIFE
Arndt, Rick. Athletes Afire. LC 85-71182. 1985. pap. 3.50 (ISBN 0-88270-590-3). Bridge Pub.

ATHOS (MONASTERIES)
Cavarnos, Constantine. Anchored in God. 2nd ed. LC 75-35432. (Illus.). 230p. 1975. 10.00 (ISBN 0-914744-30-5). Inst Byzantine.
Mount Athos: An Illustrated Guide to the Monasteries & their Histories. (Illus.). 200p. pap. 20.00 (ISBN 0-89241-369-7). Caratzas.
Patriarchal Institute for Patristic Studies, et al. The Treasures of Mount Athos, Volume 2: The Monasteries of Iveron, St. Panteleimon, Esphigmenou & Chilandari. (Illus.). 400p. 1976. cancelled (ISBN 0-89241-004-3). Caratzas.

ATLANTIS
Donnelly, Ignatius. Atlantis: The Antediluvian World. lib. bdg. 100.00 (ISBN 0-87968-055-5). Krishna Pr.
Drown, Ruth B. Wisdom from Atlantis. 153p. 1981. pap. 9.00 (ISBN 0-686-78074-4, SB-098). Sun Pub.
Elliott, Scott. Story of Atlantis & the Lost Lemuria. 8.95 (ISBN 0-8356-5509-1). Theos Pub Hse.

ATOMIC BOMB–MORAL AND RELIGIOUS ASPECTS
see Nuclear Warfare–Moral and Religious Aspects

ATONEMENT
see also Jesus Christ–Priesthood; Redemption; Servant of Jehovah
Ballou, Hosea. Treatise on Atonement. Cassara, Ernest, ed. 1986. pap. 7.95 (ISBN 0-933840-26-8, 0495000). Unitarian Univ.
Barnes, Albert. The Atonement. LC 80-65582. 1980. pap. 7.95 (ISBN 0-87123-016-X, 210016). Bethany Hse.
Clark, Gordon H. The Atonement. (The Trinity Papers: No. 17). 175p. (Orig.). 1987. pap. 8.95 (ISBN 0-940931-17-6). Trinity Found.
Fogelklou-Norlind, Emilia. Atonement of George Fox. Mather, Eleanore P., ed. LC 75-84675. (Orig.). 1969. pap. 2.50x (ISBN 0-87574-166-5). Pendle Hill.
Letch, Ralph A. Myths of the Atonement. 1985. 20.00x (ISBN 0-7223-1657-7, Pub. by A H Stockwell England). State Mutual Bk.
Lidgett, John S. The Biblical Doctrine of the Atonement. 522p. 1983. 19.50 (ISBN 0-86524-145-7, 8801). Klock & Klock.

McDonald, H. D. The Atonement of the Death of Christ. 352p. 1985. pap. 19.95 (ISBN 0-8010-6194-6). Baker Bk.

--Forgiveness & Atonement. 1984. 5.95p (ISBN 0-8010-6165-2). Baker Bk.

Maxwell, L. E. Born Crucified. (Moody Classic Ser.). 1984. pap. 3.95 (ISBN 0-8024-0038-8). Moody.

Murray, Andrew. Blood of the Cross. 1968. pap. 2.95 (ISBN 0-87508-374-9). Chr Lit.

--Power of the Blood. 1984. pap. 3.50 (ISBN 0-87508-428-1). Chr Lit.

Murray, John. Atonement. pap. 1.50 (ISBN 0-87552-342-0). Presby & Reformed.

Neie, Herbert. The Doctrine of the Atonement in the Theology of Wolfhart Panneberg. (Theologische Bibliothek Toepelmann: Vol. 36). 1978. 40.00x (ISBN 3-11-007506-7). De Gruyter.

Pink, Arthur W. Atonement. 10.95 (ISBN 0-685-19822-7). Reiner.

ATONEMENT–BIBLICAL TEACHING

Culpepper, Robert H. Interpreting the Atonement. 170p. 1986. pap. 6.95 (ISBN 0-913029-13-0). Stevens Bk Pr.

ATONEMENT–HISTORY OF DOCTRINE

Peterson, Robert A. Calvin's Doctrine of the Atonement. 1983. pap. 4.95 (ISBN 0-87552-369-2). Presby & Reformed.

Tull, James E. The Atoning Gospel. LC 81-18732. 221p. 1982. 15.50 (ISBN 0-86554-029-2, MUP-H28). Mercer Univ Pr.

Wallace, Ronald. The Atoning Death of Christ. LC 81-65758. (Foundations for Faith Ser.). 192p. (Orig.). 1981. pap. 8.95 (ISBN 0-89107-222-5, Crossway Bks). Good News.

ATONEMENT, DAY OF

see Yom Kippur

ATTRIBUTES OF GOD

see God–Attributes

ATTRITION

see Penance; Repentance

AUDIO-VISUAL MATERIALS

Simpson, Floyd & Hill, Glynn, eds. How to Repair Books & Maintain Audiovisuals. LC 84-9618. (Orig.). 1984. pap. 2.95 (ISBN 0-8054-3708-8). Broadman.

AUGSBURG CONFESSION

Burgess, Joseph A., ed. The Role of the Augsburg Confession: Catholic & Lutheran Views. LC 79-7373. 224p. 1980. 14.95 (ISBN 0-8006-0549-7, 1-549). Fortress.

Forell, George W. Augsburg Confession: A Contemporary Commentary. LC 68-25798. (Orig.). 1968. pap. 6.95 (ISBN 0-8066-0815-3, 10-0518). Augsburg.

Grane, Leif, ed. The Augsburg Confession: A Commentary. Rasmussen, John H., tr. from Ger. LC 86-28832. Tr. of Die Confessio Augustana. 272p. (Orig.). 1987. pap. 14.95 (ISBN 0-8066-2252-0, 10-0519). Augsburg.

Maurer, Wilhelm. Historical Commentary on the Augsburg Confession. Anderson, H. George, tr. from Ger. LC 86-45214. Tr. of Historischer Kommentar zur Confessio Augustana. 464p. 1986. 24.95 (ISBN 0-8006-0781-3). Fortress.

Reu, Johann M. The Augsburg Confession. LC 83-45650. Date not set. Repr. of 1930 ed. 76.50 (ISBN 0-404-19859-7). AMS Pr.

Schwenckfeld, Caspar. Commentary on the Augsburg Confession. Grater, Fred A., tr. 182p. 1982. pap. 5.00 (ISBN 0-935980-02-4). Schwenkfelder Lib.

Tappert, Theodore G., tr. Augsburg Confession: Anniversary Edition. 64p. 1980. pap. 1.75 (ISBN 0-8006-1385-6, 1-1385). Fortress.

AUGUSTANA COLLEGE

Bergendoff, Conrad. Augustana - A Profession of Faith: A History of Augustana College, 1860-1935. LC 76-92170. (Augustana College Library Ser.: No. 33). (Illus.). 220p. 1969. 5.95x (ISBN 0-910182-33-7). Augustana Coll.

Sneen, Donald. Through Trials & Triumphs: A History of Augustana College. 192p. 1985. 17.00 (ISBN 0-931170-29-X). Ctr Western Studies.

AUGUSTINE, SAINT, ABP. OF CANTERBURY, d. 604

Bathory, Peter D. Political Theory As Public Confession. LC 80-15667. 180p. 1981. 24.95 (ISBN 0-87855-405-X). Transaction Bks.

Benjamin, A. & Hackstaff, L. H. On Free Choice of the Will: Augustine. 1964. pap. text ed. write for info. (ISBN 0-02-308030-2). Macmillan.

Bently-Taylor, David. Augustine: Wayward Genius. 1981. pap. 5.95 (ISBN 0-8010-0807-7). Baker Bk.

Brady, Jules, ed. An Augustine Treasury: Selections from the Writings of St. Augustine. 1981. 5.00 (ISBN 0-8198-0706-0); pap. 4.00 (ISBN 0-686-73823-3). Dghtrs St Paul.

Brunn, Emilie Z. St. Augustine: Being & Nothingness in the Dialogs & Confessions. 210p. 1987. 21.95 (ISBN 0-913729-17-5). Paragon Hse.

Burghardt, W. J., et al, eds. St. Augustine, Against the Academics. LC 78-62461. (ACW Ser.: No. 12). 220p. 1950. 10.95 (ISBN 0-8091-0252-8). Paulist Pr.

--St. Augustine, the Lord's Sermon on the Mount. LC 78-62451. (ACW Ser.: No. 5). 227p. 1948. 13.95 (ISBN 0-8091-0246-3). Paulist Pr.

--St. Augustine, the Problem of Free Choice. LC 78-62469. (ACW Ser.: No. 22). 298p. 1955. 11.95 (ISBN 0-8091-0259-5). Paulist Pr.

Carnicelli, Thomas A., ed. King Alfred's Version of St. Augustine's Soliloquies. LC 69-12719. 1969. 7.50x (ISBN 0-674-50360-0). Harvard U Pr.

Chadwick, Henry. Augustine. (Past Masters Ser.). 128p. 1986. 14.95x (ISBN 0-19-287535-3); pap. 4.95 (ISBN 0-19-287534-5). Oxford U Pr.

Easwaran, Eknath. Love Never Faileth: The Inspiration of St. Francis, St. Augustine, St. Paul & Mother Teresa. (Illus.). 208p. (Orig.). 1985. 15.00 (ISBN 0-915132-31-1); pap. 8.00 (ISBN 0-915132-32-X). Nilgiri Pr.

Hand, Thomas A. Augustine on Prayer. rev. ed. (Orig.). 1986. pap. 3.95 (ISBN 0-89942-171-7, 171-04). Catholic BK Pub.

Hawkins, Anne O. Archetypes of Conversion: The Spiritual Autobiographies of St. Augustine, John Bunyan, & Thomas Merton. LC 83-46156. 192p. 1985. 25.00 (ISBN 0-8387-5079-6). Bucknell U Pr.

Helms, Hal. Confessions of St. Augustine: Modern English Version. 304p. 1986. pap. 8.95 (ISBN 0-941478-55-6). Paraclete Pr.

Henry, Paul. The Path to Transcendence: From Philosophy to Mysticism in Saint Augustine. Burch, Francis F., tr. (Pittsburgh Theological Monographs: No. 37). 1981. pap. 12.50 (ISBN 0-915138-49-2). Pickwick.

Institut des Etudes Augustiniennes, Paris. Fichier Augustinien, First Supplement. 1981. lib. bdg. 125.00 (ISBN 0-8161-0365-8, Hall Library). G K Hall.

Kuasten, J. & Plumpe, J., eds. St. Augustine, Faith, Hope & Charity. Arand, Louis A., tr. LC 78-62450. (Ancient Christian Writers Ser.: No. 3). 165p. 1947. 10.95 (ISBN 0-8091-0045-2). Paulist Pr.

Marshall, Michael. The Restless Heart: The Life & Influence of St. Augustine. (Illus.). 192p. 1987. 19.95 (ISBN 0-8028-3632-1). Eerdmans.

O'Connell, Robert. Imagination & Metaphysics in St. Augustine. LC 85-82595. (Aquinas Lecture). 70p. 1986. 7.95 (ISBN 0-87462-227-1). Marquette.

O'Donnell, James J. Augustine. LC 84-28133. (World Author Ser.). 1985. lib. bdg. 19.95 (ISBN 0-8057-6609-X, Twayne). G K Hall.

O'Meara, John J. The Young Augustine: An Introduction to the Confessions of St. Augustine. 224p. 1980. pap. text ed. 10.95x (ISBN 0-582-49110-X). Longman.

Rotelle, John. Augustine Day by Day. (Orig.). 1986. pap. 4.50 (ISBN 0-89942-170-9, 170-09). Catholic BK Pub.

St. Augustine. St. Augustine on the Psalms: Vol. 2. Quasten, J. & Burghardt, W. J., eds. Hebgin, D. Scholastica & Corrigan, D. Felicitas, trs. LC 60-10722. (Ancient Christian Writers Ser.: No. 30). 425p. 1961. 14.95 (ISBN 0-8091-0105-X). Paulist Pr.

Stevenson, William R., Jr. Christian Love & Just War: Moral Paradox & Political Life in St. Augustine & His Modern Interpreters. 256p. 1987. 29.95 (ISBN 0-86554-272-4, H235). Mercer Univ Pr.

Thompson, George N., ed. Saint Augustine on the End of the World. 55p. (Orig.). pap. text ed. 5.95 (ISBN 0-940564-15-7). Directions Pr.

Trape, Augustine. Saint Augustine: Man, Pastor, Mystic. (Orig.). 1985. pap. 6.95 (ISBN 0-89942-172-5, 172/02). Catholic BK Pub.

Warfield, Benjamin B. Calvin & Augustine. 12.95 (ISBN 0-8010-9585-9). Baker Bk.

Zumkeller, Adolar. Augustine's Ideal of the Religious Life. xii, 468p. 1986. 40.00 (ISBN 0-8232-1105-3); pap. 20.00 (ISBN 0-8232-1106-1). Fordham.

AUGUSTINIANS

Kaufman, Peter I. Augustinian Piety & Catholic Reform: Augustine, Colet, & Erasmus. LC 82-12491. 161p. 1982. text ed. 9.45 (ISBN 0-86554-047-0, MUP-H46). Mercer Univ Pr.

St. Augustine. The City of God. Dods, Marcus, tr. LC 54-5465. 1950. 10.95 (ISBN 0-394-60397-4). Modern Lib.

AUGUSTINUS, AURELIUS, SAINT, BP. OF HIPPO, 354-430

Augustine. Confessions of St. Augustine. abr. ed. (Summit Books). 1977. pap. 4.95 (ISBN 0-8010-0118-8). Baker Bk.

Augustine, St. Aurelius. Select Letters. Baxter, James H., tr. LC 75-41012. Repr. of 1930 ed. 37.50 (ISBN 0-404-14503-5). AMS Pr.

Augustinian Educational Conferences Staff. Augustinian Studies: Papers Read at Recent Augustinian Educational Conferences. facs. ed. LC 67-22052. (Essay Index Reprint Ser.). 1937. 16.00 (ISBN 0-8369-0163-0). Ayer Co Pubs.

Bechtel, Paul, ed. The Confessions of St. Augustine. LC 81-11163. 1981. 8.95 (ISBN 0-8024-1618-7). Moody.

Bogan, Mary Inez. Vocabulary & Style of the Soliloquies & Dialogues of St. Augustine, Vol. 42. (Patristic Studies). 238p. 1984. Repr. of 1935 ed. 28.00x (ISBN 0-939738-27-9). Zubal Inc.

Brown, Peter. Augustine of Hippo. 463p. 1987. 22.50 (ISBN 0-88029-098-6, Pub. by Dorset Pr). Hippocrene Bks.

--Augustine of Hippo: A Biography. 1967. pap. 9.95 (ISBN 0-520-01411-1, CAL179). U of Cal Pr.

Brown, Ruth A. S. Aureli Augustini: De Beata Vita: A Translation with an Introduction & Commentary, Vol. 72. (Patristic Studies). 211p. 1984. Repr. of 1944 ed. 30.00x (ISBN 0-939738-30-9). Zubal Inc.

Burghardt, W. J., et al, eds. St. Prosper of Aquitaine, Defense of St. Augustine. LC 78-62463. (Ancient Christian Writers Ser.: No. 32). 235p. 1963. 10.95 (ISBN 0-8091-0263-3). Paulist Pr.

Burke, Kenneth. The Rhetoric of Religion: Studies in Logology. 1970. pap. 9.95x (ISBN 0-520-01610-6, CAMPUS 341). U of Cal Pr.

Deane, Herbert A. The Political & Social Ideas of St. Augustine. LC 63-9809. 356p. 1963. pap. 14.00x (ISBN 0-231-08569-9). Columbia U Pr.

Evans, G. R. Augustine on Evil. LC 81-21793. 220p. 1983. 34.50 (ISBN 0-521-24526-5). Cambridge U Pr.

Fuchs, Harald. Augustin und der Antike Friendensgedanke. LC 72-147669. (Library of War & Peace; Relig. & Ethical Positions on War). 1973. lib. bdg. 46.00 (ISBN 0-8240-0427-2). Garland Pub.

Gibb, John & Montgomery, William. The Confessions of Augustine. 2nd ed. LC 78-66639. (Ancient Philosophy Ser.). 554p. 1980. lib. bdg. 67.00 (ISBN 0-8240-9597-9). Garland Pub.

Gilson, Etienne. The Christian Philosophy of St. Augustine. xii, 398p. 1983. Repr. of 1960 ed. lib. bdg. 35.00 (ISBN 0-88254-873-5, Octagon). Hippocrene Bks.

Gotte, Johannes. Augustine's Concept of Providence. 1.00 (ISBN 0-686-23373-5). Classical Folia.

Hatzfeld, Adolphe. Saint Augustine. LC 71-168252. 155p. 1975. Repr. of 1903 ed. 16.00 (ISBN 0-404-03155-2). AMS Pr.

Hill, Edmund. The Mystery of God: St. Augustine on the Trinity. (Catholic Theology Ser.). 200p. pap. 14.95 (ISBN 0-225-66470-4, HarpR). Har-Row.

Hohensee, Herbert. The Augustinian Concept of Auctoritas. 3.00 (ISBN 0-686-23374-3). Classical Folia.

Hugo, John. St. Augustine on Nature, Sex & Marriage. 249p. 1969. pap. 8.95 (ISBN 0-933932-23-5). Scepter Pubs.

Jaspers, Karl. Plato & Augustine: Taken from Vol. 1 of the Great Philosophers. Manheim, Karl, tr. LC 67-38117. Orig. Title: Great Philosophers, Vol. 1 (Pt. 2) 1966. pap. 4.95 (ISBN 0-15-672035-3, Harv). HarBraceJ.

Keyes, G. L. Christian Faith & the Interpretation of History: A Study of St. Augustine's Philosophy of History. LC 66-10314. xiv, 206p. 1966. 17.50x (ISBN 0-8032-0091-9). U of Nebr Pr.

Markus, R. A. Saeculum: History & Society in the Theology of St Augustine. LC 71-87136. 1970. 54.50 (ISBN 0-521-07621-8). Cambridge U Pr.

Meagher, Robert. An Introduction to Augustine. LC 77-99085. 1978. 30.00x (ISBN 0-8147-5423-6). NYU Pr.

Montgomery, W. St. Augustine: Aspects of His Life & Thought. 1977. lib. bdg. 34.95 (ISBN 0-8490-2556-7). Gordon Pr.

Mordell, Albert. Dante & Other Waning Classics. LC 68-8219. 1969. Repr. of 1915 ed. 18.50x (ISBN 0-8046-0322-7, Pub. by Kennikat). Assoc Faculty Pr.

Nash, Ronald H. The Light of the Mind: St. Augustine's Theory of Knowledge. LC 69-19765. Repr. of 1969 ed. 39.80 (ISBN 0-8357-9790-2, 2016099). Bks Demand UMI.

O'Connell, Robert J. Art & the Christian Intelligence in St. Augustine. LC 78-546. 1978. 18.00x (ISBN 0-674-04675-7). Harvard U Pr.

--Saint Augustine's Early Theory of Man, A. D. 386-391. LC 68-21981. 1968. text ed. 20.00x (ISBN 0-674-78520-7, Belknap Pr). Harvard U Pr.

Portalie, Eugene. A Guide to the Thought of Saint Augustine. Bastian, Ralph J., tr. from Fr. LC 75-1182. 428p. 1975. Repr. of 1960 ed. lib. bdg. 25.50x (ISBN 0-8371-7992-0, POGS). Greenwood.

Preus, Mary. Eloquence & Ignorance in Augustine's "On the Nature & Origin of the Soul". (AAR Academy Ser.). 1986. 19.95 (ISBN 0-89130-927-6, 01-01-51); pap. 15.25 (ISBN 0-89130-928-4). Scholars Pr Ga.

Quinn, John M. Praise in St. Augustine: Readings & Reflections. 220p. pap. 8.95 (ISBN 0-8158-0430-X). Chris Mass.

Rolston, Holmes, III. Religious Inquiry: Participation & Detachment. LC 83-24602. 323p. 1985. 22.50 (ISBN 0-8022-2450-4). Philos Lib.

St. Augustine. The City of God. LC 58-5717. pap. 6.50 (ISBN 0-385-02910-1, Im). Doubleday.

--Letters: 165-203. (Fathers of the Church Ser.: Vol. 30). 421p. 1955. 21.95x (ISBN 0-8132-0030-X). Cath U Pr.

--Letters: 204-270. (Fathers of the Church Ser.: Vol. 32). 317p. 1956. 17.95x (ISBN 0-8132-0032-6). Cath U Pr.

Saint Augustine. The Confessions of Saint Augustine. LC 60-13725. 6.50 (ISBN 0-385-02955-1, Im). Doubleday.

--Rule of Saint Augustine. Canning, Raymond, tr. LC 85-20760. 128p. 1986. pap. 3.95 (ISBN 0-385-23241-1, Im). Doubleday.

Sheed, F. J. Our Hearts Are Restless: The Prayer of St. Augustine. 96p. 1976. pap. 4.95 (ISBN 0-8164-2127-7, HarpR). Har-Row.

Ulanov, Barry, tr. from Lat. Prayers of St. Augustine: A Contemporary Anthology. 160p. (Orig.). 1984. pap. 7.95 (ISBN 0-86683-881-3, 7460, HarpR). Har-Row.

Warfield, Benjamin B. Studies in Tertullian & Augustine. Repr. of 1930 ed. lib. bdg. 29.00x (ISBN 0-8371-4490-6, WATT). Greenwood.

West, Rebecca. St. Augustine. 174p. 1979. Repr. of 1938 ed. lib. bdg. 22.50 (ISBN 0-89987-853-9). Darby Bks.

Willis, Gladys J. The Penalty of Eve: John Milton & Divorce. LC 83-49352. (American University Studies IV (English Language & Literature): Vol. 6). 164p. (Orig.). 1985. text ed. 21.55 (ISBN 0-8204-0094-7). P Lang Pubs.

Wirt, Sherwood E. The Confessions of Augustine in Modern English. Link, Julie, ed. 144p. 1986. pap. 5.95 (ISBN 0-310-34641-X). Zondervan.

AUGUSTINUS, AURELIUS, SAINT, BP. OF HIPPO, 354-430–BIBLIOGRAPHY

Institut Des Etudes Augustiniennes, Paris. Fichier Augustinien, 4 vols. (Augustine Bibliography). 1972. Set. 355.00 (ISBN 0-8161-0947-8, Hall Library). G K Hall.

Smith, W. Thomas. Augustine: His Life & Thought. LC 79-92071. (Illus.). 190p. (Orig.). 1980. pap. 10.95 (ISBN 0-8042-0871-9). John Knox.

AURICULAR CONFESSION

see Confession

AUROBINDO, SRI, 1872-1950

Aurobindo, Sri. Sri Aurobindo on Himself. 513p. 1985. 14.95 (ISBN 0-89071-317-0, Pub. by Sri Aurobindo Ashram India); pap. 11.75 (ISBN 0-89071-316-2, Pub. by Sri Aurobindo Ashram India). Matagiri.

Champaklal. Champaklal Speaks. (Illus.). 275p. 1975. pap. 7.25 (ISBN 0-89071-278-6). Matagiri.

--Champaklal's Treasures. (Illus.). 234p. 1976. pap. 5.25 (ISBN 0-89071-279-4). Matagiri.

Das, Manoj. Sri Aurobindo. 3rd ed. 1982. pap. 4.00x (ISBN 0-8364-1585-X, Pub. by National Sahitya Akademi). South Asia Bks.

Dhar, Niranjan. Aurobindo, Gandhi & Roy: A Yogi, a Mahatma & a Rationalist. 1986. 13.50x (ISBN 0-8364-1578-7, Pub. by Minerva India). South Asia Bks.

Gokak, Vinayak K. Sri Aurobindo-Seer & Poet. LC 73-900907. 185p. 1974. 8.00x (ISBN 0-89684-454-4). Orient Bk Dist.

Goswami, Chitta R. Sri Aurobindo's Concept of the Superman. 260p. 1976. 8.00 (ISBN 0-89071-211-5). Matagiri.

Joshi, V. C., ed. Sri Aurobindo: An Interpretation. 1973. 7.50 (ISBN 0-686-20308-9). Intl Bk Dist.

McDermott, Robert A., et al. Six Pillars: Introduction to the Major Works of Sri Aurobindo. McDermott, Robert A., ed. LC 74-77411. 300p. 1974. pap. 5.95 (ISBN 0-89012-001-3). Anima Pubns.

Minor, Robert N. Sri Aurobindo: The Perfect & the Good. 1978. 15.00x (ISBN 0-8364-0033-X). South Asia Bks.

Nirodbaran. Twelve Years with Sri Aurobindo. 306p. 1973. 5.00 (ISBN 0-89071-245-X); pap. 4.00 (ISBN 0-89071-244-1). Matagiri.

Purani, A. B. The Life of Sri Aurobindo. (Illus.). 1978. 13.50 (ISBN 0-89071-230-1); pap. 11.25 (ISBN 0-89071-229-8). Matagiri.

Rishabchand. Sri Aurobindo: His Life Unique. (Illus.). 427p. 1981. 20.00 (ISBN 0-89071-326-X, Pub. by Sri Aurobindo Ashram India); pap. 15.00 (ISBN 0-89071-325-1, Pub. by Sri Aurobindo Ashram India). Matagiri.

Sri Aurobindo. Guidance from Sri Aurobindo: Letters to a Young Disciple. Doshi, Nagin, ed. 285p. 1974. 6.00 (ISBN 0-89071-205-0). Matagiri.

--The Immortal Fire. Jhunjhuniwala, Shyam S., ed. 216p. (Orig.). 1974. pap. 4.50 (ISBN 0-89071-209-3). Matagiri.

--Sri Aurobindo on Himself. 1979. 20.00 (ISBN 0-89744-917-7). Auromere.

Themi. Sri Aurobindo: The Story of His Life. 95p. 1983. pap. 2.95 (ISBN 0-89071-327-8, Pub. by Sri Aurobindo Ashram India). Matagiri.

Varma, V. P. The Political Philosophy of Sri Aurobindo. 2nd rev. ed. 1976. 12.50 (ISBN 0-8426-0873-7). Orient Bk Dist.

AUSTRALIA–CHURCH HISTORY

Barrett, John. That Better Country. 1966. 15.50x (ISBN 0-522-83525-2, Pub. by Melbourne U Pr). Intl Spec Bk.

AUSTRALIA–RELIGION

Border, Ross. Church & State in Australia, 1788-1872: A Constitutional Study of the Church of England in Australia. LC 64-56989. 1962. text ed. 15.00x (ISBN 0-8401-0226-7). A R Allenson.

Charlesworth, Max, et al, eds. Religion in Aboriginal Australia: An Anthology. LC 83-23437. (Illus.). 458p. 1984. text ed. 39.50x (ISBN 0-7022-1754-9). U of Queensland Pr.

Kolig, Erich. Silent Revolution: The Effects of Modernization on Australian Aboriginal Religion. LC 81-6430. (Illus.). 224p. 1981. text ed. 27.50 (ISBN 0-89727-020-7). ISHI PA.

Mol, Hans. The Faith Of Australians. (Studies In Society: No. 25). 220p. 1985. text ed. 27.50x (ISBN 0-86861-628-1); pap. text ed. 12.50x (ISBN 0-86861-636-2). Allen Unwin.

Montagu, Ashley. Coming into Being among the Australian Aborigines. LC 75-41195. (Illus.). Repr. of 1937 ed. 27.45 (ISBN 0-404-14573-6). AMS Pr.

Salvado, Rosendo. The Salvado Memoirs: Historical Memoirs of Australia & Particularly of the Benedictine Mission of New Norcia & of the Habits & Customs of the Australian Natives. Stormon, E. J., tr. 1978. pap. 10.95x (ISBN 0-85564-114-2, Pub. by U of W Austral Pr). Intl Spec Bk.

Suttor, T. L. Hierarchy & Democracy in Australia, 1788-1870: The Formation of Australian Catholicism. 1965. 22.00x (ISBN 0-522-83753-0, Pub. by Melbourne U Pr). Intl Spec Bk.

Tillett, Gregory. Religious Minorities in Australia. 1985. 27.95x (ISBN 0-19-554555-9). Oxford U Pr.

Wilson, Bruce. Can God Survive in Australia. 224p. (Orig.). 1983. pap. 7.95 (ISBN 0-86760-009-8, Pub. by Albatross Bks). ANZ Religious Pubns.

AUSTRALIAN ABORIGINES–MYTHOLOGY

see Mythology, Australian (Aboriginal)

AUSTRALIAN MYTHOLOGY

see Mythology, Australian (Aboriginal)

AUSTRIA–CHURCH HISTORY

Epp, Margaret. Eight, Tulpengasse: A Church Blossom's in Vienna. 276p. (Orig.). 1978. pap. 4.95 (ISBN 0-919797-01-6, Dist. by Herald Pr.). Kindred Pr.

Friedmann, Robert. Glaubenszeugnisse Oberdeutscher Taufgesinnter, Band Zwei. (Tauferakten Kommission Ser., Vol. 12). 318p. (Ger). 9.50x (ISBN 0-8361-1186-9). Herald Pr.

AUTHORITY (RELIGION)

see also Bible–Evidences, Authority, Etc.; Catholic Church–Infallibility; Church–Authority; Church–Teaching Office; Conciliar Theory; Experience (Religion); Inner Light; Liberty of Speech in the Church; Popes–Infallibility; Tradition (Theology)

Annese, Lucius. The Purpose of Authority? LC 78-72295. (Orig.). 1978. 50.00 (ISBN 0-933402-12-0). Charisma Pr.

Cameron, James M. Images of Authority: A Consideration of the Concepts of "Regnum" & "Sacerdotium". LC 66-12489. pap. 24.30 (ISBN 0-8357-9261-7, 2016769). Bks Demand UMI.

Carson, D. A. & Woodbridge, John D., eds. Hermeneutics, Authority & Canon. 480p. 1986. pap. 14.95 (ISBN 0-310-43991-4, 12644P). Zondervan.

Davies, Rupert E. The Problems of Authority in the Continental Reformers: A Study of Luther, Zwingli, & Calvin. LC 78-5871. 1978. Repr. of 1946 ed. lib. bdg. cancelled (ISBN 0-313-20487-X, DAPA). Greenwood.

Garrigou-Lagrange, R. The Three Ways of the Spiritual Life. 1977. pap. 3.00 (ISBN 0-89555-017-2). TAN Bks Pubs.

Kemp, Eric W. Canonization & Authority in the Western Church. LC 78-63467. Repr. of 1948 ed. 20.00 (ISBN 0-404-16397-1). AMS Pr.

Lash, Nicholas. Voices of Authority. LC 76-29603. viii, 119p. 1976. pap. 3.95x (ISBN 0-915762-03-X). Patmos Pr.

Lloyd-Jones, D. Martyn. Authority. 94p. pap. 3.45x (ISBN 0-85151-386-7). Banner of Truth.

Nee, Watchman. Spiritual Authority. Kaung, Stephen, tr. 1972. 4.75 (ISBN 0-935008-34-9); pap. 3.75 (ISBN 0-935008-35-7). Christian Fellow Pubs.

Reik, Theodor. Dogma & Compulsion. LC 72-9369. 332p. 1973. Repr. of 1951 ed. lib. bdg. 45.00x (ISBN 0-8371-6577-6, REDC). Greenwood.

Rousseau, Phillip. Ascetics, Authority, & the Church in the Age of Jerome & Cassian. (Historical Monographs). 1978. 39.95x (ISBN 0-19-821870-2). Oxford U Pr.

Russell, Letty M. Household of Freedom: Authority in Feminist Theology. 132p. (Orig.). 1987. pap. 8.95 (ISBN 0-664-24017-8). Westminster.

Shaw, Graham. The Cost of Authority: Manipulation & Freedom in the New Testament. LC 82-48545. 320p. 1983. pap. 16.95 (ISBN 0-8006-1707-X). Fortress.

Skinner, John E. The Meaning of Authority. LC 82-25098. 88p. (Orig.). 1983. lib. bdg. 22.00 (ISBN 0-8191-3044-3, Co-pub. by Episcopal Div Sch); pap. text ed. 8.50 (ISBN 0-8191-3045-1). U Pr of Amer.

Southgate, Wyndham M. John Jewel & the Problem of Doctrinal Authority. LC 62-9430. (Historical Monographs: No. 49). (Illus.). 1962. 16.50x (ISBN 0-674-47750-2). Harvard U Pr.

Steele, David A. Images of Leadership & Authority for the Church: Biblical Principles & Secular Models. LC 86-24589. 206p. (Orig.). 1987. lib. bdg. 23.50 (ISBN 0-8191-5710-4); pap. text ed. 13.25 (ISBN 0-8191-5711-2). U Pr of Amer.

Tavard, George H. Holy Writ or Holy Church: The Crisis of the Protestant Reformation. LC 78-17085. 1978. Repr. of 1959 ed. lib. bdg. 22.75x (ISBN 0-313-20584-1, TAHO). Greenwood.

AUTHORS, CATHOLIC

see Catholic Authors

AVATARS

see also Incarnation

Adriel, Jean. Avatar. 285p. 1972. 8.95 (ISBN 0-940700-02-6); pap. 4.95 (ISBN 0-940700-01-8). Meher Baba Info.

De Nicolas, Antonio T. Avatara: The Humanization of Philosophy Through the Bhagavad Gita. LC 76-152. 1976. 12.50 (ISBN 0-89254-001-X); pap. 8.50 (ISBN 0-89254-002-8). Nicolas-Hays.

Parrinder, Geoffrey. Avatar & Incarnation. 1982. Repr. of 1970 ed. 15.95 (ISBN 0-19-520361-5). Oxford U Pr.

AVERROES, 1126-1198

Butterworth, C. E. & A. Abd Al-Magid Haridi, eds. Averroes's Middle Commentary on Aristotle's Topics. (American Research Center in Egypt, Publications Ser.: Vol. 4). (Arabic & Eng.). 247p. (Orig.). 1979. pap. 5.00x (ISBN 0-686-30893-X, Pub. by Am Res Ctr Egypt). Eisenbrauns.

Zedler, Beatrice H., ed. Saint Thomas Aquinas: On the Unity of the Intellect Against the Averroists. (Medieval Philosophical Texts in Translation: No. 19). 1968. pap. 7.95 (ISBN 0-87462-219-0). Marquette.

AVESTA

see also Zoroastrianism

Avesta. The Hymns of Zarathustra. Henning, M., tr. LC 78-20446. 1985. Repr. of 1952 ed. 21.00 (ISBN 0-88355-826-2). Hyperion Conn.

Bleeck, Arthur H. Avesta: The Religious Books of the Parsees. lib. bdg. 79.95 (ISBN 0-87968-133-0). Krishna Pr.

Busch, Ernestine G., ed. The Avesta: Major Portions from the Holy Book of the Magi. LC 85-90618. 440p. (Orig.). 1985. pap. 17.50 (ISBN 0-9614750-0-5). E G Busch.

Darmesteter, J. & Mills, L. H., trs. Zend-Avesta, 3 vols. Repr. 125.00 (ISBN 0-87902-154-3). Orientalia.

Darmesteter, James & Mills, L. H. The Zend-Avesta, 3 vols. 1974. lib. bdg. 300.00 (ISBN 0-87968-509-3). Krishna Pr.

Darmesteter, James, tr. Zend-Avesta: Selections. 1984. pap. 6.95 (ISBN 0-916411-41-9, Near Eastern). Holmes Pub.

Geiger, Wilhelm & Windischmann, Friedrich, eds. Zarathushtra in the Gathas & in the Greek & Roman Classics. 2nd ed. LC 74-21260. Repr. of 1899 ed. 24.50 (ISBN 0-404-12810-6). AMS Pr.

Mills, Lawrence H. Zarathushtra, Philo, the Achaemenids & Israel. LC 74-21261. Repr. of 1906 ed. 34.50 (ISBN 0-404-12815-7). AMS Pr.

Reichelt, Hans. Avesta Reader. 1968. Repr. of 1911 ed. 38.80x (ISBN 3-11-000159-4). De Gruyter.

Schuyler, Montgomery. Index Verborum of the Fragments of the "Avesta". LC 2-15630. (Columbia University. Indo-Iranian Ser.: No. 4). Repr. of 1901 ed. 14.50 (ISBN 0-404-50474-4). AMS Pr.

Szekely, Edmond B. The Zend-Avesta of Zarathustra. (Illus.). 100p. 1973. pap. 4.80 (ISBN 0-89564-058-9). IBS Intl.

The Zend-Avesta. (Sacred Bks. of the East: Vols. 4, 23, 31). 3 vols. 45.00 (ISBN 0-686-97477-8); 15.00 ea. Asian Human Pr.

AWAKENING, GREAT

see Great Awakening

AXIOLOGY

see Values

AYLWARD, GLADYS

Aylward, Gladys & Hunter, Christine. Gladys Aylward. 1970. pap. 3.50 (ISBN 0-8024-2986-6). Moody.

Burgess, Alan. THe Small Woman: The Story of Gladys Aylward of China. 266p. 1985. pap. 5.95 (ISBN 0-89283-232-0, Pub. by Vine Books). Servant.

Davey, Cyril. Never Say Die: Story of Gladys Aylward. 1964. pap. 2.95 (ISBN 0-87508-616-0). Chr Lit.

AZTECS

Brundage, Burr C. The Fifth Sun: Aztec Gods, Aztec World. (Texas Pan American Ser.). (Illus.). 283p. 1979. pap. 8.95 (ISBN 0-292-72438-1). U of Tex Pr.

Caso, Alfonso. Aztecs: People of the Sun, Vol. 50. Dunham, Lowell, tr. (Civilization of the American Indian Ser.: No. 50). (Illus.). 142p. 1978. Repr. of 1958 ed. 24.95 (ISBN 0-8061-0414-7). U of Okla Pr.

Conrad, Geoffrey W. & Demarest, Arthur A. Religion & Empire: The Dynamics of Aztec & Inca Expansionism. LC 83-14414. (New Studies in Archaeology). 256p. 1984. 52.50 (ISBN 0-521-24357-2); pap. 17.95 (ISBN 0-521-31896-3). Cambridge U Pr.

Duverger, Christian. L' Esprit du Jeu Chez les Azteques. (Civilisations et Societes Ser.: No. 59). (Illus.). 1978. pap. 26.00 (ISBN 90-279-7664-3). Mouton.

Heyden, Doris & Villasenor, Luis F. The Great Temple & the Aztec Gods. (Illus.). 72p. 1984. pap. 4.50 (ISBN 968-7074-12-4). Ocelot Pr.

Sahagun, Bernardino de. Florentine Codex, General History of the Things of New Spain, 13 bks. Anderson, Arthur J. & Dibble, Charles E., trs. Incl. Introductory Volume: Introductions, Sahagun's Prologues & Interpolations, General Bibliography, General Indices. 1982. 35.00x (ISBN 0-87480-165-6); Bk. 1. Gods. rev., 2nd ed. 1970. 17.50 (ISBN 0-87480-000-5); Bk. 2. Ceremonies. rev., 2nd ed. 1981. 40.00x (ISBN 0-87480-194-X); Bk. 3. Origins of the Gods. rev., 2nd ed. 1979. 17.50x (ISBN 0-87480-002-1); Bks. 4 & 5. The Soothsayers, the Omens. Repr. of 1979 ed. 40.00x (ISBN 0-87480-003-X); Bk. 6. Rhetoric & Moral Philosophy. 1976. 40.00x (ISBN 0-87480-010-2); Bk. 7. Sun, Moon & Stars, & the Binding of the Years. Repr. of 1977 ed. 17.50 (ISBN 0-87480-004-8); Bk. 8. Kings & Lords. Repr. of 1979 ed. 20.00x (ISBN 0-87480-005-6); Bk. 9. Merchants. Repr. of 1976 ed. 20.00x (ISBN 0-87480-006-4); Bk. 10. People. Repr. of 1974 ed. 30.00x (ISBN 0-87480-007-2); Bk. 11. Earthly Things. Repr. of 1975 ed. 45.00x (ISBN 0-87480-008-0); Bk. 12. Conquest of Mexico. rev., 2nd ed. 1975. 27.50x (ISBN 0-87480-096-X). 1982. Set. 350.00x (ISBN 0-87480-082-X). U of Utah Pr.

AZTECS–ART

Nicholson, H. B. & Berger, Rainer. Two Aztec Wood Idols: Iconographic & Chronologic Analysis. LC 68-58701. (Studies in Pre-Columbian Art & Archaeology: No.5). (Illus.). 28p. 1968. pap. 3.00x (ISBN 0-88402-026-6). Dumbarton Oaks.

B

BAAL (DEITY)

Habel, Norman C. Vahweh vs. Baal. 128p. 1964. write for info. Concordia Schl Grad Studies.

Landersdorfer, Simon K., ed. Der Bael Tatpauopoos und Die Kerube Des Ezechiel. pap. 8.00 (ISBN 0-384-31200-4). Johnson Repr.

BABISM

see also Bahaism

Balyuzi, H. M. The Bab: The Herald of the Day of Days. (Illus.). 272p. 1973. 14.95 (ISBN 0-85398-048-9). G Ronald Pub.

--Baha'u'llah: The Word Made Flesh. 134p. 1963. 10.95 (ISBN 0-85398-014-4); pap. 5.95 (ISBN 0-85398-001-2). G Ronald Pub.

Furutan, Ali-Akbar. Stories of Baha'u'llah. 128p. 1986. 12.95; pap. 5.95. G Ronald Pub.

Heggie, James. Baha'i References to Judaism, Christianity & Islam. 272p. 1986. 11.95. G Ronald Pub.

Khanum, Munirih. Munirih Khanum: Memoirs & Letters. Smith, Sammireh A., tr. (Persian., Illus.). 1987. 7.95 (ISBN 0-933770-51-0). Kalimat.

MacEoin, Denis. Studies in Babi & Baha'i History, Vol. 5: A Survey of Sources for Early Babi History & Doctorine. 1987. 19.95 (ISBN 0-933770-63-4). Kalimat.

Momen, Moojan. Selections from the Writings of E. G. Browne on the Babi & Baha'i Religions. 528p. 1987. 29.50 (ISBN 0-85398-246-5); pap. 16.95 (ISBN 0-85398-247-3). G Ronald Pub.

Momen, Moojan, ed. The Babi & Baha'i Religions Eighteen Forty-Four to Nineteen Forty-Four: Some Contemporary Western Accounts. (Illus.). 608p. 29.50 (ISBN 0-85398-102-7). G Ronald Pub.

--Studies in Babi & Baha'i History, Vol. 1. (Illus.). 1983. text ed. 19.95 (ISBN 0-933770-16-2). Kalimat.

Smith, Peter. The Babi & Baha'i Religions: From Messianic Sh'ism to a World Religion. (Illus.). 225p. Date not set. price not set (ISBN 0-521-30128-9). Cambridge U Pr.

Smith, Peter, ed. & intro. by. Studies in Babi & Baha'i History Volume 3: In Iran. (Illus.). 1986. 19.95 (ISBN 0-933770-46-4). Kalimat.

Smith, Peter, ed. Studies in Babi & Baha'i History, Vol. 6: Baha'is in the West. Date not set. 19.95 (ISBN 0-933770-64-2). Kalimat.

BABYLON

Mystical Babylon. 31p. (Orig.). pap. 0.95 (ISBN 0-937408-21-2). GMI Pubns Inc.

Political Babylon. 32p. (Orig.). 1982. pap. 0.95 (ISBN 0-937408-16-6). GMI Pubns Inc.

BABYLONIA

King, Leonard W. Babylonian Religion & Mythology. LC 77-94592. 1978. Repr. of 1899 ed. lib. bdg. 25.00 (ISBN 0-89341-311-9). Longwood Pub Group.

Thompson, R. C. The Devils & Evil Spirits of Babylonia, 2 vols. Set. 200.00 (ISBN 0-8490-0026-2). Gordon Pr.

Van Dijk, Jan, et al. Early Mesopotamian Incantations & Rituals. LC 84-13064. (Yale Oriental Ser., Babylonian Texts: Vol. 11). 200p. 1985. text ed. 35.00x (ISBN 0-300-03147-5). Yale U Pr.

BABYLONIA–ANTIQUITIES

Myhrman, David V. Babylonian Hymns & Prayers. 59.95 (ISBN 0-87968-691-X). Gordon Pr.

BABYLONIAN MYTHOLOGY

see Mythology, Assyro-Babylonian

BACH, JOHANN SEBASTIAN, 1685-1750

Stiller, Gunther. J. S. Bach & Liturgical Life in Liepzig. Leaver, Robin A., ed. Boutman, Herbert J., et al, trs. from Ger. Tr. of Johann Sebastian Bach und das Leipziger Gottesdienstliche Leben Seiner Zeit. (Illus.). 312p. (Orig.). 1984. pap. 24.95 (ISBN 0-570-01320-8, 99-1247). Concordia.

BACKUS, ISAAC, 1724-1806

Backus, Isaac. The Diary of Isaac Backus, 3 vols. McLoughlin, William G., ed. LC 76-12018. (Illus.). 1834p. 1979. Set. 120.00x (ISBN 0-87057-148-6). U Pr of New Eng.

Grenz, Stanley. Isaac Backus - Puritan & Baptist. (Dissertation Ser.: No. 4). vii, 346p. 1983. pap. 21.95 (ISBN 0-86554-067-5). NABPR.

Hovey, Alvah. Memoir of the Life & Times of the Reverend Isaac Backus. LC 73-148598. (Era of the American Revolution Ser.). 367p. 1972. Repr. of 1858 ed. lib. bdg. 47.50 (ISBN 0-306-70415-3). Da Capo.

BAHA ULIAH, 1817-1892

Balyuzi, H. M. Baha'u'llah: The King of Glory. (Illus.). 552p. 1980. 28.50 (ISBN 0-85398-090-X). G Ronald Pub.

Effendi, Shoghi. The World Order of Baha'u'llah. 2nd rev. ed. LC 56-17685. 1974. 16.95 (ISBN 0-87743-031-4, 108-020); pap. 8.95 (ISBN 0-87743-004-7, 108-021). Baha'i.

Hatcher, John. Ali's Dream: The Story of Baha'u'llah. (Illus.). 260p. 14.95 (ISBN 0-85398-092-6); pap. 8.95 (ISBN 0-85398-093-4). G Ronald Pub.

Hoffman, David. A Commentary on the Will & Testament of Abdu'l-Baha. 56p. pap. 2.95 (ISBN 0-85398-158-2). G Ronald Pub.

Honnold, Annamarie. Vignettes from the Life of Abdu'l-Baha. (Illus.). 224p. pap. 8.95 (ISBN 0-85398-129-9). G Ronald Pub.

Muhammad-'Aliy-Salmani, Ustad. My Memories of Baha'u'llah: Ustad Muhammad-'Aliy-Salmani, the Barber. Gail, Marzieh, tr. from Persian. (Illus.). xii, 148p. 1982. 11.95 (ISBN 0-933770-21-9). Kalimat.

Taherzadeh, Adib. Revelation of Baha'u'llah, Vol. I: Baghdad 1853-1863. (Illus.). 384p. 1974. 18.95 (ISBN 0-85398-052-7); pap. 11.95 (ISBN 0-85398-057-8). G Ronald Pub.

--The Revelation of Baha'u'llah, Vol. II: Adrianople, 1863-1868. (Illus.). 492p. 1977. 17.95 (ISBN 0-85398-070-5). G Ronald Pub.

Townshend, George. Christ & Baha'u'llah. LC 68-168. 116p. 1966. pap. 3.95 (ISBN 0-85398-005-5). G Ronald Pub.

BAHA'I FAITH

see Bahaism

BAHAISM

see also Babism

Abdu'l-Baha. Memorials of the Faithful. Gail, Marzieh, tr. LC 77-157797. 1971. 10.95 (ISBN 0-87743-041-1, 106-012). Baha'i.

--Secret of Divine Civilization. 2nd ed. Gail, Marzieh, tr. LC 56-12427. 1970. 15.95 (ISBN 0-87743-008-X, 106-006). Baha'i.

--Selections from the Writings of Abdu'l-Baha. Effendi, Shoghi & Gail, Marzieh, trs. 1978. 14.95 (ISBN 0-85398-081-0, 106-025); pap. 7.95 (ISBN 0-85398-084-5, 106-026); Lightweight. pap. 6.00 (ISBN 0-85398-136-1). Baha'i.

--Some Answered Questions. Barney, Laura C., tr. from Persian. LC 81-2467. xviii, 324p. 1981. 17.95 (ISBN 0-87743-162-0). Baha'i.

--Some Answered Questions. Barney, Laura C., tr. from Persian. LC 83-21353. xviii, 324p. 1984. Pocket sized. pap. 5.95 (ISBN 0-87743-190-6). Baha'i.

--Tablets of the Divine Plan. rev. ed. LC 76-10624. 1977. o.s.i 10.95 (ISBN 0-87743-107-8, 106-010); pap. 5.95 (ISBN 0-87743-116-7, 106-011). Baha'i.

--A Traveler's Narrative: Written to Illustrate the Episode of the Bab. rev. ed. Browne, Edward G., tr. from Persian. LC 79-19025. 1980. 10.95 (ISBN 0-87743-134-5, 106-027); pap. 5.95 (ISBN 0-686-96668-6, 106-028). Baha'i.

Abul-Fadl, Mirza. The Baha'i Proofs & A Short Sketch of the History & Lives of the Leaders of This Religion. Khan, Ali-Kuli, tr. from Arabic. LC 83-22486. (Illus.). xi, 305p. 1983. 17.95 (ISBN 0-87743-191-4). Baha'i.

Afrukhtih, Yunis Khan. Khatirat-i Nuh Salih. (Persian., Illus.). 1983. 15.95 (ISBN 0-933770-20-0, P-31). Kalimat.

Arjmand, Mihdi. Gulshan-i Haqayiq. (Persian.). 320p. 1982. Repr. 12.95 (ISBN 0-933770-15-4). Kalimat.

Bab. Selections from the Writings of the Bab. LC 79-670141. 1976. 14.95 (ISBN 0-85398-066-7, 105-050); pap. 7.95 (ISBN 0-85398-135-3). Baha'i.

Baha'u'llah. Epistle to the Son of the Wolf. rev. ed. Effendi, Shoghi, tr. LC 53-18798. 1976. 12.95 (ISBN 0-87743-048-9, 103-001). Baha'i.

--Gleanings from the Writings of Baha'u'llah. 2nd rev. ed. Shoghi Effendi, tr. from Persian. LC 76-45364. (Illus.). 346p. 1976. 16.95 (ISBN 0-87743-111-6, 103-003). Baha'i.

--Gleanings from the Writings of Baha'u'llah. Effendi, Shoghi, tr. from Persian. 346p. 1983. pap. 5.95 pocket size (ISBN 0-87743-187-6). Baha'i.

--The Hidden Words of Baha'u'llah. rev. ed. Effendi, Shoghi, tr. LC 54-7328. 1985. 7.95 (ISBN 0-87743-007-1, 103-005); pap. 3.50 (ISBN 0-87743-002-0, 103-006). Baha'i.

Bahaullah. Prayers & Meditations. Effendi, Shoghi, tr. 1978. 14.95 (ISBN 0-900125-39-X). Baha'i.

Baha'u'llah. The Proclamation of Baha'u'llah. LC 72-237435. 1967. 8.95 (ISBN 0-87743-064-0, 103-012); pap. 4.95 (ISBN 0-87743-065-9, 103-013). Baha'i.

--Selected Writings of Baha'u'llah. LC 79-15136. 1979. 10.95 (ISBN 0-87743-133-7, 303-024); pap. 1.00 (ISBN 0-87743-077-2, 303-023). Baha'i.

--Tablets of Baha'u'llah Revealed after the Kitab-i-Aqdas. Effendi, Shoghi & Taherzadeh, Habib, trs. LC 79-670079. 1978. 14.95 (ISBN 0-85398-077-2, 103-021, Pub. by Universal Hse. of Justice); pap. 7.95 (ISBN 0-85398-137-X). Baha'i.

Bahaullah & Bab. O God, Guide Me: A Selection of Prayers Revealed. (Illus.). 1986. pap. 4.75 (ISBN 0-87743-202-3). Baha'i.

Baha'u'llah, et al. The Pattern of Baha'i Life. 3rd ed. 1963. pap. 2.95 (ISBN 0-900125-15-2, 315-030-10). Baha'i.

Baha'u'llah, Bab & Abdu'l-Baha. Baha'i Prayers: A Selection of Prayers Revealed by Baha'u'llah, the Bab & Abdu'l-Baha. LC 82-11502. 1985. 11.95 (ISBN 0-87743-175-2, 115-070); pap. 4.95 (ISBN 0-87743-176-0, 115-071). Baha'i.

Baha'u'llah, the Bab & Abdu'l-Baha. Baha'i Prayers. LC 54-10901. 6.95 (ISBN 0-87743-012-8, 315-005). Baha'i.

Balyazi, H. M. Eminent Baha'is in the Time of Baha'u'llah. (Illus.). 400p. 1986. 28.50 (ISBN 0-85398-151-5); pap. 15.95 (ISBN 0-85398-152-3). G Ronald Pub.

Balyuzi, H. M. Edward Granville Browne & the Baha'i Faith. (Illus.). 152p. 1970. 14.95 (ISBN 0-85398-023-3). G Ronald Pub.

--Khadijih Bagum: The Wife of the Bab. (Illus.). 52p. 7.95 (ISBN 0-85398-100-0); pap. 3.75 (ISBN 0-85398-101-9). G Ronald Pub.

Beckwith, Francis. Bahai. 64p. 1985. saddle stitched 2.95 (ISBN 0-87123-848-9). Bethany Hse.

Bjorling, Joel. The Baha'i Faith: An Historical Bibliography. Melton, J. G, ed. LC 84-49294. (Reference Library of Social Science- Sects & Cults in America: Bibliographic Guides). 250p. 1985. lib. bdg. 35.00 (ISBN 0-8240-8974-X). Garland Pub.

Braun, Eunice. From Strength to Strength: The First Half Century of the Formative Age of the Baha'i Faith. LC 78-9424. 1978. pap. 2.95 (ISBN 0-87743-125-6, 332-030). Baha'i.

--A Reader's Guide: The Development of Baha'i Literature in English. 176p. 1986. 14.95 (ISBN 0-85398-228-7); pap. 8.95 (ISBN 0-85398-229-5). G Ronald Pub.

Braun, Eunice & Chance, Hugh E. A Crown of Beauty: The Baha'i Faith & the Holy Land. (Illus.). 104p. 16.95 (ISBN 0-85398-139-6); pap. 11.95 (ISBN 0-85398-140-X). G Ronald Pub.

Brown, Ramona A. Memories of Abdu'l-Baha: Recollections of the Early Days of the Baha'i Faith in California. LC 79-16412. (Illus.). 1980. 10.95 (ISBN 0-87743-128-0, 332-010); pap. 6.95 (ISBN 0-87743-139-6, 332-011). Baha'i.

Caton, Peggy, ed. Equal Circles: Baha'i Views of Women & Men. (Orig.). 1987. pap. 9.95 (ISBN 0-933770-60-X). Kalimat.

Chase, Thornton. In Galilee. Facsimile reprint ed. (Illus.). 98p. 1985. Repr. of 1921 ed. 7.95 (ISBN 0-933770-38-3). Kalimat.

Cole, Juan R. & Momen, Moojan, eds. Studies in Babi & Baha'i History: Vol. 2: From Iran East & West. (Illus.). 205p. 1984. 19.95 (ISBN 0-933770-40-5). Kalimat.

Coy, Genevieve. Counsels of Perfection: A Baha'i Guide to Mature Living. 192p. 1979. 6.95 (ISBN 0-85398-079-9). G Ronald Pub.

Effendi, Shoghi. Call to the Nations: Extracts from the Writings of Shoghi Effendi. LC 79-670140. 1978. 6.95 (ISBN 0-85398-068-3, 108-050); pap. 3.00 o. s. i. (ISBN 0-85398-069-1, 108-051). Baha'i.

--The Promised Day Is Come. rev. ed. 1980. 10.95 (ISBN 0-87743-132-9, 108-017); pap. 5.50 (ISBN 0-87743-138-8, 108-018). Baha'i.

--Selected Writings of Shoghi Effendi. rev. ed. 1975. pap. 1.95 (ISBN 0-87743-079-9, 308-043). Baha'i.

--The World Order of Baha'u'llah. 2nd rev. ed. LC 56-17685. 1974. 16.95 (ISBN 0-87743-031-4, 108-020); pap. 8.95 (ISBN 0-87743-004-7, 108-021). Baha'i.

Esslemont, J. E. Baha'u'llah & the New Era: An Introduction to the Baha'i Faith. 5th rev. ed. LC 80-24305. 1980. pap. 4.50 (ISBN 0-87743-160-4, 231-005). Baha'i.

--Baha'u'llah & the New Era: An Introduction to the Baha'i Faith. 4th rev. ed. LC 79-21937. 1980. 16.95 (ISBN 0-87743-136-1, 231-004). Baha'i.

Faizi, A. Q. Stories from The Delight of Hearts: The Memoirs of Haji Mirza Haydar-'Ali. LC 79-91219. (Illus.). 176p. 1980. 11.95 (ISBN 0-933770-11-1). Kalimat.

Freeman, Dorothy. From Copper to Gold: The Life of Dorothy Baker. (Illus.). 368p. 17.50 (ISBN 0-85398-177-9); pap. 10.95 (ISBN 0-85398-178-7). G Ronald Pub.

Furutan, Ali A. The Story of My Heart. (Illus.). 272p. 14.95 (ISBN 0-85398-114-0); pap. 8.95 (ISBN 0-85398-115-9). G Ronald Pub.

Gail, Marzieh. Khanum: The Greatest Holy Leaf. (Illus.). 48p. 6.95 (ISBN 0-85398-112-4); pap. 3.50 (ISBN 0-85398-113-2). G Ronald Pub.

--Other People, Other Places. 288p. 14.95 (ISBN 0-85398-122-1); pap. 8.95 (ISBN 0-85398-123-X). G Ronald Pub.

--The Sheltering Branch. 101p. 1959. 7.95 (ISBN 0-87743-022-5). G Ronald Pub.

Garis, M. R. Martha Root: Lioness at the Threshold. LC 83-3913. (Illus.). 500p. 1983. 22.95 (ISBN 0-87743-184-1); pap. 15.95 (ISBN 0-87743-185-X). Baha'i.

Giachery, Ugo. Shoghi Effendi: Recollections. (Illus.). 248p. 1973. 16.95 (ISBN 0-85398-050-0). G Ronald Pub.

Gotlieb, Randie & Gotlieb, Steven. Once to Every Man & Nation: Stories about Becoming a Baha'i. 160p. 1985. pap. 5.95 (ISBN 0-85398-211-2). G Ronald Pub.

Grundy, Julia M. Ten Days in the Light of 'Akka. rev. ed. LC 79-12177. 1979. pap. 6.95 (ISBN 0-87743-131-0, 332-040). Baha'i.

Hainsworth, Phillip & Perkins, Mary. The Baha'i Faith. 1985. 13.00x (ISBN 0-7062-3939-3, Pub. by Ward Lock Educ Co Ltd). State Mutual Bk.

Handy, Carol. The Dragons of Rizvania. (Illus.). 64p. 1984. 8.95 (ISBN 0-85398-192-2). G Ronald Pub.

Hatcher, John. Ali's Dream: The Story of Baha'u'llah. (Illus.). 260p. 14.95 (ISBN 0-85398-092-6); pap. 8.95 (ISBN 0-85398-093-4). G Ronald Pub.

Hatcher, William & Martin, James D. The Baha'i Faith: The Emerging Global Religion. LC 84-42743. 224p. 1985. 14.45 (ISBN 0-06-065441-4, HarpR). Har-Row.

Heggie, James. Index of Quotations From the Baha'i Scared Writings. 824p. 39.50 (ISBN 0-85398-145-0). G Ronald Pub.

Holley, Horace. Religion for Mankind. 248p. 1956. 12.95 (ISBN 0-87743-011-X); pap. 5.95 (ISBN 0-85398-000-4). G Ronald Pub.

Honnald, Annamarie. Divine Therapy: Pearls of Wisdom from the Bahai Writings. 1986. 14.95 (ISBN 0-85398-236-8); pap. 6.95 (ISBN 0-85398-237-6). G Ronald Pub.

Ives, Howard C. Portals to Freedom. 256p. 1937. pap. 8.95 (ISBN 0-87743-013-6). G Ronald Pub.

Labib, Muhammad. The Seven Martyrs of Hurmuzak. Momen, Moojan, tr. & frwd. by. (Illus.). 80p. 9.95 (ISBN 0-85398-105-1); pap. 4.95 (ISBN 0-85398-104-3). G Ronald Pub.

Lee, Anthony A., ed. Circle of Unity: Baha'i Approaches to Current Social Issues. 268p. (Orig.). 1984. pap. 9.95 (ISBN 0-933770-28-6). Kalimat.

Mahmoudi, Jalil. A Concordance to the Hidden Words of Baha'u'llah. LC 80-21346. (Orig.). 1980. pap. 2.95 (ISBN 0-87743-148-5, 368-052). Baha'i.

Maxwell, May. An Early Pilgrimage. 45p. pap. 2.95 (ISBN 0-85398-004-7). G Ronald Pub.

Miller, William M. The Baha'i Faith: Its History & Teachings. LC 74-8745. (Illus.). 464p. 1984. pap. 10.95 (ISBN 0-87808-137-2). William Carey Lib.

Momen, Moojan, ed. The Babi & Baha'i Religions Eighteen Forty-Four to Nineteen Forty-Four: Some Contemporary Western Accounts. (Illus.). 608p. 29.50 (ISBN 0-85398-102-7). G Ronald Pub.

--Studies in Babi & Baha'i History, Vol. 1. (Illus.). 1983. text ed. 19.95 (ISBN 0-933770-16-2). Kalimat.

Muhlschlegel, Peter. Auguste Forel & the Baha'i Faith. Neri, Helene, tr. from Ger. 64p. 1979. pap. 3.50 (ISBN 0-85398-076-4). G Ronald Pub.

Nakhjavani, Bahiyyih. Four on an Island. 144p. 10.95 (ISBN 0-85398-173-6); pap. 5.95 (ISBN 0-85398-174-4). G Ronald Pub.

--Response. 144p. pap. 4.95 (ISBN 0-85398-107-8). G Ronald Pub.

--When We Grow up. 120p. 1979. 9.95 (ISBN 0-85398-085-3); pap. 4.95 (ISBN 0-85398-086-1). G Ronald Pub.

Nash, Geoffrey. The Phoenix & the Ashes. 160p. 1985. pap. 6.95 (ISBN 0-85398-199-X). G Ronald Pub.

Nelson, Lee & Nelson, Miriam. Concordance to the Kitab-i-Iqan. 350p. (Orig.). 1984. pap. 9.95 (ISBN 0-933770-29-4). Kalimat.

Nerenberg, Arnie. Love & Estrangement in the Baha'i Community. (Orig.). 1986. 9.95 (ISBN 0-933770-47-2). Kalimat.

Paine, Mabel H. & Fisher, Betty J., eds. The Divine Art of Living. 272p. 1986. pap. 9.95 (ISBN 0-87743-194-9). Baha'i.

Prayer, a Baha'i Approach. Incl. Part I. Man's Link with God. Hellaby, William; Part II. Prayer as a Living Reality. Hellaby, William & Hellaby, Madeline.. 1985. 9.95 (ISBN 0-85398-212-0); pap. 4.95 (ISBN 0-85398-213-9). G Ronald Pub.

Rabbani, Ruhiyyih. Prescription for Living. 2nd, rev. ed. 272p. 4.75 (ISBN 0-85398-002-0). G Ronald Pub.

--The Priceless Pearl. (Illus.). 1969. pap. 8.95 (ISBN 0-900125-03-9, 331-048). Baha'i.

Raj, Veni. A Diamond in the Darkness. (Illus.). 32p. 1984. pap. 3.50 (ISBN 0-85398-161-2). G Ronald Pub.

Ruhe, David S. Door of Hope: A Century of the Baha'i Faith in the Holy Land. 254p. 19.95 (ISBN 0-85398-149-3); pap. 13.50 (ISBN 0-85398-150-7). G Ronald Pub.

Rutstein, Nathan. He Loved & Served: The Story of Curtis Kelsey. (Illus.). 208p. 12.95 (ISBN 0-85398-120-5); pap. 7.95 (ISBN 0-85398-121-3). G Ronald Pub.

--Teaching the Baha'i Faith: Spirit in Action. 192p. 11.95 (ISBN 0-85398-175-2); pap. 6.95 (ISBN 0-85398-176-0). G Ronald Pub.

Sabet, Huschmand. The Heavens Are Cleft Asunder. rev. ed. Coburn, Oliver, tr. from Ger. Orig. Title: Gespaltene Himmel. (Eng.). 1975. pap. 6.25 (ISBN 0-85398-055-1, 332-014). G Ronald Pub.

Saiedi, Nader, ed. Beyond Marxism: Baha'i Perspectives on a New World Order. (Orig.). 1988. pap. 9.95 (ISBN 0-933770-59-6). Kalimat.

Schaefer, Udo. The Imperishable Dominion. 320p. pap. 11.95 (ISBN 0-85398-142-6). G Ronald Pub.

--The Light Shineth in Darkness: Five Studies in Revelation after Christ. Neri, Helene M. & Coburn, Oliver, trs. 208p. 1977. 15.95 (ISBN 0-85398-091-8); pap. 9.95 (ISBN 0-85398-072-1). G Ronald Pub.

Sears, William. A Cry from the Heart: The Baha'is in Iran. (Illus.). 224p. 1982. pap. 3.95 (ISBN 0-85398-134-5). G Ronald Pub.

--God Loves Laughter. 182p. 1960. o.p. (ISBN 0-85398-018-7); pap. 6.95 (ISBN 0-85398-019-5). G Ronald Pub.

--Thief in the Night. 320p. 1961. 8.95 (ISBN 0-85398-096-9); pap. 3.95 (ISBN 0-85398-008-X). G Ronald Pub.

Sears, William & Quigley, Robert. The Flame. 144p. 1972. 7.95 (ISBN 0-85398-031-4); pap. 3.50 (ISBN 0-85398-030-6). G Ronald Pub.

Smith, Peter. The Babi & Baha'i Religions: From Messianic Sh'ism to a World Religion. (Illus.). 225p. Date not set. price not set (ISBN 0-521-30128-9). Cambridge U Pr.

Smith, Peter, ed. Studies in Babi & Baha'i History, Vol. 6: Baha'is in the West. Date not set. 19.95 (ISBN 0-933770-64-2). Kalimat.

Smith, Peter & Lee, Anthony A., eds. Faith & Reason: Some Baha'i Perspectives. (Orig.). 1987. pap. 9.95 (ISBN 0-933770-56-1). Kalimat.

Sprague, Sidney. A Year with the Baha'is of India & Burma. (Historical Reprint Ser.). (Illus.). 1986. 8.95 (ISBN 0-933770-57-X). Kalimat.

Star of the West, 8 vols. (Illus.). 544p. Set. 125.00x (ISBN 0-85398-078-0). G Ronald Pub.

Stockman, Robert H. The Baha'i Faith in America: Origins, 1892-1900, Vol. 1. (Illus.). 225p. 1985. 24.95 (ISBN 0-87743-199-X). Baha'i.

Taafaki, Irene. The Horse of the Moonlight. (Illus.). 40p. pap. 3.50 (ISBN 0-85398-111-6). G Ronald Pub.

Taherzaden, Ad. Revelation of Baha'u'llah Vol. III: Akka',the Early Years 1868-77. (Illus.). 544p. 19.95 (ISBN 0-85398-143-4). G Ronald Pub.

Thompson, Juliet. Diary of Juliet Thompson. 396p. 1983. 14.95 (ISBN 0-933770-27-8). Kalimat.

Townshend, George. Christ & Baha'u'llah. LC 68-168. 116p. 1966. pap. 3.95 (ISBN 0-85398-005-5). G Ronald Pub.

--The Heart of the Gospel. 2nd rev. ed. 160p. (ISBN 0-85398-025-X); pap. 3.95 (ISBN 0-85398-020-9). G Ronald Pub.

--The Mission of Baha'u'llah & Other Literary Pieces. 160p. 1952. 10.95 (ISBN 0-85398-021-7). G Ronald Pub.

--The Promise of All Ages. 3rd, rev. ed. 192p. 1972. 10.95 (ISBN 0-85398-044-6); pap. 3.50 (ISBN 0-85398-006-3). G Ronald Pub.

Universal House of Justice. The Baha'i World: An International Record 1954-1963, Vol. XIII. LC 27-5882. (Illus.). 1970. 27.95 (ISBN 0-87743-042-X, 233-013). Baha'i.

--The Baha'i World: An International Record 1963-1968, Vol. XIV. LC 27-5882. (Illus.). 1974. 18.95 (ISBN 0-87743-099-3, 233-014). Baha'i.

--The Baha'i World: An International Record 1968-1973, Vol. XV. (Illus.). 1976. o. s. i. 22.95 (ISBN 0-85398-059-4, 233-015). Baha'i.

--The Baha'i World: An International Record 1973-1976, Vol. XVI. (Illus.). 1979. 24.95 (ISBN 0-85398-075-6, 233-016). Baha'i.

--Bahai World: An International Record 1976-1979, Vol. XVII. (Illus.). 1981. 29.95 (ISBN 0-87743-130-2). Baha'i.

--Baha'i World: An International Record 1976-79, Vol. XVII. (Illus.). 1981. 29.95 (ISBN 0-85398-130-2). Baha'i.

--Messages from the Universal House of Justice: 1968-1973. LC 75-11795. 1976. 9.95 (ISBN 0-87743-076-4, 225-005); pap. 4.95 (ISBN 0-87743-096-9, 225-006). Baha'i.

--Wellspring of Guidance: Messages 1963-1968. rev. ed. LC 76-129996. 1976. 9.95 (ISBN 0-87743-032-2, 225-005); pap. 4.95 (ISBN 0-87743-033-0, 225-006). Baha'i.

Vader, John P. For the Good of Mankind: August Forel & Baha'i Faith. (Illus.). 144p. 10.95 (ISBN 0-85398-171-X); pap. 5.95 (ISBN 0-85398-172-8). G Ronald Pub.

Ward, Allan L. Two Hundred & Thirty-Nine Days: Abdu'l-Baha's Journey in America. LC 79-14713. (Illus.). 1979. 10.95 (ISBN 0-87743-129-9, 332-005). Baha'i.

White, Roger. Another Song, Another Season: Poems & Portrayals. 184p. 1979. cloth o.p. 4.00 (ISBN 0-85398-087-X); pap. 8.95 (ISBN 0-85398-088-8). G Ronald Pub.

--A Sudden Music. 200p. 12.95 (ISBN 0-85398-162-0); pap. 7.95 (ISBN 0-85398-163-9). G Ronald Pub.

Whitehead, O. Z. Some Baha'is to Remember. (Illus.). 304p. 14.95 (ISBN 0-85398-147-7); pap. 8.95 (ISBN 0-85398-148-5). G Ronald Pub.

--Some Early Baha'is of the West. (Illus.). 240p. 1976. 14.95 (ISBN 0-85398-065-9). G Ronald Pub.

Whitmore, Bruce W. The Dawning Place: The Building of a Temple, the Forging of the North American Baha'i Community. LC 83-25852. (Illus.). xi, 331p. 1984. 24.95 (ISBN 0-87743-192-2); pap. 12.95 (ISBN 0-87743-193-0). Baha'i.

Wilson, Samuel G. Bahaism & Its Claims. LC 79-131493. Repr. of 1915 ed. 22.50 (ISBN 0-404-06995-9). AMS Pr.

Wittman, Debbie D. The Birth of the Baha'i Faith. (Illus., Orig.). 1980. pap. 1.95 (ISBN 0-87743-146-9, 352-055). Baha'i.

Yazdi, Marion C. Youth in the Vanguard: Memoirs & Letters Collected by the First Baha'i Student at Berkeley & at Stanford University. LC 82-6793. (Illus.). xx, 211p. 1982. 14.95 (ISBN 0-87743-173-6, 332-089). Baha'i.

Zarqani, Mahmud-i. Abdu'l-Baha in America: Mahmud's Diary. 1978. 22.50 (ISBN 0-933770-61-8). Kalimat.

BAHAISM–JUVENILE LITERATURE

Heller, Wendy. My Name Is Nabil. (Illus.). 48p. 1981. 5.95 (ISBN 0-933770-17-0). Kalimat.

Lee, Anthony A. The Scottish Visitors: A Story about 'Abdu'l-Baha in Britain. (Stories About 'Abdu'l-Baha Ser.). (Illus.). 24p. (Orig.). 1981. pap. 2.50 (ISBN 0-933770-05-7). Kalimat.
--The Unfriendly Governor. (Stories About 'Abdu'l-Baha Ser.). (Illus.). 24p. 1980. pap. 2.50 (ISBN 0-933770-02-2). Kalimat.

BALAAM (BIBLICAL CHARACTER)

Vermes, Geza. Scripture & Tradition in Judaism. 2nd rev. ed. (Studia Post Biblica: No. 4). 1973. text ed. 9.95x (ISBN 90-040-3626-1). Humanities.

BALE, JOHN, BP. OF OSSORY, 1495-1563

Fairfield, Leslie P. John Bale: Mythmaker for the English Reformation. LC 75-19953. 250p. 1976. 9.75 (ISBN 0-911198-42-3). Purdue U Pr.
Harris, Jesse W. John Bale. facs. ed. LC 72-119958. (Select Bibliographies Reprint Ser). 1940. 17.00 (ISBN 0-8369-5401-7). Ayer Co Pubs.
--John Bale. LC 73-12898. 1940. Repr. lib. bdg. 20.00 (ISBN 0-8414-4742-X). Folcroft.
McCusker, Honor C. John Bale: Dramatist & Antiquary. facsimile ed. LC 79-148890. (Select Bibliographies Reprint Ser). Repr. of 1942 ed. 17.00 (ISBN 0-8369-5678-8). Ayer Co Pubs.

BALI (ISLAND)–RELIGION

Belo, Jane. Trance in Bali. LC 77-6361. 1977. Repr. of 1960 ed. lib. bdg. 35.75x (ISBN 0-8371-9652-3, BETR). Greenwood.
Monroe, Elvira. A Guide to Places of Worship in & Around San Francisco. 186p. (Orig.). 1984. pap. 6.95 (ISBN 0-933174-24-1). Wide World-Tetra.

BALTIMORE CATECHISM

Kinkead, Thomas L. An Explanation of the Baltimore Catechism. LC 78-74571. (Baltimore Catechism Ser.: No. 4). 1978. pap. text ed. 8.50 (ISBN 0-89555-085-7). TAN Bks Pubs.
The New Saint Joseph Baltimore Catechism, 2 bks. (Official Baltimore Catechism Ser.: Nos. 1 & 2). (Illus.). No. 1, Gr. 3-5. 1.80 (ISBN 0-89942-241-1, 241/05); No. 2, Gr. 6-8. 1.95 (ISBN 0-89942-242-X, 242/05). Catholic Bk Pub.

BANCROFT, RICHARD, ABP. OF CANTERBURY, 1544-1610

Babbage, Stuart B. Puritanism & Richard Bancroft. LC 63-2799. (Church Historical Society Ser.: No. 84). 1962. 20.00x (ISBN 0-8401-5084-9). A R Allenson.

BAPTISM

see also Baptisteries; Infant Baptism

Adams, Jay E. The Meaning & Mode of Baptism. 63p. 1975. pap. 3.75 (ISBN 0-87552-043-X). Presby & Reformed.
Armour, Rollin S. Anabaptist Baptism. LC 66-19026. (Study in Anabaptist & Mennonite History No. 11). 1966. 16.95x (ISBN 0-8361-1178-8). Herald Pr.
Baptism of a Child. (In Envelope). Set of 10 16.95 (ISBN 0-664-29066-3). Westminster.
Basham, Don. A Handbook on Holy Spirit Baptism. (Handbk. Ser: No. 1). 118p. 1969. pap. 2.95 (ISBN 0-88368-003-3). Whitaker Hse.
Beasley-Murray, G. R. Baptism in the New Testament. 434p. 1973. pap. 8.95 (ISBN 0-8028-1493-X). Eerdmans.
Bennett, Dennis J. Nine O'Clock in the Morning: An Episcopal Priest Discovers the Holy Spirit. LC 72-85205. 1970. pap. 5.95 (ISBN 0-912106-41-7). Bridge Pub.
Bothwell, H. Roger. My First Book about Baptism. (My Church Teaches Ser.). (Illus.). 1978. pap. 1.95 (ISBN 0-8127-0179-8). Review & Herald.
Brians, Pearl. Indecision about Baptism. large print ed. 34p. 1985. pap. 5.00 (ISBN 0-914009-41-9). VHI Library.
Burghardt, W. J., et al, eds. St. John Chrysostom, Baptismal Instructions. LC 62-21489. (Ancient Christian Writers Ser.: No. 31). 381p. 1963. 14.95 (ISBN 0-8091-0262-5). Paulist Pr.
Byrum, R. R. Holy Spirit Baptism & the Second Cleansing. 108p. pap. 0.75 (ISBN 0-686-29114-X); pap. 2.00 3 copies (ISBN 0-686-29115-8). Faith Pub Hse.
Cantelon, Willard. The Baptism in the Holy Spirit. 34p. 1951. pap. 1.00 (ISBN 0-88243-697-9, 02-0692). Gospel Pub.
Carson, Alexander. Baptism: It's Mode & Subjects. Young, John, ed. LC 80-8067. 550p. 1981. 18.95 (ISBN 0-8254-2324-4). Kregel.
Criswell, W. A. The Baptism, Filling & Gifts of the Holy Spirit. 192p. 1973. pap. 4.95 (ISBN 0-310-22751-8, 18351P). Zondervan.
Davis, Susan. A Way to Remember. Davis, Tom, ed. 32p. 1980. pap. 2.95 (ISBN 0-8280-0023-9). Review & Herald.
Eastman, A. Theodore. The Baptizing Community: Christian Initiation & the Local Congregation. 144p. (Orig.). 1982. pap. 9.95 (ISBN 0-8164-2419-5, HarpR). Har-Row.
Ervin, Howard M. Conversion-Initiation & the Baptism in the Holy Spirit. 108p. 1985. pap. 9.95 (ISBN 0-913573-12-4). Hendrickson MA.
Eynon, Dana. My New Life with Christ: Baptismal Certificate. (Certificate Booklets Ser.). (Illus.). 16p. 1982. pap. 0.95 six-cover (ISBN 0-87239-529-4, 1177). Standard Pub.
Fahey, Michael A., ed. Catholic Perspectives on Baptism, Eucharist & Ministry: A Study Commissioned by the Catholic Theological Society of America. 240p. (Orig.). 1986. lib. bdg. 24.50 (ISBN 0-8191-5431-8, Pub. by Catholic Theological Soc of Amer); pap. text ed. 11.75 (ISBN 0-8191-5432-6). U Pr of Amer.
Fogle, Jeanne S. Signs of God's Love: Baptism & Communion. Duckert, Mary J. & Lane, W. Ben, eds. (Illus.). 32p. (Orig.). 1984. pap. 4.50 (ISBN 0-664-24636-2). Geneva Pr.
Freburger, William. Baptism. 1970. pap. 0.95 (ISBN 0-8189-0425-9). Alba.
Frost, Robert. Set My Spirit Free. LC 73-84475. 234p. 1973. pap. 4.95 (ISBN 0-88270-058-8). Bridge Pub.
Gibbs, A. P. Christian Baptism. 1982. pap. 5.00 (ISBN 0-937396-62-1). Walterick Pubs.
Gillies, George & Gillies, Harriet. Scriptural Outline of the Baptism of the Holy Spirit. 32p. 1972. pap. 1.50 (ISBN 0-88368-062-9). Whitaker Hse.
Halverson, Sandy. Preparing for Baptism. 48p. 1983. pap. 3.95 (ISBN 0-88290-233-4). Horizon-Utah.
Hayford, Jack W. Water Baptism: Sealed by Christ, the Lord. LC 84-80750. (Orig.). 1984. pap. 2.95 (ISBN 0-916847-01-2). Living Way.
Hildeburn, Charles R. Baptisms & Burials From the Records of Christ Church, Philadelphia, 1709-1760. LC 81-86323. 231p. 1982. Repr. of 1893 ed. 15.00 (ISBN 0-8063-0979-2). Genealog Pub.
Hodge, Ian. Baptized Inflation: A Critique of "Christian" Keynesian. Date not set. price not set (ISBN 0-930462-13-0). Am Bur Eco Res.
Holy Baptism & Services for the Renewal of Baptism: The Worship of God. LC 85-3137. (Supplemental Liturgical Resource: No. 2). 114p. 1985. pap. 5.95 (ISBN 0-664-24647-8). Westminster.
Ironside, H. A. Baptism. pap. 1.50 (ISBN 0-87213-345-1). Loizeaux.
Jeschke, Marlin. Believers Baptism for Children of the Church. LC 82-23406. 160p. (Orig.). 1983. pap. 7.95 (ISBN 0-8361-3318-8). Herald Pr.
John, Da Free. The Fire Gospel. 224p. (Orig.). 1982. pap. 8.95 (ISBN 0-913922-73-0). Dawn Horse Pr.
Johnsson, William G. Clean: The Meaning of Christian Baptism. LC 80-15681. (Horizon Ser.). 96p. 1980. pap. 5.95 (ISBN 0-8127-0293-X). Review & Herald.
Kavanagh, Aidan. The Shape of Baptism: The Rite of Christian Initiation. (Studies in the Reformed Rites of the Catholic Church: Vol. 1). 1978. pap. 9.95 (ISBN 0-916134-36-9). Pueblo Pub Co.
Keating, Charles J. Infant Baptism & the Christian Community. LC 76-25620. (Illus.). 1977. pap. 2.95 (ISBN 0-89622-022-2). Twenty-Third.
Kelly, Henry A. The Devil at Baptism: Ritual, Theology, & Drama. LC 85-404. 304p. 1985. text ed. 29.95x (ISBN 0-8014-1806-2). Cornell U Pr.
Korth, Bob, ed. Baptism. (Discipleship Booklets Ser.). (Illus., Orig.). 1984. pap. 0.95 (ISBN 0-87239-787-4, 1151). Standard Pub.
Linzey, Stanford E. Why I Believe in the Baptism with the Holy Spirit. 1962. pap. 0.75 (ISBN 0-88243-764-X, 02-0764). Gospel Pub.
Luebering, Carol. What Do You Ask for Your Child. 64p. (Orig.). 1980. pap. 1.35 (ISBN 0-912228-64-4). St Anthony Mess Pr.
McCormick, Joe & McKenney, Tom. Holy Spirit Baptism. (Illus.). 23p. (Orig.). 1982. pap. 2.95 (ISBN 0-934527-02-4). Words Living Minis.
Marsh, Thomas A. Gift of Community: Baptism & Confirmation. (Message of the Sacraments Ser.: Vol. 2). 13.95 (ISBN 0-89453-392-4); pap. 9.95 (ISBN 0-89453-228-6). M Glazier.
Marty, Martin E. Baptism. LC 77-78635. 1977. pap. 3.95 (ISBN 0-8006-1317-1, 1-1317). Fortress.
Mauro, Philip. Baptism: A Bible Defense of Believer's Immersion. pap. 2.95 (ISBN 0-685-88367-1). Reiner.
Merrell, Karen D. Baptism. 24p. pap. 4.95 (ISBN 0-87747-559-8). Deseret Bk.
Mjorud, Herbert. What's Baptism All about? LC 77-80413. 1978. pap. 2.95 (ISBN 0-88419-173-7). Creation Hse.
Montague, George T. The Spirit & His Gifts. LC 74-77425. 72p. (Orig.). 1974. pap. 1.95 (ISBN 0-8091-1829-7, Deus). Paulist Pr.
Morris, Henry M., 3rd. Baptism: How Important Is It? LC 77-87954. 1978. pap. 1.95 (ISBN 0-916406-72-5). Accent Bks.
Muller, Lydia, ed. Glaubenszeugnisse Oberdeutscher. (Ger). 34.00 (ISBN 0-384-40404-9); pap. 28.00 (ISBN 0-384-40403-0). Johnson Repr.
Mundfrom, Gerald F. Baptism, a Covenant. (Illus.). 140p. (Orig.). 1985. pap. text ed. 4.00x (ISBN 0-9615494-0-8). Mercy & Truth.
Murphy Center for Liturgical Research. Made, Not Born: New Perspectives on Christian Initiation & the Catechumenate. 192p. 1976. pap. 6.95 (ISBN 0-268-01337-3). U of Notre Dame Pr.
Murray, John. Christian Baptism. 1980. pap. 3.95 (ISBN 0-87552-343-9). Presby & Reformed.
Myers, Margaret E. Meyersville, Md., Lutheran Baptisms. Russell, Donna V., ed. (Illus.). 70p. 1986. pap. 10.00 (ISBN 0-914385-04-6). Catoctin Pr.
Naglee, David I. From Font to Faith: John Wesley on Infant Baptism & the Nurture of Children. (American University Studies VII-Theology & Religion: Vol. 24). 272p. 1987. text ed. 26.00 (ISBN 0-8204-0375-X). P Lang Pubs.
Norbie, D. L. Baptism: The Church's Troubled Water. 1985. pap. 1.75 (ISBN 0-937396-66-4). Walterick Pubs.
Paget, John. An Answer to the Unjust Complaints of W. Best: Also an Answer to Mr. John Davenport. LC 76-57403. (English Experience Ser.: No. 819). 1977. Repr. of 1635 ed. lib. bdg. 16.00 (ISBN 90-221-0819-8). Walter J Johnson.
Payne, Joseph E., et al. Together at Baptism. LC 73-144040. (Illus.). 80p. (Orig.). 1971. pap. 1.50 (ISBN 0-87793-031-7). Ave Maria.
Popoff, Peter. Ye Shall Receive Power: The Amazing Miracle of Holy Spirit Baptism. Tanner, Don, ed. LC 82-71629. (Illus.). 96p. 1982. pap. 2.00 (ISBN 0-938544-14-4). Faith Messenger.
Pritchard, Gretchen W. New Life: The Sunday Paper's Baptism Book. (Illus.). 80p. (Orig.). 1986. pap. 5.75x (ISBN 0-9614022-2-9). Sunday Paper.
Rahner, Karl. Baptism. 1.50 (ISBN 0-87193-120-6). Dimension Bks.
Riggle, H. M. Christian Baptism, Feet Washing & the Lord's Supper. 264p. 3.50 (ISBN 0-686-29105-0). Faith Pub Hse.
Roguet, A. M. Homilies for the Celebration of Baptism. Du Charme, Jerome, tr. from Fr. LC 76-53546. 1977. pap. 2.75 (ISBN 0-8199-0655-7). Franciscan Herald.
Ross, Bob L. Baptism & Restoration Movement. 1979. pap. 1.00 (ISBN 0-686-28281-7). Pilgrim Pubns.
Schlink, Edmund. The Doctrine of Baptism. Bouman, Herbert, tr. from Ger. LC 78-159794. 256p. 1972. pap. 10.95 (ISBN 0-570-03726-3, 12-2628). Concordia.
Schmemann, Alexander. Of Water & the Spirit: A Liturgical Study of Baptism. LC 74-30061. 170p. 1974. pap. 7.95 (ISBN 0-913836-10-9). St Vladimirs.
Searle, Mark. Christening: The Making of Christians. LC 80-19454. (Illus.). 185p. (Orig.). 1980. pap. text ed. 6.50 (ISBN 0-8146-1183-4). Liturgical Pr.
Spencer, Duane E. Holy Baptism: Word Keys Which Unlock the Covenant. LC 84-81663. 170p. 1984. 9.95 (ISBN 0-939404-08-7). Geneva Ministr.
Spurgeon, C. H. Baptism. 1976. pap. 1.50 (ISBN 0-686-18091-7). Pilgrim Pubns.
--Baptismal Regeneration. 1979. 1.50 (ISBN 0-686-09097-7). Pilgrim Pubns.
Stookey, Lawrence H. Baptism: Christ's Act in the Church. LC 81-17590. 208p. (Orig.). 1982. pap. 9.95 (ISBN 0-687-02364-5). Abingdon.
Strege, Merle D., ed. Baptism & Church: A Believers' Church Vision. LC 85-43567. 224p. (Orig.). 1986. pap. 12.50 (ISBN 0-937021-00-8). Sagamore Bks MI.
Thurian, Max & Wainwright, Geoffrey, eds. Baptism & Eucharist: Ecumenical Convergence in Celebration. LC 84-169338. 268p. (Orig.). 1984. pap. 11.95 (ISBN 0-8028-0005-X). Eerdmans.
Verheyden, A. L. Anabaptism in Flanders 1530-1650. LC 61-13872. (Studies in Anabaptist & Mennonite History, No. 9). 126p. 1961. 12.95x (ISBN 0-8361-1102-8). Herald Pr.
Voorehoeve, H. C. & Bennett, Gordon H. El Bautismo. 2nd ed. Bautista, Sara, tr. from Eng. (La Serie Diamante). Tr. of Baptism. (Span., Illus.). 36p. 1982. pap. 0.85 (ISBN 0-942504-06-2). Overcomer Pr.
Wagner, Johannes, ed. Adult Baptism & the Catechumenate. LC 67-19979. (Concilium Ser.: Vol. 22). 204p. 1967. 7.95 (ISBN 0-8091-0000-2). Paulist Pr.
Weber, Gerard P., et al. Baptism & the Family. 1972. pap. 2.64 (ISBN 0-02-649000-5). Benziger Pub Co.
Willimon, William H. Remember Who You Are: Baptism, a Model for Christian Life. LC 79-93359. (Illus.). 128p. (Orig.). 1980. pap. 4.95x (ISBN 0-8358-0399-6). Upper Room.
Yoder, John H. Taufertum Und Reformation Im Gesprach. 221p. 1969. 29.00x (ISBN 0-8361-1164-8). Herald Pr.

BAPTISM–BIBLICAL TEACHING

Barclay, William. Communicating the Gospel. 1978. pap. 3.25x (ISBN 0-7152-0401-7). Outlook.
Brooks, Oscar S. The Drama of Decision: Baptism in the New Testament. 280p. 1986. 11.95 (ISBN 0-913573-40-X). Hendrickson MA.
Christenson, Larry. What about Baptism? 24p. (Orig.). 1986. pap. 1.35 (ISBN 0-8066-2257-1, 23-3009). Augsburg.
Cullmann, Oscar. Baptism in the New Testament. LC 78-6937. 84p. 1978. pap. 5.95 (ISBN 0-664-24219-7). Westminster.
Egan, John P. & Colford, Paul D. Baptism of Resistance-Blood & Celebration: A Road to Wholeness in the Nuclear Age. 1983. pap. 5.95 (ISBN 0-89622-164-4). Twenty-Third.
Gaspard, Perry A. The Baptism with the Holy Spirit. 1983. pap. 1.00 (ISBN 0-931867-02-9). Abundant Life Pubns.
Gee, Donald. Now That You've Been Baptized in the Spirit. 176p. 1972. pap. 1.50 (ISBN 0-88243-461-6, 02-0461). Gospel Pub.
Levinson, Frederick. The Gospel at Infant Baptism. pap. 4.95x (ISBN 0-7152-0443-2). Outlook.
Marcel, Pierre. The Biblical Doctrine of Infant Baptism. Hughes, Philip E., tr. from Fr. 256p. 1983. pap. 11.95 (ISBN 0-227-67855-9, Pub. by J Clarke UK). Attic Pr.
Rite of Baptism for Children. green cloth 8.50 (ISBN 0-89942-136-9, 136/22). Catholic Bk Pub.
Todd, Richard E., ed. Baptism. (Grace Bible Ser.). (Illus.). 16p. (Orig.). 1980. pap. 0.50 (ISBN 0-9605324-0-4). R E Todd.

BAPTISTERIES

Goettelmann, Paul A. The Baptistry of Frejus: A Restoration Based on the Architectural & Historical Evidence. (Illus.). 75p. 1984. Repr. of 1933 ed. 25.00x (ISBN 0-939738-23-6). Zubal Inc.

BAPTISTS

see also Anabaptists; Mennonites

Allison, William H. & Barnes, W. W. Baptist Ecclesiology: An Original Anthology. Gaustad, Edwin S., ed. LC 79-52582. (The Baptist Tradition Ser.). 1980. lib. bdg. 21.00x (ISBN 0-405-12449-X). Ayer Co Pubs.
Asplund, John. The Annual Register of the Baptist Denomination in North America to 1970. 1979. Repr. 10.00 (ISBN 0-317-01254-1). Church History.
--The Universal Register of the Baptist Denomiation in North America for the Years 1790, 1791, 1792, 1793, & Part of 1794. Gaustad, Edwin S., ed. LC 79-52581. (The Baptist Tradition Ser.). 1980. Repr. of 1794 ed. lib. bdg. 14.00x (ISBN 0-405-12448-1). Ayer Co Pubs.
Baker, A. Baptist Source Book. LC 66-22076. 1974. pap. 7.50 (ISBN 0-8054-6519-7). Broadman.
Baker, Robert A. Relations Between Northern & Southern Baptists. rev. ed. Gaustad, Edwin S., ed. LC 79-52590. (The Baptist Tradition Ser.). 1980. Repr. of 1954 ed. lib. bdg. 23.00x (ISBN 0-405-12457-0). Ayer Co Pubs.
Bopp, Virgil. When the Word Dwells Richly: Baptists in Perspective. 192p. (Orig.). 1987. pap. 5.95 (ISBN 0-87227-119-6). Reg Baptist.
Brown, J. Newton. Baptist Church Manual. pap. 1.25 (ISBN 0-8170-0015-1). Judson.
Bruce, Carrol. The Commitment Factor. LC 84-5005. 1984. pap. 3.95 (ISBN 0-8054-5541-8). Broadman.
Brumbaugh, Martin G. A History of the German Baptist Brethren in Europe & America. LC 73-134377. (Communal Societies in America Ser.). (Illus.). Repr. of 1899 ed. 37.50 (ISBN 0-404-08425-7). AMS Pr.
Bryan, G. McLeod. Dissenter in the Baptist Southland: Fifty Years in the Career of William Wallace Finlator. (Illus.). xi, 198p. 1985. 17.95 (ISBN 0-86554-176-0, MUP-H166). Mercer Univ Pr.
Bryan, G. McLeod, et al. Documents Concerning Baptism & Church Membership: A Controversy Among North Carolina Baptists. LC 76-45687. (Special Studies Ser.: No. 1). vii, 81p. 1977. pap. 2.00 (ISBN 0-932180-00-0). NABPR.
Cobb, J. E. Cobb's Baptist Church Manual. 193p. 1979. pap. 2.50 (ISBN 0-89114-056-5). Baptist Pub Hse.
Cox, Norman W., ed. Encyclopedia of Southern Baptists, Vols. I & II. LC 58-5417. (Illus.). 1958. 39.95 (ISBN 0-8054-6501-4). Broadman.
Davis, Lawrence B. Immigrants, Baptists & the Protestant Mind in America. LC 72-81264. pap. 60.00 (ISBN 0-8357-9682-5, 2019040). Bks Demand UMI.
De Lerin, Olivia S. Enviame a Mi: Aventuras de los esposos Davis, fundadores de la C. B. P. 64p. 1980. pap. 1.75 (ISBN 0-311-01062-8). Casa Bautista.
Deweese, Charles W. Prayer in Baptist Life. LC 85-21301. 1986. pap. 4.95 (ISBN 0-8054-6941-9). Broadman.
Gaustad, Edwin S., ed. Baptists: The Bible, Church Order & the Churches. original anthology ed. LC 79-52587. (The Baptist Tradition Ser.). 1980. lib. bdg. 46.00x (ISBN 0-405-12454-6). Ayer Co Pubs.

--Baptists Tradition Series, 40 bks, Vols. 1-22. (Illus.). 1980. Repr. Set. lib. bdg. 1323.00x (ISBN 0-405-12437-6). Ayer Co Pubs.

Glazier, Stephen D. Marchin' the Pilgrims Home: Leadership & Decision-Making in an Afro-Caribbean Faith. LC 82-24179. (Contributions to the Study of Religion Ser.: No. 10). (Illus.). xx, 165p. 1983. lib. bdg. 29.95 (ISBN 0-313-23464-7, GPI/). Greenwood.

Gragg, Alan. George Burman Foster: Religious Humanist. LC 77-92499. (Special Studies Ser.: No. 3). v, 79p. 1978. pap. 3.50 (ISBN 0-932180-02-7). NABPR.

Grenz, Stanley J. The Baptist Congregation. 128p. 1985. pap. 7.95 (ISBN 0-8170-1083-1). Judson.

Harrison, H. D., ed. Who's Who among Free Will Baptists. 1978. 18.95 (ISBN 0-89265-052-4). Randall Hse.

Hastings, C. B. Introducing Southern Baptists. LC 81-80052. 168p. (Orig.). 1981. pap. 7.95 (ISBN 0-8091-2364-9). Paulist Pr.

Hays, Brooks & Steely, John E. The Baptist Way of Life. rev ed. LC 81-11245. 220p. 1981. 14.95 (ISBN 0-86554-008-X, MUP-H13). Mercer Univ Pr.

Hiscox, Edward T. Principles & Practices for Baptist Churches. LC 80-8083. 598p. (Orig.). 1985. pap. 11.95 (ISBN 0-8254-2860-2). Kregel.

Jensen, Vi. Blessed Is the Woman. Silvey, James L., ed. 95p. (Orig.). 1983. pap. 3.50 (ISBN 0-89114-116-2). Baptist Pub Hse.

Jewett, Paul K. Baptist Catechism. pap. 0.85x (ISBN 0-9602638-4-5). Fuller Theol Soc.

Jordan, Lewis G. Up the Ladder in Foreign Missions. Gausted, Edwin S., ed. LC 79-52596. (The Baptist Tradition Ser.). (Illus.). 1980. Repr. of 1901 ed. lib. bdg. 27.50x (ISBN 0-405-12463-5). Ayer Co Pubs.

Lofton, Fred C. Teach Us To Pray: The Disciples Request Cast Anew. 96p. 1983. pap. 4.00 (ISBN 0-89191-751-9). Prog Bapt Pub.

Loucks, Celeste & Hullum, Everett. American Montage. Furlow, Elaine S., ed. (Human Touch Ser.: No. 3). (Illus.). 1976. 6.95 (ISBN 0-686-16312-5); lib. bdg. 6.95 (ISBN 0-937170-10-0). Home Mission.

McBeth, Leon. Women in Baptist Life. LC 78-54245. 1979. 7.95 (ISBN 0-8054-6925-7). Broadman.

MacDonald, Gail. High Call, High Privilege. 1981. pap. 6.95 (ISBN 0-8423-1424-5). Tyndale.

Morris, Elias C. Sermons, Addresses & Reminiscences & Important Correspondence, with a Picture Gallery of Eminent Ministers & Scholars. Gaustad, Edwin S., ed. LC 79-52598. (The Baptist Tradition Ser.). (Illus.). 1980. Repr. of 1901 ed. lib. bdg. 27.50x (ISBN 0-405-12465-1). Ayer Co Pubs.

Murrah, David J. C. C. Slaughter: Rancher, Banker, Baptist. (M. K. Brown Range Life Ser.: No. 15). (Illus.). 191p. 1981. 14.95 (ISBN 0-292-71067-4). U of Tex Pr.

Olson, Adolf. A Centenary History As Related to the Baptist General Conference of America. Ganstad, Edwin S., ed. LC 79-52602. (The Baptist Tradition Ser.). (Illus.). 1980. Repr. of 1952 ed. lib. bdg. 55.50x (ISBN 0-405-12467-8). Ayer Co Pubs.

Owens, Lillian. Handbook for Counselors: GMA. 161p. 1979. pap. 3.00 (ISBN 0-89114-023-9). Baptist Pub Hse.

Paschal, Mrs. W. N. Life of a Rich Man. (Illus.). 180p. 1976. pap. 2.50 (ISBN 0-89114-075-1). Baptist Pub Hse.

Peters, Mrs. Edwin. Echoes from Beautiful Feet. (Illus.). 168p. 1975. pap. 1.95 (ISBN 0-89114-073-5). Baptist Pub Hse.

Powell, Terry. You Want Me to Know What? 2nd ed. (Foundation Ser.). (Illus.). 142p. (Orig.). 1986. pap. 2.95 (ISBN 0-935797-04-1). Harvest IL.

Robinson, H. Wheeler. The Life & Faith of the Baptists. 158p. 1985. pap. 6.95 (ISBN 0-913029-09-2). Stevens Bk Pr.

Robinson, H. Wheeler & Payne, Ernest A. British Baptists: An Original Anthology. Gaustad, Edwin S., ed. LC 79-52583. (The Baptist Tradition Ser.). 1980. lib. bdg. 30.00x (ISBN 0-405-12450-3). Ayer Co Pubs.

Ross, Bob L. Old Landmarkism & the Baptists. 1979. pap. 3.95 (ISBN 0-686-26196-8). Pilgrim Pubns.

Russell, Lester F. Black Baptist Secondary Schools in Virginia, 1887-1957: A Study in Black History. LC 80-22414. 218p. 1981. 18.00 (ISBN 0-8108-1373-4). Scarecrow.

Shurden, Walter B., ed. The Life of Baptists in the Life of the World. LC 85-1401. 1985. pap. 7.95 (ISBN 0-8054-6582-0). Broadman.

Skoglund, John E. The Baptists. 1967. pap. 1.50 (ISBN 0-8170-0386-X). Judson.

Smith, Alfred J. Deacon's Upholding the Pastor's Arms. 96p. 1983. pap. 4.00 (ISBN 0-686-46044-8). Prog Bapt Pub.

Starr, Edward C. A Baptist Bibliography, Vols. 1-25. Incl. Vol. 1. Authors A. 1947. 13.25x (ISBN 0-910056-00-5); Vol. 2. Authors B-Biloxi. 1952. 16.55x (ISBN 0-910056-01-3); Vol. 3. Authors Bin-Bz. 1953. 21.20x (ISBN 0-910056-02-1); Vol. 4. Authors C-Colby. 1954. 16.55x (ISBN 0-910056-03-X); Vol. 5. Authors Colchester-Cz. 1957. 13.25x (ISBN 0-910056-04-8); Vol. 6. Authors D. 1958. 13.25x (ISBN 0-910056-05-6); Vol. 7. Authors E-Flynt. 1961. 13.25x (ISBN 0-910056-06-4); Vol. 8. Authors Fo-Glazier. 1963. 16.55x (ISBN 0-910056-07-2); Vol. 9. Authors Gleason-Halko. 1964. 16.55x (ISBN 0-910056-08-0); Vol. 10. Authors Hall-Hill, Joseph. 1965. 16.55x (ISBN 0-910056-09-9); Vol. 11. Authors Hill, Kizard. 1966. 13.25x (ISBN 0-910056-10-2); Vol. 12. Authors J. 1967. 13.25x (ISBN 0-910056-11-0); Vol. 13. Authors K-Layton. 1968. 16.55x (ISBN 0-910056-12-9); Vol. 14. Authors Lea-McGuire. 1969. 16.55x (ISBN 0-910056-13-7); Vol. 15. Authors McIlvain-Merrill. 1970. 16.55x (ISBN 0-910056-14-5); Vol. 16. Authors Merrimac-Nevin. 1971. 16.55x (ISBN 0-910056-15-3); Vol. 17. Authors New-Pastors. 1972. 16.55x (ISBN 0-910056-16-1); Vol. 18. Authors Pate-Poynton. 1972. 16.55x (ISBN 0-910056-17-X); Vol. 19. Authors Pra-Rives. 1973. 16.55x (ISBN 0-910056-18-8); Vol. 20. Authors Ro-Sardis. 1974. 13.25x (ISBN 0-685-24442-3); Vol. 21. Authors Sare-Smith, S. 1974. 16.55x (ISBN 0-685-24443-1); Vol. 22. Authors Smith, T.-Steude. 1975. 16.55x (ISBN 0-685-24444-X); Vol. 23. Authors Steven-Torbet. 1976. 16.55x (ISBN 0-685-24445-8); Vol. 24. Authors Torey-Wa. 1976. 16.55x (ISBN 0-685-24446-6); Vol. 25. Authors We-Z. 1976. 21.20x (ISBN 0-910056-24-2). Set. 400.00. Am Baptist.

Stealey, Sydnor L. & Gaustad, Edwin S., eds. A Baptist Treasury. LC 79-52607. (The Baptist Tradition Ser.). 1980. Repr. of 1958 ed. lib. bdg. 27.50x (ISBN 0-405-12472-4). Ayer Co Pubs.

Sullivan, James L. Baptist Polity as I See It. LC 83-70940. 1983. 9.95 (ISBN 0-8054-6575-8). Broadman.

Swafford, Mrs. Z. W. This We Believe. (Illus.). 109p. (Orig.). 1983. pap. 2.50 (ISBN 0-89114-115-4). Baptist Pub Hse.

Thom, W. T. The Struggle for Religious Freedom in Virginia: The Baptists. Repr. of 1900 ed. 13.00 (ISBN 0-384-60163-4). Johnson Repr.

Thomas, Roy. Planting & Growing a Fundamental Church. 1979. pap. 5.95 (ISBN 0-89265-070-2). Randall Hse.

Thomson, E. Roberts. Baptists & Disciples of Christ. 195p. 1948. pap. 2.95 (ISBN 0-87921-004-4). Attic Pr.

Tollett, T. O., compiled by. Church Roll & Record. 1979. 11.95 (ISBN 0-89114-017-4). Baptist Pub Hse.

Townsend, Leah. South Carolina Baptists: 1670-1805. LC 74-6312. (Illus.). 391p. 1978. Repr. of 1935 ed. 20.00 (ISBN 0-8063-0621-1). Genealog Pub.

Tull, James E. Shapers of Baptist Thought. LC 84-6545. (Reprints of Scholarly Excellence Ser.: No. 8). 255p. 1984. Repr. of 1972 ed. 14.50 (ISBN 0-86554-125-6, MUP-H116). Mercer Univ Pr.

Wayland, Francis. Notes on the Principles & Practices of Baptist Churches. Gaustad, Edwin S., ed. LC 79-52610. (Baptist Tradition Ser.). 1980. Repr. of 1857 ed. lib. bdg. 27.50x (ISBN 0-405-12475-9). Ayer Co Pubs.

BAPTISTS–CATECHISMS AND CREEDS

Lumpkin, William L. Baptist Confessions of Faith. (Illus.). 1959. 17.95 (ISBN 0-8170-0016-X). Judson.

BAPTISTS–CLERGY

Burnett, J. J. Sketches of Tennessee's Pioneer Baptist Preachers: History of Baptist Beginnings in the Several Associations in the State. (Illus.). 576p. 1985. Repr. of 1919 ed. 21.95 (ISBN 0-932807-11-9). Overmountain Pr.

James, Allix B. Calling a Pastor to a Baptist Church. rev. ed. Jones, Amos, Jr., ed. 50p. (Orig.). 1983. pap. 4.95 (ISBN 0-910683-00-X). Sunday School.

Lasher, George W., ed. Baptist Ministerial Directory. 1987. 45.00. Banner Pr Al.

McSwain, Larry L. & Treadwell, William C., Jr. Conflict Ministry in the Church. LC 80-67781. 1981. pap. 7.95 (ISBN 0-8054-2540-3). Broadman.

Melvin, Billy A. Free Will Baptist Minister's Manual. 1974. ringbinder 8.95 (ISBN 0-89265-024-9). Randall Hse.

Miller, Calvin. If This Be Love: The Journey of Two People Toward Each Other in Christian Love & Marriage. LC 83-48433. 112p. 1984. 11.45 (ISBN 0-06-065755-3, HarpR). Har-Row.

Nettles, Joseph E. So Beloved Cousins: The Life & Times of Solon B. Cousins, Jr. LC 82-23986. x, 178p. 1983. 12.95x (ISBN 0-86554-070-5, H53). Mercer Univ Pr.

Nichols, Harold. The Work of the Deacon & Deaconess. (Orig.). pap. 4.95 (ISBN 0-8170-0328-2). Judson.

Rich, George. God Pursues a Priest. 60p. (Orig.). 1986. pap. 2.95 (ISBN 0-87227-109-9). Reg Baptist.

Sullivan, Clayton. Called to Preach, Condemned to Survive: The Education of Clayton Sullivan. xiv, 237p. 1985. 19.95 (ISBN 0-86554-173-6, MUP-H163). Mercer Univ Pr.

BAPTISTS–DOCTRINAL AND CONTROVERSIAL WORKS

Ban, Arline J. & Ban, Joseph D. The New Disciple: Church Membership Junior-Junior High. LC 75-35898. 96p. 1976. pap. 1.95 (ISBN 0-8170-0658-3). Judson.

Davis, R. Dowd. Baptist Distinctives: A Pattern for Service. 64p. (Orig.). 1986. pap. 3.95 (ISBN 0-913029-11-4). Stevens Bk Pr.

Foshee, Howard. Broadman Church Manual. LC 72-94629. 192p. 1973. 8.95 (ISBN 0-8054-2525-X). Broadman.

Giles, James E. Esto Creemos los Bautistas. 111p. 1981. pap. 2.50 (ISBN 0-311-09091-5). Casa Bautista.

Grenz, Stanley J. The Baptist Congregation. 128p. 1985. pap. 7.95 (ISBN 0-8170-1083-1). Judson.

Hiscox, Edward T. Hiscox Guide for Baptist Churches. 12.95 (ISBN 0-8170-0329-0). Judson.

--Hiscox Standard Baptist Manual. 1965. pap. 5.95 (ISBN 0-8170-0340-1). Judson.

Hobbs, Herschel H. What Baptists Believe. LC 64-12411. 1963. bds. 4.25 (ISBN 0-8054-8101-X). Broadman.

Hobbs, Herschel H. & Mullins, E. Y. The Axioms of Religion. LC 78-50799. 1978. 8.50 (ISBN 0-8054-1707-9). Broadman.

Howington, Nolan P. A Royal Priesthood. LC 85-22376. 1986. pap. 4.95 (ISBN 0-8054-1622-6). Broadman.

Hudson, Winthrop S. Baptist Convictions. pap. 1.50 (ISBN 0-8170-0295-2). Judson.

Jackson, D. N. Baptist Doctrines & History. 1974. pap. 3.50 (ISBN 0-89114-003-4). Baptist Pub Hse.

Jackson, Paul R. The Doctrine & Administration of the Church. rev. ed. LC 68-28699. 1980. pap. 3.95 (ISBN 0-87227-072-6). Reg Baptist.

Leonard, Bill J. The Nature of the Church. (Orig.). 1986. 5.95 (ISBN 0-8054-1642-0). Broadman.

Mullins, Edgar Y. Baptist Beliefs. 5.95 (ISBN 0-8170-0014-3); pap. 4.95. Judson.

O'Donnell, J. D. Free Will Baptist Doctrines. 1974. pap. 4.95 (ISBN 0-89265-019-2). Randall Hse.

Shurden, Walter B. Not a Silent People: Controversies That Have Shaped Southern Baptists. LC 79-178066. 128p. 1972. 6.50 (ISBN 0-8054-8801-4). Broadman.

Smyth, John. The Differences of the Churches of the Seperation Containing a Description of the Leitourgie & Ministerie of the Visible Church. LC 73-6161. (English Experience Ser.: No. 624). 32p. 1973. Repr. of 1608 ed. 5.00 (ISBN 90-221-0624-1). Walter J Johnson.

BAPTISTS–EDUCATION

Brackney, William, ed. Baptist Life & Thought: Sixteen Hundred to Nineteen Eighty. 448p. 1983. 12.95 (ISBN 0-8170-0959-0). Judson.

Pegues, Albert W. Our Baptist Ministers & Schools. Repr. of 1892 ed. 44.00 (ISBN 0-384-45660-X). Johnson Repr.

Whalen, William J. Reaching Out to the Baptists with Heart & Mind. (Reaching Out to...Ser.). 32p. 1984. pap. 1.50 (ISBN 0-89243-209-8). Liguori Pubns.

BAPTISTS–GOVERNMENT

Agar, Frederick A. The Deacon at Work. 1923. 4.95 (ISBN 0-8170-0783-0). Judson.

Dale, Robert D. To Dream Again. LC 81-65386. 1981. pap. 5.95 (ISBN 0-8054-2541-1). Broadman.

Foshee, Howard. Broadman Church Manual. LC 72-94629. 192p. 1973. 8.95 (ISBN 0-8054-2525-X). Broadman.

Grenz, Stanley J. The Baptist Congregation. 128p. 1985. pap. 7.95 (ISBN 0-8170-1083-1). Judson.

Harrison, Paul M. Authority & Power in the Free Church Tradition: A Social Case Study of the American Baptist Convention. (Arcturus Bks.). 267p. 1971. lib. bdg. 7.00x (ISBN 0-8093-0503-8); pap. 2.45x (ISBN 0-8093-0499-6). S Ill U Pr.

Hiscox, Edward T. Hiscox Guide for Baptist Churches. 12.95 (ISBN 0-8170-0329-0). Judson.

--Hiscox Standard Baptist Manual. 1965. pap. 5.95 (ISBN 0-8170-0340-1). Judson.

Hobbs, James R. Pastor's Manual. 1940. 8.95 (ISBN 0-8054-2301-X). Broadman.

Maring, Norman H. & Hudson, Winthrop S. Baptist Manual of Polity & Practice. 10.95 (ISBN 0-8170-0299-5). Judson.

--Short Baptist Manual of Polity & Practice. 1965. pap. 4.95 (ISBN 0-8170-0338-X). Judson.

Naylor, Robert E. Baptist Deacon. 1955. 7.50 (ISBN 0-8054-3501-8). Broadman.

Pendleton, James M. Baptist Church Manual. rev. ed. 1966. Repr. of 1867 ed. 8.50 (ISBN 0-8054-2510-1). Broadman.

Pitman, Walter G. The Baptists & Public Affairs in the Province of Canada: 1840-1867. Gaustad, Edwin S., ed. LC 79-52576. (The Baptist Tradition Ser.). 1980. lib. bdg. 21.00x (ISBN 0-405-12444-9). Ayer Co Pubs.

BAPTISTS–HISTORY

Anderson, Justo C. Historia de los Bautistas Tomo I: Sus Bases y Principios. 1978. pap. 5.75 (ISBN 0-311-15036-5). Casa Bautista.

Associationalism among Baptists in America: 1707-1814. Gaustad, Edwin S., ed. LC 79-52577. (The Baptist Tradition Ser.). 1980. lib. bdg. 22.00x (ISBN 0-405-12445-7). Ayer Co Pubs.

Backus, Isaac. History of New England. LC 76-83410. (Religion in America, Ser. 1). 1969. Repr. of 1871 ed. 54.00 (ISBN 0-405-00231-9). Ayer Co Pubs.

Baker, J. C. Baptist History of the North Pacific Coast. Gaustad, Edwin S., ed. LC 79-52589. (The Baptist Tradition Ser.). (Illus.). 1980. Repr. of 1912 ed. lib. bdg. 48.50x (ISBN 0-405-12456-2). Ayer Co Pubs.

Bakke, Raymond J. & Roberts, Samuel K. The Expanded Mission of "Old First" Churches. 128p. 1986. pap. 8.95 (ISBN 0-8170-1100-5). Judson.

Barnes, Irwin. Truth Is Immortal: The Story of Baptists in Europe. 127p. 1950. 2.95 (ISBN 0-87921-015-X); pap. 1.95 (ISBN 0-87921-019-2). Attic Pr.

Beale, David O. S. B. C.: House on the Sand? 246p. (Orig.). 1985. pap. 4.95 (ISBN 0-89084-281-7). Bob Jones Univ Pr.

Benedict, David. Fifty Years among the Baptists. Repr. of 1860 ed. 13.00 (ISBN 0-317-38297-7). Church History.

--A General History of the Baptist Denomination in America, 2 vols. 1985. Repr. of 1813 ed. 64.00 (ISBN 0-317-31642-7). Church History.

--General History of the Baptist Denomination in America & Other Parts of the World, 2 vols. facsimile ed. LC 73-152974. (Select Bibliographies Reprint Ser). Repr. of 1813 ed. Set. 60.00 (ISBN 0-8369-5726-1). Ayer Co Pubs.

Broadus, Boyce. History of First Baptist Church Russellville. 1967. 10.00 (ISBN 0-317-13830-8); pap. 7.00. Banner Pr AL.

Brown, Louise F. Political Activities of the Baptists & the Fifth Monarchy Men in England During the Interregnum. 1964. Repr. of 1911 ed. 20.50 (ISBN 0-8337-0399-4). B Franklin.

Burkitt, Lemuel & Read, Jesse. A Concise History of the Kehukee Baptist Association from Its Original Rise to the Present Time. rev. ed. Gaustad, Edwin S., ed. LC 79-52591. (The Baptist Tradition Ser.). 1980. Repr. of 1850 ed. lib. bdg. 28.50x (ISBN 0-405-12458-9). Ayer Co Pubs.

Bush, Russ & Nettles, Tom. Baptists & the Bible. LC 80-11694. 1980. pap. 10.95 (ISBN 0-8024-0474-X). Moody.

Clarke, John & McLoughlin, William G. Colonial Baptists: Massachusetts & Rhode Island. original anthology ed. Gaustad, Edwin S., ed. LC 79-52586. (The Baptist Tradition Ser.). 1980. lib. bdg. 17.00x (ISBN 0-405-12453-8). Ayer Co Pubs.

Crook, Roger H. Our Heritage & Our Hope: A History of Pullen Memorial Baptist Church 1884-1984. LC 84-62984. (Illus.). 252p. 1985. 10.00 (ISBN 0-9614485-0-4). Pullen Mem Baptist.

Crosby, Thomas. History of the English Baptists: 1740 Ed, 4 vols. in 2 vols. Set. 45.00 (ISBN 0-686-12405-7). Church History.

Davidson, William F. An Early History of Free Will Baptists, Vol. 1. (Free Will Baptist History Ser.). 1974. 7.95 (ISBN 0-89265-037-0); pap. 4.95 (ISBN 0-89265-022-2). Randall Hse.

--The Free Will Baptists in America, 1727-1984. 462p. 1985. text ed. 14.95 (ISBN 0-89265-093-1). Randall Hse.

Davis, J. History of the Welsh Baptist: AD Sixty-Three to Seventeen Seventy. 1982. Repr. of 1835 ed. 15.00 (ISBN 0-686-91934-3). Church History.

Dawson, Joseph M. Baptists & the American Republic. Gaustad, Edwin S., ed. LC 79-52584. (The Baptist Tradition Ser.). 1980. Repr. of 1956 ed. lib. bdg. 21.00x (ISBN 0-405-12451-1). Ayer Co Pubs.

Devin, Robert. A History of the Grassy Creek Baptist Church. Repr. 15.00 (ISBN 0-686-12337-9); vinyl back 8.00 (ISBN 0-686-12338-7). Church History.

Dubovy, Andrew. Pilgrims of the Prairie: Pioneer Ukrainian Baptists in North Dakota. Bloch, Marie H., ed. (Illus.). 72p. (Orig.). 1983. lib. bdg. 8.50; pap. 4.50. Ukrainian Cult Inst.

Duncan, R. S. A History of the Baptists in Missouri. 1981. Repr. of 1882 ed. 38.00 (ISBN 0-686-77695-X). Church History.

Edwards, Morgan. Materials Toward a History of the Baptists, 2 vols. 1984. 36.00 (ISBN 0-317-38301-9). Church History.

Eighmy, John L. Churches in Cultural Captivity: A History of the Social Attitudes of Southern Baptists. Hill, Samual S., Jr., intro. by. LC 70-111047. pap. 67.00 (2029374). Bks Demand UMI.

Evans, B. The Early English Baptists, 2 vols. (Illus.). 1977. Repr. of 1862 ed. Vol. 1, 298 pp. 9.50 (ISBN 0-87921-041-9); Vol. 2, 362 pp. 9.50 (ISBN 0-87921-045-1). Attic Pr.

Fast, Heinhold. Quellen zur Geschichte der Taufer in der Schweiz, Vol. 2: Ostschweiz. (Ger.). 1974. 59.00x (ISBN 0-8361-1197-4). Herald Pr.

Gaustad, Edwin S. Baptist Piety: The Last Will & Testimony of Obadiah Holmes. LC 79-52570. (The Baptist Tradition Ser.). 1980. lib. bdg. 17.00x (ISBN 0-405-12439-2). Ayer Co Pubs.

Goertz, Hans-Jurgen, ed. Umstrittenes Taufertum 1525-1975. 1975. 22.50x (ISBN 0-8361-1128-1). Herald Pr.

Hollis, Daniel W., III. A History of First Baptist Church, Jacksonville Alabama, 1836-1986. (Illus.). 241p. 1986. 10.00 (ISBN 0-9616158-0-X). First Bapt AL.

Jeter, Jeremiah B. Recollections of a Long Life. Gaustad, Edwin S., ed. LC 79-52595. (The Baptist Tradition Ser.). 1980. Repr. of 1891 ed. lib. bdg. 24.00x (ISBN 0-405-12462-7). Ayer Co Pubs.

Knight, Richard. History of the General or Six Principle in Europe & America. Gaustad, Edwin S., ed. LC 79-52597. (The Baptist Tradition Ser.). 1980. Repr. of 1827 ed. lib. bdg. 30.50x (ISBN 0-405-12464-3). Ayer Co Pubs.

Krebs, Manfred. Quellen zur Geschichte der Taufer, Band IV. 61.00 (ISBN 0-384-30425-7); pap. 55.00 (ISBN 0-384-30424-9). Johnson Repr.

Lambert, Byron C. The Rise of the Anti-Mission Baptists: Sources & Leaders, 1800-1840. Gaustad, Edwin S., ed. LC 79-52573. (The Baptist Tradition Ser.). 1980. lib. bdg. 39.00x (ISBN 0-405-12441-4). Ayer Co Pubs.

Lambert, J. H. History of Siloam Missionary Baptist Church. pap. 2.50x (ISBN 0-686-12399-9). Church History.

Lasher, George W., ed. Baptist Ministerial Directory. 1987. 45.00. Banner Pr Al.

Lumpkin, William L. & Butterfield, Lyman. Colonial Baptists & Southern Revivals: An Original Anthology. Gaustad, Edwin S., ed. LC 79-52585. (The Baptist Tradition Ser.). 1980. lib. bdg. 25.50x (ISBN 0-405-12452-X). Ayer Co Pubs.

McBeth, H. Leon. The Baptist Heritage: Four Centuries of Baptist Witness. (Orig.). 1987. 24.95 (ISBN 0-8054-6569-3). Broadman.

--English Baptist Literature on Religious Liberty to Sixteen Eighty Nine: Doctoral Dissertation. Gaustad, Edwin S., ed. LC 79-52575. (The Baptist Tradition Ser.). 1980. lib. bdg. 39.00x (ISBN 0-405-12443-0). Ayer Co Pubs.

McBeth, Leon H. History of Baptists. LC 81-68736. 1983. cancelled 17.95 (ISBN 0-8054-6569-3). Broadman.

McKibbens, Thomas R., Jr. & Smith, Kenneth. The Life & Work of Morgan Edwards: First Baptist Historian in the United States. Gaustad, Edwin S., ed. LC 79-5269. (The Baptist Tradition Ser.). 1980. lib. bdg. 23.00x (ISBN 0-405-12438-4). Ayer Co Pubs.

McLoughlin, William G. New England Dissent, 1630-1833: The Baptists & the Separation of Church & State, 2 vols. LC 70-131464. (Center for the Study of the History of Liberty in America Ser). (Illus.). 1971. Set. 80.00x (ISBN 0-674-61175-6). Harvard U Pr.

Morris, Bryon T. A Charge to Keep. 1971. 4.00 (ISBN 0-87012-092-1). McClain.

Newman, Robert C. Baptists & the American Tradition. LC 76-7166. 1976. pap. 1.95 (ISBN 0-87227-008-4). Reg Baptist.

Pater, Calvin A. Karlstadt As the Father of the Baptist Movements. 350p. 1984. 37.50x (ISBN 0-8020-5555-9). U of Toronto Pr.

Patterson, Morgan W. Baptist History Sourcebook. cancelled (ISBN 0-8054-6568-5). Broadman.

Picirilli, Robert E., ed. History of Free Will Baptist State Associations. 1976. pap. 2.50 (ISBN 0-89265-061-3). Randall Hse.

Purefoy, George W. History of the Sandy Creek Baptist Association, from Its Organization in A. D. 1758 to 1858. Gaustad, Edwin S., ed. LC 79-52604. (The Baptist Tradition Ser.). (Illus.). 1980. Repr. of 1859 ed. lib. bdg. 26.50x (ISBN 0-405-12469-4). Ayer Co Pubs.

Rawlyk, G. A. Ravished by the Spirit: Religious Revivals, Baptists, & Henry Alline. 190p. 1984. 19.95x (ISBN 0-7735-0439-7); pap. 7.95 (ISBN 0-7735-0440-0). McGill-Queens U Pr.

Ray, D. B. The Baptist Succession. 1984. Repr. of 1912 ed. 22.00 (ISBN 0-317-11348-8). Church History.

Sandifer, Kevin. Facts, Baptist History: Sixteen Hundred to Nineteen Eighty. Bryan, Lydia & Gill, Rowland, eds. LC 83-80441. (Illus.). 144p. (Orig.). 1983. pap. 6.50 (ISBN 0-910653-01-1). Archival Servs.

Sandifer, Kevin W. A Fellowship of Love, the Heritage of First Baptist Church of Blanchard, Louisiana. Tippett, Donald C., ed. (Illus.). 1986. lib. bdg. 2.50 (ISBN 0-910653-02-X). Archival Servs.

Schmid, Walter & Von Murat, Leonhard. Quellen zur Geschichte der Taufer in der Schweiz, Vol. 1: Zurich. 428p. 1952. PLB 9.00x (ISBN 0-8361-1152-4). Herald Pr.

Schornbaum, Karl. Quellen zur Geschichte der Taufer. 34.00 (ISBN 0-384-54246-8); pap. 28.00 (ISBN 0-384-54245-X). Johnson Repr.

Semple, Robert. History of the Rise & Progress of the Baptists in Virginia. 1976. Repr. of 1894 ed. 15.00 (ISBN 0-686-12331-X). Church History.

Skinner, Craig. Lamplighter & Son. LC 82-82947. 1984. 13.95 (ISBN 0-8054-5705-4). Broadman.

Smith, Elias. The Life, Conversion, Preaching, Travels & Suffering of Elias Smith. Gaustad, Edwin S., ed. LC 79-52606. (The Baptist Tradition Ser.). 1980. Repr. of 1816 ed. lib. bdg. 34.50x (ISBN 0-405-12471-6). Ayer Co Pubs.

Spencer, J. H. The History of the Kentucky Baptists from 1769 to 1885, 2 vols. 1984. Repr. of 1886 ed. 54.00 (ISBN 0-686-12335-2). Church History.

Startup, Kenneth M. See His Banner Go: A Centennial History of the First Baptist Church, Paragould, Arkansas. LC 84-73475. (Illus.). 100p. 1985. write for info. (ISBN 0-935304-93-2). August Hse.

Stiansen, Peder. History of the Norwegian Baptists in America. Gaustad, Edwin S., ed. LC 79-52608. (The Baptist Tradition Ser.). (Illus.). 1980. Repr. of 1939 ed. lib. bdg. 32.50x (ISBN 0-405-12473-2). Ayer Co Pubs.

Storey, John W. Texas Baptist Leadership & Social Christianity, 1900-1980. LC 85-40747. (Texas A&M Southwestern Studies: No. 5). (Illus.). 237p. 1986. 22.50x (ISBN 0-89096-251-0). Tex A&M Univ Pr.

Taylor, John. A History of Ten Baptist Churches, of Which the Author Has Been Alternately a Member. 2nd ed. Gaustad, Edwin S., ed. LC 79-5609. (The Baptist Tradition Ser.). 1980. Repr. of 1827 ed. lib. bdg. 25.50x (ISBN 0-405-12474-0). Ayer Co Pubs.

Thomas, Joshua. The American Baptist Heritage in Wales, Vol. 1. 1976. 15.00 (ISBN 0-686-12332-8). Church History.

Torbet, Robert G. A History of the Baptists. rev. ed. LC 63-8225. 592p. 1973. 21.95 (ISBN 0-8170-0074-7). Judson.

Valentine, Foy D. & Gaustad, Edwin S., eds. A Historical Study of Southern Baptists & Race Relations 1917-1947: Doctoral Dissertation. LC 79-52579. (The Baptist Tradition Ser.). 1980. lib. bdg. 23.00x (ISBN 0-405-12447-3). Ayer Co Pubs.

Vanderpool. History of New Bethel Missionary Baptist Church. 5.00x (ISBN 0-686-12400-6). Church History.

Vedder, Enrique C. Breve Historia de los Bautistas Hasta 1900. Barocio, Teofilo, tr. 272p. 1985. Repr. of 1978 ed. 4.50 (ISBN 0-311-15039-X). Casa Bautista.

Vedder, H. C. History of the Baptists. 1977. lib. bdg. 59.95 (ISBN 0-8490-1988-5). Gordon Pr.

Vedder, Henry C. Short History of the Baptists. 12.95 (ISBN 0-8170-0162-X). Judson.

Wagner, Clarence M. Profiles of Black Georgia Baptists. Bennett Brother's Printing, ed. (Illus.). 268p. 1981. pap. 12.95 (ISBN 0-686-30456-X). Tru-Faith.

Wardin, Albert W., Jr. Baptist Atlas. LC 79-52541. (Illus.). 1980. 5.50 (ISBN 0-8054-6551-0). Broadman.

Whitsitt, William H. A Question in Baptist History: Whether the Anabaptists in England Practiced Immersion Before the Year 1641? Gaustad, Edwin S., ed. LC 79-52611. (The Baptist Tradition Ser.). 1980. Repr. of 1896 ed. lib. bdg. 14.00x (ISBN 0-405-12476-7). Ayer Co Pubs.

Wood, Nathan E. History of the First Baptist Church of Boston: Sixteen Sixty-Five to Eighteen Ninty Nine. Gaustad, Edwin S., ed. LC 79-52612. (The Baptist Tradition Ser.). (Illus.). 1980. Repr. of 1899 ed. lib. bdg. 34.50x (ISBN 0-405-12477-5). Ayer Co Pubs.

Wylie, J. A. History of the Waldenses. 1985. Repr. of 1870 ed. 15.00 (ISBN 0-317-38296-9). Church History.

Yance, Norman A. Religion Southern Style: Southern Baptists & Society in Historical Perspective. LC 78-61185. (Special Studies: No. 4). vi, 66p. 1978. pap. 3.95 (ISBN 0-932180-03-5). NABPR.

BAPTISTS–HISTORY–HISTORIOGRAPHY

Grenz, Stanley. Isaac Backus: Puritan & Baptist; His Place in History, His Thought, & the Implications for Modern Baptist Theology. LC 83-12140. vii, 346p. pap. 21.95 (ISBN 0-86554-067-5, P12). Mercer Univ Pr.

BAPTISTS–HYMNS

Heaton, Charles H., ed. Hymnbook for Christian Worship. LC 69-14339. 1970. Red. 7.95x (ISBN 0-8272-8020-3). Blue. 7.95x (ISBN 0-8272-8021-1); Beige. 7.95x (ISBN 0-8272-8024-6); 19.50x (ISBN 0-8272-8023-8); 8.95x (ISBN 0-8272-8022-X); brown gift 8.50x (ISBN 0-8272-8027-0). CBP.

Reynolds, William J. Companion to Baptist Hymnal: 1975 Edition. LC 75-39449. 480p. 1976. bds. 16.95 (ISBN 0-8054-6808-0). Broadman.

--Hymns of Our Faith. LC 64-14049. 1964. 18.95 (ISBN 0-8054-6805-6). Broadman.

BAPTISTS–MISSIONS

Corley, Winnie. Echoes from the Hills. 1981. lib. bdg. 14.95x (ISBN 0-934188-06-8). Evans Pubns.

Furlow, Elaine. Love with No Strings: The Human Touch in Christian Social Ministries. Hullum, Everett, ed. (The Human Touch Photo-Text Ser.: Volume IV). (Illus.). 1977. 6.95 (ISBN 0-937170-15-1). Home Mission.

Jones, Bill. Free Will Baptist Missions, Missionaries, & Their Message. (Way of Life Ser.). 1972. pap. 1.50 (ISBN 0-89265-008-7, Free Will Baptist Dept); tchr's guide 3.95 (ISBN 0-89265-007-9). Randall Hse.

Loucks, Celeste, et al. And a Cast of Thousands. Furlow, Elaine S., ed. (The Human Touch Photo-Text Ser.). (Illus.). 1978. 6.95 (ISBN 0-937170-11-9). Home Mission.

McCoy, Isaac. History of Baptist Indian Missions. LC 19-11605. 1970. Repr. of 1840 ed. 36.00 (ISBN 0-384-36590-6). Johnson Repr.

Puthenpurakal, Joseph. Baptist Missions in Nagaland. 1984. 22.50x (ISBN 0-8364-1138-2, Pub. by Mukhopadhyaya). South Asia Bks.

Tanner, William G. From Sea to Shining Sea. LC 86-9609. 1986. pap. 4.95 (ISBN 0-8054-5667-8). Broadman.

BAPTISTS–SERMONS

Allen, Charles L. Touch of the Master's Hand: Christ's Miracles for Today. 160p. 1956. pap. 2.75 (ISBN 0-8007-8093-0, Spire Bks). Revell.

Angell, C. Roy. God's Gold Mines. LC 62-9194. 1962. 7.95 (ISBN 0-8054-5113-7). Broadman.

--Price Tags of Life. LC 59-9692. 1959. 6.95 (ISBN 0-8054-5108-0). Broadman.

Brawley, Edward M., ed. Negro Baptist Pulpit. facs. ed. LC 74-154072. (Black Heritage Library Collection Ser). 1890. 19.25 (ISBN 0-8369-8783-7). Ayer Co Pubs.

Criswell, W. A. Expository Sermons on Revelation, 5 Vols. in 1. 1961-66. 24.95 (ISBN 0-310-22840-9, 9442). Zondervan.

King, Martin Luther, Jr. Strength to Love. 208p. 1985. pap. 11.95 (ISBN 0-8027-2472-8). Walker & Co.

Lovette, Roger. Questions Jesus Raised. LC 85-15137. 1986. 4.95 (ISBN 0-8054-2259-5). Broadman.

Maclaren, Alexander. Best of Alexander Maclaren. Atkins, Gaius G., ed. LC 74-179733. (Biography Index Reprint Ser). Repr. of 1949 ed. 14.00 (ISBN 0-8369-8101-4). Ayer Co Pubs.

Morgan, Howard M. & Morgan, John C. The God-Man of Galilee: Studies in Christian Living. 100p. 1986. Repr. of 1983 ed. 4.95 (ISBN 0-913029-14-9). Stevens Bk Pr.

Palmer, Gordon. By Freedom's Holy Light. 1964. 9.95 (ISBN 0-8159-5110-8). Devin.

Redpath, Alan. Blessings Out of Buffetings: Studies in Second Corinthians. 256p. 1965. 11.95 (ISBN 0-8007-0026-0). Revell.

Spurgeon, C. H. New Park Street Pulpit Index. 1976. pap. 1.50 (ISBN 0-686-16848-8). Pilgrim Pubns.

Spurgeon, C H. New Park Street Pulpit 1855-1860, 6 vols. 1981. Set. 60.00 (ISBN 0-686-16847-X). Pilgrim Pubns.

Thurman, Howard. The Growing Edge. LC 74-14866. 192p. 1974. pap. 6.95 (ISBN 0-913408-14-X). Friends United.

BAPTISTS, AFRO-AMERICAN

see Afro-American Baptists

BAR MITZVAH

Bar Mitzvah Book. (Illus.). 64p. 1987. 15.95 (ISBN 0-88363-088-5). H L Levin.

Efron, Benjamin & Rubin, Alvan D. Coming of Age: Your Bar or Bat Mitzvah. LC 77-78031. (Illus.). 1977. 5.00 (ISBN 0-8074-0084-X, 142530). UAHC.

Katsh, Abraham I., ed. Bar Mitzvah Illustrated. 8th ed. LC 76-23713. (Illus.). 1976. 18.95 (ISBN 0-88400-048-6). Shengold.

Lanckton, Alice K. Bar Mitzvah Mother's Manual. (Illus.). 304p. 1986. pap. 6.95 (ISBN 0-87052-283-3). Hippocrene Bks.

Lewit, Jane & Epstein, Ellen R. The Bar-Bat Mitzvah Planbook. LC 81-48459. (Illus.). 176p. 1982. 18.95 (ISBN 0-8128-2861-5). Stein & Day.

Metter, Bert. Bar Mitzvah, Bat Mitzvah: How Jewish Boys & Girls Come of Age. LC 83-23230. (Illus.). 64p. (Orig.). 1984. PLB 10.95 (ISBN 0-89919-149-5, Clarion); pap. 4.95 (ISBN 0-89919-292-0). HM.

Neusner, Jacob. Mitzvah: Basic Jewish Ideas. (Ser.). (Orig.). 1981. pap. 4.95 (ISBN 0-940646-25-0). Rossel Bks.

Rosenblum, Richard. My Bar Mitzvah. LC 84-16685. (Illus.). 32p. 1985. 10.25 (ISBN 0-688-04143-4, Morrow Junior Books); PLB 10.88 (ISBN 0-688-04144-2, Morrow Junior Books). Morrow.

Schoenfeld, Stuart, et al. Bar Mitzvah. LC 85-4412. (Illus.). 192p. 1985. 50.00 (ISBN 0-385-19826-4). Doubleday.

BARABBAS–FICTION

Lagerkvist, Par. Barabbas. Blair, Alain, tr. (YA) 1955. pap. 2.95 (ISBN 0-394-70134-8, Vin). Random.

BARONIUS, CESARE, 1538-1607

Pullapilly, Cyriac K. Caesar Baronius: Courtier-Reformation Historian. 1975. 21.95x (ISBN 0-268-00501-X). U of Notre Dame Pr.

BAROQUE ARCHITECTURE

see Architecture, Baroque

BAROQUE SCULPTURE

see Sculpture, Baroque

BARREN FIG TREE (PARABLE)

see Jesus Christ–Parables

BARTH, KARL, 1886-1968

Barth, Karl. Letters, Nineteen Sixty-One to Nineteen Sixty-Eight. Fangmeier, Jurgen & Stoevesand, Hinrich, eds. LC 80-29140. pap. 99.50 (ISBN 0-317-41616-2, 2023208). Bks Demand UMI.

Barth, Karl & Bultmann, Rudolf. Barth-Bultmann Letters, Nineteen Twenty-Two to Nineteen Sixty-Six. Bromiley, Geoffrey W., tr. 224p. 1981. 13.95 (ISBN 0-8028-3560-0). Eerdmans.

Barth, Karl & Zuckmayer, Carl. A Late Friendship: The Letters of Carl Zuckmayer & Karl Barth. Bromiley, Geoffrey W., tr. 80p. 1983. 8.95 (ISBN 0-8028-3574-0). Eerdmans.

Bloesch, Donald G. Jesus Is Victor! Karl Barth's Doctrine of Salvation. LC 76-14360. Repr. of 1976 ed. 33.50 (ISBN 0-8357-9013-4, 2016373). Bks Demand UMI.

Bolich, Gregory G. Karl Barth & Evangelicalism. (Orig.). 1979. pap. 6.95 (ISBN 0-87784-615-4). Inter-Varsity.

Bromiley, G. W., ed. & tr. Karl Barth: Letters 1961-1968. 288p. Date not set. 21.75 (ISBN 0-567-09321-2, Pub. by T & T Clark Ltd UK). Fortress.

Bromiley, Geoffrey W. An Introduction to the Theology of Karl Barth. LC 79-15397. (Orig.). pap. 8.95 (ISBN 0-8028-1804-8). Eerdmans.

Davaney, Sheila G. Divine Power: A Study of Karl Barth & Charles Hartshorne. LC 85-45502. (Harvard Dissertions in Religion Ser.). 224p. 1986. pap. 16.95 (ISBN 0-8006-7072-8, 1-7072). Fortress.

Gollwitzer, Helmut. Karl Barth: Church Dogmatics - A Selection with Introduction. Bromiley, G. W., ed. & tr. 272p. Date not set. pap. 8.50 (ISBN 0-567-29051-4, Pub. by T & T Clark Ltd UK). Fortress.

Gunton, Colin E. Becoming & Being: The Doctrine of God in Charles Hartshorne & Karl Barth. (Theological Monographs). 1978. text ed. 39.95x (ISBN 0-19-826713-4). Oxford U Pr.

Haerle, Wilfried. Sein und Gnade: Die Ontologie in Karl Barths Kirchlicher Dogmatik. (Theologische Bibliothek Toepelmann, Vol. 27). (Ger.). 428p. 1975. 45.60x (ISBN 3-11-005706-9). De Gruyter.

Hartwell, Herbert. The Theology of Karl Barth: An Introduction. (Studies in Theology). 201p. 1964. pap. 13.50 (ISBN 0-7156-0356-6, Pub. by Duckworth London). Longwood Pub Group.

Hausmann, William J. Karl Barth's Doctrine of Election. LC 74-81812. 1969. 5.95 (ISBN 0-8022-2281-1). Philos Lib.

Henry, David P. The Early Development of the Hermeneutic of Karl Barth. (Dissertation Ser.: No. 5). ix, 215p. pap. 18.95 (ISBN 0-86554-130-2). NABPR.

--The Early Development of the Hermeneutic of Karl Barth As Evidenced by His Appropriation of Romans Chapter Five, Twelve to Twenty-One. ix, 275p. 1985. 18.95 (ISBN 0-86554-130-2, MUP/P16). Mercer Univ Pr.

Hunsinger, George, ed. Karl Barth & Radical Politics. LC 76-976. 236p. 1976. softcover 6.45 (ISBN 0-664-24797-0). Westminster.

Jungel, Eberhard. Karl Barth, a Theological Legacy. Paul, Garrett E., tr. LC 86-7793. 96p. (Orig.). 1986. pap. 13.95 (ISBN 0-664-24031-3). Westminster.

McConnachie, John. Barthian Theology. LC 72-2493. (Select Bibliography Reprint Ser). 1972. Repr. of 1933 ed. 19.00 (ISBN 0-8369-6861-1). Ayer Co Pubs.

McKim, Donald K., ed. How Karl Barth Changed My Mind. 216p. (Orig.). 1986. pap. 9.95 (ISBN 0-8028-0099-8). Eerdmans.

McLean, Stuart. Humanity in the Thought of Karl Barth. 240p. 1981. 20.95 (ISBN 0-567-09304-2, Pub. by T&T Clark Ltd UK). Fortress.

Mallow, Vernon. The Demonic: A Selected Theological Study: An Examination into the Theology of Edwin Lewis, Karl Barth, & Paul Tillich. LC 83-1143. 192p. (Orig.). 1983. lib. bdg. 26.00 (ISBN 0-8191-3069-9); pap. text ed. 11.50 (ISBN 0-8191-3070-2). U Pr of Amer.

Matczak, Sebastian A. Le Probleme de Dieu dans la Pensee de Karl Barth. (Philosophical Questions Ser.: No. 1). 1968. pap. 19.50 (ISBN 0-912116-00-5). Learned Pubns.

Mueller, David. Karl Barth. Patterson, Bob E., ed. LC 70-188066. (Makers of the Modern Theological Mind Ser). 1972. 8.95 (ISBN 0-87680-254-4, 80254). Word Bks.

Mueller, David L. Karl Barth. 172p. 1984. pap. text ed. 8.95 (ISBN 0-8499-3002-2, 3002-2). Word Bks.

Polman, A. D. Barth. (Modern Thinkers Ser.). pap. 2.25 (ISBN 0-87552-580-6). Presby & Reformed.

Rumscheidt, H. Martin. Karl Barth in Review: Posthumous Works Introduced & Assessed. (Pittsburgh Theological Monograph: No. 30). xxviii, 118p. (Orig.). 1981. pap. 11.75 (ISBN 0-915138-33-6). Pickwick.

Rumscheidt, H. Martin, ed. The Way of Theology in Karl Barth: Essays & Comments. (Princeton Theological Monograph Ser.: No. 8). 1986. pap. 9.90 (ISBN 0-915138-61-1). Pickwick.

Schmitt, Keith R. Death & After-Life in the Theologies of Karl Barth & John Hick: A Comparative Study. (Amsterdam Studies in Theology Ser.: Vol. 5). 230p. 1985. pap. 32.50x (ISBN 90-6203-528-0, Pub. by Rodopi Holland). Humanities.

Scott, Waldron. Karl Barth's Theology of Mission. Bockmuehl, Klaus, ed. (World Evangelical Fellowship: Outreach & Identity Theological Monograph). 40p. 1978. pap. 1.95 (ISBN 0-87784-541-7). Inter-Varsity.

Sykes, S. W. Karl Barth: Studies of His Theological Method. 1979. text ed. 34.95x (ISBN 0-19-826649-9). Oxford U Pr.

Van Til, Cornelius. Christianity & Barthianism. 1960. pap. 10.95 (ISBN 0-87552-481-8). Presby & Reformed.

Whitehouse, W. A. The Authority of Grace. 272p. 1981. pap. 14.95 (ISBN 0-567-09028-0, Pub. by T&T Clark Ltd UK). Fortress.

Williamson, Rene De Visme. Politics & Protestant Theology: An Interpretation of Tillich, Barth, Bonhoeffer, & Brunner. LC 76-20817. 1976. 20.00x (ISBN 0-8071-0193-1). La State U Pr.

Zellweger-Barth, Max. My Father-in-Law: Memories of Karl Barth. Rumscheidt, Martin, tr. from Ger. (Princeton Theological Monograph Ser.: No. 5). Tr. of Mein Schwiegervater. (Orig.). 1986. pap. 6.00 (ISBN 0-915138-84-0). Pickwick.

BARTHIANISM

see Dialectical Theology

BASEL, COUNCIL OF, 1431-1449

Burns, J. H. Scottish Churchmen & the Council of Basle. LC 64-7472. 1962. 15.00 (ISBN 0-8023-9034-X). Dufour.

BASHFULNESS

Pugh, Nathanael. Running Free: Conquering Fear & Shyness. Wallace, Mary H., ed. 96p. (Orig.). 1984. pap. 4.50 (ISBN 0-912315-69-5). Word Aflame.

Rohrer, Norman B. & Sutherland, S. Philip. Why Am I Shy? Turning Shyness into Confidence. LC 78-52182. 1978. pap. 6.95 (ISBN 0-8066-1656-3, 10-7130). Augsburg.

BASIL, SAINT, 329-379

Basilius. The Ascetic Works of Saint Basil. Clarke, W. K., tr. & intro. by. LC 80-2352. Repr. of 1925 ed. 47.50 (ISBN 0-404-18902-4). AMS Pr.

Murphy, Sr. M. Gertrude. Saint Basil & Monasticism. LC 70-144661. Repr. of 1930 ed. 14.75 (ISBN 0-404-04543-X). AMS Pr.

BATH AND WELLS (DIOCESE)

Hunter, Joseph, ed. Ecclesiastical Documents. 1840. 19.00 (ISBN 0-384-24935-3). Johnson Repr.

BAUR, FERDINAND CHRISTIAN, 1792-1860

Fitzer, Joseph. Moehler & Baur in Controversy Eighteen Thirty-Two to Thirty-Eight: Romantic-idealist Assesment of the Reformation & Counter-Reformation. LC 74-77619. (American Academy of Religion. Studies in Religion). 1974. 9.95 (ISBN 0-88420-111-2, 010007). Scholars Pr GA.

BAXTER, RICHARD, 1615-1691

Keeble, N. H. Richard Baxter: Puritan Man of Letters. 1982. 45.00x (ISBN 0-19-811716-7). Oxford U Pr.

BAY PSALM BOOK

Eames, Wilberforce. The Bay Psalm Book. 1978. pap. 53.95 (ISBN 0-89102-098-5, Artemis). B Franklin.

Winship, George P. Cambridge Press, Sixteen Thirty-Eight to Sixteen Ninety-Two. facs. ed. LC 68-57346. (Essay Index Reprint Ser). 1945. 22.50 (ISBN 0-8369-1004-4). Ayer Co Pubs.

BEADS (IN RELIGION, FOLK-LORE, ETC.)

Erikson, Joan M. Universal Bead. LC 68-20819. (Illus.). 1969. 13.95 (ISBN 0-393-04233-2). Norton.

BEATIFIC VISION

Lossky, Vladimir. The Vision of God. 139p. 1963. 7.95 (ISBN 0-913836-19-2). St Vladimirs.

BEATITUDES

Barclay, William. The Beatitudes & the Lord's Prayer for Everyman. LC 75-9309. 256p. 1975. pap. 7.95 (ISBN 0-06-060393-3, RD112, HarpR). Har-Row.

Barnabas, Bentley. Beatitudes for the Balmy: And Other Poems. 1985. 6.95 (ISBN 0-682-40211-7). Exposition Pr FL.

The Beatitudes. (The Inspirational Library). 24p. 3.95 (ISBN 0-8326-2003-3, 3250). World Bible.

The Beautitudes. 20p. 1983. pap. 7.55 Dup Masters (ISBN 0-88479-037-1). Arena Lettres.

Bloem, Diane. A Woman's Workshop on the Beautitudes. (Orig.). 1981. Leader's Manual, 160 Pages. pap. 3.95 (ISBN 0-310-42641-3, 112160); Student's Manual, 96 Pages. pap. 2.95 (ISBN 0-310-42651-0, 11217). Zondervan.

Crosby, Michael H. The Spirituality of the Beatitudes: Matthew's Challenge for First World Christians. LC 80-24755. 254p. (Orig.). 1981. pap. 7.95 (ISBN 0-88344-465-8). Orbis Bks.

Denny, Randal. The Habit of Happiness. 102p. 1976. 2.50 (ISBN 0-8341-0399-0). Beacon Hill.

Drew, George. The Beatitudes: Attitudes for a Better Future. 63p. (Orig.). 1980. pap. 6.95 (ISBN 0-940754-03-7). Ed Ministries.

Haring, Bernard. Blessed Are the Pure in Heart: The Beatitudes. (Illus.). 1977. pap. 4.95 (ISBN 0-8245-0204-3). Crossroad NY.

Hughes, R. Kent. Blessed Are the Born Again. 132p. 1986. pap. 4.95 (ISBN 0-89693-369-5). Victor Bks.

Kappeler, Max. Compendium for the Study of Christian Science: No. 3, The Commandments, the Beatitudes, the Lord's Prayer. 29p. 1951. pap. 3.50 (ISBN 0-85241-057-3). Kappeler Inst Pub.

Keller, Phillip. Salt for Society. 1986. 5.95 (ISBN 0-8499-3059-6). Word Bks.

King, Pat & Wood, George. The Beatitudes-Expressing the Character of Jesus. (Bible Study Enrichment Ser.). 64p. 1985. pap. 2.95 (ISBN 0-930756-92-4). Aglow Pubns.

Kissinger, Warren S. Sermon on the Mount: A History of Interpretation & Bibliography. LC 75-29031. (ATLA Bibliography Ser.: No. 3). 309p. 1975. 22.50 (ISBN 0-8108-0843-9). Scarecrow.

Mitchell, Joan & O'Neill, Irene. Beatitudes for Today. Fisher, Carl, ed. (Illus.). 1985. dupl. masterbook 9.95 (ISBN 0-89837-102-3, Pub. by Pflaum Pr). Peter Li.

Muto, Susan. Blessings That Make Us Be: Living the Beatitudes. LC 82-13102. 176p. 1982. 7.95 (ISBN 0-8245-0516-6). Crossroad NY.

Norquist, Marilyn. Jesus' Pattern for a Happy Life: The Beatitudes. 112p. 1986. pap. 3.50 (ISBN 0-89243-136-9). Liguori Pubns.

Norris, John. Christian Blessedness (with) Reflections upon a Late Essay Concerning Human Understanding. Wellek, Rene, ed. LC 75-11241. (British Philosophers & Theologians of the 17th & 18th Centuries Ser.). 1978. Repr. of 1690 ed. lib. bdg. 51.00 (ISBN 0-8240-1793-5). Garland Pub.

Perry, Jack. Light from Light. 208p. 1987. 11.95 (ISBN 0-310-23850-1). Zondervan.

Pink, Arthur W. The Beatitudes & the Lord's Prayer. 140p. 1982. pap. 4.95 (ISBN 0-8010-7073-2). Baker Bk.

The Secret of Happiness: Matthew 5, the Beatitudes. 7.95 (ISBN 0-86683-850-3, HarpR). Har-Row.

Spurgeon, C. H. The Beatitudes. 1978. pap. 2.75 (ISBN 0-686-00504-X). Pilgrim Pubns.

Tuck, William P. The Way for All Seasons. 1987. 9.95 (ISBN 0-8054-1541-6). Broadman.

Tugwell, Simon. The Beatitudes: Soundings in Christian Traditions. 192p. 1980. 8.95 (ISBN 0-87243-098-7). Templegate.

Van Rijckenborgh, Jan. Mystery of the Beatitudes. 104p. (Orig.). 1987. pap. 10.50. Rosycross Pr.

Watson, Thomas. The Beatitudes. 307p. 1981. kivar bdg. 9.95 (ISBN 0-85151-035-3). Banner of Truth.

Wood, George O. & Krutza, William J. You Can't Beat the Beatitudes. LC 78-58721. 1978. pap. 1.25 (ISBN 0-88243-719-4, 02-0719, Radiant Bks). Gospel Pub.

BEATITUDES–MEDITATIONS

Kirby, Wallace H. Programs & Promises: Reflections on the Beatitudes. 1980. 3.50 (ISBN 0-89536-414-X, 1640). CSS of Ohio.

BEATITUDES–SERMONS

Morris, Daniel. Beatitude Saints. LC 83-62423. 128p. (Orig.). 1984. pap. 4.95 (ISBN 0-87973-615-1, 615). Our Sunday Visitor.

BEAUTY, PERSONAL

Steinhart, Lawrence M. Beauty Through Health: From the Edgar Cayce Readings. LC 73-91501. 1974. 7.95 (ISBN 0-87795-078-4). Arbor Hse.

Wlodyga, Ronald R. Health Secrets from the Bible. LC 79-64042. 1979. pap. 5.95 (ISBN 0-917182-12-X). Triumph Pub.

BEDE, THE VENERABLE, 673-735

Brown, George H. Bede the Venerable. (Twayne's English Authors Ser.). 144p. 1987. lib. bdg. 19.95 (ISBN 0-8057-6940-4, TEAS 443, Twayne). G K Hall.

Browne, G. F. The Venerable Bede: His Life & Writings. LC 76-52505. 1972. Repr. of 1919 ed. lib. bdg. 35.00 (ISBN 0-8414-1652-4). Folcroft.

Duckett, Eleanor S. Anglo-Saxon Saints & Scholars. x, 484p. 1967. Repr. of 1947 ed. 35.00 (ISBN 0-208-00200-6, Archon). Shoe String.

Hurst, David. The Venerable Bede: Commentary on the Catholic Epistles. 1985. 24.95 (ISBN 0-317-18074-6); pap. 9.00 (ISBN 0-317-18075-4). Cistercian Pubns.

Isidorus. Isidors Geschichte der Gothen, Vandalen, Sueven, Nebst Ausuzegen Aus der Kirchengeschichte Des Beda Venerablis. pap. 8.00 (ISBN 0-384-25980-4). Johnson Repr.

Leclercq, Jean, et al. St. Bede: A Tribute. LC 85-8214. (Word & Spirit Ser.: Vol. VII). 1985. pap. 7.00. St Bedes Pubns.

Lumby, F. R., ed. Be Domes Daege (Bede's de Die Judicii) (EETS OS Ser.: Vol. 65). Repr. of 1876 ed. 15.00 (ISBN 0-8115-3419-7). Kraus Repr.

Werner, Karl. Beda der Ehrwuerdige und Seine Zeit. new ed. 1963. Repr. of 1881 ed. 24.50 (ISBN 0-8337-3730-9). B Franklin.

BEDELL, WILLIAM, BP., 1571-1642

Bedell, William. True Relation of the Life & Death of the Right Reverend Father in God William Bedell, Lord Bishop of Kilmore in Ireland. Jones, Thomas W., ed. Repr. of 1872 ed. 27.00 (ISBN 0-384-03740-2). Johnson Repr.

BEECHER, LYMAN, 1775-1863

Beecher, Lyman. Autobiography of Lyman Beecher, 2 vols. Cross, Barbara M., ed. LC 61-6348. (The John Harvard Library). (Illus.). 896p. 1961. Set. 55.00x (ISBN 0-674-05400-8). Harvard U Pr.

Goodell, John. The Triumph of Moralism in New England Piety: A Study of Lyman Beecher, Harriet Beecher Stowe & Henry Ward Beecher. 50.00 (ISBN 0-405-14113-0). Ayer Co Pubs.

Henry, Stuart C. Unvanquished Puritan: A Portrait of Lyman Beecher. LC 85-30520. 299p. 1986. Repr. of 1973 ed. lib. bdg. 45.00x (ISBN 0-313-25097-9, HEUN). Greenwood.

BEGINNING

see also Creation

Stump, Gladys S. About the Beginning, Bk. 1. LC 78-78070. 1979. pap. 7.95 (ISBN 0-8163-0380-0, 01055-3). Pacific Pr Pub Assn.

BEHAVIOR

see Conduct of Life

BEING

see Ontology

BEISSEL, JOHANN CONRAD, 1690-1768

Jacoby, John E. Two Mystic Communities in America. LC 75-326. (The Radical Tradition in America Ser). 104p. 1975. Repr. of 1931 ed. 15.00 (ISBN 0-88355-230-2). Hyperion Conn.

Klein, Walter C. Johann Conrad Beissel: Mystic & Martinet 1690-1768. LC 74-187453. (The American Utopian Adventure Ser.). 218p. 1973. Repr. of 1942 ed. lib. bdg. 22.50x (ISBN 0-87991-012-7). Porcupine Pr.

BEKTASHI

Birge, John K. The Bektashi Order of Dervishes. LC 77-87662. Repr. of 1937 ed. 35.00 (ISBN 0-404-16400-5). AMS Pr.

BEL

see Baal (Deity)

BELIEF AND DOUBT

Here are entered works treating the subject from the philosophical standpoint. Works on religious belief are entered under the heading Faith.

see also Agnosticism; Faith; Rationalism; Skepticism; Truth

Armstrong, Allen. Belief, Truth & Knowledge. LC 72-83586. 240p. 1973. 42.50 (ISBN 0-521-08706-6); pap. 13.95 (ISBN 0-521-09737-1). Cambridge U Pr.

Baker, Albert E. Prophets for a Day of Judgment. facsimile ed. LC 72-90605. (Essay Index Reprint Ser). 1944. 17.00 (ISBN 0-8369-1390-6). Ayer Co Pubs.

Brown, Frank B. Transfiguration: Poetic Metaphor & the Languages of Religious Belief. LC 82-24714. (Studies in Religion). x, 230p. 1983. 25.00x (ISBN 0-8078-1560-8). U of NC Pr.

Caporale, Rocco & Grumelli, Antonio, eds. The Culture of Unbelief: Studies & Proceedings from the First International Symposium on Belief, Held in Rome, March 22-27, 1969. LC 75-138513. 1971. 39.50x (ISBN 0-520-01856-7). U of Cal Pr.

Cardiff, Ira D. What Great Men Think of Religion. LC 71-161322. (Atheist Viewpoint Ser). 504p. 1972. Repr. of 1945 ed. 29.00 (ISBN 0-405-03625-6). Ayer Co Pubs.

Cocoris, G. Michael. Questioning Christianity. 67p. (Orig.). 1985. pap. text ed. 1.00 (ISBN 0-935729-00-3). Church Open Door.

Collins, Gary. Beyond Easy Believism. 197p. 1985. pap. 8.95 (ISBN 0-8499-3025-1, 3025-1). Word Bks.

Connolly, John R. Dimensions of Belief & Unbelief. LC 80-67241. 373p. 1981. lib. bdg. 30.50 (ISBN 0-8191-1389-1); pap. text ed. 15.75 (ISBN 0-8191-1390-5). U Pr of Amer.

Da Free, John. The Transmission of Doubt. 475p. (Orig.). 1984. pap. 10.95 (ISBN 0-913922-77-3). Dawn Horse Pr.

D'Arcy, Martin C. The Nature of Belief. facsimile ed. (Select Bibliographies Reprint Ser). Repr. of 1931 ed. 21.00 (ISBN 0-8369-5930-2). Ayer Co Pubs.

Diggle, John W. Religious Doubt: Its Nature, Treatment, Causes, Difficulties, Consequences & Dissolution. 1978. Repr. of 1895 ed. lib. bdg. 25.00 (ISBN 0-8495-1030-9). Arden Lib.

Drews, Arthur. The Witnesses to the Historicity of Jesus. McCabe, Joseph, tr. LC 70-161327. (Atheist Viewpoint Ser.). 332p. 1972. Repr. of 1912 ed. 23.50 (ISBN 0-405-03811-9). Ayer Co Pubs.

Evans, Stephens. Subjectivity & Religious Belief. LC 82-40062. 238p. 1982. pap. text ed. 12.50 (ISBN 0-8191-2665-9). U Pr of Amer.

Ferreira, M. Jamie. Doubt & Religious Commitment: The Role of the Will in Newman's Thought. 1980. 29.95x (ISBN 0-19-826654-5). Oxford U Pr.

Fey, William R. Faith & Doubt: The Unfolding of Newman's Thought on Certainty. LC 75-38101. xxii, 229p. 1976. 22.95x (ISBN 0-915762-02-1). Patmos Pr.

Grant, Patrick. Six Modern Authors & Problems of Belief. LC 79-14511. 175p. 1979. text ed. 28.50x (ISBN 0-06-492515-3). B&N Imports.

Green, Ronald M. Religious Reason: The Rational & Moral Basis of Religious Belief. 1978. text ed. 18.95x (ISBN 0-19-502388-9); pap. text ed. 7.95x (ISBN 0-19-502389-7). Oxford U Pr.

Griffiths, A. Philips, ed. Knowledge & Belief. 1967. pap. 9.95x (ISBN 0-19-875003-X). Oxford U Pr.

Gutting, Gary. Religious Belief & Religious Skepticism. LC 82-50287. xi, 192p. 1983. pap. text ed. 9.95x (ISBN 0-268-01618-6, 85-16189). U of Notre Dame Pr.

Hill, Carole E., ed. Symbols & Society: Essays on Belief Systems in Action. LC 74-21905. (Southern Anthropological Society Proceedings Ser: No. 9). 150p. 1975. pap. 6.50x (ISBN 0-8203-0371-2). U of Ga Pr.

James, William. The Will to Believe & Human Immortality. pap. 5.95 (ISBN 0-486-20291-7). Dover.

--Will to Believe & Other Essays in Popular Philosophy & Human Immortality. 15.75 (ISBN 0-8446-2313-X). Peter Smith.

Jastrow, Joseph. The Psychology of Conviction: A Study of Beliefs & Attitudes. 1979. Repr. of 1918 ed. lib. bdg. 40.00 (ISBN 0-8495-2744-9). Arden Lib.

Koffarnus, Richard. Why Believe? LC 80-53673. 96p. (Orig.). 1981. pap. 2.25 (ISBN 0-87239-425-5, 40090). Standard Pub.

Laird, John. Knowledge, Belief & Opinion. LC 72-6560. 515p. 1972. Repr. of 1930 ed. 37.50 (ISBN 0-208-01215-X, Archon). Shoe String.

Lamm, Norman. Faith & Doubt. 1986. 11.95x (ISBN 0-87068-138-9). Ktav.

Laurence, Theoder. The Miracle Power of Believing. 1976. (Parker). P-H.

McCarthy, Gerald. The Ethics of Belief Debate. (AAR Studies in Religion). 1986. 20.95 (ISBN 0-89130-892-X, 01-00-41); pap. 15.95 (ISBN 0-89130-893-8). Scholars Pr GA.

McCarthy, William. Bible, Church & God. 2nd ed. LC 70-169211. (Atheist Viewpoint Ser). (Illus.). 736p. 1972. Repr. of 1946 ed. 41.00 (ISBN 0-405-03805-4). Ayer Co Pubs.

MacMillan, J. A. Authority of the Believer. 96p. 1981. pap. 2.25 (ISBN 0-87509-152-0). Chr Pubns.

Mooney, Christopher F., ed. Presence & Absence of God. LC 68-8748. 1969. 20.00 (ISBN 0-8232-0810-9). Fordham.

Nozick, M., ed. Miguel De Unamuno: The Agony of Belief. 1982. 23.50 (ISBN 0-691-06498-9); pap. 10.50x (ISBN 0-691-01366-7). Princeton U Pr.

Pieper, Josef. Belief & Faith: A Philosophical Tract. Winston, Richard & Winston, Clara, trs. from German. LC 75-31841. 106p. 1976. Repr. of 1963 ed. lib. bdg. 22.50x (ISBN 0-8371-8490-8, PIBF). Greenwood.

Pojman, Louis P. Religious Belief & the Will. (Problems of Philosophy Ser.). 256p. 1986. text ed. 32.50 (ISBN 0-7102-0399-3). Methuen Inc.

Pontas, J. Dictionnaire de Cas de Conscience ou Decisions, 2 vols. Migne, J. P., ed. (Encyclopedie Theologique Ser.: Vols. 18-19). (Fr.). 1326p. Repr. of 1847 ed. lib. bdg. 169.00x (ISBN 0-89241-238-0). Caratzas.

Quine, W. V. & Ullian, J. S. The Web of Belief. 2nd ed. 1978. pap. text ed. 7.00 (ISBN 0-394-32179-0, RanC). Random.

Radhakrishnan, Sarvepalli. Recovery of Faith. Repr. of 1955 ed. lib. bdg. 22.50x (ISBN 0-8371-0197-2, RARF). Greenwood.

Riggs, Ralph M. We Believe. 184p. 1954. 3.50 (ISBN 0-88243-780-1, 02-0780). Gospel Pub.

Rokeach, Milton. Beliefs, Attitudes & Values: A Theory of Organization & Change. LC 68-21322. (Social & Behavioral Science Ser.). 1968. 25.95x (ISBN 0-87589-013-X). Jossey-Bass.

Rusch, William G., ed. The Trinitarian Controversy. LC 79-8889. (Sources of Early Christian Thought Ser.). 192p. 1980. pap. 7.95 (ISBN 0-8006-1410-0, 1-1410). Fortress.

St. Romain, Philip. Faith & Doubt Today. LC 85-82033. 128p. (Orig.). 1986. pap. 3.25 (ISBN 0-89243-245-4). Liguori Pubns.

Santayana, George. Scepticism & Animal Faith. 14.75 (ISBN 0-8446-2863-8). Peter Smith.

--Scepticism & Animal Faith: Introduction to a System of Philosophy. 1955. pap. text ed. 6.00 (ISBN 0-486-20236-4). Dover.

Smith, Kent D. Faith: Reflections on Experience, Theology & Fiction. 114p. (Orig.). 1984. lib. bdg. 22.00 (ISBN 0-8191-3634-4); pap. text ed. 9.25 (ISBN 0-8191-3635-2). U Pr of Amer.

Smith, Wilfred C. Belief & History. LC 75-50587. 138p. 1977. pap. 7.95x (ISBN 0-8139-1086-2). U Pr of Va.

Tinder, Glenn. Against Fate. LC 81-50462. 173p. 1981. text ed. 16.95 (ISBN 0-268-00595-8). U of Notre Dame Pr.

Wiersbe, Warren W., compiled by. Classic Sermons on Faith & Doubt. LC 85-9767. (Classic Sermon Ser.). 160p. 1985. pap. 8.95 (ISBN 0-8254-4028-9). Kregel.

Wilder-Smith, A. E. He Who Thinks Has to Believe. LC 81-65988. 1981. pap. 2.95 (ISBN 0-89051-073-3). Master Bks.

BELLARMINO, ROBERTO FRANCESCO ROMOLO, SAINT, 1542-1621

Whitaker, William. Disputation on Holy Scripture Against the Papists. 55.00 (ISBN 0-384-68010-0). Johnson Repr.

BELLOC, HILAIRE, 1870-1953

Braybrook, Patrick. Some Thoughts on Hilaire Belloc: Ten Studies. 1973. 17.50 (ISBN 0-8274-1717-9). R West.

Braybrooke, Patrick. Some Thoughts on Hilaire Belloc: Ten Studies. LC 68-1140. (Studies in Irish Literature, No. 16). 1969. Repr. lib. bdg. 48.95x (ISBN 0-8383-0649-7). Haskell.

Jebb, Eleanor & Jebb, Reginald. Testimony to Hilaire Belloc. 1956. 25.00 (ISBN 0-8274-3587-8). R West.

Las Vergnas, Raymond. Chesterton, Belloc, Baring. LC 73-4884. 1938. lib. bdg. 27.00 (ISBN 0-8414-2268-0). Folcroft.

McCarthy, John P. Hilaire Belloc: Edwardian Radical. LC 78-5635. (Illus.). 1979. 8.00 (ISBN 0-913966-43-6, Liberty Pr); pap. 3.00 (ISBN 0-913966-44-4). Liberty Fund.

Morton, John B. Hilaire Belloc: A Memoir. LC 74-19265. 1974. Repr. of 1955 ed. lib. bdg. 25.00 (ISBN 0-8414-6149-X). Folcroft.

Speaight, Robert. Life of Hilaire Belloc. facs. ed. LC 78-136655. (Biography Index Reprint Ser.). 1957. 29.00 (ISBN 0-8369-8050-6). Ayer Co Pubs.

--The Life of Hilaire Belloc. 552p. 1981. Repr. of 1957 ed. lib. bdg. 35.00 (ISBN 0-89987-773-7). Darby Bks.

Wilhelmsen, Frederick. Hilaire Belloc: No Alienated Man. 1953. 20.00 (ISBN 0-8274-2495-7). R West.

BELLS

Cockett, M. Bells in Our Lives. 1985. 17.50x (ISBN 0-317-54266-4, Pub. by J Richardson UK). State Mutual Bk.

Eisel, J. The Bells of Hereford Cathedral. 1985. 12.50x (ISBN 0-317-54268-0, Pub. by J Richardson UK). State Mutual Bk.

Goodman, L. Ringing in Hertfordshire. 1985. 15.00x (ISBN 0-317-54314-8, Pub. by J Richardson UK). State Mutual Bk.

Harte, B. Bell Ringer of Angel's. 1985. 10.00x (Pub. by J Richardson UK). State Mutual Bk.

Hilton, J. Bells & Bellringing. 1977. 12.50x (ISBN 0-317-54264-8, Pub. by J Richardson UK). State Mutual Bk.

--Joseph Hatch, the Ulcombe Bellfounder. 1985. 11.25x (ISBN 0-317-54278-8, Pub. by J Richardson UK). State Mutual Bk.

Holmes, D. A. Towers with Three Bells or Less: Basingstoke. 1985. 11.25x (ISBN 0-317-54325-3, Pub. by J Richardson UK). State Mutual Bk.

Jennings, T. The Bells of Haslemere Parish Church, Surrey. 1985. 11.25x (ISBN 0-317-54272-9, Pub. by J Richardson UK). State Mutual Bk.

--A History of Staffordshire Bells. 1985. 22.50x (ISBN 0-317-54277-X, Pub. by J Richardson UK). State Mutual Bk.

Jones, R. H. About Bells & Bell Ringing. 1985. 11.25x (ISBN 0-317-54257-5, Pub. by J Richardson Uk). State Mutual Bk.

Lewis, H. Bell Ringing Minimus Three & Four Bell Methods. 1985. 18.75x (ISBN 0-317-54263-X, Pub. by J Richardson UK). State Mutual Bk.

Morris, E. The Bells of St. Mary's Twickenham. 1985. 11.25x (ISBN 0-317-54270-2, Pub. by J Richardson UK). State Mutual Bk.

Newing, A. A Peal of Puzzles. 1985. 16.25x (ISBN 0-317-54301-6, Pub. by J Richardson UK). State Mutual Bk.

BENEDICTINES

see also Cluniacs

Benedict, Saint Rule of Saint Benedict. Gasquet, Cardinal, tr. LC 66-30730. (Medieval Library). (Illus.). 130p. 1966. Repr. of 1926 ed. 18.50x (ISBN 0-8154-0022-5). Cooper Sq.

Benedictus, Saint Middle High German Translations of the Regula Sancti Benedicti. Selmer, Carl, ed. & intro. by. (Mediaeval Academy of America Publications). 1933. 28.00 (ISBN 0-527-01689-6). Kraus Repr.

Campbell, Stephanie, ed. As We Seek God: International Reflections on Contemporary Benedictine Monasticism. (Cistercian Studies Ser.: No. 70). 1983. pap. 7.95 (ISBN 0-87907-868-5). Cistercian Pubns.

Collett, Barry. Italian Benedictine Scholars & the Reformation: The Congregation of Santa Giustina of Padua. (Historical Monographs). 300p. 1985. 48.00x (ISBN 0-19-822934-8). Oxford U Pr.

English Benedictine Congregation Members & Rees, Daniel. Consider Your Call. (Cistercian Studies Ser.: No. 20). 447p. 1980. 17.95 (ISBN 0-87907-820-0). Cistercian Pubns.

Fry, Timothy, et al, eds. RB Nineteen Eighty. LC 81-1013. 627p. 1981. 24.95 (ISBN 0-8146-1211-3); pap. 17.50 (ISBN 0-8146-1220-2). Liturgical Pr.

--RB Nineteen-Eighty: The Rule of St. Benedict in Latin & English with Notes & Thematic Index. abr. ed. LC 81-12434. xii, 198p. 1981. pap. 8.95 (ISBN 0-8146-1243-1). Liturgical Pr.

Giles, John A., ed. Benedicti Abbatis Petriburgenis De Vita et Miraculis S. Thomae Cantuar. Repr. of 1850 ed. 24.00 (ISBN 0-8337-1341-8). B Franklin.

Heufelder, Emmanuel. The Way to God According to the Rule of Saint Benedict. Eberle, Luke, tr. from Ger. (Cistercian Studies: No. 49). 1983. 25.95 (ISBN 0-87907-849-9); pap. 8.00 (ISBN 0-87907-949-5). Cistercian Pubns.

Kapsner, Oliver L., ed. A Benedictine Bibliography: An Author-Subject Union List. LC 81-20790. 832p. 1982. first suppl. 22.50 (ISBN 0-8146-1258-X). Liturgical Pr.

Lunn, David. The English Benedictines, Fifteen Forty to Sixteen Eighty-Eight: From Reformation to Revolution. (Illus.). 282p. 1980. 28.50x (ISBN 0-06-494411-5). B&N Imports.

McCrank, Lawrence J., compiled by. Mt. Angel Abbey: A Centennial History of the Benedictine Community & Its Library, 1882-1982. LC 83-10536. 176p. 1983. pap. 15.00 (ISBN 0-8420-2212-0). Scholarly Res Inc.

Meisel, Anthony C. & Del Mastro, M. L., trs. The Rule of St. Benedict. LC 74-33611. 120p. 1975. pap. 2.95 (ISBN 0-385-00948-8, Im). Doubleday.

Mork, Wulston. The Benedictine Way. 1987. pap. write for info. (ISBN 0-932506-48-8). St Bedes Pubns.

Oury, Guy-Marie. St. Benedict: Blessed by God. Otto, John A., tr. from Fr. LC 80-13253. Orig. Title: Ce que croyait Benoit. 92p. (Orig.). 1980. pap. text ed. 4.50 (ISBN 0-8146-1181-8). Liturgical Pr.

Parry, David. Households of God. (Cistercian Studies: No. 39). (Orig.). 1980. pap. 7.95 (ISBN 0-87907-939-8). Cistercian Pubns.

Saal-Buch Des Benedictiner-Stiftes Gottweig (Benedictine Abbey) Repr. of 1855 ed. 23.00 (ISBN 0-384-19080-4). Johnson Repr.

Turner & Rogers. The Benedictines in Britain. 1980. 12.95 (ISBN 0-8076-0992-7). Braziller.

Van Speybrouck, Edward. Father Paul of Moll. LC 79-53695. 1979. pap. 6.00 (ISBN 0-89555-122-5). TAN Bks Pubs.

BENEDICTUS, SAINT, ABBOT OF MONTE CASSINO, 480-550

Benedictus: Studies in Honor of St. Benedict. (Cistercian Studies: No. 67). 8.95 (ISBN 0-87907-867-7). Cistercian Pubns.

Chapman, John. Saint Benedict & the Sixth Century. LC 79-109719. 239p. 1972. Repr. of 1929 ed. lib. bdg. 22.50x (ISBN 0-8371-4209-1, CHSB). Greenwood.

De Vogue, Adalbert. The Rule of Saint Benedict: A Doctrinal & Spiritual Commentary. Hasbrouck, John B., tr. from Fr. (Cistercian Studies: No. 54). Tr. of La Regle de saint Benoit, VII, Commentaire doctrinal et spirituel. 1983. pap. 25.95 (ISBN 0-87907-845-6). Cistercian Pubns.

De Waal, Esther. Seeking God: The Way of St. Benedict. 160p. 1984. pap. 4.95 (ISBN 0-8146-1388-8). Liturgical Pr.

Fry, Timothy & Baker, Imogene, eds. The Rule of St. Benedict in English. 96p. (Orig.). 1982. pap. 2.25 (ISBN 0-8146-1272-5). Liturgical Pr.

Goberna, M. Regina. Our Father Saint Benedict. Green, Maurus, tr. from Catalan. Tr. of El Pare Sant Benet. (Illus.). 128p. (Orig.). 1983. pap. 4.95 (ISBN 0-911782-45-1). New City.

Gregory The Great. The Life of Saint Benedict: Book II of the Dialogues of Gregory the Great. Uhlfelder, Myra L., tr. LC 66-30611. (Orig.). 1967. pap. 3.56 scp (ISBN 0-672-60468-X, LLA216). Bobbs.

Kock, Ernst A. Benedictus, Saint: Abbot of Monte Cassino. (EETS, OS Ser.: No. 120). (Three Middle-English Versions of the Rule of St. Benet). Repr. of 1902 ed. 50.00 (ISBN 0-527-00118-X). Kraus Repr.

Logeman, H., ed. Benedictus, Saint, Abbot of Monte Cassino: The Rule of S. Benet. (EETS, OS Ser.: No. 90). Repr. of 1888 ed. 18.00 (ISBN 0-527-00089-2). Kraus Repr.

Mork, Wulston. The Benedictine Way. 1987. pap. write for info. (ISBN 0-932506-48-8). St Bedes Pubns.

Oury, Guy-Marie. St. Benedict: Blessed by God. Otto, John A., tr. from Fr. LC 80-13253. Orig. Title: Ce que croyait Benoit. 92p. (Orig.). 1980. pap. text ed. 4.50 (ISBN 0-8146-1181-8). Liturgical Pr.

Uhlfelder, Myra L. Life of St. Benedict: St. Gregory's Dialogues, Book 2. 1967. pap. text ed. write for info. (ISBN 0-02-422100-7). Macmillan.

Vogue, Adalbert de. Community & Abbot in the Rule of Saint Benedict, Vol. I. Perkins, Ethel R., ed. Philippi, Charles, tr. from Fr. (Cistercian Studies). 1979. 22.95 (ISBN 0-87907-905-3). Cistercian Pubns.

BENEFIT OF CLERGY

see Privilegium Fori

BENEVOLENT INSTITUTIONS

see Charities

BENJAMIN, BIBLICAL CHARACTER

Paamoni, Zev. Benjamin, the Littlest Brother. (Biblical Ser.). (Illus.). 1970. 4.00 (ISBN 0-914080-28-8). Shulsinger Sales.

BENNO 2ND, BP. OF OSNABRUCK, 1020-1088

Norbert. Das Leben des Bischofs Benno der Zweiter von Osnabruck. Bd. with Ausfuehrliches Namenregister und Sachregister Mit Genauem Inhalsverzeichnis der Seither Erschienene Baende 1-90. (Die Geschichtschreiber der Deutschen Vorzeit Ser: Vol. 91). (Ger.). 12.00 (ISBN 0-384-41895-3). Johnson Repr.

BEN-YEHUDA, ELIEZER, 1858-1922

St. John, Robert. Tongue of the Prophets: The Life Story of Eliezer Ben Yehuda. LC 77-97303. 377p. 1972. Repr. of 1952 ed. lib. bdg. 22.50x (ISBN 0-8371-2631-2, STTP). Greenwood.

BERDIAEV, NIKOLAI ALEKSANDROVICH, 1874-1948

Allen, E. L. Freedom in God: A Guide to the Thought of Nicholas Berdyaev. LC 73-5751. lib. bdg. 12.50 (ISBN 0-8414-1740-7). Folcroft.

Attwater, Donald, ed. Modern Christian Revolutionaries. facsimile ed. LC 76-156608. (Essay Index Reprint Ser). Repr. of 1947 ed. 23.00 (ISBN 0-8369-2304-9). Ayer Co Pubs.

Lowrie, Donald A. Rebellious Prophet: A Life of Nicolai Berdgaev. LC 73-11867. (Illus.). 310p. 1974. Repr. of 1960 ed. lib. bdg. 35.00x (ISBN 0-8371-7095-8, LORP). Greenwood.

BEREAVEMENT

see also Consolation; Grief

Carter, James E. Facing the Final Foe. LC 85-19517. 1986. pap. 2.25 (ISBN 0-8054-5433-0). Broadman.

Griffin, Graeme M., ed. Bereavement. (Illus.). 59p. (Orig.). 1977. pap. 5.95 (ISBN 0-85819-314-0, Pub. by JBCE). ANZ Religious Pubns.

Holmes, Marjorie. To Help You Through the Hurting. 176p. 1985. pap. 8.95 (ISBN 0-8027-2508-2). Walker & Co.

Silverman, Phyllis R. Widow-to-Widow. 240p. 1986. text ed. 19.95 (ISBN 0-8261-5030-6). Springer Pub.

Spiro, Jack. A Time to Mourn. LC 67-30744. 160p. 1985. pap. text ed. 8.95 (ISBN 0-8197-0497-0). Bloch.

Wiersbe, Warren W. & Wiersbe, David W. Comforting the Bereaved. (Orig.). 1985. pap. 5.95 (ISBN 0-8024-5293-0). Moody.

Winter, David. Living Through Loss: God's Help in Bereavement. 96p. (Orig.). 1986. pap. 3.50 (ISBN 0-87788-507-9). Shaw Pubs.

BERKELEY, GEORGE, BP. OF CLOYNE, 1685-1753

Bracken, Harry M. Berkeley. LC 74-15569. 176p. 1975. 19.95 (ISBN 0-312-07595-2). St Martin.

Broad, C. D. Berkeley's Argument. LC 75-1069. (Studies in Philosophy: No. 40). 1975. lib. bdg. 22.95x (ISBN 0-8383-0113-4). Haskell.

Foster, J. & Robinson, H., eds. Essays on Berkeley: A Tercentennial Celebration. 1985. 38.00x (ISBN 0-19-824734-6). Oxford U Pr.

Fraser, Alexander C. Berkeley. 1899. 12.50 (ISBN 0-8274-1926-0). R West.

Hicks, George D. Berkeley. LC 68-15129. 1968. Repr. of 1932 ed. 9.00x (ISBN 0-8462-1235-8). Russell.

Jessop, Thomas E. Bibliography of George Berkeley. LC 68-56592. (Bibliography & Reference Ser: No. 234). 1968. Repr. of 1934 ed. 14.50 (ISBN 0-8337-1840-1). B Franklin.

Johnston, George A. Development of Berkeley's Philosophy. LC 65-17903. 1965. Repr. of 1923 ed. 10.00x (ISBN 0-8462-0686-2). Russell.

Mill, John S. Three Essays on Religion. LC 76-130995. Repr. of 1874 ed. 23.45 (ISBN 0-404-04325-9). AMS Pr.

--Three Essays on Religion. Repr. of 1874 ed. lib. bdg. 37.50x (ISBN 0-8371-1986-3, MIER). Greenwood.

Pitcher, George. Berkeley. (The Arguments of the Philosophers Ser.). 300p. 1977. 24.95x (ISBN 0-7100-8685-7); pap. 14.95 (ISBN 0-7102-0391-8). Methuen Inc.

Steinkraus, Warren E., ed. New Studies in Berkeley's Philosophy. LC 81-40866. 218p. 1982. lib. bdg. 27.75 (ISBN 0-8191-2006-5); pap. text ed. 12.75 (ISBN 0-8191-2007-3). U Pr of Amer.

Warnock, G. J. Berkeley. 240p. 1983. 14.95 (ISBN 0-268-00670-9); pap. 7.95 (ISBN 0-268-00671-7). U of Notre Dame Pr.

BERNADETTE, SAINT (BERNADETTE SOUBIROUS), 1844-1879

Cristiani, Leon. Saint Bernadette. LC 65-15727. (Illus.). 181p. 1981. pap. 3.95 (ISBN 0-8189-0421-6). Alba.

Daughters of St. Paul. Light in the Grotto. 1972. 3.00 (ISBN 0-8198-4409-8); pap. 2.00 (ISBN 0-8198-4410-1). Dghtrs St Paul.

Lynch, John W. Bernadette: The Only Witness. 5.00 (ISBN 0-8198-1104-1); pap. 4.00 (ISBN 0-8198-1105-X). Dghtrs St Paul.

Trochu, Francois. Saint Bernadette Soubirous. LC 84-51819. 432p. 1985. pap. 12.00 (ISBN 0-89555-253-1). Tan Bks Pubs.

BERNANOS, GEORGE, 1888-1948

Balthasar. Le Chretien Bernanos. 27.90 (ISBN 0-685-37226-X). French & Eur.

Heppenstall, Rayner. Double Image: Mutations of Christian Mythology in the Works of Four French Catholic Writers of Today & Yesterday. LC 72-93063. 1969. Repr. of 1947 ed. 23.00 (ISBN 0-8046-0676-5, Pub. by Kennikat). Assoc Faculty Pr.

Maubrey, Pierre. L' Expression de la Passion Interieure dans le Style de Bernanos Romancier. LC 70-94195. (Catholic University of America Studies in Romance Languages & Literatures Ser: No. 59). (Fr). Repr. of 1959 ed. 25.00 (ISBN 0-404-50359-4). AMS Pr.

BERNARD DE CLARIVAUX, SAINT, 1091?-1153

Bernard of Clairvaux & the Cistercian Spirit. LC 76-15487. (Cistercian Studies Ser.: No. 16). (Illus.). 1976. 10.95 (ISBN 0-87907-816-2). Cistercian Pubns.

Bernard of Clairvaux: Studies Presented to Dom Jean Leclercq. LC 73-8099. (Cistercian Studies: No. 23). 1973. 5.50 (ISBN 0-87907-823-5). Cistercian Pubns.

Bernard of Clairvaux, Treatises II: The Steps of Humility & Pride, on Loving God. LC 74-7147. (Cistercian Fathers Ser.: No. 13). 1974. pap. 5.00 (ISBN 0-87907-713-1). Cistercian Pubns.

Bernard de Clairvaux, Saint Letters. James, Bruno S., tr. LC 78-63344. (The Crusades & Military Orders: Second Ser.). Repr. of 1953 ed. 47.50 (ISBN 0-404-17004-8). AMS Pr.

Coulton, G. G. Two Saints: St. Bernard & St. Francis. 1923. lib. bdg. 15.00 (ISBN 0-8414-3513-8). Folcroft.

Cristiani, Leon. St. Bernard of Clairvaux. 1977. 3.95 (ISBN 0-8198-0463-0); pap. 2.95 (ISBN 0-8198-0464-9). Dghtrs St Paul.

Evans, G. Rosemary. The Mind of St. Bernard of Clairvaux. 1983. text ed. 37.00x (ISBN 0-19-826667-7). Oxford U Pr.

Mayer, Robert T., tr. Bernard of Clairvaux: The Irishman. LC 78-768. (Cistercian Fathers Ser.). 1978. 7.95 (ISBN 0-685-87078-2); pap. 4.00 (ISBN 0-87907-910-X). Cistercian Pubns.

Meadows, Denis. A Saint & a Half. 1963. 5.00 (ISBN 0-8159-6803-5). Devin.

Merton, Thomas. Last of the Fathers: Saint Bernard of Clairvaux & the Encyclical Letter, Doctor Mellifluus. Repr. of 1954 ed. lib. bdg. 22.50x (ISBN 0-8371-4434-5, MELF). Greenwood.

Morison, James C. The Life & Times of St. Bernard of Clairvaux. 1977. lib. bdg. 59.95 (ISBN 0-8490-2162-6). Gordon Pr.
Pennington, M. Basil, ed. Saint Bernard of Clairvaux: Essays Commemorating the Eighth Centenary of His Canonization. LC 77-4487. (Cistercian Studies: No. 28). 1977. 14.95 (ISBN 0-87907-828-6). Cistercian Pubns.
Storrs, Richard S. Bernard of Clairvaux: The Times, the Man & His Work. 598p. 1981. Repr. of 1893 ed. lib. bdg. 65.00 (ISBN 0-8495-4974-4). Arden Lib.

BERNARDINO DA SIENA, SAINT, 1380-1444

Allies, Mary H. Three Catholic Reformers of the Fifteenth Century. facsimile ed. LC 73-38755. (Essay Index Reprint Ser). Repr. of 1878 ed. 13.00 (ISBN 0-8369-2633-1). Ayer Co Pubs.

BERNINI, GIOVANNI LORENZO, 1598-1680

Mezzatesta, Michael. The Art of Gianlorenzo Bernini: Selected Sculpture. LC 82-81080. (Illus.). 63p. (Orig.). 1982. pap. 8.50 (ISBN 0-912804-05-X). Kimbell Art.

BERNWARD, SAINT, BP. OF HILDESHEIM, 993-1022

Tschan, Francis J. Saint Bernward of Hildesheim, 3 vols. Incl. His Life & Times. 242p. 1942; His Works of Art. 503p. 1951. 30.00 (ISBN 0-268-00242-8); Album of All Extant Works. 1952. 30.00 (ISBN 0-268-00240-1). (Mediaeval Studies Ser.: Vols. 6, 12, 13). U of Notre Dame Pr.

BERRIGAN, DANIEL, 1921-

Klejment, Anne. The Berrigans: A Bibliography of Published Works by Daniel, Philip, & Elizabeth Berrigan. LC 78-68214. (Garland Reference Library of Humanities: No. 154). 1979. lib. bdg. 36.00 (ISBN 0-8240-9788-2). Garland Pub.

BERRIGAN, PHILIP, 1923-

Klejment, Anne. The Berrigans: A Bibliography of Published Works by Daniel, Philip, & Elizabeth Berrigan. LC 78-68214. (Garland Reference Library of Humanities: No. 154). 1979. lib. bdg. 36.00 (ISBN 0-8240-9788-2). Garland Pub.

BERRY, MARTHA

Byers, Tracy. Martha Berry, the Sunday Lady of Possum Trot. LC 72-159905. 1971. Repr. of 1932 ed. 40.00x (ISBN 0-8103-3783-5). Gale.

BERTHOLD VON REGENSBURG, d. 1272

Ianucci, R. J. Treatment of the Capital Sins. LC 70-140024. (Catholic University Studies in German: No. 17). Repr. of 1942 ed. 21.00 (ISBN 0-404-50237-7). AMS Pr.

BET EL-WALI (TEMPLE)

Ricke, Herbert, et al. Beit El-Wali Temple of Ramesses Second. portfolio ed. LC 67-18437. (Oriental Institute Nubian Expedition Pubns. Ser.: Vol. 1). (Illus.). 1967. 30.00x (ISBN 0-226-62365-3, OINE1). U of Chicago Pr.

BETHENCOURT, JEAN DE, BARON DE SAINT-MARTIN-LE-GAILLARD, 1360-1425

Bontier, Pierre & Le Verrier, Jean. The Canarian; or Book of the Conquest & Conversion of the Canarians, in the Year 1402, by Messire Jean de Bethencourt. Major, Richard H., ed. LC 70-286234. (Hakluyt Society Ser.: No. 46). 300p. 1972. lib. bdg. 32.00 (ISBN 0-8337-2188-7). B Franklin.

BETHLEHEM, STAR OF

see Star of Bethlehem

BETHUNE, MARY JANE (MCCLEOD), 1875-1955

Carruth, Ella K. She Wanted to Read: The Story of Mary Macleod Bethune. (Illus.). 1966. 6.75 (ISBN 0-687-38353-6). Abingdon.
Greenfield, Eloise. Mary McLeod Bethune. LC 76-11522. (Biography Ser.). (Illus.). 1977. PLB 12.89 (ISBN 0-690-01129-6, Crowell Jr Bks). HarpJ.
Hicks, Florence J. Mary McLeod Bethune: Her Own Words of Inspiration. LC 75-18004. 96p. 1975. 4.95 (ISBN 0-912444-00-2). Gaus.
Johnson, Jan. Mary Bethune & Her Somedays. (Stories About Christian Heroes Ser.). (Illus.). 1979. pap. 1.95 (ISBN 0-03-049421-4, HarpR). Har-Row.

BETRONE, CONSOLATA, SISTER, 1903-1946

Sales, Lorenzo. Jesus Appeals to the World. 1955. 5.95 (ISBN 0-8189-0069-5). Alba.

BEZE, THEODORE DE, 1519-1605

Backus, Irena. The Reformed Roots of the English New Testament: The Influence of Theodore Beza on the English New Testament. (Pittsburgh Theological Monographs: No. 28). 1980. pap. 10.00 (ISBN 0-915138-36-0). Pickwick.
Baird, Henry M. Theodore Beza, The Counsellor of the French Reformation, 1519-1605. LC 76-121596. 1970. Repr. of 1899 ed. 25.50 (ISBN 0-8337-0151-7). B Franklin.
Raitt, Jill. The Eucharistic Theology of Theodore Beza: Development of the Reformed Doctrine. LC 74-188907. (American Academy of Religion. Studies in Religion). 1972. pap. 9.95 (ISBN 0-89130-156-9, 010004). Scholars Pr GA.

BHAGAVADGITA

see also Mahabharata, Bhagavadgita

Abhedananda, Swami. Bhagavad Gita: The Divine Message, 2 vols. 25.00 set (ISBN 0-87481-625-4). Vedanta Pr.
Aurobindo, Sri. Bhagavad Gita in Light of Sri Aurobindo. Maheshwar, ed. 1979. 20.00 (ISBN 0-89744-902-9); pap. 15.00 (ISBN 0-89744-903-7). Auromere.
--Essays on the Gita. 1979. 20.00 (ISBN 0-89744-907-X); lib. bdg. 30.00 (ISBN 0-89744-906-1); pap. 16.00 (ISBN 0-89744-908-8). Auromere.
--Essays on the Gita. 588p. 1983. 12.50 (ISBN 0-89071-297-2, Pub. by Sri Aurobindo Ashram India); pap. 8.75 (ISBN 0-89071-296-4, Pub. by Sri Aurobindo Ashram India). Matagiri.
--The Gita with Text, Translation & Sri Aurobindo's Comments. rev. ed. Jhunjhunwala, Shyam S., ed. 270p. 1974. 9.45 (ISBN 0-89071-207-7); pap. 4.50 (ISBN 0-89071-200-X). Matagiri.
--The Message of the Gita: With Text, Translation & Notes. Roy, Anilbaran, ed. (Sanskrit & Eng.). 1979. (Pub. by Sri Aurobindo Ashram Trust India); pap. 9.00 (ISBN 0-89744-977-0, Pub. by Sri Aurobindo Ashramtrust India). Auromere.
Besant. Hints on the Study of the Bhagavad Gita. 4.50 (ISBN 0-8356-7079-1). Theos Pub Hse.
Bhave, Vinoba. Talks on the Gita. 241p. 1983. 10.00 (ISBN 0-934676-37-2). Greenlf Bks.
Call of the Gita. 192p. 1987. pap. 2.95 (ISBN 0-87481-537-1, Pub. by Ramakrishna Math Madras India). Vedanta Pr.
Callewaert, Winand M. Bhagavadgitanuvada: A Study in Transcultural Translation. 1984. 26.00x (ISBN 0-8364-1148-X, Pub. by Satya Bharati Pub). South Asia Bks.
Chaitanya Yati, Guru N. Bhagavad Gita: A Sublime Hymn of Yoga. Nataraja Guru, tr. 550p. 1980. text ed. 50.00x (ISBN 0-7069-1129-6, Pub. by Vikas India). Advent NY.
Desai, Moraji. A View of the Gita. 1974. text ed. 10.00x. Coronet Bks.
Feuerstein, Georg. Bhagavad Gita: An Introduction. LC 82-42702. 191p. 1983. pap. 6.75 (ISBN 0-8356-0575-2, Quest). Theos Pub Hse.
Gandhi, M. K. Discourses on the Gita. 73p. (Orig.). 1983. pap. 1.50 (ISBN 0-934676-55-0). Greenlf Bks.
--The Gospel of Selfless Action or the Gita According to Gandhi. Desai, Mahadev, ed. 1985. pap. 11.00x (ISBN 0-8364-1397-0, Pub. by Navajivan). South Asia Bks.
Gandhi, M. K., pref. by. The Bhagavadgita. 14.50 (ISBN 0-86516-179-8). Bolchazy-Carducci.
Gandhi, Mohandas K. The Bhagavad Gita: An Interpretation. Parikh, Narahari D., ed. 309p. (Orig.). 1984. pap. 8.00 (ISBN 0-934676-65-8). Greenlf Bks.
Gauchhwal, B. S. Concept of Perfection in the Teachings of Kant & the Gita. 1967. 4.95 (ISBN 0-89684-186-3). Orient Bk Dist.
Gupta, S. K. Madhusudan Saraswati on the Bhagavaddita. 1977. 28.00 (ISBN 0-89684-246-0, Pub. by Motilal Banarsidass India). Orient Bk Dist.
Jnanadev. Jnaneshwari. Bhagwat, Ramachandra K., tr. (Illus.). 1979. 36.00 (ISBN 0-89744-188-5). Auromere.
Judge, W. Q. Notes on the Bhagavad-Gita. 69.95 (ISBN 0-8490-0739-9). Gordon Pr.
Judge, William Q. & Crosbie, Robert. Notes on the Bhagavad-Gita. 237p. 1918. Repr. 4.00 (ISBN 0-938998-10-2). Theosophy.
Judge, William Q., tr. from Sanskrit. & intro. by. The Bhagavad-Gita: The Book of Devotion Dialogue Between Krishna, Lord of Devotion, & Arjuna, Prince of India. xviii, 133p. 1930. Repr. of 1891 ed. 3.50 (ISBN 0-938998-09-9). Theosophy.
Kapoor, Jagdish C. Bhagavad-Gita: An International Bibliography of Imprints, 1785-1979. LC 82-24253. 425p. 1983. lib. bdg. 66.00 (ISBN 0-8240-9266-X). Garland Pub.
Kaveeshwar, G. W. The Ethics of Gita. 1971. 8.50 (ISBN 0-89684-203-7). Orient Bk Dist.
Kriyananda, Goswami. The Bhagavad Gita: The Song of God. 2nd ed. (Illus.). 137p. pap. text ed. 5.95 (ISBN 0-9613099-3-8). Temple Kriya Yoga.
LaViolette, Wesley. The New Gita. (Illus.). 1973. pap. 4.95 (ISBN 0-87516-172-3). De Vorss.
McArthur, Tom. Yoga & the Bhagavad-Gita. 128p. 1986. pap. 11.95 (ISBN 0-85030-479-2). Newcastle Pub.
--Yoga & the Bhagavad-Gita. 1986. Repr. lib. bdg. 19.95x (ISBN 0-8095-7037-8). Borgo Pr.
Mahabharata: Bhagvat-Geeta. LC 59-6527. (Eng.). 174p. 1972. Repr. of 1785 ed. 25.00x (ISBN 0-8201-1109-0). Schol Facsimiles.
Miller, Barbara S., tr. The Bhagavad-Gita: Krishna's Counsel in Time of War. LC 86-13725. (Illus.). 176p. 1986. 20.00x (ISBN 0-231-06468-3). Columbia U Pr.
Minor, Robert. Bhagavad Gita: An Exegetical Commentary. 1982. 38.00x (ISBN 0-8364-0817-9); text ed. 18.50x (ISBN 0-8364-0862-4). South Asia Bks.
Minor, Robert N., ed. Modern Indian Interpreters of the Bhagavadgita. (Religious Studies Ser.). 288p. (Orig.). 1986. 44.50x (ISBN 0-88706-297-0); pap. 14.95x (ISBN 0-88706-298-9). State U NY Pr.
Murray, Kim & Murray, Christopher. Illuminations from the Bhagavad-Gita. LC 79-3834. (Illus.). 64p. (Orig.). pap. 8.95 (ISBN 0-06-090763-0, CN 763, PL). Har-Row.
Row, T. Subba. Notes on the Bhagavad-Gita. LC 77-88628. 1978. 6.00 (ISBN 0-911500-81-2); pap. 3.50 (ISBN 0-911500-82-0). Theos U Pr.
Roy, Dilipkumar. Bhagavad Gita, a Revelation. 190p. 1975. 9.95 (ISBN 0-88253-698-2). Ind-US Inc.
Sankaracharya. Bhagavad Gita with Commentary of Sri Sankaracharya. Sastry, Alladi M., tr. 1979. 16.00 (ISBN 0-89744-188-5). Auromere.
Saraydarian, Haroutiun, tr. Bhagavad Gita. LC 74-11759. 1974. 9.00 (ISBN 0-911794-36-0); pap. 7.00 (ISBN 0-911794-37-9). Aqua Educ.
Sargeant, Winthrop. The Bhagavad Gita. Chapple, Christopher, ed. (SUNY Ser. in Cultural Perspectives). 777p. 1984. 44.50x (ISBN 0-87395-831-4); pap. 14.95x (ISBN 0-87395-830-6). State U NY Pr.
Saroja, G. V. Tilak & Sankara on Bhagvad Gita. 200p. 1985. text ed. 20.00x (ISBN 0-86590-571-1, Pub. by Sterling Pubs India). Apt Bks.
Shankar, Bhavani. The Doctrine of the Bhagavad Gita: Sangam Texts Ser. Iyer, Raghavan, ed. 131p. (Orig.). 1984. pap. 8.75 (ISBN 0-88695-031-7). Concord Grove.
Shankara. Bhagavad Gita, Srimad Bhasya of Sri Sankaracarya. Warrier, A. G., tr. from Sanskrit. 652p. (Orig.). 1984. pap. 16.00x (ISBN 0-87481-526-6, Pub. by Ramakrishna Math Madras India). Vedanta Pr.
Sharma, Arvind. The Hindu Gita: Ancient & Classical Interpretations of the Bhagavadgita. LC 85-21520. 250p. 1986. 28.95 (ISBN 0-8126-9013-3). Open Court.
Sircar, M. N. Mysticism in the Bhagavad-Gita. 1977. 12.00x (ISBN 0-686-22667-4). Intl Bk Dist.
Sri Aurobindo. The Message of the Gita: With Text, Translation & Notes As Interpreted by Sri Aurobindo. Roy, Anilbaran, ed. 1984. pap. 7.95 (ISBN 0-89071-225-5). Matagiri.
Sri Swami Satchidananda. The Living Gita. LC 84-27861. (Orig.). Date not set. pap. price not set (ISBN 0-932040-27-6). Integral Yoga Pubns.
Swami, Bhaktivedanta. Bhagavat Gita As It Is. 6.95 (ISBN 0-89213-134-9). Bhaktivedanta.
Swami Jyotir Maya Nanda. Srimad Bhagavad Gita: Pocket Book Edition. (Illus.). 384p. 1986. pap. 3.00 (ISBN 0-934664-44-7). Yoga Res Foun.
Swami Kriyananda. Keys to the Bhagavad Gita. 48p. 1979. pap. 3.00 (ISBN 0-916124-15-0). Dawn Pubns CA.
Van Buitenen, J. A., ed. The Bhagavadgita in the Mahabharata: A Bilingual Edition. LC 79-13021. 184p. 1981. lib. bdg. 19.00x (ISBN 0-226-84660-1); pap. 8.95 (ISBN 0-226-84662-8, Phoen). U of Chicago Pr.
Vyas, R. N. The Bhagavadgita & Jivana Yoga. 1986. 14.00x (ISBN 81-7017-203-9, Pub. by Abhinav India). South Asia Bks.
Zaehner, Robert C., ed. The Bhagavad-Gita. 492p. 1969. 45.00x (ISBN 0-19-826522-0); pap. 12.95 (ISBN 0-19-501666-1). Oxford U Pr.

BHAGAVATAS

Bhaktivedanta Swami. Light of the Bhagavat. 1985. 12.95 (ISBN 0-89213-135-7). Bhaktivedanta.
--Srimad Bhagavatam: 12th Canto, Vol. 1. 1985. 12.95 (ISBN 0-89213-129-2). Bhaktivedanta.
--Srimad Bhagavatam: 12th Canto, Vol. 2. 1985. 12.95 (ISBN 0-89213-130-6). Bhaktivedanta.
Krishna Sri, Prem. The Yoga of the Bhagavat Gita. 1982. Repr. 15.00x (ISBN 0-318-20320-0, Pub. by New Order Bk Co India). Humanities.
Puri, Vishnu. Bhakti Ratnavali: An Anthology from the Bhagavata. Tapasyananda, Swami, tr. from Sanskrit. 256p. 1980. pap. 5.95 (ISBN 0-87481-499-5). Vedanta Pr.

BHAKTI

see also God–Worship and Love; Hinduism

Bhakti in Religions of the World: With Special Reference to Dr. Sri Bankey Behariji. 268p. 1987. text ed. 32.50x (ISBN 81-7018-371-5, Pub. by B R Pub Corp Delhi). Apt Bks.
Bhaktivedanta, Swami A. C. Srimad Bhagavatam: First Canto, 3 vols. LC 73-169353. (Illus.). 1972. 12.95 ea. Vol. 1 (ISBN 0-912776-27-7). Vol. 2 (ISBN 0-912776-29-3). Vol. 3 (ISBN 0-912776-34-X). Bhaktivedanta.
--Srimad Bhagavatam: Fourth Canto, 4 vols. LC 73-169353. (Illus.). 1974. 12.95 ea. Vol. 1 (ISBN 0-912776-38-2). Vol. 2 (ISBN 0-912776-47-1). Vol. 3 (ISBN 0-912776-48-X). Vol. 4 (ISBN 0-912776-49-8). Bhaktivedanta.
--Srimad Bhagavatam: Second Canto, 2 vols. LC 73-169353. (Illus.). 1972. 12.95 ea. Vol. 1 (ISBN 0-912776-28-5). Vol. 2 (ISBN 0-912776-35-8). Bhaktivedanta.
--Srimad Bhagavatam: Third Canto, 4 vols. LC 73-169353. (Illus.). 1974. 12.95 ea. Vol. 1 (ISBN 0-912776-37-4). Vol. 2 (ISBN 0-912776-44-7). Vol. 3 (ISBN 0-912776-46-3). Vol. 4 (ISBN 0-912776-75-7). Bhaktivedanta.
Kinsley, David R. The Divine Player: A Study of Krishna Lila. 1978. 17.95 (ISBN 0-89684-019-0, Pub. by Motilal Barnarsidass India). Orient Bk Dist.
Narada. The Bhakti Sutras of Narada. Sinha, Nandalal, tr. & intro. by. LC 73-3792. (Sacred Books of the Hindus: No. 7, Pt. 1). Repr. of 1911 ed. 17.00 (ISBN 0-404-57807-1). AMS Pr.
Seth, S. J. The Divinity of Krishna. 1984. text ed. 14.00x. Coronet Bks.

BIBLE–ADDRESSES, ESSAYS, LECTURES

Ben-Gurion, David. Ben-Gurion Looks at the Bible. Kolatch, Jonathan, tr. LC 70-167600. 320p. 1972. 12.50 (ISBN 0-8246-0127-0). Jonathan David.
Benoit, Pierre, et al, eds. Dynamism of Biblical Tradition. LC 67-15983. (Concilium Ser.: Vol. 20). 226p. 1967. 7.95 (ISBN 0-8091-0035-5). Paulist Pr.
--Human Reality of Sacred Scripture. LC 65-28869. (Concilium Ser.: Vol. 10). 220p. 7.95 (ISBN 0-8091-0075-4). Paulist Pr.
Bruce, F. F. The Time Is Fulfilled. LC 78-7373. 1978. pap. text ed. 3.95 (ISBN 0-8028-1756-4). Eerdmans.
Ehrhardt, Arnold A. Framework of the New Testament Stories. LC 65-79. 1964. 22.50t (ISBN 0-674-31700-9). Harvard U Pr.
Evans, Carl D., et al, eds. Scripture in Context: Essays on the Comparative Method. LC 80-10211. (Pittsburgh Theological Monograph Ser.: No. 34). 1980. pap. 15.00 (ISBN 0-915138-43-3). Pickwick.
Goedicke, Hans. Near Eastern Studies: In Honor of William Foxwell Albright. LC 70-142817. 504p. 1971. 42.50x (ISBN 0-8018-1235-6). Johns Hopkins.
Gunn, Giles. The Bible & American Arts & Letters. LC 83-5634. (SBL Bible in American Culture Ser.). 256p. 1983. 15.95 (ISBN 0-89130-625-0, 06 12 03). Scholars Pr GA.
Hadidian, Dikran Y., ed. From Faith to Faith, Essays in Honor of Donald G. Miller, on His Seventieth Birthday. LC 79-23408. (Pittsburgh Theological Monographs: No. 31). 1979. 18.00 (ISBN 0-915138-38-7). Pickwick.
Hobbs, Edward C., ed. Stubborn Faith: Papers on Old Testament & Related Subjects Presented to Honor William Andrew Irwin. LC 56-12567. 1956. 13.95x (ISBN 0-87074-079-2). SMU Press.
McConnell, Frank, ed. The Bible & Narrative Tradition. 168p. 1986. 16.95x (ISBN 0-19-503698-0). Oxford U Pr.
Orlinsky, Harry M. Essays in Biblical & Jewish Culture & Bible Translation. 1973. 25.00x (ISBN 0-87068-218-0). Ktav.
--International Organization for Masoretic Studies, 1972 & 1973 Proceedings & Papers. LC 74-16568. (Society of Biblical Literature, Masoretic Studies). Repr. of 1974 ed. 33.30 (ISBN 0-8357-9573-X, 2017535). Bks Demand UMI.
Preiss, Theo. Life in Christ. LC 55-1608. (Studies in Biblical Theology: No. 13). 1954. pap. 10.00x (ISBN 0-8401-3013-9). A R Allenson.
Rendsburg, Gary, et al. The Bible World: Essays in Honor of Cyrus H. Gordon. 1981. 45.00x (ISBN 0-87068-758-1). Ktav.
Rylaarsdam, J. Coert, ed. Transitions in Biblical Scholarship. LC 68-9135. (Essays in Divinity Ser: Vol. 6). 1968. 25.00x (ISBN 0-226-73287-8). U of Chicago Pr.
Wenger, John C. God's Word Written. LC 66-24292. (Conrad Grebel Lecture Ser.). (Illus., Essays on the nature of biblical revelation, inspiration, & authority). 1966. pap. 6.95 (ISBN 0-8361-1900-2). Herald Pr.
Wingard, Ruth. The Spoken Words of Love. 1986. 6.95 (ISBN 0-533-06768-5). Vantage.

BIBLE–ANIMALS

see Bible–Natural History

BIBLE–ANTHROPOLOGY

see Man (Theology)

BIBLE–ANTIQUITIES

see also Christian Antiquities; Jews–Antiquities; Palestine–Antiquities;
also subdivision Antiquities under names of Biblical countries and cities

Adler, Rudolph J. Biblical Beginnings: Archaeology & the Roots of Scripture. LC 85-16970. (Illus.). 320p. 1985. 17.95 (ISBN 0-13-076233-4). P-H.
Baez-Camargo, Gonzalo. Archaeological Commentary on the Bible. LC 82-45473. (Illus.). 336p. 1986. pap. 9.95 (ISBN 0-385-17969-3, Galilee). Doubleday.
--Comentario Arqueologico de la Biblia. (Span.). 339p. (Orig.). 1979. pap. 7.95 (ISBN 0-89922-148-3). Edit Caribe.
Bartlett, John A. Jericho. Davies, Graham I., ed. (Cities of the Biblical World Ser.). 128p. (Orig.). 1983. pap. 6.95 (ISBN 0-8028-1033-0). Eerdmans.

Bimson, John J. Redating the Exodus & Conquest. 2nd ed. 288p. 1981. pap. text ed. 14.95x (ISBN 0-907459-04-8, Pub. by Almond Pr England). Eisenbrauns.

Blaiklock, E. M. The Bible & I. 128p. (Orig.). 1983. pap. 3.95 (ISBN 0-87123-298-7). Bethany Hse.

Blaiklock, E. M. & Harrison, R. K., eds. The New International Dictionary of Biblical Archaeology. 1986. 24.95 (ISBN 0-310-21250-2, 9277). Zondervan.

Bowden, John. Archeology & the Bible. 24p. 1982. pap. 3.00 (ISBN 0-910309-00-0). Am Atheist.

Bronner, Leah. Biblical Personalities & Archaeology. (Illus.). 216p. 1975. 7.95x (ISBN 0-685-58308-2). Bloch.

Capt, E. Raymond. King Solomon's Temple. LC 79-54774. (Illus.). 96p. 1979. pap. 3.00 (ISBN 0-934666-05-9). Artisan Sales.

Cole, Dan P. Shechem I: Middle Bronze IIB Pottery. (Excavation Reports of the American Schools of Oriental Research). xiv, 203p. 1984. text ed. 30.00 (ISBN 0-89757-047-2, Dist.by Eisenbrauns). Am Sch Orient Res.

Driver, S. R. Modern Research As Illustrating the Bible. (British Academy, London, Schweich Lectures on Biblical Archaeology, 1908). pap. 19.00 (ISBN 0-8115-1250-9). Kraus Repr.

Finegan, Jack. The Archaeology of the New Testament: The Mediterranean World of the Early Christian Apostles. (Illus.). 400p. 1981. 40.00x (ISBN 0-86531-064-5). Westview.

--Archeology of the New Testament: The Life of Jesus & the Beginning of the Early Church. LC 69-18059. (Illus.). 1970. 60.00x (ISBN 0-691-03534-2); pap. 10.50x (ISBN 0-691-02000-0). Princeton U Pr.

--Light from the Ancient Past, 2 vols. 2nd ed. (Illus.). 1959. Vol. 1 2nd Ed. 52.50 (ISBN 0-691-03550-4); Vol. 1 2nd Edition. pap. 16.50 (ISBN 0-691-00207-X); Vol. 2. 50.00 (ISBN 0-691-03551-2); Vol. 2. pap. 15.50x (ISBN 0-691-00208-8); Set. 90.00 (ISBN 0-686-76901-5). Princeton U Pr.

Freedman, D. N. & Campbell, E. F., Jr., eds. The Biblical Archaeologist Reader, No. 4. (Illus.). xiii, 390p. 1983. text ed. 24.95x (ISBN 0-907459-34-X, Pub. by Almond Pr England); pap. text ed. 9.95x (ISBN 0-907459-35-8). Eisenbrauns.

Gilbertson, Merrill T. Way It Was in Bible Times. LC 59-10759. (Illus.). 1959. pap. 6.95 (ISBN 0-8066-1442-0, 10-7000). Augsburg.

Hopkins, David C. The Highlands of Canaan: Agricultural Life in the Early Iron Age. (The Social World of Biblical Antiquity Ser.). 315p. 1985. text ed. 29.95x (ISBN 0-907459-38-2, Pub. by Almond Pr England); pap. text ed. 15.95 (ISBN 0-907459-39-0). Eisenbrauns.

Hoppe, Leslie J. What Are They Saying about Biblical Archaeology? LC 83-63110. (WATSA Ser.). 1984. pap. 4.95 (ISBN 0-8091-2613-3). Paulist Pr.

Howard, Dale A. Scroll of Remembrance. (Illus.). 48p. 1987. pap. 5.00 (ISBN 0-940517-02-7). JCMC Louisiana.

--Tribulation Temple. (Illus.). 80p. 1987. pap. 5.00 (ISBN 0-940517-03-5). JCMC Louisiana.

Kelso, James L. & Baramki, Dimitri. Excavations at New Testament Jericho & Khirbet en-Nitla. (Annual of the American Schools of Oriental Research: Vols. 29 & 30). 60p. 1955. text ed. 10.00x (ISBN 0-89757-030-8, Am Sch Orient Res). Eisenbrauns.

Kenyon, Dame Kathleen. The Bible & Recent Archaeology. LC 78-4089. (Illus.). 1979. pap. 8.95 (ISBN 0-8042-0010-6). John Knox.

Kyle, Melvin G. Excavating Kirjath-Sepher's Ten Cities. 19.00 (ISBN 0-405-10262-3, 14452). Ayer Co Pubs.

Lance, H. Darrell. The Old Testament & the Archaeologist. Tucker, Gene M., ed. LC 80-2387. (Guides to Biblical Scholarship: Old Testament Ser.). 112p. (Orig.). 1981. pap. 4.50 (ISBN 0-8006-0467-9, 1-467). Fortress.

Lewis, Jack. The Archaeology & Bible. LC 75-20804. (Way of Life Ser: No. 113). 112p. 1975. pap. 3.95 (ISBN 0-89112-113-7, Bibl Res Pr). Abilene Christ U.

McGovern, Patrick E. Late Bronze Palestinian Pendants: Innovation in a Cosmopolitian Age. (JSOT-ASOR Monographs: No. 1). (Illus.). xx, 184p. 1985. text ed. 35.00x (ISBN 0-905774-90-6, Pub. by JSOT Pr England). Eisenbrauns.

Makay, D. Bruce, compiled by. A Comprehensive Index to Biblical Archaeologist, Vol. 36-45. 225p. 1986. pap. 11.95 (ISBN 0-89757-008-1, Dist. by Eisenbrauns). Am Sch Orient Res.

Meyers, Carol L. The Tabernacle Menorah: A Synthetic Study of a Symbol from the Biblical Cult. LC 76-17105. (Amerian Schools of Oriental Research, Dissertation Ser.: Vol. 2). 243p. 1976. (Am Sch Orient Res); pap. text ed. 6.00x (ISBN 0-89757-101-0). Eisenbrauns.

Millard, A. R. The Bible B. C. What Can Archaeology Prove? 1982. pap. 1.75 (ISBN 0-87552-291-2). Presby & Reformed.

Moorey, P. R. Archaeology, Artefacts & the Bible: The Bible Lands in Ancient Times. (Ancient Ser.). (Illus.). 71p. (Orig.). 1969. pap. 4.50x (ISBN 0-900090-00-6, Pub. by Ashmolean Museum). State Mutual Bk.

Orlinsky, Harry M. Understanding the Bible Through History & Archaeology. 1969. 12.50x (ISBN 0-87068-096-X). Ktav.

Pfeiffer, Charles F. Ras Shamra & the Bible. (Baker Studies in Biblical Archaeology). 1976. pap. 2.95 (ISBN 0-8010-7003-1). Baker Bk.

--Tell El-Amarna & the Bible. (Baker Studies in Biblical Archaeology). 1976. pap. 2.95 (ISBN 0-8010-7002-3). Baker Bk.

Powell, Ivor. Bible Treasures. LC 84-25090. 192p. (Orig.). 1985. pap. 5.95 (ISBN 0-8254-3518-8). Kregel.

Pritchard, James B. Archaeology & the Old Testament. LC 58-10053. pap. 69.80 (ISBN 0-317-08485-2, 2016011). Bks Demand UMI.

--Gibeon, Where the Sun Stood Still: The Discovery of a Biblical City. 1962. 31.50 (ISBN 0-691-03517-2); pap. 9.50x (ISBN 0-691-00210-X). Princeton U Pr.

Pritchard, James B., ed. Ancient Near East in Pictures with Supplement. 2nd ed. Incl. Ancient Near Eastern Texts Relating to the Old Testament with Supplement. 3rd ed. Set. text ed. 60.50x ea. (ISBN 0-691-03503-2, 035032T); pictures 66.25x (032024T). 1969. deluxe ed. 68.50x ea. (ISBN 0-691-03502-4); Set. 126.75x (ISBN 0-686-66606-2). Princeton U Pr.

Ramsay, William M. Letters to the Seven Churches. (William M. Ramsay Library). 476p. 1985. pap. 12.95 (ISBN 0-8010-7681-1). Baker Bk.

Rogerson, J. W. Anthropology & the Old Testament. (The Biblical Seminar Ser.: No. 1). 128p. 1984. pap. text ed. 8.95x (ISBN 0-905774-82-5, Pub. by JSOT Pr England). Eisenbrauns.

Rowley, H. H. From Joseph to Joshua: Biblical Traditions in the Light of Archaeology. (Schweich Lectures on Biblical Archaeology). 212p. 1970. Repr. of 1948 ed. 8.25 (ISBN 0-85672-720-2, Pub. by British Acad). Longwood Pub Group.

Saulcy, L. F. Dictionnaire les Antiquites Bibligues. Migne, J. P., ed. (Troisieme et Derniere Encyclopedie Theologique Ser.: Vol. 45). (Fr.). 516p. Repr. of 1859 ed. lib. bdg. 66.50x (ISBN 0-89241-319-0). Caratzas.

Schoville, Keith N. Biblical Archaeology in Focus. LC 78-62914. 24.95 (ISBN 0-8010-8112-2). Baker Bk.

Szekely, Edmond B. The Great Experiment. (Search for the Ageless Ser.: Vol. 2). (Illus.). 328p. 1977. pap. 8.80 (ISBN 0-89564-023-6). IBS Intl.

--My Unusual Adventures on the Five Continents in Search for the Ageless. (Search for the Ageless Ser.: Vol. 1). (Illus.). 212p. 1977. pap. 7.80 (ISBN 0-89564-022-8). IBS Intl.

Thomas, D. Winton, ed. Documents from Old Testament Times. pap. 7.95x (ISBN 0-06-130085-3, TB85, Torch). Har-Row.

Thompson, J. A. The Bible & Archaeology. wnd, rev. ed. 512p. 1981. 24.95 (ISBN 0-8028-3545-7). Eerdmans.

Van Deursen, A. Illustrated Dictionary of Bible Manners & Customs. (Illus.). 1967. 6.95 (ISBN 0-8022-1762-1). Philos Lib.

Vos, Howard. Archaeology in Bible Lands. LC 77-2981. (Illus.). 1977. 11.95 (ISBN 0-8024-0289-5). Moody.

Vos, Howard F. Genesis & Archaeology. rev. & enl. ed. 1986. pap. 6.95 (ISBN 0-310-33901-4, 11154P). Zondervan.

--An Introduction to Bible Archaeology. Rev. ed. 1983. pap. 5.95 (ISBN 0-8024-0325-5). Moody.

Wight, Fred H. Manners & Customs of Bible Lands. 1953. 10.95 (ISBN 0-8024-5175-6). Moody.

Wiseman, D. J. Nebuchadrezzar & Babylon. (British Academy - Schweich Lectures). (Illus.). 144p. 1986. 34.50x (ISBN 0-19-726040-3). Oxford U Pr.

Woude, A. S. van der, ed. The World of the Bible. Woudstra, Sierd, tr. from Dutch. (Illus.). 496p. 1986. 34.95 (ISBN 0-8028-2405-6). Eerdmans.

Wright, G. Ernest. Biblical Archaeology. rev. ed. LC 57-5020. (Illus.). 292p. 1963. 27.50 (ISBN 0-664-20420-1). Westminster.

Wright, G. Ernest, ed. The Bible & the Ancient Near East: Essays in Honor of William Foxwell Albright. 1979. Repr. of 1961 ed. 15.00x (ISBN 0-931464-03-X). Eisenbrauns.

Yamauchi, Edwin. The Archaeology of New Testament Cities in Western Asia Minor. LC 80-66991. (Baker Studies in Biblical Archaeology). 160p. 1980. pap. 7.95 (ISBN 0-8010-9915-3). Baker Bk.

--Foes from the Northern Frontiers. (Baker Studies in Biblical Archaeology). 128p. (Orig.). 1982. pap. 6.95 (ISBN 0-8010-9918-8). Baker Bk.

Yamauchi, Edwin M. Las Excavaciones Y las Escrituras. 224p. 1978. 4.50 (ISBN 0-311-03658-9). Casa Bautista.

BIBLE–APPRECIATION

Bullinger, E. W. How to Enjoy the Bible. LC 83-71411. 436p. 1983. 9.95 (ISBN 0-910068-48-8). Am Christian.

Colbaugh, Lloyd N. The Gospel Behind Bars. LC 79-53942. (Radiant Life Ser.). 96p. (Orig.). 1979. pap. 1.50 (ISBN 0-88243-503-5, 02-0503). Gospel Pub.

Efird, James M. Biblical Books of Wisdom. 96p. 1983. pap. 4.95 (ISBN 0-8170-0999-X). Judson.

Hastings, James & Hastings, Edward, eds. Speaker's Bible, 18 vols. 1979. 275.00 (ISBN 0-8010-4036-1). Baker Bk.

Kohlenberger, John R., III. Read Through the Bible in a Year. (Orig.). 1986. pap. 1.95 (ISBN 0-8024-7168-4). Moody.

London Times. The Bible Today: Historical, Social, & Literary Aspects of the Old & New Testaments. LC 78-6130. 1978. Repr. of 1955 ed. lib. bdg. cancelled (ISBN 0-313-20449-7, TIBT). Greenwood.

Pryor, Neale. You Can Trust Your Bible. 3.95 (ISBN 0-89137-524-4). Quality Pubns.

Shotwell, Berenice M. Getting Better Acquainted with Your Bible. LC 75-173349. (Illus.). 1972. 24.95 (ISBN 0-9603026-0-3). Shadwold.

Ulmer, L. The Bible That Wouldn't Burn. LC 39-1094. 1983. pap. 3.95 (ISBN 0-570-03634-8). Concordia.

BIBLE–ARCHAEOLOGY

see Bible–Antiquities

BIBLE–ATLASES

see Bible–Geography–Maps

BIBLE–BIBLIOGRAPHY

Aune, David E. Jesus & the Synoptic Gospels: A Bibliographic Study Guide. Branson, Mark L., ed. (TSF - IBR Bibliographic Study Guides Ser.). 99p. (Orig.). 1981. pap. 2.95 (ISBN 0-8308-5498-3). Inter-Varsity.

The Bible: Texts & Translations of the Bible & the Apocrypha & Their Books from the National Union Catalog, 5 vols, Vol. 5. (700 pages per volume). 1980. 113.00x (ISBN 0-7201-1575-2); Set. 456.00 (ISBN 0-7201-1567-1). Mansell.

Bowden, Edwin T. & Farmer, David, eds. The Holy Bible at the University of Texas. rev. ed. Orig. Title: The Holy Bible, an Exhibit. (Illus.). 1967. 8.00 (ISBN 0-87959-027-0). U of Tex H Ransom Ctr.

Childs, Brevard S. Old Testament Books for Pastor and Teacher. LC 76-52457. 120p. 1977. pap. 4.95 (ISBN 0-664-24120-4). Westminster.

Ecole Biblique et Archeologique Francaise. Jerusalem. Catalogue de la Bibliotheque de l'ecole Biblique et Archeologique Francaise (Catalog of the Library of the French Biblical & Archaeological School, 13 vols. 1975. lib. bdg. 1405.00 (ISBN 0-8161-1154-5, Hall Library). G K Hall.

Harrington, Daniel J. The New Testament: A Bibliography. (Theological & Biblical Resources Ser.: Vol. 2). 1985. pap. 8.95 (ISBN 0-89453-535-8). M Glazier.

Herbert, A. S. Historical Catalogue of Printed Editions of the English Bible: 1525-1961. 589p. 1968. 40.00 (ISBN 0-686-87735-7). A Wofsy Fine Arts.

Kissinger, Warren S. The Parables of Jesus: A History of Interpretation & Bibliography. LC 78-23271. (American Theological Library Association (ATLA) Bibliography Ser.: No. 4). 463p. 1979. lib. bdg. 30.00 (ISBN 0-8108-1186-3). Scarecrow.

Kohlenberger, John R., III. Books about the Book: A Guide to Biblical Reference Works. 272p. 1986. pap. 10.95 (ISBN 0-310-39341-8). Zondervan.

O'Callaghan, Edmund B. List of Editions of the Holy Scriptures & Parts Thereof Printed in American Previous to 1860. LC 66-25690. 1966. Repr. of 1861 ed. 43.00x (ISBN 0-8103-3313-9). Gale.

Prime, Wendell. Fifteenth Century Bibles. LC 77-85626. 1977. Repr. of 1888 ed. lib. bdg. 15.00 (ISBN 0-89341-320-8). Longwood Pub Group.

Scholer, David M. Basic Bibliographic Guide for New Testament. pap. 3.95 (ISBN 0-8028-1503-0). Eerdmans.

Shea, John D. A Bibliographical Account of Catholic Bibles, Testaments & Other Portions of Scripture Translated from the Latin Vulgate. 1980. lib. bdg. 49.95 (ISBN 0-8490-3114-1). Gordon Pr.

Wagner, Guenter. An Exegetical Bibliography of the New Testament: Vol. 1-Matthew & Mark. LC 83-969. (Bibliographical Tools for New Testament Studies). xviii, 668p. 1983. 35.00 (ISBN 0-86554-013-6, MUP-H26). Mercer Univ Pr.

Wagner, Gunter, ed. An Exegetical Bibliography of the New Testament, Vol. 2: Luke-Acts. xiv, 550p. 1986. 49.50 (ISBN 0-86554-140-X, MUP-H131). Mercer Univ Pr.

--An Exegetical Bibliography of the New Testament: Volume 3: John-1-2-3 John. 600p. 1987. 55.00 (ISBN 0-86554-157-4). Mercer Univ Pr.

BIBLE–BIOGRAPHY

see also Apostles; Children in the Bible; Patriarchs (Bible); Prophets; Women In the Bible; also names of individuals mentioned in the Bible, e.g. Moses; Mary, Virgin

Alexander, George M. The Handbook of Biblical Personalities. 320p. 1981. pap. 6.95 (ISBN 0-8164-2316-4, HarpR). Har-Row.

Alexander, Myrna. After God's Heart. (Woman's Workshop Ser.). 160p. (Orig.). 1982. pap. 3.95p (ISBN 0-310-37141-4, 10921). Zondervan.

Auchmuty, James A., Jr. Brothers of the Bible. LC 84-17510. 1985. pap. 4.50 (ISBN 0-8054-2254-4). Broadman.

Baring-Gould, S. Legends of the Patriarchs & Prophets & Other Old Testament Characters. LC 74-9741. 1872. lib. bdg. 42.00 (ISBN 0-8414-3205-8). Folcroft.

Barker, William P. Everyone in the Bible. 384p. 1966. 15.95 (ISBN 0-8007-0084-8). Revell.

Barlow, Fred M. Heaven's Hall of Heroes. LC 78-16887. (Illus.). 1978. pap. 3.95 (ISBN 0-87227-062-9). Reg Baptist.

Barrett, Marsha. Early Christians: Workers for Jesus. (BibLearn Ser.). (Illus.). 1979. 5.95 (ISBN 0-8054-4247-2, 4242-47). Broadman.

Barron, Sr. Mary C. Unveiled Faces: Men & Women of the Bible. LC 80-27728. 95p. 1981. softcover 4.50 (ISBN 0-8146-1212-1). Liturgical Pr.

Blaiklock, E. M. Today's Handbook of Bible Characters. 848p. 1987. 17.95 (ISBN 0-87123-948-5). Bethany Hse.

Brestin, Dee. Friendship: Portraits in God's Family Album. (Fisherman Bible Studyguide Ser.). 96p. (Orig.). 1986. pap. 2.95 (ISBN 0-87788-287-8). Shaw Pubs.

Bronner, Leah. Biblical Personalities & Archaeology. (Illus.). 216p. 1975. 7.95x (ISBN 0-685-58308-2). Bloch.

Buechner, Frederick. Peculiar Treasures: A Biblical Who's Who. Buechner, Katherine A., tr. LC 78-20586. 1979. 12.45 (ISBN 0-06-061157-X, HarpR). Har-Row.

Burgess, E. T. Interesting Men of the Bible. 1970. pap. 0.50 (ISBN 0-89114-007-7). Baptist Pub Hse.

Character Sketches: From the Pages of Scripture, Illustrated in the World of Nature, 3 vols. LC 76-3050. (Illus.). 382p. 1976. Vol. 1. 25.00 (ISBN 0-916888-01-0); Vol. 2. 25.00 (ISBN 0-916888-02-9); Vol. 3, 1985. 30.00 (ISBN 0-916888-10-X). Inst Basic Youth.

Churgin, Pinchas & Smolar, Leivy. Studies in Targum Jonathan to the Prophets. 59.50x (ISBN 0-87068-109-5). Ktav.

Clift, Jeannette. Some Run with Feet of Clay. 127p. Repr. of 1978 ed. 7.95 (ISBN 0-318-20047-3). Manor of Grace.

Crouch, Brodie. Study of Minor Prophets. pap. 2.50 (ISBN 0-89315-291-9). Lambert Bk.

Deen, Edith. All of the Women of the Bible. LC 55-8621. 1955. 18.45 (ISBN 0-06-061810-8, HarpR). Har-Row.

De La Fuente, Tomas. Abraham y Jose el Patriarca: Personas Importantes de la Biblia. (Span., Illus.). 76p. 1982. pap. 2.50 (ISBN 0-940048-03-5). Austin Bilingual Lang Ed.

Dugan, LeRoy. Heroes of the Old Testament. 96p. (Orig.). 1981. No. 1. pap. 1.95 oversized, saddle stitched (ISBN 0-87123-704-0, 220704); No. 2. pap. 2.95 (ISBN 0-87123-705-9, 220705). Bethany Hse.

Estrada, Leobardo. Grandes Hombres de la Biblia. 235p. 1975. pap. 5.25 (ISBN 0-311-04656-8). Casa Bautista.

Falwell, Jerry. Champions for God. 132p. 1985. pap. 4.95 (ISBN 0-89693-534-5). Victor Bks.

Foster, Harry. Daily Thoughts on Bible Characters. 2nd ed. Living Spring Publications Staff, tr. (Chinese.). 1982. write for info. (ISBN 0-941598-99-3); pap. write for info (ISBN 0-941598-00-4). Living Spring Pubns.

Gangel, Kenneth O. Lessons in Leadership from the Bible. 1980. pap. 5.95 (ISBN 0-88469-109-8). BMH Bks.

Gilliland, Dolores S. Selected Women of the Scriptures of Stamina & Courage. (Illus.). 1978. pap. 3.95 (ISBN 0-931446-02-3). Honor Bks.

Harbour, Brian L. Famous Singles of the Bible. LC 79-56309. 1980. pap. 4.95 (ISBN 0-8054-5640-6). Broadman.

Herr, Ethel. Chosen Women of the Bible. LC 75-36503. 96p. (Orig.). 1976. pap. 4.95 (ISBN 0-8024-1297-1). Moody.

Hirst, Wolf Z. The Romantic Hero & His Biblical Sources. Hogg, James, ed. (Romantic Reassessment ser.). (Orig.). 1985. pap. 15.00 (ISBN 3-7052-0573-0, Pub. by Salzburg Studies). Longwood Pub Group.

Hurley, James B. Man & Woman in Biblical Perspective. 288p. (Orig.). 1981. pap. 9.95 (ISBN 0-310-42731-2, 10460P). Zondervan.

Lohfink, Gerhard. The Work of God Goes On. LC 86-45202. (The Bible for Christian Life Ser.). 80p. 1987. pap. 4.95 (ISBN 0-8006-2026-7). Fortress.

McElrath, William E. Judges & Kings: God's Chosen Leaders. (Illus.). 1979. 5.95 (ISBN 0-8054-4249-9, 4242-49). Broadman.

Mahany, Patricia, ed. Bible Babies. (Classroom Activity Bks.). (Illus.). 48p. (Orig.). 1984. pap. 2.95 (ISBN 0-87239-716-5, 2446). Standard Pub.

--Bible Children. (Classroom Activity Bks.). (Illus.). 48p. (Orig.). 1984. pap. 2.95 (ISBN 0-87239-717-3, 2447). Standard Pub.

Maniscalco, Joe. Bible Hero Stories. LC 74-28725. (Illus.). 144p. 1975. 6.95 (ISBN 0-87239-036-5, 2746). Standard Pub.

Matheson, George. Portraits of Bible Men. LC 86-7428. (First Series (Adam to Job)). Orig. Title: Representative Men of the Bible. 384p. 1986. pap. 8.95 (ISBN 0-8254-3251-0). Kregel.

--Portraits of Bible Men. LC 86-27221. (Ishmael to David, Second Ser.). 368p. 1987. pap. 8.95 (ISBN 0-8254-3252-9). Kregel.

Matthews, Robert J. A Plainer Translation: Joseph Smith's Translation of the Bible, a History & Commentary. LC 75-5937. 1975. 15.95 (ISBN 0-8425-1411-2). Brigham.

Meyer, F. B. Great Men of the Bible, 2 vols. 1986. Set. pap. 20.90 (ISBN 0-310-44288-5, 12362P). Zondervan.

Meyer, F. B. & Cumbers, Frank. Great Men of the Bible, Vol. 1. 384p. (Orig.). 1981. pap. 10.95 (ISBN 0-310-44271-0, 12360P). Zondervan.

--Great Men of the Bible, Vol. 2. 320p. 1982. pap. 10.95 (ISBN 0-310-44281-8, 12361P). Zondervan.

Packer, J. I., et al, eds. All the People & Places of the Bible. LC 82-12564. 1982. pap. 6.95 (ISBN 0-8407-5819-7). Nelson.

Petty, Thurman, Jr. Siege. (Orion Ser.). 144p. 1980. pap. 3.95 (ISBN 0-8127-0302-2). Review & Herald.

Reader's Digest Editors. Great People of the Bible & How They Lived. LC 73-86027. (Illus.). 1974. 21.99 (ISBN 0-89577-015-6). RD Assn.

Ridenour, Fritz. Faith It or Fake It? LC 73-120783. 176p. 1978. pap. 3.50 (ISBN 0-8307-0441-8, S114186). Regal.

Sanders, J. Oswald. Just Like Us: Twenty-One Character Studies from the Bible. 1985. pap. 6.95 (ISBN 0-8024-6516-1). Moody.

Scott, Ralph W. A New Look at Biblical Crime. LC 78-27535. 232p. 1979. 18.95x (ISBN 0-88229-416-4). Nelson-Hall.

Scripture Birthday Book. 128p. 1986. 9.95 (ISBN 0-529-06363-8). World Bible.

Sims, Albert E. & Dent, George. Who's Who in the Bible. 1979. pap. 2.95 (ISBN 0-8065-0705-5). Citadel Pr.

--Who's Who in the Bible. 1982. pap. 4.95 (ISBN 0-8022-1577-7). Philos Lib.

Steinsaltz, Adin. Biblical Images: Men & Women of the Book. LC 83-46081. (Illus.). 256p. 1984. 16.95 (ISBN 0-465-00670-1). Basic.

Stifle, J. M. ABC Bible Characters. 1982. pap. 3.95 (ISBN 0-570-04062-0, 56-1365). Concordia.

Strauss, Richard. Famous Couples of the Bible. 1982. pap. 4.95 (ISBN 0-8423-0836-9); pap. 2.95 leader's guide (ISBN 0-8423-0837-7). Tyndale.

Turner, J. J. Study of Bible Leaders. pap. 2.50 (ISBN 0-89315-290-0). Lambert Bk.

Waddey, John. An Album of Bible Characters. pap. 5.50 (ISBN 0-89137-542-2). Quality Pubns.

Whyte, Alexander. Bible Characters from the New Testament, Vol. 1. LC 81-81099. (The Shepherd Illustrated Classics Ser.). (Illus.). 276p. 1982. pap. 7.95 (ISBN 0-87983-256-8). Keats.

--Bible Characters from the New Testament, Vol. 2. LC 81-81099. (The Shepherd Illustrated Classics Ser.). (Illus.). 324p. 1982. pap. 7.95 (ISBN 0-87983-257-6). Keats.

--Whyte's Bible Characters: From the Old Testament & the New Testament. (Illus.). 1968. 24.95 (ISBN 0-310-34410-7, 11008). Zondervan.

Wiesel, Elie. Five Biblical Portraits. LC 81-40458. 168p. 1981. 9.95 (ISBN 0-268-00957-0). U of Notre Dame Pr.

--Five Biblical Portraits. LC 81-40458. vii, 157p. 1983. pap. 4.95 (ISBN 0-268-00962-7, 85-09622). U of Notre Dame Pr.

Winkler, Jude. Great People of the Bible. (Illus.). 160p. 1985. 11.95 (ISBN 0-89942-715-4). Catholic Bk Pub.

Wright, Elliott. Holy Company: Christian Heros & Heroines. 1980. 12.95 (ISBN 0-02-631590-4). Macmillan.

Youngman, Bernard R. Prophets & Rulers. (Background to the Bible Ser.: Vol. 2). pap. 8.95 (ISBN 0-7175-0416-6). Dufour.

BIBLE–BIOGRAPHY–N. T.

Cook, Madison D. Biographical Concordance of the New Testament. 216p. 1984. pap. 8.95 (ISBN 0-87213-089-4). Loizeaux.

Corvin, Raymond O. New Testament Characters. (The Alpha & Omega Bible Studies). 94p. (Orig.). 1986. pap. text ed. 5.95 (ISBN 0-89221-137-7). New Leaf.

Grollenberg, Lucas. Paul. Bowden, John, tr. LC 78-14372. 186p. 1979. pap. 4.50 (ISBN 0-664-24234-0). Westminster.

Kuyper, Abraham. Women of the New Testament. pap. 4.95 (ISBN 0-310-36751-4, 9996P). Zondervan.

Marquart, M. Jesus' Second Family. (Arch Book Series Fourteen). 1977. pap. 0.99 (ISBN 0-570-06111-3, 59-1229). Concordia.

Morris, Leon. The Atonement. LC 83-20649. 204p. 1984. pap. 8.95 (ISBN 0-87784-826-2). Inter-Varsity.

Picirilli, Robert E. Paul the Apostle. (Orig.). 1986. pap. 7.95 (ISBN 0-8024-6325-8). Moody.

BIBLE–BIOGRAPHY–O. T.

Corvin, R. O. David & His Mighty Men. facs. ed. LC 74-136646. (Biography Index Reprint Ser.). 1950. 17.00 (ISBN 0-8369-8041-7). Ayer Co Pubs.

Corvin, Raymond O. Old Testament Characters. (The Alpha & Omega Bible Studies). 94p. (Orig.). 1986. pap. text ed. 5.95 (ISBN 0-89221-136-9). New Leaf.

Fraade, Steven D. Enosh & His Generation: Pre-Israelite Hero & History in Post-Biblical Interpretation. LC 83-27137. (Society of Biblical Literature-Monograph Ser.). 1984. 29.95 (ISBN 0-89130-724-9, 06 00 30); pap. 19.95 (ISBN 0-89130-725-7). Scholars Pr GA.

Fulbright, Robert G. Old Testament Friends: Men of Courage. (BibLearn Ser.). (Illus.). 1979. 5.95 (ISBN 0-8054-4251-0, 4242-51). Broadman.

Getz, Gene A. When You're Confused & Uncertain. rev. ed. LC 86-477. (Biblical Renewal Ser.). 160p. 1986. pap. 5.95 (ISBN 0-8307-1122-8, 5418749). Regal.

Jonah. LC 76-11275. (Sunshine Bks). (Illus.). 20p. 1976. pap. 1.50 (ISBN 0-8006-1577-8, 1-1577). Fortress.

Keller, W. Phillip. David II: The Shepherd King. 224p. 1986. 11.95 (ISBN 0-8499-0559-1). Word Bks.

Knapp, Christopher. Kings of Judah & Israel. Rev. ed. 1982. pap. 5.95 (ISBN 0-87213-461-X). Loizeaux.

Kolbrek, Loyal. The Day God Made It Rain. (Arch Books Series Fourteen). 1977. pap. 0.99 (ISBN 0-570-06108-3, 59-1226). Concordia.

Kunz, Marilyn. Patterns for Living with God. pap. 2.95 (ISBN 0-87784-409-7). Inter-Varsity.

Kuyper, Abraham. Women of the Old Testament. pap. 5.95 (ISBN 0-310-36761-1, 9997P). Zondervan.

McMinn, Tom. Prophets: Preachers for God. (BibLearn Ser.). (Illus.). 1979. 5.95 (ISBN 0-8054-4250-2, 4242-50). Broadman.

Meyer, F. B. Old Testament Men of Faith. 1979. pap. 5.95 (ISBN 0-89107-170-9). Good News.

Neff, Lavonne. God's Gift Baby. (Arch Bks.: No. 14). 1977. pap. 0.99 (ISBN 0-570-06113-X, 59-1230). Concordia.

Nickelsburg, George W. Jewish Literature Between the Bible & the Mishnah: A Historical & Literary Introduction. LC 80-16176. 352p. 1981. 19.95 (ISBN 0-8006-0649-3, 1-649). Fortress.

Ogilvie, Lloyd J. Lord of the Impossible. 224p. (Orig.). 1984. pap. 9.95 (ISBN 0-687-22710-0). Abingdon.

Palau, Luis. Schemer & the Dreamer: God's Way to the Top. LC 77-4589. 1976. pap. 3.50 (ISBN 0-930014-12-X). Multnomah.

Ponder, Catherine. The Millionaires of Genesis. (The Millionaires of the Bible Ser.). 1976. pap. 4.95 (ISBN 0-87516-215-0). De Vorss.

Purves. King David. (Ladybird Ser.). 1980. 2.50 (ISBN 0-87508-843-0). Chr Lit.

Samuel, Maurice. Certain People of the Book. 1977. pap. 7.50 (ISBN 0-8074-0082-3, 388350). UAHC.

Shearburn, Wally M. Jacob's Ladder: A Choral Reading. 1980. 4.00 (ISBN 0-89536-441-7, 1014). CSS of Ohio.

Wiesel, Elie. Messengers of God: Biblical Portraits & Legends. 224p. 1985. 16.95 (ISBN 0-671-52333-3); pap. 7.95 (ISBN 0-671-54134-X). Summit Bks.

BIBLE–BIRDS

see Bible–Natural History

BIBLE–BOTANY

see Bible–Natural History

BIBLE–CANON

Barr, James. Holy Scripture: Canon, Authority, Criticism. LC 82-20123. 190p. 1983. 18.95 (ISBN 0-664-21395-2); pap. 9.95 (ISBN 0-664-24477-7). Westminster.

Blenkinsopp, Joseph. Prophecy & Canon: A Contribution to the Study of Jewish Origins. LC 76-22411. 1977. text ed. 14.95 (ISBN 0-268-01522-8). U of Notre Dame Pr.

Gamble, Harry Y. The New Testament Canon: Its Making & Meaning. LC 85-4509. (Guides to Biblical Scholarship Ser.). 96p. 1985. pap. 4.50 (ISBN 0-8006-0470-9). Fortress.

Harris, R. Laird. Inspiration & Canonicity of the Bible. (Contemporary Evangelical Perspectives Ser.). kivar 8.95 (ISBN 0-310-25891-X, 9766P). Zondervan.

MacDonald, Dennis R. The Legend & the Apostle: The Battle for Paul in Story & Canon. LC 82-21953. 144p. (Orig.). 1983. pap. 9.95 (ISBN 0-664-24464-5). Westminster.

Reid, John K. The Authority of Scripture: A Study of the Reformation & Post-Reformation Understanding of the Bible. LC 79-8716. 286p. 1981. Repr. of 1962 ed. lib. bdg. 25.00x (ISBN 0-313-22191-X, REAS). Greenwood.

Sanders, James A. Canon & Community: A Guide to Canonical Criticism. LC 83-18483. (Guides to Biblical Scholarship). 96p. 1984. pap. 4.50 (ISBN 0-8006-0468-7, 1-468). Fortress.

--From Sacred Story to Sacred Text: Canon As Paradigm. LC 85-45483. 240p. 1987. 18.95 (ISBN 0-8006-0805-4). Fortress.

Sundberg, A. C., Jr. Old Testament of the Early Church: A Study of Canon. (Harvard Theological Studies). 1964. 24.00 (ISBN 0-527-01020-0). Kraus Repr.

BIBLE–CATECHISMS, QUESTION-BOOKS, ETC.

see also Bible Games and Puzzles

Beegle, Shirley. Through the Bible Quizzes for Children. 64p. (Orig.). 1974. pap. 2.50 (ISBN 0-87239-324-0, 3249). Standard Pub.

Bible Quiz Book Nos. 1 & 2. 1.50 ea. No. 1 (ISBN 0-529-05715-8, BQ-1). No. 2 (ISBN 0-529-05716-6, BQ-2). World Bible.

DeHaan, M. R. Five Hundred Eight Answers to Bible Questions. 1979. pap. 7.95 (ISBN 0-310-23341-0, 9495P). Zondervan.

Fifty-Five Hundred Questions & Answers on the Holy Bible. 192p. 1974. pap. 3.95 (ISBN 0-310-24361-0, 9666P). Zondervan.

Lambert, Gussie. One Thousand Questions on Genesis. 2.50 (ISBN 0-89315-188-2). Lambert Bk.

Lindsay, Gordon. Difficult Questions About the Bible Answered. 1.25 (ISBN 0-89985-114-2). Christ Nations.

Makrakis, Apostolos. Divine & Sacred Catechism. Orthodox Christian Educational Society, ed. 224p. 1946. 5.50x (ISBN 0-938366-15-7). Orthodox Chr.

Morris, Henry M. Bible Has the Answer. pap. 8.95 (ISBN 0-8010-5905-4). Baker Bk.

Overduin, Daniel. Reflections Books, 4 vols. 1980. Set. pap. 6.95 (ISBN 0-570-03817-0, 12-2785). Concordia.

Redemptorist Pastoral Publication. The Illustrated Catechism. LC 80-84312. 112p. (Orig.). 1981. pap. 3.95 (ISBN 0-89243-135-0). Liguori Pubns.

Thompson, James C. Notes on the Catechism: An Outline of the Faith. 1979. pap. 4.95 (ISBN 0-8192-1249-0). Morehouse.

Vander Meer, Charles. Quickie Quizzes from the Bible. (Quiz & Puzzles Bks.). 48p. 1976. pap. 2.50 (ISBN 0-8010-9252-3). Baker Bk.

BIBLE–CHARACTERS

see Bible–Biography

BIBLE–CHILDREN

see Children in the Bible

BIBLE–CHRONOLOGY

Calmet, A. Dictionnaire Historique, Archeologique, Philologique, Chronologique Geographique et Literal de la Bible, 4 vols. Migne, J. P., ed. (Encyclopedie Theologique First Ser.: Vols. 1-4). (Fr.). 2602p. Repr. of 1846 ed. lib. bdg. 332.50x (ISBN 0-89241-231-3). Caratzas.

Chronology of the Bible. 1980. lib. bdg. 49.95 (ISBN 0-8490-3140-0). Gordon Pr.

Frye, Roland M., ed. The Reader's Bible, A Narrative: Selections from the King James Version. LC 77-311. 638p. 1979. pap. 13.50 (ISBN 0-691-01995-9). Princeton U Pr.

Kirby, Scott. Dating: Guidelines from the Bible. 1979. pap. 2.95 (ISBN 0-8010-5400-1). Baker Bk.

Lanier, Roy, Sr. Outlines of Bible History. 2.50 (ISBN 0-89315-189-0). Lambert Bk.

Parmelee, Alice. Highlights of the Story of Christianity, Bk. 5. LC 80-81098. (All About the Bible Ser.). 136p. (Orig.). 1980. pap. 5.95 (ISBN 0-8192-1274-1). Morehouse.

Reese, Edward, compiled by. The Reese Chronological Bible. 1620p. 1980. Repr. of 1977 ed. 26.95 (ISBN 0-87123-115-8, 230115). Bethany Hse.

Smith, F. LaGard. The Narrated Bible in Chronological Order. 1984. text ed. 34.95 (ISBN 0-89081-408-2). Harvest Hse.

Smith, William. Old Testament History. Fields, Wilbur, ed. LC 78-1072. (The Bible Study Textbook Ser.). (Illus.). 1967. Repr. of 1901 ed. 17.50 (ISBN 0-89900-001-0). College Pr Pub.

Urberg, S. S. Introducing Old Testament Books: With an Emphasis on Their Chronological Relationship. 1979. pap. 5.95 (ISBN 0-8010-9203-5). Baker Bk.

Walton, John W. Chronological & Background Charts of the Old Testament. 1977. spiral bdg. 8.95 (ISBN 0-310-36291-1, 11300P). Zondervan.

Wardle, William L. The History & Religion of Israel. LC 78-11741. (The Clarendon Bible, Old Testament Ser.: Vol. I). (Illus.). 1979. Repr. of 1942 ed. lib. bdg. 24.75x (ISBN 0-313-21016-0, WAHR). Greenwood.

BIBLE–CODICES

see Bible–Manuscripts

BIBLE–COINS

see Bible–Numismatics

BIBLE–COLPORTAGE

see Bible–Publication and Distribution

BIBLE–COMMENTARIES

Here are entered only commentaries on the whole Bible. Commentaries on the New Testament, and portions of the New Testament, precede commentaries on the Old Testament, and portions of the Old Testament.

see also Scholia

Abba, R. Nature & Authority of the Bible. 349p. 1958. 8.95 (ISBN 0-227-67539-8). Attic Pr.

Ackland, Donald F. Broadman Comments, January-March, 1987. (Orig.). 1986. pap. 2.50 (ISBN 0-8054-1554-8). Broadman.

--Broadman Comments, 1987-88. (Orig.). 1987. pap. 5.95 (ISBN 0-8054-1558-0). Broadman.

Ackland, Donald F., et al. Broadman Comments: April-June 1987. (Orig.). 1987. pap. 2.50 (ISBN 0-8054-1555-6). Broadman.

Adams, Charles R. & Seno, William J., eds. Success in God's Word: Bible Scriptures for a Fulfilling Life. 112p. 1986. pap. 2.95 (ISBN 0-933437-01-3). Round River Pub.

Alexander, Ralph. Ezequiel (Comentario Biblico Portavoz) Orig. Title: Ezekiel (Everyman's Bible Commentary) (Span.). 128p. 1979. pap. 4.50 (ISBN 0-8254-1002-9). Kregel.

Allen, Clifton J., et al, eds. Broadman Bible Commentary, 12 vols. Incl. Vol. 1, General Articles, Genesis-Exodus. rev. ed (ISBN 0-8054-1125-9); Vol. 2 (ISBN 0-8054-1102-X); Vol. 3 (ISBN 0-8054-1103-8); Vol. 4 (ISBN 0-8054-1104-6); Vol. 5 (ISBN 0-8054-1105-4); Vol. 6 (ISBN 0-8054-1106-2); Vol. 7 (ISBN 0-8054-1107-0); Vol. 8, General Articles, Matthew-Mark. rev. ed (ISBN 0-8054-1108-9); Vol. 9 (ISBN 0-8054-1109-7); Vol. 10 (ISBN 0-8054-1110-0); Vol. 11 (ISBN 0-8054-1111-9); Vol. 12 (ISBN 0-8054-1112-7). LC 78-93918. 1969. lib. bdg. 16.95 ea.; 195.00 set (ISBN 0-8054-1100-3). Broadman.

Allis, Oswald T. Bible Numerics. 1949. pap. 0.95 (ISBN 0-87552-100-2). Presby & Reformed.

Alter, Robert. The Art of Biblical Narrative. LC 80-68958. 195p. 1983. pap. 7.95 (ISBN 0-465-00427-X, CN-5099). Basic.

Anderson, Bernhard W. The Living Word of the Bible. LC 78-27108. 118p. 1979. pap. 4.95 (ISBN 0-664-24247-2). Westminster.

Archer, Gleason L. & Chirichigno, G. C. Old Testament Quotations in the New Testament: A Complete Survey. 1983. 21.95 (ISBN 0-8024-0236-4). Moody.

Archer, Jr., et al. The Expositor's Bible Commentary, Vol. 7. 1986. 24.95 (ISBN 0-88469-194-2). BMH Bks.

Arnold, Eberhard. Innenland: Ein Wegweiser In Die Seele Der Bibel und In Den Kampf Um Die Wirklichkeit. (Ger.). 492p. 1936. 9.00 (ISBN 0-87486-150-0). Plough.

Augustinus, Saint Aurelius. Spurious & Doubtful Works, Pseudo-Augustini Quaestiones Veteris et Novi Testamenti CXXVII. Souter, A., ed. (Corpus Scriptorum Ecclesiasticorum Latinorum Ser: Vol. 50). 40.00 (ISBN 0-384-02575-7). Johnson Repr.

Barnes, Albert. Barnes' Notes on the Old & New Testaments, 14 vols. 249.50 (ISBN 0-8010-0834-4). Baker Bk.

Barnstone, Willis, ed. The Other Bible. LC 83-48416. 768p. 1984. 24.45 (ISBN 0-06-250031-7, HarpR); pap. 14.95 (ISBN 0-06-250030-9, CN 4087). Har-Row.

Bash, Ewald. Legends from the Future. (Illus., Orig.). 1972. pap. 1.75 (ISBN 0-377-02101-6). Friend Pr.

Baumann, Dan. Confronted by Love. LC 85-2364. (Bible Commentary for Laymen Ser.). 144p. 1985. pap. 3.95 (ISBN 0-8307-1050-7, S391101). Regal.

Beacon Bible Commentary, 10 vols. 125.00 set (ISBN 0-8010-0675-9). Baker Bk.

Beichner, Paul E. Petri Riage Biblia Versificato: Petri Rigue Biblia Versificato, a Verse Commentary on the Bible, 2 vols. (Mediaeval Studies Ser.: No. 19). 1965. 50.00 set (ISBN 0-268-00016-6). U of Notre Dame Pr.

Bennion, Lowell L. Understanding the Scriptures. LC 81-66422. 88p. 1981. 6.95 (ISBN 0-87747-863-5). Deseret Bk.

Benson, Dennis C. Creative Bible Studies. LC 85-71044. (Illus.). 660p. (Orig.). 1985. pap. 19.95 (ISBN 0-931529-01-8). Group Bks.

Berry, R. L. Steps Heavenward. 123p. pap. 1.00 (ISBN 0-686-29142-5). Faith Pub Hse.
Bible Knowledge Commentary: New Testament. 1983. 24.95 (ISBN 0-88207-812-7). Victor Bks.
Black, Matthew & Rowley, H. H. Peake's Commentary on the Bible. 1962. 39.95 (ISBN 0-8407-5019-6). Nelson.
Bloem, Diane B. & Bloem, Robert C. A Women's Workshop on Bible Marriages. (Woman's Workshop Series of Study Books). 128p. (Orig.). 1980. pap. 2.95 student's manual (ISBN 0-310-21391-6, 10687); pap. 3.95 leader's manual (ISBN 0-310-21401-7, 10688). Zondervan.
Boenig, Robert. Biblical Commentaries by Richard Rolle. Hogg, James, ed. (Elizabethan & Renaissance Studies). (Orig.). 1984. pap. 15.00 (ISBN 0-317-40122-X, Pub. by Salzburg Studies). Longwood Pub Group.
Bowden, John. The Bible Contradicts Itself. 36p. 1982. Repr. of 1968 ed. saddle-stitched 3.00 (ISBN 0-911826-46-7). Am Atheist.
Brooks, Keith L. Christian Character Course. (Teach Yourself the Bible Ser). 1961. pap. 2.75 (ISBN 0-8024-1301-3). Moody.
Brown, Raymond E., et al, eds. Jerome Biblical Commentary. 1969. 59.95 (ISBN 0-13-509612-X). P-H.
Bruce, F. F., ed. International Bible Commentary. rev. ed. 1664p. 1986. text ed. 24.95 (ISBN 0-310-22020-3, 6404). Zondervan.
Brymer, Harvey P. The Most Memorable Passages of the New Testament Fully & Dramatically Illustrated. (Promotion of the Arts Library). (Illus.). 141p. 1982. 69.85 (ISBN 0-86650-039-1). Gloucester Art.
Buttrick, George A. The Interpreter's Bible, 12 vols. Incl. Vol. 1. General Articles, Genesis, Exodus. 1952 (ISBN 0-687-19207-2); Vol. 2. Leviticus - Samuel. 1953 (ISBN 0-687-19208-0); Vol. 3. Kings - Job. 1954 (ISBN 0-687-19209-9); Vol. 4. Psalms, Proverbs. 1955 (ISBN 0-687-19210-2); Vol. 5. Ecclesiastes - Jeremiah. 1956 (ISBN 0-687-19211-0); Vol. 6. Lamentations - Malachi. 1956 (ISBN 0-687-19212-9); Vol. 7. General Articles, Matthew, Mark. 1951 (ISBN 0-687-19213-7); Vol. 8. Luke, John. 1952 (ISBN 0-687-19214-5); Vol. 9. The Acts, Romans. 1954 (ISBN 0-687-19215-3); Vol. 10. Corinthians, Ephesians. 1953 (ISBN 0-687-19216-1); Vol. 11. Philippians - Hebrews. 1955 (ISBN 0-687-19217-X); Vol. 12. James - Revelation. 1957 (ISBN 0-687-19218-8). LC 51-12276. 1957. 22.95 (ISBN 0-686-76914-7); 260.00 (ISBN 0-687-19206-4). Abingdon.
Carson, D. A. God with Us. LC 85-10849. (Bible Commentary for Laymen Ser.). 168p. (Orig.). 1985. pap. 3.95 (ISBN 0-8307-1051-5, S392106). Regal.
Carson, D. A., et al. The Expositor's Bible Commentary, Vol. 8. 1986. 29.95 (ISBN 0-88469-188-8). BMH Bks.
Carter, Charles W. The Wesleyan Bible Commentary, 6 vols. 4484p. 1986. 149.50 (ISBN 0-913573-33-7). Hendrickson MA.
--The Wesleyan Bible Commentary, Vol. 1. 1060p. 1986. 27.95 (ISBN 0-913573-34-5). Hendrickson MA.
--The Wesleyan Bible Commentary, Vol. 2. 660p. 1986. 27.95 (ISBN 0-913573-35-3). Hendrickson MA.
--The Wesleyan Bible Commentary, Vol. 4. 752p. 1986. 27.95 (ISBN 0-913573-37-X). Hendrickson MA.
--The Wesleyan Bible Commentary, Vol. 5. 676p. 1986. 27.95 (ISBN 0-913573-38-8). Hendrickson MA.
--The Wesleyan Bible Commentary, Vol. 6. 528p. 1986. 27.95 (ISBN 0-913573-39-6). Hendrickson MA.
Carter, Charles W., ed. The Wesleyan Bible Commentary, 2 vols. 808p. 1986. 24.95 (ISBN 0-913573-36-1). Hendrickson MA.
Clarke, Adam, ed. Adam Clarke's Commentary on the Entire Bible. 29.95 (ISBN 0-8010-2321-1). Baker Bk.
Complete Layman's Bible Book Commentary Set, 24 vols. 1984. Set. 129.95 (ISBN 0-8054-1170-4). Broadman.
Concetta. In the Light of the Bible, Vols. 1 & 2. 1976. Vol. 1. 2.00 (ISBN 0-8198-0426-6); Vol. 2. pap. 2.00 (ISBN 0-8198-0427-4). Dghtrs St Paul.
Conn, Charles W. The Bible: Books of Books. 1977. pap. 4.25 (ISBN 0-87148-102-2). Pathway Pr.
Cook, F. C., ed. The Bible Commentary, 10 vols. 6803p. 1981. Repr. 195.00 (ISBN 0-8010-2431-5). Baker Bk.
Cowan, Richard O. Doctrine & Covenants: Our Modern Scripture. rev. ed. LC 78-19190. (Illus.). 1978. pap. 7.95 (ISBN 0-8425-1316-7). Brigham.
Criswell, W. A. Great Doctrines of the Bible: Christology, Vol. 2. 192p. 1982. 9.95 (ISBN 0-310-43860-8, 11660). Zondervan.
Daily Devotional Bible Commentary: Romans--Revelation, Vol. 4. LC 76-46442. 1982. Repr. of 1974 ed. 10.95 (ISBN 0-8054-1227-1). Broadman.
Darby, J. N. Notes & Comments on Scripture, 7 vols. Set. 30.00 (ISBN 0-88172-068-2); 4.95 ea. Believers Bkshelf.
--Notes & Jottings on Scripture. 5.95 (ISBN 0-88172-069-0). Believers Bkshelf.
Dean, Robert J. Layman's Bible Book Commentary: Luke, Vol. 17. 1983. 5.95 (ISBN 0-8054-1187-9). Broadman.
DeHaan, M. R. The Tabernacle. 1979. pap. 6.95 (ISBN 0-310-23491-3, 9502P). Zondervan.
Draper, James T., Jr. Foundations of Biblical Faith. LC 78-67001. 1979. 8.95 (ISBN 0-8054-1951-9). Broadman.
Dummelow, John R. Commentary on the Holy Bible. 1909. 19.95 (ISBN 0-02-533770-X). Macmillan.
Dunnett, Walter M. New Testament Survey. LC 63-7410. 96p. 1963. pap. text ed. 4.95 (ISBN 0-910566-03-8); Perfect bdg. instr's. guide 5.95 (ISBN 0-910566-19-4). Evang Tchr.
Dyrness, William A. Let the Earth Rejoice! 192p. (Orig.). 1983. pap. 6.95 (ISBN 0-89107-282-9, Crossway Bks). Good News.
Ebeling, Gerhard, et al. The Bible As a Document of the University. Betz, H. D., ed. 1981. pap. 10.00 (ISBN 0-89130-422-3, 00-03-03). Scholars Pr GA.
Eiselen, Frederick Carl, et al, eds. The Abingdon Bible Commentary. 1979. pap. 19.95 (ISBN 0-385-14877-1, Galilee). Doubleday.
Etheridge, Truman H. Rightly Dividing. 1955. 6.00 (ISBN 0-88027-017-9). Firm Foun Pub.
Eusebius. Preparation for the Gospel, 2 vols. Gifford, Edwin H., tr. from Gr. (Twin Brooks Ser.). 948p. 1982. pap. 24.95 (ISBN 0-8010-3369-1). Baker Bk.
The Expositor's Bible Commentary, Vol. I. 1986. cloth 29.95 (ISBN 0-88469-189-6). BMH Bks.
Falwell, Jerry & Hindson, Edward E., eds. The Liberty Bible Commentary. LC 83-7280. (Illus.). 2736p. 1983. 29.95 (ISBN 0-8407-5295-4). Nelson.
Franklin, J. E. Black Girl from Genesis to Revelations. LC 74-30386. 1977. 9.95 (ISBN 0-88258-019-1). Howard U Pr.
Friederichsen, Kay H. Las Profundas Verdades de la Biblia. Orig. Title: God's World Made Plain. (Span.). 256p. 1958. pap. 4.75 (ISBN 0-8254-1248-X). Kregel.
Fuller, David O., ed. Which Bible? 6th, rev. ed. LC 70-129737. 360p. 1975. pap. 8.95 (ISBN 0-8254-2612-X). Kregel.
Gaebelein, Arno C. Gaebelein's Concise Commentary on the Whole Bible. rev. ed. 1237p. 1985. Repr. of 1970 ed. 29.95 (ISBN 0-87213-209-9). Loizeaux.
Gaebelein, Frank E. The Expositor's Bible Commentary, 5 vols. 1979. Set. 107.75 (ISBN 0-310-36568-6, 11183). Zondervan.
Gaebelein, Frank E., ed. Expositor's Bible Commentary, Vol. 6. 1986. text ed. 29.95 (ISBN 0-88469-182-9). BMH Bks.
--Expositor's Bible Commentary, Vol. 9. (John & Acts). 464p. 1980. 19.95 (ISBN 0-310-36510-4, 11178). Zondervan.
--The Expositor's Bible Commentary, Vol. 12. (Hebrews - Revelation). 624p. 1981. 19.95 (ISBN 0-310-36540-6, 11181). Zondervan.
Gerstenberger, Erhard S. & Schrage, Wolfgang. Woman & Man: Biblical Encounter Ser. Stott, Douglas W., tr. from Ger. LC 81-10898. 256p. (Orig.). 1982. pap. 10.95 (ISBN 0-687-45920-6). Abingdon.
Gispen, W. H. The Bible Student's Commentary: Exodus. (The Bible Student's Commentary). 352p. 1982. 16.95 (ISBN 0-310-43970-1). Zondervan.
Goodboy, Eadie. God's Daughter. rev. ed. (Bible Study: Basic Ser.). 60p. (Orig.). 1985. pap. 2.95 (ISBN 0-932305-45-8, 521002). Aglow Pubns.
Grant, F. W. Numerical Structure of Scripture. 1956. pap. 4.95 (ISBN 0-87213-269-2). Loizeaux.
Grant, F. W., ed. The Numerical Bible, 7 vols. Incl. Vol. 1. Genesis to Deuteronomy (ISBN 0-87213-262-5); Vol. 2. Joshua to Second Samuel (ISBN 0-87213-263-3); Vol. 3. Psalms (ISBN 0-87213-264-1); Vol. 4. Ezekiel (ISBN 0-87213-265-X); Vol. 5. Matthew to John (ISBN 0-87213-266-8); Vol. 6. Acts to Philemon (ISBN 0-87213-267-6); Vol. 7. Hebrews to Revelation (ISBN 0-87213-268-4). 1890-1932. Set. 79.95 (ISBN 0-87213-261-7); 12.95 ea. Loizeaux.
Gray, James M. Home Bible Study Commentary. LC 85-9750. 448p. 1985. pap. 12.95 (ISBN 0-8254-2727-4). Kregel.
Greathouse, William, et al, eds. Beacon Bible Expositions, 12 vols. 1984. Set. 89.95 (ISBN 0-8341-0323-0). Beacon Hill.
Guthrie, et al. Nuevo Comentario Biblico. Orig. Title: The New Bible Commentary Revised. 972p. 1986. pap. 39.95 (ISBN 0-311-03001-7). Casa Bautista.
Guthrie, Donald. New Bible Commentary. rev. ed. 1970. 24.95 (ISBN 0-8028-2281-9). Eerdmans.
--New Testament Introduction. rev. ed. 1971. 34.95 (ISBN 0-87784-953-6). Inter-Varsity.
Haddad, Hassan & Wagner, Donald, eds. All in the Name of the Bible. 2nd ed. 130p. 1986. pap. 7.95 (ISBN 0-915597-42-X). Amana Bks.
Hamilton, Victor P. Handbook on the Pentateuch. LC 82-70466. 392p. 1982. 15.95 (ISBN 0-8010-4259-3). Baker Bk.
Harkovy, Alexander. Family Bible Holy Scriptures Commentary, 2 vols. Set. 62.50 (ISBN 0-317-30501-8). Shalom.
--The Holy Scriptures Holy Bible Commentary. 32.50 (ISBN 0-317-30500-X). Shalom.
Harper, William R. A Critical & Exegetical Commentary on Amos & Hosea. Driver, Samuel R., et al, eds. LC 5-7893. (International Critical Commentary Ser.). 608p. 1905. 24.95 (ISBN 0-567-05018-1, Pub. by T & T Clark Ltd UK). Fortress.
Harrison, Buddy & Gale, Van. Count It All Joy. rev. ed. 32p. 1981. pap. 2.50 (ISBN 0-89274-198-8). Harrison Hse.
Harrison, Everett & Pfeiffer, Charles F., eds. Wycliffe Bible Commentary. 29.95 (ISBN 0-8024-9695-4). Moody.
Harrison, Everett F., et al. The Expositor's Bible Commentary, Vol. 10. 1986. 19.95 (ISBN 0-88469-196-9). BMH Bks.
Havner, Vance. Moments of Decision. 128p. 1980. 8.95 (ISBN 0-8007-1091-6). Revell.
Hayes, John H. & Holladay, Carl. Biblical Exegesis: A Beginner's Handbook. LC 82-17999. 132p. 1982. pap. 7.95 (ISBN 0-8042-0030-0). John Knox.
Henry, Mathew & Scott, Thomas. Matthew Henry Concise Commentary on the Whole Bible. (Affordable Ser.). 1024p. 13.95 (ISBN 0-8024-0417-0). Moody.
Henry, Matthew. A Commentary on the Whole Bible, 6 vols. 7100p. 89.95 (ISBN 0-8007-0196-8); reference lib. ed. 74.95 (ISBN 0-8007-0968-3). Revell.
--A Commentary on the Whole Bible, 6 vols, Vols. 1-6. (Reference Library Edition). 7152p. 1986. Repr. Set. text ed. 59.95 (ISBN 0-529-06371-9). World Bible.
--A Commentary on the Whole Bible, Vol. 2: Joshua to Esther. (Reference Library Edition). 1160p. 1986. Repr. text ed. 10.95 (ISBN 0-529-06366-2). World Bible.
--A Commentary on the Whole Bible, Vol. 3: Job to Song of Solomon. (Reference Library Edition). 1112p. 1986. Repr. text ed. 10.95 (ISBN 0-529-06367-0). World Bible.
--A Commentary on the Whole Bible, Vol. 4: Isaiah to Malachi. (Reference Library Edition). 1520p. 1986. Repr. text ed. 10.95 (ISBN 0-529-06368-9). World Bible.
--A Commentary on the Whole Bible, Vol. 6: Acts to Revelation. (Reference Library Edition). 1200p. 1986. Repr. text ed. 10.95 (ISBN 0-529-06370-0). World Bible.
--Matthew Henry's Commentary in One Volume. Church, Leslie F., ed. 1966. 29.95 (ISBN 0-310-26010-8, 9802). Zondervan.
--Matthew Henry's Commentary on the Whole Bible, 6 vols. 7152p. Date not set. Set. 79.95 (ISBN 0-917006-21-6). Hendrickson MA.
Henry, Matthew & Scott, Thomas. Commentary on the Holy Bible, 3 vols. 1979. 59.95 (ISBN 0-8407-5163-X). Nelson.
--Matthew Henry Concise Commentary on the Whole Bible. 25.95 (ISBN 0-8024-5190-X). Moody.
Henry, Matthew, ed. Matthew Henry's Commentary on the New Testament, 10 vols. 1983. 59.95 (ISBN 0-8010-4277-1). Baker Bk.
Henry, Matthew, et al. The Bethany Parallel Commentary on the New Testament. 1500p. 1983. 39.95 (ISBN 0-87123-474-2). Bethany Hse.
Hibler, Lincoln A. Four Thousand Questions & Answers on the Old & New Testament, Vol. 1. 1986. 8.95 (ISBN 0-8062-2431-2). Carlton.
Hobbs & Paschall, eds. Teacher's Bible Commentary. LC 75-189505. 24.95 (ISBN 0-8054-1116-X). Broadman.
Hora, Thomas. Commentaries on the Scriptures. 35p. 1987. pap. 4.00 (ISBN 0-913105-10-4). PAGL Pr.
Hort, F. J. & Hort, A. F. Expository & Exegetical Studies. 1980. 29.50 (ISBN 0-86524-021-3, 7103). Klock & Klock.
Huey, F. B., Jr. Layman's Bible Book Commentary: Ezekiel, Daniel, Vol. 12. LC 81-66848. 1984. 5.95 (ISBN 0-8054-1182-8). Broadman.
Humbertson, James E., ed. Evangelical Sunday School Lesson Commentary: 1983-1984. 1983. text ed. 7.95 (ISBN 0-87148-301-7). Pathway Pr.
Hunt, Don. What the Bible Says about the Unfolded Plan of God. LC 81-82988. (What the Bible Says Ser.). 500p. 1981. 13.95 (ISBN 0-89900-084-3). College Pr Pub.
Hyatt, J. P. The Heritage of Biblical Faith. LC 64-13404. 1977. pap. 9.95 (ISBN 0-8272-1416-2). CBP.
Ironside, H. A. The Best of H. A. Ironside. (Best Ser.). 296p. (Orig.). 1981. pap. 4.95 (ISBN 0-8010-5033-2). Baker Bk.
--Complete Set of Commentaries, 22 vols. 244.90 (ISBN 0-87213-350-8). Loizeaux.
--Doctor Ironside's Bible. (Illus.). pap. 4.25 (ISBN 0-87213-393-1). Loizeaux.
Irwin, C. H. The Every Day Bible Commentary. Orig. Title: Irwin's Bible Commentary. 582p. 1983. pap. 8.95 (ISBN 0-310-26531-2, 9906P). Zondervan.
Jamieson, et al. Unabridged Bible Commentary, 3 vols. 1974. 75.00 (ISBN 0-8028-8033-9). Eerdmans.
Jamieson, Fausset & Brown's Commentary on the Whole Bible. 1957. 24.95 (ISBN 0-310-26570-3, 9930). Zondervan.
Johnson, S. Lewis. The Old Testament in the New: An Argument for Biblical Inspiration. (Contemporary Evangelical Perspectives Ser.). 128p. (Orig.). 1980. pap. 4.95 (ISBN 0-310-41851-8, 18244P). Zondervan.
Kaler, Patrick. You & The Bibles: Tough Questions & Straight Answers. 64p. (Orig.). 1985. pap. 1.95 (ISBN 0-89243-240-3). Liguori Pubns.
Karris, Robert J., ed. Collegeville Bible Commentary Series, 11 Vols. 1983. Set. pap. 28.00. Liturgical Pr.
Keeble, Marshall. From Muleback to Super Jet with the Gospel. 2.50 (ISBN 0-89225-091-7). Gospel Advocate.
Kelley, Page H. Layman's Bible Book Commentary: Micah, Nahum, Habbakuk, Zephaniah, Haggai, Zechariah, Malachi, Vol. 14. LC 83-26288. 1984. 5.95 (ISBN 0-8054-1184-4). Broadman.
Kent, Dan G. Lamentations. (Bible Study Commentary Ser.). 80p. 1983. pap. 3.95 (ISBN 0-310-44011-4, 12482P). Zondervan.
Kitto, John. Kitto's Daily Bible Illustrations, 2 vols. LC 80-8069. 1934p. 1982. 64.95 (ISBN 0-8254-3025-9). Kregel.
Kraft, Robert A. Septuagintal Lexicography. LC 75-15894. (Society of Biblical Literature. Septuagint & Cognate Studies). 1975. pap. 9.95 (ISBN 0-89130-008-2, 060401). Scholars Pr GA.
Kretzmann, Paul E. Popular Commentary of the Bible, 4 Vols. 2 Pts. Set. 70.95 (ISBN 0-570-06735-9, 15-1201). Concordia.
Layman's Bible Commentary, 25 vols. Incl. Vol. 1. Introduction to the Bible; Vol. 2. Genesis; Vol. 3. Exodus; Vol. 4. Leviticus, Numbers; Vol. 5. Deuteronomy, Joshua; Vol. 6. Judges - 2 Samuel; Vol. 7. 1 Kings - 2 Chronicles; Vol. 8. Ezra - Job; Vol. 9. Psalms; Vol. 10. Proverbs - Song of Solomon; Vol. 11. Isaiah; Vol. 12. Jeremiah, Lamentations; Vol. 13. Ezekiel, Daniel; Vo. 14. Hosea - Jonah; Vol. 15. Micah - Malachi; Vol. 16. Matthew; Vol. 17. Mark; Vol. 18. Luke; Vol. 19. John; Vol. 20. Acts of the Apostles; Vol. 21. Romans - Second Corinthians; Vol. 22. Galatians - Colossians; Vol. 23. First Thessalonians - Philemon; Vol. 24. Hebrews - Second Peter; Vol. 25. First John - Revelation. LC 59-10454. 1959-64. 4.95 ea.; Set. 115.00 (ISBN 0-8042-3086-2). John Knox.
Laymon, Charles M., ed. Interpreter's One-Volume Commentary on the Bible. (Illus.). 1971. 24.95 (ISBN 0-687-19299-4); thumb indexed 28.95 (ISBN 0-687-19300-1). Abingdon.
Leeser, Isaac. The Holy Scriptures Holy Bible Commentary. 32.50 (ISBN 0-317-30499-2). Shalom.
Lewis, Gordon R. & Demarest, Bruce, eds. Challenges to Inerrancy: A Theological Response. 458p. (Orig.). 1984. pap. 13.95 (ISBN 0-8024-0237-2). Moody.
Lockyer, Herbert, ed. Light to Live By (Wedding Edition) 384p. 1981. graduation ed. 9.95 (ISBN 0-310-28230-6, 10145); pap. 9.95 all-occasion ed. (ISBN 0-310-28211-X, 10124P). Zondervan.
MacDonald, Donald. Biblical Doctrine of Creation & the Fall: Genesis 1-3. 502p. 1984. lib. bdg. 18.95 (ISBN 0-86524-165-1, 0104). Klock & Klock.
McDowell, Gordon. Jesus Christ Returns by 1988? LC 83-90836. 66p. 1984. 5.95 (ISBN 0-533-05838-4). Vantage.
McKarns, James. Go Tell Everyone: A Commentary on the Sunday Readings - Cycles A-B & C. LC 85-20036. 279p. 1985. 9.95 (ISBN 0-8189-0488-7). Alba.
McKim, Donald K., ed. The Authoritative Word: Essays on the Nature of Scripture. 270p. 1983. pap. 10.95 (ISBN 0-8028-1948-6). Eerdmans.
MacKintosh, C. H. Short Papers on Scriptural Subjects, 2 vols. Set. 15.95 (ISBN 0-88172-115-8). Believers Bkshelf.
McQuilkin, Robertson. Understanding & Applying the Bible. (Orig.). 1983. pap. 8.95 (ISBN 0-8024-0457-X). Moody.

Marshall, I. Howard. First & Second Thessalonians. (New Century Bible Commentary Ser.). 240p. 1983. pap. 6.95 (ISBN 0-8028-1946-X). Eerdmans.

Mathis, Mary E. A Scriptural Treasury of Eternal Life. 1981. pap. 0.40 (ISBN 0-570-08357-5, 12-2937). Concordia.

--A Scriptural Treasury of Forgiveness. 1981. pap. 0.40 (12-2935). Concordia.

--A Scriptural Treasury of Guidance. 1981. pap. 0.40 (ISBN 0-570-08350-8, 12-2930). Concordia.

--A Scriptural Treasury of Hope. LC 12-2931. 1981. pap. 0.40 (ISBN 0-570-08351-6). Concordia.

--A Scriptural Treasury of Joy. 1981. pap. 0.40 (ISBN 0-570-08353-2, 12-2933). Concordia.

--A Scriptural Treasury of Love. 1981. pap. 0.40 (ISBN 0-570-08356-7, 12-2936). Concordia.

Mears, Henrietta C. What the Bible is All About. Rev. ed. 642p. 1987. pap. 9.95 (ISBN 0-8423-7902-9). Tyndale.

Melville, Cuthbert. The Rolling Files: A Study of the Bible. 1980. 7.95 (ISBN 0-682-48165-3). Exposition Pr FL.

Meyer, F. B. F. B. Meyer Bible Commentary. 1979. cloth 15.95 (ISBN 0-8423-4250-8). Tyndale.

Mize, Terry. More Than Conquerors. rev ed. 224p. 1981. pap. text ed. 3.95 (ISBN 0-89274-200-3, HH-200). Harrison Hse.

Morgan, G. Campbell. Exposition of the Whole Bible. 544p. 1959. 17.95 (ISBN 0-8007-0088-0). Revell.

Morin, Jean. Commentarius de Sacris Ecclesiae Ordinationibus. 740p. Repr. of 1695 ed. text ed. 165.60 (ISBN 0-576-99716-1, Pub. by Gregg Intl Pubs England). Gregg Intl.

Morris, Leon, et al. The Expositor's Bible Commentary, Vol. 12. 1986. cloth 19.95 (ISBN 0-88469-198-5). BMH Bks.

Naylor, Thomas H. Strategic Planning Management. 156p. 1980. pap. 13.00 (ISBN 0-912841-15-X, 03). Planning Forum.

Neil, William. Harper's Bible Commentary. LC 63-7607. 544p. 1975. pap. 7.95 (ISBN 0-06-066090-2, RD 92, HarpR). Har-Row.

O'Donovan, Daniel, tr. Bernard of Clairvaux, Treatises III: On Grace & Free Choice, in Praise of the New Knighthood. (Cistercian Studies Ser.: No. 3). 1977. 10.95 (ISBN 0-87907-119-2); pap. 4.95 (ISBN 0-87907-719-0). Cistercian Pubns.

Opatz, Patricia G. Be Still & Know That I Am God. 64p. 1981. softcover 2.95 (ISBN 0-8146-1231-8). Liturgical Pr.

Packard, Dennis J. & Packard, Sandra. Feasting Upon the Word. LC 81-12446. 242p. 7.95 (ISBN 0-87747-879-1). Deseret Bk.

Packer, J. I. God Has Spoken. rev. ed. LC 80-7789. (Orig.). 1980. pap. 4.95 (ISBN 0-87784-656-1). Inter-Varsity.

Penelope, Sr., tr. William of St. Thierry: On Contemplating God, Prayer, Meditations. (Cistercian Fathers Ser.: No. 3). 1970. pap. 5.00 (ISBN 0-87907-903-7). Cistercian Pubns.

Pink, Arthur W. Gleanings from the Scriptures. LC 73-80942. 1970. pap. 10.95 (ISBN 0-8024-3006-6). Moody.

Poole, Matthew. A Commentary on the Holy Bible, 3 vols. 1979. Set. 92.95 (ISBN 0-85151-211-9); 35.95 ea. Vol.1, Genesis through Job (ISBN 0-85151-054-X). Vol. 2, Psalms through Malachi (ISBN 0-85151-134-1). Vol. 3, Matthew through Revelation (ISBN 0-85151-135-X). Banner of Truth.

Powell, Ivor. Bible Highways. LC 85-8097. 192p. 1985. pap. 5.95 (ISBN 0-8254-3521-8). Kregel.

--Bible Windows. LC 85-8103. 188p. 1985. pap. 5.95 (ISBN 0-8254-3522-6). Kregel.

Price, Eugenia. Another Day. LC 84-7697. 168p. 1984. 9.95 (ISBN 0-385-27660-5, Dial). Doubleday.

Randolph, Boris. Bible Verses in Verse. LC 80-67992. 144p. 1980. pap. 3.95 (ISBN 0-87516-424-2). De Vorss.

Regehr, Margaret. The Golden Thread. (Illus.). 209p. (Orig.). 1985. pap. text ed. 7.00 (ISBN 0-9614486-0-1). M Regehr.

Ridderbos, J. Bible Student's Commentary: Isaiah. (Bible Student's Commentary Ser.). 528p. 1985. 24.95 (ISBN 0-310-45270-8, 11761). Zondervan.

Robinson, James M., et al. Bultmann School of Biblical Interpretation: New Directions. Funk, Robert W. & Ebeling, Gerhard, eds. 1965. lib. bdg. 17.50x (ISBN 0-88307-242-4). Gannon.

Roehrs & Franzmann. Concordia Self-Study Commentary. LC 15-2721. 1979. 21.95 (ISBN 0-570-03277-6). Concordia.

Roesel, Carol. Impressions. (Illus., Orig.). 1982. pap. 3.95 (ISBN 0-89081-317-5). Harvest Hse.

Rybolt, John E. Wisdom. (Collegeville Bible Commentary: Old Testament Ser.: Vol. 20). 112p. 1986. pap. 2.95 (ISBN 0-8146-1477-9). Liturgical Pr.

St. Thomas Aquinas. Commentary on St. Paul's Epistle to the Ephesians. Lamb, M. L., tr. LC 66-19307. (Aquinas Scripture Ser.). 1966. Vol. 2. 10.00x (ISBN 0-87343-022-0). Magi Bks.

--Commentary on St. Paul's Epistle to the Galatians. Larcher, F. R., tr. LC 66-19306. (Aquinas Scripture Ser.). 1966. Vol. 1. 10.00x (ISBN 0-87343-021-2). Magi Bks.

Salmond, S. D. The Biblical Doctrine of Immortality. 718p. 1984. lib. bdg. 26.95 (ISBN 0-86524-164-3, 8804). Klock & Klock.

Sanford, Ruth. Do You Feel Alone in the Spirit? 1978. pap. 1.95 (ISBN 0-89283-056-5). Servant.

Saucy, Richard L. Is Bible Reliable, Bk. 2. Wong, Ernest, tr. (Basic Doctrine Ser.). (Chinese.). 1985. pap. write for info. (ISBN 0-941598-28-4). Living Spring Pubns.

Seagren, Daniel R. Love Carved in Stone. LC 82-23195. 1983. pap. text ed. 3.50 (ISBN 0-8307-0840-5, S371101). Regal.

Shank, Stanley, ed. Test Your Bible Power: A Good Book Quiz. (Epiphany Bks.). 1983. pap. 1.95 (ISBN 0-345-30663-5). Ballantine.

Sharp, C. J. New Training for Service. rev. ed. (Illus.). 128p. (Orig.). 1942. pap. 2.95 (ISBN 0-87239-334-8, 3059). Standard Pub.

Shaw, W. Frank. Chapters of Symbolism. 1979. Repr. of 1897 ed. lib. bdg. 45.00 (ISBN 0-8495-4902-7). Arden Lib.

Shetler, Sanford G. Paul's Letter to the Corinthians 55 A.D. (Compact Commentary Ser). 1971. 7.80 (ISBN 0-87813-504-9); pap. 4.65 (ISBN 0-87813-503-0). Christian Light.

Smith, F. G. What the Bible Teaches. 576p. Repr. of 1914 ed. 5.50 (ISBN 0-686-29174-3). Faith Pub Hse.

Sparkman, G. Temp. The Salvation & Nurture of the Child of God. 1983. 9.95 (ISBN 0-8170-0985-X). Judson.

Speck, Von S. & Riggle, H. M. Biblische Lehren. 343p. 1982. pap. 4.00 (ISBN 0-686-36267-5). Faith Pub Hse.

Speiser, Ephraim A. Oriental & Biblical Studies: Collected Writings of E. A. Speiser. Greenberg, Moshe & Finkelstein, Jacob J., eds. LC 65-21779. pap. 154.00 (ISBN 0-317-08338-4, 2003802). Bks Demand UMI.

Spence, H. D. & Exell, T. S. The Pulpit Commentary, 23 vols. Incl. Old Testament only, 14 Vols. 320.00 (ISBN 0-8028-8056-8, 2209); New Testament only, 8 Vols. 200.00 (ISBN 0-8028-8057-6, 2210). 1959. Repr. Set. 520.00 (ISBN 0-8028-8055-X); 0er vol 22.95. Eerdmans.

Spence, H. D. & Exell, Joseph S., eds. The Pulpit Commentary, 23 vols. 26612p. Date not set. Set. 520.00 (ISBN 0-917006-32-1). Hendrickson MA.

Spohn, William C. What Are They Saying about Scripture & Ethics? (WATSA Ser.). (Orig.). 1984. pap. 4.95 (ISBN 0-8091-2624-9). Paulist Pr.

Spurgeon, C. H. The Golden Alphabet (on Psalm 119) 1980. pap. 4.25 (ISBN 0-686-09094-2). Pilgrim Pubns.

--Scriptures. 1978. pap. 1.95 (ISBN 0-686-23027-2). Pilgrim Pubns.

Spurgeon, Charles H. Guide to Commentaries. 0.50 (ISBN 0-85151-400-6). Banner of Truth.

--Metropolitan Tabernacle Pulpit. 1971. Vol. 31. 14.95. Banner of Truth.

Stanton, Elizabeth C. The Woman's Bible, 2 vols. in 1. LC 72-2626. (American Women Ser: Images & Realities). 380p. 1972. Repr. of 1895 ed. 25.50 (ISBN 0-405-04481-X). Ayer Co Pubs.

Steele, David. God Must Have a Sense of Humor, He Made Aadvarks & Orangutans..., & Me! LC 82-84780. (Illus., Orig.). 1983. pap. 6.00 (ISBN 0-937088-09-9). Illum Pr.

Steinsaltz, Adin. Biblical Images: Men & Women of the Book. LC 83-46081. 256p. 1985. pap. 6.95 (ISBN 0-465-00671-X, PL-5158). Basic.

Stott, John R. The Authority of the Bible. pap. 0.75 (ISBN 0-87784-147-0). Inter-Varsity.

Sumner, Robert L. Armstrongism: The Worldwide Church of God Examined in the Searching Light of Scripture. 424p. 1974. 12.95 (ISBN 0-914012-15-0, Pub. by Bibl Evang Pr). Sword of Lord.

Swank, George W. Living in God's Power. 112p. 1983. pap. 5.95 (ISBN 0-8170-0968-X). Judson.

Tassell, Paul. Sweeter Than Honey. 1978. pap. 2.95 (ISBN 0-87227-068-8). Reg Baptist.

Taubes, Hella. Bible Speaks, 3 vols. Bloch, Lolla, tr. (Illus.). 1974. 14.95x ea. (ISBN 0-686-76831-0). Set. Bloch.

Tenney, Merrill C. & Longenecker, Richard N. The Expositor's Bible Commentary, Vol. 9. 1986. 19.95 (ISBN 0-88469-195-0). BMH Bks.

Thomas, Leslie G. What the Bible Teaches, 2 vols. 1962. Vol. 1. 5.95 (ISBN 0-88027-023-3). Vol. II (ISBN 0-88027-024-1). Firm Foun Pub.

Tickle, John. Un Estudio de la Biblia, Libro II. Diaz, Olimpia, tr. (Span.). 96p. 1983. 3.95 (ISBN 0-89243-184-9). Liguori Pubns.

Tolbert, Malcolm O. Layman's Bible Book Commentary: Phillppians - Philemon, Vol. 22. LC 79-51998. 1980. 5.95 (ISBN 0-8054-1192-5). Broadman.

Tomlinson, M. A. Basic Bible Beliefs. 1961. pap. 3.25 (ISBN 0-934942-01-3). White Wing Pub.

Torrey, R. A. The Treasury of Scripture Knowledge. 778p. Date not set. 17.95 (ISBN 0-917006-22-4). Hendrickson MA.

Tournier, Paul. The Whole Person in a Broken World: A Biblical Remedy for Today's World. LC 81-6885. 192p. 1981. pap. 6.95 (ISBN 0-06-068312-0, HarpR, RD 360). Har-Row.

Traylor, John H., Jr. Layman's Bible Book Commentary: One & Two Kings, Two Chronicles, Vol. 6. LC 80-67148. 1982. 5.95 (ISBN 0-8054-1176-3). Broadman.

Tunyogi, Andrew C. Divine Struggle for Human Salvation: Biblical Convictions in Their Historical Settings. LC 78-65852. 1979. pap. text ed. 19.75 (ISBN 0-8191-0676-3). U Pr of Amer.

Turrettin, Thomas. The Doctrine of Scripture: Locus 2 of Institutio Theologiae Elencticae. Beardslee, John W., III, ed. 200p. (Orig.). 1981. pap. 7.95 (ISBN 0-8010-8857-7). Baker Bk.

Unger, Merill F. Unger's Survey of the Bible. LC 81-82675. 432p. 1981. pap. 12.95 (ISBN 0-89081-298-5). Harvest Hse.

Vawter, Bruce. Sirach. (Bible Ser.). Pt. 1. pap. 1.00 (ISBN 0-8091-5138-3); Pt. 2. pap. 1.00 (ISBN 0-8091-5139-1). Paulist Pr.

Vincent, Thomas. The Shorter Catechism Explained from Scripture. (Puritan Paperbacks). 282p. (Orig.). 1980. pap. 4.95 (ISBN 0-85151-314-X). Banner of Truth.

Weaver, Horace R. International Lesson Annual, 1987-1988. 448p. 1987. pap. 7.95 (ISBN 0-687-19151-3). Abingdon.

Wells, Paul R. James Barr & the Bible: Critique of a New Liberalism. 1980. pap. 12.00 (ISBN 0-87552-546-6). Presby & Reformed.

Wesberry, James P. Bread in a Barren Land. LC 81-8668. 1982. pap. 4.95 (ISBN 0-8054-5103-X). Broadman.

Wesley's Old & New Testament Notes. 200.00 (ISBN 0-686-12928-8). Schmul Pub Co.

Westcott, Brooke F. The Bible in the Church. (Canterbury Bks.). 1980. pap. 6.95 (ISBN 0-8010-9627-8). Baker Bk.

Westcott, Frederick B. The Biblical Doctrine of Justification. 407p. 1983. lib. bdg. 15.25 (ISBN 0-86524-160-0, 8803). Klock & Klock.

Whedon, D. D. Whedon's Commentary Revised, 2 vols. 1981. Vol. Matthew Mark. 7.65 (ISBN 0-87813-917-6); Vol. Luke John. 7.65 (ISBN 0-87813-918-4). Christian Light.

Whitelaw, Robert. The Gospel Millennium & Obedience to the Scripture. pap. 0.75 (ISBN 0-685-88376-0). Reiner.

Williams, George. The Student's Commentary on the Holy Scriptures. LC 75-13929. 1971. 29.95 (ISBN 0-8254-4001-7). Kregel.

Winter, David. Believing the Bible. LC 82-62582. 116p. (Orig.). 1983. pap. 5.95 (ISBN 0-8192-1325-X). Morehouse.

Wood, A. Skevington, et al. The Expositor's Bible Commentary, Vol. 11. 1986. 19.95 (ISBN 0-88469-197-7). BMH Bks.

Yamauchi, Edwin. Stones & the Scriptures. 1981. pap. 5.95 (ISBN 0-8010-9916-1). Baker Bk.

BIBLE–COMMENTARIES–N. T.

Here are entered only Commentaries on the New Testament as a whole.

Anderson, Julian G. The Story of Jesus the Messiah: Acts & Letters. (New Testament Wkbk.). (Illus.). 1979. pap. text ed. 3.95 (ISBN 0-9602128-3-3). Anderson Publ.

Barclay, William. Great Themes of the New Testament. LC 79-18213. 122p. 1979. pap. 4.95 (ISBN 0-664-24286-3). Westminster.

Barnes, Albert. Barnes' Notes on the New Testament. LC 62-8727. 1776p. 1966. 39.95 (ISBN 0-8254-2200-0). Kregel.

Bengel, John A. New Testament Commentary, 2 Vols. LC 70-155250. 1910p. 1982. Set. 59.95 (ISBN 0-8254-2242-6). Kregel.

Bolding, Amy. Cheerful Devotions to Give. (Amy Bolding Library). 96p. 1984. pap. 4.50 (ISBN 0-8010-0868-9). Baker Bk.

Bratcher, R. G., ed. Marginal Notes for the New Testament. 125p. 1980. softcover 2.50x (ISBN 0-8267-0026-8, 08558, Pub. by United Bible). Am Bible.

Briscoe, Stuart. Bound for Joy. LC 84-17778. (Bible Commentary for Laymen Ser.). 192p. 1984. pap. 3.95 (ISBN 0-8307-1004-3, S383107). Regal.

Calvin, John. Calvin's New Testament Commentaries, 12 vols. Torrance, David W. & Torrance, Thomas F., eds. Incl. The Gospel According to St. John; Chapters 1-10. Parker, T. H., tr. 10.95 (ISBN 0-8028-2044-1); The Gospel According to St. John; Chapters 11-21. Parker, T. H., tr. 10.95 (ISBN 0-8028-2045-X); Acts of the Apostles, Vol. 1. McDonald, W. J., tr. 10.95 (ISBN 0-8028-2046-8); Acts of the Apostles, Vol. 2. Fraser, John W., tr. 10.95 (ISBN 0-8028-2047-6); The Epistle to the Romans & the Thessalonians. Mackenzie, R., tr. 9.95 (ISBN 0-8028-2048-4); The First Epistle to the Corinthians. Fraser, John W., tr. 10.95 (ISBN 0-8028-2049-2); Galatians, Ephesians, Philippians, Colossians. Parker, T. H., tr. 10.95 (ISBN 0-8028-2051-4); Hebrews and Peter First & Second. Johnson, W. B., tr. 10.95 (ISBN 0-8028-2052-2); Second Corinthians, Timothy, Titus. & Philemon. Smail, T. A. 10.95 (ISBN 0-8028-2050-6); Harmony of the Gospels, 3 Vols. Parker, T. H., tr. 10.95 ea. (ISBN 0-685-22779-0). Vol. 1 (ISBN 0-8028-2038-7). Vol. 2 (ISBN 0-8028-2039-5). Vol. 3 (ISBN 0-8028-2040-9). 1960. Set. 131.40 (ISBN 0-8028-2053-0). Eerdmans.

Childs, Brevard S. The New Testament as Canon: An Introduction. LC 84-21169. 640p. 1985. 22.95 (ISBN 0-8006-0739-2, 1-739). Fortress.

Clarke, Adam. Clarke's Commentary, 3 vols. Incl. Vol. 1. Genesis-Esther (ISBN 0-687-09119-5); Vol. 2. Job-Malachi (ISBN 0-687-09120-9); Vol. 3. Matthew-Revelation (ISBN 0-687-09121-7). 1977. Set. 95.00 (ISBN 0-687-09118-7); 34.50 ea. Abingdon.

Collins, Raymond F. Introduction to the New Testament. LC 82-45070. (Illus.). 480p. 1983. 24.95 (ISBN 0-385-18126-4). Doubleday.

Cullmann, Oscar. The Christology of the New Testament. rev. ed. Guthrie, Shirley C. & Hall, Charles A. M., trs. LC 59-10178. 364p. 1980. pap. 12.95 (ISBN 0-664-24351-7). Westminster.

Davids, Peter. Commentary on James: New International Greek Testament Commentary. 226p. 1982. 15.95 (ISBN 0-8028-2388-2). Eerdmans.

Elliott, John H. & Martin, R. A. Augsburg Commentary on the New Testament. LC 82-70962. 192p. (Orig.). 1982. 8.95 (ISBN 0-8066-1937-6, 10-9042). Augsburg.

Erdman's Commentary on New Testament, 17 vols. (Erdmans Commentaries Ser.). 65.00 (ISBN 0-8010-3409-4). Baker Bk.

Farmer, William R. & Farkasfalvy, Denis. The Formation of the New Testament Canon: An Ecumenical Approach. LC 82-62417. (Theological Inquiries Ser.). 1983. pap. 8.95 (ISBN 0-8091-2495-5). Paulist Pr.

Farstad, Arthur L. & Hodges, Zane C., eds. The Greek New Testament According to the Majority Text. 78p. 1982. 14.95 (ISBN 0-8407-4963-5). Nelson.

Fehl, Jim, ed. Standard Lesson Commentary, 1986-87. 450p. 1986. text ed. 9.50 (ISBN 0-87403-010-2, 74017); pap. text ed. 7.95 (ISBN 0-87403-009-9, 1987). Standard Pub.

Fernandez, Domingo S. Una Interpretacion Del Apocalipsis. (Span.). 234p. 1985. pap. 3.50 (ISBN 0-311-04312-7). Casa Bautista.

Fitzmyer, J. A. To Advance the Gospel: New Testament Essays. 320p. 1981. 19.50x (ISBN 0-8245-0008-3). Crossroad NY.

Ford, Desmond. The Abomination of Desolation in Biblical Eschatology. LC 79-64195. 1979. pap. text ed. 14.25 (ISBN 0-8191-0757-3). U Pr of Amer.

Forestell, J. T. Targumic Traditions. LC 79-19293. (Society of Biblical Literature Aramaic Studies: No. 4). 151p. 1984. pap. 12.00 (ISBN 0-89130-352-9, 06-13-04). Scholars Pr GA.

Freyne, Sean. The World of the New Testament. (New Testament Message Ser.: Vol. 2). 12.95 (ISBN 0-89453-190-5); pap. 8.95 (ISBN 0-89453-125-5). M Glazier.

Fromer, Margaret & Keyes, Sharrel. Letters to Timothy: Discipleship in Action. LC 74-19763. (Fisherman Bible Study Guide Ser.). 80p. 1974. saddle-stitched 2.95 (ISBN 0-87788-490-0). Shaw Pubs.

Fuller, Reginald H. Foundations of New Testament Christology. 1965. lib. bdg. 25.00x (ISBN 0-684-15532-X, ScribT); pap. 1.50 (ISBN 0-684-15537-0, SL772, ScribT). Scribner.

Gospel Advocate. Commentaries on the New Testament. Incl. Matthew. Boles, H. Leo (ISBN 0-89225-001-1); Mark. Dorris, C. E (ISBN 0-89225-002-X); Luke. Boles, H. Leo (ISBN 0-89225-003-8); John. Dorris, C. E (ISBN 0-89225-004-6); Acts. Boles, H. Leo (ISBN 0-89225-005-4); Romans. Lipscomb, David & Shepherd, J. W. (ISBN 0-89225-006-2); Corinthians I. Lipscomb, David & Shepard, J. W. (ISBN 0-89225-007-0); Corinthians II - Galatians. Lipscomb, David & Shepherd, J. W. (ISBN 0-89225-008-9); Ephesians - Colossians. Shepherd, J. W (ISBN 0-89225-009-7); Thess. I, II; Tim. I, II; Titus; Philomen. Shepherd, J. W (ISBN 0-89225-010-0); Hebrews. Milligan, Robert (ISBN 0-89225-011-9); James. Woods, Guy N (ISBN 0-89225-012-7); Peter I, II; John I, II, III; Jude. Woods, Guy N (ISBN 0-89225-013-5); Revelation. Hinds, John T (ISBN 0-89225-014-3). Set. 135.00 (ISBN 0-89225-000-3); 10.95 ea. Gospel Advocate.

Gromacki, Robert G. New Testament Survey. LC 74-83793. 1974. 9.95 (ISBN 0-87227-018-1). Reg Baptist.

Gundry, Robert H. Somain Biblical Theology: With Emphasis on Pauline Anthropology. LC 75-22975. (Society for New Testament Studies: No. 29). pap. 69.50 (ISBN 0-317-28002-3, 2025584). Bks Demand UMI.

--A Survey of the New Testament. (Illus.). 432p. 1982. 17.95 (ISBN 0-310-25410-8, 18280). Zondervan.

Guthrie, Donald. The Epistle to the Hebrews: An Introduction & Commentary. (Tyndale New Testament Commentaries: Vol. 15). 288p. 1983. pap. 5.95 (ISBN 0-8028-1427-1). Eerdmans.

Hadwin, M. R. The Role of New Testament Examples As Related to Biblical Authority. 1974. pap. 2.75 (ISBN 0-88027-038-1). Firm Foun Pub.

Harrington, Daniel. Light of All Nations: Essays on the Church in New Testament Research. (Good News Studies Ser.: Vol. 3). 1982. pap. 7.95 (ISBN 0-89453-291-X). M Glazier.

Harris, F. Donald & Harris, Ronald A. The Trinity: Is the Doctrine Biblical-Is It Important? LC 77-123613. 1971. pap. 1.50 (ISBN 0-87213-310-9). Loizeaux.

Harvey, A. E. Companion to the New Testament: The New English Bible. 858p. 1970. 49.50x (ISBN 0-19-826160-8); pap. 24.95x (ISBN 0-19-213229-6). Oxford U Pr.

--The New English Bible Companion to the New Testament: The Gospels. (Orig.). 1972. pap. 13.95x (ISBN 0-19-826168-3). Oxford U Pr.

Hennecke, Edgar. New Testament Apocrypha, 2 vols. Incl. Vol. 1. Gospels & Related Writings. 532p. 1963. 18.95 (ISBN 0-664-20385-X); Vol. 2. Writings Relating to the Apostles; Apocalypses & Related Subjects. LC 63-7492. 852p. 1966. 32.50 (ISBN 0-664-20680-8). Westminster.

Hester, H. I. The Heart of the New Testament. 1980. Repr. of 1950 ed. 12.95 (ISBN 0-8054-1386-3). Broadman.

Howard, Fred D. Layman's Bible Book Commentary: First, Second, Third John, Jude & Revelation, Vol. 24. LC 80-66807. 1982. 5.95 (ISBN 0-8054-1194-1). Broadman.

Hunter, Archibald M. Preaching the New Testament. LC 81-19482. pap. 39.00 (ISBN 0-317-30145-4, 2025328). Bks Demand UMI.

International Congress on Biblical Studies, 6th, Oxford, 3-7 April,1978. Studia Biblica Nineteen Seventy-Eight, III: Papers on Paul & Other New Testament Authors. Livingstone, E. A., ed. (Journal for the Study of the New Testament, Supplement Ser.: No. 3). 468p. 1981. text ed. 37.50x (ISBN 0-905774-27-2, Pub. by JSOT Pr England). Eisenbrauns.

Jeremias, Joachim. The Eucharistic Words of Jesus. Perrin, Norman, tr. from Ger. LC 77-78633. 280p. 1977. pap. 12.95 (ISBN 0-8006-1319-8, 1-1319). Fortress.

Jesus Chist's One Hundred Rule Communication Program: An Axumatyation of the New Testament. (Analysis Ser.: No. 12). 1983. pap. 10.00 (ISBN 0-686-42848-X). Inst Analysis.

Johnson, B. W., ed. People's New Testament with Notes, 1 vol. 1971. 14.95 (ISBN 0-89225-141-7). Gospel Advocate.

Juel, Donald, et al. An Introduction to New Testament Literature. LC 77-18036. (Illus.). 1978. 16.50 (ISBN 0-687-01360-7); pap. 10.95 (ISBN 0-687-01361-5). Abingdon.

Kaiser, Walter C. The Uses of the Old Testament in the New. 1985. 13.95 (ISBN 0-8024-9085-9). Moody.

Knoch, A. E. Concordant Commentary on the New Testament. rev. ed. 407p. 1968. 10.00 (ISBN 0-910424-48-9). Concordant.

Knox, John. Marcion & the New Testament. LC 78-63168. (Heresies of the Early Christian & Medieval Era: Second Ser.). Repr. of 1942 ed. 31.00 (ISBN 0-404-16183-9). AMS Pr.

Kretzmann, Paul E. Popular Commentary of the Bible, 4 Vols. 2 Pts. Set. 70.95 (ISBN 0-570-06735-9, 15-1201). Concordia.

Kuemmel, Werner G. Introduction to the New Testament. rev. ed. Kee, Howard C., tr. from Ger. LC 74-26804. 624p. 1975. 16.95 (ISBN 0-687-19575-6). Abingdon.

Ladd, George E. A Theology of the New Testament. 1974. 24.95 (ISBN 0-8028-3443-4). Eerdmans.

Lambert, Gussie. Facts from Acts. 1.50 (ISBN 0-89315-056-8). Lambert Bk.

Lane, William L. Highlights of the Bible: New Testament. LC 80-50543. 160p. 1980. pap. 3.50 (ISBN 0-8307-0676-3, S343118). Regal.

Lane, William L., et al. The New Testament Speaks. 1969. 16.95 (ISBN 0-06-064917-8, HarpR). Har Row.

Lefevre, Jacques. Le Nouveau Testament, 2 Vols. 1970. Repr. of 1523 ed. 135.00 (ISBN 0-384-32082-1). Johnson Repr.

Lenski, Richard C. Interpretation of the New Testament, 12 Vols. 1933-46. Set. 235.00 (ISBN 0-8066-9012-7, 10-3360). Augsburg.

Luther, Martin. Sermons of Martin Luther: On the New Testament, 8 vols. Lenker, John N., ed. 1983. Repr. of 1904 ed. 95.00 (ISBN 0-8010-5626-8). Baker Bk.

Machem, J. Gresham. The New Testament: An Introduction to Its History & Literature. 1976. 11.95 (ISBN 0-85151-240-2). Banner of Truth.

McKeating, Henry, ed. The Books of Amos, Hosea, Micah. (Cambridge Bible Commentary on the New English Bible, Old Testament Ser.). (Illus.). 1971. 22.95 (ISBN 0-521-08133-5); pap. 10.95 (ISBN 0-521-09647-2). Cambridge U Pr.

McKenzie, J. L., ed. New Testament for Spiritual Reading, 25 vols. Incl. Vol. 1. Gospel According to St. Matthew, Pt. 1 (ISBN 0-8245-0334-1); Vol. 2. Gospel According to St. Matthew, Pt. 2 (ISBN 0-8245-0335-X) (ISBN 0-8245-0111-X); Vol. 3. Gospel According to St. Mark, Pt. 1 (ISBN 0-8245-0336-8) (ISBN 0-8245-0112-8); Vol. 4. Gospel According to St. Mark, Pt. 2 (ISBN 0-8245-0337-6) (ISBN 0-8245-0113-6); Vol. 5. Gospel According to St. Luke, Pt. 1 (ISBN 0-8245-0338-4) (ISBN 0-8245-0114-4); Vol. 6. Gospel According to St. Luke, Pt. 2 (ISBN 0-8245-0339-2) (ISBN 0-8245-0115-2); Vol. 7. Gospel According to St. John, Pt. 1 (ISBN 0-8245-0340-6) (ISBN 0-8245-0116-0); Vol. 8. Gospel According to St. John, Pt. 2 (ISBN 0-8164-1079-8) (ISBN 0-8245-0117-9); Vol. 9. Gospel According to St. John, Pt. 3 (ISBN 0-8245-0342-2) (ISBN 0-8245-0118-7); Vol. 10. Acts of the Apostles, Pt. 1 (ISBN 0-8245-0343-0) (ISBN 0-8245-0119-5); Vol. 11. Acts of the Apostles, Pt. 2 (ISBN 0-8245-0344-9) (ISBN 0-8245-0120-9); Vol. 12. Epistle to the Romans (ISBN 0-8245-0345-7) (ISBN 0-8245-0121-7); Vol. 13. First Epistle to the Corinthians (ISBN 0-8245-0346-5) (ISBN 0-8245-0122-5); Vol. 14. Second Epistle to the Corinthians (ISBN 0-8245-0347-3) (ISBN 0-8245-0123-3); Vol. 15. Epistle to the Galatians (ISBN 0-8245-0348-1) (ISBN 0-8245-0124-1); Vol. 16. Epistle to the Ephesians (ISBN 0-8245-0349-X) (ISBN 0-8245-0125-X); Vol. 17. Epistle to the Philippians. Epistle to the Colossians (ISBN 0-8164-1088-7) (ISBN 0-8245-0126-8); Vol. 18. First Epistle to the Thessalonians. Second Epistle to the Thessalonians (ISBN 0-8245-0352-X) (ISBN 0-8245-0127-6); Vol. 19. First Epistle to Timothy. Second Epistle to Timothy (ISBN 0-8245-0353-8) (ISBN 0-8245-0128-4); Vol. 20. Epistle to Titus. Epistle to Philemon (ISBN 0-8245-0354-6) (ISBN 0-8245-0129-2); Vol. 21. Epistle to the Hebrews. Epistle to James (ISBN 0-8245-0355-4) (ISBN 0-8245-0130-6); Vol. 22. First Epistle to Peter. Second Epistle to Peter (ISBN 0-8245-0356-2) (ISBN 0-8245-0131-4); Vol. 23. Epistle to Jude. Three Epistles of John (ISBN 0-8245-0357-0) (ISBN 0-8245-0132-2); Vol. 24. The Revelation of St. John, Pt. 1 (ISBN 0-8245-0358-9) (ISBN 0-8245-0133-0); Vol. 25. The Revelation of St. John, Pt. 2 (ISBN 0-8245-0359-7) (ISBN 0-8245-0134-9). 10.00 ea.; Set. 123.75 (ISBN 0-8245-0135-7); pap. 4.95 ea. Crossroad NY.

McNamara, Martin. Targum & Testament: Aramaic Paraphrases of the Hebrew Bible: a Light on the New Testament. 226p. 1972. 17.50x (ISBN 0-7165-0619-X, BBA 02203, Pub. by Irish Academic Pr Ireland). Biblio Dist.

Malina, Bruce J. The New Testament World: Insights from Cultural Anthropology. LC 80-84650. (Illus.). 169p. 1981. pap. 10.95 (ISBN 0-8042-0423-3). John Knox.

Malmin, Ken. New Testament Survey. 1975. 4.25 (ISBN 0-914936-22-0). Bible Temple.

Marshall, Alfred. NIV Interliear Greek-English New Testament. 1976. 21.95 (ISBN 0-310-28680-8). Zondervan.

Martin, Ralph P. New Testament Foundations: A Guide for Christian Students, Vol. 2. 1986. pap. 9.95 (ISBN 0-8028-0076-9). Eerdmans.

Meyer, Heinrich A. New Testament Commentary, 11 vols. 7050p. 250.00 (ISBN 0-913573-04-3). Hendrickson MA.

Moore, John & Neff, Kenneth. New Testament Blueprint for the Church. 1985. pap. 7.95 (ISBN 0-8024-5901-3). Moody.

Moule, C. F. The Birth of the New Testament. rev. ed. LC 81-47432. 336p. 1981. pap. 9.50 (ISBN 0-06-066029-5, RD 365, HarpR). Har-Row.

Murphy, Richard T. Background to the Bible: An Introduction to Scripture Study. (Illus.). 1978. pap. 5.95 (ISBN 0-89283-055-7). Servant.

New Testament: A Study Aid. (Book Notes). (Orig.). 1985. pap. text ed. 2.50 (ISBN 0-8120-3530-5). Barron.

Nicoll, W. Robertson, ed. Expositor's Greek New Testament, 5 Vols. 1952. Set. 60.00 (ISBN 0-8028-2108-1). Eerdmans.

Nilsen, Mary Y. Real Living: A Small Group Life Experience with the Gospel of Luke, Pt. 2. (Illus.). 1978. pap. text ed. 5.65 (ISBN 0-03-022141-2, HarpR); tchr's. guide 7.95 (ISBN 0-03-022146-3). Har-Row.

Norbie, Don. New Testament Church Organization. pap. 2.50 (ISBN 0-937396-28-1). Walterick Pubs.

Osiek, Carolyn. What Are They Saying about the Social Setting of the New Testament? (WATSA Ser.). (Orig.). 1984. pap. 4.95 (ISBN 0-8091-2625-7). Paulist Pr.

Packer, J. I. & Tenney, Merrill C., eds. The World of the New Testament. LC 82-12548. 1982. pap. 6.95 (ISBN 0-8407-5821-9). Nelson.

Perkins, Pheme. Love Commands in the New Testament. 144p. (Orig.). 1982. pap. 5.95 (ISBN 0-8091-2450-5). Paulist Pr.

--Reading the New Testament: An Introduction. LC 78-51892. 352p. 1978. pap. 5.95 (ISBN 0-8091-9535-6). Paulist Pr.

--Resurrection: New Testament Witness & Contemporary Reflection. LC 83-25473. 564p. 1984. 19.95 (ISBN 0-385-17256-7). Doubleday.

Powell, Terry. Nobody's Perfect. LC 78-65556. 116p. 1979. pap. 3.95 (ISBN 0-88207-577-2). Victor Bks.

Price, James L. The New Testament. 544p. 1986. lib. bdg. write for info. (ISBN 0-02-396610-6). Macmillan.

Pruitt, Fred. The New Testament Church & Its Symbols. 131p. 1.00 (ISBN 0-686-29157-3). Faith Pub Hse.

Reference Passage Bible, New Testament: With Old Testament References. LC 78-56146. 1978. 9.95 (ISBN 0-88270-275-0). Bridge Pub.

Reuchlin, Abelard. The True Authorship of the New Testament. 1979. pap. 4.00 (ISBN 0-930808-02-9). Vector Assocs.

Rife, J. Merle. The Nature & Origin of the New Testament. LC 74-80276. 1975. 9.95 (ISBN 0-8022-2148-3). Philos Lib.

Scheidler, Bill. New Testament Church & Its Ministries. (Illus.). 120p. 1980. pap. 8.95 (ISBN 0-914936-43-3). Bible Temple.

Schell, William G. The Ordinances of the New Testament. 67p. pap. 0.50 (ISBN 0-686-29158-1). Faith Pub Hse.

Segovia, Fernando F., ed. Discipleship in the New Testament. LC 85-47730. 240p. 1985. pap. 16.95 (ISBN 0-8006-1873-4, 1-1873). Fortress.

Southern, Paul. New Testament in Survey. pap. 2.70 (ISBN 0-89137-550-3). Quality Pubns.

Spence, H. D. & Exell, T. S. The Pulpit Commentary, 23 vols. Incl. Old Testament only, 14 Vols. 320.00 (ISBN 0-8028-8056-8, 2209); New Testament only, 8 Vols. 200.00 (ISBN 0-8028-8057-6, 2210). 1959. Repr. Set. 520.00 (ISBN 0-8028-8055-X); 0er vol 22.95. Eerdmans.

Tan, Paul L. The New Jerusalem. LC 78-73221. 1978. pap. text ed. 1.95 (ISBN 0-932940-05-6). Assurance Pubs.

Trites, Allison A. New Testament Witness in Today's World. 144p. 1982. pap. 8.95 (ISBN 0-8170-0988-4). Judson.

Tyndale, William. Expositions & Notes on Sundry Portions of the Holy Scriptures. Repr. of 1849 ed. 31.00 (ISBN 0-384-62260-7). Johnson Repr.

Tyson, Joseph B. The New Testament & Early Christianity. 480p. 1984. text ed. write for info. (ISBN 0-02-421890-1). Macmillan.

Verhey, Allen. The Great Reversal: Ethics & the New Testament. 288p. (Orig.). 1984. pap. 13.95 (ISBN 0-8028-0004-1). Eerdmans.

Vincent, Marvin. Word Studies in the New Testament, 4 Vols. 1957. 49.95 (ISBN 0-8028-8083-5). Eerdmans.

Warren, Thomas B. & Elkins, Garland, eds. The Living Messages of the Books of the New Testament. 1976. 13.00 (ISBN 0-934916-35-7). Natl Christian Pr.

Wartick, Wallace. Lessons on New Testament Evidences. 250p. 1980. pap. 4.95 (ISBN 0-89900-141-6). College Pr Pub.

Weinrich, William C., ed. The New Testament Age: Essays in Honor of Bo Reicke, 2 vols. LC 84-713. 606p. 1984. 44.95x (ISBN 0-86554-097-7, MUP/H89). Mercer Univ Pr.

Wesley's New Testament Notes. 14.95 (ISBN 0-686-12927-X). Schmul Pub Co.

Westermann, Claus. Handbook to the New Testament. Boyd, Robert H., ed. & tr. LC 69-14190. 1977. pap. 9.95 (ISBN 0-8066-1600-8, 10-2946). Augsburg.

Weymouth, R. F. New Testament in Modern Speech. 3rd ed. LC 78-9536. 750p. 1978. kivar 14.95 (ISBN 0-8254-4025-4). Kregel.

Weymouth, Richard F. The New Testament in Modern Speech. 6th ed. 457p. 1983. 9.50 (ISBN 0-227-67550-9, Pub. by J Clarke UK). Attic Pr.

Wilkins, Ronald J. Reading the New Testament. (To Live Is Christ Ser.). 160p. 1983. pap. 5.50 extended study (ISBN 0-697-01810-5); tchr's. manual 4.00 (ISBN 0-697-01811-3); spirit masters 12.95 (ISBN 0-697-01674-9); pap. 3.95 short ed. (ISBN 0-697-01673-0); tchr's. manual 3.75 (ISBN 0-697-01680-3). Wm C Brown.

Williams, Rowan. Christian Spirituality: A Theological History from the New Testament to Luther & St. John of the Cross. LC 80-82190. 193p. 1980. 10.95 (ISBN 0-8042-0660-0); pap. 8.95 (ISBN 0-8042-0508-6). John Knox.

Wilson, T. Ernest. Mystery Doctrines of the New Testament: God's Sacred Secrets. LC 74-78881. 128p. 1975. pap. text ed. 2.50 (ISBN 0-87213-962-X). Loizeaux.

Wolter, Michael. Rechtfertigung und zukuenftiges Heil. Untersuchungen zu Roemer 5, 1-11. (Beihefte zur Zeitschrift fuer die Neutestamentliche Wissenschaft: No. 43). 1978. 29.20x (ISBN 3-11-007579-2). De Gruyter.

Wuest, Kenneth S. Word Studies in the Greek New Testament, for the English Reader, 16 bks. Incl. Bk. 1. Golden Nuggets. pap. 4.95 (ISBN 0-8028-1242-2); Bk. 2. Bypaths. pap. 3.95 (ISBN 0-8028-1318-6); Bk. 3. Treasures. pap. 3.95 (ISBN 0-8028-1243-0); Bk. 4. Untranslatable Riches. pap. 4.95 (ISBN 0-8028-1241-4); Bk. 5. Studies in Vocabulary. pap. 3.95 (ISBN 0-8028-1240-6); Bk. 6. Great Truths to Live by. pap. 4.95 (ISBN 0-8028-1246-5); Bk. 7. Mark. pap. 5.95 (ISBN 0-8028-1230-9); Bk. 8. Romans. pap. 4.95 (ISBN 0-8028-1231-7); Bk. 9. Galatians. pap. 4.95 (ISBN 0-8028-1232-5); Bk. 10. Ephesians & Colossians. pap. 5.95 (ISBN 0-8028-1233-3); Bk. 11. Philippians. pap. 4.95 (ISBN 0-8028-1234-1); Bk. 12. The Pastoral Epistles. pap. 6.95 (ISBN 0-8028-1236-8); Bk. 13. Hebrews. pap. 6.95 (ISBN 0-8028-1235-X); Bk. 14. First Peter. pap. 4.95 (ISBN 0-8028-1237-6); Bk. 15. In These Last Days. pap. 4.95 (ISBN 0-8028-1238-4); Bk. 16. Prophetic Light in the Present Darkness. pap. 2.95 (ISBN 0-8028-1239-2). Set. pap. 80.20 (ISBN 0-8028-1248-1); Current 4 vols. 69.95 (ISBN 0-8028-2280-0). Eerdmans.

Zahn, Theodor. Introduction to the New Testament, 3 vols. 1977. 48.00 (ISBN 0-86524-119-8, 8003). Klock & Klock.

Zerwick, Max. Analysis Philogica Novi Testamenti Graeci: Editio Tertia. (Scripta Pontificii Instituti Biblici,: Vol.107). (Lat.). 1966. pap. 12.00 (ISBN 88-7653-551-9). Loyola.

BIBLE–COMMENTARIES–N. T. ACTS

Acts. (Erdmans Commentaries Ser.). 4.50 (ISBN 0-8010-3392-6). Baker Bk.

Airhart, Arnold E. Beacon Bible Expositions: Vol. 5, Acts. Greathouse, William M. & Taylor, Willard H., eds. (Beacon Bible Exposition Ser.). 1977. 8.95 (ISBN 0-8341-0316-8). Beacon Hill.

Alexander, J. A. Acts of the Apostles, 2 vols. in 1. (Banner of Truth Geneva Series Commentaries). 1980. 23.95 (ISBN 0-85151-309-3). Banner of Truth.

Alexander, Joseph. Commentary on the Acts of the Apostles. 1979. 27.50 (ISBN 0-86524-025-6, 4401). Klock & Klock.

Anderson, Julian G. The Story of Jesus the Messiah: Acts & Letters. (New Testament Wkbk.). (Illus.). 1979. pap. text ed. 3.95 (ISBN 0-9602128-3-3). Anderson Publ.

Arnot, William. Studies in Acts: The Church in the House. LC 78-59141. 464p. 1978. 12.95 (ISBN 0-8254-2120-9). Kregel.

Beringer, Robert. The Easter People. 1984. 4.75 (ISBN 0-89536-682-7, 4858). CSS of Ohio.

Bruce, Frederick F., ed. The Book of the Acts. (New International Commentary on the New Testament). 1954. 16.95 (ISBN 0-8028-2182-0). Eerdmans.

Carlson, G. Raymond. The Acts Story. LC 78-57178. (Radiant Life Ser.). 128p. (Orig.). 1978. pap. 2.50 (ISBN 0-88243-913-8, 02-0913); tchr's. ed 3.95 (ISBN 0-88243-184-6, 32-0184). Gospel Pub.

Christensen, Chuck & Christensen, Winnie. Acts 1-12: God Moves in the Early Church. rev. ed. (Fisherman Bible Study Guide Ser.). 68p. 1979. saddle stitch 2.95 (ISBN 0-87788-007-7). Shaw Pubs.

Coffman, James B. Commentary on Acts. (Firm Foundation Commentary Ser). 1976. cancelled 10.95 (ISBN 0-88027-069-1). Firm Foun Pub.

Conn, Charles W. The Acts of the Apostles. 1966. pap. 4.25 (ISBN 0-87148-010-7). Pathway Pr.

Conner, Kevin. Acts. 3rd ed. 136p. 1975. 7.95 (ISBN 0-914936-16-6). Bible Temple.

Cunningham, Robert C. Getting Together with Luke & Acts. 47p. 1972. pap. 0.50 (ISBN 0-88243-930-8, 02-0930). Gospel Pub.

Dalpadado, J. Kingsley. Reading the Acts, Epistles & Revelations. 1977. 6.95 (ISBN 0-8198-0450-9); pap. 5.95 (ISBN 0-8198-0451-7). Dghtrs St Paul.

Danker, Frederick W. Luke. Krodel, Gerhard, ed. LC 76-5954. (Proclamation Commentaries: the New Testament Witnesses for Preaching Ser.). 128p. 1976. pap. 4.95 (ISBN 0-8006-0583-7, 1-583). Fortress.

Dunnett, Walter M. The Book of Acts. (Shield Bible Study Ser.). 144p. (Orig.). 1981. pap. 3.95 (ISBN 0-8010-2915-5). Baker Bk.

Ford, W. Herschel. Sermons You Can Preach on Acts. 352p. Date not set. pap. 10.95 (ISBN 0-310-38461-3). Zondervan.

From Behind Closed Doors: Acts A. (Illus.). 48p. 1981. pap. 1.95 leader's guide (ISBN 0-89367-066-9). Light & Life.

From Behind Closed Doors: Acts A. (Illus.). 68p. 1981. pap. 2.50 student's guide (ISBN 0-686-79738-8). Light & Life.

Gaebelein, Arno C. Acts of the Apostles. rev. ed. LC 61-17224. 1965. 10.95 (ISBN 0-87213-215-3). Loizeaux.

Gloag, Paton J. A Critical & Exegetical Commentary on the Acts of the Apostles, 2 vols. 1979. 29.95 (ISBN 0-86524-006-X, 4402). Klock & Klock.

Gutzke, Manford G. Plain Talk on Acts. 224p. 1972. pap. 7.95 (ISBN 0-310-25501-5, 9725P). Zondervan.

Haenchen, Ernst. The Acts of the Apostles, A Commentary. LC 78-161218. 762p. 1971. 29.95 (ISBN 0-664-20919-X). Westminster.

Hengel, Martin. Acts & the History of Earliest Christianity. LC 79-8893. 160p. 1980. 9.95 (ISBN 0-8006-0630-2, 1-630); pap. 7.50 (ISBN 0-8006-1876-9, 1-1876). Fortress.

Horton, Stanley M. The Book of Acts: A Radiant Commentary on the New Testament. LC 80-65892. 304p. (Orig.). 1981. 10.95 (ISBN 0-88243-317-2, 02-0317). Gospel Pub.

Ironside, H. A. Acts. 13.95 (ISBN 0-87213-351-6). Loizeaux.

Jensen, Irving L. Acts: An Inductive Study. 256p. 1973. pap. 7.95 (ISBN 0-8024-0138-4). Moody.

Jordan, Bernice C. Acts: 14 Lessons, Vol. 1. (Footsteps of Faith Ser.). 1954. pap. text ed. 2.50 (ISBN 0-86508-039-9); figure text 11.45 (ISBN 0-86508-040-2). BCM Intl Inc.

--Acts: 15 Lessons, Vol. 2. (Footsteps of Faith Ser.). 1954. pap. text ed. 2.50 (ISBN 0-86508-041-0); figure text 11.45 (ISBN 0-86508-042-9). BCM Intl Inc.

Keck, Leander E. & Martyn, J. Louis, eds. Studies in Luke-Acts. LC 79-8886. 324p. 1980. pap. 9.95 (ISBN 0-8006-1379-1, 1-1379). Fortress.

Krodel, Gerhard A. Augsburg Commentary on the New Testament: Acts. LC 86-10796. 500p. (Orig.). 1986. pap. 19.95 (ISBN 0-8066-8884-X, 10-9046). Augsburg.

Kurz, William S. & Karris, Robert J. The Acts of the Apostles, No. 5. LC 82-20872. (Collegeville Bible Commentary Ser.). (Illus.). 112p. 1983. pap. 2.95 (ISBN 0-8146-1305-5). Liturgical Pr.

Lenski, Richard C. Interpretation of Acts. 1934. 22.95 (ISBN 0-8066-9009-7, 10-3365). Augsburg.

Lindsay, Gordon. Acts in Action, 5 vols. (Book of Acts Ser.). 1.25 ea. Christ Nations.

--Acts in Action, Christs Great Commission. (Acts in Action Ser.: Vol. 1). pap. 1.25 (ISBN 0-89985-962-3). Christ Nations.

Lindsay, Thomas M. Acts II. (Handbooks for Bible Classes & Private Students Ser.). 168p. 1885. 8.95 (ISBN 0-567-08117-6, Pub. by T & T Clark Ltd UK). Fortress.

Lord, F. Townley. Acts of the Apostles (Missionary Message of the New Testament) 119p. 1946. 2.95 (ISBN 0-87921-003-6). Attic Pr.

Lovett, C. S. Lovett's Lights on Acts. 1972. pap. 6.95 (ISBN 0-938148-28-1). Personal Christianity.

McCumber, W. E. The Widening Circle: Sermons in Acts. 80p. (Orig.). 1983. pap. 2.95 (ISBN 0-8341-0838-0). Beacon Hill.

McLaughlin. Commentary on Acts. kivar 5.95 (ISBN 0-686-12858-3). Schmul Pub Co.

Maddox, Robert L., Jr. Layman's Bible Book Commentary: Acts, Vol. 19. LC 78-67926. 1979. 5.95 (ISBN 0-8054-1189-5). Broadman.

Marshall, I. Howard. Acts of the Apostles. (Tyndale New Testament Commentaries Ser.). (Orig.). 1980. pap. 7.95 (ISBN 0-8028-1423-9). Eerdmans.

Morrison, George H. Morrison on Acts. rev. ed. Zodhiates, Joan, ed. LC 80-69541. (Glasgow Pulpit Ser.). 1981. pap. 4.95 (ISBN 0-89957-050-X). AMG Pubs.

Neil, William. The Acts of the Apostles. rev. ed. Black, Matthew, ed. (New Century Bible Commentary Ser.). 272p. 1981. pap. 9.95 (ISBN 0-8028-1904-4). Eerdmans.

Nickell, Judy. New Testament Herald. 1985. 1.25 (ISBN 0-89536-733-5, 5878). CSS of Ohio.

Nystrom, Carolyn & Fromer, Margaret. Acts 13-28: Missions Accomplished. (Young Fisherman Bible Studyguide). (Illus.). 93p. 1979. tchrs. ed. 4.95 (ISBN 0-87788-011-5); student ed. 2.95 (ISBN 0-87788-010-7). Shaw Pubs.

Ogilvie, Lloyd J. The Communicator's Commentary-Acts, Vol. 5. (The Communicator's Commentaries Ser.). 1982. 18.95 (ISBN 0-8499-0158-8). Word Bks.

Packer, John W. Acts of the Apostles. (Cambridge Bible Commentary on the New English Bible, New Testament Ser.). (Orig.). 1966. pap. 10.95 (ISBN 0-521-09383-X). Cambridge U Pr.

Pentz, Croft M. Sermon Outlines from Acts. (Sermon Outline Ser.). 1978. pap. 2.50 (ISBN 0-8010-7039-2). Baker Bk.

Phillips, John. Exploring Acts, Vol. 1. (Exploring Ser.). (Orig.). 1986. pap. 11.95 (ISBN 0-8024-2435-X). Moody.

Ryrie, Charles. Acts of the Apostles. (Everyman's Bible Commentary Ser.). 1967. pap. 5.95 (ISBN 0-8024-2044-3). Moody.

Ryrie, Charles C. Los Hechos de los Apostoles (Comentario Biblico Portavoz) Orig. Title: The Acts of the Apostles (Everyman's Bible Commentary) (Span.). 96p. 1981. pap. 2.95 (ISBN 0-8254-1631-0). Kregel.

Smith, Bailey E. Real Christianity. LC 79-50336. 1980. 9.95 (ISBN 0-8054-5168-4). Broadman.

Smith, Thomas. Alive in the Spirit: The Church in the Acts of the Apostles. (Orig.). 1976. pap. text ed. 5.65x (ISBN 0-88489-081-3); tchr's. ed. 3.00x (ISBN 0-88489-083-X). St Marys.

Stagg, Frank. Book of Acts. 1955. 14.50 (ISBN 0-8054-1311-1). Broadman.

Talbert, Charles, ed. Perspectives on Luke-Acts. LC 78-51610. (Special Studies: No. 5). ix, 269p. 1978. pap. 10.00 (ISBN 0-932180-04-3). NABPR.

Talbert, Charles H. Literary Patterns, Theological Themes & the Genre of Luke-Acts. LC 74-78620. (Society of Biblical Literature. Monograph: No. 20). Repr. of 1974 ed. 42.00 (ISBN 0-8357-9577-2, 2017509). Bks Demand UMI.

Thomas, David. Acts of the Apostles. LC 79-2543. (Kregel Bible Study Classics Ser.). 512p. 1980. 22.95 (ISBN 0-8254-3810-1). Kregel.

Thomas, Roger W. After the Spirit Comes. LC 77-83659. 1979. pap. 2.25 (ISBN 0-87239-194-9, 40049). Standard Pub.

Thomsen, Helen S. That the World May Believe: The Acts of the Apostles. 1978. pap. 2.25x (ISBN 0-8192-4085-0); tchrs guide 2.25x (ISBN 0-8192-4084-2). Morehouse.

Trenchard, Ernesto. Hechos de los Apostoles. (Span.). 686p. 1963. 13.95 (ISBN 0-8254-1742-2). Kregel.

Van Ryn, August. Acts of the Apostles. LC 61-14601. 1961. pap. 1.95 (ISBN 0-87213-883-6). Loizeaux.

Vaughan, Curtis. Acts-A Study Guide Commentary. 160p. (Orig.). 1974. pap. 5.95 (ISBN 0-310-33513-2, 10958P). Zondervan.

Wheston's Commentaries on Acts, Romans, Vol. 3. 13.95 (ISBN 0-686-13906-2). Schmul Pub Co.

Wilson, S. G. Luke & the Law. LC 83-7263. (Society for New Testament Studies Monograph: No. 50). 200p. 1984. 29.95 (ISBN 0-521-25284-9). Cambridge U Pr.

BIBLE–COMMENTARIES–N. T. CATHOLIC EPISTLES

Here are entered commentaries on the Catholic Epistles as a whole, as well as on one or more of the following Epistles: James, John, Jude, Peter.

Adamson, James. Commentary on the Epistle of James. (New International Commentary on the New Testament). 480p. 1976. 13.95 (ISBN 0-8028-2377-7). Eerdmans.

Augsburg Sermons: Epistles - Series C. LC 76-3868. 228p. 1976. 15.95 (ISBN 0-8066-1523-0, 10-0524). Augsburg.

Barbieri, Louis. First & Second Peter. (Everyman's Bible Commentary Ser.). 1977. pap. 5.95 (ISBN 0-8024-2061-3). Moody.

Barbieri, Louis A. Primera y Segunda Pedro, Comentario Biblico Portavoz. Orig. Title: First & Second Peter, Everyman's Bible Commentary. (Span.). 1981. pap. 3.95 (ISBN 0-8254-1051-7). Kregel.

Bernard, J. H. The Pastoral Epistles: Timothy & Titus. (Thornapple Commentaries Ser.). 272p. 1980. pap. 6.95 (ISBN 0-8010-0797-6). Baker Bk.

Best, Ernest. I Peter. Black, Matthew, ed. (The New Century Bible Commentary Ser.). 188p. 1982. pap. 6.95 (ISBN 0-8028-1909-5). Eerdmans.

Blair, Allen J. Epistles of John: Living Confidently. LC 82-15196. pap. 4.95 (ISBN 0-87213-028-2). Loizeaux.

Blair, J. Allen. Living Peacefully: First Peter. 1959. pap. 3.50 (ISBN 0-87213-052-5). Loizeaux.

Bowman, John W. Hebrews-Second Peter. LC 59-10454. (Layman's Bible Commentary Ser: Vol. 24). 1962. pap. 4.95 (ISBN 0-8042-3084-6). John Knox.

Bratcher, Robert G. A Translator's Guide to the Letters from James, Peter, & Jude. LC 83-18159. (Helps for Translators Ser.). viii, 200p. 1984. 2.30x (ISBN 0-8267-0192-2, 08572, Pub. by United Bible). Am Bible.

Brooke, A. E. A Critical & Exegetical Commentary on the Johannine Epistles. Driver, Samuel R., et al, eds. LC 13-170. (International Critical Commentary Ser.). 336p. 1912. 24.95 (ISBN 0-567-05037-8, Pub. by T & T Clark Ltd UK). Fortress.

Brooks, Keith L. James: Belief in Action. (Teach Yourself the Bible Ser.). 1961. pap. 2.75 (ISBN 0-8024-4227-7). Moody.

Brown, John. First Peter, 2 vols. 1980. 32.95 (ISBN 0-85151-204-6); Vol. 1, 577 Pp. (ISBN 0-85151-205-4); Vol. 2, 640 Pp. (ISBN 0-85151-206-2). Banner of Truth.

--Parting Counsels: Exposition of II Peter 1. (Banner of Truth Geneva Series Commentaries). 1980. 13.95 (ISBN 0-85151-301-8). Banner of Truth.

Brown, Raymond E., et al. Peter in the New Testament. LC 73-83787. 1973. 7.95 (ISBN 0-8066-1401-3, 10-4930). Augsburg.

Burdick, Donald. Epistles of John. (Everyman's Bible Commentary Ser.). 1970. pap. 5.95 (ISBN 0-8024-2062-1). Moody.

Burdick, Donald W. Letters of John the Apostle. (Orig.). 1985. pap. 13.95 (ISBN 0-8024-2356-6). Moody.

Cedar, Paul A. The Communicator's Commentary-James First; Second, Peter, Jude, Vol. 2. Ogilvie, Lloyd J., ed. (The Communicator's Commentaries Ser.). 1983. 16.95 (ISBN 0-8499-0164-2). Word Bks.

Clowney, Edmund P. Preaching & Biblical Theology. 1956. pap. 3.95 (ISBN 0-87552-145-2). Presby & Reformed.

Coder, Maxwell S. Judas: Los Hechos de los Apostatas (Comentario Biblico Portavoz) Orig. Title: Jude: the Acts of the Apostates (Everyman's Bible Commentary. (Span.). 134p. 1980. pap. 3.95 (ISBN 0-8254-1125-4). Kregel.

Coder, S. Maxwell. Jude: The Acts of the Apostates. (Everyman's Bible Commentary Ser). 1967. pap. 5.95 (ISBN 0-8024-2065-6). Moody.

Coffman, Burton. Commentary on James, First & Second; Peter, First, Second & Third, John, Jude. (Firm Foundation Commentary Ser.). 1979. cancelled 10.95 (ISBN 0-88027-075-6). Firm Foun Pub.

Conn, Charles W. A Survey of the Epistles. 112p. 1969. 5.25 (ISBN 0-87148-007-7); pap. 4.25 (ISBN 0-87148-008-5). Pathway Pr.

Dalpadado, J. Kingsley. Reading the Acts, Epistles & Revelations. 1977. 6.95 (ISBN 0-8198-0450-9); pap. 5.95 (ISBN 0-8198-0451-7). Dghtrs St Paul.

Delitzsch, Franz. Commentary on the Epistle to the Hebrews, 2 vols. 1978. Set. 31.50 (ISBN 0-86524-110-4, 5801). Klock & Klock.

Doerkson, Vernon. James. (Everyman's Bible Commentaries Ser.). (Orig.). 1983. pap. 5.95 (ISBN 0-8024-0242-9). Moody.

Eastman, Addison J. A Handful of Pearls: The Epistle of James. LC 78-5797. 106p. 1978. pap. 5.50 (ISBN 0-664-24202-2). Westminster.

Elliot, John. Peter One, Estrangement & Community. (Herald Biblical). 1979. 1.25 (ISBN 0-8199-0728-6). Franciscan Herald.

Fairweather, William. Background of the Epistles. 1977. 16.50 (ISBN 0-86524-118-X, 8002). Klock & Klock.

Fream, Donald. Thirteen Lessons on James & Jude. (Bible Student Study Guides). 1979. pap. 2.95 (ISBN 0-89900-161-0). College Pr Pub.

General Epistles. (Erdmans Commentaries Ser.). 5.95 (ISBN 0-8010-3398-5). Baker Bk.

Green, M. Second Epistle Peter & Epistle of Jude. (Tyndale Bible Commentaries: Vol. 18). 1968. pap. 4.95 (ISBN 0-8028-1417-4). Eerdmans.

Green, Michael. Second Peter & Jude. rev. ed. (Tyndale New Testament Commentaries Ser.). 1987. pap. 5.95 (ISBN 0-8028-0078-5). Eerdmans.

Gutzke, Manford G. Plain Talk on the Epistles of John. 1977. pap. 5.95 (ISBN 0-310-25631-3, 9857P). Zondervan.

Houlden, J. L. The Johannine Epistles. LC 74-4634. (New Testament Commentary Ser.). 176p. 1974. 10.95 (ISBN 0-06-064020-0, HarpR). Har-Row.

Hoyt, Herman A. Commentary on Second Peter. 136p. 1983. pap. 4.95 (ISBN 0-88469-153-5). BMH Bks.

Hurst, David. The Venerable Bede: Commentary on the Catholic Epistles. 1985. 24.95 (ISBN 0-317-18074-6); pap. 9.00 (ISBN 0-317-18075-4). Cistercian Pubns.

Ironside, H. A. John & Jude, Epistles. 9.95 (ISBN 0-87213-372-9). Loizeaux.

--Timothy, Titus & Philemon. 9.95 (ISBN 0-87213-391-5). Loizeaux.

Jensen, Irving L. Hebrews & the Pastoral Epistles. (Irving Jensen's Do-It-Yourself Bible Study Ser.). 139p. (Orig.). 1985. wkbk. 5.95 (ISBN 0-89840-077-5). Heres Life.

Jenson, Irving L. Epistles of John & Jude. (Bible Self-Study Ser.). 128p. (Orig.). 1971. pap. 3.25 (ISBN 0-8024-1062-6). Moody.

Johnstone, Robert. James. (Geneva Commentaries Ser.). 1977. 15.95 (ISBN 0-85151-257-7). Banner of Truth.

--Lectures on the Epistle of James. 1977. 16.50 (ISBN 0-86524-111-2, 5901). Klock & Klock.

Kelly, J. N. A Commentary on the Epistles of Peter & Jude. (Thornapple Commentaries). 397p. 1981. pap. 9.95 (ISBN 0-8010-5430-3). Baker Bk.

--A Commentary on the Pastoral Epistles. (Thornapple Commentaries Ser.). 272p. 1981. pap. 7.95 (ISBN 0-8010-5428-1). Baker Bk.

Kelly, W. Lectures on the Epistle of Jude. 6.95 (ISBN 0-88172-101-8). Believers Bkshelf.

Knowles, Victor. Thirteen Lessons in I & II Peter. (Bible Study Guide Ser.). 105p. (Orig.). pap. 2.95 (ISBN 0-89900-175-0). College Pr Pub.

Kugelman, Richard. James & Jude. (New Testament Message Ser.: Vol. 19). 10.95 (ISBN 0-89453-207-3); pap. 5.95 (ISBN 0-89453-142-5). M Glazier.

Lachs, Samuel T. Rabbinic Commentary on the New Testament: The Gospels of Matthew, Mark & Luke. 600p. 1987. 39.50 (ISBN 0-88125-089-9); pap. 19.95. Ktav.

Law, Robert. Tests of Life. 3rd ed. (Thornapple Commentary Ser.). 1978. pap. 11.95 (ISBN 0-8010-5501-6). Baker Bk.

Leaney, Alfred R. Letters of Peter & Jude. (Cambridge Bible Commentary on the New English Bible, New Testament Ser.). (Orig.). 16.95 (ISBN 0-521-04216-X); pap. 8.95x (ISBN 0-521-09403-8). Cambridge U Pr.

Leighton, Robert. Commentary on First Peter. LC 74-165058. 512p. 16.95 (ISBN 0-8254-3103-4). Kregel.

Lenski, Richard C. Interpretation of First & Second Peter, First, Second & Third John, Jude. 1938. 21.95 (ISBN 0-8066-9011-9, 10-3371). Augsburg.

--Interpretation of Hebrews & James. 1938. 21.95 (ISBN 0-8066-9010-0, 10-3370). Augsburg.

Lewis, E. Ridley. Johannine Writings & Other Epistles. (London Divinity Ser). 144p. 1961. 3.95 (ISBN 0-227-67663-7). Attic Pr.

Lillie, John. Lectures on the First & Second Epistles of Peter. 1978. 19.75 (ISBN 0-86524-116-3, 7102). Klock & Klock.

Luther, Martin. Commentary on First and Second Peter & Jude. LC 82-4652. 320p. 1982. 12.95 (ISBN 0-8254-3125-5). Kregel.

--Luther's Works: Catholic Epistles, Vol. 30. Pelikan, Jaroslav, ed. LC 55-9893. 1967. 14.95 (ISBN 0-570-06430-9, 15-1772). Concordia.

MacDuff, John R. The Footsteps of St. Peter. 648p. 1982. lib. bdg. 24.25 Smythe Sewn (ISBN 0-86524-149-X, 8406). Klock & Klock.

Macknight, James. Macknight on the Epistles. 784p. 1984. Repr. of 1966 ed. 24.95 (ISBN 0-8010-6031-1). Baker Bk.

Marshall, I. Howard. The New International Commentary on the New Testament: The Epistles of John. 1978. 14.95 (ISBN 0-8028-2189-8). Eerdmans.

Mayor, Joseph B. The Epistle of Saint James. 1977. 20.25 (ISBN 0-86524-971-7, 5902). Klock & Klock.

Moffatt, James. A Critical & Exegetical Commentary on the Epistle to the Hebrews. Driver, Samuel R. & Plummer, Alfred, eds. LC 24-21703. (International Critical Commentary Ser.). 336p. 1924. 22.95 (ISBN 0-567-05034-3, Pub. by T & T Clark Ltd UK). Fortress.

Moo, Douglas. James. Tasker, R. V., ed. (Tyndale New Testament Commentary Ser.). 176p. (Orig.). 1987. pap. 4.95 (ISBN 0-8028-0079-3). Eerdmans.

Morgan, J. & Cox, S. The Epistles of John. 612p. 1982. lib. bdg. 22.95 Smythe Sewn (ISBN 0-86524-133-3, 6202). Klock & Klock.

Morris, Leon. Commentary on the Revelation of John. Tasker, R. V., ed. (Tyndale Bible Commentaries). 1957. pap. 5.95 (ISBN 0-8028-1419-0). Eerdmans.

Munro, Winsome. Authority in Paul & Peter: The Identification of a Pastoral Stratum in the Pauline Corpus & Peter 1. LC 81-12216. (Society of New Testament Studies: No. 45). (Illus.). 230p. 1983. 32.50 (ISBN 0-521-23694-0). Cambridge U Pr.

Nisbet, Alexander. First & Second Peter. (Geneva Series Commentaries). 14.95 (ISBN 0-85151-338-7). Banner of Truth.

Nystrom, Carolyn & Fromer, Margaret. A Woman's Workshop on James. (Woman's Workshop Ser.). 144p. (Orig.). 1980. pap. 2.95 (ISBN 0-310-41901-8, 11273P). Zondervan.

Phillips, J. B. Peter's Portrait of Jesus. (Festival Ser.). 192p. 1981. pap. 1.95 (ISBN 0-687-30850-X). Abingdon.

Plummer, Alfred. The Epistles of Saint John. (Thornapple Commentaries Ser.). 302p. 1980. pap. 7.95 (ISBN 0-8010-7058-9). Baker Bk.
Reeder, W. Donald. Letters of John & Jude. (Teach Yourself the Bible Ser.). 1965. pap. 2.75 (ISBN 0-8024-4674-4). Moody.
Reicke, Bo I., ed. Epistles of James, Peter & Jude. LC 63-8221. (Anchor Bible Ser.: Vol. 37). 1964. 14.00 (ISBN 0-385-01374-4, Anchor Pr). Doubleday.
Richards, Larry. Pass It on. LC 77-87260. (Bible Alive Ser.). (Illus.). 1978. pap. text ed. 2.95 (ISBN 0-89191-089-1); tchr's ed. 3.95 (ISBN 0-89191-090-5). Cook.
Ropes, James H. A Critical & Exegetical Commentary on the Epistle of St. James. LC 16-6543. (International Critical Commentary Ser.). 336p. 1916. 22.95 (ISBN 0-567-05035-1, Pub. by T & T Clark Ltd UK). Fortress.
Runk, Wesley T. Captivating Object Lessons. (Object Lesson Ser). 1979. pap. 3.95 (ISBN 0-8010-7671-4). Baker Bk.
Selwyn, Edward G. The First Epistle of St. Peter. 2nd ed. (Thornapple Commentaries Ser.). 517p. 1981. pap. 10.95 (ISBN 0-8010-8199-8). Baker Bk.
Senior, Donald. First & Second Peter. (New Testament Message Ser.: Vol. 20). 10.95 (ISBN 0-89453-208-1); pap. 6.95 (ISBN 0-89453-143-3). M Glazier.
Sherer, Michael L. Good News for Children: Object Lessons on Epistle Texts. LC 81-65655. (Series B). 128p. (Orig.). 1981. pap. 6.95 (ISBN 0-8066-1891-4, 10-2809). Augsburg.
Sidebottom, E. M. James, Jude & II Peter. (New Century Bible Ser). 142p. 1967. 7.50 (ISBN 0-551-00590-4). Attic Pr.
--James, Jude, II Peter. Black, Matthew, ed. (The New Century Bible Commentary Ser.). 130p. 1982. pap. 5.95 (ISBN 0-8028-1936-2). Eerdmans.
Stibbs, Alan M. First Epistle of Peter. (Tyndale Bible Commentaries). 1959. 4.95 (ISBN 0-8028-1416-6). Eerdmans.
Stier, Rudolf E. Commentary on the Epistle of James. 278p. 1982. lib. bdg. 10.25 Smythe Sewn (ISBN 0-86524-157-0, 5903). Klock & Klock.
Stott, John R. Epistles of John. (Tyndale Bible Commentaries). Orig. Title: Johannine Epistles. 1964. pap. 4.95 (ISBN 0-8028-1418-2). Eerdmans.
Strauss, Lehman. Epistles of John. LC 62-17542. 1962. pap. 3.95 (ISBN 0-87213-821-6). Loizeaux.
--James. 1956. 8.95 (ISBN 0-87213-818-6). Loizeaux.
Tasker, Randolph V. General Epistle of James. (Tyndale Bible Commentaries). 1957. pap. 3.95 (ISBN 0-8028-1415-8). Eerdmans.
Taylor, Robert. Studies in James & Jude. 2.50 (ISBN 0-89315-293-5). Lambert Bk.
Taylor, Robert R., Jr. Studies in First, Second Peter. pap. 2.50 (ISBN 0-89315-294-3). Lambert Bk.
Turner, J. J. Book of James. pap. 5.50 (ISBN 0-89137-548-1). Quality Pubns.
Van Elderen, Bastiaan. The First & Second Epistle to Timothy & the Epistle to Titus. Bruce, F. F., ed. (New International Commentary on the New Testament Ser.). 256p. cancelled (ISBN 0-8028-2346-7). Eerdmans.
Vaughan, Charles J. Epistle to the Philippians. 318p. 1984. smythe sewn 11.50 (ISBN 0-86524-180-5, 5002). Klock & Klock.
Vaughan, Curtis. James: Bible Study Commentary. pap. 4.95 (ISBN 0-310-33553-1, 10955P). Zondervan.
Westcott, Brooke F. Commentary on the Epistles of Saint John. (Gr). 8.95 (ISBN 0-8028-3290-3). Eerdmans.
--The Gospel According to Saint John: The Greek Text with Introduction & Notes, 2 vols. in 1. Westcott, Arthur, ed. 877p. 1980. pap. 16.95 (ISBN 0-8010-9644-8). Baker Bk.
Williams, Ronald R., ed. Letters of John & James. (Cambridge Bible Commentary on the New English Bible, New Testament Ser.). (Orig.). 1965. 17.95 (ISBN 0-521-04206-2); pap. 8.95 (ISBN 0-521-09250-7, 250). Cambridge U Pr.
Zodhiates, Spiros. The Behavior of Belief. 1966. 19.95 (ISBN 0-89957-505-6). AMG Pubs.

BIBLE–COMMENTARIES–N. T. COLOSSIANS

Abbott, T. K. A Critical & Exegetical Commentary on the Epistles to the Ephesians & Colossians. Driver, Samuel R., et al, eds. LC 40-15742. (International Critical Commentary Ser.). 392p. 1897. 24.95 (ISBN 0-567-05030-0, Pub. by T & T Clark Ltd UK). Fortress.
Baynes, Paul. A Commentarie upon the First & Second Chapters of Saint Paul to the Colossians. 396p. Repr. of 1635 ed. text ed. 74.52X (ISBN 0-576-99737-4, Pub. by Gregg Intl Pubs England). Gregg Intl.
Boles, Kenny. Thirteen Lessons on Philippians, Colossians & Philemon. LC 79-53714. (Bible Student Study Guides). (Orig.). 1979. pap. 2.95 (ISBN 0-89900-163-7). College Pr Pub.
Bruce, F. F. The Epistles to the Colossians, to Philemon, & to the Ephesians. (New International Commentary on the New Testament Ser.). 464p. 1984. 18.95 (ISBN 0-8028-2401-3). Eerdmans.
Cannon, George C. The Use of Traditional Materials in Colossians: Their Significance for the Problem of Authenticity. LC 83-8181. viii, 253p. 1983. 17.95 (ISBN 0-86554-074-8, H51). Mercer Univ Pr.
Carson, Herbert M. Epistles of Paul to the Colossians & to Philemon. (Tyndale Bible Commentaries). 1960. pap. 3.95 (ISBN 0-8028-1411-5). Eerdmans.
Coffman, James B. Commentary on Galatians, Ephesians, Phillipians, Colossians. (Firm Foundation Commentary Ser.). 1977. cancelled 10.95 (ISBN 0-88027-072-1). Firm Foun Pub.
Colossians & Philemon. (Erdmans Commentaries Ser.). 3.50 (ISBN 0-8010-3393-4). Baker Bk.
Daille, Jean. Exposition of Colossians. 698p. 1983. lib. bdg. 24.95 (ISBN 0-86524-141-4, 5104). Klock & Klock.
Eadie, John. Colossians. 1981. 10.50 (ISBN 0-86524-067-1, 5103). Klock & Klock.
Gromacki, Robert G. Stand Perfect in Wisdom: Colossians & Ephesians. 1981. pap. 5.95 (ISBN 0-8010-3767-0). Baker Bk.
Guthrie, Donald. Exploring God's World: A Guide to Ephesians, Philippians, & Colossians. 224p. (Orig.). 1985. pap. 6.95 (ISBN 0-8028-0084-X). Eerdmans.
Harrison, Everett. Colossians. (Everyman's Bible Commentary Ser). 128p. (Orig.). 1971. pap. 5.95 (ISBN 0-8024-2051-6). Moody.
Havener, Ivan & Karris, Robert J. First Thessalonians, Philippians, Philemon, Second Thessalonians, Colossians, Ephesians, No. 8. (Collegeville Bible Commentary Ser.). (Illus.). 112p. 1983. pap. 2.95 (ISBN 0-8146-1308-X). Liturgical Pr.
Hendriksen, William. Philippians, Colossians, & Philemon. (New Testament Commentary). 243p. 1979. 17.95 (ISBN 0-8010-4212-7). Baker Bk.
Houlden, J. L., ed. Paul's Letters from Prison: Philippians, Colossians, Philemon & Ephesians. LC 77-24028. (Westminister Pelican Commentaries). 358p. 1978. 11.50 (ISBN 0-664-21347-2); pap. 6.95 (ISBN 0-664-24182-4). Westminster.
Lenski, Richard C. Interpretation of Colossians, Thessalonians First & Second, Timothy First & Second, Titus, & Philemon. 1937. 21.95 (ISBN 0-8066-9006-2, 10-3369). Augsburg.
Lightfoot, J. B. Commentaries on Galatians, Philippians, Colossians & Philemon, 3 vols. 1208p. 1981. 39.95 (ISBN 0-913573-02-7). Hendrickson MA.
Lohse, Eduard. Colossians & Philemon. Koester, Helmut, ed. Poehlman, William R. & Karris, Robert J., trs. from Ger. LC 76-157550. (Hermeneia: A Critical & Historical Commentary on the Bible Ser). 256p. 1971. 22.95 (ISBN 0-8006-6001-3, 20-6001). Fortress.
Lucas, R. J. The Message of Colossians & Philemon. Motyer, J. A. & Stott, J. R., eds. LC 79-3635. (The Bible Speaks Today Ser.). 1980. pap. 6.95 (ISBN 0-87784-284-1). Inter-Varsity.
Martin, Ralph P. Colossians & Philemon. rev. ed. (New Century Bible Commentary Ser.). 192p. 1981. pap. 5.95 (ISBN 0-8028-1908-7). Eerdmans.
--Colossians: The Church's Lord & the Christian's Liberty. 192p. 1972. 8.95 (ISBN 0-85364-125-0). Attic Pr.
Moule, Charles F. Epistles of Paul the Apostle to the Colossians & to Philemon. (Cambridge Greek Testament Ser.). 1959. text ed. 32.50 (ISBN 0-521-04252-6); pap. text ed. 10.95 (ISBN 0-521-09236-1). Cambridge U Pr.
Moule, H. C. G. Colossian & Philemon Studies. 1981. 12.00 (ISBN 0-86524-052-3, 7106). Klock & Klock.
--Studies in Colossians & Philemon. LC 77-79185. (Kregel Popular Commentary Ser.). 196p. 1977. kivar 6.95 (ISBN 0-8254-3217-0). Kregel.
Moule, Handley. Colossians. 1975. pap. 4.95 (ISBN 0-87508-361-7). Chr Lit.
Rogers, Patrick V. Colossians. (New Testament Message Ser.: Vol. 15). 10.95 (ISBN 0-89453-138-7); pap. 5.95 (ISBN 0-89453-203-0). M Glazier.
Schweizer, Edward. The Letter to the Colossians: A Commentary. Chester, Andrew, tr. LC 81-65657. 352p. (Orig.). 1982. pap. 14.95 (ISBN 0-8066-1893-0, 10-3823). Augsburg.
Taylor, Walter F., Jr. & Reumann, John H., eds. Augsburg Commentary on the New Testament: Ephesians, Colossians. LC 85-7479. 176p. (Orig.). 1985. kivar 8.95 (ISBN 0-8066-2165-6, 10-9030). Augsburg.
Thompson, G. H. Letters of Paul to the Ephesians, Colossians & Philemon. (Cambridge Bible Commentary on the New English Bible, New Testament Ser.). 18.95 (ISBN 0-521-04227-5); pap. 9.95x (ISBN 0-521-09410-0, 410). Cambridge U Pr.
Vaughan, Curtis. Colossians & Philemon: A Study Guide Commentary. (Study Guide Commentary Ser.). 144p. (Orig.). 1981. pap. 4.95 (ISBN 0-310-33583-3, 10965P). Zondervan.
Wilson, Geoffrey B. Colossians & Philemon. (Wilson'a New Testament Commentaries). 111p. (Orig.). 1980. pap. 4.95 (ISBN 0-85151-313-1). Banner of Truth.

BIBLE–COMMENTARIES–N. T. CORINTHIANS

Barrett, Charles K. The First Epistle to the Corinthians. LC 68-17594. (New Testament Commentaries Ser., Vol. 9). 1968. 18.00 (ISBN 0-06-060551-0, HarpR). Har-Row.
Barth, Karl. The Resurrection of the Dead. Kastenbaum, Robert, ed. LC 76-19559. (Death and Dying Ser.). 1977. Repr. of 1933 ed. lib. bdg. 23.50x (ISBN 0-405-09555-4). Ayer Co Pubs.
Best, Ernest. Second Corinthians. Mays, James L. & Achtemeier, Paul J., eds. LC 86-45404. (Interpretation: A Bible Commentary for Teaching & Preaching Ser.). 156p. 1987. 15.95 (ISBN 0-8042-3135-4). John Knox.
Betz, Hans D. Second Corinthians Eight & Nine: A Commentary on Two Administrative Letters of the Apostle Paul. LC 84-48904. (Hermeneia Ser.). 288p. 1985. 27.95 (ISBN 0-8006-6014-5, 20-6014). Fortress.
Bratcher, R. G. Translator's Guide to Paul's First Letter to the Corinthians. LC 82-6951. (Helps for Translators Ser.). 1982. pap. 3.50x (ISBN 0-8267-0185-X, 08566). Am Bible.
Bratcher, Robert G. Translator's Guide to Paul's Second Letter to the Corinthians. LC 83-1383. (Helps for Translators Ser.). vii, 160p. 1983. pap. 3.00x (ISBN 0-8267-0186-8, 08571, Pub. by United Bible). Am Bible.
Bridger, Gordon. First Corinthians-Galatians. (Bible Study Commentaries Ser.). 95p. 1985. pap. 4.95 (ISBN 0-317-43383-0). Chr Lit.
Brooks, Keith L. First Corinthians. (Teach Yourself the Bible Ser.). 1964. pap. 2.75 (ISBN 0-8024-2649-2). Moody.
Brown, John. The Resurrection of Life. 1978. 15.50 (ISBN 0-86524-962-8, 4601). Klock & Klock.
Bruce, F. F. Commentary on First & Second Corinthians. Black, Matthew, ed. (New Century Bible Commentary Ser.). 224p. 1980. pap. 8.95 (ISBN 0-8028-1839-0). Eerdmans.
Bultmann, Rudolf. The Second Letter to the Corinthians. Linss, Wilhelm C., tr. LC 83-70517. 272p. 1985. pap. 17.95 (ISBN 0-8066-2023-4, 10-5633). Augsburg.
Butler, Paul T. Studies in First Corinthians. (Bible Study Textbook Ser.). 416p. text ed. 14.30 (ISBN 0-89900-063-0). College Pr Pub.
Carson, Donald A. From Triumphalism to Maturity: An Exposition of II Corinthians 10-13. 1984. 12.95 (ISBN 0-8010-2489-7). Baker Bk.
Chafin, Kenneth L. & Ogilvie, Lloyd J. The Communicator's Commentary: Corinthians First; Second, Vol. 7. 1983. 18.95 (ISBN 0-8499-0347-5). Word Bks.
Colet, John. John Colet's Commentary on First Corinthians. O'Kelly, Bernard, ed. & tr. from Lat. LC 82-12403. (Medieval & Renaissance Texts & Studies: Vol. 21). (Illus.). 352p. 1985. 20.00 (ISBN 0-86698-056-3). Medieval & Renaissance NY.
Conzelmann, Hans. First Corinthians. MacRae, George W., ed. Leitch, James W., tr. from Ger. LC 73-88360. (Hermeneia: a Critical & Historical Commentary on the Bible). 352p. 1975. 25.95x (ISBN 0-8006-6005-6, 20-6005). Fortress.
Edwards, Thomas C. A Commentary on the First Epistle to the Corinthians. 1979. 18.00 (ISBN 0-86524-013-2, 4602). Klock & Klock.
Ellingworth, Paul & Hatton, Howard. A Translator's Handbook on Paul's First Letter to the Corinthians. LC 85-1142. (Helps for Translators Ser.). viii, 352p. 1985. flexible 4.20x (ISBN 0-8267-0140-X, 08578, Dist. by American Bible Society). United Bible.
Fallon, Francis T. Second Corinthians. (New Testament Message Ser.: Vol. 11). 12.95 (ISBN 0-89453-199-9); pap. 7.95 (ISBN 0-89453-134-4). M Glazier.
First Corinthians. (Erdmans Commentaries Ser.). 3.95 (ISBN 0-8010-3394-2). Baker Bk.
Foreman, Kenneth J. Romans, First & Second Corinthians. LC 59-10454. (Layman's Bible Commentary Ser: Vol. 21). 1961. pap. 4.95 (ISBN 0-8042-3081-1). John Knox.
Furnish, Victor P., intro. by. Corinthians II, Vol 32A. LC 83-2056. (Anchor Bible Ser.). (Illus.). 648p. 1984. 18.00 (ISBN 0-385-11199-1). Doubleday.
George, David C. Layman's Bible Book Commentary: Second Corinthians, Galatians, Ephesians, Vol. 21. LC 78-74202. 1980. 5.95 (ISBN 0-8054-1191-7). Broadman.
Getty, Mary A. & Karris, Robert J. First Corinthians, Second Corinthians, No. 7. (Collegeville Bible Commentary Ser.). 128p. 1983. pap. 2.95 (ISBN 0-8146-1307-1). Liturgical Pr.
Godet, Frederic L. Commentary on First Corinthians. LC 77-79190. (Kregel Reprint Library). 928p. 1977. 29.95 (ISBN 0-8254-2716-9). Kregel.
Gromacki, Robert G. Called to Be Saints. 1977. pap. 5.95 (ISBN 0-87227-014-9). Reg Baptist.
--Called to Be Saints (I Corinthians) 1977. pap. 5.95 (ISBN 0-8010-3715-8). Baker Bk.
Grosheide, Frederick W. Commentary on First Corinthians. (New International Commentary on the New Testament). 1953. 14.95 (ISBN 0-8028-2185-5). Eerdmans.
Gutzke, Manford G. Plain Talk on Corinthians. 1978. pap. 7.95 (ISBN 0-310-25641-0, 9858P). Zondervan.
Hamar, Paul. The Book of First Corinthians. LC 80-65305. 192p. (Orig.). 1980. 6.95 (ISBN 0-88243-316-4, 02-0316). Gospel Pub.
Hodge, Charles. Corinthians 1 & 2. (Geneva Commentaries Ser.). 1978. 15.95 (ISBN 0-85151-185-6). Banner of Truth.
Hughes, Philip. Commentary on the Second Epistle to the Corinthians. (New International Commentary on the New Testament). 1962. 19.95 (ISBN 0-8028-2186-3). Eerdmans.
Hughes, Robert B. First Corinthians. (Everyman's Bible Commentary Ser.). (Orig.). 1985. pap. 5.95 (ISBN 0-8024-0447-2). Moody.
Ishee, John A. God's Wisdom-God's Way: Studies in First Corinthians. 35p. (Orig.). 1983. pap. 3.50 (ISBN 0-939298-20-1). J M Prods.
Jensen, Irving. Second Corinthians. (Bible Self-Study Ser). (Illus.). 108p. 1972. pap. 3.25 (ISBN 0-8024-1047-2). Moody.
Jensen, Irving L. First Corinthians. (Bible Self-Study). 98p. 1972. pap. 3.25 (ISBN 0-8024-1046-4). Moody.
Jones, John D. Exposition of First Corinthians Thirteen. 253p. 1982. lib. bdg. 9.50 Smythe Sewn (ISBN 0-86524-144-9, 4603). Klock & Klock.
Kelly, W. Notes on First Corinthians. 8.50 (ISBN 0-88172-094-1). Believers Bkshelf.
Laurin, Roy L. Second Corinthians: Where Life Endures. LC 85-8154. 248p. 1985. pap. 9.95 (ISBN 0-8254-3129-8). Kregel.
Lenski, Richard C. Interpretation of First & Second Corinthians. 1935. 22.95 (ISBN 0-8066-9008-9, 10-3367). Augsburg.
MacArthur, John, Jr. First Corinthians: MacArthur New Testament Commentary. 1984. 14.95 (ISBN 0-8024-0754-4). Moody.
MacGorman, J. W. The Layman's Bible Commentary: Romans, I Corinthians, Vol. 20. LC 79-51501. 1980. 5.95 (ISBN 0-8054-1190-9). Broadman.
Meyer, John P. Ministers of Christ. 1963. 6.95 (ISBN 0-8100-0042-3, 15N0328). Northwest Pub.
Morgan, G. Campbell. Corinthian Letters of Paul. 288p. 1946. 15.95 (ISBN 0-8007-0051-1). Revell.
Morris, Leon. The First Epistle of Paul to the Corinthians. (Tyndale New Testament Commentary). 1958. pap. 5.95 (ISBN 0-8028-1406-9). Eerdmans.
Moule, Handley. Two, Corinthians. 1976. pap. 4.95 (ISBN 0-87508-359-5). Chr Lit.
Picirilli, Robert E. Randall House Bible Commentary (1, 2 Corinthians) Harrison, H. D., ed. (Bible Commentary Ser.). 350p. 1986. 19.95 (ISBN 0-89265-118-0). Randall Hse.
Plummer, Alfred. A Critical & Exegetical Commentary on the Second Epistle of St. Paul to the Corinthians. Driver, Samuel R. & Briggs, Charles A., eds. (International Critical Commentary Ser.). 462p. 1915. 24.95 (ISBN 0-567-05028-9, Pub. by T & T Clark Ltd UK). Fortress.
Prior, David. The Message of I Corinthians. Stott, John R. & Motyer, J. A., eds. LC 85-239. (The Bible Speaks Today Ser.). 270p. 1985. pap. 7.95 (ISBN 0-87784-297-3). Inter-Varsity.
Randall House Bible Commentary Series. Picirilli, Robert E. & Harrison, H. D., eds. Date not set. price not set (ISBN 0-89265-115-6). Randall Hse.
Redpath, Alan. Royal Route to Heaven: Studies in First Corinthians. 256p. 1960. 12.95 (ISBN 0-8007-0279-4). Revell.
Reed, Oscar F. Beacon Bible Expositions: Vol. 7, Corinthians. Greathouse, William M. & Taylor, Willard H., eds. 1976. 8.95 (ISBN 0-8341-0318-4). Beacon Hill.
Robertson, Archibald & Plummer, Alfred. A Critical & Exegitical Commentary on the First Epistle of St. Paul to the Corinthians. Driver, Samuel R. & Briggs, Charles A., eds. (International Critical Commentary Ser.). 496p. 1914. 24.95 (ISBN 0-567-05027-0, Pub. by T & T Clark Ltd UK). Fortress.

Ruef, John. Paul's First Letter to Corinth. LC 77-24086. (Westminster Pelican Commentaries). 224p. 1978. 10.00 (ISBN 0-664-21348-0); softcover 5.45 (ISBN 0-664-24183-2). Westminster.

Second Corinthians. (Erdmans Commentaries Ser.). 3.50 (ISBN 0-8010-3395-0). Baker Bk.

Smedes, Lewis B. Love Within Limits: A Realist's View of I Corinthians 13. 1978. pap. 4.95 (ISBN 0-8028-1753-X). Eerdmans.

Talbert, Charles H. Reading Corinthians: A Literary & Theological Commentary on 1 and 2 Corinthians. 224p. 1987. 15.95 (ISBN 0-8245-0804-1). Crossroad NY.

Tasker, Randolph V. Second Epistle of Paul to the Corinthians. (Tyndale Bible Commentaries). 1958. pap. 4.95 (ISBN 0-8028-1407-7). Eerdmans.

Thomas, J. D. Second Corinthians: Message of the New Testament. (Way of Life Ser.). 60p. 1986. pap. text ed. 3.95 (ISBN 0-915547-92-9, 929). Abilene Christ U.

--Self-Study Guide to the Corinthian Letters. (Way of Life Ser: No. 123). (Orig.). 1972. pap. text ed. 3.95 (ISBN 0-89112-123-4, Bibl Res Pr). Abilene Christ U.

Trenchard, Ernesto. Primera Epistola a los Corintios. (Span.). 348p. 1970. 9.95 (ISBN 0-8254-1728-7); pap. 8.95 (ISBN 0-8254-1727-9). Kregel.

Whedon's Commentary on First Corinthians, Vol. 4. 13.95 (ISBN 0-686-13331-5). Schmul Pub Co.

Wickham, Pablo. Segunda Epistola a los Corintos. (Span.). 320p. 1985. pap. 9.95 (ISBN 0-8254-1870-4). Kregel.

Williamson, Audrey. Love Is the Greatest. (Direction Bks). 64p. 1976. pap. 1.25 (ISBN 0-8010-9579-4). Baker Bk.

Wilson, Geoffrey. First Corinthians. 1978. pap. 4.95 (ISBN 0-85151-277-1). Banner of Truth.

--Second Corinthians. 1979. pap. 4.95 (ISBN 0-85151-295-X). Banner of Truth.

Zodhiates, Spiros. Getting the Most Out of Life. (I Corinthians). (Illus.). 1976. pap. 4.95 (ISBN 0-89957-515-3). AMG Pubs.

--A Revolutionary Mystery. (I Corinthians). (Illus.). 1974. pap. 6.95 (ISBN 0-89957-507-2). AMG Pubs.

--A Richer Life: I Corinthians. Orig. Title: A Richer Life for You in Christ. 1972. 8.95 (ISBN 0-89957-501-3); kivar 5.95 (ISBN 0-89957-502-1). AMG Pubs.

--To Love Is to Live. (I Corinthians). 1967. 8.95 (ISBN 0-89957-503-X). AMG Pubs.

--You & Public Opinion: I Corinthians. (Illus.). 1977. pap. 2.95 (ISBN 0-89957-522-6). AMG Pubs.

BIBLE–COMMENTARIES–N. T. EPHESIANS

Abbott, T. K. A Critical & Exegetical Commentary on the Epistles to the Ephesians & Colossians. Driver, Samuel R., et al, eds. LC 40-15742. (International Critical Commentary Ser.). 392p. 1897. 24.95 (ISBN 0-567-05030-0, Pub. by T & T Clark Ltd UK). Fortress.

Boles, Kenny. Thirteen Lessons on Ephesians. (Bible Student Study Guides). 1978. pap. 2.95 (ISBN 0-89900-159-9). College Pr Pub.

Bratcher, Robert G. & Nida, Eugene A. A Translator's Handbook on Paul's Letter to the Ephesians. LC 81-19691. (Helps for Translators Ser.). viii, 199p. 1982. pap. 3.50x (ISBN 0-8267-0143-4, 08780, Pub. by United Bible). Am Bible.

Briscoe, D. Stuart. Let's Get Moving. LC 77-91773. 160p. 1978. pap. 3.50 (ISBN 0-8307-0538-4, S322102). Regal.

Brooks, Keith L. Ephesians, the Epistle of Christian Maturity. (Teach Yourself the Bible Ser.). 1944. pap. 2.75 (ISBN 0-8024-2333-7). Moody.

Brooks, Noel. Ephesians. pap. 5.95 (ISBN 0-911866-02-7). Advocate.

Bruce, F. F. Epistle to the Ephesians. 144p. 1962. 10.95 (ISBN 0-8007-0083-X). Revell.

--The Epistles to the Colossians, to Philemon, & to the Ephesians. (New International Commentary on the New Testament Ser.). 464p. 1984. 18.95 (ISBN 0-8028-2401-3). Eerdmans.

Calvin, John. Sermons on Ephesians. 1979. 19.95 (ISBN 0-85151-170-8). Banner of Truth.

Coffman, James B. Commentary on Galatians, Ephesians, Phillipians, Colossians. (Firm Foundation Commentary Ser.). 1977. cancelled 10.95 (ISBN 0-88027-072-1). Firm Foun Pub.

Ephesians. (Erdmans Commentaries Ser.). 3.50 (ISBN 0-8010-3396-9). Baker Bk.

Gaebelein, Frank E., ed. The Expositor's Bible Commentary Vol. 11 (Ephesians-Philemon) 1978. 19.95 (ISBN 0-310-36530-9, 11180). Zondervan.

George, David C. Layman's Bible Book Commentary: Second Corinthians, Galatians, Ephesians, Vol. 21. LC 78-74202. 1980. 5.95 (ISBN 0-8054-1191-7). Broadman.

Gromacki, Robert G. Stand Perfect in Wisdom: Colossians & Ephesians. 1981. pap. 5.95 (ISBN 0-8010-3767-0). Baker Bk.

Guthrie, Donald. Exploring God's World: A Guide to Ephesians, Philippians, & Colossians. 224p. (Orig.). 1985. pap. 6.95 (ISBN 0-8028-0084-X). Eerdmans.

Gutzke, Manford G. Plain Talk on Ephesians. 224p. 1973. pap. 6.95 (ISBN 0-310-25511-2, 9729P). Zondervan.

Havener, Ivan & Karris, Robert J. First Thessalonians, Philippians, Philemon, Second Thessalonians, Colossians, Ephesians, No. 8. (Collegeville Bible Commentary Ser.). (Illus.). 112p. 1983. pap. 2.95 (ISBN 0-8146-1308-X). Liturgical Pr.

Hendriksen, William. Galatians & Ephesians. (New Testament Commentary Ser.). 290p. 1979. 18.95 (ISBN 0-8010-4211-9). Baker Bk.

Hodge, Charles. Commentary on the Epistle to the Ephesians. (Thornapple Commentaries Ser.). 1980. pap. 8.95 (ISBN 0-8010-4221-6). Baker Bk.

Houlden, J. L., ed. Paul's Letters from Prison: Philippians, Colossians, Philemon & Ephesians. LC 77-24028. (Westminister Pelican Commentaries). 358p. 1978. 11.50 (ISBN 0-664-21347-2); pap. 6.95 (ISBN 0-664-24182-4). Westminster.

Ironside, H. A. Galatians & Ephesians. 11.95 (ISBN 0-87213-397-4). Loizeaux.

Jensen, Irving L. Ephesians. (Bible Self-Study Ser.). 1973. pap. 3.25 (ISBN 0-8024-1049-9). Moody.

Julien, Tom. Inherited Wealth: Studies in Ephesians. pap. 4.95 (ISBN 0-88469-034-2). BMH Bks.

Kent, Homer, Jr. Efesios: La Gloria de la Iglesia (Comentario Biblico Portavoz) Orig. Title: Ephesians: The Glory of the Church (Everyman's Bible Commentary) (Span.). 144p. 1981. pap. 3.95 (ISBN 0-8254-1405-9). Kregel.

--Ephesians: The Glory of the Church. (Everyman's Bible Commentary Ser.). 1971. pap. 5.95 (ISBN 0-8024-2049-4). Moody.

Lenski, Richard C. Interpretation of Galatians, Ephesians, & Philippians. 1937. 21.95 (ISBN 0-8066-9007-0, 10-3368). Augsburg.

Le Peau, Andrew T. & Le Peau, Phyllis J. Ephesians. (Lifefuilder Bible Studies). 60p. (Orig.). 1985. pap. text ed. 2.95 (ISBN 0-8308-1012-9). Inter-Varsity.

Lloyd-Jones, D. Martyn. Christian Unity: An Exposition of Ephesians 4: 1-16. 280p. 1981. 12.95 (ISBN 0-8010-5607-1). Baker Bk.

--Lloyd-Jones Expositions of Ephesians, 8 Vols. 1983. 95.00 (ISBN 0-8010-5623-3). Baker Bk.

--Unsearchable Riches of Christ. 1980. 12.95 (ISBN 0-8010-5597-0). Baker Bk.

Meyer, F. B. Ephesians. 1968. pap. 4.50 (ISBN 0-87508-344-7). Chr Lit.

Mitton, C. Leslie. Ephesians. Black, Matthew, ed. (New Century Bible Commentary Ser.). 256p. 1981. pap. 6.95 (ISBN 0-8028-1907-9). Eerdmans.

Moule, H. C. G. Studies in Ephesians. LC 77-79179. (Kregel Popular Commentary Ser.). 176p. 1977. kivar 7.95 (ISBN 0-8254-3218-9). Kregel.

Moule, Handley. Ephesians. 1975. pap. 4.95 (ISBN 0-87508-363-3). Chr Lit.

Pattison, R. & Moule, H. Exposition of Ephesians: Lessons in Grace & Godliness. 390p. 1983. lib. bdg. 14.75 Smythe Sewn (ISBN 0-86524-153-8, 4902). Klock & Klock.

Paxson, Ruth. Wealth, Walk & Warfare of the Christian. 224p. 1939. 11.95 (ISBN 0-8007-0340-5). Revell.

Robinson, J. Armitage. Commentary on Ephesians. LC 78-59143. (Kregel Ltd Ed. Library). 320p. 1979. 14.95 (ISBN 0-8254-3612-5). Kregel.

Rocke, Herman H. Check Your Panoply. 240p. 1977. pap. text ed. 4.00 (ISBN 0-910424-71-3). Concordant.

Stott, John R. The Message of Ephesians. Motyer, J. A., ed. (The Bible Speaks Today Ser.). 1980. pap. text ed. 7.95 (ISBN 0-87784-287-6). Inter-Varsity.

Strauss, Lehman. Galatians & Ephesians. 1957. 8.95 (ISBN 0-87213-817-8). Loizeaux.

Swain, Lionel. Ephesians. (New Testament Message Ser.: Vol. 13). 10.95 (ISBN 0-89453-201-4); pap. 5.95 (ISBN 0-89453-136-0). M Glazier.

Taylor, Walter F., Jr. & Reumann, John H., eds. Augsburg Commentary on the New Testament: Ephesians, Colossians. LC 85-7479. 176p. (Orig.). 1985. kivar 8.95 (ISBN 0-8066-2165-6, 10-9030). Augsburg.

Thompson, G. H. Letters of Paul to the Ephesians, Colossians & Philemon. (Cambridge Bible Commentary on the New English Bible, New Testament Ser.). 18.95 (ISBN 0-521-04227-5); pap. 9.95x (ISBN 0-521-09410-0, 410). Cambridge U Pr.

Tucker, W. Leon. Studies in Ephesians. LC 83-6115. 136p. 1983. pap. 4.95 (ISBN 0-8254-3828-4). Kregel.

Van Note, Gene. Beacon Small-Group Bible Studies, Ephesians. 88p. (Orig.). 1981. pap. 2.50 (ISBN 0-8341-0722-8). Beacon Hill.

Vaughan, Curtis. Comentario Biblico Efesios. Orig. Title: Ephesians. (Port.). 1986. write for info. (ISBN 0-8297-1608-4). Life Pubs Intl.

--Ephesians: A Study Guide Commentary. (Study Guide Commentary Ser.). 1977. pap. 4.95 (ISBN 0-310-33533-7, 10962P). Zondervan.

--Ephesians (Efesios-Comemtario y Estudios) (Span.). 1986. write for info. (ISBN 0-8297-0904-5). Life Pubs Intl.

Westcott, Brooke F. St. Paul's Epistle to the Ephesians. 281p. 1983. lib. bdg. 10.50 (ISBN 0-86524-171-6, 4901). Klock & Klock.

Wiersbe, Warren W. Be Rich. LC 76-6833. 175p. 1976. pap. 5.95 (ISBN 0-88207-730-9). Victor Bks.

Wilson, Geoffrey. Ephesians. 1978. pap. 4.95 (ISBN 0-85151-263-1). Banner of Truth.

BIBLE–COMMENTARIES–N. T. EPISTLES OF PAUL

Anderson, Richard L. Understanding Paul. LC 83-72103. 448p. 1983. 10.95 (ISBN 0-87747-984-4). Deseret Bk.

Banks, Robert. Paul's Idea of Community: The Early House Churches in the Historical Setting. 1980. pap. 5.95 (ISBN 0-8028-1830-7). Eerdmans.

Barrett, Charles K. The Second Epistle to the Corinthians. LC 73-18682. 366p. 1974. 17.95 (ISBN 0-06-060552-9, HarpR). Har-Row.

Bigg, Charles. A Critical & Exergetical Commentary on the Epistles of St. Peter & St. Jude. Driver, Samuel R., et al, eds. (International Critical Commentary Ser.). 376p. 1902. 24.95 (ISBN 0-567-05036-X, Pub. by T & T Clark Ltd UK). Fortress.

Bonnet, L. & Schroeder, A. Epistolas De Pablo Tomo III. Cativiela, A., tr. from Fr. (Comentario del Nuevo Testamento). 538p. 1986. pap. 14.95 (ISBN 0-311-03052-1). Casa Bautista.

Coniaris, A. M. Treasures from Paul's Letters, Vol. I. 1978. pap. 7.95 (ISBN 0-937032-05-0). Light&Life Pub Co MN.

--Treasures from Paul's Letters, Vol. II. 1979. pap. 7.95 (ISBN 0-937032-06-9). Light&Life Pub Co MN.

Corinthians: A Commentary on the New Testament in Modern English. (J. B. Phillips New Testament Commentaries Ser). 102p. 1973. Repr. of 1972 ed. 1.50 (ISBN 0-685-29328-9). Macmillan.

Daughters of St. Paul, ed. Drawing Near Him with Confidence. (Chinese.). 1978. 3.95 (ISBN 0-8198-1801-1); pap. 2.95 (ISBN 0-8198-1802-X). Dghtrs St Paul.

Ellicott, Charles. Ellicott's Commentaries, Critical & Grammatical on the Epistles of Saint Paul, 2 vol. 1986. Repr. of 1879 ed. lib. bdg. 45.00 (ISBN 0-89941-506-7). W S Hein.

Epistles of Paul: Hebrews. (Banner of Truth Geneva Series Commentaries). 1978. 24.95 (ISBN 0-85151-271-2). Banner of Truth.

Forlines, Leroy & Picirilli, Robert. A Survey of the Pauline Epistles. 1976. pap. 3.75 (ISBN 0-89265-035-4). Randall Hse.

Godet, Frederic L. Studies in Paul's Epistles. LC 84-7138. 352p. 1984. 14.95 (ISBN 0-8254-2723-1). Kregel.

Hunter, Archibald M. Galatians-Colossians. LC 59-10454. (Layman's Bible Commentary Ser.: Vol. 22). 1959. pap. 4.95 (ISBN 0-8042-3082-X). John Knox.

Jeremiah, David. Philippians: Twenty-Six Daily Bible Studies. (Steps to Higher Ground Ser.). 1983. pap. 1.95 (ISBN 0-86508-208-1). BCM Intl Inc.

Leggett, Gary. Letters to Timothy. LC 80-82830. (Radiant Life Ser.). 128p. (Orig.). 1981. 2.50 (ISBN 0-88243-877-8, 02-0877); teacher's ed. 3.95 (ISBN 0-88243-189-7, 32-0189). Gospel Pub.

Lightfoot, J. B. Notes on Epistles of Saint Paul. Harmer, J. R., ed. (Thornapple Commentaries Ser.). 345p. 1980. pap. 8.95 (ISBN 0-8010-5602-0). Baker Bk.

Loudy, Aldai. The Gospel of Our Salvation. 122p. 1973. text ed. 4.00 (ISBN 0-910424-60-8). Concordant.

Lovett, C. S. Lovett's Lights on Galatians, Ephesians, Philippians, Colossians, 1 & 2 Thessalonians. 1970. pap. 5.95 (ISBN 0-938148-25-7). Personal Christianity.

Milligan, George. St. Paul's Epistle to the Thessalonians. 144p. 1980. 12.95 (ISBN 0-8007-1098-3). Revell.

--St. Paul's Epistles to the Thessalonians. 1980. 12.00 (ISBN 0-86524-022-1, 7104). Klock & Klock.

Morton, A. Q. & Michaelson, Sidney. Critical Concordance to the Letter of Paul to the Romans. Baird, J. Arthur & Freedman, David Noel, eds. (Computer Bible Ser: Vol. XIII). 1977. pap. 27.50 (ISBN 0-935106-08-1). Biblical Res Assocs.

Nelson, P. C. The Letters of Paul: Complete Outlines & Notes on the Epistles of Paul. 144p. 1976. pap. 2.00 (ISBN 0-88243-546-9, 02-0546). Gospel Pub.

Olshausen, Hermann. A Commentary on Paul's First & Second Epistle to the Corinthians. 388p. 1984. 14.75 (ISBN 0-86524-184-8, 4604). Klock & Klock.

Patte, Daniel. Preaching Paul. LC 84-47931. (Fortress Resources for Preaching Ser.). 96p. 1984. pap. 4.95 (ISBN 0-8006-1140-3). Fortress.

Pentecost, J. Dwight. The Joy of Living: A Study of Philippians. 160p. 1973. pap. text ed. 6.95 (ISBN 0-310-30871-2, 17012P). Zondervan.

Petersen, Norman. Rediscovering Paul: Philemon & the Sociology of Paul's Narrative World. LC 84-48730. 320p. 1985. 24.95 (ISBN 0-8006-0741-4, 1-741). Fortress.

Pobee, John S. Persecution & Martyrdom: From Experience to Theology in Paul. (JSNT Supplement Ser.: No. 6). 150p. 1984. text ed. 28.50x (ISBN 0-905774-52-3, Pub. by JSOT Pr. England); pap. text ed. 13.50x (ISBN 0-905774-53-1, Pub. by JSOT Pr. England). Eisenbrauns.

Ramsay, William H. Historical Commentary on the Epistle to the Galatians. 1978. 17.75 (ISBN 0-86524-107-4, 4801). Klock & Klock.

Robinson, John A. The Body: A Study in Pauline Theology. LC 77-7221. 96p. 1977. pap. 3.95 (ISBN 0-664-24149-2). Westminster.

Sampley, J. Paul. Pauline Partnership in Christ: Christian Community & Commitment in Light of Roman Law. LC 79-8895. 144p. 1980. 2.00 (ISBN 0-8006-0631-0, 1-631). Fortress.

Seripando, Girolamo. In D. Pauli Epistolas ad Romanos et Galatas Commentaria. 568p. Repr. of 1601 ed. text ed. 99.36 (ISBN 0-576-99309-3, Pub. by Gregg Intl Pubs England). Gregg Intl.

Sibbes, Richard. Exposition of St. Paul's Epistles. (Works of Sibbes: Vol. 5). 1978. Repr. 16.95 (ISBN 0-85151-246-1). Banner of Truth.

Souter, A. Pegaluis's Expositions on Thirteen Epistles of St. Paul, 3 pts. in 1 vol. (Texts & Studies Ser. 1: Vol. 9). pap. 83.00 (ISBN 0-8115-1712-8). Pt. 1: Introduction. Kraus Repr.

Stanley, Arthur P. Epistles of Paul to the Corinthians. 1981. 20.95 (ISBN 0-86524-051-5, 7105). Klock & Klock.

Stendahl, Krister. Paul Among Jews & Gentiles & Other Essays. LC 75-36450. 144p. 1976. pap. 4.95 (ISBN 0-8006-1224-8, 1-1224). Fortress.

Taylor, Michael J., ed. A Companion to Paul. 200p. 1975. pap. 6.95 (ISBN 0-8189-0304-X). Alba.

BIBLE–COMMENTARIES–N. T. GALATIANS

Betz, Hans D. Galatians. LC 77-78625. (Hermenia: A Critical & Historical Commentary on the Bible Ser.). 384p. 1979. 28.95 (ISBN 0-8006-6009-9, 20-6009). Fortress.

Boles, Kenny. Thirteen Lessons on Galatians. (Bible Student Study Guides). 1978. pap. 2.95 (ISBN 0-89900-158-0). College Pr Pub.

Bridger, Gordon. First Corinthians-Galatians. (Bible Study Commentaries Ser.). 95p. 1985. pap. 4.95 (ISBN 0-317-43383-0). Chr Lit.

Brooks, Keith L. Galatians, the Epistle of Christian Maturity. (Teach Yourself the Bible Ser.). 1963. pap. 2.75 (ISBN 0-8024-2925-4). Moody.

Burton, Ernest De Witt. A Critical & Exegetical Commentary on the Epistle to the Galatians. Driver, Samuel R. & Briggs, Charles A., eds. (International Critical Commentary Ser.). 632p. 1921. 24.95 (ISBN 0-567-05029-7, Pub. by T & T Clark Ltd UK). Fortress.

Cole, Alan. The Epistle of Paul to the Galatians. (Tyndale Bible Commentaries). 1964. pap. 4.95 (ISBN 0-8028-1408-5). Eerdmans.

Cousar, Charles. Galatians: The Bible Commentary for Teaching & Preaching. LC 81-82354. (Interpretation Ser.). 168p. (James Mays General Editor of the series, Paul Achtemeier New Testament editor). 1982. 13.95 (ISBN 0-8042-3138-9). John Knox.

Erasmus, Desiderius. Paraphrases on Romans & Galatians. Sider, Robert D., ed. Payne, John B., et al, trs. (Collected Works of Erasmus Ser.: Vol. 42). 232p. 1984. 29.50x (ISBN 0-8020-2510-2). U of Toronto Pr.

Galatians. (Erdman's Commentaries Ser.). 3.50 (ISBN 0-8010-3397-7). Baker Bk.

Gelesnoff, Vladimir M. Paul's Epistle to the Galatians. 1977. pap. text ed. 3.00 (ISBN 0-910424-73-X). Concordant.

George, David C. Layman's Bible Book Commentary: Second Corinthians, Galatians, Ephesians, Vol. 21. LC 78-74202. 1980. 5.95 (ISBN 0-8054-1191-7). Broadman.

Guthrie, Donald. Galatians. rev. ed. Black, Matthew, ed. (New Century Bible Commentary Ser.). 176p. 1981. pap. 5.95 (ISBN 0-8028-1906-0). Eerdmans.

Hendriksen, William. Galatians & Ephesians. (New Testament Commentary Ser.). 290p. 1979. 18.95 (ISBN 0-8010-4211-9). Baker Bk.

Hogg, C. F. & Vine, W. E. Epistle to the Galatians. 360p. (Orig.). pap. cancelled (ISBN 0-8254-2858-0). Kregel.

Keller, Phillip. A Gardener Looks at the Fruits of the Spirit. 1983. 6.95 (ISBN 0-8499-2958-X). Word Bks.

Koehler, J. The Epistle of Paul to the Galatians. Sauer, E. E., tr. 1957. 2.95 (ISBN 0-8100-0038-5, 15N0315). Northwest Pub.

Lenski, Richard C. Interpretation of Galatians, Ephesians, & Philippians. 1937. 21.95 (ISBN 0-8066-9007-0, 10-3368). Augsburg.

Lightfoot, J. B. Commentaries on Galatians, Philippians, Colossians & Philemon, 3 vols. 1208p. 1981. 39.95 (ISBN 0-913573-02-7). Hendrickson MA.

Luther, Martin. Commentary on Galatians. LC 78-59151. (Kregel Reprint Library). Orig. Title: A Commentary on St. Paul's Epistle to the Galatians. 408p. 1979. 14.95 (ISBN 0-8254-3121-2). Kregel.

--Commentary on the Epistle to the Galatians. Watson, P. S., tr. from Ger. 573p. 1978. Repr. of 1972 ed. 15.95 (ISBN 0-227-67437-5). Attic Pr.

--Luther's Works: Lectures on Galatians, Vols. 26 & 27. Incl. Vol. 26. Pelikan, Jaroslav, ed. 1962; Vol. 27. Pelikan, Jaroslav, ed. Jungkuntz, Richard, tr. 1963. 16.95 (ISBN 0-570-06427-9, 15-1769). LC 55-9893. 16.95 (ISBN 0-570-06426-0, 15-1768). Concordia.

Neil, William. Letter of Paul to the Galatians. (Cambridge Commmentary on the New English Bible, New Testament Ser.). (Orig.). 1967. pap. 6.95x (ISBN 0-521-09402-X). Cambridge U Pr.

Osiek, Carolyn. Galatians. (New Testament Message Ser.: Vol. 12). 8.95 (ISBN 0-89453-200-6); pap. 5.95 (ISBN 0-89453-135-2). M Glazier.

Pilch, John J. & Karris, Robert J. Galatians & Romans, No. 6. (Collegeville Bible Commentary Ser.). 80p. 1983. pap. 2.95 (ISBN 0-8146-1306-3). Liturgical Pr.

Ridderbos, Herman N. Epistle of Paul to the Churches of Galatia. (New International Commentary on the New Testament Ser.). 1953. 12.95 (ISBN 0-8028-2191-X). Eerdmans.

Seripando, Girolamo. In D. Pauli Epistolas ad Romanos et Galatas Commentaria. 568p. Repr. of 1601 ed. text ed. 99.36 (ISBN 0-576-99309-3, Pub. by Gregg Intl Pubs England). Gregg Intl.

Strauss, Lehman. Galatians & Ephesians. 1957. 8.95 (ISBN 0-87213-817-8). Loizeaux.

Van Harn, Roger. Galatians: A Study Guide. (Revelation Series for Adults). 1984. pap. 2.50 (ISBN 0-933140-93-2). CRC Pubns.

Vos, Howard F. Galatas: Una Llamada a la Libertad Cristiana (Comentarion Biblico Portavoz) Orig. Title: Galatians (Everyman's Bible Commentary) (Span.). 1981. pap. 3.50 (ISBN 0-8254-1825-9). Kregel.

--Galatians. (Everyman's Bible Commentary Ser.). 1970. pap. 5.95 (ISBN 0-8024-2048-6). Moody.

Wiersbe, Warren W. Be Free. LC 74-33824. 160p. 1975. pap. 5.95 (ISBN 0-88207-716-3). Victor Bks.

Wilson, Geoffrey. Galatians. 1979. pap. 4.95 (ISBN 0-85151-294-1). Banner of Truth.

BIBLE–COMMENTARIES–N. T. GOSPELS

Here are entered commentaries on the Gospels as a whole, as well as on the Individual Gospels, Matthew, Mark, Luke, John.

Achtemeier, Paul J. Mark. rev., enl., 2nd ed. Krodel, Gerhard, ed. LC 85-46020. (Proclamation Commentaries: The New Testament Witnesses for Preaching Ser.). 144p. 1986. pap. 4.50 (ISBN 0-8006-1916-1, 1-1916). Fortress.

Ackland, Donald F. Day by Day with John. LC 81-67374. 1982. pap. 4.95 (ISBN 0-8054-5187-0). Broadman.

Albright, William F. & Mann, C. S., eds. Matthew. LC 77-150875. (Anchor Bible Ser.: Vol. 26). 1971. 18.00 (ISBN 0-385-08658-X, Anchor Pr). Doubleday.

Alexander, J. A. Mark. (Geneva Series Commentaries). 1984. 15.95 (ISBN 0-85151-422-7). Banner of Truth.

Alexander, Joseph. Commentary on the Gospel of Mark. 1980. 16.75 (ISBN 0-86524-018-3, 4101). Klock & Klock.

Alexander, Joseph A. Mark. (Thornapple Commentaries Ser.). 1980. pap. 8.95 (ISBN 0-8010-0150-1). Baker Bk.

Anderson, Hugh. The Gospel of Mark. rev. ed. (New Century Bible Commentary Ser.). 384p. 1981. pap. 8.95 (ISBN 0-8028-1887-0). Eerdmans.

Anderson, Robert. The Gospel & Its Ministry. LC 78-9539. (Sir Robert Anderson Library). 224p. 1978. pap. 4.95 (ISBN 0-8254-2126-8). Kregel.

Argyle, Aubrey W., ed. Gospel According to Matthew. (Cambridge Bible Commentary on the New Testament Ser.). (Orig.). 1963. o. p. 19.95 (ISBN 0-521-04197-X); pap. 10.95 (ISBN 0-521-09198-5). Cambridge U Pr.

Barnabas. Gospel of Barnabas. 1981. pap. 9.95 (ISBN 0-686-77427-2). Kazi Pubns.

Barth, Karl. Great Promise. LC 61-15239. 70p. 1963. 6.00 (ISBN 0-8022-0074-5). Philos Lib.

Barthes, Roland, et al. Analyse Structurale et Exegese Biblique. 128p. 1973. 17.50 (ISBN 0-686-53927-3). French & Eur.

Beare, F. W. The Gospel According to Matthew: Translation, Commentary, & Notes. LC 81-47837. 575p. 1982. 29.45 (ISBN 0-06-060731-9, HarpR). Har-Row.

Belo, Fernando. A Materialist Reading of the Gospel of Mark. O'Connell, Matthew, tr. from Fr. LC 80-24756. Tr. of Lectero Materialiste de L'evangele de Marc. 384p. (Orig.). 1981. pap. 12.95 (ISBN 0-88344-323-6). Orbis Bks.

Benware, Paul. Luke: Gospel of the Son of Man. (Everyman's Bible Commentary Ser.). 1985. pap. 5.95 (ISBN 0-8024-2074-5). Moody.

Bernard, J. H. A Critical & Exegetical Commentary on the Gospel According to St. John, 2 vols. Driver, Samuel R. & Plummer, Alfred, eds. (International Critical Commentary Ser.). 24.95 ea. (Pub. by T & T ClarK Ltd UK). Vol. I, 480p (ISBN 0-567-05024-6). Vol. II, 456p (ISBN 0-567-05025-4). Fortress.

Bernard, Thomas D. The Central Teaching of Christ: A Study of John 13-17. 426p. 1985. Repr. lib. bdg. 16.25 (ISBN 0-86524-176-7, 9519). Klock & Klock.

Best, E. A. Following Jesus: Discipleship in the Gospel of Mark. (Journal for the Study of the New Testament, Supplement Ser.: No. 4). 283p. 1981. text ed. 25.95 (ISBN 0-905774-28-0, Pub. by JSOT Pr England); pap. text ed. 12.50x (ISBN 0-905774-29-9, Pub. by JSOT Pr England). Eisenbrauns.

Blair, J. Allen. John: Living Eternally. LC 77-28529. 1978. pap. 4.95 (ISBN 0-87213-046-0). Loizeaux.

Boice, James M. Witness & the Revelation in the Gospel of John. 192p. 1970. pap. 4.95 (ISBN 0-85364-099-8). Attic Pr.

Bowker, John. Jesus & the Pharisees. 240p. 1973. 42.50 (ISBN 0-521-20055-5). Cambridge U Pr.

Bratcher, R. G. Translator's Guide to the Gospel of Luke. (Helps for Translators Ser.). 388p. 1982. pap. 4.50x (ISBN 0-8267-0181-7, 08712, Pub. by United Bible). Am Bible.

Brianchaninov, Ignatius. Three Essays: On Reading the Gospel, on Reading the Holy Fathers, on Shunning Reading of Books Containing False Teachings. pap. 0.25 (ISBN 0-686-16365-6). Eastern Orthodox.

Bright, Laurence, et al. Paul Two. LC 71-173033. (Scripture Discussion Commentary Ser.: Pt. 11). 224p. 1971. pap. text ed. 4.50 (ISBN 0-87946-010-5). ACTA Found.

Briscoe, D. Stuart. Patterns for Power. LC 78-68850. (Bible Commentary for Laymen Ser.). 160p. 1979. pap. 3.50 (ISBN 0-8307-0701-8, S331101). Regal.

Brooks, Keith L. Mark: Gospel of God's Servant. (Teach Yourself the Bible Ser.). 64p. 1961. pap. 2.75 (ISBN 0-8024-5183-7). Moody.

--Matthew, the Gospel of God's King. (Teach Yourself the Bible Ser.). 1963. pap. 2.75 (ISBN 0-8024-5212-4). Moody.

Brown, David. The Four Gospels. 20.95 (ISBN 0-85151-016-7). Banner of Truth.

Brown, Raymond E., tr. Gospel According to John One - Twelve. LC 66-12209. (Anchor Bible Ser.: Vol. 29). 1966. 20.00 (ISBN 0-385-01517-8, Anchor Pr). Doubleday.

--Gospel According to John Thirteen - Twenty-One. LC 66-12209. (Anchor Bible Ser.: Vol. 29A). 1970. 18.00 (ISBN 0-385-03761-9, Anchor Pr). Doubleday.

Bruce, F. F. The Epistles of John. LC 78-22069. 1978. pap. 5.95 (ISBN 0-8028-1783-1). Eerdmans.

--The Gospel of John. 440p. 1984. 13.95 (ISBN 0-8028-3407-8). Eerdmans.

Bruner, Dale. Commentary on Matthew (One) 500p. 1987. 24.95 (ISBN 0-8499-0526-5). Word Bks.

Bunyan, John. Pharisee & the Publican. pap. 3.95 (ISBN 0-685-19840-5). Reiner.

--The Water of Life. pap. 1.50 (ISBN 0-685-88397-3). Reiner.

Burgess, John. Black Gospel, White Church. 128p. 1982. pap. 7.95 (ISBN 0-8164-2380-6, HarpR). Har-Row.

Byrum, R. R. Shadows of Good Things, or the Gospel in Type. (Illus.). 144p. pap. 1.50 (ISBN 0-686-29141-7). Faith Pub Hse.

Cadbury, Henry J. Behind the Gospels. LC 68-8591. (Orig.). 1968. pap. 2.50x (ISBN 0-87574-160-6). Pendle Hill.

Caird, G. B. Saint Luke. LC 77-81622. (Westminster Pelican Commentaries Ser.). 272p. 1978. 10.95 (ISBN 0-664-21345-6). Westminster.

Caird, George B. The Gospel of St. Luke: Commentaries. (Orig.). 1964. pap. 7.95 (ISBN 0-14-020490-3, Pelican). Penguin.

Campbell, R. K. Parables in Matthew's Gospel. 1978. pap. 1.95 (ISBN 0-915374-42-0, 42-0). Rapids Christian.

--Parables in Matthew's Gospel: Matthew 13. tchr's lesson outline 3.95 (ISBN 0-88172-011-9). Believers Bkshelf.

Carson, D. A. The Farewell Discourse & the Final Prayer of Jesus: An Exposition of John 14-17. LC 80-68769. 196p. 1981. 9.95 (ISBN 0-8010-2460-9). Baker Bk.

--Sermon on the Mount: An Evangelical Exposition of Matthew 5-7. LC 77-93260. 1978. 4.95 (ISBN 0-8010-2480-3). Baker Bk.

Carter, James E. Layman's Bible Book Commentary: John, Vol. 18. LC 81-65391. 1984. 5.95 (ISBN 0-8054-1188-7). Broadman.

Cassidy, Richard J. Jesus, Politics, & Society: A Study of Luke's Gospel. LC 78-735. 238p. (Orig.). 1978. 15.95 (ISBN 0-88344-238-8); pap. 7.95 (ISBN 0-88344-237-X). Orbis Bks.

Chantry, Walter. Today's Gospel. 1980. pap. 3.45 (ISBN 0-85151-027-2). Banner of Truth.

Chantry, Walter J. God's Righteous Kingdom. 151p. (Orig.). 1980. pap. 4.95 (ISBN 0-85151-310-7). Banner of Truth.

Chappell, Clovis G. The Sermon on the Mount. (Pulpit Libarary Ser). 1979. pap. 4.95 (ISBN 0-8010-2363-7). Baker Bk.

Clymer, R. Swinburne. Interpretation of St. John. 266p. 1953. 9.95 (ISBN 0-932785-23-9). Philos Pub.

Coffman, James B. Commentary on John. (Firm Foundation Commentary Ser.). 1974. cancelled 10.95 (ISBN 0-88027-068-3). Firm Foun Pub.

--Commentary on Luke. (Firm Foundation Commentary Ser.). 1975. cancelled 10.95 (ISBN 0-88027-067-5). Firm Foun Pub.

--Commentary on Mark. (Firm Foundation Commentary Ser.). 1975. cancelled 10.95 (ISBN 0-88027-066-7). Firm Foun Pub.

--Commentary on Matthew. (Firm Foundation Commentary Ser.). 1968. cancelled 10.95 (ISBN 0-88027-065-9). Firm Foun Pub.

Cole, Alan. Gospel According to St. Mark. (Tyndale Bible Commentaries Ser.). 1962. pap. 5.95 (ISBN 0-8028-1401-8). Eerdmans.

Coniaris, A. M. The Message of the Sunday Gospel Readings, Vol. 1. 1982. pap. 7.95 (ISBN 0-937032-26-3). Light&Life Pub Co MN.

Cooper, Harold. Doctrines from the Beloved Disciple: Outlined Gospel of John. 137p. 1972. pap. 1.00 (ISBN 0-89114-054-9). Baptist Pub Hse.

Cox, Frank L. According to Luke. 1941. pap. 2.75 (ISBN 0-88027-030-6). Firm Foun Pub.

Craddock, Fred B. John. Hayes, John H., ed. LC 82-48095. (Knox Preaching Guides Ser.). 149p. 1982. pap. 6.95. John Knox.

Crane, Thomas E. The Message of St. John: The Spiritual Teachings of the Beloved Disciple. LC 80-11779. 184p. (Orig.). 1980. pap. 5.95 (ISBN 0-8189-0402-X). Alba.

Crissey, Clair M. Layman's Bible Book Commentary: Matthew, Vol. 15. LC 79-56691. 1981. 5.95 (ISBN 0-8054-1185-2). Broadman.

Cunningham, Robert C. Getting Together with Luke & Acts. 47p. 1972. pap. 0.50 (ISBN 0-88243-930-8, 02-0930). Gospel Pub.

Dalpadado, J. Kinglsey. Reading the Gospels. 1975. pap. 4.00 (ISBN 0-8198-0454-1). Dghtrs St Paul.

Danker, Frederick W. Jesus & the New Age According to St. Luke. 1983. pap. text ed. 12.00 (ISBN 0-915644-25-8). Clayton Pub Hse.

--Luke. Krodel, Gerhard, ed. LC 76-5954. (Proclamation Commentaries: the New Testament Witnesses for Preaching Ser.). 128p. 1976. pap. 4.95 (ISBN 0-8006-0583-7, 1-583). Fortress.

--Luke. 2nd, rev. ed. LC 86-45905. (Proclamation Commentary, New Testament Ser.). 144p. 1987. pap. 7.95 (ISBN 0-8006-0598-5, 1-598). Fortress.

Denny, James. Jesus & the Gospel. 1977. lib. bdg. 59.95 (ISBN 0-8490-2095-6). Gordon Pr.

Dewey, Arthur J. The Word in Time. 204p. (Orig.). 1986. pap. 14.95 (ISBN 0-941850-18-8). Sunday Pubns.

Dibelius, Martin. From Tradition to Gospel. Wooff, Bertram L., tr. 328p. 1971. 27.50 (ISBN 0-227-67752-8). Attic Pr.

Dietrich, Suzanne. Matthew. LC 59-10454. (Layman's Bible Commentary Ser.: Vol. 16). 1961. pap. 4.95 (ISBN 0-8042-3076-5). John Knox.

Doohan, Leonard. Mark: Visionary of Early Christianity. LC 86-72485. 192p. (Orig.). 1986. pap. 9.95 (ISBN 0-939680-33-5). Bear & Co.

--Matthew: Spirituality for the 80's & 90's. LC 85-70838. 199p. (Orig.). 1985. pap. 9.95 (ISBN 0-939680-19-X). Bear & Co.

Drane, John. Jesus & the Gospels. LC 77-20448. 1979. pap. 9.95 (ISBN 0-06-062066-8, RD264, HarpR). Har-Row.

Duckworth, Robin, ed. This Is the Word of the Lord: Year A: The Year of Matthew. 1980. pap. 9.95 (ISBN 0-19-213248-2). Oxford U Pr.

Earle, Ralph. Mark: Gospel of Action. LC 73-15084. (Everyman's Bible Commentary Ser.). 1970. pap. 5.95 (ISBN 0-8024-2041-9). Moody.

--Word Meanings: Matthew-Luke, Vol. 1. 9.95 (ISBN 0-8010-3362-4). Baker Bk.

Edwards, Richard A. Matthew's Story of Jesus. LC 84-48711. 96p. 1985. pap. 4.50 (ISBN 0-8006-1619-7, 1-1619). Fortress.

Fairweather, William. Background of the Gospels. 1977. 17.00 (ISBN 0-86524-117-1, 8001). Klock & Klock.

Fallon, Michael. The Winston Commentary on the Gospels. 470p. 1982. pap. 12.95 (ISBN 0-86683-680-2, JHarpR). Har-Row.

Fenton, J. C. Saint Matthew. LC 77-81620. (Westminster Pelican Commentaries Ser.). 488p. 1978. Westminster.

Fenton, John. The Gospel of St. Matthew: Commentaries. (Orig.). 1964. pap. 7.95 (ISBN 0-14-020488-1, Pelican). Penguin.

Fillmore, Charles. Mysteries of John. 1946. 5.95 (ISBN 0-87159-105-7). Unity School.

Filson, Floyd V. John. LC 59-10454. (Layman's Bible Commentary Ser: Vol. 19). 1963. pap. 4.95 (ISBN 0-8042-3079-X). John Knox.

Fitzmyer, Joseph A. Gospel According to Luke I-IX, Vol. 28. LC 80-702. (Anchor Bible Ser.). 1981. 20.00 (ISBN 0-385-00515-6). Doubleday.

Foster, Lewis. The Only Way. LC 77-83658. 96p. (Orig.). 1978. pap. 2.25 (ISBN 0-87239-193-0, 40048). Standard Pub.

--The True Life. LC 77-83656. 96p. (Orig.). 1978. pap. 2.25 (ISBN 0-87239-192-2, 40047). Standard Pub.

Fox, Douglas J. The Matthew-Luke Commentary of Philoxenus. LC 78-12852. 1979. 14.50 (ISBN 0-89130-350-2); pap. 9.95 (ISBN 0-89130-266-2, 060143). Scholars Pr GA.

France, R. T. & Wenham, David, eds. Gospel Perspectives: Studies of History & Tradition in the Four Gospels, Vol. II. 375p. 1981. text ed. 14.75x (ISBN 0-905774-31-0, Pub. by JSOT Pr England). Eisenbrauns.

Franzen, Lavern G. Good News from Luke: Visual Messages for Children. LC 76-3869. 112p. (Orig.). 1976. pap. 6.95 (ISBN 0-8066-1528-1, 10-2813). Augsburg.

Freburger, William. This Is the Word of the Lord. rev. ed. LC 83-72480. 176p. 1984. spiral bound 6.95 (ISBN 0-87793-309-X). Ave Maria.

Fredrikson, Roger L. The Communicator's Commentary-John, Vol. 4. Ogilvie, Lloyd J., ed. (The Communicator's Commentaries Ser.). 1983. 18.95 (ISBN 0-8499-0157-X). Word Bks.

Freyne, Sean & Wansbrough, Henry. Mark & Matthew. Bright, Laurence, ed. LC 71-173033. (Scripture Discussion Commentary Ser.: Pt. 7). 256p. 1971. pap. text ed. 4.50 (ISBN 0-87946-006-7). ACTA Found.

Funk, Robert W. New Gospel Parallels, Vol. 1. LC 84-48727. (Foundations & Facets Ser.). 512p. 1985. 29.95 (ISBN 0-8006-2104-2, 1-2104). Fortress.

Gaebelein, Frank E., ed. The Expositors' Bible Commentary: Matthew, Mark, Luke, Vol. 8. LC 83-11177. 1056p. (Orig.). 1984. 29.95 (ISBN 0-310-36500-7, 11177). Zondervan.

Geldenhuys, J. Norval. Commentary on Luke. (New International Commentary on the New Testament). 1951. 17.95 (ISBN 0-8028-2184-7). Eerdmans.

Godet, F. L. Commentary on the Gospel of Saint Luke, 2 vols, Vol. 1. Shalders, E. W., ed. 448p. 1870. 13.95 (ISBN 0-567-27445-4, Pub. by T & T Clark Ltd UK). Fortress.

Godet, Frederic L. Commentary John's Gospel, 2 vols. in 1. LC 78-59145. (Kregel Reprint Library). 1132p. 1980. Repr. of 1885 ed. 34.95 (ISBN 0-8254-2714-2). Kregel.

--Commentary on Luke. 3rd ed. LC 81-18614. (Kregel Reprint Library). 586p. 1981. Repr. of 1887 ed. 24.95 (ISBN 0-8254-2720-7). Kregel.

Godwin, Johnnie C. Layman's Bible Book Commentary: Mark, Vol. 16. LC 78-54774. 1979. 5.95 (ISBN 0-8054-1186-0). Broadman.

Gospel of the King (Matthew) Leader's Guide. (New Horizons Bible Study Ser.). 47p. (Orig.). 1986. pap. 1.95 (ISBN 0-89367-116-9). Light & Life.

Gospel of the King (Matthew) Student Guide. (New Horizons Bible Study Ser.). 64p. (Orig.). 1986. pap. 2.50 (ISBN 0-89367-115-0). Light & Life.

Gould, Ezra P. A Critical & Exegetical Commentary on the Gosped According to St. Mark. Driver, Samuel R., et al, eds. (International Critical Commentary Ser.). 376p. 1896. 24.95 (ISBN 0-567-05022-X, Pub. by T & T Clark Ltd UK). Fortress.

Gundry, Robert. Matthew: A Commentary on His Literary & Theological Art. 600p. 1982. 24.95 (ISBN 0-8028-3549-X). Eerdmans.

Gutzke, Manford G. Plain Talk on John. LC 69-11646. (Prog. Bk.). 1969. pap. 7.95 (ISBN 0-310-25571-6, 9726P). Zondervan.

--Plain Talk on Luke. 1966. pap. 5.95 (ISBN 0-310-25581-3, 9097P). Zondervan.
--Plain Talk on Mark. 295p. 1975. pap. 6.95 (ISBN 0-310-25591-0, 9762P). Zondervan.
--Plain Talk on Matthew. pap. 6.95 (ISBN 0-310-25601-1, 9727P). Zondervan.
Haenchen, Ernst, tr. from Ger. The Gospel of John, Vol. 2. Funk, Robert W., ed. LC 82-48756. (Hermeneia Ser.). 384p. 34.95 (ISBN 0-8006-6015-3). Fortress.
Hall, Jean. Out of Easter, the Gospels. (YA) 1979. pap. text ed. 4.25 (ISBN 0-03-021301-0, 321, HarpR); tchr's ed 2.95 (ISBN 0-03-021306-1, 322). Har-Row.
Hall, Manly P. Apocalypse Attributed to St. John. pap. 2.95 (ISBN 0-89314-810-5). Philos Res.
Harris, Rendel. Boanerges. 1978. Repr. of 1913 ed. lib. bdg. 50.00 (ISBN 0-8482-4381-1). Norwood Edns.
Harrison, Everett F. John: The Gospel of Faith. (Everyman's Bible Commentary Ser.). 1967. pap. 5.95 (ISBN 0-8024-2043-5). Moody.
--Juan: El Evangelio de la Fe (Comentario Biblico Portavoz) Orig. Title: John: The Gospel of Faith (Everyman's Bible Commentary) (Span.). 128p. 1981. pap. 3.50 (ISBN 0-8254-1304-4). Kregel.
Haury, Samuel S. Letters Concerning the Spread of the Gospel. 50p. 1982. pap. 3.95 (ISBN 0-8361-1252-0). Herald Pr.
Hendrickx, Herman. The Infancy Narratives. (Commentary on Synoptic Gospels Ser.). 144p. 1984. pap. 9.95 (ISBN 0-225-66398-8, 8523, HarpR). Har-Row.
--The Passion Narratives. (Commentary on the Synoptic Gospels Ser.). 210p. 1984. pap. 9.95 (ISBN 0-225-66400-3, 8524, HarpR). Har-Row.
--The Resurrection Narratives. (Commentary on the Synoptic Gospels Ser.). 168p. 1984. pap. 9.95 (ISBN 0-225-66401-1, 8525, HarpR). Har-Row.
--The Sermon on the Mount. (Commentary on the Synoptic Gospels Ser.). 228p. 1984. pap. 9.95 (ISBN 0-225-66399-6, 8526, HarpR). Har-Row.
Hendriksen, William. John. (New Testament Commentary Ser.). 1961. 24.95 (ISBN 0-8010-4051-5). Baker Bk.
--Mark. (New Testament Commentary Ser). 708p. 1975. 21.95 (ISBN 0-8010-4114-7). Baker Bk.
--Matthew. (New Testament Commentary Ser.). 1973. 24.95 (ISBN 0-8010-4066-3). Baker Bk.
Hengstenberg, E. W. Commentary on the Gospel of John, 2 vols. 1980. Set. 34.95 (ISBN 0-86524-047-7, 4302). Klock & Klock.
Henry, Matthew. A Commentary on the Whole Bible, Vol. 5: Matthew to John. (Reference Library Edition). 1248p. 1986. Repr. text ed. 10.95 (ISBN 0-529-06369-7). World Bible.
Hibbert, Giles, et al. John. LC 71-173033. (Scripture Discussion Commentary Ser.: Pt. 9). 256p. 1972. pap. text ed. 4.50 (ISBN 0-87946-008-3). ACTA Found.
Hill, David. The Gospel of Matthew. rev. ed. (New Century Bible Commentary Ser.). 368p. 1981. pap. 8.95 (ISBN 0-8028-1886-2). Eerdmans.
Hill, J. R. John. (Bible Study Commentaries Ser.). 112p. 1980. pap. 4.95 (ISBN 0-87508-169-X). Chr Lit.
Hoefler, Richard C. A Sign in the Straw. 128p. (Orig.). 1980. pap. text ed. 6.95 (ISBN 0-89536-465-4, 1969). CSS of Ohio.
Holloway, Richard. Signs of Glory. 96p. 1983. pap. 5.95 (ISBN 0-8164-2412-8, HarpR). Har-Row.
Hoover, James. Mark. (Lifebuilder Bible Studies). 96p. (Orig.). 1985. pap. text ed. 2.95 (ISBN 0-8308-1004-8). Inter-Varsity.
Hubner, Hans. Law in Paul's Thought. Riches, John, ed. Greig, James, tr. 186p. 26.95 (ISBN 0-567-09313-1, Pub. by T & T Clark Ltd UK). Fortress.
Huckle, John. The Gospel According to St. John Vols. I, II & III, the New Testament for Spiritual Reading Vols. 7, 8, & 9. 1978. Vol. I. pap. 4.95 (ISBN 0-8245-0116-0); Vol. II. pap. 4.95 (ISBN 0-8245-0117-9); Vol. III. pap. 4.95 (ISBN 0-8245-0118-7). Crossroad NY.
Hughes, R. Kent. Behold the Lamb. 180p. 1984. pap. 5.95 (ISBN 0-88207-623-X). Victor Bks.
Humphrey, Hugh M. A Bibliography for the Gospel of Mark: 1954-1980. LC 81-18717. (Studies in the Bible & Early Christianity: Vol. 1). 176p. 1982. 49.95x (ISBN 0-88946-916-4). E Mellen.
Hunter, Archibald M. Gospel According to John. (Cambridge Bible Commentary on the New English Bible, New Testament Ser.). (Orig.). 1965. pap. 11.95x (ISBN 0-521-09255-8). Cambridge U Pr.
Hurtado, Larry. Text-Critical Methodology & the Pre-Caesarean Text. 112p. (Orig.). 1981. pap. 15.00x (ISBN 0-8028-1872-2). Eerdmans.
Hutcheson, George. John. (Geneva Commentary Ser.). 448p. 1985. Repr. of 1657 ed. 17.95 (ISBN 0-85151-155-4). Banner of Truth.
Hyde, Gordon. The Gospel of the Here & Now. Wheeler, Gerald, ed. (Illus.). 128p. (Orig.). 1984. pap. 4.95 (ISBN 0-8280-0247-9). Review & Herald.
The Interpreter's Concise Commentary, Vol. VI: The Gospels, 8 vols. 368p. (Orig.). 1983. pap. 4.95 (ISBN 0-687-19237-4). Abingdon.
Ironside, H. A. Gospel of Matthew. 9.95 (ISBN 0-87213-378-8). Loizeaux.
Jensen, Irving L. John. (Bible Self-Study Guide). 1970. pap. 3.25 (ISBN 0-8024-1043-X). Moody.
--Luke. (Bible Self Study Ser.). 1970. pap. 3.25 (ISBN 0-8024-1042-1). Moody.
--Mark. (Bible Self-Study Ser.). (Illus.). 1972. pap. 3.25 (ISBN 0-8024-1041-3). Moody.
Jeremiah, David. John I, II, III: Twenty-Six Daily Bible Studies. (Steps to Higher Ground Ser.). 1983. pap. 1.95 (ISBN 0-86508-206-5). BCM Intl Inc.
John. (Erdmans Commentaries Ser.). 4.50 (ISBN 0-8010-3400-0). Baker Bk.
Johnsson, William. Religion in Overalls. LC 77-22464. (Anvil Ser.). 1977. pap. 8.95 (ISBN 0-8127-0143-7). Review & Herald.
Jordan, Bernice C. Gospels: 14 Lessons, Vol. 1. (Footsteps of Faith Ser.). 1955. pap. text ed. 2.50 (ISBN 0-86508-035-6); figures text 11.45 (ISBN 0-86508-036-4). BCM Intl Inc.
--Gospels: 14 Lessons, Vol. 2. (Footsteps of Faith Ser.). 1956. pap. text ed. 2.50 (ISBN 0-86508-037-2); figures text 11.45 (ISBN 0-86508-038-0). BCM Intl Inc.
Jozwiak, William G. Meetings with the Master. LC 84-91374. 118p. 1985. 10.00 (ISBN 0-533-06459-7). Vantage.
Keck, Leander E. & Martyn, J. Louis, eds. Studies in Luke-Acts. LC 79-8886. 324p. 1980. pap. 9.95 (ISBN 0-8006-1379-1, 1-1379). Fortress.
Kee, Howard C. Jesus in History: An Approach to the Study of the Gospels. 2nd ed. LC 77-75349. 312p. 1977. pap. text ed. 13.95 (ISBN 0-15-547382-4, HC). HarBraceJ.
Keegan, Terence. A Commentary on the Gospel of Mark. LC 81-82332. 224p. (Orig.). 1981. pap. 7.95 (ISBN 0-8091-2359-2). Paulist Pr.
Keller, Phillip. A Shepherd Looks at the Good Shepherd & His Sheep. 1979. 9.95 (ISBN 0-310-26800-1, 6784); large print kivar 7.95 (ISBN 0-310-26807-9, 12568L). Zondervan.
Kelly, W. Lectures on the Gospel of Matthew. 6.95 (ISBN 0-88172-104-2). Believers Bkshelf.
Kelly, William. The Gospel of Luke. 1981. 18.50 (ISBN 0-86524-046-9, 4201). Klock & Klock.
Kim, Seyoon. The Origin of Paul's Gospel. 2nd., rev., enl. ed. 426p. (Orig.). 1984. pap. 52.00x (ISBN 3-16-144836-7, Pub. by J C B Mohr BRD). Coronet Bks.
Kingsbury, Jack D. Jesus Christ in Matthew, Mark, & Luke. Krodel, Gerhard, ed. LC 80-69755. (Proclamation Commentaries Ser.: The New Testament Witnesses for Preaching). 144p. (Orig.). 1981. pap. 4.95 (ISBN 0-8006-0596-9, 1-596). Fortress.
Kirk, Albert & Obach, Robert E. Commentary on the Gospel of Matthew. LC 78-65715. 300p. 1978. pap. 8.95 (ISBN 0-8091-2173-5). Paulist Pr.
Kistemaker, Simon. The Gospels in Current Study. rev. ed. 192p. 1980. pap. 7.95 (ISBN 0-8010-5316-1). Baker Bk.
Klug, Ron. Mark: A Daily Dialogue with God. (Personal Bible Studyguide Ser.). 156p. 1984. pap. 5.95 (ISBN 0-87788-539-7). Shaw Pubs.
Kysar, Robert. Augsburg Commentary on the New Testament- John. LC 85-26736. (Augsburg Commentaries on the New Testament Ser.). 336p. (Orig.). 1986. kivar 14.95 (ISBN 0-8066-8860-2, 10-9018). Augsburg.
--Augsburg Commentary on the New Testament: 1, 2, 3 John. LC 86-17416. 176p. (Orig.). 1986. pap. 9.95 Kivar (ISBN 0-8066-8862-9, 10-9044). Augsburg.
Lane, William L. Commentary on the Gospel of Mark. (New International Commentary on the New Testament). 1973. 18.95 (ISBN 0-8028-2340-8). Eerdmans.
Lattimore, Richmond, tr. from Greek. The Four Gospels & the Revelation. 320p. 1979. 14.95 (ISBN 0-374-15801-0). FS&G.
Lauterbach, William. The Crucial Hours. 1977. pap. 5.95 (ISBN 0-8100-0050-4, 15-0358). Northwest Pub.
LaVerdiere, Eugene. Luke. (New Testament Message Ser.: Vol. 5). 15.95 (ISBN 0-89453-193-X); pap. 10.95 (ISBN 0-89453-128-X). M Glazier.
Lloyd-Jones, D. M. El Sermon del Monte, Vol. 1. 1978. 4.75 (ISBN 0-85151-414-6). Banner of Truth.
Lorber, Jakob. The Dream of Zorel. Ozols, Violet, tr. from Ger. 124p. 1985. pap. cancelled (ISBN 0-934616-17-5). Valkyrie Pub Hse.
Lovett, C. S. Lovett's Lights on John. 1970. pap. 6.45 (ISBN 0-938148-24-9). Personal Christianity.
Ludlow, Daniel H. Companion to Your Study of the New Testament: The Four Gospels. 454p. 1982. 9.95 (ISBN 0-87747-945-3). Deseret Bk.
Luke. (Erdmans Commentaries Ser.). 4.95 (ISBN 0-8010-3401-9). Baker Bk.
Luke the Physician. I, Luke. LC 81-80713. (Illus.). 120p. 1981. pap. 3.25 (ISBN 0-87973-665-8, 665). Our Sunday Visitor.
MacArthur, John, Jr. Matthew Eight-Fifteen. (MacArthur New Testament Commentary Ser.). 1986. text ed. 14.95 (ISBN 0-8024-0763-3). Moody.
--Matthew 1-7. (MacArthur New Testament Commentary Ser.). 1985. text ed. 14.95 (ISBN 0-8024-0755-2). Moody.
McCumber, William E., et al. Beacon Bible Expositions: Vol. 1, Matthew. (Beacon Bible Expositions Ser.). 1975. 8.95 (ISBN 0-8341-0312-5). Beacon Hill.
McEleney, Neil J. The Growth of the Gospels. LC 79-90141. 96p. (Orig.). 1979. pap. 4.95 (ISBN 0-8091-2243-X). Paulist Pr.
McGinlay, Hugh, ed. The Year of Luke. 96p. (Orig.). 1982. pap. 8.95 (Pub. by JBCE). ANZ Religious Pubns.
--The Year of Mark. 86p. (Orig.). 1984. text ed. 8.95 (ISBN 0-85819-477-5, Pub. by JBCE). ANZ Religious Pubns.
--The Year of Matthew. 94p. (Orig.). 1983. pap. 8.95 (ISBN 0-85819-454-6, Pub. by JBCE). ANZ Religious Pubns.
McKenna, David L. The Communicator's Commentary-Mark, Vol. 2. Ogilvie, Lloyd, ed. (The Communicator's Commentaries Ser.). 1982. 18.95 (ISBN 0-8499-0155-3). Word Bks.
McLaughlin. Commentary on Luke. kivar 5.95 (ISBN 0-686-12859-1). Schmul Pub Co.
--Commentary on Mark. kivar 5.95 (ISBN 0-686-12860-5). Schmul Pub Co.
--Commentary on Matthew. kivar 5.95 (ISBN 0-686-12861-3). Schmul Pub Co.
--Commentary on St. John. kivar 5.95 (ISBN 0-686-12863-X). Schmul Pub Co.
McNeile, A. H. Gospel According to St. Matthew. (Thornapple Commentaries Ser.). 484p. 1980. pap. 8.95 (ISBN 0-8010-6099-0). Baker Bk.
Macpherson, Duncan, et al. Paul One. Bright, Laurence, ed. LC 71-173033. (Scripture Discussion Ser.: Pt. 10). 224p. 1972. pap. text ed. 4.50 (ISBN 0-87946-009-1). ACTA Found.
--Luke. LC 71-173033. (Scripture Discussion Commentary Ser.: Pt. 8). 192p. 1971. pap. text ed. 4.50 (ISBN 0-87946-007-5). ACTA Found.
Macrae, George W. Invitation to John: A Commentary on the Gospel of John with Complete Text from the Jerusalem Bible. LC 77-91559. 1978. pap. 3.95 (ISBN 0-385-12212-8, Im). Doubleday.
Malinski, Mieczyslaw. Faith to Move Mountains: Reflections on the Gospels of the Lectionary (A, B, C,) LC 82-61194. 144p. 1982. 5.95 (ISBN 0-8245-0509-3). Crossroad NY.
Mann, C. S. Mark: A New Translation with Introduction & Commentary, Vol. 27. LC 85-4433. (Illus.). 744p. 1986. 20.00 (ISBN 0-385-03253-6, Anchor). Doubleday.
Mark. (Erdmans Commentaries Ser.). 4.50 (ISBN 0-8010-3410-8). Baker Bk.
Marrow, Stanley B. The Words of Jesus in Our Gospel. LC 79-52105. 160p. 1979. pap. 5.95 (ISBN 0-8091-2215-4). Paulist Pr.
Marsh, John. The Gospel of Saint John: Commentaries. (Orig.). 1968. pap. 8.95 (ISBN 0-14-020491-1, Pelican). Penguin.
Marshall, I. Howard. The Gospel of Luke. (New International Greek Testament Commentary Ser.). 1978. 35.00 (ISBN 0-8028-3512-0). Eerdmans.
Martyn, J. Louis. The Gospel of John in Christian History. LC 78-70821. 160p. 1979. pap. 5.95 (ISBN 0-8091-2170-0). Paulist Pr.
Matthew. (Erdmans Commentaries Ser.). 4.95 (ISBN 0-8010-3402-7). Baker Bk.
Maurice, Frederick D. The Gospel of the Kingdom of Heaven. 416p. 1977. Repr. of 1864 ed. 12.50 (ISBN 0-87921-037-0). Attic Pr.
Meagher, John C. Clumsy Construction in Mark's Gospel: A Critique of Form & Redaktionsgeschichte. LC 79-66373. (Toronto Studies in Theology: Vol. 3). xii, 178p. 1979. 39.95x (ISBN 0-88946-876-1). E Mellen.
Meier, John P. Matthew. (New Testament Message Ser.: Vol. 3). 15.95 (ISBN 0-89453-191-3); pap. 12.95 (ISBN 0-89453-126-3). M Glazier.
--The Vision of Matthew: Christ, Church & Morality in the First Gospel. LC 78-70820. 1979. pap. 8.95 (ISBN 0-8091-2171-9). Paulist Pr.
Meyer, F. B. Gospel of John. 1970. pap. 6.95 (ISBN 0-87508-346-3). Chr Lit.
Meyer, Marvin W. Who Do People Say I Am? The Interpretation of Jesus in the New Testament Gospels. LC 82-24229. pap. 23.80 (ISBN 0-317-30155-1, 2025337). Bks Demand UMI.
Miguens, Manuel. Gospels for Sundays & Feasts: Cycle A. 1981. 7.50 (ISBN 0-8198-3015-1); pap. 6.00 (ISBN 0-8198-3016-X). Dghtrs St Paul.
--Gospels for Sundays & Feasts: Cycle C. 1980. 7.50 (ISBN 0-8198-3000-3); pap. 6.00 (ISBN 0-8198-3001-1). Dghtrs St Paul.
Miller, Donald G. Luke. LC 59-10454. (Layman's Bible Commentary Ser.: Vol. 18). 1959. pap. 4.95 (ISBN 0-8042-3078-1). John Knox.
Mills, Richard C. Workbook on the Four Gospels. (Illus.). 128p. (Orig.). 1948. pap. 3.95 (ISBN 0-87239-327-5, 3347). Standard Pub.
Minear, Paul S. Mark. LC 59-10454. (Layman's Bible Commentary, Vol. 17). 1962. pap. 4.95 (ISBN 0-8042-3077-3). John Knox.
Mitchell, John G. An Everlasting Love: A Devotional Commentary on the Gospel of John. LC 82-22285. 1982. 13.95 (ISBN 0-88070-005-X). Multnomah.
Moloney, Francis J. The Living Voice of the Gospel: The Gospels Today. 1987. pap. 10.95. Paulist Pr.
Montague, George T. Mark: Good News for Hard Times. 200p. (Orig.). 1981. pap. 6.95 (ISBN 0-89283-096-4). Servant.
Morgan, G. Campbell. The Gospel According to John. Fang, Carl, tr. (G. Campbell Morgan's Expository Ser.). 1985. write for info. (ISBN 0-941598-94-2); pap. write for info. (ISBN 0-941598-18-7). Living Spring Pubns.
--The Gospel According to Luke. Chao, Lorna, tr. (G. Campbell Morgan's Expository Ser.). 1985. write for info. (ISBN 0-941598-95-0); pap. write for info. (ISBN 0-941598-17-9). Living Spring Pubns.
--The Gospel According to Mark. Chan, Silas, tr. from Eng. (G. Campbell Morgan's Expository Ser.). (Chinese.). 1984. write for info. (ISBN 0-941598-96-9); pap. write for info. (ISBN 0-941598-16-0). Living Spring Pubns.
--The Gospel According to Matthew. Chang, David, tr. from Eng. (G. Campbell Morgan's Expository Ser.). (Chinese.). 1984. write for info. (ISBN 0-941598-97-7); pap. write for info. (ISBN 0-941598-15-2). Living Spring Pubns.
--Studies in the Four Gospels, 4 vols. Incl. The Gospel According to Matthew. 320p (ISBN 0-8007-0122-4); The Gospel According to Mark. 352p (ISBN 0-8007-0121-6); The Gospel According to Luke. 288p (ISBN 0-8007-0120-8); The Gospel According to John. 336p (ISBN 0-8007-0119-4). Set. 49.95 (ISBN 0-8007-0373-1); one-volume ed. 27.95 (ISBN 0-8007-0297-2); 13.95 ea. Revell.
Morris, Leon. The Gospel According to St. Luke. (Tyndale New Testament Commentaries Ser.). 1974. pap. 5.95 (ISBN 0-8028-1402-6). Eerdmans.
--Gospel of John. (New International Commentary of the New Testament Ser.). 1970. 24.95 (ISBN 0-8028-2296-7). Eerdmans.
Morrison, G. H. Morrison on John, Vol. I. new ed. (The Glasgow Pulpit Ser.). 1979. pap. 4.95 (ISBN 0-89957-534-X). AMG Pubs.
--Morrison on John, Vol. II. new ed. (The Glasgow Pulpit Ser.). 1979. pap. 4.95 (ISBN 0-89957-535-8). AMG Pubs.
--Morrison on Luke, Vol. I. new ed. (The Glasgow Pulpit Ser.). 1979. pap. 4.95 (ISBN 0-89957-532-3). AMG Pubs.
--Morrison on Luke, Vol. II. new ed. (The Glasgow Pulpit Ser.). 1979. pap. 4.95 (ISBN 0-89957-533-1). AMG Pubs.
--Morrison on Mark. new ed. (The Glasgow Pulpit Ser.). 1979. pap. 4.95 (ISBN 0-89957-531-5). AMG Pubs.
--Morrison on Matthew, Vol. I. new ed. (The Glasgow Pulpit Ser.). 1979. pap. 4.95 (ISBN 0-89957-528-5). AMG Pubs.
--Morrison on Matthew, Vol. II. new ed. (The Glasgow Pulpit Ser.). 1979. pap. 4.95 (ISBN 0-89957-529-3). AMG Pubs.
--Morrison on Matthew, Vol. III. new ed. (The Glasgow Pulpit Ser.). 1979. pap. 4.95 (ISBN 0-89957-530-7). AMG Pubs.
Morrison, Mary C. Approaching the Gospels Together: A Leader's Guide to Group Gospels Study. LC 78-51385. 32p. (Orig.). 1978. pap. 2.50x (ISBN 0-87574-219-X, 219). Pendle Hill.
--Approaching the Gospels Together: A Leaders' Guide to Group Gospels Study. (Orig.). 1987. pap. 10.95 (ISBN 0-87574-910-0). Pendle Hill.
Moule, Charles F. Gospel According to Mark. (Cambridge Bible Commentary on the New English Bible, New Testament Ser.). (Orig.). 1965. 15.50 (ISBN 0-521-04210-0); pap. 7.95x (ISBN 0-521-09288-4). Cambridge U Pr.
Mounce, Robert H. Matthew: A Good News Commentary. LC 84-48775. (Good News Commentary Ser.). 288p. (Orig.). 1985. pap. 9.95 (ISBN 0-06-066032-5, HarpR). Har-Row.
Munn, Sherrill. Beacon Small-Group Bible Studies, Luke: Lessons on Discipleship, Vol. 2. 68p. (Orig.). 1981. pap. 2.50 (ISBN 0-8341-0689-2). Beacon Hill.
Nilsen, Mary Y. Real Living: A Small-Group Life Experience with the Gospel of Luke, Pt. 3. (Illus.). 1978. pap. text ed. 5.65 (ISBN 0-03-045696-7, HarpR); tchr's. guide 7.95 (ISBN 0-03-045701-7). Har-Row.

Nineham, Dennis E. The Gospel of St. Mark: Commentaries. (Orig.). 1964. pap. 7.95 (ISBN 0-14-020489-X, Pelican). Penguin.

Obach, Robert E. & Kirk, Albert. A Commentary on the Gospel of John. LC 80-84505. 272p. 1981. pap. 7.95 (ISBN 0-8091-2346-0). Paulist Pr.

--A Commentary on the Gospel of Luke. 272p. (Orig.). 1986. pap. 8.95 (ISBN 0-8091-2763-6). Paulist Pr.

O'Collins, Gerald. Finding Jesus: Living Through Lent with John's Gospel. 64p. 1984. pap. 3.95 (ISBN 0-8091-2565-X). Paulist Pr.

O'Donnell, Desmond. Meet Jesus in Luke. LC 80-67126. (Praying the Scriptures Ser.). 56p. (Orig.). 1980. pap. 1.75 (ISBN 0-87793-206-9). Ave Maria.

Ogilvie, Lloyd J. When God First Thought of You. 1980. pap. 9.95 (ISBN 0-8499-2945-8). Word Bks.

Orchard, John B. A Synopsis of the Four Gospels in a New Translation: Arranged According to the Two Gospel Hypothesis. LC 81-18753. 319p. 1982. English 9.95 (ISBN 0-86554-024-1, MUP-H22); Greek 21.00 (ISBN 0-86554-061-6, MUP-H70). Mercer Univ Pr.

Outlaw, Stanley & Thigpen, Charles. A Survey of the Gospels. 1976. pap. 1.95 (ISBN 0-89265-031-1). Randall Hse.

Pallares, Jose C. A Poor Man Called Jesus: Reflections on the Gospel of Mark. Barr, Robert R., tr. from Span. LC 85-15339. 144p. (Orig.). 1986. pap. 8.95 (ISBN 0-88344-398-8). Orbis Bks.

Palmer, Earl F. The Intimate Gospel: Studies in John. 1978. pap. 5.95 (ISBN 0-8499-2941-5). Word Bks.

Patte, Daniel. Paul's Faith & the Power of the Gospel: A Structural Introduction to the Pauline Letters. LC 82-7416. 432p. (Orig.). 1983. 21.95 (ISBN 0-8006-0683-3, 1-1682). Fortress.

Pentecost, J. Dwight. The Joy of Fellowship: A Study of First John. 1977. pap. 5.95 (ISBN 0-310-30921-2, 17013P). Zondervan.

Perkins, Pheme. Gospel of St. John. (Read & Pray Ser.). 96p. 1975. pap. 1.75 (ISBN 0-685-55958-0). Franciscan Herald.

Philaretos, Sotirios D. The Decalogue & the Gospel. Orthodox Christian Educational Society, ed. Cummings, D., tr. from Hellenic. 62p. (Orig.). 1957. pap. 2.00x (ISBN 0-938366-43-2). Orthodox Chr.

Phillips, J. B. Peter's Portrait of Jesus. (Festival Ser.). 192p. 1981. pap. 1.95 (ISBN 0-687-30850-X). Abingdon.

Pink, Arthur W. Exposition of the Gospel of John, 4 Vols. in 1. 1945. 29.95 (ISBN 0-310-31180-2, 10566). Zondervan.

Plummer, Alfred. A Critical & Exegetical Commentary on the Gospel According to St. Luke. Driver, Samuel R. & Plummer, Alfred, eds. (International Critical Commentary Ser.). 688p. 1901. 24.95 (ISBN 0-567-05023-8, Pub. by T & T Clark Ltd UK). Fortress.

--The Gospel According to St. John. (Thornapple Commentaries Ser.). 380p. 1981. pap. 9.95 (ISBN 0-8010-7068-6). Baker Bk.

Powell, Ivor. Luke's Thrilling Gospel. LC 84-9637. 508p. 1984. 18.95 (ISBN 0-8254-3513-7). Kregel.

Pryor, R. Louis, ed. One Gospel: Taken Literally from the Four Gospels in the Authorized King James Version of the Bible. LC 85-42545. 381p. 1985. 29.95x (ISBN 0-89950-184-2); pap. 19.95x (ISBN 0-89950-192-3). McFarland & Co.

Raymond, John. Twenty-Six Lessons on Matthew, Vol. II. (Bible Student Study Guide Ser.). 130p. 1981. pap. 2.95 (ISBN 0-89900-171-8). College Pr Pub.

Reicke, Bo. The Roots of the Synoptic Gospels. LC 85-45485. 224p. 1986. 22.95 (ISBN 0-8006-0766-X, 1-766). Fortress.

Reist, Thomas. Saint Bonaventure As a Biblical Commentator: A Translation & Analysis of His "Commentary on Luke," XVIII,34-XIX,42. 284p. (Orig.). 1985. lib. bdg. 24.00 (ISBN 0-8191-4578-5); pap. text ed. 12.75 (ISBN 0-8191-4579-3). U Pr of Amer.

Reith, George. St. John, 2 vols, Vol. I & 2. Whyte, A. & Moffatt, J., eds. (Handbooks for Bible Classes & Private Students Ser.). 1889. 8.95 ea. (Pub. by T & T Clark Ltd UK). Vol. 1, 200 pgs (ISBN 0-567-08114-1). Vol. 2, 180 pgs (ISBN 0-567-08115-X). Fortress.

Robertson, A. T. A Harmony of the Gospels. 1932. 12.45i (ISBN 0-06-066890-3, HarpR). Har-Row.

Robertson, Arthur. Matthew. (Everyman's Bible Commentary Ser.). (Orig.). 1983. pap. 5.95 (ISBN 0-8024-0233-X). Moody.

Robinson, Forbes, tr. Coptic Apocryphal Gospels. (Texts & Studies: No. 1, Vol. 4-Pt. 2). pap. 19.00 (ISBN 0-8115-1693-8). Kraus Repr.

Ross, Charles. The Inner Sanctuary. 1967. pap. 2.95 (ISBN 0-85151-042-6). Banner of Truth.

Rutenber, Culbert G. The Price & the Prize. LC 81-65392. 1981. 6.95 (ISBN 0-8054-6230-9). Broadman.

Ryle, J. C. Luke. (Expository Thoughts on the Gospel Ser.: Vol. 2). 530p. 1986. pap. 6.95 (ISBN 0-85151-498-7). Banner of Truth.

--Luke. (Expository Thoughts on the Gospel Ser.: Vol. 1). 390p. 1986. pap. 5.95 (ISBN 0-85151-497-9). Banner of Truth.

St. Thomas Aquinas. Commentary on the Gospel of St. John, Pt. 1. Weisheipl, James A., ed. Larcher, Fabian R., tr. from Lat. LC 66-19306. (Aquinas Scripture Ser.: Vol. 4). (Illus.). 512p. 1980. 35.00x (ISBN 0-87343-031-X). Magi Bks.

Schein, Bruce E. Following the Way: The Setting of John's Gospel. LC 79-54121. 224p. 1980. 14.95 (ISBN 0-8066-1758-6, 10-2348). Augsburg.

Schnackenburg, Rudolf. The Gospel According to St. John, 2 vols. 1980. 39.50x ea. Vol. 1 (ISBN 0-8245-0311-2). Vol. 2 (ISBN 0-8245-0312-0). Crossroad NY.

Schramm, Tim. Der Markus-Stoff Bei Lukas. LC 79-96099. (New Testament Studies Monographs: No. 14). (Ger). 1971. 34.50 (ISBN 0-521-07743-5). Cambridge U Pr.

Schroeder, L. Bonnet A. Juan y Hechos: Tomo II. Cativiela, A., tr. 1986. Repr. of 1983 ed. 14.95 (ISBN 0-311-03051-3). Casa Bautista.

Schweizer, Eduard. Good News According to Mark. Madvig, Donald, tr. LC 77-93828. 1970. 18.95 (ISBN 0-8042-0250-8). John Knox.

--Good News According to Matthew. Green, David E., tr. LC 74-3717. 1975. 19.95 (ISBN 0-8042-0251-6). John Knox.

Scragg, Walter R. L. The God Who Says Yes. Wheeler, Gerald, ed. 128p. (Orig.). 1986. pap. 6.95 (ISBN 0-8280-0376-9). Review & Herald.

Shepherd, J. Barrie. Prayers from the Mount. LC 85-26400. 144p. 1986. pap. 8.95 (ISBN 0-664-24699-0). Westminster.

Skeireins. Gothic Commentary on the Gospel of John. Bennett, W. H., tr. (MLA MS). 1960. 14.00 (ISBN 0-527-83350-9). Kraus Repr.

Smith, Thomas. The Good News about Jesus As Told by Mark. Pluth, Alphonsus, ed. LC 77-89324. (Illus.). 1977. pap. 3.95 (ISBN 0-88489-095-3); tchrs' ed 1.00 (ISBN 0-88489-116-X). St Mary's.

Spurgeon, C. H. The Gospel of the Kingdom (Matthew) 1978. pap. 4.95 (ISBN 0-686-09110-8). Pilgrim Pubns.

Stanley, David M. I Encountered God! The Spiritual Exercises with the Gospel of St. John. Ganss, George E., ed. LC 84-82164. (Original Studies, Composed in English: Ser. III, No. 7). 348p. 1986. 14.00 (ISBN 0-912422-72-6); pap. 11.00 Smyth sewn (ISBN 0-912422-71-8). Inst Jesuit.

Staton, Knofel. The Servant's Call. LC 75-7462. (Illus.). 96p. 1976. pap. 2.25 (ISBN 0-87239-051-9, 40024). Standard Pub.

Steiner, Rudolf. Gospel of St. John. (Russian Language Ser.). 294p. 1985. pap. 12.00 (ISBN 0-89345-900-3, Steiner). Garber Comm.

--Gospel of St. John. (Russian Language Ser.). 196p. 1985. pap. 10.00 (ISBN 0-89345-906-2, Steiner). Garber Comm.

--The Gospel of St. John & In Relation to the Other Gospels. rev. ed. Easton, Stewart, ed. Lockwood, Samuel & Lockwood, Loni, trs. from Ger. 298p. 1982. 14.00 (ISBN 0-88010-015-X); pap. 8.95 (ISBN 0-88010-014-1). Anthroposophic.

--Gospel of St. Luke. 1964. 14.95 (ISBN 0-85440-042-7). Anthroposophic.

--Gospel of St. Luke. (Russian Language Ser.). 202p. 1985. pap. 10.00 (ISBN 0-89345-902-X, Steiner). Garber Comm.

Stonehouse, Ned B. Witness of the Synoptic Gospels to Christ. (Twin Brooks Ser.). 1979. pap. 8.95 (ISBN 0-8010-8181-5). Baker Bk.

Stylianopoulos, Theodore. The Gospel of Christ. 32p. 1981. pap. 1.95 (ISBN 0-916586-84-7). Hellenic Coll Pr.

Sullivan, James L. Juan Testifica de Jesus. Quarles, J. C., tr. from Eng. Orig. Title: John's Witness to Jesus. 128p. 1986. pap. 3.25 (ISBN 0-311-04324-0). Casa Bautista.

Swartley, Willard M. Mark: The Way for All Nations. rev. ed. LC 78-27917. 224p. 1981. pap. 9.95 (ISBN 0-8361-1977-0). Herald Pr.

Swete, Henry B. Commentary on Mark. LC 77-79193. (Kregel Reprint Library). 554p. 1978. 18.95 (ISBN 0-8254-3715-6). Kregel.

--Commentary on Revelation. LC 77-79192. (Kregel Reprint Library). Orig. Title: Apocalypse of John. 562p. 1979. text ed. 18.95 (ISBN 0-8254-3716-4). Kregel.

Talbert, Charles, ed. Perspectives on Luke-Acts. LC 78-51610. (Special Studies: No. 5). ix, 269p. 1978. pap. 10.00 (ISBN 0-932180-04-3). NABPR.

Talbert, Charles H. Literary Patterns, Theological Themes & the Genre of Luke-Acts. LC 74-78620. (Society of Biblical Literature. Monograph: No. 20). Repr. of 1974 ed. 42.00 (ISBN 0-8357-9577-2, 2017509). Bks Demand UMI.

--Reading Luke: A Literary & Theological Commentary on the Third Gospel. LC 82-12737. 288p. 1982. 17.95 (ISBN 0-8245-0532-8). Crossroad NY.

--Reading Luke: A Literary & Theological Commentary on the Third Gospel. 256p. 1984. pap. 10.95 (ISBN 0-8245-0668-5). Crossroad NY.

Tasker, Randolph V. Gospel According to St. John. (Tyndale Bible Commentaries Ser.). 1960. pap. 4.95 (ISBN 0-8028-1403-4). Eerdmans.

--Gospel According to St. Matthew. (Tyndale Bible Commentaries Ser.). 1962. pap. 5.95 (ISBN 0-8028-1400-X). Eerdmans.

Taylor, Robert R., Jr. Studies in First, Second, Third John. pap. 2.50 (ISBN 0-89315-295-1). Lambert Bk.

Temple, William. Readings in St. John's Gospel. 391p. 1985. pap. 8.95 (ISBN 0-8192-1360-8). Morehouse.

Tenney, Helen. Mark's Sketch Book of Christ. 1975. spiral bound 6.45 (ISBN 0-85151-075-2). Banner of Truth.

Tenney, Merrill C. John: The Gospel of Belief. 1948. 14.95 (ISBN 0-8028-3252-0). Eerdmans.

Thomas, David. Gospel of John, 2 vols. in 1. LC 79-15415. (Kregel Bible Study Classics Ser.). 846p. 1980. 24.95 (ISBN 0-8254-3809-8). Kregel.

Throckmorton, Burton H. Gospel Parallels: A Synopsis of the First Three Gospels. 4th ed. 1979. 10.95 (ISBN 0-8407-5150-8). Nelson.

Timmer, John. Mark: A Study Guide. (Revelation Series for Adults). (Orig.). 1980. pap. 2.50 (ISBN 0-933140-13-4). CRC Pubns.

Tinsley, E. J. Gospel According to Luke. (Cambridge Bible Commentary on the New English Bible, New Testament Ser.). (Orig.). 1965. pap. 10.95x (ISBN 0-521-09252-3). Cambridge U Pr.

Trenchard, Ernesto. Evangelio Segun Marcos. (Span.). 226p. 1957. 6.95 (ISBN 0-8254-1740-6); pap. 5.75 (ISBN 0-8254-1739-2). Kregel.

--Introduccion a los Cuatro Evangelios. (Span.). 686p. 1961. 9.95 (ISBN 0-8254-1744-9); pap. 8.75 (ISBN 0-8254-1743-0). Kregel.

Trimiew, Oliver, Jr. John: The Gospel of Life. (Orig.). 1987. pap. text ed. 4.95 (ISBN 0-940955-00-8); tchr's. ed. 3.95 (ISBN 0-940955-01-6). Urban Ministries.

Vanderlip, D. George. John: The Gospel of Life. 1979. pap. 5.95 (ISBN 0-8170-0826-8). Judson.

Van Doren, W. H. Gospel of John, 2 vols. in 1. rev. ed. LC 80-8080. (Kregel Bible Study Classics Ser.). 1454p. 1981. text ed. 34.50 (ISBN 0-8254-3953-1). Kregel.

Van Ryn, August. Mark: Meditations. 1957. pap. 2.25 (ISBN 0-87213-892-5). Loizeaux.

Vaughan, Curtis. One, Two, Three John. (Bible Study Commentary Ser.). 140p. 1984. pap. 4.95 (ISBN 0-310-33563-9). Zondervan.

Vos, Howard F. Matthew: A Bible Study Commentary. (Study Guide Commentary Ser.). 1979. pap. 6.95 (ISBN 0-310-33883-2, 11152P). Zondervan.

Welch, Reuben. Beacon Bible Expositions: Vol. 3, Luke. Greathouse, William M. & Taylor, Willard H., eds. 1974. 8.95 (ISBN 0-8341-0314-1). Beacon Hill.

--We Really Do Need Each Other. 112p. 1982. pap. 4.95 (ISBN 0-310-70221-6, 14012P). Zondervan.

Westcott, Brooke F. Commentary on Gospel According to St. John. 1950. 7.95 (ISBN 0-8028-3288-1). Eerdmans.

Whedon's Commentary on Luke, Vol. 2. 13.95 (ISBN 0-686-13330-7). Schmul Pub Co.

Whedon's Commentary on Matthew, Vol. 1. 13.95 (ISBN 0-686-13329-3). Schmul Pub Co.

White Eagle. The Living Word of St. John. new ed. 208p. 1979. pap. 13.95 (ISBN 0-85487-044-X). De Vorss.

Wiersbe, Warren. Be Alive. 156p. 1986. pap. 5.95 (ISBN 0-89693-359-8). Victor Bks.

Wilcock, Michael. The Message of Luke. Motyer, J. A. & Stott, John R., eds. LC 79-2720. (Bible Speaks Today Ser.). (Orig.). 1979. pap. 6.95 (ISBN 0-87784-291-4). Inter-Varsity.

Wilson, S. G. Luke & the Law. LC 83-7263. (Society for New Testament Studies Monograph: No. 50). 200p. 1984. 29.95 (ISBN 0-521-25284-9). Cambridge U Pr.

Wilson, Stephen G. The Gentiles & the Gentile Mission In Luke-Acts. LC 72-90489. (Society for New Testament Studies, Monograpn Ser.: Vol. 23). pap. 76.80 (ISBN 0-317-26365-X, 2024566). Bks Demand UMI.

Woods, Guy N. John. 1981. 10.95 (ISBN 0-89225-261-8). Gospel Advocate.

Ylvisaker, J. The Gospels. 1977. Repr. 24.95 (ISBN 0-8100-0052-0, 15N0363). Northwest Pub.

Young, Samuel. Beacon Bible Expositions, Vol. 4: John. Greathouse, William M. & Taylor, Willard H., eds. 196p. 1979. 8.95 (ISBN 0-8341-0315-X). Beacon Hill.

Zodhiates, Spiros. A Christian View of War & Peace. 1979. pap. 1.45 (ISBN 0-89957-509-9). AMG Pubs.

--The Song of the Virgin. LC 82-71643. (Illus.). 1974. pap. 3.95 (ISBN 0-89957-510-2). AMG Pubs.

--Was Christ God? 1966. 7.95 (ISBN 0-89957-504-8). AMG Pubs.

BIBLE–COMMENTARIES–N. T. HEBREWS

Anderson, Robert. Types in Hebrews. LC 78-9545. (Sir Robert Anderson Library). 192p. 1978. pap. 4.95 (ISBN 0-8254-2129-2). Kregel.

The Better Way (Hebrews) (New Horizons Bible Study Ser.). 68p. (Orig.). pap. 2.50 student guide (ISBN 0-89367-103-7); pap. 1.95 leader's guide (ISBN 0-89367-104-5). Light & Life.

Bowman, John W. Hebrews-Second Peter. LC 59-10454. (Layman's Bible Commentary Ser: Vol. 24). 1962. pap. 4.95 (ISBN 0-8042-3084-6). John Knox.

Brooks, Keith L. Hebrews: The Beauty of Christ Unveiled. (Teach Yourself the Bible Ser.). 1961. pap. 2.75 (ISBN 0-8024-3507-6). Moody.

Bruce, A. B. The Epistle to the Hebrews. 1980. 17.25 (ISBN 0-86524-028-0, 5802). Klock & Klock.

Bruce, Frederick F., ed. The Epistle to the Hebrews. (New International Commentary on the New Testament Ser.). 1964. 19.95 (ISBN 0-8028-2183-9). Eerdmans.

Buchanan, George W., tr. To the Hebrews. LC 72-76127. (Anchor Bible Ser.: Vol. 36). 1972. 14.00 (ISBN 0-385-02995-0, Anchor Pr). Doubleday.

Bullinger, Ethelbert W. Great Cloud of Witnesses in Hebrews Eleven. LC 79-14425. 462p. 1986. pap. 12.95 (ISBN 0-8254-2247-7). Kregel.

Casey, Juliana. Hebrews. (New Testament Message Ser.: Vol. 18). 10.95 (ISBN 0-89453-206-5); pap. 6.95 (ISBN 0-89453-141-7). M Glazier.

Chilstrom, Herbert W. Hebrews: A New & Better Way. LC 83-5600. 80p. 1984. pap. 3.95 (ISBN 0-8006-1717-7, 1-1717). Fortress.

Coffman, James B. Commentary on Hebrews. (Firm Foundation Commentary Ser.). 1971. cancelled 10.95 (ISBN 0-88027-074-8). Firm Foun Pub.

Crouch, Owen. Expository Preaching & Teaching-Hebrews. LC 83-71985. 454p. (Orig.). 1983. pap. 9.95 (ISBN 0-89900-197-1). College Pr Pub.

Crowson, Milton. The Epistle to the Hebrews. 1974. pap. 4.95 (ISBN 0-89265-021-4). Randall Hse.

D'Angelo, Mary R. Moses in the Letter to the Hebrews. LC 78-12917. (Society of Biblical Literature, Dissertation Ser.: No. 42). 1979. pap. 9.95 (ISBN 0-89130-333-2). Scholars Pr GA.

Davies, J. H., ed. Letter to the Hebrews. (Cambridge Bible Commentary on the New English Bible, New Testament Ser.). 1967. 16.95 (ISBN 0-521-04222-4); pap. 9.95x (ISBN 0-521-09408-9). Cambridge U Pr.

Dering, Edward. M. Derings Workes: More at Large Than Ever Hath Heer-to-Fore Been Printed, 3 pts. LC 74-38171. (English Experience Ser.: No. 448). 692p. 1972. Repr. of 1597 ed. 95.00 (ISBN 90-221-0448-6). Walter J Johnson.

Edwards, Thomas C. The Epistle to the Hebrews. 394p. 1982. lib. bdg. 13.00 Smythe Sewn (ISBN 0-86524-154-6, 5803). Klock & Klock.

Ellingworth, Paul & Nida, Eugene A. A Translator's Handbook on the Letter to the Hebrews. LC 83-17947. (Helps for Translators Ser.). viii, 364p. 1983. 5.00x (ISBN 0-8267-0150-7, 08782, Pub. by United Bible). Am Bible.

Filson, Floyd V. Yesterday: A Study of Hebrews in the Light of Chapter 13. LC 67-7015. (Studies in Biblical Theology: 2nd Ser., No. 4). 1967. pap. text ed. 10.00x (ISBN 0-8401-3054-6). A R Allenson.

Ford, Charles W. Learning from Hebrews. LC 80-67467. (Radiant Life Ser.). 127p. (Orig.). 1980. 2.50 (ISBN 0-88243-915-4, 02-0915); teacher's ed 3.95 (ISBN 0-88243-188-9, 32-0188). Gospel Pub.

Gerber, Aaron. Abraham: The First Hebrew. 180p. 1981. 12.50 (ISBN 0-89962-208-9). Todd & Honeywell.

Gutzke, Manford G. Plain Talk on Hebrews. 160p. 1976. pap. 5.95 (ISBN 0-310-25541-4, 9852P). Zondervan.

Hagner, Donald A. Hebrews: A Good News Commentary. LC 82-48410. (Good News Commentary Ser.). 288p. 1983. pap. 9.95 (ISBN 0-06-063555-X, RD-425, HarpR). Har-Row.

Hebrews. (Erdmans Commentaries Ser.). 3.95 (ISBN 0-8010-3399-3). Baker Bk.

Henrichsen, Walter A. After the Sacrifice. 1979. pap. 5.95 (ISBN 0-310-37711-0, 11231P). Zondervan.

Hobbs, Herschel H. Hebrews. LC 81-65388. 1981. pap. 4.95 (ISBN 0-8054-1323-5). Broadman.

Hughes, Philip E. Commentary on the Epistle to the Hebrews. LC 82-90554. 1977. text ed. 18.95 (ISBN 0-8028-3495-7). Eerdmans.
Hunt, Gladys. Hebrews: From Shadows to Reality. (Fisherman Bible Studyguides). 79p. 1979. saddle stitch 2.95 (ISBN 0-87788-338-6). Shaw Pubs.
Jensen, Irving L. Hebrews. (Bible Self-Study Ser.). 1970. pap. 3.25 (ISBN 0-8024-1058-8). Moody.
Jewett, Robert. Letter to Pilgrims. LC 80-28102. 244p. (Orig.). 1981. pap. 7.95 (ISBN 0-8298-0425-0). Pilgrim NY.
Johnsson, William G. In Absolute Confidence. LC 79-1387. (Anvil Ser.). 1979. pap. 8.95 (ISBN 0-8127-0225-5). Review & Herald.
Kent, Homer A., Jr. Epistle to the Hebrews. 1972. pap. 8.95 (ISBN 0-8010-5458-3). Baker Bk.
Kistemaker, Simon J. Hebrews. 350p. 1984. 18.95 (ISBN 0-8010-5460-5). Baker Bk.
Lenski, Richard C. Interpretation of Hebrews & James. 1938. 21.95 (ISBN 0-8066-9010-0, 10-3370). Augsburg.
MacRae, George W. Hebrews. Karris, Robert J., ed. (Collegeville Bible Commentary Ser.: No. 10). 64p. 1983. pap. 2.95 (ISBN 0-8146-1310-1). Liturgical Pr.
Meyer, F. B. Way into the Holiest. 1968. pap. 4.50 (ISBN 0-87508-353-6). Chr Lit.
Moffatt, James. A Critical & Exegetical Commentary on the Epistle to the Hebrews. Driver, Samuel R. & Plummer, Alfred, eds. LC 24-21703. (International Critical Commentary Ser.). 336p. 1924. 22.95 (ISBN 0-567-05034-3, Pub. by T & T Clark Ltd UK). Fortress.
Morris, Leon. Hebrews: Bible Study Commentary. 1986. pap. 5.95 (ISBN 0-310-45183-3, 12390P). Zondervan.
Moule, H. C. G. Studies in Hebrews. LC 77-79181. (Kregel Popular Commentary Ser.). 120p. 1977. kivar 5.95 (ISBN 0-8254-3223-5). Kregel.
Murray, Andrew. Holiest of All: An Exposition of the Epistle to the Hebrews. 576p. 17.95 (ISBN 0-8007-0138-0). Revell.
Owen, John. Hebrews, the Epistle of Warning. LC 68-57719. 1973. pap. 9.95 (ISBN 0-8254-3407-6). Kregel.
Peterson, David. Hebrews & Perfection: An Examination of the Concept of Perfection in the Epistle to the Hebrews. LC 82-4188. (Society for New Testament Monograph 47). 260p. 1982. 47.50 (ISBN 0-521-24408-0). Cambridge U Pr.
Pfeiffer, Charles F. Epistle to the Hebrews. (Everyman's Bible Commentary Ser.). (Orig.). 1968. pap. 5.95 (ISBN 0-8024-2058-3). Moody.
Phillips, John. Exploring Hebrews. LC 76-39908. 1977. pap. 9.95 (ISBN 0-8024-2431-7). Moody.
Pink, Arthur W. Exposition of Hebrews. 1954. 29.95 (ISBN 0-8010-6857-6). Baker Bk.
Saphir, Adolph. Epistle to the Hebrews, 2 vols. in 1. LC 83-4390. 924p. 1983. 21.95 (ISBN 0-8254-3728-8). Kregel.
Schrolder, A. & Bonnet, L. Hebreos-Apocalipsis: Tomo IV. Cotiviela, A., tr. from Eng. (Comentario Sobre el Nuevo Testamento). 540p. 1986. Repr. of 1983 ed. 14.95 (ISBN 0-311-03053-X). Casa Bautista.
Smith, Robert H. Augsburg Commentary on the New Testament: Hebrews. LC 83-72125. (Augsburg Commentary New Testament Ser.). 192p. (Orig.). 1984. pap. 8.95 kivar (ISBN 0-8066-8876-9, 10-9034). Augsburg.
Thomas, W. Griffith. Hebrews: A Devotional Commentary. 1962. pap. 4.95 (ISBN 0-8028-1552-9). Eerdmans.
Wartick, Wallace. Twenty-Six Lessons on Hebrews. LC 79-53713. (Bible Student Study Guides Ser.). 1979. pap. 3.95 (ISBN 0-89900-160-2). College Pr Pub.
Way, Arthur S. Letters of Paul, Hebrews & Psalms. LC 81-1092. 504p. 1981. text ed. 14.95 (ISBN 0-8254-4016-5). Kregel.
Westcott, Brooke F. Commentary on Epistle to the Hebrews. (Gr). 1950. 14.95 (ISBN 0-8028-3289-X). Eerdmans.
Wilson, Geoffrey. Hebrews. 1976. pap. 4.95 (ISBN 0-85151-278-X). Banner of Truth.

BIBLE-COMMENTARIES-N. T. JAMES
see Bible-Commentaries-N. T. Catholic Epistles

BIBLE-COMMENTARIES-N. T. JOHN
see Bible-Commentaries-N. T. Gospels

BIBLE-COMMENTARIES-N. T. JUDE
see Bible-Commentaries-N. T. Catholic Epistles

BIBLE-COMMENTARIES-N. T. LUKE
see Bible-Commentaries-N. T. Gospels

BIBLE-COMMENTARIES-N. T. MARK
see Bible-Commentaries-N. T. Gospels

BIBLE-COMMENTARIES-N. T. MATTHEW
see Bible-Commentaries-N. T. Gospels

BIBLE-COMMENTARIES-N. T. PASTORAL EPISTLES
Here are entered commentaries on the Pastoral epistles as a whole as well as those on Titus or Timothy.

Beacon Small-Group Bible Studies, I & II Timothy, Titus: Being Christian in Today's World. 72p. 1983. pap. 2.50 (ISBN 0-8341-0622-1). Beacon Hill.
Blaiklock, E. M. The Pastoral Epistles. 128p. 1972. pap. 4.95 (ISBN 0-310-21233-2, 9232). Zondervan.
Coffman, James B. Commentary on First & Second Thessalonians, I & II Timothy, Titus & Philemon. (Firm Foundation Commentary Ser.). 1978. 10.95 (ISBN 0-88027-073-X). Firm Foun Pub.
Dibelius, Martin & Conzelmann, Hans. The Pastoral Epistles. Koester, Helmut, ed. Buttolph, Philip & Yarbro, Adela, trs. from Ger. LC 71-157549. (Hermeneia: a Critical & Historical Commentary on the Bible). 1972. 19.95 (ISBN 0-8006-6002-1, 20-6002). Fortress.
Fairbairn, Patrick. The Pastoral Epistles. 1980. 17.25 (ISBN 0-86524-053-1, 7107). Klock & Klock.
Guthrie, Donald. Pastoral Epistles. (Tyndale Bible Commentary). 1957. pap. 4.95 (ISBN 0-8028-1413-1). Eerdmans.
Gutzke, Manford G. Plain Talk on Timothy, Titus, & Philemon. (Plain Talk Ser.). 1978. pap. 6.95 (ISBN 0-310-25661-5, 9861P). Zondervan.
Hanson, Anthony T., ed. Pastoral Letters. (Cambridge Bible Commentary on the New English Bible, New Testament Ser.). (Orig.). 1966. 17.95 (ISBN 0-521-04214-3); pap. 7.50x (ISBN 0-521-09380-5, 380). Cambridge U Pr.
Hendriksen, William. Thessalonians, Timothy & Titus. 404p. 1979. 21.95 (ISBN 0-8010-4213-5). Baker Bk.
Hiebert, D. Edmond. First Timothy. (Everyman's Bible Commentary Ser.). 1967. pap. 5.95 (ISBN 0-8024-2054-0). Moody.
--Second Timothy. (Everyman's Bible Commentary Ser). 1958. pap. 5.95 (ISBN 0-8024-2055-9). Moody.
--Titus & Philemon. (Everyman's Bible Commentary Ser.). 1957. pap. 5.95 (ISBN 0-8024-2056-7, MBP). Moody.
Hiebert, Edmond. Tito y Filemon: Comentario Biblico Portavoz. Orig. Title: Titus & Philemon (Everyman's Bible Commentary) (Span.). 136p. 1981. pap. 3.95 (ISBN 0-8254-1317-6). Kregel.
Holbein, Hans. Images of the Old Testament. (Children's Books from the Past: Vol. 1). 100p. 1973. Repr. of 1549 ed. 32.65 (ISBN 3-261-01003-7). P Lang Pubs.
Hultgren, Arland J. & Aus, Roger. Augsburg Commentary on the New Testament: 1 Timothy 2 Timothy, Titus, 2 Thessalonians. LC 83-72126. (Augsburg Commentary New Testament Ser.). 224p. 1984. kivar 8.95 (ISBN 0-8066-8874-2, 10-9032). Augsburg.
Karris, Robert J. Pastoral Epistles. (New Testament Message Ser.: Vol. 17). 9.95 (ISBN 0-89453-205-7); pap. 5.95 (ISBN 0-89453-140-9). M Glazier.
Kent, Homer, Jr. Pastoral Epistles. rev. ed. 1958. 10.95 (ISBN 0-8024-6357-6). Moody.
Knight, George W., III. The Faithful Sayings in the Pastoral Letters. (Baker Biblical Monographs). 1979. pap. 6.95 (ISBN 0-8010-5402-8). Baker Bk.
Lenski, Richard C. Interpretation of Colossians, Thessalonians First & Second, Timothy First & Second, Titus, & Philemon. 1937. 21.95 (ISBN 0-8066-9006-2, 10-3369). Augsburg.
Liddon, Henry P. The First Epistle to Timothy. 1978. 6.00 (ISBN 0-86524-109-0, 5401). Klock & Klock.
Lock, Walter. A Critical & Exegetical Commentary on The Pastoral Epistles. Driver, Samuel R., et al, eds. (International Critical Commentary Ser.). 212p. 1928. 22.95 (ISBN 0-567-05033-5, Pub. by T & T Clark Ltd UK). Fortress.
Moule, H. C. G. Studies in Second Timothy. LC 77-79182. (Kregel Popular Commentary Ser.). 180p. 1977. kivar 6.95 (ISBN 0-8254-3219-7). Kregel.
Mounce, Robert H. Pass It on. LC 78-68851. (Bible Commentary for Layman Ser.). 160p. 1979. pap. 3.50 (ISBN 0-8307-0667-4, S332108). Regal.
Neyrey, Jerome H. First Timothy, Second Timothy, Titus, James, First Peter, Second Peter, Jude, No. 9. Karris, Robert J., ed. (Collegeville Bible Commentary Ser.). 112p. 1983. pap. 2.95 (ISBN 0-8146-1309-8). Liturgical Pr.
Pastoral Epistles. (Erdmans Commentaries Ser.). 3.95 (ISBN 0-8010-3403-5). Baker Bk.
Pommert, John. Thirteen Lessons on Timothy & Titus. (Bible Student Study Guides). 2.95 (ISBN 0-89900-162-9). College Pr Pub.
Scarborough, Peggy. Hallelujah Anyway, Tim. 1976. pap. 3.95 (ISBN 0-87148-405-6). Pathway Pr.
Sciaparelli, Giovanni. Astronomy in the Old Testament. 59.95 (ISBN 0-87968-673-1). Gordon Pr.
Sparks, Irving A. The Pastoral Epistles: Introduction & Commentary. LC 85-10925. (Orig.). 1985. pap. 6.00 (ISBN 0-934743-01-0). Inst Biblical.
Stock, Eugene. Practical Truths from the Pastoral Epistles. LC 83-6113. 352p. 1983. 14.95 (ISBN 0-8254-3746-6). Kregel.
Taylor, Thomas. An Exposition of Titus. 1970. 20.75 (ISBN 0-86524-027-2, 5601). Klock & Klock.
Whedon's Commentary on Titus & Revelations, Vol. 5. 13.95 (ISBN 0-686-13332-3). Schmul Pub Co.
Woychuk, N. A. Exposicion de Segunda Timoteo. Orig. Title: Exposition of Second Timothy. (Span.). 1976. pap. 3.95 (ISBN 0-8254-1879-8). Kregel.

BIBLE-COMMENTARIES-N. T. PETER
see Bible-Commentaries-N. T. Catholic Epistles

BIBLE-COMMENTARIES-N. T. PHILEMON

Boles, Kenny. Thirteen Lessons on Philippians, Colossians & Philemon. LC 79-53714. (Bible Student Study Guides). (Orig.). 1979. pap. 2.95 (ISBN 0-89900-163-7). College Pr Pub.
Bruce, F. F. The Epistles to the Colossians, to Philemon, & to the Ephesians. (New International Commentary on the New Testament Ser.). 464p. 1984. 18.95 (ISBN 0-8028-2401-3). Eerdmans.
Carson, Herbert M. Epistles of Paul to the Colossians & to Philemon. (Tyndale Bible Commentaries). 1960. pap. 3.95 (ISBN 0-8028-1411-5). Eerdmans.
Cocoris, G. Michael. Philemon. 22p. (Orig.). 1985. pap. 1.00 (ISBN 0-935729-08-9). Church Open Door.
Coffman, James B. Commentary on First & Second Thessalonians, I & II Timothy, Titus & Philemon. (Firm Foundation Commentary Ser.). 1978. 10.95 (ISBN 0-88027-073-X). Firm Foun Pub.
Colossians & Philemon. (Erdmans Commentaries Ser.). 3.50 (ISBN 0-8010-3393-4). Baker Bk.
Cox, S. & Drysdale, A. H. The Epistle to Philemon. 246p. 1982. lib. bdg. 9.25 Smythe Sewn (ISBN 0-86524-134-1, 7108). Klock & Klock.
Gaebelein, Frank E., ed. The Expositor's Bible Commentary Vol. 11 (Ephesians-Philemon) 1978. 19.95 (ISBN 0-310-36530-9, 11180). Zondervan.
Getty, Mary A. Philippians & Philemon. (New Testament Message Ser.: Vol. 14). 10.95 (ISBN 0-89453-202-2); pap. 5.95 (ISBN 0-89453-137-9). M Glazier.
Gutzke, Manford G. Plain Talk on Timothy, Titus, & Philemon. (Plain Talk Ser.). 1978. pap. 6.95 (ISBN 0-310-25661-5, 9861P). Zondervan.
Hendriksen, William. Philippians, Colossians, & Philemon. (New Testament Commentary). 243p. 1979. 17.95 (ISBN 0-8010-4212-7). Baker Bk.
Hiebert, D. Edmond. Titus & Philemon. (Everyman's Bible Commentary Ser.). 1957. pap. 5.95 (ISBN 0-8024-2056-7, MBP). Moody.
Hiebert, Edmond. Tito y Filemon: Comentario Biblico Portavoz. Orig. Title: Titus & Philemon (Everyman's Bible Commentary) (Span.). 136p. 1981. pap. 3.95 (ISBN 0-8254-1317-6). Kregel.
Houlden, J. L., ed. Paul's Letters from Prison: Philippians, Colossians, Philemon & Ephesians. LC 77-24028. (Westminister Pelican Commentaries). 358p. 1978. 11.50 (ISBN 0-664-21347-2); pap. 6.95 (ISBN 0-664-24182-4). Westminster.
Ironside, H. A. Timothy, Titus & Philemon. 9.95 (ISBN 0-87213-391-5). Loizeaux.
Krentz, Edgar, et al, eds. Augsburg Commentary on the New Testament: Galatians, Philippians, Philemon. LC 85-11116. 256p. (Orig.). 1985. kivar 9.95 (ISBN 0-8066-2166-4, 10-9028). Augsburg.
Lenski, Richard C. Interpretation of Colossians, Thessalonians First & Second, Timothy First & Second, Titus, & Philemon. 1937. 21.95 (ISBN 0-8066-9006-2, 10-3369). Augsburg.
Lightfoot, J. B. Commentaries on Galatians, Philippians, Colossians & Philemon, 3 vols. 1208p. 1981. 39.95 (ISBN 0-913573-02-7). Hendrickson MA.
Lohse, Eduard. Colossians & Philemon. Koester, Helmut, ed. Poehlman, William R. & Karris, Robert J., trs. from Ger. LC 76-157550. (Hermeneia: A Critical & Historical Commentary on the Bible Ser). 256p. 1971. 22.95 (ISBN 0-8006-6001-3, 20-6001). Fortress.
Lucas, R. J. The Message of Colossians & Philemon. Motyer, J. A. & Stott, J. R., eds. LC 79-3635. (The Bible Speaks Today Ser.). 1980. pap. 6.95 (ISBN 0-87784-284-1). Inter-Varsity.
Martin, Ralph P. Colossians & Philemon. rev. ed. (New Century Bible Commentary Ser.). 192p. 1981. pap. 5.95 (ISBN 0-8028-1908-7). Eerdmans.
Moule, Charles F. Epistles of Paul the Apostle to the Colossians & to Philemon. (Cambridge Greek Testament Ser.). 1959. text ed. 32.50 (ISBN 0-521-04252-6); pap. text ed. 10.95 (ISBN 0-521-09236-1). Cambridge U Pr.
Moule, H. C. G. Colossian & Philemon Studies. 1981. 12.00 (ISBN 0-86524-052-3, 7106). Klock & Klock.
Muller, Jacobus J. Epistles of Paul to the Philippians. (New International Commentary on the New Testament). 1985. 12.95 (ISBN 0-8028-2188-X). Eerdmans.
Scroggie, W. Graham. Studies in Philemon. LC 77-79186. (W. Graham Scroggie Library). 136p. 1982. pap. 4.50 (ISBN 0-8254-3739-3). Kregel.
Thompson, G. H. Letters of Paul to the Ephesians, Colossians & Philemon. (Cambridge Bible Commentary on the New English Bible, New Testament Ser.). 18.95 (ISBN 0-521-04227-5); pap. 9.95x (ISBN 0-521-09410-0, 410). Cambridge U Pr.
Vaughan, Curtis. Colossians & Philemon: A Study Guide Commentary. (Study Guide Commentary Ser.). 144p. (Orig.). 1981. pap. 4.95 (ISBN 0-310-33583-3, 10965P). Zondervan.
Vincent, Marvin R. A Critical & Exegetical Commentary on the Philippians & Philemon. Driver, Samuel R. & Briggs, Charles A., eds. (International Critical Commentary Ser.). 248p. 1897. 22.95 (ISBN 0-567-05031-9, Pub. by T & T Clark Ltd UK). Fortress.
Wilson, Geoffrey B. Colossians & Philemon. (Wilson'a New Testament Commentaries). 111p. (Orig.). 1980. pap. 4.95 (ISBN 0-85151-313-1). Banner of Truth.

BIBLE-COMMENTARIES-N. T. PHILIPPIANS

Baker, Don. Philippians. (Lifebuilder Bible Studies). 60p. (Orig.). 1985. pap. text ed. 2.95 (ISBN 0-8308-1013-7). Inter-Varsity.
Beacon Bible Commentary Staff. Galatians-Philemon, Vol. IX. 13.95 (ISBN 0-8010-0696-1). Baker Bk.
Blair, J. Allen. Living Victoriously: Philippians. LC 62-290. 1962. pap. 2.75 (ISBN 0-87213-056-8). Loizeaux.
Boice, James M. Philippians: An Expositional Commentary. 320p. 1982. pap. 10.95 (ISBN 0-310-21501-3, 10310). Zondervan.
Boles, Kenny. Thirteen Lessons on Philippians, Colossians & Philemon. LC 79-53714. (Bible Student Study Guides). (Orig.). 1979. pap. 2.95 (ISBN 0-89900-163-7). College Pr Pub.
Brooks, Keith L. Philippians, The Epistle of Christian Joy. (Teach Yourself the Bible Ser.). 1964. pap. 2.75 (ISBN 0-8024-6506-4). Moody.
Bruce, F. F. Philippians: A Good News Commentary. LC 82-48919. 176p. (Orig.). 1983. pap. 7.95 (ISBN 0-06-061138-3, RD/446, HarpR). Har-Row.
Carballosa, Evis L. Filipenses: Un Comentario Exegetico y Practico. Orig. Title: Phillippians: Commentary. (Span.). 140p. 1973. pap. 1.95 (ISBN 0-8254-1105-X). Kregel.
Caudill, Paul R. Seven Steps to Peace. LC 81-71254. 1982. pap. 3.95 (ISBN 0-8054-1527-0). Broadman.
Caudill, R. Paul. Philippians: A Translation with Notes. LC 80-70403. (Orig.). 1981. pap. 2.25 (ISBN 0-938980-00-9). Blue Ridge.
Coffman, James B. Commentary on Galatians, Ephesians, Phillipians, Colossians. (Firm Foundation Commentary Ser.). 1977. cancelled 10.95 (ISBN 0-88027-072-1). Firm Foun Pub.
Eddleman, H. Leo. By Life or By Death: A Practical Commentary on Paul's Letter to the Philippians. 176p. (Orig.). 1981. pap. 3.75 (ISBN 0-682-49700-2, Testament). Exposition Pr FL.
Getty, Mary A. Philippians & Philemon. (New Testament Message Ser.: Vol. 14). 10.95 (ISBN 0-89453-202-2); pap. 5.95 (ISBN 0-89453-137-9). M Glazier.
Grayston, Kenneth. Philippians & Thessalonians. (Cambridge Bible Commentary on the New English Bible, New Testament Ser.). 1967. 16.95 (ISBN 0-521-04224-0); pap. 8.95 (ISBN 0-521-09409-7, 409). Cambridge U Pr.
Grunlan, Stephen A. Serving with Joy: A Study in Philippians. LC 85-71352. 107p. (Orig.). 1985. pap. 4.95 (ISBN 0-87509-371-X); leader's guide 2.95 (ISBN 0-87509-372-8). Chr Pubns.
Guthrie, Donald. Exploring God's World: A Guide to Ephesians, Philippians, & Colossians. 224p. (Orig.). 1985. pap. 6.95 (ISBN 0-8028-0084-X). Eerdmans.

Havener, Ivan & Karris, Robert J. First Thessalonians, Philippians, Philemon, Second Thessalonians, Colossians, Ephesians, No. 8. (Collegeville Bible Commentary Ser.). (Illus.). 112p. 1983. pap. 2.95 (ISBN 0-8146-1308-X). Liturgical Pr.

Hendriksen, William. Philippians, Colossians, & Philemon. (New Testament Commentary). 243p. 1979. 17.95 (ISBN 0-8010-4212-7). Baker Bk.

Hocking, David L. How to Be Happy in Difficult Situations: Studies in Philippians. pap. 4.95 (ISBN 0-88469-027-X). BMH Bks.

Houlden, J. L., ed. Paul's Letters from Prison: Philippians, Colossians, Philemon & Ephesians. LC 77-24028. (Westminster Pelican Commentaries). 358p. 1978. 11.50 (ISBN 0-664-21347-2); pap. 6.95 (ISBN 0-664-24182-4). Westminster.

Ironside, H. A. Philippians, Colossians, Thessalonians. 433p. 11.95 (ISBN 0-87213-398-2). Loizeaux.

Klug, Ron. Philippians: Living Joyfully. (Young Fisherman Bible Studyguide Ser.). (Illus.). 64p. 1983. tchr's ed. 4.95 (ISBN 0-87788-682-2); saddle-stitched student's ed. 2.95 (ISBN 0-87788-681-4). Shaw Pubs.

Krentz, Edgar, et al, eds. Augsburg Commentary on the New Testament: Galatians, Philippians, Philemon. LC 85-11116. 256p. (Orig.). 1985. kivar 9.95 (ISBN 0-8066-2166-4, 10-9028). Augsburg.

Lemke, Steve. Joy in Christ: Studies in Philippians. 36p. 1981. pap. 3.50 (ISBN 0-939298-10-4). J M Prods.

Lenski, Richard C. Interpretation of Galatians, Ephesians, & Philippians. 1937. 21.95 (ISBN 0-8066-9007-0, 10-3368). Augsburg.

Lightfoot, J. B. Commentaries on Galatians, Philippians, Colossians & Philemon, 3 vols. 1208p. 1981. 39.95 (ISBN 0-913573-02-7). Hendrickson MA.

Martin, Ralph P. Commentary on Philippians. (New Century Bible Commentary Ser.). 192p. 1980. pap. 6.95 (ISBN 0-8028-1840-4). Eerdmans.

--Epistle of Paul to the Philippians. (Tyndale Bible Commentaries). 1960. pap. 4.95 (ISBN 0-8028-1410-7). Eerdmans.

Menzies, William W. Philippians: The Joyful Life. LC 81-80302. (Radiant Life Ser.). 128p. (Orig.). 1981. pap. 2.50 (ISBN 0-88243-880-8, 02-0880); tchr's ed. 3.95 (ISBN 0-88243-191-9, 32-0191). Gospel Pub.

Meyer, F. B. Devotional Commentary on Philippians. LC 78-59146. 1978. pap. 7.95 (ISBN 0-8254-3227-8). Kregel.

Miller, Calvin. The Philippian Fragment. LC 82-15. (Illus.). 175p. 1982. pap. 5.95 (ISBN 0-87784-805-X). Inter-Varsity.

Moran, John. Joy in a Roman Jail. 208p. (Orig.). 1984. pap. 6.25 (ISBN 0-934998-17-5). Bethel Pub.

Moule, H. C. G. Studies in Philippians. LC 77-79184. (Kregel Popular Commentary Ser.). 136p. 1977. kivar 6.95 (ISBN 0-8254-3216-2). Kregel.

Moule, Handley. Philippians. 1975. pap. 4.95 (ISBN 0-87508-364-1). Chr Lit.

Muller, Jacobus J. Epistles of Paul to the Philippians. (New International Commentary on the New Testament). 1985. 12.95 (ISBN 0-8028-2188-X). Eerdmans.

Philippians. (Erdmans Commentaries Ser.). 3.95 (ISBN 0-8010-3404-3). Baker Bk.

St. Thomas Aquinas. Commentary on Saint Paul's Epistle to the Philippians & First Thessalonians. LC 66-19306. (Aquinas Scripture Ser.: Vol. 3). 1969. lib. bdg. 10.00x (ISBN 0-87343-047-6); pap. 6.00x (ISBN 0-87343-028-X). Magi Bks.

Strauss, Lehman. Philippians: Studies. 1959. 7.50 (ISBN 0-87213-823-2). Loizeaux.

Vincent, Marvin R. A Critical & Exegetical Commentary on the Philippians & Philemon. Driver, Samuel R. & Briggs, Charles A., eds. (International Critical Commentary Ser.). 248p. 1897. 22.95 (ISBN 0-567-05031-9, Pub. by T & T Clark Ltd UK). Fortress.

Vos, Howard F. Philippians: A Bible Study Commentary. (Study Guide Commentary Ser.). 96p. (Orig.). 1980. pap. 3.95 (ISBN 0-310-33863-8, 10967P). Zondervan.

Walvoord, John F. Filipenses: Triunfo en Cristo (Comentario Biblico Portavoz) Orig. Title: Philippinas: Triumph in Christ (Everyman's Bible Commentary) (Span.). 1980. pap. 3.50 (ISBN 0-8254-1852-6). Kregel.

Watson, Tom, Jr. How to Be Happy No Matter What. LC 77-73559. 160p. 1978. pap. 3.50 (ISBN 0-8307-0465-5, S103125). Regal.

Wilson, Geoffrey B. Philippians. 109p. (Orig.). 1983. pap. 4.95 (ISBN 0-85151-363-8). Banner of Truth.

BIBLE–COMMENTARIES–N. T. REVELATION

Bale, John. The Image of Bothe Curches, After the Moste Wonderfull & Heavenly Revelation of Sainct John the Evangelist. LC 72-5965. (English Experience Ser.: No. 498). 872p. 1973. Repr. of 1548 ed. 51.00 (ISBN 90-221-0498-2). Walter J Johnson.

--Select Works of John Bale, Bishop of Ossory. 51.00 (ISBN 0-384-03135-8). Johnson Repr.

Barrett, J. O. The Book of Revelation: Missionary Message of the New Testament. 123p. 1947. Repr. 2.95 (ISBN 0-87921-005-2). Attic Pr.

Beasley-Murray, G. R. The Book of Revelation. (New Century Bible Commentay Ser.). 1981. pap. 7.95 (ISBN 0-8028-1885-4). Eerdmans.

Brooks, Keith L. Revelation, the Future Foretold. (Teach Yourself the Bible Ser.). 1962. pap. 2.75 (ISBN 0-8024-7308-3). Moody.

Caird, G. B. The Revelation of St. John the Divine. LC 66-20774. (New Testament Commentaries Ser.). 1966. 17.95 (ISBN 0-06-061296-7, HarpR). Har-Row.

Cayce, Edgar. Revelation: A Commentary on the Book, Based on the Study of Twenty Four Psychic Discourses of Edgar Cayce. (Twenty-Six Interpretive Readings). 1969. pap. 8.95 (ISBN 0-87604-003-2). ARE Pr.

Charles, R. H. A Critical & Exegetical Commentary on the Revalation of St. John, 2 vols, Vol. I. Plummer, Alfred & Briggs, Charles A., eds. LC 21-5413. (International Critical Commentary Ser.). 568p. 1920. 24.95x (ISBN 0-567-05038-6, Pub. by T & T Clark Ltd UK). Fortress.

--A Critical & Exegetical Commentary on the Revalation of St. John, 2 vols, Vol. II. LC 21-5413. (International Critical Commentary Ser.). 506p. 1920. 24.95 (ISBN 0-567-05039-4, Pub. by T & T Clark Ltd UK). Fortress.

Dalpadado, J. Kingsley. Reading the Acts, Epistles & Revelations. 1977. 6.95 (ISBN 0-8198-0450-9); pap. 5.95 (ISBN 0-8198-0451-7). Dghtrs St Paul.

Easu & Rodehaver, Gladys K., eds. Book II of Revelations for the Aquarian Age. 1983. pap. 7.00 (ISBN 0-930208-14-5). Mangan Bks.

Edwards, Jonathan. Apocalyptic Writings. LC 57-2336. (The Works of Jonathan Edwards: Vol. 5). (Illus.). 1977. 50.00x (ISBN 0-300-01945-9). Yale U Pr.

Eller, Vernard. The Most Revealing Book of the Bible: Making Sense Out of Revelation. 1974. pap. 4.95 (ISBN 0-8028-1572-3). Eerdmans.

--War & Peace from Genesis to Revelation. LC 80-26280. (Christian Peace Shelf Ser.). 232p. 1981. pap. 9.95 (ISBN 0-8361-1947-9). Herald Pr.

Fiorenza, Elisabeth S. The Book of Revelation: Justice & Judgment. LC 84-47920. 224p. 1984. pap. 11.95 (ISBN 0-8006-1793-2). Fortress.

Ford, J. Massyngberde, tr. Revelation. LC 74-18796. (Anchor Bible Ser.: Vol. 38). (Illus.). 504p. 1975. 18.00 (ISBN 0-385-00895-3). Doubleday.

Franzmann, Martin H. The Revelation to John. 148p. 1986. pap. 7.95 (ISBN 0-570-03728-X, 12-2630). Concordia.

Freligh, H. M. Studies in Revelation, 4 Vols. Schroeder, E. H., ed. 327p. 1969. pap. text ed. 2.50 ea.; Vol. 1. (ISBN 0-87509-140-7); Vol. 2. (ISBN 0-87509-141-5); Vol. 3. (ISBN 0-87509-142-3); Vol. 4. (ISBN 0-87509-143-1). Chr Pubns.

Fuller, Reginald H. The Formation of the Resurrection Narratives. LC 79-8885. 240p. 1980. pap. 7.95 (ISBN 0-8006-1378-3, 1-1378). Fortress.

Glasson, Thomas F., ed. Revelation of John. (Cambridge Bible Commentary on the New English Bible, New Testament Ser.). (Orig.). 1965. 16.95 (ISBN 0-521-04208-9); pap. 9.95x (ISBN 0-521-09256-6). Cambridge U Pr.

Grimm, Jacob & Grimm, Wilhelm K. Lucky Hans. LC 86-2520. (Illus.). 32p. 1986. 12.45 (ISBN 0-8050-0009-7, North South Bks). H Holt & Co.

Gutzke, Manford G. Plain Talk on Revelation. (Orig.). 1979. pap. 5.95 (ISBN 0-310-25681-X, 9863P). Zondervan.

Hailey, Homer. Revelation. LC 78-62441. 1979. 14.95 (ISBN 0-8010-4201-1). Baker Bk.

Hendriksen, William. More Than Conquerors. Commeritive ed. 11.95 (ISBN 0-8010-4026-4). Baker Bk.

Ironside, H. A. Revelation. 9.95 (ISBN 0-87213-384-2). Loizeaux.

Kelly, W. Revelation Expounded. 5.95 (ISBN 0-88172-106-9). Believers Bkshelf.

Kirban, Salem & Cohen, Gary. Revelation Visualized. 1971. pap. 14.95 (ISBN 0-912582-08-1). Kirban.

Kuyvenhoven, Andrew. Romans: A Study Guide. (Revelation Series for Adults). 1976. pap. text ed. 2.50 (ISBN 0-933140-04-5). CRC Pubns.

Ladd, George E. El Apocalipsis de Juan: Un Comentario. Canclini, Arnoldo, tr. from Eng. LC 78-50625. Tr. of A Commentary on the Revelation of John. (Span.). 269p. (Orig.). pap. 6.95 (ISBN 0-89922-111-4). Edit Caribe.

--Commentary on the Book of Revelation of John. 1971. pap. 8.95 (ISBN 0-8028-1684-3). Eerdmans.

Lahaye, Tim. Revelation-Illustrated & Made Plain. rev. ed. 456p. 1975. 7.95 (ISBN 0-310-26991-1, 18073P). Zondervan.

Lattimore, Richmond, tr. from Greek. The Four Gospels & the Revelation. 320p. 1979. 14.95 (ISBN 0-374-15801-0). FS&G.

Lewis, Arthur H. Dark Side of the Millennium: The Problem of Evil in Revelation 20: 1-10. 96p. (Orig.). 1980. pap. 3.95 (ISBN 0-8010-5596-2). Baker Bk.

Lindsay, Gordon. Armageddon. (Revelation Ser.). 1.25 (ISBN 0-89985-047-2). Christ Nations.

--The Beast from the Bottomless Pit. (Revelation Ser.). 1.25 (ISBN 0-89985-043-X). Christ Nations.

--The One Hundred Forty-Four Thousand on Mt. Zion & the First-Fruits. (Revelation Ser.). 1.25 (ISBN 0-89985-044-8). Christ Nations.

--The Seven Churches of Prophecy, 2 vols. (Revelation Ser.). 1.25 ea. Vol. 1 (ISBN 0-89985-977-1). Vol. 2 (ISBN 0-89985-978-X). Christ Nations.

--The Sun-Clothed Woman & the Manchild. (Revelation Ser.). 1.25 (ISBN 0-89985-040-5). Christ Nations.

--A Thousand Years of Peace. (End of the Age Ser.: Vol. 8). 1.25 (ISBN 0-89985-074-X). Christ Nations.

--The Tribulation Temple. (Revelation Ser.). 1.25 (ISBN 0-89985-038-3). Christ Nations.

--The Two Babylons. (Revelation Ser.). 1.25 (ISBN 0-89985-046-4). Christ Nations.

--The Two Witnesses. (Revelation Ser.). 1.25 (ISBN 0-89985-039-1). Christ Nations.

Loane, Marcus L. They Overcame: An Exposition of the First Three Chapters of Revelation. (Canterbury Books). 144p. 1981. pap. 3.95 (ISBN 0-8010-5609-8). Baker Bk.

Lo Bue, F., ed. The Turin Fragments of Tyconius' Commentary on Revelation. (Texts & Studies, N. S.: Vol. 7). Repr. of 1963 ed. 28.00 (ISBN 0-8115-1720-9). Kraus Repr.

Love, Julian P. First John-Revelation. LC 59-10454. (Layman's Bible Commentary, Vol. 25). pap. 4.95 (ISBN 0-8042-3085-4). John Knox.

Lucas, DeWitt B. Visions of the New Life. 1963. pap. 2.50 (ISBN 0-910140-11-1). C & R Anthony.

McDonald, H. D. Theories of Revelation. 1979. pap. 10.95 (ISBN 0-8010-6081-8). Baker Bk.

Mauro, Philip. Things Which Soon Must Come to Pass: Commentary on Revelation. 1984. Repr. 14.95 (ISBN 0-317-11813-7). Reiner.

Morris, Leon. Creo En la Revelacion. Blanch, Miguel, tr. from Eng. (Serie Creo). Tr. of I Believe in the Revelation. (Span.). 223p. 1979. pap. 5.95 (ISBN 0-89922-140-8). Edit Caribe.

Mounce, Robert H. The Book of Revelation. LC 77-7664. (New International Commentary on New Testament Ser.). 1977. 16.95 (ISBN 0-8028-2348-3). Eerdmans.

Neal, Marshall. Seven Churches. (Illus.). 108p. (Orig.). 1977. pap. 2.95 (ISBN 0-89084-062-8). Bob Jones Univ Pr.

Onstad, Esther. Courage for Today-Hope for Tomorrow: A Study of the Revelation. LC 75-2829. 144p. 1975. pap. 6.95 (ISBN 0-8066-1474-9, 10-1695). Augsburg.

Pack, Frank. Message of the New Testament: Revelation I & II, 2 vols. (Way of Life Ser.: No. 176 & 177). 1984. pap. 3.95 ea. (Bibl Res Pr). Vol. I (ISBN 0-89112-176-5). Vol. II (ISBN 0-89112-177-3). Abilene Christ U.

Perkins, Pheme. The Book of Revelation. Karris, Robert J., ed. (Collegeville Bible Commentary Ser.: No. 11). 96p. 1983. Vol. 11. pap. 2.95 (ISBN 0-8146-1311-X). Liturgical Pr.

Ramsey, James B. Revelation: An Exposition of the First Eleven Chapters. (Geneva Commentary Ser.). 1977. 17.95 (ISBN 0-85151-256-9). Banner of Truth.

Rand, Howard B. Study in Revelation. 1941. 12.00 (ISBN 0-685-08817-0). Destiny.

Revelation. (Erdmans Commentaries Ser.). 4.50 (ISBN 0-8010-3405-1). Baker Bk.

Rogers, Richard. Hallelujah Anyway. 57p. (Orig.). 1980. pap. text ed. 2.50 (ISBN 0-931097-03-7). Sentinel Pub.

Ryrie, Charles C. Revelation. (Everyman's Bible Commentary Ser.). (Orig.). 1968. pap. 5.95 (ISBN 0-8024-2066-4). Moody.

Sena, Patrick. The Apocalypse: Biblical Revelation Explained. LC 83-22299. 116p. (Orig.). 1983. pap. 6.95 (ISBN 0-8189-0454-2). Alba.

Shorter, Aylward. Revelation & Its Interpretation. 280p. 1984. pap. text ed. 14.95 (ISBN 0-225-66356-2, AY8482, HarpR). Har-Row.

Strauss, Lehman. Revelation. LC 64-8641. Orig. Title: Book of the Revelation. 9.95 (ISBN 0-87213-825-9). Loizeaux.

Summers, Ray. Worthy Is the Lamb. 1951. 11.95 (ISBN 0-8054-1314-6). Broadman.

Sweet, J. P. Revelation. LC 78-26383. (Westminster Pelican Commentaries). 378p. 1979. 14.95 (ISBN 0-664-21375-8); softcover 9.95 (ISBN 0-664-24262-6). Westminster.

Tenney, Merrill C. Interpreting Revelation. 1957. 15.95 (ISBN 0-8028-3254-7). Eerdmans.

Tucker, W. Leon. Studies in Revelation. LC 80-16206. (Kregel Bible Study Classics Ser.). 400p. 1980. 14.95 (ISBN 0-8254-3826-8). Kregel.

Van Impe, Jack. Revelation Revealed. 282p. 1982. pap. 6.95 (ISBN 0-934803-09-9); 8-cassette set 29.95 (ISBN 0-934803-35-8). J Van Impe.

Walhout, Edwin. Revelation: A Study Guide. (Revelation Series for Adults). 1978. pap. text ed. 2.50 (ISBN 0-933140-07-X). CRC Pubns.

Walvoord, John F. Revelation of Jesus Christ. LC 66-16227. 1966. 15.95 (ISBN 0-8024-7310-5). Moody.

Welch, Adam C. Visions of the End: A Study in Daniel & Revelation. 260p. 1958. Repr. of 1922 ed. 10.95 (ISBN 0-227-67631-9). Attic Pr.

Whedon's Commentary on Titus & Revelations, Vol. 5. 13.95 (ISBN 0-686-13332-3). Schmul Pub Co.

Wieand, David J. Visions of Glory. 144p. (Orig.). 1980. pap. 4.95 (ISBN 0-87178-905-1). Brethren.

Wilcock, M. The Message of Revelation. LC 74-31845. (Bible Speaks Today Ser.). 1975. pap. 6.95 (ISBN 0-87784-293-0). Inter-Varsity.

Wilson, David A. Apocalypse! (Illus.). 175p. (Orig.). 1973. pap. 8.00 (ISBN 0-934852-10-3). Lorien Hse.

BIBLE–COMMENTARIES–N. T. ROMANS

Barney, Kenneth D. Freedom: A Guarantee for Everybody. LC 75-34644. (Radiant Life Ser.). 128p. 1976. pap. 2.50 (ISBN 0-88243-891-3, 02-0891, Radiant Bks); teacher's ed 3.95 (ISBN 0-88243-165-X, 32-0165). Gospel Pub.

Barrett, C. K. Reading Through Romans. LC 76-55828. 96p. 1977. pap. 3.95 (ISBN 0-8006-1250-7, 1-1250). Fortress.

Barrett, Charles K. The Epistle to the Romans. LC 57-12722. 1958. 17.95 (ISBN 0-06-060550-2, HarpR). Har-Row.

Barth, Karl. Epistle to the Romans. 6th ed. Hoskyns, Edwyn C., tr. 1968. pap. 12.95 (ISBN 0-19-500294-6). Oxford U Pr.

Bell, Robert S. Paul's Letter to the Romans. 1970. pap. 2.75 (ISBN 0-88027-036-5). Firm Foun Pub.

Best, Ernest, ed. Letter of Paul to the Romans: Cambridge Bible Commentary on the New English Bible. (New Testament Ser.). (Orig.). 1967. 21.95 (ISBN 0-521-04213-5); pap. 8.95x (ISBN 0-521-09401-1, 401). Cambridge U Pr.

Black, Matthew. Romans. (New Century Bible Series). 191p. 1973. 7.50 (ISBN 0-551-00447-9). Attic Pr.

--Romans. rev. ed. (New Century Bible Commentary Ser.). 192p. 1981. pap. 6.95 (ISBN 0-8028-1905-2). Eerdmans.

Brokke, Harold J. A Guide to Understanding Romans. LC 80-67446. 211p. 1980. pap. 5.95 (ISBN 0-87123-193-X, 210193). Bethany Hse.

Brooks, Keith L. Romans: The Gospel for All. (Teach Yourself the Bible Ser.). 1962. pap. 2.75 (ISBN 0-8024-7372-5). Moody.

Coffman, James B. Commentary on Romans. (Firm Foundation Commentary Ser.). cancelled (ISBN 0-88027-070-5). Firm Foun Pub.

Cranfield, C. E. Commentary on Romans. abr. ed. 320p. 1985. pap. 10.95 (ISBN 0-8028-0012-2). Eerdmans.

Cranfield, Charles E. A Critical & Exegetical Commentary on the Epistle to the Romans, 2 vols, Vol. 1 & 2. Emerton, John A., ed. (International Critical Commentary Ser.). 29.95 ea. (Pub. by T & T Clark Ltd UK). Vol. I, 472 pgs., 1975 (ISBN 0-567-05040-8). Vol. II, 476 pgs., 1979 (ISBN 0-567-05041-6). Fortress.

Earle, Ralph. Word Meanings in the New Testament, Vol. 3: Romans. 264p. 1974. 9.95 (ISBN 0-8341-0512-8). Beacon Hill.

Erasmus, Desiderius. Paraphrases on Romans & Galatians. Sider, Robert D., ed. Payne, John B., et al, trs. (Collected Works of Erasmus Ser.: Vol. 42). 232p. 1984. 29.50x (ISBN 0-8020-2510-2). U of Toronto Pr.

Foreman, Kenneth J. Romans, First & Second Corinthians. LC 59-10454. (Layman's Bible Commentary Ser: Vol. 21). 1961. pap. 4.95 (ISBN 0-8042-3081-1). John Knox.

Forlines, F. Leroy. Randall House Bible Commentary: Romans. (Bible Commentary Ser.). 350p. 1986. 19.95 (ISBN 0-89265-116-4). Randall Hse.

Godet, Frederic L. Commentary on Romans. LC 77-79189. (Kregel Reprint Library). 542p. 1977. 24.95 (ISBN 0-8254-2715-0). Kregel.

Grant, L. Comments on the Book of Romans. pap. 3.95 (ISBN 0-88172-078-X). Believers Bkshelf.

Greathouse, Willam M. Beacon Bible Expositions: Vol. 6, Romans. Taylor, Willard H., ed. (Beacon Bible Exposition Ser.). 1975. 8.95 (ISBN 0-8341-0317-6). Beacon Hill.
Harrisville, Roy A. Augsburg Commentary on the New Testament-Romans. LC 80-65550. 246p. (Orig.). 1980. pap. 9.95 (ISBN 0-8066-8864-5, 10-9022). Augsburg.
Hodge, Charles. Romans. (Geneva Commentaries Ser.). 1975. 13.95 (ISBN 0-85151-213-5). Banner of Truth.
Ironside, H. A. Romans. 7.95 (ISBN 0-87213-386-9). Loizeaux.
Ishee, John A. Everyman's Gospel: Studies in Romans. 34p. (Orig.). 1983. pap. 3.50 (ISBN 0-939298-19-8). J M Prods.
Johnson, Alan. Romans, Vol. 1. rev. ed. (Everyman's Bible Commentary Ser.). 1984. pap. 5.95 (ISBN 0-8024-0446-4). Moody.
Kasemann, Ernst. Commentary on Romans. Bromiley, Geoffrey W., tr. 1978. 25.95 (ISBN 0-8028-3499-X). Eerdmans.
Kenyon, Don J. Romans, 2 vols. Incl. Vol. 1. Triumph of Truth. pap. text ed. 4.95 (ISBN 0-87509-147-4); leader's guide 2.95 (ISBN 0-87509-265-9); student's manual 1.00 (ISBN 0-87509-262-4); Vol 2. Glory of Grace. pap. text ed. 4.95 (ISBN 0-87509-148-2); leader's guide 2.95 (ISBN 0-87509-266-7); student's manual 1.00 (ISBN 0-87509-263-2). 1978. pap. Chr Pubns.
Landes, Paula F. Augustine on Romans: Propositions From the Epistle to the Romans & Unfinished Commentary on the Epistle to the Romans. LC 82-10259. (Society of Biblical Literature, Texts & Translations Ser.). 124p. 1982. pap. 12.75 (ISBN 0-89130-583-1, 06-02-23). Scholars Pr GA.
Lenski, Richard C. Interpretation of Romans. 1936. 21.95 (ISBN 0-8066-9005-4, 10-3366). Augsburg.
Lloyd-Jones, D. Martin. Romans: The Final Perseverance of the Saints (8: 17-39) 458p. 1976. text ed. 15.95 (ISBN 0-310-27930-5, 10592). Zondervan.
Lloyd-Jones, D. Martyn. Romans: Assurance, Vol. 2. 272p. 1972. 14.95 (ISBN 0-310-27890-2, 10542). Zondervan.
--Romans: Atonement & Justification; an Exposition of Chapters 3: 20 - 4: 35, Vol. 1. 13.95 (ISBN 0-310-27880-5, 10561). Zondervan.
--Romans Five: Sons of God - Chapter 8: 17 - 39. 448p. 1975. 15.95 (ISBN 0-310-27920-8, 10592). Zondervan.
Lovett, C. S. Lovett's Lights on Romans. 1975. pap. 6.95 (ISBN 0-938148-30-3). Personal Christianity.
Luther, Martin. Romans. Mueller, J. Theodore, tr. LC 76-12077. Orig. Title: Commentary on the Epistle to the Romans. 1976. kivar 8.95 (ISBN 0-8254-3119-0). Kregel.
MacArthur, John, Jr. Unity in Action: Romans Fourteen vs One Through Fifteen-Thirteen. (John MacArthur Bible Studies Ser.). 1987. pap. 3.95 (ISBN 0-8024-5307-4). Moody.
MacDonald, William. Romans: Justification by Faith. (Orig.). 1981. pap. 5.95 (ISBN 0-937396-36-2). Walterick Pubs.
MacGorman, J. W. The Layman's Bible Commentary: Romans, I Corinthians, Vol. 20. LC 79-51501. 1980. 5.95 (ISBN 0-8054-1190-9). Broadman.
McLaughlin. Commentary on Romans. kivar 5.95 (ISBN 0-686-12862-1). Schmul Pub Co.
Moule, H. C. G. Studies in Romans. LC 77-79180. (Kregel Popular Commentary Ser.). 270p. 1977. kivar 8.95 (ISBN 0-8254-3215-4). Kregel.
Moule, Handley. Romans. 1975. pap. 4.95 (ISBN 0-87508-362-5). Chr Lit.
Murray, John. Epistle of Paul to the Romans. (New International Commentary on the New Testament). 1960. 19.95 (ISBN 0-8028-2286-X). Eerdmans.
Newell, William R. Romans Verse by Verse. 1938. 19.95 (ISBN 0-8024-7385-7). Moody.
Nygren, Anders. Commentary on Romans. Rasmussen, Carl, tr. LC 49-48317. 472p. 1949. pap. 6.95 (ISBN 0-8006-1684-7, 1-1684). Fortress.
Olshausen, Hermann. Studies in the Epistle to the Romans. 438p. 1983. lib. bdg. 16.50 (ISBN 0-86524-163-5, 4503). Klock & Klock.
Parker, T. H. Commentaries on Romans Fifteen Thirty-Two to Fifteen Forty-Two. 250p. 1986. 25.50 (ISBN 0-567-09366-2, Pub. by T & T Clark Ltd Uk). Fortress.
Pentz, Croft M. Expository Outlines from Romans. (Sermon Outline Ser.). 48p. (Orig.). 1980. pap. 2.50 (ISBN 0-8010-7057-0). Baker Bk.
Phillips, John. Exploring Romans. 250p. 1971. pap. 9.95 (ISBN 0-8024-2433-3). Moody.
Picirilli, Robert. The Book of Romans. 324p. 1975. 8.95 (ISBN 0-89265-026-5). Randall Hse.
Pilch, John J. & Karris, Robert J. Galatians & Romans, No. 6. (Collegeville Bible Commentary Ser.). 80p. 1983. pap. 2.95 (ISBN 0-8146-1306-3). Liturgical Pr.
Plumer, William S. Commentary on Romans. LC 73-155251. (Kregel Reprint Library). 646p. 1971. 18.95 (ISBN 0-8254-3501-3). Kregel.
Pridham, Arthur. Notes on Romans. 1983. 13.95 (ISBN 0-8254-3519-6). Kregel.
Randall House Bible Commentary Series. Picirilli, Robert E. & Harrison, H. D., eds. Date not set. price not set (ISBN 0-89265-115-6). Randall Hse.
Resources for Renewal (Romans) Leader's Guide. 48p. (Orig.). 1982. pap. 1.95 (ISBN 0-89367-080-4). Light & Life.
Resources for Renewal (Romans) Student Guide. 64p. (Orig.). 1982. pap. 2.50 (ISBN 0-89367-079-0). Light & Life.
Robinson, Thomas. Studies in Romans: A Suggestive Commentary on Paul's Epistle to the Romans, 2 vols. in 1. LC 82-7795. (Kregel Bible Study Classics Ser.). 912p. 1982. 24.95 (ISBN 0-8254-3625-7). Kregel.
Romans. (Erdmans Commentaries Ser.). 3.95 (ISBN 0-8010-3407-8). Baker Bk.
Rosenius, C. O. Romans, a Devotional Commentary. 1978. pap. 5.45 (ISBN 0-910452-42-3). Covenant.
Sanday, William & Headlam, Arthur C. A Critical & Exegetical Commentary on the Epistle to the Romans. Driver, Samuel R. & Plummer, Alfred, eds. (International Critical Commentary Ser.). 568p. 1902. 22.95 (ISBN 0-567-05026-2, Pub. by T & T Clark Ltd UK). Fortress.
Smith, Sherwood. Thirteen Lessons on Romans, Vol. II. LC 81-65030. (Bible Student Study Guides Ser.). 114p. 1981. pap. 2.95 (ISBN 0-89900-170-X). College Pr Pub.
--Thirteen Lessons on Romans, Vol. I. LC 79-55509. (Bible Student Study Guides). 113p. (Orig.). 1980. pap. 2.95 (ISBN 0-89900-164-5). College Pr Pub.
Stedman, Ray C. From Guilt to Glory: The Message of Romans 9-16. LC 85-29659. (Authentic Christianity Bks.). 1986. pap. 7.95 (ISBN 0-88070-124-2). Multnomah.
--From Guilt to Glory: The Message of Romans 1-8. LC 85-29657. (Authentic Christianity Bks.). 1985. pap. 8.95 (ISBN 0-88070-123-4). Multnomah.
Thomas, J. D. The Message of the New Testament-Romans. LC 82-70933. (Way of Life Ser.: 166). (Illus.). 108p. 1982. pap. 3.95 (ISBN 0-89112-166-8, Bibl Res Pr). Abilene Christ U.
Thomas, W. Griffith. St. Paul's Epistle to the Romans. 1946. pap. 9.95 (ISBN 0-8028-1582-0). Eerdmans.
Tucker, W. Leon. Studies in Romans. LC 83-6114. 112p. 1983. pap. 4.95 (ISBN 0-8254-3827-6). Kregel.
Vaughan, Curtis & Corley, Bruce. Romans: A Study Guide Commentary. 1976. pap. 4.95 (ISBN 0-310-33573-6, 10960P). Zondervan.
Warren, Thomas B. & Elkins, Garland, eds. The Book of Romans. 1983. 15.00 (ISBN 0-934916-03-9). Natl Christian Pr.
Wenger, J. C. A Lay Guide to Romans. LC 82-15789. 160p. (Orig.). 1983. pap. 8.95 (ISBN 0-8361-3316-1). Herald Pr.
Wheston's Commentaries on Acts, Romans, Vol. 3. 13.95 (ISBN 0-686-13906-2). Schmul Pub Co.
Wilson, Geoffrey. Romans. 254p. 1977. pap. 5.45 (ISBN 0-85151-238-0). Banner of Truth.

BIBLE-COMMENTARIES-N. T. THESSALONIANS

Brooks, Keith L. First & Second Thessalonians. (Teach Yourself the Bible Ser). 1961. pap. 2.75 (ISBN 0-8024-2645-X). Moody.
Coffman, James B. Commentary on First & Second Thessalonians, I & II Timothy, Titus & Philemon. (Firm Foundation Commentary Ser.). 1978. 10.95 (ISBN 0-88027-073-X). Firm Foun Pub.
Frame, James E. A Critical & Exegetical Commentary on the Epistles of St. Paul to the Thessalonians. Driver, Samuel R. & Briggs, Charles A., eds. (International Critical Commentary Ser.). 336p. 1912. 22.95 (ISBN 0-567-05032-7, Pub. by T & T Clark Ltd UK). Fortress.
Getz, Gene A. Standing Firm When You'd Rather Retreat. LC 86-429. (Biblical Renewal Ser.). 168p. (Orig.). 1986. pap. 5.95 (ISBN 0-8307-1093-0, 5418594). Regal.
Grayston, Kenneth. Philippians & Thessalonians. (Cambridge Bible Commentary on the New English Bible, New Testament Ser.). 1967. 16.95 (ISBN 0-521-04224-0); pap. 8.95 (ISBN 0-521-09409-7, 409). Cambridge U Pr.
Havener, Ivan & Karris, Robert J. First Thessalonians, Philippians, Philemon, Second Thessalonians, Colossians, Ephesians, No. 8. (Collegeville Bible Commentary Ser.). (Illus.). 112p. 1983. pap. 2.95 (ISBN 0-8146-1308-X). Liturgical Pr.
Hendriksen, William. Thessalonians, Timothy & Titus. 404p. 1979. 21.95 (ISBN 0-8010-4213-5). Baker Bk.
Hendrix, John D. To Thessalonians with Love. LC 81-70974. (Orig.). 1983. pap. 6.50 (ISBN 0-8054-1312-X). Broadman.
Hogg, C. F. & Vine, W. E. Epistle to the Thessalonians. (Orig.). pap. cancelled (ISBN 0-8254-2859-9). Kregel.
Hultgren, Arland J. & Aus, Roger. Augsburg Commentary on the New Testament: 1 Timothy 2 Timothy, Titus, 2 Thessalonians. LC 83-72126. (Augsburg Commentary New Testament Ser.). 224p. 1984. kivar 8.95 (ISBN 0-8066-8874-2, 10-9032). Augsburg.
Jensen, Irving L. First & Second Thessalonians. (Bible Self-Study Ser.). 112p. 1974. pap. 3.25 (ISBN 0-8024-1053-7). Moody.
Lenski, Richard C. Interpretation of Colossians, Thessalonians First & Second, Timothy First & Second, Titus, & Philemon. 1937. 21.95 (ISBN 0-8066-9006-2, 10-3369). Augsburg.
Morris, Leon. First & Second Epistles to the Thessalonians. (New International Commentary of the New Testament). 1959. 14.95 (ISBN 0-8028-2187-1). Eerdmans.
--First & Second Thessalonians. rev. ed. Tasker, R. V., ed. (Tyndale New Testament Commentaries Ser.). 160p. 1984. pap. 4.95 (ISBN 0-8028-0034-3). Eerdmans.
Palmer, Earl. First & Second Thessalonians: A Good News Commentary. LC 82-48409. (Good News Commentary Ser.). 128p. (Orig.). 1983. pap. 6.95 (ISBN 0-06-066455-X, RD426, HarpR). Har-Row.
Rolston, Holmes. First Thessalonians-Philemon. LC 59-10454. (Layman's Bible Commentary Ser: Vol. 23). pap. 4.95 (ISBN 0-8042-3083-8). John Knox.
Ryrie, Charles C. First & Second Thessalonians. (Everyman's Bible Commentary Ser.). 1968. pap. 5.95 (ISBN 0-8024-2052-4). Moody.
--Primera y Segunda Tesalonicenses (Comentario Biblico Portavoz) Orig. Title: First & Second Thessalonians (Everyman's Bible Commentary) (Span.). 104p. 1981. pap. 2.95 (ISBN 0-8254-1634-5). Kregel.
St. Thomas Aquinas. Commentary on Saint Paul's Epistle to the Philippians & First Thessalonians. LC 66-19306. (Aquinas Scripture Ser.: Vol. 3). 1969. lib. bdg. 10.00x (ISBN 0-87343-047-6); pap. 6.00x (ISBN 0-87343-028-X). Magi Bks.
Tarazi, Paul N. First Thessalonians: A Commentary. LC 82-16952. (Orthodox Biblical Studies). 186p. (Orig.). 1982. pap. 7.95 (ISBN 0-913836-97-4). St Vladimirs.
Thessalonians. (Erdmans Commentaries Ser.). 2.95 (ISBN 0-8010-3408-6). Baker Bk.
Walvoord, John F. Thessalonian Epistles. 1958. pap. 4.95 (ISBN 0-310-34071-3, 6392P). Zondervan.
Whiteley, D. E. Thessalonians. (New Clarendon Bible Ser). (Illus.). 1969. 8.95x (ISBN 0-19-836906-9). Oxford U Pr.
Wiersbe, Warren W. Be Ready. LC 78-65555. 175p. 1979. pap. 5.95 (ISBN 0-88207-782-1). Victor Bks.

BIBLE-COMMENTARIES-N. T. TIMOTHY
see Bible-Commentaries-N. T. Pastoral Epistles

BIBLE-COMMENTARIES-N. T. TITUS
see Bible-Commentaries-N. T. Pastoral Epistles

BIBLE-COMMENTARIES-O. T.
Here are entered only Commentaries on the Old Testament as a whole.

Baly, Dennis. God: History & the Old Testament. LC 76-9984. 256p. 1976. pap. 10.95x (ISBN 0-06-060369-0, RD 186, HarpR). Har-Row.
Bartlett, J. R., ed. The First & Second Books of the Maccabees: Cambridge Bible Commentary on the New English Bible. LC 72-87436. (Old Testament Ser.). (Orig.). 1973. 42.50 (ISBN 0-521-08658-2); pap. 15.95 (ISBN 0-521-09749-5). Cambridge U Pr.
Benson, Clarence H. Old Testament Survey: Poetry & Prophecy. rev. ed. 96p. 1972. pap. text ed. 4.95 (ISBN 0-910566-02-X); Perfect bdg. instr's. guide 5.95 (ISBN 0-910566-21-6). Evang Tchr.
Bratcher, R. G., ed. Marginal Notes for the Old Testament. 186p. 1980. softcover 5.00x (ISBN 0-8267-0025-X, 08557, Pub. by United Bible). Am Bible.
Brown, Jamieson-Fausett. Comentario Exegetico y Explicativo de la Biblia Tomo II. Quarles, Jaime C. & Quarles, Lemuel C., trs. from Eng. 382p. 1982. Repr. of 1959 ed. 15.75 (ISBN 0-311-03004-1). Casa Bautista.
Bruce, W. S. The Ethics of the Old Testament. 1909. 17.95 (ISBN 0-567-02058-4, Pub. by T & T Clark Ltd UK). Fortress.
Brueggemann, Walter & Wolff, Hans W. The Vitality Old Testament Traditions. 2nd ed. LC 82-7141. pap. 7.95 (ISBN 0-8042-0112-9). John Knox.
Charlesworth, James H., ed. Old Testament Pseudepigrapha, Vol. I: Apocalyptic Literature & Testaments. LC 80-2443. 1056p. 1983. 40.00 (ISBN 0-385-09630-5). Doubleday.
Clarke, Adam. Clarke's Commentary, 3 vols. Incl. Vol. 1. Genesis-Esther (ISBN 0-687-09119-5); Vol. 2. Job-Malachi (ISBN 0-687-09120-9); Vol. 3. Matthew-Revelation (ISBN 0-687-09121-7). 1977. Set. 95.00 (ISBN 0-687-09118-7); 34.50 ea. Abingdon.
Coggins, R. J. & Knibb, M. A. The First & Second Books of Esdras: Cambridge Bible Commentary on the New English Bible. LC 78-16420. (Old Testament Ser.). 1979. pap. 15.95 (ISBN 0-521-09757-6). Cambridge U Pr.
Cohen, Mortimer J. Pathways Through the Bible. rev. ed. (Illus.). 574p. 1946. 10.95 (ISBN 0-8276-0155-7, 167). Jewish Pubns.
Crenshaw, James L. Story & Faith: A Guide to the Old Testament. 539p. 1986. text ed. write for info. (ISBN 0-02-325600-1). Macmillan.
Davis, Susan. When God Lived in a Tent. (My Church Teaches Ser.). (Illus.). 1978. 1.95 (ISBN 0-8127-0181-X). Review & Herald.
De Jonge, Marinus. Outside the Old Testament. (Camridge Commentaries on the Writings of the Jewish & Christian World 200 B.C. to 200 A.D. Ser.: No. 4). 264p. 1985. 49.50 (ISBN 0-521-24249-5); pap. 18.95 (ISBN 0-521-28554-2). Cambridge U Pr.
Durham, John I. & Porter, J. R., eds. Proclamation & Presence: Old Testament Essays in Honor of Gwynne Henton Davies. LC 83-17445. xx, 315p. 1983. 17.95 (ISBN 0-86554-101-9, MUP/H93). Mercer Univ Pr.
Feinberg, John S. & Feinberg, Paul D. Tradition & Testament. LC 81-11223. 1982. 14.95 (ISBN 0-8024-2544-5). Moody.
Francisco, C. T. Introduccion Al Antiguo Testamento. Lacue, Juan J., tr. from Eng. Tr. of Introducing the Old Testament. (Span.). 350p. 1983. pap. 5.25 (ISBN 0-311-04010-1). Casa Bautista.
Gaebelein, Frank E., ed. Expositor's Bible Commentary, Vol. 4: Kings-Job. (Expositor's Bible Commentary Ser.). 1987. 29.95 (ISBN 0-310-36460-4). Zondervan.
Goldsworthy, Graeme. Gospel & Kingdom: A Christian Interpretation of the Old Testament. pap. cancelled (ISBN 0-85364-218-4, Pub. by Paternoster U K). Attic Pr.
Gordon, Dane R. The Old Testament: A Beginning Survey. (Illus.). 400p. 1985. pap. text ed. 23.33 (ISBN 0-13-634031-8). P-H.
Harrelson, Walter J. From Fertility Cult to Worship: A Reassessment for the Modern Church. LC 66-14929. (Scholars Press Reprint Ser.: No. 4). pap. 10.25x (ISBN 0-89130-379-0, 00 07 04). Scholars Pr GA.
Heaton, Eric W. Hebrew Kingdoms. (New Clarendon Bible Ser.). 1968. 10.95x (ISBN 0-19-836922-0). Oxford U Pr.
Hecke, Karl-Heinz. Die Alttestamentlichen Perikopen der Reihen III-VI. (European University Studies Twenty-Three: Vol. 180). (Ger.). 203p. 1982. 24.20 (ISBN 3-8204-5759-3). P Lang Pubs.
Henry, Matthew, et al. The Bethany Parallel Commentary on the Old Testament. 1500p. 1985. 49.95 (ISBN 0-87123-617-6). Bethany Hse.
Hester, H. I. The Heart of Hebrew History. 1980. Repr. of 1949 ed. 12.95 (ISBN 0-8054-1217-4). Broadman.
Hightower, James E., Jr. Voices from the Old Testament. LC 81-68611. (Orig.). 1983. pap. 3.95 (ISBN 0-8054-2245-5). Broadman.
Jacob & Esau. LC 78-133688. (Tudor Facsimile Texts. Old English Plays: No. 40). Repr. of 1908 ed. 49.50 (ISBN 0-404-53340-X). AMS Pr.
Johnson, L. D. Layman's Bible Book Commentary: Proverbs, Ecclesiastes, Song of Solomon, Vol. 9. LC 80-66543. 1982. 5.95 (ISBN 0-8054-1179-8). Broadman.
Jones, Clifford M. Old Testament Illustrations. LC 76-142131. (Cambridge Bible Commentary on the New English Bible, Old Testament Ser.). (Illus.). 1971. 29.95 (ISBN 0-521-08007-X); pap. 12.95 (ISBN 0-521-09646-4). Cambridge U Pr.
Keil, Carl F. & Delitzsch, Franz. Old Testament Commentaries, 10 vols. Incl. Vol. 1. Pentateuch (ISBN 0-8028-8035-5); Vol. 2. Joshua - Second Samuel (ISBN 0-8028-8036-3); Vol. 3. First Kings - Esther (ISBN 0-8028-8037-1); Vol. 4. Job (ISBN 0-8028-8038-X); Vol. 5. Psalms (ISBN 0-8028-8039-8); Vol. 6. Proverbs - Song of Solomon (ISBN 0-8028-8040-1); Vol. 7. Isaiah (ISBN 0-8028-8041-X); Vol. 8. Jeremiah-Lamentations (ISBN 0-8028-8042-8); Vol. 9. Ezekiel-Daniel (ISBN 0-8028-8043-6); Vol. 10. Minor Prophets (ISBN 0-8028-8044-4). 1971. Repr. Set. 225.00 (ISBN 0-8028-8034-7); 22.50 ea. Eerdmans.
Kent, Charles F. The Origin & Permanent Value of the Old Testament. 270p. 1981. Repr. of 1906 ed. lib. bdg. 30.00 (ISBN 0-89760-429-6). Telegraph Bks.
Kretzmann, Paul E. Popular Commentary of the Bible, 4 Vols. 2 Pts. Set. 70.95 (ISBN 0-570-06735-9, 15-1201). Concordia.

Kurtz, J. H. Sacrificial Worship of the Old Testament. Martin, James, tr. (Twin Brooks Ser.). 454p. 1980. pap. 8.95 (ISBN 0-8010-5419-2). Baker Bk.

Kurtz, John H. Sacrificial Worship of the Old Testament. 1979. 16.50 (ISBN 0-86524-012-4, 8703). Klock & Klock.

Lace, O. Jessie, ed. Understanding the Old Testament. LC 75-178282. (Cambridge Bible Commmentary on the New English Bible, Old Testament Ser.). (Illus.). 200p. 1972. 18.95 (ISBN 0-521-08415-6); pap. 9.95 (ISBN 0-521-09691-X). Cambridge U Pr.

Lawlor, George. Almah: Virgin or Young Woman? LC 73-76072. 1973. pap. 1.50 (ISBN 0-87227-036-X). Reg Baptist.

L'Heureux, Conrad E. In & Out of Paradise: The Book of Genesis From Adam & Eve to the Tower of Babel. LC 82-62415. 128p. 1983. pap. 3.95 (ISBN 0-8091-2530-7). Paulist Pr.

Lindsay, Gordon. The Four Hundred Silent Years. (Old Testament Ser.). 1.25 (ISBN 0-89985-158-4). Christ Nations.

--Lot & Lots Wife. (Old Testament Ser.: Vol. 4). pap. 1.25 (ISBN 0-89985-958-5). Christ Nations.

Lohfink, Norbert. Great Themes from the Old Testament. 1981. 10.95 (ISBN 0-8199-0801-0). Franciscan Herald.

Long, Burke O. I Kings, with an Introduction to Historical Literature, 24 Vols, Vol. 9. Knierim, Rolf & Tucker, Gene, eds. (The Forms of the Old Testament Literature Ser.). 288p. (Orig.). 1984. pap. 20.95 (ISBN 0-8028-1920-6). Eerdmans.

MacDonald, William. Old Testament Digest: Vol. 3, Job-Malachi. 1981. pap. 7.50 (ISBN 0-937396-29-X). Walterick Pubs.

MacDonald, William & Hamel, Mike. Old Testament Digest: Gen-Deut, Vol. 1. 1981. pap. 7.50 (ISBN 0-937396-59-1). Walterick Pubs.

MacKenzie, R. A. Sirach. (Old Testament Message Ser.: Vol. 19). 12.95 (ISBN 0-89453-419-X); pap. 8.95 (ISBN 0-89453-253-7). M Glazier.

Malmin, Ken. Old Testament Survey. 1974. 4.25 (ISBN 0-914936-21-2). Bible Temple.

Mears, Henrietta C. What the Old Testament Is All About. LC 76-51196. (Illus.). 1977. pap. 3.50 (ISBN 0-8307-0466-3, S111128). Regal.

Merrill, Eugene H. Historical Survey of the Old Testament. pap. 7.95 (ISBN 0-8010-5884-8). Baker Bk.

Metzger, Bruce M., ed. A Textual Commentary on the Greek New Testament. 776p. 1975. 5.45x (ISBN 3-438-06010-8, 08515, Pub. by United Bible). Am Bible.

Millett, Robert & Jackson, Kent. Studies in Scripture: The Old Testament, Vol. III. 345p. 1985. 13.95 (ISBN 0-934126-81-X). Randall Bk Co.

Miscall, Peter D. The Workings of Old Testament Narrative. LC 82-48570. (Semeia Studies). 160p. 1983. pap. 8.95 (ISBN 0-8006-1512-3). Fortress.

Morgan, Donn F. Wisdom in the Old Testament Traditions. LC 80-84653. 180p. 1982. 17.50 (ISBN 0-8042-0188-9); pap. 9.50 (ISBN 0-8042-0189-7). John Knox.

Napier, Davie. Song of the Vineyard: A Guide Through the Old Testament. rev. ed. LC 78-14672. 360p. 1981. pap. 12.95 (ISBN 0-8006-1352-X, 1-1352). Fortress.

Oehler, Gustave. Theology of the Old Testament. 1978. 22.50 (ISBN 0-86524-125-2, 8702). Klock & Klock.

Olbricht, Thomas H. He Loves Forever. LC 80-52461. (Journey Bks). (Orig.). 1980. pap. 3.50 (ISBN 0-8344-0117-7). Sweet.

Old Testament Message (Series, 23 vols. 1981. Set. 235.00 (ISBN 0-89453-400-9); Set. pap. text ed. 165.00 (ISBN 0-89453-235-9). M Glazier.

Packer, J. I., et al, eds. The World of the Old Testament. LC 82-12563. 1982. pap. 6.95 (ISBN 0-8407-5820-0). Nelson.

Parker, T. H. Calvin's Old Testament Commentaries. 256p. 1986. 28.95 (ISBN 0-567-09365-4, Pub. by T & T Clark Ltd UK). Fortress.

Patterson, Ward. Wonders in the Midst. LC 78-62709. 96p. (Orig.). 1979. pap. 2.25 (ISBN 0-87239-237-6, 40076). Standard Pub.

Pomazansky, Michael. The Old Testament in the New Testament Church. 40p. (Orig.). 1977. pap. 2.00 (ISBN 0-317-30281-7). Holy Trinity.

Protopresbyter Michael Pomazansky. Vjetkhij Zavjet v Novozavjetnoi Tserkvi. Tr. of The Old Testament in the New Testament Church. 38p. 1961. pap. 2.00 (ISBN 0-317-29101-7). Holy Trinity.

Reference Passage Bible, New Testament: With Old Testament References. LC 78-56146. 1978. 9.95 (ISBN 0-88270-275-0). Bridge Pub.

Robinson, J., ed. The First Book of Kings. LC 72-80592. (Cambridge Bible Commentary on the New English Bible, Old Testament Ser.). (Illus.). 228p. 1972. pap. 12.95 (ISBN 0-521-09734-7). Cambridge U Pr.

Saward, John. Perfect Fools. 1980. text ed. 29.95x (ISBN 0-19-213230-X). Oxford U Pr.

Schultz, Samuel J. Old Testament Survey: Law & History. rev. ed. LC 64-10037. 96p. 1968. pap. text ed. 4.95 (ISBN 0-910566-01-1); Perfect bdg. instr's. guide 5.95 (ISBN 0-910566-20-8). Evang Tchr.

Sheppard, Gerald T. Wisdom as a Hermeneutical Construct: A Study in the Sapientalizing of the Old Testament. (Beihefte Zur Zeitschrift Fuer Die Alttestamentliche Wissenschaft: No. 151). 1979. 41.00x (ISBN 3-1100-7504-0). De Gruyter.

Sparks, H. F. The Apocryphal Old Testament. 990p. 1984. 44.50x (ISBN 0-19-826166-7); pap. 19.95x (ISBN 0-19-826177-2). Oxford U Pr.

Spence, H. D. & Exell, T. S. The Pulpit Commentary, 23 vols. Incl. Old Testament only, 14 Vols. 320.00 (ISBN 0-8028-8056-8, 2209); New Testament only, 8 Vols. 200.00 (ISBN 0-8028-8057-6, 2210). 1959. Repr. Set. 520.00 (ISBN 0-8028-8055-X); 0er vol 22.95. Eerdmans.

Spiritual Letters of Madame Guyon. 1983. pap. 6.95 (ISBN 0-940232-14-6). Christian Bks.

Sprengling, Martin & Graham, William C., eds. Barhebraeus' Scholia on the Old Testament Pt. 1: Genesis 2nd Samuel. LC 32-461. (Oriental Institute Pubns. Ser: No. 13). 1931. 28.00x (ISBN 0-226-62107-3). U of Chicago Pr.

Spurrell, Helen. Old Testament Translation. 840p. 1987. 29.95 (ISBN 0-8254-3757-1). Kregel.

Stuart, Douglas. Favorite Old Testament Passages: A Popular Commentary for Today. LC 85-5148. 130p. 1985. pap. 8.95 (ISBN 0-664-24676-1). Westminster.

Suring, Margit L. The Horn-Motif in the Hebrew Bible & Related Ancient Near Eastern Literature & Iconography. (Andrews University Seminary Doctoral Dissertation Ser.: Vol. 4). (Illus.). xxvi, 533p. 1982. pap. 12.95 (ISBN 0-943872-36-7). Andrews Univ Pr.

Tos, John. Teachings of Old Testament. (Bible Study Commentaries Ser.). 128p. 1984. pap. 4.50 (ISBN 0-317-43392-X). Chr Lit.

Tromp, Nicholas J. Primitive Conceptions of Death & the Nether World in the Old Testament. (Biblica et Orientalia: Vol. 21). 1969. pap. 18.00 (ISBN 88-7653-321-4). Loyola.

Unger, Merrill F. Unger's Commentary on the Old Testament: Vol. 2 (Isaiah-Malachi) LC 81-2542. 1000p. 1982. 25.95 (ISBN 0-8024-9029-8). Moody.

Verhoef, Pieter A. The Books of Haggai & Malachi. Harrison, R. K., ed. (New International Commentary on the Old Testament Ser.). 384p. 1987. 21.95 (ISBN 0-8028-2376-9). Eerdmans.

Von Rad, Gerhard. God at Work in Israel. Marks, John, tr. LC 79-26281. 1980. pap. 7.75 (ISBN 0-687-14960-6). Abingdon.

Wagner, Volker. Rechtssaetze in gebundener Sprache und Rechtssatzreihen im israelitischen Recht: Ein Beitrag zur Gattungsforschung. (Beiheft 127 zur Zeitschrift fuer die alttestamentliche Wissenschaft). 1972. 16.80x (ISBN 3-11-003945-1). De Gruyter.

Walvoord, John & Zuck, Roy. The Bible Knowledge Commentary, Old Testament. 1985. 29.95. Victor Bks.

Warren, Thomas B. & Elkins, Garland, eds. The Living Messages of the Books of the Old Testament. 1977. 14.00 (ISBN 0-934916-36-5). Natl Christian Pr.

Whitley, C. F. Koheleth: His Language & Thought. (Beihefte zur Zeitschrift fuer die Alttestamentliche Wissenschaft: 148). 1979. 50.50x (ISBN 3-11-007602-0). De Gruyter.

Whybray, R. N. The Intellectual Tradition in the Old Testament. LC 73-78236. (Beiheft zur Zeitschrift fuer die Alttestamentliche Wissenschaft). 1974. 44.25x (ISBN 3-11-004424-2). De Gruyter.

Wiersbe, Warren W. Be Confident. 176p. 1982. pap. 5.95 (ISBN 0-88207-269-2). Victor Bks.

Wilde, Gary, ed. Old Testament Royalty: History of a Nation. (Basic Bible Ser.). 96p. 1986. pap. 4.95 (ISBN 0-89191-481-1). Cook.

Willis, John T. The Message of the Old Testament. Incl. Vol. I, No. 141. Adam to Moses (ISBN 0-89112-141-2); Vol. II, No. 142. Joshua to Ruth (ISBN 0-89112-142-0); Vol. III, No. 143. Samuel to Solomon (ISBN 0-89112-143-9); Vol. IV, No. 144. Rehoboam to Nehemiah (ISBN 0-89112-144-7). (Way of Life Ser.). 1977. pap. 3.95 ea. (Bibl Res Pr). Abilene Christ U.

BIBLE–COMMENTARIES–O. T. AMOS

see Bible–Commentaries–O. T. Minor Prophets

BIBLE–COMMENTARIES–O. T. APOCRYPHA

Coggins, R. J. & Knibb, M. A. The First & Second Books of Esdras: Cambridge Bible Commentary on the New English Bible. LC 78-16420. (Old Testament Ser.). 1979. pap. 15.95 (ISBN 0-521-09757-6). Cambridge U Pr.

Moore, Carey A. Daniel, Esther, & Jeremiah: The Additions. LC 76-42376. (Anchor Bible Ser.: Vol. 44). (Illus.). 1977. 16.00 (ISBN 0-385-04702-9, Anchor Pr). Doubleday.

Muraoka, T. A Greek-Hebrew - Aramaic Index to I Esdras. LC 83-8690. (SBL-Septuagint & Cognate Studies). 94p. 1984. pap. 8.75 (ISBN 0-89130-631-5, 06 04 16). Scholars Pr GA.

Odeberg, Hugo. Enoch Three, or the Hebrew Book of Enoch. rev. ed. (Library of Biblical Studies). 1970. 39.50x (ISBN 0-87068-093-5). Ktav.

Schodde, George H., intro. by. The Book of Enoch Translated from the Ethiopic. 1982. Repr. of 1882 ed. 39.00x (ISBN 0-403-08997-2, Regency). Scholarly.

BIBLE–COMMENTARIES–O. T. CHRONICLES

see Bible–Commentaries–O. T. Historical Books

BIBLE–COMMENTARIES–O. T. DANIEL

see Bible–Commentaries–O. T. Prophets

BIBLE–COMMENTARIES–O. T. DEUTERONOMY

see Bible–Commentaries–O. T. Pentateuch

BIBLE–COMMENTARIES–O. T. ECCLESIASTES

see Bible–Commentaries–O. T. Poetical Books

BIBLE–COMMENTARIES–O. T. ESTHER

see Bible–Commentaries–O. T. Historical Books

Hertzberg, Hans. I & II Samuel: A Commentary. (The Old Testament Library Ser.). 22.95. Westminster.

BIBLE–COMMENTARIES–O. T. EXODUS

see Bible–Commentaries–O. T. Pentateuch

BIBLE–COMMENTARIES–O. T. EZEKIEL

see Bible–Commentaries–O. T. Prophets

BIBLE–COMMENTARIES–O. T. EZRA

see Bible–Commentaries–O. T. Historical Books

BIBLE–COMMENTARIES–O. T. FIVE SCROLLS

Midrash Rabbah: Midrashim on the Pentateuch & the Five Scrolls with the Matnoth Kehunah Commentary, 5 Vols. (Hebrew & Yiddish.). Set. leatherette 95.00 (ISBN 0-87559-096-9). Shalom.

BIBLE–COMMENTARIES–O. T. GENESIS

see Bible–Commentaries–O. T. Pentateuch

BIBLE–COMMENTARIES–O. T. HABAKKUK

see Bible–Commentaries–O. T. Minor Prophets

BIBLE–COMMENTARIES–O. T. HAGGAI

see Bible–Commentaries–O. T. Minor Prophets

BIBLE–COMMENTARIES–O. T. HISTORICAL BOOKS

Ackroyd, Peter R. First Book of Samuel: Cambridge Bible Commentary on the New English Bible. LC 77-128636. (Old Testament Ser.). (Illus.). 1971. 27.95 (ISBN 0-521-07965-9); pap. 9.95x (ISBN 0-521-09635-9). Cambridge U Pr.

--The Second Book of Samuel: Cambridge Bible Commentary on the New English Bible. LC 76-58074. (Old Testament Ser.). (Illus.). 1977. 32.50 (ISBN 0-521-08633-7); pap. 11.95 (ISBN 0-521-09754-1). Cambridge U Pr.

Adeney, Walter D. The Books of Ezra & Nehemiah. 1980. 13.00 (ISBN 0-86524-050-7, 7004). Klock & Klock.

Auld, A. Graeme. Joshua, Moses & the Land. 158p. 1981. 19.95 (ISBN 0-567-09306-9, Pub. by T & T Clark Ltd UK). Fortress.

Baldwin, Joyce G. Esther. Wiseman, D. J., ed. LC 84-15670. (Tyndale Old Testament Commentaries Ser.). 122p. 1984. 12.95 (ISBN 0-87784-964-1); pap. 6.95 (ISBN 0-87784-262-0). Inter-Varsity.

Batten, Loring W. A Critical & Exegetical Commentary on Ezra & Nehemiah. Driver, Samuel R., et al, eds. LC 13-12806. (International Critical Commentary Ser.). 400p. 1913. 22.95 (ISBN 0-567-05008-4, Pub. by T & T Clark Ltd UK). Fortress.

Bennett, William H. An Exposition of the Books of Chronicles. 467p. 1983. lib. bdg. 17.50 (ISBN 0-86524-169-4, 1401). Klock & Klock.

Blaikie, William G. The Book of Joshua. 416p. 1983. lib. bdg. 15.75 (ISBN 0-86524-173-2, 0601). Klock & Klock.

--First Book of Samuel. 440p. 1983. lib. bdg. 16.50 (ISBN 0-86524-174-0, 0901). Klock & Klock.

Blair, Edward P. Deuteronomy, Joshua. LC 59-10454. (Layman's Bible Commentary Ser: Vol. 5). 1964. pap. 4.95 (ISBN 0-8042-3065-X). John Knox.

Bowes, Paula. The First & Second Samuel. (Bible Commentary Ser.). 128p. 1985. pap. text ed. 2.95 (ISBN 0-8146-1415-9). Liturgical Pr.

Brockington, L. H. Ezra, Nehemiah & Esther. (New Century Bible Ser.). 262p. 1969. text ed. 9.50 (ISBN 0-551-00530-0). Attic Pr.

Broughton, Peter. Joshua & Samuel. (Bible Study Commentaries Ser.). 126p. 1984. pap. 4.95 (ISBN 0-317-43371-7). Chr Lit.

Brueggemann, Walter. Kings I. (Knox Preaching Guide Ser.). 132p. 1983. pap. 4.95 (ISBN 0-8042-3212-1). John Knox.

--Kings II. Hayes, John, ed. LC 82-48094. (Knox Preaching Guide Ser.). 120p. 1983. pap. 4.95 (ISBN 0-8042-3214-8). John Knox.

Burns, Rita. Ezra Nehemiah. (Bible Commentary Ser.). 96p. 1985. pap. 2.95 (ISBN 0-8146-1418-3). Liturgical Pr.

Clines, D. J. Ezra, Nehemiah, Esther. Clements, Ronald, et al, eds. (New Century Bible Commentary Ser.). 384p. 1984. pap. 8.95 (ISBN 0-8028-0017-3). Eerdmans.

Cocoris, G. Michael. Nehemiah. rev. ed. 37p. 1984. pap. 1.00 (ISBN 0-935729-14-3). Church Open Door.

--Nehemiah. rev. ed. 37p. 1984. pap. 1.00 (ISBN 0-935729-15-1). Church Open Door.

Coggins, R. J. The Books of Ezra & Nehemiah. LC 75-26278. (Cambridge Bible Commentary on the New English Bible, Old Testament Ser.). (Illus.). 200p. 1976. 22.95 (ISBN 0-521-08648-5); pap. 9.95x (ISBN 0-521-09759-2). Cambridge U Pr.

--The First & Second Book of the Chronicles. LC 75-17117. (Cambridge Bible Commentary on the New English Bible, Old Testament Ser.). (Illus.). 256p. 1976. 39.50 (ISBN 0-521-08647-7); pap. 16.95x (ISBN 0-521-09758-4). Cambridge U Pr.

Conroy, Charles. First & Second Samuel, First & Second Kings, with Excursus on Davidic Dynasty & Holy City Zion. (Old Testament Message Ser.: Vol. 6). 12.95 (ISBN 0-89453-406-8); pap. 8.95 (ISBN 0-89453-241-3). M Glazier.

Cundall, Arthur E. & Morris, Leon. Judges & Ruth. LC 68-31426. (Tyndale Old Testament Commentary Ser). (Illus.). 1968. 12.95 (ISBN 0-87784-896-3); pap. 6.95 (ISBN 0-87784-257-4). Inter-Varsity.

Curtis, Edward L. & Madsen, Albert A. A Critical & Exegetical Commentary on Chronicles I & II. Driver, Samuel R., et al, eds. LC 10-14958. (International Critical Commentary Ser.). 560p. 1910. 24.95 (ISBN 0-567-05007-6, Pub. by T & T Clark Ltd UK). Fortress.

Deane, W. J. & Kirt, T. Studies in the First Book of Samuel. 509p. 1983. lib. bdg. 19.00 Smythe Sewn (ISBN 0-86524-150-3, 0902). Klock & Klock.

Dentan, Robert C. First, Second Kings & First, Second Chronicles. LC 59-10454. (Layman's Bible Commentary Ser., Vol. 7). 1964. pap. 4.95 (ISBN 0-8042-3067-6). John Knox.

Elliott-Binns, Leonard E. From Moses to Elisha: Israel to the End of the Ninth Century B. C. LC 78-10639. (Illus.). 1979. Repr. of 1929 ed. lib. bdg. 27.50x (ISBN 0-313-21015-2, EBFM). Greenwood.

Enns, Paul P. Judges: A Bible Study Commentary. (Bible Study Commentary Ser.). 160p. (Orig.). 1982. pap. 5.95 (ISBN 0-310-44051-3, 11831P). Zondervan.

--Ruth: A Bible Study Commentary. 96p. (Orig.). 1982. pap. 3.95 (ISBN 0-310-44061-0, 11832P). Zondervan.

Fensham, F. Charles. The Books of Ezra & Nehemiah. (The New International Commentary on the Old Testament Ser.). 288p. 1983. 14.95 (ISBN 0-8028-2362-9). Eerdmans.

Fischer, James A. Song of Songs, Ruth, Lamentations, Ecclesiastes, Esther. (Collegeville Bible Commentary Ser.). 112p. 1986. pap. 2.95 (ISBN 0-8146-1480-9). Liturgical pr.

Fuerst, W. J. Ruth, Esther, Ecclesiastes, the Song of Songs, Lamentations. LC 74-82589. (Cambridge Bible Commentary on the New English Bible, Old Testament Ser.). 250p. 1975. 32.50 (ISBN 0-521-20651-0); pap. 11.95 (ISBN 0-521-09920-X). Cambridge U Pr.

Garstang, John. Joshua-Judges. LC 78-9518. (Kregel Limited Edition Library). 464p. 1978. 19.95 (ISBN 0-8254-2719-3). Kregel.

Getz, Gene. Joshua: Defeat to Victory. LC 78-53358. 176p. 1979. pap. 5.95 (ISBN 0-8307-0643-7, 5410509). Regal.

Gordis, Robert. Megillat Esther: The Mascretic Hebrew Text with Introduction, New Translation & Commentary. 1977. 3.95x (ISBN 0-87068-763-8). Ktav.

Gordon, Robert P. One & Two Samuel. (Old Testament Guides Ser.). 102p. 1984. pap. text ed. 3.95x (ISBN 0-905774-64-7, Pub. by JSOT Pr England). Eisenbrauns.

Goslinga, C. J. Bible Student's Commentary: Joshua, Judges, Ruth. Tr. of Korte Verklaring. 544p. 1986. 24.95 (ISBN 0-310-45280-5). Zondervan.

Gray, John. First & Second Kings, a Commentary. rev. ed. 2nd ed. LC 73-134271. (Old Testament Library). (Illus.). 826p. 1978. 27.50 (ISBN 0-664-20898-3). Westminster.

--I & II Kings: A Commentary. 2nd rev. ed. (The Old Testament Library Ser.). 27.50. Westminster.

--Joshua, Judges & Ruth. rev. ed. (New Century Bible Ser). 337p. 1977. 14.50 (ISBN 0-551-00784-2). Attic Pr.

--Joshua, Judges, Ruth. rev. ed. (New Century Bible Commentary Ser.). 432p. 1986. pap. 12.95 (ISBN 0-8028-0018-1). Eerdmans.

Green, Roberta. Joshua: Promises to Keep. (Young Fisherman Bible Studyguide Ser.). (Illus.). 70p. 1982. tchr's ed. 4.95 (ISBN 0-87788-434-X); student ed. 2.95 (ISBN 0-87788-433-1). Shaw Pubs.

Green, Ruth H. The Book of Ruth. 1982. 7.00. Freedom Rel Found.

Grindel, John. Joshua, Judges. (Bible Commentary Ser.). 120p. 1985. pap. 2.95 (ISBN 0-8146-1414-0). Liturgical Pr.

Hamlin, E. J. The International Theological Commentary on Joshua. Holmgren, Frederick & Knight, George A., eds. (The International Theological Commentary Ser.). 200p. (Orig.). 1983. pap. 8.95 (ISBN 0-8028-1041-1). Eerdmans.

Heading, John. Understanding Chronicles One & Two. pap. 7.95 (ISBN 0-937396-10-9). Walterick Pubs.

Heijkoop, H. L. The Book of Ruth. 6.95 (ISBN 0-88172-086-0). Believers Bkshelf.

Hertzberg, Hans W. First & Second Samuel, A Commentary. LC 65-10074. (Old Testament Library). 416p. 1965. 22.95 (ISBN 0-664-20541-0). Westminster.

Holmgren, Fredrick C. Israel Alive Again: Ezra & Mehemiah. Knight, G. A., ed. (International Theological Commentary Ser.). 200p. (Orig.). 1987. pap. 9.95 (ISBN 0-8028-0259-1). Eerdmans.

Huffman, John. Joshua (CC, Vol. 6. 320p. 1986. 18.95 (ISBN 0-8499-0411-0). Word Bks.

Ironside, H. A. Ezra: Joshua, Nehemiah & Esther. 11.95 (ISBN 0-87213-396-6). Loizeaux.

Jennings, F. C. Judges & Ruth. 9.95 (ISBN 0-88172-152-2). Believers Bkshelf.

Jensen, Irving L. Ezra, Nehemiah & Esther. (Bible Self-Study Ser.). 1970. pap. 3.25 (ISBN 0-8024-1015-4). Moody.

--First & Second Samuel. (Bible Self-Study Ser.). 1970. pap. 3.25 (ISBN 0-8024-1009-X). Moody.

--Joshua: Rest-Land Won. (Everyman's Bible Commentary Ser.). (Orig.). 1966. pap. 5.95 (ISBN 0-8024-2006-0). Moody.

--Josue: La Tierra de Reposo, Conquistada (Comentario Biblico Portavoz) Orig. Title: Joshua: Rest-Land Won (Everyman's Bible Commentary) (Span.). 118p. 1980. pap. 3.50 (ISBN 0-8254-1353-2). Kregel.

Jensen, Irving L., ed. First Kings & Chronicles. (Bible Self-Study Ser.). (Illus.). 1968. pap. 3.25 (ISBN 0-8024-1011-1). Moody.

Jones, G. H. First Kings. (New Century Bible Commentary Ser.). 384p. 1984. pap. 8.95 (ISBN 0-8028-0019-X). Eerdmans.

--Second Kings. (New Century Bible Commentary Ser.). 352p. 1984. pap. 8.95 (ISBN 0-8028-0040-8). Eerdmans.

Jordan, James B. Judges: God's War Against Humanism. (Trinity Biblical Commentary Ser.). xxi, 333p. 1985. 14.95 (ISBN 0-939404-10-9). Geneva Ministr.

Kelly, Balmer H. Ezra-Job. LC 59-10454. (Layman's Bible Commentary, Vol. 8). 1962. 4.95 (ISBN 0-8042-3008-0); pap. 3.95 (ISBN 0-8042-3068-4). John Knox.

Kent, Dan G. Layman's Bible Book Commentary: Joshua, Judges, Ruth, Vol. 4. LC 79-51136. 1980. 5.95 (ISBN 0-8054-1174-7). Broadman.

Kidner, Derek. Ezra & Nehemiah. Wiseman, D. J., ed. (Tyndale Old Testament Commentaries Ser.). 1979. text ed. 12.95 (ISBN 0-87784-962-5); pap. 6.95 (ISBN 0-87784-261-2). Inter-Varsity.

Kirk, T. & Rawlinson, G. Studies in the Books of Kings. 556p. 1983. lib. bdg. 20.75 Smythe Sewn (ISBN 0-86524-155-4, 1301). Klock & Klock.

Laffey, Alice. The First & Second Books of Chronicles. (Bible Commentary Ser.). 96p. 1985. pap. 2.95 (ISBN 0-8146-1417-5). Liturgical Pr.

--The First & Second Kings. (Bible Commentary Ser.). 112p. 1985. pap. text ed. 2.95 (ISBN 0-8146-1416-7). Liturgical Pr.

Laney, J. Carl. Ezra, Nehemiah. (Everyman's Bible Commentary Ser.). (Orig.). 1982. pap. 5.95 (ISBN 0-8024-2014-1). Moody.

Lang, John M. Studies in the Book of Judges. 473p. 1983. Repr. lib. bdg. 17.75 Smythe Sewn (ISBN 0-86524-151-1, 0603). Klock & Klock.

Lewis, Arthur. Judges & Ruth. (Everyman's Bible Commentary Ser.). 1979. pap. 5.95 (ISBN 0-8024-2007-9). Moody.

Lewis, Arthur H. Jueces y Rut (Comentario Biblico Portavoz) Orig. Title: Judges & Ruth (Everyman's Bible Commentary) (Span.). 128p. 1982. pap. 3.50 (ISBN 0-8254-1434-2). Kregel.

Lewis, Joe O. Layman's Bible Book Commentary: First & Second Samuel & First Chronicles, Vol. 5. LC 79-54796. 1981. 5.95 (ISBN 0-8054-1175-5). Broadman.

Lieberman, David. The Eternal Torah: A Commentary Integrating All the Prophets into the Books of Kings, Bk. 3. 600p. 1986. 25.00x (ISBN 0-9609840-2-X). Twin Pines Pr.

MacDonald, William & Hamel, Mike. Old Testament Digest: Vol. 2, Joshua - Esther. 1982. pap. 8.50 (ISBN 0-937396-61-3). Walterick Pubs.

McEleney, Neil J. First Book of Maccabees. (Bible Ser.: No. 22). (Orig.). 1974. pap. 1.00 (ISBN 0-8091-5166-9). Paulist Pr.

--Oracle of the Lord. (Bible Ser.: No. 24). (Orig.). 1974. pap. 1.00 (ISBN 0-8091-5174-X). Paulist Pr.

--Second Book of Maccabees. (Bible Ser.: Vol. 23). (Orig.). 1974. pap. 1.00 (ISBN 0-8091-5167-7). Paulist Pr.

Marcus, David. Jephthah & His Vow. 80p. 1986. 25.00 (ISBN 0-89672-136-1); pap. 15.00 (ISBN 0-89672-135-3). Tex Tech Univ Pr.

Martin, J. D. The Book of Judges. LC 74-31797. (Cambridge Bible Commentary on the New English Bible, Old Testament Ser.). (Illus.). 272p. 1975. 24.95 (ISBN 0-521-08639-6); pap. 10.95x (ISBN 0-521-09768-1). Cambridge U Pr.

Meyer, F. B. Choice Notes on Joshua to Second Kings. LC 84-27869. (F. B. Meyer Memorial Library). 224p. 1985. pap. text ed. 8.95 (ISBN 0-8254-3241-3). Kregel.

Millard, Alan. First Kings, Second Chronicles. (Bible Study Commentaries Ser.). 126p. 1985. pap. 4.95 (ISBN 0-317-43372-5). Chr Lit.

Miller, J. M. & Tucker, G. M. The Book of Joshua. (Cambridge Bible Commentary on the New English Bible, Old Testament Ser.). (Illus.). 218p. 1974. 22.95 (ISBN 0-521-08616-7); pap. 9.95 (ISBN 0-521-09777-0). Cambridge U Pr.

Miscall, Peter D. A Reading of I Samuel. (Literary Bible Ser.). 256p. 1985. cancelled (ISBN 0-8245-0662-6). Crossroad NY.

Montague, George T. Books of Judith & Esther. (Pamphlet Bible Ser.: Vol. 21). (Orig.). 1973. pap. 1.00 (ISBN 0-8091-5173-1). Paulist Pr.

--Books of Ruth & Tobit. (Pamphlet Bible Ser.: Vol. 20). (Orig.). 1974. pap. 1.00 (ISBN 0-8091-5172-3). Paulist Pr.

Montgomery, James A. A Critical & Exegetical Commentary on Kings I & II. Driver, Samuel R., et al, eds. LC 52-8522. (International Critical Commentary Ser.). 624p. 1951. 24.95 (ISBN 0-567-05006-8, Pub. by T & T Clark Ltd UK). Fortress.

Moore, Carey A., ed. Esther. LC 75-140615. (Anchor Bible Ser.: Vol. 7B). 14.00 (ISBN 0-385-00472-9, Anchor Pr). Doubleday.

Moore, George F. A Critical & Exegetical Commentary on Judges. Driver, Samuel R., et al, eds. LC 25-19368. (International Critical Commentary Ser.). 528p. 1895. 24.95 (ISBN 0-567-05004-1, Pub. by T & T Clark Ltd UK). Fortress.

Moriarty, Frederic L. First Book of Samuel. (Bible Ser.). 1971. pap. 1.00 (ISBN 0-8091-5135-9). Paulist Pr.

Myers, Jacob M., ed. Ezra & Nehemiah. LC 65-23788. (Anchor Bible Ser.: Vol. 14). 1965. 16.00 (ISBN 0-385-04695-2, Anchor Pr). Doubleday.

Nawsome, James D. Samuel One & Two. Hayes, James D., ed. (Knox Preaching Guide Ser.). 1983. pap. 5.95 (ISBN 0-8042-3211-3). John Knox.

Newell, William R. Studies in Joshua-Job. LC 83-19899. (Old Testament Studies). 224p. 1983. kivar 7.95 (ISBN 0-8254-3314-2). Kregel.

O'Donnell, J. D. & Hampton, Ralph, Jr. A Survey of the Books of History. 1976. pap. 3.25 (ISBN 0-89265-032-X). Randall Hse.

Paton, Lewis B. A Critical & Exegetical Commentary on Esther. Driver, Samuel R., et al, eds. LC 8-30156. (International Critical Commentary Ser.). 360p. 1908. 22.95 (ISBN 0-567-05009-2, Pub. by T & T Clark Ltd UK). Fortress.

Payne, David F. First & Second Samuel. LC 82-16009. (The Daily Study Bible-Old Testament). 292p. 1982. 12.95 (ISBN 0-664-21806-7); pap. 6.95 (ISBN 0-664-24573-0). Westminster.

Pollak, P. S. Marbin Besimho. (Heb). 9.50 (ISBN 0-87559-083-7); pap. 5.00 saddle stitched (ISBN 0-87559-084-5). Shalom.

Raleigh, Alexander. The Book of Esther. 1980. 9.75 (ISBN 0-86524-037-X, 1701). Klock & Klock.

Ratzlaff, Ruben M. & Butler, Paul T. Ezra-Nehemiah-Esther. (Bible Study Textbook Ser.). 1979. 14.30 (ISBN 0-89900-014-2). College Pr Pub.

Redpath, Alan. Victorious Christian Service: Studies in the Book of Nehemiah. 192p. 9.95 (ISBN 0-8007-0337-5). Revell.

Robinson, J., ed. The Second Book of Kings. LC 75-39371. (Cambridge Bible Commentary on the New English Bible, Old Testament Ser.). (Illus.). 1976. pap. 12.95x (ISBN 0-521-09774-6). Cambridge U Pr.

Robinson, T. H. Decline & Fall of the Hebrew Kingdoms. LC 74-137284. Repr. of 1926 ed. 21.50 (ISBN 0-404-05376-9). AMS Pr.

Robinson, T. H., et al, eds. Megilloth. (Biblia Hebraica Stuttgartensia Ser.). 62p. 1975. pap. 2.50x (ISBN 3-438-05213-X, 61304, Pub. by United Bible). Am Bible.

Rossier, H. Meditations on Joshua. 7.25 (ISBN 0-88172-119-0). Believers Bkshelf.

Rust, Eric C. Judges, Ruth, First & Second Samuel. LC 59-10454. (Layman's Bible Commentary Ser: Vol. 6). 1961. pap. 4.95 (ISBN 0-8042-3066-8). John Knox.

Sailhamer, John. First & Second Chronicles. (Everyman's Bible Commentary Ser.). (Orig.). 1983. pap. 5.95 (ISBN 0-8024-2012-5). Moody.

Smith, Henry P. A Critical & Exegetical Commentary on First & Second Samuel. Driver, Samuel R., et al, eds. LC 99-1607. (International Critical Commentary Ser.). 462p. 1898. 22.95 (ISBN 0-567-05005-X, Pub. by T & T Clark Ltd UK). Fortress.

Soggin, J. Alberto. Joshua: A Commentary. Wilson, R. A., tr. LC 72-76954. (Old Testament Library). 264p. 1972. 14.95 (ISBN 0-664-20938-6). Westminster.

--Judges: A Commentary. Bowden, John, tr. from Ital. LC 81-7600. (Old Testament Library). 324p. 1981. text ed. 21.95 (ISBN 0-664-21368-5). Westminster.

Spilly, Alphonse. The First & Second Maccabees. (Bible Commentary Ser.). 136p. 1985. pap. 2.95 (ISBN 0-8146-1419-1). Liturgical Pr.

Spurgeon, Charles H. Treasury of David, 2 vols. 1983. Set. 45.00 (ISBN 0-8010-8256-0). Baker Bk.

Szyk, Arthur. Megillah: Book of Esther. 1974. 25.00x (ISBN 0-685-84454-4). Bloch.

Thompson, Robert. The Land of Promise. pap. 5.95 (ISBN 0-89728-042-3, 670209). Omega Pubns OR.

Toms, Paul E. Winning the Battles of Life: This Land Is Your Land. LC 75-23512. 1977. pap. 2.50 (ISBN 0-8307-1161-9, S413129). Regal.

Vawter, Bruce. Ezra-Nehemiah. (Bible Ser.). pap. 1.00 (ISBN 0-8091-5047-6). Paulist Pr.

Vos, Howard F. Bible Study Commentary: Ezra, Nehemiah & Esther. (Bible Study Commentary Ser.). 224p. 1987. pap. 7.95 (ISBN 0-310-33911-1). Zondervan.

--One, Two Samuel: Bible Study Commentary. (Bible Study Commentary Ser.). 1986. pap. 5.95 (ISBN 0-310-33893-X, 11153P). Zondervan.

Whitcomb, John C. Ester: El Triunfo de la Soberania de Dios (Comentario Biblico Portavoz) Orig. Title: Esther (Everyman's Bible Commentary) (Span.). 1982. pap. 4.50 (ISBN 0-8254-1866-6). Kregel.

--Esther, the Triumph of God's Sovereignty. 128p. (Orig.). 1979. pap. 4.95 (ISBN 0-88469-081-4). BMH Bks.

--Esther: Triumph of God's Sovereignty. (Everyman's Bible Commentary Ser.). 1979. pap. 5.95 (ISBN 0-8024-2016-8). Moody.

Wiseman, Luke H. Practical Truths From Judges. LC 85-8096. 354p. 1985. 14.95 (ISBN 0-8254-4034-3). Kregel.

Wood, Geoffrey. First Book of Kings. (Bible Ser.: No. 15). (Orig.). 1974. pap. 1.00 (ISBN 0-8091-5168-5). Paulist Pr.

--Second Book of Kings. (Bible Ser.: Vol. 16). (Orig.). 1974. pap. 1.00 (ISBN 0-8091-5169-3). Paulist Pr.

Woudstra, Marten H. The Book of Joshua. LC 80-23413. (New International Commentary on the Old Testament). 400p. 1981. 21.95 (ISBN 0-8028-2356-4). Eerdmans.

BIBLE–COMMENTARIES–O. T. HOSEA

see Bible–Commentaries–O. T. Minor Prophets

BIBLE–COMMENTARIES–O. T. ISAIAH

see Bible–Commentaries–O. T. Prophets

BIBLE–COMMENTARIES–O. T. JEREMIAH

see Bible–Commentaries–O. T. Prophets

Collected Writings of S. R. Hirsch, Vol. 4: Commentary on Isaiah & Additional Commentary on Psalms. 1986. 15.75 (ISBN 0-87306-950-1). Feldheim.

BIBLE–COMMENTARIES–O. T. JOB

see Bible–Commentaries–O. T. Poetical Books

BIBLE–COMMENTARIES–O. T. JOEL

see Bible–Commentaries–O. T. Minor Prophets

BIBLE–COMMENTARIES–O. T. JONAH

see Bible–Commentaries–O. T. Minor Prophets

BIBLE–COMMENTARIES–O. T. JOSHUA

see Bible–Commentaries–O. T. Historical Books

BIBLE–COMMENTARIES–O. T. JUDGES

see Bible–Commentaries–O. T. Historical Books

BIBLE–COMMENTARIES–O. T. KINGS

see Bible–Commentaries–O. T. Historical Books

BIBLE–COMMENTARIES–O. T. LAMENTATIONS

see Bible–Commentaries–O. T. Prophets

BIBLE–COMMENTARIES–O. T. LEVITICUS

see Bible–Commentaries–O. T. Pentateuch

BIBLE–COMMENTARIES–O. T. MALACHI

see Bible–Commentaries–O. T. Minor Prophets

BIBLE–COMMENTARIES–O. T. MICAH

see Bible–Commentaries–O. T. Minor Prophets

BIBLE–COMMENTARIES–O. T. MINOR PROPHETS

Allen, Leslie. Joel, Obadiah, Jonah, Micah. (New International Commentary on Old Testament Ser.). 16.95 (ISBN 0-8028-2373-4). Eerdmans.

Anderson, Bernhard W. The Eighth Century Prophets: Amos, Hosea, Isaiah, Micah. McCurley, Foster R., ed. LC 78-54545. (Proclamation Commentaries: the Old Testament Witnesses for Preaching). 128p. 1978. pap. 5.95 (ISBN 0-8006-0595-0, 1-595). Fortress.

Barber, Cyril J. Habakkuk & Zephaniah. (Everyman's Bible Commentary Ser.). 1985. pap. 5.95 (ISBN 0-8024-2069-9). Moody.

Blaikie, William G. Second Book of Samuel. 400p. 1983. lib. bdg. 15.00 (ISBN 0-86524-175-9, 0903). Klock & Klock.

Blair, J. Allen. Jonah: Living Obediently. LC 63-18265. 1963. pap. 3.95 (ISBN 0-87213-050-9). Loizeaux.

Boice, James M. The Minor Prophets: An Expositional Commentary (Hosea-Jonah, Vol. 1. 272p. 1983. 12.95 (ISBN 0-310-21550-1, 10423). Zondervan.

Clark, D. J. & Mundhenk, N. Translator's Handbook on the Books of Obadiah & Micah. LC 82-8481. (Helps for Translators Ser.). viii, 208p. 1982. pap. 3.50x (ISBN 0-8267-0129-9, 08567, Pub. by United Bible). Am Bible.

Cocoris, G. Michael. Jonah. 74p. 1986. pap. text ed. 2.00 (ISBN 0-935729-32-1). Church Open Door.

--Obadiah. 19p. (Orig.). 1983. pap. 1.00 (ISBN 0-935729-29-1). Church Open Door.

Coffman, James B. Commentary on the Minor Prophets, Vol. 1. (Firm Foundation Commentary Ser.). 360p. 1981. cancelled 8.95 (ISBN 0-88027-078-0). Firm Foun Pub.

--Commentary on the Minor Prophets, Vol. 2. (Firm Foundation Commentary Ser.). 383p. 1981. cancelled 8.95 (ISBN 0-88027-079-9). Firm Foun Pub.

--Commentary on the Minor Prophets, Vol. 3. (Commmentary Ser.). 322p. 1983. cancelled 10.95 (ISBN 0-88027-107-8). Firm Foun Pub.

Coote, Robert B. Amos among the Prophets: Composition & Theology. LC 80-8054. 144p. 1981. pap. 5.95 (ISBN 0-8006-1400-3, 1-1400). Fortress.

Crouch, Brodie. Study of Minor Prophets. pap. 2.50 (ISBN 0-89315-291-9). Lambert Bk.

Delaughter, Thomas J. Malachi: Messenger of Divine Love. LC 75-40410. 160p. (Orig.). 1976. 6.00 (ISBN 0-914520-08-3); pap. text ed. 5.00 (ISBN 0-914520-07-5). Insight Pr.

De Waard, J. & Smalley, W. A. Translator's Handbook on the Book of Amos. LC 80-490970. (Helps for Translators Ser.). 274p. 1979. 4.00x (ISBN 0-8267-0128-0, 08577, Pub. by United Bible). Am Bible.

Feinberg, Charles L. God Remembers: A Study of Zechariah. 4th ed. LC 79-88530. 1979. 8.95 (ISBN 0-930014-33-2). Multnomah.

--The Minor Prophets. rev ed. LC 76-44088. 384p. 1976. 17.95 (ISBN 0-8024-5306-6). Moody.

Freeman, Hobart. Nahum, Sofonias, Habacuc (Comentario Biblico Portavoz) Orig. Title: Nahum, Zephaniah & Habakkuk (Everyman's Bible Commentary) (Span.). 112p. 1980. pap. 3.50 (ISBN 0-8254-1246-3). Kregel.

Fretheim, Terence E. The Message of Jonah: A Theological Commentary. LC 77-72461. pap. 8.95 (ISBN 0-8066-1591-5, 10-4350). Augsburg.

Fromer, Margaret & Keyes, Sharrel. Jonah, Habakkuk, Malachi: Living Responsibly. (Fisherman Bible Studyguide Ser.). 68p. 1982. saddle-stitch 2.95 (ISBN 0-87788-432-3). Shaw Pubs.

Gaebelein, Frank E., ed. Expositor's Bible Commentary: Daniel & the Minor Prophets, Vol. 7. 752p. 1985. text ed. 24.95 (ISBN 0-310-36490-6, 11176). Zondervan.

Gailey, James H., Jr. Micah-Malachi. LC 59-10454. (Layman's Bible Commentary Ser: Vol. 15). 1962. pap. 4.95 (ISBN 0-8042-3075-7). John Knox.

Garland, D. David. Hosea: Bible Study Commentary. 128p. 1975. pap. 4.95 (ISBN 0-310-24843-4, 10234P). Zondervan.

Gelston, A. The Peshitta of the Twelve Prophets. 272p. 1985. 34.50x (ISBN 0-19-826179-9). Oxford U Pr.

Ginn, Roman. Jonah: The Spirituality of a Reluctant Prophet. (Orig.). pap. 2.95 (ISBN 0-914544-21-7). Living Flame Pr.

Gorman, Hugh. Beacon Small-Group Bible Studies: Hosea, "The Triumph of God". 88p. (Orig.). 1984. pap. 2.50 (ISBN 0-8341-0914-X). Beacon Hill.

Grayston, Kenneth. The Johannine Epistles. Clements, Ronald & Black, Matthew, eds. (New Century Bible Commentary Ser.). 180p. (Orig.). 1984. pap. 5.95 (ISBN 0-8028-1981-8). Eerdmans.

Hailey, Homer. Commentary on the Minor Prophets. 1972. 14.95 (ISBN 0-8010-4049-3). Baker Bk.

Heflin, J. Boo. Nahum, Habakkuk, Zephaniah & Haggai. (Bible Study Commentary). 240p. (Orig.). 1986. pap. text ed. 7.95 (ISBN 0-310-27531-8, 18385P). Zondervan.

Henderson, E. Harold. Triumph of Trust: Habakkuk. (Illus.). 96p. (Orig.). 1980. pap. 2.00 (ISBN 0-89114-092-1); study guide 0.75 (ISBN 0-89114-138-3). Baptist Pub Hse.

Hutton, Warwick. Jonah & the Great Fish. LC 83-15477. (Illus.). 32p. 1984. 12.95 (ISBN 0-689-50283-4, McElderly Bk). Macmillan.

Inman, V. Kerry. Prophets of Doom in an Age of Optimism. (Orig.). 1981. pap. 4.95 (ISBN 0-934688-02-8). Great Comm Pubns.

Ironside, H. A. Minor Prophets. 11.95 (ISBN 0-87213-379-6). Loizeaux.

Isbell, Charles D. Malachi: Bible Study Commentary. (Bible Study Commentary Ser.). 128p. (Orig.). 1980. pap. 4.95 (ISBN 0-310-41673-6, 9350P). Zondervan.

Jensen, Irving L. Minor Prophets of Israel. (Bible Self-Study Guides Ser.). 112p. (Orig.). 1975. pap. 3.25 (ISBN 0-8024-1028-6). Moody.

--Minor Prophets of Judah. (Bible Self-Study Guide Ser.). 112p. 1976. pap. 3.25 (ISBN 0-8024-1029-4). Moody.

Jeremiah, David. Malachi: Twenty-Six Daily Bible Studies. (Steps to Higher Ground Ser.). 1983. pap. 1.95 (ISBN 0-86508-207-3). BCM Intl Inc.

Kidner, Derek. The Message of Hosea. Motyer, J. A. & Stott, John R., eds. (Bible Speaks Today Ser.). 132p. (Orig.). 1982. text ed. 5.95 (ISBN 0-87784-290-6). Inter-Varsity.

Kimchi, David B. Commentary of Rabbi David Kimchi on Hosea. Cohen, Harry, ed. LC 30-27876. (Columbia University. Oriental Studies: No. 20). Repr. of 1929 ed. 17.00 (ISBN 0-404-50510-4). AMS Pr.

Kirk, Thomas. Jonah: His Life & Mission. 344p. 1983. lib. bdg. 12.95 (ISBN 0-86524-166-X, 3202). Klock & Klock.

Kunz, Marilyn & Schell, Catherine. Amos (Neighborhood Bible Study) 1978. pap. 2.50 (ISBN 0-8423-0067-8). Tyndale.

Laetsch, Theodore. Minor Prophets. 1956. 16.95 (ISBN 0-570-03249-0, 15-1719). Concordia.

Laney, J. Carl. Zechariah. (Everyman's Bible Commentary Ser.). (Orig.). 1984. pap. 5.95 (ISBN 0-8024-0445-6). Moody.

Leupold, Herbert C. Exposition of Zechariah. 1965. 9.95 (ISBN 0-8010-5512-1). Baker Bk.

Levine, Etan. The Aramaic Version of Jonah. 2nd ed. LC 76-27614. 1979. pap. 12.75 (ISBN 0-87203-068-7). Hermon.

Lloyd-Jones, D. Martyn. From Fear to Faith: Studies in the Book of Habakkuk. (Summit Bks.). 80p. 1982. pap. 2.95 (ISBN 0-8010-5620-9). Baker Bk.

McKeating, Henry, ed. The Books of Amos, Hosea, Micah. (Cambridge Bible Commentary on the New English Bible, Old Testament Ser.). (Illus.). 1971. 22.95 (ISBN 0-521-08133-5); pap. 10.95 (ISBN 0-521-09647-2). Cambridge U Pr.

Maier, Walter A. The Book of Nahum. (Thornapple Commentaries). 392p. 1980. pap. 6.95 (ISBN 0-8010-6098-2). Baker Bk.

Marbury, Edward. Obadiah & Habakkuk. 1979. 23.95 (ISBN 0-86524-007-8, 7003). Klock & Klock.

Martin, Hugh. Jonah. (Geneva Series Commentaries). 1978. 12.95 (ISBN 0-85151-115-5). Banner of Truth.

Martin-Achard, R. & Re'emi, P. The International Theological Commentary on Amos & Lamentations. (The International Theological Commentary Ser.). 160p. (Orig.). 1983. pap. 8.95 (ISBN 0-8028-1040-3). Eerdmans.

Mays, James L. Amos: A Commentary. LC 79-76885. (Old Testament Library). 176p. 1969. 15.95 (ISBN 0-664-20863-0). Westminster.

--Hosea: A Commentary. LC 75-79618. (Old Testament Library). 202p. 1969. 15.95 (ISBN 0-664-20871-1). Westminster.

--Micah: A Commentary. LC 76-2599. (Old Testament Library). 180p. 1976. 15.95 (ISBN 0-664-20817-7). Westminster.

Meyer, F. B. Zacaras-el Profeta Esperanza: Zacarias-El Probeta de Esperanza. Orig. Title: The Prophet of Hope - Zechariah. (Span.). 1986. write for info. (ISBN 0-8297-0895-2). Life Pubs Intl.

Mitchell, H. G., et al. A Critical & Exegetical Commentary on Haggai, Zechariah, Malachi & Jonah. (International Critical Commentary Ser.). 544p. 1912. 24.95 (ISBN 0-567-05020-3, Pub. by T & T Clark Ltd UK). Fortress.

Moore, T. V. Haggai, Malachi, & Zechariah. (Banner of Truth Geneva Series Commentaries). 1979. 13.95 (ISBN 0-85151-288-7). Banner of Truth.

Morgan, G. Campbell. Malachi's Message for Today. (Morgan Library). 131p. 1972. pap. 3.95 (ISBN 0-8010-5912-7). Baker Bk.

Myers, Jacob M. Hosea-Jonah. LC 59-10454. (Layman's Bible Commentary: Vol. 14). 1959. pap. 4.95 (ISBN 0-8042-3074-9). John Knox.

Nowell, Irene. Jonah, Tobit, Judith. (Collegeville Bible Commentary: Old Testament Ser.: Vol. 25). 112p. 1986. pap. 2.95 (ISBN 0-8146-1481-7). Liturgical Pr.

Orelli, Hans C. von. The Twelve Minor Prophets. 1977. 15.50 (ISBN 0-86524-114-7, 7001). Klock & Klock.

Oswald, H., ed. Luther's Works: Lectures on the Minor Prophets, 2: Jonah & Habakkuk, Vol. 19. LC 55-9893. 1974. 13.95 (ISBN 0-570-06419-8, 15-1761). Concordia.

Pazdan, Mary M. Joel, Obadiah, Haggai, Zechariah, Malachi. (Collegevile Bible Commentary Ser.). 128p. 1986. pap. 2.95 (ISBN 0-8146-1424-8). Liturgical Pr.

Petersen, David L. Haggai & Zechariah 1-8, a Commentary. LC 84-7477. (Old Testament Library). 320p. 1984. 24.95 (ISBN 0-664-21830-X). Westminster.

Pusey, Edward B. The Minor Prophets: With a Commentary Explanatory & Practical & Introductions to the Several Books, 2 vols. 1986. Repr. of 1885 ed. Set. lib. bdg. 45.00 (ISBN 0-89941-505-9). W S Hein.

Riggs, Jack R. Hosea's Heartbreak. 1984. pap. 5.95 (ISBN 0-87213-724-4). Loizeaux.

Sant Bani Ashram School Children, tr. Book of Jonah. LC 84-50924. (Illus.). 1984. pap. 6.95 (ISBN 0-89142-044-4). Sant Bani Ash.

Simpson, William. The Jonah Legend: A Suggestion of Interpretation. LC 72-177422. (Illus.). vi, 182p. 1971. Repr. of 1899 ed. 35.00x (ISBN 0-8103-3820-3). Gale.

Smith, Billy K. Layman's Bible Book Commentary: Vol. 13 Hosea, Joel, Amos, Abadiah, Jonah. LC 80-68536. 1982. 5.95 (ISBN 0-8054-1183-6). Broadman.

Smith, John M., et al. A Critical & Exegetical Commentary on Micah, Zephaniah, Nahum, Habakkuk, Obadiah & Joel. Driver, Samuel R. & Plummer, Alfred, eds. (International Critical Commentary Ser.). 560p. 1895. 24.95 (ISBN 0-567-05019-X, Pub. by T & T Clark Ltd UK). Fortress.

Stuhlmueller, Carroll. Amos, Hosea, Micah, Nahum, Zephaniah, Habakkuk. (Collegeville Bible Commentary Ser.). 120p. 1986. pap. 2.95 (ISBN 0-8146-1422-1). Liturgical Pr.

Tatford, Frederick A. The Minor Prophets, 3 vols. 1214p. 1982. Set. lib. bdg. 44.95 Smythe Sewn (ISBN 0-86524-135-X, 7000). Klock & Klock.

Ungerer, Walter. Habakkuk: The Man with Honest Answers. (Contemporary Discussion Ser.). 80p. 1976. pap. 1.45 (ISBN 0-8010-9202-7). Baker Bk.

Watts, John D. The Books of Joel, Obadiah, Jonah, Naham, Habakkuk & Zehaniah. LC 74-80355. (Cambridge Bible Commentary on the New English Bible, Old Testament Ser.). 300p. 1975. 22.95 (ISBN 0-521-20505-0); pap. 10.95 (ISBN 0-521-09870-X). Cambridge U Pr.

--Obadiah: A Critical & Exegetical Commentary. 78p. 1981. pap. 4.95x (ISBN 0-686-79148-7). Eisenbrauns.

Wolf, Hans W. Obadiah & Jonah: A Commentary. Kohl, Margaret, tr. from German. LC 86-22256. Orig. Title: Obadja, Jona. 192p. 1986. text ed. 19.95 (ISBN 0-8066-2244-X, 10-4710). Augsburg.

Wolf, Herbert. Hageo y Malaquias: Rededicacion y Renovacion. Orig. Title: Haggai & Malachi. (Span.). 1980. pap. 3.95 (ISBN 0-8254-1875-5). Kregel.

Wolff, Hans W. Hosea. Hanson, Paul D., ed. Stansell, Gary, tr. from Ger. LC 70-179634. (Hermeneia: A Critical & Historical Commentary on the Bible). Orig. Title: Dodekapropheton-Hosea. 292p. 1973. 24.95 (ISBN 0-8006-6004-8, 20-6004). Fortress.

--Micah the Prophet. Gehrke, Ralph D., tr. from Ger. LC 80-2380. Tr. of Mit Micha reden: Prophetie einst und jetzt. 240p. 1981. 19.95 (ISBN 0-8006-0652-3, 1-652). Fortress.

Wolff, Hans W., Jr. Joel & Amos. McBride, Dean, ed. Janzen, Waldemar, tr. from Ger. LC 75-76932. (Hermeneia: a Critical & Historical Commentary on the Bible). 416p. 1977. 29.95 (ISBN 0-8006-6007-2, 20-6007). Fortress.

Wood, Leon J. Commentary on Daniel. 320p. 1972. 16.95 (ISBN 0-310-34710-6, 10871). Zondervan.

Wright, Charles H. Zechariah & His Prophecies. 1980. 24.95 (ISBN 0-86524-020-5, 3801). Klock & Klock.

Yandian, Bob. Joel: The Outpouring of God's Glory. (Commentaries for Laymen Ser.). 160p. (Orig.). 1986. pap. 5.95 (ISBN 0-89274-402-2). Harrison Hse.

BIBLE–COMMENTARIES–O. T. NEHEMIAH

see Bible–Commentaries–O. T. Historical Books

BIBLE–COMMENTARIES–O. T. NUMBERS

see Bible–Commentaries–O. T. Pentateuch

BIBLE–COMMENTARIES–O. T. OBADIAH

see Bible–Commentaries–O. T. Minor Prophets

BIBLE–COMMENTARIES–O. T. PENTATEUCH

Aalders, C. C. Student's Commentary - Genesis, 2 vols. Set. 29.95 (ISBN 0-310-43968-X, 11755). Zondervan.

Abarbenel, Don I. Abarbenel Al Hatorah, 3 Vols. (Hebrew.). Set. 45.00 (ISBN 0-87559-078-0). Shalom.

Alford, Dean H. The Book of Genesis & Part of the Book of Exodus. 1979. 12.50 (ISBN 0-86524-001-9, 7002). Klock & Klock.

Allis, Oswald T. God Spake by Moses: An Exposition of the Pentateuch. 1951. pap. 5.95 (ISBN 0-8010-0109-9). Baker Bk.

Baer, S. Tikkun. 332p. 1900. Repr. text ed. 41.40x (ISBN 0-576-80143-7, Pub. by Gregg Intl Pubs England). Gregg Intl.

Bamberger, Bernard J. Commentary on Leviticus. Plaut, W. Gunther, ed. (The Torah: a Modern Commentary Ser.). 1979. 20.00 (ISBN 0-8074-0011-4, 3816). UAHC.

Baughen, Michael. The Moses Principle: Leadership & the Venture of Faith. LC 78-27498. 118p. 1978. pap. 2.95 (ISBN 0-87788-558-3). Shaw Pubs.

Bible Student's Commentary: Pentateuch Set, 5 vols. 1984. text ed. 95.75 (ISBN 0-310-45168-X, 11759). Zondervan.

Blair, Edward P. Deuteronomy, Joshua. LC 59-10454. (Layman's Bible Commentary Ser: Vol. 5). 1964. pap. 4.95 (ISBN 0-8042-3065-X). John Knox.

Blenkinsopp, Joseph & Challenor, John. Pentateuch. Bright, Laurence, ed. LC 71-173033. (Scripture Discussion Commentary Ser.: Pt. 1). 248p. 1971. pap. text ed. 4.50 (ISBN 0-87946-000-8). ACTA Found.

Blocher, Henri. In the Beginning: The Opening Chapters of Genesis. Preston, David G., tr. from Fr. LC 84-12800. 180p. 1984. pap. 8.95 (ISBN 0-87784-325-2). Inter-Varsity.

Boice, James M. Genesis: An Expositional Commentary, Vol. 2. 352p. 1985. 16.95 (ISBN 0-310-21560-9, 10487). Zondervan.

Bonar, Andrew. Leviticus. (Banner of Truth Geneva Series Commentaries). 1978. 15.95 (ISBN 0-85151-086-8). Banner of Truth.

Bonhoeffer, Dietrich. Creation & Fall: Temptation. 1983. 13.00 (ISBN 0-8446-5962-2). Peter Smith.

Briscoe, Stuart. Genesis (CC) 1986. 18.95 (ISBN 0-8499-0406-4). Word Bks.

Brueggemann, Walter. Genesis. LC 81-82355. (Interpretation: the Bible Commentary for Teaching & Preaching). 432p. 1982. 23.95 (ISBN 0-8042-3101-X). John Knox.

Burns, Rita. Exodus, Leviticus, Numbers, with Excursus on Feasts, Ritual, Typology. (Old Testament Message Ser.: Vol. 3). 15.95 (ISBN 0-89453-403-3); pap. 9.95 (ISBN 0-89453-238-3). M Glazier.

Bush, George. Exodus. 1981. 22.50 (ISBN 0-86524-097-3, 0202). Klock & Klock.

--Genesis, 2 vols. 1981. 29.95 (ISBN 0-86524-094-9, 0103). Klock & Klock.

--Leviticus. 1981. 10.50 (ISBN 0-86524-098-1, 0302). Klock & Klock.

--Numbers. 1981. 17.95 (ISBN 0-86524-099-X, 0401). Klock & Klock.

Calvin, John. Genesis. (Geneva Commentaries Ser.). 1979. 22.95 (ISBN 0-85151-093-0). Banner of Truth.

Candlish, Robert S. Studies in Genesis, 2 vols. in one. LC 79-14084. (Kregel Bible Study Classics Ser.). 854p. 1979. 22.95 (ISBN 0-8254-2315-5). Kregel.

Cassuto, U. A Commentary on the Book of Exodus. 2nd ed. Abrahams, Israel, tr. from Hebrew. 509p. 1974. Repr. of 1967 ed. text ed. 35.00x (ISBN 965-223-456-7, Pub. by Magnes Pr Israel). Humanities.

--From Adam to Noah: A Commentary on the Book of Genesis, Part 1. 3rd ed. 323p. 1978. Repr. of 1961 ed. text ed. 35.00x (Pub. by Magnes Pr Israel). Humanities.

--From Noah to Abraham: A Commentary on the Book of Genesis, Pt. 2. 3rd ed. 386p. 1974. Repr. of 1964 ed. text ed. 35.00x (Pub. by Magnes Pr Israel). Humanities.

Cate, Robert L. Layman's Bible Book Commentary: Exodus, Vol. 2. LC 78-59976. 1979. 5.95 (ISBN 0-8054-1172-0). Broadman.

Childs, Brevard S. The Book of Exodus: A Critical, Theological Commentary. LC 73-23120. (Old Testament Library). 686p. 1974. 26.50 (ISBN 0-664-20985-8). Westminster.

Clements, R. E., ed. Exodus: Cambridge Bible Commentary on the New English Bible. (Old Testament Ser.). 1972. 32.50 (ISBN 0-521-08218-8); pap. 10.95 (ISBN 0-521-09656-1). Cambridge U Pr.

Coats, George W. Genesis: With an Introduction to Narrative. (Forms of the Old Testament Literature Ser.: Vol. 1). 368p. (Orig.). 1984. pap. 21.95 (ISBN 0-8028-1954-0). Eerdmans.

Cochrane, Charles C. The Gospel According to Genesis. 96p. (Orig.). 1984. pap. 4.95 (ISBN 0-8028-1971-0). Eerdmans.

Coffman, James B. Commentary on Exodus. 1986. 19.95 (ISBN 0-915547-49-X). Abilene Christ U.

--Commentary on Genesis. 1986. 19.95 (ISBN 0-915547-48-1). Abilene Christ U.

--Commentary on Leviticus & Numbers. 580p. 1987. 19.95 (ISBN 0-915547-75-9). Abilene Christ U.

Cole, R. Alan. Exodus: Tyndale Old Testament Commentary. LC 72-97952. 243p. 1973. 12.95 (ISBN 0-87784-865-3); pap. 6.95 (ISBN 0-87784-252-3). Inter-Varsity.

Craghan, John F. Exodus. (Bible Commentary Ser.). 112p. 1985. pap. 2.95 (ISBN 0-8146-1371-3). Liturgical Pr.

Craigie, P. C. Commentary on the Book of Deuteronomy. (New International Commentary of the Old Testament). 520p. 1976. 16.95 (ISBN 0-8028-2355-6). Eerdmans.

Cundall, A. E. Genesis & Exodus. (Bible Study Commentaries Ser.). 126p. 1980. pap. 4.95 (ISBN 0-87508-150-9). Chr Lit.

DeHaan, M. R. Portraits of Christ in Genesis. 1978. pap. 6.95 (ISBN 0-310-23431-X, 9516P). Zondervan.

Delitzsch, Franz. A New Commentary on Genesis, 2 vols. 1978. Set. 30.50 (ISBN 0-86524-131-7, 0101). Klock & Klock.

Driver, Samuel R. A Critical & Exegetical Commentary on Deuteronomy. LC 2-25926. (International Critical Commentary Ser.). 556p. 1902. 24.95 (ISBN 0-567-05003-3, Pub. by T & T Clark Ltd UK). Fortress.

Dunnam, Maxie. Exodus: (CC, Vol. 2. 320p. 1987. 18.95 (ISBN 0-8499-0407-2). Word Bks.

Edwards, F Henry. Studies in Genesis, Vol. 1. 1987. pap. 3.50 (ISBN 0-8309-0482-4). Herald Hse.

Finkelstein, Louis. Sifre on Deuteronomy. 1969. 25.00x (ISBN 0-685-31422-7, Pub. by Jewish Theol Seminary). Ktav.

Fritsch, Charles T. Genesis. LC 59-10454. (Layman's Bible Commentary Ser: Vol. 2). 1959. pap. 4.95 (ISBN 0-8042-3062-5). John Knox.

Fromer, Margaret & Keyes, Sharrel. Genesis I Through 25: Walking with God. rev. ed. (Fisherman Bible Studyguide Ser.). 80p. 1979. saddle-stitched 2.95 (ISBN 0-87788-297-5). Shaw Pubs.

--Genesis 26 through 50: Called by God. rev. ed. (Fisherman Bible Studyguide Ser.). 66p. 1979. pap. 2.95 saddle-stitched (ISBN 0-87788-298-3). Shaw Pubs.

Fuss, Werner. Die Deuteronomistische Pentateuchredaktion in Exodus 3-17. (Beiheft 126 zur Zeitschrift fuer die alttestamentliche Wissenschaft). xii, 406p. 1972. 48.40x (ISBN 3-11-003854-4). De Gruyter.

Gardner, Leonard. Genesis: The Teacher's Guide. 1966. pap. 6.50 (ISBN 0-8381-0401-0). United Syn Bk.

Goldberg, Louis. Deuteronomy. (Bible Study Commentary Ser.). 208p. 1986. pap. 7.95 (ISBN 0-310-20201-9, 11412P). Zondervan.

Goldsmith, M. Leviticus-Deuteronomy. (Bible Study Commentary Ser.). 126p. 1980. pap. 4.95 (ISBN 0-87508-151-7). Chr Lit.

Grant, F. W. Lessons from Exodus. 6.25 (ISBN 0-88172-074-7). Believers Bkshelf.

Gray, G. Buchanan. A Critical & Exegetical Commentary on Numbers. Driver, Samuel R. & Plummer, Alfred, eds. LC 3-31887. (International Critical Commentary Ser.). 544p. 1903. 24.95 (ISBN 0-567-05002-5, Pub. by T & T Clark Ltd UK). Fortress.

Guyon, Jeanne. Genesis. 1983. pap. 5.95 (ISBN 0-940232-15-4). Christian Bks.

Hall, Brian P. The Genesis Effect: Personal & Organizational Transformations. (Illus.). 376p. (Orig.). 1986. pap. 14.95 (ISBN 0-8091-2741-5). Paulist Pr.

Ham, Wayne. Studies in Genesis, Vol. 2. (Bible Study Ser.). 1987. pap. 3.50 (ISBN 0-8309-0483-2). Herald Hse.

Hammer, Reuven, tr. from Hebrew. & Sifre: A Tannaitic Commentary on the Book of Deuteronomy. LC 85-29556. (Yale Judaica Ser.: No. 24). 560p. 1986. text ed. 45.00x (ISBN 0-300-03345-1). Yale U Pr.

Harrison, R. K. & Wiseman, D. J. Leviticus: An Introduction & Commentary. LC 80-7985. (Tyndale Old Testament Commentaries Ser.). 180p. 1980. 12.95 (ISBN 0-87784-890-4); pap. 6.95 (ISBN 0-87784-253-1). Inter-Varsity.

Hartley, William. In the Beginning God: Jottings from Genesis. 96p. 1975. pap. 1.45 (ISBN 0-8010-4132-5). Baker Bk.

Henry, Matthew. A Commentary on the Whole Bible, Vol. 1: Genesis to Deuteronomy. (Reference Library Edition). 912p. 1986. Repr. text ed. 10.95 (ISBN 0-529-06365-4). World Bible.

Hepburn, Daisy. Get Up & Go. LC 84-3362. (Life with Spice Bible Study Ser.). 64p. 1984. 2.95 (ISBN 0-8307-0946-0, 6101833). Regal.

Heslop, W. G. Gems from Genesis. LC 75-13661. (W. G. Heslop Bible Study Aids). 136p. 1975. pap. 4.50 (ISBN 0-8254-2825-4). Kregel.

--Nuggets From Numbers. LC 75-13660. (W. G. Heslop Bible Study Aids). 192p. 1975. pap. 4.50 (ISBN 0-8254-2828-9). Kregel.

Hoppe, Leslie J. Deuteronomy. (Bible Commentary Ser.). 104p. 1985. pap. 2.95 (ISBN 0-8146-1374-8). Liturgical Pr.

Huey, F. B., Jr. Exodus. (Bible Study Commentary Ser.). 1977. pap. 4.95 (ISBN 0-310-36053-6, 11021P). Zondervan.

Hummel, Charles & Hummel, Anne. Genesis. (Lifebuilder Bible Studies). 96p. (Orig.). 1985. pap. text ed. 3.50 (ISBN 0-8308-1022-6). Inter-Varsity.

Hunt, Ignatius. Genesis, 2 Bks. (Bible Ser.). Bk. 1. pap. 1.00 (ISBN 0-8091-5048-4); Bk. 2. pap. 1.00 (ISBN 0-8091-5049-2). Paulist Pr.

Hyatt, J. P. Commentary on Exodus. Clements, Ronald E., ed. (New Century Bible Commentary Ser.). 1980. pap. 8.95 (ISBN 0-8028-1844-7). Eerdmans.

Jensen, Irving L. Exodus. (Bible Self-Study Ser.). 1970. pap. 3.25 (ISBN 0-8024-1002-2). Moody.

--Genesis. (Bible Self-Study Ser.). 1967. pap. 3.25 (ISBN 0-8024-1001-4). Moody.

--Leviticus. (Bible Self Study Ser.). 1970. pap. 3.25 (ISBN 0-8024-1003-0). Moody.

--Numbers & Deuteronomy. (Bible Self Study Ser.). 1970. pap. 3.25 (ISBN 0-8024-1004-9). Moody.

--Numbers: Journey to God's Rest-Land. (Everyman's Bible Commentary Ser.). 1968. pap. 5.95 (ISBN 0-8024-2004-4). Moody.

--Numeros: Viaje a la Tierra de Reposo (Comentario Biblico Portavoz) Orig. Title: Numbers(Everyman's Bible Commentary) (Span.). 112p. 1980. pap. 3.50 (ISBN 0-8254-1355-9). Kregel.

Jordan, Bernice C. El Almacen de Dios: Exodo, 16 Lecciones, Vol. 2. (Pasos De Fe Ser.). (Span.). pap. text ed. 2.50 tchrs'. manual (ISBN 0-86508-403-3); figuras 8.95 (ISBN 0-86508-404-1). BCM Intl Inc.

--Genesis: Fifteen Lessons, Vol. 1. (Footsteps of Faith Ser.). 1960. pap. text ed. 2.50 (ISBN 0-86508-027-5); figures text 11.45 (ISBN 0-86508-028-3). BCM Intl Inc.

--Genesis: Quinze Lecciones, Tomo 1. (Pasos De Fe Ser.). (Span.). pap. text ed. 2.50 (ISBN 0-86508-401-7); figuras 8.95 (ISBN 0-86508-402-5). BCM Intl Inc.

--God's Storehouse: Exodus 16 Lessons, Vol. 2. (Footsteps of Faith Ser.). (Illus.). 1961. pap. text ed. 2.50 (ISBN 0-86508-029-1); 11.45 (ISBN 0-86508-030-5). BCM Intl Inc.

Julien, Tom. Spiritual Greatness: Studies in Exodus. (Orig.). 1979. pap. 4.95 (ISBN 0-88469-121-7). BMH Bks.

Kellogg, Samuel H. The Book of Leviticus. 1978. 21.00 (ISBN 0-86524-132-5, 0301). Klock & Klock.

Kidner, F. Derek. Genesis. LC 75-23851. (Tyndale Old Testament Commentary). 1968. 12.95 (ISBN 0-87784-881-5); pap. 6.95 (ISBN 0-87784-251-5). Inter-Varsity.

Leupold, Herbert C. Exposition of Genesis, 2 Vols. Vol. 1. 15.95 (ISBN 0-8010-5549-0); Vol. 2. 15.95 (ISBN 0-8010-5522-9). Baker Bk.

Lindsay, Gordon. The Story of Adam & Eve. (Old Testament Ser.). 1.25 (ISBN 0-89985-124-X). Christ Nations.

Luther, Martin. Luther's Works: Lectures on Galatians, Vols. 26 & 27. Incl. Vol. 26. Pelikan, Jaroslav, ed. 1962; Vol. 27. Pelikan, Jaroslav, ed. Jungkuntz, Richard, tr. 1963. 16.95 (ISBN 0-570-06427-9, 15-1769). LC 55-9893. 16.95 (ISBN 0-570-06426-0, 15-1768). Concordia.

McConville, J. G. Law & Theology in Deuteronomy. (JSOT Supplement Ser.: No. 33). 200p. 1985. text ed. 28.50x (ISBN 0-905774-78-7, Pub. by JSOT Pr England); pap. text ed. 13.50x (ISBN 0-905774-79-5, Pub. by JSOT Pr England). Eisenbrauns.

McCurley, Foster R. Genesis, Exodus, Leviticus, Numbers. LC 78-14670. (Proclamation Commentaries: the Old Testament Witness for Preaching). 128p. 1979. pap. 4.95 (ISBN 0-8006-0593-4, 1-593). Fortress.

Mackintosh, C. H. Genesis to Deuteronomy: Notes on the Pentateuch, 6 vols. in 1. LC 72-75082. 928p. 1972. 19.95 (ISBN 0-87213-617-5). Loizeaux.

Mainelli, Helen K. Numbers. (Bible Commentary Ser.). 136p. 1985. pap. 2.50 (ISBN 0-8146-1373-X). Liturgical Pr.

Mayes, A. D. Deuteronomy. (New Century Bible Ser.). 352p. 1979. 15.95 (ISBN 0-551-00804-0). Attic Pr.

--Deuteronomy. Clements, Ronald E., ed. (New Century Bible Commentary Ser.). (Orig.). 1981. pap. 9.95 (ISBN 0-8028-1882-X). Eerdmans.

Mays, James L. Leviticus, Numbers. LC 59-10454. (Layman's Bible Commentary Ser: Vol. 4). 1963. pap. 4.95 (ISBN 0-8042-3064-1). John Knox.

Meyer, F. B. Devotional Commentary on Exodus. LC 78-9530. 476p. 1978. pap. 12.95 (ISBN 0-8254-3244-8). Kregel.

Meyer, Lester. The Message of Exodus. LC 83-70519. 176p. (Orig.). 1983. pap. 8.95 (ISBN 0-8066-2025-0, 10-4347). Augsburg.

Midrash Rabbah: Midrashim on the Pentateuch & the Five Scrolls with the Matnoth Kehunah Commentary, 5 Vols. (Hebrew & Yiddish.). Set. leatherette 95.00 (ISBN 0-87559-096-9). Shalom.

Moberly, R. W. At the Mountain of God: Story & Theology in Exodus 32-34. (Journal for the Study of the Old Testament Monograph Ser.: No. 22). 258p. 1983. text ed. 22.50x (ISBN 0-905774-44-2, Pub. by JSOT Pr England); pap. text ed. 14.95x (ISBN 0-905774-45-0, Pub. by JSOT Pr England). Eisenbrauns.

Moriarty. Numbers. (Bible Ser.). Pt. 1. pap. 1.00 (ISBN 0-8091-5101-4); Pt. 2. pap. 1.00 (ISBN 0-8091-5102-2). Paulist Pr.

Morris, Henry M. History of Modern Creationism. LC 84-60865. 1984. 12.95 (ISBN 0-89051-107-1); pap. 9.95 (ISBN 0-89051-102-0). Master Bks.

Murphy, James G. Commentary on the Book of Exodus. 1979. 14.50 (ISBN 0-86524-014-0, 0201). Klock & Klock.

--Commentary on the Book of Genesis. xvi, 535p. 1986. Repr. of 1873 ed. lib. bdg. 27.50 (ISBN 0-89941-508-3). W S Hein.

Murphy, Roland E. Exodus. (Bible Ser.). Pt. 1. pap. 1.00 (ISBN 0-8091-5043-3); Pt. 2. pap. 1.00 (ISBN 0-8091-5044-1). Paulist Pr.

Napier, B. Davie. Come Sweet Death: A Quintet from Genesis. LC 67-17793. 96p. 1975. 2 rec album 11.95 (ISBN 0-8298-0375-0). Pilgrim NY.

--Exodus. LC 59-10454. (Layman's Bible Commentary Ser: Vol. 3). 1963. write for info. (ISBN 0-8042-3003-X); pap. 4.95 (ISBN 0-8042-3063-3). John Knox.

Neuser, Jacob. Sifre to Numbers, Part I. (Brown Judaic Studies). 1986. text ed. 27.95 (ISBN 1-55540-008-6, 14-01-18); pap. 22.95 (ISBN 1-55540-009-4). Scholars Pr GA.

--Sifre to Numbers, Part II. (Brown Judaic Studies). 1986. text ed. 24.95 (ISBN 1-55540-010-8, 14-01-19); pap. 19.95 (ISBN 1-55540-011-6). Scholars Pr GA.

Neusner, Jacob. Genesis Rabbah: The Judaic Commentary to the Book of Genesis, Vol. II. 1985. 34.95 (ISBN 0-89130-933-0, 14-01-05); pap. 29.55 (ISBN 0-89130-934-9). Scholars Pr GA.

--Genesis Rabbah: The Judaic Commentary to the Book of Genesis, Vol. III. 1985. 33.95 (ISBN 0-89130-935-7, 14-01-06); pap. 28.55 (ISBN 0-89130-936-5). Scholars Pr GA.

--Genesis Rabbah: The Judaic Commentary to the Book of Genesis, Vol. 1. 1985. 35.75 (ISBN 0-89130-931-4, 14-01-04); pap. 26.75 (ISBN 0-89130-932-2). Scholars Pr GA.

Neusner, Jacob & Brooks, Roger, trs. Sifra: The Rabbinic Commentary on Leviticus. (Brown Judaic Studies). 1985. 22.95 (ISBN 0-89130-913-6, 14-01-02); pap. 18.25 (ISBN 0-89130-914-4). Scholars Pr GA.

Newell, William R. Studies in the Pentateuch. LC 83-19903. (Old Testament Studies). 272p. 1983. kivar 7.95 (ISBN 0-8254-3313-4). Kregel.

Newman, Robert C. & Eckelmann, Herman J., Jr. Genesis One & the Origin of the Earth. 156p. 1981. pap. 4.95 (ISBN 0-8010-6735-9). Baker Bk.

Noordtzij, A. Bible Student's Commentary: Leviticus. (Bible Student's Commentary Ser.). 288p. 1982. 16.95 (ISBN 0-310-45090-X, 11757). Zondervan.

--Bible Student's Commentary: Numbers. (Bible Student's Commentary Ser.). 1986. 16.95 (ISBN 0-310-43980-9, 11758). Zondervan.

North, Gary. Moses & Pharaoh: Dominion Religion vs. Power Religion. 430p. 1985. pap. text ed. 12.50 (ISBN 0-930464-05-2). Inst Christian.

Noth, Martin. Exodus, a Commentary. LC 62-7940. (Old Testament Library). 284p. 1962. 17.95 (ISBN 0-664-20370-1). Westminster.

Origen. Homilies on Genesis & Exodus. LC 82-4124. (Fathers of the Church Ser.: Vol. 71). 422p. 1982. 29.95x (ISBN 0-8132-0071-7). Cath U Pr.

Origins of Faith & Life: Genesis A. (New Horizons Bible Study Ser.). 1981. pap. 1.95 leader's guide (ISBN 0-89367-052-9); pap. 2.50 study guide (ISBN 0-89367-053-7). Light & Life.

Outlaw, Stanley & O'Donnell, J. D. A Survey of the Pentateuch. 93p. 1975. pap. 2.95 (ISBN 0-89265-027-3). Randall Hse.

Payne, David F. Deuteronomy. LC 85-13653. (Daily Study Bible - Old Testament). 210p. 1985. 14.95 (ISBN 0-664-21832-6); pap. 7.95 (ISBN 0-664-24580-3). Westminster.

Peckham, Brian. The Composition of the Deuteronomic History. (Harvard Semitic Museum Monographs). 1985. 13.95 (ISBN 0-89130-909-8, 04-00-35). Scholars Pr GA.

Phillips, Anthony. Deuteronomy. LC 73-77172. (Cambridge Bible Commentary on the New English Bible, Old Testament Ser.). (Illus.). 224p. 1973. pap. 29.95 (ISBN 0-521-08636-1); pap. 12.95 (ISBN 0-521-09772-X). Cambridge U Pr.

Phillips, John. Exploring Genesis. LC 80-23685. 582p. 1980. pap. 9.95 (ISBN 0-8024-2430-9). Moody.

Pink, Arthur W. Gleanings in Exodus. 1964. pap. 10.95 (ISBN 0-8024-3001-5). Moody.

--Gleanings in Genesis. 1922. pap. 10.95 (ISBN 0-8024-3002-3). Moody.

Pinner, Mary T. & Shuard, Hilary. In-Service Education in Primary Mathematics. 208p. 1985. pap. 15.00x (ISBN 0-335-15023-3, Open Univ Pr). Taylor & Francis.

Pixley, George V. On Exodus: An Evangelical & Popular Commentary. Barr, Robert R., tr. from Span. 256p. (Orig.). 1987. 19.95 (ISBN 0-88344-560-3); pap. 9.95 (ISBN 0-88344-559-X). Orbis Bks.

Plaut, W. Gunther. Commentary on Genesis. (Pardes Torah; Jewish Commentary on the Torah Ser.). 1974. 20.00 (ISBN 0-8074-0001-7, 381611). UAHC.

--Deuteronomy: The Torah. (A Modern Commentary Ser.). 528p. 1983. 20.00 (ISBN 0-8074-0045-9). UAHC.

Pollak, P. S. Minhas Marheshes: Commentary on Genesis. (Heb). 9.50 (ISBN 0-87559-101-9). Shalom.

Porter, J. R. Leviticus. LC 75-20831. (Cambridge Bible Commentary on the New English Bible, Old Testament Ser.). (Illus.). 250p. 1976. 29.95 (ISBN 0-521-08638-8); pap. 11.95x (ISBN 0-521-09773-8). Cambridge U Pr.

Ridderbos, J. Bible Student's Commentary: Deuteronomy. (Bible Student's Commentary Ser.). 336p. 1984. 16.95 (ISBN 0-310-45260-0, 11760). Zondervan.

Sarna, Nahum M. Understanding Genesis: The Heritage of Biblical Israel. LC 66-23626. 1970. pap. 7.50 (ISBN 0-8052-0253-6). Schocken.

Schmitt, Hans-Christoph. Die Nichtpriesterliche Josephsgeschichte (Gen 37-50) 1979. 34.40 (ISBN 3-11-007834-1). De Gruyter.

Scholem, Gershom, ed. Zohar-The Book of Splendor: Basic Readings from the Kabbalah. LC 63-11040. 1963. pap. 3.95 (ISBN 0-8052-0045-2). Schocken.

Schultz, Samuel J. The Gospel of Moses. 1979. 6.95 (ISBN 0-8024-3198-4). Moody.

--Leviticus. (Everyman's Bible Commentary Ser.). (Orig.). 1983. pap. 5.95 (ISBN 0-8024-0247-X). Moody.

Silbermann, A. M. & Rosenbaum, M. Pentateuch with Rashi, 5 vols. LC 30-11064. 1973. 44.95 (ISBN 0-87306-019-9); slipcased ed. 46.95. Feldheim.

Skinner, John. A Critical & Exegetical Commentary on Genesis. Driver, Samuel R., et al, eds. (International Critical Commentary Ser.). 640p. 1930. 24.95 (ISBN 0-567-05001-7, Pub. by T & T Clark Ltd UK). Fortress.

Speiser, E. A., ed. Genesis. LC 64-21724. (Anchor Bible Ser.: Vol. 1). 1964. 16.00 (ISBN 0-385-00854-6, Anchor Pr). Doubleday.

Staack, Hagen. A Study Guide for Genesis. 1984. pap. 3.95 (ISBN 0-9613270-0-6). G McBride.

Stevens, Sherrill. Layman's Bible Book Commentary: Genesis, Vol.1. LC 78-50377. 1978. 5.95 (ISBN 0-8054-1171-2). Broadman.

Stone, Michael. Signs of the Judgement, Onomastica Sacra & the Generations from Adam. LC 80-28371. (University of Pennsylvania Armenian Texts & Studies). 1981. text ed. 16.50 (ISBN 0-89130-460-6, 21-02-03); pap. 12.00 (ISBN 0-89130-461-4). Scholars Pr GA.

Stuhlmueller, Carroll. Leviticus. (Bible Ser.). pap. 1.00 (ISBN 0-8091-5082-4). Paulist Pr.

Sturdy, John. Numbers. LC 75-39373. (Cambridge Bible Commentary on the New English Bible, Old Testament Ser.). 1976. pap. 11.95 (ISBN 0-521-09776-2). Cambridge U Pr.

Thomas, W. H. Genesis: A Devotional Commentary. 507p. 1988. pap. 12.95 (ISBN 0-8254-3817-9). Kregel.

Thomas, W. H. Griffith. Through the Pentateuch Chapter by Chapter. LC 85-10076. 192p. 1985. pap. 6.95 (ISBN 0-8254-3833-0). Kregel.

Thompson, J. Deuteronomy. Wiseman, D. J., ed. LC 74-14303. (Tyndale Old Testament Commentary Ser.). 320p. 1975. 12.95 (ISBN 0-87784-882-3); pap. 6.95 (ISBN 0-87784-255-8). Inter-Varsity.

Turner, Wayne A. Leviticus. (Bible Commentary Ser.). 112p. 1985. pap. 2.95 (ISBN 0-8146-1372-1). Liturgical Pr.

Viviano, Pauline A. Genesis. (Bible Commentary Ser.). 136p. 1985. pap. 2.95 (ISBN 0-8146-1370-5). Liturgical Pr.

Von Rad, Gerhard. Deuteronomy: A Commentary. LC 66-23088. (Old Testament Library). 212p. 1966. 15.95 (ISBN 0-664-20734-0). Westminster.

--Genesis, a Commentary. rev ed. LC 72-6413. (Old Testament Library). 440p. 1973. 17.95 (ISBN 0-664-20957-2). Westminster.

Vos, Howard F. Genesis. (Everyman's Bible Commentary Ser.). 1982. pap. 5.95 (ISBN 0-8024-2001-X). Moody.

Webber, Robert E. I Believe: A Woman's Workshop on Relational Doctrine. (Woman's Workshop Ser.). 160p. 1986. pap. 3.95 (ISBN 0-310-36701-8). Zondervan.

Wenham, Gordon. The Book of Leviticus (Nicot) (New International Commentary on the Old Testament Ser.). 1979. text ed. 16.95 (ISBN 0-8028-2353-X). Eerdmans.

--Genesis I (WBC, Vol. 1. 400p. 1987. 24.95 (ISBN 0-8499-0200-2). Word Bks.

Westermann, Claus. Genesis One-Eleven. Scullion, John J., tr. LC 82-72655. 692p. cloth 34.95 (ISBN 0-8066-1962-7, 10-2543). Augsburg.

--Genesis 12-36: A Commentary. Scullion, John J., tr. from Ger. LC 85-7449. Tr. of Genesis: Kapitel 12-36. 608p. 1985. text ed. 34.95 (ISBN 0-8066-2172-9, 10-2542). Augsburg.

--Genesis 37-50: A Commentary. Scullion, John S., tr. from Ger. LC 85-26802. 274p. 1986. 21.95 (ISBN 0-8066-2197-4, 10-2546). Augsburg.

--The Promises to the Fathers: Studies on the Patriarchal Narratives. Green, David E., tr. from Ger. LC 79-7395. 208p. 1980. 13.95 (ISBN 0-8006-0580-2, 1-580). Fortress.

Whitcomb, John C. The Early Earth. pap. 4.50 (ISBN 0-88469-060-1). BMH Bks.

Wiseman, P. J. Ancient Records & the Structure of Genesis. Wiseman, D. J., ed. 160p. 1985. pap. 6.95 (ISBN 0-8407-7502-4). Nelson.

Wolf, Earl C. Beacon Small-Group Bible Studies: Exodus: "Set Free". 86p. (Orig.). 1984. pap. 2.50. Beacon Hill.

Wood, Leon J. Genesis: A Bible Study Commentary. 160p. 1975. pap. 4.95 (ISBN 0-310-34743-2, 10233P). Zondervan.

Young, E. J. In the Beginning. 1976. pap. 3.95 (ISBN 0-85151-235-6). Banner of Truth.

Youngblood, Ronald. How It All Began: (Genesis 1-11) LC 80-50539. (Bible Commentary for Laymen Ser.). 160p. 1980. pap. 3.50 (ISBN 0-8307-0675-5, S342103). Regal.

Youngblood, Ronald F. Exodus. (Everyman's Bible Commentary Ser.). (Orig.). 1983. pap. 5.95 (ISBN 0-8024-2002-8). Moody.

Zlotowitz, Meir. Bereishis-Genesis, Vol. 5. (Art Scroll Tanach Ser.). 1980. 16.95 (ISBN 0-89906-358-6); pap. 13.95 (ISBN 0-89906-359-4). Mesorah Pubns.

--Bereishis-Genesis: Vol. 4, Vayeitzei-Vayishlach. (Art Scroll Tanach Ser.). 400p. 1979. 16.95 (ISBN 0-89906-356-X); pap. 13.95 (ISBN 0-89906-357-8). Mesorah Pubns.

BIBLE–COMMENTARIES–O. T. POETICAL BOOKS

Alden, Robert L. Proverbs: A Commentary on an Ancient Book of Timeless Advice. 222p. 1984. 12.95 (ISBN 0-8010-0194-3). Baker Bk.

--Psalms: Songs of Discipleship, 3 vols. (Everyman's Bible Commentary Ser.). 1975. pap. 5.95 ea. Vol. 1 (ISBN 0-8024-2018-4). Vol. 2 (ISBN 0-8024-2019-2). Vol. 3 (ISBN 0-8024-2020-6). Moody.

Allen, R. Praise: A Matter of Life & Breath. Chan, Silas, tr. (Chinese.). 204p. 1982. pap. write for info. (ISBN 0-941598-04-7). Living Spring Pubns.

Allen, Ronald B. Praise! A Matter of Life & Breath. LC 80-23894. 248p. 1980. pap. 5.95 (ISBN 0-8407-5733-6). Nelson.

Andersen, Francis I. Job. Wiseman, D. J., ed. LC 76-12298. (Tyndale Old Testament Commentary Ser.). 1976. 12.95 (ISBN 0-87784-869-6); pap. 6.95 (ISBN 0-87784-263-9). Inter-Varsity.

Anderson, Don. Ecclesiastes: The Mid-Life Crisis. (Kingfisher Ser.). 268p. (Orig.). 1987. pap. 7.95 (ISBN 0-87213-001-0). Loizeaux.

Baker, J. & Nicholson, E. W., eds. The Commentary of Rabbi David Kimhi on Psalms 120-150. (Cambridge Oriental Publications Ser.: No. 22). 44.50 (ISBN 0-521-08670-1). Cambridge U Pr.

Bales, James D. The Psalm for the Frightened & Frustrated Sheep. 1977. pap. 1.50 (ISBN 0-89315-216-1). Lambert Bk.

Barclay, William. The Lord Is My Shepherd: Expositions of Selected Psalms. LC 79-27096. 154p. 1980. pap. 5.95 (ISBN 0-664-24317-7). Westminster.

Barton, George A. A Critical & Exegetical Commentary on Ecclesiastes. Driver, Samuel R. & Plummer, Alfred, eds. LC 8-15777. (International Critical Commentary Ser.). 236p. 1912. 22.95 (ISBN 0-567-05014-9, Pub. by T & T Clark Ltd UK). Fortress.

Beals, Ivan A. Beacon Small-Group Bible Studies: Psalms: Keeping the Heart Aglow. 96p. (Orig.). 1984. pap. 2.50 (ISBN 0-8341-0885-2). Beacon Hill.

Beckwith, Merle R. A New List of Proverbs. LC 79-92430. cancelled (ISBN 0-8022-2361-3). Philos Lib.

Bellinger, W. H. Psalmody & Prophecy. (JSOT Supplement Ser.: No. 27). 146p. 1984. text ed. 28.50x (ISBN 0-905774-60-4, Pub. by JSOT Pr England); pap. text ed. 11.95x (ISBN 0-905774-61-2, Pub. by JSOT England). Eisenbrauns.

Bennett, Georgann. Soulshine. 1978. pap. cancelled (ISBN 0-89900-133-5). College Pr Pub.

Bernard Of Clairvaux. Bernard of Clairvaux on the Song of Songs, Vol. II. Walsh, Kilian, tr. (Cistercian Fathers Ser.: No. 7). pap. 5.00 (ISBN 0-87907-707-7). Cistercian Pubns.

Bessarion, Agioantonides. The House of Holy Wisdom: A Commentary on Proverbs 9. (Illus.). 60p. (Orig.). 1986. pap. 4.95 (ISBN 0-936649-12-7). St Anthony Orthodox.

Beyerlin, Walter. Werden und Wesen Des 107 Psalms. (Beiheft 153 Zur Zeitschrift Fur Die Alttestamentliche Wissenschaft). 1979. 29.20 (ISBN 3-11-007755-8). De Gruyter.

Blair, J. Allen. Job: Living Patiently. LC 66-25720. 1966. pap. 5.95 (ISBN 0-87213-051-7). Loizeaux.

Bloem, Diane. A Womans Workshop on Proverbs. 1978. leader's manual 5.95 (ISBN 0-310-21371-1, 10684); student manual 2.95 (ISBN 0-310-21361-4, 10683). Zondervan.

Boadt, Lawrence E. Introduction to Wisdom Literature, Proverbs. (Collegeville Bible Commentary: Old Testament Ser.: Vol. 18). 104p. 1986. pap. 2.95 (ISBN 0-8146-1475-2). Liturgical Pr.

Bonhoeffer, Dietrich. Psalms: The Prayer Book of the Bible. 2nd ed. Burtness, James H., tr. from Ger. LC 73-101111. Tr. of Das Gebetbuch der Bibel. 88p. 1974. 4.95 (ISBN 0-8066-1439-0, 10-5321). Augsburg.

The Book of Job: A New Translation According to the Traditional Hebrew Text. LC 79-25323. 88p. 1980. 7.50 (ISBN 0-8276-0172-7, 447). Jewish Pubns.

Botz, Paschal. Runways to God. LC 79-24756. 346p. (Orig.). 1979. pap. 3.50 (ISBN 0-8146-1059-5). Liturgical Pr.

Bradley, George G., ed. Lectures on the Book of Job Delivered in Westminster Abbey. 334p. 1981. Repr. of 1888 ed. lib. bdg. 50.00 (ISBN 0-89984-069-8). Century Bookbindery.

Brestin, Dee. Ecclesiastes: God's Wisdom for Evangelism. (Fisherman Bible Studyguide Ser.). 93p. 1980. saddle stitch 2.95 (ISBN 0-87788-212-6). Shaw Pubs.

Brestin, Dee & Brestin, Steve. Proverbs & Parables: God's Wisdom for Living. (Fisherman Bible Studyguide Ser.). 75p. 1975. saddle-stitch 2.95 (ISBN 0-87788-694-6). Shaw Pubs.

Bridges, C. Exposition of Psalm 119. 504p. 1986. 16.95 (ISBN 0-8254-2257-4). Kregel.

Bridges, Charles. Ecclesiastes. 319p. 1981. Repr. 12.95 (ISBN 0-85151-322-0). Banner of Truth.

--Proverbs. (Geneva Commentaries Ser.). 1979. 15.95 (ISBN 0-85151-088-4). Banner of Truth.

--Psalm One Hundred Nineteen. 1977. 13.95 (ISBN 0-85151-176-7). Banner of Truth.

Briggs, Charles & Briggs, Emile G. A Critical & Exegetical Commentary on Psalms, 2 vols. Driver, Samuel R., et al, eds. (International Critical Commentary). 24.95 ea. (Pub. by T & T Clark Ltd UK). Vol. 1, 1906, 580 pgs (ISBN 0-567-05011-4). Vol. 2, 1907, 580 pgs (ISBN 0-567-05012-2). Fortress.

Brown, John. The Sufferings & the Glories of the Messiah. (Giant Summit Bks.). 352p. 1981. pap. 5.95 (ISBN 0-8010-0792-5). Baker Bk.

Brownlow, Leroy. Living with the Psalms. 386p. 1976. 7.95 (ISBN 0-915720-17-5). Brownlow Pub Co.

Brueggemann, Walter. Praying the Psalms. LC 81-86045. (Illus.). 90p. (Orig.). 1982. pap. 6.95 (ISBN 0-88489-143-7). St Mary's.

Bullock, C. Hassell. Introduction to Old Testament Poetic Books. 1979. 11.95 (ISBN 0-8024-4143-2). Moody.

Bush, Barbara. Walking in Wisdom: A Woman's Workshop on Ecclesiastes. (Woman's Workshop Ser.). 128p. (Orig.). 1982. pap. 3.50 (ISBN 0-310-43041-0, 12014P). Zondervan.

Buttenwieser, Moses. The Psalms: Chronologically Treated with a New Translation. rev. ed. (Library of Biblical Studies Ser.). 1969. 59.50x (ISBN 0-87068-044-7). Ktav.

Campbell, Murdoch. From Grace to Glory: Meditations of the Psalms. 1979. pap. 5.45 (ISBN 0-85151-028-0). Banner of Truth.

Carr, G. Lloyd & Wiseman, D. J. The Song of Solomon. LC 83-22651. (Tyndale Old Testament Commentaries Ser.). 240p. 1984. 12.95 (ISBN 0-87784-918-8); pap. 6.95 (ISBN 0-87784-268-X). Inter-Varsity.

Champion, Richard G. Go on Singing. LC 76-20889. (Radiant Life). 128p. 1976. tchr's ed 3.95 (ISBN 0-88243-169-2, 32-0169); pap. 2.50 (ISBN 0-88243-895-6, 02-0895). Gospel Pub.

Chandler, Maggie. Seek Ye First: Song of Solomon. 128p. 1979. pap. 2.50 (ISBN 0-89114-089-1). Baptist Pub Hse.

Clarke Arthur G. Analytical Studies in the Psalms. LC 79-2518. 376p. 1979. 14.95 (ISBN 0-8254-2322-8). Kregel.

Clifford, Richard J. Psalms 1-72. (Collegeville Bible Commentary: Old Testament Ser.: Vol. 22). 80p. 1986. pap. 2.95. Liturgical Pr.

--Psalms 73-150. (Collegeville Bible Commentary: Old Testament Ser.: Vol. 23). 88p. 1986. pap. 2.95 (ISBN 0-8146-1479-5). Liturgical Pr.

Cox, Samuel. Commentary on Job. 562p. 1986. 18.95 (ISBN 0-8254-2328-7); pap. 14.95 (ISBN 0-8254-2330-9). Kregel.

Dahood, Mitchell, ed. Psalms One, One - Fifty. (Anchor Bible Ser.: Vol. 16). 1966. 16.00 (ISBN 0-385-02765-6, Anchor Pr). Doubleday.

--Psalms Three, One Hundred One - One Hundred Fifty. LC 66-11766. (Anchor Bible Ser.: Vol. 17A). 18.00 (ISBN 0-385-00607-1, Anchor Pr). Doubleday.

--Psalms Two, Fifty-One to One Hundred. LC 66-11766. (Anchor Bible Ser.: Vol. 17). 1966. 16.00 (ISBN 0-385-03759-7, Anchor Pr). Doubleday.

Davidson, Robert. Ecclesiastes & the Song of Solomon. LC 86-15659. (The Daily Study Bible - Old Testament Ser.). 168p. 1986. 14.95 (ISBN 0-664-21838-5); pap. 7.95 (ISBN 0-664-24589-7). Westminster.

Deegan, Paul J. Stickhandling & Passing. LC 76-8444. (Sports Instruction Ser.). (Illus.). 1976. PLB 8.95 (ISBN 0-87191-520-0); pap. 3.95 (ISBN 0-686-67437-5). Creative Ed.

Dickson, David. A Commentary on the Psalms, 2 vols. 1980. 32.50 (ISBN 0-86524-017-5, 1901). Klock & Klock.

--Psalms. (Geneva Commentary Ser.). 1064p. 1985. Repr. of 1653 ed. 21.95 (ISBN 0-85151-481-2). Banner of Truth.

Driver, Samuel R. A Critical & Exegetical Commentary on Job. Plummer, Alfred & Briggs, Charles, eds. LC 21-15647. (International Critical Commentary Ser.). 816p. 1921. 24.95 (ISBN 0-567-05010-6, Pub. by T & T Clark Ltd UK). Fortress.

Duquoc, Christian & Floristan, Casiano. Job & the Silence of God. (Concilium Ser. 1983: Vol. 169). 128p. (Orig.). 1983. pap. 6.95 (ISBN 0-8164-2449-7, HarpR). Har-Row.

Eaton, Michael A. Ecclesiastes. Wiseman, D. J., ed. (Tyndale Old Testament Commentary Ser.). 1983. 12.95 (ISBN 0-87784-963-3); pap. 6.95 (ISBN 0-87784-267-1). Inter-Varsity.

Fischer, James A. Song of Songs, Ruth, Lamentations, Ecclesiastes, Esther. (Collegeville Bible Commentary Ser.). 112p. 1986. pap. 2.95 (ISBN 0-8146-1480-9). Liturgical pr.

Fogle, Willa. Beside the Still Waters. 1979. pap. 4.00 (ISBN 0-87516-282-7). De Vorss.

Fuerst, W. J. Ruth, Esther, Ecclesiastes, the Song of Songs, Lamentations. LC 74-82589. (Cambridge Bible Commentary on the New English Bible, Old Testament Ser.). 250p. 1975. 32.50 (ISBN 0-521-20651-0); pap. 11.95 (ISBN 0-521-09920-X). Cambridge U Pr.

Gibson, Edgar C. The Book of Job. 266p. 1983. lib. bdg. 10.00 (ISBN 0-86524-170-8, 1801). Klock & Klock.

Gibson, John C. Job. LC 85-13652. (Daily Study Bible - Old Testament). 294p. 1985. 16.95 (ISBN 0-664-21815-6); pap. 8.95 (ISBN 0-664-24584-6). Westminster.

Ginsburg, David C. Coheleth & Song of Songs, with a Commentary Historical & Critical, 2 Vols. in 1. rev. ed. (Library of Biblical Studies Ser). 1970. 59.50x (ISBN 0-87068-059-5). Ktav.

God's Wisdom for Daily Living. LC 84-4817. 352p. 1984. 16.95 (ISBN 0-8407-5373-X). Nelson.

Goldberg, Louis. Ecclesiastes: Bible Study Commentary. 1986. pap. 4.95 (ISBN 0-310-41823-2, 18199P). Zondervan.

Gordis, Robert. The Book of God & Man. LC 65-25126. 1978. pap. 12.95x (ISBN 0-226-30410-8, P771, Phoen). U of Chicago Pr.

--The Book of Job: Commentary, New Translation & Special Studies. LC 78-2305. (Moreshet Ser.: No. 2). 1977. 45.00 (ISBN 0-87334-003-5). Ktav.

--Koheleth: The Man & His World: A Study of Ecclesiastes. rev. ed. LC 67-26988. 1968. pap. 10.95 (ISBN 0-8052-0166-1). Schocken.

Greene, Carol. Proverbs-Important Things to Know. 1980. pap. 0.99 (ISBN 0-570-06140-7, 59-1303, Arch Bk). Concordia.

Guinan, Michael D. Job. (Collegeville Bible Commentary: Old Testament Ser.: Vol. 19). 88p. 1986. pap. 2.95 (ISBN 0-8146-1476-0). Liturgical Pr.

Gutierrez, Rolando C. El Mensaje de los Salmos en Nuestro Contexto, Tomo II. 160p. 1980. pap. 4.95 (ISBN 0-311-04025-X). Casa Bautista.

Guyon, Jeanne. Song of Songs. 1983. pap. 5.95 (ISBN 0-940232-16-2). Christian Bks.

Habel, N. C. Book of Job. LC 74-82588. (Cambridge Bible Commentary on the New English Bible, Old Testament Ser.). 250p. 1975. 27.95 (ISBN 0-521-20653-7); pap. 12.95 (ISBN 0-521-09943-9). Cambridge U Pr.

Habel, Norman C. The Book of Job, a Commentary. LC 84-21580. (The Old Testament Library). 586p. 1985. 39.95 (ISBN 0-664-21831-8). Westminster.

Hadley, E. C. The Song of Solomon. pap. 3.95 (ISBN 0-88172-080-1). Believers Bkshelf.

Hansen, Carlton D. Beacon Small-Group Bible Studies: Proverbs, Wisdom for Today's Challenges. 80p. (Orig.). 1984. pap. 2.50 (ISBN 0-8341-0905-0). Beacon Hill.

Hepburn, Daisy. Never Underestimate the Power of God's Woman. LC 84-3337. (Life with Spice Bible Study Ser.). 1984. 2.95 (ISBN 0-8307-0948-7, 6101856). Regal.

Hirschler, Gertrude, tr. from German. The Psalms: Translation & Commentary by Rabbi Samson Raphael Hirsch. (Compact Ser.). 1978. 16.95 (ISBN 0-87306-135-7). Feldheim.

Holland, G. A. A True Love Story. Date not set. 14.95 (ISBN 0-533-06799-5). Vantage.

Hubbard, David. Beyond Futility. 2nd ed. Semarians, Beer-Shiba, tr. (Chinese.). 106p. 1982. pap. write for info (ISBN 0-941598-02-0). Living Spring Pubns.

Ironside, H. A. Psalms, Studies on Book One. 8.95 (ISBN 0-87213-383-4). Loizeaux.

Jansen, J. Gerald, et al, eds. Job: A Bible Commentary for Teaching & Preaching. LC 84-48512. (Interpretation Ser.). 288p. 1985. 18.95 (ISBN 0-8042-3114-1). John Knox.

Jastrow, Morris. A Gentle Cynic: Being a Translation of the Book of Koheleth Commonly Known As Ecclesiastes Stripped of Later Additions Also Its Origin, Growth & Interpretation. 255p. 1985. Repr. of 1919 ed. 50.00 (ISBN 0-8495-2810-0). Arden Lib.

--A Gentle Cynic: Translation of the Book of Koheleth Commonly Known As Ecclesiastes Stripped of Later Additions Also Its Origins, Growth, & Interpretation. 1978. Repr. of 1919 ed. lib. bdg. 35.00 (ISBN 0-8495-2733-3). Arden Lib.

Jastrow, Morris, Jr. A Gentle Cynic. 242p. 1980. Repr. of 1919 ed. lib. bdg. 35.00 (ISBN 0-89984-258-5). Century Bookbindery.

Jensen, Irving L. Ecclesiastes & the Song of Solomon. (Bible Self Study Guide Ser.). 1974. pap. 3.25 (ISBN 0-8024-1021-9). Moody.

John Of Ford. Sermons on the Final Verses of the Song of Songs, Vol. 2. Beckett, Wendy M., tr. from Latin. (Cistercian Fathers Ser.: No. 39). 1982. 21.95 (ISBN 0-87907-639-9). Cistercian Pubns.

Johnston, Leonard & Smith, Michael. Psalms & Wisdom. Bright, Laurence, ed. LC 71-173033. (Scripture Discussion Commentary Ser.: Pt. 6). 256p. 1972. pap. text ed. 4.50. ACTA Found.

Johnston, Robert. Psalms for God's People. LC 82-5344. (Bible Commentary for Laymen Ser.). 160p. 1982. pap. 3.50 (ISBN 0-8307-0820-0, S362105). Regal.

Kaiser, Walter C., Jr. Ecclesiastes: Total Life. (Everyman's Bible Commentary Ser.). 1979. pap. 5.95 (ISBN 0-8024-2022-2). Moody.

Keel, Othmar. The Symbolism of the Biblical World Ancient Near Eastern Iconography & the Book of Psalms. (Illus.). 1978. 39.50x (ISBN 0-8245-0376-7). Crossroad NY.

Keller, Phillip. A Shepard's Look at Psalm 23. 1976. 8.95 (ISBN 0-310-26790-0, 6780); large print 6.95 (ISBN 0-310-26797-8, 12553L). Zondervan.

--La Vida en el Redil. Vargas, Carlos A., tr. from Eng. LC 76-14500. Tr. of A Shepherd Looks at Psalm Twenty-Three. (Span.). 141p. 1976. pap. 3.50 (ISBN 0-89922-073-8). Edit Caribe.

Kelly, Balmer H. Ezra-Job. LC 59-10454. (Layman's Bible Commentary, Vol. 8). 1962. 4.95 (ISBN 0-8042-3008-0); pap. 3.95 (ISBN 0-8042-3068-4). John Knox.

Kidner, Derek. The Message of Ecclesiastes. LC 76-21460. (Bible Speaks Today Ser.). 1976. pap. 5.95 (ISBN 0-87784-286-8). Inter-Varsity.

Kidner, F. Derek. Proverbs. LC 75-23850. (Tyndale Old Testament Commentary Ser.). 12.95 (ISBN 0-87784-861-0); pap. 6.95 (ISBN 0-87784-266-3). Inter-Varsity.

Kirkpatrick, A. F. Psalms. (Thornapple Commentaries Ser.). 964p. 1982. pap. 19.95 (ISBN 0-8010-5453-2). Baker Bk.

Klug, Ron. Job: God's Answer to Suffering. (Fisherman Bible Studyguide Ser.). 61p. 1982. saddle-stitched 2.95 (ISBN 0-87788-430-7). Shaw Pubs.

Knoch, A. E. Concordant Studies in the Book of Daniel. rev. ed. 1968. pap. 4.00 (ISBN 0-910424-53-5). Concordant.

Kretz, Thomas. North American Psalms. LC 81-69454. 166p. 1981. pap. 4.95 (ISBN 0-933402-24-4). Charisma Pr.

Lane, Laura B. Praise the Lord with Psalms: Metrical Paraphrases of Selected Psalms. 1986. 5.95 (ISBN 0-533-06823-1). Vantage.

Larsen, Paul E. Wise up & Live. 2nd ed. LC 73-86222. 256p. pap. 3.50 (ISBN 0-8307-0453-1, S274124). Regal.

Lawrence, Anthony. The Psalm Locator. 2nd ed. (Orig.). 1985. pap. 10.95 (ISBN 0-89390-063-X). Resource Pubns.

Leiman, Harold I. Koheleth. 1978. 8.95 (ISBN 0-87306-143-8); pap. 2.95. Feldheim.

Leupold, Herbert C. Exposition of Ecclesiastes. 1966. 12.95 (ISBN 0-8010-5505-9). Baker Bk.

--Exposition of Psalms. 1970. 24.95 (ISBN 0-8010-5521-0). Baker Bk.

Limburg, James. Psalms for Sojourners. LC 86-2621. (Illus.). 112p. (Orig.). 1986. pap. 5.95 (ISBN 0-8066-2206-7, 10-5306). Augsburg.

Luther, Martin. Luther's Works, Vol. 12 Psalms. LC 55-9893. 1955. 15.95 (ISBN 0-570-06412-0, 15-1754). Concordia.

--Luther's Works, Vol. 14 Selected Psalms 3. LC 55-9893. 1958. 14.95 (ISBN 0-570-06414-7, 15-1756). Concordia.

--Luther's Works: Selected Psalms 2, Vol. 13. Pelikan, Jaroslav, ed. LC 55-9893. 1956. 16.95 (ISBN 0-570-06413-9, 15-1755). Concordia.

Luther's Works: Genesis Chapters 26-30, Vol. 5. LC 55-9893. 1967. 15.95 (ISBN 0-570-06405-8, 15-1747). Concordia.

McEachern, Alton H. Layman's Bible Book Commentary: Psalms Vol. 8. LC 79-56593. 1981. 5.95 (ISBN 0-8054-1178-X). Broadman.

McKane, William. Proverbs: A New Approach. LC 75-108185. (Old Testament Library). 692p. 1970. Westminster.

McKenna, David. Job (CC) 320p. 1986. 18.95 (ISBN 0-317-43277-X). Word Bks.

--Job (CC, Vol. 12. 320p. 1986. 18.95 (ISBN 0-8499-0418-8). Word Bks.

Makrakis, Apostolos. Commentary on the Psalms of David. Orthodox Christian Educational Society, ed. Cummings, Denver, tr. from Hellenic. 990p. 1950. 16.00x (ISBN 0-938366-19-X). Orthodox Chr.

Meyer, F. B. Choice Notes on the Psalms. LC 84-17109. (F. B. Meyer Memorial Library). 192p. 1984. pap. text ed. 7.95 (ISBN 0-8254-3242-1). Kregel.

Montgomery, Herb & Montgomery, Mary. The Joy of the Psalms. (Illus.). 64p. (Orig.). 1982. pap. 7.95 (ISBN 0-86683-631-4, HarpR). Har-Row.

Morgan, G. Campbell. Notes on the Psalms. 288p. 1947. 14.95 (ISBN 0-8007-0241-7). Revell.

Morris, Henry M. Sampling the Psalms. LC 78-55613. 1978. pap. 5.95 (ISBN 0-89051-049-0). Master Bks.

Muehlenberg, Ekkehard. Psalmenkommentare aus der Katenenueberlieferung: Untersuchungen zu den Psalmenkatenen, Vol. 3. (Patristische Texte und Studien: No. 19). 1978. 41.20x (ISBN 3-11-006959-8). De Gruyter.

--Psalmenkommentware aus Katenenveberlieferung, Vol. 2. (Patristische Texte und Studien: Vol. 16). 1977. 59.60x (ISBN 3-11-005717-4). De Gruyter.

Murphy, Joseph. Living Without Strain. 157p. 1973. pap. 3.95 (ISBN 0-87516-187-1). De Vorss.

Murphy, Roland E. The Psalms, Job. LC 77-78637. (Proclamation Commentaries: the Old Testament Witnesses for Preaching). (Orig.). 1977. pap. 4.95 (ISBN 0-8006-0588-8, 1-588). Fortress.

Neale, John M., ed. A Commentary on the Psalms from Primitive & Mediaeval Writers. LC 78-130990. 1976. Repr. of 1887 ed. 205.00 (ISBN 0-404-04680-0). AMS Pr.

Nee, Watchman. Song of Songs. 1965-1967. pap. 2.95 (ISBN 0-87508-420-6). Chr Lit.

O'Donnell, J. D. & Hampton, Ralph, Jr. A Survey of the Books of Poetry. 1976. pap. 2.25 (ISBN 0-89265-033-8). Randall Hse.

Office of Worship for the Presbyterian Church (U. S. A.) & Cumberland Presbyterian Church. A Psalm Sampler. LC 85-753089. (Illus.). 48p. 1986. pap. 4.95 ea. (ISBN 0-664-24681-8). Westminster.

Oglivie, Lloyd J. Falling into Greatness. LC 84-1946. 224p. 1984. 11.95 (ISBN 0-8407-5326-8). Nelson.

Owens, Mary F. Salt from the Psalter. LC 80-67147. 1981. pap. 4.95 (ISBN 0-8054-1218-2). Broadman.

Pahl, Paul D., tr. Luther's Works, Vol 7. LC 55-9893. 1964. 15.95 (ISBN 0-570-06407-4, 15-1749). Concordia.

--Luther's Works: Genesis Chapters 45-50, Vol. 8. LC 55-9893. 1965. 14.95 (ISBN 0-570-06408-2, 15-1750). Concordia.

Patterson, Paige. Song of Solomon. (Everyman's Bible Commentary Ser.). (Orig.). 1986. pap. 5.95 (ISBN 0-8024-2057-5). Moody.

Pelikan, Jaroslav, ed. Luther's Works, Vol. 9. LC 55-9893. 1960. 14.95 (ISBN 0-570-06409-0, 15-1751). Concordia.

--Luther's Works, Vol. 22. Bertram, Martin, tr. LC 55-9893. 1957. 17.95 (ISBN 0-570-06422-8, 15-1764). Concordia.

--Luther's Works, Vol. 24. Bertram, Martin H., tr. LC 55-9893. 1961. 16.95 (ISBN 0-570-06424-4, 15-1766). Concordia.

--Luther's Works: Genesis Chapters 1-5, Vol. 1. Schick, George V., tr. LC 55-9893. 1958. 15.95 (ISBN 0-570-06401-5, 15-1743). Concordia.

--Luther's Works: Genesis Chapters 15-20, Vol. 3. Schick, George V., tr. LC 55-9893. 1961. 15.95 (ISBN 0-570-06403-1, 15-1745). Concordia.

--Luther's Works: Genesis Chapters 6-11, Vol. 2. Schick, George V., tr. LC 55-9893. 1960. 16.95 (ISBN 0-570-06402-3, 15-1744). Concordia.

Pelikan, Jaroslav, et al, trs. from Lat. Luther's Works, Vol. 15, Letters On Ecclesiastes, Song Of Solomon, & The Last Words Of David. LC 55-9893. 1971. 15.95 (ISBN 0-570-06415-5, 15-1757). Concordia.

Peterson, Eugene H. A Long Obedience in the Same Direction. LC 79-2715. 1980. pap. 6.95 (ISBN 0-87784-727-4). Inter-Varsity.

Pillai, K. C. Orientalisms of the Bible, Vol. 2. 1974. 4.95x (ISBN 0-912178-04-3). Mor-Mac.

Plumer, W. S. Psalms. (Geneva Commentaries Ser.). 1978. 32.95 (ISBN 0-85151-209-7). Banner of Truth.

Pope, Marvin H., ed. Job. rev. ed. (Anchor Bible Ser.: Vol. 15). 1973. 18.00 (ISBN 0-385-00894-5, Anchor Pr). Doubleday.

Pope, Marvin H., tr. Song of Songs. LC 72-79417. (Anchor Bible Ser.: Vol. 7C). (Illus.). 1977. 18.00 (ISBN 0-385-00569-5, Anchor Pr). Doubleday.

Rhodes, Arnold B. Psalms. LC 59-10454. (Layman's Bible Commentary Ser: Vol. 9). 1960. 4.25 (ISBN 0-8042-3009-9); pap. 4.95 (ISBN 0-8042-3069-2). John Knox.

Ricker, Robert S. & Pitkin, Ron. Soulsearch: Hope for Twenty-First Century Living from Ecclesiastes. rev. ed. LC 85-21594. (Bible Commentary for Laymen Ser.). 168p. 1985. pap. 4.25 (ISBN 0-8307-1100-7, S393118). Regal.

Ridderbos, N. H. Die Psalmen: Stilistische Verfahren und Aufbau mit besonderer Beruecksichtigung von Ps. 1-41. Mittring, Karl E., tr. from Dutch. (Beiheft 117 zur Zeitschrift fuer die alttestamentliche Wissenschaft). 305p. 1972. 41.60x (ISBN 3-11-001834-9). De Gruyter.

Ridout, Samuel. Job. 1919. pap. 3.95 (ISBN 0-87213-719-8). Loizeaux.

Rogerson, John W. Psalms, 1-50. LC 76-27911. (Cambridge Bible Commentary on the New English Bible, Old Testament Ser.). 1977. 37.50 (ISBN 0-521-21463-7); pap. 11.95 (ISBN 0-521-29160-7). Cambridge U Pr.

--Psalms, 101-150. LC 76-27911. (Cambridge Bible Commentary on the New English Bible, Old Testament Ser.). 1977. 37.50 (ISBN 0-521-21465-3); pap. 11.95 (ISBN 0-521-29162-3). Cambridge U Pr.

--Psalms, 51-100. LC 76-27911. (Cambridge Bible Commentary on the New English Bible, Old Testament Ser.). 1977. 37.50 (ISBN 0-521-21464-5); pap. 11.95 (ISBN 0-521-29161-5). Cambridge U Pr.

Rowley, H. H. Job. rev. ed. (New Century Bible Ser.). 302p. 1976. 9.95 (ISBN 0-551-00596-3). Attic Pr.

Rylaarsdam, J. Coert. Proverbs, Ecclesiastes, Song of Solomon. LC 59-10454. (Layman's Bible Commentary Ser: Vol. 10). 1964. pap. 4.95 (ISBN 0-8042-3070-6). John Knox.

Sabourin, Leopold. The Psalms: Their Origin & Meaning. LC 73-16459. 560p. (Orig.). 1974. pap. 12.95 (ISBN 0-8189-0121-7). Alba.

Santa, George F. A Modern Study in the Book of Proverbs: Charles Bridges Classic Revised for Today's Reader. LC 78-7667. (Illus.). 1978. kiver bdg. 17.95 (ISBN 0-915134-27-6); incl. study guide (ISBN 0-915134-49-7). Mott Media.

Scammon, John H. Proverbs: Good Advice for Good Living. LC 78-24505. 1979. pap. 3.95 (ISBN 0-8170-0819-5). Judson.

Schreck, Nancy & Leach, Maureen. Psalms Anew. 208p. (Orig.). 1986. pap. 6.95 (ISBN 0-88489-174-7). St Mary's.

Scott, R. B., ed. Proverbs & Ecclesiastes. LC 65-13988. (Anchor Bible Ser.: No. 18). 1965. 14.00 (ISBN 0-385-02177-1, Anch). Doubleday.

Seals, Thomas L. Proverbs: Wisdom for All Ages. 5.50 (ISBN 0-89137-529-5). Quality Pubns.

Shakhnazarov, G. Socialist Democracy. 150p. 1974. pap. 2.95 (ISBN 0-8285-0412-1, Pub. by Progress Pubs USSR). Imported Pubns.

Simundson, Daniel J. The Message of Job: A Theological Commentary. LC 84-24214. (Augsburg Old Testament Studies). 192p. (Orig.). 1986. pap. 9.95 (ISBN 0-8066-2218-0, 10-4349). Augsburg.

Snaith, John G., ed. Ecclesiasticus: Or, the Wisdom of Jesus Son of Sirach. LC 73-82459. (Cambridge Bible Commentary on the New English Bible, Old Testament Ser.). 180p. 1974. 32.50 (ISBN 0-521-08657-4); pap. 10.95 (ISBN 0-521-09775-4). Cambridge U Pr.

Spurgeon, Charles H. The Treasury of David - A Commentary on the Psalms, 3 vols. 2912p. Date not set. 49.95 (ISBN 0-917006-25-9). Hendrickson MA.

Sputnik Psalomtschika-odnogolosnij obikhod. Tr. of The Psalm-Readers Companion, Unison & Obikhod. 624p. 1959. pap. 30.00 (ISBN 0-317-30389-9). Holy Trinity.

Stamm, Millie. Beside Still Waters: Meditation Moments on the Psalms. 144p. 1983. gift edition 9.95 (ISBN 0-310-33060-2, 10743). Zondervan.

Stuhlmueller, Carroll. Psalms One. (Old Testament Message Ser.: Vol. 21). 16.95 (ISBN 0-89453-421-1); pap. 12.95 (ISBN 0-89453-255-3). M Glazier.

--Psalms Two. (Old Testament Message Ser.: Vol. 22). 15.95 (ISBN 0-89453-422-X); pap. 10.95 (ISBN 0-89453-257-X). M Glazier.

Tassell, Paul. Secrets of the Blessed Man. 1971. pap. 2.95 (ISBN 0-87227-033-5). Reg Baptist.

Taylor, Hudson. Union & Communion. 96p. 1971. pap. 2.95 (ISBN 0-87123-571-4, 200571). Bethany Hse.

Trenchard, Ernesto. Introduccion a los Libros de Sabiduria y Job. (Span.). 152p. 1972. 4.50 (ISBN 0-8254-1746-5); pap. 3.50 (ISBN 0-8254-1745-7). Kregel.

Twombly, Gerald H. The Penetrating Poets. 112p. 1982. pap. 4.95 (ISBN 0-88469-151-9). BMH Bks.

Vander Ark, Nelle A. Sharing from the Psalms. 64p. 1984. pap. 2.95 (ISBN 0-8010-9295-7). Baker Bk.

Waddey, John. Ecclesiastes & Song of Solomon. 1986. pap. 5.50 (ISBN 0-89137-565-1). Quality Pubns.

Walsh, Kilian, tr. Bernard of Clairvaux on the Song of Songs, Vol. I. (Cistercian Fathers Er.: No. 4). pap. 5.00 (ISBN 0-87907-104-4). Cistercian Pubns.

Wardlaw, Ralph. Exposition of Ecclesiastes. 432p. 1982. lib. bdg. 16.25 Smythe Sewn (ISBN 0-86524-147-3, 2102). Klock & Klock.

Warner, Anna. The Melody of the Twenty-Third Psalm. pap. 1.95 (ISBN 0-685-88385-X). Reiner.

Watson. Divine Love Song. pap. 3.50 (ISBN 0-686-12866-4). Schmul Pub Co.

Way, Arthur S. Letters of Paul, Hebrews & Psalms. LC 81-1092. 504p. 1981. text ed. 14.95 (ISBN 0-8254-4016-5). Kregel.

Weiser, Artur. Psalms: A Commentary. LC 62-16760. (Old Testament Library). 842p. 1962. 29.50 (ISBN 0-664-20418-X). Westminster.

Westermann, Claus. The Structure of the Book of Job: A Form-Critical Analysis. Muenchow, Charles A., tr. from Ger. LC 80-2379. Tr. of Der Aufbau des Buches Hiob. 160p. 1981. 14.95 (ISBN 0-8006-0651-5, 1-651). Fortress.

Whybray, R. N. The Book of Proverbs. LC 70-171687. (New English Bible Commentaries, Old Testament). (Illus.). 192p. 1972. 24.95 (ISBN 0-521-08364-8); pap. 10.95x (ISBN 0-521-09679-0). Cambridge U Pr.

Willis, John T. Insights from the Psalms, Vol. 2. LC 73-93946. (Way of Life Ser.: No. 132). 111p. 1974. pap. 3.95 (ISBN 0-89112-132-3, Bibl Res Pr). Abilene Christ U.

--Insights from the Psalms, Vol. 3. LC 73-93946. (Way of Life Ser: No. 133). 114p. 1974. pap. 3.95 (ISBN 0-89112-133-1, Bibl Res Pr). Abilene Christ U.

Willis, John Thomas. Insights from the Psalms, Vol. 1. LC 73-93946. (Way of Life Ser: No. 131). 1974. pap. text ed. 3.95 (ISBN 0-89112-131-5, Bibl Res Pr). Abilene Christ U.

Yates, Kyle M. Psalms of Joy & Faith. 216p. 1984. pap. 7.95 (ISBN 0-913029-03-3). Stevens Bk Pr.

Zuck, Roy. Job. (Everyman's Bible Commentary Ser.). 1978. pap. 5.95 (ISBN 0-8024-2017-6). Moody.

BIBLE–COMMENTARIES–O. T. PROPHETS

see also Bible–Commentaries–O. T. Minor Prophets

Achtemeier, Elizabeth. Nahum-Malachi. LC 85-45458. (Interpretation Ser.). 216p. 1986. 17.95 (ISBN 0-8042-3129-X). John Knox.

Alexander, Ralph. Ezekiel. (Everyman's Bible Commentary Ser). 160p. (Orig.). 1976. pap. 5.95 (ISBN 0-8024-2026-5). Moody.

Anderson, R. A. The International Theological Commentary on Daniel. Knight, George A., ed. (The International Theological Commentary Ser.). 192p. (Orig.). 1984. pap. 7.95 (ISBN 0-8028-1038-1). Eerdmans.

Andre, G. Jeremiah, the Prophet. (Let's Discuss It Ser.). pap. 1.95 (ISBN 0-88172-135-2). Believers Bkshelf.

Ash, Anthony. Commentary on Jeremiah & Lamentations. 500p. 1987. 16.95 (ISBN 0-915547-94-5). Abilene Christ U.

Baldwin, Joyce. Lamentations-Daniel. (Bible Study Commentaries Ser.). 128p. 1984. pap. 4.95 (ISBN 0-317-43378-4). Chr Lit.

Baldwin, Joyce G. Daniel. Wiseman, D. J., ed. LC 78-18547. (Tyndale Old Testament Commentary Ser.). 1978. 12.95 (ISBN 0-87784-961-7); pap. 6.95 (ISBN 0-87784-273-6). Inter-Varsity.

Beacon Bible Commentary Staff. Hosea-Malachi, Vol. V. 13.95 (ISBN 0-8010-0692-9). Baker Bk.

Blair, J. Allen. Daniel: Living Courageously. LC 70-140898. 1971. pap. 4.95 (ISBN 0-87213-044-4). Loizeaux.

Braverman, Jay. Jerome's Commentary on Daniel: A Study of Comparative Jewish & Christian Interpretations of the Hebrew Bible. LC 78-55726. (Catholic Biblical Quarterly Monographs: No. 7). xvi, 162p. 1978. 4.00 (ISBN 0-915170-06-X). Catholic Biblical.

Bright, John, tr. Jeremiah. LC 65-13603. (Anchor Bible Ser.: Vol. 21). 1965. 20.00 (ISBN 0-385-00823-6, Anchor Pr). Doubleday.

Brown, John. The Sufferings & the Glories of the Messiah. (Giant Summit Bks.). 352p. 1981. pap. 5.95 (ISBN 0-8010-0792-5). Baker Bk.

Brownlee, William. Ezekiel: (WBC, Vol. 28. 384p. 1986. 22.95 (ISBN 0-8499-0227-4). Word Bks.

Buchan, James, et al, eds. Jeddah Old & New. rev. ed. (Illus.). 144p. 1986. Repr. of 1980 ed. 32.50 (ISBN 0-905743-22-9, Pub. by Stacey Intl UK). Humanities.

Bultema, Harry. Commentary on Isaiah. LC 81-11795. 650p. 1981. 16.95 (ISBN 0-8254-2258-2). Kregel.

Butler, Paul. Isaiah, Vol. III. (The Bible Study Textbook). (Illus.). 1978. 14.30 (ISBN 0-89900-022-3). College Pr Pub.

Butler, Trent C. Layman's Bible Book Commentary: Isaiah, Vol. 10. LC 80-68890. 1983. 5.95 (ISBN 0-8054-1180-1). Broadman.

Calvin, John. Daniel. Myers, Thomas, ed. (Geneva Commentary Ser.). 816p. 1986. Repr. of 1853 ed. 19.95 (ISBN 0-85151-092-2). Banner of Truth.

Carley, K. W. The Book of the Prophet Ezekiel. LC 73-94352. (Cambridge Bible Commentary on the New English Bible Ser.). (Illus.). 340p. (Orig.). 1974. 34.50 (ISBN 0-521-08653-1); pap. 13.95 (ISBN 0-521-09755-X). Cambridge U Pr.

Carroll, Robert P. Jeremiah, a Commentary. LC 85-13655. (Old Testament Library). 880p. 1986. 38.95 (ISBN 0-664-21835-0). Westminster.

Clifford, Richard J. Fair-Spoken & Persuading: An Interpretation of Second Isaiah. (Theological Inquiries Ser.). (Orig.). 1984. pap. 8.95. Paulist Pr.

Cody, Aelred. Ezekiel: With Excursus on Old Testament Priesthood. (Old Testament Message Ser.: Vol. 11). 1984. 12.95 (ISBN 0-89453-411-4); pap. 9.95 (ISBN 0-89453-245-6). M Glazier.

Collins, John J. Daniel: With an Introduction to Apocalyptic Literature. Knierim, Rolf, et al, eds. (The Forms of the Old Testament Literature Ser.: Vol. XX). 160p. (Orig.). 1984. pap. 12.95 (ISBN 0-8028-0020-3). Eerdmans.

--Isaiah. (Collegeville Bible Commentary Ser.). 144p. 1986. pap. 2.95 (ISBN 0-8146-1420-5). Liturgical Pr.

Cooke, G. A. A Critical & Exegetical Commentary on Ezekiel. Driver, Samuel R., et al, eds. LC 38-1268. (International Critical Commentary Ser.). 608p. 1936. 24.95 (ISBN 0-567-05016-5, Pub. by T & T Clark Ltd UK). Fortress.

Craven, Toni. Ezekiel, Daniel. (Collegeville Bible Commentary Ser.). 144p. 1986. pap. 2.95 (ISBN 0-8146-1423-X). Liturgical Pr.

Criswell, W. A. Expository Sermons on the Book of Ezekiel. 272p. 1987. 12.95 (ISBN 0-310-23010-1, 18352). Zondervan.

Culver, Robert D. The Histories & Prophecies of Daniel. 192p. (Orig.). 1980. pap. 4.95 (ISBN 0-88469-131-4). BMH Bks.

Cunliffe-Jones, H., ed. Book of Jeremiah. 1961. 8.95 (ISBN 0-02-529260-9). Macmillan.

Dalglish, Edward H. Layman's Bible Book Commentary: Jeremiah, Lamentations, Vol. 11. LC 81-65801. 1984. 5.95 (ISBN 0-8054-1181-X). Broadman.

Dasbach, Fernando L. Blight or Bloom. 198p. 1981. 12.50 (ISBN 0-686-28998-6). Regenbogen-Verlag.

Davis, Moshe, ed. Call to America to Build Zion: An Original Anthology. LC 77-70723. (America & the Holy Land Ser.). 1977. lib. bdg. 20.00x (ISBN 0-405-10306-9). Ayer Co Pubs.

Dickinson, George T. Jeremiah: The Iron Prophet. (Horizon Ser.). 1978. pap. 5.95 (ISBN 0-8127-0183-6). Review & Herald.

Eisemann, Moshe. Yechezkel-Ezekiel, 3 vols. (Art Scroll Tanach Ser.). (Illus.). 832p. 1980. Set. 55.95 (ISBN 0-89906-085-4); Set. pap. 45.95 (ISBN 0-89906-086-2). Mesorah Pubns.

--Yechezkel-Ezekiel, Vol. 2. (Art Scroll Tanach Ser.). 272p. 1980. 17.95 (ISBN 0-89906-077-3); pap. 14.95 (ISBN 0-89906-078-1). Mesorah Pubns.

--Yechezkel-Ezekiel, Vol. 3. (Art Scroll Tanach Ser.). (Illus.). 208p. 1980. 17.95 (ISBN 0-89906-083-8); pap. 14.95 (ISBN 0-89906-084-6). Mesorah Pubns.

Elliger, K., ed. Twelve Prophets. (Biblia Hebraica Stuttgartensia Ser.). x, 96p. 1970. pap. 2.50x (ISBN 3-438-05210-5, 61261, Pub. by German Bible Society). Am Bible.

Ellis, Peter F. Jeremiah, Baruch. (Collegeville Bible Commentary Ser.). 136p. 1986. pap. 2.95 (ISBN 0-8146-1421-3). Liturgical Pr.

Ellison, Harold. Portavoces del Eterno. Orig. Title: Old Testament Prophets. (Span.). 214p. 1982. pap. 7.50 (ISBN 0-8254-1201-3). Kregel.

Enns, Paul P. Ezekiel. (Bible Study Commentary Ser.). 224p. 1986. pap. 7.95 (ISBN 0-310-44071-8). Zondervan.

Feinberg, Charles L. Prophecy of Ezekiel. 1984. 11.95 (ISBN 0-8024-6908-6). Moody.

Fischer, James A. Song of Songs, Ruth, Lamentations, Ecclesiastes, Esther. (Collegeville Bible Commentary Ser.). 112p. 1986. pap. 2.95 (ISBN 0-8146-1480-9). Liturgical pr.

Following God's Trailblazers: Kings & Prophets 14 Lessons, Vol. 4. (Footsteps of Faith Ser.). 1958. pap. text ed. 2.50 (ISBN 0-86508-033-X); figures text 11.45 (ISBN 0-86508-034-8). BCM Intl Inc.

Freehof, Solomon B. The Book of Jeremiah: A Commentary. LC 77-8259. 1977. 15.00 (ISBN 0-8074-0008-4, 381610). UAHC.

--Ezekiel: A Commentary. 1979. 15.00 (ISBN 0-8074-0033-5, 380010). UAHC.

--Isaiah: A Commentary. 1972. 15.00 (ISBN 0-8074-0042-4, 383015). UAHC.

Fuerst, W. J. Ruth, Esther, Ecclesiastes, the Song of Songs, Lamentations. LC 74-82589. (Cambridge Bible Commentary on the New English Bible, Old Testament Ser.). 250p. 1975. 32.50 (ISBN 0-521-20651-0); pap. 11.95 (ISBN 0-521-09920-X). Cambridge U Pr.

Gaebelein, Frank E., ed. Expositor's Bible Commentary: Daniel & the Minor Prophets, Vol. 7. 752p. 1985. text ed. 24.95 (ISBN 0-310-36490-6, 11176). Zondervan.

--The Expositor's Bible Commentary: Isaiah, Jeremiah, Lamentations, Ezekiel, Vol. 6. 1088p. 1986. 29.95 (ISBN 0-310-36480-9, 11175). Zondervan.

Goldwurm, Hersh. Daniel. (The Art Scroll Tanach Ser.). 352p. 1979. 16.95 (ISBN 0-89906-079-X); pap. 13.95 (ISBN 0-89906-080-3). Mesorah Pubns.

Gray, George B. A Critical & Exegetical Commentary on Isaiah. Driver, Samuel R., et al, eds. (International Critical Commentary Ser.). 567p. 1912. 24.95 (ISBN 0-567-05015-7, Pub. by T & T Clark Ltd UK). Fortress.

Greenberg, Moshe. Ezekiel, 1-20: A New Translation with Introduction & Commentary. LC 77-12855. (Anchor Bible Ser.: Vol. 22). (Illus.). 408p. 1983. 16.00 (ISBN 0-385-00954-2, Anchor Pr). Doubleday.

Gutzke, Manford G. Plain Talk on Isaiah. 1977. pap. 6.95 (ISBN 0-310-25551-1, 9854P). Zondervan.

Hailey, Homer. A Commentary on Isaiah. 544p. 1985. 17.95 (ISBN 0-8010-4292-5). Baker Bk.

Harrison, R. K. Jeremiah & Lamentations. LC 72-97951. 240p. 1973. 12.95 (ISBN 0-87784-864-5); pap. 6.95 (ISBN 0-87784-271-X). Inter-Varsity.

Hartman, Louis F. & Di Lella, Alexander A. The Book of Daniel: A New Translation with Introduction & Commentary. LC 77-82762. (Anchor Bible Ser.: Vol. 23). 1978. 18.00 (ISBN 0-385-01322-1, Anchor Pr). Doubleday.

Herald of Hope (Isaiah) Leader's Guide. (New Horizons Bible Study Ser.). 48p. (Orig.). 1984. pap. 1.95 (ISBN 0-89367-101-0). Light & Life.

Herbert, A. S. The Book of the Prophet Isaiah. LC 74-16997. (Cambridge Bible Commentary on the New English Bible, Old Testament Ser.). (Illus.). 250p. 1975. Bks. 1-39. pap. 12.95 (ISBN 0-521-09766-5); Bks. 40-66. 27.95 (ISBN 0-521-20721-5); pap. 12.95 (ISBN 0-521-09933-1). Cambridge U Pr.

--The Book of the Prophet Isaiah, 1-39. LC 73-79495. (Cambridge Bible Commentary on the New English Bible Ser.: NEB Old Testament). 232p. 1973. pap. 10.95. Cambridge U Pr.

Heslop. Diamonds in Daniel. pap. 2.95 (ISBN 0-686-12865-6). Schmul Pub Co.

Hillers, Delbert R., tr. Lamentations. LC 70-176347. (Anchor Bible Ser: Vol. 7A). (Illus.). 168p. 1972. 14.00 (ISBN 0-385-00738-8, Anchor Pr). Doubleday.

Howie, Carl G. Ezekiel, Daniel. LC 59-10454. (Layman's Bible Commentary, Vol. 13). 1961. pap. 4.95 (ISBN 0-8042-3073-0). John Knox.

Huey, F. B., Jr. Jeremiah: Bible Study Commentary. (Bible Study Commentary Ser.). 144p. (Orig.). 1981. pap. 4.95 (ISBN 0-310-36063-3, 11063P). Zondervan.

Ibn Ezra. Commentary of Ibn Ezra on Isaiah. Friedlander, Michael, tr. LC 66-15771. 1966. 15.00 (ISBN 0-87306-013-X). Feldheim.

Ironside, H. A. Ezekiel. 9.95 (ISBN 0-87213-359-1). Loizeaux.

--Isaiah. 9.95 (ISBN 0-87213-369-9). Loizeaux.

--Jeremiah: Prophecy & Lamentations. 10.95 (ISBN 0-87213-371-0). Loizeaux.

Jennings, F. C. Isaiah. rev. ed. LC 55-41748. 1935. 14.95 (ISBN 0-87213-420-2). Loizeaux.

Jensen, Irving L. Ezekiel & Daniel. (Bible Self Study Ser.). 1970. pap. 2.95 (ISBN 0-8024-1026-X). Moody.

--Jeremiah & Lamentations. (Everyman' Bible Commentary Ser.). (Orig.). 1966. pap. 5.95 (ISBN 0-8024-2024-9). Moody.

--Jeremias y Lamentaciones (Commentario Biblico Portavoz) Orig. Title: Jeremiah & Lamentations (Everyman's Bible Commentary) (Span.). 142p. 1979. pap. 3.95 (ISBN 0-8254-1352-4). Kregel.

Jensen, Joseph. Isaiah One to Thirty-Nine. (Old Testament Message Ser.: Vol. 8). 1984. 15.95 (ISBN 0-89453-408-4); pap. 10.95 (ISBN 0-89453-243-X). M Glazier.

Joyce, Paul. Divine Initiative & Human Response in Ezekiel. (JSOT Supplement Ser.: No. 51). 200p. 1987. text ed. 30.00x (ISBN 1-85075-041-6, Pub. by JSOT Pr England); pap. text ed. 14.95x (ISBN 1-85075-042-4, Pub. by JSOT Pr England). Eisenbrauns.

Kaiser, Otto. Isaiah, One to Twelve, A Commentary. 2nd ed. LC 82-23785. (The Old Testament Library Ser.). 288p. 1983. 19.95 (ISBN 0-664-21827-X). Westminster.

--Isaiah Thirteen to Thirty-Nine, A Commentary. LC 73-21949. (Old Testament Library). 432p. 1974. 19.95 (ISBN 0-664-20984-X). Westminster.

Kelly, William. An Exposition of the Book of Isaiah. 1979. 15.25 (ISBN 0-86524-003-5, 2301). Klock & Klock.

Knight, George A. The International Theological Commentary on Isaiah 40-55. Holmgren, Frederick, ed. (The International Theological Commentary Ser.). 208p. (Orig.). 1983. pap. 9.95 (ISBN 0-8028-1039-X). Eerdmans.

Knoch, A. E. Concordant Studies in the Book of Daniel. rev. ed. 464p. 1968. 7.00 (ISBN 0-910424-52-7). Concordant.

Krutza, William J. & Dicicco, Philip P. Facing the Issues, No. 2. (Contemporary Discussion Ser.). pap. 3.50 (ISBN 0-8010-5326-9). Baker Bk.

--Facing the Issues, No. 3. (Contemporary Discussion Ser.). (Orig.). 1970. pap. 3.50 (ISBN 0-8010-5300-5). Baker Bk.

--Facing the Issues, No. 4. (Contemporary Discussion Ser.). (Orig.). 1971. pap. 3.50 (ISBN 0-8010-5310-2). Baker Bk.

Kuist, Howard T. Jeremiah, Lamentations. LC 59-10454. (Layman's Bible Commentary Ser: Vol. 12). 1960. pap. 4.95 (ISBN 0-8042-3072-2). John Knox.

Laetsch, Theodore. Jeremiah. pap. 13.95 (ISBN 0-570-03218-0, 15-2003). Concordia.

Leupold, Herbert C. Exposition of Daniel. 1969. 13.95 (ISBN 0-8010-5531-8). Baker Bk.

--Exposition of Isaiah, 1 vol. ed. 1977. 22.95 (ISBN 0-8010-5577-6). Baker Bk.

Levenson, Jon D. Theology of the Program of Restoration of Ezekiel Forty to Forty-Eight. LC 76-3769. (Harvard Semitic Museum, Monographs). 1976. 9.00 (ISBN 0-89130-105-4, 040010). Scholars Pr GA.

Limburg, James. The Prophets & the Powerless. LC 76-12397. 1976. pap. 6.95 (ISBN 0-8042-0156-0). John Knox.

Lindsay, Gordon. Prophecies of Daniel. (Daniel Ser.). 4.00 (ISBN 0-89985-052-9). Christ Nations.

McDonagh, Francis, et al. Prophets Two. LC 71-173033. (Scripture Discussion Commentary Ser.: Pt. 4). 184p. 1972. pap. text ed. 4.50 (ISBN 0-87946-003-2). ACTA Found.

McKenzie, John L., ed. Isaiah Two. LC 68-10565. (Anchor Bible Ser.: Vol. 20). 1968. 14.00 (ISBN 0-385-05390-8, Anchor Pr). Doubleday.

Macpherson, Ann, et al. Prophets One. Bright, Laurence, ed. LC 71-173033. (Scripture Discussion Commentary Ser.: Pt. 2). 214p. 1971. pap. text ed. 4.50 (ISBN 0-87946-001-6). ACTA Found.

Martens, Elmer A. Jeremiah. LC 86-9958. (A Believers Church Bible Commentary Ser.). 328p. (Orig.). 1986. pap. 17.95 (ISBN 0-8361-3405-2). Herald Pr.

Martin, Alfred. Isaiah: The Salvation of Jehovah. (Everyman's Bible Commentary Ser.). 1967. pap. 5.95 (ISBN 0-8024-2023-0). Moody.

--Isaias: La Salvacion del Senor (Comentario Biblico Portavoz) Orig. Title: Isaiah: The Salvation of Jehovah (Everyman's Bible Commentary) (Span.). 112p. 1979. pap. 3.50 (ISBN 0-8254-1455-5). Kregel.

Martin-Achard, R. & Re'emi, P. The International Theological Commentary on Amos & Lamentations. (The International Theological Commentary Ser.). 160p. (Orig.). 1983. pap. 8.95 (ISBN 0-8028-1040-3). Eerdmans.

Mays, James L. Ezekiel, Second Isaiah. McCurley, Foster R., ed. LC 77-15239. (Proclamation Commentaries, The Old Testament Witnesses for Preaching). 96p. (Orig.). 1978. pap. 4.95 (ISBN 0-8006-0592-6, 1-592). Fortress.

Montgomery, James A. A Critical & Exegetical Commentary on Daniel. Driver, Samuel R. & Plummer, Alfred, eds. LC 27-14200. (International Critical Commentary Ser.). 520p. 1926. 24.95 (ISBN 0-567-05017-3, Pub. by T & T Clark Ltd UK). Fortress.

Morgan, G. Campbell. Isaiah. Chao, Lorna, tr. (G. Campbell Morgan's Expository Ser.). 1985. write for info (ISBN 0-941598-93-4); pap. write for info. (ISBN 0-941598-20-9). Living Spring Pubns.

Mouw, Richard. When Kings Come Marching In: Isaiah & the New Jerusalem. 96p. (Orig.). 1983. pap. 3.95 (ISBN 0-8028-1935-4). Eerdmans.

Napier, Davie. Word of God, Word of Earth. LC 75-45312. 120p. 1976. 5.95 (ISBN 0-8298-0304-1); pap. 3.25 (ISBN 0-8298-0307-6). Pilgrim NY.

Newsome, James D., Jr. The Hebrew Prophets. LC 84-7601. 252p. (Orig.). 1984. pap. 12.95 (ISBN 0-8042-0113-7). John Knox.

Nicholson, E. W. The Book of the Prophet Jeremiah: Chapters 1-25. LC 73-80477. (Cambridge Bible Commentary on the New English Bible, Old Testament Ser.). 200p. 1973. 27.95 (ISBN 0-521-08625-6); pap. 11.95 (ISBN 0-521-09769-X). Cambridge U Pr.

--The Book of the Prophet Jeremiah: Chapters 26-52. LC 74-80357. (Cambridge Bible Commentary on the New English Bible, Old Testament Ser.). 250p. 1975. 27.95 (ISBN 0-521-20497-6); pap. 12.95 (ISBN 0-521-09867-X). Cambridge U Pr.

Orelli, Hans C. von. The Prophecies of Jeremiah. 1977. 15.25 (ISBN 0-86524-102-3, 2401). Klock & Klock.

Oswalt, John N. The Book of Isaiah, Chapters 1-39. (New International Commentary on the Old Testament Ser.). 672p. 29.95 (ISBN 0-8028-2368-8). Eerdmans.

Owens, Mary F. Layman's Bible Book Commentary: Ezra, Nehemiah, Esther, Job, Vol. 7. 1984. 5.95 (ISBN 0-8054-1177-1). Broadman.

Picirilli, Robert & Hampton, Ralph, Jr. A Survey of the Major Prophets. 1976. pap. 1.50 (ISBN 0-89265-034-6). Randall Hse.

Pink, Arthur W. Gleanings from Elisha. LC 79-181591. 288p. 1972. pap. 10.95 (ISBN 0-8024-3000-7). Moody.

--Gleanings in Joshua. LC 64-20991. 1964. pap. 10.95 (ISBN 0-8024-3004-X). Moody.

Polk, Timothy. The Prophetic Persona: The Language of Self-Reference in Jeremiah. (JSOT Supplement Ser.: No. 32). 240p. 1985. text ed. 28.50x (ISBN 0-905774-70-1, Pub. by JSOT Pr England); pap. text ed. 13.50x (ISBN 0-905774-71-X, Pub. by JSOT Pr England). Eisenbrauns.

Porteous, Norman W. Daniel, a Commentary. LC 65-21071. (Old Testament Library). 174p. 1965. 14.95 (ISBN 0-664-20663-8). Westminster.

Robinson, T. H. Decline & Fall of the Hebrew Kingdoms. LC 74-137284. Repr. of 1926 ed. 21.50 (ISBN 0-404-05376-9). AMS Pr.

Rosenberg, Avrohom Y. The Mishnah-Seder Moed, Vol. 4. (Art Scroll Mishnah Ser.). 352p. 1979. 14.95 (ISBN 0-89906-258-X); pap. 11.95 (ISBN 0-89906-259-8). Mesorah Pubns.

Siegman, Edward F. Ezechiel. (Bible Ser.). pap. 1.00 ea.; Pt. 1. pap. (ISBN 0-8091-5045-X); Pt. 2. pap. (ISBN 0-8091-5046-8). Paulist Pr.

Simpson, Douglas J. The Book of Daniel. 1974. pap. 3.95 (ISBN 0-89265-023-0). Randall Hse.

Smith, F. G. Prophetic Lectures on Daniel & Revelations. 260p. pap. 3.50 (ISBN 0-686-29136-0). Faith Pub Hse.

Smith, James E. Ezekiel. (Bible Study Textbook Ser.). 1979. 14.30 (ISBN 0-89900-024-X). College Pr Pub.

Strauss, Lehman. Daniel: Prophecies. LC 70-85293. Orig. Title: Prophecies of Daniel. 1969. 9.95 (ISBN 0-87213-812-7). Loizeaux.

Stuhlmueller, Carroll. Isaiah. 1976. 1.75 (ISBN 0-8199-0628-X). Franciscan Herald.

Tatford, Frederick. Daniel & His Prophecy. 1980. 9.25 (ISBN 0-86524-045-0, 2702). Klock & Klock.

Taylor, John B. Ezekiel. LC 75-98503. (Tyndale Old Testament Commentaries Ser). 1969. 12.95 (ISBN 0-87784-884-X); pap. 6.95 (ISBN 0-87784-272-8). Inter-Varsity.

--Preaching Through the Prophets. LC 84-23773. 110p. 1985. pap. 7.95 (ISBN 0-8272-2929-1). CBP.

Trenchard, Ernesto. Introduccion a los Libros Profeticos e Isaias. (Span.). 192p. 1974. 4.95 (ISBN 0-8254-1748-1); pap. 3.95 (ISBN 0-8254-1747-3). Kregel.

Vander Ark, Nelle. Inspirations from Isaiah. (Good Morning Lord Ser.). 96p. 1980. 3.95 (ISBN 0-8010-9281-7). Baker Bk.

Varner, William. The Chariot of Israel: Exploits of the Prophet of Elijah. LC 84-80766. 1984. pap. text ed. 4.95 (ISBN 0-915540-33-9). Frnds Israel.

Vine, W. E. Isaiah: Prophecies, Promises, Warnings. pap. 7.95 (ISBN 0-310-33771-2, 6621P). Zondervan.

Wallace, Ronald S. The Message of Daniel. LC 79-1996. (Bible Speaks Today Ser.). 1979. pap. 6.95 (ISBN 0-87784-285-X). Inter-Varsity.

Walton, John H. Jonah: A Bible Study Commentary. 80p. (Orig.). 1982. pap. 3.95 (ISBN 0-310-36303-9, 11616P). Zondervan.

Walvoord, John. Daniel. LC 75-123161. 1970. 17.95 (ISBN 0-8024-1752-3). Moody.

Welch, Adam C. Visions of the End: A Study in Daniel & Revelation. 260p. 1958. Repr. of 1922 ed. 10.95 (ISBN 0-227-67631-9). Attic Pr.

Westermann, Claus. Isaiah Forty to Sixty-Six: A Commentary. Stalker, David M., tr. LC 69-18647. (Old Testament Library). 446p. 1969. 19.95 (ISBN 0-664-20851-7). Westminster.

Wevers, John W. Ezekiel. (New Century Bible Ser). 253p. 1976. 8.95 (ISBN 0-551-00755-9). Attic Pr.

--Ezekiel. Clements, Ronald E., ed. (The New Century Bible Commentary Ser.). 243p. 1982. pap. 7.95 (ISBN 0-8028-1910-9). Eerdmans.

Whitcomb, John. Daniel. (Everyman's Bible Commentary Ser.). (Orig.). 1985. pap. 5.95 (ISBN 0-8024-2067-2). Moody.

White, K. Owen. Book of Jeremiah. (New Shield Ser.). 1981. pap. 3.45 (ISBN 0-8010-9517-4). Baker Bk.

Whybray, R. N. Isaiah Forty to Sixty-Six. Clements, Ronald E., ed. (New Century Bible Commentary). 320p. (Orig.). 1981. pap. 8.95 (ISBN 0-8028-1884-6). Eerdmans.

--Second Isaiah. (Old Testament Guides Ser.). xiv, 84p. 1984. pap. text ed. 3.95x (ISBN 0-905774-59-0, Pub. by JSOT Pr England). Eisenbrauns.

Willis, John T. My Servants the Prophets, Vol. 1. LC 76-180789. (Way of Life Ser.: No. 116). 1971. pap. 3.95 (ISBN 0-89112-116-1, Bibl Res Pr). Abilene Christ U.

--My Servants the Prophets, Vol. 3. LC 76-180789. (Way of Life Ser.: No. 118). (Orig.). 1972. pap. 3.95 (ISBN 0-89112-118-8, Bibl Res Pr). Abilene Christ U.

Wood, Fred M. Coming Home. LC 86-20775. (Orig.). 1987. pap. 6.95 (ISBN 0-8054-1236-0). Broadman.

--God of Grace, God of Glory. LC 81-68364. 1982. pap. 4.95 (ISBN 0-8054-1221-2). Broadman.

Wood, Leon J. Daniel: A Study Guide. 160p. 1975. pap. 6.95 (ISBN 0-310-34723-8, 10872P). Zondervan.

Wright, Charles H. Studies in Daniel's Prophecy. 368p. 1983. lib. bdg. 13.95 (ISBN 0-86524-162-7, 2703). Klock & Klock.

Wright, G. Ernest. Isaiah. LC 59-10454. (Layman's Bible Commentary, Vol. 11). 1964. pap. 4.95 (ISBN 0-8042-3071-4). John Knox.

Yates, K. M. Los Profetas Del Antiguo Testamento. Corona, Simon, tr. from Eng. Orig. Title: Preaching from the Prophets. (Span.). 336p. 1985. pap. 4.95 (ISBN 0-311-04026-8). Casa Bautista.

Yates, Kyle M. Preaching from the Prophets. 1953. text ed. 12.50 (ISBN 0-8054-1502-5). Broadman.

Young, E. J. Daniel. (The Geneva Series of Commentaries). 320p. 13.95 (ISBN 0-85151-154-6). Banner of Truth.

Young, Edward J. Book of Isaiah, Vol. 1. 1964. 19.95 (ISBN 0-8028-2179-0). Eerdmans.

Youngblood, Ronald. Themes from Isaiah. LC 83-19128. (Bible Commentary for Laymen Ser.). 1983. pap. text ed. 3.50 (ISBN 0-8307-0906-1, S373106). Regal.

BIBLE-COMMENTARIES-O. T. PROVERBS

see Bible-Commentaries-O. T. Poetical Books

BIBLE-COMMENTARIES-O. T. PSALMS

see Bible-Commentaries-O. T. Poetical Books

BIBLE-COMMENTARIES-O. T. RUTH

see Bible-Commentaries-O. T. Historical Books

BIBLE-COMMENTARIES-O. T. SAMUEL

see Bible-Commentaries-O. T. Historical Books

BIBLE-COMMENTARIES-O. T. SONG OF SOLOMON

see Bible-Commentaries-O. T. Poetical Books

BIBLE-COMMENTARIES-O. T. WISDOM LITERATURE

Boadt, Lawrence E. Introduction to Wisdom Literature, Proverbs. (Collegeville Bible Commentary: Old Testament Ser.: Vol. 18). 104p. 1986. pap. 2.95 (ISBN 0-8146-1475-2). Liturgical Pr.

Reese, James. The Book of Wisdom, Song of Songs. (Old Testament Message Ser.: Vol. 20). 12.95 (ISBN 0-89453-420-3); pap. 8.95 (ISBN 0-89453-254-5). M Glazier.

Rybolt, John E. Wisdom. (Collegeville Bible Commentary: Old Testament Ser.: Vol. 20). 112p. 1986. pap. 2.95 (ISBN 0-8146-1477-9). Liturgical Pr.

BIBLE-COMMENTARIES-O. T. ZECHARIAH

see Bible-Commentaries-O. T. Minor Prophets

BIBLE-COMMENTARIES-O. T. ZEPHANIAH

see Bible-Commentaries-O. T. Minor Prophets

BIBLE-CONCORDANCES

Abingdon's Strong Exhaustive Concordance of the Bible: Red Letter Edition. 1986. 26.95 (ISBN 0-687-40032-5); (thumb index) 28.95 (ISBN 0-687-40033-3). Abingdon.

Andersen, Francis I. & Forbes, A. Dean. Eight Minor Prophets: A Linguistic Concordance. (Computer Bible Ser.: Vol. X). 1976. pap. 25.00 (ISBN 0-935106-11-1). Biblical Res Assocs.

--A Linguistic Concordance of Ruth & Jonah: Hebrew Vocabulary & Idiom. (Computer Bible Ser.: Vol. IX). 1976. pap. 15.00 (ISBN 0-935106-12-X). Biblical Res Assocs.

Bagster, Samuel. Bagster's Keyword Concordance. 96p. 1983. Repr. 5.95 (ISBN 0-8007-1335-4). Revell.

Baker's Pocket Bible Concordance. (Direction Bks.). 1973. pap. 5.95 (ISBN 0-8010-0616-3). Baker Bk.

Branbsby, Carlos, tr. from Eng. Concordancia Tematica De la Biblia. 199p. 1986. pap. 3.50 (ISBN 0-311-42043-5). Casa Bautista.

Bullinger, E. W. Critical Lexicon & Concordance to the English & Greek New Testament. 1040p. 1975. text ed. 26.95 (ISBN 0-310-20310-4, 6253P, Pub. by Bagster). Zondervan.

Clow, W. Bible Reader's Encyclopedia & Concordance. (Illus.). 9.95 (ISBN 0-529-05899-5, RT1). World Bible.

The Complete Concordance to the Bible: New King James Version. LC 83-13271. 1120p. 1983. 19.95 (ISBN 0-8407-4959-7); indexed 23.95 (ISBN 0-8407-4953-8). Nelson.

Concordancia Breve De la Biblia. 280p. 1985. pap. 3.50 (ISBN 0-311-42055-9, Edit Mundo). Casa Bautista.

Cook, Madison D. Biographical Concordance of the New Testament. 216p. 1984. pap. 8.95 (ISBN 0-87213-089-4). Loizeaux.

Cruden, Alexander. Cruden's Compact Concordance. 1968. 9.95 (ISBN 0-310-22910-3, 9440). Zondervan.

--Cruden's Complete Concordance. 1949. 14.95 (ISBN 0-310-22920-0, 9441). Zondervan.

--Cruden's Complete Concordance. 1976. pap. 9.95 (ISBN 0-310-22921-9, 9441P). Zondervan.

--Cruden's Concordance. 1982. pap. 3.95 (ISBN 0-515-06741-5). Jove Pubns.

--Cruden's Handy Concordance. pap. 3.95 (ISBN 0-310-22931-6, 6767P). Zondervan.

Denyer, Carlos. Concordancia de las Sagradas Escrituras. LC 74-21722. (Span.). 936p. 1969. 28.95 (ISBN 0-89922-004-5); pap. 21.95 (ISBN 0-89922-121-1). Edit Caribe.

Edwards, Richard A. A Concordance to Q. LC 75-6768. (Society of Biblical Literature. Sources for Biblical Study). iv, 186p. 1975. pap. 13.95 (ISBN 0-89130-880-6, 060307). Scholars Pr GA.

--A Concordance to Q. LC 75-6768. (Society of Biblical Literature. Sources for Biblical Study: No. 7). Repr. of 1975 ed. 36.90 (ISBN 0-8357-9568-3, 2017677). Bks Demand UMI.

Ellison, John W. Nelson's Complete Concordance of the Revised Standard Version. 2nd ed. 1136p. 1985. 29.95 (ISBN 0-8407-4954-6). Nelson.

English Dictionary Supplement to the Concordance to the Peshitta Version Of the Aramaic New Testament. 59p. 1985. 2.95 (ISBN 0-910068-67-4). Am Christian.

The Englishman's Hebrew & Chaldee Concordance of the Old Testament. (Hebrew & Eng.). 1980. pap. 35.95 (ISBN 0-8054-1387-1). Broadman.

Even-Shoshan, Abraham, ed. A New Concordance of the Old Testament: Using the Hebrew & Aramaic Text. 1328p. 51.00 (ISBN 0-8010-3417-5). Baker Bk.

Fillmore, Charles. Charles Fillmore Concordance. 1975. 5.95 (ISBN 0-87159-015-8). Unity School.

Findeisen, Barbara. A Course in Miracles Concordance. 457p. 15.00 (ISBN 0-942494-45-8). Coleman Pub.

Gall, James. Bible Student's English-Greek Concordance & Greek-English Dictionary. (Paperback Reference Library). 376p. 1983. pap. 9.95 (ISBN 0-8010-3795-6). Baker Bk.

Goodrick, Edward W. & Kohlenberger, John P. The NIV Complete Concordance. 1056p. 1981. 22.95 (ISBN 0-310-43650-8, 12100). Zondervan.

Goodrick, Edward W. & Kohlenberger, John R., III. The NIV Handy Concordance. 384p. (Orig.). 1982. pap. 5.95 (ISBN 0-310-43662-1, 12101P). Zondervan.

The Hand-Size Giant Print Reference Bible. Incl. Black Genuine Leather. (semi-overlap binding, gold edges, ribbon marker). 39.95 (ISBN 0-317-18887-9, 6710S); Feora Bonded Leather. (semi-overlap binding, gold edges, ribbon marker, gift boxed). 24.95 (ISBN 0-317-18888-7); black (6708S); brown (N6708S); burgundy (R6807S); Imitation Leather. (semi-overlap binding, antique gold edges, gift boxed). 17.95 (ISBN 0-317-18889-5); black (6704S); brown (N6704S); burgundy (R6704S). 2016p. (incl. giant print concordance, harmony of the Gospels, words of Christ in red, presentation page, family record section, maps, gift boxed). thumb indexing avail. 5.00 addnl. Holman Bible Pub.

Hatch, Edwin & Redpath, Henry A. A Concordance to the Septuagint & Other Greek Versions of the Old Testament (Including the Apocryphal Books, 3 vols. in 2. 1088p. 1983. Repr. of 1906 ed. Set. 75.00 (ISBN 0-8010-4270-4). Baker Bk.

Hazelton, Charles J. Pocket Concordance to the New Testament. 1984. leather flex 4.95 (ISBN 0-8407-5824-3). Nelson.

Holman Bible Publishers. Holman Topical Concordance: An Index to the Bible Arranged by Subjects in Alphabetical Order. LC 73-7656. 288p. 1973. 8.95 (ISBN 0-87981-019-X). Holman Bible Pub.

Holman Company. Holman Bible Concordance. Hitt, Russell, ed. 1979. pap. 3.95 (ISBN 0-87981-093-9). Holman Bible Pub.

Joy, Charles R., ed. Harper's Topical Concordance. LC 62-11129. 640p. 1976. pap. 10.95 (ISBN 0-06-064229-7, RD 132, HarpR). Har-Row.

Kasten, Lloyd & Anderson, Jean. Concordance to the Celestina. 1977. 12.50 (ISBN 0-87535-124-7). Hispanic Soc.

Katz, Eliezer. A Classified Concordance, 4 vols. Incl. Vol. 1. The Torah. 415p. 1964. 30.00x (ISBN 0-8197-0382-6); Vol. 2. The Early Prophets. 702p. 1967. 30.00x (ISBN 0-8197-0383-4); Vol. 3. The Later Prophets. 683p. 1970. 30.00x (ISBN 0-8197-0384-2). Bloch.

--Classified Concordance: To the Bible & Its Various Subjects, Vol. 4. (Hebrew & Eng.). 1000p. 1974. 40.00x (ISBN 0-8197-0385-0). Bloch.

Klein, Chuck. So You Want to Get into the Race. 1980. concordance study guide 4.95 (ISBN 0-8423-6082-4). Tyndale.

Knoch, A E., compiled by. Concordant Greek Text. rev. ed. 735p. 1975. leather bdg. o.p. 25.00 (ISBN 0-910424-32-2); 12.00 (ISBN 0-910424-31-4). Concordant.

Knoch, A. E., compiled by. Concordant Literal New Testament. 624p. 1978. pap. text ed. 5.00 (ISBN 0-910424-09-8). Concordant.

--Concordant Literal New Testament with Keyword Concordance. 992p. 1983. text ed. 15.00 (ISBN 0-910424-14-4). Concordant.

Kubo, Sakae. A Reader's Greek-English Lexicon of the New Testament & Benjamin's Guide. 1975. text ed. 15.95 (ISBN 0-310-26920-2, 6269). Zondervan.

Mandelkern, S. Heichal Hakodesh Concordance to the Old Testament, 1 vol. 95.00 (ISBN 0-87559-163-9). Shalom.

Manson, T. W. A Companion to the Bible. Rowley, H. H., ed. 592p. 1963. 19.95x (ISBN 0-567-02197-1, Pub. by T & T Clark Ltd UK). Fortress.

Martin, R. A. Syntactical & Critical Concordance to the Greek Text of Baruch & the Epistle of Jeremiah. (Computer Bible Ser.: Vol. XII). (Gr.). 1977. pap. 15.00 (ISBN 0-935106-09-X). Biblical Res Assocs.

Mendelkern, Solomon. Concordance of the Bible. (Hebrew & Lat.). 1985. Repr. of 1896 ed. 25.00 (ISBN 0-685-81426-2). Feldheim.

Metzger, Bruce M., compiled by. Oxford Concise Concordance to the Revised Standard of the Holy Bible. 1962. 7.95 (ISBN 0-19-528388-0). Oxford U Pr.

Morris, Peter M. & James, Edward. A Critical Word Book of Leviticus, Numbers, Deuteronomy. (Computer Bible Ser.: Vol. VIII). 1975. pap. 20.00 (ISBN 0-935106-13-8). Biblical Res Assocs.

Morrish, George. Concordance of the Septuagint. 17.95 (ISBN 0-310-20300-7, 6512). Zondervan.

Morrison, Clinton. An Analytical Concordance to the Revised Standard Version of the New Testament. LC 77-26210. 800p. 1979. 45.00 (ISBN 0-664-20773-1). Westminster.

Morton, A. Q. & Michaelson, S. Critical Concordance to the Pastoral Epistles, I, II Timothy, Titus, Philemon. Baird, J. Arthur & Freedman, David N., eds. (The Computer Bible Ser.: Vol. XXV). 1982. pap. 35.00 (ISBN 0-935106-20-0). Biblical Res Assocs.

Morton, A. Q. & Michaelson, Sidney. A Critical Concordance to the Acts of the Apostles. (Computer Bible Ser.: Vol. VII). 1976. pap. 15.00 (ISBN 0-935106-14-6). Biblical Res Assocs.

Morton, A. Q., et al. Critical Concordance to the Letter of Paul to the Colossians. Baird, J. Arthur & Freedman, David, eds. (Computer Bible Ser.: Vol. 24). (Orig.). 1981. pap. text ed. 20.00 (ISBN 0-935106-19-7). Biblical Res Assocs.

--Critical Concordance to the Letter of Paul to the Philippians. Baird, J. Arthur & Freedman, David, eds. (Computer Bible Ser.: Vol. 23). (Orig.). 1980. pap. text ed. 20.00 (ISBN 0-935106-18-9). Biblical Res Assocs.

--A Critical Concordance to I & II Corinthians. (Computer Bible Ser.: Vol. XIX). 1979. pap. 30.00 (ISBN 0-935106-01-4). Biblical Res Assocs.

NASB Handy Concordance. 272p. (Orig.). 1984. pap. text ed. 5.95 (ISBN 0-310-45252-X, 12395P). Zondervan.

Nelson's Complete Concordance of the New American Bible. LC 77-22170. 1977. 44.95 (ISBN 0-8407-4900-7). Nelson.

New Combined Bible Dictionary & Concordance. (Direction Bks). 1973. pap. 5.95 (ISBN 0-8010-6680-8). Baker Bk.

The New Englishman's Hebrew Concordance. 1424p. 1984. 39.95 (ISBN 0-913573-21-3). Hendrickson MA.

The New World Dictionary Concordance to the New American Bible. 12.95 (ISBN 0-529-06094-9, 2418); pap. 4.95 (ISBN 0-529-04540-0, 2416). World Bible.

Ogilvie, Lloyd J., frwd. by. The Guideposts Family Topical Concordance to the Bible. LC 82-12412. 1982. 17.95 (ISBN 0-8407-4962-7). Nelson.

The Oxford Bible Reader's Dictionary & Concordance: Cyclopedic Concordance. (Illus.). 1984. 7.95 (ISBN 0-19-143442-6); pap. 4.95 (ISBN 0-19-143441-8). Oxford U Pr.

Oxford Concordance: King James Version. write for info. Oxford U Pr.

Parker, George. Lexico-Concordancia del Nuevo Testamento en Griego y Espanol. (Span.). 1000p. 1982. pap. 19.95 (ISBN 0-311-42066-4). Casa Bautista.

The Phrase Concordance of the Bible. 736p. 1986. 17.95 (ISBN 0-8407-4948-1). Nelson.

Radday, Yehuda & Levi, Yaakov. An Analytical Linguistic Key-Word-in-Context Concordance to the Book of Exodus. Baird, Arthur J. & Freedman, David, eds. (The Computer Bible Ser.: Vol. 28). (Orig.). 1985. 45.00 (ISBN 0-935106-23-5). Biblical Res Assocs.

Radday, Yehuda T. An Analytical Linguistic Concordance to the Book of Isaiah. (Computer Bible Ser: Vol. II). 1975. 20.00 (ISBN 0-935106-15-4). Biblical Res Assocs.

--An Analytical, Linguistic Key-Word-in-Context Concordance to the Book of Judges. (Computer Bible Ser.: Vol. XI). 1977. pap. 20.00 (ISBN 0-935106-10-3). Biblical Res Assocs.

Robinson, David, ed. Concordance to the Good News Bible: Today's English Version. 1416p. 1984. 24.95 (ISBN 0-8407-4956-2). Nelson.

Sloan, W. H. & Lerin, A. Concordancia Alfabetica De la Biblia. 1024p. 1981. pap. 14.95 (ISBN 0-311-42054-0). Casa Bautista.

Smith, J. B. Greek-English Concordance. LC 55-12260. 430p. 1955. 29.95 (ISBN 0-8361-1368-3). Herald Pr.

Strong, James. Strong's Exhaustive Concordance. LC 78-73138. 1978. pap. 15.95 (ISBN 0-8054-1134-8). Broadman.

--Strong's Exhaustive Concordance of the Bible with the Exclusive Key-Word Comparison. rev. ed. 1980. 23.95 (ISBN 0-687-40030-9); thumb-indexed 28.95 (ISBN 0-687-40031-7). Abingdon.

--Strong's Exhaustive Concordance of the Bible. 1552p. Date not set. 20.95 (ISBN 0-917006-01-1). Hendrickson MA.

--The Strong's New Concordance of the Bible: Popular Edition. 784p. 1985. text ed. 10.95 (ISBN 0-8407-4951-1). Nelson.

Strong, James, ed. The New Strong's New Exhaustive Concordance of the Bible. 2nd ed. 1984. 24.95 (ISBN 0-8407-5360-8); indexed 28.95 (ISBN 0-8407-5442-6). Nelson.

--Strong's Exhaustive Concordance of the Bible. 1552p. 1986. text ed. 10.95 (ISBN 0-529-06334-4); Thumb indexed ed. text ed. 13.95 (ISBN 0-529-06335-2). World Bible.

Tenney, Merrill C. & Cruden, Alexander. The Handy Bible Dictionary & Concordance. 1986. pap. 6.95 (ISBN 0-310-33271-0, 11147P). Zondervan.

Thayer, Joseph H. Greek-English Lexicon of the New Testament: A Dictionary Numerically Coded to Strong's Exhaustive Concordance. (Gr. & Eng.). 1977. pap. 15.95 (ISBN 0-8010-8838-0). Baker Bk.

Thomas, Robert L., ed. New American Standard Exhaustive Concordance of the Bible: Hebrew-Aramaic & Greek Dictionaries. LC 80-39626. 1695p. 1981. 29.95 (ISBN 0-87981-197-8, 4690-98); thumb-indexed 34.95 (ISBN 0-87981-503-5). Holman Bible Pub.

Tov, Emanuel. The Book of Baruch. LC 75-30775. (Society of Biblical Literature. Texts & Translation-Pseudepigrapha Ser.). 1975. pap. 9.75 (ISBN 0-89130-043-0, 060208). Scholars Pr GA.

Vigram, George V. The Englishman's Greek Concordance of the New Testament. rev. ed. (Gr. & Eng.). 1982. pap. 29.95 (ISBN 0-8054-1388-X). Broadman.

Walker, J. B. Walker's Comprehensive Bible Concordance. LC 76-15841. 1976. kivar 14.95 (ISBN 0-8254-4012-2). Kregel.

Way International Research Team, ed. Concordance to the Peshitta Version of the Aramaic New Testament. LC 85-51248. 494p. 1985. 19.95 (ISBN 0-910068-61-5). Am Christian.

Whitaker, Richard W., compiled by. Eerdmans' Analytical Concordance to the Revised Standard Version. 1488p. 1987. 49.95 (ISBN 0-8028-2403-X). Eerdmans.

Wigoder, Geoffrey, et al. The Illustrated Dictionary & Concordance of the Bible. (Illus.). 1000p. 1986. text ed. 100.00 (ISBN 0-02-916380-3). Macmillan.

Wigram, George V. Englishman's Greek Concordance of the New Testament. 34.95 (ISBN 0-310-20320-1, 6258). Zondervan.

--Englishman's Greek Concordance of the New Testament. 1984. 29.95 (ISBN 0-8010-3416-7). Baker Bk.

--Englishman's Hebrew & Chaldee Concordance of the Old Testament. 39.95 (ISBN 0-310-20340-6, 6265). Zondervan.

--New Englishmans Greek Concordance & Lexicon. 960p. 1982. 34.95 (ISBN 0-913573-23-X). Hendrickson MA.

Williams, Thomas D., ed. A Textual Concordance of the Holy Scriptures: (Bible Passages Taken from the Douay-Rheims Bible) LC 85-52025. 848p. (Orig.). 1985. Repr. of 1908 ed. pap. 30.00 (ISBN 0-89555-286-8). Tan Bks Pubs.

Winter, Ralph. Word Study New Testament & Concordance. 1978. text ed. 39.95 (ISBN 0-8423-8390-5). Tyndale.

Young, Robert. Young's Analytical Concordance to the Bible. rev. ed. 1220p. 1986. 22.95 (ISBN 0-8407-4945-7). Nelson.

--Young's Analytical Concordance to the Bible. 1216p. Date not set. 18.95 (ISBN 0-917006-29-1). Hendrickson MA.

BIBLE–CONCORDANCES–DATA PROCESSING

Parunak, Van Dyke H. Linguistic Density Plots in Ezekiel: The Computer Bible, Vol. XXVII A & B. Baird, Arthur J. & Freedman, David, eds. 528p. 1984. pap. 70.00x (ISBN 0-935106-22-7). Biblical Res Assocs.

BIBLE–COVENANTS

see Covenants (Theology)

BIBLE–CRITICISM, FORM

Bultmann, Rudolf. History of the Synoptic Tradition. LC 62-7282. 1963. pap. 9.50 (ISBN 0-06-061172-3, RD 187, HarpR). Har-Row.

McKnight, Edgar V. What Is Form Criticism. Via, Dan O., Jr., ed. LC 71-81526. (Guides to Biblical Scholarship: New Testament Ser.). 96p. (Orig.). 1969. pap. 4.50 (ISBN 0-8006-0180-7, 1-180). Fortress.

Tucker, Gene M. Form Criticism of the Old Testament. Rylaarsdam, J. Coert, ed. LC 72-154487. (Guides to Biblical Scholarship: Old Testament Ser.). 96p. 1971. pap. 4.50 (ISBN 0-8006-0177-7, 1-177). Fortress.

BIBLE–CRITICISM, HIGHER

see Bible–Criticism, Interpretation, etc.; Bible–Introductions

BIBLE–CRITICISM, INTERPRETATION, ETC.

Here are entered works on the Bible as a whole. Works on the New Testament as a whole and on portions of the New Testament precede works on the Old Testament.

see also Bible As Literature; Modernist-Fundamentalist Controversy; Sex in the Bible

Abba, R. Nature & Authority of the Bible. 349p. 1958. 8.95 (ISBN 0-227-67539-8). Attic Pr.

Achtemeier, Paul J. Society of Biblical Literature: Seminar Papers Nineteen Eighty. (SBL Seminar Papers & Abstracts). pap. 9.00 (ISBN 0-89130-357-X, 06-09-19). Scholars Pr GA.

Aland, Kurt & Aland, Barbara. The Text of the New Testament. Rhodes, Erroll F., tr. from Ger. (Illus.). 344p. 1987. 29.95x (ISBN 0-8028-3620-8). Eerdmans.

Alexander, Pat, ed. The Lion Encyclopedia of the Bible. 352p. 1986. 24.95 (ISBN 0-7459-1113-7). Lion USA.

Alfaro, Juan. Preguntas y Respuestas sobre la Biblia. (Span.). 64p. 1982. pap. 1.50 (ISBN 0-89243-162-8). Liguori Pubns.

Allen, Horace T., Jr. A Handbook for the Lectionary. LC 80-19735. 254p. 1980. softcover 8.95 (ISBN 0-664-24347-9, A Geneva Press Pub.). Westminster.

Anacker, Christopher A. Exhaustive Outline of the Entire Bible. LC 81-90358. (Orig.). 1981. 10.95 (ISBN 0-9607942-5-5); lib. bdg. 12.95 (ISBN 0-9607942-7-1); pap. 8.95 (ISBN 0-9607942-0-4). Ref Guide Bks.

Apple, Jody L. Hermeneutical Agnosticism: A Critique of Subjectivism in Biblical Interpretation. LC 84-62067. 195p. (Orig.). 1985. pap. 7.95 (ISBN 0-931247-00-4). New Testament Christ Pr.

Arnold, Matthew. God & the Bible: A Review of Objections to "Literature & Dogma". LC 75-129382. Repr. of 1875 ed. 15.00 (ISBN 0-404-00386-9). AMS Pr.

--Literature & Dogma. Repr. of 1873 ed. lib. bdg. 20.00 (ISBN 0-8414-3076-4). Folcroft.

--Literature & Dogma. Livingston, James C., ed. LC 79-107032. (Milestones of Thought Ser). 1970. pap. 3.95x (ISBN 0-8044-6011-6). Ungar.

--Literature & Dogma: An Essay Towards a Better Apprehension of the Bible. LC 78-126650. 1970. Repr. of 1883 ed. 15.00 (ISBN 0-404-00387-7). AMS Pr.

Balchin, John F. Understanding Scripture: What Is the Bible & How Does It Speak? LC 81-8271. 98p. (Orig.). 1981. pap. 2.95 (ISBN 0-87784-875-0). Inter-Varsity.

Barnes, W. Emery. Gospel Criticism & Form Criticism. 84p. 1936. pap. text ed. 6.95 (ISBN 0-567-02020-7, Pub. by T & T Clark Ltd UK). Fortress.

Barthel, Manfred. What the Bible Really Says: Casting New Light on the Book of Books. Howson, Mark, tr. LC 81-18679. Orig. Title: Was Wirklich in der Bibel Steht. (Illus.). 416p. 1982. 15.50 (ISBN 0-688-00821-6). Morrow.

--What the Bible Really Says: Casting New Light on the Book of Books. Howson, Mark, tr. from Ger. LC 83-3001. Tr. of Was Wirklich in der Bibel Steht. (Illus.). 416p. 1983. pap. 10.95 (ISBN 0-688-01979-X, Quill). Morrow.

Barton, John. Reading the Old Testament: Method in Biblical Study. LC 84-3640. 272p. 1984. pap. 12.95 (ISBN 0-664-24555-2). Westminster.

Baxter, J. Sidlow. The Master Theme of the Bible, Pt. I: The Doctrine of the Lamb. (Living Studies). 160p. 1985. pap. 5.95 (ISBN 0-8423-4187-0); study guide 2.95 (ISBN 0-8423-4191-9). Tyndale.

Beegle, Dewey M. Scripture, Tradition & Infallibility. LC 79-84557. Orig. Title: The Inspiration of Scripture. 332p. pap. text ed. 8.95 (ISBN 0-933462-04-2). Pryor Pettengill.

Bell, Martin. Way of the Wolf: The Gospel in New Images. LC 77-120366. (Illus.). 128p. 1970. pap. 8.95 (ISBN 0-8164-0202-7, AY6445, HarpR); 2 records 8.95 ea. Har-Row.

Best, Ernest & Wilson, R. McL., eds. Text & Interpretation: Studies in the New Testament. LC 78-2962. pap. 71.50 (ISBN 0-317-26088-X, 2024416). Bks Demand UMI.

Billheimer, Paul E. Don't Waste Your Sorrows. LC 83-15821. 144p. (Orig.). 1983. pap. 4.95 (ISBN 0-87123-310-X, 210310). Bethany Hse.

Blake, William. Annotations to Richard Watson: An Apology for the Bible in a Series of Letters Addressed to Thomas Paine, 8th Edition, 1797. James, G. Ingli, ed. (Regency Reprints Ser.: No. III). 144p. (Orig.). 1984. pap. 9.00 (ISBN 0-906449-67-7, Pub. by UC Cardiff Pr). Longwood Pub Group.

Blankenbaker, Frances. What the Bible Is All about for Young Explorers. (Illus.). 364p. 1987. pap. 12.95 (ISBN 0-8307-1179-1, 5111647). Regal.

Bloore, John. Alternative Views of the Bible. 1978. Repr. of 1925 ed. lib. bdg. 20.00 (ISBN 0-8495-0366-3). Arden Lib.

Bowden, John. Bible Absurdities. 24p. 1982. Repr. of 1968 ed. 2.50 (ISBN 0-911826-45-9, 5036). Am Atheist.

Bowker, John. Targums & Rabbinic Literature. LC 71-80817. 1969. 67.50 (ISBN 0-521-07415-0). Cambridge U Pr.

Brooks, R. T. A Place to Start: The Bible As a Guide for Today. 120p. 1983. pap. 4.95 (ISBN 0-86683-708-6, HarpR). Har-Row.

Bro. Stanley. Pure Grace. 96p. 1984. 6.95 (ISBN 0-89962-414-6). Todd & Honeywell.

Brown, Douglas E. When Past & Present Meet. 112p. 1986. 4.95 (ISBN 0-913573-46-9). Hendrickson MA.

Brown, Raymond E. The Critical Meaning of the Bible. LC 81-82333. 160p. (Orig.). 1981. pap. 5.95 (ISBN 0-8091-2406-8). Paulist Pr.

--Recent Discoveries & the Biblical World. (Background Books Ser.: Vol. 1). 4.95 (ISBN 0-89453-363-0). M Glazier.

Brown, Robert M. The Bible Speaks to You. LC 84-19578. 324p. 1985. pap. 8.95 (ISBN 0-664-24597-8). Westminster.

--Unexpected News: Reading the Bible with Third World Eyes. LC 84-2380. 166p. 1984. pap. 7.95 (ISBN 0-664-24552-8). Westminster.

Brown, Robert McAfee. Saying Yes & Saying No: On Rendering to God & Caesar. LC 85-29575. 144p. (Orig.). 1986. pap. 7.95 (ISBN 0-664-24695-8). Westminster.

Bruce, Frederick F., ed. New Testament Development of Old Testament Themes. 1969. pap. 6.95 (ISBN 0-8028-1729-7). Eerdmans.

Brueggemann, Walter. The Bible Makes Sense. LC 76-29883. (Biblical Foundation Ser.). 1977. pap. 7.95 (ISBN 0-8042-0063-7). John Knox.

--The Bible Makes Sense. LC 76-29883. 1977. pap. 6.95 (ISBN 0-88489-087-2). St Mary's.

Bublitz, Ruth M. ONE-drous Light. 128p. (Orig.). 1985. pap. 5.95 (ISBN 0-87516-556-7). De Vorss.

Cambell, Alexander. The Covenant Story of the Bible. rev. & enl. ed. 256p. 1986. pap. 10.95 (ISBN 0-8298-0734-9). Pilgrim NY.

Cameron, Nigel M. Biblical Higher Criticism & the Defense of Infallibilism in 19th Century Britain. (Texts & Studies in Religion: Vol. 33). 440p. 1987. text ed. 69.96 (ISBN 0-88946-821-4). E Mellen.

Campbell, R. K. Our Wonderful Bible. 417p. 12.95 (ISBN 0-88172-009-7); pap. 10.50 (ISBN 0-88172-010-0). Believers Bkshelf.

Carson, D. A. Exegetical Fallacies. 1984. text ed. 7.95p (ISBN 0-8010-2499-4). Baker Bk.

Carson, D. A., ed. Biblical Interpretation & the Church: The Problem of Contextualization. 232p. 1985. pap. 7.95 (ISBN 0-8407-7501-6). Nelson.

Carter, Nicholas. The Late Great Book: The Bible. McCalden, David, ed. 230p. (Orig.). 1985. pap. 10.00 (ISBN 0-910607-01-X). Truth Missions.

Cate, Robert L. Old Testament Roots for New Testament Faith. LC 80-70914. 1982. pap. 7.95 (ISBN 0-8054-1220-4). Broadman.

Chafer, Lewis S. & Walvoord, John F. Major Bible Themes. rev. ed. 11.95 (ISBN 0-310-22390-3, 6203P). Zondervan.

Chapman, Benjamin. Card-Guide to New Testament Exegesis. 2.95 (ISBN 0-8010-2396-3). Baker Bk.

Chappell, Clovis G. The Best of C. G. Chappell. (Best Ser.). 240p. 1984. pap. 5.95 (ISBN 0-8010-2500-1). Baker Bk.

Charity, Alan. Events & Their Afterlife: The Dialectics of Christian Typology in the Bible & Dante. 300p. Date not set. pap. price not set (ISBN 0-521-34923-0). Cambridge U Pr.

Cheever, George B. Guilt of Slavery & the Crime of Slaveholding. LC 69-16586. Repr. of 1860 ed. cancelled (ISBN 0-8371-1380-6, CHG&, Pub. by Negro U Pr). Greenwood.

Clark, Gordon H. God's Hammer: The Bible & Its Critics. 2nd rev. ed. 200p. 1987. pap. 6.95 (ISBN 0-940931-99-0). Trinity Found.

Clevenger, Ernest, Jr., ed. Bible Survey. 1973. pap. 1.50 (ISBN 0-88428-005-5, 141). Parchment Pr.

Clevenot, Michel. Materialist Approaches to the Bible. Nottingham, William, tr. LC 84-14711. 160p. (Orig.). 1985. pap. 8.95 (ISBN 0-88344-343-0). Orbis Bks.

Cocoris, G. Michael. Untangling Bible Doctrine. rev. ed. 107p. 1985. pap. text ed. 2.00 (ISBN 0-935729-03-8). Church Open Door.

Coggan, D. Relevance of the Bible for Today. 1967. pap. 1.75x (ISBN 0-85564-005-7, Pub. by U of W Austral Pr). Intl Spec Bk.

Cohen, Gary G. Biblical Separation Defended. 1966. pap. 3.50 (ISBN 0-87552-147-9). Presby & Reformed.

Cole, David S. The Wrath of God. 1986. 11.95 (ISBN 0-533-06517-8). Vantage.

Collins, Adela, ed. Feminist Perspectives on Biblical Scholarship. (Society of Bliblical Literature Centennial Biblical Scholarship in North America Ser.: No. 10). 152p. 13.95_o.s. (ISBN 0-89130-774-5, 06 11 10); pap. 9.50 (ISBN 0-89130-773-7). Scholars Pr GA.

Conn, Charles W., ed. La Biblia, el Libro de los Libros. (Span.). 116p. 1979. pap. 3.95 (ISBN 0-87148-523-0). Pathway Pr.

Conner, Kevin J. & Malmin, Ken P. Interpreting the Scriptures. 1976. pap. 9.95 (ISBN 0-914936-20-4). Bible Temple.

Cooper, Thomas J. Guidebook to Biblical Truth. Cooper, Willia S., ed. (The Master of Light & Darkness Ser.: Vol. 5). 70p. (Orig.). 1985. pap. 4.75 (ISBN 0-931429-05-6). Cooper & Cooper Pub.

Cooper, Thomas J. & Cooper, Willia S. Guidebook to Biblical Truth. (Stewardship Ser.: Vol. 4). 60p. (Orig.). 1985. Set. write for info. (ISBN 0-931429-00-5); Vol. 4. pap. 4.50 (ISBN 0-931429-04-8). Cooper & Cooper Pub.

Countryman, William. Biblical Authority or Biblical Tyranny? Scripture & the Christian Pilgrimage. LC 81-70591. 96p. 1982. pap. 6.95 (ISBN 0-8006-1630-8, 1-1630). Fortress.

Cowles, N. Robert. Opening the New Testament. LC 84-72468. 158p. (Orig.). 1985. pap. 4.95 (ISBN 0-87509-357-4); leader's guide 2.95 (ISBN 0-87509-358-2). Chr Pubns.

Crawford, C. C. What the Bible Says about Faith. LC 82-72621. (What the Bible Says Ser.). 380p. 1982. cancelled (ISBN 0-89900-089-4). College Pr Pub.

Cronk, George. The Message of the Bible: An Orthodox Christian Perspective. LC 82-7355. 293p. (Orig.). 1982. pap. 8.95 (ISBN 0-913836-94-X). St Vladimirs.

Curry, S. E. Vocal & Literary Interpretation of the Bible. 1979. Repr. of 1903 ed. 30.00 (ISBN 0-8414-9988-8). Folcroft.

Daniel, R. P. Let's Play Bible Detective. 36p. pap. 2.95 (ISBN 0-88172-017-8). Believers Bkshelf.

Darby, J. N. Synopsis of the Books of the Bible, 5 vols. Set. 27.50 (ISBN 0-88172-070-4). Believers Bkshelf.

Dawes, Walter A. The Ghost of Old Capernaum. (Illus.). 358p. (Orig.). 1980. pap. text ed. 24.95 (ISBN 0-938792-00-8). New Capernaum.

--Impact: The Religion of the Twenty-First Century. (Illus.). 79p. (Orig.). 1980. pap. text ed. 8.95 (ISBN 0-938792-05-9). New Capernaum.

Deal, William S. Pictorial Introduction to the Bible. (Baker's Paperback Reference Library). 440p. 1982. pap. 12.95 (ISBN 0-8010-2926-0). Baker Bk.

Detweiler, Robert, ed. Semeia Thirty-One: Reader Response Approaches to Biblical & Secular Texts. (Semeia Ser.). 1985. pap. 9.95 (ISBN 0-317-38640-9, 06-20-31). Scholars Pr GA.

--Semeia Twenty-Three: Derrida & Biblical Studies. (Semeia Ser.). pap. 9.95 (06 20 23). Scholars Pr GA.

Deutsch, Alfred H. Still Full of Sap, Still Green. LC 79-21558. 130p. 1979. pap. 2.50 (ISBN 0-8146-1051-X). Liturgical Pr.

Dibelius, Martin. James. Koester, Helmut, ed. Willims, Michael A., tr. LC 74-80428. (Hermeneia: a Critical & Historical Commentary on the Bible). 308p. 1975. 24.95 (ISBN 0-8006-6006-4, 20-6006). Fortress.

Dickson, Roger. Millennial Mistake. 2.50 (ISBN 0-89315-160-2). Lambert Bk.

Diel, Paul. Symbolism in the Bible. 1986. 17.95 (ISBN 0-317-52369-4, HarpR). Har-Row.

Dolman, Dirk H. The Tabernacle. 525p. 1982. Repr. lib. bdg. 19.75 smythe sewn (ISBN 0-86524-152-X, 0203). Klock & Klock.

Dowley, Tim, ed. Discovering the Bible. (Illus.). 144p. 1986. 14.95 (ISBN 0-8028-3624-0). Eerdmans.

Draper, James T. The Conscience of a Nation. LC 82-73420. 1983. pap. 7.95 (ISBN 0-8054-1530-0). Broadman.

Drews, Arthur. The Witnesses to the Historicity of Jesus. 69.95 (ISBN 0-8490-1313-5). Gordon Pr.

Drury, Ronan, ed. New Testament as Personal Reading. 158p. 1983. pap. 7.95 (ISBN 0-87243-122-3). Templegate.

Eastman, Dick. The University of the Word. LC 83-17763. 1983. pap. 3.95 (ISBN 0-8307-0903-7, 5018301). Regal.

Efird, James M. How to Interpret the Bible. LC 83-49051. 144p. 1984. pap. 7.95 (ISBN 0-8042-0069-6). John Knox.

Emerton, J. A. & Reif, Stefan C., eds. Interpreting the Hebrew Bible. LC 81-21668. (University of Cambridge Oriental Publication Ser.: No. 32). 1982. 52.50 (ISBN 0-521-24424-2). Cambridge U Pr.

English, E. Schuyler. A Companion to the New Scofield Reference Bible. 1972. 6.95 (ISBN 0-19-526872-5). Oxford U Pr.

Errico, Rocco A. Let There Be Light: The Seven Keys. 180p. (Orig.). 1985. pap. 9.95 (ISBN 0-87516-555-9). De Vorss.

Evans, G. R. The Language & Logic of the Bible: The Road to Reformation. 200p. 1985. 32.50 (ISBN 0-521-30548-9). Cambridge U Pr.

Ewert, David. The Holy Spirit in the New Testament. LC 82-95089. 336p. 1983. pap. 12.95 (ISBN 0-8361-3309-9). Herald Pr.

Ferguson, Nina. In the Beginning God. 1985. 6.95 (ISBN 0-8062-2430-4). Carlton.

Fiorenza, Elisabeth S. Bread Not Stone: The Challenge of Feminist Biblical Interpretation. LC 84-14669. 208p. 1986. pap. 8.95 (ISBN 0-8070-1103-7, BP 717). Beacon Pr.

Fishbane, Michael. Biblical Interpretation in Ancient Israel. 1985. 49.95x (ISBN 0-19-826325-2). Oxford U Pr.

Flanders, Henry J., Jr., et al. Introduction to the Bible. 588p. 1973. text ed. 25.75 (ISBN 0-394-34416-2, RandC). Random.

Flood, Robert G. Thirty Minute Panorama of the Bible. (Orig.). 1984. pap. 1.95 (ISBN 0-8024-8747-5). Moody.

Flynn, Leslie B. Holy Contradictions. 156p. 1987. pap. 5.95 (ISBN 0-89693-239-7). Victor Bks.

Foote, G. W. & Ball, W. P., eds. The Bible Handbook: For Freethinkers & Inquiring Christians. 11th ed. LC 71-161330. (Atheist Viewpoint Ser). 176p. 1972. Repr. of 1961 ed. 20.00 (ISBN 0-405-03797-X). Ayer Co Pubs.

Forlines, Leroy. Inerrancy & the Scriptures. 26p. 1978. pap. 0.95 (ISBN 0-89265-107-5). Randall Hse.

Fosdick, Harry E. The Modern Use of the Bible. 1925. 35.00 (ISBN 0-8274-2758-1). R West.

Fox, Emmet. Diagrams for Living: The Bible Unveiled. LC 69-10475. 1968. 12.45 (ISBN 0-06-062851-0, HarpR). Har-Row.

Friederichsen, Kay. God's Word Made Plain. 1958. pap. 4.95 (ISBN 0-8024-3041-4). Moody.

Friedman, Richard E. Who Wrote The Bible. 1987. 16.95. Summit Bks.

Froehlich, Karlfried, ed. & tr. Biblical Interpretation in the Early Church. LC 84-47922. (Sources of Early Christian Thought Ser.). 128p. 1985. pap. 7.95 (ISBN 0-8006-1414-3, 1-1414). Fortress.

Fudge, Edward W. The Fire That Consumes: A Biblical & Historical Study of Final Punishment. 1983. 19.95 (ISBN 0-89890-018-2). Providential Pr.

Fuller, R. C. Alexander Geddes: A Forerunner of Biblical Criticism. (Historic Texts & Interperters Ser.: No. 3). 186p. 1985. text ed. 25.95x (ISBN 0-907459-26-9, Pub. by Almond Pr England); pap. text ed. 12.95x (ISBN 0-907459-27-7). Eisenbrauns.

Gaebelein, Frank E., ed. Expositor's Bible Commentary, Vol. 1. (Introductory Actilces). 1979. 22.95 (ISBN 0-310-36430-2, 11170). Zondervan.

Gaffin, Richard B., Jr., ed. Redemptive History & Biblical Interpretation: The Shorter Writings of Geerhardus Vos. 1980. 17.50 (ISBN 0-87552-270-X). Presby & Reformed.

Gardner, Helen. Limits of Literary Criticism. LC 74-16242. 1956. lib. bdg. 8.00 (ISBN 0-8414-4558-3). Folcroft.

Gaudin, Thierry. The Secret Code: The Lost & Hidden Language of the Bible, Vol. 1. LC 85-70031. 300p. (Orig.). 1985. pap. 12.95 (ISBN 0-933357-05-2). Bret Pubns.

Gaventa, Beverly R. From Darkness to Light: Aspects of Conversion in the New Testament. LC 85-16309. (Overtures to Biblical Theology Ser.). 176p. 1986. pap. 8.95 (ISBN 0-8006-1545-X, 1-1545). Fortress.

Gladden, Lee & Gladden, Vivianne C. Heirs of the Gods: A Space Age Interpretation of the Bible. LC 78-53852. (Illus.). 324p. Repr. of 1979 ed. 15.95 (ISBN 0-686-37960-8). Bel-Air.

Gladden, Washington. Who Wrote the Bible? A Book for the People. LC 72-5435. (Select Bibliographies Reprint Ser.). 1972. Repr. of 1891 ed. 22.00 (ISBN 0-8369-6909-X). Ayer Co Pubs.

Gnuse, Robert. You Shall Not Steal: Community & Property in the Biblical Tradition. LC 85-4810. 176p. (Orig.). 1985. pap. 9.95 (ISBN 0-88344-799-1). Orbis Bks.

Gobbel, A. Roger, et al. Helping Youth Interpret the Bible: A Teaching Resource. LC 84-3916. 204p. 1984. pap. 9.95 (ISBN 0-8042-1580-4). John Knox.

Gonzales, Bertha, tr. from Span. The Bible & the Message to the Men of the "New Earth". (Illus.). 144p. (Orig.). 1986. pap. write for info. (ISBN 0-9607590-5-0). Action Life Pubns.

Goodboy, Eadie. God's Daughter. rev. ed. (Bible Study: Basic Ser.). 60p. (Orig.). 1985. pap. 2.95 (ISBN 0-932305-45-8, 521002). Aglow Pubns.

Goodis, Karen L. The Learning Center Book of Bible People. LC 81-67026. (Learning Center Book Ser.). (Illus.). 123p. (Orig.). 1981. pap. 14.50 (ISBN 0-86705-005-5). AIRE.

Gordis, Robert. Poets, Prophets, & Sages: Essays in Biblical Interpretation. LC 79-98984. pap. 111.50 (ISBN 0-317-37273-4, 2055498). Bks Demand UMI.

Graesser, Erich. Das Problem der Parusieverzoegerung in den Synoptischen Evangelien und in der Apostelgeschichte. 3rd ed. (Beihefte zur Zeitschrift fuer die Alttestamentliche Wissenschaft 22). 1977. 36.40x (ISBN 3-11-007512-1). De Gruyter.

Grant, L. M. The Bible: It's Sixty Six Books in Brief. 70p. pap. 3.95 (ISBN 0-88172-160-3). Believers Bkshelf.

Green, Ruth H. The Born Again Skeptic's Guide to the Bible. 1979. 9.00. Freedom Rel Found.

Gresham, Charles R. What the Bible Says about Resurrection. LC 82-7411. (What the Bible Says Ser.). 351p. 1983. 13.95 (ISBN 0-89900-090-8). College Pr Pub.

Gunderson, Vivian. What's the Bible Like: New Testament. (Illus.). 1983. pap. 1.25 (ISBN 0-8323-0418-2). Binford-Metropolitan.

Haley, John W. Alleged Discrepancies of the Bible. (Direction Bks.). 1977. pap. 7.95 (ISBN 0-8010-4171-6). Baker Bk.

--Alleged Discrepancies of the Bible. 480p. 1984. pap. text ed. 3.95 (ISBN 0-88368-157-9). Whitaker Hse.

Hallam, Arthur F. Concurrences Between Dio Chrysostom's First Discourse & the New Testament. 91p. (Orig.). 1985. pap. 9.95 (ISBN 0-938770-04-7). Capitalist Pr OH.

Hallo, W. W., et al, eds. Scripture in Context II: More Essays on the Comparative Method. 1983. text ed. 17.50 (ISBN 0-931464-14-5). Eisenbrauns.

Halpern, Baruch & Levenson, Jon D., eds. Traditions in Transformation: Turning Points in Biblical Faith. 1981. 22.50 (ISBN 0-931464-06-4). Eisenbrauns.

Harbour, Brian L. Famous Parents of the Bible. LC 82-73079. 1983. pap. 4.95 (ISBN 0-8054-5655-4). Broadman.

Harris, Ralph W. The Incomparable Story. LC 77-75602. (Radiant Life Ser.). 128p. 1977. pap. 2.50 (ISBN 0-88243-907-3, 02-0907); tchr's ed. 3.95 (ISBN 0-88243-177-3, 32-0177). Gospel Pub.

Harris, Stephen L. Understanding the Bible. 2nd ed. 1985. pap. 19.95 (ISBN 0-87484-696-X). Mayfield Pub.

Heline, Corinne. Mystic Masonry & the Bible. pap. 1.00 (ISBN 0-87613-017-1). New Age.

--Mythology & the Bible. 1972. pap. 4.50 (ISBN 0-87613-018-X). New Age.

--Mythology & the Bible. 75p. pap. text ed. 4.50 (ISBN 0-933963-13-0). New Age Bible.

--New Age Bible Interpretation, Vol. 1. (Illus.). 496p. 1985. Repr. of 1935 ed. lib. bdg. 16.00 (ISBN 0-933963-01-7). New Age Bible.

--New Age Bible Interpretation, Vol. 2. (Illus.). 469p. Repr. lib. bdg. 16.00 (ISBN 0-933963-02-5). New Age Bible.

--New Age Bible Interpretation, Vol. 3. (Illus.). 516p. Repr. text ed. 16.00 (ISBN 0-87613-046-5). New Age Bible.

--New Age Bible Interpretation, Vol. 4. 144p. 1985. Repr. of 1935 ed. lib. bdg. 8.00 (ISBN 0-87613-089-9). New Age Bible.

--New Age Bible Interpretation, Vol. 5. 230p. Repr. lib. bdg. 11.00 (ISBN 0-933963-05-X). New Age Bible.

--New Age Bible Interpretation, Vol. 6. (Illus.). 255p. lib. bdg. 12.00 (ISBN 0-933963-06-8). New Age Bible.

--New Age Bible Interpretation, Vol. 7. (Illus.). 298p. lib. bdg. 14.00 (ISBN 0-933963-07-6). New Age Bible.

Hendriksen, William. Bible on the Life Hereafter. (Direction Books). 1971. pap. 6.95 (ISBN 0-8010-4022-1). Baker Bk.

--Survey of the Bible. rev. ed. LC 76-507. 515p. 1976. 17.95 (ISBN 0-8010-4288-7). Baker Bk.

Henrichsen, Walter A. Entendamos. Cook, David A., tr. from Eng. Tr. of Understand. (Span.). 112p. 1979. pap. 2.95 (ISBN 0-89922-131-9). Edit Caribe.

--A Layman's Guide to Interpreting the Bible. 112p. (Orig.). 1985. pap. 5.95 (ISBN 0-310-37681-5). Zondervan.

Hicks, Robert & Bewes, Richard. The Christian. (Understanding Bible Truth Ser.). (Orig.). 1981. pap. 0.95 (ISBN 0-89840-023-6). Heres Life.

Hills, Edward F. The King James Version Defended. 4th ed. (Illus.). 280p. 1984. pap. 8.95x (ISBN 0-915923-00-9). Christian Res Pr.

Howard, Elsie. Basic Bible Survey. LC 82-19686. 96p. (Orig.). 1983. pap. 2.95 (ISBN 0-87239-572-3, 3210). Standard Pub.

Hruska, Eva J. The Alpha thru Omega Bible Survey. LC 85-90314. 1985. pap. 3.95 (ISBN 0-9614616-1-6); tchr's. ed 7.95 (ISBN 0-9614616-0-8). Eva Hruska.

Hyers, Conrad. And God Created Laughter: The Bible As Divine Comedy. LC 86-46037. 132p. (Orig.). 1987. pap. 9.95 (ISBN 0-8042-1653-3). John Knox.

Iannarelli, S. Joseph. The Third Testament of the Holy Bible. 1985. 5.95 (ISBN 0-533-06645-X). Vantage.

Inch, Morris A. & Bullock, C. Hassell, eds. The Literature & Meaning of Scripture. 360p. 1981. 14.95 (ISBN 0-8010-5032-4). Baker Bk.

Innes, Kathleen E. The Bible As Literature. 255p. 1980. Repr. of 1930 ed. lib. bdg. 25.00 (ISBN 0-8492-1222-7). R West.

The Interpreter's Concise Commentary, 8 vols. Set. slipcased 34.95 (ISBN 0-687-19231-5). Abingdon.

Jefferson, Thomas. American Christian Bible. LC 82-80548. 128p. 1982. pap. 5.00 (ISBN 0-914752-14-6). Sovereign Pr.

Johnson, Luke T. The Writings of the New Testament: An Interpretation. LC 85-16202. 640p. 1986. 34.95 (ISBN 0-8006-0886-0, 1-886); pap. 18.95 (ISBN 0-8006-1886-6, 1-1886). Fortress.

Johnson, S. Lewis. The Old Testament in the New: An Argument for Biblical Inspiration. (Contemporary Evangelical Perspectives Ser.). 128p. (Orig.). 1980. pap. 4.95 (ISBN 0-310-41851-8, 18244P). Zondervan.

Jones, Shirley M. The Coming of Yahweh. (Illus.). 600p. 1985. 17.50 (ISBN 0-9615111-0-9). Sandbird Pub.

Jordan, Bernice. Footsteps to God: Six Basic Bible Truth Lessons. (Illus.). 1970. pap. text ed. 6.50 (ISBN 0-86508-025-9). BCM Intl Inc.

Kasher, M. M. Encyclopedia of Biblical Interpretation, 9 vols. Set. 35.00 ea. (ISBN 0-87068-315-2). Ktav.

Keet, Cuthbert C. Study of the Psalms of Ascents: A Critical & Exegetical Commentary Upon Psalms 120-134. (Illus.). 200p. 1969. 9.50 (ISBN 0-7051-0041-3). Attic Pr.

Kemper, Frederick W. The Lamb. LC 12-2983. (Christian Education & the Church Ser.). 1983. pap. 5.95 (ISBN 0-570-03901-0). Concordia.

Kimball, William. What the Bible Says about the Great Tribulation. LC 83-71918. (What the Bible Says Ser.). (Illus.). 291p. 1983. 13.95 (ISBN 0-89900-093-2). College Pr pub.

Kingsbury, Jack D. The Christology of Mark's Gospel. LC 83-5576. 224p. 1983. 19.95 (ISBN 0-8006-0706-6, 1-706). Fortress.

Kirby, John & Thompson, William M., eds. Voegelin & the Theologian: Ten Studies in Interpretation. LC 82-22914. (Toronto Studies in Theology: Vol. 10). 392p. 1983. 59.95x (ISBN 0-88946-751-X). E Mellen.

Kirk, Thomas. The Life of Joseph. 319p. 1985. smythe sewn 12.75 (ISBN 0-86524-193-7, 8408). Klock & Klock.

Klem, Herbert V. Oral Communication of the Scripture: Insights from African Oral Art. LC 81-10052. (Applied Cultural Anthropology Ser.). (Illus.). 280p. (Orig.). 1982. pap. text ed. 9.95x (ISBN 0-87808-332-4). William Carey Lib.

Klinsing, P. David, et al. Is There Life after High School. LC 79-53677. 116p. 1979. pap. 2.50 (ISBN 0-87509-264-0). Chr Pubns.

Knight, George & Edwards, James R., eds. The Layman's Overview of the Bible. 224p. 1987. pap. text ed. 8.95 (ISBN 0-8407-3109-4). Nelson.

Knoch, A. E. The Mystery of the Gospel. 297p. 1976. pap. text ed. 4.00 (ISBN 0-910424-55-1). Concordant.

Koenig, John. New Testament Hospitality: Partnership with Strangers As Promise & Mission. LC 85-47725. (Overtures to Biblical Theology Ser.). 176p. 1985. pap. 9.95 (ISBN 0-8006-1543-3, 1-1543). Fortress.

Kung, Hans & Moltmann, Jurgen, eds. Conflicting Ways of Interpreting the Bible, Concilium 138. (New Concilium 1980). 128p. 1981. pap. 5.95 (ISBN 0-8245-4771-3, HarpR). Har-Row.

Lamsa, George. Idioms in the Bible Explained & a Key to the Original Gospels. LC 85-42782. 128p. 1985. pap. 8.95 (ISBN 0-06-064927-5, HarpR). Har-Row.

Lamsa, George M. Old Testament Light. LC 84-48774. 1008p. 1985. 34.95 (ISBN 0-06-064924-0, HarpR); pap. 19.95 (ISBN 0-06-064925-9, HarpR). Har-Row.

Lamsa, George M., tr. Holy Bible. 29.45 (ISBN 0-317-52395-3, HarpR); pap. 19.95 (ISBN 0-317-52396-1, RD 423). Har-Row.

--Holy Bible: From the Ancient Eastern Text. 1248p. 1986. 29.95 (ISBN 0-06-064922-4, HarpR); pap. 19.95 (ISBN 0-06-064923-2, HarpR). Har-Row.

Landy, Francis. Paradoxes of Paradise: Identity & Difference in the Song of Songs. (Bible & Literature Ser.: No. 7). 1983. text ed. 29.95x (ISBN 0-907459-16-1, Pub. by Almond Pr England); pap. text ed. 16.95x (ISBN 0-907459-17-X, Pub. by Almond Pr England). Eisenbrauns.

Larkin, Ernest & Broccolo, Gerald T., eds. The Priest & Sacred Scripture. cancelled (ISBN 0-686-18989-2, V-226). US Catholic.

Lasley, Don & Lasley, Kay. Scripture Handbook on Business & Finance. 1985. pap. 6.95 (ISBN 0-89274-317-4). Harrison Hse.

Lategan, Bernard C. & Vorster, Willem S. Text & Reality: Aspects of Reference in Biblical Texts. LC 85-47735. 144p. 1985. pap. 9.95 (ISBN 0-8006-1514-X). Fortress.

Law, Terry. The Power of Praise & Worship. (Illus.). 256p. (Orig.). 1985. pap. 6.95 (ISBN 0-932081-01-0). Victory Hse.

Leach, Edmund & Aycock, Alan. Structuralist Interpretations of Biblical Myth. LC 82-25263. (Illus.). 176p. 1983. 34.50 (ISBN 0-521-25491-4); pap. 11.95 (ISBN 0-521-27492-3). Cambridge U Pr.

Lemons, Paul G. A Message for the Human Race. 1984. 15.95 (ISBN 0-533-06058-3). Vantage.

Lewis, Gordon. Bible, Christian & Latter Day Saints. pap. 1.25 (ISBN 0-8010-5567-9). Baker Bk.

--Bible, Christian & Seventh Day Adventists. pap. 1.25 (ISBN 0-8010-5573-3). Baker Bk.

--Bible, Christians & Jehovah's Witnesses. pap. 1.25 (ISBN 0-8010-5568-7). Baker Bk.

Lindsay, Gordon. Bible Days Are Here Again. pap. 4.00 (ISBN 0-89985-194-0). Christ Nations.

Lohfink, Gerhard. The Bible, Now I Get It: A Form Criticism Handbook. LC 78-1209. (Illus.). 1979. pap. 7.95 (ISBN 0-385-13432-0). Doubleday.

Longacre, Robert E., ed. OPTAT: Occasional Papers in Translation & Textlinguistics, Studies in Translation, Discourse Analysis, & Related Areas of Biblical Research. 88p. (Orig.). 1986. pap. 5.00 (ISBN 0-88312-668-0). Summer Inst Ling.

Louis, Kenneth R. Literary Interpretations of Biblical Narratives 11. LC 74-12400. 320p. (Orig.). 1982. pap. 10.95 (ISBN 0-687-22132-3). Abingdon.

Luck, G. C. The Bible Book by Book: An Introduction to Bible Synthesis. 1955. pap. text ed. 3.95 (ISBN 0-8024-0045-0). Moody.

Lyons, L. Bible in Everyday Speech. 1986. cancelled (ISBN 0-442-25325-7). Van Nos Reinhold.

MacArthur, John F., Jr. Take God's Word for It. LC 79-91704. 160p. 1980. pap. 2.50 (ISBN 0-8307-0674-7, S341107). Regal.

--Why Believe the Bible. LC 79-91704. 160p. 1980. 5.95 (ISBN 0-8307-0750-6, 5413818). Regal.

Macarthur, John, Jr. Why I Trust the Bible. 120p. 1983. pap. 4.95 (ISBN 0-88207-389-3). Victor Bks.

McAuley, Marilyn. What Did God Make? (Peek & Find Bks.). (Illus.). 28p. 1984. board book 3.95 (ISBN 0-89191-878-7, 58784). Cook.

McConnell, Frank, ed. The Bible & Narrative Tradition. 168p. 1986. 16.95x (ISBN 0-19-503698-0). Oxford U Pr.

McDonald, C. L. In the Likeness of God or, of Moses, of Pride & of Thorns. 1986. 10.95 (ISBN 0-533-07031-7). Vantage.

MacDonald, Dennis R. There Is No Male & Female: The Fate of a Dominical Saying in Paul & Gnosticism. LC 86-45200. (Harvard Dissertations in Religion Ser.). 160p. 1987. pap. 14.95 (ISBN 0-8006-7076-0, 1-7076). Fortress.

McIntosh, Hugh. Is Christ Infallible & the Bible True? 1981. lib. bdg. 27.00 (ISBN 0-86524-076-0, 8603). Klock & Klock.

Madeley, Hulon M. The Other Revelation for Christians. (Illus.). 48p. 1985. 7.95 (ISBN 0-89962-434-0). Todd & Honeywell.

Malone, Willie. Your New Beginning: Step Two. 64p. (Orig.). 1983. pap. 2.50 (ISBN 0-88144-008-6). Christian Pub.

March, W. Eugene, ed. Texts & Testaments: Critical Essays on the Bible & Early Church Fathers. LC 79-92585. 321p. 1980. 15.00 (ISBN 0-911536-80-9). Trinity U Pr.

Mayhue, Richard L. How to Interpret the Bible for Yourself. 1986. pap. 3.95 (ISBN 0-88469-178-0). BMH Bks.

Menzies, William W. Understanding the Times of Christ. 128p. 1969. 1.50 (ISBN 0-88243-622-8, 02-0622). Gospel Pub.

Merrill, Arthur L. & Overholt, Thomas W., eds. Scripture in History & Theology: Essays in Honor of J. Coert Rylaarsdam. LC 77-12106. (Pittsburgh Theological Monographs: No. 17). 1977. pap. 10.00 (ISBN 0-915138-32-8). Pickwick.

Metcalfe, J. C. Bible & the Human Mind. pap. 2.95 (ISBN 0-87508-913-5). Chr Lit.

Metz, Donald. Studies in Biblical Holiness. 284p. 1971. 10.95 (ISBN 0-8341-0117-3). Beacon Hill.

Metzger, Will. Tell the Truth. 2nd ed. LC 83-25304. 187p. (Orig.). 1981. pap. 6.95 (ISBN 0-87784-934-X). Inter Varsity.

Mini-Guide to the Contents of the Books of the Bible. pap. 0.50 (ISBN 0-686-70364-2). Reiner.

Montgomery, John W., ed. God's Inerrant Word. pap. 8.95 (ISBN 0-87123-292-8, 210292). Bethany Hse.

Moorman, Jere. All Things Are Possible: Humorous Interpretations of Scripture. 96p. (Orig.). 1983. pap. 3.00 (ISBN 0-915561-00-X). Crane Pubns CA.

Morgan, G. Campbell. Answers of Jesus to Job. (Morgan Library). 1973. pap. 3.95 (ISBN 0-8010-5917-8). Baker Bk.

Morris, Leon. Apocalyptic. 88p. 1977. pap. 4.95 (ISBN 0-8028-1455-7). Eerdmans.

--Testaments of Love: A Study of Love in the Bible. (Orig.). 1981. 12.95 (ISBN 0-8028-3502-3). Eerdmans.

Most, William G. Free from All Error: Authorship, Inerrancy, Historicity of Scripture, Church Teaching, & Modern Scripture Scholars. 179p. (Orig.). 1985. pap. 11.95 (ISBN 0-913382-51-5, 101-31). Prow Bks-Franciscan.

Moulton, Richard G. A Short Introduction to the Literature of the Bible. 1978. Repr. of 1900 ed. lib. bdg. 25.00 (ISBN 0-8495-3729-0). Arden Lib.

Murray, Andrew. The Believer's New Covenant. LC 83-21408. 128p. 1983. pap. 3.95 (ISBN 0-87123-406-8, 210406). Bethany Hse.

Nane, Orville J. Nave's Topical Bible. 1616p. Date not set. 19.95 (ISBN 0-917006-02-X). Hendrickson MA.

Nineham, Dennis. The Use & Abuse of the Bible. LC 76-15690. (Library of Philosophy & Religion Ser.). (Illus.). 295p. 1976. text ed. 28.50x (ISBN 0-06-495178-2). B&N Imports.

Nottage, Isiah L. The Biblical Mysteries Revealed. 1984. 9.95 (ISBN 0-8062-2315-4). Carlton.

El Nuevo Testamento: Reina-Valera Actualizada. (Span.). 320p. (Orig.). 1986. pap. 0.95 (ISBN 0-311-48753-X). Casa Bautista.

El Nuevo Testamento: "Venid a Mi" Rva. (Span.). 320p. (Orig.). 1986. pap. 0.60 (ISBN 0-311-48752-1). Casa Bautista.

Omer, Mordechai. Turner & the Bible. 48p. 1981. 5.50x (ISBN 0-900090-79-0, Pub. by Ashmolean Museum). State Mutual Bk.

Orlinsky, Harry M. Understanding the Bible Through History & Archaeology. 1969. 12.50x (ISBN 0-87068-096-X). Ktav.

Osden, Russell. A Capsule View of the Bible. 1979. pap. 1.00 (ISBN 0-88469-045-8). BMH Bks.

Outlaw, et al. A Survey of the New Testament. Harrison, Harrold D., ed. (Orig.). 1984. pap. 4.95 (ISBN 0-89265-090-7). Randall Hse.

Packer, J. I. Beyond the Battle for the Bible. LC 80-68331. 160p. 1980. text ed. 9.95 (ISBN 0-89107-195-4, Crossway Bks). Good News.

Parmalee, Alice. Introducing the Bible. (Epiphany Ser.). 128p. 1983. pap. 2.25 (ISBN 0-345-30575-2). Ballantine.

Parmenter, Bruce. What the Bible Says about Self Esteem. LC 86-70211. (What the Bible Says Ser.). 405p. 13.95 (ISBN 0-89900-251-X). College Pr Pub.

Pearlman, Myer. Seeing the Story of the Bible. 128p. 1930. pap. 2.95 (ISBN 0-88243-581-7, 02-0581). Gospel Pub.

--Through the Bible Book by Book, 4 vols. 1935. pap. 2.95 ea.; Vol. 1. (ISBN 0-88243-660-0, 02-0660); Vol. 2. (ISBN 0-88243-661-9, 02-0661); Vol. 3. (ISBN 0-88243-662-7, 02-0662); Vol. 4. (ISBN 0-88243-663-5, 02-0663). Gospel Pub.

Penniman, Josiah H. A Book about the English Bible. 1977. Repr. of 1920 ed. lib. bdg. 27.50 (ISBN 0-8492-2101-3). R West.

Pettingill, William L. Bible Questions Answered. 1932. 8.95 (ISBN 0-310-31131-4, Pub. by Dunham). Zondervan.

Phillips, Wade H. Perplexing Scriptures. 135p. (Orig.). 1984. pap. 4.50 (ISBN 0-934942-44-7, 2034). White Wing Pub.

The Pilgrim Study Bible. 1984. write for info. Oxford U Pr.

Pillai, K. C. Light Through an Eastern Window. pap. 4.95 (ISBN 0-8315-0057-3). Speller.

--Orientalisms of the Bible, Vol. II. LC 84-50935. 141p. 1984. 3.95 (ISBN 0-910068-56-9). Am Christian.

--Orientalisms of the Bible, Vol. 1. 1969. 4.95x (ISBN 0-912178-02-7). Mor-Mac.

Pinnock, Clark H. The Scripture Principle. LC 84-37732. 288p. 1985. 15.45i (ISBN 0-06-066620-X); 15.95. Har-Row.

Priest, James E. Governmental & Judicial Ethics in the Bible & Rabbinic Literature. LC 79-23423. 312p. 1980. 17.95x (ISBN 0-87068-697-6). Pepperdine U Pr.

Prime, Derek. Baker's Bible Study Guide. (Baker's Paperback Reference Library). 296p. 1982. pap. 8.95 (ISBN 0-8010-7076-7). Baker Bk.

Purkiser, W. T. Beacon Bible Expositions: Hebrews, James, Peter, Vol. 11. Greathouse, William M. & Taylor, Willard H., eds. 1974. 8.95 (ISBN 0-8341-0322-2). Beacon Hill.

Ramm, Bernard. Protestant Biblical Interpretation. Chan, Silas, tr. from Eng. (Chinese.). 1984. pap. write for info. (ISBN 0-941598-10-1). Living Spring Pubns.

Richards, Kent, ed. Society of Biblical Literature Nineteen Eighty-One: Seminar Papers. (SBL Seminar Papers & Abstracts). pap. 9.00 (ISBN 0-89130-548-3, 06-09-20). Scholars Pr GA.

Richards, Kent H., ed. Society of Biblical Literature: Seminar Papers Nineteen Eighty-Four. 412p. 1984. pap. 15.00 (ISBN 0-89130-810-5, 06 09 23). Scholars Pr GA.

--Society of Biblical Literature: Seminar Papers Nineteen Eighty-Three. (SBL Seminar Papers). 490p. 1983. pap. 15.00 (ISBN 0-89130-607-2, 06 09 22). Scholars Pr GA.

Ricoeur, Paul. Essays on Biblical Interpretation. Mudge, Lewis S., ed. LC 80-8052. 192p. (Orig.). 1980. pap. 8.95 (ISBN 0-8006-1407-0, 1-1407). Fortress.

Riley, William. Tale of Two Testaments. 176p. 1985. pap. 5.95 (ISBN 0-89622-240-3). Twenty Third.

Rogerson, John, ed. Beginning Old Testament Study. LC 82-20210. 164p. 1983. pap. 8.95 (ISBN 0-664-24451-3). Westminster.

Root, Orrin. Training for Service: A Survey of the Bible. Daniel, Eleanor, rev. by. 128p. 1983. pap. 3.95 (ISBN 0-87239-704-1, 3212); tchr's. ed. 4.95 (ISBN 0-87239-703-3, 3211). Standard Pub.

Rowland, Alfred. Studies in First Timothy. 302p. 1985. smythe sewn 12.00 (ISBN 0-86524-194-5, 5402). Klock & Klock.

Rowley, Harold H. The Unity of the Bible. LC 78-2684. 1978. Repr. of 1953 ed. lib. bdg. 22.50x (ISBN 0-313-20346-6, ROUB). Greenwood.

Ruch, Dr. Velma. The Signature of God. 1986. pap. 25.00 (ISBN 0-8309-0428-X). Herald Hse.

Ruskin, John. The Bible References of John Ruskin. LC 77-13181. 1977. Repr. lib. bdg. 30.00 (ISBN 0-8414-4608-3). Folcroft.

Russell, Letty M., ed. Feminist Interpretation of the Bible. LC 84-17342. 166p. (Orig.). 1985. pap. 10.95 (ISBN 0-664-24639-7). Westminster.

--The Liberating Word: A Guide to Non-Sexist Interpretation of the Bible. LC 76-18689. 120p. 1976. pap. 7.95 (ISBN 0-664-24751-2). Westminster.

Sadowski, Frank, ed. The Church Fathers on the Bible. 1987. pap. write for info. (ISBN 0-8189-0510-7). Alba.

Sanford, Agnes. The Healing Power of the Bible. LC 83-48999. 1984. pap. 6.95 (ISBN 0-06-067053-3, RD 520, HarpR). Har-Row.

Saucy, Richard L. Is Bible Reliable, Bk. 2. Wong, Ernest, tr. (Basic Doctrine Ser.). (Chinese.). 1985. pap. write for info. (ISBN 0-941598-28-4). Living Spring Pubns.

Saunders, Ernest W. Searching the Scriptures: A History of the Society of Biblical Literature 1880-1980. LC 82-10818. (Society of Biblical Literature - Biblical Scholarship in North America Ser.). 15.00 (ISBN 0-89130-591-2, 06-11-08). Scholars Pr GA.

Schlink, Basilea. Allah or the God of the Bible: What Is the Truth? 1984. pap. 2.50 (ISBN 0-551-01140-8, Pub. by Marshall Morgan & Scott UK). Evang Sisterhood Mary.

Scott, John H. God Reveals Himself. 1987. 7.95 (ISBN 0-533-07061-9). Vantage.

Seale, M. S. Qur'an & Bible: Studies in Interpretation & Dialogue. 124p. 1978. 23.50 (ISBN 0-85664-818-3, Pub. by Croom Helm Ltd). Methuen Inc.

Senior, Donald & Stuhlmueller, Carroll. The Biblical Foundations for Mission. LC 82-22430. 384p. (Orig.). 1983. 12.50 (ISBN 0-88344-046-6); pap. 14.95 (ISBN 0-88344-047-4). Orbis Bks.

Shotwell, Willis A. Biblical Exegesis of Justin Martyr. LC 66-8998. 1965. pap. 10.00x (ISBN 0-8401-2173-3). A R Allenson.

Simpson, Albert B. Old Faith & the New Gospels. pap. 1.25 (ISBN 0-87509-031-1). Chr Pubns.

Slusser, Gerald H. From Jung to Jesus: Myth & Consciousness in the New Testament. LC 85-45792. 180p. 1986. pap. 10.95 (ISBN 0-8042-1111-6). John Knox.

Smith, F. G. What the Bible Teaches. 1970. pap. 4.95 (ISBN 0-87162-104-5, D8850). Warner Pr.

Soncino Books of the Bible, 14 vols. Incl. Chumash. 22.50 (ISBN 0-900689-24-2); Daniel. 10.95 (ISBN 0-900689-36-6); Hoshua & Judges. 10.95 (ISBN 0-900689-25-0); Samuel I-II. 10.95 (ISBN 0-900689-26-9); Chronicles. 10.95 (ISBN 0-900689-37-4); King I-II. 10.95 (ISBN 0-900689-27-7); Isaiah. 10.95 (ISBN 0-900689-28-5); Jeremiah. 10.95 (ISBN 0-900689-29-3); Ezekiel. 10.95 (ISBN 0-900689-30-7); Twelve Prophets. 10.95 (ISBN 0-900689-31-5); Psalms. 10.95 (ISBN 0-900689-32-3); Proverbs. 10.95; Job. 10.95; Five Meeillah. 10.95 (ISBN 0-900689-35-8). Set. 149.95x (ISBN 0-900689-23-4). Bloch.

The Song of Songs. (Modern Critical Interpretations--Ancient, Medieval, & Renaissance Ser.). 1987. 19.95 (ISBN 0-87754-917-6). Chelsea Hse.

Soulen, Richard N. Handbook of Biblical Criticism. rev. ed. LC 76-12398. 225p. 1981. pap. 11.95 (ISBN 0-8042-0045-9). John Knox.

Spencer, Richard A., ed. Orientation by Disorientation: Studies on Literary Criticism & Biblical Literary Criticism Presented in Honor of William A. Beardslee. (Pittsburgh Theological Monograph Ser.: No. 35). 1980. pap. text ed. 15.00 (ISBN 0-915138-44-1). Pickwick.

Stegall, Neil & Bernard, David. A New Birth: A Study Guide. 120p. (Orig.). 1987. pap. 5.95 spiral bd. (ISBN 0-932581-15-3). Word Aflame.

Stein, Robert H. Difficult Sayings in the Gospels: Jesus's Use of Overstatement & Hyperbole. 96p. pap. 4.95 (ISBN 0-8010-8262-5). Baker Bk.

Steinsaltz, Adin. Biblical Images: Men & Women of the Book. LC 83-46081. 256p. 1985. pap. 6.95 (ISBN 0-465-00671-X, PL-5158). Basic.

Stendahl, Krister. Meanings: The Bible As Document & Guide. LC 83-5601. 240p. 1984. pap. 14.95 (ISBN 0-8006-1752-5, 1-1752). Fortress.

Stott, John R. Understanding the Bible. 2nd ed. 192p. 1985. pap. 6.95 (ISBN 0-310-41431-8). Zondervan.

Swartley, Willard. Slavery, Sabbath, War & Women: Case Issues in Biblical Interpretation. LC 82-23417. (Conrad Grebel Lecture Ser.). 320p. (Orig.). 1983. pap. 15.95 (ISBN 0-8361-3330-7). Herald Pr.

Swetmon. Does the Bible Contradict Itself. 1985. pap. 3.95 (ISBN 0-89225-276-6). Gospel Advocate.

Tan, Paul L. Literal Interpretation of the Bible. LC 78-73220. 1978. pap. text ed. 2.95 (ISBN 0-932940-04-8). Assurance Pubs.

--Literal Interpretation of the Bible. 114p. 1979. pap. 3.95 (ISBN 0-88469-098-9). BMH Bks.

Terry, Milton S. Bible Hermeneutics. 784p. 1974. kivar 14.95 (ISBN 0-310-36831-6, 6672P). Zondervan.

Thoma, Clemens & Wyschgrod, Michael, eds. Understanding Scripture: Explorations of Jewish & Christian Traditions of Interpretation. 1987. pap. 7.95 (ISBN 0-8091-2873-X). Paulist Pr.

Thomas, J. D. Heaven's Window: Sequel to We Be Brethren. LC 74-28950. 159p. 1975. 11.95 (ISBN 0-89112-002-5, Bibl Res Pr). Abilene Christ U.

Thompson, Henry O., ed. The Answers Lie Below: Essays in Honor of Lawrence Edmund Toombs. LC 83-23376. (Illus.). 428p. (Orig.). 1984. lib. bdg. 32.50 (ISBN 0-8191-3745-6); pap. text ed. 17.75 (ISBN 0-8191-3746-4). U Pr of Amer.

Trail, W. The Literary Characteristics & Achievements of the Bible. 335p. 1983. Repr. of 1863 ed. lib. bdg. 85.00 (ISBN 0-89984-471-5). Century Bookbindery.

Trenchard, Ernesto. Bosquejos de Doctrina Fundamental. (Span.). 144p. 1972. pap. 3.95 (ISBN 0-8254-1725-2). Kregel.

--Normas de Interpretacion Biblica. (Span.). 150p. 1958. pap. 3.95 (ISBN 0-8254-1749-X). Kregel.

Trible, Phyllis. Texts of Terror: Literary-Feminist Readings of Biblical Narratives. LC 83-48906. (Overtures to Biblical Theology Ser.). 144p. 1984. pap. 8.95 (ISBN 0-8006-1537-9, 1-1537). Fortress.

Tucker, Gene & Knight, Douglas, eds. Humanizing America's Iconic Book. LC 82-836. (SBL Biblical Scholarship in North America Ser.). 188p. 1982. 29.95 (ISBN 0-89130-654-4, 06-11-06); pap. 17.50 (ISBN 0-89130-570-X). Scholars Pr GA.

Tyndale, William. Doctrinal Treatises, an Introduction to Different Portions of the Holy Scriptures. Repr. of 1848 ed. 51.00 (ISBN 0-384-62250-X). Johnson Repr.

Ulmer, Louise. Bringing Bible People to Life. 1982. 2.95 (ISBN 0-89536-574-X, 0217). CSS of Ohio.

Underwood, B. E. Spirit's Sword: God's Infallible Book. 1969. 3.95 (ISBN 0-911866-50-7); pap. 2.95 (ISBN 0-911866-91-4). Advocate.

Upchurch, Stanley. Arguments Against the Bible: An Expose of the Verbal Plenary Inspiration of the Bible. 10.00x (ISBN 0-686-27700-7). Freedom Univ-FSP.

Van Benschoten, A. Q., Jr. What the Bible Says about Stewardship. 96p. 1983. pap. 4.95 (ISBN 0-8170-0993-0). Judson.

Vander Goot, Henry V. Interpreting the Bible in Theology & the Church. LC 84-9027. (Symposium Ser.: Vol. II). 128p. 1984. pap. 19.95 (ISBN 0-88946-701-3). E Mellen.

Van Till, Howard J. The Fourth Day: What the Bible & the Heavens Are Telling Us about the Creation. LC 85-29400. (Illus.). 286p. (Orig.). 1986. pap. 9.95 (ISBN 0-8028-0178-1). Eerdmans.

Vawter, Bruce. The Path of Wisdom: Biblical Investigations. (Background Bks.: Vol. 3). 1986. pap. 12.95 (ISBN 0-89453-466-1). M Glazier.

Vine, William E. Vine's Expository Dictionary of New Testament Words. 1376p. Date not set. 14.95 (ISBN 0-917006-03-8). Hendrickson MA.

Von Campenhausen, Hans. The Formation of the Christian Bible. Baker, J. A., tr. from Ger. LC 73-171495. 360p. 1977. pap. 10.95 (ISBN 0-8006-1263-9, 1-1263). Fortress.

Vos, Geerhardus. Redemptive History & Biblical Interpretation. Gaffin, Richard B., Jr., ed. 584p. 1981. 17.50 (ISBN 0-8010-9286-8). Baker Bk.

Walters, Eva M. Christian Witness: That They Might Know Him. 1987. 7.95 (ISBN 0-533-07011-2). Vantage.

Ward, Miriam, ed. A Companion to the Bible. LC 85-15817. 419p. (Orig.). 1985. pap. 14.95 (ISBN 0-8189-0487-9). Alba.

Warren, Thomas B. Logic & the Bible. 1983. 11.00 (ISBN 0-934916-01-2). Natl Christian Pr.

Warren, Virgil. What the Bible Says about Salvation. LC 82-73345. (What the Bible Says Ser.). 640p. 1982. 13.95 (ISBN 0-89900-088-6). College Pr Pub.

Weaver, Horace R. Getting Straight about the Bible: The Creation, Interpreting Scripture, the Apocalypse, Life on Other Planets. LC 75-2342. 160p. (Orig.). 1975. pap. 6.95 (ISBN 0-687-14138-9). Abingdon.

Weisser, Thomas H. Three Persons from the Bible: Or Babylon. (Illus.). 44p. pap. 2.00 (ISBN 0-317-17477-0). Tom Weisser.

Wesley, John. Explanatory Notes on the New Testament. 29.95 (ISBN 0-317-07537-3, 96510). Baker Bk.

Westman, Heinz. The Structure of Biblical Myths: The Ontogenesis of the Psyche. LC 83-19132. (Seminar Ser.: No. 16). v, 477p. (Orig.). 1983. pap. 18.50 (ISBN 0-88214-116-3). Spring Pubns.

Whitaker, William. Disputation on Holy Scripture Against the Papists. 55.00 (ISBN 0-384-68010-0). Johnson Repr.

White, J. Benton. From Adam to Armageddon: A Survey of the Bible. LC 85-8921. 320p. 1985. pap. text ed. write for info. (ISBN 0-534-05111-1). Wadsworth Pub.

White, John. The Book of Books. 1978. 7.50 (ISBN 0-87552-545-8). Presby & Reformed.

White, Leland J. Christ & the Christian Movement: Jesus in the New Testament, the Creeds & Modern Theology. LC 85-11190. 296p. (Orig.). 1985. pap. 10.95 (ISBN 0-8189-0484-4). Alba.

Whiteside, Elena S. The Way: Living in Love. LC 72-89132. 284p. 1972. 5.95 (ISBN 0-910068-06-2). Am Christian.

Wiersbe, Warren W. Run with the Winners. Weese, Wightman, ed. 160p. (Orig.). 1985. pap. 4.95 (ISBN 0-8423-5798-X); study guide 2.95 (ISBN 0-8423-5799-8). Tyndale.

Williams, Burtis. Gospel in the Feasts of Israel. 32p. 1968. pap. 0.50 (ISBN 0-89114-011-5). Baptist Pub Hse.

Willis, John T. Insights from the Psalms, Vol. 2. LC 73-93946. (Way of Life Ser.: No. 132). 111p. 1974. pap. 3.95 (ISBN 0-89112-132-3, Bibl Res Pr). Abilene Christ U.

--Insights from the Psalms, Vol. 3. LC 73-93946. (Way of Life Ser: No. 133). 114p. 1974. pap. 3.95 (ISBN 0-89112-133-1, Bibl Res Pr). Abilene Christ U.

Wink, Walter. The Bible in Human Transformation: Towards a New Paradigm for Biblical Study. LC 73-79047. 96p. (Orig.). 1980. pap. 4.95 (ISBN 0-8006-1034-2, 1-1034). Fortress.

Wright, Sara M. Brief Survey of the Bible. 1958. pap. 5.95 (ISBN 0-87213-971-9). Loizeaux.

Writings-Kethubim: A New Translation of the Holy Scriptures According to the Traditional Hebrew Text. 624p. blue cloth 10.95 (ISBN 0-8276-0202-2); black leatherette, boxed, gold edges 19.95 (ISBN 0-8276-0203-0). Jewish Pubns.

Young, Robert. Young's Literal Translation of the Bible. pap. 24.95 (ISBN 0-8010-9921-8). Baker Bk.

Yusseff, M. A. The Dead Sea Scrolls, The Gospel of Barnabas & the New Testament. LC 85-73210. 154p. (Orig.). 1986. pap. 8.00 (ISBN 0-89259-061-0). Am Trust Pubns.

Zehr, Paul M. Biblical Criticism in the Life of the Church. LC 85-24762. 112p. (Orig.). 1986. pap. 6.95 (ISBN 0-8361-3404-4). Herald Pr.

BIBLE–CRITICISM, INTERPRETATION, ETC.–HISTORY

Bentley, Jerry H. Humanists & Holy Writ. LC 83-42547. 264p. 1983. 25.50x (ISBN 0-691-05392-8). Princeton U Pr.

Bird, Phyllis A. The Bible As the Church's Book. LC 82-7049. (Library of Living Faith: Vol. 5). 118p. 1982. pap. 5.95 (ISBN 0-664-24427-0). Westminster.

Chrysostomos, Archimandrite & Auxentios, Hieromonk. Scripture & Tradition. 96p. 1984. pap. 5.00 (ISBN 0-911165-04-5). Ctr Trad Orthodox.

Ellis, E. Earle. Prophecy & Hermeneutics in Early Christianity: New Testament Essays. 306p. 1978. lib. bdg. 54.00x. Coronet Bks.

Gill, David W. The Word of God in the Ethics of Jacques Ellul. LC 83-20165. (ATLA Monograph Ser.: No. 20). 231p. 1984. 19.00 (ISBN 0-8108-1667-9). Scarecrow.

Grant, Robert M. & Tracy, David. A Short History of the Interpretation of the Bible. 2nd, rev. & enlarged ed. LC 83-18485. 224p. 1984. pap. 10.95 (ISBN 0-8006-1762-2, 1-1762). Fortress.

Greenwood, David C. Structuralism & the Biblical Text. (Religion & Reason Ser.: No. 32). xi, 155p. 1985. 37.75x (ISBN 0-89925-103-X). Mouton.

Hamann, H. P. A Popular Guide to New Testament Criticism. 1977. pap. 4.75 (ISBN 0-570-03760-3, 12-2671). Concordia.

Kelly, George A. The Church's Problem with Bible Scholars. LC 85-1507. 60p. 1985. 2.50 (ISBN 0-8199-0929-7). Franciscan Herald.

Kinns, Samuel. Graven in the Rock or the Historical Accuracy of the Bible. LC 77-85611. 1977. Repr. of 1891 ed. lib. bdg. 65.00 (ISBN 0-89341-319-4). Longwood Pub Group.

Knight, Douglas A. Rediscovering the Traditions of Israel. LC 75-6868. (Society of Biblical Literature. Dissertation Ser.: No. 9). pap. 86.50 (ISBN 0-317-07884-4, 2017515). Bks Demand UMI.

Koch, Klaus. Growth of the Biblical Tradition. 1968. lib. bdg. 24.50x (ISBN 0-684-14524-3, ScribT). Scribner.

Krodel, Gottfried G. & Lehman, Helmut T., eds. Luther's Works: Letters I, Vol. 48. LC 55-9893. 1963. 19.95 (ISBN 0-8006-0348-6). Fortress.

Kuenning, Larry. Exiles in Babylon. LC 77-85708. 1978. pap. 2.25 (ISBN 0-930682-00-9). Friends Truth.

Kugel, James L. & Greer, Rowan A. Early Biblical Interpretation. LC 85-26397. (Library of Early Christianity: Vol. 3). 214p. 1986. 16.95 (ISBN 0-664-21907-1). Westminster.

McNally, Robert. The Bible in the Early Middle Ages. (Reprints & Translations Ser.). 1986. pap. 9.95 (ISBN 0-89130-912-8, 00-07-14). Scholars Pr GA.

Maier, Gerhard. End of the Historical Critical Method. 1977. pap. 6.25 (ISBN 0-570-03752-2, 12-2656). Concordia.

Motyer, Alec. The Message of Philippians. Stott, John R., ed. LC 83-22684. (The Bible Speaks Today Ser.). 252p. 1983. pap. 7.95 (ISBN 0-87784-310-4). Inter-Varsity.

Neill, Stephen. Interpretation of the New Testament, 1861-1961. 1964. pap. 10.95x (ISBN 0-19-283005-8). Oxford U Pr.

Olsen, V. N. The New Testament Logia on Divorce: A Study of their Interpretation from Erasmus to Milton. 167p. (Orig.). 1971. pap. 40.00x (Pub. by J. C. B. Mohr BRD). Coronet Bks.

Prickett, Stephen. Words & the Word: Language Poetics, & Biblical Interpretation. 288p. 1986. 39.50 (ISBN 0-521-32248-0). Cambridge U Pr.

Reventlow, Henning G. The Authority of the Bible & the Rise of the Modern World. Bowden, John, tr. from German. LC 83-48921. 688p. 1984. 42.95 (ISBN 0-8006-0288-9, 1-288). Fortress.

Riesen, Richard A. Criticism & Faith in Late Victorian Scotland: A. B. Davidson, William Robertson Smith & George Adam Smith. LC 85-5388. 490p. (Orig.). 1985. lib. bdg. 30.50 (ISBN 0-8191-4655-2); pap. text ed. 18.75 (ISBN 0-8191-4656-0). U Pr of Amer.

Rollins, Wayne G. Jung & the Bible. LC 82-48091. 156p. 1983. pap. 10.95 (ISBN 0-8042-1117-5). John Knox.

Sanders, James A. God Has a Story Too: Biblical Sermons in Context. LC 77-15244. 160p. 1979. pap. 6.95 (ISBN 0-8006-1353-8, 1-1353). Fortress.

Talmage, Frank E. David Kimhi: The Man & the Commentaries. LC 75-1747. (Harvard Judaic Monographs: No. 1). 224p. 1976. text ed. 16.50x (ISBN 0-674-19340-7). Harvard U Pr.

Woodbridge, John D. Biblical Authority: A Critique of the Rogers-McKim Proposal. 256p. (Orig.). 1982. pap. 9.95 (ISBN 0-310-44751-8, 12647P). Zondervan.

BIBLE–CRITICISM, INTERPRETATION, ETC.–N. T.

see also Demythologization

Alford, Henry. The New Testament for English Readers, 4 vols. 1983. Repr. of 1976 ed. 54.95 (ISBN 0-8010-0195-1). Baker Bk.

Anderson, Julian G. The New Testament in Everyday American English (EAE) LC 84-194786. (Illus.). 896p. 1984. pap. 4.95 (ISBN 0-9602128-4-1). Anderson Publ.

The Aramaic New Testament. LC 83-71100. 524p. 1983. 24.95 (ISBN 0-910068-47-X). Am Christian.

Bammel, E & Barrett, C. K., eds. Donum Gentilicium: New Testament Studies in Honor of David Daube. 1978. 59.00x (ISBN 0-19-826629-4). Oxford U Pr.

Barclay, William. The Master's Men. LC 85-6395. 224p. 1985. pap. 8.95 (ISBN 0-8027-2496-5). Walker & Co.

Barth, Markus. The People of God. (Journal for the Study of the New Testament, Supplement Ser.: No. 5). 100p. 1983. text ed. 15.95x (ISBN 0-905774-54-X, Pub. by JSOT Pr England); pap. text ed. 7.95x (ISBN 0-905774-55-8, Pub. by JSOT Pr England). Eisenbrauns.

Beardslee, William A. Literary Criticism of the New Testament. Via, Dan O., Jr., ed. LC 77-94817. (Guides to Biblical Scholarship: New Testament Ser.). 96p. (Orig.). 1970. pap. 4.50 (ISBN 0-8006-0185-8, 1-185). Fortress.

Beck, Norman A. Mature Christianity: The Recognition & Repudiation of the Anti-Jewish Polemic of the New Testament. LC 83-51047. (Illus.). 328p. 1985. 19.50 (ISBN 0-941664-03-1). Assoc Univ Prs.

Beckwith, Roger. The Old Testament Canon of the New Testament Church. 536p. 1986. 35.00 (ISBN 0-8028-3617-8). Eerdmans.

Berry, Nancee. Jesus Cares for Me. (Come Unto Me Ser.). 16p. 1979. pap. 1.65 (ISBN 0-8127-0252-2). Review & Herald.

Best, Ernest. From Text to Sermon: Responsible Use of the New Testament in Preaching. LC 77-79584. 1978. 8.95 (ISBN 0-8042-0245-1). John Knox.

Black, Matthew. The Scrolls & Christian Origins: Studies in the Jewish Background of the New Testament. LC 83-11519. (Brown Judaic Studies). 232p. 1983. pap. 14.00 (ISBN 0-89130-639-0, 14 00 48). Scholars Pr GA.

Blanch, Stuart. For All Mankind: A New Approach to the Old Testament. pap. 4.95 (ISBN 0-19-520025-X). Oxford U Pr.

Boers, Hendrikus. What Is New Testament Theology? The Rise of Criticism & the Problem of a Theology of the New Testament. Via, Dan O., Jr., ed. LC 79-7372. (Guides to Biblical Scholarship: New Testament Ser.). 96p. 1979. pap. 4.50 (ISBN 0-8006-0466-0, 1-466). Fortress.

Briggs, R. C. Interpreting the New Testament Today. rev. ed. LC 73-8024. 288p. (Orig.). 1973. pap. 9.95 (ISBN 0-687-19327-3). Abingdon.

Brooks, Oscar S. The Drama of Decision: Baptism in the New Testament. 280p. 1986. 11.95 (ISBN 0-913573-40-X). Hendrickson MA.

Brown, Schuyler. The Origins of Christianity: A Historical Introduction to the New Testament. (Oxford Bible Ser.). (Orig.). 1984. pap. 8.95 (ISBN 0-19-826202-7). Oxford U Pr.

Bruce, F. F. What the Bible Teaches about What Jesus Did. 1979. pap. 3.95 (ISBN 0-8423-7885-5). Tyndale.

Bultmann, Rudolf. History of the Synoptic Tradition. LC 62-7282. 1963. pap. 9.50 (ISBN 0-06-061172-3, RD 187, HarpR). Har-Row.

Chapman, Benjamin. New Testament: Greek Notebook Exegesis Filler. 1.00 (ISBN 0-8010-2425-0). Baker Bk.

Charlesworth, J. Old Testament Pseudepigrapha & the New Testament. (Society for New Testament Studies Monographs: No. 54). 213p. 1985. 34.50 (ISBN 0-521-30190-4). Cambridge U Pr.

Clemen, Carl. Religionsgeschichtliche Erklaerung des Neuen Testamentes: Die Abhaengigkeit des aeltesten Christentums von nichtjuedischen Religionen und philosophischen Systemen. 440p. 1973. Repr. of 1924 ed. text ed. 59.20x (ISBN 3-11-002412-8). De Gruyter.

Conzelmann, Hans & Lindemann, Andreas. Arbeitsbuch zum Neuen Testament. 8th ed. 474p. (Orig.). 1986. pap. 22.00x (ISBN 3-16-145007-8, Pub. by J C B Mohr BRD). Coronet Bks.

Crapps, Robert W., et al. Introduction to the New Testament. 566p. 1969. text ed. 25.00 (ISBN 0-394-34415-4, RandC). Random.

Cruden, Alexander. Cruden's Complete Concordance. 796p. Date not set. 13.95 (ISBN 0-917006-31-3). Hendrickson MA.

Culpepper, R. Alan. Anatomy of the Fourth Gospel: A Study in Literary Design. LC 82-16302. (Foundations & Facets Ser.). 256p. 1983. 19.95 (ISBN 0-8006-2102-6, 1-2102). Fortress.

Darton, Michael, ed. A Modern Concordance to the New Testament. LC 75-34831. 1977. 12.95 (ISBN 0-385-07901-X). Doubleday.

Dibelius, Martin. Fresh Approach to the New Testament & Early Christian Literature. LC 78-32096. 1979. Repr. of 1936 ed. lib. bdg. 24.75x (ISBN 0-8371-4219-9, DINT). Greenwood.

Donne, Brian K. Christ Ascended: A Study in the Significance of the Ascension of Jesus Christ in the New Testament. 1983. pap. text ed. 7.95 (ISBN 0-85364-336-9). Attic Pr.

Draper, Maurice L., ed. Restoration Studies III. 1986. pap. 15.00 (ISBN 0-8309-0432-8, Pub. by Reidel Holland). Kluwer Academic.

Drumwright, Huber L. & Vaughan, Curtis, eds. New Testament Studies: Essays in Honor of Ray Summers in His Sixty-fifth Year. LC 75-29815. 195p. 1975. 7.95 (ISBN 0-918954-15-0). Baylor Univ Pr.

Dunn, James D. The Evidence for Jesus. LC 85-22540. 128p. (Orig.). 1986. pap. 8.95 (ISBN 0-664-24698-2). Westminster.

--Unity & Diversity in the New Testament: An Inquiry into the Character of Earliest Christianity. LC 77-22598. 488p. 1984. pap. 14.95 (ISBN 0-664-24525-0). Westminster.

Earle, Ralph. Word Meanings in the New Testament. 374p. 1987. text ed. 24.95 (ISBN 0-8010-3434-5). Baker Bk.

--Word Meanings in the New Testament: Hebrews-Revelation, Vol. 6. 174p. 1984. 9.95 (ISBN 0-8341-0943-3). Beacon Hill.

--Word Meanings in the New Testament, Vol. 1: Matthew, Mark, Luke. 285p. 1980. 9.95 (ISBN 0-8341-0683-3). Beacon Hill.

--Word Meanings in the New Testament, Vol. 5: Philemon-Philippians. 1977. 9.95 (ISBN 0-8341-0493-8). Beacon Hill.

--Word Meanings in the New Testament: 1 & 2 Corinthians, Ephesians, Vol. 4. 350p. 1979. 9.95 (ISBN 0-8341-0567-5). Beacon Hill.

Eaton, John. Kingship & the Psalms. (The Biblical Seminar Ser.: No. 3). 240p. 1986. pap. text ed. 9.95x (ISBN 0-905774-89-2, Pub. by JSOT Pr England). Eisenbrauns.

Efird, James M. The New Testament Writings: History, Literature, Interpretation. LC 79-87750. (Biblical Foundation Ser.). 1980. pap. 7.95 (ISBN 0-8042-0246-X). John Knox.

Elliott, John H., ed. Social-Scientific Criticism of the New Testament. (Semeia Ser.: No. 35). pap. 9.95 (06 20 35). Scholars Pr GA.

Epp, Eldon J. & Gordon, Fee D., eds. New Testament Textual Criticism: Its Significance for Exegesis. (Illus.). 94.00x (ISBN 0-19-826175-6). Oxford U Pr.

Erasmus, Desiderius. The First Tome or Volume of the Paraphrase of Erasmus Upon the Newe Testamente. LC 75-23361. 1350p. 1975. Repr. of 1548 ed. lib. bdg. 100.00x (ISBN 0-8201-1159-7). Schol Facsimiles.

Fallis, William J. Points for Emphasis, Nineteen Eighty-Seven to Eighty-Eight. (Orig.). 1987. pap. 3.95 (ISBN 0-8054-1560-2). Broadman.

--Points for Emphasis, Nineteen Eighty-Seven to Eighty-Eight. 1987. pap. 2.95 (ISBN 0-8054-1559-9). Broadman.

Ferguson, Everett. Demonology of the Early Christian World. LC 84-16681. (Symposium Ser.: Vol. 12). 190p. 1984. 19.95 (ISBN 0-88946-703-X). E Mellen.

--Message of the New Testament: The Letters of John. (Way of Life Ser.: No. 175). 1984. pap. 3.95 (ISBN 0-89112-175-7, Bibl Res Pr). Abilene Christ U.

Fitzmyer, Joseph A. Essays on the Semitic Background of the New Testament. LC 74-83874. (Society of Biblical Literature. Sources for Biblical Study). 1974. pap. 13.50 (060305). Scholars Pr GA.

Flanagan, Neal M. The Gospel According to John VII the Johannine Epistles, No. 4. Karris, Robert J., ed. LC 82-22908. (Collegeville Bible Commentary Ser.). 128p. 1983. pap. 2.95 (ISBN 0-8146-1304-7). Liturgical Pr.

Fowler, Everett W. Evaluating Versions of the New Testament. LC 80-81607. (Illus.). 80p. (Orig.). 1981. pap. 2.95 (ISBN 0-937136-03-4). Maranatha Baptist.

France, R. T., ed. A Bibliographical Guide to New Testament Research. 56p. (Orig.). 1979. pap. text ed. 3.95x (ISBN 0-905774-19-1, Pub. by JSOT Pr England). Eisenbrauns.

Fuller, Reginald H. A Critical Introduction to the New Testament. 221p. 1979. pap. 9.95 (ISBN 0-7156-0582-8, Pub. by Duckworth London). Longwood Pub Group.

--New Testament in Current Study. (Hudson River Editions). 1976. 15.00x (ISBN 0-684-14843-9, ScribT). Scribner.

Gafni, Shlomo S., ed. The Glory of the New Testament. LC 83-840322. 1984. 25.00 (ISBN 0-394-53659-2, Pub. by Villard Bks). Random.

Gietzen, Jean J. A People Set Apart. LC 83-61452. 1983. pap. 6.95 (ISBN 0-89390-047-8). Resource Pubns.

Gilles, Anthony E. The People of the Way: The Story Behind the New Testament. (Illus.). 142p. (Orig.). 1984. pap. 5.95 (ISBN 0-86716-036-5). St Anthony Mess Pr.

Goldsmith, Dale. New Testament Ethics. 196p. (Orig.). 1987. pap. 9.95 (ISBN 0-87178-605-2). Brethren.

Goldsworthy, Graeme. Gospel & Kingdom: A Christian's Guide to the Old Testament. 128p. 1983. pap. 6.95 (ISBN 0-86683-686-1, HarpR). Har-Row.

Grant, Frederick C. Ancient Judaism & the New Testament. LC 77-18848. 1978. Repr. of 1959 ed. lib. bdg. cancelled (ISBN 0-313-20204-4, GRAJ). Greenwood.

Grogan, Geoffrey W. What the Bible Teaches about Jesus. 1979. pap. 3.95 (ISBN 0-8423-7884-7). Tyndale.

Groh, Dennis E. & Jewett, Robert, eds. The Living Text: Essays in Honor of Ernest W. Saunders. (Illus.). 272p. (Orig.). 1985. lib. bdg. 27.50 (ISBN 0-8191-4584-X); pap. text ed. 14.25 (ISBN 0-8191-4585-8). U Pr of Amer.

Gunderson, Vivian. What's the Bible Like: New Testament. (Illus.). 1983. pap. 1.25 (ISBN 0-8323-0418-2). Binford-Metropolitan.

Guthrie, Donald. Teaching of the New Testament. 1983. pap. 4.95 (ISBN 0-87508-179-7). Chr Lit.

Hall, Terry. New Testament Express. 160p. 1986. pap. 3.95 (ISBN 0-88207-598-5). Victor Bks.

Hallam, Arthur F. William Lloyd's Life of Pythagoras, with a New Thesis on the Origin of the New Testament. 84p. (Orig.). 1982. pap. 8.50 (ISBN 0-938770-01-2). Capitalist Pr OH.

Harrington, Daniel J. God's People in Christ: New Testament Perspectives on the Church & Judaism, No. 7. Brueggemann, Walter & Donahue, John R., eds. LC 79-7380. (Overtures to Biblical Theology Ser.). 144p. 1980. pap. 8.95 (ISBN 0-8006-1531-X, 1-1531). Fortress.

--Interpreting the New Testament: A Practical Guide. (New Testament Message Ser.: Vol. 1). 1979. 10.95 (ISBN 0-89453-189-1); pap. 6.95 (ISBN 0-89453-124-7). M Glazier.

Harris, Murray J. Raised Immortal: Resurrection & Immortality in the New Testament. 320p. (Orig.). 1985. pap. 10.95 (ISBN 0-8028-0053-X). Eerdmans.

Harrison, Everett F. El Comentario Biblico Moody: Nuevo Testamento. Orig. Title: Wycliffe Bible Commentary: N. T: (Span.). 568p. 1965. 16.95 (ISBN 0-8254-1307-9). Kregel.

Hazelton, Charles J. Pocket Concordance to the New Testament. 1984. leather flex 4.95 (ISBN 0-8407-5824-3). Nelson.

Hengel, Martin. The Son of God: The Origin of Christology & the History of Jewish-Hellenistic Religion. Bowden, John, tr. from Ger. LC 75-37151. 112p. 1976. pap. 5.50 (ISBN 0-8006-1227-2, 1-1227). Fortress.

Horbury, W. & McNeil, B., eds. Suffering & Martyrdom in the New Testament. LC 80-40706. 240p. 1981. 49.50 (ISBN 0-521-23482-4). Cambridge U Pr.

Horvath, Tibor. Sacrificial Interpretation of Jesus' Achievement in the New Testament. 1980. 9.95 (ISBN 0-8022-2240-4). Philos Lib.

House, H. Wayne. Chronological & Background Charts of the New Testament. 160p. (Orig.). 1981. pap. 10.95 spiral bdg. (ISBN 0-310-41641-8, 11149P). Zondervan.

Hultgren, Arland J. Christ & His Benefits: Christology & Redemption in the New Testament. LC 86-45917. 288p. 1987. text ed. 24.95 (ISBN 0-8006-0861-5). Fortress.

Jeremias, Joachim. The Central Message of the New Testament. LC 81-66890. pap. 23.80 (2027865). Bks Demand UMI.

Jervell, Jacob. The Unknown Paul: Essays on Luke-Acts & Early Christian History. LC 84-24605. 192p. (Orig.). 1984. pap. 10.95 (ISBN 0-8066-2119-2, 10-6815). Augsburg.

Kee, Howard C. Medicine, Miracle & Magic in New Testament Times. (Society for New Testament Studies Monographs: No. 55). 200p. 1986. 29.95 (ISBN 0-521-32309-6). Cambridge U Pr.

Kenny, Anthony. A Stylometric Study of the New Testament. 160p. 1986. text ed. 38.00 (ISBN 0-19-826178-0). Oxford U Pr.

Kissinger, Warren S. The Parables of Jesus: A History of Interpretation & Bibliography. LC 78-23271. (American Theological Library Association (ATLA) Bibliography Ser.: No. 4). 463p. 1979. lib. bdg. 30.00 (ISBN 0-8108-1186-3). Scarecrow.

Kunz, Marilyn & Schell, Catherine. Psalms & Proverbs, Neighborhood Bible Study. 1971. pap. 2.95 (ISBN 0-8423-4991-X). Tyndale.

--They Met Jesus, Neighborhood Bible Study. 1971. pap. 2.95 (ISBN 0-8423-7080-3). Tyndale.

Lace, O. Jessie. Understanding the New Testament. (Cambridge Bible Commentary on the New English Bible, New Testament Ser.). 16.95 (ISBN 0-521-04205-4); pap. 9.95 (ISBN 0-521-09281-7). Cambridge U Pr.

Ladd, George E. New Testament & Criticism. 1966. pap. 6.95 (ISBN 0-8028-1680-0). Eerdmans.

Lasserre, Jean. War & the Gospel. Coburn, O., tr. 248p. 1962. 9.95 (ISBN 0-227-67635-1). Attic Pr.

Lawson, LeRoy. The New Testament Church Then & Now Workbook. 48p. 1983. pap. 1.75 (ISBN 0-87239-609-6, 88586). Standard Pub.

Leary, James F. A Light to the Nations: A Guide to the New Testament. 144p. 1986. pap. 4.95 (ISBN 0-88479-036-3). Chr Classics.

Leon-Dufour, Xavier. Life & Death in the New Testament. 1986. 18.45 (ISBN 0-317-52379-1, HarpR). Har-Row.

--Sharing the Eucharistic Bread: The Witness of the New Testament. 368p. (Orig.). 1987. pap. 12.95 (ISBN 0-8091-2865-9). Paulist Pr.

Liefeld, Walter L. New Testament Exposition: From Text to Sermon. 176p. 1984. 11.95 (ISBN 0-310-45910-9, 12607P). Zondervan.

Lohse, Edward. The Formation of the New Testament. Boring, M. Eugene, tr. LC 80-27032. 256p. (Orig.). 1981. pap. 9.95 (ISBN 0-687-13294-0). Abingdon.

Ludwig, Charles. Ludwig's Handbook of New Testament Cities & Rulers. LC 83-71619. 244p. (Orig.). 1983. pap. 6.95 (ISBN 0-89636-111-X). Accent Bks.

Lussier, Ernest. Jesus Christ Is Lord: Adoration Viewed Through the New Testament. LC 79-15581. 1980. 7.95 (ISBN 0-8189-0382-1). Alba.

McCray, Walter A. Who Says? A Black Perspective on the Authority of New Testament Exegesis Highlighting the Foundation for Its Interpretations & Applications. Bentley, William H., ed. 75p. (Orig.). pap. write for info. (ISBN 0-933176-35-X). Black Light Fellow.

McSorley, Richard. New Testament Basis of Peacemaking. LC 84-25121. 160p. 1985. pap. 7.95 (ISBN 0-8361-3383-8). Herald Pr.

Makrakis, Apostolos. Interpretation of the Entire New Testament (Revelation Not Incl), 2 vols. Orthodox Christian Educational Society, ed. Alexander, Albert G., tr. from Hellenic. 2052p. (Vol. 1, 1127 pp.;vol. 2, 925 pp.). 1949. Set. 28.00x (ISBN 0-938366-08-4). Orthodox Chr.

Matthews, William R., Sr. Background Information for New Testament Students. Jones, Amos, Jr., ed. 250p. (Orig.). 1985. pap. cancelled (ISBN 0-910683-05-0). Sunday School.

Mears, Henrietta C. What the New Testament Is All About. 288p. pap. 3.95 (ISBN 0-8307-0525-2, 5015618). Regal.

Mercer, Calvin R. Norman Perrin's Interpretation of the New Testament. Mabee, Charles, ed. (Studies in American Biblical Hermeneutics). 192p. 1986. 19.95 (ISBN 0-86554-219-8, MUP-H197). Mercer Univ Pr.

Metzger, Bruce. The Early Versions of the New Testament. 1977. 24.95x (ISBN 0-19-826170-5). Oxford U Pr.

Metzger, Bruce M. The New Testament: Its Background, Growth & Content. enl. ed. 310p. 1965. 16.50 (ISBN 0-687-27914-3). Abingdon.

Millet, Robert L., ed. Studies in Scripture, Vol. Six: Acts to Revelation. 1987. 15.95 (ISBN 0-87579-084-4). Deseret Bk.

Mills, Watson E. Index of Reviews of New Testament Books Between 1900-1950. repr. ed. LC 77-72827. (Special Studies: No. 2). viii, 69p. 1984. pap. 3.50 (ISBN 0-932180-01-9). NABPR.

Minear, Paul S. Images of the Church in the New Testament. LC 60-11331. 294p. 1970. pap. 9.95 (ISBN 0-664-24903-5). Westminster.

Moffatt, James. The Approach to the New Testament. LC 77-27150. (Hibbert Lectures: 1921). Repr. of 1921 ed. 28.00 (ISBN 0-404-60420-X). AMS Pr.

--An Introduction to the Literature of the New Testament. 630p. 1983. Repr. of 1911 ed. lib. bdg. 75.00 (ISBN 0-89984-820-6). Century Bookbindery.

Mohrlang, Roger. Matthew & Paul: A Comparison of Ethical Perspectives. LC 83-10147. (Society for New Testament Studies Monograph: No. 48). 220p. 1984. 37.50 (ISBN 0-521-25093-5). Cambridge U Pr.

Morrice, William G. Joy in the New Testament. 144p. (Orig.). 1982. pap. 11.95 (ISBN 0-85364-340-7). Attic Pr.

Moule, Charles F. Essays in New Testament Interpretation. LC 81-10141. (Illus.). 260p. 1982. 42.50 (ISBN 0-521-23783-1). Cambridge U Pr.

Neill, Stephen. Jesus Through Many Eyes: Introduction to the Theology of the New Testament. LC 75-36455. 228p. 1976. pap. 7.95 (ISBN 0-8006-1220-5, 1-1220). Fortress.

Neyrey, Jerome H. Christ Is Community: The Christologies of the New Testament. (Good News Studies: Vol. 13). 1985. pap. 12.95 (ISBN 0-89453-465-3). M Glazier.

Orchard, D. B. & Longstaff, R. W., eds. J. J. Griesbach. LC 77-27405. (Society for New Testament Studies Monographs: No. 34). 1979. 32.50 (ISBN 0-521-21706-7). Cambridge U Pr.

Osborn, E. C. Word & History. 1967. pap. 2.60x (ISBN 0-85564-020-0, Pub. by U of W Austral Pr). Intl Spec Bk.

Parker, James. The Concept of Apokatastasis in Acts: A Study in Primitive Christian Theology. 140p. 1981. pap. text ed. 5.95 (ISBN 0-931016-01-0). Schola Pr TX.

Parsons, Richard E. Sir Edwyn Hoskyns As a Biblical Theologian. LC 85-25038. 152p. 1986. 25.00 (ISBN 0-312-72647-3). St Martin.

Partridge, Eric. A New Testament Word Book: A Glossary. facsimile ed. LC 70-117907. (Select Bibliographies Reprint Ser). Repr. of 1940 ed. 19.00 (ISBN 0-8369-5359-2). Ayer Co Pubs.

Patzia, Arthur G. Colossians, Philemon, Ephesians. LC 83-48996. (Good News Commentary Ser.). 256p. (Orig.). 1984. pap. 8.95 (ISBN 0-06-066479-7, RD 506). Har-Row.

Peake, Arthur S. A Critical Introduction to the New Testament. 242p. 1979. Repr. of 1909 ed. lib. bdg. 25.00 (ISBN 0-89987-009-0). Darby Bks.

Penn, William. Fruits of Solitude. pap. 5.95 (ISBN 0-913408-39-5). Friends United.

Pennock, Michael. The New Testament: Student Text. LC 82-70088. (Illus.). 256p. (Orig.). 1982. pap. 5.50 (ISBN 0-87793-246-8). Ave Maria.

--The New Testament: Teacher's Manual. 112p. (Orig.). 1982. 2.95 (ISBN 0-87793-247-6). Ave Maria.

Petersen, Norman R. Literary Criticism for New Testament Critics. Via, Dan O., Jr., ed. LC 77-15241. (Guides to Biblical Scholarship: New Testament Ser.). 96p. (Orig.). 1978. pap. 4.50 (ISBN 0-8006-0465-2, 1-465). Fortress.

Pickering, Wilbur N. The Identity of the New Testament Text. rev. ed. LC 80-17369. 192p. 1980. pap. 8.95 (ISBN 0-8407-5744-1). Nelson.

Pritchard, John P. A Literary Approach to the New Testament. (Illus.). 350p. 1972. 17.95x (ISBN 0-8061-1011-2); pap. 11.95x (ISBN 0-8061-1710-9). U of Okla Pr.

Reese, James M. Experiencing the Good News: The New Testament as Communication. (Good News Studies Ser.: Vol. 10). 1984. pap. 9.95 (ISBN 0-89453-448-3). M Glazier.

Reicke, Bo. The New Testament Era: The World of the Bible from 500 B.C. to A.D. 100. LC 68-15864. 352p. 1974. pap. 8.95 (ISBN 0-8006-1080-6, 1-1080). Fortress.

Reumann, John. Righteousness in the New Testament: Justification in Lutheran-Catholic Dialogue. LC 81-43086. 320p. 1982. pap. 13.95 (ISBN 0-8006-1616-2, 1-1616). Fortress.

Rhein, Francis B. Understanding the New Testament. LC 65-23532. 1974. pap. text ed. 6.95 (ISBN 0-8120-0027-7). Barron.

Robbins, John W. Scripture Twisting in the Seminaries, Part 1: Feminism. (Trinity Papers: No. 10). 116p. (Orig.). 1985. pap. 5.95 (ISBN 0-940931-10-9). Trinity Found.

Robertson, A. T. Word Pictures in the New Testament, 6 vols. 1982. 75.00 (ISBN 0-8010-7710-9). Baker Bk.

Robinson, Donald. Faith's Framework: The Structure of New Testament Theology. 152p. 1986. pap. 9.95 (ISBN 0-85364-317-2, Pub. by Paternoster UK). Attic Pr.

Ryan, Thomas J., ed. Critical History & Biblical Faith: New Testament Perspectives. (Annual Publication of the College Theology Society Ser.). 242p. 1984. pap. text ed. 8.25 (ISBN 0-8191-4157-7). U Pr of Amer.

Sandmel, Samuel. A Jewish Understanding of the New Testament. 1974. 11.95x (ISBN 0-87068-102-8); pap. 9.95x (ISBN 0-87068-262-8). Ktav.

--A Jewish Understanding of the New Testament. 356p. pap. 9.95 (ISBN 0-686-95179-4). ADL.

Sands, Percy C. Literary Genius of the New Testament. Repr. of 1932 ed. lib. bdg. 22.50x (ISBN 0-8371-4328-4, SANT). Greenwood.

Schneider, Johannes. Church & World in the New Testament. 59p. 1983. pap. 5.45 (ISBN 0-86554-063-2, P11). Mercer Univ Pr.

Schonfield, Hugh J., ed. & tr. from Gr. The Original New Testament: A Radical Translation & Reinterpretation. LC 85-42792. 628p. 1985. 19.45 (ISBN 0-06-250776-1, HarpR). Har-Row.

Schulz, Thomas. Charis: The Meaning of Grace in the New Testament. 78p. 1971. pap. 3.95 (ISBN 0-911620-06-0). Westcott.

Scott, Ernest F. The Literature of the New Testament. Evans, Austin P., ed. LC 84-25243. (Records of Civilization Sources & Studies: No. xv). xv, 312p. 1985. Repr. of 1936 ed. lib. bdg. 45.00x (ISBN 0-313-24743-9, SCNT). Greenwood.

Selby, D. J. Introduction to the New Testament: The Word Became Flesh. 1971. text ed. write for info. (ISBN 0-02-408870-6). Macmillan.

Skilton, John H. The New Testament Student & Bible Translation. (New Testament Student Ser.). 1978. pap. 5.00 (ISBN 0-87552-436-2). Presby & Reformed.

Slomowitz, Samuel W. Jesus Christ-Sam. 1987. 7.95 (ISBN 0-533-07158-5). Vantage.

Smith, Chuck. New Testament Study Guide. 224p. (YA) 1982. pap. 2.95 (ISBN 0-936728-33-7). Word For Today.

Smitty, William H. Three Hundred Sermon Outlines From the New Testament. LC 81-86666. (Orig.). 1983. pap. 4.50 (ISBN 0-8054-2246-3). Broadman.

Spivey, Robert A. & Smith, Moody D. Anatomy of the New Testament: A Guide to Its Structure & Meaning. 3rd ed. 544p. 1981. text ed. write for info. (ISBN 0-02-415300-1). Macmillan.

Stagg, Frank. Teologia del Nuevo Testamento. Canclini, Arnoldo, tr. 346p. 1985. pap. 9.95 (ISBN 0-311-09077-X). Casa Bautista.

Stambaugh, John E. & Balch, David L. The New Testament in Its Social Environment. LC 85-15516. (Library of Early Christianity: Vol. 2). (Illus.). 208p. 1986. 16.95 (ISBN 0-664-21906-3). Westminster.

Sturz, Harry A. The Byzantine Text-Type & New Testament Textual Criticism. 320p. 1984. 18.95 (ISBN 0-8407-4958-9). Nelson.

Telford, Shirley. The Prince of Peace: Returns to Fulfill All Prophecy. (Illus.). 56p. (Orig.). 1984. 5.50 (ISBN 0-9600202-0-9); Audio-Video Cassette. 12.00 (ISBN 0-9613706-1-0). William & Rich.

Tenney, Merrill C. New Testament Survey. rev. ed. Dunnett, Walter M., rev. by. 480p. 1985. 19.95 (ISBN 0-8028-3611-9). Eerdmans.

--Nuestro Nuevo Testamento. Orig. Title: New Testament Survey. (Span.). 492p. 1981. pap. 12.95 (ISBN 0-8254-1716-3). Kregel.

Tidball, Derek. An Introduction to the Sociology of the New Testament. 1982. pap. text ed. 9.95 cancelled (ISBN 0-85364-301-6). Attic Pr.

--The Social Context of the New Testament: A Sociological Analysis. 160p. 1984. pap. 7.95 (ISBN 0-310-45391-7, 12602P). Zondervan.

Tolbert, Malcolm, et al. Perspectives on the New Testament: Essays in Honor of Frank Stagg. Talbert, Charles H., ed. vi, 108p. 1985. lib. bdg. 9.95x (ISBN 0-86554-152-3, MUP-H121). Mercer Univ Pr.

Travis, Stephen H. Christ & the Judgement of God: Divine Retribution in the New Testament. 240p. Date not set. pap. 12.95 (ISBN 0-8407-5958-4). Nelson.

Tremmel, William C. The Twenty-Seven Books That Changed the World: A Guide to Readng the New Testament. LC 80-27930. 1981. text ed. 21.95 (ISBN 0-03-052631-0, HoltC). H Holt & Co.

Trench, Robert C. Synonyms of the New Testament. 1950. pap. 8.95 (ISBN 0-8028-1520-0). Eerdmans.

Tripole, Martin R. The Jesus Event & Our Response. LC 79-27896. 248p. (Orig.). 1980. pap. 7.95 (ISBN 0-8189-0399-6). Alba.

Vanhoye, Albert. Old Testament Priests & the New Priest. Orchard, Bernard, tr. from Fr. LC 85-2171. (Studies in Scripture: Vol. II). Tr. of Pretres anciens, pretre nouveau selon le nouveau testament. 1986. pap. 24.95 (ISBN 0-932506-38-0). St Bedes Pubns.

Van Ness Goetchius, Eugene. The Language of the New Testament. 349p. 1966. text ed. write for info. (ISBN 0-02-344530-0, Pub. by Scribner). Macmillan.

Viertel, Weldon E. Vida y Ministerio de Cristo: Texto Programado. Zorzoli, Ruben O., tr. from Span. Tr. of The Life & Ministry of Christ. 192p. 1985. pap. text ed. write for info. (ISBN 0-311-04356-9). Casa Bautista.

Waggener, Florence E. The New Testament Simply Told. LC 86-90523. 160p. 1986. 11.95x (ISBN 0-9617339-0-X). Waggener Publ Co.

Wansbrough, Henry. New Testament of the New Jerusalem Bible. LC 86-11680. (Illus.). 552p. 1986. pap. 6.95 (ISBN 0-385-23706-5, Im). Doubleday.

Watson, Francis. Paul, Judaism, & the Gentiles: A Sociological Approach. (Society for New Testament Studies Monographs: No. 56). 266p. Date not set. 32.50 (ISBN 0-521-32573-0). Cambridge U Pr.

Wendland, Ernst H. God's Mission in the New Testament. Fischer, William E., ed. (Bible Class Course Ser.). 40p. (Orig.). (YA) 1986. pap. 2.50 (ISBN 0-938272-55-1). WELS Board.

Wesley, John. Explanatory Notes on the New Testament, 2 vols. 1056p. Date not set. 29.95 (ISBN 0-913573-06-X). Hendrickson MA.

Wetzel, Robert, compiled by. Essays on New Testament Christianity. LC 78-55881. 1978. text ed. 12.95 (ISBN 0-87239-208-2, 2856). Standard Pub.

Wigram, George V. Englishman's Greek Concordance of the New Testament. 1984. 29.95 (ISBN 0-8010-3416-7). Baker Bk.

Wink, Walter. Naming the Powers: The Language of Power in the New Testament. LC 83-48905. (The Power Ser.: Vol. 1). 192p. 1984. pap. 14.95 (ISBN 0-8006-1786-X, 1-1786). Fortress.

The Word, The New Century Version: New Testament. LC 84-51094. (Illus.). 556p. 1984. 13.95 (ISBN 0-8344-0123-1, BB400C). Sweet.

Wuellner, Wilhelm H. & Leslie, Robert C. The Surprising Gospel: Intriguing Psychological Insights from the New Testament. 176p. (Orig.). 1983. pap. 11.95 (ISBN 0-687-40724-9). Abingdon.

Wuest, Kenneth. Practical Use of the Greek New Testament. Wise, Donald, rev. by. 160p. 1982. text ed. 11.95 (ISBN 0-8024-6737-7). Moody.

Yaeger, Randolph O. Renaissance New Testament, Vols. 1-9. Incl. Vol. 1. 25.00 (ISBN 0-88289-957-0); Vol. 2 (ISBN 0-88289-657-1); Vol. 3 (ISBN 0-88289-357-2); Vol. 4 (ISBN 0-88289-857-4); Vol. 5 (ISBN 0-88289-257-6); Vol. 6 (ISBN 0-88289-757-8); Vol. 7. 1982. 22.50 (ISBN 0-88289-457-9); Vol. 8. 1982. 22.50 (ISBN 0-88289-358-0); Vol. 9. 1982. 22.50 (ISBN 0-88289-858-2). 590p. 1980. each 22.50 (ISBN 0-686-77622-4). Pelican.

Yamauchi, Edwin. Harper's World of the New Testament. LC 80-8606. (Illus.). 144p. (Orig.). 1981. pap. 9.95i (ISBN 0-06-069708-3, RD349, HarpR). Har-Row.

Yeager, Randolph O. The Renaissance New Testament, Vol. 10. LC 79-28652. 660p. 1982. 22.50 (ISBN 0-88289-258-4). Pelican.

--The Renaissance New Testament, Vol. 11. 660p. 22.50 (ISBN 0-88289-758-6). Pelican.

BIBLE–CRITICISM, INTERPRETATION, ETC.–N. T. ACTS

Achtemeier, Paul J. The Quest for Unity in the New Teatament Church: A Study in Paul & Acts. LC 86-45911. 128p. 1987. pap. 7.95 (ISBN 0-8006-1972-2, 1-1972). Fortress.

Armstrong, D. Wade. Evangelistic Growth in Acts One & Two. LC 83-70375. (Orig.). 1983. pap. 4.95 (ISBN 0-8054-6242-2). Broadman.

Barnes, Albert. Acts & Romans. 18.95 (ISBN 0-8010-0844-1). Baker Bk.

Beacon Bible Commentary Staff. Acts, Vol. V. 6.95 (ISBN 0-8010-0679-1). Baker Bk.

--John: Acts, Vol. VII. 13.95 (ISBN 0-8010-0694-5). Baker Bk.

Black, Matthew. Aramaic Approach to the Gospels & Acts. 3rd ed. 1967. 32.50x (ISBN 0-19-826157-8). Oxford U Pr.

Boer, Harry R. The Four Gospels & Acts: A Short Introduction. 112p. 1982. pap. 3.95 (ISBN 0-8028-1901-X). Eerdmans.

Bruce, F. F. Acts. 1983. pap. 4.95 (ISBN 0-87508-170-3). Chr Lit.

Capt, E. Raymond. Lost Chapter of Acts of the Apostles. 32p. 1982. pap. 2.00 (ISBN 0-934666-09-1). Artisan Sales.

Cassidy, Richard J. & Scharper, Philip J., eds. Political Issues in Luke-Acts. LC 82-19060. 192p. (Orig.). 1983. 16.95 (ISBN 0-88344-390-2); pap. 9.95 (ISBN 0-88344-385-6). Orbis Bks.

Coleman, Robert E. The Master Plan of Discipleship. 9.95; pap. 5.95. Revell.

Conzelmann, Hans. Acts. LC 86-45203. 368p. 1987. pap. 37.95 (ISBN 0-8006-6018-8, 20-6018). Fortress.

Criswell, W. A. Acts: An Exposition. 948p. 1983. Repr. 19.95 (ISBN 0-310-44150-1, 11666). Zondervan.

Crowe, Jerome. The Acts. (New Testament Message Ser.: Vol. 8). 204p. 1980. 12.95 (ISBN 0-89453-196-4); pap. 8.95 (ISBN 0-89453-131-X). M Glazier.

Denny, Randal E. Wind in the Rigging. 120p. 1985. pap. 4.50 (ISBN 0-8341-0937-9). Beacon Hill.

Easter, Frances. Bible Study. (Studies in Acts: vol. I). 1986. pap. 3.50 (ISBN 0-8309-0436-0). Herald Hse.

--Studies in Acts, Vol. II. (Bible Study Ser.). 1986. pap. 3.50 (ISBN 0-8309-0442-5). Herald Hse.

Esler, Philip S. Community & Gospel in Luke-Acts: The Social & Political Motivations of Lucan Theory. (Society for New Testament Studies Monographs: No. 57). 224p. Date not set. price not set (ISBN 0-521-32965-5). Cambridge U Pr.

Faraone, Joseph J. & Stewart, Jane L. Paraclete Power: A Study Guide for the Acts of the Apostles. LC 77-16475. 1978. pap. 3.50 (ISBN 0-8189-0361-9). Alba.

Gasque, Ward. A History of the Criticism of the Acts of the Apostles. 334p. 1975. lib. bdg. 52.00x (Pub. by J C B Mohr BRD). Coronet Bks.

Gettys, Joseph M. How to Study Acts. 219p. 1976. pap. 4.50x (ISBN 0-87921-028-1). Attic Pr.

Green, Joel B. How to Read the Gospels & Acts. LC 87-5572. (The How to Read Ser.). 180p. (Orig.). 1987. pap. 6.95 (ISBN 0-87784-940-4). Inter-Varsity.

Guthrie, Donald. The Apostles. 432p. 1981. pap. 12.95 (ISBN 0-310-25421-3, 12235P). Zondervan.

Harper, Alfred F. Beacon Small-Group Bible Studies, Acts, Pt, I: The Spirit-Filled Church. 96p. 1982. pap. 2.50 (ISBN 0-8341-0800-3). Beacon Hill.

Harrison, Everett F. Interpreting Acts. (Interpreting Ser.: No. 2). 352p. 1986. pap. 14.95 (ISBN 0-310-31850-5). Zondervan.

The Interpreter's Concise Commentary, Vol. VII: Acts & Paul's Letters. 4.95 (ISBN 0-687-19238-2). Abingdon.

Jacobs, J. Vernon & Wade, John W. Workbook on the Book of Acts. 112p. 1986. pap. 3.95 (ISBN 0-87403-095-1, 3346). Standard Pub.

Johnson, Luke T. Decision Making in the Church: A Biblical Model. LC 82-17675. 112p. 1983. pap. 6.95 (ISBN 0-8006-1694-4). Fortress.

--The Literary Function of Possession in Luke-Acts. LC 77-21055. (Society of Biblical Literature. Dissertation Ser.: No. 39). 1985. pap. 11.25 (ISBN 0-89130-200-X, 060139). Scholars Pr GA.

Juel, Donald. Luke-Acts: The Promise of History. LC 82-25845. 136p. 1983. pap. 8.95 (ISBN 0-8042-0321-0). John Knox.

Kelly, William. The Acts, Catholic Epistles & Revelation. (Introductory Lecture Ser.). 580p. 6.95 (ISBN 0-88172-096-8). Believers Bkshelf.

Kent, Homer A., Jr. Jerusalem to Rome: Studies in Acts. (Illus.). pap. 5.95 (ISBN 0-88469-056-3). BMH Bks.

Krodel, Gerhard. Acts. LC 80-2395. (Proclamation Commentaries: the New Testament Witnesses for Preaching). 128p. (Orig.). 1981. pap. 5.95 (ISBN 0-8006-0585-3, 1-585). Fortress.

Kurzinger, Josef. The Acts of the Apostles, Vol. I. McKenzie, John L., ed. LC 81-605. (The New Testament for Spiritual Reading Ser.). 227p. 1981. pap. 4.95 (ISBN 0-8245-0119-5). Crossroad NY.

--The Acts of the Apostles, Vol. II. McKenzie, John L., ed. LC 81-605. (The New Testament for Spiritual Reading Ser.). 227p. 1981. pap. 4.95 (ISBN 0-8245-0120-9). Crossroad NY.

LaFargue, J. Michael. Language & Gnosis: Form & Meaning in the Acts of Thomas Chapters 1-10. LC 84-45191. (Harvard Dissertations in Religion Ser.). 288p. 1984. pap. 14.95 (ISBN 0-8006-7016-7, 1-7016). Fortress.

Laurin, Roy L. Acts of the Apostles: Life in Action. LC 85-8158. 408p. 1985. pap. 11.95 (ISBN 0-8254-3127-1). Kregel.

Lohfink, Gerhard. The Conversion of Saint Paul: Narrative & History in Acts. Malina, Bruce J., ed. & tr. 156p. 1976. 5.95 (ISBN 0-8199-0572-0). Franciscan Herald.

Maddox, Robert. Purpose of Luke-Acts. Riches, John, ed. 220p. 1982. 26.95 (ISBN 0-567-09312-3, Pub. by T&T Clark Ltd UK). Fortress.

Morgan, G. Campbell. Acts of the Apostles. 560p. 1924. 17.95 (ISBN 0-8007-0000-7). Revell.

Munck, Johannes, ed. Acts of the Apostles. LC 66-20918. (Anchor Bible Ser.: Vol. 31). 1967. 18.00 (ISBN 0-385-00914-3, Anchor Pr). Doubleday.

Phillips, John. Exploring Acts, Vol. 1. (Exploring Ser.). (Orig.). 1986. pap. 11.95 (ISBN 0-8024-2435-X). Moody.

Powell, Ivor. The Amazing Acts. 1987. 18.95 (ISBN 0-8254-3526-9). Kregel.

Reese, Gareth. New Testament History-Acts. 5th ed. (The Bible Study Textbook Ser.). (Illus.). 1976. 19.95 (ISBN 0-89900-055-X). College Pr Pub.

Richard, Earl. Acts Six: One to Eight, Four - The Authors Method of Composition. LC 78-12926. (Society of Biblical Literature. Dissertation Ser.: No. 41). (Orig.). 1978. pap. 10.95 (ISBN 0-89130-261-1, 06-01-41). Scholars Pr GA.

Sanders, Jack T. The Jews in Luke-Acts. LC 86-45926. 432p. 1987. pap. 19.95 (ISBN 0-8006-0837-2, 1-1969). Fortress.

Scragg, W. R. The In-Between God. Wheeler, Gerald, ed. 128p. pap. price not set (ISBN 0-8280-0374-2). Review & Herald.

Talbert, Charles H. Acts. Hayes, John, ed. (Preaching Guides). 120p. (Orig.). 1984. pap. 6.95 (ISBN 0-8042-3231-8). John Knox.

Thurman, Thomas D. Acts: The Genesis of the New Testament. Evans, H. Sherwood, ed. 60p. (Orig.). 1985. pap. 2.25 (ISBN 0-9614213-0-4). Chr Restor Assn.

Tiede, David L. Prophecy & History in Luke-Acts. LC 79-8897. pap. 44.00 (2029616). Bks Demand UMI.

Timmer, John. Acts, A Study Guide. (Revelation Series for Adults). 1981. pap. text ed. 2.50 (ISBN 0-933140-20-7). CRC Pubns.

To Rome & Beyond (Acts B) Student Guide. (New Horizons Bible Study). 68p. (Orig.). 1982. pap. 2.50 (ISBN 0-89367-069-3). Light & Life.

Torrey, C. C. Composition & Date of Acts. (Harvard Theological Studies). 1916. pap. 15.00 (ISBN 0-527-01001-4). Kraus Repr.

Turner, Elizabeth S. Be Ye Transformed. 1969. 5.95 (ISBN 0-87159-008-5). Unity School.

Tyson, Joseph B. The Death of Jesus in Luke-Acts. 212p. 1986. text ed. 17.95 (ISBN 0-87249-461-6). U of SC Pr.

Underwood, Dan. Acts. (Standard Bible Study Workbooks Ser.). 80p. 1987. wkbk. 1.95 (ISBN 0-87403-185-0, 40205). Standard Pub.

Vaughan, Charles J. Studies in the Book of Acts. 620p. 1985. smythe sewn 24.95 (ISBN 0-86524-189-9, 4404). Klock & Klock.

Wade, John. Acts. (Standard Bible Studies). (Illus.). 288p. 1987. pap. price not set (ISBN 0-87403-165-6, 40105). Standard Pub.

Wade, John W. Dear Theophilus. 256p. 1985. pap. 4.95 (ISBN 0-87239-968-0, 41036). Standard Pub.

Wartick, Wallace. Studies in Acts, Vol. II. (Bible Student Study Guides Ser). 1978. pap. 2.95 (ISBN 0-89900-154-8). College Pr Pub.

--Studies in Acts, Vol. I. (Bible Student Study Guides Ser). 1977. pap. 2.95 (ISBN 0-89900-153-X). College Pr Pub.

Wilde, Gary, ed. Acts: Powered by the Spirit. (Basic Bible Ser.). 112p. 1986. pap. 4.95 (ISBN 0-89191-519-2). Cook.

Witherspoon, Jet. Acts. LC 86-25414. 192p. (Orig.). 1972. pap. 4.95 (ISBN 0-912315-34-2). Word Aflame.

BIBLE–CRITICISM, INTERPRETATION, ETC.–N. T. APOCRYPHA

Cameron, Ron. Sayings Traditions in the Apocryphon of James. LC 84-45189. (Harvard Theological Studies). 160p. 1984. pap. 12.95 (ISBN 0-8006-7015-9). Fortress.

Cameron, Ron, ed. The Other Gospels: Non-Canonical Gospel Texts. LC 82-8662. 192p. 1982. pap. 11.95 (ISBN 0-664-24428-9). Westminster.

Charlesworth, James H. & Mueller, James R. The New Testament Apocrypha & Pseudepigrapha: A Guide to Publications, with Excursueses on Apacalypses. LC 85-18350. (ATLA Bibliographer Ser.: No. 17). 468p. 1987. 42.50 (ISBN 0-8108-1845-0). Scarecrow.

Davies, Stevan L. The Revolt of the Widows: The Social World of the Apocryphal Acts. LC 80-11331. 150p. 1980. 12.95x (ISBN 0-8093-0958-0). S Ill U Pr.

Goodspeed, Edgar J. Strange New Gospels. facsimile ed. LC 70-156652. (Essay Index Reprint Ser). Repr. of 1931 ed. 12.00 (ISBN 0-8369-2364-2). Ayer Co Pubs.

Goodspeed, Edgar J., ed. Apocrypha. 1959. pap. 5.95 (ISBN 0-394-70163-1, V163, Vin). Random.

The Lost Books of the Bible & the Forgotten Books of Eden. 562p. 9.95 (ISBN 0-529-03385-2); pap. 7.95 (ISBN 0-529-02061-0). World Bible.

Metzger, Bruce M., ed. Oxford Annotated Apocrypha: Revised Standard Version. 1977. text ed. write for info. Oxford U Pr.

Minear, Paul S. New Testament Apocalyptic. LC 81-4721. (Interpreting Biblical Texts Ser.). 160p. (Orig.). 1981. pap. 8.95 (ISBN 0-687-27890-2). Abingdon.

Rivera, Roberto A., ed. Apocalipsis. (Span.). 96p. 1980. pap. 3.25 (ISBN 0-87148-028-X). Pathway Pr.

Turner, Henry E. & Montefiore, Hugh. Thomas & the Evangelists. LC 63-59763. (Studies in Biblical Theology: No. 35). 1962. pap. 10.00x (ISBN 0-8401-3035-X). A R Allenson.

BIBLE–CRITICISM, INTERPRETATION, ETC.–N. T. COLOSSIANS

see Bible–Criticism, Interpretation, etc.–N. T. Epistles

BIBLE–CRITICISM, INTERPRETATION, ETC.–N. T. CORINTHIANS

see Bible–Criticism, Interpretation, Etc.–N. T. Epistles

BIBLE–CRITICISM, INTERPRETATION, ETC.–N. T. EPHESIANS

see Bible–Criticism, Interpretation, Etc.–N. T. Epistles

BIBLE–CRITICISM, INTERPRETATION, ETC.–N. T. EPISTLES

Here are entered books on the Epistles as a whole, or on one or more of the following, Colossians, Corinthians, Ephesians, Galatians, Hebrews, James, Epistles of John, Jude, Peter, Philemon, Romans, Thessalonians, Timothy, Titus.

Achtemeier, Paul J. The Quest for Unity in the New Teatament Church: A Study in Paul & Acts. LC 86-45911. 128p. 1987. pap. 7.95 (ISBN 0-8006-1972-2, 1-1972). Fortress.

--Romans: Interpretation: A Bible Commentary for Teaching & Preaching. Mays, James L., ed. LC 84-47796. 240p. 1985. 17.95 (ISBN 0-8042-3137-0). John Knox.

Adams, Jay E. How to Overcome Evil. (Direction Bks). 1978. pap. 1.95 (ISBN 0-8010-0126-9). Baker Bk.

Adamson, James B. James: The Man & His Message. 432p. (Orig.). 1987. pap. 16.95 (ISBN 0-8028-0167-6). Eerdmans.

Aderman, James A. You Can't Lose. Fischer, William E., ed. (Bible Class for Young Adults Ser.). (Illus.). 64p. (Orig.). 1987. pap. 2.95 (ISBN 0-938272-28-4). Wels Board.

Ahern, Barnabas M. The Epistle to the Romans. 1979. 1.75 (ISBN 0-8199-0629-8). Franciscan Herald.

At Ease under Pressure: James I, II Peter. (New Horizons Bible Study). 64p. 1982. Student's Guide 2.50 (ISBN 0-89367-073-1). Light & Life.

At Ease under Pressure: James I, II Peter. (New Horizons Bible Study). 48p. 1982. pap. 1.95 Leaders' Guide (ISBN 0-89367-072-3). Light & Life.

Austgen, Robert J. Natural Motivation in the Pauline Epistles. rev. ed. 1969. 10.95 (ISBN 0-268-00374-2). U of Notre Dame Pr.

Badenas, Robert. Christ the End of the Law: Romans 10-4 in Pauline Perspective. (JSoT Supplement Ser.: No. 10). 312p. 1985. text ed. 36.50x (ISBN 0-905774-93-0, Pub. by JSOT Pr England); pap. text ed. 15.95x (ISBN 0-905774-94-9). Eisenbrauns.

Balch, David. Let Wives Be Submissive: The Domestic Code in 1 Peter. LC 80-21203. (Society of Biblical Literature Monograph). 196p. 1981. pap. 21.00 (ISBN 0-89130-429-0). Scholars Pr GA.

Bales, James. Romans. 2.50 (ISBN 0-89315-241-2). Lambert Bk.

Barclay, William. All-Sufficient Christ: Studies in Paul's Letter to the Colossians. LC 63-18385. 142p. 1963. pap. 6.95 (ISBN 0-664-24480-7). Westminster.

Barnes, Albert. Ephesians-Philemon. 15.95 (ISBN 0-8010-0847-6). Baker Bk.

--First Corinthians, Galatians. 18.95 (ISBN 0-8010-0846-8). Baker Bk.

--Hebrews-Jude. 18.95 (ISBN 0-8010-0848-4). Baker Bk.

Barney, Kenneth D. A Faith to Live by. LC 76-27929. (Radiant Life Ser.). 128p. 1977. pap. 2.50 (ISBN 0-88243-899-9, 02-0899); teacher's ed. 3.95 (ISBN 0-88243-171-4, 32-0171). Gospel Pub.

Barrett, C. K. Essays on Paul. LC 82-2764. 180p. 1982. 18.95 (ISBN 0-664-21390-1). Westminster.

Bartchy, S. Scott. First-Century Slavery & the Interpretation of I Corinthians 7: 21. LC 73-83723. (Society of Biblical Literature. Dissertation Ser.). 1973. pap. 12.00 (ISBN 0-89130-220-4, 060111). Scholars Pr GA.

Barth, Karl, et al. Christ & Adam: Man & Humanity in Romans Five. Small, T. A., tr. 96p. 1983. Repr. of 1957 ed. lib. bdg. 12.00 (ISBN 0-88254-864-6, Octagon). Hippocrene Bks.

Bassler, Jouette M. Divine Impartiality: Paul & a Theological Axiom. Baird, William, ed. LC 81-1367. (Society of Biblical Literature Dissertation Ser.). 1981. pap. text ed. 13.50 (ISBN 0-89130-475-4, 0-06-01-59). Scholars Pr GA.

Baughen, Michael. Strengthened by Struggle: The Stress Factor in 2 Corinthians. 128p. 1984. pap. 5.95 (ISBN 0-87788-792-6). Shaw Pubs.

Baylis, Robert. Ephesians: Living in God's Household. LC 76-43523. (Fisherman Bible Studyguide). 45p. 1976. saddle stitched 2.95 (ISBN 0-87788-223-1). Shaw Pubs.

Beacon Bible Commentary Staff. Corinthians, Vol. VII. 6.95 (ISBN 0-8010-0681-3). Baker Bk.

--Galatians-Philemon, Vol. IX. 13.95 (ISBN 0-8010-0696-1). Baker Bk.

--Hebrews, James, I-II Peter, Vol. XI. 6.95 (ISBN 0-8010-0677-5). Baker Bk.

--Hebrews-Revelation, Vol. X. 13.95 (ISBN 0-8010-0698-8). Baker Bk.

--Romans, Vol. VI. 8.95 (ISBN 0-8010-0680-5). Baker Bk.

--Romans, II-Corinthians, Vol. VIII. 13.95 (ISBN 0-8010-0695-3). Baker Bk.

--Thessalonians, Vol. X. 6.95 (ISBN 0-8010-0743-7). Baker Bk.

Beacon Hill Staff. Beacon Small-Group Bible Studies, I Corinthians, Living As a Responsible Christian. 60p. 1982. pap. 2.50 (ISBN 0-8341-0755-4). Beacon Hill.

Becker, Calvin W. First & Second Timothy & Titus: Letters to Two Young Men. (Teach Yourself the Bible Ser.). 1961. pap. 2.75 (ISBN 0-8024-2646-8). Moody.

Bell, R. C. Studies in Ephesians. 1971. pap. 2.75 (ISBN 0-88027-041-1). Firm Foun Pub.

--Studies in Galatians. 1954. pap. 2.75 (ISBN 0-88027-042-X). Firm Foun Pub.

--Studies in Philippians. 1956. pap. 2.75 (ISBN 0-88027-043-8). Firm Foun Pub.

--Studies in Romans. 1957. pap. 2.75 (ISBN 0-88027-025-X). Firm Foun Pub.

Bluhm, Heinz. Luther Translator of Paul: Studies in Romans & Galatians. 580p. 1984. text ed. 49.80 bndg. text (ISBN 0-8204-0186-2). P Lang Pubs.

Boatman, Don E. Helps from Hebrews. LC 75-1066. (The Bible Study Textbook Ser.). (Illus.). 1960. 14.30 (ISBN 0-89900-044-4). College Pr Pub.

Boatman, Don E. & Boles, Kenny. Galatians. rev. ed. LC 70-1141. (The Bible Study Textbook Ser.). (Illus.). 1976. 12.20 (ISBN 0-89900-039-8). College Pr Pub.

Boice, James M. The Epistles of John. 224p. 1983. pap. 7.95 (ISBN 0-310-21531-5, 10421). Zondervan.

Boyer, James L. For a World Like Ours: Studies in I Corinthians. pap. 4.95 (ISBN 0-88469-057-1). BMH Bks.

Breisch, Francis. Ephesians: A Study Guide. (Revelation Series for Adults). 1976. pap. text ed. 2.50 (ISBN 0-317-39618-8). CRC Pubns.

Brinsmead, Bernard. Galatians: A Dialogical Response to Opponents. LC 81-18535. (SBL Dissertation Ser.). 1982. pap. 17.25 (ISBN 0-89130-549-1, 06 01 65). Scholars Pr GA.

Brown, John. Galatians. 1982. lib. bdg. 16.00 (ISBN 0-86524-083-3, 4802). Klock & Klock.

--Hebrews. (Geneva Ser.). 329p. 1983. Repr. of 1862 ed. text ed. 15.95 (ISBN 0-85151-099-X). Banner of Truth.

Brown, Raymond. Timothy-James. 1983. pap. 4.95 (ISBN 0-87508-174-6). Chr Lit.

Brown, Raymond E. The Epistles of John. LC 81-43380. (Anchor Bible Ser.: Vol. 30). 840p. 1982. 20.00 (ISBN 0-385-05686-9). Doubleday.

Brown, Richard. Studies in Romans, Vol. 1. (Bible Study Ser.). 1986. pap. 3.50 (ISBN 0-8309-0452-2). Herald Hse.

Brown, Richard A. Studies in Romans, Vol. 2. (Bible Study Ser.). 1986. pap. 3.50 (ISBN 0-8309-0454-9). Herald Hse.

Bruce, A. B. The Epistle to the Hebrews. 1980. 17.25 (ISBN 0-86524-028-0, 5802). Klock & Klock.

Bultmann, Rudolf. The Johannine Epistles. Funk, Robert W., ed. O'Hara, R. Philip, et al, trs. from Gr. LC 75-171510. (Hermeneia: a Critical & Historical Commentary on the Bible). 158p. 1973. 19.95 (ISBN 0-8006-6003-X, 20-6003). Fortress.

Burghardt, W. J., et al, eds. The Didache, the Epistle of Barnabas, the Epistle & Martyrdom of St. Polycarp, the Fragments of Papias, the Epistle of Diognetus. LC 78-62453. (ACW Ser.: No. 6). 241p. 1948. 13.95 (ISBN 0-8091-0247-1). Paulist Pr.

Butt, Herbert W. Tests of Eternal Life: Studies in First John. pap. 0.50 (ISBN 0-685-00745-6). Reiner.

Calvin, John. Sermons on Timothy & Titus. 1983. 37.95 (ISBN 0-85151-374-3). Banner of Truth.

Camara, Dom H. Through the Gospel with Dom Helder. Neame, Alan, tr. from Fr. 160p. (Orig.). 1986. pap. 8.95 (ISBN 0-88344-266-3). Orbis Bks.

Campbell, Richard D. Signs of a Lively Congregation. 1984. 3.95 (ISBN 0-89536-701-7, 4886). CSS of Ohio.

Capps, Charles. Hebrews. 39p. (Orig.). 1985. wkbk. 4.95 (ISBN 0-914307-36-3). Word Faith.

Carson, D. A. Showing the Spirit: A Theological Exposition of 1 Corinthians 12-14. 256p. 1987. pap. 12.95 (ISBN 0-8010-2521-4). Baker Bk.

Caudill, Paul R. First Corinthians: A Translation with Notes. LC 82-71220. 1983. 4.95 (ISBN 0-8054-1391-X). Broadman.

--Hebrews: A Translation with Notes. LC 84-21415. 1985. pap. 4.95 (ISBN 0-8054-1395-2). Broadman.

Clark, Gordon H. Ephesians. (Trinity Papers: No. 11). 225p. (Orig.). 1985. pap. 8.95 (ISBN 0-940931-11-7). Trinity Found.

--First & Second Thessolonians. (Trinity Papers: No. 14). 152p. (Orig.). 1986. pap. 5.95 (ISBN 0-940931-14-1). Trinity Found.

--The Pastoral Epistles. (Trinity Papers: No. 6). 294p. (Orig.). 1983. pap. 9.95 (ISBN 0-940931-06-0). Trinity Found.

A Closer Walk: Reflections of John 14 Through 17 from the Edgar Cayce Readings. 74p. (Orig.). 1974. pap. 3.95 (ISBN 0-87604-078-4). ARE Pr.

Cocoris, G. Michael. Colossians. rev. ed. 35p. 1985. pap. 1.00 (ISBN 0-935729-05-4). Church Open Door.

--Colossians, Pt. 1. rev. ed. 41p. 1985. pap. text ed. 1.00 (ISBN 0-935729-04-6). Church Open Door.

--Ephesians. (Orig.). Date not set. pap. text ed. price not set (ISBN 0-935729-37-2). Church Open Door.

--Galatians. (Orig.). 1986. pap. text ed. write for info. (ISBN 0-935729-33-X). Church Open Door.

--James, Pt. 1. rev. ed. 51p. 1984. pap. text ed. 1.00 (ISBN 0-935729-12-7). Church Open Door.

--James, Pt. 2. rev. ed. 43p. 1984. pap. text ed. 1.00 (ISBN 0-935729-13-5). Church Open Door.

--John. rev. ed. 181p. 1985. pap. text ed. 3.00 (ISBN 0-935729-07-0). Church Open Door.

--Joshua, Pt. 1. 44p. (Orig.). 1984. pap. text ed. 1.00 (ISBN 0-935729-18-6). Church Open Door.

--Joshua, Pt. 2. 42p. (Orig.). 1984. pap. text ed. 1.00 (ISBN 0-935729-19-4). Church Open Door.

--Joshua, Pt. 3. 44p. (Orig.). 1984. pap. text ed. 1.00 (ISBN 0-935729-20-8). Church Open Door.

--Titus. 99p. (Orig.). 1985. pap. text ed. 2.00 (ISBN 0-935729-31-3). Church Open Door.

Compier, Don. Studies in First Corinthians. (Bible Study Ser.). 1987. pap. 3.50 (ISBN 0-8309-0448-4). Herald Hse.

--Studies in Second Corinthians. (Bible Study Ser.). 1987. pap. 3.50 (ISBN 0-8309-0479-4). Herald Hse.

Couchman, Bob & Couchman, Win. James: Hear It! Live It! (Carpenter Studyguide Ser.). 1982. saddle-stitched leader's handbook, 61p 2.95 (ISBN 0-87788-423-4); member's handbook, 64p 1.95 (ISBN 0-87788-422-6). Shaw Pubs.

Cox, S. & Drysdale, A. H. The Epistle to Philemon. 246p. 1982. lib. bdg. 9.25 Smythe Sewn (ISBN 0-86524-134-1, 7108). Klock & Klock.

Craddock, Fred. Philippians: Interpretation: A Bible Commentary for Teaching & Preaching. Mays, James L. & Miller, Patrick D., eds. LC 84-47797. 96p. 1984. 12.95 (ISBN 0-8042-3140-0). John Knox.

Crouch, Owen. Expository Preaching & Teaching-Hebrews. LC 83-71985. 454p. (Orig.). 1983. pap. 9.95 (ISBN 0-89900-197-1). College Pr Pub.

Cundy, Ian. Ephesians-Thessalonians. 1981. pap. 4.95 (ISBN 0-87508-173-8). Chr Lit.

Dahl, Nils A. Studies in Paul. LC 77-84083. 1977. pap. 10.95 (ISBN 0-8066-1608-3, 10-6100). Augsburg.

Daille, Jean. Exposition of Colossians. 698p. 1983. lib. bdg. 24.95 (ISBN 0-86524-141-4, 5104). Klock & Klock.

Davids, Peter H. James: A Good News Commentary. LC 83-47720. (The Good News Commentary Ser.). 176p. (Orig.). 1983. pap. 7.95 (ISBN 0-06-061697-0, RD-499, HarpR). Har-Row.

Davis, James A. Wisdom & Spirit: An Investigation of 1 Corinthians 1.18-3.20 Against the Background of Jewish Sapiential. (Traditions in the Greco-Roman Period Ser.). 270p. (Orig.). 1984. lib. bdg. 27.25 (ISBN 0-8191-4210-7); pap. text ed. 13.75 (ISBN 0-8191-4211-5). U Pr of Amer.

Demarest, Bruce. A HIstory of Interpretation of Hebrews 7, 1-10 from the Reformation to the Present. 154p. 1976. pap. text ed. 28.50x (Pub. by J C B Mohr BRD). Coronet Bks.

DeWelt, Don. Romans Realized. LC 72-1068. (The Bible Study Textbook Ser.). (Illus.). 1959. 12.20 (ISBN 0-89900-037-1). College Pr Pub.

Dey, Lala K. The Intermediary World & Patterns of Perfection in Philo & Hebrews. LC 75-22457. (Society of Biblical Literature Dissertation Ser.: No.25). pap. 62.80 (ISBN 0-317-12981-3, 2017524). Bks Demand UMI.

Donelson, Lewis R. Pseudoepigraphy & Ethical Arguments in the Pastoral Epistles. 260p. 1986. lib. bdg. 52.50x (ISBN 3-16-145009-4, Pub. by J C B Mohr BRD). Coronet Bks.

Donfried, Karl P., ed. The Romans Debate: Essays on the Origin & Purpose on the Epistle. LC 77-84082. 1977. pap. 10.95 (ISBN 0-8066-1607-5, 10-5542). Augsburg.

Doyle, Stephen. Thessalonians & Galations. (Read & Pray Ser.). 1980. 1.75 (ISBN 0-8199-0635-2). Franciscan Herald.

Eadie, John. Colossians. 1981. 10.50 (ISBN 0-86524-067-1, 5103). Klock & Klock.

--The Words of the Apostle Paul. 462p. 1985. smythe sewn 18.50 (ISBN 0-86524-191-0, 4405). Klock & Klock.

Earle, Ralph. Word Meanings in the New Testament: Romans, Vol. 3. 9.95 (ISBN 0-8010-3322-5). Baker Bk.

--Word Meanings: Philippians-Philemon, Vol. 5. 9.95 (ISBN 0-8010-3330-6). Baker Bk.

Ebeling, Gerhard. Truth of the Gospel: An Exposition of Galatians. LC 84-47918. 288p. 1985. 19.95 (ISBN 0-8006-0728-7, 1-728). Fortress.

Edwards, Thomas C. A Commentary on the First Epistle to the Corinthians. 1979. 18.00 (ISBN 0-86524-013-2, 4602). Klock & Klock.

--The Epistle to the Hebrews. 394p. 1982. lib. bdg. 13.00 Smythe Sewn (ISBN 0-86524-154-6, 5803). Klock & Klock.

Eisele, Carol. Christ in You. (Aglow Bible Study Basic Ser.: Bk. 10). 64p. 1977. 2.95 (ISBN 0-930756-22-3, 521010). Aglow Pubns.

Erasmus, Desiderius. An Exhortation to the Diligent Studye of Scripture. Roy, W., tr. LC 72-5983. (English Experience Ser.: No. 510). 156p. 1973. Repr. of 1529 ed. 11.50 (ISBN 90-221-0510-5). Walter J Johnson.

Eubanks, David L. & Shannon, Robert C. Hebrews. (Standard Bible Studies). 128p. 1986. pap. text ed. 5.95 (ISBN 0-87403-171-0, 40111). Standard Pub.

Evans, Coleen. Living True. 132p. 1985. pap. 4.95 (ISBN 0-89693-321-0). Victor Bks.

Evans, Colleen T. Love Is an Everyday Thing. rev. ed. 128p. 1984. pap. 4.95 (ISBN 0-8007-5157-4, Power Bks). Revell.

Fairbanks, LeBron. Beacon Small-Group Bible Studies, Philippians, Colossians, Experiencing His Peace. 100p. 1982. pap. 2.50 (ISBN 0-8341-0778-3). Beacon Hill.

Fee, Gordon D. The First Epistle to the Corinthians. Bruce, F. F., ed. (New International Commentary on the New Testament Ser.). 736p. 1987. pap. 27.95 (ISBN 0-8028-2288-6). Eerdmans.

Ferguson, Roger. Experiencing Fullness in Christian Living: Studies in Colossians. 36p. 1982. pap. 3.50 (ISBN 0-939298-08-2). J M Prods.

Fetterhoff, Dean. The Making of a Man of God: Studies in I & II Timothy. pap. 4.95 (ISBN 0-88469-030-X). BMH Bks.

Fields, Wilbur. The Glorious Church-Ephesians. 2nd ed. LC 71-1065. (The Bible Study Textbook Ser.). (Illus.). 1960. 10.60 (ISBN 0-89900-040-1). College Pr Pub.

--Philippians, Colossians, Philemon. LC 78-8763. (The Bible Study Textbook Ser.). (Illus.). 1969. 10.60 (ISBN 0-89900-041-X). College Pr Pub.

--Thinking Through Thessalonians. LC 77-1794. (The Bible Study Textbook Ser.). (Illus.). 1963. 12.20 (ISBN 0-89900-042-8). College Pr Pub.

Findlay, G. G. The Epistles of Paul the Apostle to the Thessalonians. (Thornapple Commentaries Ser.). 319p. 1982. pap. 9.95 (ISBN 0-8010-3503-1). Baker Bk.

Flanagan, Neal M. The Gospel According to John VII the Johannine Epistles, No. 4. Karris, Robert J., ed. LC 82-22908. (Collegeville Bible Commentary Ser.). 128p. 1983. pap. 2.95 (ISBN 0-8146-1304-7). Liturgical Pr.

Francis, Fred O. & Sampley, J. Paul. Pauline Parallels. rev. ed. LC 83-48920. (Foundations & Facets: New Testament Ser.). 416p. 1984. 29.95 (ISBN 0-8006-2103-4, 1-2103). Fortress.

Friskney, Tom. Thirteen Lessons on I & II Thessalonians. LC 82-71253. (Bible Student Study Guide Ser.). 122p. 1982. pap. 2.95 (ISBN 0-89900-172-6). College Pr Pub.

Fromer, Margaret & Fromer, Paul. Putting Christ First: A Woman's Workshop on Colossians. Kobobel, Janet, ed. (Woman's Workshop Ser.). 128p. 1986. pap. 5.95 (ISBN 0-310-44801-8, 11313P). Zondervan.

--A Woman's Workshop on Philippians. (Woman's Workshop Ser.). 128p. 1982. pap. 2.95 (ISBN 0-310-44771-2, 11312P). Zondervan.

Fudge, Edward. Expository Outlines on Ephesians. 2.00 (ISBN 0-686-12688-2). E Fudge.

Fuller, Reginald H., et al. Hebrews, James, 1 & 2 Peter, Jude, Revelation. Krodel, Gerhard, ed. LC 76-7864. (Proclamation Commentaries). 132p. 1977. pap. 4.95 (ISBN 0-8006-0584-5, 1-584). Fortress.

Gaebelein, Frank E., ed. The Expositor's Bible Commentary, (Romans - Galatians, Vol. 10. 600p. 1976. 19.95 (ISBN 0-310-36520-1, 11179). Zondervan.

Gardiner, George E. La Catastrofe de Corinto. Orig. Title: The Corinthian Catastrophe. (Span.). 64p. 1976. pap. 2.25 (ISBN 0-8254-1254-4). Kregel.

Georgi, Dieter. The Opponents of Paul in Second Corinthians: A Study of Religious Propaganda in Late Antiquity. LC 84-47917. 464p. 1985. 32.95 (ISBN 0-8006-0729-5, 1-729). Fortress.

Getty, Mary A. Ephesians, Philippians, Colassians. (Read & Pray Ser.). 1980. pap. 1.95 (ISBN 0-8199-0636-0). Franciscan Herald.

Gettys, Joseph M. How to Study Ephesians. rev. ed. 64p. 1976. pap. 4.00x (ISBN 0-87921-056-7). Attic Pr.

--How to Study I Corinthians. 128p. 1968. pap. 4.50x (ISBN 0-8042-3532-5). Attic Pr.

Getz, Gene A. Believeing God When You Are Tempted To Doubt. LC 83-4440. (The Measure of...Ser.). 160p. 1983. pap. 5.95 (ISBN 0-8307-0881-2, 5417930). Regal.

Gilbert. Gilbert of Hoyland: Treasties, Epistles, & Sermons. Braceland, Lawrence C., tr. (Fathers Ser.: No. 34). 1981. 12.95 (ISBN 0-87907-434-5). Cistercian Pubns.

Gilmer, Arden E. Romans: The Gospel According to Paul. LC 85-72274. 1985. pap. 4.50x (ISBN 0-934970-05-X). Brethren Ohio.

Gingrich, Raymond E. The Epistles of the Blessed Hope: First & Second Thessalonians. 1986. pap. 5.95 (ISBN 0-88469-176-4). BMH Bks.

Gnilka, Joachim & Mussner, Franz. The Epistle to the Phillipians & the Epistle to the Colossians. McKenzie, John L., ed. LC 81-605. (New Testament for Spiritual Reading Ser.). 180p. 1981. pap. 4.95 (ISBN 0-8245-0126-8). Crossroad NY.

Gooch, Paul W. Partial Knowledge: Philosophical Studies in Paul. LC 86-40589. 224p. 1987. text ed. 22.95x (ISBN 0-268-01567-8, Dist. by Har-Row). U of Notre Dame Pr.

Gorday, Peter. Principles of Patristic Exegesis: Romans 9-11 in Origen, John Chrysostom & Augustine. LC 83-20588. (Studies in the Bible & Early Christianity: Vol. 4). 424p. 1984. 69.95x (ISBN 0-88946-602-5). E Mellen.

Gottwald, Norman K. The Hebrew Bible-A Socio-Literary Introduction. LC 84-48719. (Illus.). 736p. 1985. 34.95 (ISBN 0-8006-0853-4, 1-853); pap. 19.95 (ISBN 0-8006-1853-X, 1-1853). Fortress.

Grant, L. M. First & Second Thessalonians. 46p. pap. 2.95 (ISBN 0-88172-079-8). Believers Bkshelf.

Griffith, Harry C. The Ways of God: Paths into the New Testament. 149p. 1986. pap. 7.95 (ISBN 0-8192-1377-2). Morehouse.

Grudem, Wayne A. The Gift of Prophecy in One Corinthians. LC 81-40583. 358p. (Orig.). 1982. lib. bdg. 32.00 (ISBN 0-8191-2083-9); pap. text ed. 15.75 (ISBN 0-8191-2084-7). U Pr of Amer.

Habeck, Irwin J. Ephesiana. 1985. 7.95 (ISBN 0-8100-0171-3, 15N0404). Northwest Pub.

Harper, A. F. Beacon Small-Group Bible Studies, James: Does God Want Faith or Obedience. 80p. (Orig.). 1980. pap. 2.50 (ISBN 0-8341-0625-6). Beacon Hill.

Harriman, Joseph B. A Harmony of Paul's Life & Letters. 77p. (Companion vol. to A Harmony of the Four gospels). 1969. 2.50 (ISBN 0-910840-13-X). Kingdom.

Hartnack, Justus. From Radical Empiricism to Absolute Idealism. LC 86-8603. (Studies in the History of Philosophy: Vol. 1). 222p. 1986. 49.95x (ISBN 0-88946-304-2). E Mellen.

Hasler, J. Ireland. The Message of Life: Studies in the Epistle of St. John (Missionary Message of the New Testament) 96p. 1949. 3.95 (ISBN 0-87921-013-3). Attic Pr.

Haugerud, Joann. The Word for Us, Gospels of John & Mark, Epistles to the Romans, & the Galations. LC 77-83418. 1977. 7.95 (ISBN 0-9603042-3-1). Coalition Women-Relig.

Hayes, John, ed. First & Second Corinthians. Baird, William. (Knox Preaching Guides Ser.). pap. 4.95 (ISBN 0-8042-3239-3). John Knox.

Hendriksen, William. NTC-Romans, 1 Vol. 1981. 19.95 (ISBN 0-8010-4265-8). Baker Bk.

Heynen, Ralph. Creative Discussions on I Corinthians 13. (Contemporary Discussion Ser.). 96p. 1982. pap. 2.95 (ISBN 0-8010-4260-7). Baker Bk.

Hiebel, Frederick. The Epistles of Paul & Rudolf Steiner's Philosophy of Freedom. 1979. pap. 4.95 (ISBN 0-916786-41-2). St George Bk Serv.

Hiebert, D. Edmond. The Epistle of James. LC 78-23925. 1979. 13.95 (ISBN 0-8024-2357-4). Moody.

Hogg, C. F. & Vine, W. E. Epistles of Paul the Apostle to the Thessalonians. 5.95 (ISBN 0-89315-040-1). Lambert Bk.

Hook, Martha. Letter of Unity: A Woman's Workshop on Ephesians. (Woman's Workshop Ser.). 1987. Leader's Guide, 80p. pap. 4.95 (ISBN 0-310-26181-3); Student's Guide, 64p. pap. 3.95 (ISBN 0-310-26191-0). Zondervan.

Horton, F. L. The Melchizedek Tradition. LC 75-32479. (Society for New Testament Studies Monographs: No. 30). 220p. 1976. 42.50 (ISBN 0-521-21014-3). Cambridge U Pr.

Hoyt, Herman A. Christ, God's Final Word to Man: An Exposition of the Epistle to the Hebrews. pap. 4.95 (ISBN 0-88469-009-1). BMH Bks.

--The First Christian Theology Studies in Romans. pap. 4.95 (ISBN 0-88469-038-5). BMH Bks.

Hufton, Richard A. Ephesians: The Mystery Within. 126p. (Orig.). 1984. pap. 3.50 (ISBN 0-933643-04-7). Grace World Outreach.

--Galatians: The Gospel of Freedom. LC 85-80103. 130p. (Orig.). 1985. pap. 4.00 (ISBN 0-933643-00-4). Grace World Outreach.

--James: Faith in Action. 146p. (Orig.). 1984. pap. 4.00 (ISBN 0-933643-03-9). Grace World Outreach.

Hughes, G. Hebrews & Hermeneutics. LC 77-84806. (Society for New Testament Studies Monographs: No. 36). 1980. 32.50 (ISBN 0-521-21858-6). Cambridge U Pr.

Hughes, Robert B. Second Corinthians. (Everyman's Bible Commentary Ser.). 1983. pap. 5.95 (ISBN 0-8024-0241-0). Moody.

Hultgren, Arland J. Paul's Gospel & Mission: The Outlook from His Letter to the Romans. LC 85-4430. 176p. 1985. pap. 9.95 (ISBN 0-8006-1871-8). Fortress.

Hummel, Charles & Hummel, Anne. I Corinthians: Problems & Solutions in a Growing Church. (Fisherman Bible Studyguide). 93p. 1981. saddle-stitched 2.95 (ISBN 0-87788-137-5). Shaw Pubs.

Hunt, Gladys. Luke: A Daily Dialogue with God. (Personal Bible Studyguide Ser.). 192p. (Orig.). 1986. pap. 5.95 (ISBN 0-87788-510-9). Shaw Pubs.

Hutchinson, John. An Exposition of Paul's Epistle to the Philippians. 328p. 1985. smythe sewn 13.00 (ISBN 0-86524-190-2, 5003). Klock & Klock.

The Interpreter's Concise Commentary, Vol. VII: Acts & Paul's Letters. 4.95 (ISBN 0-687-19238-2). Abingdon.

The Interpreter's Concise Commentary, Vol. VIII: Revelation & the General Epistles. 4.95 (ISBN 0-687-19239-0). Abingdon.

Ironside, H. A. Ephesians: Galatians. 11.95 (ISBN 0-87213-397-4). Loizeaux.

--Esther: Joshua, Ezra, Nehemiah. 11.95 (ISBN 0-87213-396-6). Loizeaux.

--Hebrews, James, Peter. 9.95 (ISBN 0-87213-399-0). Loizeaux.

--James: Hebrews, Peter. 9.95 (ISBN 0-87213-399-0). Loizeaux.

--Joshua, Ezra, Nehemiah, Esther. 11.95 (ISBN 0-87213-396-6). Loizeaux.

--Jude: John. 9.95 (ISBN 0-87213-372-9). Loizeaux.

--Philemon: Timothy, Titus. 9.95 (ISBN 0-87213-391-5). Loizeaux.

Ishee, John A. God's Purpose-God's People: Studies in Ephesians. 36p. 1982. pap. 3.50 (ISBN 0-939298-03-1). J M Prods.

James, Edgar C. Epistles of Peter. (Teach Yourself the Bible Ser.). 1964. pap. 2.75 (ISBN 0-8024-2355-8). Moody.

Jensen, Irving. Romans. (Irving Jensen's Do-It Yourself Bible Study). 114p. (Orig.). 1983. pap. 5.95 wkbk. (ISBN 0-89840-036-8). Heres Life.

Jensen, Irving L. Colossians & Philemon. (Bible Self-Study Ser.). 80p. 1973. pap. 3.25 (ISBN 0-8024-1052-9). Moody.

--First & Second Peter. (Bible Self-Study Ser.). 1971. pap. 3.25 (ISBN 0-8024-1060-X). Moody.

--First & Second Timothy & Titus. (Bible Self-Study Ser.). 1973. pap. 3.25 (ISBN 0-8024-1054-5). Moody.

--Philippians. (Bible Self-Study Ser.). 80p. 1973. pap. 3.25 (ISBN 0-8024-1051-0). Moody.

--Romans. (Bible Self-Study Ser.). 1970. pap. 3.25 (ISBN 0-8024-1045-6). Moody.

Jewett, Robert. Christian Tolerance: Paul's Message to the Modern Church. LC 82-13480. (Biblical Perspectives on Current Issues Ser.). 168p. 1982. pap. 9.95 (ISBN 0-664-24444-0). Westminster.

--The Thessalonian Correspondence: Pauline Rhetoric & Millenarian Piety. LC 86-45204. (Foundations & Facets Ser.). 256p. 1986. text ed. 17.95 (ISBN 0-8006-2111-5, 1-2111). Fortress.

Johnson, Alan F. Romans: The Freedom Letter, Vol. 2. rev. ed. (Everyman's Bible Commentary Ser.). Date not set. pap. 5.95 (ISBN 0-8024-2079-6). Moody.

Johnson, Ben. Blueprint for Sainthood: A Study of the Series C Epistles for Lent. 1980. 4.25 (ISBN 0-89536-416-6, 0234). CSS of Ohio.

Johnson, Luke T. First & Second Timothy, Titus. Hayes, John H., ed. LC 86-45403. (Preaching Guides). 132p. (Orig.). 1987. pap. 7.95 (ISBN 0-8042-3242-3). John Knox.

Jones, Amos, Jr. Paul's Message of Freedom: What Does It Mean to the Black Church? 256p. 1984. 12.95 (ISBN 0-8170-0840-3). Judson.

Julian, Helen. Key to Abundant Living. 1977. tchr's manual 2.00 (ISBN 0-87509-099-0); student manual 1.25 (ISBN 0-87509-100-8). Chr Pubns.

Julien, Tom. Inherited Wealth: Studies in Ephesians. pap. 4.95 (ISBN 0-88469-034-2). BMH Bks.

Kackelman, John, Jr. Studies in Colossiani. 1986. pap. 5.50 (ISBN 0-89137-562-7). Quality Pubns.

Kaiser, Bill. No Other Gospel. 153p. (Orig.). 1984. pap. 6.95 (ISBN 0-914307-16-9, Dist. by Harrison Hse). Word Faith.

Kappeler, Max. The Epistles in the Light of Christian Science. LC 72-200094. 253p. 1962. 14.00 (ISBN 0-85241-042-5). Kappeler Inst Pub.

Kasemann, Ernst. The Wandering People of God: An Investigation of the Letter to the Hebrews. Harrisville, Roy A., tr. LC 84-20523. 272p. (Orig.). 1984. 21.95 (ISBN 0-8066-2121-4, 10-6940). Augsburg.

Kaye, Bruce N. The Thought Structure of Romans with Special Reference to Chapter Six. 203p. (Orig.). 1979. pap. 5.95 (ISBN 0-931016-03-7). Schola Pr TX.

Keck, Leander, et al. Pauline Letters. 160p. (Orig.). 1984. pap. 9.50 (ISBN 0-687-30494-6). Abingdon.

Kelly, W. Epistle to the Hebrews. 272p. pap. 8.50 (ISBN 0-88172-155-7). Believers Bkshelf.

--Exposition of the Epistles of John. 6.25 (ISBN 0-88172-100-X). Believers Bkshelf.

--Notes on Romans. 8.50 (ISBN 0-88172-107-7). Believers Bkshelf.

--Titus & Philemon. 6.50 (ISBN 0-88172-110-7). Believers Bkshelf.

Kelly, William. The Acts, Catholic Epistles & Revelation. (Introductory Lecture Ser.). 580p. 6.95 (ISBN 0-88172-096-8). Believers Bkshelf.

--The Pauline Epistles. (Introductory Lecture Ser.). 551p. 6.95 (ISBN 0-88172-098-4). Believers Bkshelf.

Kent, Homer A., Jr. Ephesians, the Glory of the Church. pap. 5.95 (ISBN 0-88469-078-4). BMH Bks.

--The Epistle to the Hebrews. pap. 11.95 (ISBN 0-88469-069-5). BMH Bks.

--Faith That Works. 1986. pap. 7.95 (ISBN 0-88469-180-2). BMH Bks.

--Faith That Works: Studies in the Epistle of James. 1986. pap. 7.95 (ISBN 0-8010-5476-1). Baker Bk.

--The Freedom of God's Sons: Studies in Galatians. (Illus.). pap. 5.95 (ISBN 0-88469-058-X). BMH Bks.

--A Heart Opened Wide: Studies in II Corinthians. (New Testament Studies). 176p. (Orig.). 1982. pap. 4.95 (ISBN 0-8010-5438-9). Baker Bk.

--A Heart Opened Wide: Studies in II Corinthians. 176p. (Orig.). 1982. pap. 4.95 (ISBN 0-88469-152-7). BMH Bks.

Kenyon, Don J. Romans, 2 vols. Incl. Vol. 1. Triumph of Truth. pap. text ed. 4.95 (ISBN 0-87509-147-4); leader's guide 2.95 (ISBN 0-87509-265-9); student's manual 1.00 (ISBN 0-87509-262-4); Vol 2. Glory of Grace. pap. text ed. 4.95 (ISBN 0-87509-148-2); leader's guide 2.95 (ISBN 0-87509-266-7); student's manual 1.00 (ISBN 0-87509-263-2). 1978. pap. Chr Pubns.

Kertlege, Karl. The Epistles to the Romans. McKenzie, John L., ed. LC 81-605. (The New Testament for Spiritual Reading Ser.). 144p. 1981. pap. 4.95 (ISBN 0-8245-0121-7). Crossroad NY.

Kiley, Mark. Colossians as Pseudepigraphy. (Biblical Seminar Ser.: No. 4). 240p. 1986. pap. text ed. 11.95x (ISBN 1-85075-024-6, Pub. by JSOT Pr England). Eisenbrauns.

King, Guy H. Belief That Behaves. 1971. pap. 3.95 (ISBN 0-87508-271-8). Chr Lit.

--Crossing the Border (Colossians) 1957. pap. 3.95 (ISBN 0-87508-274-2). Chr Lit.

--Fellowship. 1972. pap. 3.95 (ISBN 0-87508-279-3). Chr Lit.

--Leader Led. 1971. pap. 3.95 (ISBN 0-87508-283-1). Chr Lit.

--To My Son (II Timothy) 1972. pap. 3.95 (ISBN 0-87508-287-4). Chr Lit.

Kistemaker, Simon J. Exposition of the Epistles of James & John. 1986. 18.95 (ISBN 0-8010-5469-9). Baker Bk.

--Expositions of the Epistles of Peter & Jude: New Testament Commentary. 1987. text ed. 19.95 (ISBN 0-8010-5484-2). Baker Bk.

Knight, John A. Beacon Bible Expositions: Philippians, Colossians, Philemon. Greathouse, William H., ed. 320p. 1985. 8.95 (ISBN 0-8341-0320-6). Beacon Hill.

Knox, John. Chapters in a Life of Paul. rev., 2nd ed. Hare, Douglas R., ed. 192p. 1987. 29.95 (ISBN 0-86554-266-X, MUP/H227/P32); pap. 14.95 (ISBN 0-86554-281-3). Mercer Univ Pr.

Kort, Ann & Morschauer, Scott, eds. Biblical & Related Studies Related to Samuel Iwry. xvii, 274p. 1985. text ed. 25.00x (ISBN 0-931464-23-4). Eisenbrauns.

Kuhatschek, Jack. Galatians: Why Christ Accepts Us. (LifeBuilder Bible Studies). (Orig.). 1986. pap. 2.95 (ISBN 0-8308-1011-0). Inter-Varsity.

--Romans: The Gift of Righteousness. (Lifebuilder Bible Studies). 96p. (Orig.). 1986. pap. 2.95 (ISBN 0-8308-1008-0). Inter-Varsity.

Kuniholm, Whitney. First & Second Thessalonians, First & Second Timothy, Titus, Philemon: A Daily Dialogue. (Personal Bible Studyguide Ser.). 120p. (Orig.). 1986. pap. 5.95 (ISBN 0-87788-809-4). Shaw Pubs.

--Galatians, Ephesians, Philippians, & Colossians: A Daily Dialogue with God. (Personal Bible Studyguide Ser.). 144p. 1983. pap. 5.95 (ISBN 0-87788-292-4). Shaw Pubs.

Kunz, Marilyn & Schell, Catherine. Corinthians One. (Neighborhood Bible Studies Ser.). 1974. pap. 2.50 (ISBN 0-8423-0441-X). Tyndale.

Kuschel, Harlyn J. A Study Guide for Philippians-Colossians & Philemon. Fischer, William E., ed. (Study Guide for People's Bible Ser.). 48p. (Orig.). 1987. pap. text ed. 1.50 (ISBN 0-938272-57-8). Wels Board.

Kuske, David P. A Study Guide for Paul's Letters to the Thessalonians. 41p. (Orig.). 1984. pap. 1.50 (ISBN 0-938272-51-9). WELS Board.

--Thessalonians. (People's Bible Ser.). 1984. pap. 4.95 (ISBN 0-8100-0193-4, 15N0406). Northwest Pub.

Larsen, Dale. Hebrews, James, 1 & 2 Peter, Jude: A Daily Dialogue with God. (Personal Bible Studyguide Ser.). 144p. 1984. pap. 5.95 (ISBN 0-87788-339-4). Shaw Pubs.

Larsen, Sandy & Larsen, Dale. Galatians: Free at Last. (Young Fisherman Bible Studyguide Ser.). (Illus.). 73p. 1982. saddle-stitched student ed. 2.95 (ISBN 0-87788-293-2); tchr's ed. 4.95 (ISBN 0-87788-294-0). Shaw Pubs.

Larson, Muriel. Living by Faith: A Study of Romans. 60p. 1984. pap. 2.95 (ISBN 0-930756-80-0, 521016). Aglow Pubns.

Lauersdorf, Richard E. A Study Guide for Hebrews. Fischer, William E., ed. (Study Guide for People's Bible Ser.). 48p. (Orig.). 1986. pap. 1.50 (ISBN 0-938272-56-X). WELS Board.

Laurin, Roy L. Colossians. 192p. 1987. pap. 9.95 (ISBN 0-8254-3135-2). Kregel.

--First Corinthians. Orig. Title: First Corinthians: Where Life Matures. 336p. 1987. pap. 10.95 (ISBN 0-8254-3132-8). Kregel.

--Romans. Orig. Title: Romans: Where Life Begins. 540p. 1988. Repr. of 1955 ed. 12.95 (ISBN 0-8254-3130-1). Kregel.

Laws, Sophie. The Epistle of James. LC 80-8349. (Harper's New Testament Commentaries Ser.). 288p. 1981. 16.00 (ISBN 0-06-064918-6, HarpR). Har-Row.

Lawson, E. L. Galatians-Ephesians. (Standard Bible Studies). (Illus.). 288p. 1987. pap. price not set (ISBN 0-87403-169-9, 40109). Standard Pub.

LePeau, Andrew T. & LePeau, Phyllis J. Faith That Works: Eleven Studies in James. 72p. (Orig.). 1980. pap. 2.25 (ISBN 0-87784-365-1). Inter Varsity.

--James: Faith That Works. (LifeGuide Bible Studies). 64p. (Orig.). 1987. pap. 2.95. Inter-Varsity.

Leyburn, John. Soldier of the Cross. 2nd ed. 339p. 1986. Repr. of 1851 ed. lib. bdg. 27.50 (ISBN 0-89941-509-1). W S Hein.

Lias, John J. First Epistle of John. 1982. lib. bdg. 15.75 (ISBN 0-86524-092-2, 6201). Klock & Klock.

Lieu, Judith. The Second & Third Epistles of John. 280p. 1987. 19.95 (ISBN 0-567-09443-X, Pub. by T & T Clark Ltd UK). Fortress.

Lloyd-Jones, D. Martyn. The Christian Warfare: An Exposition of Ephesians 6: 10-13. 1977. Repr. of 1976 ed. 12.95 (ISBN 0-8010-5574-1). Baker Bk.

--Darkness & Light: An Exposition of Ephesians 4 17-5 17. 408p. 1983. Repr. of 1965 ed. 12.95 (ISBN 0-8010-5617-9). Baker Bk.

--II Peter. 15.95 (ISBN 0-85151-379-4). Banner of Truth.

--The Plight of Man & the Power of God. (Summit Bks.). 96p. 1982. pap. 2.95 (ISBN 0-8010-5621-7). Baker Bk.

--Romans- The Gospel of God: An Exposition of Chapter 1. 416p. 1986. 16.95 (ISBN 0-310-27950-X, 10571). Zondervan.

--Romans: The New Man, Vol. 3. 1973. text ed. 14.95 (ISBN 0-310-27900-3, 10534). Zondervan.

Loane, Marcus L. Godliness & Contentment: Studies in the Three Pastoral Epistles. (Canterbury Bks.). 128p. (Orig.). 1982. pap. 5.95 (ISBN 0-8010-5619-5). Baker Bk.

Locke, John. A Paraphrase & Notes on the Epistles of St. Paul, 2 vols. (The Clarendon edition of the Works of John Locke). (Illus.). 800p. 1986. Set. 125.00x (ISBN 0-19-824801-6). Oxford U Pr.

Lull, David J. The Spirit in Galatia: Paul's Interpretation of Pneuma As Divine Power. LC 79-26094. (Society of Biblical Literature Dissertation: No. 49). 15.95 (ISBN 0-89130-367-7, 06-01-49); pap. 10.95 (ISBN 0-89130-368-5). Scholars Pr GA.

Lyall, Francis. Slaves, Citizens, Sons: Legal Metaphors in the Epistles. 320p. 1984. pap. 9.95 (ISBN 0-310-45191-4, 12452P). Zondervan.

Lyons, George. Pauline Autobiography: Toward a New Understanding. (Society of Biblical Literature Dissertation Ser.). 1985. 23.50 (ISBN 0-89130-730-3, 06-01-73); pap. 15.50 (ISBN 0-89130-765-6). Scholars Pr GA.

MacArthur, John. Hebrews. (The MacArthur New Testament Commentary Ser.). (Orig.). 14.95 (ISBN 0-8024-0753-6). Moody.

MacArthur, John F., Jr. Ephesians. 1986. 14.95 (ISBN 0-88469-171-3). BMH Bks.

--Liberated for Life a Christian Declaration of Indepence. LC 75-23511. 1984. pap. 4.95 (ISBN 0-8307-0931-2, 5418165). Regal.

MacArthur, John, Jr. The Christian & Government. (John MacArthur's Bible Studies). (Orig.). 1986. pap. 3.50 (ISBN 0-8024-5095-4). Moody.

--Entering God's Rest: Hebrew Three Through Four. (John MacArthur Bible Studies). 1987. pap. 3.50 (ISBN 0-8024-5316-3). Moody.

--Ephesians. (MacArthur New Testament Commentary Ser.). 1986. text ed. 14.95 (ISBN 0-8024-2358-2). Moody.

--First Corinthians. 1984. 14.95 (ISBN 0-88469-161-6). BMH Bks.

--Freedom from Sin: Romans Six Through Seven. (John MacArthur Bible Studies Ser.). 1987. pap. 4.50 (ISBN 0-8024-5309-0). Moody.

--God's High Calling for Women: First Timothy Two Verses Nine through Fifteen. (John MacArthur Bible Studies Ser.). 1987. pap. 3.50 (ISBN 0-8024-5308-2). Moody.

--Justification by Faith. (John MacArthur's Bible Studies). 1985. pap. 4.95 (ISBN 0-8024-5120-9). Moody.

--Living in the Spirit: Ephesians Five Eighteen Through Twenty. (John MacArthur Bible Studies Ser.). 1987. pap. 3.95 (ISBN 0-8024-5315-5). Moody.

--The Lord's Supper: Mattew Twenty-six Vs Seventeen to Thirty, Corinthians Eleven Seventeen Through Thirty-four. (John MacArthur Bible Studies). 1987. pap. 3.50 (ISBN 0-8024-5310-4). Moody.

--Love's Humility. (John MacArthur's Bible Studies). (Orig.). 1986. pap. 3.95 (ISBN 0-8024-5097-0). Moody.

--The Wrath of God. (John MacArthur's Bible Studies). (Orig.). 1986. pap. 3.50 (ISBN 0-8024-5096-2). Moody.

McCann, Michael D. Hebrews. (Standard Bible Study Workbooks). 64p. 1986. pap. text ed. 1.95 (ISBN 0-87403-191-5, 40211). Standard Pub.

McCann, Mike. Galatians-Ephesians. (Standard Bible Study Workbooks Ser.). 80p. 1987. wkbk. 1.95 (ISBN 0-87403-189-3, 40209). Standard Pub.

McClain, Alva J. Romans Outlined & Summarized. 1979. pap. 1.95 (ISBN 0-88469-015-6). BMH Bks.

--Romans, the Gospel of God's Grace. 11.95 (ISBN 0-88469-080-6). BMH Bks.

--Romans: The Gospel of God's Grace. 1979. 11.95 (ISBN 0-8024-7373-3). BMH Bks.

MacDonald, William. Letter to Titus. pap. 2.50 (ISBN 0-937396-46-X). Walterick Pubs.

McDonald, William. Letters to the Thessalonians. rev. ed. 1982. pap. 3.50 (ISBN 0-937396-43-5). Walterick Pubs.

MacDonald, William. Thessalonians. 5.00 (ISBN 0-686-27147-5); pap. 3.95 (ISBN 0-937396-43-5). Walterick Pubs.

McWhorter, Jane. Caterpillars or Butterflies. (Illus.). 1977. pap. 4.95 (ISBN 0-89137-410-8). Quality Pubns.

Mahan, Henry T. Galatians. 1983. pap. 1.50 (ISBN 0-686-40819-5). Pilgrim Pubns.

Malherbe, Abraham. Paul & the Thessalonians: The Philosophic Tradition of Pastoral Care. LC 86-45918. 144p. 1987. 8.95 (ISBN 0-8006-0863-1, 1-863). Fortress.

Maly, Eugene H. Romans. (New Testament Message Ser.: Vol. 9). 160p. 1980. 12.95 (ISBN 0-89453-197-2); pap. 7.95 (ISBN 0-89453-132-8). M Glazier.

Manton, Thomas. Exposition of the Epistle of Jude. 375p. 14.00 (ISBN 0-86524-172-4, 6501). Klock & Klock.

--James. 1983. 15.95 (ISBN 0-85151-074-4). Banner of Truth.

Marsh, F. E. Practical Truths from First Thessalonians. LC 86-2742. Orig. Title: Flashes from the Lighthouse of Truth. 272p. 1986. Repr. 12.95 (ISBN 0-8254-3234-0). Kregel.

Martin, Ralph & Toon, Peter, eds. Reconciliation: A Study of Paul's Theology. LC 80-16340. (New Foundations Theological Library). 272p. 1981. 12.95 (ISBN 0-8042-3709-3); pap. 11.95 (ISBN 0-8042-3729-8). John Knox.

Martin, Ralph P. Second Corinthians, Vol. 40, WBC. 380p. 1985. 25.95 (ISBN 0-8499-0239-8, 0239-8). Word Bks.

Maynard-Reid, Pedrito U. Poverty & Wealth in James. LC 86-23506. 128p. (Orig.). 1987. pap. 8.95 (ISBN 0-88344-417-8). Orbis Bks.

Meyer, Marvin W. The Letter of Peter to Philip. Kee, Howard C., ed. LC 80-28612. (Society of Biblical Literature Dissertation Ser.). 1981. pap. text ed. 13.50 (ISBN 0-89130-463-0, 06-01-53). Scholars Pr GA.

Miller, Stephen M. Beacon Small-Group Bible Studies, II Corinthians, Galatians: Reckless Freedom, Responsible Living. Wolf, Earl C., ed. 96p. (Orig.). 1985. pap. 2.50 (ISBN 0-8341-0957-3). Beacon Hill.

Mitchell, Phyllis. With Christ in Heavenly Realms: A Study of Ephesians. (Enrichment Bible Studies). 60p. 1986. pap. 2.95 (ISBN 0-932305-22-9, 522007). Aglow Pubns.

Moran, John C., et al, eds. The Romanist, No. 4-5. 1981. 10.00 (ISBN 0-318-20641-2). F M Crawford.

--The Romanist, No. 6-8. 1984. 10.00 (ISBN 0-318-20642-0). F M Crawford.

Morgan, J. & Cox, S. The Epistles of John. 612p. 1982. lib. bdg. 22.95 Smythe Sewn (ISBN 0-86524-133-3, 6202). Klock & Klock.

Morrison, G. H. Morrison on Galations through Hebrews. LC 82-71841. (Glasgow Pulpit Ser.). 1982. pap. 4.95 (ISBN 0-89957-557-9). AMG Pubs.

--Morrison on Romans & Corinthians. (Glasgow Pulpit Ser.). 96p. 1982. pap. 4.95 (ISBN 0-89957-547-1). AMG Pubs.

Morton, A. Q. & Michaelson, S. A Critical Concordance to I, II Thessalonians. Baird, J. Arthur & Freedman, David N., eds. (The Computer Bible: Vol XXVI). 136p. (Orig.). 1983. pap. 25.00x (ISBN 0-935106-21-9). Biblical Res Assocs.

--Critical Concordance to the Pastoral Epistles, I, II Timothy, Titus, Philemon. Baird, J. Arthur & Freedman, David N., eds. (The Computer Bible Ser.: Vol. XXV). 1982. pap. 35.00 (ISBN 0-935106-20-0). Biblical Res Assocs.

Morton, A. Q., et al. A Critical Concordance to I & II Corinthians. (Computer Bible Ser.: Vol. XIX). 1979. pap. 30.00 (ISBN 0-935106-01-4). Biblical Res Assocs.

--A Critical Concordance to the Epistle of Paul to the Galatians. Baird, J. Arthur & Freedman, David, eds. (The Computer Bible Ser.: Vol. XXI). (Orig.). 1980. pap. text ed. 20.00 (ISBN 0-935106-16-2). Biblical Res Assocs.

--A Critical Concordance to the Letter of Paul to the Ephesians. Baird, J. Arthur & Freedman, David, eds. (The Computer Bible Ser.: Vol. XXII). (Orig.). 1980. pap. text ed. 20.00 (ISBN 0-935106-17-0). Biblical Res Assocs.

Motyer, Alec. The Message of James. Stott, John R., ed. LC 85-4316. (Bible Speaks Today Ser.). 156p. 1985. pap. 6.95 (ISBN 0-87784-292-2). Inter-Varsity.

Moule, H. C. Romans. 1982. lib. bdg. 16.25 (ISBN 0-86524-086-8, 4502). Klock & Klock.

Mounce, Robert. A Living Hope: A Commentary on I & II Peter. 1982. pap. 4.95 (ISBN 0-8028-1915-X). Eerdmans.

Murphy-O'Connor, Jerome. First Corinthians. (New Testament Message Ser.: Vol. 10). 172p. 1980. 12.95 (ISBN 0-89453-198-0); pap. 7.95 (ISBN 0-89453-133-6). M Glazier.

--St. Paul's Corinth: Texts & Archaeology. (Good News Studies: Vol. 6). 1983. pap. 9.95 (ISBN 0-89453-303-7). M Glazier.

Myers, Bill. Faith Workout. (Illus.). 144p. 1986. 3.95 (ISBN 0-89693-265-6). Victor Bks.

Nee, Watchman. Sit, Walk, Stand. 1977. pap. 2.95 (ISBN 0-8423-5893-5). Tyndale.

Nickle, Keith. Collection: A Study in Paul's Strategy. LC 66-72379. (Studies in Biblical Theology: No. 48). 1966. pap. 10.00x (ISBN 0-8401-3048-1). A R Allenson.

Nielson, Bill. Beacon Small-Group Bible Studies, I & II Thessalonians: The Distinguishing Marks of a Christian. 56p. 1982. pap. 2.50 (ISBN 0-8341-0738-4). Beacon Hill.

Nielson, John M. Beacon Small-Group Bible Studies, Romans: More than Conquerors. Wolf, Earl C., ed. 96p. (Orig.). 1984. pap. 2.50 (ISBN 0-8341-0944-1). Beacon Hill.

Norden, Rudolph F. Radiant Faith. Feucht, Oscar E., ed. 1966. pap. 1.60 study guide (ISBN 0-570-03527-9, 14-1330); pap. 1.95 leader's manual (ISBN 0-570-03528-7, 14-1331). Concordia.

Noth, Martin. The Chronicler's History. (JSOT Supplement Ser.). 120p. 1987. text ed. 22.50x (ISBN 1-85075-043-2, Pub. by JSOT Pr England); pap. text ed. 9.50x (ISBN 1-85075-044-0, Pub. by JSOT Pr England). Eisenbrauns.

Nystrom, Carolyn. A Woman's Workshop on Romans-Leader's Manual. 112p. (Orig.). 1981. pap. 3.95 (ISBN 0-310-41911-5, 11274P). Zondervan.

--A Woman's Workshop on Romans-Student's Manual. 144p. (Orig.). 1981. pap. 3.95 (ISBN 0-310-41921-2, 11275P). Zondervan.

Oberst, Bruce. Letters from Peter. LC 74-1071. (The Bible Study Textbook Ser.). (Illus.). 1962. 10.60 (ISBN 0-89900-046-0). College Pr Pub.

Ogilvie, Lloyd John. You Are Loved & Forgiven. rev. ed. LC 86-10186. 192p. 1986. text ed. 12.95 (ISBN 0-8307-1168-6, 5111616); pap. text ed. 4.95 (ISBN 0-8307-1110-4, S412117). Regal.

Olbricht, Thomas H. Message of the New Testament-Ephesians & Colossians. LC 82-74323. (Way of Life Ser.: No. 170). 91p. 1983. pap. 3.95 (ISBN 0-89112-170-6, Biblo Res Pr). Abilene Christ U.

Orr, Anna M. Proving Yourself: A Study of James. (Basic Bible Study Ser.). 64p. pap. 2.95 (ISBN 0-930756-75-4, 521015). Aglow Pubns.

Osiek, Carolyn A. First Corinthians. (Read & Pray Ser.). 1980. 1.75 (ISBN 0-8199-0634-4). Franciscan Herald.

Palau, Luis. Time to Stop Pretending. 156p. 1985. pap. 5.95 (ISBN 0-89693-332-6). Victor Bks.

Park, James. An Existential Interpretation of Paul's Letters to the Romans. LC 83-8852. 1983. pap. 4.00x (ISBN 0-89231-200-9). Existential Bks.

Pauck, Wilhelm, ed. Luther: Lectures on Romans. LC 61-13626. (Library of Christian Classics). 502p. 1977. pap. 11.95 (ISBN 0-664-24151-4). Westminster.

Paul's Letters to Timothy & Titus. LC 78-1143. (The Bible Study Textbook Ser.). (Illus.). 1962. 12.20 (ISBN 0-89900-043-6). College Pr Pub.

Pearson, Birger A. The Pneumatikos-Psychikos Terminology in First Corinthians. LC 73-92202. (Society of Biblical Literature. Dissertation Ser.). 1975. pap. 8.95 (ISBN 0-88414-034-2, 060112). Scholars Pr GA.

Petersen, William J. O Discipulado de Timoteo. Orig. Title: The Discipling of Timothy. (Port.). 1986. write for info. (ISBN 0-8297-0685-2). Life Pubs Intl.

Pfeiffer, Charles R. La Epistola a los Hebreos (Comentario Biblico Portavoz) Orig. Title: Epistle to the Hebrews (Everyman's Bible Commentary) (Span.). 128p. 1981. pap. 3.50 (ISBN 0-8254-1564-0). Kregel.

Phillips, John. Exploring Romans. rev. ed. (Exploring Ser.). 1987. pap. 11.95 (ISBN 0-8024-2429-5). Moody.

Phipps, William E. Encounter Through Questioning Paul: A Fresh Approach to the Apostle's Life & Letters. LC 82-17580. (Illus.). 114p. (Orig.). 1983. lib. bdg. 24.25 (ISBN 0-8191-2785-X); pap. text ed. 9.50 (ISBN 0-8191-2786-8). U Pr of Amer.

Picirilli, Robert. The Book of Galatians. 1973. pap. 3.95 (ISBN 0-89265-012-5). Randall Hse.

--The Book of Romans, 3 vols. 1974. Set. pap. 3.50 ea.; Vol. 1. pap. (ISBN 0-89265-015-X); Vol. 2. pap. (ISBN 0-89265-016-8); Vol. 3. pap. (ISBN 0-89265-017-6). Randall Hse.

Piper, John. The Justification of God: An Exegetical & Theological Study of Romans 9: 1-23. 312p. (Orig.). 1983. pap. 8.95 (ISBN 0-8010-7079-1). Baker Bk.

Plummer, Alfred. The Gospel According to St. Mark. (Thornapple Commentaries Ser.). 448p. 1982. pap. 12.95 (ISBN 0-8010-7072-4). Baker Bk.

Powell, Margaret J., ed. Bible, N. T. Epistles of Paul: The Pauline Epistles Contained in Ms. (EETS, ES Ser.: No. 116). Repr. of 1916 ed. 35.00 (ISBN 0-527-00320-4). Kraus Repr.

Reapsome, James. Romans: A Daily Dialogue With God. (Personal Bible Studyguide Ser.). 120p. pap. 4.95 (ISBN 0-87788-731-4). Shaw Pubs.

Reese, James M. First & Second Thessalonians. (New Testament Message Ser.: Vol. 16). 130p. 1980. 10.95 (ISBN 0-89453-204-9); pap. 5.95 (ISBN 0-89453-139-5). M Glazier.

Reicke, Bo I. The Disobedient Spirits & Christian Baptism: Study of First Peter, III-19 & Its Context. LC 79-8117. 288p. 1984. Repr. of 1946 ed. 41.50 (ISBN 0-404-18430-8). AMS Pr.

Reid, John C. The Grumpy Prophet & 22 other Bible Stories to Read & Tell. 80p. 1986. casebound 7.95 (ISBN 0-87239-917-6, 3370). Standard Pub.

Reuss, Josef. The First Epistle to Timothy & the Second Epistle to Timothy. McKenzie, John L., ed. LC 81-605. (New Testament for Spiritual Reading Ser.). 171p. 1981. pap. 4.95 (ISBN 0-8245-0128-4). Crossroad NY.

Rhyne, C. Thomas. Faith Establishes the Law. Kee, Howard, ed. LC 81-1794. (Society of Biblical Literature Dissertation Ser.). 1981. pap. 13.50 (ISBN 0-89130-483-5, 06-01-55). Scholars Pr GA.

Richards, William L. The Classification of the Greek Manuscripts of the Johannine Epistles. LC 77-23469. (Society of Biblical Literature. Dissertation Ser.). 1977. pap. 9.95 (ISBN 0-89130-140-2, 060135). Scholars Pr GA.

Roberts, Roy R. Life in the Pressure Cooker: Studies in James. pap. 4.95 (ISBN 0-88469-033-4). BMH Bks.

Robinson, John A. Wrestling with Romans. LC 79-11645. 160p. 1979. pap. 5.95 (ISBN 0-664-24275-8). Westminster.

Roetzel, Calvin J. The Letters of Paul: Conversations in Context. 2nd ed. LC 81-85334. (Biblical Foundations Ser.). 144p. 1982. pap. 9.95 (ISBN 0-8042-0209-5). John Knox.

Ropes, James H. Singular Problem of the Epistle to the Galatians. (Harvard Theological Studies). 1929. pap. 15.00 (ISBN 0-527-01014-6). Kraus Repr.

Rust, Henry R. James: The Most American Book in the Bible. 70p. (Orig.). 1985. pap. 6.95 (ISBN 0-940754-31-2). Ed Ministries.

St. Paul. The Epistles of Paul in Modern English: A Paraphrase. Stevens, George B., tr. from Gr. 1980. Repr. of 1898 ed. 10.95 (ISBN 0-939464-03-9). Labyrinth Pr.

Sampley, J. Paul, et al. Ephesians, II Colossians, Thessalonians: Pastoral Epistles. LC 77-78652. (Proclamation Commentaries: the New Testament Witness for Preaching). 128p. 1978. pap. 4.95 (ISBN 0-8006-0589-6, 1-589). Fortress.

Sanders, E. P. Paul, the Law & the Jewish People. LC 82-17487. 240p. 1983. pap. 9.95 (ISBN 0-8006-1878-5, 1-1878). Fortress.

Saunders, Ernest W. Thessalonians, Philippians, & Philemon One & Two. Hayes, John, ed. (Knox Preaching Guides Ser.). 1983. pap. 4.95. John Knox.

Schierse, F. J. The Epistle to the Hebrews & the Epistle of St. James. McKenzie, John L., ed. LC 81-605. (New Testament for Spiritual Reading Ser.). 246p. 1981. pap. 4.95 (ISBN 0-8245-0130-6). Crossroad NY.

Schiffman, Harvey R. Sensation & Perception: An Integrated Approach. 2nd ed. LC 81-19770. 540p. 1982. write for info. (ISBN 0-471-08208-2). Wiley.

Schneider, Gerhard. The Epistle to the Galatians. McKenzie, John L., ed. LC 81-605. (New Testament for Spiritual Reading Ser.). 142p. 1981. pap. 4.95 (ISBN 0-8245-0124-1). Crossroad NY.

Schuller, Robert H. Be Happy - You Are Loved! 224p. 1986. 15.95 (ISBN 0-8407-5517-1). Nelson.

Schurmann, Heinz, et al. The First & Second Epistle to the Thessalonians. McKenzie, John L., ed. LC 81-605. (New Testament for Spiritual Reading Ser.). 168p. 1981. pap. 4.95 (ISBN 0-8245-0127-6). Crossroad NY.

Schwank, Bernedikt. First & Second Epistles of St. Peter. McKenzie, John T., ed. LC 81-605. (New Testament for Spiritual Reading Ser.). 192p. 1981. pap. 4.95 (ISBN 0-8245-0131-4). Crossroad NY.

Scott, Ernest F. Paul's Epistle to the Romans. LC 79-4204. 1979. Repr. of 1947 ed. lib. bdg. 22.50x (ISBN 0-313-20800-X, SCPE). Greenwood.

Scroggs, Robin. Paul for a New Day. LC 76-9719. 96p. 1977. pap. 3.95 (ISBN 0-8006-1242-6, 1-1242). Fortress.

Set Free to Serve (Galatians-I, II Thessalonians) Leader's Guide. (New Horizons Bible Study). 47p. (Orig.). 1985. pap. 1.95 (ISBN 0-317-37972-0). Light & Life.

Set Free to Serve (Galatians-I, II Thessalonians) Student Guide. (New Horizons Bible Study). 64p. (Orig.). 1985. pap. 2.50 (ISBN 0-89367-106-1). Light & Life.

Shaw, Graham. The Cost of Authority: Manipulation & Freedom in the New Testament. LC 82-48545. 320p. 1983. pap. 16.95 (ISBN 0-8006-1707-X). Fortress.

Shaw, Luci. Colossians: Focus on Christ. (Fisherman Bible Studyguide). 56p. 1982. saddle-stitched 2.95 (ISBN 0-87788-132-4). Shaw Pubs.

Shelly, Rubel. In Step with the Spirit: A Study of the Fruit of the Spirit, Galatians 5: 22-23. 1987. pap. price not set (ISBN 0-8010-8276-5). Baker Bk.

Sherer, Michael L. Good News for Children: Object Lessons on Epistle Texts. LC 82-70957. (Series C). 128p. (Orig.). 1982. pap. 6.95 (ISBN 0-8066-1932-5, 10-2810). Augsburg.

Simmons, Billy E. Galatians. 128p. 1983. pap. 3.00 (ISBN 0-914520-20-2). Insight Pr.

Spradley, Ruth. Women's Bible Studies--Colossians. (Women's Bible Studies Ser.). (Illus.). 144p. 1987. pap. 4.95 (ISBN 0-87403-232-6, 39932). Standard Pub.

--Women's Bible Studies--Philippians. (Women's Bible Studies Ser.). (Illus.). 144p. 1987. pap. 4.95 (ISBN 0-87403-231-8, 39931). Standard Pub.

Staton, Knofel. First Corinthians. (Standard Bible Studies). (Illus.). 272p. 1987. pap. price not set (ISBN 0-87403-167-2, 40107). Standard Pub.

Stedman, Ray C. What More Can God Say? 2nd ed. LC 74-176002. 256p. 1977. pap. 3.95 (ISBN 0-8307-0457-4, S283123). Regal.

Steele, David N. & Thomas, Curtis C. Romans. pap. 5.95 (ISBN 0-8010-8018-5). Baker Bk.

Stevens, George B. The Epistles of Paul in Modern English: A Paraphrase. viii, 331p. 1980. Repr. of 1898 ed. 10.95 (ISBN 0-940033-26-7). R O Roberts.

Stier, Rudolf E. Commentary on the Epistle of James. 278p. 1982. lib. bdg. 10.25 Smythe Sewn (ISBN 0-86524-157-0, 5903). Klock & Klock.

Stott, John R. Men Made New: An Exposition of Romans 5-8. 108p. 1984. pap. 4.95 (ISBN 0-8010-8244-7). Baker Bk.

--The Message of Galatians. pap. 6.95 (ISBN 0-87784-288-4). Inter-Varsity.

--The Message of Second Timothy. LC 73-75890. (Bible Speaks Today Ser.). 144p. 1973. text ed. 5.95 (ISBN 0-87784-295-7). Inter-Varsity.

Sullender, R. Scott. Peter: A Journey in Faith. 47p. (Orig.). 1986. pap. 6.95 (ISBN 0-940754-37-1). Ed Ministries.

Summers, Ray. Ephesians: Pattern for Christian Living. LC 73-87069. pap. 4.25 (ISBN 0-8054-1345-6). Broadman.

Swank, J. Grant, Jr. Beacon Small-Group Bible Studies, I & II Peter: A Faith for Testing Times. (Beacon Small-Group Bible Studies). 80p. 1982. pap. 2.50 (ISBN 0-8341-0790-2). Beacon Hill.

Sweeting, George. Faith that Works: Study of the Book of James. 1983. pap. 3.95 (ISBN 0-8024-0276-3). Moody.

Swindoll, Charles. Living above the Level of Mediocrity: A Commitment to Excellence. 256p. 1987. 14.95 (ISBN 0-8499-0564-8). Word Bks.

Talbert, Charles H., ed. Perspectives on First Peter. LC 86-8772. (NABPR (National Association of Baptist Professors of Religion0 Special Studies: No. 9). 151p. (Orig.). 1986. pap. 15.95 (ISBN 0-86554-198-1, MUP-M11). Mercer Univ Pr.

Taylor, Robert, Jr. Studies in First & Second Timothy. 2.50 (ISBN 0-89315-286-2). Lambert Bk.

--Studies in Titus & Philemon. 2.50 (ISBN 0-89315-287-0). Lambert Bk.

Taylor, Robert R., Jr. Studies in First & Second Thessalonians. 1977. pap. 2.50 (ISBN 0-89315-285-4). Lambert Bk.

Tenney, Merrill C. Galatians: The Charter of Christian Liberty. rev. ed. 1960. 10.95 (ISBN 0-8028-3253-9). Eerdmans.

Theissen, Gerd. The Social Setting of Pauline Christianity: Essays on Corinth. Schutz, John H., tr. LC 81-43087. 1982. 19.95 (ISBN 0-8006-0669-8). Fortress.

Thomas, J. D. Message of the New Testament-First Corinthians. (Way of Life Ser.: No. 167). 1984. pap. 3.95 (ISBN 0-89112-167-6, Bibl Res Pr). Abilene Christ U.

Thomas, Roger. The Perfect Church. LC 81-14544. 96p. (Orig.). 1982. pap. 2.25 (ISBN 0-87239-479-4, 41012). Standard Pub.

Thomas, W. H. Studies in Colossians to Philemon. LC 86-7178. 192p. 1986. pap. 6.95 (ISBN 0-8254-3834-9). Kregel.

Thrall, Margaret E., ed. First & Second Letters of Paul to the Corinthians. (Cambridge Bible Commentary on the New English Bible, New Testament Ser.). (Orig.). 1965. pap. 10.95x (ISBN 0-521-09251-5). Cambridge U Pr.

Thusing, Wilhelm, et al. The Epistle of St. Jude & the Three Epistles of St. John. McKenzie, John L., ed. LC 81-605. (New Testament for Spiritual Reading Ser.). 148p. 1981. pap. 4.95 (ISBN 0-8245-0132-2). Crossroad NY.

Timmons, Tim. Radical Christianity. 144p. 1986. pap. 4.95 (ISBN 0-89693-531-0). Victor Bks.

Townsend, Jim. Colossians & Philemon: A Runaway Church & a Runaway Slave. (Bible Mastery Ser.). 144p. 1987. pap. 5.95 (ISBN 1-55513-849-7). Cook.

--Hebrews: Pilgrim's Progress or Regress? (Bible Mastery Ser.). 144p. 1987. pap. 5.95 (ISBN 1-55513-846-2). Cook.

--Old Testament Highlights: Survey of the Hebrew Scriptures. (Bible Mastery Ser.). 144p. 1987. pap. 5.95 (ISBN 1-55513-847-0). Cook.

Trenchard, Ernesto. Epistola a los Galatas. (Span.). 224p. 1964. 6.75 (ISBN 0-8254-1732-5); pap. 5.50 (ISBN 0-8254-1731-7). Kregel.

--Epistola a los Hebreos. (Span.). 290p. 1974. 6.95 (ISBN 0-8254-1734-1); pap. 5.75 (ISBN 0-8254-1733-3). Kregel.

--Epistola a los Romanos. (Span.). 1969. 7.95 (ISBN 0-8254-1736-8); pap. 6.95 (ISBN 0-8254-1735-X). Kregel.

Trenchard, Ernesto & Wickham, Pablo. Epistola a los Efesios. (Span.). 220p. 1980. 6.75 (ISBN 0-8254-1730-9). Kregel.

Tullis, Edward L. Shaping the Church from the Mind of Christ: A Study of Paul's Letter to the Philippians. LC 84-50837. 80p. (Orig.). 1984. pap. 3.95 (ISBN 0-8358-0494-1). Upper Room.

Turner, Elizabeth S. Be Ye Transformed. 1969. 5.95 (ISBN 0-87159-008-5). Unity School.

Underwood, Jonathan. First Corinthians. (Standard Bible Study Workbooks Ser.). 80p. 1987. wkbk. 1.95 (ISBN 0-87403-187-7, 40207). Standard Pub.

Van Horn, Roger. Philippians: A Study Guide. (Revelation Series for Adults). 1983. pap. text ed. 2.50 (ISBN 0-933140-84-3). CRC Pubns.

Van Note, Gene. Beacon Small-Group Bible Studies, Hebrews: He is Here at Last. 64p. (Orig.). 1980. pap. 2.50 (ISBN 0-8341-0623-X). Beacon Hill.

Vaughan, Curtis. Galatians Bible Study Commentary. 128p. 1972. pap. 4.95 (ISBN 0-310-33543-4, 10856P). Zondervan.

Vaughan, Curtis & Lea, Thomas D. Corinthians 1: Bible Study Commentary. (Bible Study Commentary Ser.). 160p. 1983. pap. 4.95 (ISBN 0-310-44021-1, 12484P). Zondervan.

Verner, David C. The Household of God & the Social World of the Pastoral Epistles. LC 82-25015. (Society of Biblical Literature Dissertation Ser.). 218p. 1983. pap. 13.50 (ISBN 0-89130-611-0, 06 01 71). Scholars Pr GA.

Vos, Geerhardus. The Teaching of the Epistle to the Hebrews. pap. 4.95 (ISBN 0-87552-503-2). Presby & Reformed.

Waggoner, E. J. The Glad Tidings: Studies in Galatians. rev. ed. LC 72-81729. 144p. pap. 5.95 (ISBN 0-912145-06-4). MMI Pr.

Wallenkampf, Arnold V. Salvation Comes from the Lord. Wheeler, Gerald, ed. LC 83-3297. 128p. (Orig.). 1983. pap. 5.95 (ISBN 0-8280-0210-X). Review & Herald.

Walter, Eugen. The First Epistle to the Corinthians. McKenzie, John L., ed. LC 81-605. (New Testament for Spiritual Reading Ser.). 200p. 1981. pap. 4.95 (ISBN 0-8245-0122-5). Crossroad NY.

Wartick, Wallace. Studies in Second Corinthians. (Bible Student Study Guides Ser.). 1977. pap. 2.95 (ISBN 0-89900-155-6). College Pr Pub.

--Twenty-Six Lessons on First Corinthians. (Bible Study Guide Ser.). 176p. (Orig.). 1980. pap. 3.95 (ISBN 0-89900-168-8). College Pr Pub.

Watson, D. J. Dedication: Nobody Said It Was Easy. 1987. pap. write for info. (ISBN 0-88469-181-0). BMH Bks.

Watson, Thomas. All Things for Good. (Puritan Paperbacks). 128p. (Orig.). 1986. pap. 3.45 (ISBN 0-85151-478-2). Banner of Truth.

Welch, Reuben R. Let's Listen to Jesus: Reflections on the Farewell Discourse. Allison, Joseph D., ed. 144p. (Orig.). 1985. pap. 5.95 (ISBN 0-310-75101-2, 17044P). Zondervan.

Westcott, Frederick B. Colossians: A Letter to Asia. 1981. lib. bdg. 7.50 (ISBN 0-86524-070-1, 5102). Klock & Klock.

White, John L. The Form & Function of the Body of the Greek Letter in the Non-Literary Papyri & in Paul the Apostle. LC 75-33088. (Society of Biblical Literature. Dissertation Ser.). (Illus.). 1975. pap. 9.95 (ISBN 0-89130-048-1, 060102). Scholars Pr GA.

Wiersbe, Warren. Be Complete. 160p. 1981. pap. 5.95 (ISBN 0-88207-257-9). Victor Bks.

Wiersbe, Warren W. Be Faithful. 1981. pap. 5.95 (ISBN 0-88207-268-4). Victor Bks.

Wilde, Gary, ed. Ephesians: Life in the Church. (Basic Bible Ser.). 112p. 1986. pap. 4.95 (ISBN 0-89191-480-3). Cook.

--One & Two Thessalonians: Hope of His Coming. (Basis Bible Ser.). 96p. 1986. pap. 4.95 (ISBN 0-89191-520-6). Cook.

--Philippians: Joy in the Lord. (Basic Bible Ser.). 96p. 1986. pap. 4.95 (ISBN 0-89191-482-X). Cook.

Wiley, H. Orton. The Epistle to the Hebrews. Weigelt, Morris, ed. 438p. 1985. text ed. 15.95 (ISBN 0-8341-0890-9). Beacon Hill.

William of St. Thierry. William of St. Thierry: Exposition on the Epistle to the Romans. Anderson, John D., ed. (Cistercian Fathers Ser.: No. 27). 1980. 17.95 (ISBN 0-87907-327-6). Cistercian Pubns.

William of St. Thierry, Golden Epistle. LC 72-152482. (Cistercian Fathers Ser.: No. 12). 1971. pap. 4.00 (ISBN 0-87907-712-3). Cistercian Pubns.

Willis, Wendell L. Idol Meat in Corinth. (Society of Biblical Literature Dissertation Ser.: No. 68). 1985. 19.50 (ISBN 0-89130-764-8, 06 01 68); pap. 12.95 (ISBN 0-89130-606-4). Scholars Pr GA.

Wimbush, Vincent L. Paul, the World Ascetic: Response to the World & Self-Understanding According to 1 Corinthians 7. 128p. 1987. 18.95 (ISBN 0-86554-263-5, H224). Mercer Univ Pr.

Wolf, Earl C. Beacon Small-Group Bible Studies, I, II & III John: Everybody Ought to Know. 80p. 1982. pap. 2.50 (ISBN 0-8341-0791-0). Beacon Hill.

Wrightman, Paul. Paul's Later Letters: From Promise to Fulfillment. LC 84-11039. 238p. (Orig.). 1984. pap. 9.95 (ISBN 0-8189-0441-0). Alba.

Yandian, Bob. Ephesians: The Maturing of the Saints. (Orig.). 1985. pap. 5.95 (ISBN 0-89274-387-5). Harrison Hse.

--Galatians: The Spirit-Controlled Life. 264p. (Orig.). 1985. pap. 6.95 (ISBN 0-89274-388-3). Harrison Hse.

Zerwick, Max. The Epistle to the Ephesians. McKenzie, John L., ed. LC 81-605. (New Testament for Spiritual Reading Ser.). 181p. 1981. pap. 4.95 (ISBN 0-8245-0125-X). Crossroad NY.

Zilonka, Paul. Romans. (Read & Pray Ser.). 1979. 1.75 (ISBN 0-8199-0633-6). Franciscan Herald.

Zuntz, G. The Text of the Epistles: A Disquisition upon the Corpus Paulinum. (Schweich Lectures on Biblical Archaeology). 306p. 1946. 8.25 (ISBN 0-85672-715-6, Pub. by British Acad). Longwood Pub Group.

BIBLE–CRITICISM, INTERPRETATION, ETC.–N. T. EPISTLES OF JOHN

see Bible–Criticism, Interpretation, Etc.–N. T. Epistles

BIBLE–CRITICISM, INTERPRETATION, ETC.–N. T. GALATIANS

see Bible–Criticism, Interpretation, Etc.–N. T. Epistles

Stronstad, Roger. The Charismatic Theology of St. Luke. 96p. 1985. pap. 4.95 (ISBN 0-913573-11-6). Hendrickson MA.

BIBLE–CRITICISM, INTERPRETATION, ETC.–N. T. GOSPELS

Here are entered works on the gospels as a whole, or on one or more of the gospels: John, Luke, Mark, Matthew.

Aland, K., ed. Synopsis of the Four Gospels (English Only) 1983. 5.95x (ISBN 0-8267-0500-6, 08564). Am Bible.

Alexander, Joseph. Commentary on the Gospel of Mark. 1980. 16.75 (ISBN 0-86524-018-3, 4101). Klock & Klock.

Anderson, H., ed. Gospel of Mark. (New Century Bible Ser.). 384p. 1976. 9.50 (ISBN 0-551-00579-3). Attic Pr.

Appold, Mark L. The Oneness Motif in the Fourth Gospel: Motif Analysis & Exegetical Probe into the Theology of John. 322p. 1976. pap. text ed. 38.50x (ISBN 0-89563-577-1, Pub. by J. C. B. Mohr BRD). Coronet Bks.

Archimandrite Simeon. Ijevangel'skije Poichjenija. Tr. of Lessons from the Gospel. 40p. 1970. pap. 2.00 (ISBN 0-317-29123-8). Holy Trinity.

Ashton, John, ed. The Interpretation of John. LC 85-45536. (Issues in Religion & Theology Ser.). 176p. 1986. pap. 7.95 (ISBN 0-8006-1774-6, 1-1774). Fortress.

Augustinus, Saint Aurelius. De Consensu Evangelistarum Librer4, Bk. 4. Weihrich, F., ed. (Corpus Scriptorum Ecclesiasticorum Latinorum Ser: Vol. 43). 40.00 (ISBN 0-384-02480-7). Johnson Repr.

Backman, Pat. Journey with Matthew. (Orig.). 1984. tchr's. ed. 4.95 (ISBN 0-931055-03-2). LuraMedia.

Bacon, Benjamin W. Is Mark a Roman Gospel? (Harvard Theological Studies: Vol. 7). 1919. 11.00 (ISBN 0-527-01007-3). Kraus Repr.

Barnes, Albert. The Gospels. 19.95 (ISBN 0-8010-0843-3). Baker Bk.

Barrett, C. K. Essays on John. LC 82-2759. 176p. 1982. 18.95 (ISBN 0-664-21389-8). Westminster.

--The Gospel According to St. John. 2nd ed. LC 78-2587. 654p. 1978. 28.95 (ISBN 0-664-21364-2). Westminster.

--The Gospel of John & Judaism. Smith, D. M., tr. LC 75-15435. 112p. 1975. 3.95 (ISBN 0-8006-0431-8, 1-431). Fortress.

Barrett, Charles K. The Gospel of John & Judaiam. Smith, D. M., tr. LC 75-15435. pap. 27.80 (2026897). Bks Demand UMI.

Barron, Bruce. The Health & Wealth Gospel: A Fresh Look at Healing, Prosperity & Positive Confession. LC 86-27503. 206p. (Orig.). 1987. pap. 6.95 (ISBN 0-87784-327-9). Inter Varsity.

Barth, Karl. Witness to the Word: A Commentary on John 1. Furst, Walther, ed. Bromiley, Geoffrey W., tr. from Ger. 160p. (Orig.). 1986. pap. 10.95 (ISBN 0-8028-0186-2). Eerdmans.

Beacon Bible Commentary Staff. John, Vol. IV. 6.95 (ISBN 0-8010-0777-1). Baker Bk.

--John: Acts, Vol. VII. 13.95 (ISBN 0-8010-0694-5). Baker Bk.

--Luke, Vol. III. 6.95 (ISBN 0-8010-0678-3). Baker Bk.

--Mark, Vol. II. 6.95 (ISBN 0-8010-0755-0). Baker Bk.

--Matthew, Vol. I. 6.95 (ISBN 0-8010-0676-7). Baker Bk.

--Matthew-Luke, Vol. VI. 13.95 (ISBN 0-8010-0693-7). Baker Bk.

Beasley-Murray, George. Matthew. (Bible Study Commentaries Ser.). 122p. 1984. pap. 4.95 (ISBN 0-317-43380-6). Chr Lit.

Beker, J. Christiaan. Paul's Apocalyptic Gospel: The Coming Triumph of God. LC 82-8670. 128p. (Orig.). 1982. pap. 7.95 (ISBN 0-8006-1649-9, 1-1649). Fortress.

Bellinzoni, Arthur J., ed. The Two-Source Hypothesis: A Critical Appraisal. x, 486p. 1985. 39.95 (ISBN 0-86554-096-9, MUP/H88). Mercer Univ Pr.

Bence, Evelyn. Following Jesus: A Woman's Workshop on Luke. (Woman's Workshop Ser.). 112p. 1986. pap. 3.95 (ISBN 0-310-44781-X, 11314P). Zondervan.

Best, Ernest. Disciples & Discipleship: Studies in the Gospel According to Mark. 272p. 1986. 19.95 (ISBN 0-567-09369-7, Pub. by T & T Clark Ltd UK). Fortress.

--Mark: The Gospel as Story. Riches, John, ed. 154p. 1983. 21.95 (ISBN 0-567-09342-5, Pub. by T&T Clark Ltd UK). Fortress.

Black, Matthew. Aramaic Approach to the Gospels & Acts. 3rd ed. 1967. 32.50x (ISBN 0-19-826157-8). Oxford U Pr.

Blackwelder, Boyce. The Four Gospels. 1980. 9.95 (ISBN 0-87162-221-1, D3768). Warner Pr.

Blackwell, John. The Passion As Story: The Plot of Mark. LC 85-16209. (Fortress Resources for Preaching Ser.). 96p. 1986. pap. 5.95 (ISBN 0-8006-1144-6, 1-1144). Fortress.

Blank, Josef. The Gospel According to St. John, Vol. II. McKenzie, John L., ed. LC 81-605. (The New Testament for Spiritual Reading Ser.). 282p. 1981. pap. 4.95. Crossroad NY.

Boer, Harry R. The Four Gospels & Acts: A Short Introduction. 112p. 1982. pap. 3.95 (ISBN 0-8028-1901-X). Eerdmans.

Boettner, Loraine. A Harmony of the Gospels. 1976. pap. 3.95 (ISBN 0-87552-132-0). Presby & Reformed.

Bogart, John L. Orthodox & Heretical Perfectionism in the Johannine Community As Evident in the First Epistle of John. LC 77-5447. (Society of Biblical Literature. Dissertation Ser.). 1977. pap. 9.95 (ISBN 0-89130-138-0, 060133). Scholars Pr GA.

Boice, James M. The Gospel of John. 1986. 34.95 (ISBN 0-310-21570-6, 10429). Zondervan.

Booth, Roger P. Jesus & the Laws of Purity: Tradition History & Legal History in Mark 7. (JSoT Supplement Ser.: No. 13). 300p. 1986. text ed. 27.50x (ISBN 1-85075-023-8, Pub. by JSOT Pr England); pap. text ed. 13.50x (ISBN 1-85075-022-X). Eisenbrauns.

Bowman, John. The Fourth Gospel & the Jews: A Study of R. Akiba, Esther, & the Gospel of John. LC 75-40461. (Pittsburgh Theological Monographs: No. 8). 1975. pap. 9.00 (ISBN 0-915138-10-7). Pickwick.

--The Samaritan Problem: Studies in the Relationship of Samaritanism, Judaism, & Early Christianity. Johnson, Alfred M., Jr., tr. from Ger. LC 75-20042. (Pittsburgh Theological Monographs: No. 4). 1975. pap. 8.75 (ISBN 0-915138-04-2). Pickwick.

Bratcher, Robert G. A Translator's Guide to the Gospel of Mark. (Helps for Translators Ser.). 236p. 1981. pap. 4.50x (ISBN 0-8267-0180-9, 08711, Pub. by United Bible). Am Bible.

--A Translator's Guide to the Gospel of Matthew. LC 82-213977. (Helps for Translators Ser.). 388p. 1981. pap. 4.50x (ISBN 0-8267-0179-5, 08710, Pub. by United Bible). Am Bible.

Brestin, Dee. How Should a Christian Live? 1, 2, & 3 John. (A Core Study in the Fisherman Bible Studyguides). 80p. 1985. pap. 2.95 (ISBN 0-87788-351-3). Shaw Pubs.

Brinton, Howard. Light & Life in the Fourth Gospel. LC 76-128679. (Orig.). 1971. pap. 2.50x (ISBN 0-87574-179-7). Pendle Hill.

Brooks, Keith. Mark: Gospel of God's Servant. rev. ed. (Teach Yourself the Bible Ser.). 1987. pap. 2.75 (ISBN 0-8024-5200-0). Moody.

Brooks, Keith L. Luke, the Gospel of God's Man. (Teach Yourself the Bible Ser.). 1964. pap. 2.75 (ISBN 0-8024-5047-4). Moody.

Buechner, Frederick. Telling the Truth: The Gospel As Tragedy, Comedy, & Fairy Tale. LC 77-7839. 1977. 12.45 (ISBN 0-06-061156-1, HarpR). Har-Row.

Bultmann, Rudolf. Gospel of John: A Commentary. LC 70-125197. 758p. 1971. 26.50 (ISBN 0-664-20893-2). Westminster.

Burnett, Fred W. The Testament of Jesus-Sophia: A Redaction-Critical Study of the Eschatological Discourse in Matthew. LC 80-67211. 491p. (Orig.). 1981. lib. bdg. 35.75 (ISBN 0-8191-1743-9); pap. text ed. 19.75 (ISBN 0-8191-1744-7). U Pr of Amer.

Butler, Paul. The Gospel of John. 3rd ed. LC 78-1789. (The Bible Study Textbook Ser.). (Illus.). 1965. 15.90 (ISBN 0-89900-035-5). College Pr Pub.

--Luke. LC 81-68817. (Bible Study Textbook Ser.). 627p. 1981. 17.50 (ISBN 0-89900-062-2). College Pr Pub.

Cadbury, H. J. Style & Literary Method of Luke, 2 Vols. in 1. (Harvard Theo. Studies: No. 6). 1919-1920. 22.00 (ISBN 0-527-01006-5). Kraus Repr.

Candlish, Robert S. First Epistle of John. LC 79-14801. (Kregel Bible Study Classics Ser.). 602p. 1979. 22.95 (ISBN 0-8254-2320-1). Kregel.

Cannon, George Q. Gospel Truth: Classics Edition. 2nd ed. 1987. 14.95 (ISBN 0-87579-094-1). Deseret Bk.

Cannon, William R. The Gospel of John. 128p. (Orig.). 1985. pap. 4.95 (ISBN 0-8358-0511-5). Upper Room.

--The Gospel of Matthew. LC 82-50948. 128p. (Orig.). 1983. pap. 4.95 (ISBN 0-8358-0450-X). Upper Room.

--Jesus the Servant: From the Gospel of Mark. LC 78-62578. 1978. pap. text ed. 2.95x (ISBN 0-8358-0376-7). Upper Room.

Carmignac, Jean. The Birth of the Synoptic Gospels. Wrenn, Michael J., tr. 1986. 9.50 (ISBN 0-8199-0887-8). Franciscan Herald.

Carson, D. A. When Jesus Confronts the World: An Exposition of Matthew 8-10. 240p. 1987. pap. price not set (ISBN 0-8010-2522-2). Baker Bk.

Carver, Frank. Beacon Small-Group Bible Studies, Matthew, Vol. I: To Be a Disciple. Wolf, Earl C., ed. (Beacon Small-Group Bible Study). 80p. (Orig.). 1984. pap. 2.50 (ISBN 0-8341-0870-4). Beacon Hill.

--Matthew, Part 2: Come & Learn from Me. Wolf, Earl, ed. (Small-Group Bible Studies). 84p. 1986. pap. 2.50 (ISBN 0-8341-1076-8). Beacon Hill.

Cassidy, Richard J. Jesus, Politics, & Society: A Study of Luke's Gospel. LC 78-735. 238p. (Orig.). 1978. 15.95 (ISBN 0-88344-238-8); pap. 7.95 (ISBN 0-88344-237-X). Orbis Bks.

Cassidy, Richard J. & Scharper, Philip J., eds. Political Issues in Luke-Acts. LC 82-19060. 192p. (Orig.). 1983. 16.95 (ISBN 0-88344-390-2); pap. 9.95 (ISBN 0-88344-385-6). Orbis Bks.

Chapman, Geoffrey. Book of Gospels. (Illus.). 672p. 1985. 95.00 (ISBN 0-225-66351-1, HarpR). Har-Row.

Chilton, Bruce. Targumic Approaches to the Gospels: Essays in the Mutual Definition of Judaism & Christianity. 200p. (Orig.). 1987. lib. bdg. 24.75 (ISBN 0-8191-5731-7, Pub. by Studies in Judaism); pap. text ed. 12.25 (ISBN 0-8191-5732-5). U Pr of Amer.

Ciuba, Edward J. Who Do You Say That I Am? An Adult Inquiry into the First Three Gospels. LC 74-10808. 155p. 1974. pap. 5.95 (ISBN 0-8189-0295-7). Alba.

Clarke, Samuel. The Works, 4 vols. LC 75-11207. (British Philosophers & Theologians of the 17th & 18th Century Ser.: Vol. 12). 3274p. 1976. Repr. of 1742 ed. Set. lib. bdg. 204.00 (ISBN 0-8240-1762-5). Garland Pub.

Coniaris, A. M. The Message of the Sunday Gospels, Vol. 2. 1983. pap. 7.95 (ISBN 0-937032-29-8). Light&Life Pub Co MN.

Conzelmann, Hans. The Theology of St. Luke. LC 82-2372. 256p. 1982. pap. 9.95 (ISBN 0-8006-1650-2, 1-1650). Fortress.

Corbin, Linda. Following Jesus. Dys, Pat, ed. (Studies for Kids Ser.: Pt. 1). (Illus.). 48p. 1985. 2.95 (ISBN 0-87239-903-6, 3303). Standard Pub.

Corbin, Linda & Dys, Pat. Following Jesus. (Studies for Kids Ser.: Pt. 2). (Illus.). 48p. 1985. 2.95 (ISBN 0-87239-904-4, 3304). Standard Pub.

Cottrell, Jack. The Gospel of Matthew, Vol. IV. LC 85-72877. (Bible Study Textbook Ser.). 996p. text ed. 18.95 (ISBN 0-89900-032-0). College Pr Pub.

Countryman, L. William. The Mystical Way in the Fourth Gospel: Crossing over into God. LC 86-45913. 160p. 1987. pap. text ed. 9.95 (ISBN 0-8006-1949-8, 1-1949). Fortress.

Cowley, Roger W. The Traditional Interpretation of the Apocalypse of St. John in the Ethiopian Orthodox Church. LC 82-19834. (University of Cambridge Oriental Publications Ser.: No. 33). 480p. 1983. 77.50 (ISBN 0-521-24561-3). Cambridge U Pr.

Craddock, Fred B. The Gospels. LC 80-26270. 160p. (Orig.). 1981. pap. 8.95 (ISBN 0-687-15655-6). Abingdon.

Crossan, John D. Four Other Gospels: Shadows on the Contour of the Canon. 208p. (Orig.). 1985. 15.95 (ISBN 0-86683-959-3, HarpR). Har-Row.

Dahmus, Joseph. The Puzzling Gospels. (Basics of Christian Thought Ser.). 1985. 10.95 (ISBN 0-88347-182-5). Thomas More.

Dale & Larsen, Sandy. Mark: Good News for Today. (Carpenter Studyguide). 80p. 1984. member's handbook 1.95 (ISBN 0-87788-540-0); saddle-stitched leader's handbook 2.95 (ISBN 0-87788-541-9). Shaw Pubs.

Daniel, Orville E. Harmony of the Four Gospels: The New International Version. 1987. pap. price not set (ISBN 0-8010-2974-0). Baker Bk.

Davies, Stevan L. The Gospel of Thomas & Christian Wisdom. 160p. 1983. pap. 9.95 (ISBN 0-8164-2456-X, HarpR). Har-Row.
Dawsey, James M. The Lukan Voice: Confusion & Irony in the Gospel of Luke. 208p. 1986. 19.50 (ISBN 0-86554-193-0, MUP-H178). Mercer Univ Pr.
De Jonge, Marinus. Jesus: Stranger from Heaven & Son of God. Steely, John E., ed. LC 77-9984. (Soceity of Biblical Literature. Sources for Biblical Studies: No. 11). Repr. of 1977 ed. 61.50 (ISBN 0-8357-9575-6, 2017532). Bks Demand UMI.
Dewey, Joanna. Markan Public Debate: Literary Technique, Concentric Structure & Theology in Mark 2: 1-3: 6. LC 79-17443. (Society of Biblical Literature Ser.: No. 48). 14.95 (ISBN 0-89130-337-5, 06-01-48); pap. 9.95 (ISBN 0-89130-338-3). Scholars Pr GA.
Dodd, Charles H. Historical Tradition in the Fourth Gospel. 1975. pap. 17.95x (ISBN 0-521-29123-2). Cambridge U Pr.
--Interpretation of the Fourth Gospel. 67.50 (ISBN 0-521-04848-6); pap. text ed. 18.95 (ISBN 0-521-09517-4). Cambridge U Pr.
Doddridge, Philip. Exposition of the Gospels, 2 vol. 1986. Set. 37.50 (ISBN 0-8254-2456-9). Vol. I, 472pgs. Vol. II, 492pgs. Kregel.
Donahue, John R. The Theology & Setting of Discipleship in the Gospel of Mark. LC 83-60749. (Pere Marquette Lecture Ser.). 1983. 7.95 (ISBN 0-87462-538-6). Marquette.
Donders, Joseph G. Beyond Jesus: Reflections on the Gospel for the B-Cycle. LC 84-5088. 320p. (Orig.). 1984. 10.95 (ISBN 0-88344-049-0). Orbis Bks.
--Christ, the Divine Network: Reflections on the Gospel for the A-Cycle. LC 86-718. 256p. (Orig.). 1986. pap. 10.95 (ISBN 0-88344-254-X). Orbis Bks.
--Jesus, Hope Drawing Near: Reflections on the Gospels for the C-Cycle. LC 85-5125. 272p. (Orig.). 1985. pap. 10.95 (ISBN 0-88344-244-2). Orbis Bks.
Doohan, Leonard. Luke: The Perennial Spirituality. LC 85-71858. 214p. (Orig.). 1985. pap. 9.95 (ISBN 0-939680-24-6). Bear & Co.
Doswald, Beverly J. Learning about God & Jesus: An Overview of the Gospel in Simple English. LC 86-81297. 50p. (Orig.). 1986. pap. 3.25 (ISBN 0-938783-00-9). Helpful Beginnings.
Drane, John. Jesus & the Gospels. LC 77-20448. 1979. pap. 9.95 (ISBN 0-06-062066-8, RD264, HarpR). Har-Row.
Draper, James T., Jr. Faith that Works: Studies in James. 1983. pap. 5.95 (ISBN 0-8423-0872-5); Leader's Guide 2.95 (ISBN 0-8423-0873-3). Tyndale.
Drury, John. Parables in Gospels. LC 84-27652. 192p. 1985. 14.95 (ISBN 0-8245-0655-3). Crossroad NY.
Dunnam, Maxie. Jesus' Claims-Our Promise: A Study of the "I Am" Sayings of Jesus. LC 84-51831. 128p. (Orig.). 1984. pap. 5.95 (ISBN 0-8358-0502-6). Upper Room.
Earle, Ralph. Mark: Gospel of Action. LC 73-15084. (Everyman's Bible Commentary Ser.). 1970. pap. 5.95 (ISBN 0-8024-2041-9). Moody.
Easter, Frances. Bible Studies Series. (Studies in Luke Ser.: Vol. II). 1985. pap. 3.50 (ISBN 0-8309-0430-1). Herald Hse.
Edwards, Richard A. Sign of Jonah in the Theology of the Evangelists & Q. LC 74-153931. (Studies in Biblical Theology, 2nd Ser.: No. 18). 1971. pap. text ed. 10.00x (ISBN 0-8401-3068-6). A R Allenson.
Ellis, Peter F. The Genius of John: A Composition-Critical Commentary on the Fourth Gospel. (Orig.). 1984. pap. 10.95 (ISBN 0-8146-1328-4). Liturgical Pr.
Enriquez, Edmund C. The Golden Gospel: A Pictorial History of the Restoration. (Illus.). 96p. 1981. pap. 5.95 (ISBN 0-88290-198-2). Horizon Utah.
Esler, Philip S. Community & Gospel in Luke-Acts: The Social & Political Motivations of Lucan Theory. (Society for New Testament Studies Monographs: No. 57). 224p. Date not set. price not set (ISBN 0-521-32965-5). Cambridge U Pr.
Eyre, Stephen & Eyre, Jackie. Matthew: Being Discipled by Jesus. (LifeBuilder Bible Studies). 64p. (Orig.). 1987. pap. 2.95 (ISBN 0-8308-1003-X). Inter-Varsity.
Fakhry, Tamer. The Gospel Unified. 1984. 15.00 (ISBN 0-533-05126-6). Vantage.
Farmer, William R. The Synoptic Problem: A Critical Analysis. LC 76-13764. xi, 308p. 1981. 18.95 (ISBN 0-915948-02-8, MUP-H005). Mercer Univ Pr.
Farris, Stephen. The Hymns of Luke's Infancy Narratives: Their Origin, Meaning & Significance. (JSoT Supplement Ser.: No. 44). 225p. 1985. text ed. 32.50x (ISBN 0-905774-91-4, Pub. by JSOT Pr England); pap. text ed. 13.95x (ISBN 0-905774-92-2). Eisenbrauns.
Ferguson, Everett. Message of the New Testament: The Letters of John. (Way of Life Ser.: No. 175). 1984. pap. 3.95 (ISBN 0-89112-175-7, Bibl Res Pr). Abilene Christ U.
Ford, W. Herschel. Sermons You Can Preach on Matthew. 240p. (Orig.). 1985. pap. 8.95 (ISBN 0-310-45521-9, 9834P). Zondervan.
Foster, Lewis. John. (Standard Bible Studies). (Illus.). 272p. 1987. pap. price not set (ISBN 0-87403-164-8, 40104). Standard Pub.
Foster, Lewis A. Luke. (Standard Bible Studies). 336p. 1986. pap. text ed. 9.95 (ISBN 0-87403-163-X, 40103). Standard Pub.
The Four Gospels. 5.00 (ISBN 0-317-46838-3); 3.50 (ISBN 0-317-46839-1). Dghtrs St Paul.
Fowler, Harold. The Gospel of Matthew, Vol. I. LC 78-1064. (The Bible Study Textbook Ser.). (Illus.). 1975. 14.30 (ISBN 0-89900-029-0). College Pr Pub.
--The Gospel of Matthew, Vol. II. (The Bible Study Textbook Ser.). (Illus.). 1972. 17.50 (ISBN 0-89900-030-4). College Pr Pub.
--The Gospel of Matthew, Vol. III. (The Bible Study Textbook Ser.). (Illus.). 1978. 18.95 (ISBN 0-89900-031-2). College Pr Pub.
Fowler, Robert M. Loaves & Fishes: The Function of the Feeding Stories in the Gospel of Mark. Baird, William, ed. LC 81-2749. (Society of Biblical Literature Dissertation Ser.). 1981. pap. 15.00 (ISBN 0-89130-486-X, 06-01-54). Scholars Pr GA.
Fox, Emmet. Sermon on the Mount. 1934. 12.45 (ISBN 0-06-062950-9, HarpR). Har-Row.
France, R. T. & Wenham, David, eds. Gospel Perspectives: Studies of History & Tradition in the Four Gospels, Vol. 1. 263p. 1980. text ed. 14.75x (ISBN 0-905774-21-3, Pub. by JSOT Pr England). Eisenbrauns.
--Gospel Perspectives, Vol. III: Studies of History & Tradition in the Four Gospels. 299p. 1983. text ed. 14.75x (ISBN 0-905774-56-6, Pub. by JSOT Press England). Eisenbrauns.
Franck, Eskil. Revelation Taught: The Paraclete in the Gospel of John. (New Testament Ser.: No. 14). 168p. (Orig.). 1985. pap. text ed. 27.50x (ISBN 91-40-05114-5, Pub. by Liber Utbildning (Stockholm Sweden)). Coronet Bks.
Frey, Louis. Analyse Ordinale Es Evangiles Synoptiques. (Mathematiques et Sciences De L'homme: No. 11). 1972. 46.50 (ISBN 0-686-21228-2); pap. 27.20x (ISBN 0-686-21229-0). Mouton.
Freze, Mike. Questions & Answers: The Gospel of Matthew. 144p. 1987. pap. 4.95 (ISBN 0-8010-3534-1). Baker Bk.
Funk, Robert W. New Gospel Parallels, Vol. 2. LC 84-48727. (Foundations & Facets Ser.). 384p. 1986. 24.95 (ISBN 0-8006-2106-9, 1-2106). Fortress.
Gaebelein, Arno C. Gospel of John. rev. ed. LC 65-26586. 1965. 9.95 (ISBN 0-87213-220-X). Loizeaux.
Gerhardsson, Birger. The Origins of the Gospel Traditions. LC 78-19634. pap. 23.80 (2029615). Bks Demand UMI.
Gettys, Joseph M. How to Study Luke. rev. ed. 153p. 1975. pap. 4.50x (ISBN 0-87921-027-3). Attic Pr.
Gilchrist, John & Andrews, Judy. Matthew's Gospel. 1.77 (ISBN 0-8091-9335-3). Paulist Pr.
Gill, Clinton. Hereby We Know: I, II, III John. LC 70-1464. (The Bible Study Textbook Ser.). (Illus.). 1966. 10.60 (ISBN 0-89900-047-9). College Pr Pub.
Gill, Jean. Images of My Self: Meditation & Self-Exploration Through the Imagery of the Gospels. 128p. 1982. pap. 3.95 (ISBN 0-8091-2463-7). Paulist Pr.
Gingrich, Raymond E. Fellowship with the Word of Life: Studies in I, II, III John. pap. 4.95 (ISBN 0-88469-042-3). BMH Bks.
Godet, F. L. Commentary on the Gospel of St. Luke, 2 vols, Vol. 2. Cusin, M. D., ed. 472p. 1870. 13.95 (ISBN 0-567-27446-2, Pub. by T&T Clark Ltd UK). Fortress.
The Gospel According to Abbie Jane Wells. 143p. 1985. 9.95 (ISBN 0-88347-175-2). Thomas More.
The Gospels. (Modern Critical Interpretations--Ancient, Medieval, & Renaissance Ser.). 1987. 24.50 (ISBN 0-87754-911-7). Chelsea Hse.
Granberg-Michaelson, Wes, ed. Tending the Garden: Essays on the Gospel & the Earth. 176p. (Orig.). 1987. pap. 8.95 (ISBN 0-8028-0230-3). Eerdmans.
Grant, Frederick C. The Gospels: Their Origin & Their Growth. vii, 216p. 1983. Repr. of 1957 ed. lib. bdg. 19.00 (ISBN 0-88254-870-0, Octagon). Hippocrene Bks.
Grant, Harold, et al. From Image To Likeness: A Jungian Path in the Gospel Journey. 224p. (Orig.). 1983. pap. 8.95 (ISBN 0-8091-2552-8). Paulist Pr.
Grant, Michael. Jesus: An Historian's Review of the Gospels. LC 77-70218. 1978. text ed. 12.50 (ISBN 0-684-14889-7, ScribT); pap. text ed. 9.95 (ISBN 0-684-17439-1). Scribner.
Green, H. Benedict. The Gospel According to Matthew in the Revised Standard Version. (New Clarendon Bible Ser). 1975. pap. 9.95x (ISBN 0-19-836911-5). Oxford U Pr.
Green, Joel B. How to Read the Gospels & Acts. LC 87-5572. (The How to Read Ser.). 180p. (Orig.). 1987. pap. 6.95 (ISBN 0-87784-940-4). Inter-Varsity.
Griffith, Harry C. The Ways of God: Paths into the New Testament. 149p. 1986. pap. 7.95 (ISBN 0-8192-1377-2). Morehouse.
Gruenler, Royce G. The Trinity in the Gospel of John. 1986. pap. 9.95 (ISBN 0-8010-3806-5). Baker Bk.
Gunderson, Vivian. Bible Learn & Do: Gospel of Mark. (Illus.). 1982. pap. 1.25 (ISBN 0-8323-0412-3); pap. 2.50 tchr's manual (ISBN 0-8323-0439-5). Binford-Metropolitan.
Guthrie, Donald. Exploring God's Word: A Guide to John's Gospel. 232p. (Orig.). pap. 7.95 (ISBN 0-8028-0256-7). Eerdmans.
Guttgemans, Erhard T. Candid Questions Concerning Gospel Form Criticism: A Methodological Sketch of Fundamental Problematics of Form & Redaction Criticism. 2nd ed. Doty, William G., tr. LC 79-10167. (Pittsburgh Theological Monographs: No. 26). 1979. pap. 15.00 (ISBN 0-915138-24-7). Pickwick.
Gutzke, Manford G. Plain Talk on Luke. 1966. pap. 5.95 (ISBN 0-310-25581-3, 9097P). Zondervan.
Habermas, Gary R. Ancient Evidence for the Life of Jesus: Historical Records of His Death & Resurrection. 1985. pap. 6.95 (ISBN 0-8407-5919-3). Nelson.
Haenchen, Ernst. The Gospel of John. FUnk, Robert W., tr. from Ger. LC 82-48756. (Hermeneia). 1984. 34.95 (ISBN 0-8006-6013-7, 20-6013). Fortress.
Hailey, Homer. That You May Believe: Studies in the Gospel of John. (Illus.). 1982. 9.95 (ISBN 0-913814-51-2). Nevada Pubns.
Harrell, Irene B. & Benson, Alie H., eds. The Manufacturer's Handbook. (Orig.). 1987. pap. 7.00 (ISBN 0-915541-04-1). Star Bks Inc.
Harrington, Daniel J. The Gospel According to Matthew, No. 1. Karris, Robert J., ed. LC 82-20333. (Collegeville Bible Commentary Ser.). (Illus.). 128p. 1983. pap. 2.95 (ISBN 0-8146-1301-2). Liturgical Pr.
Harrington, Daniel J. & Gordon, Edmund F. Luke: An Access Guide for Scripture Study. (Access Guides for Scripture Study). 1983. pap. 3.20 (ISBN 0-8215-5929-X); leader's ed. 3.45 (ISBN 0-8215-5934-6). Sadlier.
--Mark: An Access for Scripture Study. (Access Guide for Scripture Study). 128p. 1983. pap. 3.45 (ISBN 0-8215-5928-1); leader's ed. 4.20 (ISBN 0-8215-5933-8). Sadlier.
Harrington, Wilfrid. Mark. (New Testament Message Ser.: Vol. 4). 270p. 1979. 14.95 (ISBN 0-89453-192-1); pap. 9.95 (ISBN 0-89453-127-1). M Glazier.
Hebart, Friedemann. One in the Gospel. 1981. pap. 4.25 (ISBN 0-570-03830-8, 12-2796). Concordia.
Hengel, Martin. The Charismatic Leader & His Followers. LC 81-9708. 124p. 1981. 10.95 (ISBN 0-8245-0137-3). Crossroad NY.
--Studies in the Gospel of Mark. Bowden, John, tr. LC 85-4508. 216p. 1985. pap. 12.95 (ISBN 0-8006-1881-5). Fortress.
Higgins, A. J. The Son of Man in the Teaching of Jesus. LC 79-42824. (Society for New Testament Studies Monographs: No. 39). 186p. 1981. 32.50 (ISBN 0-521-22363-6). Cambridge U Pr.
Hillis, Don W. John: Gospel of Light & Life. rev. & expanded ed. (Teach Yourself the Bible Ser.). Date not set. pap. 2.75 (ISBN 0-8024-4375-3). Moody.
Hobbs, Herschel H. John: A Study Guide Commentary. 96p. 1973. pap. 4.95 (ISBN 0-310-26113-9). Zondervan.
Holwerda, David E. John: A Study Guide. (Revelation Series for Adults). 1977. pap. text ed. 2.50 (ISBN 0-933140-06-1). CRC Pubns.
Holy Gospel. 1963. 6.00 (ISBN 0-8198-0503-3); pap. 5.00 (ISBN 0-8198-0504-1). Dghtrs St Paul.
Hooker, Morna. The Son of Man in Mark: A Study of the Background of the Term "Son of Man" & Its Use in St. Mark's Gospel. LC 67-4912. pap. 60.00 (ISBN 0-317-26028-6, 2023832). Bks Demand UMI.
Huckle, John & Visokay, Paul. The Gospel According to St. John, Vol. I. McKenzie, John L., ed. LC 81-605. (The New Testament for Spiritual Reading Ser.). 282p. 1981. 10.00; pap. 4.95. Crossroad NY.
Hull, Jerry. Beacon Small-Group Bible Studies, Luke: Good News for All of Us, Vol. 1. 72p. (Orig.). 1980. pap. 2.50 (ISBN 0-8341-0657-4). Beacon Hill.
Hull, John. Hellenistic Magic & the Synoptic Tradition. LC 73-77369. (Studies in Biblical Theology, 2nd Ser.: No. 28). 1974. pap. text ed. 12.00x (ISBN 0-8401-3078-3). A R Allenson.
Hurtado, Larry. Mark: A Good News Commentary. LC 82-48930. 288p. (Orig.). 1983. pap. 9.95 (ISBN 0-06-064085-5, RD/447, HarpR). Har-Row.
--Text-Critical Methodology & the Pre-Caesarean Text. 112p. (Orig.). 1981. pap. 15.00x (ISBN 0-8028-1872-2). Eerdmans.
Hutchinson, Gloria. Jesus' Saving Questions. 118p. (Orig.). 1984. pap. text ed. 4.95 (ISBN 0-86716-028-4). St Anthony Mess Pr.
Ice, Rhoderick. Thirteen Lessons on the Gospel of Mark. (Bible Student Study Guides Ser). 1977. pap. 2.95 (ISBN 0-89900-151-3). College Pr Pub.
The Illustrated Gospel of St. John. (Illus.). 128p. 1986. 14.95 (ISBN 0-86350-068-4). Salem Hse Pubs.
International Congress on Biblical Studies. Studia Biblica Nineteen Seventy-Eight II: Papers on the Gospels. Livingston, E. A., ed. (Journal for the Study of the New Testament Supplement Ser.: No. 2). 350p. 1980. text ed. 37.50x (ISBN 0-905774-22-1, Pub. by JSOT Pr England). Eisenbrauns.
Interpretation of St. Matthew, 2 Vols. 1945. Set. 16.95 (ISBN 0-686-00813-8). Vol. I, 285 pp (ISBN 0-932785-24-7). Vol. II, 284 pp (ISBN 0-932785-25-5). Philos Pub.
Ironside, H. A. Jude: John. 9.95 (ISBN 0-87213-372-9). Loizeaux.
Ishee, John A. Design for Living: The Sermon on the Mount. 36p. 1982. pap. 3.50 (ISBN 0-939298-07-4). J M Prods.
Jensen, Irving L. John. (Irving Jensen's Do-It-Yourself Bible Study Ser.). 160p. (Orig.). 1983. wkbk. 5.95 (ISBN 0-89840-051-1). Heres Life.
--Luke. (Bible Self Study Ser.). 1970. pap. 3.25 (ISBN 0-8024-1042-1). Moody.
Jervell, Jacob. Jesus in the Gospel of John. Cleven, Harry T., tr. LC 84-14547. 96p. (Orig.). 1984. pap. 5.95 (ISBN 0-8066-2089-7, 10-3516). Augsburg.
Jim & Reapsome, Martha. Discipleship: The Growing Christians Lifestyle. (Fisherman Bible Studyguide). 64p. 1984. pap. 2.95 (ISBN 0-87788-175-8). Shaw Pubs.
Johnson, B. W. & DeWelt, Don. The Gospel of Mark. LC 76-1069. (The Bible Study Textbook Ser.). (Illus.). 1965. 15.90 (ISBN 0-89900-033-9). College Pr Pub.
Johnson, Luke T. The Literary Function of Possession in Luke-Acts. LC 77-21055. (Society of Biblical Literature. Dissertation Ser.: No. 39). 1985. pap. 11.25 (ISBN 0-89130-200-X, 060139). Scholars Pr GA.
--Luke Acts: A Story of Prophet & People. LC 81-4520. 65p. 1.75 (ISBN 0-8199-0524-0). Franciscan Herald.
Juel, Donald. Luke-Acts: The Promise of History. LC 82-25845. 136p. 1983. pap. 8.95 (ISBN 0-8042-0321-0). John Knox.
--Messiah & Temple: The Trial of Jesus in the Gospel of Mark. LC 76-46397. (Society of Biblical Literature. Dissertation Ser.: No. 31). Repr. of 1977 ed. 43.60 (ISBN 0-8357-9578-0, 2017527). Bks Demand UMI.
Kaiser, Bill. Gospel of Jesus & Paul. 152p. (Orig.). 1985. pap. text ed. 5.95 (ISBN 0-914307-37-1). Word Faith.
Karris, Robert. Following Jesus: A Guide to the Gospels. (Biblical Ser.). 1973. pap. 1.25 (ISBN 0-8199-0514-3). Franciscan Herald.
--The Gospel of St. Luke. (Read & Pray Ser.). 1974. 1.75 (ISBN 0-8199-0626-3). Franciscan Herald.
Keach, Benjamin. Exposition of the Parables. LC 73-85297. (Kregel Reprint Library). 918p. 1988. 29.95 (ISBN 0-8254-3016-X). Kregel.
Kealy, Sean. Mark's Gospel: A History of Its Interpretation. LC 81-84384. 144p. (Orig.). 1982. pap. 8.95 (ISBN 0-8091-2417-3). Paulist Pr.
Kee, Howard C. Community of the New Age: Studies in Mark's Gospel. LC 83-17416. xii, 225p. 1983. 16.95 (ISBN 0-86554-100-0, MUP/H92). Mercer Univ Pr.
Kelber, Werner H. The Oral & the Written Gospel: The Hermeneutics of Speaking & Writing in the Synoptic Tradition, Mark, Paul, & Q. LC 82-7450. 272p. 1983. 23.95 (ISBN 0-8006-0689-2, 1-689). Fortress.
Kelly, W. Exposition of the Gospel of Luke. 6.25 (ISBN 0-88172-102-6). Believers Bkshelf.
--Exposition of the Gospel of Mark. 5.50 (ISBN 0-88172-103-4). Believers Bkshelf.
Kelly, William. The Gospels. (Introductory Lecture Ser.). 567p. 6.95 (ISBN 0-88172-097-6). Believers Bkshelf.
Kemmer, Alfons. The Creed in the Gospels. Schnaus, Urban, tr. 144p. (Orig.). 1986. pap. 7.95 (ISBN 0-8091-2830-6). Paulist Pr.
Kent, Homer A., Jr. Light in the Darkness: Studies in the Gospel of John. (Illus.). pap. 5.95 (ISBN 0-88469-055-5). BMH Bks.
Keyes, Sharrel. Luke: Following Jesus. (Fisherman Bible Studyguide Ser.). 96p. 1983. pap. 2.95 saddlestitched (ISBN 0-87788-511-7). Shaw Pubs.

Kingsbury, Jack D. Matthew. 2nd, enl. & rev. ed. LC 84-45212. (Proclamation Commentaries Ser.). 144p. 1986. pap. 6.95 (ISBN 0-8006-0597-7). Fortress.

--Matthew As Story. LC 85-16204. 160p. 1986. pap. 9.95 (ISBN 0-8006-1891-2). Fortress.

--The Parables of Jesus in Matthew 13. LC 76-40850. 1976. pap. text ed. 12.95 (ISBN 0-915644-08-8). Clayton Pub Hse.

Kodell, Jerome. The Gospel According to Luke, No. 3. Karris, Robert J., ed. LC 82-20350. (Collegeville Bible Commentary Ser.). (Illus.). 128p. 1983. pap. 2.95 (ISBN 0-8146-1303-9). Liturgical Pr.

Kraeling, Carl H. Anthropos & Son of Man. LC 27-23162. (Columbia University. Oriental Studies: No. 25). Repr. of 1927 ed. 18.50 (ISBN 0-404-50515-5). AMS Pr.

Kuniholm, Whitney. John: A Daily Dialogue with God. (Personal Bible Studyguide Ser.). 155p. 1982. pap. 4.95 (ISBN 0-87788-431-5). Shaw Pubs.

Kunst, H. Evangelisches Staatslexikon. 2nd rev. ed. (Ger.). 1975. 125.00 (ISBN 3-7831-0463-7, M-7373, Pub. by Kreuz Vlg.). French & Eur.

Kunz, Marilyn & Schell, Catherine. John, Book One. 1978. pap. 2.95 (ISBN 0-8423-1895-X). Tyndale.

--John, Book Two. 1979. pap. 2.95 (ISBN 0-8423-1896-8). Tyndale.

--Matthew Book One. 1980. pap. 2.50 (ISBN 0-8423-4188-9). Tyndale.

--Matthew Book Two. 1980. pap. 2.95 (ISBN 0-8423-4189-7). Tyndale.

Kysar, Robert. The Fourth Evangelist & His Gospel: An Examination of Contemporary Scholarship. LC 75-22711. 320p. (Orig.). 1975. pap. 11.95 (ISBN 0-8066-1504-4, 10-2365). Augsburg.

--John, the Maverick Gospel. LC 76-12393. (Biblical Foundations Ser.). 1976. pap. 7.95 (ISBN 0-8042-0302-4). John Knox.

--John's Story of Jesus. LC 83-16537. 96p. 1984. pap. 4.50 (ISBN 0-8006-1775-4, 1-1775). Fortress.

Lamsa, George M. Gospel Light: An Indispensable Guide to the Teachings of Jesus & the Customs of His Time. LC 86-45020. 416p. 1986. pap. 12.95 (ISBN 0-06-064928-3, HarpR). Har-Row.

Larson, Bruce. The Communicator's Commentary-Luke, Vol. 3. Ogilvie, Lloyd J., ed. (The Communicator's Commentaries Ser.). 1984. 18.95 (ISBN 0-8499-0156-1). Word Bks.

Lattimore, Richard, tr. The Four Gospels & the Revelation. 288p. 1981. pap. 3.95 (ISBN 0-671-50441-X). WSP.

Laurin, Roy L. First John. LC 86-27394. Orig. Title: Epistle of John: Life at its Best. 200p. 1987. pap. 8.95 (ISBN 0-8254-3136-0). Kregel.

Lawson, E. Leroy. Matthew. (Standard Bible Studies). 352p. 1986. pap. 9.95 (ISBN 0-87403-161-3, 40101). Standard Pub.

Lenski, R. C. Interpretation of St. John's Gospel. 1936. 22.95 (ISBN 0-8066-9000-3, 10-3364). Augsburg.

--Interpretation of St. John's Revelation. 1935. 21.95 (ISBN 0-8066-9001-1, 10-3372). Augsburg.

--Interpretation of St. Luke's Gospel. 1934. 22.95 (ISBN 0-8066-9002-X, 10-3363). Augsburg.

--Interpretation of St. Mark's Gospel. 1946. 21.95 (ISBN 0-8066-9003-8, 0-3362). Augsburg.

--Interpretation of St. Matthew's Gospel. 1933. 22.95 (ISBN 0-8066-9004-6, 10-3361). Augsburg.

Lineberry, John. That We May Have Fellowship: Studies in First John. 112p. 1986. pap. 4.95 (ISBN 0-87227-115-3). Reg Baptist.

Lipman, Matthew. Mark. LC 80-80849. (Philosophy for Children Ser.). 86p. 1980. pap. 8.00 (ISBN 0-916834-13-1, TX 752-903). First Mntn Foun.

Longstaff, Thomas R. Evidence of Conflation in Mark? A Study in the Synoptic Problem. LC 76-40001. (Society of Biblical Literature. Dissertation Ser.: No. 28). (Illus.). 1977. pap. 9.95 (ISBN 0-89130-086-4, 060128). Scholars Pr GA.

Lowry, Charles W. The First Theologians. 200p. (Orig.). 1986. pap. 7.95 (ISBN 0-89526-804-3). Regnery Bks.

MacArthur, John F., Jr. Matthew One-Seven. 1985. 14.95 (ISBN 0-88469-168-3). BMH Bks.

MacArthur, John, Jr. Jesus Silences His Critics: Mattew Twenty-Two Verses Fifteen Through Forty-Six. (John MacArthur Bible Studies Ser.). 1987. pap. 3.50 (ISBN 0-8024-5313-9). Moody.

--The Lord's Supper: Mattew Twenty-six Vs Seventeen to Thirty, Corinthians Eleven Seventeen Through Thirty-four. (John MacArthur Bible Studies). 1987. pap. 3.50 (ISBN 0-8024-5310-4). Moody.

--Love Not the World. (John MacArthur's Bible Studies). (Orig.). 1986. pap. 3.50 (ISBN 0-8024-5098-9). Moody.

--Love's Humility. (John MacArthur's Bible Studies). (Orig.). 1986. pap. 3.95 (ISBN 0-8024-5097-0). Moody.

--Marks of a True Believer: First John Two Vs Eighteen Through Four Twenty-One. (John MacArthur Bible Studies Ser.). 1987. pap. 3.95 (ISBN 0-8024-5312-0). Moody.

--The Master's Men. (John MacArthur's Bible Studies). 1985. pap. text ed. 3.50 (ISBN 0-8024-5106-3). Moody.

--Matthew 8-15. 1986. 14.95 (ISBN 0-88469-172-1). BMH Bks.

--Overcoming Materialism. (John MacArthur's Bible Studies). (Orig.). 1986. pap. 3.50 (ISBN 0-8024-5099-7). Moody.

--Signs of Christ's Return: Matthew Twenty-Four Through Twenty-Five. (John MacArthur Bible Studies Ser.). 1987. pap. 5.95 (ISBN 0-8024-5311-2). Moody.

--Your Completeness in Christ. (John MacArthur's Bible Studies). 1985. pap. 3.50 (ISBN 0-8024-5114-4). Moody.

Macaulay, J. C. Behold Your King. LC 81-22580. 256p. 1982. pap. 9.95 (ISBN 0-8024-2417-1). Moody.

Mackintosh, H. R. The Doctrine of the Person of Jesus Christ. 560p. 1913. pap. 15.95 (ISBN 0-567-27218-4, Pub. by T&T Clark Ltd UK). Fortress.

McPolin, James. John. (New Testament Message Ser.: Vol. 6). 244p. 1979. 14.95 (ISBN 0-89453-194-8); pap. 9.95 (ISBN 0-89453-129-8). M Glazier.

Maddox, Robert. Purpose of Luke-Acts. Riches, John, ed. 220p. 1982. 26.95 (ISBN 0-567-09312-3, Pub. by T&T Clark Ltd UK). Fortress.

Magness, Lee. Sense & Absence. (Semeia Studies). 1986. text ed. 14.95 (ISBN 1-55540-006-X, 06-06-15); pap. 10.95 (ISBN 1-55540-007-8). Scholars Pr GA.

Makrakis, Apostolos. The Interpretation of the Gospel Law. Orthodox Christian Educational Society, ed. Cummings, Denver, tr. from Hellenic. 453p. 1955. 9.00x (ISBN 0-938366-10-6). Orthodox Chr.

Malbon, Elizabeth S. Narrative Space & Mythic Meaning in Mark. 208p. (Orig.). 1986. 24.95 (ISBN 0-06-254540-X, HarpR). Har-Row.

Maloney, Elliott C. Semitic Interference in Marcan Syntax. LC 80-13016. (Society of Biblical Literature Dissertation Ser.: No. 51). pap. 15.00 (ISBN 0-89130-406-1, 06-01-51). Scholars Pr GA.

Marcus, Joel. The Mystery of the Kingdom of God. (Dissertation Ser.). 270p. 1986. 17.95 (ISBN 0-89130-983-7, 06-01-90); pap. 12.95 (ISBN 0-89130-984-5). Scholars Pr GA.

Marion-Wild, E. C. The Prologue of the Gospel of St. John: Esoteric Studies. Roboz, Helga & Roboz, Steven, trs. from Ger. 19p. 1984. pap. 3.75 (ISBN 0-919924-22-0). Anthroposophic.

Marshall, I. Howard. Luke: Historian & Theologian. (Contemporary Evangelical Perspective Ser). 1971. kivar 7.95 (ISBN 0-310-28761-8, 10105P). Zondervan.

Martin, Ralph & Toon, Peter, eds. Reconciliation: A Study of Paul's Theology. LC 80-16340. (New Foundations Theological Library). 272p. 1981. 12.95 (ISBN 0-8042-3709-3); pap. 11.95 (ISBN 0-8042-3729-8). John Knox.

Martin, Ralph P. Mark: Evangelist & Theologian. (Contemporary Evangelical Perspective Ser.). 249p. 1973. kivar 7.95 (ISBN 0-310-28801-0). Zondervan.

Martinez Dalmau, Eduardo. Study on the Synoptic Gospels. 1964. 5.95 (ISBN 0-8315-0013-1). Speller.

Matera, Frank. The Kingship of Jesus: Composition & Theology in Mark Fifteen. LC 82-708. (SBL Dissertation Ser.). 1982. pap. 12.75 (ISBN 0-89130-564-5, 060166). Scholars Pr GA.

Matera, Frank J. Passion Narratives & Gospel Theologies: Interpreting the Synoptics Through Their Passion Stories. 320p. 1986. pap. 12.95 (ISBN 0-8091-2775-X). Paulist Pr.

--What Are They Saying about Mark? 1987. pap. 5.95. Paulist Pr.

Mauro, Philip. Gospel of the Kingdom. 6.95 (ISBN 0-685-19829-4). Reiner.

Mays, James L., ed. Interpreting the Gospels. LC 80-8057. pap. 79.30 (2027872). Bks Demand UMI.

Meagher, John C. Five Gospels: An Account of How the Good News Came to Be. 324p. 1983. 24.50 (ISBN 0-86683-731-0, HarpR); pap. 11.95 (ISBN 0-86683-691-8). Har-Row.

Meier, John P. & Gordon, Edmund F. Matthew: An Access Guide for Scripture Study. 174p. 1983. pap. 4.20 (ISBN 0-8215-5932-X); manual 3.45 (ISBN 0-8215-5935-4). Sadlier.

Michaels, J. Ramsey. John: A Good News Commentary. LC 83-47729. (The Good News Commentary Ser.). 288p. (Orig.). 1983. pap. 9.95 (ISBN 0-06-065575-5, RD-462, HarpR). Har-Row.

Miller, Charles E., et al. The Word Made Flesh: Homilies for the Sundays of the Three Cycles. LC 83-8819. 353p. 1983. pap. 14.95 (ISBN 0-8189-0436-4). Alba.

Minear, Paul S. John: The Martyr's Gospel. 192p. (Orig.). 1985. pap. 8.95 (ISBN 0-8298-0718-7). Pilgrim NY.

--Matthew: The Teacher's Gospel. LC 82-10178. 160p. (Orig.). 1982. pap. 7.95 (ISBN 0-8298-0617-2). Pilgrim NY.

Mitchell, John G. Fellowship: A Devotional Study of the Epistles of John. LC 84-193801. (Orig.). 1974. pap. text ed. 6.95 (ISBN 0-930014-06-5). Multnomah.

Mohrlang, Roger. Matthew & Paul: A Comparison of Ethical Perspectives. LC 83-10147. (Society for New Testament Studies Monograph: No. 48). 220p. 1984. 37.50 (ISBN 0-521-25093-5). Cambridge U Pr.

Morgan. Gospel According to John. 1984. 13.95 (ISBN 0-8007-0119-4). Revell.

--Gospel According to Luke. 1984. 13.95 (ISBN 0-8007-0120-8). Revell.

--Gospel According to Mark. 1984. 13.95 (ISBN 0-8007-0121-6). Revell.

--Gospel According to Matthew. 1984. 13.95 (ISBN 0-8007-0122-4). Revell.

Morgan, Campbell G. Analyzed Bible. Matthew. 6.95 (ISBN 0-8010-6159-8); Romans. pap. 5.95 (ISBN 0-8010-6149-0). Baker Bk.

--Analyzed Bible: John. 280p. 1984. pap. 6.95 (ISBN 0-8010-6173-3). Baker Bk.

Morison, James. Mark. 1981. lib. bdg. 21.00 (ISBN 0-86524-069-8, 4102). Klock & Klock.

--Matthew. 1981. lib. bdg. 24.95 (ISBN 0-86524-068-X, 4001). Klock & Klock.

Morris, Leon. Reflections on the Gospel of John, Vol. 2. 208p. 1987. pap. 8.95 (ISBN 0-8010-6215-2). Baker Bk.

Morrison, Mary C. Approaching the Gospels Together: A Leaders' Guide to Group Gospels Study. (Orig.). 1987. pap. 10.95 (ISBN 0-87574-910-0). Pendle Hill.

Nellen, Josephine F. Jesus & You. 1987. 8.95 (ISBN 0-533-07355-3). Vantage.

Newman, B. M. & Nida, E. A. Translator's Handbook on the Gospel of John. LC 81-452133. (Helps for Translators Ser.). 681p. 1980. 7.00x (ISBN 0-8267-0137-X, 08620, Pub. by United Bible). Am Bible.

Nilsen, Mary. Real Living: A Small-Group Life Experience with the Gospel of Luke, Pt. 1. (Illus.). 1977. pap. text ed. 5.65 (ISBN 0-03-021856-X, HarpR); tchr's. ed. 7.95 (ISBN 0-03-021861-6). Har-Row.

Nilsen, Mary Y. Real Living: A Small-Group Life Experience with the Gospel of Luke, Pt. 4. Winston Press Editorial Staff, ed. (Illus.). 1979. pap. text ed. 5.65 (ISBN 0-03-045706-8, HarpR); tchr's. guide 7.95 (ISBN 0-03-045711-4). Har-Row.

Norquist, Marilyn. How to Read & Pray the Gospels. (Handbook of the Bible Ser.). 1979. pap. 1.95 (ISBN 0-89243-099-0). Liguori Pubns.

Nutt, Grady. The Gospel According to Norton. LC 73-91610. pap. 4.50 (ISBN 0-8054-5322-9, 4253-22). Broadman.

Nystrom, Carolyn. Mark: God on the Move. (Young Fisherman Bible Studyguide Ser.). 96p. 1978. pap. 4.95 tchr's ed. (ISBN 0-87788-312-2); student ed. 2.95 (ISBN 0-87788-311-4). Shaw Pubs.

--Who Is Jesus? A Woman's Workshop on Mark. (Woman's Workshop Ser.). 144p. 1987. pap. 3.95 (ISBN 0-310-42001-6). Zondervan.

O'Quinn, J. Frank, ed. Jesus' Lost Gospels: The Discovery at Nag Hammadi. (Illus.). 48p. 1981. pap. text ed. 6.95 (ISBN 0-9609802-0-2). Life Science.

Orchard, Bernard & Riley, Harold. The Order of the Synoptics: Why Three Synoptic Gospels? 384p. 1987. 38.95 (ISBN 0-86554-222-8, MUP H-199). Mercer Univ Pr.

O'Toole, Robert F. The Unity of Luke's Theology: An Analysis of Luke-Acts. (Good News Studies Ser.: Vol. 9). 1984. pap. 8.95 (ISBN 0-89453-438-6). M Glazier.

Outler, Albert C., et al. The Relationships Among the Gospels: An Interdisciplinary Dialogue. Walker, William O., Jr., ed. LC 78-52845. (Monograph Series in Religion). 359p. 1978. text ed. 15.00 (ISBN 0-911536-73-6). Trinity U Pr.

Paregien, Stan. Twenty-Six Lessons on the Gospel of John. (Bible Student Study Guides Ser.). 1977. pap. 3.95 (ISBN 0-89900-152-1). College Pr Pub.

Patte, Daniel. The Gospel According to Matthew: A Structural Commentary on Matthew's Faith. LC 86-45218. 432p. 1986. pap. 19.95 (ISBN 0-8006-1978-1, 1-1978). Fortress.

Patton, Carl S. Sources of the Synoptic Gospels. 263p. 1980. Repr. of 1915 ed. lib. bdg. 50.00 (ISBN 0-89984-385-9). Century Bookbindery.

--Sources of the Synoptic Gospels. Repr. of 1915 ed. 37.00 (ISBN 0-384-38805-1). Johnson Repr.

Pennington, M. Basil. Breaking Bread: The Table Talk of Jesus. LC 85-51008. 160p. 1986. 10.95 (ISBN 0-86683-489-3, HarpR). Har-Row.

Perkins, Pheme. The Gospel According to St. John: A Theological Commentary. LC 77-12896. (Herald Scriptural Library). pap. 66.80 (ISBN 0-317-28173-9, 2022571). Bks Demand UMI.

Perpich, Sandra W. A Hermeneutic Critique of Structuralist Exegesis: With Specific Reference to Lk. 10.29-37. LC 83-21737. (Illus.). 264p. (Orig.). 1984. lib. bdg. 25.25 (ISBN 0-8191-3668-9); pap. text ed. 13.25 (ISBN 0-8191-3669-7). U Pr of Amer.

Perrin, Norman. Resurrection According to Matthew, Mark, & Luke. LC 76-47913. 96p. (Orig.). 1977. pap. 3.95 (ISBN 0-8006-1248-5, 1-1248). Fortress.

--What Is Redaction Criticism? Via, Dan O., Jr., ed. LC 72-81529. (Guides to Biblical Scholarship). 96p. (Orig.). 1969. pap. 4.50 (ISBN 0-8006-0181-5, 1-181). Fortress.

Plummer, Alfred. An Exegetical Commentary on The Gospel According To Matthew. (Thornapple Commentaries Ser.). 497p. 1982. pap. 12.95 (ISBN 0-8010-7078-3). Baker Bk.

Plunkett, Mark. John. (Standard Bible Study Workbooks Ser.). 80p. 1987. wkbk. 1.95 (ISBN 0-87403-184-2, 40204). Standard Pub.

Powell, Ivor. John's Wonderful Gospel. LC 83-16192. 448p. 1983. 16.95 (ISBN 0-8254-3514-5). Kregel.

--Matthew's Majestic Gospel. LC 86-10401. 528p. 1986. 18.95 (ISBN 0-8254-3525-0). Kregel.

Powell, Ivor C. Mark's Superb Gospel. LC 85-25615. 432p. 1986. 16.95 (ISBN 0-8254-3523-4). Kregel.

Raymond, John. Twenty-Six Lessons on Matthew, Vol. 1. LC 80-67734. (Bible Student Study Guides). 130p. (Orig.). 1980. pap. 2.95 (ISBN 0-89900-167-X). College Pr Pub.

Rice, George. Luke, a Plagiarist. (Anchor Ser.). 1984. pap. 6.95 (ISBN 0-8163-0542-0). Pacific Pr Pub Assn.

Richards, Hubert J. The Miracles of Jesus: What Really Happened? (What Really Happened? Ser.). 128p. 1986. pap. 5.95 (ISBN 0-89622-287-X). Twenty-Third.

Ricks, Chip. John & One John. 1982. pap. 2.50 (ISBN 0-8423-1890-9). Tyndale.

Ringe, Sharon H. Jesus, Liberation & the Biblical Jubilee: Images for Ethics & Christology. LC 85-4609. (Overtures to Biblical Theology Ser.). 144p. 1985. pap. 8.95 (ISBN 0-8006-1544-1). Fortress.

Rist, J. M. On the Independence of Matthew & Mark. LC 76-40840. (Society for New Testament Studies Monographs: No. 22). 1978. 24.95 (ISBN 0-521-21476-9). Cambridge U Pr.

Ritchie, John. Five Hundred Gospel Sermon Illustrations. LC 86-27201. 152p. 1987. pap. 5.95 (ISBN 0-8254-3620-6). Kregel.

Robbins, Vernon K. Jesus the Teacher: A Socio-Rhetorical Interpretation of Mark. LC 83-16504. 256p. 1984. 23.95 (ISBN 0-8006-0719-8, 1-719). Fortress.

Robertson, A. T. Una Armonia De los Cuatro Evangelios. Patterson, W. F., tr. from Eng. Orig. Title: Harmony of the Four Gospels. (Span.). 259p. 1986. pap. 4.95 (ISBN 0-311-04302-X). Casa Bautista.

Robinson, John A. The Priority of John. 464p. 1987. pap. 19.95 (ISBN 0-940989-01-8). Meyer Stone Bks.

Rosenstock-Huessy, Eugen. The Fruit of Lips or Why Four Gospels? LC 78-8524. (Pittsburgh Theological Monographs: No. 19). 1978. pap. 6.25 (ISBN 0-915138-31-X). Pickwick.

Ryle, J. C. Expository Thoughts on the Gospels, 3 vols. Incl. St. Matthew. 426p. 1974. Repr. 9.95 (ISBN 0-227-67697-1); St. Mark. 384p. 1973. Repr. 9.95 (ISBN 0-227-67698-X); St. Luke. 540p. Repr. of 1983 ed. 19.95 (ISBN 0-227-67877-X); St. John. write for info. (ISBN 0-227-67453-7); Vol. 2. 9.95 (ISBN 0-227-67454-5); Matthew-Mark. 380p. Repr. of 1983 ed. 19.95 (ISBN 0-227-67874-5). Set. 65.00 (ISBN 0-227-67874-5). Attic Pr.

--Mark. 370p. 1984. pap. 5.95 (ISBN 0-85151-441-3). Banner of Truth.

--Matthew. (Expository Thoughts on the Gospel Ser.). 368p. 1986. pap. 5.95 (ISBN 0-85151-483-9). Banner of Truth.

Sanders, Jack T. The Jews in Luke-Acts. LC 86-45926. 432p. 1987. pap. 19.95 (ISBN 0-8006-0837-2, 1-1969). Fortress.

Schaberg, Jane. The Father, the Son & the Holy Spirit: An Investigation of the Origin & Meaning of the Triadic Phrase in Matt 28: 19b. LC 81-14466. (SBL Dissertation Ser.). 1982. pap. 18.00 (ISBN 0-89130-543-2, 060161). Scholars Pr GA.

Schillebeeckx, Edward. God among Us: The Gospel Proclaimed. LC 82-23575. 278p. 1983. 12.95 (ISBN 0-8245-0575-1). Crossroad NY.

Schmidt, Dan. Follow the Leader. 144p. 1986. pap. 3.95 (ISBN 0-89693-629-5). Victor Bks.

Schnackenburg, Rudolf. The Gospel According to St. John, Vol. 3. 566p. 1982. 39.50x (ISBN 0-8245-0098-9). Crossroad NY.
--The Gospel According to St. Mark, Vol. II. McKenzie, John L., ed. LC 81-605. (The New Testament for Spiritual Reading Ser.). 182p. 1981. pap. 4.95 (ISBN 0-686-85824-7). Crossroad NY.
Schnakenburg, Rudolf. The Gospel According to St. Mark, Vol. I. McKenzie, John L., ed. LC 81-605. (The New Testament for Spiritual Reading Ser.). 182p. pap. 4.95 (ISBN 0-8245-0112-8). Crossroad NY.
Schramm, Tim. Der Markus-Stoff Bei Lukas. LC 79-96099. (New Testament Studies Monographs: No. 14). (Ger). 1971. 34.50 (ISBN 0-521-07743-5). Cambridge U Pr.
Schweizer, Eduard. The Good News According to Luke. Green, David E., tr. LC 83-22237. 1984. 23.95 (ISBN 0-8042-0249-4). John Knox.
Schwizer, Eduard. Luke: A Challenge to Present Theology. LC 81-85332. 144p. 1982. pap. 10.50 (ISBN 0-8042-0686-4). John Knox.
Scotland, Nigel. Can We Trust the Gospels? 54p. 1979. pap. 1.95 (ISBN 0-85364-249-4). Attic Pr.
Scroggie, William G. Luke-John. 1981. pap. 4.95 (ISBN 0-87508-485-0). Chr Lit.
Scrogie, William G. Matthew-Mark. 1981. pap. 4.95 (ISBN 0-87508-484-2). Chr Lit.
Scrogin, Michael. Does the Gospel Make Sense Today? 128p. 1983. pap. 7.95 (ISBN 0-8170-0967-1). Judson.
The Secret of Happiness: Matthew 5, the Beatitudes. 7.95 (ISBN 0-86683-850-3, HarpR). Har-Row.
Senior, Donald. The Gospel of Matthew. (Read & Pray Ser.). 1974. 1.75 (ISBN 0-8199-0518-6). Franciscan Herald.
--Jesus: A Gospel Portrait. 192p. (Orig.). 1975. pap. 2.95 (ISBN 0-8278-9003-6, Pub. by Pflaum Pr). Peter Li.
--Mathew: A Gospel for the Church. 1976. pap. 1.25 (ISBN 0-685-77500-3). Franciscan Herald.
--Passion of Jesus in the Gospel of Matthew. (Passion Ser.: Vol. 1). 1985. pap. 8.95 (ISBN 0-89453-460-2). M Glazier.
--What Are They Saying about Matthew? LC 82-62967. (WATSA Ser.). 96p. (Orig.). 1983. pap. 3.95 (ISBN 0-8091-2541-2). Paulist Pr.
The Servant Story (Mark) Leader's Guide. (New Horizons Bible Study Ser.). 48p. 1980. pap. 1.95 (ISBN 0-89367-050-2). Light & Life.
The Servant Story (Mark) Study Guide. (New Horizons Bible Study Ser.). 64p. 1980. pap. 2.50 (ISBN 0-89367-049-9). Light & Life.
Shaver, Charles. Beacon Small-Group Bible Studies, Gospel of John, Pt. II: That You Might Have Life. Wolf, Earl C., ed. 64p. (Orig.). 1984. pap. 2.50 (ISBN 0-8341-0881-X). Beacon Hill.
--Beacon Small-Group Bible Studies, John: That All Might Believe, Vol. 1. 68p. (Orig.). 1980. pap. 2.50 (ISBN 0-8341-0651-5). Beacon Hill.
Sherman, Cecil E. A Kingdom of Surprises. LC 85-4699. (Orig.). 1985. pap. 3.75 (ISBN 0-8054-1533-5). Broadman.
Shuler, Philip L. A Genre for the Gospels: The Biographical Character of Matthew. LC 81-71384. 144p. 1982. 3.50 (ISBN 0-8006-0677-9). Fortress.
--A Genre for the Gospels: The Biographical Character of Matthew. LC 81-71384. pap. 35.30 (2029606). Bks Demand UMI.
Sigal, Phillip. The Halakah of Jesus of Nazareth According to the Gospel of Matthew. 282p. (Orig.). 1986. lib. bdg. 23.75 (ISBN 0-8191-5210-2); pap. text ed. 13.25 (ISBN 0-8191-5211-0). U Pr of Amer.
Simpson, Albert B. Four-Fold Gospel. rev. ed. 1984. pap. 4.95 (ISBN 0-87509-347-7). Chr Pubns.
Sloan, Robert B. The Favorable Year of the Lord: A Study of Jubilary Theology in the Gospel of Luke. 213p. (Orig.). 1977. pap. 6.95 (ISBN 0-931016-02-9). Schola Pr TX.
Smith, D. Moody. John. 2nd, rev., & enl. ed. Krodel, Gerhard, ed. LC 75-13046. (Proclamation Commentaries: The New Testament Witnesses for Preaching Ser.). 144p. 1986. pap. 7.95 (ISBN 0-8006-1917-X, 1-1917). Fortress.
Smith, Dwight M. Interpreting the Gospels for Preaching. LC 79-8900. pap. 32.00 (2029609). Bks Demand UMI.
Smith, Joseph F. Gospel Doctrine. 1986. text ed. 10.95 (ISBN 0-87579-063-1). Deseret Bk.
Smith, Joyce M. Demons, Doubters & Dead Men. (Good Life Bible Studies Book). 64p. (Orig.). 1986. 2.95wkbk. (ISBN 0-8423-0542-4). Tyndale.
Smith, Thomas J. Jesus Alive! The Mighty Message of Mark. LC 73-81824. 1973. pap. 6.00x (ISBN 0-88489-015-5); teaching guide 3.00x (ISBN 0-88489-117-8). St Marys.
Soards, Marion L. The Passion According to Luke: The Special Material of Luke 22. (JSOT Supplement Ser.: No. 14). 150p. 1987. text ed. 24.50x (ISBN 1-85075-036-X, Pub. by JSOT Pr England); pap. text ed. 11.95x (ISBN 1-85075-037-8, Pub. by JSOT Pr England). Eisenbrauns.
Sorlien, Sandra. Bulletin Board Ideas: Creative Ways to Communicate the Gospel. (Illus.). 40p. (Orig.). 1980. pap. 4.95 (ISBN 0-8066-1778-0, 10-0949). Augsburg.
Souter, John C. The All-New Super Incredible Bible Study Book on Mark. 144p. (Orig.). 1985. pap. 3.95 (ISBN 0-310-45881-1, 12475P). Zondervan.
Sperry Symposium Staff, ed. Principles of the Gospel in Practice. 257p. Date not set. 10.95 (ISBN 0-934126-75-5). Randall Bk Co.
Spruce, Jim. Beacon Small-Group Bible Studies, Mark: Getting in on the Action. 80p. (Orig.). 1980. pap. 2.50 (ISBN 0-8341-0650-7). Beacon Hill.
Stanton, Graham, ed. The Interpretation of Matthew. LC 83-5508. (Issues in Religion & Theology Ser.). 176p. 1983. pap. 7.95 (ISBN 0-8006-1766-5, 1-1766). Fortress.
Staton, Knofel. Check Your Commitment: Instructor. 160p. 1985. pap. 3.50 (ISBN 0-87239-828-5, 39982). Standard Pub.
--Check Your Commitment: Student. 128p. 1985. pap. 2.95 (ISBN 0-87239-829-3, 39983). Standard Pub.
--Thirteen Lessons on I, II, III John. LC 80-69722. (Bible Student Study Guide Ser.). 149p. 1980. pap. 2.95 (ISBN 0-89900-169-6). College Pr Pub.
Stegemann, Wolfgang. The Gospel & the Poor. Elliott, Dietlinde, tr. from Ger. LC 83-48915. 80p. 1984. pap. 3.95 (ISBN 0-8006-1783-5, 1-1783). Fortress.
Stein, Robert H. Difficult Passages in the Gospels. 139p. 1984. pap. 6.95 (ISBN 0-8010-8249-8). Baker Bk.
Steiner, Rudolf. Apocalypse of St. John. 2nd ed. Tr. of Die Apokalypse des Johannes. 227p. 1985. pap. 12.95 (ISBN 0-88010-131-8). Anthroposophic.
--Background to the Gospel of St. Mark. 2nd ed. Tr. of Exkurse in das Gebiet des Markus-Evangeliums. 200p. 1986. pap. 10.95 (ISBN 0-88010-145-8). Anthroposophic.
--Deeper Secrets in Human History in the Light of the Gospel of St. Matthew. 2nd ed. Tr. of Die tieferen Geheimmnisse des Menschheitswerdens im Lichte der Evangelien. 60p. 1985. pap. 6.95 (ISBN 0-88010-132-6). Anthroposophic.
--The Fifth Gospel. Davy, C. & Osmond, D. S., trs. from Ger. Tr. of Aus der Akkasha Forschung: Das Fuenfte Evangelium. 168p. 1985. pap. 9.95 (ISBN 0-85440-520-8, Pub. by Steinerbooks). Anthroposophic.
--The Gospel of St. John. Monges, Maud B., tr. from Ger. LC 63-1084. (Illus.). 192p. 1984. 14.95 (ISBN 0-88010-107-5); pap. 8.95 (ISBN 0-910142-13-0). Anthroposophic.
Stevens, William A. & Burton, Ernest D. A Harmony of the Gospels for Historical Study. 283p. 1930. text ed. write for info. (ISBN 0-02-417240-5, Pub. by Scribner). Macmillan.
Stock, Augustine. Call to Discipleship: A Literary Study of Mark's Gospel. (Good News Studies: Vol. 1). 1982. pap. 9.95 (ISBN 0-89453-273-1). M Glazier.
Stoger, Alois. The Gospel According to St. Luke, Vol. I. McKenzie, John L., ed. LC 81-605. (New Testament for Spiritual Reading Ser.). 182p. 1981. pap. 4.95 (ISBN 0-8245-0114-4). Crossroad NY.
--The Gospel According to St. Luke, Vol. II. McKenzie, John L., ed. LC 81-605. (New Testament for Spiritual Reading Ser.). 182p. 1981. pap. 4.95 (ISBN 0-8245-0115-2). Crossroad NY.
Stonehouse, Ned B. Origins of the Synoptic Gospels. (Twin Brooks Ser.). 1979. pap. 5.95 (ISBN 0-8010-8180-7). Baker Bk.
Strauss, Lehman. Prophetic Mysteries Revealed: The Prophetic Significance of the Parables of Matthew 13 & the Letters of Revelation 2-3. LC 80-17540. 256p. 1980. 9.95 (ISBN 0-87213-832-1). Loizeaux.
Stronstad, Roger. The Charismatic Theology of St. Luke. 96p. 1985. pap. 4.95 (ISBN 0-913573-11-6). Hendrickson MA.
Suggs, M. Jack. Wisdom, Christology, & Law in Matthew's Gospel. LC 75-95930. Repr. of 1970 ed. 36.00 (ISBN 0-8357-9185-8, 2017749). Bks Demand UMI.
Summers, Ray. Behold the Lamb. LC 78-67924. 1979. 12.95 (ISBN 0-8054-1374-X). Broadman.
Swanson, Reuben J. The Horizontal Line Synopsis of the Gospels. LC 75-20997. 608p. 1984. Repr. of 1980 ed. 24.95 (ISBN 0-87808-744-3). William Carey Lib.
--The Horizontal Line Synopsis of the Gospels: Volume I, The Gospel of Mathew. 1982. 29.95 (ISBN 0-915948-10-9). Bks Distinction.
Sydnor, William. Jesus According to Luke. 144p. (Orig.). 1982. pap. 7.95 (ISBN 0-8164-2393-8, HarpR). Har-Row.
Talbot, John M. Reflections on the Gospels, 3 vols, Vol. 2. 196p. (Orig.). 1987. pap. 5.95 (ISBN 0-89283-349-1). Servant.
Tannehill, Robert C. The Narrative Unity of Luke-Acts: A Literary Interpretation Vol. 1. LC 86-45224. (The Gospel According to Luke Series). 352p. 1986. 19.95 (ISBN 0-8006-2112-3, 1-2112). Fortress.
Taylor, Edward. Harmony of the Gospels, 4 Vols. LC 82-5452. 2688p. 1983. Set. 300.00x (ISBN 0-8201-1379-4). Schol Facsimiles.
Taylor, Michael J. John: The Different Gospel... A Reflective Commentary. LC 83-15485. 269p. 1983. pap. 9.95 (ISBN 0-8189-0456-9). Alba.
Teeple, Howard M. The Literary Origin of the Gospel of John. LC 73-87487. x, 297p. (Orig.). 1974. pap. 6.00 (ISBN 0-914384-00-7). Religion & Ethics.
Telford, William R. The Barren Temple & the Withered Tree. (Journal for the Study of the New Testament, Supplement Ser.: No. 1). 336p. 1980. text ed. 21.95x (ISBN 0-905774-20-5, Pub by JSOT Pr England). Eisenbrauns.
Telford, William R., ed. The Interpretation of Mark. LC 84-18708. (Issues in Religion & Theology Ser.). 176p. 1985. pap. 7.95 (ISBN 0-8006-1772-X, 1-1772). Fortress.
Theissen, Gerd. The Miracle Stories of the Early Christian Tradition. Riches, John, ed. McDonagh, Francis, tr. LC 82-48546. 416p. 1983. 29.95 (ISBN 0-8006-0700-7). Fortress.
Thiemann, Ronald F. Revelation & Theology: The Gospel As Narrated Promise. LC 84-40822. 208p. 1985. text ed. 23.95 (ISBN 0-268-01629-1, 85-16296). U of Notre Dame Pr.
Thomas, Robert L. & Gundry, Stanley N. A Harmony of the Gospels: New American Standard Version. 14.95x (ISBN 0-317-52392-9, HarpR). Har-Row.
Thompson, William G. The Gospels for Whole Life. 228p. (Orig.). 1983. pap. 9.95 (ISBN 0-86683-645-4, AY8336, HarpR). Har-Row.
Tiede, David L. Prophecy & History in Luke-Acts. LC 79-8897. pap. 44.00 (2029616). Bks Demand UMI.
Toussaint, Stanley D. Behold the King: A Study of Matthew. LC 80-13410. 1980. text ed. 16.95 (ISBN 0-930014-39-1). Multnomah.
Townsend, Jim. Gospel Themes: Four Portraits of Christ's Life. (Bible Mastery Ser.). 144p. 1987. pap. 5.95 (ISBN 1-55513-848-9). Cook.
Trilling, Wolfgang. The Gospel According to St. Matthew, Vol. I. McKenzie, John L., ed. LC 81-605. (New Testament for Spiritual Reading Ser.). 182p. 1981. pap. 4.95 (ISBN 0-8245-0110-1). Crossroad NY.
--The Gospel According to St. Matthew, Vol. II. McKenzie, John L., ed. LC 81-605. (The New Testament for Spiritual Reading Ser.). 182p. 1981. pap. 4.95 (ISBN 0-8245-0111-X). Crossroad NY.
Trompf, G. W., ed. The Gospel Is Not Western: Black Theologies from Aboriginal Australia & Melanesia. LC 86-23539. (Illus.). 224p. (Orig.). 1987. pap. 17.95 (ISBN 0-88344-269-8). Orbis Bks.
Tuckett, C. M. The Revival of the Griesbach Hypothesis: An Analysis & Appraisal. LC 81-6128. (Society for New Testament Studies Monographs: No. 44). 230p. 1983. 37.50 (ISBN 0-521-23803-X). Cambridge U Pr.
Tuckett, Christopher. Nag Hammadi & the Gospel Tradition: Synoptic Tradition in the Nag Hammadi Library. 190p. 1986. 21.50 (ISBN 0-567-09364-6, Pub. by T & T Clark Ltd UK). Fortress.
Turner, Henry E. & Montefiore, Hugh. Thomas & the Evangelists. LC 63-59763. (Studies in Biblical Theology: No. 35). 1962. pap. 10.00x (ISBN 0-8401-3035-X). A R Allenson.
Tyson, Joseph B. & Longstaff, Thomas R. W. Synoptic Abstract. Baird, J. Arthur & Freedman, David Noel, eds. (The Computer Bible Ser.: Vol. XV). 1978. pap. 15.00 (ISBN 0-935106-05-7). Biblical Res Assocs.
Underwood, David A. Luke. (Standard Bible Study Workbooks Ser.). 64p. 1986. pap. text ed. 1.95 (ISBN 0-87403-183-4, 40203). Standard Pub.
Underwood, Jonathan. Matthew. (Standard Bible Study Workbooks Ser.). 64p. 1986. pap. text ed. 1.95 (ISBN 0-87403-181-8, 40201). Standard Pub.
Van Doren, W. H. Gospel of Luke, 2 vols. in 1. LC 80-8079. (Kregel Bible Study Classics Ser.). 1100p. 1981. 29.95 (ISBN 0-8254-3952-3). Kregel.
Van Linden, Philip. The Gospel According to Mark, No. 2. Karris, Robert J., ed. LC 82-20356. (Collegeville Bible Commentary Ser.). (Illus.). 96p. 1983. pap. 2.95 (ISBN 0-8146-1302-0). Liturgical Pr.
Via, Dan O., Jr. The Ethics of Mark's Gospel-In the Middle of Time. LC 84-48733. 256p. 1985. 19.95 (ISBN 0-8006-0746-5, 1-746). Fortress.
Walaskay, Paul W. And So We Came to Rome: The Political Perspectives of St. Luke. LC 82-19835. (Society for New Testament Studies Monograph: No. 49). (Illus.). 120p. 1984. 29.95 (ISBN 0-521-25116-8). Cambridge U Pr.
Wartick, Wallace. Twenty-Six Lessons on the Four Gospels. 2nd ed. (Bible Student Study Guides Ser.). 1977. pap. 9.95 (ISBN 0-89900-157-2). College Pr Pub.
Wells, Edmund. More Gospel According to Mother Goose. 159p. (Orig.). 1981. pap. 2.95 (ISBN 0-8341-0727-9). Beacon Hill.
Wenham, David. The Jesus Tradition Outside the Gospels. (Gospel Perspectives Ser.: No. 5). 419p. 1985. text ed. 24.50x (ISBN 1-85075-006-8, Pub by JSOT Pr England); pap. text ed. 13.50x (ISBN 1-85075-007-6). Eisenbrauns.
Wenham, David & Blomberg, Craig. The Miracles of Jesus. (Gospel Perspectives Ser.: No. 6). 1986. text ed. 30.00x (ISBN 1-85075-008-4, Pub. by JSOT Pr England); pap. text ed. 14.95x (ISBN 1-85075-009-2, Pub. by JSOT Pr England). Eisenbrauns.
Wesner, Marlene & Wesner, Miles E. A Fresh Look at the Gospel. LC 82-72231. (Orig.). 1983. pap. 5.95 (ISBN 0-8054-1955-1). Broadman.
Whitacre, Rodney A. Johannine Polemic: The Role of Tradition & Theology. LC 82-5457. (SBL Dissertation Ser.). 292p. 1982. pap. 13.00 (ISBN 0-89130-579-3, 06-01-67). Scholars Pr GA.
Whitley, B. J., Jr. Sharing God's Feelings. LC 84-51661. 201p. (Orig.). 1985. pap. 9.95 (ISBN 0-9615536-0-X). Spirit Christ.
Whitlock, Baird W., ed. The Gospel: The Life of Jesus. LC 83-40471. 160p. 1984. 11.95 (ISBN 0-8052-3875-1). Schocken.
Wiersbe, Warren W. Be Transformed. 156p. 1986. pap. 5.95 (ISBN 0-89693-352-0). Victor Bks.
Wijngaards, John. Handbook to the Gospels: A Guide to the Gospel Writings & the Life & Times of Jesus. (Illus.). 300p. 1983. pap. 8.95 (ISBN 0-89283-118-9). Servant.
Wilcock, Michael. Mark. 1983. pap. 4.50 (ISBN 0-87508-167-3). Chr Lit.
Williams, James G. Gospel Against Parable: Mark's Language of Mystery. (Bible & Literature Ser.: No. 12). 246p. 1985. text ed. 24.95x (ISBN 0-907459-44-7, Pub. by Almond Pr England); pap. text ed. 10.95x (ISBN 0-907459-45-5). Eisenbrauns.
Williamson, Lamar, Jr. Mark: A Bible Commentary for Teaching & Preaching. Mays, James L. & Achtemeier, Paul J., eds. LC 82-17161. (Interpretation Ser.). 289p. 1983. 17.95 (ISBN 0-8042-3121-4). John Knox.
Wilson, Ernest T. The Farewell Ministry of Christ: John 13-17. LC 81-316. 96p. (Orig.). 1981. pap. 2.50 (ISBN 0-87213-965-4). Loizeaux.
Winstone, Harold. Gospel for Young Christians. (Illus.). 192p. 1985. 3.95 (ISBN 0-225-27392-6, HarpR). Har-Row.
Witherby, H. Forbes. The Gospel of Our Salvation. 254p. 1986. 9.95 (ISBN 0-8254-4026-2). Kregel.
Woll, D. Bruce. Johannine Christianity in Conflict: Authority, Rank & Succession in the First Farwell Discourse. LC 81-1795. (SBL Dissertation Ser.). 1981. pap. 12.00 (ISBN 0-89130-471-1, 060160). Scholars Pr GA.
Wormhoudt, Arthur, tr. Gospel & Qasida. (Arab Translation Ser.: No. 84). (Illus.). 180p. (Orig.). 1985. pap. 6.50x (ISBN 0-916358-36-4). Wormhoudt.
Wright, John W. And Then There Was One. 120p. (Orig.). 1985. pap. 4.95 (ISBN 0-8341-1057-1). Beacon Hill.

BIBLE–CRITICISM, INTERPRETATION, ETC.–N. T. HEBREWS

see Bible–Criticism, Interpretation, Etc.–N. T. Epistles

BIBLE–CRITICISM, INTERPRETATION, ETC.–N. T. JAMES

see Bible–Criticism, Interpretation, Etc.–N. T. Epistles

BIBLE–CRITICISM, INTERPRETATION, ETC.–N. T. JOHN

see Bible–Criticism, Interpretation, etc.–N. T. Gospels

BIBLE–CRITICISM, INTERPRETATION, ETC.–N. T. JUDE

see Bible–Criticism, Interpretation, Etc.–N. T. Epistles

BIBLE–CRITICISM, INTERPRETATION, ETC.–N. T. LUKE

see Bible–Criticism, Interpretation, Etc.–N. T. Gospels

Schottroff, Luise & Stegemann, Wolfgang. Jesus & the Hope of the Poor. O'Connell, Matthew, tr. from Ger. LC 86-5435. (Jesus von Nazareth-Hoffnung der Armen Ser.). 144p. (Orig.). 1986. pap. 9.95 (ISBN 0-88344-255-8, CIP). Orbis Bks.

BIBLE–CRITICISM, INTERPRETATION, ETC.–N. T. MARK

see Bible–Criticism, Interpretation, Etc.–N. T. Gospels

BIBLE–CRITICISM, INTERPRETATION, ETC.–N. T. MATTHEW
see Bible–Criticism, Interpretation, Etc.–N. T. Gospels

BIBLE–CRITICISM, INTERPRETATION, ETC.–N. T. PETER
see Bible–Criticism, Interpretation, Etc.–N. T. Epistles

BIBLE–CRITICISM, INTERPRETATION, ETC.–N. T. PHILEMON
see Bible–Criticism, Interpretation, Etc.–N. T. Epistles

BIBLE–CRITICISM, INTERPRETATION, ETC.–N. T. REVELATION

Anglin, E. Warren. Seven Thunderers Utter Their Voices: History & Verse by Verse Study in the Book of Revelation of the Bible. 2nd ed. 176p. (Orig.). pap. 7.95 (ISBN 0-318-04199-5). Total Comm Ministries.

Barclay, William. Letters to the Seven Churches. LC 82-2760. 128p. 1982. pap. 6.95 (ISBN 0-664-24433-5). Westminster.

Barnes, Albert. Revelation. 12.95 (ISBN 0-8010-0849-2). Baker Bk.

Beacon Bible Commentary Staff. Hebrews-Revelation, Vol. X. 13.95 (ISBN 0-8010-0698-8). Baker Bk.

Beale, G. K. The Use of Daniel in Jewish Apocalyptic Literature & in the Relevation of St. John. 364p. (Orig.). 1985. lib. bdg. 26.00 (ISBN 0-8191-4290-5); pap. text ed. 15.25 (ISBN 0-8191-4291-3). U Pr of Amer.

Becker, Judy. The Missing Message of Revelation: Natural Catastrophes Ordained by God. Campbell, Evelyn, ed. (Illus.). 374p. (Orig.). 1986. pap. 9.95 (ISBN 0-9617493-0-X). Landmark Pr GA.

Becker, Siegbert W. Revelation. 1985. 16.95 (ISBN 0-8100-0190-X, 15N0410). Northwest Pub.

Berger, Klaus. Die Amen-Worte Jesu: Eine Untersuchung zum Problem der Legitimation in Apokalyptischer Rede. (Beiheft 39 Zur Zeitschrift fuer Die neutestamentliche Wissenschaft Ser.). (Ger). 1970. 20.80x (ISBN 3-11-006445-6). De Gruyter.

Berrigan, Daniel. The Nightmare of God. LC 81-51877. (Sunburst Originals Ser.: No. 9). (Illus.). 144p. (Orig.). 1983. pap. 6.00 (ISBN 0-934648-08-5). Sunburst Pr.

Blevins, James L. Revelation. Hayes, John, ed. LC 84-4387. (Preaching Guides Ser.). 132p. (Orig.). 1984. pap. 6.95 (ISBN 0-8042-3250-4). John Knox.

--Revelation As Drama. LC 84-4986. 1984. pap. 6.95 (ISBN 0-8054-1393-6). Broadman.

Brady, David. The Contribution of British writers Between 1560 & 1830 to the Interpretation of Revelation 13. 16-18. 341p. 1983. lib. bdg. 60.00x (ISBN 3-16-144497-3, Pub. by J C B Mohr BRD). Coronet Bks.

Brandt, Leslie F. Prophets Now. 1979. 8.50 (ISBN 0-570-03278-4, 15-2722). Concordia.

Bulter, Paul T. Twenty-Six Lessons on Revelation, Pt. 1. LC 82-71688. (Bible Student Study Guide Ser.). 133p. 1982. pap. 2.95 (ISBN 0-89900-173-4). College Pr Pub.

--Twenty-Six Lessons on Revelation, Pt. 2. LC 82-71688. (Bible Student Study Guide Ser.). 284p. 1982. pap. 4.95 (ISBN 0-89900-176-9). College Pr Pub.

Burch, V. Anthropology & the Apocalypse: An Interpretation of "the Book of Revelation" in Relation to the Archaeology, Folklore & Religious Literature & Ritual of the Near East. 1977. lib. bdg. 59.95 (ISBN 0-8490-1437-9). Gordon Pr.

Burns, Patricia H. The Book of Revelation Explained, Vol. 1. LC 82-90898. iv, 57p. 1986. pap. 9.95 (ISBN 0-9611368-0-4). B R E Pub.

Butterworth, F. Edward. Return of the Ancients. (Orig.). 1987. pap. 10.00 (ISBN 0-941227-00-6). Cosmic Pr Chico.

Copeland, John A. A Study of the Revelation. 1971. pap. 4.50 (ISBN 0-89137-702-6). Quality Pubns.

Cox, Clyde C. Evangelical Precepts of the Revelation. 1972. 5.95 (ISBN 0-87148-278-9). Pathway Pr.

Davis, W. M. Studies in Revelation. 1976. pap. 2.75 (ISBN 0-88027-044-6). Firm Foun Pub.

Dawkins, Lee. The Beast of Revelation Thirteen: The Number of a Man Six Threescore & Six? or Six Threescore to the Power & Six? Equals Nine? 68p. 1982. 5.00 (ISBN 0-682-49887-4). Exposition Pr FL.

Demarest, Bruce A. General Revelation: Historical Views & Contemporary Issues. 320p. 1982. 14.95 (ISBN 0-310-44550-7, 12706). Zondervan.

Ellul, Jacques. The Subversion of Christianity. Bromiley, Geoffrey W., tr. from Fr. 224p. (Orig.). 1986. pap. 9.95 (ISBN 0-8028-0049-1). Eerdmans.

Evans, Charles W., Jr. Babylon: The Oldest & Most Corrupt Harlot. 1984. 12.95 (ISBN 0-533-05914-3). Vantage.

Farrar, Austin. Rebirth of Images: The Making of St. John's Apocalypse. 13.25 (ISBN 0-8446-0617-0). Peter Smith.

Farrer, Austin. A Rebirth of Images: The Making of St. John's Apocalypse. 352p. (Orig.). 1986. 39.50 (ISBN 0-88706-271-7); pap. 12.95 (ISBN 0-88706-272-5). State U NY Pr.

Feinberg, Charles L. Revelation. 1985. 9.95 (ISBN 0-88469-162-4). BMH Bks.

Fitch, Alger M., Jr. Revelation. (Standard Bible Studies). 112p. 1986. pap. 5.95 (ISBN 0-87403-173-7, 40113). Standard Pub.

Fuller, Reginald H., et al. Hebrews, James, 1 & 2 Peter, Jude, Revelation. Krodel, Gerhard, ed. LC 76-7864. (Proclamation Commentaries). 132p. 1977. pap. 4.95 (ISBN 0-8006-0584-5, 1-584). Fortress.

Geoffrey of Auxerre. Geoffrey of Auxerre: On the Apocalypse, No. 42. Gibbons, Joseph, tr. from Latin. (Cistercian Fathers Ser.). write for info (ISBN 0-87907-642-9). Cistercian Pubns.

Gettys, Joseph M. How to Study the Revelation. rev. ed. 117p. 1973. pap. 4.50x (ISBN 0-87921-029-X). Attic Pr.

Guyon, Jeanne. Christ Our Revelation. (Orig.). 1985. pap. 7.95 (ISBN 0-940232-21-9). Christian Bks.

Harris, Thomas L. Arcana of Christianity, 3 pts. in 2 vols. LC 72-2955. Repr. of 1867 ed. Set. 92.00 (ISBN 0-404-10720-6). AMS Pr.

Heck, Timothy A. Revelation. (Standard Bible Study Workbooks Ser.). 64p. 1986. pap. text ed. 1.95 (ISBN 0-87403-193-1, 40213). Standard Pub.

Hendley, Jesse M. The Fifth Horseman of the Apocalypse. LC 85-19795. 236p. (Orig.). 1985. pap. 10.95 (ISBN 0-8254-2849-1). Kregel.

Hoyt, Herman A. Studies in Revelation. pap. 5.95 (ISBN 0-88469-118-7). BMH Bks.

The Interpreter's Concise Commentary, Vol. VIII: Revelation & the General Epistles. 4.95 (ISBN 0-687-19239-0). Abingdon.

Jensen, Irving L. Revelation. (Bible Self-Study Ser.). 124p. (Orig.). 1971. pap. 3.25 (ISBN 0-8024-1066-9). Moody.

--Revelation. (Irving Jensen's Do-It-Yourself Bible Study Ser.). 110p. (Orig.). 1985. wkbk. 5.95 (ISBN 0-89840-081-3). Heres Life.

Jernigan, Wade. The Unsealed Book: An Amillennial View of Revelation. 1975. pap. 3.50 (ISBN 0-89265-028-1). Randall Hse.

Jeske, Richard L. Revelation for Today: Images of Hope. LC 82-16079. 144p. 1983. pap. 6.95 (ISBN 0-8006-1693-6). Fortress.

Johnson, Alan F. Revelation: Bible Study Commentary. (Bible Study Commentary Ser.). 1986. pap. 7.95 (ISBN 0-310-45173-6, 12386P). Zondervan.

Kelly, William. The Acts, Catholic Epistles & Revelation. (Introductory Lecture Ser.). 580p. 6.95 (ISBN 0-88172-096-8). Believers Bkshelf.

Lattimore, Richard, tr. The Four Gospels & the Revelation. 288p. 1981. pap. 3.95 (ISBN 0-671-50441-X). WSP.

Lyons, Harold D. The Final Prophet. Graves, Helen, ed. LC 86-40282. 288p. 1987. 12.95 (ISBN 1-55523-037-7). Winston-Derek.

McKeever, Jim. Revelation for Layman. 1980. 10.95 (ISBN 0-931608-07-4); pap. 5.95 (ISBN 0-931608-08-2). Omega Pubns OR.

Makrakis, Apostolos. Interpretation of the Book of Revelation. Orthodox Christian Educational Society, ed. Alexander, A. G., tr. from Hellenic. 564p. 1972. 11.00x (ISBN 0-938366-12-2). Orthodox Chr.

Meyer, Nathan M. From Now to Eternity: Sermons from Revelation. pap. 6.00 (ISBN 0-88469-035-0). BMH Bks.

Morris, Henry M. The Revelation Record. 1983. 18.95 (ISBN 0-8423-5511-1). Tyndale.

Morris, S. L. The Drama of Christianity: An Interpretation of the Book of Revelation. 152p. 1982. pap. 4.95 (ISBN 0-8010-6136-9). Baker Bk.

Newport, John P. The Lion & the Lamb. LC 85-29887. 1986. 11.95 (ISBN 0-8054-1324-3). Broadman.

O'Brien, Bonnie B & C, Chester. The Victory of the Lamb. 182p. 1982. pap. 12.75 (ISBN 0-311-72280-6). Casa Bautista.

O'Day, Gail R. Revelation in the Fourth Gospel: Narrative Mode & Theological Claim. LC 86-45217. 160p. 1986. pap. 9.95 (ISBN 0-8006-1933-1). Fortress.

Phillips, John. Exploring Revelation. LC 74-15330. 288p. 1974. pap. 9.95 (ISBN 0-8024-2432-5). Moody.

--Exploring Revelation. rev. ed. (Exploring Ser.). 1987. pap. 11.95 (ISBN 0-8024-2497-X). Moody.

Portillo, Carlos E. His Revelation from Apocalypses. LC 85-52117. 150p. (Orig.). 1987. pap. write for info. (ISBN 0-937365-02-5). WCP Pubns.

The Revelation of Saint John the Divine. (Modern Critical Interpretations--Ancient, Medieval, & Renaissance Ser.). 1987. 19.95 (ISBN 0-87754-916-8). Chelsea Hse.

Revelation: Three Viewpoints. LC 77-74512. 1977. pap. 9.95 (ISBN 0-8054-1363-4). Broadman.

Robbins, Ray F. The Revelation of Jesus Christ. LC 75-1739. 240p. 1976. bds. 6.50 (ISBN 0-8054-1354-5). Broadman.

Rowland, F. V. Daniel & the Revelation. 1984. 11.95 (ISBN 0-533-05996-8). Vantage.

Russell, Marjorie H. Revelation: Your Future Prophesied. (Illus.). 60p. (Orig.). 1985. pap. 7.98 (ISBN 0-9614745-0-5). Arcadia Corp.

Sage, Gerald S. The End of False Religion-When? LC 87-80323. (Illus.). 192p. (Orig.). 1987. pap. 9.95 (ISBN 0-941813-00-2). Elite Pubs.

Saint's Revelation. LC 84-90117. 51p. 1985. 6.95 (ISBN 0-533-06193-8). Vantage.

Schick, Eduard. The Revelation of St. John, Vol. I. McKenzie, John L., ed. LC 81-605. (New Testament for Spiritual Reading Ser.). 112p. 1981. pap. 4.95 (ISBN 0-8245-0133-0). Crossroad NY.

--The Revelation of St. John, Vol. II. McKenzie, John L., ed. LC 81-605. (New Testament for Spiritual Reading Ser.). 112p. 1981. 10.00 (ISBN 0-8245-0359-7); pap. 4.95 (ISBN 0-8245-0134-9). Crossroad NY.

Schick, Edwin A. Revelation - the Last Book of the Bible. LC 76-62602. pap. 20.00 (2029617). Bks Demand UMI.

Seiss, Joseph. The Apocalypse. LC 86-27393. 536p. 1987. Repr. 24.95 (ISBN 0-8254-3754-7). Kregel.

Simpson, Douglas. The Apocalypse: A Premillennial Interpretation of the Book of Revelation. 1975. pap. 3.95 (ISBN 0-89265-029-X). Randall Hse.

Smith, F. G. The Revelation Explained. 464p. Repr. 5.50 (ISBN 0-686-29163-8). Faith Pub Hse.

Stevens, Paul. Revelation: The Triumph of God. (LifeBuilder Bible Studies). 64p. (Orig.). 1987. pap. 2.95 (ISBN 0-8308-1021-8). Inter-Varsity.

Strauss, James D. Revelation - the Seer, the Saviour, & the Saved. rev. ed. (The Bible Study Textbook Ser.). (Illus.). 1972. 15.90 (ISBN 0-89900-048-7). College Pr Pub.

Strauss, Lehman. Prophetic Mysteries Revealed: The Prophetic Significance of the Parables of Matthew 13 & the Letters of Revelation 2-3. LC 80-17540. 256p. 1980. 9.95 (ISBN 0-87213-832-1). Loizeaux.

Sutton, Hilton. Revelation: God's Grand Finale. 280p. (Orig.). 1984. pap. 6.95 (ISBN 0-89274-298-4). Harrison Hse.

--Revelation Teaching Syllabus. 1985. 10.00 (ISBN 0-89274-318-2). Harrison Hse.

Swedenborg, Emanuel. Spiritual Life - the Word of God. pap. 1.95 (ISBN 0-87785-083-6). Swedenborg.

Thompson, Steven. The Apocalypse & Semitic Syntax. LC 84-12081. (Society for New Testament Studies Monograph: No. 52). 160p. 1985. 32.50 (ISBN 0-521-26031-0). Cambridge U Pr.

Turner, Elizabeth S. Be Ye Transformed. 1969. 5.95 (ISBN 0-87159-008-5). Unity School.

Van Hartingsveld, L. Text & Interpretation: A Practical Commentary, Revelation. Van Der Woude, A. S., ed. (Text & Interpretation Ser.). (Dutch.). 128p. (Orig.). 1985. pap. 6.95 (ISBN 0-8028-0100-5). Eerdmans.

Venden, Morris. Return of Elijah. (Harv Ser.). 1983. pap. 4.50 (ISBN 0-8163-0453-X). Pacific Pr Pub Assn.

The Victorious Christ (Revelation) Leader's Guide. (New Horizons Bible Study Ser.). 48p. 1983. pap. 1.95 (ISBN 0-89367-089-8). Light & Life.

The Victorious Christ (Revelation) Student Guide. 68p. 1983. pap. 2.50 (ISBN 0-89367-088-X). Light & Life.

Wiersbe, Warren W. Be Victorious. 156p. 1985. pap. 5.95 (ISBN 0-89693-547-7). Victor Bks.

BIBLE–CRITICISM, INTERPRETATION, ETC.–N. T. ROMANS
see Bible–Criticism, Interpretation, Etc.–N. T. Epistles

BIBLE–CRITICISM, INTERPRETATION, ETC.–N. T. THESSALONIANS
see Bible–Criticism, Interpretation, Etc.–N. T. Epistles

BIBLE–CRITICISM, INTERPRETATION, ETC.–N. T. TIMOTHY
see Bible–Criticism, Interpretation, Etc.–N. T. Epistles

BIBLE–CRITICISM, INTERPRETATION, ETC.–N. T. TITUS
see Bible–Criticism, Interpretation, Etc.–N. T. Epistles

BIBLE–CRITICISM, INTERPRETATION, ETC.–O. T

Ackroyd, Peter R. Israel under Babylon & Persia. (New Clarendon Bible Ser.). 1970. 15.95x (ISBN 0-19-836917-4). Oxford U Pr.

Adamiak, Richard. Justice & History in the Old Testament: The Evolution of Divine Retribution in the Historiographies of the Wilderness Generation. 1982. 14.95x (ISBN 0-939738-08-2). Zubal Inc.

Alter, Robert. The Art of Biblical Narrative. LC 80-68958. 208p. 1981. 14.95 (ISBN 0-465-00424-5). Basic.

Anderson, G. W. A Critical Introduction to the Old Testament. (Studies in Theology). 262p. 1979. pap. 13.50 (ISBN 0-7156-0077-X, Pub. by Duckworth London). Longwood Pub Group.

Archer, Gleason L. Resena Critica De Una Introduccion al Antiguo Testament (Survey of Old Testament Introduction) (Span.). 507p. 1982. pap. 14.95 (ISBN 0-8254-1033-9). Kregel.

--A Survey of Old Testament Introduction. LC 64-20988. 582p. 1973. 16.95 (ISBN 0-8024-8447-6). Moody.

Archpriest Michael Kheraskov & Athanasiev, D. Rukovodstvo k Izucheniju Svijashchennago Pisanija Vjetkhago Zavjeta, 3 vols. Tr. of A Guide for Study of the Holy Scriptures of the Old Testament. 942p. pap. text ed. 32.00 (ISBN 0-317-29295-1). Holy Trinity.

Armeding, Carl E. The Old Testament & Criticism. 144p. 1983. pap. 6.95 (ISBN 0-8028-1951-6). Eerdmans.

Asimov, Isaac. Asimov's Guide to the Bible: The Old Testament. 720p. 1971. pap. 10.95 (ISBN 0-380-01032-1). Avon.

Bacher, Wilhelm. Abraham Ibn Esra Als Grammatiker: Ein Beitrag zur Geschichte der Hebraischen Sprachwissenschaft. Katz, Steven, ed. LC 79-7125. (Jewish Philosophy, Mysticism & History of Ideas Ser.). 1980. Repr. of 1882 ed. lib. bdg. 16.00x (ISBN 0-405-12239-X). Ayer Co Pubs.

Balentine, Samuel E. The Hidden God: The Hiding of the Face of God in the Old Testament. (Oxford Theological Monographs). 1983. 34.00x (ISBN 0-19-826719-3). Oxford U Pr.

Becker, Joachim. Messianic Expectation in the Old Testament. Green, David E., tr. LC 79-8891. pap. 24.00 (2027875). Bks Demand UMI.

Benagh, Christine L. Meditations on the Book of Job. LC 64-25262. 1964. 3.95 (ISBN 0-686-05041-X). St Thomas.

Ben-Israel, Manasseh. The Conciliator: A Reconcilement of the Apparent Contradictions in Holy Scripture. Lindo, E. H., tr. from Span. LC 72-83942. (The Library of Judaic Studies: No. SHP 10). 688p. 1987. Repr. of 1904 ed. 23.50 (ISBN 0-87203-115-2). Hermon.

Berkeley, James P. Knowing the Old Testament. (Illus.). (YA) 1954. pap. text ed. 5.95 (ISBN 0-8170-0088-7). Judson.

Best, Thomas F., ed. Hearing & Speaking the Word: An Anthology of the Works of James Muilenburg. (Scholars Press Homage Ser.: No. 7). 464p. 1985. 26.95 (ISBN 0-89130-665-X, 00 16 07). Scholars Pr GA.

Birch, Bruce C. What Does the Lord Require? The Old Testament Call to Social Witness. LC 85-610. 120p. 1985. pap. 8.95 (ISBN 0-664-24630-3). Westminster.

Black, James. The Old Testament: Student Text. LC 82-70087. (Illus.). 160p. (Orig.). 1982. pap. 4.95 (ISBN 0-87793-248-4). Ave Maria.

--The Old Testament: Teacher's Manual. 80p. (Orig.). 1982. tchrs. ed. 2.25 (ISBN 0-87793-249-2). Ave Maria.

Blenkinsopp, Joseph. Prophecy & Canon: A Contribution to the Study of Jewish Origins. LC 76-22411. 206p. 1986. pap. 9.95 (ISBN 0-268-01559-7). U of Notre Dame Pr.

--Wisdom & Law in the Old Testament: The Ordering of Life in Israel & Early Judaism. (The Oxford Bible Ser.). (Orig.). 1983. pap. 9.95 (ISBN 0-19-213253-9). Oxford U Pr.

Boadt, Lawrence. Reading the Old Testament: An Introduction. LC 84-60723. 416p. (Orig.). 1984. pap. 7.95 (ISBN 0-8091-2631-1). Paulist Pr.

Bock, Darrell L. Proclamation from Prophecy & Pattern: Lucan Old Testament Christiology. (JSOT Supplement Ser.: No. 12). 350p. 1986. text ed. 28.50x (ISBN 1-85075-000-9, Pub. by JSOT Pr England); pap. text ed. 13.50x (ISBN 1-85075-001-7). Eisenbrauns.

Brenner, Athalya. Colour Terms in the Old Testament. (Journal for the Study of the Old Testament, Supplement Ser.: No. 21). 296p. 1983. text ed. 29.95x (ISBN 0-905774-42-6, Pub. by JSOT Pr England); pap. text ed. 21.95 (ISBN 0-905774-43-4, Pub. by JSOT Pr England). Eisenbrauns.

Bronstein, Herbert & Friedlander, Albert, eds. The Five Scrolls. 324p. 1984. 19.95 (ISBN 0-916694-80-1); deluxe ed. 60.00 (ISBN 0-916694-81-X); special ltd. ed., leatherbound 675.00 (ISBN 0-916694-82-8). Central Conf.

Butler, James T., et al. Understanding the Word: Essays in Honor of Bernhard W. Anderson. (JSOT Supplement Ser.: No. 37). 390p. 1986. text ed. 37.50x (ISBN 0-905774-88-4, Pub. by JSOT Pr England). Eisenbrauns.

Cantleberry, Lillian. Jacob: God's Plain Man. 1984. pap. 7.95 (ISBN 0-570-03928-2, 12-2863). Concordia.

Charles, R. H., et al. Apocrypha & Pseudepigrapha of the Old Testament, 2 Vols. Vol. 1. 69.00x (ISBN 0-19-826155-1); Vol. 2. 69.00x (ISBN 0-19-826152-7). Oxford U Pr.

Charlesworth, J. Old Testament Pseudepigrapha & the New Testament. (Society for New Testament Studies Monographs: No. 54). 213p. 1985. 34.50 (ISBN 0-521-30190-4). Cambridge U Pr.

Charlesworth, James H. The Pseudepigrapha & Modern Research, with a Supplement. LC 76-25921. (Society Biblical Literature Septuagint & Cognate Studies). 344p. 1981. pap. 12.75 (ISBN 0-89130-440-1, 06 0707S). Scholars Pr GA.

Childs, Brevard S. Old Testament Theology in a Canonical Context. LC 85-45503. 272p. 1986. 16.95 (ISBN 0-8006-0772-4, 1-772). Fortress.

Christian, Owen L. Faith in Conflict. 192p. 1986. 12.50 (ISBN 0-89962-519-3). Todd & Honeywell.

Claassen, W. Text & Context: Old Testament & Semitic Studies for F.C. Fensham. (JSOT Supplement Ser.: No. 48). 220p. 1987. text ed. 28.50x (ISBN 1-85075-040-8, Pub. by JSOT Pr England). Eisenbrauns.

Clements, Ronald E. One Hundred Years of Old Testament Interpretation. LC 76-23236. 160p. 1976. pap. 7.95 (ISBN 0-664-24747-4). Westminster.

Clines, D. J. & Gunn, D. M. Art & Meaning: Rhetoric in Biblical Literature. (Journal for the Study of the Old Testament, Supplement Ser.: No. 19). viii, 266p. 1982. text ed. 25.00x (ISBN 0-905774-38-8, Pub. by JSOT Pr England); pap. text ed. 13.95x (ISBN 0-905774-39-6). Eisenbrauns.

Cooper, Eli L. Insights to Scripture. 196p. (Orig.). 1986. lib. bdg. 24.00 (ISBN 0-8191-5121-1); pap. text ed. 10.25 (ISBN 0-8191-5122-X). U Pr of Amer.

Craghan, John F. Love & Thunder: A Sprituality of the Old Testament. 248p. 1983. pap. text ed. 11.00 (ISBN 0-8146-1279-2). Liturgical Pr.

Creelman, H. S. History & Literature of the Old Testament, 2 vols. (Illus.). 1987. Set. 189.45 (ISBN 0-89266-573-4). Am Classical Coll Pr.

Crenshaw, J. L. & Crenshaw, Willis. Essays on Old Testament Ethics: J. P. Hyatt in Memoriam. 1974. 35.00x (ISBN 0-87068-233-4). Ktav.

Crenshaw, James L. Old Testament Wisdom: An Introduction. LC 80-82183. 262p. 1981. 16.95 (ISBN 0-8042-0143-9); pap. 12.95 (ISBN 0-8042-0142-0). John Knox.

Crenshaw, James L., ed. Theodicy in the Old Testament. LC 83-8885. (Issues in Religion & Theology Ser.). 176p. 1983. pap. 7.95 (ISBN 0-8006-1764-9). Fortress.

Daube, David. The Exodus Pattern in the Bible. LC 78-9920. 1979. Repr. of 1963 ed. lib. bdg. 24.75 (ISBN 0-313-21190-6, DAEX). Greenwood.

Davidson, Benjamin. Analytical Hebrew & Chaldee Lexicon. 784p. Date not set. 24.95 (ISBN 0-913573-03-5). Hendrickson MA.

Davies, Philip R. The Damascus Covenant: An Interpretation of the "Damascus Document". (Journal for the Study of the Old Testament, Supplement Ser.: No. 25). 267p. 1983. text ed. 28.00x (ISBN 0-905774-50-7, Pub. by JSOT Pr England); pap. text ed. 18.50x (ISBN 0-905774-51-5, Pub. by JSOT Pr England). Eisenbrauns.

De Lange, N. R. Origen & the Jews. LC 75-36293. (Oriental Publications Ser.: No. 25). 160p. 1977. 39.50 (ISBN 0-521-20542-5). Cambridge U Pr.

Dickerhoff, Heinrich. Wege ins Alte Testament - und Zurueck: Vom Sinn und den Moeglichkeiten einer "Theologie mit dem Alten Testament" in der Arbeit mit Erwachsenen, Vol 211. (European University Studies: No. 23). (Ger.). 409p. 1983. 40.55 (ISBN 3-8204-7734-9). P Lang Pubs.

Dyrness, William A. Themes in Old Testament Theology. LC 79-2380. 1979. pap. 8.95 (ISBN 0-87784-726-6). Inter-Varsity.

Efird, James M. Old Testament Writings: History, Literature, Interpretation. LC 81-82352. (Biblical Foundations Ser.). (Illus.). 324p. 1982. pap. 11.95 (ISBN 0-8042-0145-5). John Knox.

Eggleton, John E. Discovering the Old Testament. 306p. 1980. pap. text ed. 7.95 (ISBN 0-933656-07-6). Trinity Pub Hse.

Eisenberg, Azriel. The Book of Books. 163p. 1976. pap. 9.95 (ISBN 0-900689-77-3). Soncino Pr.

Elliott, Maurice. Spiritualism in the Old Testament. 59.95 (ISBN 0-8490-1117-5). Gordon Pr.

Engnell, Ivan. Rigid Scrutiny: Critical Essays on the Old Testament. Willis, John T., tr. LC 70-76166. 1969. 15.00x (ISBN 0-8265-1133-3). Vanderbilt U Pr.

--A Rigid Scrutiny: Critical Essays on the Old Testament. Willis, John T., ed. (Vanderbilt University Press Bks.). 303p. 1969. 15.00 (ISBN 0-8265-1133-3). U of Ill Pr.

Faur, Jose. Golden Doves with Silver Dots: Semiotics & Textuality in Rabbinic Tradition. LC 84-47967. (Jewish Literature & Culture Ser.). 256p. 1986. 27.50x (ISBN 0-253-32600-1). Ind U Pr.

Fohrer, Georg. Theologische Grundstrukturen des Alten Testaments. (Theologische Bibliothek Toepelmann, 24). 1972. pap. 23.20x (ISBN 3-11-003874-9). De Gruyter.

Foley, Leonard. From Eden to Nazareth: Finding Our Story in the Old Testament. (Illus.). 103p. (Orig.). 1983. pap. text ed. 3.50 (ISBN 0-86716-020-9). St Anthony Mess Pr.

Fontaine, Carol R. Traditional Sayings in the Old Testament: A Contextual Study. (Bible & Literature Ser.: No. 5). 1982. text ed. 24.95x (ISBN 0-907459-08-0, Pub. by Almond Pr England); pap. text ed. 14.95x (ISBN 0-907459-09-9, Pub. by Almond Pr England). Eisenbrauns.

Francisco, Clyde T. Introducing the Old Testament. rev. ed. LC 76-24060. 1977. bds. 13.95 (ISBN 0-8054-1213-1, 4212-13). Broadman.

Frick, Frank S. The Formation of the State in Ancient Israel: A Survey of Models & Theories. (The Social World of Biblical Antiquity Ser.). 219p. 1985. text ed. 24.95x (ISBN 0-907459-51-X, Pub. by Almond Pr England); pap. text ed. 10.95 (ISBN 0-907459-52-8). Eisenbrauns.

Fromm, Erich. You Shall Be As Gods: A Radical Interpretation of the Old Testament & Its Tradition. 1977. pap. 2.50 (ISBN 0-449-30763-8, Prem). Fawcett.

Gafni, Shlomo S., ed. The Glory of the Old Testament. LC 83-848323. 256p. 1984. 25.00 (ISBN 0-394-53658-4, Pub. by Villard Bks). Random.

Gall, A. Von, ed. Der Hebraeische Pentateuch der Samaritaner, 5 pts. (Ger.). xciv, 440p. 1966. Repr. of 1918 ed. Set. 45.60x (ISBN 3-11-009258-1). De Gruyter.

Gaster, Theodore H. Myth, Legend & Custom in the Old Testament: A Comparative Study with Chapters from Sir James G. Frazer's Folklore in the Old Testament, 2 vols. Set. 36.00 (ISBN 0-8446-5189-3). Peter Smith.

Geisler, Norman L. A Popular Survey of the Old Testament. LC 77-78578. 1977. pap. 8.95 (ISBN 0-8010-3684-4). Baker Bk.

Gileadi, Avraham, ed. Israel's Apostasy & Restoration in Prophetic Thought: Essays in Honor of Roland Kenneth Harrison. 336p. 1986. 26.95 (ISBN 0-8407-7532-6). Nelson.

Ginsburg, Christian D. Introduction to the Massoretico Critical Edition of the Hebrew Bible. rev. ed. 1966. 79.50x (ISBN 0-87068-060-9). Ktav.

Girdlestone, Robert B. Synonyms of the Old Testament: Numerically Coded to Strong's Exhaustive Concordance. White, Donald R., ed. 400p. 1983. deluxe ed. 22.95 (ISBN 0-8010-3798-0); pap. 17.95 kivar bdg. (ISBN 0-8010-3789-1). Baker Bk.

Goldingay, John. Old Testament Commentary Survey. 2nd ed. Hubbard, Robert & Branson, Mark L., eds. 66p. 1981. pap. 3.50 (ISBN 0-8308-5499-1). Inter-Varsity.

--Theological Diversity & the Authority of the Old Testament. 240p. (Orig.). 1987. pap. 14.95 (ISBN 0-8028-0229-X). Eerdmans.

Good, Edwin M. Irony in the Old Testament. (Bible & Literature Ser.: No. 3). (Orig.). 1981. pap. text ed. 9.95x (ISBN 0-907459-05-6, Pub. by Almond Pr England). Eisenbrauns.

Gooding, D. W. The Account of the Tabernacle. (Texts & Studies, New Ser.: Vol. 6). Repr. of 1959 ed. 28.00 (ISBN 0-8115-1719-5). Kraus Repr.

Gordon, Cyrus H. Homer & Bible: The Origin & Character of East Mediterranean Literature. 1967. pap. 4.95 (ISBN 0-911566-03-1). Ventnor.

Gottwald, Norman K., ed. SEMEIA: Social Scientific Criticism of the Hebrew Bible & Its Social World: The Israelite Monarchy. 152p. 1986. pap. 9.95 (ISBN 0-317-52980-3, 06-20-37). Scholars Pr GA.

Gowan, Donald E. Eschatology in the Old Testament. LC 85-4550. 160p. 1985. pap. 9.95 (ISBN 0-8006-1906-4, 1-1906). Fortress.

--Reclaiming the Old Testament for the Christian Pulpit. 176p. Date not set. pap. 10.95 (ISBN 0-567-29106-5, Pub. by T & T Clark Ltd UK). Fortress.

--When Man Becomes God: Humanism & Hybris in the Old Testament. LC 75-17582. (Pittsburgh Theological Monographs: No. 6). 1975. pap. 8.75 (ISBN 0-915138-06-9). Pickwick.

Gray, George B. A Critical Introduction to the Old Testament. 1978. Repr. of 1936 ed. lib. bdg. 25.00 (ISBN 0-8495-1939-X). Arden Lib.

Gunneweg, A. H. Understanding the Old Testament. Bowden, John, tr. LC 78-6696. (Old Testament Library). 272p. 1978. Westminster.

Hall, Terry. Old Testament Express. 160p. 1985. pap. 3.95 (ISBN 0-88207-599-3). Victor Bks.

Hanne, Tony. A New Old Testament. LC 84-90178. 105p. 1986. 8.95 (ISBN 0-533-06228-4). Vantage.

Harralson, David M. Stories from the Old Testament. (Literacy Volunteers of America Readers Ser.). 48p. (Orig.). 1983. pap. 1.95 (ISBN 0-8428-9607-4). Cambridge Bk.

Harrington, Daniel J. Interpreting the Old Testament: A Practical Guide. (Old Testament Message Ser.: Vol. 1). 1981. 10.95 (ISBN 0-89453-401-7); pap. 6.95 (ISBN 0-89453-236-7). M Glazier.

Hawkins, O. S. Clues to a Successful Life. LC 82-71561. (Orig.). 1982. pap. 6.95 (ISBN 0-8054-5515-9). Broadman.

Hayes, John H., ed. Old Testament Form Criticism. LC 72-97351. (Trinity University Monograph Series in Religion: Vol. 2). pap. 77.50 (ISBN 0-317-28182-8, 2022566). Bks Demand UMI.

Heaton, E. W. Solomon's New Men. LC 74-13412. (Illus.). 216p. 1975. 15.00x (ISBN 0-87663-714-4, Pica Pr). Universe.

Heidel, Alexander. Gilgamesh Epic & Old Testament Parallels. 2nd ed. LC 49-5734. 1963. 8.95 (ISBN 0-226-32398-6, P136, Phoen). U of Chicago Pr.

Holladay, William L. A Concise Hebrew & Aramaic Lexicon of the Old Testament. (Hebrew & Aramaic.). 1971. 27.95 (ISBN 0-8028-3413-2). Eerdmans.

Honor, Leo L. Sennacherib's Invasion of Palestine. LC 26-20926. (Columbia University. Contributions to Oriental History & Philology: No. 12). Repr. of 1926 ed. 15.00 (ISBN 0-404-50542-2). AMS Pr.

James, M. R., ed. The Testament of Abraham. (Texts & Studies: No. 1, Vol. 2, Pt. 2). pap. 19.00 (ISBN 0-8115-1685-7). Kraus Repr.

Jensen, Irving L. Jensen's Survey of the Old Testament. 1978. text ed. 19.95 (ISBN 0-8024-4307-9). Moody.

Jensen, Joseph. God's Word to Israel: An Introduction to the Old Testament. 400p. 1982. pap. 9.95 (ISBN 0-89453-289-8). M Glazier.

Kaiser, Walter C., Jr. Classical Evangelical Essays in Old Testament Interpretation. 1972. pap. 9.95 (ISBN 0-8010-5314-5). Baker Bk.

Kaplan, Louis E. Gates of Mercy. LC 79-64616. (Orig.). 1979. pap. 3.75 (ISBN 0-87203-085-7). Hermon.

Knight, Douglas A. Rediscovering the Traditions of Israel. LC 75-6868. (Society of Biblical Literature. Dissertation Ser.: No. 9). pap. 86.50 (ISBN 0-317-07884-4, 2017515). Bks Demand UMI.

Kramer, Herman B. The Book of Destiny. LC 75-13556. (Illus.). 1975. pap. 12.50 (ISBN 0-89555-046-6). TAN Bks Pubs.

Kurtz, John H. Sacrificial Worship of the Old Testament. 1979. 16.50 (ISBN 0-86524-012-4, 8703). Klock & Klock.

Lang, Bernhard, ed. Anthropological Approaches to the Old Testament. LC 84-48723. (Issues in Religion & Theology Ser.). 176p. 1985. pap. 7.95 (ISBN 0-8006-1771-1, 1-1771). Fortress.

La Sor, W. S. & Hubbard, David A. Old Testament Survey: The Message, Form, & Background of the Old Testament. 698p. 1982. 24.95 (ISBN 0-8028-3556-2). Eerdmans.

Leary, James F. Hear, O Israel: A Guide to the Old Testament. 144p. 1986. pap. 4.95 (ISBN 0-88479-029-0). Chr Classics.

Loader, J. A. Ecclesiastes. Van Der Woude, A. S., ed. Vriend, John, tr. from Dutch. (Text & Interpretation Commentary Ser.). 120p. (Orig.). 1986. pap. 6.95 (ISBN 0-8028-0102-1). Eerdmans.

Long, Burke O., ed. Images of Man & God: Old Testament Short Stories in Literary Focus. (Bible & Literature Ser.: No. 1). 128p. 1981. text ed. 19.95x (ISBN 0-907459-00-5, Pub. by Almond Pr England); pap. text ed. 6.95x (ISBN 0-907459-01-3). Eisenbrauns.

Ludlow, Daniel H. A Companion to Your Study of the Old Testament. LC 80-28088. 437p. 1981. 9.95 (ISBN 0-87747-853-8). Deseret Bk.

Ludlow, Victor L. Unlocking the Old Testament. LC 81-68266. (Illus.). 239p. 1981. 8.95 (ISBN 0-87747-873-2). Deseret Bk.

Ludwig, Charles. Ludwig's Handbook of Old Testament Rulers & Cities. LC 84-70426. 244p. (Orig.). 1984. pap. 6.95 (ISBN 0-89636-130-6). Accent Bks.

McAlpine, Thomas H. Sleep, Divine & Human, in the Old Testament. (JSOT Supplement Ser.: No. 38). 232p. 1986. text ed. 32.50x (ISBN 0-317-46791-3, Pub. by JSOT Pr England); pap. text ed. 14.95x (ISBN 0-317-46792-1). Eisenbrauns.

Martens, Elmer A. God's Design: A Focus on Old Testament Theology. pap. 10.95 (ISBN 0-8010-6209-8). Baker Bk.

Mayo, S. M. The Relevance of the Old Testament for the Christian Faith: Biblical Theology & Interpretive Methodology. 220p. (Orig.). 1982. lib. bdg. 27.75 (ISBN 0-8191-2656-X); pap. text ed. 12.50 (ISBN 0-8191-2657-8). U Pr of Amer.

Mellor, E. B., ed. The Making of the Old Testament. (Cambridge Bible Commentary on the New English Bible, Old Testament Ser.). (Illus.). 226p. 1972. 22.95 (ISBN 0-521-08184-X); pap. 10.95 (ISBN 0-521-09673-1). Cambridge U Pr.

Melnick. Old Testament. (Book Note). 1985. pap. 2.50 (ISBN 0-8120-3531-3). Barron.

Millett, Robert & Jackson, Kent. Studies in Scripture: The Old Testament, Vol. III. 345p. 1985. 13.95 (ISBN 0-934126-81-X). Randall Bk Co.

Miscall, Peter D. The Workings of Old Testament Narrative. LC 82-48570. (Semeia Studies). 160p. 1983. pap. 8.95 (ISBN 0-8006-1512-3). Fortress.

--The Workings of Old Testament Narrative. LC 82-5993. (SBL Semeia Studies). 158p. 1983. pap. 8.95 (ISBN 0-89130-584-X, 06-06-12). Scholars Pr GA.

Mistere Du Viel Testament, 6 Vols. (Illus.). 200.00 (ISBN 0-384-39180-X); pap. 165.00 (ISBN 0-384-39179-6). Johnson Repr.

Monarch Notes on the Old Testament As Living Literature. 1976. pap. 3.95 (ISBN 0-671-00964-8). Monarch Pr.

Neusner, Jacob. Judaism & Scripture: The Evidence of Leviticus Rabbah. LC 85-20497. (CSHJ Ser.). 664p. 1986. 50.00x (ISBN 0-226-57614-0). U of Chicago Pr.

--The Religious Study of Judaism: Description, Analysis & Interpretation. LC 85-30411. (Studies in Judaism Ser.: Vol. 1). 188p. (Orig.). 1986. lib. bdg. 22.50 (ISBN 0-8191-5393-1, Pub. by Studies in Judaism); pap. text ed. 9.75 (ISBN 0-8191-5394-X). U Pr of Amer.

--The Religious Study of Judaism: Description, Analysis, Interpretation-The Centrality of Context. LC 85-30411. (Studies in Judaism: Vol. 2). 230p. (Orig.). 1986. lib. bdg. 24.50 (ISBN 0-8191-5450-4, Pub. by Studies in Judaism); pap. text ed. 12.75 (ISBN 0-8191-5451-2). U Pr of Amer.

Nibley, Hugh. Old Testament & Related Studies. LC 85-27544. (Collected Works of Hugh Nibley Ser.). 304p. 1986. 15.95 (ISBN 0-87579-032-1). Deseret Bk.

Nicholson, Ernest W. God & His People: Covenant & Theology in the Old Testament. 240p. 1986. 36.00x (ISBN 0-19-826684-7). Oxford U Pr.

Noth, Martin. The Deuteronomistic History. (Journal for the Study of the Old Testament, Supplement Ser.: No. 15). 1981. text ed. 20.95x (ISBN 0-905774-25-6, Pub. by JSOT Pr England); pap. text ed. 10.95x (ISBN 0-905774-30-2, Pub. by JSOT Pr England). Eisenbrauns.

Ohler, Annemarie. Studying the Old Testament. 400p. 33.95 (ISBN 0-567-09335-2, Pub. by T & T Clard Ltd UK). Fortress.

Ohlsen, Woodrow. Perspectives on Old Testament Literature. LC 77-91012. (Illus.). 450p. 1978. 14.95 (ISBN 0-15-570484-2, HC). HarBraceJ.

Otwell, John H. And Sarah Laughed: The Status of Woman in the Old Testament. LC 76-54671. 222p. 1977. pap. 8.95 (ISBN 0-664-24126-3). Westminster.

Outlaw, et al. A Survey of the Old Testament. Harrison, Harrold D., ed. (Orig.). 1984. pap. 5.95 (ISBN 0-89265-089-3). Randall Hse.

Polzin, Robert M. & Rothman, Eugene, eds. The Biblical Mosaic: Changing Perspectives. LC 81-67307. (Semeia Studies). 1982. pap. 9.95 (ISBN 0-8006-1510-7, Co-Pub by Fortress Pr). Fortress.

Pomazansky, Michael. The Old Testament in the New Testament Church. 40p. (Orig.). 1977. pap. 2.00 (ISBN 0-317-30281-7). Holy Trinity.

Reventlow, Henning G. Problems of Old Testament Theology in the Twentieth Century. Bowden, John, tr. LC 84-21178. 96p. 1985. 14.95 (ISBN 0-8006-1875-0, 1-1875). Fortress.

Riesener, Ingrid. Der Stamm Awad in Alten Testament. (Beiheft zur Zeitschrift Fuer die Alttestamentliche Wissenschaft: Vol. 149). 1979. 62.00x (ISBN 3-11-007260-2). De Gruyter.

Ringe, Sharon H. Jesus, Liberation & the Biblical Jubilee: Images for Ethics & Christology. LC 85-4609. (Overtures to Biblical Theology Ser.). 144p. 1985. pap. 8.95 (ISBN 0-8006-1544-1). Fortress.

Ringgren, Helmer. Israelite Religion. Green, David E., tr. from Ger. LC 66-10757. 408p. 1975. pap. 7.95 (ISBN 0-8006-1121-7, 1-1121). Fortress.

Rogers, Robert W., ed. Cuneiform Parallels to the Old Testament. 1977. lib. bdg. 69.95 (ISBN 0-8490-1695-9). Gordon Pr.

Rogerson, J. W. Myth in Old Testament Interpretation. LC 73-78234. (Beiheft zur Zeitschrift fuer die Alttestamentliche Wissenschaft). 1974. 50.00x (ISBN 3-11-004220-7). De Gruyter.

Rogerson, John W. Old Testament Criticism in the Nineteenth Century. LC 84-47933. 448p. 1985. 29.95 (ISBN 0-8006-0737-6, 1-737). Fortress.

Rowley, H. H. Rediscovery of the Old Testament. 224p. 1946. 14.00 (ISBN 0-227-67576-2). Attic Pr.

Rowley, Harold H. Re-Discovery of the Old Testament. facs. ed. LC 75-76912. (Essay Index Reprint Ser). 1946. 19.00 (ISBN 0-8369-1154-7). Ayer Co Pubs.

Sandmel, Samuel. Enjoyment of Scripture: The Law, the Prophets, & the Writings. (Illus.). 1972. pap. 8.95 (ISBN 0-19-501783-8). Oxford U Pr.

--The Hebrew Scriptures: An Introduction to Their Literature & Religious Ideas. 1978. pap. 16.95x (ISBN 0-19-502369-2). Oxford U Pr.

Sands, Percy C. Literary Genius of the Old Testament. LC 75-35756. 1975. Repr. of 1924 ed. lib. bdg. 27.50 (ISBN 0-8414-7646-2). Folcroft.

Schaefer-Lichtenberger, Christa. Stadt und Eidgenossenschaft im Alten Testament: Eine Auseinandersetzung mit Max Webers Studie "Das Antike Judentum". (Ger.). 485p. 1983. 43.20 (ISBN 3-11-008591-7). De Gruyter.

Schmidt, Werner H. Einfuehrung in das Alte Testament: Dritte, Erweiterte Auflage. (Ger.). x, 394p. 1985. 19.20x (ISBN 3-11-010403-2). De Gruyter.

Schwartzbach, B. E. Voltaire's Old Testament Criticism. 275p. (Orig.). 1970. pap. text ed. 24.00x (Pub. by Droz Switzerland). Coronet Bks.

Scroggie, W. Graham. Fascination of Old Testament Story. Date not set. 7.95 (ISBN 0-8254-3726-1). Kregel.

Slingerland, H. Dixon. The Testaments of the Twelve Patriarchs: A Critical History of Research. LC 75-34233. (Society of Biblical Literature. Monograph). 1977. 13.50 (ISBN 0-89130-084-8, 060021); pap. 9.95 (ISBN 0-89130-062-7). Scholars Pr GA.

Sternberg, Meir. The Poetics of Biblical Narrative: Ideological Literature & the Drama of Reading. LC 85-42752. (Indiana Studies in Biblical Literature). 596p. 1985. 57.50x (ISBN 0-253-34521-9). Ind U Pr.

Stuart, Douglas. Old Testament Exegesis: A Primer for Students & Pastors. 2nd, rev. & enl. ed. LC 84-10431. 142p. 1984. pap. 7.95 (ISBN 0-664-24559-5). Westminster.

Tatham, Julie C. The Old Testament Made Easy. (Illus.). 540p. (Orig.). 1986. limp leatherette 20.00 (ISBN 0-9617543-0-3). J C Tatham.

Taubes, Hellen. The Bible Speaks By, 3 Vols. 1965. Set. 14.95. Soncino Pr.

Taylor, Edward. Upon the Types of the Old Testament. Mignon, Charles W., ed. 1988. price not set (ISBN 0-8032-3075-3). U of Nebr Pr.

Thompson, Michael E. W. Situation & Theology: Old Testament Interpretations of the Syro-Ephraimite War. (Prophets & Historians Ser.: No. 1). 1983. text ed. 25.95x (ISBN 0-907459-14-5, Pub. by Almond Pr England); pap. text ed. 12.95x (ISBN 0-907459-15-3, Pub. by Almond Pr England). Eisenbrauns.

Tigay, Jeffrey H. Empirical Models for Biblical Criticism. LC 84-20951. 304p. 1985. 37.50 (ISBN 0-8122-7976-X). U of Pa Pr.

Troeger, Thomas H. Rage! Reflect. Rejoice! Praying with the Psalmists. LC 77-22755. 96p. 1977. pap. 3.95 (ISBN 0-664-24293-6). Westminster.

Tullock, John H. The Old Testament Story. 2nd ed. (Illus.). 432p. 1987. text ed. 28.67 (ISBN 0-13-633892-5). P-H.

UBS Committee, ed. Preliminary & Interim Report on the Hebrew Old Testament Text Project, Vol. 5. (Prophetical Bks.: No. II). (Eng. & Fr.). xxxiii, 443p. 1980. pap. 5.00x (ISBN 0-8267-0012-8, 08559, Pub. by United Bible). Am Bible.

Unger, Merrill F. Unger's Commentary On The Old Testament: Genesis-Song of Solomon, Vol. 1. 360p. 1981. 25.95 (ISBN 0-8024-9028-X). Moody.

Von Nordheim, Eckhard. Die Lehre der Alten: II Das Testament als Literaturgattung im Alten Testament und im Alten Vorderen Orient. (Arbeiten zur Literatur und Geschichte des hellenistischen Judentums Ser.: No. 18). (Ger.). xii, 184p. 1986. 25.50 (ISBN 90-04-07313-2, Pub. by E J Brill). Heinman.

Waggener, Florence E. Story of the Old Testament Simply Told. (Illus.). 1979. 5.50 (ISBN 0-682-49375-9). Exposition Pr FL.

Weingreen, Jacob. From Bible to Mishna: The Continuity of Tradition. LC 75-37728. 250p. 1976. text ed. 27.00x (ISBN 0-8419-0249-6). Holmes & Meier.

Wellhausen, Julius. Prolegomena to the History of Ancient Israel. 14.25 (ISBN 0-8446-3147-7). Peter Smith.

Wendland, E. H., ed. Sermon Studies on the Old Testament. (Series B). 1984. 12.95 (ISBN 0-8100-0192-6, 15N0412). Northwest Pub.

Wendland, Ernst H. God's Mission in the Old Testament. Fischer, William E., ed. (Bible Class Course Ser.). 40p. (Orig.). 1986. pap. text ed. 2.50 (ISBN 0-938272-54-3). WELS Board.

Wigram, George V. The Englishman's Hebrew & Chaldee Concordance of the Old Testament. (Reference Set). 1760p. 1982. Repr. of 1980 ed. 34.95 (ISBN 0-88062-105-2). Mott Media.

Williamson, H. G. Israel in the Book of Chronicles. LC 76-11096. 1977. 42.50 (ISBN 0-521-21305-3). Cambridge U Pr.

Willmington, Harold L. Willmington's Survey of the Old Testament. 624p. 1987. 19.95. Victor Bks.

Wilson, Robert R. Sociological Approaches to the Old Testament. LC 83-16607. (Guides to Biblical Scholarship). 96p. 1984. pap. 4.50 (ISBN 0-8006-0469-5, 1-469). Fortress.

Wilson, William. New Wilson's Old Testament Word Studies: Keyed to Strong's Numbering System & to the Theological Wordbook of Old Testament. rev. ed. LC 86-7210. 584p. 1987. 27.95 (ISBN 0-8254-4030-0); prepub. 24.95 until Oct. 1987. Kregel.

Wright, Christopher J. An Eye for an Eye: The Place of Old Testament Ethics Today. LC 83-18651. 180p. 1983. pap. 8.95 (ISBN 0-87784-821-1). Inter-Varsity.

Wurthwein, Ernst. The Text of the Old Testament. Rhodes, Erroll F., tr. LC 79-15492. Tr. of Text Des Alten Testaments. (Illus.). 1980. text ed. 16.95 (ISBN 0-8028-3530-9). Eerdmans.

Youngblood, Ronald. Heart of the Old Testament. 1971. pap. 4.50 (ISBN 0-8010-9900-5). Baker Bk.

Zlotowitz, Meir. The Five Megillos, 5 vols. (The Art Scroll Tanach Ser.). 928p. 1977. Boxed Set. 59.95 (ISBN 0-89906-010-2); Boxed Set. pap. 44.95 (ISBN 0-89906-011-0). Mesorah Pubns.

BIBLE–CRITICISM, INTERPRETATION, ETC.–O. T. AMOS

see Bible–Criticism, Interpretation, Etc.–O. T. Minor Prophets

BIBLE–CRITICISM, INTERPRETATION, ETC.–O. T. APOCRYPHAL BOOKS

Charlesworth, James H., ed. Old Testament Pseudepigrapha, 2 vols. 1056p. 1986. slipcased set 80.00 (ISBN 0-385-19491-9). Doubleday.

Cole, C. Donald. I Believe... 160p. 1983. pap. 3.95 (ISBN 0-8024-0353-0). Moody.

Craven, Toni. Artistry & Faith in the Book of Judith. LC 82-25000. (Society of Biblical Literature Dissertation Ser.). 150p. 1983. pap. 11.25 (ISBN 0-89130-612-9, 06 01 70). Scholars Pr GA.

Dancy, J. C. Shorter Books of the Apochrypha: Cambridge Bible Commentary on the New English Bible. LC 72-76358. (Old Testament Ser.). 224p. (Orig.). 1972. pap. 9.95 (ISBN 0-521-09729-0). Cambridge U Pr.

Gaster, Moses. Studies & Texts in Folklore, Magic, Medieval Romance, Hebrew Apocrypha & Samaritan Archaeology, 3 Vols. rev. ed. 1970. Set. 45.00x (ISBN 0-87068-056-0). Ktav.

Jeppesen, Knud & Otzen, Benedikt, eds. The Productions of Time: Tradition History in the Old Testament Scholarship. 169p. 1984. 24.95x (ISBN 0-907459-36-6, Pub. by Almond Pr England); pap. text ed. 10.95x (ISBN 0-907459-37-4). Eisenbrauns.

Kee, Howard C. The Origins of Christianity: Sources & Documents. LC 73-4830. 320p. 1973. P-H.

Lee, Thomas R. Studies in the form of Sirach 44-50. (Dissertation Ser.). 284p. 1986. 17.95 (ISBN 0-89130-834-2, 06-01-75); pap. 13.95 (ISBN 0-89130-835-0). Scholars Pr GA.

Mack, Burton L. Wisdom & the Hebrew Epic: Ben Sira's Hymn in Praise of the Fathers. LC 85-8564. (Chicago Studies in the History of Judiasm). xiv, 264p. 1986. lib. bdg. 25.00x (ISBN 0-226-50049-7). U of Chicago Pr.

Marcus, Ralph. Law in the Apocrypha. LC 29-9822. (Columbia University. Oriental Studies: No. 26). Repr. of 1927 ed. 15.00 (ISBN 0-404-50516-3). AMS Pr.

Murphy, Frederick J. The Structure & Meaning of Second Baruch. 1985. 16.50 (ISBN 0-89130-844-X, 06-01-78); pap. 10.95 (ISBN 0-89130-845-8). Scholars Pr GA.

Nickelsburg, George W., Jr., ed. Studies on the Testament of Abraham. LC 76-44205. (Society of Biblical Literature. Septuagint & Cognate Studies). 1976. pap. 13.50 (ISBN 0-89130-117-8, 060406). Scholars Pr GA.

Sayler, Gwendolyn B. Have the Promises Failed: A Literary Analysis of 2 Baruch. LC 83-16336. (SBL Dissertation Ser.). 180p. 15.75 (ISBN 0-89130-651-X, 060172); pap. 10.50 (ISBN 0-89130-781-8). Scholars Pr GA.

Slingerland, H. Dixon. The Testaments of the Twelve Patriarchs: A Critical History of Research. LC 75-34233. (Society of Biblical Literature. Monograph). 1977. 13.50 (ISBN 0-89130-084-8, 060021); pap. 9.95 (ISBN 0-89130-062-7). Scholars Pr GA.

Tov, Emanual. The Book of Baruch: A Discussion of an Early Revision of the IXX of Jeremiah 29-52 & Baruch 1: 1-3: 8. LC 75-43872. (Harvard Semitic Monographs). 1976. pap. 9.75 (ISBN 0-89130-070-8, 06-02-08). Scholars Pr GA.

BIBLE–CRITICISM, INTERPRETATION, ETC.–O. T. CHRONICLES

see Bible–Criticism, Interpretation, Etc.–O. T. Historical Books

BIBLE–CRITICISM, INTERPRETATION, ETC.–O. T. DANIEL

see Bible–Criticism, Interpretation, Etc.–O. T. Prophets

BIBLE–CRITICISM, INTERPRETATION, ETC.–O. T. DEUTERONOMY

see Bible–Criticism, Interpretation, Etc.–O. T. Pentateuch

BIBLE–CRITICISM, INTERPRETATION, ETC.–O. T. ECCLESIASTES

see Bible–Criticism, Interpretation, etc.–O. T. Poetical Books

BIBLE–CRITICISM, INTERPRETATION, ETC.–O. T. ESTHER

see Bible–Criticism, Interpretation, Etc.–O. T. Historical Books

BIBLE–CRITICISM, INTERPRETATION, ETC.–O. T. EXODUS

see Bible–Criticism, Interpretation, Etc.–O. T. Pentateuch

BIBLE–CRITICISM, INTERPRETATION, ETC.–O. T. EZEKIEL

see Bible–Criticism, Interpretation, Etc.–O. T. Prophets

McGregor, Leslie J. The Greek Text of Ezekiel: An Examination of it's Homogeneity. (SBL & SCS Ser.). 1985. 18.25 (ISBN 0-89130-902-0, 06-0418); pap. 13.95 (ISBN 0-89130-903-9). Scholars Pr GA.

BIBLE–CRITICISM, INTERPRETATION, ETC.–O. T. EZRA

see Bible–Criticism, Interpretation, Etc.–O. T. Historical Books

BIBLE–CRITICISM, INTERPRETATION, ETC.–O. T. GENESIS

see Bible–Criticism, Interpretation, Etc.–O. T. Pentateuch

BIBLE–CRITICISM, INTERPRETATION, ETC.–O. T. HABAKKUK

see Bible–Criticism, Interpretation, Etc.–O. T. Minor Prophets

BIBLE–CRITICISM, INTERPRETATION, ETC.–O. T. HAGGAI

see Bible–Criticism, Interpretation, Etc.–O. T. Minor Prophets

BIBLE–CRITICISM, INTERPRETATION, ETC.–O. T. HISTORICAL BOOKS

Here are entered works on the historical Books as a whole, as well as on one or more of the following: Chronicles, Esther, Ezra, Joshua, Judges, Kings, Nehemiah, Ruth, Samuel.

Ackroyd, Peter R. First Book of Samuel: Cambridge Bible Commentary on the New English Bible. LC 77-128636. (Old Testament Ser.). (Illus.). 1971. 27.95 (ISBN 0-521-07965-9); pap. 9.95x (ISBN 0-521-09635-9). Cambridge U Pr.

Ahlstrom, Gosta W. Who Were the Israelites? x, 134p. 1986. text ed. 12.50x (ISBN 0-931464-24-2). Eisenbrauns.

Alexander, Myrna. With Him in the Struggle: A Woman's Workshop on II Samuel. (Woman's Workshop Ser.). 128p. 1986. pap. 3.95 (ISBN 0-310-37211-9, 10918P). Zondervan.

Allan, Leslie. Chronicles First & Second, Vol. 10. 400p. 1987. 24.95 (ISBN 0-8499-0415-3). Word Bks.

Andrews, Gini. Esther: The Star & the Sceptre. 288p. 1981. pap. 7.95 (ISBN 0-310-20181-0, 10859). Zondervan.

Augustinus, Saint Aurelius. Quaestionum in Heptateuchum Libri 7, Adnotationum in Iob Liber Unus. (Corpus Scriptorum Ecclesiasticorum Latinorum Ser: Vol. 38, Pt. 2). 50.00 (ISBN 0-384-02515-3). Johnson Repr.

Auld, A. Graeme. First & Second Kings. LC 86-15658. (The Daily Study Bible - Old Testament Ser.). 266p. 1986. 15.95 (ISBN 0-664-21836-9); pap. 8.95 (ISBN 0-664-24585-4). Westminster.

--Joshua, Judges, & Ruth. LC 84-22076. (The Daily Study Bible-Old Testament). 290p. 1985. 15.95 (ISBN 0-664-21809-1); pap. 8.95 (ISBN 0-664-24576-5). Westminster.

Bal, Mieke. Murder & Difference: Gender, Genre & Scholarship Sisera's Death. (Indiana Studies in Biblical Literature). (Illus.). Date not set. price not set. Ind U Pr.

Barber, Cyril J. Nehemiah & the Dynamics of Effective Leadership: Study Guide. (Illus.). 56p. 1980. pap. text ed. 3.25 (ISBN 0-87213-022-3). Loizeaux.

--Nehemiah & the Dynamics of Effective Leadership. LC 76-22567. 1976. pap. 3.95 (ISBN 0-87213-021-5). Loizeaux.

Barnes, Albert. Exodus-Esther. 24.95 (ISBN 0-8010-0836-0). Baker Bk.

Barrett, Ethel. Ruth. LC 80-52961. (Bible Biography Ser.). 128p. 1980. pap. 1.95 (ISBN 0-8307-0764-6, 5810418). Regal.

Beacon Bible Commentary Staff. Joshua-Esther, Vol. II. 13.95 (ISBN 0-8010-0689-9). Baker Bk.

Berg, Sandra B. The Book of Esther: Motifs, Themes & Structure. LC 78-32035. (SBL Dissertation Ser.). 1979. pap. 9.95 (ISBN 0-89130-279-4, 060144). Scholars Pr GA.

Bickerman, Elias. Four Strange Books of the Bible: Jonah, Daniel, Koheleth, Esther. (Illus.). 252p. 1984. pap. 8.95 (ISBN 0-8052-0774-0). Schocken.

Bimson, John J. Redating the Exodus & Conquest. 2nd ed. 288p. 1981. pap. text ed. 14.95x (ISBN 0-907459-04-8, Pub. by Almond Pr England). Eisenbrauns.

Boadt, Lawrence. Jeremiah Twenty-Six to Fifty-Two, Habakkuk, Zephaniah, Nahum. (Old Testament Message Ser.: Vol. 10). 1982. 15.95 (ISBN 0-89453-410-6); pap. 9.95 (ISBN 0-89453-244-8). M Glazier.

Bob & Couchman, Win. Ruth & Jonah: People in Process. (Carpenter Studyguide). 80p. 1983. saddle-stiched member's handbk. 1.95 (ISBN 0-87788-736-5); leader's handbook 2.95 (ISBN 0-87788-737-3). Shaw Pubs.

Bodine, Walter R. The Greek Text of Judges: Recensional Developments. LC 80-12578. (Harvard Semitic Monographs: No. 23). 15.00x (ISBN 0-89130-400-2, 04-00-23). Scholars Pr GA.

Boling, Robert G., tr. & intro. by. Judges, Vol. 6A. LC 72-96229. (Anchor Bible Ser). (Illus.). 360p. 1975. 18.00 (ISBN 0-385-01029-X). Doubleday.

Bos, Johanna W. Ruth, Esther, Jonah. LC 85-45793. (Preaching Guides Ser.). 108p. 1986. pap. 4.95 (ISBN 0-8042-3227-X). John Knox.

Bostrom, Otto H. Alternative Readings in the Hebrew of the Books of Samuel. LC 18-8964. (Augustana College Library Publication Ser.: No. 8). 60p. 1918. pap. 0.75 (ISBN 0-910182-05-1). Augustana Coll.

Bowman, John. The Fourth Gospel & the Jews: A Study of R. Akiba, Esther, & the Gospel of John. LC 75-40461. (Pittsburgh Theological Monographs: No. 8). 1975. pap. 9.00 (ISBN 0-915138-10-7). Pickwick.

Brueggemann, Walter. Revelation & Violence: A Study in Contextualization. LC 86-60473. (Pere Marquette Ser.). 72p. 1986. 7.95 (ISBN 0-87462-541-6). Marquette.

Burney, C. F. The Book of Judges with Introduction & Notes. 528p. Repr. of 1920 ed. lib. bdg. 100.00 (ISBN 0-8495-0481-3). Arden Lib.

Carlson, R. A. David, the Chosen King: A Traditio-Historical Approach to the 2nd Book of Samuel. 304p. (Orig.). 1964. pap. text ed. 23.50x. Coronet Bks.

Cocoris, G. Michael. Joshua. rev. ed. 125p. 1986. pap. text ed. 3.00 (ISBN 0-935729-34-8). Church Open Door.

Cohen, A. Kings One & Two. 337p. 1950. 10.95 (ISBN 0-900689-27-7). Soncino Pr.

Cohen, A., ed. Chronicles. 358p. 1952. 10.95 (ISBN 0-900689-37-4). Soncino Pr.

--Joshua & Judges. 332p. 1950. 10.95 (ISBN 0-900689-20-X). Soncino Pr.

--Samuel. 361p. 1949. 10.95 (ISBN 0-900689-26-9). Soncino Pr.

Cohen, Bydr A., ed. The Five Megilloth. 252p. 1946. 10.95 (ISBN 0-900689-35-8). Soncino Pr.

Craghan, John. Esther, Judith, Tobit, Jonah, Ruth. (Old Testament Message Ser.: Vol. 16). 1982. 12.95 (ISBN 0-89453-416-5); pap. 8.95 (ISBN 0-89453-249-9). M Glazier.

Craven, Toni. Artistry & Faith in the Book of Judith. LC 82-25000. (Society of Biblical Literature Dissertation Ser.). 150p. 1983. pap. 11.25 (ISBN 0-89130-612-9, 06 01 70). Scholars Pr GA.

Crises at the Crossroads: Ruth-Esther. (New Horizons Bible Study). 48p. (Orig.). 1982. pap. 1.95 Leader's Guide (ISBN 0-89367-074-X); student guide 2.50 (ISBN 0-89367-075-8). Light & Life.

Crockett, William D. A Harmony of Samuel, Kings, & Chronicles. 1985. pap. 9.95 (ISBN 0-8010-2511-7). Baker Bk.

Davis, John J. The Birth of a Kingdom: Studies in I & II Samuel & I Kings I-II. pap. 5.95 (ISBN 0-88469-053-9). BMH Bks.

--Conquest & Crisis: Studies in Joshua, Judges & Ruth. (Illus.). pap. 5.95 (ISBN 0-88469-052-0). BMH Bks.

Driver, S. R. Notes on the Hebrew Text of Samuel. 1986. 24.95 (ISBN 0-88469-163-2). BMH Bks.

Edersheim, Alfred, et al. Practical Truth Series, 6 Vols. Incl. Elisha; Jonah; Thessalonians; Pastoral Epistles; Israel's Wanderings; Judges. 1940p. 1986. Set. 74.70 (ISBN 0-8254-3529-3). Kregel.

Eslinger, Lyle. The Ringship of God in Crisis: A Close Reading of 1 Samuel 1-12. (Bible & Literature Ser.: No. 35). 515p. 1985. text ed. 29.95x (ISBN 0-907459-40-4, Pub. by Almond Pr England); pap. text ed. 15.95 (ISBN 0-907459-41-2). Eisenbrauns.

Fairbanks, Lebron. Beacon Small-Group Bible Studies, Acts, Pt. II: The Continuing Mission of the Church. Wolf, Earl C., ed. 90p. (Orig.). 1985. pap. 2.50 (ISBN 0-8341-0947-6). Beacon Hill.

Fokkelman, J. P. Narrative & the Poetry in the Books of Samuel; Vol. 2: The Crossing Fates. (Studia Semitica Neerlandica: No. 20). 744p. 1986. 50.00 (ISBN 90-232-2175-3, Pub. by Van Gorcum Holland). Longwood Pub Group.

--Narrative Art & Poetry in the Books of Samuel: A Full Interpretation on Stylistic & Structural Analysis, Volume 1. (King David-Studia Semitica Neerlandica: No. 20). 534p. 1981. text ed. 50.00 (ISBN 90-232-1852-3). Longwood Pub Group.

Follis, Elaine R. Directions in Biblical Hebrew Poetry. (JSOT Supplement Ser.: No. 40). 340p. 1986. text ed. 33.50x (ISBN 1-85075-013-0, Pub. by JSOT Pr England); pap. text ed. 15.95x (ISBN 1-85075-012-2). Eisenbrauns.

Gettys, Joseph M. Surveying the Historical Books. 164p. 1963. pap. 4.00x (ISBN 0-8042-3664-X). Attic Pr.

Greenspoon, Leonard. Textual Studies in the Book of Joshua. LC 83-3434. (Harvard Semitic Monographs). 412p. 1983. 21.75 (ISBN 0-89130-622-6, 04 00 28). Scholars Pr GA.

Grindel, John A. First Book of Chronicles. (Bible Ser.: No. 17). (Orig.). 1974. pap. 1.00 (ISBN 0-8091-5170-7). Paulist Pr.

--Second Book of Chronicles. (Bible Ser.: Vol. 18). (Orig.). 1974. pap. 1.00 (ISBN 0-8091-5171-5). Paulist Pr.

Grossfeld, Bernard. Concordance of the First Targum to the Book of Esther. LC 83-11550. (SBL Aramaic Studies). 186p. 1984. pap. 11.25 (ISBN 0-89130-635-8, 06 13 05). Scholars Pr GA.

Gunn, D. M. The Fate of King Saul. (Journal for the Study of the Old Testament, Supplement Ser.: No. 14). 1980. text ed. 18.95x (ISBN 0-905774-24-8, Pub. by JSOT Pr England); pap. text ed. 10.95 (ISBN 0-905774-63-9). Eisenbrauns.

Harper, A. F. Beacon Small-Group Bible Studies, I & II Samuel: David-A Man after God's Own Heart". Wolf, Earl C., ed. 102p. (Orig.). 1985. pap. 2.50 (ISBN 0-8341-0934-4). Beacon Hill.

Heslop, William G. Rubies from Ruth. LC 76-12078. (W. G. Heslop Bible Study Aids Ser.). 116p. 1976. pap. 4.50 (ISBN 0-8254-2830-0). Kregel.

Hoppe, Leslie. Joshua, Judges, with Excursus on Charismatic Leadership in Israel. (Old Testament Message Ser.: Vol. 5). 1982. text ed. 12.95 (ISBN 0-89453-405-X); pap. 8.95 (ISBN 0-89453-240-5). M Glazier.

Inrig, Gary, ed. Hearts of Iron, Feet of Clay. 1979. pap. 7.95 (ISBN 0-8024-3487-8). Moody.

Kackelman, John, Jr. Studies in Judges. 1986. pap. 5.95 (ISBN 0-89137-564-3). Quality Pubns.

Katz, Mordechai. Lilmod Ulelamade: From the Teachings of Our Sages on Judges. (Rothman Foundation Ser.). 1986. 8.95 (ISBN 0-87306-207-8); pap. 6.95 (ISBN 0-87306-928-5). Feldheim.

King, Philip J. Judges. (Bible Ser.). pap. 1.00 (ISBN 0-8091-5077-8). Paulist Pr.

Laney, J. Carl. First & Second Samuel. (Everyman's Bible Commentary Ser.). 1982. pap. 5.95 (ISBN 0-8024-2010-9). Moody.

McCarter, P. Kyle, Jr., ed. Samuel II. LC 81-43919. (Anchor Bible Ser.: No. 9). (Illus.). 576p. 1984. 18.00 (ISBN 0-385-06808-5, Anchor Pr). Doubleday.

McConville, J. G. Ezra, Nehemiah, & Esther. LC 84-25825. (The Daily Study Bible-Old Testament Ser.). 210p. 1985. 14.95 (ISBN 0-664-21814-8); pap. 7.95 (ISBN 0-664-24583-8). Westminster.

McGee, J. Vernon. Esther: The Romance of Providence. LC 81-22362. 140p. 1982. pap. 4.95 (ISBN 0-8407-5796-4). Nelson.

McNeely, Richard I. First & Second Kings. (Everyman's Bible Commentary Ser.). 1978. pap. 5.95 (ISBN 0-8024-2011-7). Moody.

Mangan, Celine. One-Two Chronicles, Ezra, Nehemiah. (Old Testament Message Ser.: Vol. 13). 1982. 12.95 (ISBN 0-89453-413-0); pap. 7.95 (ISBN 0-89453-247-2). M Glazier.

Martin, James D. & Davies, Phillip R. A Word in Season: Essays in Honour of William McKane. (JSOT Supplement Ser.: No. 42). 225p. 1986. text ed. 30.00x (ISBN 1-85075-016-5, Pub. by JSOT Pr England); pap. text ed. 15.95x (ISBN 1-85075-047-5). Eisenbrauns.

Mayes, A. D. Judges. (Old Testament Guides Ser.). 98p. 1985. pap. text ed. 3.95x (ISBN 0-905774-58-2, Pub. by JSOT Pr England). Eisenbrauns.

Moriarty, Frederick. Second Book of Samuel. (Bible Ser.). pap. 1.00 (ISBN 0-8091-5136-7). Paulist Pr.

Myers, Jacob M., ed. Chronicles One. LC 65-17226. (Anchor Bible Ser.: Vol. 12). 1965. 14.00 (ISBN 0-385-01259-4, Anchor Pr). Doubleday.

--Chronicles Two. (Anchor Bible Ser.: Vol. 13). 1965. 14.00 (ISBN 0-385-03757-0, Anchor Pr). Doubleday.

Newsome, James D., Jr. A Synoptic Harmony of Samuel, Kings, & Chronicles. 272p. 1986. text ed. 16.95 (ISBN 0-8010-6744-8). Baker Bk.

Ollenburger, Ben C. Zion, the City of the Great King: A Theological Symbol of the Jerusalem Cult. (JSOT Supplement Ser.: No. 41). 240p. 1986. text ed. 28.50x (ISBN 1-85075-015-7, Pub. by JSOT Pr England); pap. text ed. 13.50x (ISBN 1-85075-014-9). Eisenbrauns.

Owen, Valarie. Possess the Land. 193p. (Orig.). 1984. pap. text ed. 6.95 (ISBN 0-914307-17-7, Dist. by Harrison Hse). Word Faith.

Palau, Luis. Grito de Victoria! Calcada, Leticia, tr. from Eng. Tr. of The Moment to Shout! (Span.). 144p. 1986. pap. 5.50 (ISBN 0-311-46106-9). Casa Bautista.

Ridout, Samuel. Judges & Ruth. rev. ed. 415p. 1981. pap. 7.25 (ISBN 0-87213-720-1). Loizeaux.

Rosenberg, A. J. Book of Kings 2. 480p. 1980. 12.95 (ISBN 0-910818-31-2). Judaica Pr.

Rosenberg, A. J., ed. Book of Joshua. 350p. 1984. 12.95 (ISBN 0-910818-08-8). Judaica Pr.

--Book of Judges. 400p. 1979. 12.95 (ISBN 0-910818-17-7). Judaica Pr.

--Book of Kings 1. 512p. 1980. 12.95 (ISBN 0-910818-30-4). Judaica Pr.

--Book of Samuel 1. 525p. 1981. 12.95 (ISBN 0-910818-07-X). Judaica Pr.

--Book of Samuel 2. 540p. 1982. 12.95 (ISBN 0-910818-11-8). Judaica Pr.

Rosenberg, Israel. The World of Words. 224p. 1973. 8.95 (ISBN 0-8022-2101-7). Philos Lib.

Rost, Leonhard. The Succession to the Throne of David. (Historic Texts & Interpreters Ser: No. 1). Orig. Title: Die Uberlieferung von der Thronnachfolge Davids. 160p. 1982. text ed. 25.95x (ISBN 0-907459-12-9, Pub. by Almond Pr England); pap. text ed. 12.95x (ISBN 0-907459-13-7, Pub. by Almond Pr England). Eisenbrauns.

Sanders, J. Oswald. Promised-Land Living. 1984. pap. 5.95 (ISBN 0-8024-0372-7). Moody.

Scroggie, W. Graham. Joshua in the Light of the New Testament. LC 80-8074. (W. Graham Scroggie Library). 88p. 1981. pap. 4.50 (ISBN 0-8254-3734-2). Kregel.

Simpson, Frances. Beacon Small-Group Bible Studies, Ruth-Esther: Faith That Risks All. Wolf, Earl C., ed. 96p. (Orig.). 1984. pap. 2.50 (ISBN 0-8341-0941-7). Beacon Hill.

Smith, H. An Outline of the Book of Nehemiah. pap. 4.25 (ISBN 0-88172-125-5). Believers Bkshelf.

Smith, Joyce M. Esther, a Woman of Courage. 1981. pap. 2.95 (ISBN 0-8423-0729-X). Tyndale.

Southwell, P. Ezra-Job. 1983. pap. 4.95 (ISBN 0-87508-156-8). Chr Lit.

Stokes, Penelope. Ruth & Daniel: God's People in an Alien Society. (Fisherman Bible Studyguide Ser.). 64p. (Orig.). 1986. pap. 2.95 (ISBN 0-87788-735-7). Shaw Pubs.

Strait, C. Neil. Beacon Small-Group Bible Studies, Ezra-Nehemiah: God's Faithfulness & Man's Obedience. Wolf, Earl C., ed. 96p. (Orig.). 1985. pap. 2.50 (ISBN 0-8341-0927-1). Beacon Hill.

Thompson, Alden. Responsibility for Evil in the Theodicy of IV Ezra: A Study Illustrating the Significance of Form & Structure for the Meaning of the Book. LC 76-40915. (Society of Biblical Literature. Dissertation Ser.). 1977. pap. 9.95 (ISBN 0-89130-091-0, 060129). Scholars Pr GA.

Toms, Paul E. Winning the Battles of Life (Joshua) rev. ed. LC 86-15417. 224p. 1986. pap. 4.95 (ISBN 0-8307-1161-9, S413129). Regal.

Ulrich, Eugene C., Jr. The Qumran Text of Samuel & Josephus. LC 78-15254. (Harvard Semitic Museum. Harvard Semitic Monographs: No. 19). 1978. 15.00 (ISBN 0-89130-256-5, 040019). Scholars Pr GA.

Van Dyne, Glen. Beacon Small-Group Bible Studies, Joshua: Never a Dull Moment. Wolf, Earl C., ed. 80p. 1986. pap. 2.50 (ISBN 0-8341-1098-9). Beacon Hill.

Van Seters, John. In Search of History: Historiography in the Ancient World & the Origins of Biblical History. LC 82-48912. 416p. 1983. text ed. 35.00x (ISBN 0-300-02877-6); pap. 12.95 (ISBN 0-300-03633-7, Y-574). Yale U Pr.

Verbrugge, Verlyn. Ezra-Nehemiah. (Five-on-One Ser.). 128p. (Orig.). 1986. pap. text ed. 3.95 (ISBN 0-930265-18-1); tchr's. guide 7.95 (ISBN 0-930265-19-X). CRC Pubns.

Webb, Barry G. The Book of the Judges: An Integrated Reading. (JSOT Supplement Ser.: No. 46). 260p. 1987. text ed. 31.50x (ISBN 1-85075-034-3, Pub. by JSOT Pr England); pap. text ed. 14.95x (ISBN 1-85075-035-1, Pub. by JSOT Pr England). Eisenbrauns.

Whitcomb, John C., Jr. Solomon to the Exile: Studies in Kings & Chronicles. pap. 4.95 (ISBN 0-88469-054-7). BMH Bks.

Wilcock, Michael. The Message of One & Two Chronicles. Stott, John R. & Motyer, J. A., eds. LC 86-27700. (The Bible Speaks Today Ser.). 240p. (Orig.). 1987. pap. 8.95 (ISBN 0-87784-299-X). Inter-Varsity.

Williamson, H. G. Ezra & Nehemiah. (Old Testament Guides Ser.). 100p. 1986. pap. text ed. 4.95x (ISBN 1-85075-045-9, Pub. by JSOT Pr England). Eisenbrauns.

--Ezra-Nehemiah: Vol. 16, WBC. 1985. 22.95 (ISBN 0-8499-0215-0, 0215-0). Word Bks.

Winter, Willard W. Studies in First & Second Samuel. LC 70-1508. (The Bible Study Textbook Ser.). 1967. 15.90 (ISBN 0-89900-011-8). College Pr Pub.

--Studies in Joshua, Judges, Ruth. (The Bible Study Textbook Ser.). (Illus.). 1969. 15.90 (ISBN 0-89900-010-X). College Pr Pub.

Wood, Leon U. Distressing Days of the Judges. 434p. 1982. pap. 11.95 (ISBN 0-310-34731-9, 10232P). Zondervan.

Zlotowitz, Meir. The Book of Ruth. (Art Scroll Tanach Ser.). 160p. 1976. 11.95 (ISBN 0-89906-002-1); pap. 8.95 (ISBN 0-89906-003-X). Mesorah Pubns.

--The Megillah-the Book of Esther. (The Art Scroll Tanach Ser.). 160p. 1976. 11.95 (ISBN 0-89906-000-5); pap. 8.95 (ISBN 0-89906-001-3). Mesorah Pubns.

BIBLE–CRITICISM, INTERPRETATION, ETC.–O. T. HOSEA

see Bible–Criticism, Interpretation, Etc.–O. T. Minor Prophets

BIBLE–CRITICISM, INTERPRETATION, ETC.–O. T. ISAIAH

see Bible–Criticism, Interpretation, Etc.–O. T. Prophets

BIBLE–CRITICISM, INTERPRETATION, ETC.–O. T. JEREMIAH

see Bible–Criticism, Interpretation, Etc.–O. T. Prophets

BIBLE–CRITICISM, INTERPRETATION, ETC.–O. T. JOB

see Bible–Criticism, Interpretation, Etc.–O. T. Poetical Books

BIBLE–CRITICISM, INTERPRETATION, ETC.–O. T. JOEL

see Bible–Criticism, Interpretation, Etc.–O. T. Minor Prophets

BIBLE–CRITICISM, INTERPRETATION, ETC.–O. T. JONAH

see Bible–Criticism, Interpretation, Etc.–O. T. Minor Prophets

BIBLE–CRITICISM, INTERPRETATION, ETC.–O. T. JOSHUA

see Bible–Criticism, Interpretation, Etc.–O. T. Historical Books

BIBLE–CRITICISM, INTERPRETATION, ETC.–O. T. JUDGES

see Bible–Criticism, Interpretation, Etc.–O. T. Historical Books

BIBLE–CRITICISM, INTERPRETATION, ETC.–O. T. KINGS

see Bible–Criticism, Interpretation, Etc.–O. T. Historical Books

BIBLE–CRITICISM, INTERPRETATION, ETC.–O. T. LAMENTATIONS

see Bible–Criticism, Interpretation, Etc.–O. T. Prophets

BIBLE–CRITICISM, INTERPRETATION, ETC.–O. T. LEVITICUS

see Bible–Criticism, Interpretation, Etc.–O. T. Pentateuch

BIBLE–CRITICISM, INTERPRETATION, ETC.–O. T. MALACHI

see Bible–Criticism, Interpretation, Etc.–O. T. Minor Prophets

BIBLE–CRITICISM, INTERPRETATION, ETC.–O. T. MICAH

see Bible–Criticism, Interpretation, Etc.–O. T. Minor Prophets

BIBLE–CRITICISM, INTERPRETATION, ETC.–O. T. MINOR PROPHETS

Here are entered works on the 12 minor prophets as a whole, as well as books on one or more of the minor prophets.

see also Bible–Criticism, Interpretation, Etc.–O. T. Prophets

Artos, Allen. Jonah. 52p. (Orig.). 1984. cancelled 10.00 (ISBN 0-934852-00-6); pap. 3.50 (ISBN 0-934852-24-3). Lorien Hse.

Auld, A. Graeme. Amos. (Old Testament Guides Ser.). 96p. 1986. pap. 3.95x (ISBN 1-85075-005-X, Pub. by JSOT Pr England). Eisenbrauns.

Bickerman, Elias. Four Strange Books of the Bible: Jonah, Daniel, Koheleth, Esther. (Illus.). 252p. 1984. pap. 8.95 (ISBN 0-8052-0774-0). Schocken.

Boice, James M. The Minor Prophets: An Expositional Commenatry (Micah-Malachi, Vol. 2. 1986. 14.95 (ISBN 0-310-21580-3, 10424). Zondervan.

Burn, Samuel C. Jonah. 1981. lib. bdg. 11.25 (ISBN 0-86524-071-X, 3201). Klock & Klock.

Buss, Martin J. The Prophetic Words of Hosea: A Morphological Study. (Beiheft 111 Zur Zeitschrift Fuer Die alttestamentliche Wissenschaft). 1969. 30.00- (ISBN 3-11-002579-5). De Gruyter.

Cathcart, Kevin J. Nahum in the Light of Northwest Semetic. (Biblica et Orientalia: Vol. 26). 1973. pap. 20.00 (ISBN 88-7653-326-5). Loyola.

Cocoris, G. Michael. Amos: The Message We Dare Not Ignore. 90p. (Orig.). 1985. pap. text ed. 1.00 (ISBN 0-935729-02-X). Church Open Door.

Coggins, R. J. Haggi, Zechariah, Malachi. (Old Testament Guides Ser.). 100p. 1986. pap. text ed. 4.95x (ISBN 1-85075-025-4, Pub. by JSOT Pr England). Eisenbrauns.

Cripps, Richard S. Amos. 1981. lib. bdg. 13.50 (ISBN 0-86524-081-7, 3001). Klock & Klock.

Crowley, Edward J. Lamentations, Baruch, Sophonia, Nahum, Habacuc. (Bible Ser.). pap. 1.00 (ISBN 0-8091-5078-6). Paulist Pr.

Di Gangi, Mariano. Twelve Prophetic Voices. 168p. 1985. pap. 5.95 (ISBN 0-89693-536-1). Victor Bks.

Feinberg, Charles L. God Remembers: A Study of Zechariah. 4th ed. LC 79-88530. 1979. 8.95 (ISBN 0-930014-33-2). Multnomah.

Garland, D. David. Amos: Bible Study Commentary. 96p. 1973. pap. 4.95 (ISBN 0-310-24833-7, 9696P). Zondervan.

Gill, Clinton R. Minor Prophets: A Study of Micah Through Malachi. (The Bible Study Textbook Ser.). (Illus.). 1971. 15.90 (ISBN 0-89900-027-4). College Pr Pub.

Kachelman, John L. Studies in Jonah. pap. 5.50 (ISBN 0-89137-319-5). Quality Pubns.

Kodell, Jerome. Lamentations, Haggai, Zechariah, Second Zechariah, Malachi, Obadiah, Joel, Baruch. (Old Testament Ser.: Vol. 14). 1982. 12.95 (ISBN 0-89453-414-9); pap. 8.95 (ISBN 0-89453-248-0). M Glazier.

Kohlenberger, John R., III. Jonah-Nahum. (Everyman's Bible Commentary Ser.). (Orig.). 1984. pap. 5.95 (ISBN 0-8024-0352-2). Moody.

Kuniholm, Whitney. Amos: Israel on Trial. (Fisherman Bible Studyguide). 67p. 1981. saddle stitch 2.95 (ISBN 0-87788-043-3). Shaw Pubs.

Magonet, Jonathan. Form & Meaning: Studies in Literary Techniques in the Book of Jonah. (Bible & Literature Ser.: No. 8). vi, 184p. 1983. pap. text ed. 10.95x (ISBN 0-907459-25-0, Pub. by Almond Pr England). Eisenbrauns.

Morgan, G. Campbell. Hosea: The Heart & Holiness of God. (Morgan Library). 1974. pap. 4.50 (ISBN 0-8010-5952-6). Baker Bk.

Nielson, John B. Zehariah-Malachi: Prisoners of Hope. 80p. (Orig.). 1986. pap. 2.50 (ISBN 0-8341-1100-4). Beacon Hill.

Petersen, Mark E. Malachi & the Great & Dreadful Day. 76p. 1983. 5.95 (ISBN 0-87747-962-3). Deseret Bk.

Prinsloo, Willem S. The Theology of the Book of Joel. (Beihefte zur Zeitschrift fur die Alttestamentliche Wissenschaft: Vol. 163). viii, 136p. 1985. 43.75x (ISBN 3-11-010301-X). De Gruyter.

Robinson, George L. The Twelve Minor Prophets. 203p. 1981. Repr. of 1926 ed. lib. bdg. 35.00 (ISBN 0-89984-434-0). Century Bookbindery.

Shelly, Rubel. Minor Prophets. pap. 2.50 (ISBN 0-89315-161-0). Lambert Bk.

Smith, Gary. A Commentary on the Book of Amos. 268p. 1986. 24.95 (ISBN 0-8407-5423-X). Nelson.

Strange, Marcian. Amos, Osee & Michae. (Bible Ser.). pap. 1.00 (ISBN 0-8091-5002-6). Paulist Pr.

Stuhlmueller, Carroll. Aggai, Zacharia, Malachia, Jona, Joel, Abdia. (Bible Ser.). pap. 1.00 (ISBN 0-8091-5000-X). Paulist Pr.

Tracy, Wesley. Beacon Small-Group Bible Studies, Micah-Obadiah: What Does the Lord Require? Wolf, Earl C., ed. 96p. (Orig.). 1985. pap. 2.50 (ISBN 0-8341-0963-8). Beacon Hill.

Twombly, Gerald H. Major Themes from the Minor Prophets. (Adult Study Guide Ser.). 144p. (Orig.). 1981. pap. 4.95 (ISBN 0-88469-132-2). BMH Bks.

Vandeman, George E. The Book That Wouldn't Go Away. (Stories That Win Ser.). 64p. 1983. pap. 1.25 (ISBN 0-8163-0537-4). Pacific Pr Pub Assn.

Vawter, Bruce. Amos, Hosea, Micah, with Introduction to Classical Prophecy. (Old Testament Message Ser.: Vol. 7). 1982. 12.95 (ISBN 0-89453-407-6); pap. 6.95 (ISBN 0-89453-242-1). M Glazier.

Ward, James. Amos & Hosea. Hayes, John, ed. (Knox Preaching Guides). 96p. 1981. pap. 4.95 (ISBN 0-8042-3225-3). John Knox.

Wolf, Herbert. Haggai & Malachi. (Everyman's Bible Commentary Ser.). 128p. (Orig.). 1976. pap. 5.95 (ISBN 0-8024-2037-0). Moody.

Zlotowitz, Meir. Yonah-Jonah. (The Art Scroll Tanach Ser.). 160p. 1978. 11.95 (ISBN 0-89906-081-1); pap. 8.95 (ISBN 0-89906-082-X). Mesorah Pubns.

BIBLE–CRITICISM, INTERPRETATION, ETC.–O. T. NAHUM

see Bible–Criticism, Interpretation, Etc.–O. T. Minor Prophets

BIBLE–CRITICISM, INTERPRETATION, ETC.–O. T. NEHEMIAH

see Bible–Criticism, Interpretation, Etc.–O. T. Historical Books

BIBLE–CRITICISM, INTERPRETATION, ETC.–O. T. NUMBERS

see Bible–Criticism, Interpretation, Etc.–O. T. Pentateuch

BIBLE–CRITICISM, INTERPRETATION, ETC.–O. T. OBADIAH

see Bible–Criticism, Interpretation, Etc.–O. T. Minor Prophets

BIBLE–CRITICISM, INTERPRETATION, ETC.–O. T. PENTATEUCH

Here are entered works on the pentateuch as a whole, as well as books on one or more of the following: Deuteronomy, Exodus, Genesis, Leviticus, Numbers.

Aberbach, M. & Grossfeld, B. Targum Onkelos to Genesis. 45.00x (ISBN 0-87068-339-X). Ktav.

Alford, Dean H. The Book of Genesis & Part of the Book of Exodus. 1979. 12.50 (ISBN 0-86524-001-9, 7002). Klock & Klock.

Allen, Eula. Creation Trilogy, 3 vols. rev. ed. Incl. Vol. 1. Before the Beginning. 1966 (ISBN 0-87604-054-7); Vol. 2. The River of Time. 1965 (ISBN 0-87604-055-5); Vol. 3. You Are Forever. 1966 (ISBN 0-87604-056-3). (Illus.). pap. 10.95 set (ISBN 0-87604-125-X); pap. 3.95 ea. ARE Pr.

Allis, Oswald T. Five Books of Moses. 1949. pap. 7.95 (ISBN 0-87552-102-9). Presby & Reformed.

--God Spake by Moses. 1951. pap. 5.95 (ISBN 0-87552-103-7). Presby & Reformed.

Augustinus, Saint Aurelius. Quaestionum in Heptateuchum Libri 7, Adnotationum in Iob Liber Unus. (Corpus Scriptorum Ecclesiasticorum Latinorum Ser: Vol. 38, Pt. 2). 50.00 (ISBN 0-384-02515-3). Johnson Repr.

Aurelio, John. Mosquitoes in Paradise. 144p. 1985. pap. 7.95 (ISBN 0-8245-0698-7). Crossroad NY.

Bailey, Lloyd R. Leviticus. Hayes, John H., ed. LC 86-46035. (Knox Preaching Guide Series). 108p. (Orig.). 1987. pap. 5.95 (ISBN 0-8042-3203-2). John Knox.

--The Pentateuch. LC 81-4495. (Interpreting Biblical Texts Ser.). 160p. (Orig.). 1981. pap. 8.95 (ISBN 0-687-30610-8). Abingdon.

Baldwin, Joyce G. The Message of Genesis 12-50: From Abraham to Joseph. Motyer, J. A. & Stott, John R., eds. LC 86-10615. (The Bible Speaks Today). 224p. (Orig.). 1986. pap. 7.95 (ISBN 0-87784-298-1). Inter Varsity.

Barnes, Albert. Exodus-Esther. 24.95 (ISBN 0-8010-0836-0). Baker Bk.

--Genesis. 13.95 (ISBN 0-8010-0835-2). Baker Bk.

Barthes, Roland, et al. Analyse Structurale et Exegese Biblique. 128p. 1973. 17.50 (ISBN 0-686-53927-3). French & Eur.

Beacon Bible Commentary Staff. Genesis-Deuteronomy, Vol. I. 13.95 (ISBN 0-8010-0688-0). Baker Bk.

Benjamin, Don C. Deuteronomy & City Life: A Form Criticism of Texts with the Word City ('ir) in Deuteronomy 4: 41 -26: 19. LC 83-3609. (Illus.). 366p. (Orig.). 1983. lib. bdg. 31.25 (ISBN 0-8191-3138-5); pap. text ed. 15.75 (ISBN 0-8191-3139-3). U Pr of Amer.

Bennett, Allan. A Note on Genesis. (Equinox Reprints: Vol. 1, No. 2). 1976. pap. 1.50 (ISBN 0-87728-338-9). Weiser.

Bible, Ken. Beacon Small-Group Bible Studies, Genesis, Pt. II: God's Hand in History. Wolf, Earl C., ed. 96p. (Orig.). 1986. pap. 2.50 (ISBN 0-8341-0958-1). Beacon Hill.

--Genesis: Faithful to His Promises, Pt. 2. Wolf, Earl, ed. (Small Group Bible Studies). 72p. (Orig.). Date not set. pap. 2.50 (ISBN 0-8341-1108-X). Beacon Hill.

Blenkinsopp, Joseph. Prophecy & Canon: A Contribution to the Study of Jewish Origins. LC 76-22411. 1977. text ed. 14.95 (ISBN 0-268-01522-8). U of Notre Dame Pr.

Boice, James M. Genesis, Vol. I. 352p. 1982. Chapter 1-11. 16.95 (ISBN 0-310-21540-4, 10486). Zondervan.

Bonar, Clayton. Beacon Small-Group Bible Studies, Deuteronomy: Words to Live By. Wolf, Earl C., ed. 100p. (Orig.). 1986. pap. 2.50 (ISBN 0-8341-0959-X). Beacon Hill.

Branson, Robert. Beacon Small-Group Bible Studies, Genesis, Pt. I: How It All Began. Wolf, Earl C., ed. 96p. (Orig.). 1984. pap. 2.50 (ISBN 0-8341-0935-2). Beacon Hill.

Bricose, Jill. Here Am I; Send Aaron! 1984. pap. 2.95 (ISBN 0-89693-712-7). Victor Bks.

Burke, John B. Studies in Genesis. 1979. pap. 4.95 (ISBN 0-88469-048-2). BMH Bks.

Bush, George. Exodus. 1981. 22.50 (ISBN 0-86524-097-3, 0202). Klock & Klock.

--Genesis, 2 vols. 1981. 29.95 (ISBN 0-86524-094-9, 0103). Klock & Klock.

Chambers, Oswald. Our Portrait in Genesis. 1973. pap. 2.25 (ISBN 0-87508-135-5). Chr Lit.

Clements, Ronald E. Abraham & David: Genesis 15 & Its Meaning for Israelite Tradition. LC 67-8569. (Studies in Biblical Theology, 2nd Ser.: No. 5). 1967. pap. 10.00x (ISBN 0-8401-3055-4). A R Allenson.

Clifford, Richard. Deuteronomy, with Excursus on Covenant & Law. (Old Testament Message Ser.: Vol. 4). 1982. 12.95 (ISBN 0-89453-404-1); pap. 7.95 (ISBN 0-89453-239-1). M Glazier.

Clines, David J. The Theme of the Pentateuch. (Journal for the Study of the Old Testament Supplement Ser.: No. 10). 152p. 1978. text ed. 22.50 (ISBN 0-905774-14-0, Pub. by JSOT Pr England); pap. text ed. 10.95x (ISBN 0-905774-15-9, Pub. by JSOT Pr England). Eisenbrauns.

Cochrane, Charles C. The Gospel According to Genesis: A Guide to Understanding Genesis 1-11. LC 84-4047. Repr. of 1984 ed. 24.00 (2027539). Bks Demand UMI.

Colclasure, Chuck. Proverbs, God's Powerhouse of Wisdom. 1981. pap. 2.50 (ISBN 0-8423-4928-6). Tyndale.

Cole, Clifford. Studies in Exodus, Vol. 1. (Bible Studies Ser.). 1986. pap. 3.50 (ISBN 0-8309-0460-3). Herald Hse.

Cole, Clifford A. Studies in Exodus, Vol. 2. (Bible Study Ser.). 1986. pap. 3.50 (ISBN 0-8309-0462-X). Herald Hse.

Conn, Charles W. A Guide to the Pentateuch. 109p. 1963. 5.25 (ISBN 0-87148-004-2); pap. 4.25 (ISBN 0-87148-005-0). Pathway Pr.

Conrad, Edgar W. Fear Not Warrior: A Study of Pericopes in the Hebrew Scriptures. (Brown Judaic Studies). 1985. 30.95 (ISBN 0-89130-864-4, 14-06-75); pap. 25.95 (ISBN 0-89130-865-2). Scholars Pr GA.

Cox, Claude E. The Armenian Translation of Deuteronomy. Stone, Michael E., ed. LC 81-5273. 1981. text ed. 16.50 (ISBN 0-89130-491-6, 21-02-02); pap. text ed. 12.00 (ISBN 0-89130-492-4). Scholars Pr GA.

Crawford, C. C. Genesis, Vol. I. LC 77-1140. (The Bible Study Textbook Ser.). 1966. 14.30 (ISBN 0-89900-002-9). College Pr Pub.

--Genesis, Vol. II. (The Bible Study Textbook Ser.). 1968. 15.90 (ISBN 0-89900-003-7). College Pr Pub.

--Genesis, Vol. III. (The Bible Study Textbook Ser.). (Illus.). 1970. 14.30 (ISBN 0-89900-004-5). College Pr Pub.

Cummings, John. Deuteronomy. 1982. lib. bdg. 16.00 (ISBN 0-86524-085-X, 0501). Klock & Klock.

Davidson, Robert, ed. Genesis, Chapters Twelve to Fifty. LC 78-12892. (Cambridge Bible Commentary on the New English Bible, Old Testament Ser.). (Illus.). 1979. 39.50 (ISBN 0-521-22485-3); pap. 14.95x (ISBN 0-521-29520-3). Cambridge U Pr.

--Genesis, Chapters 1-11. LC 72-93675. (Cambridge Bible Commentary on the New English Bible, Old Testament Ser.). 200p. (Orig.). 1973. pap. 8.95x (ISBN 0-521-09760-6). Cambridge U Pr.

Davies, G. I. The Way of the Wilderness. LC 77-95442. (Society for Old Testament Monographs). (Illus.). 1979. 32.50 (ISBN 0-521-22057-2). Cambridge U Pr.

Davis, John D. Genesis & Semitic Tradition. (Twin Brooks Ser.). 1980. pap. 4.95 (ISBN 0-8010-2902-3). Baker Bk.

Davis, John J. Moses & Gods of Egypt. (Old Testament Studies). pap. 11.95 (ISBN 0-8010-2957-0). Baker Bk.

--Moses & the Gods of Egypt: Studies in Exodus. Rev. ed. (Illus.). 1985. pap. 11.95 (ISBN 0-88469-177-2). BMH Bks.

--Paradise to Prison: Studies in Genesis. LC 74-30753. (Old Testament Studies). 384p. 1975. 14.95 (ISBN 0-8010-2838-8). Baker Bk.

--Paradise to Prison: Studies in Genesis. 14.95 (ISBN 0-88469-050-4). BMH Bks.

DeWelt, Don. Leviticus. LC 75-328945. (The Bible Study Textbook Ser.). (Illus.). 1975. 14.95 (ISBN 0-89900-007-X). College Pr Pub.

Doty, Brant L. Numbers. (The Bible Study Textbook Ser.). 1973. 14.30 (ISBN 0-89900-008-8). College Pr Pub.

Doukhan, Jacques B. The Genesis Creation Story: Its Literary Structure. (Andrews University Seminary Doctoral Dissertation Ser.: Vol. 5). xii, 303p. 1982. pap. 10.95 (ISBN 0-943872-37-5). Andrews Univ Pr.

Drazin, Israel. Targum Onkelos on Deuteronomy. 1981. 45.00x (ISBN 0-87068-755-7). Ktav.

Durham, John. Exodus (WBC, Vol. 3. 448p. 1986. 25.95 (ISBN 0-8499-0202-9). Word Bks.

Eckstein, Stephen D., Jr. The Purpose of Genesis. 1976. pap. 2.75 (ISBN 0-88027-037-3). Firm Foun Pub.

Ellison, H. L. Exodus. LC 81-12917. (Daily Study Bible Old Testament Ser.). 216p. 1982. 12.95 (ISBN 0-664-21803-2); pap. 7.95 (ISBN 0-664-24570-6). Westminster.

Erdman, Charles. El Pentateuco. Casanova, Humberto & Casanova, Viviana, trs. Tr. of The Pentateuch. 396p. 1986. 12.95 (ISBN 0-939125-14-5). Evangelical Lit.

Erdman, Charles R. Deuteronomy. 96p. 1982. pap. 3.50 (ISBN 0-8010-3379-9). Baker Bk.

--Genesis. 128p. 1982. pap. 4.95 (ISBN 0-8010-3375-6). Baker Bk.

--Numbers. 144p. 1982. pap. 4.50 (ISBN 0-8010-3378-0). Baker Bk.

Ferch, Arthur. In the Beginning. Wheeler, Gerald, ed. LC 85-1946. 128p. (Orig.). 1985. pap. 5.95 (ISBN 0-8280-0282-7). Review & Herald.

Fleck, Ludwig. Genesis & Development of a Scientific Fact. Trenn, Thaddeus J. & Merton, Robert K., eds. Bradley, Fred, tr. from Ger. LC 79-12521. 224p. 1981. pap. 8.00x (ISBN 0-226-25325-2). U of Chicago Pr.

Fohr, S. D. Adam & Eve: The Spiritual Symbolism of Genesis & Exodus. LC 86-1497. 162p. (Orig.). 1986. lib. bdg. 25.75 (ISBN 0-8191-5267-6); pap. text ed. 10.25 (ISBN 0-8191-5268-4). U Pr of Amer.

Fox, Everett. In the Beginning: A New English Rendition of the Book of Genesis. 288p. 1983. 14.95 (ISBN 0-8052-3870-0). Schocken.

Fraade, Steven D. Enosh & His Generation: Pre-Israelite Hero & History in Post-Biblical Interpretation. LC 83-27137. (Society of Biblical Literature-Monograph Ser.). 1984. 29.95 (ISBN 0-89130-724-9, 06 00 30); pap. 19.95 (ISBN 0-89130-725-7). Scholars Pr GA.

Fretheim, Terence E. Deuteronomic History. Bailey, Lloyd R. & Furnish, Victory P., eds. 160p. (Orig.). 1983. pap. 9.95 (ISBN 0-687-10497-1). Abingdon.

Friedman, Richard E. The Exile & Biblical Narrative: The Formation of the Deuteronomistic & Priestly Works. LC 80-28836. 1981. 12.00 (ISBN 0-89130-457-6, 04 00 22). Scholars Pr GA.

Genesis. (Modern Critical Interpretations--Ancient, Medieval, & Renaissance Ser.). 1987. 19.95 (ISBN 0-87754-910-9). Chelsea Hse.

Gerbrandt, Gerald E. Kingship According to Deuteronomistic History. (Society of Biblical Literature Dissertation Ser.). 1986. 17.95 (ISBN 0-89130-968-3, 06 01 87); pap. 12.95 (ISBN 0-89130-969-1). Scholars Pr GA.

Gettys, Joseph M. Surveying the Pentateuch. 147p. 1962. pap. 4.50x (ISBN 0-8042-3676-3). Attic Pr.

Gibson, John C. L. Genesis, Vol. 1 chs. 1-11. LC 81-7477. (Daily Study Bible-Old Testament Ser.). 224p. 1981. 12.95 (ISBN 0-664-21801-6); pap. 6.95 (ISBN 0-664-24568-4). Westminster.

--Genesis, Vol. 2, chs. 12-50. LC 81-7477. (Daily Study Bible-Old Testament Ser.). 336p. 1982. 12.95 (ISBN 0-664-21804-0); pap. 7.95 (ISBN 0-664-24571-4). Westminster.

Glanzman, George S. Deuteronomy. Pt. 1. pap. 1.00 (ISBN 0-8091-5028-X); Pt. 2. pap. 1.00 (ISBN 0-8091-5029-8). Paulist Pr.

Goldberg, Louis. Leviticus: Bible Study Commentary. (A Study Guide Commentary Ser.). 128p. (Orig.). 1980. pap. 4.95 (ISBN 0-310-41813-5, 18198P). Zondervan.

Graves, Robert & Patai, Raphael. Hebrew Myths. 1966. pap. 5.95 (ISBN 0-07-024125-2). McGraw.

Gray, Elizabeth Dodson. Green Paradise Lost. LC 79-89193. x, 166p. 1979. pap. 8.95 (ISBN 0-934512-02-7). Roundtable Pr.

--Why the Green Nigger? Re-Mything Genesis. LC 79-89193. x, 166p. 1979. 12.95 (ISBN 0-934512-01-9). Roundtable Pr.

Grazia, Alfred de. God's Fire: Moses & the Management of Exodus. (Quantavolution Ser.). (Illus.). 340p. 1983. pap. 20.00 (ISBN 0-940268-03-5). Metron Pubns.

Green, William H. The Higher Criticism of the Pentateuch. (Twin Brooks Ser.). 1978. pap. 4.95 (ISBN 0-8010-3723-9). Baker Bk.

Grossfeld, Bernard. A Critical Commentary on Targum Neofiti I to Genesis. Schiffman, L. H., ed. 75.00x (ISBN 0-87068-333-0). Ktav.

Gunderson, Vivian. Bible Learn & Do: Exodus. (Illus.). 1981. pap. 1.25 (ISBN 0-8323-0394-1); tchr's manual 2.50 (ISBN 0-8323-0435-2). Binford-Metropolitan.

--Bible Learn & Do: Genesis, Pt. I. (Illus.). 1979. pap. 1.25 (ISBN 0-8323-0368-2); tchr's. manual 2.50 (ISBN 0-8323-0376-3). Binford-Metropolitan.

--Bible Learn & Do: Genesis, Pt. II. (Illus.). 1980. pap. 1.25 (ISBN 0-8323-0369-0); tchr's. manual 2.50 (ISBN 0-8323-0377-1). Binford-Metropolitan.

--Bible Learn & Do: Numbers. (Illus.). 1981. pap. 1.25 (ISBN 0-8323-0393-3); tchr's. manual 2.50 (ISBN 0-8323-0436-0). Binford-Metropolitan.

Gunkel, Hermann. The Legends of Genesis: The Biblical Saga & History. LC 64-22609. 1984. pap. 5.50 (ISBN 0-8052-0086-X). Schocken.

Guyon, Jeanne. The Way Out. (Orig.). 1985. pap. 6.95 (ISBN 0-940232-20-0). Christian Bks.

Habel, Norman C. Literary Criticism of the Old Testament. Rylaarsdam, Coert, ed. LC 78-157548. (Guides to Biblical Scholarship: Old Testament Ser.). 96p. 1971. pap. 4.50 (ISBN 0-8006-0176-9, 1-176). Fortress.

Hadas, Pamela W. In Light of Genesis. LC 80-13129. (Jewish Poetry Ser.). 128p. 1980. 10.95 (ISBN 0-8276-0177-8, 462); pap. 6.95 (ISBN 0-8276-0178-6, 461). Jewish Pubns.

Harris, Thomas L. Arcana of Christianity, 3 pts. in 2 vols. LC 72-2955. Repr. of 1867 ed. Set. 92.00 (ISBN 0-404-10720-6). AMS Pr.

Hasel, Gerhard F. The Remnant: The History & Theology of the Remnant Idea from Genesis to Isaiah. 3rd ed. (Andrews University Monographs, Studies in Religion: Vol. V). x, 474p. 1980. pap. 10.95 (ISBN 0-943872-05-7). Andrews Univ Pr.

Hertz, J. H. Penateuch & Haftorahs. 1067p. 1960. 25.00 (ISBN 0-900689-21-8). Soncino Pr.

Hooke, Samuel H. In the Beginning. LC 78-10638. (The Clarendon Bible Old Testament Ser.: Vol. VI). (Illus.). 1979. Repr. of 1947 ed. lib. bdg. 22.50x (ISBN 0-313-21014-4, HOIB). Greenwood.

Huey, F. B., Jr. Numbers: Bible Study Commentary. (Bible Study Commentary Ser.). 144p. (Orig.). 1981. pap. 4.95 (ISBN 0-310-36073-0, 11064P). Zondervan.

Ibn Ezra on Leviticus: The Straightforward Meaning. pap. 9.95 (ISBN 0-88125-109-7). Ktav.

Ingersoll, Robert G. Some Mistakes of Moses. 270p. 1986. pap. 12.95 (ISBN 0-87975-361-7). Prometheus Bks.

The Interpreter's Concise Commentary, Vol. I: The Pentateuch, 8 vols. 368p. (Orig.). 1983. pap. 4.95 (ISBN 0-687-19232-3). Abingdon.

Jacob, Benno. Das Erste Buch der Tora Genesis. (Ger.). 1934. 100.00 (ISBN 0-87068-247-4). Ktav.

Janzen, Waldemar. By Faith Abraham & Sarah: Genesis 12-25. Shelly, Maynard, ed. LC 86-83035. (Faith & Life Bible Studies). 70p. (Orig.). 1987. pap. 4.95 (ISBN 0-87303-108-3). Faith & Life.

Jukes, Andrew. The Law of the Offerings. LC 68-19198. 220p. 1976. pap. 6.95 (ISBN 0-8254-2957-9). Kregel.

Kang, C. H. & Nelson, Ethel. The Discovery of Genesis. 1979. pap. 4.95 (ISBN 0-570-03792-1, 12-2755). Concordia.

Kappeler, Max. The Four Levels of Spiritual Consciousness. LC 72-883567. 198p. 1970. 14.00 (ISBN 0-85241-091-3). Kappeler Inst Pub.

Kelly, William. The Pentateuch. (Introductory Lecture Ser.). 524p. 6.95 (ISBN 0-88172-099-2). Believers Bkshelf.

Knight, George A. Leviticus. LC 81-3007. (Daily Study Bible-Old Testament Ser.). 182p. 1981. 12.95 (ISBN 0-664-21802-4); pap. 6.95 (ISBN 0-664-24569-2). Westminster.

Koch, R. Riddle of Genesis. pap. 0.75 (ISBN 0-8199-0395-7). Franciscan Herald.

Kunz, Marilyn & Schell, Catherine. Genesis. 1981. pap. 2.95 (ISBN 0-8423-0995-0). Tyndale.

Lambert, Gussie. One Thousand Questions on Genesis. 2.50 (ISBN 0-89315-188-2). Lambert Bk.

Leach, David A. Genesis: The Book of Beginnings. 96p. 1984. pap. 4.95 (ISBN 0-8170-1047-5). Judson.

Lee, J. A. A Lexical Study of the Septuagint Version of the Pentateuch. LC 82-5460. (Septuagint & Cognate Studies). 186p. 1983. pap. 12.50 (ISBN 0-89130-576-9, 06 04 14). Scholars Pr GA.

Lund, Shirley & Foster, Julia A. Variant Versions of Targumic Traditions Within Codex Neofiti 1. LC 77-5389. (Society of Biblical Literature. Aramaic Studies). 1977. pap. 10.50 (ISBN 0-89130-137-2, 061302). Scholars Pr GA.

Maarsingh, B. Numbers. Van der Woude, A. S., ed. Vriend, John, tr. from Dutch. (Text & Interpretation Commentary Ser.). 128p. (Orig.). 1987. pap. 6.95 (ISBN 0-8028-0104-8). Eerdmans.

McKenzie, Steven L. The Chronicler's Use of the Deuteronomistic History. (Harvard Semitic Monograph Ser.: No. 33). 1985. 16.50 (ISBN 0-89130-828-8, 04 00 33). Scholars Pr GA.

Maher, Michael. Genesis. (Old Testament Message Ser.: Vol. 2). 1982. 15.95 (ISBN 0-89453-402-5); pap. 9.95 (ISBN 0-89453-237-5). M Glazier.

Meyering, Robert A. Genesis One-Eleven. (Five-on-One Ser.). 96p. (Orig.). 1986. pap. text ed. 3.95 (ISBN 0-930265-16-5); tchr's. guide 7.95 (ISBN 0-930265-17-3). CRC Pubns.

Miller, William T. Mysterious Encounters at Mamre & Jabbok. (Brown Judaic Studies: No. 50). 252p. 1985. 24.95 (ISBN 0-89130-816-4, 14 00 50); pap. 18.25 (ISBN 0-89130-817-2). Scholars Pr GA.

Morgan, G. Campbell. Ten Commandments. (Morgan Library). 1974. pap. 3.95 (ISBN 0-8010-5954-2). Baker Bk.

Morris, Henry M. Genesis Record. 24.95 (ISBN 0-8010-6004-4). Baker Bk.

Morris, Peter M. & James, Edward. A Critical Word Book of the Pentateuch. (Computer Bible Ser.: Vol. XVII). 1980. pap. 25.00 (ISBN 0-935106-03-0). Biblical Res Assocs.

Morrison, G. H., ed. Morrison on Genesis. (Glasgow Pulpit Ser.). 72p. 1976. pap. 4.95 (ISBN 0-89957-520-X). AMG Pubs.

Murphy, James G. Commentary on the Book of Exodus. 1979. 14.50 (ISBN 0-86524-014-0, 0201). Klock & Klock.

Newman, Louis. Genesis: The Student's Guide, Pt. 2. pap. 4.95 (ISBN 0-8381-0404-5). United Syn Bk.

--Teacher's Supplement to Genesis the Student's Guide Pt. 1. pap. 2.95 (ISBN 0-8381-0403-7). United Syn Bk.

North, Gary. The Dominion Covenant: Genesis. 1982. 14.95 (ISBN 0-930464-03-6). Inst Christian.

Olson, Dennis T. The Death of the Old & the Birth of the New: Framework of the Book of Numbers & the Pentateuch. (Brown Judaic Ser.). 1985. 29.95 (ISBN 0-89130-885-7, 14-00-71); pap. 22.95 (ISBN 0-89130-886-5). Scholars Pr Ga.

Owen, Valarie. In the Beginning God. 224p. (Orig.). 1983. pap. text ed. 6.95 (ISBN 0-914307-00-2, Dist. by Harrion Hse). Word Faith.

--Let My People Go. 395p. (Orig.). 1983. pap. text ed. 9.95 (ISBN 0-914307-10-X, Dist. by Harrison Hse). Word Faith.

Payne, David F. Deuteronomy. LC 85-13653. (Daily Study Bible - Old Testament). 210p. 1985. 14.95 (ISBN 0-664-21832-6); pap. 7.95 (ISBN 0-664-24580-3). Westminster.

Peacock, Heber F. A Translator's Guide to Selections from the First Five Books of the Old Testament. (Helps for Translators Ser.). 323p. 1982. pap. 4.30x (ISBN 0-8267-0298-8, 08765, Pub. by United Bible). Am Bible.

Peckham, Brian. The Composition of the Deuteronomic History. (Harvard Semitic Museum Monographs). 1985. 13.95 (ISBN 0-89130-909-8, 04-00-35). Scholars Pr GA.

Peters, Melvin K. A Critical Edition of the Coptic (Bohairic) Pentateuch: Septuagint & Cognate Studies, Vol. 2, Exodus. 122p. 1986. 11.95 (ISBN 1-55540-030-2, 06-04-22); pap. 8.95 (ISBN 1-55540-031-0). Scholars Pr GA.

Philip, James. Numbers, Vol. 4. 300p. 1987. 18.95 (ISBN 0-8499-0409-9). Word Bks.

Pico Della Mirandola, Giovanni. On the Dignity of Man. Wallis, Charles G., et al, trs. Bd. with On Being & Unity; Heptaplus. LC 65-26540. 1965. pap. 7.87 scp (ISBN 0-672-60483-3, LLA227). Bobbs.

Polzin, Robert M. Moses & the Deuteronomist: A Literary Study of the Deuteronomic History. 224p. 1981. 17.95 (ISBN 0-8164-0456-9, HarpR); pap. 8.95 (ISBN 0-8164-2284-2). Har-Row.

Pope John Paul II. Original Unity of Man & Woman. 184p. 1981. 4.00 (ISBN 0-8198-5405-0); pap. 3.00 (ISBN 0-686-78419-7). Dghtrs St Paul.

Radday, Yehuda & Levi, Yaakov. An Analytical Linguistic Key-Word-in-Context Concordance to the Book of Exodus. Baird, Arthur J. & Freedman, David, eds. (The Computer Bible Ser.: Vol. 28). (Orig.). 1985. 45.00 (ISBN 0-935106-23-5). Biblical Res Assocs.

Rendsburg, Gary A. Redaction of Genesis. xii, 132p. 1986. text ed. 12.50x (ISBN 0-931464-25-0). Eisenbrauns.

Riggans, Walter. Numbers. LC 83-7007. (Daily Study Bible-Old Testament). 262p. (Orig.). 1983. 14.95 (ISBN 0-664-21393-6); pap. 7.95 (ISBN 0-664-24474-2). Westminster.

Rodriguez, Angel M. Substitution in the Hebrew Cultus, Vol. 3. (Andrews University Seminary Doctoral Dissertation Ser.). xiv, 339p. (Orig.). 1982. pap. 10.95 (ISBN 0-943872-35-9). Andrews Univ Pr.

Roop, Eugene F. Genesis. (The Believers Church Bible Comentary Ser.: No. 2). 344p. (Orig.). 1987. pap. 17.95 (ISBN 0-8361-3443-5). Herald Pr.

St. John Chrysostom. Homilies on Genesis 1-17. Hill, Robert C., tr. from Gr. (The Fathers of the Church Ser.: Vol. 74). 1986. 29.95 (ISBN 0-8132-0074-1). Cath U Pr.

Sanderson, Judith E. An Exodus Scroll from Qumran: 4QpaleoExodm & the Samaritan Tradition. (Harvard Semitic Studies). 378p. 1986. 20.95 (ISBN 1-55540-036-1, 04-04-30). Scholars Pr GA.

Schaeffer, Francis A. Genesis in Space & Time. LC 72-78406. 144p. 1972. pap. 6.95 (ISBN 0-87784-636-7). Inter-Varsity.

Scherman, Nosson. Bircas Hamazon-Grace after Meals. (Art Scroll Mesorah Ser.). 96p. 1977. 7.50 (ISBN 0-89906-152-4); pap. 5.50 (ISBN 0-89906-153-2). Mesorah Pubns.

Schmidt, Ludwig. De Deo: Studien Zur Literaturkritik und Thelogie des Buches Jona, des Gespraechs zwischen Abraham und Jahiwe in Gen. 18, 22ff. (Beiheft 143 zur Zeitschrift Fuer die Alttestamentliche Wissenschaft Ser.). 1976. 41.60x (ISBN 3-11-006618-1). De Gruyter.

Schneider, Bernard N. Deuteronomy: A Favored Book of Jesus. pap. 5.95 (ISBN 0-88469-051-2). BMH Bks.

Schreur, Clarence. Genesis & Common Sense. 109p. 1983. 12.50 (ISBN 0-942078-03-9). R Tanner Assocs Inc.

Schultz, Albert L. God's Call: Exodus Second Part. Bartlett, Kenneth, ed. (Books of Oral Tradition: No. 4). 80p. (Orig.). 1986. pap. 9.85 (ISBN 0-936596-11-2). Quantal.

Seiss, Joseph. Gospel in Leviticus. LC 80-8078. 408p. 1981. 12.95 (ISBN 0-8254-3743-1). Kregel.

Siegel, Jonathan P. The Severus Scroll & 1Q1SA. LC 75-28372. (Society of Biblical Literature, Masoretic Studies). 1975. pap. 8.95 (ISBN 0-89130-028-7, 060502). Scholars Pr GA.

Skeem, Kenneth A. In the Beginning... Skeem, Jeanette L., ed. LC 81-68054. (Illus.). 256p. 1981. 12.00 (ISBN 0-9606782-0-4). Behemoth Pub.

Slemming, Charles W. Made According to Pattern. 1964. pap. 2.95 (ISBN 0-87508-506-7). Chr Lit.

Smith, George. The Chaldean Account of Genesis. LC 77-73714. (Secret Doctrine Reference Ser.). (Illus.). 340p. 1977. Repr. of 1876 ed. 15.00 (ISBN 0-913510-26-2). Wizards.

Stedman, Ray C. Understanding Man. LC 86-16463. (Authentic Christianity Ser.). (Orig.). 1986. pap. 6.95 (ISBN 0-88070-156-0). Multnomah.

Steiner, Rudolf. Genesis: Secrets of the Bible Story of Creation. Lenn, Dorothy, et al, trs. from Ger. 139p. 1982. pap. 9.95 (ISBN 0-85440-391-4, Pub by Steinerbooks). Anthroposophic.

Strahan, James. Hebrew Ideals in Genesis (Genesis 11-50) LC 82-7785. 360p. 1982. 14.95 (ISBN 0-8254-3729-6). Kregel.

Talbot, Gordon. A Study of the Book of Genesis. LC 81-65578. 288p. (Orig.). 1981. pap. 6.95 (ISBN 0-87509-253-5); leader's guide 2.95 (ISBN 0-87509-311-6). Chr Pubns.

Taylor, John H., tr. & annotations by. St. Augustine: The Literal Meaning of Genesis, Vol. 1. (Ancient Christian Writers Ser.: Vol. 41). 292p. 1983. 19.95 (ISBN 0-8091-0326-5). Paulist Pr.

--St. Augustine: The Literal Meaning of Genesis, Vol. 2. (Ancient Christian Writers Ser.: Vol. 42). 358p. 1983. 22.95 (ISBN 0-8091-0327-3). Paulist Pr.

Teubal, Savina J. Sarah the Priestess: The First Matriarch of Genesis. LC 84-96. xx, 201p. 1984. 16.95 (ISBN 0-8040-0843-4, Swallow); pap. 8.95 (ISBN 0-8040-0844-2, Swallow). Ohio U Pr.

Thielicke, Helmut. How the World Began. Doberstein, J. W., tr. from Ger. 308p. 1978. Repr. 13.95 (ISBN 0-227-67484-7). Attic Pr.

Tobin, Thomas H. The Creation of Man: Philo & the History of Interpretation. Vawter, Bruce, ed. LC 82-19891. (Catholic Biblical Quarterly Monographs: No. 14). viii, 199p. (Orig.). 1983. pap. 6.00x (ISBN 0-915170-13-2). Catholic Biblical.

Versteeg, J. P. Is Adam a "Teaching Model" in the New Testament? pap. 1.75 (ISBN 0-8010-9276-0). Baker Bk.

Wallace, Howard N. The Eden Narrative. (Harvard Semitic Museum Monograph). 1985. 16.95 (ISBN 0-89130-838-5, 04-00-32). Scholars Pr GA.

Walzer, Michael. Exodus & Revolution. LC 84-45306. 177p. 1985. 15.95 (ISBN 0-465-02164-6). Basic.

--Exodus & Revolution. LC 84-45306. 192p. 1986. pap. 6.95 (ISBN 0-465-02165-4, PL 5168). Basic.

Weimar, Peter. Untersuchungen zur Redaktionsgeschichte des Pentateuch. 1977. 34.40x (ISBN 3-11-006731-5). De Gruyter.

Weinfeld, M. Deuteronomy & the Deuteronomic School. 1972. 53.00x (ISBN 0-19-826626-X). Oxford U Pr.

Weiss, Jess E. The Adam & Eve Fantasy. 80p. 1985. 8.00 (ISBN 0-682-40262-1). Exposition Pr FL.

Wendland, Ernst H. Exodus. (People's Bible Ser.). 1984. pap. 6.95 (ISBN 0-8100-0180-2, 15N0405); study guide, 52p 1.50 (ISBN 0-938272-50-0). Northwest Pub.

Whitcomb, John C. The World That Perished. pap. 4.95 (ISBN 0-88469-059-8). BMH Bks.

Whitcomb, John C. & Morris, Henry M. The Genesis Flood. pap. 8.95 (ISBN 0-8010-9501-8). Baker Bk.

--The Genesis Flood. pap. 8.95 (ISBN 0-88469-067-9). BMH Bks.

White, Gail. The Last Eve. LC 85-91011. 160p. 1985. 10.00 (ISBN 0-682-40244-3). Exposition Pr FL.

Wiester, John. The Genesis Connection. LC 83-13409. (Illus.). 320p. 1983. 14.95 (ISBN 0-8407-5296-2). Nelson.

Wilson, Ian. Exodus: The True Story. LC 85-45727. 208p. 1986. 19.45 (ISBN 0-06-250969-1, HarpR). Har-Row.

Young, E. J. Genesis 3. 1984. pap. 4.45 (ISBN 0-85151-148-1). Banner of Truth.

Young, Edward J. Studies in Genesis One. pap. 4.95 (ISBN 0-87552-550-4). Presby & Reformed.

Zachary, Jean. The Holy Days, As Outlined in Leviticus Twenty-Three. 72p. (Orig.). 1987. pap. 3.75 (ISBN 0-9617733-0-8). Pneuma Pub.

BIBLE–CRITICISM, INTERPRETATION, ETC.–O. T. POETICAL BOOKS

Here are entered works on the poetical books as a whole, as well as books on one or more of the following: Job, Ecclesiastes, Psalms, Proverbs, Song of Solomon; For works on Lamentations see Bible–Criticism, Interpretation, Etc–O. T. Prophets.

Ackley, Phil. Get Wise: Studies in Proverbs. (Young Fisherman Bible Studyguides). (Illus.). 80p. 1985. tchr's. ed. 4.95 (ISBN 0-87788-696-2); student ed. 2.95 (ISBN 0-87788-695-4). Shaw Pubs.

Aitken, Kenneth T. Proverbs. LC 86-15660. (The Daily Study Bible-Old Testament). 276p. 1986. 15.95 (ISBN 0-664-21837-7); pap. 8.95 (ISBN 0-664-24586-2). Westminster.

Alexander, Joyce & Alexander, Dorsey, illus. David: Psalm Twenty-Four. (Illus., Calligraphy & Illus.). 1970. pap. 5.00 (ISBN 0-912020-17-2). Turtles Quill.

Allen, Charles L. Twenty-Third Psalm. (Illus.). 64p. 1961. 7.95 (ISBN 0-8007-0330-8). Revell.

Allen, Ronald B. Rediscovering Prophecy: A New Song for a New Kingdom. 1987. pap. 7.95. Multnomah.

Anderson, Bernhard W. Out of the Depths: The Psalms Speak for Us Today. Revised & Expanded ed. LC 83-19801. 254p. 1983. pap. 11.95 (ISBN 0-664-24504-8). Westminster.

Andrews, Samuel J. & Gifford, E. H. Man & the Incarnation: The Study of Philippians 2 & Psalm 110. 1981. lib. bdg. 15.00 (ISBN 0-86524-078-7, 9510). Klock & Klock.

Archer, Gleason L., Jr. The Book of Job: God's Answer to the Problem of Undeserved Suffering. 128p. (Orig.). 1983. pap. 5.95 (ISBN 0-8010-0190-0). Baker Bk.

Aufrecht, Walter, ed. Studies in the Book of Job. (SR Supplements Ser.: No. 16). 104p. 1985. pap. text ed. 8.95x (ISBN 0-88920-179-X, Pub. by Wilfrid Laurier Canada). Humanities.

Augustine, St. St. Augustine on the Psalms, Vol. 1. Quasten, J. & Burghardt, W. J., eds. Hebgin, Scholastica & Corrigan, Felicitas, trs. LC 60-10722. (Ancient Christian Writers Ser.: No. 29). 360p. 1960. 12.95 (ISBN 0-8091-0104-1). Paulist Pr.

Augustinus, Saint Aurelius. Quaestionum in Heptateuchum Libri 7, Adnotationum in Iob Liber Unus. (Corpus Scriptorum Ecclesiasticorum Latinorum Ser: Vol. 38, Pt. 2). 50.00 (ISBN 0-384-02515-3). Johnson Repr.

Barnes, Albert. Job. 18.95 (ISBN 0-8010-0837-9). Baker Bk.

--Proverbs-Ezekiel. 10.95 (ISBN 0-8010-0839-5). Baker Bk.

--Psalms. 29.95 (ISBN 0-8010-0838-7). Baker Bk.

Beacon Bible Commentary Staff. Job-Song of Solomon, Vol. III. 13.95 (ISBN 0-8010-0690-2). Baker Bk.

Bergant, Dianne. Job, Ecclesiastes. (Old Testament Message Ser.: Vol. 18). 1982. 12.95 (ISBN 0-89453-418-1); pap. 9.95 (ISBN 0-89453-252-9). M Glazier.

Bernard Of Clairvaux. Bernard of Clairvaux: Sermons on the Song of Songs, Vol. IV. Edmonds, Irene, tr. (Cistercian Fathers Ser.: N0. 40). 1980. 15.95 (ISBN 0-87907-140-0). Cistercian Pubns.

Beyerlin, Walter. We Are Like Dreamers. Livingstone, Dinah, tr. from Ger. Tr. of Wir Sind Wie Traumende. 76p. 1982. 13.95 (ISBN 0-567-09315-8, Pub. by T&T Clark Ltd). Fortress.

Bloem, Diane B. Into the Midst of Suffering: A Woman's Workshop on Job. (Woman's Workshop Ser.). (Orig.). 1985. Leader's ed., 64pp. pap. 3.95 (ISBN 0-310-42771-1, 11213P); Student's ed., 112pp. pap. 2.95 (ISBN 0-310-42781-9, 11213P). Zondervan.

Blommerde, Anton C. Northwest Semetic Grammar & Job. (Biblica et Orientalia Ser.: Vol. 22). 1969. pap. 13.00 (ISBN 88-7653-322-2). Loyola.

The Book of Job. (Modern Critical Interpretations--Ancient, Medieval, & Renaissance Ser.). 19.95 (ISBN 0-87754-913-3). Chelsea Hse.

Bourke, Myles M. Job. (Bible Ser.). Pt. 1. pap. 1.00 (ISBN 0-8091-5073-5); Pt. 2. pap. 1.00 (ISBN 0-8091-5074-3). Paulist Pr.

Broyles, Craig C. The Conflict of Faith & Experience in the Psalms: A Form-Critical & Theological Study. (JSOT Supplement Ser.: No. 52). 200p. 1986. text ed. 27.50x (ISBN 1-85075-052-1, Pub. by JSOT Pr England); pap. text ed. 19.95x (ISBN 1-85075-053-X, Pub. by JSOT Pr England). Eisenbrauns.

Bunyan, John. Israel's Hope Encouraged. pap. 1.95 (ISBN 0-685-19836-7). Reiner.

Camp, Claudia. Wisdom & the Faminine in the Book of Proverbs. (Bible & Literature Ser.: No. II). 360p. 1985. text ed. 29.95x (ISBN 0-907459-42-0, Pub. by Almond Pr England); pap. text ed. 15.95x (ISBN 0-907459-43-9). Eisenbrauns.

Camp, Sylvia. I Wonder from Job. pap. 3.50 (ISBN 0-89315-127-0). Lambert Bk.

Carder, David. Promises from Proverbs. 1986. pap. 2.50 (ISBN 0-310-36782-4, 12732P). Zondervan.

Cargile, Wayne. Bible Melodies Chosen. 1971. pap. 1.00 (ISBN 0-87012-106-5). McClain.

Chamberlain, Gary, tr. The Psalms: A New Translation for Prayer & Worship. LC 84-50842. 192p. (Orig.). 1984. pap. 6.95 (ISBN 0-8358-0485-2). Upper Room.

Chambers, Oswald. Shade of His Hand. 1961. pap. 2.95 (ISBN 0-87508-127-4). Chr Lit.

Cohen, A. Job. 233p. 1946. 10.95 (ISBN 0-900689-34-X). Soncino Pr.

--Proverbs. 223p. 1946. 10.95 (ISBN 0-900689-33-1). Soncino Pr.

--The Psalms. 488p. 1945. 10.95 (ISBN 0-900689-32-3). Soncino Pr.

Cole, C. Donald. Thirsting for God: A Devotional Study of the Psalms in Light of Their Historical Background. LC 85-72918. 350p. 1986. pap. 8.95 (ISBN 0-89107-376-0, Crossway Bks). Good News.

Cooper, Dale J. Psalms: A Study Guide. (Revelation Series for Adults). 1979. pap. text ed. 2.50 (ISBN 0-933140-08-8). CRC Pubns.

Cox, Dermot. Proverbs, with Introduction to Sapiential Books. (Old Testament Ser.: Vol. 17). 1982. 12.95 (ISBN 0-89453-417-3); pap. 9.95 (ISBN 0-89453-251-0). M Glazier.

Crossan, John D., ed. Semeia Nineteen: The Book of Job & Ricoeur's Hermeneutics. (Semeia Ser.). pap. 9.95 (06 20 19). Scholars Pr GA.

Cumming, Charles G. Assyrian & Hebrew Hymns of Praise. LC 34-3318. (Columbia University. Oriental Studies: No. 12). Repr. of 1934 ed. 16.50 (ISBN 0-404-50502-3). AMS Pr.

Deal, William S. New Light on the Shepherd Psalm. 1982. 3.95. Crusade Pubs.

Drakeford, John W. Wisdom for Today's Family. LC 77-94449. 1978. pap. 5.50 (ISBN 0-8054-5592-2). Broadman.

Draper, James T., Jr. Proverbs: Practical Directions for Living. (Living Studies). pap. 4.95 (ISBN 0-8423-4922-7); leader's guide 2.95 (ISBN 0-8423-4923-5). Tyndale.

Dunlop, Laurence. Patterns of Prayer in the Psalms. 160p. (Orig.). 1982. pap. 9.95 (ISBN 0-8164-2377-6, HarpR). Har-Row.

Durham, James. Song of Solomon. 1981. lib. bdg. 17.25 (ISBN 0-86524-075-2, 2201). Klock & Klock.

--Song of Solomon. (Geneva Ser.). 460p. 1982. Repr. of 1840 ed. 13.95 (ISBN 0-85151-352-2). Banner of Truth.

Eames, Wilberforce, ed. A List of Editions of the Bay Psalm Book or New England Version of the Psalms, 2 vols. in 1. Incl. Bible. O. T. Psalms. English. Paraphrases. 1912 Bay Psalm Book. facsimile ed. New England Society. 1912. Repr. LC 1-538. 1885. Repr. 23.50 (ISBN 0-8337-0987-9). B Franklin.

Eaton, J. H. Job. (Old Testament Guides Ser.). 69p. 1985. pap. text ed. 3.95x (ISBN 0-905774-97-3, Pub by. JSOT Pr England). Eisenbrauns.

Eaton, John H. The Psalms Come Alive: Capturing the Voice & the Art of Israel's Songs. LC 86-20115. (Illus.). 180p. 1986. pap. 6.95 (ISBN 0-87784-387-2). Inter-Varsity.

Falwell, Jerry. Wisdom for Living. 156p. 1984. pap. 5.95 (ISBN 0-89693-370-9). Victor Bks.

Forestell, J. Terrence. Proverbs. (Bible Ser.). 1.00 (ISBN 0-8091-5122-7). Paulist Pr.

Francisco, Clyde T. Un Varon Llamado Job. Glaze, Jack A., tr. from Eng. (Reflexiones Teologicas Ser.). Orig. Title: A Man Called Job. 64p. 1981. pap. 1.95 (ISBN 0-311-04659-2). Casa Bautista.

Freligh, Harold M. Job. pap. 1.95 (ISBN 0-87509-097-4). Chr Pubns.

Fruchtenbaum, Arnold G. Biblical Lovemaking: A Study of the Song of Solomon. 70p. 1983. pap. 3.50 (ISBN 0-914863-03-7). Ariel Pr CA.

Garland, D. David. Job: Bible Study Commentary. 160p. 1971. pap. 4.95 (ISBN 0-310-24863-9, 9671P). Zondervan.

Gerstenberger, Erhard, ed. Psalms: With Introduction to Cultic Poetry, Prt. I. (The Forms of the Old Testament Literature Ser.: Vol. XIV). 224p. (Orig.). 1987. pap. 21.95 (ISBN 0-8028-0255-9). Eerdmans.

Gibson, John C. Job. LC 85-13652. (Daily Study Bible - Old Testament). 294p. 1985. 16.95 (ISBN 0-664-21815-6); pap. 8.95 (ISBN 0-664-24584-6). Westminster.

Gilbert Of Hoyland. Gilbert of Hoyland: Sermons on the Song of Songs, 1. Braceland, Lawrence C., tr. from Latin. LC 77-23026. (Fathers Ser.: No. 14). 1978. 15.95 (ISBN 0-87907-414-0). Cistercian Pubns.

Gladson, Jerry. Who Said Life Is Fair? Wheeler, Gerald, ed. 128p. 1985. pap. 6.95 (ISBN 0-8280-0242-8). Review & Herald.

Glatzer, Nahum N. The Dimensions of Job: A Study & Selected Readings. LC 69-11936. 320p. 1973. pap. 7.95 (ISBN 0-8052-0378-8). Schocken.

Glickman, S. Craig. A Song for Lovers. LC 75-21454. 204p. (Orig.). 1976. pap. 6.95 (ISBN 0-87784-768-1). Inter-Varsity.

Gordis, Robert. The Song of Songs & Lamentations: A Commentary & Translation. 1974. 25.00x (ISBN 0-87068-256-3). Ktav.

Goulder, Michael D. The Psalms of the Sons of Korah. (Journal for the Study of the Old Testament, Supplement Ser.: No. 20). xiv, 302p. 1983. 27.50x (ISBN 0-905774-40-X, Pub. by JSOT Pr England); pap. text ed. 14.95x (ISBN 0-905774-41-8). Eisenbrauns.

Gregory the Great. Remediarium Conversorum: A Synthesis in Latin of "Moralia in Job". Peter of Waltham & Gildea, Joseph, eds. LC 84-3693. 504p. 1984. 25.00 (ISBN 0-8453-4507-9). Assoc Univ Prs.

Grosse, David G. Beacon Small-Group Bible Studies, Job: The Trial & Triumph of Faith. Wolf, Earl C., ed. 88p. (Orig.). 1986. pap. 2.50 (ISBN 0-8341-1109-8). Beacon Hill.

--Job: The Trial & Triumph of Faith. (Small Group Bible Studies). 88p. (Orig.). 1986. pap. 2.50 (ISBN 0-8341-1138-1). Beacon Hill.

Gunkel, Hermann. Psalms: A Form-Critical Introduction. Reumann, John, ed. Horner, Thomas M., tr. from Ger. LC 67-22983. (Facet Bks.). 64p. (Orig.). 1967. pap. 2.50 (ISBN 0-8006-3043-2, 1-3043). Fortress.

Guthrie, Harvey H., Jr. Israel's Sacred Songs: A Study of Dominant Themes. 256p. 1984. pap. text ed. 11.50 (ISBN 0-8191-4027-9, Co-Pub. by Episcopal Div Sch). U Pr of Amer.

Guyon, Jeanne. The Book of Job. 1985. pap. 7.95 (ISBN 0-940232-23-5). Christian Bks.

Habel, Norman C. Job. LC 80-82193. (Knox Preaching Guides). 100p. (Orig., John Hayes series editor). 1981. pap. 4.95 (ISBN 0-8042-3216-4). John Knox.

Hann, Robert R. The Manuscript History of the Psalms of Solomon. LC 81-21212. (SBL Septuagint & Cognate Studies). 1982. pap. 15.00 (ISBN 0-89130-557-2, 06-04-13). Scholars Pr GA.

Hawkins, Thomas R. The Unsuspected Power of the Psalms. LC 84-51828. 128p. (Orig.). 1985. pap. 5.95 (ISBN 0-8358-0499-2). Upper Room.

Hayhoe, D. The Creation Psalms of David. 40p. pap. 2.95 (ISBN 0-88172-148-4). Believers Bkshelf.

Heslop, William G. Sermon Seeds from Psalms. LC 76-12080. (W. G. Heslop Bible Study Aids Ser.). 144p. 1976. pap. 4.50 (ISBN 0-8254-2831-9). Kregel.

Huffman, Vicki. The Best of Times: Ecclesiastes 3: 1-8. LC 85-29087. 1986. pap. 5.95 (ISBN 0-8054-1234-4). Broadman.

Hunt, Donald. Pondering the Proverbs. (The Bible Study Textbook Ser.). (Illus.). 1974. 14.30 (ISBN 0-89900-018-5). College Pr Pub.

Ironside, H. A. Proverbs, Song of Solomon. 12.95 (ISBN 0-87213-395-8). Loizeaux.

Jackson, Wayne. Book of Job. pap. 5.50 (ISBN 0-89137-541-4). Quality Pubns.

Jastrow, Morris. A Gentle Cynic: Being a Translation of the Book of Koheleth Commonly Known As Ecclesiastes Stripped of Later Additions also Its Origin, Growth & Interpretation. 255p. 1985. Repr. of 1919 ed. 50.00 (ISBN 0-8495-2810-0). Arden Lib.

Jastrow, Morris, Jr. The Book of Job. 1920. 40.00 (ISBN 0-8274-1953-8). R West.

Jennings, F. C. Meditations on Ecclesiastes. 143p. 5.95 (ISBN 0-88172-090-9). Believers Bkshelf.

Jensen, Irving L. Job. (Bible Self Study Guide Ser.). 1975. pap. 3.25 (ISBN 0-8024-1018-9). Moody.

--Proverbs. (Bible Self-Study Guide Ser.). (Illus.). 96p. 1976. pap. 3.25 (ISBN 0-8024-1020-0). Moody.

--Psalms. (Bible Self-Study Guides). 1968. pap. 3.25 (ISBN 0-8024-1019-7). Moody.

Keller, Phillip. A Shepherd Looks at Psalm 23. (Illus.). 160p. 1987. padded gift ed. 19.95 (ISBN 0-310-35670-9). Zondervan.

Kidner, Derek. The Wisdom of Proverbs, Job & Ecclesiastes. LC 85-11826. 176p. 1985. pap. 5.95 (ISBN 0-87784-405-4). Inter-Varsity.

Klug, Ron. The Real Questions: Searching the Psalms for Answers. (Young Fisherman Bible Studyguide Ser.). 64p. 1984. saddle-stitched tchr's. ed. 4.95 (ISBN 0-87788-702-0); saddle-stitched student ed. 2.95 (ISBN 0-87788-701-2). Shaw Pubs.

Knight, George A. Psalms: Nos. 1-72, Vol. 1. LC 82-20134. (Daily Study Bible Old Testament Ser.). 350p. 1982. 12.95 (ISBN 0-664-21805-9); pap. 7.95 (ISBN 0-664-24572-2). Westminster.

--Psalms: Nos. 73-150, Vol. 2. LC 82-20134. (Daily Study Bible Old Testament Ser.). 384p. 1983. 15.95 (ISBN 0-664-21808-3); pap. 8.95 (ISBN 0-664-24575-7). Westminster.

Kraft, Robert A. The Testament of Job. LC 74-15201. (Society of Biblical Literature. Text & Translation-Psuedepigrapha Ser.: No. 5). pap. 17.70 (ISBN 0-8357-9580-2, 2017530). Bks Demand UMI.

Kraus, Hans J. Theology of the Psalms. Crim, Keith, tr. from Ger. LC 86-17267. 240p. 1986. 24.95 (ISBN 0-8066-2225-3, 10-6292). Augsburg.

Kroll, Woodrow M. Psalms: The Poetry of Palestine. 464p. (Orig.). 1987. lib. bdg. 37.50 (ISBN 0-8191-5750-3); pap. text ed. 24.75 (ISBN 0-8191-5751-1). U Pr of Amer.

Lang, Bernhard. Wisdom & the Book of Proverbs. 192p. 1985. pap. 10.95 (ISBN 0-8298-0568-0). Pilgrim NY.

Lawson, George. Exposition of Proverbs, 2 vols. in 1. LC 80-8070. (Kregel Timeless Classics Ser.). 904p. 1981. 27.50 (ISBN 0-8254-3123-9). Kregel.

Lewis, C. S. Reflections on the Psalms. LC 58-10910. 1964. pap. 3.95 (ISBN 0-15-676248-X, Harv). HarBraceJ.

--Reflections on the Psalms. 224p. 1985. pap. 9.95 (ISBN 0-8027-2512-0). Walker & Co.

Lloyd-Jones, D. Martyn. Faith on Trial: Studies in Psalm 73. 128p. 1982. pap. 4.50 (ISBN 0-8010-5618-7). Baker Bk.

MacDonald, James M. Ecclesiastes. 1982. lib. bdg. 15.50 (ISBN 0-86524-091-4, 2101). Klock & Klock.

MacDonald, William. Enjoying the Psalms, 2 vols. 1977. pap. 7.00 ea. Vol. 1 (ISBN 0-937396-34-6). Vol. 2 (ISBN 0-937396-35-4). Walterick Pubs.

Mack, Burton L. Wisdom & the Hebrew Epic: Ben Sira's Hymn in Praise of the Fathers. LC 85-8564. (Chicago Studies in the History of Judaism). xiv, 264p. 1986. lib. bdg. 25.00x (ISBN 0-226-50049-7). U of Chicago Pr.

McKee, David & Woo, Nancy E. Ecclesiastes in A. S. L. - Chapter Three, Verses 1-4: Written in Sutton Sign Writing. text ed. 3.00x. Ctr Sutton Movement.

MacLarsen, Alexander. The Psalms, 3 Vols. 1981. smythe sewn 45.00 (ISBN 0-86524-038-8, 1902). Klock & Klock.

McLemore, Clinton W. Good Guys Finish First: Success Strategies from the Book of Proverbs for Business Men & Women. LC 83-14708. 142p. 1983. pap. 7.95 (ISBN 0-664-26004-7, A Bridgebooks Publication). Westminster.

Maloney, George A. Singers of the New Song: A Mystical Interpretation of the Song of Songs. LC 85-71639. 176p. (Orig.). 1985. pap. 4.95 (ISBN 0-87793-292-1). Ave Maria.

Meredith, Maurice. Studies in Proverbs. pap. 2.50 (ISBN 0-89315-261-7). Lambert Bk.

Meyer, F. B. Shepherd Psalm. 1972. pap. 2.95 (ISBN 0-87508-351-X). Chr Lit.

More Precious Than Gold: Psalm 19. 48p. (Orig.). 7.95 (ISBN 0-86683-845-7, HarpR). Har-Row.

Murphy, Roland E. Ecclesiastes & Canticle of Canticles. (Bible Ser.). pap. 1.00 (ISBN 0-8091-5036-0). Paulist Pr.

--Wisdom Literature & Psalms: Interpreting Biblical Texts. Bailey, Lloyd R. & Furnish, Victor P., eds. 160p. (Orig.). 1983. pap. 8.95 (ISBN 0-687-45759-9). Abingdon.

Murray, Andrew. Confession & Forgiveness. 176p. 1984. pap. 5.95 (ISBN 0-310-29731-1, 10366P, Clarion Class). Zondervan.

Muse, Dan T. The Song of Songs. 5.95 (ISBN 0-911866-78-7). Advocate.

Nandy, Pritish, ed. The Lord is My Shepherd: Selections from the Psalms. (Vikas Library of Modern Morian Writing: No. 12). (Orig.). 1982. text ed. 5.95x (ISBN 0-7069-1492-9, Pub. by Vikas India). Advent NY.

North, Robert. Psalms. (Bible Ser.). Pt. 3. pap. 1.00 (ISBN 0-8091-5125-1); Pt. 4. pap. 1.00 (ISBN 0-8091-5126-X); Pt. 5. pap. 1.00 (ISBN 0-8091-5127-8); Pt. 6. pap. 1.00 (ISBN 0-8091-5128-6). Paulist Pr.

Nystrom, Carolyn. A Woman's Workshop on David & His Psalms. (Woman's Workshop Ser.). 144p. 1982. pap. 3.95 (ISBN 0-310-41931-X, 11276P). Zondervan.

Olsen, Erling C. Psalms, Meditations in the Psalms. 1050p. 1975. Repr. 19.95 (ISBN 0-87213-680-9). Loizeaux.

Ortiz, Marcelino. Verdades que Cambian Vidas. (Span.). 96p. (Orig.). 1981. pap. 2.50 (ISBN 0-89922-173-4). Edit Caribe.

Peacock, Heber F. A Translator's Guide to Selected Psalms. (Helps for Translators Ser.). 154p. 1981. pap. 3.30x (ISBN 0-8267-0299-6, 08737, Pub. by United Bible). Am Bible.

Penn-Lewis, Jessie. Story of Job. 1965. pap. 4.95 (ISBN 0-87508-954-2). Chr Lit.

Peterson, Eugene. Psalms: Prayers of the Heart. (LifeGuide Bible Studies). 64p. (Orig.). 1987. pap. 2.95. Inter-Varsity.

Phillips, John. Exploring the Song of Solomon. 157p. 1984. pap. 6.95 (ISBN 0-87213-683-3). Loizeaux.

Pierson, Arthur T. George Muller of Bristol. 336p. 1984. pap. 7.95 (ISBN 0-310-47091-9, 11669P, Clarion Class). Zondervan.

Power, P. B. The I Wills of the Psalms. 395p. 1985. pap. 5.95 (ISBN 0-85151-445-6). Banner of Truth.

Rich, Charles. The Embrace of the Soul: Reflections on the Song of Songs. LC 83-23066. 1984. pap. 3.50 (ISBN 0-932506-31-3). St Bedes Pubns.

Riva, Anna. Powers of the Psalms. 128p. (Orig.). 1982. pap. 3.95 (ISBN 0-943832-07-1). Intl Imports.

Rotherham, Joseph B. Studies in Psalms, Vol. I. DeWelt, Don, ed. (The Bible Study Textbook Ser.). (Illus.). 1970. Repr. 14.30 (ISBN 0-89900-016-9). College Pr Pub.

--Studies in Psalms, Vol. II. rev. ed. DeWelt, Don, ed. (The Bible Study Textbook Ser.). (Illus.). 1971. Repr. of 1901 ed. 14.30 (ISBN 0-89900-017-7). College Pr Pub.

Routley, Erik. Exploring the Psalms. LC 74-20674. 170p. 1975. pap. 3.95 (ISBN 0-664-24999-X). Westminster.

Rowley, H. H. New Century Bible Commentary on Job. rev. ed. Clements, Ronald E., ed. 304p. 1980. pap. 7.95 (ISBN 0-8028-1838-2). Eerdmans.

St. Augustine. St. Augustine on the Psalms: Vol. 2. Quasten, J. & Burghardt, W. J., eds. Hebgin, D. Scholastica & Corrigan, D. Felicitas, trs. LC 60-10722. (Ancient Christian Writers Ser.: No. 30). 425p. 1961. 14.95 (ISBN 0-8091-0105-X). Paulist Pr.

Smith, Joyce M. A Listening Heart. 1981. pap. 2.95 (ISBN 0-8423-2375-9). Tyndale.

Southwell, P. Ezra-Job. 1983. pap. 4.95 (ISBN 0-87508-156-8). Chr Lit.

Spurgeon, Charles H. The Treasury of David, 2 vols. 1984. Repr. Psalms 1-78, Vol. I, 1440p. 39.95 set (ISBN 0-8407-5425-6). Psalms 79-150, Vol. II, 1464p. Nelson.

Stenbock, Evelyn A. Beacon Small-Group Bible Studies, Ecclesiastes: "Faith or Futility?". Wolf, Earl C., ed. 96p. (Orig.). 1985. pap. 2.50 (ISBN 0-8341-0964-6). Beacon Hill.

Strauss, James D. Job Shattering of Silence. LC 77-155412. (The Bible Study Textbook Ser.). (Illus.). 1976. 15.90 (ISBN 0-89900-015-0). College Pr Pub.

Stummer, Friedrich. Summerisch-Akkadische Parallelen Zum Aufbau Alttestamentlicher Psalmen. Repr. of 1922 ed. 15.00 (ISBN 0-384-58710-0). Johnson Repr.

Swindoll, Charles. Living on the Ragged Edge: Ecclesiastes. 224p. 1985. 12.95 (ISBN 0-8499-0463-3, 0463-3). Word Bks.

Tengbom, Mildred. Sometimes I Hurt: Reflections on the Book of Job. 192p. (Orig.). 1986. pap. 7.95 (ISBN 0-570-03981-9, 12-2897). Concordia.

Thomas, David. Book of Job. LC 82-7767. (Bible Study Classics). 500p. 1982. 22.95 (ISBN 0-8254-3814-4). Kregel.

--Book of Proverbs, 2 Vols. in 1. LC 82-18682. (Kregel Bible Classics Ser.). 836p. 1983. 24.95 (ISBN 0-8254-3813-6). Kregel.

--Sermon Notes on the Psalms. Lockyer, Herbert, ed. Tr. of The Homilist. 320p. (Orig.). Date not set. pap. 10.95 (ISBN 0-8254-3116-6). Kregel.

Toy, Crawford H. A Critical & Exegetical Commentary on Proverbs. Driver, Samuel R., et al, eds. (International Critical Commentary Ser.). 592p. 1899. 24.95 (ISBN 0-567-05013-0, Pub. by T & T Clark Ltd UK). Fortress.

Tsevat, Matitiahu. The Meaning of Job & Other Biblical Studies: Essays on the Literature & Religion of the Hebrew Bible. 1981. 25.00x (ISBN 0-87068-714-X). Ktav.

Turner, Charles W. Wise Words in a Wicked World: Studies in Proverbs. pap. 4.95 (ISBN 0-88469-028-8). BMH Bks.

Van Selms, A. Job: A Practical Commentary. Van Der Woude, A. S., ed. (Text & Interpretation Ser.). (Dutch.). 192p. (Orig.). 1985. pap. 8.95 (ISBN 0-8028-0101-3). Eerdmans.

Watters, William R. Formula Criticism & the Poetry of the Old Testament. (Beiheft 138 zur Zeitschrift fur die Alttestamentliche Wissenschaft). 1976. 43.20x (ISBN 3-11-005730-1). De Gruyter.

Weiss, Meir. The Story of Job's Beginning. 84p. 1983. text ed. 15.00x (ISBN 9-652-23438-9, Pub. by Magnes Pr Israel). Humanities.

Westermann, Claus. Praise & Lament in the Psalms. rev. enl. ed. Crim, Keith & Soulen, Richard, trs. from German. LC 65-10553. 1981. 12.95 (ISBN 0-8042-1791-2); pap. 9.95 (ISBN 0-8042-1792-0). John Knox.

--The Psalms: Structure, Content, & Message. Gehrke, Ralph D., tr. from Ger. LC 79-54127. Tr. of Der Psalter. 136p. (Orig.). 1980. pap. 7.95 (ISBN 0-8066-1762-4, 10-5300). Augsburg.

--The Structure of the Book of Job: A Form-Critical Analysis. LC 80-2379. pap. 40.00 (2029297). Bks Demand UMI.

Wiersbe, Warren W. Meet Yourself in the Psalms. 192p. 1983. pap. 5.95 (ISBN 0-88207-740-6). Victor Bks.

Williams, Donald. Psalms (CC, Vol. 13. 448p. 1986. 23.95 (ISBN 0-8499-0419-6). Word Bks.

Williams, James G. Those Who Ponder Proverbs: Aphoristic Thinking & Biblical Literature. (Bible & Literature Ser.: No. 2). 1981. text ed. 19.95x (ISBN 0-907459-02-1, Pub. by Almond Pr England); pap. text ed. 9.95x (ISBN 0-907459-03-X, Pub. by Almond Pr England). Eisenbrauns.

Winston, David. The Wisdom of Solomon. LC 78-18150. (Anchor Bible Ser.: Vol. 43). 1979. 16.00 (ISBN 0-385-01644-1, Anchor Pr). Doubleday.

Wither, George. Preparation to the Psalter. 1884. Repr. of 1619 ed. 30.50 (ISBN 0-8337-3850-X). B Franklin.

Wood, Fred M. The Sunnier Side of Doubt. LC 83-24020. 1984. pap. 4.95 (ISBN 0-8054-2253-6). Broadman.

Wright, Christopher. Proverbs-Isaiah 39. 1983. pap. 4.95 (ISBN 0-87508-158-4). Chr Lit.

Wright, Stafford. Psalms. (Bible Study Commentaries Ser.). 152p. 1982. pap. 4.95 (ISBN 0-317-43374-1). Chr Lit.

Yoder, Sanford C. Poetry of the Old Testament. 426p. 1948. pap. 9.95 (ISBN 0-8361-1709-3). Herald Pr.

Zimmerman, Frank. The Inner World of Qoehelet. 1972. 15.00x (ISBN 0-87068-181-8). Ktav.

Zlotowitz, Meir. Koheles-Ecclesiastes. (The Art Scroll Ser.). 224p. 1976. 11.95 (ISBN 0-89906-006-4); pap. 8.95 (ISBN 0-686-63976-6). Mesorah Pubns.

BIBLE–CRITICISM, INTERPRETATION, ETC.–O. T. PROPHETS

Here are entered works on the prophets as a whole as well as those on one or more of the following: Isaiah, Daniel, Lamentations, Ezekiel, Jeremiah.

Achtemeier, Elizabeth. The Community & Message of Isaiah Fifty Six-Sixty Six: A Theological Commentary. LC 81-52284. 160p. (Orig.). 1982. pap. 8.95 (ISBN 0-8066-1916-3, 10-1610). Augsburg.

--Jeremiah. Hayes, John H., ed. LC 86-45402. (Preaching Guides). 120p. (Orig.). 1987. pap. 7.95 (ISBN 0-8042-3222-9). John Knox.

Alexander, Joseph A. Isaiah, 2 Vols. 1981. Set. lib. bdg. 29.95 (ISBN 0-86524-072-8, 2302). Klock & Klock.

Allis, Oswald T. Unity of Isaiah. 1952. pap. 4.50 (ISBN 0-87552-105-3). Presby & Reformed.

Allison, Winn O. Jeremiah, Lamentations: God's Unfailing Love. Wolf, Earl C., ed. (Small-Group Bible Studies). 96p. (Orig.). 1986. pap. text ed. 2.50 (ISBN 0-8341-1106-3). Beacon Hill.

Austin, Bill. When God Has Put You on Hold. 112p. 1986. pap. 4.95 (ISBN 0-8423-7989-4). Tyndale.

Baltzer, Dieter. Ezechiel und Deuterojesaja: Beruehrungen in der Heilserwartung der beiden grossen Exilspropheten. (Beiheft 121 Zur Zeitschrift fuer die alttestamentliche Wissenschaft Ser.). 1971. 28.40x (ISBN 3-11-001756-3). De Gruyter.

Barnes, Albert. Daniel. 16.95 (ISBN 0-8010-0841-7). Baker Bk.

--Isaiah. 23.95 (ISBN 0-8010-0840-9). Baker Bk.

--Minor Prophets. 23.95 (ISBN 0-8010-0842-5). Baker Bk.

--Proverbs-Ezekiel. 10.95 (ISBN 0-8010-0839-5). Baker Bk.

Beacon Bible Commentary Staff. Isaiah-Daniel, Vol. IV. 13.95 (ISBN 0-8010-0691-0). Baker Bk.

Beale, G. K. The Use of Daniel in Jewish Apocalyptic Literature & in the Relevation of St. John. 364p. (Orig.). 1985. lib. bdg. 26.00 (ISBN 0-8191-4290-5); pap. text ed. 15.25 (ISBN 0-8191-4291-3). U Pr of Amer.

Bickerman, Elias. Four Strange Books of the Bible: Jonah, Daniel, Koheleth, Esther. (Illus.). 252p. 1984. pap. 8.95 (ISBN 0-8052-0774-0). Schocken.
Blank, Sheldon. Understanding the Prophets. 144p. 1983. pap. text ed. 4.00 (ISBN 0-8074-0250-8, 382755). UAHC.
Blenkinsopp, Joseph. Prophecy & Canon: A Contribution to the Study of Jewish Origins. LC 76-22411. 1977. text ed. 14.95 (ISBN 0-268-01522-8). U of Notre Dame Pr.
Boadt, Lawrence. Jeremiah One to Twenty-Five. (Old Testament Message Ser.: Vol. 9). 1982. 15.95 (ISBN 0-89453-409-2); pap. 9.95 (ISBN 0-89453-262-6). M Glazier.
Brandt, Leslie F. Prophets Now. 1979. 8.50 (ISBN 0-570-03278-4, 15-2722). Concordia.
Branson, Robert. Beacon Small-Group Bible Studies, Isaiah: Preparing the Way of the Lord. Wolf, Earl C., ed. 96p. (Orig.). 1985. pap. 2.50 (ISBN 0-8341-0961-1). Beacon Hill.
Bright, John. Covenant & Promise: The Prophetic Understanding of the Future in Pre-Exilic Israel. LC 76-13546. 208p. 1976. 10.00 (ISBN 0-664-20752-9). Westminster.
Briscoe, Stuart. Dry Bones. 168p. 1985. pap. 5.95 (ISBN 0-89693-522-1). Victor Bks.
Brown, Raymond E. Daniel. (Bible Ser.). pap. 1.00 (ISBN 0-8091-5024-7). Paulist Pr.
Brueggemann, Walter. Hopeful Imagination: Prophectic Voices in Exile. LC 86-45207. 160p. 1986. pap. 7.95 (ISBN 0-8006-1925-0). Fortress.
Buchanan, Edward A. Broken Jars & Empty Cisterns: Studies in Jeremiah. 32p. 1982. pap. 3.50 (ISBN 0-939298-09-0). J M Prods.
Butler, Paul. Isaiah, Vol. I. LC 75-328170. (The Bible Study Textbook Ser.). (Illus.). 1980. cancelled (ISBN 0-89900-020-7). College Pr Pub.
--Isaiah, Vol. II. (The Bible Study Textbook Ser.). (Illus.). 1976. cancelled (ISBN 0-89900-021-5). College Pr Pub.
--Isaiah, Vol. I, II. (Bible Study Textbook). 694p. 1980. 15.90 (ISBN 0-89900-061-4). College Pr Pub.
Campbell, G. & Morgan. Studies in the Prophecy of Jeremiah. 288p. 13.95 (ISBN 0-8007-0298-0). Revell.
Campbell-Morgan, G. Minor Prophets. 160p. 1960. 10.95 (ISBN 0-8007-0208-5). Revell.
Carroll, Robert P. From Chaos to Covenant: Prophecy in the Book of Jeremiah. 288p. 1981. 14.95 (ISBN 0-8245-0106-3). Crossroad NY.
--Jeremiah, a Commentary. LC 85-13655. (Old Testament Library). 880p. 1986. 38.95 (ISBN 0-664-21835-0). Westminster.
Clements, R. E. Isaiah & the Deliverance of Jerusalem. (Journal for the Study of the Old Testament, Supplement Ser.: No. 13). 1980. text ed. 18.95x (ISBN 0-905774-23-X, Pub. by JSOT Pr England); pap. text ed. 10.95 (ISBN 0-905774-62-0). Eisenbrauns.
--New Century Bible Commentary on Isaiah 1-39. rev. ed. 320p. 1980. pap. 8.95 (ISBN 0-8028-1841-2). Eerdmans.
Clifford, R. J. Book of Daniel. pap. 1.25 (ISBN 0-317-46870-7). Franciscan Herald.
Clines, David J. I, He, We & They: A Literary Approach to Isaiah Fifty-Three. (JSOT Supplement Ser.: No. 1). 65p. 1976. pap. text ed. 4.95x (ISBN 0-905774-00-0, Pub. by JSOT Pr England). Eisenbrauns.
Cocoris, G. Michael. Daniel. rev. ed. 150p. 1985. pap. text ed. 3.00 (ISBN 0-935729-06-2). Church Open Door.
Coggins, Richard, et al, eds. Israel's Prophetic Tradition: Essays in Honour of Peter Ackroyd. 294p. 1985. 18.95 (ISBN 0-521-31886-6). Cambridge U Pr.
Cohen, A. Ezekiel. 350p. 1950. 10.95 (ISBN 0-900689-30-7). Soncino Pr.
--Isaiah One & Two. 330p. 1949. 10.95 (ISBN 0-900689-28-5). Soncino Pr.
--Jeremiah. 369p. 1949. 10.95 (ISBN 0-900689-29-3). Soncino Pr.
--The Twelve Prophets. 368p. 1948. 10.95 (ISBN 0-900689-31-5). Soncino Pr.
Cole, Alan. Isaiah Forty-Jeremiah. 1983. pap. 4.95 (ISBN 0-87508-161-4). Chr Lit.
Collins, John. Daniel, One-Two Maccabees, with Excursus on Apocalyptic Genre. (Old Testament Message Ser.: Vol. 15). 1982. 15.95 (ISBN 0-89453-415-7); pap. 12.95 (ISBN 0-89453-250-2). M Glazier.
Collins, John J. The Apocalyptic Vision of the Book of Daniel. LC 77-23124. (Harvard Semitic Monograph). 1977. text ed. 11.95 (ISBN 0-89130-133-X, 040016). Scholars Pr GA.
Copeland, John A. A Study of Daniel. 1973. pap. 4.50 (ISBN 0-89137-703-4). Quality Pubns.
Craigie, Peter C. Ezekiel. LC 83-7044. (Daily Study Bible-Old Testament). 332p. 1983. 14.95 (ISBN 0-664-21807-5); pap. 7.95 (ISBN 0-664-24574-9). Westminster.
--Twelve Prophets, Vol. 1. LC 84-2372. (Daily Study Bible-Old Testament Ser.). 1984. 14.95 (ISBN 0-664-21810-5); pap. 7.95 (ISBN 0-664-24577-3). Westminster.
--Twelve Prophets, Vol. 2. LC 84-2372. (The Daily Study Bible-Old Testament). 260p. 1985. 15.95 (ISBN 0-664-21813-X); pap. 8.95 (ISBN 0-664-24582-X). Westminster.
Crenshaw, James L. Prophetic Conflict: Its Effect upon Israelite Religion. (Beiheft 124 zur Zeitschrift fuer die alttestamentliche Wissenschaft). 134p. 1971. 33.00x (ISBN 3-11-003363-1, 3-11-003363-1). De Gruyter.
Criswell, W. A. Expository Sermons on the Book of Daniel. 651p. 19.95 (ISBN 0-310-22800-X, 9461). Zondervan.
Croatto, J. Severino. Exodus: A Hermeneutics of Freedom. LC 80-26148. 112p. (Orig.). 1981. pap. 4.95 (ISBN 0-88344-111-X). Orbis Bks.
Croft, Steven J. The Identity of the Individual in the Psalms. (JSOT Supplement Ser.: No. 44). 280p. 1986. text ed. 34.00x (ISBN 1-85075-021-1, Pub. by JSOT Pr England); pap. text ed. 15.95x (ISBN 1-85075-020-3). Eisenbrauns.
Crowther, Duane S. Prophets & Prophecies of the Old Testament. 2nd ed. LC 66-25508. (Comprehensive Bible Ser.). (Illus.). 644p. 1973. Repr. of 1967 ed. 12.95 (ISBN 0-88290-022-6). Horizon Utah.
Davidson, Robert. Jeremiah, Vol. 1: Chapters 1 to 20. LC 83-14598. (Daily Study Bible - Old Testament Ser.). 176p. 1983. 12.95 (ISBN 0-664-21394-4); pap. 6.95 (ISBN 0-664-24476-9). Westminster.
Davies, Eryl. Prophecy & Ethics: Isaiah & the Ethical Traditions of Israel. (Journal for the Study of the Old Testament, Supplement: No. 16). 1981. 19.95 (ISBN 0-905774-26-4, Pub. by JSOT Pr England). Eisenbrauns.
Davies, P. R. Daniel. (Old Testament Guides Ser.). 133p. 1985. pap. text ed. 3.95x (ISBN 1-85075-002-5, Pub. by JSOT Pr England). Eisenbrauns.
De Almeida, Abraao. Visiones Profecticas de Daniel. Tr. of Prophetic Visions of Daniel. (Span.). 224p. 1986. pap. 3.95 (ISBN 0-8297-0497-3). Life Pubs Intl.
DeMott, Harold. Beacon Small-Group Bible Studies, Daniel: Daring to Live by Faith. Wolf, Earl C., ed. 96p. (Orig.). 1985. pap. 2.50 (ISBN 0-8341-0962-X). Beacon Hill.
Devault, Joseph J. Josue. (Bible Ser.). pap. 1.00 (ISBN 0-8091-5075-1). Paulist Pr.
DeVries, James. The Kingdom of Christ. LC 84-90313. 155p. (Orig.). 1984. pap. 3.50 (ISBN 0-9613181-0-4). Kingdom Bks.
Diamond, A. R. The Confessions of Jeremiah in Context: Scenes of Prophetic Drams. (JSOT Supplement Ser.: No. 45). 250p. 1987. text ed. 29.50x (ISBN 1-85075-032-7, Pub. by JSOT Pr England); pap. text ed. 19.95x (ISBN 1-85075-033-5, Pub. by JSOT Pr England). Eisenbrauns.
Efird, James M. The Old Testament Prophets Then & Now. 128p. 1982. pap. 4.95 (ISBN 0-8170-0960-4). Judson.
Eichrodt, Walther. Ezekiel: A Commentary. LC 71-117646. (Old Testament Library). 608p. 1970. 18.95 (ISBN 0-664-20872-X). Westminster.
Eisermann, Moshe. Yechezkel-Ezekiel, Vol. 1. (The Art Scroll Tanach Ser.). 352p. 1977. 17.95 (ISBN 0-89906-075-7); pap. 14.95 (ISBN 0-89906-076-5). Mesorah Pubns.
Ellis, Charles & Ellis, Norma. Wells of Salvation: Meditations of Isaiah. 224p. (Orig.). 1986. pap. 5.95 (ISBN 0-85151-457-X). Banner of Truth.
Erdman, Charles R. Isaiah. 160p. 1982. pap. 4.50 (ISBN 0-8010-3380-2). Baker Bk.
Feinberg, Charles L. Daniel, the Kingdom of the Lord. 1984. 9.95 (ISBN 0-88469-157-8). BMH Bks.
Ferch, Arthur J. The Son of Man in Daniel Seven. (Andrews University Seminary Doctoral Dissertation Ser.: Vol. 6). x, 237p. 1983. pap. 9.95 (ISBN 0-943872-38-3). Andrews Univ Pr.
Fettke, Steven M. Messages to a Nation in Crisis: An Introduction to the Prophecy of Jeremiah. LC 82-19997. (Illus.). 72p. (Orig.). 1983. pap. text ed. 7.75 (ISBN 0-8191-2839-2). U Pr of Amer.
Flanagan, Neal. Jeremiah, 2 pts. (Bible Ser.). Pt. 1. pap. 1.00 (ISBN 0-8091-5071-9); Pt. 2. pap. 1.00 (ISBN 0-8091-5072-7). Paulist Pr.
Gaebelein, Arno C. The Prophet Daniel. LC 55-9465. 218p. 1968. pap. 5.95 (ISBN 0-8254-2701-0). Kregel.
Gerbrandt, Gerald E. Kingship According to Deuteronomistic History. (Society of Biblical Literature Dissertation Ser.). 1986. 17.95 (ISBN 0-89130-968-3, 06 01 87); pap. 12.95 (ISBN 0-89130-969-1). Scholars Pr GA.
Gileadi, Avraham. The Book of Isaiah. 264p. 1987. 12.95 (ISBN 0-87579-076-3). Deseret Bk.
Goldingay, John. God's Prophet God's Servant: A Study in Jeremiah & Isaiah 40-56. 160p. 1986. pap. 11.95 (ISBN 0-85364-338-5, Pub. by Paternoster UK). Attic Pr.
Gordis, Robert. The Song of Songs & Lamentations: A Commentary & Translation. 1974. 25.00x (ISBN 0-87068-256-3). Ktav.
Hamilton, Edith. Spokesmen for God. 1962. pap. 3.95 (ISBN 0-393-00169-5, Norton Lib). Norton.
Harper, H. B. Prophet Potpourri: H. B. & His-Her Bible Adventures, Vol. 6. LC 86-81422. 216p. (Orig.). 1986. pap. 5.95 (ISBN 0-934318-91-3). Falcon Pr MT.
Herald of Hope (Isaiah) Student Guide. (New Horizons Bible Study Ser.). 68p. (Orig.). 1984. pap. 2.50 (ISBN 0-89367-100-2). Light & Life.
Heslop, William G. Diamonds From Daniel. LC 76-12082. (W. G. Heslop Bible Study Aids Ser.). 184p. 1976. pap. text ed. 4.50 (ISBN 0-8254-2833-5). Kregel.
--Pearls from the Prophet Ezekiel. LC 76-12081. (W. G. Heslop Bible Study Aids). 160p. 1976. pap. 4.50 (ISBN 0-8254-2832-7). Kregel.
Holladay, William L. Architecture of Jeremiah, 1-20. 204p. 1976. 20.00 (ISBN 0-8387-1523-0). Bucknell U Pr.
--Isaiah: Scroll of a Prophetic Heritage. 270p. 1987. pap. 9.95 (ISBN 0-8298-0658-X). Pilgrim NY.
--Jeremiah One. LC 85-45498. (Hermeneia Ser.). 752p. 1986. 44.95 (ISBN 0-8006-6017-X, 20-6017). Fortress.
Huesman, John S. Isaiah, 2 pts. (Bible Ser.). Pt. 1. pap. 1.00 (ISBN 0-8091-5069-7); Pt. 2. pap. 1.00 (ISBN 0-8091-5070-0). Paulist Pr.
The Interpreter's Concise Commentary, Vol. IV: The Major Prophets. 4.95 (ISBN 0-687-19235-8). Abingdon.
The Interpreter's Concise Commentary, Vol. V: The Minor Prophets & the Apocrypha. 4.95 (ISBN 0-687-19236-6). Abingdon.
Jensen, Joseph. The Use of Tora by Isaiah: His Debate with the Wisdom Tradition. LC 73-83134. (Catholic Biblical Quarterly Monographs: No. 3). 3.00 (ISBN 0-915170-02-7). Catholic Biblical.
Jeske, John C. Daniel. (People's Bible Ser.). 1985. pap. 6.50 (ISBN 0-8100-0197-7, 15N0407); study guide, 32p 1.50 (ISBN 0-938272-52-7). Northwest Pub.
Kappeler, Max. The Minor Prophets in the Light of Christian Science. LC 64-36062. 214p. 1962. 14.00 (ISBN 0-85241-041-7). Kappeler Inst Pub.
Kennett, R. H. The Composition of the Book of Isaiah in the Light of History & Archaeology. (British Academy, London, Schweich Lectures on Biblical Archaeology Series, 1909). pap. 19.00 (ISBN 0-8115-1251-7). Kraus Repr.
Kimchi, David B. Commentary of David Kimchi on Isaiah. Finkelstein, Louis, ed. LC 27-4417. (Columbia University. Oriental Studies: No. 19). Repr. of 1926 ed. 24.50 (ISBN 0-404-50509-0). AMS Pr.
Knight, George A. Isaiah Fifty-Six to Sixty-Six. Holmgern, Frederick, ed. (International Theological Commentary Ser.). 148p. (Orig.). 1985. pap. 5.95 (ISBN 0-8028-0021-1). Eerdmans.
Koch, Klaus. The Prophets, Volume One. Kohl, Margaret, tr. from Ger. LC 79-8894. 224p. 1982. pap. 10.95 (ISBN 0-8006-1648-0, 1-1648). Vol. 1, The Assyrian Age. Fortress.
Kodell, Jerome. Lamentations, Haggai, Zechariah, Second Zechariah, Malachi, Obadiah, Joel, Baruch. (Old Testament Ser.: Vol. 14). 1982. 12.95 (ISBN 0-89453-414-9); pap. 8.95 (ISBN 0-89453-248-0). M Glazier.
Landersdorfer, Simon K., ed. Der Bael Tatpauopoos und Die Kerube Des Ezechiel. pap. 8.00 (ISBN 0-384-31200-4). Johnson Repr.
LaRondelle, Hans K. The Israel of God in Prophecy: Principles of Prophetic Interpretation. LC 82-74358. (Andrews University Monographs, Studies in Religion: Vol.13). viv, 226p. 1983. 14.95 (ISBN 0-943872-13-8); pap. 8.50 (ISBN 0-943872-14-6). Andrews Univ Pr.
Lickley, W. A. Malachi: Lessons for Today. pap. 3.95 (ISBN 0-88172-114-X). Believers Bkshelf.
Lindblom, J. Prophecy in Ancient Israel. LC 63-907. 480p. 1962. 17.95 (ISBN 0-8006-0916-6, 1-916). Fortress.
Lundbom, Jack R. Jeremiah: A Study in Ancient Hebrew Rhetoric. LC 75-15732. (Society of Biblical Literature. Dissertation Ser.: No. 18). Repr. of 1975 ed. 39.80 (ISBN 0-8357-9574-8, 2017520). Bks Demand UMI.
McCall, Thoma S. & Levitt, Zola. The Coming Russian Invasion of Israel, Updated. 96p. 1987. pap. 4.95 (ISBN 0-8024-1624-1). Moody.
McClain, Alva J. Daniel's Prophecy of the Seventy Weeks. pap. 3.95 (ISBN 0-88469-076-8). BMH Bks.
Macintosh, A. A. Isaiah XXI: A Palimpsest. LC 79-41375. 160p. 1980. 34.50 (ISBN 0-521-22943-X). Cambridge U Pr.
McKane, William. Jeremiah: Chapters 1-25, Vol. 1. Cranfield, Charles E. & Emerton, John A., eds. (International Critical Commentary Ser.). 784p. 1986. 39.95 (ISBN 0-567-05042-4, Pub. by T & T Clark Ltd UK). Fortress.
McKeating, Henry, ed. The Books of Amos, Hosea, Micah. (Cambridge Bible Commentary on the New English Bible, Old Testament Ser.). (Illus.). 1971. 22.95 (ISBN 0-521-08133-5); pap. 10.95 (ISBN 0-521-09647-2). Cambridge U Pr.
Martin, Alfred. Isaiah: The Salvation of Jehovah. (Everyman's Bible Commentary Ser.). 1967. pap. 5.95 (ISBN 0-8024-2023-0). Moody.
Mays, James L. & Achtemeier, Paul J., eds. Interpreting the Prophets. LC 86-45223. 336p. 1987. pap. 16.95 (ISBN 0-8006-1932-3). Fortress.
Melugin, Roy F. Formation of Isaiah 40-55. (Beiheft 141 Zur Zeitschrift fuer die Altestamentliche Wissenschaft). 1976. text ed. 42.00 (ISBN 3-11-005820-0). De Gruyter.
Millar, William R. Isaiah Twenty-Four to Twenty-Seven & the Origin of Apocalyptic. LC 76-3561. (Harvard Semetic Museum Ser.). 1976. pap. 11.95 (ISBN 0-89130-102-X, 04-00-11). Scholars Pr GA.
Miller, Patrick D. Sin & Judgment in the Prophets. LC 81-8950. (SBL Monograph Ser.). 1982. 19.50 (ISBN 0-89130-514-9, 06-00-27); pap. 16.00 (ISBN 0-89130-515-7). Scholars Pr GA.
Mintz, Alan. Hurban: Responses to Catastrophe in Hebrew Literature. LC 83-23979. 288p. 1984. 27.50x (ISBN 0-231-05634-6). Columbia U Pr.
Montgomery, James. Isaiah, 2 vols. 2.50 ea. (ISBN 0-686-73329-0); Vol. 1. (ISBN 0-89315-125-4); Vol. 2. (ISBN 0-89315-126-2). Lambert Bk.
Morgan, Campbell G. Analyzed Bible. 256p. 1984. Isaiah I. pap. 5.95 (ISBN 0-8010-6171-7); Isaiah 2. pap. 5.95 (ISBN 0-8010-6172-5). Baker Bk.
Nehemiah, Ezra. Daniel. Cohen, A., ed. 278p. 1951. 10.95 (ISBN 0-900689-36-6). Soncino Pr.
Niditch, Susan. The Symbolic Vision in Biblical Tradition. LC 83-8643. (Harvard Semitic Monographs). 270p. 1983. 15.00 (ISBN 0-89130-627-7, 04 00 30). Scholars Pr GA.
Overholt, Thomas. Threat of Falsehood: A Study in Jeremiah. LC 71-131589. (Studies in Biblical Theology, 2nd Ser: No. 16). pap. 10.00x (ISBN 0-8401-3066-X). A R Allenson.
Parunak, Van Dyke H. Linguistic Density Plots in Ezekiel: The Computer Bible, Vol. XXVII A & B. Baird, Arthur J. & Freedman, David, eds. 528p. 1984. pap. 70.00x (ISBN 0-935106-22-7). Biblical Res Assocs.
Perdue, Leo G. & Kovacs, Brian W., eds. A Prophet to the Nations: Essays in Jeremiah Studies. xii, 391p. 1984. text ed. 25.00x (ISBN 0-931464-20-X). Eisenbrauns.
Pervo, Richard I. Profit with Delight: The Literary Genre of the Acts of the Apostles. LC 86-45220. 224p. 1987. 16.95 (ISBN 0-8006-0782-1). Fortress.
Petersen, William J. Jeremiah: The Prophet Who Wouldn't Quit. 168p. 1984. pap. 5.95 (ISBN 0-88207-243-9). Victor Bks.
Peterson, David L. The Roles of Israel's Prophets. (Journal for the Study of the Old Testament: Supplement Ser. 17). 131p. 1982. text ed. 14.95 (ISBN 0-905774-32-9, Pub. by JSOT Pr England); (Pub. by JSOT Pr England). Eisenbrauns.
Petrie, Arthur. Message of Daniel. pap. 2.95 (ISBN 0-87509-103-2). Chr Pubns.
Rast, Walter E. Joshua, Judges, Samuel, Kings. McCurley, Foster R., ed. LC 78-54559. (Proclamation Commentaries: the Old Testament Witnesses for Preaching). 132p. 1978. pap. 4.95 (ISBN 0-8006-0594-2, 1-594). Fortress.
Rosenberg, A. J. Book of Jeremiah, Vol. 1. (Books of the Prophet Ser.). 460p. 1985. 12.95 (ISBN 0-910818-59-2). Judaica Pr.
Rosenberg, A. J., ed. Book of Isaiah 1. 261p. 1982. 12.95 (ISBN 0-910818-50-9). Judaica Pr.
--Book of Isaiah 2. 554p. 1983. 12.95 (ISBN 0-910818-52-5). Judaica Pr.
--Book of Jeremiah, Bk. II. 442p. 1985. 12.95 (ISBN 0-910818-60-6). Judaica Pr.
--Book of Twelve Prophets, Vol. 1. (Books of the Prophets Ser). 465p. 1986. 14.95 (ISBN 0-910818-70-3). Judaica Pr.
Rowland, F. V. Daniel & the Revelation. 1984. 11.95 (ISBN 0-533-05996-8). Vantage.
Rushdoony, Rousas J. Thy Kingdom Come: Studies in Daniel & Revelation. pap. 7.95 (ISBN 0-87552-413-3). Presby & Reformed.
Russell, D. S. Daniel. LC 81-1777. (The Daily Study Bible - Old Testament Ser.). 244p. 1981. 12.95 (ISBN 0-664-21800-8); pap. 6.95 (ISBN 0-664-24567-6). Westminster.

Sawyer, John F. Isaiah, Vol. I, Chs. 1-32. LC 84-22098. (The Daily Study Bible Ser. Old Testament). 280p. 1984. 14.95 (ISBN 0-664-21812-1); pap. 7.95 (ISBN 0-664-24579-X). Westminster.

Scullion, John. Isaiah Forty to Sixty-Six. (Old Testament Message Ser.: Vol. 12). 1982. 12.95 (ISBN 0-89453-412-2); pap. 9.95 (ISBN 0-89453-246-4). M Glazier.

Smith, James E. Jeremiah & Lamentations. LC 72-97951. (The Bible Study Textbook Ser.). (Illus.). 1972. 18.95 (ISBN 0-89900-023-1). College Pr Pub.

Smith, John M. Prophets & Their Times. rev ed. Irwin, William A., ed. LC 25-6864. 1941. 20.00x (ISBN 0-226-76356-0). U of Chicago Pr.

Smith, Sidney. Isaiah Chapters XL-LV: Literary Criticism & History. (British Academy, London, Schweich Lectures on Biblical Archaeology Series, 1940). pap. 28.00 (ISBN 0-8115-1282-7). Kraus Repr.

Soderlund, Sven. The Greek Text of Jeremiah: A Revised Hypothesis. (JSOT Supplement Ser.: No. 47). 304p. 1986. text ed. 27.50x (ISBN 1-85075-028-9, Pub. by JSOT Pr England); pap. text ed. 13.50 (ISBN 0-317-46787-5). Eisenbrauns.

Stavroulakis, Nikos, illus. Jeremiah: A New Translation. (Illus.). 92p. 1973. 12.50 (ISBN 0-8276-0027-5). Jewish Pubns.

Stevens, W. C. The Book of Daniel. 190p. 1915. pap. 3.25 (ISBN 0-87509-061-3). Chr Pubns.

Stokes, Penelope. Ruth & Daniel: God's People in an Alien Society. (Fisherman Bible Studyguide Ser.). 64p. (Orig.). 1986. pap. 2.95 (ISBN 0-87788-735-7). Shaw Pubs.

Strauss, Lehman. Daniel: Prophecies. LC 70-85293. Orig. Title: Prophecies of Daniel. 1969. 9.95 (ISBN 0-87213-812-7). Loizeaux.

Stulman, Louis. The Other Text of Jeremiah: A Reconstruction of the Hebrew Text Underlying the Greek Version of the Prose Sections of Jeremiah with English Translation. LC 85-20278. 178p. (Orig.). 1986. lib. bdg. 25.75 (ISBN 0-8191-4988-8); pap. text ed. 12.75 (ISBN 0-8191-4989-6). U Pr of Amer.

Thompson, John A. The Book of Jeremiah. LC 79-16510. (New International Commentary on the Old Testament Ser.). 1980. 27.95 (ISBN 0-8028-2369-6). Eerdmans.

Torrey, Charles C. & Spiegel, Shalom. Book of Ezekiel: Critical Studies. rev. ed. (Library of Biblical Studies). 1970. 29.50x (ISBN 0-87068-116-8). Ktav.

Tov, Emanual. The Book of Baruch: A Discussion of an Early Revision of the IXX of Jeremiah 29-52 & Baruch 1: 1-3: 8. LC 75-43872. (Harvard Semitic Monographs). 1976. pap. 9.75 (ISBN 0-89130-070-8, 06-02-08). Scholars Pr GA.

Towner, W. Sibley. Daniel. Mays, James L. & Miller, Patrick D., eds. LC 83-18791. (Interpretation Ser.). 228p. 1984. 16.95 (ISBN 0-8042-3122-2). John Knox.

Ward, James M. The Prophets. LC 81-20575. (Interpreting Biblical Texts). 160p. (Orig.). 1982. pap. 8.95 (ISBN 0-687-34370-4). Abingdon.

Watts, John. Isaiah Two (WBC, Vol. 25. 400p. 1987. 24.95 (ISBN 0-8499-0224-X). Word Bks.

Weippert, Helga. Die Prosareden des Jeremiabuches. LC 72-76045. (Beiheft 132 zur Zeitschrift fuer die alttestamentliche Wissenschaft). (Ger.). 1973. 55.00x (ISBN 3-11-003867-6). De Gruyter.

Whitcomb, John C. Daniel: The Coming of Christ's Kingdom. 1985. pap. 5.95 (ISBN 0-88469-165-9). BMH Bks.

Whitcomb, John C., Jr. Darius the Mede. pap. 2.50 (ISBN 0-88469-064-4). BMH Bks.

Whybray, R. N. Thanksgiving for a Liberated Prophet: An Interpretation of Isaiah Chapter Fifty-Three. (Journal for the Study of the Old Testament Supplement Ser.: No. 4). 184p. 1978. (Pub. by JSOT Pr England); pap. text ed. 10.95 (ISBN 0-905774-04-3, Pub. by JSOT Pr England). Eisenbrauns.

Whybray, R. N., ed. Isaiah Forty to Sixty-Six. (New Century Bible Ser.). 304p. 1975. 9.95 (ISBN 0-551-00573-4). Attic Pr.

Wiesel, Elie. Five Biblical Portraits. LC 81-40458. vii, 157p. 1983. pap. 4.95 (ISBN 0-268-00962-7, 85-09622). U of Notre Dame Pr.

Wilson, Dan. Promise of Deliverance. 1983. pap. 2.50x (ISBN 0-87574-060-X, 060). Pendle Hill.

Wolf, Herbert M. Interpreting Isaiah: The Suffering & Glory of the Messiah. 272p. (Orig.). 1985. pap. 9.95 (ISBN 0-310-39061-3, 12713P). Zondervan.

Wright, Ludie J. The Closing of Man's History. (Bible Prophecy Ser.: No. 1). (Illus.). 209p. (Orig.). 1986. 15.95 (ISBN 0-9617290-0-7); pap. 12.95 (ISBN 0-9617290-1-5). Hse Better Sales.

Young, Edward J. My Servants the Prophets. 1952. pap. 8.95 (ISBN 0-8028-1697-5). Eerdmans.

Youngblood, Ronald. Temas de Isaias. Orig. Title: Themes from Isaiah. (Span.). 1986. write for info. (ISBN 0-8297-0896-0). Life Pubs Intl.

Zimmerli, Walther. Ezekiel I. Cross, Frank M., Jr. & Baltzer, Klaus, eds. LC 75-21540. (Hermenia: A Critical & Historical Commentary on the Bible). 558p. 1979. 39.95 (ISBN 0-8006-6008-0, 20-6008). Fortress.

--Ezekiel II. LC 72-1540. (Hermeneia-A Critical & Historical Commentary on the Bible). 576p. 1983. 39.95 (ISBN 0-8006-6010-2, 20-6010). Fortress.

--I Am Yahweh. Brueggemann, Walter, ed. Scott, Doug, tr. from German. LC 81-85326. 160p. 1982. 15.95 (ISBN 0-8042-0519-1). John Knox.

Zlotowitz, Meir. Eichah-Lamentations. (The Art Scroll Tanach Ser.). 160p. 1976. 11.95 (ISBN 0-89906-004-8); pap. 8.95 (ISBN 0-89906-005-6). Mesorah Pubns.

BIBLE–CRITICISM, INTERPRETATION, ETC.–O. T. PROVERBS

see Bible–Criticism, Interpretation, Etc.–O. T. Poetical Books

BIBLE–CRITICISM, INTERPRETATION, ETC.–O. T. PSALMS

see Bible–Criticism, Interpretation, Etc.–O. T. Poetical Books

BIBLE–CRITICISM, INTERPRETATION, ETC.–O. T. RUTH

see Bible–Criticism, Interpretation, Etc.–O. T. Historical Books

BIBLE–CRITICISM, INTERPRETATION, ETC.–O. T. SAMUEL

see Bible–Criticism, Interpretation, Etc.–O. T. Historical Books

BIBLE–CRITICISM, INTERPRETATION, ETC.–O. T. SONG OF SOLOMON

see Bible–Criticism, Interpretation, Etc.–O. T. Poetical Books

BIBLE–CRITICISM, INTERPRETATION, ETC.–O. T. WISDOM LITERATURE

Macdonald, Duncan B. Hebrew Philosophical Genius. LC 65-18819. 1965. Repr. of 1936 ed. 7.50x (ISBN 0-8462-0688-9). Russell.

Maly, Eugene H. Wisdom. (Bible Ser.). pap. 1.00 (ISBN 0-8091-5156-1). Paulist Pr.

Murphy, Roland E. Wisdom Literature: Ruth, Esther, Job, Proverbs, Ecclesiastes, Canticles. (The Forms of the Old Testament Literature Ser.). (Orig.). 1981. pap. 12.95 (ISBN 0-8028-1877-3). Eerdmans.

Scott, R. B. Way of Widsom. 1972. pap. 7.95 (ISBN 0-02-089280-2, Collier). Macmillan.

BIBLE–CRITICISM, INTERPRETATION, ETC.–O. T. ZECHARIAH

see Bible–Criticism, Interpretation, Etc.–O. T. Minor Prophets

BIBLE–CRITICISM, INTERPRETATION, ETC. O. T. ZEPHANIAH

see Bible–Criticism, Interpretation, Etc.–O. T. Minor Prophets

BIBLE–CRITICISM, INTERPRETATION, ETC.–THEORY, METHODS, ETC.

see Bible–Hermeneutics

BIBLE–CRITICISM, TEXTUAL

see also Bible–Quotations, Early; Bible–Versions

Cohen, Harold R. Biblical Hapax Legomena in the Light of Akkadian & Ugaritic: Society of Biblical Literature, No.37. LC 77-13422. (Dissertation Ser.). pap. 50.30 (ISBN 0-8357-9565-9, 2017528). Bks Demand UMI.

Eclov, Lee. The Church: Pictures of Christ's Body. (Fisherman Bible Studyguide Ser.). 55p. 1981. saddle stitched 2.95 (ISBN 0-87788-155-3). Shaw Pubs.

Friedman, Richard E., ed. The Creation of Sacred Literature: Composition & Redaction of the Biblical Text. (U.C. Publications in Near Eastern Studies: Vol. 22). 1981. pap. 21.50x (ISBN 0-520-09637-1). U of Cal Pr.

Greenlee, J. Harold. Introduction to New Testament Textual Criticism. 1964. pap. 7.95 (ISBN 0-8028-1724-6). Eerdmans.

--Scribes, Scrolls, & Scripture: A Layperson's Guide to Textual Criticism. 112p. (Orig.). 1985. pap. 6.95 (ISBN 0-8028-0082-3). Eerdmans.

Kenyon, F. G. Recent Developments in the Textual Criticism of the Greek Bible. (British Academy of London Ser.). pap. 19.00 (ISBN 0-8115-1274-6). Kraus Repr.

Koch, Klaus. Growth of the Biblical Tradition. 1968. lib. bdg. 24.50x (ISBN 0-684-14524-3, ScribT). Scribner.

Lategan, Bernard C. & Vorster, Willem S. Text & Reality: Aspects of Reference in Biblical Texts. 14.95 (ISBN 0-89130-822-9, 06 06 14); pap. 9.95 (ISBN 0-89130-823-7). Scholars Pr GA.

McCarter, P. Kyle, Jr. Textual Criticism: Recovering the Text of the Hebrew Bible. LC 86-4388. (Guides to Biblical Scholarship, Old Testament Ser.). 96p. 1986. pap. 4.95 (ISBN 0-8006-0471-7, 1-471). Fortress.

Olley, John W. Righteousness in the Septuagint of Isaiah: A Contextual Study. LC 78-3425. (Society of Biblical Literature, Septuagint & Cognate Studies: No. 8). 1979. pap. 9.95 (ISBN 0-89130-226-3, 06-04-08). Scholars Pr GA.

Van Til, Cornelius. The Doctrine of Scripture. 1967. pap. 5.50 syllabus (ISBN 0-87552-484-2). Presby & Reformed.

Woude, A. S. van der, ed. The World of the Bible. Woudstra, Sierd, tr. from Dutch. (Illus.). 496p. 1986. 34.95 (ISBN 0-8028-2405-6). Eerdmans.

BIBLE–CRITICISM, TEXTUAL–N. T.

Barnard, P. M., ed. The Biblical Text of Clement of Alexandria in the Four Gospels & the Acts of the Apostles. (Texts & Studies Ser.: No. 1, Vol. 5, Pt. 5). pap. 13.00 (ISBN 0-8115-1700-4). Kraus Repr.

Barrett, C. K. Church, Ministry, & Sacraments in the New Testament. 112p. (Orig.). 1985. pap. 6.95 (ISBN 0-8028-1994-X). Eerdmans.

Burton, Ernest D. Syntax of the Moods & Tenses of New Testament Greek. LC 76-25360. 238p. 1976. 12.95 (ISBN 0-8254-2256-6). Kregel.

Clark, Gordon H. Logical Criticisms of Textual Criticism. (Trinity Papers: No. 16). 49p. (Orig.). 1986. pap. 2.95 (ISBN 0-940931-16-8). Trinity Found.

Dearing, Vinton A. A Manual of Textual Analysis. LC 82-20947. ix, 108p. 1983. Repr. of 1959 ed. lib. bdg. 32.50x (ISBN 0-313-23734-4, DEMA). Greenwood.

Glunz, Hans. Die Lateinische Vorlage der Westsaechsischen Evangelienversion. pap. 8.00 (ISBN 0-384-18955-5). Johnson Repr.

Harris, J. R. Codex Bezae: A Study of the So-Called Western Text of the New Testament. (Texts & Studies Ser.: No. 1, Vol. 2, Pt. 1). pap. 19.00 (ISBN 0-8115-1684-9). Kraus Repr.

Hurtado, Larry. Text-Critical Methodology & the Pre-Caesarean Text. 112p. (Orig.). 1981. pap. 15.00x (ISBN 0-8028-1872-2). Eerdmans.

Johnson, Alfred M., Jr., ed. & tr. The New Testament & Structuralism: A Collection of Essays. LC 76-25447. (Pittsburgh Theological Monographs: No. 11). 1976. pap. text ed. 11.50 (ISBN 0-915138-13-1). Pickwick.

Lake, K. Codex One of the Gospels & Its Allies. (Texts & Studies Ser.: No. 1, Vol. 7, Pt. 3). pap. 19.00 (ISBN 0-8115-1705-5). Kraus Repr.

Metzger, Bruce M. Text of the New Testament: Its Transmission, Corruption, & Restoration. 2nd ed. 1968. 13.95x (ISBN 0-19-500391-8). Oxford U Pr.

Orchard, D. B. & Longstaff, R. W., eds. J. J. Griesbach. LC 77-27405. (Society for New Testament Studies Monographs: No. 34). 1979. 32.50 (ISBN 0-521-21706-7). Cambridge U Pr.

Zerwick, Max. A Grammatical Analysis of Greek New Testament. (Scripta Pontificii Instituti Biblici Ser.: Vol. 1). 1974. pap. 16.00 (ISBN 88-7653-553-5). Loyola.

BIBLE–CRITICISM, TEXTUAL–O. T.

Allgeier, Arthur. Die Chester Beatty-Papyri Zum Pentateuch. 12.00 (ISBN 0-384-00860-7). Johnson Repr.

Dillon, E. J. Sceptics of the Old Testament. LC 73-16064. (Studies in Comparative Literature, No. 35). 1974. Repr. of 1895 ed. lib. bdg. 51.95x (ISBN 0-8383-1723-5). Haskell.

Eitan, Israel. Contribution to Biblical Lexicography. (Columbia University. Contributions to Oriental History & Philology: No. 10). Repr. of 1924 ed. 12.50 (ISBN 0-404-50540-6). AMS Pr.

Gordis, Robert. The Biblical Text in the Making: A Study of the Kethibh-Qere. rev. ed. 1971. 29.95x (ISBN 0-87068-157-5). Ktav.

Grabbe, Lester L. Comparative Philology & the Text of Job: A Study in Methodology. LC 77-23489. (Society of Biblical Literature. Dissertation Ser.). 1977. pap. 9.95 (ISBN 0-89130-139-9, 060134). Scholars Pr GA.

Jacob, Ben Chayyim. Introduction to the Rabbinic Bible of 1525. rev. ed. (Library of Biblical Studies Ser). 1969. 39.50x (ISBN 0-87068-067-6). Ktav.

Katz, Peter. The Text of the Septuagint: Its Corruptions & Their Emendation. Gooding, D. W., ed. LC 74-161292. pap. 110.00 (ISBN 0-317-28405-3, 2022451). Bks Demand UMI.

Klein, Ralph W. Textual Criticism of the Old Testament: The Septuagint After Qumran. Tucker, Gene M., ed. LC 74-80420. (Guides to Biblical Scholarship: Old Testament Ser.). 96p. (Orig.). 1974. pap. 3.95 (ISBN 0-8006-1087-3, 1-1087). Fortress.

Levy, B. B. Targun Neophyti One: A Textual Study: Introduction, Genesis, Exodus. LC 86-11117. (Studies in Judaism). 470p. (Orig.). 1986. lib. bdg. 36.50 (ISBN 0-8191-5464-4, Pub. by Studies in Judaism); pap. text ed. 21.75 (ISBN 0-8191-5465-2). U Pr of Amer.

O'Connell, Kevin G. The Theodotionic Revision of the Book of Exodus. LC 70-160026. (Semitic Monographs Ser: No. 3). 509p. 1972. 20.00x (ISBN 0-674-87785-3). Harvard U Pr.

Revell, E. J. Biblical Texts with Palestinian Pointing & Their Accents. LC 77-8893. (Society of Biblical Literature. Masoretic Studies). 1977. pap. 10.95 (ISBN 0-89130-141-0, 060504). Scholars Pr GA.

Shenkel, James D. Chronology & Recensional Development in the Greek Text of Kings. LC 68-21983. (Semitic Monographs: No. 1). (Illus.). 1968. text ed. 10.00x (ISBN 0-674-13050-2). Harvard U Pr.

Talbert, Charles H., ed. Reimarus: Fragments. Fraser, Ralph S., tr. (Reprints & Translations). 1985. pap. 13.95 (ISBN 0-89130-858-X, 00-07-07). Scholars Pr Ga.

Zandstra, Sidney. Witness of "The Vulgate," "Peshitta" & "Septuagint" to the Text of "Zephaniah". LC 72-948. (Columbia University. Contributions to Oriental History & Philology Ser.: No. 4). Repr. of 1909 ed. 12.50 (ISBN 0-404-50534-1). AMS Pr.

Zeitlin, Irving M. Ancient Judaism: Biblical Criticism from Max Weber to the Present. 328p. 1986. pap. 12.95 (ISBN 0-7456-0297-5). Basil Blackwell.

BIBLE–DEVOTIONAL LITERATURE

see Bible–Meditations

BIBLE–DICTIONARIES

Alexander, Patricia, ed. Eerdmans' Family Encyclopedia of the Bible. (Illus.). 1978. 18.95 (ISBN 0-8028-3517-1). Eerdmans.

Allmen, Jean-Jacques Von, ed. Vocabulaire Biblique. (Fr.). 320p. 1964. pap. 24.95 (ISBN 0-686-57248-3, M-6759). French & Eur.

Androgeus, John C., ed. The Lost Gospel of the Ages: Key to Immortality & Companion to the Holy Bible. (Illus.). 979p. 1978. pap. text ed. 95.00 (ISBN 0-9609802-3-7). Life Science.

Archer, Gleason L. The Encyclopedia of Bible Difficulties. 352p. 1982. 19.95 (ISBN 0-310-43570-6, 112252). Zondervan.

Armstrong, Terry, et al, eds. A Reader's Hebrew-English Lexicon of the Old Testament: Genesis-II Kings. (Hebrew & Eng.). 1982. 16.95 (ISBN 0-310-37040-X, 6291). Zondervan.

Balthazar, Vera & Batista, Joao, eds. Dictionario Biblico Buckland. Orig. Title: Buckland Bible Dictionary. (Illus.). 453p. text ed. 6.50 (ISBN 0-8297-0836-7); pap. 4.50 (ISBN 0-686-97837-4). Life Pubs Intl.

Barker, William P. Everyone in the Bible. 384p. 1966. 15.95 (ISBN 0-8007-0084-8). Revell.

Bauer. Diccionario De Teologia Biblica. 2nd ed. (Span.). 582p. 1976. 38.95 (ISBN 84-254-0360-X, S-50203). French & Eur.

Botterweck, G. Johannes & Ringgren, Helmer, eds. Theological Dictionary of the Old Testament, 5 vols. 560p. 1978. Set. 137.50 (ISBN 0-8028-2338-6); Vol. I. 27.50 ea. (ISBN 0-8028-2325-4). Vol. II (ISBN 0-8028-2326-2). Vol. III (ISBN 0-8028-2327-0). Vol. IV (ISBN 0-8028-2328-9). Vol. V (ISBN 0-8028-2329-7). Eerdmans.

Boyd, James P. Boyd's Bible Dictionary. Orig. Title: Vest Pocket Bible Dictionary, Orig. pap. 3.75 (ISBN 0-87981-087-4). Holman Bible Pub.

Bratcher, R. G., ed. Short Bible Reference System. 148p. 1961. 4.80x (ISBN 0-8267-0030-6, 08506, Pub. by United Bible). Am Bible.

Bromiley, Geoffrey W., ed. The International Standard Bible Encyclopedia, Vol. III, K-P. rev. ed. (International Standard Bible Encyclopedia Ser.). (Illus.). 1080p. 1986. 37.50 (ISBN 0-8028-8163-7). Eerdmans.

--The International Standard Bible Encyclopedia, Vol. 2: E-J. rev. ed. 1132p. 1981. 37.50 (ISBN 0-8028-8162-9). Eerdmans.

Brown, Colin. The New International Dictionary of New Testament Theology, 3 vols. Set. 109.95 (ISBN 0-310-21928-0, 11137P). Zondervan.

Brown, Francis, et al, eds. The New Brown-Driver-Briggs Hebrew - Lexicon of the Old Testament. 1200p. 1979. 34.95 (ISBN 0-913573-20-5). Hendrickson MA.

Bryant, T. A. New Compact Bible Dictionary. 1967. 9.95 (ISBN 0-310-22080-7, 6726P); pap. 5.95 (ISBN 0-310-22082-3). Zondervan.

Bryant, T. A., compiled by. Today's Dictionary of the Bible. LC 82-12980. 678p. (Orig.). 1982. 15.95 (ISBN 0-87123-569-2, 230569). Bethany Hse.

Buttrick, George A. & Crim, Keith R., eds. The Interpreter's Dictionary of the Bible, 5 vols. LC 62-9387. 1976. Set. 112.00 (ISBN 0-687-19268-4). Abingdon.

Calmet, A. Dictionnaire Historique, Archeologique, Philologique, Chronologique Geographique et Literal de la Bible, 4 vols. Migne, J. P., ed. (Encyclopedie Theologique First Ser.: Vols. 1-4). (Fr.). 2602p. Repr. of 1846 ed. lib. bdg. 332.50x (ISBN 0-89241-231-3). Caratzas.

Carrez, Maurice & Morel, Francois. Dictionnaire Grec-Francais du Nouveau Testament. (Fr.-Gr.). 276p. 37.50 (ISBN 0-686-56940-7, M-6062). French & Eur.

Cazelles, H., et al. Supplement au Dictionnaire de la Bible, 7 vols. (Fr.). 128p. 1967. Set. 595.50 (ISBN 0-686-56943-1, M-6065). French & Eur.

Cheyne, T. K. & Black, J. S., eds. Encyclopedia Biblica, 4 vols. 1977. lib. bdg. 425.95 (ISBN 0-8490-1764-5). Gordon Pr.

Concordia Bible Dictionary. 176p. 1963. text ed. 4.95 (ISBN 0-570-03186-9, 12-2213). Concordia.

Crim, Keith R., et al, eds. The Interpreter's Dictionary of the Bible, Supplementary Volume. LC 62-9387. (Illus.). 1976. 22.95 (ISBN 0-687-19269-2). Abingdon.

Custer, Stewart. A Treasury of New Testament Synonyms. 161p. 1975. 7.95 (ISBN 0-89084-025-3). Bob Jones Univ Pr.

David Ben Abraham. The Hebrew-Arabic Dictionary of the Bible, Known As Kitab Jami al-Alfaz (Agron, 2 vols. Skoss, Solomon L., ed. LC 78-63565. (Yale Oriental Ser. Researches: Nos. 20-21). (Hebrew & Arabic.). Repr. of 1945 ed. Set. 97.50 (ISBN 0-404-60290-8). AMS Pr.

Davidson, Benjamin. Analytical Hebrew & Chaldee Lexicon. (Hebrew.). 27.95 (ISBN 0-310-20290-6, 6263, Pub. by Bagster). Zondervan.

Davies, Benjamin. Baker's Harmony of the Gospels. (Baker's Paperback Reference Library). 192p. 1983. pap. 6.95 (ISBN 0-8010-2928-7). Baker Bk.

Davis. Davis Dictionary of the Bible. 24.95 (ISBN 0-8054-1124-0). Broadman.

Davis, John D. Davis Dictionary of the Bible. 1954. 24.95 (ISBN 0-8010-2805-1). Baker Bk.

Detzler, Wayne. New Testament Words in Today's Language. 408p. 1986. 14.95 (ISBN 0-89693-528-0). Victor Bks.

Dheilly, Joseph. Dictionnaire Biblique. (Fr.). 1284p. 1964. 22.50 (ISBN 0-686-57092-8, M-6114). French & Eur.

Dictionnaire des Noms Propres de la Bible. (Fr.). 536p. 1978. 59.95 (ISBN 0-686-56850-8, M-6628). French & Eur.

Douglas, J. D., ed. The New Bible Dictionary. 1344p. 1982. 24.95 (ISBN 0-8423-4667-8). Tyndale.

Dow, James L., ed. World's Handy Dictionary of the Bible. 640p. 1986. pap. 4.95 (ISBN 0-529-06320-4). World Bible.

Earle, Ralph. Word Meanings in the New Testament. 374p. 1987. text ed. 24.95 (ISBN 0-8010-3434-5). Baker Bk.

--Word Meanings in the New Testament: Hebrews-Revelation, Vol. 6. 174p. 1984. 9.95 (ISBN 0-8341-0943-3). Beacon Hill.

--Word Meanings in the New Testament: I & II Corinthians, Galatians & Ephesians, Vol. 4. 1979. 9.95 (ISBN 0-8010-3349-7). Baker Bk.

Easton, M. G. Illustrated Bible Dictionary. (Baker's Paperback Reference Library). 760p. 1983. pap. 12.95 (ISBN 0-8010-3386-1). Baker Bk.

Eastwood, J. & Wright, W. Aldis. A Glossary of the English Bible Words. 564p. 1981. Repr. of 1866 ed. lib. bdg. 75.00 (ISBN 0-89760-210-2). Telegraph Bks.

Ellenbogen, M. Foreign Words in the Old Testament: Their Origin & Terminology. 190p. 1972. 50.00x (ISBN 0-317-39068-6, Pub. by Luzac & Co Ltd). State Mutual Bk.

Enlow, Jack. Glosario de Nombres Biblicos. 96p. 1981. pap. 2.25 (ISBN 0-311-03655-4). Casa Bautista.

Fausset, A. R. Fausset's Bible Dictionary. (Illus.). 1970. 9.95 (ISBN 0-310-24311-4, 9616P). Zondervan.

Finnegan, Edward G., ed. Windsor Bible Dictionary. (Illus.). 1979. pap. 1.25 (ISBN 0-685-02398-2). World Bible.

Fohrer, Georg, et al, eds. Hebrew & Aramaic Dictionary of the Old Testament. Johnstone, W. A., tr. from Ger. LC 73-82430. (Hebrew & Aramaic.). viii, 344p. 1973. text ed. 16.75 (ISBN 3-11-004572-9). De Gruyter.

Furst, Gesenius. Hebrew-English Dictionary: Hebrew & Chaldee Lexicon to the Old Testament. rev. ed. Mitchell, Edward C., ed. (Hebrew & Eng.). 47.50 (ISBN 0-87559-021-7); thumb indexed 52.50 (ISBN 0-87559-022-5). Shalom.

Gehman, Henry S., ed. The New Westminster Dictionary of the Bible. LC 69-10000. (Illus.). 1064p. 1982. thumb indexed 25.95 (ISBN 0-664-21388-X); 22.95. Westminster.

Gentz, William H., ed. The Dictionary of Bible & Religion. (Illus.). 1152p. 1986. 26.95 (ISBN 0-687-10757-1). Abingdon.

Gesenius, Wilhelm. Hebrew & Chaldee Lexicon: Keyed to Strong's Exhaustive Concordance. Tregelles, Samuel P., tr. (Hebrew & Chaldee.). kivar 24.95 (ISBN 0-8010-3801-4); pap. 19.95 (ISBN 0-8010-3736-0). Baker Bk.

Gesenius, William. Hebrew & English Lexicon to the Old Testament. 2nd ed. Brown, Francis, et al, eds. Robinson, Edward, tr. (Hebrew & Eng.). 1959. Repr. of 1907 ed. 34.95x (ISBN 0-19-864301-2). Oxford U Pr.

Gingrich, Wilbur F., et al. Greek-English Lexicon of the New Testament & Other Early Christian Literature. rev 2nd. ed. 1979. 45.00 (ISBN 0-310-20570-0, 6768). Zondervan.

Grabner Haider, Anton. Vocabulario Practico De la Biblia. (Span.). 892p. 1975. 41.95 (ISBN 84-254-0964-0, S-50206). French & Eur.

Haag, Herbert. Diccionario De la Biblia. 7th ed. (Span.). 1080p. 1977. 50.00 (ISBN 84-254-0077-5, S-50196). French & Eur.

Hastings, James, ed. Dictionary of the Bible. 1963. lib. bdg. 55.00x (ISBN 0-684-15556-7, ScribT). Scribner.

Hebrew English Dictionary to the Bible. 27.50 (ISBN 0-87559-161-2). Shalom.

Hebrew-English Lexicon of the Bible. LC 74-26705. (Hebrew & Eng.). 296p. (Orig.). 1975. pap. 7.50 (ISBN 0-8052-0481-4). Schocken.

Huey, F. B., Jr. & Corley, Bruce. A Student's Dictionary for Biblical & Theological Studies. 1986. pap. 6.96 (ISBN 0-310-45951-6, 12726P). Zondervan.

The Illustrated Bible Dictionary, 3 vols. 1980. 99.95 (ISBN 0-8423-7525-2). Tyndale.

An Inclusive-Language Lectionary: Readings for Year A. LC 83-16779. 192p. 1983. pap. 7.95 (ISBN 0-664-24506-4). Westminster.

Inglis, James. A Topical Dictionary of Bible Texts. (Paperback Reference Library). 528p. 1985. pap. 12.95 (ISBN 0-8010-5038-3). Baker Bk.

International Bible Dictionary. 1977. (Pub. by Logos); pap. 6.95 (ISBN 0-88270-235-1). Bridge Pub.

Jackson, J. B. Dictionary of Scripture Proper Names of the Old & New Testaments. 1909. pap. 3.95 (ISBN 0-87213-410-5). Loizeaux.

Jamieson, Fausset & Brown's Commentary on the Whole Bible. 1957. 24.95 (ISBN 0-310-26570-3, 9930). Zondervan.

Jones, Alfred. Jones' Dictionary of Old Testament Proper Names: Keyed to Strong's Numbering System. rev. ed. Archer, Gleason L., Jr., ed. & frwd. by. LC 86-3001. 400p. 1988. Repr. of 1856 ed. 24.95 (ISBN 0-8254-2961-7). Kregel.

Kittel, Gerhard & Friedrich, Gerhard, eds. Theological Dictionary of the New Testament, 10 vols. Incl. Vol. 1. 1964. 29.95 (ISBN 0-8028-2243-6); Vol. 2. 1965. 29.95 (ISBN 0-8028-2244-4); Vol. 3. 1966. 29.95 (ISBN 0-8028-2245-2); Vol. 4. 1967. 29.95 (ISBN 0-8028-2246-0); Vol. 5. 1968. 29.95 (ISBN 0-8028-2247-9); Vol. 6. 1969. 29.95 (ISBN 0-8028-2248-7); Vol. 7. 1970. 29.95 (ISBN 0-8028-2249-5); Vol. 8. 1972. 29.95 (ISBN 0-8028-2250-9); Vol. 9. 1973. 29.95 (ISBN 0-8028-2322-X); Vol; Vol. 10. 1976. 29.95 (ISBN 0-8028-2323-8); Vol. 10. 1976. 29.95 (ISBN 0-8028-2323-8). Set. 299.50 (ISBN 0-8028-2324-6). Eerdmans.

--Theological Dictionary of the New Testament. abridged ed. Bromiley, Geoffrey, tr. from Ger. 1300p. 1985. pap. 49.95 cloth (ISBN 0-8028-2404-8). Eerdmans.

Lass, Abraham H., et al. The Facts on File Dictionary of Classical, Biblical, & Literary Allusions. 240p. 1987. 18.95 (ISBN 0-8160-1267-9). Facts on File.

Leon-Dufour, Xavier. Dictionary of the New Testament. LC 79-3004. 464p. 1983. pap. 12.95 (ISBN 0-06-065242-X, RD-486, HarpR). Har-Row.

--Dictionnaire du Nouveau Testament. (Fr.). 1975. 29.95 (ISBN 0-686-57011-1, M-6352). French & Eur.

Lexicon to the Syriac New Testament. LC 79-91407. 243p. 1979. 4.95 (ISBN 0-910068-18-6). Am Christian.

Lockyer, Herbert, Sr., ed. Nelson's Illustrated Bible Dictionary. 1088p. 1986. 26.95 (ISBN 0-8407-4955-4). Nelson.

Lueker, Erwin. Companion Dictionary of the Bible. 192p. 1985. pap. 5.95 (ISBN 0-570-03947-9, 12-2880). Concordia.

McClintock, John & Strong, James. Cyclopaedia of Biblical, Theological, & Ecclesiastical Literature: Cyclopaedia of Biblical Literature, Vol. 1-10. 250.00 (ISBN 0-405-00020-0, 11917). Ayer Co Pubs.

McElrath, William N. Bible Dictionary for Young Readers. LC 65-15604. (Illus.). 1965. 9.95 (ISBN 0-8054-4404-1, 4244-04). Broadman.

--Mi Primer Diccionario Biblico. McElrath, Ruth G., tr. from Eng. (Span., Illus.). 128p. 1985. pap. 2.95 (ISBN 0-311-03656-2). Casa Bautista.

--Mi Primer Diccionario Biblico. (Span.). 122p. 1978. pap. 4.95 (S-37577). French & Eur.

McFarlan, Dr. Donald M. Concise Bible Dictionary. 2nd ed. 208p. 1986. pap. 3.95 (ISBN 0-89622-301-9). Twenty-Third.

Mackenzie, John. Dictionary of Bible. 1967. pap. 14.95 (ISBN 0-02-087720-X, Collier). Macmillan.

--Dictionary of Bible. 1965. 29.95 (ISBN 0-02-583470-3). Macmillan.

Matthews, Velda & Beard, Ray. Basic Bible Dictionary. Korth, Bob, ed. (Illus.). 128p. (Orig.). 1984. pap. 7.95 (ISBN 0-87239-720-3, 2770). Standard Pub.

Mickelsen, Alvera & Mickelsen, Berkley. Family Bible Encyclopedia, 2 vols. Incl. Volume I (A-K (ISBN 0-89191-100-6); Volume II (L-Z (ISBN 0-89191-127-8). LC 78-55384. (Illus.). 1978. 9.95 ea.; Set. 12.95 (ISBN 0-89191-201-0). Cook.

Miller, Madeleine S. & Lane, J. Harper's Bible Dictionary. rev. ed. 1973. 18.95i (ISBN 0-06-065673-5, HarpR). Har-Row.

--Harper's Bible Dictionary. Rev. ed. 1974. 22.07 (ISBN 0-06-065674-3, HarpR); indexed 21.95i. Har-Row.

Miller, Madeleine S. & Miller, J. Lane. Harper's Encyclopedia of Bible Life. Bennet, Boyce M., Jr. & Scott, David H., eds. LC 78-4752. (Illus.). 416p. 1983. pap. 10.95 (ISBN 0-06-065677-8, RD-436, HarpR). Har-Row.

Muybridge, Eadweard. Muybridge's Complete Human & Animal Locomotion: All 781 Plates from the 1887 Animal Locomotion, 3 vols. Incl. Vol. 1. 33.34 (ISBN 0-486-23792-3); Vol. 2. 33.33 (ISBN 0-486-23793-1); Vol. 3. 33.33 (ISBN 0-486-23794-X). (Illus.). 1979. Repr. of 1887 ed. Set. 100.00. Dover.

NAS Thinline Bible. 1983. Brown cloth edition. text ed. 17.95 (ISBN 0-8024-6283-9); Brown. deluxe ed. 29.95 (ISBN 0-8024-6281-2); Burgundy. deluxe ed. 29.95 (ISBN 0-8024-6282-0). Moody.

Negev, Abraham, ed. Dictionnaire Archeologique de la Bible. (Fr.). 350p. 1970. 47.50 (ISBN 0-686-57094-4, M-6117). French & Eur.

Nelson, Wilton M., ed. Diccionario Ilustrado de la Biblia. (Span., Illus.). 735p. 1974. 29.95 (ISBN 0-89922-033-9); pap. 21.95 (ISBN 0-89922-099-1). Edit Caribe.

Nelson's New Compact Illustrated Bible Dictionary. (Illus.). 1978. 2.95 (ISBN 0-8407-5636-4). Nelson.

New Combined Bible Dictionary & Concordance. (Direction Bks). 1973. pap. 5.95 (ISBN 0-8010-6680-8). Baker Bk.

New Webster's Bible Dictionary & Concordance. (Deluxe Pocket Editions Ser.). 288p. pap. 2.50 (ISBN 0-8326-0066-0, 6531). World Bible.

The New World Dictionary Concordance to the New American Bible. 12.95 (ISBN 0-529-06094-9, 2418); pap. 4.95 (ISBN 0-529-04540-0, 2416). World Bible.

Newman, Barclay M. A Concise Greek-English Dictionary of the New Testament. 203p. 1971. 3.25x (ISBN 3-438-06008-6, 56493, Pub. by United Bible). Am Bible.

Obermayer, Heinz. Diccionario Biblico Manual. (Span.). 352p. 1975. pap. 7.95 (ISBN 84-7263-094-3, S-50212). French & Eur.

Orr, James, ed. International Standard Bible Encyclopedia, 4 vols. 1930. 89.95 (ISBN 0-8028-8045-2). Eerdmans.

Osburn, William, Jr. A Hebrew & English Lexicon to the Old Testament. 287p. 1981. pap. 6.95 (ISBN 0-310-20361-9, 6264P). Zondervan.

The Oxford Bible Reader's Dictionary & Concordance: Cyclopedic Concordance. (Illus.). 1984. 7.95 (ISBN 0-19-143442-6); pap. 4.95 (ISBN 0-19-143441-8). Oxford U Pr.

Peloubet, Francis N. Everyday Bible Dictionary. 816p. 1967. 14.95 (ISBN 0-310-30850-X, 10551). Zondervan.

Pfeiffer, Charles F., et al, eds. Wycliffe Bible Encyclopedia, 2 vols. (Illus.). 1875p. 1975. 54.95 (ISBN 0-8024-9697-0). Moody.

Pick, Aaron. Dictionary of Old Testament Words for English Readers. LC 76-16230. 602p. 1977. kivar 14.95 (ISBN 0-8254-3511-0). Kregel.

Rand, W. W. Diccionario de la Santa Biblia. (Span., Illus.). 768p. 1969. pap. 15.50 (ISBN 0-89922-003-7). Edit Caribe.

Richards, Larry. The Dictionary of Basic Bible Truths. 528p. 1987. pap. 14.95 (ISBN 0-310-43521-8). Zondervan.

Richards, Lawrence O. Expository Dictionary of Bible Words. 596p. 1985. 24.95 (ISBN 0-310-39000-1, 18300). Zondervan.

Richardson, Alan. Theological Word Book of the Bible. 1962. 7.95 (ISBN 0-02-603060-8). Macmillan.

--Theological Wordbook of the Bible. 1962. pap. 7.95 (ISBN 0-02-089090-7, Collier). Macmillan.

Rienecker, Fritz. Lexikon Zur Bibel. 3rd ed. (Ger.). 1974. 40.00 (ISBN 3-417-00403-9, M-7192). French & Eur.

Rouet, Albert. A Short Dictionary of the New Testament. (Illus.). 128p. 1982. pap. 6.95 (ISBN 0-8091-2400-9). Paulist Pr.

Skoss, Solomon, ed. Hebrew-Arabic Dictionary of the Bible Known As Kitab Jami-Al-Alfaz, 2 vols. (Yale Oriental Researches Ser.: No. XX, XXI). (Hebrew & Arabic.). 1945. 50.00x ea.; 95.00x set (ISBN 0-686-57837-6). Elliots Bks.

Smith, Barbara. The Westminster Concise Bible Dictionary. LC 80-25771. (Illus.). 188p. 1981. pap. 5.95 (ISBN 0-664-24363-0). Westminster.

Smith, William. New Smith's Bible Dictionary. rev. ed. LC 78-69668. 1979. pap. 9.95 (ISBN 0-385-14652-3, Galilee). Doubleday.

--Smith's Bible Dictionary. rev. ed. 9.95 (ISBN 0-87981-033-5); thumb-indexed 14.95 (ISBN 0-87981-035-1); pap. 6.95 (ISBN 0-87981-489-6). Holman Bible Pub.

--Smith's Bible Dictionary. (Family Library). (YA) 1984. pap. 5.95 (ISBN 0-515-08507-3). Jove Pubns.

--Smith's Bible Dictionary. Peloubet, F. N. & Peloubet, M. A., eds. 1979. 8.95 (ISBN 0-8407-5542-2); pap. 5.95 (ISBN 0-8407-3085-3). Nelson.

--Smith's Bible Dictionary. 800p. pap. 4.95 (ISBN 0-8007-8039-6, Spire Bks). Revell.

--Smith's Bible Dictionary. (Illus.). 818p. 1981. pap. 7.95 (ISBN 0-310-32871-3, 10820P). Zondervan.

--Smith's Bible Dictionary. (Illus.). 1955. 10.95 (ISBN 0-310-32870-5, 10820). Zondervan.

--Smith's Bible Dictionary. 912p. Date not set. 10.95 (ISBN 0-917006-24-0). Hendrickson MA.

Society of Biblical Literature & Achtemeier, Paul J., eds. Harper's Bible Dictionary. LC 85-42767. (Illus.). 1194p. 1985. thumb indexed 29.95 (ISBN 0-06-069863-2, HarpR); 27.50 (ISBN 0-06-069862-4). Har-Row.

Staudacher, Joseph M. Lector's Guide to Biblical Pronunciations. LC 75-14609. 72p. (Orig.). 1975. pap. 2.95 (ISBN 0-87973-773-5). Our Sunday Visitor.

Tenney, Merrill C. Handy Dictionary of the Bible. (Orig.). pap. 4.95 (ISBN 0-310-33151-X, 10898P). Zondervan.

--Handy Dictionary of the Bible. 1986. write for info. (ISBN 0-8297-0683-6). Life Pubs Intl.

Tenney, Merrill C. & Cruden, Alexander. The Handy Bible Dictionary & Concordance. 1986. pap. 6.95 (ISBN 0-310-33271-0, 11147P). Zondervan.

Tenney, Merrill C., ed. The Zondervan Pictorial Bible Dictionary. (Illus.). 1969. 21.95 (ISBN 0-310-33160-9, 6750); indexed o.p. 23.95 (ISBN 0-310-33170-6). Zondervan.

--The Zondervan Pictorial Encyclopedia of the Bible, 5 vols. new ed. (Illus.). 1974. Set. text ed. 149.95 (ISBN 0-310-33188-9, 6700). Zondervan.

Thayer, John. The New Thayer's Greek Lexicon. 784p. 1981. 19.95 (ISBN 0-913573-22-1). Hendrickson MA.

Thayer, Joseph, ed. Thayer's Greek-English Lexicon of the New Testament. 1984. 22.95 (ISBN 0-8010-8872-0). Baker Bk.

Thayer, Joseph H., ed. & tr. Greek-English Lexicon of the New Testament. (Gr.). 746p. 1901. 19.95 (ISBN 0-567-01015-5, Pub. by T & T Clark Ltd UK). Fortress.

Thomas, Robert L., ed. New American Standard Exhaustive Concordance of the Bible: Hebrew-Aramaic & Greek Dictionaries. LC 80-39626. 1695p. 1981. 29.95 (ISBN 0-87981-197-8, 4690-98); thumb-indexed 34.95 (ISBN 0-87981-503-5). Holman Bible Pub.

Truesdale, Albert, et al, eds. A Dictionary of the Bible & Christian Doctrine in Everyday English. 200p. (Orig.). 1985. 14.95 (ISBN 0-8341-1075-X). Beacon Hill.

Unger, Merrill F. Unger's Bible Dictionary. 1961. 22.95 (ISBN 0-8024-9035-2). Moody.

--Unger's Bible Dictionary. (Affordables Ser.). (Illus.). 1200p. 13.95 (ISBN 0-8024-0418-9). Moody.

--Unger's Concise Bible Dictionary: With Complete Pronunciation Guide to Bible Names by W. Murray Severance. 296p. 1985. pap. 7.95 (ISBN 0-8010-9208-6). Baker Bk.

Unity School Of Christianity. Metaphysical Bible Dictionary. 1931. 10.00 (ISBN 0-87159-098-0). Unity School.

Van Deursen, A. Illustrated Dictionary of Bible Manners & Customs. (Illus.). 1979. pap. 3.95 (ISBN 0-8065-0707-1). Citadel Pr.

Vincent, M. R. Vincent's Word Studies in th New Testament, 4 vols. 2720p. 49.95 (ISBN 0-917006-30-5). Hendrickson MA.

Vine, W. E. The Expanded Vine's Expository Dictionary of New Testament Words. rev. ed. 1376p. 1984. pap. 14.95 (ISBN 0-87123-619-2, 230619). Bethany Hse.

--Expository Dictionary of New Testament Words. 1392p. (Orig.). 1981. pap. 12.95 (ISBN 0-310-33781-X, 6795P). Zondervan.

--An Expository Dictionary of New Testament Words. (Affordables Ser.). 1985. pap. 9.95 (ISBN 0-8024-0435-9). Moody.

--Vines Expository Dictionary of New Testament Words. (Barbour Bks). 351p. 1985. 14.95 (ISBN 0-916441-31-8); pap. 10.95 (ISBN 0-916441-34-2). Barbour & Co.

--Vine's Expository Dictionary of Old & New Testament Words. 1568p. 1981. 19.95 (ISBN 0-8007-1282-X). Revell.

Vine, W. E. & Bruce, F. F. Vine's Expository Dictionary of Old & New Testament Words. (Reference Library Edition). 1568p. 1987. Repr. text ed. 14.95 (ISBN 0-529-06374-3). World Bible.

Webster's Concise Dictionary of Modern English. 608p. 1987. pap. 5.95 (ISBN 0-8407-3110-8). Nelson.

Wigoder, Geoffrey, et al. The Illustrated Dictionary & Concordance of the Bible. (Illus.). 1000p. 1986. text ed. 100.00 (ISBN 0-02-916380-3). Macmillan.
Wigram, George V. New Englishmans Greek Concordance & Lexicon. 960p. 1982. 34.95 (ISBN 0-913573-23-X). Hendrickson MA.
Wilson, Walter L. Wilson's Dictionary of Bible Types. 1957. pap. 10.95 (ISBN 0-8028-1453-0). Eerdmans.
Wood, Richard H. A Cyclopedic Dictionary of Ecclesiastical Terms According to the Use of the Episcopal Church. 1984. 10.95 (ISBN 0-8062-2141-0). Carlton.
Young, G. Douglas. Young's Bible Dictionary. 608p. 1984. 9.95 (ISBN 0-8423-8598-3). Tyndale.

BIBLE–DRAMA

see Bible As Literature; Bible Plays; Mysteries and Miracle-Plays

BIBLE–ECONOMICS

see also Christianity and Economics

Lockman, Vic. Biblical Economics in Comics. (Illus.). 112p. (Orig.). 1985. pap. 6.00 (ISBN 0-936175-00-1). V Lockman.
North, Gary. Honest Money. (The Biblical Blueprint Ser.). Date not set. pap. 6.95 (ISBN 0-8407-3094-2). Nelson.

BIBLE–ETHICS

see also Sociology, Biblical

Bridges, Julian C. & Estudio, Guias de. Guia De Estudios Sobre Bases Biblicas De la Etica. 96p. 1982. Repr. of 1973 ed. 4.50 (ISBN 0-311-43505-X). Casa Bautista.
Bruce, W. S. The Ethics of the Old Testament. 1909. 17.95 (ISBN 0-567-02058-4, Pub. by T & T Clark Ltd UK). Fortress.
Chambers, Oswald. Biblical Ethics. 1964. 2.95 (ISBN 0-87508-102-9). Chr Lit.
Crenshaw, J. L. & Crenshaw, Willis. Essays on Old Testament Ethics: J. P. Hyatt in Memoriam. 1974. 35.00x (ISBN 0-87068-233-4). Ktav.
Duke, David N. The Biblical View of Reality: The Bible & Christian Ethics. ii, 59p. 1985. pap. text ed. 6.95x (ISBN 0-932269-05-2). Wyndham Hall.
Everding, H. Edward, Jr. & Wilbanks, Dana M. Decision Making & the Bible. LC 75-11656. 160p. 1975. pap. 5.95 (ISBN 0-8170-0668-0). Judson.
Forlines, Leroy. Biblical Ethics. 1973. pap. 5.95 (ISBN 0-89265-014-1). Randall Hse.
Furnish, Victor P. Theology & Ethics in Paul. LC 68-17445. 1978. pap. 12.95 (ISBN 0-687-41499-7). Abingdon.
Giles, J. E. Bases Biblicas De la Etica. 1983. Repr. of 1979 ed. 4.25 (ISBN 0-311-46028-3). Casa Bautista.
Haas, Peter, ed. Biblical Hermeneutics in Jewish Moral Discourse. (Semeia Ser.: No. 34). pap. 9.95 (06 20 34). Scholars Pr GA.
Kaiser, Walter C., Jr. Toward Old Testament Ethics. 1986. 16.95 (ISBN 0-310-37110-4, 12321). Zondervan.
Mackie, George M. Bible Manners & Customs. LC 84-230883. (Illus.). 192p. 1984. 6.95 (ISBN 0-8007-5179-5, Power Bks.). Revell.
Maston, T. B. Biblical Ethics -- A Survey: A Guide to the Ethical Message of the Scriptures from Genesis Through Revelation. LC 82-6470. 320p. 1982. 13.95 (ISBN 0-86554-051-9, MUP-H32). Mercer Univ Pr.
Murray, John. Principles of Conduct. 1957. pap. 7.95 (ISBN 0-8028-1144-2). Eerdmans.
Payne, Franklin E., Jr. Biblical-Medical Ethics. 1986. text ed. 19.95 (ISBN 0-8010-7099-6). Baker Bk.
Schnackenburg, Rudolf. Moral Teaching of the New Testament. pap. 7.95 (ISBN 0-8245-0329-5). Crossroad NY.
Schrage, Wolfgang. Ethics of the New Testament. Green, David E., tr. LC 86-45922. 384p. 1987. pap. 29.95 (ISBN 0-8006-0835-6, 1-835). Fortress.
Wenham, John W. The Enigma of Evil: Can We Believe in the Goodness of God? 224p. (Orig.). 1985. pap. 7.95 (ISBN 0-310-29871-7, 12449P). Zondervan.
White, R. E. Biblical Ethics. pap. 9.95 (ISBN 0-8042-0787-9). John Knox.

BIBLE–ETHNOLOGY

see also Lost Tribes of Israel

Hanks, Thomas D. God So Loved the Third World: The Bible, the Reformation & Liberation Theologies. Dekker, James C., tr. from Span. LC 83-8076. Tr. of Opresion, Podreza y Liberacion: Reflexiona Biblicas. 176p. (Orig.). 1983. pap. 8.95 (ISBN 0-88344-152-7). Orbis Bks.
Montgomery, James A. Arabia & the Bible. rev. ed. (Library of Biblical Studies). 1969. 25.00x (ISBN 0-87068-090-0). Ktav.

BIBLE–EVIDENCES, AUTHORITY, ETC.

see also Bible–Quotations, Early; Miracles

Alexander, Archibald. Evidences of the Authenticity, Inspiration, & Canonical Authority of the Holy Scriptures. LC 70-38431. (Religion in America, Ser. 2). 314p. 1972. Repr. of 1836 ed. 23.50 (ISBN 0-405-04052-0). Ayer Co Pubs.
Bartlett, David L. The Shape of Scriptural Authority. LC 83-48009. 176p. 1983. pap. 8.95 (ISBN 0-8006-1713-4, 1-1713). Fortress.
Bennett, Dennis. Moving Right Along in the Spirit. 160p. 1982. 5.95 (ISBN 0-8007-5184-1, Power Bks). Revell.
Bird, Phyllis A. The Bible As the Church's Book. LC 82-7049. (Library of Living Faith: Vol. 5). 118p. 1982. pap. 5.95 (ISBN 0-664-24427-0). Westminster.
Bruce, Frederick F. New Testament Documents: Are They Reliable. pap. 3.95 (ISBN 0-87784-691-X). Inter-Varsity.
Carman, George. Science Proves the Bible. De Witt, Mason, ed. 190p. 1986. 12.00 (ISBN 0-936749-00-8). Zytech Western Pub.
Clark, Gordon H. Concept of Biblical Authority. 1979. 0.75 (ISBN 0-87552-143-6). Presby & Reformed.
Clevenger, Ernest, Jr. & Hill, Samuel G. Bible Evidences. (Bible Centered Studies). (Illus.). 73p. (Orig.). 1973. pap. 1.50 (ISBN 0-88428-009-8). Parchment Pr.
Criswell, W. A. Why I Preach That the Bible Is Literally True. LC 69-13142. 1969. pap. 3.95 (ISBN 0-8054-5536-1). Broadman.
Dulles, Avery. Apologetics & the Biblical Christ. LC 63-22027. 88p. (Orig.). 1963. pap. 4.95 (ISBN 0-8091-1505-0). Paulist Pr.
Forstman, H. Jackson. Word & Spirit: Calvin's Doctrine of Biblical Authority. 1962. 20.00x (ISBN 0-8047-0070-2). Stanford U Pr.
Geisler, Norman. Inerrancy. 1980. pap. 11.95 (ISBN 0-310-39281-0, 18157P). Zondervan.
Hagerty, Cornelius. The Authenticity of the Sacred Scriptures. 339p. 1969. 10.00 (ISBN 0-912414-00-6). Lumen Christi.
Jackson, Wayne. Biblical Studies in the Light of Archaeology. 69p. (Orig.). 1982. pap. 2.50 (ISBN 0-932859-00-3). Apologetic Pr.
--Fortify Your Faith. 74p. (Orig.). 1974. pap. text ed. 2.50 (ISBN 0-932859-07-7). Apologetic Pr.
Johnston, Robert G. The Scriptures: Sacred Fact or Pious Fiction? 1970. pap. 2.25 (ISBN 0-8100-0024-5, 12-0337). Northwest Pub.
Kenyon, Frederic G. The Bible & Modern Scholarship. LC 78-9892. 1979. Repr. of 1948 ed. lib. bdg. 22.50x (ISBN 0-313-21009-8, KEBI). Greenwood.
Lindsay, Gordon. Thirty Bible Reasons Why Christ Heals Today. (Divine Healing & Health Ser.). 1.25 (ISBN 0-89985-031-6). Christ Nations.
McCord, Hugo. From Heaven or from Men. 1970. pap. 2.75 (ISBN 0-88027-033-0). Firm Foun Pub.
Maier, Gerhard. End of the Historical Critical Method. 1977. pap. 6.25 (ISBN 0-570-03752-2, 12-2656). Concordia.
Mollenkott, Virginia. Godding: The Bible & Human Responsibility. 1987. 12.95. Crossroad NY.
Pache, Rene. Inspiration & Authority of Scripture. 1970. pap. 10.95 (ISBN 0-8024-4091-6). Moody.
Pinnock, Clark. Defense of Biblical Infallibility. pap. 1.75 (ISBN 0-8010-6863-0). Baker Bk.
Pinnock, Clark H. Defense of Biblical Infallibility. 1967. pap. 1.75 (ISBN 0-87552-350-1). Presby & Reformed.
Stott, John R. God's Book for God's People. LC 82-21203. 96p. 1982. pap. 2.95 (ISBN 0-87784-396-1). Inter-Varsity.
Taylor, Richard S. Biblical Authority & Christian Faith. 95p. (Orig.). 1980. pap. 2.95 (ISBN 0-8341-0633-7). Beacon Hill.
Warfield, B. B. Inspiration & Authority of Bible. 12.95 (ISBN 0-8010-9586-7). Baker Bk.
Warfield, Benjamin B. Inspiration & Authority of the Bible. 2nd ed. 1948. 12.95 (ISBN 0-87552-527-X). Presby & Reformed.
Westminster Seminary Faculty Symposium. Infallible Word. Woolley, Paul, ed. pap. 9.95 (ISBN 0-87552-543-1). Presby & Reformed.
Wolseley, Charles. The Reasonableness of Scripture-Belief. LC 73-2618. 488p. 1973. Repr. of 1672 ed. lib. bdg. 75.00x (ISBN 0-8201-1113-9). Schol Facsimiles.

BIBLE–EVIDENCES, AUTHORITY, ETC.–N. T.

Bruce, Frederick F., ed. New Testament Documents: Are They Reliable? (Orig.). 1959. pap. 2.95 (ISBN 0-8028-1025-X). Eerdmans.

BIBLE–EVIDENCES, AUTHORITY, ETC.–O. T.

Allis, Oswald T. Five Books of Moses. 1949. pap. 7.95 (ISBN 0-87552-102-9). Presby & Reformed.
Carmichael, Calum M. Law & Narrative in the Bible: The Evidence of the Deuteronomic Laws & the Decalogue. LC 85-4214. 352p. 1985. text ed. 35.00x (ISBN 0-8014-1792-9). Cornell U Pr.
The Literary Man's Bible: A Selection of Passages from the Old Testament, Historic, Poetic & Philosophic, Illustrating Hebrew Literature. 414p. 1982. Repr. of 1908 ed. lib. bdg. 40.00 (ISBN 0-89987-133-X). Darby Bks.
Thomas, D. Winton, ed. Documents from Old Testament Times. pap. 7.95x (ISBN 0-06-130085-3, TB85, Torch). Har-Row.

BIBLE–EXAMINATIONS, QUESTION-BOOKS, ETC.

see Bible–Catechisms, Question-Books, etc.

BIBLE–EXEGESIS

see Bible–Commentaries; Bible–Hermeneutics

BIBLE–FESTIVALS

see Fasts and Feasts

BIBLE–FICTION

see Bible–History of Biblical Events–Fiction

BIBLE–FOLK-LORE

see Folk-Lore, Jewish

BIBLE–FORM CRITICISM

see Bible–Criticism, Form

BIBLE–GARDENS

see Bible–Natural History

BIBLE–GEOGRAPHY

see also Ecclesiastical Geography

Aharoni, Yohanan. The Land of the Bible: A Historical Geography. rev. & enlarged ed. Rainey, Anson F., tr. LC 80-14168. 496p. 1980. pap. 19.95 (ISBN 0-664-24266-9). Westminster.
Baly, Denis. Basic Biblical Geography. LC 86-45206. 80p. 1987. pap. 4.95 (ISBN 0-8006-1922-6, 1-1922). Fortress.
Beitzel, Barry J. The Moody Atlas of Bible Lands. 1985. text ed. 31.95 (ISBN 0-8024-0438-3). Moody.
Blaiklock, E. M. Zondervan Pictorial Bible Atlas. (Illus.). 1969. 24.95 (ISBN 0-310-21240-5). Zondervan.
Callaway, Joseph A. & Adams, J. McKee, eds. Biblical Backgrounds. rev. ed. 1966. 14.95 (ISBN 0-8054-1113-5). Broadman.
Canfield, Betty M. The Bible World Maps of the Old & New Testaments. (Illus.). 24p. (Orig.). 1983. pap. text ed. 4.95 (ISBN 0-9611756-0-5). Humble Pub Co.
Chapman, Marie. Fun with Bible Geography. LC 80-65055. (Teaching Aid Ser.). 65p. 1980. plastic spiral 5.95 (ISBN 0-89636-044-X). Accent Bks.
Clevenger & Hill, eds. Bible Geography. 1973. pap. 1.50 (ISBN 0-88428-003-9, 111). Parchment Pr.
Cohn, Robert L. The Shape of Sacred Space: Four Biblical Studies. LC 80-11086. (Studies in Religion: No. 23). pap. 8.50 (ISBN 0-89130-384-7, 01-00-23). Scholars Pr GA.
Compact Bible Atlas with Gazetteer. (Illus.). 1979. pap. 4.95 (ISBN 0-8010-2432-3). Baker Bk.
Dowley, Tim. The Moody Guide to Bible Lands. 1987. text ed. 7.95 (ISBN 0-8024-5563-8). Moody.
Duffield, Guy P. Handbook of Bible Lands. 192p. 1985. pap. 7.95 (ISBN 0-8010-2948-1). Baker Bk.
Field, Frank M. Where Jesus Walked: Through the Holy Land with the Master. Davis, Moshe, ed. LC 77-70681. (America & the Holy Land Ser.). (Illus.). 1977. Repr. of 1951 ed. lib. bdg. 20.00x (ISBN 0-405-10244-5). Ayer Co Pubs.
Gale, William. I Sat Where They Sat. pap. 2.50 (ISBN 0-686-12884-2). Schmul Pub Co.
Gonen, Rivka. Biblical Holy Places. (Illus.). 192p. pap. cancelled (ISBN 0-915361-67-1). Adama Pubs Inc.
Harrison, R. K., ed. Major Cities of the Biblical World. 320p. 1985. 15.95 (ISBN 0-8407-7520-2). Nelson.
Kent, Charles F. Biblical Geography & History. 296p. 1981. Repr. of 1911 ed. lib. bdg. 30.00 (ISBN 0-89760-431-8). Telegraph Bks.
Kesich, Veselin & Kesich, Lydia W. Treasures of the Holy Land: A Visit to the Places of Christian Origins. LC 85-18403. (Illus., Orig.). 1985. pap. 6.95 (ISBN 0-88141-045-4). St Vladimirs.
May, Herbert G., ed. Oxford Bible Atlas. 3rd. ed. 1985. 18.95 (ISBN 0-19-143452-3); pap. 10.95x (ISBN 0-19-143451-5). Oxford U Pr.
Mazar, Benjamin & Avi-Yonah, Michael. Illustrated World of the Bible Library, 5 vols. Incl. Vol. 1. The Laws. 40.00 (ISBN 0-8088-1167-3); Vol. 2. The Early Prophets. 40.00 (ISBN 0-8088-1168-1); Vol. 3. The Late Prophets. 40.00 (ISBN 0-8088-1169-X); Vol. 4. The Writings. 40.00 (ISBN 0-8088-1170-3); Vol. 5. The New Testament. Avi-Yonah, Michael. 40.00 (ISBN 0-8088-1171-1). 1961. Vols. 1-4. old testament ed. 160.00 (ISBN 0-8088-1080-4); Vols. 1-5. new testament ed. 200.00 (ISBN 0-8088-1081-2). Davey.
Packer, J. I., et al, eds. All the People & Places of the Bible. LC 82-12564. 1982. pap. 6.95 (ISBN 0-8407-5819-7). Nelson.
Parmelee, Alice. The Holy Land. LC 81-80630. (All About the Bible Ser.: Bk. 6). 136p. (Orig.). 1981. pap. 5.95 (ISBN 0-8192-1290-3). Morehouse.
Pfeiffer, Charles F. & Vos, Howard F. Wycliffe Historical Geography of Bible Lands. 1967. 25.95 (ISBN 0-8024-9699-7). Moody.
Ritter, K. Comparative Geography of Palestine & the Sinaitic Peninsula, 4 Vols. LC 68-26367. (Reference Ser., No. 44). 1969. Repr. of 1865 ed. Set. lib. bdg. 159.95x (ISBN 0-8383-0180-0). Haskell.
Ritter, Karl. The Comparative Geography of Palestine, 4 vols. 1865. Set. 65.00x (ISBN 0-403-03564-3). Scholarly.
--Comparative Geography of Palestine & the Sinaitic Peninsula, 4 Vols. Gage, William L., tr. LC 69-10151. 1969. Repr. of 1866 ed. Set. lib. bdg. 71.00x (ISBN 0-8371-0638-9, RISP). Greenwood.
Tidwell, J. B. Geografia Biblica. Pierson, Carlos C., tr. (Span., Illus.). 144p. 1982. pap. 5.50 (ISBN 0-311-15031-4). Casa Bautista.
Vos, Howard F. An Introduction to Bible Geography. Rev. ed. 1983. pap. 6.95 (ISBN 0-8024-0326-3). Moody.
Wild, Laura H. Geographic Influences in Old Testament Masterpieces. 182p. 1980. Repr. of 1915 ed. lib. bdg. 30.00 (ISBN 0-8414-9701-X). Folcroft.
--Geographic Influences in Old Testament Masterpieces. 1915. 27.00 (ISBN 0-8274-2396-9). R West.

BIBLE–GEOGRAPHY–MAPS

Aharoni, Yohanon & Avi-Yonah, Michael. The Macmillan Bible Atlas. rev. ed. LC 77-4313. (Illus.). 183p. 1977. 25.95 (ISBN 0-02-500590-1). Macmillan.
Allen, J. Catling. Pictorial Bible Atlas. 14.95 (ISBN 0-7175-0991-5); pap. 9.95 (ISBN 0-7175-0857-9). Dufour.
American Map Corp. Staff. Student Atlas of the Bible. (Series 9500: No. 9559). (Illus.). 1978. 2.95 (ISBN 0-8416-9559-8); Span. lang. ed. write for info. Am Map.
Archbishop of York. Palmer's Bible Atlas (Facsimile Edition) 84p. 1982. 14.95 (ISBN 0-686-43010-7, Carta Pub Isreal). Hippocrene Bks.
Filson, Wright. Atlas Historico Westminster de la Biblia. 134p. 1981. pap. 19.95 (ISBN 0-311-15030-6). Casa Bautista.
Frank, Harry T. Atlas of the Bible Lands. rev. ed. LC 77-6292. (Illus.). 48p. 1984. 7.95 (ISBN 0-8437-7056-2); pap. 4.99 (ISBN 0-8437-7055-4). Hammond Inc.
Frank, Harry T., ed. Atlas of the Bible Lands. 1979. pap. 4.95 (ISBN 0-8054-1136-4). Broadman.
Grollenberg, Luc H. The Penguin Shorter Atlas of the Bible. Hedlund, Mary F., tr. (Reference Ser). (Illus.). 1978. pap. 7.95 (ISBN 0-14-051056-7). Penguin.
Holman Bible Publishers. The Holman Bible Atlas. Hooper, Jerry L., ed. (Illus.). 1978. pap. 6.95 (ISBN 0-87981-099-8). Holman Bible Pub.
Laney, J. Carl. Baker's Concise Bible Atlas. (Illus.). 192p. (Orig.). 1987. pap. 10.95 (ISBN 0-8010-5638-1). Baker Bk.
Laor, Eran. Maps of the Holy Land: Cartobibliography of Printed Maps, 1475-1900. LC 86-15298. 224p. 1986. 77.50 (ISBN 0-8451-1705-X). A R Liss.
Montgomery, James A. Arabia & the Bible. rev. ed. (Library of Biblical Studies). 1969. 25.00x (ISBN 0-87068-090-0). Ktav.
Moody Bible Atlas. 1985. 29.95 (ISBN 0-88469-169-1). BMH Bks.
Paterson, J. H. & Wiseman, D. J., eds. New Bible Atlas. 128p. 1985. 14.95 (ISBN 0-8423-4675-9). Tyndale.
Pfeiffer, Charles F. Baker's Bible Atlas. rev. ed. (Illus.). 1961. Repr. 15.95 (ISBN 0-8010-6930-0). Baker Bk.
--The Bible Atlas. LC 60-15536. 1975. 16.95 (ISBN 0-8054-1129-1). Broadman.
Reader's Digest Editors. Atlas of the Bible: An Illustrated Guide to the Holy Land. LC 80-53426. (Illus.). 256p. 1981. 21.95 (ISBN 0-89577-097-0, Pub. by RD Assn). Random.
Rogerson, John. Atlas of the Bible. 240p. 1985. text ed. 40.00 (ISBN 0-8407-5462-0). Nelson.
Root, Orrin. Standard Bible Atlas. (Illus.). 32p. 1973. pap. 3.50 (ISBN 0-87239-251-1, 3169). Standard Pub.
Rowley, H. H., ed. Student's Bible Atlas. 40p. 1984. pap. 3.95 (ISBN 0-8170-1022-X). Judson.
Smith, George A. Historical Geography of the Holy Land. 13.25 (ISBN 0-8446-2956-1). Peter Smith.
Wright, G. Ernest & Filson, F. V., eds. Westminster Historical Maps of Bible Lands. 24p. pap. 2.50 (ISBN 0-664-29077-9). Westminster.
Wright, G. Ernest & Filson, Floyd V., eds. Westminster Historical Atlas to the Bible. rev. ed. LC 56-9123. 130p. 1956. 18.95 (ISBN 0-664-20535-6). Westminster.

BIBLE–GLOSSARIES, VOCABULARIES, ETC.

see Bible–Dictionaries

BIBLE–HANDBOOKS, MANUALS, ETC.

Alexander, David & Alexander, Pat, eds. Eerdmans' Concise Bible Handbook. LC 80-20131. (Illus.). 384p. (Orig.). 1981. pap. 9.95 (ISBN 0-8028-1875-7). Eerdmans.

--Eerdmans' Handbook to the Bible. rev. ed. (Illus.). 680p. 1983. 24.95 (ISBN 0-8028-3486-8). Eerdmans.

Alexander, Pat, ed. Eerdmans' Concise Bible Encyclopedia. LC 80-19885. (Illus.). 256p. (Orig.). 1981. pap. 8.95 (ISBN 0-8028-1876-5). Eerdmans.

Bagster, Samuel. Bagster's Bible Handbook. Elwell, Walter, intro. by. 264p. 1983. Repr. 9.95 (ISBN 0-8007-1334-6). Revell.

Bennett, Boyce M. Bennett's Guide to the Bible: Graphic Aids & Outlines. (Illus.). 128p. (Orig.). 1982. pap. 9.95 (ISBN 0-8164-2397-0, HarpR). Har-Row.

Blair, Edward P. Manual Biblico de Abingdon. LC 81-12774. Tr. of Abingdon Bible Handbook. (Span.). 400p. (Orig.). 1982. pap. 12.95 (ISBN 0-687-23170-1). Abingdon.

Boyd, Robert T. Boyd's Bible Handbook. LC 82-81088. 800p. 1983. 26.95 (ISBN 0-89081-352-3). Harvest Hse.

Chapman, Benjamin. Card-Guide to New Testament Exegesis. 2.95 (ISBN 0-8010-2396-3). Baker Bk.

Clevenger, Ernest, Jr. General Bible Knowledge Bible Drill: Flash Cards Flipbook. (Bible Drill Flash Cards Flipbook Ser.). 104p. 1983. pap. 4.25 (ISBN 0-88428-017-9). Parchment Pr.

Cully, Iris V. & Cully, Kendig B. A Guide to Biblical Resources. LC 81-80625. 160p. (Orig.). 1981. pap. 7.95 (ISBN 0-8192-1286-5). Morehouse.

Danker, Frederick W. Multipurpose Tools for Bible Study. rev. ed. 1970. pap. 12.50 (ISBN 0-570-03734-4, 12-2638). Concordia.

Davis, John J. Handbook of Basic Bible Texts: Every Key Passage for the Study of Doctrine & Theology. 1986. pap. 6.95 (ISBN 0-310-43711-3, 12103P). Zondervan.

Elwell, Walter A., ed. The Shaw Pocket Bible Handbook. 400p. 1984. 9.95 (ISBN 0-87788-683-0). Shaw Pubs.

Foote, G. W. & Ball, W. P. The Bible Handbook. 372p. 1983. pap. 7.00 (ISBN 0-910309-26-4). Am Atheist.

Freeman. Handbook of Bible Manners & Customs. Repr. of 1870 ed. cancelled. Guildhall Pubs.

Halley, Henry H. Compendio Manual de la Biblia. Orig. Title: Halley's Bible Handbook. (Span.). 768p. 1955. 14.95 (ISBN 0-8254-1300-1); pap. 12.95. Kregel.

--Halley's Bible Handbook. 1976. 9.95 (ISBN 0-310-25720-4, 9744); pap. 13.95 Large print (ISBN 0-310-25727-1, 12564L); large print Kivar 19.95 (ISBN 0-310-41390-7, 9840). Zondervan.

Hann, Robert R. The Bible: An Owner's Manual, What You Need to Know Before You & Read Your Own Bible. 160p. 1983. pap. 6.95 (ISBN 0-8091-2503-X). Paulist Pr.

Hutchins, John. Hutchins' Guide to Bible Reading. LC 83-102876. (Illus.). 608p. 1983. 25.00x (ISBN 0-938386-00-X). Button Gwin.

Jensen, Irving. Disfrute Su Biblia. Orig. Title: Enjoy Your Bible. (Span.). 1981. pap. 3.50 (ISBN 0-8254-1350-8). Kregel.

Larsen, Dale & Larsen, Sandy. Getting to Know God. (Carpenter Studyguide). 80p. 1985. memb. ed. 1.95 (ISBN 0-87788-317-3); leader ed. 2.95 (ISBN 0-87788-318-1). Shaw Pubs.

Lawrence, Anthony. The Psalm Locator. 2nd ed. (Orig.). 1985. pap. 10.95 (ISBN 0-89390-063-X). Resource Pubns.

Leigh, Ronald W. Direct Bible Discovery. LC 81-67203. 1982. pap. 7.95 (ISBN 0-8054-1139-9). Broadman.

Little, Henry. YHWH: Tetragrammaton. LC 84-90091. 177p. 1985. 12.95 (ISBN 0-533-06173-3). Vantage.

Maredsous, Monks of. Guide to the Bible. 2.25 (ISBN 0-87243-016-2). Templegate.

Mills, Dick. Quick Reference Scripture Handbook. 50p. (Orig.). 1984. pap. 1.95 (ISBN 0-89274-323-9). Harrison Hse.

Morgan, G. Campbell. Handbook for Bible Teachers & Preachers. (Paperback Reference Library). 312p. 1985. pap. 8.95 (ISBN 0-8010-6190-3). Baker Bk.

Norquist, Marilyn. Como Leer y Orar los Evangelios. McPhee, John, ed. Diaz, Olimpia, tr. from Eng. (Handbook of the Bible Ser.). Orig. Title: Hand. 64p. 1980. pap. 1.50 (ISBN 0-89243-127-X). Liguori Pubns.

Teaching Visuals from Willmington's Guide to the Bible. 1981. pap. 14.95 (ISBN 0-8423-6939-2). Tyndale.

Torrey, R. A. The Treasury of Scripture Knowledge. 784p. 1973. 21.95 (ISBN 0-8007-0324-3). Revell.

Turner, Nicholas. Handbook for Biblical Studies. LC 82-7111. 156p. 1982. pap. 6.95 (ISBN 0-664-24436-X). Westminster.

Unger, Merrill F. Manual Biblico de Unger. Orig. Title: Unger's Bible Handbook. (Span.). 954p. 1976. pap. 12.95 (ISBN 0-8254-1778-3). Kregel.

--The New Unger's Bible Handbook. rev. ed. Larson, Gary N., ed. (Illus.). 1984. 24.95 (ISBN 0-8024-9049-2). Moody.

--Unger's Bible Handbook. LC 66-16224. 1966. 9.95 (ISBN 0-8024-9039-5). Moody.

Weed, Michael & Weed, Libby. Bible Handbook: A Guide for Basic Bible Learning. LC 73-91023. 1978. student's ed. 5.95 (ISBN 0-8344-0101-0). Sweet.

Willmington, H. L. Willmington's Guide to the Bible. 1981. 29.95 (ISBN 0-8423-8804-4). Tyndale.

Wilson, C. Vincent. The Westminster Concise Handbook for the Bible. LC 79-15498. (Illus.). 112p. 1979. pap. 4.50 (ISBN 0-664-24272-3). Westminster.

BIBLE–HARMONIES

Farmer, William R., ed. Synopticon. 1969. 80.00 (ISBN 0-521-07464-9). Cambridge U Pr.

Kerr, John H. Harmony of the Gospels. 236p. 10.95 (ISBN 0-8007-0131-3). Revell.

Wieand, Albert C. New Harmony of the Gospels. 1947. 15.95 (ISBN 0-8028-3299-7). Eerdmans.

BIBLE–HERMENEUTICS

Here are entered works on the principles of Biblical Criticism. Critical works on the Bible are entered under Bible–Criticism, Interpretation, Etc.

Apple, Jody L. Hermeneutical Agnosticism: A Critique of Subjectivism in Biblical Interpretation. LC 84-62067. 195p. (Orig.). 1985. pap. 7.95 (ISBN 0-931247-00-4). New Testament Christ Pr.

Barthes, R., et al. Structural Analysis & Biblical Exegesis. Johnson, Alfred M., Jr., tr. LC 74-31334. (Pittsburgh Theological Monographs: No. 3). 1974. pap. 9.95 (ISBN 0-915138-02-6). Pickwick.

Benoit, Pierre, ed. How Does the Christian Confront the Old Testament. (Concilium Ser.: Vol. 30). 1967. 7.95 (ISBN 0-8091-0074-6). Paulist Pr.

Berkhof, Louis. Principles of Biblical Interpretation. 1950. 9.95 (ISBN 0-8010-0549-3). Baker Bk.

Birdsong, Robert E. The Hermetic Commandments in Today's World. (Aquarian Academy Monograph, Ser. F: Lecture No. 7). 1977. pap. 1.25 (ISBN 0-917108-19-1). Sirius Bks.

Bleicher, Josef. Contemporary Hermeneutics: Hermeneutics As Method, Philosophy & Critique. 224p. 1980. 28.00x (ISBN 0-7100-0551-2); pap. 14.00x (ISBN 0-7100-0552-0). Methuen Inc.

Branson, Mark L. & Padilla, C. Rene, eds. Conflict & Context: Hermeneutics in the Americas. 304p. (Orig.). 1986. pap. 13.95 (ISBN 0-8028-0172-2). Eerdmans.

Brenneman, Walter L., Jr., et al. The Seeing Eye: Hermeneutical Phenomenology in the Study of Religion. LC 81-47174. 168p. 1982. 22.50x (ISBN 0-271-00291-3). Pa St U Pr.

Crossan, John D., ed. Semeia Nineteen: The Book of Job & Ricoeur's Hermeneutics. (Semeia Ser.). pap. 9.95 (06 20 19). Scholars Pr GA.

Davidson, Richard M. Typology in Scripture: A Study of Hermeneutical Tupos Structures. (Andrews University Seminary Doctoral Dissertation Ser.: Vol. 2). 496p. (Orig.). 1981. pap. 10.95 (ISBN 0-943872-34-0). Andrews Univ Pr.

Ferguson, Duncan S. Biblical Hermeneutics: An Introduction. LC 85-45456. 204p. 1986. pap. 12.95 (ISBN 0-8042-0050-5). John Knox.

Flinn, Frank K., ed. Hermeneutics & Horizons: The Shape of the Future. LC 82-50053. (Conference Ser.: No. 11). xvii, 445p. (Orig.). 1982. pap. text ed. 11.95 (ISBN 0-932894-11-9, Pub. by New Era Bks). Paragon Hse.

Fountain, Thomas. Claves de Interpretacion Biblica. 148p. 1985. pap. 4.25 (ISBN 0-311-03653-8). Casa Bautista.

Hahn, Ferdinand. Historical Investigation & New Testament Faith. Krentz, Edgar, ed. Maddox, Robert, tr. from Ger. LC 82-48547. 112p. 1983. pap. 7.50 (ISBN 0-8006-1691-X, 1-1691). Fortress.

Hartill, J. Edwin. Principles of Biblical Hermeneutics. 13.95 (ISBN 0-310-25900-2, 9774). Zondervan.

Hughes, G. Hebrews & Hermeneutics. LC 77-84806. (Society for New Testament Studies Monographs: No. 36). 1980. 32.50 (ISBN 0-521-21858-6). Cambridge U Pr.

Johnson, Alfred M., Jr., ed. & tr. Structuralism & Biblical Hermeneutics. LC 79-9411. (Pittsburgh Theological Monographs: No. 22). 1979. pap. 12.95 (ISBN 0-915138-18-2). Pickwick.

Krentz, Edgar. The Historical-Critical Method. LC 74-26345. (Guides to Biblical Scholarship: Old Testament Ser.). 96p. 1975. pap. 4.50 (ISBN 0-8006-0460-1, 1-460). Fortress.

Kung, Hans & Moltmann, Jurgen, eds. Conflicting Ways of Interpreting the Bible. (Concilium Ser.: Vol. 138). 128p. (Orig.). 1980. pap. 5.95 (ISBN 0-8164-2280-X, HarpR). Har-Row.

McKim, Donald K., ed. A Guide to Contemporary Hermeneutics: Major Trends in Biblical Interpretation. 312p. (Orig.). 1986. pap. 14.95 (ISBN 0-8028-0094-7). Eerdmans.

McKnight, Edgar V. The Bible & the Reader: An Introduction to Literary Criticism. LC 85-4603. 176p. 1985. pap. 8.95 (ISBN 0-8006-1872-6). Fortress.

Mickelsen, A. Berkeley. Interpreting the Bible. 1963. 20.95 (ISBN 0-8028-3192-3). Eerdmans.

Olthuis, James H., et al. A Hermeneutics of Ultimacy: Peril or Promise? (Christian Studies Today). 90p. (Orig.). 1987. lib. bdg. 19.75 (ISBN 0-8191-5800-3, Pub. by Inst Chris Stud); pap. text ed. 8.25 (ISBN 0-8191-5801-1). U Pr of Amer.

Panikkar, Raimundo. Myth, Faith & Hermeneutics: Toward Cross-Cultural Religious Understanding. LC 77-99306. 528p. 1980. 22.95 (ISBN 0-8091-0232-3). Paulist Pr.

Patte, Daniel. What Is Structural Exegesis? Via, Dan O., Jr., ed. LC 75-36454. (Guides to Biblical Scholarship: New Testament Ser.). 96p. (Orig.). 1976. pap. 4.50 (ISBN 0-8006-0462-8, 1-462). Fortress.

Phillips, John. The Bible Explorer's Guide. 320p. 1987. 9.95 (ISBN 0-87213-682-5). Loizeaux.

Poland, Lynn M. Literary Criticism & Biblical Hermeneutics. (American Academy of Religion Academy Ser.: No. 48). 1985. 15.25 (ISBN 0-89130-825-3, 01 01 48); pap. 10.25 (ISBN 0-89130-836-9). Scholars Pr GA.

Prickett, Stephen. Words & the Word: Language Poetics, & Biblical Interpretation. 288p. 1986. 39.50 (ISBN 0-521-32248-0). Cambridge U Pr.

Radmacher, Earl D. & Preus, Robert D., eds. Hermeneutics, Inerrancy, & the Bible: Papers from ICBI Summit II. LC 83-12314. 928p. (Orig.). 1984. pap. 16.95 (ISBN 0-310-37081-7, 12314P). Zondervan.

Ramm, Bernard. Hermeneutics. (Practical Theology Ser.). pap. 3.95 (ISBN 0-8010-7605-6). Baker Bk.

--Protestant Biblical Interpretation. 9.95 (ISBN 0-8010-7600-5). Baker Bk.

Reese, James M. Experiencing the Good News: The New Testament as Communication. (Good News Studies Ser.: Vol. 10). 1984. pap. 9.95 (ISBN 0-89453-448-3). M Glazier.

Reumann, John, et al, eds. Studies in Lutheran Hermeneutics. LC 78-14673. 352p. 1979. 15.95 (ISBN 0-8006-0534-9, 1-534). Fortress.

Saint Augustine. On Christian Doctrine. Robertson, D. W., Jr., tr. LC 58-9956. 1958. pap. 7.20 scp (ISBN 0-672-60262-8). Bobbs.

Silva, Moises. Biblical Interpretation: Its History. (Foundations in Hermeneutics Ser.: Vol. 1). 176p. Date not set. pap. 7.95 (ISBN 0-8407-7524-5). Nelson.

Smart, James D. The Strange Silence of the Bible in the Church: A Study in Hermeneutics. LC 72-118323. 184p. 1970. pap. 8.95 (ISBN 0-664-24894-2). Westminster.

Sproul, R. C. Knowing Scripture. LC 77-11364. 1977. pap. text ed. 5.95 (ISBN 0-87784-733-9). Inter-Varsity.

Thiselton, Anthony C. The Two Horizons. LC 79-14387. 1984. 12.95 (ISBN 0-8028-0006-8). Eerdmans.

Torjesen, Karen Jo. Hermeneutical Procedure & Theological Method in Origen's Exegesis. (Patristische Texts und Studien: Vol. 28). xii, 183p. 1985. 41.00x (ISBN 3-11-010202-1). De Gruyter.

Virkler, Henry A. Hermeneutics: Principles & Processes of Biblical Interpretation. LC 80-70530. 200p. 1981. 12.95 (ISBN 0-8010-9282-5). Baker Bk.

Warren, Thomas B. When Is an Example Binding? (Biblical Hermeneutics Ser.). 1975. pap. 7.00 (ISBN 0-934916-43-8). Natl Christian Pr.

BIBLE–HERMENEUTICS–HISTORY

see Bible–Criticism, Interpretation, Etc.–History

BIBLE–HIGHER CRITICISM

see Bible–Criticism, Interpretation, etc.; Bible–Introductions

BIBLE–HISTORIOGRAPHY

Adamiak, Richard. Justice & History in the Old Testament: The Evolution of Divine Retribution in the Historiographies of the Wilderness Generation. 1982. 14.95x (ISBN 0-939738-08-2). Zubal Inc.

Blomberg, Craig. The Historical Reliability of the Gospels. 288p. 1987. pap. 9.95 (ISBN 0-87784-992-7). Inter-Varsity.

Dulles, Avery. Apologetics & the Biblical Christ. LC 63-22027. 88p. (Orig.). 1963. pap. 4.95 (ISBN 0-8091-1505-0). Paulist Pr.

Peckham, Brian. The Composition of the Deuteronomic History. (Harvard Semitic Museum Monographs). 1985. 13.95 (ISBN 0-89130-909-8, 04-00-35). Scholars Pr GA.

Wallis, Louis. The Bible Is Human. LC 74-149677. Repr. of 1942 ed. 24.00 (ISBN 0-404-06814-6). AMS Pr.

BIBLE–HISTORY

This head is used for work on the History of Bible texts or versions. For works on historical events see Bible–History of Biblical Events, or Bible–History of Contemporary Events.

Aling, Charles F. Egypt & Bible History: From Earliest Times to 1000 B.C. (Baker Studies in Biblical Archaeology). 144p. (Orig.). 1981. pap. 5.95 (ISBN 0-8010-0174-9). Baker Bk.

Baker, Charles. The Book of Bible History. 1980. lib. bdg. 59.95 (ISBN 0-8490-3159-1). Gordon Pr.

--Manual of Bible History: Reading Lessons, Explanations, Questions & Geographical Notes, 2 vols. 1980. lib. bdg. 195.95 (ISBN 0-8490-3117-6). Gordon Pr.

Becker, J. Formation of the Old Testament. 1.25 (ISBN 0-8199-0513-5). Franciscan Herald.

Bigelow, John. The Bible That Was Lost & Is Found. 4th ed. LC 78-65549. pap. 1.95 (ISBN 0-87785-159-X). Swedenborg.

Bruce, F. F. History of the Bible in English. 3rd ed. 1978. pap. 8.95 (ISBN 0-19-520088-8). Oxford U Pr.

Bruce, Frederick F. The Books & the Parchments. rev. & updated ed. (Illus.). 320p. (Orig.). 13.95 (ISBN 0-8007-1214-5). Revell.

Butterworth, Charles C. The English Primers, Fifteen Twenty-Nine to Fifteen Forty-Five: Their Publication & Connection with the English Bible & the Reformation in England. 1970. lib. bdg. 26.00x (ISBN 0-374-91131-2, Octagon). Hippocrene Bks.

Calmet, A. Dictionnaire Historique, Archeologique, Philologique, Chronologique Geographique et Literal de la Bible, 4 vols. Migne, J. P., ed. (Encyclopedie Theologique First Ser.: Vols. 1-4). (Fr.). 2602p. Repr. of 1846 ed. lib. bdg. 332.50x (ISBN 0-89241-231-3). Caratzas.

Cambridge History of the Bible, 3 vols. Incl. Vol. 1. From the Beginnings to Jerome. Ackroyd, P. R. & Evans, C. F., eds. pap. 23.95 (ISBN 0-521-09973-0); Vol. 2. The West from the Fathers to the Reformation. Lampe, G. W., ed. 65.00 (ISBN 0-521-04255-0); pap. 23.95 (ISBN 0-521-29017-1); Vol. 3. The West from the Reformation to the Present Day. Greenslade, S. L., ed. 72.50 (ISBN 0-521-04254-2); pap. 21.95 (ISBN 0-521-29016-3). LC 63-24435. 57.50 ea.; Set. 155.00 (ISBN 0-521-08778-3). Set. pap. 47.50 (ISBN 0-521-29018-X). Cambridge U Pr.

Clay, Albert T. The Origin of Biblical Tradition. LC 78-63556. (Yale Oriental Ser. Researches: No. 12). Repr. of 1923 ed. 37.50 (ISBN 0-404-60282-7). AMS Pr.

Clevenger & Hill. History of the Bible Church. 1973. pap. 1.50 (ISBN 0-88428-006-3, 171). Parchment Pr.

Clifford, David. The Two Jerusalems in Prophecy. LC 78-14922. (Illus.). 1978. pap. 3.50 (ISBN 0-87213-081-9). Loizeaux.

Curtis, Adrian H. Ugarit. (Cities of the Biblical World Ser.). 128p. (Orig.). 1985. pap. 8.95 (ISBN 0-8028-0166-8). Eerdmans.

Daiches, David. The King James Version of the English Bible. LC 68-16338. vii, 228p. 1968. Repr. of 1941 ed. 21.50 (ISBN 0-208-00493-9, Archon). Shoe String.

Deloe, Jesse B. Sweeter Than Honey. pap. 4.95 (ISBN 0-88469-105-5). BMH Bks.

Earle, Ralph. How We Got Our Bible. 119p. 1972. 2.95 (ISBN 0-8341-0226-9). Beacon Hill.

Ewert, David. From Ancient Tablets to Modern Translations: A General Introduction to the Bible. 1986. 15.95 (ISBN 0-310-45370-4, 12384). Zondervan.

Foley, Helen S. Bible Records, Barbour County, Ala, Vol. 1. 80p. 1983. pap. 10.00 (ISBN 0-89308-180-9). Southern Hist Pr.

--Bible Records, Barbour County, Ala, Vol. 2. 84p. 1983. pap. 10.00 (ISBN 0-89308-181-7). Southern Hist Pr.

Fontana, John M. Mankind's Greatest Invention. LC 64-5232. 112p. 1964. 4.95 (ISBN 0-9600034-1-X). J M Fontana.

Forster, Roger T. & Marston, V. Paul. God's Strategy in Human History. 304p. 1984. pap. 7.95 (ISBN 0-87123-434-3, 210434). Bethany Hse.

Franzmann, Werner H. Bible History Commentary: Old Testament. LC 80-53145. (Illus.). 616p. 1981. 15.95 (ISBN 0-938272-04-7). WELS Board.

Gilles, Anthony E. People of the Book: The Story Behind the Old Testament. (Illus.). 178p. (Orig.). 1983. pap. text ed. 5.95 (ISBN 0-86716-026-8). St Anthony Mess Pr.

Glashouwer, Willem J. How the Bible Came to Be. 1980. cancelled (ISBN 0-310-42130-6). Zondervan.

Goodspeed, Edgar J. How Came the Bible ? (Festival Books). 1976. pap. 1.95 (ISBN 0-687-17524-0). Abingdon.

Graham, Henry G. Where We Got the Bible... Our Debt to the Catholic Church. 153p. 1977. pap. 3.00 (ISBN 0-89555-137-3). TAN Bks Pubs.

Grunze, Richard. Bible History: Teachers' Manual. 228p. 1985. suedene vinyl 3-ring binder 12.95 (ISBN 0-938272-15-2). WELS Board.

Grunze, Richard, ed. Bible History. (WELS Lutheran Elementary Schools' Religion Curriculum Ser.). (Illus.). 556p. 1984. 11.95 (ISBN 0-938272-14-4). WELS Board.

Ishida, T., ed. Studies in the Period of David & Solomon & Other Essays: Papers Read at the International Symposium for Biblical Studies, 6-7 December 1979. LC 82-11183. 409p. 1982. text ed. 35.00x (ISBN 0-931464-16-1). Eisenbrauns.

Keller, Werner. The Bible As History. 2nd, rev. ed. Rehork, Joachim, ed. Neil, William & Rasmussen, B. H., trs. from Ger. LC 80-22218. Orig. Title: Und Die Bibel Hat Docht Recht. (Illus.). 448p. 1981. 14.95 (ISBN 0-688-03724-0). Morrow.

Kent, Charles F. The Origin & Permanent Value of the Old Testament. 270p. 1981. Repr. of 1906 ed. lib. bdg. 30.00 (ISBN 0-89760-429-6). Telegraph Bks.

Koch, Klaus. The Book of Books: The Growth of the Bible. LC 69-12299. 192p. 1969. pap. 2.65 (ISBN 0-664-24840-3). Westminster.

Lang, Bernhard. Monotheism & the Prophetic Minority: An Essay in Biblical History & Sociology. (Social World of Biblical Antiquity: No. 1). 191p. 1983. text ed. 22.95x (ISBN 0-907459-30-7, Pub. by Almond Pr England); pap. text ed. 10.95x (ISBN 0-907459-31-5). Eisenbrauns.

Lightfoot, Neil R. How We Got the Bible. 1962. 7.95 (ISBN 0-8010-5502-4). Baker Bk.

--How We Got the Bible. rev. ed. (Way of Life Ser.). 95p. 1986. pap. 3.95. Abilene Christ U.

--How We Got the Bible. rev. ed. 1987. price not set (ISBN 0-8010-5644-6). Baker Bk.

McAfee, Cleland B. The Greatest English Classic. LC 77-18104. 1977. Repr. of 1912 ed. lib. bdg. 30.00 (ISBN 0-8414-6231-3). Folcroft.

MacGregor, Geddes. The Bible in the Making. LC 82-17499. 318p. 1983. pap. 14.50 (ISBN 0-8191-2810-4). U Pr of Amer.

Mackay, H. G. Story of Your Bible. 1985. pap. 2.95 (ISBN 0-937396-65-6). Walterick Pubs.

Metzger, Bruce M. Text of the New Testament: Its Transmission, Corruption, & Restoration. 2nd ed. 1968. 13.95x (ISBN 0-19-500391-8). Oxford U Pr.

Miller, J. Maxwell. The Old Testament & the Historian. Tucker, Gene M., ed. LC 75-10881. (Guides to Biblical Scholarship: Old Testament Ser.). 96p. 1976. pap. 4.50 (ISBN 0-8006-0461-X, 1-461). Fortress.

Nicholas, David R. Foundations of Biblical Inerrancy. pap. 2.50 (ISBN 0-88469-104-7). BMH Bks.

Oakshott, Walter. The Two Winchester Bibles. (Illus.). 1981. 350.00x (ISBN 0-19-818235-X). Oxford U Pr.

Packer, James I., et al, eds. Public Life in Bible Times. 224p. 1985. pap. 6.95 (ISBN 0-8407-5984-3). Nelson.

Pieters, A. Can We Trust Bible History? 2.50 (ISBN 0-686-23481-2). Rose Pub MI.

Ramsey, Johnny, ed. Story of the Bible. pap. 3.95 (ISBN 0-89137-543-0). Quality Pubns.

Read, Lenet H. How We Got the Bible. LC 85-72842. 140p. 1985. 8.95 (ISBN 0-87747-799-X). Deseret Bk.

Rogers, Jack & McKim, Donald. The Authority & Interpretation of the Bible: An Historical Approach. LC 78-20584. 1979. 23.50 (ISBN 0-06-066696-X, HarpR). Har-Row.

Saint Joseph Concise Bible History. (Capsule Comments, Catechetical Aids). flexible bdg. 2.25 (ISBN 0-89942-770-7, 770). Catholic Bk Pub.

Schmidt, Werner H. The Faith of the Old Testament: A History. Sturdy, John, tr. LC 82-21780. 312p. (Orig.). 1983. 25.00 (ISBN 0-664-21826-1); pap. 12.95 (ISBN 0-664-24456-4). Westminster.

Schulte, Hannelis. Die Entstehung der Geschichtsschreibung Im Alten Israel. (Beiheft 128 zur Zeitschrift fuer die altestamentliche Wissenschaft). 1972. 36.40x (ISBN 3-11-003960-5). De Gruyter.

Schultz, Samuel J. Old Testament Survey: Law & History. rev. ed. LC 64-10037. 96p. 1968. pap. text ed. 4.95 (ISBN 0-910566-01-1); Perfect bdg. instr's. guide 5.95 (ISBN 0-910566-20-8). Evang Tchr.

Smuth, J. Paterson. The Ancient Documents & the Modern Bible. 212p. 1979. Repr. of 1920 ed. lib. bdg. 40.00 (ISBN 0-8495-4885-3). Arden Lib.

Smyth, John P. How We Got Our Bible. LC 77-24190. 1977. Repr. of 1912 ed. lib. bdg. 20.00 (ISBN 0-8414-7793-0). Folcroft.

Swartley, Willard M., ed. Essays on War & Peace: Bible & Early Church. (Occasional Papers Ser.: No. 9). 154p. 1986. pap. text ed. 6.50 (ISBN 0-936273-09-7). Inst Mennonite.

Teeple, Howard M. The Historical Approach to the Bible. LC 81-85275. (Truth in Religion Ser.: No. 2). 323p. (Orig.). 1982. pap. 7.50 (ISBN 0-914384-02-3). Religion & Ethics.

Thompson, Craig R. Bible in English, Fifteen Twenty-Five to Sixteen Eleven. LC 59-1241. (Folger Guides to the Age of Shakespeare). 1958. pap. 3.95 (ISBN 0-918016-22-3). Folger Bks.

Underwood, Jonathan. A History of the English Bible. LC 83-577. 96p. 1983. pap. 3.50 (ISBN 0-87239-644-4, 39974). Standard Pub.

Walsh, Katherine & Wood, Diana, eds. The Bible in the Medieval World: Essays in Memory of Beryl Smalley. (Studies in Church History: Subsidia 4). 352p. 1985. 45.00x (ISBN 0-631-14275-4). Basil Blackwell.

Willey, Herbert L. The Bible Through the Centuries. 1929. 37.50 (ISBN 0-8274-1935-X). R West.

Woodrow, Ralph. Amazing Discoveries Within the Book of Books. (Illus.). 1979. pap. 4.95 (ISBN 0-916938-04-2). R Woodrow.

--Noah's Flood, Joshua's Long Day, & Lucifer's Fall: What Really Happened? (Illus.). 1984. 4.95 (ISBN 0-916938-07-7). R Woodrow.

BIBLE–HISTORY OF BIBLICAL EVENTS

see also Palestine–History

Adams, Sebastian C. A Chronological Chart of Ancient, Modern & Biblical History. 1982. Repr. of 1877 ed. educational chart 14.95 (ISBN 0-943388-04-X). South Oregon.

Buksbazen, Victor. Feasts of Israel. 1976. pap. 2.95 (ISBN 0-87508-043-X). Chr Lit.

Cornfeld & Gaalyah, eds. Josephus: The Jewish War. 560p. 1982. 44.95 (ISBN 0-310-39210-1, 10265). Zondervan.

De Dietrich, Suzanne. God's Unfolding Purpose: A Guide to the Study of the Bible. Brown, Robert M., tr. LC 60-6169. 1960. Westminster.

Earle, Arthur. The Bible Dates Itself. LC 73-88548. 1974. 12.50 (ISBN 0-9600788-1-9). A Earle.

Frank, Harry T. Discovering the Biblical World. rev. ed. LC 74-7044. (Illus.). 228p. 1977. 19.95 (ISBN 0-8437-3624-0). Hammond Inc.

Frank, Harry T. & Strange, James F. Discovering the Biblical World. rev. ed. (Illus.). 288p. 1987. pap. 14.95 (ISBN 0-8437-3626-7). Hammond Inc.

Grant, Michael. Jesus: An Historian's View of the Gospels. 261p. 1978. pap. text ed. write for info. (ISBN 0-02-345630-2, Pub. by Scribner). Macmillan.

Hindson, Edward E. The Philistines & the Old Testament. (Baker Studies in Biblical Archaeology). pap. 6.95 (ISBN 0-8010-4034-5). Baker Bk.

Kee, Howard C. Understanding the New Testament. 4th ed. (Illus.). 464p. 1983. text ed. 33.00 (ISBN 0-13-936591-5). P-H.

Keller, Werner. The Bible As History. (Illus.). 544p. 1974. pap. 4.95 (ISBN 0-553-25438-3). Bantam.

Kent, Charles F. Biblical Geography & History. 296p. 1981. Repr. of 1911 ed. lib. bdg. 30.00 (ISBN 0-89760-431-8). Telegraph Bks.

Lemche, Niels P. Ancient Israel: A New History of Israelite Society. (The Biblical Seminar Ser.: No. 5). 250p. 1987. pap. text ed. 9.50x (ISBN 1-85075-017-3, Pub. by JSOT Pr England). Eisenbrauns.

McDowell, Josh. More Evidence That Demands a Verdict. rev. ed. 425p. 1981. pap. 7.95 (ISBN 0-918956-73-0). Campus Crusade.

Maelzer, G., ed. Bibliographie zur Geschichte des Pietismus, Vol. 1, Die Werke Der Wuerttembergischen Pietisten des 17. Und 18. Jahrhunderts. 415p. 1972. 41.60 (ISBN 3-11-002219-2). De Gruyter.

Mendenhall, George E. The Tenth Generation: The Origins of the Biblical Tradition. 266p. 1973. 25.00x (ISBN 0-8018-1267-4); pap. 8.95x (ISBN 0-8018-1654-8). Johns Hopkins.

Nettleton, David. Our Infallible Bible. LC 77-15540. (Illus.). 1978. pap. 1.75 (ISBN 0-87227-055-6); tchr's guide 4.50 (ISBN 0-87227-056-4). Reg Baptist.

Peale, John S. Biblical History As the Quest for Maturity. LC 85-5067. (Symposium Ser.: Vol. 15). 120p. 1985. 39.95x (ISBN 0-88946-706-4). E Mellen.

Rhodes, Arnold B. Mighty Acts of God. (Orig.). 1964. pap. 7.95 (ISBN 0-8042-9010-5); tchrs' ed. 6.95 (ISBN 0-8042-9012-1). John Knox.

Schaeffer, Edith. Christianity Is Jewish. 1977. pap. 6.95 (ISBN 0-8423-0242-5). Tyndale.

Skousen, W. Cleon. The First Two Thousand Years. 1953. 8.95 (ISBN 0-88494-029-2). Bookcraft Inc.

--The Fourth Thousand Years. LC 66-29887. 1966. 13.95 (ISBN 0-88494-147-7). Bookcraft Inc.

--The Third Thousand Years. 1964. 12.95 (ISBN 0-88494-122-1). Bookcraft Inc.

Spittler, Russell P. Corinthian Correspondence. LC 75-43157. (Radiant Life Ser.). 128p. 1976. pap. 2.50 (ISBN 0-88243-892-1, 02-0892); tchr's. ed. 3.95 (ISBN 0-88243-166-8, 32-0166). Gospel Pub.

Strobel, August. Der Spaetbronzezeitliche Seevoelkersturm: Ein Forschungsueberblick mit Folgerungen zur biblischen Exodusthematik. (Beiheft 145 Zur Zeitschrift fuer die Alttestamentliche Wissenschaft Ser). 1976. 61.00x (ISBN 3-11-006761-7). De Gruyter.

Tadmor, H. History Historiography & Interpretation: Studies in Biblical & Cuneiform Literatures. Weinfeld, M., ed. 192p. 1983. pap. text ed. 22.50 (ISBN 965-223-459-1, Pub by Magnes Pr Israel). Humanities.

Wilson, Michael L. Outline of Bible History & Major Christian Movements. 1974. pap. 4.95 (ISBN 0-88027-014-4). Firm Foun Pub.

Woodrow, Ralph. Noah's Flood, Joshua's Long Day, & Lucifer's Fall: What Really Happened? (Illus.). 1984. 4.95 (ISBN 0-916938-07-7). R Woodrow.

BIBLE–HISTORY OF BIBLICAL EVENTS–CHRONOLOGY

see Bible–Chronology

BIBLE–HISTORY OF BIBLICAL EVENTS–FICTION

Blackburn, Francis A., ed. Exodus & Daniel. LC 76-144440. (Belles Lettres Ser., Section I: No. 6). Repr. of 1907 ed. 16.50 (ISBN 0-404-53607-7). AMS Pr.

Levine, Faye. Solomon & Sheba. 240p. 1986. pap. 9.95 (ISBN 0-312-74283-5). St Martin.

Tyndale Library of Great Biblical Novels, 6 vols. 23.95 (ISBN 0-8423-7643-7). Tyndale.

BIBLE–HISTORY OF BIBLICAL EVENTS–HISTORIOGRAPHY

see Bible–Historiography

BIBLE–HISTORY OF BIBLICAL EVENTS–JUVENILE LITERATURE

see Bible Stories

BIBLE–HISTORY OF BIBLICAL EVENTS–N. T.

Barrett, Ethel. The People Who Couldn't Be Stopped. LC 70-96703. (Illus., Orig.). 1970. pap. 1.95 (ISBN 0-8307-0007-2, S063107). Regal.

Bruce, F. F. New Testament History. LC 78-144253. 462p. 1972. pap. 9.95 (ISBN 0-385-02533-5, Anch). Doubleday.

Dana, H. E. El Mundo Del Nuevo Testamento. Villarello, Ildefonso, tr. 288p. 1982. pap. 4.95 (ISBN 0-311-04342-9). Casa Bautista.

Denny, Randal E. Wind in the Rigging. 120p. 1985. pap. 4.50 (ISBN 0-8341-0937-9). Beacon Hill.

Eller, Meredith F. The Beginnings of the Christian Religion: A Guide to the History & Literature of Judaism & Christianity. 1958. 16.95x (ISBN 0-8084-0392-3); pap. 12.95x (ISBN 0-8084-0393-1). New Coll U Pr.

Filson, Floyd V. A New Testament History: The Story of the Emerging Church. LC 64-15360. (Illus.). 464p. 1964. 12.95 (ISBN 0-664-20525-9). Westminster.

Fowler, Henry T. The History & Literature of the New Testament. LC 78-12516. 1979. Repr. of 1925 ed. lib. bdg. cancelled (ISBN 0-313-21188-4, FOHL). Greenwood.

Hanson, John & Horsley, Richard A. Bandits, Prophets, & Messiahs: Popular Movements at the Time of Jesus. 220p. 1985. 28.35 (ISBN 0-86683-992-5, HarpR). Har-Row.

Harrop, Clayton. History of the New Testament in Plain Language. 192p. 1984. 9.95 (ISBN 0-8499-0432-3, 0432-3). Word Bks.

Roetzel, Calvin J. The World That Shaped the New Testament. LC 85-12492. 180p. 1985. pap. 11.95 (ISBN 0-8042-0455-1). John Knox.

Tenney, Merrill C. New Testament Times. 1965. 21.95 (ISBN 0-8028-3250-4). Eerdmans.

BIBLE–HISTORY OF BIBLICAL EVENTS–O. T.

Ackroyd, Peter R. Exile & Restoration: A Study of Hebrew Thought of the Sixth Century B. C. LC 68-27689. (Old Testament Library). 302p. 1968. 14.95 (ISBN 0-664-20843-6). Westminster.

Albright, William F. Biblical Period from Abraham to Ezra: A Historical Survey. pap. 4.95x (ISBN 0-06-130102-7, TB102, Torch). Har-Row.

Bennett, Robert. God's Work of Liberation: A Journey Through the Old Testament with the Liberation Heroes of Israel. (Illus., Orig.). 1976. pap. text ed. 5.95 (ISBN 0-8192-4067-2); tchr's guide 2.25x (ISBN 0-8192-4068-0). Morehouse.

Christian, Mary B. & Van Woerkom, Dorothy. Bible Heroes, Kings & Prophets. 1982. pap. 3.75 (ISBN 0-570-04066-3, 56-1718). Concordia.

Cogan, Morton. Imperialism & Religion: Assyria, Judah & Israel in the Eighth & Seventh Centuries B.C.E. LC 73-83723. (Society of Biblical Literature. Monograph). 1974. 13.50 (ISBN 0-89130-330-8, 060019); pap. 9.95 (ISBN 0-89130-331-6, 00-06-19). Scholars Pr GA.

Conn, Charles W. Highlights of Hebrew History. 1975. pap. 4.25 (ISBN 0-87148-401-3); instrs. guide 5.25 (ISBN 0-87148-404-8). Pathway Pr.

Craigie, Peter C. Problem of War in the Old Testament. LC 78-17698. 1979. pap. 5.95 (ISBN 0-8028-1742-4). Eerdmans.

Creelman, H. S. History & Literature of the Old Testament, 2 vols. (Illus.). 1987. Set. 189.45 (ISBN 0-89266-573-4). Am Classical Coll Pr.

Edersheim, Alfred. Old Testament Bible History. 1972. 24.95 (ISBN 0-8028-8028-2). Eerdmans.

Fison, J. E. Understanding the Old Testament: The Way of Holiness. LC 78-21116. 1979. Repr. of 1952 ed. lib. bdg. 24.75x (ISBN 0-313-20839-5, FIUO). Greenwood.

Halpern, Baruch. The Emergence of Israel in Canaan. LC 82-24030. (Society of Biblical Literature Monographic Ser.: No. 29). 352p. 1984. 36.75 (ISBN 0-89130-649-8, 06 00 29); pap. 24.50 (ISBN 0-89130-609-9). Scholars Pr GA.

Hare, D. S. The Story of St. Paul. (Ladybird Ser.). (YA) 1969. pap. 2.50 (ISBN 0-87508-869-4). Chr Lit.

Harrison, Roland K. Old Testament Times. (Illus.). 1970. 16.95 (ISBN 0-8028-3334-9). Eerdmans.

Heaton, Eric W. Hebrew Kingdoms. (New Clarendon Bible Ser.). 1968. 10.95x (ISBN 0-19-836922-0). Oxford U Pr.

Herrmann, Siegfried. A History of Israel in Old Testament Times. 2nd, rev. & enl. ed. Bowden, John, tr. from Ger. LC 81-43092. Tr. of Geschichte Israels in alttestamentlicher Zeit. 456p. 1981. pap. 16.95 (ISBN 0-8006-1499-2, 1-1499). Fortress.

The Interpreter's Concise Commentary, Vol. II: Old Testament History. 4.95 (ISBN 0-687-19233-1). Abingdon.

Kennett, R. H. The Composition of the Book of Isaiah in the Light of History & Archaeology. (British Academy, London, Schweich Lectures on Biblical Archaeology Series, 1909). pap. 19.00 (ISBN 0-8115-1251-7). Kraus Repr.

MacKenzie, R. A. Faith & History in the Old Testament. LC 63-10585. 1963. 8.95 (ISBN 0-8166-0297-2). U of Minn Pr.

Merrill, Eugene. Historical Survey of Old Testament. 1966. pap. 7.95 (ISBN 0-934532-16-8). Presby & Reformed.

Orlinsky, Harry M. Ancient Israel. LC 82-2937. (The Development of Western Civilization Ser.). xii, 164p. 1982. Repr. of 1954 ed. lib. bdg. 24.75x (ISBN 0-313-23559-7, ORAN). Greenwood.

Patterson, Ward. Wonders in the Midst. LC 78-62709. 96p. (Orig.). 1979. pap. 2.25 (ISBN 0-87239-237-6, 40076). Standard Pub.

Pfeiffer, Charles F. Old Testament History. 1973. 22.95 (ISBN 0-8010-6945-9). Baker Bk.

Rand, Howard B. Primogenesis. 1953. 15.00 (ISBN 0-685-08813-8). Destiny.

Sandford, Frank W. Art of War for the Christian Soldier. 2nd ed. LC 66-29707. 1966. 4.00 (ISBN 0-910840-12-1). Kingdom.

Staton, Knofel. Struggle for Freedom. LC 76-18381. 96p. 1977. pap. 2.25 (ISBN 0-87239-063-2, 40034). Standard Pub.

Unger, Merrill F. Israel & the Aramaeans of Damascus. (BSBA Ser.). 1980. pap. 5.95 (ISBN 0-8010-9204-3). Baker Bk.

Wade, G. W. Old Testament History. 1904. lib. bdg. 20.00 (ISBN 0-8482-9973-6). Norwood Edns.

Wallis, Louis. The Bible Is Human. LC 74-149677. Repr. of 1942 ed. 24.00 (ISBN 0-404-06814-6). AMS Pr.

Wood, Leon J. Israel's United Monarchy. 1980. 12.95 (ISBN 0-8010-9622-7). Baker Bk.

BIBLE–HISTORY OF BIBLICAL EVENTS–SOURCES

see Bible–Evidences, Authority, etc.

BIBLE–HISTORY OF CONTEMPORARY EVENTS, ETC.

see also Palestine–History

Adams, Sebastian C. A Chronological Chart of Ancient, Modern & Biblical History. 1982. Repr. of 1877 ed. educational chart 14.95 (ISBN 0-943388-04-X). South Oregon.

Blaiklock, E. M. Zondervan Pictorial Bible Atlas. (Illus.). 1969. 24.95 (ISBN 0-310-21240-5). Zondervan.

Callaway, Joseph A. & Adams, J. McKee, eds. Biblical Backgrounds. rev. ed. 1966. 14.95 (ISBN 0-8054-1113-5). Broadman.

Coleman, William L. Today's Handbook of Bible Times & Customs. (Illus.). 306p. 1984. 11.95 (ISBN 0-87123-594-3, 230594). Bethany Hse.

Dixon, James W. Reading the Bible As History. 605p. 1986. 21.90 (ISBN 0-533-06192-X). Vantage.

Finegan, Jack. Light from the Ancient Past, 2 vols. 2nd ed. (Illus.). 1959. Vol. 1 2nd Ed. 52.50 (ISBN 0-691-03550-4); Vol. 1 2nd Edition. pap. 16.50 (ISBN 0-691-00207-X); Vol. 2. 50.00 (ISBN 0-691-03551-2); Vol. 2. pap. 15.50x (ISBN 0-691-00208-8); Set. 90.00 (ISBN 0-686-76901-5). Princeton U Pr.
Harrison, Roland K. Old Testament Times. (Illus.). 1970. 16.95 (ISBN 0-8028-3334-9). Eerdmans.
Kenyon, Frederic G. The Bible & Modern Scholarship. LC 78-9892. 1979. Repr. of 1948 ed. lib. bdg. 22.50x (ISBN 0-313-21009-8, KEBI). Greenwood.
Mackie, George M. Bible Manners & Customs. (Illus.). 176p. 1956. (Power Bks); pap. 6.95 (ISBN 0-8007-5179-5). Revell.
Montgomery, James A. Arabia & the Bible. rev. ed. (Library of Biblical Studies). 1969. 25.00x (ISBN 0-87068-090-0). Ktav.
Pritchard, James B., ed. Ancient Near East in Pictures with Supplement. 2nd ed. Incl. Ancient Near Eastern Texts Relating to the Old Testament with Supplement. 3rd ed. Set. text ed. 60.50x ea. (ISBN 0-691-03503-2, 035032T); pictures 66.25x (032024T). 1969. deluxe ed. 68.50x ea. (ISBN 0-691-03502-4); Set. 126.75x (ISBN 0-686-66606-2). Princeton U Pr.
Spurgeon, C. H. The Bible & the Newspaper. 1973. pap. 2.50 (ISBN 0-686-09104-3). Pilgrim Pubns.
Thompson, J. A. The Bible & Archaeology. wnd, rev. ed. 512p. 1981. 24.95 (ISBN 0-8028-3545-7). Eerdmans.
Ullendorff, Edward. Ethiopia & the Bible. (British Academy Ser). 1968. 29.95x (ISBN 0-19-725904-9). Oxford U Pr.

BIBLE–HISTORY OF CONTEMPORARY EVENTS–N. T.

Barrett, Charles K., ed. New Testament Background: Selected Documents. pap. 6.95x (ISBN 0-06-130086-1, TB86, Torch). Har-Row.
Blaiklock, E. M. World of the New Testament. (Bible Study Commentary Ser.). 127p. 1983. pap. 4.95 (ISBN 0-87508-176-2). Chr Lit.
Bruce, F. F. New Testament History. LC 78-144253. 462p. 1972. pap. 9.95 (ISBN 0-385-02533-5, Anch). Doubleday.
Fowler, Henry T. The History & Literature of the New Testament. LC 78-12516. 1979. Repr. of 1925 ed. lib. bdg. cancelled (ISBN 0-313-21188-4, FOHL). Greenwood.
Jones, Clifford M. New Testament Illustrations. (Cambridge Bible Commentary on the New English Bible, New Testament Ser.). 27.95 (ISBN 0-521-05446-X); pap. 12.95x (ISBN 0-521-09376-7, 376). Cambridge U Pr.
Kee, Howard C. The New Testament in Context: Sources & Documents. (Illus.). 256p. 1984. pap. text ed. 20.33 (ISBN 0-13-615774-2). P-H.
Lohse, Edward. The New Testament Environment. Steely, John E., tr. from Ger. LC 75-43618. 320p. 1976. pap. 10.95 (ISBN 0-687-27944-5). Abingdon.
Nickell, Judy. New Testament Herald. 1985. 1.25 (ISBN 0-89536-733-5, 5878). CSS of Ohio.
Pfeiffer, Robert H. History of New Testament Times. LC 77-138125. 561p. 1972. Repr. of 1949 ed. lib. bdg. 23.00x (ISBN 0-8371-3559-1, PFNT). Greenwood.
Tenney, Merrill C. New Testament Times. 1965. 21.95 (ISBN 0-8028-3250-4). Eerdmans.
Vermes, Geza. Jesus & the World of Judaism. LC 83-16535. 224p. 1984. pap. 10.95 (ISBN 0-8006-1784-3, 1-1784). Fortress.

BIBLE–HISTORY OF CONTEMPORARY EVENTS–O. T.

Anderson, G. W. The History & Religion of Israel. (New Clarendon Bible-OT Ser.). (Illus.). 1966. pap. 11.95x (ISBN 0-19-836915-8). Oxford U Pr.
Gordon, Cyrus H. Ancient Near East. 1965. pap. 8.95 (ISBN 0-393-00275-6, Norton Lib). Norton.

BIBLE–HOMILETICAL USE

Adams, Jay E. Essays on Biblical Preaching. (Jay Adams Library). 160p. 1986. pap. 7.95 (ISBN 0-310-51041-4, 12116P). Zondervan.
Allen, Horace T., Jr. A Handbook for the Lectionary. LC 80-19735. 254p. 1980. softcover 8.95 (ISBN 0-664-24347-9, A Geneva Press Pub.). Westminster.
Allen, Ronald J. Contemporary Biblical Interpretation for Preaching. 160p. 1984. pap. 5.95 (ISBN 0-8170-1002-5). Judson.
Appelman, Hyman. Sermon Outlines on Key Bible Themes. (Sermon Outline Ser.). pap. 1.95 (ISBN 0-8010-0003-3). Baker Bk.
Blevins, James L. Revelation. Hayes, John, ed. LC 84-4387. (Preaching Guides Ser.). 132p. (Orig.). 1984. pap. 6.95 (ISBN 0-8042-3250-4). John Knox.
Burghardt, Walter J. Still Proclaiming Your Wonders: Homilies for the Eighties. 256p. (Orig.). 1984. pap. 9.95 (ISBN 0-8091-2632-X). Paulist Pr.
Coniaris, A. Gems from the Sunday Gospel Lessons in the Orthodox Church, Vol. II. pap. 5.95 (ISBN 0-937032-13-1). Light&Life Pub Co MN.
Cox, James W., ed. Biblical Preaching: An Expositor's Treasury. LC 83-10518. 368p. (Orig.). 1983. 19.95 (ISBN 0-664-21397-9). Westminster.
Craddock, Fred B. John. Hayes, John H., ed. LC 82-48095. (Knox Preaching Guides Ser.). 149p. 1982. pap. 6.95. John Knox.
Crouch, Owen. Expository Preaching & Teaching-Hebrews. LC 83-71985. 454p. (Orig.). 1983. pap. 9.95 (ISBN 0-89900-197-1). College Pr Pub.
Demaray, Donald E. Introduction to Homiletics. 140p. 1978. pap. 5.95 (ISBN 0-8010-2892-2). Baker Bk.
--Proclaiming the Truth. 1980. pap. 6.95 (ISBN 0-8010-2898-1). Baker Bk.
Fee, Gordon D. New Testament Exegesis: A Handbook for Students & Pastors. LC 82-24829. (Illus.). 154p. (Orig.). 1983. pap. 8.95 (ISBN 0-664-24469-6). Westminster.
Freeman, Harold. Variety in Biblical Preaching. 192p. 1986. 12.95 (ISBN 0-8499-0562-1). Word Bks.
Fuller, Reginald H. The Use of the Bible in Preaching. LC 80-2377. 80p. (Orig.). 1981. pap. 3.95 (ISBN 0-8006-1447-X, 1-1447). Fortress.
Hawkins, Tomas. Homiletica Practica. 1986. Repr. of 1985 ed. 1.95 (ISBN 0-311-42041-9). Casa Bautista.
Hayden, Edwin V. Preaching Through the Bible. 2nd ed. LC 81-82987. 557p. 1981. pap. 8.95 (ISBN 0-89900-145-9). College Pr Pub.
Jackson, Samuel T. Lincoln's Use of the Bible. LC 74-26790. 1974. Repr. of 1909 ed. lib. bdg. 17.00 (ISBN 0-8414-5329-2). Folcroft.
Keach, Benjamin. Preaching from the Types & Metaphors of the Bible. LC 78-165059. (Kregel Reprint Library). 1038p. 1975. 31.95 (ISBN 0-8254-3008-9). Kregel.
Keck, Leander E. The Bible in the Pulpit: The Renewal of Biblical Preaching. LC 77-12015. 1978. pap. 8.95 (ISBN 0-687-03160-5). Abingdon.
MacLaren, Alexander. Expositions of Holy Scripture, 17 vols. 12830p. 1975. Repr. Set. 295.00 (ISBN 0-8010-5967-4). Baker Bk.
Martin, Ralph P. New Testament Books for Pastor & Teacher. LC 83-21654. 152p. (Orig.). 1984. pap. 8.95 (ISBN 0-664-24511-0). Westminster.
Parker, Joseph. Preaching Through the Bible, 14 vols. 189.50 (ISBN 0-8010-7032-5). Baker Bk.
Robinson, Haddon. Biblical Preaching. LC 80-66776. 1980. 10.95 (ISBN 0-8010-7700-1). Baker Bk.
Spurgeon, Charles H. My Sermon Notes, 4 vols. (Spurgeon Library). 1981. Set. pap. 21.95 (ISBN 0-8010-8201-3); pap. 5.95 ea. Baker Bk.
Talbert, Charles H. Acts. Hayes, John, ed. (Preaching Guides). 120p. (Orig.). 1984. pap. 6.95 (ISBN 0-8042-3231-8). John Knox.
Ward, James. Amos & Hosea. Hayes, John, ed. (Knox Preaching Guides). 96p. 1981. pap. 4.95 (ISBN 0-8042-3225-3). John Knox.
Wardlaw, Don M., ed. Preaching Biblically. LC 83-1276. 174p. (Orig.). 1983. pap. 10.95 (ISBN 0-664-24478-5). Westminster.

BIBLE–ILLUSTRATIONS

see Bible–Pictures, Illustrations, etc.

BIBLE–INDEXES, TOPICAL

Bratcher, R. G., ed. New Testament Index. 37p. 1963. pap. 1.15x (ISBN 0-8267-0003-9, 08507, Pub. by United Bible). Am Bible.
Bratcher, R. G. & Thompson, J. A., eds. Bible Index. 136p. 1970. pap. 2.15x (ISBN 0-8267-0005-5, 08511, Pub. by United Bible). Am Bible.
Crowther, Duane S. Come unto Christ. LC 70-173393. (Scripture Guide Ser.). 240p. 1971. pap. 5.95 (ISBN 0-88290-007-2). Horizon Utah.
--God & His Church. LC 76-173392. (Scripture Guide Ser.). 244p. 1971. pap. 5.95 (ISBN 0-88290-006-4). Horizon Utah.
--The Plan of Salvation & the Future in Prophecy. LC 72-173391. (Scripture Guide Ser.). 228p. 1971. pap. 5.95 (ISBN 0-88290-005-6). Horizon Utah.
Cruden, Alexander. Cruden's Concordance: Handy Reference Edition. (Baker's Paperback Reference Library). 344p. 1982. pap. 7.95 (ISBN 0-8010-2478-1). Baker Bk.
DeHaan, M. R. & Bosch, H. G. Bread for Each Day. large print ed. 1979. Kivar 10.95 (ISBN 0-310-23267-8, 1257L); 13.95 (ISBN 0-310-23260-0, 9510). Zondervan.
Harold Shaw Publishers. Bible Index Pocketbook. LC 81-8940. 192p. 1981. pap. 2.95 (ISBN 0-87788-077-8). Shaw Pubs.
El Indice Biblico de Bolsillo. (PocketPac Ser.). (Span.). 192p. 1984. pap. 2.95 (ISBN 0-87788-219-3). Shaw Pubs.
Katz, Eliezer. A Classified Concordance, 4 vols. Incl. Vol. 1. The Torah. 415p. 1964. 30.00x (ISBN 0-8197-0382-6); Vol. 2. The Early Prophets. 702p. 1967. 30.00x (ISBN 0-8197-0383-4); Vol. 3. The Later Prophets. 683p. 1970. 30.00x (ISBN 0-8197-0384-2). Bloch.
Nave, Orville. Nave's Topical Bible. condensed ed. Moody Press Staff, ed. pap. 4.95 (ISBN 0-8024-0030-2). Moody.
Nave, Orville J. & Coder, S. Maxwell. Nave's Topical Bible. enlarged ed. 1384p. 1975. 21.95 (ISBN 0-8024-5861-0). Moody.
A Periodical & Monographic Index to the Literature on the Gospels & Acts Based on the Files of Ecole Biblique in Jerusalem. LC 78-27276. (Bibliographia Tripotamopolitana: No.3). 1971. 12.00x (ISBN 0-931222-02-8). Pitts Theolog.
Tenney, Merrill C., ed. The Zondervan Pictorial Bible Dictionary. (Illus.). 1969. 21.95 (ISBN 0-310-33160-9, 6750); indexed o.p. 23.95 (ISBN 0-310-33170-6). Zondervan.
Vichas, Robert. Annotated Handbook of Biblical Quotations, Verses, & Parables. LC 85-19346. 411p. 1985. 29.95 (ISBN 0-13-037870-4, Busn). P-H.

BIBLE–INFLUENCE

Gunn, Giles. The Bible & American Arts & Letters. LC 83-5634. (SBL Bible in American Culture Ser.). 256p. 1983. 15.95 (ISBN 0-89130-625-0, 06 12 03). Scholars Pr GA.
Hanson, Paul D. The People Called: The Growth of Community in the Bible. LC 84-47725. 448p. 1986. 29.45 (ISBN 0-06-063700-5, HarpR). Har-Row.
Hatch, Nathan O. & Noll, Mark A., eds. The Bible in America: Essays in Cultural History. LC 81-18751. 1982. 22.50x (ISBN 0-19-503099-0); pap. 6.95 (ISBN 0-19-503100-8). Oxford U Pr.
Johnson, James T., ed. The Bible in American Law, Politics, & Political Rhetoric. LC 83-16327. (The Bible in American Culture Ser.). 1984. pap. 15.95 (ISBN 0-89130-652-8, 06 12 04). Scholars Pr GA.
Lohfink, Gerhard. The Work of God Goes On. LC 86-45202. (The Bible for Christian Life Ser.). 80p. 1987. pap. 4.95 (ISBN 0-8006-2026-7). Fortress.
Mueller, Janel. The Native Tongue & the Word: Developments in English Prose Style, 1380-1580. LC 83-15817. 512p. 1984. lib. bdg. 27.50x (ISBN 0-226-54562-8). U of Chicago Pr.
Phy, Allene S., ed. The Bible & Popular Culture in America. LC 83-11548. (Bible in American Culture Ser.). 1985. 15.95 (ISBN 0-89130-640-4, 06 12 02). Scholars Pr GA.
Roston, Murray. Prophet & Poet: The Bible & the Growth of Romanticism. 1979. Repr. of 1965 ed. lib. bdg. 27.50 (ISBN 0-8495-4610-9). Arden Lib.
Sande, Gene. Bible - Man's Book of Realization. 1981. pap. 2.50 (ISBN 0-87613-095-3). New Age.
Sandeen, Ernest R., ed. The Bible & Social Reform. LC 81-71386. (The Bible in American Culture Ser.). 196p. 1982. 12.95 (ISBN 0-8006-0611-6, 1-611). Fortress.
Schoffler, Herbert. Abendland und Altes Testament. pap. 10.00 (ISBN 0-384-54210-7). Johnson Repr.
Ullendorff, Edward. Ethiopia & the Bible. (British Academy Ser). 1968. 29.95x (ISBN 0-19-725904-9). Oxford U Pr.
Warshaw, Thayer S. A Compact Guide to Bible Based Beliefs. LC 80-19820. 49p. (Orig.). 1981. pap. 2.25 (ISBN 0-687-09254-X). Abingdon.

BIBLE–INSPIRATION

see also Bible–Evidences, Authority, etc.; Inspiration; Revelation

Abraham, William J. Divine Inspiration of Holy Scripture. 1981. 32.00x (ISBN 0-19-826659-6). Oxford U Pr.
Achtemeier, Paul J. The Inspiration of Scripture: Problems & Proposals. LC 80-10286. (Biblical Perspectives on Current Issues). 188p. 1980. pap. 8.95 (ISBN 0-664-24313-4). Westminster.
Bender, H. S. Biblical Revelation & Inspiration. pap. 1.45 (ISBN 0-8361-1322-5). Herald Pr.
Betzer, Dan. Countdown. LC 79-53943. 112p. 1979. pap. 1.95 (ISBN 0-88243-481-0, 02-0481). Gospel Pub.
Boling, Robert G. & Wright, Ernest. Joshua, Vol. 6. LC 79-6583. (Anchor Bible Ser.). (Illus.). 432p. 1982. 18.00 (ISBN 0-385-00034-0). Doubleday.
The Bowl Judgments. Date not set. pap. 0.95 (ISBN 0-937408-11-5). GMI Pubns Inc.
Bratcher, R. G. A Translator's Guide to the Revelation to John. LC 84-8670. (Helps for Translators Ser.). viii, 204p. 1984. flexible bdg. 3.50x (ISBN 0-8267-0195-7, 08790, Pub. by United Bible). Am Bible.
Buckingham, Jamie. Risky Living: The Key to Inner Healing. LC 76-12033. 1976. (Pub. by Logos); pap. 4.95 (ISBN 0-88270-177-0). Bridge Pub.
Clark, Vivian. God's Remedy for Depression. (Direction Bks.). (Orig.). 1980. pap. 3.50 (ISBN 0-8010-2444-7). Baker Bk.
Clevenger & Hill, eds. Bible Characters. 1973. pap. 1.50 (ISBN 0-88428-008-X, 161). Parchment Pr.
Collins, Adela Y. Crisis & Catharsis: The Power of the Apocalypse. LC 83-26084. 180p. 1984. pap. 11.95 (ISBN 0-664-24521-8). Westminster.
Gaussen, L. Divine Inspiration of the Bible. LC 75-155249. (Kregel Reprint Library). 382p. 1971. 12.95 (ISBN 0-8254-2707-X). Kregel.
Getz, Gene A. When You Feel You Haven't Got It. rev. ed. LC 86-540. (Biblical Renewal Ser.). 160p. 1986. pap. 5.95 (ISBN 0-8307-1123-6, 5418757). Regal.
Godfrey, W. Robert & Boyd, Jesse L., III, eds. Through Christ's Word: A Festschrift for Philip E. Hughes. 272p. (Orig.). 1985. pap. 10.95 (ISBN 0-87552-274-2). Presby & Reformed.
Harris, R. Laird. Inspiration & Canonicity of the Bible. (Contemporary Evangelical Perspectives Ser.). kivar 8.95 (ISBN 0-310-25891-X, 9766P). Zondervan.
Hodges, Serena M. Look on the Fields. 202p. 1956. pap. 2.00 (ISBN 0-88243-540-X, 02-0540). Gospel Pub.
Huffman, Vicki. The Best of Times: Ecclesiastes 3: 1-8. LC 85-29087. 1986. pap. 5.95 (ISBN 0-8054-1234-4). Broadman.
Humphreys, Alice L. Heaven in My Hand. 5.95 (ISBN 0-8042-2352-1). John Knox.
Hunter, John E. Jesus Speaks Today. LC 81-68042. 1982. pap. 4.25 (ISBN 0-8054-5184-6). Broadman.
Infant Joe. 128p. Date not set. pap. 4.95 (ISBN 0-937408-24-7). GMI Pubns Inc.
Lewis, John M. Revelation, Inspiration, Scripture. LC 83-71822. (Layman's Library of Christian Doctrine Ser.). 1985. 5.95 (ISBN 0-8054-1633-1). Broadman.
Maston, T. B. Treasures from the Holy Scripture. (Orig.). 1987. pap. 3.25 (ISBN 0-8054-5043-2). Broadman.
Newman, John H. The Theological Papers of John Henry Newman: On Biblical Inspiration & on Infallibility, Vol. 2. Holmes, J. Derek, ed. 1979. text ed. 22.50x (ISBN 0-19-920081-5). Oxford U Pr.
Orchard, R. E. This Is Our Hope. 150p. 1966. 3.95 (ISBN 0-88243-617-1, 02-0617). Gospel Pub.
Pache, Rene. Inspiration & Authority of Scripture. 1970. pap. 10.95 (ISBN 0-8024-4091-6). Moody.
Phillips, Wade H. God the Church & Revelation. 376p. (Orig.). 1986. pap. 8.95 (ISBN 0-934942-60-9, 4048). White Wing Pub.
Pink, Arthur W. Divine Inspiration of the Bible. pap. 4.50 (ISBN 0-685-19827-8). Reiner.
Pinnock, Clark H. Biblical Revelation. 2nd ed. 272p. (Orig.). 1985. pap. 7.95 (ISBN 0-87552-371-4). Presby & Reformed.
--Defense of Biblical Infallibility. 1967. pap. 1.75 (ISBN 0-87552-350-1). Presby & Reformed.
Price, Eugenia. Early Will I Seek Thee: Journal of a Heart That Longed & Found. LC 82-22179. 188p. 1983. pap. 6.95 (ISBN 0-385-27864-0, Dial). Doubleday.
Ravenhill, Leonard. Tried & Transfigured. LC 81-71752. 144p. 1982. pap. 4.95 (ISBN 0-87123-544-7, 210544). Bethany Hse.
The Seven Seal Judgements. Date not set. pap. 0.95 (ISBN 0-686-88510-4). GMI Pubns Inc.
Stalker, James. Living the Christ Life. LC 81-81097. (The Shepherd Illustrated Classics Ser.). (Illus.). 1981. pap. 5.95 (ISBN 0-87983-259-2). Keats.
Stott, John R. God's Book for God's People. LC 82-21203. 96p. 1982. pap. 2.95 (ISBN 0-87784-396-1). Inter-Varsity.
Sun Clothed Woman. Date not set. pap. 0.95 (ISBN 0-937408-08-5). GMI Pubns Inc.
Taylor, Robert R., Jr. Jesus Christ Hope of the Homes. 2.50 (ISBN 0-89315-131-9). Lambert Bk.
The Trumpet Judgments. Date not set. pap. 0.95 (ISBN 0-937408-10-7). GMI Pubns Inc.
The Two Witnesses. Date not set. pap. 0.95 (ISBN 0-937408-12-3). GMI Pubns Inc.
Warfield, Benjamin B. Inspiration & Authority of the Bible. 2nd ed. 1948. 12.95 (ISBN 0-87552-527-X). Presby & Reformed.
Westminster Seminary Faculty Symposium. Infallible Word. Woolley, Paul, ed. pap. 9.95 (ISBN 0-87552-543-1). Presby & Reformed.
Whaley, K. A. Basic Bible Doctrines for Victorious Living. 87p. 1981. pap. 7.95 (ISBN 0-686-35778-7). First Baptist.
Williams, Ernest S. Word of Encouragement. 25p. pap. 0.40 (ISBN 0-88243-840-9, 02-0840). Gospel Pub.
Williams, Maxine. Eyes Have It. LC 62-15648. 1962. pap. 1.75 (ISBN 0-88243-495-0, 02-0495). Gospel Pub.
Young, Edward J. Thy Word Is Truth. 1957. pap. 5.95 (ISBN 0-8028-1244-9). Eerdmans.

BIBLE–INTERLINEAR TRANSLATIONS

Kohlenberger, John R., III. The NIV Interlinear Hebrew-English Old Testament. 544p. 1980. Vol. 1. 24.95 (ISBN 0-310-38880-5, 6280); Vol. 2. 24.95 (ISBN 0-310-38890-2, 6281); Vol. 3. 24.95 (ISBN 0-310-44200-1, 6282). Zondervan.

Marshall, Alfred. Interlinear Greek-English New Testament. 27.95 (ISBN 0-310-20380-5, 6254, Pub. by Bagster). Zondervan.

--RSV Interlinear Greek, New Testament. 24.95 (ISBN 0-310-20410-0, 10108). Zondervan.

BIBLE–INTERPRETATION

see Bible–Commentaries; Bible–Criticism, Interpretation, etc.; Bible–Hermeneutics

BIBLE–INTRODUCTIONS

Arnold, Eberhard. Inner Land: A Guide into the Heart & Soul of the Bible. LC 74-30356. 608p. 1976. 12.00 (ISBN 0-87486-152-7). Plough.

Baxter, J. Sidlow. Explore the Book. 36.95 (ISBN 0-310-20620-0, 6729). Zondervan.

Bergant, Dianne. Introduction to the Bible. (Bible Commentary Ser.). 72p. 1985. pap. 2.95 (ISBN 0-8146-1369-1). Liturgical Pr.

Blair, Edward P. Abingdon Bible Handbook. rev. ed. (Illus.). 528p. 1982. pap. 23.95 (ISBN 0-687-00170-6). Abingdon.

Chase, Mary E. Bible & the Common Reader. rev. ed. 1962. pap. 4.95 (ISBN 0-02-084390-9, Collier). Macmillan.

Cook, Stanley A. An Introduction to the Bible. LC 78-12762. 1979. Repr. of 1945 ed. lib. bdg. 22.50x (ISBN 0-313-21028-4, COIB). Greenwood.

Cronk, George. The Message of the Bible: An Orthodox Christian Perspective. LC 82-7355. 293p. (Orig.). 1982. pap. 8.95 (ISBN 0-913836-94-X). St Vladimirs.

Dentan, Robert C. Holy Scriptures: A Survey. (Orig.). 1949. pap. 5.95 (ISBN 0-8164-2031-9, SP1, HarpR). Har-Row.

Drewes, C. F. Introduction to the Books of the Bible. 1929. 4.95 (ISBN 0-570-03185-0, 12-2110). Concordia.

Eller, Meredith F. The Beginnings of the Christian Religion: A Guide to the History & Literature of Judaism & Christianity. 1958. 16.95x (ISBN 0-8084-0392-3); pap. 12.95x (ISBN 0-8084-0393-1). New Coll U Pr.

Farrell, Melvin L. Getting to Know the Bible: An Introduction to Sacred Scripture for Catholics. 112p. 1986. pap. 5.95 (ISBN 0-937997-01-3). HI-Time Pub.

Fesperman, Francis I. From Torah to Apocalypse: An Introduction to the Bible. 334p. 1983. pap. text ed. 15.25 (ISBN 0-8191-3555-0). U Pr of Amer.

Foreman, Kenneth J., et al. Introduction to the Bible. Kelly, Balmer H., et al, eds. LC 59-10454. (Layman's Bible Commentary, Vol. 1). 1959. pap. 4.95 (ISBN 0-8042-3061-7). John Knox.

Geisler, Norman L. & Nix, William E. General Introduction to the Bible. rev. ed. LC 68-18890. 1968. 29.95 (ISBN 0-8024-2916-5). Moody.

Goodspeed, Edgar J. Story of the Bible. LC 36-21666. Repr. of 1967 ed. 44.00 (ISBN 0-8357-9657-4, 2013612). Bks Demand UMI.

Harris, R. Laird. Your Bible: An Introduction to the Word. rev. ed. 96p. 1976. pap. text ed. 4.95 (ISBN 0-910566-12-7); instr's. guide 5.95 (ISBN 0-910566-29-1). Evang Tchr.

Hauer, Christian E. & Young, William A. An Introduction to the Bible: A Journey into Three Worlds. (Illus.). 400p. 1985. text ed. 29.67 (ISBN 0-13-478488-X). P-H.

Hayes, John H. Introduction to the Bible. LC 76-105395. (Illus.). 556p. 1971. pap. 13.95 (ISBN 0-664-24883-7). Westminster.

Hughes, Gerald & Travis, Stephen. Harper's Introduction to the Bible. LC 80-8607. (Illus.). 144p. (Orig.). 1981. pap. 11.95 (ISBN 0-06-064078-2, RD 350, HarpR). Har-Row.

Introduction to Books of the Bible. 7.00 (ISBN 0-8198-3605-2); 6.00 (ISBN 0-8198-3606-0). Dghtrs St Paul.

Jenkins, Simon. Kick-Starting the Bible. (Illus.). 160p. 1987. pap. 5.95 (ISBN 0-7459-1004-1). Lion USA.

Jensen, Irving L. How to Profit from Bible Reading. (Orig.). 1985. pap. 5.95 (ISBN 0-8024-0460-X). Moody.

Kilgallen, John J. First Corinthians: An Introduction & Study Guide. (Illus.). 128p. (Orig.). 1987. pap. 5.95 (ISBN 0-8091-2847-0). Paulist Pr.

Landis, Benson Y. Outline of the Bible: Book by Book. (Orig.). 1963. pap. 5.95 (ISBN 0-06-463263-6, EH 263, B&N Bks). Har-Row.

McElrath, William N. Bible Guidebook. LC 72-79174. 144p. 1972. 9.95 (ISBN 0-8054-4410-6, 4244-10). Broadman.

Phillips, John. Exploring the Scriptures. 1965. pap. 9.95 (ISBN 0-8024-2434-1). Moody.

Richards, Lawrence O. The Word Bible Handbook. 1982. 10.95 (ISBN 0-8499-0279-7). Word Bks.

Ryrie, Charles. Ryrie's Concise Guide to the Bible. LC 83-71924. 163p. (Orig.). 1983. pap. 5.95 (ISBN 0-86605-121-X). Heres Life.

Ryrie, Charles C. You Mean the Bible Teaches That. 1974. pap. 5.95 (ISBN 0-8024-9828-0). Moody.

Scroggie, W. Graham. Know Your Bible. 608p. 1965. 23.95 (ISBN 0-8007-0169-0). Revell.

Selby, D. J. & West, J. K. Introduction to the Bible, 2 Vols. 1971. Set. text ed. write for info. (ISBN 0-02-408850-1). Macmillan.

Taylor, Justin. As It Was Written: An Introduction to the Bible. 176p. 1987. pap. 7.95 (ISBN 0-8091-2843-8). Paulist Pr.

Timbuktu, Adib K. What Every Christian Should Know about the Bible. 1984. 6.95 (ISBN 0-8062-2308-1). Carlton.

BIBLE–INTRODUCTIONS–APOCRYPHA AND APOCRYPHAL BOOKS

Eissfeldt, Otto. The Old Testament: An Introduction. LC 65-15399. 1965. 14.95xi (ISBN 0-06-062171-0, RD162, HarpR). Har-Row.

James, M. R., ed. Apocrypha Anecdota. (Texts & Studies Ser.: No. 1, Vol. 2, Pt. 3). pap. 19.00 (ISBN 0-8115-1686-5). Kraus Repr.

--Apocrypha Anecdota: Second Series. (Texts & Studies Ser.: No. 1, Vol. 5, Pt. 1). pap. 19.00 (ISBN 0-8115-1696-2). Kraus Repr.

Pfeiffer, Robert H. History of New Testament Times. LC 77-138125. 561p. 1972. Repr. of 1949 ed. lib. bdg. 23.00x (ISBN 0-8371-3559-1, PFNT). Greenwood.

BIBLE–INTRODUCTIONS–N. T.

Here are entered Introductions to the New Testament as a whole, or to any part except the Gospels, which are listed separately below.

Barclay, William. Introduction to John & the Acts of the Apostles. LC 75-38902. 352p. 1976. softcover 5.95 (ISBN 0-664-24771-7). Westminster.

--The Men, the Meaning, the Message of the New Testament Books. LC 77-22184. 156p. 1978. pap. 4.95 (ISBN 0-664-24188-3). Westminster.

Bauman, Edward W. An Introduction to the New Testament. LC 61-10616. 190p. 1979. pap. 5.95 (ISBN 0-664-24279-0). Westminster.

Collins, Raymond F. Introduction to the New Testament. 480p. 1987. pap. 10.95 (ISBN 0-385-23534-8, Im). Doubleday.

Cullmann, Oscar. New Testament: An Introduction for the General Reader. LC 68-12796. 138p. 1968. pap. 8.95 (ISBN 0-664-24817-9). Westminster.

Daughters of St. Paul. Introductions to the Books of the New Testament. 1977. pap. 1.00 (ISBN 0-8198-0421-5). Dghtrs St Paul.

Dunnett, Walter. Outline of New Testament Survey. (Orig.). 1960. pap. 5.95 (ISBN 0-8024-6245-6). Moody.

Dunnett, Walter M. New Testament Survey. LC 63-7410. 96p. 1963. pap. text ed. 4.95 (ISBN 0-910566-03-8); Perfect bdg. instr's. guide 5.95 (ISBN 0-910566-19-4). Evang Tchr.

Harrison, Everett F. Introduction to the New Testament. 1964. 22.95 (ISBN 0-8028-3106-0). Eerdmans.

Harvey, A. E. New English Bible Companion to the New Testament: The Gospels. 400p. 1972. pap. 9.95 (ISBN 0-521-09689-8). Cambridge U Pr.

Hunter, Archibald M. Introducing the New Testament. 3rd. rev. ed. LC 72-7110. 224p. 1973. pap. 7.95 (ISBN 0-664-24965-5). Westminster.

Kee, Howard C. Understanding the New Testament. 4th ed. (Illus.). 464p. 1983. text ed. 33.00 (ISBN 0-13-936591-5). P-H.

Koester, Helmut. Introduction to the New Testament. 1982. Vol. 1: History, Culture, & Religion of the Hellenistic Age. 24.95 (ISBN 0-89925-198-6); Vol. 2: History & Literature of Early Christianity. 22.95 (ISBN 0-89925-199-4). De Gruyter.

Marxsen, Willi. Introduction to the New Testament: An Approach to Its Problems. Buswell, G., tr. from Ger. LC 68-15419. 304p. 1968. pap. 8.50 (ISBN 0-8006-1181-0, 1-1181). Fortress.

Miller, Adam W. Introduction to the New Testament. rev. ed. 1984. pap. 1.50 (ISBN 0-87162-141-X, D2403). Warner Pr.

Moffatt, James. An Introduction to the Literature of the New Testament. 704p. 1981. 19.95 (ISBN 0-567-07213-4, Pub. by T & T Clark Ltd UK). Fortress.

Morgan, Carl H. Layman's Introduction to the New Testament. LC 68-22756. (Illus.). 1968. pap. text ed. 4.95 (ISBN 0-8170-0399-1). Judson.

Peake, Arthur S. A Critical Introduction to the New Testament. 1914. lib. bdg. 25.00 (ISBN 0-8482-9974-4). Norwood Edns.

Pfeiffer, Robert H. History of New Testament Times. LC 77-138125. 561p. 1972. Repr. of 1949 ed. lib. bdg. 23.00x (ISBN 0-8371-3559-1, PFNT). Greenwood.

Stott, John R. Basic Introduction to the New Testament. pap. 5.95 (ISBN 0-8028-1190-6). Eerdmans.

Thiessen, Henry C. Introduction to the New Testament. 1943. 14.95 (ISBN 0-8028-3259-8). Eerdmans.

Tyndale, William. A Compendious Introduccion Unto the Pistle off Paul to the Romayns. LC 74-28890. (English Experience Ser.: No. 767). 1975. Repr. 3.50 (ISBN 90-221-0767-1). Walter J Johnson.

BIBLE–INTRODUCTIONS–N. T. GOSPELS

Barclay, William. Introduction to the First Three Gospels: A Revised Edition of the First Three Gospels. LC 75-37545. 314p. 1976. pap. 9.95 (ISBN 0-664-24798-9). Westminster.

Green, Joel B. How to Read the Gospels & Acts. LC 87-5572. (The How to Read Ser.). 180p. (Orig.). 1987. pap. 6.95 (ISBN 0-87784-940-4). Inter-Varsity.

Heim, Ralph D. Harmony of the Gospels. LC 47-2807. 228p. 1974. pap. 6.95 (ISBN 0-8006-1494-1, 1-1494). Fortress.

Nickle, Keith F. The Synoptic Gospels: An Introduction. LC 79-92069. (Orig.). 1980. pap. 9.95 (ISBN 0-8042-0422-5). John Knox.

Scroggie, W. Graham. Guide to the Gospels. 664p. 1975. 23.95 (ISBN 0-8007-0127-5). Revell.

BIBLE–INTRODUCTIONS–O. T.

Here are listed Introductions to the Old Testament as a whole, or to any part except Apocryphal writings, which are listed separately under Bible–Introductions–Apocrypha and Apocryphal Books.

Archer, Gleason L. A Survey of Old Testament Introduction. LC 64-20988. 582p. 1973. 16.95 (ISBN 0-8024-8447-6). Moody.

Bullock, C. Hassell. An Introduction to the Old Testament Prophetic Books. 1986. text ed. 19.95 (ISBN 0-8024-4142-4). Moody.

Cate, Robert L. An Introduction to the Old Testament & Its Study. (Orig.). 1987. 19.95 (ISBN 0-8054-1233-6). Broadman.

Childs, Brevard S. Introduction to the Old Testament As Scripture. LC 78-14665. 688p. 1979. 29.95 (ISBN 0-8006-0532-2, 1-532). Fortress.

Driver, S. R. An Introduction to the Literature of the Old Testament. 640p. 1913. 19.95 (ISBN 0-567-07205-3, Pub. by T & T Clark Ltd UK). Fortress.

--Introduction to the Literature of the Old Testament. 16.50 (ISBN 0-8446-1998-1). Peter Smith.

Eissfeldt, Otto. The Old Testament: An Introduction. LC 65-15399. 1965. 14.95xi (ISBN 0-06-062171-0, RD162, HarpR). Har-Row.

Green, William H. General Introduction to the Old Testament: The Canon. (Twin Brooks Ser.). 1980. pap. 6.95 (ISBN 0-8010-3755-7). Baker Bk.

Hayes, John H. Understanding the Psalms. LC 75-22034. 128p. 1976. pap. 4.95 (ISBN 0-8170-0683-4). Judson.

Hummel, Horace. The Word Becoming Flesh. 1979. 22.95 (ISBN 0-570-03273-3, 15-2718). Concordia.

Laurin, Robert B. The Layman's Introduction to the Old Testament. 1970. pap. 4.95 (ISBN 0-8170-0451-3). Judson.

Miller, Adam W. Introduction to the Old Testament. 1981. pap. 1.75 (ISBN 0-87162-193-2, D2401). Warner Pr.

Rendtorff, Rolf. The Old Testament: An Introduction. Bowden, John, tr. LC 85-47728. (Ger.). 1986. 22.95 (ISBN 0-8006-0750-3). Fortress.

Robinson, George L. Twelve Minor Prophets. 5.95 (ISBN 0-8010-7669-2). Baker Bk.

Schwartzman, Sylvan D. & Spiro, Jack D. Living Bible: A Topical Approach to the Jewish Scriptures. (Illus.). 1962. text ed. 5.00 (ISBN 0-8074-0097-1, 161751). UAHC.

Sundberg, A. C., Jr. Old Testament of the Early Church: A Study of Canon. (Harvard Theological Studies). 1964. 24.00 (ISBN 0-527-01020-0). Kraus Repr.

Trawick, Buckner B. Bible As Literature: Old Testament & the Apocrypha. 2nd ed. 1970. pap. 5.95 (ISBN 0-06-460056-4, CO 56, B&N Bks). Har-Row.

West, James. Introduction to the Old Testament. 2nd ed. 1981. text ed. write for info. (ISBN 0-02-425920-9). Macmillan.

Williams, Jay G. Understanding the Old Testament. LC 74-162825. 1972. pap. 6.95 (ISBN 0-8120-0424-8). Barron.

Winward, Stephen F. Guide to the Prophets. LC 68-55819. 1976. pap. 8.95 (ISBN 0-8042-0131-5). John Knox.

Wood, James D. Wisdom Literature: An Introduction. LC 67-108276. (Studies in Theology: No. 64). 1967. text ed. 8.50x (ISBN 0-8401-6064-X). A R Allenson.

Yoder, Sanford C. He Gave Some Prophets: The Old Testament Prophets & Their Message. LC 64-18733. 256p. 1964. 7.95 (ISBN 0-8361-1496-5). Herald Pr.

Young, Edward J. Introduction to the Old Testament. rev ed. 1958. 14.95 (ISBN 0-8028-3310-1). Eerdmans.

BIBLE–JUVENILE LITERATURE

see also Bible Stories

Alden, Laura. I Read about God's Care: Grade 2. rev. ed. (Basic Bible Readers Ser.). (Illus.). 128p. 1983. text ed. 7.95 (ISBN 0-87239-662-2, 2952). Standard Pub.

Alexander, Pat, retold by. Nelson Children's Bible. 6.95 (ISBN 0-8407-5238-5). Nelson.

Allen, J. Catling. Pictorial Bible Atlas. 14.95 (ISBN 0-7175-0991-5); pap. 9.95 (ISBN 0-7175-0857-9). Dufour.

Allen, J. F., et al. Illustrated Bible for Children. (Illus.). 9.95 (ISBN 0-8407-5264-4). Nelson.

Amstutz, Beverly. Benjamin & the Bible Donkeys. (Illus.). 36p. 1981. pap. 2.50x (ISBN 0-937836-03-6). Precious Res.

Auld, A. Graeme. First & Second Kings. LC 86-15658. (The Daily Study Bible - Old Testament Ser.). 266p. 1986. 15.95 (ISBN 0-664-21836-9); pap. 8.95 (ISBN 0-664-24585-4). Westminster.

Barr, Robert R. What Is the Bible? A Nazareth Book. 128p. 1984. pap. 4.95 (ISBN 0-86683-727-2, HarpR). Har-Row.

Barrett, Marsha. Early Christians: Workers for Jesus. (BibLearn Ser.). (Illus.). 1979. 5.95 (ISBN 0-8054-4247-2, 4242-47). Broadman.

Bartholomew. The Bible Tells Me. 1982. pap. 0.85 (ISBN 0-570-04074-4, 56-1377). Concordia.

Baw, Cindy & Brownlow, Paul C. Children of the Bible: Twenty-Six Exciting Stories about Children of the Bible. (Illus.). 1984. 10.95 (ISBN 0-915720-19-1). Brownlow Pub Co.

Baxendale, Jean. Preschool Bible Activities, 4 vols. (Illus.). 24p. (Orig.). 1982. No. 1. pap. 1.50 (ISBN 0-87239-487-5, 2459); No. 2. pap. 1.50 (ISBN 0-87239-488-3, 2460); No. 3. pap. 1.25 (ISBN 0-87239-489-1, 2461); No. 4. pap. 1.50 (ISBN 0-87239-490-5, 2462). Standard Pub.

Beers, V. Gilbert. Little Talks about God & You. 224p. (Orig.). 1986. pap. 7.95 (ISBN 0-89081-519-4). Harvest Hse.

--My Picture Bible to See & to Share. 1982. text ed. 12.95 (ISBN 0-88207-818-6). Victor Bks.

Beers, V. Gilbert & Beers, Ronald A. Bible Stories to Live By. LC 82-84616. (Illus.). 192p. 1983. 12.95 (ISBN 0-89840-044-9). Heres Life.

Behnke, John. Ten Plus One Bible Stories from Creation to Samson, Retold in Everyday Language for Today's Children. LC 83-82022. (Orig.). 1984. pap. 2.95 (ISBN 0-8091-6552-X). Paulist Pr.

Bennett, Marian. Bible Numbers. (Little Happy Day Bks.). (Illus.). 24p. (Orig.). 1983. pap. 0.49 (ISBN 0-87239-653-3, 2123). Standard Pub.

Bennett, Marian, compiled by. Bible Memory Verses. (Little Happy Day Bks.). (Illus.). 24p. (Orig.). 1983. pap. 0.49 (ISBN 0-87239-652-5, 2122). Standard Pub.

Berube, Francoise D. & Berube, John-Paul. Sacrament of Peace. Ages 7-8. childs bk. 2.95 (ISBN 0-8091-9166-0); Ages 9-12. childs bk. 2.95 (ISBN 0-8091-9167-9); director's guide 4.95 (ISBN 0-8091-9169-5). Paulist Pr.

Biblelearn, 24 vol. set. 1979. 129.95 (ISBN 0-8054-4257-X, 4242-57). Broadman.

Birky, Lela. Truth for Life Bible Studies. pap. write for info (ISBN 0-686-15481-9). Rod & Staff.

Boehlke, Neal A. Man Who Met Jesus at Bethesda. (Arch Bk.). 1981. pap. 0.99 (ISBN 0-570-06143-1, 59-1260). Concordia.

Booth, Julianne. Books of the New Testament. (Arch Book Supplement Ser.). 1981. pap. 0.99 (ISBN 0-570-06150-4, 59-1305). Concordia.

Bretschneider, Diana. Bible Puzzle Time, Friends of God. 16p. 1983. pap. 0.60 (ISBN 0-87239-655-X, 2303). Standard Pub.

Bull, Norman. Church of Jesus Begins. (Bible Story & Its Background Ser.: Vol. 7). pap. 9.95 (ISBN 0-7175-0983-4). Dufour.

--Church of Jesus Grows. (Bible Story & Its Background Ser.: Vol. 8). pap. 9.95 (ISBN 0-7175-0454-9). Dufour.

Burgess, Beverly C. God Is My Best Friend. (Illus.). 32p. (Orig.). 1986. pap. 1.98 (ISBN 0-89274-293-3). Harrison Hse.

Burrage, Barbara. The Bible Quiz Book. 1979. pap. 2.95 (ISBN 0-8192-1256-3). Morehouse.

--Bible Quizzerama Puzzle Book. 48p. (Orig.). 1981. pap. 1.95 (ISBN 0-87239-446-8, 2836). Standard Pub.

Carl, Angela R. & Holmes, Alice C. Growing with Bible Heroes: Grade 4. rev. ed. Miller, Marge, ed. (Basic Bible Readers Ser.). (Illus.). 128p. 1983. text ed. 7.95 (ISBN 0-87239-664-9, 2954). Standard Pub.

Carlson, John. Getting More From Your Bible Reading. LC 82-14563. 137p. (Orig.). 1982. pap. 3.95 (ISBN 0-87123-256-1, 210256). Bethany Hse.

Carwell, L'Ann. Baby's First Book About Creation. (Illus.). 1979. 1.25 (ISBN 0-570-08000-2, 56-1325). Concordia.

Coleman, William. How, Why, When, Where, Bks. 1 & 2. 23p. 1984. Bk. 1. pap. 2.95 (ISBN 0-89191-717-9, 57174, Chariot Bks.); Bk. 2. pap. 2.95 (ISBN 0-89191-942-2, 59428, Chariot Bks.). Cook.
--The Who, What, When, Where Bible Busy Book. 32p. 1984. pap. 1.50 (ISBN 0-89191-853-1). Cook.
Collins, Marjorie. Bible Quizzes on Bible Themes. 48p. 1983. pap. 1.95 (ISBN 0-87239-658-4, 3138). Standard Pub.
Conn, Charles P. & Conn, Charles W. The Relevant Record. LC 76-2969. (Illus.). 1976. pap. 1.99 (ISBN 0-87148-732-2). Pathway Pr.
Corbin, Linda & Dys, Pat. Following Jesus: The Book of Acts, Pt. 1. (Illus.). 48p. 1986. wkbk. 2.95 (ISBN 0-87403-053-6, 3197). Standard Pub.
--Following Jesus: The Book of Acts, Pt. 2. (Illus.). 48p. 1986. wkbk. 2.95 (ISBN 0-87403-054-4, 3308). Standard Pub.
Coriell, Ron & Coriell, Rebekah. A Child's Book of Character Building, Bk. Two. 128p. 1981. 10.95 (ISBN 0-8007-1265-X). Revell.
Crain, Steve. Bible Fun Book, No. 8. (Activity Book Ser.). 32p. (Orig.). 1981. pap. 0.99 saddle-stitched (ISBN 0-87123-772-5, 220772). Bethany Hse.
Daniel, Rebecca. Book VIII-More Parables. (Life of Jesus Ser.). 32p. (YA) 1984. wkbk. 3.95 (ISBN 0-86653-229-3). Good Apple.
Daniels, Rebecca. Book I-His Birth. (Life of Jesus Ser.). 32p. (YA) 1984. wkbk. 3.95 (ISBN 0-86653-213-7). Good Apple.
--Book II-His Boyhood. (Life of Jesus Ser.). 32p. (YA) 1984. wkbk. 3.95 (ISBN 0-86653-223-4). Good Apple.
--Book III-Gathering His Disciples. (Life of Jesus Ser.). 32p. (YA) 1984. wkbk. 3.95 (ISBN 0-86653-224-2). Good Apple.
--Book IV-the Teacher. (Life of Jesus Ser.). 32p. (YA) 1984. wkbk. 3.95 (ISBN 0-86653-225-0). Good Apple.
--Book IX-Prophacies Fulfilled. (Life of Jesus Ser.). 32p. (YA) 1984. wkbk. 3.95 (ISBN 0-86653-230-7). Good Apple.
--Book V-The Healer. (Life of Jesus Ser.). 32p. (YA) wkbk. 3.95 (ISBN 0-86653-226-9). Good Apple.
--Book VI-His Miracles. (Life of Jesus Ser.). 32p. (YA) 1984. wkbk. 3.95 (ISBN 0-86653-227-7). Good Apple.
--Book VII-Parables. (Life of Jesus Ser.). 32p. (YA) 1984. wkbk. 3.95 (ISBN 0-86653-228-5). Good Apple.
--Book XI-His Last Hours. (Life of Jesus Ser.). 32p. (YA) 1984. wkbk. 3.95 (ISBN 0-86653-232-3). Good Apple.
--Book XII-His Resurection. (Life of Jesus Ser.). 32p. (YA) 1984. wkbk. 3.95 (ISBN 0-86653-233-1). Good Apple.
Daughters of St. Paul. Adventures of Peter & Paul. (Illus.). 120p. 1984. 10.00 (ISBN 0-8198-0726-5). Dghtrs St Paul.
Davidson, Alice J. Psalms & Proverbs. (Alice in Bibleland Ser.). (Illus.). 32p. 1984. 4.95 (ISBN 0-8378-5069-X). Gibson.
--The Story of Baby Jesus. (Alice in Bibleland Ser.). (Illus.). 32p. 1985. 4.95 (ISBN 0-8378-5072-X). Gibson.
--The Story of Baby Moses. (Alice in Bibleland Ser.). (Illus.). 32p. 1985. 4.95 (ISBN 0-8378-5071-1). Gibson.
--The Story of David & Goliath. (Alice in Bibleland Ser.). (Illus.). 32p. 1985. 4.95 (ISBN 0-8378-5070-3). Gibson.
--The Story of the Loaves & Fishes. (Alice in Bibleland Ser.). (Illus.). 32p. 1985. 4.95 (ISBN 0-8378-5073-8). Gibson.
Davidson, Robert. Ecclesiastes & the Song of Solomon. LC 86-15659. (The Daily Study Bible - Old Testament Ser.). 168p. 1986. 14.95 (ISBN 0-664-21838-5); pap. 7.95 (ISBN 0-664-24589-7). Westminster.
Degering, Etta B. Once upon a Bible Time. Van Dolson, Bobbie J., ed. LC 76-14118. (Illus.). 1976. 7.95 (ISBN 0-8280-0052-2). Review & Herald.
De la Mare, Walter. Stories from the Bible. (Illus.). 418p. 1985. pap. 6.95 (ISBN 0-571-11086-X). Faber & Faber.
DePaola, Tomie. Noah & the Ark. (Illus.). 40p. (Orig.). 1983. 12.95 (ISBN 0-86683-699-3, AY8268, HarpR); pap. 5.95. Har-Row.
De Vries, Anne. Story Bible for Young Children. (Illus.). 1986. pap. 9.95 (ISBN 0-8010-2963-5). Baker Bk.
Draper, Edythe. Wonder. 448p. 1984. 5.95 (ISBN 0-8423-8385-9). Tyndale.
Dugan, LeRoy, illus. Heroes of the New Testament Coloring Book. (Illus.). 96p. (Orig.). 1981. saddle-stitched 2.95 (ISBN 0-87123-701-6). Bethany Hse.
--Heroes of the Old Testament, No. 3. (Illus.). 96p. (Orig.). 1981. pap. 2.95 saddle stitched (ISBN 0-87123-703-2). Bethany Hse.
DuPree, Sherry S. & Noble, E. Myron, eds. Bible Lessons for Youth, Bk. I. 40p. (Orig.). 1987. pap. text ed. 2.95 (ISBN 0-9616056-4-2). Mid Atl Reg Pr.
Ellis, Joyce & Lynn, Claire. Bible Bees. (Illus.). 36p. 1981. 1.25 (ISBN 0-89323-049-9). Bible Memory.
Evslin, Bernard. Signs & Wonders: Tales from the Old Testament. (Illus.). 352p. 1982. 17.95 (ISBN 0-02-734100-3, Four Winds). Macmillan.
Falk, Cathy. God's Care. (Bible Activities for Little People Ser.: Bk. 1). 24p. (Orig.). 1983. pap. 1.50 (ISBN 0-87239-676-2, 2451). Standard Pub.
--God's Friends. (Bible Activities for Little People Ser.: BK. 2). 24p. (Orig.). 1983. pap. 1.50 (ISBN 0-87239-677-0, 2452). Standard Pub.
--God's Son. (Bible Activities for Little People Ser.: Bk. 3). 24p. (Orig.). 1983. pap. 1.50 (ISBN 0-87239-678-9, 2453). Standard Pub.
--We Love God. (Bible Lessons for Little People Ser.: Bk. 2). 144p. (Orig.). 1983. pap. 7.95 (ISBN 0-87239-613-4, 3360). Standard Pub.
--We Please God. (Bible Activities Ser.: Bk. 4). 24p. (Orig.). 1983. pap. 1.50 (ISBN 0-87239-679-7, 2454). Standard Pub.
Finnegan, Edward G. Children's Bible Stories. LC 75-18758. (Treasure House Bks). (Illus.). 256p. 1978. 7.95 (ISBN 0-8326-1803-9, 3602); deluxe ed. 8.95 (ISBN 0-686-66397-7). World Bible.
--Historias De la Biblia. LC 75-18758. (Treasure House Bks). (Span., Illus.). 1978. 9.95 (ISBN 0-8326-2601-5, 5180). World Bible.
Frank, Penny. Daniel in the Lion's Den. Alexander, P., ed. (Lion Story Bible Ser.). 24p. 1987. 2.95 (ISBN 0-85648-752-X). Lion USA.
--Jesus on Trial. Alexander, P., ed. (Lion Story Bible Ser.). 24p. 1987. 2.95. Lion USA.
--Jesus the Teacher. Alexander, P., ed. (Lion Story Bible Ser.). 24p. 1987. 2.95 (ISBN 0-85648-760-0). Lion USA.
--King David. Alexander, P., ed. (Lion Story Bible Ser.). 24p. 1987. 2.95 (ISBN 0-85648-744-9). Lion USA.
--Naaman's Dreadful Secret. Alexander, P., ed. (Lion Story Bible Ser.). 24p. 1987. 2.95 (ISBN 0-85648-748-1). Lion USA.
--Paul & His Friends. Alexander, P., ed. (Lion Story Bible Ser.). 24p. 1987. 2.95 (ISBN 0-85648-776-7). Lion USA.
--The Story of the Two Brothers. Alexamder, P., ed. (Lion Story Bible Ser.). 24p. 1987. 2.95 (ISBN 0-85648-765-1). Lion USA.
Freeman, Margaret. Hidden Treasure: Parables for Kids. LC 81-16669. (Illus.). 96p. (Orig.). 1982. pap. 3.95 (ISBN 0-87239-499-9, 2728). Standard Pub.
Fulbright, Robert G. Old Testament Friends: Men of Courage. (BibLearn Ser.). (Illus.). 1979. 5.95 (ISBN 0-8054-4251-0, 4242-51). Broadman.
Gamm, David. Child's Play. LC 78-51069. (Illus.). 96p. 1978. pap. 4.95 (ISBN 0-87793-150-X). Ave Maria.
Garrison, Eileen & Albanese, Gayle. Eucharistic Manual for Children. LC 84-60217. (Illus.). 28p. (Orig.). 1984. pap. 3.95 (ISBN 0-8192-1343-8). Morehouse.
Gay, Marcina. Bible Quizzes for Kids. 48p. (Orig.). 1982. pap. 1.95 (ISBN 0-87239-594-4, 3136). Standard Pub.
Gillum, Perry & Allen, Rob, eds. Getting a Grip: Bible Study for Young Teens. 41p. (Orig.). (YA) 1986. pap. 3.95 (ISBN 0-934942-55-2); tchr's. ed. 2.95 (ISBN 0-934942-56-0). White Wing Pub.
Graeber, Charlotte. Jonah, Speak for God. (Speak for Me Ser.). (Illus.). 24p. 1986. 3.95 (ISBN 0-8407-6702-1). Nelson.
--Moses, Speak for God! (Speak for Me Ser.). (Illus.). 24p. 1986. 3.95 (ISBN 0-8407-6704-8). Nelson.
--Paul, Speak for God. (Speak for Me Ser.). (Illus.). 24p. 1986. 3.95 (ISBN 0-8407-6700-5). Nelson.
--Peter, Speak for God. (Speak for Me Ser.). (Illus.). 24p. 1986. 3.95 (ISBN 0-8407-6701-3). Nelson.
Grishaver, Joel L. Being Torah. LC 85-50219. (Illus.). 224p. (Orig.). 1985. pap. text ed. 7.95 (ISBN 0-933873-00-X). Torah Aura.
Grogg, Evelyn. Bible Lessons for Little People: Revised with Learning Centers. rev. ed. Eberle, Sarah, rev. by. LC 80-53878. 144p. 1981. pap. 7.95 (ISBN 0-87239-430-1, 3368). Standard Pub.
Grunze, Richard. Searching in God's Word-New Testament. (Lutheran Elementary Schools' Religion Curriculum Ser.). 142p. 1986. 4.95 (ISBN 0-938272-41-1). WELS Board.
--Searching in God's Word-Old Testament. (Lutheran Elementary Schools' Religion Curriculum Ser.). 140p. 1986. 4.95 (ISBN 0-938272-40-3). WELS Board.
Hagan, Lowell & Westerhof, Jack. Theirs Is the Kingdom. LC 86-11679. (Illus.). 336p. 1986. 16.95 (ISBN 0-8028-5013-8). Eerdmans.
Hand, Phyllis. Breaking into Bible Games. (Helping Hand Ser.). 48p. (YA) 1984. wkbk. 4.95 (ISBN 0-317-43001-7). Good Apple.
Harrison, Marc, illus. The Alphabet Book. (Bible Look 'N Learn Bks.). (Illus.). 24p. 1985. bds. 3.95 (ISBN 0-8407-6685-8). Nelson.
--The Animal Book. (Bible Look-n-Learn Ser.). 1986. 3.95 (ISBN 0-8407-6708-0). Nelson.
--The Color Book. (Bible Look 'N Learn Bks.). (Illus.). 24p. 1985. bds. 3.95 (ISBN 0-8407-6687-4). Nelson.
--The Counting Book. (Bible Look 'N Learn Bks.). (Illus.). 24p. 1985. bds. 3.95 (ISBN 0-8407-6686-6). Nelson.
--The Opposite Book. (Bible Look-n-Learn Ser.). 1986. 3.95 (ISBN 0-8407-6710-2). Nelson.
--The Shape Book. (Bible Look-n-Learn Ser.). 1986. 3.95 (ISBN 0-8407-6709-9). Nelson.
Hartweg, Judy. Faithful Followers. (Helping Hand Ser.). 48p. 1984. wkbk. 4.95 (ISBN 0-86653-237-4). Good Apple.
Hayes & Hook. Meu Livro de Historias Biblicas. (Portugese Bks.). Tr. of My Book of Bible Stories. (Port.). 1979. 3.00 (ISBN 0-8297-0758-1). Life Pubs Intl.
Hayes, Wanda. A Child's First Book of Bible Stories. LC 83-664. (Illus.). 128p. 1983. text ed. 7.95 (ISBN 0-87239-659-2, 2949). Standard Pub.
Haywood, Carolyn. Make a Joyful Noise! Bible Verses for Children. LC 84-2401. (Illus.). 96p. 1984. 11.95 (ISBN 0-664-32711-7). Westminster.
Heath, Lou & Taylor, Beth. Reading My Bible in Fall. LC 85-30947. (Orig.). 1986. pap. 4.50 (ISBN 0-8054-4322-3). Broadman.
--Reading My Bible in Winter. LC 85-30940. (Orig.). 1986. pap. 4.50 (ISBN 0-8054-4323-1). Broadman.
Helgeson, Donald V. Handbook for Writing Technical Proposals That Win Contracts. LC 85-3549. 178p. 1985. pap. 24.95 (ISBN 0-13-379686-8). P-H.
Heppenstall, Margit S. Deborah. new ed. LC 67-19497. (Crown Ser.). 1977. pap. 4.95 (ISBN 0-8127-0169-0). Review & Herald.
Hill, Harold. Bible Answers for King's Kids. rev. ed. 224p. 1983. pap. 5.95 (ISBN 0-8007-5131-0, Power Bks). Revell.
Hollingsworth, T. R. Ezra of Galilee. 80p. (Orig.). 1987. pap. text ed. 6.95 (ISBN 0-9617668-0-8). Hollybridge Pubns.
Hughes, Barbara & Dwiggins, Gwen. God Loves Children. (God Loves...Coloring Book Ser.). (Illus.). 0.75 (ISBN 0-8091-6562-7). Paulist Pr.
--God Loves Colors. (God Loves...Coloring Book Ser.). (Illus.). 0.60 (ISBN 0-8091-6566-X). Paulist Pr.
--God Loves Fun. (God Loves...Coloring Book Ser.). (Illus.). 0.75t (ISBN 0-8091-6564-3). Paulist Pr.
--God Loves Love. (God Loves...Coloring Book Ser.). (Illus.). 0.60 (ISBN 0-8091-6565-1). Paulist Pr.
Hutson, Joan. Love Never Ever Ends. LC 82-6737. (Happy Day Bks.). (Illus.). 24p. 1983. 1.59 (ISBN 0-87239-641-X, 3561). Standard Pub.
Hutton, Warwick. Noah & the Great Flood. LC 77-3217. (Illus.). 32p. 1977. 8.95 (ISBN 0-689-50098-X, McElderry Bk). Macmillan.
Ife, Elaine & Sutton, Rosalind, eds. David & Goliath. (Now You Can Read Stories from the Bible Ser.). (Illus.). 24p. 1985. 2.50 (ISBN 0-8407-5392-6). Nelson.
--Noah & the Ark. (Now You Can Read Stories from the Bible Ser.). (Illus.). 24p. 1985. 2.50 (ISBN 0-8407-5390-X). Nelson.
The Illustrated Childern's Bible. (Illus.). 480p. 12.95 (ISBN 0-448-14494-8). Putnam Pub Group.
Jessie, Karen. O. T. Books of the Bible. 48p. (Orig.). (YA) 1983. 1.95 (ISBN 0-87239-674-6, 2774). Standard Pub.
Kauffman, Suzanne. God Comforts His People: Activity Book. (Story Bible Ser.). (Illus.). 84p. (Orig.). 1986. pap. 3.00 (ISBN 0-8361-3411-7). Herald Pr.
Keller, W. Phillip. A Child's Look at the Twenty-Third Psalm. LC 80-976. (Illus.). 96p. 1981. 8.95 (ISBN 0-385-15456-9, Galilee). Doubleday.
--A Child's Look at the Twenty-Third Psalm. LC 84-13718. (Illus.). 96p. 1985. pap. 5.95 (ISBN 0-385-15457-7, Galilee). Doubleday.
Krein, Linda. Bible Crosswords. (Bible Baffler Ser.). 48p. 1986. wkbk. 4.95 (ISBN 0-86653-366-4). Good Apple.
Lalo, Laurent. David & Goliath. LC 83-24975. (Illus.). 24p. 1985. 4.95 (ISBN 0-88070-044-0). Multnomah.
--Jesus & John the Baptist. LC 83-25075. (Illus.). 24p. 1985. 4.95 (ISBN 0-88070-045-9). Multnomah.
Latham, Judy. Women in the Bible: Helpful Friends. (BibLearn Ser.). (Illus.). 1979. 5.95 (ISBN 0-8054-4248-0, 4242-48). Broadman.
Layton, Karen & Layton, Ron. Bible Word Fun. (Bible Baffler Ser.). 48p. 1986. wkbk. 4.95 (ISBN 0-86653-367-2). Good Apple.
LeCours, Zoe S. Exit Here Please: Puzzles, Games & Mazes about the Book of Exodus. (Illus.). 64p. (Orig.). 1986. pap. 4.95 (ISBN 0-934661-01-4, 7078). Lions Head Pr.
--To Begin with Puzzles, Games & Mazes about the Book of Genesis. (Illus.). 48p. (Orig.). 1985. pap. 4.49 (ISBN 0-934661-00-6, 7077). Lions Head Pr.
LeFevre, G. L. Stories from Acts. (Bible Quiz 'N Tattletotals Ser.). 16p. (Orig.). 1982. pap. 0.98 (ISBN 0-87239-581-2, 2808). Standard Pub.
Lehman, Carolyn. God's Wonderful World: Thirteen Pupil Activities, Bk. 1. (God's Wonderful World Ser.). (Illus.). 32p. 1985. wkbk 1.50 (ISBN 0-87239-837-4, 3317). Standard Pub.
Lehman, Elsie. God's Wisdom & Power Activity Book. (Story Bible Ser.). 80p. 1985. pap. 3.00 (ISBN 0-8361-3391-9). Herald Pr.
Lehman, Elsie E. God Sends His Son Activity Book. (Bible Story Ser.: Bk. 8). 80p. (Orig.). 1987. pap. 3.00 (ISBN 0-8361-3429-X). Herald Pr.
Lepon, Shoshana. The Ten Tests of Abraham. (Bible Series for Young Children). (Illus.). 32p. (Orig.). 1986. 7.95 (ISBN 0-317-52412-7); pap. 5.95 (ISBN 0-910818-67-3). Judaica Pr.
Lewis, Shari. One-Minute Bible Stories: Old Testament. LC 86-2011. (Illus.). 48p. 1986. 6.95 (ISBN 0-385-19565-6); PLB 6.95 (ISBN 0-385-19566-4). Doubleday.
Lewis, Shari & Henderson, Florence. One-Minute Bible Stories: New Testament. LC 86-6401. (Illus.). 48p. 1986. 6.95 (ISBN 0-385-23286-1); PLB 6.95 (ISBN 0-385-23287-X). Doubleday.
Lindvall, Ella K. The Bible Illustrated for Little Children. (Illus.). 1985. text ed. 11.95 (ISBN 0-8024-0596-7). Moody.
--Noah & His Ark. (People of the Bible Ser.). 4.95 (ISBN 0-8024-0396-4). Moody.
--Read-Aloud Bible Stories, Vol. 1. LC 82-2114. 160p. 1982. 16.95 (ISBN 0-8024-7163-3). Moody.
Lutz, Kathryn. God Wants Us to Listen. Lemon, Patricia H., ed. (Christian Storybooks Ser.). 1986. pap. 5.95 (ISBN 0-939697-03-3). Graded Pr.
--God's Gift of Touch. Lemon, Patricia H., ed. (Christian Storybooks Ser.). 24p. (Orig.). 1986. pap. 5.95 packaged with audio cass. (ISBN 0-939697-02-5). Graded Pr.
--The Smells in God's World. Lemon, Patricia H., ed. (Christian Storybooks). 24p. (Orig.). 1986. pap. 5.95 packaged with audio cassette (ISBN 0-939697-01-7); audio cassette incl. Graded Pr.
Lynn, Claire. B-I-B-L-E That's the Book for Me! (A Doctrinal Series for Children: Bk. 1). (Illus.). 18p. (Orig.). 1981. pap. 1.50 (ISBN 0-89323-013-8). Bible Memory.
Lysne, Mary E. Bible Activity Fun for Kids. 24p. 1983. pap. 1.50 (ISBN 0-87239-693-2, 2363). Standard Pub.
--Bible Learning Fun for Kids. 24p. 1983. pap. 1.50 (ISBN 0-87239-694-0, 2364). Standard Pub.
McElrath, William E. Judges & Kings: God's Chosen Leaders. (Illus.). 1979. 5.95 (ISBN 0-8054-4249-9, 4242-49). Broadman.
MacKenthun, Carole & Dwyer, Paulinus. Faith. (Fruit of the Spirit Ser.). (Illus.). 48p. 1986. wkbk. 4.95 (ISBN 0-86653-361-3). Good Apple.
--Goodness. (Fruit of the Spirit Ser.). (Illus.). 48p. 1986. wkbk. 4.95 (ISBN 0-86653-363-X). Good Apple.
--Joy. (Fruit of the Spirit Ser.). (Illus.). 48p. 1986. wkbk. 4.95 (ISBN 0-86653-360-5). Good Apple.
--Love. (Fruit of the Spirit Ser.). (Illus.). 48p. Date not set. wkbk. 4.95 (ISBN 0-86653-359-1). Good Apple.
--Patience. (Fruit of the Spirit Ser.). (Illus.). 48p. Date not set. wkbk. 4.95 (ISBN 0-86653-364-8). Good Apple.
--Peace. (Fruit of the Spirit Ser.). (Illus.). 48p. 1986. wkbk. 4.95 (ISBN 0-86653-365-6). Good Apple.
MacKenzie, Joy. The Big Book of Bible Crafts & Projects. (Illus.). 212p. (Orig.). 1981. pap. 12.95 (ISBN 0-310-70151-1, 14019P). Zondervan.
McMinn, Tom. Prophets: Preachers for God. (BibLearn Ser.). (Illus.). 1979. 5.95 (ISBN 0-8054-4250-2, 4242-50). Broadman.
Mahany, Patricia, ed. Bible Animals. (Classroom Activity Bks.). (Illus., Orig.). 1984. pap. 2.95 (ISBN 0-87239-715-7, 2445). Standard Pub.
--Bible Babies. (Classroom Activity Bks.). (Illus.). 48p. (Orig.). 1984. pap. 2.95 (ISBN 0-87239-716-5, 2446). Standard Pub.
--Bible Children. (Classroom Activity Bks.). (Illus.). 48p. (Orig.). 1984. pap. 2.95 (ISBN 0-87239-717-3, 2447). Standard Pub.
--Bible Verses in Action. (Stick-On Activity & Coloring Bks.). (Illus.). 16p. 1983. pap. 1.50 (ISBN 0-87239-686-X, 2366). Standard Pub.

--Jesus' Helpers Classroom Dot-to-Dot Book. (Classroom Activity Bks.). (Illus.). 96p. pap. 2.95 (ISBN 0-87239-503-0, 2334). Standard Pub.

Mahany, Patricia S. Bible Who Am I? (Stick-On Activity & Coloring Bks.). (Illus.). 16p. 1983. pap. 1.50 (ISBN 0-87239-687-8, 2367). Standard Pub.

Martin, Dianne & Heller, Rachelle. Bible BASIC: Advanced. (Illus.). 64p. 1986. 5.95 (ISBN 0-87403-052-8, 3192). Standard Pub.

Martin, Wayne W., tr. The Gospel of Mark: A Translation for Children. LC 84-50838. 112p. (Orig.). 1984. pap. 9.95 (ISBN 0-8358-0493-3). Upper Room.

Maschke, Ruby. Bible People Story-N-Puzzle Book. 48p. (Orig.). 1983. pap. 2.50 (ISBN 0-87239-673-8, 2773). Standard Pub.

--Disciples of Christ Story-N-Puzzle Book. 48p. (Orig.). 1983. pap. 2.50 (ISBN 0-87239-675-4, 2775). Standard Pub.

Matranga, Frances. Good Times Bible Activities. 24p. 1983. pap. 1.50 (ISBN 0-87239-692-4, 2362). Standard Pub.

--Happy Time Bible Activities. 24p. 1983. pap. 1.50 (ISBN 0-87239-691-6, 2361). Standard Pub.

Matthews, Velda. Bible Places. (Illus.). 1985. 1.95 (ISBN 0-87239-254-6, 2782). Standard Pub.

Matthews, Velda & Beard, Ray. Basic Bible Dictionary. Korth, Bob, ed. (Illus.). 128p. (Orig.). 1984. pap. 7.95 (ISBN 0-87239-720-3, 2770). Standard Pub.

Maves, Paul B. & Maves, Mary C. Finding Your Way Through the Bible. (Orig.). 1971. pap. 3.50 (ISBN 0-687-13049-2). Abingdon.

Michaels, Larry. Bible Object Talks for Children. (Illus.). 48p. (Orig.). 1982. pap. 2.95 (ISBN 0-87239-532-4, 2888). Standard Pub.

Miles, A. Marie. Bible: Chain of Truth. 168p. pap. 1.25 (ISBN 0-686-29101-8). Faith Pub Hse.

Mitchell, Joan & Sherlock, Therese. Celebrating the Gospel. Fisher, Carl, ed. (Illus.). 1985. dupl. masterbook 9.95 (ISBN 0-89837-105-8, Pub. by Pflaum Pr). Peter Li.

Moncure, Jane B. I Learn to Read about Jesus: Primer. rev. ed. (Basic Bible Readers Ser.). 128p. 1983. text ed. 7.95 (ISBN 0-87239-660-6, 2950). Standard Pub.

Murphy, Elspeth C. It's My Birthday, God: Psalm 90. (David & I Talk to God Ser.). (Illus.). 1982. misc. format 2.50 (ISBN 0-89191-580-X). Cook.

Myers, Bill. Faith Workout. (Illus.). 144p. 1986. 3.95 (ISBN 0-89693-265-6). Victor Bks.

Neely, Keith. Daddy's Letter. (Color & Learn Bks.). (Orig.). pap. 2.25 (ISBN 0-8024-0502-9). Moody.

Newman, Shirley. Introduction to Kings, Later Prophets & Writings, Vol. 3. Rossel, Seymour, ed. (The Child's Introduction to Bible Ser.). (Illus.). 160p. (Orig.). 1981. pap. text ed. 6.95x (ISBN 0-87441-336-2); wkbk. by Morris Sugarman 3.50x; tchr's ed. 12.50x. Behrman.

Nystrom, Carolyn. Acts 1-12: Church on the Move. (Young Fisherman Bible Study Guide Ser.). 59p. 1979. tchrs. ed. 4.95 (ISBN 0-87788-126-X); student ed. 2.95 (ISBN 0-87788-125-1). Shaw Pubs.

--Angels & Me. (Children's Bible Basics Ser.). (Illus.). 1984. 4.95 (ISBN 0-8024-6017-8). Moody.

--What Is the Bible? (Children's Bible Basics Ser.). 32p. 1982. 4.95 (ISBN 0-8024-0157-0). Moody.

Nystrom, Carolyn & Fromer, Margaret. Acts 13-28: Missions Accomplished. (Young Fisherman Bible Studyguide). (Illus.). 93p. 1979. tchrs. ed. 4.95 (ISBN 0-87788-011-5); student ed. 2.95 (ISBN 0-87788-010-7). Shaw Pubs.

Pape, Donna L., et al. Bible Activities for Kids, No. 3. (Illus.). 63p. (Orig.). 1981. pap. 1.95 (ISBN 0-87123-172-7, 210172). Bethany Hse.

--Bible Activities for Kids, No. 4. (Illus.). 59p. 1981. pap. 1.95 (ISBN 0-87123-173-5, 210173). Bethany Hse.

Paterson, John & Paterson, Katherine. Consider the Lilies: Flowers of the Bible. LC 85-43603. (Illus.). 96p. (YA) 1986. 13.70i (ISBN 0-690-04461-5, Crowell Jr Bks); PLB 13.89 (ISBN 0-690-04463-1). HarpJ.

Patterson, Lillie. David, the Story of a King. (Illus.). 96p. 1985. PLB 7.95 (ISBN 0-687-10280-4). Abingdon.

Peifer, Jane & Nolt, Marilyn. Good Thoughts about Me. (Good Thoughts Ser.: No. 1). (Illus.). 24p. (Orig.). 1985. pap. 2.95 (ISBN 0-8361-3389-7). Herald Pr.

--Good Thoughts about People. (Good Thoughts Ser.: No. 3). (Illus.). 24p. (Orig.). 1985. pap. 2.95 (ISBN 0-8361-3390-0). Herald Pr.

--Good Thoughts at Bedtime. (Good Thoughts Ser.: No. 2). (Illus.). 24p. (Orig.). 1985. pap. 2.95 (ISBN 0-8361-3388-9). Herald Pr.

Phillips, Cheryl & Harvey, Bonnie C., eds. My Jesus Pocketbook of God's Fruit. LC 83-50194. (My Jesus Pocketbook Ser.). (Illus.). 32p. 1983. pap. 0.49 (ISBN 0-937420-08-5). Stirrup Assoc.

Phillips, Cheryl M. & Harvey, Bonnie C., eds. My Jesus Pocketbook of the Lord's Prayer. LC 83-50193. (My Jesus Pocketbook Ser.). (Illus.). 32p. 1983. pap. 0.49 (ISBN 0-937420-07-7). Stirrup Assoc.

Powell, Ruth. Walking with a Hero: Children's Bible Studies for Children's Church. 96p. (Orig.). 1982. pap. 7.95 (ISBN 0-87239-593-6, 3375). Standard Pub.

Priddy, Linda. The Bible & Me: Writing Fun for Kids Series. (Illus.). 24p. (Orig.). 1982. pap. 1.50 (ISBN 0-87239-482-4, 2101). Standard Pub.

Quinn, Mark. Jesus of the Gospels: A Worktext Approach to Understanding Scripture. (YA) 1987. pap. text ed. write for info. (ISBN 0-697-02233-1); write for info. tchr's. ed. (ISBN 0-697-02234-X). Wm C Brown.

Rakel, Michael & Bremke, Maryann. New Testament Times. 1984. 9.95 (ISBN 0-89837-100-7, Pub. by Pflaum Press). Peter Li.

--Old Testament Times. 1984. 9.95 (ISBN 0-89837-099-X, Pub. by Pflaum Press). Peter Li.

Randall, Louise A. Scripture Stories for Tiny Tots: Read-Aloud Stories from the Bible for Children 1 to 6. LC 83-83429. 38p. (Orig.). 1983. pap. 3.95 (ISBN 0-88290-209-1). Horizon Utah.

Reid, John C. Thirty Favorite Bible Stories with Discussion Questions. LC 81-21514. (Illus.). 192p. (Orig.). 1982. pap. 4.95 (ISBN 0-87239-498-0, 3373). Standard Pub.

Richards, Larry. International Children's Bible Handbook. LC 86-5995. (Illus.). 1986. 13.95 (ISBN 0-8344-0133-9, BB600C). Sweet.

Roberts, Cara. Teaching with Object Talks. (Illus.). 48p. (Orig.). 1982. pap. 2.95 (ISBN 0-87239-533-2, 2889). Standard Pub.

Rogers, Barbara. God Rescues His People Activity Book. 72p. (Orig.). 1983. pap. 3.00 (ISBN 0-8361-3338-2). Herald Pr.

--God's Chosen King Activity Book. 88p. (Orig.). 1984. pap. 3.00 (ISBN 0-8361-3370-6). Herald Pr.

Rottschafer, Joyce. My Bible Number Book. LC 81-50675. (A Happy Day Book). (Illus.). 24p. (Orig.). 1981. pap. 1.59 (ISBN 0-87239-465-4, 3598). Standard Pub.

Russell. My First Bible Wordbook. 1984. 8.95 (ISBN 0-528-82421-X). Macmillan.

Ryrie, Charles C. Making the Most of Life. 1983. pap. 3.95 (ISBN 0-88207-587-X). SP Pubns.

Sant Bani Ashram School Children, tr. Book of Jonah. LC 84-50924. (Illus.). 1984. pap. 6.95 (ISBN 0-89142-044-4). Sant Bani Ash.

Schlegl, William. Bible Trivia. (Bible Baffler Ser.). 48p. 1986. wkbk. 4.95 (ISBN 0-86653-368-0). Good Apple.

Schoolland, Marian M. Leading Little Ones to God: A Child's Book of Bible Teaching. rev., 2nd ed. (Illus.). 96p. 1981. 14.95 (ISBN 0-8028-4035-3). Eerdmans.

Schultz, Samuel. Deuteronomy. (Everyman Bible Commentary Ser). 128p. (Orig.). 1971. pap. 5.95 (ISBN 0-8024-2005-2). Moody.

Sherlock, Connie. Bible Families. (Think 'n Check Quizzes Ser.). (Illus.). 16p. (Orig.). 1983. pap. 1.95 (ISBN 0-87239-688-6, 2792). Standard Pub.

Silverman, Maida. My Bible Alphabet. (Golden Storytime Book). (Illus.). 24p. 1987. pap. 2.95 (ISBN 0-307-11968-8, Golden Bks). Western Pub.

Skinner, Donna. File Folder Learning Centers. LC 81-84001. 160p. (Orig.). 1982. pap. 7.95 (ISBN 0-87239-492-1, 3071). Standard Pub.

Smith, Joyce M. Demons, Doubters & Dead Men. (Good Life Bible Studies Book). 64p. (Orig.). 1986. 2.95wkbk. (ISBN 0-8423-0542-4). Tyndale.

--Young Disciples. 50p. 1983. pap. 2.95 (ISBN 0-8423-8599-1). Tyndale.

Sorenson, Stephen. Lord, Teach Me Your Ways: Children's Stories with Biblical Parallels. LC 81-2067. 96p. 1982. 6.95 (ISBN 0-687-22660-0). Abingdon.

Souter, John C. The All-New Super Incredible Bible Study Book on Mark. 144p. (Orig.). 1985. pap. 3.95 (ISBN 0-310-45881-1, 12475P). Zondervan.

Speelman, Marlene & Adams, Janiece. Bible Busy Book. 10p. 1986. 15.95 (ISBN 0-8407-6711-0). Nelson.

Stafford, Linda. Mind Invaders. (YA) 1982. pap. 1.95. Victor Bks.

Stanford, Sylvia. I'm Growing. (Bible & Me Ser.). (Illus.). 1986. 5.95 (ISBN 0-8054-4167-0). Broadman.

Steen, Shirley & Edwards, Anne. A Child's Bible. 1986. 9.95 (ISBN 0-8091-2867-5). Paulist Pr.

Steiner, Rudolf. And It Came to Pass: An Old Testament, Reader for Children. 1973. lib. bdg. 79.95 (ISBN 0-87968-556-5). Krishna Pr.

Stirrup Associates Inc. My Jesus Pocketbook of a Very Special Birth Day. Harvey, Bonnie C. & Phillips, Cheryl M., eds. LC 84-50919. (My Jesus Pocketbook Ser.). (Illus.). 32p. 1984. pap. 0.49 (ISBN 0-937420-15-8). Stirrup Assoc.

--My Jesus Pocketbook of Daniel in the Lion's Den. Harvey, Bonnie C. & Phillips, Cheryl M., eds. LC 84-50916. (My Jesus Pocketbook Ser.). (Illus.). 32p. (Orig.). 1984. pap. text ed. 0.49 (ISBN 0-937420-12-3). Stirrup Assoc.

--My Jesus Pocketbook of the Beginning. Harvey, Bonnie C. & Phillips, Cheryl M., eds. LC 84-50918. (Jesus Pocketbook Ser.). (Illus.). 32p. (Orig.). 1984. pap. 0.49 (ISBN 0-937420-14-X). Stirrup Assoc.

--My Jesus Pocketbook of the Big Little Person: The Story of Zacchaeus. Phillips, Cheryl M. & Harvey, Bonnie C., eds. LC 84-50917. (My Jesus Pocketbook Ser.). (Illus.). 32p. 1984. pap. 0.49 (ISBN 0-937420-13-1). Stirrup Assoc.

Stirrup Associates, Inc. Staff. My Jesus Pocketbook of Li'l Critters. Phillips, Cheryl M., ed. LC 82-63139. (Illus.). 32p. (Orig.). 1983. pap. text ed. 0.49 (ISBN 0-937420-05-0). Stirrup Assoc.

--My Jesus Pocketbook of Manners. Phillips, Cheryl M., ed. LC 82-63141. (Illus.). 32p. 1983. pap. 0.49 (ISBN 0-937420-06-9). Stirrup Assoc.

--My Jesus Pocketbook of the 23rd Psalm. Phillips, Cheryl M., ed. LC 82-63140. (Illus.). 32p. (Orig.). 1983. pap. text ed. 0.49 (ISBN 0-937420-04-2). Stirrup Assoc.

Stoddard, Sandol. Doubleday Illustrated Children's Bible. LC 82-45340. (Illus.). 384p. 1984. deluxe ed. 22.95 (ISBN 0-385-18541-3). Doubleday.

--Doubleday Illustrated Children's Bible. LC 82-45340. (Illus.). 384p. 1983. 14.95 (ISBN 0-385-18521-9). Doubleday.

Storr, Catherine. Abraham & Isaac. LC 84-18076. (People of the Bible Ser.). (Illus.). 32p. 1985. PLB 10.65 (ISBN 0-8172-1994-3). Raintree Pubs.

--David & Goliath. LC 84-18138. (People of the Bible Ser.). (Illus.). 32p. 1985. PLB 10.65 (ISBN 0-8172-1995-1). Raintree Pubs.

--Jesus Begins His Work. LC 82-9037. (People of the Bible). (Illus.). 32p. 1982. PLB 10.65 (ISBN 0-8172-1978-1). Raintree Pubs.

--Moses & the Plagues. LC 84-18077. (People of the Bible Ser.). (Illus.). 32p. 1985. PLB 10.65 (ISBN 0-8172-1999-4). Raintree Pubs.

--Noah & His Ark. Storr, Catherine, retold by. LC 82-7712. (People of the Bible Ser.). (Illus.). 32p. 1982. PLB 10.65 (ISBN 0-8172-1975-7). Raintree Pubs.

Storr, Catherine, retold by. Joseph & His Brothers. LC 82-9087. (People of the Bible). (Illus.). 32p. 1982. PLB 10.65 (ISBN 0-8172-1976-5). Raintree Pubs.

Stump, Gladys S. Baby Jesus. (Books I Can Read Ser.). (Illus.). 1978. pap. 1.95 (ISBN 0-8127-0160-7). Review & Herald.

--Baby Moses. (Books I Can Read Ser.). (Illus.). 1978. pap. 1.95 (ISBN 0-8127-0164-X). Review & Herald.

--Elisha's Room. (Books I Can Read). (Illus.). 1978. pap. 1.95 (ISBN 0-8127-0162-3). Review & Herald.

--Mordecai's Ride. (Books I Can Read). (Illus.). 1978. pap. 1.95 (ISBN 0-8127-0161-5). Review & Herald.

--Paul. (Books I Can Read). (Illus.). 1978. pap. 1.95 (ISBN 0-8127-0165-8). Review & Herald.

Swihart, Judson J. How to Treat Your Family As Well As You Treat Your Friends. LC 82-11234. 1982. pap. 5.95 (ISBN 0-8307-0855-3, 5417605). Regal.

Taggart, George. Bible Promises for Tiny Tots, No. 3. Coffen, Richard W., ed. 32p. (Orig.). 1987. pap. 3.95 (ISBN 0-8280-0375-0). Review & Herald.

--Bible Promises for Tiny Tots, II. Coffen, Richard W., ed. 32p. (Orig.). 1985. pap. 3.95 (ISBN 0-8280-0246-0). Review & Herald.

Thomsen, Helen S. That the World May Believe: The Acts of the Apostles. 1978. pap. 2.25x (ISBN 0-8192-4085-0); tchrs guide 2.25x (ISBN 0-8192-4084-2). Morehouse.

Truitt, Gloria. People of the New Testament: Arch Book Supplement. LC 59-1311. 1983. pap. 0.99 (ISBN 0-570-06173-3). Concordia.

--People of the Old Testament: Arch Book Supplement. LC 59-1310. 1983. pap. 0.99 (ISBN 0-570-06172-5). Concordia.

Uhl, Harold J. Good News from John: Visual Messages for Children. LC 79-50094. 1979. pap. 6.95 (ISBN 0-8066-1712-8, 10-2811). Augsburg.

Voorhies, Alice F. Believe It or Not It's in the Bible. 38p. (Orig.). 1985. pap. 3.00 (ISBN 0-931494-77-X). Brunswick Pub.

Wangerin, Walter, Jr. The Bible: Its Story for Children. (Illus.). 416p. 1981. 12.95. Macmillan.

Ward, Elaine M. Growing with the Bible. 64p. (Orig.). 1986. pap. 6.95 (ISBN 0-940754-36-3). Ed Ministries.

Watson, E. Elaine. I Wish, I Wish. LC 82-62733. (Happy Day Bks.). (Illus.). 24p. 1983. 1.59 (ISBN 0-87239-637-1, 3557). Standard Pub.

Waybill, Marjorie. God's Family Activity Book. 64p. (Orig.). 1983. pap. 3.00 (ISBN 0-8361-3336-6). Herald Pr.

Weed, Libby, ed. Read 'n Grow Picture Bible. LC 84-51093. (Illus.). 319p. 1984. 14.95 (ISBN 0-8344-0124-X, BB200C). Sweet.

Weisheit, Eldon. The Gospel for Kids: Series C. 1979. 6.75 (ISBN 0-570-03279-2, 15-2723). Concordia.

--The Psalms for Children: Series C. LC 85-11154. 128p. (Orig.). 1985. pap. 6.95 (ISBN 0-8066-2169-9, 10-5305). Augsburg.

Wendland, Ernst H. God's Mission in the New Testament. Fischer, William E., ed. (Bible Class Course Ser.). 40p. (Orig.). (YA) 1986. pap. 2.50 (ISBN 0-938272-55-1). WELS Board.

What the Bible Tells Us: A Series for Young Children. Incl. Jesus Heals a Blind Man (ISBN 0-8066-1684-9, 10-3514); Jesus Heals a Sick Man (ISBN 0-8066-1685-7, 10-3515); Jesus & the Storm (ISBN 0-8066-1683-0, 10-3485); Zacchaeus (ISBN 0-8066-1699-7, 10-7550). (Second Ser.). (Illus.). 1979. pap. 2.95 ea. Augsburg.

Wiersbe, Warren. Be Challenged! rev. ed. LC 82-12404. 1982. pap. 3.50 (ISBN 0-8024-1080-4). Moody.

Woggon, Guillermo. Versiculos "Llave". Granberry, Nola, tr. (Libros Para Colorear). Tr. of Key Bible Verses. (Span., Illus.). 16p. 1985. pap. 1.25 (ISBN 0-311-38565-6). Casa Bautista.

World Book Inc. Best-Loved Bible Stories: Old Testament & New Testament, 2 vols. LC 79-55309. (Illus.). 90p. 1980. write for info. (ISBN 0-7166-2059-6). World Bk.

Zabriskie, Pat. The Puppet People. LC 79-53725. 80p. (Orig.). 1979. pap. 2.95 (ISBN 0-88243-753-4, 02-0753). Gospel Pub.

BIBLE–LANGUAGE, STYLE

see also Bible–Parables; Bible As Literature; Greek Language, Biblical; Hebrew Language

Boring, W. Eugene. Truly Human-Truly Divine: Christological Language & the Gospel Form. Lambert, Herbert, ed. LC 84-11382. 144p. 1984. pap. 11.95 (ISBN 0-8272-3625-5). CBP.

Bullinger, E. W. Figures of Speech Used in the Bible. 24.95 (ISBN 0-8010-0559-0). Baker Bk.

Burke, Kenneth. The Rhetoric of Religion: Studies in Logology. 1970. pap. 9.95x (ISBN 0-520-01610-6, CAMPUS 341). U of Cal Pr.

Caird, G. B. The Language & Imagery of the Bible. LC 79-27586. 288p. 1980. 20.00 (ISBN 0-664-21378-2). Westminster.

Dana, H. E. & Mantey, J. R. Gramatica Griega Del Nuevo Testamento. Robleto, Adolfo & De Clark, Catalina, trs. 1984. pap. 9.95 (ISBN 0-311-42010-9). Casa Bautista.

Danker, Frederick W. Benefactor: Epigraphic Study of a Graeco-Roman & New Testament Semantic Field. LC 81-70419. 1982. 29.95x (ISBN 0-915644-23-1). Clayton Pub Hse.

Davies, T. L. Bible English: Chapters on Old & Disused Expressions. 1875. 25.00 (ISBN 0-8274-1932-5). R West.

Duke, James O. Horace Bushnell: On the Vitality of Biblical Language. LC 83-16312. (SBL-Biblical Schlolarship in North America). 138p. 1984. pap. 13.50 (ISBN 0-89130-650-1, 06 11 09). Scholars Pr GA.

Dunning, Stephen N. The Tongues of Men: Hegel & Hamann on Religious Language & History. LC 79-10729. (American Academy of Religion, Dissertation Ser.: No. 27). 1979. 14.00 (ISBN 0-89130-283-2, 010127); pap. 9.95 (ISBN 0-89130-302-2). Scholars Pr GA.

Earle, Ralph. Word Meanings in the New Testament, Vol. 3: Romans. 264p. 1974. 9.95 (ISBN 0-8341-0512-8). Beacon Hill.

--Word Meanings in the New Testament, Vol. 5: Philemon-Philippians. 1977. 9.95 (ISBN 0-8341-0493-8). Beacon Hill.

Eller, Vernard. The Language of Canaan & the Grammar of Feminism: An Exercise in Wittgensteinian Analysis. 64p. 1982. pap. 2.95 (ISBN 0-8028-1902-8). Eerdmans.

Gibson, Arthur. Biblical Semantic Logic. 1981. 32.50 (ISBN 0-312-07796-3). St Martin.

Girdlestone, Robert B. Synonyms of the Old Testament. 1948. pap. 6.95 (ISBN 0-8028-1548-0). Eerdmans.

Good, Robert M. The Sheep of His Pasture: A Study of the Hebrew Noun 'AM(M) & its Semitic Cognates. LC 83-90934. (Harvard Semitic Monographs). 214p. 1984. 15.00 (ISBN 0-89130-628-5, 04 00 29). Scholars Pr GA.

Hardesty, Nancy A. Inclusive Language in the Church. LC 86-46036. 108p. (Orig.). 1987. pap. 7.95 (ISBN 0-8042-1686-X). John Knox.

Jacques, Xavier. List of New Testament Words Sharing Common Elements. (Scripta Pontificci Instituti Biblici: Vol. 119). 1969. pap. 13.00 (ISBN 88-7653-497-0). Loyola.

Johnson, Luke T. The Writings of the New Testament: An Interpretation. LC 85-16202. 640p. 1986. 34.95 (ISBN 0-8006-0886-0, 1-886); pap. 18.95 (ISBN 0-8006-1886-6, 1-1886). Fortress.

Keach, Benjamin. Preaching from the Types & Metaphors of the Bible. LC 78-165059. (Kregel Reprint Library). 1038p. 1975. 31.95 (ISBN 0-8254-3008-9). Kregel.
Kennedy, George A. New Testament Interpretation Through Rhetorical Criticism. LC 83-23577. x, 171p. 1984. 14.00x (ISBN 0-8078-1601-9); pap. 6.95 (ISBN 0-8078-4120-X). U of NC Pr.
McEvenne, Sean E. Narrative Style of the Priestly Writer. (Analecta Biblica: Vol. 50). 1971. pap. 17.00 (ISBN 88-7653-050-9). Loyola.
Macuch, Rudolf. Grammatik des Samaritanischen Hebraeisch. (Studia Samaritana 1). (Ger). 1969. 110.00x (ISBN 3-11-000133-0). De Gruyter.
Mansoor, Menahem. Biblical Hebrew Step by Step II: Readings from the Book of Genesis. 230p. (Orig.). 1984. pap. 13.95 (ISBN 0-8010-6151-2); cassette 7.95 (ISBN 0-8010-6198-9). Baker Bk.
Marin, Louis. The Semiotics of the Passion Narratives. Johnson, Alfred M., Jr., tr. (Pittsburgh Theological Monographs: No. 25). 1980. 12.95 (ISBN 0-915138-23-9). Pickwick.
Morris, Leon. Apostolic Preaching of the Cross. 1956. pap. 5.95 (ISBN 0-8028-1512-X). Eerdmans.
Moulton, James H. Style, Vol. 4. (Moulton's Grammar of New Testament Greek Ser.). 184p. 1976. 14.95 (ISBN 0-567-01018-X, Pub. by T & T Clark Ltd Uk). Fortress.
Partridge, Eric. A New Testament Word Book: A Glossary. facsimile ed. LC 70-117907. (Select Bibliographies Reprint Ser). Repr. of 1940 ed. 19.00 (ISBN 0-8369-5359-2). Ayer Co Pubs.
Pritchard, John P. A Literary Approach to the New Testament. (Illus.). 350p. 1972. 17.95x (ISBN 0-8061-1011-2); pap. 11.95x (ISBN 0-8061-1710-9). U of Okla Pr.
Pryke, E. J. Redactional Style in the Marcan Gospel. LC 76-52184. (Society for New Testament Studies Monographs: No. 33). 1978. 44.50 (ISBN 0-521-21430-0). Cambridge U Pr.
Rosenau, William. Hebraisms in the Authorized Version of the Bible. LC 76-9047. 1976. Repr. of 1903 ed. lib. bdg. 25.00 (ISBN 0-8414-7247-5). Folcroft.
Sands, Percy C. Literary Genius of the New Testament. Repr. of 1932 ed. lib. bdg. 22.50x (ISBN 0-8371-4328-4, SANT). Greenwood.
--Literary Genius of the Old Testament. LC 75-35756. 1975. Repr. of 1924 ed. lib. bdg. 27.50 (ISBN 0-8414-7646-2). Folcroft.
Sawyer, John F. Semantics in Biblical Research: New Methods of Defining Hebrew Words for Salvation. LC 72-75901. (Studies in Biblical Theology, Second Ser.: No. 24). 1972. pap. text ed. 12.00x (ISBN 0-8401-3074-0). A R Allenson.
Stein, Robert H. Difficult Sayings in the Gospels: Jesus's Use of Overstatement & Hyperbole. 96p. pap. 4.95 (ISBN 0-8010-8262-5). Baker Bk.
Thompson, Leonard L. Introducing Biblical Literature: A More Fantastic Country. LC 78-6632. (Illus.). ref. ed. 28.95 (ISBN 0-13-498824-8). P-H.
Tomback, Richard S. A Comparative Semitic Lexicon of the Phoenician & Punic Languages. LC 76-55377. (Society of Biblical Literature. Dissertation Ser.: No. 32). pap. 94.80 (ISBN 0-8357-9567-5, 2017672). Bks Demand UMI.
Trawick, Buckner B. Bible As Literature: Old Testament & the Apocrypha. 2nd ed. 1970. pap. 5.95 (ISBN 0-06-460056-4, CO 56, B&N Bks). Har-Row.
Turner, Nigel. Grammatical Insights into the New Testament. 208p. 1965. 15.95 (ISBN 0-567-01017-1, Pub. by T & T Clark Ltd UK). Fortress.
Voelz, James W. Fundamental Greek Grammar. 320p. 1986. 14.95 (ISBN 0-570-04226-7, 15-2185). Concordia.
Wilder, Amos N. Early Christian Rhetoric: The Language of the Gospel. LC 78-131949. 1971. 10.00x (ISBN 0-674-22002-1). Harvard U Pr.

BIBLE–LAW
see Jewish Law; Law (Theology)

BIBLE–LITERARY CRITICISM
see Bible–Criticism, Interpretation, etc.; Bible–Introductions; Bible As Literature

BIBLE–LITURGICAL USE
see also Lectionaries

Barrois, Georges A. Scripture Readings in Orthodox Worship. 197p. 1977. pap. 6.95 (ISBN 0-913836-41-9). St Vladimirs.
Gospel for Sundays & Feasts: Cycle B. 1979. 7.50 (ISBN 0-8198-0573-4); pap. 6.00 (ISBN 0-8198-0574-2). Dghtrs St Paul.
Mann, Jacob. The Bible As Read & Preached in the Old Synagogue, Vol. 1. rev. ed. (Library of Biblical Studies). 1970. 59.50x (ISBN 0-87068-083-8). Ktav.

BIBLE–MANUSCRIPTS
see also Dead Sea Scrolls

Allgeier, Arthur. Die Chester Beatty-Papyri Zum Pentateuch. 12.00 (ISBN 0-384-00860-7). Johnson Repr.
Barns, J. W. & Kilpatrick, G. D. A New Psalms Fragment. 1957. pap. 2.25 (ISBN 0-85672-621-4, Pub. by British Acad). Longwood Pub Group.
Beza, Theodore. Bezae Codex Cantabrigiensis: Being an Exact Copy, in Ordinary Type of the Celebrated Uncial Graeco-Latin Manuscript of the Four Gospels & Acts of the Apostles. Scrivener, Frederick H., ed. LC 78-4144. (Pittsburgh Reprint Ser.: No. 5). 1978. pap. 19.95 (ISBN 0-915138-39-5). Pickwick.
Edmunds, C. C. & Hatch, W. H. Gospel Manuscripts of the General Theological Seminary. (Harv Theol Studies). 1918. pap. 15.00 (ISBN 0-527-01004-9). Kraus Repr.
Gordis, Robert. The Biblical Text in the Making: A Study of the Kethibh-Qere. rev. ed. 1971. 29.95x (ISBN 0-87068-157-5). Ktav.
Hann, Robert R. The Manuscript History of the Psalms of Solomon. LC 81-21212. (SBL Septuagint & Cognate Studies). 1982. pap. 15.00 (ISBN 0-89130-557-2, 06-04-13). Scholars Pr GA.
Lake, Kirsopp & New, Silva, eds. Six Collations of New Testament Manuscripts. (Harvard Theol Studies). 1932. 24.00 (ISBN 0-527-01017-0). Kraus Repr.
MacGregor, Geddes. The Bible in the Making. LC 82-17499. 318p. 1983. pap. 14.50 (ISBN 0-8191-2810-4). U Pr of Amer.
Metzger, Bruce M. Manuscripts of the Greek Bible: An Introduction to Paleography. (Illus.). 1981. 19.95x (ISBN 0-19-502924-0). Oxford U Pr.
Pattie, T. S. Manuscripts of the Bible. (Illus.). 32p. (Orig.). 1979. pap. 2.95 (ISBN 0-904654-13-3, Pub. by British Lib). Longwood Pub Group.
Pieterisma, Albert. Chester Beatty Biblical Papyri IV & V: A New Edition with Text-Critical Analysis. LC 74-84103. 1974. 24.00 (ISBN 0-88866-016-2, 310016). Scholars Pr GA.
Read, William M. Michigan Manuscript 18 of the Gospels. LC 44-13750. (Publications in Language & Literature Ser.: No. 11). (Illus.). 75p. 1942. pap. 5.00x (ISBN 0-295-95219-9). U of Wash Pr.
Smith, Morton. The Secret Gospel: The Discovery & Interpretation of the Secret Gospel According to Mark. LC 82-73215. 157p. pap. 7.95 (ISBN 0-913922-55-2). Dawn Horse Pr.
Strack, Hermann L. Petrograd Codex of the Hebrew Bible: The Latter Prophets, Prophetarum Posteriorum. rev. ed. (Library of Biblical Studies Ser). 1970. 50.00x (ISBN 0-87068-111-7). Ktav.
Wisse, Frederik. The Profile Method for Classifying & Evaluating Manuscript Evidence. 140p. 1982. pap. 17.00x (ISBN 0-8028-1918-4). Eerdmans.
Yadin, Yigael. Message of the Scrolls. 1957. (Touchstone Bks); pap. 3.95 (ISBN 0-686-66285-7). S&S.

BIBLE–MAPS
see Bible–Geography–Maps

BIBLE–MEDICINE, HYGIENE, ETC.

Brummel, George H. Bible Medicine with Healing Verses. LC 83-91263. 172p. (Orig.). 1984. pap. 9.95 (ISBN 0-9613041-0-3). G Brummel Pub.
Duke, James A. Medicinal Plants of the Bible. (Traditional Healing Ser.: No. 10). (Illus.). 300p. 1983. lib. bdg. 49.95 (ISBN 0-932426-23-9). Trado-Medic.
Josephson, Elmer A. God's Key to Health & Happiness. 224p. 1976. pap. 6.95 (ISBN 0-8007-5018-7, Power Bks). Revell.
Kee, Howard C. Medicine, Miracle & Magic in New Testament Times. (Society for New Testament Studies Monographs: No. 55). 200p. 1986. 29.95 (ISBN 0-521-32309-6). Cambridge U Pr.
Lindsay, Gordon. The Bible Secret of Divine Health. (Divine Healing & Health Ser.). 1.25 (ISBN 0-89985-023-5). Christ Nations.
--Twenty-Five Objections to Divine Healing & the Bible Answers. (Divine Healing & Health Ser.). 1.25 (ISBN 0-89985-030-8). Christ Nations.
McMillen, S. I. None of These Diseases. 160p. 1963. pap. 2.95 (ISBN 0-8007-8030-2, Spire Bks). Revell.
Preuss, Julius. Biblical & Talmudic Medicine. Rosner, Fred, tr. from Ger. 1978. 45.00x (ISBN 0-88482-861-1, Sandhedrin Pr). Hebrew Pub.
Rosner, F. Medicine in the Bible & the Talmud: Selections from Classical Jewish Sources. (Library of Jewish Law & Ethics: Vol. 5). 9.95x (ISBN 0-87068-326-8). Ktav.

BIBLE–MEDITATIONS

Ashlag, R. Yehuda. A Gift of the Bible. 160p. 1984. pap. 9.95 (ISBN 0-943688-22-1). Res Ctr Kabbalah.
Becker, Siegbert W. The Scriptures: Inspired of God. 1971. pap. 2.25 (ISBN 0-8100-0027-X, 12-0340). Northwest Pub.
The Bible Promise Book. (Barbour Bks). 1986. bonded leather 10.95 (ISBN 0-916441-44-X); pap. 3.95 (ISBN 0-916441-43-1). Barbour & Co.
Birkey, Verna. You Are Very Special: A Biblical Guide to Self-Worth. 160p. 1977. pap. 5.95 (ISBN 0-8007-5032-2, Power Bks). Revell.
Booth, Julianne. Bible Verses to Remember. 1982. pap. 2.95 (ISBN 0-570-04061-2, 56-1364). Concordia.
Byers, Paul. Unto Him Be Glory. 220p. 1974. 4.95 (ISBN 0-89114-047-6); pap. 2.95 (ISBN 0-89114-046-8). Baptist Pub Hse.
Carretto, Carlo. Love Is for Living. Moiser, Jeremy, tr. from Ital. LC 76-49878. Orig. Title: Cio Che Conta E Amare. 158p. 1977. pap. 7.95 (ISBN 0-88344-293-0). Orbis Bks.
Ford, Charles W. The Inspired Scriptures. LC 78-60267. (Radiant Life Ser.). 128p. 1978. pap. 2.50 (ISBN 0-88243-914-6, 02-0914); tchr's ed. 3.95 (ISBN 0-88243-185-4, 32-0185). Gospel Pub.
Hyde, Clarence. Search the Scriptures. (Illus.). 112p. (Orig.). 1986. pap. 9.95 (ISBN 1-55630-014-X). Brentwood Comm.
Kersten, John C. Bible Meditations for Every Day: A Guide to Living the Year in the Spirit of the Scriptures. flexible bdg. 4.95 (ISBN 0-89942-277-2, 277/04). Catholic Bk Pub.
Kolden, Marc. Called by the Gospel: An Introduction ot the Christian Faith. LC 82-72651. 112p. 1983. pap. 5.95 (ISBN 0-8066-1958-9, 10-0967). Augsburg.
Krebs, Robert G. Why We're Here. 1987. 7.95 (ISBN 0-533-07098-8). Vantage.
Laurin, Roy L. Philippians. 208p. 1987. pap. 8.95 (ISBN 0-8254-3134-4). Kregel.
McAlister, Walter E, compiled By. Listen to the King: Meditations Just from the Scriptures. (Direction Bks.). 96p. (Orig.). 1980. pap. 2.95 (ISBN 0-8010-6104-0). Baker Bk.
McAlpine, Campbell. Alone with God: A Manual of Biblical Meditation. 1981. pap. 5.95 (ISBN 0-87123-000-3, 210000). Bethany Hse.
McBride, Neal. Equipping Adults Through Bible Study. 32p. 1977. pap. 1.50 (ISBN 0-8307-0505-8, 9970118). Regal.
McDowell, Josh & Bellis, Dale. Evidence Growth Guide, Vol. 3: Trustworthiness of the Bible. (Truth Alive Ser.: Pt. III). 120p. (Orig.). 1983. pap. 4.95 (ISBN 0-86605-020-5). Campus Crusade.
Meyer, F. B. Great Verses Through the Bible. 144p. 1982. pap. 13.95 (ISBN 0-310-29131-3, 10212P). Zondervan.
Michael, Chester P. Scripture Themes & Texts for Meditation & Study. 1981. pap. 2.00. Open Door Inc.
Packer, James I. God's Words. LC 81-18683. 192p. (Orig.). 1982. pap. 5.95 (ISBN 0-87784-367-8). Inter-Varsity.
Plantinga, Theodore. Wait for the Lord: Meditations on the Christian Life. 137p. (Orig.). 1981. pap. 5.75 (ISBN 0-932914-12-8). Dordt Coll Pr.
Sanford, Agnes. The Healing Power of the Bible. 1983. pap. 2.50 (ISBN 0-8007-8475-8, Spire Bks). Revell.
Schlink, Basilea. At the Side of Our Saviour: A Walk Through the Garden of Jesus' Sufferings. First English ed. (Illus.). 28p. (Orig.). 1982. pap. 1.50 gift edition (ISBN 3-87209-627-3). Evang Sisterhood Mary.
Sire, James W. Beginning with God. LC 81-14305. 128p. (Orig.). 1981. pap. 3.50 (ISBN 0-87784-369-4). Inter-Varsity.
Spurgeon, C. H. Evening by Evening. 368p. 1984. pap. text ed. 3.95 (ISBN 0-88368-154-4). Whitaker Hse.
Stuhlmeuller, Carroll. Biblical Meditations for Ordinary Time. 416p. (Orig.). 1984. Pt. II, Weeks 10-22. pap. 5.95 (ISBN 0-8091-2645-1); Pt. III, Weeks 23-34. pap. 5.95 (ISBN 0-8091-2648-6). Paulist Pr.
--Biblical Meditations for Ordinary Time: Pt. I, Weeks 1-9. 320p. (Orig.). 1984. pap. 4.95 (ISBN 0-8091-2644-3). Paulist Pr.
Stuhlmueller, Carroll. Biblical Meditations for Advent & the Christmas Season. LC 80-82083. (Biblical Meditations Ser.: Vol. 3). 288p. (Orig.). 1980. pap. 4.95 (ISBN 0-8091-2318-5). Paulist Pr.
Swafford, Z. W. Bible Gems. 1974. pap. 0.75 (ISBN 0-89114-034-4). Baptist Pub Hse.
Swindoll, Charles R. Growing Strong in the Seasons of Life. LC 83-11466. 350p. 1983. 14.95 (ISBN 0-88070-026-2). Multnomah.
Taylor, Sharon A. The Book: That Which Has Been & That Which Shall Be, Bk. I. LC 84-91294. 74p. 1985. 7.95 (ISBN 0-533-06386-8). Vantage.
The Upper Room Disciplines 1987. 382p. (Orig.). 1986. pap. 4.50 (ISBN 0-8358-0531-X). Upper Room.

BIBLE–MEDITATIONS–N. T.

Blair, J. Allen. First Corinthians: Living Wisely. LC 68-58844. 1969. pap. 5.50 (ISBN 0-87213-057-6). Loizeaux.
--Second Peter: Living Faithfully. LC 61-14600. 1961. pap. 4.95 (ISBN 0-87213-047-9). Loizeaux.
Burrows, Ruth. Living Love: Meditations on Texts from the New Testament. 1985. 5.95 (ISBN 0-87193-243-1). Dimension Bks.
Comblin, Jose. Sent from the Father: Meditations on the Fourth Gospel. Kabat, Carl, tr. from Port. LC 78-16750. Orig. Title: O Enviado do Pai. 115p. (Orig.). 1979. pap. 2.48 (ISBN 0-88344-453-4). Orbis Bks.
Gaebelein, Arno C. Gospel of Matthew. LC 61-17223. 1961. Repr. of 1910 ed. 12.95 (ISBN 0-87213-221-8). Loizeaux.
Gutzke, Manford G. Plain Talk on James. 1969. pap. 5.95 (ISBN 0-310-25561-9, 9728P). Zondervan.
Keating, Thomas. Crisis of Faith. LC 79-13036. 1979. pap. 4.00 (ISBN 0-932506-05-4). St Bedes Pubns.
Killinger, John. A Devotional Guide to the Gospels: Three Hundred Sixty-Six Meditations. 588p. 1984. Repr. 14.95 (ISBN 0-8499-3008-1, 3008-1). Word Bks.
Linden, Philip Van. The Gospel of Mark. 1976. 1.75 (ISBN 0-8199-0630-1). Franciscan Herald.
Meyer, F. B. Great Thoughts from the Upper Room. 160p. 1983. pap. 5.95 (ISBN 0-310-44601-5, 12364P, Clarion Class). Zondervan.
Sheil, Leonard. Pray Like This: Pray with Saint Paul. 1963. 3.00 (ISBN 0-8198-0128-3). Dghtrs St Paul.
Sims, Edward R. A Season with the Savior: Meditations on Mark. 1979. 6.95 (ISBN 0-8164-0413-5, HarpR); pap. 3.95 (ISBN 0-8164-2195-1). Har-Row.
Talbot, John M. Reflections on the Gospels: Daily Devotions for Radical Christian Living. 196p. (Orig.). 1986. pap. 5.95 (ISBN 0-89283-306-8). Servant.
Taylor, Kenneth N. Living Letter for the Children's Hour. LC 68-26407. (Illus.). 192p. 1968. pap. 3.95 (ISBN 0-8024-0062-0). Moody.

BIBLE–MEDITATIONS–O. T.

Berrigan, Daniel. A Book of Parables. 160p. 1977. 3.00 (ISBN 0-8164-0328-7, HarpR). Har-Row.
Blair, J. Allen. Living Reliantly: Twenty-Third Psalm. 1958. pap. 2.75 (ISBN 0-87213-054-1). Loizeaux.
Brandt, Leslie F. God Is Here-Let's Celebrate. LC 73-89877. 1969. pap. 2.95 (ISBN 0-570-03102-8, 12-2320). Concordia.
Cate, Robert. Help in Ages Past, Hope for Years to Come: Daily Devotions from the Old Testament. 201p. 1983. pap. 5.95 (ISBN 0-13-387431-1). P-H.
Holland, G. A. A True Love Story. Date not set. 14.95 (ISBN 0-533-06799-5). Vantage.
Poll, Solomon. Ancient Thoughts in Modern Perspective: A Contemporary View of the Bible. LC 68-22349. 136p. 1968. 6.95 (ISBN 0-8022-1998-5). Philos Lib.
Shepherd, J. Barrie. Encounters: Poetic Meditations on the Old Testament. LC 82-22422. 176p. (Orig.). 1983. pap. 8.95 (ISBN 0-8298-0637-7). Pilgrim NY.
Stedman, Ray C. Highlights of the Bible: Genesis-Nehemiah. LC 79-65423. 256p. 1979. pap. 3.50 (ISBN 0-8307-0656-9, S333147). Regal.

BIBLE–MIRACLES
see Jesus Christ–Miracles; Miracles

BIBLE–MISCELLANEA

Auldtomes, Niles. Deathly Trivia from the Bible. (Odd Books for Odd Moments Ser.: No. 6). (Illus.). 120p. (Orig.). 1986. pap. 5.95 (ISBN 0-930937-34-1). Winds World Pr.
Beegle, Shirley. Easy Bible Quizzes for All Ages. rev. ed. 1983. pap. 1.95 (ISBN 0-87239-657-6, 3137). Standard Pub.
Bostrom, Alice. Search the Word Bible Puzzles. (Illus.). 48p. 1983. pap. 2.50 (ISBN 0-87239-589-8, 2787). Standard Pub.
Bowen, Barbara M. Strange Scriptures That Perplex the Western Mind. 1940. pap. 3.95 (ISBN 0-8028-1511-1). Eerdmans.
Dempsey, Elbert A. God's Other Books. 1987. pap. 12.75 (ISBN 0-8309-0464-6). Herald Hse.
DeVries, Betty. Bible Activity Capsule. (Pelican Activity Ser.). pap. 0.89 (ISBN 0-8010-2896-5). Baker Bk.
--Bible Treasures Activity Book. (Pelican Activity Ser.). pap. 0.89 (ISBN 0-8010-2895-7). Baker Bk.
Dougherty, James. The Fivesquare City. 178p. 1980. 15.95 (ISBN 0-268-00946-5). U of Notre Dame Pr.
Downing, David C., compiled by. Two Hundred Twenty Misconceptions about the Bible: A Handbook of Misinformation, Misquotation, & Misinterpretations of the Bible. 1987. pap. price not set (ISBN 0-8010-2975-9). Baker Bk.
Fillmore, Charles. Mysteries of Genesis. 1936. 5.95 (ISBN 0-87159-104-9). Unity School.
Fischman, Joyce. Bible Work & Play, Vol. 2. rev. ed. (Illus.). 80p. 1984. wkbk. 5.00 (ISBN 0-8074-0256-7). UAHC.

Gay, Marcina. The Bible Puzzle Book. 128p. (Orig.). 1984. pap. 2.25 (ISBN 0-8007-8487-1, Spire Bks). Revell.

Gramelsbach, Helen. Seventy-One Creative Bible Story Projects: Patterns for Crafts, Visuals, & Learning Centers. (Illus.). 64p. 1983. pap. 4.95 (ISBN 0-87239-607-X, 2103). Standard Pub.

Harper, George. Kings on the Hill. (H. B. Bible Adventures Ser.). 224p. (Orig.). 1985. pap. 5.95 (ISBN 0-934318-70-0). Falcon Pr MT.

Heline, Corinne. New Testament, 3 Vols. Vol. 4. 8.00 (ISBN 0-87613-086-4); Vol. 5. 12.00 (ISBN 0-87613-082-1); Vol. 6. 12.00 (ISBN 0-87613-083-X). New Age.

--Occult Anatomy & the Bible. 1985. pap. 9.95 (ISBN 0-87613-093-7). New Age.

--Questions & Answers, Biblical. pap. 2.50 (ISBN 0-87613-026-0). New Age.

Johnson, Irene. Prophecy Foretold-Fulfilled: Puzzle Book. (Illus.). 48p. 1983. pap. 2.50 (ISBN 0-87239-590-1, 2788). Standard Pub.

Lanier, Roy H., Jr. Cross Questions Scripture Answers. pap. 1.75 (ISBN 0-89137-618-6). Quality Pubns.

Leary, William. Hidden Bible. 1955. 19.95 (ISBN 0-910140-07-3). C & R Anthony.

MacKemzie, Joy & Bledsoe, Shirley. The Bible Book of Lists. 128p. 1984. pap. 5.95 (ISBN 0-310-70321-2, 14035P). Zondervan.

MacKenzie, Joy & Bledsoe, Shirley. A Big Book of Bible Games & Puzzles. 192p. 1982. pap. 9.95 (ISBN 0-310-70271-2, 14029P). Zondervan.

Meredith, J. M. Meredith's Second Book of Bible Lists. LC 83-3807. 192p. (Orig.). 1983. pap. 5.95 (ISBN 0-87123-319-3, 210319). Bethany Hse.

Meredith, Joel L. Meredith's Book of Bible Lists. LC 80-14486. 288p. (Orig.). 1980. text ed. 10.95 (ISBN 0-87123-022-4, 230022); pap. 6.95 (ISBN 0-87123-023-2, 210023). Bethany Hse.

Murphy, Joseph. Pray Your Way Through It. 171p. 1973. pap. 4.00 (ISBN 0-87516-190-1). De Vorss.

Null & Watts. A Little Bit of Everything Good. pap. 5.50 (ISBN 0-89137-619-4). Quality Pubns.

Paterson, Ruby. Fun with Bible Facts. pap. 1.75 (ISBN 0-89137-620-8). Quality Pubns.

--More Fun with Bible Facts. pap. 1.75 (ISBN 0-89137-617-8). Quality Pubns.

Perkins, Percy H., Jr. Gemstones of the Bible. 2nd ed. 1986. 17.95 (ISBN 0-9603090-2-0). P H Perkins Jr.

Phillips, Bob. In Search of Bible Trivia. (Orig.). 1985. pap. 4.95 (ISBN 0-89081-458-9). Harvest Hse.

Reeds, Roger C. Biblical Graphics. 1977. 7.95 (ISBN 0-89265-058-3); pap. 5.95 (ISBN 0-89265-042-7). Randall Hse.

Sheppard, Jennifer M. The Giffard Bible. Freedberg, S. J., ed. (Outstanding Dissertations in Fine Arts Ser.). (Illus.). 450p. 1985. Repr. of 1983 ed. 60.00 (ISBN 0-8240-6867-X). Garland Pub.

Souter, John C. The Word. 96p. 1985. 4.95 (ISBN 0-8423-8394-8). Tyndale.

Stenerson, Ruth. Bible Readings for Students. LC 85-30771. 112p. (Orig.). 1986. pap. 3.95 (ISBN 0-8066-2190-7, 10-0691). Augsburg.

Stewart, Don. Ninety-Nine Questions People Ask Most about the Bible. 160p. (Orig.). 1987. pap. 5.95 (ISBN 0-8423-5107-8). Tyndale.

Stiefel, Janice. How to Plan a Bible Treasure Hunt. (Illus.). 50p. (Orig.). 1981. pap. 3.50 (ISBN 0-9605858-0-X). Second Hand.

Wlodyga, Ronald R. Health Secrets from the Bible. LC 79-64042. 1979. pap. 5.95 (ISBN 0-917182-12-X). Triumph Pub.

Yereance, Robert A. Strangers, All Strangers. LC 79-27016. 1981. 14.95 (ISBN 0-87949-151-5). Ashley Bks.

BIBLE-MUSIC

Here are entered works on musical instruments and music in the Bible (whole or parts). Works dealing with the singing of psalms in churches are entered under the heading Psalmody.

see also Music, Jewish

Johansson, Calvin M. Music & Ministry: A Biblical Counterpoint. 152p. 1984. pap. 6.95 (ISBN 0-913573-07-8). Hendrickson MA.

Stainer, John. Music of the Bible. LC 74-100657. (Music Ser). (Illus.). 1970. Repr. of 1914 ed. lib. bdg. 32.50 (ISBN 0-306-71862-6). Da Capo.

BIBLE-NAMES

see also God-Name; Jesus Christ-Name

Buechner, Frederick. Peculiar Treasures: A Biblical Who's Who. Buechner, Katherine A., tr. LC 78-20586. 1979. 12.45 (ISBN 0-06-061157-X, HarpR). Har-Row.

Fowler, Jeaneane D. Theophoric Personal Names in Ancient Hebrew: A Comparative Study. (JSOT Supplement Ser.: No. 49). 400p. 1987. text ed. 37.50x (ISBN 1-85075-038-6, Pub. by JSOT Pr England); pap. text ed. 18.95x (ISBN 1-85075-039-4, Pub. by JSOT Pr England). Eisenbrauns.

Kayne, Joseph D. Pencils & Sticks: Scripture Word-Searches for LDS Families. 32p. (Orig.). 1983. pap. 3.95 (ISBN 0-88290-218-0). Horizon Utah.

Meier, Arnold. Alttestamentliche Namengebung in England. pap. 9.00 (ISBN 0-685-13337-0). Johnson Repr.

Scott-Craig, T. S. K. A Guide to Pronouncing Biblical Names. LC 81-84713. 112p. (Orig.). 1982. pap. 3.50 (ISBN 0-8192-1292-X). Morehouse.

Severance, W. Murray. Pronouncing Bible Names. rev. ed. 96p. 5.95 (ISBN 0-87981-657-0, 4691-03). Holman Bible Pub.

Singerman, Robert. Jewish & Hebrew Onomastics: A Bibliography. (Reference Library of the Humanities: Vol. 92). (LC 76-052684). 1977. lib. bdg. 23.00 (ISBN 0-8240-9881-1). Garland Pub.

BIBLE-NATURAL HISTORY

see also Nature-Religious Interpretations

Chancellor, John. Flowers & Fruits of the Bible. LC 81-69042. (Illus.). 64p. 1982. 14.95 (ISBN 0-8253-0085-1). Beaufort Bks NY.

Duke, James A. Medicinal Plants of the Bible. (Traditional Healing Ser.: No. 10). (Illus.). 300p. 1983. lib. bdg. 49.95 (ISBN 0-932426-23-9). Trado-Medic.

Fauna & Flora of the Bible. 2nd ed. 224p. 1980. pap. 4.50x (ISBN 0-8267-0021-7, 08513, Pub. by United Bible). Am Bible.

France, Peter, et al. An Encyclopedia of Bible Animals. (Illus.). 168p. 1986. 26.95 (ISBN 0-7099-3737-7). Salem Hse Pubs.

Guest, Dean. Trees of Restoration. cancelled (ISBN 0-533-05752-3). Vantage.

James, Wilma. Gardening with Biblical Plants. LC 83-2290. (Illus.). 272p. 1983. 24.95x (ISBN 0-8304-1009-0). Nelson-Hall.

Janovy, John, Jr. Back in Keith County. LC 83-17003. (Illus.). x, 179p. 1983. pap. 5.95 (ISBN 0-8032-7560-9, BB 875, Bison). U of Nebr Pr.

Mahany, Patricia, ed. Bible Animals. (Classroom Activity Bks.). (Illus., Orig.). 1984. pap. 2.95 (ISBN 0-87239-715-7, 2445). Standard Pub.

Newton, Richard. Bible Animals & the Lessons Taught by Them. 1978. Repr. of 1888 ed. lib. bdg. 42.50 (ISBN 0-8492-1958-2). R West.

O'Brien, Marian M. Herbs & Spices of the Bible: How to Grow & Use Them. Lambert, Herbert, ed. LC 84-256. 128p. 1984. pap. 8.95 (ISBN 0-8272-1420-0). CBP.

Parmelee, Alice. The Holy Land. LC 81-80630. (All About the Bible Ser.: Bk. 6). 136p. (Orig.). 1981. pap. 5.95 (ISBN 0-8192-1290-3). Morehouse.

Paterson, John & Paterson, Katherine. Consider the Lilies: Flowers of the Bible. LC 85-43603. (Illus.). 96p. (YA) 1986. 13.70i (ISBN 0-690-04461-5, Crowell Jr Bks); PLB 13.89 (ISBN 0-690-04463-1). HarpJ.

Porter, Gene S. Birds of the Bible. 1986. Repr. lib. bdg. 35.95x (ISBN 0-89966-529-2). Buccaneer Bks.

Rabinowitz, Louis I. Torah & Flora. (Illus.). 1977. 11.95 (ISBN 0-88482-917-0, Sanhedrin Pr). Hebrew Pub.

Ragg, Lonsdale. Tree Lore in the Bible. Repr. of 1935 ed. lib. bdg. 30.00 (ISBN 0-8495-4528-5). Arden Lib.

Shoemaker, Albert M. Birds & Scripture. (Illus.). 1984. pap. 2.50 (ISBN 0-913976-07-5). Discovery Bks.

Walker, Winifred. All the Plants of the Bible. LC 78-22802. (Illus.). 1979. Repr. of 1957 ed. 15.95 (ISBN 0-385-14964-6). Doubleday.

Wood, J. G. Animals in the Bible: A Description of Their Meaning, Importance, Uses, Symbolical Value, 3 vols. (Illus.). 670p. 1986. Repr. Set. 337.45 (ISBN 0-89901-278-7). Found Class Reprints.

Zohary, Michael. Plants of the Bible: A Complete Handbook to all the Plants with 200 Full-Color Plates taken in the Natural Habitat. LC 82-4535. (Illus.). 224p. 1982. 17.95 (ISBN 0-521-24926-0). Cambridge U Pr.

BIBLE-NATURAL HISTORY-JUVENILE LITERATURE

Ferguson, Walter W. Living Animals of the Bible. (Encore Edition). 1974. 3.95 (ISBN 0-684-15245-2, ScribT). Scribner.

Peelman, Nancy. The Beasts, Birds & Fish of the Bible. LC 75-14605. (Illus.). 40p. (Orig.). 1975. pap. 4.50 (ISBN 0-8192-1197-4). Morehouse.

--The Plants of the Bible. LC 75-14607. (Illus.). 40p. (Orig.). 1975. pap. 4.50 (ISBN 0-8192-1196-6). Morehouse.

Rostron, Hilda L. Animals, Birds & Plants of the Bible. (Ladybird Ser). (Illus.). 1964. bds. 2.50 (ISBN 0-87508-830-9). Chr Lit.

BIBLE-NUMBERS

see Numbers in the Bible

BIBLE-NUMISMATICS

Madden, Frederic W. History of Jewish Coinage & of Money in the Old & New Testaments. LC 66-26486. (Library of Biblical Studies). (Illus.). 1968. 39.50x (ISBN 0-87068-082-X). Ktav.

Meshorer, Ya'akov. Coins of the Ancient World. Currier, Richard L., ed. LC 72-10795. (The Lerner Archaeology Ser.: Digging up the Past). (Illus.). 96p. 1975. PLB 8.95 (ISBN 0-8225-0835-4). Lerner Pubns.

Yeoman, R. S. Moneys of the Bible. (Illus.). 1982. Repr. of 1961 ed. softcover 7.00 (ISBN 0-915262-77-0). S J Durst.

BIBLE-OUTLINES, SYLLABI, ETC.

see Bible-Study

BIBLE-PARABLES

see also Jesus Christ-Parables

Arnot, William. The Lesser Parables of Our Lord. LC 80-8066. 464p. 1981. 12.95 (ISBN 0-8254-2121-7). Kregel.

--The Parables of Our Lord. LC 80-8065. 532p. 1981. 14.95 (ISBN 0-8254-2119-5). Kregel.

Boucher, Madeleine I. The Parables. (New Testament Message Ser.: Vol. 7). 12.95 (ISBN 0-89453-195-6); pap. 7.95 (ISBN 0-89453-130-1). M Glazier.

De La Fuente, Tomas R. Jesus Nos Habla Por Medio De Sus Parabolas. 160p. 1978. 2.95 (ISBN 0-311-04344-5). Casa Bautista.

Dodd, C. H. The Parables of the Kingdom. 176p. 1977. pap. text ed. write for info. (ISBN 0-02-330460-X, Pub. by Scribner). Macmillan.

Drew, George. The Parables in Depth. 55p. (Orig.). 1982. pap. 6.95 (ISBN 0-940754-18-5). Ed Ministries.

Drury, John. Parables in Gospels. LC 84-27652. 192p. 1985. 14.95 (ISBN 0-8245-0655-3). Crossroad NY.

Drysdale. Holiness in the Parables. pap. 2.50 (ISBN 0-686-12879-6). Schmul Pub Co.

Habershon, Ada R. Study of the Parables. LC 62-19175. 392p. 1967. 12.95 (ISBN 0-8254-2802-5); pap. 9.95 (ISBN 0-8254-2852-1). Kregel.

Jones, Peter R. The Teachings of the Parables. LC 78-654367. 1982. 13.95 (ISBN 0-8054-1371-5). Broadman.

Laidlaw, John. Studies in the Parables of Our Lord. 352p. 1984. 13.25 (ISBN 0-86524-183-X, 9521). Klock & Klock.

MacArthur, John, Jr. The Parables of the Kingdom. (John MacArthur's Bible Studies). (Orig.). 1985. pap. 3.50 (ISBN 0-8024-5112-8). Moody.

Miller, John W. Step by Step Through the Parables. LC 81-80046. 176p. (Orig.). 1981. pap. 7.95 (ISBN 0-8091-2379-7). Paulist Pr.

Morgan, G. Campbell. The Parable of the Father's Heart. (Morgan Library). 96p. 1981. pap. 2.95 (ISBN 0-8010-6118-0). Baker Bk.

Nee, Watchman. Grace for Grace. Kaung, Stephen, tr. from Chinese. 1983. pap. text ed. 2.75 (ISBN 0-935008-59-4). Christian Fellow Pubs.

Opal, Lyon. Parables. 1984. pap. 1.95 (ISBN 0-317-30409-7). Pacific Pr Pub Assn.

Schindler, Regine. The Lost Sheep. LC 80-68546. Orig. Title: Das Verlorene Shaf. (Illus.). 32p. 1982. Repr. 7.95g (ISBN 0-687-22780-1). Abingdon.

Snodgrass, Klyne. The Parable of the Wicked Tenants: An Inquiry into Parable Interpretation. 150p. 1983. pap. 48.00x (Pub. by J. C. B. Mohr BRD). Coronet Bks.

BIBLE-PARAPHRASES

Bale, John. The Image of Bothe Curches, After the Moste Wonderfull & Heavenly Revelation of Sainct John the Evangelist. LC 72-5965. (English Experience Ser.: No. 498). 872p. 1973. Repr. of 1548 ed. 51.00 (ISBN 90-221-0498-2). Walter J Johnson.

Brandt, Leslie F. Epistles Now. LC 75-38711. (Illus.). 176p. 1976. 8.50 (ISBN 0-570-03258-X, 15-2166). Concordia.

Etheridge, J. W. Targums of Onkelos & Jonathan Ben Uzziel on the Pentateuch with the Fragments of the Jerusalem Targum from the Chaldee. 1969. Repr. of 1865 ed. 59.50x (ISBN 0-87068-045-5). Ktav.

Glass, Henry A. Story of the Psalters. LC 72-1635. Repr. of 1888 ed. 18.50 (ISBN 0-404-08308-0). AMS Pr.

Jordan, Clarence. Cotton Patch Version of Luke & Acts. LC 69-18840. 1969. pap. 4.95 (ISBN 0-8329-1173-9, Assn Pr). New Century.

--Cotton Patch Version of Matthew & John. LC 83-61334. 1970. pap. 4.95 (ISBN 0-8329-1062-7, Assn Pr). New Century.

--Cotton Patch Version of Paul's Epistles. LC 68-11487. 1968. pap. 4.95 (ISBN 0-8329-1041-4, Assn Pr). New Century.

McKenzie, E. C. Mac's Giant Book of Quips & Quotes. 1983. pap. 12.95 (ISBN 0-8010-6164-4). Baker Bk.

Melander, Ingrid. Middle English Metrical Paraphrase on the Old Testament. 116p. (Orig.). 1971. pap. text ed. 30.00x. Coronet Bks.

Nevins, Albert J. The Deuterocanonical Books (Paraphrase) 1976. pap. 1.25 (ISBN 0-87973-721-2). Our Sunday Visitor.

The Way: Catholic Edition. LC 72-84415. 1116p. 1973. pap. 11.95 (ISBN 0-87973-831-6). Our Sunday Visitor.

Winship, George P. Cambridge Press, Sixteen Thirty-Eight to Sixteen Ninety-Two. facs. ed. LC 68-57346. (Essay Index Reprint Ser). 1945. 22.50 (ISBN 0-8369-1004-4). Ayer Co Pubs.

Wither, George. Exercises Upon the First Psalm. 1882. 29.50 (ISBN 0-8337-3836-4). B Franklin.

BIBLE-PATRISTIC QUOTATIONS

see Bible-Quotations, Early

BIBLE-PERIODICALS

Hebrew Union College Annual, 10 Vols. 1969. 650.00x (ISBN 0-87068-065-X). Ktav.

BIBLE-PHILOLOGY

see Greek Language, Biblical; Hebrew Language

BIBLE-PHILOSOPHY

Elliott, Charles. The Bible & Slavery: In Which the Abrahamic & Mosaic Discipline is Considered. 17.25 (ISBN 0-8369-9167-2, 9042). Ayer Co Pubs.

Fahey, Michael A. Cyprian & the Bible: A Study of Third-Century Exegesis. 701p. 1971. lib. bdg. 65.00 (Pub. by J C B Mohr BRD). Coronet Bks.

Hill, Donald E. God's Plan for the Local Church. 32p. 1982. pap. 2.49 (ISBN 0-88151-022-X). Lay Leadership.

Niceta of Remesiana, Sulp. Severus, Vincent of Lerins, Prosper. LC 50-5703. (Fathers of the Church Ser: Vol. 7). 443p. 1949. 22.95x (ISBN 0-8132-0007-5). Cath U Pr.

Polka, Brayton. The Dialectic of Biblical Critique: Interpretation & Existence. LC 84-26216. 192p. 1986. 25.00 (ISBN 0-312-19874-4). St Martin.

Runner, E. H. The Relation of the Bible to Learning. 1974. pap. 4.95 (ISBN 0-686-11988-6). Wedge Pub.

Thiselton, Anthony C. The Two Horizons. LC 79-14387. 1984. 12.95 (ISBN 0-8028-0006-8). Eerdmans.

Trigg, Joseph W. Origen: The Bible & Philosophy in the Third Century Church. (Illus.). 280p. 1983. pap. 16.95 (ISBN 0-8042-0945-6). John Knox.

BIBLE-PICTURES, ILLUSTRATIONS, ETC.

see also subdivisions Art under names of Bible characters and Biblical subjects, e.g. Jesus Christ-Art

Baynes, Pauline, illus. The Song of the Three Holy Children. LC 86-11952. (Illus.). 32p. 1986. 12.95 (ISBN 0-8050-0134-4). H Holt & Co.

Beers, V. Gilbert. My Picture Bible to See & to Share. 1982. text ed. 11.95 (ISBN 0-88207-818-6, Sonflower Bks). SP Pubns.

Bernard, Bruce. The Bible & Its Painters. LC 84-9740. (Illus.). 300p. 1984. 24.95 (ISBN 0-02-510130-7). Macmillan.

Bible Stories Coloring Book. 48p. 1973. pap. 2.50 (ISBN 0-486-20623-8). Dover.

Bible, Story of a Book. 1985. pap. 3.95 (ISBN 0-89314-818-0). Philos Res.

The Biblical Illustrator, 23 vols. 1978. 595.00 set (ISBN 0-8010-3280-6). Baker Bk.

Blake, William. Blake's Job: William Blake's Illustrations of the Book of Job. Damon, S. Foster, ed. LC 82-13585. (Illus.). 76p. 1982. pap. 8.95 (ISBN 0-87451-241-7). U Pr of New Eng.

Brymer, Harvey P. The Most Memorable Passages of the New Testament Fully & Dramatically Illustrated. (Promotion of the Arts Library). (Illus.). 141p. 1982. 69.85 (ISBN 0-86650-039-1). Gloucester Art.

Cahn, Walter. Romanesque Bible Illumination. LC 82-71593. (Illus.). 308p. 1982. 95.00x (ISBN 0-8014-1446-6). Cornell U Pr.

Chick, Jack T. King of Kings. (Sword Ser.: Vol. 1). (Illus.). 64p. (Orig.). 1980. pap. 1.65 (ISBN 0-937958-07-7). Chick Pubns.

Church Administration Department Staff. Illustrating the Gospel of Matthew. LC 81-68044. 1982. pap. 5.25 (ISBN 0-8054-2243-9). Broadman.

Coen, Rena N. Old Testament in Art. LC 77-84410. (Fine Art Books). (Illus.). 1970. PLB 5.95 (ISBN 0-8225-0168-6). Lerner Pubns.

Culbertson, Paul. Living Portraits from the Old Testament. 192p. 1978. pap. 2.95 (ISBN 0-8341-0507-1). Beacon Hill.

Davidson, Bernice F. Raphael's Bible: A Study of the Vatican Logge. LC 84-43088. (College Art Association Monographs: Vol. 39). (Illus.). 198p. 1985. 30.00 (ISBN 0-271-00388-X). Pa St U Pr.

Deal, William S. Pictorial Introduction to the Bible. large print 12.95 (ISBN 0-686-13725-6); pap. 7.95. Crusade Pubs.

--A Pictorial Introduction to the Bible. LC 67-20517. 438p. 1982. pap. 12.95 (ISBN 0-89081-363-9). Harvest Hse.

De Suassure, Eric, ed. Taize Picture Bible. LC 69-11860. (Illus.). 298p. 1968. 9.95 (ISBN 0-8006-0005-3, 1-5). Fortress.

Dillenberger, John. Benjamin West: The Context of His Life's Work. LC 76-42004. (Illus.). 238p. 1977. 25.00 (ISBN 0-911536-65-5). Trinity U Pr.

Dore, Gustave. Dore Bible Illustrations. (Illus.). 256p. 1974. pap. 8.95 (ISBN 0-486-23004-X). Dover.

Eleen, Luba. The Illustration of the Pauline Epistles in French & English Bibles of the Twelfth & Thirteenth Century. (Illus.). 1982. 89.00x (ISBN 0-19-817344-X). Oxford U Pr.

Gaines, M. C., ed. Picture Stories from the Bible: The Old Testament in Full-Color Comic-Strip Form. LC 79-66064. (Illus.). 224p. 1979. Repr. of 1943 ed. 9.95 (ISBN 0-934386-01-3). Scarf Pr.

Gutmann, Joseph. No Graven Images: Studies in Art & the Hebrew Bible. (Library of Biblical Studies). 1970. 50.00x (ISBN 0-87068-063-3). Ktav.

Habershon, Ada R. Hidden Pictures in the Old Testament. LC 82-18676. 304p. 1983. pap. 8.95 (ISBN 0-8254-2855-6). Kregel.

Hall, Terry. Bible Panorama. 1983. text ed. 9.95 (ISBN 0-88207-273-0). Victor Bks.

Hamm, Jack. Illustrated Clip Art Bible Verses. 48p. (Orig.). 1985. pap. 9.95 (ISBN 0-933545-01-0). Knight Media.

Haney, Kristine E. The Winchester Psalter: An Iconographic Study. (Illus.). 204p. 1986. text ed. 60.00x (ISBN 0-7185-1260-X, Pub. by Leicester U Pr). Humanities.

Hindman, Sandra. Text & Image in Fifteenth-Century Illustrated Dutch Bibles (1977) (Corpus Sacrae Scripturae Neerlandicae Medii Aevi Ser.: Miscellanea: Vol. 1). (Illus.). 35.00 (ISBN 90-04-04901-0). Heinman.

Hook, Frances, illus. Frances Hook Picture Book. Hayes, Wanda. (Illus.). 1963. 7.95 (ISBN 0-87239-243-0, 2868). Standard Pub.

Kessler, Herbert L. The Illustrated Bibles from Tours. LC 76-45902. (Studies in Manuscript Illumination: No. 7). (Illus.). 236p. 1977. 61.00 (ISBN 0-691-03923-2). Princeton U Pr.

Krause, Johann U. Bible Illustration. (Printed Sources of Western Art Ser.). (Ger., Illus.). 50p. 1981. pap. 35.00 slipcase (ISBN 0-915346-54-0). A Wofsy Fine Arts.

Krauss, Johann U. Baroque Cartouches for Designers & Artists. (Pictorial Archive Ser). (Illus.). 1970. pap. 6.50 (ISBN 0-486-22222-5). Dover.

Kup, Karl. Christmas Story in Medieval & Renaissance Manuscripts from the Spencer Collection, the New York Public Library. LC 70-98680. (Illus.). 128p. 1969. pap. 10.00 (ISBN 0-87104-053-0). NY Pub Lib.

Little, Charles. Ten Thousand Illustrations from the Bible. pap. 15.95 (ISBN 0-8010-5606-3). Baker Bk.

Lockman, Vic. Biblical Economics in Comics. (Illus.). 112p. (Orig.). 1985. pap. 6.00 (ISBN 0-936175-00-1). V Lockman.

--God's Law for Modern Man: God's Law or Chaos. (Illus.). 150p. (Orig.). Date not set. pap. 9.95 (ISBN 0-936175-05-2). V Lockman.

Luzwick, Dierdre. The Surrealist's Bible. LC 75-44001. (Illus.). 128p. 1976. 10.00 (ISBN 0-8246-0206-4). Jonathan David.

Marien, Matthaeus. Iconum Biblicarum. (Illus.). 320p. 1981. Repr. of 1630 ed. 34.95 (ISBN 0-939688-06-9). Directed Media.

Marks, Alfred. I've Taken a Page in the Bible. 208p. 1987. 14.95 (ISBN 0-86051-348-3). Parkwest Pubns.

Oakshott, Walter. The Two Winchester Bibles. (Illus.). 1981. 350.00x (ISBN 0-19-818235-X). Oxford U Pr.

Petersham, Maud & Petersham, Miska. Christ Child. 63p. 1931. 12.95 (ISBN 0-385-07260-0); PLB (ISBN 0-385-07319-4); pap. 5.95 (ISBN 0-385-15841-6, Zephyr). Doubleday.

Rice, Don, ed. The New Testament: A Pictorial Archive from Nineteenth-Century Sources. (Pictorial Archive Ser.). (Illus.). 192p. (Orig.). 1986. pap. 7.95 (ISBN 0-486-25073-3). Dover.

Robertson, Archibald. Word Pictures in the New Testament, 6 vols. Incl. Vol. 1. Matthew & Mark (ISBN 0-8054-1301-4); Vol. 2. Luke (ISBN 0-8054-1302-2); Vol. 3. Acts (ISBN 0-8054-1303-0); Vol. 4. Epistles of Paul (ISBN 0-8054-1304-9); Vol. 5. John & Hebrews (ISBN 0-8054-1305-7); Vol. 6. Genesis, Epistles, Revelation & John (ISBN 0-8054-1306-5). 1943. 11.95 ea.; Set. 67.50 (ISBN 0-8054-1307-3). Broadman.

Rosensaft, Jean. Chagall & the Bible. (Illus.). 160p. 1987. 24.95 (ISBN 0-87663-653-9). Universe.

Schorsch, Anita & Greif, Martin. The Morning Stars Sang: The Bible in Popular & Folk Art. LC 78-52197. (Illus.). 128p. 1980. 12.95x (ISBN 0-87663-316-5); pap. 8.95 (ISBN 0-87663-985-6). Universe.

Schwebel, Ivan. The Arena of Jerusalem. LC 86-3570. (Illus.). 1987. 39.95 (ISBN 0-915361-43-4, Dist. by Watts). Adama Pubs Inc.

Shissler, Barbara. New Testament in Art. LC 70-84411. (Fine Art Books). (Illus.). 1970. PLB 5.95 (ISBN 0-8225-0169-4). Lerner Pubns.

Strachan, James. Early Bible Illustrations: A Short Study Based on Some Fifteenth & Early Sixteenth Century Printed Texts. LC 58-571. pap. 44.80 (ISBN 0-317-10120-X, 2050748). Bks Demand UMI.

Swanson, Steve. Biblical Pictures of Water. 1986. 3.95 (ISBN 0-89536-784-X, 6802). CSS of Ohio.

Swanson, Steven. Biblical Pictures of Bread. 1985. 3.95 (ISBN 0-89536-718-1, 5802). CSS of Ohio.

Taylor, Kenneth N. Bible in Pictures for Little Eyes. (Illus.). 1956. 11.95 (ISBN 0-8024-0595-9). Moody.

--La Biblia en Cuadros para Ninos. Orig. Title: The Bible in Pictures for Little Eyes. (Span.). 190p. 1956. 13.95 (ISBN 0-8254-1706-6). Kregel.

Wees, J. Dustin & Campbell, Michael J. Darkness Visible: The Prints of John Martin. LC 86-61656. (Illus.). 88p. (Orig.). 1986. pap. 14.95 (ISBN 0-931102-20-0). S & F Clark Art.

BIBLE–POETRY

see Hebrew Poetry

BIBLE–POLITICAL SCIENCE

Johnson, James T., ed. The Bible & American Law, Politics, & Political Rhetoric. LC 83-16327. (Bible in American Culture Ser.: No. 4). 216p. 1985. 14.95 (ISBN 0-8006-0614-0, 1-614). Fortress.

--The Bible in American Law, Politics, & Political Rhetoric. LC 83-16327. (The Bible in American Culture Ser.). 1984. pap. 15.95 (ISBN 0-89130-652-8, 06 12 04). Scholars Pr GA.

Katsh, A. I. The Biblical Heritage of American Democracy. pap. 9.95x (ISBN 0-87068-488-4). Ktav.

Mouw, Richard J. Politics & the Biblical Drama. 1983. pap. 5.95 (ISBN 0-8010-6153-9). Baker Bk.

Rosenberg, Joel. King & Kin: Political Allegory in the Hebrew Bible. LC 85-45160. (Indiana Studies in Biblical Literature: Midland Bks: No. 396). 256p. 1986. 29.50x (ISBN 0-253-14624-0); pap. 10.95x (ISBN 0-253-20396-1). Ind U Pr.

BIBLE–PRAYERS

see also Jesus Christ–Prayers; Lord's Prayer; Prayer–Biblical Teaching

Boom, Corrie ten. Prayers & Promises for Every Day from the Living Bible. 272p. 1985. pap. 9.95 (ISBN 0-8027-2505-8). Walker & Co.

--Prayers & Promises for Every Day: With Corrie Ten Boom. Shaw, Luci, ed. LC 77-92352. (Day Star Devotional). 144p. 1977. pap. 2.95 (ISBN 0-87788-689-X). Shaw Pubs.

Canham, Elizabeth. Praying the Bible: A Parish Life Sourcebook. LC 86-32976. 98p. (Orig.). 1987. pap. 6.95 (ISBN 0-936384-46-8). Cowley Pubns.

Gallagher, Maureen, et al. Praying with Scripture Handbook. LC 82-62923. 176p. (Orig.). 1984. pap. 7.95 (ISBN 0-8091-2544-7); leader's manual with slides 22.95 (ISBN 0-8091-7751-X). Paulist Pr.

Geissler, Eugene S., ed. Bible Prayer Book. LC 80-71052. 528p. (Orig.). 1981. pap. 4.95 (ISBN 0-87793-218-2). Ave Maria.

Greenberg, Moshe. Biblical Prose Prayer: As a Window to the Popular Religion of Ancient Israel. LC 83-47662. (Taubman Lectures in Jewish Studies: No. 6). 78p. 1983. 16.50x (ISBN 0-520-05011-8); pap. 3.95 (ISBN 0-520-05012-6, CAL 680). U of Cal Pr.

Hintz, Debra T. Gathering Prayers. 80p. (Orig.). 1986. pap. 7.95 (ISBN 0-89622-296-9). Twenty-Third.

Liturgical Prayer Magazine. Prayers of the Faithful. Fehren, Henry, ed. 1977. pap. 11.50 (ISBN 0-916134-29-6). Pueblo Pub Co.

MacDonald, William. Old Testament Digest: Vol. 3, Job-Malachi. 1981. pap. 7.50 (ISBN 0-937396-29-X). Walterick Pubs.

Murray, Andrew. Insights for Daily Living: A Guide to Scriptural Prayer. rev. ed. 208p. Date not set. pap. 3.95 (ISBN 0-89283-329-7, Pub. by Vine Books). Servant.

Pink, Arthur W. Gleanings from Paul. LC 67-14379. 1967. pap. 10.95 (ISBN 0-8024-3005-8). Moody.

Rosage, David. Rejoice in Me: A Pocket Guide to Daily Scriptural Prayer. 256p. 1986. pocket-size 3.95 (ISBN 0-89283-298-3). Servant.

Rosage, David E. Abide in Me: A Pocket Guide to Daily Scriptural Prayer. 240p. (Orig.). 1985. pap. 3.95 (ISBN 0-89283-243-6). Servant.

--The Lord Is My Shepherd: Praying the Psalms. 196p. (Orig.). 1984. pap. 3.50 (ISBN 0-89283-196-0). Servant.

--The Pocket Book of Bible Prayers. 224p. (Orig.). 1987. compact ed. 5.95 (ISBN 0-89283-320-3). Servant.

--Scriptural Prayer Journal. 150p. (Orig.). 1987. pap. 4.95 (ISBN 0-89283-341-6). Servant.

Soderholm, Marjorie. Prayers That Make a Difference. rev. ed. Orig. Title: A Study Guide to Bible Prayers. 96p. 1980. pap. 2.50 (ISBN 0-911802-49-5). Free Church Pubns.

Stravinskas, Peter M. Prayer Book of the Bible: Reflection on the Old Testament. LC 83-63171. 160p. 1984. pap. 5.95 (ISBN 0-87973-606-2, 606). Our Sunday Visitor.

BIBLE–PRINTING

see Bible–History; Bible–Publication and Distribution

BIBLE–PROPHECIES

see also Apocalyptic Literature; Messiah–Prophecies; Prophets

Allis, Oswald T. Prophecy & the Church. 1945. pap. 5.95 (ISBN 0-87552-104-5). Presby & Reformed.

Beegle, Dewey M. Prophecy & Prediction. 274p. 1978. write for info. (ISBN 0-933462-00-X); pap. text ed. 8.95 (ISBN 0-933462-01-8). Pryor Pettengill.

Benson, Clarence H. Old Testament Survey: Poetry & Prophecy. rev. ed. 96p. 1972. pap. text ed. 4.95 (ISBN 0-910566-02-X); Perfect bdg. instr's. guide 5.95 (ISBN 0-910566-21-6). Evang Tchr.

Bloomfield, Arthur E. All Things New. LC 42-5300. 1959. pap. 7.95 (ISBN 0-87123-007-0); study guide 1.95 (ISBN 0-87123-520-X). Bethany Hse.

--The End of the Days. LC 51-9505. 288p. 1961. 8.95 (ISBN 0-87123-122-0, 210122). Bethany Hse.

Boyer, James L. Prophecy, Things to Come. pap. 4.95 (ISBN 0-88469-006-7). BMH Bks.

Brooks, Keith L. Great Prophetic Themes. (Teach Yourself the Bible Ser.). 1962. pap. 2.75 (ISBN 0-8024-3320-0). Moody.

Cantelon, Willard. The Day the Dollar Dies: Biblical Prophecy of a New World System in the End Times. LC 72-94186. 190p. 1973. (Haven Bks); pap. 2.95 (ISBN 0-88270-170-3). Bridge Pub.

Christianson, Arne. The Future Is Now. 1983. 8.95 (ISBN 0-533-05552-0). Vantage.

Clement, George H. The ABC's of the Prophetical Scriptures. pap. 2.25 (ISBN 0-685-61832-3). Reiner.

Coder, S. Maxwell. The Final Chapter. 318p. 1984. pap. 7.95 (ISBN 0-8423-0866-0). Tyndale.

Culley, Robert C. & Overholt, Thomas W., eds. Semeia Twenty-One: Anthropological Perspectives on Old Testament Prophecy. pap. 9.95 (06 20 21). Scholars Pr GA.

De Haan, M. R. Days of Noah. 5.95 (ISBN 0-310-23331-3, 9512P). Zondervan.

De Haan, Martin R. Coming Events in Prophecy. 5.95 (ISBN 0-310-23301-1). Zondervan.

Gaebelein, Arno C. The Prophet Daniel. LC 55-9465. 218p. 1968. pap. 5.95 (ISBN 0-8254-2701-0). Kregel.

--Revelation. LC 61-17225. 1960. 7.95 (ISBN 0-87213-223-4). Loizeaux.

Grudem, Wayne A. The Gift of Prophecy in One Corinthians. LC 81-40583. 358p. (Orig.). 1982. lib. bdg. 32.00 (ISBN 0-8191-2083-9); pap. text ed. 15.75 (ISBN 0-8191-2084-7). U Pr of Amer.

Hadley, E. C. Prophetic Events. 74p. pap. 4.25 (ISBN 0-88172-146-8). Believers Bkshelf.

Harris, Charles. What's Ahead? LC 80-84173. (Radiant Life Ser.). 128p. (Orig.). 1982. pap. 2.50 (ISBN 0-88243-897-2, 02-0897); teacher's ed. 3.95 (ISBN 0-88243-195-1, 32-0195). Gospel Pub.

Harris, Ralph W. Pictures of Truth. LC 76-58081. (Radiant Life Ser.). 128p. 1977. pap. 2.50 (ISBN 0-88243-905-7, 02-0905); teacher's ed 3.95 (ISBN 0-88243-175-7, 32-0175). Gospel Pub.

Haynes, Aliene M. What after World War III. 1987. 11.95 (ISBN 0-533-06842-8). Vantage.

Hengstenberg, E. W. Christology of the Old Testament. Arnold, T. K., tr. from Ger. LC 77-129739. (Kregel Reprint Library). 716p. 1988. pap. 16.95 (ISBN 0-8254-2812-2). Kregel.

Hoekema, Anthony A. The Bible & the Future. 1979. 24.95 (ISBN 0-8028-3516-3). Eerdmans.

Ironside, H. A. Daniel the Prophet. with chart 9.95 (ISBN 0-87213-357-5); chart only 0.15. Loizeaux.

Iverson, Percy E. What Is Life All About. 1985. 10.95 (ISBN 0-533-06511-9). Vantage.

Lindsay, Gordon. Israel, the False Prophet & the Two Witnesses, Vol. 5. (End of the Age Ser.). 1.25 (ISBN 0-89985-071-5). Christ Nations.

--Israel's Forty-Eight Signs of Christ Return. 2.25 (ISBN 0-89985-186-X). Christ Nations.

--Prophecies of Daniel. (Daniel Ser.). 4.00 (ISBN 0-89985-052-9). Christ Nations.

--Those Amazing Prophecies That Prove the Bible. (Prophecy Ser.). 1.25 (ISBN 0-89985-053-7). Christ Nations.

--Twenty-One Things Shortly to Come to Pass in Israel. 1.25 (ISBN 0-89985-192-4). Christ Nations.

Lindsay, Gordon & Autry, Jarry. Israel: Prophetic Signs. 72p. (Orig.). 1982. Repr. of 1968 ed. 2.95 (ISBN 0-89985-189-4). Christ Nations.

Lindsey, Hal & Carlson, C. C. The Late Great Planet Earth. 192p. 1980. pap. 3.50 (ISBN 0-553-23958-9). Bantam.

--Late Great Planet Earth. 1976. pap. 3.95 mass market (ISBN 0-310-27772-8, 18093P); pap. 5.95 (ISBN 0-310-27771-X, 18089P); study guide o.p. 0.75 (ISBN 0-310-27773-6). Zondervan.

Long, Marvin R. God's Works Through Elvis. 1979. 4.00 (ISBN 0-682-49294-9). Exposition Pr FL.

Lucas, DeWitt B. Secret Bible Prophecies. 1965. pap. 2.50 (ISBN 0-910140-10-3). C & R Anthony.

Ludwigson, Raymond. A Survey of Bible Prophecy. (Contemporary Evangelical Perspective Ser.). Orig. Title: Outlines to Bible Eschatology. 192p. 1973. Repr. 6.95 (ISBN 0-310-28421-X, 10100P). Zondervan.

Lundstrom, Lowell. Certain Hope for Uncertain Times. Orig. Title: What's Coming Next? 368p. 1984. pap. text ed. 5.95 (ISBN 0-88368-152-8). Whitaker Hse.

Mabie, C. W. Behold I Show You a Mystery. LC 80-82229. 150p. (Orig.). 1980. pap. 4.95 (ISBN 0-9601416-5-0). J C Print.

McCall, Thomas S. & Levitt, Zola. The Coming Russian Invasion of Israel. 96p. 1976. pap. 4.95 (ISBN 0-8024-1607-1). Moody.

McClain, Alva J. Daniel's Prophecy of the Seventy Weeks. pap. 3.95 (ISBN 0-310-29011-2, 10177P). Zondervan.

Meresco, Donald. New Light on the Rapture. LC 80-67028. (Orig.). 1980. pap. 6.95 (ISBN 0-937078-00-X). Bible Light.

Norquist, Marilyn. How to Read & Pray the Prophets. (Handbook of the Bible Ser.). (Orig.). 1980. pap. 1.50 (ISBN 0-89243-122-9, 44900). Liguori Pubns.

Payne, J. Barton. Encyclopedia of Biblical Prophecy. 784p. 1980. pap. 18.95 (ISBN 0-8010-7051-1). Baker Bk.

Pentecost, J. Dwight. Prophecy for Today. 224p. 1984. pap. 5.95 (ISBN 0-310-30981-6, 17018P). Zondervan.

Phillips, John. Exploring the Future. LC 82-557. 400p. 1983. 14.95 (ISBN 0-8407-5275-X). Nelson.

Plueger, Aaron L. Things to Come for Planet Earth. 1977. pap. 3.95 (ISBN 0-570-03762-X, 12-2691). Concordia.

Portillo, Carlos E. That Unknown Day. LC 85-52117. (Illus.). 400p. (Orig.). 1986. 14.95 (ISBN 0-937365-00-9); pap. 9.95 (ISBN 0-937365-01-7). WCP Pubns.

Rand, Howard B. Marvels of Prophecy. 1959. 5.00 (ISBN 0-685-08810-3). Destiny.

--Study in Daniel. 1948. 12.00 (ISBN 0-685-08814-6). Destiny.

Reinertson, Kristen E. The Holy City with Signs & Wonders. LC 86-90554. (Illus.). 150p. (Orig.). 1987. pap. text ed. 11.95 (ISBN 0-9617564-5-4). Skoglie Storevik Pubs.

Relfe, Mary S. The New Money System. 271p. 1982. pap. 6.95 (ISBN 0-9607986-1-7). Ministries.

--When Your Money Fails. 234p. (Orig.). 1981. pap. text ed. 5.95 (ISBN 0-9607986-0-9). Ministries.

Smith, Chuck. Future Survival. (Illus.). 112p. (Orig.). 1980. pap. 1.50 (ISBN 0-936728-02-7). Word for Today.

Strauss, Lehman. Prophetic Mysteries Revealed: The Prophetic Significance of the Parables of Matthew 13 & the Letters of Revelation 2-3. LC 80-17540. 256p. 1980. 9.95 (ISBN 0-87213-832-1). Loizeaux.

Swafford, Mrs. Z. W. He Will Come. 3rd ed. (Illus.). 128p. 1974. pap. 2.00 (ISBN 0-89114-009-3). Baptist Pub Hse.

Swinger, Marlys. Kingdom of God's Justice: As Foretold by Isaiah. 60p. (Choral edition). 1972. pap. 2.50 (ISBN 0-87486-012-1); L.P. Record-Mono 4.95. Plough.

Taber, William. The Prophetic Stream. LC 84-61291. (Orig.). 1984. pap. 2.50x (ISBN 0-87574-256-4). Pendle Hill.

Tan, Paul L. The Interpretation of Prophecy. 1975. 8.95 (ISBN 0-88469-000-8). BMH Bks.

Tatford, Frederick A. God's Program of the Ages. LC 67-26075. 160p. (Orig.). 1967. 4.95 (ISBN 0-8254-3800-4). Kregel.

Taylor, Charles R. Beware America! Orig. Title: A Message to the President. (Illus.). 48p. (Orig.). 1983. pap. 3.50 (ISBN 0-937682-06-3). Today Bible.

--Death of Sadat...Start of World War III. (Illus.). 96p. (Orig.). 1982. pap. 3.95 (ISBN 0-937682-05-5). Today Bible.

Taylor, G. F. Rainbow. pap. 2.00 (ISBN 0-911866-61-2). Advocate.

Urquhart, John. Wonders of Prophecy. pap. 3.95 (ISBN 0-87509-155-5). Chr Pubns.

Walker, Paul L. Knowing the Future. LC 76-710. 1976. pap. 1.99 (ISBN 0-87148-477-3). Pathway Pr.

Walvoord, John F. Israel in Prophecy. 1978. pap. 4.95 (ISBN 0-310-34081-0, 10970P). Zondervan.

--Nations in Prophecy. 1967. pap. 5.95 (ISBN 0-310-34101-9, 12159P). Zondervan.

Westermann, Claus. A Thousand Years & a Day. LC 62-8544. 292p. 1982. pap. 8.95 (ISBN 0-8006-1913-7, 1-1913). Fortress.

Wittreich, Joseph A., Jr. Visionary Poetics: Milton's Tradition & His Legacy. LC 78-52569. (Illus.). 324p. 1979. 29.95 (ISBN 0-87328-101-2). Huntington Lib.

Woodrow, Ralph. Great Prophecies of the Bible. (Illus.). 200p. 1971. 4.95 (ISBN 0-916938-02-6). R Woodrow.

--His Truth Is Marching On! Advanced Studies on Prophecy in the Light of History. (Illus.). 1977. pap. 4.95 (ISBN 0-916938-03-4). R Woodrow.

BIBLE–PSYCHOLOGY

see also Christianity–Psychology; Psychology, Religious

Chambers, Oswald. Biblical Psychology. 1973. pap. 3.95 (ISBN 0-87508-099-5). Chr Lit.

Cohen, Edmund D. The Mind of the Bible-Believer. 425p. 1986. 19.95 (ISBN 0-87975-341-2). Prometheus Bks.

Krutza, William J. Facing Yourself in the Bible: Studies in Human Personalities from the Bible. (Contemporary Discussion Ser.). 128p. 1976. pap. 1.25 (ISBN 0-8010-5369-2). Baker Bk.

Reik, Tneodor. Dogma & Compulsion. LC 72-9369. 332p. 1973. Repr. of 1951 ed. lib. bdg. 45.00x (ISBN 0-8371-6577-6, REDC). Greenwood.

Theissen, Gerd. Psychological Aspects of Pauline Theology. Galvin, John P., tr. from Ger. LC 86-45196. 512p. 1986. 34.95 (ISBN 0-8006-0789-9). Fortress.

Walsh, J. P. The Mighty from Their Thrones: Power in the Biblical Tradition. LC 86-45198. (Overtures to Biblical Theology Ser.). 224p. 1987. pap. 12.95 (ISBN 0-8006-1546-8). Fortress.

Wuellner, Wilhelm H. & Leslie, Robert C. The Surprising Gospel: Intriguing Psychological Insights from the New Testament. 176p. (Orig.). 1983. pap. 11.95 (ISBN 0-687-40724-9). Abingdon.

BIBLE–PUBLICATION AND DISTRIBUTION

Holt, Pat. Gideon: God's Warrior. 32p. 1986. 7.95 (ISBN 0-687-14220-2). Abingdon.

Kohlenberger, John R. All about Bibles. (Illus.). 76p. 1985. pap. 0.95 (ISBN 0-19-526951-9). Oxford U Pr.

BIBLE–QUOTATIONS, EARLY

see also Bible–Criticism, Textual

Barnard, P. M., ed. The Biblical Text of Clement of Alexandria in the Four Gospels & the Acts of the Apostles. (Texts & Studies Ser.: No. 1, Vol. 5, Pt. 5). pap. 13.00 (ISBN 0-8115-1700-4). Kraus Repr.

Burkitt, F. C. S. Ephraim's Quotations from the Gospel. (Texts & Studies Ser.: No. 1, Vol. 7, Pt. 2). pap. 13.00 (ISBN 0-8115-1704-7). Kraus Repr.

Cook, Albert S. Biblical Quotations in Old English Prose Writers: Second Series. LC 74-7275. 1903. lib. bdg. 40.00 (ISBN 0-686-96720-8). Folcroft.

Kimball, William R. What the Bible Says about the Great Tribulation. 304p. 1985. pap. 7.95 (ISBN 0-8010-5466-4). Baker Bk.

Levine, Mark & Rachlis, Eugene, eds. The Complete Book of Bible Quotations. pap. 12.95 (ISBN 0-671-49864-9). PB.

Puritan Treasury of Quotations. pap. 6.45 (ISBN 0-85151-249-6). Banner of Truth.

Savran, George. Quoted Direct Speech. (Studies in Biblical Literature). Date not set. price not set. Ind U Pr.

Speake, Jennifer, ed. Biblical Quotations. LC 83-1511. 208p. 1983. 17.95 (ISBN 0-87196-241-1). Facts on File.

BIBLE–RACE PROBLEMS

see Bible–Ethnology

BIBLE–READERS

see Readers–Bible

BIBLE–READING

Bennett, Robert A. & Edwards, O. C. The Bible for Today's Church. (The Church's Teaching Ser.: Vol. 2). 320p. 1979. 5.95 (ISBN 0-8164-0419-4, HarpR); pap. 4.95 (ISBN 0-8164-2215-X); users guide 1.50 (ISBN 0-8164-2222-2). Har-Row.

Birky, Lela. The Bible Nurture & Reader Ser. 1969. write for info. (ISBN 0-686-05603-5); Span. ed. write for info.; tchr's. ed. avail. (ISBN 0-686-05604-3). Rod & Staff.

Brandt, Leslie F. Bible Readings for Troubled Times. LC 84-18617. 112p. (Orig.). 1984. pap. 3.95 (ISBN 0-8066-2130-3, 10-0686). Augsburg.

Eshbaugh, Howard. Hearing the Word: Scripture in Worship. 1980. 4.50 (ISBN 0-89536-413-1, 0833). CSS of Ohio.

Evelan, R. R. How to Read the Bible: A Step by Step Manual. 1984. 5.95 (ISBN 0-89536-700-9, 4883). CSS of Ohio.

--How to Read the Bible: Leader's Guide. 1984. 2.25 (ISBN 0-89536-716-5, 4891). CSS of Ohio.

Hoerber, Robert G. Reading the New Testament for Understanding. 192p. 1986. pap. 7.50 (ISBN 0-570-03988-6, 12-3016). Concordia.

Hort, Erasmus. The Bible Book: Resources for Reading the New Testament. 172p. 1983. pap. 12.95x (ISBN 0-8245-0557-3). Crossroad NY.

Huggett, Joyce. The Joy of Listening to God. LC 86-27689. 240p. (Orig.). 1987. pap. 6.95 (ISBN 0-87784-729-0). Inter-Varsity.

Huxhold, Harry N. Bible Readings for Church Workers. LC 84-21574. 112p. (Orig.). 1984. pap. 3.95 (ISBN 0-8066-2132-X, 10-0684). Augsburg.

Klug, Ron & Klug, Lyn. Bible Readings for Parents. LC 81-52277. (Bible Readings Ser.). 112p. (Orig.). 1982. pap. 3.95 (ISBN 0-8066-1909-0, 10-0679). Augsburg.

McKeever, James. Victory Bible Reading Plan. 1984. 1.00 (ISBN 0-86694-102-9). Omega Pubns OR.

Maly, Eugene H. The Word Alive: Reflections & Commentaries on the Sunday Readings Cycles A, B, & C. LC 81-20571. (Illus.). 322p. 1982. pap. 12.95 (ISBN 0-8189-0416-X). Alba.

Mueller, Charles S. Bible Reading for Teenagers. LC 81-52274. (Bible Readings Ser.). 112p. (Orig.). 1981. pap. 3.95 (ISBN 0-8066-1906-6, 10-0681). Augsburg.

No Volvera a Mi Vacia. LC 76-55490. (Span.). 365p. (Orig.). 1976. pap. 3.75 (ISBN 0-89922-080-0). Edit Caribe.

Not by Bread Alone: Bible Readings for the Weekdays of Lent. (Illus.). 112p. 1972. pap. 2.45 (ISBN 0-87793-087-2). Ave Maria.

The Office of Readings. 1952p. 1984. 26.95 (ISBN 0-8198-5407-7). Dghtrs St Paul.

Paul, Cathy. God's Inspired Holy Word Says... 1981. 4.95 (ISBN 0-8062-1785-5). Carlton.

Ruffcorn, Kevin E. Bible Readings for Growing Christians. LC 84-18424. 112p. (Orig.). 1984. pap. 3.95 (ISBN 0-8066-2131-1, 10-0685). Augsburg.

Seerveld, Calvin. Balaam's Apocalyptic Prophecies: A Study in Reading Scripture. pap. 3.95 (ISBN 0-88906-110-6). Wedge Pub.

Shotwell, Berenice M. Getting Better Acquainted with Your Bible. LC 75-173349. (Illus.). 1976. pap. 16.50 (ISBN 0-9603026-1-1). Shadwold.

Stenerson, Ruth. Bible Reading for Singles. LC 80-65543. (Bible Reading Ser.). 112p. (Orig.). 1980. pap. 3.95 (ISBN 0-8066-1788-8, 10-0678). Augsburg.

--Bible Reading for Teachers. LC 81-52275. (Bible Readings Ser.). 112p. (Orig.). 1982. pap. 3.95 (ISBN 0-8066-1907-4, 10-0680). Augsburg.

Syverson, Betty G. Bible Readings for Caregivers. (Bible Readings Ser.). 112p. (Orig.). 1987. pap. 3.95 (ISBN 0-8066-2276-8, 10-0695). Augsburg.

Tengbom, Mildred & Tengbom, Luverne. Bible Readings for Families. LC 80-65542. (Bible Readings Ser.). 112p. (Orig.). 1980. pap. 3.95 (ISBN 0-8066-1787-X, 10-0677). Augsburg.

Watkins, Morris. Literacy, Bible Reading & Church Growth Through the Ages. LC 78-15315. (Illus.). 1978. pap. 5.95 (ISBN 0-87808-325-1). William Carey Lib.

Williamson, Denise J. Bible Readings on God's Creation. (Bible Readings Ser.). 112p. (Orig.). 1987. pap. 3.95 (ISBN 0-8066-2277-6, 10-0696). Augsburg.

Wold, Margaret & Wold, Erling. Bible Readings for Couples. LC 80-65541. (Bible Reading Ser.). 112p. (Orig.). 1980. pap. 3.95 (ISBN 0-317-40483-0, 10-0676). Augsburg.

BIBLE–RELATION OF N. T. TO O. T.

Bruce, Frederick F., ed. New Testament Development of Old Testament Themes. 1969. pap. 6.95 (ISBN 0-8028-1729-7). Eerdmans.

Collins, Adela Y. Crisis & Catharsis: The Power of the Apocalypse. LC 83-26084. 180p. 1984. pap. 11.95 (ISBN 0-664-24521-8). Westminster.

Meyer, F. B. Christ in Isaiah. 1970. pap. 3.95 (ISBN 0-87508-341-2). Chr Lit.

BIBLE–REVELATION

see Bible–Inspiration

BIBLE–SCIENCE

see Bible and Science

BIBLE–SERMONS

Here are entered works containing sermons which are successively based on at least one whole book of the Bible, virtually forming a commentary in sermon form.

Almirudus, Hiram, ed. Antologia de Homilias Biblicas, Vol. IV. (Span.). 162p. 1981. 6.95 (ISBN 0-87148-025-5). Pathway Pr.

--Antologia de Homilias Biblicas, Vol. V. (Span.). 158p. 1982. 6.95 (ISBN 0-87148-026-3). Pathway Pr.

--Antologia de Homilias Biblicas, Vol. VI. (Span.). 158p. 1982. 6.95 (ISBN 0-87148-027-1). Pathway Pr.

--Antologia de Homilias Biblicas, Vol. III. (Span.). 148p. 1980. 6.95 (ISBN 0-87148-024-7). Pathway Pr.

--Antologia de Homilias Biblicas, Vol. I. (Span.). 159p. 1977. 6.95 (ISBN 0-87148-022-0). Pathway Pr.

--Antologia de Homilias Biblicas, Vol. II. (Span.). 159p. 1979. 6.95 (ISBN 0-87148-023-9). Pathway Pr.

Augsburg Sermons, Epistles, Series B: Sermons on Epistle Texts from the New Lectionary & Calendar. LC 78-52205. 1978. 15.95 (ISBN 0-8066-1666-0, 10-0523). Augsburg.

Boles, H. Leo. Questions & Answers: Sermon Outlines & Bible Study Notes. 1985. pap. 8.95 (ISBN 0-89225-274-X). Gospel Advocate.

Braga, James. Como Preparar Mensajes Biblicos. Orig. Title: How to Prepare Bible Messages. Tr. of How to Prepare Bible Messages. (Span.). 320p. 1986. pap. 9.50 (ISBN 0-8254-1072-X). Kregel.

Cornils, Stanley. Thirty-Four Two-Minute Talks for Youth & Adults. 64p. 1985. pap. 2.95 (ISBN 0-87239-868-4, 2883). Standard Pub.

Korth, Bob, compiled by. Object Talks for Special Days. (Illus.). 48p. (Orig.). 1984. pap. 2.95 (ISBN 0-87239-723-8, 2859). Standard Pub.

Macartney, Clarence E. Woman of Tekoah & Other Sermons on Bible Characters. (Macartney Bible Characters Library). 1977. pap. 2.95 (ISBN 0-8010-6020-6). Baker Bk.

Mayhue, Richard. How to Interpret the Bible for Yourself. (Moody Press Electives Ser.). (Orig.). 1986. pap. text ed. 3.95 (ISBN 0-8024-0732-3); leader's guide 4.95 (ISBN 0-8024-0733-1). Moody.

Michaels, Larry. Easy Bible Object Talks. (Illus.). 48p. 1985. pap. 2.95 (ISBN 0-87239-846-3, 2886). Standard Pub.

Robertson, Frederick W. Sermons on the Bible. 1978. Repr. of 1906 ed. lib. bdg. 35.00 (ISBN 0-8482-2315-2). Norwood Edns.

Spray, Russell E. Scriptural Sermon Outlines. 64p. 1987. pap. price not set (ISBN 0-8010-8277-3). Baker Bk.

BIBLE–SERMONS–N. T.

Campderros, Daniel. Bosquejos Biblicos, Tomo III. 96p. 1986. pap. 2.50 (ISBN 0-311-43033-3). Casa Bautista.

Criswell, W. A. Expository Sermons on Revelation, 5 Vols. in 1. 1961-66. 24.95 (ISBN 0-310-22840-9, 9442). Zondervan.

De Haan, Mr. R. Hebrews. pap. 6.95 (ISBN 0-310-23371-2, 9506P). Zondervan.

Finney, Charles G. & Parkhurst, L. B. Principles of Liberty. rev. ed. LC 82-20705. (Finney's Sermons on Romans Ser.). 194p. (Orig.). 1983. pap. 5.95 (ISBN 0-87123-475-0, 210475). Bethany Hse.

Ford, W. Herschel. Sermons You Can Preach on Acts. 352p. Date not set. pap. 10.95 (ISBN 0-310-38461-3). Zondervan.

--Sermons You Can Preach on John: Simple Sermons. 432p. pap. 12.95 (ISBN 0-310-38451-6, 9835P). Zondervan.

--Sermons You Can Preach on Matthew. 240p. (Orig.). 1985. pap. 8.95 (ISBN 0-310-45521-9, 9834P). Zondervan.

--Simple Sermons on the New Testament Texts. 112p. 1985. pap. 3.95 (ISBN 0-8010-3517-1). Baker Bk.

Hooker, Richard. Two Sermons Upon S. Judes Epistle. LC 70-26033. (English Experience Ser.: No. 195). 56p. 1969. Repr. of 1614 ed. 8.00 (ISBN 90-221-0195-9). Walter J Johnson.

Ironside, H. A. Corinthians One. 12.95x (ISBN 0-87213-354-0). Loizeaux.

--Corinthians Two. 8.95 (ISBN 0-87213-355-9). Loizeaux.

--Gospel of John. 16.95 (ISBN 0-87213-373-7). Loizeaux.

--Gospel of Luke. 14.95 (ISBN 0-87213-376-1). Loizeaux.

--Gospel of Mark. 8.95 (ISBN 0-87213-377-X). Loizeaux.

Lovette, Roger. Questions Jesus Raised. LC 85-15137. 1986. 4.95 (ISBN 0-8054-2259-5). Broadman.

Meyer, Nathan M. From Now to Eternity: Sermons from Revelation. pap. 6.00 (ISBN 0-88469-035-0). BMH Bks.

Morrison, G. H. Morrison on John, Vol. I. new ed. (The Glasgow Pulpit Ser.). 1979. pap. 4.95 (ISBN 0-89957-534-X). AMG Pubs.

--Morrison on John, Vol. II. new ed. (The Glasgow Pulpit Ser.). 1979. pap. 4.95 (ISBN 0-89957-535-8). AMG Pubs.

--Morrison on Luke, Vol. I. new ed. (The Glasgow Pulpit Ser.). 1979. pap. 4.95 (ISBN 0-89957-532-3). AMG Pubs.

--Morrison on Luke, Vol. II. new ed. (The Glasgow Pulpit Ser.). 1979. pap. 4.95 (ISBN 0-89957-533-1). AMG Pubs.

--Morrison on Mark. new ed. (The Glasgow Pulpit Ser.). 1979. pap. 4.95 (ISBN 0-89957-531-5). AMG Pubs.

--Morrison on Matthew, Vol. I. new ed. (The Glasgow Pulpit Ser.). 1979. pap. 4.95 (ISBN 0-89957-528-5). AMG Pubs.

--Morrison on Matthew, Vol. II. new ed. (The Glasgow Pulpit Ser.). 1979. pap. 4.95 (ISBN 0-89957-529-3). AMG Pubs.

--Morrison on Matthew, Vol. III. new ed. (The Glasgow Pulpit Ser.). 1979. pap. 4.95 (ISBN 0-89957-530-7). AMG Pubs.

Redpath, Alan. Blessings Out of Buffetings: Studies in Second Corinthians. 256p. 1965. 11.95 (ISBN 0-8007-0026-0). Revell.

Thomas, W. Griffith. Outline Studies in Acts. 1956. pap. 10.95 (ISBN 0-8028-1570-7). Eerdmans.

BIBLE–SERMONS–O. T.

Augsburg Sermons: Old Testament Lessons - Series C. LC 79-50092. 264p. 1979. 15.95 (ISBN 0-8066-1703-9, 10-0529). Augsburg.

Bechett, Wendy M., tr. John of Ford: Sermons on the Song of Songs I. LC 77-3697. (Cistercian Fathers Ser.: No. 29). 1977. 14.95 (ISBN 0-87907-629-1). Cistercian Pubns.

Criswell, W. A. Expository Sermons on the Book of Ezekiel. 272p. 1987. 12.95 (ISBN 0-310-23010-1, 18352). Zondervan.

De Haan, M. R. Revelation. 1956. 13.95 (ISBN 0-310-23440-9, 9498P). Zondervan.

Gilbert Of Hoyland. Gilbert of Hoyland, Sermons on the Song of Songs, II. (Fathers Ser.: No. 20). 1979. 8.95 (ISBN 0-87907-420-5). Cistercian Pubns.

Hooper, John. The Early Writings of John Hooper. 1843. 51.00 (ISBN 0-384-24210-3). Johnson Repr.

--The Later Writings of Bishop Hooper. 1852. 55.00 (ISBN 0-384-24211-1). Johnson Repr.

McCurley, Foster R., Jr. Proclaiming the Promise: Christian Preaching from the Old Testament. LC 74-76921. 176p. (Orig.). 1974. pap. 5.75 (ISBN 0-8006-1083-0, 1-1083). Fortress.

Rabinowitz, Louis I. Torah & Flora. (Illus.). 1977. 11.95 (ISBN 0-88482-917-0, Sanhedrin Pr). Hebrew Pub.

Redpath, Alan. Victorious Christian Living: Studies in the Book of Joshua. 256p. 1955. 10.95 (ISBN 0-8007-0336-7). Revell.

Sermons on the Final Verses of the Song of Songs. (Cistercian Fathers Ser.: Nbr. 43). 1982. 21.95 (ISBN 0-87907-643-7). Cistercian Pubns.

Stulman, Louis. The Prose Sermons of the Book of Jeremiah: A Redescription of the Correspondence with Deuteronomistic Literature in Light of Recent Text-Critical Research. (Society of Biblical Literature Dissertation Ser.). 166p. 1987. 17.25 (ISBN 0-89130-960-8, 06-01-83); pap. 13.25 (ISBN 0-89130-961-6). Scholars Pr GA.

Thielicke, Helmut. How the World Began: Man in the First Chapters of the Bible. Doberstein, John W., tr. from Ger. LC 61-6756. 324p. 1961. pap. 6.95 (ISBN 0-8006-1894-7, 1-1894). Fortress.

Thomas, David. Sermon Notes on the Psalms. Lockyer, Herbert, ed. Tr. of The Homilist. 320p. (Orig.). Date not set. pap. 10.95 (ISBN 0-8254-3116-6). Kregel.

Wolff, Hans W. Old Testment & Christian Preaching. Kohl, Margaret, tr. LC 85-45477. 112p. 1986. pap. 8.95 (ISBN 0-8006-1905-6, 1-1905). Fortress.

Wood, Charles R. Sermon Outlines on the Psalms. LC 85-23735. 64p. (Orig.). 1986. pap. 2.95 (ISBN 0-8254-4033-5). Kregel.

BIBLE–SOCIOLOGY

see Sociology, Biblical

BIBLE–STORIES

see Bible Stories

Jackson, Forrest W. Their Story-Our Story. LC 85-6623. 1985. pap. 4.95 (ISBN 0-8054-3618-9, 4236-18). Broadman.

BIBLE–STUDY

see also Bible Stories

Ackland, Donald F., et al. Broadman Comments, 1986-87. (Orig.). 1986. pap. 5.95 (ISBN 0-8054-1553-X). Broadman.

Adar, Zvi. Humanistic Values in the Bible. Tcherikover, Victor, tr. from Hebrew. LC 67-24730. 429p. 1967. 11.00 (ISBN 0-935457-02-X). Reconstructionist Pr.

Adeney, Carol, ed. This Morning with God. LC 68-28080. 1978. pap. 9.95 (ISBN 0-87784-870-X). Inter-Varsity.

Aderman, James. Challeging Christianity: Leader's Guide. Fischer, William E., ed. (Bible Class Course Ser.). 48p. 1986. pap. 2.95 (ISBN 0-938272-25-X). WELS Board.

--I'm Listening, Lord: Leader's Guide. Fischer, William E., ed. (Bible Class Course for Young Adults Ser.). 64p. 1984. pap. text ed. 2.95 (ISBN 0-938272-19-5). Wels Board.

--I'm Listening, Lord: Student's Guide. Fischer, William E., ed. (Bible Class Course for Young Adults Ser.). (Illus.). 48p. 1984. pap. text ed. 2.95 (ISBN 0-938272-18-7). Wels Board.

Aderman, James & Fischer, William E. Challenging Christianity: Student's Guide. (Bible Class Course Ser.). (Illus.). 40p. 1986. pap. 2.95 (ISBN 0-938272-24-1). WELS Board.

Aderman, James A. A Survival Guide to the Last Times. Fischer, William E., ed. (Bible Class Course for Young Adults Ser.). (Illus.). 64p. (Orig.). 1987. pap. text ed. 2.95 (ISBN 0-938272-30-6); tchr's ed. 2.95 (ISBN 0-938272-29-2). Wels Board.

Alexander, J. W. Plan Para Memorizar las Escrituras. Orig. Title: Fire in My Bones. 48p. 1981. Repr. of 1979 ed. 1.75 (ISBN 0-311-03660-0). Casa Bautista.
Alexander, John W. Scripture Memory One Hundred One. 1975. pap. 0.75 (ISBN 0-87784-153-5). Inter-Varsity.
Anderson, Ann K. My Favorite Verse: Favorite Ser. LC 85-70000. 24p. 1986. pap. 4.95 (ISBN 0-89636-209-4). Accent Bks.
Anderson, Bernhard W. The Unfolding Drama of the Bible. rev. ed. LC 78-14057. 1971. pap. 3.95 (ISBN 0-8329-1068-6, Assn Pr). New Century.
Arndt, William F. Bible Difficulties & Seeming Contradictions. 1987. pap. 8.95 (ISBN 0-570-04470-7). Concordia.
Augsburger, David W. The Book that Reads You. (New Life Ser.). pap. 3.00 (ISBN 0-8361-1685-2). Herald Pr.
Bailey, Ron & Bailey, Betty. Team Teaching Children in Bible Class. 1972. 4.95 (ISBN 0-931097-05-3). Sentinel Pub.
Barber, Cyril J. How to Gain Life: Changing Insights from the Book of Books. 1979. pap. 1.00 (ISBN 0-88469-100-4). BMH Bks.
Barnhouse, Donald C. Expositions of Bible Doctrines, 10 vols. in four. (Bible Study). 1952-64. Set. 49.95 (ISBN 0-8028-3014-5). Eerdmans.
Barr, James. The Scope & Authority of the Bible. LC 80-21394. 164p. 1981. pap. 7.95 (ISBN 0-664-24361-4). Westminster.
Basic Bible Study Library, 2 vols. Incl. Zondervan Pictorial Bible Dictionary. Tenney, Merrill C., ed. (Illus.); Matthew Henry's Commentary on the Whole Bible. Henry, Matthew. Set. slip case 48.90. Zondervan.
Baughman, Ray E. Abundant Life. 1959. pap. 3.50 (ISBN 0-8024-0047-7). Moody.
Be Strong & Courageous (Joshua) Leader's Guide. (New Horizons Bible Study Ser.). 47p. 1986. pap. 1.95 (ISBN 0-89367-112-6). Light & Life.
Be Strong & Courageous (Joshua) Student Guide. (New Horizons Bible Study Ser.). 64p. (Orig.). 1986. pap. 2.50 (ISBN 0-89367-111-8). Light & Life.
Beers, Gilbert. Victor Handbook of Bible Knowledge. Popular ed. LC 81-50695. 640p. 1981. 29.95 (ISBN 0-88207-811-9); pap. 21.95 (ISBN 0-88207-808-9). Victor Bks.
Bennett, et al. Twenty-Six Bible Programs for Preschools. (Illus.). 96p. 1987. 8.95 (ISBN 0-87403-147-8, 3417). Standard Pub.
Bennett, Georgaan. What the Bible Says About Goodness. LC 80-69626. (What the Bible Says Ser.). 405p. 1981. 13.50 (ISBN 0-89900-080-0). College Pr Pub.
Bensen, D. R. Bibical Limericks. 1986. pap. 6.95 (Pub. by Ballantine-Epiphany). Ballantine.
Berg, Miguel. El Placer De Estudiar la Biblia. (Span.). 127p. (Orig.). 1973. pap. 2.95 (ISBN 0-89922-026-6). Edit Caribe.
The Bible Companion. (Illus.). 1985. 17.95 (ISBN 0-687-03148-6). Abingdon.
The Bible: God's Wonderful Book. (Teaching Bks.). (Illus.). 10p. 1968. pap. text ed. 2.95 (ISBN 0-86508-150-6). BCM Intl Inc.
Bisagno, John R. Great Mysteries of the Bible. LC 81-67997. 1982. 7.95 (ISBN 0-8054-1952-7). Broadman.
Blaiklock, E. M. Blaiklock's Handbook to the Bible. 256p. 1981. pap. 6.95 (ISBN 0-8007-5055-1, Power Bks). Revell.
Blomgren, David K. Bible Survey. (Illus.). 70p. 1979. pap. 6.25 (ISBN 0-914936-39-5). Bible Temple.
Boadt, Lawrence, et al, eds. Biblical Studies: Meeting Ground of Jews & Christians. LC 80-82812. (Stimulus Bk). 232p. (Orig.). 1981. pap. 7.95 (ISBN 0-8091-2344-4). Paulist Pr.
Boerma, Conrad. The Rich, the Poor & the Bible. rev. ed. Bowden, John, tr. from Dutch. LC 80-15337. 120p. 1980. pap. 5.95 (ISBN 0-664-24349-5). Westminster.
Boice, James M. Standing on the Rock: The Importance of Biblical Inerrancy. (Orig.). 1984. leader's guide 2.95 (ISBN 0-8423-6604-0); pap. 4.95 (ISBN 0-8423-6603-2). Tyndale.
Bolton, Barbara & Smith, Charles. Creative Bible Learning for Children, Grades 1-6. LC 77-74532. 208p. 1977. pap. 3.95 (ISBN 0-8307-0478-7, 9100105). Regal.
Boone, Julia R. Getting to Know Your Bible. LC 81-69259. 176p. 1984. pap. 9.95 (ISBN 0-8054-1140-2). Broadman.
Bovon, Francois & Rouiller, Gregoire, eds. Exegesis: Problems of Method & Exercises in Reading. Miller, Donald G, tr. from Fr. LC 78-27622. (Pittsburgh Theological Monographs: No. 21). Orig. Title: Exegesis; Problemes de Methode et Exercices de Lecture. 1978. pap. 15.00 (ISBN 0-915138-25-5). Pickwick.
Braga, James. How to Prepare Bible Messages. rev. ed. LC 81-14132. 1982. pap. 6.95 (ISBN 0-930014-71-5). Multnomah.
Breneman, Mervin, ed. Biblia con Notas. (Span.). 1696p. 1981. black imitation leather 15.95 (ISBN 0-89922-164-5); black imitation leather 19.95 (ISBN 0-89922-364-8); red imitation leather 15.95 (ISBN 0-89922-264-1); red imitation leather 19.95 (ISBN 0-89922-464-4). Edit Caribe.
Brettschneider, Diana, et al. Twenty-Six Bible Programs for Preschoolers. 96p. 1987. tchr's wkbk. 8.95 (ISBN 0-87403-213-X, 3413). Standard Pub.
Brewer, Ralph J. Journey Through the Bible. 167p. (Orig.). 1983. pap. text ed. 5.95 (ISBN 0-87148-450-1); instrs. guide 2.50 (ISBN 0-87148-451-X). Pathway Pr.
Bright, Bill. Handbook for Christian Maturity. 360p. (Orig.). 1981. pap. 8.95 (ISBN 0-86605-010-8). Campus Crusade.
--Handbook of Concepts for Living. 545p. (Orig.). 1981. pap. 8.95 (ISBN 0-86605-011-6). Campus Crusade.
--Ten Basic Steps Teachers Manual. 2nd ed. 512p. 1983. pap. 8.95 (ISBN 0-918956-97-8). Campus Crusade.
Briscoe, Jill. Evergrowing, Evergreen. 96p. 1986. pap. 4.95 (ISBN 0-89693-255-9). Victor Bks.
Briscoe, Stuart & Briscoe, Jill. Our Favorite Verse. LC 86-71753. (My Favorite Verse Ser.). 24p. 1987. pap. 4.95 (ISBN 0-89636-224-8). Accent Bks.
Bromiley, Geoffrey W., ed. The International Standard Bible Encyclopedia, Vol. III, K-P. rev. ed. (International Standard Bible Encyclopedia Ser.). (Illus.). 1080p. 1986. 37.50 (ISBN 0-8028-8163-7). Eerdmans.
--International Standard Bible Encyclopedia, Vol. 1, A-D. rev. ed. LC 79-12280. (Illus.). 1979. 37.50 (ISBN 0-8028-8161-0). Eerdmans.
Brooks, D. P. Bible: How to Understand & Teach It. LC 68-14365. 1969. pap. 4.25 (ISBN 0-8054-1118-6). Broadman.
Brooks, Keith L. Basic Bible Study. (Teach Yourself the Bible Ser.). 1961. pap. 2.75 (ISBN 0-8024-0478-2). Moody.
Brooks, R. T., ed. Ask the Bible. LC 83-3841. 400p. 1983. 19.95 (ISBN 0-672-52765-0). Bobbs.
Brown, Milton P. To Hear the Word: Invitation to Serious Study of the Bible. 256p. 1987. 29.95 (ISBN 0-86554-251-1, MUP H-216); pap. 14.95 (ISBN 0-86554-252-X, MUP P-40). Mercer Univ Pr.
Brueggemann, Walter. The Creative Word: Canon as a Model for Biblical Education. LC 81-71387. 176p. 1982. pap. 9.95 (ISBN 0-8006-1626-X, 1-1626). Fortress.
--Living Toward a Vision: Biblical Reflections on Shalom. rev. ed. LC 76-22172. (Shalom Resource Ser.). 1982. pap. 6.95 (ISBN 0-8298-0613-X). Pilgrim NY.
Brug, John F. A Study Guide for Ezra, Nehemiah, Esther. (Study Guide for People's Bible Ser.). 60p. (Orig.). 1985. pap. 1.50 (ISBN 0-938272-53-5). Wels Board.
Bruinsma, Sheryl. Easy-to-Use Object Lessons. (Object Lesson Ser.). 96p. (Orig.). 1983. pap. 3.95 (ISBN 0-8010-0832-8). Baker Bk.
Buber, Martin. On the Bible: Eighteen Studies. Glatzer, Nahum N., ed. LC 81-16555. 288p. 1982. 17.95x (ISBN 0-8052-3796-8); pap. 7.95 (ISBN 0-8052-0691-4). Schocken.
Bull, Geoffrey. Love Song in Harvest. 1977. pap. 3.95 (ISBN 0-87508-042-1). Chr Lit.
Burgess, Allan K. How to Understand & Enjoy the Scriptures. LC 85-29212. (Illus.). 80p. 1986. 5.95 (ISBN 0-87579-030-5). Deseret Bk.
Burke, John. Beginners' Guide to Bible Sharing I. 192p. 1985. pap. 8.95 (ISBN 0-697-02014-2). Wm C Brown.
--Beginners' Guide to Bible Sharing II. 240p. 1984. pap. 9.95 (ISBN 0-697-02015-0). Wm C Brown.
Burns, Jim. The Ninety Day Experience. 112p. 1984. wkbk. 5.95 (ISBN 0-915929-12-0). Merit Bks.
Burns, Ralph O. Basic Bible Truths for New Converts. 30p. 1978. pap. 0.60 (ISBN 0-87227-007-6). Reg Baptist.
Burron, Arnold H. Discipline That Can't Fail. 1986. pap. 4.95 (ISBN 0-8010-0940-5). Baker Bk.
Carlson, G. Raymond. Preparing to Teach God's Word. LC 75-5221. (Illus.). 128p. 1975. pap. 1.25 (ISBN 0-88243-579-5, 02-0579). Gospel Pub.
Carmelite Sisters of Noto, Italy Staff. God's Word to His Church. Carmelite Sisters of Cristo Rey Carmel, San Francisco Staff, tr. from Ital. LC 81-83568. Tr. of Alla Sorgente Della Parola di Dio. 144p. (Orig.). 1982. pap. text ed. 7.95 (ISBN 0-89870-016-7). Ignatius Pr.
Cartlidge, David R. & Dungan, David L. Documents for the Study of the Gospels. LC 79-21341. 300p. (Orig.). 1980. 16.95 (ISBN 0-8006-0640-X, 1-640); pap. 10.95 (ISBN - 08006-1640-5, 1-1640). Fortress.
Chapman, Gary. Now That You Are Single Again. 80p. 1985. wkbk. 3.95 (ISBN 0-89840-087-2). Heres Life.
Charley, Julian. Cincuenta Palabras Claves de la Biblia. Diaz, Jorge E. & Diaz, Myriam, trs. from Eng. Orig. Title: Fifty Key Words-The Bible. (Span., Illus.). 80p. Date not set. pap. price not set (ISBN 0-311-04029-2). Casa Bautista.
Clanton, A. L., ed. Through the Bible Study Series, 7 vol. set. 2688p. 1982. text ed. 54.95 per set (ISBN 0-912315-51-2). Word Aflame.
--Through the Bible Study Series, Vol. VII. 384p. 1982. text ed. 6.95 (ISBN 0-912315-58-X). Word Aflame.
--Through the Bible Study Series, Vol. VI. 384p. 1981. text ed. 6.95 (ISBN 0-912315-57-1). Word Aflame.
--Through the Bible Study Series, Vol. V. 384p. 1981. text ed. 6.95 (ISBN 0-912315-56-3). Word Aflame.
--Through the Bible Study Series, Vol. IV. 384p. 1981. text ed. 6.95 (ISBN 0-912315-55-5). Word Aflame.
--Through the Bible Study Series, Vol. III. 384p. 1981. text ed. 6.95 (ISBN 0-912315-54-7). Word Aflame.
--Through the Bible Study Series, Vol. 1. 384p. 1981. text ed. 6.95 (ISBN 0-912315-52-0). Word Aflame.
Clapp, Steve & Mauck, Sue I. Through the Bible, Vol. I. (C-Four Youth Bible Materials Ser.). (Illus.). 138p. (Orig.). 1982. pap. 10.00 (ISBN 0-914527-15-0). C-Four Res.
Clark, Gordon H. First & Second Peter. 1980. pap. 5.95 (ISBN 0-87552-167-3). Presby & Reformed.
Clarke, E. G. The Wisdom of Solomon. (Cambridge Bible Commentary on the New English Bible, Old Testament Ser.). 148p. 1973. 18.95 (ISBN 0-521-08635-3); pap. 8.95 (ISBN 0-521-09756-8). Cambridge U Pr.
Clawson, Cynthia. My Favorite Verse. LC 86-73189. (My Favorite Verse Ser.). 24p. 1987. pap. 4.95 (ISBN 0-89636-222-1). Accent Bks.
Claypool, John. Glad Reunion. 144p. 1985. 8.95 (ISBN 0-8499-0469-2, 0469-2). Word Bks.
Clevenger, Ernest A., Jr. The Church. (Bible Drill Flash Card Flipbook Ser.). 104p. 1983. pap. 4.25 (ISBN 0-88428-016-0). Parchment Pr.
Coalition on Women & Religion Staff. The Women's Bible: Study Guide. 1975. 5.95 (ISBN 0-9603042-2-3). Coalition Women-Relig.
Cockman, Nelda. Is Bible Reliable? Leader's Guide. Chao, Loran Y., tr. (Basic Doctrine Ser.). (Chinese.). 1986. pap. write for info. (ISBN 0-941598-34-9). Living Spring Pubns.
Cohn, Robert L. The Shape of Sacred Space: Four Biblical Studies. LC 80-11086. (Studies in Religion: No. 23). pap. 8.50 (ISBN 0-89130-384-7, 01-00-23). Scholars Pr GA.
Coleman, Lucien E., Jr. Como Ensenar la Biblia. Diaz, Jorge E., tr. Orig. Title: How to Teach the Bible. (Span.). 265p. 1985. Repr. of 1982 ed. 6.50 (ISBN 0-311-11039-8). Casa Bautista.
--How to Teach the Bible. LC 79-52001. 1980. 9.95 (ISBN 0-8054-3428-3). Broadman.
Coleman, Lyman. Body Building. (Free University Ser.). (Orig.). 1981. pap. 4.95 leader's guide (ISBN 0-687-37306-9); pap. 1.25 student's bk. (ISBN 0-687-37307-7). Abingdon.
Coleman, Lyman, et al, eds. The Serendipity Group Study Book. 496p. 1986. kivar 9.95 (ISBN 0-310-25081-1, 12032P). Zondervan.
Colwell, Ernest C. The Study of the Bible. rev. ed. LC 64-23411. (Midway Reprint Ser.). pap. 54.50 (2026769). Bks Demand UMI.
Conn, Robert & Clapp, Steve. Methods of Bible Study. (C-Four Youth Bible Materials Ser.). (Illus.). 91p. (Orig.). 1982. pap. 8.00 (ISBN 0-914527-14-2). C-Four Res.
Conyers, A. J. How to Read the Bible. LC 85-23173. (How to Read Ser.). 216p. (Orig.). 1986. pap. 6.95 (ISBN 0-87784-944-7). Inter-Varsity.
Cook, Robert A. Now That I Believe: New King James Version. 1986. pap. text ed. 2.95 (ISBN 0-8024-5983-8). Moody.
Cooper, Thomas J. Guidebook to Biblical Truth. Cooper, Willia S., ed. (The Ministry of Women in God's Plan Ser.: Vol. 6). 50p. (Orig.). 1985. pap. 4.00 (ISBN 0-931429-06-4). Cooper & Cooper Pub.
Corvin, Raymond O. Great Themes of the Bible. (The Alpha & Omega Bible Studies). 90p. (Orig.). 1986. pap. 5.95 (ISBN 0-89221-138-5). New Leaf.
--Great Truths of the Bible. (The Alpha & Omega Bible Studies). 90p. (Orig.). 1986. pap. text ed. 5.95 (ISBN 0-89221-139-3). New Leaf.
Cottvell, Jack. Tough Questions: Biblical Answers Part Two. Orig. Title: The Bible Says. 128p. 1986. pap. 3.95 (ISBN 0-89900-213-7). College Pr Pub.
Craghan, John F. Yesterday's Word Today. LC 82-12648. 496p. 1982. pap. 14.95 (ISBN 0-8146-1273-3). Liturgical Pr.
Craig, James D. New Life Studies: Group Leader's Guide. 2nd rev. abr. ed. 48p. 1983. 4.00 (ISBN 0-88151-025-4). Lay Leadership.
Crowther, Duane S. A Guide to Effective Scripture Study. LC 75-5321. (Scripture Guide Ser). 147p. 1975. pap. 4.95 (ISBN 0-88290-004-8). Horizon Utah.
Curso Biblico por Correspondencia, Vol. III. 538p. 1975. pap. 15.95 (ISBN 0-87148-179-0). Pathway Pr.
Dale, Alan T. The Bible in the Classroom. 96p. (Orig.). 1973. pap. 4.95 (ISBN 0-8192-1151-6). Morehouse.
--The Winding Quest. (Illus.). 432p. (Orig.). 1973. pap. 9.95 (ISBN 0-8192-1150-8). Morehouse.
Dalpadado, J. Kingsley. Reading the Bible. 1973. 5.95 (ISBN 0-8198-0338-3); pap. 4.95 (ISBN 0-8198-0339-1). Dghtrs St Paul.
David the Anointed: Leader's Guide. (Orig.). 1984. pap. text ed. 3.95 (ISBN 0-934688-10-9). Great Comm Pubns.
Davis, Earl C. Forever, Amen. LC 81-67199. 1982. pap. 4.50 (ISBN 0-8054-1953-5). Broadman.
Deal, William S. Pictorial Introduction to the Bible. large print 12.95 (ISBN 0-686-13725-6); pap. 7.95. Crusade Pubs.
--A Pictorial Introduction to the Bible. LC 67-20517. 438p. 1982. pap. 12.95 (ISBN 0-89081-363-9). Harvest Hse.
DeHaan, M. R. The Chemistry of the Blood. 160p. 1983. pap. 5.95 (ISBN 0-310-23291-0, 9282P). Zondervan.
Deloe, Jesse B. Sweeter Than Honey. pap. 4.95 (ISBN 0-88469-105-5). BMH Bks.
De Surgy, Paul. Mystery of Salvation. Sheed, Rosemary, tr. 1966. pap. 6.95 (ISBN 0-268-00185-5). U of Notre Dame Pr.
De Vaux, R. & Milik, J. T. Discoveries in the Judaean Desert: Qumran Grotte 4-11, Vol. 6. (Illus.). 1977. text ed. 52.00x (ISBN 0-19-826317-1). Oxford U Pr.
Doane, T. W. Bible Myths & Their Parallels in Other Religions. 589p. spiral bdg. 12.00. Truth Seeker.
Dole, Anita S. Bible Study Notes, Vols. 1-3. Woofenden, William R., ed. LC 76-24081. 1976-78. lib. bdg. write for info. (ISBN 0-685-92171-9). Vol 1 (ISBN 0-917426-01-0). Vol. 2 (ISBN 0-917426-02-9). Vol. 3 (ISBN 0-917426-03-7). Am New Church Sunday.
--Bible Study Notes, Vol. 4. Woofenden, William R., ed. LC 76-24081. 1979. write for info. (ISBN 0-917426-04-5). Am New Church Sunday.
--Bible Study Notes, Vol. 5. Woofenden, William R., ed. LC 76-24081. 1979. write for info (ISBN 0-917426-05-3). Am New Church Sunday.
Dorsett, Judy. Handbook of Creativity. (Illus.). 128p. 1985. pap. 7.95 (ISBN 0-87239-729-7, 3226). Standard Pub.
Douglass, Stephen B. & Roddy, Lee. Making the Most of Your Mind. 250p. (Orig.). 1982. pap. 6.95 (ISBN 0-86605-109-0). Heres Life.
Dowley, Tim. The Moody Guide to the Bible. 1986. Repr. text ed. 7.95 (ISBN 0-8024-5562-X). Moody.
Draper, James T., Jr. Discover Joy: Studies in Philippians. 1983. pap. 4.95 (ISBN 0-8423-0606-4); leader's guide 2.95 (ISBN 0-8423-0607-2). Tyndale.
Drew, George. Making the Bible Our Own. 65p. 1985. pap. 6.95 (ISBN 0-940754-29-0). Ed Ministries.
Dukes, H. N. The Bible: Fact, Fiction, Fantasy, Faith. 178p. (Orig.). 1987. pap. 8.00 (ISBN 0-682-40337-7). Exposition Pr Fl.
Eade, Alfred T. The New Panorama Bible Study Course. Incl. No. 1. A Study of Dispensational Truth. (Illus.). 28p (ISBN 0-8007-0221-2); No. 2. The Study of Angelology. 32p (ISBN 0-8007-0222-0); No. 3. The Second Coming of Christ. 36p (ISBN 0-8007-0223-9); No. 4. The Book of Revelation. (Illus.). 28p (ISBN 0-8007-0434-7). pap. 6.95 ea. Revell.
--Panorama de la Biblia. Orig. Title: New Panorama Bible Study Course. 32p. 1986. pap. 3.75 (ISBN 0-311-03657-0). Casa Bautista.
Earle, Ralph. How to Study the Bible. (Christian Living Ser.). 32p. (Orig.). 1987. pap. write for info. (ISBN 0-8341-1187-X). Beacon Hill.
Easter, Frances. Bible Studies Series. (Studies in Luke: Vol. 1). 1985. pap. 3.50 (ISBN 0-8309-0424-7). Herald Hse.
Eastman, Dick. La Universidad de la Palabra. Silva, Jose D., tr. from English. (Span.). 239p. 1986. pap. text ed. 3.50 (ISBN 0-8297-0443-4). Life Pubs Intl.
Eby, Ray. Bakers Bible Atlas Study Guide. 1977. 4.95 (ISBN 0-686-25535-6); test 1.75 (ISBN 0-686-31725-4); map 1.55 (ISBN 0-686-31726-2). Rod & Staff.
Edwards, F. Henry. A Students Guide to the Doctrine & Covenants. 1980. pap. 9.00 (ISBN 0-8309-0267-8). Herald Hse.
Efird, James M. These Things Are Written: An Introduction to the Religious Ideas of the Bible. LC 77-15749. (Biblical Foundations Ser.). 1978. pap. 8.95 (ISBN 0-8042-0073-4). John Knox.

Eisenberg, Azriel. The Book of Books: The Story of the Bible Text. 1976. 9.95x (ISBN 0-685-84453-6). Bloch.

Elliott, Douglas. As You Recover. 32p. 1984. pap. 1.25 (ISBN 0-8010-3414-0). Baker Bk.

Entrevernes Group. Signs & Parables: Semiotics & Gospel Texts. Phillips, Gary, tr. from Fr. LC 78-12840. (Pittsburgh Theological Monographs: No. 23). Orig. Title: Signes et Paraboles. 1978. pap. 10.00 (ISBN 0-915138-35-2). Pickwick.

Enyi, Donatus O. Thirty Seconds with Your Bible: Learn How to Chart Your Horoscope, Predict Your Destiny, Luck, Fortune... LC 86-70272. (Illus.). 80p. 1986. 9.95 (ISBN 0-937171-00-X); pap. 6.95 (ISBN 0-937171-01-8). D Enyi.

Estudio Biblico para Exhortador. (Span.). 33p. 1975. pap. 0.95 (ISBN 0-87148-305-X). Pathway Pr.

Estudio Biblico para Licenciado. (Span.). 43p. 1975. pap. 1.25 (ISBN 0-87148-310-6). Pathway Pr.

Evans, G. Rosemary. Old Arts & New Theology: The Beginnings of Theology As an Academic Discipline. 1980. text ed. 34.95x (ISBN 0-19-826653-7). Oxford U Pr.

Evans, M. J. Progress of God's People. (Discovering the Bible Ser.). pap. 8.95 (ISBN 0-7175-1161-8). Dufour.

Exploring the Bible. rev. ed. (Time of Life Learning Ser.). (Illus.). 32p. 1985. pap. 2.95 (ISBN 0-89622-243-8). Twenty-Third.

Eynon, Dana. Adventures Through the Bible. rev. ed. LC 79-1031. 176p. 1980. pap. 7.95 tchr's book (ISBN 0-87239-378-X, 3234). Standard Pub.

--Through the Bible in a Year: Pupil Workbook. 64p. 1975. wkbk. 1.95 (ISBN 0-87239-011-X, 3239). Standard Pub.

--Through the Bible in a Year: Teacher. LC 74-27239. 176p. 1975. tchr's manual 7.95 (ISBN 0-87239-028-4, 3237). Standard Pub.

Fairweather, William. From Exile to Advent. Moffatt, J., ed. (Handbooks for Bible Classes & Private Students Ser.). 210p. 1894. 8.95 (ISBN 0-567-28128-0, Pub. by T & T Clark Ltd Uk). Fortress.

Falwell, Jerry. My Favorite Verse. LC 86-72750. (My Favorite Verse Ser.). 24p. 1987. pap. 4.95 (ISBN 0-89636-235-3). Accent Bks.

Fee, Gordon & Stuart, Douglas. How to Read the Bible for All it's Worth. 272p. 1982. pap. 7.95 (ISBN 0-310-37361-1, 11146P). Zondervan.

Fellows, Carmen, et al. Twenty-Six Programs for Preschoolers (Spring & Summer) 96p. 1986. wkbk. 8.95 (ISBN 0-87403-011-0, 3404). Standard Pub.

Finzel, Hans. Opening the Book. 352p. 1986. pap. 11.95 (ISBN 0-89693-277-X). Victor Bks.

--Unlocking the Scriptures. 144p. 1986. 7.95 (ISBN 0-89693-276-1). Victor Bks.

Fischer, James A. How to Read the Bible. rev. ed. 1987. 14.95 (ISBN 0-396-08986-0); pap. 8.95 (ISBN 0-396-09028-1). Dodd.

Fischman, Joyce. Bible Work & Play, Vol. 1. rev. ed. (Illus.). 80p. (Orig.). 1985. pap. text ed. 5.00 (ISBN 0-8074-0304-0). UAHC.

Fishbane, Michael. Text & Texture: Close Readings of Selected Biblical Texts. LC 79-14083. 154p. 1982. pap. 7.95 (ISBN 0-8052-0726-0). Schocken.

Fishel, Kent. Cornerstones: Believing the Bible. 112p. 1987. pap. 4.95 (ISBN 0-310-39761-8). Zondervan.

Flanders, Henry J., Jr., et al. Introduction to the Bible. 588p. 1973. text ed. 25.75 (ISBN 0-394-34416-2, RandC). Random.

Following God's Trailblazers: Kings & Prophets 14 Lessons, Vol. 4. (Footsteps of Faith Ser.). 1958. pap. text ed. 2.50 (ISBN 0-86508-033-X); figures text 11.45 (ISBN 0-86508-034-8). BCM Intl Inc.

Ford, Charles W. How to Study the Bible. LC 77-99213. (Radiant Life Ser.). 128p. 1978. pap. text ed. 2.50 (ISBN 0-88243-912-X, 02-0912); tchr's ed. 3.95 (ISBN 0-88243-183-8, 32-0183). Gospel Pub.

Freeman, James M. Manners & Customs of the Bible. (Illus.). 515p. 1972. (Pub. by Logos); pap. 8.95 (ISBN 0-88270-022-7). Bridge Pub.

Fromer, Margaret & Nystrom, Carolyn. James: Roadmap for Down-to-Earth Christians. (Young Fisherman Bible Studyguide Ser.). (Illus.). 89p. 1982. saddle-stiched tchr's. ed. 4.95 (ISBN 0-87788-420-X); student ed. 2.95 (ISBN 0-87788-419-6). Shaw Pubs.

Fugita, Neil. Introducing the Bible. LC 81-80874. 224p. (Orig.). 1981. pap. 5.95 (ISBN 0-8091-2392-4). Paulist Pr.

Furnish, Dorothy J. Exploring the Bible with Children. LC 74-34486. 176p. 1975. pap. 6.95 (ISBN 0-687-12426-3). Abingdon.

Gama, Roberto, tr. from Eng. Diccionario Biblico Arqueologico. Pfeiffer, Charles F., ed. Tr. of The Biblical World - A Dictionary of Biblical Archaelolgy. (Span.). 768p. 1982. 29.95 (ISBN 0-311-03667-8). Casa Bautista.

Garstang, John. Joshua Judges: The Foundations of Bible History. 1977. lib. bdg. 59.95 (ISBN 0-8490-2109-X). Gordon Pr.

Gates, John E. An Analysis of the Lexicographic Resources Used by American Biblical Scholars Today. LC 72-88670. (Society of Biblical Literature. Dissertation Ser.: No. 8). pap. 49.00 (ISBN 0-317-10146-3, 2017664). Bks Demand UMI.

Gaudin, Thierry. The Secret Code: The Lost & Hidden Language of the Bible, Vol. 1. LC 85-70031. 300p. (Orig.). 1985. pap. 12.95 (ISBN 0-933357-05-2). Bret Pubns.

Geiger, Lura J. Astonish Me, Yahweh! Leader's Guide. (Illus.). 101p. (Orig.). 1984. 12.95 (ISBN 0-931055-02-4). LuraMedia.

Geiger, Lura J., et al. Astonish Me, Yahweh! (Illus.). 106p. (Orig.). 1983. wkbk. 11.95 (ISBN 0-931055-01-6). LuraMedia.

Geisler, Norman L. & Nix, William E. From God to Us. 302p. (Orig.). 1974. pap. 9.95 (ISBN 0-8024-2878-9). Moody.

Gerbrandt, Gerald. Better Than Rivers of Oil. LC 85-81305. (Faith & Life Bible Studies). 78p. (Orig.). pap. 4.95 (ISBN 0-87303-105-9). Faith & Life.

Gerlach, Joel & Bolge, Richard. Preach the Gospel. 1982. 8.95 (ISBN 0-8100-0153-5, 15NO387). Northwest Pub.

Gerstner, John. Bible Inerrancy Primer. 1981. pap. 2.50 (ISBN 0-88469-144-6). BMH Bks.

Gervais, Marcel, ed. Journey: A Home & Group Bible Study Program. (Illus.). Set. 60.00; Old Testament, Set 20 Bklts. 30.00 (ISBN 0-8091-9279-9); New Testament Set, 20 Bklts. 30.00 (ISBN 0-8091-9280-2); bklt. 1.50 ea. Paulist Pr.

Gibbs, A. P. Through the Scriptures. pap. 5.95 (ISBN 0-937396-45-1). Walterick Pubs.

Gleaves, Les. Building Your Bible School. 1986. 4.95 (ISBN 0-931097-10-X). Sentinel Pub.

Gobbel, A. Roger, et al. Helping Youth Interpret the Bible: A Teaching Resource. LC 84-3916. 204p. 1984. pap. 9.95 (ISBN 0-8042-1580-4). John Knox.

Gobbel, Roger A. & Gobbel, Gertrude G. The Bible: A Child's Playground. LC 85-45501. 192p. 1986. pap. 9.95 (ISBN 0-8006-1887-4). Fortress.

Gonzalez, Justo & Gonzalez, Catherine. In Accord-Let Us Worship. (Orig.). 1981. pap. 3.95 (ISBN 0-377-00110-4). Friend Pr.

Good, Lou-Ann. Bible Readings for Office Workers. 112p. (Orig.). 1987. pap. 3.95 (ISBN 0-8066-2250-4, 10-0693). Augsburg.

Goodgame, Louis R. Delightful Discipline. Date not set. pap. 3.00 (ISBN 0-8010-3815-4). Baker Bk.

Gordon, Cyrus. The Pennsylvania Tradition of Semitics: A Century of Near Eastern & Biblical Studies at the University of Pennsylvania. (Biblical Scholarship in North America Ser.). 85p. 1987. 13.95 (ISBN 1-55540-022-1); pap. 11.95 (ISBN 1-55540-023-X). Scholars Pr GA.

Gospel Magic: Easy Made & Self Contained, No. 2. 1982. pap. 4.95 (ISBN 0-915398-20-6). Visual Evangels.

Green, Jay P., Sr. The Interlinear Bible, 4 vols. 2952p. 1986. 89.95 (ISBN 0-913573-31-0). Hendrickson MA.

--The Interlinear Bible. 736p. 1986. 21.95 (ISBN 0-913573-29-9). Hendrickson MA.

--The Interlinear Bible. 960p. 1986. 44.95 (ISBN 0-913573-25-6). Hendrickson MA.

Griggs, Donald L. Twenty New Ways of Teaching the Bible. (Griggs Educational Resources Ser.). 1979. pap. 7.25 (ISBN 0-687-42740-1). Abingdon.

Griggs, Patricia. Opening the Bible with Children: Beginning Bible Skills. 64p. (Orig.). 1986. pap. 7.50 (ISBN 0-687-29210-7). Abingdon.

Grimsley, R. W. The Church That Jesus Built. 1969. pap. 2.75 (ISBN 0-88027-031-4). Firm Foun Pub.

Gunderson, Vivian. Bible Learn & Do: The Bible Is the Best Book, Why? 1985. pap. 1.25 (ISBN 0-8323-0442-5). Binford-Metropolitan.

Gustafson, J. Louise & Poziemski, Christine L. Step-by-Step Through the Bible: Puzzles, Quizzes & Writing Experiences for Teaching Important Biblical Passages. (The Learning Connections Ser.). 160p. (Orig.). 1984. pap. 9.95 (ISBN 0-86683-835-X, 8442, HarpR). Har-Row.

Hagin, Kenneth E. Bible Faith Study Course. 1974. pap. 5.00 (ISBN 0-89276-080-X). Hagin Ministries.

--Bible Prayer Study Course. 1974. pap. 5.00 (ISBN 0-89276-081-8). Hagin Ministries.

--The Bible Way to Receive the Holy Spirit. 1981. pap. 0.50 mini bk. (ISBN 0-89276-255-1). Hagin Ministries.

Haldane, Robert. The Authenticity & Inspiration of the Holy Scriptures. 210p. 1985. Repr. lib. bdg. 9.00 (ISBN 0-86524-182-1, 8604). Klock & Klock.

Hall. Getting More from Your Bible. 1984. 5.95 (ISBN 0-88207-300-1). Victor Bks.

--Off the Shelf & Into Your Self. 1982. 3.95 (ISBN 0-88207-589-6). Victor Bks.

Hall, J. L., ed. Through the Bible Study Series, Vol. II. 384p. 1981. text ed. 6.95 (ISBN 0-912315-53-9). Word Aflame.

Hall, Terry. Dynamic Bible Teaching with Overhead Transparencies. 80p. 1985. pap. 9.95 (ISBN 0-89191-584-2). Cook.

Halley, Henry H. Compendio Manual de la Biblia. Denyer, C. P., tr. (Span., Illus.). 768p. 1985. Repr. of 1984 ed. 14.95 (ISBN 0-311-03666-X). Casa Bautista.

Hanke, Howard. The Thompson Chain Reference Bible Survey. 1981. 19.95 (ISBN 0-8499-0272-X). Word Bks.

Hanks, Joyce M. Ronsard & Biblical Tradition. (Etudes litteraires francaises: 17). 199p. (Orig.). 1982. pap. 19.00x (ISBN 3-87808-896-5). Benjamins North Am.

Hansel, G. Understanding the Living Word. 1980. pap. 8.95 (ISBN 0-8163-0372-X). Pacific Pr Pub Assn.

Harbour, Brian L. A New Look at the Book. LC 84-27479. 1985. pap. 5.95 (ISBN 0-8054-1535-1). Broadman.

Harrington, Daniel, ed. The Bible in the Churches: How Different Christians Interpret the Scriptures. 1985. pap. 8.95 (ISBN 0-8091-2676-1). Paulist Pr.

Harrington, Wilfrid. The New Guide to Reading & Studying the Bible. enl. ed. pap. 7.95 (ISBN 0-89453-092-5). M Glazier.

Haystead, Wesley. Creative Bible Learning for Early Childhood: Birth Through 5 Years. LC 77-77030. 192p. 1977. pap. 3.95 (ISBN 0-8307-0477-9, 9000100). Regal.

Hendricks, William C. & Den Bleyker, Merle. Object Lessons That Teach Bible Truths. (Object Lessons Ser.). 1977. pap. 3.95 (ISBN 0-8010-4172-4). Baker Bk.

Henrichsen, Walter A. A Layman's Guide to Interpreting the Bible. 112p. (Orig.). 1985. pap. 5.95 (ISBN 0-310-37681-5). Zondervan.

--A Layman's Guide to Studying the Bible. 144p. (Orig.). 1985. pap. 6.95 (ISBN 0-310-37631-9, 11236P). Zondervan.

Henrichsen, Walter A. & Jackson, Gayle. A Layman's Guide to Applying the Bible. 224p. (Orig.). 1985. pap. 7.95 (ISBN 0-310-37691-2, 11233P, Pub. by Lamplight); Set pack. pap. 19.95 (ISBN 0-310-37698-X, 11238P, Pub. by Lamplight). Zondervan.

Hepburn, Daisy. Be It Ever So Humble. LC 83-24603. (Life with Spice Bible Study Ser.). 1984. 2.95 (ISBN 0-8307-0943-6, 6101805). Regal.

--Be Mine. LC 83-24618. (Life with Spice Bible Study Ser.). 1984. 2.95 (ISBN 0-8307-0944-4, 6101817). Regal.

--Color Me Christian. LC 83-24624. (Life with Spice Bible Study Ser.). 1984. 2.95 (ISBN 0-8307-0949-5, 6101867). Regal.

--Consider Christ. LC 83-24623. (Life with Spice Bible Study Ser.). 1984. 2.95 (ISBN 0-8307-0945-2, 6101829). Regal.

--Living Simply. LC 84-3360. (Life with Spice Bible Study Ser.). 1984. 2.95 (ISBN 0-8307-0947-9, 6101848). Regal.

Herlick, Stanford. What You Should Know about the Bible: A Practical Guide to Bible Basics. LC 85-82137. (Illus.). 255p. 1985. 12.50 (ISBN 0-9616026-0-0). FBF Pubns.

Herr, Ethel. Bible Study for Busy Women. 160p. 1983. pap. 6.95 (ISBN 0-8024-0147-3). Moody.

Herring, Ralph, et al. How to Understand the Bible. LC 74-75674. 1974. 8.95 (ISBN 0-8054-1127-5). Broadman.

Heslop, W. G. Heslop Bible Study Aids, 6 vols. 1979. Set. pap. 24.00 (ISBN 0-8254-2858-0). Kregel.

Hession, Roy. From Shadow to Substance. 1976. pap. 3.95 (ISBN 0-87508-260-2). Chr Lit.

--Our Nearest Kinsman. 1976. pap. 2.95 (ISBN 0-87508-229-7). Chr Lit.

Hestenes, Roberta. Using the Bible in Groups. LC 84-15291. 118p. (Orig.). 1985. pap. 6.95 (ISBN 0-664-24561-7). Westminster.

Hill, Donald E. Pathway of Discipleship One Hundred One: Group Leader's Guide. 2nd rev. ed. 48p. 1983. 4.00 (ISBN 0-88151-028-9). Lay Leadership.

--Pathway of Discipleship One Hundred One: Home Study Guide. 2nd rev. ed. 56p. 1983. 8.00 (ISBN 0-88151-027-0). Lay Leadership.

Hills, Edward F. Believing Bible Study. 2nd ed. (Illus.). 258p. pap. 4.50 (ISBN 0-915923-01-7). Christian Res Pr.

Hirschmann, Maria A. & Pershing, Betty. Learn of Me: A Study of the Teachings of Christ. LC 79-90958. (Bible Study & Sharing Ser.: No. 3). 144p. (Orig.). 1980. pap. 4.95 (ISBN 0-932878-02-4, HB-02). Hansi.

Hoggard, Robert. Surveying the Scriptures. 1981. pap. 2.95 (ISBN 0-86544-013-1). Salv Army Suppl South.

Hook, Martha. A Woman's Workshop on Faith. (A Woman's Workshop Ser.). 1977. leaders 3.95 (ISBN 0-310-26231-3, 11681P); students 2.95 (ISBN 0-310-26241-0, 11682P). Zondervan.

Horn, Geoffrey, illus. Bible Studies for Children. Cavanaugh, Arthur. LC 79-27811. (Illus.). 336p. 1980. 12.95 (ISBN 0-02-554060-2). Macmillan.

Hort, F. J. & Hort, A. F. Expository & Exegetical Studies. 1980. 29.50 (ISBN 0-86524-021-3, 7103). Klock & Klock.

Howard, George. Think It Through. 48p. (Orig.). 1984. pap. 2.95 (ISBN 0-89109-163-7). NavPress.

Huegel, F. J. Bone of His Bone. (Christian Classic Ser.). 96p. 1980. pap. 3.95 (ISBN 0-310-26321-2, 9955P). Zondervan.

Huggins, Larry. Believer's Bible Companion. 32p. (Orig.). 1984. pap. 1.95 (ISBN 0-89274-314-X, HH-314). Harrison Hse.

Hunt, Gladys. Relationships. (Fisherman Bible Studyguide Ser.). 64p. 1983. saddle stitched 2.95 (ISBN 0-87788-721-7). Shaw Pubs.

--You Can Start a Bible Study Group: Making Friends, Changing Lives. rev. ed. (Resource for Fisherman Bible Studyguides). 96p. 1984. Repr. of 1971 ed. lib. bdg. 2.95 (ISBN 0-87788-974-0). Shaw Pubs.

Hybels, Lynne. Joy of Personal Worship. 156p. 1984. pap. 5.95 (ISBN 0-89693-373-3). Victor Bks.

Hyde, Kathy. Teaching the Bible to Change Lives. LC 84-47801. 143p. (Orig.). 1984. pap. 6.95 (ISBN 0-89840-064-3). Heres Life.

Ingersoll, Robert. What Can You Believe in the Bible. 106p. 1987. 4.00. Am Atheist.

Ironside, H. A. & Ottman, F. Studies in Biblical Eschatology. 426p. 1983. lib. bdg. 16.00 Smythe Sewn (ISBN 0-86524-143-0, 9806). Klock & Klock.

Ishee, John A. New Beginning: Studies in John's Gospel. 35p. (Orig.). 1982. pap. 3.50 (ISBN 0-939298-13-9, 139). J. M. Prods.

Iverson, Edie, et al. Bible Study Leadership Training. (Illus.). 53p. 1980. pap. 6.75 (ISBN 0-914936-46-8). Bible Temple.

Jackson, Forrest W., compiled by. Bible Studies for Special Occasions in Youth Ministry. LC 82-70109. 1982. pap. 4.95 (ISBN 0-8054-3617-0, 4236-17). Broadman.

Jackson, Kent P. & Millet, Robert, eds. Studies in Scripture: The Gospels, Vol. 5. 1986. text ed. 15.95 (ISBN 0-87579-064-X). Deseret Bk.

Jensen, Irving. Irving Jensen's Do-It-Yourself Bible Study: Mark. (Irving Jensen's Do-It-Yourself Bible Study Ser.). 118p. (Orig.). 1983. wkbk 5.95 (ISBN 0-89840-035-X). Heres Life.

Jensen, Irving L. Enjoy Your Bible. 1969. pap. 5.95 (ISBN 0-8024-2347-7). Moody.

--First & Second Peter. (Bible Self-Study Ser.). 1971. pap. 3.25 (ISBN 0-8024-1060-X). Moody.

--Independent Bible Study. LC 68-12114. 1972. pap. 6.95 (ISBN 0-8024-4050-9). Moody.

--James. (Bible Self-Study Ser). (Illus.). 1972. pap. 3.25 (ISBN 0-8024-1059-6). Moody.

Jeske, Richard L. Understanding & Teaching the Bible. Rast, Harold W., ed. LC 80-69756. (A Lead Book). 128p. (Orig.). 1981. pap. 3.95 (ISBN 0-8006-1601-4, 1-1601). Fortress.

Johns, Cheryl B. Finding Eternal Treasures. (International Correspondence Program Ser.). (Orig.). 1985. pap. text ed. 6.95 (ISBN 0-87148-340-8). Pathway Pr.

Johnsen, Henry. People of the Way: Biblical Ecumenism. 5.95 (ISBN 0-685-00743-X). Reiner.

Jones, Bob, III. Biblical Answers to Bothersome Questions. 71p. (Orig.). 1981. pap. 2.00 (ISBN 0-89084-150-0). Bob Jones Univ Pr.

Jordan, Bernice. Guia de la Ensenanza Efectiva. Tr. of Guidebook to Better Teaching. (Span.). 1976. pap. text ed. 5.95 (ISBN 0-86508-420-3). BCM Intl Inc.

--Guidebook to Better Teaching. 126p. 1980. pap. text ed. 5.95 (ISBN 0-86508-090-9). BCM Intl Inc.

Jordan, Bernice C. Acts: 14 Lessons, Vol. 1. (Footsteps of Faith Ser.). 1954. pap. text ed. 2.50 (ISBN 0-86508-039-9); figure text 11.45 (ISBN 0-86508-040-2). BCM Intl Inc.

--Acts: 15 Lessons, Vol. 2. (Footsteps of Faith Ser.). 1954. pap. text ed. 2.50 (ISBN 0-86508-041-0); figure text 11.45 (ISBN 0-86508-042-9). BCM Intl Inc.

--En las Huellas de los Heroes: 14 Lecciones, Tomo 4. (Pasos De Fe Ser.). (Span.). pap. text ed. 2.50 (ISBN 0-86508-407-6); figuras 8.95 (ISBN 0-86508-408-4). BCM Intl Inc.

--Genesis: Fifteen Lessons, Vol. 1. (Footsteps of Faith Ser.). 1960. pap. text ed. 2.50 (ISBN 0-86508-027-5); figures text 11.45 (ISBN 0-86508-028-3). BCM Intl Inc.

--Los Gigantes en Canaan: 14 Lecciones, Tomo 3. (Pasos de Fe Ser.). (Span.). pap. text ed. 2.50 (ISBN 0-86508-405-X); figuras 8.95 (ISBN 0-86508-406-8). BCM Intl Inc.

Kaiser, Walter C., Jr. Quality Living. rev. ed. (MP Electives Ser.). 1986. pap. text ed. 3.95 (ISBN 0-8024-7069-6); tchr's ed. 4.95 (ISBN 0-8024-7070-X). Moody.
--Quest for Renewal: Personal Revival in the Old Testament. (Orig.). 1986. pap. 6.95 (ISBN 0-8024-7050-5). Moody.
Kaufman, Daniel. Doctrines of the Bible. 639p. 1928. 12.95 (ISBN 0-8361-1358-6). Herald Pr.
Keegan, Terence J. Interpreting the Bible: A Popular Introduction to Biblical Hermeneutics. 224p. (Orig.). 1986. pap. 8.95 (ISBN 0-8091-2747-4). Paulist Pr.
Kelm, Paul. Christianity Is All Talk. Fischer, William, ed. (Bible Class Course for Young Adults Ser.: Student's Guide). (Illus.). 44p. 1984. pap. text ed. 2.95 (ISBN 0-938272-16-0). Wels Board.
--Christianity Is All Talk. Fischer, William, ed. (Bible Class Course for Young Adults Ser.: Leader's Guide). 64p. 1984. pap. text ed. 2.95 (ISBN 0-938272-17-9). Wels Board.
Kersten, Phyllis N. & Williams, E. Louise. Talented, Tired, Beautiful Feet: A Bible Study for Women. 64p. (Orig.). 1985. pap. 2.95 (ISBN 0-570-03967-3, 12-3002). Concordia.
Keyes, Nelson B. El Fascinante Mundo de la Biblia. Orig. Title: Story of the Bible World. (Span., Illus.). 216p. 1980. 20.95 (ISBN 0-311-03664-3, Edit Mundo); pap. 16.95 (ISBN 0-311-03665-1, Edit Mundo). Casa Bautista.
Keyes, Sharrel. Working Out Together: Keeping Your Group in Shape. (Fisherman Bible Studyguides). 64p. (Orig.). 1985. pap. 1.00 (ISBN 0-87788-263-0). Shaw Pubs.
Kimball, William. Book of Books. LC 86-71101. 160p. (Orig.). 1986. pap. 6.95 (ISBN 0-89900-211-0). College Pr Pub.
Klein, Chuck. So You Want to Lead Students. 96p. 1982. pap. 4.95 leader's guide (ISBN 0-8423-6084-0). Tyndale.
--So You Want to Set the Pace. 96p. 1982. pap. 4.95 (ISBN 0-8423-6083-2). Tyndale.
Klim, Mary K. Bible Studies for Senior Citizens. 91p. 1986. pap. 5.95x (ISBN 0-932910-59-9). Potentials Development.
Knight, George W. & Edwards, James R., eds. The Layman's Overview of the Bible. 1987. 14.95 (ISBN 0-8407-7560-1). Nelson.
Knowles, Victor. What the Bible Says about Angels & Demons. LC 86-71104. (What the Bible Says Ser.). 405p. 1986. 13.95 (ISBN 0-89900-252-8). College Pr Pub.
Kodell, Jerome. The Catholic Bible Study Handbook: A Popular Introduction to Studying Scripture. 266p. (Orig.). 1985. pap. 7.95 (ISBN 0-89283-185-5). Servant.
Korth, Russ & Wormser, Ron, Jr. Going up! rev. ed. 82p. 1980. pap. text ed. 5.00 (ISBN 0-934396-26-4). Churches Alive.
Kruis, John G. Quick Scripture Reference for Counseling. 80p. 1987. pap. price not set (ISBN 0-8010-5488-5). Baker Bk.
Krupp, Nate. Bible Studies for Christian Discipleship. 2nd ed. 1979. Repr. 1.45 (ISBN 0-89221-052-4). New Leaf.
--Bible Studies for New Christians. 2nd ed. 1979. Repr. 1.45 (ISBN 0-89221-053-2). New Leaf.
--Bible Studies for Soul Winners. 1979. Repr. 1.45 (ISBN 0-89221-054-0). New Leaf.
Krutza, William J. The Second Coming Bible Study Guide, No. 2. (Contemporary Discussion Ser.). (Orig.). 1973. pap. 0.95 (ISBN 0-8010-5330-7). Baker Bk.
Kuiper, R. B. The Bible Tells Us So: Twelve Short Chapters on Major Themes of the Bible. 1978. pap. 3.45 (ISBN 0-85151-001-9). Banner of Truth.
Kunz, Marilyn & Schell, Catherine. Celebrate. (Neighborhood Bible Studies). 48p. (Orig.). 1984. pap. 2.95 (ISBN 0-8423-0218-2). Tyndale.
--Courage to Cope. (Neighborhood Bible Studies). 48p. (Orig.). 1984. pap. 2.50 (ISBN 0-8423-0446-0). Tyndale.
--Efesios y Filemon. Orozco, Julio, tr. from Eng. LC 77-83811. (Encuentros Biblicos Ser.). Tr. of Ephesians & Philemon. (Span.). 55p. 1977. pap. 1.25 (ISBN 0-89922-095-9). Edit Caribe.
--How to Start a Neighborhood Bible Study. (Neighborhood Bible Studies). 1970. pap. 2.00 (ISBN 0-8423-1540-3). Tyndale.
--How to Start a Neighborhood Bible Study. incl. cassette 8.95 (ISBN 0-8423-1533-0). Tyndale.
--John, One, & James: Neighborhood Bible Study. 1978. pap. 2.95 (ISBN 0-8423-1930-1). Tyndale.
--Prophets of Hope. (Neighborhood Bible Studies). 48p. (Orig.). 1984. pap. 2.50 (ISBN 0-8423-4908-1). Tyndale.
--Set Free. 1982. pap. 2.95 (ISBN 0-8423-5867-6). Tyndale.
Kwak, Chung H., ed. Principle of Creation. (Home Study Course Ser.). 60p. 1980. pap. 4.00. HSA Pubns.
--Resurrection (Five) (Home Study Course Ser.). 40p. (Orig.). 1980. pap. 4.00 (ISBN 0-910621-14-4). HSA Pubns.
Kwak, Chung Hwan, ed. The Fall of Man (2) (Home Study Course Ser.). 60p. (Orig.). 1980. pap. 4.00 (ISBN 0-910621-11-X). HSA Pubns.
--The Mission of The Messiah (Three) (Home Study Course Ser.). 40p. (Orig.). 1980. pap. 4.00 (ISBN 0-910621-12-8). HSA Pubns.
Kwak, Chung Hwan Rev., ed. Consummation of Human History (4) (Home Study Course Ser.). 40p. 1980. pap. 4.00 (ISBN 0-910621-13-6). HSA Pubns.
LaHaye, Tim. How to Study the Bible for Yourself. LC 76-5568. 1976. pap. 4.95 (ISBN 0-89081-021-4, 0214). Harvest Hse.
Larsen, Sandy. Eye Opening Bible Studies. (Bible Discovery Guide for Campers Ser.). 32p. 1986. pap. 1.95 (ISBN 0-87788-247-9). Shaw Pubs.
--Sticking Together: Friendships for Life. (Bible Discovery Guides for Teen Campers Ser.). 32p. (Orig.). (YA) 1987. pap. 1.50 camper (ISBN 0-87788-787-X); pap. 1.50 counselor (ISBN 0-87788-788-8). Shaw Pubs.
Lebar, Lois & Berg, Miguel. Llamados a Ensenar. Blanch, Jose M., tr. from Eng. LC 77-5183. (Span., Illus.). 160p. 1970. pap. 3.95 (ISBN 0-89922-006-1). Edit Caribe.
Lehman, Carolyn. God's Wonderful World: Twenty Six Lessons for Primary Church. (Children's Church Ser.). (Illus.). 144p. 1985. wkbk 8.95 (ISBN 0-87239-839-0, 3316). Standard Pub.
--Twenty-Six Complete Programs for Children's Church: Traveling with Bible People. (Children's Church Ser.). 144p. 1986. tchr's ed. 8.95 (ISBN 0-87403-060-9, 3324). Standard Pub.
Lemke, Steve. Living Hope: Studies in I Peter. 35p. (Orig.). 1982. pap. 3.50 (ISBN 0-939298-12-0, 120). J M Prods.
LeRoy, Douglas. Basic Bible Study. LC 78-65822. 72p. (Orig.). 1978. pap. text ed. 1.25 (ISBN 0-87148-699-7). Pathway Pr.
Levenson, Jon D. Sinai & Zion: An Entry into the Jewish Bible. 240p. (Orig.). 1985. 16.95 (ISBN 0-86683-961-5, AY8551, HarpR). Har-Row.
Licht, Jacob. Storytelling in the Bible. 2nd ed. 156p. 1986. Repr. of 1978 ed. text ed. 22.50 (ISBN 965-223-542-3, Pub. by Magnes Pr Israel). Humanities.
Lincoln, William C. Personal Bible Study. LC 75-2345. 160p. 1975. pap. 4.95 (ISBN 0-87123-458-0, 210458). Bethany Hse.
Lindgren. Teaching Bible Truths with Single Objects. 1979. 3.50 (ISBN 0-88207-036-3). Victor Bks.
Lockyer, Herbert. The All Series, Bks. 1-14. Incl. Bk. 1. All the Apostles of the Bible. 15.95 (ISBN 0-310-28010-9, 10052); Bk. 2. All the Books & Chapters of the Bible; Bk. 3. All the Doctrines of the Bible. 15.95 (ISBN 0-310-28050-8, 10082); Bk. 4. All the Children of the Bible; Bk. 5. All the Holy Days & Holidays; Bk. 6. All the Kings & Queens of the Bible; Bk. 7. All the Men of the Bible. 15.95 (ISBN 0-310-28080-X, 10054); Bk. 8. All the Women of the Bible. 14.95 (ISBN 0-310-28150-4, 10038); Bk. 9. All the Miracles of the Bible. 16.95 (ISBN 0-310-28100-8, 10066); Bk. 10. All the Parables of the Bible. 15.95 (ISBN 0-310-28110-5, 10075); Bk. 11. All the Prayers of the Bible. 15.95 (ISBN 0-310-28120-2, 10041); Bk. 12. All the Promises of the Bible. 16.95 (ISBN 0-310-28130-X, 10074); Bk. 13. All the Trades & Occupations of the Bible; Bk. 14. All the Messianic Prophecies of the Bible. 19.95 (ISBN 0-310-28090-7, 10076). Zondervan.
Love One Another Bible Study Series, 7 vols. LC 79-52132. 1979. pap. 16.80 (ISBN 0-934396-00-0). Churches Alive.
Lowry, Mark. The Temple of Divine Truth. 1986. 6.95 (ISBN 0-8062-2423-1). Carlton.
Lum, Ada. How to Begin an Evangelistic Bible Study. pap. 2.50 (ISBN 0-87784-317-1). Inter-Varsity.
Maas, Robin. The Church Bible Study Handbook. 208p. (Orig.). 1982. pap. 11.95 (ISBN 0-687-08146-7). Abingdon.
MacArthur, John J. Liberty in Christ. (John MacArthur's Bible Studies). (Orig.). 1986. pap. 3.50 (ISBN 0-8024-5094-6). Moody.
MacArthur, John, Jr. Abiding in Christ. (John MacArthur's Bible Studies). (Orig.). 1986. pap. 3.50 (ISBN 0-8024-5128-4). Moody.
--Acting on the Good News. (John MacArthur's Bible Studies). (Orig.). 1987. pap. 3.95 (ISBN 0-8024-5348-1). Moody.
--Assurance of Victory. (John MacArthur's Bible Studies). (Orig.). 1986. pap. 3.50 (ISBN 0-8024-5130-6). Moody.
--The Believers Armor. (John MacArthur's Bible Studies). 1986. pap. 4.95 (ISBN 0-8024-5092-X). Moody.
--Condemned & Crucified. (John MacArthur's Bible Studies). (Orig.). 1987. pap. 3.95 (ISBN 0-8024-5349-X). Moody.
--The Disciples' Prayer. (John MacArthur's Bible Studies). (Orig.). 1986. pap. 4.95 (ISBN 0-8024-5129-2). Moody.
--Empowered to Serve: Acts one Verses one to two Verses Thirteen. (John Mac Arthur Bible Studies Ser.). 1987. pap. 3.95 (ISBN 0-8024-5314-7). Moody.
--How to Study the Bible. (John MacArthur's Bible Studies). 1985. pap. 3.50 (ISBN 0-8024-5105-5). Moody.
--Paul on Trial. (John MacArthur's Bible Studies). (Orig.). 1986. pap. 3.95 (ISBN 0-8024-5131-4). Moody.
--Paul's Perilous Journey. (John MacArthur's Bible Studies). (Orig.). 1987. pap. 3.50 (ISBN 0-8024-5350-3). Moody.
--The Resurrection & the Life. (John MacArthur's Bible Studies). 1986. pap. 3.50 (ISBN 0-8024-5091-1). Moody.
--Your Family. rev. & expanded ed. (Moody Press Electives Ser.). 1983. pap. 3.95 (ISBN 0-8024-0257-7). Moody.
McClain, Alva J. Bible Truths. 1981. pap. 1.25 (ISBN 0-88469-013-X). BMH Bks.
--The Inspiration of the Bible. 1980. pap. 1.00 (ISBN 0-88469-115-2). BMH Bks.
Maccoby, Hyam. The Sacred Executioner: Human Sacrifice & the Legacy of Guilt. LC 82-80492. (Illus.). 208p. 1983. 19.95 (ISBN 0-500-01281-4). Thames Hudson.
McConville, J. G. First & Second Chronicles. LC 84-2371. (Daily Study Bible-Old Testament Ser.). 280p. 1984. 14.95 (ISBN 0-664-21811-3); pap. 7.95 (ISBN 0-664-24578-1). Westminster.
McCreary, W. Burgess. One Thousand Bible Drill Questions. 1980. pap. 1.75 (ISBN 0-87162-263-7, WP#D5899). Warner Pr.
MacDonald, William. Here's the Difference. pap. 2.95 (ISBN 0-937396-55-9). Walterick Pubs.
--Let Me Introduce You to the Bible. 1980. pap. 2.50 (ISBN 0-937396-22-2). Walterick Pubs.
McDowell, Josh. Guide to Understanding Your Bible. LC 82-73526. 221p. 1982. pap. 6.95 (ISBN 0-86605-087-6). Here's Life.
McDowell, Josh & Bellis, Dale. Evidence Growth Guide, Vol. 2: Uniqueness of the Bible. 80p. (Orig.). 1981. 4.95 (ISBN 0-86605-019-1). Campus Crusade.
Mackay, Harold. How to Study Your Bible. Date not set. pap. 2.95 (ISBN 0-937396-68-0). Walterick Pubs.
McKim, Donald K. What Christians Believe about the Bible. 183p. 1985. pap. 8.95 (ISBN 0-8407-5968-1). Nelson.
McKinney, et al. A Through the Bible Reading Program. (Illus.). 112p. (Orig.). 1983. pap. 3.95 (ISBN 0-87239-647-9, 3076). Standard Pub.
Madsen, Norman P. Bible Readers Tool Box. LC 86-24523. 168p. (Orig.). 1987. pap. 7.95 (ISBN 0-8272-0214-8). CBP.
Magers, Mary A. Bible Moments with Motions. Zapel, Arthur L., ed. Zapel, Michelle, tr. (Illus.). 53p. (Orig.). 1984. pap. 3.95 (ISBN 0-916260-27-5). Meriwether Pub.
Mains, David. Making Scripture Yours. (Chapel Talks Ser.). 64p. 0.95 (ISBN 0-89191-272-X, 52720). Cook.
Mains, David & Mains, Karen. Our Favorite Verse. LC 86-73188. (My Favorite Verse Ser.). 24p. 1987. pap. 4.95 (ISBN 0-89636-232-9). Accent Bks.
Makrakis, Apostolos. The Bible & the World & Triluminal Science. Orthodox Christian Educational Society, ed. Cummings, Denver, tr. from Hellenic. 531p. 1950. 10.00x (ISBN 0-938366-18-1). Orthodox Chr.
Malmin, Kenneth P. Bible Research. rev. ed. (Illus.). 149p. 1979. Repr. of 1976 ed. notebk. 11.95 (ISBN 0-914936-33-6). Bible Temple.
Manni, Alvin. Take & Read: Gems from the Bible. 280p. (Orig.). 1981. pap. 7.50 (ISBN 0-89944-054-1). Don Bosco Multimedia.
Marinelli, Anthony J. Yahweh & Son: A Teenager's Guide to the Bible. 160p. (Orig.). 1986. pap. 7.95 (ISBN 0-8091-9568-2). Paulist Pr.
Marino, Joseph S., ed. Biblical Themes in Religious Education. LC 83-16124. 294p. (Orig.). 1983. pap. 14.95 (ISBN 0-89135-038-1). Religious Educ.
Marlowe, Monroe & Reed, Bobbie. Creative Bible Learning for Adults. LC 77-76206. (International Center for Learning Handbooks). 192p. 1977. pap. 3.95 (ISBN 0-8307-0480-9, 9900152). Regal.
Marsh, F. E. Devotional Bible Studies. LC 79-2548. 304p. 1980. 10.95 (ISBN 0-8254-3230-8). Kregel.
--Illustrated Bible Study Outlines. LC 79-125116. 268p. 1979. pap. 8.95 (ISBN 0-8254-3245-6). Kregel.
Martin, George. Reading Scripture As the Word of God. Rev. ed. 200p. 1982. pap. 4.95 (ISBN 0-89283-152-9). Servant.
Martin, John R. Keys to Successful Bible Study. LC 81-6459. 184p. 1981. pap. 6.95 (ISBN 0-8361-1963-0). Herald Pr.
Martin, Sydney. Beacon Bible Expositions, Vol. 10: Thessalonians, Timothy, Titus. Greathouse, William M & Taylor, Willard H., eds. 1978. 8.95 (ISBN 0-8341-0321-4). Beacon Hill.
Martin, T. E. Beacon Bible Expositions, Vol. 12: John, Jude, Revelation. Greathouse, M., ed. 230p. 1983. 8.95 (ISBN 0-8341-0809-7). Beacon Hill.
Matek, Ord. The Bible Through Stamps. LC 73-23126. 240p. 1974. 7.50x (ISBN 0-87068-397-7). Ktav.
Matthews, Carole. Through the Bible with Preschoolers. 144p. 1985. 8.95 (ISBN 0-87239-945-1, 3330). Standard Pub.
Mears, Henrietta C., et al. What the Bible Is All About. rev. ed. Youngblood, Ronald & Tenney, Merrill C., eds. LC 83-4333. 1982. 13.95 (ISBN 0-8307-0902-9, 5110704); pap. 9.95 (ISBN 0-8307-0862-6, 5417202). Regal.
Merton, Thomas. Opening the Bible. LC 85-24722. 96p. 1986. pap. 4.95 (ISBN 0-8006-1910-2). Fortress.
Meyer, F. B. Great Verses of the Bible. 1984. gift ed. 6.95 (ISBN 0-915720-82-5). Brownlow Pub Co.
Michael, Chester P. Scripture Themes & Texts for Meditation & Study. 1981. pap. 2.00. Open Door Inc.
Mickelsen, A. Berkeley & Mickelsen, Alvera M. Understanding Scripture. 2nd ed. LC 81-52231. (Better Bible Study Ser.). 1982. pap. 3.50 (ISBN 0-8307-0795-6, 5017302). Regal.
Miller, Herb. Building a Meaningful Life with the Carpenter's Twenty Megatruths. 108p. (Orig.). 1968. pap. write for info. (ISBN 0-937462-03-9). Net Pr.
Milner, Wanda. How to Use Your Bible. (Illus.). 24p. (Orig.). 1983. pap. 2.95 (ISBN 0-87239-690-8, 3200). Standard Pub.
Mitchell, Phyllis. How to Study the Bible. (Workbook Ser.). (Illus.). 95p. 1982. pap. 4.95 (ISBN 0-930756-67-3, 581003). Aglow Pubns.
Moir, John S. A History of Biblical Studies in Canada: A Sense of Proportion. LC 82-5979. (Society of Biblical Literature: Biblical Scholarship in North America Ser.). 132p. 1982. pap. 17.95 (ISBN 0-89130-581-5, 06 11 07). Scholars Pr GA.
Monser, Harold E. & Robertson, A. T. Topical Index & Digest of the Bible. (Paperback Reference Library). 688p. 1983. pap. 14.95 (ISBN 0-8010-6160-1). Baker Bk.
Moorehead, Bob. Free at Last. LC 86-71102. 88p. (Orig.). 1986. pap. 3.95 (ISBN 0-89900-212-9). College Pr Pub.
Morissey, Kirkie. In His Name. 132p. 1985. pap. 4.95 (ISBN 0-89109-056-8). NavPress.
Morris, Henry, 3rd. Explore the Word! LC 78-55611. 1978. pap. 7.95 (ISBN 0-89051-047-4). Master Bks.
Morrissey, Kirkie. On Holy Ground. 144p. (Orig.). 1983. pap. 4.95 (ISBN 0-89109-051-7). NavPress.
Moulton, Richard G. The Literary Study of the Bible. LC 70-4534. 1898. 59.00x (ISBN 0-403-00113-7). Scholarly.
Murray, Dick. Teaching the Bible to Adults & Youth. (Creative Leadership Ser.). 176p. 1987. pap. 8.95 (ISBN 0-687-41082-7). Abingdon.
Nave, Orville J. Nave's Study Bible. 24.95 (ISBN 0-8010-6696-4). Baker Bk.
--Nave's Topical Bible. LC 79-14111. 1979. 19.95 (ISBN 0-8407-4992-9). Nelson.
Navigators Staff. The Navigator Bible Studies Handbook. x1979 ed. LC 79-87654. (Illus.). 132p. 1974. pap. 5.95 (ISBN 0-89109-075-4). Navpress.
Navigators Staff, ed. How to Lead Small Group Bible Studies. 72p. 1982. pap. 3.95 (ISBN 0-89109-124-6). NavPress.
Nee, Watchman. Ye Search the Scriptures. Kaung, Stephen, tr. 1974. 4.75 (ISBN 0-935008-46-2); pap. 3.75 (ISBN 0-935008-47-0). Christian Fellow Pubs.
Neighbour, Ralph W., Jr. Sigueme. 128p. 1986. Repr. of 1983 ed. reader ed. 2.75 (ISBN 0-311-13837-3); student ed. 2.65 (ISBN 0-311-13836-5). Casa Bautista.
Nelson, Thomas. What Christians Believe about the Bible. 183p. 1985. pap. 7.95 (ISBN 0-317-43242-7). Ideals.
The New Catholic Study Bible: St. Jerome Edition. 1786p. 1985. 29.95 (ISBN 0-87973-542-2). Our Sunday Visitor.
Norden, Rudolph. Introducing the Books of the Bible: A Devotional Summary. 64p. 1987. pap. 3.95 (ISBN 0-570-04452-9, 12-3061). Concordia.
Norquist, Marilyn. Biblical Guidelines for Discovering God's Kingdom. LC 82-81769. 64p. 1982. pap. 4.25 (ISBN 0-89243-160-1). Liguori Pubns.
North, Gary. Seventy-Five Bible Questions Your Instructors Pray You Won't Ask. 280p. (Orig.). 1984. pap. 4.95 (ISBN 0-930462-03-3). Am Bur Eco Res.
Nyquist, James F. & Kuhatschek, Jack. Leading Bible Discussions. rev. ed. 60p. 1985. pap. 2.95 (ISBN 0-8308-1000-5). Inter-Varsity.

Nystrom, Carolyn. At the Starting Line: Beginning a New Life. (Young Fisherman Bible Studyguides). 48p. 1985. pap. 2.95 student (ISBN 0-87788-053-0); pap. text ed. 4.95 Tchr's. (ISBN 0-87788-054-9). Shaw Pubs.
--Basic Beliefs: A Woman's Workshop on the Christian Faith. (Woman's Workshop Ser.). 124p. 1986. pap. 3.95 (ISBN 0-310-41971-9). Zondervan.
O'Connor, M. & Freedman, David N. Backgrounds for the Bible. 1987. text ed. 17.50x (ISBN 0-931464-30-7). Eisenbrauns.
O'Heron, Edward J. Biblical Companions. LC 78-74625. 1979. pap. 3.95 (ISBN 0-87973-647-X). Our Sunday Visitor.
O'Ree. Bible Games & Fun for Everyone. 1966. 0.60 (ISBN 0-88027-103-5). Firm Foun Pub.
Osborne, Grant R. & Woodward, Stephen B. Handbook for Bible Study. 188p. 1983. pap. 5.95 (ISBN 0-8010-6701-4). Baker Bk.
Our Father. (Illus.). 48p. 1983. 7.95 (ISBN 0-86683-745-0, AY8398, HarpR). Har-Row.
Packer, J. I. Meeting God. (LifeBuilder Bible Studies). 64p. (Orig.). 1986. pap. 2.95. Inter-Varsity.
Packer, James I., et al, eds. The Bible Almanac: A Comprehensive Handbook of the People of the Bible & How They Lived. LC 79-23475. 792p. 1980. 16.95 (ISBN 0-8407-5162-1). Nelson.
Palmer, W. Robert. How to Understand the Bible. 2nd ed. 118p. 1980. pap. 3.95 (ISBN 0-89900-140-8). College Pr Pub.
Parmelee, Alice. Introducing the Bible. (All About the Bible Ser.: Bk. 1). (Illus.). 1979. pap. 5.95 (ISBN 0-8192-1253-9). Morehouse.
Paxson, Ruth. Life on the Highest Plane: A Study of the Spiritual Nature & Needs of Man. pap. 12.95 (ISBN 0-8010-7091-0). Baker Bk.
Pendleton, Joe. The Joy of Bible Study. (Illus.). 64p. (Orig.). 1981. pap. 1.95 (ISBN 0-89114-106-5); P. 32. tchr's ed. 1.50 (ISBN 0-89114-107-3). Baptist Pub Hse.
Perry, Lloyd M. & Culver, Robert D. How to Get More from Your Bible. (Direction Bks). 1979. pap. 3.95 (ISBN 0-8010-7048-1). Baker Bk.
Perschke, Louis M. Helps & Hints at Bible Study. 176p. 1981. 8.50 (ISBN 0-682-49733-9, Testament). Exposition Pr FL.
Peters, F. E. The Children of Abraham: Judaism, Christianity, Islam. LC 81-47941. 240p. 1983. 23.50 (ISBN 0-691-07267-1); pap. 8.50x (ISBN 0-691-02030-2). Princeton U Pr.
Phillips, John. Exploring the World of the Jew. LC 81-16844. 288p. 1982. pap. 9.95 (ISBN 0-8024-2411-2). Moody.
Piatt, Larry. One Thousand One More Questions on the Bible. 96p. 1986. pap. 4.95 (ISBN 0-8010-7094-5). Baker Bk.
--One Thousand One Questions on the Bible. 50p. 1984. pap. 3.95 (ISBN 0-8010-7085-6). Baker Bk.
Pierce, Rice A. How to Enjoy Bible Study with Others. LC 72-5250. 1972. 3.95 (ISBN 0-8407-5043-9). Religious Activ.
--Leading Dynamic Bible Study. LC 74-78835. 1979. 3.95 (ISBN 0-8054-3420-8). Religious Activ.
Piet, John H. A Path Through the Bible. LC 81-2258. (Illus.). 318p. 1981. pap. 14.95 (ISBN 0-664-24369-X). Westminster.
The Pilgrim Study Bible. 1984. write for info. Oxford U Pr.
Pink, A. W. Studies in the Scriptures, 1946. pap. 9.45 (ISBN 0-85151-346-8). Banner of Truth.
--Studies in the Scriptures, 1947. 298p. pap. 9.45 (ISBN 0-85151-347-6). Banner of Truth.
Pixley, George V. God's Kingdom: A Guide for Biblical Study. Walsh, Donald E., tr. from Sp. LC 81-3946. Tr. of Reino de Dios. 128p. (Orig.). 1981. pap. 5.95 (ISBN 0-88344-156-X). Orbis Bks.
Plantinga, Theodore. Reading the Bible As History. 110p. (Orig.). 1980. pap. 4.25 (ISBN 0-932914-04-7). Dordt Coll Pr.
Plueddemann, Carol, ed. Great Passages of the Bible. (Fisherman Bible Studyguide Ser.). 64p. (Orig.). 1987. pap. 2.95 (ISBN 0-87788-332-7). Shaw Pubs.
Pocketpac Bks. Promises for the Golden Years. 96p. 1983. pap. 2.50 (ISBN 0-87788-320-3). Shaw Pubs.
Powell, Ivor C. Bible Gems. LC 86-27525. 172p. (Orig.). 1987. pap. 5.95 (ISBN 0-8254-3527-7). Kregel.
Prince, Derek. Self Study Bible Course. 1969. pap. 5.95 (ISBN 0-934920-08-7, B-90). Derek Prince.
Ramsey, Boniface. Beginning to Read the Fathers. 288p. (Orig.). 1985. pap. 9.95 (ISBN 0-8091-2691-5). Paulist Pr.
Reader's Digest Editors. Family Guide to the Bible: A Concordance & Reference Companion to the King James Version. LC 84-13261. (Illus.). 832p. 1984. 24.50 (ISBN 0-89577-192-6, Pub. by RD Assn). Random.
Reed, C. Edward & Reed, Bobbie. A Creative Bible Learning for Youth: Grades 7-12. LC 77-76205. 1977. pap. 3.95 (ISBN 0-8307-0479-5, 9700102). Regal.
Reid, Muriel F. Speak the Thought: How to Read & Speak in Public, with Bible-Lesson Applications. 2nd, exp. ed. 64p. 1984. 7.00 (ISBN 0-915878-05-4). Joseph Pub Co.
Reis, Elizabeth M. A Deeper Kind of Truth: Biblical Tales for Life & Prayer. 112p. (Orig.). 1987. pap. 5.95 (ISBN 0-8091-2858-6). Paulist Pr.
Retzer, Fernon. You Can Understand the Bible. 1984. pap. 1.95 (ISBN 0-317-28295-6). Pacific Pr Pub Assn.
Richards, Ken. Walking Through the Bible with H. M. S. Richards. 384p. 1983. 9.95 (ISBN 0-8163-0433-5). Pacific Pr Pub Assn.
Richards, Lawrence O. Creative Bible Study. 1979. pap. 5.95 (ISBN 0-310-31911-0, 10711P). Zondervan.
--Creative Bible Teaching. LC 74-104830. 1970. 12.95 (ISBN 0-8024-1640-3). Moody.
Riley, William. The Bible Study Group: An Owner's Manual. LC 85-70362. (Illus.). 152p. 1985. pap. 7.95 (ISBN 0-87793-286-7). Ave Maria.
Ritchie, John. Five Hundred Children's Sermon Outlines. LC 86-27396. 128p. 1987. pap. 4.95 (ISBN 0-8254-3623-0). Kregel.
--Five Hundred Gospel Sermon Outlines. LC 86-27760. 128p. 1987. pap. 4.95 (ISBN 0-8254-3621-4). Kregel.
--Five Hundred Sermon Outlines on Basic Bible Truths. LC 86-27541. 128p. 1987. pap. 4.95 (ISBN 0-8254-3618-4). Kregel.
Roach, Michael L. Outreach Through Neighborhood Bible Study. 54p. 1986. 3.50 (ISBN 0-317-52739-8). Herald Hse.
Robinson, James H. & Darline, R. One Hundred Bible Quiz Activities for Church School Classes. 1981. pap. 3.95 (ISBN 0-570-03829-4, 12-2794). Concordia.
Robinson, John A. T. Redating the New Testament. LC 76-17554. 384p. 1976. 15.00 (ISBN 0-664-21336-7). Westminster.
Robinson, Russell D. Teaching the Scriptures: A Syllabus for Bible Study. (Illus.). 156p. 1977. 11.95 (ISBN 0-9600154-3-4); pap. 9.95 (ISBN 0-9600154-4-2). Bible Study Pr.
Robinson, Wayne B. The Transforming Power of the Bible. LC 83-23680. 240p. (Orig.). 1984. pap. 9.95 (ISBN 0-8298-0706-3). Pilgrim NY.
Rolls, Charles J. The World's Greatest Name, Names & Titles of Jesus Christ Beginning with H-K. rev. ed. 183p. 1985. pap. 5.95 (ISBN 0-87213-732-5). Loizeaux.
Roth, Wolfgang & Ruether, Rosemary R. The Liberating Bond: Covenants Biblical & Contemporary. (Orig.). 1978. pap. 2.95 (ISBN 0-377-00076-0). Friend Pr.
RSV Handy Concordance. 192p. 1972. pap. 5.95 (ISBN 0-310-32391-6, 6765P). Zondervan.
Russell, Joseph. The Daily Lectionary-Year 1: Advent-Easter. (Orig.). 1986. pap. 2.50 (ISBN 0-88028-057-3). Forward Movement.
Ryken, Leland. Worlds of Delight: A Literary Introduction to the Bible. 372p. 1987. pap. 17.95 (ISBN 0-8010-7743-5). Baker Bk.
Ryrie, Charles C. Object Lessons. 96p. 1981. pap. 3.95 (ISBN 0-8024-6024-0). Moody.
--Understanding Bible Doctrine. rev. ed. (Elective Ser.). 1983. pap. 3.95 (ISBN 0-8024-0258-5). Moody.
Sala, Harold. My Favorite Verse. LC 86-72986. (My Favorite Verse Ser.). 24p. 1987. pap. 4.95 (ISBN 0-89636-228-0). Accent Bks.
Salem Kirban Reference Bible. (Illus.). 1979. skivertex flexible bdg. 49.95 (ISBN 0-912582-31-6); leather ed. 69.95 (ISBN 0-686-52197-8). Kirban.
Salem, Luis. Hogares de la Biblia. (Span.). 107p. (Orig.). pap. 2.50 (ISBN 0-89922-079-7). Edit Caribe.
Samms, Robert L. How to Study the Bible, Pt. I. (Lay Action Ministry Program Ser.). 96p. 1987. pap. 4.95 (ISBN 0-89191-516-8). Cook.
--How to Study the Bible, Pt. II. (Lay Action Ministry Program Ser.). 96p. 1987. pap. 4.95 (ISBN 0-89191-517-6). Cook.
Sanner, A. Elwood & Greathouse, William M. Beacon Bible Expositions, Vol. 2: Mark. 1978. 8.95 (ISBN 0-8341-0313-3). Beacon Hill.
Santa Biblia Dios Habla Hoy. 1504p. 1980. pap. 15.95 (ISBN 0-311-48716-5, Edit Mundo). Casa Bautista.
Saphir, Adolph. The Divine Unity of Scripture. LC 84-9642. (Adolph Saphir Study Ser.). 376p. 1984. pap. 10.95 (ISBN 0-8254-3747-4). Kregel.
Schacher, James A. Conversational Bible Studies. (Contemporary Discussion Ser). 112p. 1975. 1.65 (ISBN 0-8010-8054-1). Baker Bk.
Schaeffer, Francis. Basic Bible Studies. 1972. pap. 2.95 (ISBN 0-8423-0103-8). Tyndale.
Schreck, Alan. Catholic & Christian Study Guide. 64p. (Orig.). 1985. pap. 2.95 (ISBN 0-89283-249-5). Servant.
Schultz, Samuel. Ley e Historia del Antiguo Testamento. Villalobos, Fernando P., tr. from Eng. (Curso Para Maestros Cristianos Ser.: No. 1). (Span., Illus.). 122p. 1972. pap. 3.50 (ISBN 0-89922-008-8); instructor's manual 1.50 (ISBN 0-89922-009-6). Edit Caribe.
Schuster, Ignatius. Bible History. Heck, H. J., ed. Schumacher, Philip, tr. (Illus.). 1974. pap. 8.00 (ISBN 0-89555-006-7). TAN Bks Pubs.
Sciacca, Francis. To Walk & Not Grow Weary. 84p. 1985. pap. 3.95 (ISBN 0-89109-034-7). NavPress.
Scofield, C. I. Rightly Dividing the Word of Truth. pap. 1.50 (ISBN 0-87213-770-8). Loizeaux.
--Rightly Dividing the Word of Truth. 72p. (Orig.). 1974. pap. 2.95 (ISBN 0-310-32662-1, 6364P). Zondervan.
Scofield, Willard A. Teaching the Bible: Creative Techniques for Bringing Scripture to Life. 112p. 1986. pap. 6.95 (ISBN 0-8170-1094-7). Judson.
Scott, Bernard B. The Word of God in Words: Reading & Preaching the Gospels. LC 85-5227. (Fortress Resources for Preaching). 96p. 1985. pap. 4.95 (ISBN 0-8006-1142-X). Fortress.
Scott, W. Bible Handbook, 2 vols. 18.00 (ISBN 0-88172-123-9). Believers Bkshelf.
The Scriptures: How Shall I Read Them? 1970. pap. 2.25 (ISBN 0-8100-0025-3, 12-0338). Northwest Pub.
Searcy, W. B. The Proper Way to Study the Bible. 1982. 6.75 (ISBN 0-8062-1943-2). Carlton.
Seashore, Gladys. I Am a Possibility. 80p. 1979. pap. 1.95 (ISBN 0-911802-44-4). Free Church Pubns.
Shedd, Charlie & Shedd, Martha. Bible Study in Duet. 144p. 1984. 8.95 (ISBN 0-310-42380-5, 18360). Zondervan.
--Bible Study Together: Making Marriage Last. 144p. 1987. pap. 5.95 (ISBN 0-310-42381-3). Zondervan.
Shelly, Maynard. New Call for Peacemakers. (Illus.). 109p. 1980. pap. text ed. 2.00 (ISBN 0-87303-031-1). Faith & Life.
Siegel, Beatrice. Sam Ellis's Island. LC 85-42799. (Illus.). 128p. 1985. PLB 11.95 (ISBN 0-02-782720-8, Four Winds). Macmillan.
Simmons, Arthur G. & Simmons, Beborah T. Create in Me: Young Adult Bible Study. 1985. 5.75 (ISBN 0-89536-765-3, 5872). CSS of Ohio.
Simundson, Daniel J. Where Is God In My Praying? Biblical Responses to Eight Searching Questions. LC 86-22294. 96p. (Orig.). 1986. pap. 5.50 (ISBN 0-8066-2241-5, 10-7096). Augsburg.
Skilton, John H. The New Testament Student & His Field. (New Testament Student Ser.). 318p. 1982. pap. 9.95 (ISBN 0-87552-437-0). Presby & Reformed.
Slay, James L. Esto Creemos Curzo de Doctrina Biblica Para Ninos. (Span., Orig.). pap. 1.00 (ISBN 0-87148-311-4). Pathway Pr.
Slemming, Charles W. Bible Digest. LC 68-27671. 906p. 1975. 27.95 (ISBN 0-8254-3706-7). Kregel.
--Bible Digest Charts. LC 64-17168. 1974. pap. 12.95 (ISBN 0-8254-3701-6). Kregel.
Smalley, Beryl. Study of the Bible in the Middle Ages. 1964. pap. 9.95x (ISBN 0-268-00267-3). U of Notre Dame Pr.
Smead, Jane. Chateaubriand et la Bible, Contribution a L'etude Des Sources Des "Martyrs". 1973. Repr. of 1924 ed. 15.00 (ISBN 0-384-56347-3). Johnson Repr.
Smith, Joyce M. Fulfillment: Bible Studies for Women. 1975. pap. 2.95 (ISBN 0-8423-0980-2). Tyndale.
--Growing When You Don't Feel Like It. (Good Life Bible Studies). 64p. (YA) 1985. pap. 2.95 (ISBN 0-8423-1229-3). Tyndale.
Smith, Thomas A. Discovering Discipleship: A Resource for Home Bible Studies. LC 80-54073. (Illus.). 64p. (Orig.). 1981. pap. 2.75 (ISBN 0-87239-438-7, 88570). Standard Pub.
Song, Grace Y., et al, eds. The Bible Compiled for A Blessed Life. LC 83-26389. 680p. (Orig.). 1984. pap. 4.95 (ISBN 0-916075-00-1). Intl Life Mess.
Souter, John & Souter, Susan. Youth Bible Study Notebook. 1977. pap. 5.95 (ISBN 0-8423-8790-0). Tyndale.
Souter, Susan J. How to Be a Confident Woman: A Bible Study Guide for Women. LC 78-51904. 80p. 1978. pap. 2.95 (ISBN 0-89081-124-5). Harvest Hse.
Spurgeon, Charles H. Metropolitan Tabernacle Pulpit. 1971. Vol. 31. 14.95. Banner of Truth.
Stacey, W. David. Groundwork of Biblical Studies. LC 82-70961. 448p. 1982. pap. 14.95 (ISBN 0-8066-1936-8, 10-2898). Augsburg.
Stanley, David M. A Modern Scriptural Approach to the Spiritual Exercises. Ganss, George E., frwd. by. LC 67-25219. (Series III: No. 1). xviii, 358p. 1986. pap. 6.95 (ISBN 0-912422-07-6). Inst Jesuit.
Staton, Knofel. Bible Keys for Today's Family. LC 83-9239. 144p. (Orig.). 1984. pap. 2.95 (ISBN 0-87239-669-X, 41024). Standard Pub.
Steidl, Paul M. Earth, the Stars, & the Bible. 1979. pap. 5.95 (ISBN 0-87552-430-3). Presby & Reformed.
Steinmueller, John E. The Sword of the Spirit. 108p. 1977. pap. 3.00 (ISBN 0-912103-00-0). Stella Maris Bks.
Stensland, Vivian, ed. Daily Light from the New American Standard Bible. 416p. 1975. 9.95 (ISBN 0-8024-1740-X). Moody.
Sterrett, T. Norton. How to Understand Your Bible. LC 74-78674. 180p. 1974. pap. 6.95 (ISBN 0-87784-638-3). Inter-Varsity.
Stibbs, Alan. How to Understand Your Bible. Wenham, David & Wenham, Clare, eds. LC 77-72351. Orig. Title: Understanding God's Word. 77p. 1978. pap. 1.95 (ISBN 0-87788-365-3). Shaw Pubs.
Stibbs, Alan M., ed. Search the Scriptures. rev. ed. 9.95 (ISBN 0-87784-856-4). Inter-Varsity.
Stobbe, Leslie H. Preteen Bible Exploration. 1987. pap. 4.95 (ISBN 0-8010-8273-0). Baker Bk.
Stott, John R. Understanding the Bible. rev. ed. 256p. 1982. pap. 6.95 (ISBN 0-310-41451-2, 12610P). Zondervan.
--Understanding the Bible. 2nd ed. 192p. 1985. pap. 6.95 (ISBN 0-310-41431-8). Zondervan.
Stout, John L. What the Bible Does Not Say. LC 80-84340. (Illus.). 208p. 1981. 10.95 (ISBN 0-8187-0042-4). Harlo Pr.
Strauss, Lehman. In God's Waiting Room. rev. ed. 1985. pap. text ed. 4.95 (ISBN 0-8024-3827-X). Moody.
Strickland, Rennard. Fire & the Spirits: Cherokee Law From Clan to Court. LC 74-15903. (Illus.). 260p. 1982. pap. 10.95 (ISBN 0-8061-1619-6). U of Okla Pr.
Sullivan, Jessie P. Object Lessons: With Easy-to-Find Objects. (Object Lesson Ser.). 128p. (Orig.). 1981. pap. 3.95 (ISBN 0-8010-8190-4). Baker Bk.
Swain, Lionel, et al. Last Writings. LC 71-173033. (Scripture Discussion Commentary Ser.: Pt. 12). 192p. 1972. pap. text ed. 4.50 (ISBN 0-87946-011-3). ACTA Found.
Swanston, Hamish. Histories Two. Bright, Laurence, ed. LC 71-173033. (Scripture Discussion Commentary Ser.: Pt. 5). 224p. 1971. pap. text ed. 4.50 (ISBN 0-87946-005-9). ACTA Found.
Swanston, Hamish & Bright, Laurence. Histories One. LC 71-173033. (Scriptures Discussion Commentary Ser.: Pt. 3). 182p. 1971. pap. text ed. 4.50 (ISBN 0-87946-002-4). ACTA Found.
Swindoll, Luci. My Favorite Verse. LC 85-73591. (My Favorite Verse Ser.). 24p. 1986. pap. 4.95 (ISBN 0-89636-204-3). Accent Bks.
Tadmor, H. History Historiography & Interpretation: Studies in Biblical & Cuneiform Literatures. Weinfeld, M., ed. 192p. 1983. pap. text ed. 22.50 (ISBN 965-223-459-1, Pub by Magnes Pr Israel). Humanities.
Tash, Sharon. Kingdom Living. (Bible Study Basic Ser.). 64p. 1984. 2.95 (521018). Aglow Pubns.
Taylor, Charles R. Pretribulation Rapture & the Bible. (Illus.). 40p. (Orig.). 1980. pap. 1.50 (ISBN 0-937682-03-9). Today Bible.
Taylor, Willard H. Beacon Bible Expositions: Galatians-Ephesians, Vol. 8. 228p. 1981. 8.95 (ISBN 0-8341-0734-1). Beacon Hill.
Tenney, Helen. Mark's Sketch Book of Christ. 1975. spiral bound 6.45 (ISBN 0-85151-075-2). Banner of Truth.
Teyler, Theodore W. Bible Basics. (Illus.). 48p. (Orig.). 1986. pap. 4.95 leader's guide (ISBN 0-933350-35-X); pap. 4.95 student manual (ISBN 0-317-46726-3). Morse Pr.
That You May Believe (John) Leader's Guide. (New Horizons Bible Study). 48p. 1983. pap. 1.95 (ISBN 0-89367-082-0). Light & Life.
Thompson, David L. Bible Study That Works. 72p. 1986. pap. 3.95 (ISBN 0-310-75001-6, 17024P). Zondervan.
Thompson, J. A. Handbook of Life in Bible Times. LC 86-3046. (Illus.). 380p. 1986. 34.95 (ISBN 0-87784-949-8). Inter-Varsity.
Thompson, Paul M. & Lillevold, Joani. The Giving Book: Creative Resources for Senior High Ministry. LC 84-47794. (Illus.). 144p. (Orig.). 1985. pap. 9.95 (ISBN 0-8042-1192-2). John Knox.
Tickle, John. Discovering the Bible, Bk. 2. 96p. (Orig.). 1980. pap. 3.95 (ISBN 0-89243-133-4). Liguori Pubns.
--Discovering the Bible: 8 Simple Keys for Learning & Praying. LC 77-94872. 1978. pap. 3.95 leader's guide, Bk. 1 (ISBN 0-89243-084-2); leader's guide, bk. 2 2.95 (ISBN 0-89243-141-5). Liguori Pubns.
--Un Estudio de la Biblia. Diaz, Olimpia, Sr., tr. from Eng. 96p. 1980. pap. 1.95 (ISBN 0-89243-131-8). Liguori Pubns.
Ting, K. H. How to Study the Bible. Tao Fong Shan Ecumenical Centre, tr. from Chinese. Tr. of Zeyang Du Shengjing. 1981. pap. 1.95 (ISBN 0-377-00122-8). Friend Pr.
Torrey, R. A. How to Study the Bible. 155p. 1985. pap. 3.50 (ISBN 0-88368-164-1). Whitaker Hse.
Torrey, R. A., ed. How to Study the Bible for Greatest Profit. 1984. pap. 3.95 (ISBN 0-8010-8875-5). Baker Bk.

Townsend, Jim. The Personal Bible Study. (Complete Teacher Training Meeting Ser.). 48p. 1986. tchr's ed 9.95 (ISBN 0-89191-320-3). Cook.

Traina, Robert A. Methodical Bible Study. 1985. 12.95 (ISBN 0-317-38919-X, 17031). Zondervan.

--Methodical Bible Study. 1985. 14.95 (ISBN 0-310-31230-2). Zondervan.

Tucker, Ronald D. Love Is. (Illus.). 76p. (Orig.). 1983. pap. 2.50 (ISBN 0-933643-10-1). Grace World Outreach.

--The New Creation. (Illus.). 34p. (Orig.). 1983. pap. 1.75 (ISBN 0-933643-11-X). Grace World Outreach.

--Righteousness. (Illus.). 48p. (Orig.). 1983. pap. 2.00 (ISBN 0-933643-09-8). Grace World Outreach.

--Vision. (Illus.). 24p. (Orig.). 1983. pap. 1.50 (ISBN 0-933643-12-8). Grace World Outreach.

Turner, Elizabeth S. Hagase la Luz. (Span.). 320p. 1985. 5.95 (ISBN 0-317-44746-7). Unity School.

Turner, J. J. How to Effectively Study the Bible. pap. 2.50 (ISBN 0-686-73328-2). Lambert Bk.

Twombly, Gerald H. An Analytical Survey of the Bible. pap. 5.95 (ISBN 0-88469-120-9). BMH Bks.

Unger, Merrill F. Nuevo Manual Biblico de Unger. Orig. Title: New Unger's Bible Handbook. (Span.). 720p. 1987. 32.95 (ISBN 0-8254-1779-1). Kregel.

Van Buren, James & Dewett, Don. What the Bible Says about Praise & Promise. LC 80-66127. (What the Bible Says Ser.). 450p. 1980. 13.95 (ISBN 0-89900-078-9). College Pr Pub.

Van Dolson, Leo. How to Get the Most Out of Bible Study. (Harvest Ser.). 122p. 1980. pap. 5.95 (ISBN 0-8163-0360-6). Pacific Pr Pub Assn.

Van Dyke Parunak, H., ed. Computer Tools for Ancient Texts: Proceedings of the 1980 Ann Arbor Symposium on Biblical Studies & the Computer. 1987. text ed. price not set (ISBN 0-931464-32-3). Eisenbrauns.

Van Ness, Bethann & De Clemente, Elizabeth M. Historias de Toda la Biblia. (Illus.). 684p. 1979. pap. 19.95 (ISBN 0-311-03600-7). Casa Bautista.

Van Note, Gene. How to Lead a Small Group Bible Study. 48p. pap. 1.75 (ISBN 0-8341-0653-1). Beacon Hill.

Viertel, Weldon. La Biblia y Su Interpretacion. Orig. Title: The Bible & Its Interpretation. 208p. 1983. pap. 8.25 (ISBN 0-311-03670-8). Casa Bautista.

Vogels, Walter. Reading & Preaching the Bible: A New Approach. (Background Bks.: Vol. 4). 1986. pap. 7.95 (ISBN 0-89453-472-6). M Glazier.

Vos, Howard F. Effective Bible Study. (Contemporary Evangelical Perspectives Ser.). 1956. kivar 6.95 (ISBN 0-310-33851-4, 10966P). Zondervan.

Wadsworth, Michael, ed. Ways of Reading the Bible. 232p. 1981. 28.50x (ISBN 0-389-20119-7). B&N Imports.

Wahlie, Albert J. Believer's Tree of Life. Ben Menachem, Shmuel, ed. (Illus.). 105p. (Orig.). 1986. pap. 6.95x (ISBN 0-9616488-0-5). Alef Bet Comns.

Wake Up O' Sleeping World. 48p. 1983. 9.95 (ISBN 0-89962-315-8). Todd & Honeywell.

Wald, Oletta. Joy of Discovery in Bible Study. rev. ed. LC 75-22710. 96p. 1975. pap. 4.95 (ISBN 0-8066-1513-3, 10-3600). Augsburg.

--Joy of Teaching Discovery Bible Study. LC 76-3857. (Orig.). 1976. pap. 4.95 (ISBN 0-8066-1530-3, 10-3603). Augsburg.

Walker, Mrs. Charles. That Ye May Abound. (Illus.). 80p. (Orig.). 1980. pap. 3.00 (ISBN 0-89114-096-4). Baptist Pub Hse.

Walvoord, John F. Philippians: Joy & Peace. (Everyman's Bible Commentary). 1971. pap. 5.95 (ISBN 0-8024-2050-8). Moody.

Warfield, B. B. Biblical & Theological Studies. 12.95 (ISBN 0-8010-9584-0). Baker Bk.

Warren, Richard. Twelve Dynamic Bible Study Methods. 252p. 1981. pap. 7.95 (ISBN 0-88207-815-1). Victor Bks.

We Believe... A Guide to a Better Understanding of the Bible As a Source Book for the Humanities. school ed. School ed. 0.75 (ISBN 0-89942-247-0, 247.05-SD). Catholic Bk Pub.

Weaver, Horace R., ed. The International Lesson Annual, 1986-1987. 448p. (Orig.). 1986. pap. 7.95 (ISBN 0-687-19150-5). Abingdon.

Weber, Hans-Ruedi. Experiments with Bible Study. LC 82-13398. 330p. 1983. pap. 12.95 (ISBN 0-664-24461-0). Westminster.

Weed, Michael & Weed, Libby. Bible Handbook: A Guide for Basic Bible Learning. LC 73-91023. 1978. student's ed. 5.95 (ISBN 0-8344-0101-0). Sweet.

Weisheit, Eldon. The Gospel for Little Kids. 1980. pap. 4.95 (ISBN 0-570-03811-1, 12-2920). Concordia.

Welbers, Thomas. Banquet of the Word: Bible Study Based on the Sunday Readings. LC 86-60891. 400p. 1986. pap. 17.95 (ISBN 0-89390-073-7). Resource Pubns.

Wendland, E. H., ed. Sermon Studies on the Gospels. (Series C). 1982. 12.95 (ISBN 0-8100-0149-7, 15NO378). Northwest Pub.

Whitaker, Lois. See & Know. 87p. (Orig.). 1980. pap. text ed. 3.95 (ISBN 0-931097-02-9). Sentinel Pub.

White, J. Benton. From Adam to Armageddon: A Survey of the Bible. LC 85-8921. 320p. 1985. pap. text ed. write for info. (ISBN 0-534-05111-1). Wadsworth Pub.

White, John. Bible Study. 1984. pap. 0.75 (ISBN 0-87784-068-7). Inter-Varsity.

White, Reginald E. The Night He Was Betrayed: Bible Studies in Our Lord's Preparation for His Passion. LC 82-13783. pap. 35.30 (ISBN 0-317-30167-5, 2025349). Bks Demand UMI.

White, William, Jr. Theological & Grammatical Phrasebook of the Bible. 1984. 12.95 (ISBN 0-8024-0218-6). Moody.

Wiersbe, Warren. Live Like a King. rev. ed. (Moody Press Elective Ser.). 1983. pap. 3.95 (ISBN 0-8024-0256-9); pap. 2.50 leaders guide (ISBN 0-8024-0306-9). Moody.

Wight, Fred H. & Gower, Ralph. The New Manners & Customs of Bible Times. rev. ed. 1986. 24.95 (ISBN 0-8024-5954-4). Moody.

Wilcox, Anne. Building Bible Study Skills. 60p. 1985. 4.95 (ISBN 0-87123-832-2); student's wkbk. 3.95 (ISBN 0-87123-821-7). Bethany Hse.

Wilkins, Ronald J. Understanding the Bible: School Edition. rev. ed. (To Live Is Christ Ser.). 212p. 1982. pap. 5.75 (ISBN 0-697-01786-9); tchr's. manual 5.00 (ISBN 0-697-01787-7); spirit masters 12.95. Wm C Brown.

--Understanding the Bible: Short Edition. (To Live Is Christ Ser.). 1977. pap. 3.95 (ISBN 0-697-01659-5); tchr's. manual 6.00 (ISBN 0-697-01665-X); spirit masters 12.95. Wm C Brown.

Wilkinson, Bruce & Boa, Kenneth. Talk Thru the Bible: A Survey of a Setting & Content of Scripture. LC 83-4130. (Illus.). 469p. 1983. Repr. of 1981 ed. 14.95 (ISBN 0-8407-5286-5). Nelson.

Willerton, Chris. Teaching the Adult Bible Class. 2.95 (ISBN 0-89137-609-7). Quality Pubns.

Wink, Walter. Transforming Bible Study: A Leader's Guide. LC 80-16019. 176p. 1980. pap. 7.95 (ISBN 0-687-42499-2). Abingdon.

Wolf, Earl C. Making the Bible Yours. 13th ed. 102p. 1984. pap. 3.95 (ISBN 0-8341-0892-5). Beacon Hill.

Wood, Fred M. Salmos: Cantos de Vida. De Gutierrez, Edna L., tr. from Span. Tr. of Psalms: Songs From Life. 160p. 1984. pap. 2.75 (ISBN 0-311-04032-2). Casa Bautista.

The World in Reading. 14.00 (ISBN 0-8198-8213-5). Dghtrs St Paul.

Wright, David. Wisdom As a Lifestyle: Building Biblical Life-Codes. 1987. pap. 6.95 (ISBN 0-310-44311-3). Zondervan.

Yarn, David H. The Four Gospels As One. 281p. 1982. 8.95 (ISBN 0-87747-948-8). Deseret Bk.

Yoder, Perry & Yoder, Elizabeth. Towards Understanding the Bible. LC 78-53649. 1978. pap. 3.95 (ISBN 0-87303-006-0). Faith & Life.

Your Kingdom Come: Bible Studies for the Church Year Based on the Wcc Mission & Evangelism Theme, Melbourne 1980. (Orig.). 1980. pap. 2.25 (ISBN 0-377-00093-0). Friend Pr.

Zodhiates, Spiros, ed. Hebrew Greek-Key Study Bible. 59.00 (ISBN 0-89957-572-2). AMG Pubs.

--The Hebrew-Greek Key Study Bible. 1985. deluxe ed. 39.95 (ISBN 0-8010-9930-7). Baker Bk.

BIBLE–STUDY–BIBLIOGRAPHY

Cully, Iris V. & Cully, Kendig B. A Guide to Biblical Resources. LC 81-80625. 160p. (Orig.). 1981. pap. 7.95 (ISBN 0-8192-1286-5). Morehouse.

Danker, Frederick W. Multipurpose Tools for Bible Study. rev. ed. 1970. pap. 12.50 (ISBN 0-570-03734-4, 12-2638). Concordia.

Harner, Philip B. An Inductive Approach to Biblical Study. LC 82-40213. 132p. (Orig.). 1982. lib. bdg. 24.00 (ISBN 0-8191-2608-X); pap. text ed. 7.75 (ISBN 0-8191-2609-8). U Pr of Amer.

Johnston, Robert K., ed. The Use of the Bible in Theology. LC 84-48513. 1985. pap. 11.95 (ISBN 0-8042-0530-2). John Knox.

Training Manual Research Division. Bible Instruction Manuals, Etc. A Bibliography. 1984. pap. text ed. 1.95 (ISBN 0-318-03127-2, Pub. by Training Manuals). Prosperity & Profits.

BIBLE–STUDY–OUTLINES, SYLLABI, ETC.

Auer, Jim. A Teenager's (Absolutely Basic) Introduction to the New Testament. 96p. 1986. pap. 2.95 (ISBN 0-89243-257-8). Liguori Pubns.

Beck, Norman A. Scripture Notes: Series C (Common Consensus Lectionary) 1985. 9.95 (ISBN 0-89536-755-6, 5861). CSS of Ohio.

Bennett, Boyce M. Bennett's Guide to the Bible: Graphic Aids & Outlines. (Illus.). 128p. (Orig.). 1982. pap. 9.95 (ISBN 0-8164-2397-0, HarpR). Har-Row.

Braga, James. How to Study the Bible. LC 82-6420. (Orig.). 1982. pap. 6.95 (ISBN 0-930014-72-3). Multnomah.

Briggs, S. R. & Elliott, J. H. Six Hundred Bible Gems & Outlines. LC 75-42955. 200p. 1976. pap. 5.95 (ISBN 0-8254-2255-8). Kregel.

Campderros, Daniel. Bosquejos Biblicos Tomo I: Antiguo Testamento. 96p. 1984. pap. 2.50 (ISBN 0-311-43025-2). Casa Bautista.

--Bosquejos Biblicos Tomo II. 96p. 1985. pap. 2.50 (ISBN 0-311-43026-0). Casa Bautista.

Carroll, Frank L. Brief Bible Studies for Busy People. LC 85-3470. 144p. 1985. 13.95 (ISBN 0-13-081993-X); pap. 6.95 (ISBN 0-13-081985-9). P-H.

Childress, Harvey. Expanding Outlines of the New Testament Books. 5.95 (ISBN 0-89137-536-8). Quality Pubns.

Clevenger, Ernest A., Jr. Bible Characters. (Bible Drill Flash Cards Flipbook Ser.). 1982. pap. 4.25 (ISBN 0-88428-018-7). Parchment Pr.

--A Pocket Bible Ready Reference for Personal Workers. (Bible Ready Reference Ser.). 24p. (Orig.). 1982. pap. 0.50 (ISBN 0-88428-011-X). Parchment Pr.

Custer, Stewart. Tools for Preaching & Teaching the Bible. 240p. (Orig.). 1979. pap. 6.95 (ISBN 0-89084-064-4). Bob Jones Univ Pr.

Daniels, Rebecca. Bible Teacher Time Savers. (Helping Hand Ser.). 48p. 1984. wkbk. 4.95 (ISBN 0-86653-235-8). Good Apple.

Dodd, C. H. A Course of Study Outlines for Bible Class Leaders. 59.95 (ISBN 0-87968-954-4). Gordon Pr.

Dole, Anita S. Bible Study Notes, Vol. 6. Woofenden, William R., ed. LC 76-24081. 1979. write for info (ISBN 0-917426-06-1). Am New Church Sunday.

Duckworth, John, et al, eds. The Bible. (Pacesetter Ser.). 64p. 1987. tchr's. ed. 7.95 (ISBN 0-318-21517-9). Cook.

Ellis, Peter F. & Ellis, Judith M. John: An Access Guide for Scripture Study. 174p. 1983. pap. 3.95 (ISBN 0-8215-5936-2); leader's guide 3.25 (ISBN 0-8215-5918-4). Sadlier.

Fehlauer, Adolph F. Bible Reader's Guide. 1981. 5.95 (ISBN 0-8100-0146-2, 06N0558). Northwest Pub.

Gettys, Joseph M. How to Study Philippians, Colossians, & Philemon. 87p. 1964. pap. text ed. 4.50x (ISBN 0-8042-3472-8). Attic Pr.

Harrington, Daniel J. & Gordon, Edmund F. Luke: An Access Guide for Scripture Study. (Access Guides for Scripture Study). 1983. pap. 3.20 (ISBN 0-8215-5929-X); leader's ed. 3.45 (ISBN 0-8215-5934-6). Sadlier.

--Mark: An Access for Scripture Study. (Access Guide for Scripture Study). 128p. 1983. pap. 3.45 (ISBN 0-8215-5928-1); leader's ed. 4.20 (ISBN 0-8215-5933-8). Sadlier.

Horton, Wade H. Sound Scriptural Outlines, No. 3. 1977. 7.25 (ISBN 0-87148-781-0); pap. 6.25 (ISBN 0-87148-780-2). Pathway Pr.

Jackson, Wayne. A Study Guide to Greater Bible Knowledge. 156p. (Orig.). 1986. pap. 5.00 (ISBN 0-932859-12-7). Apologetic Pr.

Jensen, Irving. Haggai, Zechariah & Malachi. (Bible Self Study Guide Ser.). 1976. pap. 3.25 (ISBN 0-8024-1037-5). Moody.

--The Layman's Bible Study Notebook. parallel new testament ed. LC 77-93518. (King James & New International Version Ser.). (Orig.). 1978. pap. 26.95 (ISBN 0-89081-116-4). Harvest Hse.

Klausmeier, Robert. Elementary Teacher Survival Kit. 80p. 1986. tchr's ed 9.95 (ISBN 0-89191-363-7). Cook.

Kunz, Marilyn & Schell, Catherine. Hebrews. (Neighborhood Bible Study). 1971. pap. 2.95 (ISBN 0-8423-1410-5). Tyndale.

Lee, Robert. The Outlined Bible. 1986. pap. 7.95 (ISBN 0-310-44821-2, 10465P). Zondervan.

LeRoy, Ford. Design for Teaching & Training: A Self-Study Guide to Lesson Planning. LC 77-87249. (Illus.). 1978. pap. 12.95 (ISBN 0-8054-3422-4). Broadman.

Marsh, F. E. Five Hundred Bible Study Outlines. LC 79-2549. 382p. 1985. pap. 10.95 (ISBN 0-8254-3248-0). Kregel.

--One Thousand Bible Study Outlines. LC 75-125115. 1970. pap. 12.95 (ISBN 0-8254-3247-2). Kregel.

Meier, John P. & Gordon, Edmund F. Matthew: An Access Guide for Scripture Study. 174p. 1983. pap. 4.20 (ISBN 0-8215-5932-X); manual 3.45 (ISBN 0-8215-5935-4). Sadlier.

Moore, C. R. & Moore, K. W. Prophecy Library. 957p. 1972. spiral bdg 19.80 (ISBN 0-914674-01-3). Freelandia.

Pipa, Joseph A. Leader's Guide for T. Norton Sterrett's "How to Understand Your Bible". A Teaching Manual for Use in Adult Study Groups. (Orig.). 1977. pap. 2.95 (ISBN 0-934688-06-0). Great Comm Pubns.

Ritchie, John. Five Hundred Sermon Outlines on the Christian Life. LC 86-27759. 120p. 1987. pap. 4.95 (ISBN 0-8254-3622-2). Kregel.

Showalter, G. H. & Davis, W. M. New Bible Studies. 1949. pap. 1.50 (ISBN 0-88027-027-6). Firm Foun Pub.

Smith, G. Dallas, ed. Outlines of Bible Study: An Easy-to-Follow Guide to Greater Bible Knowledge. 120p. 1986. pap. text ed. 3.95 (ISBN 0-89225-287-1). Gospel Advocate.

Sr. Carole MacKenthun. Biblical Bulletin Boards. (Helping Hand Ser.). 48p. 1984. wkbk. 4.95 (ISBN 0-86653-197-1). Good Apple.

Steele, David H. & Thomas, Curtis C. Interpretive Outline of Romans. (Illus.). 1963. pap. 5.95 (ISBN 0-87552-443-5). Presby & Reformed.

Swanson, Reuben J. The Horizontal Line Synopsis of the Gospels: Volume I, The Gospel of Mathew. 1982. 29.95 (ISBN 0-915948-10-9). Bks Distinction.

Teaching Visuals from Willmington's Guide to the Bible. 1981. pap. 14.95 (ISBN 0-8423-6939-2). Tyndale.

Townsend, Lucy. Bible Trek-athon. (Complete Teacher Training Meeting Ser.). 48p. 1986. tchr's ed 9.95 (ISBN 0-89191-314-9). Cook.

Uhl, Catherine. Gospel Lesson Plans. LC 79-65918. 136p. 1979. pap. 7.95 (ISBN 0-8091-2211-1). Paulist Pr.

Zimmerli, Walther. Old Testament Theology in Outline. Green, David, tr. Tr. of Grundriss der Alttestamentlichen Theologie. 258p. 1978. pap. 12.95 (ISBN 0-567-22353-1, Pub. by T&T Clark Ltd UK). Fortress.

BIBLE–STUDY–N. T.

Adams, Jay E. The Christian Counselor's New Testament. 1977. 24.95 (ISBN 0-8010-0119-6). Baker Bk.

Aderman, James. Is He the One? Fischer, William E., ed. (Bible Class Course for Young Adults Ser.). (Illus.). 64p. 1985. pap. 2.95 leaders guide (ISBN 0-938272-21-7); pap. 2.95 students guide (ISBN 0-938272-20-9). WELS Board.

Allen, Carlos & Estudios, Guias de. Guia De Estudios Sobre Estudios En el Nuevo Testamento. (Illus.). 96p. 1981. pap. 3.25 (ISBN 0-311-43502-5). Casa Bautista.

Archbishop Averky Taushev. Rukovodstvo k Izuchjeniju Svjashchennago Pisanija Novago Zavjeta-Tchetvjerojevangelija. Tr. of A Guide for Study of the Holy Scriptures of the New Testament-The Four Gospels. 345p. 1974. pap. text ed. 12.00 (ISBN 0-317-29299-4). Holy Trinity.

Ascroft, Winifred. The Quickening Flame: A Scriptural Study of Revival. (Basic Bible Study). 64p. 1985. pap. 2.95 (ISBN 0-932305-20-2, 521020). Aglow Pubns.

Asimov, Isaac. Asimov's Guide to the Bible: The New Testament. 640p. 1971. pap. 8.95 (ISBN 0-380-01031-3, 60255-5). Avon.

Barclay, William. New Testament Words. LC 73-12737. 302p. 1976. softcover 5.95 (ISBN 0-664-24761-X). Westminster.

--Palabras Griegas Del Nuevo Testamento. Marin, Javier J., tr. 220p. 1985. pap. 4.50 (ISBN 0-311-42052-4). Casa Bautista.

Beck, Madeline H. & Williamson, Lamar, Jr. Mastering New Testament Facts, 4 bks. Incl. Bk. 1. Introduction & Synoptic Gospels (ISBN 0-8042-0326-1); Bk. 2. The Fourth Gospel & Acts (ISBN 0-8042-0327-X); Bk. 3. Pauline Letters (ISBN 0-8042-0328-8); Bk. 4. The General Letters & Revelation (ISBN 0-8042-0329-6). (Illus., Orig.). 1973. pap. 4.95 ea.; pap. 14.95 set. John Knox.

Benson, C. H. Arte de Ensenar. Villalobos, Fernando P., tr. from Eng. (Curso Para Maestros Cristianos: No. 5). (Span.). 128p. 1971. pap. 3.50 (ISBN 0-89922-016-9). Edit Caribe.

Besson, Pablo, tr. from Greek. Nuevo Testamento de Nuestro Senor Jesucristo. (Span.). 576p. 1981. pap. 6.50 (ISBN 0-311-48710-6, Edit Mundo). Casa Bautista.

The Better Way (Hebrews) (New Horizons Bible Study Ser.). 68p. (Orig.). pap. 2.50 student guide (ISBN 0-89367-103-7); pap. 1.95 leader's guide (ISBN 0-89367-104-5). Light & Life.

Bible Puzzler No. Two: Stories from Mark. 1985. 2.95 (ISBN 0-89536-768-8, 5876). CSS of Ohio.

Bivens, Forest & Vallesky, David. New Life in Christ. Fischer, William E., ed. (Bible Class Course Ser.). 120p. (Orig.). 1986. pap. text ed. 4.95 (ISBN 0-938272-07-1). WELS Board.

--New Life in Christ: Teacher's Guide. (Bible Class Course Ser.). 40p. (Orig.). 1986. pap. text ed. 2.50 (ISBN 0-938272-03-9). WELS Board.

Borland, James A. A General Introduction to the New Testament. (Illus.). viii, 216p. 1986. pap. 14.95x (ISBN 0-936461-00-4). Univ Book Hse.

Brestin, Dee. Examining the Claims of Jesus. (A Core Study in the Fisherman Bible Studyguides). 48p. 1985. pap. 2.95 (ISBN 0-87788-246-0). Shaw Pubs.

Brown, Raymond B. Marcos Presenta Al Salvador. Lerin, Olivia Y Alfredo, tr. Orig. Title: Mark - the Saviour for Sinners. 160p. 1982. pap. 4.25 (ISBN 0-311-04346-1). Casa Bautista.

Bruce, Frederick F. The Message of the New Testament. 120p. 1973. pap. 4.95 (ISBN 0-8028-1525-1). Eerdmans.

Bryson, Harold T. Increasing the Joy: Studies in I John. LC 81-67200. 1982. pap. 5.95 (ISBN 0-8054-1390-1). Broadman.

Campderros, Daniel. Bosquejos Biblicos Tomo II. 96p. 1985. pap. 2.50 (ISBN 0-311-43026-0). Casa Bautista.

Carmody, John, et al. Exploring the New Testament. (Illus.). 448p. 1986. text ed. 31.00 (ISBN 0-13-297276-X). P-H.

Carr, A. W. Angels & Principalities. (Society for the New Testament Studies Monographs: No. 42). 240p. 1982. 32.50 (ISBN 0-521-23429-8). Cambridge U Pr.

Carver, Frank. Matthew, Part 2: Come & Learn from Me. Wolf, Earl, ed. (Small-Group Bible Studies). 84p. 1986. pap. 2.50 (ISBN 0-8341-1076-8). Beacon Hill.

Chilton, Bruce. Beginning New Testament Study. 208p. (Orig.). 1987. pap. 9.95 (ISBN 0-8028-0254-0). Eerdmans.

Christensen, Chuck & Christensen, Winnie. Mark: God in Action. LC 72-88935. (Fisherman Bible Studyguide Ser.). 94p. 1972. saddle-stitched 2.95 (ISBN 0-87788-309-2). Shaw Pubs.

Clark, Walter J. How to Use New Testament Greek Study Aids. 256p. 1984. pap. 6.95 (ISBN 0-87213-079-7). Loizeaux.

Coleman, Lyman. Serendipity New Testament for Groups: New International Version. 9.95 (ISBN 0-8091-2863-2). Paulist Pr.

Corley, Bruce C., ed. Colloquy on New Testament Studies: A Time for Reappraisal & Fresh Approaches. LC 83-8192. xiv, 370p. 1983. 21.50 (ISBN 0-86554-082-9, H54). Mercer Univ Pr.

Dale, Alan T. New World. (Illus.). 429p. (Orig.). 1973. pap. 9.95 (ISBN 0-8192-1149-4). Morehouse.

Dodd, Damon C. The Book of Revelation, Study Guide. 1973. pap. 2.95 (ISBN 0-89265-013-3). Randall Hse.

Dunnett, W. M. Sintesis del Nuevo Testamento. Blanch, Jose M., tr. from Eng. (Curso Para Maestros Cristianos: No. 3). (Span.). 128p. 1972. pap. 3.50 (ISBN 0-89922-012-6). Edit Caribe.

Earle, Ralph. Word Meanings in the New Testament: I & II Corinthians, Galatians & Ephesians, Vol. 4. 1979. 9.95 (ISBN 0-8010-3349-7). Baker Bk.

Foulkes, Francis. Pocket Guide to the New Testament. LC 77-27742. 1978. pap. 2.95 (ISBN 0-87784-580-8). Inter-Varsity.

Frazen, Lavern G. Good News from Matthew: Visual Messages for Children. LC 77-72463. 1977. pap. 6.95 (ISBN 0-8066-1597-4, 10-2814). Augsburg.

Fromer, Margaret & Keyes, Sharrel. Letters to the Thessalonians. LC 75-33441. (Fisherman Bible Studyguide Ser.). 47p. 1975. saddle-stitched 2.95 (ISBN 0-87788-489-7). Shaw Pubs.

Gettys, Joseph M. How to Study John. 153p. 1960. pap. 4.50x (ISBN 0-8042-3568-6). Attic Pr.

Gideon, Virtus E. Luke: Study Guide Commentary. (Orig.). 1967. pap. 4.95 (ISBN 0-310-24973-2, 9084P). Zondervan.

Gilley, Robert. God's Plan for the World, New Testament Survey. (International Correspondence Program Ser.). 169p. (Orig.). 1984. pap. 6.95 (ISBN 0-87148-362-9). Pathway Pr.

Gingrich, Raymond E. The Epistles of the Blessed Hope: First & Second Thessalonians. 1986. pap. 5.95 (ISBN 0-88469-176-4). BMH Bks.

Gospel of the King (Matthew) Leader's Guide. (New Horizons Bible Study Ser.). 47p. (Orig.). 1986. pap. 1.95 (ISBN 0-89367-116-9). Light & Life.

Gospel of the King (Matthew) Student Guide. (New Horizons Bible Study Ser.). 64p. (Orig.). 1986. pap. 2.50 (ISBN 0-89367-115-0). Light & Life.

Gromacki, Robert G. New Testament Survey. 16.95 (ISBN 0-8010-3677-1). Baker Bk.

Hamblin, Robert L. Triumphant Strangers: A Contemporary Look at First Peter. LC 81-67206. 1982. pap. 5.95 (ISBN 0-8054-1389-8). Broadman.

Harvey, A. E. New English Bible Companion to the New Testament. 1979. 65.00 (ISBN 0-521-07705-2). Cambridge U Pr.

Hawkes, John D. New Testament Digest. 160p. 1968. pap. 3.95 (ISBN 0-89036-014-6). Hawkes Pub Inc.

Henderlite, Rachel. Exploring the New Testament. (Orig.). 1946. pap. 5.95 (ISBN 0-8042-0240-0). John Knox.

Henry, Patrick. New Directions in New Testament Study. LC 79-16267. 300p. 1979. 19.95 (ISBN 0-664-21376-6); pap. 10.95 (ISBN 0-664-24283-9). Westminster.

Hester, H. I. Introduccion Al Estudio Del Nuevo Testamento. Benlliure, Felix, tr. from Eng. Tr. of The Heart of the New Testament. (Span.). 366p. 1980. pap. 7.95 (ISBN 0-311-04330-5). Casa Bautista.

Honeycutt, Roy L., Jr. Layman's Bible Book Commentary: Leviticus, Numbers, Deuteronomy, Vol. 3. LC 78-73278. 1979. 5.95 (ISBN 0-8054-1173-9). Broadman.

Hooker, Morna D. Studying the New Testament. LC 82-70959. 224p. (Orig.). 1982. pap. 10.95 (ISBN 0-8066-1934-1, 10-6140). Augsburg.

Hunt, Gladys. The God Who Understands Me: The Sermon on the Mount. LC 75-181992. (Fisherman Bible Studyguide Ser.). 87p. 1971. saddle-stitched 2.95 (ISBN 0-87788-316-5). Shaw Pubs.

--John: Eyewitness. LC 70-158130. (Fisherman Bible Studyguide Ser.). 87p. 1971. pap. 2.95 saddle stitch (ISBN 0-87788-245-2). Shaw Pubs.

--Luke: A Daily Dialogue with God. (Personal Bible Studyguide Ser.). 192p. (Orig.). 1986. pap. 5.95 (ISBN 0-87788-510-9). Shaw Pubs.

--Revelation: The Lamb Who Is the Lion. (Fisherman Bible Studyguide). 73p. 1973. saddle-stitched 2.95 (ISBN 0-87788-486-2). Shaw Pubs.

James, Edgar C. Second Corinthians: Keys to Triumphant Living. (Teach Yourself the Bible Ser.). 1964. pap. 2.75 (ISBN 0-8024-7680-5). Moody.

Jasper, David. The New Testament & the Literary Imagination. 128p. 1987. text ed. 19.95 (ISBN 0-391-03482-0). Humanities.

Jensen, Irving L. Acts. (Bible Self-Study Ser). 1970. pap. 3.25 (ISBN 0-8024-1044-8). Moody.

--Galatians. (Bible Self Study Ser). 1973. pap. 3.25 (ISBN 0-8024-1048-0). Moody.

--Hebrews. (Bible Self-Study Ser.). 1970. pap. 3.25 (ISBN 0-8024-1058-8). Moody.

--Jensen's Survey of the New Testament. 608p. 1981. text ed. 19.95 (ISBN 0-8024-4308-7). Moody.

--Matthew. (Bible Self Study Ser.). 1974. pap. 3.25 (ISBN 0-8024-1040-5). Moody.

--Romans. (Bible Self-Study Ser.). 1970. pap. 3.25 (ISBN 0-8024-1045-6). Moody.

Jensen, Irving R. Life of Christ. (Bible Self Study Ser.). pap. 3.25 (ISBN 0-8024-1067-7). Moody.

Jones, G. E. Twenty-Six New Testament Lessons. 111p. 1978. pap. 2.00 (ISBN 0-89114-080-8). Baptist Pub Hse.

Jones, J. Estill. Hechos: Colaborando en la Mision de Cristo. Canclini, Arnoldo, tr. from Eng. (Estudios Biblicos Basicos Ser.). Orig. Title: Acts: Working Together in Christ's Mission. 157p. 1981. pap. 2.50 (ISBN 0-311-04339-9). Casa Bautista.

Juelicher, A., et al, eds. Itala: Das Neue Testament in Altlateinischer Ueberlieferung, Vol. 3. 2nd ed. viii, 282p. 1976. 162.25x (ISBN 3-11-002255-9). De Gruyter.

Kent, Homer A., Jr. Jerusalem to Rome: Studies in the Book of Acts. (New Testament Studies Ser.). pap. 5.95 (ISBN 0-8010-5313-7). Baker Bk.

--Light in the Darkness. (New Testament Studies Ser.). 1974. pap. 5.95 (ISBN 0-8010-5343-9). Baker Bk.

Kunz, Marilyn & Schell, Catherine. Acts. (Neighborhood Bible Study Ser.). 1972. pap. 2.95 (ISBN 0-8423-0030-9). Tyndale.

--Mark, Neighborhood Bible Study. 1970. pap. 2.95 (ISBN 0-8423-4101-3). Tyndale.

--Peter, One & Two. (Neignborhood Bible Studies). 1973. pap. 2.95 (ISBN 0-8423-4820-4). Tyndale.

--Romans, Neighborhood Bible Study. 1970. pap. 2.95 (ISBN 0-8423-5701-7). Tyndale.

Kuschel, Harlyn J. A Study Guide for Philippians-Colossians & Philemon. Fischer, William E., ed. (Study Guide for People's Bible Ser.). 48p. (Orig.). 1987. pap. text ed. 1.50 (ISBN 0-938272-57-8). Wels Board.

Lane, G. W. Doctrine of the New Testament in Ten Great Subjects. 127p. 1964. pap. 1.95 (ISBN 0-87148-250-9). Pathway Pr.

LaVerdiere, Eugene. The New Testament in the Life of the Church. LC 80-67403. 192p. (Orig.). 1980. pap. 4.95 (ISBN 0-87793-213-1). Ave Maria.

Lewis, E. Ridley. Acts of the Apostles & the Letters of St. Paul. (London Divinity Ser.). 160p. 1964. Repr. of 1960 ed. 3.95 (ISBN 0-227-67401-4). Attic Pr.

Lightfoot, J. B. Biblical Essays. (Canterbury Books Ser.). 1979. pap. 8.95 (ISBN 0-8010-5586-5). Baker Bk.

Linden, Philip Van. Knowing Christ Through Mark's Gospel. 1977. pap. 1.25 (ISBN 0-8199-0727-8). Franciscan Herald.

Lockerbie, Jeanette. Twenty-Four Women's Programs: Please Pass the Fruit. 96p. (Orig.). 1986. pap. 4.95 (ISBN 0-87403-226-1, 2979). Standard Pub.

Logan, A. H. & Wedderburn, A. J., eds. New Testament & Gnosis. 272p. 1983. 22.95 (ISBN 0-567-09344-1, Pub. by T&T Clark Ltd UK). Fortress.

Lum, Ada. Jesus the Life Changer. 40p. 1978. pap. 2.25 (ISBN 0-87784-316-3). Inter-Varsity.

MacArthur, John, Jr. Christ Displays His Glory: Matthew Sixteen Verse Twenty Four to Seventeen Verses Thirteen. (John MacArthur Bible Studies Ser.). 1987. pap. 3.50 (ISBN 0-8024-5317-1). Moody.

McKenzie, John L. The New Testament Without Illusion. (The Crossroad Paperback Ser.). 256p. 1982. pap. 6.95 (ISBN 0-8245-0451-8). Crossroad NY.

Malone, J. W. A New Testament Study Guide. kivar 4.95 (ISBN 0-686-12848-6). Schmul Pub Co.

Morgan, G. Campbell. God's Last Word to Man: Studies in Hebrew. (Morgan Library). pap. 4.95 (ISBN 0-8010-5955-0). Baker Bk.

Murphy, Richard T. Background to the Bible: An Introduction to Scripture Study. (Illus.). 1978. pap. 5.95 (ISBN 0-89283-055-7). Servant.

Nicholson, W. R. Colossians. LC 73-81742. 284p. 1973. 7.95 (ISBN 0-8254-3301-0); pap. 5.95 (ISBN 0-8254-3300-2). Kregel.

Nystrom, Carolyn. Mark: God on the Move. (Young Fisherman Bible Studyguide Ser.). 96p. 1978. pap. 4.95 tchr's ed. (ISBN 0-87788-312-2); student ed. 2.95 (ISBN 0-87788-311-4). Shaw Pubs.

Open Letters from a Roman Prison: Philippians, Colossians, Philemon, Leader's Guide. (New Horizons Bible Study Ser.). 48p. 1980. pap. 1.95 (ISBN 0-89367-047-2). Light & Life.

Open Letters from a Roman Prison: Philippians, Colossians, Philemon Study Guide. (New Horizons Bible Study Ser.). 64p. 1980. pap. 2.50 (ISBN 0-89367-046-4). Light & Life.

Outlaw, Stanley. Questions from the Text of the New Testament. 36p. 1977. pap. 2.95 (ISBN 0-89265-050-8). Randall Hse.

Parmelee, Alice. Guide to the New Testament. (All About the Bible Ser.: Bk. 3). (Illus.). 1980. pap. 5.95 (ISBN 0-8192-1255-5). Morehouse.

Patterson, Charles H. New Testament Notes. (Orig.). 1965. pap. 3.25 (ISBN 0-8220-0880-7). Cliffs.

Pentz, Croft M. Sermon Outlines from Acts. (Sermon Outline Ser.). 1978. pap. 2.50 (ISBN 0-8010-7039-2). Baker Bk.

Perrin, Norman & Duling, Dennis C. The New Testament: An Introduction. 2nd ed. (Illus.). 516p. (Orig.). 1982. pap. text ed. 15.95 (ISBN 0-15-565726-7, HC). HarBraceJ.

Pickell, Charles N. Epistle to the Colossians: A Study Manual. (Shield Bible Study Ser). (Orig.). 1965. pap. 1.00 (ISBN 0-8010-6942-4). Baker Bk.

Powell, Paul W. The Saint Peter Principle. LC 81-67372. 1982. 5.50 (ISBN 0-8054-5299-0). Broadman.

Ramsay, William M. The Layman's Guide to the New Testament. LC 79-87742. (Layman's Bible Commentary Ser.). 273p. (Orig.). 1980. pap. 11.95 (ISBN 0-8042-0322-9). John Knox.

Richards, M. Ross & Richards, Marie C. New Testament Charts. pap. 2.95 (ISBN 0-87747-446-X). Deseret Bk.

Robertson, A. T. Estudios en el Nuevo Testamento. Hale, Sara A., tr. from Eng. Orig. Title: Studies in the New Testament. (Span.). 224p. 1983. pap. 3.50 (ISBN 0-311-03629-5). Casa Bautista.

Robertson, Archibald. Word Pictures in the New Testament, 6 vols. Incl. Vol. 1. Matthew & Mark (ISBN 0-8054-1301-4); Vol. 2. Luke (ISBN 0-8054-1302-2); Vol. 3. Acts (ISBN 0-8054-1303-0); Vol. 4. Epistles of Paul (ISBN 0-8054-1304-9); Vol. 5. John & Hebrews (ISBN 0-8054-1305-7); Vol. 6. Genesis, Epistles, Revelation & John (ISBN 0-8054-1306-5). 1943. 11.95 ea.; Set. 67.50 (ISBN 0-8054-1307-3). Broadman.

Rochais, G. Les Recits de Resurrection des Morts dans le Nouveau Testament. LC 79-41615. (Society for New Testament Studies Monographs: No. 40). (Fr.). 240p. 1981. 39.50 (ISBN 0-521-22381-4). Cambridge U Pr.

Segerman, Sue K. Hiding the Word in Your Heart: How to Memorize Scripture. (Cornerstone Ser.). 40p. 1986. pap. 2.95 (ISBN 0-932305-24-5, 533012). Aglow Pubns.

Showalter, G. H. & Davis, W. M. Simplified Bible Lessons on the Old & New Testaments. 1944. pap. 2.75 (ISBN 0-88027-039-X). Firm Foun Pub.

Stadler, Richard H. Meet the Lord & His Church. Fischer, William E., ed. (Bible Class Course for Young Adults Ser.). (Illus.). 64p. (Orig.). 1987. pap. text ed. 2.95 (ISBN 0-938272-26-8); tchr's ed. 2.95 (ISBN 0-938272-27-6). Wels Board.

Steele, David H. & Thomas, Curtis C. Interpretive Outline of Romans. (Illus.). 1963. pap. 5.95 (ISBN 0-87552-443-5). Presby & Reformed.

Stevens, William W. A Guide for New Testament Study. LC 76-62920. 1977. pap. 13.95 (ISBN 0-8054-1360-X). Broadman.

Thomas, J. D. Self-Study Guide to Galatians & Romans. rev. ed. (Way of Life Ser: No. 122). Orig. Title: Self-Study Guide to Romans. (Orig.). 1971. pap. text ed. 3.95 (ISBN 0-89112-122-6, Bibl Res Pr). Abilene Christ U.

To Rome & Beyond (Acts B) Leader's Guide. (New Horizons Bible Study). 46p. (Orig.). 1982. pap. 1.95 (ISBN 0-89367-068-5). Light & Life.

Viertel, Weldon E. Los Hechos de los Apostoles: Texto Programado. Tr. of Early Church Growth: a Study of the Book of Acts. (Span.). 208p. 1985. pap. write for info. (ISBN 0-311-04348-8). Casa Bautista.

Violi, Unicio J. Monarch Notes on the New Testament. (Orig.). pap. 4.50 (ISBN 0-671-00625-8). Monarch Pr.

Walker, Catherine B. Bible Workbook: New Testament, Vol. 2. 1951. pap. 5.95 (ISBN 0-8024-0752-8). Moody.

Winter, Ralph. Word Study New Testament & Concordance. 1978. text ed. 39.95 (ISBN 0-8423-8390-5). Tyndale.

Wolff, Hans W. The Old Testament: A Guide to Its Writings. Crim, Keith R., tr. from Gr. LC 73-79010. 160p. (Orig.). 1973. pap. 4.95 (ISBN 0-8006-0169-6, 1-169). Fortress.

Woods, Guy N. How to Read the Greek New Testament. 5.00 (ISBN 0-89225-103-4). Gospel Advocate.

Wright, John W. And Then There Was One. 120p. (Orig.). 1985. pap. 4.95 (ISBN 0-8341-1057-1). Beacon Hill.

Ziesler, J. A. The Meaning of Righteousness in Paul: A Linguistic & Theological Enquiry. LC 75-164455. (Society for New Testament Studies, Monograph Ser.: Vol. 20). pap. 66.80 (ISBN 0-317-26359-5, 2024567). Bks Demand UMI.

BIBLE–STUDY–O. T.

Anderson, Bernhard W. Understanding the Old Testament. 4th ed. (Illus.). 672p. 1986. text ed. write for info (ISBN 0-13-935925-7). P-H.

Anderson, G. W. Tradition & Interpretation. 1979. 34.50x (ISBN 0-19-826315-5). Oxford U Pr.

Auer, Jim. A Teenager's (Absolutely Basic) Introduction to the New Testament. 96p. 1986. pap. 2.95 (ISBN 0-89243-257-8). Liguori Pubns.

Auld, A. Graeme. First & Second Kings. LC 86-15658. (The Daily Study Bible - Old Testament Ser.). 266p. 1986. 15.95 (ISBN 0-664-21836-9); pap. 8.95 (ISBN 0-664-24585-4). Westminster.

Barber, Cyril J. Dynamic Personal Bible Study: Principles of Inductive Bible Study Based on the Life of Abraham. LC 81-8443. 1981. pap. 4.95 (ISBN 0-87213-023-1). Loizeaux.

--Nehemiah & the Dynamics of Effective Leadership: Study Guide. (Illus.). 56p. 1980. pap. text ed. 3.25 (ISBN 0-87213-022-3). Loizeaux.

Beck, Madeline H. & Williamson, Lamar, Jr. Mastering Old Testament Facts, Bk. 4: Isaiah-Malachi. (Mastering Old Testament Facts Ser.). (Illus.). 112p. (Orig.). 1981. pap. 4.95 (ISBN 0-8042-0137-4). John Knox.

Benson, C. H. Poesia y Profecia del Antiquo Testamento. Villalobos, Fernando P., tr. from Eng. (Curso Para Maestros Cristianos: No. 2). (Span.). 122p. 1972. pap. 3.50 (ISBN 0-89922-010-X). Edit Caribe.

Benson, Clarence H. Old Testament Survey: Poetry & Prophecy. rev. ed. 96p. 1972. pap. text ed. 4.95 (ISBN 0-910566-02-X); Perfect bdg. instr's. guide 5.95 (ISBN 0-910566-21-6). Evang Tchr.

Bewer, Julius A. & Kraeling, Emil G. The Literature of the Old Testament. 3rd ed. LC 62-17061. (Records of Civilization: Sources & Studies: No. 5). pap. 128.00 (ISBN 0-317-26423-0, 2024975). Bks Demand UMI.

Black, Robert E. The Books of Chronicles. (The Bible Study Textbook Ser.). (Illus.). 1973. College Pr Pub.

Bornkamm, Gunther. The New Testament: A Guide to Its Writings. Fuller, Reginald H. & Fuller, Ilse, trs. from Ger. LC 73-79009. 176p. (Orig.). 1973. pap. 4.95 (ISBN 0-8006-0168-8, 1-168). Fortress.

Bream, Howard N., et al, eds. A Light unto My Path: Old Testament Studies in Honor of Jacob M. Myers. LC 73-85042. (Gettysburg Theological Studies, No. 4). 576p. 1974. 27.95 (ISBN 0-87722-026-3). Temple U Pr.

Brown, Raymond. Let's Read the Old Testament. 1972. pap. 2.95 (ISBN 0-87508-034-0). Chr Lit.

Campderros, Daniel. Bosquejos Biblicos Tomo I: Antiguo Testamento. 96p. 1984. pap. 2.50 (ISBN 0-311-43025-2). Casa Bautista.

Castleman, Robbie. Elijah: Obedience in a Threatening World. (Fisherman Bible Studyguide Ser.). 64p. (Orig.). 1986. pap. 2.95 (ISBN 0-87788-218-5). Shaw Pubs.

Charpentier, Etienne. How to Read the Old Testament. LC 82-12728. 128p. 1982. pap. 10.95 (ISBN 0-8245-0540-9). Crossroad NY.

Computer Concordance to the Norum Testamentum Graece. 2nd ed. 1985. 72.00 (ISBN 3-11-010528-4). De Gruyter.

Cowles, H. Robert. Opening the Old Testament. LC 80-65149. (Illus.). 158p. (Orig.). 1980. pap. 4.50 (ISBN 0-87509-279-9); Leader's Guide. 2.95 (ISBN 0-87509-283-7). Chr Pubns.

Davidson, Robert. Ecclesiastes & the Song of Solomon. LC 86-15659. (The Daily Study Bible - Old Testament Ser.). 168p. 1986. 14.95 (ISBN 0-664-21838-5); pap. 7.95 (ISBN 0-664-24589-7). Westminster.

Davies, Benjamin & Mitchell, Edward. Hebrew & Lexicon to the Old Testament. 800p. Date not set. 22.95 (ISBN 0-8254-2453-4). Kregel.

Davis, O. B. Introduction to Biblical Literature. 1976. pap. text ed. 9.25x (ISBN 0-8104-5834-9). Boynton Cook Pubs.

Fields, Wilbur. Exploring Exodus. LC 78-301089. (The Bible Study Textbook Ser.). (Illus.). 1977. 18.95 (ISBN 0-89900-006-1). College Pr Pub.

Fromer, Margaret & Keyes, Sharrel. Jonah, Habakkuk, Malachi: Living Responsibly. (Fisherman Bible Studyguide Ser.). 68p. 1982. saddle-stitch 2.95 (ISBN 0-87788-432-3). Shaw Pubs.

Garland, D. David. Isaiah: Bible Study Commentary. (Orig.). 1968. pap. 4.95 (ISBN 0-310-24853-1, 9672P). Zondervan.

Gregory, Sadie. A New Dimension in Old Testament Study. 103p. (Orig.). 1980. pap. 5.00 (ISBN 0-917479-05-X). Guild Psy.

Groth, Jeanette. Little Journeys Through the Old Testament. 128p. (Orig.). 1986. pap. 5.95 (ISBN 0-570-03985-1, 12-3012). Concordia.

Harris, R. Laird, et al, eds. Theological Wordbook of the Old Testament, 2 Vols. LC 80-28047. 1800p. 1980. text ed. 39.95 (ISBN 0-8024-8631-2). Moody.

Hayes, John H. An Introduction to Old Testament Study. LC 78-20993. 1979. pap. text ed. 14.50 (ISBN 0-687-01363-1). Abingdon.

Henderlite, Rachel. Exploring the Old Testament. (Orig.). 1945. pap. 5.95 (ISBN 0-8042-0120-X). John Knox.

Herald of Hope (Isaiah) Leader's Guide. (New Horizons Bible Study Ser.). 48p. (Orig.). 1984. pap. 1.95 (ISBN 0-89367-101-0). Light & Life.

Hodson, Geoffrey. The Hidden Wisdom in the Holy Bible, Vol. 4. LC 67-8724. 375p. (Orig.). 1981. pap. 5.95 (ISBN 0-8356-0548-5, Quest). Theos Pub Hse.

Hoffmann, Hans W. Die Intention der Verkuendigung Jesajas. LC 74-80632. (Beiheft 136 zur Zeitschrift fuer die alttestamentliche Wissenschaft). 125p. 1974. 30.00 (ISBN 3-11-004672-5). De Gruyter.

Honeycutt, Roy L., Jr. Layman's Bible Book Commentary: Leviticus, Numbers, Deuteronomy, Vol. 3. LC 78-73278. 1979. 5.95 (ISBN 0-8054-1173-9). Broadman.

Janzen, Waldemar. Mourning Cry & Woe Oracle. (Beiheft 125 zur Zeitschrift fuer die alttestamentliche Wissenschaft). 120p. 1972. 27.50x (ISBN 3-11-003848-X). De Gruyter.

Jarvis, F. Washington. Prophets, Poets, Priests, & Kings: The Old Testament Story. 288p. 1975. pap. 6.95 (ISBN 0-8164-2089-0, HarpR). Har-Row.

Jensen, Irving L. Genesis. (Bible Self-Study Ser.). 1967. pap. 3.25 (ISBN 0-8024-1001-4). Moody.

--Isaiah & Jeremiah. rev. ed. (Bible Self-Study Ser.). (Illus., Orig.). 1968. pap. 3.25 (ISBN 0-8024-1023-5). Moody.

--Joshua. rev. ed. (Bible Self-Study Ser). (Illus.). 80p. 1967. pap. 3.25 (ISBN 0-8024-1006-5). Moody.

--Judges & Ruth. rev. ed. (Bible Self-Study Ser). (Illus.). 96p. 1967. pap. 3.25 (ISBN 0-8024-1007-3). Moody.

Jensen, Irving L., ed. Second Kings with Chronicles. rev. ed. (Bible Self-Study Ser.). (Illus., Orig.). 1968. pap. 3.25 (ISBN 0-8024-1012-X). Moody.

Jeremiah, David. Abraham: Twenty-Six Daily Bible Studies. (Steps to Higher Ground Ser.). 1982. pap. 1.95 (ISBN 0-86508-201-4). BCM Intl Inc.

Kunz, Marilyn. Patterns for Living with God. pap. 2.95 (ISBN 0-87784-409-7). Inter-Varsity.

Kunz, Marilyn & Schell, Catherine. Ephesians & Philemon. (Neighborhood Bible Studies). 1973. pap. 2.95 (ISBN 0-8423-0695-1). Tyndale.

--Luke. (Neighborhood Bible Studies). 1973. pap. 2.95 (ISBN 0-8423-3880-2). Tyndale.

--Philippians & Colossians. (Neighborhood Bible Studies). 1974. pap. 2.95 (ISBN 0-8423-4825-5). Tyndale.

Larsen, Sandy. Standing Strong: Notes from Joseph's Journal. (Bible Discovery Guides for Teen Campers Ser.). (Illus.). 32p. (Orig.). (YA) 1986. pap. 1.50 camper (ISBN 0-87788-784-5); pap. 1.50 counselor (ISBN 0-87788-785-3). Shaw Pubs.

Layne, James N. Old Testament Study Simplified. new ed. LC 77-23715. 1978. pap. 3.95 (ISBN 0-87148-656-3). Pathway Pr.

Lewis, Jack P. Minor Prophets. 1966. pap. 3.95 (ISBN 0-8010-5509-1). Baker Bk.

Link, Mark. These Stones Will Shout: A New Voice for the Old Testament. LC 82-74383. (Illus.). 300p. 1983. pap. 7.95x (ISBN 0-89505-117-6). Argus Comm.

Livingston, G. Herbert. The Pentateuch in Its Cultural Environment. pap. 12.95 (ISBN 0-8010-5630-6). Baker Bk.

Long, Burke O. The Problem of Etiological Narrative in the Old Testament. (Beiheft 108 zur Zeitschrift fuer die alttestamentliche Wissenschaft). 1968. 15.50x (ISBN 3-11-005590-2). De Gruyter.

Macdonald, John. Samaritan Chronicle No. 2 (or, Sepher Ha-Yamim) from Joshua to Nebuchadnezzar. (Beiheft 107 zur Zeitschrift fuer die alttestamentliche Wissenschaft). 1969. 34.80 (ISBN 3-11-002582-5). De Gruyter.

McKeating, Henry. Studying the Old Testament. LC 82-70960. 224p. (Orig.). 1982. pap. 10.95 (ISBN 0-8066-1935-X, 10-6141). Augsburg.

Miller, J. Maxwell. The Old Testament & the Historian. Tucker, Gene M., ed. LC 75-10881. (Guides to Biblical Scholarship: Old Testament Ser.). 96p. 1976. pap. 4.50 (ISBN 0-8006-0461-X, 1-461). Fortress.

Naville, E. The Text of the Old Testament. (British Academy, London, Schweich Lectures in Biblical Archaeology Series, 1915). pap. 19.00 (ISBN 0-8115-1257-6). Kraus Repr.

Outlaw, Stanley. Questions from Text of Old Testament. 1977. pap. 2.95 (ISBN 0-89265-049-4). Randall Hse.

--Survey of the Old Testament. 1977. pap. 2.75 (ISBN 0-89265-048-6). Randall Hse.

Palau, Luis. Grito de Victoria! Calcada, Leticia, tr. from Eng. Tr. of The Moment to Shout! (Span.). 144p. 1986. pap. 5.50 (ISBN 0-311-46106-9). Casa Bautista.

Parmelee, Alice. Guide to the Old Testament & Apocrypha. (All About the Bible Ser.: Bk. 2). (Illus.). 1980. pap. 5.95 (ISBN 0-8192-1254-7). Morehouse.

Patterson, Charles H. Old Testament Notes. (Orig.). 1965. pap. 3.25 (ISBN 0-8220-0949-8). Cliffs.

Pfeiffer, Charles F. Book of Genesis. (Shield Bible Study). (Orig.). pap. 2.95 (ISBN 0-8010-6906-8). Baker Bk.

--Book of Leviticus: A Study Manual. (Shield Bible Study). (Orig.). pap. 2.95 (ISBN 0-8010-6889-4). Baker Bk.

Richards, Larry. Years of Darkness, Days of Glory. LC 76-6582. (Bible Alive Ser). (Illus.). 1977. pap. text ed. 2.95 (ISBN 0-912692-97-9); tchr's. ed. o.p. 3.95 (ISBN 0-912692-96-0). Cook.

Richards, M. Ross & Richards, Marie C. Old Testament Charts. pap. 1.95 (ISBN 0-87747-447-8). Deseret Bk.

Robinson, George L. Book of Isaiah. pap. 4.50 (ISBN 0-8010-7609-9). Baker Bk.

Rogerson, John, ed. Beginning Old Testament Study. LC 82-20210. 164p. 1983. pap. 8.95 (ISBN 0-664-24451-3). Westminster.

Sampey, R. Estudios sobre el Antiguo Testamento. 226p. 1983. pap. 3.50 (ISBN 0-311-03627-9). Casa Bautista.

Schleiermacher, Friedrich D. Kritische Gesamtausgabe: Erste Abteilung (Schriften und Entwuerfe), Band 7, Teil 3 - Der Christliche Glaube, 1821-1822. (Ger.). 1984. 128.00 (ISBN 3-11-008593-3). De Gruyter.

Schultz, Samuel J. The Old Testament Speaks. 3rd ed. LC 80-7740. (Illus.). 448p. 1980. 17.95xi (ISBN 0-06-067134-3, HarpR). Har-Row.

--Old Testament Survey: Law & History. rev. ed. LC 64-10037. 96p. 1968. pap. text ed. 4.95 (ISBN 0-910566-01-1); Perfect bdg. instr's. guide 5.95 (ISBN 0-910566-20-8). Evang Tchr.

Seybold, Klaus & Mueller, Ulrich B. Sickness & Healing. Stott, Douglas W., tr. from Ger. LC 81-3663. (Biblical Encounter Ser.). 208p. (Orig.). 1981. pap. 9.95 (ISBN 0-687-38444-3). Abingdon.

Showalter, G. H. & Davis, W. M. Simplified Bible Lessons on the Old & New Testaments. 1944. pap. 2.75 (ISBN 0-88027-039-X). Firm Foun Pub.

Soggin, J. Alberto. Introduction to the Old Testament. Rev. ed. Bowden, John, tr. LC 81-3422. (Old Testament Library). 544p. 1982. 27.50 (ISBN 0-664-21385-5). Westminster.

Songs of the Ages (Psalms) Leader's Guide. (New Horizons Bible Study). 48p. (Orig.). 1984. pap. 1.95 (ISBN 0-89367-091-X). Light & Life.

Songs of the Ages (Psalms) Student Guide. (New Horizon Bible Study). 68p. (Orig.). 1984. pap. 2.50 (ISBN 0-89367-090-1). Light & Life.

Spangenberg, Wolfhart. Samtliche Werke: Anbind- oder Fangbriefe. Gelegenheitsdichtungen. Beschreibung des Gluckhafens, Vol. 4, Pt. 1. Vizkelety & Bircher, eds. (Ger.). iv, 393p. 1981. 120.00 (ISBN 3-11-008030-3). De Gruyter.

Sperry, Sidney B. The Spirit of the Old Testament. LC 70-119330. (Classics in Mormon Literature Ser.). 246p. 1980. Repr. 6.95 (ISBN 0-87747-832-5). Deseret Bk.

Starr, Frank. Light for the Way: Old Testament, 2 bks. (Illus.). 96p. 1987. pap. 2.95 ea. Bk. 3 (ISBN 0-570-04450-2, 12-3057). Bk. 4 (ISBN 0-570-04451-0, 12-3058). Concordia.

Tatham, Julie C. The Old Testament Made Easy. LC 85-90957. (Illus.). 720p. 1985. 25.00 (ISBN 0-682-40263-X). Exposition Pr FL.

Temporini, Hildegard & Haase, Wolfgang, eds. Aufstieg und Niedergang der Roemischen Welt: Section 2, Principat. Incl. Vol. 25, Pt. 1. Religion (Vorkonstantinisches Christentum: Leben und Umwelt Jesu; Neues Testament Kanonische Schriften und Apokryphen) 1982. 221.00 (ISBN 3-11-008700-6); Vol. 25, Pt. 2. Religion (Vorkonstantinisches Christentum: Leben und Umwelt Jesu; Neues Testament, Fortsetzung Kanonische Schriften und Apokryphen) 1984. 258.00 (ISBN 3-11-009523-8); Vol. 25, Pt. 3. Religion (Vorkonstantinisches Christentum: Leben und Umwelt Jesu; Neues Testament, Fortsetzung Kanonische Schriften und Apokryphen) 1985. 232.00 (ISBN 3-11-010370-2); Vol. 29, Pt. 1. Sprache und Literatur (Sprachen und Schriften) 1983. 147.00 (ISBN 3-11-009524-6); Vol. 29, Pt. 2. Sprache und Literatur (Sprachen und Schriften) (Fortsetzung) 1983. 216.00 (ISBN 3-11-009525-4); Vol. 30, Pt. 1. Sprache und Literatur (Literatur der augusteischen Zeit: Allgemeines, einzelne Autoren) 1982. 216.00 (ISBN 3-11-008469-4); Vol. 30, Pt. 2. Sprache und Literatur (Literatur der augusteischen Zeit: Allgemeines, einzelne Autoren, Fortsetzung) 1982. 147.00 (ISBN 3-11-008699-9); Vol. 30, Pt. 3. Sprache und Literatur (Literatur der augusteischen Zeit: Allgemeines, einzelne Autoren, Fortsetzung) 1983. 190.00 (ISBN 3-11-009526-2); Vol. 31, Pt. 1. Sprache und Literatur (Literatur der augusteischen Zeit: Einzelne Autoren - Vergil, Horaz, Ovid) 1980. 166.00 (ISBN 3-11-008123-7); Vol. 31, Pt. 2. Sprache und Literatur (Literatur der ausgusteischen Zeit: Einzelne Autoren, Fortsetzung Vergil, Horaz, Ovid) 1981. 155.00 (ISBN 3-11-008288-8); Vol. 31, Pt. 3. Sprache und Literatur (Literatur der ausgusteischen Zeit); Einzelne Autoren - Fortsetzung, Vergil, Horaz, Ovid. 1981. 179.00 (ISBN 3-11-008467-8); Vol. 31, Pt. 4. Sprache und Literatur (Literatur der augusteischen Zeit: Einzelne Autoren, Fortsetzung Vergil, Horaz, Ovid) 1981. 142.00 (ISBN 3-11-008555-0); Vol. 32, Pt. 1. Sprache und Literatur (Literatur der julisch-claudischen und der flavischen Zeit) 1984. 190.00 (ISBN 3-11-010363-X); Vol. 32, Pt. 2. Sprache und Literatur (Literatur der julisch-claudischen und der flavischen Zeit) (Fortsetzung) 1985. 242.00 (ISBN 3-11-010374-5); Vol. 32, Pt. 3. Sprache und Literatur (Literatur der julisch-claudischen und der flavischen Zeit) (Fortsetzung) 1985. 190.00 (ISBN 3-11-010388-5). (Ger.). De Gruyter.

Trial & Triumph Genesis B: Leader's Guide. (New Horizons Bible Study Ser.). 1981. pap. 1.95 (ISBN 0-89367-054-5). Light & Life.

Trial & Triumph Genesis B: Study Guide. (New Horizons Bible Study Ser.). 68p. 1981. pap. 2.50 (ISBN 0-89367-055-3). Light & Life.

Urberg, S. S. Introducing Old Testament Books: With an Emphasis on Their Chronological Relationship. 1979. pap. 5.95 (ISBN 0-8010-9203-5). Baker Bk.

Van Dyne, Glen. Beacon Small-Group Bible Studies, Joshua: Never a Dull Moment. Wolf, Earl C., ed. 80p. 1986. pap. 2.50 (ISBN 0-8341-1098-9). Beacon Hill.

Walker, Catherine B. Bible Workbook: Old Testament, Vol. 1. 1943. pap. 5.95 (ISBN 0-8024-0751-X). Moody.

Walton, Robert C., ed. Bible Study Sourcebook. LC 80-26358. Vol. 1: Old Testament. pap. 54.00 (2027296); Vol. 2: New Testament. pap. 59.30. Bks Demand UMI.

Westermann, Claus. Handbook to the Old Testament. Boyd, Robert H., tr. LC 67-25362. 1967. pap. 11.95 (ISBN 0-8066-1529-X, 10-2951). Augsburg.

Willi-Plein, Ina. Vorformen der Schriftexegese innerhalb des Alten Testaments. 286p. 1971. 43.20x (ISBN 3-11-001897-7). De Gruyter.

Willis, John T., ed. The World & Literature of the Old Testament. (The Bible Study Textbook Ser.). 1979. Repr. of 1978 ed. 11.60 (ISBN 0-89900-058-4). College Pr Pub.

Wood, Charles R. Sermon Outlines from Proverbs. LC 83-25569. 88p. (Orig.). 1984. pap. 3.95 (ISBN 0-8254-4023-8). Kregel.

Youngblood, Ronald & Kaiser, Walter C., Jr., eds. A Tribute to Gleason Archer. 1986. text ed. 15.95 (ISBN 0-8024-8780-7). Moody.

Youngman, Bernard R. Patriarchs, Judges, & Kings. (Background to the Bible Ser.: Vol. 1). pap. 8.95 (ISBN 0-7175-0414-X). Dufour.

Zimmerli, Walther. Old Testament Theology in Outline. Green, David, tr. Tr. of Grundriss der Alttestamentlichen Theologie. 258p. 1978. pap. 12.95 (ISBN 0-567-22353-1, Pub. by T&T Clark Ltd UK). Fortress.

BIBLE–STUDY–TEXT-BOOKS

see also Bible Stories

Black, Robert E. The Books of Chronicles. (The Bible Study Textbook Ser.). (Illus.). 1973. College Pr Pub.

Boatman, Don E. & Boles, Kenny. Galatians. rev. ed. LC 70-1141. (The Bible Study Textbook Ser.). (Illus.). 1976. 12.20 (ISBN 0-89900-039-8). College Pr Pub.

Childress, Harvey. My Wonderful Salvation. 1978. pap. 1.75 (ISBN 0-88027-088-8). Firm Foun Pub.

Conn, Charles W. Highlights of Hebrew History. 1975. pap. 4.25 (ISBN 0-87148-401-3); instrs. guide 5.25 (ISBN 0-87148-404-8). Pathway Pr.

DeWelt, Don. Acts Made Actual. rev. ed. LC 59-20263. (The Bible Study Textbook Ser.). (Illus.). 1975. 14.30 (ISBN 0-89900-036-3). College Pr Pub.

Eakin, Patsy. God Said, Part I. 65p. (Orig.). 1981. pap. 2.95 (ISBN 0-931097-06-1). Sentinel Pub.

--God Said, Part II. 89p. 1981. pap. text ed. 2.95 (ISBN 0-931097-11-8). Sentinel Pub.

Fields, Wilbur. Exploring Exodus. LC 78-301089. (The Bible Study Textbook Ser.). (Illus.). 1977. 18.95 (ISBN 0-89900-006-1). College Pr Pub.

Fream, Donald. A Chain of Jewels from James & Jude. LC 71-1073. (The Bible Study Textbook Ser.). (Illus.). 1965. 12.20 (ISBN 0-89900-045-2). College Pr Pub.

Kidwell, R. J. & DeWelt, Don. Ecclesiastes; Song of Solomon. LC 78-301088. (The Bible Study Textbook Ser.). 1977. 14.30 (ISBN 0-89900-019-3). College Pr Pub.

Lee, Peter, et al. Food for Life. LC 77-27693. 1978. pap. 3.95 (ISBN 0-87784-489-5). Inter-Varsity.

Oberst, Bruce. Deuteronomy. LC 70-1070. (The Bible Study Textbook Ser.). 1968. 14.30 (ISBN 0-89900-009-6). College Pr Pub.

Peabody, Larry. Secular Word Is Full-Time Service Study Guide. 1976. pap. 1.50 (ISBN 0-87508-449-4). Chr Lit.

Richards, Larry. Years of Darkness, Days of Glory. LC 76-6582. (Bible Alive Ser). (Illus.). 1977. pap. text ed. 2.95 (ISBN 0-912692-97-9); tchr's. ed. o.p. 3.95 (ISBN 0-912692-96-0). Cook.

Robinson, James D. How to Use The Bible. 1982. pap. 3.25 (ISBN 0-570-03853-7, 12-2808). Concordia.

Shannon, Foster H. Green Leaf Bible Series, Year Two. (Orig.). 1984. pap. 12.50 (ISBN 0-938462-11-3). Green Leaf CA.

Souter, John. What's the Good Word? The All New Super Incredible Bible Study Book for Junior Highs. 64p. 1983. pap. 3.50 (ISBN 0-310-45891-9, 12474P). Zondervan.

Spencer, Geoffrey. The Burning Bush. LC 74-84762. 1974. pap. 6.50 (ISBN 0-8309-0129-9). Herald Hse.

Vander Klay, Grace. Bible Activity Safari. (Pelican Activity Ser.). pap. 0.89 (ISBN 0-8010-9280-9). Baker Bk.

White, Willie W. The Greatest Work in the World. rev. ed. 1975. pap. 1.95 (ISBN 0-89900-108-4). College Pr Pub.

Willis, John T., ed. The World & Literature of the Old Testament. (The Bible Study Textbook Ser.). 1979. Repr. of 1978 ed. 11.60 (ISBN 0-89900-058-4). College Pr Pub.

BIBLE–SYMBOLISM

see Symbolism in the Bible

BIBLE–TEACHINGS

see Bible–Theology

BIBLE–TEXTUAL CRITICISM

see Bible–Criticism, Textual

BIBLE–THEOLOGY

see also names of specific doctrines, with or without the subdivision Biblical Teaching

Allen, Diogenes. Philosophy for Understanding Theology. LC 84-48510. 252p. 1985. pap. 14.95 (ISBN 0-8042-0688-0). John Knox.

Bales, James. Biblical Doctrine of God. pap. 2.50 (ISBN 0-89315-021-5). Lambert Bk.

Bauer, Johannes B. Bibeltheologisches Woerterbuch, 2 vols. 3rd ed. (Ger.). 1967. Set. 150.00 (ISBN 3-222-10240-6, M-7308, Pub. by Styria). French & Eur.

Bavinck, Herman. Our Reasonable Faith: A Survey of Christian Doctrine. Zylstra, Henry, tr. (Twin Brooks Ser). 1977. pap. 13.95 (ISBN 0-8010-0513-2). Baker Bk.

Berrie, W. W. A Theology of Generosity: Principles & Practice of Giving Based on Bible Teaching. 32p. 1982. pap. 2.50 (ISBN 0-8192-1293-8). Morehouse.

Biblical Beliefs. 96p. 1982. pap. text ed. 4.95 (ISBN 0-910566-10-0); Perfect bdg. instr's. guide 5.95 (ISBN 0-910566-17-8). Evang Tchr.

Brooks, Keith L. Practical Bible Doctrine. (Teach Yourself the Bible Ser.). 1962. pap. 2.75 (ISBN 0-8024-6733-4). Moody.

Brueggemann, Walter. The Land: Place As Gift, Promise & Challenge in Biblical Faith. Donahue, John R., ed. LC 76-15883. (Overtures to Biblical Theology Ser.: No. 1). 228p. 1977. pap. 8.95 (ISBN 0-8006-1526-3, 1-1526). Fortress.

Bultmann, Rudolf. Theology of the New Testament. (Contemporary Theology Ser.). 278p. 1951. pap. text ed. write for info. (ISBN 0-02-305580-4, Pub. by Scribner). Macmillan.

Capps, Charles. Why Tragedy Happens to Christians. 187p. (Orig.). 1980. pap. 3.75 (ISBN 0-89274-175-9, HH-175). Harrison Hse.

Chafer, Lewis S. Systematic Theology, 8 vols. 2700p. 1981. Repr. 94.95 (ISBN 0-310-22378-4). Zondervan.

Churchill, John G. What the Bible Tells Me. 60p. 1976. pap. 1.50 (ISBN 0-8341-0412-1). Beacon Hill.

Clowney, Edmund P. Preaching & Biblical Theology. 1956. pap. 3.95 (ISBN 0-87552-145-2). Presby & Reformed.

Cooper, Thomas J. Guidebook to Biblical Truth. Cooper, Willia S., ed. (The Master of Light & Darkness Ser.: Vol. 5). 70p. (Orig.). 1985. pap. 4.75 (ISBN 0-931429-05-6). Cooper & Cooper Pub.

Cooper, Thomas J. & Cooper, Willia S. Guidebook to Biblical Truth. (Stewardship Ser.: Vol. 4). 60p. (Orig.). 1985. Set. write for info. (ISBN 0-931429-00-5); Vol. 4. pap. 4.50 (ISBN 0-931429-04-8). Cooper & Cooper Pub.

Criswell, W. A. Great Doctrines of the Bible, Vol. 7. Ruark, J., ed. 1987. price not set (ISBN 0-310-43960-4). Zondervan.

--Great Doctrines of the Bible: Ecclesiology, Vol. 3. 128p. 1983. 8.95 (ISBN 0-310-43900-0, 11661). Zondervan.

Day, Millard F. Basic Bible Doctrines. 1953. pap. 3.50 (ISBN 0-8024-0239-9). Moody.

Denney, James. The Biblical Doctrine of Reconciliation. 348p. 1985. smythe sewn 14.00 (ISBN 0-86524-192-9, 8806). Klock & Klock.

Evans, William. Las Grandes Doctrinas de la Biblia. Orig. Title: Great Doctrines of the Bible. (Span.). 1986. pap. 4.75 (ISBN 0-8254-1222-6). Kregel.

Fahey, Michael A. Cyprian & the Bible: A Study of Third-Century Exegesis. 701p. 1971. lib. bdg. 65.00 (Pub. by J C B Mohr BRD). Coronet Bks.

Gnuse, Robert. Authority of the Bible, Theories of Inspiration Revelation & the Canon of Scripture. (Theological Inquirers Ser.). 160p. (Orig.). 1985. pap. 6.95 (ISBN 0-8091-2692-3). Paulist Pr.

Grant, George. In the Shadow of Plenty. 1986. pap. 6.95 (ISBN 0-8407-3095-0). Nelson.

Hanson, Paul D. Dynamic Transcendence: The Correlation of Confessional Heritage & Contemporary Experience in Biblical Model of Divine Activity. LC 78-54552. pap. 27.30 (2026940). Bks Demand UMI.

Herrmann, Siegfried. Israel in Egypt. LC 73-77371. (Studies in Biblical Theology, Second Ser.: No. 27). (Orig.). 1973. pap. text ed. 10.00x (ISBN 0-8401-3077-5). A R Allenson.

Hodges, Zane C. The Gospel under Siege: A Study on Faith & Works. 124p. (Orig.). 1981. pap. 4.95 (ISBN 0-9607576-0-0). Redencion Viva.

Janzen, Waldemar. Still in the Image: Essays in Biblical Theology & Anthrpology. LC 82-83886. (Institute of Mennonite Studies: No.6). 226p. (Orig.). 1982. pap. 10.95 (ISBN 0-87303-076-1). Faith & Life.

Johnston, Robert K., ed. The Use of the Bible in Theology. LC 84-48513. 1985. pap. 11.95 (ISBN 0-8042-0530-2). John Knox.

Kirwan, Willia. Biblical Concepts for Christian Counseling: A Case for Integrating Psychology & Theology. 240p. (Orig.). 1984. pap. 9.95 (ISBN 0-8010-5454-0). Baker Bk.

Knoch, A. E. All in All. rev. ed. 222p. 1978. pap. text ed. 4.00 (ISBN 0-910424-74-8). Concordant.

Lane, Belden C. Storytelling: Study Guide, The Enchantment of Theology Cassette Tapes. LC 86-6079. 24p. (Orig.). 1982. pap. 2.50 (ISBN 0-8272-3419-8, 10S2113). CBP.

Lewis, Gordon. Bible, the Christian & Jehovah's Witnesses. 1966. pap. 1.25 (ISBN 0-87552-324-2). Presby & Reformed.

--Bible, the Christian & Latter Day Saints. 1966. pap. 1.25 (ISBN 0-87552-325-0). Presby & Reformed.

--Bible, the Christian & Seventh Day Adventists. 1966. pap. 1.25 (ISBN 0-87552-326-9). Presby & Reformed.

Loren, Mary E. Leader's Guide: Meeting the Forgiving Jesus. 48p. 1985. pap. 2.95 (ISBN 0-89243-225-X). Liguori Pubns.

Mayhew, Eugene J., ed. Shalom: Essays in Honor of Dr. Charles H. Shaw. 231p. 1983. pap. 11.95 (ISBN 0-912407-01-8). William Tyndale Col Pr.

Payne, Peggy. Teaching for Life-Changing Learning. (C. E. Ministries Ser.). 94p. (Orig.). 1984. pap. 3.50 (ISBN 0-89367-092-8). Light & Life.

Queck, Lynn. Leader's Guide: Meeting Jesus in Holy Communion. 96p. 1985. pap. 3.95 (ISBN 0-89243-224-1). Liguori Pubns.

Reventlow, Henning G. Problems of Biblical Theology in the 20th Century. LC 86-4722. 1986. pap. 14.95 (ISBN 0-8006-1935-8, 1-1935). Fortress.

Ryrie, Charles C. Sintesis de Doctrina Biblica. Orig. Title: Survey of Bible Doctrine. (Span.). 208p. 1979. pap. 4.95 (ISBN 0-8254-1637-X). Kregel.

--Survey of Bible Doctrine. LC 72-77958. 192p. 1972. pap. 5.95 (ISBN 0-8024-8435-2). Moody.

St. John, P. Infant & Junior Scripture Lesson. 274p. 1956. 4.00 (ISBN 0-227-67493-6). Attic Pr.

Schaeffer, Francis. True Spirituality. 1972. pap. 6.95 (ISBN 0-8423-7351-9). Tyndale.

Schoonenberg, Piet. Covenant & Creation. LC 74-75119. 1969. 11.95 (ISBN 0-268-00311-4). U of Notre Dame Pr.

Schuetze, A. Basic Doctrines of the Bible. 1969. pap. 2.50 (ISBN 0-8100-0016-4, 09N0921). Northwest Pub.

Shoemaker, H. Stephen. Retelling the Biblical Story. LC 85-16650. 1985. pap. 6.95 (ISBN 0-8054-2114-9). Broadman.

Smart, James D. The Past, Present, & Future of Biblical Theology. LC 79-16943. 162p. 1979. softcover 8.95 (ISBN 0-664-24284-7). Westminster.

Taylor, Richard & Taylor, Willard. God, Man & Salvation. 724p. 1977. 16.95 (ISBN 0-8341-0440-7). Beacon Hill.

Terrien, Samuel. The Elusive Presence: The Heart of Biblical Theology. LC 78-4424. 544p. 1983. pap. 12.95 (ISBN 0-06-068234-5, RD-487, HarpR). Har-Row.

Torrey, Reuben A. What the Bible Teaches. 20th ed. 544p. 1984. 15.95 (ISBN 0-8007-0344-8). Revell.

Trenchard, Ernesto. Estudios de Doctrina Biblica. (Span.). 406p. 1976. pap. 9.95 (ISBN 0-8254-1738-4). Kregel.

Vos, Geerhardus. Notes on Biblical Theology. 1948. pap. 10.95 (ISBN 0-8028-1209-0). Eerdmans.

Wakefield. Bible Basis for Christian Security. pap. 1.50 (ISBN 0-686-12851-6). Schmul Pub Co.

Walsh, J. P. The Mighty from Their Thrones: Power in the Biblical Tradition. LC 86-45198. (Overtures to Biblical Theology Ser.). 224p. 1987. pap. 12.95 (ISBN 0-8006-1546-8). Fortress.

White, Marian. Bible Teaching Finger Plays. (Teaching Helps Ser). 1977. pap. 4.50 (ISBN 0-8010-9592-1). Baker Bk.

Wilson, T. Ernest. Mystery Doctrines of the New Testament: God's Sacred Secrets. LC 74-78881. 128p. 1975. pap. text ed. 2.50 (ISBN 0-87213-962-X). Loizeaux.

BIBLE-THEOLOGY-N. T.

Auer, Jim. A Teenager's (Absolutely Basic) Introduction to the New Testament. 96p. 1986. pap. 2.95 (ISBN 0-89243-257-8). Liguori Pubns.

Beardslee, William A. Human Achievement & Divine Vocation in the Message of Paul. LC 61-4760. (Studies in Biblical Theology: No. 31). 1961. pap. 10.00x (ISBN 0-8401-3031-7). A R Allenson.

Bender, Harold S. These Are My People: The New Testament Church. LC 62-12947. (Conrad Grebel Lecture Ser.). 136p. 1962. pap. 6.95 (ISBN 0-8361-1479-5). Herald Pr.

Berkhof, Hendrik. Christ & the Powers. LC 62-13713. 80p. 1962. pap. 5.95 (ISBN 0-8361-1820-0). Herald Pr.

Boers, Hendrikus. What Is New Testament Theology? The Rise of Criticism & the Problem of a Theology of the New Testament. Via, Dan O., Jr., ed. LC 79-7372. (Guides to Biblical Scholarship: New Testament Ser.). 96p. 1979. pap. 4.50 (ISBN 0-8006-0466-0, 1-466). Fortress.

Bornkamm, Gunther. Paul. Stalker, D. M., tr. from Ger. LC 70-85068. 1971. short disc 15.95xi (ISBN 0-06-060933-8, HarpR). Har-Row.

Bornkamm, Gunther, et al. Tradition & Interpretation in Matthew. LC 63-10495. 308p. 1963. 13.95 (ISBN 0-664-20453-8). Westminster.

Brown, Colin, ed. The New International Dictionary of New Testament Theology, 4 vols. 1986. 109.95 (ISBN 0-310-33238-9, 11137). Zondervan.

Brox, Norbert. Understanding the Message of Paul. Blenkinsopp, Joseph, tr. (Orig.). 1968. pap. 1.45x (ISBN 0-268-00286-X). U of Notre Dame Pr.

Bruce, F. F. The Defence of the Gospel in the New Testament. rev. ed. LC 77-2282. 1977. pap. 4.95 (ISBN 0-8028-1024-1). Eerdmans.

Fitzmyer, Joseph F. Pauline Theology: A Brief Sketch. (Orig.). 1967. pap. text ed. write for info. (ISBN 0-13-654525-4). P-H.

Glasson, T. Francis. Moses in the Fourth Gospel. LC 63-5666. (Studies in Biblical Theology: No. 40). 1963. pap. 10.00x (ISBN 0-8401-3040-6). A R Allenson.

Goppelt, Leonard. Theology of the New Testament: Jesus & the Gospels, Vol I. Alsup, John E., tr. LC 80-28947. 316p. 1981. 15.95 (ISBN 0-8028-2384-X). Eerdmans.

Goppelt, Leonhard. Theology of the New Testament: The Variety & Unity of the Apostolic Witness to Christ, Vol. II. 248p. 1983. 17.95 (ISBN 0-8028-2385-8). Eerdmans.

Grollenberg, Lucas. Paul. Bowden, John, tr. LC 78-14372. 186p. 1979. pap. 4.50 (ISBN 0-664-24234-0). Westminster.

Gundry, Robert H. Soma in Biblical Theology: With Emphasis on Pauline Anthropology. LC 75-22975. (Society for New Testament Studies. Monograph: 29). pap. 69.50 (ISBN 0-317-41736-3, 2025584). Bks Demand UMI.

Guthrie, Donald. New Testament Theology. 1056p. 1981. text ed. 34.95 (ISBN 0-87784-965-X). Inter-Varsity.

Hamerton-Kelly, Robert. God the Father: Theology & Patriarchy in the Teaching of Jesus, No. 4. Brueggemann, Walter & Donahue, John R., eds. LC 78-54551. (Overtures to Biblical Theology Ser.). 144p. 1979. pap. 8.95 (ISBN 0-8006-1528-X, 1-1528). Fortress.

Hasel, Gerhard. New Testament Theology. pap. 5.95 (ISBN 0-8028-1733-5). Eerdmans.

Hull, John. Hellenistic Magic & the Synoptic Tradition. LC 73-77369. (Studies in Biblical Theology, 2nd Ser.: No. 28). 1974. pap. text ed. 12.00x (ISBN 0-8401-3078-3). A R Allenson.

Hunter, Archibald M. The Gospel According to St. Paul. rev. ed. LC 67-10511. Orig. Title: Interpreting Paul's Gospel. 126p. 1967. pap. 7.95 (ISBN 0-664-24742-3). Westminster.

Jeremias, Joachim. New Testament Theology. LC 70-143936. lib. rep. ed. 30.00x (ISBN 0-684-15157-X, ScribT). Scribner.

Kennedy, Harry A. Theology of the Epistles. LC 20-15157. (Studies in Theology: No. 13). 1919. 6.00x (ISBN 0-8401-6013-5). A R Allenson.

Morris, Leon. New Testament Theology. 448p. 1986. text ed. 19.95 (ISBN 0-310-45570-7, 12391, Pub. by Academie Bks). Zondervan.

Morrison, Clinton D. Powers That Be: Earthly Rulers & Demonic Powers in Romans, Chapter 13, 1-7. LC 60-4219. (Studies in Biblical Theology: No. 29). 1960. pap. 10.00x (ISBN 0-8401-3029-5). A R Allenson.

Pomazansky, Michael. The Old Testament in the New Testament Church. 40p. (Orig.). 1977. pap. 2.00 (ISBN 0-317-30281-7). Holy Trinity.

Preiss, Theo. Life in Christ. LC 55-1608. (Studies in Biblical Theology: No. 13). 1954. pap. 10.00x (ISBN 0-8401-3013-9). A R Allenson.

Raisanen, Heikki. Paul & the Law. 330p. 1983. lib. bdg. 67.50x (ISBN 3-16-144629-1, Pub. by J C B Mohr BRD). Coronet Bks.

Ribberbos, Herman N. Coming of the Kingdom. 1962. pap. 11.95 (ISBN 0-87552-408-7). Presby & Reformed.

Ridderbos, Herman N. Paul. DeWitt, J. Richard, tr. 587p. 1975. 23.95 (ISBN 0-8028-3438-8). Eerdmans.

Ryrie, Charles C. Biblical Theology of the New Testament. LC 59-11468. 1959. 12.95 (ISBN 0-8024-0712-9). Moody.

Schnackenburg, Rudolf. Present & Future: Modern Aspects of New Testament Theology. 1966. 11.95x (ISBN 0-268-00215-0). U of Notre Dame Pr.

Schoeps, Hans J. Paul: The Theology of the Apostle in the Light of Jewish Religious History. Knight, Harold, tr. LC 61-10284. 304p. 1979. Repr. of 1961 ed. softcover 7.95 (ISBN 0-664-24273-1). Westminster.

Stagg, Frank. New Testament Theology. LC 62-15328. 1962. 13.95 (ISBN 0-8054-1613-7). Broadman.

Stevens, George B. The Theology of the New Testament. 636p. 1918. 19.95 (ISBN 0-567-07215-0, Pub. by T & T Clark Ltd UK). Fortress.

Taylor, Michael J., ed. A Companion to John: Readings in Johannine Theology. LC 77-7042. 1977. pap. 6.95 (ISBN 0-8189-0348-1). Alba.

Townsley, David & Bjork, Russell. Scripture Index to the New International Dictionary of New Testament Theology: And Index to Selected Extrabiblical Literature. Brown & Colin, eds. 208p. 1985. pap. 10.95 (ISBN 0-310-44501-9, 11315P). Zondervan.

Williams, Rowan. Christian Spirituality: A Theological History from the New Testament to Luther & St. John of the Cross. LC 80-82190. 193p. 1980. 10.95 (ISBN 0-8042-0660-0); pap. 8.95 (ISBN 0-8042-0508-6). John Knox.

BIBLE-THEOLOGY-O. T.

Achtemeier, Paul J. & Achtemeier, Elizabeth. The Old Testament Roots of Our Faith. LC 78-14659. 160p. 1979. pap. 5.95 (ISBN 0-8006-1348-1, 1-1348). Fortress.

Baldwin, Joyce. Haggai, Zechariah, Malachi. LC 72-75980. (Tyndale Old Testament Commentary Ser.). 256p. 1972. 12.95 (ISBN 0-87784-908-0); pap. 6.95 (ISBN 0-87784-276-0). Inter-Varsity.

Botterweck, G. Johannes. Diccionario Teologico del Antiguo Testamento, 4 vols. (Span.). 1116p. 1978. Set. pns (S-50106). French & Eur.

Botterweck, G. Johannes & Ringgren, Helmer, eds. Theological Dictionary of the Old Testament, 5 vols. 560p. 1978. Set. 137.50 (ISBN 0-8028-2338-6); Vol. I. 27.50 ea. (ISBN 0-8028-2325-4). Vol. II (ISBN 0-8028-2326-2). Vol. III (ISBN 0-8028-2327-0). Vol. IV (ISBN 0-8028-2328-9). Vol. V (ISBN 0-8028-2329-7). Eerdmans.

Craigie, Peter. Ugarit & the Old Testament. 110p. (Orig.). 1983. pap. 5.95 (ISBN 0-8028-1928-1). Eerdmans.

Crenshaw, James L. A Whirlpool of Torment: The Oppressive Presence of God in Ancient Israel. LC 83-18479. (Overtures to Biblical Theology Ser.). 144p. 1984. pap. 7.95 (ISBN 0-8006-1536-0, 1-1536). Fortress.

Davidson, A. B. The Theology of the Old Testament. Salmond, S. D., ed. 572p. 1904. 16.95 (ISBN 0-567-27206-0, Pub. by T & T Clark Ltd UK). Fortress.

De Vries, Simon J. The Achievements of Biblical Religion: A Prolegomenon to Old Testament Theology. LC 83-3614. 558p. (Orig.). 1983. lib. bdg. 40.75 (ISBN 0-8191-3140-7); pap. text ed. 22.25 (ISBN 0-8191-3141-5). U Pr of Amer.

Dumbrell, W. J. Covenant & Creation: A Theology of Old Testament Covenants. 220p. 1986. pap. 8.95 (ISBN 0-8407-3053-5). Nelson.

Eichrodt, Walther. Theology of the Old Testament, 2 Vols. Baker, J., tr. LC 61-11867. (Old Testament Library). 1967. 22.95 ea. Vol. 1, 542p (ISBN 0-664-20352-3). Vol. 2, 574p (ISBN 0-664-20769-3). Westminster.

Gelin, Albert. Key Concepts of the Old Testament. Lamb, George, tr. 96p. pap. 2.95 (ISBN 0-8091-1610-3, Deus). Paulist Pr.

Getz, Gene A. When You Feel You Haven't Got It. rev. ed. LC 86-540. (Biblical Renewal Ser.). 160p. 1986. pap. 5.95 (ISBN 0-8307-1123-6, 5418757). Regal.

Gottwald, Norman K. The Tribes of Yahweh: A Sociology of the Religion of Liberated Israel, 1250-1050 B.C. LC 78-24333. 944p. (Orig.). 1979. pap. 19.95 (ISBN 0-88344-499-2). Orbis Bks.

Hasel, Gerhard F. Old Testament Theology: Basic Issues in the Current Debate. rev. ed. 168p. 1975. pap. 5.95 (ISBN 0-8028-1478-6). Eerdmans.

Jenni, Ernst. Diccionario Teologico Manual del Antiguo Testamento, 2 vols. (Span.). 642p. 1978. Set. 75.00 (S-50105). French & Eur.

Kaiser, Walter C., Jr. Toward an Old Testament Theology. 1978. 16.95 (ISBN 0-310-37100-7, 12320). Zondervan.

McKenzie, John L. A Theology of the Old Testament. LC 86-9230. 336p. 1986. pap. text ed. 12.00 (ISBN 0-8191-5354-0). U Pr of Amer.

MacKenzie, R. A. Faith & History in the Old Testament. LC 63-10585. 1963. 8.95 (ISBN 0-8166-0297-2). U of Minn Pr.

Miller, Patrick D., Jr. & Roberts, J. J. The Hand of the Lord: A Reassessment of the "Ark Narrative" of 1 Samuel. LC 76-48737. (Near Eastern Studies). 128p. 1977. 12.50x (ISBN 0-8018-1920-2). Johns Hopkins.

Moon, Cyris H. A Korean Minjung Theology: An Old Testament Perspective. 96p. (Orig.). 1986. pap. 7.95 (ISBN 0-88344-250-7). Orbis Bks.

Muybridge, Eadweard. Muybridge's Complete Human & Animal Locomotion: All 781 Plates from the 1887 Animal Locomotion, 3 vols. Incl. Vol. 1. 33.34 (ISBN 0-486-23792-3); Vol. 2. 33.33 (ISBN 0-486-23793-1); Vol. 3. 33.33 (ISBN 0-486-23794-X). (Illus.). 1979. Repr. of 1887 ed. Set. 100.00. Dover.

Payne, J. Barton. Theology of the Older Testament. 1962. 12.95 (ISBN 0-310-30721-X, 10545P). Zondervan.

Pomazansky, Michael. The Old Testament in the New Testament Church. 40p. (Orig.). 1977. pap. 2.00 (ISBN 0-317-30281-7). Holy Trinity.

Prinsloo, Willem S. The Theology of the Book of Joel. (Beihefte zur Zeitschrift fur die Alttestamentliche Wissenschaft: Vol. 163). viii, 136p. 1985. 43.75x (ISBN 3-11-010301-X). De Gruyter.

Robinson, Henry W. Inspiration & Revelation in the Old Testament. LC 78-9891. 1979. Repr. of 1946 ed. lib. bdg. 24.75x (ISBN 0-313-21068-3, ROIR). Greenwood.

Schmidt, Werner H. The Faith of the Old Testament: A History. Sturdy, John, tr. LC 82-21780. 312p. (Orig.). 1983. 25.00 (ISBN 0-664-21826-1); pap. 12.95 (ISBN 0-664-24456-4). Westminster.

Stevens, William W. A Guide for Old Testament Study. LC 73-91606. pap. 10.50 (ISBN 0-8054-1210-7). Broadman.

Stone, Nathan. Names of God. 1944. pap. 3.50 (ISBN 0-8024-5854-8). Moody.

Von Rad, Gerhard. The Message of the Prophets. Stalker, D. M., tr. from Ger. LC 72-183633. 288p. 1972. pap. 10.95xi (ISBN 0-06-068929-3, RD45, HarpR). Har-Row.

--Old Testament Theology, 2 vols. LC 62-7306. Vol. 1. S.D. 17.95 (ISBN 0-06-068930-7, HarpR); Vol. 2. 16.95 (ISBN 0-06-068931-5, HarpR). Har-Row.

Westermann, Claus. Elements of Old Testament Theology. Stott, Doug, tr. LC 81-82346. Tr. of Theologie Des Alten Testaments in Grundzuegen. 249p. 1982. 20.95 (ISBN 0-8042-0191-9); pap. 15.95 (ISBN 0-8042-0193-5). John Knox.

BIBLE–TRANSLATING

Arichea, D. C., Jr. & Nida, E. A. Translator's Handbook on Paul's Letter to the Galatians. LC 79-115359. (Helps for Translators Ser.). 176p. Repr. of 1976 ed. soft cover 3.65x (ISBN 0-8267-0142-6, 08527, Pub. by United Bible). Am Bible.

Beegle, Dewey M. God's Word into English. LC 79-84556. 1965. pap. 8.95 (ISBN 0-933462-02-6). Pryor Pettengill.

Bratcher, R. G. & Nida, E. A. Translator's Handbook on the Gospel of Mark. LC 61-19352. (Helps for Translators Ser.). 534p. 1961. soft cover 5.90x (ISBN 0-8267-0135-3, 08501, Pub. by United Bible). Am Bible.

Bratcher, Robert G. & Nida, Eugene A. A Translator's Handbook on Paul's Letters to the Colossians & to Philemon. (Helps for Translators Ser.). 149p. soft cover 3.30x (ISBN 0-8267-0145-0, 08529, Pub. by United Bible). Am Bible.

Commission Christian Lit. Bible Translations. 1981. pap. 0.79 (ISBN 0-8100-0132-2, 04N1212). Northwest Pub.

Dahlquist, Anna M. Trailblazers for Translators: The Influence of the "Chichicastenago Twelve". Date not set. pap. price not set (ISBN 0-87808-205-0). William Carey Lib.

De Waard, J. & Nida, E. A. Translator's Handbook on the Book of Ruth. (Helps for Translators Ser.). 111p. 1973. 3.30x (ISBN 0-8267-0107-8, 08518, Pub. by United Bible). Am Bible.

Earle, Ralph. Word Meanings in the New Testament, Vol. 1: Matthew, Mark, Luke. 285p. 1980. 9.95 (ISBN 0-8341-0683-3). Beacon Hill.

Eclov, Lee. The Church: Pictures of Christ's Body. (Fisherman Bible Studyguide Ser.). 55p. 1981. saddle stitched 2.95 (ISBN 0-87788-155-3). Shaw Pubs.

Ellingworth, P. & Nida, E. A. Translator's Handbook on Paul's Letter to the Thessalonians. (Helps for Translators Ser.). 229p. 1975. 4.50x (ISBN 0-8267-0146-9, 08526, Pub. by United Bible). Am Bible.

Haas, C., et al. Translator's Handbook on the Letters of John. LC 74-102407. (Helps for Translators Ser.). 171p. 1972. 3.30x (ISBN 0-8267-0154-X, 08516, Pub. by United Bible). Am Bible.

Harrisville, Roy A. Benjamin Wisner Bacon: Pioneer in American Biblical Criticism. LC 76-16178. (Society of Biblical Literature. Studies in Biblical Scholarship). 1976. pap. 8.95 (ISBN 0-89130-110-0, 061102). Scholars Pr GA.

--Frank Chamberlain Porter: Pioneer in American Biblical Interpretation. LC 76-4498. (Society of Biblical Literature. Study in Biblical Scholarship). 1976. pap. 8.95 (ISBN 0-89130-104-6, 061101). Scholars Pr GA.

Hoare, H. W. Our English Bible. 1925. 27.00 (ISBN 0-8274-3083-3). R West.

Loh, I. & Nida, E. A. Translator's Handbook on Paul's Letter to the Philippians. LC 82-17585. (Helps for Translators Ser.). 167p. 1977. 3.30x (ISBN 0-8267-0144-2, 08528, Pub. by United Bible). Am Bible.

Newman, B. M. & Nida, E. A. Translator's Handbook on Paul's Letter to the Romans. LC 75-2229. (Helps for Translators Ser.). 325p. 1973. 5.00x (ISBN 0-8267-0139-6, 08517, Pub. by United Bible). Am Bible.

Newman, B. M., Jr. & Nida, E. A. Translator's Handbook on the Acts of the Apostles. LC 73-162720. (Helps for Translators Ser.). 542p. 1972. 6.00x (ISBN 0-8267-0138-8, 08514, Pub. by United Bible). Am Bible.

Nida, Eugene A. Toward a Science of Translating: With Special Reference to Principles & Procedures Involved in Bible Translating. 1964. text ed. 39.95x (ISBN 0-391-02063-3). Humanities.

Price, Brynmor F. & Nida, Eugene A. A Translator's Handbook on the Book of Jonah. (Helps for Translators Ser.). 95p. 1978. 3.30x (ISBN 0-8267-0199-X, 08552, Pub. by United Bible). Am Bible.

Reiling, J. & Swellengrebel, J. L. Translator's Handbook on the Gospel of Luke. LC 72-856530. (Helps for Translators Ser.). 798p. 1971. 8.40x (ISBN 0-8267-0198-1, 08512, Pub. by United Bible). Am Bible.

Waard, Jan de & Nida, Eugene A. From One Language to Another: Functional Equivalence in Bible Translation. 224p. 1986. 15.95 (ISBN 0-8407-7555-5). Nelson.

BIBLE–TRANSLATIONS

see Bible–Versions

BIBLE–TYPOLOGY

see Typology (Theology)

BIBLE–USE

see also Bible–Homiletical Use; Bible–Liturgical Use

Adams, Jay E. Use of Scripture in Counseling. 1975. pap. 2.95 (ISBN 0-87552-063-4). Presby & Reformed.

Benoit, Pierre, ed. How Does the Christian Confront the Old Testament. (Concilium Ser.: Vol. 30). 1967. 7.95 (ISBN 0-8091-0074-6). Paulist Pr.

Dickson, Nicholas. Bible in Waverley: Or, Sir Walter Scott's Use of the Sacred Scripture. 311p. 1980. Repr. of 1884 ed. lib. bdg. 30.00 (ISBN 0-8495-1123-2). Arden Lib.

Kelsey, David H. Uses of Scripture in Recent Theology. LC 74-26344. 240p. 1975. pap. 7.95 (ISBN 0-8006-1374-0, 1-1374). Fortress.

Mollenkott, Virginia R. Women, Men, & the Bible. LC 76-40446. 1977. pap. 8.95 (ISBN 0-687-45970-2) (ISBN 0-687-81914-8). Abingdon.

BIBLE–VERSIONS

Here are entered works on Versions of the Bible in any language except English. For English Version see subdivision Versions, English.

see also Language Question in the Church

Adomeit, Ruth. Three Centuries of Thumb Bibles. LC 78-68238. (Garland Reference Library of Humanities). (Illus.). 435p. 1980. 73.00 (ISBN 0-8240-9818-8). Garland Pub.

Aland, Kurt, ed. Die Alten Uebersetzungen des Neuen Testaments, die Kirchenvaeterzitate und Lektionare: Der Gegenwaertige Stand Ihrer Erforschung und Ihre Bedeutung fuer die Griechische Textgeschichte. (Arbeiten zur neutestamentlichen Textforschung 5). xxiv, 590p. 1972. 62.40x (ISBN 3-11-004121-9). De Gruyter.

Allgeier, Arthur. Die Psalmen der Vulgata: Ihre Eigenart. 22.00 (ISBN 0-384-00870-4). Johnson Repr.

American & British Committee for the International Greek New Testament Project. The New Testament in Greek: The Gospel According to St. Luke, Vol. 3, Pt. 1. (The New Testament in Greek Ser.). 1983. 98.00x (ISBN 0-19-826167-5). Oxford U Pr.

Armstrong, D., et al. The Old Church Slavonic Translation of the Andron Hagion Biblos in the Edition of Nikolas Van Wijk. Van Schooneveld, C. H., ed. (Slavistic Printings & Reprintings Ser: No. 1). 310p. 1975. text ed. 67.20x (ISBN 90-2793-196-8). Mouton.

Beck, William F. The Holy Bible in the Language of Today: An American Translation. 1977. 16.95 (ISBN 0-87981-082-3). Holman Bible Pub.

Behrends, Rainer, et al. Biblia Pauperum: Apocalypsis. (Illus., LC 77-088869). 1978. boxed 500.00 (ISBN 0-87817-239-4). Hacker.

Bell, P. G. Essentials of New Testament: Greek. 1983. pap. 9.95 Wkbk. (ISBN 0-89957-569-2); answer bk. for wkbk. 4.95 (ISBN 0-89957-570-6); answers for essentials 2.95. AMG Pubs.

Berry, George R. Interlinear Greek-English New Testament. LC 78-54242. 1978. pap. 15.95 (ISBN 0-8054-1372-3). Broadman.

--Interlinear Greek-English New Testament. 24.95 (ISBN 0-310-21170-0, 9216). Zondervan.

Berry, George R. & Strong, James. Interlinear Greek-English New Testament. (Reference Set). 1187p. 24.95 (ISBN 0-915134-74-8). Mott Media.

Bloomfield, Samuel T. The Greek Testament: With English Notes, 2 vols. 1986. Repr. of 1843 ed. Set. lib. bdg. 45.00 (ISBN 0-89941-507-5). W S Hein.

Boehmer, Eduard. Bibliotheca Wiffeniana: Bibliotheca Wiffeniana: Spanish Reformers of Two Centuries from Fifteen Twenty, 3 Vols. 1964. Repr. of 1904 ed. Set. 62.00 (ISBN 0-8337-0330-7). B Franklin.

Bostrom, Otto H. Alternative Readings in the Hebrew of the Books of Samuel. LC 18-8964. (Augustana College Library Publication Ser.: No. 8). 60p. 1918. pap. 0.75 (ISBN 0-910182-05-1). Augustana Coll.

Bouterwek, K. W. Cademon's Des Angelsachsen Biblishce Dictungen, 2 Vols. 393p. 1983. Repr. of 1854 ed. Set. lib. bdg. 400.00 (ISBN 0-8495-0636-0). Arden Lib.

Bowker, John. Targums & Rabbinic Literature. LC 71-80817. 1969. 67.50 (ISBN 0-521-07415-0). Cambridge U Pr.

Bratcher, Robert G. A Translator's Guide to the Gospel of Mark. (Helps for Translators Ser.). 236p. 1981. pap. 4.50x (ISBN 0-8267-0180-9, 08711, Pub. by United Bible). Am Bible.

--A Translator's Guide to the Gospel of Matthew. LC 82-213977. (Helps for Translators Ser.). 388p. 1981. pap. 4.50x (ISBN 0-8267-0179-5, 08710, Pub. by United Bible). Am Bible.

Bratcher, Robert G. & Nida, Eugene A. Manuel du Traducteur pour l'Evangile de Marc. Weber, C., tr. (Auxiliaires Du Traducteur Ser.). 542p. 1963. pap. 7.05x (ISBN 0-8267-0250-3, 51972, Pub. by United Bible). Am Bible.

Bratcher, Robert G., ed. Old Testament Quotations in the New Testament. 2nd, rev. ed. LC 84-8493. (Helps for Translators Ser.). xii, 80p. 1984. flexible bdg. 2.60x (ISBN 0-8267-0029-2, 08530, Pub. by United Bible). Am Bible.

Brenton, Charles. The Septuagint & Apocrypha in Greek & English. 1390p. 1972. 39.95 (ISBN 0-310-20430-5, 6234). Zondervan.

Bronstein, Herbert & Friedlander, Albert, eds. The Five Scrolls. 324p. 1984. 19.95 (ISBN 0-916694-80-1); deluxe ed. 60.00 (ISBN 0-916694-81-X); special ltd. ed., leatherbound 675.00 (ISBN 0-916694-82-8). Central Conf.

Budge, Ernest A., ed. Coptic Apocrypha in the Dialect of Upper Egypt. LC 77-3589. (Coptic Texts: Vol. 3). (Illus.). Repr. of 1913 ed. 55.00 (ISBN 0-404-11553-5). AMS Pr.

--Coptic Biblical Texts in the Dialect of Upper Egypt. LC 77-3590. (Coptic Texts: Vol. 2). (Illus.). 1977. Repr. of 1912 ed. 45.00 (ISBN 0-404-11552-7). AMS Pr.

Chambers, B. Bibliography of French Bibles: Fifteenth & Sixteenth Century French Language Editions of the Bible. 572p. (Orig.). 1983. pap. text ed. 67.50x (Pub. by Droz Switzerland). Coronet Bks.

Chapman, Benjamin. Greek New Testament Insert. 1.95 (ISBN 0-8010-2405-6). Baker Bk.

--New Testament: Greek Notebook Exegesis Filler. 1.00 (ISBN 0-8010-2425-0). Baker Bk.

Chu, John W. Selections from the New Testament in Chinese. 6.00 (ISBN 0-88710-083-X); tapes avail. (ISBN 0-88710-084-8). Far Eastern Pubns.

Chupco, Lee & Coachman, Ward. Creek (Muscogee) New Testament Concordance. 167p. 1982. spiral bdg. 12.50x (ISBN 0-940392-10-0). Indian U Pr OK.

Clark, J. Reuben, Jr. Why the King James Version. LC 79-15008. (Classics in Mormon Literature Ser.). 535p. 1979. 7.95 (ISBN 0-87747-773-6). Deseret Bk.

Conybeare, F. C. & Stock, George, eds. Selections from the Septuagint. (College Classical Ser.). vi, 313p. 1981. lib. bdg. 25.00x (ISBN 0-89241-366-2); pap. 12.50 (ISBN 0-89241-114-7). Caratzas.

Conybeare, Frederick C. & Stock, G. A Grammar of Septuagint Greek. 80p. 1980. pap. 6.95 (ISBN 0-310-43001-1, 6652P). Zondervan.

Cox, Claude E. Hexaplaric Materials Preserved in the Armenian Version. (Septuagint & Cognate Studies). 1986. text ed. 12.95 (ISBN 1-55540-028-0, 06-04-21); pap. 9.95 (ISBN 1-55540-029-9). Scholars Pr GA.

Danker, Frederick W. Shorter Lexicon of the Greek New Testament. 2nd, rev. ed. Gingrich, F. Wilbur, rev. by. LC 82-10933. 256p. 1983. lib. bdg. 22.00x (ISBN 0-226-13613-2). U of Chicago Pr.

Deanesly, Margaret. The Lollard Bible & Other Medieval Biblical Versions. LC 77-84722. Repr. of 1920 ed. 49.50 (ISBN 0-404-16125-1). AMS Pr.

Ellingworth, Paul & Hatton, Howard. A Translator's Handbook on Paul's First Letter to the Corinthians. LC 85-1142. (Helps for Translators Ser.). viii, 352p. 1985. flexible 4.20x (ISBN 0-8267-0140-X, 08578, Dist. by American Bible Society). United Bible.

Falk, Marcia. Love Lyrics from the Bible: A Translation & Literary Study of the Song of Songs. (Bible & Literature Ser.: No. 4). 1981. text ed. 19.95x (ISBN 0-907459-06-4, Pub. by Almond Pr England); pap. text ed. 9.95x (ISBN 0-907459-07-2, Pub. by Almond Pr England). Eisenbrauns.

Forman, Charles C. Four Early Bibles in Pilgrim Hall. (Pilgrim Society Notes: No. 9). 1959. 1.00 (ISBN 0-940628-17-1). Pilgrim Soc.

Foster, Lewis & Stedman, Jon. Selecting a Translation of the Bible. LC 83-4689. (Illus.). 128p. (Orig.). 1983. pap. 3.95 (ISBN 0-87239-645-2, 39975). Standard Pub.

Fowler, Everett W. Evaluating Versions of the New Testament. LC 80-81607. (Illus.). 80p. (Orig.). 1981. pap. 2.95 (ISBN 0-937136-03-4). Maranatha Baptist.

Friberg, Timothy & Friberg, Barbara, eds. Analytical Greek New Testament. 1000p. 1981. 24.95 (ISBN 0-8010-3496-5). Baker Bk.

Fristedt, Sven L. The Wycliffe Bible, 2 vols. LC 78-63195. (Heresies of the Early Christian & Medieval Era: Second Ser.). Repr. of 1953 ed. 45.00 set (ISBN 0-404-16370-X). AMS Pr.

Frye, Northrop. The Secular Scripture: A Study of the Structure of Romance. (Charles Eliot Norton Lectures Ser.). 192p. 1976. 15.00x (ISBN 0-674-79675-6); pap. 5.95x (ISBN 0-674-79676-4, HP 127). Harvard U Pr.

Glassman, Eugene H. The Translation Debate. LC 80-29286. 128p. (Orig.). 1981. pap. 4.25 (ISBN 0-87784-467-4). Inter Varsity.

Glunz, Hans. Britannien und Bibeltext. Repr. of 1930 ed. 16.00 (ISBN 0-384-18950-4). Johnson Repr.

--Die Lateinische Vorlage der Westsaechsischen Evangelienversion. pap. 8.00 (ISBN 0-384-18955-5). Johnson Repr.

Goodspeed, Edgar J. The Student's New Testament: The Greek Text & the American Translation. pap. 160.00 (ISBN 0-317-20700-8, 2024115). Bks Demand UMI.

--The Student's New Testament: The Greek Text & the American Translation, 2 vols. (Midway Reprint Ser.). Vol. 1. pap. 121.80 (2026775); Vol. 2. pap. 146.00. Bks Demand UMI.

Gordis, Robert. Megillat Esther: The Mascretic Hebrew Text with Introduction, New Translation & Commentary. 1977. 3.95x (ISBN 0-87068-763-8). Ktav.

Greenstein, Edward L. & Preminger, Alex, eds. Hebrew Bible in Literary Criticism. (Library of Literary Criticism). 635p. 1986. 65.00x (ISBN 0-8044-3266-X). Ungar.

Hatch, Edwin & Redpath, Henry A. A Concordance to the Septuagint & Other Greek Versions of the Old Testament (Including the Apocryphal Books, 3 vols. in 2. 1088p. 1983. Repr. of 1906 ed. Set. 75.00 (ISBN 0-8010-4270-4). Baker Bk.

Hawley, Charles A. Critical Examination of the Peshitta Version of the Book of Ezra. LC 24-1925. (Columbia University. Contributions to Oriental History & Philology: No. 8). Repr. of 1922 ed. 12.50 (ISBN 0-404-50538-4). AMS Pr.

Heuman, Fred S. The Uses of Hebraisms in Recent Bible Translations. 154p. 1977. 9.95 (ISBN 0-8022-2190-4). Philos Lib.

Hitchcock, Roswell D. Baker's Topical Bible. 768p. 1984. pap. 11.95 (ISBN 0-8010-4284-4). Baker Bk.

Interlinear Greek-English New Testament: Coded to Strong's. 1984. deluxe ed. 24.95 (ISBN 0-8010-5036-7). Baker Bk.

Interlinear Greek-English New Testament: With Greek-English Lexicon & New Testament Synonyms. 1977. pap. 14.95 (ISBN 0-8010-0700-3). Baker Bk.

Jackson, Wayne. The Bible Translation Controversy. (That You May Believe Ser.). 20p. (Orig.). 1985. pap. 1.50 (ISBN 0-932859-01-1). Apologetic Pr.

Jellicoe, Sidney. The Septuagint & Modern Study. 1978. Repr. of 1968 ed. 12.50x (ISBN 0-931464-00-5). Eisenbrauns.

Juelicher, A., et al, eds. Itala: Das Neue Testament in Altlateinischer Ueberlieferung, Vols. 1-2 & 4. Incl. Vol. 1. Matthaeus-Evangelium. rev. 2nd ed. viii, 160p. 1972. 84.00 (ISBN 3-11-002256-7); Vol. 2. Marcus-Evangelium. x, 230p. 1970. 76.00 (ISBN 3-11-001244-8); Vol. 4. Johannes-Evangelium. x, 230p. 1963. 96.00x (ISBN 3-11-001243-X). (Ger.). De Gruyter.

Katz, Peter. The Text of the Septuagint: Its Corruptions & Their Emendation. Gooding, D. W., ed. LC 74-161292. pap. 110.00 (ISBN 0-317-28405-3, 2022451). Bks Demand UMI.

Kenyon, F. G. Recent Developments in the Textual Criticism of the Greek Bible. (British Academy of London Ser.). pap. 19.00 (ISBN 0-8115-1274-6). Kraus Repr.

--The Text of the Greek Bible. 3rd, rev. ed. 1975. 40.50 (ISBN 0-7156-0641-7, Pub. by Duckworth London); pap. 13.50 (ISBN 0-7156-0652-2). Longwood Pub Group.

Kessler, Herbert L. The Illustrated Bibles from Tours. LC 76-45902. (Studies in Manuscript Illumination: No. 7). (Illus.). 236p. 1977. 61.00 (ISBN 0-691-03923-2). Princeton U Pr.

Kimball, William. Book of Books. LC 86-71101. 160p. (Orig.). 1986. pap. 6.95 (ISBN 0-89900-211-0). College Pr Pub.

Knight, Douglas A. & Tucker, Gene M., eds. The Hebrew Bible & Its Modern Interpreters. LC 83-49216. (The Bible & Its Modern Interpreters Ser.). 496p. 1984. 24.95 (ISBN 0-8006-0721-X, 1-721). Fortress.

Kohlenberger, John, III. NIV Interlinear Hebrew-English Old Testament: Isaiah-Malachi, Vol. 4. 640p. 1985. 24.95 (ISBN 0-310-44210-9, 6283). Zondervan.

Kohlenberger, John R. All about Bibles. (Illus.). 76p. 1985. pap. 0.95 (ISBN 0-19-526951-9). Oxford U Pr.

Kohlenberger, John R., III. The NIV Interlinear Hebrew-English Old Testament: Genesis-Malachi, 4 vols. 1985. Set. text ed. 95.80 (ISBN 0-310-38948-8, 6284). Zondervan.

Kubo, Sakae & Specht, Walter. So Many Versions? rev. enlarged ed. 320p. 1983. pap. 9.95 (ISBN 0-310-45691-6, 12458P). Zondervan.

Levine, Etan. The Aramaic Version of Lamentations. LC 76-276212. 203p. 1981. pap. 14.75 (ISBN 0-87203-065-2). Hermon.

--The Aramaic Version of Qohelet. new ed. 1979. pap. 14.75 (ISBN 0-87203-087-3). Hermon.

Littlefield, Mark G., ed. Biblia Romanceada I.I.8: The Thirteenth-Century Spanish Bible Contained in Escorial MS. I. I. 8. (Dialect Ser.: No. 4). (Illus.). xiv, 334p. 1983. inc. 10 microfiches 35.00x (ISBN 0-942260-34-1). Hispanic Seminary.

The Lost Books of the Bible & the Forgotten Books of Eden. 562p. 9.95 (ISBN 0-529-03385-2); pap. 7.95 (ISBN 0-529-02061-0). World Bible.

Lowden, John. Illuminated Prophet Books: A Study of Byzantine Manuscripts of the Major & Minor Prophets. LC 86-43164. 250p. 1987. 49.75x (ISBN 0-271-00604-8). Pa St U Pr.

McCarter, P. Kyle, Jr. Textual Criticism: Recovering the Text of the Hebrew Bible. LC 86-4388. (Guides to Biblical Scholarship, Old Testament Ser.). 96p. 1986. pap. 4.95 (ISBN 0-8006-0471-7, 1-471). Fortress.

McComb, S. The Making of the English Bible. 59.95 (ISBN 0-8490-0578-7). Gordon Pr.

McKibben-Stockwell. Nuevo Lexico Griego Espanol. (Span.). 316p. 1985. pap. 6.95 (ISBN 0-311-42072-9, Edit Mundo). Casa Bautista.

Mansoor, Menahem. Key to Biblical Hebrew Step by Step, No. 1. pap. 7.95 (ISBN 0-8010-6100-8). Baker Bk.

Marshall, Alfred. The NASB Interlinear Greek-English New Testament. 1056p. 1984. text ed. 27.95 (ISBN 0-310-45240-6, 12394). Zondervan.

Metzger, Bruce. The Early Versions of the New Testament. 1977. 24.95x (ISBN 0-19-826170-5). Oxford U Pr.

Mille, Carol E. Which Translation Do You Prefer. 1975. pap. 1.00 (ISBN 0-915374-52-8, 52-8). Rapids Christian.

Neusner, Jacob. In Search of Talmudic Biography: The Problem of the Attributed Saying. LC 84-10526. (Brown Judaic Studies). 148p. 1984. 19.95 (ISBN 0-89130-752-4, 14 00 70); pap. 14.95 (ISBN 0-89130-758-3). Scholars Pr GA.

Newman, B. M. & Nida, E. A. Translator's Handbook on the Gospel of John. LC 81-452133. (Helps for Translators Ser.). 681p. 1980. 7.00x (ISBN 0-8267-0137-X, 08620, Pub. by United Bible). Am Bible.

Nida, Eugene A. Comment Traduire la Bible. Margot, J. C., tr. 279p. 1967. pap. 4.05x (ISBN 0-8267-0024-1, 51970, Pub. by United Bible). Am Bible.

Nida, Eugene A. & Reyburn, William D. Meaning Across Cultures: A Study on Bible Translating. LC 81-38374. 96p. (Orig.). 1981. pap. 2.98 (ISBN 0-88344-326-0). Orbis Bks.

El Nuevo Testamento. (Span.). 1970. pap. 2.00 (ISBN 0-8198-2301-5). Dghtrs St Paul.

O'Connell, Kevin G. The Theodotionic Revision of the Book of Exodus. LC 70-160026. (Semitic Monographs Ser: No. 3). 509p. 1972. 20.00x (ISBN 0-674-87785-3). Harvard U Pr.

Orlinsky, Harry M. Essays in Biblical & Jewish Culture & Bible Translation. 1973. 25.00x (ISBN 0-87068-218-0). Ktav.

Peacock, Heber F. A Translator's Guide to Selected Psalms. (Helps for Translators Ser.). 154p. 1981. pap. 3.30x (ISBN 0-8267-0299-6, 08737, Pub. by United Bible). Am Bible.

--A Translator's Guide to Selections from the First Five Books of the Old Testament. (Helps for Translators Ser.). 323p. 1982. pap. 4.30x (ISBN 0-8267-0298-8, 08765, Pub. by United Bible). Am Bible.

Powers, Ward. Learn to Read the Greek New Testament. 336p. 1982. 19.95 (ISBN 0-8028-3578-3). Eerdmans.

Robertson, A. T. & Davis, W. Hersey. New Short Grammar of the Greek New Testament. 10th ed. 1977. pap. 12.95 (ISBN 0-8010-7656-0). Baker Bk.

Sanders, Henry A. New Testament Manuscripts in the Freer Collection. Repr. of 1918 ed. 37.00 (ISBN 0-384-38809-4). Johnson Repr.

--Old Testament Manuscripts in the Freer Collection. Repr. of 1917 ed. 37.00 (ISBN 0-384-38808-6). Johnson Repr.

Santa Biblia: Edicion Bilingue Espanol-Ingles. 1812p. bonded leather 39.95 (ISBN 0-311-48748-3). Casa Bautista.

Shenkel, James D. Chronology & Recensional Development in the Greek Text of Kings. LC 68-21983. (Semitic Monographs: No. 1). (Illus.). 1968. text ed. 10.00x (ISBN 0-674-13050-2). Harvard U Pr.

Smith, Richard H. A Concise Coptic-English Lexicon. 81p. 1983. 10.95x (ISBN 0-8028-3581-3). Eerdmans.

Stokes, Mack B. The Bible in the Wesleyan Heritage. LC 80-23636. 96p. (Orig.). 1981. pap. 4.95 (ISBN 0-687-03100-1). Abingdon.

Stulman, Louis. The Other Text of Jeremiah: A Reconstruction of the Hebrew Text Underlying the Greek Version of the Prose Sections of Jeremiah with English Translation. LC 85-20278. 178p. (Orig.). 1986. lib. bdg. 25.75 (ISBN 0-8191-4988-8); pap. text ed. 12.75 (ISBN 0-8191-4989-6). U Pr of Amer.

Szirmai, Julia C. La Bible Anonyme du Ms. Paris B. N. F. Fr, No. 763. (Faux Titre Ser.: No. 22). 402p. 1985. pap. text ed. 55.00x (ISBN 90-6203-927-8, Pub. by Rodopi Holland). Humanities.

Taber, Charles R. & Nida, Eugene A. La Traduction: Theorie et Methode. 1971. pap. 3.30x (ISBN 0-8267-0022-5, 51971, Pub. by United Bible). Am Bible.

Thayer, Joseph H., tr. A Greek-English Lexicon of the New Testament. (Reference Set). Orig. Title: Grimm's Wilkes Clavis Novi Testamonti. 726p. 1982. Repr. of 1977 ed. 22.95 (ISBN 0-915134-73-X). Mott Media.

Theological Faculty, University of Navarre, ed. The Navarre Bible: St. Mark. 202p. 1986. 10.00 (ISBN 0-906127-92-0). Lumen Christi.

Tov, Emanual. The Book of Baruch: A Discussion of an Early Revision of the IXX of Jeremiah 29-52 & Baruch 1: 1-3: 8. LC 75-43872. (Harvard Semitic Monographs). 1976. pap. 9.75 (ISBN 0-89130-070-8, 06-02-08). Scholars Pr GA.

Trafton, Joseph L. The Syriac Version of the Psalms of Solomon. (SBL Septuagint & Cognate Studies). 1985. 22.95 (ISBN 0-89130-910-1, 06-04-11); pap. 15.95 (ISBN 0-89130-911-X). Scholars Pr GA.

Tucker, Gene M. & Knight, Douglas A. The Hebrew Bible & Its Modern Interpreters. LC 83-49216. (SBL-The Bible & Its Modern Interpreters Ser.). 1985. 22.50 (ISBN 0-89130-671-4, 06 14 01); pap. 14.95 (ISBN 0-89130-784-2). Scholars Pr GA.

Two New Scriptures. pap. 1.00 (ISBN 0-89036-079-0). Hawkes Pub Inc.

UBS Committee, ed. Preliminary & Interim Report on the Hebrew Old Testament Text Project, Vols. 1-5. Incl. Vol. 1. (Pentateuch). xxxiii, 317p. 1973. pap. 4.00x (ISBN 0-8267-0008-X, 08520); Vol. 2. (Historical Bks.). xxxiv, 556p. 1976. pap. 6.60x (ISBN 0-8267-0009-8, 08521); Vol. 3. (Poetical Books). xxxiii, 620p. 1977. pap. 7.00x (ISBN 0-8267-0010-1, 08522); Vol. 4. (Prophetical Books: No. 1). xxxiii, 335p. 1979. pap. 4.50x (ISBN 0-8267-0011-X, 08523); (Prophetical Books: No. 2). xxxiii, 443p. 1980. pap. 5.00x (ISBN 0-8267-0012-8, 08559). (Eng. & Fr., Pub. by United Bible). Am Bible.

--Preliminary & Interim Report on the Hebrew Old Testament Text Project, Vol. 2. (Historical Bks.). (Eng. & Fr.). xxiv, 556p. 1976. pap. 6.60x (ISBN 0-8267-0009-8, 08521, Pub. by United Bible). Am Bible.

--Preliminary & Interim Report on the Hebrew Old Testament Text Project, Vol. 3. (Poetical Books). (Eng. & Fr.). xxxiii, 620p. 1977. pap. 7.00x (ISBN 0-8267-0010-1, 08522, Pub. by United Bible). Am Bible.

Weingreen, Jacob. An Introduction to the Critical Study of the Text of the Hebrew Bible. 1982. 8.95x (ISBN 0-19-815453-4). Oxford U Pr.

Wellington, Paul A., ed. Joseph Smith's New Translation of the Bible. LC 74-127097. 1970. 16.00 (ISBN 0-8309-0032-2). Herald Hse.

Woods, Guy N. How to Read the Greek New Testament. 5.00 (ISBN 0-89225-103-4). Gospel Advocate.

Worrell, William H. The Coptic Manuscripts in the Freer Collection. Repr. of 1923 ed. 37.00 (ISBN 0-384-38810-8). Johnson Repr.

Wright, C. D. Translations of the Gospel Back into Tongues. LC 82-17047. (SUNY Poetry Ser.). 84p. 1982. 24.50x (ISBN 0-87395-652-4) (ISBN 0-87395-685-0). State U NY Pr.

Wuest, Kenneth S., tr. The New Testament: An Expanded Translation. 1961. 14.95 (ISBN 0-8028-3306-3); pap. 9.95 (ISBN 0-8028-1229-5). Eerdmans.

Yaeger, Randolph. Renaissance New Testament, Vol. 14. 660p. 1983. 22.50 (ISBN 0-88289-859-0). Pelican.

Zandstra, Sidney. Witness of "The Vulgate," "Peshitta" & "Septuagint" to the Text of "Zephaniah". LC 72-948. (Columbia University. Contributions to Oriental History & Philology Ser.: No. 4). Repr. of 1909 ed. 12.50 (ISBN 0-404-50534-1). AMS Pr.

Zimmerman, Frank. Biblical Books Translated from Arabic. 1974. 25.00x (ISBN 0-87068-252-0). Ktav.

Zlotowitz, Bernard M. The Septuagint Translation of the Hebrew Terms in Relation to God in the Book of Jeremiah. 1981. 25.00x (ISBN 0-87068-704-2). Ktav.

Zohrapian, Hovhann, ed. Astuatsashunch Matean Hin ew Nor Ktakarants. LC 84-14281. (Classical Armenian Texts Ser.). (Armenian.). 912p. 1985. Repr. of 1805 ed. 150.00 (ISBN 0-88206-054-6). Caravan Bks.

Zuntz, G. The Ancestry of the Harklean New Testament. 1965. pap. 2.25 (ISBN 0-85672-677-X, Pub. by British Acad). Longwood Pub Group.

BIBLE–VERSIONS–THEORY, METHODS, ETC.

see Bible–Translating

BIBLE–VERSIONS, ENGLISH

Adomeit, Ruth. Three Centuries of Thumb Bibles. LC 78-68238. (Garland Reference Library of Humanities). (Illus.). 435p. 1980. 73.00 (ISBN 0-8240-9818-8). Garland Pub.

Barker, Kenneth, ed. The NIV: The Making of a Contemporary Translation. 240p. 1986. pap. 8.95 (ISBN 0-310-24181-2). Zondervan.

Barry, Lloyd E., intro. by. Geneva Bible: A Facsimile of the Fifteen-Sixty Edition. 1274p. 1969. 95.00x (ISBN 0-299-05251-6). U of Wis Pr.

Beale, David. A Pictorial History of Our English Bible. (Illus.). 79p. (Orig.). 1982. pap. 2.95 (ISBN 0-89084-149-7). Bob Jones Univ Pr.

The Book of Job: A New Translation According to the Traditional Hebrew Text. LC 79-25323. 88p. 1980. 7.50 (ISBN 0-8276-0172-7, 447). Jewish Pubns.

Brown, John. The History of the English Bible. LC 77-13187. 1977. Repr. lib. bdg. 15.00 (ISBN 0-8414-9929-2). Folcroft.

Byington, Steven T., tr. The Bible in Living English: Written by an Anarchist. (Men & Movements in the History & Philosophy of Anarchism Ser.). 1979. lib. bdg. 59.95 (ISBN 0-686-59576-9). Revisionist Pr.

Cartwright, Thomas. A Confutation of the Rhemists Translation, Glosses & Annotations on the New Testament. LC 71-171737. (English Experience Ser.: No. 364). 830p. 1971. Repr. of 1618 ed. 114.00 (ISBN 90-221-0364-1). Walter J Johnson.

Charles, R. H., ed. The Book of Jubilees: The Little Genesis. 1984. Repr. of 1902 ed. 39.00x (ISBN 0-403-08996-4, Regency). Scholarly.

Charles, R. H., intro. by. The Apoclypse of Baruch. 1976. Repr. of 1896 ed. 39.00x (ISBN 0-685-71069-6, Regency). Scholarly.

Coverdale, Myles. Remains of Myles Coverdale, Bishop of Exeter. 1846. 51.00 (ISBN 0-384-09950-5). Johnson Repr.

Daiches, David. The King James Version of the English Bible. LC 68-16338. vii, 228p. 1968. Repr. of 1941 ed. 21.50 (ISBN 0-208-00493-9, Archon). Shoe String.

Duthie, Alan S. Bible Translations & How to Choose Between Them. 127p. 1986. pap. 10.95 (ISBN 0-85364-400-4, Pub. by Paternoster UK). Attic Pr.

Fowler, Everett W. Evaluating Versions of the New Testament. LC 80-81607. (Illus.). 80p. (Orig.). 1981. pap. 2.95 (ISBN 0-937136-03-4). Maranatha Baptist.

Fulke, William. Defence of the Sincere & True Translations of the Holy Scriptures into the English Tongue. Repr. of 1843 ed. 51.00 (ISBN 0-384-17230-X). Johnson Repr.

Gasquet, Francis C. Old English Bible & Other Essays. LC 68-26209. 1969. Repr. of 1897 ed. 28.50x (ISBN 0-8046-0166-6, Pub. by Kennikat). Assoc Faculty Pr.

Hammond, Gerald. The Making of the English Bible. LC 83-13264. 249p. 1983. 19.95 (ISBN 0-8022-2419-9). Philos Lib.

Herbert, A. S., ed. Historical Catalogue of Printed Editions of the English Bible 1525-1961. rev. ed. 1968. 12.75 (ISBN 0-564-00130-9, 17066, Pub. by United Bible). Am Bible.

Hills, M. T. & Eisenhart, E. J., eds. Concise History of the English Bible. 7th ed. 1983. pap. 3.50x (ISBN 0-8267-0326-7, 16228, Pub. by United Bible). Am Bible.

Hunt, G. N. About the New English Bible. 1970. 1.25 (ISBN 0-521-07938-1). Cambridge U Pr.

Jordan, Clarence. Cotton Patch Version of Hebrews & the General Epistles. LC 73-14856. (Cotton Patch Translations of the Bible Ser.). 1973. pap. 4.95 (ISBN 0-8329-1879-2, Assn Pr). New Century.

Kauffman, Nancy J. & Kauffman, Elizabeth J. Heavy Bread. LC 73-75087. (Pivot Family Reader Ser). 192p. (Orig.). 1973. pap. 1.25 (ISBN 0-87983-030-1). Keats.

King James-Simple English Parallel: New Testament. 19.00 (ISBN 0-89957-571-4). AMG Pubs.

Kleps, Arthur J. Boo Hoo Bible: The Neo-American Church Catechism & Handbook. rev. ed. LC 73-29356. Orig. Title: Neo-American Church Catechism. (Illus.). 218p. 1971. pap. 5.00 (ISBN 0-9600388-1-7). Neo-Am Church.

Kohlenberger, John R., III. Words about the Word: A Guide to Choosing & Using Your Bible. 176p. 1986. pap. 9.95 (ISBN 0-310-39361-2, 6287P). Zondervan.

Lewis, C. S. Literary Impact of the Authorized Version. Reumann, John, ed. LC 63-17883. (Facet Bks). 48p. (Orig.). 1963. pap. 2.50 (ISBN 0-8006-3003-3, 1-3003). Fortress.

Lindberg, Conrad. The Middle English Bible: Prefatory Epistles of St. Jerome. 172p. 1978. text ed. 19.50x. Oxford U Pr.

--The Middle English Bible: The Book of Baruch. 174p. 1986. 45.00 (ISBN 82-00-06057-8); pap. 23.00x. Oxford U Pr.

McComb, S. The Making of the English Bible. 59.95 (ISBN 0-8490-0578-7). Gordon Pr.

MacGregor, Geddes. The Bible in the Making. LC 82-17499. 318p. 1983. pap. 14.50 (ISBN 0-8191-2810-4). U Pr of Amer.

Metzger, Bruce. The Early Versions of the New Testament. 1977. 24.95x (ISBN 0-19-826170-5). Oxford U Pr.

Newton, A. Edward. Greatest Book in the World & Other Papers. LC 78-86572. (Essay & General Literature Index Reprint Ser). (Illus.). 1969. Repr. 31.50x (ISBN 0-8046-0579-3, Pub. by Kennikat). Assoc Faculty Pr.

Opfell, Olga S. The King James Bible Translators. LC 81-20885. (Illus.). 179p. 1982. lib. bdg. 18.95x (ISBN 0-89950-041-2). McFarland & Co.

Pattison, T. Harwood. The History of the English Bible. 1894. 20.00 (ISBN 0-8274-2521-X). R West.

Phillips, J. B. The New Testament in Modern English. 1973. 8.95 (ISBN 0-02-088490-7). Macmillan.

Schodde, George H., intro. by. The Book of Enoch Translated from the Ethiopic. 1982. Repr. of 1882 ed. 39.00x (ISBN 0-403-08997-2, Regency). Scholarly.

Segraves, Daniel. The Search For the Word of God: A Defense of King James Version. Wallace, Mary, ed. 328p. (Orig.). 1984. pap. 7.95 (ISBN 0-912315-70-9). Word Aflame.

Segraves, Daniel L. The Search for the Word of God: A Defense of the King James Versions. 1982. pap. 6.00x (ISBN 0-912315-70-9). Freedom Univ-FSP.

Stanton, Elizabeth C. The Woman's Bible. 1974. Repr. 12.95 (ISBN 0-9603042-1-5). Coalition Women-Relig.

Tyndale, William. Five Books of Moses Called the Pentateuch. LC 67-23739. (Centaur Classics Ser.). 791p. 1967. 32.50x (ISBN 0-8093-0259-4). S Ill U Pr.

Underwood, Jonathan. A History of the English Bible. LC 83-577. 96p. 1983. pap. 3.50 (ISBN 0-87239-644-4, 39974). Standard Pub.

Vernon, Louise A. The King's Book. LC 80-18998. (Illus.). 128p. 1980. pap. 4.50 (ISBN 0-8361-1933-9). Herald Pr.

Wigram, George V. Englishman's Greek Concordance of the New Testament. 1984. 29.95 (ISBN 0-8010-3416-7). Baker Bk.

Wilson, David A. Apocalypse! (Illus.). 175p. (Orig.). 1973. pap. 8.00 (ISBN 0-934852-10-3). Lorien Hse.

Winship, George P. Cambridge Press, Sixteen Thirty-Eight to Sixteen Ninety-Two. facs. ed. LC 68-57346. (Essay Index Reprint Ser). 1945. 22.50 (ISBN 0-8369-1004-4). Ayer Co Pubs.

Worrell, A. S. The Worrell New Testament. 1980. Repr. of 1904 ed. 11.95 (ISBN 0-88243-392-X, 01-0392). Gospel Pub.

BIBLE–WOMEN

see Women in the Bible

BIBLE–ZOOLOGY

see Bible–Natural History

BIBLE AND ASTROLOGY

Custer, Stewart. The Stars Speak: Astronomy in the Bible. (Illus.). 203p. (Orig.). 1977. pap. 6.95 (ISBN 0-89084-059-8). Bob Jones Univ Pr.

Dobin, Joel C. The Astrological Secrets of the Hebrew Sages: To Rule Both Day & Night. LC 77-8288. 256p. 1983. pap. 9.95 (ISBN 0-89281-052-1). Inner Tradit.

BIBLE AND FEMINISM

Tolbert, Mary A., ed. The Bible & Feminist Hermeneutics. (Semeia Ser.: No. 28). 9.95 (06 20 28). Scholars Pr GA.

BIBLE AND LAW

Johnson, James T., ed. The Bible & American Law, Politics, & Political Rhetoric. LC 83-16327. (Bible in American Culture Ser.: No. 4). 216p. 1985. 14.95 (ISBN 0-8006-0614-0, 1-614). Fortress.

BIBLE AND POLITICAL SCIENCE

see Bible–Political Science

BIBLE AND SCIENCE

see also Creation; Modernist-Fundamentalist Controversy; Nature–Religious Interpretations

Brams, Steven J. Biblical Games: A Strategic Analysis of Stories in the Old Testament. 1980. text ed. 22.00x (ISBN 0-262-02144-7); pap. 7.95 (ISBN 0-262-52074-5). MIT Pr.

Bucaille, Maurice. The Bible, the Quran & Science. Beg, Anwer, ed. Bucaille, Maurice & Pannell, Alastair D., trs. from Fr. LC 77-90336. 253p. 1978. 11.95 (ISBN 0-89259-010-6); pap. 8.50. Am Trust Pubns.

Cantonwine, Charles R. Science, Religion & Tradition. 1986. 7.95 (ISBN 0-533-06727-8). Vantage.

Carman, George. Science Proves the Bible. De Witt, Mason, ed. 190p. 1986. 12.00 (ISBN 0-936749-00-8). Zytech Western Pub.

Clark, Harold W. Fossils, Flood & Fire. (Illus.). 1968. 8.95 (ISBN 0-911080-16-3). Outdoor Pict.

Commission For Christian Literature, ed. Is Evolutionism the Answer. (Truth Unchanging Series). (Illus.). 1968. pap. 2.50 (ISBN 0-8100-0023-7, 12-0331). Northwest Pub.

Crouch, W. W. Science & the Bible in a Troubled World. LC 84-90294. 102p. 1985. 8.95 (ISBN 0-533-06326-4). Vantage.

Glick, Thomas, compiled by. Darwinism in Texas. LC 72-185614. (Illus.). 38p. 1972. 7.00 (ISBN 0-87959-032-7). U of Tex H Ransom Ctr.

Heinze, Thomas F. Creation vs. Evolution Handbook. (Direction Books). 1973. pap. 3.50 (ISBN 0-8010-4002-7). Baker Bk.

Katter, Reuben L. History of Creation & Origin of the Species: A Scientific Theological Viewpoint (How the Universe Came into Being) 3rd ed. 480p. 1984. 16.95 (ISBN 0-911806-01-6, C13374); pap. 11.95 (ISBN 0-911806-00-8). Theotes.

Lindsay, Gordon. The Bible Is a Scientific Book. 1.50 (ISBN 0-89985-117-7). Christ Nations.

Morris, Henry M. The Biblical Basis of Modern Science. 1984. 24.95 (ISBN 0-8010-6178-4). Baker Bk.

--Evolution & the Modern Christian. 1967. pap. 2.95 (ISBN 0-87552-337-4). Presby & Reformed.

--Science & the Bible. rev., expanded ed. 1986. pap. 5.95 (ISBN 0-8024-0656-4). Moody.

Morris, Henry M. & Clark, Martin. The Bible Has the Answer. LC 76-20206. 1976. pap. 9.95 (ISBN 0-89051-018-0). Master Bks.

Nelkin, Dorothy. The Creation Controversy: Science or Scripture in the Schools? LC 83-45954. 242p. 1984. pap. 9.95x (ISBN 0-8070-3155-0, BP 675). Beacon Pr.

Nelson, Byron C. Deluge Story in Stone. (Illus.). 1968. Repr. of 1931 ed. 5.95 (ISBN 0-87123-095-X, 210095). Bethany Hse.

Ramm, Bernard. Christian View of Science & Scripture. 1954. pap. 4.95 (ISBN 0-8028-1429-8). Eerdmans.

Ray, John. Three Physico-Theological Discourses: Primitive Chaos, & Creation of the World, the General Deluge, Its Causes & Effects. Albritton, Claude C., Jr., ed. LC 77-6538. (History of Geology Ser.). 1978. Repr. of 1713 ed. lib. bdg. 34.50x (ISBN 0-405-10457-X). Ayer Co Pubs.

Read, John. Humour & Humanism in Chemistry. LC 79-8621. Repr. of 1947 ed. 42.50 (ISBN 0-404-18487-1). AMS Pr.

Rehwinkel, Alfred M. Flood. 2nd ed. (Orig.). (YA) 1951-1957. pap. 9.95 (ISBN 0-570-03183-4, 12-2103). Concordia.

Reid, James. Dios, el Atomo, y el Universo. Orozco, Julio, tr. from Eng. LC 76-55491. Tr. of God, the Atom & the Universe. (Span.). 240p. (Orig.). 1977. pap. 5.95 (ISBN 0-89922-083-5). Edit Caribe.

Schmeling, William A. Creation Versus Evolution--Not Really. 2nd ed. LC 76-19997. (Illus.). 1977. pap. text ed. 5.25 (ISBN 0-915644-12-6). Clayton Pub Hse.

Thomas, J. D. Evolution & Antiquity. 2nd ed. (Way of Life Ser: No. 120). Orig. Title: Doctrine of Evolution & the Antiquity of Man. (Orig.). 1959. pap. 3.95 (ISBN 0-89112-120-X, Bibl Res Pr). Abilene Christ U.

Walker, Paul L. Understanding the Bible & Science. LC 75-25343. (Illus.). 1976. pap. 1.99 (ISBN 0-87148-878-7). Pathway Pr.

Wheeler, Gerald W. Deluge. LC 78-8404. (Flame Ser.). 1978. pap. 0.99 (ISBN 0-8127-0191-7). Review & Herald.

Whiston, William. A New Theory of the Earth: Its Original, to the Consummation of All Things Wherein the Creation of the World in Six Days. Albritton, Claude C., Jr., ed. LC 77-6545. (History of Geology Ser.). 1978. lib. bdg. 37.50x (ISBN 0-405-10463-4). Ayer Co Pubs.

BIBLE AND SPIRITUALISM

Cox, Michael. Handbook of Christian Spirituality: The Major Figures & Teachings from the New Testament to the 20th Century. LC 84-48236. 288p. 1985. 14.45 (ISBN 0-06-061601-6, HarpR). Har-Row.

Prince, Derek. Philosophy, the Bible & the Supernatural. 1969. pap. 0.10 (ISBN 0-934920-22-2, B71). Derek Prince.

Wallis, E. W. Spiritualism in the Bible. 59.95 (ISBN 0-8490-1116-7). Gordon Pr.

BIBLE AS LITERATURE

see also Bible–Criticism, Interpretation, etc.; Bible–Parables; Religious Literature

Aune, David E. The New Testament in Its Literary Environment. Meeks, Wayne A., ed. (Library of Early Christianity: Vol. 8). 262p. 1987. 22.95 (ISBN 0-664-21912-8). Westminster.

Berlin, Adele. Poetics & Interpretation of Biblical Narrative. (Bible & Literature Ser.: No. 9). 180p. 1983. text ed. 22.95x (ISBN 0-907459-23-4, Pub. by Almond Pr England); pap. text ed. 10.95x (ISBN 0-907459-24-2). Eisenbrauns.

Bulthaupt, Fritz. Milstater Genesis und Exodus: Eine Grammatisch-Stillistische Ist Untersuchung. (Ger). 21.00 (ISBN 0-384-06341-1); pap. 16.00 (ISBN 0-685-02228-5). Johnson Repr.

Chase, Mary E. Bible & the Common Reader. rev. ed. 1962. pap. 4.95 (ISBN 0-02-084390-9, Collier). Macmillan.

Cook, Albert S. The Bible & English Prose Style. LC 72-192049. Repr. of 1892 ed. lib. bdg. 8.50 (ISBN 0-8414-1134-4). Folcroft.

Curry, S. S. Vocal & Literary Interpretation of the Bible. 1909. 32.50 (ISBN 0-8274-3677-7). R West.

Dinsmore, Charles A. The English Bible as Literature. 1931. Repr. 30.00 (ISBN 0-8274-3832-X). R West.

Edge, Henry T. Esoteric Keys to the Christian Scriptures. rev. 2nd ed. Small, W. Emmett & Todd, Helen, eds. Bd. with The Universal Mystery-Language of Myth & Symbol. Orig. Title: The Universal Mystery-Language & Its Interpretations. Orig. Title: Theosophical Light on the Christian Bible. 1973. pap. 3.00 (ISBN 0-913004-12-X, 913004-12). Point Loma Pub.

Exum, J. Cheryl, ed. Tragedy & Comedy in the Bible. (Semeia Ser.: No. 32). pap. 9.95 (06 20 32). Scholars Pr GA.

Farrar, Austin. Rebirth of Images: The Making of St. John's Apocalypse. 13.25 (ISBN 0-8446-0617-0). Peter Smith.

Frye, Northrop. The Great Code: The Bible in Literature. LC 81-47303. 261p. 1983. pap. 5.95 (ISBN 0-15-636480-8, Harv). HarBraceJ.

Fullington, James F., ed. The Bible: Prose & Poetry from the Old Testament. LC 50-9988. (Crofts Classics Ser.). 1950. pap. text ed. 4.95x (ISBN 0-88295-013-4). Harlan Davidson.

Gabel, John B. & Wheeler, Charles. The Bible As Literature: An Introduction. 320p. 1986. 24.50x (ISBN 0-19-503993-9); pap. 9.95x (ISBN 0-19-503994-7). Oxford U Pr.

Gardner, Helen. Limits of Literary Criticism. LC 74-16242. 1956. lib. bdg. 8.00 (ISBN 0-8414-4558-3). Folcroft.

Geller, Stephen A., et al. A Sense of Text: The Art of Language in the Study of Biblical Literature. 113p. 1983. pap. text ed. 12.50 (ISBN 0-9602686-1-8). Dropsie Coll.

Gottcent, John H. The Bible: A Literary Study. 120p. 1986. 10.50 (ISBN 0-8057-7951-5, Twayne); pap. 5.95 (ISBN 0-8057-8003-3). G K Hall.

--The Bible As Literature: A Selective Bibliography. 1979. lib. bdg. 26.00 (ISBN 0-8161-8121-7, Hall Reference). G K Hall.

Greenstein, Edward L. & Preminger, Alex, eds. Hebrew Bible in Literary Criticism. (Library of Literary Criticism). 635p. 1986. 65.00x (ISBN 0-8044-3266-X). Ungar.

Gunn, D. M. The Story of King David: Genre & Interpretation. (Journal for the Study of the Old Testament Supplement Ser.: No. 6). 164p. 1978. (Pub. by JSOT Pr England); pap. text ed. 16.95x (ISBN 0-905774-05-1, Pub. by JSOT Pr England). Eisenbrauns.

Hallam, Arthur F. Concurrences Between Dio Chrysostom's First Discourse & the New Testament. 91p. (Orig.). 1985. pap. 9.95 (ISBN 0-938770-04-7). Capitalist Pr OH.

Johnson, Luke T. The Writings of the New Testament: An Interpretation. LC 85-16202. 640p. 1986. 34.95 (ISBN 0-8006-0886-0, 1-886); pap. 18.95 (ISBN 0-8006-1886-6, 1-1886). Fortress.

Lewis, C. S. Literary Impact of the Authorized Version. Reumann, John, ed. LC 63-17883. (Facet Bks). 48p. (Orig.). 1963. pap. 2.50 (ISBN 0-8006-3003-3, 1-3003). Fortress.

McConnell, Frank, ed. The Bible & Narrative Tradition. 168p. 1986. 16.95x (ISBN 0-19-503698-0). Oxford U Pr.

McKnight, Edgar V. The Bible & the Reader: An Introduction to Literary Criticism. LC 85-4603. 176p. 1985. pap. 8.95 (ISBN 0-8006-1872-6). Fortress.

McNamara, Martin. Intertestamental Literature. (Old Testament Message Ser.: Vol. 23). 16.95 (ISBN 0-89453-423-8); pap. 12.95 (ISBN 0-89453-256-1). M Glazier.

Mensendiek, Mark. Grace to You. 20p. (Orig.). 1985. pap. 0.75 (ISBN 0-933643-22-5). Grace World Outreach.

Miller, Donald E. The Gospel & Mother Goose. 112p. (Orig.). 1987. pap. 6.95 (ISBN 0-87178-320-7). Brethren.

Moffatt, James. An Introduction to the Literature of the New Testament. 630p. 1983. Repr. of 1911 ed. lib. bdg. 75.00 (ISBN 0-89984-820-6). Century Bookbindery.

Moulton, R. G. The Literary Study of the Bible. 34.95 (ISBN 0-8490-0544-2). Gordon Pr.

Moulton, Richard G. The Literary Study of the Bible. LC 70-4534. 1898. 59.00x (ISBN 0-403-00113-7). Scholarly.

--A Short Introduction to the Literature of the Bible. 1901. 25.00 (ISBN 0-8274-3404-9). R West.

Moulton, Richard G. & Bruce, A. B. The Bible As Literature. LC 78-1666. Repr. of 1899 ed. lib. bdg. 47.50 (ISBN 0-8414-6242-9). Folcroft.

Mouw, Richard J. Politics & the Biblical Drama. 1983. pap. 5.95 (ISBN 0-8010-6153-9). Baker Bk.

Prickett, Stephen. Words & the Word: Language Poetics, & Biblical Interpretation. 288p. 1986. 39.50 (ISBN 0-521-32248-0). Cambridge U Pr.

Purinton, Herbert R. Literature of the Old Testament. 1926. 20.00 (ISBN 0-8274-2966-5). R West.

Ryken, Leland. How to Read the Bible As Literature. 200p. (Orig.). 1985. pap. text ed. 7.95 (ISBN 0-310-39021-4, 11158P). Zondervan.

Ryken, Leland, ed. The New Testament in Literary Criticism. (A Library of Literary Criticism). 450p. 1985. 45.00 (ISBN 0-8044-3271-6). Ungar.

Sands, P. C. Literary Genius of the New Testament. 1932. 20.00 (ISBN 0-8274-2953-3). R West.

Sands, Percy C. Literary Genius of the New Testament. Repr. of 1932 ed. lib. bdg. 22.50x (ISBN 0-8371-4328-4, SANT). Greenwood.

Stein, Robert H. Difficult Sayings in the Gospels: Jesus's Use of Overstatement & Hyperbole. 96p. pap. 4.95 (ISBN 0-8010-8262-5). Baker Bk.

Sternberg, Meir. Poetics of Biblical Narrative. (Literary Biblical Ser.). 380p. cancelled (ISBN 0-8245-0640-5). Crossroad NY.

Stoddart, Janet T. The New Testament in Life & Literature. 1973. 40.00 (ISBN 0-8274-0860-9). R West.

Stott, John R. Bible Book for Today. Chan, Silas, tr. (Chinese.). 1985. pap. write for info. (ISBN 0-941598-23-3). Living Spring Pubns.

Tigay, Jeffrey H. Empirical Models for Biblical Criticism. LC 84-20951. 304p. 1985. 37.50 (ISBN 0-8122-7976-X). U of Pa Pr.

Trail, W. The Literary Characteristics & Achievements of the Bible. 335p. 1983. Repr. of 1863 ed. lib. bdg. 85.00 (ISBN 0-89984-471-5). Century Bookbindery.

Wallace, Robert Burns. An Introduction to the Bible As Literature. 1929. 20.00 (ISBN 0-8274-2583-X). R West.

Wild, Laura H. A Literary Guide to the Bible. LC 74-9861. 1976. lib. bdg. 35.00 (ISBN 0-8414-9533-5). Folcroft.

Wood, Irving. The Bible As Literature: An Introduction. LC 79-441. (Bible Study Textbook Series). 1979. Repr. of 1914 ed. lib. bdg. 42.50 (ISBN 0-8414-9712-5). Folcroft.

Wood, Irving F. The Bible as Literature. 346p. 1980. Repr. of 1914 ed. lib. bdg. 43.50 (ISBN 0-8482-7073-8). Norwood Edns.

Wood, Irving F. & Grant, E. The Bible As Literature. 1914. Repr. 4.00 (ISBN 0-8274-3802-8). R West.

BIBLE GAMES AND PUZZLES

see also Bible–Catechisms, Question-Books, etc.

Allen, Edith B. One Hundred Bible Games. (Paperback Program Ser). (YA) 1968. pap. 3.95 (ISBN 0-8010-0033-5). Baker Bk.

Bangley, Bernard K. Bible BASIC: Bible Games for Personal Computers. LC 83-48461. 128p. (Orig.). 1983. pap. 9.95 (ISBN 0-06-250042-2, CN 4092, HarpR). Har-Row.

Becker, Joyce. Bible Crafts. LC 82-80820. (Illus.). 128p. 1982. 12.95 (ISBN 0-8234-0467-6); pap. 6.95 (ISBN 0-8234-0469-2). Holiday.

Beegle, Shirley. Bible Quizzes. 1985. pap. 0.69 pocket size (ISBN 0-87239-823-4, 2813). Standard Pub.

--Favorite Bible Verses. (Double Trouble Puzzles Ser.). (Illus.). 48p. 1987. pap. 2.50 (ISBN 0-87403-325-X, 2765). Standard Pub.

--Friends of God. (Double Trouble Puzzles Ser.). (Illus.). 48p. 1987. pap. 2.50 (ISBN 0-87403-328-4, 2768). Standard Pub.

--Friends of Jesus. (Double Trouble Puzzles Ser.). (Illus.). 48p. 1987. pap. 2.50 (ISBN 0-87403-327-6, 2767). Standard Pub.

--Life of Jesus. (Double Trouble Puzzles Ser.). (Illus.). 48p. 1987. pap. 2.50 (ISBN 0-87403-326-8, 2766). Standard Pub.

Bible Calculator Word Games. 1986. pap. 3.95 (ISBN 0-8010-7741-9). Baker Bk.

Bible Puzzler, No. 1. 1985. 2.95 (ISBN 0-89536-741-6, 5825). CSS of Ohio.

Borchardt, Lois M. Learning about God's Love: Word-Picture Activities for Children in Grades 1 & 2. 48p. 1986. pap. 2.95 (ISBN 0-570-04354-9). Concordia.

Cachiaras, D., et al. Twenty-Six Bible Programs for Preschoolers. (Illus.). 96p. 1986. wkbk. 8.95 (ISBN 0-87403-063-3, 3408). Standard Pub.

Calculator Word Games. 1986. pap. 3.95 (ISBN 0-8010-7742-7). Baker Bk.

Crain, Steve. Bible Fun Book, No. 7. (Activity Book Ser.). 32p. (Orig.). 1981. oversized saddle stitched .99 (ISBN 0-87123-766-0, 220766). Bethany Hse.

Crisci, Elizabeth. Ninety-Nine Fun Ideas for Teaching Bible Verses. (Illus.). 112p. 1985. pap. 3.95 (ISBN 0-87239-869-2, 3072). Standard Pub.

Daniel, Rebecca. Book VIII-More Parables. (Life of Jesus Ser.). 32p. (YA) 1984. wkbk. 3.95 (ISBN 0-86653-229-3). Good Apple.

Daniels, Rebecca. Book I-His Birth. (Life of Jesus Ser.). 32p. (YA) 1984. wkbk. 3.95 (ISBN 0-86653-213-7). Good Apple.

--Book II-His Boyhood. (Life of Jesus Ser.). 32p. (YA) 1984. wkbk. 3.95 (ISBN 0-86653-223-4). Good Apple.

--Book VI-His Miracles. (Life of Jesus Ser.). 32p. (YA) 1984. wkbk. 3.95 (ISBN 0-86653-227-7). Good Apple.

--Book VII-Parables. (Life of Jesus Ser.). 32p. (YA) 1984. wkbk. 3.95 (ISBN 0-86653-228-5). Good Apple.

--Book XI-His Last Hours. (Life of Jesus Ser.). 32p. (YA) 1984. wkbk. 3.95 (ISBN 0-86653-232-3). Good Apple.

--Book XII-His Resurection. (Life of Jesus Ser.). 32p. (YA) 1984. wkbk. 3.95 (ISBN 0-86653-233-1). Good Apple.

Davis, S. K. Bible Crossword Puzzle Book. (Quiz & Puzzle Bks). 1969. pap. 2.95 (ISBN 0-8010-2812-4). Baker Bk.

Dawson, George A. Scripture Scrambles. 48p. 1987. pap. 2.50 (ISBN 0-87403-235-0, 2685). Standard Pub.

Deffner, Wenonah S. Scripture Word Search. (Quiz & Puzzle Bks.). 1980. pap. 2.45 (ISBN 0-8010-2897-3). Baker Bk.

DeYoung, Gordon. Dial-a-Word from the Bible. (Quiz & Puzzle Bks.). 1977. pap. 0.95 (ISBN 0-8010-2862-0). Baker Bk.

Edwards, Rosemary W. Cut & Color Patterns for Young Children. rev. ed. (Illus.). 112p. 1985. pap. 4.95 (ISBN 0-912315-93-8). Word Aflame.

Falk, Cathy. Action Rhymes: Bible Learning Through Movement. 48p. 1985. pap. 2.50 (ISBN 0-87239-920-6, 3202). Standard Pub.

Filipi, Emily. One Hundred & One Word Puzzles on the Bible. LC 84-21445. 1985. pap. 2.95 (ISBN 0-8054-9110-4). Broadman.

--One Hundred Word Puzzles on the Bible. LC 81-68367. 1982. pap. 2.95 (ISBN 0-8054-9107-4). Broadman.

--Scripture Facts the Easy Way. (Quiz & Puzzle Books). 1980. pap. 1.95 (ISBN 0-8010-3491-4). Baker Bk.

Finley, Tom. Good Clean Fun: Fifty Nifty Bible Games for Junior Highers. 112p. 1986. pap. 8.95 (ISBN 0-310-31251-5, 18389). Zondervan.

Gasperson, David. Seek-the-Verses Bible Puzzles. 48p. 1986. pap. 2.50 (ISBN 0-87403-045-5, 2689). Standard Pub.

Gise, Wayne T. Biblical Personality Puzzlebook. LC 86-14720. (Orig.). 1987. pap. 2.95 (ISBN 0-8054-9112-0). Broadman.

--Searching for Answers. LC 85-14993. (Orig.). 1985. pap. 2.95 (ISBN 0-8054-9111-2). Broadman.

Gordon, William C. Bible Word Search. (Quiz & Puzzle Bks.). 112p. 1983. 2.95 (ISBN 0-8010-3679-8). Baker Bk.

Graham, Kathy. Hope for a Troubled Nation. (Bible Puzzle Time). (Illus.). 16p. (Orig.). 1982. pap. 0.60 (ISBN 0-87403-016-1, 2176). Standard Pub.

Griffhorn, Thelma. Things for Kids to Do. 132p. 1985. pap. 6.95 (ISBN 0-89693-525-6). Victor Bks.

Hall, Frederick. Bible Quizzes for Everybody. (Quiz & Puzzle Bks.). 150p. 1980. pap. 3.95 (ISBN 0-8010-4032-9). Baker Bk.

Hand, Phyllis. Breaking into Bible Games. (Helping Hand Ser.). 48p. (YA) 1984. wkbk. 4.95 (ISBN 0-317-43001-7). Good Apple.

Hartweg, Judy. Faithful Followers. (Helping Hand Ser.). 48p. 1984. wkbk. 4.95 (ISBN 0-86653-237-4). Good Apple.

Hendricks, William C. & Noord, Glenn Van. Bible Word Chain Puzzles. (Quiz & Puzzle Bks.). 96p. (Orig.). 1981. pap. 2.95 (ISBN 0-8010-4238-0). Baker Bk.

Honors, Mildred O. One Thousand Bible Questions in Rhymes, Puzzles, Quizzes & Games. (Quiz & Puzzle Bks.). pap. 2.95 (ISBN 0-8010-4136-8). Baker Bk.

Houck, Fannie L. Proverbs Puzzle. 48p. 1986. pap. 2.50 (ISBN 0-87403-048-X, 2692). Standard Pub.

Houmes, Lola H. Sword Drill Games Can Be Fun. 48p. pap. 2.95 (ISBN 0-87403-126-5, 2778). Standard Pub.

Kamiya, Artie & Kamiya, Elizabeth. Mobiles, Banners & Chariots. (Helping Hand Ser.). (Illus.). 48p. (YA) 1984. wkbk 4.95 (ISBN 0-86653-184-X). Good Apple.

Keeler, Ronald F. Bible Games & Activities. (Game & Party Bks.). Orig. Title: The Bible Game Book. 96p. 1982. pap. 2.95 (ISBN 0-8010-5436-2). Baker Bk.

King, U. R. Bible Mystery Word Puzzle. 64p. 1986. pap. text ed. 3.00 (ISBN 0-935545-02-6). Land & Land.

Korty, Margaret B. Bible Bits & Relevant Rhymes. LC 84-71870. 117p. 1984. spiral binding 5.95 (ISBN 0-9603060-1-3). Church Lib.

Leon, Judene. Bible Games for Teams & Groups. (Illus.). 64p. 1984. pap. 6.95 (ISBN 0-86683-832-5, HarpR). Har-Row.

Marks, Thomas J. Bible Study Puzzle Book. 1981. pap. 2.95 saddlewire (ISBN 0-8054-9106-6). Broadman.

--More Bible Study Puzzles. (Orig.). 1983. pap. 2.95 (ISBN 0-8054-9108-2). Broadman.

Maschke, Ruby. Children's Bible Stories Puzzle Book. 48p. 1986. pap. 2.50 (ISBN 0-87403-046-3, 2690). Standard Pub.

Pape, Donna L. & Mueller, Virginia. Bible Activities for Kids, No. 2. (Illus.). 60p. (Orig.). 1980. pap. 1.95 (ISBN 0-87123-149-2, 21049). Bethany Hse.

Pape, Donna L., et al. Bible Activities for Kids, No. 1. (Illus.). 64p. (Orig.). 1980. pap. 1.95 (ISBN 0-87123-148-4, 210148). Bethany Hse.

Pettigrew, Helen. Bible Word Quest. new ed. 96p. 1975. pap. 2.95 (ISBN 0-8010-6965-3). Baker Bk.

Phillips, Bob. In Search of Bible Trivia II. pap. 4.95 (ISBN 0-89081-464-3). Harvest Hse.

Reynolds, Erma. Bible Events Quiz Book. (Quiz & Puzzle Bks.). 96p. 1985. pap. 3.50 (ISBN 0-8010-7734-6). Baker Bk.

--Bible People Quiz Book. (Quiz & Puzzle Books). 1979. pap. 2.95 (ISBN 0-8010-7692-7). Baker Bk.

--Intriguing Bible Quizzes. (Quiz & Puzzle Books). 112p. 1976. pap. 2.95 (ISBN 0-8010-7640-4). Baker Bk.

--One Hundred One Bible Action Games. 64p. 1986. pap. 3.95 (ISBN 0-87403-017-X, 2801). Standard Pub.

Rhodes, Bennie. Calculator Word Games. LC 77-8870. 1977. pap. 2.95 (ISBN 0-915134-39-X). Mott Media.

Shofner, Myra. The Ark Book of Riddles. LC 79-57214. (Illus.). 1980. pap. 2.50 (ISBN 0-89191-250-9). Cook.

Short, Beth. Memorizing Bible Verses with Games & Crafts. LC 12-2872. 1984. pap. 4.95 teacher's material (ISBN 0-570-03937-1). Concordia.

Stiefel, Janice. How to Plan a Bible Treasure Hunt. (Illus.). 50p. (Orig.). 1981. pap. 3.50 (ISBN 0-9605858-0-X). Second Hand.

Stilson, Max. Who? What? Where? Bible Quizzes. (Quiz & Puzzle Bks.). 96p. 1980. pap. 2.95 (ISBN 0-8010-8012-6). Baker Bk.

Sychterz, Terre. The Bible & Me! Zapel, Arthur L., ed. (Illus.). 40p. 1986. pap. 3.95 (ISBN 0-916260-39-9). Meriwether Pub.

Tonothy, Ruth. Bible Crossword Puzzles. 48p. 1986. pap. 2.50 (ISBN 0-87403-050-1, 2694). Standard Pub.

Warner, Diane. Bible Puppet Scripts for Busy Teachers. LC 81-69783. 1983. pap. 4.95 (ISBN 0-89636-076-8). Accent Bks.

Wells, Amos R. Go till You Guess Bible Games. (Quiz & Puzzle Book Ser.). 128p. (Orig.). 1980. pap. 2.95 (ISBN 0-8010-9502-6). Baker Bk.

Westphal, Arnold C. Bible Magic Trick Talks for Childrens Church. 1987. pap. 4.95 (ISBN 0-915398-26-5). Visual Evangels.

--Fold 'n Snip Bible Bits, No. 7. 1974. 4.95 (ISBN 0-915398-06-0). Visual Evangels.

--Gospel Surprise Paper Tears. (No. 13). 1986. pap. 4.95 (ISBN 0-915398-25-7). Visual Evangels.

Whitlow, Gretchen. New Bible Crossword Puzzles, No. 5. 128p. (Orig.). 1983. pap. 2.25 (ISBN 0-8007-8471-5, Spire Bks.). Revell.

BIBLE IN LITERATURE

see also Religion in Literature

Ackerman, Carl. The Bible in Shakespeare. 1978. lib. bdg. 18.00 (ISBN 0-8495-0134-2). Arden Lib.

Arnold, Matthew. God & the Bible: A Review of Objections to Literature & Dogma. 1973. Repr. of 1875 ed. 14.75 (ISBN 0-8274-1704-7). R West.

Bloch, Chana. Spelling the Word: George Herbert & the Bible. LC 84-123. 375p. 1985. 37.50x (ISBN 0-520-05121-1). U of Cal Pr.

Brown, James Buchan. Bible Truths with Shakespearian Parallels. 6th ed. LC 74-19106. Repr. of 1886 ed. 15.00 (ISBN 0-404-01136-5). AMS Pr.

Cook, A. S. Biblical Quotations in Old English Prose Writers. 59.95 (ISBN 0-87968-731-2). Gordon Pr.

Cook, Albert S. Biblical Quotations in Old English Prose Writers. LC 74-2465. 1898. lib. bdg. 40.00 (ISBN 0-8414-3552-9). Folcroft.

Cook, Stanley A. The Old Testament. 1936. 39.50 (ISBN 0-8274-3060-4). R West.

Cornelius, R. M. Christopher Marlowe's Use of the Bible. LC 84-21280. (American University Studies IV (English Language & Literature): Vol. 23). (Illus.). 335p. 1984. text ed. 32.00 (ISBN 0-8204-0193-5). P Lang Pubs.

Dickson, Nicholas. The Bible in Waverley. 1973. Repr. of 1884 ed. write for info. (ISBN 0-8274-1586-9). R West.

--Or, Sir Walter Scott's Use of Sacred Scriptures. 1979. Repr. of 1884 ed. lib. bdg. 30.00 (ISBN 0-8414-3830-7). Folcroft.

Fairman, Marion A. Biblical Patterns in Modern Literature. LC 72-85235. 128p. 1972. 2.95 (ISBN 0-913228-04-4). Dillon-Liederbach.

Fletcher, H. Use of the Bible in Milton's Prose. LC 75-95425. (Studies in Milton, No. 22). 1970. Repr. of 1929 ed. lib. bdg. 39.95x (ISBN 0-8383-0974-7). Haskell.

Fowler, David C. The Bible in Early English Literature. LC 76-7786. (Illus.). 274p. 1976. 18.95x (ISBN 0-295-95438-8). U of Wash Pr.

Friedman, Clarence W. Prefigurations in Meistergesang. LC 75-140020. (Catholic University of America Studies in German Ser.: No. 18). Repr. of 1943 ed. 22.00 (ISBN 0-404-50238-5). AMS Pr.

Hirsch, David H. & Aschkenasy, Nehama, eds. Biblical Patterns in Modern Literature. (Brown Judaic Studies: No. 77). 252p. 1985. o.s. 21.95 (ISBN 0-89130-813-X, 14 00 77); pap. 17.95 (ISBN 0-89130-814-8). Scholars Pr GA.

Hirst, Wolf Z. The Romantic Hero & His Biblical Sources. Hogg, James, ed. (Romantic Reassessment ser.). (Orig.). 1985. pap. 15.00 (ISBN 3-7052-0573-0, Pub. by Salzburg Studies). Longwood Pub Group.

Jacobson, Howard. The Exagoge of Ezekiel. LC 82-4410. 240p. 1983. 49.50 (ISBN 0-521-24580-X). Cambridge U Pr.

Joseph, O. L. The Influence of the English Bible Upon the English Language & Upon English & American Literature. 59.95 (ISBN 0-8490-0409-8). Gordon Pr.

Kuhn, Alvin B. The Red Sea Is Your Blood. 66p. 1976. pap. 5.95 (ISBN 0-88697-007-5). Life Science.

Liptzin, Sol. Biblical Themes in World Literature. LC 84-19457. 316p. 1985. 20.00 (ISBN 0-88125-063-5). Ktav.

Moffatt, James. The Bible in Scots Literature. LC 73-14835. 1924. Repr. lib. bdg. 35.00 (ISBN 0-8414-6048-5). Folcroft.

Montgomery, John W., ed. Myth, Allegory, & Gospel. LC 74-1358. Orig. Title: Names & Titles of Christ. 160p. 1974. pap. 5.95 (ISBN 0-87123-358-4, 210358). Bethany Hse.

Moore, Edward. Studies in Dante, First Series: Scriptures & Classical Authors in Dante. LC 68-57627. (Illus.). 1969. Repr. of 1896 ed. lib. bdg. 22.50x (ISBN 0-8371-0909-4, MODF). Greenwood.

--Studies in Dante, Second Series: Miscellaneous Essays. LC 68-57628. (Illus.). 1969. Repr. of 1899 ed. lib. bdg. 22.50x (ISBN 0-8371-0908-6, MOSD). Greenwood.

--Studies in Dante, Third Series: Miscellaneous Essays. LC 68-57629. (Illus.). 1969. Repr. of 1903 ed. lib. bdg. 22.50x (ISBN 0-8371-0917-5, MODT). Greenwood.

Murphy, G. Ronald. Brecht & the Bible: A Study of Religious Nihilism & Human Weakness in Brecht's Plays. LC 80-20207. (Studies in Germanic Languages & Literatures: No. 96). xi, 107p. 12.50x (ISBN 0-8078-8096-5). U of NC Pr.

Noble, Richmond. Shakespeare's Biblical Knowledge & Use of the Book of Common Prayer. 1970. lib. bdg. 20.00x (ISBN 0-374-96115-8, Octagon). Hippocrene Bks.

Purdy, Dwight H. Joseph Conrad's Bible. LC 83-40331. 160p. 1984. 16.95x (ISBN 0-8061-1876-8). U of Okla Pr.

Robinson, Edna M. Tennyson's Use of the Bible. 119p. 1968. Repr. of 1917 ed. 12.50x (ISBN 0-87752-093-3). Gordian.

Sims, James H. Dramatic Uses of Biblical Allusions in Marlowe & Shakespeare. LC 66-64917. (University of Florida Humanities Monographs: No. 24). 1966. pap. 3.50 (ISBN 0-8130-0206-0). U Presses Fla.

Sims, James H. & Ryken, Leland, eds. Milton & Scriptural Tradition: The Bible into Poetry. LC 83-16781. 192p. 1984. text ed. 19.50x (ISBN 0-8262-0427-9). U of MO Pr.

Smyth, Mary Co. Biblical Quotations in Middle English Literature Before 1350. LC 74-18317. 1974. Repr. of 1910 ed. lib. bdg. 37.50 (ISBN 0-8414-7825-2). Folcroft.

Smyth, Mary W. Biblical Quotations in Middle English Literature, 2 vols. 105.00 (ISBN 0-87968-730-4). Gordon Pr.

Tannenbaum, Leslie. Biblical Tradition in Blake's Early Prophecies: The Great Code of Art. LC 81-47158. 368p. 1982. 30.50x (ISBN 0-691-06490-3). Princeton U Pr.

Weaver, Bennett. Toward the Understanding of Shelley. 1967. lib. bdg. 18.50x (ISBN 0-374-98284-8, Octagon). Hippocrene Bks.

Wock, E. W. The Bible in English Literature. 69.95 (ISBN 0-87968-727-4). Gordon Pr.

Wordsworth, Charles. Shakespeare's Knowledge & Use of the Bible. 3rd ed. LC 73-144706. Repr. of 1880 ed. 27.50 (ISBN 0-404-07039-6). AMS Pr.

Zink, Harriet R. Emerson's Use of the Bible. LC 77-7882. 1977. lib. bdg. 20.00 (ISBN 0-8414-9805-9). Folcroft.

BIBLE IN LITERATURE–BIBLIOGRAPHY

Coleman, Edward D. Bible in English Drama: An Annotated Bibliography. rev. ed. 1969. 25.00x (ISBN 0-87068-034-X). Ktav.

--Bible in English Drama: An Annotated List of Plays. 1969. 6.95 (ISBN 0-87104-021-2, Co-Pub by Ktav). NY Pub Lib.

BIBLE IN THE SCHOOLS

see Religion in the Public Schools

BIBLE PLAYS

Here are entered works on the dramatization of Biblical events, collections of such dramatizations, and such individual plays as are not entered under the name of a principal character or other specific heading.

see also Liturgical Drama;

also subdivision Drama under names of Biblical characters

Bailey, Kenneth. The Cross & the Prodigal. LC 72-90957. 176p. 1973. pap. 5.25 (ISBN 0-570-03139-7, 12-2523). Concordia.

DeAngelis, William. Acting Out the Gospels. LC 81-84919. 96p. 1982. pap. 9.95 (ISBN 0-89622-136-9). Twenty-Third.

Dramatized New Testament. 1987. 34.95 (280006). Bethany Hse.

Gamm, David. Child's Play. LC 78-51069. (Illus.). 96p. 1978. pap. 4.95 (ISBN 0-87793-150-X). Ave Maria.

Hayes, Theresa. Getting Your Act Together. LC 85-16548. 112p. 1986. pap. 4.95 (ISBN 0-87239-998-2, 3358). Standard Pub.

Huges, Robert D. Plays That'll Preach. LC 85-365. 1985. pap. 4.95 (ISBN 0-8054-6812-9). Broadman.

Ison, Colleen. Goliath's Last Stand. LC 85-17315. 112p. 1986. pap. 4.95 (ISBN 0-87239-997-4, 3357). Standard Pub.

Miller, Sarah W. Bible Dramas for Older Boys & Girls. LC 75-95409. 1970. pap. 4.95 (ISBN 0-8054-7506-0). Broadman.

Pasachoff, Naomi E. Playwriters, Preachers & Politicians: A Study of Testament Dramas. Hogg, James, ed. (Elizabethan & Renaissance Studies). 162p. (Orig.). 1975. pap. 15.00 (ISBN 3-7052-0691-5, Pub. by Salzburg Studies). Longwood Pub Group.

Richardson, Carol. Bible Programs & Dramas for Children. 64p. (Orig.). 1983. pap. 2.95 (ISBN 0-87239-665-7, 3350). Standard Pub.

Sparks, Judith A., compiled by. Bible Programs & Dramas for Youth & Adults. 64p. (Orig.). 1983. pap. 2.95 (ISBN 0-87239-671-1, 3351). Standard Pub.

Spence, Hersey E. Old Testament Dramas. LC 74-175994. 1976. Repr. of 1936 ed. 15.50 (ISBN 0-404-06176-1). AMS Pr.

Stuart, Jamie. A Scots Gospel. LC 86-45544. 87p. (Orig.). 1986. pap. 4.95 (ISBN 0-8042-0421-7); 60 min. cassette 7.95 (ISBN 0-8042-0424-1). John Knox.

Sullivan, Jessie P. Puppet Scripts for Children's Church. (Paperback Program Ser.). 1978. pap. 4.50 (ISBN 0-8010-8124-6). Baker Bk.

Townsend, L., et al, eds. Parade of Plays III. 96p. 1987. pap. 5.95 (ISBN 0-89191-281-9). Cook.

Von Speyr, Adrienne. Three Women & the Lord. Harrison, Graham, tr. LC 86-80789. (Illus.). 115p. 1986. pap. 7.95 (ISBN 0-89870-059-0). Ignatius Pr.

Wamberg, Steve & Wamberg, Annie. Acting Up: A Complete Introduction to Biblical Drama for Junior High Youth Groups. (The Best of Young Teen Action Ser.). 32p. 1985. pap. 4.95 (ISBN 0-89191-379-3). Cook.

Zabriskie, Pat. Pointing the Way with Puppets. LC 81-81240. 80p. 1981. pap. 3.95 (ISBN 0-88243-574-4, 02-0574). Gospel Pub.

BIBLE PUZZLES

see Bible Games and Puzzles

BIBLE STORIES

Abram Talked with God. (Little Learner Ser.). 24p. 1985. 5.95 (ISBN 0-570-08950-6, 56-1541). Concordia.

Anthony, William. Bible Stories. LC 77-71655. (Illus., Orig.). pap. 5.00 (ISBN 0-912330-25-2, Dist. by Inland Bk). Jargon Soc.

Asch, Sholem. In the Beginning: Stories from the Bible. Cunningham, Caroline, tr. from Yiddish. LC 66-24907. (Illus.). 1979. pap. 3.95 (ISBN 0-8052-0626-4). Schocken.

Baden, Robert. Adam & His Family. (Arch Bks.). (Illus.). 24p. 1986. pap. 0.99 saddlestitched (ISBN 0-570-06198-9, 59-1421). Concordia.

Barrett, Ethel. Ethel Barrett Tells Favorite Bible Stories, Vol.3. LC 77-93051. (Bible Biography Ser.). 128p. 1978. pap. 3.95 (ISBN 0-8307-0615-1, 5605806). Regal.

Baw, Cindy & Brownlow, Paul C. Children of the Bible: Twenty-Six Exciting Stories about Children of the Bible. (Illus.). 1984. 10.95 (ISBN 0-915720-19-1). Brownlow Pub Co.

Baxendale, Jean. First Bible Lessons: A Course for Two and Three-Year-Olds. rev. ed. LC 81-53021. (Illus.). 144p. 1982. pap. 7.95 (ISBN 0-87239-486-7, 3369). Standard Pub.

Beers, V. Gilbert. Along Thimblelane Trails. LC 81-14197. (Muffin Family Ser.). 96p. 1981. 11.95 (ISBN 0-8024-0298-4). Moody.

--Captain Maxi's Secret Island. (Muffin Family Ser.: No. 11). 96p. 1983. 11.95 (ISBN 0-8024-9573-7). Moody.

Beers, V. Gilbert & Beers, Ronald. The Victor Family Story Bible. 640p. 1985. 19.95 (ISBN 0-88207-822-4). Victor Bks.

Beers, V. Gilbert & Beers, Ronald A. Walking with Jesus. (Illus.). 192p. 1984. 14.95 (ISBN 0-89840-069-4). Heres Life.

Bennett, Marian. David, the Shepherd. (Happy Day Bible Stories Bks.). (Illus.). 24p. 1984. 1.59 (ISBN 0-87239-763-7, 3723). Standard Pub.

--My Bible Book. (Wipe-Clean Bks.). (Illus.). 12p. 1985. pap. 1.39 (ISBN 0-87239-956-7, 3516). Standard Pub.

Bentley, James, retold by. The Children's Bible. (Illus.). 237p. 1983. 7.95 (ISBN 0-531-03592-1). Watts.

Bergey, Alyce. David & Jonathan. (Arch Bks.). (Illus.). 24p. 1987. pap. 00.99 (ISBN 0-570-09006-7, 59-01434). Concordia.

--Young Jesus in the Temple. (Arch Bks.). (Illus.). 24p. 1986. pap. 0.99 saddlestitched (ISBN 0-570-06203-9, 59-1426). Concordia.

Bible Stories for Children. 32p. 1981. pap. 3.95 (ISBN 0-8249-8017-4). Ideals.

Bible Stories for Children. (Illus.). 20p. 1985. incl. cassette 8.95 (ISBN 0-8249-8121-9). Ideals.

Birth of the Savior. (The Inspirational Library). 24p. 3.95 (ISBN 0-8326-2004-1, 3251). World Bible.

Borsh, Frederick H. Power in Weakness: New Hearing for Gospel Stories of Healing & Discipleship. LC 82-15997. 160p. 1983. pap. 8.95 (ISBN 0-8006-1703-7, 1-1703). Fortress.

Boruch, Behn. In the Beginning. 1958. 4.00 (ISBN 0-88482-727-5). Hebrew Pub.

Brem, M. M. La Historia de Maria. (Libros Arco Ser.). Tr. of Mary's Story. (Span., Illus.). 32p. 1979. pap. 0.95 (ISBN 0-89922-145-9). Edit Caribe.

Brewer, Tina. Big & Little in the Bible. (Happy Day Bks.). (Illus.). 1.59 (ISBN 0-87403-022-6, 3482). Standard Pub.

Brincat, Matthew De. Salt & Light. 56p. 1983. pap. 3.00 (ISBN 0-911423-00-1). Bible-Speak.

Briscoe, Jill. There's a Snake in My Garden. 1977. pap. 5.95 (ISBN 0-310-21821-7, 9256P). Zondervan.

Burke, Pratricia A, et al. Adventures from God's Word. rev. ed. Miller, Marge, ed. (Basic Bible Readers Ser.). (Illus.). 128p. 1983. text ed. 7.95 (ISBN 0-87239-663-0, 2953). Standard Pub.

Burl Ives Bible-Time Stories, 12 bks. Set. incl. lp. 14.95 (ISBN 0-89191-299-1, 52993); Set. incl. cassette 14.95 (ISBN 0-89191-297-5, 52977). Cook.

Burrow, Dan. When Jesus Was a Baby. LC 84-70244. (Augsburg Open Window Bks.). (Illus.). 12p. (Orig.). 1984. pap. 4.95 (ISBN 0-8066-2078-1, 10-7082). Augsburg.

Cameron, William E. Great Dramas of the Bible. LC 81-71560. 305p. 1982. 5.95 (ISBN 0-87159-047-6). Unity School.

Carter, Will. The Accounts to Caesar Tiberius Concerning Jesus of Nazareth. 142p. (Orig.). 1986. pap. 3.99 (ISBN 0-9617190-0-1). Drame Pr.

Carwell, L'Ann. Baby's First Bible Story Book. (Illus.). 1979. 1.25 (ISBN 0-570-08003-7, 56-1328). Concordia.

Chapman, Marie M. Puppet Animals Tell Bible Stories. LC 77-75134. (Illus.). 1977. tchr's ed. spiral bdg. 4.95 (ISBN 0-916406-74-1). Accent Bks.

Ching Yee, Janice. God's Busiest Angels. (Illus.). 1975. pap. 3.00 (ISBN 0-931420-09-1). Pi Pr.

--God's Purest Angels. (Illus.). 1976. pap. 3.00 (ISBN 0-931420-11-3). Pi Pr.

Coats, George W. Saga, Legend, Tale, Novella, Fable. (JSOT Supplement Ser.). 159p. 1985. text ed. 18.50x (ISBN 0-905774-84-1, Pub by JSOT Pr England); pap. text ed. 8.95x (ISBN 0-905774-85-X). Eisenbrauns.

Coe, Joyce. Jesus Rides into Jerusalem. (Illus.). 24p. 1987. pap. 00.99 (ISBN 0-570-09007-5, 59-1435). Concordia.

Conrod, John. Computer Bible Games, Bk. 2. LC 83-91269. 160p. (Orig.). (YA) 1984. pap. 6.95 (ISBN 0-89636-141-1). Accent Bks.

The Creation. (Burl Ives Bible-Time Stories). incl. tape 4.95 (ISBN 0-89191-804-3, 98046). Cook.

Crockett, Maline C. Stories to See & Share. 80p. 1980. pap. 4.50 (ISBN 0-87747-828-7). Deseret Bk.

Crompton, T., illus. The Good Samaritan: Retold by Catherine Storr. (People of the Bible Ser.). (Illus.). 32p. 1984. 10.65 (ISBN 0-8172-1988-9, Raintree Childrens Books Belitha Press Ltd. - London). Raintree Pubs.
Cross, Luther S. Easy Object Stories. 114p. 1984. pap. 3.95 (ISBN 0-8010-2502-8). Baker Bk.
Dale, Alan T. The Crowd Is Waiting. (Rainbow Books, Bible Story Books for Children). 1976. pap. 1.00 (ISBN 0-8192-1208-3). Morehouse.
--I've Found the Sheep. (Rainbow Books, Bible Story Books for Children). 1976. pap. 1.00 (ISBN 0-8192-1206-7). Morehouse.
--Jesus Is Really Alive Again! (Rainbow Books, Bible Story Books for Children). 1976. pap. 1.00 (ISBN 0-8192-1209-1). Morehouse.
--Paul the Traveler. (Rainbow Books, Bible Story Books for Children). 1976. pap. 1.00 (ISBN 0-8192-1211-3). Morehouse.
Dampier, Joseph H. Workbook on Christian Doctrine. 64p. (Orig.). 1943. pap. 1.95 (ISBN 0-87239-072-1, 3343). Standard Pub.
Daniel. (Burl Ives Bible-Time Stories). incl. tape 4.95 (ISBN 0-89191-800-0, 98004). Cook.
Daniel, Rebecca. Abraham. (Our Greatest Heritage Ser.). (Illus.). 32p. 1983. wkbk. 3.95 (ISBN 0-86653-133-5, SS 802). Good Apple.
--Adam & Eve. (Our Greatest Heritage Ser.). (Illus.). 32p. 1983. wkbk. 3.95 (ISBN 0-86653-131-9, SS 800). Good Apple.
--Daniel. (Our Greatest Heritage Ser.). (Illus.). 32p. 1983. wkbk. 3.95 (ISBN 0-86653-140-8, SS 809). Good Apple.
--David. (Our Greatest Heritage Ser.). (Illus.). 1983. wkbk. 3.95 (ISBN 0-86653-138-6, SS 807). Good Apple.
--Jonah. (Our Greatest Heritage Ser.). (Illus.). 32p. 1983. wkbk. 3.95 (ISBN 0-86653-141-6, SS 810). Good Apple.
--Joseph. (Our Greatest Heritage Ser.). (Illus.). 32p. 1983. wkbk. 3.95 (ISBN 0-86653-134-3, SS 803). Good Apple.
--Joshua. (Our Greatest Heritage Ser.). (Illus.). 32p. 1983. wkbk. 3.95 (ISBN 0-86653-136-X, SS 805). Good Apple.
--Moses. (Our Greatest Heritage Ser.). (Illus.). 32p. 1983. wkbk. 3.95 (ISBN 0-86653-135-1, SS 804). Good Apple.
--Noah. (Our Greatest Heritage Ser.). (Illus.). 1983. wkbk. 3.95 (ISBN 0-86653-132-7, SS 801). Good Apple.
--Samson. (Our Greatest Heritage Ser.). (Illus.). 32p. 1983. wkbk. 3.95 (ISBN 0-86653-137-8, SS 806). Good Apple.
--Solomon. (Our Greatest Heritage Ser.). (Illus.). 32p. 1983. wkbk. 3.95 (ISBN 0-86653-139-4, SS 808). Good Apple.
--Women of the Old Testament. (Our Greatest Heritage Ser.). (Illus.). 32p. 1983. wkbk. 3.95 (ISBN 0-86653-142-4, SS 811). Good Apple.
Daughters of St. Paul, ed. Bible Stories for Everyone. 1956. 6.00 (ISBN 0-8198-0008-2); pap. 5.00 (ISBN 0-8198-0009-0). Dghtrs St Paul.
David. (Burl Ives Bible-Time Stories). incl. tape 4.95 (ISBN 0-89191-803-5, 98038). Cook.
Davidson, Alice J. The Story of Daniel & the Lions. (Alice in Bibleland Ser.). 32p. 1986. 4.95 (ISBN 0-8378-5079-7). Gibson.
--The Story of Jonah. (The Alice in Bibleland Storybooks). (Illus.). 32p. 1984. 4.95 (ISBN 0-8378-5068-1). Gibson.
--The Story of Noah. (The Alice in Bibleland Storybooks). (Illus.). 32p. 1984. 4.95 (ISBN 0-8378-5067-3). Gibson.
Davidson, Robert G. Gathering the Pieces. 88p. (Orig.). 1985. pap. 9.95 (ISBN 0-940754-30-4). Ed Ministries.
Dede, Vivian H. Elizabeth's Christmas Story. LC 59-1430. (Arch Bks.). (Illus.). 24p. 1987. pap. 0.99 (ISBN 0-570-09002-4, 59/1430). Concordia.
De Kort, Kees, illus. What the Bible Tells Us: Third Series, 4 bks. Incl. A Baby Called John. 28p (ISBN 0-8066-1770-5, 10-0538); Jesus & a Little Girl. 28p (ISBN 0-8066-1771-3, 10-3479); The Son Who Left Home. 28p (ISBN 0-8066-1773-X, 10-5852); Jesus Goes Away. 28p (ISBN 0-8066-1774-8, 10-3510). 1980. pap. 2.95 ea. Augsburg.
Demaree, Doris C. Bible Boys & Girls. (Bible Stories for Children Ser.). (Illus.). 1970. pap. 1.50 (ISBN 0-87162-002-2, D1443). Warner Pr.
--Bible Heroes. (Bible Stories for Children Ser.). 1970. pap. 1.50 (ISBN 0-87162-004-9, D1444). Warner Pr.
--Exciting Adventures. (Bible Stories for Children Ser.). 1974. pap. 1.50 (ISBN 0-87162-235-1, D1445). Warner Pr.
--Followers of God. (Bible Stories for Children Ser.). 1974. pap. 1.50 (ISBN 0-87162-236-X, D1446). Warner Pr.
--Helping Others. (Bible Stories for Children Ser.). 1970. pap. 1.50 (ISBN 0-87162-237-8, D1447). Warner Pr.
--Living for Jesus. (Bible Stories for Children Ser.). 1974. pap. 1.50 (ISBN 0-87162-238-6, D1448). Warner Pr.
DePaola, Tomie, illus. David & Goliath. (Bible Story Cutout Bks.). (Illus., Orig.). 1984. 32 pages 12.95, (ISBN 0-86683-820-1, 8452, HarpR); pap. 5.95, 40 pages (ISBN 0-86683-700-0, 8469). Har-Row.
--Queen Esther. (Bible Story Cutout Bks.). (Illus., Orig.). 1984. 32p 12.95, (ISBN 0-86683-822-8, 8454, HarpR); pap. 4.95, 40p (ISBN 0-86683-702-7, 8271). Har-Row.
DeVries, Betty. One Hundred One Bible Activity Sheets. 144p. 1983. pap. 5.95 (ISBN 0-8010-2931-7). Baker Bk.
Doney, Meryl. The Two Houses. (Illus.). 16p. 1982. pap. 0.99 (ISBN 0-86683-664-0, AY8246, HarpR). Har-Row.
Donovan, John B. The Family Book of Bible Stories. 120p. 1986. pap. 8.95 (ISBN 0-8192-1381-0). Morehouse.
Donze, Mary T. Down Gospel Byways: Eighteen Stories of People Who Met Jesus. 80p. 1984. pap. 2.95 (ISBN 0-89243-198-9). Liguori Pubns.
Durepo, Martha. Our Bible. LC 86-17571. (Bible-&-Me Ser.). 1987. 5.95 (ISBN 0-8054-4175-1). Broadman.
Easterly, Lane, ed. Great Bible Stories for Children. (Illus.). 7.95 (ISBN 0-8407-5351-9). Nelson.
Edward, Gene. A Tale of Three Kings. 120p. 1980. pap. 5.95 (ISBN 0-940232-03-0). Christian Bks.
Efron, Marshall & Olsen, Alfa B. Bible Stories You Can't Forget No Matter How Hard You Try. (Illus.). 1976. 9.95 (ISBN 0-525-26500-7, 0966-290). Dutton.
Egermeier, Elsie E. Egermeier's Bible Story Book. 5th ed. LC 68-23397. (Illus.). 1969. 14.95 (ISBN 0-87162-006-5, D2005); deluxe ed. 15.95 (ISBN 0-87162-007-3, D2006); pap. 8.95 (ISBN 0-87162-229-7, D2008). Warner Pr.
--Egermeier's Favorite Bible Stories. 1965. 7.95 (ISBN 0-87162-014-6, D3695). Warner Pr.
--Picture Story Bible ABC Book. rev. ed. (Illus.). 1963. 5.95 (ISBN 0-87162-262-9, D1703). Warner Pr.
Enns, Peter & Forsberg, Glen. Daniel & the Lions & Five Other Stories. (Stories that Live Ser.: Bk. 4). (Illus.). 24p. 1985. book & cassette 4.95 (ISBN 0-936215-04-6). STL Intl.
--Stories That Live, 6 vols. (Series I). (Illus.). 144p. 1985. books & cassettes 29.70 (ISBN 0-936215-00-3). STL Intl.
Esther. (Burl Ives Bible-Time Stories). incl. tape 4.95 (ISBN 0-89191-802-7, 98020). Cook.
Eudaly, Maria S. De. El Cuidado de Dios. Villasenor, Emma Z., tr. (Illus.). 1983. pap. 0.95 (ISBN 0-311-38555-9). Casa Bautista.
Evans, Shirlee. A Life in Her Hands. 192p. (Orig.). 1987. pap. 5.95 (ISBN 0-8361-3441-9). Herald Pr.
--Tree Tall to the Rescue. (Tree Tall Ser.: No. 3). (Illus.). 144p. (Orig.). 1987. pap. 4.50 (ISBN 0-8361-3444-3). Herald Pr.
Farber, Norma. All Those Mothers at the Manger. LC 85-42610. (Illus.). 32p. 1985. 11.25i (ISBN 0-06-021869-X); PLB 10.89g (ISBN 0-06-021870-3). HArpJ.
--How the Hibernators Came to Bethlehem. LC 80-7685. (Illus.). 32p. 1980. PLB 7.85 (ISBN 0-8027-6353-7). Walker & Co.
Faris. My Bible Story Reader, 5 vols. pap. 2.95 ea. Schmul Pub Co.
Father Augustine. Some Loves of the Seraphic Saint. 1979. 5.95 (ISBN 0-8199-0776-6). Franciscan Herald.
Favorite Bible Stories, Vol. 1. 1.95 (ISBN 0-89954-378-2). Antioch Pub Co.
Ferntheil, Carol. Bible Adventures Basic Bible Reader. 128p. 1985. pap. 4.95 (2757). Standard Pub.
Finnegan, Edward G. Children's Bible Stories. LC 75-18758. (Treasure House Bks). (Illus.). 256p. 1978. 7.95 (ISBN 0-8326-1803-9, 3602); deluxe ed. 8.95 (ISBN 0-686-66397-7). World Bible.
--Historias De la Biblia. LC 75-18758. (Treasure House Bks). (Span., Illus.). 1978. 9.95 (ISBN 0-8326-2601-5, 5180). World Bible.
Fishy Story. 1.75 (ISBN 0-8198-0197-6). Dghtrs St Paul.
Fletcher, Mary. My Very First Prayer-Time Book. (Very First Bible Stories Ser.). 1984. 1.59 (ISBN 0-87162-274-2, D8503). Warner Pr.
Frank, Penny. Daniel in the Lion's Den. Alexander, P., ed. (Lion Story Bible Ser.). 24p. 1987. 2.95 (ISBN 0-85648-752-X). Lion USA.
--Jesus on Trial. Alexander, P., ed. (Lion Story Bible Ser.). 24p. 1987. 2.95. Lion USA.
--Jesus the Teacher. Alexander, P., ed. (Lion Story Bible Ser.). 24p. 1987. 2.95 (ISBN 0-85648-760-0). Lion USA.
--King David. Alexander, P., ed. (Lion Story Bible Ser.). 24p. 1987. 2.95 (ISBN 0-85648-744-9). Lion USA.
--Naaman's Dreadful Secret. Alexander, P., ed. (Lion Story Bible Ser.). 24p. 1987. 2.95 (ISBN 0-85648-748-1). Lion USA.
--Paul & His Friends. Alexander, P., ed. (Lion Story Bible Ser.). 24p. 1987. 2.95 (ISBN 0-85648-776-7). Lion USA.
--The Story of the Two Brothers. Alexamder, P., ed. (Lion Story Bible Ser.). 24p. 1987. 2.95 (ISBN 0-85648-765-1). Lion USA.
Frost, S. E., Jr., ed. Favorite Stories from the Bible. 176p. 1986. pap. 2.95 (ISBN 0-345-33125-7, Pub. by Ballantine Epiphany). Ballantine.
Geller, Norman. The First Seven Days. (Illus.). 32p. 1983. pap. 6.95 (ISBN 0-915753-00-6). N Geller Pub.
Ginzberg, Louis. Legends of the Bible. LC 56-9915. 620p. 1956. 14.95 (ISBN 0-8276-0036-4, 168). Jewish Pubns.
Golann, Cecil P. Mission on a Mountain: The Story of Abraham & Isaac. LC 73-7498. (Foreign Lands Ser.). (Illus.). 32p. 1975. PLB 5.95 (ISBN 0-8225-0363-8). Lerner Pubns.
Grant, Amy, et al. Amy Grant's Heart to Heart Bible Stories. LC 85-62143. (Illus.). 96p. 1985. 9.95x (ISBN 0-8344-0130-4, BB500C). Sweet.
Gray, Nicolette, ed. Jacob's Ladder: Bible Picture Book from Anglo-Saxon & 12th Century English MSS. 1978. Repr. of 1949 ed. lib. bdg. 25.00 (ISBN 0-8495-1948-9). Arden Lib.
Greenberg, Sidney. Lessons for Living: Reflections on the Weekly Bible Readings & on the Festivals. 236p. 1985. 15.95x (ISBN 0-87677-157-6). Hartmore.
Greene, Carol. The Easter Women. (Arch Bks.). (Illus.). 24p. 1987. pap. 0.99 (ISBN 0-570-09003-2, 59-1432). Concordia.
Grimsrud, Ted. Triumph of the Lamb. LC 87-409. 192p. (Orig.). 1987. pap. 14.95 (ISBN 0-8361-3438-9). Herald Pr.
Groff, Cora M. Crown of Jewels. 144p. 1985. pap. 6.00 (ISBN 0-682-40210-9). Exposition Pr FL.
Gross, Arthur W. Child's Garden of Bible Stories. (Concordia Primary Religion Ser.). 1981. 9.95 (ISBN 0-570-03414-0, 56-1001); pap. 5.95 (ISBN 0-570-03402-7, 56-1012). Concordia.
Groth, Lynn. With You, Dear Child, in Mind. (A Cradle Roll Program Ser.). 16p. (Orig.). 1985. pap. 1.25 (ISBN 0-938272-77-2). Wels Board.
Gunkel, Hermann. The Folktale in the Old Testament. (Historic Texts & Interpreters Ser.: No. 5). 224p. 1985. text ed. 24.95x (ISBN 1-85075-031-9, Pub. by Almond Pr England); pap. text ed. 10.95x (ISBN 1-85075-030-0). Eisenbrauns.
Haan, Sheri D. Good News for Children. 1969. pap. 5.95 (ISBN 0-8010-4073-6). Baker Bk.
Hanna-Barbera, illus. Daniel & the Lion's Den. (The Greatest Adventure: Ser.Stories from the Bible.). (Illus., Orig.). Date not set. 5.95 (ISBN 0-687-15746-3). Abingdon.
--David & Goliath. (The Greatest Adventure Ser.Stories from the Bible). (Illus., Orig.). 1986. 5.95 (ISBN 0-687-15741-2). Abingdon.
--Joshua & the Battle of Jericho. (The Greatest Adventure: Stories from the Bible). (Illus., Orig.). Date not set. 5.95 (ISBN 0-687-15743-9). Abingdon.
--Moses Let My People Go. (The Greatest Adventure: Stories from the Bible). (Illus.). 48p. (Orig.). Date not set. 5.95 (ISBN 0-687-15740-4). Abingdon.
--Noah's Ark. (The Greatest Adventure: Stories from the Bible). (Illus., Orig.). Date not set. 5.95 (ISBN 0-687-15744-7). Abingdon.
--Samson & Delilah. (The Greatest Adventure: Stories from the Bible). (Illus., Orig.). Date not set. 5.95 (ISBN 0-687-15745-5). Abingdon.
Hannon, Ruth. Children's Bible Stories from the Old Testament. (Illus.). 1978. 4.95 (ISBN 0-307-13740-6, 13740, Golden Bks). Western Pub.
Harper, George. The Race to Grace. (H. B. Bible Adventures Ser.). 216p. (Orig.). 1986. pap. 5.95 (ISBN 0-934318-74-3). Falcon Pr MT.
Harper, George H. A God in the Bush is Worth Two in the Hand. (Bible Adventure Ser.). 216p. (Orig.). 1985. pap. 5.95 (ISBN 0-934318-48-4). Falcon Pr MT.
Hayes, Wanda. My Book of Bible Stories. (Illus.). 1964. board cover 5.95 (ISBN 0-87239-240-6, 3047). Standard Pub.
Head, Constance. Jeremiah & the Fall of Jerusalem. (Arch Bks.). (Illus.). 24p. 1986. pap. 0.99 saddlestitched (ISBN 0-570-06201-2, 59-1424). Concordia.
Heine, Helme. One Day in Paradise. LC 85-72492. (Illus.). 32p. 1986. 12.95 (ISBN 0-689-50394-6, McElderry Bk). Macmillan.
Henry, Avril. The Mirour of Mans Saluacioune: A Middle English Translation of Speculum Humanae Salvationis. LC 86-19364. (Middle Ages Ser.). (Illus.). 347p. 1987. text ed. 49.95x (ISBN 0-8122-8054-7). U of Pa Pr.
Hodges. Moses & the Ten Plagues. (Arch Bks.). 24p. (Orig.). 1985. pap. 0.99 (ISBN 0-570-06190-3, 59-1291). Concordia.
Hodges, Turner. Bible Story Library. 1963. 12.95 (ISBN 0-672-23099-2, Pub. by Audel). Macmillan.
Hollender, Betty. Bible Stories for Little Children, Bk. 1. rev. ed. (Illus.). 80p. (Orig.). 1985. pap. text ed. 6.00 (ISBN 0-8074-0309-1, 103100). UAHC.
Hollender, Betty R. Bible Stories for Little Children, Vol. 2. rev. ed. (Illus.). 80p. 1987. pap. text ed. 6.00 (ISBN 0-8074-0324-5). UAHC.
Hook, Richard & Hook, Frances. Jesus: El Amigo De los Ninos. Tr. of Jesus, the Friend of Children. (Illus.). 112p. 1981. 19.50 (ISBN 0-311-38552-4, Edit Mundo); pap. 14.95 (ISBN 0-311-38553-2). Casa Bautista.
Humphrey, Ruth. Bible Story & Color Book. (Illus.). 64p. (Orig.). 1982. pap. 2.95 (ISBN 0-87239-582-0, 2397). Standard Pub.
Hurlbut, Jesse L. Hurlbut's Story of the Bible. rev. ed. (Illus.). 15.95 (ISBN 0-310-26520-7, 6524). Zondervan.
Hutton, Warwick. Jonah & the Great Fish. LC 83-15477. (Illus.). 32p. 1984. 12.95 (ISBN 0-689-50283-4, McElderly Bk). Macmillan.
--Moses in the Bulrushes. LC 85-72261. (Illus.). 32p. 1986. 12.95 (ISBN 0-689-50393-8, McElderry Bk). Macmillan.
Ife, Elaine & Sutton, Rosalind. Now You Can Read Stories from the Bible. (Illus.). 208p. 1984. 9.95 (ISBN 0-8407-5396-9). Nelson.
Ife, Elaine & Sutton, Rosalind, eds. David & Jonathan. (Now You Can Read Stories from the Bible Ser.). (Illus.). 24p. 1985. 2.50 (ISBN 0-8407-5448-5). Nelson.
--Moses in the Bulrushes. (Now You Can Read Stories from the Bible Ser.). (Illus.). 24p. 1985. 2.50 (ISBN 0-8407-5481-7). Nelson.
--Samuel. (Now You Can Read Stories from the Bible Ser.). (Illus.). 24p. 1985. 2.50 (ISBN 0-8407-5449-3). Nelson.
--Stories Jesus Told. (Now You Can Read Stories from the Bible Ser.). (Illus.). 24p. 1984. 2.50 (ISBN 0-8407-5395-0). Nelson.
Ingram, Kristen J. Bible Stories for the Church Year. Russell, Joseph P., ed. LC 83-20135. 184p. (Orig.). 1986. pap. 10.95 (ISBN 0-86683-537-7, HarpR). Har-Row.
Jahsmann, Allan H. My Favorite Bible Stories. LC 67-15957. 1967. 5.95 (ISBN 0-570-03415-9, 56-1064). Concordia.
Jennings, A. Day the Little Children Came. (Arch Bks.). 1984. pap. 0.99 (ISBN 0-570-06092-3, 59-1210). Concordia.
Jewels from the Bible. (The Inspirational Library). 24p. 3.95 (ISBN 0-8326-2008-4, 3255). World Bible.
Jobling, David. THe Sense of Biblical Narrative II: Stuctural Analyses in the Hebrew Bible. (JSOT Supplement Ser.: No. 39). 120p. 1986. text ed. 21.00x (ISBN 1-85075-010-6, Pub. by JSOT Pr England); pap. text ed. 8.95x (ISBN 1-85075-011-4, Pub. by JSOT Pr England). Eisenbrauns.
Jonah. (Burl Ives Bible-Time Stories). incl. tape 4.95 (ISBN 0-89191-799-3, 97998). Cook.
Jonah. LC 76-11275. (Sunshine Bks). (Illus.). 20p. 1976. pap. 1.50 (ISBN 0-8006-1577-8, 1-1577). Fortress.
Jones, Mary A. Favorite Bible Stories & Verses. 112p. 1986. 9.95 (ISBN 0-02-689034-8). Macmillan.
Joshua. (Burl Ives Bible-Time Stories). incl. tape 4.95 (ISBN 0-89191-610-5, 26104). Cook.
Joyce, Jon L. Stories We Love, Vol. 2. (Orig.). 1983. pap. 14.95 (ISBN 0-937172-52-9). JLJ Pubs.
Kaiser, Judith B. Quick-Line Stories for Young Children. 1975. spiral bdg. 3.95 (ISBN 0-916406-12-1). Accent Bks.
Kendall, Joan. The Story of Samuel. (Very First Bible Stories Ser.). 1984. 1.59 (ISBN 0-87162-271-8, D8500). Warner Pr.
Kepes, Joanne L. Life in Bible Times & Places. 1982. 9.95 (Pub. by Pflaum Pr). Peter Li.
Knapp, John, II. My Book of Bible Rhymes. (Illus.). 1987. 11.95. Cook.
Knecht, F. J. Child's Bible History. Schumacher, Philip, tr. (Illus.). 1973. pap. 2.00 (ISBN 0-89555-005-9). TAN Bks Pubs.
Knowles, Andrew. The Crossroad Children's Bible. (Illus.). 448p. 1981. 12.95 (ISBN 0-8245-0138-1); pap. 7.95 (ISBN 0-8245-0473-9). Crossroad NY.
Kolbrek, Loyal. Paul Believes in Jesus. (Illus.). 24p. 1987. pap. 00.99 (ISBN 0-570-09008-3, 59-1436). Concordia.
Kopper, Philip, ed. & intro. by. A Christmas Testament. LC 82-5843. (Illus.). 144p. 1982. slipcased 25.00 (ISBN 0-941434-23-0). Stewart Tabori & Chang.
Kort, Kees De, illus. What the Bible Tells Us: A Series for Young Children. Incl. Jesus Is Born (ISBN 0-8066-1576-1, 10-3520); Jesus at the Wedding (ISBN 0-8066-1577-X, 10-3490); The Good Samaritan (ISBN 0-8066-1578-8, 10-2815); Jesus Is Alive (ISBN 0-8066-1579-6, 10-3518). (Illus.). 1977. pap. 2.95 ea. Augsburg.
Korty, Margaret B. Bible Bits & Relevant Rhymes. LC 84-71870. 117p. 1984. spiral binding 5.95 (ISBN 0-9603060-1-3). Church Lib.

Kroll, Woodrow. Bible Country. 1982. 22.95 (ISBN 0-89636-060-1). Accent Bks.

Kuykendall, Carolyn. Babies of the Bible. (Happy Day Bks.). (Illus.). 24p. 1986. 1.59 (ISBN 0-87403-021-8, 3481). Standard Pub.

Land, Sipke van der. Stories from the Bible-Newly Retold. LC 79-10049. pap. 51.30 (ISBN 0-317-39654-4, 2023224). Bks Demand UMI.

Lane, A. C. Bible Truths. pap. 0.50 (ISBN 0-88243-696-1, 02-0696). Gospel Pub.

Larson, Robert L. Bible Stories Reader. 1985. 8.95 (ISBN 0-533-06749-9). Vantage.

Le Blanc, Andre, illus. Great Adventures from the Bible. (Illus.). 200p. (Orig.). 1984. pap. 3.95 (ISBN 0-89191-848-5). Cook.

Leeper, John H. The Riddle of the Outlaw Bear & Other Faith-Building Stories. (Illus.). 1984. pap. 4.95 (ISBN 0-8024-7352-0). Moody.

LeFever, Marlene & Weyna, Kathy. Creative Kid Books, No. 1. 1984. pap. 1.95 (ISBN 0-89191-935-X, 59352). Cook.

--Creative Kid Books, No. 2. 1984. pap. 1.95 (ISBN 0-89191-936-8, 59360). Cook.

LeFevre, G. L. Favorite Bible Stories. (Bible Quiz 'N Tattletotals Ser.). 16p. (Orig.). 1982. pap. 0.98 (ISBN 0-87239-578-2, 2805). Standard Pub.

Lehman, Elsie E. God Sends His Son Activity Book. (Bible Story Ser.: Bk. 8). 80p. (Orig.). 1987. pap. 3.00 (ISBN 0-8361-3429-X). Herald Pr.

Lehn, Cornelia. God Keeps His Promise: A Bible Story Book for Young Children. LC 76-90377. (Illus.). 1970. 11.95x (ISBN 0-87303-291-8). Faith & Life.

Lewis, Jim. Biblical Favorites. LC 85-50948. 134p. (Orig.). 1985. pap. 7.95 (ISBN 0-942482-08-5). Unity Church Denver.

Licht, Jacob. Storytelling in the Bible. 154p. 1978. text ed. 18.50x (ISBN 965-223-301-3, Pub. by Magnes Pr Israel). Humanities.

Lindvall, Ella. Miracles by the Sea. (People of the Bible Ser.). (Illus.). 1984. 4.95 (ISBN 0-8024-0397-2). Moody.

Lindvall, Ella K. Jonah & the Great Fish. 2nd ed. (People of the Bible Ser.). (Illus.). 1984. 4.95 (ISBN 0-8024-0398-0). Moody.

--Joseph & the King. 2nd ed. (People of the Bible Ser.). (Illus.). 1984. 4.95 (ISBN 0-8024-0400-6). Moody.

--The Lost Son & Other Stories. (People of the Bible Ser.). (Illus.). 1984. 4.95 (ISBN 0-8024-0399-9). Moody.

--Read-Aloud Bible Stories, Vol. 2. (Illus.). 1985. text ed. 16.95 (ISBN 0-8024-7164-1). Moody.

Lovik, Craig J. The Exodus. (Arch Bks.). (Illus.). 24p. 1987. pap. 0.99 (ISBN 0-570-09001-6, 59-1429). Concordia.

McCall, Yvonne H. The Story of Jacob, Rachel & Leah. (Arch Bks.). (Illus.). 24p. 1986. pap. 0.99 saddlestitched (ISBN 0-570-06205-5, 59-1428). Concordia.

McDonald, Mary R. Little Stories About God. (Illus.). 1964. 5.50 (ISBN 0-8198-0080-5). pap. 4.50 (ISBN 0-8198-0081-3). Dghtrs St Paul.

McElroy. Jesus Forgives Peter. (Arch Bks.). 24p. (Orig.). 1985. pap. 0.99 (ISBN 0-570-06192-X, 59-1293). Concordia.

MacHaster, Eve B. God Comforts His People. LC 95-835. (Story Bible Ser: No. 7). (Illus.). 176p. (Orig.). 1985. pap. 5.95 (ISBN 0-8361-3393-5). Herald Pr.

McKarns, James. Seldom-Told Bible Tales. 1985. 4.95 (ISBN 0-89536-738-6, 5821). CSS of Ohio.

McKellar, Shona. The Beginning of the Rainbow. LC 81-7954. (Illus.). 1982. 8.95g (ISBN 0-687-02770-5). Abingdon.

MacMaster, Eve. God's Chosen King. LC 83-12736. (Story Bible Ser.: Vol. 4). (Illus.). 190p. (Orig.). 1983. pap. 5.95 (ISBN 0-8361-3344-7). Herald Pr.

McMaster, Eve. God's Wisdom & Power. LC 84-8974. (Story Bible Ser.: No. 5). (Illus.). 168p. (Orig.). 1984. pap. 5.95 (ISBN 0-8361-3362-5). Herald Pr.

MacMaster, Eve B. God Builds His Church. (Story Bible Ser.: No. 10). (Illus.). 184p. (Orig.). 1987. pap. 5.95 (ISBN 0-8361-3446-X). Herald Pr.

--God Sends His Son. LC 86-18342. (Story Bible Ser.: Bk. 8). (Illus.). 160p. (Orig.). 1986. pap. 5.95 (ISBN 0-8361-3420-6). Herald Pr.

Magnet, Charles E. Puppet Dialogues. LC 78-53323. 1978. spiral bdg. 4.95 (ISBN 0-916406-99-7). Accent Bks.

Mahany, Patricia. Animals in the Ark. (My Shape Bk.). (Illus.). 12p. 1984. 2.95 (ISBN 0-87239-781-5, 2721). Standard Pub.

--Baby Moses in a Basket. (Happy Day Bible Stories Bks.). (Illus.). 24p. 1984. 1.59 (ISBN 0-87239-761-0, 3721). Standard Pub.

--Bible Story Favorites. (My Shape Bk.). (Illus.). 1984. 2.95 (ISBN 0-87239-782-3, 2722). Standard Pub.

Mahany, Patricia, ed. Favorite Bible Stories. (Classroom Activity Bks.). (Illus.). 48p. (Orig.). 1984. pap. 2.95 (ISBN 0-87239-718-1, 2448). Standard Pub.

Mahany, Patricia, compiled by. God Can Do Anything-Bible Miracles. (Story & Color Bks.). (Illus.). 64p. (Orig.). 1984. pap. 2.95 (ISBN 0-87239-796-3, 2372). Standard Pub.

--Through the Bible with ABC's. (Story & Color Bks.). (Illus.). 64p. (Orig.). 1984. pap. 2.95 (ISBN 0-87239-798-X, 2374). Standard Pub.

Mann, Victor. He Remembered to Say "Thank You". (Arch Bks: No. 13). (Illus.). 32p. 1976. pap. 0.99 (ISBN 0-570-06103-2, 59-1221). Concordia.

Marquardt, Mervin A. The Temptation of Jesus. (Arch Bks.). (Illus.). 24p. 1986. pap. 0.99 saddlestitched (ISBN 0-570-06204-7, 59-1427). Concordia.

Marshall, Catherine. Catherine Marshall's Story Bible. 200p. 1985. pap. 9.95 (ISBN 0-380-69961-3). Avon.

Martin, Bill. Fit for the King. Haynes, Glenda, ed. (Illus.). 384p. (Orig.). (YA) pap. 11.50 (ISBN 0-89114-154-5). Baptist Pub Hse.

Marxhausen, Evelyn. Simeon & the Baby Jesus. (Arch Bks.). (Illus.). 24p. 1986. pap. 0.99 saddlestitched (ISBN 0-570-06202-0, 59-1425). Concordia.

Matheny, Ruth A. Scripture Stories for Today. 1983. 9.95 (ISBN 0-89837-089-2, Pub. by Pflaum Pr). Peter Li.

Mazziotta, Richard. Jesus In the Gospels: Old Stories Told Anew. LC 86-70132. 200p. (Orig.). 1986. pap. 5.95 (ISBN 0-87793-336-7). Ave Maria.

Merrell, JoAnn. Bible Stories for Family Devotions. (Illus.). 80p. 1982. pap. 4.95 (ISBN 0-87123-196-4, 210196). Bethany Hse.

Meyer, F. B. Great Verses of the Bible. 1984. gift ed. 6.95 (ISBN 0-915720-82-5). Brownlow Pub Co.

Mills, Brenda. My Bible Story Picture Book. (Illus.). 128p. 1982. text ed. 12.95 (ISBN 0-89081-319-1). Harvest Hse.

Miyoshi, Sekiya. Jonah & the Big Fish. LC 81-3635. 1982. 8.95g (ISBN 0-687-20541-7). Abingdon.

Molan, Chris, illus. Joseph the Dream Teller: Retold by Catererine Storr. (People of the Bible Ser.). (Illus.). 32p. 1984. 10.65 (ISBN 0-8172-1989-7, Raintree Children's Books Belitha Press Ltd. - London). Raintree Pubs.

Moody, Dwight L. Doscientas Anecdotas e Ilustraciones. Orig. Title: Two Hundred Anecdotes & Illustrations. (Span.). 1983. pap. 3.25 (ISBN 0-8254-1491-1). Kregel.

Mueller, A. C. My Good Shepherd Bible Story Book. LC 70-89876. 1969. bds. 12.50 (ISBN 0-570-03400-0, 56-1126). Concordia.

Murphy, Elspeth. Jesus & the Big Storm. (Tubable Hugable Ser.). (Illus.). 1984. pap. 2.95 (ISBN 0-89191-816-7). Cook.

--Noah's Ark. (Tubable Hugable Ser.). (Illus.). 1984. pap. 2.95 (ISBN 0-89191-820-5). Cook.

My First Bible Board Books. Incl. Noah & the Ark (ISBN 0-528-82490-2); Baby Jesus (ISBN 0-528-82491-0); Daniel in the Lion's Den (ISBN 0-528-82492-9); Joseph & His Brothers (ISBN 0-528-82493-7); Jesus Our Friend (ISBN 0-528-82494-5); Jonah & the Great Fish (ISBN 0-528-82495-3). 14p. 1984. pap. 2.95 ea. Macmillan.

Noah. (Burl Ives Bible-Time Stories). incl. tape 4.95 (ISBN 0-89191-801-9, 98012). Cook.

Noah's Ark. (Illus.). 1986. 2.95 (ISBN 1-55513-177-8, Chariot Bks). Cook.

Norquist, Marilyn. The Bible: Its Heroes & Its Message. 96p. 1985. pap. 2.95 (ISBN 0-89243-227-6). Liguori Pubns.

Noth, Martin. The Laws in the Pentateuch. 304p. pap. 13.95 (ISBN 0-317-31484-X, 30-870-259). Fortress.

Odor, Ruth. Bible Adventures. (Flip-a-Bible-Story Bks.). (Illus.). 16p. (Orig.). 1982. pap. 3.95 (ISBN 0-87239-561-8, 2735). Standard Pub.

--Bible Heroes. (Flip-a-Bible-Story Bks.). (Illus.). 16p. (Orig.). 1982. pap. 3.95 (ISBN 0-87239-562-6, 2736). Standard Pub.

--The Happiest Day. 1985. 5.95 (ISBN 0-89565-085-1, R4915). Standard Pub.

--Jesus & His Friends. (Flip-a-Bible-Story Bks.). (Illus.). 16p. (Orig.). 1982. pap. 3.95 (ISBN 0-87239-560-X, 2734). Standard Pub.

One Hundred Bible Stories. rev. ed. LC 66-10838. (Illus., King James Ed). 1966. 6.95 (ISBN 0-570-03461-2, 56-1063); wkbk. 3.85 (ISBN 0-570-01519-7, 22-1201). Concordia.

Parker, Gary. Life Before Birth. (Orig.). 1987. 9.95 (ISBN 0-89051-115-2); read-along cassette 5.95. Master Bks.

Patten, Donald W. The Biblical Flood & the Ice Epoch. 1966. 9.00 (ISBN 0-686-70598-X); pap. 7.50 (ISBN 0-686-70599-8). Pacific Mer.

Patterson, Kathy C. & Niklaus, Phyllis M. Stories for Communication. Communication & Learning Innovators, Ltd. Staff, et al, eds. (Bible Ser.). (Illus.). 13p. 1985. 6.00 (ISBN 0-932361-01-3). Comm & Learning.

Patterson, Yvonne. Happy Hannah. (Happy Day Bible Stories Bks.). (Illus.). 24p. 1984. 1.59 (ISBN 0-87239-764-5, 3724). Standard Pub.

Paul. (Burl Ives Bible-Time Stories). incl. tape 4.95 (ISBN 0-89191-601-6, 26013). Cook.

Petach, Heidi. Daniel & the Lions. (Happy Day Bible Stories Bks.). (Illus.). 24p. 1984. 1.59 (ISBN 0-87239-762-9, 3722). Standard Pub.

--The Lost Sheep. (Happy Day Bible Stories Bks.). (Illus.). 24p. 1984. 1.59 (ISBN 0-87239-765-3, 3725). Standard Pub.

Picture Stories from the Bible. pap. 5.00 (ISBN 0-87068-598-8). Ktav.

Pixner, Bargil, et al. The Glory of Bethlehem. 75p. 1986. 11.95 (ISBN 0-8170-1109-9). Judson.

Polyzoides, G. Stories from the New Testament. (Illus.). 112p. 3.20 (ISBN 0-686-83966-8). Divry.

Ponder, Catherine. The Millionaire Joshua. LC 77-86719. (The Millionaires of the Bible Ser.). 1978. pap. 5.95 (ISBN 0-87516-253-3). De Vorss.

Prescott, D. M. Noah & His Ark. (Very First Bible Stories Ser.). 1984. 1.59 (ISBN 0-87162-273-4, D8502). Warner Pr.

Price, Carl E. Through Other Eyes: Vivid Narratives of Some of the Bible's Most Notable Characters. 144p. (Orig.). 1987. pap. 6.95 (ISBN 0-8358-0555-7). Upper Room.

Price, Eugenia. Beloved World: The Story of God & People. (Illus.). 1979. pap. 9.95 (ISBN 0-310-31271-X, 10540P). Zondervan.

Procter, Marjorie. The Little Grey Donkey. (Very First Bible Stories Ser.). 1984. 1.59 (ISBN 0-87162-272-6, D8501). Warner Pr.

--The Little Lost Lamb. (Very First Bible Stories Ser.). 1984. 1.59 (ISBN 0-87162-276-9, D8505). Warner Pr.

Ramsay, DeVere. God's People Our Story: Bible Stories from the New Testament. LC 83-51404. 128p. 1984. 12.95 (ISBN 0-8358-0480-1). Upper Room.

Raub, Joyce. Cain & Abel. (Arch Bks.). (Illus.). 24p. 1986. pap. 0.99 saddlestitched (ISBN 0-570-06199-7, 59-1422). Concordia.

Regehr, Lydia. Bible Riddles of Birds & Beasts & Creeping Things. (Illus.). 36p. (Orig.). 1982. pap. 1.50 (ISBN 0-89323-030-8). Bible Memory.

Reid, John C. The Grumpy Prophet & 22 other Bible Stories to Read & Tell. 80p. 1986. casebound 7.95 (ISBN 0-87239-917-6, 3370). Standard Pub.

Robbins, Richard S. Bible Stories in Action for Children. 1981. 4.50 (ISBN 0-89536-475-1, 0209). CSS of Ohio.

Roberts, Jim & Scheck, Joann. Bible Pop-O-Rama Books, 2 vols. Incl. The Brightest Star (ISBN 0-8066-1601-6, 10-0915); When Jesus Was a Boy (ISBN 0-8066-1602-4, 10-7064). (Illus.). 1978. laminated 1.95 ea. Augsburg.

Robertson, Jenny. Enciclopedia de Historias Biblicas. LaValle, Maria T., tr. Tr. of Encyclopedia of Bible Stories. (Span., Illus.). 272p. 1984. 12.95 (ISBN 0-311-03671-6). Casa Bautista.

--The Landybird Bible Storybook. (Illus.). 384p. 1983. 14.95 (ISBN 0-310-44440-3, 11361). Zondervan.

Rostron, Hilda L. Stories About Children of the Bible. (Ladybird Ser). (Illus.). 1962. bds. 2.50 (ISBN 0-87508-860-0). Chr Lit.

Round, Graham, illus. Elijah & the Great Drought. (Illus.). 16p. 1982. pap. 0.99 (ISBN 0-86683-662-4, AY8239, HarpR). Har-Row.

--Nehemiah Builds a City. (Illus.). 16p. 1982. pap. 0.99 (ISBN 0-86683-661-6, AY8241, HarpR). Har-Row.

Russell, Jim, illus. Moses of the Bullrushes: Retold by Catherine Storr. (People of the Bible Ser.). (Illus.). 32p. 1984. 10.65 (ISBN 0-8172-1990-0, Raintree Children's Books Belitha Press Ltd. - London). Raintree Pubs.

Schoolland, Marian M. Leading Little Ones to God: A Child's Book of Bible Teaching. rev., 2nd ed. (Illus.). 96p. 1981. 14.95 (ISBN 0-8028-4035-3). Eerdmans.

--Marian's Big Book of Bible Stories. 1947. 12.95 (ISBN 0-8028-5003-0). Eerdmans.

--Marian's Favorite Bible Stories. 1948. 5.95 (ISBN 0-8028-5002-2); pap. 3.95 (ISBN 0-8028-5007-3). Eerdmans.

Sevidge, Marla J. Daughters of Jerusalem. LC 87-7437. 176p. (Orig.). 1987. pap. 9.95 (ISBN 0-8361-3440-0). Herald Pr.

Seymour, Peter. Peter Spier's Little Bible Storybooks. (Illus.). 1983. 7.95 (ISBN 0-385-19061-1). Doubleday.

Sheldon, Charles M. Bible Stories. LC 74-4817. (Illus.). 1978. pap. 4.95 (ISBN 0-448-14612-6, G&D). Putnam Pub Group.

Sisters of the Community of Jesus. Jericho Walls. (Illus.). 72p. (Orig.). 1984. pap. 7.95 incl. cassette (ISBN 0-941478-18-1). Paraclete Pr.

--Miracle at the Manger. LC 84-62045. (Illus., Orig.). 1984. pap. 9.95 (ISBN 0-941478-32-7). Paraclete Pr.

--Red Sea Waters. LC 82-61465. (Illus.). 72p. (Orig.). 1983. pap. 7.95 incl. cassette (ISBN 0-941478-08-4). Paraclete Pr.

Spier, Peter. Noah's Ark. LC 76-43630. (Illus.). 44p. 1977. 11.95 (ISBN 0-385-09473-6); PLB 11.95 (ISBN 0-385-12730-8). Doubleday.

Stangl, Jean. Bible Cut & Tell Stories: Old & New Testaments. (Illus.). 40p. 1987. pap. 2.95 (ISBN 0-87403-154-0, 2874 (OLD TESTAMENT)); pap. 2.95 (ISBN 0-87403-155-9, 2875 (NEW TESTAMENT)). Standard Pub.

Stedman, Ray C. Highlights of the Bible: Poets & Prophets. LC 81-50589. (Bible Commentary for Laymen Ser.). 224p. 1981. pap. text ed. 3.50 (ISBN 0-8307-0774-3, S352108). Regal.

Steele, Philip. Joseph & the Coat of Many Colors. LC 85-40309. (Bible Stories Ser.). (Illus.). 24p. 1985. 5.45 (ISBN 0-382-09091-8); PLB 6.96 (ISBN 0-382-09088-8). Silver.

Steele, Philip, adapted by. Joseph & His Brothers. LC 85-40308. (Bible Stories Ser.). (Illus.). 24p. 1985. 5.45 (ISBN 0-382-09092-6); PLB 6.96 (ISBN 0-382-09089-6). Silver.

Stifle, J. M. ABC Bible Stories. 1982. pap. 3.95 (ISBN 0-570-04063-9, 56-1366). Concordia.

Storr, Catherine, retold by. The Prodigal Son. LC 82-23011. (People of the Bible). (Illus.). 32p. 1983. PLB 10.65 (ISBN 0-8172-1982-X). Raintree Pubs.

Stowell, Gordon. Jesus Alimenta. De Martinez, Violeta S., tr. from Span. (Libros Pescaditos Sobre Jesus). Tr. of Jesus Feeds the People. (Illus.). 24p. pap. 0.60 (ISBN 0-311-38614-8). Casa Bautista.

--Jesus Ama. De Martinez, Violeta S., tr. from Span. (Libros Pescaditos Sobre Jesus). Tr. of Jesus Loves. (Illus.). 24p. 1984. pap. 0.60 (ISBN 0-311-38611-3). Casa Bautista.

--Jesus Cuenta. De Martinez, Violeta S., tr. from Span. (Libros Pescaditos Sobre Jesus). Tr. of Jesus Tells Stories. (Illus.). 24p. 1984. pap. 0.60 (ISBN 0-311-38613-X). Casa Bautista.

--Jesus Ensena. De Martinez, Violeta S., tr. from Span. (Libros Pescaditos Sobre Jesus). Tr. of Jesus Teaches. (Illus.). 24p. 1984. pap. 0.60 (ISBN 0-311-38609-1). Casa Bautista.

--Jesus Llama. De Martinez, Violeta S., tr. from Span. (Libros Pescaditos Sobre Jesus). Tr. of Jesus & the Fisherman. (Illus.). 24p. 1984. pap. 0.60 (ISBN 0-311-38612-1). Casa Bautista.

--Jesus Nace. De Martinez, Violeta S., tr. from Span. (Libros Pescaditos Sobre Jesus). Tr. of Jesus Is Born. (Illus.). 24p. 1984. pap. 0.60 (ISBN 0-311-38608-3). Casa Bautista.

--Jesus Sana. De Martinez, Violeta S., tr. from Eng. (Libros Pescaditos Sobre Jesus). Tr. of Jesus Heals. (Illus.). 24p. 1984. pap. 0.60 (ISBN 0-311-38610-5). Casa Bautista.

--Jesus Vive. De Martinez, Violeta S., tr. from Span. (Libros Pescaditos Sobre Jesus). Tr. of Jesus Lives. (Illus.). 24p. 1984. pap. 0.60 (ISBN 0-311-38615-6). Casa Bautista.

Sutton, Rosalind & Ife, Elaine, eds. Moses the Leader. (Now You Can Read Stories from the Bible Ser.). (Illus.). 24p. 1985. 2.50 (ISBN 0-8407-5391-8). Nelson.

Svensson, Borje. Great Stories from the Bible. (Change-the-Picture Storybooks). (Illus.). 10p. 1985. 6.95 (ISBN 0-89191-939-2, 59394, Chariot Bks). Cook.

Sylwester, Roland. Teaching Bible Stories More Effectively with Puppets. (Illus.). 64p. 1976. pap. 3.95 (ISBN 0-570-03731-X, 12-2633). Concordia.

Tarrant, Christ. Life in Bible Times. 48p. (Orig.). 1986. pap. 5.95 (ISBN 0-687-21850-0). Abingdon.

Taylor, Kenneth, tr. The Book for Children. 640p. 1985. 9.95 (ISBN 0-8423-2145-4). Tyndale.

Taylor, Kenneth N. Bible in Pictures for Little Eyes. (Illus.). 1956. 11.95 (ISBN 0-8024-0595-9). Moody.

--The Living Bible Story Book. 7.95 (ISBN 0-8423-2307-4). Tyndale.

Taylor, Paul. The Great Dinosaur Mystery & the Bible. (Illus.). 63p. 1987. 9.95 (ISBN 0-89051-114-4). Master Bks.

Thompson, Jean B. Bible Stories in Rhyme. 1986. text ed. 12.95 (ISBN 0-8024-0651-3). Moody.

Trapido, Barbara. Noah's Ark: A Novel. 264p. 1985. 16.95 (ISBN 0-531-09704-8). Watts.

Truit, Gloria A. Events of the Bible (Arch Bks) 1984. pap. 0.99 (59-1312). Concordia.

--Places of the Bible. 1984. pap. 0.99 (59-1313). Concordia.

Ulmer, Louise. Samuel, the Judge. (Arch Bks.). (Illus.). 24p. 1986. pap. 0.99 saddlestitched (ISBN 0-570-06200-4, 59-1423). Concordia.

Vargesko, Edward B. It Happened This Way. (Orig.). 1982. pap. 2.25 (ISBN 0-937172-35-9). JLJ Pubs.

Vos, Catherine F. The Child's Story Bible. (Illus.). 432p. 1983. Repr. of 1934 ed. PLB 14.95 (ISBN 0-8028-5011-1). Eerdmans.

VOS Story Bible, 3 vols. Set. pap. 27.50 (ISBN 0-85151-442-1). Banner of Truth.

VOS Story Bible: New Testament. pap. 9.50 (ISBN 0-85151-237-2). Banner of Truth.

VOS Story Bible: Old Testament (Samuel-Malachi) pap. 9.50 (ISBN 0-85151-251-8). Banner of Truth.

Waddell, Helen. Stories from Holy Writ. LC 74-25538. 280p. 1975. Repr. of 1949 ed. lib. bdg. 22.50x (ISBN 0-8371-7872-X, WAHW). Greenwood.

Wahl, Jan, retold by. Runaway Jonah & Other Biblical Adventures Including Little Joseph, Singing David & Captain Noah. (Illus.). 96p. 1985. 13.95 (ISBN 0-89845-421-2). Caedmon.

Walton, John & Walton, Kim. Abraham & His Big Family. (Early Bible Foundations Ser.). (Illus.). 1986. pap. 2.95 (ISBN 1-55513-031-3, Chariot Bks). Cook.

--Daniel & the Lion's Den. (Early Foundations in the Bible Ser.). (Illus.). 1987. pap. 2.95 (ISBN 1-55513-045-3, Chariot Press). Cook.

--God & the World He Made. (Early Bible Foundations Ser.). (Illus.). 1986. pap. 2.95 (ISBN 1-55513-030-5, Chariot Bks). Cook.

--Jonah & the Big Fish. (Early Bible Foundations Ser.). (Illus.). 1986. pap. 2.95 (ISBN 1-55513-035-6, Chariot Bks). Cook.

--Moses & the Awful Plagues. (Early Bible Foundations Ser.). (Illus.). 1986. pap. 2.95 (ISBN 1-55513-041-0, Chariot Bks). Cook.

Wangerin, W., Jr. O Happy Day! (Arch Bks.: No. 12). 1981. pap. 0.99 (ISBN 0-570-06093-1, 59-1211). Concordia.

Wangerin, Walter, Jr. The Baby God Promised. (Arch Bks.: No. 13). (Illus.). 32p. 1976. pap. 0.99 (ISBN 0-570-06105-9, 59-1223). Concordia.

Ward, Elaine M. More Old Testament Stories. 65p. 1984. pap. 6.95 (ISBN 0-940754-23-1). Ed Ministries.

Waybill, Marjorie. God's Justice: Activity Book. (Story Bible Ser.: Vol. 6). 88p. (Orig.). 1985. pap. 3.00 (ISBN 0-8361-3397-8). Herald Pr.

Where Do We Live? (Illus.). 1986. 2.95 (ISBN 1-55513-176-X, Chariot Bks). Cook.

White, William R. Stories for Telling: A Treasury for Christian Storytellers. LC 85-28980. 144p. (Orig.). 1986. pap. 6.95 (10-6023). Augsburg.

Wilkerson, David. Promesas de Jesus. (Span.). 95p. 1974. pap. 2.50 (ISBN 0-89922-027-4). Edit Caribe.

Wolf, Bob. Bible Animal Stories, Bk. 1. (Illus.). 86p. 1983. pap. 3.95 (ISBN 0-89323-044-8). Bible Memory.

--Uncle Bob's Bible Stories. (Illus.). 108p. (Orig.). 1982. pap. 1.75 (ISBN 0-89323-028-6). Bible Memory.

The Worry Pill & Other Stories Based on Proverbs. 4.95 (2850001). CEF Press.

Youd, Pauline. Adopted for a Purpose: Bible Stories of Joseph, Moses, Samuel, & Esther. 144p. (Orig.). 1986. pap. 7.95 (ISBN 0-687-00770-4). Abingdon.

Zehr, Paul. God Dwells with His People. LC 80-22701. 216p. 1981. pap. 7.95 (ISBN 0-8361-1939-8). Herald Pr.

BIBLE STORIES–N. T.

see also Jesus Christ–Biography–Juvenile Literature

Barnwell, William H. Our Story According to St. Mark. 288p. (Orig.). 1982. pap. 9.95 (ISBN 0-86683-634-9, HarpR). Har-Row.

Bible Puzzler No. Two: Stories from Mark. 1985. 2.95 (ISBN 0-89536-768-8, 5876). CSS of Ohio.

Broughton, Pamela, retold by. The Prodigal Son. (Golden Bible Stories Ser.). (Illus.). 32p. 1986. 3.95 (ISBN 0-307-11623-9, Pub. by Golden Bks). Western Pub.

Buck, Pearl S. The Story Bible: New Testament, Vol. 2. 1972. pap. 3.95 (ISBN 0-451-14639-5, AE2694, Sig). NAL.

Bull, Norman. One Hundred New Testament Stories. 160p. (Orig.). 1984. pap. 7.95 (ISBN 0-687-29073-2). Abingdon.

Children of the New Testament. (Arch Book Anthology Ser.). (Illus.). 160p. 1986. 7.95 (ISBN 0-570-06206-3, 59-7000). Concordia.

Children of the Old Testament. (Arch Book Anthology Ser.). (Illus.). 152p. 1986. 7.95 (ISBN 0-570-06207-1, 59-7001). Concordia.

Child's Bible: New Testament: Rewritten for Children by Shirley Steen. LC 78-51445. 288p. 1978. pap. 4.95 (ISBN 0-8091-2118-2). Paulist Pr.

Coe, Joyce. The Donkey Who Served the King. (Arch Bk. Ser.: No. 15). (Illus.). 1978. 0.99 (ISBN 0-570-06120-2, 59-1238). Concordia.

Colina, Tessa, ed. Jesus, My Friend. (Jesus & Me Pupil Activities Books: No. 3). (Illus.). 1978. pap. 1.50 (ISBN 0-87239-270-8, 2442). Standard Pub.

--Jesus, My Lord. (Jesus & Me Pupil Activities Books: No. 4). (Illus.). 1978. pap. 1.50 (ISBN 0-87239-271-6, 2443). Standard Pub.

--Jesus, My Saviour. (Jesus & Me Pupil Activities Books: No. 1). (Illus.). 1978. pap. 1.50 (ISBN 0-87239-268-6, 2440). Standard Pub.

Dolch, Edward W. & Dolch, M. P. Gospel Stories. (Pleasure Reading Ser.). 176p. 1951. PLB 6.57 (ISBN 0-8116-2608-3). Garrard.

Doney, Meryl. The Kind Stranger. (Illus.). 16p. 1982. pap. 0.99 (ISBN 0-86683-666-7, AY8244, HarpR). Har-Row.

--The Lost Sheep. (Illus.). 16p. 1982. pap. 0.99 (ISBN 0-86683-663-2, AY8243, HarpR). Har-Row.

--The Loving Father. (Illus.). 16p. 1982. pap. 0.99 (ISBN 0-86683-665-9, AY8245, HarpR). Har-Row.

The First Christmas. (Read, Show & Tell Ser.). (Eng. & Span., Illus.). 1977. Eng. ed. 2.52 (ISBN 0-8326-2603-1, 3621); Span. ed. 2.95 (ISBN 0-685-52280-6, 5621). World Bible.

Fletcher, Sarah. Bible Story Book: New Testament. LC 56-1427. (Continued Applied Christianity Ser.). 1983. 10.50 (ISBN 0-570-04080-9). Concordia.

Garfield, Leon. The King in the Garden. LC 84-10064. (Illus.). 32p. 1985. 11.75 (ISBN 0-688-04106-X). Lothrop.

Gibson, Katherine. The Tall Book of Bible Stories. LC 57-10952. (Tall Bks.). (Illus.). 128p. 1980. 5.70i (ISBN 0-06-021935-1); PLB 7.89 (ISBN 0-06-021936-X). HarpJ.

Groth, Jeanette L. Little Journeys with Jesus. pap. 5.95 (ISBN 0-570-03924-X, 12-2858). Concordia.

Heeg, Aloysius J. Jesus & I. pap. text ed. 1.00 (ISBN 0-8294-0214-4). Loyola.

Johnson, Pamela F., illus. The Miracle of the Loaves & Fishes. (Golden Bible Stories Ser.). (Illus.). 32p. 1986. 3.95 (ISBN 0-307-11622-0, Pub. by Golden Bks). Western Pub.

Kingston, Robert. See & Share Stories about Jesus, 4 bks. Orig. Title: Bible Stories. (Illus.). 40p. Repr. Set. 7.95 (ISBN 0-687-37132-5). Abingdon.

Klus, Ronald. John the Baptist. (Arch Book Ser.: No. 21). 1984. pap. 0.99 (ISBN 0-570-06189-X, 59-1290). Concordia.

Lewis, Shari & Henderson, Florence. One-Minute Bible Stories: New Testament. LC 86-6401. (Illus.). 48p. 1986. 6.95 (ISBN 0-385-23286-1); PLB 6.95 (ISBN 0-385-23287-X). Doubleday.

Lusk, David T. Within the Halls of Pilate. 4.50 (ISBN 0-89137-538-4). Quality Pubns.

MacDonald, William C. Glossolalia in the New Testament. 22p. 1964. pap. 1.50 (ISBN 0-88243-508-6, 02-0508). Gospel Pub.

MacMaster, Eve B. God's Suffering Servant. LC 86-19526. (Story Bible Ser.: Bk. 9). (Illus.). 120p. (Orig.). 1987. pap. 5.95 (ISBN 0-8361-3422-2). Herald Pr.

Marquart, M. Jesus' Second Family. (Arch Book Series Fourteen). 1977. pap. 0.99 (ISBN 0-570-06111-3, 59-1229). Concordia.

Marshall, Catherine. Catherine Marshall's Story Bible. (Illus.). 216p. 1984. pap. 10.95 (ISBN 0-8245-0596-4). Crossroad NY.

Rasi, Humberto. Life of Jesus. 9.95 ea. (ISBN 0-8163-0573-0). No.1, 1984. No.2, 1985 (ISBN 0-8163-0602-8). No. 3, 1985 (ISBN 0-8163-0607-9). Pacific Pr Pub Assn.

Reis, Elizabeth M. A Deeper Kind of Truth: Biblical Tales for Life & Prayer. 112p. (Orig.). 1987. pap. 5.95 (ISBN 0-8091-2858-6). Paulist Pr.

Roberts, D. S. Faith, Hope & Love: Learning about I Corinthians 13. LC 56-1397. (Concept Books Series Four). 1983. pap. 3.95 (ISBN 0-570-08526-8). Concordia.

Round, Graham, illus. Miriam & the Princess of Egypt. (Illus.). 16p. 1982. pap. 0.99 (ISBN 0-86683-659-4, AY8240, HarpR). Har-Row.

--Naaman & the Little Servant Girl. (Illus.). 1982. pap. 0.99 (ISBN 0-86683-660-8, AY8242, HarpR). Har-Row.

Stortz, Diane. Zaccheus Meets Jesus. (Happy Day Bible Stories Bks.). (Illus.). 24p. 1984. 1.59 (ISBN 0-87239-766-1, 3726). Standard Pub.

Tiner, John H. Favorite Stories from Acts Word Search. 48p. 1986. pap. 2.50 (ISBN 0-87403-047-1, 2691). Standard Pub.

Uhl, Harold J. The Gospel for Children: Object Messages from the Gospel of Mark. LC 75-14695. 128p. 1975. pap. 6.95 (ISBN 0-8066-1493-5, 10-2830). Augsburg.

The Wise Men. (Read, Show & Tell Ser.). (Eng. & Span., Illus.). 1977. Eng. Ed. 2.25 (ISBN 0-8326-2606-6, 3624). Span. Ed (5624). World Bible.

BIBLE STORIES–O. T.

Barrett, Ethel. The Strangest Thing Happened. LC 76-84599. 144p. 1971. pap. 1.95 (ISBN 0-8307-0005-6, S061104). Regal.

Behnke, John. Ten Plus One Bible Stories from Creation to Samson, Retold in Everyday Language for Today's Children. LC 83-82022. (Orig.). 1984. pap. 2.95 (ISBN 0-8091-6552-X). Paulist Pr.

Boggs, Sue H. The Secret of Hind's Feet. 2.95 (ISBN 0-89137-537-6). Quality Pubns.

Boruch, Behn. Coat of Many Colors. 1959. 3.95 (ISBN 0-88482-728-3). Hebrew Pub.

Broughton, Pamela. The Creation. (Golden Bible Stories Ser.). (Illus.). 32p. 1985. 3.95 (ISBN 0-307-11620-4, Pub. by Golden Bks). Western Pub.

--Noah's Ark. (Golden Bible Stories Ser.). (Illus.). 32p. 1985. 3.95 (ISBN 0-307-11621-2, Pub. by Golden Bks). Western Pub.

Broughton, Pamela, retold by. David & Goliath. LC 85-81161. (Golden Bible Stories). (Illus.). 32p. 1986. 3.95 (ISBN 0-307-11625-5, Pub. by Golden Bks). Western Pub.

Buck, Pearl S. The Story Bible: Old Testament, Vol. 1. 1972. pap. 3.95 (ISBN 0-451-13458-3, Sig). NAL.

Bull, Norman. Prophets of the Jews. (Bible Story & Its Background Ser.: Vol. 3). pap. 9.95 (ISBN 0-7175-0979-6). Dufour.

Caffrey, Stephanie & Kenslea, Timothy, eds. The Boy in the Striped Coat. (Rainbow Books). 1978. pap. 1.00 (ISBN 0-8192-1234-2). Morehouse.

Chaikin, Miriam. Exodus. LC 85-27361. (Illus.). 32p. 1987. reinforced bdg. 14.95 (ISBN 0-8234-0607-5). Holiday.

Child's Bible: Old Testament: Rewritten for Children by Anne Edwards. LC 78-51444. 384p. 1978. pap. 4.95 (ISBN 0-8091-2117-4). Paulist Pr.

Clarke, M. J., et al. Copper, Molybdenum, & Vanadium in Biological Systems: Structure & Bonding, Vol. 53. (Illus.). 166p. 1983. 39.50 (ISBN 0-387-12042-4). Springer-Verlag.

Colina, Tessa. Ark Full of Animals. (Illus.). 1985. comb bdg. 4.95 (ISBN 0-317-30647-2, R2707). Standard Pub.

Cone, Molly. About Learning. (Shema Primary Ser: No. 2). (Illus., Orig.). 1972. pap. 5.00 (ISBN 0-8074-0127-7, 101082). UAHC.

Craig, Diana. Moses & the Flight from Egypt. LC 84-50448. (Bible Stories Ser.). (Illus.). 24p. 1984. 5.45 (ISBN 0-382-06945-5); PLB 6.96 (ISBN 0-382-06797-5). Silver.

--The Young Moses. LC 84-50449. (Bible Stories Ser.). (Illus.). 24p. 1984. PLB 6.96 (ISBN 0-382-06797-5); 5.45 (ISBN 0-382-06946-3). Silver.

Craig, Diana, adapted by. Elijah: Messenger of God. LC 84-51683. (Bible Stories Ser.). (Illus.). 24p. 1984. 5.45 (ISBN 0-382-06943-9); PLB 6.96 (ISBN 0-382-06794-0). Silver.

--Jacob & Esau. LC 84-51684. (Bible Stories Ser.). (Illus.). 24p. 1984. 5.45 (ISBN 0-382-06944-7); PLB 5.96 (ISBN 0-382-06795-9). Silver.

David & Goliath. (Read, Show & Tell Ser.). (Eng. & Span., Illus.). 1977. Eng. Ed. pap. 2.25 (ISBN 0-8326-2602-3, 3620). Span. Ed (5620). World Bible.

DePaola, Tomie. Noah & the Ark. (Illus.). 32p. 1983. 12.95 (ISBN 0-86683-819-8, AY8451, HarpR). Har-Row.

Dimond, Jasper. Noah's Ark. (Illus.). 48p. 1983. 8.95 (ISBN 0-13-622951-4). P-H.

Enns, Peter & Forsberg, Glen. Adam & Eve & Five Other Stories. (Stories that Live Ser.: Bk. 1). (Illus.). 24p. 1985. book & Cassette 4.95 (ISBN 0-936215-01-1). STL Intl.

--David & Goliath & Five Other Stories. (Stories that Live Ser.: Bk. 3). (Illus.). 24p. 1985. book & Cassette 4.95 (ISBN 0-936215-03-8). STL Intl.

--Joseph the Dreamer & Five Other Stories. (Stories that Live Ser.: Bk. 2). (Illus.). 24p. 1985. book & cassette 4.95 (ISBN 0-936215-02-X). STL Intl.

Fant, Louie, Jr., ed. Noah-in Sign Language. pap. 5.00 (ISBN 0-917002-10-5). Joyce Media.

Fischman, Joyce. Bible Work & Play, 3 vols. (Illus., Orig.). 1966. pap. text ed. 2.50 ea. Vol. 1 o.p (102610). Vol. 2 o.p (102620). Vol. 3 (102640). UAHC.

Fletcher, Sarah. Bible Story Book: Old Testament. LC 83-1801. (Continued Applied Christianity Ser.). 1983. 10.50 (ISBN 0-570-04079-5, 56-1426). Concordia.

Gibson, Katherine. The Tall Book of Bible Stories. LC 57-10952. (Tall Bks.). (Illus.). 128p. 1980. 5.70i (ISBN 0-06-021935-1); PLB 7.89 (ISBN 0-06-021936-X). HarpJ.

Golphenee, Lucille B. Isaac's Chosen Wife. (Arch Book Ser.: No. 21). 1984. pap. 0.99 (59-1282). Concordia.

Head, Constance. The Story of Deborah. (Arch Bk Ser.: No. 15). (Illus.). 1978. 0.99 (ISBN 0-570-06116-4, 59-1234). Concordia.

Hollyer, Belinda. David & Goliath. LC 84-50452. (Bible Stories Ser.). (Illus.). 24p. 1984. 5.45 (ISBN 0-382-06940-4); PLB 6.96 (ISBN 0-382-06791-6). Silver.

--Jonah & the Great Fish. LC 84-50451. (Bible Stories Ser.). (Illus.). 24p. 1984. 5.45 (ISBN 0-382-06792-4); pap. 5.96 (ISBN 0-382-06941-2). Silver.

--Noah & the Ark. LC 84-50450. (Bible Stories Ser.). (Illus.). 24p. 1984. PLB 6.96 (ISBN 0-382-06793-2); pap. 5.45 (ISBN 0-382-06942-0). Silver.

Hollyer, Belinda, adapted by. Daniel in the Lions' Den. LC 84-50453. (Bible Stories Ser.). (Illus.). 24p. 1984. 6.96 (ISBN 0-382-06939-0); PLB 5.96 (ISBN 0-382-06939-0). Silver.

Hunt, P. Bible Stories from the Old Testament. (Illus.). 4.98 (ISBN 0-517-43909-3). Outlet Bk Co.

Hutton, Warwick. Jonah & the Great Fish. LC 83-15477. (Illus.). 32p. 1984. 12.95 (ISBN 0-689-50283-4, McElderly Bk). Macmillan.

Ife, Elaine & Sutton, Rosalind, eds. David & Goliath. (Now You Can Read Stories from the Bible Ser.). (Illus.). 24p. 1985. 2.50 (ISBN 0-8407-5392-6). Nelson.

Jones, Howard A. Hooked on Horses: Bits of This & That about People & Horses after 21 Years in the Racing Game. (Illus.). 144p. 1982. 12.50 (ISBN 0-682-49792-4, Banner). Exposition Pr FL.

Kauffman, Suzanne. God Gives the Land Activity Book. (Story Bible Ser.: Bk. 3). 64p. 1984. pap. 3.00 (ISBN 0-8361-3359-5). Herald Pr.

Kolbrek, Loyal. The Day God Made It Rain. (Arch Books Series Fourteen). 1977. pap. 0.99 (ISBN 0-570-06108-3, 59-1226). Concordia.

Levinger, Elma E. Beautiful Garden & Other Bible Tales. (Illus.). 5.95 (ISBN 0-8197-0253-6). Bloch.

Lewis, Shari. One-Minute Bible Stories: Old Testament. LC 86-2011. (Illus.). 48p. 1986. 6.95 (ISBN 0-385-19565-6); PLB 6.95 (ISBN 0-385-19566-4). Doubleday.

Limburg, James. Old Stories for a New Time. LC 82-49019. 127p. 1983. pap. 8.95 (ISBN 0-8042-0148-X). John Knox.

Macmaster, Eve. God Gives the Land. LC 83-182. (Story Bible Ser.: Vol. 3). (Illus.). 168p. (Orig.). 1983. pap. 5.95 (ISBN 0-8361-3332-3). Herald Pr.

--God Rescues His People: Stories of God & His People: Exodus, Leviticus, Numbers & Deuteronomy. LC 82-2849. (Story Bible Ser.: No. 2). (Illus.). 176p. (Orig.). 1982. pap. 5.95 (ISBN 0-8361-1994-0). Herald Pr.

McWhorter, Jane. Meet My Friend David. 4.95 (ISBN 0-89137-420-5). Quality Pubns.

Mahany, Patricia S. Hurry Up, Noah. (Happy Day Bks.). (Illus.). 24p. 1986. 1.59 (ISBN 0-87403-028-5, 3488). Standard Pub.

Marjorie, Palmer. God Saves Noah. (My Bible Story Reader Ser.: Vol. 2). (Illus., Orig.). 1983. pap. 1.95 (ISBN 0-8024-0192-9). Moody.

Mitchell, Robert. Abraham, Sarah & the Promised Son. (Arch Book Ser.: No. 21). 1984. pap. 0.99 (59-1284). Concordia.

Napier, B. Davie. Come Sweet Death. rev. ed. LC 80-27301. 64p. 1981. pap. 4.95 (ISBN 0-8298-0422-6). Pilgrim NY.

Neff, Lavonne. God's Gift Baby. (Arch Bks.: No. 14). 1977. pap. 0.99 (ISBN 0-570-06113-X, 59-1230). Concordia.

Noah's Boat. (Read, Show & Tell Ser). (Eng. & Span., Illus.). 1977. Eng. Ed. 2.25 (ISBN 0-8326-2605-8, 3623). Span. Ed (5623). World Bible.

Omer, Devorah. The Gideonites. 256p. 1968. 3.50 (ISBN 0-88482-750-X). Hebrew Pub.

Paamoni, Zev. Yitzchak, Son of Abraham. (Biblical Ser.). (Illus.). 1970. 4.00 (ISBN 0-914080-25-3). Shulsinger Sales.

Palmer, Marjorie. God Helps David. (My Bible Story Reader Ser.: Vol. 1). (Illus.). 1983. pap. 1.95 (ISBN 0-8024-0191-0). Moody.

Pfrimmer, Mildred. Books to Learn & Live by, 5 bks. Incl. Bk. 1. The ABC's of Creation; Bk. 2. The ABC's of the Flood; Bk. 3. The Aardvark in the Art; Bk. 4. Elephant in Eden; Bk. 5. The Tale of the Whale. (The Little Talkers Ser.). 1977. Set. 17.50 (ISBN 0-685-80546-8). Triumph Pub.

Polyzoides, G. Stories from the Old Testament. (Gr., Illus.). 71p. 3.20 (ISBN 0-686-80434-1). Divry.

Ramsay, DeVere. The Old Testament: God's People-Our Story. LC 84-51829. (Illus.). 1985. 12.95 (ISBN 0-8358-0500-X). Upper Room.

Robison, Pamela. Abinadi, Man of God. (Orig.). 1981. pap. 4.00 (ISBN 0-8309-0324-0). Herald Hse.

Samson. (Read, Show & Tell Ser.). (Eng. & Span., Illus.). 1977. Eng. Ed. 2.25 (ISBN 0-8326-2607-4, 3625). Span. Ed (5625). World Bible.

Samuels, Ruth. Bible Stories for Jewish Children, 2 vols, No. 1. (Illus.). 1958. 7.95x (ISBN 0-87068-356-X). Ktav.

--Bible Stories for Jewish Children, 2 vols, No. 2. (Illus.). 1973. 7.95x (ISBN 0-87068-965-7). Ktav.

Scruggs, Rachael I. Come Follow Me. LC 80-52620. 142p. 1983. 7.95 (ISBN 0-533-04769-2). Vantage.

Seven Archangels. The Vials of the Seven Last Plagues. LC 76-28083. 156p. (Orig.). 1977. pap. 5.95 (ISBN 0-916766-23-3). Summit Univ.

Stern, Menahem. The Sun & the Clouds. 1972. 6.95x (ISBN 0-87068-389-6). Ktav.

Stewart, Frances T. & Stewart, Charles P. Noah & the Rainbow Promise. (Stick & L Book Ser.). (Illus.). 1986. pap. 6.95 (ISBN 0-8054-4187-5). Broadman.

Stirrup Associates, Inc. My Jesus Pocketbook of Jonah & the Big Fish. Harvey, Bonnie C. & Phillips, Cheryl M., eds. LC 83-51679. (My Jesus Pocketbook Ser.). (Illus.). 32p. 1984. pap. 0.49 (ISBN 0-937420-09-3). Stirrup Assoc.

--My Jesus Pocketbook of Noah & the Floating Zoo. Harvey, Bonnie C. & Phillips, Cheryl M., eds. LC 83-51680. (My Jesus Pocketbook Ser.). (Illus.). 32p. 1984. pap. 0.49 (ISBN 0-937420-10-7). Stirrup Assoc.

Storr, Catherine, retold by. Adam & Eve. LC 82-23060. (People of the Bible). (Illus.). 32p. 1983. PLB 10.65 (ISBN 0-8172-1981-1). Raintree Pubs.

Tiner, John H. Word Search: Favorite Bible Stories from Genesis. pap. 2.70 (ISBN 0-89137-615-1). Quality Pubns.

Tower of Babel. (Read, Show & Tell Ser.). (Eng. & Span., Illus.). 1977. Eng. Ed. 2.25 (ISBN 0-8326-2604-X, 3622). Span. Ed (5622). World Bible.

Traylor, Ellen G. Noah. 256p. 1985. pap. 6.95 (ISBN 0-8423-4703-8). Tyndale.

VOS Story Bible: Old Testament (Genesis-Ruth) pap. 9.50 (ISBN 0-85151-250-X). Banner of Truth.

Ward, Elaine M. More Old Testament Stories. 65p. 1984. pap. 6.95 (ISBN 0-940754-23-1). Ed Ministries.

--Old Testament Stories: For Church & Home. 70p. (Orig.). 1984. pap. 6.95 (ISBN 0-940754-19-3). Ed Ministries.

Waterman, Paul. Great Adventures of the Old Testament. (Activity Book Ser.). Vol. 1. pap. 0.99 (ISBN 0-87123-751-2, 220751); Vol. 2. pap. 0.99 (ISBN 0-87123-769-5). Bethany Hse.

Weil, Lisl. Esther. LC 79-22543. (Illus.). 48p. 1980. 9.95 (ISBN 0-689-30761-6, Childrens Bk). Macmillan.

Weisheit, Eldon. God's Promise for Children: Object Lessons on Old Testament Texts. LC 82-70956. (Series C). 128p. (Orig.). 1982. pap. 6.95 (ISBN 0-8066-1931-7, 10-2694). Augsburg.

BIBLE TRANSLATING

see Bible–Translating; Bible–Versions

BIBLICAL ANTHROPOLOGY

see Man (Theology)

BIBLICAL ARCHAEOLOGY

see Bible–Antiquities

BIBLICAL CHARACTERS

see Bible–Biography

BIBLICAL GREEK

see Greek Language, Biblical

BIBLICAL LAW

see Jewish Law

BIBLICAL NAMES

see Bible–Names

BIBLICAL NUMEROLOGY

see Numbers in the Bible

BIBLICAL RESEARCH

see Bible–Criticism, Interpretation, etc.

BIBLICAL SOCIOLOGY

see Sociology, Biblical

BIGAMY

see also Polygamy

Deer, John. Bigamy, Polygamy & Polyandry: A Comprehensive Bibliography. 108p. (Orig.). 1986. pap. 11.95 (ISBN 0-940519-08-9). Res Discover Pubns.

BIGOTRY

see Toleration

BILLINGS, WILLIAM, 1746-1800

Barbour, James M. The Church Music of William Billings. LC 72-39000. 167p. 1972. Repr. of 1960 ed. lib. bdg. 22.50 (ISBN 0-306-70434-X). Da Capo.

--The Church Music of William Billings. 167p. Repr. of 1960 ed. lib. bdg. 29.00 (Pub. by Am Repr Serv). Am Biog Serv.

McKay, David & Crawford, Richard. William Billings of Boston: Eighteenth-Century Composer. LC 74-2971. (Illus.). 320p. 1975. 37.00x (ISBN 0-691-09118-8). Princeton U Pr.

Nathan, Hans. William Billings: Data & Documents. LC 75-33593. (Bibliographies in American Music: No. 2). 1976. 10.00 (ISBN 0-911772-67-7). Info Coord.

BIOGRAPHY

see also Christian Biography; Epitaphs

also names of individuals, and subdivision biography under particular subjects and under names of countries, cities, etc.

Bertaux, Daniel, ed. Biography & Society: The Life History Approach in the Social Sciences. (Sage Studies in International Sociology: Vol. 23). 308p. 1981. pap. 14.00 (ISBN 0-8039-9801-5). Sage.

Carre, E. G. Praying Hyde. LC 82-73972. 183p. 1983. pap. 4.95 (ISBN 0-88270-541-5). Bridge Pub.

Clark, Barrett H. Great Short Biographies of the World: A Collection of Short Biographies. 1979. Repr. of 1929 ed. lib. bdg. 40.00 (ISBN 0-8492-4037-9). R West.

Cochrane, Robert. The Treasury of Modern Biography: A Gallery of Literary Sketches of Eminent Men & Women of the 19th Century. 1881. Repr. 50.00 (ISBN 0-8274-3645-9). R West.

Eastman, Fred. Men of Power: Benjamin Franklin, Ralph Waldo Emerson, George Fox, Charles Darwin, Vol. 3. facs. ed. LC 74-128236. (Essay Index Reprint Ser). 1939. 18.00 (ISBN 0-8369-1993-9). Ayer Co Pubs.

--Men of Power: Francis of Assisi, Leonardo Da Vinci, Oliver Cromwell, John Milton, Vol. 2. facs. ed. LC 74-128236. (Essay Index Reprint Ser). 1938. 18.00 (ISBN 0-8369-1992-0). Ayer Co Pubs.

--Men of Power: Nicolai Lenin, Mahatma Gandhi, Edward Livingston Trudeau, Robest Louis Stevenson, Vol. 5. facs. ed. LC 74-128236. (Essay Index Reprint Ser). 1940. 18.00 (ISBN 0-8369-1995-5). Ayer Co Pubs.

Fraser, Amy S. The Hills of Home. (Illus.). 250p. 1973. pap. 8.95 (ISBN 0-7102-0540-6). Methuen Inc.

Friedson, Anthony M., ed. New Directions in Biography. (Biography Monographs: No. 2). 125p. 1982. pap. text ed. 7.95x (ISBN 0-8248-0783-9). UH Pr.

Kingsmill, Hugh. The Progress of a Biographer. 1973. lib. bdg. 25.00 (ISBN 0-8414-5588-0). Folcroft.

Langness, L. L. & Frank, Gelya F. Lives: An Anthropological Approach to Biography. Edgerton, R. B., ed. LC 81-15460. (Chandler & Sharp Publications in Anthropology Ser.). 232p. (Orig.). 1981. pap. 9.95x (ISBN 0-88316-542-2). Chandler & Sharp.

Lownsbery, Eloise. Saints & Rebels. facsimile ed. LC 72-156682. (Essay Index Reprint Ser). Repr. of 1937 ed. 22.00 (ISBN 0-8369-2322-7). Ayer Co Pubs.

Macmurray, John, ed. Some Makers of the Modern Spirit: A Symposium. facs. ed. LC 68-22926. (Essay Index Reprint Ser). Repr. of 1933 ed. 16.25 (ISBN 0-8369-0658-6). Ayer Co Pubs.

Oliver, Peter. Saints of Chaos. facs. ed. LC 67-23255. (Essay Index Reprint Ser). 1934. 17.00 (ISBN 0-8369-0752-3). Ayer Co Pubs.

Pachter, Marc, ed. Telling Lives: The Biographer's Art. LC 81-10312. 151p. 1981. pap. 10.95 (ISBN 0-8122-1118-9). U of Pa Pr.

Pinto, Vivan De Sola. English Biography. 1973. lib. bdg. 10.00 (ISBN 0-8414-9259-X). Folcroft.

Roberts, S. C. Doctor Watson: Prolegomena to the Study of a Biographical Problem. LC 73-16388. lib. bdg. 10.00 (ISBN 0-8414-7268-8). Folcroft.

Stevenson, Burton. A Guide to Biography. 1973. Repr. of 1910 ed. 25.00 (ISBN 0-8274-0867-6). R West.

BIOLOGY–STUDY AND TEACHING

Liberty, Gene. The Meaning of Life. (Orig.). 1975. pap. text ed. 8.67 (ISBN 0-87720-010-6). AMSCO Sch.

BIRTH (IN RELIGION, FOLK-LORE, ETC.)

The New Technologies of Birth & Death: Medical, Legal & Moral Dimensions. LC 80-83425. xvi, 196p. (Orig.). 1980. pap. 8.95 (ISBN 0-935372-07-5). Pope John Ctr.

BIRTH CONTROL

see also Abortion

Bouvier, Leon & Rao, Sethu. Socioreligious Factors in Fertility Decline. LC 75-26602. 224p. 1975. text ed. 25.00x prof ref (ISBN 0-88410-352-8). Ballinger Pub.

Field, Marilyn J. The Comparative Politics of Birth Control: Determinants of Policy Variation & Change in the Developed Nations. (Landmark Dissertations in Women's Studies). (Illus.). 320p. 1983. 42.95 (ISBN 0-03-069527-9). Praeger.

Friesen, Duane. Moral Issues in the Control of Birth. new ed. LC 74-76587. (Illus.). 64p. 1974. pap. 1.95 (ISBN 0-87303-561-5). Faith & Life.

Gordon, Linda. Woman's Body, Woman's Right: Birth Control in America. 1977. pap. 8.95 (ISBN 0-14-004683-6). Penguin.

Hardin, Garrett, ed. Population, Evolution, & Birth Control: A Collage of Controversial Ideas. 2nd ed. LC 69-16921. (Biology Ser.). (Illus.). 386p. 1969. pap. text ed. 13.95x (ISBN 0-7167-0670-9). W H Freeman.

Hodann, Max. History of Modern Morals. LC 72-9651. Repr. of 1937 ed. 47.50 (ISBN 0-404-57460-2). AMS Pr.

Knowlton, Charles & Owen, Robert D. Birth Control & Morality in Nineteenth Century America: Two Discussions. (Family in America Ser.). 1972. cancelled (ISBN 0-405-03883-6, 13318). Ayer Co Pubs.

Musallam, Basim. Sex & Society in Islam: Birth Control Before the Nineteenth Century. LC 82-23539. (Cambridge Studies in Islamic Civilization). 240p. 1983. 34.50 (ISBN 0-521-24874-4). Cambridge U Pr.

Musallam, Basim F. Sex & Society in Islam: Birth Control Before the Nineteenth Century. (Cambridge Studies in Islamic Civilization). 176p. 1986. pap. 12.95 (ISBN 0-521-33858-1). Cambridge U Pr.

Reining, Priscilla & Tinker, Irene, eds. Population: Dynamics, Ethics & Policy. 1975. pap. 19.00 (ISBN 0-12-586751-4). Acad Pr.

Schwartz, Michael. The Case Against Planned Parenthood. 200p. (Orig.). Date not set. pap. cancelled (ISBN 0-87973-539-2, 539). Our Sunday Visitor.

Tychsen, Laurie. Too Many People? Answers & Hope for the Human Family. 46p. (Orig.). 1986. pap. 3.25 (ISBN 0-937779-03-2). Greenlawn Pr.

BIRTH CONTROL–RELIGIOUS ASPECTS

Atkinson, Gary M. & Moraczewski, Albert S. Genetic Counseling, the Church & the Law. LC 79-92084. xvii, 259p. (Orig.). 1980. pap. 9.95 (ISBN 0-935372-06-7). Pope John Ctr.

--A Moral Evaluation of Contraception & Sterilization: A Dialogical Study. LC 79-90971. viii, 115p. (Orig.). 1979. pap. 4.95 (ISBN 0-935372-05-9). Pope John Ctr.

Bouvier, Leon & Rao, Sethu. Socioreligious Factors in Fertility Decline. LC 75-26602. 224p. 1975. text ed. 25.00x prof ref (ISBN 0-88410-352-8). Ballinger Pub.

Collins, Mary J., ed. A Church Divided: Catholics' Attitudes about Family Planning, Abortion, & Teenage Sexuality. (The Bishops Watch Ser.). (Orig.). 1986. pap. 5.00 (ISBN 0-915365-12-X). Cath Free Choice.

DeJong, Peter & Smit, William. Family Planning: How To Decide What's Best for You. 208p. 1987. pap. 6.95 (ISBN 0-310-37961-X). Zondervan.

Feldman, David M. Birth Control in Jewish Law: Marital Relations, Contraception, & Abortion As Set Forth in the Classic Texts of Jewish Law. LC 79-16712. 1980. Repr. of 1968 ed. lib. bdg. 27.50x (ISBN 0-313-21297-X, FEBC). Greenwood.

--Marital Relations, Birth Control, & Abortion in Jewish Law. LC 68-15338. 336p. 1974. pap. 8.95 (ISBN 0-8052-0438-5). Schocken.

Field, Marilyn J. The Comparative Politics of Birth Control: Determinants of Policy Variation & Change in the Developed Nations. (Landmark Dissertations in Women's Studies). (Illus.). 320p. 1983. 42.95 (ISBN 0-03-069527-9). Praeger.

Mumford, Stephen D. The Pope & the New Apocalypse: The Holy War Against Family Planning. (Illus.). 82p. (Orig.). 1986. 6.95 (ISBN 0-937307-00-9); pap. 3.95 (ISBN 0-937307-01-7). CRPS.

O'Reilly, James. The Moral Problems of Contraception. (Synthesis Ser). 62p. 1975. pap. 0.75 (ISBN 0-8199-0363-9). Franciscan Herald.

Quesnell, John Q. The Family Planning Dilemma Revisited. (Synthesis Ser.). 64p. 1975. pap. 1.75 (ISBN 0-8199-0364-7). Franciscan Herald.

Ramirez de Arellano, Annette B. & Seipp, Conrad. Colonialism, Catholicism, & Contraception: A History of Birth Control in Puerto Rico. LC 82-13646. xiv, 219p. 1983. 25.00x (ISBN 0-8078-1544-6). U of NC Pr.

BIRTH RECORDS

see Registers of Births, Deaths, Marriages, etc.

BIRTHS, REGISTERS OF

see Registers of Births, Deaths, Marriages, etc.

BISHOPS

see also Apostolic Succession; Church Polity; Conciliar Theory; Dioceses; Episcopacy; Investiture; Ordination; Popes–Primacy

Abbey, Charles J. The English Church & Its Bishops, 1700-1800, 2 Vols. LC 77-130230. Repr. of 1887 ed. Set. 74.50 (ISBN 0-404-00290-0). AMS Pr.

Akenson, Donald H. A Protestant in Purgatory: Richard Whately, Archbishop of Dublin. LC 81-3522. (Conference on British Studies (CBS) Biography: Vol. II). xiii, 276p. 1981. 25.00 (ISBN 0-208-01917-0, Archon). Shoe String.

Archbishop Averky Taushev. Visokopreosvjashennij Theofan, Arkhiepiskop Poltavsky i Perejaslavsky. Tr. of His Eminance Theophan, Archbishop of Poltava & Perejaslavl. 88p. 1974. pap. 5.00 (ISBN 0-317-29284-6). Holy Trinity.

Archbishop Vitaly Maximenko. Motivi Moijej Zhizni. Tr. of Motives of My Life. 205p. 1955. pap. 7.00 (ISBN 0-317-29054-1). Holy Trinity.

As One Who Serves: Reflections on the Pastoral Ministry of Priests in the United States. 86p. 1977. pap. 3.25 (ISBN 1-55586-549-6). US Catholic.

Benson, Robert L. The Bishop-Elect: A Study in Medieval Ecclesiastical Office. LC 65-17130. pap. 115.00 (ISBN 0-317-07842-9, 2010535). Bks Demand UMI.

The Bishop & the Liturgy: Highlights of the New Ceremonial of Bishops. 104p. (Orig.). 1986. pap. 8.95 (ISBN 1-55586-996-3). US Catholic.

Boece, Hector. Hectoris Boetii Murthlacensium Et Aberdonensium Episcoporum Vitae, Iterum in Lucem Editae. LC 76-39462. (Bannatyne Club, Edinburgh. Publications: No. 11). Repr. of 1825 ed. 20.00 (ISBN 0-404-52711-6). AMS Pr.

Boland, T. P. James Duhig. LC 86-15654. (Illus.). 435p. 1987. text ed. 37.50x (ISBN 0-7022-2011-6). U of Queensland Pr.

Bouchard, Constance B. Spirituality & Administration: The Role of the Bishop in Twelfth-Century Auxerre. LC 78-55889. 1979. 11.00x (ISBN 0-910956-79-0, SAM5); pap. 5.00x (ISBN 0-910956-67-7). Medieval Acad.

Bronder, Saul E. Social Justice & Church Authority: The Public Life of Archbishop Robert E. Lucey. 215p. 1982. 29.95 (ISBN 0-87722-239-8). Temple U Pr.

Cabestrero, Teofilo. Mystic of Liberation: A Portrait of Bishop Pedro Casaldaliga of Brazil. Walsh, Donald D., tr. from Span. & Fr. LC 80-25402. Orig. Title: Dialogos en Mato Grosso con Pedro Casadaliga. (Illus.). 176p. (Orig.). 1981. pap. 7.95 (ISBN 0-88344-324-4). Orbis Bks.

Calendars & Indexes to the Letters & Papers of Edward White Benson, Archbishop of Canterbury, 1883-1896 in Lambeth Palace Library, Vol. 3. (Calenders & Indexes to Letters & Papers of Archbishops of Canterbury on Lambeth Palace Library). 252p. 1980. text ed. 52.00x (ISBN 0-7201-1615-5). Mansell.

Catechetics in Our Time: Synod of Bishops, 1977. 1978. pap. 3.50 (ISBN 1-55586-575-5, V575). US Catholic.

Collinson, Patrick. Archbishop Grindal, 1519-1589: The Struggle for a Reformed Church in England. LC 78-65474. 1979. 46.00x (ISBN 0-520-03831-2). U of Cal Pr.

Cunningham, Agnes. The Bishop in the Church: Patristic Texts on the Role of the Episkopos. (Theology & Life Ser.: Vol. 13). 1985. pap. 3.95 (ISBN 0-89453-469-6). M Glazier.

Dark, Sidney. Seven Archbishops. Repr. of 1944 ed. 25.00 (ISBN 0-686-19840-9). Ridgeway Bks.

Davies, Michael. Archbishop Lefebvre & Religious Liberty. 17p. 1980. pap. 1.00 (ISBN 0-89555-143-8). TAN Bks Pubs.

Denny, Barbara. Kings Bishop. 376p. 1986. 49.00 (ISBN 0-946619-16-6, Pub. by Alderman Pr). State Mutual Bk.

Directives for the Mutual Relations Between Bishops & Religions in the Church. pap. cancelled (ISBN 0-686-15367-7, V-591). US Catholic.

Dunbar, Newell. Phillip Brooks: The Man, the Preacher, & the Author. 1978. Repr. of 1893 ed. lib. bdg. 35.00 (ISBN 0-8492-0668-5). R West.

Ellis, John T. Catholic Bishops: A Memoir. 1983. pap. 6.95 (ISBN 0-89453-463-7). M Glazier.

Erdozain, Placido. Archbishop Romero: Martyr of Salvador. McFadden, John & Warner, Ruth, trs. from Sp. LC 81-2007. Orig. Title: Monsenor Romero: Martis de la Iglesia Popular. (Illus.). 128p. (Orig.). 1981. pap. 4.95 (ISBN 0-88344-019-9). Orbis Bks.

Francesconi, Mario. Bishop John B. Scalabrini: An Insight into His Spirituality. Cinquino, J. & Monaco, Vincent, trs. from It. LC 73-75230. (Illus.). 107p. 1973. pap. 3.00 (ISBN 0-913256-50-1). Ctr Migration.

Gardner, A. Synesius of Cyrene: Philosopher & Bishop. 1977. lib. bdg. 59.95 (ISBN 0-8490-2697-0). Gordon Pr.

Gibson, Margaret. Lanfranc of Bec. 1978. 47.00x (ISBN 0-19-822462-1). Oxford U Pr.

Gladish, Richard R. Bishop William Henry Benade: Founder & Reformer. (Illus.). 400p. 1983. 15.00 (ISBN 0-910557-07-1). Acad New Church.

Granjon, Henry. Along the Rio Grande: A Pastoral Visit to Southern New Mexico in 1902. Taylor, Michael R., ed. De Lopez, Mary W., tr. from Fr. LC 86-11390. (Illus.). 153p. 1986. 17.50x (ISBN 0-8263-0903-8); pap. 8.95 (ISBN 0-8263-0904-6, Co-pub. by Historical Society of New Mexico). U of NM Pr.

Guy, B. Domestic Correspondance of Dominique-Marie Varlet: Bishop of Babylon 1678-1742. (Studies in the History of Christian Thought: No. 36). ix, 150p. 1986. 22.00 (ISBN 90-04-07671-9, Pub. by E J Brill). Heinman.

Haines, R. M. The Church & Politics in Fourteenth Century England. LC 76-54062. (Studies in Medieval Life & Thought: No. 10). 1978. 49.50 (ISBN 0-521-21544-7). Cambridge U Pr.

James, Francis G. North Country Bishop: A Biography of William Nicolson. 1956. 59.50x (ISBN 0-686-51425-4). Elliots Bks.

Jezernik, Maksimiljan. Frederick Baraga: A Portrait of the First Bishop of Marquette Based on the Archives of the Congregatio De Propaganda Fide. LC 68-16856. 155p. 1968. 8.00 (ISBN 0-686-28380-5); pap. 6.00 (ISBN 0-686-28381-3). Studia Slovenica.

Johnson, Joseph A., Jr. The Soul of the Black Preacher. LC 70-162411. 176p. 1971. 4.95 (ISBN 0-8298-0193-6). Pilgrim NY.

Lawler, Philip F. How Bishops Decide: An American Catholic Case Study. 45p. (Orig.). pap. 4.00 (ISBN 0-89633-101-6). Ethics & Public Policy.

Liederbach, Clarence A. America's Thousand Bishops: From 1513 to 1974, from Abramowicz to Zuroweste. LC 73-94081. 80p. 1974. pap. 3.50 (ISBN 0-913228-09-5). R J Liederbach.

--Canada's Bishops: Sixteen Fifty-Eight to Nineteen Seventy-Five. LC 73-94082. 1976. pap. 2.95 (ISBN 0-913228-10-9). R J Liederbach.

--Mexico's Bishops: From Fifteen Twenty-eight to Nineteen Seventy-six from Abad to Zumarraga. LC 76-29279. 80p. 1977. pap. 2.95 (ISBN 0-913228-18-4). R J Liederbach.

McCabe, Richard A. Joseph Hall: A Study in Satire & Meditation. (Illus.). 1982. 72.00x (ISBN 0-19-812807-X). Oxford U Pr.
Macdonald, Frederick. Bishop Stirling of the Falklands. 1976. lib. bdg. 59.95 (ISBN 0-8490-1509-X). Gordon Pr.
McKee, John. A Martyr Bishop: The Life of St. Oliver Plunkett. 181p. 1975. 7.95 (ISBN 0-912414-21-9). Lumen Christi.
Mills, Frederick V., Sr. Bishops by Ballot: An Eighteenth-Century Ecclesiastical Revolution. 1978. 19.95x (ISBN 0-19-502411-7). Oxford U Pr.
Morgan, John H. Who Becomes a Bishop? A Study of Priests Who Become Bishops in the Episcopal Church (1960 to 1980) 65p. (Orig.). 1985. pap. 6.95x (ISBN 0-932269-28-1). Wyndham Hall.
Nemec, Ludvik. Antonin Cyril Stojan: Apostle of Unity. LC 83-70817. (Illus.). 256p. 1983. pap. 11.95 (ISBN 0-89944-068-1). Don Bosco Multimedia.
O'Donnell, John H. The Catholic Hierarchy of the United States, 1790-1922. LC 73-3558. (Catholic University of America. Studies in American Church History: No. 4). Repr. of 1922 ed. 28.00 (ISBN 0-404-57754-7). AMS Pr.
Otto Bishop of Freising. Der Chronik des Bischofs Otto, Von Freising, Sechstes und Siebentes Buch. Kohl, H., tr. (Ger.). pap. 10.00 (ISBN 0-384-43965-9). Johnson Repr.
Page, Jesse. The Black Bishop: Samuel Adjai Crowther. LC 75-106783. (Illus.). 1979. Repr. of 1908 ed. 32.00x (ISBN 0-8371-4610-0, PBB&, Pub. by Negro U Pr). Greenwood.
Pope John Paul II. To the U. S. Bishops at Their Ad Ldmina Visita. 108p. 1984. 3.50 (ISBN 0-8198-0723-0); pap. 2.50 (ISBN 0-8198-0724-9). Dghtrs St Paul.
Priest Nikolai Deputatov. Revnitel' Blagotchestija 19-go vjeka, Episkop Theofan Zatvornik. Tr. of A Zealot for Piety in the 19th Century Bishop Theophan the Recluse. 71p. 1971. pap. 3.00 (ISBN 0-317-29261-7). Holy Trinity.
Pruter, Karl. Bishops Extraordinary. LC 86-2284. 60p. 1985. Repr. lib. bdg. 19.95x (ISBN 0-89370-544-6). Borgo Pr.
--Directory of Autocephalous Anglican, Catholic, & Orthodox Bishops. 3rd ed. LC 86-34289. 53p. 1986. lib. bdg. 19.95x (ISBN 0-89370-528-4). Borgo Pr.
Puhalo, Lazar. Innokenty of Alaska. 86p. (Orig.). 1986. pap. 5.00 (ISBN 0-913026-86-7). Synaxis Pr.
Ravitch, Norman. Sword & Mitre: Government & Episcopate in France & England in the Age of Aristocracy. 1966. text ed. 18.40x (ISBN 0-686-22467-1). Mouton.
Sergijevsky, N. Svjatitel' Tikhon, Episkop Voronjezhskij i Zadonskij. Tr. of St. Tikhon, Bishop pf Voronezh & Zadonsk. 213p. pap. 8.00 (ISBN 0-317-29184-X). Holy Trinity.
Sivric, Ivo. Bishop J. G. Strossmayer: New Light on Vatican I. 1975. 7.95 (ISBN 0-8199-0491-0). Franciscan Herald.
Spooner, W. A. Bishop Butler. 1979. Repr. of 1901 ed. lib. bdg. 30.00 (ISBN 0-8492-8086-9). R West.
Svjatejshij Tikhon, Patrijarkh Moskovskij i Vseja Rossij. Tr. of His Holiness Tikhon, Patriarch of Moscow & all Russia. 80p. 1965. pap. 3.00 (ISBN 0-317-29216-1). Holy Trinity.
Tillard, J. M. The Bishop of Rome. (Theology & Life Ser.: Vol. 5). 1983. 12.95 (ISBN 0-89453-304-5); pap. 9.95 (ISBN 0-89453-298-7). M Glazier.
Tyndale-Biscoe, J. For God Alone: The Life of George West, Bishop of Rangoon. 1985. 30.00x (ISBN 0-317-43630-9, Pub. by Amate Pr. Ltd). State Mutual Bk.
Walsh, Katherine. A Fourteenth-Century Scholar & Primate: Richard FitzRalph in Oxford, Avignon, & Armagh. (Illus.). 1981. 65.00x (ISBN 0-19-822637-3). Oxford U Pr.

BLACK ART (WITCHCRAFT)
see Witchcraft

BLACK FRIARS
see Dominicans

BLACK MASS
see Satanism

BLACK MONKS
see Benedictines

BLACK MUSLIMS

Baldwin, James. Fire Next Time. 1985. pap. 3.95 (ISBN 0-440-32542-0, LE). Dell.
Lomax, Louis E. When the Word Is Given... A Report on Elijah Muhammad, Malcolm X, & the Black Muslim World. LC 78-14002. (Illus.). 1979. Repr. of 1964 ed. lib. bdg. 22.50x (ISBN 0-313-21002-0, LOWW). Greenwood.
Malcolm X. Autobiography of Malcolm X. 1977. pap. 2.75 (ISBN 0-345-29420-3). Ballantine.
Marsh, Clifton E. From Black Muslims to Muslims: The Transition from Separatism to Islam, 1930-1980. LC 84-5611. 159p. 1984. 16.50 (ISBN 0-8108-1705-5). Scarecrow.
Shalaby, Ibrahim. Education of a Black Muslim. 1980. pap. 1.25 (ISBN 0-686-32639-3). Impresora Sahuaro.

BLACKS–RELIGION

Bruce, Calvin E. & Jones, William R., eds. Black Theology II: Essays on the Formation & Outreach of Contemporary Black Theology. LC 75-39113. 285p. 1978. 25.00 (ISBN 0-8387-1893-0). Bucknell U Pr.
Buckner, John E. Son of Man. 1981. 4.95 (ISBN 0-8062-1796-0). Carlton.
Cone, James H. Speaking the Truth: Ecumenism, Liberation, & Black Theology. 176p. (Orig.). 1986. pap. 8.95 (ISBN 0-8028-0226-5). Eerdmans.
Erskine, Noel L. Decolonizing Theology: A Caribbean Perspective. LC 80-21784. 144p. (Orig.). 1981. pap. 6.95 (ISBN 0-88344-087-3). Orbis Bks.
Ives, Kenneth, et al. Black Quakers: Brief Biographies. (Studies in Quakerism: 12). (Illus.). 118p. (Orig.). 1986. pap. 8.00 (ISBN 0-89670-015-1). Progresiv Pub.
Jones, Major J. Christian Ethics for Black Theology. LC 74-8680. pap. cancelled (ISBN 0-317-30065-2, 2020267). Bks Demand UMI.
Moyd, Olin P. Redemption in Black Theology. LC 78-23816. 1979. soft cover 8.95 (ISBN 0-8170-0806-3). Judson.
Roberts, J. Deotis. Black Theology in Dialogue. LC 86-15665. 132p. (Orig.). 1987. pap. 12.95 (ISBN 0-664-24022-4). Westminster.
--Roots of a Black Future: Family & Church. LC 80-16788. 152p. 1980. pap. 8.95 (ISBN 0-664-24333-9). Westminster.
Shockley, Grant S., et al. Black Pastors & Churches in United Methodism. 1976. pap. 1.00 (ISBN 0-89937-005-5). Ctr Res Soc Chg.
Simpson, George E. Black Religions in the New World. LC 78-16892. (Illus.). 1978. 40.00x (ISBN 0-231-04540-9). Columbia U Pr.
Smith, John, Jr. The Relational Self: Ethics & Therapy from a Black Church Perspective. 256p. (Orig.). 1982. pap. 11.95 (ISBN 0-687-35945-7). Abingdon.
Williams, Melvin D. Community in a Black Pentecostal Church: An Anthropological Study. LC 74-5108. pap. 53.50 (ISBN 0-317-42278-2, 2024332). Bks Demand UMI.
Williams, Walter L. Black Americans & the Evangelization of Africa, 1877-1900. LC 81-69830. 282p. 1982. text ed. 32.50x (ISBN 0-299-08920-7). U of Wis Pr.
Wilmore, Gayraud S. & Cone, James H., eds. Black Theology: A Documentary History, 1966-1979. LC 79-12747. 672p. 1979. pap. 14.95 (ISBN 0-88344-042-3). Orbis Bks.

BLAKE, WILLIAM, 1757-1827

Altizer, Thomas J. New Apocalypse: The Radical Christian Vision of William Blake. 1967. 8.50 (ISBN 0-87013-108-7). Mich St U Pr.
Aubrey, Bryan. Watchmen of Eternity: Blake's Debt to Jacob Boehme. (Illus.). 208p. (Orig.). 1986. PLB 27.00 (ISBN 0-8191-5220-X); pap. text ed. 13.25 (ISBN 0-8191-5221-8). U Pr of Amer.
Ba Han, Maung. William Blake: His Mysticism. 1978. Repr. of 1924 ed. lib. bdg. 35.00 (ISBN 0-8495-0377-9). Arden Lib.
--William Blake: His Mysticism. LC 72-13650. 1974. Repr. of 1924 ed. lib. bdg. 30.00 (ISBN 0-8414-1234-0). Folcroft.
Bandy, Melanie. Mind Forg'd Manacles: Evil in the Poetry of Blake & Shelley. LC 80-18779. (Illus.). 210p. 1981. text ed. 19.95 (ISBN 0-8173-0046-5). U of Ala Pr.
Berger, P. William Blake: Poet & Mystic. LC 67-31287. (Studies in Blake, No. 3). 1969. Repr. of 1914 ed. lib. bdg. 75.00x (ISBN 0-8383-0778-7). Haskell.
Bertholf, Robert J. & Levitt, Annette S., eds. William Blake & the Moderns. 352p. 1982. 44.50x (ISBN 0-87395-615-X); pap. 18.95x (ISBN 0-87395-616-8). State U NY Pr.
Butterworth, Adeline M. William Blake: Mystic. LC 74-8017. 1911. lib. bdg. 15.00 (ISBN 0-8414-3186-8). Folcroft.
Clark, John H. God of Shelley & Blake. (English Literature Ser., No. 33). 1970. Repr. of 1930 ed. lib. bdg. 39.95x (ISBN 0-8383-0342-0). Haskell.
Clarke, John H. God of Shelley & Blake. LC 73-12459. 1973. lib. bdg. 10.00 (ISBN 0-8414-3425-5). Folcroft.
--William Blake on the Lord's Prayer: 1757-1827. LC 70-95421. (Studies in Blake, No. 3). 1971. Repr. of 1927 ed. lib. bdg. 48.95x (ISBN 0-8383-0967-4). Haskell.
Curran, Stuart & Wittreich, Joseph A., Jr., eds. Blake's Sublime Allegory: Essays on the "Four Zoas," "Milton," & "Jerusalem". LC 72-1377. (Illus.). 404p. 1973. 35.00x (ISBN 0-299-06180-9). U of Wis Pr.
DiSalvo, Jackie. War of Titans: Blake's Critique of Milton & the Politics of Religion. LC 82-11136. 403p. 1983. 38.95x (ISBN 0-8229-3804-9). U of Pittsburgh Pr.
Doskow, Minna. William Blake's Jerusalem. LC 81-65463. (Illus.). 388p. 1982. 37.50 (ISBN 0-8386-3090-1). Fairleigh Dickinson.
Erdman, David V. Blake: Prophet Against Empire. rev. ed. LC 69-18055. 1969. pap. 17.00x (ISBN 0-691-01329-2). Princeton U Pr.
Gilchrist, Alexander. Life of William Blake: With Selections from His Poems & Other Writings, 2 vols. enl. ed. (Illus.). 993p. 1969. Set. 75.00x (ISBN 0-87753-017-3). Phaeton.
Gleckner, Robert F. Blake's Prelude: "Poetical Sketches". LC 82-47976. 216p. 1983. text ed. 20.00x (ISBN 0-8018-2850-3). Johns Hopkins.
Goddard, Harold C. Blake's Fourfold Vision. LC 56-7354. (Orig.). 1956. pap. 2.50x (ISBN 0-87574-086-3). Pendle Hill.
Hamblen, Emily S. The Interpretaton of William Blake's Job. LC 70-100759. 1970. pap. 39.95x (ISBN 0-8383-0037-5). Haskell.
Howard, John. Infernal Poetics: Poetic Structure in Blake's Lambeth Prophecies. LC 82-49319. (Illus.). 256p. 1984. 34.50 (ISBN 0-8386-3176-2). Fairleigh Dickinson.
Kortelling, Jacomina. Mysticism in Blake & Wordsworth. LC 68-2111. (Studies in Poetry, No. 38). 1969. Repr. of 1928 ed. lib. bdg. 39.95x (ISBN 0-8383-0577-6). Haskell.
Kremen, Kathryn R. The Imagination of the Resurrection: The Poetic Continuity of a Religious Motif in Donne, Blake, & Yeats. LC 71-168812. (Illus.). 344p. 1972. 26.50 (ISBN 0-8387-7940-9). Bucknell U Pr.
Morton, A. L. The Everlasting Gospel. 1978. Repr. of 1958 ed. lib. bdg. 15.00 (ISBN 0-8495-3736-3). Arden Lib.
--Everlasting Gospel. (Studies in Blake, No. 3). 1958. pap. 39.95x (ISBN 0-8383-0098-7). Haskell.
Nurmi, Martin. Blake's Marriage of Heaven & Hell. LC 72-6067. (Studies in Blake, No. 3). 1972. Repr. of 1957 ed. lib. bdg. 75.00x (ISBN 0-8383-1599-2). Haskell.
Percival, Milton O. William Blake's Circle of Destiny. 1964. lib. bdg. 27.50x (ISBN 0-374-96384-3, Octagon). Hippocrene Bks.
Pinto, Vivian De Sola, ed. The Divine Vision. LC 68-24905. (Studies in Blake, No. 3). 1973. Repr. of 1957 ed. lib. bdg. 75.00x (ISBN 0-8383-0790-6). Haskell.
Scholz, Joachim J. Blake & Novalis. (European University Studies: Series 18, Comparative Literature, Vol. 19). 404p. 1978. 40.40 (ISBN 3-261-02576-X). P Lang Pubs.
Singh, Charu S. & Hogg, James. The Chariot of Fire: A Study of William Blake In the Light of Hindu Thought. (Romantic Reassessment Ser.). 194p. (Orig.). 1981. pap. 15.00 (ISBN 3-7052-0577-3, Pub. by Salzburg Studies). Longwood Pub Group.
Stevenson, Warren. Divine Analogy: A Study of the Creation Motif in Blake & Coleridge. Hogg, James, ed. (Romantic Reassessment Ser.). 403p. (Orig.). 1972. pap. 15.00 (ISBN 0-317-40044-4, Pub. by Salzburg Studies). Longwood Pub Group.
Tannenbaum, Leslie. Biblical Tradition in Blake's Early Prophecies: The Great Code of Art. LC 81-47158. 368p. 1982. 30.50x (ISBN 0-691-06490-3). Princeton U Pr.
Webster, Brenda. Blake's Prophetic Psychology. LC 84-114638. (Illus.). 336p. 1983. 27.50x (ISBN 0-8203-0658-4). U of Ga Pr.
Wittreich, Joseph A., Jr. Angel of Apocalypse: Blake's Idea of Milton. LC 74-27316. 358p. 1975. 37.50x (ISBN 0-299-06800-5). U of Wis Pr.
Young, Mildred B. Woolman & Blake: Prophets of Today. LC 72-170018. (Orig.). 1971. pap. 2.50x (ISBN 0-87574-177-0). Pendle Hill.

BLAVATSKY, HELENE PETROVNA (HAHN-HAHN), 1831-1891

Barborka, Geoffrey. Divine Plan: Commentary on the Secret Doctrine. 3rd ed. 1972. 19.95 (ISBN 0-8356-7167-4). Theos Pub Hse.
Barker, A. Trevor, compiled by. The Letters of H. P. Blavatsky to A. P. Sinnett. facsimile of 1925 ed. LC 73-84138. 1973. 12.00 (ISBN 0-911500-23-5). Theos U Pr.
Blavatsky, Helena P. Esoteric Writings of H. P. Blavatsky. LC 79-6547. (Illus.). 500p. (Orig.). 1980. pap. 8.75 (ISBN 0-8356-0535-3, Quest). Theos Pub Hse.
--H. P. Blavatsky Collected Writings, Vol. XII. De Zirkoff, Boris, ed. LC 80-53953. (Illus.). 849p. 1981. 16.50 (ISBN 0-8356-0228-1). Theos Pub Hse.
De Purucker, G. & Tingley, Katherine. H. P. Blavatsky: The Mystery. rev. ed. Small, W. Emmett & Todd, Helen, eds. (Illus.). 256p. 1974. pap. 5.25 (ISBN 0-913004-14-6). Point Loma Pub.
Hanson, Virginia, ed. H. P. Blavatsky & the Secret Doctrine Commentaries on Her Contributions to World Thought. LC 71-112039. (Orig.). 1971. pap. 2.25 (ISBN 0-8356-0031-9, Quest). Theos Pub Hse.
Leichtman, Robert R. H. P. Blatavsky Returns. (From Heaven to Earth Ser.). (Illus.). 95p. (Orig.). 1980. pap. 3.50 (ISBN 0-89804-059-0). Ariel OH.
Murphet, Howard. When Daylight Comes. LC 74-18958. (Illus.). 304p. (Orig.). 1975. cloth 8.95 (ISBN 0-8356-0461-6). Theos Pub Hse.
Prem, Sri K. & Ashish, Sri Madhava. Man: The Measure of All Things. LC 74-87256. 1969. 8.50 (ISBN 0-8356-0006-8). Theos Pub Hse.
Robb, Richard I., ed. The Secret Doctrine of H. P. Blavatsky: First International Symposium, July 1984. 112p. 1984. pap. 7.00 (ISBN 0-913510-52-1). Wizards.
Ryan, Charles J. H. P. Blavatsky & the Theosophical Movement. 2nd,rev. ed. Knoche, Grace F., ed. LC 75-4433. (Illus.). 1975. 9.00 (ISBN 0-911500-79-0); pap. 6.00 (ISBN 0-911500-80-4). Theos U Pr.
--H. P. Blavatsky & the Theosophical Movement: With 7 Appendixes. Small, W. Emmett & Todd, Helen, eds. (Illus.). 484p. 1975. pap. 7.00 (ISBN 0-913004-25-1). Point Loma Pub.
Sinnett, Alfred P., ed. Incidents in the Life of Madame Blavatsky. facsimile ed. LC 75-36919. (Occult Ser.). Repr. of 1886 ed. 25.50x (ISBN 0-405-07974-5). Ayer Co Pubs.
Solovyoff, Vsevolod S. A Modern Priestess of Isis. Leaf, Walter, tr. LC 75-36921. (Occult Ser.). 1976. Repr. of 1895 ed. 26.50x (ISBN 0-405-07976-1). Ayer Co Pubs.
Wachtmeister, Constance. Reminiscences of H. P. Blavatsky. rev. new ed. LC 76-44810. 1977. pap. 3.75 (ISBN 0-8356-0488-8, Quest). Theos Pub Hse.

BLESSING AND CURSING
see also Exorcism

Aman, Reinhold, ed. Maledicta 1980. LC 77-649633. (Maledicta: International Journal of Verbal Aggression Ser.: Vol. 4, No. 1 & 2). (Illus.). 320p. 1980. pap. 20.00 (ISBN 0-916500-55-1). Maledicta.
Berquist, Maurice. Miracle & Power of Blessing. 1984. pap. 2.95 (ISBN 0-87162-408-7, D8556). Warner Pr.
Westermann, Claus. Blessing: In the Bible & the Life of the Church, No. 3. Brueggeman, Walter & Donahue, John R., eds. Crim, Keith, tr. from Ger. LC 78-54564. (Overtures to Biblical Theology Ser.). 144p. 1978. pap. 8.95 (ISBN 0-8006-1529-8, 1-1529). Fortress.

BLESSINGS, TABLE
see Grace at Meals

BLOOD (IN RELIGION, FOLK-LORE, ETC.)

Rusche, Franz. Blut, Leben und Seele, Ihr Verhaeltnis Nach Auffassung der Griechischen und Hellenistischen Antike, der Bibel und der Alten Alexandrinischen Theologen. Repr. of 1930 ed. 34.00 (ISBN 0-384-52515-6). Johnson Repr.

BLOY, LEON, 1846-1917

Beguin, Albert. Leon Bloy: A Study in Impatience. Riley, Edith M., tr. from Fr. 247p. 1982. Repr. of 1947 ed. lib. bdg. 45.00 (ISBN 0-89984-081-7). Century Bookbindery.
Brady, Sr. M. Rosalie. Thought & Style in the Works of Leon Bloy. LC 70-94176. (Catholic Universtiy of America Studies in Romance Languages & Literatures Ser: No. 30). Repr. of 1945 ed. 19.00 (ISBN 0-404-50330-6). AMS Pr.
Heppenstall, Rayner. Double Image: Mutations of Christian Mythology in the Works of Four French Catholic Writers of Today & Yesterday. LC 72-93063. 1969. Repr. of 1947 ed. 23.00 (ISBN 0-8046-0676-5, Pub. by Kennikat). Assoc Faculty Pr.

BLUE LAWS
see Sunday Legislation

BLUMHARDT, CHRISTOPH, 1842-1919

Blumhardt's Battle. 1970. pap. 1.65 (ISBN 0-913926-01-9). T E Lowe.

BOA-HO
see Bon (Tibetan Religion)

BODY, HUMAN (IN RELIGION, FOLK-LORE, ETC.)

Ashley, Benedict M. Theologies of the Body: Humanist & Christian. (Illus.). 770p. (Orig.). 1985. pap. 20.95 (ISBN 0-935372-15-6). Pope John Ctr.
Barral, Mary R. The Body in Interpersonal Relations: Merleau-Ponty. 312p. 1984. pap. text ed. 14.50 (ISBN 0-8191-3755-3). U Pr of Amer.
Kreml, Patricia B. Slim for Him. LC 78-53422. 1978. pap. 4.95 (ISBN 0-88270-300-5). Bridge Pub.
Monks of Solesmes. The Human Body. 1960. 6.50 (ISBN 0-8198-3309-6). Dghtrs St Paul.

BODY AND MIND
see Mind and Body

BODY AND SOUL (PHILOSOPHY)
see Mind and Body

BODY AND SOUL (THEOLOGY)
see Man (Theology)

BOEHME, JAKOB, 1575-1624

Aubrey, Bryan. Watchmen of Eternity: Blake's Debt to Jacob Boehme. (Illus.). 208p. (Orig.). 1986. PLB 27.00 (ISBN 0-8191-5220-X); pap. text ed. 13.25 (ISBN 0-8191-5221-8). U Pr of Amer.
Erb, Peter C. Jacob Boehme, "The Way to Christ". LC 77-95117. (Classics of Western Spirituality). 336p. 1978. 13.95 (ISBN 0-8091-0237-4); pap. 7.95 o. p. (ISBN 0-8091-2102-6). Paulist Pr.

Hartmann, Franz. Life of Jacob Boehme. 1985. pap. 4.95 (ISBN 0-916411-97-4, Pub by Sure Fire). Holmes Pub.
Koyre, Alexandre. Philosophie De Jacob Boehme. 1929. 32.00 (ISBN 0-8337-1953-X). B Franklin.
Liem, Ann. Jacob Boehme: Insights into the Challenge of Evil. LC 77-79823. 32p. (Orig.). 1977. pap. 2.50x (ISBN 0-87574-214-9). Pendle Hill.
Walsh, David. The Mysticism of Innerworldly Fulfillment: A Study of Jacob Boehme. LC 83-6554. (University of Florida Humanities Monographs: No. 53). x, 142p. (Orig.). 1983. pap. 12.50 (ISBN 0-8130-0751-8). U Presses Fla.

BOETHIUS, d. 524

Barrett, Helen M. Boethius: Some Aspects of His Times & Works. LC 65-18789. 1965. Repr. of 1940 ed. 7.50x (ISBN 0-8462-0653-6). Russell.
Gruber, Joachim. Kommmentar Zu Boethius De Consolatione Philosophiae. (Texte und Kommentare: Vol. 9). 1978. 62.00x (ISBN 3-11-007223-8). De Gruyter.
James, H. J. The Consolation of Philosophy of Boethius. 1897. 25.00 (ISBN 0-8274-2093-5). R West.
Masi, Michael. Boethius & the Liberal Arts: A Collection of Essays. (Utah Studies in Literature & Linguistics: Vol. 18). 220p. 1982. pap. 27.35 (ISBN 3-261-04722-4). P Lang Pubs.
Reiss, Edmund. Boethius. (World Authors Ser.). 1982. lib. bdg. 19.95 (ISBN 0-8057-6519-0, Twayne). G K Hall.
Stewart, Hugh F. Boethius: An Essay. LC 74-20524. 1975. Repr. of 1891 ed. 23.50 (ISBN 0-8337-4935-8). B Franklin.

BOHEMIAN BRETHREN

see also Moravians

Bittinger, Emmet F. Heritage & Promise: Perspectives on the Church of the Brethren. rev. ed. 1983. pap. 6.95 (ISBN 0-87178-357-6). Brethren.
Brown, Dale. Simulations on Brethren History. pap. 6.95 (ISBN 0-87178-794-6). Brethren.
Durnbaugh, Donald F. The Church of the Brethren Yesterday & Today. Eller, David, ed. 192p. (Orig.). 1986. pap. 9.95 (ISBN 0-87178-151-4). Brethren.
Fink, Benjamin. Life of John Kline. 7.95 (ISBN 0-87178-516-1). Brethren.
Mezezers, Valdis. The Herrnhuterian Pietism in the Baltic. (Illus.). 160p. 1975. 8.95 (ISBN 0-8158-0322-2); pap. 6.95 (ISBN 0-8158-0413-X). Chris Mass.
Snyder, Graydon & Shaffer, Kenneth. Texts in Transit. (Orig.). 1976. pap. 2.95 (ISBN 0-685-61334-8). Brethren.
Wine, J. Floyd. A History of Calvary Church of the Brethren. LC 72-95960. (Illus.). 1972. pap. 3.95 (ISBN 0-9604350-1-8). J F Wine.

BON (TIBETAN RELIGION)

see also Lamaism

Hoffmann, Helmut. The Religions of Tibet. LC 78-11420. (Illus.). 1979. Repr. of 1961 ed. lib. bdg. 24.75x (ISBN 0-313-21120-5, HORT). Greenwood.

BONAVENTURA, SAINT, CARDINAL, 1221-1274

Bettoni, Efrem. Saint Bonaventure. Scuola, Editrice, Brescia, Italy, tr. from Ital. LC 81-13371. (The Notre Dame Pocket Library). Tr. of Santa Bonaventura. 127p. 1982. Repr. of 1964 ed. lib. bdg. 22.50x (ISBN 0-313-23271-7, BESB). Greenwood.
Boehner, Philotheus. Itinerarium Mentis in Deum. (Works of Saint Bonaventure Ser.). 1956. 3.50 (ISBN 0-686-11591-0). Franciscan Inst.
Bougerol, Guy J. Introduction to the Works of St. Bonaventure. 1964. 7.50 (ISBN 0-8199-0525-9). Franciscan Herald.
Cousins, Ewert, ed. Bonaventure: The Soul's Journey into God: the Tree of Life, the Life of Francis. LC 78-60723. (Classics of Western Spirituality). 380p. 1978. 13.95 (ISBN 0-8091-0240-4); pap. 10.95 (ISBN 0-8091-2121-2). Paulist Pr.
Faccin, Dominic. Spiritual Exercises According to Saint Bonaventure. Colligan, Owen A., tr. (Spirit & Life Ser). 1955. 3.00 (ISBN 0-686-11568-6). Franciscan Inst.
Gilson, Etienne. The Philosophy of St. Bonaventure. 1965. 7.50 (ISBN 0-8199-0526-7). Franciscan Herald.
Hayes, Zachary, tr. Saint Bonaventure's Disputed Questions on the Mystery of the Trinity. (Works of Saint Bonaventure Ser.). 1980. 11.00 (ISBN 0-686-28123-3). Franciscan Inst.
Healy, Sr. Emma T. De Reductione Artium Ad Theologiam. (Works of Saint Bonaventure Ser). (Translated). 1955. 4.50 (ISBN 0-686-11590-2). Franciscan Inst.
McLean, George F., ed. Thomas & Bonaventure: A Septicentenary Commemoration. LC 75-319639. (Proceedings of the American Catholic Philosophical Association: Vol. 48). 1974. pap. 15.00 (ISBN 0-918090-08-3). Am Cath Philo.
Prentice, Robert P. Psychology of Love According to St. Bonaventure. (Philosophy Ser). 1957. 8.00 (ISBN 0-686-11536-8). Franciscan Inst.
Reist, Thomas. Saint Bonaventure As a Biblical Commentator: A Translation & Analysis of His "Commentary on Luke," XVIII,34-XIX,42. 284p. (Orig.). 1985. lib. bdg. 24.00 (ISBN 0-8191-4578-5); pap. text ed. 12.75 (ISBN 0-8191-4579-3). U Pr of Amer.
Shahan, Robert W. & Kovach, Francis J. Bonaventure & Aquinas: Enduring Philosophers. LC 75-40963. (Illus.). 200p. 1976. pap. 8.95x (ISBN 0-8061-1349-9). U of Okla Pr.
Spargo, Emma J. The Category of the Aesthetic in the Philosophy of Saint Bonaventure. (Philosophy Ser). 1953. 8.00 (ISBN 0-686-11541-4). Franciscan Inst.
Tavard, G. H. Transiency & Permanence: The Nature of Theology According to Saint Bonaventure. 1974. Repr. of 1954 ed. 15.00 (ISBN 0-686-11588-0). Franciscan Inst.
Werner, Karl. Psychologie und Erkenntnisslehre D. Johannes Bonaventura. (Ger.). 70p. 1973. Repr. of 1876 ed. lib. bdg. 18.50 (ISBN 0-8337-3739-2). B Franklin.

BONBO

see Bon (Tibetan Religion)

BONHOEFFER, DIETRICH, 1906-1945

Bethge, Eberhard. Costly Grace: An Illustrated Introduction to Dietrich Bonhoeffer in His Own Words. LC 78-19492. (Illus.). 1979. pap. 4.95i (ISBN 0-06-060773-4, RD294, HarpR). Har-Row.
Bethge, Ederhard. Dietrich Bonhoeffer. LC 70-10975. 1977. pap. 19.95 (ISBN 0-06-060771-8, RD 165, HarpR). Har-Row.
Burtness, James. Shaping the Future: The Ethics of Dietrich Bonhoeffer. LC 85-47723. 208p. 1985. pap. 16.95 (ISBN 0-8006-1869-6, 1-1869). Fortress.
Day, Thomas I. Dietrich Bonhoeffer on Christian Community & Common Sense. LC 83-25900. (Toronto Studies in Theology: Vol. 11). 248p. 1983. 49.95x (ISBN 0-88946-752-8). E Mellen.
Feil, Ernst. The Theology of Dietrich Bonhoeffer. Rumscheidt, H. Martin, tr. LC 84-47919. 272p. 1985. 19.95 (ISBN 0-8006-0696-5, 1-696). Fortress.
Godsey, John D. Preface to Bonhoeffer: The Man & Two of His Shorter Writings. LC 79-7378. 80p. 1979. pap. 3.50 (ISBN 0-8006-1367-8, 1-1367). Fortress.
Morris, Kenneth E. Bonhoeffer's Ethic of Discipleship: A Study in Social Psychology, Political Thought, & Religion. LC 85-31949. 144p. 1986. 17.95 (ISBN 0-271-00428-2). Pa St U Pr.
Peck, William J., ed. New Studies in Bonhoeffer's Ethics. (Toronto Studies in Theology: Vol. 31). 284p. 1987. lib. bdg. 49.95 (ISBN 0-88946-775-7). E Mellen.
Roark, Dallas M. Dietrich Bonhoeffer. Patterson, Bob E., ed. LC 72-76439. (Makers of the Modern Theological Mind Ser.). 140p. 1972. 8.95 (ISBN 0-87680-253-6, 80253). Word Bks.
Williamson, Rene De Visme. Politics & Protestant Theology: An Interpretation of Tillich, Barth, Bonhoeffer, & Brunner. LC 76-20817. 1976. 20.00x (ISBN 0-8071-0193-1). La State U Pr.

BONIFACE, ORIGINALLY WINFRED, SAINT, BP. OF MAINZ, 680-755

Boniface, Saint Letters of Saint Boniface. Emerton, Ephraim, ed. 1967. lib. bdg. 21.50x (ISBN 0-374-92584-4, Octagon). Hippocrene Bks.
Duckett, Eleanor S. Anglo-Saxon Saints & Scholars. x, 484p. 1967. Repr. of 1947 ed. 35.00 (ISBN 0-208-00200-6, Archon). Shoe String.

BONIFACE 8TH, POPE, d. 1303

Wood, C. T. Philip the Fair & Boniface VIII: State vs. Papacy. LC 76-23207. (European Problem Ser.). 124p. 1976. pap. 5.95 (ISBN 0-88275-454-8). Krieger.

BOOK CENSORSHIP

see Censorship

BOOK OF COMMON PRAYER

see Church of England–Book of Common Prayer; Protestant Episcopal Church in the U. S. a.–Book of Common Prayer

BOOK OF JUBILEES

Endres, John C. Biblical Interpretation in the Book of Jubilees. Karris, Robert J., ed. LC 86-6845. (Catholic Biblical Quarterly-Monograph: no. 18). 284p. (Orig.). 1987. pap. 8.50 (ISBN 0-915170-17-5). Catholic Bibl Assn.

BOOK OF MORMON

Bennion, Lowell L. The Book of Mormon: A Guide to Christian Living. LC 85-16104. 138p. 1985. 8.95 (ISBN 0-87747-866-X). Deseret Bk.
Book of Mormon: Eighteen Thirty. (Heritage Reprints Ser.). 1970. 12.00 (ISBN 0-8309-0025-X). Herald Hse.
Cheville, Roy A. Scriptures from Ancient America. LC 64-12944. 1964. pap. 10.00 (ISBN 0-8309-0252-X). Herald Hse.
Crowther, Duane S. Reading Guide to the Book of Mormon: A Simplified Program Featuring Brief Outlines & Doctrinal Summaries. LC 75-5322. 169p. 1975. 7.95 (ISBN 0-88290-045-5). Horizon Utah.
Etzenhouser, R. From Palmyra, New York, Eighteen Thirty to Independence, Missouri, Eighteen Ninety-Four. LC 73-134393. Repr. of 1894 ed. 29.50 (ISBN 0-404-08435-4). AMS Pr.
Hawkes, John D. Book of Mormon Digest. 240p. 1966. pap. 4.95 (ISBN 0-89036-010-3). Hawkes Pub Inc.
Larson, Clinton F. & Revill, Joseph N. Illustrated Stories of the Book of Mormon, 16 vols. (Illus.). write for info 0.00 (ISBN 0-911712-38-0). Promised Land.
Ludlow, Dan. A Companion to Your Study of the Book of Mormon. LC 76-27139. 1976. 9.95 (ISBN 0-87747-610-1). Deseret Bk.
Nibley, Hugh C. Since Cumorah. 11.95 (ISBN 0-87747-240-8). Deseret Bk.
Persuitte, David. Joseph Smith & the Origins of "The Book of Mormon". LC 84-42734. (Illus.). 303p. 1985. lib. bdg. 19.95x (ISBN 0-89950-134-6). McFarland & Co.
Reynolds, George & Sjodahl, Janne M. Commentary on the Book of Mormon, 7 vols. Vol. 1. 9.95 (ISBN 0-87747-039-1); Vol. 2. 9.95 (ISBN 0-87747-040-5); Vol. 3. 9.95 (ISBN 0-87747-041-3); Vol. 4. 9.95 (ISBN 0-87747-042-1); Vol. 5. 9.95 (ISBN 0-87747-043-X); Vol. 6. 9.95 (ISBN 0-87747-044-8); Vol. 7. 9.95 (ISBN 0-87747-045-6). Deseret Bk.
Ricks, Eldin. Book of Mormon Study Guide. 1976. pap. 4.95 (ISBN 0-87747-567-9). Deseret Bk.
Roberts, B. H. Studies of the Book of Mormon. Madsen, Brigham D., ed. LC 84-236. (Illus.). 412p. 1985. 21.95 (ISBN 0-252-01043-4). U of Ill Pr.
Smith, Joseph, Jr., tr. Book of Mormon: First Edition Facsimile. 590p. 1980. 9.99 (ISBN 0-87747-808-2). Deseret Bk.
Taves, Ernest H. Trouble Enough: Joseph Smith & the Book of Mormon. LC 84-42790. (Illus.). 280p. 1984. 20.95 (ISBN 0-87975-261-0). Prometheus Bks.
Vestal, Kirk H. & Wallace, Arthur. The Firm Foundation of Mormonism. LC 81-80795. xii, 306p. 1981. 8.95x (ISBN 0-937892-06-8). LL Co.
Vogel, Dan. Indian Origins & the Book of Mormon. LC 86-61016. 154p. 1986. pap. 8.95 (ISBN 0-941214-42-7). Signature Bks.

BOOK OF THE DEAD

Andrews, Carol. The Ancient Egyptian Book of the Dead. Faulkner, R. O., tr. (Illus.). 268p. 1985. text ed. 40.00x (ISBN 0-02-901470-0). Macmillan.
Budge, E. A. Egyptian Book of the Dead: The Papyrus of Ani. 16.25 (ISBN 0-8446-1764-4). Peter Smith.
Budge, E. A., intro. by. The Book of the Dead. 1977. pap. 9.95 (ISBN 0-8065-0591-5). Citadel Pr.
Budge, E. A. Wallis. Egyptian Book of the Dead: The Papyrus of Ani in the British Museum. 1967. pap. 8.95 (ISBN 0-486-21866-X). Dover.
Fremantle, Francesca & Trungpa, Chogyam, trs. from Tibetan. The Tibetan Book of the Dead: The Great Liberation Through Hearing in the Bardo. LC 74-29615. (Clear Light Ser.). (Illus.). 256p. 1975. pap. 7.95 (ISBN 0-87773-074-1). Shambhala Pubns.
Wallis-Budge, E. A., tr. The Bandlet of Righteousness: An Ethiopian Book of the Dead. (Coptic.). 1984. pap. 3.95 (ISBN 0-916411-23-0, Near Eastern). Holmes Pub.

BOOK OF THE DEAD–DICTIONARIES, INDEXES, ETC.

Budge, Ernest A. A Hieroglyphic Vocabulary to the Theban Recension of the Book of the Dead. LC 73-18846. Repr. of 1911 ed. 26.50 (ISBN 0-404-11335-4). AMS Pr.

BOOKS–CENSORSHIP

see Censorship

BOOKS, SACRED

see Sacred Books

BOOKS OF HOURS

see Hours, Books Of

BOSCO, GIOVANNI, SAINT, 1815-1888

Aubry, Joseph, ed. The Spiritual Writings of St. John Bosco. Caselli, Joseph, tr. from Italian. LC 83-71820. Tr. of Giovanni Bosco, Scritti Spirituali. 412p. 1984. pap. 12.95 (ISBN 0-89944-049-5). Don Bosco Multimedia.
Avallone, Paul. Reason, Religion, & Kindness. 3rd, rev. ed. LC 77-83952. 1977. pap. 4.75 (ISBN 0-89944-030-4). Don Bosco Multimedia.
Brown, Eugene. Dreams, Visions & Prophecies of Don Bosco. LC 86-13533. 344p. 1986. lib. bdg. 13.95 (ISBN 0-89944-085-1); pap. 9.95 (ISBN 0-89944-086-X). Don Bosco Multimedia.
Ceria, Eugenio. The Biographical Memoirs of Saint John Bosco, Vol. XIV (1879-80) Borgatello, Diego, ed. LC 65-3104. Tr. of Memorie Biografiche di Don Giovanni Bosco. 628p. 1985. 19.95 (ISBN 0-89944-014-2). Don Bosco Multimedia.
Desramaut, Francis. Don Bosco & the Spiritual Life. Luna, Roger M., tr. from Fr. LC 79-52674. (Orig.). 1979. pap. text ed. 10.95 (ISBN 0-89944-022-3). Don Bosco Multimedia.
Isoardi, Gian C. Don Bosco the Catechist. Cornell, Wallace L., tr. from Ital. 89p. 1981. pap. 4.75 (ISBN 0-89944-053-3). Don Bosco Multimedia.
Lappin, Peter. Stories of Don Bosco. 2nd ed. LC 78-72525. (Illus.). 1979. pap. 2.95 (ISBN 0-89944-036-3). Don Bosco Multimedia.
Lemoyne, G. B., et al. The Biographical Memoirs of Saint John Bosco, 14 vols. Borgatello, Diego, tr. from Ital. Incl. Vol. I. lib. bdg. 14.95 (ISBN 0-89944-001-0); Vol. II. lib. bdg. 15.95 (ISBN 0-89944-002-9); Vol. III. lib. bdg. 16.95 (ISBN 0-89944-003-7); Vol. IV. lib. bdg. 19.95 (ISBN 0-89944-004-5); Vol. V. lib. bdg. 21.95 (ISBN 0-89944-005-3); Vol. VI. lib. bdg. 22.95 (ISBN 0-89944-006-1); Vol. VII. lib. bdg. 18.95 (ISBN 0-89944-007-X); Vol. VIII. lib. bdg. 15.95 (ISBN 0-89944-008-8); Vol. IX. lib. bdg. 16.95 (ISBN 0-89944-009-6); Vol. X. lib. bdg. 20.95 (ISBN 0-89944-010-X); Vol. XI. lib. bdg. 18.95 (ISBN 0-89944-011-8); Vol. XII. lib. bdg. 17.95 (ISBN 0-89944-012-6); Vol. XIII. Rev. ed. 1983. lib. bdg. 24.95 (ISBN 0-89944-013-4). LC 65-3104. Orig. Title: Memorie Biografiche di Don Giovanni Bosco. 1981. Set. lib. bdg. write for info. (ISBN 0-89944-000-2). Don Bosco Multimedia.
Morrison, John A. The Educational Philosophy of Saint John Bosco. LC 79-54817. 258p. (Orig.). 1979. pap. 8.95 (ISBN 0-89944-050-9). Don Bosco Multimedia.
Rinaldi, Peter M. Man with a Dream. (Illus.). 1978. pap. 2.95 (ISBN 0-89944-035-5). Don Bosco Multimedia.
Stella, Pietro. Don Bosco & the Death of Charles. Drury, John, tr. from Italian. (Don Bosco in the History of Catholic Religious Thought & Practice Ser.). 56p. (Orig.). 1985. pap. 5.95 (ISBN 0-89944-080-0). Don Bosco Multimedia.
--Don Bosco: Life & Work. Drury, John, tr. from Italian. (Don Bosco in the History of Catholic Religious Thought & Practice Ser.). Tr. of Don Bosco Nella Storia della Religiosita Cattolica: Vita e Opere. 336p. (Orig.). 1985. 24.95 (ISBN 0-89944-081-9). Don Bosco Multimedia.
Wirth, Morand. Don Bosco & the Salesians. DeBurgh, David, tr. from Italian. LC 82-72675. Orig. Title: Don Bosco e i Salesiani. 432p. (Orig.). 1982. pap. 10.95 (ISBN 0-89944-065-7). Don Bosco Multimedia.

BOSSUET, JACQUES BENIGNE, BP. OF MEAUX, 1627-1704

Gotaas, Mary C. Bossuet & Vieira. LC 75-128929. (Catholic Univ. of American Studies in Romance Lang. & Lit. Ser.: No. 46). Repr. of 1953 ed. 21.00 (ISBN 0-404-50346-2). AMS Pr.
Goyet. L' Humanisme de Bossuet. 48.25 (ISBN 0-685-34207-7). French & Eur.
Simpson, William J. A Study of Bossuet. (Church Historical Society London N. S. Ser.: No. 22). pap. 23.00 (ISBN 0-8115-3146-5). Kraus Repr.
Terstegge, Georgiana. Providence As "Idee-Maitresse" in the Works of Bossuet. LC 73-128931. (Catholic University of America. Studies in Romance Languages & Literature: No. 43). 1970. Repr. of 1948 ed. 29.00 (ISBN 0-404-50334-9). AMS Pr.

BOSTON–FIRST CHURCH OF CHRIST, SCIENTIST

Eddy, Mary B. The First Church of Christ, Scientist, & Miscellany. German Ed. pap. 8.50 (ISBN 0-87952-155-4). First Church.

BOSTON–TRINITY CHURCH

Oliver, Andrew & Peabody, James B. The Records of Trinity Church, Boston: Vol. II - 1728-1830. LC 80-68230. 571p. 1982. 30.00x (ISBN 0-8139-0982-1, Colonial Soc MA). U Pr of Va.

BOURGES, SAINT-ETIENNE (CATHEDRAL)

Bayard, Tania. Bourges Cathedral: The West Portals. LC 75-23780. (Outstanding Dissertations in the Fine Arts Ser. - Medieval). (Illus.). 1976. lib. bdg. 55.00 (ISBN 0-8240-1977-6). Garland Pub.

BOY CHOIR TRAINING

see Choirboy Training

BOYD, ROBERT, 1578-1627

Wodrow, Robert. Collections Upon the Lives of the Reformers & Most Eminent Ministers of the Church of Scotland, 2 Vols. in 3 Pts. LC 70-178317. (Maitland Club, Glasgow. Publications: No. 32). Repr. of 1848 ed. Set. 105.00 (ISBN 0-404-52993-3). AMS Pr.

BOYS–PRAYER-BOOKS AND DEVOTIONS
Jones, Chris. Lord, I Want to Tell You Something: Prayers for Boys. LC 73-78266. (Illus.). 96p. (Orig.). 1973. pap. 3.95 (ISBN 0-8066-1330-0, 10-4100). Augsburg.
BOYS–RELIGIOUS LIFE
Wallis, Reginald. New Boy. pap. 1.00 (ISBN 0-87213-910-7). Loizeaux.
BOYS IN THE BIBLE
see Children in the Bible
BRADSHAW, TERRY
Hasegawa, Sam. Terry Bradshaw. (Sports Superstars Ser.). (Illus.). 1977. pap. 3.95 (ISBN 0-89812-212-0). Creative Ed.
BRAHMAN MYTHOLOGY
see Mythology, Hindu; Vedas
BRAHMANANDA, SWAMI, 1863-1922
Prabhavananda, Swami. Eternal Companion: Brahmananda, His Life & Teachings. 3rd ed. LC 72-113256. 1960. pap. 7.95 (ISBN 0-87481-024-8). Vedanta Pr.
BRAHMANAS
Drury, Naama. The Sacrificial Ritual in the Satapatha Brahmana. 137p. 1981. text ed. 8.25 (ISBN 0-8426-1759-0). Verry.
Heesterman, J. C. Ancient Indian Royal Consecration: The Rajasuya Described According to the Yajus Texts & Annotated. (Disputationes Rheno-Trajectinae Ser: No. 2). (Orig.). 1957. pap. text ed. 25.60x (ISBN 90-2790-028-0). Mouton.
Keith, Arthur, ed. Rigveda Brahmanas. lib. bdg. 100.00 (ISBN 0-87968-440-2). Krishna Pr.
Khare, R. S. The Changing Brahmans: Association & Elites among the Kanya-Kybjas of North India. LC 72-128711. (Illus.). 1970. text ed. 21.00x (ISBN 0-226-43433-8). U of Chicago Pr.
Oman, J. C. Brahmans, Theists & Muslims of India. 1973. 24.00 (ISBN 0-89684-371-8). Orient Bk Dist.
Sharma, R. N. Brahmins Through the Ages. 1977. 18.00x (ISBN 0-686-22659-3). Intl Bk Dist.
BRAHMANISM
see also Hindu Sects; Hinduism; Jains
Bailey, G. M. The Mythology of Brahma. 1983. 27.00x (ISBN 0-19-561411-9). Oxford U Pr.
Barnett, L. D. Brahma-Knowledge, Philosophy of Vedanta. 59.95 (ISBN 0-87968-780-0). Gordon Pr.
Biardeau, Madeleine. Theorie De la Connaissance et Philosophie De la Parole Dans le Brahmanisme Classique. (Le Monde D'outre-Mer Passe et Present, Etudes: No. 23). 1963. pap. 34.80x (ISBN 90-2796-178-6). Mouton.
Christy, Arthur. The Transmigration of the Seven Brahmans. Thoreau, Henry D., tr. LC 72-3516. (American Literature Ser., No. 49). Orig. Title: Harivansa. 1972. Repr. of 1931 ed. lib. bdg. 29.95x (ISBN 0-8383-1563-1). Haskell.
Daweewarn, D. Brahamism in Southeast Asia. 322p. 1982. text ed. 40.00x (ISBN 0-391-02581-3, Pub. by Sterling India). Humanities.
Donato, Sri. The Day of Brahma. Morningland Publications, Inc., ed. (Illus.). 377p. 1981. pap. 10.00 (ISBN 0-935146-20-2). Morningland.
Oman, John C. The Brahmans, Theists & Muslims of India. LC 76-179231. (Illus.). Repr. of 1907 ed. 31.50 (ISBN 0-404-54858-X). AMS Pr.
Saraswati, Baidyanath. Brahmanic Ritual Traditions. Malik, S. C., ed. LC 78-901135. (Illus.). 1977. 15.00 (ISBN 0-89684-478-1). Orient Bk Dist.
Subramaniam, K. Brahmin Priest of Tamil Nadu. LC 74-13072. 183p. 1975. 19.95x (ISBN 0-470-83535-4). Halsted Pr.
BRAINERD, DAVID, 1718-1747
Edwards, Jonathan. The Life of David Brainerd: The Works of Jonathan Edwards, Vol. 7. Pettit, Norman, ed. LC 83-23445. (Illus.). 640p. 1984. text ed. 50.00x (ISBN 0-300-03004-5). Yale U Pr.
Tallach, John. God Made Them Great. 144p. 1982. pap. 5.45 (ISBN 0-85151-190-2). Banner of Truth.
BRAND, PAUL WILSON, 1914-
Wilson, Dorothy C. Ten Fingers for God: The Complete Biography of Dr. Paul Brand. LC 82-24600. 288p. 1982. pap. 5.95 (ISBN 0-8407-5834-0). Nelson.
BRAY, THOMAS, 1656-1730
Bray, Thomas. Reverend Thomas Bray: His Life & Selected Works Relating to Maryland. Steiner, Bernard C., ed. LC 72-14420. (Maryland Historical Society. Fund-Publications Ser.: No. 37). Repr. of 1901 ed. 15.00 (ISBN 0-404-57637-0). AMS Pr.
Thompson, Henry P. Thomas Bray. LC 54-32504. 1954. 12.50x (ISBN 0-8401-2335-3). A R Allenson.
BRAZIL–RELIGION
Bastide, Roger. The African Religions of Brazil: Toward a Sociology of the Interpenetration of Civilizations. Sebba, Helen, tr. (Johns Hopkins Studies in Atlantic History & Culture Ser.). 1978. text ed. 45.00x (ISBN 0-8018-2056-1); pap. text ed. 14.95x (ISBN 0-8018-2130-4). Johns Hopkins.
Boff, Clodovis. Feet-on-the-Ground Theology: Pastoral Ministry in Western Brazil. Berryman, Phillip, tr. from Port. 288p. (Orig.). 1987. 19.95 (ISBN 0-88344-579-4); pap. 8.95 (ISBN 0-88344-554-9). Orbis Bks.
Brown, Diana D. Umbanda: Religion & Politics in Urban Brazil. Kottak, Conrad, ed. LC 85-20962. (Studies in Cultural Anthropology: No. 7). 270p. 1985. 44.95 (ISBN 0-8357-1556-6). UMI Res Pr.
Bruneau, Thomas E. The Church in Brazil: The Politics of Religion. LC 81-16391. (University of Texas at Austin, Institute of Latin American Studies-Latin American Monographs: No. 56). pap. 63.30 (2026564). Bks Demand UMI.
Cook, Guillermo. The Expectation of the Poor: Latin American Base Ecclesial Communities in Protestant Perspective. LC 85-5131. 256p. (Orig.). 1985. pap. 13.95 (ISBN 0-88344-209-4). Orbis Bks.
Mizuki, John. The Growth of Japanese Churches in Brazil. LC 78-5415. (Illus.). 1978. pap. 8.95 (ISBN 0-87808-323-5). William Carey Lib.
BREATH AND BREATHING (IN RELIGION, FOLK-LORE, ETC.)
see also Yoga, Hatha
Fletcher, Ella A. The Law of the Rhythmic Breath. LC 80-19750. 372p. 1980. Repr. of 1979 ed. lib. bdg. 19.95x (ISBN 0-89370-644-2). Borgo Pr.
Sivapriyananda, S. Secret Power of Tantrik Breathing. 80p. 1983. text ed. 15.00 (ISBN 0-391-02899-5, Pub. by Abhinav Pubs India). Humanities.
BRENDAN, SAINT–LEGEND
O'Meara, John J. The Voyage of Saint Brendan: Journey to the Promised Land. (Dolmen Texts: No. 1). (Illus.). 1978. pap. text ed. 9.95x (ISBN 0-85105-384-X). Humanities.
BRETHREN, UNITED
see Moravians
BREWSTER, WILLIAM, 1566?-1644
Steele, Ashbel. Chief of the Pilgrims: Or, the Life & Time of William Brewster. facs. ed. LC 72-133535. (Select Bibliographies Reprint Ser). (Illus.). 1857. 23.50 (ISBN 0-8369-5567-6). Ayer Co Pubs.
BRIDAL CUSTOMS
see Marriage Customs and Rites
BRIGHAM YOUNG UNIVERSITY
Bergera, Gary J. & Priddis, Ronald. Brigham Young University: A House of Faith. 513p. (Orig.). 1985. pap. 19.95 (ISBN 0-941214-34-6). Signature Bks.
BRONTE, PATRICK, 1777-1861
Bronte, Patrick. Bronteana: The Rev. Patrick Bronte, His Collected Works & Life. LC 77-148320. Repr. of 1898 ed. 16.00 (ISBN 0-404-08920-8). AMS Pr.
BROOK FARM
Cooke, George W. John Sullivan Dwight: A Biography. LC 79-90210. (Music Reprint Ser). 1969. Repr. of 1898 ed. 39.50 (ISBN 0-306-71818-9). Da Capo.
Sams, Henry W., ed. Autobiography of Brook Farm. 15.25 (ISBN 0-8446-4056-5). Peter Smith.
BROTHELS
see Prostitution
BROTHERLINESS
Gandhi, M. K. All Men Are Brothers. (Modern Classics of Peace Ser). pap. 7.95 (ISBN 0-912018-15-1). World Without War.
Holland, Muhtar, tr. Al Ghazali: On the Duties of Brotherhood. LC 76-8057. 96p. 1976. 10.00 (ISBN 0-87951-046-3); pap. 7.95 (ISBN 0-87951-083-8). Overlook Pr.
Rahner, Karl. The Love of Jesus & the Love of Neighbor. LC 82-23523. 96p. 1983. pap. 5.95 (ISBN 0-8245-0570-0). Crossroad NY.
Sweeney, Frances. Every Man My Brother. 1976. 4.00 (ISBN 0-8198-0410-X); pap. 3.00 (ISBN 0-8198-0411-8). Dghtrs St Paul.
BROTHERS OF THE COMMON LIFE
Bowman, S. Loren. Power & Polity among the Brethren. (Orig.). 1987. pap. 5.95. Brethren.
BROWNISTS
see also Pilgrims (New Plymouth Colony)
Ainsworth, Henry & Johnson, Francis. An Apologie or Defence of Such True Christians as Are Commonly Called Brownists. LC 70-25742. (English Experience Ser.: No. 217). Repr. of 1604 ed. 16.00 (ISBN 90-221-0424-9). Walter J Johnson.
Alison, Richard. A Confutation of Brownisme. LC 68-54608. (English Experience Ser.: No. 9). 130p. 1968. Repr. of 1590 ed. 16.00 (ISBN 90-221-0009-X). Walter J Johnson.
Gifford, George. A Plaine Declaration That Our Brownists Be Full Donatists. LC 74-80180. (English Experience Ser.: No. 661). 1974. Repr. of 1590 ed. 14.00 (ISBN 90-221-0661-6). Walter J Johnson.
Lawne, Christopher. Brownisme Turned the In-Side Out-Ward. LC 76-6282. (English Experience Ser: No. 74). 40p. 1968. Repr. of 1613 ed. 7.00 (ISBN 90-221-0074-X). Walter J Johnson.
White, Thomas. A Discoverie of Brownisme. LC 74-80226. (English Experience Ser.: No. 701). (Illus.). 30p. 1974. Repr. of 1605 ed. 5.00 (ISBN 90-221-0701-9). Walter J Johnson.
BROWNLOW, WILLIAM GANNAWAY, 1805-1877
Coulter, E. Merton. William G. Brownlow: Fighting Parson of the Southern Highlands. LC 71-136309. (Tennesseana Editions Ser.). (Illus.). pap. 114.50 (ISBN 0-8357-9767-8, 2016173). Bks Demand UMI.
BROWNSON, ORESTES AUGUSTUS, 1803-1876
Gilhooley, Leonard. Contradiction & Dilemma: Orestes Brownson & the American Idea. LC 78-158738. xvi, 231p. 1972. 25.00 (ISBN 0-8232-0930-X). Fordham.
BRUDERHOF COMMUNITIES
Arnold, Eberhard. Children's Education in Community: The Basis of Bruderhof Education. Mow, Merrill, ed. LC 76-27728. 1976. pap. 3.25 (ISBN 0-87486-164-0). Plough.
--Foundation & Orders of Sannerz & the Rhon Bruderhof: Introductory History: The Basis for Our Orders, Vol. 1. LC 76-5856. 1976. pap. 2.50 (ISBN 0-87486-162-4). Plough.
--Living Churches: The Essence of Their Life - Love to Christ & Love to the Brothers, Vol. 1. LC 73-21273. 1974. pap. 2.50 (ISBN 0-87486-116-0). Plough.
--Sendbrief from the Alm Bruderhof to the Rhoen Bruderhof. LC 74-23145. 1974. pap. 2.50 (ISBN 0-87486-148-9). Plough.
Arnold, Eberhard & Arnold, Emmy. Seeking for the Kingdom of God: Origins of the Bruderhof Communities. LC 74-6317. 200p. 1974. 6.50 (ISBN 0-87486-133-0). Plough.
Arnold, Eberhard, et al. When the Time Was Fulfilled: Talks & Writings on Advent & Christmas. LC 65-17599. 1965. 7.00 (ISBN 0-87486-104-7). Plough.
Arnold, Emmy. Torches Together: The Beginning & Early Years of the Bruderhof Communities. LC 63-23426. 1971. 8.95 (ISBN 0-87486-109-8). Plough.
--Torches Together: The Beginning & Early Years of the Bruderhof Communities. Society of Brothers, tr. from Ger. LC 77-166341. (Illus.). 1976. pap. 6.00 (ISBN 0-87486-171-3). Plough.
Kleinsasser, Jacob, et al. For the Sake of Divine Truth: 1974 Visit of Four Brothers to Central Europe. LC 74-23787. 1974. pap. 1.20 (ISBN 0-87486-146-2). Plough.
Zablocki, Benjamin. The Joyful Community: An Account of the Bruderhof, a Communal Movement Now in Its Third Generation. 1980. pap. 5.95 (ISBN 0-226-97749-8, P885, Phoen). U of Chicago Pr.
BRUNNER, HEINRICH EMIL, 1889-
Humphrey, J. Edward. Emil Brunner. Patterson, Bob E., ed. LC 75-36186. (Maker's of the Modern Theological Mind Ser.). 1976. 8.95 (ISBN 0-87680-453-9). Word Bks.
--Emil Brunner. 183p. 1984. pap. text ed. 8.95 (ISBN 0-8499-3006-5, 3006-5). Word Bks.
Williamson, Rene De Visme. Politics & Protestant Theology: An Interpretation of Tillich, Barth, Bonhoeffer, & Brunner. LC 76-20817. 1976. 20.00x (ISBN 0-8071-0193-1). La State U Pr.
BUBER, MARTIN, 1878-1965
Boni, Sylvain. The Self & the Other in the Ontologies of Sartre & Buber. LC 82-20130. 202p. (Orig.). 1983. lib. bdg. 27.50 (ISBN 0-8191-2852-X); pap. text ed. 12.50 (ISBN 0-8191-2853-8). U Pr of Amer.
Buber, Martin. Ecstatic Confessions: The Heart of Mysticism. Mendes-Flor, Paul, ed. LC 84-48212. 224p. 1985. 16.45 (ISBN 0-06-061154-5, HarpR). Har-Row.
--The Way of Response: Selections from His Writings. Glatzer, Nahum N., ed. LC 66-26977. 1971. pap. 5.95 (ISBN 0-8052-0292-7). Schocken.
Cohen, Adir. The Educational Philosophy of Martin Buber. LC 81-68074. 350p. 1983. 32.50 (ISBN 0-8386-3098-7). Fairleigh Dickinson.
Diamond, Malcolm L. Martin Buber: Jewish Existentialist. 1968. lib. bdg. 17.50x (ISBN 0-88307-077-4). Gannon.
Friedman, Maurice. Martin Buber: The Life of Dialogue. 3rd, rev. ed. 1976. pap. 13.00x (ISBN 0-226-26356-8). U of Chicago Pr.
Jewish Peace Fellowship, ed. Martin Buber & the Covenant of Peace. 1984. lib. bdg. 79.95 (ISBN 0-87700-629-6). Revisionist Pr.
Kohanski, Alexander. Martin Buber's Philosophy of Interhuman Relation. LC 80-70626. 300p. 1981. 28.50 (ISBN 0-8386-3085-5). Fairleigh Dickinson.
Murphy, John W. The Social Philosophy of Martin Buber: The Social World as a Human Dimension. LC 82-21779. 176p. (Orig.). 1983. lib. bdg. 26.25 (ISBN 0-8191-2940-2); pap. text ed. 11.50 (ISBN 0-8191-2941-0). U Pr of Amer.
Oesterreicher, John M. The Unfinished Dialogue: Martin Buber & the Christian Way. LC 85-12410. 128p. 1986. 14.95 (ISBN 0-8022-2495-4). Philos Lib.
Osterreicher, John M. The Unfinished Dialogue: Martin Buber & the Christian Way. 136p. 1987. pap. 5.95 (ISBN 0-8065-1050-1). Citadel Pr.
Panko, Stephen M. Martin Buber. Patterson, Bob E., ed. LC 76-2869. (Markers of the Modern Theological Mind Ser.). 1976. 8.95 (ISBN 0-87680-470-9, 80470). Word Bks.
Pfuetze, Paul. Self, Society, Existence: Human Nature & Dialogue in the Thought of George Herbert Mead & Martin Buber. 400p. 1973. Repr. of 1961 ed. lib. bdg. 22.50x (ISBN 0-8371-6708-6, PFSS). Greenwood.
Schaeder, Grete. The Hebrew Humanism of Martin Buber. Jacobs, Noah J., tr. from Ger. LC 70-39691. (Schaver Publication Fund for Jewish Studies Ser.). 504p. 1973. 29.95x (ISBN 0-8143-1483-X). Wayne St U Pr.
Schilpp, Paul A. & Friedman, Maurice, eds. The Philosophy of Martin Buber. LC 65-14535. (The Library of Living Philosophers: Vol. XII). 831p. 1967. 37.95 (ISBN 0-87548-129-9). Open Court.
Vermes, Pamela. Buber on God & the Perfect Man. Neusner, J., et al, eds. LC 80-23406. (Brown Judaic Studies). 1981. pap. 10.50 (ISBN 0-89130-427-4). Scholars Pr GA.
Wood, Robert E. Martin Buber's Ontology: An Analysis of I & Thou. LC 73-82510. (Studies in Phenomenology & Existential Philosophy). 160p. 1969. 19.95 (ISBN 0-8101-0256-0); pap. 10.95 (ISBN 0-8101-0650-7). Northwestern U Pr.
BUCER, MARTIN, 1491-1551
Bucer, Martin. A Briefe Treatise Concerning the Burnynge of Bucer & Phagius at Cambridge. LC 76-57362. (English Experience Ser.: No. 780). 1977. Repr. of 1562 ed. lib. bdg. 14.00 (ISBN 90-221-0780-9). Walter J Johnson.
Eells, Hastings. The Attitudes of Martin Bucer Toward the Bigamy of Philip of Hesse. LC 83-45611. Date not set. Repr. of 1924 ed. 32.50 (ISBN 0-404-19829-5). AMS Pr.
BUDDHISM
see also Lamaism; Mahayana Buddhism; Meditation (Buddhism); Monasticism and Religious Orders, Buddhist; Pali Literature; Tantric Buddhism; Zen Buddhism
also headings beginning with the word Buddhist
Abhayadatta. Buddha's Lions. Robinson, James, tr. from Tibean. (Tibetan Translation Ser.). (Illus.). 1979. 19.95 (ISBN 0-913546-60-7). Dharma Pub.
A. C. Bhaktivedanta Prabhupada. Sri Namamrta: The Holy Nectar of the Holy Name. (Illus.). 586p. 1982. pap. 12.95 (ISBN 0-89213-113-6). Bhaktivedanta.
Ajaya, Swami, ed. Living with the Himalayan Masters: Spiritual Experiences of Swami Rama. LC 80-82974. 490p. 1980. pap. 12.95 (ISBN 0-89389-070-7). Himalayan Pubs.
Akiyama, Aisaburo. Buddhist Hand-Symbol. LC 78-72367. Repr. of 1939 ed. 22.50 (ISBN 0-404-17214-8). AMS Pr.
Alexander, P. C. Buddhism in Kerala. LC 78-72369. Repr. of 1949 ed. 37.50 (ISBN 0-404-17216-4). AMS Pr.
Allione, Tsultrim. Women of Wisdom. (Illus.). 224p. (Orig.). 1985. pap. 12.95 (ISBN 0-7102-0240-7). Methuen Inc.
Andersen, Dines & Smith, Helmer, eds. The Sutta-Nipata. LC 78-70124. Repr. of 1913 ed. 27.00 (ISBN 0-404-17383-7). AMS Pr.
Arnold, Edwin. The Light of Asia or, the Great Renunciation (Mahabhinishkramana) Being the Life & Teaching of Gautama, Prince of India, Founder of Buddhism. x, 176p. 1972. pap. 5.00 (ISBN 0-7100-7006-3). Methuen Inc.
Aronson, Harvey B. Love & Sympathy in Theravada Buddhism. cancelled (ISBN 0-8364-0627-3, Pub. by Motilal Banarsidass). South Asia Bks.
Asvaghosa. The Buddhacharita or Acts of the Buddha, 2 vols. in 1. Johnson, E. H., ed. & tr. Repr. of 1936 ed. text ed. 25.00x. Coronet Bks.
Asvaghosha, B. A Life of Buddha. lib. bdg. 79.95 (ISBN 0-87968-473-9). Krishna Pr.
Bancroft, Anne. The Buddhist World. LC 84-51193. (Religions of the World Ser.). (Illus.). 48p. 1985. 9.25 (ISBN 0-382-06928-5); PLB 14.96 (ISBN 0-382-06747-9). Silver.
Barrington, E. The Great Teachings of the Buddha, 2 vols. (Illus.). 211p. 1986. Set. 147.50 (ISBN 0-89901-273-6). Found Class Reprints.
Bechert, Heinz & Gombrich, Richard, eds. The World of Buddhism: Buddhist Monks & Nuns in Society & Culture. LC 84-8125. 1984. 49.95 (ISBN 0-87196-982-3). Facts on File.
Berry, Thomas. Buddhism. LC 75-10518. 1967. pap. 5.95 (ISBN 0-89012-017-X). Anima Pubns.

Bethlenfalvy, Geza. A Hand-List of the Ulan Bator Manuscript of the Kanjur-Rtse Them Spans-Ma. 112p. 1982. pap. text ed. 12.50 (ISBN 963-05-3260-3, Pub. by Akademiai Kiado Hungary). Humanities.

Bhattacharya, Gouriswar, ed. Deyadharma: Studies in Memory of Dr. D. C. Sircar. (Illus.). 276p. 1986. lib. bdg. 75.00x (ISBN 81-7030-021-5, Pub. by Sri Satguru Pubns India). Orient Bk Dist.

Biography of Master Hsuan Hua Publication Committee. Records of the Life of Tripitaka Master Hua, Vol. 1. (Illus.). 90p. (Orig.). 1981. pap. 5.00 (ISBN 0-917512-78-2). Buddhist Text.

--Records of the Life of Tripitaka Master Hua, Vol. 2. (Illus.). 229p. (Orig.). 1976. pap. 8.00 (ISBN 0-917512-10-3). Buddhist Text.

Bloom, Alfred. Tannisho: A Resource for Modern Living. LC 80-39523. 112p. (Orig.). 1981. pap. 6.95 (ISBN 0-938474-00-6). Buddhist Study.

Bloom, Alred. Shoshinge: The Heart of Shin Buddhism. Nagatani, T. & Tabrah, Ruth, trs. 108p. (Orig.). 1986. pap. 6.95 (ISBN 0-938474-06-5). Buddhist Study.

Books on Buddhism. 1986. pap. 4.95 (ISBN 0-317-46501-5). Dharma Pub.

Buddha, Gautama. Dhammapada. Babbitt, Irving, tr. LC 64-23655. Tr. of The Path of Truth. 1965. pap. 5.95 (ISBN 0-8112-0004-3, NDP188). New Directions.

Buddhadatta. Buddhadatta's Manuals, 2 vols. in 1. Buddhadatta, A. P., ed. LC 78-72382. Repr. of 1928 ed. 47.50 (ISBN 0-404-17244-X). AMS Pr.

Buddhadharma. Upasaka Two & One. 1981. pap. 3.95 (ISBN 0-87881-078-1). Mojave Bks.

Buddhavamsa. The Buddavamsa & the Carlya-Pitaka, Pt. 1. Morris, Richard, ed. LC 78-72391. Repr. of 1882 ed. 17.00 (ISBN 0-404-17249-0). AMS Pr.

Buddhist Text Translation Society Staff. Cherishing Life, Vol. 2. Bhikshuni Heng Tao & Bhikshuni Heng Ch'ih, trs. from Chinese. (Illus.). 160p. 1983. pap. 7.00 (ISBN 0-88139-015-1). Buddhist Text.

--Filiality, the Human Source, Vol. 1. 132p. 1983. pap. 7.00 (ISBN 0-88139-006-2). Buddhist Text.

--Filiality, the Human Source, Vol. 2. 120p. (Orig.). 1983. pap. 7.00 (ISBN 0-88139-020-8). Buddhist Text.

Buddhist Text Translation Society Staff, tr. from Chinese. Flower Adornment Sutra, Chapter 39: Entering the Dharma Realm, Part VII. 160p. (Orig.). 1983. pap. 9.00 (ISBN 0-88139-050-X). Buddhist Text.

--A Pictorial Biography of the Venerable Master Hsu Yun, Vol. 1. (Illus.). 236p. (Orig.). 1983. pap. 8.00 (ISBN 0-88139-008-9). Buddhist Text.

--Pictorial Biography of the Venerable Master Hsu Yun, Vol. 2. (Illus.). 236p. (Orig.). 1985. pap. 8.00 (ISBN 0-88139-116-6). Buddhist Text.

Burland, C. A. Way of the Buddha. (The Way Ser.). pap. 5.95 (ISBN 0-7175-0590-1). Dufour.

Carter, John R. & Bond, George D. The Threefold Refuge in the Theravada Buddhist Tradition. LC 82-26467. 1982. 4.95x (ISBN 0-89012-030-7). Anima Pubns.

Carus, Paul. Amitabha: A Story of Buddhist Theology. 1977. Repr. 29.00x (ISBN 0-403-07255-7). Scholarly.

--Der Buddha. 100p. 1913. pap. 3.95 (ISBN 0-317-40410-5). Open Court.

--Gospel of Buddha. (Illus.). 1979. pap. 6.95 (ISBN 0-89744-195-8). Auromere.

--Gospel of Buddha. rev. & enl. ed. LC 17-29837. (Illus.). 331p. 1915. deluxe ed. 24.95 (ISBN 0-87548-226-0); pap. 9.95 (ISBN 0-87548-228-7). Open Court.

Chang, C. C. Buddhist Teaching of Totality. LC 70-136965. 1971. 24.50x (ISBN 0-271-01179-3); pap. 14.95x (ISBN 0-271-01142-4). Pa St U Pr.

Chang, Garma C., tr. from Tibetan. The Hundred Thousand Songs of Milarepa, 2 Vols. LC 76-55120. 1977. pap. 14.95 ea.; Vol. 1, 356p. (ISBN 0-87773-095-4, 73346-0); Vol. 2, 374p. (ISBN 0-87773-096-2, 72996-X). Shambhala Pubns.

Ch'en, Kenneth K. Buddhism: The Light of Asia. LC 67-30496. 1968. pap. text ed. 5.95 (ISBN 0-8120-0272-5). Barron.

Chopra, P. N., ed. Contributions of Buddhism to World Civilization & Culture. 408p. 50.00X (ISBN 0-317-52136-5, Pub. by S Chand India). State Mutual Bk.

Chung-Yuan, Chang. Original Teachings of Cha'an Buddhism. pap. 9.95 (ISBN 0-394-62417-3, V-333, Vin). Random.

Cleary, Thomas, tr. The Book of Serenity. 464p. 1986. cancelled (ISBN 0-89281-072-6); pap. cancelled (ISBN 0-89281-074-2). Inner Tradit.

Collins, Steven. Selfless Persons: Imagery & Thought in Theravada Buddhism. LC 81-16998. 1982. 47.50 (ISBN 0-521-24081-6). Cambridge U Pr.

Constandse, William. Why I Became a Buddhist. 130p. (Orig.). 1985. pap. 6.95 (ISBN 0-911527-02-8). Utama Pubns Inc.

Conze, Edward. Buddha's Law among the Birds. 1986. Repr. 8.00 (ISBN 81-208-0198-9, Pub. by Motilal Banarsidass). South Asia Bks.

--Buddhism: Its Essence & Development. 17.50 (ISBN 0-8446-1889-6). Peter Smith.

--Buddhism: It's Essence & Development. 1982. pap. 6.95x (ISBN 0-06-130058-6, TB 58, Torch). Har-Row.

--Buddhism: Its Essence & Development. 221p. 1975. 25.00x (ISBN 0-317-39041-4, Pub. by Luzac & Co Ltd). State Mutual Bk.

--Buddhist Studies Nineteen Thirty-Four to Nineteen Seventy-Two. 512p. 1977. Repr. 20.00 (ISBN 0-686-48400-2). Wheelwright Pr.

--Buddhist Thought in India. 1967. pap. 8.95 (ISBN 0-472-06129-1, 129, AA). U of Mich Pr.

--Further Buddhist Studies: Selected Essays. 238p. 1975. 40.00x (ISBN 0-317-39071-6, Pub. by Luzac & Co Ltd). State Mutual Bk.

--Thirty Years of Buddhist Studies. 274p. 1967. 40.00x (ISBN 0-317-39172-0, Pub. by Luzac & Co Ltd). State Mutual Bk.

Cook, Francis H. Hua-Yen Buddhism: The Jewel Net of Indra. LC 76-43288. (Institute for Advanced Study of World Religions Ser.). 1977. 19.95x (ISBN 0-271-01245-5). Pa St U Pr.

Coomara, Swamy M., intro. by. Sutta Nipata: Or Dialogues & Discourses of Gotama Buddha. LC 78-70125. 1980. Repr. of 1874 ed. 23.00 (ISBN 0-404-17384-5). AMS Pr.

Coomaraswamy, Ananda K. Buddha & the Gospel of Buddhism. (Illus.). 1975. text ed. 17.00x. Coronet Bks.

--Hinduism & Buddhism. LC 78-138215. 1971. Repr. of 1943 ed. lib. bdg. 22.50x (ISBN 0-8371-5570-3, COHB). Greenwood.

Coomaraswamy, Ananda K. & Nivedita, Sr. Myths of the Hindus & Buddhists. (Illus.). 400p. pap. 6.95 (ISBN 0-486-21759-0). Dover.

Cousins, L., et al, eds. Buddhist Studies in Honour of I. B. Horner. LC 74-77963. 275p. 1974. lib. bdg. 45.00 (ISBN 90-277-0473-2, Pub. by Reidel Holland). Kluwer Academic.

Cummings, Mary. Lives of the Buddha in the Art & Literature of Asia. LC 80-67341. (Michigan Papers on South & Southeast Asia: No. 20). (Illus.). xiii, 225p. 1982. 19.95 (ISBN 0-89148-022-6); pap. 10.95 (ISBN 0-89148-023-4). Ctr S&SE Asian.

Dahlke, Paul. Buddhism & Its Place in the Mental Life of Mankind. LC 78-72403. Repr. of 1927 ed. 29.00 (ISBN 0-404-17265-2). AMS Pr.

--Buddhist Stories. facsimile ed. Silacara, Bhikkhu, tr. LC 71-106285. (Short Story Index Reprint Ser.). 1913. 19.00 (ISBN 0-8369-3322-2). Ayer Co Pubs.

Dalai Lama, IV. The Opening of the Wisdom-Eye. Rinpoche, Thubten K., et al, trs. from Tibetan. LC 70-152367. (Illus.). 1972. 7.50 (ISBN 0-8356-0202-8). Theos Pub Hse.

Dauer, Dorothea W. Schopenhauer As Transmitter of Buddhist Ideas. (European University Studies: Series 1, German Language & Literature: Vol. 15). 39p. 1969. 6.55 (ISBN 3-261-00014-7). P Lang Pubs.

David-Neel, Alexandra. Buddhism. 1979. pap. 3.50 (ISBN 0-380-46185-4, 63594-1, Discus). Avon.

--Buddhism. LC 77-10308. 1978. 8.95 (ISBN 0-312-10680-7). St Martin.

Davids, C. Rhys, ed. Khuddaka-Nikaya: The Minor Anthologies of the Pali Canon, 4 vols. Repr. of 1931 ed. 105.00 set (ISBN 0-404-17640-2). AMS Pr.

Davids, Carolina A. Buddhism: A Study of the Buddhist Norm. LC 78-72408. Repr. of 1912 ed. 25.00 (ISBN 0-404-17269-5). AMS Pr.

--A Manual of Buddhism for Advanced Students. LC 78-72410. Repr. of 1932 ed. 32.50 (ISBN 0-404-17274-1). AMS Pr.

Davids, Rhys. Buddhist Suttas. lib. bdg. 79.95 (ISBN 0-87968-511-5). Krishna Pr.

--Sakya of Buddhist Origins. lib. bdg. 79.95 (ISBN 0-87968-512-3). Krishna Pr.

De Bary, W. Theodore, ed. The Unfolding of Neo-Confucianism. LC 74-10929. (Neo-Confucian Series & Studies in Oriental Culture: No. 10). 593p. 1975. 38.00x (ISBN 0-231-03828-3); pap. 18.50x (ISBN 0-231-03829-1). Columbia U Pr.

Denwood, Philip & Piatigorsky, Alexander, eds. Buddhist Studies: Ancient & Modern. (Collected Papers on South Asia: No. 4). (Illus.). 206p. 1983. 24.50x (ISBN 0-389-20264-9, 07082). B&N Imports.

De Silva, Padmasiri. An Introduction to Buddhist Psychology. (Library of Philosophy & Religion Ser.). 134p. 1979. text ed. 28.50x (ISBN 0-06-491666-9). B&N Imports.

Dharma Realm Buddhist Association Staff. World Peace Gathering. (Illus.). 128p. (Orig.). pap. 5.00 (ISBN 0-917512-05-7). Buddhist Text.

Dhiravamsa. A New Approach to Buddhism. LC 74-81623. 1974. pap. 3.95 (ISBN 0-913922-08-0). Dawn Horse Pr.

Dube, S. N. Cross Currents in Early Buddhism. 1981. 22.50x (ISBN 0-8364-0686-9, Pub. by Manohar India). South Asia Bks.

Dumoulin, Heinrich. Christianity Meets Buddhism. Maraldo, John C., tr. from Ger. LC 73-82783. 212p. 1974. 19.95 (ISBN 0-87548-121-3). Open Court.

Dwivedi, A. N. Essentials of Hinduism, Jainism & Buddhism. 148p. 1979. 12.00 (ISBN 0-88065-083-4, Pub. by Messers Today & Tomorrows Printers & Publishers India). Scholarly Pubns.

Edgerton, Franklin, ed. Buddhist Hybrid Sanscrit Reader. 1953. 49.50x (ISBN 0-685-69814-9). Elliots Bks.

Education in Human Development. 400p. 1987. pap. 12.95 (ISBN 0-89800-134-X). Dharma Pub.

Ellwood, Rober S., ed. Eastern Spirituality in America: Selected Writings. (Sources of American Spirituality Ser.). 256p. 1987. pap. 16.95 (ISBN 0-8091-0388-5). Paulist Pr.

Eppsteiner, Fred & Maloney, Dennis, eds. The Path of Compassion: Contemporary Writings on Engaged Buddhism. 1985. 9.95 (ISBN 0-934834-52-0). White Pine.

Evans & Matilal, eds. Buddhist Logic & Epistemology. 1986. lib. bdg. 59.50 (ISBN 90-277-2222-6, Pub. by Reidel Holland). Kluwer Academic.

Fa-hsien, Fl. The Travels of Fa-hsien, 399 to 144 A.D. Or Record of the Buddhistic Kingdoms. Giles, M. A. & Giles, H. A., trs. from Fr. LC 81-13362. xx, 96p. 1982. Repr. of 1956 ed. lib. bdg. 22.50x (ISBN 0-313-23240-7, FATR). Greenwood.

Fausset, Hugh A. Flame & the Light: Meanings in Vedanta & Buddhism. LC 69-10089. Repr. of 1969 ed. lib. bdg. 22.50x (ISBN 0-8371-0996-5, FAVB). Greenwood.

Fernando, Antony & Swidler, Leonard. Buddhism Made Plain: An Introduction for Christians & Jews. LC 84-18880. 176p. (Orig.). 1985. pap. 9.95 (ISBN 0-88344-198-5). Orbis Bks.

Fielding-Hall, Harold. The Inward Light. LC 78-72431. Repr. of 1908 ed. 27.00 (ISBN 0-404-17294-6). AMS Pr.

Five Hundred & Fifty Books on Buddhism: Translations, Studies, General Readings. (Nyingma Reference Ser.). 95p. pap. 4.95 (ISBN 0-913546-97-6). Dharma Pub.

Fox, Douglas A. The Heart of Buddhist Wisdom: A Translation of the Heart Sutra with Historical Introduction & Commentary. (Studies in Asian Thought & Religion: Vol. 3). 195p. 1986. lib. bdg. 39.95x (ISBN 0-88946-053-1). E Mellen.

Franck, Frederick. The Buddha Eye: An Anthology of the Kyoto School. 256p. 1982. 14.95 (ISBN 0-8245-0410-0). Crossroad NY.

Frazier, Allie M., ed. Readings in Eastern Religious Thought, 3 vols. Incl. Vol. 1. Hinduism; Vol. 2. Buddhism; Vol. 3. Chinese & Japanese Religions. (ISBN 0-664-24848-9). LC 69-14197. 1969. Westminster.

Gard, Richard A., ed. Buddhism. LC 61-15499. (Great Religions of Modern Man Ser). 1976. 8.95 (ISBN 0-8076-0166-7). Braziller.

Gimello, Robert M. & Gregory, Peter N., eds. Studies in Ch'an & Hua-Yen. (Studies in East Asian Buddhism: No. 1). 406p. 1983. pap. text ed. 14.95x (ISBN 0-8248-0835-5). UH Pr.

Goddard, Dwight. The Buddha's Golden Path. 214p. 1981. pap. 12.00 (ISBN 0-89540-074-X, SB-074). Sun Pub.

Goddard, Dwight, ed. A Buddhist Bible. LC 72-105327. 677p. 1970. pap. 11.95 (ISBN 0-8070-5951-X, BP357). Beacon Pr.

Gokhale, Balkrishna G. Buddhism & Asoka. LC 78-72443. Repr. of 1948 ed. 41.50 (ISBN 0-404-17298-9). AMS Pr.

Goldstein, Joseph. The Experience of Insight: A Simple & Direct Guide to Buddhist Meditation. LC 82-42682. 185p. (Orig.). 1983. pap. 7.95 (ISBN 0-87773-226-4). Shambhala Pubns.

Gour, Hari S. The Spirit of Buddhism. LC 78-72432. Repr. of 1929 ed. 57.50 (ISBN 0-404-17299-7). AMS Pr.

Govinda, Lama A. Psycho-Cosmic Symbolism of the Buddhist Stupa. 102p. 1976. 20.00x (ISBN 0-317-39141-0, Pub. by Luzac & Co Ltd). State Mutual Bk.

--The Way of the White Clouds. (Illus.). 305p. 1970. pap. 10.95 (ISBN 0-87773-007-5). Shambhala Pubns.

Grimm, G. Doctrine of the Buddha. 2nd ed. 1984. Repr. 32.00 (ISBN 0-8426-0489-8). Orient Bk Dist.

Guenther, Herbert, et al. Questions & Answers on Guru & Disciple. (Illus.). 1978. pap. text ed. 3.00 (ISBN 0-931454-02-6). Timeless Bks.

Guenther, Herbert V. Matrix of Mystery: Scientific & Humanistic Aspects of rDzogs-chen Thought. LC 83-2306. (Illus.). 317p. 1984. 22.50 (ISBN 0-87773-291-4, 54073-5). Shambhala Pubns.

Gupta, Sunil K., ed. Insights into Buddhism. 212p. 1986. 15.00 (ISBN 81-7030-022-3, Pub. by Sri Satguru Pubns India). Orient Bk Dist.

Gyalpo, Tangtong. A Technique for Developing Enlightened Consciousness: A Traditional Buddhist Meditation on Avalokiteshvara. Gyatso, Janet, tr. from Tibetan. (Basic Buddhism Ser.). 26p. (Orig.). 1980. pap. 1.50 (ISBN 0-915078-02-3, P-01). Buddhist Assn US.

Hall, Isaac. The Growth & the Essence of Buddhism. (Illus.). 148p. 1982. Repr. of 1883 ed. 89.75 (ISBN 0-89901-060-1). Found Class Reprints.

Hall, Manly P. Arhats of Buddhism. pap. 3.95 (ISBN 0-89314-529-7). Philos Res.

--Buddha's Sermon on the Mount. pap. 2.50 (ISBN 0-89314-307-3). Philos Res.

--Buddhism & Psychotherapy. pap. 7.95 (ISBN 0-89314-394-4). Philos Res.

--Koyasan: Sanctuary of Buddhism. pap. 2.50 (ISBN 0-89314-326-X). Philos Res.

--Noble Eightfold Path. pap. 2.50 (ISBN 0-89314-337-5). Philos Res.

Hamsa, Bhagwan. The Holy Mountain: Being the Story of a Pilgrimage to Lake Manas & of Initiation on Mount Kailas in Tibet. LC 78-72437. Repr. of 1934 ed. 27.50 (ISBN 0-404-17303-9). AMS Pr.

Hardy, Robert S. Eastern Monachism: An Account of the Origin, Laws, Discipline, Sacred Writings, Mysterious Rites, Religious Ceremonies, & Present Circumstances, of the Order of Mendicants Founded by Gotama Budha. LC 78-72438. Repr. of 1850 ed. 40.00 (ISBN 0-404-17304-7). AMS Pr.

--A Manual of Buddhism in Its Modern Development. LC 78-72439. Repr. of 1853 ed. 46.50 (ISBN 0-404-17305-5). AMS Pr.

Hearn, Lafcadio. Gleanings in Buddha-Fields. LC 73-172539. Repr. of 1897 ed. 20.00 (ISBN 0-405-08609-1). Ayer Co Pubs.

--Gleanings in Buddha-Fields: Studies of Hand & Soul in the Far East. LC 72-146523. 1971. pap. 6.25 (ISBN 0-8048-0978-X). C E Tuttle.

Heng Sure & Heng Chau. News from True Cultivators, Vol. I. 128p. (Orig.). 1983. pap. 5.00 (ISBN 0-88139-016-X). Buddhist Text.

--News from True Cultivators, Vol. 2. 130p. (Orig.). 1983. pap. 5.00 (ISBN 0-88139-024-0). Buddhist Text.

--With One Heart Bowing to the City of Ten Thousand Buddhas, Vol. I. (Illus.). 180p. (Orig.). 1977. pap. 6.00 (ISBN 0-917512-21-9). Buddhist Text.

--With One Heart Bowing to the City of Ten Thousand Buddhas, Vol. II. (Illus.). 322p. (Orig.). 1979. pap. 7.00 (ISBN 0-917512-23-5). Buddhist Text.

--With One Heart Bowing to the City of Ten Thousand Buddhas, Vol. IX. 220p. (Orig.). 1983. pap. 7.50 (ISBN 0-88139-016-X). Buddhist Text.

Heng Sure, et al. Open Your Eyes. (Illus.). 347p. (Orig.). 1979. pap. 7.50 (ISBN 0-917512-32-4). Buddhist Text.

Heng Yin, et al. Songs for Awakening. (Illus.). 112p. (Orig.). 1979. pap. 8.00 (ISBN 0-917512-31-6). Buddhist Text.

Holmes, Edmond. The Creed of Buddha. LC 72-9918. 260p. 1973. Repr. of 1957 ed. lib. bdg. 22.50x (ISBN 0-8371-6606-3, HOCB). Greenwood.

Horniman, R. The Living Buddha. LC 78-72441. Repr. of 1903 ed. 33.00 (ISBN 0-404-17307-1). AMS Pr.

Hua, Husan. Sutra of the Past Vows of Earthstore Bodhisattva: The Collected Lectures of Tripitaka Master Hsuan Hua. Ching, Heng, tr. from Chinese. (IASWR Ser.). 235p. 1974. 12.75 (ISBN 0-686-47598-4, S-10); pap. 6.75 (ISBN 0-915078-00-7, S-11). Inst Adv Stud Wld.

Hua, Tripitaka Master. Heart Sutra & Verses Without a Stand, With Prose Commentary. Buddhist Text Translation Society, tr. from Chinese. (Illus.). 160p. (Orig.). 1980. pap. 7.50 (ISBN 0-917512-27-8). Buddhist Text.

Humphreys, Christmas. Buddhism. (Pelican Ser.). 256p. (Orig.). 1951. pap. 6.95 (ISBN 0-14-020228-5). Penguin.

--Exploring Buddhism. LC 74-12206. 188p. (Orig.). 1975. pap. 2.50 (ISBN 0-8356-0454-3, Quest). Theos Pub Hse.

--A Popular Dictionary of Buddhism. 224p. 1984. pap. 8.95 (ISBN 0-7007-0184-2). Salem Hse Pubs.

Humphreys, Christmas, ed. The Wisdom of Buddhism. 2nd, rev. ed. 280p. 1987. pap. text ed. 9.95 (ISBN 0-391-03464-2, Pub. by Humanities Press & Curzon Pr England). Humanities.

Iijima, Kanjitsu. Buddhist Yoga. (Illus.). 184p. 1975. pap. 8.95 (ISBN 0-87040-349-4). Japan Pubns USA.

Ikeda, Daisaku. Buddhism: The First Millennium. Watson, Burton, tr. LC 77-84915. 1978. 12.95x (ISBN 0-87011-321-6). Kodansha.

Illion, Theodore. Darkness over Tibet. 192p. 1983. pap. 6.95 (ISBN 0-912181-03-6). East School Pr.

--In Secret Tibet: In Disguise Amongst Lamas, Robbers & Wise Men. A Key to the Mysteries of Tibet. 190p. 1983. pap. 6.95 (ISBN 0-912181-01-X). East School Pr.

Isaacson, Harold J., tr. The Throat of the Peacock: Japanese Senryu on Filial Devotion. (Bhaisajaguru Ser.). 1977. pap. 1.85 (ISBN 0-87830-557-2). Theatre Arts.

Itivuttaka. Sayings of Buddha: The Iti-Vuttaka. LC 9-4569. (Columbia University. Indo-Iranian Ser.: No. 5). Repr. of 1908 ed. 16.50 (ISBN 0-404-50475-2). AMS Pr.

Jacobson, Nolan P. Buddhism & the Contemporary World: Change & Self Correction. LC 82-5909. 203p. 1982. 18.95x (ISBN 0-8093-1052-X); pap. 9.95 (ISBN 0-8093-1071-6). S Ill U Pr.

--Buddhism: The Religion of Analysis. LC 66-71124. (Arcturus Books Paperbacks). 202p. 1970. pap. 7.95x (ISBN 0-8093-0463-5). S Ill U Pr.

--Understanding Buddhism. 224p. (Orig.). 1985. text ed. 19.95x (ISBN 0-8093-1224-7); pap. text ed. 10.95x (ISBN 0-8093-1225-5). S Ill U Pr.

Jamspal, Lozang, et al. Nagarjuna's Letter to King Gautamiputra. 1978. 9.95 (ISBN 0-89684-022-0, Pub. by Motilal Banarsidass India). Orient Bk Dist.

Jayatilleke, K. N. The Message of the Buddha. Smart, Ninian, ed. LC 75-15431. 1975. 12.95 (ISBN 0-02-916350-1). Free Pr.

Jennings, J. G. Vedantic Buddhism of Buddha. 1974. Repr. 28.00 (ISBN 0-8426-0683-1). Orient Bk Dist.

Jinapriya, Ginige. Buddhist Education in Ceylon, & Other Essays. LC 78-72901. Repr. of 1931 ed. 18.50 (ISBN 0-404-17313-6). AMS Pr.

Johansson, Rune. The Dynamic Psychology of Early Buddhism. (Scandinavian Institute of Asian Studies Monographs: No. 37). (Illus.). 1979. pap. text ed. 15.00x (ISBN 0-7007-0114-1). Humanities.

John Damascene, Saint Barlaam & Iosaph. (Loeb Classical Library: No. 34). 13.95x (ISBN 0-674-99038-2). Harvard U Pr.

John-Roger. The Buddha Consiousness. LC 76-17344. 1976. pap. 5.00 (ISBN 0-914829-03-3). Baraka Bk.

Johnston, E. R. Buddhacarita: Acts of Buddha. 1978. Repr. 26.00 (ISBN 0-8426-0474-X). Orient Bk Dist.

Jones, Richard H. Science & Mysticism: A Comparative Study of Western Natural Science, Theravada Buddhism, & Advaita Vedanta. LC 84-46098. 272p. 1986. 35.00x (ISBN 0-8387-5093-1, Pub. by Bucknell U Pr). Assoc Univ Prs.

Jong, J. W. De. Buddhist Studies. Schopen, Gregory, ed. 1980. 35.00 (ISBN 0-89581-002-6). Asian Human Pr.

Jorgensen, Hans, ed. Vicitrakarnika-Vadanoddhrta: A Collection of Buddhistic Legends. LC 78-70134. Repr. of 1931 ed. 34.50 (ISBN 0-404-17404-3). AMS Pr.

Junankar, N. S. Gautama: The Nyaya Philosophy. 1979. 34.00x (ISBN 0-89684-002-6). South Asia Bks.

Kahawai Collective Staff, ed. Not Mixing up Buddhism: Essays on Women & Buddhist Practice. 1987. 10.00 (ISBN 0-934834-71-7). White Pine.

Kalupahana, David J. The Principles of Buddhist Psychology. (Buddhist Studies). 256p. 1987. 39.50 (ISBN 0-88706-404-3); pap. 12.95 (ISBN 0-88706-403-5). State U NY Pr.

Kasawara, Kenju. The Dharma-Samgraha, an Ancient Collection of Buddhist Technical Terms. Muller, F. Max & Wenzel, H., eds. LC 78-72425. Repr. of 1885 ed. 17.50 (ISBN 0-404-17286-5). AMS Pr.

Kashima, Tetsuden. Buddhism in America: The Social Organization of an Ethnic Religious Institution. LC 76-57837. (Contributions in Sociology: No. 26). (Illus.). 1977. lib. bdg. 29.95 (ISBN 0-8371-9534-9, KSO/). Greenwood.

Kaviratna, Harischandra, tr. Dhammapada, Wisdom of the Buddha. LC 80-52031. 1980. 12.50 (ISBN 0-911500-39-1); pap. 7.50 (ISBN 0-911500-40-5). Theos U Pr.

Kawamura, Leslie S. & Scott, Keith, eds. Buddhist Thought & Asian Civilization: Essays in Honor of Herbert V. Genther on His Sixtieth Birthday. LC 77-71194. 1977. 25.00 (ISBN 0-913546-51-8). Dharma Pub.

Keith, Arthur B. The Karma-Mimamsa. LC 78-72451. Repr. of 1921 ed. 27.00 (ISBN 0-404-17318-7). AMS Pr.

Kennedy, Alex. The Buddhist Vision. (Illus.). 216p. (Orig.). 1987. pap. 8.95 (ISBN 0-87728-620-5). Weiser.

King, Winston L. Theravada Meditation: The Buddhist Transformation of Yoga. LC 79-25856. 192p. 1980. 22.75x (ISBN 0-271-00254-9). Pa St U Pr.

Kiyota, Minoru. Shingon Buddhism. LC 77-27894. 1978. text ed. 9.95x (ISBN 0-914910-09-4); pap. 7.95x (ISBN 0-914910-10-8). Buddhist Bks.

Kunjavihari, Vasu. Lord Buddha & His Doctrine. LC 78-72458. Repr. of 1927 ed. 39.50 (ISBN 0-404-17326-8). AMS Pr.

Lakshmi Narasu, Pokala. The Essence of Buddhism. 3rd rev. & enl. ed. LC 78-72459. Repr. of 1948 ed. 32.50 (ISBN 0-404-17327-6). AMS Pr.

Landaw, Jonathan. Prince Siddhartha. (Illus.). 144p. 1984. 15.95 (ISBN 0-318-04415-3, Wisdom Pubns). Great Traditions.

--The Story of Buddha. (Illus.). 1979. 7.50 (ISBN 0-89744-140-0). Auromere.

Law, Bimala C. The Buddhist Conception of Spirits. 2nd rev. & enl. ed. LC 78-72462. Repr. of 1936 ed. 21.50 (ISBN 0-404-17334-9). AMS Pr.

Law, Bimala C., ed. Buddhistic Studies. LC 78-72463. Repr. of 1931 ed. 74.50 (ISBN 0-404-17335-7). AMS Pr.

--Geography of Early Buddhism. LC 78-72464. Repr. of 1932 ed. 21.00 (ISBN 0-404-17336-5). AMS Pr.

--A Study of the Mahavastu. LC 78-72469. Repr. of 1930 ed. 26.50 (ISBN 0-404-17339-X). AMS Pr.

Layman, Emma M. Buddhism in America. LC 76-4566. (Illus.). 364p. 1976. pap. 13.95x (ISBN 0-88229-436-9). Nelson-Hall.

Leland, Charles G. Fusang or the Discovery of America by Chinese Buddhist Priests. 212p. 1981. pap. 12.00 (ISBN 0-89540-094-4, SB-094). Sun Pub.

Lester, Robert C. Theravada Buddhism in Southeast Asia. LC 71-185154. 1973. 7.95 (ISBN 0-472-06184-4). U of Mich Pr.

Lillie, Arthur. Buddha & Buddhism. LC 76-100573. 1975. 11.25x (ISBN 0-89684-372-6). Orient Bk Dist.

Lindtner, Christian, tr. from Sanskrit, Chinese, Tibetan. Master of Wisdom: Writings of the Buddhist Master Nagarjuna. (Tibetan Translation Ser.). 420p. 1987. 28.00 (ISBN 0-89800-139-0). Dharma Pub.

Ling, T. O. A Dictionary of Buddhism. LC 72-37231. 244p. 1972. 7.95 (ISBN 0-684-12763-6, ScribT). Scribner.

Ling, Trevor. Buddha, Marx & God: Some Aspects of Religion in the Modern World. 2nd ed. 1979. 26.00 (ISBN 0-312-10679-3). St Martin.

--Buddism. 1985. 13.00x (ISBN 0-7062-3594-0, Pub. by Ward Lock Educ Co Ltd). State Mutual Bk.

--A Dictionary of Buddhism. 1985. 15.00x (ISBN 0-8364-1436-5, Pub. by KP Bagchi India). South Asia Bks.

Ling, Trevor, ed. The Buddha's Philosophy of Man: Early Indian Buddhist Dialogues. 229p. 1981. pap. 5.95x (ISBN 0-460-01247-9, Evman). Biblio Dist.

Maitriya. The Buddha Mimansa. Maharaja Yogiraja, ed. LC 78-70098. Repr. of 1925 ed. 23.50 (ISBN 0-404-17347-0). AMS Pr.

Malalasekera, George P. & Jayatilleke, K. N. Buddhism & the Race Question. LC 77-18853. (The Race Question in Modern Thought). 1978. Repr. of 1958 ed. lib. bdg. 22.50x (ISBN 0-313-20208-7, MABU). Greenwood.

March, A. C. A Glossary of Buddhist Terms. 99p. 1986. Repr. of 1937 ed. lib. bdg. 10.50 (ISBN 81-7030-025-8, Pub. by Sri Satguru Pubns India). Orient Bk Dist.

Mariah, Paul. For the Vietnamese Buddhists. Man-Root.

Master Hua, Tripitaka. Listen to Yourself: Think Everything Over, Vol. II. Buddhist Text Translation Society, tr. from Chinese. 172p. 1983. pap. 7.00 (ISBN 0-88139-010-0). Buddhist Text.

--Records of High Sanghans, Vol. I. Buddhist Text Translation Society, tr. from Chinese. 160p. (Orig.). 1983. pap. 7.00 (ISBN 0-88139-012-7). Buddhist Text.

Matsunami, Kodo. Introducing Buddhism. LC 75-28970. (Illus.). 304p. 1976. pap. 7.50 (ISBN 0-8048-1192-X). C E Tuttle.

Matthews, Bruce. Craving & Salvation: A Study in Buddhist Soteriology. (SR Supplements). 138p. 1984. pap. text ed. 9.25x (ISBN 0-88920-147-1). Humanities.

Mistry, Freny. Nietzsche & Buddhism. (Monographien und Texte zur Nietzsche-Forschung, Vol. 6). 211p. 1981. 43.25 (ISBN 3-11-008305-1). De Gruyter.

Miyamoto, Kazuo, ed. One Man's Journey. 120p. (Orig.). 1981. pap. 6.95 (ISBN 0-938474-02-2). Buddhist Study.

Mojica Sandoz, Luis. La Meditacion Segun la Mas Antigua Tradicion Budista. (Coleccion Uprex; Serie Manuales: No. 54). (Span., Illus.). 1979. pap. text ed. 1.85 (ISBN 0-8477-0054-2). U of PR Pr.

Monier-Williams. Buddhism, in Its Connection with Brahmanism & Hinduism, & in Contrast with Christianity. 2nd ed. LC 78-70101. Repr. of 1890 ed. 57.50 (ISBN 0-404-17349-7). AMS Pr.

Mookerjee, S. Buddhist Philosophy of Universal Flux. 1975. Repr. 20.00 (ISBN 0-8426-0852-4). Orient Bk Dist.

Morgan, Kenneth W. The Path of the Buddha: Buddhism Interpreted by Buddhists. 1986. 24.00X (ISBN 81-208-0030-3, Pub. by Motilal Banarsidass). South Asia Bks.

Morgan, Peggy. Buddhism. (World Religions Ser.). (Illus.). 72p. 1987. 16.95 (ISBN 0-7134-5203-X, Pub. by Batsford England). David & Charles.

--Buddhism in the Twentieth Century. 1985. pap. 5.95 (ISBN 0-7175-1394-7). Dufour.

Mori, Masatoshi G. Buddhism & Faith. LC 78-70102. Repr. of 1928 ed. 21.50 (ISBN 0-404-17353-5). AMS Pr.

Morris, Richard, ed. The Puggala-Pannatti. LC 78-70109. Repr. of 1883 ed. 20.00 (ISBN 0-404-17359-4). AMS Pr.

Moses, Larry W. The Political Role of Mongol Buddhism. LC 81-622859. (Indiana University Uralic & Altaic Ser.: Vol. 133). x, 299p. 1977. 15.00 (ISBN 0-933070-01-2). Ind U Res Inst.

Nagarjuna. She-rab Dong-bu, or Prajnya Danda: A Metrical Translation in Tibetan of a Sanskirt Ethical Work. Campbell, W. L., ed. LC 78-70103. Repr. of 1919 ed. 22.00 (ISBN 0-404-17354-3). AMS Pr.

Nakamura, Hajime. Gotama Buddha. LC 77-8589. 1977. 8.95x (ISBN 0-914910-05-1); pap. 6.95x (ISBN 0-914910-06-X). Buddhist Bks.

Nakamura, Hijime. Buddhism in Comparative Light. 1986. 15.00 (ISBN 81-208-0184-9, Pub. by Motilal Banarsidass). South Asia Bks.

Narasu, P. Lakshmi. The Essence of Buddhism with an Introduction by Anagarika H. Dharmmapals. 212p. 1986. Repr. of 1907 ed. 15.00X (ISBN 0-8364-1748-8, Pub. by Manohar India). South Asia Bks.

Narayan, R. K. Swami & Friends. LC 80-16119. 192p. 1980. lib. bdg. 13.00x (ISBN 0-226-56829-6); pap. 6.95 (ISBN 0-226-56831-8). U of Chicago Pr.

National Master Ch'ing Liang. Flower Adornment Sutra Prologue: Vol. I, The First Door. Master Hua, Tripitaka, commentary by. Buddhist Text Translation Society, tr. from Chinese. (Illus.). 252p. (Orig.). 1981. pap. 10.00 (ISBN 0-917512-66-9). Buddhist Text.

Newland, Guy. Compassion in Madhyamika Buddhism. (A Wisdom Advanced Book, Blue Ser.). 160p. (Orig.). 1984. pap. 10.95 (ISBN 0-86171-024-X, Wisdom Pubns). Great Traditions.

Niwano, Nikkyo. Buddhism for Today: A Modern Interpretation of the Threefold Lotus Sutra. LC 79-22383. 476p. 1976. pap. 10.95 (ISBN 0-8348-0147-7). Weatherhill.

--A Buddhist Approach to Peace. Nezu, Masuo, tr. from Japanese. (Illus.). 162p. 1977. 7.95 (ISBN 4-333-00308-3, Pub. by Kosei Publishing Co). C E Tuttle.

Nyana, U. The Vipassana Dipani; or the Manual of Insight. LC 78-70107. Repr. of 1930 ed. 22.00 (ISBN 0-404-17357-8). AMS Pr.

Nyanatiloka. Buddhist Dictionary. LC 77-87508. Repr. of 1950 ed. 20.00 (ISBN 0-404-16846-9). AMS Pr.

Nyingpo, Namkhay. Mother of Knowledge: The Enlightenment of Ye-shes Mtsho-Rgyal. Tulka, Tarthang, tr. (Translation Ser.). Orig. Title: Tibetan. (Illus.). 250p. 1983. 21.95 (ISBN 0-913546-90-9); pap. 12.95 (ISBN 0-913546-91-7). Dharma Pub.

Obeyesekere, Gananath. Medusa's Hair: An Essay on Personal Symbols & Religious Experiences. LC 80-27372. (Illus.). 252p. 1981. lib. bdg. 22.50x (ISBN 0-226-61600-2). U of Chicago Pr.

Odin, Steve. Process Metaphysics & Hua-Yen Buddhism: A Critical Study of Cumulative Penetration vs. Interpretation. LC 81-9388. 256p. 1982. 44.50 (ISBN 0-87395-568-4); pap. 16.95 (ISBN 0-87395-569-2). State U NY Pr.

Olcott, Henry S. Buddhist Catechism. 1971. pap. 2.75 (ISBN 0-8356-0027-0, Quest). Theos Pub Hse.

--The Buddhist Catechism. 44th ed. xv, 115p. 1983. pap. 4.95 (ISBN 0-912181-07-9). East School Pr.

O'Neil, Kevin. American Buddhist Directory. 2nd ed. 116p. (Orig.). 1985. pap. 20.00 (ISBN 0-86627-012-4). Crises Res Pr.

--The American Buddhist Directory, 1982. 96p. 1982. pap. 7.00 (ISBN 0-86627-003-5). Crises Res Pr.

--Basic Buddhism. 41p. (Orig.). 1981. pap. 5.00 (ISBN 0-86627-006-X). Crises Res Pr.

--An Introduction to Nichiren Shoshu Buddhism. 111p. 1980. pap. 5.00 (ISBN 0-86627-002-7). Crises Res Pr.

--Realm of Totality. 49p. (Orig.). 1984. pap. 6.00 (ISBN 0-86627-011-6). Crises Res Pr.

Otani, Kosho K. The Successor: My Life. LC 84-23016. (Illus.). 114p. 1985. 16.95x (ISBN 0-914910-50-7). Buddhist Bks.

Out of Curiosity: Spirit of Nyingma in America. 350p. 1987. pap. 12.95 (ISBN 0-89800-135-8). Dharma Pub.

Pande, G. C. Studies in the Origin of Buddhism. 2nd rev. ed. 1974. 30.00 (ISBN 0-8426-0547-9). Orient Bk Dist.

Parrinder, Geoffrey. The Wisdom of the Early Buddhists. LC 77-7945. (New Directions Wisdon Ser.). 1977. pap. 4.95 (ISBN 0-8112-0667-X, NDP444). New Directions.

Peiris, William. The Western Contribution to Buddhism. 372p. 1974. lib. bdg. 79.95 (ISBN 0-87968-550-6). Krishna Pr.

--Western Contribution to Buddhism. 1973. 11.25 (ISBN 0-8426-0537-1). Orient Bk Dist.

Percheron, Maurice. Buddha & Buddhism. Stapleton, Edmund, tr. from Fr. LC 82-3471. (The Overlook Spiritual Masters Ser.). (Illus.). 192p. 1982. cloth 18.95 (ISBN 0-87951-157-5). Overlook Pr.

--Buddha & Buddhism. Stapleton, Edmund, tr. from Fr. LC 82-3471. (Spiritual Masters Ser.). (Illus.). 192p. 1983. pap. 9.95 (ISBN 0-87951-193-1). Overlook Pr.

Pratt, James B. The Pilgrimage of Buddhism & a Buddhist Pilgrimage. 758p. 1982. Repr. of 1928 ed. lib. bdg. 45.00 (ISBN 0-89984-828-1). Century Bookbindery.

Prebish, Charles S., ed. Buddhism: A Modern Perspective. LC 74-300085. 346p. 1975. 24.95x (ISBN 0-271-01185-8); pap. 14.95x (ISBN 0-271-01195-5). Pa St U Pr.

Pruett, Gordon E. The Meaning & End of Suffering for Freud & the Buddhist Tradition. LC 86-26735. 524p. 1987. lib. bdg. 34.50 (ISBN 0-8191-5758-9). U Pr of Amer.

Rahula, Bhikku T. A Critical Study of the Mahavastu. 1978. 24.95 (ISBN 0-89684-018-2, Pub. by Motilal Banarsidass India). Orient Bk Dist.

Rahula, Walpola. Buddhist Studies in Honour of Walpola Rahula. 308p. 1981. 75.00x (ISBN 0-86092-030-5, Pub. by Fraser Bks). State Mutual Bk.

--What the Buddha Taught. rev. ed. (Illus.). 168p. 1974. pap. 6.95 (ISBN 0-394-17827-0, E641, Ever). Grove.

--Zen & the Taming of the Bull: Towards the Definition of Buddhist Thought. 1978. text ed. 17.50x (ISBN 0-900406-69-0). Humanities.

Rajneesh, Bhagwan S. The Book of the Books, Vol. 1. Rajneesh Foundation International, ed. LC 82-50462. (Buddha Ser.). 360p. (Orig.). 1982. pap. 15.95 (ISBN 0-88050-513-3). Chidvilas Found.

--The Book of the Books, Vol. 4. Krishna, Swami P., ed. LC 82-50462. (Buddha Ser.). 384p. (Orig.). 1985. pap. 4.95 (ISBN 0-88050-516-8). Chidvilas Found.

--The Secret of Secrets, Vol. 1. Rajneesh Foundation International, ed. LC 82-50464. (Tao Ser.). 588p. (Orig.). 1982. pap. 16.95 (ISBN 0-88050-628-8). Chidvilas Found.

--Zorba the Buddha. Maneesha, Ma Prem, ed. LC 82-50463. (Initiation Talks Ser.). (Illus.). 344p. 1982. pap. 21.95 (ISBN 0-88050-694-6). Chidvilas Found.

Ramakrishna Gopala Bhanddarkar. Commemorative Essays Presented to Sir Ramakrishna Gopal Bhandarkar. LC 78-70111. Repr. of 1917 ed. 44.00 (ISBN 0-404-17366-7). AMS Pr.

Rawding, F. W. The Buddha. LC 74-14436. (Cambridge Introduction to the History of Mankind Ser.). (Illus.). 48p. (YA) 1975. pap. 5.95 (ISBN 0-521-20368-6). Cambridge U Pr.

Reynolds, Frank E., et al. Guide to Buddhist Religion. 440p. 1981. lib. bdg. 57.50 (ISBN 0-8161-7900-X, Hall Reference). G K Hall.

Richards, Harriet. Light Your Own Lamp. LC 66-26971. 1967. 5.95 (ISBN 0-8022-1333-2). Philos Lib.

Rinpoche, Bikshu. Buddhism: An Introduction to the Living Spiritual Tradition. 160p. (Orig.). 1987. pap. 8.95 (ISBN 0-913757-71-3, Pub. by New Era Bks). Paragon Hse.

Rinpoche, Patrul. The Propitious Speech from the Beginning, Middle & End. Norbu, Thinley, tr. from Tibetan. 46p. (Orig.). 1984. pap. 7.00 (ISBN 0-9607000-6-4). Jewel Pub Hse.

Robinson, Richard H. & Johnson, Willard L. The Buddhist Religion: A Historical Introduction. 3rd ed. 304p. 1982. pap. text ed. write for info (ISBN 0-534-01027-X). Wadsworth Pub.

Roerich, Helena. Foundations of Buddhism. 1971. Repr. index 8.00 (ISBN 0-686-79661-6). Agni Yoga Soc.

Roerich, Nicholas. Shambhala. softcover 12.00 (ISBN 0-686-79666-7); 16.00. Agni Yoga Soc.

Ross, Nancy W. Buddhism: A Way of Life & Thought. LC 80-7652. (Illus.). 224p. 1980. 15.95 (ISBN 0-394-49286-2). Knopf.

--Buddhism: A Way of Life & Thought. LC 81-40081. (Illus.). 224p. 1981. pap. 6.95 (ISBN 0-394-74754-2, Vin). Random.

--Three Ways of Asian Wisdom: Hinduism, Buddhism, Zen. (Illus.). 1978. pap. 12.95 (ISBN 0-671-24230-X, Touchstone Bks). S&S.

Rowland, Benjamin, Jr. The Evolution of the Buddha Image. LC 74-27420. (Asia Society Ser.). (Illus.). 1979. Repr. of 1963 ed. lib. bdg. 31.00x (ISBN 0-405-06568-X). Ayer Co Pubs.

Saint-Hilaire, J. B. Buddha & His Religion. 59.95 (ISBN 0-87968-798-3). Gordon Pr.

Sakakibara, Tokuso, et al. Bodhisattvas Everywhere. Tabrah, Ruth, ed. Arai, Toshikazu, tr. from Japanese. 120p. (Orig.). 1983. pap. 6.95 (ISBN 0-938474-03-0). Buddhist Study.

Santideva. The Path of Light. LC 78-70117. Repr. of 1909 ed. 20.00 (ISBN 0-404-17374-8). AMS Pr.

Saso, Michael & Chappell, David W., eds. Buddhist & Taoist Studies Number One. (Asian Studies at Hawaii: No. 18). (Illus.). 174p. 1977. pap. text ed. 10.50x (ISBN 0-8248-0420-1). UH Pr.

Satyaprakash. Buddhism: A Select Bibliography. 1986. Repr. of 1976 ed. 28.50x (ISBN 0-8364-1828-X, Pub. by Indian Doc Serv India). South Asia Bks.

Satyaprakash, ed. Buddhism: A Selection Bibliography. 1977. 11.00 (ISBN 0-88386-956-X). South Asia Bks.

Saunders, E. Dale. Mudra: A Study of Symbolic Gestures in Japanese Buddhist Sculpture. (Bollingen Ser.: Vol. 58). (Illus.). 1960. 37.00x (ISBN 0-691-09796-8). Princeton U Pr.

Saunders, K. J. Story of Buddhism. 69.95 (ISBN 0-8490-1129-9). Gordon Pr.

Schweitzer, Albert. Indian Thought & Its Development. 1962. 11.00 (ISBN 0-8446-2893-X). Peter Smith.

Seneviratne, H. L. Rituals of the Kandyan State. LC 77-80842. (Cambridge Studies in Social Anthropology: No. 22). (Illus.). 1978. 37.50 (ISBN 0-521-21736-9). Cambridge U Pr.

Shaku, Soyen. Sermons of a Buddhist Abbot. 35.00 (ISBN 0-8490-1026-8). Gordon Pr.

Shen, C. T. Mayflower II: On Buddhist Voyage to Liberation. LC 83-81198. (Basic Buddhism Ser.). (Illus.). 1983. pap. 4.95 (ISBN 0-915078-03-1, P-02). Inst Adv Stud Wld.

Shen Fu. Six Records of a Floating Life. Pratt, Leonard, tr. 176p. 1983. pap. 3.95 (ISBN 0-14-044429-7). Penguin.

Shigaraki, Takamaro. The World of Buddhist Awakening. 96p. 1983. pap. 6.95 (ISBN 0-938474-03-0). Buddhist Study.

Sinnett. Esoteric Buddhism. 11.25 (ISBN 0-8356-5230-0). Theos Pub Hse.

Sinnett, A. P. Esoteric Buddhism. 5th ed. LC 73-76091. (Secret Doctrine Reference Ser.). 240p. 1981. pap. 8.00 (ISBN 0-913510-45-9). Wizards.

Smith, Helmer, ed. The Khuddaka-Patha. LC 78-72454. Repr. of 1915 ed. 28.50 (ISBN 0-404-17323-3). AMS Pr.

Snelling, John. Buddhism. (Religions of the World Ser.). (Illus.). 48p. 1986. PLB 10.90 (ISBN 0-531-18065-4, Pub. by Bookwright). Watts.

Southwold, Martin. Buddhism in Life: The Anthropological Study of Religion & the Sinhalese Practice of Buddhism. LC 83-9890. (Themes in Social Anthropology Ser.). 232p. 1984. 36.00 (ISBN 0-7190-0971-5, Pub. by Manchester Univ Pr). Longwood Pub Group.

Spiegelman, J. Marvin & Miyuki, Mokusen. Buddhism & Jungian Psychology. 224p. (Orig.). 1985. pap. 8.95 (ISBN 0-941404-37-4). Falcon Pr AZ.

Spiro, Melford E. Buddhism & Society: A Great Tradition & Its Burmese Vicissitudes. 2nd, exp. ed. LC 81-18522. 530p. 1982. 40.00x (ISBN 0-520-04671-4); pap. 10.95x (ISBN 0-520-04672-2, CAMPUS 298). U of Cal Pr.

Sprung, G. M., ed. The Problems of Two Truths in Buddism & Vedanta. LC 73-83570. 1973. lib. bdg. 26.00 (ISBN 90-277-0335-3, Pub. by Reidel Holland). Kluwer Academic.

Sri Aurobindo. Essays on the Gita. 1976. 12.50 (ISBN 0-89071-231-X). Matagiri.

Stambaugh, Joan. The Real Is Not the Rational. (Buddhist Studies). 142p. (Orig.). 1986. 34.50 (ISBN 0-88706-166-4); pap. 10.95 (ISBN 0-88706-167-2). State U NY Pr.

Stcherbatskoi, F. I. The Conception of Buddhist Nirvana. lib. bdg. 100.00 (ISBN 0-87968-058-X). Krishna Pr.

Stcherbatsky, T. Central Conception of Buddhism. 1979. Repr. 12.50 (ISBN 0-89684-183-9). Orient Bk Dist.

Stcherbatsky, Theodore. Conception of Buddhist Nirvana. 2nd rev. ed. 1977. 13.95 (ISBN 0-89684-187-1). Orient Bk Dist.

Strauss, C. T. Buddha & His Doctrine. LC 70-102584. 1970. Repr. of 1923 ed. 16.50x (ISBN 0-8046-0744-3, Pub. by Kennikat). Assoc Faculty Pr.

Strong, D. M., tr. from Pali. The Udana, or the Solemn Utterances of the Buddha. LC 78-70131. Repr. of 1902 ed. 20.50 (ISBN 0-404-17399-3). AMS Pr.

Subramaniam, V. Buddhism, Dance & Drama. 1985. 12.00x (ISBN 0-8364-1322-9, Pub. by Ashish India). South Asia Bks.

Sure, Heng & Chau, Heng. With One Heart Bowing to the City of Ten Thousand Buddhas, Vol. VIII. (Illus.). 232p. (Orig.). 1982. pap. 7.50 (ISBN 0-917512-53-7). Buddhist Text.

--With One Heart Bowing to the City of Ten Thousand Buddhas, Vol. V. (Illus.). 127p. (Orig.). 1981. pap. 4.00 (ISBN 0-917512-91-X). Buddhist Text.

Sutra, Buddhist. The Voice of the Buddha: The Beauty of Compassion, 2 vols. Bays, Gwendolyn, tr. from Fr. (Translation Ser.). (Illus.). 704p. 1983. Set. 60.00. Vol. I (ISBN 0-913546-84-4). Vol. II (ISBN 0-913546-85-2). Dharma Pub.

Suttapitaka. Prakrit Dhammapada. LC 78-70127. Repr. of 1921 ed. 31.50 (ISBN 0-404-17386-1). AMS Pr.

Syama-Sankara, Hara C. Buddha & His Sayings. LC 78-70128. Repr. of 1914 ed. 18.00 (ISBN 0-404-17387-X). AMS Pr.

Takakusa, Junjiro. The Essentials of Buddhist Philosophy. 236p. 1978. pap. 6.95 (ISBN 0-87728-426-1). Weiser.

Taylor, Arnold C., ed. Kathavatthu, 2 vols. in one. LC 78-72450. Repr. of 1894 ed. 56.00 (ISBN 0-404-17317-9). AMS Pr.

--Patisambhidamagga, 2 vols. in one. LC 78-70108. Repr. of 1905 ed. 43.50 (ISBN 0-404-17358-6). AMS Pr.

Tendzin, Osel. Buddha in the Palm of Your Hand. LC 81-84450. (Dragon Ser.). (Illus.). 120p. (Orig.). 1982. pap. 6.95 (ISBN 0-87773-223-X). Shambhala Pubns.

--Buddha in the Palm of Your Hand. 1987. pap. 8.95. Shambhala Pubns.

Thera, N. Heart of Buddhist Meditation. 1973. pap. 7.95 (ISBN 0-87728-073-8). Weiser.

Thomas, E. J., tr. Early Buddhist Scriptures. lib. bdg. 79.95 (ISBN 0-87968-563-8). Krishna Pr.

Tin, Maung, ed. Khudaka Patha. LC 78-70126. Repr. of 1913 ed. 18.00 (ISBN 0-404-17385-3). AMS Pr.

Trenckner, V., ed. The Majjhima-Nikaya, 4 vols. LC 78-70099. Repr. of 1888 ed. 137.50 set (ISBN 0-404-17660-7); Vol. 1. (ISBN 0-404-17661-5); Vol. 2. (ISBN 0-404-17662-3); Vol. 3. (ISBN 0-404-17663-1); Vol. 4. (ISBN 0-404-17664-X). AMS Pr.

Tripitaka Master Hua. Buddha Root Farm. Buddhist Text Translation Society, et al, trs. from Chinese. (Illus.). 72p. (Orig.). 1976. pap. 4.00 (ISBN 0-917512-08-1). Buddhist Text.

--Flower Adornment Sutra: Names of Thus Come Ones & the Four Holy Truths, Chapters 7 & 8. Buddhist Text Translation Society, tr. from Chinese. 175p. (Orig.). 1983. pap. 8.50 (ISBN 0-88139-014-3). Buddhist Text.

--Listen to Yourself; Think Everything Over, Vol 1. Buddhist Text Translation Society Staff, tr. from Chinese. (Illus.). 153p. (Orig.). 1978. pap. 7.00 (ISBN 0-917512-24-3). Buddhist Text.

Tripitaka Master Hua, commentary by. The Dharani Sutra. Buddhist Text Translation Society, tr. from Chinese. (Illus.). 352p. (Orig.). 1976. pap. 12.00 (ISBN 0-917512-13-8). Buddhist Text.

--Flower Adornment Sutra, Chapter 39: Entering the Dharma Realm, Part III. Buddhist Text Translation Society, tr. from Chinese. (Illus.). 250p. (Orig.). 1981. pap. 8.50 (ISBN 0-917512-73-1). Buddhist Text.

Tsering, Nawang. Buddhism in Ladakh. 112p. 1979. text ed. 9.95 (ISBN 0-89684-263-0, Pub. by Sterling India). Orient Bk Dist.

Tulku, Tarthang. Love of Knowledge. (Psychology Ser.). 300p. (Orig.). 1987. pap. 12.95 (ISBN 0-89800-138-2). Dharma Pub.

--Reflections of Mind: Western Psychology Meets Tibetan Buddhism. LC 75-5254. (Illus.). 1975. 14.95 (ISBN 0-913546-15-1); pap. 7.95 (ISBN 0-913546-14-3). Dharma Pub.

Tulku, Tarthang, ed. Annals of the Nyingma Lineage, Vol. 11. (Illus.). 1977. pap. 12.00 (ISBN 0-913546-32-1). Dharma Pub.

Tushita Meditation Centre, compiled by. International Buddhist Directory 1985. (A Wisdom Reference Bk.). 150p. (Orig.). 1985. pap. write for info. (ISBN 0-86171-025-8, Wisdom Bks). Great Traditions.

U Kyaw Min. Buddhist Adhidhamma: Meditation & Concentration. 192p. Date not set. pap. 6.95 (ISBN 0-89346-287-X). Heian Intl.

Van Zile, Judy. The Japanese Bon Dance in Hawaii. (Illus.). 96p. 1982. pap. 5.95 (ISBN 0-916630-27-7). Pr Pacifica.

Verdu, A. The Philosophy of Buddhism: A "Totalistic" Synthesis. 264p. 1981. 34.50 (ISBN 90-247-2224-1, Pub. by Martinus Nijhoff Netherlands). Kluwer Academic.

Verdu, Alfonso. Early Buddhist Philosophy in the Light of the Four Noble Times. 241p. 1985. 24.00 (ISBN 81-208-0001-X, Pub. by Motilal Banarsidass India). Orient Bk Dist.

Wangal, Geshe. The Door of Liberation. rev. ed. 235p. 1979. pap. 4.75 (ISBN 0-932156-01-0). Lotsawa.

Warder, Anthony K., ed. New Paths in Buddhist Research. LC 82-83594. x, 137p. 1985. 15.95x (ISBN 0-89386-008-5); pap. 9.95 (ISBN 0-89386-009-3). Acorn NC.

Warren, Henry C. Buddhism in Translations. LC 78-70138. Repr. of 1896 ed. 47.50 (ISBN 0-404-17408-6). AMS Pr.

Warren, Henry C., tr. Everyman's Life of the Buddha: Translated from Pali Sacred Scriptures. Westburg, John E., ed. (Comparative Literature Studies Ser). (Illus.). 138p. 1966. pap. 5.00 (ISBN 0-87423-003-9). Westburg.

Watters, Thomas. On Yuan Chwang's Travels in India 629-645 A. D. LC 74-158213. Repr. of 1905 ed. Set. 45.00 (ISBN 0-404-06878-2). AMS Pr.

Yamaguchi, Susumu. The Mahayana Way to Buddhahood. Buddhist Books International, tr. from Japanese. LC 82-4416. 1982. 10.95x (ISBN 0-914910-11-6). Buddhist Bks.

Ye-Shes Rgyal-Mtshan. Mind in Buddhist Psychology: The Necklace of Clear Understanding, an Elucidation of the Workings of Mind & Mental Events. Guenther, Herbert V. & Kawamura, Leslie S., trs. from Tibetan. LC 74-24373. (Tibetan Translation Ser.: Vol. 3). (Illus.). 168p. 1975. 12.95 (ISBN 0-913546-07-0); pap. 7.95 (ISBN 0-913546-06-2). Dharma Pub.

Yoshinori, Takeuchi. The Heart of Buddhism: In Search of the Timeless Spirit of Primitive Buddhism. LC 82-23453. 192p. (Orig.). 1983. 17.50 (ISBN 0-8245-0577-8). Crossroad NY.

BUDDHISM–HISTORY

Bhattacharya, Dipak C. Studies in Buddhist Iconography. 1978. 22.50x (ISBN 0-8364-0016-X). South Asia Bks.

Buddhist Sutra. How the Thousand Buddhas Become Enlightened, 3 vols. 1987. 35.00 ea. (ISBN 0-89800-136-6). Dharma Pub.

Chai-Shin, Yu. Early Buddhism & Christianity. xv, 241p. 1986. Repr. 17.50 (ISBN 81-208-0050-8, Pub. by Motilal Banarsidass). South Asia Bks.

Cleary, Thomas. Entry into the Inconceivable: An Introduction to Hua-yen Buddhism. LC 83-3613. 227p. 1983. text ed. 16.95x (ISBN 0-8248-0824-X). UH Pr.

Davids, Carolina A. Buddhism: Its Birth & Dispersal. rev. ed. LC 78-72407. Repr. of 1934 ed. 25.00 (ISBN 0-404-17268-7). AMS Pr.

Davids, Caroline A. Outines of Buddhism: A Historical Sketch. 126p. 1934. Repr. text ed. 12.50x. Coronet Bks.

--Sakya or Buddhist Origins. 444p. 1931. Repr. text ed. 32.50x. Coronet Bks.

Denwood, Philip & Piatigorsky, Alexander. Buddhist Studies: Ancient & Modern. 220p. 1981. 30.00x (ISBN 0-7007-0153-2, Pub. by Curzon England). State Mutual Bk.

Floyer, A. M. Evolution of Ancient Buddhism. 59.95 (ISBN 0-8490-0143-9). Gordon Pr.

Garret-Jones, John. Tales & Teaching of the Buddha. 1979. 18.95 (ISBN 0-04-294104-0). Allen Unwin.

Grousset, Rene. In the Footsteps of the Buddha. facs. ed. Leon, Mariette, tr. from Fr. LC 77-124235. (Select Bibliographies Reprint Ser). 1932. 19.50 (ISBN 0-8369-5423-8). Ayer Co Pubs.

Herman, A. L. An Introduction to Buddhist Thought: A Philosophic History of Indian Buddhism. (Illus.). 480p. (Orig.). 1984. lib. bdg. 35.75 (ISBN 0-8191-3594-1); pap. text ed. 13.50 (ISBN 0-8191-3595-X). U Pr of Amer.

Horner, I. B. Women under Primitive Buddhism. 1975. Repr. 12.50 (ISBN 0-8426-0955-5). Orient Bk Dist.

Ikeda, Daisaku. Buddhism: The First Millennium. LC 82-80739. 172p. 1982. pap. 5.25 (ISBN 0-87011-534-0). Kodansha.

Jayatilleke, K. Early Buddhist Theory of Knowledge. 1981. 22.00x (ISBN 0-8364-0795-4, Pub. by Motilal Banarsidass). South Asia Bks.

Kimura, Ryukan. A Historical Study of the Terms Hinayana & Mahayana & the Origin of Mahayana Buddhism. LC 78-72455. Repr. of 1927 ed. 26.50 (ISBN 0-404-17324-1). AMS Pr.

La Vallee Poussin, Louis de. The Way to Nirvana: Six Lectures on Ancient Buddhism As a Discipline of Salvation. LC 77-27154. (Hibbert Lectures Ser.: 1916). Repr. of 1917 ed. 24.50 (ISBN 0-404-60417-X). AMS Pr.

Lyons, Elizabeth & Peters, Heather. Buddhism: History & Diversity of a Great Tradition. (Illus.). 64p. 1985. pap. 8.95 (ISBN 0-934718-76-8). Univ Mus of U PA.

--Buddhism: History & Diversity of a Great Tradition. LC 85-28817. (University of Pennsylvaina Museum Ser.). (Illus.). 64p. 1985. pap. 12.95 (ISBN 0-317-46953-3). U of Pa Pr.

Mus, Paul. Barabudur: Esquisse d'une histoire du bouddhisme fondee sur la critique archeologique des textes, 2 vols. in 1. Bolle, Kees W., ed. LC 77-79146. (Mythology Ser.). (Fr.). 1978. Repr. of 1935 ed. lib. bdg. 82.50x (ISBN 0-405-10555-X). Ayer Co Pubs.

Overmyer, Daniel L. Folk Buddhist Religion: Dissenting Sects in Late Traditional China. (Harvard East Asian Ser.: No.83). 256p. 1976. 15.00x (ISBN 0-674-30705-4). Harvard U Pr.

Paul, Diana. The Buddhist Feminine Ideal: Queen Srimala & the Tathagatagarbha American Academy of Religion. LC 79-12031. (Dissertation Ser.: No. 30). 1980. o.s. 14.00 (ISBN 0-89130-284-0, 01-01-30); pap. 9.95 (ISBN 0-89130-303-0). Scholars Pr GA.

--Women in Buddhism: Images of the Feminine in the Mahayana Tradition. 1985. 35.00x (ISBN 0-520-05445-8); pap. 10.95 (ISBN 0-520-05428-8, CAL 740). U of Cal Pr.

Perez-Ramon, Joacquin. Self & Non-Self in Early Buddhism. (Religon & Society Ser.: No. 17). 1980. 58.00x (ISBN 90-279-7987-1). Mouton.

Powell, William F. The Record of Tung Shan. LC 86-4305. (Classics in East Asian Buddism: No. 1). 112p. 1986. pap. text ed. 8.50x (ISBN 0-8248-1070-8). UH Pr.

Pratt, James B. The Pilgrimage of Buddhism & a Buddhist Pilgrimage. LC 75-3325. (Philosophy of America Ser.). Repr. of 1928 ed. 57.50 (ISBN 0-404-59320-8). AMS Pr.

Robinson, Richard H. Early Madhyamika in India & China. 346p. 1978. pap. 6.95 (ISBN 0-87728-433-4). Weiser.

Rockhill, William W., ed. The Life of Buddha & the Early History of His Order. 285p. Repr. of 1884 ed. text ed. 19.50x (ISBN 0-89563-149-0, Pub. by Chinese Matl Ctr). Coronet Bks.

Sadler, A. W. In Quest of the Historical Buddha & the White Cranes of Sri Ramakrishna. LC 84-48565. (Illus.). 1984. pap. 6.50x sewn bdg. (ISBN 0-910913-02-1). Laughing B P.

Saunders, Kenneth J. Epochs in Buddhist History; the Haskell Lectures, 1921. LC 78-70118. Repr. of 1924 ed. 32.00 (ISBN 0-404-17375-6). AMS Pr.

Szekely, Edmond B. Pilgrim of the Himalayas. (Illus.). 32p. 1974. pap. 2.95 (ISBN 0-89564-061-9). IBS Intl.

Taranath. Taranatha's History of Buddhism in India. Chattopadhyaya, Debiprsdad & Chattopadhyaya, A., eds. 1980. Repr. of 1970 ed. 27.00x (ISBN 0-8364-1597-3, Pub. by KP Bagchi & Co.). South Asia Bks.

Thomas, Edward J. The History of Buddhist Thought. 316p. 1981. pap. 17.00 (ISBN 0-89540-100-2, SB-100). Sun Pub.

Tsukamoto, Zenryi. A History of Early Chinese Buddhism: From Its Introduction to the Death of Hui-Yuan, 2 vols. Hurvitz, Leon, tr. from Japanese. (Illus.). 648p. 1985. Boxed Set. 175.00x (ISBN 0-87011-635-5). Kodansha.

Tsybikov, G. T. The Buddist Pilgrim at the Holy Places of Tibet Based on Diaries Kept over the Years 1899-1902. 482p. Repr. of 1919 ed. text ed. 74.52x (ISBN 0-576-03102-X). Gregg Intl.

Varma, V. P. Early Buddhism & Its Origin. 1973. text ed. 20.00x. Coronet Bks.

Yu, Chai-Shin. Early Buddhism & Christianity. 1981. 20.00x (ISBN 0-8364-0797-0, Pub. by Motilal Banarsidass). South Asia Bks.

BUDDHISM–POETRY

Arnold, Edwin. Light of Asia. LC 79-4436. 1969. pap. 4.50 (ISBN 0-8356-0405-5, Quest). Theos Pub Hse.

BUDDHISM–RELATIONS–CHRISTIANITY

Dumoulin, Heinrich. Christianity Meets Buddhism. Maraldo, John C., tr. from Ger. LC 73-82783. 212p. 1974. 19.95 (ISBN 0-87548-121-3). Open Court.

Johnston, William. The Mirror Mind: Spirituality & Transformation. LC 80-8350. 192p. 1984. pap. 6.95 (ISBN 0-06-064206-8, RD 516, HarpR). Har-Row.

Lillie, Arthur. The Influence of Buddhism on Primitive Christianity. LC 78-70094. 1980. Repr. of 1893 ed. 58.75 (ISBN 0-404-17343-8). AMS Pr.

Lopez, Donald S., Jr. & Rockefeller, Stephen C., eds. The Christ & the Bodhisattva. (Buddhist Studies). 304p. (Orig.). 1987. 44.50X (ISBN 0-88706-401-9); pap. 14.95X (ISBN 0-88706-402-7). State U NY Pr.

Streeter, Burnett H. Buddha & the Christ. LC 72-102585. 1970. Repr. of 1932 ed. 29.50x (ISBN 0-8046-0745-1, Pub. by Kennikat). Assoc Faculty Pr.

Swearer, Donald K. Dialogue: The Key to Understanding Other Religions. LC 77-3964. (Biblical Perspectives on Current Issues). 172p. 1977. soft cover 4.95 (ISBN 0-664-24138-7). Westminster.

BUDDHISM–RELATIONS–SHINTO

Matsunaga, Alicia. Buddhist Philosophy of Assimilation. LC 68-57058. (Illus.). 1969. 29.50 (ISBN 0-8048-0730-2). C E Tuttle.

BUDDHISM–SACRED BOOKS

Beal, Samuel. A Catena of Buddhist Scriptures from the Chinese. 448p. Repr. of 1871 ed. text ed. 37.50x (ISBN 0-89644-188-1, Pub. by Chinese Matl Ctr). Coronet Bks.

Bowden, E. The Imitation of Buddha: Quotations from Buddhist Literature for Each Day. 59.95 (ISBN 0-8490-0386-5). Gordon Pr.

Buddhaghosa. The Padyacudamani of Buddhaghosacarya. LC 78-72387. Repr. of 1921 ed. 32.50 (ISBN 0-404-17248-2). AMS Pr.

--Papancasudani Majjhimanikayatthakatha of Buddhaghosacariya, 5 vols. in 4. LC 78-72388. Repr. of 1938 ed. Set. 165.00 (ISBN 0-404-17560-0). AMS Pr.
--The Sumangala-Vilasini, 3 vols. LC 78-72390. Repr. of 1886 ed. Set. 110.00 (ISBN 0-404-17580-5). Vol. 1 (ISBN 0-404-17581-3). Vol. 2 (ISBN 0-404-17582-1). Vol. 3 (ISBN 0-404-17583-X). AMS Pr.
Buddhist Text Translation Society, tr. from Chinese. Brahma Net Sutra, Vol. II Commentary by Hui Seng, Elder Master. (Illus.). 210p. (Orig.). 1982. pap. 10.00 (ISBN 0-917512-88-X). Buddhist Text.
--Brahma Net Sutra, text only. 70p. (Orig.). 1982. pap. 5.00 (ISBN 0-917512-56-1). Buddhist Text.
Buddhist Text Translation Society Staff, tr. Flower Adornment Sutra, Chapter 22: The Ten Inexhaustible Treasuries Commentary by Tripitka Master Hua. (Illus.). 184p. (Orig.). 1983. pap. 7.00 (ISBN 0-917512-38-3). Buddhist Text.
Buddhist Text Translation Society Staff, tr. from Chinese. Flower Adornment Sutra, Chapter 36: Universal Worthy's Conduct. (Illus.). 75p. (Orig.). 1983. pap. 5.00 (ISBN 0-88139-011-9). Buddhist Text.
--Flower Adornment Sutra, Chapter 39: Entering the Dharma Realm, Part VI. (Illus.). 320p. (Orig.). 1982. pap. 9.00 (ISBN 0-917512-48-0). Buddhist Text.
--Sutra of the Past Vows of Earth Store Bodhisattva. (Illus.). 120p. (Orig.). 1982. pap. 6.00 (ISBN 0-88139-502-1). Buddhist Text.
Burtt, Edwin A., ed. Teachings of the Compassionate Buddha. (Orig.). 1955. pap. 3.95 (ISBN 0-451-62450-5, ME2282, Ment). NAL.
Carus, Paul. The Dharma; or, the Religious Enlightenment; an Exposition of Buddhism. 5th rev. & enl. ed. LC 78-72393. Repr. of 1907 ed. 24.00 (ISBN 0-404-17253-9). AMS Pr.
Chih-hsu, Ou-i. The Buddhist I Ching. Cleary, Thomas, tr. from Chinese. LC 86-31460. (Dragon Ser.). 290p. 1987. pap. 10.95 (ISBN 0-87773-408-9). Shambhala Pubns.
Cleary, Thomas, tr. The Flower Ornament Scripture: A Translation of the Avatamsaka Sutra, Vol. 1. LC 83-2370. 703p. 1984. 40.00 (ISBN 0-87773-767-3, 53690-8). Shambhala Pubns.
Conze, Edward & Lancaster, Lewis, eds. Buddhist Scriptures: A Bibliography. LC 77-83380. (Reference Library of the Humanities: Vol. 113). 161p. 1982. lib. bdg. 31.00 (ISBN 0-8240-9848-X). Garland Pub.
Conze, Edward, tr. Buddhist Scriptures. (Classics Ser.). (Orig.). 1959. pap. 5.95 (ISBN 0-14-044088-7). Penguin.
Conze, Edward, et al. Buddhist Texts Through the Ages. 322p. 1985. Repr. of 1964 ed. 20.00x (ISBN 0-317-39042-2, Pub. by Luzac & Co Ltd). State Mutual Bk.
Cowell, E. B. & Muller, F. Max. Buddhist Mahayana Texts. (Sacred Bks. of the East: Vol. 49). 15.00 (ISBN 0-89581-534-6). Asian Human Pr.
Crosbie, Robert. The Language of the Soul. (Sangam Texts). 130p. 1986. pap. 8.75 (ISBN 0-88695-026-0). Concord grove.
Davids, Rhys. Poems of Cloister & Jungle, a Buddhist Anthology. 59.95 (ISBN 0-8490-0849-2). Gordon Pr.
Davids, T. W. Buddhist Suttas. (Sacred Bks. of the East: Vol. 11). 15.00 (ISBN 0-89581-520-6). Asian Human Pr.
The Dhammapada. ix, 139p. 1955. 3.00 (ISBN 0-938998-16-1). Cunningham Pr.
Dhammapada. (Life Companion Library). 116p. (Orig.). 1983. pap. 5.95 (ISBN 0-89744-016-1). Auromere.
Dhammapada. Texts from the Buddhist Canon. Beal, Samuel, tr. from Chin. LC 78-72420. Repr. of 1878 ed. 22.50 (ISBN 0-404-17284-9). AMS Pr.
Dhammapadatthakatha. The Commentary on the Dhammapada, 5 vols. in 4. Norman, H. C., ed. LC 78-72423. Repr. of 1915 ed. Set. 155.00 (ISBN 0-404-17620-8). AMS Pr.
Fausboll, V., ed. Buddhist Birth Stories; or Jataka Tales, Vol. 1. Davids, Rhys T., tr. LC 78-72443. Repr. of 1880 ed. 42.50 (ISBN 0-404-17309-8). AMS Pr.
Gooneratne, Edmund R., ed. The Dhatu Katha Pakarana & Its Commentary. LC 78-72426. Repr. of 1892 ed. 21.50 (ISBN 0-404-17287-3). AMS Pr.
Hridayananda dasa Goswami Acaryadeva. Srimad-Bhagavatam: Eleventh Canto, Vol. 1. (Illus.). 450p. 1982. 12.95 (ISBN 0-89213-112-8); text ed. 9.95 (ISBN 0-686-98021-2). Bhaktivedanta.
Hua, Tripitaka Master. The Shurangama Sutra, Vol. 7. Buddhist Text Translation Society, tr. from Chinese. (Illus.). 270p. (Orig.). 1982. pap. 8.50 (ISBN 0-917512-97-9). Buddhist Text.
Hurvitz, Leon, tr. from Chin & Sanskrit. Scripture of the Lotus Blossom of the Fine Dharma: The Lotus Sutra. LC 75-45381. 1976. pap. 16.00x (ISBN 0-231-03920-4). Columbia U Pr.
Judge, W. Q. Hit the Mark. (Sangam Texts Ser.). 126p. 1986. pap. 8.75 (ISBN 0-88695-024-4). Concord Grove.
Kern, H. The Saddharma-Pundarika or the Lotus of the Good Law. (Sacred Bks. of the East: Vol. 21). 15.00 (ISBN 0-89581-524-9). Asian Human Pr.
Lancaster, Lewis R., ed. The Korean Buddhist Canon: A Descriptive Catalogue. LC 75-40662. (Center for Korean Studies, UC Berkeley). 1980. 60.00x (ISBN 0-520-03159-8). U of Cal Pr.
Maitreya, Aryasanga. Uttaratantra, or Ratnagotravibhaga: Sublime Science of the Great Vehicle to Salvation. Obermiller, E., tr. from Tibetan. 225p. 1984. Repr. of 1931 ed. lib. bdg. 22.50x (ISBN 0-88181-001-0). Canon Pubns.
Master Hua, Tripitaka. The Shurangama Mantra: A Commentary, Vol. III. Buddhist Text Translation Society, tr. from Chinese. (Illus.). 156p. (Orig.). 1982. pap. 6.50 (ISBN 0-917512-36-7). Buddhist Text.
Master Hua, Tripitaka, commentary by. Flower Adornment (Avatamsaka) Sutra: Chapter 26, The Ten Grounds, Pt. One. Buddhist Text Translation Society, tr. from Chinese. (Illus.). 234p. (Orig.). 1980. pap. 7.00 (ISBN 0-917512-87-1). Buddhist Text.
Master Hua, Triptaka. Herein Lies the Treasure-Trove, Vol. 1. Buddhist Text Translation Society, tr. from Chinese. (Illus.). 160p. (Orig.). 1983. pap. 6.50 (ISBN 0-88139-001-1). Buddhist Text.
Mavalankar, Damodar K. The Service of Humanity. (Sangam Texts). 132p. 1986. pap. 8.75 (ISBN 0-88695-025-2). Concord Grove.
Monto Hikkei Kai. The Jodoshinshu Book. (Illus.). 92p. 1973. pap. 2.50 (ISBN 0-685-65547-4). Nembutsu Pr.
Mueller, Friedrich M. Buddhist Texts from Japan, 3 pts. in 1 vol. LC 73-18824. (Illus.). Repr. of 1884 ed. 34.50 (ISBN 0-404-11430-X). AMS Pr.
Nagarjuna & Pandit, Sakya. Elegant Sayings. LC 77-23433. (Tibetan Translation Ser.: Vol. 8). 1977. 10.95 (ISBN 0-913546-12-7); pap. 6.95 (ISBN 0-913546-13-5). Dharma Pub.
National Master Ch'ing Liang. Flower Adornment Sutra Prologue: Vol. III: The Second Door, Part II. Tripitaka Master Hua, commentary by. Buddhist Text Translation Society Staff, tr. from Chinese. (Illus.). 220p. (Orig.). 1983. pap. 10.00 (ISBN 0-917512-98-7). Buddhist Text.
Rajneesh, Bhagwan S. The Book of Wisdom, Vol. 2. Swami Krishna Prabhu, ed. LC 82-23142. (Buddhist Masters Ser.). 416p. (Orig.). 1984. pap. 5.95 (ISBN 0-88050-531-1). Chidvilas Found.
Regamey, Constantin, tr. from Sanskrit & Tibetan. Three Chapters from the Samadhirajasutra. 112p. 1984. Repr. of 1938 ed. lib. bdg. 17.50x (ISBN 0-88181-003-7). Canon Pubns.
Rockhill, William H., ed. Udanavarga: A Collection of Verses from the Buddhist Canon. Repr. of 1883 ed. text ed. 20.00 (ISBN 0-89644-342-6, Pub. by Chinese Matl Ctr). Coronet Bks.
Sure, Heng & Chau, Heng. With One Heart Bowing to the City of Ten Thousand Buddhas, Vol. VII. (Illus.). 160p. (Orig.). 1982. pap. 5.00 (ISBN 0-917512-99-5). Buddhist Text.
Suzuki, D. T. Manual of Zen Buddhism. (Orig.). 1960. pap. 5.95 (ISBN 0-394-17224-8, E231, Ever). Grove.
Talib, Gurbachan S., tr. Sri Guru Granth Sahib in English Translation, Vol. 1. 1985. 30.00x (ISBN 0-8364-1507-8, Pub. by Punjabi U India). South Asia Bks.
Thomas, E. J., tr. from Sanskrit. The Quest of Enlightenment: A Selection of the Buddhist Scriptures. LC 78-70130. Repr. of 1950 ed. 17.50 (ISBN 0-404-17389-6). AMS Pr.
Thomas, Edward J. Early Buddhist Scriptures. LC 78-70129. Repr. of 1935 ed. 31.00 (ISBN 0-404-17388-8). AMS Pr.
Tripitaka Master Hua, commentary by. Dharma Flower Sutra, Vol. X. Buddhist Text Translation Society Staff, tr. from Chinese. 150p. (Orig.). 1983. pap. 7.50 (ISBN 0-917512-34-0). Buddhist Text.
--Flower Adornment (Avatamsaka) Sutra: Chapter 15, The Ten Dwellings. Buddhist Text Translation Society, tr. from Chinese. (Illus.). 185p. (Orig.). 1981. pap. 8.00 (ISBN 0-917512-77-4). Buddhist Text.
--Flower Adornment Sutra, Chapter 11: Pure Conduct. Buddhist Text Translation Society Staff, tr. from Chinese. (Illus.). 255p. (Orig.). 1983. pap. 9.00 (ISBN 0-917512-37-5). Buddhist Text.
--Flower Adornment Sutra, Chapter 24: Praises in the Tushita Heaven. Buddhist Text Translation Society, tr. from Chinese. (Illus.). 130p. (Orig.). 1982. pap. 5.00 (ISBN 0-917512-39-1). Buddhist Text.
--Flower Adornment Sutra, Chapter 5: Flower Adorned Sea of Worlds, Part 1. Buddhist Text Translation Society Staff, tr. from Chinese. (Illus.). 250p. (Orig.). 1983. pap. 8.50 (ISBN 0-917512-54-5). Buddhist Text.
--Flower Adornment Sutra, Chapter 9: Light Enlightenment. Buddhist Text Translation Society Staff, tr. from Chinese. (Illus.). 225p. (Orig.). 1983. pap. text ed. 8.50 (ISBN 0-88139-005-4). Buddhist Text.
--The Shurangama Sutra, Vol. 2. Buddhist Text Translation Society, tr. from Chinese. (Illus.). 212p. (Orig.). 1979. pap. 8.00 (ISBN 0-917512-25-1). Buddhist Text.
Tucci, Giuseppe. Minor Buddhist Texts, 2 parts in 1. 1986. Repr. 28.00 (ISBN 81-208-0190-3, Pub. by Motilal Banarsidass). South Asia Bks.
Tucci, Giuseppe, ed. The Nyayanukha of Dignaga. LC 78-72427. Repr. of 1930 ed. 17.50 (ISBN 0-404-17288-1). AMS Pr.
Upham, Edward. The Mahavansi. the Raja-Ratnacari. & the Raja-Vali, Forming the Sacred & Historical Books of Ceylon, 3 vols. LC 78-70132. Repr. of 1833 ed. 115.00 set (ISBN 0-404-17670-4). AMS Pr.
Vasubhandu, Bodhisattva. The Hundred Dharmas. Master Hua, Tripitaka, commentary by. Buddhist Text Translation Society, tr. from Chinese. 130p. (Orig.). 1983. pap. 6.50 (ISBN 0-88139-003-8). Buddhist Text.
Warren, Henry C. Buddhism in Translations. LC 5-17082. 1963. pap. text ed. 7.95x (ISBN 0-689-70200-0, 19). Atheneum.
Wayman, Alex. Analysis of the Sravakabhumi Manuscript. LC 61-64259. (University of California Publications in Classical Philology: Vol. 17). pap. 48.00 (ISBN 0-317-09845-4, 2021172). Bks Demand UMI.
Woodeward, F. L. Some Sayings of the Buddha. 69.95 (ISBN 0-8490-2629-6). Gordon Pr.

BUDDHISM–BURMA

Bigandet, Paul A. The Life, or Legend of Gaudama: The Buddha of the Burmese, 2 vols. 4th ed. LC 77-8749. Repr. of 1912 ed. Set. 52.50 (ISBN 0-404-16800-0). AMS Pr.
E Maung. Burmese Buddhist Law. LC 77-87483. Repr. of 1937 ed. 25.00 (ISBN 0-404-16812-4). AMS Pr.
Htin Aung, U. Folk Elements in Burmese Buddhism. LC 77-29231. 1978. Repr. of 1962 ed. lib. bdg. 22.50x (ISBN 0-313-20275-3, HTFE). Greenwood.
Ling, Trevor. Buddhism, Imperialism & War. (Illus.). 1979. text ed. 13.95x (ISBN 0-04-294105-9). Allen Unwin.
Ray, Nihar-Ranjan. An Introduction to the Study of Theravada Buddhism in Burma: A Study of Indo-Burmese Historical & Cultural Relations from the Earliest Times to the British Conquest. LC 77-87021. Repr. of 1946 ed. 25.00 (ISBN 0-404-16853-1). AMS Pr.

BUDDHISM–CHINA

Beal, Samuel. Buddhism in China. lib. bdg. 79.95 (ISBN 0-87968-479-8). Krishna Pr.
--Buddhism in China. 16.75 (ISBN 0-8369-7129-9, 7963). Ayer Co Pubs.
Blofeld, John E. The Jewel in the Lotus: Outline of Present Day Buddhism in China. LC 74-10096. (China Studies: from Confucius to Mao Ser). 193p. 1986. Repr. of 1948 ed. 20.50 (ISBN 0-88355-161-6). Hyperion Conn.
Chan, Sin-wai. Buddhism in Late Ch'ing Political Thought. 191p. 1985. 31.50x (ISBN 0-8133-0256-0). Westview.
Chappell, David W., ed. Buddhist & Taoist Practice in Medieval Chinese Society: Buddhist & Taoist Studies II. (Asian Studies at Hawaii: No. 34). 256p. 1987. pap. text ed. 18.00x (ISBN 0-8248-0957-2). UH Pr.
Ch'en, Kenneth. Buddhism in China: A Historical Survey. (Studies in History of Religion: Vol. 1). 1974. pap. 13.50x (ISBN 0-691-00015-8). Princeton U Pr.
Cheng, Hsueh-li. Empty Logic: Madhyamika Buddhism from Chinese Sources. LC 83-13246. 220p. 1984. 17.95 (ISBN 0-8022-2442-3). Philos Lib.
Chun-fang Yu. The Renewal of Buddhism in China: Chu-Hung & the Late Ming Synthesis. LC 79-28073. (Buddhist Studies). (Illus.). 1981. 34.00x (ISBN 0-231-04972-2). Columbia U Pr.
Covell, Ralph R. Confucius, the Buddha, & Christ: A History of the Gospel in Chinese. LC 86-8615. 304p. (Orig.). 1986. pap. 14.95 (ISBN 0-88344-267-1, CIP). Orbis Bks.
De Bary, William T., ed. The Buddhist Tradition: In India, China & Japan. 448p. 1972. pap. 4.76 (ISBN 0-394-71696-5, V702, Vin). Random.
Edkins, Joseph. Chinese Buddhism: A Volume of Sketches, Historical, Descriptive & Critical. 2nd, rev. ed. 487p. Repr. of 1893 ed. text ed. 27.50x (Pub. by Chinese Matl Ctr). Coronet Bks.
Hodous, Lewis. Buddhism & Buddhists in China. LC 78-72440. Repr. of 1924 ed. 17.50 (ISBN 0-404-17306-3). AMS Pr.
Hurvitz, Leon & Shotaro, Lida, eds. Chinese Buddhism at Sixes & Sevens: A Study of the First Systematization of Buddhist Thought in China. 1987. 30.00 (ISBN 0-89581-906-6). Asian Human Pr.
Ikeda, Daisaku. The Flower of Chinese Buddhism. (Illus.). 216p. 1986. 19.95 (ISBN 0-8348-0208-2). Weatherhill.
Li, Shao-ch'Ang. Popular Buddhism in China. lib. bdg. 79.95 (ISBN 0-87968-539-5). Krishna Pr.
McRae, John R. The Northern School of & the Formation of Early Ch'an Buddhism. LC 86-4062. (Studies in East Asian Buddhism: No. 3). 456p. 1987. 40.00x (ISBN 0-8248-1056-2). UH Pr.
Pachow, W. Chinese Buddhism: Aspects of Interaction & Reinterpretation. LC 80-5432. 275p. 1980. lib. bdg. 27.00 (ISBN 0-8191-1090-6). U Pr of Amer.
Powell, William F. The Record of Tung Shan. LC 86-4305. (Classics in East Asian Buddism: No. 1). 112p. 1986. pap. text ed. 8.50x (ISBN 0-8248-1070-8). UH Pr.
Reichelt, Karl. Truth & Tradition in Chinese Buddhism. 59.95 (ISBN 0-8490-1234-1). Gordon Pr.
Reischauer, Edwin O., tr. Ennin's Diary: The Record of a Pilgrimage to China in Search of the Law. LC 55-5553. (Illus.). pap. 119.50 (ISBN 0-8357-9521-7, 2012366). Bks Demand UMI.
Robinson, Richard H. Early Madhyamika in India & China. 1976. Repr. 18.50 (ISBN 0-8426-0904-0). Orient Bk Dist.
Snellgrove, David. Indo-Tibetan Buddhism: Indian Buddhists & Their Tibetan Successors. LC 85-2453. (Illus.). 550p. 1986. Vol. I. pap. 18.95 (ISBN 0-87773-311-2); Vol. II. pap. 18.95 (ISBN 0-87773-379-1). Shambhala Pubns.
Soothill, W. E. The Lotus of the Wonderful Law, or the Lotus Gospel. (Illus.). 288p. 1987. pap. 9.95 (ISBN 0-391-03465-0, Pub. by Curzon Pr England). Humanities.
Suzuki, D. T. Essays in Zen Buddhism. 1961. pap. 5.95 (ISBN 0-394-17230-2, E309, Ever). Grove.
--Manual of Zen Buddhism. (Orig.). 1960. pap. 5.95 (ISBN 0-394-17224-8, E231, Ever). Grove.
--Zen Buddhism: Selected Writings of D. T. Suzuki. 1956. pap. 5.50 (ISBN 0-385-09300-4, A90, Anch). Doubleday.
Tsukamoto, Zenryi. A History of Early Chinese Buddhism: From Its Introduction to the Death of Hui-Yuan, 2 vols. Hurvitz, Leon, tr. from Japanese. (Illus.). 648p. 1985. Boxed Set. 175.00x (ISBN 0-87011-635-5). Kodansha.
Van Oort, H. A. The Iconography of Chinese Buddhism in Traditional China, 2 pts. (Iconography of Religions Ser.: XII-5). (Illus.). 1986. Pt. 1, xii, 30p. pap. 25.50 (ISBN 90-04-07822-3, Pub. by E J Brill); Pt. 2, viii, 27p. pap. 24.75 (ISBN 90-04-07823-1). Heinman.
Watts, Alan W. The Spirit of Zen: A Way of Life, Work & Art in the Far East. 1958. pap. 2.95 (ISBN 0-394-17418-6, E219, Ever). Grove.
Weinstein, Stanley. Buddhism under the T'ang. (Cambridge Studies in Chinese History, Literature & Institutions). 200p. 1987. 39.50 (ISBN 0-521-25585-6). Cambridge U Pr.
Welch, Holmes H. Practice of Chinese Buddhism, 1900-1950. LC 67-13256. pap. 9.95x (ISBN 0-674-69701-4). Harvard U Pr.
Wright, Arthur F. Buddhism in Chinese History. LC 59-7432. (Illus.). 1959. 13.50x (ISBN 0-8047-0546-1); pap. 6.95 (ISBN 0-8047-0548-8, SP118). Stanford U Pr.
Zucher, E. The Buddhist Conquest of China: The Spread & Adaptation of Buddhism in Early Medieval China, 2 vols. 470p. 1973. Set. text ed. 99.00x (ISBN 0-391-01961-9). Humanities.

BUDDHISM–EAST (FAR EAST)

Alabaster, Henry. The Wheel of the Law: Buddhism Illustrated from Siamese Sources. 384p. Repr. of 1871 ed. text ed. 49.68x (ISBN 0-576-03126-7, Pub. by Gregg Intl Pubs England). Gregg Intl.
Lessmann, Heinrich. Aufgaben und Ziele der Vergleichenden Mythenforschung: Tasks & Goals of Comparative Mythology. Bolle, Kees W., ed. LC 77-79138. (Mythology Ser.). (Ger.). 1978. Repr. of 1908 ed. lib. bdg. 17.00x (ISBN 0-405-10548-7). Ayer Co Pubs.
McDermott, Robert A., ed. Focus on Buddhism. LC 81-8084. (Focus on Hinduism & Buddhism Ser.). 160p. 1981. text ed. 14.50 (ISBN 0-89012-020-X); pap. 7.95 (ISBN 0-89012-021-8). Anima Pubns.
Malagoda, Kirsiri. Buddhism in Sinhalese Society, 1750-1900: A Study of Religious Revival & Change. LC 74-22966. 1976. 42.00x (ISBN 0-520-02873-2). U of Cal Pr.
Nhat Hanh, Thich. Being Peace. (Illus.). 120p. (Orig.). 1987. pap. 8.50 (ISBN 0-938077-00-7). Parallax Pr.

Ray, Nihar-Ranjan. Sanskrit Buddhism in Burma. LC 78-70112. Repr. of 1936 ed. 22.00 (ISBN 0-404-17367-5). AMS Pr.

Swearer, Donald K. Buddhism & Society in Southeast Asia. LC 81-8048. (Focus on Hinduism & Buddhism Ser.). 64p. 1981. pap. 4.95x (ISBN 0-89012-023-4). Anima Pubns.

Thien-An, Thieh. Buddhism & Zen in Vietnam: In Relation to the Development in Asia. LC 74-83391. (Illus.). 300p. 1975. 12.50 (ISBN 0-8048-1144-X). C E Tuttle.

Vogel, J. P. Buddhist Art in India, Ceylon, & Java. (Illus.). 187p. 1977. Repr. of 1936 ed. text ed. 19.00x. Coronet Bks.

BUDDHISM–GREAT BRITAIN

Humphreys, Christmas. The Development of Buddhism in England. LC 78-72442. Repr. of 1937 ed. 17.50 (ISBN 0-404-17308-X). AMS Pr.

Mackenzie, Donald A. Buddhism in Pre-Christian Britain. 1977. lib. bdg. 59.95 (ISBN 0-8490-1558-8). Gordon Pr.

BUDDHISM–INDIA

Ahir, D. C. Buddhist Shrines in India. (Illus.). xii, 132p. 1986. text ed. 25.00x (ISBN 81-7018-326-X, Pub. by D K Pub Corp Delhi). Apt Bks.

Bhattacharyya, Benoytosh. An Introduction to Buddhist Esoterism. 1980. Repr. of 1931 ed. 19.00x (ISBN 0-686-69019-2, Pub. by Motilal Banarsidas). South Asia Bks.

Carrithers, Michael. The Buddha. LC 83-8004. (Past Masters Ser.). 1983. 13.95x (ISBN 0-19-287590-6); pap. 4.95 (ISBN 0-19-287589-2). Oxford U Pr.

Chattopadhyaya, Debiprasad, ed. Taranatha's History of Buddhism in India. Chattopadhyay, Alaka, tr. 1980. 28.00x (ISBN 0-8364-1484-5, Pub. by KP Bagchi India). South Asia Bks.

Davids, Thomas W. Buddhist India. LC 78-38349. (Select Bibliographies Reprint Ser). Repr. of 1903 ed. 28.00 (ISBN 0-8369-6766-6). Ayer Co Pubs.

De Bary, William T., ed. The Buddhist Tradition: In India, China & Japan. 448p. 1972. pap. 4.76 (ISBN 0-394-71696-5, V702, Vin). Random.

Dutt, N. Buddhist Sects in India. 2nd ed. 1977. 9.00x (ISBN 0-88386-971-3). South Asia Bks.

Dutt, Nalinaksha. Buddhist Sects in India. 1978. (Pub. by Motilal Banarsidas India); pap. 7.50 (ISBN 0-89684-044-1). Orient Bk Dist.

Ghosh, Mallar. Development of Buddhist Iconography in Eastern India. (Illus.). 1980. text ed. 44.00x. Coronet Bks.

Grimm, George. Buddhist Wisdom: The Mystery of the Self. 2nd, rev. ed. Keller-Grimm, M., ed. Aikins, Carrol, tr. from Ger. 1982. 11.50 (ISBN 0-89684-041-7, Pub. by Motilal Banarsidass India). Orient Bk Dist.

Grunwedel, Albert. Buddhist Art in India. Gibson, Agnes C., tr. (Ger., Illus.). 236p. Repr. of 1901 ed. text ed. 37.50x. Coronet Bks.

Hindery, Roderick. Comparative Ethics in Hindu & Buddhist Traditions. 1978. 18.95 (ISBN 0-89684-017-4, Pub. by Motilal Banarsidass India). Orient Bk Dist.

Holt, John C. Discipline: The Canonical Buddhism of the Vinayapataka. 1983. 16.00x (ISBN 0-8364-0951-5). South Asia Bks.

Joshi, Lal M. Studies in the Buddhistic Culture of India (During the 7th & 8th Centuries A.D.) 1977. text ed. 35.00x (ISBN 0-8426-1056-1). Verry.

Joshi, Lalman. Studies in the Buddhistic Culture of India. 2nd rev. ed. 1977. 28.00 (ISBN 0-89684-325-4, Pub. by Motilal Banarsidass India). Orient Bk Dist.

Kail, Owen C. Buddist Cave Temples of India. (Illus.). xi, 138p. 1981. text ed. 25.00x (ISBN 0-86590-043-4, Pub. by Taraporevala India). Apt Bks.

Keith, A. B. Buddhist Philosophy in India & Ceylon. lib. bdg. 90.00 (ISBN 0-87968-181-0). Krishna Pr.

Kern, H. Manual of Indian Buddhism. 1974. Repr. 6.95 (ISBN 0-8426-0674-2). Orient Bk Dist.

Lal, Hazra Kanai. Royal Patronage of Buddhism in Ancient India. 1984. text ed. 55.00x (ISBN 0-86590-167-8). Apt Bks.

Ling, Trevor. Buddhist Revival in India: Aspects of the Sociology of Buddhism. LC 79-20167. 1980. 26.00 (ISBN 0-312-10681-5). St Martin.

Marshall, John. The Buddhist Art of Gandhara. (Illus.). 1981. Repr. of 1960 ed. text ed. 30.00x. Coronet Bks.

Nakamura, Hijime. Indian Buddhism: A Survey with Bibliographical Notes. 440p. 1986. 28.00 (Pub. by Motilal Banarsidass). South Asia Bks.

Obermiller, E. The History of Buddhism in India & Tibet. 231p. 1986. Repr. of 1932 ed. 27.00 (ISBN 81-7030-026-6, Pub. by Sri Satguru Pubns India). Orient Bk Dist.

Pandeya, R. C. Buddhist Studies in India. 1975. 12.50 (ISBN 0-8426-0806-0). Orient Bk Dist.

Rajneesh, Bhagwan S. Book of the Books, Vol. 2. Asha, Ma P., ed. LC 82-50462. (Buddha Ser.). 352p. (Orig.). 1983. pap. 4.95 (ISBN 0-88050-514-1). Chidvilas Found.

--Book of the Secrets, Vol. V. 2nd ed. Ma Prema Veena, ed. LC 75-36733. (Tantra Ser.). 400p. 1984. pap. 4.95 (ISBN 0-88050-529-X). Chidvilas Found.

Rajneesh, Bhagwan Shree. Hsin Hsin Ming: The Book of Nothing. 2nd ed. Punito, Ma, ed. LC 83-17783. (Zen Master Ser.). 320p. 1983. pap. 4.95 (ISBN 0-88050-597-4). Chidvilas Found.

--Philosophia Ultima. Anurag, Ma Yoga, ed. LC 83-43216. (Upanishads Ser.). 384p. (Orig.). 1983. pap. 4.95 (ISBN 0-88050-617-2). Chidvilas Found.

--Sacred Yes. Ma Prem Maneesha, ed. LC 83-17665. (Initiation Talks Ser.). 448p. (Orig.). 1983. pap. 4.95 (ISBN 0-88050-624-5). Chidvilas Found.

--Tantra, Spirituality & Sex. 2nd ed. Anurag, Ma Yoga, ed. LC 83-16036. (Tantra Ser.). 160p. 1983. pap. 3.95 (ISBN 0-88050-696-2). Chidvilas Found.

--Won't You Join the Dance. Maneesha, Ma Prem, ed. LC 83-43217. (Initiation Talks Ser.). 320p. (Orig.). 1983. pap. 4.95 (ISBN 0-88050-676-8). Chidvilas Found.

Robinson, Richard H. Early Madhyamika in India & China. 1976. Repr. 18.50 (ISBN 0-8426-0904-0). Orient Bk Dist.

Saint-Hilaire, J. Barthelemy. Buddhism in India & Sri Lanka. LC 75-907912. 1975. Repr. of 1975 ed. 10.50x (ISBN 0-89684-373-4). Orient Bk Dist.

Singh, Fauja, ed. Perspectives on Guru Amardas. 1985. 8.50x (ISBN 0-8364-1518-3, Pub. by Punjabi U India). South Asia Bks.

Taranath. Taranatha's History of Buddhism in India. Chattopadhyaya, Debiprsdad & Chattopadhyaya, A., eds. 1980. Repr. of 1970 ed. 27.00x (ISBN 0-8364-1597-3, Pub. by KP Bagchi & Co.). South Asia Bks.

Tripitaka. The Quest of Enlightenment. Thomas, E. J., tr. from Sanskrit. LC 85-24863. (The Wisdom of the East Ser.). 95p. 1986. Repr. of 1950 ed. lib. bdg. 29.75x (ISBN 0-313-22185-5, TRQE). Greenwood.

Tsing, I. A Record of the Buddhist Religion as Practised in India & the Malay Archipelago. Takakusu, J., tr. Repr. of 1896 ed. text ed. 22.50x (ISBN 0-89644-178-4). Coronet Bks.

Vogel, J. P. Buddhist Art in India, Ceylon, & Java. (Illus.). 187p. 1977. Repr. of 1936 ed. text ed. 19.00x. Coronet Bks.

Warder, A. K. Indian Buddhism. rev. 2nd ed. 580p. 1980. text ed. 22.00 (ISBN 0-89684-094-8, Pub. by Motilal Banarsidass India). Orient Bk Dist.

BUDDHISM–JAPAN

Anesaki, Masharu. Nichiren: The Buddhist Prophet. 1916. 11.25 (ISBN 0-8446-1029-1). Peter Smith.

Covell, Jon Carter & Yamada, Abbot S. Unraveling Zen's Red Thread: Ikkyu's Controversial Way. LC 80-81040. (Illus.). 341p. 1980. 21.50x (ISBN 0-930878-19-1). Hollym Intl.

De Bary, William T., ed. The Buddhist Tradition: In India, China & Japan. 448p. 1972. pap. 4.76 (ISBN 0-394-71696-5, V702, Vin). Random.

Gibson, Morgan. Among Buddhas of Japan. 1987. 10.00. White Pine.

Kiyota, Minoru, et al, eds. Japanese Buddhism: Its Tradition, New Religions & Interaction with Christianity. 1987. 24.50 (ISBN 0-914910-76-0). Buddhist Bks.

LaFleur, William R. The Karma of Words: Buddhism & the Literary Arts in Medieval Japan. LC 82-45909. 232p. 1983. text ed. 30.00x (ISBN 0-520-04600-5); pap. 9.95 (ISBN 0-520-05622-1, CAL764). U of Cal Pr.

Lloyd, Arthur. The Creed of Half Japan: Historical Sketches of Japanese Buddhism. LC 78-70095. Repr. of 1912 ed. 40.50 (ISBN 0-404-17344-6). AMS Pr.

McMullin, Neil. Buddhism & the State in Sixteenth Century Japan. LC 84-42572. (Illus.). 408p. 1984. 45.00x (ISBN 0-691-07291-4). Princeton U Pr.

Matsunaga, Alicia & Matsunaga, Daigan. Foundation of Japanese Buddhism: The Mass Movement, Vol. 2. LC 74-83654. 1976. 16.95x (ISBN 0-914910-27-2); pap. 9.50 (ISBN 0-914910-28-0). Buddhist Bks.

Matsunaga, Daigan & Matsunaga, Alicia. Foundation of Japanese Buddhism: The Aristocratic Age, Vol. I. LC 74-83654. 1974. 14.95x (ISBN 0-914910-25-6); pap. 8.50x (ISBN 0-914910-26-4). Buddhist Bks.

Murata, Kiyoaki. Japan's New Buddhism: An Objective Account of Soka Gakkai. LC 74-83640. (Illus.). 216p. 1969. 8.50 (ISBN 0-8348-0040-3). Weatherhill.

Nakarai, Toyozo W. The Study of the Impact of Buddhism Upon Japanese Life As Revealed in the Order of Kokin-Shu. 59.95 (ISBN 0-8490-1156-6). Gordon Pr.

Nanjio, Bunyiu, tr. from Japanese. Short History of the Twelve Buddhist Sects. (Studies in Japanese History & Civilization). 1979. Repr. of 1886 ed. 19.75 (ISBN 0-89093-252-2). U Pubns Amer.

Picken, Stuart D. Buddhism: Japan's Cultural Identity. LC 81-84800. (Illus.). 80p. 1982. 19.95 (ISBN 0-87011-499-9). Kodansha.

Pilgrim, Richard B. Buddhism & the Arts of Japan. LC 81-8063. (Focus on Hinduism & Buddhism Ser.). 64p. (Orig.). 1981. pap. 4.95x (ISBN 0-89012-026-9). Anima Pubns.

Reischauer, A. K. Studies in Japanese Buddhism. LC 73-107769. Repr. of 1917 ed. 24.50 (ISBN 0-404-05237-1). AMS Pr.

Reischauer, August. Studies in Japanese Buddhism. 75.00 (ISBN 0-8490-1147-7). Gordon Pr.

Roth, Martin & Stevens, John. Zen Guide: Where to Meditate in Japan. (Illus.). 152p. pap. 7.50 (ISBN 0-8348-0202-3). Weatherhill.

Saunders, E. Dale. Buddhism in Japan: With an Outline of Its Origins in India. LC 77-24539. 1977. Repr. of 1964 ed. lib. bdg. 25.75x (ISBN 0-8371-9746-5, SABJ). Greenwood.

Shaner, David E. The Bodymind Experience in Japanese Buddhism: A Phenomenological Study of Kukai & Dogen. (Series in Buddhist Studies). 202p. 1986. 44.50x (ISBN 0-88706-061-7); pap. 14.95x (ISBN 0-88706-062-5). State U NY Pr.

Steinilber-Oberlin, Emile. The Buddhist Sects of Japan, Their History, Philosophical Doctrines & Sanctuaries. Loge, Marc, tr. LC 78-109854. (Illus.). 303p. Repr. of 1938 ed. lib. bdg. 22.50x (ISBN 0-8371-4349-7, STBS). Greenwood.

Streeter, Burnett H. Buddha & the Christ. LC 72-102585. 1970. Repr. of 1932 ed. 29.50x (ISBN 0-8046-0745-1, Pub. by Kennikat). Assoc Faculty Pr.

Suzuki, David A. Crisis in Japanese Buddhism: Case of the Otani Sect. 285p. 1985. 19.50 (ISBN 0-914910-51-5). Buddhist Bks.

Takada, Koin. Spirit of Buddhism Today. Yampolsky, Philip, tr. (Illus.). 1973. 9.95 (ISBN 0-89346-095-8, Pub. by Tokuma Shoten); pap. 2.95 (ISBN 0-89346-043-5). Heian Intl.

Thelle, Notto R. Buddhism & Christianity in Japan: From Conflict to Dialogue, 1854-1899. (Illus.). 384p. 1987. text ed. 30.00x. UH Pr.

Watts, Alan W. The Spirit of Zen: A Way of Life, Work & Art in the Far East. 1958. pap. 2.95 (ISBN 0-394-17418-6, E219, Ever). Grove.

Yuki. Yuki, Temple Dog: How a California Pound Dog Became Guardian of a Japanese Buddhist Temple. (Illus.). 1986. 16.95 (ISBN 0-914910-37-X). Buddhist Bks.

BUDDHISM–KOREA

Lancaster, Lewis R., ed. The Korean Buddhist Canon: A Descriptive Catalogue. LC 75-40662. (Center for Korean Studies, UC Berkeley). 1980. 60.00x (ISBN 0-520-03159-8). U of Cal Pr.

Starr, Frederick. Korean Buddhism: History-Condition-Art: Three Lectures. LC 78-70123. Repr. of 1918 ed. 25.00 (ISBN 0-404-17379-9). AMS Pr.

Sunim, Kusan. The Way of Korean Zen. Fages, Martine, tr. (Illus.). 182p. pap. 12.50 (ISBN 0-8348-0201-5). Weatherhill.

BUDDHISM–NEPAL

Fantin, Mario. Mani Rimdu-Nepal: The Buddhist Dance Drama of Tengpoche (1976) (Illus.). 1978. 40.00. Heinman.

Von Furer-Haimendorf, Christoph. The Sherpas of Nepal Buddhist Highlanders. 298p. 1982. 49.00x (ISBN 0-85692-020-7, Pub. by E-W Pubns England). State Mutual Bk.

BUDDHISM–SRI LANKA

Vogel, J. P. Buddhist Art in India, Ceylon, & Java. (Illus.). 187p. 1977. Repr. of 1936 ed. text ed. 19.00x. Coronet Bks.

BUDDHISM–THAILAND

Anuman, Rajadhon Phraya. Life & Ritual in Old Siam: Three Studies of Thai Life & Customs. Gedney, William J., ed. LC 78-23833. (Illus.). 1979. Repr. of 1961 ed. lib. bdg. 24.75x (ISBN 0-313-21193-0, ARLF). Greenwood.

Ishii, Yoneo. Sangha, State, & Society: Thai Buddhism in History. Hawkes, Peter, tr. from Japanese. (Monographs, Center for Southeast Asian Studies, Kyoto University). 224p. 1985. text ed. 25.00x (ISBN 0-8248-0993-9); pap. text ed. 16.00x (ISBN 0-8248-0994-7). UH Pr.

Keyes, Charles F. Thailand: Buddhist Kingdom As Modern Nation State. (Profiles-Nations of Contemporary Asia Ser.). 240p. 1987. 32.50 (ISBN 0-86531-138-2). Westview.

Ling, Trevor. Buddhism, Imperialism & War. (Illus.). 1979. text ed. 13.95x (ISBN 0-04-294105-9). Allen Unwin.

Mole, Robert L. Thai Values & Behavior Patterns. LC 71-130419. (Illus.). 1971. 4.75 (ISBN 0-8048-0947-X). C E Tuttle.

Suksamran, Somboon. Buddhism & Politics in Thailand. 180p. (Orig.). 1982. pap. text ed. 25.00 (ISBN 9971-902-43-5, Pub. by Inst Southeast Asian Stud). Gower Pub Co.

--Political Buddhism in Southeast Asia: The Role of the Sangha in the Modernization of Thailand. LC 77-77606. (Illus.). 1977. 20.00x (ISBN 0-312-62137-X). St Martin.

Suriyabongs, Luang. The Buddhas' Doctrine of Truth: Dhamma & Buddhist Religion As Practiced by the Holy Brotherhood in Siam. Bunnag, Krachang, tr. LC 77-87512. Repr. of 1936 ed. 14.50 (ISBN 0-404-16870-1). AMS Pr.

Tambiah, S. J. Buddhism & the Spirit Cults in Northeast Thailand. LC 73-108112. (Cambridge Studies in Social Anthropology: No. 2). (Illus.). 1970. pap. 19.95 (ISBN 0-521-09958-7). Cambridge U Pr.

Tambiah, Stanley J. The Buddhist Saints of the Forest & the Cult of Amulets: A Study in Charisma, Hagiography, Sectarianism & Millenial Buddhism. LC 83-15113. (Cambridge Studies in Social Anthropology: No. 49). (Illus.). 432p. 1984. 57.50 (ISBN 0-521-25984-3); pap. 18.95 (ISBN 0-521-27787-6). Cambridge U Pr.

Tulku, Tarthang, ed. Annals of the Nyingma Lineage, Vol. 11. (Illus.). 1977. pap. 12.00 (ISBN 0-913546-32-1). Dharma Pub.

Wells, Kenneth E. Thai Buddhism: Its Rites & Activities. LC 77-87081. (Illus.). viii, 320p. Repr. of 1960 ed. 34.50 (ISBN 0-404-16876-0). AMS Pr.

BUDDHISM–TIBET

Chang, Garma C. The Six Yogas of Naropa & Mahamudra. 2nd ed. LC 86-10020. 128p. 1986. pap. 9.95 (ISBN 0-937938-33-5). Snow Lion.

Dalai Lama. The Opening of the Wisdom Eye. LC 70-152732. 178p. 1981. pap. 6.95 (ISBN 0-8356-0549-3, Quest). Theos Pub Hse.

Dalai Lama, IV. The Opening of the Wisdom-Eye. Rinpoche, Thubten K., et al, trs. from Tibetan. LC 70-152732. (Illus.). 1972. 7.50 (ISBN 0-8356-0202-8). Theos Pub Hse.

Dargyay, Eva M. The Rise of Esoteric Buddhism in Tibet. 1977. 14.00 (ISBN 0-8426-0915-6, Pub by Molilal Banarsidass India). Orient Bk Dist.

Darqyay, Eva. The Rise of Esoteric Buddhism in the Tibet. 272p. 1979. pap. 5.95 (ISBN 0-87728-432-6). Weiser.

Dowman, Keith. Masters of Mahamudra: Songs & Histories of Eighty-Four Siddhas. (Buddhist Studies). 320p. 1986. 44.50x (ISBN 0-88706-158-3); pap. 10.95x (ISBN 0-88706-160-5). State U NY Pr.

Gold, Peter. Tibetan Reflections. (Illus.). 112p. (Orig.). 1984. pap. 11.95 (ISBN 0-86171-022-3, Wisdom Pubns). Great Traditions.

Guenther, Herbert V. Tibetan Buddhism in Western Perspective. LC 76-47758. (Illus.). 1977. pap. 8.95 (ISBN 0-913546-50-X). Dharma Pub.

Gyatso, Geshe K. Buddhism in the Tibetan Tradition: A Guide. (Illus.). 144p. (Orig.). 1984. pap. 9.95 (ISBN 0-7102-0242-3). Methuen Inc.

Gyatso, Tenzin. My Land & My People. 3rd ed. (Illus.). 271p. 1983. Repr. of 1962 ed. 6.95. Potala.

Heruka, Tsang N. The Life of Marpa the Translator. Nalanda Translation Committee & Trungpa, Chogyam, trs. from Tibetan. LC 86-11837. 320p. 1986. pap. 12.95 (ISBN 0-87773-377-5). Shambhala Pubns.

Kalu Rinpoche. The Dharma: That Benefits All Beings Impartially Like the Light of the Sun & Moon. 256p. (Orig.). 1986. 34.50x (ISBN 0-88706-156-7); pap. 10.95x (ISBN 0-88706-157-5). State U NY Pr.

Klong-chen rab-byams pa. Looking Deeper. Guenther, Herbert V., tr. from Tibetan. (Illus.). 64p. (Orig.). 1984. pap. 3.50 (ISBN 0-931454-09-3). Timeless Bks.

Ligeti, L., ed. Tibetan & Buddhist Studies Commemorating the Two Hundreth Anniversary of the Birth of Alexander Csoma de Koros, 2 vols. (Bibliotheca Orientalis Hungarica: No. 29). 827p. 1984. Set. text ed. 115.00x (ISBN 963-05-3573-4, Pub. by Akademiai Kiado Hungary). Vol. 1 (ISBN 963-05-3902-0). Vol. 2 (ISBN 963-05-3903-9). Humanities.

Nagarjuna & Gyatso, Tenzin. The Buddhism of Tibet & the Precious Garland. 212p. 1983. pap. 12.50 (ISBN 0-04-294127-X). Allen Unwin.

Obermiller, E. The History of Buddhism in India & Tibet. 231p. 1986. Repr. of 1932 ed. 27.00 (ISBN 81-7030-026-6, Pub. by Sri Satguru Pubns India). Orient Bk Dist.

Paul, Robert A. The Tibetan Symbolic World: Psychoanalytic Explorations. LC 81-16505. (Chicago Originals Ser.). (Illus.). 360p. 1982. lib. bdg. 14.00x (ISBN 0-226-64987-3). U of Chicago Pr.

Rabten, Geshe. Echoes of Voidness. Batchelor, Stephen, ed. (Intermediate Book: White Ser.). (Illus.). 148p. (Orig.). 1983. pap. 8.95 (ISBN 0-86171-010-X, Pub. by Wisdom Pubns). Great Traditions.

Rinbochay, Lati & Hopkins, Jeffrey. Death, Intermediate State & Rebirth in Tibetan Buddhism. LC 80-80130. 86p. 1979. lib. bdg. cancelled (ISBN 0-937938-01-7); pap. 6.95 (ISBN 0-937938-00-9). Snow Lion.

Rinbochay, Lati, et al. Meditative Status in Tibetan Buddhism. Zahler, Leah, ed. Hopkins, Jeffrey, tr. from Tibetan. (Wisdom Advanced Book: Blue Ser.). (Illus.). 288p. (Orig.). 1983. pap. 10.95 (ISBN 0-86171-011-8, Pub. by Wisdom Pubns). Great Traditions.

Schlagintweit, Emil. Buddhism in Tibet. 69.95 (ISBN 0-87968-802-5). Gordon Pr.

SGam po pa. The Jewel Ornament of Liberation. Guenther, Herbert V., tr. LC 86-11839. 353p. (off). 1986. pap. 14.95 (ISBN 0-87773-378-3). Shambhala Pubns.

Sopa, Geshe Lhundup & Hopkins, Jeffrey. The Practice & Theory of Tibetan Buddhism. LC 75-42898. 1976. pap. 4.95 (ISBN 0-394-17905-6, E672, Ever). Grove.

Tharchin, Sermey G., et al. King Udrayana & the Wheel of Life: The History & Meaning of the Buddhist Teaching of Dependent Origination. LC 84-61266. (Illus.). 248p. (Orig.). 1984. 14.50 (ISBN 0-918753-06-6); pap. 9.50 (ISBN 0-918753-05-8). Mahayana.

Trungpa, Chogyam. Born in Tibet. LC 85-8174. (Illus.). 280p. 1985. pap. 9.95 (ISBN 0-87773-333-3, 74219-2). Shambhala Pubns.

--Cutting Through Spiritual Materialism. LC 73-86145. (Dragon Ser.). (Illus.). 212p. (Orig.). 1973. pap. 8.95 (ISBN 0-87773-050-4). Shambhala Pubns.

Tsogyal, Yeshe. The Life & Liberation of Padmasambhava, 2 vols. Toussaint, G. C. & Douglas, Kenneth, trs. (Tibetan Translation Ser.). (Illus.). 1978. 60.00 set (ISBN 0-685-80849-1). Vol. I (ISBN 0-913546-18-6). Vol. II (ISBN 0-913546-20-8). Dharma Pub.

Tulku, Tarthang. Crystal Mirror, Vol. V. (Illus.). 1977. pap. 12.95 (ISBN 0-913546-47-X). Dharma Pub.

Waddell, Austine. Buddhism & Lamaism of Tibet. 1985. text ed. 40.00x (ISBN 0-86590-615-7, Pub. by Sterling Pubs India). Apt Bks.

Yeshe, Lama & Rinpoche, Zopa. Wisdom Energy: Basic Buddhist Teachings. Landaw, Jonathan & Berzin, Alexander, eds. (Wisdom Basic Book: Orange Ser.). (Illus.). 151p. 1982. pap. 7.95 (ISBN 0-86171-008-8, Pub. by Wisdom Pubns). Great Traditions.

BUDDHISM AND CHRISTIANITY

see Christianity and Other Religions–Buddhism

BUDDHISM AND STATE

Ishii, Yoneo. Sangha, State, & Society: Thai Buddhism in History. Hawkes, Peter, tr. from Japanese. (Monographs, Center for Southeast Asian Studies, Kyoto University). 224p. 1985. text ed. 25.00x (ISBN 0-8248-0993-9); pap. text ed. 16.00x (ISBN 0-8248-0994-7). UH Pr.

Smith, Bardwell L., ed. Religion & Legitimation of Power in Sri Lanka. LC 77-7449. 1978. pap. 7.95 (ISBN 0-89012-008-0). Anima Pubns.

--Religion & Legitimation of Power in Thailand, Laos & Burma. LC 77-7444. 1978. pap. 7.95 (ISBN 0-89012-009-9). Anima Pubns.

Tambiah, S. J. World Conqueror & World Renouncer. LC 76-8290. (Cambridge Studies in Social Anthropology: No. 15). 1976. 65.00 (ISBN 0-521-21140-9); pap. 19.95 (ISBN 0-521-29290-5). Cambridge U Pr.

BUDDHIST ARCHITECTURE

see Architecture, Buddhist

BUDDHIST ART

see Art, Buddhist

BUDDHIST CONVERTS FROM CHRISTIANITY

Nydahl, Ole. Entering the Diamond Way: My Path among the Lamas. Aronoff, Carol A. & Clemens, Paul M., eds. LC 85-73182. (Illus.). 256p. (Orig.). 1985. pap. 12.95 (ISBN 0-931892-03-1). B Dolphin Pub.

BUDDHIST DOCTRINES

Amore, Roy C., ed. Developments in Buddhist Thought: Canadian Contributions to Buddhist Studies. 196p. 1979. pap. text ed. 9.95x (ISBN 0-919812-11-2, Pub. by Wilfred Laurier Canada). Humanities.

Asvaghosa. The Principle & Practice of Mahayana Buddhism: An Interpretation of Professor Suzuki's Translation of Ashvaghosa's Awakening of Faith. Goodard, Dwight, ed. LC 78-72373. Repr. of 1933 ed. 18.00 (ISBN 0-404-17223-7). AMS Pr.

Bendall, Cecil & Rouse, W. H., eds. Siksa Samuccaya: A Compendium of Buddhist Doctrine. 1981. 18.50x (ISBN 0-8364-0793-8, Pub. by Motilal Banarsidass). South Asia Bks.

Bigelow, William S. Buddhism & Immortality. LC 78-72379. Repr. of 1908 ed. 16.50 (ISBN 0-404-17228-8). AMS Pr.

Buddhaghosa. The Path of Purity, 3 vols. Pe Maung Tin, tr. LC 78-72389. Repr. of 1931 ed. Set. 95.00 (ISBN 0-404-17570-8). AMS Pr.

Carus, Paul. Nirvana, a Story of Buddhist Psychology. LC 78-72395. (Illus.). Repr. of 1902 ed. 22.00 (ISBN 0-404-17254-7). AMS Pr.

Coomaraswamy, Ananda K. & Horner, I. B. The Living Thoughts of Gotama, the Buddha. LC 78-72397. Repr. of 1948 ed. 34.50 (ISBN 0-404-17256-3). AMS Pr.

Davids, C. Rhys. What Was the Original Gospel in 'Buddhism'? LC 78-72416. Repr. of 1938 ed. 17.00 (ISBN 0-404-17277-6). AMS Pr.

Dhammapada. The Buddha's Path of Virtue. 2nd ed. Woodward, F. L., tr. LC 78-72419. Repr. of 1929 ed. 21.50 (ISBN 0-404-17283-0). AMS Pr.

Goddard, Dwight. The Buddha's Golden Path. 2nd rev. ed. LC 78-72435. Repr. of 1931 ed. 27.00 (ISBN 0-404-17296-2). AMS Pr.

Great Master Lyan Chr, commentary by. Essentials of the Shramanera Vinaya & Rules of Deportment: A General Explanation. Buddhist Text Translation Society Staff, tr. from Chinese. (Eng., Illus.). 112p. (Orig.). 1975. pap. 5.00 (ISBN 0-917512-04-9). Buddhist Text.

Heng Sure & Heng Chau. With One Heart Bowing to the City of Ten Thousand Buddhas, Vol. IV. (Illus.). 136p. (Orig.). 1980. pap. 4.00 (ISBN 0-917512-90-1). Buddhist Text.

Jinarajadasa, Curuppumullage. The Reign of Law (Buddhist Essays) LC 78-72902. Repr. of 1923 ed. 22.50 (ISBN 0-404-17314-4). AMS Pr.

Kapleau, Roshi P. To Cherish All Life: A Buddhist View of Animal Slaughter & Meat Eating. LC 81-51149. (Illus., Orig.). 1981. pap. text ed. 4.25 (ISBN 0-940306-00-X). Zen Ctr.

Maitreya, Sthiramati. Madhyantavibhagatika: An Analysis of the Middle Path & the Extremes. Friedman, David L., tr. from Sanskrit. 154p. 1984. Repr. of 1937 ed. lib. bdg. 19.50x (ISBN 0-88181-004-5). Canon Pubns.

Marcus, Russell, commentary by. Forms of Man: The Buddhist Vision of Thawan Duchanee. (Illus.). 1974. pap. 15.00 (ISBN 0-8048-1234-9). C E Tuttle.

Masefield, Peter. Divine Revelation in Pali Buddhism. 216p. 1986. 27.95 (ISBN 0-04-294132-6). Allen Unwin.

Obermiller, E. The Doctrine of Prajna-Paramita As Exposed in the Abhisamayalamkara of Maitreya. 153p. 1984. Repr. of 1932 ed. lib. bdg. 19.50x (ISBN 0-88181-002-9). Canon Pubns.

O'Neil, Kevin. The Diamond Sutra. 1978. pap. 5.00 (ISBN 0-86627-004-3). Crises Res Pr.

Ross, Nancy W. Buddhism: A Way of Life & Thought. LC 80-7652. (Illus.). 224p. 1980. 15.95 (ISBN 0-394-49286-2). Knopf.

Santideva, compiled by. Siksha-Samuccaya, a Compendium of Buddhist Doctrine. Bendall, Cecil & Rouse, W. D., trs. LC 78-70114. Repr. of 1922 ed. 33.50 (ISBN 0-404-17368-3). AMS Pr.

Schumann, Hans W. Buddhism. Fenerstein, Georg, tr. from Ger. LC 74-6302. (Illus.). 200p. 1974. pap. 7.95 (ISBN 0-8356-0457-8). Theos Pub Hse.

Shantaraksita. Tattva-Sangraha of Santaraksita with Commentary of Kamalasila. Jha, Ganganath, tr. 1593p. 1986. Repr. of 1937 ed. Set. 85.00 (ISBN 0-317-46526-0, Pub. by Motilal Banarsidass India); Vol. 1. 50.00 (ISBN 81-208-0059-1); Vol. 2. 50.00 (ISBN 81-208-0060-5). South Asia Bks.

Sure, Heng & Chau, Heng. With One Heart Bowing to the City of Ten Thousand Buddhas, Vol. III. (Illus.). 154p. (Orig.). 1980. pap. 5.00 (ISBN 0-917512-89-8). Buddhist Text.

Tulku, Tarthang, ed. Nyingma Edition of the sDe-dge bKa-gyur & bsTun-gyur, 120 vols. (Tibetan Buddhist Canon). 65000p. 1981. Set. 17250.00 (ISBN 0-89800-129-3). Dharma Pub.

Vasu-Mitra. Origin & Doctrines of Early Indian Buddhist Schools. Masuda, Jiryo, tr. LC 78-70133. Repr. of 1925 ed. 17.00 (ISBN 0-404-17403-5). AMS Pr.

BUDDHIST ETHICS

Aitken, Robert. The Mind of Clover: Essays in Zen Buddhist Ethics. 224p. (Orig.). 1984. pap. 11.50 (ISBN 0-86547-158-4). N Point Pr.

King, Winston L. In the Hope of Nibbana: The Ethics of Theravada Buddhism. LC 62-9575. 308p. 1964. 22.95 (ISBN 0-87548-230-9); pap. 9.95 (ISBN 0-87548-231-7). Open Court.

Misra, G. S. Development of Buddhist Ethics. 1984. text ed. 14.00x. Coronet Bks.

Tachibana, Shundo, pref. by. The Ethics of Buddhism. LC 74-20477. 288p. 1975. Repr. of 1926 ed. text ed. 24.50x (ISBN 0-06-496720-4). B&N Imports.

Tharchin, Sermey G. Methods of Achieving the Paths: Stages of Philosophical & Ethical Development According to the Madhyamika Svatantrika School of Buddhism. Taylor, Barbara D., ed. Tr. of Lam-thob-tsul. 59p. (Orig.). 1981. pap. 5.00 (ISBN 0-918753-02-3). Mahayana.

BUDDHIST LEGENDS

see Legends, Buddhist

BUDDHIST LITERATURE

see also Buddhism–Sacred Books

Buddhaghosa. The Atthasalini, Buddhaghosa's Commentary on the Dhammasangani. Muller, Edward, ed. LC 78-72383. Repr. of 1897 ed. 39.50 (ISBN 0-404-17245-8). AMS Pr.

--Buddhaghosa's Parables. Rogers, T., tr. from Burmese. LC 78-72384. Repr. of 1870 ed. 37.50 (ISBN 0-404-17246-6). AMS Pr.

--Expositor (Atthasalini, 2 vols. in 1. rev. ed. Maung Tin, tr. Davis, Carolina A., rev. by. LC 78-72385. Repr. of 1920 ed. 49.50 (ISBN 0-404-17247-4). AMS Pr.

Cranmer-Byng, J. L., ed. Chinese Buddhist Verse. Robinson, Richard H., tr. from Chinese. LC 79-8725. 1980. Repr. of 1954 ed. lib. bdg. 18.75x (ISBN 0-313-22168-5, ROCB). Greenwood.

Crown, W. The Heritage of Buddhist Poetry. 1986. 6.95 (ISBN 0-533-06003-6). Vantage.

Cummings, Mary. Lives of the Buddha in the Art & Literature of Asia. LC 80-67341. (Michigan Papers on South & Southeast Asia: No. 20). (Illus.). xiii, 225p. 1982. 19.95 (ISBN 0-89148-022-6); pap. 10.95 (ISBN 0-89148-023-4). Ctr S&SE Asian.

Dhammapada. (Life Companion Library). 116p. (Orig.). 1983. pap. 5.95 (ISBN 0-89744-016-1). Auromere.

Easwaran, Eknath, tr. from Pali. The Dhammapada. 1986. 13.95 (ISBN 0-915132-38-9); pap. 6.95 (ISBN 0-915132-37-0). Nilgiri Pr.

Ijima, Kanjitsu. The Lotus Textbook. 62p. (Orig.). 1984. pap. 10.00 (ISBN 0-86627-010-8). Crises Res Pr.

Johansson, Rune E. Pali Buddhist Texts. 160p. 1982. 30.00x (ISBN 0-7007-0063-3, Pub. by Curzon England). State Mutual Bk.

--Pali Buddhist Texts Explained to the Beginner. 1981. pap. 12.00 (ISBN 0-8364-0329-0, Pub. by Curzon Pr). South Asia Bks.

Mistry, Jim. Letters from the Mandali of Avatar Meher Baba, Vol. 2. LC 83-142831. 176p. (Orig.). 1983. pap. 7.95 (ISBN 0-913078-46-8). Sheriar Pr.

Nariman, Gushtaspshah K. Literary History of Sanskrit Buddhism. LC 78-70106. Repr. of 1920 ed. 37.50 (ISBN 0-404-17356-X). AMS Pr.

Nariman, J. K. Literary History of Sanskrit Buddhism. 2nd ed. 1972. 13.95 (ISBN 0-8426-0453-7). Orient Bk Dist.

Newland, Guy. Compassion: A Tibetan Analysis. (A Wisdom Advanced Book: Blue Ser.). 168p. (Orig.). 1985. pap. 12.95 (ISBN 0-318-04680-6, Wisdom Pubns). Great Traditions.

Norbu, Thinley. The Small Golden Key to the Treasure of the Various Essential Necessities of General & Extraordinary Buddhist Dharma. rev. ed. LC 84-29724. 111p. 1985. pap. 10.00 (ISBN 0-9607000-2-1). Jewel Pub Hse.

O'Neil, Kevin R., ed. American Buddhist Newsletter: 1981-82, Vol. I. 136p. (Orig.). 1982. pap. 35.00 (ISBN 0-86627-000-0). Crises Res Pr.

Pruden, Leo, tr. Karmasiddhi Prakarana of Vasubandhu. 1987. 20.00 (ISBN 0-89581-907-4). Asian Human Pr.

Rajneesh, Bhagwan S. A Cup of Tea. 2nd ed ed. Somendra, Swami Anand, ed. LC 83-43215. (Early Discourses & Writings Ser.). 272p. 1983. pap. 4.95 (ISBN 0-88050-538-9). Chidvilas Found.

--Just Around the Corner. Mahasattva, Swami Krishna, ed. LC 84-42870. (Initiation Talks Ser.). 224p. (Orig.). 1984. pap. 3.95 (ISBN 0-88050-588-5). Chidvilas Found.

Rajneesh, Bhagwan Shree. And Now, & Here, Vol. 1. Mahasattva, Swami Satya, ed. LC 84-42798. (Early Discourses & Writings Ser.). 320p. (Orig.). 1984. pap. 4.95 (ISBN 0-88050-709-8). Chidvilas Found.

--I Am That. Ma Prem Apa, ed. LC 84-42809. (Upanishads Ser.). 416p. (Orig.). 1984. pap. 5.95 (ISBN 0-88050-580-X). Chidvilas Found.

--Tao: The Golden Gate, Vol. 1. Asha, Ma Prem, ed. LC 84-42615. (Tao Ser.). 336p. (Orig.). 1984. pap. 4.95 (ISBN 0-88050-646-6). Chidvilas Found.

--You Ain't Seen Nothing Yet. Maneesha, Ma Prem, ed. LC 84-42614. (Initiation Talks Ser.). 304p. (Orig.). 1984. pap. 4.95 (ISBN 0-88050-687-3). Chidvilas Found.

Richman, Paula. Women, Branch Stories, & Religious Rhetoric in a Tamil Buddhist Text. (Foreign & Comparative Studies-South Asian Ser.: No. 12). (Orig.). 1987. pap. write for info. (ISBN 0-915984-90-3). Syracuse U Foreign Comp.

Saunders, Kenneth J., ed. The Heart of Buddhism: Being an Anthology of Buddhist Verse. LC 78-70120. Repr. of 1915 ed. 17.00 (ISBN 0-404-17377-2). AMS Pr.

Shaku, Soyen. Zen for Americans: Including the Sutra of Forty-Two Chapters. Suzuki, D. T., tr. 220p. 1974. pap. 6.95 (ISBN 0-87548-273-2). Open Court.

Stryk, Lucien. World of the Buddha: An Introduction to Buddhist Literature. 1982. pap. 9.95 (ISBN 0-394-17974-9, E803, Ever). Grove.

Thera, Nyanaponika. The Vision of Dhamma: The Buddhist Writings of Nyanaponika Thera. Bodhi, Bhikkhu, ed. 296p. (Orig.). 1986. pap. 12.50 (ISBN 0-87728-669-8). Weiser.

Tripitaka Master Hua. Shuramana Mantra: A Commentary, Vol. IV. Buddhist Text Translation Society, tr. from Chinese. 140p. (Orig.). pap. 6.50 (ISBN 0-88139-022-4). Buddhist Text.

--Shurangama Mantra: A Commentary, Vol. II. Buddhist Text Translation Society, tr. (Illus.). 210p. (Orig.). 1982. pap. 7.50 (ISBN 0-917512-82-0). Buddhist Text.

Tripitaka Master Hua, commentary by. Flower Adornment Sutra: Chapter 17, Merit & Virture from First Bringing Forth the Mind. Buddhist Text Translation Society, tr. from Chinese. (Illus.). 196p. (Orig.). 1982. pap. 7.00 (ISBN 0-917512-83-9). Buddhist Text.

--Flower Adornment Sutra, Chapter 39: Entering the Dharma Realm, Part V. Buddhist Text Translation Society, tr. from Chinese. (Illus.). 310p. 1982. pap. 9.00 (ISBN 0-917512-81-2). Buddhist Text.

--Flower Adornment Sutra, Chapter 40: Universal Worthy's Conduct & Vows. Buddhist Text Translation Society, tr. from Chinese. (Illus.). 316p. (Orig.). 1982. pap. 10.00 (ISBN 0-917512-84-7). Buddhist Text.

Tsiang, Hiuen. Si-Yu-Ki, Buddhist Records of th Western World, 2 vol. in 1. Beal, Samuel, tr. 618p. Repr. of 1884 ed. 38.50x (ISBN 0-89644-454-6, Pub. by Chinese Matl Ctr). Coronet Bks.

Unno, Taitetsu & Tabrah, Ruth. Tannisho: A Shin Buddhist Classic. 73p. (Orig.). 1985. 12.50 (ISBN 0-938474-05-7); pap. 6.95 (ISBN 0-938474-04-9). Buddhist Study.

Waley, Arthur, tr. The Temple, & Other Poems. LC 78-70137. Repr. of 1923 ed. 25.00 (ISBN 0-404-17407-8). AMS Pr.

Woodward, F. L., tr. from Pali. Buddhist Stories. LC 78-70141. Repr. of 1925 ed. 20.00 (ISBN 0-404-17414-0). AMS Pr.

BUDDHIST LOGIC

Guha, D. C. Navya Nyaya System of Logic. 3rd enlarged ed. 1979. 15.50 (ISBN 0-89684-059-X, Pub. by Motilal Banarsidass India). Orient Bk Dist.

McDermott, A. C., ed. An Eleventh-Century Buddhist Logic of 'Exists' Ratnakirti's Ksanabhangasiddih Vyatirekatmika. (Foundations of Language Supplementary Ser: No. 11). 88p. 1969. 18.50 (ISBN 90-277-0081-8, Pub. by Reidel Holland). Kluwer Academic.

Shantaraksita. Tattva-Sangraha of Santaraksita with Commentary of Kamalasila. Jha, Ganganath, tr. 1593p. 1986. Repr. of 1937 ed. Set. 85.00 (ISBN 0-317-46526-0, Pub. by Motilal Banarsidass India); Vol. 1. 50.00 (ISBN 81-208-0059-1); Vol. 2. 50.00 (ISBN 81-208-0060-5). South Asia Bks.

Stcherbatsky, T. Buddhist Logic, 2 Vols. 1958. Repr. of 1932 ed. Set. text ed. 74.00x (ISBN 90-2790-060-4). Mouton.

Stcherbatsky, Theodore. Buddhist Logic, 2 vols. 1930. pap. text ed. 8.95 ea.; Vol. 1. pap. text ed. (ISBN 0-486-20955-5); Vol. 2. pap. text ed. (ISBN 0-486-20956-3). Dover.

Tharchin, Sermey G. Methods of Achieving the Paths: Stages of Philosophical & Ethical Development According to the Madhyamika Svatantrika School of Buddhism. Taylor, Barbara D., ed. Tr. of Lam-thob-tsul. 59p. (Orig.). 1981. pap. 5.00 (ISBN 0-918753-02-3). Mahayana.

Tucci, Giuseppe, tr. Pre-Dinnaga Buddhist Texts on Logic from Chinese Sources. 368p. 1929. Repr. text ed. 32.00 (ISBN 0-89644-478-3, Pub. by Chinese Matl Ctr). Coronet Bks.

BUDDHIST MONASTICISM AND RELIGIOUS ORDERS

see Monasticism and Religious Orders, Buddhist

BUDDHIST PHILOSOPHY

see Philosophy, Buddhist

BUDDHIST SECTS

see also Mahayana Buddhism

Hardacre, Helen. Lay Buddhism in Contemporary Japan. LC 83-43075. (Illus.). 328p. 1984. 35.00x (ISBN 0-691-07284-1). Princeton U Pr.

Nanjio, Bunyiu, compiled by. A Short History of the Twelve Japanese Buddhist Sects. LC 78-70104. Repr. of 1886 ed. 23.00 (ISBN 0-404-17355-1). AMS Pr.

O'Neil, Kevin. An Introduction to Nichiren Shoshu Buddhism. 111p. 1980. pap. 5.00 (ISBN 0-86627-002-7). Crises Res Pr.

Steinilber-Oberlin, Emile. Buddhist Sects of Japan: Their Histories, Philosophical Doctrines & Sanctuaries. Loge, Marc, tr. 1977. lib. bdg. 39.95 (ISBN 0-8490-1559-6). Gordon Pr.

Williams, George M., ed. Victory in Faith: Experiences of NSA Members. 100p. (Orig.). 1985. pap. text ed. 5.00 (ISBN 0-915678-14-4). World Tribune Pr.

BUDDHIST TANTRISM

see Tantric Buddhism

BUDDHIST THEOLOGY

see Buddhist Doctrines

BULGAKOV, MIKHAIL, 1891-1940

Proffer, Ellendea. Mikhail Bulgakov: Life & Work. LC 83-16199. 1984. 45.00 (ISBN 0-88233-198-1). Ardis Pubs.

Proffer, Ellendea, ed. Bulgakov Photographic Bibliography. 140p. 1984. 35.00 (ISBN 0-88233-812-9); pap. 15.00 (ISBN 0-88233-813-7). Ardis Pubs.

Sahni, K. A Mind in Ferment: Mikhail Bulgakov's Prose. 251p. 1984. text ed. 12.50x (ISBN 0-391-03201-1, Pub. by Arnold Heinemann). Humanities.

BULLETIN BOARDS IN RELIGIOUS EDUCATION

Dorsett, Judy. Bulletin Board Builders, No. 3. (Illus.). 64p. 1986. 3.95 (ISBN 0-87403-020-X, 3240). Standard Pub.

Paris, Janelle A. Planning Bulletin Boards for Church & Synagogue Libraries. LC 83-7331. (CSLA Guide Two Ser. No. 11). (Orig.). 1983. pap. 6.95 (ISBN 0-915324-20-2); pap. 5.50 members. CSLA.

Smelser, Georgia & Enloe, Eilene. Two Hundred Two Bulletin Boards for All Ages. LC 85-26522. (Illus.). 176p. (Orig.). 1986. pap. 5.50 (ISBN 0-912315-96-2). Word Aflame.

Sorlien, Sandra. Bulletin Boards That Communicate: Creative Ideas for the Congregation. 56p. (Orig.). 1984. pap. 4.95 (ISBN 0-8066-2073-0, 10-0950). Augsburg.

Staffeld, Jean, et al. Thirty-Eight Recipes for Bulletin Boards & Art Projects That Christian Kids Can Make. (Illus.). 1978. pap. 4.95 (ISBN 0-570-03774-3, 12-2721). Concordia.

BULTMANN, RUDOLF KARL, 1884-

Barth, Karl & Bultmann, Rudolf. Barth-Bultmann Letters, Nineteen Twenty-Two to Nineteen Sixty-Six. Bromiley, Geoffrey W., tr. 224p. 1981. 13.95 (ISBN 0-8028-3560-0). Eerdmans.

Eisenbeis, Walter. A Translation of the Greek Expressions in the Text of The Gospel of John, A Commentary by Rudolf Bultmann. 160p. (Orig.). 1984. lib. bdg. 22.00 (ISBN 0-8191-3884-3); pap. text ed. 11.25 (ISBN 0-8191-3885-1). U Pr of Amer.

Jones, Geraint V. Christology & Myth in the New Testament. LC 56-4228. 1956. A R Allenson.

Ridderbos, H. N. Bultmann. (Modern Thinkers Ser.). 1960. pap. 2.00 (ISBN 0-87552-581-4). Presby & Reformed.

BUNYAN, JOHN, 1628-1688

Arnott, Anne. Valiant for Truth: The Story of John Bunyan. 160p. (Orig.). 1986. pap. 5.95 (ISBN 0-8028-0192-7). Eerdmans.

Bacon, Ernest W. Bunyan Pilgrim & Dreamer: John Bunyan - His Life & Work. 186p. 1984. pap. 5.95 (ISBN 0-8010-0869-7). Baker Bk.

--Pilgrim & Dreamer: John Bunyan: His Life & Work. 176p. pap. text ed. 8.95 cancelled (ISBN 0-85364-309-1). Attic Pr.

Batson, E. Beatrice. John Bunyan: Allegory & Imagination. LC 83-21341. 168p. 1984. 27.50x (ISBN 0-389-20442-0, 08004). B&N Imports.

Brittain, Vera. In the Steps of John Bunyan. (Illus.). 1973. 30.00 (ISBN 0-8274-1456-0). R West.

--Valiant Pilgrim: The Story of John Bunyan & Puritan England. 1950. 30.00 (ISBN 0-8274-3665-3). R West.

Buckland, Augustus R. John Bunyan: The Man & His Work. LC 76-16025. 1976. Repr. of 1928 ed. lib. bdg. 20.00 (ISBN 0-8414-3319-4). Folcroft.

Bunyan, John. Grace Abounding to the Chief of Sinners. (Summit Bks). 132p. 1986. pap. 4.95 (ISBN 0-8010-0925-1). Baker Bk.

Bunyan, John & Parkhurst, Louis G., Jr. John Bunyan: Pilgrim's Prayer Book. rev. ed. 136p. 1986. pap. 5.95 (ISBN 0-8423-4933-2). Tyndale.

Coats, Robert B. John Bunyan. LC 77-9277. 1977. lib. bdg. 15.00 (ISBN 0-8414-1804-7). Folcroft.

Froude, James A. Bunyan. LC 73-11369. 1880. lib. bdg. 12.00 (ISBN 0-8414-1985-X). Folcroft.

Griffith, Gwilym O. John Bunyan. 1973. Repr. of 1927 ed. lib. bdg. 20.00 (ISBN 0-8414-4623-7). Folcroft.

Harding, Richard W. John Bunyan: His Life & Times. LC 76-27749. 1976. Repr. of 1928 ed. lib. bdg. 20.00 (ISBN 0-8414-4933-3). Folcroft.

Harding, William H. John Bunyan, Pilgrim & Dreamer. LC 77-9369. 1977. 25.00 (ISBN 0-8414-4782-9). Folcroft.

Harrison, Frank M. A Bibliography of the Works of John Bunyan. 1977. lib. bdg. 59.95 (ISBN 0-8490-1502-2). Gordon Pr.

Hawkins, Anne O. Archetypes of Conversion: The Spiritual Autobiographies of St. Augustine, John Bunyan, & Thomas Merton. LC 83-46156. 192p. 1985. 25.00 (ISBN 0-8387-5079-6). Bucknell U Pr.

Hutton, W. H. John Bunyan. LC 77-24947. Repr. of 1927 ed. lib. bdg. 15.00 (ISBN 0-8414-4861-2). Folcroft.

Newey, Vincent, ed. The Pilgrim's Progress: Critical & Historical Views. (English Texts & Studies). 302p. 1980. 30.00x (ISBN 0-389-20016-6). B&N Imports.

Sharrock, Roger. John Bunyan. LC 84-6728. 163p. 1984. Repr. lib. bdg. 25.00x (ISBN 0-313-24528-2, SHJO). Greenwood.

Speight, Harold E. The Life & Writings of John Bunyan. 1928. 40.00 (ISBN 0-8274-2916-9). R West.

--The Life & Writings of John Bunyan. 224p. 1983. lib. bdg. 50.00 (ISBN 0-8495-5063-7). Arden Lib.

Stevevson, Robert. Exposition of the Pilgrim's Progress, with Illustrative Quotations from Bunyan's Minor Works. LC 77-24243. 1977. Repr. of 1912 ed. lib. bdg. 27.50 (ISBN 0-8414-7933-X). Folcroft.

Talon, Henri A. John Bunyan: The Man & His Works. 1978. lib. bdg. 35.00 (ISBN 0-8495-5114-5). Arden Lib.

--John Bunyan: The Man & His Works. 340p. 1980. Repr. of 1951 ed. lib. bdg. 35.00 (ISBN 0-89987-810-5). Darby Bks.

--John Bunyan: The Man & His Works. LC 76-8161. 1976. lib. bdg. 47.50 (ISBN 0-8414-8611-5). Folcroft.

Venables, Edmund. Life of John Bunyan. LC 77-20805. 1977. Repr. of 1888 ed. lib. bdg. 35.00 (ISBN 0-8414-9157-7). Folcroft.

Willcocks, M. P. Bunyan Calling: A Voice from the Seventeenth Century. 1979. Repr. of 1943 ed. lib. bdg. 30.00 (ISBN 0-8414-9718-4). Folcroft.

--Bunyan Calling: A Voice from the Seventeenth Century. 1943. 17.50 (ISBN 0-8274-1984-8). R West.

Williams, Charles W. A Bi-Centenary Memorial of John Bunyan Who Died A.D. 1688. LC 76-27709. 1976. Repr. of 1888 ed. lib. bdg. 17.50 (ISBN 0-8414-9510-6). Folcroft.

Wright, Clifford K. Bunyan As a Man of Letters. LC 77-4072. 1977. Repr. lib. bdg. 9.50 (ISBN 0-8414-9601-3). Folcroft.

BUNYAN, JOHN, 1628-1688–FICTION

Deal, William S. The Tinker of Bedford: A Historical Fiction on the Life & Times of John Bunyan. 1977. pap. 2.95 (ISBN 0-686-19330-X). Crusade Pubs.

BUNYAN, JOHN, 1628-1688–STUDY

Backscheider, Paula R. A Being More Intense: A Study of the Prose Works of Bunyan, Swift, & Defoe. LC 83-45274. (Studies in the Eighteenth Century: No. 7). 222p. 1984. 32.50 (ISBN 0-404-61473-6). AMS Pr.

Brown, John. John Bunyan, (1628-1688) His Life, Times & Work. Harrison, Frank M., ed. (Illus.). xxiv, 515p. 1969. Repr. of 1928 ed. 37.50 (ISBN 0-208-00726-1, Archon). Shoe String.

Firth, Charles H. John Bunyan. LC 74-11062. 1911. lib. bdg. 10.00 (ISBN 0-8414-4212-6). Folcroft.

Froude, James A. Bunyan. Morley, John, ed. LC 68-58379. (English Men of Letters). Repr. of 1888 ed. lib. bdg. 12.50 (ISBN 0-404-51711-0). AMS Pr.

Greaves, Richard L., compiled by. Annotated Bibliography of John Bunyan Studies. LC 72-177693. 1972. 7.00 (ISBN 0-318-03615-0). Pitts Theolog.

Harrison, Frank M. Bibliography of the Works of John Bunyan. LC 76-28174. 1932. lib. bdg. 12.50 (ISBN 0-8414-4934-1). Folcroft.

Kelman, John. Road: A Study of John Bunyan's Pilgrim's Progress, 2 Vols. LC 77-113339. 1970. Repr. of 1912 ed. Set. 50.00x (ISBN 0-8046-1025-8, Pub. by Kennikat). Assoc Faculty Pr.

Knox, Edmund A. John Bunyan in Relation to His Times. 1928. lib. bdg. 12.50 (ISBN 0-8414-5598-8). Folcroft.

Lindsay, Jack. John Bunyan: Maker of Myths. LC 77-85138. 1969. Repr. of 1937 ed. 25.00x (ISBN 0-678-00523-0). Kelley.

--John Bunyan: Maker of Myths. LC 73-86039. 1969. Repr. of 1937 ed. 23.00x (ISBN 0-8046-0623-4, Pub. by Kennikat). Assoc Faculty Pr.

Mordell, Albert. Dante & Other Waning Classics. LC 68-8219. 1969. Repr. of 1915 ed. 18.50x (ISBN 0-8046-0322-7, Pub. by Kennikat). Assoc Faculty Pr.

Reason, Joyce. To Be a Pilgrim (John Bunyan) 1961. pap. 2.95 (ISBN 0-87508-625-X). Chr Lit.

Wharey, James B. Study of the Sources of Bunyan's Allegories(with Special Reference to Deguileville's Pilgrimage of Man. LC 68-59038. 136p. 1968. Repr. of 1904 ed. 15.00x (ISBN 0-87752-120-4). Gordian.

Zimmerman, Diane, ed. Pilgrim's Progress Guides. (LifeView: a Christian Approachto Literature Studies). 1977. pap. 0.85 student guide (ISBN 0-915134-32-2); tchrs. ed. 1.50 (ISBN 0-915134-36-5). Mott Media.

BURIAL

see also Catacombs; Cremation; Epitaphs; Funeral Rites and Ceremonies; Funeral Service; Sepulchral Monuments; Tombs

Bushnell, David L., Jr. Native Cemeteries & Forms of Burial East of the Mississippi. Repr. of 1920 ed. 29.00x (ISBN 0-403-03658-5). Scholarly.

Galley, Howard, ed. The Burial of the Dead: Rite One. 1977. pap. 0.95 (ISBN 0-8164-2152-8, HarpR). Har-Row.

--The Burial of the Dead: Rite Two. 1977. pap. 0.95 (ISBN 0-8164-2153-6, HarpR). Har-Row.

Hildeburn, Charles R. Baptisms & Burials From the Records of Christ Church, Philadelphia, 1709-1760. LC 81-86323. 231p. 1982. Repr. of 1893 ed. 15.00 (ISBN 0-8063-0979-2). Genealog Pub.

Morgan, Ernest. Dealing Creatively with Death: A Manual of Death Education & Simple Burial. 10th ed. 1984. pap. 6.50. Continent Assn Funeral.

Rush, Alfred C. Death & Burial in Christian Antiquity. 59.59 (ISBN 0-8490-0009-2). Gordon Pr.

Walker, George A. Gatherings from Graveyards Particularly Those of London: With a Concise History of the Modes of Interment among Different Nations, from the Earliest Periods. Kastenaum, Robert, ed. LC 76-19591. (Death & Dying Ser.). 1977. Repr. of 1977 ed. lib. bdg. 25.50x (ISBN 0-405-09586-4). Ayer Co Pubs.

Zelevansky, Paul. The Case for the Burial of Ancestors, Bk. 1. LC 80-54692. 1981. 27.00 (ISBN 0-9605610-3-X); pap. 18.00 (ISBN 0-9605610-2-1). Zartscorp.

BURIAL STATISTICS

see Registers of Births, Deaths, Marriages, etc.

BURMA–RELIGION

Ananda-Maitreya. The Religion of Burma & Other Papers. LC 77-87482. Repr. of 1929 ed. 31.50 (ISBN 0-404-16790-X). AMS Pr.

Luce, Gordon H. Old Burma-Early Pagan, 3 Vols. 1969. 120.00 set (ISBN 0-686-92654-4). J J Augustin.

Pe, Hla. Burma: Literature, Historiography, Scholarship, Language, Life & Buddhism. 224p. 1986. pap. text ed. 17.50 (ISBN 9971-988-00-3, Pub. by Inst Southeast Asian Stud). Gower Pub Co.

Ray, Nihar-Ranjan. Brahmanical Gods in Burma: A Chapter of Indian Art & Iconography. LC 77-87020. Repr. of 1932 ed. 16.50 (ISBN 0-404-16852-3). AMS Pr.

Spiro, Melford E. Burmese Supernaturalism. enlarged ed. LC 77-17280. pap. 84.00 (ISBN 0-317-42082-8, 2025708). Bks Demand UMI.

Trager, Frank N. & Koenig, William J. Burmese Sit-Tans, Seventeen Sixty-Four to Eighteen Twenty-Six: Records of Rural Life & Administration. (Association for Asian Studies Monographs: No. 36). 440p. 1979. 9.50x (ISBN 0-8165-0672-8). U of Ariz Pr.

BURNING OF THE DEAD

see Cremation

BURNT OFFERING

see Sacrifice

BURY ST. EDMUNDS ABBEY

Douglas, D. C., ed. Feudal Documents from the Abbey of Bury St. Edmunds. (British Academy, London, Records of the Social & Economic History of England & Wales: Vol. 8). pap. 45.00 (ISBN 0-8115-1248-7). Kraus Repr.

Jocelin De Brakelond. Chronica Jocelini De Brakelonda. LC 17-17164. (Camden Society, London. Publications, First Series: No. 13). Repr. of 1840 ed. 19.00 (ISBN 0-404-50113-3). AMS Pr.

Jocelin De Brakelonda. Chronica Jocelini De Brakelonda, De Rebus Gestis Samsonis. 1840. 19.00 (ISBN 0-384-27530-3). Johnson Repr.

McLachlan, Elizabeth P. The Scriptorium of Bury St. Edmunds in the Twelfth Century. LC 83-48695. (Theses from the Courtauld Institute of Art Ser.). (Illus.). 515p. 1984. lib. bdg. 60.00 (ISBN 0-8240-5983-2). Garland Pub.

BURYING GROUNDS

see Burial; Cemeteries

BUSHIDO

Nitobe, Inazo. Bushido: The Soul of Japan. LC 77-83070. 1969. Repr. of 1905 ed. 7.25 (ISBN 0-8048-0693-4). C E Tuttle.

Seward, Jack. Hara-Kiri: Japanese Ritual Suicide. LC 68-11973. 1968. pap. 7.95 (ISBN 0-8048-0231-9). C E Tuttle.

BUSINESS ETHICS

see also Success; Wealth, Ethics Of

Cumbler, John T. A Moral Response to Industrialism: The Lectures of Reverend Cook in Lynn, Massachusetts. LC 81-9338. (American Social History Ser.). 180p. 1982. 39.50 (ISBN 0-87395-558-7); pap. 10.95 (ISBN 0-87395-559-5). State U NY Pr.

Eckman, Lester. Jewish Tradition & Corporate Morality. LC 85-63013. 96p. 1986. 10.95. Shengold.

Jeremy, David. Business & Religion in Britain, Vol. 5. (Business and History Ser.). 220p. 1987. text ed. 60.00 (ISBN 0-566-05096-X). Gower Pub Co.

Jung, Leo & Levine, Aaron. Business Ethics in Jewish Law. LC 86-22889. Date not set. 27.50x (ISBN 0-88482-918-9). Hebrew Pub.

Morano, Roy W. The Protestant Challenge to Corporate America: Issues of Social Responsibility. Farmer, Richard, ed. LC 84-8514. (Research for Business Decisions Ser.: No. 69). 256p. 1984. 44.95 (ISBN 0-8357-1592-2). UMI Res Pr.

Natale, Samuel M. Ethics & Morals in Business. LC 83-3200. 183p. 1983. text ed. 19.95 (ISBN 0-89135-036-5, Pub. by REP Bks). Religious Educ.

Rush, Myron. Lord of the Marketplace. 192p. 1986. pap. 7.95 (ISBN 0-89693-278-8). Victor Bks.

Solowsky, Alan S. God & the American Corporation. (International Council for Excellence in Management Library). (Illus.). 1980. deluxe ed. 69.95 (ISBN 0-89266-266-2). Am Classical Coll Pr.

Stevens, Edward. Business Ethics. LC 79-91409. 248p. (Orig.). 1979. pap. 9.95 (ISBN 0-8091-2244-8). Paulist Pr.

Williams, Oliver F. & Houck, John M. Full Value: Cases in Christian Business Ethics. LC 78-3143. 1978. pap. 8.95x S.D. (ISBN 0-06-069515-3, RD 279, HarpR). Har-Row.

BUSINESSMEN–RELIGIOUS LIFE

Urwick, Lyndall. The Golden Book of Management: A Historical Record of the Life & Work of Seventy Pioneers. Chandler, Alfred D., ed. LC 79-7557. (History of Management Thought & Practice Ser.). (Illus.). 1980. Repr. of 1956 ed. lib. bdg. 21.00x (ISBN 0-405-12343-4). Ayer Co Pubs.

Wade, Marion E. & Kittler, Glenn D. The Lord Is My Counsel: A Businessman's Personal Experiences with the Bible. 192p. 1984. pap. 4.95 (ISBN 0-13-540658-7). P-H.

BUSY WORK

see Creative Activities and Seatwork

BUTLER, JOSEPH, BP. OF DURHAM, 1692-1752

Butler, Joseph. Five Sermons. Darwall, Stephen, ed. LC 83-12577. (HPC Philosophical Classics Ser.). 86p. 1983. pap. text ed. 3.45 (ISBN 0-915145-61-8). Hackett Pub.

Mossner, Ernest C. Bishop Butler & the Age of Reason. LC 69-13247. 1969. Repr. of 1936 ed. 15.00 (ISBN 0-405-08807-8, Pub. by Blom). Ayer Co Pubs.

BUTTON, THOMAS DE, BP. OF EXETER, d. 1307

Hale, William H. & Ellacombe, H. T., eds. Account of the Executors of Richard Bishop of London 1303, & of the Executors of Thomas Bishop of Exeter 1310. 1874. 27.00 (ISBN 0-384-20950-5). Johnson Repr.

BYLES, MATHER, 1707-1788

Eaton, Arthur W. The Famous Mather Byles, the Noted Boston Tory Preacher, Poet, & Wit. facsimile ed. LC 72-8697. (American Revolutionary Ser.). Repr. of 1914 ed. lib. bdg. 19.00x (ISBN 0-8398-0458-X). Irvington.

BYZANTINE ANTIQUITIES

see also Christian Antiquities

Harvard University Dumbarton Oaks Research Library. Dictionary Catalogue of the Byzantine Collection of the Dumbarton Oaks Research Library, 12 vols. 1975. Set. lib. bdg. 1390.00 (ISBN 0-8161-1150-2, Hall Library). G K Hall.

Matzulewitsch, Leonid. Byzantinische Antike: Studien auf Grund der Silbergefaesse der Ermitage. (Archaeologische Mitteilungen aus Russischen Sammlungen, Vol. 2). (Ger., Illus.). xi, 150p. 1974. Repr. of 1929 ed. 216.00 (ISBN 3-1100-2245-1). De Gruyter.

Raya, Joseph & Vinck, Jose D. Byzantine Altar Gospel. 350p. 1979. 87.50x (ISBN 0-911726-34-9). Alleluia Pr.

BYZANTINE ARCHITECTURE

see Architecture, Byzantine

BYZANTINE ART

see Art, Byzantine

BYZANTINE CHANTS

see Chants (Byzantine)

BYZANTINE EMPIRE–HISTORY

Agathias. Agathiae Myrinaei Historiarum Libri quinque. Keydell, Rudolfus, ed. (Corpus Fontium Historiae Byzantinae Ser. Berolinensis Vol. 2). 232p. (Lat). 1967. 40.40x (ISBN 3-11-001348-7). De Gruyter.

Bowman, Steven B. The Jews of Byzantium: Twelve Four to Fourteen Fifty-Three. LC 83-17230. (Judaic Studies Ser.). (Illus.). 400p. 1985. 42.50 (ISBN 0-8173-0198-4). U of Ala Pr.

Dvornik, Francis. Legendes de Constantin et de methode vues de Byzance. (Russian Ser: No. 12). 1969. Repr. of 1933 ed. 35.00 (ISBN 0-87569-009-2). Academic Intl.

Frendo, J. D., tr. from Lat. Agathias: The Histories. (Corpus Fontium Historiae Byzantinae: Vol. 2a). Tr. of Agathiae Myrinaei Historiarum libri quinque. iv, 170p. 1975. 51.00x (ISBN 3-11-003357-7). De Gruyter.

Gadolin, A. A. A Theory of History & Society, with Special Reference to the Chronographia of Michael Psellus: Eleventh Century Byzantium. 2nd ed. (Illus.). 244p. 1986. lib. bdg. 45.00x (ISBN 90-256-0906-6, Pub. by A M Hakkert). Coronet Bks.

Geankoplos, Deno J. Byzantine East & Latin West: Two Worlds of Christendom in Middle Ages & Renaissance. LC 76-20685. (Illus.). xii, 206p. 1976. Repr. of 1966 ed. 17.50 (ISBN 0-208-01615-5, Archon). Shoe String.

Gerostergios, Asterios. Justinian the Great: The Emperor & Saint. LC 82-82095. (Illus.). 312p. 1982. 15.95 (ISBN 0-914744-58-5); pap. 11.95 (ISBN 0-914744-59-3). Inst Byzantine.
Gruhn, Albert. Die Byzantinische Politik Zur der Zeit Kreuzzuege. 1904. 12.50 (ISBN 0-8337-1479-1). B Franklin.
Hussey, J. M. The Orthodox Church in the Byzantine Empire. (History of the Christian Church Ser.). 320p. 1986. 59.00x (ISBN 0-19-826901-3). Oxford U Pr.
Nicol, D. M. Church & Society in the Last Centuries of Byzantium. LC 78-72092. (The Birkbeck Lectures, 1977). 1979. 32.50 (ISBN 0-521-22438-1). Cambridge U Pr.
Norden, Walter. Papsttum Und Byzanz: Das Problem Ihrer Wiedervereinigung Bis Zum Untergange Des Byzantinischen Reichs (1453) 1903. 40.50 (ISBN 0-8337-2571-8). B Franklin.
Oeconomos, Lysimaque. La Vie Religieuse Dans l'Empire Byzantin Au Temps Des Comnenes et Des Anges. LC 77-184705. (Research & Source Works Ser.). (Fr.). 252p. 1972. Repr. of 1918 ed. lib. bdg. 23.50 (ISBN 0-8337-2602-1). B Franklin.
Ramsay, W. M. & Bell, Gertrude L. The Thousand & One Churches. (Illus.). xvi, 580p. 1985. Repr. of 1905 ed. lib. bdg. 80.00x (ISBN 0-89241-121-X). Caratzas.
Regel, Vasilii E., ed. Analecta Byzantino-Russica. 1964. Repr. of 1891 ed. 23.50 (ISBN 0-8337-2919-5). B Franklin.
Sharf, Andrew. Byzantium Jewry from Justinian to the Fourth Crusade. (Littman Library of Jewish Civilization). (Illus.). 1971. 24.00x (ISBN 0-19-710021-X). Oxford U Pr.
Tsakonas, Demetrios. A Man Sent by God: The Life of Patriarch Athenagoras of Constantinople. Angeloglou, George, tr. from Greek. LC 77-77699. (Illus.). 99p. 1977. pap. 3.95 (ISBN 0-916586-07-3). Holy Cross Orthodox.
Van Dieten, Ioannes, ed. Nicetae Choniatae Historiae, 2 vols. (Corpus Fontium Historiae Byzantinae Vol. XI: Series Berolinensis). 1975. 242.00x (ISBN 3-11-004528-1). De Gruyter.
Van Dieten, Jan-Louis. Niketas Choniates: Erlaeuterungen Zu Den Reden und Briefen Nebst Einer Biographie. (Supplementa Byzantina, 2). 1971. 43.20x (ISBN 3-11-002290-7). De Gruyter.

C

CABALA

Abelson, Joshua. Jewish Mysticism: An Introduction to Kabbalah. LC 80-54593. (The Judaic Studies Library: SHP 7). 192p. 1981. pap. 6.95 (ISBN 0-87203-096-2). Hermon.
Ashlag, Yehuda. An Entrance to the Tree of Life of Rabbi Isaac Luria. Berg, Philip S., ed. 1977. 13.95 (ISBN 0-943688-05-1); pap. 10.95 (ISBN 0-943688-35-3). Res Ctr Kabbalah.
--Etz Chaim: Hebrew Text, 2 vols. condensed ed. 40.00 (ISBN 0-943688-18-3). Res Ctr Kabbalah.
--Ten Luminous Emanations, Vol. 1. 1970. 11.95 (ISBN 0-943688-08-6); pap. 9.95 (ISBN 0-943688-29-9). Res Ctr Kabbalah.
--Ten Luminous Emanations, Vol. 2. Berg, Philip S., ed. 1972. 11.95 (ISBN 0-943688-09-4); pap. 9.95 (ISBN 0-943688-25-6). Res Ctr Kabbalah.
Banes, Daniel. Shakespeare, Shylock & Kabbalah. LC 78-58912. 1978. 9.99 (ISBN 0-686-10284-3); pap. 3.60 (ISBN 0-686-10285-1). Malcolm Hse.
Berg, Philip S. The Kabbalah Connection. 224p. 1983. 12.95 (ISBN 0-943688-02-7); pap. 9.95 (ISBN 0-943688-03-5). Res Ctr Kabbalah.
--Kabbalah for the Layman. (Span.). 224p. 1986. 12.95 (ISBN 0-943688-43-4); pap. 9.95 (ISBN 0-943688-44-2). Res Ctr Kabbalah.
--Kabbalah for the Layman II. 224p. 1987. 14.95 (ISBN 0-943688-24-8); pap. 9.95 (ISBN 0-943688-26-4). Res Ctr Kabbalah.
--Kabbalah for the Layman III. 1987. 14.95 (ISBN 0-943688-69-8); pap. 9.95 (ISBN 0-943688-70-1). Res Ctr Kabbalah.
--Power of the Aleph Beth, Vol. 1. 288p. 1986. 14.95 (ISBN 0-943688-11-6); pap. 9.95 (ISBN 0-943688-10-8). Res Ctr Kabbalah.
Berg, Phillip S. Power of the Aleph Beth, Vol. II. 1987. 14.95 (ISBN 0-943688-56-6); pap. 9.95 (ISBN 0-943688-57-4). Res Ctr Kabbalah.
Bernstein, Henrietta. Cabalah Primer: Introduction to English-Hebrew Cabalah. 192p. 1984. pap. 9.95 (ISBN 0-87516-526-5). De Vorss.
Bischoff, Erich. The Kabbala: An Introduction to Jewish Mysticism & Secret Doctrine. LC 84-52262. 96p. 1985. pap. 5.95 (ISBN 0-87728-564-0). Weiser.
Bloom, Harold. Kabbalah & Criticism. LC 75-12820. 100p. 1975. 8.95 (ISBN 0-8264-0124-4). Continuum.
--Kabbalah & Criticism. LC 82-4674. 126p. 1983. pap. 7.95 (ISBN 0-8245-0487-9). Crossroad NY.
Book Raziel. (Heb). 7.50 (ISBN 0-87559-105-1). Shalom.
Butler, W. E. Magic & the Qabbalah. 1972. pap. 8.95 (ISBN 0-85030-155-6). Weiser.
Cleghorn, Spencer. Kabbalistic Discoveries into Hebrew & Aegyptian Mysteries, 2 Vols. (Illus.). 121p. 1983. 177.75 (ISBN 0-89920-057-5). Am Inst Psych.
Cordavero, Moses. Or Nerev: Hebrew Text. 1980. 10.00 (ISBN 0-943688-17-5). Res Ctr Kabbalah.
Cordovero, Moses. The Palm Tree of Deborah. Jacobs, Louis, tr. from Heb. LC 80-54594. (The Judaic Studies Library: No. SPH8). 133p. 1981. pap. 7.95 (ISBN 0-87203-097-0). Hermon.
Crowley, Aleister. Seven Seven Seven: A Study of the Kabbalah. 1973. lib. bdg. 80.00 (ISBN 0-87968-105-5). Krishna Pr.
Dale, Rodney, ed. Kabbalah Decoded. Sassoon, George, tr. 240p. 1978. 55.00 (ISBN 0-7156-1289-1, Pub. by Duckworth London); pap. 17.00 (ISBN 0-7156-1374-X). Longwood Pub Group.
Dan, Joseph & Kiener, Ronald C., eds. The Early Kabbalah. (Classics of Western Spirituality Ser.: Vol. 51). 224p. 1986. 13.95 (ISBN 0-8091-0373-7); pap. 10.95 (ISBN 0-8091-2769-5). Paulist Pr.
Davies, Ann. This Is Truth about the Self. 3rd ed. 1984. 4.50 (ISBN 0-938002-03-1). Builders of Adytum.
Eisen, William. The English Cabalah, 2 vols, Vol. 1. (Illus.). 608p. 1980. text ed. 16.95 (ISBN 0-87516-390-4). De Vorss.
--The English Cabalah Volume 2: The Mysteries of Phi. LC 79-57053. (Agashan Teachings Ser.). 652p. 1982. 26.95 (ISBN 0-87516-459-5). De Vorss.
--The Essence of the Cabalah. (Illus.). 480p. 1984. 22.95 (ISBN 0-87516-524-9). De Vorss.
Fortune, Dion. Mystical Qabalah. 311p. 1984. 8.95 (ISBN 0-87728-596-9). Weiser.
Franck, Adolphe. The Kabbalah. 1979. pap. 5.95 (ISBN 0-8065-0708-X). Citadel Pr.
Gamache, H. Eighth, Ninth & Tenth Books of Moses. 4.95x (ISBN 0-685-21888-0). Wehman.
Gaster, M. The Origin of the Kabbala. 1976. lib. bdg. 69.95 (ISBN 0-8490-2386-6). Gordon Pr.
Gewurz, Elias. Hidden Treasures of the Ancient Qabalah. 1922. 4.50 (ISBN 0-911662-31-6). Yoga.
--Mysteries of the Qabalah. 1922. 4.50 (ISBN 0-911662-32-4). Yoga.
Godwin, David. Godwin's Practical Encyclopedia of Cabalistic Magick. 2nd, rev. & expanded ed. Weschcke, Carl L., ed. (Sourcebook Ser.). 500p. 1987. pap. 15.00 (ISBN 0-87542-292-6, L-292). Llewellyn Pubns.
Gonzalez-Wippler, Migene. A Kabbalah for the Modern World. 2nd, rev. & expanded ed. LC 83-80133. (New Age Ser.). 250p. 1987. pap. 9.95 (ISBN 0-87542-294-2). Llewellyn Pubns.
Gray, William G. Concepts of Qabalah. LC 82-62848. (The Sangreal Sodality Ser.: Vol.3). 384p. 1984. pap. 9.95 (ISBN 0-87728-561-6). Weiser.
Hakdamot: Hebrew Text of Entrance to the Tree of Life. 1970. 10.00 (ISBN 0-943688-19-1). Res Ctr Kabbalah.
Halevi, Z'ev B. The Work of the Kabbalist. (Illus.). 223p. (Orig.). 1985. pap. 9.95 (ISBN 0-87728-637-X). Weiser.
Halevi, Z'ev Ben Shimon. Kabbalah & Psychology. (Illus.). 260p. (Orig.). 1986. pap. 12.50 (ISBN 0-87728-671-X). Weiser.
--School of Kabbalah. LC 85-50635. (Illus.). 288p. (Orig.). 1985. pap. 8.95 (ISBN 0-87728-648-5). Weiser.
--The Way of the Kabbalah. 1976. pap. 6.50 (ISBN 0-87728-305-2). Weiser.
Highfield, A. C. Book of Celestial Images: Angelic & Godform Images in Ritual Magic. LC 86-16209. 192p. 1986. lib. bdg. 19.95 (ISBN 0-8095-7004-1). Borgo Pr.
Hoffman, Edward. The Way of Splendor: Jewish Mysticism & Modern Psychology. LC 81-50967. (Illus.). 224p. 1981. pap. 10.95 (ISBN 0-87773-210-8). Shambhala Pubns.
Idel, Moshe. The Mystical Experience in Abraham Abulafia. (SUNY Series in Judaica: Hermeneutics, Mysticism & Religion). 240p. 1987. text ed. 39.50x (ISBN 0-88706-552-X); pap. 12.95x (ISBN 0-88706-553-8). State U NY Pr.
Jellinek, Adolph. Beitrage zur Geschichte der Kabbala. Katz, Steven, ed. LC 79-7138. (Jewish Philosophy, Mysticism, & History of Ideas Ser.). 1980. Repr. of 1852 ed. lib. bdg. 16.00x (ISBN 0-405-12264-0). Ayer Co Pubs.
Kaplan, Aryeh. Meditation & Kabbalah. LC 81-70150. 368p. (Orig.). 1985. pap. 12.50 (ISBN 0-87728-616-7). Weiser.
Knight, Gareth. Practical Guide to Qabalistic Symbolism. 1978. 22.50 (ISBN 0-87728-397-4). Weiser.
Krakovsky, Levi. Kabbalah: The Light of Redemption. 1970. 14.95 (ISBN 0-943688-06-X); pap. 11.95 (ISBN 0-943688-32-9). Res Ctr Kabbalah.
--The Omnipotent Light Revealed: Wisdom of the Kabbalah. 4.00 (ISBN 0-686-13335-8). Yesod Pubs.
Lancer, Bob. Inner Freedom Through Qabala. (Illus.). 134p. (Orig.). 1986. pap. 6.95 (ISBN 0-917913-02-7). Limitless Light.
Levi, Eliphas. The Mysteries of the Qabalah, or the Occult Agreement of the Two Testaments. (Studies in Hermetic Tradition Ser.: Vol. 2). (Illus.). 1974. pap. 12.95 (ISBN 0-85030-274-9). Weiser.
Luria. Kitve Ari: Hebrew Text, 17 vols. 1985. 340.00 set (ISBN 0-943688-16-7); 25.00 ea. Res Ctr Kabbalah.
Luzzatto, Moses. General Principles of Kabbalah. 288p. 1970. 13.75 (ISBN 0-943688-07-8); pap. 11.95 (ISBN 0-943688-31-0). Res Ctr Kabbalah.
Mathers, S. L. The Kabbalah Unveiled. LC 71-16504. 373p. (Orig.). 1983. pap. 12.50 (ISBN 0-87728-557-8). Weiser.
Myer, Isaac. Qabbalah: The Philosophical Writings of Solomon Ben Yehudah Ibn Gabirol. 69.95 (ISBN 0-8490-0922-7). Gordon Pr.
Ophiel. The Art & Practice of Caballa Magic. 1977. pap. 8.95 (ISBN 0-87728-303-6). Weiser.
Papus. The Qabalah. 1977. pap. 12.95 (ISBN 0-85030-340-0). Weiser.
Pick, Bernhard. The Cabala. LC 13-26188. 115p. 1974. pap. 4.95 (ISBN 0-87548-199-X). Open Court.
Ponce, Charles. Kabbalah. LC 78-7385. (Illus.). 1978. pap. 6.50 (ISBN 0-8356-0510-8, Quest). Theos Pub Hse.
Reuchlin, Johann. De Arte Cabbalistica. Goodman, Martin, tr. LC 77-86231. (Bilingual Editions of Classics in Philosophy & Science Ser.: No. 1). 1983. 20.00 (ISBN 0-913870-56-0). Abaris Bks.
Richardson, Alan. An Introduction to the Mystical Qabalah. (Paths to Inner Power Ser). 1974. pap. 3.50 (ISBN 0-85030-264-1). Weiser.
Rowlands, Henry. Mona Antiqua Restaurata. Feldman, Burton & Richardson, Robert D., eds. LC 78-60894. (Myth & Romanticism Ser.: Vol. 21). 399p. 1979. lib. bdg. 80.00 (ISBN 0-8240-3570-4). Garland Pub.
Sassoon, George. The Kabbalah Decoded. Dale, Rodney, ed. 240p. 1978. pap. 9.95 (ISBN 0-7156-1289-1). US Games Syst.
Schaya, Leo. The Universal Meaning of the Kabbalah. 1972. 6.95 (ISBN 0-8216-0167-9). Univ Bks.
Scholem, Gershom. Kabbalah. 1978. pap. 10.95 (ISBN 0-452-00791-7, Mer). NAL.
--On the Kabbalah & Its Symbolism. LC 65-11575. 1969. pap. 6.95 (ISBN 0-8052-0235-8). Schocken.
--Origins of the Kabbalah. Werblowsky, R. J., ed. Arkush, Allan, tr. 500p. 1987. 47.50 (ISBN 0-691-07314-7). Princeton U Pr.
--Sabbatai Sevi: The Mystical Messiah. Werblowski, R. Zwi, tr. from Hebrew. LC 75-166389. (Bollingen Series, Vol. 93). (Illus.). 1040p. 1973. 71.00x (ISBN 0-691-09916-2); pap. 22.50x (ISBN 0-691-01809-X). Princeton U Pr.
Scholem, Gershom, ed. Zohar-The Book of Splendor: Basic Readings from the Kabbalah. LC 63-11040. 1963. pap. 3.95 (ISBN 0-8052-0045-2). Schocken.
Schutz, Albert L. Call Adonoi: Manual of Practical Cabalah & Gestalt Mysticism. LC 80-50264. (Illus.). 200p. (Orig.). 1980. 11.95 (ISBN 0-936596-01-5); pap. 8.95 (ISBN 0-936596-00-7). Quantal.
--Exodus-Exodus, Cabalistic Bible: Part I, Slavery & the Coming of Moses. (Orig.). 1984. pap. 6.95 (ISBN 0-936596-10-4). Quantal.
Schweid, ELiezer. Judaism & Mysticism According to Gershom Scholem: A Critical Analysis & Programmatic Discussion. Weiner, David A., tr. (Reprints & Translations). 1985. 22.95 (ISBN 0-89130-982-9, 00-07-09); pap. 16.95 (ISBN 0-89130-887-3). Scholars Pr Ga.
Sheinkin, David. The Path of the Kabbalah: An Introduction to the Living Jewish Spiritual Tradition. (Patterns of World Spirituality Ser.). 224p. 1986. pap. 9.95 (ISBN 0-913757-69-1, Pub. by New Era Bks). Paragon Hse.
Spector, Sheila A. Jewish Mysticism: An Annotated Bibliography on the Kabbalah in English. LC 83-48224. (Reference Library of Social Science Ser.). 1984. lib. bdg. 45.00 (ISBN 0-8240-9042-X). Garland Pub.
Straughn, R. A. The Realization of Neter Nu: A Kabalistical Guide to the Realization of Self. 1975. pap. 8.00 (ISBN 0-917650-01-8). Maat Pub.
Suares, Carlo. The Qabala Trilogy. Stuart, Micheline & Stuart, Vincent, trs. from Fr. LC 85-8179. 565p. 1985. pap. 17.95 (ISBN 0-87773-337-6, 74220-6). Shambhala Pubns.
Waite, Arthur E. The Holy Kabbalah. 636p. 1976. pap. 9.95 (ISBN 0-8065-0522-2). Citadel Pr.
--Holy Kabbalah: A Study of the Secret Tradition in Israel. 1960. 20.00 (ISBN 0-8216-0025-7). Univ Bks.
Z'Ev ben Shimon Halevi. Kabbalah: Tradition of Hidden Knowledge. (Art & Imagination Ser.). (Illus.). 1980. pap. 10.95 (ISBN 0-500-81023-0). Thames Hudson.

CABRINI, FRANCES XAVIER, SAINT, 1850-1917

Daughters of St. Paul. Mother Cabrini. 1977. 3.50 (ISBN 0-8198-0440-1); pap. 2.50 (ISBN 0-8198-0441-X). Dghtrs St Paul.
Sullivan, Mary L. Mother Cabrini: Italian Immigrant of the Century. 250p. 1987. 19.50 (ISBN 0-934733-06-6). Ctr Migration.

CAIN

Bretscher, Paul G. Cain, Come Home! LC 76-1810. (Illus.). 144p. 1976. pap. text ed. 4.25 (ISBN 0-915644-05-3). Clayton Pub Hse.
Eichhorn, David M. Cain: Son of the Serpent. (Limited Editions Reprints). 160p. 1985. 14.95 (ISBN 0-940646-24-2); pap. 8.95 (ISBN 0-940646-19-6). Rossel Bks.

CAIRO GENIZAH

Schecter, Solomon. Documents of Jewish Sectaries, 2 Vols. in 1. rev. ed. (Library of Biblical Studies Ser). (Illus.). 1970. 35.00 (ISBN 0-87068-016-1). Ktav.

CALENDAR

see also Church Calendar; Days; Time

Bond, John J. Handy-Book of Rules & Tables for Verifying Dates with the Christian Era. LC 66-29473. 1966. Repr. of 1889 ed. 10.00x (ISBN 0-8462-1795-3). Russell.
Brindze, Ruth. Story of Our Calendar. (Illus.). 1949. 9.95 (ISBN 0-8149-0278-2). Vanguard.
Kennedy, J. M. The Pater Calendar. LC 73-606. 1973. lib. bdg. 12.50 (ISBN 0-8414-1531-5). Folcroft.
Nuttall, Zelia. Fundamental Principles of Old & New World Civilization. (HU PMP Ser.). 1901. 51.00 (ISBN 0-527-01190-8). Kraus Repr.

CALENDAR, ECCLESIASTICAL

see Church Calendar

CALENDAR, JEWISH

see also Chronology, Jewish

Burnaby, Sherrard B. Elements of the Jewish Muhammadan Calendars. 1976. lib. bdg. 59.95 (ISBN 0-8490-1757-2). Gordon Pr.
Langdon, Stephen H. Babylonian Menologies & the Semitic Calendars. LC 78-72744. (Ancient Mesopotamian Texts & Studies). Repr. of 1935 ed. 21.50 (ISBN 0-404-18192-9). AMS Pr.

CALENDAR REFORM

Boudreau, Amy. Story of the Christian Year. 1971. 4.50 (ISBN 0-685-27196-X). Claitors.
Makris, Kallistos. The God-Inspired Orthodox Julian Calendar VS. the False Gregorian Papal Calendar. Vlesmas, Jerry, tr. from Hellenic. 118p. (Orig.). 1971. pap. 3.25x (ISBN 0-938366-36-X). Orthodox Chr.

CALIPHATE

Bakshi, S. R. Gandhi & Khilafat. 1985. 18.00x (ISBN 0-8364-1491-8, Pub. by Gitanjali Prakashan). South Asia Bks.
Chejne, A. Succession to the Rule in Islam. 1960. 5.30x (ISBN 0-87902-158-6). Orientalia.
Dixon, Abd'al-Ameer'Abd. The Umayyad Caliphate: A Political Study. 222p. 1971. 95.00x (ISBN 0-317-39182-8, Pub. by Luzac & Co Ltd). State Mutual Bk.
Husain, S. A. Glorious Caliphate. 15.50 (ISBN 0-686-18626-5). Kazi Pubns.
Kennedy, Hugh. The Early Abbasid Caliphate: A Political History. 238p. 1981. 28.50x (ISBN 0-389-20018-2, 06791). B&N Imports.
Lewis, Wyndham. The Caliph's Design. (Illus.). 188p. (Orig.). 1986. 20.00 (ISBN 0-87685-665-2); pap. 9.50 (ISBN 0-87685-664-4); deluxe ed. 30.00 (ISBN 0-87685-666-0). Black Sparrow.
Muir, W. The Caliphate: Its Rise, Decline & Fall. 624p. 1984. Repr. of 1891 ed. 90.00x (ISBN 0-317-39168-2, Pub. by Luzac & Co Ltd). State Mutual Bk.
Muir, William. Annals of the Early Caliphate from Original Sources. 1977. lib. bdg. 59.95 (ISBN 0-8490-1434-4). Gordon Pr.
Sattar, M. A. It Removes the Misconceptions about Caliphs' Caliphate. 416p. 1985. pap. 19.00 (ISBN 0-941724-36-0). Islamic Seminary.
Siddiqi, Amir H. Caliphate & Kingship in Mediaeval Persia. LC 77-10621. (Studies in Islamic History: No. 14). 112p. 1978. Repr. of 1937 ed. lib. bdg. 17.50x (ISBN 0-87991-463-7). Porcupine Pr.

CALLING

see Vocation

CALVIN, JEAN, 1509-1564

Armstrong, Brian G. Calvinism & the Amyraut Heresy: Protestant Scholasticism & Humanism in Seventeenth-Century France. LC 72-84949. (Illus.). 350p. 1969. 30.00 (ISBN 0-299-05490-X). U of Wis Pr.

Armstrong, William P., ed. Calvin & the Reformation: Four Studies. (Twin Brooks Ser.). 1980. pap. 6.95 (ISBN 0-8010-2901-5). Baker Bk.

Banks, Charles W. The Life & Times of John Calvin: With an Earnest Appeal for the Adoption of Open-Air Preaching. LC 83-45599. Date not set. Repr. of 1891 ed. 21.50 (ISBN 0-404-19867-8). Ams Pr.

Blackburn, William W. Young Calvin in Paris: Or, the Scholar & the Cripple. LC 83-45602. Date not set. Repr. of 1868 ed. 30.00 (ISBN 0-404-19869-4). AMS Pr.

Calvin, John. The Best of John Calvin. Dunn, Samuel, compiled by. (Best Ser.). 416p. 1981. pap. 5.95 (ISBN 0-8010-2467-6). Baker Bk.

--Calvin's Letters. pap. 5.95 (ISBN 0-85151-323-9). Banner of Truth.

--Concerning Scandals. Fraser, John W., tr. LC 78-8675. Repr. of 1978 ed. 24.90 (ISBN 0-8357-9126-2, 2012802). Bks Demand UMI.

Cuthbertson, David. A Tragedy of the Reformation: Being the Authentic Narrative of the History & Burning of the "Christianismi Restitution", 1953, with a Succinct Account of the Theological Controversy Between Michael Servetus, Its Author, & the Reformer, John Calvin. LC 83-45608. Date not set. Repr. of 1912 ed. 20.00 (ISBN 0-404-19826-0). AMS Pr.

Davies, Alfred T. John Calvin: Many Sided Genius. LC 83-45609. Date not set. Repr. of 1947 ed. 18.50 (ISBN 0-404-19827-9). AMS Pr.

De Beze, Theodore. A Discourse Conteyning the Life & Death of John Calvin. LC 77-38153. (English Experience Ser.: No. 433). 80p. 1972. Repr. of 1564 ed. 11.50 (ISBN 90-221-0433-8). Walter J Johnson.

Fillingham, Patricia. John Calvin. (Illus.). 42p. 1983. pap. 5.00 (ISBN 0-942292-04-9). Warthog Pr.

Forstman, H. Jackson. Word & Spirit: Calvin's Doctrine of Biblical Authority. 1962. 20.00x (ISBN 0-8047-0070-2). Stanford U Pr.

Hansen, William P. & Haney, John, eds. Calvin. (World's Leaders--Past & Present Ser.). (Illus.). 112p. 1987. lib. bdg. 16.95 (ISBN 0-87754-515-4). Chelsea Hse.

Harkness, Georgia E. John Calvin: The Man & His Ethics. 1977. lib. bdg. 59.95 (ISBN 0-8490-2106-5). Gordon Pr.

--John Calvin: The Man & His Ethics. LC 83-45612. Date not set. Repr. of 1931 ed. 32.50 (ISBN 0-404-19830-9). AMS Pr.

Haroutunian, Joseph, ed. Calvin: Commentaries. LC 58-5060. (Library of Christian Classics). 410p. 1979. softcover 8.95 (ISBN 0-664-24160-3). Westminster.

Helm, Paul. Calvin & the Calvinists. 84p. (Orig.). 1982. pap. 5.95 (ISBN 0-85151-344-1). Banner of Truth.

Henderson, Henry F. Calvin in His Letters. 59.95 (ISBN 0-87968-810-6). Gordon Pr.

Henry, Paul E. The Life & Times of John Calvin, 2 vols. Stebbing, Henry, tr. from Ger. LC 83-45613. Date not set. Repr. of 1851 ed. Set. 95.00 (ISBN 0-404-19831-7). AMS Pr.

Hunt, Robert N. Calvin. LC 83-45617. Date not set. Repr. of 1933 ed. 37.50 (ISBN 0-404-19835-X). AMS Pr.

Hunter, Adam M. The Teaching of Calvin: A Modern Interpretation. LC 83-45618. Date not set. Repr. of 1950 ed. 37.50 (ISBN 0-404-19836-8). AMS Pr.

Jansen, J. F. Calvin's "Doctrine of the Work of Christ". 120p. 1956. 10.00 (ISBN 0-227-67425-1). Attic Pr.

McCrie, Thomas. The Early Years of John Calvin: A Fragment, 1509-1536. LC 83-45622. Date not set. Repr. of 1880 ed. 28.00 (ISBN 0-404-19840-6). AMS Pr.

McKim, Donald K. Readings in Calvin's Theology. 304p. (Orig.). 1984. pap. 15.95 (ISBN 0-8010-6150-4). Baker Bk.

Mackinnon, James. Calvin & the Reformation. LC 83-45648. Date not set. Repr. of 1936 ed. 37.50 (ISBN 0-404-19841-4). AMS Pr.

McNeill, John T., ed. Calvin: Institutes of the Christian Religion, 2 vols. LC 60-5379. (Library of Christian Classics). 1812p. 1960. Set. 34.95 (ISBN 0-664-22028-2). Westminster.

Miles, Robert W. That Frenchman, John Calvin. LC 83-45625. Date not set. Repr. of 1939 ed. 29.00 (ISBN 0-404-19843-0). AMS Pr.

Palm, Franklin C. Calvinisim & the Religious Wars. LC 78-80579. 1971. Repr. 24.50x (ISBN 0-86527-020-1). Fertig.

Parker, T. H. John Calvin. Jenkins, Simon, ed. 240p. 1987. pap. 7.95 (ISBN 0-7459-1219-2). Lion USA.

--John Calvin: A Biography. LC 75-33302. (Illus.). 208p. 1976. 10.95 (ISBN 0-664-20810-X). Westminster.

Peterson, Robert A. Calvin's Doctrine of the Atonement. 1983. pap. 4.95 (ISBN 0-87552-369-2). Presby & Reformed.

Potter, G. R. & Greengrass, M., eds. John Calvin. LC 82-23088. (Documents of Modern History Ser.). 180p. 1983. 20.00x (ISBN 0-312-44277-7). St Martin.

Quistorp, Heinrich. Calvin's Doctrine of the Last Things. John Knox.

--Calvin's Doctrine of the Last Things. Knight, Harold, tr. LC 83-45629. Date not set. Repr. of 1955 ed. 27.50 (ISBN 0-404-19846-5). AMS Pr.

Reid, J. K., ed. Calvin: Theological Treatises. LC 54-9956. (Library of Christian Classics). 352p. 1978. softcover 8.95 (ISBN 0-664-24156-5). Westminster.

Reyburn, Hugh Y. John Calvin: His Life, Letters & Work. LC 83-45630. Date not set. Repr. of 1914 ed. 45.00 (ISBN 0-404-19847-3). AMS Pr.

Rilliet, Albert. Calvin & Servetus: The Reformer's Share in the Trial of Michael Servetus Historically Ascertained. Tweedie, W. K., tr. from Fr. LC 83-45631. Date not set. Repr. of 1846 ed. 31.50 (ISBN 0-404-19848-1). AMS Pr.

Rolston, Holmes, III. John Calvin Vs. the Westminster Confession. LC 75-37422. (Orig.). 1972. pap. 4.95 (ISBN 0-8042-0488-8). John Knox.

Selinger, Suzanne. Calvin Against Himself: An Inquiry in Intellectual History. LC 83-21330. 238p. 1984. 29.50 (ISBN 0-208-01948-0, Archon). Shoe String.

Shepherd, Victor A. The Nature & Function of Faith in the Theology of John Calvin. LC 82-24899. vii, 248p. 1983. pap. 17.45 (ISBN 0-86554-066-7, P07). Mercer Univ Pr.

--The Nature & Function of Faith in the Theology of John Calvin. (Dissertation Ser.: No. 2). viii, 248p. 1982. pap. 17.45 (ISBN 0-86554-066-7). NABPR.

Smyth, Thomas. Calvin & His Enemies: A Memoir of the Life, Character & Principles of Calvin. rev. & enl. ed. LC 83-45632. Date not set. Repr. of 1909 ed. 28.00 (ISBN 0-404-19849-X). AMS Pr.

Stickelberger, E. Calvin. Gelser, David, tr. 174p. 1977. Repr. of 1959 ed. 12.95 (ISBN 0-227-67424-3). Attic Pr.

Torrance, Thomas F. Calvin's Doctrine of Man. LC 77-5615. 1977. Repr. lib. bdg. 22.50x (ISBN 0-8371-9639-6, TOCD). Greenwood.

Van Halsema, Thea B. This Was John Calvin. (Christian Biography Ser.). 184p. 1981. pap. 4.95 (ISBN 0-8010-9283-3). Baker Bk.

Walker, Williston. John Calvin: The Organiser of Reformed Protestantism, 1509-1564. Repr. of 1906 ed. 27.50 (ISBN 0-404-06807-3). AMS Pr.

Warfield, Benjamin B. Calvin & Augustine. 12.95 (ISBN 0-8010-9585-9). Baker Bk.

--Calvin & Augustine. 1954. 12.95 (ISBN 0-87552-526-1). Presby & Reformed.

Zweig, Stefan. The Right to Heresay-Castellio Against Calvin. 2nd ed. LC 84-40514. (History & Biography Ser.). (Illus.). 300p. 1985. pap. cancelled (ISBN 0-910129-27-4). Wiener Pub Inc.

CALVINISM

see also Antinomianism; Arminianism; Congregationalism; Covenants (Theology); Mercersburg Theology; New England Theology; Perseverance (Theology); Predestination; Presbyterianism; Puritans

Adams, Jay E. Counseling & the Five Points of Calvinism. 1981. pap. 0.75 (ISBN 0-87552-072-3). Presby & Reformed.

Armstrong, Brian G. Calvinism & the Amyraut Heresy: Protestant Scholasticism & Humanism in Seventeenth-Century France. LC 72-84949. (Illus.). 350p. 1969. 30.00 (ISBN 0-299-05490-X). U of Wis Pr.

Balke, William. Calvin & the Anabaptist Radicals. Heynen, William, tr. LC 81-12438. pap. 87.50 (ISBN 0-317-30132-2, 2025315). Bks Demand UMI.

Battles, Ford L. & Walchenbach, John. An Analysis of "The Institute of the Christian Religion" of John Calvin. LC 79-57385. 1980. pap. 12.95 (ISBN 0-8010-0766-6). Baker Bk.

Boesak, Allan A. Black & Reformed: Apartheid, Liberation, & the Calvinist Tradition. LC 84-7212. 192p. (Orig.). 1984. pap. 8.95 (ISBN 0-88344-148-9). Orbis Bks.

Boulger, James D. The Calvinistic Temper in English Poetry. (De Proprietatibus Litterarum, Ser. Major: No. 21). 1980. text ed. 71.00x (ISBN 90-279-7575-2). Mouton.

Bratt, James D. Dutch Calvinism in Modern America: A History of a Conservative Subculture. (Illus.). 368p. (Orig.). 1984. pap. 13.95 (ISBN 0-8028-0009-2). Eerdmans.

Calvin, Jean. Letters, Compiled from the Original Manuscripts & Edited with Historical Notes, 4 vols. Bonnet, Jules, ed. Gilchrist, M. R. & Constable, David, trs. from Lat. & Fr. LC 70-185936. 1973. Repr. of 1858 ed. Set. 110.00 (ISBN 0-8337-4021-0). B Franklin.

Calvin, John. Calvin's Commentaries, 22 vols. 1979. Repr. Set. 495.00 (ISBN 0-8010-2440-4). Baker Bk.

--Calvin's Selected Works: Tracts & Letters, 7 vols. Beveridge, Henry & Bonnet, Jules, eds. 1983. Repr. 99.95 (ISBN 0-8010-2493-5). Baker Bk.

--John Calvin's Treatises Against the Anabaptists & Against the Libertines. Farley, Benjamin W., tr. 360p. (Orig.). 1982. pap. 16.95 (ISBN 0-8010-2476-5). Baker Bk.

Calvinistic Paths Retraced. 240p. 1985. pap. 7.95 (ISBN 0-914012-25-8, Pub. by Bibl Evang Pr). Sword of Lord.

Crew, P. Mack. Calvinist Preaching & Iconoclasm in the Netherlands, 1544-1569. LC 77-77013. (Studies in Early Modern History). 1978. 37.50 (ISBN 0-521-21739-3). Cambridge U Pr.

Dakin, Arthur. Calvinism. LC 72-153211. 1971. Repr. of 1940 ed. 23.00x (ISBN 0-8046-1521-7, Pub. by Kennikat). Assoc Faculty Pr.

Gerrish, Brian, ed. Reformatio Perennis: Essays on Calvin & the Reformation in Honor of Ford Lewis Battles. (Pittsburgh Theological Monograph Ser.: No. 32). 1981. pap. 15.00 (ISBN 0-915138-41-7). Pickwick.

Hart, Hendrik & Van Der Hoeven, Johan, eds. Rationality in the Calvinian Tradition. LC 83-19672. (Christian Studies Today). 420p. (Orig.). 1984. lib. bdg. 32.25 (ISBN 0-8191-3616-6); pap. text ed. 16.75 (ISBN 0-8191-3617-4). U Pr of Amer.

Heller, H. The Conquest of Poverty: The Calvinist Revolt in Sixteenth-Century France. (Studies in Medieval & Reformation Thought: No. 35). xiv, 281p. 1986. 40.00 (ISBN 90-04-07598-4, Pub. by E J Brill). Heinman.

Helm, Paul. Calvin & the Calvinists. 84p. (Orig.). 1982. pap. 5.95 (ISBN 0-85151-344-1). Banner of Truth.

Herbert, T. Walter, Jr. Moby Dick & Calvinism: A World Dismantled. 1977. 27.00x (ISBN 0-8135-0829-0). Rutgers U Pr.

Hood, Fred J. Reformed America: The Middle & Southern States, Seventeen Eighty-Three to Eighteen Thirty-Seven. LC 79-28834. 304p. 1980. 21.50 (ISBN 0-8173-0034-1). U of Ala Pr.

Hopfl, Harro. The Christian Polity of John Calvin. (Cambridge Studies in the History & Theory of Politics). 320p. 1985. pap. 14.95 (ISBN 0-521-31638-3). Cambridge U Pr.

Hunter, Adam M. The Teaching of Calvin: A Modern Interpretation. LC 83-45618. Date not set. Repr. of 1950 ed. 37.50 (ISBN 0-404-19836-8). AMS Pr.

Keesecker, William F., ed. & selected by. A Calvin Reader: Reflections on Living. LC 85-15237. 144p. 1985. pap. 9.95 (ISBN 0-664-24667-2). Westminster.

Kelly, Kent. Inside the Tuplic Contoversy: Calvinism Rebuked & Revisited. LC 86-70927. (Illus.). 264p. 1986. 9.95 (ISBN 0-9604138-4-7). Calvary Pr.

Kuyper, Abraham. Lectures on Calvinism. pap. 3.95 (ISBN 0-8028-1607-X). Eerdmans.

Leith, John H. Introduction to the Reformed Tradition: A Way of Being the Christian Community. rev. ed. LC 81-5968. (Illus.). 253p. 1981. pap. 10.95 (ISBN 0-8042-0479-9). John Knox.

McDonnell, Kilian. John Calvin, the Church, & the Eucharist. LC 65-17149. pap. 105.00 (ISBN 0-317-08461-5, 2010572). Bks Demand UMI.

McNeil, John T. On God & Political Duty: Calvin. 1956. pap. text ed. write for info. (ISBN 0-02-379760-6). Macmillan.

McNeill, J. T. The History & Character of Calvinism. 1954. pap. 12.95 (ISBN 0-19-500743-3). Oxford U Pr.

Marshall, Gordon. Presbyteries & Profits: Calvinism & the Development of Capitalism in Scotland, 1560 - 1707. 1980. 54.00x (ISBN 0-19-827246-4). Oxford U Pr.

Martin, Albert N. Practical Implications of Calvinism. 1979. pap. 1.00 (ISBN 0-85151-296-8). Banner of Truth.

Palm, Franklin C. Calvinisim & the Religious Wars. LC 78-80579. 1971. Repr. 24.50x (ISBN 0-86527-020-1). Fertig.

--Calvinism & the Religious Wars. LC 83-45628. Date not set. Repr. of 1932 ed. 22.50 (ISBN 0-404-19880-5). AMS Pr.

Palmer, Edwin H. Doctrinas Claves. 2.95 (ISBN 0-85151-407-3). Banner of Truth.

--Five Points of Calvinism: A Study Guide. 1972. pap. 4.95 (ISBN 0-8010-6926-2). Baker Bk.

Partee, Charles, ed. Calvin & Classical Philosophy 1977. (Studies in the History of Christian Thought: Vol. 14). 30.00 (ISBN 90-04-04839-1). Heinman.

Poggi, Gianfranco. Calvinism & the Capitalist Spirit: Max Weber's "Protestant Ethic". LC 83-40103. 136p. 1983. lib. bdg. 13.50x (ISBN 0-87023-417-X); pap. text ed. 6.95x (ISBN 0-87023-418-8). U of Mass Pr.

Pope, Earl. New England Calvinism & the Disruption of the Presbyterian Church. Kuklick, Bruce, ed. (American Religious Thought of the 18th & 19th Centuries Ser.). 400p. 1987. lib. bdg. 50.00 (ISBN 0-8240-6969-2). Garland Pub.

Prestwich, Menna, ed. International Calvinism. (Illus.). 414p. 1985. 49.95x (ISBN 0-19-821933-4). Oxford U Pr.

Ross, Bob L. Killing Effects of Calvinism. 1980. pap. 1.25 (ISBN 0-686-29039-9). Pilgrim Pubns.

Seaton, Jack. The Five Points of Calvinism. 1979. pap. 1.20 (ISBN 0-85151-264-X). Banner of Truth.

Shedd, William G. Commentary on Romans: A Classic Commentary from the Reformed Perspective. (Thornapple Commentaries Ser.). 1980. pap. 8.95 (ISBN 0-8010-8175-0). Baker Bk.

Shurr, William H. Rappaccini's Children: American Writers in a Calvinist World. LC 79-57573. 176p. 1981. 16.00x (ISBN 0-8131-1427-6). U Pr of Ky.

Spencer, Duane E. Tulip: Five Points of Calvinism. LC 78-73445. (Direction Bks). pap. 2.95 (ISBN 0-8010-8161-0). Baker Bk.

Steele, David H. & Curtis, Thomas C. Five Points of Calvinism. 1963. pap. 2.50 (ISBN 0-87552-444-3). Presby & Reformed.

Steele, David N. & Thomas, Curtis C. Five Points of Calvinism. (Biblical & Theological Studies). pap. 2.50 (ISBN 0-8010-7919-5). Baker Bk.

Van der Walt, B., ed. Calvinus Reformator: His Contribution to Theology, Church & Society. Date not set. pap. 12.50x cancelled (ISBN 0-86990-686-0). Radix Bks.

Wallace, Ronald S. Calvin's Doctrine of the Word & Sacraments. xii, 253p. 1982. pap. 12.95 (ISBN 0-939404-02-8). Geneva Ministr.

Warfield, Benjamin B. Calvin & Augustine. 1954. 12.95 (ISBN 0-87552-526-1). Presby & Reformed.

Wendel, Francois. Calvin: Origins & Development of His Religious Thought. Mairet, Philip, tr. 384p. 1987. pap. 14.95 (ISBN 0-939464-44-6). Labyrinth Pr.

Whittemore, Robert C. The Transformation of the New England Theology. (American University Studies VII-Theology & Religion: Vol. 23). 441p. 1987. text ed. 42.00 (ISBN 0-8204-0374-1). P Lang Pubs.

Williams, David R. Wilderness Lost: The Religious Origins of the American Mind. LC 85-43475. 296p. 1987. 38.50x (ISBN 0-941664-21-X). Susquehanna U Pr.

Wilterdink, Garret. Tyrant or Father? A Study of Calvin's Doctrine of God. 185p. (Orig.). 1985. pap. 9.95 (ISBN 0-932269-19-2). Wyndham Hall.

CAMBRIDGE PLATONISTS

Cassirer, Ernst. Platonic Renaissance in England. LC 71-128186. 207p. 1970. Repr. of 1954 ed. 19.50x (ISBN 0-87752-128-X). Gordian.

De Pauley, William C. Candle of the Lord. facsimile ed. LC 75-107693. (Essay Index Reprint Ser). 1937. 16.00 (ISBN 0-8369-1496-1). Ayer Co Pubs.

--The Candle of the Lord: Studies in the Cambridge Platonists. (Church Historical Society, London, New Ser.: No. 28). pap. 23.00 (ISBN 0-8115-3152-X). Kraus Repr.

Howard, Claud. Coleridge's Idealism. LC 72-191125. 1924. lib. bdg. 17.50 (ISBN 0-8414-5131-1). Folcroft.

Powicke, Frederick J. The Cambridge Platonists. LC 79-151196. (Illus.). x, 219p. 1971. Repr. of 1926 ed. 23.00 (ISBN 0-208-01088-2, Archon). Shoe String.

--Cambridge Platonists, a Study. Repr. of 1926 ed. lib. bdg. 22.50x (ISBN 0-8371-3999-6, POPL). Greenwood.

CAMP-MEETINGS

see also Church Camps

Brians, Pearl. My First SDA Camp Meeting. large print ed. 44p. 1985. pap. 6.00 (ISBN 0-914009-27-3). VHI Library.

Bruce, Dickson D., Jr. And They All Sang Hallelujah: Plain-Folk Camp-Meeting Religion, 1800-1845. LC 74-11344. (Illus.). 1974. 13.50x (ISBN 0-87049-157-1); pap. 5.95x (ISBN 0-87049-310-8). U of Tenn Pr.

Johnson, Charles A. The Frontier Camp Meeting: Religion's Harvest Time. LC 55-8783. (Illus.). xiv, 325p. 1985. 21.95x (ISBN 0-87074-201-9). SMU Press.

Shaw, Naomi. Let the Hallelujahs Roll. LC 76-52280. (YA) 1977. pap. 1.95 (ISBN 0-89221-028-1). New Leaf.

CAMPBELL, BEATRICE STELLA (TANNER), 1865-1940

Davies, Horton. Mirror of the Ministry in Modern Novels. facsimile ed. LC 70-111824. (Essay Index Reprint Ser.). 1959. 19.00 (ISBN 0-8369-1601-8). Ayer Co Pubs.

CAMPBELLITES

see Disciples of Christ

CAMPMEETINGS

see Camp-Meetings

CAMPS (CHURCH)

see Church Camps

CAMUS, ALBERT, 1913-1960

Akeroyd, Richard H. The Spiritual Quest of Albert Camus. LC 76-3324. 1976. 7.50 (ISBN 0-916620-03-4). Portals Pr.

Lottman, Herbert. Albert Camus: A Biography. LC 80-68394. (Illus.). 753p. 1981. pap. 8.95 (ISBN 0-8076-0998-6). Braziller.

Petersen, Carol. Albert Camus. Gode, Alexander, tr. LC 68-31455. (Literature & Life Ser.). 1969. 12.95 (ISBN 0-8044-2691-0). Ungar.

Suther, Judith D. Essays on Camus' Exile & the Kingdom. LC 80-36800. (Romance Monographs: No. 41). 329p. 1982. 30.00x (ISBN 84-499-4725-1). Romance.

Vargas, Mario. Entre Sartre y Camus. LC 81-68707. (Coleccion la Nave y el Puerto Ser.). 144p. 1981. pap. 5.50 (ISBN 0-940238-48-9). Ediciones Hura.

CANAANITE MYTHOLOGY

see Mythology, Canaanite

CANADA-CHURCH HISTORY

Liederbach, Clarence A. Canada's Bishops: Sixteen Fifty-Eight to Nineteen Seventy-Five. LC 73-94082. 1976. pap. 2.95 (ISBN 0-913228-10-9). R J Liederbach.

Lupul, M. R. The Roman Catholic Church & the North-West School Question: A Study in Church-State Relations in Western Canada, 1875-1905. LC 73-89844. 1974. 27.50x (ISBN 0-8020-5301-7). U of Toronto Pr.

Wilkins, Ronald J. Religion in North America. (To Live Is Christ Ser.). 208p. 1984. pap. 5.75 (ISBN 0-697-01930-6); tchr's manual 4.95 (ISBN 0-697-01931-4); spirit masters 10.95 (ISBN 0-697-01735-4). Wm C Brown.

CANADA-RELIGION

Halpert, Herbert & Story, G. M., eds. Christmas Mumming in Newfoundland: Essays in Anthropology, Folklore, & History. LC 71-391290. pap. 64.50 (ISBN 0-317-42289-8, 2055819). Bks Demand UMI.

Jacquet, Constant H., Jr., ed. Yearbook of American & Canadian Church 1986. 304p. (Orig.). 1986. pap. 17.95 (ISBN 0-687-46641-5). Abingdon.

Jacquet, H. Constant, ed. Yearbook of American & Canadian Churches, 1987. 304p. 1987. pap. 18.95 (ISBN 0-687-46642-3). Abingdon.

Johnston, A. J. Religion in Life at Louisbourg, 1713-1758. 288p. 1984. 30.00x (ISBN 0-7735-0427-3). McGill-Queens U pr.

Neufeldt, Ronald. Religious Studies in Alberta: A State-of-the-Art Review. (Study of Religion in Canada Ser.). 145p. 1983. pap. text ed. 10.00x (ISBN 0-317-03613-0, Pub. by Wilfrid Laurier Canada). Humanities.

Roy, Maurice. The Parish & Democracy in French Canada. LC 52-1123. (University of Toronto, Duncan & John Gray Memorial Lecture Ser.). pap. 20.00 (2026546). Bks Demand UMI.

CANCER-PERSONAL NARRATIVES

see Cancer Patients-Personal Narratives

CANCER-PSYCHOLOGICAL ASPECTS

Moster, Mary B. When the Doctor Says "It's Cancer". abr. ed. (Pocket Guides Ser.). 96p. 1986. 1.95 (ISBN 0-8423-7981-9). Tyndale.

Platt, Nancy V. Pastoral Care to the Cancer Patient. 100p. 1980. pap. 9.75x (ISBN 0-398-04051-6). C C Thomas.

CANCER PATIENTS-PERSONAL NARRATIVES

Becton, Randy. The Gift of Life: A Message of Hope for the Seriously Ill. (Illus.). 1978. pap. 4.75 (ISBN 0-89137-309-8). Quality Pubns.

Curtas, Ted. Tears of Joy. cancelled (ISBN 0-686-12741-2); pap. 3.95 (ISBN 0-686-12742-0). Grace Pub Co.

Helman, Ethel. An Autumn Life: How a Surgeon Faced His Fatal Illness. 120p. (Orig.). 1986. pap. 6.95 (ISBN 0-571-13704-0). Faber & Faber.

Higginbotham, Mary. With Each Passing Moment. pap. 1.25 (ISBN 0-686-12748-X). Grace Pub Co.

Loeffler, Chris & Hunsberger, Eydie M. Eydie Mae: How I Conquered Cancer Naturally. pap. 2.95 (ISBN 0-932638-01-5). Prod Hse.

Pelgrin, Mark. And a Time to Die. Moon, Sheila & Howes, Elizabeth, eds. LC 75-26836. 159p. 1976. pap. 2.95 (ISBN 0-8356-0305-9, Quest). Theos Pub Hse.

Stargel, Gloria C. The Healing. (Orig.). 1982. pap. 2.50 (ISBN 0-8423-1425-3). Tyndale.

CANISIUS, PETER, SAINT, 1524-1597

Brodrick, James. Saint Peter Canisius. (Request Reprint). (Illus.). 1962. 19.95 (ISBN 0-8294-0008-7). Loyola.

--Saint Peter Canisius, S. J., 1521-1597. LC 83-45589. Date not set. Repr. of 1935 ed. 65.00 (ISBN 0-404-19882-1). AMS Pr.

CANON (MUSIC)

Norden, Hugo. The Technique of Canon. 1982. pap. 9.00 (ISBN 0-8283-1839-5). Branden Pub Co.

Prout, E. Double Counterpoint & Canon. LC 68-25300. (Studies in Music, No. 42). 1969. Repr. of 1893 ed. lib. bdg. 48.95x (ISBN 0-8383-0312-9). Haskell.

Prout, Ebenezer. Double Counterpoint & Canon. Repr. of 1893 ed. lib. bdg. 22.50x (ISBN 0-8371-2265-1, PRDC). Greenwood.

CANON LAW

see also Church Orders, Ancient; Ecclesiastical Courts; Ecclesiastical Law

also special legal headings with Canon Law added in parentheses, e.g. Marriage (Canon Law)

Alexander, Archibald. Evidence of the Authenticity, Inspiration & Canonical Authority of the Holy Scriptures. (Works of Reverend Archibald Alexander). 308p. Repr. of 1842 ed. lib. bdg. 39.00 (ISBN 0-932051-73-1, Pub. by Am Repr Serv). Am Biog Serv.

Amram, David W. Leading Cases in the Bible. ix, 220p. 1985. Repr. of 1905 ed. lib. bdg. 22.50x (ISBN 0-8377-0218-6). Rothman.

Beckwith, Roger. The Old Testament Canon of the New Testament Church. 536p. 1986. 35.00 (ISBN 0-8028-3617-8). Eerdmans.

Box, Hubert S. The Principles of Canon Law. LC 86-3163. 1986. Repr. of 1949 ed. 32.75x (ISBN 0-313-25204-1, BPRC/). Greenwood.

Canon Law Society of America Staff, tr. from Latin. The Code of Canon Law: Latin-English Edition. Orig. Title: Codex Iuris Canonici. xlii, 668p. (Orig.). 1983. 15.00 (ISBN 0-943616-20-4); pap. 12.00 (ISBN 0-943616-19-0). Canon Law Soc.

Canon Law Society of America Staff. Proceedings of the Forty-Sixth Annual Convention. 308p. (Orig.). 1985. pap. 8.00 (ISBN 0-943616-29-8). Canon Law Soc.

Canon Law Society of Great Britain & Ireland Staff, ed. Index to the Code of Canon Law. 104p. (Orig.). 1985. pap. 3.50 (ISBN 0-8028-0067-X). Eerdmans.

Canon Law Society of Great Britain, Ireland Staff, ed. The Code of Canon Law in English Translation. 1983. pap. 9.95 (ISBN 0-8028-1978-8). Eerdmans.

Carleton, George. Jurisdiction Regall, Episcopall, Papall. LC 68-54625. (English Experience Ser.: No. 34). 302p. 1969. Repr. of 1610 ed. 30.00 (ISBN 90-221-0034-0). Walter J Johnson.

CLSA Staff. Annual Convention Proceedings, 45th: 1983. 354p. 1984. pap. 7.00 (ISBN 0-943616-22-0). Canon Law Soc.

Coriden, James A., et al. The Art of Interpretation: Selected Studies on the Interpretation of Canon Law. v, 79p. (Orig.). 1983. pap. 3.75 (ISBN 0-943616-18-2). Canon Law Soc.

Coriden, James A., et al, eds. The Code of Canon Law: A Text & Commentary. 39.95 (ISBN 0-8091-0345-1). Paulist Pr.

--The Code of Canon Law: A Text & Commentary, Study Edition. 1184p. 1986. pap. text ed. 29.95 (ISBN 0-8091-2837-3). Paulist Pr.

Cunningham, Richard G. Annotated Bibliography of the Work of the Canon Law Society of America 1965-1980. 121p. (Orig.). 1982. pap. 4.50 (ISBN 0-943616-06-9). Canon Law Soc.

Dietzen, John J. The New Question Box. rev. ed. 606p. 1987. pap. 9.95 (ISBN 0-940518-01-5). Guildhall Pubs.

Doyle, Thomas P. Rights & Responsibilities. 64p. (Orig.). 1983. pap. 2.50 (ISBN 0-916134-58-X). Pueblo Pub Co.

Edelby, Neophytos. Future of Canon Law. LC 78-100004. (Concilium Ser.: No. 48). 188p. 7.95 (ISBN 0-8091-0049-5). Paulist Pr.

Ferreira-Ibarra, Dario C., ed. The Canon Law Collection of the Library of Congress: A General Bibliography with Selective Annotations. LC 81-607964. (Illus.). xiv, 210p. 1981. 11.00 (ISBN 0-8444-0367-9). Lib Congress.

Gallen, Joseph F. Cannon Law for Religious: An Explanation. LC 83-15883. 218p. (Orig.). 1983. pap. 9.95 (ISBN 0-8189-0461-5). Alba.

Gibson, Edmund. Codex Juris Ecclesiastici Anglicani, 2 Vols. 1761. text ed. 372.60x (ISBN 0-576-99471-5, Pub. by Gregg Intl Pubs England). Gregg Intl.

Gorecki, Danuta M. & Wajenberg, Arnold. Cannon Law: History, Sources, & a Proposed Classification Scheme. Date not set. price not set. Am Assn Law Libs.

Hite, Jordan F., et al. Readings, Cases, Materials in Canon Law: A Textbook for Ministerial Students. LC 79-24977. 370p. (Orig.). 1980. pap. text ed. 8.50 (ISBN 0-8146-1081-1). Liturgical Pr.

Huels, J. M. The Faithful of Christ: The New Canon Law for the Laity. 1983. 5.50 (ISBN 0-8199-0873-8). Franciscan Herald.

Huels, John M. The Pastoral Companion: A Canon Law Handbook for Catholic Ministry. LC 85-29316. 1986. 25.00 (ISBN 0-8199-0900-9); pap. 15.00. Franciscan Herald.

--The Pastoral Companion: A Canon Law Handbook for Pastoral Ministry. 1986. 25.00 (ISBN 0-8199-0900-9); pap. 15.00. Franciscan Herald.

Huizing, Peter & Walf, Knut, eds. The Revised Code of Canon Law: A Missed Opportunity, Vol. 147. (Concilium 1981). 128p. (Orig.). 1981. pap. 6.95 (ISBN 0-8164-2347-4, HarpR). Har-Row.

Kelly, Henry A. Canon Law & the Archpriest of Hita. LC 82-12403. (Medieval & Renaissance Texts & Studies: Vol. 27). 204p. 1984. 16.00 (ISBN 0-86698-058-X). Medieval & Renaissance NY.

Laeuchli, Samuel. Power & Sexuality: The Emergence of Canon Law at the Synod of Elvira. LC 72-83671. 143p. 1972. 9.95 (ISBN 0-87722-015-8). Temple U Pr.

Levine, Mark S. Canonical Analysis & Factor Comparison. LC 77-75941. (University Papers: Quantitative Applications in the Social Sciences, No. 6). 62p. 1977. 6.00 (ISBN 0-8039-0655-2). Sage.

Liptak, David Q. The New Code & the Sacraments. 140p. 1983. pap. 7.95 (ISBN 0-941850-12-9). Sunday Pubns.

Liptak, David Q. & Sheridan, Philip A. The New Code: Laity & Deacons. 128p. (Orig.). 1986. pap. 7.95 (ISBN 0-941850-20-X). Sunday Pubns.

Lowery, Daniel L. Catholic Beliefs, Laws, Practices: Twenty-Six Questions & Answers. 64p. 1984. pap. 1.50 (ISBN 0-89243-213-6). Liguori Pubns.

Maitland, Frederic W. Roman Canon Law in the Church of England. 1969. Repr. of 1898 ed. 21.00 (ISBN 0-8337-2186-0). B Franklin.

Mathis, Marcian & Bonner, Dismas, eds. Pastoral Companion. 14th ed. 1976. 17.50 (ISBN 0-8199-0084-2, L38625). Franciscan Herald.

Naz, R. Dictionnaire de Droit Canonique, 7 vols. (Fr.). 1965. Set. 695.00 (ISBN 0-686-57057-X, M-6423). French & Eur.

The New Canon Law: Perspectives on the Law, Religious Life & the Laity. LC 82-17889. (Orig.). 1983. pap. 11.00 (ISBN 0-87125-076-4). Cath Health.

Ogle, Arthur. Canon Law in Mediaeval England: An Examination of William Lyndwood's Provinciale. LC 78-156390. (Research & Source Works Ser.: No. 731). 1971. Repr. of 1912 ed. lib. bdg. 20.50 (ISBN 0-8337-2603-X). B Franklin.

Provost, James & Walf, Knut, eds. Canon Law--Church Reality. (Concilium Nineteen Eighty-Six Ser.). 120p. 1986. pap. 6.95 (ISBN 0-567-30065-X, Pub. by T & T Clark Ltd UK). Fortress.

Provost, James H., ed. Code, Community, Ministry: Selected Studies for the Revised Code of Canon Law. vi, 116p. (Orig.). 1983. pap. 4.50 (ISBN 0-943616-15-8). Canon Law Soc.

Rinere, Elissa. New Law & Life: Sixty Practical Questions & Answers on the New Code of Canon Law. 103p. (Orig.). 1985. pap. 4.50 (ISBN 0-943616-28-X). Canon Law Soc.

Schumacher, William A. & Cuneo, J. James, eds. Roman Replies & CLSA Advisory Opinions, 1985. 68p. (Orig.). 1985. pap. 5.50 (ISBN 0-943616-30-1). Canon Law Soc.

Shumacher, William A. Roman Replies, 1982. 42p. (Orig.). 1982. pap. 3.00 (ISBN 0-943616-13-1). Canon Law Soc.

Somerville, Robert & Pennington, Kenneth, eds. Law, Church, & Society: Essays in Honor of Stephan Kuttner. LC 76-53199. 1977. 27.95x (ISBN 0-8122-7726-0). U of Pa Pr.

Urresti, Teodoro-J & Edelby, Neophytos, eds. Pastoral Reform in Church Government. LC 65-28464. (Concilium Ser.: Vol. 8). 192p. 7.95 (ISBN 0-8091-0109-2). Paulist Pr.

Urresti, Teodoro J., et al. Renewal & Reform of Canon Law. Edelby, Neophytos, ed. LC 67-30868. (Concilium Ser.: Vol. 28). 191p. 1967. 7.95 (ISBN 0-8091-0125-4). Paulist Pr.

Wrenn, Lawrence G. Decisions. 2nd, rev. ed. vi, 200p. (Orig.). 1983. pap. 4.50 (ISBN 0-943616-17-4). Canon Law Soc.

CANONIZATION

see also Saints

Kemp, Eric W. Canonization & Authority in the Western Church. LC 78-63467. Repr. of 1948 ed. 20.00 (ISBN 0-404-16397-1). AMS Pr.

--Canonization & Authority in the Western Church. LC 78-20474. 1980. Repr. of 1948 ed. 20.35 (ISBN 0-88355-852-1). Hyperion Conn.

CANTATA

see also Choral Music; Church Music

Bach, Johann Sebastian. Eleven Great Cantatas in Full Vocal & Instrumental Score. Date not set. 16.50 (ISBN 0-8446-5459-0). Peter Smith.

CANTERBURY CATHEDRAL

Caviness, Madeline H. The Early Stained Glass of Canterbury Cathedral: 1175-1220. (Illus.). 1978. text ed. 68.50x (ISBN 0-691-03927-5). Princeton U Pr.

Hill, Canon D. Canterbury Cathedral. (The New Bell's Cathedral Guides Ser.). 1986. cancelled (ISBN 0-918678-13-7). Historical Times.

Ingram-Hill, Canon D. Canterbury Cathedral. (The New Bell Cathedral Guides Ser.). (Illus.). 192p. (Orig.). 1987. pap. 14.95 (ISBN 0-7135-2619-X, Pub. by Automobile Assn Brit). Salem Hse Pubs.

Keates, Jonathan & Hornak, Angelo. Canterbury Cathedral. (Illus.). pap. 13.95 (ISBN 0-935748-17-2). Scala Books.

Runcie, Robert A. Seasons of the Spirit: The Archbishop of Canterbury at Home & Abroad. LC 83-1734. pap. 68.00 (ISBN 0-317-30160-8, 2025342). Bks Demand UMI.

Taylor, George R. The Story of Canterbury. LC 78-63479. (Illus.). Repr. of 1912 ed. 38.50 (ISBN 0-404-16545-1). AMS Pr.

CANVASSING (CHURCH WORK)

see Visitations (Church Work)

CAPITAL SINS

see Deadly Sins

CAPUCHINS

Cuthbert. The Capuchins: A Contribution to the History of the Counter Reformation, 2 vols. 1977. lib. bdg. 250.00 (ISBN 0-8490-1571-5). Gordon Pr.

Vogel, Claude. The Capuchins in French Louisiana (1722-1766) LC 73-3561. (Catholic University of America. Studies in American Church History: No. 7). Repr. of 1928 ed. 20.00 (ISBN 0-404-57757-1). AMS Pr.

CARDINALS

Bargrave, John. Pope Alexander the Seventh & the College of Cardinals. Robertson, James C., ed. LC 78-160001. (Camden Society, London. Publications, First Ser.: No. 92). Repr. of 1867 ed. 19.00 (ISBN 0-404-50192-3). AMS Pr.

--Pope Alexander the Seventh & the College of Cardinals. 19.00 (ISBN 0-384-03435-7). Johnson Repr.

Berton, C. Dictionnaire des Cardinaux. Migne, J. P., ed. (Troisieme et Derniere Encyclopedie Theologique Ser.: Vol. 31). (Fr.). 912p. Repr. of 1857 ed. lib. bdg. 115.00x (ISBN 0-89241-310-7). Caratzas.

--Dictionnaire des Cardinaux. 912p. Date not set. Repr. of 1866 ed. text ed. 186.30x (ISBN 0-576-78521-0, Pub. by Gregg Intl Pubs England). Gregg Intl.

Buehrle, Marie C. Rafael: Cardinal Merry del Val. 308p. (Orig.). 1980. pap. 7.00 (ISBN 0-912414-28-6). Lumen Christi.

Gray, Robert. Cardinal Manning: A Biography. LC 85-10687. 366p. 1985. 29.95 (ISBN 0-312-12032-X). St Martin.

Hallman, Barbara M. Italian Cardinals, Reform, & the Church As Property, 1492-1563. LC 84-8501. (Center for Medieval & Renaissance Studies, UCLA Publications: No. 22). 1985. 35.00x (ISBN 0-520-04937-3). U of Cal Pr.

Hutton, Richard H. Cardinal Newman. LC 75-30029. Repr. of 1891 ed. 21.00 (ISBN 0-404-14033-5). AMS Pr.

McCormack, Ellen. Cuomo vs. O'Connor: Did a Catholic Politician Make an Anti-Catholic Appeal? LC 85-71482. 100p. (Orig.). 1985. pap. 5.95 (ISBN 0-934117-00-4). Dolores Pr.

Moloney, Thomas. Westminster, Whitehall, & the Vatican: The Role of Cardinal Hinsley, 1935-43. LC 85-19381. (Illus.). 263p. 1985. text ed. 24.95x (ISBN 0-268-01938-X, Pub. by Burns & Oates London). U of Notre Dame Pr.

Morgan, Thomas B. Speaking of Cardinals. facs. ed. LC 70-134119. (Essay Index Reprint Ser). 1946. 18.00 (ISBN 0-8369-2002-3). Ayer Co Pubs.

Noel, Gerard. Cardinal Basil Hume. (Profiles Ser.). (Illus.). 64p. 1984. 8.95 (ISBN 0-241-11204-4, Pub. by Hamish Hamilton England). David & Charles.

Walsh, James J. Our American Cardinals. facs. ed. LC 68-58815. (Essay Index Reprint Ser). 1926. 23.75 (ISBN 0-8369-1072-9). Ayer Co Pubs.

Zekowski, Arlene & Berne, Stanley. Cardinals & Saints. LC 58-11713. (Illus.). 1958. 45.00 (ISBN 0-913844-10-1). Am Canadian.

CARE OF SOULS

see Pastoral Counseling; Pastoral Theology

CAREY, WILLIAM, 1761-1834

Clinton, Iris. Young Man in a Hurry (William Carey) 1961. pap. 2.95 (ISBN 0-87508-630-6). Chr Lit.

Miller, Basil. William Carey. 154p. 1985. pap. 3.50 (ISBN 0-87123-850-0, 200850). Bethany Hse.

CARMELITE NUNS-FICTION

Von Le Fort, Gertrud. The Song at the Scaffold. rev. ed. McMurtrey, Martin & Knopp, Robert, eds. (Illus., Orig.). 1954. pap. text ed. 3.95 (ISBN 0-910334-24-2). Cath Authors.

CARMELITES

Bernanos, Georges. Dialogue Des Carmelites. (Coll. Le Livre de Vie). pap. 3.95 (ISBN 0-685-37216-2). French & Eur.

Hogg, James. L' Ancienne Chartreuse du Reposoir Aujourd'hui Carmel, et les Chartruses de la Savoie. (Analecta Cartusiana Ser.: No. 39-2). (Illus.). 110p. (Orig.). 1979. pap. 25.00 (ISBN 3-7052-0047-X, Pub by Salzburg Studies). Longwood Pub Group.

--L' Ancienne Chartreuse du Reposior, Aujourd'hui Carmel, et les Chartreusesde la Savoie, Introduction. (Analecta Cartusiana Ser.: No. 39-1). (Orig.). 1986. pap. 25.00 (ISBN 3-7052-0046-1, Pub by Salzburg Studies). Longwood Pub Group.

CARMELITES–DRAMA

Bernanos, Georges. Dialogue Des Carmelites. 1960. 13.50 (ISBN 0-685-11136-9). French & Eur.

CAROLS

see also Christmas–Poetry; Christmas Music

Bartok. Carols & Christmas Songs: Colinde, Vol. 4. (Rumanian Folk Music Ser). 1975. lib. bdg. 131.50 (ISBN 90-247-1737-X, Pub. by Martinus Nijhoff Netherlands). Kluwer Academic.

Choirs of Angels in Stained Glass. (Illus.). 1985. pap. 5.95 (ISBN 0-8027-7136-X). Walker & Co.

Christmas Carols. pap. 1.50 (ISBN 0-685-22654-9). Polanie.

Cofone, Charles J., ed. Favorite Christmas Carols. (Illus.). 64p. 1975. pap. 3.50 (ISBN 0-486-20445-6). Dover.

Cox, Heather & Rickard, Garth. Carols to Sing, Clap & Play: A Companion to the Soprano Recorder Tuition Books. (Illus.). 1984. pap. 4.50 (ISBN 0-918812-36-4). MMB Music.

Cusack, Margaret. The Christmas Carol Sampler. (Illus.). 10.95 (ISBN 0-15-217752-3, HJ). HarBraceJ.

Dearmer, Percy, et al, eds. Oxford Book of Carols. 1928. 21.00 (ISBN 0-19-353314-6); pap. 13.95 (ISBN 0-19-353315-4); Words & Melody. pap. 6.95 (ISBN 0-19-313118-8). Oxford U Pr.

--Oxford Book of Carols for Schools. 1956. piano ed. 6.75 (ISBN 0-19-330830-4); melody ed. 2.50 (ISBN 0-19-330831-2). Oxford U Pr.

De Paola, Tomie. The Friendly Beasts: An Old English Christmas Carol. (Illus.). 32p. 1981. 10.95 (ISBN 0-399-20739-2); pap. 4.95 (ISBN 0-399-20777-5). Putnam Pub Group.

Ehret, Walter & Evans, George K. International Book of Christmas Carols. LC 80-13105. (Illus.). 352p. 1980. pap. 14.95 (ISBN 0-8289-0378-6). Greene.

Gillington, Alice E. Old Christmas Carols of the Southern Counties. LC 76-25121. 1976. Repr. of 1910 ed. lib. bdg. 17.50 (ISBN 0-8414-4534-6). Folcroft.

Greene, Richard L., ed. The Early English Carols. 2nd ed. 1977. 129.00x (ISBN 0-19-812715-4). Oxford U Pr.

--A Selection of English Carols. LC 77-13760. 1978. Repr. of 1962 ed. lib. bdg. 24.75x (ISBN 0-313-20002-5, GREC). Greenwood.

Husk, William A. Songs of the Nativity. LC 73-9861. (Folklore Ser). 32.50 (ISBN 0-88305-258-X). Norwood Edns.

Ideals Staff. Book of Christmas Carols. (Illus.). 24p. 1984. pap. 2.95 (ISBN 0-8249-8072-7). Ideals.

Jacques, Reginald & Willcocks, David. Carols for Choirs: Fifty Christmas Carols, Bk. 1. (YA) 1961. 12.00 (ISBN 0-19-353221-2); pap. 7.00 (ISBN 0-19-353222-0). Oxford U Pr.

Jacques, Reginald, ed. Oxford S-A-B Carol Book: Forty Carols. (YA) 1960. limp linen 7.25x (ISBN 0-19-330514-3). Oxford U Pr.

The Keepsake Book of Christmas Carols: Complete Lyrics to the Most Beloved Yuletide Songs. (Illus.). 48p. 1984. pap. 4.95 (ISBN 0-89471-281-0); lib. bdg. 12.90 (ISBN 0-89471-282-9). Running Pr.

Leary, Norma. Portraits of Customs & Carols. 1983. pap. 2.95 (ISBN 0-937172-54-5). JLJ Pubs.

McKuen, Rod. The Carols of Christmas. 1971. 3.95 (ISBN 0-394-47420-1). Random.

Oberndorfer, Marx & Oberndorfer, Anne. Noels: A Collection of Christmas Carols. 144p. 1932. complete gift edition 8.50 (ISBN 0-912222-05-0, R2582751); pap. 4.00 choral ed., carols only (ISBN 0-912222-06-9). FitzSimons.

Phillips, William J. Carols, Their Origin, Music, & Connection with Mystery-Plays: A Greenwood Archival Edition. (Illus.). Repr. of 1921 ed. lib. bdg. 40.00x (ISBN 0-8371-4312-8, PHCA). Greenwood.

Pyle, Hershal. America's Favorite Carols. Date not set. 2.50 (ISBN 0-317-20179-4). Campus.

--Carols for the Holidays. Date not set. 2.25 (ISBN 0-317-20177-8). Campus.

--A Festival of Holiday Songs. Date not set. pap. 2.95 (ISBN 0-317-20180-8). Campus.

Reed, Will L., ed. Second Treasury of Christmas Music. LC 68-16193. 1968. 12.95 (ISBN 0-87523-165-9). Emerson.

--Treasury of Easter Music & Music for Passiontide. 1963. 12.95 (ISBN 0-87523-142-X). Emerson.

Roseberry, Eric, ed. The Faber Book of Carols & Christmas Songs. 118p. 1983. 8.95 (ISBN 0-571-09249-7); pap. 6.95 (ISBN 0-571-13189-1). Faber & Faber.

Rosenkrans, B., compiled by. My Book of Christmas Carols. (All Aboard Bks.). (Illus.). 32p. 1986. pap. 1.95 (ISBN 0-448-19079-6, G&D). Putnam Pub Group.

Sandys, William. Christmas Carols, Ancient & Modern. LC 76-30740. 1977. Repr. of 1833 ed. lib. bdg. 32.50 (ISBN 0-8414-7779-5). Folcroft.

--Christmas Carols: Ancient & Modern. 69.95 (ISBN 0-87968-866-1). Gordon Pr.

Shinn, Duane. How to Play Twelve Christmas Carols on the Piano - This Christmas - with the Visualized Chord System. 1976. pap. 6.95 (ISBN 0-912732-19-9). Duane Shinn.

--Super-Chords Made Super-Simple. 1976. pap. 6.95 (ISBN 0-912732-20-2). Duane Shinn.

Studwell, William E. Christmas Carols: A Reference Guide. LC 84-48240. 320p. 1984. lib. bdg. 29.00 (ISBN 0-8240-8899-9). Garland Pub.

Tennyson, Noel, illus. Christmas Carols: A Treasury of Holiday Favorites with Words & Pictures. LC 83-60412. (Illus.). 24p. 1983. 1.95 (ISBN 0-394-86125-6). Random.

The Ultimate Christmas Fake Book. (Fake Bk. Ser.). 84p. 1985. 9.95 (ISBN 0-88188-381-6, HL00240063). H Leonard Pub Corp.

Willcocks, David, ed. Carols for Choirs: Bk. 3, Fifty Carols. 1978. pap. text ed. 7.00 (ISBN 0-19-353570-X). Oxford U Pr.

--Carols for Christmas. (Illus.). 96p. 1983. 25.00 (ISBN 0-03-064044-X). H Holt & Co.

Woods, Sylvia. Fifty Christmas Carols for All Harps: Each Arranged for Beginning & Advanced Harpers. (Sylvia Woods Multi-Level Harp Bks.). (Illus.). 96p. 1984. pap. 13.95 (ISBN 0-9602990-5-X). Woods Mus Bks Pub.

The World's Best Christmas Carols. rev. ed. 64p. 1987. pap. 2.95 (ISBN 0-87403-212-1, 9848). Standard Pub.

CAROLS–HISTORY AND CRITICISM

Gilbert, David. Some Ancient Christmas Carols with the Tunes to Which They Were Formally Sung in the West of England. LC 72-6976. 1972. lib. bdg. 12.50 (ISBN 0-88305-249-0). Norwood Edns.

Greene, Richard L. The Early English Carols. LC 76-161945. 461p. 1935. Repr. 79.00x (ISBN 0-403-01342-9). Scholarly.

Routley, Erik. The English Carol. LC 73-9129. (Illus.). 272p. 1973. Repr. of 1959 ed. lib. bdg. 22.50x (ISBN 0-8371-6989-5, ROEC). Greenwood.

St. Amour, Sr. M. Paulina. Study of the "Villancico" up to Lope De Vega. LC 78-94170. (Catholic University of America Studies in Romance Languages & Literatures Ser: No. 21). Repr. of 1940 ed. 22.00 (ISBN 0-404-50321-7). AMS Pr.

Warren, Nathan B. Christmas in the Olden Time. LC 76-58002. 1977. Repr. of 1859 ed. lib. bdg. 22.50 (ISBN 0-8414-1656-7). Folcroft.

CARROLL FAMILY

Ives, J. Moss. Ark & the Dove: The Beginnings of Civil & Religious Liberties in America. LC 76-79200. (Illus.). 1969. Repr. of 1936 ed. 32.50x (ISBN 0-8154-0293-7). Cooper Sq.

CARTER, JIMMY, PRES. U. S., 1924-

Allen, Gary. Jimmy Carter-Jimmy Carter. 96p. pap. 1.00 (ISBN 0-686-31145-0). Concord Pr.

Vincent, Stephen, ed. Omens from the Flight of Birds: The First 101 Days of Jimmy Carter. (Illus.). 1978. pap. 4.95x (ISBN 0-917672-05-4). Momos.

CARTHUSIANS

Bauer, Erika. Heinrich Hallers Uberstzung Der'Imitatio Christi. Hogg, James, ed. (Analecta Cartusiana Ser.: No. 88). 224p. (Orig.). 1982. pap. 25.00 (ISBN 3-7052-0145-X, Pub by. Salzburg Studies). Longwood Pub Group.

Beltrutti, Georgio. Le Certose D'Italia (Liguria) La Certosa di Toirano. Hogg, James, ed. (Analecta Cartusiana Ser.: No. 101). 95p. (Orig.). 1982. pap. 25.00 (ISBN 0-317-42563-3, Pub. by Salzburg Studies). Longwood Pub Group.

Bodenstedt, Mary I. Praying the Life of Christ. Hogg, James, ed. (Analecta Cartusiana Ser.: No. 15). 184p. (Orig.). 1983. pap. 25.00 (ISBN 3-7052-0017-8, Pub by Salzburg Studies). Longwood Pub Group.

Boyer, Raymond & Brisson, Marie. Miscellanea Cartusiensia, Vol. 3. Hogg, James, ed. (Analecta Cartusiana Ser.: No. 42). (Fr. & Lat.). 101p. (Orig.). 1978. pap. 25.00 (ISBN 3-7052-0058-5, Pub by Salzburg Studies). Longwood Pub Group.

Brauer, Wilhelm. Einleitung Zu Den Werken Des Dom Georgius Schwengel. Hogg, James, ed. (Analecta Cartusiana Ser.: No. 90). 27p. (Orig.). 1982. pap. 25.00 (ISBN 3-7052-0147-6, Pub. by Salzburg Studies). Longwood Pub Group.

--Karthaus Und Sein Kloster "Marienparadies", Ein "Bildband" Zum Heimatbuch Des Kreises Karthaus. Hogg, James, ed. (Analecta Cartusiana Ser.: No. 93). 178p. (Orig.). 1980. pap. 25.00 (ISBN 3-7052-0162-X, Pub. by Salzburg Studies). Longwood Pub Group.

Bruno, Soeur & Osb, Barrier. Les Activities Du Solitaire En Chartreuse D'Apres Plus Anciens Temoins. (Analecta Cartusiana: No. 87). 159p. 1981. pap. 25.00 (ISBN 3-7052-0144-1, Pub. by Salzburg Studies). Longwood Pub Group.

Chiarelli, Caterina. Le Attivita Artistiche & il Patrimonio Librario della Certosa di Firenze, 2 vols. Hogg, James, ed. (Analecta Cartusiana Ser.: No. 102). 491p. (Orig.). 1984. pap. 50.00 (ISBN 0-317-42557-9, Pub. by Salzburg Studies). Longwood Pub Group.

De Grauwe, Jan. Histoire de la Chartreuse Sheen Anglorum au Continent: Bruges, Louvain, Malines, Nieuport (1559-1783) Hogg, James, ed. (Analecta Cartuaiana Ser.: No. 48). (Fr.). 254p. (Orig.). 1985. pap. 25.00 (ISBN 3-7052-0068-2, Pub by Salzburg Studies). Longwood Pub Group.

--Historia Cartusiana Belgica: Esquisse Historique et Apercu des Archives, des Bibliotheques et des Oeuvres D'Art. Hogg, James, ed. (Analecta Cartusiana: No. 51). (Orig.). 1985. pap. 25.00 (ISBN 3-7052-0071-2, Pub. by Salzburg Studies). Longwood Pub Group.

--Prosopographia Cartuaiana Belgica: 1314-1796. Hogg, James, ed. (Analecta Cartusiana Ser.: No. 28). (Flemish & Fr.). 360p. (Orig.). 1976. pap. 25.00 (ISBN 3-7052-0029-1, Pub by Salzburg Studies). Longwood Pub Group.

Devaux, Augustin. La Chartreuse de Selignac. Hogg, James, ed. (Analecta Cartusiana Ser.: No. 24). (Fr.). 313p. (Orig.). 1975. pap. 25.00 (ISBN 3-7052-0024-0, Pub by Salzburg Studies). Longwood Pub Group.

Dupont, Dom P. Sermons Capitulaires de la Chartreuse de Mayence du Debut du XV Siecle. Hogg, James, ed. (Analecta Cartusiana Ser.: No. 46). (Fr.). 193p. (Orig.). 1978. pap. 25.00 (ISBN 3-7052-0062-3, Pub by Salzburg Studies). Longwood Pub Group.

Du Pont, Guigo. Della Contemplazione. Hogg, James, ed. Piovesan, Emilio, tr. & intro. by. (Analecta Cartusiana Ser.: No. 45). (Ital. & Lat.). 123p. (Orig.). 1979. pap. 25.00 (ISBN 3-7052-0061-5, Pub by Salzburg Studies). Longwood Pub Group.

Englert, Robert W. Scattering & Oneing: A Study of Conflict in the Works of the Author of the Cloud of Unknowing. Hogg, James, ed. (Analecta Cartusiana Ser.: No. 105). 184p. (Orig.). 1983. pap. 25.00 (ISBN 0-317-42594-3, Pub. by Salzburg Studies). Longwood Pub Group.

Giacometti, Mario. Pregare in Certosa Oggi. Hogg, James, ed. (Analecta Cartusiana Ser.: No. 97). 141p. (Orig.). 1980. pap. 25.00 (ISBN 3-7052-0168-9, Pub. by Salzburg Studies). Longwood Pub Group.

Gilhodes, Abbe L. La Chartreuse Saint-Sauveur de Villefranche-de-Rouergue 1459-1791. Hogg, James, ed. (Analecta Cartusiana Ser.: No. 14). (Fr.). 236p. (Orig.). 1973. pap. 25.00 (ISBN 3-7052-0016-X, Pub by Salzburg Studies). Longwood Pub Group.

Gomez, Ildefonso. La Cartuja en Espana. Hogg, James, ed. (Analecta Cartusiana Ser.: No. 114). 499p. (Orig.). 1984. pap. 25.00 (ISBN 0-317-42560-9, Pub. by Salzburg Studies). Longwood Pub Group.

Hantschk, Rolanda. Die Geschichte der Kartause Mauerbach. Hogg, James, ed. (Analecta Cartusiana Ser.: No. 7). (Ger.). 164p. (Orig.). 1972. pap. 25.00 (ISBN 3-7052-0008-9, Pub by Salzburg Studies). Longwood Pub Group.

Hocquard, Gaston. Les Meditations du Bienheureux de Guigues de Saint Romain: Cinquieme Prieur de Chartreuse (1109-1136) Hogg, James, ed. (Analecta Cartusiana Ser.: No. 112). 311p. (Orig.). 1984. pap. 25.00 (ISBN 0-317-42589-7, Pub. by Salzburg Studies). Longwood Pub Group.

Hogg, James. Adam of Witham De Quadripartito Exercitio Cellae. (Analecta Cartusiana Ser.: No. 98). (Orig.). 1986. pap. 25.00 (ISBN 3-7052-0169-7, Pub. by Salzburg Studies). Longwood Pub Group.

--The Cartae of the Carthusian General Chapter of the Urbanist Observance During the Great Schism. (Analecta Cartusiana Ser.: No. 119). (Orig.). 1988. pap. 25.00 (ISBN 0-317-42562-5, Pub. by Salzburg Studies). Longwood Pub Group.

--La Cartuja De Aniago. (Analecta Cartusiana Ser.: No. 94/2). 204p. (Orig.). 1980. pap. 25.00 (ISBN 3-7052-0164-6, Pub. by Salzburg Studies). Longwood Pub Group.

--La Cartuja De Aniago: Introduction, Vol. 1. (Analecta Cartusiana: No. 94/1). 1987. pap. 25.00 (ISBN 3-7052-0163-8, Pub. by Salzburg Studies). Longwood Pub Group.

--La Cartuja de Scala Dei: (The Charterhouse of Scala Dei) (Analecta Cartusiana Ser.: No. 41-3). (Span. & Eng., Illus.). 54p. (Orig.). 1980. pap. 25.00 (ISBN 3-7052-0051-8, Pub by Salzburg Studies). Longwood Pub Group.

--La Cartuja de Val de Cristo: (The Charterhouse of Val de Cristo) (Analecta Cartusiana Ser.: No. 41-5). (Span. & Eng., Illus.). 50p. (Orig.). 1979. pap. 25.00 (ISBN 3-7052-0053-4, Pub by Salzburg Studies). Longwood Pub Group.

--Las Cartujas de las Cuevas, Cazalla de la Sierra y Granada: (The Charterhouses of las Cuevas, Cazalla de la Sierra & Granada) (Analecta Cartuasiana Ser.: No. 47-3). (Span., Illus.). 110p. (Orig.). 1979. pap. 25.00 (ISBN 3-7052-0065-8, Pub by Salzburg Studies). Longwood Pub Group.

--Las Cartujas de Montalegre, Sant Pol de Maresme, Vallparadis, Ara Coeli y Via Coeli. (Analecta Cartusiana Ser.: No. 41-2). (Span., Illus.). 140p. (Orig.). 1983. pap. 25.00 (ISBN 3-7052-0050-X, Pub by Salzburg Studies). Longwood Pub Group.

--La Certosa di Serra San Bruno. (Analecta Cartusiana Ser.: No. 26-2). (Ital. & Eng., Illus.). 61p. (Orig.). 1980. pap. 25.00 (ISBN 3-7052-0027-5, Pub by Salzburg Studies). Longwood Pub Group.

--The Charterhouses of Buxheim, Ittingen & la Valsainte. (Analecta Cartusiana Ser.: No. 38). (Illus.). 220p. (Orig.). 1977. pap. 25.00 (ISBN 3-7052-0045-3, Pub by Salzburg Studies). Longwood Pub Group.

--The Charterhouses of las Cuevas, Jerez de la Frontera, Cazalla & Granada: Introduction. (Analecta Cartusiana Ser.: No. 47-1). (Orig.). 1986. pap. 25.00 (ISBN 3-7052-0063-1, Pub by Salzburg Studies). Longwood Pub Group.

--The Charterhouses of the Carthusian Provinces of Catalonia. (Analecta Cartusiana Ser.: No. 41-1). (Orig.). 1986. pap. 25.00 (ISBN 3-7052-0049-6, Pub by Salzburg Studies). Longwood Pub Group.

--The Evolution of the Carthusian Statutes from the Consuetudines Guigonis to the Teria Compilatio, 2 Vols. (Analecta Cartusiana: No. 99). (Orig.). 1988. pap. 50.00 (ISBN 3-7052-0170-0, Pub. by Salzburg Studies). Longwood Pub Group.

--The Fyrst Boke of the Introduction of Knowledge by Andrew Borde, Vol. 2 Text. (Analecta Cartusiana Ser.: No. 92/2). 103p. (Orig.). 1979. pap. 25.00 (ISBN 3-7052-0161-1, Pub. by Salzburg Studies). Longwood Pub Group.

--The Fyrst Boke of the Introduction of Knowledge by Andrew Borde: Introduction, Vol. 1. (Analecta Cartusiana Ser.: No. 92/1). (Orig.). 1987. pap. 25.00 (ISBN 3-7052-0160-3, Pub. by Salzburg Studies). Longwood Pub Group.

--Gugleilmo di Saint-Thierry: La Lettera d'Oro. (Analecta Cartusiana Ser.: No. 37). 144p. (Orig.). 1977. pap. 25.00 (ISBN 3-7052-0044-5, Pub by Salzburg Studies). Longwood Pub Group.

--An Illustrated Yorkshire Carthusian Religious Miscellany, 2 Vols. (Analecta Cartusiana Ser.: No. 95/1-2). (Orig.). 1985. pap. 50.00 (ISBN 3-7052-0165-4, Pub. by Salzburg Studies). Longwood Pub Group.

--An Illustrated Yorkshire Carthusian Religious Miscellany, Vol. 3. (Analecta Cartusiana Ser.: No. 95/3). 140p. (Orig.). 1981. pap. 25.00 (ISBN 3-7052-0166-2, Pub. by Salzburg Studies). Longwood Pub Group.

--Die Kartauser und die Reformation: Internationaler Kongress Vom 24 bis 27 1983, 2 vols. (Analecta Cartusiana Ser.: No. 108). 320p. (Orig.). 1984. pap. 50.00 (ISBN 0-317-42576-5, Pub. by Salzburg Studies). Longwood Pub Group.

--Leopold Brenner, Historia Cartusia Mauerancensis. (Analecta Cartusiana Ser.: No. 32). (Orig.). 1987. pap. 25.00 (ISBN 3-7052-0033-X, Pub by Salzburg Studies). Longwood Pub Group.

--Medieval Carthisian Costomaries, Pt. 2. (Analecta Carusiana Ser.: No. 2). (Orig.). 1986. pap. 25.00 (ISBN 3-7052-0002-X, Pub by Salzburg Studies). Longwood Pub Group.

--Passio XVIII Cartusianorum in Anglia Martyrum a Domo Maurito Chauncy: A Critical Study. (Analecta Cartusiana Ser.: No. 86). (Orig.). 1987. pap. 25.00 (ISBN 3-7052-0143-3, Pub. by Salzburg Studies). Longwood Pub Group.

--La Real Caruja de Jesus Nazareno de Valldemossa. (Analecta Cartusiana Ser.: No. 41-9). (Span., Illus.). 66p. (Orig.). 1983. pap. 25.00 (ISBN 3-7052-0057-7, Pub by Salzburg Studies). Longwood Pub Group.

--The Register of the Charterhouse of London: Land Rev. Misc Book 61 of the London Public Record Office. (Analecta Cartusiana Ser.: No. 89). (Orig.). 1987. 25.00 (ISBN 3-7052-0146-8, Pub. by Salzburg Studies). Longwood Pub Group.

--El Santo Rosario en la Cartuja. (Analecta Cartusiana Ser.: No. 103). 134p. (Orig.). 1983. pap. 25.00 (ISBN 0-317-42593-5, Pub. by Salzburg Studies). Longwood Pub Group.

--The Speculum Devotorum of an Anonymous Carhusian of Sheen: From the manuscripts Cambridge University Library (Gg. I.6 & Foyle Vol.2) (Analecta Carusiana Ser.: No. 12). (Eng.). 173p. (Orig.). 1973. pap. 25.00 (ISBN 3-7052-0013-5, Pub by Salzburg Studies). Longwood Pub Group.
--The Speculum Devotorum of an Anonymous Carthusian of Sheen: Introduction. (Analceta Cartusiana Ser.: No. 11). (Orig.). 1985. pap. 25.00 (ISBN 3-7052-0012-7, Pub by Salzburg Studies). Longwood Pub Group.
--The 'Speculum Inclusorum' MS. British Library London Harley 2372: A Critical Edition, Vol. 1. (Analecta Cartusiana Ser.: No. 59-1). (Orig.). 1985. pap. 25.00 (ISBN 3-7052-0086-0, Pub. by Salzburg Studies). Longwood Pub Group.
--The 'Speculum Incusorum' MS. British Library London Harley 2372. (Analecta Cartusiana Ser.: No. 59-2). (Lat.). 139p. (Orig.). 1981. pap. 25.00 (ISBN 3-7052-0087-9, Pub. by Salzburg Studies). Longwood Pub Group.
--The Statuta Jancelini Twelve Twenty-Two & the De Reformatione of Prior Bernard Twelve Forty-Eight. (Analecta Cartusiana Ser.: No. 65-2). 162p. (Orig.). 1978. pap. 25.00 (ISBN 3-7052-0096-8, Pub. by Salzburg Studies). Longwood Pub Group.
--The 'Statuta Jancelini' Twelve Twenty-Two & The 'De Reformatione of Prior Bernard Twelve Forty-Eight: A Critical Edition, Vol. 1. (Analecta Cartusiana Ser.: No. 65-1). (Orig.). 1985. pap. 25.00 (ISBN 3-7052-0095-X, Pub. by Salzburg Studies). Longwood Pub Group.
--Trisulti: Art & Architecture. (Analecta Cartusiana Ser.: No. 74-2). (Orig.). 1984. pap. 25.00 (ISBN 3-7052-0110-7, Pub. by Salzburg Studies). Longwood Pub Group.
Hogg, James & Sargent, Michael. The Chartae Of The Carthusian General Chapter, Vol. 1. (Analecta Catusiana Ser.: No. 100/1). 186p. (Orig.). 1983. pap. 25.00 (ISBN 3-7052-0171-9, Pub. by Salzburg Studies). Longwood Pub Group.
--The Chartae of the Carthusian General Chapter, Vol. 2. (Analecta Cartusiana Ser.: No. 100/2). 229p. (Orig.). 1983. pap. 25.00 (ISBN 3-7052-0172-7, Pub. by Salzburg Studies). Longwood Pub Group.
--The Chartae of the Carthusian General Chapter, Vol. 3. (Analecta Cartusiana Ser.: No. 100/3). 209p. (Orig.). 1984. pap. 25.00 (ISBN 3-7052-0173-5, Pub. by Salzburg Studies). Longwood Pub Group.
--The Chartae of the Carthusian General Chapter, Vol. 4. (Analecta Cartusiana Ser.: No. 100/4). 241p. (Orig.). 1984. pap. 25.00 (ISBN 0-317-42565-X, Pub. by Salzburg Studies). Longwood Pub Group.
--The Chartae of the Carthusian General Chapter, Vol. 5. (Analecta Cartusiana Ser.: No. 100/5). 229p. (Orig.). 1985. pap. 25.00 (ISBN 0-317-42566-8, Pub. by Salzburg Studies). Longwood Pub Group.
--The Chartae of the Carthusian General Chapter, Vol. 6. (Analecta Cartusiana Ser.: No. 100/6). 1985. pap. 25.00 (ISBN 0-317-42567-6, Pub. by Salzburg Studies). Longwood Pub Group.
--The Chartae of the Carthusian General Chapter, Vol. 7. (Analecta Cartusiana Ser.: No. 100/7). (Orig.). 1985. pap. 25.00 (ISBN 0-317-42569-2, Pub. by Salzburg Studies). Longwood Pub Group.
--The Chartae of the Carthusian General Chapter, Vol. 8. (Analecta Cartusiana Ser.: No. 100/8). (Orig.). 1986. pap. 25.00 (ISBN 0-317-42570-6, Pub. by Salzburg Studies). Longwood Pub Group.
--The Chartae of the Carthusian General Chapter, Vol. 9. (Analecta Cartusiana Ser.: No. 100/9). (Orig.). 1987. pap. 25.00 (ISBN 0-317-42571-4, Pub. by Salzburg Studies). Longwood Pub Group.
Hogg, James, ed. La Cultura Artistica Nelle Certose Europee. (Analecta Cartusiana Ser.: No. 115). (Orig.). 1986. pap. 25.00 (ISBN 0-317-42572-2, Pub. by Salzburg Studies). Longwood Pub Group.
--Kartauserliturgie. (Analecta Cartusiana Ser.: No. 116). (Orig.). 1987. pap. 25.00 (ISBN 3-7052-0196-4, Pub. by Salzburg Studies). Longwood Pub Group.
--Kartausermystik und Mystiker, Vol. 1. (Analecta Cartusiana Ser.: No. 55-1). 238p. (Orig.). 1981. pap. 25.00 (ISBN 0-317-40525-X, Pub. by Salzburg Studies). Longwood Pub Group.
--Kartausermystik und Mystiker, Vol. 2. (Analecta Cartusiana Ser.: No. 55-2). 226p. (Orig.). 1981. pap. 25.00 (ISBN 3-7052-0077-1, Pub. by Salzburg Studies). Longwood Pub Group.
--Kartausermystik und Mystiker, Vol. 3. (Analecta Carusiana Ser.: No. 55-3). 198p. 1982. pap. 25.00 (ISBN 3-7052-0078-X, Pub. by Salzburg Studies). Longwood Pub Group.
--Kartausermystik und Mystiker, Vol. 4. (Analecta Cartusiana Ser.: No. 55-4). 172p. (Orig.). 1982. pap. 25.00 (ISBN 3-7052-0079-8, Pub. by Salzburg Studies). Longwood Pub Group.
--Kartausermystik und Mystiker, Vol. 5. (Analecta Cartusiana Ser.: No. 55-5). 103p. (Orig.). 1982. pap. 25.00 (ISBN 3-7052-0080-1, Pub. by Salzburg Studies). Longwood Pub Group.
--Kartauserregel und Kartauserleben: Internationaler Kongress Vom XX, 30 Mai bis 3 Juni 1984, Sift Heilgenkrezv, 3 vols. (Analecta Cartusiana Ser.: No. 113/1-3). 744p. (Orig.). 1984. pap. 85.00 (ISBN 0-317-42577-3, Pub. by Salzburg Studies). Longwood Pub Group.
--Kartauserschriftsteller. (Analecta Cartusiana Ser.: No. 117). (Orig.). 1988. pap. 25.00 (ISBN 0-317-42580-3, Pub. by Salzburg Studies). Longwood Pub Group.
Hogg, James, ed. & intro. by. Late Fifteenth Century Carthusian Rubrics for the Deacon & The Sacristan: (From the Ms. Valsainte 42-T.I.8) (Analecta Cartusiana Ser.: No. 4). (Lat. & Eng.). 169p. (Orig.). 1971. pap. 25.00 (ISBN 3-7052-0004-6, Pub by Salzburg Studies). Longwood Pub Group.
Hogg, James, ed. Mauerbach und die Kartauser: Symposium Uber die Kartausegeschichte und - Spiritualitat 27, 28 May 1983. (Analecta Cartusiana Ser.: No. 110). 98p. (Orig.). 1984. pap. 25.00 (ISBN 0-317-42585-4, Pub. by Salzburg Studies). Longwood Pub Group.
--Mittelalterliche Caerimonialia der Kartauser, Pr. 1. (Analecta Cartusiana Ser.: No. 2). (Ger. & Lat.). 354p. 1971. pap. 25.00 (ISBN 3-7052-0001-1, Pub by Salzburg Studies). Longwood Pub Group.
--Spatmittelalterliche Geistliche Literatur in der Nationalsprache, Vol. 1. (Analecta Cartusiana Ser.: No. 106/1). 236p. (Orig.). 1983. pap. 25.00 (ISBN 0-317-42595-1, Pub. by Salzburg Studies). Longwood Pub Group.
--Spatmittelalterliche Geistliche Literatur in der Nationalsprache, Vol. 2. (Analecta Cartusiana Ser.: No. 106/2). 190p. (Orig.). 1984. pap. 25.00 (ISBN 0-317-42596-X, Pub. by Salzburg Studies). Longwood Pub Group.
--The Speculum Devotorum of an Anonymous Carhusian of Sheen: From the Manuscripts Cambridge University Library (Gg. I.6 & Foyle Vol.3, Pt. 2) (Analecta Carusiana Ser.: No. 13). (Eng.). 174p. (Orig.). 1974. pap. 25.00 (ISBN 3-7052-0014-3, Pub by Salzburg Studies). Longwood Pub Group.
--Spiritualitat Heute und Gestern, Vol. 1. (Analceta Carusiana Ser.: No. 35). (Eng, Ger, & Fr.). 236p. (Orig.). 1982. pap. 25.00 (ISBN 3-7052-0037-2, Pub by Salzburg Studies). Longwood Pub Group.
--Spiritualitat Heute und Gestern, Vol. 3. (Analecta Carusiana Ser.: No. 35). (Ital, Ger, & Eng.). 174p. (Orig.). 1983. pap. 25.00 (ISBN 3-7052-0039-9, Pub by Salzburg Studies). Longwood Pub Group.
--Spiritualitat Heute und Gestern, Vol. 4. (Analecta Carusiana Ser.: No. 35). (Fr, Ital, Ger, & Eng., Illus.). 131p. (Orig.). 1984. pap. 25.00 (ISBN 3-7052-0040-2, Pub by Salzburg Studies). Longwood Pub Group.
--Spiritualitat Heute und Gestern, Vol. 5. (Analecta Cartusiana Ser.: No. 35). (Orig.). 1984. pap. 25.00 (ISBN 3-7052-0041-0, Pub by Salzburg Studies). Longwood Pub Group.
--Spiritualitiat Heute und Gestern, Vol. 2. (Analecta Cartusiana Ser.: No. 35). (Ger. & Eng.). 200p. (Orig.). 1983. pap. 25.00 (ISBN 3-7052-0038-0, Pub by Salzburg Studies). Longwood Pub Group.
Kempf, Nicolas. Tractatus de Mystica Theologia, Vol. 2. Hogg, James, ed. (Analecta Cartusiana Ser.: No. 9). (Lat. & Fr.). 574p. (Orig.). 1973. pap. 50.00 (ISBN 3-7052-0010-0, Pub by Salzburg Studies). Longwood Pub Group.
Legendre, Jaquelin. La Chartruese de Lugne des Origines au Debut 14e Siecle 1172-1332. Hogg, James, ed. (Analecta Cartusiana Ser.: No. 27). (Fr., Illus.). 204p. (Orig.). 1975. pap. 25.00 (ISBN 3-7052-0028-3, Pub by Salzburg Studies). Longwood Pub Group.
Macken, Raymond. Denys the Carthusian: Commentator on Boethius's De Consolatione Philosophiae. Hogg, James, ed. (Analecta Cartusiana Ser.: No. 118). 94p. (Orig.). 1984. pap. 25.00 (ISBN 0-317-42573-0, Pub. by Salzburg Studies). Longwood Pub Group.
Marks, Richard B. The Medieval Manuscript Library of the Charterhouse of St. Barbara in Cologne, Vols. 1 & 2. Hogg, James, ed. (Analecta Cartusiana Ser.: Nos. 21 & 22). (Illus.). 473p. (Orig.). 1974. Set. pap. 50.00 (ISBN 3-7052-0022-4, Pub by Salzburg Studies). Longwood Pub Group.
Mayer, Erwin. Die Geschichte der Kartause Seitz. Hogg, James, ed. (Analecta Cartusiana Ser.: No. 104). 116p. (Orig.). 1983. pap. 25.00 (ISBN 0-317-42574-9, Pub. by Salzburg Studies). Longwood Pub Group.
Orban, A. P. Die Korrespondenz und die Liber Exhortacionis des Heinrich Von Kalkar: Eine Kritische Ausgabe. Hogg, James, ed. (Analecta Cartusiana Ser.: No. 111). 303p. (Orig.). 1984. pap. 25.00 (ISBN 0-317-42581-1, Pub. by Salzburg Studies). Longwood Pub Group.
Pisani, Maria S. La Certosa di Serra San Bruno Nella Storia del Monachesimo. Hogg, James, ed. (Analcecta Cartusiana Ser.: No. 26-1). (Ital.). 131p. (Orig.). 1976. pap. 25.00 (ISBN 3-7052-0026-7, Pub. by Salzburg Studies). Longwood Pub Group.
Propago Sacri Ordinis Cartusiensis-Apparatus ad Annales Carytusiae Paradisi B.M.V, 2 Vols. (Analecta Cartusiana Ser.: No. 90/10). 454p. 1982. pap. 50.00 (ISBN 3-7052-0157-3, Pub. by Salzburg Studies). Longwood Pub Group.
Salter, Elizabeth. Nicolas Love's Myrrour of the Blessed Lyf of Jesu Christ. Hogg, James, ed. (Analecta Carusiana Ser.: No. 10). (Orig.). 1974. pap. 25.00 (ISBN 3-7052-0011-9, Pub by Salzburg Studies). Longwood Pub Group.
Sargent, Michael & Hogg, James. Nicholas Love: The Myrrour of the Blessed LYF of Jesu Christ, 2 Vols. (Analecta Cartusiana Ser.: No. 91). (Orig.). 1987. pap. 50.00 (ISBN 3-7052-0159-X, Pub. by Salzburg Studies). Longwood Pub Group.
Sargent, Michael G. James Grenehalgh As Textual Critic. Hogg, James, ed. (Analecta Cartusiana Ser.: No. 85/1&2). 589p. (Orig.). 1984. pap. 50.00 (ISBN 3-7052-0142-5, Pub. by Salzburg Studies). Longwood Pub Group.
Savary, Louis M. Psychological Themes in the Golden Epistle of William Saint-Thierry to the Carthusians of Mont-Dieu. Hogg, James, ed. (Analecta Cartusiana Ser.: No. 8). 198p. (Orig.). 1973. pap. 25.00 (ISBN 3-7052-0009-7, Pub by Salzburg Studies). Longwood Pub Group.
Schwengel, Georgius. Propago Sacri Ordinis Cartusienses per Germaniam Pars 2, 2 Vols. Hogg, James, ed. (Analecta Cartusiana Ser.: No. 90/4). 378p. 1982. pap. 50.00 (ISBN 3-7052-0151-4, Pub. by Salzburg Studies). Longwood Pub Group.
--Propago Sacri Ordinis Cartusiensis-Appartus Annales Sacri Ordinis Cartusiensis, 3 Vols. Hogg, James, ed. (Analecta Cartusiana Ser.: No. 90/9). 534p. (Orig.). 1983. pap. 85.00 (ISBN 3-7052-0156-5, Pub. by Salzburg Studies). Longwood Pub Group.
--Propago Sacri Ordinis Cartusiensis: Appendix ad Tom I, 2 Vols. Hogg, James, ed. (Analecta Cartusiana Ser.: No. 90/5). 440p. (Orig.). 1983. pap. 50.00 (ISBN 3-7052-0152-2, Pub. by Salzburg Studies). Longwood Pub Group.
--Propago Sacri Ordinis Cartusiensis: Appendis ad Tom II, 2 Vols. Hogg, James, ed. (Analecta Cartusiana: No. 90/6). 397p. (Orig.). 1983. pap. 50.00 (ISBN 0-317-42583-8, Pub. by Salzburg Studies). Longwood Pub Group.
--Propago Sacri Ordinis Cartusiensis: Appendix ad Tom III, 2 vols. Hogg, James, ed. (Analecta Cartusiana Ser.: No. 90/7). 357p. (Orig.). 1983. pap. 50.00 (ISBN 3-7052-0154-9, Pub. by Salzburg Studies). Longwood Pub Group.
--Propago Sacri Ordinis Cartusiensis: Appendix ad Tom IV, 2 Vols. Hogg, James, ed. (Analecta Cartusiana: No. 90/8). 412p. (Orig.). 1983. pap. 50.00 (ISBN 3-7052-0155-7, Pub. by Salzburg Studies). Longwood Pub Group.
--Propago Sacri Ordinis Cartusiensis de Provinciis Burgundiae, Franciae, Picardiae, Teutoniae et Angliae. Hogg, James, ed. (Analecta Cartusiana Ser.: No. 90/2). 276p. (Orig.). 1981. pap. 25.00 (ISBN 3-7052-0149-2, Pub. by Salzburg Studies). Longwood Pub Group.
--Propago Sacri Ordinis Cartusiensis-Diplomata Poloniae et Prussiae, 2 Vols. Hogg, James, ed. (Analecta Cartusiana Ser.: No. 90/11). 256p. (Orig.). 1982. pap. 50.00 (ISBN 3-7052-0158-1, Pub. by Salzburg Studies). Longwood Pub Group.
--Propago Sacri Ordinis Cartusiensis per Franciam, 2 Vols. Hogg, James, ed. (Analecta Cartusiana Ser.: No. 90/1). 300p. (Orig.). 1984. pap. 50.00 (ISBN 3-7052-0148-4, Pub. by Salzburg Studies). Longwood Pub Group.
--Propago Sacri Ordinis Cartusiensis per Germaniam. Hogg, James, ed. (Analecta Cartusiana Ser.: No. 90/3). 480p. (Orig.). 1981. pap. 25.00 (ISBN 3-7052-0150-6, Pub. by Salzburg Studies). Longwood Pub Group.
Stohlker, Friedrich. Die Kartause Buxheim, 2 Vols. Hogg, James, ed. (Analecta Cartusiana Ser.: No. 96). (Orig.). 1985. pap. 50.00 (ISBN 3-7052-0167-0, Pub. by Salzburg Studies). Longwood Pub Group.
Thompson, E. Margaret. The Carthusian Order in England. (Church Historical Society London N. S. Ser.: No. 3). Repr. of 1930 ed. 80.00 (ISBN 0-8115-3127-9). Kraus Repr.
Tromby, Benedetto. Storia Critico Chronologica Diplomatica del Patriarca S. Brunone e del Suo Ordine Cartusiano, 2 pts, Vol. 1. Hogg, James, ed. (Analecta Cartusiana Ser.: No. 84-1). 523p. (Orig.). 1981. pap. 50.00 (ISBN 3-7052-0131-X, Pub. by Salzburg Stiudies). Longwood Pub Group.
--Storia Critico Chronologica Diplomatica del Patriarca S. Brunone e del Suo Ordine Cartusiano, 2 pts, Vol. 3. Hogg, James, ed. (Analecta Cartusiana Ser.: No. 84-3). 522p. 1982. pap. 50.00 (ISBN 3-7052-0133-6, Pub. by Salzburg Studies). Longwood Pub Group.
--Storia Critico-Chronologica-Diplomatica del Patriarca S. Brunone E Del Suo Ordine Cartusiano, Vol. 4 (2 pts.) Hogg, James, ed. (Analecta Cartusiana Ser.: No. 84-4). 632p. (Orig.). 1982. pap. 50.00 (ISBN 3-7052-0134-4, Pub. by Salzburg Studies). Longwood Pub Group.
--Storia Critico-Chronologica-Diplomatica del Patriarca S. Brunone E. del Suo Ordine Cartusiano, 2 pts, Vol. 6. Hogg, James, ed. (Analecta Cartusiana Ser.: No. 84/6). 632p. (Orig.). 1982. pap. 50.00 (ISBN 3-7052-0136-0, Pub. by Salzburg Studies). Longwood Pub Group.
--Storia Critico-Chronologica-Diplomatica del Patriarca S. Brunone E del Suo Ordine Cartusiano, 2 pts, Vol. 7. Hogg, James, ed. (Analecta Cartusiana Ser.: No. 84/7). 637p. (Orig.). 1982. pap. 50.00 (ISBN 3-7052-0137-9, Pub. by Salzburg Studies). Longwood Pub Group.
--Storia Critico-Chronologica-Diplomatica del Patriarca S. Brunone E del Suo Ordine Carusiano, 2 pts, Vol. 8. Hogg, James, ed. (Analecta Cartusiana: No. 84-8). 574p. (Orig.). 1982. pap. 50.00 (ISBN 3-7052-0138-7, Pub. by Salzburg Studies). Longwood Pub Group.
--Storia-Critico-Chronologica-Diplomatica del Patriarca S. Brunone E. del Suo Cartusiano, 2 pts, Vol. 9. Hogg, James, ed. (Analecta Cartusiana: No. 84-9). 638p. (Orig.). 1982. pap. 50.00 (ISBN 3-7052-0139-5, Pub. by Salzburg Studies). Longwood Pub Group.
--Storia Critico-Chronologica-Diplomatica del Patriarca S. Brunone E. del Suo Ordine Cartusiano, 3 pts, Vol. 10. Hogg, James, ed. (Analecta Cartusiana Ser.: No. 84-10). 730p. (Orig.). 1982. pap. 85.00 (ISBN 3-7052-0140-9, Pub. by Salzburg Studies). Longwood Pub Group.
--Storia Critico-Chronologica-Diplomatica del Patriarca S. Brunone E. del Suo Ordine Cartusiano, Vol. 11. Hogg, James, ed. (Analecta Cartusiana Ser.: No. 84-11). 31p. (Orig.). 1981. pap. 7.50 (ISBN 3-7052-0141-7, Pub. by Salzburg Studies). Longwood Pub Group.
Whatmore, L. E. The Carthusians under King Henry the Eighth. Hogg, James, ed. (Analecta Cartusiana Ser.: No. 109). 227p. (Orig.). 1983. pap. 25.00 (ISBN 0-317-42558-7, Pub. by Salzburg Studies). Longwood Pub Group.

CARTWRIGHT, THOMAS, 1535-1603

Sutcliffe, Matthew. The Examination of T. Cartwrights Late Apologie. LC 72-7837. (English Experience Ser.: No. 558). 120p. 1973. Repr. of 1596 ed. 13.00 (ISBN 90-221-0558-X). Walter J Johnson.

CASAS, BARTOLOME DE LAS, BP. OF CHIAPA, 1474-1566

MacNutt, F. A. Bartolome de las Casas. 59.95 (ISBN 0-87968-708-8). Gordon Pr.
MacNutt, Francis A. Bartholomew De Las Casas: His Life, His Apostolate, & His Writings. LC 70-172712. Repr. of 1909 ed. 32.45 (ISBN 0-404-07146-5). AMS Pr.

CASES OF CONSCIENCE

see Casuistry

CASILDA, SAINT, fl. 1050–JUVENILE LITERATURE

Trevino, Elizabeth B. De. Casilda of the Rising Moon. LC 67-10389. 224p. 1967. 3.95 (ISBN 0-374-31188-9). FS&G.

CASUISTRY

see also Conscience; Pastoral Counseling; Responsa

Cathcart, Dwight. Doubting Conscience: Donne & the Poetry of Moral Argument. LC 74-78985. 1975. 10.00x (ISBN 0-472-08198-5). U of Mich Pr.
Merrill, Thomas F. Willian Perkins 1558-1602, English Puritanist--His Pioneer Works on Casuistry: Discourse on Conscience & the Whole Treatise of Cases of Conscience. xx, 242p. 1966. text ed. 28.50x (Pub. by B De Graaf Netherlands). Coronet Bks.
Perkins, William. The Whole Treatise of the Cases of Conscience. LC 74-38218. (English Experience Ser.: No. 482). 690p. 1972. Repr. of 1606 ed. 43.00 (ISBN 90-221-0482-6). Walter J Johnson.
Starr, G. A. Defoe & Casuistry. LC 75-113010. 1971. 25.50x (ISBN 0-691-06192-0). Princeton U Pr.

CATABAPTISTS

see Anabaptists

CATACOMBS
see also Christian Art and Symbolism
Adams, William H. Famous Caves & Catacombs. facsimile ed. LC 70-37773. (Essay Index Reprint Ser). Repr. of 1886 ed. 23.00 (ISBN 0-8369-2577-7). Ayer Co Pubs.
Aringhi, Paolo. The Catacombs of Rome, 2 vols. (Printed Sources of Western Ser.). (Lat., Illus.). 1981. pap. 120.00 slipcase (ISBN 0-915346-61-3). A Wofsy Fine Arts.
Davisson, Emmett D. Art & Mysteries in Tombs, Mummies & Catacombs. (Illus.). 1980. deluxe ed. 97.45 deluxe binding (ISBN 0-930582-63-2). Gloucester Art.
Giffin, Rodney & Giffin, Sara. In the Catacombs of Rome. 1982. pap. 3.00 (ISBN 0-89536-524-3, 0902). CSS of Ohio.
Stevenson, J. The Catacombs: Rediscovered Monuments of Early Christianity. (Ancient Peoples & Places Ser.). (Illus.). 1978. 19.95 (ISBN 0-500-02091-4). Thames Hudson.

CATECHETICAL ILLUSTRATIONS
see Homiletical Illustrations

CATECHETICAL SERMONS
Augustine, St. St. Augustine, the First Catechetical Instruction. Quasten, J. & Plumpe, J., eds. Christopher, Joseph P., tr. LC 78-62449. (Ancient Christian Writers Ser.: No. 2). 170p. 1946. 10.95 (ISBN 0-8091-0047-9). Paulist Pr.
Kurth, Edwin W. Catechetical Helps. 1981. pap. text ed. 4.95 (ISBN 0-570-03507-4, 14-1261). Concordia.
Williams, F. Chenhalls. Captain Sebastian: Fifty-Two Talks to Boys & Girls. 96p. 1961. pap. 2.75 (ISBN 0-87921-007-9). Attic Pr.

CATECHETICS
see also Catechetical Sermons; Catechisms; Christian Education; Confirmation–Instruction and Study; First Communion
also subdivision Catechisms and Creeds under names of Christian denominations, e.g. Catholic Church–Catechisms and Creeds
Anselm of Canterbury. Why God Became Man & the Virgin Conception & Original Sin. Colleran, Joseph M., tr. from Latin. & intro. by. LC 71-77166. 256p. (Orig.). 1982. pap. text ed. 4.95x (ISBN 0-87343-025-5). Magi Bks.
Boucher, Therese. Becoming a Sensuous Catechist: Using the Arts in Religion Classes. (Illus.). 80p. 1984. pap. 5.95 (ISBN 0-89622-216-0). Twenty-Third.
Boyd, Don & Sedano, Maruja. Master Catechist Guide for the Catechist Formation Book. LC 82-60853. 1982. pap. 3.95 (ISBN 0-8091-2471-8). Paulist Pr.
Edwards, O. C., Jr. & Westerhoff, John H., 3rd, eds. A Faithful Church: Issues in the History of Catechesis. LC 80-81099. 320p. (Orig.). 1981. pap. 14.95 (ISBN 0-8192-1278-4). Morehouse.
An Explanation of Dr. Martin Luther's Small Catechism. 265p. 1982. write for info. (ISBN 0-89279-043-1). Board Pub Evang.
Foley, Rita. Create! 2nd ed. (Catechist Training Ser.). 1982. 3.95 (ISBN 0-8215-1230-7). Sadlier.
Jean, Rael & Issac, Erich. The Coercive Utopians. (Christian Activist Ser.). 1985. pap. 7.95 (ISBN 0-89526-815-9). Regnery Bks.
Lange, A. H. Catechetical Review. pap. 0.55 (ISBN 0-570-03520-1, 14-1102). Concordia.
Leary, Michael. Christ & the Catechist: The Spiritual Life of the Christian Teacher. LC 86-83017. 128p. 1987. pap. 6.95 (ISBN 0-89870-139-2). Ignatius Pr.
Malloy, Joseph L., ed. Catechism for Inquirers. 4th ed. 1984. pap. 2.50 (ISBN 0-8091-5012-3). Paulist Pr.
On Catechesis in Our Time. 100p. 1976. pap. 3.95 (ISBN 1-55586-654-9). US Catholic.
Sork, David, et al. The Catechist Formation Book. LC 80-84507. 200p. (Orig.). 1981. pap. 7.95 (ISBN 0-8091-2365-7). Paulist Pr.
Tucker, Beverley D. Questions on the Way. 160p. (Orig.). 1987. pap. price not set (ISBN 0-88028-056-5). Forward Movement.
Warren, Michael, ed. Sourcebook for Modern Catechetics. LC 83-50246. 496p. (Orig.). 1983. pap. 15.95 (ISBN 0-88489-152-6). St Mary's.
Zanzig, Thomas. Sharing the Christian Message: A Program Manual for Volunteer Catechists, Ninth Grade. 1977. pap. 9.95 (ISBN 0-88489-086-4); duplicating masters 5.95 (ISBN 0-88489-128-3). St Mary's.

CATECHETICS–CATHOLIC CHURCH
Brown, Raymond E. Biblical Exegesis & Church Doctrine. 5.95 (ISBN 0-8091-2750-4). Paulist Pr.
Catholic Bishops of England & Wales Staff. A Catechism of Christian Doctrine. LC 82-50599. 72p. 1982. pap. 2.00 (ISBN 0-89555-176-4). TAN Bks Pubs.
Council of Trent Staff. The Catechism of the Council of Trent. LC 82-50588. 603p. 1983. pap. 15.00 (ISBN 0-89555-185-3). TAN Bks Pubs.
Daughters of St Paul. Basic Catechism. 1980. 3.00 (ISBN 0-8198-0622-6); pap. 2.00 (ISBN 0-8198-0623-4). Dghtrs St Paul.
Douglas, J. D. & Cairns, Earle E., eds. The New International Dictionary of the Christian Church. rev. ed. 1978. 29.95 (ISBN 0-310-23830-7, 11100). Zondervan.
Falvan, Michael, et al, eds. Faith & Culture: A Multicultural Catechetical Resource. 96p. (Orig.). 1987. pap. 5.95 (ISBN 1-55586-994-7). US Catholic.
Father James F. Hawker. Catechetics in the Catholic School. 61p. 1986. 6.60 (ISBN 0-318-20569-6). Natl Cath Educ.
Hofinger, Johannes. Art of Teaching Christian Doctrine. rev. ed. 1962. 14.95 (ISBN 0-268-00015-8). U of Notre Dame Pr.
Introduction to Sharing the Light of Faith. 48p. 1979. pap. 2.75 (ISBN 1-55586-685-9). US Catholic.
Kelley, Francis D., pref. by. Media & Catechetics Today: Towards the Year 2000. 24p. 1980. 3.60 (ISBN 0-686-29243-X). Natl Cath Educ.
Kelly, George A. Catechetical Instruction & the Catholic Faithful. 226p. 1982. 5.95 (ISBN 0-8198-1418-0, RA0015); pap. 4.95 (ISBN 0-8198-1419-9). Dghtrs St Paul.
Marthaler, Berard L. An Official Commentary for Sharing the Light of Faith. 119p. 1981. pap. 7.50 (ISBN 1-55586-694-8). US Catholic.
Norms & Guidelines for Catechetical Planners. 112p. 1980. pap. 3.75 (ISBN 1-55586-686-7). US Catholic.
Ott, Ludwig. Fundamentals of Catholic Dogma. Bastible, James C., ed. Lynch, Patrick, tr. from Ger. Orig. Title: Grundriss der Katholischen Dogmatik. 1974. pap. 15.00 (ISBN 0-89555-009-1). TAN Bks Pubs.
Pelikan, Jaroslav. The Christian Tradition: A History of the Development of Doctrine, Vol. 4: Reformation of Church & Dogma (1300-1700) LC 79-142042. lii, 426p. 1985. 27.50x (ISBN 0-226-65376-5); pap. 14.95 (ISBN 0-226-65377-3). U of Chicago Pr.
Sacred Congregation of the Clergy, Official English Translation of the Latin Document April 11, 1971. General Catechetical Directory. pap. 3.75 (ISBN 1-55586-173-3, V-173). US Catholic.
St. Mary's College, Kansas, Jesuit Fathers. The Church Teaches: Documents of the Church in English Translation. Clarkson, John F., et al, eds. 1973. pap. 10.00 (ISBN 0-89555-011-3). TAN Bks Pubs.
Sharing the Light of Faith: National Catechetical Directory for Catholics of the United States. (Illus.). 182p. (Orig.). 1979. pap. 6.50 (ISBN 1-55586-001-X). US Catholic.
Tobin, William, ed. International Catechetical Congress: Selected Documentation: Rome, 1971. cancelled (ISBN 0-686-18988-4, V-199). US Catholic.
United States Catholic Conference, Conference of Catholic Bishops, Department of Education. Sharing the Light of Faith: National Catechetical Directory for Catholics of the United States. (Illus., Orig.). 1979. pap. 6.50 (ISBN 1-55586-001-X). US Catholic.
A Vision for the Catechetical Ministry: An Instrument for Diocesan & Parish Planning. 1985. 5.30 (ISBN 0-318-18576-8); 4.00. Natl Cath Educ.

CATECHISMS
see also Bible–Catechisms, Question-Books, etc.; Catechetical Sermons; Catechetics; Creeds; also subdivision Catechisms and Creeds under names of religions, religious denominations, etc., e.g. Catholic Church–Catechisms and Creeds
Daughters of St. Paul. Basic Catechism Manual, Vol. I. 1981. pap. 5.95 (ISBN 0-8198-1107-6). Dghtrs St Paul.
--Basic Catechism Manual, Vol. II. 1981. pap. 5.95 (ISBN 0-8198-1106-8). Dghtrs St Paul.
--Giae Ly Can Ban. Tueng, Andrew, tr. Orig. Title: Basic Catachism. (Vietnamese.). 202p. (Orig.). 1983. pap. text ed. 2.00 (ISBN 0-8198-3035-6). Dghtrs St Paul.
--God Loves Me. 1982. pap. 1.95 (ISBN 0-8198-3032-1); tchr's. manual 3.95 (ISBN 0-8198-3031-3). Dghtrs St Paul.
Dyer, George, ed. An American Catholic Catechism. LC 75-7786. 320p. 1975. (HarpR); pap. 7.95 (ISBN 0-8164-2588-4). Har-Row.
Fehlauer, Adolph. Catechism Lessons: Pupil's Book. Grunze, Richard, ed. (Illus.). 336p. 1981. 6.95 (ISBN 0-938272-09-8). WELS Board.
Feiner, Johannes & Vischer, Lukas, eds. The Common Catechism: A Book of Christian Faith. LC 75-1070. 690p. 1975. 10.95 (ISBN 0-8245-0211-6). Crossroad NY.
Gentile, Ernest B. The Charasmatic Catechism. LC 76-22255. 1977. pap. 4.95 (ISBN 0-89221-025-7). New Leaf.
Hardon, John A. Question & Answer Catholic Catechism. LC 80-2961. 408p. 1981. (Im); pap. 9.95 (ISBN 0-385-13664-1). Doubleday.
Janz, Denis, ed. Three Reformation Catechisms: Catholic, Anabaptist, Lutheran. LC 82-20799. (Texts & Studies in Religion: Vol. 13). viii, 224p. 1982. 49.95x (ISBN 0-88946-800-1). E Mellen.
Kreuziger, Frederick A. Church & Catechism: The Baltimore Catechism Revisited. xiii, 126p. 1986. pap. 8.95 (ISBN 0-9616430-0-5). Reflex Bks.
Kuske, David P. Catechism Handbook. 228p. 1982. three ring binder 19.95 (ISBN 0-938272-12-8). WELS Board.
--Luther's Catechism. (Illus.). 383p. 1982. text ed. 7.50 (ISBN 0-938272-11-X); pap. 2.50 catechism aid bklet. (ISBN 0-938272-13-6). WELS Board.
Lemius, J. B. Catechism of Modernism. LC 81-52536. 160p. 1981. pap. 3.00 (ISBN 0-89555-167-5). TAN Bks Pubs.
Lockman, Vic. The Catechism for Young Children with Cartoon, Bk. 1. (Illus., Orig.). 1984. pap. 1.00 (ISBN 0-936175-01-X); pap. text ed. 1.00 (ISBN 0-936175-03-6). V Lockman.
Lovasik, Lawrence. Saint Joseph New American Catechism. (Illus.). flexible bdg. 3.00 (ISBN 0-89942-253-5, 253/05). Catholic Bk Pub.
McGuire, Michael A. Father McGuire's New, Modern Catechism Know, Love, & Serve: The Holy Father, Our God-Given Supreme Teacher. LC 73-158919. (Know, Love, & Serve Catechisms Ser.). (Illus.). 222p. 1973. pap. 11.00 (ISBN 0-913382-43-4, 103-5). Prow Bks-Franciscan.
--Father McGuire's New, Modern Catechism Know, Love, & Serve, Bk. 1. LC 73-158919. (Know, Love & Serve Catechisms). (Illus.). 58p. 1971. pap. 5.25 (ISBN 0-913382-39-6, 103-1). Prow Bks-Franciscan.
--Father McGuire's New, Modern Catechism Know, Love, & Serve: Preparing for First Holy Communion, BK. 2. LC 73-158919. (Know, Love, & Serve Catechisms Ser.). (Illus.). 90p. 1971. pap. 6.50 (ISBN 0-913382-40-X, 103-2). Prow Bks-Franciscan.
--Father McGuire's New, Modern Catechism Know, Love, & Serve, Bk. 3. LC 73-158919. (Know, Love, & Serve Catechisms Ser.). (Illus.). 175p. 1972. pap. 9.50 (ISBN 0-913382-41-8, 103-3). Prow Bks-Franciscan.
--Father McGuire's New, Modern Catechism Know, Love, & Serve, Bk. 4. LC 73-158919. (Know, Love, & Serve Catechisms Ser.). (Illus.). 192p. 1973. pap. 10.00 (ISBN 0-913382-42-6, 103-4). Prow Bks-Franciscan.
McGuire, Michael A. & Mangieri, Rose M. Know, Love & Serve: General Principles & the Christo-Centric Method. (Know, Love & Serve Cathechism Ser.). 30p. (Orig.). 1973. pap. 2.50 (ISBN 0-913382-44-2). Prow Bks-Franciscan.
Malone, Mary T. Step-by-Step: A Cathechetical Handbook for the RCIA. 1986. pap. 19.95 (ISBN 0-697-02204-8). Wm C Brown.
Mangieri, Rose M. My Companion to Know, Love, & Serve. LC 73-158919. (Know, Love, & Serve Catechisms Ser.). (Illus.). 85p. (Orig.). 1977. pap. 5.50 (ISBN 0-913382-45-0, 103-7). Prow Bks-Franciscan.
Metropolitan Philaret Of Moscow. Catechism of the Orthodox Church. 1901. pap. 2.95 (ISBN 0-686-00252-0). Eastern Orthodox.
Mole, John W. The ABC Catechism: Ordinary Sundays & Solemnities, Vol. II. LC 81-15227. 278p. 1983. 9.50 (ISBN 0-8199-0863-0). Franciscan Herald.
--The A.B.C. Catechism, Vol. 1: Advent to Pentecost. 262p. 1980. 9.50 (ISBN 0-8199-0814-2). Franciscan Herald.
Murphy Center for Liturgical Research. Made, Not Born: New Perspectives on Christian Initiation & the Catechumenate. 192p. 1976. pap. 6.95 (ISBN 0-268-01337-3). U of Notre Dame Pr.
Nowell, Alexander. A Catechisme, or First Instruction & Learning of Christian Religion. LC 74-23570. 185p. 1975. Repr. of 1570 ed. lib. bdg. 30.00x (ISBN 0-8201-1143-0). Schol Facsimiles.
Oddi, Silvie C. The Right of the Catechized to the Truth. 102p. 1983. pap. 2.00 (ISBN 0-8198-6407-2). Dghtrs St Paul.
O'Mahoney, Gerald. Abba! Father! A Personal Catechism. 160p. 1982. 10.95 (ISBN 0-8245-0546-8); pap. 5.95 (ISBN 0-8245-0519-0). Crossroad NY.
Pederson, Phillip E., ed. What Does This Mean? Luther's Catechisms Today. LC 79-50082. 1979. pap. 7.95 (ISBN 0-8066-1723-3, 10-7047). Augsburg.
Proten, C. Introduction to the Fante & Accra (GA) Languages & J. E. J. (Capiteins Fante Catechism Ser.). 69p. 1971. 19.00x (ISBN 0-317-39089-9, Pub. by Luzac & Co Ltd). State Mutual Bk.
Quesnell, Quentin. The Gospel in the Church: A Catechetical Commentary on the Lectionary Cycle C: the Creed. LC 82-9951. 176p. 1982. 12.95 (ISBN 0-8245-0454-2); pap. 5.95 (ISBN 0-8245-0476-3). Crossroad NY.
Redemptorist Pastoral Publication Staff. Jesus Loves You: A Catholic Catechism for the Primary Grades. LC 82-8000658. 96p. 1982. pap. 4.95 (ISBN 0-89243-157-1). Liguori Pubns.
Roberts, Kenneth J. You Better Believe It. LC 77-84944. (Illus.). 1977. pap. 5.95 (ISBN 0-87973-750-6). Our Sunday Visitor.
Sedano, Maruja, et al. El Libro De Formacion De Catequistas: Creciendo y Compartiendo. 1982. pap. 7.95 (ISBN 0-8091-2439-4). Paulist Pr.
Spurgeon, C. H. A Catechism. 32p. 1985. pap. 0.95. Pilgrim Pubns.
Westminster Assembly. Shorter Catechism with Scripture Proofs. 0.75 (ISBN 0-85151-265-8). Banner of Truth.

CATECHISMS–BIBLIOGRAPHY
Eames, Wilberforce. Early New England Catechisms. 1898. 16.00 (ISBN 0-8337-0989-5). B Franklin.
--Early New England Catechisms. LC 68-31081. 1969. Repr. of 1898 ed. 35.00x (ISBN 0-8103-3478-X). Gale.

CATHARINA, SAINT, OF ALEXANDRIA
Capgrave, John. The Life of St. Katharine of Alexandria. Horstmann, Carl, ed. (EETS, OS Ser.: No. 100). Repr. of 1893 ed. 70.00 (ISBN 0-527-00102-3). Kraus Repr.
Einenkel, E., ed. Catharina, Saint, of Alexandria: The Life of St. Katherine. (EETS, OS Ser.: No. 80). Repr. of 1884 ed. 20.00 (ISBN 0-527-00080-9). Kraus Repr.
Logan, H. M. The Dialect of the "Life of Saint Katherine". A Linguistic Study of the Phonology & Inflections. (Janua Linguarum Ser. Practica: No. 130). 1973. pap. text ed. 34.40x (ISBN 0-686-22600-3). Mouton.
Papadopulos, Leonidas J. & Lizardos, Georgia, trs. from Gr. The Life & Sufferings of Saint Catherine the Great Martyr. (Illus.). 1986. pap. 3.00 (ISBN 0-913026-63-8). St Nectarios.

CATHEDRALS
see also Architecture, Gothic;
also subdivision Churches under names of cities, e.g. New York (City)–Churches
Aubert & Goubet. Cathedrales Abbatiales, Collegiales et Prieures Romans en France. 153.25 (ISBN 0-685-34010-4). French & Eur.
--Cathedrales et Tresors Gothiques en France. 153.25 (ISBN 0-685-34011-2). French & Eur.
Barnard, E. K. The Windows of Portsmouth Cathedral. 1977. 42.00x (ISBN 0-317-43731-3, Pub. by City of Portsmouth). State Mutual Bk.
Baxter, Lucy E. The Cathedral Builders: The Story of a Great Masonic Guild. LC 78-58191. 1978. pap. 50.00 (ISBN 0-89341-354-2). Longwood Pub Group.
Bono, F. English Cathedrals. 1976. lib. bdg. 234.95 (ISBN 0-8490-1771-8). Gordon Pr.
Burman, Peter. St. Paul's Cathedral. (The New Bell's Cathedral Guides Ser.). 1986. cancelled 24.95 (ISBN 0-918678-15-3). Historical Times.
Burrell, Arthur. Cathedral on the Nile: The History of All Saints Cathedral, Cairo. 120p. 1985. 30.00x (ISBN 0-317-43629-5, Pub. by Amate Pr. Ltd.). State Mutual Bk.
Carthy, Margaret. A Cathedral of Suitable Magnificence: St. Patrick's Cathedral, New York. 1983. 15.00 (ISBN 0-89453-372-X); pap. 6.95 (ISBN 0-89453-373-8). M Glazier.
Carthy, Mary P. Old St. Patrick's: New York's First Cathedral. (Monograph Ser.: No. 23). (Illus.). 1947. 10.00x (ISBN 0-930060-05-9). US Cath Hist.
Clifton-Taylor, Alec. The Cathedrals of England. (Illus.). 1980. pap. 8.95 (ISBN 0-500-20062-9). Thames Hudson.
Collingswood, Hermann. A Collection of Fifty-Five Dramatic Illustrations in Full Colours of the Cathedral Cities of Italy. (The Masterpieces of World Architectural Library). (Illus.). 107p. 1983. Repr. of 1911 ed. 287.75 (ISBN 0-89901-081-4). Found Class Reprints.
Competitive Designs for the Cathedral of St. John the Divine in New York City. (Architecture & Decorative Art Ser.). 57p. 1982. Repr. lib. bdg. 95.00 (ISBN 0-306-76139-4). Da Capo.
Cormack, Patrick. English Cathedrals. (Illus.). 1984. 14.95 (ISBN 0-517-55409-7, Harmony). Crown.
Denny, Barbara. Kings Bishop. 376p. 1986. 49.00 (ISBN 0-946619-16-6, Pub. by Alderman Pr). State Mutual Bk.
Ditchfield, P. H. The Cathedrals of Great Britain: Their History & Architecture. (Illus.). 1979. Repr. of 1916 ed. lib. bdg. 45.00 (ISBN 0-8495-1112-7). Arden Lib.
Dunlop, Ian. The Cathedrals' Crusade. LC 81-14431. (Illus.). 256p. 1982. 20.00 (ISBN 0-8008-1316-2). Taplinger.
Ellis, Bruce T. Bishop Lamy's Santa Fe Cathedral. LC 85-8551. (Historical Society of New Mexico Publication Ser.). (Illus.). 208p. 1985. 19.95 (ISBN 0-8263-0824-4); pap. 10.95 (ISBN 0-8263-0850-3). U of NM Pr.
Fitchen, John. The Construction of Gothic Cathedrals: A Study of Medieval Vault Erection. LC 80-26291. (Illus.). 1977. pap. 12.95 (ISBN 0-226-25203-5, Phoen). U of Chicago Pr.

Florisoone, Michel. Dictionnaire des Cathedrales de France. (Fr.). 256p. 1971. pap. 6.95 (ISBN 0-686-56834-6, M-6612). French & Eur.
Franzwa, Gregory M. The Old Cathedral. 2nd ed. LC 80-15885. (Illus.). 1980. 14.95 (ISBN 0-935284-18-4). Patrice Pr.
Gallagher, Maureen. The Cathedral Book. LC 82-60592. 1983. pap. 2.95 (ISBN 0-8091-2485-8). Paulist Pr.
Gilbert, George. The Sixty Dramatic Illustrations in Full Colours of the Cathedral Cities of England. (A Promotion of the Arts Library). (Illus.). 99p. 1983. 297.85 (ISBN 0-86650-046-4). Gloucester Art.
Hardy, Paul E. & Bishop of Exeter. A Guide to the Preservation of Medieval Cathedrals & Churches. LC 82-14257. (Illus.). 160p. 1983. pap. text ed. 16.95 (ISBN 0-582-30514-4, Construction Press). Longman.
Hutchinson, John & O'Connor, David. York Minister. (The New Bell's Cathedral Guides Ser.). 1986. cancelled 24.95 (ISBN 0-918678-14-5). Historical Times.
Huysmans, J. K. The Cathedral. 59.95 (ISBN 0-87968-815-7). Gordon Pr.
Huysmans, Joris K. The Cathedral. Paul, C. Kegan, ed. Bell, Clara, tr. from Fr. LC 77-10270. Repr. of 1922 ed. 32.50 (ISBN 0-404-16322-X). AMS Pr.
Jantzen, Hans. High Gothic. LC 83-43099. (Illus.). 196p. 1984. 25.00x (ISBN 0-691-04026-5); pap. 7.95x (ISBN 0-691-00372-6). Princeton U Pr.
Kraus, Henry. Gold Was the Mortar: The Economics of Cathedral Building. (Illus.). 1979. 37.95x (ISBN 0-7100-8728-4). Methuen Inc.
Levine, Lee I., ed. The Jerusalem Cathedra: Studies in the History, Archaeology, Geography & Ehthnography of the Land of Israel, Vol. 2. 355p. 1983. 35.00x (ISBN 0-8143-1715-4). Wayne St U Pr.
Macray, W. D., ed. Charters & Documents Illustrating the History of the Cathedral: City & Diocese of Salisbury in the 12th & 13th Centuries. (Rolls Ser.: No. 97). Repr. of 1891 ed. 44.00 (ISBN 0-8115-1176-6). Kraus Repr.
Maines, Clark. The Western Portal of Saint-Loup-De-Naud. LC 78-74373. (Fine Arts Dissertations, Fourth Ser.). (Illus.). 511p. 1979. lib. bdg. 53.00 (ISBN 0-8240-3960-2). Garland Pub.
Murray, Stephen. Building Troyes Cathedral: The Late Gothic Campaigns. LC 85-45744. (Illus.). 272p. 1986. 47.50x (ISBN 0-253-31277-9). Ind U Pr.
Parkhurst, Helen H. Cathedral: A Gothic Pilgrimage. 304p. 1980. Repr. of 1936 ed. lib. bdg. 40.00 (ISBN 0-8492-2174-9). R West.
Pepin, David. Discovering Cathedrals. 5th. ed. (Discovering Ser.: No. 112). (Illus.). 1985. pap. 4.95 (ISBN 0-85263-718-7, Pub. by Shire Pubns England). Seven Hills Bks.
Pevsner, Nikolaus & Metcalf, Priscilla. The Cathedrals of England: Midland, Eastern & Northern England, Vol. 2. 400p. 1985. 40.00 (ISBN 0-670-80125-9). Viking.
--The Cathedrals of England: Southern England, Vol. 1. 384p. 1985. 40.00 (ISBN 0-670-80124-0). Viking.
Prior, Edward S. The Cathedral Builders in England. LC 77-94613. 1978. Repr. of 1905 ed. lib. bdg. 25.00 (ISBN 0-89341-247-3). Longwood Pub Group.
Rodin, Auguste. Cathedrals of France. rev. ed. Geissbuhler, Elisabeth C., tr. from Fr. (Art of the Middle Ages Ser.). Tr. of Cathedrales de France. (Illus.). 278p. 1981. 25.00 (ISBN 0-933806-07-8). Black Swan CT.
Ruskin, John, et al. An Illustrated Architectural History of the Greatest Cathedrals of the World, 2 vols. (Illus.). 311p. 1986. Set. 187.75 (ISBN 0-86650-201-7). Gloucester Art.
Saalman, Howard. Filippo Brunelleschi: The Cupola of Santa Maria del Fiore. Harris, John & Laing, Alastair, eds. (Studies in Architecture: No. XX). (Illus.). 420p. 1986. 95.00 (ISBN 0-302-02784-X, Pub. by Zwemmer Bks UK). Sotheby Pubns.
Spence, Keith & McVeigh, Shaun. Cathedrals & Abbeys of England & Wales. (Blue Guides Ser.). (Illus.). 1984. 29.95 (ISBN 0-393-01664-1); pap. 16.95 (ISBN 0-393-30071-4). Norton.
Thorold, Henry. Collins Guide to Cathedrals, Abbeys & Priories of England & Wales. (Illus.). 332p. 1987. 24.95 (ISBN 0-00-217241-0). Salem Hse Pubs.
Watson, P. Building the Medieval Cathedrals. LC 74-19525. (Introduction to the History of Mankind). 48p. 1976. pap. 4.95 limp bdg. (ISBN 0-521-08711-2). Cambridge U Pr.
Watson, Percy. Building the Medieval Cathedrals. LC 78-56794. (Cambridge Topic Bks). (Illus.). 1978. PLB 8.95 (ISBN 0-8225-1213-0). Lerner Pubns.
Wilson, Christopher, et al. Westminster Abbey: The New Bell's Cathedral Guides. (The New Bell's Cathedral Guides). 1986. cancelled 24.95 (ISBN 0-918678-12-9). Historical Times.

CATHERINE OF GENOA, SAINT, 1447-1510

Catherine of Genoa: Purgation & Purgatory, the Spiritual Dialogue. Hughes, Serge, ed. LC 79-88123. (Classics of Western Spirituality Ser). 190p. 1979. 12.95 (ISBN 0-8091-0285-4); pap. 8.95 (ISBN 0-8091-2207-3). Paulist Pr.
Kaye-Smith, Sheila. Quartet in Heaven. facs. ed. LC 75-136649. (Biography Index Reprint Ser.). 1952. 18.00 (ISBN 0-8369-8044-1). Ayer Co Pubs.
Von Huegel, F. The Mystical Element of Religion As Studied in Saint Catherine of Genoa & Her Friends, 2 vols. 1977. lib. bdg. 200.00 (ISBN 0-8490-2317-3). Gordon Pr.

CATHERINE OF SIENA, SAINT, 1347-1380

Curtayne, Alice. St. Catherine of Siena. LC 80-53745. 1980. pap. 7.50 (ISBN 0-89555-162-4). Tan Bks Pubs.
Daughters of St. Paul. Catherine of Siena. (Encounter Ser.). 1975. 3.00 (ISBN 0-8198-0395-2). Dghtrs St Paul.
Gardner, E. Saint Catherine of Siena: A Study in the Religion, Literature & History of the Fourteenth Century in Italy. 1976. lib. bdg. 59.95 (ISBN 0-8490-2557-5). Gordon Pr.
Giordani, Igino. Saint Catherine of Siena. 1981. 8.00 (ISBN 0-8198-0493-2); pap. 7.00 (ISBN 0-8198-6809-4). Dghtrs St Paul.
Noffke, Suzanne, ed. Catherine of Siena: The Dialogue. LC 79-56755. (Classics of Western Spirituality Ser.). 416p. 1980. 13.95 (ISBN 0-8091-0295-1); pap. 10.95 (ISBN 0-8091-2233-2). Paulist Pr.

CATHOLIC ACTION

see also Christian Democracy; Laity

Lenta, Clementine. What Can I Do for Christ? 5.50 (ISBN 0-910984-17-4). Montfort Pubns.
Philips, Gerard. Achieving Christian Maturity. 4.95 (ISBN 0-685-10957-7, L37990). Franciscan Herald.
Poggi, Gianfranco. Catholic Action in Italy: Sociology of a Sponsored Organization. 1967. 25.00x (ISBN 0-8047-0292-6). Stanford U Pr.

CATHOLIC AUTHORS

see also subdivision Catholic Authors under names of literatures, e.g. English Literature–Catholic Authors

Braybrooke, P. Some Catholic Novelists: Their Art & Outlook. 59.95 (ISBN 0-8490-1075-6). Gordon Pr.
Friedman, Melvin J., ed. Vision Obscured: Perceptions of Some Twentieth-Century Catholic Novelists. LC 72-126130. 1970. 25.00 (ISBN 0-8232-0890-7). Fordham.
Hoehn, Matthew, ed. Catholic Authors: Contemporary Biographical Sketches, 1930-1947. 800p. 1981. Repr. of 1947 ed. 75.00x (ISBN 0-8103-4314-2). Gale.
Keeler, Sr. Mary J. Catholic Literary France from Verlaine to the Present Time. LC 76-90649. (Essay Index Reprint Ser). 1938. 19.00 (ISBN 0-8369-1219-5). Ayer Co Pubs.
Kellogg, Gene. The Vital Tradition: The Catholic Novel in a Period of Convergence. LC 74-108375. 1970. 8.35 (ISBN 0-8294-0192-X). Loyola.
Romig, Walter, ed. Book of Catholic Authors, Fourth Series: Informal Self-Portraits of Famous Modern Catholic Writers. LC 70-179740. (Biography Index Reprint Ser.). Repr. of 1948 ed. 27.50 (ISBN 0-8369-8108-1). Ayer Co Pubs.
Sonnenfeld, Albert. Crossroads: Essays on the Catholic Novelists. 138p. 1982. 13.95 (ISBN 0-917786-24-6). Summa Pubns.
Thorp, Willard. Catholic Novelists in Defense of Their Faith, 1829-1865. 14.00 (ISBN 0-405-10862-1, 11860). Ayer Co Pubs.

CATHOLIC CHURCH

see also Anglo-Catholicism; Canon Law; Councils and Synods; Fasts and Feasts; Inquisition; Oxford Movement; Salvation outside the Catholic Church

Appel, David L. Marketing. (How to Ser.). 43p. 1986. 5.65 (ISBN 0-318-20575-0). Natl Cath Educ.
Augustine, St. The Catholic & Manichaean Ways of Life. LC 66-11337. (Fathers of the Church Ser.: Vol. 56). 128p. 1966. 14.95x (ISBN 0-8132-0056-3). Cath U Pr.
Balcom, Mary G. The Catholic Church in Alaska. LC 78-97897. (Illus.). 1970. 2.50 (ISBN 0-685-47728-2). Balcom.
Boettner, Loraine. Roman Catholicism. 8.95 (ISBN 0-8010-0685-6). Baker Bk.
Bord, Richard J. & Faulkner, Joseph E. The Catholic Charismatics: Anatomy of a Modern Religious Movement. LC 82-42782. 160p. 1983. 19.95x (ISBN 0-271-00340-5). Pa St U Pr.
Breathett, George, ed. The Catholic Church in Haiti 1704-1785: Selected Letters, Memoirs & Documents. 1983. 34.95x (ISBN 0-89712-103-1). Documentary Pubns.
Browne, Henry J. The Catholic Church & the Knights of Labor. LC 76-6326. (Irish Americans Ser). (Illus.). 1976. Repr. of 1949 ed. 32.00 (ISBN 0-405-09323-3). Ayer Co Pubs.
Burghardt, W. J., et al, eds. St. Cyprian, the Lapsed, the Unity of the Catholic Church. LC 57-7364. (Ancient Christian Writers Ser.: No. 25). 132p. 1957. 10.95 (ISBN 0-8091-0260-9). Paulist Pr.
Carey, George. A Tale of Two Churches: Can Protestants & Catholics Get Together? LC 84-28858. 180p. (Orig.). 1985. pap. 5.95 (ISBN 0-87784-972-2). Inter-Varsity.
Chilson, Richard. Catholic Christianity: A Guide to the Way, the Truth, & the Life. 1987. pap. 7.95. Paulist Pr.
--Faith of Catholics: An Introduction. rev. ed. LC 72-81229. 320p. 1975. pap. 4.95 (ISBN 0-8091-1873-4, Deus). Paulist Pr.
Collins, Mary J., ed. A Church Divided: Catholics' Attitudes about Family Planning, Abortion, & Teenage Sexuality. (The Bishops Watch Ser.). (Orig.). 1986. pap. 5.00 (ISBN 0-915365-12-X). Cath Free Choice.
Connolly, Charles. On Being Catholics. 96p. 1983. pap. 5.00 (ISBN 0-912414-37-5). Lumen Christi.
Cunningham, Lawrence. Catholic Heritage. 240p. 1985. pap. 9.95 (ISBN 0-8245-0685-5). Crossroad NY.
Curran, Charles E. Transition & Tradition in Moral Theology. LC 78-20877. 272p. 1980. pap. text ed. 6.95 (ISBN 0-268-01838-3). U of Notre Dame Pr.
Deedy, John. The Catholic Fact Book. 1986. 23.95 (ISBN 0-88347-186-8). Thomas More.
D'Elia, Donald. The Spirits of Seventy-Six: A Catholic Inquiry. 182p. (Orig.). pap. 6.95 (ISBN 0-931888-10-7). Christendom Pubns.
Dietrich, Donald J. The Goethezeit & the Metamorphosis of Catholic Theology in the Age of Idealism: Theology, Vol. 128. (European University Studies: Ser. 23). 261p. 1979. pap. 26.25 (ISBN 3-261-04703-8). P Lang Pubs.
Dietzen, John J. The New Question Box. rev. ed. 606p. 1987. pap. 9.95 (ISBN 0-940518-01-5). Guildhall Pubs.
Dolan, John P. Catholicism. LC 67-28536. (Orig.). 1968. pap. text ed. 5.95 (ISBN 0-8120-0273-3). Barron.
Duffy, Regis A. On Becoming a Catholic: The Challenge of Christian Initiation. LC 84-47721. 176p. (Orig.). 1984. pap. 7.95 (ISBN 0-06-062106-0, RD 525, HarpR). Har-Row.
Dulles, Avery. The Catholicity of the Church & the Structure of Catholicism. 210p. 1985. 22.50 (ISBN 0-19-826676-6). Oxford U Pr.
--A Church to Believe In: Discipleship & the Dynamics of Freedom. LC 81-17520. 208p. 1983. pap. 8.95 (ISBN 0-8245-0593-X). Crossroad NY.
Environment & Art in Catholic Worship. 100p. 1978. pap. 7.95 (ISBN 1-55586-563-1, V563). US Catholic.
Father Sheedy. Questions Catholics Ask. LC 78-58466. 1978. pap. 4.95 (ISBN 0-87973-738-7). Our Sunday Visitor.
Fellowship of Catholic Scholars. Faith & the Sources of Faith: The Sixth Convention of the Fellowship of Catholic Scholars. Williams, Paul L., ed. 120p. (Orig.). 1985. pap. 5.95 (ISBN 0-937374-00-8). NE Bks.
Forrest, M. D. Chats with Converts: Complete Explanation of Catholic Belief. 31st ed. LC 78-56979. 1978. pap. 5.00 (ISBN 0-89555-069-5). TAN Bks Pubs.
Foy, Felician A. & Avato, Rose M., eds. Catholic Almanac, 1986. LC 73-64101. 650p. (Orig.). 1985. pap. 13.95 (ISBN 0-87973-256-3, 256). Our Sunday Visitor.
--Catholic Almanac 1987. LC 73-64101. 600p. (Orig.). 1986. pap. 13.95 (ISBN 0-87973-257-1, 257). Our Sunday Visitor.
--Concise Guide to the Catholic Church, Vol. II. 165p. (Orig.). 1986. pap. 6.95 (ISBN 0-87973-585-6, 585). Our Sunday Visitor.
Garrigou-Lagrange, R. The Three Ways of the Spiritual Life. 1977. pap. 3.00 (ISBN 0-89555-017-2). TAN Bks Pubs.
Gathering God's People: Signs of a Successful Parish. 265p. 1982. 9.55 (ISBN 0-318-00782-7). Natl Cath Educ.
Greeley, Andrew. The Catholic Why? Book. 167p. 1983. 10.95 (ISBN 0-88347-154-X). Thomas More.
--How to Save the Catholic Church. 288p. 1984. 16.95 (ISBN 0-670-38475-5, Elizabeth Sifton Bks). Viking.
Griesbach, Marc F. & Carmichael, John P., eds. The ACPA in Today's Intellectual World: Proceedings, 1983, Vol. 57. LC 82-73233. 250p. 1984. pap. 15.00 (ISBN 0-918090-17-2). Am Cath Philo.
Happel, Stephen & Tracy, David. A Catholic Vision. LC 83-5687. 196p. 1984. pap. 10.95 (ISBN 0-8006-1719-3). Fortress.
Hayes, Edward J., et al. Catholicism & Society. (Catholicism Catechism Ser.). 1982. pap. 5.95 (ISBN 0-913382-26-4, 103-16); tchr's manual 3.00 (ISBN 0-913382-27-2, 103-17). Prow Bks-Franciscan.
Hellwig, Monika. Tradition: The Catholic Story Today. 96p. (Orig.). 1974. pap. 2.95 (ISBN 0-8278-9060-5, Pub. by Pflaum Pr). Peter Li.
Hellwig, Monika K. Understanding Catholicism. LC 81-80047. 200p. (Orig.). 1981. pap. 5.95 (ISBN 0-8091-2384-3). Paulist Pr.
Henri, De Lubac. The Splendor of the Church. LC 86-82080. 382p. 1986. pap. 12.95 (ISBN 0-89870-120-1). Ignatius Pr.
Hitchcock, James. Catholicism & Modernity. 250p. 1983. pap. 8.95 (ISBN 0-89283-179-0). Servant.
Huelin, Gordon, ed. Old Catholics & Anglicans: 1931-81. (Illus.). 1983. text ed. 27.50x (ISBN 0-19-920129-3). Oxford U Pr.
Kaschmitter, William A. The Spirituality of the Catholic Church. 980p. 1982. 20.00 (ISBN 0-912414-33-2). Lumen Christi.
Kelley, Bennet. Catholic Faith Today. green, flexible bdg. 3.00 (ISBN 0-89942-243-8, 243-04). Catholic Bk Pub.
Kelly, Peter. Roman Catholicism. 1985. 13.00x (ISBN 0-7062-3601-7, Pub. by Ward Lock Educ Co Ltd). State Mutual Bk.
Kloppenburg, Bonaventure. The People's Church. 1978. 8.95 (ISBN 0-8199-0692-1). Franciscan Herald.
Lehmann, L. H. Out of the Labyrinth. 252p. 1983. pap. 6.95 (ISBN 0-937958-13-1). Chick Pubns.
Likoudis, James & Whitehead, K. D. The Pope, the Council, & the Mass. 1981. 13.95 (ISBN 0-8158-0400-8). Chris Mass.
Lowery, Daniel L. Catholic Beliefs, Laws, Practices: Twenty-Six Questions & Answers. 64p. 1984. pap. 1.50 (ISBN 0-89243-213-6). Liguori Pubns.
Lubich, Chiara. May They All Be One. Tr. of Tutti Siano Uno. 96p. (Orig.). 1983. pap. 3.95 (ISBN 0-911782-46-X). New City.
McDonnell, John J. The World Council of Churches & the Catholic Church. (Toronto Studies in Theology: Vol. 21). 479p. 1985. lib. bdg. 49.95x (ISBN 0-88946-765-X). E Mellen.
McLoughlin, Emmett. Crime & Immorality in the Catholic Church. LC 62-7778. 1962. 4.95 (ISBN 0-910294-19-4). Brown Bk.
Martin, Ralph. A Crisis of Truth: The Attack on Faith, Morality & Mission in the Catholic Church. 245p. 1983. pap. 6.95 (ISBN 0-89283-146-4). Servant.
Miscitelli, Peter. Savonarola, Protestantism & the Church of Rome, 2 vols. (Illus.). 247p. 1985. Set. 187.50 (ISBN 0-89901-230-2). Found Class Reprints.
Molnar, Thomas. Dialogues & Ideologues. 1977. Repr. of 1964 ed. 6.95 (ISBN 0-8199-0679-4). Franciscan Herald.
A New Catechism: Catholic Faith for Adults. 1977. pap. 8.95 (ISBN 0-8245-0332-5). Crossroad NY.
Nichols, Peter. The Pope's Divisions. 16.95 (ISBN 0-03-047576-7). Brown Bk.
O'Hagan, Thomas. Essays on Catholic Life. facs. ed. LC 67-22106. (Essay Index Reprint Ser). 1916. 17.00 (ISBN 0-8369-1333-7). Ayer Co Pubs.
Panzion, Leo. The Pleasures of Being a Catholic. new ed. (Human Development Library Bk.). (Illus.). 1979. Set. 49.75 (ISBN 0-89266-155-0). Am Classical Coll Pr.
Pruter, Hugo R. Neo-Congregationalism. LC 85-13416. 90p. 1985. Repr. lib. bdg. 19.95x (ISBN 0-89370-598-5). Borgo Pr.
Pruter, Karl. Bishops Extraordinary. LC 86-2284. 60p. 1985. Repr. lib. bdg. 19.95x (ISBN 0-89370-544-6). Borgo Pr.
Putnam, George H. The Censorship of the Church of Rome, 2 vols. 200.00 (ISBN 0-87968-826-2). Gordon Pr.
Ratcliffe, A. The Truth about Hitler & the Roman Catholic Church. 1982. lib. bdg. 59.95 (ISBN 0-87700-362-9). Revisionist Pr.
Ratzinger, Joseph, et al. Church Today. Ignatius, May, tr. 79p. pap. 1.25 (ISBN 0-8199-0396-5). Franciscan Herald.
Ratzinger, Joseph C. Principles of Catholic Theology: Building Stones for Fundamental Theology. McCarthy, Mary F., tr. from Ger. LC 86-83133. Tr. of Theologische Prinzipienlehre. 320p. (Orig.). 1986. 24.95 (ISBN 0-89870-133-3). Ignatius Pr.
Ray, Mary A. American Opinion of Roman Catholicism in the Eighteenth Century. 456p. 1974. Repr. of 1936 ed. lib. bdg. 26.00x (ISBN 0-374-96723-7, Octagon). Hippocrene Bks.
Robleto, Un Adolfo. Un Vistazo a la Doctrina Romana. 128p. 1984. pap. 2.95 (ISBN 0-311-05319-X). Casa Bautista.
Rodrigue, Beryl. A Convert Looks at the Catholic Church & the World Crisis. 1981. 6.50 (ISBN 0-8062-1833-9). Carlton.
Schumacher, William A. Roman Replies, 1983. 24p. (Orig.). 1983. pap. 3.00 (ISBN 0-943616-21-2). Canon Law Soc.
Sparagna, Aniceto. Personal Evangelism among Roman Catholics. (Orig.). 1978. pap. 3.95 (ISBN 0-89900-122-X). College Pr Pub.

Staley, Vernon. The Catholic Religion. 320p. 1983. pap. 9.95 (ISBN 0-8192-1327-6). Morehouse.
Straus, Carrie. The Catholic Church. 288p. 1987. 14.95 (ISBN 0-87052-312-0). Hippocrene Bks.
Stutfield, Hugh E. Mysticism & Catholicism. 1977. lib. bdg. 59.95 (ISBN 0-8490-2318-1). Gordon Pr.
Szarnicki, Zygmunt V. Mankind's Greatest Life. 188p. (Orig.). 1985. pap. 9.95 (ISBN 0-939332-12-4). J Pohl Assocs.
Von Hildebrand, Dietrich. The New Tower of Babel. LC 76-998. 1977. Repr. 5.95 (ISBN 0-8199-0600-X). Franciscan Herald.
Welch, Jerome A. Catholicism Today. LC 76-29584. (Illus.). 1977. 7.95 (ISBN 0-917728-01-7); pap. 6.95 (ISBN 0-917728-02-5). Jewel Pubns.
Whitcomb, Paul. The Catholic Church Has the Answer. 60p. (Orig.). 1986. pap. 1.25 (ISBN 0-89555-282-5). Tan Bks Pubs.
Wright, Dudley. Roman Catholicism & Freemasonry. 1977. lib. bdg. 69.95 (ISBN 0-8490-2531-1). Gordon Pr.
Yeager, Robert J. Volunteers. (How to Ser.). 28p. 1986. 5.65 (ISBN 0-318-20573-4). Natl Cath Educ.

CATHOLIC CHURCH–ADDRESSES, ESSAYS, LECTURES

The Addresses of His Holiness Pope John Paul II to the United States Bishops During Their Ad Limina Visits: Ad Limina Addresses. 60p. 1983. pap. 4.95 (ISBN 1-55586-926-2). US Catholic.
American Catholic Historic Association Staff. Catholic Philosophy of History, Vol. 3. facs. ed. LC 67-23190. (Essay Index Reprint Ser). 1936. 16.00 (ISBN 0-8369-0285-8). Ayer Co Pubs.
Barry, William F. Roma Sacra: Essays on Christian Rome. facs. ed. LC 68-14896. (Essay Index Reprint Ser). 1927. 18.00 (ISBN 0-8369-0174-6). Ayer Co Pubs.
Belloc, Hilaire. Essays of a Catholic. facs. ed. LC 67-26713. (Essay Index Reprint Ser). 1931. 18.00 (ISBN 0-8369-0188-6). Ayer Co Pubs.
Bindley, T. Herbert, ed. The Ecumenical Documents of the Faith: The Creed of Nicea; Three Epistles of Cyril; The Tome of Leo; The Chalcedonian Definition. 4th ed. LC 79-8708. viii, 246p. 1980. Repr. of 1950 ed. lib. bdg. 24.75x (ISBN 0-313-22197-9, BIOD). Greenwood.
Catholic Health Association Staff. The Ministry of Healing: Readings in the Catholic Health Care Ministry. LC 81-12201. 120p. 1981. pap. 7.50 (ISBN 0-686-85771-2). Cath Health.
Claudel, Paul. Ways & Crossways. facs. ed. O'Conner, Fr. J., tr. LC 67-28732. (Essay Index Reprint Ser.). 1933. 20.00 (ISBN 0-8369-0313-7). Ayer Co Pubs.
--Ways & Crossways. LC 68-15820. 1968. Repr. of 1933 ed. 21.50 (ISBN 0-8046-0079-1, Pub. by Kennikat). Assoc Faculty Pr.
Duquoc, Christian. Opportunities for Belief & Behavior. LC 67-31523. (Concilium Ser: Vol. 29). 186p. 1967. 7.95 (ISBN 0-8091-0106-8). Paulist Pr.
Erasmus, Desiderius. The Historical Significance of Desiderius Erasmus in the Light of the Protestant Revolution & the Catholic Church As Revealed by His Most Famous Pronouncements, 2 vols. (Illus.). 396p. 1985. Set. 207.50. Am Classical Coll Pr.
Faber, Frederick W. Spiritual Conferences. LC 78-66304. 1978. pap. 9.00 (ISBN 0-89555-079-2). TAN Bks Pubs.
Fesquet, Henri. Has Rome Converted. Salemson, Harold J., tr. 1968. 9.50 (ISBN 0-685-11959-9). Heineman.
Greenbaum, Howard H. & Falcione, Raymond L. Organizational Communication Nineteen Seventy-Seven: Abstracts, Analysis, & Overview. new ed. 1979. pap. 9.00 (ISBN 0-931874-08-4). Assn Busn Comm.
Gremillion, Joseph, ed. The Gospel of Peace & Justice: Catholic Social Teaching Since Pope John. LC 75-39892. 637p. (Orig.). 1976. pap. 14.95 (ISBN 0-88344-166-7). Orbis Bks.
Hogan, Richard M. & Levoir, John M. Covenant of Love: Pope John Paul II on Sexuality, Marriage & Family in the Modern World. LC 84-18666. 264p. 1985. 15.95 (ISBN 0-385-19540-0). Doubleday.
Huizing, Peter & Walf, Knut, eds. Electing Our Own Bishops. (Concilium Ser.: Vol. 137). 128p. (Orig.). 1980. pap. 5.95 (ISBN 0-8164-2279-6, HarpR). Har-Row.
Johnson, David M., ed. Justice & Peace Education: Models for College & University Faculty. LC 85-25808. 256p. (Orig.). 1986. pap. 16.95 (ISBN 0-88344-247-7). Orbis Bks.
Maritain, Jacques. Ransoming the Time. Binsse, Harry L., tr. LC 70-165665. 322p. 1972. Repr. of 1941 ed. 25.00x (ISBN 0-87752-153-0). Gordian.
--Religion et Culture. 176p. 1968. 3.95 (ISBN 0-686-56366-2). French & Eur.
Matheison, Moira, ed. Consulting the American Catholic Laity: A Decade of Dialogue. 40p. (Orig.). 1986. pap. 2.95 (ISBN 1-55586-999-8). US Catholic.
Meslier, Jean. Superstition in All Ages. Knopp, Anna, tr. 346p. 1974. pap. 13.95 (ISBN 0-88697-008-3). Life Science.
Pope John Paul II. The Far East Journey of Peace & Brotherhood. write for info. Dghtrs St Paul.
Pope Pius Eleventh. Essays in History, Written Between the Years 1896-1912. facs. ed. LC 67-26771. (Essay Index Reprint Ser.). 1934. 17.00 (ISBN 0-8369-0791-4). Ayer Co Pubs.
Pope Pius Twelfth. Addresses of Pius the Twelfth to Cloistered Religious. pap. 1.25 (ISBN 0-8198-0006-6). Dghtrs St Paul.
Ruthler, George W. Beyond Modernity: Reflections of a Post-Modern Catholic. LC 86-82636. 227p. (Orig.). 1986. pap. 11.95 (ISBN 0-89870-135-X). Ignatius Pr.
Ryan, John K. & Benard, Edmond, eds. American Essays for the Newman Centennial. LC 47-30528. pap. 64.50 (ISBN 0-317-07851-8, 2005379). Bks Demand UMI.
Strange, Roderick. The Catholic Faith. 192p. 1986. 24.95 (ISBN 0-19-826685-5); pap. 8.95 (ISBN 0-19-283051-1). Oxford U Pr.
Talks of John Paul II. 1979. 7.95 (ISBN 0-8198-0599-8); pap. 6.95 (ISBN 0-8198-0600-5). Dghtrs St Paul.
Timmerman, S. F., Jr. Timmerman's Lectures on Catholicism. 1952. 3.95 (ISBN 0-88027-085-3). Firm Foun Pub.

CATHOLIC CHURCH–APOLOGETIC WORKS

Benko, Stephen. Los Evangelicos, los Catolicos y la Virgen Maria, Los. Olmedo, Alfonso, tr. from Eng. Orig. Title: Protestants, Catholics & Mary. 1985. pap. 6.95 (ISBN 0-311-05041-7). Casa Bautista.
Cavanaugh, Joseph H. Evidence for Our Faith. 3rd ed. 1959. 8.00x (ISBN 0-268-00092-1). U. of Notre Dame Pr.
Chesterton, G. K. The Everlasting Man. 280p. 1974. pap. 4.50 (ISBN 0-385-07198-1, Im). Doubleday.
Furfey, Paul H. Fire on the Earth. 17.00 (ISBN 0-405-10830-3, 11837). Ayer Co Pubs.
Gibbons, James. The Faith of Ours Fathers: Being a Plain Exposition & Vindication of the Church Founded by Our Lord Jesus Christ. 33.00 (ISBN 0-405-10832-X, 11839). Ayer Co Pubs.
Horvath, Tibor. Faith under Scrutiny. LC 75-1179. 343p. 1975. pap. text ed. 5.95 (ISBN 0-8190-0073-6). Loyola.
Riches, Pierre. Back to Basics: Catholic Faith in Today's World. 176p. 1984. pap. 7.95 (ISBN 0-8245-0646-4). Crossroad NY.
Sheen, Fulton J. Moral Universe: A Preface to Christian Living. facs. ed. LC 67-28766. (Essay Index Reprint Ser). 1936. 15.00 (ISBN 0-8369-0873-2). Ayer Co Pubs.
--Peace of Soul. 1954. pap. 4.95 (ISBN 0-385-02871-7, D8, Im). Doubleday.
Tertullian. Apologetical Works. (Father of the Church Ser.: Vol. 10). 430p. 1950. 34.95x (ISBN 0-8132-0010-5). Cath U Pr.

CATHOLIC CHURCH–BIBLIOGRAPHY

see also Catholic Literature

Annette, Miserendino, ed. Catholic Telephone Guide. 296p. 1986. 22.00 (ISBN 0-910635-54-4). Cath News Pub Co.
Finotti, Joseph. Bibliographia Catholica Americana: A List of Works by Catholic Authors & Published in the United States. LC 74-149232. (Bibliography & Reference Ser.: No. 401). 1971. Repr. of 1872 ed. lib. bdg. 23.50 (ISBN 0-8337-1128-8). B Franklin.
Foy, Felician A. & Avato, Rose, eds. Concise Guide to the Catholic Church. LC 83-63170. 80p. (Orig.). 1984. pap. 6.95 (ISBN 0-87973-616-X, 616). Our Sunday Visitor.
Gorman, Robert. Catholic Apologetical Literature in the United States (1784-1858) LC 73-3582. (Catholic University of America. Studies in American Church History: No. 28). Repr. of 1939 ed. 23.00 (ISBN 0-404-57778-4). AMS Pr.
Hurter, Hugo. Nomenclator Litterarius Theologiae Catholicae Theologo Sexhibens Aetate, Natione, Disciplins Distinctos, 5 Vols. in 6. 1903. Set. 294.00 (ISBN 0-8337-1772-3). B Franklin.
Perennes, F M. Dictionnaire de Bibliographie Catholique, Presentant l'Indication et les Titres Complets de tous les Ouvrages qui Ontetes Publies dans les Trois Lanques Grecque, Latine et Francaise... Suivi d'un Dictionnaire de Bibliologie par G. Brunet (the Last 2 Vols., 6 vols. Migne, J. P., ed. (Troisieme et Derniere Encyclopedie Theologique Ser.: Vols. 39-44). (Fr.). 4001p. Repr. of 1866 ed. lib. bdg. 510.00x (ISBN 0-89241-318-2). Caratzas.

CATHOLIC CHURCH–BIOGRAPHY

Anderson, Margaret L. Windthorst: A Political Biography. 1981. 75.00x (ISBN 0-19-822578-4). Oxford U Pr.
Blunt, Hugh F. Great Magdelens. facs. ed. LC 71-86731. (Essay Index Reprint Ser). 1928. 18.50 (ISBN 0-8369-1122-9). Ayer Co Pubs.
Caponigri, Aloysius R. Modern Catholic Thinkers: An Anthology. (Essay Index Reprint Ser.). 650p. Repr. of 1960 ed. lib. bdg. 37.50 (ISBN 0-8290-0784-9). Irvington.
Cowie, Frederick J. Pioneers of Catholic Europe. LC 84-62160. 190p. 1985. pap. 6.95 (ISBN 0-87973-713-1, 713). Our Sunday Visitor.
Delany, Selden P. Married Saints. facs. ed. LC 69-17573. (Essay Index Reprint Ser). 1935. 18.00 (ISBN 0-8369-0071-5). Ayer Co Pubs.
DiOrio, Ralph A. & Gropman, Donald. The Man Beneath the Gift: The Story of My Life. LC 80-17619. (Illus.). 239p. 1981. 9.95 (ISBN 0-688-03740-2); pap. 7.95 (ISBN 0-688-00795-3). Morrow.
Hallett, Paul. Witness to Permanence. LC 86-82637. 279p. (Orig.). 1986. pap. 11.95 (ISBN 0-89870-134-1). Ignatius Pr.
Helming, Dennis M. Footprints in the Snow: A Pictorial Biography of the Founder of Opus Dei, Josemaria Escriva. (Illus.). 80p. (Orig.). 1986. pap. write for info. (ISBN 0-933932-50-2). Scepter Pubs.
Hogan, John G. Heralds of the King. LC 79-107714. (Essay Index Reprint Ser.). 1934. 17.00 (ISBN 0-8369-1516-X). Ayer Co Pubs.
Lovato, Carol N. Brother Mathias: Founder of the Little Brothers of the Good Shepherd. LC 86-62454. 288p. 1987. pap. 8.95 (ISBN 0-87973-485-X, 485). Our Sunday Visitor.
McNulty, Kenneth K., Sr. Street or Pulpit? The Witness of Activist Monsignor Charles Owen Rice of Pittsburgh. (The Answers Ser.). 288p. (Orig.). 1985. pap. 9.95 (ISBN 0-935025-00-6). Data & Res Tech.
Maynard, Theodore. Pillars of the Church. LC 76-136763. (Essay Index Reprint Ser). 1945. 19.00 (ISBN 0-8369-1940-8). Ayer Co Pubs.
Nevins, Albert J. Builders of Catholic America. LC 85-72363. 250p. (Orig.). 1985. pap. 7.95 (ISBN 0-87973-582-1, 582). Our Sunday Visitor.
O'Connor, Thomas H. Fitzpatrick's Boston, 1846-1866: John Bernard Fitzpatrick, Third Bishop of Boston. LC 83-23806. 308p. 1984. text ed. 22.95x (ISBN 0-930350-56-1). NE U Pr.
Osburn, Charlie & Lilly, Fred. The Charlie Osburn Story: You Gotta Give It All to Jesus. 140p. 1986. pap. 4.95 (ISBN 0-89283-287-8). Servant.
Proctor, William. An Interview with Chiara Lubich. 72p. (Orig.). 1983. pap. 4.95 (ISBN 0-911782-44-3). New City.
Ryan, George E. Figures in Our Catholic History. 1979. 4.00 (ISBN 0-8198-0608-0); pap. 2.50 (ISBN 0-8198-0609-9). Dghtrs St Paul.
Spalding, Martin. Sketches of the Early Catholic Missions of Kentucky; from Their Commencement in 1787 to the Jubilee of 1826-7. LC 70-38548. (Religion in America, Ser. 2). 328p. 1972. Repr. of 1844 ed. 22.00 (ISBN 0-405-04087-3). Ayer Co Pubs.
Stauter, Patrick C. & Delaney, Howard L. The Willging Years: Seventeen Years with the First Catholic Bishop of Pueblo. (Illus., Orig.). 1987. pap. text ed. 24.95 (ISBN 0-9617847-0-9). P C Stauter.
Steuart, Robert H. Diversity in Holiness. facs. ed. LC 67-28770. (Essay Index Reprint Ser). 1937. 17.00 (ISBN 0-8369-0906-2). Ayer Co Pubs.
Undset, Sigrid. Stages on the Road. facs. ed. Chater, A. G., tr. LC 70-80404. (Essay Index Reprint Ser). 1934. 16.50 (ISBN 0-8369-1068-0). Ayer Co Pubs.
Walsh, James J., compiled by. These Splendid Priests. facs. ed. LC 68-29252. (Essay Index Reprint Ser). 1968. Repr. of 1926 ed. 17.00 (ISBN 0-8369-0973-9). Ayer Co Pubs.
--These Splendid Sisters. LC 75-128326. (Essay Index Reprint Ser). 1927. 18.00 (ISBN 0-8369-1856-8). Ayer Co Pubs.
Ward, Maisie, ed. English Way: Studies in English Sanctity from St. Bede to Newman. facs. ed. LC 68-29253. (Essay Index Reprint Ser). 1968. Repr. of 1933 ed. 17.75 (ISBN 0-8369-0975-5). Ayer Co Pubs.
Watson, D. Jeanene. Teresa of Calcutta. LC 84-60313. (The Sowers Ser.). 1984. 8.95 (ISBN 0-88062-013-7); pap. 4.95 (ISBN 0-88062-012-9). Mott Media.
Weisheipl, James A. Friar Thomas d'Aquino: His Life, Thought, & Work. LC 83-14326. 487p. 1983. pap. 16.95 (ISBN 0-8132-0590-5). Cath U Pr.

CATHOLIC CHURCH–CATECHISMS AND CREEDS

see also Baltimore Catechism

Avento, Genarro P. The Church's Moral Teaching, Bk. III. pap. 3.95 (ISBN 0-941850-08-0). Sunday Pubns.
Badia, Leonard F. Basic Catholic Beliefs for Today: The Creed Explained. LC 84-14632. 170p. (Orig.). 1984. pap. 8.95 (ISBN 0-8189-0469-0). Alba.
Baltimore Plenary Council Staff. Baltimore Catechism, No. 1. 1977. pap. 3.00 (ISBN 0-89555-010-5). TAN Bks Pubs.
--Baltimore Catechism, No. 2. 1977. pap. 1.75 (ISBN 0-89555-008-3). TAN Bks Pubs.
--Baltimore Catechism: Cathechism of Christian Doctrine. 1974. pap. 3.50 (ISBN 0-89555-007-5, 147). TAN Bks Pubs.
Bell, D. Rayford. Apostolic Catechism. LC 84-90806. 60p. 1984. 1.50 (ISBN 0-317-39381-2). D R Bell.
Cardinal Gibbons. Faith of Our Fathers. LC 80-51331. 352p. 1980. pap. 9.00 (ISBN 0-89555-158-6). Tan Bks Pubs.
Catecismo Basico. (Span.). 3.00 (ISBN 0-8198-1444-X); 2.00 (ISBN 0-8198-1445-8). Dghtrs St Paul.
Church-Papal Teachings. 12.00 (ISBN 0-317-46826-X). Dghtrs St Paul.
Credo: A Catholic Catechism. 296p. 1984. pap. 8.95 (ISBN 0-225-66343-0, HarpR). Har-Row.
Creed & Catechetics. 10.95 (ISBN 0-8198-1430-X); 9.50 (ISBN 0-8198-1431-8). Dghtrs St Paul.
Davies, Benedict. Credo: A Catholic Catechism. 300p. 1985. pap. 5.95 (ISBN 0-86683-901-1, HarpR); pap. 3.95 leaders guide (ISBN 0-86683-743-4). Har-Row.
De Cordoba, Pedro. Christian Doctrine for the Instruction & Information of the Indians. Stoudemire, Sterling A., tr. LC 79-121681. 1970. 7.95x (ISBN 0-87024-159-1). U of Miami Pr.
Deharbe, Joseph. A Full Catechism of the Catholic Religion. 1979. lib. bdg. 59.95 (ISBN 0-8490-2924-4). Gordon Pr.
DeVito, Michael. The Church's Faith, Bk. I. pap. 3.95 (ISBN 0-941850-06-4). Sunday Pubns.
Faerber, W. Catholic Catechism. LC 78-68498. 122p. 1978. pap. 3.00 (ISBN 0-89555-086-5, 307). TAN Bks Pubs.
Gallagher, Joseph V. Para Ser Catolico: Un Catecismo Para Hoy. new, spanish ed. 1976. pap. 1.50 (ISBN 0-8091-1939-0). Paulist Pr.
Geiermann, Peter. The Convert's Catechism of Catholic Doctrine. 1977. pap. 2.00 (ISBN 0-89555-029-6). TAN Bks Pubs.
Greeley, Andrew. The Bottom Line Catechism for Contemporary Catholics. 304p. 1982. pap. 10.95 (ISBN 0-88347-135-3). Thomas More.
Handbook for Today's Catholic: Beliefs, Practices, Prayers. A Redemptorist Pastoral Publication. 1978. pap. 1.50 (ISBN 0-89243-076-1). Liguori Pubns.
Hardon, John A. The Catholic Catechism. LC 73-81433. 1973. pap. 10.95 (ISBN 0-385-08045-X). Doubleday.
John Paul II. A Commentary on "Catechesi Trandendae: The New Chsrter for Religious Education in Our Time. LC 80-26792. 243p. 1980. 4.50 (ISBN 0-8199-0815-0). Franciscan Herald.
Johnson, Gary. The Illustrated Catechism: Leader's Guide. (Illus.). 96p. 1981. pap. 4.95 (ISBN 0-89243-150-4). Liguori Pubns.
Lamdon, Michele. How to Live with Jesus - Leader's Guide. 64p. 1981. pap. 4.95 (ISBN 0-89243-148-2). Liguori Pubns.
Lawler, Ronald, et al, eds. The Catholic Catechism. 200p. (Orig.). 1986. pap. 6.50 (ISBN 0-87973-802-2, 802). Our Sunday Visitor.
Lovasik, Lawrence G. What Catholics Believe. (Illus.). 1977. pap. 2.50 (ISBN 0-89555-027-X). TAN Bks Pubs.
Metropolitan Philaret Drozdov. Prostrannij Khristijanskij Katekhisis. Tr. of The Complete Christian Catechism. 170p. pap. text ed. 6.00 (ISBN 0-317-29305-2). Holy Trinity.
Mole, John W. The A.B.C. Catechism, Vol. 1: Advent to Pentecost. 262p. 1980. 9.50 (ISBN 0-8199-0814-2). Franciscan Herald.
New Catechism. 1967. 10.00 (ISBN 0-8245-0331-7). Crossroad NY.
The New Saint Joseph First Communion Cathechism. rev. ed. (Official Baltimore Catechism Ser.). (Illus.). 1.60 (ISBN 0-89942-240-3, 240/05). Catholic Bk Pub.
Pope John Paul II: Catechist. 1980. 4.50 (ISBN 0-317-46877-4). Franciscan Herald.
Pro-Life Catechism. 3.25 (ISBN 0-8198-5818-8); 2.00 (ISBN 0-8198-5819-6). Dghtrs St Paul.
Redemptorist Pastoral Publication. How You Live with Jesus: Catechism for Today's Young Catholic. LC 81-80097. 96p. 1981. pap. 3.50 (ISBN 0-89243-137-7). Liguori Pubns.
The Roman Catechism. 15.00 (ISBN 0-8198-6408-0); 14.00 (ISBN 0-8198-6413-7). Dghtrs St Paul.
St. Paul Family Catechism. 5.95 (ISBN 0-8198-7329-2); 4.50 (ISBN 0-8198-7330-6). Dghtrs St Paul.

Schmaus, Michael. Dogma, 6 vols. Incl. Vol. 1. God in Revelation (ISBN 0-87061-098-8); Vol. 2. God & Creation (ISBN 0-87061-099-6); Vol. 3. God & His Christ (ISBN 0-87061-100-3); Vol. 4. The Church (ISBN 0-87061-101-1); Vol. 5. Church As Sacrament (ISBN 0-87061-102-X); Vol. 6. Justification & the Last Things (ISBN 0-87061-103-8). 1984. Set. pap. 60.00 (ISBN 0-87061-095-3); pap. 10.00 ea. Chr Classics.

Tynan, Michael. Catechism For Catholics. 96p. (Orig.). 1983. pap. 5.95 (ISBN 0-87061-088-0). Chr Classics.

We Believe... A Guide to a Better Understanding of the Bible As a Source Book for the Humanities. school ed. School ed. 0.75 (ISBN 0-89942-247-0, 247.05-SD). Catholic Bk Pub.

CATHOLIC CHURCH–CEREMONIES AND PRACTICES

Gibbons, Joseph C. Whatever Happened to Friday? & Other Questions Catholics Ask. LC 79-91275. (Orig.). 1980. pap. 3.95 (ISBN 0-8091-2278-2). Paulist Pr.

Handbook for Today's Catholic Family A Redemptorist Pastoral Publication. (Orig.). 1979. pap. 1.50 (ISBN 0-89243-112-1). Liguori Pubns.

Holy Communion & Worship of the Eucharist Outside Mass. gold cloth 8.50 (ISBN 0-89942-648-4, 648/22). Catholic Bk Pub.

Hughes, Philip E. Confirmation in the Church Today. pap. 20.00 (ISBN 0-317-08439-9, 2012949). Bks Demand UMI.

McNulty, Arthur F. Co-Creators with God. 88p. (Orig.). 1985. pap. 4.95 (ISBN 0-934134-29-4, Leaven Pr). Sheed & Ward MO.

McPhee, John, ed. Tu Fe. Diaz, Olimpia, tr. (Span.). (YA) 1980. pap. 1.95 (ISBN 0-89243-124-5, 48290). Liguori Pubns.

St. Romain, Philip. Catholic Answers to Fundamentalists' Questions. 64p. 1984. pap. 1.95 (ISBN 0-89243-220-9). Liguori Pubns.

CATHOLIC CHURCH–CHARITIES

O'Brien, Joachim. Parish Family Life & Social Action. LC 77-3573. 1977. pap. 1.50 (ISBN 0-8199-0673-5). Franciscan Herald.

O'Grady, John. Catholic Charities in the United States: History & Problems. LC 71-137180. (Poverty U. S. A. Historical Record Ser). 1971. Repr. of 1930 ed. 32.00 (ISBN 0-405-03118-1). Ayer Co Pubs.

CATHOLIC CHURCH–CLERGY

see also Apostolic Succession; Bishops; Cardinals; Episcopacy; Priests; Retreats; Theological Seminaries, Catholic

As One Who Serves: Reflections on the Pastoral Ministry of Priests in the United States. 86p. 1977. pap. 3.25 (ISBN 1-55586-549-6). US Catholic.

Bausch, William J. Take Heart, Father: A Hope-Filled Vision for Today's Priest. 216p. (Orig.). 1986. pap. 9.95 (ISBN 0-89622-309-4). Twenty-Third.

Berrigan, Daniel. The Mission: A Film Journal. LC 86-45012. 160p. 1986. 14.95 (ISBN 0-06-250056-2, HarpR). Har-Row.

Casey, Gerard. Natural Reason: A Study of the Notions of Inference, Assent, Intuition, & First Principles in the Philosophy of John Henry Cardinal Newman. (American University Studies V Philosophy: Vol. 4). 345p. 1984. 37.00 (ISBN 0-8204-0078-5). P Lang Pubs.

The Continuing Formation of Priests (Growing in Wisdom, Age & Grace) 44p. 1984. pap. 2.50 (ISBN 1-55586-954-8). US Catholic.

Doherty, Catherine D. Dear Father: A Message of Love to Priests. LC 78-31389. 1979. pap. 3.50 (ISBN 0-8189-0377-5). Alba.

Doohan, Helen. The Minister of God: Effective & Fulfilled. LC 86-14099. 127p. (Orig.). 1986. pap. 6.95 (ISBN 0-8189-0507-7). Alba.

Ellard, G. Ordination Anointings in the Western Church Before 1000 A. D. (Med Acad of Amer Pubns). 1932. 18.00 (ISBN 0-527-01688-8). Kraus Repr.

Fathers of the Church. 4.00 (ISBN 0-317-46836-7); 3.00 (ISBN 0-8198-2612-X). Dghtrs St Paul.

Fullness in Christ (A Report on a Study of Clergy Retirement) 92p. 1979. pap. 2.95 (ISBN 1-55586-607-7). US Catholic.

Guareschi, Giovanni. Little World of Don Camillo. LC 86-8845. (Illus.). 144p. 1986. pap. 5.95 (ISBN 0-385-23242-X, Im). Doubleday.

The Health of American Catholic Priests: A Report & a Study. 104p. 1985. pap. text ed. 3.95 (ISBN 1-55586-948-3). US Catholic.

Hoffman, Philip T. Church & Community in the Diocese of Lyon: 1500-1789. LC 83-23404. (Historical Publications Ser.: No. 132). 256p. 1984. text ed. 22.50x (ISBN 0-300-03141-6). Yale U Pr.

Kelly, George A., ed. Catholic Ministries in Our Times. 1981. 4.00 (ISBN 0-8198-1400-8); pap. 3.00 (ISBN 0-8198-1401-6). Dghtrs St Paul.

Law, Thomas G., ed. The Archpriest Controversy, 2 Vols. Repr. of 1898 ed. 54.00 (ISBN 0-384-31730-8). Johnson Repr.

McNulty, Kenneth K., Sr. Street or Pulpit? The Witness of Activist Monsignor Charles Owen Rice of Pittsburgh. (The Answers Ser.). 288p. (Orig.). 1985. pap. 9.95 (ISBN 0-935025-00-6). Data & Res Tech.

Malone, David M. The Church Cannot Ordain Women to the Priesthood. 1978. 0.75 (ISBN 0-8199-0724-3). Franciscan Herald.

Marriage & Priesthood: Six Sermons on Commitment. (Sermon Ser.: No. 3). 33p. (Orig.). 1984. pap. 5.00 (ISBN 0-936384-16-6). Cowley Pubns.

Menard, Eusebe. At All Times, in Every Age. 1977. 4.95 (ISBN 0-8199-0663-8). Franciscan Herald.

Mercier, Desire. Selected Writings by Cardinal Mercier. (Illus.). 128p. 1984. 57.85 (ISBN 0-89901-136-5). Found Class Reprints.

Mohler, James A. The Origin & Evolution of the Priesthood. 137p. 1976. pap. 3.95 (ISBN 0-8189-0342-2). Alba.

Molnar, Thomas. Dialogues & Ideologues. 1977. Repr. of 1964 ed. 6.95 (ISBN 0-8199-0679-4). Franciscan Herald.

Muggeridge, Anne R. The Desolate City: Revolution in the Catholic Church. 256p. 1986. 16.95 (ISBN 0-06-066038-4, HarpR). Har-Row.

Murnion, Philip J. The Catholic Priest & the Changing Structure of Pastoral Ministry. 40.00 (ISBN 0-405-10845-1, 11822). Ayer Co Pubs.

Norms for Priestly Formation: A Compendium of Official Documents on Training of Candidates for the Priesthood. 344p. 1982. pap. 17.50 (ISBN 1-55586-838-X). US Catholic.

A Photo Directory of the United States Catholic Hierarchy. pap. cancelled (ISBN 0-686-15371-5, V-576). US Catholic.

The Priest & Stress. 26p. 1982. pap. 2.25 (ISBN 1-55586-832-0). US Catholic.

Pruter, Karl. Directory of Autocephalous Anglican, Catholic, & Orthodox Bishops. 3rd ed. LC 86-34289. 53p. 1986. lib. bdg. 19.95x (ISBN 0-89370-528-4). Borgo Pr.

Quinn, Bernard. Distribution of Catholic Priests in the United States: 1971. 1975. pap. 3.50x (ISBN 0-914422-04-9). Glenmary Res Ctr.

Rulla, Luigi M. Depth Psychology & Vocation: A Psycho-Social Perspective. LC 70-146938. 1971. 28.00 (ISBN 88-7652-374-X). Loyola.

Russell, H. Africa's Twelve Apostles. 1980. 6.95 (ISBN 0-8198-0702-8); pap. 5.50 (ISBN 0-8198-0703-6). Dghtrs St Paul.

St. Joseph Cafasso. The Priest the Man of God: His Dignity & Duties. O'Connell, Patrick, tr. from It. LC 79-112472. 1971. Repr. of 1892 ed. 7.00 (ISBN 0-89555-041-5). TAN Bks Pubs.

Schillebeeckx, Edward. Church with a Human Face: New & Expanded Theology of Ministry. Bowden, John, tr. 400p. 1985. 19.95 (ISBN 0-8245-0693-6). Crossroad NY.

Spiritual Formation in the Catholic Seminary. 64p. 1984. pap. 4.95 (ISBN 1-55586-920-3). US Catholic.

Von Hilderbrand, Dietrich. Celibacy & the Crisis of Faith. 1971. 4.95 (ISBN 0-8199-0428-7). Franciscan Herald.

Watson, Thomas E. The Roman Catholic Hierarchy. (Studies in Populism). 1980. lib. bdg. 69.95 (ISBN 0-686-68883-X). Revisionist Pr.

CATHOLIC CHURCH–CLERGY–APPOINTMENT, CALL AND ELECTION

Fichter, Joseph H. Religion As an Occupation. (Orig.). 1966. pap. 3.95x (ISBN 0-268-00229-0). U of Notre Dame Pr.

Laborers for the Vineyard: Proceedings of a Conference on Church Vocations. 180p. 1984. pap. 7.50 (ISBN 1-55586-908-4). US Catholic.

National Conference of Religious Vocation Directors. Ministries for the Lord: A Resource Guide & Directory of Catholic Church Vocations for Men, 1985. 128p. (Orig.). 1985. pap. 4.95 (ISBN 0-8091-2724-5). Paulist Pr.

Vera, Hernan. Professionalization & Professionalism of Catholic Priests. LC 82-6886. (University of Florida Social Sciences Monographs: No. 68). xii, 116p. 1982. pap. 7.00x (ISBN 0-8130-0713-5). U Presses Fla.

CATHOLIC CHURCH–CLERGY–CORRESPONDENCE, REMINISCENCES, ETC.

Boyd, Malcolm. Half Laughing, Half Crying: Songs for Myself. 306p. 1985. 15.95 (ISBN 0-312-35663-3). St Martin.

Burtsell, Richard L. & Callahan, Nelson J. The Diary of Richard L. Burtsell, Priest of New York the Early Years, 1865-1868. 37.50 (ISBN 0-405-10813-3). Ayer Co Pubs.

Chiniquy, Charles. Fifty Years in the "Church" of Rome. abr. ed. 366p. 1985. pap. 7.95 (ISBN 0-937958-21-2). Chick Pubns.

Greeley, Andrew M. Confessions of a Parish Priest. 448p. 1986. 18.95. S&S.

Hendrickson, Paul. Seminary: A Search. 320p. 1987. pap. 6.95 (ISBN 0-671-63586-7). Summit Bks.

Ironside, H. A. Letters to a Roman Catholic Priest. pap. 1.25 (ISBN 0-87213-349-4). Loizeaux.

Lord, Daniel A. Played by Ear. LC 56-7099. (Illus.). 1956. 11.95 (ISBN 0-8294-0049-4). Loyola.

Maguire, Daniel C. Reflections of a Catholic Theologian on Visiting an Abortion Clinic. 11p. pap. 1.50 (ISBN 0-915365-10-3). Cath Free Choice.

Merton, Thomas. Seeds of Destruction. 1983. 14.00 (ISBN 0-8446-5988-6). Peter Smith.

Scanlan, Michael. Let the Fire Fall. 180p. 1986. pap. 6.95 (ISBN 0-89283-296-7). Servant.

Sheehan, Lawrence. A Blessing of Years: The Memoirs of Lawrence Cardinal Sheehan. LC 82-19965. (Illus.). 314p. 1984. pap. text ed. 9.95 (ISBN 0-317-11856-0, 85-06743). U of Notre Dame Pr.

CATHOLIC CHURCH–COLLECTED WORKS

Chesterton, G. K. Collected Works of G. K. Chesterton II: The Everlasting Man, St. Francis of Assisi, St. Thomas Aquinas. Marlin, George, ed. 480p. 1986. 29.95 (ISBN 0-89870-116-3); pap. 17.95 (ISBN 0-89870-117-1). Ignatius Pr.

--The Collected Works of G. K. Chesterton: The Illustrated London News, Vol. xxvii. Marlin, George, ed. LC 85-81511. 622p. 1986. 29.95 (ISBN 0-89870-118-X); pap. 17.95 (ISBN 0-89870-119-8). Ignatius Pr.

Dollen, Charles. The Book of Catholic Wisdom. LC 86-60327. 205p. (Orig.). 1986. pap. 7.95 (ISBN 0-87973-535-X, 535). Our Sunday Visitor.

Lexau, Henry. A Treasury of Catholic Digest: Favorite Stories of Fifty Years, 1936-1986. LC 86-81597. 598p. 1986. 24.95 (ISBN 0-89870-115-5). Ignatius Pr.

Lonergan, Bernard J. A Second Collection. LC 74-14798. 314p. 1975. 12.00 (ISBN 0-664-20721-9). Westminster.

McCool, Gerald, ed. Rahner Reader. (Orig.). 1975. pap. 10.95 (ISBN 0-8245-0370-8). Crossroad NY.

Newman, John H. Essays & Sketches. Harrold, Charles F., ed. Repr. of 1948 ed. lib. bdg. 41.00x (ISBN 0-8371-2842-0, NEER). Greenwood.

CATHOLIC CHURCH–DICTIONARIES

Amanne, E. Dictionnaire de Theologie Catholigue. (Fr.). Set. pap. 1995.00 (ISBN 0-686-56893-1, M-6003). French & Eur.

Broderick, Robert C., ed. The Catholic Encyclopedia. 1983. pap. 14.95 (ISBN 0-87973-700-X). Our Sunday Visitor.

--The Catholic Encyclopedia. rev. & updated ed. 612p. pap. 18.95 (ISBN 0-8407-5787-5). Nelson.

Catholic University of America Staff. New Catholic Encylopedia, 17 vols. LC 66-22292. 712p. 1981. Repr. of 1967 ed. Set. 750.00 (ISBN 0-07-010235-X). Publishers Guild.

Daughters of St. Paul. A Brief Catholic Dictionary for Young People. 1977. pap. text ed. 1.00 (ISBN 0-8198-0389-8). Dghtrs St Paul.

Hardon, John A. Modern Catholic Dictionary. LC 77-82945. 624p. 1980. 22.95 (ISBN 0-385-12162-8). Doubleday.

--Pocket Catholic Dictionary. LC 85-5790. 528p. 1985. pap. 6.95 (ISBN 0-385-23238-1, Im). Doubleday.

Loth, Bernard & Michel, Albert. Dictionnaire de Theologie Catholique, Tables Generales: De Raison a Stolz, 3 vols. (Fr.). 256p. 1970. Set. 295.00 (ISBN 0-686-57021-9, M-6379). French & Eur.

Lowery, Daniel L. A Basic Catholic Dictionary. LC 85-80600. (Orig.). 1986. pap. 3.95 (ISBN 0-89243-241-1). Liguori Pubns.

Reynolds, R. & Ekstrom, Rosemary. Concise Catholic Dictionary Shortened Titles on Reprints. 224p. 1982. pap. 3.95 (ISBN 0-89622-159-8). Twenty-Third.

CATHOLIC CHURCH–DIPLOMATIC RELATIONS

see Catholic Church–Relations (Diplomatic)

CATHOLIC CHURCH–DISCIPLINE

see also Casuistry; Indulgences; Marriage (Canon Law); Marriage, Mixed; Penance; Penitentials

Curran, Charles E. Transition & Tradition in Moral Theology. LC 78-20877. 1979. text ed. 18.95x (ISBN 0-268-01837-5, Dist. by Har Row). U of Notre Dame Pr.

Edelby, Neophytos & Urresti, Teodoro-J., eds. Religious Freedom. LC 66-29260. (Concilium Ser.: Vol. 18). 191p. 7.95 (ISBN 0-8091-0124-6). Paulist Pr.

Lea, Henry C. History of Auricular Confession & Indulgences in the Latin Church, 3 Vols. LC 68-19287. 1968. Repr. of 1896 ed. lib. bdg. 67.25x (ISBN 0-8371-0140-9, LEHC). Greenwood.

Morrissey, Gerard. The Crisis of Dissent. 128p. (Orig.). 1985. pap. 4.95 (ISBN 0-931888-19-0). Christendom Pubns.

Urban, Leonard. Look What They've Done to My Church. 1985. pap. 5.95 (ISBN 0-8294-0499-6). Loyola.

CATHOLIC CHURCH–DOCTRINAL AND CONTROVERSIAL WORKS

see also Encyclicals, Papal

Allen, William. Libri Tres, Id Est: De Sacramentis in Genere, De Sacramento Eucharistiae, De Sacrificio Eucharistiae. 699p. Repr. of 1576 ed. text ed. 124.20x (ISBN 0-576-99475-8, Pub. by Gregg Intl Pubs England). Gregg Intl.

An Answere to a Letter (Saint German, Christopher) LC 73-6097. (English Experience Ser.: No. 566). 1973. Repr. of 1535 ed. 8.00 (ISBN 90-221-0566-0). Walter J Johnson.

Baldwin, Robert F. The End of the World: A Catholic View. LC 83-63166. 192p. 1984. pap. 5.95 (ISBN 0-87973-608-9, 608). Our Sunday Visitor.

Brantl, George. Catholicism. LC 61-15501. (Great Religions of Modern Man Ser). 1961. 8.95 (ISBN 0-8076-0162-4). Braziller.

Brown, Raymond E. Biblical Reflections on Crises Facing the Church. LC 75-19861. 132p. 1975. pap. 4.95 (ISBN 0-8091-1891-2). Paulist Pr.

Carey, Patrick, ed. American Catholic Religious Thought. 1987. pap. 12.95. Paulist Pr.

Chillingworth, William. Works of William Chillingworth, 3 Vols. Repr. of 1838 ed. Set. lib. bdg. 95.00 (ISBN 0-404-01570-0). Vol. 1 (ISBN 0-404-01571-9). Vol. 3 (ISBN 0-404-01572-7). Vol. 4 (ISBN 0-404-01573-5). AMS Pr.

Corbett, James A. & Garvin, Joseph N., eds. Summa Contra Haereticos. (Mediaeval Studies Ser.: No. 15). (Lat). 1968. 23.95 (ISBN 0-268-00268-1). U of Notre Dame Pr.

Cruickshank, John. PASCAL: Pensees. (Critical Guides to French Texts Ser.: No. 23). 79p. 1983. pap. 3.95 (ISBN 0-7293-0154-0, Pub. by Grant & Cutler). Longwood Pub Group.

Cyprian, St. Selected Treatises. LC 77-81349. (Fathers of the Church Ser.: Vol. 36). 372p. 1958. 19.95x (ISBN 0-8132-0036-9). Cath U Pr.

Daughters of St. Paul, ed. Catechism of Modern Man. 3rd rev. ed. 1971. 7.95 (ISBN 0-8198-0015-5); pap. 6.95 (ISBN 0-8198-0016-3). Dghtrs St Paul.

--Church's Amazing Story. rev. ed. LC 68-59043. (Divine Master Ser., Vol. 2). 1969. 6.00 (ISBN 0-8198-0028-7); pap. 5.00 (ISBN 0-8198-0029-5); teacher's manual 8.50 (ISBN 0-8198-0030-9). Dghtrs St Paul.

De Lubac, Henry. Paradoxes & Further Paradoxes. Simon, Paule, et al, trs. LC 86-62928. Orig. Title: Paradoxes, Nuveaux Paradoxes. (Fr.). 222p. (Orig.). 1986. pap. 11.95 (ISBN 0-89870-132-5). Ignatius Pr.

Dewan, Wilfred F. Catholic Belief & Practice in an Ecumenical Age. (Orig.). 1966. pap. 1.95 (ISBN 0-8091-1510-7, Deus). Paulist Pr.

Falardeau, Ernest. One Bread & Cup: Source of Communion. 1987. pap. 7.95. M Glazier.

Finkelstein, et al. Religions of Democracy. 1941. 9.50 (ISBN 0-8159-6708-X). Devin.

Flynn, Eileen P. Human Fertilization "In Vitro". A Catholic Moral Perspective. LC 83-27343. 202p. (Orig.). 1984. lib. bdg. 25.00 (ISBN 0-8191-3819-3); pap. text ed. 12.25 (ISBN 0-8191-3820-7). U Pr of Amer.

Fransen, P. Intelligent Theology, Vol. 2: Confirmation & Priesthood. 157p. pap. 2.50 (ISBN 0-8199-0401-5). Franciscan Herald.

Fuller, Reginald C., et al, eds. A New Catholic Commentary on Holy Scripture. rev. ed. 1378p. 1984. 34.95 (ISBN 0-8407-5017-X). Nelson.

Gardiner, Stephen. Obedience in Church & State: Three Political Tracts. Janelle, Pierre, ed. LC 68-19272. 1968. Repr. of 1930 ed. lib. bdg. 22.50x (ISBN 0-8371-0081-X, GABW). Greenwood.

Geiermann, Peter. The Convert's Catechism of Catholic Doctrine. 1977. pap. 2.00 (ISBN 0-89555-029-6). TAN Bks Pubs.

Gratsch, Edward, et al. Principles of Catholic Theology: A Synthesis of Dogma & Morals. LC 80-26272. 401p. (Orig.). 1981. pap. 12.95 (ISBN 0-8189-0407-0). Alba.

Gregory The Great, St. Dialogues. (Fathers of the Church Ser.: Vol. 39). 287p. 1959. 29.95x (ISBN 0-8132-0039-3). Cath U Pr.

Grob, Gerald, ed. Pope, or President? Startling Disclosures of Romanism As Revealed by Its Own Writers: Facts for Americans. LC 76-46094. (Anti-Movements in America). 1977. lib. bdg. 27.50x (ISBN 0-405-09967-3). Ayer Co Pubs.

Halligan, Nicholas. The Sacraments & Their Celebration. LC 85-23031. 284p. (Orig.). 1986. pap. 14.95 (ISBN 0-8189-0489-5). Alba.

Hamilton, Elizabeth. I Stay in the Church. 183p. 1973. 4.95 (ISBN 0-85478-053-X). Attic Pr.

Haughton, Rosemary. The Catholic Thing. 1980. pap. 8.95 (ISBN 0-87243-116-9). Templegate.

Hesburgh, Theodore M. The God & the World of Man. 2nd ed. 1960. 8.95x (ISBN 0-268-00112-X). U of Notre Dame Pr.

Hubert, Marie L. Pascal's Unfinished Apology. LC 70-153272. 165p. 1973. Repr. of 1952 ed. 21.50 (ISBN 0-8046-1699-X, Pub. by Kennikat). Assoc Faculty Pr.

Hume, Basil. To Be a Pilgrim: A Spiritual Notebook. LC 84-47726. 240p. 1984. 13.45 (ISBN 0-06-064081-2, HarpR). Har-Row.

Hurst, Jane. La Historia de las Ideas sobre el Aborto en la Iglesia Catolica: Una Relacion Desconocida. Boyd, Susan J. & Peterson, Jan, eds. Inda, Caridad, tr. from Eng. (Aborto de Buena Fe Ser.). (Span., Illus.). 31p. 1985. pap. 1.00 (ISBN 0-915365-11-1). Cath Free Choice.

Jouhanneaud, P. Dictionnaire Dogmatique, Historique, Ascetique et Pratique, des Indulgences des Confreries et Associations Catholiques. Migne, J. P., ed. (Nouvelle Encyclopedie Theologique Ser.: Vol. 27). (Fr.). 686p. Repr. of 1852 ed. lib. bdg. 87.50x (ISBN 0-89241-270-4). Caratzas.

Kavanaugh, Kiernan, ed. & intro. by. John of the Cross: Selected Writings. (Classics of Western Spirituality Ser.: No. 53). 1987. 16.95 (ISBN 0-8091-0384-2); pap. 12.95 (ISBN 0-8091-2839-X). Paulist Pr.

Kelly, George A. The Church's Problem with Bible Scholars. LC 85-1507. 60p. 1985. 2.50 (ISBN 0-8199-0929-7). Franciscan Herald.

--An Uncertain Church: The New Catholic Problem. (Synthesis Ser.). 1977. pap. 1.25 (ISBN 0-8199-0705-7). Franciscan Herald.

Lay Commission on Catholic Social Teaching & the U. S. Economy. Toward the Future: Catholic Social Thought & the U. S. Economy, a Lay Letter. 120p. 1985. pap. text ed. 4.75 (ISBN 0-8191-4860-1). U Pr of Amer.

Lepicier, A. M. Unseen World: Catholic Theology & Spiritualism. 69.95 (ISBN 0-8490-1251-1). Gordon Pr.

Levy, Rosalie M. What Think You of Christ. 1962. 1.50 (ISBN 0-8198-0172-0). Dghtrs St Paul.

McCormick, Richard A. & Curran, Charles, eds. Readings in Moral Theology, No. 5: Official Catholic Social Teaching. 400p. (Orig.). 1986. pap. 9.95 (ISBN 0-8091-2738-5). Paulist Pr.

McLoughlin, Emmett. American Culture & Catholic Schools. 288p. 1973. pap. 2.75 (ISBN 0-8065-0356-4). Citadel Pr.

Martos, Joseph. Doors to the Sacred: A Historical Introduction to Sacraments in the Catholic Church. LC 82-45148. 552p. 1982. pap. 10.95 (ISBN 0-385-18180-9, Im). Doubleday.

Melzer, Sara E. Discourses of the Fall: A Study of Pascal's Pensees. LC 85-24519. 128p. 1986. text ed. 22.95x (ISBN 0-520-05540-3). U of Cal Pr.

Moore, Philip S. & Dulong, Marthe. Sententiae Petri Pictaviensis 1. (Mediaeval Studies Ser.: No. 7). (Lat). 1943. 21.95 (ISBN 0-268-00250-9). U of Notre Dame Pr.

More, Thomas. The Apolyge of Syr Thomas More. LC 72-221. (English Experience Ser.: No. 228). 1970. Repr. of 1533 ed. 42.00 (ISBN 90-221-0228-9). Walter J Johnson.

--The Supplycacyon of Soulys: Agaynst the Supplycacyon of Beggars. LC 72-220. (English Experience Ser.: No. 353). 88p. 1971. Repr. of 1529 ed. 14.00 (ISBN 90-221-0353-6). Walter J Johnson.

More, Sir Thomas. A Dyaloge of Syr T. More...Wherein Be Treatyd Dyvers Maters, As of the Veneration & Worshyp of Ymagys. LC 74-28873. (English Experience Ser.: No. 752). 1975. Repr. of 1529 ed. 26.50 (ISBN 90-221-0752-3). Walter J Johnson.

Morneau, Robert F. Themes & Theses of Six Recent Papal Documents: A Commentary. 160p. (Orig.). 1985. pap. 5.95 (ISBN 0-8189-0482-8). Alba.

Neuner, J. & Dupuis, J., eds. The Christian Faith. rev. ed. LC 82-22700. 740p. 1983. pap. 13.95 (ISBN 0-8189-0453-4). Alba.

Nevins, Albert J., ed. Father Smith Instructs Jackson. rev. ed. LC 75-628. 278p. 1975. pap. 6.50 (ISBN 0-87973-864-2). Our Sunday Visitor.

Newman, John H. Apologia Pro Vita Sua. Culler, A. D., ed. LC 56-2548. (YA) 1956. pap. 6.50 (ISBN 0-395-05109-6, RivEd). HM.

--Apologia Pro Vita Sua. DeLaura, David, ed. (Critical Editions Ser). 1968. pap. text ed. 11.95x (ISBN 0-393-09766-8, 9766, NortonC). Norton.

Novak, Michael. Confession of a Catholic. LC 85-20367. 232p. 1986. pap. text ed. 12.25 (ISBN 0-8191-5023-1). U Pr of Amer.

O'Brien, John A. The Faith of Millions. rev. ed. LC 74-82119. 416p. 1974. pap. 6.50 (ISBN 0-87973-830-8). Our Sunday Visitor.

Pascal, Blaise. Maximes et Pensees. 4.95 (ISBN 0-686-54848-5). French & Eur.

--Pensees, 2 vols. (Folios 936 & 937). 4.50 ea. French & Eur.

--Pensees. Desgranges, ed. 1962. pap. 9.95 (ISBN 0-685-11485-6). French & Eur.

--Pensees. Krailsheimer, A. J., tr. (Classics Ser.). (Orig.). 1966. pap. 3.95 (ISBN 0-14-044171-9). Penguin.

--The Thoughts of Blaise Pascal. LC 78-12814. 1978. Repr. of 1961 ed. lib. bdg. 24.25 (ISBN 0-313-20530-2, PATH). Greenwood.

Pastoral Constitution on the Church in the Modern World (Gaudium et Spes) 138p. 1965. pap. 3.95 (ISBN 1-55586-015-X). US Catholic.

St. Augustine. Against Julian. LC 77-81347. (Fathers of the Church Ser.: Vol. 35). 407p. 1957. 21.95x (ISBN 0-8132-0035-0). Cath U Pr.

St. Thomas Aquinas. Middle High German Translation of the "Summa Theologica". Morgan, Bayard Q. & Strothmann, Friedrich W., eds. LC 50-8471. (Stanford University. Stanford Studies in Language & Literature: No. 8). (Lat. & Ger., Glossary). Repr. of 1950 ed. 42.50 (ISBN 0-404-51816-8). AMS Pr.

Saint German, Christopher. The Addicion of Salem & Byzance. LC 73-6157. (English Experience Ser.: No. 619). 152p. 1973. Repr. of 1534 ed. 10.50 (ISBN 90-221-0619-5). Walter J Johnson.

Schneider, Reinhold. Messages from the Depths: (Selections from the Writings of Reinhold Schneider) Winterhalter, Curt, ed. Cunningham, Robert, tr. from Ger. 1977. pap. 2.50 (ISBN 0-8199-0683-2). Franciscan Herald.

Seculoff, James F. Catholic Home Devotions. LC 85-72535. 160p. (Orig.). 1986. pap. 5.50 (ISBN 0-87973-584-8, 584). Our Sunday Visitor.

Segundo, Juan L. Theology & the Church: A Response to Cardinal Ratzinger. LC 85-51459. 175p. 1985. 14.95 (ISBN 0-86683-491-5, HarpR). Har-Row.

Silbermann, Eileen Z. The Savage Sacrament: A Theology of Marriage after American Feminism. 128p. (Orig.). 1983. pap. 5.95 (ISBN 0-89622-165-2). Twenty-Third.

Stravinskas, Peter M. The Catholic Church & the Bible. LC 87-60217. 120p. (Orig.). 1987. pap. 5.95 (ISBN 0-87973-515-5). Our Sunday Visitor.

Swidler, Leonard. Aufklarung Catholicism Seventeen Eighty to Eighteen Fifty: Liturgical & Other Reforms in the Catholic Aufklarung. LC 78-2736. 1978. pap. 9.95 (ISBN 0-89130-227-1, 01-00-17). Scholars Pr GA.

Swidler, Leonard, ed. Consensus in Theology? A Dialogue with Hans Kung & Edward Schillebeeckx. LC 80-65385. 180p. 1980. 12.95 (ISBN 0-664-21379-0). Westminster.

Undset, Sigrid. Stages on the Road. facs. ed. Chater, A. G., tr. LC 70-80404. (Essay Index Reprint Ser). 1934. 16.50 (ISBN 0-8369-1068-0). Ayer Co Pubs.

Van Zeller, Hubert. Spirituality Recharted. 1985. pap. 4.95 (ISBN 0-932506-39-9). St Bedes Pubns.

Vatican Council II, Staff. Dogmatic Constitution on the Church (Lumen Gentium) 94p. 1964. pap. 3.25 (ISBN 1-55586-000-1). US Catholic.

Winzet, Ninian. Certane Tractatis for Reformatioun of Doctryne & Maneris in Scotland. LC 79-178311. (Maitland Club, Glasgow Publications: No. 33). Repr. of 1835 ed. 20.00 (ISBN 0-404-53001-X). AMS Pr.

Worgul, George S. From Magic to Metaphor: A Validation of Christian Sacraments. 248p. 1986. pap. text ed. 11.75 (ISBN 0-8191-4983-7). U Pr of Amer.

Woznicki, Andrew N. Journey to the Unknown: Catholic Doctrine on Ethnicity & Migration. LC 82-83230. 105p. (Orig.). 1982. pap. text ed. 3.95 (ISBN 0-910727-01-5). Golden Phoenix.

Zacchello, Joseph. Secrets of Romanism. 232p. 1981. pap. 4.95 (ISBN 0-87213-981-6). Loizeaux.

CATHOLIC CHURCH–DOCTRINAL AND CONTROVERSIAL WORKS–DEBATES, ETC.

Hanson, James E. If I'm a Christian Why Be a Catholic? The Biblical Roots of a Catholic Faith. (Orig.). 1984. pap. 5.95 (ISBN 0-8091-2633-8). Paulist Pr.

Nolan, Hugh J., ed. Pastoral Letters of the United States Catholic Bishops: 1792-1983, 4 vols. 1890p. 1984. pap. 95.00 (ISBN 1-55586-897-5). US Catholic.

Pinard, C. Dictionnaire des Objections Populaires contre le Dogme, la Morale, la Discipline et L'histoire de Eglise Catholique. Migne, J. P., ed. (Troisieme et Derniere Encyclopedie Theologique Ser.: Vol. 33). (Fr.). 756p. Repr. of 1858 ed. lib. bdg. 96.50x (ISBN 0-89241-312-3). Caratzas.

CATHOLIC CHURCH–DOCTRINAL AND CONTROVERSIAL WORKS–MISCELLANEOUS AUTHORS

De Leon, Daniel. The Vatican in Politics. 4th ed. 1962. pap. text ed. 0.50 (ISBN 0-935534-31-8). NY Labor News.

Hardon, John A. Treasury of Catholic Wisdom. LC 86-19648. 768p. 1987. 27.50 (ISBN 0-385-23079-6). Doubleday.

McLoughlin, Emmett. Letters to an Ex-Priest. 1965. 4.95 (ISBN 0-8184-0050-1). Lyle Stuart.

Wells, H. G. Crux Ansata: An Indictment of the Roman Catholic Church. LC 73-161344. (Atheist Viewpoint Ser). (Illus.). 114p. 1972. Repr. of 1944 ed. 13.00 (ISBN 0-405-03798-8). Ayer Co Pubs.

CATHOLIC CHURCH–DOCTRINAL AND CONTROVERSIAL WORKS–PROTESTANT AUTHORS

see also Anti-Clericalism

Beecher, Edward. The Papal Conspiracy Exposed & Protestantism Defended. LC 76-46066. (Anti-Movements in America). (Illus.). 1977. Repr. of 1885 ed. lib. bdg. 32.00x (ISBN 0-405-09940-1). Ayer Co Pubs.

Beecher, Lyman. A Pleas for the West. Grob, Gerald, ed. LC 76-46067. (Anti-Movements in America). 1977. lib. bdg. 17.00x (ISBN 0-405-09941-X). Ayer Co Pubs.

Bilson, Thomas. The True Difference Between Christian Subjection & Unchristian Rebellion. LC 70-38154. (English Experience Ser.: No. 434). 854p. 1972. Repr. of 1585 ed. 143.00 (ISBN 90-221-0434-6). Walter J Johnson.

Blanshard, Paul. Communism, Democracy, & Catholic Power. LC 75-156175. 340p. 1972. Repr. of 1952 ed. lib. bdg. 35.00x (ISBN 0-8371-6118-5, BLCD). Greenwood.

Boettner, Loraine. Roman Catholicism. 1962. 8.95 (ISBN 0-87552-130-4). Presby & Reformed.

Chemnitz, Martin. Examination of the Council of Trent. Kramer, Fred, tr. from Lat. LC 79-143693. 1971. 29.95 (ISBN 0-570-03213-X, 15-2113). Concordia.

Crashaw, William. The Sermon Preached at the Cross, February 14, 1607. Repr. of 1608 ed. 27.00 (ISBN 0-384-10125-9). Johnson Repr.

A Discovery of the Great Subtiltie & Wonderful Wisdom of the Italians. LC 74-80221. (English Experience Ser.: No. 656). 1974. Repr. of 1591 ed. 10.50 (ISBN 90-221-0656-X). Walter J Johnson.

Favour, John. Antiquitie Triumphing over Noveltie. LC 76-171757. (English Experience Ser.: No. 325). 602p. 1971. Repr. of 1619 ed. 72.00 (ISBN 90-221-0325-0). Walter J Johnson.

Fulton, Justin D. The Fight with Rome. LC 76-46077. (Anti-Movements in America). 1977. Repr. of 1889 ed. lib. bdg. 30.00x (ISBN 0-405-09950-9). Ayer Co Pubs.

Gordon, John. Englands & Scotlands Happiness in Being Reduced to Unitie of Religion. LC 75-38190. (English Experience Ser.: No. 461). 50p. 1972. Repr. of 1604 ed. 7.00 (ISBN 90-221-0461-3). Walter J Johnson.

Grob, Gerald, ed. Anti-Catholicism in America, 1841-1851. Three Sermons: An Original Anthology. (Anti-Movements in America Ser.). 1977. Repr. of 1977 ed. lib. bdg. 17.00x (ISBN 0-405-09980-0). Ayer Co Pubs.

Hislop, Alexander. The Two Babylons. 9.95 (ISBN 0-87213-330-3). Loizeaux.

Jewel, John. Works, 4 Vols. 1845-1850. Set. 204.00 (ISBN 0-384-27217-7). Johnson Repr.

King, James M. Facing the Twentieth Century. Grob, Gerald, ed. LC 76-46085. (Anti-Movements in America Ser.). (Illus.). 1977. Repr. of 1899 ed. lib. bdg. 54.00x (ISBN 0-405-09958-4). Ayer Co Pubs.

Lambert, O. C. Catholicism Against Itself, Vol. 1. abr. ed. 1963. pap. 1.50 (ISBN 0-89315-012-6). Lambert Bk.

Montagu, Richard. Appello Caesarem: A Just Appeale from Two Unjust Informers. LC 75-38210. (English Experience Ser.: No. 475). 348p. 1972. Repr. of 1625 ed. 49.00 (ISBN 90-221-0475-3). Walter J Johnson.

--A Gagg for the New Gospell? No: A New Gagg for an Old Goose. LC 74-28872. (English Experience Ser.: No. 751). 1975. Repr. of 1624 ed. 26.00 (ISBN 90-221-0751-5). Walter J Johnson.

Morison, Richard. An Exhortation to Styre All Englyshe Men to the Defense of Theyr Countreye. LC 79-38211. (English Experience Ser.: No. 476). 64p. 1972. Repr. of 1539 ed. 9.50 (ISBN 90-221-0476-1). Walter J Johnson.

--An Inuective Agenste Treason. LC 72-38212. (English Experience Ser.: No. 477). 104p. 1972. Repr. of 1539 ed. 9.50 (ISBN 90-221-0477-X). Walter J Johnson.

Murray, Nicholas. Letters to the Right Rev. John Hughes, Roman Catholic Bishop of New York. Grob, Gerald, ed. LC 76-46091. (Anti-Movements in America). 1977. Repr. of 1855 ed. 29.00 (ISBN 0-405-09964-9). Ayer Co Pubs.

Nevins, William. Thoughts on Popery. Grob, Gerald, ed. LC 76-46093. (Anti-Movements in America). 1977. Repr. of 1836 ed. lib. bdg. 17.00x (ISBN 0-405-09966-5). Ayer Co Pubs.

Ormerod, Oliver. The Picture of a Papist: Whereunto Is Annexed a Certain Treatise, Intituled Pagano-Papismus. LC 74-28878. (English Experience Ser.: No. 756). 1975. Repr. of 1606 ed. 18.50 (ISBN 90-221-0756-6). Walter J Johnson.

Owen, Lewis. The Running Register: Recording the State of the English Colledges in All Forraine Parts. LC 68-54654. (English Experience Ser.: No. 19). 118p. 1968. Repr. of 1626 ed. 13.00 (ISBN 90-221-0019-7). Walter J Johnson.

Tyndale, William. Expositions & Notes on Sundry Portions of the Holy Scriptures. Repr. of 1849 ed. 31.00 (ISBN 0-384-62260-7). Johnson Repr.

Wadsworth, James. The English Spanish Pilgrime. LC 71-25682. (English Experience Ser.: No. 275). 96p. 1970. Repr. of 1629 ed. 11.50 (ISBN 90-221-0275-0). Walter J Johnson.

Wright, Charles & Neil, Charles, eds. The Protestant Dictionary: Containing Articles on the History, Doctrines, & Practices of the Christian Church. LC 73-155436. 1971. Repr. of 1933 ed. 65.00x (ISBN 0-8103-3388-0). Gale.

CATHOLIC CHURCH–DOCTRINAL AND CONTROVERSIAL WORKS, POPULAR

Badia, Leonard F. & Sarno, Ronald. Morality: How to Live It Today. LC 79-20498. 1980. pap. 9.95 (ISBN 0-8189-0391-0). Alba.

Devine, George. Transformation in Christ. LC 70-39884. 125p. 1972. pap. 3.95 (ISBN 0-8189-0240-X). Alba.

Knight, David M. Chastity: Who Lives It. LC 85-19516. 32p. (Orig.). 1985. pap. 3.95 (ISBN 0-915488-10-8, BV4647.C5K57). Clarity Pub.

Kung, Hans. The Church-Maintained in Truth: A Theological Meditation. LC 81-69569. 88p. 1982. pap. 2.95 (ISBN 0-394-70816-4, Vin). Random.

Myers, Rawley. God & Man: The Basic Truths. 1976. 0.50 (ISBN 0-8199-0606-9). Franciscan Herald.

O'Connell, Timothy E. Principles for a Catholic Morality. 1978. (HarpR); pap. 9.95 (ISBN 0-86683-885-6). Har-Row.

Regan, Cronan. Signpost: Questions About the Church & Religion You Always Wanted Answered. LC 70-169056. (Illus.). 340p. 1972. 7.50 (ISBN 0-8199-0432-5). Franciscan Herald.

Shaw, Russell. Signs of the Times: Questions Catholics Ask Today. (Orig.). 1985. pap. 8.95 (ISBN 0-87061-133-X). Chr Classics.

CATHOLIC CHURCH–EDUCATION

see also Catholic Church in the United States–Education; Catholic Universities and Colleges; Theological Seminaries, Catholic

Augustinian Educational Conferences Staff. Augustinian Studies: Papers Read at Recent Augustinian Educational Conferences. facs. ed. LC 67-22052. (Essay Index Reprint Ser.). 1937. 16.00 (ISBN 0-8369-0163-0). Ayer Co Pubs.

Benson, Peter L. & Guerra, Michael J. Sharing the Faith: The Beliefs & Values of Catholic High School Teachers. 85p. 1985. 11.40 (ISBN 0-318-18578-4); member 8.55. Natl Cath Educ.

Bredeweg, Frank H. United States Catholic Elementary & Secondary Schools, 1984-85. 1985. 6.60; member 4.95. Natl Cath Educ.

Brent, Daniel & Jurkowitz, Carolyn. School Board Study Programs: Board Members Manual, Series I. 1983. 6.00 (ISBN 0-318-00790-8). Natl Cath Educ.

Burgess, Robert G. Experiencing Comprehensive Education: A Study of Bishop McGregor School. 288p. 1983. 24.00 (ISBN 0-416-35150-6, NO. 4037); pap. 11.95 (ISBN 0-416-35160-3, NO. 4038). Methuen Inc.

Burke, Richard J. Understanding & Implementing Development. 1985. 4.80 (ISBN 0-318-18573-3). Natl Cath Educ.

Campbell, Cathy. Public Relations. 1985. 4.80 (ISBN 0-318-18572-5). Natl Cath Educ.

The Catholic High School: A National Portrait. 254p. 1985. 23.75 (ISBN 0-318-04383-1). Natl Cath Educ.

Catholic High Schools: Their Impact on Low-Income Students. 254p. 1985. 26.50. Natl Cath Educ.

The Catholic School. 1978. pap. 1.95 (ISBN 1-55586-550-X, V550). US Catholic.

Challenging Gifted Students in the Catholic School. 41p. 1985. 6.00. Natl Cath Educ.

Chandler, Phyllis & Burney, Joan. Sharing the Faith with Your Child: From Birth to Age Six. 96p. 1984. pap. 2.25 (ISBN 0-89243-205-5). Liguori Pubns.

Coakley, Mary L. How to Live Life to the Fullest: A Handbook for Seasoned Citizens. LC 83-63167. 168p. 1984. pap. 4.95 (ISBN 0-87973-628-3, 628). Our Sunday Visitor.

Colwell, Stephen. The Position of Christianity in the United States, in Its Relations with Our Political Institutions, & Specially with Reference to Religious Instruction in the Public Schools. LC 78-38444. (Religion in America, Ser. 2). 180p. 1972. Repr. of 1854 ed. 17.00 (ISBN 0-405-04063-6). Ayer Co Pubs.

Current Issues in Catholic Higer Education: Trends in Enrollment & Finances 1978-1982, Vol. 4, No. 1. 32p. 1983. 6.00 (ISBN 0-318-00780-0). Natl Cath Educ.

Current Issues in Catholic Higher Education: Facing the Future, Vol.3, No. 2. 31p. 1983. 3.60 (ISBN 0-318-00779-7). Natl Cath Educ.

Deferrari, Roy J., ed. Essays on Catholic Education in the U. S. facsimile ed. LC 71-90629. (Essay Index Reprint Ser.). 566p. Repr. of 1942 ed. lib. bdg. 32.00 (ISBN 0-8290-0814-4). Irvington.
Directory of Development. (How To Ser.). 28p. 1986. 10.95. Natl Cath Educ.
Elementary School Finance Manual. 126p. 1984. 12.00 (ISBN 0-318-03690-8). Natl Cath Educ.
Fostering Discipline & Discipleship Within the Catholic Educational Community. 70p. 1985. 34.30 (ISBN 0-318-18579-2). Natl Cath Educ.
Fox, Robert J. The Catholic Faith. LC 83-61889. 360p. (Orig.). 1983. pap. 7.95 (ISBN 0-87973-614-3, 614). Our Sunday Visitor.
Ganss, George E. Saint Ignatius' Idea of a Jesuit University. 2nd ed. (Illus.). 1956. pap. 16.95 (ISBN 0-87462-437-1). Marquette.
Gary, Barbara S. Seeking Foundation Grants. 1985. 5.65 (ISBN 0-318-18574-1). Natl Cath Educ.
Gilbert, John R. Pastor As Shepherd of the School Community. 52p. 1983. 4.80 (ISBN 0-318-00788-6). Natl Cath Educ.
Harper, Mary-Angela. Ascent to Excellence in Catholic Education: A Guide to Effective Decision-Making. 278p. 1980. 9.55 (ISBN 0-318-00777-0). Natl Cath Educ.
Harpers, Ferry W. & Fogle, Sonja. Recent Advances in Leather Conservation: Proceedings of a Refresher Course Sponsored by FAIC, June,1984. 15.00 (ISBN 0-318-18700-0). Am Inst Conser Hist.
Hesburgh, Theodore M. Patterns for Educational Growth. 1958. 5.95x (ISBN 0-268-00202-9). U of Notre Dame Pr.
Hollenbach, David. Claims in Conflict: Retrieving & Renewing the Catholic Human Rights Tradition. LC 79-84239. (Woodstock Ser.: No. 4). (Orig.). 1979. pap. 7.95 (ISBN 0-8091-2197-2). Paulist Pr.
Kealey, Robert J. Everyday Issues Related to Justice & Other Gospel Values. 80p. 1984. 4.80 (ISBN 0-318-17779-X). Natl Cath Educ.
Kirsch, Felix M., ed. Classics: Their History & Present Status in Education: A Symposium of Essays. facs. ed. LC 68-22104. (Essay Index Reprint Ser). 1928. 20.00 (ISBN 0-8369-0600-4). Ayer Co Pubs.
Kirwen, Michael C., ed. A Model Four Semester Syllabus for Transcultural Theology Overseas. LC 86-8618. 224p. 1986. 49.95 (ISBN 0-88946-047-7). E Mellen.
Leahy, John A. Eagle's Chase: The Agony of Success. LC 85-21644. (Illus.). 192p. 1986. 13.95 (ISBN 0-88280-114-7). ETC Pubns.
Lee, James M., ed. Catholic Education in the Western World. 1967. 17.95x (ISBN 0-268-00030-1). U of Notre Dame Pr.
McBride, Alfred. Interviewing & Supporting the Catholic Educator. 1983. 3.35 (ISBN 0-318-00784-3). Natl Cath Educ.
McGaw, Martha M. Sixty Ways to Let Yourself Grow. 64p. 1984. pap. 1.50 (ISBN 0-89243-211-X). Liguori Pubns.
Marique, Pierre J. Philosophy of Christian Education. Repr. of 1939 ed. lib. bdg. 22.50x (ISBN 0-8371-4271-7, MAED). Greenwood.
Meiring, Bernard J. Educational Aspects of the Legislation of the Councils of Baltimore, 1829-1884. 25.50 (ISBN 0-405-10844-3, 11821). Ayer Co Pubs.
Mittelstaadt, Claudio O. The Essence of the Catholic Approach to Education. (Illus.). 134p. 1982. 59.15 (ISBN 0-89266-356-1). Am Classical Coll Pr.
National Conference of Directors of Religious Education. That They All May Be One. 1977. 3.60 (ISBN 0-318-00800-9). Natl Cath Educ.
NCEA. (Keynote Ser.). 1985. write for info. Natl Cath Educ.
NPCD Handbook for DREs. 88p. 1983. 6.00 (ISBN 0-318-00786-X). Natl Cath Educ.
Occasional Papers on Catholic Higher Education. Incl. Vol. 1, No. 1. 20p. 1975. 1.20 (ISBN 0-318-18249-1); Vol. I, No. 2. 49p. 1975. 2.40 (ISBN 0-318-18250-5); Vol. II, No. 1. 11p. 1976. 1.20 (ISBN 0-318-18251-3); Vol. II, No. 2. 23p. 1976. 1.20 (ISBN 0-318-18252-1); Vol. III, No. 1. 19p. 1977. 1.20 (ISBN 0-318-18253-X); Vol. III, No. 2. 32p. 1977. 1.20 (ISBN 0-318-18254-8); Vol. IV, No. 1. 35p. 1978. 1.80 (ISBN 0-318-18255-6); Vol. IV, No. 2. 35p. 1978. 2.40 (ISBN 0-318-18256-4); Vol. V, No. 1. 35p. 1979. 2.40 (ISBN 0-318-18257-2). Natl Cath Educ.
Peace Education Council & Sister Loretta Carey. Directions for Justice-Peace Education in the Catholic Elementary School. 44p. 1985. 4.80 (ISBN 0-318-20608-0). Natl Cath Educ.
Podgorski, John. Empowering the Catholic Teacher. 1987. pap. write for info. (ISBN 0-697-02242-0). Wm C Brown.
Podhaizer, Mary E. Jesus Our Life: Activity Book. Puccetti, Patricia I., ed. (Faith & Life Ser.: bk. 2). 76p. (Orig.). 1984. pap. 2.50 (ISBN 0-89870-063-9). Ignatius Pr.
Powell, Carol & Powell, David. How to Bring Up Children in the Catholic Faith. 240p. 1984. 12.95 (ISBN 0-13-402537-7). P-H.
Praetz, Helen. Building a School System. 178p. 1980. 28.00x (ISBN 0-522-84213-5, Pub. by Melbourne U Pr Australia). Intl Spec Bk.
The Qualities & Competencies of the Catechist. rev. ed. 1983. 4.80 (ISBN 0-318-00789-4). Natl Cath Educ.
Reck, Carleen & Coreil, Judith. School Evaluation for the Catholic Elementary School: An Overview. 56p. 1983. 3.00 (ISBN 0-318-00791-6). Natl Cath Educ.
--Verifying the Vision: A Self-Evaluation Instrument for the Catholic Elementary School. 160p. 1984. 12.00 (ISBN 0-318-17778-1). Natl Cath Educ.
Reverend James Hawker & Sr. Thea Bowman. The Non-Catholic in the Catholic School. 1984. 4.20 (ISBN 0-318-18580-6); member 3.15. Natl Cath Educ.
Saint Mary's College - Holy Cross - Indiana. College Goes to School. facs. ed. LC 68-58811. (Essay Index Reprint Ser). 1945. 15.00 (ISBN 0-8369-0125-8). Ayer Co Pubs.
Schultheis, Michael J., et al. Our Best Kept Secret: The Rich Heritage of Catholic Social Teaching. (Illus.). 60p. (Orig.). 1985. pap. text ed. 3.50 (ISBN 0-934255-01-6). Center Concern.
A Self-Study Guide for Catholic High Schools. 76p. 1981. 9.00 (ISBN 0-318-00792-4). Natl Cath Educ.
Stochl, Susan, et al, eds. Easter People, Grade 1: Welcome. (Easter People Ser.). 1977. pap. text ed. 3.34 (ISBN 0-03-020356-2, 161, HarpR); tchr's. ed. 7.60 (ISBN 0-03-020366-X, 163); activity pack 3.90 (ISBN 0-03-020371-6, 162); parent bk. 2.25 (ISBN 0-03-020361-9, 164). Har-Row.
--Easter People, Grade 2: Belong. (Easter People Ser). 1977. pap. text ed. 3.34 (ISBN 0-03-020376-7, 165, HarpR); tchr's. ed. 7.60 (ISBN 0-03-020386-4, 167); activity pack 3.90 (ISBN 0-03-020391-0, 166); parent bk. 2.25 (ISBN 0-03-020381-3, 168). Har-Row.
Stuhr, Robert L. & Jarc, Jerry A. Annual Fund Estate Planning. (How to Ser.). 1984. 4.80. Natl Cath Educ.
That They All May Be One. 26p. 1977. 3.60 (ISBN 0-318-20611-0). Natl Cath Educ.
Thompson, Andrew. That They May Know You. 112p. 1982. 10.55 (ISBN 0-318-00801-7). Natl Cath Educ.
Those Who Would Be Catholic School Principals: Their Recruitment, Preparation, & Evaluation. 1985. 8.00 (ISBN 0-318-18577-6). Natl Cath Educ.
United States Catholic Conference, Conference of Catholic Bishops, Department of Education. Sharing the Light of Faith: National Catechetical Directory for Catholics of the United States. (Illus., Orig.). 1979. pap. 6.50 (ISBN 1-55586-001-X). US Catholic.
United States Catholic Elementary Schools & Their Finances 1984. 6.00 (ISBN 0-318-03695-9). Natl Cath Educ.
Van Merrienboer, Edward, et al. Seeking a Just Society: An Educational Design. Incl. Elementary Edition. 42.00 (ISBN 0-318-00795-9); Secondary Edition. 42.00 (ISBN 0-318-00796-7). Total Edition. 72.00 (ISBN 0-318-00793-2); faculty unit 4.00 (ISBN 0-318-00794-0). Natl Cath Educ.
Yeager, Robert J. The Case Statement. 1984. 4.80 (ISBN 0-318-18571-7). Natl Cath Educ.
--Resources for Development. (How to Ser.). 46p. 1986. 8.95. Natl Cath Educ.

CATHOLIC CHURCH–ENCYCLOPEDIAS
see Catholic Church–Dictionaries

CATHOLIC CHURCH–FASTS AND FEASTS
see Fasts and Feasts–Catholic Church

CATHOLIC CHURCH–FINANCE
Lunt, W. E. Financial Relations of the Papacy with England to 1327. 1967. Repr. of 1939 ed. 20.00X (ISBN 0-910956-13-8). Medieval Acad.
--Financial Relations of the Papacy with England, 1327-1534. 1962. 25.00X (ISBN 0-910956-48-0). Medieval Acad.
Maida, Adam J. & Carfardi, Nicholas P. Church Property, Church Finances, & Church-Related Corporations: A Canon Law Handbook. LC 83-20946. 1984. 28.00 (ISBN 0-87125-090-X). Cath Health.

CATHOLIC CHURCH–FOREIGN RELATIONS
see Catholic Church–Relations (Diplomatic)

CATHOLIC CHURCH–GOVERNMENT
see also Bishops; Cardinals; Dioceses; Investiture; Papacy; Popes
Dahm, Charles & Ghelardi, Robert. Power & Authority in the Catholic Church: Cardinal Cody in Chicago. LC 81-40453. 334p. 1982. text ed. 22.95 (ISBN 0-268-01546-5). U of Notre Dame Pr.
Edelby, Neophytos, et al, eds. Sacraments in Theology & Canon Law. LC 68-58308. (Concilium Ser.: Vol. 38). 191p. 1968. 7.95 (ISBN 0-8091-0132-7). Paulist Pr.
Fisher, Eugene J. & Polish, Daniel F., eds. The Formation of Social Policy in the Catholic & Jewish Tradition. new ed. LC 80-50268. 208p. text ed. 17.95 (ISBN 0-268-00953-8); pap. text ed. 8.95 (ISBN 0-268-00951-1). U of Notre Dame Pr.
Hale, Robert. Canterbury & Rome, Sister Churches: A Roman Catholic Monk Reflects on Reunion in Diversity. 7.95 (ISBN 0-8091-2480-7). Paulist Pr.
Hebblethwaite, Peter. Synod Extraordinary: An Evaluation of the Catholic Church on the 20th Anniversary of Vatican Council II. LC 85-27160. 144p. 1986. 15.95 (ISBN 0-385-23466-X). Doubleday.
Muggeridge, Anne R. The Desolate City: Revolution in the Catholic Church. 256p. 1986. 16.95 (ISBN 0-06-066038-4, HarpR). Har-Row.
Quinn, Bernard & Bookser-Feister, John. Apostolic Regions of the United States: 1980. LC 78-67012. (Illus.). 1985. pap. text ed. 4.00x (ISBN 0-914422-08-1). Glenmary Res Ctr.
Schnell, Ursula. Das Verhaeltnis von Amt und Gemeinde im Neueren Katholizismus. (Theologische Bibliothek Toepelmann: Vol. 29). 1977. pap. 41.20x (ISBN 3-11-004929-5). De Gruyter.
Ullman, Walter. Medieval Papalism: The Political Theories of the Medieval Canonists. LC 79-1644. 1981. Repr. of 1949 ed. 21.50 (ISBN 0-88355-946-3). Hyperion Conn.
Urresti, Teodoro-J & Edelby, Neophytos, eds. Pastoral Reform in Church Government. LC 65-28464. (Concilium Ser.: Vol. 8). 192p. 7.95 (ISBN 0-8091-0109-2). Paulist Pr.

CATHOLIC CHURCH–HISTORY
see also Catholic Church in the United States–History; Councils and Synods; Counter-Reformation; Schism–Eastern and Western Church; Schism, the Great Western, 1378-1417; also names of specific councils of the Catholic Church
Aumann, Jordan. Christian Spirituality in the Catholic Tradition. 336p. 1985. pap. 11.95 (ISBN 0-89870-068-X). Ignatius Pr.
Baldwin, Summerfield. Organization of Medieval Christianity. 1986. 11.25 (ISBN 0-8446-1051-8). Peter Smith.
Bamonte, Louis J. Your Faith: Leader's Guide. 1978. tchr's ed 2.95 (ISBN 0-89243-085-0). Liguori Pubns.
Baynes, Norman H. Constantine the Great & the Christian Church. 1974. lib. bdg. 59.95 (ISBN 0-87968-934-X). Gordon Pr.
Bellini, Enzo, et al. The Catholic Church Today, 1920-1981. Drury, John, ed. & tr. from Ital. (Illustrated History of the Church). (Illus.). 126p. 1982. 12.95 (ISBN 0-86683-160-6, HarpR). Har-Row.
Boer, Harry R. A Short History of the Early Church. LC 75-25742. pap. 6.95 (ISBN 0-8028-1339-9). Eerdmans.
Bokenkotter, Thomas. A Concise History of the Catholic Church. LC 78-20269. 1979. pap. 6.50 (ISBN 0-385-13015-5, Im). Doubleday.
Brauer, Jerald C., ed. Westminster Dictionary of Church History. LC 69-11071. 900p. 1971. 27.50 (ISBN 0-664-21285-9). Westminster.
Buhlmann, Walbert. The Coming of the Third Church: An Analysis of the Present & Future. Woodhall, Ralph & Woodhall, A. N., eds. LC 76-23237. Orig. Title: Es Kommt die dritte Kirche. 430p. 1977. pap. 9.95x (ISBN 0-88344-070-9). Orbis Bks.
Cadoux, Cecil J. Philip of Spain & the Netherlands: An Essay on Moral Judgments in History. LC 69-15788. xv, 251p. 1969. Repr. of 1947 ed. 27.50 (ISBN 0-208-00735-0, Archon). Shoe String.
Capetti, Giselda, ed. Cronistoria, 5 vols. LC 80-68484. 400p. (Orig.). 1980. Set. pap. 40.00 (ISBN 0-89944-043-6); Vol. 1. pap. (ISBN 0-89944-044-4); Vol. 2. pap. (ISBN 0-89944-045-2); Vol. 3. pap. (ISBN 0-89944-046-0); Vol. 4. pap. (ISBN 0-89944-047-9); Vol. 5. pap. (ISBN 0-89944-048-7). Don Bosco Multimedia.
Chapman, H. John. Studies on the Early Papacy. LC 76-118517. 1971. Repr. of 1928 ed. 23.00x (ISBN 0-8046-1139-4, Pub. by Kennikat). Assoc Faculty Pr.
Cockerham, Allan W. The Apostolic Succession in the Liberal Catholic Church. 2nd ed. (Illus.). 1980. pap. text ed. 2.80 (ISBN 0-918980-09-7). St Alban Pr.
Creighton, Mandell. History of the Papacy from the Great Schism to the Sack of Rome, 6 Vols. rev. ed. LC 74-77897. Repr. of 1897 ed. Set. 165.00 (ISBN 0-404-01870-X); 27.50 ea. AMS Pr.
Cunningham, Lawrence S. The Catholic Heritage: Martyrs, Ascetics, Pilgrims, Warriors, Mystics, Theologians, Artists, Humanists, Activists, Outsiders & Saints. 256p. 1983. 14.95 (ISBN 0-8245-0592-1). Crossroad NY.
Day, Edward. The Catholic Church Story. rev ed. LC 78-73834. (Illus.). 192p. (Orig.). 1975. pap. 3.95 (ISBN 0-89243-105-9, 65300). Liguori Pubns.
De Wohl, Louis. Founded on a Rock: A History of the Catholic Church. LC 81-6557. 248p. 1981. Repr. lib. bdg. 23.50x (ISBN 0-313-23168-0, DEF0). Greenwood.
Dunney, Joseph A. Church History in the Light of the Saints. LC 74-2196. (Essay Index Reprint Ser.). Repr. of 1944 ed. 25.00 (ISBN 0-518-10162-2). Ayer Co Pubs.
Fenwick, Benedict J. Memoirs to Serve for the Future Ecclesiastical History of the Diocese of Boston. McCarthy, Joseph M., ed. LC 78-64366. (Monograph: No. 35). (Illus.). 270p. 1979. 10.95x (ISBN 0-686-65388-2). US Cath Hist.
Fox, Robert F. Catechism of the Catholic Church. 1979. 8.95 (ISBN 0-685-94958-3). Franciscan Her.
Franck, Frederick. Exploding Church. pap. 2.95 (ISBN 0-440-52432-6). Dell.
Frazee, Charles A. Catholics & Sultans: The Church & the Ottoman Empire 1453-1923. LC 82-4562. 384p. 1983. 67.50 (ISBN 0-521-24676-8). Cambridge U Pr.
Goodich, Michael. The Unmentionable Vice: Homosexuality in the Later Medieval Period. LC 78-13276. 179p. 1980. pap. 7.95 (ISBN 0-87436-300-4). Ross-Erikson.
Harney, Martin P. Catholic Church Through the Ages. LC 73-76312. 1974. 12.00 (ISBN 0-8198-0500-9); pap. 11.00 (ISBN 0-8198-0501-7). Dghtrs St Paul.
Holmes, Derek J. & Bickers, Bernard W. A Short History of the Catholic Church. LC 83-63193. 315p. 1984. pap. 8.95 (ISBN 0-8091-2623-0). Paulist Pr.
Johnson, Gary. Catholic Church Story: Leader's Guide. 1978. tchr's ed 2.95 (ISBN 0-89243-092-3). Liguori Pubns.
Johnson, George, et al. The Story of the Church. LC 80-51329. 521p. 1980. pap. 12.50 (ISBN 0-89555-156-X). Tan Bks Pubs.
Jouhanneaud, P. Dictionnaire Dogmatique, Historique, Ascetique et Pratique, des Indulgences des Confreries et Associations Catholiques. Migne, J. P., ed. (Nouvelle Encyclopedie Theologique Ser.: Vol. 27). (Fr.). 686p. Repr. of 1852 ed. lib. bdg. 87.50x (ISBN 0-89241-270-4). Caratzas.
Kington-Oliphant, Thomas L. Rome & Reform, 2 Vols. LC 76-118541. 1971. Repr. of 1902 ed. Set. 47.50x (ISBN 0-8046-1165-3, Pub. by Kennikat). Assoc Faculty Pr.
Lovasik, Lawerence G. Concise Church History: St. Joseph Edition. (Orig.). 1986. pap. 5.95 (ISBN 0-89942-262-4). Catholic BK Pub.
MacCaffrey, James. History of the Catholic Church from the Renaissaince to the French Revolution, 2 vols. facsimile ed. LC 75-130558. (Select Bibliographies Reprint Ser.). Repr. of 1915 ed. Set. 53.00 (ISBN 0-8369-5531-5); Vol. 1. 26.50 (ISBN 0-8369-9984-3); Vol. 2. 26.50 (ISBN 0-8369-9985-1). Ayer Co Pubs.
McKenna, Marian. Concise History of Catholicism. (Quality Paperback: No. 143). 285p. 1962. pap. 2.95 (ISBN 0-8226-0143-5). Littlefield.
Meadows, Denis. A Short History of the Catholic Church. 1959. 12.95 (ISBN 0-8159-6813-2). Devin.
Milman, Henry H. History of Latin Christianity, 9 Vols. LC 71-172734. Repr. of 1887 ed. Set. lib. bdg. 145.00 (ISBN 0-404-04360-7). AMS Pr.
Minnich, Nelson H., ed. Studies in Catholic History. 1985. 35.00 (ISBN 0-89453-530-7). M Glazier.
Nevins, Albert J. Builders of Catholic America. LC 85-72363. 250p. (Orig.). 1985. pap. 7.95 (ISBN 0-87973-582-1, 582). Our Sunday Visitor.
Orlandis, Jose. A Short History of the Catholic Church. 163p. 1985. pap. 7.50 (ISBN 0-912414-43-X). Lumen Christi.
--A Short History of the Catholic Church. Adams, Michael, tr. from Span. Tr. of Historia breve del Cristianismo. 163p. (Orig.). 1985. pap. 7.95 (ISBN 0-906127-86-6, Pub. by Four Courts Pr Ireland). Scepter Pubs.
Pelikan, Jaroslav. The Christian Tradition: A History of the Development of Doctrine, Vol. 1: Emergence of the Catholic Tradition, 100-600. LC 79-142042. 1971. 25.00x (ISBN 0-226-65370-6). U of Chicago Pr.
Phelan, Thomas P. Catholics in Colonial Days. LC 74-145706. Repr. of 1935 ed. 40.00x (ISBN 0-8103-3685-5). Gale.
Pluth, Alphonsus & Koch, Carl. The Catholic Church: Our Mission in History. (Illus.). 330p. (Orig.). 1985. pap. text ed. 11.00x (ISBN 0-88489-161-5); teaching manual 18.95x (ISBN 0-88489-162-3). St Mary's.
Previtali, David R. The Life of Grace. (Faith & Life). (Illus.). 176p. (Orig.). 1985. pap. 7.50 (ISBN 0-89870-083-3); pap. 2.50 activity bk. (ISBN 0-89870-084-1). Ignatius Pr.

The Roman Catholic Church Index of Prohibited Books As Issued by Pope Leo XIII. 201p. 1985. Repr. of 1907 ed. 127.55 (ISBN 0-89901-199-3). Found Class Reprints.

Ruffin, C. Bernard. The Days of the Martyrs. LC 85-60517. 200p. (Orig.). 1985. pap. 7.95 (ISBN 0-87973-595-3, 595). Our Sunday Visitor.

Schreck, Alan. The Compact History of the Catholic Church. 192p. (Orig.). 1987. pap. 5.95 (ISBN 0-89283-328-9). Servant.

Sullivan, Francis A. Magisterium: Teaching Authority in the Catholic Church. 1984. pap. 9.95 (ISBN 0-8091-2577-3). Paulist Pr.

Taves, Ann. The Household of Faith: Roman Catholic Devotions in Mid-Nineteenth Century America. LC 85-41008. 192p. 1986. text ed. 17.95x (ISBN 0-268-01082-X). U of Notre Dame Pr.

Taylor, Mark L. God Is Love: A Study in the Theology of Karl Rahner. (AAR-Academy Ser.). 1986. 24.95 (ISBN 0-89130-925-X, 01-01-50); pap. 18.25 (ISBN 0-89130-926-8). Scholars Pr GA.

Von Ranke, Leopold. History of the Popes: Their Church & State, 3 vols. 1205p. 1986. Repr. of 1901 ed. lib. bdg. 150.00 (ISBN 0-8495-4730-X). Arden Lib.

Werner, Karl. Geschichte Der Katholischen Theologie. 2nd ed. 50.00 (ISBN 0-384-66815-1). Johnson Repr.

CATHOLIC CHURCH–HISTORY–SOURCES

Brugge, David M. Navajos in the Catholic Church Records of New Mexico 1694-1875. LC 84-60510. 1986. 12.50x (ISBN 0-912586-59-1). Navajo Coll Pr.

Historical Documents of Central Christian Church 1848-1979. 100p. (Orig.). 1980. pap. write for info. T H Peters.

Innocent Third, Pope Register Innocenz' 3rd Uber Die Reichsfrage, 1198-1209. Tangl, Georgine, ed. 1923. 23.00 (ISBN 0-384-07885-0). Johnson Repr.

Loomis, Louise R., tr. Book of the Popes. 1965. lib. bdg. 19.50x (ISBN 0-374-95093-8, Octagon). Hippocrene Bks.

Mathews, Shailer. Select Medieval Documents & Other Material Illustrative in the History of Church & Empire, 754 A.D.-1254 A.D. LC 70-178566. (Lat.). Repr. of 1900 ed. 21.00 (ISBN 0-404-56628-6). AMS Pr.

CATHOLIC CHURCH–HISTORY–MIDDLE AGES, 600-1500

Wilson, Stanley G. With the Pilgrims to Canterbury: And the History of the Hospital of St. Thomas. LC 70-178306. Repr. of 1934 ed. 14.50 (ISBN 0-404-06997-5). AMS Pr.

CATHOLIC CHURCH–HISTORY–MODERN PERIOD, 1500-

Boxer, C. R. The Church Militant & Iberian Expansion: 1440-1770. LC 77-18386. (Johns Hopkins Symposia in Comparative History Ser.: No. 10). (Illus.). 1978. text ed. 17.50x (ISBN 0-8018-2042-1). Johns Hopkins.

Bridgewater, John. Concerto Ecclesiae Catholicae in Anglia Adversus Calvinopapistas et Puritanos. 886p. Repr. of 1588 ed. text ed. 149.04 (ISBN 0-576-78532-6, Pub. by Gregg Intl Pubs England). Gregg Intl.

Callahan, W. J. & Higgs, D. Church & Society in Catholic Europe of the Eighteenth Century. LC 78-12165. 1979. 27.95 (ISBN 0-521-22424-1). Cambridge U Pr.

Campbell, Kenneth L. The Intellectual Struggle of the English Catholics in the Seventeenth Century: The Catholic Dilemma. LC 86-23893. (Texts & Studies in Religion Ser.: Vol. 30). 256p. 1986. text ed. 49.95 (ISBN 0-88946-818-4). E Mellen.

Chesterton, G. K. Orthodoxy. 160p. 1973. pap. 3.50 (ISBN 0-385-01536-4, Im). Doubleday.

Cohen, Paul M. Piety & Politics: Catholic Revival & the Generation of 1905-1914 in France. McNeill, William H. & Pinkney, David H., eds. (Modern European History Ser.). 348p. 1987. lib. bdg. 50.00 (ISBN 0-8240-8034-3). Garland Pub.

Delumeau, Jean. Catholicism Between Luther & Voltaire: A New View of the Counter-Reformation. Moiser, Jeremy, tr. LC 77-4005. 314p. 1977. 21.50 (ISBN 0-664-21341-3). Westminster.

Kurtz, Lester R. The Politics of Heresy: The Modernist Crisis in Roman Catholicism. LC 85-1179. 256p. 1986. text ed. 32.50x (ISBN 0-520-05537-3). U of Cal Pr.

MacCaffrey, James. History of the Catholic Church: From the Renaissance to the French Revolution, Vol. II. facsimile ed. LC 75-130558. 470p. Repr. of 1915 ed. lib. bdg. 25.50 (ISBN 0-8290-0464-5). Irvington.

--History of the Catholic Church: From the Renaissance to the French Revolution, Vol. I. facsimile ed. LC 75-130558. 419p. Repr. of 1915 ed. lib. bdg. 25.50 (ISBN 0-8290-0463-7). Irvington.

McShane, Joseph M. Sufficiently Radical: Catholicism, Progressivism, & the Bishops Program of 1919. 1986. 38.95 (ISBN 0-8132-0631-6). Cath U Pr.

O'Shaughnessy, Laura & Serra, Luis. The Church & Revolution in Nicaragua. LC 82-92625. (Monographs in International Studies, Latin America Ser.: No. 11). 118p. pap. 11.00x (ISBN 0-89680-126-8, Ohio U Ctr Intl). Ohio U Pr.

Pawsey, Margaret M. The Demon of Discord: Tensions in the Catholic Church of Victoria, 1853-1864. (Illus.). 200p. 1983. 25.00x (ISBN 0-522-84249-6, Pub. by Melbourne U Pr). Intl Spec Bk.

Ray, Mary A. American Opinion of Roman Catholicism in the Eighteenth Century. 456p. 1974. Repr. of 1936 ed. lib. bdg. 26.00x (ISBN 0-374-96723-7, Octagon). Hippocrene Bks.

Scott, William & Scott, Frances M. The Church Then & Now: Cultivating a Sense of Tradition. 108p. (Orig.). 1985. pap. 3.95 (ISBN 0-934134-30-8, Leaven Pr). Sheed & Ward MO.

Stravinskas, Peter M. & McBain, Robert A. The Church After the Council: A Primer for Adults. LC 75-4720. 113p. (Orig.). 1975. pap. 2.95 (ISBN 0-8189-0316-3). Alba.

CATHOLIC CHURCH–HYMNS

Blume, Clemens, ed. Hymnodia Gotica. Repr. of 1909 ed. 60.00 ea. Vol. 1. (ISBN 0-384-04766-1); Vol. 2. (ISBN 0-384-04767-X). Johnson Repr.

--Thesauri Hymnologica Hymnarium, 2 Vols. Repr. of 1909 ed. 60.00 ea. Johnson Repr.

--Thesauri Hymnologica Prosarium, 2 Vols in 3. (Illus.). Repr. of 1922 ed. 60.00 ea. Johnson Repr.

Boncore Di Santa Vittoria Staff. Boncore Di Santa Victoria Novus Liber Hymnorum Ac Orationum. Repr. of 1903 ed. 60.00 (ISBN 0-384-12867-X). Johnson Repr.

Dreves, Guido M., ed. Cantiones Bohemicae. 1886. 60.00 (ISBN 0-384-12860-2). Johnson Repr.

--Cantiones et Muteti, 3 vols. (Illus.). 1895-1904. 60.00 ea. (ISBN 0-384-12865-3). Johnson Repr.

--Historiae Rhythmicae, 8 Vols. 1889-1904. 60.00 ea. (ISBN 0-384-12880-7). Johnson Repr.

--Hymni Inediti, 7 Vols. 1888-1903. 60.00 ea. Johnson Repr.

--Hymnodia Hiberica: Liturgische Reimofficien, Aus Spanischen Brevieren. (Illus.). 1894. 60.00 (ISBN 0-384-12915-3). Johnson Repr.

--Hymnodia Hiberica: Spanische Hymnen Des Mittelalters. 1894. 60.00 (ISBN 0-384-12920-X). Johnson Repr.

--Pia Dictamina, 7 Vols. 1893-1905. 60.00 ea. (ISBN 0-384-12950-1). Johnson Repr.

--Psalteria Rhythmica, 2 Vols. 1900-01. 60.00 ea. (ISBN 0-384-12960-9) (ISBN 0-384-12961-7). Johnson Repr.

Messenger, Ruth E. Ethical Teachings in the Latin Hymns of Medieval England. LC 30-20975. (Columbia University. Studies in the Social Sciences: No. 321). Repr. of 1930 ed. 18.50 (ISBN 0-404-51321-2). AMS Pr.

Moissac France Benedictine Abbey. Hymnarius Moissiacensis. 1888. 60.00 (ISBN 0-384-39520-1). Johnson Repr.

Stocklin, Ulrich V. Psalteria Wessofontana. Dreves, Guido M., ed. Repr. of 1902 ed. 60.00 (ISBN 0-384-58320-2). Johnson Repr.

--Udalricus Wessofontanus. Dreves, Guido M., ed. Repr. 60.00 (ISBN 0-384-58330-X). Johnson Repr.

CATHOLIC CHURCH–INFALLIBILITY

see also Popes–Infallibility

Chirico, Peter. Infallibility: The Crossroads of Doctrine. (Theology & Life Ser.: Vol. 1). pap. 9.95 (ISBN 0-89453-296-0). M Glazier.

Hodge, A. A. & Warfield, B. B. Inspiration. 1979. pap. 2.95 (ISBN 0-8010-4222-4). Baker Bk.

Kirvan, John J., ed. Infallibility Debate. LC 76-168745. Repr. of 1971 ed. 40.00 (ISBN 0-8357-9485-7, 2013529). Bks Demand UMI.

Kung, Hans. Infallible? An Inquiry. LC 82-45641. 288p. 1983. pap. 10.95 (ISBN 0-385-18483-2). Doubleday.

Newman, John H. The Theological Papers of John Henry Newman: On Biblical Inspiration & on Infallibility, Vol. 2. Holmes, J. Derek, ed. 1979. text ed. 22.50x (ISBN 0-19-920081-5). Oxford U Pr.

Ryre, Charles C. What You Should Know about Inerrancy. (Current Christian Issues Ser.). pap. 4.50 (ISBN 0-8024-8785-8). Moody.

CATHOLIC CHURCH–LITURGICAL MOVEMENT

see Liturgical Movement–Catholic Church

CATHOLIC CHURCH–LITURGY AND RITUAL

see also Chants (Plain, Gregorian, etc.); Church Music–Catholic Church; Liturgical Movement–Catholic Church; Sequences (Liturgy); Stations of the Cross

Aridas, Christopher. Your Catholic Wedding: A Complete Plan-Book. LC 81-43250. (Illus.). 192p. 1982. pap. 2.95 (ISBN 0-385-17731-3, Im). Doubleday.

As One Who Serves: Reflections on the Pastoral Ministry of Priests in the United States. 86p. 1977. pap. 3.25 (ISBN 1-55586-549-6). US Catholic.

Assamani, Joseph A. De Catholicis Seu Patriarchis Chaldaeorum et Nestorianorum Commentarius: De Unione et Communione Ecclesiastica. 410p. Repr. of 1775 ed. text ed. 82.80x (ISBN 0-576-99702-1, Pub. by Gregg Intl Pubs England). Gregg Intl.

Austin, Gerard. Anointing with the Spirit. (Reformed Rites of the Catholic Church Ser.: Vol. 2). 192p. (Orig.). 1985. pap. 10.95 (ISBN 0-916134-70-9). Pueblo Pub Co.

The Bishop & the Liturgy: Highlights of the New Ceremonial of Bishops. 104p. (Orig.). 1986. pap. 8.95 (ISBN 1-55586-996-3). US Catholic.

Bouyer, Louis. Liturgical Piety. (Liturgical Studies Ser). 1965. 10.95x (ISBN 0-268-00158-8). U of Notre Dame Pr.

Boyack, Kenneth, et al. Catholic Faith Inventory. write for info. Paulist Pr.

Catholic Church, Liturgy & Ritual: Prosarium Lemovicense. Repr. of 1889 ed. 60.00 (ISBN 0-384-07880-X). Johnson Repr.

Champlin, Joseph. Healing in the Catholic Church: Mending Wounded Hearts & Bodies. LC 84-62226. 160p. 1985. pap. 5.50 (ISBN 0-87973-719-0, 719). Our Sunday Visitor.

Cooper, Irving S. Ceremonies of the Liberal Catholic Rite. 2nd ed. (Illus.). 225p. 1981. Repr. of 1934 ed. 16.50 (ISBN 0-935461-07-8). St Alban Pr CA.

Cruz, Joan C. Relics. LC 84-60744. (Illus.). 352p. 1984. pap. 10.95 (ISBN 0-87973-701-8, 701). Our Sunday Visitor.

Davies, Michael. Open Lesson to a Bishop. 1980. pap. 1.00 (ISBN 0-89555-142-X). Tan Bks Pubs.

Ellard, Gerald. Master Alcuin, Liturgist. LC 56-8943. (Jesuit Studies). 1956. 2.95 (ISBN 0-8294-0027-3). Loyola.

Ferretti, Paolo A. Estetica Gregoriana. LC 77-5498. (Music Reprint Ser.). 1977. Repr. of 1934 ed. lib. bdg. 45.00 (ISBN 0-306-77414-3). Da Capo.

Gallen, Joseph F. Conforming Constitutions to the New Code. 58p. 1984. pap. 2.00 (ISBN 0-317-18638-8). Dghtrs St Paul.

Georgi, D. De Liturgia Romani Pontificis in Solemni Celebratione Missarum, 3 vols. 1822p. Repr. of 1731 ed. text ed. 372.60 (ISBN 0-576-99174-0, Pub. by Gregg Intl Pubs England). Gregg Intl.

Good News for Lit. Comm. Cycle A. 5.95 (ISBN 0-8198-3011-9); 4.95 (ISBN 0-8198-3012-7). Dghtrs St Paul.

Handbook for Today's Catholic Family A Redemptorist Pastoral Publication. (Orig.). 1979. pap. 1.50 (ISBN 0-89243-112-1). Liguori Pubns.

Hebert, Albert, compiled by. A Prayerbook of Favorite Litanies: 116 Favorite Catholic Litanies & Responsory Prayers. LC 84-51818. 192p. 1985. pap. 7.50 (ISBN 0-89555-252-3). Tan Bks Pubs.

Hittorpius, Melchior. De Divinsis Catholicae Ecclesiae Officiis et Mysteriis. 796p. Repr. of 1610 ed. text ed. 207.00 (ISBN 0-576-99170-8, Pub. by Gregg Intl Pubs England). Gregg Intl.

Howard, Thomas. The Liturgy Explained. (Illus.). 48p. (Orig.). 1981. pap. 2.95 (ISBN 0-8192-1285-7). Morehouse.

Huck, Gabe & Sloyan, Virginia, eds. Parishes & Families: A Model for Christian Formation Through Liturgy. 1973. pap. 5.00 (ISBN 0-918208-11-4). Liturgical Conf.

Hucke, H. & Wagner, Johannes, eds. Church Worships. LC 66-17730. (Concilium Ser.: Vol. 12). 196p. 1966. 7.95 (ISBN 0-8091-0020-7). Paulist Pr.

Italian Ritual. (Rubrics in Italian & English). Blue Cloth 4.95 (ISBN 0-89942-111-3, 111/22). Catholic Bk Pub.

Kwatera, Michael. The Ministry of Servers. (Illus.). 48p. (Orig.). 1982. pap. 1.25 (ISBN 0-8146-1300-4). Liturgical Pr.

Lang, Jovian. Dictionary of the Liturgy. 1986. 8.00 (ISBN 0-89942-273-X). Catholic BK Pub.

Lawler, Ronald. Light from Light: What Catholics Believe about Jesus. 240p. (Orig.). 1987. pap. 7.50 (ISBN 0-87973-547-3, 547). Our Sunday Visitor.

Liturgical Calendar & Ordo, 1987, United States of America. 128p. 1986. pap. 6.95 (ISBN 1-55586-986-6). US Catholic.

Liturgical Formation in Seminaries: A Commentary. 120p. 1984. pap. 4.95 (ISBN 1-55586-917-3). US Catholic.

Mahony, Roger. The Bible in the Life of the Catholic Church. 32p. (Orig.). 1983. pap. 0.50 (ISBN 0-8146-1317-9). Liturgical Pr.

May, William E., ed. Principles of Catholic Moral Life. LC 80-10969. 456p. 1981. 10.50 (ISBN 0-8199-0793-6). Franciscan Herald.

Merton, Thomas. Seasons of Celebration. 1983. 13.50 (ISBN 0-8446-5990-8). Peter Smith.

Migne, J. P., ed. Origines et Raison De la Liturgie Catholique En Forme De Dictionnaire... Suivies De la Liturgie Armenienne Traduite En Francais. Avedichian, Gabriel & Pascal, E., trs. (Encyclopedie Theologique Ser.: Vol. 8). (Fr.). 652p. Repr. of 1833 ed. lib. bdg. 83.00x (ISBN 0-89241-233-X). Caratzas.

Night Prayer, From the Liturgy of the Hours. 86p. 1976. pap. 2.95 (ISBN 1-55586-480-5). US Catholic.

O'Connor, Francine M. & Boswell, Kathryn. The ABC'S of the Rosary. (Illus.). 32p. 1984. pap. 1.95 (ISBN 0-89243-221-7). Liguori Pubns.

Order of Christian Funerals: General Introduction & Pastoral Notes. (Liturgy Documentary Ser.: No. 8). 72p. (Orig.). Date not set. pap. 5.95 (ISBN 1-55586-990-4). US Catholic.

Penance & Reconciliation in the Church. (Liturgy Documentary Ser.: No. 7). 96p. (Orig.). 1986. pap. 5.95 (ISBN 1-55586-104-0). US Catholic.

Power, David N. Gifts That Differ: Lay Ministries Established & Unestablished. (Studies in the Reformed Rites of the Catholic Church: Vol. 8). (Orig.). 1980. pap. 9.95 (ISBN 0-916134-43-1). Pueblo Pub Co.

Ratzinger, Cardinal J. Seek That Which Is Above. Harrison, Graham, tr. from German. LC 86-81553. Tr. of Suchen was Droben Ist. 132p. 1986. 9.95 (ISBN 0-89870-101-5). Ignatius Pr.

Redemptorist Pastoral Publication. Manual para el Catolico de Hoy. 1978. pap. 1.95 (ISBN 0-89243-091-5). Liguori Pubns.

Rev. Gene Ulses. The Wisdom of the Lord: Homilies for Weekdays & Feast Days. LC 86-60910. 254p. (Orig.). 1986. 12.95 (ISBN 0-87973-512-0, 512). Our Sunday Visitor.

Rite of Anointing & Pastoral Care of the Sick. pocket ed. 6.95 (ISBN 0-89942-156-3, 156/04). Catholic Bk Pub.

Ryrie, Charles C. What You Should Know about the Rapture. LC 81-4019. (Current Christian Issues Ser.). 128p. 1981. pap. 4.50 (ISBN 0-8024-9416-1). Moody.

Sacred Congregation for Divine Worship. Rites of the Catholic Church, Vol. 1. rev. ed. International Committee on English in the Liturgy, tr. from Lat. 1983. 14.50 (ISBN 0-916134-15-6). Pueblo Pub Co.

--The Rites of the Catholic Church, Vol. 2. International Commission on English in the Liturgy, tr. from Lat. 1980. pap. 11.50 (ISBN 0-916134-37-7). Pueblo Pub Co.

St. Romain, Philip. Catholic Answers to Fundamentalists' Questions. 64p. 1984. pap. 1.95 (ISBN 0-89243-220-9). Liguori Pubns.

Tiso, Francis & Catholic Heritage Press. A Young Person's Book of Catholic Signs & Symbols. LC 81-43459. 128p. 1982. pap. 3.50 (ISBN 0-385-17951-0, Im). Doubleday.

Vagaggini, Cipriano. Canon of the Mass & Liturgical Reform. Coughlan, Peter, tr. 1967. 4.50 (ISBN 0-8189-0019-9). Alba.

Von Allmen, et al. Roles in the Liturgical Assembly. O'Connell, Matthew J., tr. from Fr. (Orig.). 1981. pap. 17.50 (ISBN 0-916134-44-X). Pueblo Pub Co.

Wathen, James F. The Great Sacrilege. LC 76-183571. 1971. pap. 5.00 (ISBN 0-89555-014-8). TAN Bks Pubs.

Weber, Gerard. The Mass: Finding Its Meaning for You & Getting More Out of It. (Illus., Orig.). 1985. pap. 4.95 (ISBN 0-86716-049-7). St Anthony Mess Pr.

Werner, Eric. The Sacred Bridge. (Music Reprint Ser.). 1979. Repr. of 1959 ed. lib. bdg. 65.00 (ISBN 0-306-79581-7). Da Capo.

CATHOLIC CHURCH–LITURGY AND RITUAL–BIBLIOGRAPHY

Charles Louis De Bourbon. Bibliotheque liturgique, 2 vols. in 1. Ales, Anatole, ed. LC 72-130592. (Fr). 1970. Repr. of 1898 ed. lib. bdg. 40.50 (ISBN 0-8337-0036-7). B Franklin.

Riano, J. F. Critical & Biographical Notes on Early Spanish Music. LC 79-158958. (Music Ser.). 1971. Repr. of 1887 ed. lib. bdg. 29.50 (ISBN 0-306-70193-6). Da Capo.

CATHOLIC CHURCH–LITURGY AND RITUAL–BREVIARY

Goossens, Mathias, ed. With the Church. 6.95 (ISBN 0-8199-0148-2, L39000). Franciscan Herald.

Monastic Breviary. 1976. 14.95x (ISBN 0-8192-1220-2). Morehouse.

Salmi, Mario, intro. by. The Grimani Breviary. LC 74-78138. (Illus.). 276p. 1974. 195.00 (ISBN 0-87951-022-6). Overlook Pr.

CATHOLIC CHURCH–LITURGY AND RITUAL–HISTORY

Ellard, G. Ordination Anointings in the Western Church Before 1000 A. D. (Med Acad of Amer Pubns). 1932. 18.00 (ISBN 0-527-01688-8). Kraus Repr.

James, Edwin O. Christian Myth & Ritual: A Historical Study. 11.25 (ISBN 0-8446-2307-5). Peter Smith.

Kucharek, Casimir. The Byzantine Slav Liturgy of St. John Chrysostom, Its Origin & Evolution. LC 74-147735. (Illus.). 840p. 1971. 18.75 (ISBN 0-911726-06-3, BSL). Alleluia Pr.

Searle, Mark, ed. Sunday Morning: A Time for Worship. LC 82-15306. 200p. (Orig.). 1982. pap. 5.95 (ISBN 0-8146-1259-8). Liturgical Pr.

CATHOLIC CHURCH–LITURGY AND RITUAL–HOURS

see also Hours, Books of

More, St. Thomas. Thomas More's Prayer Book: A Facsimile Reproduction of the Annotated Pages. Martz, Louis L. & Sylvester, Richard S., trs. LC 69-15454. (Elizabethan Club Ser.: No. 4). (Lat. & Eng., Illus.). 1969. 26.00x (ISBN 0-300-00179-7). Yale U Pr.

Scotto, Dominic. The Liturgy of the Hours. 1986. pap. 9.95 (ISBN 0-932506-48-8). St Bedes Pubns.

CATHOLIC CHURCH–LITURGY AND RITUAL–MISSAL

see also Masses

Goode, Teresa C. Gonzalo De Berceo. (Carl Ser.: No. 7). Repr. of 1933 ed. 21.00 (ISBN 0-404-50307-1). AMS Pr.

Goossens, Mathias, ed. With the Church. 6.95 (ISBN 0-8199-0148-2, L39000). Franciscan Herald.

Lovasik, Lawrence G. My Picture Missal. (Saint Joseph Picture Bks.). (Illus.). flexible bdg. 0.95 (ISBN 0-89942-275-6, 275). Catholic Bk Pub.

The New First Mass Book. (Illus.). black leaherette, hard bd. 2.25 (ISBN 0-89942-808-8, 808/67-B); white leatherette, hard bd. 2.25 (ISBN 0-89942-809-6, 808/67W); black soft simulated lea., colered edges 2.75 (ISBN 0-89942-810-X, 808/42-B); white soft sim. lea., colored edges 2.75 (ISBN 0-89942-811-8, 808/42W); dlx. black sim. pearl, gold edges 8.95 (ISBN 0-89942-812-6, 808/82B); dlx. white sim. pearl, gold edges 8.95 (ISBN 0-89942-813-4, 808/82W). Catholic Bk Pub.

The New Saint Joseph Sunday Missal: Prayer Book & Hymnal. regular, annual 1986 ed. (Two Color Large Type Ordinary, Year "C" Only, Introduction). blue flexible bdg. 1.70 (ISBN 0-89942-886-X, 886/04). Catholic Bk Pub.

The New Saint Joseph Weekday Missal, 2 vols. Incl. Vol. 1. Advent to Pentecost (ISBN 0-89942-920-3, 920/09); Vol. 2. Pentecost to Advent (ISBN 0-89942-921-1, 921/09). 9.25 ea.; annual guide o.s.i. 1.00 (ISBN 0-686-14349-3, 920-G). Catholic Bk Pub.

Ogrodowski, William. A Catholic Book of the Mass. LC 84-60752. 168p. 1985. pap. 6.95 (ISBN 0-87973-600-3, 600). Our Sunday Visitor.

Roguet, A. M. The New Mass. 2.95 (ISBN 0-89942-130-X, 130/05). Catholic Bk Pub.

Simmons, T. F., ed. The Lay Folks Mass Book: Four Texts. (EET OS Ser.: Vol. 71). Repr. of 1879 ed. 63.00 (ISBN 0-8115-3359-X). Kraus Repr.

CATHOLIC CHURCH–LITURGY AND RITUAL–OFFICE OF THE BLESSED VIRGIN MARY

Little Office of the Blessed Virgin. cloth o.p. 3.00 (ISBN 0-8199-0063-X, L38395); pap. 2.25 (ISBN 0-8199-0062-1, 38396). Franciscan Herald.

CATHOLIC CHURCH–LITURGY AND RITUAL–PSALTER

see also Psalms (Music); Psalters

More, St. Thomas. Thomas More's Prayer Book: A Facsimile Reproduction of the Annotated Pages. Martz, Louis L. & Sylvester, Richard S., trs. LC 69-15454. (Elizabethan Club Ser.: No. 4). (Lat. & Eng., Illus.). 1969. 26.00x (ISBN 0-300-00179-7). Yale U Pr.

CATHOLIC CHURCH–LITURGY AND RITUAL–TROPER

Blume, Clemens, ed. Tropi Graduales, 2 Vols. (Illus.). Repr. of 1906 ed. 60.00 ea. Johnson Repr.

Planchart, Alejandro. The Repertory of Tropes at Winchester, 2 vols. LC 76-3033. 1976. text ed. 63.00x (ISBN 0-691-09121-8). Princeton U Pr.

CATHOLIC CHURCH–MISSIONS

American Catholic Missionary Staff. The First American Catholic Missionary Congress: Proceedings of the American Catholic Missionary, 1st, Chicago, 1908. 51.00 (ISBN 0-405-10837-0, 11844). Ayer Co Pubs.

Breslin, Thomas A. China, American Catholicism, & the Missionary. LC 79-27857. (Illus.). 1980. text ed. 19.75x (ISBN 0-271-00259-X). Pa St U Pr.

Casteneda, Carlos E. Our Catholic Heritage in Texas, 1519-1936, 7 vols. LC 76-1471. (Chicano Heritage Ser.). (Illus.). 1976. Repr. Set. 248.00 (ISBN 0-405-09488-4). Ayer Co Pubs.

Danielou, Jean. Salvation of the Nations. 1962. pap. 1.25x (ISBN 0-268-00244-4). U of Notre Dame Pr.

Degrijse, Omer. Going Forth: Missionary Consciousness in Third World Catholic Churches. LC 83-19337. 112p. (Orig.). 1984. pap. 6.95 (ISBN 0-88344-427-5). Orbis Bks.

De Smet, Pierre-Jean. Origin, Progress & Prospects of the Catholic Mission to the Rocky Mountains. 1971. pap. 1.00 (ISBN 0-87770-044-3). Ye Galleon.

Ellis, Marc. A Year of the Catholic Worker. LC 78-61722. 144p. 1978. pap. 3.50 (ISBN 0-8091-2140-9). Paulist Pr.

Faraud, Henri J. Dix-Huit Ans Chez Les Sauvages: Voyages Et Missions De Monseigneur Henry Faraud. Repr. of 1866 ed. 28.00 (ISBN 0-384-15135-3). Johnson Repr.

Gillard, John T. The Catholic Church & the Negro. (Basic Afro-American Reprint Library). 1969. Repr. of 1929 ed. 19.00 (ISBN 0-384-18550-9). Johnson Repr.

Hastings, Adrian. Church & Mission in Modern Africa. LC 67-30321. (Orig.). 1967. 25.00 (ISBN 0-8232-0770-6). Fordham.

Hickey, Edward J. The Society for the Propagation of the Faith: Its Foundation, Organization & Success (1822-1922) LC 73-3557. (Catholic University of America. Studies in American Church History: No. 3). Repr. of 1922 ed. 25.00 (ISBN 0-404-57753-9). AMS Pr.

Hsiang, Paul Stanislaus. The Catholic Missions in China During the Middle Ages: 1294-1368, No. 37. (Studies in Sacred Theology, Second Series). 57p. 1983. Repr. of 1949 ed. 12.00x (ISBN 0-939738-32-5). Zubal Inc.

Laracy, Hugh. Marists & Melanesians: A History of Catholic Missions in the Solomon Islands. 222p. 1976. text ed. 15.00x (ISBN 0-8248-0361-2). UH Pr.

Leger, Sr. Mary C. The Catholic Indian Missions in Maine (1611-1820) LC 73-3563. (Catholic University of America. Studies in American Church History: No. 8). Repr. of 1929 ed. 26.00 (ISBN 0-404-57758-X). AMS Pr.

Liguori, Alfonso M. & Redemptorists. The Mission-Book of the Congregation of the Most Holy Redeemer. 38.50 (ISBN 0-405-10843-5, 11848). Ayer Co Pubs.

Linden, Ian & Linden, Jane. Catholics, Peasants & Chewa Resistance in Nyasaland, 1889-1939. 1974. 38.50x (ISBN 0-520-02500-8). U of Cal Pr.

McNamara, William. The Catholic Church on the Northern Indiana Frontier, 1789-1844. LC 73-3567. (Catholic University of America. Studies in American Church History: No. 12). Repr. of 1931 ed. 19.00 (ISBN 0-404-57762-8). AMS Pr.

Menger, Matt. Valley of Mekong. 1970. 4.95 (ISBN 0-685-79412-1); pap. 3.95 (ISBN 0-685-79413-X). Guild Bks.

Menger, Matt J. In the Valley of the Mekong. LC 79-115966. 1970. pap. 3.95 (ISBN 0-686-18632-X). Oblate.

Pritchett, John P. Black Robe & Buckskin. 1960. 12.95x (ISBN 0-8084-0063-0); pap. 8.95 (ISBN 0-8084-0064-9). New Coll U Pr.

Rippy, J. Fred & Nelson, Jean T. Crusaders of the Jungle. LC 76-123495. 1971. Repr. of 1936 ed. 31.50x (ISBN 0-8046-1382-6, Pub. by Kennikat). Assoc Faculty Pr.

Savage, Alma H. Dogsled Apostles. facs. ed. LC 68-55857. (Essay Index Reprint Ser). 1942. 18.00 (ISBN 0-8369-0851-1). Ayer Co Pubs.

Shea, John D. History of the Catholic Missions Among the Indian Tribes of the United States, 1529-1854. LC 73-175853. Repr. of 1855 ed. 28.50 (ISBN 0-404-07176-7). AMS Pr.

Shea, John G. History of the Catholic Missions Among the Indian Tribes of the United States, 1529-1854. LC 70-83436. (Religion in America, Ser. 1). 1969. Repr. of 1857 ed. 26.50 (ISBN 0-405-00263-7). Ayer Co Pubs.

Stott, John R. & Meeking, Basil, eds. The Evangelical-Roman Catholic Dialogue on Mission, 1977-1984. 80p. (Orig.). 1986. pap. 4.95 (ISBN 0-8028-0184-6). Eerdmans.

Tache, Alexandre A. Vingt Annees De Missions Dans le Nord-Ouest De L'amerique. (Canadiana Before 1867 Ser). (Fr). Repr. of 1866 ed. 18.00 (ISBN 0-384-59425-5). Johnson Repr.

--Vingt Annees De Missions Dans le Nord-Ouest De L'amerique Par Mgr. Alex. Tache Eveque De Saint-Boniface (Montreal, 1866) (Canadiana Avant 1867: N0. 21). 1970. 16.80x (ISBN 90-2796-343-6). Mouton.

Williams, Theodore, ed. World Missions: Building Bridges or Barriers. 101p. (Orig.). 1979. pap. 2.00 (ISBN 0-936444-02-9). World Evang Fellow.

CATHOLIC CHURCH–MODERNISM

see Modernism–Catholic Church

CATHOLIC CHURCH–MUSIC

see Church Music–Catholic Church

CATHOLIC CHURCH–MYSTICISM

see Mysticism–Catholic Church

CATHOLIC CHURCH–PASTORAL LETTERS AND CHARGES

Gannon, Thomas S., ed. The Catholic Challenge to the American Economy: Reflections on the Bishops' Pastoral Letter on Catholic Social Teaching & the U. S. Economy. 352p. 1987. pap. 14.95 (ISBN 0-02-911270-2, Collier). Macmillan.

Hug, James E. Renew the Earth: A Guide to the Second Draft of the U. S. Bishops' Pastoral Letter on Catholic Social Teachings & the U. S. Economy. (Illus.). 32p. (Orig.). 1985. pap. text ed. 1.50 (ISBN 0-934255-02-4). Center Concern.

Pervan, Tomislav. Queen of Peace, Echo of the Eternal Word. (Illus.). 58p. (Orig.). 1986. pap. 3.50 (ISBN 0-940535-05-X). Franciscan U Pr.

CATHOLIC CHURCH–PASTORAL THEOLOGY

see Pastoral Theology–Catholic Church

CATHOLIC CHURCH–PERIODICALS

Catholic Biblical Quarterly: Washington D.C. 1939-1968, Vols. 1-30. Set. lib. bdg. 1350.00 (ISBN 0-685-77254-3); lib. bdg. 45.00 ea. AMS Pr.

Catholic Periodical & Literature Index, Vol. 20. 1980. 90.00 (ISBN 0-87507-022-1). Cath Lib Assn.

Doyle, James A. Catholic Press Directory. 184p. 1985. pap. 25.00 (ISBN 0-686-30366-0). Cath Pr Assn.

Griffin, Robert F. The Continuing Conversation. LC 85-80352. 200p. (Orig.). 1985. pap. 7.50 (ISBN 0-87973-828-6, 828). Our Sunday Visitor.

Holland, Mary G. The British Catholic Press & the Eductional Controversy, 1847-1865. McNeill, William H. & Stanksy, Peter, eds. (Modern European History Ser.). 400p. 1987. lib. bdg. 60.00 (ISBN 0-8240-7817-9). Garland Pub.

Logan, Natale, ed. The Catholic Periodical & Literature Index. Incl. Vol. 2 1934-38. 50.00 (ISBN 0-87507-010-8); Vol. 4. 1943-48. 50.00 (ISBN 0-87507-011-6); Vol. 10. 1959-60. 30.00 (ISBN 0-87507-012-4); Vol. 11. 1961-62; Vol. 12. 1963-64. 40.00 (ISBN 0-87507-014-0); Vol. 14. 1967-68. 40.00 (ISBN 0-87507-015-9); Vol. 15. 1969-70. 45.00 (ISBN 0-87507-016-7); Vol. 16. 1971-72. 60.00 (ISBN 0-87507-017-5); Vol. 17. 1973-1974. 55.00 (ISBN 0-87507-018-3); Vol. 18. 60.00 (ISBN 0-87507-019-1, 1975-1976); Vol. 19. 70.00 (ISBN 0-87507-020-5, 1977-1978); Vol. 21. 90.00 (ISBN 0-87507-025-6, 1981-1982). LC 70-649588. Orig. Title: The Catholic Periodical Index & The Guide to Catholic Literature. Cath Lib Assn.

Moran, Patrick R. Day by Day with the Saints. 214p. (Orig.). 1985. pap. 7.95 (ISBN 0-87973-714-X, 714). Our Sunday Visitor.

CATHOLIC CHURCH–PERIODICALS–HISTORY

Baumgartner, Apollinaris W. Catholic Journalism. LC 75-159997. (BCL Ser. I). Repr. of 1931 ed. 11.50 (ISBN 0-404-00693-0). AMS Pr.

CATHOLIC CHURCH–PRAYER-BOOKS AND DEVOTIONS

see also Hours, Books Of

Bierbaum, Athanasius. Pusillum, 4 vols. 7.50 (ISBN 0-685-10971-2, L38675). Franciscan Herald.

Boncore Di Santa Vittoria Staff. Boncore Di Santa Victoria Novus Liber Hymnorum Ac Orationum. Repr. of 1903 ed. 60.00 (ISBN 0-384-12867-X). Johnson Repr.

Bryant, Christopher. The Heart in Pilgrimage: Christian Guidelines for the Human Journey. 208p. 1980. 9.95 (ISBN 0-8164-0457-7, HarpR). Har-Row.

Buckley, Michael & Castle, Tony, eds. The Catholic Prayer Book. 272p. (Orig.). 1986. pap. 6.95 (ISBN 0-89283-283-5). Servant.

A Catholic Prayerbook. 80p. (Compiled from Approved Sources). 1985. pap. 1.50 (ISBN 0-89555-280-9). Tan Bks Pubs.

Curley, Maureen. First Prayers for Young Catholics. (Children of the Kingdom Activities Ser.). 1978. 9.95 (ISBN 0-89837-008-6, Pub. by Pflaum Pr). Peter Li.

Dreves, Guido M., ed. Pia Dictamina, 7 Vols. 1893-1905. 60.00 ea. (ISBN 0-384-12950-1). Johnson Repr.

--Psalteria Rhythmica, 2 Vols. 1900-01. 60.00 ea. (ISBN 0-384-12960-9) (ISBN 0-384-12961-7). Johnson Repr.

Fox, Robert J. A Catholic Prayer Book. LC 74-75133. 128p. 1974. pap. 3.95 (ISBN 0-87973-771-9). Our Sunday Visitor.

--Prayerbook for Catholics. 112p. (Orig.). 1982. 6.00 (ISBN 0-931888-08-5); pap. 3.95. Christendom Pubns.

Konstant, David. Treasured Catholic Prayers & Devotions. 1987. pap. 4.95 (ISBN 0-89622-312-4). Twenty-Third.

McNally, Thomas & Storey, William. Day by Day: The Notre Dame Prayerbook for Students. (Illus.). 208p. 1975. pap. 2.95 (ISBN 0-87793-100-3). Ave Maria.

Moore, George. Hail & Farewell: Ave, Salve, Vale. Cave, Richard, ed. 1985. pap. 16.95 (ISBN 0-8132-0602-2). Cath U Pr.

O'Connell, Daniel M. A Cardinal Newman Prayerbook: Kindly Light. 352p. 1985. pap. 14.95 (ISBN 0-87193-220-2). Dimension Bks.

O'Malley, John W., et al. Challenge. LC 58-6622. 1958. 4.95 (ISBN 0-8294-0062-1). Loyola.

Sinclair, Keith V., compiled by. French Devotional Texts of the Middle Ages: A Bibliographic Manuscript Guide. LC 79-7587. 1979. lib. bdg. 49.95x (ISBN 0-313-20649-X, SFT/). Greenwood.

Stocklin, Ulrich V. Psalteria Wessofontana. Dreves, Guido M., ed. Repr. of 1902 ed. 60.00 (ISBN 0-384-58320-2). Johnson Repr.

Tudor, Tasha. First Prayers. LC 59-9631. (Illus.). 1952. protestant ed. 4.50 (ISBN 0-8098-1952-X). McKay.

Van Lierde, Peter C., ed. Prayers & Devotions from Pope John Paul II. 472p. 1984. 10.95 (ISBN 0-89526-601-6). Regnery Bks.

CATHOLIC CHURCH–RELATION TO THE STATE

see Church and State–Catholic Church

CATHOLIC CHURCH–RELATIONS

Aveling, J. C., et al. Rome & The Anglicans: Historical & Doctrinal Aspects of Anglican-Roman Catholic Relations. Haase, Wolfgang, ed. 301p. 1982. 81.50 (ISBN 3-11-008267-5). De Gruyter.

Bagiackas, Joseph. The Future Glory. LC 83-70962. 130p. (Orig.). 1983. pap. 3.95 (ISBN 0-943780-02-0, 8020). Charismatic Ren Servs.

Bodin, Jean. Colloquium of the Seven About Secrets of the Sublime. Daniels, Marion L., tr. from Lat. & intro. by. LC 73-2453. 480p. 1975. 63.00x (ISBN 0-691-07193-4). Princeton U Pr.

Kung, Hans. Do We Know the Others? LC 66-20895. (Concilium Ser.: Vol. 14). 196p. 1966. 7.95 (ISBN 0-8091-0033-9). Paulist Pr.

Pinay, M. The Plot Against the Catholic Church: Communism, Free Masonry & the Jewish Fifth Column in the Clergy. 1979. lib. bdg. 69.95 (ISBN 0-8490-2984-8). Gordon Pr.

Ranaghan, Kevin & Ranaghan, Dorothy. Catholic Pentecostals Today. rev. ed. LC 83-70963. 196p. 1983. pap. 4.95 (ISBN 0-943780-03-9, 8039). Charismatic Ren Servs.

Vatican Council Two. Decree on Ecumenism. Stransky, Thomas, ed. (Orig.). 1965. pap. 1.95 (ISBN 0-8091-5027-1). Paulist Pr.

CATHOLIC CHURCH–RELATIONS–JUDAISM

Feldblum, E. Y. The American Catholic Press & the Jewish State: 1917-1959. 25.00x (ISBN 0-87068-325-X). Ktav.

Marx, Victor. Catholicism, Judaism & the Effort at World Domination. (Illus.). 1980. 65.00 (ISBN 0-89266-216-6). Am Classical Coll Pr.

Pinay, Maurice. The Plot Against the Church. 1978. 15.00x (ISBN 0-911038-39-6). Noontide.

Poliakov, Leon. Jewish Barbers & the Holy See: From the Thirteenth to the Seventeenth-Century. Kochan, Miriam, tr. from Fr. (Littman Library of Jewish Civilization). 288p. 1977. 29.00x (ISBN 0-19-710028-7). Oxford U Pr.

Pope John Paul, II. Pope John Paul II: On Jews & Judiasm, 1979-1986. (Orig.). Date not set. pap. price not set (ISBN 1-55586-151-2). US Catholic.

Zerin, Edward. What Catholics Should Know About Jews: And Other Christians. 1980. pap. 3.25 (ISBN 0-697-01739-7). Wm C Brown.

CATHOLIC CHURCH–RELATIONS–ORTHODOX EASTERN CHURCH

see also Schism–Eastern and Western Church

Chrysostomos, Archimandrite. Orthodoxy & Papism. Williams, Theodore M., ed. LC 82-73693. 70p. 1982. pap. 4.50 (ISBN 0-911165-00-2). Ctr Trad Orthodox.

Halecki, Oscar. From Florence to Brest, Fourteen Thirty-Nine to Fifteen Ninety-Six. 2nd ed. LC 68-26103. 456p. 1968. 35.00 (ISBN 0-208-00702-4, Archon). Shoe String.

Norden, Walter. Papsttum Und Byzanz: Das Problem Ihrer Wiedervereinigung Bis Zum Untergange Des Byzantinischen Reichs (1453) 1903. 40.50 (ISBN 0-8337-2571-8). B Franklin.

Rogers, Francis M. The Quest for Eastern Christians: Travels & Rumor in the Age of Discovery. LC 62-18138. pap. 58.30 (ISBN 0-317-41750-9, 2055901). Bks Demand UMI.

CATHOLIC CHURCH–RELATIONS–PROTESTANT CHURCHES

Avis, Paul. Truth Beyond Words: Problems & Prospects for Anglican-Roman Catholic Unity. 142p. (Orig.). 1985. pap. 7.95 (ISBN 0-936384-26-3). Cowley Pubns.

LaFontaine, Charles V. & Stone, Glenn C., eds. Exploring the Faith We Share. LC 79-92856. 144p. 1980. pap. 3.50 (ISBN 0-8091-2301-0). Paulist Pr.

Marty, Myron A. Lutherans & Roman Catholicism: The Changing Conflict, 1917-1963. 1968. 14.95 (ISBN 0-268-00162-6). U of Notre Dame Pr.

Minus, Paul M., Jr. The Catholic Rediscovery of Protestantism: A History of Ecumenical Pioneering. LC 75-44804. 276p. 1976. pap. 6.95 (ISBN 0-8091-1944-7). Paulist Pr.

Snderson, H. George, et al, eds. Justification by Faith: Lutherans & Catholics in Dialogue VII. LC 84-28412. 320p. (Orig.). 1984. pap. 6.95 (ISBN 0-8066-2103-6, 10-3626). Augsburg.

Tavard, George H. Holy Writ or Holy Church: The Crisis of the Protestant Reformation. LC 78-17085. 1978. Repr. of 1959 ed. lib. bdg. 22.75x (ISBN 0-313-20584-1, TAHO). Greenwood.

Underwood, Kenneth W. Protestant & Catholic. LC 72-9051. (Illus.). 484p. 1973. Repr. of 1957 ed. lib. bdg. 22.50x (ISBN 0-8371-6567-9, UNPC). Greenwood.

Witmer, Joseph W. & Wright, J. Robert, eds. Called to Full Unity: Documents on Anglican-Roman Catholic Relations 1966-1983. 358p. 1986. pap. 14.95 (ISBN 1-55586-937-8). US Catholic.

CATHOLIC CHURCH–RELATIONS (DIPLOMATIC)

Dunn, Dennis J. The Catholic Church & the Soviet Government. (East European Monographs: No. 30). 267p. 1977. 25.00x (ISBN 0-914710-23-0). East Eur Quarterly.

Gasquet, Francis A. Monastic Life in the Middle Ages, 1792-1806. facs. ed. LC 76-137377. (Select Bibliographies Reprint Ser). 1922. 16.00 (ISBN 0-8369-5578-1). Ayer Co Pubs.

Hachey, Thomas, ed. Anglo-Vatican Relations, 1914-1939: Confidential Annual Reports of the British Ministers to the Holy See. 1972. lib. bdg. 23.00 (ISBN 0-8161-0991-5, Hall Reference). G K Hall.

Lukacs, Lajos. The Vatican & Hungary 1846-1878: Reports & Correspondence on Hungary of the Apostolic Nuncios in Vienna. Kormos, Zsofia, tr. 795p. 1981. text ed. 65.00x (ISBN 963-05-2446-5, Pub. by Akademiai Kiado UK). Humanities.

Ridley, Francis A. The Papacy & Fascism: The Crisis of the 20th Century. LC 72-180422. (Studies in Fascism, Ideology & Practice). Repr. of 1937 ed. 24.50 (ISBN 0-404-56156-X). AMS Pr.

Sayers, Jane E. Papal Government & England During the Pontificate of Honorius III (1216-1227) LC 84-1853. (Cambridge Studies in Medieval Life & Thought: 3rd Ser., Vol. 21). 1985. 49.50 (ISBN 0-521-25911-8). Cambridge U Pr.

Setton, Kenneth M. The Papacy & the Levant, Twelve Hundred Four to Fifteen Seventy-One, Vols. III & IV. LC 75-25476. (Memoirs Ser.: Vols. 161 & 162). 1984. Vol. 161. 45.00 (ISBN 0-87169-161-2); Vol. 162. 45.00 (ISBN 0-87169-162-0). Am Philos.

Von Balthasar, Has U. The Office of Peter. Emery, Andree, tr. from German. LC 86-80787. Tr. of Der Antiromische Affekt. 368p. 1986. pap. 12.95 (ISBN 0-89870-020-5). Ignatius Pr.

Walsh, Henry H. Concordat of 1801. LC 34-12835. (Columbia University. Studies in the Social Sciences: No. 387). Repr. of 1933 ed. 21.00 (ISBN 0-404-51387-5). AMS Pr.

Wilkie, W. E. The Cardinal Protectors of England: Rome & the Tudors Before the Reformation. LC 73-82462. 224p. 1974. 44.50 (ISBN 0-521-20332-5). Cambridge U Pr.

CATHOLIC CHURCH–RELATIONS (ECCLESIASTICAL)

see Catholic Church–Relations

CATHOLIC CHURCH–SERMONS

Bechett, Wendy M., tr. John of Ford: Sermons on the Song of Songs I. LC 77-3697. (Cistercian Fathers Ser.: No. 29). 1977. 14.95 (ISBN 0-87907-629-1). Cistercian Pubns.

Caesarius Of Arles, St. Sermons-One to Eighty. (Fathers of the Church Ser.: Vol. 31). 1956. 34.95x (ISBN 0-8132-0031-8). Cath U Pr.

Donders, Joseph G. Jesus, the Stranger. LC 77-21783. 298p. (Orig.). 1978. pap. 8.95x (ISBN 0-88344-235-3). Orbis Bks.

Fichtner, Joseph. Proclaim His Word: Homiletic Themes for Sundays & Holy Days - Cycle C, Vol. 1. new ed. LC 73-5726. 238p. (Orig.). 1973. pap. 3.95 (ISBN 0-8189-0274-4). Alba.

Jarrett, Bede. No Abiding City. 1.95 (ISBN 0-87243-012-X). Templegate.

Manton, Joseph. Straws from the Crib. (Orig.). 1964. 5.95 (ISBN 0-8198-0150-X); pap. 4.95 (ISBN 0-8198-0151-8). Dghtrs St Paul.

Manton, Joseph E. Pennies from a Poor Box. 1962. 6.50 (ISBN 0-8198-0119-4). Dghtrs St Paul.

Newman, John H. The Kingdom Within: Discourses to Mixed Congregations. 1984. pap. 14.95 (ISBN 0-87193-216-4). Dimension Bks.

--Parochial & Plain Sermons. LC 86-62927. 1734p. (Orig.). 1987. pap. 49.00 (ISBN 0-89870-136-8). Ignatius Pr.

O'Sullivan, Kevin. Sunday Readings. Incl. Cycle A. 428p. 1971. (ISBN 0-8199-0481-3); Cycle B. 487p. 1972. (ISBN 0-8199-0482-1); Cycle C. 444p. 1970. (ISBN 0-8199-0483-X). LC 74-141766. 9.00 ea. Franciscan Herald.

Pope John Paul II. Lord & Giver of Life. 144p. (Orig.). 1986. pap. 3.95 (ISBN 1-55586-103-2). US Catholic.

Roguet, A. M. Homilies for the Celebration of Marriage. Du Charme, Jerome, tr. from Fr. LC 76-53538. 1977. pap. 3.50 (ISBN 0-8199-0656-5). Franciscan Herald.

St. Augustine. Sermons on the Liturgical Seasons. (Fathers of the Church Ser.: Vol. 38). 1959. 29.95x (ISBN 0-8132-0038-5). Cath U Pr.

Wallace, James A. Preaching Through the Saints. LC 82-7745. 80p. 1982. pap. 2.50 (ISBN 0-8146-1271-7). Liturgical Pr.

CATHOLIC CHURCH–SOCIETIES, ETC.

see also Monasticism and Religious Orders; Monasticism and Religious Orders for Women

Macdonald, Fergus. The Catholic Church & the Secret Societies in the United States. LC 46-8049. (Monograph Ser.: No. 22). 1946. 12.50x (ISBN 0-930060-04-0). US Cath Hist.

CATHOLIC CHURCH AND LABOR

see Church and Labor

CATHOLIC CHURCH AND SALVATION

see Salvation outside the Catholic Church

CATHOLIC CHURCH AND SOCIAL PROBLEMS

see Church and Social Problems–Catholic Church

Ratzinger, Joseph & Messori, Vittorio. The Ratzinger Report. Attanasio, Salvator & Harrison, Graham, trs. LC 85-81218. Tr. of Rapporto sulla Fede. (Ger. & Ital.). 197p. (Orig.). 1985. pap. 9.95 (ISBN 0-89870-080-9). Ignatius Pr.

CATHOLIC CHURCH AND SOCIALISM

see Socialism and Catholic Church

CATHOLIC CHURCH AND STATE

see Church and State–Catholic Church

CATHOLIC CHURCH IN AFRICA

De Craemer, Willy. The Jamaa & the Church: A Bantu Catholic Movement in Zaire. (Oxford Studies in African Affairs). 1977. 58.00x (ISBN 0-19-822708-6). Oxford U Pr.

Hastings, Adrian. Church & Mission in Modern Africa. LC 67-30321. (Orig.). 1967. 25.00 (ISBN 0-8232-0770-6). Fordham.

Healey, Joseph G. A Fifth Gospel: The Experience of Black Christian Values. LC 80-25033. (Illus.). 220p. (Orig.). 1981. pap. 3.98 (ISBN 0-88344-013-X). Orbis Bks.

Linden, Ian & Linden, Jane. Church & Revolution in Rwanda. LC 76-58329. 295p. 1977. text ed. 39.50x (ISBN 0-8419-0305-0, Africana). Holmes & Meier.

CATHOLIC CHURCH IN AMERICA

Carey, Patrick W. People, Priests, & Prelates: Ecclesiastical Democracy & the Tensions of Trusteeism. LC 86-40243. (Studies in American Catholicism: Vol. 8). 392p. 1987. text ed. 26.95x (ISBN 0-268-01563-5). U of Notre Dame Pr.

McAvoy, Thomas T., ed. Roman Catholicism & the American Way of Life. LC 72-13177. (Essay Index Reprint Ser.). Repr. of 1960 ed. 14.75 (ISBN 0-8369-8167-7). Ayer Co Pubs.

Murray, John O. Catholic Heros & Heroines of America. 35.00 (ISBN 0-87968-818-1). Gordon Pr.

--Catholic Pioneers of America. 35.00 (ISBN 0-87968-819-X). Gordon Pr.

Smithson, Sandra. To Be the Bridge: A Black Perspective on White Catholicism in America. LC 84-50080. 200p. 1984. pap. 8.95 (ISBN 0-938232-48-7). Winston-Derek.

Spalding, Martin. Sketches of the Early Catholic Missions of Kentucky; from Their Commencement in 1787 to the Jubilee of 1826-7. LC 70-38548. (Religion in America, Ser. 2). 328p. 1972. Repr. of 1844 ed. 22.00 (ISBN 0-405-04087-3). Ayer Co Pubs.

CATHOLIC CHURCH IN AUSTRALIA

Boland, T. P. James Duhig. LC 86-15654. (Illus.). 435p. 1987. text ed. 37.50x (ISBN 0-7022-2011-6). U of Queensland Pr.

Molony, J. N. Roman Mould of the Australian Catholic Church. 1969. 17.50x (ISBN 0-522-83934-7, Pub by Melbourne U Pr). Intl Spec Bk.

Suttor, T. L. Hierarchy & Democracy in Australia, 1788-1870: The Formation of Australian Catholicism. 1965. 22.00x (ISBN 0-522-83753-0, Pub. by Melbourne U Pr). Intl Spec Bk.

CATHOLIC CHURCH IN CANADA

see also Catholics in Canada

Brasseur De Bourbourg, Charles E. Histoire du Canada, De Son Eglise et De Ses Missions Depuis la Decouverte De L'Amerique Jusqu'a Nos Jours, 2 vols. (Canadiana Before 1867 Ser). (Fr). Repr. of 1852 ed. Set. 50.00 (ISBN 0-384-05570-2). Johnson Repr.

Munnick, Harriet D. Catholic Church Records of the Pacific Northwest: Vancouver & Stellamaris Mission. LC 72-83958. (Illus.). 1972. 25.00 (ISBN 0-8323-0375-5). Binford-Metropolitan.

Pope John Paul II. Canada: Celebrating Our Faith. 370p. 1985. 7.00 (ISBN 0-317-18636-1); pap. 6.00 (ISBN 0-8198-1441-5). Dghtrs St Paul.

Saint-Vallier, Jean B. Estat Present De L'eglise & De la Colonie Francoise Dans la Nouvelle France Par M. L'eveque De Quebec. (Canadiana Avant 1867: No. 20). 1967. 18.40x (ISBN 90-2796-332-0). Mouton.

Sellar, Robert. Tragedy of Quebec. LC 72-1429. (Select Bibliographies Reprint Ser.). 1972. Repr. of 1907 ed. 17.25 (ISBN 0-8369-6836-0). Ayer Co Pubs.

CATHOLIC CHURCH IN EUROPE

Callahan, W. J. & Higgs, D. Church & Society in Catholic Europe of the Eighteenth Century. LC 78-12165. 1979. 27.95 (ISBN 0-521-22424-1). Cambridge U Pr.

Coleman, John A. The Evolution of Dutch Catholicism, Nineteen Fifty-Eight to Nineteen Seventy-Four. LC 74-22958. 1979. 42.50x (ISBN 0-520-02885-6). U of Cal Pr.

Sherry, Gerard E. The Catholic Shrines of Europe. LC 86-62664. (Illus.). 119p. 1986. pap. 5.95 (ISBN 0-87973-548-1, 548). Our Sunday Visitor.

Wolff, Richard, ed. Catholics, the State & the European Radical Right, 1919-1945. (Atlantic Studies: No. 50). write for info (ISBN 0-88033-101-1). Brooklyn Coll Pr.

CATHOLIC CHURCH IN FRANCE

see also Americanism (Catholic Controversy); Catholics in France

Acomb, Evelyn M. French Laic Laws: 1879-1889. LC 67-18747. 1968. Repr. lib. bdg. 21.50 (ISBN 0-374-90038-8, Octagon). Hippocrene Bks.

Baumgartner, F. J. Radical Reactionaries: The Political Thought of the French Catholic League. 320p. (Orig.). 1976. pap. text ed. 37.50x (Pub. by Droz Switzerland). Coronet Bks.

Cohen, Paul M. Piety & Politics: Catholic Revival & the Generation of 1905-1914 in France. McNeill, William H. & Pinkney, David H., eds. (Modern European History Ser.). 348p. 1987. lib. bdg. 50.00 (ISBN 0-8240-8034-3). Garland Pub.

Collins, Ross W. Catholicism & the Second French Republic, 1848-1852. 1980. lib. bdg. 27.50x (ISBN 0-374-91868-6, Octagon). Hippocrene Bks.

Kselman, Thomas A. Miracles & Prophecies in Nineteenth-Century France. (Illus.). 312p. 1983. 30.00 (ISBN 0-8135-0963-7). Rutgers U Pr.

Moser, Mary T. The Evolution of the Option for the Poor in France, 1880-1965. (Illus.). 216p. (Orig.). 1985. lib. bdg. 24.00 (ISBN 0-8191-4814-8); pap. text ed. 11.75 (ISBN 0-8191-4815-6). U Pr of Amer.

Spencer, Philip. Politics of Belief in Nineteenth-Century France. LC 77-80592. 284p. 1973. Repr. of 1954 ed. 24.50x (ISBN 0-86527-156-9). Fertig.

Walsh, Henry H. Concordat of 1801. LC 34-12835. (Columbia University. Studies in the Social Sciences: No. 387). Repr. of 1933 ed. 21.00 (ISBN 0-404-51387-5). AMS Pr.

CATHOLIC CHURCH IN GERMANY

see also Catholics in Germany

Waibel, Paul R. Politics of Accommodation: German Social Democracy & the Catholic Church, 1945-1959. (European University Studies: No. 31, Vol. 35). 161p. 1983. pap. 23.15 (ISBN 3-8204-7270-3). P Lang Pubs.

CATHOLIC CHURCH IN GREAT BRITAIN

see also Catholics in England

Arnstein, Walter L. Protestant vs. Catholic in Mid-Victorian England: Mr. Newdegate & the Nuns. LC 81-11451. 272p. text ed. 20.00x (ISBN 0-8262-0354-X). U of Mo Pr.

Bridgewater, John. Concerto Ecclesiae Catholicae in Anglia Adversus Calvinopapistas et Puritanos. 886p. Repr. of 1588 ed. text ed. 149.04 (ISBN 0-576-78532-6, Pub. by Gregg Intl Pubs England). Gregg Intl.

Catholic Emancipation Eighteen Twenty-Nine to Nineteen Twenty-Nine: Essays by Various Writers. facs. ed. LC 67-22084. (Essay Index Reprint Ser). 1929. 20.00 (ISBN 0-8369-0284-X). Ayer Co Pubs.

Chinnici, Joseph P. The English Catholic Enlightenment: John Lingard & the Cisalpine Movement, 1780 to 1850. LC 79-20250. (Illus.). xiv, 262p. 1980. 24.95x (ISBN 0-915762-10-2). Patmos Pr.

England: Unity God's Gift. 3.50 (ISBN 0-8198-2302-3); 2.50 (ISBN 0-8198-2307-4). Dghtrs St Paul.

Holland, Mary G. The British Catholic Press & the Eductional Controversy, 1847-1865. McNeill, William H. & Stanksy, Peter, eds. (Modern European History Ser.). 400p. 1987. lib. bdg. 60.00 (ISBN 0-8240-7817-9). Garland Pub.

Holmes, J. Derek. More Roman Than Rome: English Catholicism in the Nineteenth Century. LC 77-92886. (Illus.). 278p. 1978. 21.95x (ISBN 0-915762-05-6). Patmos Pr.

Hornsby-Smith, Michael P. Roman Catholics in England: Studies in Social Structure Since the Second World War. (Illus.). 288p. 1987. 29.50 (ISBN 0-521-30313-3). Cambridge U Pr.

Klaus, Robert J. The Pope, the Protestants, & the Irish: Papal Aggression & Anti-Catholicism in Mid-Nineteenth Century England. McNeill, William H. & Stansky, Peter, eds. (Modern European History Ser.). 400p. 1987. lib. bdg. 60.00 (ISBN 0-8240-7820-9). Garland Pub.

Law, Thomas G., ed. The Archpriest Controversy, 2 Vols. Repr. of 1898 ed. 54.00 (ISBN 0-384-31730-8). Johnson Repr.

Mathew, David. Catholicism in England, Fifteen Thirty-Five to Nineteen Thirty-Five. 1977. lib. bdg. 59.95 (ISBN 0-8490-1587-1). Gordon Pr.

Matthew, David. Catholicism in England: The Portraits of a Minority, Its Culture & Tradition. 295p. 1984. Repr. of 1948 ed. lib. bdg. 45.00 (ISBN 0-89984-946-6). Century Bookbindery.

Messenger, Ruth E. Ethical Teachings in the Latin Hymns of Medieval England. LC 30-20975. (Columbia University. Studies in the Social Sciences: No. 321). Repr. of 1930 ed. 18.50 (ISBN 0-404-51321-2). AMS Pr.

Pollen, John H. English Catholics in the Reign of Queen Elizabeth: A Study of Their Politics, Civil Life & Government. 1971. Repr. of 1920 ed. lib. bdg. 24.50 (ISBN 0-8337-2798-2). B Franklin.

Schiefen, Richard J. Nicholas Wiseman & the Transformation of English Catholicism. (Illus.). 416p. 1984. 32.50x (ISBN 0-915762-15-3). Patmos Pr.

Shuster, George N. Catholic Spirit in Modern English Literature. facs. ed. LC 67-26785. (Essay Index Reprint Ser). 1922. 20.00 (ISBN 0-8369-0878-3). Ayer Co Pubs.

Williams, Michael C. St. Alban's College, Valladolid: Four Centuries of English Catholic Presence in Spain. LC 86-17787. 278p. 1986. 35.00 (ISBN 0-312-69736-8). St Martin.

CATHOLIC CHURCH IN GREAT BRITAIN–BIBLIOGRAPHY

Gillow, Joseph. Literary & Biographical History; or Bibliographical Dictionary of English Catholics from the Breach with Rome, in 1534, to the Present Time, 5 Vols. 1962. Repr. of 1892 ed. 205.00 (ISBN 0-8337-1356-6). B Franklin.

Norman, Edward. The English Catholic Church in the Nineteenth Century. 1984. pap. 13.95x (ISBN 0-19-822955-0). Oxford U Pr.

CATHOLIC CHURCH IN INDIA

Becker, C. History of the Catholic Missions in Northeast India. 1980. 32.00x (ISBN 0-8364-0600-1, Pub. by Mukhopadhyay India). South Asia Bks.

Koilparampil, George. Caste in the Catholic Community in Kerala. 289p. 1986. 14.50X (Pub. by Macmillan India). South Asia Bks.

CATHOLIC CHURCH IN IRELAND

Keenan, Desmond J. The Catholic Church in Nineteenth-Century Ireland: A Sociological Study. LC 83-11941. 300p. 1984. 29.50X (ISBN 0-389-20426-9, 07312). B&N Imports.

Kerr, Donal A. Peel, Priests & Politics: Sir Robert Peel's Administration & the Roman Catholic Church in Ireland, 1841-1846. (Oxford Historical Monographs). 400p. 1982. pap. 15.95x (ISBN 0-19-822932-1). Oxford U Pr.

Kirby, Peadar. Is Irish Catholicism Dying? 93p. 1984. pap. 5.95 (ISBN 0-87061-112-7). Chr Classics.

Klaus, Robert J. The Pope, the Protestants, & the Irish: Papal Aggression & Anti-Catholicism in Mid-Nineteenth Century England. McNeill, William H. & Stansky, Peter, eds. (Modern European History Ser.). 400p. 1987. lib. bdg. 60.00 (ISBN 0-8240-7820-9). Garland Pub.

Larkin, Emmet. The Historical Dimensions of Irish Catholicism. LC 76-6350. (Irish Americans Ser.). 1976. 20.00 (ISBN 0-405-09344-6). Ayer Co Pubs.

--The Making of the Roman Catholic Church in Ireland, 1850-1860. LC 79-19650. xxiv, 520p. 1980. 32.50x (ISBN 0-8078-1419-9). U of NC Pr.

--The Roman Catholic Church in Ireland & the Fall of Parnell, 1888-1891. LC 78-22056. xxi, 316p. 1979. 30.00x (ISBN 0-8078-1352-4). U of NC Pr.

Larkin, Emmet J. The Roman Catholic Church & the Creation of the Modern Irish State, 1878-1886. LC 75-7169. (American Philosophical Society Memoirs Ser.: Vol. 108). pap. 109.00 (ISBN 0-317-29437-7, 2024293). Bks Demand UMI.

Pochin-Mould, Daphne. Irish Pilgrimage. 1957. 12.95 (ISBN 0-8159-5816-1). Devin.

CATHOLIC CHURCH IN ITALY

Hay, Denys. The Church in Italy in the Fifteenth Century. LC 76-47409. (Birkbeck Lectures: 1971). 1977. 37.50 (ISBN 0-521-21532-3). Cambridge U Pr.

Munday, Anthony. The Englishe Romayne Lyfe. LC 76-38213. (English Experience Ser.: No. 478). 84p. 1972. Repr. of 1582 ed. 6.00 (ISBN 90-221-0478-8). Walter J Johnson.

CATHOLIC CHURCH IN JAPAN

Boxer, C. R. The Christian Century in Japan: Fifteen Forty-Nine to Sixteen Fifty. (California Library Reprint Ser: No. 51). (Illus.). 552p. 1974. Repr. of 1967 ed. 49.50x (ISBN 0-520-02702-7). U of Cal Pr.

Laures, John. Catholic Church in Japan: A Short History. Repr. of 1954 ed. lib. bdg. 22.50x (ISBN 0-8371-2974-5, LACC). Greenwood.

CATHOLIC CHURCH IN LATIN AMERICA

Boff, Leonardo. Ecclesiogenesis: The Base Communities Reinvent the Church. Barr, Robert R., tr. from Port. LC 85-15600. 128p. (Orig.). 1986. pap. 9.95 (ISBN 0-88344-214-0). Orbis Bks.

Bruneau, Thomas C. The Political Transformation of the Brazilian Catholic Church. LC 73-79318. (Perspective on Development Ser.: Vol. 2). pap. 71.00 (ISBN 0-317-28009-0, 2025579). Bks Demand UMI.

Comblin, Jose. The Church & the National Security State. LC 79-10881. 256p. (Orig.). 1979. pap. 12.95 (ISBN 0-88344-082-2). Orbis Bks.

Costello, Gerald M. Mission to Latin America: The Successes & Failures of a Twentieth-Century Crusade. LC 78-12974. 319p. (Orig.). 1979. pap. 2.49 (ISBN 0-88344-312-0). Orbis Bks.

Greenleaf, Richard E. The Roman Catholic Church in Colonial Latin America. LC 77-76836. 284p. 1977. pap. 6.50x (ISBN 0-87918-034-X). ASU Lat Am St.

Klaiber, Jeffrey L. Religion & Revolution in Peru, 1824-1976. LC 76-51616. 1977. text ed. 22.95x (ISBN 0-268-01599-6). U of Notre Dame Pr.

Landsberger, Henry A., ed. Church & Social Change in Latin America. LC 77-85355. 1970. 21.95x (ISBN 0-268-00356-4). U of Notre Dame Pr.

Levine, Daniel H., ed. Religion & Political Conflict in Latin America. LC 85-24525. xiii, 266p. 1986. 24.95x (ISBN 0-8078-1689-2); pap. 9.95x (ISBN 0-8078-4150-1). U of NC Pr.

Mecham, J. Lloyd. Church & State in Latin America: A History of Politico-Ecclesiastical Relations. rev. ed. xi, 465p. 1969. pap. 7.95x (ISBN 0-8078-4042-4). U of NC Pr.

Thornton, Mary C. The Church & Freemasonry in Brazil, 1872-1875. LC 73-2647. 287p. 1973. Repr. of 1948 ed. lib. bdg. 22.50x (ISBN 0-8371-6816-3, THCF). Greenwood.

Van Oss, Adriaan C. Catholic Colonialism: A Parish History of Guatemala, 1524-1821. (Cambridge Latin American Studies: No. 57). (Illus.). 320p. 1986. 44.50 (ISBN 0-521-32072-0). Cambridge U Pr.

CATHOLIC CHURCH IN MEXICO

Braden, Charles S. Religious Aspects of the Conquest of Mexico. LC 74-181914. Repr. of 1930 ed. 37.50 (ISBN 0-404-00925-5). AMS Pr.

Mounce, Virginia N. An Archivists Guide to the Catholic Church in Mexico. LC 78-62226. 1979. perfect bdg. 10.95 (ISBN 0-88247-570-3). R & E Pubs.

Quirk, Robert E. The Mexican Revolution & the Catholic Church, 1910-1929. LC 85-30209. 276p. 1986. Repr. of 1973 ed. lib. bdg. 45.00x (ISBN 0-313-25121-5, QUMC). Greenwood.

Schultz, Paul. A History of the Apostolic Succession of Archbishop Emile F. Rodriguez-Fairfield from the Mexican National Catholic Church. 100p. Date not set. Repr. lib. bdg. 19.95x (ISBN 0-89370-557-8). Borgo Pr.

Schwaller, John F. The Origins of Church Wealth in Mexico: Ecclesiastical Revenues & Church Finances, 1523-1600. LC 85-1122. (Illus.). 241p. 1985. 22.50x (ISBN 0-8263-0813-9). U of NM Pr.

CATHOLIC CHURCH IN POLAND

Monticone, Ronald C. The Catholic Church in Communist Poland, 1945-1985: Forty Years of Church-State Relations. (East European Monographs: No. 205). 256p. 1986. 25.00 (ISBN 0-88033-102-X). East Eur Quarterly.

Szajkowski, Bogdan. Next to God...Poland: Politics & Religion in Contemporary Poland. LC 83-40151. 258p. 1983. 25.00 (ISBN 0-312-57233-6). St Martin.

Zatko, James J., ed. Valley of Silence: Catholic Thought in Contemporary Poland. 1967. 21.95x (ISBN 0-268-00290-8). U of Notre Dame Pr.

CATHOLIC CHURCH IN SCOTLAND

Gunnin, Gerry C. John Wheatley, Catholic Socialism, & Irish Labour in the West of Scotland, 1906-1924. McNeil, William H. & Stansky, Peter, eds. (Modern European History Ser.). 375p. 1987. lib. bdg. 55.00 (ISBN 0-8240-7811-X). Garland Pub.

Mackenzie, Compton. Catholicism & Scotland. LC 75-118486. 1971. Repr. of 1936 ed. 23.50x (ISBN 0-8046-1235-8, Pub. by Kennikat). Assoc Faculty Pr.

Robertson, Joseph, ed. Concilia Scotiae, 2 Vols. LC 77-39875. (Bannatyne Club, Edinburgh. Publications: No. 113). Repr. of 1866 ed. 65.00 (ISBN 0-404-52866-X). AMS Pr.

CATHOLIC CHURCH IN SPAIN

Callahan, William J. Church, Politics, & Society in Spain, 1750-1874. (Harvard Historical Monographs: No. 73). (Illus.). 336p. 1984. text ed. 25.00x (ISBN 0-674-13125-8). Harvard U Pr.

Sanchez, Jose M. The Spanish Civil War As a Religious Tragedy. LC 86-40581. 272p. 1987. text ed. 22.95x (ISBN 0-268-01726-3, Dist. by Har-Row). U of Notre Dame Pr.

Williams, Michael C. St. Alban's College, Valladolid: Four Centuries of English Catholic Presence in Spain. LC 86-17787. 278p. 1986. 35.00 (ISBN 0-312-69736-8). St Martin.

CATHOLIC CHURCH IN THE NETHERLANDS

Bakvis, Herman. Catholic Power in the Netherlands. (Illus.). 254p. 1981. 26.50x (ISBN 0-7735-0361-7). McGill-Queens U Pr.

CATHOLIC CHURCH IN THE PHILIPPINE ISLANDS

Phelan, John L. Hispanization of the Philippines: Spanish Aims & Filipino Responses, 1565-1700. (Illus.). 234p. 1959. 30.00x (ISBN 0-299-01810-5). U of Wis Pr.

CATHOLIC CHURCH IN THE SOVIET UNION

Labunka, Miroslav & Rudnytzky, Leonid, eds. The Ukrainian Catholic Church: 1945-1975. LC 76-26753. 1976. 7.50 (ISBN 0-686-28475-5). St Sophia Religious.

Murav'Ev, Andrei N. A History of the Church of Russia. LC 76-133816. Repr. of 1842 ed. 29.45 (ISBN 0-404-04541-3). AMS Pr.

Stehle, Hansjakob. Eastern Politics of the Vatican, 1917-1979. Smith, Sandra, tr. from Ger. LC 80-15236. Orig. Title: Die Ostpolitik Des Vatikans, 1917-1975. (Illus.). 1981. 28.95x (ISBN 0-8214-0367-2); pap. 14.95 (ISBN 0-8214-0564-0). Ohio U Pr.

CATHOLIC CHURCH IN THE UNITED STATES

see also Americanism (Catholic Controversy); Catholics in the United States

Abell, Aaron I. American Catholicism & Social Action: A Search for Social Justice, 1865-1950. LC 80-16876. 306p. 1980. Repr. of 1963 ed. lib. bdg. 27.50x (ISBN 0-313-22513-3, ABAC). Greenwood.

Bryce, Mary C. Place of Pride: The Role of the Bishops in the Development of Catechesis in the United States. LC 84-17065. 227p. 1985. 25.95x (ISBN 0-8132-0595-6). Cath U Pr.

Bugg, Leila H. The People of Our Parish. 20.00 (ISBN 0-405-10811-7). Ayer Co Pubs.

Building the Local Church, Shared Responsibiity in Diocesan Pastoral Councils. 88p. 1984. pap. 6.95 (ISBN 1-55586-907-6). US Catholic.

Burnett, Betty. A Time of Favor: The Story of the Catholic Family of Southern Illinois. Franzwa, Gregory M., ed. xvi, 305p. 1987. 10.00 (ISBN 0-935284-48-6). Patrice Pr.

Burton, Katherine K. In No Strange Land. facsimile ed. LC 72-99619. (Essay Index Reprint Ser). 1942. 19.50 (ISBN 0-8369-1551-8). Ayer Co Pubs.

Byers, David, ed. The Parish in Transition: Proceedings of a Conference on the American Catholic Parish. 120p. 1986. pap. 8.95 (ISBN 1-55586-967-X). US Catholic.

Carey, Patrick, ed. American Catholic Religious Thought. 1987. pap. 12.95. Paulist Pr.

Curley, Michael J. Church & State in the Spanish Floridas (1783-1822) LC 73-3584. (Catholic University of America. Studies in American Church History: No. 30). Repr. of 1940 ed. 36.00 (ISBN 0-404-57780-6). AMS Pr.

Curran, Charles E. Toward an American Catholic Moral Theology. LC 86-40583. 256p. 1987. text ed. 18.95x (ISBN 0-268-01862-6, Dist. by Har-Row). U of Notre Dame Pr.

Davidson, J. L. Prophets of Deceit. 1960. 5.25 (ISBN 0-88027-016-0). Firm Foun Pub.

Delanglez, Jean. The French Jesuits in Lower Louisiana (1700-1763) LC 73-3576. (Catholic University of America. Studies in American Church History: No. 21). Repr. of 1935 ed. 46.00 (ISBN 0-404-57771-7). AMS Pr.

De Smet, Pierre-Jean. Origin, Progress & Prospects of the Catholic Mission to the Rocky Mountains. 1971. pap. 1.00 (ISBN 0-87770-044-3). Ye Galleon.

Desmond, Humphrey. A. P. A. Movement: A Sketch. LC 69-18772. (American Immigration Collection Ser., No. 1). 1969. Repr. of 1912 ed. 10.00 (ISBN 0-405-00519-9). Ayer Co Pubs.

Dignan, Patrick J. A History of the Legal Incorporation of Catholic Church Property in the United States (1784-1932) LC 73-3569. (Catholic University of America. Studies in American Church History: No. 14). Repr. of 1933 ed. 31.00 (ISBN 0-404-57764-4). AMS Pr.

Evans, Hiram W. The Rising Storm: An Analysis of the Growing Conflict Over the Political Dilemma of Roman Catholics in America. Grob, Gerald, ed. LC 76-46075. (Anti-Movements in America). 1977. lib. bdg. 27.50x (ISBN 0-405-09948-7). Ayer Co Pubs.

Gabert, Glen, Jr. In Hoc Signo? A Brief History of Catholic Parochial Education in America. LC 72-89992. 1973. 19.95x (ISBN 0-8046-9028-6, Pub. by Kennikat). Assoc Faculty Pr.

Gallup, George, Jr. & Castelli, Jim. American Catholic People: Their Beliefs, Practices, & Values. LC 86-16576. 216p. 1987. 15.95 (ISBN 0-385-23122-9). Doubleday.

Gannon, Michael V. Cross in the Sand: The Early Catholic Church in Florida, 1513-1870. LC 83-10498. 1965. pap. 12.00 (ISBN 0-8130-0776-3). U Presses Fla.

Gleason, Philip. Conservative Reformers: German-American Catholics & the Social Order. 1968. 22.95x (ISBN 0-268-00061-1). U of Notre Dame Pr.

Gorman, Robert. Catholic Apologetical Literature in the United States (1784-1858) LC 73-3582. (Catholic University of America. Studies in American Church History: No. 28). Repr. of 1939 ed. 23.00 (ISBN 0-404-57778-4). AMS Pr.

Guilday, Peter K. History of the Councils of Baltimore, 1791-1884. LC 77-83421. (Religion in America, Ser. 1). 1969. Repr. of 1932 ed. 25.50 (ISBN 0-405-00246-7). Ayer Co Pubs.

--Life & Times of John England. LC 70-83422. (Religion in America, Ser. 1). 1969. Repr. of 1927 ed. 54.00 (ISBN 0-405-00247-5). Ayer Co Pubs.

Hoge, Dean R., et al. Research on Men's Vocations to the Priesthood & the Religious Life. 104p. 1984. pap. 6.50 (ISBN 1-55586-904-1). US Catholic.

Hug, James E. Renew the Earth: A Guide to the Second Draft of the U. S. Bishops' Pastoral Letter on Catholic Social Teachings & the U. S. Economy. (Illus.). 32p. (Orig.). 1985. pap. text ed. 1.50 (ISBN 0-934255-02-4). Center Concern.

Jacoby, George P. Catholic Child Care in Nineteenth Century New York: With a Correlated Summary of Public & Protestant Child Welfare. LC 74-1686. (Children & Youth Ser.: Vol. 10). 284p. 1974. Repr. of 1941 ed. 23.90x (ISBN 0-405-05963-9). Ayer Co Pubs.

Kelly, George A. The Crisis of Authority: John Paul II & the American Bishops. LC 81-52143. 116p. 1982. 10.95 (ISBN 0-89526-666-0). Regnery Bks.

Keyser, Les & Keyser, Barbara. Hollywood & the Catholic Church: The Image of Roman Catholicism in American Movies. LC 84-12556. 294p. 1984. 12.95 (ISBN 0-8294-0468-6). Loyola.

Kohn, Richard. The Church in a Democracy. McKenna, Constance, ed. (Illus.). 23p. 1981. pap. 1.00 (ISBN 0-915365-03-0). Cath Free Choice.

Lane, Francis E. American Charities & the Child of the Immigrant: Study of Typical Child Caring Institutions New York & Massachusetts-1845-1880, Vol. 6. LC 74-1691. (Children & Youth Ser.). 188p. 1974. Repr. of 1932 ed. 18.00x (ISBN 0-405-05967-1). Ayer Co Pubs.

Leckey, Dolores R., ed. Journeying Together: Proceedings of Three Regional Convocations on Shared Responsibility in America. 48p. 1986. pap. 4.95 (ISBN 1-55586-975-0). US Catholic.

Lucey, William L. Catholic Church in Maine. (Illus.). 372p. 1957. 7.50x (ISBN 0-686-00233-4). O'Brien.

Meconis, Charles. With Clumsy Grace: The American Catholic Left, 1961-1975. 1979. 9.95 (ISBN 0-8264-0175-9). Continuum.

Morse, Samuel F. Foreign Conspiracy Against the Liberties of the United States: The Numbers of Brutus. LC 76-46090. (Anti-Movements in America Ser.). 1977. lib. bdg. 18.00 (ISBN 0-405-09963-0). Ayer Co Pubs.

Mulvey, Sr. Mary D. French Catholic Missionaries in the Present United States (1604-1791) LC 73-3578. (Catholic University of America. Studies in American Church History: No. 23). Repr. of 1936 ed. 23.00 (ISBN 0-404-57773-3). AMS Pr.

Munnick, Harriet D. Catholic Church Records of the Pacific Northwest: Vancouver & Stellamaris Mission. LC 72-83958. (Illus.). 1972. 25.00 (ISBN 0-8323-0375-5). Binford-Metropolitan.

Nolan, Hugh J., ed. Pastoral Letters of the United States Catholic Bishops, 1975-1983, Vol. IV. 616p. 1984. pap. 24.95 (ISBN 1-55586-875-4). US Catholic.

--Pastoral Letters of the United States Catholic Bishops, 1962-1974, Vol. III. 511p. 1984. pap. 24.95 (ISBN 1-55586-870-3). US Catholic.

--Pastoral Letters of the United States Catholic Bishops, 1941-1961, Vol. II. 271p. 1984. pap. 24.95 (ISBN 1-55586-885-1). US Catholic.

--Pastoral Letters of the United States Catholic Bishops, 1792-1940, Vol. I. 487p. 1984. pap. 24.95 (ISBN 1-55586-880-0). US Catholic.

O'Hara, Edwin V. The Church & the Country Community. 14.00 (ISBN 0-405-10846-X, 11849). Ayer Co Pubs.

O'Neill, James M. Catholicism & American Freedom. LC 78-21495. 1979. Repr. of 1952 ed. lib. bdg. cancelled (ISBN 0-313-21153-1, ONCA). Greenwood.

Parish Life in the United States, Final Report to the Bishops of the United States by the Parish Project, November, 1982. 90p. 1983. pap. 7.50 (ISBN 1-55586-876-2). US Catholic.

The Parish Self-Study Guide. 97p. 1982. pap. 7.95 (ISBN 1-55586-842-8). US Catholic.

Parsons, Wilfrid. Early Catholic Americana. LC 77-91536. 1977. Repr. of 1939 ed. lib. bdg. 25.00 (ISBN 0-89341-469-7). Longwood Pub Group.

Permanent Deacons in the United States: Guidelines on Their Formation & Ministry. rev. ed. 60p. 1985. pap. 3.95 (ISBN 1-55586-974-2). US Catholic.

A Photo Directory of the United States Catholic Hierarchy. pap. cancelled (ISBN 0-686-15371-5, V-576). US Catholic.

Quinn, Bernard & Bookser-Feister, John. Apostolic Regions of the United States: 1980. LC 78-67012. (Illus.). 1985. pap. text ed. 4.00x (ISBN 0-914422-08-1). Glenmary Res Ctr.

Ryan, John A. Questions of the Day. facs. ed. LC 67-26779. (Essay Index Reprint Ser). 1931. 20.00 (ISBN 0-8369-0846-5). Ayer Co Pubs.

Safranski, Scott R. Managing God's Organization: The Catholic Church in Society. Farmer, Richard, ed. LC 85-16540. (Research for Business Decisions: No. 79). 200p. 1985. 44.95 (ISBN 0-8357-1669-4). UMI Res Pr.

Salpointe, J. B. Soldiers of the Cross. 1977. Repr. of 1898 ed. lib. bdg. 24.95x (ISBN 0-89712-063-9). Documentary Pubns.

Schiavo, Giovanni E. Italian-American History: The Italian Contribution to the Catholic Church in America. LC 74-17948. (Italian American Experience Ser: Vol. No. 2). (Illus.). 1975. Repr. 70.50x (ISBN 0-405-06429-2). Ayer Co Pubs.

Shaughnessy, Gerald. Has the Immigrant Kept the Faith. LC 76-83438. (Religion in America Ser). 1969. Repr. of 1925 ed. 20.00 (ISBN 0-405-00262-9). Ayer Co Pubs.

Shea, John G. History of the Catholic Missions Among the Indian Tribes of the United States, 1529-1854. LC 70-83436. (Religion in America, Ser. 1). 1969. Repr. of 1857 ed. 26.50 (ISBN 0-405-00263-7). Ayer Co Pubs.

Spalding, John L. The Religious Mission of the Irish People & Catholic Colonization. 17.00 (ISBN 0-405-10859-1, 11857). Ayer Co Pubs.

Stewart, James H. American Catholic Leadership: A Decade of Turmoil, 1966-76. (Religon & Society Ser.: No. 13). 1978. pap. 13.00x (ISBN 90-279-7884-0). Mouton.

To Do the Work of Justice: A Plan of Action for the Catholic Community in the United States. pap. 1.95 (ISBN 1-55586-132-6, B-132). US Catholic.

To the Church in America. 4.00 (ISBN 0-8198-7313-6); 3.00 (ISBN 0-8198-7314-4). Dghtrs St Paul.

Varacalli, Joseph A. Toward the Establishment of Liberal Catholicism in America. LC 82-23811. 326p. (Orig.). 1983. lib. bdg. 30.00 (ISBN 0-8191-2974-7); pap. text ed. 14.75 (ISBN 0-8191-2975-5). U Pr of Amer.

Vogel, Claude. The Capuchins in French Louisiana (1722-1766) LC 73-3561. (Catholic University of America. Studies in American Church History: No. 7). Repr. of 1928 ed. 20.00 (ISBN 0-404-57757-1). AMS Pr.

Wakin, Edward & Scheuer, Joseph F. The De-Romanization of the American Catholic Church. LC 78-10157. 1979. Repr. of 1966 ed. lib. bdg. 24.75x (ISBN 0-313-21238-4, WADE). Greenwood.

Walsh, James J. American Jesuits. facs. ed. LC 68-29251. (Essay Index Reprint Ser). 1934. 18.25 (ISBN 0-8369-0970-4). Ayer Co Pubs.

Weber, Francis J. California's Reluctant Prelate: The Life & Times of Thaddeus Amat. (Illus.). 1964. 6.75 (ISBN 0-87093-061-3). Dawsons.

Whitney, Thomas R. A Defence of the American Policy As Opposed to the Encroachments of Foreign Influence, & Especially to the Interference of the Papacy in the Political Interests & Affairs of the United States. LC 75-145496. (The American Immigration Library). 372p. 1971. Repr. of 1856 ed. lib. bdg. 22.95x (ISBN 0-89198-029-6). Ozer.

CATHOLIC CHURCH IN THE UNITED STATES–BIBLIOGRAPHY

Weber, Francis J. Select Guide to California Catholic History. 12.50 (ISBN 0-87026-001-4). Westernlore.

CATHOLIC CHURCH IN THE UNITED STATES–EDUCATION

Bollig, Richard Joseph. History of Catholic Education in Kansas: 1836-1932. 131p. 1984. 24.00x (ISBN 0-939738-22-8). Zubal Inc.

Burns, J. A. Growth & Development of the Catholic School System in the United States. LC 78-89156. (American Education: Its Men, Institutions & Ideas, Ser. 1). 1969. Repr. of 1912 ed. 21.00 (ISBN 0-405-01394-9). Ayer Co Pubs.

--The Principles, Origin & Establishment of the Catholic School System in the United States. LC 74-89155. (American Education: Its Men, Institutions & Ideas Ser). 1969. Repr. of 1908 ed. 21.00 (ISBN 0-405-01393-0). Ayer Co Pubs.

The Catholic High School: A National Portrait. 254p. 1985. 23.75 (ISBN 0-318-04383-1). Natl Cath Educ.

A Day in the Life of a Director of Religious Education. 36p. 1977. 3.60. Natl Cath Educ.

Evangelization: Mission & Ministry for Catholic Educators. 25p. 1979. 3.60. Natl Cath Educ.

Greeley, Andrew M. & Rossi, Peter H. Education of Catholic Americans. LC 66-10867. (NORC Monographs in Social Research Ser.: No. 6). 1966. 8.95x (ISBN 0-202-09003-5). NORC.

Hofinger, Johannes. Prayer Services for the Christian Educator. 1983. 5.35 (ISBN 0-686-40164-6). Natl Cath Educ.

Lannie, Vincent. Public Money & Parochial Education: Bishop Hughes, Governor Seward & the New York School Controversy. 294p. (Pub. by Press of Case Western University). 1968. 16.95 (ISBN 0-268-00565-6). U of Notre Dame Pr.

Lapati, Americo D. A High School Curriculum for Leadership. 1961. 14.95x (ISBN 0-8084-0375-3). New Coll U Pr.

Lee, James M., ed. Catholic Education in the Western World. 1967. 17.95x (ISBN 0-268-00030-1). U of Notre Dame Pr.

McGucken, William J. The Catholic Way in Education. (Request Reprint). 1962. 3.00 (ISBN 0-8294-0052-4). Loyola.

McLoughlin, Emmett. American Culture & Catholic Schools. 288p. 1973. pap. 2.75 (ISBN 0-8065-0356-4). Citadel Pr.

National Catholic Educational Associations & National Conference of Directors of Religious Education. Hear the Word, Share the Word, Guide Your People. 48p. 1978. 4.80. Natl Cath Educ.

The National Conference on Catholic School Finance III. 84p. 1977. 3.60 (ISBN 0-686-29258-8). Natl Cath Educ.

The National Conference on Catholic School Finance I. 75p. 1974. 3.60 (ISBN 0-686-29260-X). Natl Cath Educ.

Noonan, Eileen. Books for Catholic Elementary Schools. pap. 2.50 (ISBN 0-87507-024-8). Cath Lib Assn.

Parent, Neil A., ed. Serving Life & Faith: Adult Religious Education & the American Catholic Community. 72p. 1986. pap. 6.95 (ISBN 1-55586-982-3). US Catholic.

Reilly, Daniel F. School Controversy Eighteen Ninety-One to Eighteen Ninety-Three. LC 76-89221. (American Education: Its Men, Institutions & Ideas, Ser. 1). 1969. Repr. of 1943 ed. 24.00 (ISBN 0-405-01460-0). Ayer Co Pubs.

The Vocation & Spirituality of the Director of Religious Education. 25p. 1980. 4.20 (ISBN 0-686-29244-8). Natl Cath Educ.

Wade, Francis C. Teaching & Morality. LC 63-17962. 1963. 2.95 (ISBN 0-8294-0080-X). Loyola.

White, James A. The Founding of Cliff Haven: Early Years of the Catholic Summer School of America. LC 53-1915. (Monograph Ser.: No. 24). 1950. 7.50x (ISBN 0-930060-06-7). US Cath Hist.

CATHOLIC CHURCH IN THE UNITED STATES–HISTORY

Baumstein, Paschal M. My Lord of Belmont: A Biography of Leo Haid. (Illus.). xxii, 396p. 1985. 20.00 (ISBN 0-9614976-0-2). Archives Belmont.

Bayard, Ralph. Lone-Star Vanguard: The Catholic Re-Occupation of Texas (1838-1848) LC 45-10779. 453p. 1982. lib. bdg. 59.95x (ISBN 0-89370-723-6). Borgo Pr.

Bayley, James R. A Brief Sketch of the Early History of the Catholic Church on the Island of New York. LC 77-359171. (Monograph Ser.: No. 29). 1973. Repr. of 1870 ed. 8.50x (ISBN 0-930060-09-1). US Cath Hist.

Becker, Martin J. A History of Catholic Life in the Diocese of Albany, 1609-1864. LC 77-359170. (Monograph: No. 31). (Illus.). 1975. 15.00x (ISBN 0-930060-11-3). US Cath Hist.

Benedict, Samuel O. Catholicism & Americanism: The Vision of a Conflict? (Illus.). 147p. 1987. 98.85 (ISBN 0-89266-590-4). Am Classical Coll Pr.

Bennett, William H. Catholic Footsteps in Old New York: A Chronicle of Catholicity in the City of New York from 1524 to 1808. LC 77-359169. (Monograph Ser.: No. 28). 1973. Repr. of 1909 ed. 10.00x (ISBN 0-930060-08-3). US Cath Hist.

Brophy, Don & Westenhaver, Edythe, eds. Story of Catholics in America. 3.95 (ISBN 0-8091-2087-9). Paulist Pr.

Cadden, John P. The Historiography of the American Catholic Church, 1785-1943. 14.00 (ISBN 0-405-10812-5). Ayer Co Pubs.

Cadden, John Paul. The Historiography of the American Catholic Church: 1785-1943, No. 82. (Studies in Sacred Theology). 134p. 1984. Repr. of 1944 ed. 35.00x (ISBN 0-939738-33-3). Zubal Inc.

Carroll, Mary A. Catholic History of Alabama & the Floridas. facs. ed. LC 70-124228. (Select Bibliographies Reprint Ser). 1908. 18.00 (ISBN 0-8369-5417-3). Ayer Co Pubs.

Casteneda, Carlos E. Our Catholic Heritage in Texas, 1519-1936, 7 vols. LC 76-1471. (Chicano Heritage Ser.). (Illus.). 1976. Repr. Set. 248.00 (ISBN 0-405-09488-4). Ayer Co Pubs.

Coleman, John A. An American Strategic Theology. 10.95 (ISBN 0-8091-2469-6). Paulist Pr.

Conley, Patrick T. Rhode Island Catholicism: A Historical Guide. 24p. (Orig.). 1984. pap. 2.95 (ISBN 0-917012-56-9). RI Pubns Soc.

Curran, Charles E. American Catholic Social Ethics: Twentieth Century Approaches. LC 82-4829. 336p. 1982. 24.95 (ISBN 0-268-00603-2). U of Notre Dame Pr.

--American Catholic Social Ethics: Twentieth-Century Approaches. LC 82-4829. 353p. 1984. text ed. 9.95 (ISBN 0-268-00609-1, 85-06099). U of Notre Dame Pr.

Curran, Robert E. Michael Augustine Corrigan & the Shaping of Conservative Catholism in America, 1878-1902. 46.50 (ISBN 0-405-10814-1). Ayer Co Pubs.

Dolan, Jay P. American Catholic Experience: A History from Colonial Times to the Present. LC 84-26026. 504p. 1985. 19.95 (ISBN 0-385-15206-X). Doubleday.

--American Catholic Experience: A History from Colonial Times to the Present. 504p. 1987. pap. 10.95 (ISBN 0-385-15207-8, Im). Doubleday.

--Catholic Revivalism: The American Experience, 1830-1900. LC 77-89755. 1978. text ed. 19.95x (ISBN 0-268-00722-5). U of Notre Dame Pr.

--The Immigrant Church: New York's Irish & German Catholics. LC 75-12552. pap. 59.30 (ISBN 0-317-08406-2, 2019817). Bks Demand UMI.

--The Immigrant Church: New York's Irish & German Catholics, 1815-1865. LC 82-23827. (Illus.). xiv, 221p. 1983. pap. text ed. 7.95x (ISBN 0-268-01151-6, 85-11511). U of Notre Dame Pr.

Dolan, Jay P., ed. The American Catholic Parish: A History from 1850 to the Present. Vol. I: The Northeast, Southeast & South Central States. 19.95t; Vol. II: The Pacific States, Intermountain West & Midwest States. 19.95t (ISBN 0-8091-2854-3). Paulist Pr.

Easterly, Frederick J. The Life of Rt. Rev. Joseph Rosati, D. M., First Bishop of St. Louis, 1789-1843. LC 73-3587. (Catholic University of America. Studies in American Church History: No. 33). Repr. of 1942 ed. 27.00 (ISBN 0-404-57783-0). AMS Pr.

Ellis, John T. & Trisco, Robert. A Guide to American Catholic History. 2nd, rev. ed. LC 81-17585. 265p. 1982. lib. bdg. 29.85 (ISBN 0-87436-318-7). ABC-Clio.

Geary, Gerald J. The Secularization of the California Missions (1810-1846) LC 73-3572. (Catholic University of America. Studies in American Church History: No. 17). Repr. of 1934 ed. 26.00 (ISBN 0-404-57767-9). AMS Pr.

Gleason, Philip. Keeping the Faith: American Catholicism Past & Present. LC 86-40579. 320p. 1987. text ed. 24.95x (ISBN 0-268-01227-X, Dist. by Har-Row). U of Notre Dame Pr.

Gower, Joseph F. & Leliaert, Richard M., eds. The Brownson-Hecker Correspondence. LC 76-20160. 1979. text ed. 25.00x (ISBN 0-268-00656-3). U of Notre Dame Pr.

Griffin, Joseph A. The Contribution of Belgium to the Catholic Church in America (1523-1857) LC 73-3568. (Catholic University of America. Studies in American Church History: No. 13). Repr. of 1932 ed. 28.00 (ISBN 0-404-57763-6). AMS Pr.

Guilday, Peter K. History of the Councils of Baltimore, 1791-1884. LC 77-83421. (Religion in America, Ser. 1). 1969. Repr. of 1932 ed. 25.50 (ISBN 0-405-00246-7). Ayer Co Pubs.

Hayman, Robert W. Catholicism in Rhode Island & the Diocese of Providence, 1780-1886. LC 82-73128. 353p. 1982. 17.95 (ISBN 0-917012-55-0). RI Pubns Soc.

Hennesey, James. American Catholics: A History of the Roman Catholic Community in the United States. 1981. pap. 10.95 (ISBN 0-19-503268-3). Oxford U Pr.

Hennesey, James J. American Catholics: A History of the Roman Catholic Community in the United States. 1981. 19.95x (ISBN 0-19-502946-1). Oxford U Pr.

Kantowicz, Edward. Corporation Sole: Cardinal Mundelein & Chicago Catholicism. LC 82-13420. (Notre Dame Studies in American Catholicism). 320p. 1983. text ed. 19.95 (ISBN 0-268-00738-1); pap. text ed. 9.95 (ISBN 0-268-00739-X). U of Notre Dame Pr.

Kenny, Michael. Romance of the Floridas. LC 70-120573. (Illus.). Repr. of 1934 ed. 15.00 (ISBN 0-404-03656-2). AMS Pr.

Kuzniewski, Anthony. Faith & Fatherland. 183p. 1980. text ed. 16.95 (ISBN 0-268-00948-1). U of Notre Dame Pr.

Linkh, Richard M. American Catholicism & European Immigrants (1900-1924) LC 74-79914. vii, 200p. 1974. pap. 9.95x (ISBN 0-913256-17-X). Ctr Migration.

Lyons, Sr. Letitia M. Francis Norbet Blanchet & the Founding of the Oregon Missions (1838-1848) LC 73-3585. (Catholic University of America. Studies in American Church History: No. 31). Repr. of 1940 ed. 28.00 (ISBN 0-404-57781-4). AMS Pr.

McAvoy, Thomas T. Catholic Church in Indiana, Seventeen Eighty-Nine to Eighteen Thirty-Four. LC 41-6425. (Columbia University. Studies in the Social Sciences: No. 471). Repr. of 1940 ed. 20.00 (ISBN 0-404-51471-5). AMS Pr.

McNamara, William. The Catholic Church on the Northern Indiana Frontier, 1789-1844. LC 73-3567. (Catholic University of America. Studies in American Church History: No. 12). Repr. of 1931 ed. 19.00 (ISBN 0-404-57762-8). AMS Pr.

Martin, Aquinata. The Catholic Church on the Nebraska Frontier: 1854-1885. LC 73-3580. (Catholic University of America. Studies in American Church History: No. 26). Repr. of 1937 ed. 26.00 (ISBN 0-404-57776-8). AMS Pr.

Marty, Martin. An Invitation to American Catholic History. (Basics of Christian Thought Ser.). 1986. 14.95 (ISBN 0-88347-189-2). Thomas More.

Mattingly, M. R. The Catholic Church on the Kentucky Frontier: 1785-1812. LC 73-3579. (Catholic University of America. Studies in American Church History: No. 25). Repr. of 1936 ed. 29.00 (ISBN 0-404-57775-X). AMS Pr.

Munnick, Harriet D., compiled by. Catholic Church Records of the Pacific Northwest: Roseburg & Portland. LC 85-63221. (Illus.). 440p. 1986. 25.00 (ISBN 0-8323-0447-6). Binford-Metropolitan.

O'Connell, Jeremiah J. Catholicity in the Carolinas & Georgia: Leaves of Its History. LC 73-187371. (Illus.). 647p. 1972. Repr. of 1879 ed. 17.50 (ISBN 0-87152-099-0). Reprint.

Pare, George. The Catholic Church in Detroit, 1701-1888. LC 83-67420. 733p. 1983. pap. 19.05x (ISBN 0-8143-1758-8). Wayne St U Pr.

Piehl, Mel. Breaking Bread: The Catholic Worker & the Origin of Catholic Radicalism in America. 314p. 1984. pap. 12.95 (ISBN 0-87722-353-X). Temple U Pr.

Porter, Jack W. & Stineman, William F. The Catholic Church in Greencastle, Putnam County, Indiana 1848-1978. LC 78-65724. (Illus.). 1979. 14.95 (ISBN 0-9602352-0-5). St Paul the Apostle.

Roemer, Theodore. The Ludwig-Missionsverein & the Church in the United States (1838-1918) LC 73-3571. (Catholic University of America. Studies in American Church History: No. 16). Repr. of 1933 ed. 22.00 (ISBN 0-404-57766-0). AMS Pr.

Saalfeld, Lawrence J. Forces of Prejudice in Oregon, Nineteen Twenty to Nineteen Twenty-Five. LC 84-14599. (Oregon Catholic History Ser.). (Orig.). 1984. pap. 8.95 (ISBN 0-9613644-0-8). Archdiocesan.

Shea, John D. History of the Catholic Church in the United States, 4 vols. 216.00 (ISBN 0-405-10852-4, 11855). Ayer Co Pubs.

Sheed, Wilfrid. Frank & Maisie: A Memoir with Parents. 304p. 1986. pap. 7.95 (ISBN 0-671-62813-5, Touchstone Bks). S&S.

Stineman, William F. & Porter, Jack W. Saint John the Evangelist Church, Indianapolis, Indiana: A Photographic Essay of the Oldest Catholic Church in Indianapolis & Marion County. LC 85-63564. (Illus.). 80p. 1986. 39.95 (ISBN 0-9616134-0-8). ST John Evang.

Taylor, Mary C. A History of the Foundations of Catholicism in Northern New York. LC 77-359034. (Monograph Ser.: No. 32). (Illus.). 13.50x (ISBN 0-930060-12-1). US Cath Hist.

Tomasi, Silvano M. Piety & Power: The Role of Italian Parishes in the New York Metropolitan Area (1889-1930) LC 74-79913. 201p. 1975. 14.95x (ISBN 0-913256-16-1). Ctr Migration.

Walker, Fintan G. The Catholic Church in the Meeting of Two Frontiers: The Southern Illinois Country (1763-1793) LC 73-3574. (Catholic University of America. Studies in American Church History: No. 19). Repr. of 1935 ed. 17.50 (ISBN 0-404-57769-5). AMS Pr.

CATHOLIC CHURCH IN THE UNITED STATES–HISTORY–SOURCES

Curran, Francis X. Catholics in Colonial Law. 1963. 2.95 (ISBN 0-8294-0016-8). Loyola.

Gleason, Philip. Documentary Reports on Early American Catholicism. 17.00 (ISBN 0-405-10833-8, 11825). Ayer Co Pubs.

McCants, Sr. Dorothea O., ed. They Came to Louisiana: Letters of a Catholic Mission, 1854-1882. LC 72-96258. (Illus.). Repr. of 1970 ed. 72.80 (ISBN 0-8357-9392-3, 2020997). Bks Demand UMI.

Munnick, Harriet D. Catholic Church Records of the Pacific Northwest: St. Louis, Gervais & Brooks. LC 72-71955. (Illus.). 1982. 25.00 (ISBN 0-8323-0408-5). Binford-Metropolitan.

Munnick, Harriet D. & Beckham, Stephen D., eds. Catholic Church Records of the Pacific Northwest: Grand Ronde Register, 2 Vols. (Illus.). 1987. Set. 25.00 (ISBN 0-8323-0455-7). Vol. I. Vol.II. Binford-Metropolitan.

Munnick, Harriet D. & Beckman, Stephan D., eds. Catholic Church Records of the Pacific Northwest: Grand Ronde Register, 2 vols. (Illus.). 1987. Set. 25.00 (ISBN 0-8323-0455-7). Vol. I, (1860-1885) Vol. II, (1885-1898) Binford-Metropolitan.

Weber, Francis J. Readings in California Catholic History. 10.00 (ISBN 0-87026-000-6). Westernlore.

CATHOLIC CHURCH IN VENEZUELA

Watters, Mary. History of the Church in Venezuela, 1810-1930. LC 70-137303. Repr. of 1933 ed. 22.00 (ISBN 0-404-06877-4). AMS Pr.

CATHOLIC CHURCH MUSIC

see Church Music–Catholic Church

CATHOLIC CONVERTS

see Converts, Catholic

CATHOLIC EMANCIPATION

Catholic Emancipation Eighteen Twenty-Nine to Nineteen Twenty-Nine: Essays by Various Writers. facs. ed. LC 67-22084. (Essay Index Reprint Ser). 1929. 20.00 (ISBN 0-8369-0284-X). Ayer Co Pubs.

Gwynn, Stephen. Henry Grattan & His Times. facsimile ed. LC 78-175699. (Select Bibliographies Reprint Ser.). Repr. of 1939 ed. 26.50 (ISBN 0-8369-6614-7). Ayer Co Pubs.

Reynolds, James A. Catholic Emancipation Crisis in Ireland, 1823-1829. Repr. of 1954 ed. lib. bdg. 22.50x (ISBN 0-8371-3141-3, RECE). Greenwood.

CATHOLIC FOREIGN MISSION SOCIETY OF AMERICA

Keller, James G. & Berger, Meyer. Men of Maryknoll. LC 78-142650. (Essay Index Reprint Ser.). Repr. of 1943 ed. 18.00 (ISBN 0-8369-2775-3). Ayer Co Pubs.

CATHOLIC JOURNALISM

see Journalism, Religious

CATHOLIC LEARNING AND SCHOLARSHIP

Burrell, David B. & Kane, Franzita, eds. Evangelization in the American Context. LC 76-22403. 1976. pap. 2.95x (ISBN 0-268-00902-3). U of Notre Dame Pr.

Fehr, Wayne L. The Birth of the Catholic Tubingen School: The Dogmatics of Johann Sebastian Drey. Raschke, Carl, ed. LC 81-14645. (American Academy of Religion, Dissertation Ser.). 1981. text ed. 14.95 (ISBN 0-89130-544-0, 01-01-37). Scholars Pr GA.

Gibbons, Joseph C. Whatever Happened to Friday? & Other Questions Catholics Ask. LC 79-91275. (Orig.). 1980. pap. 3.95 (ISBN 0-8091-2278-2). Paulist Pr.

Schoenl, William J. The Intellectual Crisis in English Catholicism: Liberal Catholics, Modernists, & the Vatican in the Late Nineteenth & Early Twentieth Centuries. Stanmsky, Peter & Hume, Leslie, eds. LC 81-48368. 360p. 1982. lib. bdg. 52.00 (ISBN 0-8240-5164-5). Garland Pub.

CATHOLIC LIBRARIES

see Libraries, Catholic

CATHOLIC LITERATURE

see also Catholic Authors

Caponigri, Aloysius R., ed. Modern Catholic Thinkers. facs. ed. LC 78-117775. (Essay Index Reprint Ser). 1960. 38.50 (ISBN 0-8369-1787-1). Ayer Co Pubs.

Diaconal Reader: Selected Articles from the Diaconal Quarterly. 112p. 1985. pap. 4.95 (ISBN 1-55586-939-4). US Catholic.

Huchede, P. History of Antichrist. 1976. pap. 2.00 (ISBN 0-89555-100-4). TAN Bks Pubs.

John Chrysostom, St. Homilies, 48-88. LC 57-1545. (Fathers of the Church Ser.: Vol. 41). 485p. 1960. 29.95x (ISBN 0-8132-0041-5). Cath U Pr.

Logan, Natale, ed. The Catholic Periodical & Literature Index. Incl. Vol. 2 1934-38. 50.00 (ISBN 0-87507-010-8); Vol. 4. 1943-48. 50.00 (ISBN 0-87507-011-6); Vol. 10. 1959-60. 30.00 (ISBN 0-87507-012-4); Vol. 11. 1961-62; Vol. 12. 1963-64. 40.00 (ISBN 0-87507-014-0); Vol. 14. 1967-68. 40.00 (ISBN 0-87507-015-9); Vol. 15. 1969-70. 45.00 (ISBN 0-87507-016-7); Vol. 16. 1971-72. 60.00 (ISBN 0-87507-017-5); Vol. 17. 1973-1974. 55.00 (ISBN 0-87507-018-3); Vol. 18. 60.00 (ISBN 0-87507-019-1, 1975-1976); Vol. 19. 70.00 (ISBN 0-87507-020-5, 1977-1978); Vol. 21. 90.00 (ISBN 0-87507-025-6, 1981-1982). LC 70-649588. Orig. Title: The Catholic Periodical Index & The Guide to Catholic Literature. Cath Lib Assn.

Masterpieces of Catholic Literature, 2 vols. 1139p. 1965. Set. 60.00x (ISBN 0-89356-154-1). Salem Pr.

Newman, John H. Blessed Art Thou among Women. 1985. 4.95 (ISBN 0-87193-076-5). Dimension Bks.

Pope John Paul II. You Are the Future You Are My Hope. 1979. pap. 3.95 (ISBN 0-8198-0633-1). Dghtrs St Paul.

White, Thomas & O'Donnell, Desmond. Renewal of Faith. LC 74-76320. 240p. 1974. pap. 2.95 (ISBN 0-87793-068-6). Ave Maria.

CATHOLIC LITERATURE (COLLECTIONS)

Kenyon, Ruth. The Catholic Faith & the Industrial Order. 1980. lib. bdg. 59.95 (ISBN 0-8490-3129-X). Gordon Pr.

Nolan, Hugh J., ed. Pastoral Letters of the United States Catholic Bishops, 1975-1983, Vol. IV. 616p. 1984. pap. 24.95 (ISBN 1-55586-875-4). US Catholic.

--Pastoral Letters of the United States Catholic Bishops, 1962-1974, Vol. III. 511p. 1984. pap. 24.95 (ISBN 1-55586-870-3). US Catholic.

--Pastoral Letters of the United States Catholic Bishops, 1941-1961, Vol. II. 271p. 1984. pap. 24.95 (ISBN 1-55586-885-1). US Catholic.

--Pastoral Letters of the United States Catholic Bishops, 1792-1940, Vol. I. 487p. 1984. pap. 24.95 (ISBN 1-55586-880-0). US Catholic.

Vitale, Philip H. Catholic Literary Opinion in the Nineteenth Century. 197p. 4.50 (ISBN 0-685-25451-8); pap. 2.50 (ISBN 0-685-25452-6). Auxiliary U Pr.

CATHOLIC LITERATURE–BIBLIOGRAPHY

Catholic Library Association Staff. Guide to Catholic Literature, 6 vols. Romig, Walter, ed. Incl. 20.00 (ISBN 0-685-22623-9); 10.00; Vols. 3-5. 1944-1955. 15.00 ea.; Vol 6. 1956-1959. 17.50 (ISBN 0-685-22626-3); Vol. 7. 1960-1963. 25.00 (ISBN 0-685-22627-1); Vol. 8. 1964-1967. 25.00 (ISBN 0-685-22628-X). Cath Lib Assn.

Catholic Periodical & Literature Index, 1983-1984, Vol. 22. 100.00 (ISBN 0-87507-036-1). Cath Lib Assn.

Clancy, Thomas H. English Catholic Books, 1641-1700. LC 74-704. 158p. 1974. pap. 8.00 (ISBN 0-8294-0231-4). Loyola.

Gillow, Joseph. Literary & Biographical History; or Bibliographical Dictionary of English Catholics from the Breach with Rome, in 1534, to the Present Time, 5 Vols. 1962. Repr. of 1892 ed. 205.00 (ISBN 0-8337-1356-6). B Franklin.

Hurter, Hugo. Nomenclator Litterarius Theologiae Catholicae Theologo Sexhibens Aetate, Natione, Disciplins Distinctos, 5 Vols. in 6. 1903. Set. 294.00 (ISBN 0-8337-1772-3). B Franklin.

Perennes, F M. Dictionnaire de Bibliographie Catholique, Presentant l'Indication et les Titres Complets de tous les Ouvrages qui Ontetes Publies dans les Trois Lanques Grecque, Latine et Francaise... Suivi d'un Dictionnaire de Bibliologie par G. Brunet (the Last 2 Vols., 6 vols. Migne, J. P., ed. (Troisieme et Derniere Encyclopedie Theologique Ser.: Vols. 39-44). (Fr.). 4001p. Repr. of 1866 ed. lib. bdg. 510.00x (ISBN 0-89241-318-2). Caratzas.

Schuster, George N. Catholic Authors, Crown Edition. (Illus.). (YA) 1952. pap. 3.95 (ISBN 0-910334-23-4). Cath Authors.

CATHOLIC LITERATURE–HISTORY AND CRITICISM

Alexander, Calvert. Catholic Literary Revival. LC 68-16288. 1968. Repr. of 1935 ed. 31.50x (ISBN 0-8046-0005-8, Pub. by Kennikat). Assoc Faculty Pr.

D'Souza, Dinesh. The Catholic Classics. LC 86-61500. 168p. (Orig.). 1986. pap. 6.95 (ISBN 0-87973-545-7, 545). Our Sunday Visitor.

Kellogg, Gene. The Vital Tradition: The Catholic Novel in a Period of Convergence. LC 74-108375. 1970. 8.35 (ISBN 0-8294-0192-X). Loyola.

Musser, Benjamin F. Franciscan Poets. facs. ed. LC 67-26768. (Essay Index Reprint Ser). 1933. 17.25 (ISBN 0-8369-0732-9). Ayer Co Pubs.

Schuster, George N. Catholic Authors, Crown Edition. (Illus.). (YA) 1952. pap. 3.95 (ISBN 0-910334-23-4). Cath Authors.

Sheed, Francis J. Sidelights on the Catholic Revival. facs. ed. LC 74-99649. (Essay Index Reprint Ser). 1940. 18.00 (ISBN 0-8369-2176-3). Ayer Co Pubs.

Vitale, Philip H. Catholic Literary Opinion of the Twentieth Century. 438p. 4.50 (ISBN 0-685-25453-4). Auxiliary U Pr.

CATHOLIC MOVEMENT (ANGLICAN COMMUNION)

see Anglo-Catholicism

CATHOLIC PERIODICALS

see Catholic Church–Periodicals

CATHOLIC PRESS ASSOCIATION

Doyle, James A. Catholic Press Directory. 184p. 1985. pap. 25.00 (ISBN 0-686-30366-0). Cath Pr Assn.

Salzmann, Regina A. Catholic Press Directory, 1986. 208p. 1986. pap. 25.00 (ISBN 0-318-18711-6). Cath Pr Assn.

CATHOLIC SCHOOLS

Bredeweg, Frank H. United States Catholic Elementary & Secondary Schools, 1985-86. 21p. 1986. 6.60. Natl Cath Educ.

Brother Robert J. Kealey. Curriculum in the Catholic School. 61p. 1986. 6.60 (ISBN 0-318-20568-8). Natl Cath Educ.

Brother Terence McLaughlin. Catholic School Finance & Church-State Relations. 81p. 1986. 6.60 (ISBN 0-318-20564-5). Natl Cath Educ.

Catholic Secondary Schools & College: Reviewing the Partnership (Proceedings of the Symposium on Secondary School College Collaboration) 76p. 1986. 5.30. Natl Cath Educ.

Current Issues in Catholic Higher Education. Incl. Vol. 1, No. 1. Registration-Draft-National Service. 40p. 1980. 2.40 (ISBN 0-318-20581-5); Vol. 1, No. 2. Peace & Justice Education. 40p. 1981. 2.40 (ISBN 0-318-20582-3); Vol. 2, No. 1. Purposes & Leadership. 50p. 1981. 2.40 (ISBN 0-318-20583-1); Vol. 2, No. 2. Campus As Context. 48p. 1982. 2.40 (ISBN 0-318-20584-X); Vol. 3, No. 1. Report on Graduate Education. 40p. 1982. 3.60 (ISBN 0-318-20585-8); Vol. 3, No. 2. Facing the Future. 31p. 1983. 3.60 (ISBN 0-318-20586-6); Vol. 4, No. 1. Trends in Enrollment & Finance, 1978-82. 32p. 1983. 6.00 (ISBN 0-318-20587-4); Vol. 4, No. 2. Sponsorship-Partnership & 1984 Annual Meeting Papers. 47p. 1984. 6.00 (ISBN 0-318-20588-2); Vol. 5, No. 1. International Perspectives. 36p. 1984. 6.00 (ISBN 0-318-20589-0); Vol. 5, No. 2. Tradition in a Changed Context. 32p. 1985. 6.00 (ISBN 0-318-20590-4); Vol. 6, No. 1. Beyond Basketball. 38p. 1985. 6.00 (ISBN 0-318-20591-2); Vol. 6, No. 2. Town & Gown. 40p. 1986. 6.50 (ISBN 0-318-20592-0). Set. 37.00 (ISBN 0-318-20580-7). Natl Cath Educ.

Development in Total Catholic Education. 1985. 4.80 (ISBN 0-318-20606-4). Natl Cath Educ.

Drahmann, Theodore. Governance & Administration in the Catholic School. 45p. 1986. 6.60 (ISBN 0-318-20563-7). Natl Cath Educ.

Father Edwin J. McDermott. Distinctive Qualities of the Catholic School. 78p. 1986. 6.60 (ISBN 0-318-20560-2). Natl Cath Educ.

Father James F. Hawker. Catechetics in the Catholic School. 61p. 1986. 6.60 (ISBN 0-318-20569-6). Natl Cath Educ.

Guidelines for Selected Personnel Practices in Catholic Schools II. 58p. 1977. 4.55 (ISBN 0-686-29246-4). Natl Cath Educ.

Jarc, Jerry A. Development & Public Relations for the Catholic School. 65p. 1986. 6.60 (ISBN 0-318-20562-9). Natl Cath Educ.

McElligott, Arlene F. & McElligott, Joseph P. The Catholic Elementary School Extension Program. 33p. 1986. 5.30 (ISBN 0-318-20576-9). Natl Cath Educ.

Raftery, Francis. The Teacher in the Catholic School. 61p. 1986. 6.60 (ISBN 0-318-20567-X). Natl Cath Educ.

A Self-Study Guide for Catholic High Schools. 76p. 1981. 9.00 (ISBN 0-318-20605-6). Natl Cath Educ.

Traviss, Mary P. Student Moral Development in the Catholic School. 96p. 1986. 6.60 (ISBN 0-318-20565-3). Natl Cath Educ.

Warrick, Keith, et al. Catholic High School Ministry. (Illus.). 224p. 1986. loose-leaf bdg. 34.95 (ISBN 0-88489-173-9). St Mary's.

Weiss, Ed. The Parent, the Parish, & the Catholic School. 1986. 6.60 (ISBN 0-318-20566-1). Natl Cath Educ.

Welch, Mary L. Methods of Teaching in the Catholic School. 1986. 6.60 (ISBN 0-318-20570-X). Natl Cath Educ.

Yeager, Robert J., compiled by. Directory of Development. 28p. 1986. 10.95 (ISBN 0-318-20571-8). Natl Cath Educ.

CATHOLIC SCHOOLS–GREAT BRITAIN

Directory of Catholic Schools & Colleges. 64p. 1982. 25.00x (ISBN 0-317-43550-7, Pub. by Truman & Knightley). State Mutual BK.

CATHOLIC SCHOOLS–UNITED STATES

Augenstein, John J. A Collaborative Approach to Personnel Relations: A Model Process for Justice in the Catholic School Community of Faith. 191p. 1980. 2.35 (ISBN 0-686-39900-5). Natl Cath Educ.

Bredweg, Frank H. United States Catholic Elementary & Secondary Schools, 1985-86. 21p. 1986. 7.30 (ISBN 0-318-20578-5). Natl Cath Educ.

--United States Catholic Elementary Schools & their Finances, 1986. 1986. 6.00 (ISBN 0-318-20577-7). Natl Cath Educ.

Cascone, Gina. Pagan Babies & Other Catholic Memories. 160p. 1982. 9.95 (ISBN 0-312-59418-6). St Martin.

--Pagan Babies & Other Catholic Memories. 160p. 1983. pap. 4.95 (ISBN 0-312-59419-4). St Martin.

Catholic Elementary Schools & Their Finances. 1980 1.50 (ISBN 0-686-39958-7); 1979 1.80 (ISBN 0-686-39959-5); 1978 1.50 (ISBN 0-686-39960-9). Natl Cath Educ.

Catholic High Schools & Their Finances. 1980 3.00 (ISBN 0-686-39953-6); 1979 3.60 (ISBN 0-686-39954-4); 1978 3.00 (ISBN 0-686-39955-2). Natl Cath Educ.

Directory-Department of Chief Administrators of Catholic Education. 75p. 3.60 (ISBN 0-686-39967-6). Natl Cath Educ.

Drahmann, Theodore. The Catholic School Principal: An Outline for Action. 50p. 1981. 4.80 (ISBN 0-686-39893-9). Natl Cath Educ.

Effective Catholic Schools: An Exploration-Executive Summary. 104p. 1984. 21.60 (ISBN 0-318-03689-4). Natl Cath Educ.

Egan, Katherine. Beginnings: The Orientation of New Teachers. 20p. 1981. 2.40 (ISBN 0-686-39892-0). Natl Cath Educ.

Father Harold A. Buetow. A History of Catholic Schooling in the United States. 89p. 1986. 6.60 (ISBN 0-318-20561-0). Natl Cath Educ.

Glathorn, Allan A. & Shields, Carmel R. Differentiated Supervision for Catholic Schools. 72p. 1983. 5.75 (ISBN 0-318-00781-9). Natl Cath Educ.

Greeley, Andrew M. Catholic High Schools & Minority Students. LC 81-23131. (Illus.). 125p. 1982. 14.95 (ISBN 0-87855-452-1). Transaction Bks.

Harper, Mary-Angela. Developing Performance Excellence in Catholic Educational Policymaking: A Handbook of Training Programs. 82p. 1982. 6.00 (ISBN 0-686-39917-X). Natl Cath Educ.

--Let Peace & Justice Prevail. 10p. 1977. 1.55 (ISBN 0-686-39920-X). Natl Cath Educ.

McBride, Alfred & Praem, O. The Christian Formation of Catholic Educators. 32p. 1981. 3.00 (ISBN 0-686-39896-3); member 2.25. Natl Cath Educ.

--The Pre-Service Formation of Teachers for Catholic Schools. 24p. 1982. 2.40 (ISBN 0-686-39890-4). Natl Cath Educ.

McLoughlin, Emmett. American Culture & Catholic Schools. 288p. 1973. pap. 2.75 (ISBN 0-8065-0356-4). Citadel Pr.

NCEA-GANLEY's Catholic Schools in America. 322p. 33.00 (ISBN 0-686-29255-3). Natl Cath Educ.

Permuth, Steve, et al. The Law, the Student, & the Catholic School. 96p. 1981. 6.00 (ISBN 0-686-39898-X). Natl Cath Educ.

Personnel Inventory & Employment Application. 1979. 25 copies 3.60 (ISBN 0-686-39902-1). Natl Cath Educ.

A Report on United States Catholic Schools, 1972-73. 98p. 1973. 2.40 (ISBN 0-686-29263-4). Natl Cath Educ.

Strommen, Merton P. Five Shaping Forces: Using Organizational Dynamics to Do More with Less. 104p. 1982. 9.60 (ISBN 0-686-39889-0). Natl Cath Educ.

Teacher as Minister Weekly Plan Book. 208p. 1979. 4.80 (ISBN 0-686-39948-X). Natl Cath Educ.

U. S. Catholic Schools: 1973 to 1974. 92p. 1974. 2.40. Natl Cath Educ.

Vision & Values in the Catholic School: Participant's Guide. 96p. 1981. 4.20 (ISBN 0-686-39942-0). Natl Cath Educ.

Vision y Valores Manual del Participante. (Span.). 96p. 1982. 4.20 (ISBN 0-686-39943-9). Natl Cath Educ.

CATHOLIC THEOLOGICAL SEMINARIES

see Theological Seminaries, Catholic

CATHOLIC UNIVERSITIES AND COLLEGES

Crocker, John R. The Student Guide to Catholic Colleges & Universties. LC 82-48923. 468p. (Orig.). 1983. pap. 9.95 (ISBN 0-06-061602-4, RD/459, HarpR). Har-Row.

Current Issues in Catholic Higher Education: Sponsorship-Partnership & 1984 Annual Meeting Papers, Vol. 4. (No. 2). 6.00 (ISBN 0-318-03688-6). Natl Cath Educ.

Directory of Catholic Schools & Colleges. 64p. 1982. 25.00x (ISBN 0-317-43550-7, Pub. by Truman & Knightley). State Mutual BK.

FitzGerald, Paul A. Governance of Jesuit Colleges in the United States, 1920-1970. LC 83-25927. 328p. 1984. text ed. 20.00 (ISBN 0-268-01010-2, 85-10109). U of Notre Dame Pr.

Greeley, Andrew M. Changing Catholic College. LC 67-27393. (NORC Monographs in Social Research Ser.: No. 13). 1967. 8.95x (ISBN 0-202-09011-6). NORC.

McCluskey, Neil S., ed. Catholic University: A Modern Appraisal. LC 70-85353. 1970. 22.95 (ISBN 0-268-00355-6). U of Notre Dame Pr.

McMahon, Thomas F., et al. Ethics on a Catholic University Campus. Barry, James D., ed. 1981. pap. 5.95 (ISBN 0-8294-0369-8). Loyola.

Padberg, John W. Colleges in Controversy: The Jesuit Schools in France from Revival to Suppression, 1815-1880. LC 75-78523. (Historical Studies: No. 83). 1969. text ed. 22.50x (ISBN 0-674-14160-1). Harvard U Pr.

Wade, Francis C. The Catholic University & the Faith. (Aquinas Lecture Ser.). 1978. 7.95 (ISBN 0-87462-143-7). Marquette.

CATHOLIC UNIVERSITY OF AMERICA

The History of the Catholic University of America, 3 vols. Incl. Vol.1. The Rectorship of John J. Keane, 1887-1896. Ahern, Patrick H. 220p. 1949 (ISBN 0-8132-0313-9); Vol.2. The Rectorship of Thomas J. Conaty, 1896-1903. Hogan, Peter E. 1949 (ISBN 0-8132-0314-7); Vol.3. The Rectorship of Denis J. O'Connell, 1903-1909. Barry, C. J. 212p. 1950 (ISBN 0-8132-0315-5). 5.95x ea. Cath U Pr.

CATHOLICITY

see also Ecumenical Movement

Adam, Karl. The Spirit of Catholicism. McCann, Dom J., tr. from German. 237p. 1981. Repr. of 1929 ed. lib. bdg. 30.00 (ISBN 0-89987-028-7). Darby Bks.

Aulen, Gustaf E. Reformation & Catholicity. Wahlstrom, Eric H., tr. from Swedish. LC 78-25981. 1979. Repr. of 1961 ed. lib. bdg. 22.50x (ISBN 0-313-20809-3, AURC). Greenwood.

Badia, Leonard F. Basic Catholic Beliefs for Today: The Creed Explained. LC 84-14632. 170p. (Orig.). 1984. pap. 8.95 (ISBN 0-8189-0469-0). Alba.

Baker, Kenneth. Fundamentals of Catholicism: Church, Grace, Sacraments & Eschatology or the Last Things, Vol. III. 1983. pap. 10.95 (ISBN 0-317-02736-0, Co-Pub. by Ignatius Pr-Catholic Polls). Guild Bks.

--Fundamentals of Catholicism: God, Trinity, Creation, Christ, Mary, Vol. II. LC 82-80297. 1983. pap. 10.95 (ISBN 0-89870-019-1, Co-Pub. by Ignatius Pr-Catholic Polls). Guild Bks.

--Fundamentals of Catholicism: Grace, the Church, the Sacraments, Eschatology, Vol. 3. LC 82-80297. 388p. (Orig.). 1983. pap. 11.95 (ISBN 0-89870-027-2). Ignatius Pr.

--Fundamentals of Catholocism: The Creed, the Commandments, Vol. I. LC 82-80297. 1982. pap. 9.95 (ISBN 0-89870-017-5, Co-Pub. by Ignatius Pr-Catholic Polls). Guild Bks.

Baker, Kenneth S. Fundamentals of Catholicism: God, Trinity, Creation, Christ, Mary, Vol. 2. LC 82-80297. 387p. (Orig.). 1983. pap. 11.95 (ISBN 0-89870-019-1). Ignatius Pr.

Benestace, J. Brian & Butler, Frances J., eds. Quest for Justice. 487p. (Orig.). 1981. pap. 17.95 (ISBN 1-55586-649-2). US Catholic.

Bokenkotter, Thomas. Essential Catholicism: Dynamics of Faith & Belief. LC 86-4390. 456p. 1986. pap. 9.95 (ISBN 0-385-23243-8, Im). Doubleday.

Bokenkotter, Thomas, tr. Essential Catholicism. LC 84-13631. 432p. 1985. 19.95 (ISBN 0-385-18357-7). Doubleday.

Boudreau, Albert. The Born-Again Catholic. (Illus., Orig.). 1979. pap. 4.95 (ISBN 0-914544-26-8). Living Flame Pr.

Butler, Christopher. The Theology of Vatican II. rev. ed. 238p. 1981. pap. 17.50 (ISBN 0-87061-062-7). Chr Classics.

Chilson, Richard. Creed for a Young Catholic. LC 80-2073. 128p. 1981. pap. 2.75 (ISBN 0-385-17436-5, Im). Doubleday.

Chinnici, Joseph P., ed. Devotion to the Holy Spirit in American Catholicism. LC 85-60956. (Sources of American Spirituality Ser.: Vol. 3). 256p. 1985. 12.95 (ISBN 0-8091-0366-4). Paulist Pr.

Cortes, Juan D. & Schramm, Edmund. Ensayo Sobre el Catolicismo, el Liberalismo y el Socialismo & Donoso Cortes, 2 vols. in one. Mayer, J. P., ed. LC 78-67342. (European Political Thought Ser.). (Span. & Ger.). 1979. Repr. of 1935 ed. lib. bdg. 39.00x (ISBN 0-405-11687-X). Ayer Co Pubs.

Daschbach, Edwin. Interpreting Scripture: A Catholic Response to Fundamentalism. 144p. 1985. pap. 6.95 (ISBN 0-697-02110-6). Wm C Brown.

Faber, Federick W. Bethlehem. LC 78-66306. 1978. pap. 10.00 (ISBN 0-89555-080-6). TAN Bks Pubs.

Hill, Brennan & Newland, Mary R., eds. Why Be a Catholic? 108p. (Orig.). 1979. pap. 2.00 (ISBN 0-697-01713-3). Wm C Brown.

Jehan, L. F. Dictionnaire de Philosophie Catholique, 3 vols. Migne, J. P., ed. (Troisieme et Derniere Encyclopedie Theologique Ser.: Vols. 48-50). (Fr.). 2047p. Repr. of 1864 ed. lib. bdg. 260.00x (ISBN 0-89241-321-2). Caratzas.

Kennedy, David G. Catholicism & the Mysticisms of the East. LC 86-62211. viii, 70p. (Orig.). 1986. pap. 4.95x (ISBN 0-934995-01-X). OLW Editions.

Kohmescher, Matthew F. Catholicism Today: A Survey of Catholic Belief & Practice. LC 80-82085. 216p. (Orig.). 1980. pap. 4.95 (ISBN 0-8091-2335-5). Paulist Pr.

--Good Morality Is Like Good Cooking... & Other Suggestions for Right Living. 112p. (Orig.). 1987. pap. 4.95 (ISBN 0-8091-2856-X). Paulist Pr.

Kollar, Nathan R., ed. Options in Roman Catholicism: An Introduction. LC 82-21823. 224p. (Orig.). 1983. lib. bdg. 27.00 (ISBN 0-8191-2958-5); pap. text ed. 12.50 (ISBN 0-8191-2959-3). U Pr of Amer.

Lambert, O. C. Catholicism Against Itself, Vol. 1. 11.95 (ISBN 0-89315-005-3). Lambert Bk.

--Catholicism Against Itself, Vol. 2. 11.95 (ISBN 0-89315-006-1). Lambert Bk.

Larkin, Emmet. The Historical Dimensions of Irish Catholicism. LC 83-23175. 139p. 1984. pap. 9.95x (ISBN 0-8132-0594-8). Cath U Pr.

Levesque, George H. Social Credit & Catholicism. 1979. lib. bdg. 39.95 (ISBN 0-8490-3006-4). Gordon Pr.

McBrien, Richard P. Catholicism, 2 vols. 1368p. 1980. Set. 45.00 (ISBN 0-03-056907-9, HarpR). Har-Row.

--Catholicism Study Edition. 1312p. (Orig.). 1981. pap. 24.50 (ISBN 0-86683-601-2, HarpR). Har-Row.

Martin, Richard M. Events, Reference, & Logical Form. LC 77-24685. pap. 67.80 (2029492). Bks Demand UMI.

Merton, Thomas. The Secular Journal. 1983. 16.00 (ISBN 0-8446-5985-1). Peter Smith.

Reedy, William J., ed. Becoming a Catholic Christian. 198p. pap. 5.95 (ISBN 0-8215-9326-9). Sadlier.

Schreck, Alan. Catholic & Christian. 240p. (Orig.). 1984. pap. 6.95 (ISBN 0-89283-181-2). Servant.

Schultenover, David G. George Tyrrell: In Search of Catholicism. LC 81-38406. (Illus.). xiv, 505p. 1981. 32.50x (ISBN 0-915762-13-7). Patmos Pr.

Stravinskas, Peter M. The Catholic Response. LC 84-62435. 208p. (Orig.). 1985. pap. 5.95 (ISBN 0-87973-594-5, 594). Our Sunday Visitor.

Your Faith: A Popular Presentation of Catholic Belief. LC 81-85557. (Redemptorist Pastoral Publication Ser.). 64p. 1982. pap. 2.95 (ISBN 0-89243-154-7). Liguori Pubns.

Znoskovo-Borovsky, Mitrophan. Pravoslavije, Rimo-Katolichestvo, Protenstatizm i Sektantstvo. Tr. of Orthodoxy, Roman-Catholicism, Protenstatism & Sectarianism. 156p. 1972. pap. text ed. 5.00 (ISBN 0-317-30254-X). Holy Trinity.

Zubiri, Xavier. On Essence. LC 78-68067. pap. 132.30 (2029514). Bks Demand UMI.

CATHOLICS

Aspell, A. L. Catholics: A Celebration. Date not set. pap. price not set (ISBN 0-940518-05-8). Guildhall Pubs.

Ball, Ann. Modern Saints: Their Lives & Faces. LC 82-50357. (Illus.). 457p. 1983. pap. 10.00 (ISBN 0-89555-222-1). TAN Bks Pubs.

Christopher, Kenneth. Ten Catholics: Lives to Remember. (Nazareth Bks). 120p. 1983. pap. 3.95 (ISBN 0-86683-715-9, HarpR). Har-Row.

Coman, Peter. Catholics & the Welfare State. LC 76-49523. pap. 32.00 (ISBN 0-317-08456-9, 2011288). Bks Demand UMI.

Cunningham, Lawrence. Catholic Experience. 270p. 1987. pap. 10.95 (ISBN 0-8245-0811-4). Crossroad NY.

Davis, Charles. Why I Left the Roman Catholic Church. 27p. 1976. 3.00 (ISBN 0-911826-11-4). Am Atheist.

Derrick, Christopher. That Strange Divine Sea: Reflections on Being a Catholic. LC 83-80190. 189p. (Orig.). 1983. pap. 8.95 (ISBN 0-89870-029-9). Ignatius Pr.

Deshon, George. Guide for Catholic Young Women. 24.50 (ISBN 0-405-10816-8). Ayer Co Pubs.

Dyrud, Keith P., et al. The Other Catholics. 33.00 (ISBN 0-405-10820-6). Ayer Co Pubs.

Gaffney, James. Newness of Life: A Modern Introduction to Catholic Ethics. LC 79-84404. 360p. 1979. pap. 6.95 (ISBN 0-8091-2202-2). Paulist Pr.

Greeley, Andrew & Durkin, Mary. Angry Catholic Women. 1984. pap. 15.95 (ISBN 0-88347-165-5). Thomas More.

Hoge, Dean R., et al. Converts, Dropouts, Returnees: A Study of Religious Change among Catholics. LC 81-15351. 200p. 1981. 14.95 (ISBN 0-8298-0483-8); pap. 7.95 (ISBN 0-8298-0487-0). Pilgrim NY.

Lawrence, Emeric A. The Ministry of Believers. 24p. (Orig.). 1982. pap. text ed. 1.25 (ISBN 0-8146-1276-8). Liturgical Pr.

Lund, Candida, ed. If I Were Pope. 1987. 11.95 (ISBN 0-88347-187-6). Thomas More.

McIntyre, Marie. Female & Catholic: A Journal of Mind & Heart. 80p. (Orig.). 1986. pap. 3.95 (ISBN 0-89622-307-8). Twenty-Third.

McNamee, Fintan, ed. Psychology of the Catholic Intellectual. (Synthesis Ser.). 1967. pap. 0.75 (ISBN 0-8199-0241-1, L38669). Franciscan Herald.

Moran, Bob. A Closer Look at Catholicism: A Guide for Protestants. 192p. 1986. 12.95 (ISBN 0-8499-0514-1, 0514-1). Word Bks.

Morriss, Frank. The Catholic As Citizen. 141p. 1980. 6.95 (ISBN 0-8199-0775-8). Franciscan Herald.

Palau, Gabriel. The Active Catholic. LC 84-50405. 224p. 1984. pap. 4.00 (ISBN 0-89555-238-8). TAN Bks Pubs.

Peyret, Raymond. Marthe Robin: The Cross & the Joy. Faulhaber, Clare W., tr. from Fr. LC 83-15591. (Illus.). 135p. 1983. pap. 6.95 (ISBN 0-8189-0464-X). Alba.

Pieper, Josef & Raskop, Heinrich. What Catholics Believe: A Primer of the Catholic Faith. Van Heurck, Jan, tr. LC 82-1411. 116p. 1983. 8.50 (ISBN 0-8199-0796-0). Franciscan Herald.

The Proceedings of the Grisons in the Year 1618. LC 78-171760. (English Experience Ser.: No. 383). 94p. Repr. of 1619 ed. 14.00 (ISBN 90-221-0383-8). Walter J Johnson.

Ratzinger, Joseph. Daughter Zion. McDermott, John M., tr. from Ger. LC 82-84579. Orig. Title: Tochter Zion. 83p. (Orig.). 1983. pap. 5.95 (ISBN 0-89870-026-4). Ignatius Pr.

Scott, Thomas. The Interpreter, Wherein Three Principal Terms of State Are Clearly Unfolded. LC 74-80194. (English Experience Ser.: No. 673). 1974. Repr. of 1624 ed. 3.50 (ISBN 90-221-0281-5). Walter J Johnson.

Simms, Carolynne. Letters from a Roman Catholic. 27p. 1987. pap. 3.00 (ISBN 0-911826-11-4). Am Atheist.

Taylor, Bill. A Tale of Two Cities: The Mormons-Catholics. 1981. pap. 5.50 (ISBN 0-933046-02-2). Little Red Hen.

To the Youth of the World. 64p. 1985. pap. 3.95 (ISBN 1-55586-962-9). US Catholic.

Tomczak, Larry. Clap Your Hands! LC 73-88241. 143p. 1973. pap. 4.95 (ISBN 0-88270-073-1). Bridge Pub.

Toon, Peter. Protestants & Catholics: A Guide to Understanding the Differences. 160p. (Orig.). 1984. pap. 5.95 (ISBN 0-89283-188-X). Servant.

Walsh, James J. Catholic Churchmen in Science, First Ser. facs. ed. LC 68-16985. (Essay Index Reprint Ser). 1906. 19.00 (ISBN 0-8369-0971-2). Ayer Co Pubs.

--Catholic Churchmen in Science, Second Ser. facs. ed. LC 67-22126. (Essay Index Reprint Ser.). 1909. 19.00 (ISBN 0-8369-1387-6). Ayer Co Pubs.

--Catholic Churchmen in Science. Third Ser. facs. ed. LC 67-22126. (Essay Index Reprint Ser). 1917. 19.00 (ISBN 0-8369-0972-0). Ayer Co Pubs.

Whitcomb, Paul. Confession of a Roman Catholic. 55p. 1985. pap. 1.25 (ISBN 0-89555-281-7). Tan Bks Pubs.

CATHOLICS IN AUSTRIA

Diamant, Alfred. Austrian Catholics & the First Republic: Democracy, Capitalism, & the Social Order, 1918-1934. LC 60-5745. pap. 84.30 (ISBN 0-317-09404-1, 2015226). Bks Demand UMI.

CATHOLICS IN CANADA

Fenwick, Benedict J. Memoirs to Serve for the Future Ecclesiastical History of the Diocese of Boston. McCarthy, Joseph M., ed. LC 78-64366. (Monograph: No. 35). (Illus.). 270p. 1979. 10.95x (ISBN 0-686-65388-2). US Cath Hist.

Pritchett, John P. Black Robe & Buckskin. 1960. 12.95x (ISBN 0-8084-0063-0); pap. 8.95 (ISBN 0-8084-0064-9). New Coll U Pr.

CATHOLICS IN ENGLAND

Bossy, John. The English Catholic Community, 1570-1850. (Illus.). 1976. 39.95x (ISBN 0-19-519847-6); pap. 5.95x (ISBN 0-19-285148-9). Oxford U Pr.

Campbell, Kenneth L. The Intellectual Struggle of the English Catholics in the Seventeenth Century: The Catholic Dilemma. LC 86-23893. (Texts & Studies in Religion Ser.: Vol. 30). 256p. 1986. text ed. 49.95 (ISBN 0-88946-818-4). E Mellen.

Clancy, Thomas H. Papist Pamphleteers. LC 64-14078. (Jesuit Studies). 1964. 4.95 (ISBN 0-8294-0013-3). Loyola.

Copley, Thomas. Letters of Sir Thomas Copley to Queen Elizabeth & Her Ministers. Christie, Richard C., ed. LC 74-80263. (Research & Source Works Ser.: No. 631). 1971. Repr. lib. bdg. 32.00 (ISBN 0-8337-0655-1). B Franklin.

Devlin, Christopher. Hamlet's Divinity & Other Essays. facs. ed. (Essay Index Reprint Ser). 1963. 15.00 (ISBN 0-8369-1915-7). Ayer Co Pubs.

Donne, John. Pseudo-Martyr. LC 74-16215. 450p. 1974. 60.00x (ISBN 0-8201-1140-6). Schol Facsimiles.

Franklin, R. W. Nineteenth-Century Churches: The History of a New Catholicism in Wurttemberg, England & France. McNeill, William H., ed. 700p. 1987. lib. bdg. 105.00 (ISBN 0-8240-8067-X). Garland Pub.

Havran, Martin J. The Catholics in Caroline England. 1962. 17.50x (ISBN 0-8047-0112-1). Stanford U Pr.

Hibbard, Caroline M. Charles I & the Popish Plot. LC 81-23075. ix, 342p. 1983. 30.00x (ISBN 0-8078-1520-9). U of NC Pr.

Holmes, Peter. Resistance & Compromise: The Political Thought of the Elizabethan Catholics. LC 81-17990. (Cambridge Studies in the History & Theory of Politics). 296p. 1982. 44.50 (ISBN 0-521-24343-2). Cambridge U Pr.

Horey, Adrian. The Catholic Subjects of Elizabeth I. LC 78-312404. pap. 60.00 (ISBN 0-317-20042-9, 2023264). Bks Demand UMI.

Hornsby-Smith, Michael P. Roman Catholics in England: Studies in Social Structure Since the Second World War. (Illus.). 288p. 1987. 29.50 (ISBN 0-521-30313-3). Cambridge U Pr.

Kirk, John. Biographies of English Catholics in the Eighteenth Century. xvi, 293p. 1985. Repr. of 1901 ed. lib. bdg. 39.00 (ISBN 0-932051-45-6, Pub. by Am Repr Serv). Am Biog Serv.

Knox, Wilfred L. The Catholic Movement in the Church of England. 1979. Repr. of 1923 ed. lib. bdg. 30.00 (ISBN 0-8495-3029-6). Arden Lib.

Leatherbarrow, J. Stanley. The Lancashire Elizabethan Recusants. Repr. of 1947 ed. 24.00 (ISBN 0-384-31910-6). Johnson Repr.

Matthew, David. Catholicism in England: The Portraits of a Minority, Its Culture & Tradition. 295p. 1984. Repr. of 1948 ed. lib. bdg. 45.00 (ISBN 0-89984-946-6). Century Bookbindery.

Norman, Edward. Roman Catholicism in England from the Elizabethan Settlement to the Second Vatican Council. (OPUS). 160p. 1985. 18.95x (ISBN 0-19-219181-0); pap. 9.95 (ISBN 0-19-281935-6). Oxford U Pr.

Rose, Elliot. Cases of Conscience: Alternatives Open to Recusants & Puritans under Elizabeth I & James I. LC 74-76947. pap. 68.50 (2027243). Bks Demand UMI.

Ward, Maisie, ed. English Way: Studies in English Sanctity from St. Bede to Newman. facs. ed. LC 68-29253. (Essay Index Reprint Ser). 1968. Repr. of 1933 ed. 17.75 (ISBN 0-8369-0975-5). Ayer Co Pubs.

Ward, Wilfrid P. Ten Personal Studies. LC 73-107742. (Essay Index Reprint Ser.). 1908. 21.00 (ISBN 0-8369-1584-4). Ayer Co Pubs.

CATHOLICS IN FRANCE

Doering, Bernard. Jacques Maritain & the French Catholic Intellectuals. LC 82-40377. 288p. 1983. text ed. 22.95. U of Notre Dame Pr.

Fitzpatrick, Brian. Catholic Royalism in the Department of the Gard: 1814-1852. LC 82-14564. (Illus.). 224p. 1983. 49.50 (ISBN 0-521-22454-3). Cambridge U Pr.

Franklin, R. W. Nineteenth-Century Churches: The History of a New Catholicism in Wurttemberg, England & France. McNeill, William H., ed. 700p. 1987. lib. bdg. 105.00 (ISBN 0-8240-8067-X). Garland Pub.

Sedgwick, Alexander C. Ralliement in French Politics, Eighteen Ninety to Eighteen Ninety-Eight. LC 65-12828. (Historical Studies: No. 74). 1965. 14.00x (ISBN 0-674-74751-8). Harvard U Pr.

Sutton, Michael. Nationalism, Positivism & Catholicism: The Politics of Charles Maurras & French Catholics, 1890-1914. LC 82-4360. (Cambridge Studies in the History & Theory of Politics). 320p. 1983. 47.50 (ISBN 0-521-22868-9). Cambridge U Pr.

CATHOLICS IN GERMANY

Dietrich, Donald J. Catholic Citizens in the Third Reich: Psyco-Social Principles & Moral Reasoning. 385p. 1987. 39.95 (ISBN 0-88738-131-6). Transaction Bks.

Franklin, R. W. Nineteenth-Century Churches: The History of a New Catholicism in Wurttemberg, England & France. McNeill, William H., ed. 700p. 1987. lib. bdg. 105.00 (ISBN 0-8240-8067-X). Garland Pub.

Sperber, Johnathan. Popular Catholicism in Nineteenth-Century Germany. LC 84-42559. 552p. 1984. text ed. 45.00x (ISBN 0-691-05432-0). Princeton U Pr.

CATHOLICS IN IRELAND

Biever, Bruce F. Religion, Culture & Values: A Cross-Cultural Analysis of Motivational Factors in Native Irish & American Irish Catholicism. LC 76-6322. (Irish Americans Ser). 1976. 62.00 (ISBN 0-405-09319-5). Ayer Co Pubs.

Biggs-Davison, John & Chowdharay-Best, George. The Cross of Saint Patrick: The Catholic Unionist Tradition in Ireland. 1985. 50.80x (ISBN 0-946041-26-1, Pub. by Kensal Pr UK). State Mutual Bk.

Corish, Patrick. The Irish Catholic Experience. 1985. 25.00 (ISBN 0-317-42754-7). M Glazier.

Kirby, Peadar. Is Irish Catholicism Dying? 93p. 1984. pap. 5.95 (ISBN 0-87061-112-7). Chr Classics.

Purcell, Mary. Matt Talbot: His Life & Times. 250p. 1977. 7.00 (ISBN 0-8199-0657-3). Franciscan Herald.

Reynolds, James A. Catholic Emancipation Crisis in Ireland, 1823-1829. Repr. of 1954 ed. lib. bdg. 22.50x (ISBN 0-8371-3141-3, RECE). Greenwood.

CATHOLICS IN ITALY

Francis, George. She Died, She Lives: In Search of Maria Orsola. 176p. 1977. pap. 3.95 (ISBN 0-232-51392-9). Attic Pr.

CATHOLICS IN LITERATURE

Carver, George. The Catholic Tradition in English Literature. 59.95 (ISBN 0-87968-820-3). Gordon Pr.

Doyle, Sr. Rosa. Catholic Atmosphere in Marie Von Ebner Eschenbach: Its Use As a Literary Device. LC 70-140040. (Catholic University Studies in German Ser.: No. 6). Repr. of 1936 ed. 18.00 (ISBN 0-404-50226-1). AMS Pr.

Hutton, Edward. Catholicism & English Literature. LC 76-26671. 1942. lib. bdg. 30.00 (ISBN 0-8414-4926-0). Folcroft.

Stratford, Philip. Faith & Fiction: Creative Process in Greene & Mauriac. 1964. pap. 9.95x (ISBN 0-268-00379-3). U of Notre Dame Pr.

CATHOLICS IN THE UNITED STATES

Benedict, Samuel O. Catholicism & Americanism: The Vision of a Conflict? (Illus.). 147p. 1987. 98.85 (ISBN 0-89266-590-4). Am Classical Coll Pr.

Biever, Bruce F. Religion, Culture & Values: A Cross-Cultural Analysis of Motivational Factors in Native Irish & American Irish Catholicism. LC 76-6322. (Irish Americans Ser). 1976. 62.00 (ISBN 0-405-09319-5). Ayer Co Pubs.

Billington, Ray A. The Origins of Nativism in the United States, 1800-1844. LC 73-19129. (Politics & People Ser.). (Illus.). 716p. 1974. Repr. 52.00x (ISBN 0-405-05854-3). Ayer Co Pubs.

Colligan, John, et al. The Extended Catholic Family: Rediscovering Our Catholic Identity Through Intimate Relationships with Fellow Catholics. LC 83-62198. 110p. (Orig.). 1983. pap. text ed. 4.95 (ISBN 0-911905-06-5). Past & Mat Rene Ctr.

Congress of Colored Catholics of the United States. Three Catholic Afro-American Congresses. 14.00 (ISBN 0-405-10863-X, 11829). Ayer Co Pubs.

Conley, Patrick T. & Smith, Matthew J. Catholicism in Rhode Island: The Formative Era. LC 76-62863. 1976. 12.50 (ISBN 0-917012-13-5). RI Pubns Soc.

Delaney, John J. Dictionary of American Catholic Biography. LC 83-25524. 624p. 1984. 24.95 (ISBN 0-385-17878-6). Doubleday.

Dolan, Jay P., ed. The American Catholic Tradition. 1893.50 (ISBN 0-405-10810-9). Ayer Co Pubs.

Ellis, John T. American Catholicism. 2nd ed. Boorstin, Daniel J., ed. LC 69-19274. (Chicago History of American Civilization Ser.). 1969. pap. 10.00x (ISBN 0-226-20556-8, CHAC5). U of Chicago Pr.

Ellis, John T. & Trisco, Robert. A Guide to American Catholic History. 2nd, rev. ed. LC 81-17585. 265p. 1982. lib. bdg. 29.85 (ISBN 0-87436-318-7). ABC-Clio.

Flynn, George Q. Roosevelt & Romanism: Catholics & American Diplomacy, 1937-1945. LC 75-35343. (Contributions in American History: No. 47). 272p. 1976. lib. bdg. 29.95 (ISBN 0-8371-8581-5, FRR/). Greenwood.

Foley, Albert S. God's Men of Color: The Colored Catholic Priest of the U. S. 1854-1954. LC 69-18569. (American Negro: His History & Literature, Ser. No. 2). 1969. Repr. of 1955 ed. 14.00 (ISBN 0-405-01864-9). Ayer Co Pubs.

Greeley, Andrew M. The American Catholic: A Social Portrait. LC 76-7683. (Illus.). pap. 9.95x (ISBN 0-465-09733-2, TB-5058). Basic.

--American Catholics Since the Council: An Unauthorized Report. (Illus.). 240p. (Orig.). 1985. pap. 14.95 (ISBN 0-88347-191-4). Thomas More.

Halsey, William M. The Survival of American Innocence: Catholicism in An Era of Disillusionment, 1920-1940. LC 79-63360. (Studies in American Catholicism: No. 2). 1979. 19.95x (ISBN 0-268-01699-2, 85-16999). U of Notre Dame Pr.
Hanna, Mary. Catholics & American Politics. LC 79-11035. 1979. text ed. 16.50x (ISBN 0-674-10325-4). Harvard U Pr.
Hennessey, James. Catholics in the Promised Land of the Saints. LC 81-80935. (Pere Marquette Lecture Ser.). 100p. 1981. 7.95 (ISBN 0-87462-536-X). Marquette.
Historical Records Survey, WPA Staff. Inventory of the Roman Catholic Church Records of New Hampshire. 19p. 1985. pap. 3.50 (ISBN 0-935207-18-X). DanBury Hse Bks.
Houtart, Francois. Aspects Sociologiques du Catholicisme Americain: Vie Urbaine et Institutions Religieuses. 30.00 (ISBN 0-405-10835-4, 11841). Ayer Co Pubs.
Ives, J. Moss. Ark & the Dove: The Beginnings of Civil & Religious Liberties in America. LC 76-79200. (Illus.). 1969. Repr. of 1936 ed. 32.50x (ISBN 0-8154-0293-7). Cooper Sq.
Kelly, Mary G. Catholic Immigrant Colonization Projects in the United States, 1815-1860. LC 74-145485. (The American Immigration Library). x, 290p. 1971. Repr. of 1939 ed. lib. bdg. 17.95x (ISBN 0-89198-016-4). Ozer.
Kennedy, Eugene. Now & Future Church. LC 83-20574. 216p. 1985. pap. 7.95 (ISBN 0-385-23236-5, Im). Doubleday.
--The Now & Future Church: The Psychology of Being an American Catholic. LC 83-20574. 216p. 1984. 13.95 (ISBN 0-385-19040-9). Doubleday.
Kotre, John N. The Best of Times, the Worst of Times: Andrew Greeley & American Catholicism, 1950-1975. LC 78-14224. 256p. 1978. 21.95x (ISBN 0-88229-380-X). Nelson-Hall.
Kuzniewski, Anthony. Faith & Fatherland. 183p. 1980. text ed. 16.95 (ISBN 0-268-00948-1). U of Notre Dame Pr.
McAvoy, Thomas T. Catholic Church in Indiana, Seventeen Eighty-Nine to Eighteen Thirty-Four. LC 41-6425. (Columbia University. Studies in the Social Sciences: No. 471). Repr. of 1940 ed. 20.00 (ISBN 0-404-51471-5). AMS Pr.
McDonald, Donald. Catholics in Conversation: Seventeen Interviews with Leading American Catholics. LC 78-5695. 1978. Repr. of 1960 ed. lib. bdg. cancelled (ISBN 0-313-20486-1, MCCC). Greenwood.
McNally, Michael J. Catholicism in South Florida, 1868-1968. LC 84-7389. 334p. (Orig.). 1984. pap. 13.95 (ISBN 0-8130-0788-7). U Presses Fla.
McNeal, Patricia F. The American Catholic Peace Movement, 1928-1972. 32.00 (ISBN 0-405-10840-0, 11820). Ayer Co Pubs.
Mosqueda, Lawrence J. Chicanos, Catholicism & Political Ideology. 228p. (Orig.). 1986. lib. bdg. 24.50 (ISBN 0-8191-5318-4); pap. text ed. 12.75 (ISBN 0-8191-5319-2). U Pr of Amer.
Munnick, Harriet D. Catholic Church Records of the Pacific Northwest: Oregon City, Salem & Jacksonville. LC 84-70844. (Illus.). 1984. 25.00 (ISBN 0-8323-0429-8). Binford-Metropolitan.
Munnick, Harriet D., compiled by. Catholic Church Records of the Pacific Northwest: Roseburg & Portland. LC 85-63221. (Illus.). 440p. 1986. 25.00 (ISBN 0-8323-0447-6). Binford-Metropolitan.
Nolan, Hugh J., ed. Pastoral Letters of the United States Catholic Bishops, 1975-1983, Vol. IV. 616p. 1984. pap. 24.95 (ISBN 1-55586-875-4). US Catholic.
--Pastoral Letters of the United States Catholic Bishops, 1962-1974, Vol. III. 511p. 1984. pap. 24.95 (ISBN 1-55586-870-3). US Catholic.
--Pastoral Letters of the United States Catholic Bishops, 1941-1961, Vol. II. 271p. 1984. pap. 24.95 (ISBN 1-55586-885-1). US Catholic.
--Pastoral Letters of the United States Catholic Bishops, 1792-1940, Vol. I. 487p. 1984. pap. 24.95 (ISBN 1-55586-880-0). US Catholic.
O'Brien, David J. The Renewal of American Catholicism. LC 72-85825. 320p. 1974. pap. 4.95 (ISBN 0-8091-1828-9). Paulist Pr.
Olson, James S. Catholic Immigrants in America. 260p. 1986. 26.95x01568129x (ISBN 0-8304-1037-6). Nelson-Hall.
Parot, Joseph J. Polish Catholics in Chicago, 1850-1920: A Religious History. LC 81-11297. 298p. 22.50 (ISBN 0-87580-081-5); pap. 10.00 (ISBN 0-87580-527-2). N Ill U Pr.
Piehl, Mel. Breaking Bread: The Catholic Worker & the Origin of Catholic Radicalism in America. LC 82-10327. 233p. 1982. 24.95 (ISBN 0-87722-257-6). Temple U Pr.
Procko, Bohdan P. Ukrainian Catholics in America: A History. LC 81-43718. 184p. (Orig.). 1982. lib. bdg. 27.75 (ISBN 0-8191-2409-5); pap. text ed. 11.50 (ISBN 0-8191-2410-9). U Pr of Amer.
Roohan, James E. American Catholics & the Social Question, 1865-1900. LC 76-6364. (Irish Americans Ser). 1976. 37.50 (ISBN 0-405-09356-X). Ayer Co Pubs.
Ruskowski, Leo F. French Emigre Priests in the United States (1791-1815) LC 73-3586. (Catholic University of America. Studies in American Church History: No. 32). Repr. of 1940 ed. 21.00 (ISBN 0-404-57782-2). AMS Pr.
Schwartz, Michael. The Persistent Prejudice: Anti-Catholicism in America. LC 84-60746. 240p. 1984. pap. 6.95 (ISBN 0-87973-715-8, 715). Our Sunday Visitor.
Shanabruch, Charles. Chicago's Catholics: An Evolution of an American Identity. LC 80-53071. (Studies in American Catholicism: Vol. 4). 288p. 1981. text ed. 22.95 (ISBN 0-268-01840-5). U of Notre Dame Pr.
Shaughnessy, Gerald. Has the Immigrant Kept the Faith. LC 76-83438. (Religion in America Ser). 1969. Repr. of 1925 ed. 20.00 (ISBN 0-405-00262-9). Ayer Co Pubs.
Sheed, Wilfrid. Frank & Maisie: A Memoir with Parents. 304p. 1986. pap. 7.95 (ISBN 0-671-62813-5, Touchstone Bks). S&S.
Thomas, John L. The American Catholic Family. LC 80-15221. (Illus.). xii, 471p. 1980. Repr. of 1956 ed. lib. bdg. 37.50x (ISBN 0-313-22473-0, THAC). Greenwood.
Tristano, Richard. What Southern Catholics Need to Know about Evangelical Religion. 1984. pap. 3.00x (ISBN 0-914422-14-6). Glenmary Res Ctr.
Whyte, John H. Catholics in Western Democracies: A Study in Political Behavior. 1981. 22.50x (ISBN 0-312-12446-5). St Martin.

CATS (IN RELIGION, FOLK-LORE, ETC.)

Howey, M. Oldfield. The Cat in the Mysteries of Religion & Magic. LC 81-51289. (Illus.). 254p. 1982. Repr. of 1930 ed. 12.50 (ISBN 0-8048-1360-4). C E Tuttle.

CAVE TEMPLES

Burgess, James & Fergusson, James. The Cave Temples of India. (Illus.). 1969. text ed. 57.50x. Coronet Bks.
Kail, Owen C. Buddist Cave Temples of India. (Illus.). xi, 138p. 1981. text ed. 25.00x (ISBN 0-86590-043-4, Pub. by Taraporevala India). Apt Bks.
Wauchope, Robert S. Buddhist Cave Temples of India. LC 78-70139. Repr. of 1933 ed. 34.50 (ISBN 0-404-17409-4). AMS Pr.

CAYCE, EDGAR, 1877-1945

Cayce, Hugh L. Venture Inward: Edgar Cayce's Story & the Mysteries of the Unconscious Mind. LC 85-42772. 256p. 1985. pap. 4.95 (ISBN 0-06-250131-3, HarpR). Har-Row.
Drummond, Richard H. Unto the Churches: Jesus Christ, Christianity, & the Edgar Cayce Readings. 1978. pap. 7.95 (ISBN 0-87604-102-0). ARE Pr.
Irion, J. Everett. Interpreting the Revelation with Edgar Cayce. 440p. 1982. 19.95 (ISBN 0-87604-137-3). ARE Pr.
Leichtman, Robert R. Edgar Cayce Returns. (From Heaven to Earth Ser.). (Illus.). 112p. (Orig.). 1978. pap. 3.50 (ISBN 0-89804-052-3). Ariel OH.
Lewis, Roger. Color & the Edgar Cayce Readings. 48p. 1973. pap. 3.50 (ISBN 0-87604-068-7). Are Pr.
Sparrow, Lynn E. Edgar Cayce & the Born Again Christian. 237p. (Orig.). 1985. pap. 6.95 (ISBN 0-87604-158-6). ARE Pr.
Turner, Gladys D. & St. Clair, Mae G. One Hundred Twenty-Three Questions & Answers: From the Edgar Cayce Readings. rev. ed. 58p. 1974. pap. 3.95 (ISBN 0-87604-073-3). ARE Pr.

CECILIA, SAINT

Buehrle, Marie C. Who Are You: The Life of St. Cecilia. LC 70-158918. 1971. pap. 2.95 (ISBN 0-913382-07-8, 101-7). Prow Bks-Franciscan.
Kirsch, Johann P. Heilige Caecilia in der Roemischen Kirche Des Altertums. 1910. pap. 8.00 (ISBN 0-384-29610-6). Johnson Repr.

CELIBACY

see also Patarines; Virginity; Vows

Baars, Conrad W. A Priest for Now: Masculine & Celibate. LC 72-87091. (Synthesis Ser). 1972. pap. 1.25 (ISBN 0-8199-0375-2). Franciscan Herald.
Brown, Gabrielle. The New Celibacy: Why More Men & Women Are Abstaining from Sex & Enjoying It. 300p. 1980. 10.95 (ISBN 0-07-008430-0). McGraw.
Clark, Keith. Being Sexual...& Celibate. LC 85-73158. 184p. (Orig.). 1986. pap. 4.95 (ISBN 0-87793-329-4). Ave Maria.
Constantelos, D. J. Marriage, Sexuality & Celibacy: A Greek Orthodox Perspective. 1975. pap. 4.95 (ISBN 0-937032-15-8). Light&Life Pub Co MN.
Ford, J. Massingberd. Trilogy on Wisdom & Celibacy. 1967. 16.95x (ISBN 0-268-00285-1). U of Notre Dame Pr.
Foresi, Pascal. Celibacy Put to the Gospel Test. 33p. 1969. pap. 1.15 (ISBN 0-911782-16-8). New City.
Gallagher, Chuch & Vandenburg, Thomas. Celibacy Myth. 144p. 1987. 12.95 (ISBN 0-8245-0814-9). Crossroad NY.
Goergen, Don. The Sexual Celibate. 272p. 1975. 5.00 (ISBN 0-8164-0268-X, HarpR). Har-Row.
Hebert, Albert J. Priestly Celibacy: Recurrent Battle & Lasting Values. 198p. 1971. 6.00 (ISBN 0-912414-01-4). Lumen Christi.
Hickey, Raymond. A Case for an Auxiliary Priesthood. LC 81-16950. 160p. (Orig.). 1982. pap. 1.99 (ISBN 0-88344-021-0). Orbis Bks.
Huddleston, Mary A., ed. Celibate Loving: Encounter in Three Dimensions. (Orig.). 1984. pap. 9.95 (ISBN 0-8091-2588-9). Paulist Pr.
Kiesling, Christopher. Celibacy, Prayer & Friendship: A Making-Sense-Out-of-Life Approach. LC 77-25084. 1978. pap. 7.95 (ISBN 0-8189-0365-1). Alba.
Knight, David M. Chastity: Who Lives It. LC 85-19516. 32p. (Orig.). 1985. pap. 3.95 (ISBN 0-915488-10-8, BV4647.C5K57). Clarity Pub.
McNamara, Jo Ann. A New Song: Celibate Women in the First Three Christian Centuries. LC 83-10852. (Women & History Ser.: Nos. 6 & 7). 154p. 1983. text ed. 29.95 (ISBN 0-86656-249-4, B249). Haworth Pr.
--A New Song: Celibate Women in the First Three Christian Centuries. LC 85-8505. 154p. 1985. pap. 8.95 (ISBN 0-918393-17-5). Harrington Pk.
Melanchthon, Philip. A Very Godly Defense, Defending the Marriage of Priests. Beuchame, L., tr. LC 76-25643. (English Experience Ser.: No. 199). 1969. Repr. of 1541 ed. 8.00 (ISBN 90-221-0199-1). Walter J Johnson.
Theology of Marriage & Celibacy. 9.00 (ISBN 0-8198-7333-0); 8.00 (ISBN 0-8198-7334-9). Dghtrs St Paul.
Thomas, Gordon. Desire & Denial: Celibacy & the Church. 1986. 19.95 (ISBN 0-316-84097-1). Little.
Von Hilderbrand, Dietrich. Celibacy & the Crisis of Faith. 1971. 4.95 (ISBN 0-8199-0428-7). Franciscan Herald.

CELTIC CHURCH

Chadwick, Nora K., et al. Studies in the Early British Church. LC 73-673. vii, 374p. 1973. Repr. of 1958 ed. 32.50 (ISBN 0-208-01315-6, Archon). Shoe String.
Glunz, Hans. Britannien und Bibeltext. Repr. of 1930 ed. 16.00 (ISBN 0-384-18950-4). Johnson Repr.
Leathem, Diana. They Built on Rock: The Story of the Celtic Christian Church. 1977. lib. bdg. 59.95 (ISBN 0-8490-2743-8). Gordon Pr.
Pochin-Mould, Daphne. Irish Pilgrimage. 1957. 12.95 (ISBN 0-8159-5816-1). Devin.
Rhys, John. Lectures on the Origin & Growth of Religion as Illustrated by Celtic Heathendom. LC 77-27165. (Hibbert Lectures: 1886). Repr. of 1898 ed. 53.00 (ISBN 0-404-60407-2). AMS Pr.
Toland, John. The History of the Celtic Religion & Learning. LC 74-16159. 1974. Repr. lib. bdg. 40.00 (ISBN 0-8414-8553-4). Folcroft.
Warren, Frederick E. Liturgy & Ritual of the Celtic Church. 1987. 39.50 (ISBN 0-85115-473-5); pap. 12.50. Eastern Orthodox.

CELTS

see also Druids and Druidism

Anwyl, Edward. Celtic Religion: In Prechristian Times. 1977. lib. bdg. 59.95 (ISBN 0-8490-1590-1). Gordon Pr.
Green, Miranda. The Gods of the Celts. LC 86-22135. (Illus.). 224p. 1986. 27.50x (ISBN 0-389-20672-5). B&N Imports.
MacCulloch, John A. The Celtic & Scandinavian Religions. LC 72-11739. 180p. 1973. Repr. of 1948 ed. lib. bdg. 22.50x (ISBN 0-8371-6705-1, MCSR). Greenwood.
--The Religion of the Ancient Celts. LC 77-4127. 1977. lib. bdg. 52.50 (ISBN 0-8414-5998-3). Folcroft.
Webster, Graham. Celtic Religion in Roman Britain. LC 86-26532. (Illus.). 176p. 1987. 30.00 (ISBN 0-389-20686-5). B&N Imports.
Wentz, W. Y. The Fairy-Faith in Celtic Countries. LC 77-12812. 1973. pap. text ed. 15.00x (ISBN 0-391-00773-4). Humanities.

CEMETERIES

see also Catacombs; Epitaphs; Tombs

Bushnell, David L., Jr. Native Cemeteries & Forms of Burial East of the Mississippi. Repr. of 1920 ed. 29.00x (ISBN 0-403-03658-5). Scholarly.
Child, Mark. Discovering Churchyards. (Discovering Ser.: No. 268). (Illus.). 80p. 1983. pap. 3.50 (ISBN 0-85263-603-2, Pub. by Shire Pubns England). Seven Hills Bks.
Curl, James S. The Victorian Celebration of Death: The Architecture & Planning of the 19th-Century Necropolis. LC 70-184048. 222p. 1972. 35.00x (ISBN 0-8103-2000-2). Gale.
Dawes, Jean D. & Magilton, J. R. Cemetery of St. Helen-on-the-Walls, Aldwark, York. (Archaeology of York Ser: Vol. 12). 132p. 1980. pap. text ed. 25.00x (ISBN 0-900312-88-2, Pub. by Coun Brit Archaeology). Humanities.
Hirsh, Ethel S. Jewish Buildings & Cemeteries Guide to Visual Resources: International Holdings in Israel, Vol. I. 75p. 1982. pap. 10.00 (ISBN 0-943376-17-3). Magnes Mus.
Hudson, Kenneth. Churchyards & Cemeteries. (Illus.). 48p. 1984. laminated boards 9.95 (ISBN 0-370-30543-4, Pub. by Bodley Head). Salem Hse Pubs.
Levy, B. H. Savannah's Old Jewish Community Cemeteries. LC 83-1045. vii, 118p. 1983. 10.95 (ISBN 0-86554-076-4, H68). Mercer Univ Pr.
Shaver, Elizabeth D. Watervliet Shaker Cemetery, Albany, N. Y. 1986. pap. 2.50. Shaker Her Soc.
Stevens, Revalee R. & Steven, Robert K. The Protestant Cemetery of Rome. LC 81-84484. (North American Records in Italy). (Illus.). 110p. (Orig.). 1982. pap. 9.00 (ISBN 0-88127-003-2). Oracle Pr LA.

CENA, ULTIMA

see Lord's Supper

CENSORSHIP

Daily, Jay E. The Anatomy of Censorship. (Books in Library & Information Science: Vol. 6). 424p. 1973. 50.50 (ISBN 0-8247-6065-4). Dekker.
Ernst, M. L. & Lindey, A. The Censor Marches on. LC 73-164512. (Civil Liberties in American History Ser.). 346p. 1971. Repr. of 1940 ed. lib. bdg. 39.50 (ISBN 0-306-70295-9). Da Capo.
Gordon, George N. Erotic Communications: Studies in Sex, Sin & Censorship. new ed. (Humanistic Studies in the Communication Arts). (Illus.). 352p. 1980. 21.00x (ISBN 0-8038-1959-5, Communication Arts); pap. 13.00x (ISBN 0-8038-1960-9). Hastings.
Ide, Arthur F. Evangelical Terrorism: Censorship, Jerry Falwell, Pat Robertson & the Seamy Side of Christian Fundamentalism. LC 86-22013. xxxi, 195p. 1986. pap. 12.95 (ISBN 0-938659-01-4). Scholars Bks.
Putnam, George H. The Censorship of the Church of Rome, 2 vols. 200.00 (ISBN 0-87968-826-2). Gordon Pr.
The Roman Catholic Church Index of Prohibited Books As Issued by Pope Leo XIII. 201p. 1985. Repr. of 1907 ed. 127.55 (ISBN 0-89901-199-3). Found Class Reprints.
Thomas, Cal. Book Burning. LC 83-70319. 180p. 1983. pap. 5.95 (ISBN 0-89107-284-5, Crossway Bks). Good News.

CENTRAL JEWISH INSTITUTE, NEW YORK

Berkson, Isaac B. Theories of Americanization: A Critical Study. LC 77-87743. (American Education: Its Men, Institutions & Ideas, Ser. 1). 1969. Repr. of 1920 ed. 15.00 (ISBN 0-405-01387-6). Ayer Co Pubs.
--Theories of Americanization: A Critical Study, with Special Reference to the Jewish Group. LC 78-176558. (Columbia University. Teachers College. Contributions to Education: No. 109). Repr. of 1920 ed. 22.50 (ISBN 0-404-55109-2). AMS Pr.

CEREMONIES

see Rites and Ceremonies

CHAGALL, MARC, 1887-

Alexander, Sidney. Marc Chagall: A Biography. (Illus.). 525p. 1979. 26.95x (ISBN 0-8464-1196-2). Beekman Pubs.
Rosensaft, Jean. Chagall & the Bible. (Illus.). 160p. 1987. 24.95 (ISBN 0-87663-653-9). Universe.

CHAKRAS (THEOSOPHY)

Gunther, Bernard. Energy Ecstasy & Your Seven Vital Shakras. LC 83-8822. 200p. 1983. lib. bdg. 21.95x (ISBN 0-89370-666-3). Borgo Pr.
Johari, Harish. Chakras: Energy Centers of Transformation. (Illus.). 192p. 1987. pap. 14.95 (ISBN 0-89281-054-8). Inner Tradit.
Lansdowne, Zachary F. The Chakras & Esoteric Healing. LC 84-51108. 1986. pap. 8.95 (ISBN 0-87728-584-5). Weiser.
Leadbeater, Charles W. Chakras. 10th ed. 1973. 7.95 (ISBN 0-8356-7016-3). Theos Pub Hse.
--The Chakras. LC 73-147976. (Illus.). 148p. 1972. pap. 5.75 (ISBN 0-8356-0422-5, Quest). Theos Pub Hse.
Motoyama, Hiroshi. Theories of the Chakras. LC 81-51165. 350p. (Orig.). 1982. pap. 8.95 (ISBN 0-8356-0551-5, Quest). Theos Pub Hse.
Rendel, Peter. Introduction to the Chakras. (Paths to Inner Power Ser). (Illus.). 1981. pap. 3.50 (ISBN 0-85030-161-0). Weiser.
Schwarz, Jack. Voluntary Controls: Exercises for Creative Meditation & for Activating the Potential of the Chakras. 1978. pap. 7.95 (ISBN 0-525-47494-3, 0772-230). Dutton.

CHANNING, WILLIAM ELLERY, 1780-1842

Mendelsohn, Jack. Channing: The Reluctant Radical. 2nd ed. 1986. pap. 10.95 (ISBN 0-933840-28-4, Skinner Hse Bks). Unitarian Univ.

CHANTING

see Chants (Buddhist); Chants (Byzantine); Chants (Jewish); Chants (Plain, Gregorian, etc.)

CHANTRIES

Kreider, Alan. English Chantries: The Road to Dissolution. LC 78-12453. (Harvard Historical Studies: No. 97). 1979. 22.50x (ISBN 0-674-25560-7). Harvard U Pr.

Wood-Legh, Kathleen. Perpetual Chantries in Britain. LC 65-28505. pap. 93.30 (ISBN 0-317-26370-6, 2024564). Bks Demand UMI.

CHANTS (BUDDHIST)

Himalayan Institute. Chants from Eternity. (Illus.). 64p. 1977. plastic comb bdg. 4.95 (ISBN 0-89389-033-2). Himalayan Pubs.

Kaufmann, Walter. Tibetan Buddhist Chant: Musical Notations & Interpretations of a Song Book by the Bkah Brgyud Pa & Sa Skya Pa Sects. Norbu, Thubten Jigme, tr. LC 72-85606. (Humanities Ser.: No. 70). 578p. 1975. 25.00x (ISBN 0-253-36017-X). Ind U Pr.

SYDA Foundation. The Nectar of Chanting. 3rd, rev. ed. LC 78-68854. 216p. 7.95 (ISBN 0-914602-16-0). SYDA Found.

CHANTS (BYZANTINE)

Conomos, Dimitri. Byzantine Hymnography & Byzantine Chant. Vaporis, N. M., intro. by. (Nicholas E. Kulukundis Lectures in Hellenism Ser.). 56p. (Orig.). 1984. pap. text ed. 4.00 (ISBN 0-917653-04-1). Hellenic Coll Pr.

CHANTS (HINDU)

see also Hindu Hymns

Chant & Be Happy: Based on Teachings of A. C. Bhaktivedanta Swami. (Illus.). 118p. 2.95 (ISBN 0-89213-118-7). Bhaktivedanta.

Gurbachan Singh Talib. Japuji: The Immortal Prayer-Chant. 1977. 7.00x (ISBN 0-88386-967-5). South Asia Bks.

Howard, Wayne. Samavedic Chant. LC 76-49854. (Illus.). 1977. 50.00x (ISBN 0-300-01956-4). Yale U Pr.

Yogananda, Paramahansa. Cosmic Chants. rev. 6th ed. LC 74-20347. (Illus.). 84p. 1974. flexible bdg 3.50 (ISBN 0-87612-131-8); German ed. 9.00x (ISBN 0-87612-132-6). Self Realization.

CHANTS (JEWISH)

Werner, Eric. The Sacred Bridge. (Music Reprint Ser.). 1979. Repr. of 1959 ed. lib. bdg. 65.00 (ISBN 0-306-79581-7). Da Capo.

CHANTS (PLAIN, GREGORIAN, ETC.)

Berry, Mary, ed. Cantors. LC 78-56178. (Resources of Music Ser.). 1979. pap. 5.95 (ISBN 0-521-22149-8). Cambridge U Pr.

D'Ortigue, J. L. Dictionnaire Liturgique, Historique, et Theorique de Plain Chante de Musique Religieuse. Migne, J. P., ed. (Nouvelle Encyclopedie Theologique Ser.: Vol. 29). (Fr.). 782p. Date not set. Repr. of 1860 ed. lib. bdg. 99.00x (ISBN 0-89241-272-0). Caratzas.

D'Ortigue, M. J. Dictionnaire Liturgique, Historique et Theorique de Plainchant et de Musique d'Eglise. LC 79-155353. (Music Ser). (Fr.). 1971. Repr. of 1854 ed. lib. bdg. 110.00 (ISBN 0-306-70165-0). Da Capo.

Graham, Carolyn. Jazz Chants for Children. (Illus.). 1979. pap. text ed. 7.50x (ISBN 0-19-502496-6); tchrs ed. 10.95x (ISBN 0-19-502497-4); cassette 12.00x (ISBN 0-19-502575-X); tchrs' ed & cassette 16.00x (ISBN 0-19-502576-8). Oxford U Pr.

Iyer, Raghavan, ed. Chants for Contemplation: Shikh Text. (Sacred Texts Ser.). Orig. Title: ADI Granth. 144p. (Orig.). 1984. pap. 8.75 (ISBN 0-88695-030-9). Concord Grove.

Klarmann, Andrew F. Gregorian Chant, a Textbook for Seminaries, Novitiates, & Secondary Schools. (Illus.). ix, 148p. Repr. of 1945 ed. lib. bdg. 22.50x (ISBN 0-8371-9019-3, KLGC). Greenwood.

Pugsley, Richard. Window into Chant. 1987. pap. 5.95 (ISBN 0-941478-50-5). Paraclete Pr.

Soderlund, G. F. & Scott, Samuel H., eds. Examples of Gregorian Chant & Other Sacred Music of the 16th Century. LC 70-129090. (Orig.). 1971. 27.95 (ISBN 0-13-293753-0). P-H.

CHANTS (PLAIN, GREGORIAN, ETC.)–HISTORY AND CRITICISM

Apel, Willi. Gregorian Chant. LC 57-10729. (Illus.). 544p. 1958. 35.00x (ISBN 0-253-32650-8). Ind U Pr.

Ferretti, Paolo A. Estetica Gregoriana. LC 77-5498. (Music Reprint Ser.). 1977. Repr. of 1934 ed. lib. bdg. 45.00 (ISBN 0-306-77414-3). Da Capo.

Gastoue, Amedee. L' Art Gregorien. 3rd ed. LC 77-178576. (Fr.). Repr. of 1920 ed. 21.50 (ISBN 0-404-56607-3). AMS Pr.

--Les Origines du chant romain: L'antiphonaire Gregorien. (Fr.). Repr. of 1907 ed. 32.50 (ISBN 0-404-56609-X). AMS Pr.

Luecke, Jane-Marie. Measuring Old English Rhythm: An Application of the Principles of Gregorian Chant Rhythm to the Meter of Beowolf. LC 66-25869. (Literary Monographs: Vol. 9). 168p. 1978. 25.00x (ISBN 0-299-07510-9). U of Wis Pr.

Randel, Don M. An Index to the Chant of the Mozarabic Rite. LC 72-5384. (Princeton Studies in Music Ser.: No. 6). pap. 160.00 (ISBN 0-317-09926-4, 2011400). Bks Demand UMI.

Robertson, Alec. Interpretation of Plainchant: A Preliminary Study. Repr. of 1937 ed. lib. bdg. 22.50x (ISBN 0-8371-4322-5, ROPL). Greenwood.

Werner, Eric. The Sacred Bridge. (Music Reprint Ser.). 1979. Repr. of 1959 ed. lib. bdg. 65.00 (ISBN 0-306-79581-7). Da Capo.

CHANTS (PLAIN, GREGORIAN, ETC.)–INSTRUCTION AND STUDY

Dechevrens, Antoine. Composition Musicale et Composition Litteraire a Propos du Chant Gregorrien. 373p. 1910. Repr. lib. bdg. 62.50x (Pub. by G Olms BRD). Coronet Bks.

Rayburn, John. Gregorian Chant: A History of Controversy Concerning Its Rhythm. LC 80-27616. xiv, 90p. 1981. Repr. of 1964 ed. lib. bdg. 22.50x (ISBN 0-313-22811-6, RAGR). Greenwood.

CHANUKAH

see Hanukkah (Feast of Lights)

CHAPELS

see also Chantries;

also subdivision Churches under names of cities, e.g. New York (City)–Churches

Johnson, L. C. Chapel Messages. 1982. pap. 5.95 (ISBN 0-89265-081-8). Randall Hse.

Wroth, William. The Chapel of Our Lady of Talpa. 1979. pap. 10.00 (ISBN 0-916537-28-5, Taylor Museum). CO Springs Fine Arts.

--The Chapel of Our Lady of Talpa. LC 78-58985. (Illus.). 104p. (Orig.). 1982. pap. 8.95 (ISBN 0-295-95920-7, Pub. by Taylor Museum). U of Wash Pr.

CHAPLAINS

Elkins, Dov P. God's Warriors: Dramatic Adventures of Rabbis in Uniform. LC 74-226. (Illus.). 92p. 1974. 7.95 (ISBN 0-8246-0168-8). Jonathan David.

Solt, Leo F. Saints in Arms. LC 74-153355. (Stanford University. Stanford Studies in History, Economics & Political Science: No. 18). Repr. of 1959 ed. 19.00 (ISBN 0-404-50976-2). AMS Pr.

Taylor, Horace M. Reminiscences of an Army Chaplain. LC 86-1472. Date not set. price not set. (ISBN 0-9617424-0-2). H M Taylor.

CHARACTER EDUCATION

see Moral Education

CHARISMATA

see Gifts, Spiritual

CHARISMATIC MOVEMENT

see Pentecostalism

CHARITABLE INSTITUTIONS

see Charities

CHARITIES

see also Church Charities; Endowments; Monasteries; Poor; Sisterhoods

Martin-Doisy, F. Dictionnaire d'Economic Charitable, 4 vols. Migne, J. P., ed. (Troisieme et Derniere Encyclopedie Theologique Ser.: Vols. 5-8). (Fr.). 3616p. Repr. of 1857 ed. lib. bdg. 456.00x (ISBN 0-89241-292-5). Caratzas.

CHARITIES–UNITED STATES

Ancona, Antoinette. St. Jude & "His People". LC 85-90095. 124p. 1985. 10.95 (ISBN 0-533-06604-2). Vantage.

CHARITY

see also Altruism; Kindness; Love (Theology)

Aelred of Rievaulx. The Mirror of Charity. Connor, Elizabeth, tr. from Latin. (Cistercian Fathers Ser.: No. 17). Orig. Title: Speculum Caritatis. Date not set. pns (ISBN 0-87907-217-2); pap. pns (ISBN 0-87907-717-4). Cistercian Pubns.

Al-Ghazzali. The Mysteries of Almsgiving. Faris, Nabik A., tr. 1966. 12.95x (ISBN 0-8156-6002-2, Am U Beirut). Syracuse U Pr.

Colwell, Stephen. New Themes for the Protestant Clergy. LC 71-83417. (Religion in America, Ser. 1). 1969. Repr. of 1851 ed. 32.00 (ISBN 0-405-00243-2). Ayer Co Pubs.

Faris, N. A. The Mysteries of Almsgiving. pap. 4.50 (ISBN 0-686-18616-8). Kazi Pubns.

Featherstone, Vaughn J. Charity Never Faileth. LC 80-10528. 121p. 1980. 7.95 (ISBN 0-87747-806-6). Deseret Bk.

Grant, George. The Dispossessed: Homelessness in America. LC 86-71355. 256p. 1986. pap. 8.95 (ISBN 0-89107-411-2, Crossways Bks). Good News.

--In the Shadow of Plenty. 1986. pap. 6.95 (ISBN 0-8407-3095-0). Nelson.

Kuasten, J. & Plumpe, J., eds. St. Augustine, Faith, Hope & Charity. Arand, Louis A., tr. LC 78-62450. (Ancient Christian Writers Ser.: No. 3). 165p. 1947. 10.95 (ISBN 0-8091-0045-2). Paulist Pr.

Morris, Woodrow W. The Greatest of These: Quotations on Fundamental Truths of Charity - The Teaching of Freemasonry. (Illus.). 132p. 1985. 8.75 (ISBN 0-88053-080-4). Macoy Pub.

Stransky, Thomas F. & Sheerin, John B., eds. Doing the Truth in Charity: Statements of Popes Paul VI, John Paul I, John Paul II & the Secretariat for Promoting Christian Unity. LC 81-85384. 400p. (Orig.). 1982. 12.95 (ISBN 0-8091-2398-3). Paulist Pr.

CHARLATANS

see Impostors and Imposture

CHARLESTOWN, MASSACHUSETTS URSULINE CONVENT

Whitney, Louise G. Burning of the Convent. LC 70-90196. (Mass Violence in America). Repr. of 1877 ed. 10.00 (ISBN 0-405-01341-8). Ayer Co Pubs.

CHARTRES, FRANCE–NOTRE-DAME (CATHEDRAL)

Adams, Roger J. The Eastern Portal of the North Transept at Chartres: Christological Rather Than Mariological. (Kultstatten der Gallisch-frankischen Kirche Vol.2). 190p. 1982. pap. 27.90 (ISBN 3-8204-6902-8). P Lang Pubs.

Branner, Robert, ed. Chartres Cathedral. (Norton Critical Studies in Art History). (Illus.). 1969. pap. 8.95x (ISBN 0-393-09851-6, NortonC). Norton.

Charpentier, Louis. The Mysteries of Chartres Cathedral. 1980. pap. 1.75 (ISBN 0-380-00386-4, 24596). Avon.

Katzenellenbogen, Adolf. Sculptural Programs of Chartres Cathedral. (Illus.). 1964. pap. 6.95x (ISBN 0-393-00233-0, Norton Lib). Norton.

Katzenellenbogen, Adolf E. The Sculptural Programs of Chartres Cathedral: Christ, Mary, Ecclesia. LC 59-14894. pap. 57.50 (ISBN 0-317-10764-X, 2007368). Bks Demand UMI.

Lillich, Meredith P. The Stained Glass of Saint-Pere de Chartres. LC 77-13926. (Illus.). 1978. 50.00x (ISBN 0-8195-5023-X). Wesleyan U Pr.

CHASIDISM

see Hasidism

CHASTITY

Burghardt, W. J., et al, eds. St. Methodius, the Symposium: A Treatise on Chastity. (Ancient Christian Writers Ser.: No. 27). 256p. 1958. 11.95 (ISBN 0-8091-0143-2). Paulist Pr.

Burrus, Virginia. Chastity As Autonomy: Women in the Stories of Apocryphal Acts. (Studies in Women & Religion). 184p. 1987. text ed. 39.95 (ISBN 0-88946-526-6). E Mellen.

Diamond, Eugene & Diamond, Rosemary. The Positive Values of Chastity. 1983. 7.50 (ISBN 0-8199-0829-0). Franciscan Herald.

Groeschel, Benedict J. The Courage to Be Chaste. 128p. (Orig.). 1985. pap. 4.95 (ISBN 0-8091-2705-9). Paulist Pr.

Knight, David M. Chastity: Who Lives It. LC 85-19516. 32p. (Orig.). 1985. pap. 3.95 (ISBN 0-915488-10-8, BV4647.C5K57). Clarity Pub.

Lewis, Dio. Chastity: Our Secret Sins. LC 73-20634. (Sex, Marriage & Society). 324p. 1974. Repr. of 1874 ed. 24.50x (ISBN 0-405-05809-8). Ayer Co Pubs.

May, William E. The Nature & Meaning of Chastity. (Synthesis Ser.). 1977. pap. 1.75 (ISBN 0-8199-0710-3). Franciscan Herald.

--Sex, Marriage & Chastity: Reflections of a Catholic Layman, Spouse & Parent. 1981. 6.95 (ISBN 0-8199-0821-5). Franciscan Herald.

CHERUBIM

see Angels

CHESTER (DIOCESE)

Gastrell, Francis. Notitia Cestriensis, 2 Vols. in 4. Repr. of 1850 ed. Set. 92.00 (ISBN 0-384-17700-X). Johnson Repr.

CHESTER PLAYS

Lumiansky, R. M. & Mills, David. The Chester Mystery Cycle: Essays & Documents. LC 82-1838. viii, 339p. 1983. 40.00x (ISBN 0-8078-1522-5); essay "Music in the Cycle" by Richard Rastall incl. U of NC Pr.

CHESTERTON, GILBERT KEITH, 1874-1936

Attwater, Donald, ed. Modern Christian Revolutionaries. facsimile ed. LC 76-156608. (Essay Index Reprint Ser). Repr. of 1947 ed. 23.00 (ISBN 0-8369-2304-9). Ayer Co Pubs.

Barker, Dudley. G. K. Chesterton. LC 72-95988. 1975. 5.95 (ISBN 0-8128-1804-0). Stein & Day.

Braybrooke, Patrick. G. K. Chesterton. LC 72-6491. (English Biography Ser., No. 31). 130p. 1972. Repr. of 1922 ed. lib. bdg. 35.95x (ISBN 0-8383-1616-6). Haskell.

Bullett, Gerald. The Innocence of G. K. Chesterton. 1973. Repr. of 1923 ed. 17.50 (ISBN 0-8274-1799-3). R West.

Chesterton, G. K. Collected Works of G. K. Chesterton, Vol. I. LC 85-81511. 1986. 24.95 (ISBN 0-89870-077-9); pap. 15.95 (ISBN 0-89870-079-5). Ignatius Pr.

--G. K. Chesterton Anthology. Kavanagh, P. J., ed. 515p. 1985. 24.95 (ISBN 0-89870-073-6); pap. 14.95 (ISBN 0-89870-096-5). Ignatius Pr.

--The G. K. Chesterton Calendar: A Quotation from the Works of G. K. Chesterton for Every Day in the Year. 75.00 (ISBN 0-87968-325-2). Gordon Pr.

Chesterton, G. K. & More, Thomas. Orthodoxy. (Books to Live Ser.). 1985. Repr. of 1908 ed. 10.95 (ISBN 0-88347-184-1). Thomas More.

Clemens, Cyril. Chesterton As Seen by His Contemporaries. 1973. 69.95 (ISBN 0-87968-027-X). Gordon Pr.

--Chesterton As Seen by His Contemporaries. LC 76-92958. (English Biography Ser., No. 31). 1969. Repr. of 1938 ed. lib. bdg. 48.95x (ISBN 0-8383-0968-2). Haskell.

Coates, John. Chesterton & the Edwardian Cultural Crisis. 280p. 1984. text ed. 28.50 (ISBN 0-85958-451-8, Pub. by U of Hull UK); pap. text ed. 19.95 (ISBN 0-85958-444-5). Humanities.

Evans, Maurice. G. K. Chesterton. LC 72-3187. (English Literature Ser., No. 33). 1972. Repr. of 1939 ed. lib. bdg. 39.95x (ISBN 0-8383-1504-6). Haskell.

Ffinch, Michael. G. K. Chesterton: A Biography. 1987. 18.95 (ISBN 0-06-252576-X, HarpR). Har-Row.

Furlong, William B. Shaw & Chesterton: The Metaphysical Jesters. LC 77-114616. 1970. 21.95 (ISBN 0-271-00110-0). Pa St U Pr.

Hollis, Christopher. The Mind of Chesterton. LC 76-130447. 1970. 14.95x (ISBN 0-87024-184-2). U of Miami Pr.

Kuhn, Heinz. Der Gemeinschaftagedanke Bei Chesterton. pap. 10.00 (ISBN 0-384-30680-2). Johnson Repr.

Las Vergnas, Raymond. Chesterton, Belloc, Baring. LC 73-4884. 1938. lib. bdg. 27.00 (ISBN 0-8414-2268-0). Folcroft.

Lea, F. A. The Wild Knight of Battersea: G. K. Chesterton. 1973. Repr. of 1945 ed. 25.00 (ISBN 0-8274-0321-6). R West.

Marlin, G., et al, eds. The Quotable Chesterton. LC 86-80788. 391p. 1986. 24.95 (ISBN 0-89870-102-3); pap. 16.95 (ISBN 0-89870-122-8). Ignatius Pr.

Rauch, Rufus W., ed. A Chesterton Celebration at the University of Notre Dame. LC 85-3592. (Illus.). 96p. 1983. 9.95 (ISBN 0-268-00744-6, 83-07444). U of Notre Dame Pr.

Slosson, Edwin E. Six Major Prophets. facsimile ed. LC 71-167421. (Essay Index Reprint Ser). Repr. of 1917 ed. 23.00 (ISBN 0-8369-2571-8). Ayer Co Pubs.

Sullivan, John. Chesterton: Contenary Appraisal. 243p. 1974. 12.50 (ISBN 0-06-496591-0). Lumen Christi.

Titterton, W. G. K. Chesterton. LC 73-14569. 1974. Repr. of 1947 ed. lib. bdg. 22.50 (ISBN 0-8414-8536-4). Folcroft.

--G. K. Chesterton: A Portrait. LC 72-8980. (English Biography Ser., No. 31). 1973. Repr. of 1936 ed. lib. bdg. 49.95x (ISBN 0-8383-1679-4). Haskell.

Ward, Maisie. Gilbert Keith Chesterton. LC 83-45860. 1944. 46.50 (ISBN 0-404-20280-2, PR4453). AMS Pr.

West, Julius. G. K. Chesterton: A Critical Study. LC 72-6120. 1973. Repr. of 1915 ed. lib. bdg. 30.00 (ISBN 0-8414-0112-8). Folcroft.

CHICANOS

see Mexican Americans

CHILD AND MOTHER

see Mother and Child

CHILD AND PARENT

see Parent and Child

CHILD REARING

Here are entered works on the principles and techniques of raising children. Works on the psycho-social interaction between parents and their minor children are entered under Parent and Child. Works on the skills, attributes and attitudes needed for parenthood are entered under Parenting.

see also Moral Education

Barber, Virginia & Skaggs, Merrill M. The Mother Person. LC 76-48850. 1977. pap. 7.95 (ISBN 0-8052-0565-9). Schocken.

Burba, Linda J. & Burba, Keith V. T-R-A-I-N up the Children. 111p. 1985. pap. 4.50 (ISBN 0-8341-1062-8). Beacon Hill.

Burgess, Allan K. Helping Your Child Stay Morally Clean. LC 84-71705. 100p. 1984. 6.95 (ISBN 0-87747-671-3). Deseret Bk.

Byers, J. W. Parent & Child. 60p. pap. 0.50 (ISBN 0-686-29132-8). Faith Pub Hse.

Carlson, Lee W., ed. Christian Parenting. 80p. 1984. pap. 6.95 (ISBN 0-8170-1072-6). Judson.

Chase, Betty N. Discipline Them, Love Them. 112p. 1982. wkbk. 6.95 (ISBN 0-89191-359-9). Cook.

Chinmoy, Sri. A Child's Heart & a Child's Dreams: Growing up with Spiritual Wisdom, a Guide for Parents & Children. 123p. 1986. pap. text ed. write for info. (ISBN 0-88497-862-1). Aum Pubns.

Cook, Barbara. How to Raise Good Kids. LC 78-7844. 192p. 1978. pap. 4.95 (ISBN 0-87123-233-2, 210233). Bethany Hse.

Cuthbertson, Duane. Raising Your Child, Not Your Voice. 168p. 1986. pap. 5.95 (ISBN 0-89693-342-3). Victor Bks.

Dobson, James. Dare to Discipline. 1973. pap. 6.95 (ISBN 0-8423-0631-5). Tyndale.

--Dare to Discipline. 1977. pap. 3.50 mass (ISBN 0-8423-0635-8). Tyndale.

Dobson, James C. The Strong-Willed Child. 1978. 10.95 (ISBN 0-8423-0664-1). Tyndale.
Gaulke, Earl H. You Can Have a Family Where Everybody Wins. LC 75-23574. 104p. 1975. pap. 3.50 (ISBN 0-570-03723-9, 12-2625). Concordia.
Gore, Tipper. Raising PG Kids in an X-Rated Society. 240p. 1987. 12.95 (ISBN 0-687-35283-5); pap. 8.95 (ISBN 0-687-35282-7). Abingdon.
Hull, Karen. The Mommy Book: Advice to New Mothers from Those Who've Been There. 240p. 1986. pap. 8.95 (ISBN 0-310-32241-3). Zondervan.
Isaacs, David. Character Building: A Guide for Parents & Teachers. Tr. of La Educacion de las Virtudes Humanas. 268p. (Orig.). 1984. write for info. (ISBN 0-906127-68-8, Pub. by Four Courts Pr Ireland); pap. 8.95 (ISBN 0-906127-67-X, Pub. by Four Courts Pr Ireland). Scepter Pubs.
Katz, Lilian G. & Ward, Evangeline H. Ethical Behavior in Early Childhood Education. LC 78-57538. 26p. 1978. pap. text ed. 2.00 (ISBN 0-912674-61-X, NAEYC #112). Natl Assn Child Ed.
Kelly, Clifton M. & Wantz, Sherman P. Train up a Child. LC 82-84318. 110p. (Orig.). 1983. pap. 4.95. Highlands Pub.
Kesler, Jay, ed. Parents & Teenagers. 696p. 1984. pap. 16.95 (ISBN 0-88207-817-8). Victor Bks.
Kesler, Jay, et al, eds. Parents & Children. 640p. 1986. 16.95 (ISBN 0-89693-809-3). Victor Bks.
Kuykendall, Carol. Learning to Let Go. 160p. (Orig.). 1985. pap. 6.95 (ISBN 0-310-33621-X, 12763P). Zondervan.
Lenz, Friedel. Celebrating the Festivals with Children. Tr. of Mit Kindren Feste feiern. 20p. (Orig.). 1986. pap. 3.95 (ISBN 0-88010-151-2). Anthroposophic.
Narramore, Bruce. Parenting with Love & Limits. 312p. 1987. pap. 9.95 (ISBN 0-310-30541-1). Zondervan.
--Why Children Misbehave. 152p. 1984. pap. 5.95 (ISBN 0-310-30361-3). Zondervan.
Narramore, S. Bruce. Help! I'm a Parent. 1972. pap. 6.95 (ISBN 0-310-30321-4). Zondervan.
Nelson, Gerald E. & Lewak, Richard W. Who's the Boss? Love, Authority & Parenting. LC 85-8184. Orig. Title: The One-Minute Scolding. (Illus.). 164p. 1985. pap. 6.95 (ISBN 0-87773-342-2, 74223-0). Shambhala Pubns.
Phillips, Mike. Building Respect, Responsibility, & Spiritual Values in Your Child. LC 81-12225. 138p. (Orig.). 1981. pap. 3.95 (ISBN 0-87123-146-8, 210146). Bethany Hse.
Roberts, Patricia, ed. Parenting Alone. 1980. pap. 4.50 (ISBN 0-8309-0297-X). Herald Hse.
Schulman, Michael & Mekler, Eva. Bringing up a Moral Child: A New Approach for Teaching Your Child to Be Kind, Just & Responsible. LC 84-18472. 1985. 19.95 (ISBN 0-201-16442-6); pap. 12.95 (ISBN 0-201-16443-4). Addison-Wesley.
Shedd, Charlie W. You Can Be a Great Parent. LC 76-128353. 1982. pap. 2.25 (ISBN 0-8499-4166-0, 98070). Word Bks.
Slater, Peter G. Children in the New England Mind: In Death & in Life. LC 77-7352. 248p. 1977. 27.50 (ISBN 0-208-01652-X, Archon). Shoe String.
Stunden, Clifford. How to Raise a Child You Can Live With: And What to Do If You Haven't. 160p. 1987. 10.95 (ISBN 0-8499-0552-4). Word Bks.
Udo de Haes, Daniel. The Young Child: Creative Living with Two to Four Year Olds. Blaxland de Lange, Simon & Blaxland de Lange, Paulamaria, trs. from Dutch. 90p. (Orig.). 1986. pap. 10.95 (ISBN 0-88010-169-5). Anthroposophic.
Wilkerson, Rich. Hold Me While You Let Me Go. LC 82-83838. 196p. (Orig.). 1983. pap. 4.95 (ISBN 0-89081-370-1). Harvest Hse.

CHILDREN–DEATH AND FUTURE STATE

Bennett, Cora N. One, Two, Three, Four, Five, Six, Seven, All Dead Children Go to Heaven. 32p. 1986. 5.95 (ISBN 0-89962-509-6). Todd & Honeywell.
Dodd, Robert V. Helping Children Cope with Death. LC 84-6713. 56p. (Orig.). 1984. pap. 1.95 (ISBN 0-8361-3368-4). Herald Pr.
Fischhoff, Joseph & Brohl, Noreen. Before & After My Child Died: A Collection of Parents' Experiences. 247p. (Orig.). 1981. pap. 7.95x (ISBN 0-9607956-0-X). Emmons-Fairfield Pub.
Hill, Mary V. Angel Children: Those Who Die Before Accountability. LC 73-75397. (Illus.). 70p. (Orig.). 1973. pap. 5.50 (ISBN 0-88290-017-X). Horizon Utah.
Lombardo, Victor S. & Lombardo, Edith F. Kids Grieve Too! (Illus.). 88p. 1986. 17.75x (ISBN 0-398-05275-1). C C Thomas.
Manney, James & Blattner, John. Death in the Nursery: The Secret Crime of Infanticide. 224p. (Orig.). 1984. pap. 6.95 (ISBN 0-89283-192-8). Servant.
Marchbanks, John B. Your Little One Is in Heaven. pap. 1.95 (ISBN 0-87213-642-6). Loizeaux.
Quezada, Adolfo. Good-Bye, My Son, Hello. LC 84-72629. 64p. (Orig.). 1985. pap. 2.95 (ISBN 0-87029-196-3). Abbey.
Slater, Peter G. Children in the New England Mind: In Death & in Life. LC 77-7352. 248p. 1977. 27.50 (ISBN 0-208-01652-X, Archon). Shoe String.
Van Eeden, Frederik. Paul's Awakening. Lake, H. S., tr. from Dutch. LC 83-81704. 96p. 1985. 6.95 (ISBN 0-86164-156-6, Pub. by Momenta Pub Ltd). Hunter Hse.

CHILDREN–PRAYER-BOOKS AND DEVOTIONS

see also Grace at Meals

Abajian, Diane. Praying & Doing the Stations of the Cross with Children. (Illus.). 24p. 1980. pap. 1.50 (ISBN 0-89622-118-0). Twenty-Third.
Alleman, Herman C. Prayers for Boys. LC 81-142145. pap. 3.95 (ISBN 0-8407-5241-5). Nelson.
--Prayers for Girls. 3.95 (ISBN 0-8407-5242-3). Nelson.
Angers, JoAnn M. My Beginning Mass Book. (Illus.). 32p. (Orig.). 1978. pap. 1.95 (ISBN 0-89622-082-6). Twenty-Third.
Armstrong, William. Health, Happiness, Humor & Holiness: As Seen Through Children's Eyes. Graves, Helen, ed. (Illus.). 150p. 1987. pap. text ed. 6.95 (ISBN 1-55523-065-2). Winston-Derek.
Bivens, Ruth. Aunt Ruth's Puppet Scripts, Bk. IV. (Orig.). 1987. three-ring binder & cassette 19.95 (ISBN 0-89265-122-9). Randall Hse.
Booth, Julianne. Bible Verses to Remember. 1982. pap. 2.95 (ISBN 0-570-04061-2, 56-1364). Concordia.
Brown, Angela. Prayers That Avail Much for Children. (Illus.). 32p. (Orig.). 1983. pap. 3.98 (ISBN 0-89274-296-8). Harrison Hse.
Carr & Paquet. God, I've Got to Talk to You Again! LC 59-1315. (Arch Bks.). 24p. (Orig.). 1985. pap. 0.99 (ISBN 0-570-06197-0, 59-1315). Concordia.
Champlin, Joseph M. & Haggerty, Brian A. Together in Peace for Children. LC 76-26348. (Illus.). 72p. 1976. 1.50 (ISBN 0-87793-119-4). Ave Maria.
Colao, Flora & Hosansky, Tamar. Your Children Should Know: Teach Your Children the Strategies That Will Keep Them Safe from Assault & Crime. LC 83-5981. (Illus.). 192p. 1983. 16.95 (ISBN 0-672-52777-4). Bobbs.
Coleman, William. Animals That Show & Tell. LC 85-15122. 144p. 1985. pap. 4.95 (ISBN 0-87123-807-1). Bethany Hse.
--Before You Tuck Me In. 128p. (Orig.). 1986. pap. 4.95 (ISBN 0-87123-830-6). Bethany Hse.
--Counting Stars. LC 76-28973. 128p. 1976. 4.95 (ISBN 0-87123-055-0, 210055). Bethany Hse.
--The Warm Hug Book. 128p. (Orig.). 1985. pap. 4.95 (ISBN 0-87123-794-6, 210794). Bethany Hse.
Coombs, Robert S. & Perry, Iris. Of Such Is the Kingdom: Sermons for Children. (Object Lesson Ser.). 96p. (Orig.). 1987. pap. 4.95 (ISBN 0-8010-2518-4). Baker Bk.
Corbin, Linda & Dys, Pat. Jesus Teaches Me. (Discipleship Workbook for Parent & Child Ser.: Bk. 4). (Illus.). 35p. Date not set. wkbk. 3.95 (ISBN 0-87509-389-2). Chr Pubns.
Darcy-Berube, Francoise & Berube, John P. Someone's There: Paths to Prayer for Young People. LC 86-82055. (Illus.). 80p. (Orig.). 1987. pap. 4.95 (ISBN 0-87793-350-2). Ave Maria.
Dear God. (First Prayer Ser.). 2.95 (ISBN 0-86112-218-6, Pub. by Brimax Bks). Borden.
Donze, Mary T. In My Heart Room. 64p. 1982. pap. 1.50 (ISBN 0-89243-161-X). Liguori Pubns.
Draper, Edythe. Stretch. 1983. kivar, girls' ed. 5.95 (ISBN 0-8423-6673-3). Tyndale.
--Stretch. 1983. kivar, boys' ed. 5.95 (ISBN 0-8423-6668-7). Tyndale.
Field, Rachel. Prayer for a Child. LC 44-47191. (Illus.). 32p. 1968. 8.95 (ISBN 0-02-735190-4). Macmillan.
Gockel, Herman W. & Saleska, Edward J., eds. Child's Garden of Prayer. (Illus.). 1981. pap. 1.50 (ISBN 0-570-03412-4, 56-1016). Concordia.
God Bless. (First Prayer Ser.). 2.95 (ISBN 0-86112-195-3, Pub. by Brimax Bks). Borden.
God Made. (First Prayer Ser.). 2.95 (ISBN 0-86112-219-4, Pub. by Brimax Bks). Borden.
God's in His Heaven: Prayers & Poems for Little Children. LC 84-2101. (God's in His Heaven Bks.). (Illus.). 32p. 1984. pap. 4.95 (ISBN 0-394-86760-2, BYR). Random.
Gregory, Sally. Poems, Prayers & Graces. (Illus.). 28p. 1987. 12.95 (ISBN 0-340-34873-9, Pub. by Hodder & Stoughton UK). David & Charles.
Hayes, Wanda. My Thank You Book. (Illus.). 32p. 1964. 5.95 (ISBN 0-87239-241-4, 3048). Standard Pub.
Heath, Lou & Taylor, Beth. Reading My Bible in Spring. (Orig.). 1987. pap. 4.50 (ISBN 0-8054-4320-7). Broadman.
--Reading My Bible in Summer. (Orig.). 1987. pap. 4.50 (ISBN 0-8054-4321-5). Broadman.
Hills, Desmond B. Light for My Life. Van Dolson, Bobbie J., ed. 384p. 1981. 7.95 (ISBN 0-8280-0041-7). Review & Herald.
Hodgson, Joan. Our Father. (Illus.). 1977. pap. 2.95 (ISBN 0-85487-040-7). De Vorss.
Holmes, Marjorie. Nobody Else Will Listen. 1976. pap. 2.95 (ISBN 0-553-23457-9). Bantam.
Hook, Richard & Hook, Frances. Jesus: El Amigo De los Ninos. Tr. of Jesus, the Friend of Children. (Illus.). 112p. 1981. 19.50 (ISBN 0-311-38552-4, Edit Mundo); pap. 14.95 (ISBN 0-311-38553-2). Casa Bautista.
Huxhold, Harry N., ed. Adventures with God. LC 66-15551. 1966. pap. 7.95 (ISBN 0-570-03736-0, 12-2640). Concordia.
Klug, Lyn. I Know I Can Trust You, Lord: Prayers for Girls. LC 83-70503. (Young Readers Ser.). 80p. 1983. pap. 3.95 (ISBN 0-8066-2009-9, 10-3192). Augsburg.
Klug, Ron. You Promised, Lord: Prayers for Boys. LC 83-70502. (Young Readers Ser.). 80p. (Orig.). 1983. pap. 3.95 (ISBN 0-8066-2008-0, 10-7417). Augsburg.
Klug, Ron & Klug, Lyn. Thank You, God: Prayers for Young Children. LC 80-67800. 32p. (Orig.). 1980. pap. 3.95 (ISBN 0-8066-1862-0, 10-6243). Augsburg.
L'Engle, Madeleine. Prayers for Sunday. (Illus.). 1974. pap. 1.95 (ISBN 0-8192-1153-2). Morehouse.
Lipman, Zev, illus. Baruch Ata Befi Hataf: Illustrated Prayers & Blessings for Young Children. (Illus.). 4.95 (ISBN 0-685-84974-0). Feldheim.
Little Folded Hands. rev. ed. LC 59-12074. 1959. 3.50 (ISBN 0-570-03417-5, 56-1038); pap. 1.85 laminated (ISBN 0-570-03416-7, 56-1037). Concordia.
McDow, Jane. Golden Thoughts for Children. (Illus.). 48p. (Orig.). 1986. pap. write for info. (ISBN 0-9616464-0-3). Candy Apple Pub.
McKissack, Patricia & McKissack, Fredrick. When Do You Talk To God? Prayers for Small Children. LC 86-71903. (Illus.). 32p. (Orig.). 1986. pap. 4.95 (ISBN 0-8066-2239-3, 10-7078). Augsburg.
Magagna, Anna M., illus. First Prayers. LC 82-60742. (Illus.). 64p. 1983. 8.95 (ISBN 0-02-762120-0). Macmillan.
Matranga, Frances. My Book of Prayers. (Happy Day Bks.). (Illus.). 24p. 1985. 1.59 (ISBN 0-87239-877-3, 3677). Standard Pub.
Meyzlisch, Saul, ed. A Child's Passover Haggadah. (Illus.). 76p. 1987. 9.95 (ISBN 0-915361-70-1, Dist. by Watts). Adama Pubs Inc.
Miles, Mary L. Daily Look at Jesus, No. 1-2. (Pre-Teen Books Ser.). 1970. No. 2. Moody.
My First Prayer Book. (Little Books To Treasure). (Illus.). 32p. 1985. 1.95 (ISBN 0-225-66387-2, HarpR). Har-Row.
Nystrom, Carolyn. What Is Prayer? (Children's Bible Basics Ser.). 32p. 1980. pap. 4.95 (ISBN 0-8024-5991-9). Moody.
Odor, Ruth. Prayers for Boys. 1985. pap. 0.69 pocket size (ISBN 0-87239-825-0, 2815). Standard Pub.
--Prayers for Girls. 1985. pap. 0.69 pocket size (ISBN 0-87239-826-9, 2816). Standard Pub.
Parker, Marjorie H. Fun Devotions for Kids, No. 2. 64p. 1985. pap. 2.50 (ISBN 0-87239-892-7, 2822). Standard Pub.
Perkins, Lee & Perkins, Jim. Healthier & Happier Children Through Bedtime Meditations & Prayers, Bks. 1 & 2. 40p. 1982. book & tape set 14.95 (ISBN 0-87604-184-5). ARE Pr.
Plantinga, Cornelius, Jr. A Sure Thing. LC 86-8280. (Illus.). 300p. 1986. lib. bdg. 11.95 (ISBN 0-930265-27-0); incl. tchr's. manual 7.95 (ISBN 0-930265-28-9). CRC Pubns.
Prayers for Children. 32p. 1981. pap. 3.95 (ISBN 0-8249-8023-9). Ideals.
Puig, Enric. Lord, I Am One of Your Little Ones. 93p. 1987. 5.95 (ISBN 0-8294-0545-3). Loyola.
Richards, Jean. We Can Share God's Love. 80p. 1984. pap. 2.95 (ISBN 0-8170-1010-6). Judson.
Richterkessing, Sue. Devotions for Your Preschool Classroom. 1983. pap. 4.95 (ISBN 0-570-03913-4, 12-2854). Concordia.
Roberts, Don. Prayers for the Young Child. 1981. pap. 7.95 (ISBN 0-570-04051-5, 56-1717). Concordia.
Rogal, Samuel J., compiled by. The Children's Jubliee: A Bibliographical Survey of Hymnals for Infants, Youth & Sunday Schools Published in Britain & American, 1655-1900. LC 83-1661. (Illus.). xliv, 91p. 1983. lib. bdg. 35.00 (ISBN 0-313-23880-4, RCJ/). Greenwood.
Ross, Uta O. The Boy Who Wanted to Be a Missionary. (Illus.). 48p. (Orig.). 1984. pap. 11.95 (ISBN 0-687-03910-X). Abingdon.
Schlesselman, R. & Ahrens, L. Dear Father in Heaven. rev. ed. (Illus.). 1977. pap. 2.25 (ISBN 0-570-03469-8, 56-1301). Concordia.
Schmidt, J. David. Graffiti: Devotions for Girls. new ed. (Illus.). 128p. (Orig.). (YA) 1983. pap. 4.95 (ISBN 0-8007-5115-9, Power Bks). Revell.
--Graffiti: Devotions for Guys. new ed. (Illus.). 128p. (Orig.). (YA) 1983. pap. 4.95 (ISBN 0-8007-5114-0, Power Bks). Revell.
Sorensen, David A. It's a Mystery to Me, Lord: Bible Devotions for Boys. LC 85-22993. (Young Readers Ser.). 112p. (Orig.). 1985. pap. 3.95 (ISBN 0-8066-2183-4, 10-3445). Augsburg.
Sorenson, Jane. Five Minutes with God, No. 2. (Illus.). 64p. 1985. pap. 2.50 (ISBN 0-87239-894-3, 2824). Standard Pub.
Stadler, Bernice. Celebrations of the Word for Children: Cycle A. Reece, Nancy, ed. 88p. (Orig.). 1986. pap. 9.95 (ISBN 0-89622-308-6). Twenty-Third.
Steiner, Rudolf. Prayers for Mothers & Children. 3rd. ed. Hersey, Eileen V. & Von Arnim, Christian, trs. from Ger. 76p. 1983. pap. 5.00 (ISBN 0-85440-195-4, Pub. by Steinerbooks). Anthroposophic.
Swanson, Steve, et al. Faith Prints: Youth Devotions for Every Day of the Year. LC 85-13466. 224p. (Orig.). 1985. pap. 4.95 (ISBN 0-8066-2178-8, 10-2189). Augsburg.
Taylor, Kenneth N. Living Letter for the Children's Hour. LC 68-26407. (Illus.). 192p. 1968. pap. 3.95 (ISBN 0-8024-0062-0). Moody.
--Living Thoughts for the Children's Hour. LC 72-77943. (Illus.). 128p. 1972. pap. 3.95 (ISBN 0-8024-0121-X). Moody.
--Meditaciones para Ninos. Orig. Title: Devotions for the Children's Hour. (Span.). 252p. 1983. pap. 4.75 (ISBN 0-8254-1707-4). Kregel.
Thank You God. (First Prayer Ser.). 2.95 (ISBN 0-86112-196-1, Pub. by Brimax Bks). Borden.
Thomas, Virginia & Miller, Betty. Children's Literature for All God's Children. LC 85-17169. 120p. 1986. pap. 11.95 (ISBN 0-8042-1690-8). John Knox.
Tudor, Tasha. First Prayers. LC 59-9631. (Illus.). 1952. protestant ed. 4.50 (ISBN 0-8098-1952-X). McKay.
--More Prayers. LC 67-19929. (Illus.). 1967. 4.95 (ISBN 0-8098-1954-6). McKay.
Webb, Barbara O. Now What, Lord? Bible Devotions for Girls. LC 85-22884. (Young Readers Ser.). 112p. (Orig.). 1985. pap. 3.95 (ISBN 0-8066-2182-6, 10-4680). Augsburg.
Weber, Hans-Ruedi. Jesus & the Children: Biblical Resources for Study & Preaching. LC 79-87754. 1980. pap. 5.95 (ISBN 0-8042-1316-X). John Knox.
Weisheit, Eldon. God's Promise for Children: Object Lessons on Old Testament Texts. LC 81-65656. (Series B). 128p. (Orig.). 1981. pap. 6.95 (ISBN 0-8066-1892-2, 10-2693). Augsburg.
Wilkin, Esther. Little Prayers. (Golden Look-Look Ser.). (Illus.). 24p. 1980. pap. 1.50 (ISBN 0-307-11858-4, Golden Bks.). Western Pub.
Wyly, Louise B. Fun Devotions for Kids. (Illus.). 64p. 1985. pap. 2.50 (ISBN 0-87239-891-9, 2821). Standard Pub.

CHILDREN–RECREATION

see Creative Activities and Seatwork; Games

CHILDREN–RELIGIOUS LIFE

see also Children–Prayer-Books and Devotions

Aaseng, Nathan. I'm Searching, Lord, but I Need Your Light. LC 82-72644. (Young Readers Ser.). 112p. 1983. pap. 3.95 (ISBN 0-8066-1950-3, 10-3203). Augsburg.
--Which Way Are You Leading Me, Lord? Bible Devotions for Boys. LC 84-21562. (Young Readers Ser.). 112p. (Orig.). 1984. pap. 3.95 (ISBN 0-8066-2113-3, 10-7099). Augsburg.
Alcott, A. Bronson, ed. Conversations with Children on the Gospels (Record of Conversations on the Gospels, Held in Mr. Alcott's School; Unfolding the Doctrine & Discipline of Human Culture, 2 vols. in 1. LC 72-4948. (The Romantic Tradition in American Literature Ser.). 616p. 1972. Repr. of 1836 ed. 40.00 (ISBN 0-405-04621-9). Ayer Co Pubs.
Anderson, Debby. All Year Long. (Sparklers Ser.). 1986. comb binding 2.95 (ISBN 1-55513-043-7, Chariot Bks). Cook.
--God Is with Me. (Sparklers Ser.). 1986. comb binding 2.95 (ISBN 0-89191-269-X, Chariot Bks). Cook.
--Thank You, God. (Sparkler Bks.). (Illus.). 1986. plastic comb bdg. 2.95 (ISBN 0-89191-931-7, 59311, Chariot Bks). Cook.
Andre, Evelyn, compiled by. Sing & Be Joyful: Enjoying Music with Young Children. LC 79-14787. 1979. pap. 8.95 (ISBN 0-687-38550-4). Abingdon.
Animals. (Feelings & Growth Development Coloring Bks.). (Illus.). 0.75 (ISBN 0-8091-6542-2). Paulist Pr.

Apostolos-Cappadona, Diane, ed. The Sacred Play of Children. 160p. 1983. pap. 9.95 (ISBN 0-8164-2427-6, HarpR). Har-Row.
Arnold, Eberhard. Children's Education in Community: The Basis of Bruderhof Education. Mow, Merrill, ed. LC 76-27728. 1976. pap. 3.25 (ISBN 0-87486-164-0). Plough.
Ashton, Leila M. My "Feel Good" Secrets. (My Church Teaches Ser.). (Illus.). 1978. pap. 1.50 (ISBN 0-8127-0178-X). Review & Herald.
Baker, Marguerite. And Then the Angels Came to the First Grade Children. 1964. pap. 1.50 (ISBN 0-685-79136-X). Summit Univ.
Ban, Arline J. Children's Time in Worship. 128p. 1981. pap. 6.95 (ISBN 0-8170-0902-7). Judson.
Bartholomew. God Loves Me. 1982. pap. 0.85 (ISBN 0-570-04073-6, 56-1376). Concordia.
--I Go To Church. 1982. pap. 0.85 (ISBN 0-570-04072-8, 56-1375). Concordia.
--Jesus Teaches Me. 1982. pap. 0.85 (ISBN 0-570-04071-X, 56-1374). Concordia.
Beckmann, Beverly. Emotions in God's World. 24p. 1986. 5.95 (ISBN 0-570-04149-X). Concordia.
Bence, Evelyn. Growing. 32p. 1985. 4.95 (ISBN 0-8378-2043-X). Gibson.
Bennett, J. G. & Montessori, Mario. The Spiritual Hunger of the Modern Child. Addison, Wendy, ed. LC 87-71204. 220p. 1985. pap. 8.95 (ISBN 0-934254-06-0). Claymont Comm.
Bennett, Marian. God's Animals. (My Shape Book Ser.). (Illus.). 10p. 1985. 2.95 (ISBN 0-87239-909-5, 2749). Standard Pub.
--God's Gifts. (My Shape Book Ser.). (Illus.). 10p. 1985. 2.95 (ISBN 0-87239-910-9, 2750). Standard Pub.
The Bird That Wouldn't Talk. (Color-a-Story Bks.). (Illus.). 1985. pap. 0.89 (ISBN 0-89191-998-8, 59980). Cook.
Blackwell, Muriel F. Called to Teach Children. LC 82-82954. 1983. 6.95 (ISBN 0-8054-3233-7). Broadman.
Bonnici, Roberta L. Your Right to Be Different. (Discovery Bks.). (Illus.). 48p. (YA) 1982. pap. text ed. 1.50 (ISBN 0-88243-842-5, 02-0842); tchr's ed 3.95 (ISBN 0-88243-333-4, 02-0333). Gospel Pub.
Boykin, Phyllis. I Like to Go to Church. (Bible-&-Me Ser.). 1987. 5.95 (ISBN 0-8054-4174-3). Broadman.
Bruinsma, Sheryl. New Object Lessons for Children of All Ages. (Object Lesson Ser.). 1980. pap. 4.95 (ISBN 0-8010-0775-5). Baker Bk.
--Object Lessons for Special Days. 80p. 1986. 4.50 (ISBN 0-8010-0920-0). Baker Bk.
Brusselmans, C., ed. Jesus Loves Children. 5.95 (ISBN 0-8215-9889-9). Sadlier.
Bushnell, Horace. Views of Christian Nurture & Subjects Related Thereto. LC 74-23297. 264p. 1975. Repr. of 1847 ed. lib. bdg. 40.00x (ISBN 0-8201-1147-3). Schol Facsimiles.
Bussard, Paula J. & Jefferson, Patti. Lessons on Praise from Critter County: Helping Children Praise God. (Critter County Ser.). 144p. 1987. pap. 9.95 (ISBN 0-87403-217-2, 3337). Standard Pub.
Call, Betty & Souther, Sheila. Children Can Worship, Bk. 3. (Orig.). 1983. pap. text ed. 10.95 (ISBN 0-87148-178-2). Pathway Pr.
Cantoni, Louise B. Leaving Matters to God. (Illus.). 164p. 1984. 3.00 (ISBN 0-8198-4424-1); pap. 2.00 (ISBN 0-8198-4425-X). Dghtrs St Paul.
Carroll, Frances. How to Talk with Your Children about God. 1985. pap. 6.95 (ISBN 0-317-18129-7). P-H.
Caswell, Helen R. God's World Makes Me Feel So Little. (Illus.). 32p. 1985. paper over board 5.95 (ISBN 0-687-15510-X). Abingdon.
Cavalletti, Sofia. The Religious Potential of the Child. 224p. 1982. pap. 10.95 (ISBN 0-8091-2389-4). Paulist Pr.
Chafin, Kenneth L. Tell All the Little Children. 1976. pap. 0.95 (ISBN 0-8054-6211-2). Broadman.
Christopherson, Victor A. Child Rearing In Today's Christian Family. (Family Life Ser.). 176p. 1985. pap. 6.95 (ISBN 0-8170-1065-3). Judson.
Clouse, Bonnidell. Moral Development. 368p. 1985. pap. 13.95 (ISBN 0-8010-2507-9). Baker Bk.
Coe, Rachel. I Have a Family. LC 86-17629. (Bible-&-Me Ser.). 1987. 5.95 (ISBN 0-8054-4172-7). Broadman.
Coffey, Rosalie L. & Glenn, John S. Completing the Promise. (Religious Awards for Boy Scouts Ser.). 1984. pap. 4.95x (ISBN 0-938758-17-9). MTM Pub Co.
Coleman, William. The Good Night Book. LC 79-20002. (Illus.). 128p. 1980. pap. 4.95 (ISBN 0-87123-187-5, 210187). Bethany Hse.
--On Your Mark. LC 79-16458. 112p. 1979. pap. 4.95 (ISBN 0-87123-490-4, 210490). Bethany Hse.
--The Palestine Herald, 4 vols. (The Palestine Herald Ser.). (Illus.). No. 1. 2.95 (ISBN 0-89191-981-3); No. 2. 2.95 (ISBN 0-89191-982-1); No. 3. 2.95 (ISBN 0-89191-983-X); No. 4. 2.95 (ISBN 0-89191-984-8). Cook.
Colton, Ann R. Precepts for the Young. 66p. 1959. pap. 2.50 (ISBN 0-917187-15-6). A R C Pub.
Coulton, G. G. Infant Perdition in the Middle Ages. 1977. lib. bdg. 59.95 (ISBN 0-8490-2058-1). Gordon Pr.
Cranor, Phoebe. Why Did God Let Grandpa Die? LC 76-17737. 128p. 1976. pap. 3.50 (ISBN 0-87123-603-6, 200603). Bethany Hse.
Crapps, Joyce W. Who Made These Things? LC 86-18773. (Bible-&-Me Ser.). 1987. 5.95 (ISBN 0-8054-4178-6). Broadman.
Cronin, Gaynell B. The Table of the Lord. LC 86-70131. (Illus., Orig.). 1986. Child's Bk, 104 pgs. pap. text ed. 4.50 (ISBN 0-87793-299-9); Director's Manual, 168 pgs. 9.75 (ISBN 0-87793-325-1); Parent's Bk, 96 pgs. 3.50 (ISBN 0-87793-326-X). Ave Maria.
Dean, Bessie. I'm Happy When I'm Good. (Children's Inspirational Coloring Bk.). (Illus.). 24p. 1979. pap. 1.25 (ISBN 0-88290-109-5). Horizon Utah.
Dean, Elizabeth P. Jodie: One Little Ewe Lamb. 96p. 1984. pap. 4.95 (ISBN 0-8010-2938-4). Baker Bk.
De Brand, Roy E. Children's Sermons for Special Occasions. LC 82-72228. (Orig.). 1983. pap. 3.95 (ISBN 0-8054-4927-2). Broadman.
DeGrote-Sorensen, Barbara. Everybody Needs a Friend: A Young Christian Book for Girls. LC 86-32152. 112p. (Orig.). 1987. pap. 4.95 (ISBN 0-8066-2247-4, 10-2120). Augsburg.
De Smith, Josie. El Hogar Que Dios Me Dio. 80p. 1986. pap. 2.25 (ISBN 0-311-46082-8). Casa Bautista.
DeVine, Bob. Uncle Bob Talks with My Digestive System. LC 85-4737. (Designed by God Ser.). (Illus.). 48p. 1985. pap. 4.95 (ISBN 0-89191-944-9, 59444, Chariot Bks). Cook.
Drescher, John M., et al. When Your Child... LC 86-4831. 144p. (Orig.). 1986. pap. 7.95 (ISBN 0-8361-3416-8). Herald Pr.
Edstrom, Lois. Contemporary Object Lessons for Children's Church. (Object Lessons Ser.). 112p. 1986. 4.50 (ISBN 0-8010-3432-9). Baker Bk.
Escape to Egypt. (Color-a-Story Bks.). (Illus.). 1985. pap. 0.89 (ISBN 0-89191-946-5, 59469). Cook.
Everett, Betty S. I Want to Be Like You, Lord: Bible Devotion for Girls. LC 84-21563. (Young Readers Ser.). 112p. (Orig.). 1984. pap. 3.95 (ISBN 0-8066-2112-5, 10-3196). Augsburg.
--Who Am I, Lord? LC 82-72645. (Young Readers Ser.). 112p. (Orig.). 1983. pap. 3.95 (ISBN 0-8066-1951-1, 10-7072). Augsburg.
Everything You Need for Children's Worship: Except Children. pap. cancelled (ISBN 0-912228-50-4). St Anthony Mess Pr.
Eyre, Linda & Eyre, Richard. Teaching Children Joy. 203p. pap. 8.95 (ISBN 0-87747-888-0, Pub. by Shadow Mountain). Deseret Bk.
The First Christmas. (Color-a-Story Bks.). (Illus.). 1985. pap. 0.89 (ISBN 0-89191-958-9, 59584). Cook.
Fitzgerald, Annie. Dear God, Bless Our Food. LC 84-71372. (Dear God Bks.). 16p. (Orig.). 1984. pap. 1.50 (ISBN 0-8066-2108-7, 10-1859). Augsburg.
--Dear God, Good Morning. LC 84-71377. (Dear God Bks.). 16p. (Orig.). 1984. pap. 1.50 (ISBN 0-8066-2104-4, 10-1860). Augsburg.
--Dear God, Good Night. LC 84-71374. (Dear God Bks.). 16p. 1984. pap. 1.50 (ISBN 0-8066-2105-2, 10-1861). Augsburg.
--Dear God, I Just Love Birthdays. LC 84-71371. (Dear God Bks.). 16p. (Orig.). 1984. pap. 1.50 (ISBN 0-8066-2107-9, 10-1862). Augsburg.
--Dear God, Thanks for Friends. LC 84-71873. (Dear God Bks.). 16p. (Orig.). 1984. pap. 1.50 (ISBN 0-8066-2109-5, 10-1863). Augsburg.
--Dear God, Thanks for Making Me. LC 83-71368. (Dear God Bks.). 16p. (Orig.). 1984. pap. 1.50 (ISBN 0-8066-2106-0, 10-1864). Augsburg.
Fleming, Jean. El Corazon de Una Madre. Araujo, Juan S., tr. from Eng. Tr. of A Mother's Heart. (Span.). 144p. 1987. pap. 4.25 (ISBN 0-88113-029-X). Edit Betania.
Frog. 1986. 2.95 (ISBN 1-55513-175-1, Chariot Bks). Cook.
Frost, Marie H. Listen to Your Children. LC 80-50320. 144p. (Orig.). 1980. pap. 2.95 (ISBN 0-87239-396-8, 3000). Standard Pub.
Gambill, Henrietta. Are You Listening? LC 85-10349. (A New Values Ser.). (Illus.). 32p. 1985. PLB 7.45 (ISBN 0-89565-332-X). Childs World.
Glass, Dorlis B. Children, Children! A Ministry Without Boundries. LC 86-50509. 72p. (Orig.). 1986. pap. 4.95 (ISBN 0-88177-033-7, DR033B). Discipleship Res.
Goldman, Ronald. Religious Thinking from Childhood to Adolescence. 1968. pap. text ed. 6.95 (ISBN 0-8164-2061-0, SP53, HarpR). Har-Row.
Gonter, Janet. Choosing Is... (I'm Growing Up Ser.). (Illus.). 1986. casebound 3.95 (ISBN 0-87403-123-0, 3603). Standard Pub.
Gray, E. Dodson & Gray, D. Dodson. Children of Joy: Raising Your Own Home-Grown Christians. LC 74-80259. xviii, 258p. (Orig.). 1975. pap. 7.95 (ISBN 0-934512-03-5). Roundtable Pr.
Grunze, Richard. The Young Christian's Life. 1979. 9.95 (ISBN 0-8100-0104-7, 06N0557). Northwest Pub.
Gruzen, Lee F. Raising Your Jewish-Christian Child: Wise Choices for Interfaith Parents. 1987. 16.95 (ISBN 0-396-08551-2). Dodd.
Haas, Dorothy. My First Communion. Tucker, Kathleen, ed. (Illus.). 48p. 1987. PLB 9.25 (ISBN 0-8075-5331-X). A Whitman.
Halverson, Delia T. Helping Your Child Discover Faith. 128p. 1982. pap. 5.95 (ISBN 0-8170-0957-4). Judson.
Hansel, Tim. You Gotta Keep Dancin' LC 85-11298. 150p. 1985. pap. 6.95 (ISBN 0-89191-722-5, 57224). Cook.
Harrison House Staff. Confessions for Kids. (Illus.). 29p. (Orig.). 1984. pap. 0.75 (ISBN 0-89274-322-0). Harrison Hse.
Hartley, Jan. Sharing Faith at Home. (SPAN Ser.). (Illus.). 31p. (Orig.). 1983. pap. 3.95 (ISBN 0-85819-450-3, Pub. by JBCE). ANZ Religious Pubns.
Hayes, Rebecca S. Grant Me a Portion. 1987. pap. 4.50 (ISBN 0-8054-6585-5). Broadman.
Heller, David. The Children's God. LC 85-24581. (Illus.). 176p. 1986. 15.95 (ISBN 0-226-32635-7). U of Chicago Pr.
Herbert, Janet. Hurray for Birthdays. (Sparklers Ser.). 1986. comb binding 2.95 (ISBN 1-55513-040-2, Chariot Bks). Cook.
Hesch, John B. Prayer & Meditation for Middle School Kids. 144p. (Orig.). 1985. pap. 7.95 (ISBN 0-8091-2723-7). Paulist Pr.
Heusser, D-B & Heusser, Phyllis. Children As Partners in the Church. LC 85-9934. 64p. 1985. pap. 3.95 (ISBN 0-8170-1054-8). Judson.
Holmes, Urban T., III. Young Children & the Eucharist. rev. ed. 128p. 1982. pap. 6.95 (ISBN 0-8164-2425-X, HarpR). Har-Row.
Homan, Walter J. Children & Quakerism. LC 70-169387. (Family in America Ser). 180p. 1972. Repr. of 1939 ed. 14.00 (ISBN 0-405-03864-X). Ayer Co Pubs.
Howard, Barbara, ed. Children: Of Such Is the Kingdom of God. LC 79-7102. 1979. pap. 8.00 (ISBN 0-8309-0243-0). Herald Hse.
Hunt, Gladys. Honey for a Child's Heart. 1969. pap. 5.95 (ISBN 0-310-26381-6, 9891P). Zondervan.
Hunter, Emily. Little Lips Shall Praise Thee. (Illus.). 96p. 1986. 11.95 (ISBN 0-89081-543-7). Harvest Hse.
Huttar, Leora W. Church Time for Preschoolers. LC 75-17368. 1975. spiral 6.95 (ISBN 0-916406-36-9). Accent Bks.
If Only I'd Listened. (Color-a-Story Bks.). (Illus.). 1985. pap. 0.89 (ISBN 0-89191-996-1, 59964). Cook.
Ingle, Clifford, ed. Children & Conversion. LC 79-113212. 160p. 1975. pap. 4.95 (ISBN 0-8054-2514-4). Broadman.
Johnson, Lois W. You're My Best Friend, Lord. LC 76-3866. 96p. (Orig.). 1976. pap. 3.95 (ISBN 0-8066-1541-9, 10-7490). Augsburg.
Johnson, Philip E. And More Celebrating the Seasons with Children. 120p. (Orig.). 1986. pap. 6.95 (ISBN 0-8298-0735-7). Pilgrim NY.
--More Celebrating the Seasons with Children. 112p. 1985. pap. 7.95 (ISBN 0-8298-0731-4). Pilgrim NY.
Jones, Chris. What Do I Do Now Lord? LC 76-3860. 96p. (Orig.). 1976. pap. 3.95 (ISBN 0-8066-1539-7, 10-7044). Augsburg.
Juknialis, Joseph J. When God Began in the Middle. (Illus.). 80p. (Orig.). 1981. pap. text ed. 7.95 (ISBN 0-89390-027-3). Resource Pubns.
Kageler, Len. Short Stops with the Lord. 104p. 1984. 5.95 (ISBN 0-87509-348-5). Chr Pubns.
Kelly, Clifton M. & Wantz, Sherman P. Train up a Child. LC 82-84318. 110p. (Orig.). 1983. pap. 4.95. Highlands Pub.
Kenneally, Christy. Strings & Things: Poems & Other Messages for Children. (Orig.). 1984. pap. 3.50 (ISBN 0-8091-6555-4). Paulist Pr.
Kohler, Christine. Help Me: I'm Lost. (Growing up Christian Ser.). 24p. (Orig.). 1985. pap. 3.95 (ISBN 0-570-04115-5, 56-1526). Concordia.
--I Help the Handicapped. (Growing Up Christian Ser.). 24p. (Orig.). 1985. pap. 3.95 (ISBN 0-570-04114-7, 56-1525). Concordia.
--Jesus Makes Me Well. (Growing up Christian Ser.). (Illus.). 24p. (Orig.). 1985. pap. 3.95 (ISBN 0-570-04113-9, 56-1524). Concordia.
Krall, Jack & Kalberer, Jan. Upside Down & Inside Out: A Study Experience in Christian Clowning. 120p. 1987. cancelled (ISBN 0-317-46796-4). Resource Pubns.
Kushner, Harold S. When Children Ask about God. LC 76-9140. 1976. pap. 4.95 (ISBN 0-8052-0549-7). Schocken.
Landau, Elliott D. & Egan, M. Winston. Guiding Your Child: A 60-Point Checklist for Parents. LC 78-70361. 48p. 1978. pap. 3.95 (ISBN 0-88290-103-6). Horizon Utah.
Landis, Mary M. Health for the Glory of God. 1976. write for info. (ISBN 0-686-15484-3); tchr's. ed. avail. (ISBN 0-686-15485-1). Rod & Staff.
Lang, J. David. Your Phone's Ringing! (Illus.). 64p. 1985. pap. 2.50 (ISBN 0-87239-897-8, 2827). Standard Pub.
Larose, Paul. Working with Children & the Liturgy. LC 81-14984. (Illus.). 95p. 1982. pap. 2.95 (ISBN 0-8189-0428-3). Alba.
Larson, Jim. Rights, Wrongs, & In-Betweens: Guiding Our Children to Christian Maturity. LC 83-72121. 144p. (Orig.). 1984. pap. 6.95 (ISBN 0-8066-2065-X, 10-5518). Augsburg.
Lashbrook, Marilyn. A Champion Is... (I'm Growing Up Ser.). (Illus.). 32p. 1986. casebound 3.95 (ISBN 0-87403-121-4, 3601). Standard Pub.
Lawton, Florrie A. God Loves Me. LC 85-24342. (Bible & Me Ser.). (Illus.). 1986. 5.95 (ISBN 0-8054-4163-8). Broadman.
Leighton, Audrey O. Fingerplay Friends. 128p. 1984. pap. 5.95 (ISBN 0-8170-1051-3). Judson.
Lewis, C. S., et al. Christian Childhoods: An Anthology of Personal Memories. Van Oss, Celia, ed. 270p. 1986. 15.95 (ISBN 0-8245-0695-2); pap. cancelled (ISBN 0-8245-0696-0). Crossroad NY.
Linville, Barbara. God Made the One & Only Me. LC 76-8737. (Illus.). 1976. pap. text ed. 3.95 (ISBN 0-916406-28-8). Accent Bks.
Loeks, Mary Foxwell. Object Lessons for Children's Worship. (Object Lesson Ser). 1979. pap. 3.50 (ISBN 0-8010-5584-9). Baker Bk.
Lost & Found Cat. (Color-a-Story Bks.). (Illus.). 1985. pap. 0.89 (ISBN 0-89191-994-5, 59949). Cook.
MacArthur, John, Jr. The Last Will Be First. (John MacArthur's Bible Studies). (Orig.). 1987. pap. 3.95 (ISBN 0-8024-5347-3). Moody.
Macaulay, Susan S. For the Children's Sake: Foundations of Education for Home & School. LC 83-72043. 192p. 1984. pap. 6.95 (ISBN 0-89107-290-X, Crossway Bks). Good News.
McCarroll, Tolbert. Guiding God's Children: A Foundation for Spiritual Growth in the Home. 240p. (Orig.). 1983. pap. 9.95 (ISBN 0-8091-2547-1). Paulist Pr.
McCay, Gracie R. & Sargent, Virginia A., eds. Children Together, Vol. 3. 128p. 1985. pap. 9.95 (ISBN 0-8170-1078-5). Judson.
McKissack, Patricia A. Lights Out, Christopher. LC 84-71375. (Christopher Bks.). (Illus.). 32p. (Orig.). 1984. pap. 3.95 (ISBN 0-8066-2110-9, 10-3870). Augsburg.
McKissack, Patricia C. It's the Truth, Christopher. LC 84-71376. (Christopher Bks.). (Illus.). 32p. (Orig.). 1984. pap. 3.95 (ISBN 0-8066-2111-7, 10-3457). Augsburg.
Marshall, Sharon. Justin: Heaven's Baby. 128p. (Orig.). 1983. pap. 3.95 (ISBN 0-8341-0833-X). Beacon Hill.
Maughan, Joyce B. Talks for Tots. LC 85-70993. 171p. 1985. 8.95 (ISBN 0-87747-804-X). Deseret Bk.
Maynard, Morlee. Happy Times with People. LC 85-25555. (Bible & Me Ser.). 1986. 5.95 (ISBN 0-8054-4165-4). Broadman.
Meier, Paul D. Christian Child Rearing & Personality Development. 1977. pap. 6.95 (ISBN 0-8010-6016-8). Baker Bk.
Mitchell, Joan. We Gather, Remember, & Eat. 1986. tchr's. ed. 2.00 (ISBN 0-89837-110-4); wkbk. 5.25 (ISBN 0-89837-109-0). Peter Li.
Mock, Dorothy. Thank You, God, for Water. (Happy Day Bks.). (Illus.). 24p. 1985. 1.59 (ISBN 0-87239-880-3, 3680). Standard Pub.
Montgomery, Herb & Montgomery, Mary. The Christian Pattern Book: Dozens of Creative Activities for Children. (Illus.). 64p. 1984. wkbk. 5.95 (ISBN 0-86683-831-7, HarpR). Har-Row.
Morentz, Jim & Morentz, Doris. Our Time Together: Children's Sermons Based on Lectionary Series A. 112p. (Orig.). 1983. pap. 8.75 (ISBN 0-687-29775-3). Abingdon.
Murphy, Elspeth C. God You Fill Us Up with Joy. (David & I Talk to God Ser.). (Illus.). 1987. pap. 2.95 (ISBN 1-55513-037-2, Chariot Bks). Cook.
Murray, Andrew. How to Bring Your Children to Christ. 320p. 1984. pap. 3.95 (ISBN 0-88368-135-8). Whitaker Hse.

Naglee, David I. From Font to Faith: John Wesley on Infant Baptism & the Nurture of Children. (American University Studies VII-Theology & Religion: Vol. 24). 272p. 1987. text ed. 26.00 (ISBN 0-8204-0375-X). P Lang Pubs.
Narramore, S. Bruce. An Ounce of Prevention: A Parent's Guide to Moral & Spiritual Growth in Children. 160p. 1973. pap. 6.95 (ISBN 0-310-30301-X, 11035P). Zondervan.
Naylor, Phyllis R. Getting Along with Your Friends. LC 79-22999. (Illus.). 1980. 8.75g (ISBN 0-687-14122-2). Abingdon.
Norweb, Jeanne. The Forbidden Door. LC 82-84552. (Illus.). 216p. 1985. pap. 5.95 (ISBN 0-89191-937-6, 59378, Chariot Bks). Cook.
The Old Log Cabin. (Color-a-Story Bks.). (Illus.). 1985. pap. 0.89 (ISBN 0-89191-993-7). Cook.
Owens, Carolyn. Color Me...Cuddly! (Illus.). 32p. 1982. pap. 0.99 (ISBN 0-87123-695-8, 220695). Bethany Hse.
Pearson, Mary Rose. More Children's Church Time. LC 82-70390. 220p. (Orig.). 1982. 14.95 (ISBN 0-89636-082-2). Accent Bks.
Perkins, Lee & Perkins, Jim. Healthier & Happier Children Through Bedtime Meditations & Stories. rev. ed. 1975. with tape 7.95 (ISBN 0-87604-106-3). ARE Pr.
Pope John Paul II. You Are My Favorites. 1980. 6.95 (ISBN 0-8198-8701-3). Dghtrs St Paul.
Powell, Carol & Powell, David. How to Bring Up Children in the Catholic Faith. 240p. 1984. 12.95 (ISBN 0-13-402537-7). P-H.
Quinn, Phil E. Renegade Saint: A Story of Hope by a Child Abuse Survivor. 1986. 12.95 (ISBN 0-687-36130-3). Abingdon.
Rathert, Donna & Prahlow, Lois. Time for Church. 24p. 1985. pap. 2.95 (ISBN 0-570-04129-5, 56-1540). Concordia.
Reece, Colleen. Honor Bound. 176p. 1983. 3.95 (ISBN 0-8024-0153-8). Moody.
Richardson, Arleta. Sixteen & Away from Home. (Grandma's Attic Ser.). 1985. pap. 3.50 (ISBN 0-89191-933-3, 59337). Cook.
Robinson, Edward. The Original Vision: A Study of the Religious Experience of Childhood. 192p. (Orig.). 1983. pap. 7.95 (ISBN 0-8164-2439-X, HarpR). Har-Row.
Robinson, Gail. God Made Only One Me. 32p. 1986. 4.95 (ISBN 0-570-04148-1). Concordia.
Rooney, Laurel. Stations of the Cross. 1984. 9.95 (ISBN 0-89837-094-9, Pub. by Pflaum Press). Peter Li.
Royer, Katherine. Happy Times with Nursery Children at Home & Church. 192p. (Orig.). 1971. pap. 7.95x (ISBN 0-8361-1275-X). Herald Pr.
Saia, Mary J. & Boyle, Judith. Our Growing Child. 112p. (Orig.). 1985. pap. 5.95 (ISBN 0-89622-221-7). Twenty-Third.
Sandberg, Jessie R. Preparing Your Children for Greatness. (Joyful Living Ser.). 1987. pap. 1.50 (ISBN 0-912623-05-5). Joyful Woman.
Schroeder, Theodore W. I Don't Want to Complain, But: Teen Conversations with God. 112p. (Orig.). 1985. pap. 4.95 (ISBN 0-570-03964-9, 12-2999). Concordia.
Scoggan, Nita. God's Plan to Enjoy Your Children. Tolliver, Alice, ed. LC 84-60581. (Illus.). 52p. 1985. pap. 2.95 (ISBN 0-910487-03-0). Royalty Pub.
Sloath, Donald E. The Dangers of Growing up in a Christian Home. 224p. 1986. pap. 8.95 (ISBN 0-8407-3064-0). Nelson.
Smith, Daniel H. How to Lead a Child to Christ. (Orig.). 1987. pap. 2.95 (ISBN 0-8024-4622-1). Moody.
Smith, Judy G. Developing a Child's Spiritual Growth: Through Sight, Sound, Taste, Touch & Smell. 80p. (Orig.). 1983. pap. 8.75 (ISBN 0-687-10499-8). Abingdon.
Sorensen, David A. The Friendship Olympics: A Young Christian Book for Boys. LC 86-32259. 112p. 1987. pap. 4.95 (ISBN 0-8066-2248-2, 10-2430). Augsburg.
Souter, John C. How to Grow New Christians. 1979. pap. 3.95 (ISBN 0-8423-1486-5). Tyndale.
Souther, Shelia. Children Can Worship, Bk. 1. (Orig.). 1986. pap. 10.95 (ISBN 0-87148-185-5). Pathway Pr.
Spurgeon, C. H. Infant Salvation. 1981. pap. 0.95 (ISBN 0-686-37176-3). Pilgrim Pubns.
Stocker, Fern N. Adoniram Judson: Following God's Plan. (Guessing Bks.). (Orig.). 1986. pap. 3.95 (ISBN 0-8024-4384-2). Moody.
Tangvald, Christine. I Can Talk to God. (I Am Special Bks.). (Illus.). 20p. 1985. 3.95 (ISBN 0-89191-907-4, 59071). Cook.
--When I Am Sick. (I Am Special Bks.). (Illus.). 20p. 1985. 3.95 (ISBN 0-89191-908-2, 59089). Cook.
Tengbom, Mildred. Does It Make Any Difference What I Do? 160p. (Orig.). 1984. pap. 4.95 (ISBN 0-87123-448-3, 210448). Bethany Hse.
Thigpen, Paul. Angels in the Air. 1986. 4.95 (ISBN 1-55513-053-4, Chariot Bks). Cook.
Uhrich, Ethel. Manners in God's House. (Illus.). 1972. pap. 3.95 (ISBN 0-87239-272-4, 2586). Standard Pub.
Van Impe, Jack. The Happy Home: Child Rearing. 34p. 1985. pap. 1.95 (ISBN 0-934803-01-3). J Van Impe.
Van Impe, Rexella. Beware: Children in Peril. 40p. 1985. pap. 1.95 (ISBN 0-934803-13-7). J Van Impe.
Vest, Lamar. The Church & Its Youth. (CTC Ser.). 1980. 5.25 (ISBN 0-87148-170-7); pap. 4.25 (ISBN 0-87148-171-5); instr's guide 7.95 (ISBN 0-87148-172-3). Pathway Pr.
Viser, William C. It's OK to Be an MK. (Orig.). 1986. pap. 7.95 (ISBN 0-8054-6337-2). Broadman.
The Warm Nest. (Color-a-Story Bks.). (Illus.). 1985. pap. 0.89 (ISBN 0-89191-997-X, 59972). Cook.
Weisheit, Eldon. God's Love for God's Children: Story Devotion for Family Time. LC 86-3397. (Illus.). 256p. (Orig.). 1986. kivar paper 9.95 (ISBN 0-8066-2213-X, 10-2680). Augsburg.
--God's Word in a Child's World: Messages & Guidelines for Sharing the Gospel with Children. LC 86-3442. 128p. (Orig.). 1986. pap. 6.95 (ISBN 0-8066-2214-8, 10-2745). Augsburg.
--To the Kid in the Pew-Series C. (To the Kid in the Pew Ser.). 128p. 1976. 6.75 (ISBN 0-570-03261-X, 15-2169). Concordia.
Westerhoff, John H., III. Will Our Children Have Faith? 144p. 1983. pap. 6.95 (ISBN 0-8164-2435-7, AY7452, HarpR). Har-Row.

CHILDREN, JEWISH
see Jewish Children

CHILDREN AND DEATH
Doleski, Teddi. A Present for Jessica. (Illus.). 48p. (Orig.). 1986. pap. 2.50 (ISBN 0-8091-6557-0). Paulist Pr.
LaVelle, Steven. Just Passing Through. (Illus.). 32p. (Orig.). 1980. pap. 1.50 (ISBN 0-87516-402-1). De Vorss.
Lombardo, Victor S. & Lombardo, Edith F. Kids Grieve Too! (Illus.). 88p. 1986. 17.75x (ISBN 0-398-05275-1). C C Thomas.
Stickney, Doris. Water Bugs & Dragonflies: Explaining Death to Children. (Illus.). 24p. 1982. pap. 1.25 (ISBN 0-8298-0609-1). Pilgrim NY.
Wolf, Anna W. Helping Your Child to Understand Death. rev. ed. 1973. pap. 2.30 (ISBN 0-87183-240-2). Jewish Bd Family.

CHILDREN IN THE BIBLE
Bourgeois, Jean-Francois. Los Ninos de la Biblia. Maecha, Alberto, ed. Orig. Title: Les Enfants de la Bible. (Span., Illus.). 40p. 1984. pap. write for info. (ISBN 0-942504-11-9). Overcomer Pr.
Fugate, J. Richard. What the Bible Says About Child Training. (What the Bible Says about...Ser.). (Illus.). 287p. 1980. pap. 5.95 (ISBN 0-86717-000-X). Aletheia Pubs.
Rostron, Hilda L. Stories About Children of the Bible. (Ladybird Ser). (Illus.). 1962. bds. 2.50 (ISBN 0-87508-860-0). Chr Lit.

CHILDREN OF GOD
Mercer, Ethel. A Child of the King. (Illus.). 80p. 1987. 8.95 (ISBN 0-89962-586-X). Todd & Honeywell.

CHILDREN'S HYMNS
see also Sunday-Schools–Hymns
Armstrong, C. F. Hymns for Little Children. 1977. lib. bdg. 59.95 (ISBN 0-8490-2030-1). Gordon Pr.
Beautiful Ways Songs. pap. 0.30 (ISBN 0-686-29099-2). Faith Pub Hse.
Cromie, Marguerite. Children Sing. 1975. pap. 1.25 (ISBN 0-8198-0390-1). Dghtrs St Paul.
Curry, W. Lawrence, ed. Songs & Hymns for Primary Children. 1978. softcover 3.95 (ISBN 0-664-10117-8). Westminster.
Gross, Arthur W. & Jahsmann, Allan H. Little Children Sing to God! 1960. 8.95 (ISBN 0-570-03471-X, 56-1036). Concordia.
Haas, James E. Rainbow Songs. 40p. (Orig.). 1975. pap. 3.95 (ISBN 0-8192-1201-6). Morehouse.
Hartzler, Arlene & Gaeddert, John, eds. Children's Hymnary. LC 67-24327. 1967. 5.95 (ISBN 0-87303-095-8). Faith & Life.
Royer, Katherine, ed. Nursery Songbook. (Illus.). 48p. 1957. pap. 2.95x (ISBN 0-8361-1278-4). Herald Pr.
Songs for Early Childhood. 1958. 3.25 ea. (ISBN 0-664-10058-9). Westminster.
Songs for Young Children. LC 75-40910. (Illus.). 1976. spiral bdg. 3.50 (ISBN 0-916406-31-8). Accent Bks.
Stelzer, Theodore G. Child's Garden of Song. (Concordia Primary Religion Ser). 1949. 9.95 (ISBN 0-570-03479-5, 56-1003). Concordia.
Wilson, Valerie & Hull, Shirley, eds. Preschoolers Sing & Say. 1976. wire spiral 2.50 (ISBN 0-87227-045-9). Reg Baptist.
Youth with a Mission. The Singing Word: Youth with a Mission Songbook. enl &rev. 2nd ed. (Illus.). 288p. 1974. plastic spiral bd. 5.95 (ISBN 0-87123-505-6, 280505). Bethany Hse.

CHILDREN'S LITERATURE (COLLECTIONS)
Holbein, Hans. Images of the Old Testament. (Children's Books from the Past: Vol. 1). 100p. 1973. Repr. of 1549 ed. 32.65 (ISBN 3-261-01003-7). P Lang Pubs.

CHILDREN'S SERMONS
see also Object-Teaching
Behnke, Daniel J. Fifty Worship Talks for Children. 1982. pap. 5.56 (ISBN 0-570-03850-2, 12-2805). Concordia.
Benjamin, Don-Paul & Miner, Ron. Come Sit with Me Again: Sermons for Children. (Illus.). 128p. (Orig.). 1987. pap. 6.95 (ISBN 0-8298-0748-9). Pilgrim NY.
Bess, C. W. Object-Centered Children's Sermons. (Object Lesson Ser.). 1978. pap. 3.95 (ISBN 0-8010-0734-8). Baker Bk.
Bess, C. W. & DeBand, Roy E. Bible-Centered Object Sermons for Children. (Object Lesson Ser.). 128p. 1985. pap. 4.95 (ISBN 0-8010-0886-7). Baker Bk.
Bosco, Ronald A., ed. Lessons for the Children of Godly Ancestors. LC 82-5844. (Sermon in America Ser.). 1982. 60.00x (ISBN 0-8201-1381-6). Schol Facsimiles.
Brennan-Nichols, Patricia. Liturgies & Lessons: Childrens Homilies. 1984. pap. 9.95 (ISBN 0-941850-13-7). Sunday Pubns.
Bruinsma, Sheryl. Object Lessons for Special Days. 80p. 1986. 4.50 (ISBN 0-8010-0920-0). Baker Bk.
Castle, Leon W. A Year of Children's Sermons. LC 76-6717. (Illus.). 144p. 1976. pap. 4.95 (ISBN 0-8054-4918-3). Broadman.
Coniaris, A. M. Eighty Talks for Orthodox Young People. 1975. pap. 4.95 (ISBN 0-937032-16-6). Light&Life Pub Co MN.
Cornils, Stanley. Twenty-Five Two-Minute Talks for Children. 48p. 1985. pap. 2.95 (ISBN 0-87239-867-6, 2882). Standard Pub.
Cross, Luther S. Story Sermons for Children. (Object Lesson Ser.). (Orig.). 1966. pap. 3.50 (ISBN 0-8010-2328-9). Baker Bk.
Dann, Bucky. Better Children's Sermons: 54 Visual Lessons, Dialogues, & Demonstrations. LC 83-6851. 124p. (Orig.). 1983. pap. 7.95 (ISBN 0-664-24481-5). Westminster.
--Creating Children's Sermons: Fifty-One Visual Lessons. LC 81-10493. 132p. pap. 7.95 (ISBN 0-664-24383-5). Westminster.
Edstrom, Lois. Contemporary Object Lessons for Children's Church. (Object Lessons Ser.). 112p. 1986. 4.50 (ISBN 0-8010-3432-9). Baker Bk.
Humbertson, James E., ed. Evangelical Sunday School Lesson Commentary 1984-1985. 424p. 1984. 4.00 (ISBN 0-87148-302-5). Pathway Pr.
Jennings, Shirley. God Is Always Near. Sherer, Michael L., ed. (Orig.). 1987. pap. 5.95 (ISBN 0-89536-857-9, 7816). CSS of Ohio.
Jones, James A., III. Conversations with Children. LC 85-40201. (Illus.). 96p. 1985. 7.95 (ISBN 0-938232-72-X). Winston-Derek.
Jordan, Jerry M. Another Brown Bag. LC 80-36849. (Illus.). 1980. pap. 6.95 (ISBN 0-8298-0406-4). Pilgrim NY.
Linam, Gail. God's People: A Book of Children's Sermons. LC 85-25736. (Orig.). 1986. pap. 4.95 (ISBN 0-8054-4928-0). Broadman.
McConnell, Cecil & McConnell, Mary. Objetos Que Ensenan de Dios. (Span.). 96p. 1986. pap. 3.50 (ISBN 0-311-44007-X). Casa Bautista.
Miner, Ron. Come Sit with Me: Sermons for Children. LC 81-10650. (Illus.). 96p. (Orig.). 1981. pap. 5.95 (ISBN 0-8298-0469-2). Pilgrim NY.
Morentz, Jim & Morentz, Doris. Children's Object Lesson Sermons Based on the New Common Lectionary: Year C. 112p. (Orig.). 1985. pap. 6.95 (ISBN 0-687-06498-8). Abingdon.
Radius, Marianne. Ninety Story Sermons for Children's Church. 286p. 1976. pap. 7.95 (ISBN 0-8010-7641-2). Baker Bk.
--One Hundred & Twenty Dramatic Story Sermons for Children's Church. 368p. 1985. pap. 8.95 (ISBN 0-8010-7730-3). Baker Bk.
Reid, John C. Twenty-Two More Object Talks for Children's Worship. (Illus.). 80p. 1987. pap. 3.50 (ISBN 0-87403-239-3, 2879). Standard Pub.
Runk, Wesley. What Color Is Your Balloon? (Orig.). 1987. pap. price not set (ISBN 0-89536-883-8, 7869). CSS of Ohio.
Runk, Wesley T. On Jesus' Team. Sherer, Michael L., ed. (Orig.). 1986. pap. 5.25 (ISBN 0-89536-809-9, 6838). CSS of Ohio.
Schmalenberger, Jerry. Saints Who Shaped the Church. Sherer, Michael L., ed. (Orig.). 1987. pap. 6.50 (ISBN 0-89536-856-0, 7815). CSS of Ohio.
Smelser, Georgia & Westberg, Barbara. Fifty-Two Visualized Talks for Children's Church. (Illus., Orig.). 1981. pap. 4.50 tchr's ed (ISBN 0-912315-13-X). Word Aflame.
Spurgeon, C. H. Come Ye Children. 1979. pap. 2.95 (ISBN 0-686-16840-2). Pilgrim Pubns.
Uhl, Harold J. The Gospel for Children: Object Messages from the Gospel of Mark. LC 75-14695. 128p. 1975. pap. 6.95 (ISBN 0-8066-1493-5, 10-2830). Augsburg.
Van Seters, Virginia A. Twenty-Two Object Talks for Children's Worship. (Illus.). 48p. 1986. pap. 2.95 (ISBN 0-87403-055-2, 2866). Standard Pub.
Weisheit, E. Sixty-One Worship Talks for Children. rev. ed. LC 68-20728. 1975. pap. 4.95 (ISBN 0-570-03714-X, 12-2616). Concordia.
Weisheit, Eldon. The Gospel for Kids: Series B. 1978. 6.75 (ISBN 0-570-03267-9, 15-2713). Concordia.
--Sixty-One Gospel Talks for Children: With Suggested Objects for Illustration. LC 70-96217. 1969. pap. 4.95 (ISBN 0-570-03713-1, 12-2615). Concordia.
--To the Kid in the Pew-Series B. LC 74-4548. 1975. 6.75 (ISBN 0-570-03252-0, 15-2160). Concordia.
Weishiet, Eldon. Gospel for Kids: Series A. 1977. 6.75 (ISBN 0-570-03265-2, 15-2711). Concordia.
Wyly, Louise B. Twenty-Six Lessons for Children's Worship: Listening When God Speaks. (Illus.). 144p. 1986. 8.95 (ISBN 0-87403-057-9, 3321). Standard Pub.

CHILDREN'S SONGS
see also Children's Hymns
Andre, Evelyn, compiled by. Rejoice & Sing Praise: A Collection of Songs & Materials to Be Used with Elementary Boys & Girls. LC 77-1604. 1977. pap. 9.95 (ISBN 0-687-35930-9). Abingdon.
Children at Sunrise Ranch, illus. Songs for the Joy of Living. (Illus.). 50p. 1985. ring-bound 11.95 (ISBN 0-932869-01-7). Eden Valley.
Clawson, Sharalee S. I Feel My Saviour's Love: Themes from LDS Children's Songs in Counted Cross-Stitch. 9p. 1986. pap. 5.00 (ISBN 0-88290-277-6). Horizon Utah.
McKernan, Llewellyn. More Songs of Gladness (Suppl.) (Arch Bks.). (Illus.). 24p. 1987. pap. 0.99 (ISBN 0-570-09004-0, 59-1432). Concordia.
Perry, Frances B., ed. Let's Sing Together: Favorite Primary Songs of Members of the Church of Jesus Christ of Latter-day Saints. (Illus.). 96p. 1981. 10.98 (ISBN 0-941518-00-0). Perry Enterprises.
Sing! Sing! Sing! Music Book for Children. 1.50 (ISBN 0-8198-6836-1). Dghtrs St Paul.
Stevens, Carolyn S. Children's Favorites: Inspirational Songs Arranged for the Piano. 40p. 1986. pap. 7.95 (ISBN 0-88290-275-X). Horizon Utah.

CHILDREN'S STORIES
see also Christmas Stories; Easter Stories; Missionary Stories; Story-Telling
Branch, Mary. Tell Me a Story. LC 78-53210. (Stories That Win Ser.). 1978. pap. 1.25 (ISBN 0-8163-0210-3, 20079-0). Pacific Pr Pub Assn.
Bunsen, Rick, ed. The Golden Christmas Treasury. LC 84-72934. (Illus.). 80p. 1986. 7.95 (ISBN 0-307-15585-4, Pub. by Golden Bks). Western Pub.
Carlson, Bernice W. Listen & Help Tell the Story. (Illus.). 1965. 9.95 (ISBN 0-687-22096-3). Abingdon.
Holt, Pat. Mommy's Lesson. 32p. 1985. pap. 3.95 (ISBN 0-570-04131-7, 56-1545). Concordia.
Kiefer, Velma B. Stories to Tell in Children's Church. (Paperback Program Ser.). Orig. Title: Please Tell Me a Story. 1976. pap. 5.95 (ISBN 0-8010-5371-4). Baker Bk.
Smith, Elva S. & Hazeltine, Alice I.compiled by. Christmas in Legend & Story: A Book for Boys & Girls Illustrated from Famous Paintings. LC 72-39390. (Granger Index Reprint Ser.). Repr. of 1915 ed. 18.00 (ISBN 0-8369-6353-9). Ayer Co Pubs.
Sparks, Judy, ed. Baby Jesus ABC Storybook. (Happy Day Bk.). (Illus.). 24p. 1979. 1.59 (ISBN 0-87239-354-2, 3624). Standard Pub.

CHILIASM
see Millennium

CHINA–ANTIQUITIES
Guangzhou Municipal Museum. Guangzhou Hanmu Excavation of the Han Tombs at Guangzhou. 526p. 1981. 150.00x (ISBN 0-317-44071-3, Pub. by Han-Shan Tang Ltd). State mutual Bk.
Laufer, Berthold. Jade: A Study in Chinese Archaeology & Religion. LC 74-81085. (Illus.). 480p. 1975. pap. 6.95 (ISBN 0-486-23123-2). Dover.
--Jade: A Study in Chinese Archaeology & Religion. (Field Museum of Natural History). (Illus.). 1912. 41.00 (ISBN 0-527-01870-8). Kraus Repr.
--Jade: A Study in Chinese Archaeology & Religion. (Illus.). 15.25 (ISBN 0-8446-5214-8). Peter Smith.
Zhenyu, Luo. Gu Mingqi Tulu. 1916. 300.00x (ISBN 0-317-44070-5, Pub. by Han-Shan Tang Ltd). State Mutual Bk.

CHINA–CHURCH HISTORY

De Groot, J. J. Sectarianism & Religious Persecution in China: A Page in the History of Religions, 2 vols. 872p. 1972. Repr. of 1903 ed. 60.00x (ISBN 0-7165-2034-6, Pub. by Irish Academic Pr Ireland). Biblio Dist.

Wurth, Elmer P. Papal Documents Relating to the New China, 1937-1984. 193p. (Orig.). 1985. pap. 10.00 (ISBN 0-88344-403-8). Orbis Bks.

CHINA–RELIGION

Baker, Dwight C. T'ai Shan: An Account of the Sacred Eastern Peak of China. lib. bdg. 79.95 (ISBN 0-87968-474-7). Krishna Pr.

Beal, Samuel. The Fo-sho-hing-tsan-king. (Sacred Books of the East: Vol. 19). 15.00 (ISBN 0-89581-523-0). Asian Human Pr.

Blofeld, John. Bodhisattva of Compassion: The Mystical Tradition of Kuan Yin. LC 77-91352. (Illus.). 155p. 1978. pap. 9.95 (ISBN 0-87773-126-8, 73609-5). Shambhala Pubns.

Broomhall, A. J. Hudson Taylor & China's Open Century: Bk. V. Refiner's Fire, Bk. V. 1985. pap. 9.95 (ISBN 0-340-36866-7). OMF Bks.

Chan, Hok-Lam & DeBary, W. Theodore, eds. Yuan Thought: Chinese Thought & Religion Under the Mongols. LC 82-1259. 512p. 1982. 39.00x (ISBN 0-231-05324-X). Columbia U Pr.

Chiu, Milton M. The Tao of Chinese Religion. (Illus.). 432p. (Orig.). 1985. lib. bdg. 29.50 (ISBN 0-8191-4263-8); pap. text ed. 17.50 (ISBN 0-8191-4264-6). U Pr of Amer.

De Groot, J. J. Le Cope du Mahayana en Chine: Amsterdam, 1892. LC 78-74288. (Oriental Religions Ser.: Vol. 15). 281p. 1980. lib. bdg. 40.00 (ISBN 0-8240-3917-3). Garland Pub.

DeGroot, J. J. The Religious System of China, 6 vols. 1982. Repr. of 1892 ed. 130.00 (ISBN 0-89986-346-9). Oriental Bk Store.

De Groot, J. J. Sectarianism & Religious Persecution in China: A Page in the History of Religions, 2 vols. 872p. 1972. Repr. of 1903 ed. 60.00x (ISBN 0-7165-2034-6, Pub. by Irish Academic Pr Ireland). Biblio Dist.

Edkins, Joseph. Chinese Buddhism: A Volume of Sketches, Historical, Descriptive & Critical. 2nd, rev. ed. 487p. Repr. of 1893 ed. text ed. 27.50x (Pub. by Chinese Matl Ctr). Coronet Bks.

Elliott, Alan J. Chinese Spirit-Medium Cults in Singapore. 1981. Repr. of 1955 ed. 15.00 (ISBN 0-89986-347-7). Oriental Bk Store.

Fung, Raymond, compiled by. Households of God on China's Soil. LC 82-18974. 84p. (Orig.). 1983. pap. 5.95 (ISBN 0-88344-189-6). Orbis Bks.

Giles, H. A. The Religions of Ancient China. 59.95 (ISBN 0-8490-0941-3). Gordon Pr.

Giles, Herbert A. Religions of Ancient China. LC 79-95067. (Select Bibliographies Reprint Ser). 1905. 17.00 (ISBN 0-8369-5069-0). Ayer Co Pubs.

--Religions of Ancient China. LC 76-20524. 1976. Repr. of 1905 ed. lib. bdg. 17.00 (ISBN 0-8414-4518-4). Folcroft.

Granet, Marcel. The Religion of the Chinese People. Freedman, Maurice, tr. from Fr. 1977. pap. 5.95x (ISBN 0-06-131905-8, TB 1905, Torch). Har-Row.

Groot, Jan J. The Religion of the Chinese. LC 79-2824. 230p. 1981. Repr. of 1910 ed. 21.50 (ISBN 0-8305-0004-9). Hyperion Conn.

Hanson, Eric O. Catholic Politics in China & Korea. LC 79-27206. 160p. (Orig.). 1980. pap. 2.49 (ISBN 0-88344-084-9). Orbis Bks.

Harvey, Edwin D. The Mind of China. LC 73-874. (China Studies: from Confucius to Mao Ser). x, 321p. 1973. Repr. of 1933 ed. 25.50 (ISBN 0-88355-069-5). Hyperion Conn.

Henderson, John B. The Development & Decline of Chinese Cosmology. LC 84-4000. (Neo-Confucian Studies). 280p. 1984. 36.00 (ISBN 0-231-05772-5); pap. cancelled (ISBN 0-231-05773-3). Columbia U Pr.

Jochim, Christian. Chinese Religions: A Cultural Perspective. (Illus.). 224p. 1986. pap. text ed. 17.00 (ISBN 0-13-132994-4). P-H.

Kao, James. Chinese Divination. pap. 26.80 (ISBN 0-317-26229-7, 2055584). Bks Demand UMI.

Keijiro, Marui. Survey of Taiwanese Religions in 1919, 2 vols. (Asian Folklore & Social Life Monograph: Nos. 56-57). (Japanese.). 428p. 1974. 25.00 (ISBN 0-89986-053-2). Oriental Bk Store.

Kwok, D. W. Scientism in Chinese Thought, Nineteen Hundred to Nineteen Fifty. LC 73-162297. 231p. 1972. Repr. of 1965 ed. 18.00 (ISBN 0-8196-0275-2). Biblo.

Laufer, Berthold. Jade: A Study in Chinese Archaeology & Religion. LC 74-81085. (Illus.). 480p. 1975. pap. 6.95 (ISBN 0-486-23123-2). Dover.

--Jade: A Study in Chinese Archaeology & Religion. (Field Museum of Natural History). (Illus.). 1912. 41.00 (ISBN 0-527-01870-8). Kraus Repr.

--Jade: A Study in Chinese Archaeology & Religion. (Illus.). 15.25 (ISBN 0-8446-5214-8). Peter Smith.

Lawrence, Carl. The Church in China. 176p. (Orig.). 1985. pap. 5.95 (ISBN 0-87123-815-2). Bethany Hse.

Legge, James. The Religions of China. LC 78-2685. 1979. Repr. of 1880 ed. lib. bdg. 45.00 (ISBN 0-8495-3313-9). Arden Lib.

--The Religions of China. LC 76-28535. 1976. Repr. of 1880 ed. lib. bdg. 40.00 (ISBN 0-8414-5809-X). Folcroft.

--The Sacred Books of China, 6 vols. 600.00. Krishna Pr.

--The Sacred Books of China. (Sacred Bks. of the East: Vols. 3, 16, 27, 28, 39, 40). 6 vols. 90.00 (ISBN 0-686-97476-X); 15.00 ea. Asian Human Pr.

Lyall, Leslie T. God Reigns in China. 1985. pap. 4.50 (ISBN 0-340-36199-9). OMF Bks.

Martin, Mary L. & MacInnis, Donald. Values & Religion in China Today: A Teaching Workbook & Lesson Series. 141p. (Orig.). 1985. pap. 12.95 (ISBN 0-88344-527-1). Orbis Bks.

Maspero, Henri. Taoism & Chinese Religion. Kierman, Frank A., Jr., tr. from Fr. LC 80-13444. Orig. Title: Le Taoisme et les religions Chinoises. 656p. 1981. lib. bdg. 40.00x (ISBN 0-87023-308-4). U of Mass Pr.

Moule, A. C. Christians in China before the Year 1550. 1972. lib. bdg. 20.00x (ISBN 0-374-95972-2, Octagon). Hippocrene Bks.

Orr, Robert G. Religion in China. (Orig.). 1980. pap. 4.95 (ISBN 0-377-00103-1). Friend Pr.

Overmyer, Daniel. The Religions of China. LC 85-42789. 128p. (Orig.). 1986. pap. 6.95 (ISBN 0-06-066401-0, HarpR). Har-Row.

Rowley, Harold H. Prophecy & Religion in Ancient China & Israel. LC 56-12074. 1956. 12.00x (ISBN 0-8401-2059-1). A R Allenson.

Sam Pollard of Yunnan. pap. 3.95 (ISBN 0-686-23584-3). Schmul Pub Co.

Shryock, John K. The Temples of Anking & Their Cults, a Study of Modern Chinese Religion. LC 70-38083. Repr. of 1931 ed. 26.00 (ISBN 0-404-56947-1). AMS Pr.

Sirr, Henry C. China & the Chinese: Their Religion, Culture, Customs, & Manufactures; The Evils Arising from the Opium Trade, 2 vols. 915p. Repr. of 1849 ed. Set. text ed. 38.00x (ISBN 0-89644-564-X, Pub. by Chinese Matl Ctr). Coronet Bks.

Smith, Carl T. Chinese Christians: Elites, Middlemen, & the Church in Hong Kong. (Illus.). 264p. 1986. 27.00x (ISBN 0-19-583973-0). Oxford U Pr.

Snow, Helen F. Totemism, the T'AO-T'iEH & the Chinese Ritual Bronzes. enl. ed. 100p. 1986. 35.00 (ISBN 0-686-64038-1). H F Snow.

Soothill, William E. The Three Religions of China. LC 73-899. (China Studies: from Confucius to Mao Ser.). (Illus.). 271p. 1973. Repr. of 1929 ed. 28.00 (ISBN 0-88355-093-8). Hyperion Conn.

Story, Grace C. Footprints on the Sands of China. pap. 2.25 (ISBN 0-686-13722-1). Crusade Pubs.

Thompson, Laurence G. Chinese Religion in Western Languages: A Comprehensive & Classified Bibliography of Publications in English, French, & German Through 1980. LC 84-24010. (Monograph of the Association for Asian Studies: No. XLI). 302p. 1985. HC Monograph 19.95x (ISBN 0-8165-0926-3). U of Ariz Pr.

Tien, Chen Fu. The Current Religious Policy of People's Republic of China (January 1, 1976 to March 15, 1979) Pt. I: An Inquiry. 73p. (Orig.). 1983. pap. 12.95. Chen Fu.

Ting, K. H., et al. Chinese Christians Speak Out. (Chinese Spotlight Ser.). (Illus.). 140p. 1984. pap. 3.95 (ISBN 0-8351-1281-0). China Bks.

Travels of an Alchemist: The Journey of the Taoist Ch'ang-Ch'un from China to the Hindukush. 1978. Repr. of 1931 ed. 12.00 (ISBN 0-89986-341-8). Oriental Bk Store.

Wagner, Rudolf G. Reenacting the Heavenly Vision: The Role of Religion in the Taping Rebellion. (China Research Monograph: No. 25). (Illus.). 146p. 1984. pap. 12.00x (ISBN 0-912966-60-2). IEAS.

Weber, Max. Religion of China. 1968. 14.95 (ISBN 0-02-934440-9); text ed. 14.95 (ISBN 0-02-934450-6). Free Pr.

Welch, Holmes. The Buddhist Revival in China: With a Section of Photos by Henri Cartier-Bresson. LC 68-15645. (Harvard East Asian Ser.: Vol. 33). pap. 80.60 (ISBN 0-317-28777-X, 2017757). Bks Demand UMI.

Welch, Holmes & Seidel, Anna, eds. Facets of Taoism: Essays in Chinese Religion. LC 77-28034. 1979. 38.00x (ISBN 0-300-01695-6); pap. 8.95x (ISBN 0-300-02673-0). Yale U Pr.

Weller, Robert P. Unities & Diversities in Chinese Religion. LC 86-9085. 250p. 1986. 22.50x (ISBN 0-295-96397-2). U of Wash Pr.

Williams, B. W. The Joke of Christianizing China. 40p. 1983. pap. 3.00 (ISBN 0-910309-13-2). Am Atheist.

Wolf, Arthur P., ed. Religion & Ritual in Chinese Society. LC 73-89863. (Studies in Chinese Society). xiv, 378p. 1974. 27.50x (ISBN 0-8047-0858-4). Stanford U Pr.

Yang, Yung-Ch'Ing. China's Religious Heritage. LC 72-4542. (Essay Index Reprint Ser.). Repr. of 1943 ed. 16.00 (ISBN 0-8369-2981-0). Ayer Co Pubs.

Yu, David C. Guide to Chinese Religion. (Reference: Asian Phil.-Rel. Ser.). 1985. lib. bdg. 45.00 (ISBN 0-8161-7902-6). G K Hall.

Yuan, Ch'u. The Nine Songs: A Study of Shamanism in Ancient China. 2nd ed. Waley, Arthur, tr. LC 73-84228. 1973. pap. 3.95 (ISBN 0-87286-075-2). City Lights.

CHINESE LEGENDS

see Legends, Chinese

CHOIR BOOKS

see Service Books (Music)

CHOIRBOY TRAINING

Osbeck, Kenneth W. Devotional Warm-ups for Church Choirs. LC 85-17222. 96p. (Orig.). 1985. pap. 2.95 (ISBN 0-8254-3421-1); pap. 29.00 dozen (ISBN 0-8254-3423-8). Kregel.

CHOIRS (MUSIC)

see also Choirboy Training; Choral Music; Choral Singing; Conducting, Choral

Hastings, Thomas. The History of Forty Choirs. LC 72-1620. Repr. of 1854 ed. 18.50 (ISBN 0-404-08313-7). AMS Pr.

Jacobs, Ruth K. The Successful Children's Choir. 64p. 1984. pap. 5.00 (ISBN 0-912222-12-3). FitzSimons.

Martin-Marrero, Vernetta. The Gospel Church Choir Organizer. 150p. 1984. 3 ring hard storage binder 29.95 (ISBN 0-9613430-0-1). Martin-Marrero.

Mees, A. Choirs & Choral Music. LC 68-25296. (Studies in Music, No. 42). 1969. Repr. of 1901 ed. lib. bdg. 49.95x (ISBN 0-8383-0308-0). Haskell.

Mees, Arthur. Choirs & Choral Music. Repr. of 1901 ed. lib. bdg. 22.50 (ISBN 0-8371-1967-7, MECM). Greenwood.

Robinson, Ray & Winold, Allen. The Choral Experience: Literature, Materials, & Methods. 1976. text ed. 25.50 scp (ISBN 0-06-161419-X, HarpC). Har-Row.

Schield, Dean C. More Effective Choir Ministry: A Manual for Church Musicians. LC 86-42932. 32p. (Orig.). 1986. pap. 4.00 (ISBN 0-937021-02-4). Sagamore Bks MI.

CH'ONDOGYO

Weems, Benjamin. Reform, Rebellion & the Heavenly Way. LC 64-17267. (Association for Asian Studies Monograph: No. 15). 122p. 1964. 7.95x (ISBN 0-8165-0144-0). U of Ariz Pr.

CHORAL MUSIC

Here are entered works on choral music. Collections of choral compositions are entered under Choruses.

see also Choirs (Music); Choral Singing; Conducting, Choral; Part-Songs

Jacobson, Betty. Blessed be God, Choral Instrumental Ensemble. pap. 20.00 (ISBN 0-317-09814-4, 2003553). Bks Demand UMI.

Mason, Lowell, ed. The Boston Handel & Haydn Society Collection of Church Music. LC 77-171078. (Earlier American Music Ser.: Vol. 15). 324p. 1973. Repr. of 1822 ed. lib. bdg. 37.50 (ISBN 0-306-77315-5). Da Capo.

Mees, A. Choirs & Choral Music. LC 68-25296. (Studies in Music, No. 42). 1969. Repr. of 1901 ed. lib. bdg. 49.95x (ISBN 0-8383-0308-0). Haskell.

Mees, Arthur. Choirs & Choral Music. Repr. of 1901 ed. lib. bdg. 22.50 (ISBN 0-8371-1967-7, MECM). Greenwood.

Moe, Daniel. Basic Choral Concepts. 31p. 1972. pap. 4.00 (ISBN 0-8066-1216-9, 11-9080). Augsburg.

Wienandt, Elwyn A. Choral Music of the Church. LC 80-12943. (Music Reprint Ser.). xi, 494p. 1980. Repr. of 1965 ed. lib. bdg. 45.00 (ISBN 0-306-76002-9). Da Capo.

CHORAL MUSIC–BIBLIOGRAPHY

Eslinger, Gary S. & Daugherty, F. Mark, eds. Sacred Choral Music in Print, 2 vols. 2nd ed. LC 85-15368. (Music in Print Ser.: Vol. 1). 1312p. 1985. lib. bdg. 180.00 (ISBN 0-88478-017-1). Musicdata.

Laster, James, compiled by. Catalogue of Choral Music Arranged in Biblical Order. LC 82-16745. 269p. 1983. 27.50 (ISBN 0-8108-1592-3). Scarecrow.

CHORAL SINGING

see also Choirboy Training; Choirs (Music); Conducting, Choral

Ehmann, Wilhelm. Choral Directing. Wiebe, George D., tr. 1968. 15.95 (ISBN 0-8066-0832-3, 11-9130). Augsburg.

Robinson, Ray & Winold, Allen. The Choral Experience: Literature, Materials, & Methods. 1976. text ed. 25.50 scp (ISBN 0-06-161419-X, HarpC). Har-Row.

CHORUSES, SACRED

see also Anthems; Sacred Vocal Music; Service Books (Music)

Batten, Adrian. Four Anthems. Evans, David, ed. LC 68-65217. (Penn State Music Series, No. 17). 232p. pap. 3.25x (ISBN 0-271-09117-7). Pa St U Pr.

Cummings, Charles. Songs of Freedom: The Psalter As a School of Prayer. 1986. pap. 6.95 (ISBN 0-87193-245-8). Dimension Bks.

Curry, W. Lawrence, ed. Anthems for the Junior Choir, 5 bks. 1.50 ea. Westminster.

--Service Music for the Adult Choir. 3.50 ea. (ISBN 0-664-10059-7). Westminster.

Davies, Walford & Ley, Henry G., eds. Church Anthem Book: One Hundred Anthems. rev. ed. 1959. 17.50x (ISBN 0-19-353106-2). Oxford U Pr.

Jacques, Reginald & Willcocks, David. Carols for Choirs: Fifty Christmas Carols, Bk. 1. (YA) 1961. 12.00 (ISBN 0-19-353221-2); pap. 7.00 (ISBN 0-19-353222-0). Oxford U Pr.

Osbeck, Kenneth W. Pocket Guide for the Church Choir Member. 48p. 1984. pap. 1.25 (ISBN 0-8254-3408-4); Per Dozen. pap. 12.95 (ISBN 0-8254-3417-3). Kregel.

Oxford Easy Anthem Book. 1957. 12.00 (ISBN 0-19-353320-0); pap. 7.00 (ISBN 0-19-353321-9). Oxford U Pr.

Ryazhsky, A. Uchjebnik Tserkovnago Penija. Tr. of Textbook of Sacred Singing. 105p. 1966. pap. 5.00 (ISBN 0-317-30382-1). Holy Trinity.

CHOSEN PEOPLE (JEWS)

see Jews–Election, Doctrine of

CHRIST

see Jesus Christ

CHRIST APOSTOLIC CHURCH

Baker, William J. Beyond Port & Prejudice. 1981. 20.00 (ISBN 0-89101-032-7). U Maine Orono.

CHRISTENING

see Baptism

CHRISTIAN ALEXANDRIAN SCHOOL

see Alexandrian School, Christian

CHRISTIAN AND MISSIONARY ALLIANCE–MISSIONS

Tozer, Aiden W. Let My People Go. pap. 4.45 (ISBN 0-87509-189-X). Chr Pubns.

CHRISTIAN ANTIQUITIES

see also Architecture, Gothic; Catacombs; Christian Art and Symbolism; Church Architecture; Church Furniture; Church Vestments; Crosses; Fasts and Feasts; Sepulchral Monuments

Bourasse, J. J. Dictionnaire d'Archeologie Sacree, 2 vols. Migne, J. P., ed. (Nouvelle Encyclopedie Theologique Ser.: Vols. 11-12). (Fr.). 1236p. Repr. of 1852 ed. lib. bdg. 157.00x (ISBN 0-89241-261-5). Caratzas.

Bowder, Diana. The Age of Constantine & Julian. (Illus.). 230p. 1978. text ed. 32.50x (ISBN 0-06-490601-9, 06359). B&N Imports.

Brand, John. Observations on the Popular Antiquities of Great Britain: Chiefly Illustrating the Origin of Our Vulgar & Provincial Customs, Ceremonies & Superstitions, 3 vols. LC 67-23896. 1969. Repr. of 1849 ed. Set. 68.00x (ISBN 0-8103-3256-6). Gale.

Finegan, Jack. Light from the Ancient Past, 2 vols. 2nd ed. (Illus.). 1959. Vol. 1 2nd Ed. 52.50 (ISBN 0-691-03550-4); Vol. 1 2nd Edition. pap. 16.50 (ISBN 0-691-00207-X); Vol. 2. 50.00 (ISBN 0-691-03551-2); Vol. 2. pap. 15.50x (ISBN 0-691-00208-8); Set. 90.00 (ISBN 0-686-76901-5). Princeton U Pr.

Hanson, Richard. Studies in Christian Antiquity. 376p. 1986. 32.95 (ISBN 0-567-09363-8, Pub. by T & T Clark Ltd UK). Fortress.

Hopkins, C. & Baur, P. V. Christian Church at Dura-Europos. (Illus.). 1934. pap. 39.50x (ISBN 0-686-50041-5). Elliots Bks.

Kirsch, Johann P. Roemischen Titelkirchen Im Altertum. 1918. 19.00 (ISBN 0-384-29614-9). Johnson Repr.

Leclercq, Dom H. & Marron, Henri. Dictionnaire d'Archeologie Chretienne et de Liturgie, 28 vols. (Fr.). 1903. Set. 1995.00 (ISBN 0-686-57001-4, M-6342). French & Eur.

Mader, Andreas E. Altchristliche Basiliken und Lokaltraditionen in Sudjudaa. pap. 19.00 (ISBN 0-384-35000-3). Johnson Repr.

Riley, Hugh M. Christian Initiation: A Comparative Study of the Interpretation of the Baptismal Liturgy in the Mystagogical Writing of Cyril of Jerusalem, John Chrysostom, Theodore of Mopsuetia, & Ambrose of Milan. LC 74-11191. (Catholic University of America Studies in Christian Antiquity: No. 17). pap. 128.80 (ISBN 0-317-27922-X, 2025126). Bks Demand UMI.

Smith, William & Cheetham, Samuel, eds. Dictionary of Christian Antiquities: Being a Continuation of the Dictionary of the Bible, 2 Vols. LC 17-21174. (LM). (Illus.). 1968. Repr. of 1880 ed. Set. 148.00 (ISBN 0-527-84150-1). Kraus Repr.

CHRISTIAN ARCHAEOLOGY

see Christian Antiquities

CHRISTIAN ART AND SYMBOLISM
see also Altarpieces; Art and Religion; Bible–Pictures, Illustrations, etc.; Catacombs; Cathedrals; Christian Antiquities; Church Architecture; Church Decoration and Ornament; Church Furniture; Church Vestments; Crib in Christian Art and Tradition; Crosses; Emblems; Fish (In Religion, Folk-Lore, etc.); Hours, Books Of; Icons; Illumination of Books and Manuscripts; Jewish Art and Symbolism; Mosaics; Symbolism in the Bible
also subdivision Art under various subjects, e.g. Jesus Christ–Art

Ahlborn, Richard. The Sculpted Saints of a Borderland Mission. LC 74-18171. (Illus.). 124p. 1974. pap. 7.50 (ISBN 0-915076-03-9). SW Mission.

Andrews, Edward D. & Andrews, Faith. Religion in Wood: A Book of Shaker Furniture. LC 66-12722. (Midland Bks Ser.: No. 286). (Illus.). 128p. 1966. 20.00 (ISBN 0-253-17360-4); pap. 7.95x (ISBN 0-253-20286-8). Ind U Pr.

Beckwith, John. Early Christian & Byzantine Art. (Pelican History of Art Ser.). 1980. pap. 18.95 (ISBN 0-14-056133-1, Pelican). Penguin.

Benson, George W. The Cross: Its History & Symbolism. LC 73-88643. 1976. Repr. of 1934 ed. lib. bdg. 25.00 (ISBN 0-87817-149-5). Hacker.

Blom, Dorothea. Art Responds to the Bible. LC 74-24006. (Illus.). 32p. (Orig.). 1974. pap. 2.50x (ISBN 0-87574-197-5). Pendle Hill.

Bowder, Diana. The Age of Constantine & Julian. (Illus.). 230p. 1978. text ed. 32.50x (ISBN 0-06-490601-9, 06359). B&N Imports.

Boyer & Zahorski. Visions of Wonders: An Anthology of Christian Fantasy. 1986. pap. 2.50 (ISBN 0-380-78824-1, 78824-1). Avon.

Brown, Stephanie. Religious Painting. LC 78-24454. (Mayflower Gallery). (Illus.). 1979. 12.50 (ISBN 0-8317-7370-7, Mayflower Bks); pap. 6.95 (ISBN 0-8317-7371-5). Smith Pubs.

Buchtal, Hugo & Kurz, Otto. Hand List of Illuminated Oriental Christian Manuscripts. (Warburg Institute Studies: Vol. 12). Repr. of 1942 ed. 20.00 (ISBN 0-8115-1389-0). Kraus Repr.

Clement, Clara E. Handbook of Legendary & Mythological Art. LC 68-26616. (Illus.). 1969. Repr. of 1881 ed. 45.00x (ISBN 0-8103-3175-6). Gale.

Coleman, Robert. The New Covenant. 132p. 1985. pap. 4.95 (ISBN 0-89109-524-1). NavPress.

Coniaris, A. Sacred Symbols That Speak, Vol. I. 1986. pap. 7.95 (ISBN 0-937032-39-5). Light&Life Pub Co MN.

Costello, Elaine. Religious Signing. (Illus.). 176p. 1986. pap. 9.95 (ISBN 0-553-34244-4). Bantam.

Cutler, Anthony. Transfigurations: Studies in the Dynamics of Byzantine Iconography. LC 75-1482. (Illus.). 226p. 1975. 32.50x (ISBN 0-271-01194-7). Pa St U Pr.

De Fleury, C. Rohault. La Sainte Vierge: Etudes Archeologiques et Iconographiques, 2 vols. (Fr., Illus.). Repr. of 1878 ed. Set. 325.00x (ISBN 0-89241-154-6). Caratzas.

De Jaegher, Paul, ed. An Anthology of Christian Mysticism. 1977. 7.95 (ISBN 0-87243-073-1). Templegate.

Diehl, Huston. An Index of Icons in English Emblem Books, 1500-1700. LC 85-40950. (Illus.). 288p. 1986. 35.00x (ISBN 0-8061-1989-6). U of Okla Pr.

Dillenberger, Jane. Style & Content in Christian Art. 320p. 1986. pap. 17.95 (ISBN 0-8245-0782-7). Crossroad NY.

--Style & Content in Christian Art: From the Catacombs to the Chapel Designed by Matisse at Vence, France. LC 65-22293. pap. 80.50 (ISBN 0-317-10399-7, 2001274). Bks Demand UMI.

Dionysius Of Fourna. Manuel d'iconographie Chretienne, Grecque et Latine. Durand, Paul, tr. 1963. Repr. of 1845 ed. 32.00 (ISBN 0-8337-0868-6). B Franklin.

Dixon, Laurinda S. Alchemical Imagery in Bosch's "Garden of Delights". Seidel, Linda, ed. LC 81-14673. (Studies in Fine Arts: Iconography: No. 2). 250p. 1981. 49.95 (ISBN 0-8357-1247-8). UMI Res Pr.

Durantis, Gulielmus. Symbolism of Churches & Church Ornaments: A Translation of the First Book of the Rationale Divinorum Officiorum. Neale, John M. & Webb, Benjamin, eds. Repr. of 1843 ed. 28.00 (ISBN 0-404-04653-3). AMS Pr.

Dyrness, W. A. Christian Art in Asia. 1979. pap. text ed. 11.50x (ISBN 0-391-01157-X). Humanities.

Elliott, Ann. Christian Folk Art: Crafts & Activities. (Illus.). 1979. pap. 4.95 (ISBN 0-8192-1250-4). Morehouse.

Evans, E. P. Animal Symbolism in Ecclesiastical Architecture. 59.95 (ISBN 0-87968-638-3). Gordon Pr.

Evans, Joan. Monastic Iconography in France from the Renaissance to the Revolution. LC 67-12317. (Illus.). 1969. 80.00 (ISBN 0-521-06960-2). Cambridge U Pr.

Farwell, Beatrice. Manet & the Nude, a Study in Iconography in the Second Empire. LC 79-57509. (Outstanding Dissertations in the Fine Arts Ser.: No. 5). 290p. 1981. lib. bdg. 61.00 (ISBN 0-8240-3929-7). Garland Pub.

Ferguson, George. Signs & Symbols in Christian Art. (Illus.). 1966. pap. 7.95 (ISBN 0-19-501432-4). Oxford U Pr.

Figueroa Y Miranda, Miguel. La Pintura Cristiana En los Tres Primeros Siglos. (UPREX, Humanidades: No. 12). pap. 1.85 (ISBN 0-8477-0012-7). U of PR Pr.

Fleury, C. Rohault. La Messe: Etudes Archeologiques sur ses Monuments, 8 vols. (Fr., Illus.). 1722p. Repr. of 1889 ed. lib. bdg. 600.00x (ISBN 0-89241-153-8). Caratzas.

Forsyth, Ilene H. The Throne of Wisdom: Wood Sculptures of the Madonna in Romanesque France. LC 72-166372. pap. 77.30 (ISBN 0-317-41726-6, 2052061). Bks Demand UMI.

Forsyth, Peter T. Religion in Recent Art. 3rd ed. LC 73-148780. Repr. of 1905 ed. 24.50 (ISBN 0-404-02515-3). AMS Pr.

Francis, Anne F. Voyage of Re-Discovery: The Veneration of St. Vincent. 1978. 15.00 (ISBN 0-682-48429-6, University). Exposition Pr FL.

Friedmann, Herbert. A Bestiary for St. Jerome: Animal Symbolism in European Religious Art. LC 79-607804. (Illus.). 378p. 1980. 39.95x (ISBN 0-87474-446-6, FRBJ). Smithsonian.

Frueh, Erne & Frueh, Florence. Chicago Stained Glass. (Illus.). 160p. 1983. 19.95 (ISBN 0-8294-0435-X). Loyola.

Gardner, Percy. Principles of Christian Art. 1977. lib. bdg. 59.95 (ISBN 0-8490-2479-X). Gordon Pr.

Geiger, Gail. The Carafa Chapel, Renaissance Art in Rome. (Sixteenth Century Essays & Studies Ser.: Vol. V). (Illus.). 210p. 1985. smyth sewn 50.00x (ISBN 0-940474-05-0). Sixteenth Cent.

Giorgi, Louis P. Windows of St. Justin Martyr. LC 80-67119. (Illus.). 136p. 1982. 25.00 (ISBN 0-87982-034-9). Art Alliance.

Goffen, Rona. Piety & Patronage in Renaissance Venice: Bellini, Titian, & Franciscans. LC 85-91280. 320p. 1986. 40.00 (ISBN 0-300-03455-5). Yale U Pr.

Goode, Teresa C. Gonzalo De Berceo. (Carl Ser.: No. 7). Repr. of 1933 ed. 21.00 (ISBN 0-404-50307-1). AMS Pr.

Grabar, Andre. Christian Iconography: A Study of Its Origins. LC 67-31114. (A. W. Mellon Lectures in the Fine Arts No. 10, Bollingen Ser: No. Xxxv). (Illus.). 432p. (Orig.). 1980. 66.00x (ISBN 0-691-09716-X); pap. 15.95x (ISBN 0-691-01830-8). Princeton U Pr.

Guicciradi, Francesco. Catholic Rome & Its Most Beautiful Paintings. (The Institute for the Promotion of the Arts Ser.). (Illus.). 1978. deluxe bdg. 75.65 (ISBN 0-930582-01-2). Gloucester Art.

Hackwood, Frederick W. Christ Lore: Being the Legends, Traditions, Myths, Symbols, Customs, & Superstitions of the Christian Church. LC 69-16064. (Illus.). 1971. Repr. of 1902 ed. 34.00x (ISBN 0-8103-3528-X). Gale.

Hamm, Jack. Custom Clip Art for Churches, Vol. 2. 48p. (Orig.). 1985. pap. 9.95 (ISBN 0-933545-00-2). Knight Media.

--Handy Clip Art for Church Bulletin Covers. 48p. (Orig.). 1985. pap. 9.95 (ISBN 0-933545-02-9). Knight Media.

Healy, E. M. Christian Art in Italy, Spain, Holland & Germany. (Illus.). 145p. 1986. 127.45 (ISBN 0-86650-193-2). Gloucester Art.

Heath, Sidney. The Romance of Symbolism & Its Relation to Church Ornament & Architecture. LC 70-174054. (Illus.). 1976. Repr. of 1909 ed. 40.00x (ISBN 0-8103-4302-9). Gale.

Heinberg, Richard. Memories & Visions of Paradise. (Illus.). 61p. (Orig.). 1985. pap. 4.95 (ISBN 0-932869-00-9). Emissaries Divine.

Henkel, Arthur, ed. Emblemata: Supplement der Erstausgabe. Schoene, Albrecht. (Ger.). 400p. 1976. 65.00 (ISBN 0-317-02568-6). Interbk Inc.

Henry, Francoise. Early Christian Irish Art. rev. ed. (Illus.). 128p. 1979. pap. 6.95 (ISBN 0-85342-462-4, Pub. by Mercier Pr Ireland). Irish Bks Media.

Hocquard, Gaston, et al. Collectanea Cartusiensa, No. 1. Hogg, James, ed. (Analecta Cartusiana Ser.: No. 82-1). (Fr., Illus.). 1980. pap. 25.00 (ISBN 3-7052-0119-0, Pub. by Salzburg Studies). Longwood Pub Group.

Hogg, James & Brauer, Wilhelm. Collectanea Cartusiensia, No. 3. Hogg, James, ed. (Analecta Cartusiana Ser.: No. 82-3). (Lat. & Ger.). 120p. (Orig.). 1980. pap. 25.00 (ISBN 3-7052-0121-2, Pub. by Salzburg Studies). Longwood Pub Group.

Hogg, James & Hogg, James. Collectanea Cartusiensia, No. 6. (Analecta Cartusiana Ser.: No. 82-6). (Orig.). 1985. pap. 25.00 (ISBN 3-7052-0124-7, Pub. by Salzburg Studies). Longwood Pub Group.

Hogg, James, ed. Collectanea Cartusiensia, No. 4. (Analecta Cartusiana Ser.: No. 82-4). (Orig.). 1985. pap. 25.00 (ISBN 3-7052-0122-0, Pub. by Salzburg Studies). Longwood Pub Group.

--Collectanea Cartusiensia, No. 5. (Analecta Cartusiana Ser.: No. 82-5). (Orig.). 1985. pap. 25.00 (ISBN 3-7052-0123-9, Pub. by Salzburg Studies). Longwood Pub Group.

--Collectanea Cartusiensia, No. 7. (Analecta Cartusiana Ser.: No. 82-7). (Orig.). 1986. pap. 25.00 (ISBN 3-7052-0125-5, Pub. by Salzburg Studies). Longwood Pub Group.

--Collectanea Cartusiensia, No. 8. (Analecta Cartusiana Ser.: No. 82-8). (Orig.). 1987. pap. 25.00 (ISBN 3-7052-0126-3, Pub. by Salzburg Studies). Longwood Pub Group.

--Collectanea Cartusiensia, No. 9. (Analecta Cartusiana Ser.: No. 82-9). (Orig.). 1987. pap. 25.00 (ISBN 3-7052-0127-1, Pub. by Salzburg Studies). Longwood Pub Group.

Hulme, F. E. History, Principles & Practice of Symbolism in Christian Art. 35.00 (ISBN 0-8490-0364-4). Gordon Pr.

Hulme, F. Edward. History, Principles, & Practice of Symbolism in Christian Art. LC 68-18027. 1969. Repr. of 1891 ed. 37.00x (ISBN 0-8103-3214-0). Gale.

Inman, Thomas. Ancient, Pagan & Modern Christian Symbolism. LC 77-6998. Repr. of 1884 ed. lib. bdg. 25.00 (ISBN 0-89341-301-1). Longwood Pub Group.

--Ancient, Pagan & Modern Christian Symbolism. 147p. 1978. Repr. of 1884 ed. 15.95 (ISBN 0-87928-101-4). Corner Hse.

Ives, Colta. Picturesque Ideas on the Flight into Egypt. LC 82-4405. (Illus.). 72p. 1982. Repr. 20.00 (ISBN 0-8076-1047-X). Braziller.

Jameson, Anna B. Legends of the Monastic Orders As Represented in the Fine Arts. LC 75-41154. 1976. Repr. of 1866 ed. 29.50 (ISBN 0-404-14767-4). AMS Pr.

--Sacred & Legendary Art, 2 Vols. LC 71-124594. Repr. of 1896 ed. 18.50 (ISBN 0-404-03551-5). AMS Pr.

Jouve, E. G. Dictionnaire d'Esthetique Chretienne ou Theorie du Beau dans l'Art Chretien. Migne, J. P., ed. (Troisieme et Derniere Encyclopedie Theologique Ser.: Vol. 17). (Fr.). 646p. Repr. of 1856 ed. lib. bdg. 82.50x (ISBN 0-89241-300-X). Caratzas.

Kalokyris, Constantine D. The Essence of Orthodox Inconography. Chamberas, Peter A., tr. from Greek. (Illus.). 129p. 1971. pap. 9.95 (ISBN 0-917651-12-X). Holy Cross Orthodox.

Keller, John E. & Kinkade, Richard P. Iconography in Medieval Spanish Literature. LC 83-2478. (Illus.). 160p. 1984. 50.00x (ISBN 0-8131-1449-7). U Pr of Ky.

Knapp, Sr. Justina. Christian Symbols & How to Use Them. LC 74-8172. (Illus.). 164p. 1975. Repr. of 1935 ed. 43.00x (ISBN 0-8103-4050-X). Gale.

Knipping, John B. Iconography of the Counter Reformation in the Netherlands: Heaven on Earth, 2 vols. LC 73-85234. (Illus.). 539p. 1974. Set. text ed. 195.00x (Pub. by B De Graaf Netherlands). Coronet Bks.

Landa, Robin. Religious Art: A Workbook for Artists & Designers. 272p. 1985. 29.95 (ISBN 0-13-773037-3); pap. 16.95 (ISBN 0-13-773029-2). P-H.

Lewis, Jim. Mystical Teachings of Christianity. 150p. 1980. pap. 7.95 (ISBN 0-942482-01-8). Unity Church Denver.

Littaur, Fred. National Directory of Christian Artists. LC 85-80487. 256p. (Orig.). 1985. pap. 9.95 (ISBN 0-89081-490-2). Harvest Hse.

Liturgical Objects in the Walters Art Gallery: A Picture Book. LC 67-9432. (Illus.). 1967. pap. 3.50 (ISBN 0-911886-11-7). Walters Art.

Lohr, Andrew. Talks on Mystic Christianity. Challgren, Patricia & Crater, Mildred, eds. LC 84-90346. (Illus.). 152p. (Orig.). 1984. pap. 6.50 (ISBN 0-9613401-0-X). Fiery Water.

Long, Charles H. Significations: Signs, Symbols & Images in the Interpretation of Religion. LC 85-45495. 208p. 1986. pap. 12.95 (ISBN 0-8006-1892-0, 1-1892). Fortress.

Lubke, Wilhelm. Ecclesiastical Art in Germany During the Middle Ages. Wheatley, L. A., tr. from Ger. LC 78-16244. 1978. Repr. of 1877 ed. lib. bdg. 35.00 (ISBN 0-89341-359-3). Longwood Pub Group.

MacCormack, Sabine. Art & Ceremony in Late Antiquity. (The Transformation of the Classical Heritage Ser.: Vol. 1). (Illus.). 450p. 1981. 45.00x (ISBN 0-520-03779-0). U of Cal Pr.

Mahr, Adolph R. Christian Art in Ancient Ireland, 2 vols. in 1. LC 75-11058. 1977. Repr. of 1932 ed. lib. bdg. 50.00 (ISBN 0-87817-173-8). Hacker.

Maldonado, Luis & Power, David, eds. Symbol & Art in Worship. (Concilium Ser.: Vol. 132). 128p. (Orig.). 1980. pap. 5.95 (ISBN 0-8164-2274-5, HarpR). Har-Row.

Male, Emile. Religious Art from the Twelfth to the Eighteenth Century. LC 82-47903. (Illus.). 256p. 1982. 31.50x (ISBN 0-691-04000-1); pap. 10.50x (ISBN 0-691-00347-5). Princeton U Pr.

--Religious Art in France: The Late Middle Ages: A Study of Medieval Iconography & Its Sources. Bober, Harry, ed. Mathews, Marthiel, tr. (Bollingen Ser. XC: No. 3). 600p. 1987. text ed. 85.00x (ISBN 0-691-09914-6). Princeton U Pr.

--Religious Art in France: The Twelfth Century. LC 72-14029. (Bollingen Ser.: No. 90). 1978. 73.50x (ISBN 0-691-09912-X). Princeton U Pr.

Martin, David. Breaking of Image: The Sociology of Christian Theory & Practice. 1980. 26.00 (ISBN 0-312-09522-8). St Martin.

Martin, F. David. Art & the Religious Experience: The Language of the Sacred. LC 75-161508. (Illus.). 288p. 1972. 27.50 (ISBN 0-8387-7935-2). Bucknell U Pr.

Martone, Thomas. The Iconography of the Conversion of Saint Paul. Freedberg, S. J., ed. (Outstanding Dissertations in Fine Arts Ser.). (Illus.). 325p. 1985. Repr. of 1978 ed. 45.00 (ISBN 0-8240-6882-3). Garland Pub.

Mercer, Henry C. The Bible in Iron. 3rd ed. (Illus.). 356p. 1961. pap. 15.00 (ISBN 0-910302-01-4). Bucks Co Hist.

Miles, Margaret R. Image As Insight: Visual Understanding in Western Christianity & Secular Culture. LC 85-47528. (Illus.). 304p. 1985. 24.95 (ISBN 0-8070-1006-5). Beacon Pr.

--Image As Insight: Visual Understanding in Western Christianity & Secular Culture. LC 85-47528. (Illus.). 200p. 1987. pap. 12.95 (ISBN 0-8070-1007-3, BP 743). Beacon Pr.

Miller, David L. Christs: Meditations on Archetypal Images in Christian Theology. 200p. 1981. 12.95x (ISBN 0-8164-0492-5, HarpR). Har-Row.

Moe, Dean L. Christian Symbols Handbook: Commentary & Patterns for Traditional & Contemporary Symbols. 96p. (Orig.). 1985. pap. 9.95 (ISBN 0-8066-2153-2, 10-1180). Augsburg.

Morey, Charles R. Christian Art. (Illus.). 1958. pap. 3.95 (ISBN 0-393-00103-2, Norton Lib). Norton.

--Christian Art. (Illus.). 14.50 (ISBN 0-8446-2606-6). Peter Smith.

Murray, R. Symbols of Church & Kingdom. LC 74-80363. 430p. 1975. 59.50 (ISBN 0-521-20553-0). Cambridge U Pr.

Nelson, Gertrud M. Clip-Art for Feasts & Seasons. expanded ed. (Illus.). 120p. (Orig.). 1982. pap. 10.95 (ISBN 0-916134-41-5). Pueblo Pub Co.

Nolan, James L. Discovery of the Lost Art Treasures of California's First Mission. Pourade, Richard F., ed. LC 78-73173. (Illus.). 128p. 1978. 20.00 (ISBN 0-913938-20-3). Copley Bks.

Oakeshott, Walter. Sigena: Romanesque Paintings in Spain & the Winchester Bible Artists. (Illus.). 1972. 49.00x (ISBN 0-19-921006-3). Oxford U Pr.

Obrennen, Junius & Smith, Nopal. The Crystal Icon. (Illus.). vii, 200p. 1981. deluxe ed. 50.00 (ISBN 0-940578-03-4). Galahand Pr.

O'Connell, Patrick F. Collectanea Cartusiensia, No. 2. Hogg, James, ed. (Analecta Cartusiana Ser.: No. 82-2). (Fr. & Ger.). 118p. (Orig.). 1980. pap. 25.00 (ISBN 3-7052-0120-4, Pub. by Salzburg Studies). Longwood Pub Group.

O'Meadhra, U. Early Christian, Viking & Romanesque Art. (Illus.). 260p. (Orig.). 1979. pap. text ed. 30.00x (ISBN 91-22-00270-7, Pub. by Almqvist & Wiksell). Coronet Bks.

Palmer, Michael. Paul Tillich's Philosophy of Art. LC 83-15056. (Theologische Bibliothek Toepelmann Ser.: Vol. 41). xxii, 217p. 1983. 49.50x (ISBN 3-11-009681-1). De Gruyter.

Pedretti, Carlo & Brown, David A. Leonardo, 3 vols. (Illus.). 1985. Set. pap. 29.95 (ISBN 0-295-96323-9, Pub. by Natl Gallery of Art). U of Wash Pr.

Pepper, Stephen. Bob Jones University Collection of Religious Art: Italian Paintings. (Illus.). 336p. (Orig.). 1984. pap. 55.00 (ISBN 0-89084-263-9). Bob Jones Univ Pr.

Porter, A. Kingsley. Romanesque Sculpture of the Pilgrimage Roads, 10 Vols. in 3. LC 67-4262. (Illus.). 1986. Repr. of 1923 ed. 250.00 set (ISBN 0-87817-020-0). Hacker.

Porter, Arthur K. Crosses & Culture of Ireland. LC 68-56480. (Illus.). 1969. Repr. of 1931 ed. 33.00 (ISBN 0-405-08860-4, Pub. by Blom). Ayer Co Pubs.

Post, W. Ellwood. Saints, Signs & Symbols. (Illus.). 96p. 1974. pap. 6.50 (ISBN 0-8192-1171-0). Morehouse.

Power, David N. Unsearchable Riches. 160p. (Orig.). 1984. pap. 9.95 (ISBN 0-916134-62-8). Pueblo Pub Co.

The Religious & Historical Paintings of Jan Steen. (Illus.). 1977. 42.50 (ISBN 0-8390-0170-3, Allanheld & Schram). Abner Schram Ltd.

Rest, Friedrich. Our Christian Symbols. LC 53-9923. (Illus.). 96p. 1954. pap. 3.25 (ISBN 0-8298-0099-9). Pilgrim NY.

Reutersward, Patrik. Forgotten Symbols of God: Five Essays Reprinted from Konsthistorisk Tidskrift. (Stockholm Studies in History of Art: No. 35). (Illus.). 152p. (Orig.). 1986. pap. text ed. 22.00x (Pub. by SPN Yugoslavia). Coronet Bks.

Ridderbos, Bernhard. Saint & Symbol: Images of Saint Jerome in Early Italian Art. (Illus.). xv, 126p. 1984. pap. 18.00x (ISBN 90-6088-087-0, Pub. by Boumas Boekhuis Netherlands). Benjamins North AM.

Ryken, Leland. Culture in Christian Perspective: A Door to Understanding & Enjoying the Arts. LC 86-1442. 1986. 13.95 (ISBN 0-88070-115-3). Multnomah.

Schapiro, Meyer. Late Antique, Early Christian & Mediaeval Art: Selected Papers, Vol. III. (Illus.). 422p. 1979. 25.00 (ISBN 0-8076-0927-7). Braziller.

Senior, John. The Restoration of Christian Culture. LC 82-83497. 244p. (Orig.). 1983. pap. 9.95 (ISBN 0-89870-024-8). Ignatius Pr.

Siegl, Helen. Clip Art-Block Prints for the Gospel of Cycles A, B, C. (Illus.). 216p. (Orig.). pap. 11.95 (ISBN 0-916134-66-0). Pueblo Pub Co.

Sill, Gertrude G. Handbook of Symbols in Christian Art. (Illus.). 1975. pap. 10.95 (ISBN 0-02-000850-3, Collier). Macmillan.

Stokes, Margaret. Early Christian Art in Ireland. LC 70-39211. (Select Bibliographies Reprint Ser.). Repr. of 1911 ed. 23.50 (ISBN 0-8369-6813-1). Ayer Co Pubs.

Swarzenski, Hanns. Monuments of Romanesque Art: The Art of Church Treasures in North-Western Europe. 2nd ed. LC 55-937. (Illus.). 1967. 40.00x (ISBN 0-226-78605-6). U of Chicago Pr.

Swift, Emerson H. Roman Sources of Christian Art. (Illus.). Repr. of 1951 ed. lib. bdg. 22.50x (ISBN 0-8371-3430-7, SWCA). Greenwood.

Theisen, Jerome. Community & Disunity: Symbols of Grace & Sin. 144p. 1985. pap. 7.50 (ISBN 0-8146-1406-X). Liturgical Pr.

Tiso, Francis & Catholic Heritage Press. A Young Person's Book of Catholic Signs & Symbols. LC 81-43459. 128p. 1982. pap. 3.50 (ISBN 0-385-17951-0, Im). Doubleday.

Treasures of the Orthodox Church Museum in Finland. (Illus.). 124p. (Orig.). 1985. pap. text ed. 57.50x (Pub. by Almqvist & Wiksell). Coronet Bks.

Van Der Meer, Frederik. Early Christian Art. Brown, Peter & Brown, Friedl, trs. from Ger. LC 67-25083. pap. 50.00 (ISBN 0-317-28145-3, 2024099). Bks Demand UMI.

Van Os, Henk. Sienese Altarpieces 1215-1460 Form, Content, Function: Vol. I 1215-1344. Van Der Ploeg, Kees, contrib. by. (Mediaevalia Groningana IV: Bk. IV). (Illus.). 163p. 1984. 28.00x (ISBN 90-6088-083-8, Pub. by Boumas Boekhuis Netherlands). Benjamins North AM.

The Vatican: Spirit & Art of Christian Rome. 1983. 60.00 (ISBN 0-8109-1711-4). Abrams.

Veith, Gene E., Jr. The Gift of Art. LC 83-18636. 120p. 1984. pap. 6.95 (ISBN 0-87784-813-0). Inter-Varsity.

Verdon, Timothy G. & Dally, John, eds. Monasticism & the Arts. (Illus.). 368p. 1984. text ed. 34.95x (ISBN 0-8156-2291-0); pap. text ed. 16.95x (ISBN 0-8156-2292-9). Syracuse U Pr.

Washington, Joseph R., Jr. Anti-Blackness in English Religion. LC 84-27334. (Texts & Studies in Religion: Vol. 19). 623p. 1985. 79.95x (ISBN 0-88946-808-7). E Mellen.

Watanabe, Sadao. Biblical Prints. (Illus.). 1987. deluxe ed. 100.00 (ISBN 0-8028-3635-6). Eerdmans.

Waters, Clara E. A Handbook of Legendary & Mythological Art. LC 76-27524. (Illus.). 1976. Repr. of 1876 ed. lib. bdg. 50.00 (ISBN 0-89341-037-3). Longwood Pub Group.

Watts, Alan W. Myth & Ritual in Christianity. (Illus.). 1968. pap. 9.95x (ISBN 0-8070-1375-7, BP301). Beacon Pr.

Weatherhead, Leslie D. The Meaning of the Cross. (Festival Ser.). 192p. 1982. pap. 2.75 (ISBN 0-687-23970-2). Abingdon.

Webber, Frederick R. Church Symbolism: An Explanation of the More Important Symbols of the Old & New Testament, the Primitive, the Mediaeval & the Modern Church. rev. 2nd ed. LC 79-107627. (Illus.). 1971. Repr. of 1938 ed. 56.00x (ISBN 0-8103-3349-X). Gale.

Weitzmann, Kurt. Late Antique-Early Christian Painting. LC 76-16444. (Magnificent Paperback Art Ser.). 128p. 1977. 19.95 (ISBN 0-8076-0830-0); pap. 11.95 (ISBN 0-8076-0831-9). Braziller.

Wetzler, Robert & Huntington, Helen. Seasons & Symbols. LC 62-9094. (Illus., Orig.). 1962. pap. 6.95 (ISBN 0-8066-0221-X, 10-5625). Augsburg.

Wildridge, Thomas T. Grotesque in Church Art. LC 68-30633. 1969. Repr. of 1899 ed. 35.00x (ISBN 0-8103-3077-6). Gale.

Willet, Andrew. Sacrorum Emblematum Centuria Una. LC 84-5360. 1984. Repr. of 1592 ed. 35.00x (ISBN 0-8201-1395-6). Schol Facsimiles.

Williamson, John. The Oak King, the Holly King, & the Unicorn: The Myths & Symbolism of the Unicorn Tapestries. LC 85-45242. (Illus.). 280p. 1987. pap. 12.95 (ISBN 0-06-096032-9, PL 6032, PL). Har-Row.

CHRISTIAN ART AND SYMBOLISM–JUVENILE LITERATURE

Konrady, Marlene. The Jesse Tree: A Cutout Book. (The Learning Connections Ser.). 48p. (Orig.). 1984. pap. 8.95 (ISBN 0-86683-830-9, 8439, HarpR). Har-Row.

CHRISTIAN ATHEISM

see Death of God Theology

CHRISTIAN BIOGRAPHY

see also Apostles; Apostolic Fathers; Bishops; Cardinals; Clergy; Fathers of the Church; Hermits; Missionaries; Monasticism and Religious Orders; Popes; Puritans; Reformers; Saints; Theologians

Agle, Nan H. A Promise Is to Keep. 160p. (Orig.). 1985. pap. 6.95 (ISBN 0-310-41591-8, 9290P). Zondervan.

Antonellis, Costanzo J. The Story of Peter Donders. 115p. 3.50 (ISBN 0-8198-6834-5, BI0217); pap. 2.50 (ISBN 0-8198-6835-3). Dghtrs St Paul.

Archbishop Konstantine Zaitsev. Pamjati Igumena Fillimona. Tr. of In Memory of Igumen Philimon. 58p. 1954. pap. 2.00 (ISBN 0-317-29287-0). Holy Trinity.

Atkins, Gaius G. Pilgrims of the Lonely Road. facs. ed. LC 67-28741. (Essay Index Reprint Ser). 1913. 18.00 (ISBN 0-8369-0162-2). Ayer Co Pubs.

Aubry, Joseph. Savio: A Study Guide. Boenzi, Joe, tr. from Ital. LC 79-50460. (Orig.). 1979. pap. 2.75 (ISBN 0-89944-038-X). Don Bosco Multimedia.

Band, Arnold. Nahman of Bratslav, the Tales. LC 78-53433. (Classics of Western Spirituality). 368p. 1978. pap. 9.95 (ISBN 0-8091-2103-4). Paulist Pr.

Barbee, A. H. Behind the Iron Curtain: The Story of John Visser. 75p. 1985. pap. 2.95 (ISBN 0-89084-280-9). Bob Jones Univ Pr.

Barber, Natalie. Dr. & Mrs. Fix-It: The Story of Frank & Bessie Beck. LC 79-130776. (Bold Believers Ser). (Orig.). 1969. pap. 0.95 (ISBN 0-377-84181-1). Friend Pr.

Barger, R. Curtis. Don't You Know? Haven't You Heard? Woolsey, Raymond H., ed. (Banner Ser.). 128p. (Orig.). 1985. pap. 5.95 (ISBN 0-8280-0278-9). Review & Herald.

Barrett, Eric C. & Fisher, David, eds. Scientists Who Believe: Twenty-One Tell Their Own Stories. 1984. pap. 4.50 (ISBN 0-8024-7634-1). Moody.

Barrett, Ethel. Steve Paxon: Can't Lose for Winning. LC 84-26238. 1985. pap. 4.95 (ISBN 0-8307-1022-1, 5418424). Regal.

Barrett, Thomas Van Braam. Great Morning of the World: The Unforgettable Story of Harry Barrett. LC 75-16416. Repr. of 1975 ed. 47.30 (ISBN 0-8357-9011-8, 2016366). Bks Demand UMI.

Basetti-Sani, Biuolio. Louis Massignon: Christian Ecumenist. 1974. 6.95 (ISBN 0-8199-0496-1). Franciscan Herald.

Batzler, Louis R. Sunlight & Shadows: Portraits of Priorities for Living & Dying. (Illus.). 60p. (Orig.). 1986. pap. 4.95 (ISBN 0-935710-09-4). Hid Valley MD.

Benton, John. Tracy. 192p. (Orig.). 1984. pap. 2.95 (ISBN 0-8007-8495-2, New Hope). Revell.

Beougher, Lois. Now Lord, How Did You Manage That? 143p. 1984. 7.95 (ISBN 0-533-05912-7). Vantage.

Berio, Paquita. Ahora Brillan las Estrellas. (Span.). 134p. (Orig.). 1981. pap. 3.75 (ISBN 0-89922-201-3). Edit Caribe.

Berrigan, Daniel. Portraits: O Those I Love. (Crossroad Paperback Ser.). 160p. 1982. pap. 6.95 (ISBN 0-8245-0416-X). Crossroad NY.

Biography of Duncan Campbell. 2.00 (ISBN 0-686-12852-4). Schmul Pub Co.

Biver, Paul. Pere Lamy. O'Connor, John, tr. from Fr. 1973. pap. 5.50 (ISBN 0-89555-055-5). TAN Bks Pubs.

Blair, Charles & Sherrill, John. The Man Who Could Do No Wrong. 1982. pap. 3.50 (ISBN 0-8423-4002-5). Tyndale.

Blamires, Harry, et al. Chosen Vessels: Portraits of Ten Outstanding Christian Men. Turner, Charles, ed. 224p. (Orig.). 1985. pap. 10.95 (ISBN 0-89283-226-6, Pub. by Vine Books). Servant.

Bolshakoff, Sergius. Russian Mystics. (Cistercian Studies: No. 26). Orig. Title: I Mistici Russi. 303p. 1981. pap. 6.95 (ISBN 0-87907-926-6). Cistercian Pubns.

Booth, L. Venchael, ed. Crowned with Glory & Honor: The Life of Rev. Lacey Kirk Williams. 1978. 8.00 (ISBN 0-682-48939-5). Exposition Pr FL.

Bosco, St. John. St. Dominic Savio. rev. ed. Aronica, Paul, tr. from Ital. LC 78-67221. (Illus.). 1979. pap. 2.95 (ISBN 0-89944-037-1). Don Bosco Multimedia.

Boyd, Nancy. Three Victorian Women Who Changed Their World: Josephine Butler, Octavia Hill, Florence Nightingale. 1982. 22.95x (ISBN 0-19-520271-6). Oxford U Pr.

Brians, Charline. Light after Ellen White. large print ed. 32p. 1985. pap. 5.00 (ISBN 0-914009-06-0). VHI Library.

Bryant, M. Darrol & Huessy, Hans R. Eugen Rosenstock-Huessy: Studies in His Life & Thought. LC 86-28469. (Toronto Studies in Theology: Vol. 28). 280p. 1987. text ed. 49.95x (ISBN 0-88946-772-2). E Mellen.

Buksbazen, Lydia. They Looked for a City. 1977. pap. 3.95 (ISBN 0-87508-041-3). Chr Lit.

Burghardt, W. J., et al, eds. Julianus Pomerius, the Contemplative Life. LC 78-62457. (ACW Ser.: No. 4). 220p. 1947. 9.95 (ISBN 0-8091-0245-5). Paulist Pr.

--St. Athanasius: The Life of St. Antony. LC 78-62454. (ACW Ser.: No. 10). 155p. 1950. 12.95 (ISBN 0-8091-0250-1). Paulist Pr.

Byers, A. L. Birth of a Reformation: Life & Labours of D. S. Warner. (Illus.). 496p. Repr. 5.50 (ISBN 0-686-29104-2). Faith Pub Hse.

Byrum, Isabel. The Poorhouse Waif & His Divine Teacher. 223p. pap. 2.00 (ISBN 0-686-29161-1). Faith Pub Hse.

Campbell, Don G. Master Teacher: Nadia Boulanger. (Illus.). 151p. 1984. text ed. 19.95 (ISBN 0-912405-03-1). Pastoral Pr.

Campbell, Faith F. Stanley Frodsham: Prophet with a Pen. LC 74-77406. 1974. pap. 1.25 (ISBN 0-88243-603-1, 02-0603). Gospel Pub.

Cantleberry, Lillian. Sarah's Story. (Continued Applied Christianity Ser.). 1983. pap. 7.95 (ISBN 0-570-03898-7, 12-2980). Concordia.

Carlson, Carole C. Corrie Ten Boom: Her Life, Her Faith. (Illus.). 224p. 1984. pap. 3.50 (ISBN 0-8007-8490-1, Spire Bks). Revell.

Carman, Stephen & Owen, Robert. Quest. 160p. (Orig.). 1986. pap. 5.95 (ISBN 0-8423-5112-4). Tyndale.

Chavez, Fray A. But Time & Chance: The Biography of Padre Martinez of Taos. LC 81-27. 176p. 1981. 35.00x (ISBN 0-913270-96-2); pap. 11.95 (ISBN 0-913270-95-4). Sunstone Pr.

Chesterton, G. K. Napoleon of Notting Hill. LC 77-99307. 228p. 1978. pap. 3.45 (ISBN 0-8091-2096-8). Paulist Pr.

Chittister, Joan, et al. Midwives of the Future: American Sisters Tell Their Story. Ware, Ann P., ed. LC 84-82554. 237p. (Orig.). 1984. pap. 8.95 (ISBN 0-934134-11-1, Leaven Pr). Sheed & Ward MO.

Choy, Leona. Andrew Murray: Apostle of Abiding Love. 1978. 8.95 (ISBN 0-87508-368-4); pap. 6.95 (ISBN 0-87508-367-6). Chr Lit.

Christopher, Kenneth. Ten Catholics: Lives to Remember. (Nazareth Bks). 120p. 1983. pap. 3.95 (ISBN 0-86683-715-9, HarpR). Har-Row.

Chrystal, William G. A Father's Mantle: The Legacy of Gustav Niebuhr. LC 81-21108. 160p. (Orig.). 1982. pap. 7.95 (ISBN 0-8298-0494-3). Pilgrim NY.

Church, Mary C., ed. Life & Letters of Dean Church. 428p. 1981. Repr. of 1897 ed. lib. bdg. 45.00 (ISBN 0-8495-0859-2). Arden Lib.

Clinton, Iris. Friend of Chiefs, Robert Moffat. (Stories of Faith & Fame). 1975. pap. 2.95 (ISBN 0-87508-608-X). Chr Lit.

Coffey, Thomas P. A Candle in the Wind: My Thirty Years in Book Publishing. 222p. 1985. pap. 5.95 (ISBN 0-87193-212-1). Dimension Bks.

Colbeck, Kay & Harrell, Irene B. The Story of Singing Waters. (Orig.). 1987. pap. 7.00 (ISBN 0-915541-21-1). Star Bks Inc.

Collins, W. Lucas. Lucian. 1877. Repr. 25.00 (ISBN 0-8274-3005-1). R West.

Colson, Charles W. Life Sentence. (Illus.). 320p. 1981. pap. 7.95 (ISBN 0-8007-5059-4, Power Bks). Revell.

Cooper, Brian G. Meeting Famous Christians. (Illus.). 111p. 1977. pap. text ed. 3.50 (ISBN 0-85597-205-X). Attic Pr.

Corley, Winnie. Echoes from the Hills. 1981. lib. bdg. 14.95x (ISBN 0-934188-06-8). Evans Pubns.

Cristiani, Leon. A Cross for Napoleon. 1980. 4.00 (ISBN 0-8198-1404-0); pap. 2.00 (ISBN 0-8198-1405-9). Dghtrs St Paul.

Crosby, Fanny J. Fanny J. Crosby: Autobiography of Fanny J Crosby. (Christian Biography Ser.). 254p. 1986. Repr. of 1906 ed. 7.95 (ISBN 0-8010-2509-5). Baker Bk.

Daniels, W. H. Dr. Cullis & His Work. Dayton, Donald W., ed. (The Higher Christian Life Ser.). 364p. 1985. 45.00 (ISBN 0-8240-6410-0). Garland Pub.

Daughters of St. Paul. Boy with a Mission. 1967. 3.00 (ISBN 0-8198-0229-8). Dghtrs St Paul.

--God's Secret Agent. 1967. 3.00 (ISBN 0-8198-0236-0). Dghtrs St Paul.

--Joey. 1980. 3.00 (ISBN 0-8198-3907-8); pap. 2.00 (ISBN 0-8198-3908-6). Dghtrs St Paul.

Davidson, Henry M. Good Christian Men. facsimile ed. LC 70-142616. (Essay Index Reprint Ser). Repr. of 1940 ed. 19.00 (ISBN 0-8369-2390-1). Ayer Co Pubs.

Dawson, Joseph M. A Thousand Months to Remember: An Autobiography. 306p. 1964. 6.95 (ISBN 0-918954-03-7). Baylor Univ Pr.

Day, Richard E. Beacon Lights of Grace: Twelve Biographical Vignettes. facs. ed. LC 71-148210. (Biography Index Reprint Ser.). 1947. 17.00 (ISBN 0-8369-8057-3). Ayer Co Pubs.

Defeller, F. X. & Perennes, F. Dictionnaire de Biographie Chretienne, 3 vols. Migne, J. P., ed. (Nouvelle Encyclopedie Theologique Ser.: Vols. 1-3). (Fr.). 2352p. Repr. of 1851 ed. lib. bdg. 298.00x (ISBN 0-89241-254-2). Caratzas.

DeHaan, Dan. Steve Bartkowski: Intercepted: A Game Plan for Spiritual Growth. (Illus.). 160p. 1981. pap. 5.95 (ISBN 0-8007-5075-6, Power Bks). Revell.

De Hueck Doherty, Catherine. Soul of My Soul: Reflections from a Life of Prayer. LC 85-72271. 128p. (Orig.). 1985. pap. 4.95 (ISBN 0-87793-298-0). Ave Maria.

Delaney, John J. Pocket Dictionary of Saints. LC 82-45479. 528p. 1983. pap. 6.95 (ISBN 0-385-18274-0, Im). Doubleday.

--Saints Are Now: Eight Portraits of Modern Sanctity. LC 82-45866. 224p. 1983. pap. 4.50 (ISBN 0-385-17356-3, Im). Doubleday.

Dennis, Lane T., ed. The Letters of Francis A. Schaeffer: Spiritual Reality in the Personal Christian Life. LC 85-70473. 264p. (Orig.). 1986. 15.95 (ISBN 0-89107-361-2, Crossway Bks); pap. 7.95 (ISBN 0-89107-409-0, Crossway Bks). Good News.

DePree, Gladis. Festival! An Experiment in Living. 208p. 1985. 12.95 (ISBN 0-310-44110-2, 9488). Zondervan.

Dodd, C. H. Founder of Christianity. 1970. pap. 5.95 (ISBN 0-02-084640-1, Collier). Macmillan.

Doherty, Catherine de Hueck. Fragments of My Life. LC 79-56889. (Illus.). 208p. (Orig.). 1979. pap. 4.95 (ISBN 0-87793-194-1). Ave Maria.

Donze, Mary T. Touching a Child's Heart: An Innovative Guide to Becoming a Good Storyteller. LC 85-71557. 88p. (Orig.). 1985. pap. 3.95 (ISBN 0-87793-290-5). Ave Maria.

Dorsett, Lyle W. And God Came In: The Extraordinary Story of Joy Davidman-Her life & Marriage to C.S. Lewis. (Illus.). 192p. 1983. 14.95 (ISBN 0-02-532250-8). Macmillan.

Dunker, Marilee P. Days of Glory, Seasons of Night. rev. ed. 176p. 1984. pap. text ed. 6.95 (ISBN 0-310-45501-4, 12040P). Zondervan.

Early Christian Biographies: Lives of St. Cyprian, St. Ambrose, St. Augustine, St. Anthony, St. Paul the first Hermit, St. Hilarion, Malchus, St. Epiphanius. LC 64-19949. (Fathers of the Church Ser: Vol. 15). 407p. 1952. 21.95x (ISBN 0-8132-0015-6). Cath U Pr.

Eby, Richard E. Caught up into Paradise. pap. 3.50 (ISBN 0-8007-8489-8, Spire Bks). Revell.

--Tell Them I Am Coming. 160p. 1984. pap. 2.50 (ISBN 0-8007-8496-0, Spire Bks). Revell.

Echols, Evaline. Climb up Through Your Valleys. 1980. 6.95 (ISBN 0-87148-174-X); pap. 5.95 (ISBN 0-87148-173-1). Pathway Pr.

Edman, V. Raymond. They Found the Secret: Twenty Lives that Reveal a Touch of Eternity. 176p. 1984. pap. 5.95 (ISBN 0-310-24051-4, 9564P, Clarion Class). Zondervan.

Eisenman, Robert H. James the Just in the Habakkuk Pesher. (Studia Post-Biblica Ser.: Vol. 35). x, 110p. 1986. pap. 17.25 (ISBN 90-04-07587-9, Pub. by E J Brill). Heinman.

Eliade, Mircea. No Souvenirs, Journal, Nineteen Fifty-Seven to Nineteen Sixty-Nine. 1983. 16.00 (ISBN 0-8446-6030-2). Peter Smith.

Elliot, Elisabeth. Passion & Purity. 160p. (Orig.). 1984. pap. 6.95 (ISBN 0-8007-5137-X, Power Bks). Revell.

Elliot, Elizabeth. Shadow of the Almighty: The Life & Testament of Jim Elliot. LC 58-10365. 1979. pap. 6.95 (ISBN 0-06-062211-3, RD 488, HarpR). Har-Row.

Emert, Joyce R. Louis Martin: Father of a Saint. LC 83-2728. 208p. (Orig.). 1983. pap. 9.95 (ISBN 0-8189-0446-1). Alba.

Estes, James M. Christian Magistrate & State Church: The Reforming Career of Johannes Brenz. 208p. 1982. 30.00x (ISBN 0-8020-5589-3). U of Toronto Pr.

Estes, Steve & Estes, Verna. Called to Die: The Story of American Linguist Chet Bitterman, Slain by Terrorists. Sloan, John, ed. 208p. pap. 6.95 (ISBN 0-310-28381-7, 12197P). Zondervan.

Fleisher, David & Freedman, David M. Death of an American: The Killing of John Singer. (Illus.). 248p. 1983. 15.95 (ISBN 0-8264-0231-3). Crossroad NY.

Ford, Sallie R. Mary Bunyan: Blind Daughter of John Bunyan. 9.95 (ISBN 0-685-00748-0). Reiner.

Fosdick, Harry E. The Man from Nazareth: As His Contemporaries Saw Him. LC 78-16469. 1978. Repr. of 1949 ed. lib. bdg. 24.25x (ISBN 0-313-20603-1, FOMN). Greenwood.
Fox, Robert J. Call of Heaven: Brother Gino, Stigmatist. (Illus.). 206p. (Orig.). 1982. pap. 3.95 (ISBN 0-931888-06-9). Christendom Pubns.
--Francisco of Fatima: His Life As He Might Tell It. 14p. 1982. pap. 1.00 (ISBN 0-911988-53-X). Ami Pr.
--Jacinta of Fatima: Her Life as She Might Tell It. 22p. 1982. pap. 1.00 (ISBN 0-911988-52-1). Ami Pr.
Francis A. Schaeffer: Portraits of the Man & His Work. LC 85-73846. 1986. pap. 7.95 (ISBN 0-89107-386-8, Crossway Bks). Good News.
Frederick, Peter J. Knights of the Golden Rule: The Intellectual As Christian Social Reformer in the 1890s. LC 76-9497. 344p. 1976. 28.00x (ISBN 0-8131-1345-8). U Pr of Ky.
Gaspar, Karl. How Long? Prison Reflections from the Philippines. Graham, Helen & Noonan, Breda, eds. LC 85-25851. 176p. (Orig.). 1986. pap. 9.95 (ISBN 0-88344-226-4). Orbis Bks.
Gaydos, Michael. Eyes to Behold. LC 73-77531. 1982. pap. 4.95 (ISBN 0-89221-069-9). New Leaf.
Gentz, William H. The World of Philip Potter. 1974. pap. 2.95 (ISBN 0-377-00006-X). Friend Pr.
Getz, Gene. A Estatura de Uma Mulher. Batista, Jaoa, ed. Ferreira, Ruth V., tr. (Port.). 144p. 1981. pap. 1.60 (ISBN 0-8297-1075-2). Life Pubs Intl.
Goforth, Rosalind. Jonathan Goforth. (Men of Faith Ser.). 3.95 (ISBN 0-87123-842-X, 200842). Bethany Hse.
Gompertz, Rolf. The Messiah of Midtown Park. LC 83-50871. 136p. 1983. velo binding 10.00 (ISBN 0-918248-05-1). Word Doctor.
Goodspeed, Edgar J. A Life of Jesus. LC 78-21540. 1979. Repr. of 1950 ed. lib. bdg. 24.75x (ISBN 0-313-20728-3, GOLJ). Greenwood.
Goronwy, Jessica. The Tree of Hope. 1985. 20.00x (ISBN 0-7223-1827-8, Pub. by A H Stockwell England). State Mutual Bk.
Graham, Franklinn & Lockerbie, Jeanette. Bob Pierce: This One Thing I Do. 1983. 10.95 (ISBN 0-8499-0097-2). Word Bks.
Green, Vivian H. From St. Augustine to William Temple. facsimile ed. LC 72-148213. (Biography Index Reprint Ser.). 1948. 18.00 (ISBN 0-8369-8060-3). Ayer Co Pubs.
Grier, Rosey. Rosey: The Gentle Giant. 1986. 17.95 (ISBN 0-89274-406-5). Harrison Hse.
Guthrie, LaWanda. His Strange Ways. LC 81-10854. 1986. pap. 10.95 (ISBN 0-87949-212-0). Ashley Bks.
Haig, J. A. Headmaster. LC 80-52617. 270p. 1982. 5.95 (ISBN 0-941478-06-8). Paraclete Pr.
Haig, J. Alastair. Al Who? LC 80-52617. 270p. (Orig.). 1980. pap. cancelled (ISBN 0-932260-05-5). Paraclete Pr.
Haines, J. Harry. Ten Hands for God. 80p. (Orig.). 1983. pap. 3.50 (ISBN 0-8358-0449-6). Upper Room.
Hajos, Mary. Removing the Stones. 1976. pap. 2.95 (ISBN 0-87508-264-5). Chr Lit.
Hale, Charles R. Metropolitan Innocent of Moscow, the Apostle of Alaska. pap. 1.25 (ISBN 0-686-05655-8). Eastern Orthodox.
Hale, Mabel. The Hero of Hill House. 224p. pap. 2.00 (ISBN 0-686-29148-4). Faith Pub Hse.
Hale, Thomas, Jr. Don't Let the Goats Eat the Loquat Trees. 304p. pap. 9.95 (ISBN 0-310-21301-0, 18318P). Zondervan.
Hall, Clarence. Miracle on the Sepik. 2nd ed. (Illus.). 100p. 1981. pap. 3.95. Gift Pubns.
Hall, Clarence W. Portrait of a Builder: William A. McIntyre. 1983. pap. 5.95 (ISBN 0-86544-020-4). Salv Army Suppl South.
Hall, Mary. The Impossible Dream: The Spirituality of Dom Helder Camara. LC 79-26888. 96p. (Orig.). 1980. pap. 2.48 (ISBN 0-88344-212-4). Orbis Bks.
Hanley, Boniface. Ten Christians: By Their Deeds You Shall Know Them. LC 79-53836. (Illus.). 272p. (Orig.). 1979. pap. 6.95 (ISBN 0-87793-183-6). Ave Maria.
Haresign, Gordon. Innocence: The Story of Steve Linscott, the Emmaus Bible School Student Convicted of Murder. 224p. 1986. 7.95 (ISBN 0-310-43801-2, 12056P). Zondervan.
Hastings, Robert J. Glorious Is Thy Name! LC 85-26948. 1986. 7.95 (ISBN 0-8054-7230-4). Broadman.
Hayes, Norvel. Winds of God. 90p. (Orig.). 1985. pap. 4.95 (ISBN 0-89274-375-1). Harrison Hse.
Hefley, James & Hefley, Marti. China: Christian Martyrs of the Twentieth Century. LC 78-6187. 1978. pap. 2.25 (ISBN 0-915134-16-0). Mott Media.
Hembree, Ron. The Mark Buntain Story. LC 83-73187. 256p. 1984. pap. 3.95 (ISBN 0-87123-593-5, 200593). Bethany Hse.
Hemleben, Johannes. Rudolf Steiner: A Documentary Biography. Twyman, Leo, tr. (Illus.). 1975. (Pub by Henry Goulden, Ltd); pap. 10.95 (ISBN 0-904822-03-6). St George Bk Serv.
Herr, Dan. Start Digging! 1987. 9.95 (ISBN 0-88347-204-X). Thomas More.
Hession, Roy. My Calvary Road. 1978. pap. 4.95 (ISBN 0-87508-262-9). Chr Lit.
Hickman, Martin. David Matthew Kennedy: Banker, Statesman, Churchman. 1987. 14.95 (ISBN 0-87579-093-3). Deseret Bk.
Hill, John H. Dear God, Pourquoi? Why Did You Born Me in Texas. LC 84-91310. 167p. 1985. 10.95 (ISBN 0-533-06400-7). Vantage.
Hodges, George. Saints & Heroes Since the Middle Ages. LC 75-107713. (Essay Index Reprint Ser.). 1912. 21.50 (ISBN 0-8369-1515-1). Ayer Co Pubs.
--Saints & Heroes to the End of the Middle Ages. facs. ed. LC 67-26749. (Essay Index Reprint Ser). 1911. 20.00 (ISBN 0-8369-0544-X). Ayer Co Pubs.
Hoehner, Harold W. Herod Antipas: A Contemporary of Jesus Christ. new ed. 456p. 1980. pap. 11.95 (ISBN 0-310-42251-5, 10842P). Zondervan.
Hoffman, Joy. With Wandering Steps & Slow. LC 81-18566. 140p. (Orig.). 1982. pap. 4.95 (ISBN 0-87784-804-1). Inter-Varsity.
Hosier, Helen K. Living Cameos. 192p. (Orig.). 1984. pap. 8.95 (ISBN 0-8007-1398-2). Revell.
Hoversten, Cheryl. Come September. 1984. 5.95 (ISBN 0-89536-961-3, 7512). CSS of Ohio.
Howell, Patrick. Reducing the Storm to a Whisper: The Story of a Breakdown. 228p. 1985. 15.95 (ISBN 0-88347-183-3). Thomas More.
Hughes, Philip E. Lefevre: Pioneer of Ecclesiastical Renewal in France. 224p. (Orig.). 1984. pap. 15.95x (ISBN 0-8028-0015-7). Eerdmans.
Hunt, Dave & Kristian, Hans. The Secret Invasion. 224p. 1987. pap. 5.95 (ISBN 0-89081-560-7). Harvest Hse.
Ives, Carolyn. Being OK. (Orig.). 1987. pap. 7.00 (ISBN 0-915541-19-X). Star Bks Inc.
Jackson, S. Trevena. Fanny Crosby's Story. (Christian Biography Ser.). 198p. 1981. pap. 3.95 (ISBN 0-8010-5127-4). Baker Bk.
Jenkins, Peter & Jenkins, Barbara. The Road Unseen. (General Ser.). 406p. 1986. lib. bdg. 18.95 (ISBN 0-317-46368-3, Large Print Bks). G K Hall.
Johnson, A. Wetherell. Created for Commitment. 1982. 12.95 (ISBN 0-8423-0484-3). Tyndale.
Johnson, Elsie. Man Who Freed Slaves: Wilberforce. (Stories of Faith, Fame Ser.). (YA) 1975. pap. 2.95 (ISBN 0-87508-615-2). Chr Lit.
Johnson, R. K. Builder of Bridges: The Biography of Dr. Bob Jones, Sr. (Illus.). 383p. 1982. pap. 5.95 (ISBN 0-89084-157-8). Bob Jones Univ Pr.
Jones, W. Paul. The Province Beyond the River: The Diary of a Protestant at a Trappist Monastery. 160p. (Orig.). 1986. pap. 6.95 (ISBN 0-8358-0546-8). Upper Room.
Jordan, Mickey & Harrell, Irene B. Let Yesterday Go. LC 84-51995. 285p. 1984. pap. 6.00 (ISBN 0-915541-01-7). Star Bks Inc.
Kabell, Margaret. Prophet of the Pacific. (Stories of Faith, Fame Ser.). (YA) 1976. pap. 2.95 (ISBN 0-87508-619-5). Chr Lit.
Keller, Phillip. Wonder O' the Wind. 1986. 7.95 (ISBN 0-8499-3061-8). Word Bks.
Kepler, Thomas S. Journey with the Saints. facs. ed. LC 70-148223. (Biography Index Reprint Ser.). 1951. 17.00 (ISBN 0-8369-8070-0). Ayer Co Pubs.
Kimball, Stanley B. Heber C. Kimball: Mormon Patriarch & Pioneer. LC 80-21923. (Illus.). 345p. 1981. pap. 13.50 (ISBN 0-252-01299-2). U of Ill Pr.
Kirsch, George B. Jeremy Belknap: A Biography. 25.00 (ISBN 0-405-14112-2). Ayer Co Pubs.
Lam, Nora & Harrell, Irene B. China Cry. LC 79-63932. 120p. (Orig.). 1984. pap. 5.95 (ISBN 0-89221-110-5). New Leaf.
Lamera, Stephen. James Alberione: A Marvel for Our Times. (Illus.). 1977. 4.00 (ISBN 0-8198-0428-2); pap. 3.00 (ISBN 0-8198-0429-0). Dghtrs St Paul.
Lantry, Eileen. Good People Get Burned Too. (Life Ser.). 1984. pap. 4.95 (ISBN 0-8163-0549-8). Pacific Pr Pub Assn.
Lappin, Peter. Conquistador. LC 69-19398. 1970. 6.95 (ISBN 0-89944-040-1). Don Bosco Multimedia.
--The Wine in the Chalice. (Orig.). 1972. pap. 3.25 (ISBN 0-89944-031-2). Don Bosco Multimedia.
Lawson, James G. Deeper Experiences of Famous Christians. 1981. pap. 2.95 (ISBN 0-87162-069-3, D3349). Warner Pr.
Lee, Luther. Autobiography of the Rev. Luther Lee. Dayton, Donald W., ed. (The Higher Christian Life Ser.). 345p. 1985. 45.00 (ISBN 0-8240-6426-7). Garland Pub.
Le Joly, Edward. Servant of Love: Mother Teresa & Her Missionaries of Charity. LC 77-15874. (Illus.). 1978. 4.95 (ISBN 0-06-065215-2, HarpR). Har-Row.
Lemmon, Sarah M. Parson Pettigrew of the "Old Church". 1744-1807. (James Sprunt Studies in History & Political Science: No. 52). vii, 168p. 1971. pap. 5.00x (ISBN 0-8078-5052-7). U of NC Pr.
Lindsay, Gordon. John G. Lake: Apostle to Africa. 1.75 (ISBN 0-89985-011-1). Christ Nations.
--Men Who Change the World, 7 vols. 0.95 ea. Christ Nations.
Linke, Maria Z & Hunt, Ruth. East Wind. 1978. pap. 2.50 (ISBN 0-310-27852-X). Zondervan.
Long, Jim, ed. How Could God Let This Happen. (Campus Life Bks). 160p. 1986. pap. 5.95 (ISBN 0-8423-1377-X). Tyndale.
Lopeshinskaya, Elena. Martyr Bishop Confessors under Communism. (Rus.). pap. 5.00 (ISBN 0-686-05413-X). Eastern Orthodox.
Lotz, Philip H., ed. Founders of Christian Movements. LC 71-111843. (Essay Index Reprint Ser). 1941. 17.00 (ISBN 0-8369-1672-7). Ayer Co Pubs.
Lutz, Lorry. Destined for Royalty: A Brahmin Priest's Search for Truth. LC 85-22681. 152p. (Orig.). 1986. pap. 5.95 (ISBN 0-87808-202-6, WCL202-6). William Carey Lib.
McCartney, Hazel S. Saga of Seven Sisters. 1985. 12.00 (ISBN 0-533-06270-5). Vantage.
McClendon, James W., Jr. Biography as Theology: How Life Stories Can Remake Today's Theology. LC 74-9715. 224p. 1974. pap. 7.75 (ISBN 0-687-03539-2). Abingdon.
MacDonald, George. The Boyhood of Ranald Bannerman. Hamilton, Dan, ed. 168p. 1987. pap. 3.95 (ISBN 0-89693-748-8). Victor Bks.
--The Genius of Willie MacMichael. Hamilton, Dan, ed. 168p. 1987. pap. 3.95 (ISBN 0-89693-750-X). Victor Bks.
--Heather & Snow. Hamilton, Dan, ed. 288p. 1987. pap. 5.95 (ISBN 0-89693-760-7). Victor Bks.
--The Wanderings of Clare Skymer. Hamilton, Dan, ed. 168p. 1987. pap. 3.95 (ISBN 0-89693-757-7). Victor Bks.
MacGregor, Geddes. Apostles Extraordinary: A Celebration of Saints & Sinners. (Illus.). 168p. (Orig.). 1986. pap. 8.95 (ISBN 0-89407-065-7). Strawberry Hill.
MacHaffie, Barbara J. Her Story: Women in Christian Tradition. LC 85-45494. 192p. 1986. pap. 9.95 (ISBN 0-8006-1893-9). Fortress.
Mackay, Henry F. Followers in the Way. LC 71-93359. (Essay Index Reprint Ser). 1934. 17.00 (ISBN 0-8369-1304-3). Ayer Co Pubs.
Mackay, Kris. No Greater Love. LC 81-22123. 99p. 1982. 6.95 (ISBN 0-87747-906-2). Deseret Bk.
McLoughlin, Emmett. Famous Ex-Priests. LC 68-18759. 1968. 4.95 (ISBN 0-8184-0030-7). Lyle Stuart.
Malone, Dumas. Saints in Action. facs. ed. LC 70-142664. (Essay Index Reprint Ser). 1939. 15.00 (ISBN 0-8369-2062-7). Ayer Co Pubs.
Malony, H. Newton. Integration Musings: Thoughts on Being A Christian Professional. LC 86-81512. (Orig.). 1986. pap. 12.95 (ISBN 0-9609928-3-9). Integ Pr.
Marty, Martin E. & Peerman, Dean G., eds. A Handbook of Christian Theologians. 736p. (Orig.). 1984. pap. 13.50 (ISBN 0-687-16563-6). Abingdon.
Massey, Marilyn C. Christ Unmasked: The Meaning of "The Life of Jesus" in German Politics. LC 82-8547. (Studies in Religion Ser.). xi, 182p. 1983. 23.00x (ISBN 0-8078-1524-1). U of NC Pr.
Medvedev, Anthony. The Young Elder: From Ambrose of Milkova. 70p. 1974. pap. 3.00 (ISBN 0-317-30442-9). Holy Trinity.
Mellows, Mary. A Lamp for Orchid. 126p. 1986. pap. 22.00X (ISBN 0-7223-1987-8, Pub. by A H Stockwell England). State Mutual Bk.
Memoirs of George E. Harmon. (Illus.). 56p. 0.60 (ISBN 0-686-29129-8); 2 copies 1.00 (ISBN 0-686-29130-1). Faith Pub Hse.
Mlodozeniec, Juventyn. I Knew St. Maximilian. 116p. 1982. pap. 2.95 (ISBN 0-911988-48-3). AMI Pr.
Montieth, Bill. Wild Bill. 164p. (Orig.). 1984. pap. 5.95 (ISBN 0-89274-324-7). Harrison Hse.
Moore, Joy H. Ted Studebaker: A Man Who Loved Peace. LC 86-19419. (Illus.). 40p. (Orig.). 1987. pap. 9.95 (ISBN 0-8361-3427-3). Herald Pr.
Mother Teresa. Words to Love By. LC 82-73373. (Illus.). 80p. (Orig.). 1983. pap. 4.95 (ISBN 0-87793-261-1). Ave Maria.
Mounce, William D. Profiles in Faith. LC 84-9961. 1984. pap. 3.95 (ISBN 0-8307-0984-3, S382102). Regal.
Moyer, Elgin. Wycliffe Biographical Dictionary of the Church. 1982. 19.95 (ISBN 0-8024-9693-8). Moody.
Murphy, Leona S. Miracles & the Sumrall Family. 205p. (Orig.). 1984. pap. 6.95 (ISBN 0-89274-325-5). Harrison Hse.
Murray, Iain. Life of John Murray. 1984. pap. 6.95 (ISBN 0-85151-426-X). Banner of Truth.
Murray, Iain H. The Life of A. W. Pink. (Illus.). 272p. (Orig.). 1981. pap. 5.95 (ISBN 0-85151-332-8). Banner of Truth.
Murray, William J. My Life Without God. LC 83-14269. 252p. 1984. pap. 5.95 (ISBN 0-8407-5884-7). Nelson.
Naylor, C. W. The Redemption of Howard Gray. 72p. pap. 0.50 (ISBN 0-686-29162-X). Faith Pub Hse.
Nemec, Ludvik. Infant Jesus of Prague. (LargeType). 2.25 (ISBN 0-89942-129-6, 129/04). Catholic Bk Pub.
Neville, Robert C. Soldier, Sage, Saint. LC 77-75798. 1978. 20.00 (ISBN 0-8232-1035-9); pap. 8.00 (ISBN 0-8232-1036-7). Fordham.
Newton, Joseph F. Some Living Masters of the Pulpit: Studies in Religious Personality. facsimile ed. LC 71-152203. (Essay Index Reprint Ser). Repr. of 1923 ed. 18.00 (ISBN 0-8369-2287-5). Ayer Co Pubs.
Nikiforoff-Volgin, V. Dorozhnij Posokh. Tr. of A Staff for the Road. 188p. 1971. pap. 6.00 (ISBN 0-317-30421-6). Holy Trinity.
Oates, Wayne E. The Struggle to Be Free: My Story & Your Story. LC 83-5904. 164p. 1983. pap. 7.95 (ISBN 0-664-24500-5). Westminster.
O'Brien, Charles F. Sir William Dawson: A Life in Science & Religion. LC 71-153381. (American Philosophical Society, Memoirs: Vol. 84). pap. 54.30 (ISBN 0-317-20673-7, 2025140). Bks Demand UMI.
Odenheimer, William H. Jerusalem & Its Vicinity: Familiar Lectures on the Sacred Localities Connected with the Week Before the Resurrection. Davis, Moshe, ed. (America & the Holy Land Ser.). (Illus.). 1977. Repr. of 1855 ed. lib. bdg. 20.00x (ISBN 0-405-10272-0). Ayer Co Pubs.
Omartian, Stormie. Stormie. 224p. (Orig.). 1986. pap. 6.95 (ISBN 0-89081-556-9). Harvest Hse.
Orr, C. E. The Hidden Life. 112p. pap. 0.75 (ISBN 0-686-29149-2). Faith Pub Hse.
Owen, Bob. Ted Engstrom: Man with a Vision. 214p. 1984. pap. 5.95 (ISBN 0-8423-6942-2). Tyndale.
Owen, Robert & Howard, David M. Victor el Victorioso. Orellana, Eugenio, tr. from Eng. Tr. of Victor. (Span.). 152p. 1981. pap. 3.25 (ISBN 0-89922-206-4). Edit Caribe.
Palmer, Bernard. My Son, My Son. (Living Bks.). 288p. (Orig.). 1987. pap. 3.95 (ISBN 0-8423-4639-2). Tyndale.
Patterson, Chuck. There Is Something Else. Wallace, Mary H., ed. (Illus., Orig.). 1982. pap. 5.95 (ISBN 0-912315-23-7). Word Aflame.
Peabody, Francis G. Reminiscences of Present-Day Saints. facsimile ed. LC 74-37525. (Essay Index Reprint Ser). Repr. of 1927 ed. 23.50 (ISBN 0-8369-2576-9). Ayer Co Pubs.
Peachment, Brian. Three Fighters for Freedom. 1974. pap. 1.60 (ISBN 0-08-017617-8). Pergamon.
Perez, J. Guillent. A Case of Conscience. 370p. (Orig.). 1985. pap. 12.95 (ISBN 0-9607590-2-6). Action Life Pubns.
Philipon, M. M. Conchita: A Mother's Diary. Owen, Aloysius, tr. LC 78-1929. 1978. pap. 6.95 (ISBN 0-8189-0368-6). Alba.
Phillips, Carolyn. Michelle. 1982. 3.95 (ISBN 0-88113-205-5). Edit Betania.
Phillips, D. Z. R. S. Thomas: Poet of the Hidden God. (Princeton Theolographical Monograph Ser.: No. 2). 192p. (Orig.). 1986. pap. 18.00 (ISBN 0-915138-83-2). Pickwick.
Phillips, Gloria & Harrell, Irene B. A Heart Set Free. (Orig.). 1985. pap. 5.00 (ISBN 0-915541-02-5); study guide: Spiritual Warfare 5.00 (ISBN 0-915541-16-5); answer bk. avail. (ISBN 0-915541-17-3). Star Bks Inc.
Pike, Eunice V. Ken Pike: Scholar & Christian. LC 81-51058. (Illus.). 270p. (Orig.). 1981. pap. 5.00 (ISBN 0-88312-920-5); microfiche (3) 6.00 (ISBN 0-88312-986-8). Summer Inst Ling.
Pink, A. W. Letters of A. W. Pink. 1978. pap. 2.95 (ISBN 0-85151-262-3). Banner of Truth.
Popoff, Peter. A New Fire Is Blazing. Tanner, Don, ed. LC 80-67993. (Illus.). 194p. (Orig.). 1980. pap. 4.95 (ISBN 0-938544-02-0). Faith Messenger.
Poulos, Nellie. Life's Story & Healings. 160p. pap. 1.50 (ISBN 0-686-29128-X). Faith Pub Hse.
Powell, Terry. Heroes & Zeroes. 144p. 1987. pap. 3.95 (ISBN 0-89693-570-1). Victor Bks.
Price, Eugenia. The Burden Is Light. 272p. 1985. pap. 11.95 (ISBN 0-8027-2514-7). Walker & Co.
Price, Harry. No Respecter of Persons. 128p. 1981. pap. 4.95 (ISBN 0-8059-2797-2). Dorrance.
Purcell, Mary. The Quiet Companion: Peter Favre S. J., 1506-1546. vi, 198p. 1981. 8.95 (ISBN 0-8294-0377-9). Loyola.
Rayburn, Jim, III. Dance, Children, Dance. 192p. 1984. 9.95 (ISBN 0-8423-0515-7). Tyndale.

Rengers, Christopher. The Youngest Prophet: The Life of Jacinta Marto, Fatima Visionary. LC 85-30789. 144p. (Orig.). 1986. pap. 5.95 (ISBN 0-8189-0496-8). Alba.
Reville, John C. Herald of Christ Louis Bourdaloue, S. J. 1978. Repr. of 1922 ed. lib. bdg. 25.00 (ISBN 0-8492-2270-2). R West.
Reynolds, Ralph V. Upon the Potter's Wheel. Wallace, Mary H., ed. LC 85-31583. 144p. (Orig.). 1981. pap. 4.95 (ISBN 0-912315-22-9). Word Aflame.
Riley, Jeannie C. & Buckingham, Jamie. From Harper Valley to the Mountain Top. (Epiphany Bks.). (Illus.). 1983. pap. 2.75 (ISBN 0-345-30481-0). Ballantine.
Rinaldi, Peter M. By Love Compelled. (Illus., Orig.). 1973. pap. 3.25 (ISBN 0-89944-032-0). Don Bosco Multimedia.
Rohrer, Norman B. Mom LeTourneau. Throop, Isabel A., ed. 144p. 1985. 6.95 (ISBN 0-8423-4502-7). Tyndale.
Rosewell, Pamela. The Five Silent Years of Corrie Ten Boom. Hazzard, David, ed. 192p. 1986. pap. 6.95 (ISBN 0-310-61121-0, 13228P). Zondervan.
Rover, Dave & Fickett, Harold. Welcome Home, Davey. 208p. 1986. 12.95 (ISBN 0-8499-0553-2). Word Bks.
Rowe, Henry K. Modern Pathfinders of Christianity: The Lives & Deeds of Seven Centuries of Christian Leaders. facs. ed. LC 68-16973. (Essay Index Reprint Ser). 1928. 15.00 (ISBN 0-8369-0839-2). Ayer Co Pubs.
Rudolph, L. C. Francis Asbury. 240p. (Orig.). 1983. pap. 8.95 (ISBN 0-687-13461-7). Abingdon.
Ruegsegger, Ronald W., ed. Reflections on Francis Schaeffer. 336p. 1986. pap. 12.95 (ISBN 0-310-37091-4, 12355P). Zondervan.
Ruffin, Bernard. Fanny Crosby. (Heroes of the Faith Ser.). 1985. Repr. of 1976 ed. 6.95 (ISBN 0-916441-16-4). Barbour & Co.
Runk, Wesley T. People Who Knew Paul. 1985. 2.00 (ISBN 0-89536-185-X, 1610). CSS of Ohio.
Rupp, Ernest G. Six Makers of English Religion, Fifteen Hundred to Seventeen Hundred. (Essay Index Reprint Ser.). Repr. of 1957 ed. 16.75 (ISBN 0-518-10159-2). Ayer Co Pubs.
Rushing, Philip. Empty Sleeves. LC 83-11322. 224p. (Orig.). 1984. 9.95 (ISBN 0-310-28820-7, 11322). Zondervan.
Russell, Arthur J. Their Religion. facs. ed. LC 78-128308. (Essay Index Reprint Ser). 1935. 20.00 (ISBN 0-8369-2131-3). Ayer Co Pubs.
Ryle, J. C. Christian Leaders of the Eighteenth Century: Includes Whitefield, Wesley, Grimshaw, Romaine, Rowlands, Berridge, Venn, Walker, Harvey, Toplady, & Fletcher. 1978. pap. 7.45 (ISBN 0-85151-268-2). Banner of Truth.
St. Nectarios Press, ed. New Martyrs of the Turkish Yoke. Papadopulos, Leonidas, et al, trs. from Gr. LC 84-50974. 400p. (Orig.). 1985. pap. 12.50x (ISBN 0-913026-57-3); pap. 15.00x after January 1986. St Nectarios.
Sandberg, Karl C. At the Crossaroads of Faith & Reason: An Essay on Pierre Bayle. LC 66-18531. pap. 33.80 (ISBN 0-317-51991-3, 2027388). Bks Demand UMI.
Sandstrom, David H. Landmarks of the Spirit: One Man's Journey. 192p. (Orig.). 1984. pap. 11.95 (ISBN 0-8298-0726-8). Pilgrim NY.
Sattler, Gary. God's Glory, Neighbor's Good: Francke's Biography & Sermons. 272p. 1982. pap. 8.95 (ISBN 0-910452-50-4). Covenant.
Schantz, Daniel D. Barton W. Stone. (Restoration Booklets Ser.). (Illus., Orig.). 1984. pap. 0.75 (ISBN 0-87239-775-0, 3295). Standard Pub.
--Raccoon John Smith. (Restoration Booklets). (Illus.). 16p. (Orig.). 1984. pap. 0.75 (ISBN 0-87239-778-5, 3298). Standard Pub.
--Walter Scott. (Restoration Booklets Ser.). (Illus.). 16p. (Orig.). 1984. pap. 0.75 (ISBN 0-87239-777-7, 3297). Standard Pub.
Schmidt, William J. Architect of Unity. 1978. cloth 14.95 (ISBN 0-377-00080-9); pap. 9.95 (ISBN 0-377-00079-5). Friend Pr.
Schmoger, Carl E. The Life of Anne Catherine Emmerich, 2 vols. 1976. Set. pap. 33.00 (ISBN 0-89555-061-X); Vol. 1. pap. 12.00 (ISBN 0-89555-059-8); Vol. 2. pap. 24.00 (ISBN 0-89555-060-1). TAN Bks Pubs.
Schwing, Sally A. Do You Think It Snows In Heaven? Graves, Helen, ed. 213p. 1987. 12.95 (ISBN 1-55523-049-0). Winston-Derek.
Scott, Carolyn. Dr. Who Never Gave up, Ida Scudder. (Stories of Faith & Fame Ser.). (YA) 1975. pap. 2.95 (ISBN 0-87508-607-1). Chr Lit.
Sheldon, Charles M. In His Steps. 243p. 1985. pap. 3.95 (ISBN 0-310-32751-2, Clarion Class). Zondervan.
Sheley, Donald B., ed. Beggar at the Banquet: The Story of Dr. Woo Jun Hong. LC 81-13971. (Illus.). 178p. (Orig.). pap. 5.95 (ISBN 0-88289-306-8). Pelican.
Sheron, Carole. The Rise & Fall of Superwoman. LC 79-26704. (Orion Ser.). 96p. 1980. pap. 3.50 (ISBN 0-8127-1270-6). Review & Herald.
Sindevitch, Heinrich. Kamo Grjadeshi: Quo Vadis. 523p. 23.00 (ISBN 0-317-30246-9); pap. 18.00 (ISBN 0-317-30247-7). Holy Trinity.
Skazanije o Khrista Radi Jurodivoj - Pelagiji Ivanovna Serebrennikva. Tr. of The Life of the Fool for Christ-Pelagia Ivanovna Serebrennikova. 183p. pap. 7.00 (ISBN 0-317-29280-3). Holy Trinity.
Skoglund, Elizabeth. Coping. LC 79-65538. 128p. 1980. pap. 3.95 (ISBN 0-8307-0727-1, 5413109). Regal.
Smelser, Georgia. Nathaniel A. Urshan: Champion of the Faith & Legend in Our Time. (Illus.). 160p. (Orig.). 1985. pap. 15.00 (ISBN 0-912315-95-4). Word Aflame.
--OMA. LC 85-31579. (Illus.). 254p. (Orig.). 1981. pap. 5.95 (ISBN 0-912315-16-4). Word Aflame.
Smith, Jane S. & Carlson, Betty. A Gift of Music. LC 83-70798. 255p. 1983. pap. 7.95 (ISBN 0-89107-293-4, Crossway Bks). Good News.
Smith, William & Wace, Henry, eds. Dictionary of Christian Biography, Literature, Sects & Doctrines: Being a Continuation of the Dictionary of the Bible, 4 Vols. LC 12-3122. 1968. Repr. of 1877 ed. Set. 375.00 (ISBN 0-527-84200-1). Kraus Repr.
Snow, Michael. Christian Pacifism. LC 81-69724. 98p. (Orig.). 1982. pap. 6.95 (ISBN 0-913408-67-0). Friends United.
Sorrill, Bobbie. Annie Armstrong: Dreamer in Action. LC 83-70842. 1984. 8.95 (ISBN 0-8054-6333-X). Broadman.
Spaeth, Barbara J. Laurie Miracle by Miracle. 48p. 1986. 6.95 (ISBN 0-317-43316-4). Todd & Honeywell.
Spangler, Ann. Bright Legacy: Portraits of Ten Outstanding Christian Women. 196p. 1985. pap. 6.95 (ISBN 0-89283-278-9, Pub. by Vine Books). Servant.
Spangler, Ann, ed. Bright Legacy: Portraits of Ten Outstanding Christian Women. 204p. 1983. 10.95 (ISBN 0-89283-167-7, Pub. by Vine Bks). Servant.
Speer, Robert E. Some Great Leaders in the World Movement. facs. ed. LC 67-26786. (Essay Index Reprint Ser). 1911. 18.00 (ISBN 0-8369-0895-3). Ayer Co Pubs.
Squire, Aelred. Aelred of Rievaulx: A Study. (Cistercian Studies Ser.: No. 50). 192p. 1981. 10.95 (ISBN 0-87907-850-2); pap. 5.00 (ISBN 0-686-85802-6). Cistercian Pubns.
Stedman, Ray C. The Man of Faith: Learning from the Life of Abraham. LC 85-21772. (Authentic Christianity Bks.). 1985. pap. 7.95 (ISBN 0-88070-125-0). Multnomah.
Steel, Valetta & Erny, Ed. Thrice Through the Valley. (Living Books). 112p. 1986. 2.95 (ISBN 0-8423-7146-X). Tyndale.
Stone, Hoyt E. Yet Will I Serve Him. 1976. pap. 3.95 (ISBN 0-87148-931-7). Pathway Pr.
Stover, Ruby E. Life's Golden Gleanings. 94p. pap. 1.00 (ISBN 0-686-29127-1). Faith Pub Hse.
Strahan, Loretta. Beside the Still Waters. Hughes, Jeff, ed. 108p. (Orig.). 1986. pap. 3.45 (ISBN 0-910653-18-6, 8101T). Archival Servs.
Strong, June. A Little Journey. Wheeler, Gerald, ed. 126p. (Orig.). 1984. pap. 5.95 (ISBN 0-8280-0236-3). Review & Herald.
Susag, S. O. Personal Experiences of S. O. Susag. 191p. pap. 1.75 (ISBN 0-686-29134-4). Faith Pub Hse.
Tada, Joni E. Choices...Changes. 240p. 1986. 14.95 (ISBN 0-310-24010-7, 12018). Zondervan.
Tallach, John. They Shall Be Mine. 128p. 1981. pap. 5.45 (ISBN 0-85151-320-4). Banner of Truth.
Taylor, Herbert J. The Herbert J. Taylor Story. 128p. 1983. pap. 4.95 (ISBN 0-87784-836-X). Inter-Varsity.
Taylor, Hudson & Thompson, Phyllis. God's Adventurer. (Illus.). 1978. pap. 2.50 (ISBN 9971-83-777-3). OMF Bks.
Thomasma, Kenneth. Soun Tetoken: Nez Perce Boy. (Voyager Ser.). 144p. 1984. 8.95 (ISBN 0-8010-8874-7); pap. 5.95 (ISBN 0-8010-8873-9). Baker Bk.
Tickle, Phyllis A. What the Heart Already Knows. (Orig.). 1985. pap. 5.95 (ISBN 0-8358-0522-0). Upper Room.
Tiltman, Marjorie. God's Adventurers. facs. ed. LC 68-16979. (Essay Index Reprint Ser.). 1933. 18.00 (ISBN 0-8369-0945-3). Ayer Co Pubs.
Tinnes, Bonnie. I Am a Woman; I Am a Person. 99p. (Orig.). 1986. pap. 4.95 (ISBN 0-9616611-0-0). Thoughts By Bonnie.
Tomlinson, A. J. The Last Great Conflict. 241p. 1984. Repr. of 1913 ed. 8.95 (ISBN 0-317-14173-2, 1925). White Wing Pub.
Traylor, Ellen G. John, Son of Thunder. 1980. pap. 4.95 (ISBN 0-8423-1903-4). Tyndale.
Trosse, George. The Life of the Reverend Mr. George Trosse. Brink, A. W., ed. LC 73-79097. pap. 37.50 (ISBN 0-317-26445-1, 2023853). Bks Demand UMI.
Tsanoff, Radoslav A. Autobiographies of Ten Religious Leaders: Alternatives in Christian Experience. LC 68-57880. 304p. 1968. 7.00 (ISBN 0-911536-34-5). Trinity U Pr.
Turbet, Paschal. The Little Bishop. 1977. 3.50 (ISBN 0-8198-0430-4); pap. 2.50 (ISBN 0-8198-0431-2). Dghtrs St Paul.
Van Cleave, Mary E. Behold the Bride. 1986. 12.95 (ISBN 0-533-07024-4). Vantage.
Van Halsema, Thea. Three Men Came to Heidelberg. (Christian Biography Ser.). 96p. 1982. pap. 3.95 (ISBN 0-8010-9289-2). Baker Bk.
Vaporis, Nomikos M., pref. by. Byzantine Ecclesiastical Personalities. (Byzantine Fellowship Lectures: No. 2). 107p. 1975. pap. 2.95 (ISBN 0-916586-04-9). Holy Cross Orthodox.
Volio, Maria F. Confesion de un Alma Idolatra. 152p. (Orig.). 1982. pap. 3.75 (ISBN 0-89922-218-8). Edit Caribe.
Walahfrid Strabo. Leben Des Heiligen Gallus & Des Abtes Otmar Von Sanktgallen. Potthast, A., tr. x, 86p. (Ger.). pap. 10.00 (ISBN 0-384-31951-3). Johnson Repr.
Walker, Williston. Great Men of the Christian Church. facs. ed. LC 68-8502. (Essay Index Reprint Ser). 1908. 22.00 (ISBN 0-8369-0966-6). Ayer Co Pubs.
Wallace, Archer. Religious Faith of Great Men. facs. ed. LC 67-26792. (Essay Index Reprint Ser). 1934. 17.00 (ISBN 0-8369-0968-2). Ayer Co Pubs.
Wallace, Mary H. It's Real. (Illus.). 224p. (Orig.). 1981. pap. 5.95 (ISBN 0-912315-17-2). Word Aflame.
Walsh, Sheila. Never Give It up. 1987. pap. 6.95. Revell.
Washburn, Henry B. Men of Conviction. facs. ed. LC 74-134152. (Essay Index Reprint Ser). 1931. 18.00 (ISBN 0-8369-2081-3). Ayer Co Pubs.
--Religious Motive in Philanthropy. LC 72-105047. (Essay Index Reprint Ser). 1931. 18.00 (ISBN 0-8369-1634-4). Ayer Co Pubs.
Watson, David. You Are My God: A Pioneer of Renewal Recounts His Pilgramage in Faith. 196p. 1984. pap. 5.95 (ISBN 0-87788-972-4). Shaw Pubs.
Watson, Vera M. The Children of Ministers Tell Us. 1983. 5.95 (ISBN 0-8062-2033-3). Carlton.
Watt, Leilani. Caught in the Conflict. LC 83-82700. 176p. 1984. text ed. 9.95 (ISBN 0-89081-411-2). Harvest Hse.
Way, Nancy L. A Second Chance. 1985. 5.95 (ISBN 0-8062-2444-4). Carlton.
Weatherspool, W. W. Those Days. 1981. 5.95 (ISBN 0-8062-1835-5). Carlton.
Welch, Rosa P. & Myers, Oma L. Rosa's Song: The Life & Ministry of Rosa Page Welch. LC 84-1882. 224p. 1984. pap. 8.95x (ISBN 0-8272-3210-1). CBP.
Westmoreland, Tony. In All Things I Am Not Alone. Graves, Helen, ed. 230p. 1987. 8.95 (ISBN 1-55523-059-8). Winston-Derek.
Whipple, Edwin P. Recollections of Eminent Men with Other Papers. 397p. 1982. Repr. of 1886 ed. lib. bdg. 45.00 (ISBN 0-8495-5840-9). Arden Lib.
White, Arthur W. Ellen G. White Biography, Vol. 2. Woolsey, Raymond H., ed. 480p. 1986. 19.95 (ISBN 0-8280-0120-0). Review & Herald.
White, Charles E. The Beauty of Holiness: Phoebe Palmer As Theologian, Revivalist, Feminist, & Humanitarian. 352p. 1986. 15.95 (ISBN 0-310-46250-9). Zondervan.
Wiebe, Katie F. Have Cart, Will Travel. (Trailblazer Ser.). 86p. (Orig.). 1974. pap. 1.00 (ISBN 0-919797-27-X). Kindred Pr.
Wiersbe, Warren W. Victorious Christians You Should Know. 176p. 1984. pap. 4.95 (ISBN 0-8010-9667-7). Baker Bk.
Wilkerson, Gwen & Schonauer, Betty. In His Strength. Rev. ed. LC 77-92619. 144p. 1982. pap. 4.95 (ISBN 0-8307-0825-1, 5416405). Regal.
Williams, Effie M. Just Mary. 96p. pap. 0.75 (ISBN 0-686-29124-7). Faith Pub Hse.
Williamsen, Glen & Anders, Isabel. Susanna. 240p. (Orig.). 1985. pap. 3.50 (ISBN 0-8423-6691-1). Tyndale.
Williamson, Glen. Brother Kawabe. 1977. pap. 1.75 (ISBN 0-89367-012-X). Light & Life.
Wilson, Ella M. My Testimony. 70p. 1986. pap. 6.95 (ISBN 1-55523-060-1). Winston-Derek.
Wilson, J. Christy. Flaming Prophet: The Story of Samuel Zwemer. LC 76-130778. (Bold Believers Ser). (Orig.). 1970. pap. 0.95 (ISBN 0-377-84201-X). Friend Pr.
Wolfger Von Prufening. Das Leben Des Bischofs Otto Von Bamberg. xxix, 78p. (Ger.). Repr. of 1928 ed. 12.00 (ISBN 0-384-69065-3). Johnson Repr.
Woodson, Meg. I'll Get to Heaven Before You Do! 96p. 1985. pap. text ed. 6.95 (ISBN 0-687-18611-0). Abingdon.
Wurmbrand, Richard. Tortured for Christ. LC 86-72054. 128p. 1987. pap. 4.95 (ISBN 0-89107-408-2, Crossway Bks). Good News.
Yanich, Voyeslav. Lives of the Serbian Saints. (Illus.). 1973. 3.95 (ISBN 0-686-05412-1). Eastern Orthodox.
Yee, Check-Hung. For My Kinsmen's Sake. 1986. 15.00 (ISBN 0-89216-066-7). Salvation Army.
Young, Fay. The Awakening. 64p. 1981. 5.00 (ISBN 0-682-49701-0). Exposition Pr FL.
Ziglar, Zig. Confessions of a Happy Christian. 199p. 1982. pap. 6.95 (ISBN 0-88289-400-5). Pelican.

CHRISTIAN BIOGRAPHY–JUVENILE LITERATURE

Benton, John. Kari. 192p. 1984. pap. 2.95 (ISBN 0-8007-8491-X, New Hope). Revell.
Bonniwell, William R. The Life of Blessed Margaret of Castello. LC 83-70524. 113p. 1983. pap. 4.00 (ISBN 0-89555-213-2). TAN Bks Pubs.
Byers, Carolyn. Mary Andrews: Companion of Sorrow. Wheeler, Gerald, ed. LC 83-21121. (A Banner Bk.). (Illus.). 91p. (Orig.). 1984. pap. 5.95 (ISBN 0-8280-0212-6). Review & Herald.
Higgins, Daniel. The Challenge: Life of Dominic Savio. (Illus.). 1959. 4.25 (ISBN 0-89944-025-8). Don Bosco Multimedia.
Kamin, Philip. Paul Young. (Illus.). 32p. 1985. pap. 4.95 (ISBN 0-88188-411-1, 00183876, Robus Bks). H Leonard Pub Corp.
Lappin, Peter. General Mickey. (Orig.). 1977. pap. 2.95 (ISBN 0-89944-029-0). Don Bosco Multimedia.
McIndoo, Ethel. Freeda Harris: Woman of Prayer. LC 84-2978. (Meet the Missionary Ser.). 1984. 5.50 (ISBN 0-8054-4286-3, 4242-86). Broadman.
Olsen, Sue. Kate Magevney & the Christmas Miracle: A Child's Christmas in Memphis (1850) Easson, Roger R., ed. LC 84-11612. (A Child's Christmas in Memphis Ser.: Vol. 2). (Illus.). 48p. 1984. 9.95 (ISBN 0-918518-34-2). St Luke TN.
Ready, Dolores. John's Magic: John Bosco. LC 77-86595. (Stories About Christian Heroes). (Illus.). 1977. pap. 1.95 (ISBN 0-86683-765-5, HarpR). Har-Row.
Thornton, Andre & Janssen, Al. Triumph Born of Tragedy. LC 82-82812. 160p. (Orig.). 1983. pap. 4.95 (ISBN 0-89081-367-1). Harvest Hse.
Watson, Jean. Watchmaker's Daughter: The Life of Corrie Ten Boom for Young People. (Illus.). 160p. 1983. pap. 4.95 (ISBN 0-8007-5116-7, Power Bks). Revell.

CHRISTIAN CHURCH IN TEXAS

Lawrence, Kenneth, ed. Classic Themes of Disciples Theology: Rethinking the Traditional Affirmations of the Christian Church (Disciples of Christ) LC 85-50712. 150p. 1986. text ed. 20.00x (ISBN 0-87565-024-4). Tex Christian.

CHRISTIAN CIVILIZATION

see Civilization, Christian

CHRISTIAN COMMUNICATION

see Communication (Theology)

CHRISTIAN CONVERTS

see Converts

CHRISTIAN DEMOCRACY

see also Catholic Action; Church and Labor; Socialism, Christian

Fogarty, Michael P. Christian Democracy in Western Europe, 1820-1953. LC 73-11997. (Illus.). 448p. 1974. Repr. of 1957 ed. lib. bdg. 26.75x (ISBN 0-8371-7114-8, FOCH). Greenwood.
Irving, Ronald E. The Christian Democratic Parties of Western Europe. LC 78-41082. pap. 90.00 (ISBN 0-317-42290-1, 2023267). Bks Demand UMI.
Maier, Hans. Revolution & Church: The Early History of Christian Democracy, 1789-1901. Schossberger, Emily M., tr. LC 68-27577. 1969. 7.95 (ISBN 0-268-00319-X). U of Notre Dame Pr.
Quantin, M. Dictionnaire Raisonne de Diplomatie Chretienne, Vol. 47. Migne, J. P., ed. (Encyclopedie Theologique Ser.). (Fr.). 578p. Repr. of 1846 ed. lib. bdg. 74.00x (ISBN 0-89241-251-8). Caratzas.
Webster, Richard A. The Cross & the Fasces: Christian Democracy and Fascism in Italy. 1960. 18.50x (ISBN 0-8047-0043-5). Stanford U Pr.

CHRISTIAN DEVOTIONAL CALENDARS

see Devotional Calendars

CHRISTIAN DEVOTIONAL LITERATURE

see Devotional Literature

CHRISTIAN DOCTRINE

see Theology, Doctrinal

CHRISTIAN DOCTRINE (CATHOLIC CHURCH)

see Catechetics–Catholic Church

CHRISTIAN EDUCATION

Here are entered works dealing with instruction in the Christian religion in schools and private life; Works on the relation of the church to education in general, and works on the history of the part that the church has taken in secular education are entered under Church and education.

see also Bible–Study; Catechetical Sermons; Catechetics; Catechisms; Christian Leadership; Church and College; Church and Education; Church Schools; Jesus Christ–Teaching Methods; Theology–Study and Teaching; Week-Day Church Schools

Acheson, Edna L. The Construction of Junior Church School Curricula. LC 73-176503. Repr. of 1929 ed. 22.50 (ISBN 0-404-55331-1). AMS Pr.

Achtemeier, Paul J. Romans: Interpretation: A Bible Commentary for Teaching & Preaching. Mays, James L., ed. LC 84-47796. 240p. 1985. 17.95 (ISBN 0-8042-3137-0). John Knox.

Aldridge, Betty. You Can Teach Preschoolers Successfully. (Training Successful Teachers Ser.). 48p. (Orig.). 1984. pap. 2.95 (ISBN 0-87239-805-6, 3205). Standard Pub.

Anderson. Teach What You Preach. 1982. pap. 8.95 (ISBN 0-8298-0481-1). Pilgrim NY.

Anderson, Dorothy P. Leader's Guide for Jay E. Adams's Christian Living in the Home: A Teaching Manual for Use in Adult Study Groups. (Orig.). 1977. pap. 2.95 (ISBN 0-934688-05-2). Great Comm Pubns.

Ashton, Leila. Checks from God. (My Church Teaches Ser.). 32p. 1981. pap. 1.95 (ISBN 0-8127-0314-6). Review & Herald.

Associated Women's Organization, Mars Hill Bible School. Something Special. Simpson, Peggy & Stanley, Linda, eds. 1977. pap. 4.95 (ISBN 0-89137-408-6). Quality Pubns.

Augustine, St. The Teacher, The Free Choice of the Will, Grace & Free Will. Bd. with Two Works on Free Will. LC 67-30350. (Fathers of the Church Ser.: Vol. 59). 232p. 1968. 17.95x (ISBN 0-8132-0059-8). Cath U Pr.

Aultman, Donald S. Contemporary Christian Education. 122p. 1968. 4.95 (ISBN 0-87148-159-6); pap. 3.95 (ISBN 0-87148-160-X). Pathway Pr.

--The Ministry of Christian Teaching. 111p. 1966. 4.95 (ISBN 0-87148-554-0); pap. 3.95 (ISBN 0-87148-555-9). Pathway Pr.

Averett, Joy & Smith, Donna. Bible Handwork Ideas for Twos & Threes. 1983. pap. 3.25 (ISBN 0-89137-613-5). Quality Pubns.

Barbour, Mary E. You Can Teach Two's & Three's. 64p. 1981. pap. 3.50 (ISBN 0-88207-149-1). Victor Bks.

Bausch, Thomas. The Spiritual Exercises & Today's CLC: Making the Exercises Come to Life. 24p. 1973. pap. text ed. 1.50x (ISBN 0-913605-01-8). NFCLC.

Bausch, Thomas A. The Spiritual Exercises & CLC: The Role of the Exercises in Today's CLC's. 24p. 1973. pap. text ed. 1.50x (ISBN 0-913605-00-X). NFCLC.

Bausch, William J. Storytelling, Imagination & Faith. 240p. (Orig.). 1984. pap. 7.95 (ISBN 0-89622-199-7). Twenty-Third.

Bayly, Joseph. Psalms of My Life. 1969. pap. 0.95 pock. pap. (ISBN 0-8423-5002-0). Tyndale.

Baynes, Richard W. God's OK-You're OK? Perspective on Christian Worship. LC 79-67440. 96p. (Orig.). 1981. pap. 2.25 (ISBN 0-87239-382-8, 40088). Standard Pub.

Bell, Sadie. Church, the State, & Education in Virginia. LC 78-89148. (American Education: Its Men, Institutions & Ideas Ser). 1969. Repr. of 1930 ed. 43.00 (ISBN 0-405-01385-X). Ayer Co Pubs.

Benson, Marilyn & Benson, Dennis. The Hard Times Catalog for Youth Ministry. LC 82-81332. (Illus.). 288p. (Orig.). 1982. pap. 14.95 (ISBN 0-936664-06-1). Group Bks.

Berg, Carolyn. Bulletin Board Designs for the Christian Classroom. 1984. pap. 5.95 tchr's. material (ISBN 0-570-03930-4, 12-2866). Concordia.

Blazier, Kenneth D. A Growing Church School. 1978. pap. text ed. 2.50 (ISBN 0-8170-0785-7). Judson.

Blazier, Kenneth D. & Huber, Evelyn M. Planning Christian Education in Your Church. LC 73-19585. 32p. (Orig.). 1974. pap. 1.00 (ISBN 0-8170-0633-8); pap. 2.95 spanish ed (ISBN 0-8170-0685-0). Judson.

Bower, Robert K. Administering Christian Education. LC 64-22018. 1964. pap. 8.95 (ISBN 0-8028-1559-6). Eerdmans.

Bower, William C. The Curriculum of Religious Education. (Educational Ser.). 1930. Repr. 30.00 (ISBN 0-8482-7353-2). Norwood Edns.

Brause, Dorsey. Expanded Ministry to Adults: Program Guidelines. 1979. pap. 3.50 (ISBN 0-89367-030-8). Light & Life.

Breeden, Terri. Teaching the Meaning of Church Ordinances to Children. (Orig.). 1986. pap. 5.95 (ISBN 0-89265-097-4). Randall Hse.

Brewer, Clifton H. A History of Religious Education in the Episcopal Church to Eighteen Thirty-Five. 1924. 14.50x (ISBN 0-686-51401-7). Elliots Bks.

--History of Religious Education in the Episcopal Church to 1835. LC 73-89152. (American Education Its Men, Institutions & Ideas, Ser. 1). 1969. Repr. of 1924 ed. 16.00 (ISBN 0-405-01390-6). Ayer Co Pubs.

Brokering, Herb. Wholly Holy. 96p. (Orig.). 1981. pap. 3.95 (ISBN 0-942562-00-3). Brokering Pr.

Brown, Marion E. & Prentice, Marjorie G. Christian Education in the Year Two Thousand. 160p. 1984. pap. 5.95 (ISBN 0-8170-1055-6). Judson.

Brubaber, Zuck & Brubaker, Joanne. Childhood Education in the Church. rev., exp. ed. 1986. text ed. 24.95 (ISBN 0-8024-1251-3). Moody.

Brubaker, J. Lester. Personnel Administration in the Christian School. 168p. (Orig.). 1980. pap. 6.95 (ISBN 0-88469-130-6). BMH Bks.

Bubeck, Mark I. Overcoming the Adversary. 1984. pap. 5.95 (ISBN 0-8024-0333-6). Moody.

Burba, Linda. Everybody Ought to Go to Learning Centers. (Teaching Helps Ser.). 80p. 1981. pap. 2.95 (ISBN 0-8010-0811-5). Baker Bk.

Bushnell, Horace. Views of Christian Nurture & Subjects Related Thereto. LC 74-23297. 264p. 1975. Repr. of 1847 ed. lib. bdg. 40.00x (ISBN 0-8201-1147-3). Schol Facsimiles.

Bussard, Paula & Wyrtzen, Christine. Lessons on Love from Critter County. 144p. 1986. wkbk. 9.95 (ISBN 0-87403-000-5, 3340). Standard Pub.

Byrne, H. W. Christian Approach to Education. 1986. pap. 9.95 (ISBN 0-8010-0941-3). Baker Bk.

Carpenter, Joel A. & Shipps, Kenneth W., eds. Making Higher Education Christian: The History & Mission of Evangelical Colleges in America. 304p. (Orig.). 1987. pap. 16.95 (ISBN 0-8028-0253-2). Eerdmans.

Carroll, Frances. How to Talk with Your Children about God. 1985. pap. 6.95 (ISBN 0-317-18129-7). P-H.

Cheney, Ruth G., ed. The Christian Education Catalog. 192p. (Orig.). 1981. pap. 10.95 (ISBN 0-8164-2328-8, HarpR). Har-Row.

Cherne, J. The Learning Disabled Child in Your Church School. LC 12-2818. (09). 1983. pap. 3.25 (ISBN 0-570-03883-9). Concordia.

China Educational Commission. Christian Education in China: A Study. LC 75-36223. Repr. of 1922 ed. 34.50 (ISBN 0-404-14474-8). AMS Pr.

Christian Education Materials for Youth & Families: Alcohol & Drugs. 54p. 1983. 6.95 (ISBN 0-89486-181-6). Hazelden.

Christ's Object Lessons. large print ed. 1980. pap. 7.25 (ISBN 0-8280-0044-1, 03364-7). Review & Herald.

Church Educational Ministries. LC 67-27288. 96p. 1980. pap. text ed. 4.95 (ISBN 0-910566-13-5); Perfect bdg. instr's. guide 5.95 (ISBN 0-910566-18-6). Evang Tchr.

Cionca, John. The Troubleshooting Guide to Christian Education. LC 85-73069. 176p. 1986. pap. 7.95 (ISBN 0-89636-191-8). Accent Bks.

Clement Of Alexandria. Christ the Educator. LC 66-20313. (Fathers of the Church Ser.: Vol. 23). 309p. 1954. 16.95x (ISBN 0-8132-0023-7). Cath U Pr.

Cober, Kenneth L. Shaping the Church's Educational Ministry. LC 75-139502. (Illus.). 1971. pap. 3.95 (ISBN 0-8170-0519-6); pap. 1.95 spanish ed (ISBN 0-8170-0603-6). Judson.

Coleman, Lucien E., Jr. Why the Church Must Teach. LC 84-4966. 1984. pap. 6.95 (ISBN 0-8054-3234-5). Broadman.

Coleman, William. Earning Your Wings. 144p. 1984. pap. 4.95 (ISBN 0-87123-311-8, 210311). Bethany Hse.

--Getting Ready for Our New Baby. LC 84-432. 112p. 1984. pap. 4.95 (ISBN 0-87123-295-2, 210295). Bethany Hse.

Colwell, Stephen. The Position of Christianity in the United States, in Its Relations with Our Political Institutions, & Specially with Reference to Religious Instruction in the Public Schools. LC 78-38444. (Religion in America, Ser. 2). 180p. 1972. Repr. of 1854 ed. 17.00 (ISBN 0-405-04063-6). Ayer Co Pubs.

Concordia Primary Religion Ser. teacher's manual wkbks. 7.35 (ISBN 0-570-01520-0, 22-1206); (4 wkbks) 1.50 ea. Concordia.

Craddock, Fred. Philippians: Interpretation: A Bible Commentary for Teaching & Preaching. Mays, James L. & Miller, Patrick D., eds. LC 84-47797. 96p. 1984. 12.95 (ISBN 0-8042-3140-0). John Knox.

Cummings, Calvin K. Confessing Christ. 3rd, rev. ed. (Orig.). 1977. pap. 1.45 (ISBN 0-934688-04-4). Great Comm Pubns.

Cummings, David, ed. The Purpose of a Christian School. 1979. pap. 4.50 (ISBN 0-87552-157-6). Presby & Reformed.

Currie, Winifred. Creative Classroom Communications. 126p. 1972. pap. 1.25 (ISBN 0-88243-507-8, 02-0507). Gospel Pub.

Curry, Allen D. Leader's Guide for John W. Sanderson's "The Fruit of the Spirit". A Teaching Manual for Use in Adult Study Groups. (Orig.). 1978. pap. 2.95 (ISBN 0-934688-07-9). Great Comm Pubns.

Daniel, et al. Introduction to Christian Education. 2nd, rev. ed. 352p. 1987. pap. text ed. price not set (ISBN 0-87403-211-3, 88591). Standard Pub.

Daniel, Eleanor, et al. Introduction to Christian Education. LC 79-92587. (Bible College Textbooks Ser.). 352p. (Orig.). 1980. pap. text ed. 6.95 (ISBN 0-87239-394-1, 88581). Standard Pub.

Dauw, Dean C. New Educational Methods for Increasing Religious Effectiveness. pap. 0.65 (ISBN 0-8199-0389-2, L38532). Franciscan Herald.

Davies, Rupert E., ed. Approach to Christian Education. 1956. 7.00 (ISBN 0-8022-0352-3). Philos Lib.

Davis, Ron, et al. You Can Teach Adults Successfully. (Training Successful Teachers Ser.). 48p. (Orig.). 1984. pap. 2.95 (ISBN 0-87239-808-0, 3208). Standard Pub.

Dayton, Edward R. God's Purpose - Man's Plans. 64p. 1982. pap. 5.95 (ISBN 0-912552-11-5). Missions Adv Res Com Ctr.

DeBoy, James J., Jr. Getting Started in Adult Religious Education: A Practical Guide. LC 79-88932. 128p. 1979. pap. 5.95 (ISBN 0-8091-2222-7). Paulist Pr.

DeJong, James A. & Van Dyke, Louis Y., eds. Building the House: Essays on Christian Education. 153p. (Orig.). 1981. pap. 5.95 (ISBN 0-932914-05-5). Dordt Coll Pr.

DeJong, Norman, ed. Christian Approaches to Learning Theory: The Nature of the Learner - Major Papers Delivered at the Second Annual Conference, Trinity Christian College, Palos Heights, Illinois, Nov. 2-3, 1984, Vol. II. 174p. (Orig.). 1986. lib. bdg. 25.00 (ISBN 0-8191-5004-5, Pub. by Trinity Christ Coll); pap. text ed. 11.75 (ISBN 0-8191-5005-3). U Pr of Amer.

Deuink, James W. & Herbster, Carl D. Effective Christian School Management. 2nd ed. (Illus.). 291p. 1986. pap. 8.95 (ISBN 0-89084-319-8). Bob Jones Univ Pr.

Dewitt, David. Answering the Tough Ones. 160p. 1980. pap. 5.95 (ISBN 0-8024-8971-0). Moody.

Diaz, Jorge & De Gonzalez, Nelly, eds. La Biblia lo Dice. (Span., Illus.). 120p. 1986. Repr. of 1984 ed. spiral bdg. 3.95 (ISBN 0-311-11453-9). Casa Bautista.

Donnelly, Dody. Team. LC 77-74584. 168p. (Orig.). 1977. pap. 5.95 (ISBN 0-8091-2013-5). Paulist Pr.

Doran, Adron & Choate, J. E. The Christian Scholar. 1985. 14.95 (ISBN 0-89225-279-0); pap. 8.95 (ISBN 0-89225-282-0). Gospel Advocate.

Dresselhaus, Richard L. Teaching for Decision. LC 73-75502. 124p. 1973. pap. 1.25 (ISBN 0-88243-616-3, 02-0616). Gospel Pub.

Dubitsky, Cora M. Building the Faith Community. LC 74-12632. 192p. 1975. pap. 2.95 (ISBN 0-8091-1848-3). Paulist Pr.

Durka, Gloria & Smith, Joanmarie. Aesthetic Dimensions of Religious Education. LC 78-65903. 252p. 1979. pap. 8.50 (ISBN 0-8091-2164-6). Paulist Pr.

Dykstra, Craig. Vision & Character: A Christian Educator's Alternative to Kohlberg. LC 81-82340. 160p. (Orig.). 1981. pap. 5.95 (ISBN 0-8091-2405-X). Paulist Pr.

Edge, Findley B. Metodologia Pedagogica. Mendoza, Celia & Molina, Sara P., trs. from Eng. Orig. Title: Helping the Teacher. 155p. 1982. pap. 3.75 (ISBN 0-311-11026-6). Casa Bautista.

--Pedagogia Fructifera. Lopez, Alberto, tr. from Eng. Tr. of Teaching for Results. (Span.). 192p. 1985. pap. 3.95 (ISBN 0-311-11025-8). Casa Bautista.

Ensenanzas, Disciplina y Gobierna de la Iglesia de Dios. (Span.). 137p. 1980. pap. 3.95 (ISBN 0-87148-304-1). Pathway Pr.

Episcopal Church. Prayer Book Guide to Christian Education. 224p. 1983. pap. 9.95 (ISBN 0-8164-2422-5, HarpR). Har-Row.

Eyre, Linda & Eyre, Richard. Teaching Children Joy. LC 84-201498. 240p. 1986. pap. 3.50 (ISBN 0-345-32704-7). Ballantine.

Fenn, William P. Christian Higher Education in Changing China, 1880-1950. LC 75-43741. (Illus.). pap. 64.00 (ISBN 0-317-07969-7, 2012769). Bks Demand UMI.

Fisher, Constance L. Dancing the Old Testament: Christian Celebrations of Israelite Heritage for Worship & Education. Adams, Doug, ed. (Illus.). 1980. pap. 5.95 (ISBN 0-941500-07-1). Sharing Co.

Fitzpatrick, Daniel J. Confusion, Call, Commitment: The Spiritual Exercises & Religious Education. LC 76-3801. 178p. 1976. pap. 4.95 (ISBN 0-8189-0327-9). Alba.

Fleming, Sanford. Children & Puritanism: The Place of Children in the Life & Thought of the New England Churches, 1620-1847. LC 70-89178. (American Education: Its Men, Institutions & Ideas Ser). 1969. Repr. of 1933 ed. 15.00 (ISBN 0-405-01416-3). Ayer Co Pubs.

Foltz, Nancy T., ed. Handbook of Adult Religious Education. 272p. (Orig.). 1986. pap. 14.95 (ISBN 0-89135-052-7). Religious Educ.

Ford, LeRoy. Modelos Para el Proceso de Ensenanza-Aprendizaje. Gaydou, Nelda B. de & Diaz, Jorge E., trs. from Eng. Tr. of Design for Teaching & Training. (Span., Illus.). 320p. (Orig.). 1986. pap. 5.95 (ISBN 0-311-11042-8). Casa Bautista.

Forster, Roger & Marston, Paul. That's a Good Question. 2nd ed. Sun, Hugo S. & Chan, Silas, trs. (Chinese.). 204p. 1982. pap. write for info (ISBN 0-941598-01-2). Living Spring Pubns.

Foster, Robert D. The Navigator. LC 83-60287. 240p. 1983. pap. 3.95 (ISBN 0-89109-495-4). NavPress.

Fox, Robert J. Religious Education: Its Effects, Its Challenges Today. 1972. pap. 0.95 (ISBN 0-8198-0344-8). Dghtrs St Paul.

Gaebelein, Frank E. Pattern of God's Truth. LC 54-6908. 1968. pap. 5.95 (ISBN 0-8024-6450-5). Moody.

Gangel, Kenneth O. & Benson, Warren S. Christian Education: Its History & Philosophy. 1983. 18.95 (ISBN 0-8024-3561-0). Moody.

Garlett, Marti W. Who Will Be My Teacher? The Christian Way to Stronger Schools. 256p. 1985. 12.95 (ISBN 0-8499-0471-4, 0471-4). Word Bks.

Gibson, Jean. Advanced Christian Training. (Orig.). 1986. pap. 7.00 (ISBN 0-937396-04-4). Walterick Pubs.

Graendorf, Werner, ed. Introduction to Biblical Christian Education. LC 81-1608. 1981. 16.95 (ISBN 0-8024-4128-9). Moody.

Greer, Clark. Multi-Media Methods for Christian Ministries. LC 82-16132. 1982. pap. 2.95 (ISBN 0-87227-085-8). Reg Baptist.

Greever, Jack. Marcos: Estudios Para un Joven En Busca De Identidad. Orig. Title: Mark: an Inductive Bible Study. (Span.). 64p. 1982. pap. 2.50 (ISBN 0-311-12325-2, Edit Mundo). Casa Bautista.

Griggs, Donald L. Basic Skills for Church Teachers. (Griggs Educational Resources Ser.). 112p. 1985. pap. 7.95 (ISBN 0-687-02488-9). Abingdon.

--Planning for Teaching Church School. LC 85-12588. 64p. 1985. pap. 5.95 (ISBN 0-8170-1079-3). Judson.

Griggs, Patricia. Creative Activities in Church Education. (Griggs Educational Resources Ser.). 1980. pap. 6.95 (ISBN 0-687-09812-2). Abingdon.

Griggs, Patricia R. Using Storytelling in Christian Education. LC 80-26468. 64p. (Orig.). 1981. pap. 7.25 (ISBN 0-687-43117-4). Abingdon.

Halverson, Delia T. Helping Your Child Discover Faith. 128p. 1982. pap. 5.95 (ISBN 0-8170-0957-4). Judson.

Hammack, Mary L. How to Organize Your Church Library & Resource Center. 128p. 1985. pap. 5.95 (ISBN 0-8170-1066-1). Judson.

Hanchey, Howard. Creative Christian Education: Teaching the Bible Through the Church Year. 224p. 1986. pap. 10.95 (ISBN 0-8192-1380-2). Morehouse.

Hanson, Grant W. Foundations for the Teaching Church. 96p. 1986. pap. 5.95 (ISBN 0-8170-1096-3). Judson.

Harbison, Elmore H. The Christian Scholar in the Age of the Reformation. LC 83-16511. Repr. of 1983 ed. 46.80 (2027546). Bks Demand UMI.

Harrison, H. D. Christian Education: Total Task of the Church. 28p. 1976. pap. 0.75 (ISBN 0-89265-101-6). Randall Hse.

Hart, Thomas N. The Art of Christian Listening. LC 80-82810. 132p. (Orig.). 1981. pap. 4.95 (ISBN 0-8091-2345-2). Paulist Pr.

Haystead, Wes. Teaching Your Child About God. LC 68-29315. 144p. 1981. text ed. 8.95 (ISBN 0-8307-0798-0, 5109406). Regal.

Heie, Harold & Wolfe, David L., eds. Reality of Christian Learning: Strategies for Faith-Discipline Integration. 448p. 1987. pap. 19.95 (ISBN 0-8028-0233-8). Eerdmans.

Hendricks, Howard G. Say It with Love. LC 72-77011. 143p. 1972. pap. 5.95 (ISBN 0-88207-050-9). Victor Bks.

Henman, J. Robert. The Child As Quest: Method & Religious Education. LC 83-19877. 70p. (Orig.). 1984. pap. text ed. 6.75 (ISBN 0-8191-3633-6). U Pr of Amer.

Henrichsen, Walter A. How to Disciple Your Children. 120p. 1981. pap. 4.95 (ISBN 0-88207-260-9). Victor Bks.

Hill, Donald E. Pathway of Discipleship One Hundred One. 2nd rev. ed. (Pathway of Discipleship Ser.). 184p. 1983. pap. text ed. 15.00 (ISBN 0-88151-026-2). Lay Leadership.
Hofinger, Johannes. Pastoral Life in the Power of the Spirit. LC 81-1439. (Illus.). 215p. 1982. pap. 6.95 (ISBN 0-8189-0427-5). Alba.
Holmes, Arthur F. The Idea of A Christian College. rev. ed. 104p. 1987. pap. 6.95 (ISBN 0-8028-0258-3). Eerdmans.
Humbertson, James E., ed. Evangelical Sunday School Lesson Commentary, 1976. 396p. 1976. 2.25 (ISBN 0-87148-281-9). Pathway Pr.
Hurst, D. V. E Ele Concedeu Uns Para Mestres. (Portuguese Bks.). Tr. of And He Gave Teachers. 1979. 2.40 (ISBN 0-8297-0838-3). Life Pubs Intl.
Hutchins, Eileen. Observation-Thinking-the Senses. 1975. pap. 1.95 (ISBN 0-916786-13-7). St George Bk Serv.
Isaac, Stephen. The Way of Discipleship to Christ. LC 76-57021. 1976. pap. 4.50 (ISBN 0-910378-12-6). Christward.
Jackson, Neta. Building Christian Relationships. 64p. 1984. pap. 3.95 (ISBN 0-87123-407-6); pap. 4.95 tchr's guide (ISBN 0-87123-429-7). Bethany Hse.
Jehle, Paul. Go Ye Therefore & Teach: Operation Manual for Christian Day School. 300p. 1982. tchr's. ed. 10.00 (ISBN 0-942516-01-X). Plymouth Rock Found.
Johnson, L. T. & Buchanan, Edward A. The Teaching Church. 2nd ed. (Enabling Ser.). (Illus.). 95p. (Orig.). 1984. pap. 5.95 (ISBN 0-935797-00-9). Harvest IL.
Johnson, R. K. Fortress of Faith. 3rd ed. (Illus.). 456p. 1984. pap. 7.95 (ISBN 0-89084-252-3). Bob Jones Univ Pr.
Johnston, O. R. Who Needs the Family? LC 80-7780. 152p. (Orig.). 1980. pap. 5.95 (ISBN 0-87784-588-3). Inter-Varsity.
Jones, Charles C. Religious Instruction of the Negroes in the United States. facs. ed. LC 70-149869. (Black Heritage Library Collection). 1842. 16.50 (ISBN 0-8369-8718-7). Ayer Co Pubs.
Joy, Donald M. Meaningful Learning in the Church. 1969. 3.25 (ISBN 0-89367-019-7). Light & Life.
The Joy of Ministry: My Role in Christian Education. (Christian Education Ministries Ser.). 1978. pap. 3.50 (ISBN 0-89367-026-X). Light & Life.
Kelly, Margaret, ed. Justice & Health Care: Christian Perspectives. LC 84-9459. 1985. pap. 16.50 (ISBN 0-87125-097-7). Cath Health.
Kelsey, Morton T. Can Christians Be Educated? Burgess, Harold W., ed. LC 77-3691. 154p. (Orig.). 1977. pap. 8.95 (ISBN 0-89135-008-X). Religious Educ.
Kevane, Eugene, ed. Teaching the Catholic Faith Today. (Resources for Catechetical Teachers). 352p. 1982. 12.00 (ISBN 0-8198-7319-5, EP1048); pap. 10.00 (ISBN 0-8198-7320-9). Dghtrs St Paul.
Kittel, Helmuth. Evangelische Religionspaedagogik. (Ger). 1970. 23.20x (ISBN 3-11-002654-6). De Gruyter.
Knight, George R. Philosophy & Education: An Introduction in Christian Perspective. LC 81-117900. (Illus.). xii, 244p. 1980. pap. text ed. 10.95 (ISBN 0-943872-79-0). Andrews Univ Pr.
Knox, Ian P. Above or Within? The Supernatural in Religious Education. LC 76-55589. 164p. (Orig.). 1977. pap. 10.95 (ISBN 0-89135-006-3). Religious Educ.
Larson, Mobby. Prayers of a Christian Educator. (Greeting Book Line Ser.). 32p. (Orig.). 1985. pap. 1.50 (ISBN 0-89622-277-2). Twenty-Third.
Lawson, LeRoy. Where Do You Grow from Here? 128p. 1985. pap. 2.95 (ISBN 0-87239-967-2, 41034). Standard Pub.
Leary, Michael. Christ & the Catechist: The Spiritual Life of the Christian Teacher. LC 86-83017. 128p. 1987. pap. 6.95 (ISBN 0-89870-139-2). Ignatius Pr.
Lee, James M. The Flow of Religious Instruction: A Social-Science Approach. LC 74-29824. (Illus.). 379p. (Orig.). 1975. pap. 14.95 (ISBN 0-89135-003-9). Religious Educ.
Lee, James M., ed. The Religious Education We Need: Toward the Renewal of Christian Education. LC 76-55587. 174p. (Orig.). 1977. pap. 7.95 (ISBN 0-89135-005-5). Religious Educ.
Lee, James Michael. The Shape of Religious Instruction: A Social-Science Approach. LC 74-29823. 330p. (Orig.). 1971. lib. bdg. 16.95 (ISBN 0-89135-000-4); pap. 14.95 (ISBN 0-89135-002-0). Religious Educ.
Lewis, Paul. Forty Ways to Teach Your Child Values. 224p. 1985. pap. 6.95 (ISBN 0-8423-0920-9). Tyndale.
Lines, Timothy A. Systemic Religious Education. LC 86-20383. 264p. (Orig.). 1987. pap. 14.95 (ISBN 0-89135-057-8). Religious Educ.
Lister, Louis & Lister, Rebecca. The Religious School Board: A Manual. 1978. pap. 5.00 (ISBN 0-8074-0014-9, 243870). UAHC.
Love, Bessie & Newey, Paul. Water, 4 bks. Incl. Bk. 1. Source of Life; Bk. 2. Destroyer; Bk. 3. Sustainer; Bk. 4. Transformer. (Illus., Orig.). 1974. Set. pap. 3.50x (ISBN 0-8192-4041-9); leaders guide 2.50x (ISBN 0-8192-4042-7). Morehouse.
Luther, Martin. Luther's Works, Vol. 28. LC 55-9893. 1973. 15.95 (ISBN 0-570-06428-7, 15-1770). Concordia.
McAllister, Dawson & Webster, Dan. El Discipulado Del Joven una Guia de Estudio. (Span.). 80p. 1986. pap. 4.50 (ISBN 0-311-12324-4, Edit Mundo). Casa Bautista.
McCarthy, David S. Practical Guide for the Christian Writer. 112p. 1983. pap. 5.95 (ISBN 0-8170-0979-5). Judson.
McCarthy, Mary. Memories of a Catholic Girlhood. LC 57-8842. 245p. 1972. pap. 5.95 (ISBN 0-15-658650-9, Harv). HarBraceJ.
McCollister, John C. The Christian Book of Why. 340p. 1983. 11.95 (ISBN 0-8246-0297-8). Jonathan David.
McDaniel, Elsiebeth, et al. Adventures in Creative Teaching. 96p. 1986. pap. 6.95 (ISBN 0-89693-557-4). Victor Bks.
Maclean, Angus H. The Idea of God in Protestant Religious Education. LC 75-177033. (Columbia University. Teachers College. Contributions to Education: No. 410). Repr. of 1930 ed. 22.50 (ISBN 0-404-55410-5). AMS Pr.
Massi, Jeri. Derwood, Inc. (English Skills for Christian Schools Ser.). 288p. (Orig.). 1986. pap. 5.95 (ISBN 0-89084-323-6). Bob Jones Univ Pr.
Mathson, Patricia. Creative Learning Activities for Religious Education: A Catalog of Teaching Ideas for Church, School, & Home. (Illus.). 192p. 1984. pap. 8.95 (ISBN 0-13-189838-8). P-H.
Michie, Donald & Rhoads, David. Mark As Story: An Introduction to the Narrative of a Gospel. LC 81-43084. 176p. 1982. pap. 8.95 (ISBN 0-8006-1614-6). Fortress.
Miller, Randolph C. The Theory of Christian Education Practice: How Theology Affects Christian Education. LC 80-15886. 312p. (Orig.). 1980. pap. 12.95 (ISBN 0-89135-049-7). Religious Educ.
Monks Of Solesmes, ed. Our Lady: Eight Hundred & Sixty-Eight Pronouncements from Benedict Fourteenth to John Twenty-Third. 5.50 (ISBN 0-8198-0111-9). Dghtrs St Paul.
Moore, Emily. Fifty-Two Sundays of Worship for Children, Bk. 2. 1972. 6.95 (ISBN 0-8341-0253-6). Beacon Hill.
Moore, Mary E. Education for Continuity & Change: A New Model for Christian Religious Education. 224p. (Orig.). 1983. pap. 10.95 (ISBN 0-687-11523-X). Abingdon.
Morris, Henry M. Education for the Real World. LC 77-78017. 1977. pap. 8.95 (ISBN 0-89051-093-8). Master Bks.
Moynahan, Michael E. Once upon a Parable: Dramas for Worship & Religious Education. (Orig.). 1984. pap. 8.95 (ISBN 0-8091-2586-2). Paulist Pr.
Nelson, Jane S. Christ-Centered Crafts for Children's Classes. LC 81-8711. 1981. pap. 2.50 (ISBN 0-87227-078-5). Reg Baptist.
Neville, Gwen K. & Westerhoff, John H., III. Learning Through Liturgy. 189p. 1983. pap. 6.95 (ISBN 0-8164-2423-3, HarpR). Har-Row.
NFCLC. NFCLC Formation Program. 150p. 1975. wkbk. 7.00x (ISBN 0-913605-02-6). NFCLC.
--NFCLC Formation Program: Leader's Manual. 80p. (Orig.). 1975. pap. 3.50x wkbk. (ISBN 0-913605-03-4). NFCLC.
O'Hare, Padraic, ed. Tradition & Transformation in Religious Education. LC 78-27506. 114p. (Orig.). 1979. pap. 6.95 (ISBN 0-89135-016-0). Religious Educ.
Olen, Dale R. Teaching Life Skills to Children: A Practical Guide for Teachers & Parents. 1984. pap. 6.95 (ISBN 0-8091-2618-4). Paulist Pr.
Orr, Dick & Bartlett, David L. Bible Journeys. 80p. 1980. pap. 4.95 (ISBN 0-8170-0898-5). Judson.
Parent, Neil A., ed. Christian Adulthood. 125p. 1985. pap. 6.95 (ISBN 1-55586-921-1). US Catholic.
--Christian Adulthood 1982. 130p. 1982. pap. 5.95 (ISBN 1-55586-827-4). US Catholic.
--Christian Adulthood 1983. 68p. 1983. pap. 4.95 (ISBN 1-55586-862-2). US Catholic.
--Christian Adulthood 1985-1986. 124p. 1985. pap. 8.95 (ISBN 1-55586-965-3). US Catholic.
Payne, Daniel A. Treatise on Domestic Education. facs. ed. LC 75-157373. (Black Heritage Library Collection Ser). 1885. 16.00 (ISBN 0-8369-8811-6). Ayer Co Pubs.
Peterson, Gilbert A. The Christian Education of Adults. 1985. text ed. 16.95 (ISBN 0-8024-0496-0). Moody.
Pfeifer, Carl J. Presences of Jesus. 2nd ed. 112p. 1984. pap. 4.95 (ISBN 0-89622-193-8). Twenty-Third.
Powers, Bruce P., ed. Christian Education Handbook. LC 80-69522. 1981. pap. 9.95 (ISBN 0-8054-3229-9). Broadman.
Purdy, John C., ed. Always Being Reformed: The Future of Church Education. LC 85-953. 120p. 1985. pap. 7.95 (ISBN 0-664-24655-9, A Geneva Press Publication). Westminster.
Reichert, Richard. Simulation Games for Religious Education. LC 75-142. 1975. pap. 4.50 (ISBN 0-88489-060-0). St Marys.
Religious Education Commission. All Are Called. 1984. pap. 5.75 (ISBN 0-8309-0391-7). Herald Hse.
Rice, Wayne, compiled by. The Youth Specialties Clip Art Book, Vol. II. 112p. 1987. pap. 14.95 (ISBN 0-310-39791-X). Zondervan.
Richards, Lawrence O. A Theology of Christian Education. 320p. 1975. 17.95 (ISBN 0-310-31940-4, 18135). Zondervan.
Ridenour, Crea. Ocupate en Ensenar. 48p. 1983. pap. 1.50 (ISBN 0-311-11031-2). Casa Bautista.
Roadcup, David. Ministering to Youth. LC 79-92586. (Bible College Textbooks Ser.). 256p. (Orig.). 1980. pap. text ed. 6.95 (ISBN 0-87239-395-X, 88582). Standard Pub.
Robertson, O. D. Sold on Sunday School. (Orig.). 1984. pap. text ed. 3.95 (ISBN 0-87148-808-6). Pathway Pr.
Rogers, Donald B. In Praise of Learning. LC 79-26829. (Into Our Third Century Ser.). (Orig.). 1980. pap. 3.95 (ISBN 0-687-18910-1). Abingdon.
Rogers, John T. Communicating Christ to the Cults. LC 83-4421. 1983. pap. 3.95 (ISBN 0-87227-091-2). Reg Baptist.
Rose, Jack H. Christianity & Education: A Manifesto. LC 86-90551. 302p. (Orig.). 1986. pap. 29.95 (ISBN 0-9617430-0-X). J H Rose.
Sanner, A. E & Harper, A. F. Exploring Christian Education. 504p. 1978. 15.95 (ISBN 0-8341-0494-6). Beacon Hill.
Savage, Thomas G. And Now a Word from Our Creator. LC 72-1370. 1972. 5.95 (ISBN 0-8294-0213-6). Loyola.
Schaal, John H. Feed My Sheep. 1972. pap. 1.95 (ISBN 0-8010-7958-6). Baker Bk.
Schaupp, Jack. Creating & Playing Games with Students. (Orig.). 1981. pap. 6.50 (ISBN 0-687-09809-2). Abingdon.
Schipani, Daniel S. Conscientization & Creativity: Paulo Freire & Christian Education. 224p. (Orig.). 1984. lib. bdg. 26.00 (ISBN 0-8191-3881-9); pap. text ed. 12.25 (ISBN 0-8191-3882-7). U Pr of Amer.
Sell, Charles M. Family Ministry: Family Life Through the Church. 272p. 15.95 (ISBN 0-310-42580-8, 12335). Zondervan.
Seymour, Jack L. From Sunday School to Church School: Continuities in Protestant Church Education in the United States, 1860-1929. LC 82-15977. 188p. 1982. lib. bdg. 26.25 o. p. (ISBN 0-8191-2726-4); pap. text ed. 11.50 (ISBN 0-8191-2727-2). U Pr of Amer.
Seymour, Jack L. & O'Gorman, Robert T. The Church in the Education of the Public: Refocusing the Task of Religious Education. 160p. 1984. pap. 10.95 (ISBN 0-687-08252-8). Abingdon.
Sias, Twila. You Can Teach Children Successfully. (Training Successful Teachers Ser.). 48p. (Orig.). 1984. pap. 2.95 (ISBN 0-87239-806-4, 3206). Standard Pub.
Simpson, Douglas J., ed. Christian Education: An Introduction to Its Scope. 1979. 7.95 (ISBN 0-89265-053-2). Randall Hse.
Skoor, Susan. Christian Education in the Family. 1984. pap. text ed. 6.00 (ISBN 0-8309-0392-5). Herald Hse.
Smart, James D. The Teaching Ministry of the Church: An Examination of Basic Principles of Christian Education. LC 54-10569. 208p. 1971. pap. 6.95 (ISBN 0-664-24910-8). Westminster.
Smirnoff, Peter. Instruction in God's Law. 1974. pap. 5.00 (ISBN 0-686-10199-5). Eastern Orthodox.
Smith, Judy G. Joyful Teaching - Joyful Learning. LC 86-71007. 104p. (Orig.). 1986. pap. 6.95 (ISBN 0-88177-031-0, DR031B). Discipleship Res.
Solignac, Pierre. Christian Neurosis. 256p. 1982. 12.95 (ISBN 0-8245-0108-X). Crossroad NY.
Sparks, Lee, ed. Try This One... Too. LC 82-81331. (Illus.). 80p. (Orig.). 1982. pap. 5.95 (ISBN 0-936664-05-3). Group Bks.
Sperry, Willard L., et al, eds. Religion in the Post-War World. facsimile ed. LC 76-142698. (Essay Index Reprints - Religion & Education Ser.: Vol. 4). Repr. of 1945 ed. 14.00 (ISBN 0-8369-2202-6). Ayer Co Pubs.
Splaine, Mike. How to Build a Christian Lecture Series. (Illus.). 50p. 1982. wkbk. & cassette 5.00x (ISBN 0-913605-05-0). NFCLC.
Strubhar, Daniel. Penmanship for Christian Writing. 1981. write for info.; tchr's. ed. avail. Rod & Staff.
Sullivan, Jessie P. Object Lessons & Stories for the Children's Church. (Object Lesson Ser.). 160p. 1974. pap. 4.95 (ISBN 0-8010-8037-1). Baker Bk.
Summers, Georgianna. Teaching as Jesus Taught. LC 83-70161. 96p. (Orig.). 1983. pap. 4.50 (ISBN 0-88177-000-0, DR000B). Discipleship Res.
Sylwester, R. The Puppet & the Word. LC 12-2966. 1982. pap. 4.95 (ISBN 0-570-03873-1). Concordia.
Taylor, Marvin J. Introduction to Christian Education. LC 66-11452. 412p. 1975. pap. 8.95 (ISBN 0-687-19498-9). Abingdon.
Taylor, Marvin J., ed. Changing Patterns of Religious Education. 320p. (Orig.). 1984. pap. 15.95 (ISBN 0-687-06046-X). Abingdon.
Thompson, Paul M. & Lillevold, Joani. The Giving Book: Creative Resources for Senior High Ministry. LC 84-47794. (Illus.). 144p. (Orig.). 1985. pap. 9.95 (ISBN 0-8042-1192-2). John Knox.
Timmons, Gary. Welcome: An Adult Education Program Based on RCIA. LC 81-84388. 64p. (Orig.). 1982. pap. 4.95 (ISBN 0-8091-2429-7). Paulist Pr.
Truman, Ruth. How to Be a Liberated Christian. LC 80-27302. 160p. 1981. 8.75 (ISBN 0-687-17710-3). Abingdon.
Van Brummelen, Harro W. Telling the Next Generation: The Educational Development in North American Calvinist Christian Schools. (Illus.). 332p. (Orig.). 1986. lib. bdg. 27.50 (ISBN 0-8191-5307-9, Pub. by Inst Christ Stud); pap. text ed. 14.75 (ISBN 0-8191-5308-7). U Pr of Amer.
Vander Ark, John A. Twenty-Two Landmark Years: Christian Schools International, 1943-65. 160p. 1983. pap. 9.95 (ISBN 0-8010-9291-4). Baker Bk.
Vander Stelt, John C., ed. The Challenge of Marxist & Neo-Marxist Ideologies for Christian Scholarship. 280p. 1982. pap. 12.95 (ISBN 0-932914-07-1). Dordt Coll Pr.
Van Pelt, Ethel. Marla. 154p. (Orig.). 1982. pap. 2.95 (ISBN 0-89084-155-1). Bob Jones Univ Pr.
Varner, Jeanne. How to Make Children's Church Come Alive. 1979. 4.95 (ISBN 0-87148-407-2). Pathway Pr.
Wagner, C. Peter, et al. Unreached Peoples, Eighty-One. (Orig.). 1981. pap. 8.95 (ISBN 0-89191-331-9). Cook.
Waldrop, C. Sybil. Guiding Your Child Toward God. LC 84-14964. 1985. pap. 4.95 (ISBN 0-8054-5660-0). Broadman.
Wallace, Mary, et al. Total Teaching for Today's Church. rev. ed. Orig. Title: Centers of Interest. (Illus.). 200p. (Orig.). 1985. pap. 6.95 (ISBN 0-912315-85-7). Word Aflame.
Ward, Waylon O. The Bible in Counseling. 1977. pap. 12.95 (ISBN 0-8024-0623-8). Moody.
Watkins, Dawn L. Jenny Wren. (English Skills for Christian Schools Ser.). (Illus., Orig.). 1986. pap. 4.95 (ISBN 0-89084-324-4). Bob Jones Univ Pr.
Weber, G. P., et al, eds. Word & Worship: CCD Ed. Incl. Our Brother Jesus. pap. 2.56 (ISBN 0-02-649370-5, 64937); Jesus with Us. pap. 2.88 (ISBN 0-02-649330-6, 64933); We Follow Jesus. pap. 3.76 (ISBN 0-02-649470-1, 64947); Father, Son & Spirit Show Their Love. pap. 3.80 (ISBN 0-02-649150-8, 64915); We Break Bread in Loving Thanksgiving. 2nd ed. pap. 3.80 (ISBN 0-02-649110-9, 64941); God's Saving Word. pap. 4.36 (ISBN 0-02-649290-3, 64929); God's Saving Mystery. 2nd ed. pap. 4.36 (ISBN 0-02-649190-7, 64919); God's Saving Presence. pap. 4.36 (ISBN 0-02-649250-4, 64925). 1966-70. tchr's manual 3.36 ea.; parent's guide 2.00 (ISBN 0-02-649140-0, 64914). Benziger Pub Co.
Weber, Hans-Ruedi. Experiments with Bible Study. LC 82-13398. 330p. 1983. pap. 12.95 (ISBN 0-664-24461-0). Westminster.
Wedderspoon, A. G., ed. Religious Education, Nineteen Forty-Four to Nineteen Eighty-Four. 238p. 1968. 3.95 (ISBN 0-87921-063-X); pap. 1.95 (ISBN 0-87921-064-8). Attic Pr.
Westerhoff, John H., ed. A Colloquy on Christian Education. LC 72-4258. 1979. pap. 5.95 (ISBN 0-8298-0365-3). Pilgrim NY.
Westerhoff, John H., III, ed. Values for Tomorrow's Children. LC 72-125961. 1979. pap. 5.95 (ISBN 0-8298-0377-7). Pilgrim NY.
Westerhoff, John H., 3rd, ed. A Colloquy on Christian Education. LC 72-4258. 1972. 6.95 (ISBN 0-8298-0238-X). Pilgrim NY.
Westing, Harold J. Evaluate & Grow. 1984. pap. 5.95 (ISBN 0-88207-624-8). Victor Bks.
Wheatcroft, Anita L. Seasons & Saints. (Illus.). 112p. (Orig.). 1974. pap. text ed. 4.25x (ISBN 0-8192-4050-8); tchrs'. ed. 4.75x (ISBN 0-8192-4049-4). Morehouse.
White, Ellen G. Counsels on Education. 1968. deluxe ed. 8.95 (ISBN 0-8163-0112-3, 03555-0). Pacific Pr Pub Assn.

--Counsels to Parents, Teachers & Students Regarding Christian Education. 1943. Repr. of 1913 ed. deluxe ed. 10.95 (ISBN 0-8163-0115-8, 03591-5). Pacific Pr Pub Assn.
--Fundamentals of Christian Education. (CHL Ser.). 1977. 8.95 (ISBN 0-8127-0307-3). Review & Herald.
Williams, Mel & Brittain, Mary A. Christian Education in Family Clusters. 80p. 1982. pap. 6.95 (ISBN 0-8170-0936-1). Judson.
Williamson, Nancy S. One Hundred Handy Ideas for Busy Teachers. (Teaching Helps Ser.). 1980. pap. 2.50 (ISBN 0-8010-9630-8). Baker Bk.
Willis, Wesley. Make Your Teaching Count! 144p. 1985. pap. 5.95 (ISBN 0-89693-324-5). Victor Bks.
Winston Staff. Joy Four. rev. ed. (Joy Religion Ser.). (Illus.). 1978. pap. text ed. 5.87 (ISBN 0-86683-034-0, HarpR); tchr's. manual 8.95 (ISBN 0-86683-044-8). Har-Row.
Wood, Andrew. Unto the Least of These: Special Education in the Church. LC 84-16077. 1984. pap. 4.95 (ISBN 0-87227-099-8). Reg Baptist.
Woodward, Luther E. Relations of Religious Training & Life Patterns to the Adult Religious Life. LC 71-177627. (Columbia University. Teachers College. Contributions to Education: No. 527). Repr. of 1932 ed. 22.50 (ISBN 0-404-55527-6). AMS Pr.
Wright, Norman. Training Christians to Counsel. 236p. 1983. Repr. 14.95 (ISBN 0-89081-422-8). Harvest Hse.
Wynne, Edward J., Jr. The Implications of Carl Michalson's Theological Method for Christian Education. Thompson, Henry O., ed. LC 82-24760. (Illus.). 400p. (Orig.). 1983. lib. bdg. 31.25 (ISBN 0-8191-3021-4); pap. text ed. 15.75 (ISBN 0-8191-3022-2). U Pr of Amer.
Yale Divinity School Faculty Members Staff & Brown, Charles R. Education for Christian Service: A Volume in Commemoration of the 100th Anniversary of the Divinity School of Yale University. 1922. 49.50x (ISBN 0-685-89749-4). Elliots Bks.
Zanzig, Thomas. Sharing: A Manual for Program Directors. (Sharing Program Ser.). 214p. 1985. pap. 54.00 (ISBN 0-88489-167-4). St Mary's.
--Sharing the Christian Message: A Program Manual for Volunteer Catechists, 11th & 12th Grade. (Illus.). 1979. pap. 38.00 (ISBN 0-88489-110-0); spiritmasters 9.95 (ISBN 0-88489-130-5). St Marys.
--Sharing 1: A Manual for Volunteer Teachers. (Sharing Program Ser.). (Illus.). 199p. 1985. pap. 18.95 (ISBN 0-88489-163-1). St Mary's.
--Sharing 4: A Manual for Volunteer Teachers. (Sharing Program Ser.). 200p. 1987. pap. 18.95 (ISBN 0-88489-166-6). St Mary's.
Ziegler, Sandra. Service Project Ideas. (Ideas Ser.). (Illus.). 48p. 1977. pap. text ed. 1.95 (ISBN 0-87239-122-1, 7962). Standard Pub.
Zuck, Roy B. The Holy Spirit in Your Teaching. 228p. 1984. pap. 7.95 (ISBN 0-88207-622-1). Victor Bks.
Zuck, Roy B. & Benson, Warren S., eds. Youth Education in the Church. 1978. 13.95 (ISBN 0-8024-9844-2). Moody.

CHRISTIAN ETHICS

see also Bible–Ethics; Casuistry; Christian Life; Christianity and Economics; Commandments, Ten; Fear of God; Guilt; Jesus Christ–Ethics; Law and Gospel; Love (Theology); Pastoral Medicine; Pastoral Psychology; Perfection; Sin; Sins; Social Ethics; Virtue and Virtues; also subdivision Moral and Religious Aspects under specific subjects, e.g. Amusements–Moral and Religious Aspects

Allen, Joseph L. Love & Conflict: A Covenantal Model of Christian Ethics. 336p. 1984. pap. 12.95 (ISBN 0-687-22806-9). Abingdon.
Andreyev, I. M. Pravoslavno-Khristijanskoe Nravstvennoje Bogoslovije. Tr. of Orthodox-Christian Moral Theology. 148p. 1966. pap. text ed. 5.00 (ISBN 0-317-30264-7). Holy Trinity.
Augsburger, David W. What Do You Fear? (New Life Ser.). pap. 3.00 (ISBN 0-8361-1687-9). Herald Pr.
Augsburger, Myron S. The Peacemaker. 208p. 1987. pap. 9.95 (ISBN 0-687-30353-2). Abingdon.
Augustinus, Saint Aurelius. De Fide et Symbolo, De Fide et Operibus, De Agone Christiano, Pt. 3. (Corpus Scriptorum Ecclesiasticorum Latinorum Ser: Vol. 41). 65.00 (ISBN 0-384-02385-1). Johnson Repr.
--Liber Qvi Appellatvr Specvlvm et Liber De Divinis Scriptvris. (Corpus Scriptorum Ecclesiasticorum Latinorum Ser: Vol. 12). 50.00 (ISBN 0-384-02505-6). Johnson Repr.
Bahnsen, Greg. Theonomy in Christian Ethics. 1977. kivar 12.50 (ISBN 0-934532-00-1). Presby & Reformed.
Ballou, Adin. Christian Non-Resistance. LC 70-121104. (Civil Liberties in American History Ser). 1970. Repr. of 1910 ed. lib. bdg. 35.00 (ISBN 0-306-71980-0). Da Capo.
Barclay, William. Christian Ethics for Today. LC 83-48994. 224p. 1984. pap. 7.95 (ISBN 0-06-060412-3, RD 512). Har-Row.
Barnette, Henlee H. Introducing Christian Ethics. LC 61-5629. 1961. 9.95 (ISBN 0-8054-6102-7). Broadman.
Barth, Karl. The Christian Life. Bromiley, Geoffrey W., ed. LC 80-39942. 328p. 1981. 17.95 (ISBN 0-8028-3523-6). Eerdmans.
Beach, Waldo & Niebuhr, H. Richard, eds. Christian Ethics-Sources of the Living Tradition. 2nd ed. 550p. 1973. text ed. 25.00 (ISBN 0-394-34414-6). Random.
Bennett, John C. The Radical Imperative: From Theology to Social Ethics. LC 75-15538. 208p. 1975. 8.50 (ISBN 0-664-20824-X). Westminster.
Berdiaev, Nikolai. The Destiny of Man. Duddington, Natalie, tr. LC 78-14100. 1987. Repr. of 1954 ed. 26.50 (ISBN 0-88355-775-4). Hyperion Conn.
Bilheimer, Robert S., ed. Faith & Ferment: An Interdisciplinary Study of Christian Beliefs & Practices. LC 83-70512. 352p. (Orig.). 1983. pap. 15.95 (ISBN 0-8066-2018-8, 10-2168). Augsburg.
Bonifazi, Conrad. A Theology of Things. LC 76-7549. 1976. Repr. of 1967 ed. lib. bdg. 22.50x (ISBN 0-8371-8838-5, BOTT). Greenwood.
Bonino, Jose M. Toward a Christian Political Ethics. LC 82-48541. 144p. 1983. pap. 6.95 (ISBN 0-8006-1697-9, 1-1697). Fortress.
Brill, Earl H. The Christian Moral Vision. (Church's Teaching Ser.: Vol. 6). 254p. 1979. 5.95 (ISBN 0-8164-0423-2, HarpR); pap. 4.95 (ISBN 0-8164-2219-2). Har-Row.
Brown, David. Choices: Ethics & the Christian. (Faith & the Future Ser.). 176p. 1984. pap. 24.95x (ISBN 0-631-13182-5); pap. 6.95 (ISBN 0-631-13222-8). Basil Blackwell.
Browne, T. & Johnson, Samuel. Christian Morals. 2nd ed. Roberts, S. C., ed. 1927. 20.00 (ISBN 0-527-12200-9). Kraus Repr.
Buber, Martin. Good & Evil. 143p. 1980. pap. text ed. write for info. (ISBN 0-02-316280-5, Pub. by Scribner). Macmillan.
Byrum, R. R. Christian Theology. rev. ed. Newell, Arlo F., ed. 1982. 14.95 (ISBN 0-87162-252-1, D3051). Warner Pr.
Cadoux, C. John. The Early Christian Attitude to War: A Contribution to the History of Christian Ethics. 304p. 1982. pap. 9.95 (ISBN 0-8164-2416-0, HarpR). Har-Row.
Cesaretti, C. A. & Commins, Stephen, eds. Let the Earth Bless the Lord: A Christian Perspective on Land Use. 160p. (Orig.). 1981. pap. 6.95 (ISBN 0-8164-2296-6, HarpR). Har-Row.
Chambers, Oswald. Moral Foundations of Life. 1961. pap. 2.95 (ISBN 0-87508-117-7). Chr Lit.
Childress, James F. Civil Disobedience & Political Obligation: A Study in Christian Social Ethics. LC 75-158137. (Yale Publication in Religion Ser.: No. 16). pap. 66.50 (ISBN 0-317-09428-9, 2021988). Bks Demand UMI.
Childress, James F. & Macquarrie, John, eds. The Westminster Dictionary of Christian Ethics. rev. ed. LC 85-22539. 704p. 1986. 34.95 (ISBN 0-664-20940-8). Westminster.
Christian Ideals. 1970. pap. 2.85 (ISBN 0-87813-501-4). Christian Light.
Clagett, John Y. Christian Conscience. LC 84-9824. 1984. pap. 3.95 (ISBN 0-87227-097-1). Reg Baptist.
Coleman, William V. Finding a Way to Follow. 1977. pap. 4.95 (ISBN 0-8192-1227-X). Morehouse.
Collins, Raymond F. Christian Morality: Biblical Foundations. LC 85-41020. 256p. 1986. 22.95 (ISBN 0-268-00758-6). U of Notre Dame Pr.
Culver, Robert D. The Peacemongers. Carpenter, Mark, ed. 160p. 1985. pap. 5.95 (ISBN 0-8423-4789-5). Tyndale.
Curran, Charles E. American Catholic Social Ethics: Twentieth Century Approaches. LC 82-4829. 336p. 1982. 24.95 (ISBN 0-268-00603-2). U of Notre Dame Pr.
--Critical Concerns in Moral Theology. LC 83-40593. 288p. 1984. text ed. 16.95 (ISBN 0-268-00747-0, 85-07477). U of Notre Dame Pr.
--Directions in Catholic Social Ethics. LC 84-28079. 304p. (Orig.). 1985. pap. text ed. 8.95 (ISBN 0-268-00853-1, 85-08533). U of Notre Dame Pr.
--Directions in Fundamental Moral Theology. LC 85-2543. 304p. 1985. pap. text ed. 8.95x (ISBN 0-268-00854-X, 85-08541, Dist. by Har-Row). U of Notre Dame Pr.
--New Perspectives in Moral Theology. LC 76-13206. 293p. 1976. text ed. 18.95 (ISBN 0-268-01449-3); pap. 6.95 (ISBN 0-268-01450-7). U of Notre Dame Pr.
--Transition & Tradition in Moral Theology. LC 78-20877. 272p. 1980. pap. text ed. 6.95 (ISBN 0-268-01838-3). U of Notre Dame Pr.
Curran, Charles E. & McCormick, Richard. Readings in Moral Theology: No. 1, Moral Norms & Catholic Tradition. LC 79-84237. 1979. pap. 9.95 (ISBN 0-8091-2203-0). Paulist Pr.
Curran, Charles E. & McCormick, Richard A., eds. Readings in Moral Theology, No. 2: The Distinctiveness of Christian Ethics. LC 79-84237. 360p. 1980. pap. 7.95 (ISBN 0-8091-2303-7). Paulist Pr.
--Readings in Moral Theology, No. 3: The Magisterium & Morality. LC 81-82436. (Orig.). 1981. pap. 7.95 (ISBN 0-8091-2407-6). Paulist Pr.
Daly, Robert J. Christian Biblical Ethics. (Orig.). 1984. pap. 9.95 (ISBN 0-8091-2592-7). Paulist Pr.
Day, Thomas I. Dietrich Bonhoeffer on Christian Community & Common Sense. LC 83-25900. (Toronto Studies in Theology: Vol. 11). 248p. 1983. 49.95x (ISBN 0-88946-752-8). E Mellen.
DeBurgh, W. G. From Morality to Religion. LC 70-102568. 1970. Repr. of 1938 ed. 31.50x (ISBN 0-8046-0728-1, Pub. by Kennikat). Assoc Faculty Pr.
De Burgh, W. G. From Morality to Religion. 352p. 1985. Repr. of 1938 ed. lib. bdg. 85.00 (ISBN 0-89984-042-6). Century Bookbindery.
Driver, Tom F. Christ in a Changing World: Toward an Ethical Christology. LC 81-5552. 224p. 1981. 12.95 (ISBN 0-8245-0105-5). Crossroad NY.
Duke, David N. The Biblical View of Reality: The Bible & Christian Ethics. ii, 59p. 1985. pap. text ed. 6.95x (ISBN 0-932269-05-2). Wyndham Hall.
Elizondo, Virgil & Greinacher, Norbert, eds. Church & Peace. (Concilium 1983: Vol. 164). 128p. (Orig.). 1983. pap. 6.95 (ISBN 0-8164-2444-6, HarpR). Har-Row.
Ellison, Marvin M. The Center Cannot Hold: The Search for a Global Economy of Justice. LC 82-23795. 330p. (Orig.). 1983. lib. bdg. 31.00 (ISBN 0-8191-2963-1); pap. text ed. 15.50 (ISBN 0-8191-2964-X). U Pr of Amer.
Finn, Daniel R. & Pemberton, Prentiss L. Toward a Christian Economic Ethic: Stewardship & Social Power. LC 83-25409. 266p. 1985. pap. 10.95 (ISBN 0-86683-876-7, 7919, HarpR). Har-Row.
Fletcher, Joseph & Montgomery, John W. Situation Ethics: True or False. 90p. (Orig.). 1972. pap. 2.95 (ISBN 0-87123-525-0, 200525). Bethany Hse.
Forell, George W. Christian Social Teachings. LC 71-159003. 1971. pap. 7.95 (ISBN 0-8066-1126-X, 10-1179). Augsburg.
--Ethics of Decision: An Introduction to Christian Ethics. LC 55-7767. 176p. 1955. pap. 4.50 (ISBN 0-8006-1770-3, 1-1770). Fortress.
--History of Christian Ethics: From the New Testament to Augustine, Vol. 1. LC 79-50096. 248p. 1979. 15.95 (ISBN 0-8066-1715-2, 10-3042). Augsburg.
Forlines, F. Leroy. Christian Standards & Convictions Without Legalism. 1981. pap. 2.25 (ISBN 0-89265-074-5). Randall Hse.
Forrer, Richard. Theodicies in Conflict: A Dilemma in Puritan Ethics & Nineteenth-Century American Literature. LC 85-27220. (Contributions to the Study of Religion: No. 17). 302p. 1986. lib. bdg. 37.95 (ISBN 0-313-25191-6, FTS/). Greenwood.
Fuchs, Josef. Christian Ethics in a Secular Arena. Hoose, Bernard & McNeil, Brian, trs. from Ital. & Ger. LC 84-7964. 164p. (Orig.). 1984. pap. 9.95 (ISBN 0-87840-411-2). Georgetown U Pr.
Fulbecke, William. A Booke of Christian Ethicks or Moral Philosophie. LC 74-28856. (English Experience Ser.: No. 737). 1975. Repr. of 1587 ed. 6.00 (ISBN 90-221-0737-X). Walter J Johnson.
Furlong, Monica. Christian Uncertainties. LC 82-72129. xii, 124p. 1982. pap. 6.95 (ISBN 0-936384-06-9). Cowley Pubns.
Gallagher, John. The Basis for Christian Ethics. 240p. (Orig.). 1985. pap. 9.95 (ISBN 0-8091-2690-7). Paulist Pr.
Gallup, George, Jr. & O'Connell, George. Who Do Americans Say That I Am? LC 85-26383. 130p. (Orig.). 1986. pap. 10.95 (ISBN 0-664-24685-0). Westminster.
Gardner, E. Clinton. Biblical Faith & Social Ethics. 1960. text ed. 23.50 scp (ISBN 0-06-042240-8, HarpC). Har-Row.
--Christocentrism in Christian Social Ethics: A Depth Study of Eight Modern Protestants. LC 82-21843. 264p. (Orig.). 1983. lib. bdg. 28.50 (ISBN 0-8191-2954-2); pap. text ed. 13.50 (ISBN 0-8191-2955-0). U Pr of Amer.
Geisler, Norman. Ethics: Alternatives & Issues. 256p. 1971. 14.95 (ISBN 0-310-24930-9, 18079). Zondervan.
--La Etica Cristiana del Amor. Canclini, Arnoldo, tr. from Eng. LC 77-15813. Tr. of The Christian Ethic of Love. (Span.). 126p. 1977. pap. 3.95 (ISBN 0-89922-103-3). Edit Caribe.
Geisler, Norman L. Options in Contemporary Christian Ethics. LC 80-69431. 128p. (Orig.). 1981. pap. 4.95 (ISBN 0-8010-3757-3). Baker Bk.
Genovesi, Vincent J. Expectant Creativity: The Action of Hope in Christian Ethics. LC 81-43807. 172p. (Orig.). 1982. lib. bdg. 27.75 (ISBN 0-8191-2407-9); pap. text ed. 11.50 (ISBN 0-8191-2408-7). U Pr of Amer.
Gill, Robin. A Textbook of Christian Ethics. 571p. 1986. pap. 19.95 (ISBN 0-567-29127-8, Pub. by T & T Clark Ltd UK). Fortress.
Goldsmith, Dale. New Testament Ethics. 196p. (Orig.). 1987. pap. 9.95 (ISBN 0-87178-605-2). Brethren.
Gonzalez-Ruiz, Jose-Maria. The New Creation: Marxist & Christian? O'Connell, Mathew J., tr. from Spanish. LC 76-10226. Orig. Title: Marximo y Cristianismo Frente Al Hombre Nuevo. 160p. (Orig.). 1976. 1.74 (ISBN 0-88344-327-9). Orbis Bks.
Gustafson, James M. Can Ethics Be Christian? LC 74-11622. 1977. pap. 7.00x (ISBN 0-226-31102-3, P734, Phoen). U of Chicago Pr.
Hall, Brian, et al. Readings in Value Development. 1982. pap. 11.95 (ISBN 0-8091-2448-3). Paulist Pr.
Hamilton, Elizabeth. Letters Addressed to the Daughter of a Nobleman on the Formation of the Religious & the Moral Principle, 2 vols. Luria, Gina, ed. (The Feminist Controversy in England, 1788-1810 Ser.). 1974. Set. lib. bdg. 121.00 (ISBN 0-8240-0865-0). Garland Pub.
Hanigan, James P. As I Have Loved You: Challenge of Christian Ethics. 240p. (Orig.). 1986. pap. 9.95 (ISBN 0-8091-2734-2). Paulist Pr.
Happel, Stephen & Walter, James J. Conversion & Discipleship: A Christian Foundation for Ethics & Doctrine. LC 85-45499. 240p. 1986. pap. 14.95 (ISBN 0-8006-1908-0, 1-1908). Fortress.
Haring, Bernard. Free & Faithful in Christ: General Moral Theology. (Free & Faithful in Christ Ser.: Vol. 1). 506p. 1987. pap. 19.50 (ISBN 0-8245-0308-2). Crossroad NY.
--Law of Christ, 3 vols. 646p. Vol. 1. 17.95 (ISBN 0-8091-0084-3). Paulist Pr.
Harris. Applying Moral Theories. 1985. pap. text ed. write for info. (ISBN 0-534-05898-1). Wadsworth Pub.
Harrison, Beverly W., et al. The Public Vocation of Christian Ethics. 400p. (Orig.). 1987. pap. 12.95 (ISBN 0-8298-0582-6). Pilgrim NY.
Hauerwas, Stanley. A Community of Character: Toward a Constructive Christian Social Ethic. LC 80-53072. 320p. 1981. text ed. 20.00 (ISBN 0-268-00733-0). U of Notre Dame Pr.
--The Peaceable Kingdom: A Primer in Christian Ethics. LC 83-14711. 224p. 1983. text ed. 17.95x (ISBN 0-268-01553-8, 85-15538); pap. text ed. 7.95x (ISBN 0-268-01554-6, 85-15546). U of Notre Dame Pr.
--Vision & Virtue: Essays in Christian Ethical Reflection. LC 80-54877. 264p. 1981. text ed. 7.95 (ISBN 0-268-01921-5). U of Notre Dame Pr.
Hauerwas, Stanley & Bondi, Richard. Truthfulness & Tragedy: Further Investigations in Christian Ethics. LC 76-30425. 1977. 18.95x (ISBN 0-268-01831-6); pap. text ed. 9.95 (ISBN 0-268-01832-4). U of Notre Dame Pr.
Hebblethwaite, Brian. Christian Ethics in the Modern Age. LC 81-13105. 144p. 1982. pap. 6.95 (ISBN 0-664-24395-9). Westminster.
Henry, Carl F. Christian Personal Ethics. (Twin Brooks Ser). 1977. pap. 12.95 (ISBN 0-8010-4165-1). Baker Bk.
Henson, Herbert H. Christian Morality, Natural, Developing, Final. LC 77-27189. (Gifford Lectures: 1935-36). Repr. of 1936 ed. 27.00 (ISBN 0-404-60494-3). AMS Pr.
Hoehn, Richard A. Up from Apathy: A Study of Moral Awareness & Social Involvement. LC 83-7057. 179p. (Orig.). 1983. pap. 10.95 (ISBN 0-687-43114-X). Abingdon.
Hollinger, Dennis P. Individualism & Social Ethics: An Evangelical Syncretism. 284p. 1984. lib. bdg. 28.50 (ISBN 0-8191-3580-1); pap. text ed. 13.50 (ISBN 0-8191-3581-X). U Pr of Amer.
Hopkins, Mark. The Law of Love & Love As a Law: Or, Christian Ethics. 3rd ed. LC 75-3196. Repr. of 1871 ed. 42.50 (ISBN 0-404-59197-3). AMS Pr.
Hornus, Jean-Michel. It Is Not Lawful for Me to Fight. LC 79-26846. (Christian Peace Shelf Ser.). 376p. 1980. pap. 15.95 (ISBN 0-8361-1911-8). Herald Pr.
Hughes, Philip E. Christian Ethics in Secular Society: An Introduction to Christian Ethics. 240p. 1983. 13.95 (ISBN 0-8010-4267-4). Baker Bk.

Hyde, Henry J. For Every Idle Silence: A Congressman Speaks Out. 140p. (Orig.). 1985. pap. 6.95 (ISBN 0-89283-282-7). Servant.

Hynson, Leon O. To Reform the Nation: Theological Foundations of Wesley's Ethics. Chapman, Ben & Terpstra, Gerard, eds. 192p. (Orig.). 1984. pap. 7.95 (ISBN 0-310-75071-7, 17030P). Zondervan.

Inge, William R. Christian Ethics & Modern Problems. Repr. of 1930 ed. lib. bdg. 22.50x (ISBN 0-8371-3960-0, INCE). Greenwood.

Ingram, J. K., ed. Imitation Christi. (EETS, ES Ser.: No. 63). Repr. of 1893 ed. 54.00 (ISBN 0-527-00268-2). Kraus Repr.

Jones, Major J. Christian Ethics for Black Theology. LC 74-8680. pap. cancelled (ISBN 0-317-30065-2, 2020267). Bks Demand UMI.

Jorstad, Erling. The Politics of Moralism: The New Christian Right in American Life. LC 81-65641. 128p. (Orig.). 1981. pap. 6.95 (ISBN 0-8066-1877-9, 10-5011). Augsburg.

Kalven, Bruce, et al. Value Development: A Practical Guide. 1982. pap. 10.00 (ISBN 0-8091-2445-9); learning summaries 2.50 (ISBN 0-8091-2520-X); time diary 3.00 (ISBN 0-8091-2519-6). Paulist Pr.

Kammer, Charles L., 3rd. The Kingdom Revisited: An Essay on Christian Social Ethics. LC 81-40045. 188p. (Orig.). 1981. lib. bdg. 26.00 (ISBN 0-8191-1737-4); pap. text ed. 12.50 (ISBN 0-8191-1738-2). U Pr of Amer.

Keane, Philip S. Christian Ethics & Imagination. 224p. (Orig.). 1984. pap. 9.95 (ISBN 0-8091-2647-8). Paulist Pr.

Kirk, Kenneth E. The Vision of God: The Christian Doctrine of the Summum Bonum. abr. ed. Dunstan, G. R., ed. 223p. 1977. Repr. of 1934 ed. 13.95 (ISBN 0-227-67830-3). Attic Pr.

Kreider, Carl. The Christian Entrepreneur. LC 80-16836. (Conrad Grebel Lectures Ser.). 214p. 1980. pap. 8.95 (ISBN 0-8361-1936-3). Herald Pr.

Langford, Thomas A. Harvest of the Spirit. LC 81-50602. 64p. 1981. pap. 3.50x (ISBN 0-8358-0428-3). Upper Room.

Lanier, Jean. Paraphrases for Pilgrims. 1977. pap. 1.75 (ISBN 0-89192-187-7). Interbk Inc.

Laurie, Greg. God's Design for Christian Dating. 2nd ed. LC 82-83836. 96p. (YA) 1983. pap. 2.25 (ISBN 0-89081-373-6). Harvest Hse.

Lebacqz, Karen. Six Theories of Justice: Perspectives from Philosophical & Theological Ethics. LC 86-26457. 144p. (Orig.). 1986. pap. 9.95 (ISBN 0-8066-2245-8, 10-5820). Augsburg.

Lehmann, Paul L. Ethics in a Christian Context. LC 78-31749. 1979. Repr. of 1963 ed. lib. bdg. 27.50x (ISBN 0-313-20971-5, LEEC). Greenwood.

--Ethics in a Christian Context. LC 63-11545. 1976. pap. 4.95x (ISBN 0-06-065231-4, RD 192, HarpR). Har-Row.

Liebman, Robert C. & Wuthnow, Robert. The New Christian Right: Mobilization & Legitimation. (Social Institutions & Social Change Ser.). 1983. lib. bdg. 26.95x (ISBN 0-202-30307-1); pap. text ed. 9.95 (ISBN 0-202-30308-X). De Gruyter Aldine.

Little, David. Religion, Order, & Law: A Study in Pre-Revolutionary England. LC 84-2611. 270p. 1984. pap. text ed. 11.00x (ISBN 0-226-48546-3). U of Chicago Pr.

Lochman, Jan M. Signposts to Freedom: The Ten Commandments of Christian Ethics. Lewis, David, tr. LC 81-52283. 192p. (Orig.). 1982. pap. 10.95 (ISBN 0-8066-1915-5, 10-5767). Augsburg.

Long, Edward L., Jr. A Survey of Christian Ethics. 1967. pap. 12.95x (ISBN 0-19-503242-X). Oxford U Pr.

--A Survey of Recent Christian Ethics. 1982. pap. 8.95x (ISBN 0-19-503160-1). Oxford U Pr.

McCormick, Richard A. Notes on Moral Theology. LC 80-5682. 902p. 1981. lib. bdg. 30.00 (ISBN 0-8191-1439-1); pap. text ed. 17.75 (ISBN 0-8191-1440-5). U Pr of Amer.

McCormick, Richard A. & Ramsey, Paul, eds. Doing Evil to Achieve Good: Moral Choice in Conflict Situations. LC 78-11316. 1978. 11.95 (ISBN 0-8294-0285-3). Loyola.

McCormick, Richard J. Notes on Moral Theology: Nineteen Eighty-One Through Nineteen Eighty-Four. 242p. 1985. lib. bdg. 22.00 (ISBN 0-8191-4351-0); pap. text ed. 9.25 (ISBN 0-8191-4352-9). U Pr of Amer.

McDonagh, E. Social Ethics & the Christian: Towards Freedom in Communion. 96p. 1979. pap. 8.00 (ISBN 0-7190-0739-9, Pub. by Manchester Univ Pr). Longwood Pub Group.

McDonagh, Edna. Doing the Truth: The Quest for Moral Theology. LC 79-63361. 1979. text ed. 14.95x (ISBN 0-268-00844-2). U of Notre Dame Pr.

MacNamara, Vincent. Faith & Ethics. 216p. (Orig.). 1985. 17.95 (ISBN 0-87840-426-0); pap. 10.95 (ISBN 0-87840-414-7). Georgetown U Pr.

Macquarrie, John, ed. Dictionary of Christian Ethics. LC 67-17412. 378p. 1967. 18.95 (ISBN 0-664-20646-8). Westminster.

Maestri, William. Choose Life & Not Death: A Primer on Abortion, Euthanasia, & Suicide. LC 85-28687. 9.95 (ISBN 0-8189-0490-9). Alba.

Manning, Doug. Comforting Those Who Grieve: A Guide for Helping Others. LC 84-48226. 112p. 1985. 10.45 (ISBN 0-06-065418-X, HarpR). Har-Row.

Marshall, Gordon. Presbyteries & Profits: Calvinism & the Development of Capitalism in Scotland, 1560 - 1707. 1980. 54.00x (ISBN 0-19-827246-4). Oxford U Pr.

Marshall, Michael E. Christian Orthodoxy Revisited. 137p. (Orig.). pap. 6.95 (ISBN 0-8192-1363-2). Morehouse.

May, William E. The Unity of the Moral & Spiritual Life. (Synthesis Ser). 1978. pap. 0.75 (ISBN 0-8199-0745-6). Franciscan Herald.

Meeks, Wayne A. The Moral World of the First Christians. LC 86-5504. (Library of Early Christianity: Vol. 6). 180p. 1986. 18.95 (ISBN 0-664-21910-1). Westminster.

Messenger, Ruth E. Ethical Teachings in the Latin Hymns of Medieval England. LC 30-20975. (Columbia University. Studies in the Social Sciences: No. 321). Repr. of 1930 ed. 18.50 (ISBN 0-404-51321-2). AMS Pr.

Mieth, Dietmar & Pohier, Jacques, eds. Christian Ethics & Economics: The North South Conflict, Concilium 140. (New Concilium 1980). 128p. 1980. pap. 5.95 (ISBN 0-8164-2282-6, HarpR). Har-Row.

Milingo, Emmanuel. The World in Between: Christian Healing & the Struggle for Spiritual Survival. Macmillan, Mona, ed. 144p. (Orig.). 1985. pap. 5.95 (ISBN 0-88344-354-6). Orbis Bks.

Mitchell, Joan & O'Neill, Irene. Making Moral Choices. Fisher, Carl, ed. (Illus.). 1985. Dupl. Masterbook 9.95 (ISBN 0-89837-103-1, Pub. by Pflaum Pr). Peter Li.

Mohler, James A. Dimensions of Faith. LC 69-13120. (Orig.). 1969. pap. 2.80 (ISBN 0-8294-0100-8). Loyola.

Moral Theology Today: Certitudes & Doubts. LC 84-11714. 372p. (Orig.). 1984. pap. 17.95 (ISBN 0-935372-14-8). Pope John Ctr.

Muelder, Walter G. Moral Law in Christian Social Ethics. LC 66-15972. 198p. lib. bdg. 19.95x (ISBN 0-88946-011-6). E Mellen.

Niebuhr, H. Richard. The Responsible Self. LC 63-15955. 1978. pap. 6.95xi (ISBN 0-06-066211-5, RD 266, HarpR). Har-Row.

Niebuhr, Reinhold. An Interpretation of Christian Ethics. 1979. pap. 8.95 (ISBN 0-8164-2206-0, HarpR). Har-Row.

O'Connell, Timothy E. Principles for a Catholic Morality. 1978. (HarpR); pap. 9.95 (ISBN 0-86683-885-6). Har-Row.

Odhner, Hugo L. The Moral Life. 142p. 1985. Repr. of 1957 ed. write for info. (ISBN 0-910557-08-X). Acad New Church.

Oglesby, Enoch H. God's Divine Arithematic. Jones, Amos, Jr., ed. LC 84-54498. 150p. (Orig.). 1986. pap. write for info. (ISBN 0-910683-06-9). Sunday School.

Ogletree, Thomas W. The Use of the Bible in Christian Ethics. LC 83-5489. 240p. 1983. 19.95 (ISBN 0-8006-0710-4, 1-710). Fortress.

Okayama, Kotaro. Zur Grundlegung Christlicher Ethik Theologische Konzeptionen der Gegenwart im Lichte des Analogie-Problems. (Theologische Bibliothek Toepelmann: Vol. 30). 1977. 24.40x (ISBN 3-11-005812-X). De Gruyter.

Osborn, E. Ethical Patterns in Early Christian Thought. LC 75-10040. 288p. 1976. 39.50 (ISBN 0-521-20835-1). Cambridge U Pr.

Osborn, Eric F. Ethical Patterns in Early Christian Thought. LC 75-10040. pap. 65.50 (2026351). Bks Demand UMI.

Paskins, Barrie, ed. Ethics & European Security. 192p. 1986. 28.95x (ISBN 0-86569-146-0). Auburn Hse.

Pennock, Michael. Christian Morality & You: Teacher Manual. Rev. ed. (High School Religion Text Program). 152p. 1984. 7.95 (ISBN 0-87793-311-1). Ave Maria.

Pennock, Michael & Finley, James. Christian Morality & You: Student Text. Rev. ed. LC 83-73085. (High School Religion Text Programs). (Illus.). 200p. 1984. pap. 5.95 (ISBN 0-87793-308-1). Ave Maria.

Ple, Albert. Duty or Pleasure? A New Appraisal of Christian Ethics. 208p. 1986. 22.95 (ISBN 0-913729-24-8); pap. 12.95 (ISBN 0-913729-25-6). Paragon Hse.

Rahner, Karl & Weger, Karl-Heinz. Our Christian Faith: Answers for the Future. 208p. (Orig.). 1980. 10.95 (ISBN 0-8245-0361-9); pap. 4.95 (ISBN 0-8245-0362-7). Crossroad NY.

Ramsey, Paul. Basic Christian Ethics. LC 78-56925. 424p. 1980. pap. text ed. 14.00x (ISBN 0-226-70383-5). U of Chicago Pr.

--Deeds & Rules in Christian Ethics. LC 83-10257. 256p. 1983. pap. text ed. 13.25 (ISBN 0-8191-3355-8). U Pr of Amer.

Rashdall, H. Conscience & Christ: Six Lectures on Christian Ethics. LC 17-2649. 1916. 26.00 (ISBN 0-527-73900-6). Kraus Repr.

Rauschenbusch, Walter. The Social Principles of Jesus. LC 76-50566. 1976. Repr. of 1916 ed. lib. bdg. 22.00 (ISBN 0-8414-7308-0). Folcroft.

Raymond, Irving W. Teaching of the Early Church on the Use of Wine & Strong Drink. LC 79-120207. (Columbia University. Studies in the Social Sciences: No. 286). Repr. of 1927 ed. 14.50 (ISBN 0-404-51286-0). AMS Pr.

Reeck, Darrell. Ethics for the Professions: A Christian Perspective. LC 81-52282. 176p. (Orig.). 1982. pap. 11.95 (ISBN 0-8066-1914-7, 10-2088). Augsburg.

Reichert, Richard. Confronting Christianity: Moral Issues. LC 78-53634. 44p. 1978. pap. 9.95 (ISBN 0-88489-099-6). St Marys.

--Making Moral Decisions. rev. ed. LC 83-60316. (Illus.). 1983. pap. text ed. 7.20x (ISBN 0-88489-150-X); tchrs. guide 9.00x (ISBN 0-88489-151-8). St Marys.

Rendtorff, Trutz. Ethics, Vol. 1: Basic Elements & Methodology in an Ethical Theology. Crimm, Keith, tr. LC 85-45484. 208p. 1986. 19.95 (ISBN 0-8006-0767-8, 1-767). Fortress.

Ridenour, Fritz. How to Be a Christian in an Unchristian World. rev. ed. LC 72-169603. 192p. (Orig.). 1972. pap. 3.50 (ISBN 0-8307-0611-9, S123150). Regal.

Ringe, Sharon H. Jesus, Liberation & the Biblical Jubilee: Images for Ethics & Christology. LC 85-4609. (Overtures to Biblical Theology Ser.). 144p. 1985. pap. 8.95 (ISBN 0-8006-1544-1). Fortress.

Roeda, Jack. Decisions: A Study of Christian Ethics. LC 80-189628. (Orig.). 1980. pap. text ed. 4.50 (ISBN 0-933140-14-2); tchr's. manual 5.95 (ISBN 0-933140-15-0). CRC Pubns.

Ross, J. Elliott. Christian Ethics. 1951. 10.50 (ISBN 0-8159-5202-3). Devin.

Rossi, Philip. Together Toward Hope: A Journey to Moral Theology. LC 83-1279. 224p. 1983. 16.95x (ISBN 0-268-01844-8, 85-18441). U of Notre Dame Pr.

Rudnick, Milton L. Christian Ethics for Today: An Evangelical Approach. LC 79-53924. 1979. pap. 8.95 (ISBN 0-8010-7738-9). Baker Bk.

Rush, Vincent E. The Responsible Christian: A Guide for Moral Decision Making According to Classical Tradition. 288p. 1984. 9.95 (ISBN 0-8294-0448-1). Loyola.

Ryrie, Charles C. What You Should Know about Social Responsibility. LC 81-16804. (Current Christian Issues Ser.). 1982. pap. 4.50 (ISBN 0-8024-9417-X). Moody.

Schaeffer, Francis A. The Complete Works of Francis A. Schaeffer. LC 84-72010. 2250p. 1985. (Crossway Bks); pap. 59.95 (ISBN 0-89107-331-0). Good News.

--How Should We Then Live? LC 83-70956. 288p. 1983. pap. 9.95 (ISBN 0-89107-292-6, Crossway BKs). Good News.

Schuller, Bruno. Wholly Human: Essays on the Theory & Language of Morality. Heinegg, Peter, tr. from Ger. Orig. Title: Der Menschliche Mensch. 256p. (Orig.). 1986. 17.95 (ISBN 0-87840-427-9); pap. 9.95 (ISBN 0-87840-422-8). Georgetown U Pr.

Scott, Lane A. & Hynson, Leon O., eds. Christian Ethics. (Wesleyan Theological Perspectives Ser.: Vol. III). 1983. 14.95 (ISBN 0-87162-267-X, D4852). Warner Pr.

Simmons, Paul D. Birth & Death: Bioethical Decision-Making. LC 82-20160. (Biblical Perspectives on Current Issues). 270p. 1983. pap. 13.95 (ISBN 0-664-24463-7). Westminster.

Simmons, Paul D., ed. Issues in Christian Ethics. LC 79-52983. 1980. pap. 8.95 (ISBN 0-8054-6122-1). Broadman.

Simpson, A. B. Danger Lines in the Deeper Life. 133p. 1966. pap. 2.00 (ISBN 0-87509-007-9). Chr Pubns.

Smedes, Lewis B. Sex for Christians. 176p. 1976. pap. 5.95 (ISBN 0-8028-1618-5). Eerdmans.

Smith, Harmon L. Ethics & the New Medicine. LC 76-124756. Repr. of 1970 ed. 43.50 (ISBN 0-8357-9005-3, 2016356). Bks Demand UMI.

Sproul, R. C. Ethics & the Christian. 94p. 1983. pap. 2.95 (ISBN 0-8423-0775-3). Tyndale.

Stamp, Josiah. Christian Ethic As An Economic Factor. facsimile ed. LC 70-102256. (Select Bibliographies Reprint Ser). 1926. 17.00 (ISBN 0-8369-5141-7). Ayer Co Pubs.

Staton, Knofel. Check Your Morality. LC 83-418. 194p. (Orig.). 1983. pap. 3.95 (ISBN 0-87239-630-4, 39971). Standard Pub.

Stevens, Edward. Making Moral Decisions. rev. ed. LC 81-80877. 96p. 1981. pap. 4.95 (ISBN 0-8091-2397-5). Paulist Pr.

Stivers, Robert L. Hunger, Technology & Limits to Growth: Christian Responsibility for Three Ethical Issues. LC 83-72120. 176p. (Orig.). 1984. pap. 9.95 (ISBN 0-8066-2064-1, 10-3184). Augsburg.

Stone, Ronald H. Realism & Hope. 1977. pap. text ed. 11.75 (ISBN 0-8191-0128-1). U Pr of Amer.

Stott, John & Miller, Nick, eds. Crime & the Responsible Community. LC 81-110661. (London Lectures in Contemporary Christianity: 1979). pap. 47.80 (ISBN 0-317-09298-7, 2019339). Bks Demand UMI.

Swindoll, Charles R. You & Your Child. 2nd ed. 1982. pap. 4.95 (ISBN 0-8407-5616-X). Nelson.

Taylor, A. E. The Faith of the Moralist: Gifford Lectures Delivered in the University of St. Andrews, 1926-1928, 2 vols. 1977. Repr. of 1932 ed. Set. lib. bdg. 50.00 (ISBN 0-8482-2663-1). Norwood Edns.

Taylor, Alfred E. Faith of a Moralist, 2 Vols. in 1. LC 37-23815. (Gifford Lectures 1926-1928). 1968. Repr. of 1937 ed. 41.00 (ISBN 0-527-89062-6). Kraus Repr.

Thielicke, Helmut. Theological Ethics, 2 vols. Incl. Foundations; Politics; Vol. III. Sex. pap. 8.95 (ISBN 0-8028-1794-7). LC 78-31858. Eerdmans.

Thompson, Kenneth W. Christian Ethics & the Dilemmas of Foreign Policy. 160p. 1983. pap. text ed. 9.75 (ISBN 0-8191-3040-0). U Pr of Amer.

--Christian Ethics & the Dilemmas of Foreign Policy. LC 59-15344. pap. 30.40 (ISBN 0-8357-9098-3, 2017937). Bks Demand UMI.

Thomson, Judith J. Rights, Restitution, & Risk: Essays in Moral Theory. Parent, William, ed. & pref. by. (Illus.). 288p. 1986. text ed. 29.95x (ISBN 0-674-76980-5); pap. text ed. 9.95x (ISBN 0-674-76981-3). Harvard U Pr.

Tillman, William M., Jr. & Gilbert, Timothy D. Christian Ethics: A Primer. LC 85-25474. 1986. pap. 5.95 (ISBN 0-8054-6128-0). Broadman.

Torrence, Rosemary. Mending Our Nets. 176p. 1980. 10.95 (ISBN 0-697-01757-5). Wm C Brown.

Turner, Philip. Sex, Money & Power: An Essay on Christian Social Ethics. LC 84-72481. 135p. (Orig.). 1985. pap. 7.95 (ISBN 0-936384-22-0). Cowley Pubns.

Underwood, Jon. Check Your Morality: Leader's Guide. 48p. (Orig.). 1984. pap. 2.95 (ISBN 0-87239-760-2, 39961). Standard Pub.

Van Til, Cornelius. Christian Theistic Ethics. 1975. pap. 7.95 syllabus (ISBN 0-87552-478-8). Presby & Reformed.

Varga, Andrew C. On Being Human: Principles of Ethics. LC 78-51589. 160p. 1978. pap. 3.95 (ISBN 0-8091-2111-5). Paulist Pr.

Warren, Thomas B. & Barnhart, Joe. Warren-Barnhart Debate on Ethics. 1981. pap. 13.00 (ISBN 0-934916-47-0). Natl Christian Pr.

Wayland, Francis. Elements of Moral Science. Blau, Joseph L., ed. LC 63-19149. (The John Harvard Library). 1963. 27.50x (ISBN 0-674-24600-4). Harvard U Pr.

Webb, Lance. Onesimus. LC 80-21306. 374p. 1980. pap. 4.95 (ISBN 0-8407-5742-5). Nelson.

Weber, Max. Protestant Ethic & the Spirit of Capitalism. rev. ed. 1977. pap. 8.95 (ISBN 0-684-16489-2, ScribT). Scribner.

Wesley, J. The Christian Pattern. pap. 2.75 (ISBN 0-686-12912-1). Schmul Pub Co.

Westermarck, Edward A. Christianity & Morals. facs. ed. LC 78-80406. (Essay Index Reprint Ser). 1939. 23.75 (ISBN 0-8369-1055-9). Ayer Co Pubs.

White, R. E. Christian Ethics: The Historical Development. pap. 11.95 (ISBN 0-8042-0791-7). John Knox.

Whitehead, John W. The Stealing of America. LC 83-70320. 180p. 1983. pap. 6.95 (ISBN 0-89107-286-1, Crossway Bks). Good News.

Wilcox, John R. Taking Time Seriously: James Luther Adams. LC 78-61391. 1978. pap. text ed. 12.25 (ISBN 0-8191-0600-3). U Pr of Amer.

Wilkins, Ronald J. Understanding Christian Morality. (To Live Is Christ Ser). 256p. 1982. pap. 5.75; tchr's. manual 5.00 (ISBN 0-697-01800-8); spirit masters 10.95 (ISBN 0-697-01801-6); kit 20.00 (ISBN 0-697-01675-7). Wm C Brown.

--Understanding Christian Morality: Short Edition. (To Live Is Christ Ser.). 112p. 1977. pap. 4.20 (ISBN 0-697-01661-7); tchr's. manual 6.00 (ISBN 0-697-01667-6). Wm C Brown.

Williams, Oliver F. & Houck, John M. Full Value: Cases in Christian Business Ethics. LC 78-3143. 1978. pap. 8.95x S.D. (ISBN 0-06-069515-3, RD 279, HarpR). Har-Row.

Willimon, William H. The Service of God. 240p. 1983. pap. 11.50 (ISBN 0-687-38094-4). Abingdon.

Wogaman, J. Philip. A Christian Method of Moral Judgment. LC 76-40108. 282p. 1977. pap. 8.95 (ISBN 0-664-24134-4). Westminster.

Woodhouse, A. S., ed. & intro. by. Puritanism & Liberty: Being the Army Debates (1647-9) from the Clarke Manuscripts with Supplementary Documents. 634p. 1986. pap. 11.95x (ISBN 0-460-01057-3, Pub. by Evman England). Biblio Dist.

Young, David P. The Speed of Love: An Exploration of Christian Faithfulness in a Technological World. 150p. (Orig.). 1986. pap. 6.95 (ISBN 0-377-00159-7). Friend Pr.

Young, Douglas. A Primer of Christianity & Ethics. Hunting, Constance, ed. 200p. (Orig.). (YA) 1985. pap. 12.95 (ISBN 0-913006-34-3). Puckerbrush.

CHRISTIAN ETHICS–ANGLICAN AUTHORS

Spong, John & Haines, Denise. Beyond Moralism. 204p. (Orig.). 1986. pap. 9.95 (ISBN 0-86683-514-8, HarpR). Har-Row.

Winter, Gibson. Liberating Creation: Foundations of Religious Social Ethics. LC 81-5364. 1981. 12.95 (ISBN 0-8245-0032-6). Crossroad NY.

CHRISTIAN ETHICS–CATHOLIC AUTHORS

Bockle, Franz, ed. Moral Problems & Christian Personalism. LC 65-24045. (Concilium Ser.: Vol. 5). 191p. 7.95 (ISBN 0-8091-0099-1). Paulist Pr.

--Understanding the Signs of the Times. LC 67-25694. (Concilium Ser.: Vol. 25). 176p. 1967. 7.95 (ISBN 0-8091-0152-1). Paulist Pr.

Curran, Charles E. Catholic Moral Theology in Dialogue. LC 76-14906. 1976. text ed. 18.95x (ISBN 0-268-00716-0); pap. 5.95 (ISBN 0-268-00717-9). U of Notre Dame Pr.

Curran, Charles E. & McCormick, Richard A. Readings in Moral Theology, No. 4: The Use of Scripture in Moral Theology. 1984. pap. 9.95 (ISBN 0-8091-2563-3). Paulist Pr.

Curran, Charles E., ed. Absolutes in Moral Theology? LC 75-3988. 320p. 1976. Repr. of 1968 ed. lib. bdg. 25.00x (ISBN 0-8371-7450-3, CUMT). Greenwood.

Daughters of St. Paul, tr. Yes to Life. 1977. 6.95 (ISBN 0-8198-0485-1); pap. 5.95 (ISBN 0-8198-0486-X). Dghtrs St Paul.

Daughters of St Paul. Morality Today: The Bible in My Life. 1979. 3.25 (ISBN 0-8198-0620-X); pap. 2.25 (ISBN 0-8198-0621-8). Dghtrs St Paul.

Fuchs, Josef. Personal Responsibility & Christian Morality. Cleves, William, et al, trs. from Ger. LC 83-1548. 240p. (Orig.). 1983. pap. 10.95 (ISBN 0-87840-405-8). Georgetown U Pr.

Glaser, John W. Caring for the Special Child. LC 84-82551. 97p. (Orig.). 1985. pap. 6.95 (ISBN 0-934134-14-6, Leaven Pr). Sheed & Ward MO.

Haring, Bernard. Toward a Christian Moral Theology. 1966. 12.95x (ISBN 0-268-00281-9). U of Notre Dame Pr.

Lawler, Philip F. How Bishops Decide: An American Catholic Case Study. 45p. (Orig.). pap. 4.00 (ISBN 0-89633-101-6). Ethics & Public Policy.

Lohkamp, Nicholas. Living the Good News: An Introduction to Moral Theology. 170p. (Orig.). 1982. pap. text ed. 4.50 (ISBN 0-86716-016-0). St Anthony Mess Pr.

Lovasik, Lawrence G. Clean Love in Courtship. 1974. pap. 1.50 (ISBN 0-89555-095-4). TAN Bks Pubs.

Schlitzer, Albert L. Our Life in Christ. (University Theology Ser.: Vols. 1 & 2). 1962. Set. 12.95 (ISBN 0-268-00201-0). U of Notre Dame Pr.

Sheen, Fulton J. Moral Universe: A Preface to Christian Living. facs. ed. LC 67-28766. (Essay Index Reprint Ser). 1936. 15.00 (ISBN 0-8369-0873-2). Ayer Co Pubs.

Spaeth, Robert L. The Church & a Catholic's Conscience. 96p. 1985. pap. 6.50 (ISBN 0-86683-869-4, 8456, HarpR). Har-Row.

Sullivan, Shaun J. Killing in Defense of Private Property: The Development of a Roman Catholic Moral Teaching, Thirteenth to Eighteenth Centuries. LC 75-38843. (American Academy of Religion. Dissertation Ser.). (Illus.). 1976. pap. 9.95 (ISBN 0-89130-067-8, 010115). Scholars Pr GA.

Thomas a Kempis. Imitation of Christ. new, rev. ed. Fitzpatrick, Clare L., ed. (Illus., Large Type). maroon, colored edges 4.95 (ISBN 0-89942-320-5, 320/00). Catholic Bk Pub.

Van Der Poel, Cornelius J. The Search for Human Values. LC 75-161445. 192p. 1973. pap. 3.95 (ISBN 0-8091-1781-9, Deus). Paulist Pr.

Westley, Dick. Morality & Its Beyond. 324p. (Orig.). 1984. pap. 8.95 (ISBN 0-89622-207-1). Twenty-Third.

CHRISTIAN ETHICS–DICTIONARIES

Macquarrie, John, ed. Dictionary of Christian Ethics. LC 67-17412. 378p. 1967. 18.95 (ISBN 0-664-20646-8). Westminster.

Pierrot. Dictionnaire de Theologie Morale, 2 vols. Migne, J. P., ed. (Encyclopedie Theologique Ser.: Vols. 31-32). (Fr.). 1486p. Repr. of 1849 ed. lib. bdg. 188.50x (ISBN 0-89241-242-9). Caratzas.

Stoeckle, Bernard, ed. The Concise Dictionary of Christian Ethics. 1979. 19.50 (ISBN 0-8245-0300-7). Crossroad NY.

CHRISTIAN ETHICS–ORTHODOX EASTERN AUTHORS

Harakas, Stanley S. For the Health of Body & Soul. 48p. (Orig.). 1980. pap. 1.95 (ISBN 0-916586-42-1). Hellenic Coll Pr.

Khrapovitsky, Antony. Moral Idea of the Main Dogmas of the Faith. Novakshonoff, V. & Puhalo, L., trs. from Rus. 96p. (Orig.). 1986. pap. 7.50. Synaxis Pr.

Yannaras, Christos. Freedom of Morality. Briere, Elizabeth, tr. from Gr. LC 84-9030. 272p. (Orig.). 1984. pap. text ed. 12.95 (ISBN 0-88141-028-4). St Vladimirs.

CHRISTIAN ETHICS–STUDY AND TEACHING

Chapin, Alice. Building Your Child's Faith. 144p. (Orig.). 1983. pap. 5.95 (ISBN 0-86605-115-5). Campus Crusade.

CHRISTIAN EVIDENCES

see Apologetics

CHRISTIAN HYMNS

see Hymns

CHRISTIAN LEADERSHIP

see also Church Officers

Anderson, Godfrey T. Spicer: Leader with the Common Touch. Wheeler, Gerald, ed. LC 83-3279. (Illus.). 128p. (Orig.). 1983. pap. 5.95 (ISBN 0-8280-0150-2). Review & Herald.

Anderson, Ray S. Minding God's Business. 176p. (Orig.). 1986. pap. 9.95 (ISBN 0-8028-0168-4). Eerdmans.

Bailey, Keith M. Servants in Charge. 123p. 1979. pap. 3.95 (ISBN 0-87509-160-1); Leader's Guide. 0.95 (ISBN 0-87509-261-6). Chr Pubns.

Baldwin, David M. Friendless American Male: Leader's Guide. LC 82-21518. 48p. 1984. pap. 3.95 (ISBN 0-8307-0991-6, 6101914). Regal.

The Best of Leader Ideabank. 110p. 1984. pap. 9.95 (ISBN 0-89191-976-7). Cook.

Bonar, Andrew. The Life of R. M. M'Cheyne. 1978. pap. 3.45 (ISBN 0-85151-085-X). Banner of Truth.

Bonar, Andrew A. Memoir & Remains of R. M. M'cheyne. 1978. 16.95 (ISBN 0-85151-084-1). Banner of Truth.

Broderick, Robert C. Your Parish - Where the Action Is. 1974. pap. 2.25 (ISBN 0-8199-0486-4). Franciscan Herald.

Brokhoff, John. This You Can Believe: Participant. (Orig.). 1987. pap. price not set (ISBN 0-89536-893-5, 7879). CSS of Ohio.

Burkhart, Rob. I Hate Witnessing Leader's Guide. LC 84-18165. 64p. 1985. pap. 3.95 (ISBN 0-8307-1011-6, 6101987). Regal.

Carroll, R. Leonard. Stewardship: Total Life Commitment. 144p. 1967. pap. 4.25 (ISBN 0-87148-755-1). Pathway Pr.

Chartier, Jan. Developing Leadership in the Teaching Church. 112p. 1985. pap. 5.95 (ISBN 0-8170-1067-X). Judson.

Chisholm, Alex & Chisholm, Sarah. Emotions: Can You Trust Them? Leader's Guide. 48p. 1984. pap. 3.95 (ISBN 0-8307-0992-4, 6101926). Regal.

Clevenger, Ernest, Jr. A Beginning Course in Church Leadership Training for Men. (Illus.). 42p. 1975. 3.25 (ISBN 0-88428-036-5). Parchment Pr.

Clowers, Don. Principles of Leadership. 40p. (Orig.). 1985. wkbk. 4.95 (ISBN 0-914307-49-5). Word Faith.

Cornwall, Judson. Profiles of a Leader. LC 80-85161. (Orig.). 1980. pap. 4.95 (ISBN 0-88270-503-2). Bridge Pub.

Couchman, Bob & Couchman, Win. Small Groups: Timber to Build up God's House. LC 82-798. (Carpenter Studyguide). 83p. 1982. pap. 2.95 (ISBN 0-87788-097-2). Shaw Pubs.

Craig, James D., ed. All about Cells. 2nd rev. ed. 32p. 1981. pap. 2.49 (ISBN 0-88151-017-3). Lay Leadership.

Crunlan, Stephen A. & Lambrides, Daniel H. Healing Relationships: A Christian's Manual of Lay Counseling. LC 83-70103. 325p. 1984. pap. 6.45 (ISBN 0-87509-329-9); Leader's Guide. 2.95 (ISBN 0-87509-354-X). Chr Pubns.

Dale, Robert D. Ministers As Leaders. LC 84-9501. (Broadman Leadership Ser.). 1984. pap. 4.95 (ISBN 0-8054-3110-1). Broadman.

Dayton, E. Resources for Christian Leaders. 8th ed. 40p. 1982. pap. 3.95 (ISBN 0-912552-16-6). Missions Adv Res Com Ctr.

Dayton, Edward R. & Engstrom, Ted W. Strategy for Leadership. 240p. 1979. 13.95 (ISBN 0-8007-0994-2). Revell.

Detwiler-Zapp, Diane & Dixon, William C. Lay Caregiving. LC 81-66519. (Creative Pastoral Care & Counseling Ser.). 1982. pap. 4.50 (ISBN 0-8006-0567-5, 1-567). Fortress.

Eims, Leroy. Be the Leader You Were Meant to Be. LC 75-5392. 132p. 1975. pap. 4.95 (ISBN 0-88207-723-6). Victor Bks.

--Laboring in the Harvest. 108p. 1985. pap. 4.95 (ISBN 0-89109-530-6). NavPress.

Ellis, Joe. The Church on Purpose: Keys to Effective Church Leadership. LC 82-3175. (Illus.). 112p. (Orig.). 1982. pap. 6.95 (ISBN 0-87239-441-7, 88584). Standard Pub.

Engstrom, Ted. Your Gift of Administration: How to Discover & Use It. LC 83-8327. 192p. 1983. 9.95 (ISBN 0-8407-5297-0). Nelson.

Engstrom, Ted W. Desafio del Liderazgo. De Bedoian, Adriana P., tr. from Eng. Tr. of Your Gift of Administration. (Span.). 128p. 1987. pap. 3.25 (ISBN 0-88113-058-3). Edit Betania.

--The Making of a Christian Leader. 1976. pap. 6.95 (ISBN 0-310-24221-5, 9573P). Zondervan.

Erickson, Kenneth A. Christian Time Management. 128p. (Orig.). 1985. pap. 4.95 (ISBN 0-570-03972-X, 12-3007). Concordia.

Fernando, Ajith. Leadership Lifestyles: A Study of 1 Timothy. (Living Studies). 224p. 1985. pap. 6.95 (ISBN 0-8423-2130-6); leader's guide 2.95 (ISBN 0-8423-2131-4). Tyndale.

Fisher, Doug, ed. Why We Serve: Personal Stories of Catholic Lay Ministers. 176p. (Orig.). 1984. pap. 6.95 (ISBN 0-8091-2640-0). Paulist Pr.

Fox, Zeni, et al. Leadership for Youth Ministry. (Illus.). 200p. (Orig.). 1984. pap. 8.95 (ISBN 0-88489-157-7). St Mary's.

Fransen, Paul. Effective Church Councils: Leadership Styles & Decision Making in the Church. (Administration Series for Churches). 56p. (Orig.). 1985. pap. 3.95 (ISBN 0-8066-2198-2, 10-2023). Augsburg.

Frost, Marie H. Frankly Feminine: Leader's Guide. 48p. (Orig.). 1984. pap. 2.95 (ISBN 0-87239-746-7, 2970). Standard Pub.

--Listen to Your Children: Leader's Guide. 48p. (Orig.). 1984. pap. 2.95 (ISBN 0-87239-747-5, 2999). Standard Pub.

Fryman, Sarah. The Measure of a Woman. LC 77-74533. (The Measure of... Ser.). 64p. 1985. pap. 3.95 (ISBN 0-8307-0988-6, 6101888). Regal.

Gangel, Kenneth O. So You Want to Be a Leader. pap. 2.95 (ISBN 0-87509-131-8); leaders guide 2.00 (ISBN 0-87509-298-5). Chr Pubns.

Gedde, Palmer. While You Can. (Orig.). 1987. pap. price not set (ISBN 0-89536-891-9, 7877). CSS of Ohio.

Gerig, Donald. Leadership in Crisis. LC 81-51741. 128p. 1981. pap. 3.95 (ISBN 0-8307-0797-2, 5415304). Regal.

Gobbel, A. Roger, et al. Helping Youth Interpret the Bible: A Teaching Resource. LC 84-3916. 204p. 1984. pap. 9.95 (ISBN 0-8042-1580-4). John Knox.

Grantham, Rudolph E. Lay Shepherding. 1980. pap. 5.95 (ISBN 0-8170-0863-2). Judson.

Greenslade, Philip. Leadership, Greatness, & Servanthood. 208p. (Orig.). 1986. pap. 5.95 (ISBN 0-87123-871-3, 210871). Bethany Hse.

Hall, Brian. Shepherds & Lovers. LC 81-84352. 144p. (Orig.). 1982. pap. 6.95 (ISBN 0-8091-2425-4). Paulist Pr.

Hall, Brian P. Leadership Through Values: A Study in Personal & Organizational Development. LC 80-81438. (Illus.). 112p. (Orig.). 1980. pap. 8.95 (ISBN 0-8091-2313-4). Paulist Pr.

Hancock, Steve. Discovering My Gifts for Service: Leader's Guide. rev. ed. 48p. 1984. pap. 2.95 (ISBN 0-87239-811-0, 39979). Standard Pub.

Harrington, Arthur. What the Bible Says about Leadership. (What the Bible Says Ser.). 425p. text ed. 13.95 (ISBN 0-89900-250-1). College Pr Pub.

Harrison, Doyle. Understanding Authority for Effective Leadership. rev. ed. 122p. (Orig.). 1985. pap. 3.50 (ISBN 0-89274-379-4). Harrison Hse.

Hayden, Marshall. God's Plan for Church Leadership: Leader's Guide. LC 82-3378. 64p. (Orig.). 1982. pap. 1.95 (ISBN 0-87239-567-7, 39986). Standard Pub.

Hayes, Norvel. You Can Be a Soulwinner. 150p. (Orig.). 1983. pap. 4.95 (ISBN 0-89274-269-0). Harrison Hse.

Hendee, John. Ambassadors for Christ. (Ambassadors Training Program Ser.). 64p. (Orig.). 1984. pap. 2.95 trainer's manual (ISBN 0-87239-812-9, 3221); student book 2.50 (ISBN 0-87239-813-7, 3222). Standard Pub.

--Peace Treaty with God. (Ambassadors Training Program Ser.). 16p. (Orig.). 1984. pap. 0.50 (ISBN 0-87239-814-5, 3223). Standard Pub.

Hendrix, Olan. Management for the Christian Leader. 1986. text ed. 8.95 (ISBN 0-8010-4313-1). Baker Bk.

Henkelmann, Ervin F. & Carter, Stephen J. How to Develop a Team Ministry & Make It Work. 1985. pap. 8.95 (ISBN 0-570-03946-0, 12-2879). Concordia.

Hepburn, Daisy. Look, You're a Leader. LC 85-19637. 284p. 1985. pap. write for info. (ISBN 0-8307-1098-1, 5418647); resource manual avail. (ISBN 0-8307-1074-4, 5203023). Regal.

Hermansen, Janet. On the Crest of the Wave: Leader's Guide. LC 83-8616. 64p. 1985. pap. 3.95 (ISBN 0-8307-1010-8, 6101974). Regal.

Hughes, R. Kent. Living on the Cutting Edge: Joshua & the Challenge of Spiritual Leadership. LC 86-72055. 176p. (Orig.). 1987. pap. 6.95 (ISBN 0-89107-414-7, Crossway Bks). Good News.

Hunter, Kent R. Your Church Has Personality. Schaller, Lyle E., ed. (Creative Leadership Ser.). 129p. (Orig.). 1985. pap. 6.95 (ISBN 0-687-46875-2). Abingdon.

Index to Leaders of Iberian Christianity. 1.00 (ISBN 0-686-23370-0). Classical Folia.

Johnson, Thomas C. The Life of Robert Lewis Dabney. 1977. 16.95 (ISBN 0-85151-253-4). Banner of Truth.

Jones, Judie. Succeeding as a Woman in Music Leadership. LC 83-7249. 202p. (Orig.). 1983. pap. text ed. 8.95 perfect binding (ISBN 0-912801-00-X). Creat Arts Dev.

Jones, Stephen D. Transforming Discipleship in the Inclusive Church. 160p. 1984. pap. 6.95 (ISBN 0-8170-1049-1). Judson.

Kettner, Elmer. Training for Leadership in the Church. 1.95 (ISBN 0-933350-09-0). Morse Pr.

Kilinski, Kenneth & Wolfert, Jerry. Organization & Leadership in the Local Church. 14.95 (ISBN 0-310-26810-9, 18132). Zondervan.

Korth, Bob, ed. Membership. (Discipleship Booklets Ser.). (Illus.). 1984. 0.95 (ISBN 0-87239-788-2, 1152). Standard Pub.

Krutza, William J. Leader's Guide to Facing the Issues, No. 3 & 4. (Contemporary Discussion Ser.). pap. 1.95 (ISBN 0-8010-5387-0). Baker Bk.

Kuhn, Barbara. The Whole Lay Ministry Catalog. (Orig.). 1979. pap. 8.95 (ISBN 0-8164-2187-0, HarpR). Har-Row.

Larson, Jim. Caring Enough to Hear & Be Heard: Leader's Guide. LC 82-403. (Caring Enough Ser.). 1984. pap. 3.95 (ISBN 0-8307-0994-0, 6101948). Regal.

--When Enough Is Enough. LC 84-11644. (Caring Enough Ser.). 64p. 1985. pap. 3.95 (ISBN 0-8307-0987-8, 6101872). Regal.

Larson, Jim & Feldmeth, Joanne. Your Spiritual Gifts Can Help Your Church Grow. 64p. 1985. pap. 3.95 (ISBN 0-8307-1008-6, 6101951). Regal.

Leas, Speed B. Leadership & Conflict. (Creative Leadership Ser.). 128p. (Orig.). 1982. pap. 7.50 (ISBN 0-687-21264-2). Abingdon.

Lefroy, William. Church Leaders in Primitive Times. 1977. lib. bdg. 69.95 (ISBN 0-8490-1628-2). Gordon Pr.

Le Peau, Andrew T. Paths of Leadership. LC 82-23221. 132p. (Orig.). 1983. pap. 3.95 (ISBN 0-87784-806-8). Inter-Varsity.

Lythgoe, Dennis L. The Sensitive Leader. 1986. text ed. 9.95 (ISBN 0-87579-061-5). Deseret Bk.

McCarty, C. Barry. A Parliamentary Guide for Church Leaders. 1987. pap. 6.95 (ISBN 0-8054-3116-0). Broadman.

Mackenzie, Robert. John Brown of Haddington. 1964. pap. 2.95 (ISBN 0-85151-113-9). Banner of Truth.

Mangham, Evelyn. Great Missionaries in a Great Work. Schroeder, E. H., ed. (Illus.). 85p. 1970. pap. 1.75 (ISBN 0-87509-091-5). Chr Pubns.

Marique, J. M., ed. Leaders of Iberian Christianity. 5.00 (ISBN 0-686-23369-7). Classical Folia.

Michno, Dennis G. A Priest's Handbook: The Ceremonies of the Church. LC 81-84716. (Illus.). 304p. 1983. 32.50 (ISBN 0-8192-1300-4). Morehouse.

Miller, Herbert. Tools for Active Christians. LC 79-14795. (P.A.C.E. Ser.). (Orig.). 1979. pap. 6.95 (ISBN 0-8272-3624-7). CBP.

Moore, Charles. The Exercise of Church Leadership. 1976. pap. 2.75 (ISBN 0-88027-032-2). Firm Foun Pub.

--Functioning Leadership in the Church. 1973. pap. 2.75 (ISBN 0-88027-034-9). Firm Foun Pub.

Morgan, Edward. John Elias: Life & Letters. 1973. 13.95 (ISBN 0-85151-174-0). Banner of Truth.

Msgr. Josemaria Escriva de Balaguer: A Profile of the Founder of Opus Dei. 360p. 1977. 14.95 (ISBN 0-933932-31-6); pap. 6.95 large ed. (ISBN 0-933932-30-8); small ed. 4.95 (ISBN 0-933932-34-0). Scepter Pubs.

Muck, Terry. When to Take a Risk. (Leadership Library). 175p. 1987. 9.95 (ISBN 0-917463-12-9). Chr Today.

Murphey, Cecil B. When in Doubt, Hug 'em: How to Develop a Caring Church. LC 77-15751. 1978. 5.95 (ISBN 0-8042-1890-0). John Knox.

Ng, David. Developing Leaders for Youth Ministry. 64p. 1984. pap. 5.95 (ISBN 0-8170-1032-7). Judson.

Parker, Margaret. Love, Acceptance & Forgiveness: Leader's Guide. LC 79-63763. 128p. 1984. pap. 3.95 (ISBN 0-8307-0989-4, 6101895). Regal.

--When You Feel Like a Failure. (Study & Grow Electives). 64p. 1985. pap. 3.95 leader's guide (ISBN 0-8307-1036-1, 6102073). Regal.

Perkins, Aeschliman. The Man Who Cried Justice. 1987. pap. 5.95 (ISBN 0-8307-1075-2, 5418545). Regal.

Peterson, Eugene, et al. Weddings, Funerals, Special Events. (Leadership Library). 175p. 1987. 9.95 (ISBN 0-917463-13-7). Chr Today.

Powers, Bruce P. Christian Leadership. LC 78-72841. 1979. 8.50 (ISBN 0-8054-3227-2). Broadman.

Resources for Christian Leaders. 1982. 1982. 2.50 (ISBN 0-912552-23-9). World Vision Intl.

Richards, Lawrence O. & Hoeldtke, Clyde. A Theology of Church Leadership. (Illus.). 352p. 1980. 17.95 (ISBN 0-310-31960-9, 18136). Zondervan.

Richardson, John. Caring Enough to Confront. LC 73-83400. (Caring Enough Ser.). 1984. pap. 3.95 (ISBN 0-8307-0990-8, 6101903). Regal.

Rickerson, Wayne. Family Fun Times: Activities That Bind Marriages, Build Families, & Develop Christian Leaders. 80p. Date not set. pap. 7.95 (ISBN 0-87403-207-5, 3187). Standard Pub.

Routley, Erik & Young, Carlton R. Music Leadership in the Church. 136p. 1985. pap. text ed. 6.95 (ISBN 0-916642-24-0). Agape IL.

Russell, Robert L. The Making of a Leader. 256p. 1987. pap. price not set (ISBN 0-87403-267-9, 3181). Standard Pub.

St. Clair, Barry. Leadership. 1984. pap. 9.95 (ISBN 0-88207-193-9). Victor Bks.

Sanders, J. Oswald. Spiritual Leadership. 5th ed. 1986. text ed. 9.95 (ISBN 0-8024-8246-5). Moody.

Schaller, Lyle E. Getting Things Done: Concepts & Skills for Leaders. 144p. (Orig.). 1986. pap. 10.95 (ISBN 0-687-14142-7). Abingdon.

Scipione, George C. Timothy, Titus & You: A Workbook for Church Leaders. 96p. 1986. pap. 3.95 (ISBN 0-87552-439-7). Presby & Reformed.

Shawchuck, Norman. How to Be a More Effective Church Leader: A Special Edition for Pastors & Other Church Leaders. (Illus.). 69p. 1981. pap. 9.95 (ISBN 0-938180-07-X). Org Resources Pr.

--How to be a More Effective Church Leader: A Special Edition for Pastors & Other Church Leaders. Orig. Title: Taking a Look at Your Leadership Styles. (Illus.). 69p. 1981. pap. 9.95 (ISBN 0-938180-07-X). Spiritual Growth.

--How to Manage Conflict in the Church: Conflict Interventions & Resources, Vol. II. (Illus.). 51p. (Orig.). 1983. pap. 9.95 (ISBN 0-938180-11-8). Org Resources Pr.

--How to Manage Conflict in the Church: Understanding & Managing Conflict, Vol. I. (Illus.). 51p. (Orig.). 1983. pap. 9.95 (ISBN 0-938180-10-X). Org Resources Pr.

--What It Means to Be a Church Leader: A Biblical Point of View. (Illus.). 71p. (Orig.). 1984. pap. 7.95 (ISBN 0-938180-13-4). Org Resources Pr.

Shawchuck, Norman & Lindgren, Alvin J. Management for Your Church: How to Realize Your Church's Potential Through a Systems Approach. (Illus.). 160p. 1985. pap. 8.95 (ISBN 0-938180-14-2). Org Resources Pr.

Shelley, Marshall. Helping Those Who Don't Want Help. (Leadership Library). 175p. 1986. 9.95 (ISBN 0-917463-10-2). Chr Today.

Slater, Michael & Nachtrieb, Eric. Stretcher Bearers. 64p. 1985. pap. 3.95 (ISBN 0-8307-1056-6, 6102137). Regal.

Smith, Fred. Learning to Lead. (Leadership Library). 182p. 1986. write for info. (ISBN 0-917463-08-0). Chr Today.

Somervill, Charles. Leadership Strategies for Ministers. Cummings, H. Wayland, ed. LC 86-26788. 132p. (Orig.). 1987. pap. 8.95 (ISBN 0-664-24062-3). Westminster.

Staton, Knofel. Discovering My Gifts for Service. rev. ed. 48p. 1984. 2.50 (ISBN 0-87239-810-2, 39978). Standard Pub.

--God's Plan for Church Leadership. LC 82-3378. 160p. (Orig.). 1982. pap. 5.95 (ISBN 0-87239-566-9, 39987). Standard Pub.

Steele, David A. Images of Leadership & Authority for the Church: Biblical Principles & Secular Models. LC 86-24589. 206p. (Orig.). 1987. lib. bdg. 23.50 (ISBN 0-8191-5710-4); pap. text ed. 13.25 (ISBN 0-8191-5711-2). U Pr of Amer.

Stone, Sam E. How to be an Effective Church Leader. (Illus.). 96p. 1987. pap. price not set (ISBN 0-87403-268-7, 3182). Standard Pub.

Stoppe, Richard L. Leadership Communication. 254p. (Orig.). 1982. pap. text ed. 5.95 (ISBN 0-87148-519-2). Pathway Pr.

Strauch, Alexander. Biblical Eldership: An Urgent Call to Restore Biblical Church Leadership. 425p. 1986. 12.95 (ISBN 0-936083-00-X). Lewis-Roth.

Sweetser, Thomas P. & Holden, Carol W. Leadership in a Successful Parish. LC 86-45386. 160p. 1986. pap. 8.95 (ISBN 0-86683-517-2, RD 569, HarpR). Har-Row.

Swindoll, Charles. Hand Me Another Brick: Principles of Effective Leadership: How to Motivate Yourself & Others. LC 78-4170. 1978. pap. 6.95 (ISBN 0-8407-5650-X). Nelson.

Thompson, Bernard. Good Samaritan Faith: A Strategy for Meeting Needs in Your Community. LC 83-24805. 210p. 1984. pap. 6.95 (ISBN 0-8307-0932-0, 5418176). Regal.

Thompson, Paul M. & Lillevold, Joani. The Giving Book: Creative Resources for Senior High Ministry. LC 84-47794. (Illus.). 144p. (Orig.). 1985. pap. 9.95 (ISBN 0-8042-1192-2). John Knox.

Trout, Janet & Walter, Diane. Reflections of Success. 1984. pap. 5.95 (ISBN 0-912315-81-4). Word Aflame.

Tyler, Bennet & Bonar, Andrew. The Life & Labours of Asahel Nettleton. 1975. 10.95 (ISBN 0-85151-208-9). Banner of Truth.

Underwood, Jon. Check Your Homelife: Leader's Guide. 64p. (Orig.). pap. 2.95 (ISBN 0-87239-759-9, 39963). Standard Pub.

--Check Your Morality: Leader's Guide. 48p. (Orig.). 1984. pap. 2.95 (ISBN 0-87239-760-2, 39961). Standard Pub.

--Triumph over Temptation: Leader's Guide. 48p. (Orig.). 1984. pap. 2.95 (ISBN 0-87239-790-4, 39977). Standard Pub.

Ward, J. Neville. The Following Plough: Meditations on Prayer. LC 84-71179. 128p. 1984. pap. 6.00 (ISBN 0-936384-18-2). Cowley Pubns.

White, John. Excellence in Leadership. LC 86-2938. 132p. (Orig.). 1986. pap. 5.95 (ISBN 0-87784-570-0). Inter-Varsity.

Whitehead, James D. & Whitehead, Evelyn E. Emerging Laity: Returning Leadership to the Community of Faith. LC 85-31201. 240p. 1986. 15.95 (ISBN 0-385-23612-3). Doubleday.

Yeakley, Flavil. Church Leadership & Organization. pap. 5.95 (ISBN 0-317-47145-7). Gospel Advocate.

Youssef, Michael. The Leadership Style of Jesus. 168p. 1986. pap. 5.95 (ISBN 0-89693-168-4). Victor Bks.

Zunkel, C. Wayne. Growing the Small Church: A Guide for Church Leaders. 109p. 1982. tchr's. ed. 12.95 (ISBN 0-89191-952-X). Cook.

--Growing the Small Church: A Guide for Church Members. 120p. 1984. pap. text ed. 2.95 (ISBN 0-89191-951-1). Cook.

CHRISTIAN LEGENDS

see Legends, Christian

CHRISTIAN LIFE

see also Asceticism; Christian Education; Christian Ethics; Conduct of Life; Conversion; Devotional Exercises; Faith; Family–Religious Life; Monastic and Religious Life; Monastic and Religious Life of Women; Peace of Mind; Perfection; Piety; Prayer; Revivals; Sanctification; Spiritual Life; Stewardship, Christian

also subdivision Religious Life under classes of persons and institutions, e.g. Children–Religious Life

Aaseng, Nathan. I'm Learning, Lord, but I Still Need Help: Story Devotions for Boys. LC 81-65652. 112p. (Orig.). 1981. pap. 3.95 (ISBN 0-8066-1888-4, 10-3202). Augsburg.

Abdu, Hani R. The True Christian Science. 64p. 1981. 5.00 (ISBN 0-682-49632-4). Exposition Pr FL.

Ackland, Donald F., et al. Broadman Comments, October-December 1987. (Orig.). 1987. pap. 2.50 (ISBN 0-8054-1557-2). Broadman.

Adams, Harry B. What Jesus Asks: Meditations on Questions in the Gospels. Lambert, Herbert, ed. LC 85-18991. 160p. (Orig.). 1986. pap. 10.95 (ISBN 0-8272-4217-4). CBP.

Adams, James E. Three to Win. LC 77-72255. (Radiant Life Ser.). 125p. pap. 2.50 (ISBN 0-88243-906-5, 02-0906); tchr's ed 3.95 (ISBN 0-88243-176-5, 32-0176). Gospel Pub.

Adams, Jay. The Biblical View of Self-Esteem, Self-Love & Self-Image. 1986. pap. 5.95 (ISBN 0-89081-553-4). Harvest Hse.

Adams, Jay E. Christian Counselor's Casebook. (Companion Vol. to Christian Counselor's Manual). 1976. pap. 5.95 (ISBN 0-8010-0075-0). Baker Bk.

--Christian Living in the Home. 1974. pap. 3.95 (ISBN 0-8010-0052-1). Baker Bk.

--Grist from Adams' Mill. 96p. 1983. pap. 2.50 (ISBN 0-87552-079-0). Presby & Reformed.

--How to Overcome Evil. 116p. 1978. pap. 2.50 (ISBN 0-87552-022-7). Presby & Reformed.

--Shepherding God's Flock. 1979. pap. 10.95 (ISBN 0-87552-058-8). Presby & Reformed.

Adams, Jennifer K. With All My Heart. Wallace, Mary, ed. (Illus.). 104p. 1984. pap. 4.95 (ISBN 0-912315-78-4). Word Aflame.

Adams, Lane. How Come Its Taking Me So Long? (Living Studies). 156p. 1985. pap. 5.95 (ISBN 0-8423-1491-1); leader's guide 2.95 (ISBN 0-8423-1492-X). Tyndale.

Adeboye, E. A., ed. The Crucified Life. 48p. (Orig.). 1985. pap. 0.95 (ISBN 0-88144-053-1, CPS022). Christian Pub.

Adolph, Harold & Bourne, David L. Stop Making Yourself Sick. 132p. 1986. pap. 4.95 (ISBN 0-89693-325-3). Victor Bks.

Aglow Staff. Aglow in the Kitchen. 160p. 1976. 4.95 (ISBN 0-930756-21-5, 532001). Aglow Pubns.

Agudo, Philomena. Affirming the Human & the Holy. LC 79-1499. (Illus.). 101p. 1979. pap. 4.95 (ISBN 0-89571-006-4). Affirmation.

Agudo, Philomena, et al. Guilt: Issues of Emotional Living in an Age of Stress for Clergy & Religious. Kelley, Kathleen E., ed. LC 80-10747. 144p. 1980. pap. 5.00 (ISBN 0-89571-008-0). Affirmation.

Ahrens, Herman C., Jr. Feeling Good about Yourself. (Orig.). 1983. pap. 1.25 (ISBN 0-8298-0644-X). Pilgrim NY.

--Life with Your Parents. (Looking Up Ser.). 24p. 1983. pap. 1.25 booklet (ISBN 0-8298-0667-9). Pilgrim NY.

Aivanhov, Omraam M. The True Meaning of Christ's Teaching, Vol. 215. (Izvor Collection Ser.). (Illus.). 186p. (Orig.). 1984. pap. 4.95 (ISBN 2-85566-322-9). Prosveta USA.

Akeroyd, Richard H. He Made Us a Kingdom: The Principles to be Applied in Establishing Christ's Kingdon Now. 1985. 5.00 (ISBN 0-916620-79-4). Portals Pr.

Alberione, James. Living Our Commitment. 1968. 4.00 (ISBN 0-8198-4411-X); pap. 3.00 (ISBN 0-8198-4412-8). Dghtrs St Paul.

--Paschal Mystery in Christian Living. Daughters Of St. Paul, tr. LC 68-28102. (St. Paul Editions). (Illus.). 1968. 3.95 (ISBN 0-8198-0114-3); pap. 2.95 (ISBN 0-8198-0115-1). Dghtrs St Paul.

Alberione, Rev. James. Growing in Perfect Union. 1964. 3.00 (ISBN 0-8198-3019-4); pap. 2.00 (ISBN 0-8198-3020-8). Dghtrs St Paul.

Alcorn, Wallace. Momentum. (Living Studies Ser.). 128p. (Orig.). 1986. pap. 5.95 (ISBN 0-8423-4538-8); guide 2.95study (ISBN 0-8423-4539-6). Tyndale.

Aldrich, Joseph C. Secrets to Inner Beauty. LC 84-9970. 142p. 1984. pap. 5.95 (ISBN 0-88070-069-6). Multnomah.

Aldworth, Thomas. Shaping a Healthy Religion. 132p. 1985. pap. 8.95 (ISBN 0-88347-200-7). Thomas More.

Alexander, Archibald. Feathers on the Moor. facs. ed. LC 67-22050. (Essay Index Reprint Ser). 1928. 17.00 (ISBN 0-8369-0145-2). Ayer Co Pubs.

Alexander, John. Your Money or Your Life: A New Look at Jesus' View of Wealth & Power. LC 86-45010. 256p. 1986. 13.95 (ISBN 0-06-060151-5, HarpR). Har-Row.

Allchin, A. M. The World Is a Wedding: Explorations in Christian Spirituality. (Crossroad Paperback Ser.). 512p. 1982. pap. 6.95 (ISBN 0-8245-0411-9). Crossroad NY.

Allen, Charles L. Faith, Hope, & Love. 192p. 1982. pap. 5.95 (ISBN 0-8007-5096-9, Power Bks). Revell.

--God's Psychiatry. 160p. 9.95 (ISBN 0-8007-0113-5); pap. 2.95 (ISBN 0-8007-8015-9, Spire Bks); pap. 5.95 (ISBN 0-8007-5010-1, Power Bks). Revell.

--Life More Abundant. pap. 2.25 (ISBN 0-515-06412-2). Jove Pubns.

--The Secret of Abundant Living. 160p. 1980. 8.95 (ISBN 0-8007-1123-8); Spire Bks. pap. 3.50 (ISBN 0-8007-8479-0). Revell.

--Victory in the Valleys of Life. 128p. 1984. pap. 2.95 (ISBN 0-8007-8488-X, Spire Bks). Revell.

--You Are Never Alone. 160p. 1984. pap. 5.95 (ISBN 0-8007-5145-0, Power Bks). Revell.

Allen, Diogenes. Love: Christian Romance, Marriage, Friendship. 149p. (Orig.). 1987. pap. 8.95 (ISBN 0-936384-47-6). Cowley Pubns.

--The Traces of God in a Frequently Hostile World. LC 80-51570. 108p. (Orig.). 1981. pap. 6.00 (ISBN 0-936384-03-4). Cowley Pubns.

Allen, Richard. The Life Experience & Gospel Labors of the Rt. Rev. Richard Allen. 96p. (Orig.). 1983. pap. 3.95 (ISBN 0-687-21844-6). Abingdon.

Allen, Ruth. What's the Matter with Christy? LC 82-8036. 110p. (Orig.). 1982. pap. 3.95 (ISBN 0-87123-629-X, 210629). Bethany Hse.

Allphin, McKay. Eternal Grit: Up-to-Heaven Insights & Down-to-Earth Wisdom. LC 78-70363. 138p. 1978. 7.95 (ISBN 0-88290-102-8). Horizon Utah.

Almand, Joan & Wooderson, Joy. Establishing Values. LC 76-17147. 1976. pap. 1.99 (ISBN 0-87148-283-5). Pathway Pr.

Alton, Wright. The Third Eye, Book I. (The Third Eye Bks.). (Illus.). 160p. (Orig.). Date not set. pap. 10.95. Creat Gospel Prod A Wright.

Always Growing. (Benziger Family Life Program Ser.). 8p. 1978. 3.00 (ISBN 0-02-651850-3); tchrs. ed. 4.15 (ISBN 0-02-651860-0); family handbook 1.80 (ISBN 0-02-651890-2). Benziger Pub Co.

Amatora, Sr. Mary. The Queen's Heart of Gold: The Complete Story of Our Lady of Beauraing. LC 78-188443. 1972. 7.50 (ISBN 0-682-47467-3, Banner); pap. 5.00 (ISBN 0-682-47480-0, Banner). Exposition Pr FL.

Amen, Carol. Teetering on the Tightrope. LC 79-18718. (Orion Ser.). 1979. pap. 2.95 (ISBN 0-8127-0250-6). Review & Herald.

Ames, William. Conscience with the Power & Cases Thereof. LC 74-28826. (English Experience Ser.: No. 708). 1975. Repr. of 1639 ed. 35.00 (ISBN 9-0221-0708-6). Walter J Johnson.

Andersen, Linda. Slices of Life. 112p. 1986. pap. 6.95 (ISBN 0-8010-0205-2). Baker Bk.

Anderson. The Lakeside Story. LC 86-70041. (Illus.). 242p. 1986. 12.50 (ISBN 0-87483-010-9). August Hse.

--Teach What You Preach. 1982. pap. 8.95 (ISBN 0-8298-0481-1). Pilgrim NY.

Anderson, Arthur W. Wild Beasts & Angels. 1979. pap. 4.50 (ISBN 0-910452-43-1). Covenant.

Anderson, C. Alan. God in a Nutshell. (Illus.). 28p. (Orig.). 1981. pap. 3.00 (ISBN 0-9607532-0-6). Squantum Pr.

Anderson, Don. Abraham: Delay Is Not Denial. (Kingfisher Ser.). 200p. 1987. pap. 6.95 (ISBN 0-87213-000-2). Loizeaux.

Anderson, Elaine. With God's Help Flowers Bloom. 1978. pap. 4.95 (ISBN 0-89137-411-6); study guide 2.85 (ISBN 0-89137-412-4). Quality Pubns.

Anderson, Paul. Building Christian Character. (Trinity Teen Curriculum Ser.). 48p. 1984. Repr. student wkbk. 3.95 (ISBN 0-87123-436-X, 210436); tchr's. guide 4.95 (ISBN 0-87123-430-0). Bethany Hse.

Anderson, William. Journeying in His Light. 160p. 1982. wire coil 4.95 (ISBN 0-697-01858-X). Wm C Brown.

Anderson, William A. In His Light. 1985. pap. 5.75 (ISBN 0-697-02111-4). Wm C Brown.

Andrews, Elsie M. Facing & Fulfilling the Later Years. LC 68-16318. (Orig.). 1968. pap. 2.50x (ISBN 0-87574-157-6). Pendle Hill.

Andrews, Gini. A Violent Grace. 112p. 1987. pap. 4.95 (ISBN 0-310-20131-4). Zondervan.

Anthony, Susan B. Sidewalk Contemplatives: A Spirituality for Concerned Christians. 160p. (Orig.). 1987. pap. 8.95 (ISBN 0-8245-0795-9). Crossroad NY.

Apel, William D. Witnesses Before Dawn. 1984. pap. 6.95 (ISBN 0-8170-1031-9). Judson.

Arbuckle, Gerald A. Strategies for Growth in Religious Life. LC 86-17359. 240p. (Orig.). 1986. pap. 11.95 (ISBN 0-8189-0505-0). Alba.

Are, Thomas L. The Gospel for the Clockaholic. 128p. 1985. pap. 5.95 (ISBN 0-8170-1075-0). Judson.

Are You Fun to Live With? Whiston, Lionel. 143p. 1985. lib. bdg. 11.95 (ISBN 0-938736-13-2); pap. 3.95 (ISBN 0-938736-14-0). Life Enrich.

Aridas, Chris. Discernment: Seeking God in Every Situation. 120p. (Orig.). 1981. pap. 3.50 (ISBN 0-914544-37-3). Living Flame Pr.

Arienda, Roger & Roque, Marichelle. Libre Dentro de la Carcel. (Span.). 176p. 1986. pap. 2.95 (ISBN 0-311-46102-6). Casa Bautista.

Armbruster, Wally. Let Me Out: I'm a Prisoner in a Stained Glass Jail. LC 85-11561. 1985. pap. 6.95 (ISBN 0-88070-111-0). Multnomah.

Armstrong, Larry. Disaster & Deliverance. LC 79-88400. 1979. pap. 3.75 (ISBN 0-933350-22-8). Morse Pr.

Armstrong, Terry R., ed. Planning to Stay Together. Armstrong, Anne. 1980. pap. 1.99 (ISBN 0-8309-0308-9). Herald Hse.

Arndt, Rick. Winning with Christ. 1982. pap. 4.95 (ISBN 0-570-03627-5, 39-1073). Concordia.

Arnold, Eberhard. Living Churches: The Essence of Their Life - the Meaning & Power of Prayer Life, Vol. 2. LC 75-42829. 1976. pap. 2.50 (ISBN 0-87486-159-4). Plough.

--Revolution Gottes. 110p. 1984. pap. 7.00 (ISBN 3-87173-689-9). Plough.

Arnold, Heini. Freedom from Sinful Thoughts: Christ Alone Breaks the Curse. LC 73-20199. 130p. 1973. 3.50 (ISBN 0-87486-115-2). Plough.

--Give Us Burning Hearts. 36p. 1985. pap. 1.50 (ISBN 0-87486-196-9). Plough.

--Lead Us on the Way. 36p. 1985. pap. 1.50 (ISBN 0-87486-194-2). Plough.

--Make Us Ready. 36p. 1985. pap. 1.50 (ISBN 0-87486-198-5). Plough.

--May the Light Shine. 36p. 1985. pap. 1.50 (ISBN 0-87486-197-7). Plough.

--Thine Is the Kingdom. 36p. 1985. pap. 1.50 (ISBN 0-87486-182-9). Plough.

--Thou Art the Vine. 36p. 1985. pap. 1.50 (ISBN 0-87486-178-0). Plough.

--We Are Thy Children. 36p. 1985. pap. 1.50 (ISBN 0-87486-193-4). Plough.

Arnold, John D. & Tompkins, Bert. How to Make the Right Decisions. 1986. pap. 5.95 (ISBN 0-8010-0209-5). Baker Bk.

Arnold, William V. The Power of Your Perceptions. LC 83-26089. (Potentials: Guides for Productive Living Ser.,: Vol. 6). 118p. (Orig.). 1984. pap. 7.95 (ISBN 0-664-24524-2). Westminster.

Arp, Dave & Arp, Claudia. Ten Dates for Mates. LC 83-3954. 176p. 1983. pap. 7.95 (ISBN 0-8407-5845-6). Nelson.

Arrupe, Pedro. Justice with Faith Today: Selected Letters & Addresses--II. Aixala, Jerome, ed. LC 80-81055. 336p. 1980. 8.00 (ISBN 0-912422-51-3); pap. 7.00 smyth sewn (ISBN 0-912422-50-5). Inst Jesuit.

Arthur, Kay. Teach Me How to Live. 384p. (Orig.). 1983. pap. 6.95 (ISBN 0-8007-5125-6, Power Bks). Revell.

Aschenbrenner, George. A God for a Dark Journey. 1984. pap. 5.95 (ISBN 0-87193-211-3). Dimension Bks.

Ash, Anthony L. Decide to Love. LC 80-80294. (Journey Bks.). 140p. (Orig.). 1980. pap. 3.50 (ISBN 0-8344-0116-9). Sweet.

Ashcraft, Nancy. At the Scent of Water. 1986. pap. 4.95 (ISBN 0-87508-049-9). Chr Lit.

Ashton, Marvin J. What Is Your Destination? LC 78-14982. 1978. 8.95 (ISBN 0-87747-719-1). Deseret Bk.

Associated Women's Organization, Mars Hill Bible School. What Are We Doing Here? 1972. pap. 4.95 (ISBN 0-89137-404-3). Quality Pubns.

Atkins, Stanley & McConnell, Theodore, eds. Churches on the Wrong Road. 270p. (Orig.). 1986. pap. 7.95 (ISBN 0-89526-803-5). Regnery Bks.

Aubry, Joseph. The Renewal of Our Salesian Life, 2 vols. Bedard, Paul & Whitehead, Kenneth, trs. from Ital. LC 84-70210. Orig. Title: Rinnovare la Nostra Vita Salesiana. 426p. 1984. pap. text ed. write for info. (ISBN 0-89944-071-1); Vol. I:The Active Apostolate. pap. 5.00; Vol. II:The Salesian Community & Family. pap. 5.50 (ISBN 0-89944-077-0). Don Bosco Multimedia.

Auer, Jim. For Teens Only: Straight Talk about Parents - Life - Love. 64p. 1985. pap. 1.95 (ISBN 0-89243-228-4). Liguori Pubns.

--What's Right? A Teenager's Guide to Christian Living. 96p. 1987. pap. 3.25 (ISBN 0-89243-265-9). Liguori Pubns.

Augsburger, David. Caring Enough to Confront. rev. ed. LC 73-83400. 144p. 1980. pap. 5.95 (ISBN 0-8307-0733-6, 5411602). Regal.

--From Here to Maturity. 1982. pap. 2.50 (ISBN 0-8423-0938-1). Tyndale.

Augsburger, David W. Like Falling in Love. (New Life Ser.). pap. 3.00 (ISBN 0-8361-1686-0). Herald Pr.

--What Do You Want? (New Life Ser.). pap. 3.00 (ISBN 0-8361-1688-7). Herald Pr.

Austin, Bill. How to Get What You Pray For. LC 83-50970. 160p. 1984. pap. 4.95 (ISBN 0-8423-1473-3); leader's guide 2.95 (ISBN 0-8423-1474-1). Tyndale.

--When God Has Put You on Hold. 112p. 1986. pap. 4.95 (ISBN 0-8423-7989-4). Tyndale.

Away in a Manger. (Illus.). 1987. 6.95 (ISBN 0-570-04166-X). Concordia.

Aycock, Don M. Walking Straight in a Crooked World. (Orig.). 1987. pap. 3.25 (ISBN 0-8054-5034-3). Broadman.

Baba, Meher. The Face of God. (Illus.). 28p. pap. 1.75 (ISBN 0-913078-00-X). Sheriar Pr.

Babris, Janina. In Human Touch. 17p. 1976. 5.95 (ISBN 0-912414-20-0). Lumen Christi.

Bach, Marcus. The Unity Way. LC 82-50085. 387p. 1982. 5.95 (ISBN 0-87159-164-2). Unity School.

Bacher, June Masters. A Mother's Joy. 128p. 1984. pap. 6.95 6x (ISBN 0-89081-415-5). Harvest Hse.

Bachman, John W. Media-Wasteland Or Wonderland: Opportunities & Dangers for Christians in the Electronic Age. LC 84-24319. 176p. (Orig.). 1984. pap. 7.95 (ISBN 0-8066-2116-8, 10-4307). Augsburg.

Backus, William & Chapian, Marie. Telling Yourself the Truth. LC 80-10136. 41p. (Orig.). 1980. pap. 5.95 (ISBN 0-87123-562-5, 210562); study guide 2.50 (ISBN 0-87123-567-6, 210567). Bethany Hse.

--Why Do I Do What I Don't Want to Do? LC 84-6336. 144p. 1984. pap. 4.95 (ISBN 0-87123-625-7, 210625). Bethany Hse.

Bacon, Daniel W. From Faith to Faith. 1984. pap. 5.95 (ISBN 9971-972-03-4). OMF Bks.

Baden, Robert. How to Understand Your Parents & Maybe Like the Ones You Love. 1987. pap. 4.95 (ISBN 0-570-04467-7). Concordia.

Bagster, Samuel. Daily Light. 1985. Repr. of 1975 ed. 6.95 (ISBN 0-916441-09-1). Barbour & Co.

Bailey, James. The Happy Hour. 1985. 6.95 (ISBN 0-89536-750-5, 5856). CSS of Ohio.

Bailey, Ney. Faith Is Not a Feeling. LC 78-60077. 1979. pap. 4.95 (ISBN 0-918956-45-5). Campus Crusade.

Bailey, Richard D. Estate Planning: A Workbook for Christians. LC 81-14907. 96p. (Orig.). 1982. pap. 7.75 (ISBN 0-687-12004-7). Abingdon.

Bailey, Waylon. As You Go. LC 81-47888. 118p. (Orig.). 1981. pap. 4.00 (ISBN 0-914520-15-6). Insight Pr.

Baillie, Donald M. God Was in Christ. 230p. 1980. pap. text ed. write for info. (ISBN 0-02-305440-9, Pub. by Scribner). Macmillan.

Baily, Keith M. Care of Converts. 95p. (Orig.). 1979. pap. 1.50 (ISBN 0-87509-156-3); leader's guide 0.75 (ISBN 0-87509-157-1). Chr Pubns.

Baird, J. Arthur. Rediscovering the Power of the Gospel: Jesus' Theology of the Kingdom. LC 82-83623. 1982. pap. 9.95 (ISBN 0-910789-00-2). Iona Pr.

Baker, Alonzo. My Sister Alma & I. (Daybreak Ser.). 1981. pap. 4.50 (ISBN 0-8163-0373-8). Pacific Pr Pub Assn.

Baker, Bo. The Lift of Love. 1986. 7.95 (ISBN 0-8054-5039-4). Broadman.

Baker, Don. Pain's Hidden Purpose: Finding Perspective in the Midst of Suffering. LC 83-22135. 1984. pap. 5.95 (ISBN 0-88070-035-1). Multnomah.

Bakker, Jim. Eight Keys to Success. LC 79-92249. 128p. 1980. pap. 2.50 (ISBN 0-89221-071-0). New Leaf.

Bakker, Tammy & Dudley, Cliff. Run to the Roar. LC 80-80656. 142p. 1980. 7.95 (ISBN 0-89221-073-7). New Leaf.

Balch, Dianne. All Joy. LC 82-72303. 169p. 1982. pap. 5.95 (ISBN 0-86605-098-1). Here's Life.

Baldwin, Stanley C. How to Build Your Own Christian Character. 1982. pap. 4.95 (ISBN 0-88207-271-4). Victor Bks.

Ball, Judy & Danich, John. The Brain, the Soul, God. 174p. 1986. pap. 6.95 (ISBN 0-88144-064-7). Christian Pub.

Ballenger, A. F. A Believer's Guide to Christian Maturity. LC 82-72493. 256p. 1982. pap. 4.95 (ISBN 0-87123-278-2, 210278). Bethany Hse.

Baly, Denis & Rhodes, Royal W. The Faith of Christians. LC 84-47914. 256p. 1984. pap. 14.95 (ISBN 0-8006-1790-8). Fortress.

Banas, Jackie. I Love Me, the Only Diet There Is: A Manual. (Orig.). 1986. spiral bdg. 7.00 (ISBN 0-9614014-3-5). Know Him Pr.

--Reflections in Righteousness. (Illus.). 56p. (Orig.). 1985. 5.00 (ISBN 0-9614014-2-7). Know Him Pr.

Banks, Bill. Alive Again! 168p. (Orig.). 1977. pap. 3.95 (ISBN 0-89228-048-4). Impact Bks MO.

Banks, Martha. The Call of Jesus: Lessons in Becoming His Disciple. rev. ed. (Bible Study: Basic Ser.). 64p. (Orig.). pap. 2.95 (ISBN 0-932305-28-8, 521009). Aglow Pubns.

Banks, Robert. The Tyranny of Time. LC 84-28855. 265p. 1985. pap. 6.95 (ISBN 0-87784-338-4). Inter-Varsity.

Barclay, Oliver R. The Intellect & Beyond: Developing a Christian Mind. 144p. (Orig.). 1985. pap. 6.95 (ISBN 0-310-33291-5, 12280P). Zondervan.

Barclay, William. The Promise of the Spirit. LC 60-11200. 120p. 1978. pap. 6.95 (ISBN 0-664-24205-7). Westminster.

Barin. Jesus Came to Me. 2nd rev. ed. LC 86-60047. (Illus.). 150p. (Orig.). 1986. Repr. of 1973 ed. 17.95 (ISBN 0-935075-06-2). Sri Aurobindo.

Barker, Raymond C. The Science of Successful Living. LC 57-11392. 145p. 1984. pap. 5.50 (ISBN 0-87516-536-2). De Vorss.

Barnett, Timothy L. & Flora, Steven R. Exploring God's Web of Life. 80p. 1982. pap. 5.25 (ISBN 0-942684-01-X). Camp Guidepts.

Barney, Kenneth D. A Faith to Live by. LC 76-27929. (Radiant Life Ser.). 128p. 1977. pap. 2.50 (ISBN 0-88243-899-9, 02-0899); teacher's ed. 3.95 (ISBN 0-88243-171-4, 32-0171). Gospel Pub.

--If You Love Me... LC 75-22611. (Radiant Life Ser.). 128p. 1977. pap. 2.50 (ISBN 0-88243-889-1, 02-0889); teacher's ed 3.95 (ISBN 0-88243-163-3, 32-0163). Gospel Pub.

--It Began in an Upper Room. LC 78-67445. 128p. 1978. pap. 1.50 (ISBN 0-88243-528-0, 02-0528, Radiant Bks). Gospel Pub.

Barrett, Ethel & Parker, Peggy. Will the Real Phony Please Stand up? rev. ed. LC 84-17777. 224p. 1984. pap. 4.95 (ISBN 0-8307-1001-9, 5418383); Leader's Guide 3.95 (ISBN 0-8307-1009-4, 6101966). Regal.

Barrett, Lois. The Way God Fights. (Peace & Justice Ser.: No. 1). 96p. (Orig.). 1987. pap. 4.95 (ISBN 0-8361-3445-1). Herald Pr.

Barsuhn, Rochelle. Sometimes I Feel. LC 85-10351. (Illus.). 32p. 1985. PLB 4.95 (ISBN 0-89693-228-1). Dandelion Hse.

Barth, Karl. The Christian Life. Bromiley, Geoffrey W., ed. LC 80-39942. 328p. 1981. 17.95 (ISBN 0-8028-3523-6). Eerdmans.

--The Doctrine of Reconciliation: The Christian Life. Bromiley, G. W. & Torrance, T. F., eds. Bromiley, G. W., tr. from Ger. (Church Dogmatics Ser.: Vol. 4, Pt. 4). 240p. 1969. 19.95 (ISBN 0-567-09045-0, Pub. by T & T Clark Ltd UK). Fortress.

Bartlett, Bob. Power Pack. LC 85-16841. 100p. 1985. pap. 4.95 (ISBN 0-89221-124-5). New Leaf.

Barton, Bruce. The Man Nobody Knows. 128p. 1987. pap. 5.95 (ISBN 0-02-083620-1, Collier). Macmillan.

Bascio, Patrick. Building a Just Society. LC 80-27238. 176p. (Orig.). 1981. pap. 5.95 (ISBN 0-88344-205-1). Orbis Bks.

Basham, Don. Face up with a Miracle. 190p. 1971. pap. 2.95 (ISBN 0-88368-002-5). Whitaker Hse.

Basler, Michael. Discipling One to One. (Pathfinder Pamphlets Ser.). 32p. (Orig.). 1986. pap. 1.95 (ISBN 0-87784-217-5). Inter-Varsity.

Bass, Charles D. Banishing Fear from Your Life. LC 85-23943. 168p. 1986. 14.95 (ISBN 0-385-23331-0). Doubleday.

Bass, George M. Plastic Flowers in the Holy Water. 1981. 4.35 (ISBN 0-89536-480-8, 1605). CSS of Ohio.

Bassett, Paul M. & Greathouse, William M. Exploring Christian Holiness: The Historical Development, Vol. 2. (Exploring Christian Holiness Ser.). 250p. 1984. 15.95 (ISBN 0-8341-0926-3). Beacon Hill.

Bastian, Donald N. Along the Way. 128p. 1977. pap. 3.95 (ISBN 0-89367-008-1). Light & Life.

Baughman, Ray. La Vida Abundante. Orig. Title: The Abundant Life. (Span.). 192p. 1959. pap. 3.95 (ISBN 0-8254-1056-8). Kregel.

Bauman, Louis. The Faith: Once for All Delivered unto the Saints. pap. 2.95 (ISBN 0-88469-026-1). BMH Bks.

Baur, Francis. Life in Abundance: A Contemporary Spirituality. 240p. 1983. pap. 7.95 (ISBN 0-8091-2507-2). Paulist Pr.

Baxter, J. Sidlow. Majesty! The God You Should Know. LC 84-47805. 228p. 1984. 12.95 (ISBN 0-89840-070-8). Heres Life.

Beals, Ivan A. What It Means to Forgive. (Christian Living Ser.). 32p. (Orig.). 1987. pap. write for info. (ISBN 0-8341-1185-3). Beacon Hill.

Beattie, Frank A., Jr. Coming down from the Mountain. (Orig.). 1982. pap. 1.95 (ISBN 0-937172-38-3). JLJ Pubs.

Beatty, Bill. Seven Steps Toward God. LC 85-82315. 102p. (Orig.). 1986. pap. 5.95 (ISBN 0-937779-01-6). Greenlawn Pr.

Bechtel, Faythelma. Creative Touch, No. 2. 1982. 5.50x (ISBN 0-87813-919-2). Christian Light.

Beckman, Beverly. Senses in God's World. 24p. 1986. 5.95 (ISBN 0-570-04150-3). Concordia.

Becton, Randy. The Beauty of God's Whisper. 1980. pap. 4.75 (ISBN 0-89137-310-1). Quality Pubns.

Beebe, Ralph K. A Garden of the Lord. LC 68-56609. (Illus.). 288p. 1968. 3.95 (ISBN 0-913342-13-0). Barclay Pr.

Beers. Choosing God's Way to See & Share. 1983. 12.95 (ISBN 0-88207-819-4). Victor Bks.

Beers, Richard G. Walk the Distant Hills: The Story of Longri Ao. (Bold Believers Ser.). 1969. pap. 0.95 (ISBN 0-377-84171-4). Friend Pr.

Being Alive. (Benziger Family Life Program Ser.). 3p. 1978. 3.00 (ISBN 0-02-651600-4); tchrs. ed. 4.15 (ISBN 0-02-651610-1); family handbook 1.80 (ISBN 0-02-651640-3). Benziger Pub Co.

Bell, Buddy. Faithfulness: The Crowbar of God. 47p. 1986. pap. 2.95 (ISBN 0-89274-350-6). Christian Pub.

Bender, Urie A. To Walk in the Way. LC 79-83511. 208p. 1979. pap. 5.95 (ISBN 0-8361-1884-7). Herald Pr.

Benjamin, Dick & Richardson, Jim. Remember the Poor. 1982. pap. 1.75 (ISBN 0-911739-26-2). Abbott Loop.

Benjamin, Rick & Richardson, Jim. God Is Greater. 1983. pap. 1.75 (ISBN 0-911739-00-9). Abbott Loop.

Bennett, Rita. I'm Glad You Asked That. rev. & updated ed. 160p. 1983. pap. 5.95 (ISBN 0-8007-5111-6, Power Bks). Revell.

Benson, Bob. He Speaks Softly. 160p. 1985. 8.95 (ISBN 0-8499-0449-8, 0449-8). Word Bks.

Benson, Dennis C. & Benson, Marilyn J. Promises to Keep: A Workbook of Experiences for Covenant Living. (Orig.). 1978. pap. 3.95 (ISBN 0-377-00077-9). Friend Pr.

Benson, Ezra T. Come unto Christ. 136p. 1984. 8.95 (ISBN 0-87747-997-6). Deseret Bk.

Benton, John. Sheila. 192p. 1982. pap. 2.95 (ISBN 0-8007-8419-7, New Hope Bks.). Revell.

--Stephanie. 1983. pap. 2.95 (ISBN 0-8007-8472-3, Spire Bks). Revell.

--Valarie. 192p. (Orig.). 1982. pap. 2.95 (ISBN 0-8007-8430-8, New Hope Bks.). Revell.

Benz, Larry L. Standards for Living. LC 77-70791. 1977. pap. 1.99 (ISBN 0-87148-779-9). Pathway Pr.

Berghoef, Gerard & DeKoster, Lester. The Believers Handbook. LC 82-72686. 295p. 1982. 15.95 (ISBN 0-934874-03-4); pap. 8.95 (ISBN 0-934874-05-0). Chr Lib Pr.

Bernard, Loretta A. & Bernard, David K. In Search of Holiness. 288p. (Orig.). 1981. pap. 6.95 (ISBN 0-912315-40-7). Word Aflame.

Bernard, Mary. Agony! Can the Church Survive Without Jesus? LC 79-84343. 1979. pap. 2.95 (ISBN 0-89221-059-1). New Leaf.

Bernard, Otis. Put a Little Starch in Your Faith. 150p. 1980. pap. 4.95 (ISBN 0-89221-095-8). New Leaf.

Bernardoni, Gus. Golf God's Way. LC 77-80414. 1978. 9.95 (ISBN 0-88419-144-3). Creation Hse.

Berquist, Maurice. Miracle & Power of Blessing. 1984. pap. 2.95 (ISBN 0-87162-408-7, D8556). Warner Pr.

Berry, Jo. Can You Love Yourself? LC 77-89395. 160p. 1978. pap. 4.95 (ISBN 0-8307-0579-1, 5407206). Regal.

--Managing Your Life & Time. 192p. 1986. pap. 6.95 (ISBN 0-310-34181-7). Zondervan.

Berry, John R. Good Words for New Christians. (Orig.). 1987. pap. 2.95 (ISBN 0-9616900-0-3). J R Berry.

Berry, Karen. Beyond Broken Dreams: A Scriptural Pathway to New Life. 1984. pap. 3.50 (ISBN 0-86716-034-9). St Anthony Mess Pr.

Bershadsky, Luba & Millington, Ada. I Know His Touch. 240p. 1985. pap. 2.95 (ISBN 0-345-32164-2). Ballantine.

Bertolucci, John. The Disciplines of a Disciple. 136p. (Orig.). 1985. pap. 4.95 (ISBN 0-89283-240-1). Servant.

Bess, C. W. Nothing Can Separate Us. 1986. pap. 4.95 (ISBN 0-8054-2263-3). Broadman.

Beyer, Douglas. Commandments for Christian Living. 96p. 1983. pap. 5.95 (ISBN 0-8170-1008-4). Judson.

--Parables for Christian Living. 112p. 1985. pap. 5.95 (ISBN 0-8170-1074-2). Judson.

Biblical Applications for Tjta. 5.95 (ISBN 0-317-15734-5). Chr Marriage.

Bickel, Margot & Steigert, Hermann. Harvest the Day. Frost, Gerhard E., ed. (Illus.). 64p. (Orig.). pap. 7.95 (ISBN 0-86683-730-2, HarpR). Har-Row.

Biegert. Looking Up...While Lying Down. (Looking Up Ser.). 1979. pap. 1.25 booklet (ISBN 0-8298-0364-5). Pilgrim NY.

Biegert, John E. Mirando Hacia Arriba en Medio de la Enfermedad: (Looking Up...While Lying Down) (Looking Up Ser.). (Span.). 24p. (Orig.). 1983. pap. 1.25 booklet (ISBN 0-8298-0663-6). Pilgrim NY.

--Staying in... (Looking Up Ser.). 1985. pap. 1.25 (ISBN 0-8298-0567-2). Pilgrim NY.

Biersdorf, John E. Healing of Purpose: God's Call to Discipleship. 192p. (Orig.). 1985. pap. 11.95 (ISBN 0-687-16741-8). Abingdon.

Billheimer, Paul E. Destined for the Cross. 1982. pap. 3.95 (ISBN 0-8423-0604-8). Tyndale.

--Destined to Overcome. 123p. 1982. pap. 4.95 (ISBN 0-87123-287-1, 210287). Bethany Hse.

Bills, Paul. Alaska. LC 80-65307. (Illus.). 160p. (Orig.). 1980. pap. 2.50 (ISBN 0-88243-462-4, 02-0462). Gospel Pub.

Bimler, Rich. Celebrating Saints. 80p. (Orig.). 1986. pap. 3.95 (ISBN 0-570-04440-5). Concordia.

Binford, Helaina L. Heart Song: Prophecies, Ponderings & Poetry. (Illus.). 50p. (Orig.). 1986. pap. 5.00 (ISBN 0-939313-11-1). Joshua-I-Minist.

Birch, Bruce C. & Rasmussen, Larry L. Bible & Ethics in the Christian Life. LC 76-3856. 208p. 1976. pap. 8.95 (ISBN 0-8066-1524-9, 10-0702). Augsburg.

Birkey, Verna & Turnquist, Jeanette. Building Happy Memories & Family Traditions. (Illus.). 128p. 1983. 4.95 (ISBN 0-8007-5109-4, Power Bks). Revell.

Birkinshaw, Elsye. Turn off Your Age. LC 79-27693. 1980. pap. 7.95 (ISBN 0-912800-77-1). Woodbridge Pr.

Birthday: Voices from the Heart. Date not set. price not set (ISBN 0-934383-13-8). Pride Prods.

Bisagno, John R. Life Without Compromise. LC 81-71253. 1983. 3.95 (ISBN 0-8054-1503-3). Broadman.

--Power of Positive Living. LC 70-93913. (Orig.). 1970. pap. 3.95 (ISBN 0-8054-1910-1). Broadman.

Bishop, Amelia. The Flame & the Candle. (Orig.). 1987. 7.50 (ISBN 0-8054-5033-5). Broadman.

--The Gift & the Giver. LC 84-2796. 1984. 6.25 (ISBN 0-8054-5106-4). Broadman.

Bjorkman, Adaline. While It Was Still Dark. (Illus.). 1978. pap. 3.95 (ISBN 0-910452-34-2). Covenant.

Black, Doris. Reach for Your Spiritual Potential. 1986. pap. 4.95 (ISBN 0-89137-438-8). Quality Pubns.

Blackwell, Muriel F. The Dream Lives On. LC 82-73865. 1984. 6.95 (ISBN 0-8054-4808-X, 4248-08). Broadman.

Blackwell, William & Blackwell, Muriel. Working Partners Working Parents. LC 79-51134. 1979. 5.95 (ISBN 0-8054-5637-6). Broadman.

Blaiklock, D. A., ed. Living Is Now. 1972. pap. 1.50 (ISBN 0-8010-0579-5). Baker Bk.

Blaiklock, E. M. & Keys, A. C., trs. from Ital. The Little Flowers of St. Francis. 176p. 1985. pap. 3.95 (ISBN 0-89283-300-9). Servant.

Blanch, Lord S. Way of Blessedness. 272p. 1987. pap. 3.50 (ISBN 0-345-34310-7, Pub. by Ballantine Epiphany). Ballantine.

Blanch, Stuart Y. Living by Faith. LC 84-10182. Repr. of 1984 ed. 39.00. Bks Demand UMI.

Blandford, Brian. Winners & Losers. LC 84-26709. 1985. pap. 3.95 (ISBN 0-8307-1012-4, S181422). Regal.

Blank, Richard. A Christian Passover Celebration. 1981. 2.95 (ISBN 0-89536-477-8, 0317). CSS of Ohio.

Blanton, Mary T. Knock on a Door. 32p. 1984. 4.95. Victor Bks.

Blattner, John. Growing in the Fruit of the Spirit. (Living As A Christian Ser.). 96p. 1984. pap. 3.95 (ISBN 0-89283-177-4). Servant.

Blish, James. The Tale That Wags the God. 1986. 15.00 (ISBN 0-911682-29-5). Advent.

Blitchington, Peter & Cruise, Robert J. Understanding Your Temperament: A Self-Analysis with a Christian Viewpoint. 38p. (Orig.). 1979. pap. 2.95 (ISBN 0-943872-67-7). Andrews Univ Pr.

Blitchington, W. Peter. Sex Roles & the Christian Family. 1983. pap. 5.95 (ISBN 0-8423-5896-X); leader's guide 2.95 (ISBN 0-8423-5897-8). Tyndale.

Blodgett, Ralph. How Will It End? (Eighty-Five-Miss Ser). 1984. pap. 1.19 (ISBN 0-8163-0567-6). Pacific Pr Pub Assn.

Blogg, Martin. Dance & the Christian Faith. (Illus.). 283p. 1987. pap. 17.95 (ISBN 0-340-35173-X, Pub. by Hodder & Stoughton UK). David & Charles.

Blomgren, David K. Song of the Lord. 70p. Date not set. pap. 6.95. Bible Temple.

Bloodworth, Venice. Key to Yourself. 1986. pap. 4.95 (ISBN 0-87516-296-7). De Vorss.

Boa, Kenneth & Moody, Larry. I'm Glad You Asked. 1982. pap. 6.95 (ISBN 0-88207-354-0). Victor Bks.

Boardman, W. E. The Higher Christian Life. Dayton, Donald W., ed. (Higher Christian Life Ser.). 330p. 1985. PLB 40.00 (ISBN 0-8240-6406-2). Garland Pub.

Bobgan, Deidre. Lord of the Dance: The Beauty of the Disciplined Life. 160p. (Orig.). 1987. pap. 5.95 (ISBN 0-89081-583-6). Harvest Hse.

Bobgan, Martin & Bobgan, Deidre. The Psychological Way: the Spiritual Way. LC 79-17884. 224p. 1979. pap. 6.95 (ISBN 0-87123-026-7, 210026). Bethany Hse.

Bockelman, Wilfred, ed. Tapestry. 128p. (Orig.). 1985. pap. 3.95 (ISBN 0-8066-2177-X, 10-6201). Augsburg.

Boff, Leonardo. Church, Charism, Power. 1986. pap. 10.95 (ISBN 0-8245-0726-6). Crossroad NY.

Boll, Shirley. At Every Gate a Pearl. 1986. 3.25 (ISBN 0-87813-525-1). Christian Light.

Bolten, Thomas A. Finding God in the Space Age. 1987. 14.95 (ISBN 0-533-06954-8). Vantage.

Bonar, Horatius. When God's Children Suffer. LC 80-84441. (Shepherd Illustrated Classics Ser.). (Illus.). 144p. 1981. pap. 5.95 (ISBN 0-87983-221-5). Keats.

--Words to Winners of Souls. (Summit Bks.). 1979. pap. 2.50 (ISBN 0-8010-0773-9). Baker Bk.

Bonhoeffer, Dietrich. Life Together. LC 54-6901. 128p. 1976. pap. 6.95 (ISBN 0-06-060851-X, RD292, HarpR). Har-Row.

Bonhoeffer, Dietrich, et al. The Christian Cornerstone Library: The Cost of Discipleship - Mere Christianity - Your God Is Too Small, 3 vols. 672p. 1987. Set. pap. 12.95 (ISBN 0-02-084440-9, Collier). Macmillan.

Bonifazi, Flavian. Yearning of a Soul. 1979. 4.95 (ISBN 0-8198-0614-5); pap. 3.50 (ISBN 0-8198-0615-3). Dghtrs St Paul.

Bonilla, Plutarco. Los Milagros Tambien Son Parabolas. LC 78-59240. (Span.). 166p. (Orig.). 1978. pap. 3.95 (ISBN 0-89922-114-9). Edit Caribe.

Bontrager, G. Edwin & Showalter, Nathan. It Can Happen Today. LC 86-15036. 96p. (Orig.). 1986. pap. 5.95 (ISBN 0-8361-3419-2); pap. 14.95x tchrs. manual (ISBN 0-8361-1286-5). Herald Pr.

Bontrager, Ida B. Ozark Parson. 1978. 5.55 (ISBN 0-87813-512-X). Christian Light.

Booker, Richard. Intimacy with God. LC 84-70055. 196p. 1983. pap. 5.95 (ISBN 0-88270-552-0). Bridge Pub.

--Radical Christian Living. LC 84-90103. (Illus.). 124p. (Orig.). 1985. pap. 4.95 (ISBN 0-932081-03-7). Victory Hse.

--Seated in Heavenly Places. LC 85-72460. 1986. pap. 5.95 (ISBN 0-88270-600-4). Bridge Pub.

Boom, Corrie T. Each New Day. (Christian Library). 1985. Repr. of 1980 ed. 6.95 (ISBN 0-916441-20-2). Barbour & Co.

Boom, Corrie ten. This Day Is the Lord's. 1982. pap. 2.75 (ISBN 0-515-06734-2). Jove Pubns.

--Tramp for the Lord. 1976. pap. 2.95 (ISBN 0-515-08993-1). Jove Pubns.

Boone, Pat. My Brothers Keeper? 1975. pap. 1.75 (ISBN 0-89129-028-1). Jove Pubns.

Booth, Catherine. Aggressive Christianity. (Writings of Catherine Booth Ser.). 1986. Repr. of 1880 ed. deluxe ed. 4.95 (ISBN 0-86544-031-X). Salvation Army.

--Highway of Our God. (Writings of Catherine Booth Ser.). 1986. Repr. of 1880 ed. deluxe ed. 4.95 (ISBN 0-86544-033-6). Salvation Army.

--Life & Death. (Writings of Catherine Booth Ser.). 1986. Repr. of 1883 ed. deluxe ed. 4.95 (ISBN 0-86544-034-4). Salvation Army.

--Papers on Godliness. (Writings of Catherine Booth Ser.). 1986. Repr. of 1890 ed. deluxe ed. 4.95 (ISBN 0-86544-032-8). Salvation Army.

--Popular Christianity. (Writings of Catherine Booth Ser.). 1986. Repr. of 1888 ed. deluxe ed. 4.95 (ISBN 0-86544-035-2). Salvation Army.

--Writings of Catherine Booth, 6 Vols. 1986. Repr. of 1880 ed. Set. deluxe ed. 19.95 (ISBN 0-86544-038-7). Salvation Army.

Boros, L. The Hidden God. 132p. 1973. 5.95 (ISBN 0-8245-0313-9). Crossroad NY.

Boros, Ladislaus. Being a Christian Today. Davies, M. Benedict, tr. LC 79-13607. 124p. 1979. 7.95 (ISBN 0-8245-0202-7). Crossroad NY.

Borsch, Frederick H. Introducing the Lessons of the Church Year: A Guide for Lay Readers & Congregations. 240p. (Orig.). 1984. pap. 8.95 (ISBN 0-8164-2496-9, 6102, HarpR). Har-Row.

Borth, Martha. Sitting at His Feet. (Illus.). 85p. (Orig.). 1985. pap. 5.95 (ISBN 0-935993-00-2). Clar Call Bks.

Botterweck, C. Michael. A Test of Faith: Challenges of Modern Day Christians. 304p. (Orig.). 1983. pap. 8.95 (ISBN 0-911541-01-2). Gregory Pub.

Bouldin, Don. Ears to Hear, Eyes to See. (Orig.). 1987. pap. 6.95 (ISBN 0-8054-3002-4). Broadman.

Bourgeois, Henri. On Becoming Christian. 2nd ed. 160p. 1985. pap. 6.95 (ISBN 0-89622-270-5). Twenty-Third.

Bove, Vincent. Playing His Game. LC 84-70985. 1984. pap. 5.95 (ISBN 0-88270-570-9). Bridge Pub.

Bowen, Desmond. The Idea of the Victorian Church: A Study of the Church of England 1833-1889. 1968. 20.00x (ISBN 0-7735-0033-2). McGill-Queens U Pr.

Bowne, Borden P. The Christian Revelation. LC 75-3069. Repr. of 1898 ed. 20.00 (ISBN 0-404-59068-3). AMS Pr.

Bo Yin Ra. The Book on Life Beyond. Reichenbach, Bodo A., tr. from Ger. LC 78-51633. 1978. pap. 5.00 (ISBN 0-915034-02-6). Kober Pr.

Boykin, John. Circumstances & the Role of God. 224p. 1986. text ed. 12.95 (ISBN 0-317-46020-X). Zondervan.

Boynes, Cyril H. Freedom Through the Balisier. LC 83-40235. 148p. (Orig.). 1984. pap. 4.75 (ISBN 0-8356-0584-1, Quest). Theos Pub Hse.

Bradley, Gerard T. Face the Light. LC 82-99822. 89p. 1983. 8.95 (ISBN 0-533-05448-6). Vantage.

Bradshaw, Charles E. Profile of Faith. 9.95 (ISBN 0-911866-01-9). Advocate.

Brady, Anne. Me & My Mustang. (Illus.). 50p. (Orig.). 1986. pap. 4.95 (ISBN 0-937689-02-5). Chisum Pub.

Brand, Paul & Yancey, Philip. In His Image. 224p. 1984. 12.95 (ISBN 0-310-35500-1, 10242). Zondervan.

Brandall, William S. The Secret of the Universe: New Discoveries on God, Man & the Eternity of Life. (Illus.). 119p. 1985. 127.45 (ISBN 0-89266-535-1). Am Classical Coll Pr.

Brandeis, Arthur, ed. Jacob's Well, an English Treatise on the Cleansing of Man's Conscience, Pt. 1. (EETS, OS Ser.: No. 115). Repr. of 1900 ed. 54.00 (ISBN 0-527-00114-7). Kraus Repr.

Brandt, Diana, ed. Being Brothers & Sisters. LC 83-83062. (Illus.). 115p. 1984. pap. 7.95 (ISBN 0-87303-091-5). Faith & Life.

Brandt, Henry R. The Struggle for Inner Peace. rev. ed. 136p. 1984. pap. 4.95 (ISBN 0-88207-245-5). Victor Bks.

Brandt, Leslie. Jesus Now. 1978. 8.50 (ISBN 0-570-03268-7, 15-2714). Concordia.

Brandt, Leslie F. Christ in Your Life. 1980. 7.50 (ISBN 0-570-03292-X, 15-2729). Concordia.

Breault, William. A Voice over the Water. LC 84-73051. 128p. (Orig.). 1985. pap. 4.95 (ISBN 0-87793-281-6). Ave Maria.

Brecheen, Carl & Faulkner, Paul. What Every Family Needs or Whatever Happened to Mom, Dad, & the Kids. LC 78-68726. (Journey Bks.). 1979. pap. 3.95 (ISBN 0-8344-0104-5). Sweet.

Bredesen, Harald. Yes, Lord. rev. ed. LC 72-91776. 199p. 1982. pap. 4.95 (ISBN 0-910311-00-5). Huntington Hse Inc.

Bredin, Eamonn. Rediscovering Jesus: Challenge of Discipleship. 300p. 1986. pap. 9.95 (ISBN 0-89622-300-0). Twenty-Third.

Breese, Dave. Know the Marks of Cults. LC 74-21907. 128p. 1975. pap. 4.95 (ISBN 0-88207-704-X). Victor Bks.

Brengle, Samuel L. Guest of the Soul. 1978. pap. 3.95 (ISBN 0-86544-001-8). Salv Army Suppl South.

--Heart Talks on Holiness. 1978. pap. 3.95 (ISBN 0-86544-002-6). Salv Army Suppl South.

--Love Slaves. 1960. Repr. of 1923 ed. 3.95 (ISBN 0-86544-004-2). Salv Army Suppl South.

--Soul Winner's Secret. 1978. pap. 3.95 (ISBN 0-86544-007-7). Salv Army Suppl South.

--Way of Holiness. 1966. Repr. of 1902 ed. 3.95 (ISBN 0-86544-008-5). Salv Army Suppl South.

Brennan, Anne & Janice, Brewi. Mid-Life Directions, Praying & Playing Sources of New Dynamism. LC 84-62157. 192p. (Orig.). 1985. pap. 7.95 (ISBN 0-8091-2681-8). Paulist Pr.

Brenneman, Helen G. But Not Forsaken. 1983. 3.25 (ISBN 0-87813-954-0). Christian Light.

Brestin, Dee. How Should a Christian Live? 1, 2, & 3 John. (A Core Study in the Fisherman Bible Studyguides). 80p. 1985. pap. 2.95 (ISBN 0-87788-351-3). Shaw Pubs.

Brestin, Steve & Brestin, Dee. Higher Ground: For the Believer Who Seeks Joy & Victory. (Fisherman Bible Studyguide Ser.). 58p. 1978. saddle-stitched 2.95 (ISBN 0-87788-345-9). Shaw Pubs.

Brewer, Bartholomew F. & Furrell, Alfred W. Peregrinaje Esde Roma. Vargas-Caba, Jose M., tr. from Eng. (Span., Illus.). 194p. 1986. pap. 5.95 (ISBN 0-89084-328-7). Bob Jones Univ Pr.

--Pilgrimage from Rome. rev. ed. (Illus.). 1986. pap. 5.95 (ISBN 0-89084-327-9). Bob Jones Univ Pr.

Brewi, Janice & Brennan, Anne, eds. Mid Life: Psyhological & Spiritual Perspectives. 224p. 1982. 12.95 (ISBN 0-8245-0417-8); pap. 8.95. Crossroad NY.

Brezik, Victor B. About Living. 156p. 1980. 4.95 (ISBN 0-912414-29-4). Lumen Christi.

Brians, Bert. Leoni Meadows Experiences. large print ed. 62p. 1984. pap. 9.00 (ISBN 0-914009-07-9). VHI Library.

Brians, Charline. Sunday Sister. large print ed. 24p. 1985. pap. 4.00 (ISBN 0-914009-53-2). VHI Library.

--Testing Myself As a Prophet. large print ed. 1985. pap. 5.00 (ISBN 0-914009-10-9). VHI Library.

Brians, Pearl. Appetite Control for Christians. large print ed. 28p. 1985. pap. 4.50 (ISBN 0-914009-30-3). VHI Library.

--During My Conversion. large print ed. 44p. 1984. pap. 8.00 (ISBN 0-914009-11-7). VHI Library.

--Ingathering Experience, Vol. 1. large print ed. 33p. 1985. pap. 5.00 (ISBN 0-914009-32-X). VHI Library.

--Mama's Life on a Missouri Farm. large print ed. 86p. pap. 8.00 (ISBN 0-914009-26-5). VHI Library.

--Out of Confusion-into the Light. large print ed. 58p. 1984. pap. 9.50 (ISBN 0-914009-12-5). VHI Library.

--Overeaters Feelings & Faith. large print ed. 40p. 1985. pap. 5.50 (ISBN 0-914009-31-1). VHI Library.

--Pleading with the Father. large print ed. 27p. 1985. pap. 4.50 (ISBN 0-914009-36-2). VHI Library.

Brians, Pearl, ed. Hangups, Health & Heaven. large print ed. 50p. pap. 9.95 (ISBN 0-9608650-0-4). VHI Library.

Bricose, Jill. Here Am I; Send Aaron! 1984. pap. 2.95 (ISBN 0-89693-712-7). Victor Bks.

Bridges, Jacqueline K. Sackcloth & Ashes. LC 84-91345. 99p. 1985. 8.95 (ISBN 0-533-06442-2). Vantage.

Bridges, Jerry. The Practice of Godliness. LC 83-61499. 272p. 1983. pap. 3.95 (ISBN 0-89109-497-0). NavPress.

--True Fellowship. 150p. 1987. pap. 3.95 (ISBN 0-89109-175-0). NavPress.

Briggs, Freda I. Mom, Can We Still Keep Roger? 96p. 1985. pap. 4.95 (ISBN 0-8010-0888-3). Baker Bk.

Bright, Bill. Believing God for the Impossible. LC 78-73565. 1979. 8.95 (ISBN 0-918956-55-2). Campus Crusade.

--Come Help Change Our World. LC 79-53543. 1979. 8.95 (ISBN 0-918956-01-3). Campus Crusade.

Briscoe, D. Stuart. Spirit Life. 160p. 1983. pap. 5.95 (ISBN 0-8007-5185-X). Revell.

--When the Going Gets Tough. LC 82-11205. 1982. 5.95 (ISBN 0-8307-0802-2, 5417507). Regal.

Briscoe, Jill. How to Follow the Shepherd When You're Being Pushed Around by the Sheep. 192p. 1984. pap. 5.95 (ISBN 0-8007-5166-3, Power Bks). Revell.

--Thank You for Being a Friend. 192p. (Orig.). 1981. pap. 5.95 (ISBN 0-310-21851-9, 9261P). Zondervan.

--Wings. 384p. 1984. 11.95 (ISBN 0-8407-5328-4). Nelson.

Briscoe, Stuart. How to Be a Motivated Christian. 192p. 1987. 9.95 (ISBN 0-89693-179-X). Victor Bks.

--Tough Truths for Today's Living. 178p. 1984. pap. text ed. 5.95 (ISBN 0-8499-2999-7, 2999-7). Word Bks.

--What Works When Life Doesn't. rev. ed. 176p. 1984. pap. 2.95 (ISBN 0-89693-709-7). Victor Bks.

Briscoe, Stuart & Briscoe, Jill. What It Means to Be a Christian. 128p. 1987. pap. 4.95 (ISBN 1-55513-803-9). Cook.

Bristol, Goldie & McGinnis, Carol. When It's Hard to Forgive. 168p. 1982. pap. 5.95 (ISBN 0-88207-311-7). Victor Bks.

Bristow, Benny. From Kneepants to Romance. pap. 1.95 (ISBN 0-89137-810-3). Quality Pubns.

Bristow, Gwen. From Pigtails to Wedding Bells. pap. 1.95 (ISBN 0-89137-811-1). Quality Pubns.

Bristow, Hennie. Something to Think about. pap. 2.50 (ISBN 0-89315-292-7). Lambert Bk.

Broadbent, Belle B. Where Flowers Grow. 16p. 1982. pap. 1.95 (ISBN 0-939298-04-X). J M Prods.

Broadus, Loren. How to Stop Procrastinating & Start Living. LC 82-72641. 128p. 1983. pap. 5.95 (ISBN 0-8066-1947-3, 10-3178). Augsburg.

Brockelman, Paul. Time & Self. 96p. 1985. pap. 10.95 (ISBN 0-8245-0703-7). Crossroad NY.

Broderick, James. The Economic Morals of the Jesuits. LC 76-38248. (The Evolution of Capitalism Ser.). 168p. 1972. Repr. of 1934 ed. 12.00 (ISBN 0-405-04113-6). Ayer Co Pubs.

Bromiley, Geoffrey W. God & Marriage. 96p. (Orig.). 1980. pap. 4.95 (ISBN 0-8028-1851-X). Eerdmans.

Brooks. Your Life in Christ. 1.95 (ISBN 0-8054-2520-9). Broadman.

Brooks, Pat. Healing of the Mind. 4th. ed. Orig. Title: Using Your Spiritual Authority. 1983. pap. text ed. 2.50 (ISBN 0-932050-00-X). New Puritan.

--Out! In the Name of Jesus. 3rd ed. LC 85-72223. 235p. 1986. pap. text ed. 5.00 (ISBN 0-932050-27-1). New Puritan.

Brooks, Vivia. Heritage of the Lord. (Illus.). 96p. 1984. 10.00 (ISBN 0-87770-314-0). Ye Galleon.

Brother Sheffey. 4.95 (ISBN 0-686-27777-5). Schmul Pub Co.

Brother Lawrence & Laubach, Frank. Practicing His Presence. 3rd ed. Edwards, Gene, ed. 1973. pap. 5.95 (ISBN 0-940232-01-4). Christian Bks.

Brown, David, ed. Bible Wisdom for Modern Living: Arranged by Subject. 400p. 1986. 17.95 (ISBN 0-671-62545-4). S&S.

Brown, Delwin. To Set at Liberty: Christian Faith & Human Freedom. LC 80-21783. 144p. (Orig.). 1981. pap. 6.95 (ISBN 0-88344-501-8). Orbis Bks.

Brown, James A. The Word & the World: God's Priorities for Today. 64p. 1984. 7.95 (ISBN 0-89962-419-7). Todd & Honeywell.

Brown, Joan W. Every Knee Shall Bow. 194p. 1984. pap. 5.95 (ISBN 0-89066-054-9). World Wide Pubs.

Brown, L. David. Take Care: A Guide for Responsible Living. LC 78-52200. 1978. pap. 6.95 (ISBN 0-8066-1665-2, 10-6190). Augsburg.

Brown, Lavonn D. The Life of the Church. 1987. 5.95 (ISBN 0-8054-1643-9). Broadman.

Brown, Marion M. & Leech, Jane K. Dreamcatcher: The Life of John Neihardt. 144p. (Orig.). 1983. pap. 6.95 (ISBN 0-687-11174-9). Abingdon.

Brown, Marion M., et al. The Silent Storm. 1985. Repr. of 1963 ed. 6.95 (ISBN 0-8010-0884-0). Baker Bk.

Brown, Pean. Gifts of Silence. 84p. 1983. pap. 6.95 (ISBN 0-942494-79-2). Coleman Pub.

Brown, Raymond E. The Community of the Beloved Disciple. LC 78-65894. 204p. 1979. 5.95 (ISBN 0-8091-0274-9); pap. 4.95 (ISBN 0-8091-2174-3). Paulist Pr.

Brown, Robert M. Making Peace in the Global Village. LC 80-27213. 118p. 1981. pap. 5.95 (ISBN 0-664-24343-6). Westminster.

Brown, Stephen. If God Is in Charge. LC 83-2240. 180p. 1983. pap. 5.95 (ISBN 0-8407-5844-8). Nelson.

--No More Mr. Nice Guy: Saying Goodbye to Doormat Christianity. 224p. 1986. 14.95 (ISBN 0-8407-5539-2). Nelson.

Brownell, Ada N. Confessions of a Pentecostal. LC 77-92887. 112p. 1978. pap. 1.25 (ISBN 0-88243-476-4, 02-0476). Gospel Pub.

Brownlow, Leroy. Christian's Everyday Problems. 1966. pap. 2.50 (ISBN 0-915720-39-6). Brownlow Pub Co.

--Today Is Mine. 1972. gift ed 7.95 (ISBN 0-915720-14-0); leather ed. 12.95 (ISBN 0-915720-57-4). Brownlow Pub Co.

Bruchez, Dardo. Mensaje a la Conciencia. (Span.). 128p. (Orig.). 1979. pap. 3.50 (ISBN 0-89922-143-2). Edit Caribe.

Brumbaugh, Thoburn T. My Marks & Scars I Carry: The Story of Ernst Kisch. (Bold Believers Ser.). 1969. pap. 0.95 (ISBN 0-377-84151-X). Friend Pr.

Brumfield, J. C. Comfort for Troubled Christians. (Moody Acorn Ser.). 1975. pap. 7.95 package of 10 (ISBN 0-8024-1400-1). Moody.

Brunner, August. New Creation: Towards a Theology of the Christian Life. 143p. 1956. 10.00 (ISBN 0-8022-0189-X). Philos Lib.

Brunner, Emil. The Divine Imperative. LC 47-2443. 728p. 1979. softcover 9.95 (ISBN 0-664-24246-4). Westminster.

--Our Faith. 153p. 1980. pap. text ed. write for info. (ISBN 0-02-315940-5, Pub. by Scribner). Macmillan.

Bruso, Dick. Bible Promises, Help & Hope for Your Finances. 156p. (Orig.). 1985. pap. 2.95 (ISBN 0-89840-075-9). Heres Life.

Bruster, Bill G. & Dale, Robert D. How to Encourage Others. LC 82-70868. (Orig.). 1983. pap. 6.95 (ISBN 0-8054-2247-1). Broadman.

Bryant, Christopher. The Heart in Pilgrimage: Christian Guidelines for the Human Journey. 208p. 1980. 9.95 (ISBN 0-8164-0457-7, HarpR). Har-Row.

--Jung & the Christian Way. 144p. (Orig.). 1984. pap. 7.95 (ISBN 0-86683-872-4, 7917, HarpR). Har-Row.

Buchanan, Jami L. Letters to My Little Sisters. LC 84-27612. (Orig.). 1985. pap. 3.95 (ISBN 0-8307-0999-1, S185100). Regal.

Buchheim, Durwood. The Power of Darkness. 1985. 6.95 (ISBN 0-89536-746-7, 5852). CSS of Ohio.

Buckingham, Jamie. Daughter of Destiny. LC 76-12034. 1976. (Pub. by Logos); pap. 2.95 pocket ed. (ISBN 0-88270-318-8). Bridge Pub.

Buechner, Frederick. The Alphabet of Grace. LC 84-48765. 128p. 1985. 12.45 (ISBN 0-06-061173-1, HarpR). Har-Row.

Buehring, David K. Acts Alive. 1986. pap. 7.95 (ISBN 0-935779-10-8). Crown Min.

Buerger, Jane & Davis, Jennie. Helping Is. 1984. 4.95 (ISBN 0-89693-218-4). Victor Bks.

--Helping Is-- LC 84-7042. (Illus.). 32p. 1984. lib. bdg. 4.95 (ISBN 0-89693-218-4). Dandelion Hse.

Buess, Bob. Deliverance from the Bondage of Fear. 1972. pap. 2.50 (ISBN 0-934244-03-0). Sweeter Than Honey.

--Discipleship Pro & Con. 1975. pap. 2.50 (ISBN 0-934244-06-5). Sweeter Than Honey.

--Favor the Road to Success. 1982. pap. 2.50 (ISBN 0-934244-17-0). Sweeter Than Honey.

--Implanted Word. 1978. pap. 2.50 (ISBN 0-934244-10-3). Sweeter Than Honey.

--The Laws of the Spirit. 1968. pap. 2.50 (ISBN 0-934244-01-4). Sweeter Than Honey.

--The Race Horse. 1978. pap. 2.50 (ISBN 0-934244-08-1). Sweeter Than Honey.

--Setting the Captives Free. LC 42-1127. 1975. pap. 2.50 (ISBN 0-934244-02-2). Sweeter Than Honey.

Building a Love That Lasts: Outstanding Articles on Marriage from the Ensign. LC 85-16011. 192p. 1985. 8.95 (ISBN 0-87747-852-X). Deseret Bk.

Bundschuh, Rick. A Shadow of a Man. LC 86-22048. (Light Force Ser.). 120p. (Orig.). (YA) 1986. pap. 4.95 (ISBN 0-8307-1143-0, S185116). Regal.

Bundschuh, Rick & Gilbert, Dave. Dating Your Mate. 144p. (Orig.). 1987. pap. 4.95 (ISBN 0-89081-598-4). Harvest Hse.

Bundschuh, Rick, compiled by. Hot Buttons. LC 85-32323. (The Light Force Ser.). (Illus.). 153p. (Orig.). 1986. pap. 4.25 (ISBN 0-8307-1092-2, S182437). Regal.

Bunyan, John. My Imprisonment. pap. 1.75 (ISBN 0-686-64391-7). Reiner.

Burbach, Maur, et al. Our Family: A Love Story. 66p. 1981. 12.50 (ISBN 0-8146-1222-9). Liturgical Pr.

Burghardt, Walter J. Seasons That Laugh or Weep: Musings on the Human Journey. LC 83-60655. 144p. (Orig.). 1983. 4.95 (ISBN 0-8091-2533-1). Paulist Pr.

Burke, Dennis. Diligence. 96p. (Orig.). 1983. pap. 2.50 (ISBN 0-89274-307-7, HH307). Harrison Hse.

Burke, John. Bible Sharing: How to Grow in the Mystery of Christ. LC 79-15006. (Orig.). 1979. pap. 5.95 (ISBN 0-8189-0386-4). Alba.

Burkett, Larry. Using Your Money Wisely: Guidelines from Scripture. 1986. pap. 7.95 (ISBN 0-8024-3425-8). Moody.

--What Husbands Wish Their Wives Knew about Money. 1977. pap. 3.95 (ISBN 0-88207-758-9). Victor Bks.

Burkhart, Rob. Yet Will I Trust Him. LC 79-91705. (Study & Grow Electives). 64p. 1985. pap. 3.95 (ISBN 0-8307-1016-7, 6102002). Regal.

Burkholder, Byron, ed. They Saw His Glory: Stories of Conversion & Service. 186p. (Orig.). 1984. pap. 5.95 (ISBN 0-919797-40-7). Kindred Pr.

Burnham, Sue. Dynamics of Christian Living for Women. LC 81-67598. 50p. (Orig.). (YA) 1981. pap. 2.95 (ISBN 0-940386-00-3). Dynamics Chr Liv.

Burnham, T. Lee. Home & School Connection. 1986. 7.95 (ISBN 0-87579-045-3, Pub. by Shadow Mountain). Deseret Bk.

Burns, Jim. Giving Yourself to God: Pursuing Excellence in Your Christian Life. (Orig.). pap. 3.95; wkbk. 3.95 (ISBN 0-89081-488-0). Harvest Hse.

--Growth Unlimited. 160p. (Orig.). 1987. pap. 5.95 (ISBN 0-89081-580-1). Harvest Hse.

--Jim Burn's Youth Series 1--Leaders' Guide. (Orig.). 1985. pap. 7.95 (ISBN 0-89081-495-3). Harvest Hse.

--Living Your Life... As God Intended. (Illus., Orig.). 1985. pap. 3.95 (ISBN 0-89081-450-3). Harvest Hse.

--Making Your Life Count. (Illus.). 64p. Wkbk 3.95 (ISBN 0-89081-392-2). Harvest Hse.

--Putting God First. (Illus.). 64p. 1983. wkbk. 3.95 (ISBN 0-89081-366-3). Harvest Hse.

Burns, Jim & Webster, Doug. Building Relationships...With God & Others. (Jim Burns Youth Ser.: No. 2). 64p. (Orig.). 1986. wkbk. 3.95 (ISBN 0-89081-479-1). Harvest Hse.

Burron, Arnold & Crews, Jerry. Guaranteed Steps to Managing Stress. (Orig.). 1986. pap. 6.95 (ISBN 0-8423-1249-8). Tyndale.

Burroughs, Jeremiah. The Rare Jewel of Christian Contentment. 1979. pap. 5.45 (ISBN 0-85151-091-4). Banner of Truth.

Burrows, Ruth. Before the Living God. 6.95 (ISBN 0-87193-155-9). Dimension Bks.

Burrows, Stephen G. God's Daughter in Nassau. 186p. 1980. 8.50 (ISBN 0-682-49497-6). Exposition Pr FL.

Burtchaell, James T. Philemon's Problem: The Daily Dilemma of the Christian. LC 73-88935. 1973. pap. 2.95 (ISBN 0-914070-05-3). ACTA Found.

Burton, Alma P. Toward the New Jerusalem. LC 85-10203. 172p. 1985. 7.95 (ISBN 0-87747-883-X). Deseret Bk.

Burton, Ella S. God's Word Is Our Only Foundation. 1983. 5.75 (ISBN 0-8062-2164-X). Carlton.

Burton, William F. Where to Go with Your Troubles. 80p. 1969. pap. 1.00 (ISBN 0-88243-627-9, 02-0627). Gospel Pub.

Burton, Wilma. Sidewalk Psalms... & Some from Country Lanes. LC 79-92015. 119p. 1980. 8.95 (ISBN 0-89107-165-2). Good News.

Bush, Bernard J., ed. Coping: Issues of Emotional Living in an Age of Stress for Clergy & Religious. LC 76-362761. 83p. 1976. pap. 2.95 (ISBN 0-89571-000-5). Affirmation.

Bush, Charles W. How to Hear God Speak. 128p. (Orig.). 1975. pap. text ed. 1.50 (ISBN 0-89228-028-X). Impact Bks MO.

Bush, Danny E. Invitation to the Feast. LC 85-13314. 1985. pap. 3.75 (ISBN 0-8054-5019-X). Broadman.

Bustanoby, Andre. Being a Success at Who You Are. 1986. pap. 4.95 (ISBN 0-310-45381-X, 9172P). Zondervan.

Butler, Ralph. Out of the Silence. 142p. 1978. pap. 2.95 (ISBN 0-7050-0059-1). Attic Pr.

Buttaci, Salvatore S. & Gerstle, Susan L., eds. Reflections of the Inward Silence. LC 76-19240. 1976. 9.95 (ISBN 0-917398-03-3); pap. 7.95 (ISBN 0-917398-04-1). New Worlds.

Butterworth, Eric. In the Flow of Life. LC 82-50121. 181p. 1982. Repr. 5.95 (ISBN 0-87159-065-4). Unity School.

--Spiritual Economics--the Prosperity Process. 220p. 1983. 5.95 (ISBN 0-87159-142-1). Unity School.

--Unity: A Quest for Truth. (Orig.). 1965. pap. 3.00 (ISBN 0-8315-0020-4). Speller.

--Unity: A Quest for Truth. 160p. 1985. 5.95 (ISBN 0-87159-165-0, X1965, ROBERT SPELLER & SONS PUB.). Unity School.

Buzzard, Lynn R. & Eck, Laurence. Tell It to the Church. 192p. (Orig.). 1985. pap. 6.95 (ISBN 0-8423-6986-4). Tyndale.

Byerly, Helen. Growing with Daily Devotions. 20p. 1964. No. 4. 1.50 ea., spiral bd., wkbk. (ISBN 0-87509-337-X). No. 5 (ISBN 0-87509-338-8). No. 6 (ISBN 0-87509-339-6). No. 7 (ISBN 0-87509-340-X). No. 8 (ISBN 0-87509-341-8). No. 9 o.p (ISBN 0-87509-342-6). No. 10 (ISBN 0-87509-343-4). No. 11 (ISBN 0-87509-344-2). No.12 (ISBN 0-87509-345-0). Chr Pubns.

Cada, Lawrence, et al. Shaping the Coming Age of Religious Life. 2nd ed. LC 78-25987. 208p. 1985. pap. 7.95 (ISBN 0-89571-023-4). Affirmation.

Cady, Emilie H. God a Present Help. rev. ed. LC 84-5002010. 1985. 5.95 (ISBN 0-87159-044-1). Unity School.

Cairns, Earle E. God & Man in Time. LC 78-73042. 1978. pap. 7.95 (ISBN 0-8010-2426-9). Baker Bk.

Caldwell, Genevieve. First Person Singular. 180p. 1986. 10.95 (ISBN 0-8407-3072-1). Nelson.

Caldwell, Louis O. A Birthday Remembrance. LC 77-7043. (Illus.). pap. 20.00 (ISBN 0-8357-9001-0, 2016349). Bks Demand UMI.

--You Can Overcome Your Fears, Phobias, & Worries. 1985. pap. 1.25 (ISBN 0-8010-2506-0). Baker Bk.

--You Can Prevent or Overcome a Nervous Breakdown. (Christian Counseling Aids Ser.). 1978. pap. 1.25 (ISBN 0-8010-2415-3). Baker Bk.

Calkin, Ruth. Lord, I Keep Running Back to You. 1983. pap. 3.50 (ISBN 0-8423-3819-5). Tyndale.

Calkin, Ruth H. Lord, You Love to Say Yes. (Living Books). 160p. (Orig.). 1985. pap. 2.95 (ISBN 0-8423-3824-1). Tyndale.

--Love Is So Much More, Lord. LC 79-51739. 1979. pap. 2.50 (ISBN 0-89191-187-1). Cook.

Callen, Barry. Where Life Begins. 128p. 1973. pap. 2.50 (ISBN 0-87162-146-0, D9026). Warner Pr.

Calvin, John. The Christian Life. Leith, John A., ed. LC 83-48978. 112p. 1984. 10.45 (ISBN 0-06-061298-3, HarpR). Har-Row.

--Golden Booklet of the True Christian Life: Devotional Classic. (Summit Bks.). 1975. pap. 3.95 (ISBN 0-8010-2366-1). Baker Bk.

Camara, Helder. It's Midnight, Lord. Gallagher, Joseph, et al, trs. (Illus., Orig.). 1984. pap. 7.95 (ISBN 0-912405-02-3). Pastoral Pr.

Cameli, Louis. Mary's Journey. 5.95 (ISBN 0-8215-9911-9). Sadlier.

Cameron, Lewis. Opportunity My Ally. (Illus.). 253p. 1965. 10.95 (ISBN 0-227-67706-4). Attic Pr.

Campbell, Alexander. Heroes Then, Heroes Now. (Illus.). 89p. (Orig.). 1981. pap. 12.95 (ISBN 0-940754-08-8). Ed Ministries.

--Stories of Jesus, Stories of Now. 80p. (Orig.). 1980. pap. 12.95 (ISBN 0-940754-04-5). Ed Ministries.

Campbell, Alexander & Haff, Gerry. Live with Moses. 90p. (Orig.). 1982. pap. 12.95 (ISBN 0-940754-13-4). Ed Ministries.

Campbell, David. Yet Not I. 88p. (Orig.). 1978. pap. 1.95 (ISBN 0-912315-39-3). Word Aflame.

Campbell, Don G. Master Teacher: Nadia Boulanger. (Illus.). 151p. 1984. text ed. 19.95 (ISBN 0-912405-03-1). Pastoral Pr.

Campbell, R. K. Divine Principles of Gathering. 40p. pap. 0.45 (ISBN 0-88172-015-1). Believers Bkshelf.

--Essentials of the Christian Life. 46p. pap. 0.50 (ISBN 0-88172-008-9). Believers Bkshelf.

--Outside the Camp. 16p. pap. 0.30 (ISBN 0-88172-087-9). Believers Bkshelf.

Campbell, Robert & Sherer, Michael. Turn Us, Lord. 1985. 2.95 (ISBN 0-89536-728-9, 5812). CSS of Ohio.

Campbell, Roger. Let's Communicate. (Orig.). 1979. pap. 3.50 (ISBN 0-87508-060-X). Chr Lit.

--You Can Win. 132p. 1985. pap. 4.95 (ISBN 0-89693-317-2). Victor Bks.

Campion, Michael & Zehr, Wilmer. Especially for Grandparents. (When Was the Last Time Ser.). (Illus.). 112p. (Orig.). 1980. pap. 5.95 (ISBN 0-87123-141-7, 210141). Bethany Hse.

Campolo, Anthony. Partly Right. 192p. 1985. 11.95 (ISBN 0-8499-0368-8, 0368-8). Word Bks.

Campus Crusade for Christ Staff. How to Make Your Mark. 540p. (Orig.). 1983. pap. 8.95 (ISBN 0-86605-142-2). Campus Crusade.

Cane, Bill. Through Crisis to Freedom. LC 79-89874. (Orig.). 1980. pap. 3.25 (ISBN 0-914070-14-2). ACTA Found.

Capper, W. M. & Johnson, D., eds. The Faith of a Surgeon: Belief & Experience in the Life of Arthur Rendle Short. 160p. 1976. pap. 5.95 (ISBN 0-85364-198-6). Attic Pr.

Capps, Charles. Authority in Three Worlds. 266p. (Orig.). 1980. pap. 3.95 (ISBN 0-89274-281-X). Harrison Hse.

--Changing the Seen & Shaping the Unseen. 1981. pap. 2.25 (ISBN 0-89274-220-8, HH-220). Harrison Hse.

--God's Image of You. 1985. 2.95 (ISBN 0-89274-376-X). Harrison Hse.

--Kicking over Sacred Cows. 132p. (Orig.). 1984. pap. 4.95 (ISBN 0-914307-18-5, Dist. by Harrison Hse). Word Faith.

Caprio, Betsy & Hedberg, Thomas. Coming Home: A Handbook for Exploring the Sanctuary Within. (Illus.). 288p. (Orig.). 1986. pap. 9.95 (ISBN 0-8091-2739-3); director's manual 9.95 (ISBN 0-8091-2787-3). Paulist Pr.

Carl, Angela R. A Matter of Choice. LC 84-7040. (Illus.). 32p. 1984. lib. bdg. 4.95 (ISBN 0-89693-223-0). Dandelion Hse.

Carlin, Cathy. Jesus, What Are You Doing Tonight? (Outreach Ser.). 32p. 1982. pap. 0.99 (ISBN 0-8163-0492-0). Pacific Pr Pub Assn.

Carlson, Dwight L. Guiltfree: How to Release the Tension in Your Life. 2nd ed. LC 83-80118. 1985. pap. 4.95 (ISBN 0-89081-375-2, 3752). Harvest Hse.

Carlson, Lee W., ed. Christian Parenting. 80p. 1984. pap. 6.95 (ISBN 0-8170-1072-6). Judson.

Carmack, Rita J. Set My Heart Free. 144p. 1984. pap. 5.00 (ISBN 0-88144-031-0). Jewel Pr.

Carmichael, Amy. Candles in the Dark. 1982. pap. text ed. 3.50 (ISBN 0-87508-085-5). Chr Lit.

--Learning of God. 1986. pap. 4.95 (ISBN 0-87508-086-3). Chr Lit.

Carmichael, Bill & Carmichael, Nancie. Answers to the Questions Christian Women Are Asking. 1984. text ed. 10.95 (ISBN 0-89081-446-5); pap. 6.95 (ISBN 0-89081-442-2). Harvest Hse.

Carmichael, Ralph. He's Everything to Me: Autobiography. 192p. 1986. 14.95 (ISBN 0-8499-0094-8). Word Bks.

Carmody, Denixe L. Double Cross. 192p. (Orig.). 1986. pap. 10.95 (ISBN 0-8245-0736-3). Crossroad NY.

Carmody, John. How to Make It Through the Day. LC 84-51826. 112p. (Orig.). 1985. pap. 5.95 (ISBN 0-8358-0491-7). Upper Room.

--Maturing a Christian Conscience. 160p. (Orig.). 1985. pap. 6.95 (ISBN 0-8358-0510-7). Upper Room.

Carothers, J. Edward. Caring for the World. (Orig.). 1978. pap. 4.95 (ISBN 0-377-00078-7). Friend Pr.

Carretto, Carlo. Letters from the Desert. 1976. pap. write for info (ISBN 0-515-09573-7). Jove Pubns.

Carroll, Frances L. Frustration: How Christians Can Deal with It. 156p. 1984. pap. 6.95 (ISBN 0-13-330804-9). P-H.

--Promises: A Guide to Christian Commitment. 228p. 1985. 14.95 (ISBN 0-13-731076-5); pap. 7.95 (ISBN 0-13-731068-4). P H.

--Temptation: How Christians Can Deal with It. 192p. 1984. 13.95 (ISBN 0-13-903229-0); pap. 5.95 (ISBN 0-13-903211-8). P-H.

Carstens, Christopher & Mahedy, William. Right Here, Right Now: Spiritual Exercises for Busy Christians. 1985. 9.95 (ISBN 0-345-31801-3, Pub. by Ballantine Epiphany). Ballantine.

Carstens, Christopher & Mahedy, William P. Starting on Monday: Christian Living in the Workplace. 176p. 1987. 11.95 (ISBN 0-345-32910-4). Ballantine.

Carter, Edward. Response to God's Love: A View of the Spiritual Life. 184p. 1984. 9.95 (ISBN 0-317-14585-1). Loyola.

Carty, Charles M. Why Squander Illness? 1974. pap. 1.50 (ISBN 0-89555-051-2). TAN Bks Pubs.

Casey, Karen & Vanceburg, Martha. The Promise of a New Day. 400p. (Orig.). 1985. pap. 5.95 (ISBN 0-86683-502-4, HarpR). Har-Row.

Caslow, Dan. Christian Disciple, No. 2. 1984. pap. 1.95 (ISBN 0-8163-0497-1). Pacific Pr Pub Assn.

--Church Fellowship. 1984. pap. 1.95 (ISBN 0-8163-0499-8). Pacific Pr Pub Assn.

--New Life, No. 1. 1984. pap. 1.95 (ISBN 0-317-30423-2). Pacific Pr Pub Assn.

--Personal Ministry, No. 3. 1984. pap. 1.95 (ISBN 0-8163-0498-X). Pacific Pr Pub Assn.

Caslow, Daniel E. Winning. 1981. pap. 5.95 (ISBN 0-8163-0462-9). Pacific Pr Pub Assn.

Cassels, Louis. Christian Primer. 112p. 1981. pap. 1.50 (ISBN 0-88028-012-3). Forward Movement.

Castro, Carol C. Welcoming God's Forgiveness. 120p. 1978. pap. text ed. 3.95 (ISBN 0-697-01681-1); leader's guide 4.50 (ISBN 0-697-01682-X); classroom tchr's guide .75 (ISBN 0-697-01907-1); adult resource book, pack/10,10.25 1.05 (ISBN 0-697-01685-4). Wm C Brown.

--Welcoming Jesus. 120p. 1979. pap. 3.95 (ISBN 0-697-01702-8); leader's guide 4.50 (ISBN 0-697-01703-6); classroom teacher's guide .75 (ISBN 0-697-01909-8); adult resource book, pack/10, 10.25 1.05 (ISBN 0-697-01704-4). Wm C Brown.

Castro, Emilio. Sent Free: Mission & Unity in the Perspective of the Kingdom. 112p. (Orig.). 1985. pap. 5.95 (ISBN 0-8028-0068-8). Eerdmans.

Catherwood, Frederick. First Things First: The Ten Commandments in the 20th Century. LC 81-51. 160p. 1981. pap. 5.95 (ISBN 0-87784-472-0). Inter Varsity.

Catoir, John. Para que Vuestro Gozo Sea colmado. Casamada, Jose, tr. from Eng. (Span.). 158p. (Orig.). 1986. pap. 5.00 (ISBN 0-317-46550-3). Chrstphrs NY.

Cattell, Everett L. Christian Mission: A Matter of Life. 160p. (Orig.). 1981. 11.95 (ISBN 0-913408-76-X); pap. 8.95 (ISBN 0-913408-68-9). Friends United.

Cavanaugh, Joan & Forseth, Pat. More of Jesus, Less of Me. 1976. pap. 3.95 (ISBN 0-88270-174-6). Bridge Pub.

Cavarnos, Constantine. Paths & Means to Holiness. 85p. (Orig.). 1986. pap. 5.00 (ISBN 0-911165-08-8). Ctr Trad Orthodox.

Cayce, Hugh L. The Jesus I Knew. 81p. (Orig.). 1984. pap. 4.95 (ISBN 0-87604-156-X). ARE Pr.

Cerart, Joan. Lord of the Horizon. 300p. 1987. pap. 7.95 (ISBN 0-89804-147-3). Ariel OH.

--Scarlet Feather. 290p. 1988. pap. 7.95 (ISBN 0-89804-148-1). Ariel OH.

--So Moses Was Born. 312p. 1988. pap. 7.95 (ISBN 0-89804-149-X). Ariel OH.

Cerling, Charles. Freedom from Bad Habits. LC 84-62384. 141p. (Orig.). 1984. pap. 5.95 (ISBN 0-89840-079-1). Heres Life.

Cerling, Charles E. Assertiveness & the Christian. 140p. 1983. pap. 4.95 (ISBN 0-8423-0083-X). Tyndale.

Chadwick, Enid M. At God's Altar. Schuler, Eugenia, ed. (Illus.). 1978. pap. 1.50x (ISBN 0-934502-00-5). Thursday Pubs.

--At God's Altar: Rite One. Schuler, Eugenia, ed. (Illus.). 1978. pap. 1.50x (ISBN 0-934502-01-3). Thursday Pubs.

Chamberlain. When Can a Child Believe. LC 73-80778. pap. 4.95 (ISBN 0-8054-6208-2). Broadman.

Chambers, Oswald. Still Higher for His Highest. 192p. 1970. 6.95 (ISBN 0-87508-142-8). Chr Lit.

Champion, Richard G. Go on Singing. LC 76-20889. (Radiant Life). 128p. 1976. tchr's ed 3.95 (ISBN 0-88243-169-2, 32-0169); pap. 2.50 (ISBN 0-88243-895-6, 02-0895). Gospel Pub.

Champlin, David. The Lord Is Present. 7.95 (ISBN 0-87193-175-3). Dimension Bks.

Chandler, Ted E. How to Have Good Health. LC 81-68045. 1982. 7.95 (ISBN 0-8054-5298-2). Broadman.

Chapian, Marie. Free to Be Thin. LC 79-15656. (Illus.). 192p. 1979. pap. 5.95 (ISBN 0-87123-560-9, 210560); study guide (No. 1) by Neva Coyle 64 pgs. 2.50 (ISBN 0-87123-163-8, 210163). Bethany Hse.

--Of Whom the World Was Not Worthy. LC 78-769. (Illus.). 256p. 1978. pap. 6.95 (ISBN 0-87123-250-2, 210417). Bethany Hse.

Charland, William A., Jr. Decide to Live. LC 79-9563. 156p. 1979. pap. 6.95 (ISBN 0-664-24277-4). Westminster.

Charles, Howard H. Alcohol & the Bible. LC 66-10970. 40p. 1981. pap. 1.50 (ISBN 0-8361-1941-X). Herald Pr.

Chattalas, Angelos M. Pearls of Wisdom. 1986. 9.50 (ISBN 0-8062-2507-6). Carlton.

Cheasebro, Margaret. Puppet Scripts by the Month. 1985. pap. 4.95 (ISBN 0-8054-7524-9). Broadman.

Cherry, Corbin L. I Have Been Here. 112p. 1987. 6.95 (ISBN 1-55523-050-4). Winston-Derek.

Chesham, Sallie. One Hand upon Another. (Illus.). 160p. (Orig.). 1978. pap. 1.50 (ISBN 0-89216-016-0). Salvation Army.

--Peace Like a River. 1981. pap. 5.95 (ISBN 0-86544-014-X). Salv Army Suppl South.

Chick, Jack T. Cortinas de Humo. (Span., Illus., Orig.). 1984. pap. 2.50 (ISBN 0-937958-20-4). Chick Pubns.

Chiganos, William S. Preparing to Serve As a God Parent. 1986. pap. 1.25 (ISBN 0-937032-44-1). Light&Life Pub Co MN.

Chilcote, Paul W. Wesley Speaks on Christian Vocation. 104p. (Orig.). 1987. pap. 6.95 (ISBN 0-88177-041-8, DR041B). Discipleship Res.

Childs, Geoffrey S. The Golden Thread. (Illus.). 200p. 1986. write for info. (ISBN 0-910557-15-2). Acad New Church.

Chilson, Richard W. Full Christianity: A Catholic Response to Fundamental Questions. 144p. (Orig.). 1985. pap. 4.95 (ISBN 0-8091-2669-9). Paulist Pr.

Chilton, David. Productive Christians in An Age of Guilt Manipulators. 3rd ed. 480p. 1985. pap. 12.50 (ISBN 0-930464-04-4). Inst Christian.

Chinn, Wilberta L. & Owyang, Gregory R. Enjoy Your Quiet Time. 52p. 1986. wkbk. 3.00 (ISBN 0-937673-01-3). Peacock Ent LA.

Cho, Paul Y. The Fourth Dimension. LC 79-65588. 1979. pap. 5.95 (ISBN 0-88270-380-3, Pub. by Logos). Bridge Pub.

--The Leap of Faith. 120p. 1984. pap. 2.95 (ISBN 0-88270-574-1). Bridge Pub.

--Solving Life's Problems. LC 80-82787. (Orig.). 1980. pap. 4.95 (ISBN 0-88270-450-8). Bridge Pub.

Cho, Paul Y. & Manzano, R. Whitney. The Fourth Dimension, Vol. 2. LC 79-65588. 183p. 1983. pap. 5.95 (ISBN 0-88270-561-X). Bridge Pub.

--Mucho Mas Que Numeros. Bernal, Luis L., ed. Lievano, M. Francisco, tr. Tr. of More Than Numbers. (Span.). 208p. 1985. pap. text ed. 2.95 (ISBN 0-8297-0531-7). Life Pubs Intl.

Chrichton, J. D. Christian Celebration: A Three-in-One Textbook. 604p. (Orig.). pap. text ed. 22.50 (ISBN 0-225-66399-6, HarpR). Har-Row.

Christenson, Evelyn. Lord, Change Me. LC 77-81219. 192p. 1977. pap. 5.95 (ISBN 0-88207-756-2). Victor Bks.

--What Happens When God Answers. 160p. 1986. 9.95 (ISBN 0-8499-0569-9). Word Bks.

Christenson, Larry. Back to Square One. LC 79-16413. 144p. 1979. pap. 3.95 (ISBN 0-87123-025-9, 210025). Bethany Hse.

--La Familia Cristiana. 238p. 1972. 3.95 (ISBN 0-88113-080-X). Edit Betania.

--Gift of Tongues. 1963. pap. 1.25 (ISBN 0-87123-184-0, 260184). Bethany Hse.

--How to Have a Daily Quiet Time. 16p. 1979. saddle stitch 0.99 (ISBN 0-87123-235-9, 200235). Bethany Hse.

--The Wonderful Way That Babies Are Made. LC 82-12813. 48p. (Orig.). 1982. 8.95 (ISBN 0-87123-627-3, 230627). Bethany Hse.

Christian Broadcasting Network Staff, ed. The Christian Counselor's Handbook. 240p. 1987. pap. 8.95 (ISBN 0-8423-0255-7). Tyndale.

Christian Character Library Staff & Rinehart, Stacy. Living in Light of Eternity. 176p. 1986. 8.95 (ISBN 0-89109-551-9). NavPress.

Christian Experience. rev. ed. (Time of Life Learning Ser.). (Illus.). 32p. pap. 2.95 (ISBN 0-89622-246-2). Twenty-Third.

The Christian Home. pap. 4.95 (ISBN 0-88172-006-2). Believers Bkshelf.

Christian Life Magazine Staff & Wagner, C. Peter. Signs & Wonders Today. 1986. write for info. (ISBN 0-8297-0709-3). Life Pubs Intl.

Christian, Robert. Common Sense Renewed. 132p. 1986. 12.50 (ISBN 0-89279-078-4). Graphic Pub.

Christian Workers NT: New American Standard. deluxe, brown 19.95 (ISBN 0-8024-5541-7). Moody.

Christie, Les. Getting a Grip on Time Management. 64p. 1984. pap. 5.95 (ISBN 0-88207-192-0). Victor Bks.

Christoff, Nicholas B. Saturday Night, Sunday Morning: Singles & the Church. LC 77-7841. 160p. 1980. pap. 4.95 (ISBN 0-06-061381-5, RD 341, HarpR). Har-Row.

Christopher. Scott. new ed. (Orig.). 1978. pap. 3.95 (ISBN 0-87243-078-2). Templegate.

Church of England, House of Bishops Staff. The Nature of Christian Belief. 60p. (Orig.). 1986. pap. 2.25 (ISBN 0-88028-062-X). Forward Movement.

Churches Alive, Inc. Staff. Communicating. LC 79-52133. (Love One Another Bible Study Ser.). (Illus.). 1979. wkbk. 3.00 (ISBN 0-934396-06-X). Churches Alive.

--Contributing. LC 79-52132. (Love One Another Bible Study Ser.). (Illus.). 1979. wkbk. 3.00 (ISBN 0-934396-05-1). Churches Alive.

--Forgiving. LC 79-52128. (Love One Another Bible Study Ser.). (Illus.). 1979. wkbk. 3.00 (ISBN 0-934396-01-9). Churches Alive.

--Growth Group Member's Notebook. LC 80-52536. (Illus.). 105p. (Orig.). 1980. pap. text ed. 5.95 (ISBN 0-934396-11-6). Churches Alive.

--Love One Another Leader's Guide. LC 79-52128. (Love One Another Ser.). (Illus.). 85p. (Orig.). 1981. pap. text ed. 4.95 (ISBN 0-934396-13-2). Churches Alive.

--Maintaining Unity. LC 79-52134. (Love One Another Bible Study Ser.). (Illus.). 1979. wkbk. 3.00 (ISBN 0-934396-07-8). Churches Alive.

--Submitting. LC 79-52131. (Love One Another Bible Study Ser.). (Illus.). 1979. wkbk. 3.00 (ISBN 0-934396-04-3). Churches Alive.

--Understanding. LC 79-52129. (Love One Another Bible Study Ser.). (Illus.). 1979. wkbk. 3.00 (ISBN 0-934396-02-7). Churches Alive.

Clapp, Steve & Mauck, Sue I. A Primer for Angry Christians. (Illus.). 138p. (Orig.). 1981. pap. 6.00 (ISBN 0-914527-09-6). C-Four Res.

--Repairing Christian Lifestyles. 2nd ed. (Repairing Christian Lifestyles Ser.). (Illus.). 174p. (YA) 1983. pap. 6.00 (ISBN 0-914527-26-6); pap. 5.00 leader's guide (ISBN 0-914527-27-4). C-Four Res.

Clapp, Steve, ed. Prayer & the Christian Life: C-4 Devotional Journal II. (The C-4 Journals Ser.). 126p. (Orig.). 1982. pap. 6.00 (ISBN 0-317-11522-7). C-Four Res.

Clark, Fay M. You Will Take It with You. 135p. 1976. pap. 5.00 (ISBN 0-686-12934-2). Hiawatha Bondurant.

Clark, Keith. An Experience of Celibacy. LC 81-69747. (Illus.). 176p. (Orig.). 1982. pap. 4.95 (ISBN 0-87793-240-9). Ave Maria.

Clark, Martin E. Choosing Your Career: The Christian's Decision Manual. 1981. pap. 3.95 (ISBN 0-87552-205-X). Presby & Reformed.

--Choosing Your Career: The Christian's Decision Manual. 120p. (Orig.). 1983. pap. 4.95 (ISBN 0-8010-2483-8). Baker Bk.

Clark, Rebecca. The Rainbow Connection. LC 82-84590. 192p. 1983. 4.95 (ISBN 0-87159-136-7). Unity School.

Clark, Stephen B. Man & Woman in Christ: An Examination of the Roles of Men & Women in Light of Scripture & the Social Sciences. 754p. (Orig.). 1980. 24.95 (ISBN 0-89283-084-0). Servant.

Clark, Stephen B., ed. Patterns of Christian Community. 98p. (Orig.). 1984. pap. 4.95 (ISBN 0-89283-186-3). Servant.

Clark, Steve B. Growing in Faith. (Living As a Christian Ser.). 1972. pap. 2.25 (ISBN 0-89283-004-2). Servant.

--Knowing God's Will. (Living As a Christian Ser.). 1974. pap. 2.50 (ISBN 0-89283-005-0). Servant.

Clawson, Virginia. The Family Symphony. LC 84-17524. 1984. 7.95 (ISBN 0-8054-5661-9). Broadman.

Clemens, David A. The Cutting Edge, Vol. 2. LC 79-52420. (Steps to Maturity Ser.). 1975. student's manual 15.95x (ISBN 0-86508-003-8); tchr's. manual 17.95x (ISBN 0-86508-004-6). BCM Intl Inc.

--God Encountered, Vol. 1. LC 79-52420. (Steps to Maturity Ser.). 1973. tchrs'. manual 17.95x (ISBN 0-86508-002-X); student's manual 15.95x (ISBN 0-86508-001-1); visuals packett 4.95x (ISBN 0-86508-007-0). BCM Intl Inc.

Clement, Jane T. Sperling. 154p. 1986. pap. 6.00 (ISBN 3-922819-36-2). Plough.

Clemmons, William P. Discovering the Depths. LC 75-22507. 140p. 1976. pap. 7.95 (ISBN 0-8054-5562-0). Broadman.

Cliffe, A. E. Let Go & Let God. 1951. pap. 5.95 (ISBN 0-13-531509-3). P-H.

Clouse, Bonnidell. Moral Development. 368p. 1985. pap. 13.95 (ISBN 0-8010-2507-9). Baker Bk.

Clowers, Don. Chastening of the Lord. 40p. (Orig.). 1986. wkbk 4.95 (ISBN 0-914307-56-8). Word Faith.

Cobb, John B., Jr. Christ in a Pluralistic Age. LC 74-820. 286p. 1984. pap. 11.95 (ISBN 0-664-24522-6). Westminster.

Coburn, John B. Christ's Life, Our Life. LC 77-17172. 112p. 1978. 4.00 (ISBN 0-8164-0384-8, HarpR); pap. 4.95 (ISBN 0-8164-2616-3). Har-Row.

Cocoris, G. Michael. Questioning Christianity. 67p. (Orig.). 1985. pap. text ed. 1.00 (ISBN 0-935729-00-3). Church Open Door.

Coggin & Spooner. How to Build a Bus Ministry. 2.25 (ISBN 0-8054-9405-7). Broadman.

Cole, C. Donald. Christian Perspectives on Controversial Issues. 128p. (Orig.). 1983. pap. 3.50 (ISBN 0-8024-0165-1). Moody.

Cole, Edwin L. Courage: A Book for Champions. 164p. (Orig.). 1985. pap. 3.95 (ISBN 0-89274-362-X). Harrison Hse.

Cole, Ginny & Durfey, Carolyn, eds. Come to the Banquet. 200p. 1983. pap. text ed. 7.00 (ISBN 0-913991-00-7). Off Christian Fellowship.

Cole, W. Douglas. When Families Hurt. LC 79-51133. 1979. 6.50 (ISBN 0-8054-5638-4). Broadman.

Coleman, Charles G. Divine Guidance: That Voice Behind You. LC 77-6796. 1977. pap. 2.50 (ISBN 0-87213-087-8). Loizeaux.

Coleman, Lucien E. The Exciting Christian Life: Bible Study on Christian Growth. 36p. 1982. pap. 3.50 (ISBN 0-939298-11-2). J M Prods.

Coleman, Lyman. Coping: O God, I'm Struggling. (Serendipity Ser.). (Orig.). 1981. pap. 4.95 leader's guide 64 pgs. (ISBN 0-687-37310-7); pap. 1.25 student's bk. 32 pgs. (ISBN 0-687-37311-5). Abingdon.

--My Calling: Here I Am Lord. (Serendipity Ser.). (Orig.). 1981. pap. 4.95 leader's guide 64 pgs (ISBN 0-687-37336-0); pap. 1.25 student's bk 32 pgs (ISBN 0-687-37337-9). Abingdon.

Coleman, Robert E. Growing in the Word. 272p. 1982. pap. 2.95 (ISBN 0-8007-8448-0, Spire Bks). Revell.

--They Meet the Master. 160p. 1979. pap. 5.95 (ISBN 0-8007-1037-1). Revell.

Coleman, William. Courageous Christians. LC 81-70519. (Wonderful World of the Bible Ser.). (Illus.). 1983. 9.95 (ISBN 0-89191-558-3). Cook.

--A Measured Pace. 144p. (Orig.). 1986. pap. 4.95 (ISBN 0-87123-671-0, 210671). Bethany Hse.

--You Can Be Creative. LC 83-80474. 160p. (Orig.). 1984. pap. 3.95 (ISBN 0-89081-387-6, 3876). Harvest Hse.

Coleman, William L. More about My Magnificent Machine. LC 79-21140. (Illus.). 128p. (Orig.). 1980. pap. 4.95 (ISBN 0-87123-386-X, 210386). Bethany Hse.

Cole-Whittaker, Terry. What You Think of Me Is None of My Business. 194p. (Orig.). 1982. pap. 9.95 (ISBN 0-86679-002-0). Oak Tree Pubns.

Collected Writings of John Murray, Vol. 3: To Serve the Living God. 24.95 (ISBN 0-85151-337-9). Banner of Truth.

Collier, Philip E. It Seems to Me. 1982. 4.95 (ISBN 0-86544-019-0). Salv Army Suppl South.

Colligan, John, et al. Calling Disciples. 54p. (Orig.). 1984. 1.95 (ISBN 0-911905-22-7). Past & Mat Rene Ctr.

--Calling Disciples, Mentality. LC 84-60459. (Calling Disciples Ser.: Bk. 2). 67p. (Orig.). 1984. pap. text ed. 2.95 (ISBN 0-911905-21-9). Past & Mat Rene Ctr.

Collins, Charlotte. Not Healed? LC 82-73707. 1983. pap. text ed. 2.50 (ISBN 0-932050-15-8). New Puritan.

Collins, Gary. How to Be a People Helper. LC 76-15112. (Orig.). 1976. pap. 5.95 (ISBN 0-88449-055-6, A424076). Vision Hse.

--People Helper Growthbook. LC 76-25752. 1976. pap. 5.95 (ISBN 0-88449-056-4, A424084). Vision Hse.

Collins, Gary R. Getting Started. 224p. (Orig.). 1984. pap. 5.95 (ISBN 0-8007-5162-0, Power Bks). Revell.

--Getting Your Life Out of Neutral. 1987. 14.95. Revell.

--The Magnificent Mind. 224p. 1985. 9.95 (ISBN 0-8499-0385-8, 0385-8). Word Bks.

--The Sixty-Second Christian. 64p. 1984. 5.95 (ISBN 0-8499-0450-1, 0450-1). Word Bks.

Colson, Charles. Dare to Be Different, Dare to Be Christian. 48p. 1986. pap. 1.95 (ISBN 0-89693-159-5). Victor Bks.

--Naci de Nuevo. Ward, Rhode, tr. from Eng. LC 77-81645. Tr. of Born Again. (Span.). 419p. 1977. pap. 6.50 (ISBN 0-89922-087-8). Edit Caribe.

--Presenting Belief in an Age of Unbelief. 48p. 1986. 1.95 (ISBN 0-89693-158-7). Victor Bks.

--The Struggle for Men's Hearts & Minds. 48p. 1986. 1.95 (ISBN 0-89693-166-8). Victor Bks.

Colson, Charles W. Loving God. 288p. 1983. 12.95 (ISBN 0-310-47030-7, 11306); study guide 3.95 (ISBN 0-310-47038-2, 11307). Zondervan.

Colton, Gary P. Praise & Prayer. 1978. 7.95 (ISBN 0-8198-0593-9). Dghtrs St Paul.

Colville, Josephine. Growing Up. 1979. 6.25 (ISBN 0-8198-0575-0); pap. 5.00 (ISBN 0-8198-0576-9). Dghtrs St Paul.

Combee, Jerry H. & Hall, Cline E. Designed for Destiny. 112p. 1985. 4.95 (ISBN 0-8423-0619-6). Tyndale.

Compton, Al. Armonia Familiar. 32p. 1981. pap. 1.30 (ISBN 0-311-46078-X). Casa Bautista.

Compton, Everald. Living with Money. 47p. (Orig.). 1983. pap. 5.95 (ISBN 0-340-34299-4, Pub. by Genesis). ANZ Religious Pubns.

Conant, Newton. Cheating God. 102p. 1985. pap. 3.50 (ISBN 0-317-43393-8). Chr Lit.

Coniaris, A. M. Making God Real in the Orthodox Christian Home. 1977. pap. 5.95 (ISBN 0-937032-07-7). Light&Life Pub Co MN.

Conn, Charles P. & Aultman, Donald S. Studies in Discipleship. LC 75-14887. 1975. pap. 1.99 (ISBN 0-87148-772-1). Pathway Pr.

Conner, Kevin J. & Iverson, K. R. Restoring the Church. (Illus.). 92p. 1977. Answer key. pap. 8.95 (ISBN 0-914936-23-9). Bible Temple.

Conscious Contact. 24p. (Orig.). 1985. pap. 0.95 (ISBN 0-89486-323-1). Hazelden.

Conway, Jim. Los Hombres En Su Crisis de Media Vida. Orig. Title: Men in Mid-Life Crisis. (Span.). 256p. 1982. pap. 5.95 (ISBN 0-311-46088-7, Edit Mundo). Casa Bautista.

Conway, Jim & Conway, Sally. La Mujer en su Crisis de Media Vida. De Zorzoli, Alicia, tr. from Span. Tr. of Women in Mid-Life Crisis. 352p. 1985. pap. 6.50 (ISBN 0-311-46105-0). Casa Bautista.

Cook, Ellen. Sharing the Journey. 1986. pap. 6.95 (ISBN 0-697-02208-0). Wm C Brown.

Cook, Jean T. Hugs for Our New Baby. (Illus.). 1987. 3.95 (ISBN 0-570-04165-1). Concordia.

Cook, William H. Success, Motivation, & the Scriptures. new ed. LC 74-82582. 192p. 1975. kivar 6.95 (ISBN 0-8054-5226-5). Broadman.

Coop, William L. Pacific People Sing Out Strong. (Orig.). 1982. pap. 4.95 (ISBN 0-377-00118-X). Friend Pr.

Cooper, Darien B. The Christian Woman's Planner. 160p. (Orig.). 1986. pap. 8.95 spiral bdg. (ISBN 0-310-44621-X, 11742P). Zondervan.

--You Can Be the Wife of a Happy Husband. LC 74-77450. 156p. 1974. pap. 5.95 (ISBN 0-88207-711-2). Victor Bks.

Cooper, Douglas. Living Spirit-Filled Life. (Red Ser.). 1985. pap. 4.95 (ISBN 0-8163-0595-1). Pacific Pr Pub Assn.

--Living We've Just Begun. (Redwood Ser.). 96p. 1983. pap. 4.95 (ISBN 0-8163-0505-6). Pacific Pr Pub Assn.

Cooper, Harold. Living Jesus. (Illus.). 1977. PBK:106. pap. text ed. 1.50 (ISBN 0-89114-077-8); PBK:48. tchrs. ed. 1.00 (ISBN 0-89114-078-6). Baptist Pub Hse.

--Loving Truth about Jesus. 136p. 1976. pap. 1.50 (ISBN 0-89114-100-6); tchr's ed 1.00 (ISBN 0-89114-101-4). Baptist Pub Hse.
--True Service. (Illus.). 111p. 1978. pap. text ed. 1.50 (ISBN 0-89114-081-6); P. 55. tchrs. ed. 1.25 (ISBN 0-89114-082-4). Baptist Pub Hse.
Cooper, Mildred & Fanning, Martha. What Every Woman Still Knows: A Celebration of the Christian Liberated Woman. LC 78-17182. 182p. 1978. 7.95 (ISBN 0-87131-271-9). M Evans.
Cooper, W. Norman. The Ultimate Destination. 95p. 1980. 7.50 (ISBN 0-87516-413-7); pap. 4.50 (ISBN 0-87516-381-5). De Vorss.
Coors, Holly. Joy Is the Promise. 1978. pap. 1.50 (ISBN 0-88419-182-6). Creation Hse.
Cope, Lamar. Faith for a New Day. Lambert, Herbert, ed. 128p. (Orig.). 1986. pap. 8.95 (ISBN 0-8272-1013-2). CBP.
Copeland, E. Luther. World Mission & World Survival. LC 84-14963. 1985. pap. 5.95 (ISBN 0-8054-6335-6). Broadman.
Coppin, Ezra. Too Proud to Die. LC 82-50238. 168p. (Orig.). 1982. pap. 4.95 (ISBN 0-88449-082-3, A424615). Vision Hse.
Corbin, Linda & Dys, Pat. Together: Jesus Helps Me Grow, Bk. 2. (Orig.). Date not set. pap. 3.95 (ISBN 0-87509-374-4). Chr Pubns.
--Together: Jesus Makes Us New, Bk. 1. (Illus.), 24p. (Orig.). 1986. pap. 3.95 (ISBN 0-87509-373-6). Chr Pubns.
Corbitt, Jackie. Our Lengthened Shadows. 110p. 1970. pap. 1.75 (ISBN 0-89114-015-8). Baptist Pub Hse.
Cording, Ruth. The Joy of Remembering Our Guests. 1982. gift padded cover 7.95 (ISBN 0-87162-258-0, J1016). Warner Pr.
Cordner, John. Dear Laddie. LC 86-71593. 300p. (Orig.). 1987. pap. 4.50 (ISBN 0-9617224-0-1). J Cordner.
Cornwall, Judson. Let Us Abide. LC 77-23143. 155p. 1984. pap. 4.95 (ISBN 0-8007-5065-9). Bridge Pub.
--Let Us Be Holy. LC 87-70993. 1978. pap. 4.95 (ISBN 0-88270-278-5). Bridge Pub.
--Let Us See Jesus. LC 80-20645. 160p. 1981. pap. 4.95 (ISBN 0-8007-5052-7). Bridge Pub.
Corson-Finnerty, Adam. World Citizen: Action for Global Justice. LC 81-16918. 178p. (Orig.). 1982. pap. 6.95 (ISBN 0-88344-715-0). Orbis Bks.
Cory, Lloyd, compiled by. Quotable Quotations. 400p. 1985. pap. 12.95 (ISBN 0-88207-823-2). Victor Bks.
Cosby, Clair G. Lord, Help Me Love My Sister. LC 86-4831. 80p. (Orig.). 1986. pap. 4.95 (ISBN 0-8361-3413-3). Herald Pr.
Cosgrove, Francis M. Essentials of Discipleship. LC 79-93015. 192p. 1980. pap. 5.95 (ISBN 0-89109-442-3). NavPress.
--Essentials of New Life. LC 78-54949. (Illus.). 180p. (Orig.). 1978. pap. 5.95 (ISBN 0-89109-427-X). NavPress.
Costas, Orlando. Christ Outside the Gate: Mission Beyond Christendom. LC 82-7892. 272p. (Orig.). 1982. pap. 12.95 (ISBN 0-88344-147-0). Orbis Bks.
Costello, Andrew. How to Deal with Difficult People. LC 80-81751. 112p. (Orig.). 1980. pap. 3.95 (ISBN 0-89243-128-8). Liguori Pubns.
Cote, Richard G. Holy Mirth: A Theology of Laughter. 100p. (Orig.). 1985. pap. 8.95 (ISBN 0-89571-031-5). Affirmation.
Cottrell, Jack. Tough Questions: Biblical Answers Part One. 122p. (Orig.). pap. 3.95 (ISBN 0-89900-208-0). College Pr Pub.
Couey, Dick. Happiness Is Being a Physically Fit Christian. LC 84-12746. 1985. 9.95 (ISBN 0-8054-7525-7). Broadman.
Couey, Richard. Lifelong Fitness & Fulfillment. LC 80-65844. 1980. 7.95 (ISBN 0-8054-5426-8). Broadman.
Countryman, Jack. God's Promises for Living. 285p. 1984. leatherbound 19.95 (ISBN 0-937347-01-9). J Countryman Pubs.
--God's Promises for Your Every Need. 334p. 1981. leatherbound 19.95 (ISBN 0-937347-00-0). J Countryman Pubs.
Cousens, Gabriel. Spiritual Nutrition. 232p. 1986. 9.95 (ISBN 0-9615875-2-0). Cassandra Pr.
Covey, R. O. Probing Our Problems. 176p. (Orig.). 1986. pap. 5.95 (ISBN 0-934942-59-5, 3950). White Wing Pub.
Cowman, Mrs. Charles E. Springs in the Valley. 1977. large-print ed. kivar 9.95 (ISBN 0-310-22517-5, 12562L). Zondervan.
Cox, Edward F. Twelve for Twelve. 64p. 1982. pap. 3.50 (ISBN 0-8341-0787-2). Beacon Hill.
Cox, William E. Sir, I Represent Christian Salesmanship. pap. 1.50 (ISBN 0-686-64392-5). Reiner.
Coyle, Neva. Free to Be Thin Study Guide Discipline, No. 2. 58p. 1982. pap. 2.25 (ISBN 0-87123-169-7, 210169). Bethany Hse.
--Perseverance for People under Pressure. 64p. (Orig.). 1986. pap. 2.50 saddle stitched (ISBN 0-87123-888-8). Bethany Hse.
Coyle, Neva & Chapian, Marie. There's More to Being Thin Than Being Thin. 170p. (Orig.). 1984. pap. 5.95 (ISBN 0-87123-443-2, 210443). Bethany Hse.
Crabb, Jr. & Lawrence, J. Encouragement. 1986. 9.95 (ISBN 0-88469-199-3). BMH Bks.
Craig, James D. New Life Studies. 2nd rev. abr. ed. 174p. 1983. pap. text ed. 15.00 (ISBN 0-88151-023-8). Lay Leadership.
--New Life Studies: Home Study Guide. 2nd rev. abr. ed. 64p. 1983. 8.00 (ISBN 0-88151-024-6). Lay Leadership.
Crane, J. D. El Espiritu Santo en la Experiencia del Cristiano. De Lerin, Olivia, tr. Orig. Title: The Christian's Esperience of the Holy Spirit. Tr. of The Christian Experience of the Holy Spirit. 128p. 1982. Repr. of 1979 ed. 5.95 (ISBN 0-311-09093-1). Casa Bautista.
Crane, James & Estudios, Guias de. Guia de Estudios Sobre Manual Para Predicadores Laicos. 88p. 1982. pap. 3.50 (ISBN 0-311-43502-5). Casa Bautista.
Crane, James D. & Diaz, Jorge E. Lecciones Para Nuevos Creyentes Student. 64p. 1984. pap. 1.65 (ISBN 0-311-13835-7); teacher ed. 2.95 (ISBN 0-311-13838-1). Casa Bautista.
Cranfield, Charles E. The Bible & Christian Life. 256p. 1985. pap. 15.95 (ISBN 0-567-29125-1, Pub. by T&T Clark Ltd UK). Fortress.
Crank, David. Godly Finances: The Bible Way to Pay off Your Home. 50p. (Orig.). 1986. pap. 4.95 (ISBN 0-936437-00-6). D Crank Pubns.
Cranor, Phoebe. Why Doesn't God Do Something? LC 78-118. 144p. (YA) 1978. pap. 3.50 (ISBN 0-87123-605-2, 200605). Bethany Hse.
Crawford, Dan R. Where One Is Gathered in His Name. LC 85-19519. 1986. 6.95 (ISBN 0-8054-5025-4). Broadman.
Creagh, Terry. Give Sorrow Words. 94p. (Orig.). 1982. pap. 9.95 (ISBN 0-85819-341-8, Pub. by JBCE). ANZ Religious Pubns.
Crean, David & Ebbeson, Eric, eds. Living Simply: An Examination of Christian Lifestyles. 128p. (Orig.). 1981. pap. 5.95 (ISBN 0-8164-2340-7, HarpR). Har-Row.
Crews, Clyde F. Fundamental Things Apply: Reflecting on Christian Basics. LC 83-71005. 104p. (Orig.). 1983. pap. 3.95 (ISBN 0-87793-272-7). Ave Maria.
Cribb, C. C. Flying High Against the Sky: If God Has It I Want It! LC 79-84881. Date not set. pap. 2.95 (ISBN 0-932046-16-9). Manhattan Ltd NC.
--Getting Ready for Heaven. LC 78-60614. (If God Has It I Want It!). 1979. pap. 2.95 (ISBN 0-685-96444-2). Manhattan Ltd NC.
--Getting Ready for the Coming Rapture. LC 79-88232. (If God Has It I Want It! Ser.). Date not set. pap. 2.95 (ISBN 0-932046-19-3). Manhattan Ltd NC.
--Getting Your Share of the Spirit's Outpouring. LC 79-88229. (If God Has It I Want It! Ser.). Date not set. pap. 2.95 (ISBN 0-932046-17-7). Manhattan Ltd NC.
--Moving the Hand That Moves the World. LC 79-88930. (If God Has It I Want It! Ser.). Date not set. pap. 2.95 (ISBN 0-932046-18-5). Manhattan Ltd NC.
--Spinning Straw into Gold. LC 79-84880. (If God Has It I Want It! Ser.). pap. 2.95 (ISBN 0-932046-15-0). Manhattan Ltd NC.
--Staking Your Claim on Healing. LC 79-83919. (If God Has It I Want It!). 1979. pap. 2.95 (ISBN 0-932046-14-2). Manhattan Ltd NC.
Crider, Virginia. Answering the Cry. (Northland Ser.). 1976. pap. 2.50 (ISBN 0-87813-510-3). Christian Light.
Crinzi, Debbie. Principles of Discipleship. 102p. 1984. pap. text ed. 5.00 (ISBN 0-8309-0394-1). Herald Hse.
Cristenson, Larry. The Renewed Mind. LC 74-12770. 144p. (Orig.). 1974. pap. 4.95 (ISBN 0-87123-479-3, 210479). Bethany Hse.
Criswell, W. A. Great Doctrines of the Bible, Vol. 6: Christian Life & Stewardship. 128p. 1986. text ed. 11.95 (ISBN 0-310-43950-7). Zondervan.
Crockett, William J. God's Way: Voices from the Heart. 15p. 1985. pap. 3.00 (ISBN 0-934383-34-0). Pride Prods.
--Mother's Day: Voices from the Heart. 15p. 1985. pap. 3.00 (ISBN 0-934383-33-2). Pride Prods.
--My Quest: Voices from the Heart. 15p. 1985. pap. 3.00 (ISBN 0-934383-32-4). Pride Prods.
Cromie, Richard M. Christ Will See You Through. 60p. (Orig.). 1985. pap. 1.50 (ISBN 0-914733-04-4). Desert Min.
Cronin, Gaynell. Sunday Throughout the Week. LC 81-68992. (Illus.). 176p. (Orig.). 1981. pap. 5.95 (ISBN 0-87793-241-7). Ave Maria.
Crook, Carol. Step out in Ministry! LC 86-71831. 203p. (Orig.). 1986. pap. 9.95 (ISBN 0-939399-07-5). Bks of Truth.
Crooks, Mrs. Boyd. Our Faith Speaks. 62p. 1962. pap. 0.35 (ISBN 0-89114-147-2). Baptist Pub Hse.
Crossin, John W. What Are They Saying about Virtue. (WATSA Ser.). pap. 4.95 (ISBN 0-8091-2674-5). Paulist Pr.
Crow, Paul A., Jr. Christian Unity: Matrix for Mission. (Orig.). 1982. pap. 4.95 (ISBN 0-377-00115-5). Friend Pr.
Cruz, Rodolfo A. Instrucciones Practicas para Nuevos Creyentes. LC 77-71308. (Span.). 78p. (Orig.). 1970. pap. text ed. 1.95 (ISBN 0-89922-002-9). Edit Caribe.
Culbertson, William. God's Provision for Holy Living. (Moody Classics Ser.). 1984. pap. 2.95 (ISBN 0-8024-3043-0). Moody.
Culliton, Joseph T. Non-Violence-Central to Christian Spirituality: Perspectives from Scriptures to the Present. LC 82-7964. (Toronto Studies in Theology: Vol. 8). 312p. 1982. 49.95x (ISBN 0-88946-964-4). E Mellen.
Cullum, Charles G. All Things Are Possible: The Charles Cullum Lessons. LC 86-5819. 176p. (Orig.). 1986. pap. 7.95 (ISBN 0-937641-00-6). Stone Canyon Pr.
Cully, Iris V. Christian Child Development. LC 78-19507. 176p. 1983. pap. 6.95 (ISBN 0-06-061654-7, RD/453, HarpR). Har-Row.
Cummings, Charles. The Mystery of the Ordinary: Discovering the Richness of Everyday Experiences. LC 81-47846. 144p. 1982. 9.57 (ISBN 0-06-061652-0, HarpR). Har-Row.
Cummins, Walter J. Demonstrating God's Power. LC 85-50446. 276p. 1985. 6.95 (ISBN 0-910068-60-7). Am Christian.
Cunningham, Loren & Rogers, Janice. Eres Tu, Senor? Araujo, Juan S., tr. from Eng. Tr. of Is That Really You, God? (Span.). 176p. 1986. pap. 3.50 (ISBN 0-88113-061-3). Edit Betania.
Curran, Dolores. Family: A Church Challenge for the 80's. (Orig.). 1980. pap. 3.50 (ISBN 0-86683-640-3, HarpR). Har-Row.
Currie, David R. On the Way! LC 81-69403. 1982. pap. 3.95 (ISBN 0-8054-5336-9, 4253-36). Broadman.
Curtin, Rosalie, et al. R. C. I. A. A Practical Approach to Christian Initiation. 136p. (Orig.). 1981. pap. 10.95 (ISBN 0-697-01759-1). Wm C Brown.
Curtis, Ken & Curtis, Nancy. Tormented? Christians Guide for Spiritual Warfare. rev. ed. (Illus.). 1985. pap. 3.95 (ISBN 0-9615445-0-3, Dist. by Spring Arbor). Spiritual Warfare.
Cuss, Gladys. I Have Been Before the Judgement Seat of Christ: A Religious Autobiography. 189p. 1980. 7.95 (ISBN 0-682-49521-2). Exposition Pr FL.
Cussen, Joseph A. World Youth & the Family. 1984. pap. 6.95 (ISBN 0-941850-14-5). Sunday Pubns.
Cutts, A. M. Dios y Sus Ayudantes. (Span., Illus.). 48p. 1981. pap. 1.25 (ISBN 0-311-38548-6). Casa Bautista.
Daane, James. Freedom of God. 5.95 (ISBN 0-8028-3421-3). Fuller Theol Soc.
Dabney, Robert L. Dabney Discussions, Vol. 1. 728p. 1982. Repr. of 1891 ed. 19.95 (ISBN 0-85151-348-4). Banner of Truth.
--Dabney Discussions, Vol. 2. (Religious Ser.). 684p. 1982. Repr. of 1891 ed. 19.95 (ISBN 0-85151-349-2). Banner of Truth.
--Dabney Discussions, Vol. 3. (Religious Ser.). 493p. 1982. Repr. of 1892 ed. 17.95 (ISBN 0-85151-350-6). Banner of Truth.
Dalrymple, John. Living the Richness of the Cross. LC 83-70945. 128p. (Orig.). 1983. pap. 3.95 (ISBN 0-87793-274-3). Ave Maria.
Dana, Mark. Lifemating: New Hope for Those Who've Loved & Lost. 1985. 7.75 (ISBN 0-8062-2447-9). Carlton.
Daniel, R. P. Outlines for Christian Youth. pap. 5.95 (ISBN 0-88172-019-4). Believers Bkshelf.
Danielou, Jean, ed. From Glory to Glory: Texts from Gregory of Nyssa's Mystical Writings. LC 79-38. 304p. 1979. pap. 9.95 (ISBN 0-913836-54-0). St Vladimirs.
Daniels, Velma S. Patches of Joy. 1979. 7.95 (ISBN 0-88289-101-4); pap. 5.95 (ISBN 0-88289-232-0). Pelican.
D'Arcy, Paula. Where the Wind Begins: Stories of Hurting People Who Said Yes to Life. 144p. 1985. pap. 5.95 (ISBN 0-87788-925-2). Shaw Pubs.
Darey-Bembe, Francoise & Bembe, John P. Day by Day with God. 1982. 4.95 (ISBN 0-8215-9908-9). Sadlier.
Darling, Harold W. Man in His Right Mind. 158p. 1977. pap. 5.95 (ISBN 0-85364-097-1). Attic Pr.
Darnall, Jean. Heaven, Here I Come. LC 77-91521. 1978. pap. 2.95 (ISBN 0-88419-148-6). Creation Hse.
Daughters of St. Paul. More Than a Knight. (Encounter Ser.). (Illus.). 100p. 1982. 3.00 (ISBN 0-8198-4714-3, EN0204); pap. 2.00 (ISBN 0-8198-4715-1). Dghtrs St Paul.
--Yes Is Forever. (Encounter Ser.). (Illus.). 109p. 1982. 3.00 (ISBN 0-8198-8700-5, EN0260); pap. 2.00 (ISBN 0-8198-8702-1). Dghtrs St Paul.
Davidson, Robert G. Held in High Value. 65p. (Orig.). 1986. pap. 9.95 (ISBN 0-940754-34-7). Ed Ministries.
--What Do They Expect of Me? 80p. 1986. pap. 9.95 (ISBN 0-940754-32-0). Ed Ministries.
Davies, Brian. Thinking about God. 1986. pap. 16.95 (ISBN 0-317-52367-8, HarpR). Har-Row.
Davis, Earl C. Somebody Cares. LC 81-71255. 1983. 7.95 (ISBN 0-8054-5211-7). Broadman.
Davis, John J. Abortion & the Christian. 128p. 1984. pap. 4.95 (ISBN 0-87552-221-1). Presby & Reformed.
--Contemporary Counterfeits. 1979. pap. 1.25 (ISBN 0-88469-003-2). BMH Bks.
--Demons, Exorcism & the Evangelical. 1979. pap. 1.00 (ISBN 0-88469-043-1). BMH Bks.
Davis, Lee E. In Charge. LC 84-4969. 1984. pap. 4.95 (ISBN 0-8054-6404-2). Broadman.
Davis, Ron L. A Forgiving God in an Unforgiving World. 1984. pap. 5.95 (ISBN 0-89081-431-7). Harvest Hse.
Davis, Roy E. Light on the Spiritual Path. 138p. 1984. pap. 3.95 (ISBN 0-317-20861-6). CSA Pr.
--My Personal Fulfillment Plan Workbook. 32p. 1984. pap. 3.95 (ISBN 0-317-20868-3). CSA Pr.
--This Is Reality. 160p. 1983. pap. 3.95 (ISBN 0-317-20863-2). CSA Pr.
--Who is the True Guru. 192p. 1981. pap. 4.95 (ISBN 0-317-20864-0). CSA Pr.
Davis, W. A. Another Generation. (Orig.). 1985. text ed. 5.25 (ISBN 0-87148-019-0); pap. 4.25 (ISBN 0-87148-020-4); instr's. guide 7.95 (ISBN 0-87148-021-2). Pathway Pr.
Davis, W. M. The Way to Get What You Want. 1941. pap. 3.50 (ISBN 0-88027-022-5). Firm Foun Pub.
Davy, Yvonne. Africa's Diamonds. Tyson-Flyn, Juanita, ed. (Daybreak Ser.). 96p. 1983. pap. 4.95 (ISBN 0-8163-0512-9). Pacific Pr Pub Assn.
--Trail of Peril. Wheeler, Gerald, ed. LC 83-17835. (A Banner Bk.). (Illus.). 94p. (Orig.). 1984. pap. 5.95 (ISBN 0-8280-0223-1). Review & Herald.
Day. If You Fight-Fight Fair. (Out Ser.). 1984. 1.25 (ISBN 0-8163-0597-8). Pacific Pr Pub Assn.
Day, Albert E. Discipline & Discovery. rev. ed. 1977. pap. 4.95x (ISBN 0-8358-0354-6). Upper Room.
Day, LeRoy J. Dynamic Christian Fellowship. rev. ed. (Orig.). pap. 2.95 (ISBN 0-8170-0226-X). Judson.
Day, N. R. Your Faith Is Growing! 51p. (Orig.). 1981. pap. 5.45 (ISBN 0-940754-10-X). Ed Ministries.
Day, N. Raymond. From Palm Sunday to Easter. 45p. (Orig.). 1979. pap. 5.45 (ISBN 0-940754-01-0). Ed Ministries.
Dayton, Edward R. What Ever Happened to Commitment? 224p. 1983. pap. 6.95 (ISBN 0-310-23161-2, 10748P). Zondervan.
Dayton, Edward R. & Engstrom, Ted W. Strategy for Living. LC 76-3935. (Orig.). 1976. pap. 6.95 (ISBN 0-8307-0424-8, 5403405); wkbk. 4.95 (ISBN 0-8307-0476-0, 5202000). Regal.
Dayton, Edward R., ed. That Everyone May Hear. 3rd ed. 91p. 1983. pap. 4.60 (ISBN 0-912552-41-7). Missions Adv Res Com Ctr.
Dayton, Howard. Your Money: Frustration or Freedom? 1979. pap. 5.95 (ISBN 0-8423-8725-0). Tyndale.
Deal, William S. Daily Christian Living. LC 62-22195. 1962. pap. 0.95 (ISBN 0-686-05840-2). Crusade Pubs.
--Heart Talks on the Deeper Life. 1960. 1.50 (ISBN 0-686-05838-0). Crusade Pubs.
--Problems of the Spirit-Filled Life. 2.95 (ISBN 0-686-13724-8). Crusade Pubs.
--What Every Young Christian Should Know. 1982. 1.95. Crusade Pubs.
--Workmen of God. 1975. pap. 0.95 (ISBN 0-686-11025-0). Crusade Pubs.
Dean, Bessie. Let's Learn God's Plan. LC 78-52114. (Illus.). 1978. pap. 3.95 (ISBN 0-88290-092-7). Horizon Utah.
De Bargh, David J. Christ in My Life. 1977. 4.50 (ISBN 0-8198-0396-0); pap. text ed. 3.50 (ISBN 0-8198-0397-9). Dghtrs St Paul.
De Brosses, Charles. Du Culte Des Dieux Fetiches, Ou Parallele de l'Ancienne Religion de l'Egypte Avec la Religion Actuelle de Nigrittie. 286p. Repr. of 1760 ed. text ed. 62.10 (ISBN 0-576-12101-0, Pub. by Gregg Intl Pubs England). Gregg Intl.
De Deguilleville, Guillaume. The Pilgrimage of the Life of Man, Pts. 1-3. Furnivall, F. J. & Locock, K. B., eds. (EETS, ES Ser.: Nos. 77, 83, & 92). Repr. of 1904 ed. 90.00 (ISBN 0-527-00279-8). Kraus Repr.
DeGroat, Florence. Resurrection. LC 81-67782. (Universal Man Ser.: Vol. 2). (Illus.). 168p. (Orig.). 1981. pap. text ed. 6.50 (ISBN 0-87516-456-0). De Vorss.
DeHaan, Daniel F. The God You Can Know. LC 81-16948. 180p. 1982. pap. 5.95 (ISBN 0-8024-3008-2). Moody.

DeHaan, Dennis J., ed. Windows on the World. 1984. pap. 4.95 (ISBN 0-8010-2946-5). Baker Bk.

DeHaan, M. R. & Bosch, Henry G. Our Daily Bread. 1986. 13.95 (ISBN 0-310-23410-7, 9505). Zondervan.

DeHaan, R. F. Return Unto Me. pap. 2.00 (ISBN 0-686-14199-7). Rose Pub MI.

De Hueck Doherty, Catherine. Soul of My Soul: Reflections from a Life of Prayer. LC 85-72271. 128p. (Orig.). 1985. pap. 4.95 (ISBN 0-87793-298-0). Ave Maria.

Deiros, P. A. Que Paso con Estos Pecados? 144p. 1979. pap. 2.50 (ISBN 0-311-42063-X). Casa Bautista.

Deiros, Pablo. El Cristiano y los Problemas Eticos. 112p. 1982. pap. 3.50 (ISBN 0-311-46064-X). Casa Bautista.

De Jong, Benjamin R. Uncle Ben's Quotebook. 1976. 11.95 (ISBN 0-8010-2851-5). Baker Bk.

De la Cruz Aymes, Maria, et al. Growing with God. (God with Us Program). 112p. (Orig.). 1983. pap. text ed. 3.69 (ISBN 0-8215-1121-1); tchr's ed. 10.86 (ISBN 0-8215-1131-9); wkbk. 1.65 (ISBN 0-8215-1151-3); compact ed 3.18 (ISBN 0-8215-1101-7). Sadlier.

--Growing with God's Forgiveness & I Celebrate Reconcilation. (Sacrament Program Ser.). 72p. 1985. pap. text ed. 3.30 (ISBN 0-8215-2371-6); tchr's. ed. 4.50 (ISBN 0-8215-2373-2); Parent Pack (10 booklets) 5.04 (ISBN 0-8215-2377-5). Sadlier.

Delafield, E. Love Prescription. (Stories That Win Ser.). 64p. 1980. pap. 0.95 (ISBN 0-8163-0410-6). Pacific Pr Pub Assn.

De La Touche, Louise M. The Book of Infinite Love. O'Connell, E. Patrick, tr. from Fr. LC 79-90488. 1979. pap. 3.00 (ISBN 0-89555-129-2). TAN Bks Pubs.

--The Little Book of the Work of Infinite Love. LC 79-90490. 1979. pap. 1.50 (ISBN 0-89555-130-6). TAN Bks Pubs.

De Lubac, Henri. Christian Faith. 1986. pap. 12.95 (ISBN 0-317-52368-6, HarpR). Har-Row.

Delve, Eric. To Boldly Go. 132p. 1986. pap. 4.95 (ISBN 0-89693-275-3). Victor Bks.

DeMarco, Donald. The Anesthetic Society. 182p. (Orig.). 1982. pap. 6.95 (ISBN 0-931888-09-3). Christendom Pubns.

De Mello, Anthony. One-Minute Wisdom. LC 85-29003. 216p. 1986. 14.95 (ISBN 0-385-23585-2). Doubleday.

Deming, Doris R. Touch of Infinity. 1984. 6.75 (ISBN 0-8062-2224-7). Carlton.

Dennis, Joe. Spreading Truth. 64p. 1979. pap. text ed. 1.95 (ISBN 0-89114-086-7); P. 78. tchrs. ed. 1.95 (ISBN 0-89114-087-5). Baptist Pub Hse.

De Poor, Betty M., tr. Dios, Tu y Tu Familia. (Dios, Tu y la Vida). Orig. Title: Deus, Voce E Sua Familia. 1981. Repr. of 1978 ed. 0.95 (ISBN 0-311-46202-2). Casa Bautista.

Derstine, Gerald. Destined to Mature. 144p. (Orig.). 1984. pap. 3.50 (ISBN 0-88368-147-1). Whitaker Hse.

De Santo, Charles. Dear Tim. LC 81-23744. 200p. (Orig.). 1982. pap. 7.95 (ISBN 0-8361-1991-6). Herald Pr.

DeStefano, Patricia. Interlude of Widowhood. (Greeting Book Line Ser.). 48p. (Orig.). 1983. pap. 1.50 (ISBN 0-89622-200-4). Twenty-Third.

Detrick, R. Blaine. Golf & the Gospel. 1985. 4.95 (ISBN 0-89536-766-1, 5873). CSS of Ohio.

De Vries, Dawn. Servant of the Word. LC 86-45902. 240p. 1987. pap. 14.95 (ISBN 0-8006-3203-6). Fortress.

DeVries, Janet M. Learning the Pacific Way: A Guide for All Ages. (Orig.). 1982. pap. 3.95 (ISBN 0-377-00119-8). Friend Pr.

DeVries, Thomas D. Discovering Our Gifts. 1.50 (ISBN 0-8091-9328-0). Paulist Pr.

De Waal, Esther. God under My Roof. 40p. (Orig.). 1985. pap. 1.50 (ISBN 0-941478-42-4). Paraclete Pr.

Dewar, Diana. All for Christ: Some Twentieth Century Martyrs. 1980. pap. 8.95x (ISBN 0-19-283024-4). Oxford U Pr.

Dewey, Barbara. As You Believe. LC 85-7370. 208p. 1985. 18.95 (ISBN 0-933123-01-9). Bartholomew Bks.

Dewitt, John R. Amazing Love. 160p. (Orig.). 1981. pap. text ed. 5.45 (ISBN 0-85151-328-X). Banner of Truth.

Dexter, Anne. View the Land. 1986. pap. 3.50 (ISBN 0-88270-609-8). Bridge Pub.

Dicharry, Warren. To Live the Word Inspired & Incarnate: An Integral Biblical Spirituality. LC 85-7386. 464p. (Orig.). 1985. pap. 12.95 (ISBN 0-8189-0476-3). Alba.

Dickerson, Grace. Jesus. 1985. 5.50 (ISBN 0-533-03936-3). Vantage.

Dickman, R. Thomas. In God We Should Trust. LC 76-53146. 1977. 6.95 (ISBN 0-87212-071-6). Libra.

Dickson, Elaine. Say No, Say Yes to Change. LC 81-67375. 1982. 6.95 (ISBN 0-8054-5210-9). Broadman.

DiCrescenza, Frances. Annihilation or Salvation? 1986. 8.95 (ISBN 0-8062-2505-X). Carlton.

Diehl & Morris. Physical Fitness & the Christian. 212p. 1986. pap. text ed. 14.95 (ISBN 0-8403-4200-4). Kendall-Hunt.

Diehl, William E. Christianity & Real Life. LC 76-7860. 128p. 1976. pap. 4.50 (ISBN 0-8006-1231-0, 1-1231). Fortress.

--Thank God, It's Monday! LC 81-71390. 192p. 1982. pap. 6.95 (ISBN 0-8006-1656-1, 1-1656). Fortress.

Diehm, William J. Finding Your Life Partner. 128p. 1984. pap. 4.95 (ISBN 0-8170-1028-9). Judson.

Diorio, MaryAnn L. Dating Etiquette for Christian Teens. (Illus.). 48p. (Orig.). 1984. pap. 3.95 (ISBN 0-930037-00-6). Daystar Comm.

Disciples of Morningland. The Way to Oneness. 4th ed. 1979. pap. 3.95 (ISBN 0-935146-00-8). Morningland.

Dittmer, Terry. Creating Contemporary Worship. 80p. (Orig.). 1985. pap. 6.95 (ISBN 0-570-03954-1, 12-2889). Concordia.

Dobbins, G. S. Aprenda a Ser Lider. Molina, S. P., tr. from Eng. Orig. Title: Learning to Lead. (Span.). 126p. 1986. pap. 2.50 (ISBN 0-311-17013-7). Casa Bautista.

Dobbins, Richard D. Su Poder Espiritual Y Emocional. Oyola, Eliezer, tr. from Eng. Orig. Title: Your Spiritual & Emotional Power. (Span.). 171p. 1985. pap. 2.95 (ISBN 0-8297-0705-0). Life Pubs Intl.

--Your Spiritual & Emotional Power. 160p. (Orig.). 1984. pap. 4.95Bks (ISBN 0-8007-5136-1, Power Bks). Revell.

Dobschutz, Ernst Von. Christian Life in the Primitive Church. 1977. lib. bdg. 59.95 (ISBN 0-8490-1615-0). Gordon Pr.

Dobson, James. Dare to Discipline. 1977. pap. 3.50 mass (ISBN 0-8423-0635-8). Tyndale.

Dobson, James C. Love for a Lifetime: Wise Words from Those Who've Gone Before. Date not set. price not set (ISBN 0-88070-174-9). Multnomah.

Dobson, Theodore. Inner Healing: God's Great Assurance. LC 78-65129. 216p. 1978. pap. 7.95 (ISBN 0-8091-2161-1). Paulist Pr.

Dockrey, Karen. Friends: Finding & Keeping Them. LC 85-12783. 1985. pap. 4.50 (ISBN 0-8054-5343-1). Broadman.

Doherty, Barbara. Make Yourself an Ark. 1984. 10.95 (ISBN 0-88347-162-0). Thomas More.

Doherty, Catherine D. The Gospel of a Poor Woman. 6.95 (ISBN 0-87193-151-6). Dimension Bks.

Doherty, Ivy D. Rainbows of Promise. Wheeler, Gerald, ed. (A Banner Bk.). (Illus.). 92p. (Orig.). 1984. pap. 5.95 (ISBN 0-8280-0213-4). Review & Herald.

Dominian, Jack. Marriage, Faith & Love. 288p. 1982. 14.95 (ISBN 0-8245-0425-9). Crossroad NY.

Donahue, Bob & Donahue, Marilyn. Don't Be a Puppet on a String. 1983. pap. 3.95 (ISBN 0-8423-0610-2). Tyndale.

--Getting Your Act Together. (No. 4). 108p. 1983. pap. 3.95 (ISBN 0-8423-1005-3). Tyndale.

Donders, Joseph G. The Global Believer: Toward a New Imitation of Christ. 144p. (Orig.). 1986. pap. 5.95 (ISBN 0-89622-294-2). Twenty-Third.

Donfried, Karl P. The Dynamic Word: New Testament Insights for Contemporary Christians. LC 80-8905. 244p. 1981. 12.95 (ISBN 0-06-061945-7, HarpR). Har-Row.

Donicht, Mark. Chrysalis: A Journey into the New Spiritual America. (Illus.). 192p. 1978. pap. 4.95 (ISBN 0-89496-011-3). Ross Bks.

Donnelly, Dorothy. The Witness of Little Things. (Orig.). Date not set. pap. price not set (ISBN 0-913382-37-X, 101-37). Prow Bks-Franciscan.

Donovan, Vincent J. Christianity Rediscovered. rev. ed. LC 81-18992. 208p. 1982. pap. 8.95 (ISBN 0-88344-096-2). Orbis Bks.

Donze, Mary T. Touching a Child's Heart: An Innovative Guide to Becoming a Good Storyteller. LC 85-71557. 88p. (Orig.). 1985. pap. 3.95 (ISBN 0-87793-290-5). Ave Maria.

Double, Don. Life in a New Dimension. 1979. pap. 2.95 (ISBN 0-88368-083-1). Whitaker Hse.

Doughty, Stephen. Answering Love's Call: Christian Love & a Life of Prayer. LC 86-81809. 128p. (Orig.). 1986. pap. 4.95 (ISBN 0-87793-348-0). Ave Maria.

Douglass, H. E. Hello Neighbor. (Outreach Ser.). 16p. 1983. pap. 0.25 (ISBN 0-8163-0523-4). Pacific Pr Pub Assn.

Doukhan, Jacques. Drinking at the Sources. 1981. 7.95 (ISBN 0-8163-0407-6). Pacific Pr Pub Assn.

Doulis, T. Journeys to Orthodoxy. 1986. pap. 6.95 (ISBN 0-937032-42-5). Light&Life Pub Co MN.

Downey, Michael. Clothed in Christ. 160p. 1987. pap. 9.95 (ISBN 0-8245-0812-2). Crossroad NY.

Downs, Thomas. The Parish As Learning Community. LC 78-70816. 128p. 1979. pap. 3.95 (ISBN 0-8091-2172-7). Paulist Pr.

Drakeford, John W. Hechos el Uno Para el Otro. De Plou, Dafne C., tr. (Sexo en la Vida Cristiana Ser.). 1983. pap. 3.50 (ISBN 0-311-46256-1). Casa Bautista.

Drakeford, John W. & Drakeford, Robina. Mothers Are Special. LC 78-73137. 1979. 8.95 (ISBN 0-8054-5636-8). Broadman.

Draper, Edythe. Cool: How a Kid Should Live. 1974. kivar 6.95 (ISBN 0-8423-0435-5). Tyndale.

--In Touch. 1983. deluxe ed. 8.95 gift ed. (ISBN 0-8423-1711-2); christmas ed. 8.95 (ISBN 0-8423-1712-0); deluxe graduation ed. 8.95 (ISBN 0-8423-1713-9); kivar 5.95 (ISBN 0-8423-1710-4). Tyndale.

Draper, James T., Jr. Live up to Your Faith: Studies in Titus. 1983. pap. 3.95 (ISBN 0-8423-3687-7); leader's guide 2.95 (ISBN 0-8423-3688-5). Tyndale.

--Proverbs: Practical Directions for Living. (Living Studies). pap. 4.95 (ISBN 0-8423-4922-7); leader's guide 2.95 (ISBN 0-8423-4923-5). Tyndale.

Draper, Maurice L. Isles & Continents. (Orig.). 1982. pap. 14.00 (ISBN 0-8309-0343-7). Herald Hse.

Dreier, Patricia, compiled by. The Gold of Friendship: A Bouquet of Special Thoughts. (Illus.). 1980. 6.95 (ISBN 0-8378-1707-2). Gibson.

Drescher, John & Drescher, Betty. If We Were Starting Our Marriage Again. 96p. (Orig.). 1985. pap. 6.50 (ISBN 0-687-18672-2). Abingdon.

Drew, Joseph W. & Hague, W. Creation of Full Human Personality. pap. 0.75 (ISBN 0-8199-0247-0, L38115). Franciscan Herald.

Drinan, Robert F. God & Caesar on the Potomac: A Pilgrimage of Conscience. 1985. 15.00 (ISBN 0-89453-458-0). M Glazier.

Drotts, Wallace D. Take up Your Cross: Invitation to Abundant Life. LC 84-61032. 80p. (Orig.). 1985. pap. 3.95 (ISBN 0-8091-2655-9). Paulist Pr.

Dubay, Thomas. Authenticity. 4.95 (ISBN 0-87193-143-5). Dimension Bks.

--Happy Are You Poor. 5.95 (ISBN 0-87193-141-9). Dimension Bks.

--What is Religious Life? 5.95 (ISBN 0-87193-116-8). Dimension Bks.

Dubois, Aberic. Conversations in Umbria. 1980. 7.95 (ISBN 0-8199-0784-7). Franciscan Herald.

Duckworth, Robin. This Is the Word of the Lord: Year C. the Year of Luke. (Orig.). 1982. pap. 9.95 (ISBN 0-19-826666-9). Oxford U Pr.

Dudley, Cliff. The Hidden Christian. LC 80-80657. 160p. 1980. 7.95 (ISBN 0-89221-074-5). New Leaf.

Dudley, Roger L. Passing on the Torch. Woolsey, Raymond H., ed. 192p. 1986. 12.95 (ISBN 0-8280-0348-3). Review & Herald.

Dugan, LeRoy. The Uncomplicated Christian. LC 78-66886. 128p. 1978. pap. 2.50 (ISBN 0-87123-572-2, 200572). Bethany Hse.

Dugan, Richard L. Building Christian Commitment. (Trinity Bible Ser.). 107p. (Orig.). 1982. wkbk. 3.95 (ISBN 0-87123-280-4, 240280). Bethany Hse.

Dumke, Edward J. The Serpent Beguiled Me & I Ate: A Heavenly Diet for Saints & Sinners. LC 86-4445. (Illus.). 1986. pap. 8.95 (ISBN 0-385-23671-9). Doubleday.

Dunaway, Patricia. Beyond the Distant Shadows. 208p. (Orig.). 1984. pap. 4.95 (ISBN 0-87123-446-7). Bethany Hse.

Duncan, Tannis. Reaching for Excellence. 67p. (Orig.). 1982. pap. text ed. 2.50 (ISBN 0-87148-737-3). Pathway Pr.

Dunn, Charles W., Sr. How to Be Happy in an Unhappy World. 141p. (Orig.). 1986. pap. 6.95 (ISBN 0-89084-318-X). Bob Jones Univ Pr.

Dunn, Jerry G. & Palmer, Bernard. God Is for the Alcoholic. rev. ed. pap. 6.95 (ISBN 0-8024-3284-0). Moody.

Dunnam, Maxie. The Workbook on Becoming Alive in Christ. 160p. (Orig.). 1986. pap. 5.50 (ISBN 0-8358-0542-5). Upper Room.

Dunnam, Maxie D. Alive in Christ: The Dynamic Process of Spiritual Formation. LC 81-20631. 160p. 1982. 8.75 (ISBN 0-687-00993-6). Abingdon.

--The Christian Way. 112p. 1987. pap. 4.95 (ISBN 0-310-20741-X). Zondervan.

Dunne, John. The House of Wisdom. LC 84-48767. 224p. 1985. 15.45 (ISBN 0-317-18550-0, HarpR). Har-Row.

Dunne, Tad. We Cannot Find Words. casebound 8.95 (ISBN 0-87193-138-9). Dimension Bks.

Dunning, H. Ray. Fruit of the Spirit. 38p. 1982. pap. 1.95 (ISBN 0-8341-0806-2). Beacon Hill.

Dunning, James B. New Wine: New Wineskins. 128p. (Orig.). 1981. pap. 5.95 (ISBN 0-8215-9807-4). Sadlier.

Durham, Charles. When You Are Feeling Lonely. LC 84-10499. 180p. (Orig.). 1984. pap. 5.95 (ISBN 0-87784-915-3). Inter-Varsity.

Durken, Daniel, ed. & pref. by. Sin, Salvation, & the Spirit. LC 79-20371. (Illus.). 368p. 1979. text ed. 6.00 (ISBN 0-8146-1078-1); pap. text ed. 10.00 (ISBN 0-8146-1079-X). Liturgical Pr.

Durkheim, Emile. The Elementary Forms of the Religious Life. 2nd ed. Swain, Joseph W., tr. LC 76-369730. pap. 117.80 (ISBN 0-317-20057-7, 2023276). Bks Demand UMI.

Durkin, Mary G. Feast of Love. 248p. 1984. 9.95 (ISBN 0-8294-0443-0). Loyola.

Durland, Frances C. Coping with Widowhood. 1979. pap. 1.50 (ISBN 0-89243-098-2). Liguori Pubns.

Durnbaugh, Donald F., ed. On Earth Peace. 1978. pap. 9.95 (ISBN 0-87178-660-5). Brethren.

Durrett, Deane. My New Sister, the Bully. 128p. 1985. 7.95 (ISBN 0-687-27551-2). Abingdon.

Duty, Guy. Escape from the Coming Tribulation. LC 75-17979. 160p. (Orig.). 1975. pap. 4.95 (ISBN 0-87123-131-X, 210131). Bethany Hse.

Dye, Dwight L. A Kingdom of Servants. 1979. 3.95 (ISBN 0-87162-218-1, D5050). Warner Pr.

Dye, Harold E. A Daily Miracle. (Orig.). 1986. pap. 3.25 (ISBN 0-8054-5026-2). Broadman.

Each Day a New Beginning. 400p. (Orig.). 1985. pap. 5.95 (ISBN 0-86683-501-6, HarpR). Har-Row.

Eager, George B. Love, Dating & Marriage. LC 86-90552. (Illus.). 136p. (Orig.). 1987. pap. 5.95 (ISBN 0-9603752-5-2). Mailbox.

--The New Life in Christ. LC 86-62669. (Illus.). 163p. 1987. pap. text ed. 4.95 (ISBN 0-9603752-6-0). Mailbox.

Eareckson, Joni & Estes, Steve. A Step Further. 192p. 1982. pap. 3.95 (ISBN 0-310-23972-9, 12008P). Zondervan.

Eareckson, Joni & Musser, Joe. Joni. 1984. pap. 2.95 (ISBN 0-553-22886-2). Bantam.

Earles, Brent D. Bouncing Back. (Life Enrichment Ser.). 144p. Date not set. pap. 5.95 (ISBN 0-8010-3435-3). Baker Bk.

--You're Worth It! But Do You Believe It? 112p. 1985. pap. 5.95 (ISBN 0-8010-3427-2). Baker Bk.

Eash, John E. Bring an Offering. 1985. pap. 1.95 (ISBN 0-317-38498-8). Brethren.

Eastman, Dick. A Celebration of Praise: Exciting Prospects for Extraordinary Praise. pap. 4.95 (ISBN 0-8010-3420-5). Baker Bk.

Eastman, Hubbard. Noyesism Unveiled. LC 72-134402. Repr. of 1849 ed. 30.00 (ISBN 0-404-08446-X). AMS Pr.

Eaton, Evelyn E. & Whitehead, James. Seasons of Strength: New Visions of Adult Christian Maturing. LC 84-4199. 240p. 1986. pap. 7.95 (ISBN 0-385-19680-6, Im). Doubleday.

Ebersole, Stella. Go Ye to Burma. 432p. 1986. 24.95 (ISBN 0-89962-556-8). Todd & Honeywell.

Eckerd, Jack & Conn, Charles P. Eckerd. (Illus.). 1987. 12.95 (ISBN 0-8007-1532-2). Revell.

Edens, David. Estoy Creciendo Estoy Cambiando. Du Plou, Dafne C., tr. (Sexo en la Vida Cristiana Ser). (Illus.). 1985. pap. 1.75 (ISBN 0-311-46252-9). Casa Bautista.

Edvardsen, Aril & Harris, Madalene. Dreaming & Achieving the Impossible. 1984. pap. 5.95 (ISBN 0-88419-192-3). Creation Hse.

Edwards, Bob. Anybody Who Needs to Be Sure Is in Trouble. LC 82-81009. 72p. 1982. pap. 5.45 (ISBN 0-941780-11-2, Parkhurst-Little). August Hse.

Edwards, Charles G. Stress. (Outreach Ser.). 32p. 1982. pap. 1.25 (ISBN 0-8163-0468-8). Pacific Pr Pub Assn.

Edwards, Gene. Church Life. 132p. 1987. text ed. 8.95 (ISBN 0-940232-25-1). Christian Bks.

--Inward Journey. 250p. 1982. pap. 5.95 (ISBN 0-940232-06-5). Christian Bks.

--Letters to a Devastated Christian. 68p. 1983. pap. 3.95 (ISBN 0-940232-13-8). Christian Bks.

--Our Mission. (Orig.). 1984. pap. 7.95 (ISBN 0-940232-11-1). Christian Bks.

--Preventing a Church Split. 1987. 8.95 (ISBN 0-940232-26-X). Christian Bks.

--The Purpose. 1987. pap. 5.95 (ISBN 0-940232-27-8). Christian Bks.

Edwards, Gene, ed. The Divine Romance. 1984. 10.95 (ISBN 0-940232-24-3); pap. 7.95. Christian Bks.

Edwards, Judson. Dancing to Zion: How to Harvest Joy on the Road to Heaven. Sloan, John, ed. 180p. 1986. pap. 5.95 avail. (ISBN 0-310-34511-1, 12066P). Zondervan.

--Running the Race. LC 85-4700. 1985. pap. 5.95 (ISBN 0-8054-5711-9). Broadman.

Edwards, Richard & Wild, Robert. The Sentences of Sextus. LC 81-13770. (Society of Biblical Literature Texts & Translations Ser.). 1981. pap. text ed. 12.00 (ISBN 0-89130-528-9, 06-02-22). Scholars Pr GA.

Edwards, Tilden. Living Simply Through the Day. 444p. 1985. pap. 9.95 large print ed. (ISBN 0-8027-2492-2). Walker & Co.

Eims, Leroy. Keeping off the Casualty List. 132p. 1986. pap. 4.95 (ISBN 0-89693-152-8). Victor Bks.

--Laboring in the Harvest. 108p. 1985. pap. 4.95 (ISBN 0-89109-530-6). NavPress.

--The Lost Art of Disciple Making. pap. 6.95 (ISBN 0-310-37281-X, 9233P). Zondervan.

--What Every Christian Should Know about Growing. LC 75-44842. 168p. 1976. pap. 5.95 (ISBN 0-88207-727-9). Victor Bks.

--Winning Ways. LC 74-77319. 160p. 1974. pap. 4.50 (ISBN 0-88207-707-4). Victor Bks.

Eisenman, Tom. Big People, Little People. (Family Ministry Ser.). (Illus.). 54p. 1985. pap. text ed. 19.95 (ISBN 0-89191-968-6). Cook.

--On My Own. (Family Ministry Ser.). (Illus.). 54p. 1985. pap. text ed. 19.95 (ISBN 0-89191-978-3). Cook.

Elbin, Paul N. Making Happiness a Habit. (Festival Ser.). 192p. 1981. pap. 2.75 (ISBN 0-687-23030-6). Abingdon.

Ellard, Gerald. Christian Life & Worship. 35.50 (ISBN 0-405-10819-2). Ayer Co Pubs.

Eller, Vernard. Towering Babble: God's People Without God's Word. LC 83-4621. (Illus.). 192p. (Orig.). 1983. pap. 7.95 (ISBN 0-87178-855-1). Brethren.

Elliot, Elisabeth. Discipline: The Glad Surrender. 1985. pap. 5.95 (ISBN 0-8007-5195-7, Power Bks). Revell.

--A Lamp for My Feet: The Bible's Light for Daily Living. 210p. (Orig.). 1985. pap. 9.95 (ISBN 0-89283-234-7, Pub. by Vine Books). Servant.

--Love Has a Price Tag. 152p. 1982. pap. 5.95 (ISBN 0-89283-153-7, Pub. by Vine Books). Servant.

--The Mark of a Man. LC 80-25108. 176p. 1981. pap. 5.95 (ISBN 0-8007-5121-3, Power Bks). Revell.

--The Savage My Kinsman. (Illus.). 149p. 1981. pap. 5.95 (ISBN 0-89283-099-9, Pub. by Vine Books). Servant.

Elliott, J. E. Once Saved Always Saved. 74p. (Orig.). 1986. pap. 2.25 (ISBN 0-934942-62-5, 4115). White Wing Pub.

Ellis, Joyce. Plug into a Rainbow. 144p. (Orig.). 1984. pap. 3.95 (ISBN 0-310-47192-3, 12495P). Zondervan.

Ellison, Craig W., ed. Your Better Self: Christianity, Psychology, & Self-Esteem. LC 82-47742. 224p. (Orig.). 1982. pap. 8.95 (ISBN 0-686-97230-9, RD/408, HarpR). Har-Row.

Ellison, H. L. The Household Church. 120p. 1979. pap. 4.95 (ISBN 0-85364-239-7). Attic Pr.

--The Servant of Jehovah. 32p. 1983. pap. 2.50 (ISBN 0-85364-254-0, Pub. by Paternoster UK). Attic Pr.

Ellul, Jacques. Money & Power. Neff, LaVonne, tr. from Fr. LC 83-22647. Orig. Title: L Homme et l'Argent. 216p. 1984. pap. 7.95 (ISBN 0-87784-916-1). Inter-Varsity.

Elsdon, Ronald. Bent World. LC 81-8261. 200p. (Orig.). 1981. pap. 4.95 (ISBN 0-87784-834-3). Inter-Varsity.

Emmons, Michael & Richardson, David. The Assertive Christian. Frost, Miriam, ed. 144p. (Orig.). 1981. pap. 6.95 (ISBN 0-86683-755-8, HarpR). Har-Row.

Engstrom, Barbie. Faith to Know. LC 77-94207. (Christian Guidebook Ser.). (Illus., Orig.). Date not set. pap. 10.50 (ISBN 0-932210-01-5). Kurios Found.

Engstrom, Ted & Larson, Robert C. A Time for Commitment. 112p. 1987. padded gift ed. 9.95 (ISBN 0-310-51010-4); pap. 4.95 (ISBN 0-310-51011-2). Zondervan.

Engstrom, Ted W. Motivation to Last a Lifetime. 96p. 1983. gift ed. 8.95 (ISBN 0-310-24250-9, 9570L); pap. 4.95 (ISBN 0-310-24251-7, 9570P). Zondervan.

Enzler, Clarence. My Other Self. pap. 5.95 (ISBN 0-87193-056-0). Dimension Bks.

Enzler, Clarence J. Let Us Be What We Are. 5.95 (ISBN 0-87193-136-2). Dimension Bks.

Epp, Margaret. The Earth is Round. 228p. (Orig.). pap. 4.00 (ISBN 0-919797-00-8). Kindred Pr.

Erickson, J. Irving. Sing It Again! 1985. 12.95 (ISBN 0-910452-58-X). Covenant.

Erickson, Mae. Quiz for Christian Wives. 32p. 1976. pap. 0.95 (ISBN 0-930756-20-7, 541003). Aglow Pubns.

Erwin, Gayle D. The Jesus Style. 211p. 1985. 9.95 (ISBN 0-8499-0509-5, 0509-5). Word Bks.

Escandon, R. Como Llegar a Ser Vencedor. (Span.). 128p. 1982. pap. 3.95 (ISBN 0-311-46092-5, Edit Mundo). Casa Bautista.

Eshleman, Paul. I Just Saw Jesus, Still Doing Miracles, Still Touching Lives. 224p. (Orig.). 1985. pap. 6.95 (ISBN 0-89840-100-3). Heres Life.

Etheridge, Myrna L. Break Forth into Joy. 179p. (Orig.). 1985. pap. 5.00x (ISBN 0-937417-01-7). Etheridge Minist.

Etling, Harold H. Our Heritage: Brethren Beliefs & Practices. pap. 4.95 (ISBN 0-88469-022-9). BMH Bks.

Evans, Coleen. Living True. 132p. 1985. pap. 4.95 (ISBN 0-89693-321-0). Victor Bks.

Evans, Gary T. & Hayes, Richard E. Equipping God's People. (Church's Teaching Ser.: Introductory). 80p. 1979. pap. 1.25 (ISBN 0-86683-896-1, HarpR). Har-Row.

Evans, Louis H., Jr. Covenant to Care. 120p. 1982. pap. 4.95 (ISBN 0-88207-355-9). Victor Bks.

Evans, Robert A., et al. Casebook for Christian Living: Value Formation for Families & Congregations. pap. 6.95 (ISBN 0-8042-2032-8). John Knox.

Evans, W. Glyn. Daily with the King. LC 79-21970. 1979. pap. 5.95 (ISBN 0-8024-1739-6). Moody.

Fabiola. 7.00 (ISBN 0-8198-2606-5); 6.00 (ISBN 0-8198-2607-3). Dghtrs St Paul.

Fairbanks, Henry G. Towards Acceptance--the Ultimates: Aging, Pain, Fear & Death from an Integral Human View. 1986. pap. 8.95 (ISBN 0-8158-0433-4). Chris Mass.

Falaturi, Abdoldjavad & Petuchowski. Three Ways to One God. 160p. 1987. 14.95 (ISBN 0-8245-0818-1). Crossroad NY.

Falwell, Jerry. Wisdom for Living. 156p. 1984. pap. 5.95 (ISBN 0-89693-370-9). Victor Bks.

Farnsworth, Kirk E. Wholehearted Integration: Harmonizing Psychology & Christianity Through Word & Deed. 160p. 1986. 6.95 (ISBN 0-8010-3513-9). Baker Bk.

Farnsworth, Kirk E. & Lawhead, Wendell H. Life Planning. 96p. (Orig.). 1981. pap. 7.95 (ISBN 0-87784-840-8). Inter-Varsity.

Farrell, Edward. Can You Drink This Cup? pap. 4.95 (ISBN 0-87193-179-6). Dimension Bks.

--Prayer Is a Hunger. 4.95 (ISBN 0-87193-031-5). Dimension Bks.

Father's Day: Voices from the Heart. Date not set. price not set (ISBN 0-934383-14-6). Pride Prods.

Fearon, Mary & Tully, Mary J. Wonder-Filled. 1983. pap. 4.00 (ISBN 0-697-01853-9); tchr's. manual 6.00 (ISBN 0-697-01854-7); parent book 3.50 (ISBN 0-697-01855-5). Wm C Brown.

Fenocketti, Mary M. Coping with Discouragement. 64p. 1985. pap. 1.50 (ISBN 0-89243-226-8). Liguori Pubns.

Fenske, S. H. My Life in Christ: A Momento of My Confirmation. LC 76-5729. 1976. pap. 2.50 (ISBN 0-8100-0056-3, 16N0514). Northwest Pub.

Ferguson, Mable L. God's High Country. 384p. (Orig.). pap. 14.95 (ISBN 0-930161-09-2). State of the Art Ltd.

Ferguson, Sinclair. A Heart for God. (Christian Character Library). 150p. 1985. hdbk. 8.95 (ISBN 0-89109-507-1). NavPress.

Ferguson, Sinclair B. Children of the Living God. LC 86-63652. 168p. (Orig.). 1987. pap. price not set (ISBN 0-89109-137-8). NavPress.

--Heart for God. 150p. 1987. pap. 3.95 (ISBN 0-89109-176-9). NavPress.

--Kingdom Life in a Fallen World: Living out the Sermon on the Mount. (Christian Character Library). 224p. 1986. 8.95 (ISBN 0-89109-492-X). NavPress.

Ferm, Dean W. Alternative Lifestyles Confront the Church. 144p. 1983. pap. 8.95 (ISBN 0-8164-2394-6, HarpR). Har-Row.

Ferrin, Martha. Moments with Martha. LC 83-60477. 1983. pap. text ed. 2.50 (ISBN 0-932050-18-2). New Puritan.

Fichtner, Joseph. To Stand & Speak for Christ. LC 81-10975. 166p. 1981. pap. 6.95 (ISBN 0-8189-0415-1). Alba.

Fick, Mike & Richardson, Jim. Control Your Thoughts. 1983. pap. 1.75 (ISBN 0-911739-01-7). Abbott Loop.

Fickett, Harold L., Jr. Keep on Keeping on. LC 75-23517. 160p. (Orig.). 1977. pap. 3.50 (ISBN 0-8307-0371-3, S311100). Regal.

Fields, Wilbur. New Testament Backgrounds. 2nd ed. (Bible Student Study Guides Ser). 1977. pap. 5.95 (ISBN 0-89900-156-4). College Pr Pub.

Fine, Robert. Great Todays - Better Tomorrows. 1976. pap. 2.95 (ISBN 0-89367-001-4). Light & Life.

Finley, James. The Awakening Call. LC 84-72094. 160p. (Orig.). 1985. pap. 4.95 (ISBN 0-87793-278-6). Ave Maria.

Finney, Charles G. Crystal Christianity: A Vital Guide to Personal Revival. Orig. Title: Lectures to Professing Christians. 330p. 1986. pap. 3.95 (ISBN 0-88368-171-4). Whitaker Hse.

--How to Experience Revival. 1986. write for info. (ISBN 0-8297-0798-0). Life Pubs Intl.

--Lectures to Professing Christians. (The Higher Christian Life Ser.). 348p. 1985. lib. bdg. 45.00 (ISBN 0-8240-6418-6). Garland Pub.

--Principles of Union with Christ. Parkhurst, Louis G., ed. 128p. 1985. pap. 4.95 (ISBN 0-87123-447-5, 210447). Bethany Hse.

--Principles of Victory. Parkhurst, G., ed. LC 81-15464. 201p. (Orig.). 1981. pap. 5.95 (ISBN 0-87123-471-8, 210471). Bethany Hse.

--The Promise of the Spirit. Smith, Timothy L., ed. LC 79-26286. 272p. (Orig.). 1980. pap. 6.95 (ISBN 0-87123-207-3, 210207). Bethany Hse.

Finsaas, Clarence B. They Marched to Heaven's Drumbeat. 1985. pap. 5.95 (ISBN 0-88419-193-1). Creation Hse.

Fire upon the Earth. 4.95 (ISBN 0-87193-142-7). Dimension Bks.

Fischer, Edward. Journeys Not Regreeted. 1986. pap. 10.95 (ISBN 0-317-42448-3). Crossroad NY.

Fischer, Kathleen R. The Inner Rainbow: The Imagination in Christian Life. 160p. 1983. pap. 6.95 (ISBN 0-8091-2498-X). Paulist Pr.

Fischer, William L. Alternatives. LC 79-67005. 1980. 5.95 (ISBN 0-87159-000-X). Unity School.

Fish, Roy J. Giving a Good Invitation. LC 74-18043. 1975. pap. 3.50 (ISBN 0-8054-2107-6). Broadman.

Fishel, Kent & Deselm, Joel. Breakthrough No. 1: Christian Assurances. 1986. pap. 2.95 (ISBN 0-310-45981-8, 12629P). Zondervan.

--Breakthrough No. 2: Christian Growth. 1986. pap. 2.95 (ISBN 0-310-45971-0, 12628P). Zondervan.

--Breakthrough No. 3: Christian Living. 1986. pap. 2.95 (ISBN 0-310-45941-9, 12627P). Zondervan.

Fisher, Neal F. Context for Discovery. LC 81-7929. (Into Our Third Century Ser.). (Orig.). 1981. pap. 4.95 (ISBN 0-687-09620-0). Abingdon.

Fisher, Robert. En Espiritu y en Verdad. (Span., Orig.). pap. text ed. 5.95 (ISBN 0-87148-313-0). Pathway Pr.

Fisher, Robert, ed. In Spirit & in Truth. (Orig.). pap. text ed. 5.95 (ISBN 0-87148-438-2). Pathway Pr.

--Pressing Toward the Mark. LC 83-63384. 176p. 1983. pap. text ed. 8.95 (ISBN 0-87148-714-4). Pathway Pr.

Fishwick, Nina M. Liberated for Life a Christian Declaration of Indepence. (Study & Grow Electives Ser.). 64p. 1985. pap. 3.95 (ISBN 0-8307-1039-6, 6102095). Regal.

Fitzhardinge, L. F. The Spartans. LC 79-66136. (Ancient Peoples & Places Ser.). (Illus.). 180p. 1985. pap. 10.95f (ISBN 0-500-27364-2). Thames Hudson.

Five Gifts from God. 1979. 1.75 (ISBN 0-8198-0616-1); pap. 1.00 (ISBN 0-8198-0617-X). Dghtrs St Paul.

Fix, Janet & Levitt, Zola. For Singles Only. 128p. 1978. pap. 5.95 (ISBN 0-8007-5034-9, Power Bks). Revell.

Flattery, George M. Teaching for Christian Maturity. 126p. 1968. 1.50 (ISBN 0-88243-618-X, 02-0618). Gospel Pub.

Flavel, John. The Mystery of Providence. 1976. pap. 3.95 (ISBN 0-85151-104-X). Banner of Truth.

Fleck, G. Peter. The Mask of Religion. LC 79-9644. (Library of Liberal Religion). 204p. 1980. 12.95 (ISBN 0-87975-125-8). Prometheus Bks.

Fleming, David A., ed. Religious Life at the Crossroads. 200p. (Orig.). 1985. pap. 8.95 (ISBN 0-8091-2709-1). Paulist Pr.

Fleming, Jean. Between Walden & the Whirlwind. (Christian Character Library). 133p. 1985. hdbk. 8.95 (ISBN 0-89109-520-9). NavPress.

Fleming, Jean M. Between Walden & the Whirlwind. 133p. 1987. pap. 3.95. NavPress.

Fletcher, Sarah. Christian Babysitter's Handbook. 1985. pap. 3.95 (ISBN 0-570-03948-7, 12-2881). Concordia.

Fletcher, William. The Second Greatest Commandment. LC 83-62501. 156p. 1983. pap. 4.95 (ISBN 0-89109-502-0). NavPress.

--The Triumph of Surrender: Responding to the Greatness of God. (Christian Character Library). 190p. Date not set. 8.95 (ISBN 0-89109-538-1). NavPress.

Fletcher, William M. El Segundo de los Grandes Mandamientos. Carrodeguas, Angel, ed. Romanenghi de Powell, Elsie R., tr. from Eng. Tr. of The Second Greatest Commandment. (Span.). 192p. Date not set. pap. text ed. 2.95 (ISBN 0-8297-0722-0). Life Pubs Intl.

Flood, Edmund. Parables for Now. 4.95 (ISBN 0-87193-186-9). Dimension Bks.

Flynn, Leslie B. You Don't Have to Go It Alone. LC 80-66722. 160p. (Orig.). 1981. pap. 4.95 (ISBN 0-89636-058-X). Accent Bks.

Fogle, Jeanne S. Signs of God's Love. pap. 4.50. Westminster.

Forbes, Cheryl. Imagination: Embracing a Theology of Wonder. LC 86-811. (Critical Concern Bks.). 1986. 12.95 (ISBN 0-88070-136-6). Multnomah.

--The Religion of Power. 176p. 1983. 9.95 (ISBN 0-310-45770-X, 12396). Zondervan.

Forlines, Leroy. Biblical Systematics. 1975. 7.95 (ISBN 0-89265-025-7); pap. 4.95 (ISBN 0-89265-038-9). Randall Hse.

Forliti, John E. Reverence for Life & Family Program: Parent-Teacher Resource. 1981. pap. 4.50 176 pp (ISBN 0-697-01789-3); tchr. training tape 9.95 (ISBN 0-697-01837-7). Wm C Brown.

Forrest, Diane. The Adventurers: Ordinary People with Special Callings. 1984. pap. 5.95 (ISBN 0-317-13951-7). Upper Room.

Forrester, Duncan, et al. Encounter with God. 192p. 1983. pap. 13.95 (ISBN 0-567-29346-7, Pub. by T&T Clark Ltd UK). Fortress.

Fortieth Anniversary: Voices from the Heart. Date not set. price not set (ISBN 0-934383-12-X). Pride Prods.

Fortune, Katie. Receive All God Has to Give. 1971. pap. write for info. color booklet (ISBN 0-930756-01-0, 541001); pap. 0.95 color booklet (ISBN 0-317-03288-7). Aglow Pubns.

Fosdick, Harry E. The Meaning of Service. 224p. 1983. pap. 4.35 (ISBN 0-687-23961-3). Abingdon.

Foster, Elvie L. The Most Important Thing in Our Lives Is... LC 86-90082. 47p. 1986. 5.95 (ISBN 0-533-07047-3). Vantage.

Foster, H. Normal Christian Life: Study Guide. rev ed. 52p. 1985. pap. 2.25 (ISBN 0-317-43399-7). Chr Lit.

Foster, John & Goldsborough, June. Christian ABC Book. (Illus.). 1982. 6.95 (ISBN 0-911346-05-8). Christianica.

Foster, Richard. Alabanza a la Disciplina. Lievano, M. Francisco, tr. from Eng. Tr. of Celebration of Discipline. (Span.). 224p. 1986. pap. 4.95 (ISBN 0-88113-012-5). Edit Betania.

Foster, Richard J. The Celebration of Discipline: Paths to Spiritual Growth. LC 77-20444. 1978. 13.45 (ISBN 0-06-062831-6, HarpR). Har-Row.

--Freedom of Simplicity. LC 80-8351. 192p. 1981. 13.45 (ISBN 0-06-062832-4, HarpR). Har-Row.

--Money, Sex & Power: Study Guide. LC 84-48785. 96p. (Orig.). 1985. pap. 4.95 (ISBN 0-06-062827-8, HarpR). Har-Row.

--Money, Sex & Power: The Challenge of the Disciplined Life. LC 84-48769. 192p. 1985. 13.45 (ISBN 0-06-062826-X, HarpR). Har-Row.

Foster, Timothy. How to Deal with Depression. 132p. 1984. pap. 4.95 (ISBN 0-88207-610-8). Victor Bks.

Foth, Margaret. Life Is Too Short. 144p. (Orig.). 1985. pap. 5.95 (ISBN 0-310-42681-2, 12779P). Zondervan.

Foundations of Unity. Ser. One. 4.50 (ISBN 0-87159-038-7); Ser. Two. 8.50 (ISBN 0-87159-039-5). Unity School.

Fourez, Gerard. Sacraments & Passages: Celebrating the Tensions of Modern Life. LC 83-71164. 168p. (Orig.). 1983. pap. 4.95 (ISBN 0-87793-301-4). Ave Maria.

Fowler, James W. Becoming Adult, Becoming Christian: Adult Development & Christian Faith. LC 83-48987. 144p. 1984. 14.45 (ISBN 0-06-062841-3, HarpR). Har-Row.

--Stages of Faith: The Psychology of Human Development & the Quest for Meaning. LC 80-7757. 224p. 1981. 18.45 (ISBN 0-06-062840-5, HarpR). Har-Row.

Fowler, Lea. Precious in the Sight of God. 1983. pap. 4.95 (ISBN 0-89137-428-0). Quality Pubns.

Fowler, Richard A. Winning by Losing: Eleven Biblical Paradoxes That Can Change Your Life. (Orig.). 1986. pap. 6.95 (ISBN 0-8024-9564-8). Moody.

France, Lillian E. Challenge, I Dare You. 1984. 5.75 (ISBN 0-8062-1803-7). Carlton.

Freeman, Bill. God's Eternal Purpose. (Illus.). 14p. 1983. pap. 0.25 (ISBN 0-914271-01-6). NW Christian Pubns.

Freeman, Carroll B. The Senior Adult Years. LC 79-51137. 1979. 7.95 (ISBN 0-8054-5421-7). Broadman.

Freeman, James D. Tu Puedes! LC 82-70490. 256p. 1982. 5.95 (ISBN 0-87159-158-8). Unity School.

Freiday, Dean. Nothing Without Christ. LC 84-70040. (Orig.). 1984. pap. 3.95 (ISBN 0-913342-44-0). Barclay Pr.

Fretz, Clarence Y. You & Your Bible-You & Your Life. (Christian Day School Ser). pap. 4.10x (ISBN 0-87813-902-8); teachrs guide 13.75x (ISBN 0-87813-903-6). Christian Light.

Freudenberger, C. Dean. Food for Tomorrow. LC 83-72119. 176p. 1984. pap. 9.95 (ISBN 0-8066-2063-3, 10-2333). Augsburg.

Friesen, Evelyn & Phu, Sam. Freedom Isn't Free. 165p. (Orig.). 1985. pap. 6.65 (ISBN 0-318-18903-8). Kindred Pr.

Friesen, Garry & Maxson, J. Robin. Decision Making & the Will of God. LC 80-24592. (Critical Concern Bks.). 1981. 13.95 (ISBN 0-930014-47-2). Multnomah.

--Decision Making & the Will of God: A Biblical Alternative to the Traditional View. expanded ed. (Critical Concern Bks.). pap. cancelled (ISBN 0-88070-100-5). Multnomah.

Frisk, Donald C. New Life in Christ. 1969. pap. 2.95 (ISBN 0-910452-03-2). Covenant.

Fritz, Mary. Take Nothing for the Journey: Solitude as the Foundation for Non-Possessive Life. 88p. (Orig.). 1985. pap. 3.95 (ISBN 0-8091-2722-9). Paulist Pr.

Frost, Gerhard E. A Second Look. (Orig.). 1984. pap. 6.95 (ISBN 0-86683-935-6, 8513, HarpR). Har-Row.

Frost, Marie H. Love Is God. (First Happy Day Bks.). (Illus.). 20p. 1986. casebound 1.29 (ISBN 0-87403-133-8, 2003). Standard Pub.

Frost, Stanley B. Standing & Understanding: A Re-Appraisal of the Christian Faith. LC 68-59095. pap. 46.80 (ISBN 0-317-26033-2, 2023834). Bks Demand UMI.

Fry, Eldon E., et al. Now We Are Three. (Family Ministry Ser.). (Illus.). 54p. 1985. pap. text ed. 19.95 (ISBN 0-89191-977-5). Cook.

Fryer, Charles. A Hand in Dialogue. 128p. 1983. 17.95 (ISBN 0-227-67841-9, Pub. by J Clarke UK). Attic Pr.

Fudge, Edward. Christianity Without Ulcers. pap. 5.00 (ISBN 0-686-12686-6). E Fudge.

Furlong, Monica. Travelling in. LC 84-71182. 125p. 1984. pap. 6.00 (ISBN 0-936384-20-4). Cowley Pubns.

Furman, Richard. The Intimate Husband. 1986. pap. 8.95 (ISBN 0-89081-557-7). Harvest Hse.

--Reaching Your Full Potential. 1984. pap. 6.95 (ISBN 0-89081-443-0). Harvest Hse.

Gabriel of St. Mary Magdalen. Divine Intimacy: A Celebration of Prayer and the Joy of Christian Life, 4 vols. 2nd ed. LC 86-83132. (Orig.). 1987. pap. 12.95 ea. Vol. 1, 285 p (ISBN 0-89870-142-2). Vol. 2, 285 p (ISBN 0-89870-143-0). Vol. 3, 285 p (ISBN 0-89870-144-9). Vol. 4, 285 p (ISBN 0-89870-145-7). Ignatius Pr.

Gaebelein, Frank E. The Pattern of God's Truth. 1985. pap. 5.95 (ISBN 0-88469-170-5). BMH Bks.

Gaede, S. D. Belonging: Our Need for Community in Church & Family. LC 85-17987. 288p. (Orig.). 1985. pap. 9.95 (ISBN 0-310-36891-X, 12294P). Zondervan.

Gage, Gloria. A Season for Glory. 144p. (Orig.). 1984. pap. 4.95 (ISBN 0-89636-143-8). Accent Bks.

Gage, Robert C. Cultivating Spiritual Fruit. 144p. (Orig.). 1986. pap. 5.25 (ISBN 0-87227-114-5). Reg Baptist.

Gaither, Gloria. Fully Alive! 208p. 1984. pap. 4.95 (ISBN 0-8407-5945-2). Nelson.

Galambos, Edith P. Loving Hands for Jesus. (Little Learner Ser.). 24p. 1985. 5.95 (ISBN 0-570-08951-4, 56-1543). Concordia.

Galilea, Segundo. Following Jesus. Phillips, Helen, tr. from Span. LC 80-24802. Orig. Title: El Seguimiento de Cristo. 128p. (Orig.). 1981. pap. 6.95 (ISBN 0-88344-136-5). Orbis Bks.

Gallagher, Chuck & Crilly, Oliver. Prayer, Saints, Scripture & Ourselves. LC 83-60189. 162p. (Orig.). 1983. pap. text ed. 6.95 (ISBN 0-911905-03-0). Past & Mat Rene Ctr.

Gallagher, Chuck, et al. Calling Disciples: Outlines. LC 84-60459. (Calling Disciples Ser.: Bk. 1). 64p. (Orig.). 1984. pap. text ed. 2.95 (ISBN 0-911905-23-5). Past & Mat Rene Ctr.

Galloway, Dale. Rebuild Your Life. 1981. pap. 4.95 (ISBN 0-8423-5323-2). Tyndale.

Galloway, John, Jr. How to Stay Christian. 144p. 1984. pap. 4.95 (ISBN 0-8170-1038-6). Judson.

Gambaci, Elio. Religious Life. 25.00 (ISBN 0-8198-6416-1). Dghtrs St Paul.

Gambill, Henrietta. Are You Listening? LC 84-7026. (Illus.). 32p. 1984. lib. bdg. 7.45 (ISBN 0-89693-221-4). Dandelion Hse.

Gangel, Kenneth & Gangel, Elizabeth. Building a Christian Family: A Guide for Parents. (Orig.). 1987. pap. 6.95 (ISBN 0-8024-1506-7). Moody.

Gangel, Kenneth O. The Family First. pap. 3.50 (ISBN 0-88469-106-3). BMH Bks.

Gannon, Thomas M. & Traub, George W. The Desert & the City: An Interpretation of the History of Christian Spirituality. 338p. 1984. 8.95 (ISBN 0-8294-0452-X). Loyola.

Garlow, Willa R. Jesus Is a Special Person. LC 85-24361. (Bible & Me Ser.). (Illus.). 1986. 5.95 (ISBN 0-8054-4166-2). Broadman.

Garrison, Jayne. The Christian Working Mother's Handbook. 144p. 1986. pap. 7.95 (ISBN 0-8423-0258-1). Tyndale.

Garrison, Omar V. Jesus Loved Them. (Illus.). 133p. 1983. 19.95 (ISBN 0-931116-06-6). Ralston-Pilot.

Garrotto, Alfred J. Christians Reconciling. 96p. (Orig.). 1982. pap. 4.95 (ISBN 0-86683-170-3, HarpR). Har-Row.

Gaspard, Perry A. Freedom from Fear. 1980. pap. 2.00 (ISBN 0-931867-06-1). Abundant Life Pubns.

--The Power of God's Word. 60p. 1981. pap. 2.00 (ISBN 0-931867-05-3). Abundant Life Pubns.

--The Power of the Tongue. 1983. pap. 1.50 (ISBN 0-931867-04-5). Abundant Life Pubns.

--Redeemed from the Curse. 64p. 1983. pap. 2.00 (ISBN 0-931867-03-7). Abundant Life Pubns.

Gattin, Dana. God Is the Answer. 1984. 5.95 (ISBN 0-317-03625-4). Unity School.

Gaub, Ken, ed. God's Got Your Number. 150p. (Orig.). 1986. pap. text ed. 3.95 (ISBN 0-88368-185-4). Whitaker Hse.

Gause, R. Hollis. Revelation: God's Stamp of Sovereignty. LC 83-63383. 286p. 1983. pap. text ed. 9.95 (ISBN 0-87148-740-3). Pathway Pr.

Geisler, Norman L. The Roots of Evil. (Christian Free University Curriculum Ser.). 1978. pap. 4.95 (ISBN 0-310-35751-9, 12655P). Zondervan.

Geisler, Ruth. The Christian Family Prepares for Easter. 96p. (Orig.). 1985. pap. 6.95 (ISBN 0-570-03977-0, 12-2893). Concordia.

George, William T. Lo Que Dios Espera de Mi. LC 82-60829. (Illus.). 157p. (Orig.). 1983. pap. text ed. 6.95 (ISBN 0-87148-517-6). Pathway Pr.

--What God Expects of Me. LC 82-60828. 175p. (Orig.). 1982. pap. text ed. 6.95 (ISBN 0-87148-918-X). Pathway Pr.

Getz, Gene. God's Plan for Building a Good Reputation. 144p. 1987. pap. 5.95 (ISBN 0-89693-010-6). Victor Bks.

--Serving One Another. 156p. 1984. pap. 5.95 (ISBN 0-88207-612-4). Victor Bks.

Getz, Gene A. Building up One Another. LC 76-19918. 120p. 1976. pap. 4.95 (ISBN 0-88207-744-9). Victor Bks.

--Doing Your Part When You'd Rather Let God Do It All: The Measure of a Christian Based on James 2-5. LC 84-17749. 1985. pap. 5.95 (ISBN 0-8307-1002-7, 5418395). Regal.

--Encouraging One Another. 1981. pap. 5.95 (ISBN 0-88207-256-0). Victor Bks.

--Living for Others When You'd Rather Live for Yourself. LC 85-24283. (Biblical Renewal Ser.). 126p. 1985. pap. write for info. (ISBN 0-8307-1125-2, 5418606). Regal.

--Measure of a Man. LC 74-175983. 224p. (Orig.). 1974. pap. 4.95 (ISBN 0-8307-0291-1, 5012104). Regal.

--Pressing on When You'd Rather Turn Back: Philippians. rev. ed. (Biblical Renewal Ser.). 200p. 1985. pap. 5.95 (ISBN 0-8307-1089-2, 5418561). Regal.

--Standing Firm When You'd Rather Retreat. LC 86-429. (Biblical Renewal Ser.). 168p. (Orig.). 1986. pap. 5.95 (ISBN 0-8307-1093-0, 5418594). Regal.

--Vivendo Sob Pressao. Orig. Title: When the Pressure Is on. (Port.). 1986. write for info. (ISBN 0-8297-0897-9). Life Pubs Intl.

Ghezzi, Bert. The Angry Christian: How to Control & Use Your Anger. (Living As a Christian Ser.). 108p. (Orig.). 1980. pap. 2.95 (ISBN 0-89283-086-7). Servant.

--Facing Your Feelings: How to Get Your Emotions to Work for You. (Living as a Christian Ser.). 112p. 1983. pap. 2.95 (ISBN 0-89283-133-2). Servant.

--Getting Free: How Christians Can Overcome the Flesh & Conquer Persistent Personal Problems. (Living As a Christian Ser.). 112p. 1982. pap. 2.95 (ISBN 0-89283-117-0). Servant.

--Transforming Problems. 140p. (Orig.). 1986. pap. 4.95 (ISBN 0-89283-294-0). Servant.

Gibson, Eva. Melissa. 137p. (Orig.). 1982. pap. 2.95 (ISBN 0-87123-575-7, 200575). Bethany Hse.

Gibson, Eva & Price, Steven. Building Christian Confidence. (Building Bks.). 64p. (Orig.). 1987. tchr's. guide 4.95 (ISBN 0-87123-935-3). Bethany Hse.

--Building Christian Confidence. (Building Bks.). 76p. (Orig.). 1987. student wkbk. 3.95 (ISBN 0-87123-934-5). Bethany Hse.

Gibson, George M. Story of the Christian Year. LC 71-142635. (Essay Index Reprint Ser.). (Illus.). Repr. of 1945 ed. 25.00 (ISBN 0-8369-2770-2). Ayer Co Pubs.

Gibson, Jean. Intermediate Christian Training. 1981. pap. 7.50 (ISBN 0-937396-60-5). Walterick Pubs.

The Gift of New Life. (Benziger Family Life Program Ser.). 5p. 1978. 2.00 (ISBN 0-02-651700-0); tchrs. ed. 4.00 (ISBN 0-02-651710-8); family handbook 1.00 (ISBN 0-02-651740-X). Benziger Pub Co.

Gifts to Share. (Benziger Family Life Program Ser.). 1978. 2.00 (ISBN 0-02-651500-8); tchrs. ed. 4.00 (ISBN 0-02-651510-5); family handbook 1.00 (ISBN 0-02-651540-7). Benziger Pub Co.

Gilbert, Marvin. God, Me, & Thee. (Discovery Bks.). 1980. 1.50 (ISBN 0-88243-841-7, 02-0841); tchr's ed 3.95 (ISBN 0-88243-331-8, 02-0331). Gospel Pub.

Gill, Jean. Unless You Become Like a Little Child. 88p. (Orig.). 1985. pap. 4.95 (ISBN 0-8091-2717-2). Paulist Pr.

Gillquist, Peter E. Love Is Now. new ed. 1970. 4.95 (ISBN 0-310-36941-X, 18054P). Zondervan.

Gillum, Perry. The Christian Life. (Whole Man Whole World Bible Lessons Ser.). 151p. (Orig.). 1983. pap. 3.95 (ISBN 0-934942-46-3, 2418). White Wing Pub.

Gilmore, Donald R. Stepping Stones of Faith. rev. ed. 88p. 1987. price not set (ISBN 0-9617810-0-9). D R Gilmore.

Gilroy, Caroline. Song of the Soul Set Free. 103p. (Orig.). 1986. pap. 3.95 (ISBN 0-8341-1138-1). Beacon Hill.

Giordani, Igino. Diary of Fire. Tr. of Diario di Fuoco. 127p. (Orig.). 1982. pap. 3.95 (ISBN 0-911782-41-9). New City.

Gish, Arthur G. Living in Christian Community. LC 79-11848. 384p. 1979. pap. 9.95 (ISBN 0-8361-1887-1). Herald Pr.

Gittings, James A. Bread, Meat & Raisins after the Dance. LC 77-83883. 1977. 10.00 (ISBN 0-89430-006-7). Palos Verdes.

Give Us This Day. (Little Remembrance Gift Edition Ser.). 4.95 (ISBN 0-87741-004-6). Makepeace Colony.

Gladden, Washington. Being a Christian. LC 72-4168. (Select Bibliographies Reprint Ser.). 1972. Repr. of 1876 ed. 14.00 (ISBN 0-8369-6880-8). Ayer Co Pubs.

--Ruling Ideas of the Present Age. 1971. Repr. of 1895 ed. 23.00 (ISBN 0-384-18865-6). Johnson Repr.

Glass, Bill & McEachern, James E. Plan to Win. 160p. 1984. 8.95 (ISBN 0-8499-0431-5, 0431-5). Word Bks.

Glenn, Alfred A. Taking Your Faith to Work. (Orig.). 1980. pap. 4.95 (ISBN 0-8010-3748-4). Baker Bk.

Glisson, Jerry. Knowing & Doing God's Will. LC 86-2617. (Orig.). 1986. pap. 5.95 (ISBN 0-8054-5027-0). Broadman.

God & Us. 2.25 (ISBN 0-8198-3029-1); 1.25 (ISBN 0-8198-3030-5). Dghtrs St Paul.

God Cares, Vol. 2. 2nd, rev. ed. 1985. pap. 14.95 (ISBN 0-8163-0611-7). Pacific Pr Pub Assn.

God Has Given Us Every Good Thing. 7.95 (ISBN 0-317-46978-9). CSA Pr.

God's Financial Partner: A Bible Course on God, Money & You. write for info. (ISBN 0-9607644-0-2). Financial.

Goehri Ethridge, Myrna L. Fearing No Evil: One Woman's Life of Tragedy & Victory. (Illus.). 108p. (Orig.). 1984. pap. 5.95 (ISBN 0-941018-12-1). Martin Pr CA.

Goff, Guillermo. El Matrimonio y la Familia en la Vida Cristiana. (Span.). 240p. 1985. pap. 7.00 (ISBN 0-311-46097-6). Casa Bautista.

Golden, Jerry & Lestarjette, Steve. Burned Alive! 176p. 1987. pap. text ed. 5.95 (ISBN 0-939079-01-1). Christlife Pubs.

Goldman, W. Darryl. Stand in the Door. LC 80-65309. 176p. 1980. pap. 2.95 (ISBN 0-88243-599-X, 02-0599). Gospel Pub.

Goldsmith, Joel S. The Infinite Way. pap. 5.95 (ISBN 0-87516-309-2). De Vorss.

Gollancz, Victor. A Year of Grace. 1950. 15.95 (ISBN 0-575-00982-9, Pub. by Gollancz England). David & Charles.

Gompertz, Rolf. A Celebration of Life: With Menachem. LC 83-50872. 160p. 1983. velo binding 10.00 (ISBN 0-918248-06-X). Word Doctor.

Gonzalez, Bertha, tr. from Span. A World According to the Heart of God. LC 85-73186. 176p. (Orig.). 1986. pap. 5.00 (ISBN 0-9607590-1-8). Action Life Pubns.

Gonzalez-Ruiz, Jose-Maria. The New Creation: Marxist & Christian? O'Connell, Mathew J., tr. from Spanish. LC 76-10226. Orig. Title: Marximo y Cristianismo Frente Al Hombre Nuevo. 160p. (Orig.). 1976. 1.74 (ISBN 0-88344-327-9). Orbis Bks.

Goodyear, Imogene, ed. The Beauty of Wholeness: Program Resource for Women 1981. 1980. pap. 5.00 (ISBN 0-8309-0294-5). Herald Hse.

Gordon, Arthur. Touch of Wonder. (Orig.). pap. 2.95 (ISBN 0-515-08987-7). Jove Pubns.

Gordon, Earnest B. Adoniram Judson Gordon. Dayton, Donald W., ed. (The Higher Christian Life Ser.). 386p. 1985. 55.00 (ISBN 0-8240-6421-6). Garland Pub.

Gordon, Joel R. Focus on Growth in the Church. rev. ed. (To Live in Christ Ser.). 1980. pap. write for info. (ISBN 0-697-01724-9); instrs.' manual avail. (ISBN 0-697-01722-2). Wm C Brown.

Gordon-Smith, Eileen L. In His Time. 1984. pap. 2.25 (ISBN 9971-972-04-2). OMF Bks.

Gore, Charles. Philosophy of Good Life. 1963. Repr. of 1935 ed. 12.95x (ISBN 0-460-00924-9, Evman). Biblio Dist.

Gospel Principles. 1978. Repr. 7.95 (ISBN 0-87747-716-7). Deseret Bk.

Gossett, Don. How to Conquer Fear. Orig. Title: How You Can Rise Above Fear. 160p. 1981. pap. 2.95 (ISBN 0-88368-092-0). Whitaker Hse.

--What You Say Is What You Get. 192p. 1976. pap. 3.95 (ISBN 0-88368-066-1). Whitaker Hse.

Goudzwaard, B. Aid for the Overdeveloped West. 1975. pap. 3.50 (ISBN 0-88906-100-9). Wedge Pub.

Goudzwaard, Bob. Idols of Our Time. Vennen, Mark V., tr. from Dutch. LC 84-652. Tr. of Genoodzaakt Goed te Wezen: Christelijke Hoop in Een Bezetenwereld. 120p. (Orig.). 1984. pap. 6.95 (ISBN 0-87784-970-6). Inter-Varsity.

Gouge, William. Of Domesticall Duties. LC 76-57385. (English Experience Ser.: No. 803). 1977. Repr. of 1622 ed. lib. bdg. 66.00 (ISBN 90-221-0803-1). Walter J Johnson.

Gould, Toby, et al. We Don't Have Any Here. 52p. 1986. pap. 4.95 (ISBN 0-88177-030-2, DR030B). Discipleship Res.

Grabbe, George. Otritsanije vmesto utverzhdenije. Tr. of Denial Instead of Affirmation. 48p. 1971. pap. 2.00 (ISBN 0-317-30377-5). Holy Trinity.

Graham, Billy. Hasta el Armagedon. Sipowicz, Edwin, tr. from Eng. Orig. Title: Till Armageddon. 272p. 1983. pap. 5.95 (ISBN 0-311-09097-4). Casa Bautista.

--El Mundo en Llamas. Orig. Title: World Aflame. (Span.). 272p. 1983. pap. 5.25 (ISBN 0-311-46091-7). Casa Bautista.

--Nacer a Una Nueva Vida. Ward, Rhode, tr. from Eng. LC 78-52622. Tr. of How to Be Born Again. (Span.). 191p. 1978. pap. 4.95 (ISBN 0-89922-110-6). Edit Caribe.

--Peace with God. rev. ed. 288p. 1985. 10.95 (ISBN 0-8499-0464-1, 0464-1); pap. text ed. 7.95 (ISBN 0-8499-2991-1, 2991-1). Word Bks.

--El Secreto de la Felicidad. Orig. Title: The Secret of Happiness. (Span.). 192p. 1981. pap. 2.75 (ISBN 0-311-04352-6). Casa Bautista.

--Till Armageddon. 224p. 1984. pap. 6.95 (ISBN 0-8499-2998-9, 2998-9). Word Bks.

Graham, Billy & Ten Boom, Corrie. To God Be the Glory. 62p. 1985. pap. text ed. 4.95 large print ed. (ISBN 0-8027-2473-6). Walker & Co.

Graham, John K. God's Gift: The Secrets of Financial Freedom, No. 1. LC 83-83273. (God's Gift Ser.). (Illus.). 112p. 1984. 12.95 (ISBN 0-916333-00-0). King's Hse Pub.

Graham, Ruth B. Sitting by My Laughing Fire. LC 77-75457. 1977. 10.95 (ISBN 0-8499-2933-4). Word Bks.

Grahame, Kenneth. Pagan Papers. LC 72-3427. (Essay Index Reprint Ser.). Repr. of 1898 ed. 15.00 (ISBN 0-8369-2903-9). Ayer Co Pubs.

Grannis, J. Christopher, et al. The Risk of the Cross: Christian Discipleship in the Nuclear Age. 128p. (Orig.). 1981. pap. 5.95 (ISBN 0-8164-2305-9, HarpR). Har-Row.

Grant, Brian W. From Sin to Wholeness. LC 81-16122. 174p. 1982. pap. 8.95 (ISBN 0-664-24399-1). Westminster.

Grant, George. The Dispossessed: Homelessness in America. LC 86-71355. 256p. 1986. pap. 8.95 (ISBN 0-89107-411-2, Crossways Bks). Good News.

Grant, Kenneth. Ponderings. 48p. 1986. 6.95 (ISBN 0-8378-5087-8). Gibson.

Grant, L. M. First & Second Corinthians. 194p. pap. 7.25 (ISBN 0-88172-154-9). Believers Bkshelf.

--God's Order: Is It Possible Today? pap. 0.95 (ISBN 0-88172-153-0). Believers Bkshelf.

Grant, Sandy. Share the Gospel. 80p. 1987. pap. 5.95 (ISBN 1-55513-825-X). Cook.

Grant, Wilson W. The Caring Father. LC 82-72990. (Orig.). 1983. pap. 5.95 (ISBN 0-8054-5654-6). Broadman.

--De Padres a Hijos Acerca del Sexo. La Valle, Maria T., et al, trs. from Eng. (Sexo en la Vida Cristiana Ser.). (Span., Illus.). 192p. 1982. pap. 3.95 (ISBN 0-311-46255-3). Casa Bautista.

--The Power of Affirming Touch. LC 86-10830. (Christian Growth Bks). 128p. (Orig.). 1986. pap. 6.95 (ISBN 0-8066-2210-5, 10-5028). Augsburg.

Gratitude. (Pocket Power Ser.). 16p. (Orig.). 1985. pap. 0.50 (ISBN 0-89486-299-5). Hazelden.

Green, Eise F. Now We Can Face the Day. 1975. 2.25 (ISBN 0-87509-112-1). Chr Pubns.

Green, Hollis L. Dynamics of Christian Discipleship. 112p. 1962. 5.25 (ISBN 0-87148-251-7); pap. 4.25 (ISBN 0-87148-252-5). Pathway Pr.

Green, Holly W. Turning Fear to Hope: Help for Marrages Troubled by Abuse. 228p. (Orig.). 1984. pap. 5.95 (ISBN 0-8407-5937-1). Nelson.

Green, Michael. New Life, New Lifestyle: A Fresh Look at the World. LC 84-25390. 159p. 1985. pap. 5.95 (ISBN 0-88070-073-4). Multnomah.

Green, Milton. The Great Falling Away Today. (Orig.). 1986. pap. 6.95 (ISBN 0-910311-40-4). Huntington Hse Inc.

Green, Thomas H. A Vacation with the Lord: A Personal, Directed Retreat. LC 86-71143. 176p. (Orig.). 1986. pap. 4.95 (ISBN 0-87793-343-X). Ave Maria.

Greenfield, Guy. The Wounded Parent. LC 82-70463. 128p. 1982. pap. 4.95 (ISBN 0-8010-3779-4). Baker Bk.
Greenman, Bill. How to Find Your Purpose in Life. 200p. (Orig.). 1987. pap. text ed. 3.95 (ISBN 0-88368-192-7). Whitaker Hse.
Greenslade, Philip. Leadership, Greatness, & Servanthood. 208p. (Orig.). 1986. pap. 5.95 (ISBN 0-87123-871-3, 210871). Bethany Hse.
Greenspahn, Frederick E. The Human Condition in the Jewish & Christian Conditions. 1985. text ed. 25.00x (ISBN 0-88125-084-8). Ktav.
Gregorian, Juanita L. Glorious Thunder. 144p. 1986. 10.95 (ISBN 0-89962-498-7). Todd & Honeywell.
Greidanus, Morris, et al. Welcome. LC 82-12907. 71p. 1982. pap. 3.50 (ISBN 0-933140-48-7); pap. 3.50 leader's guide (ISBN 0-933140-49-5). CRC Pubns.
Grgic, Bob. Journey to the Father. (YA) 1987. pap. text ed. write for info. (ISBN 0-697-02225-0); write for info. tchr's. ed. (ISBN 0-697-02226-9). Wm C Brown.
Grierson, Denham. Transforming a People of God. 161p. (Orig.). 1984. pap. 11.95 (ISBN 0-85819-464-3, Pub. by JBCE). ANZ Religious Pubns.
Griffin, Bryan F. Panic among the Phillistines. (Christian Activist Ser.). 259p. 1985. pap. 5.95 (ISBN 0-89526-817-5). Regnery Bks.
Griffin, Em. The Mind Changers. 1976. pap. 7.95 (ISBN 0-8423-4290-7). Tyndale.
Griffin, Gayle. Food for Temple & Table. 1981. spiral bdg. 9.95 (ISBN 0-89323-018-9). Bible Memory.
Griffin, Henry E., Jr. Brethern, I Would Not Have You Ignorant. 64p. (Orig.). 1986. pap. 2.25 (ISBN 0-934942-63-3, 2262). White Wing Pub.
Griffiss, James E. A Silent Path to God. LC 79-8903. pap. 27.50 (2029620). Bks Demand UMI.
Griffith, Anna. Balance: A Modern Christian Challenge. pap. 4.95 (ISBN 0-89137-425-6). Quality Pubns.
Griffith, Harry C. The Ways of God: Paths into the New Testament. 149p. 1986. pap. 7.95 (ISBN 0-8192-1377-2). Morehouse.
Griffith, Leonard. Take Hold of the Treasure. 128p. 1983. pap. 5.95 (ISBN 0-8170-0997-3). Judson.
Grisbrooke, Jardine W., ed. Spiritual Counsels of Father John of Kronstadt: Select Passages from "My Life in Christ". 256p. 1983. pap. 10.95 (ISBN 0-227-67856-7, Pub. by J Clarke UK). Attic Pr.
Groff, Warren F. God's Story-& Ours! 148p. (Orig.). 1986. pap. 7.95 (ISBN 0-317-52618-9). Brethren.
Groomer, Vera. Obedience Brings Happiness. (Come Unto Me Ser.). 16p. 1979. pap. 1.65 (ISBN 0-8127-0251-4). Review & Herald.
Groothuis, Douglas R. The New Age Movement. 32p. (Orig.). 1986. pap. 0.75 (ISBN 0-87784-079-2). Inter-Varsity.
--Unmasking the New Age. LC 85-23832. 200p. (Orig.). 1986. pap. 6.95 (ISBN 0-87784-568-9). Inter-Varsity.
Groten, Dallas. Will the Real Winner Please Stand Up. 160p. 1985. pap. 4.95 (ISBN 0-87123-819-5, 210819). Bethany Hse.
Grounds, Vernon. Radical Commitment: Getting Serious about Christian Growth. LC 84-3344. 1984. pap. 5.95 (ISBN 0-88070-051-3). Multnomah.
Grubb, L. L. How to Discover God. 1979. pap. write for info. (ISBN 0-88469-002-4). BMH Bks.
Grubb, Norman P. Spontaneous You. 1970. pap. 3.50 (ISBN 0-87508-224-6). Chr Lit.
--Summit Living. 368p. 1985. 9.95 (ISBN 0-317-43397-0); pap. 7.95 (ISBN 0-87508-267-X). Chr Lit.
--Yes, I Am. 1982. pap. text ed. 4.95 (ISBN 0-87508-206-8). Chr Lit.
Gruen, Ernest J. Freedom to Choose. 224p. 1976. pap. 2.95 (ISBN 0-88368-072-6). Whitaker Hse.
Guinness, Michele. Child of the Covenant. 160p. 1985. pap. 2.95 (ISBN 0-345-32715-2). Ballantine.
Gurnall, William. Christian in Complete Armour: A Modernised Abridgement, Vol. 1. rev., abr. ed. 320p. 1986. pap. 5.95 (ISBN 0-85151-456-1). Banner of Truth.
Gustafson, James M. Christ & the Moral Life. 1979. 8.00x (ISBN 0-226-31109-0, P830, Phoen). U of Chicago Pr.
Gustaveson, David. Personal Life Notebook. 192p. 1980. pap. 8.95 spiral bdg. (ISBN 0-87123-467-X, 210467). Bethany Hse.
Gutherie, Shirley C., Jr. Diversity in Faith-Unity in Christ. LC 86-9157. 144p. (Orig.). 1986. pap. 10.95 (ISBN 0-664-24013-5). Westminster.
Gutierrez-Cortes, Rolando. Cuando la Familia Enfrenta Problemas. (Serie de la Familia). (Span.). 96p. 1985. pap. 3.50 (ISBN 0-311-46261-8). Casa Bautista.
Guyon, Jeanne. Final Steps in Christian Maturity. 1985. pap. 6.95 (ISBN 0-940232-22-7). Christian Bks.
Guzie, Tad & Guzie, Noreen M. About Men & Women: How Your Great Story Shapes Your Destiny. 176p. (Orig.). 1986. pap. 7.95 (ISBN 0-8091-2813-6). Paulist Pr.
Gvillo, Doris. Musing, Meditations, & Meanderings. 1984. 5.95 (ISBN 0-89536-982-6, 7531). CSS of Ohio.
Gyan, Gopi. Morningland Color Book. 1979. pap. 7.95 (ISBN 0-935146-09-1). Morningland.
Haas, Harold I. El Cristiano Frente a los Problemas Mentales. De Molina, Sara Pais, tr. 110p. 1977. Repr. of 1975 ed. 2.50 (ISBN 0-311-42500-3). Casa Bautista.
Hacking, W. Smith Wigglesworth Remembered. 107p. 1981. pap. 3.95 (ISBN 0-89274-203-8). Harrison Hse.
Hackman, Ruth. God in the Midst of Every Day: Reflections on Life's Simple Gifts. LC 86-7888. (Illus.). 128p. 1986. kivar paper 6.50 (ISBN 0-8066-2207-5, 10-2643). Augsburg.
Hadidian, Allen. Discipleship: Helping Other Christians Grow. 1987. pap. 6.95 (ISBN 0-8024-3362-6). Moody.
Hagin, Kenneth E. The Believer's Authority. 2nd ed. 1985. pap. 2.50 (ISBN 0-89276-406-6). Hagin Ministries.
--El Cristiano Intercesor. 1985. 1.00 (ISBN 0-89276-118-0). Hagin Ministries.
--The Interceding Christian. 2nd ed. 1983. pap. 1.00 (ISBN 0-89276-018-4). Hagin Ministries.
--Kenneth E. Hagin's Fifty Years in the Ministry, 1934-1984. 1984. pap. write for info. (ISBN 0-89276-093-1). Hagin Ministries.
--Love Never Fails. 1984. pap. 0.50 mini bk. (ISBN 0-89276-264-0). Hagin Ministries.
Hagin, Kenneth, Jr. Commanding Power. 1985. pap. 0.50 (ISBN 0-317-40350-8). Hagin Ministries.
Hailey, Homer. From Creation to the Day of Eternity. (Illus.). 1982. 11.95 (ISBN 0-913814-42-3). Nevada Pubns.
Haines, Madge. You, Too, Can Find Peace. Woolsey, Raymond H., ed. (Banner Ser.). 128p. (Orig.). 1987. pap. 6.50 (ISBN 0-8280-0366-1). Review & Herald.
Haiven, Judith. Faith, Hope, No Charity: An Inside Look at the Born Again Movement in Canada & the United States. (Illus.). 221p. 1984. lib. bdg. 14.95 (ISBN 0-919573-32-0); pap. 7.95 (ISBN 0-919573-33-9). Left Bank.
Hajos, Mary. Removing the Stones. 1976. pap. 2.95 (ISBN 0-87508-264-5). Chr Lit.
Hakenewerth, Quentin. The Grain of Wheat. 88p. 1966. pap. 1.75 (ISBN 0-9608124-0-7). Marianist Com Ctr.
Halbrook, D. L. & Halbrook, Becky. Wait Guys & Girls. pap. 4.25 (ISBN 0-89137-805-7). Quality Pubns.
Hald, Marie M. Jesus Jewels. 118p. 1983. pap. 5.00 (ISBN 0-682-49963-3). Exposition Pr FL.
Hale, Anita. My Room at Church. LC 85-24344. (Bible & Me Ser.). (Illus.). 1986. 5.95 (ISBN 0-8054-4168-9). Broadman.
Hale, Mabel. Emma Bailey Seeks Truth. 24p. 1982. pap. 0.25 (ISBN 0-686-36258-6); pap. 1.00 5 copies (ISBN 0-686-37283-2). Faith Pub Hse.
Hall, Brian & Tonna, Benjamin. God's Plan for Us: A Practical Strategy for Communal Discernment of Spirits. LC 80-81439. 128p. 1980. pap. 8.95 (ISBN 0-8091-2311-8). Paulist Pr.
Hall, Brian P. The Personal Discernment Inventory: An Instrument for Spiritual Guides. pap. 5.95 (ISBN 0-8091-2312-6). Paulist Pr.
Hall, Brian P. & Tonna, Benjamin. The Hall-Tonna Inventory of Values. write for info. Paulist Pr.
Hall, Carolyn. Does God Give Interviews? 56p. 1985. 7.95 (ISBN 0-533-06644-1). Vantage.
Hall, Eugene E. & Heflin, James L. Proclaim the Word. LC 84-17458. 1985. 9.95 (ISBN 0-8054-2102-5). Broadman.
Hall, Marion P. The Healing Coin. 86p. 1984. pap. 5.50 (ISBN 0-87516-542-7). De Vorss.
Hall, Mary. The Impossible Dream: The Spirituality of Dom Helder Camara. LC 79-26888. 96p. (Orig.). 1980. pap. 2.48 (ISBN 0-88344-212-4). Orbis Bks.
--A Quest for the Liberated Christian. (IC-Studies in the Intercultural History of Christianity: Vol. 19). 341p. 1978. pap. 37.25 (ISBN 3-261-02668-5). P Lang Pubs.
Hallam, Arthur F. Total Surrender to God. 236p. (Orig.). 1985. pap. 19.95 (ISBN 0-938770-05-5). Capitalist Pr OH.
Hallesby, O. Temperament & the Christian Faith. LC 62-9093. 106p. 1978. pap. 3.95 (ISBN 0-8066-1660-1, 10-6237). Augsburg.
Halpin, Marlene. Imagine That! 144p. 1982. pap. 4.95 (ISBN 0-697-01812-1); videotapes avail. Wm C Brown.
Halverson, Delia T. Helping Your Teen Develop Faith. 112p. 1985. pap. 5.95 (ISBN 0-8170-1046-7). Judson.
Halverson, K. & Hess, Karen. The Wedded Unmother. LC 79-54123. 128p. 1980. pap. 5.95 (ISBN 0-8066-1768-3, 10-7015). Augsburg.
Hambrick, John. The High Cost of Indifference: Leader's Guide. (Study & Grow Electives). 64p. 1985. pap. 3.95 (ISBN 0-8307-1019-1, 6102038). Regal.
Hamerton-Kelly, Robert G. Sprung Time: Seasons of the Christian Year. LC 79-56162. 144p. (Orig.). 1980. pap. 4.50 (ISBN 0-8358-0397-X). Upper Room.
Hamilton, Elizabeth. Letters Addressed to the Daughter of a Nobleman on the Formation of the Religious & the Moral Principle, 2 vols. Luria, Gina, ed. (The Feminist Controversy in England, 1788-1810 Ser.). 1974. Set. lib. bdg. 121.00 (ISBN 0-8240-0865-0). Garland Pub.
Hamilton, LeRoy L. Jogging with God. 56p. 1985. 5.95 (ISBN 0-8059-2983-5). Dorrance.
Hamilton, Neill Q. Maturing in the Christian Life: A Pastor's Guide. LC 83-20661. 192p. (Orig.). 1984. pap. 10.95 (ISBN 0-664-24515-3). Westminster.
Hammond, Frank & Hammond, Ida M. Pigs in the Parlor. 153p. (Orig.). 1973. pap. 4.95 (ISBN 0-89228-027-1). Impact Bks MO.
Hammond, Frank & Hammond, Ida Mae. Kingdom Living for the Family. 175p. (Orig.). 1985. pap. 4.95 (ISBN 0-89228-100-6). Impact Bks MO.
Hampton, Diane. The Diet Alternative. Orig. Title: Scriptural Eating Patterns. 144p. (Orig.). 1984. pap. 3.95 (ISBN 0-88368-148-X). Whitaker Hse.
Hancock, Maxine. Living on Less & Liking It More. 160p. 1982. pap. 4.95 (ISBN 0-89081-414-7). Harvest Hse.
Hand, Marcus V. Put Your Arms Around the World. LC 78-66976. 112p. (Orig.). 1978. pap. text ed. 1.25 (ISBN 0-87148-698-9). Pathway Pr.
Handford, Elizabeth R. Forgiving the Unforgivable. (The "Joyful Living" Ser.). 31p. (Orig.). 1985. pap. 1.50 (ISBN 0-912623-02-0). Joyful Woman.
Handford, Elizabeth R. & Martin, Joy R. The Mysterious Alabaster Bottle. 28p. (Orig.). 1987. pap. 1.50 (ISBN 0-912623-04-7). Joyful Woman.
Haney, Anita. Battling Anorexia. (Orig.). 1986. pap. 5.95 (ISBN 0-89265-111-3). Randall Hse.
Haney, David. El Senor y Sus Laicos. Martinez, Jose Luis, ed. (Span.). 84p. 1986. pap. 2.50 (ISBN 0-311-09095-8). Casa Bautista.
Hanon, Bill. The Eternal Church. 398p. (Orig.). 1981. 12.95 (ISBN 0-939868-01-6); pap. 8.95 (ISBN 0-939868-00-8). Chr Intl Pubs.
Hansel, Tim. When I Relax I Feel Guilty. LC 78-73460. 1979. pap. 6.95 (ISBN 0-89191-137-5). Cook.
Hansen, Lillian E. The Double Yoke. (Illus.). 268p. 1979. pap. 2.95 (ISBN 0-89216-020-9). Salvation Army.
Harakas, S. Living the Liturgy. 1974. pap. 4.95 (ISBN 0-937032-17-4). Light&Life Pub Co MN.
--Toward Transfigured Life. 1983. pap. 12.95 (ISBN 0-937032-28-X). Light&Life Pub Co MN.
Harbaugh, Gary L. The Faith-Hardy Christian: How to Face the Challenges of Life with Confidence. LC 86-7966. (Christian Growth Ser.). 128p. 1986. pap. 6.95 (ISBN 0-8066-2212-1, 10-2184). Augsburg.
Harbour, Brian L. A New Look at the Book. LC 84-27479. 1985. pap. 5.95 (ISBN 0-8054-1535-1). Broadman.
Harder, Helmut. Living As God's People. LC 86-80675. (Faith & Life Bible Studies). 64p. (Orig.). 1986. pap. 4.95 (ISBN 0-87303-108-3). Faith & Life.
Hardin, Joyce. Three Steps Behind. 320p. (Orig.). 1986. pap. 10.95 (ISBN 0-915547-91-0). Abilene Christ U.
Hardinge, Leslie. The Victors. (Anchor Ser.). 112p. 1982. pap. 5.95 (ISBN 0-8163-0490-4). Pacific Pr Pub Assn.
Hare, Eric B. Fullness of Joy. 1985. pap. 5.95 (ISBN 0-8163-0586-2). Pacific Pr Pub Assn.
Haring, Bernard. Dare to Be Christian: Developing a Social Conscience. 160p. 1983. pap. 4.25 (ISBN 0-89243-180-6). Liguori Pubns.
--Free & Faithful in Christ: Light to the World, Vol. 3. 500p. 1981. 19.50 (ISBN 0-8245-0009-1). Crossroad NY.
--Free & Faithful in Christ: The Truth Will Set You Free, Vol. 2. 560p. 1979. 19.50 (ISBN 0-8245-0309-0). Crossroad NY.
Harnish, James A. Jesus Makes the Difference! The Gospel in Human Experience. 144p. (Orig.). 1987. pap. 6.95 (ISBN 0-8358-0554-9). Upper Room.
Harper, Michael. Walking in the Spirit. 112p. (Orig.). 1983. pap. 3.95 (ISBN 0-87123-614-1, 210614). Bethany Hse.
Harpur, Tom. For Christ's Sake. LC 86-47866. 118p. 1987. 17.95 (ISBN 0-8070-1012-X); pap. 8.95 (ISBN 0-8070-1013-8, BP 756). Beacon Pr.
Harries, Richard. Prayer & the Pursuit of Happiness. 160p. (Orig.). 1985. pap. 6.95 (ISBN 0-8028-0089-0). Eerdmans.
Harrington, W., et al. The Saving Word, Years A, B & C. 370p. 1982. pap. 12.00 ea. (ISBN 0-89453-266-9); Set. pap. 30.00. M Glazier.
Harris, Huffman T. Open the Door Wide to Happy Living. 1985. 12.95 (ISBN 0-8062-2523-8). Carlton.
Harrison, Norman B. New Testament Living. 1972. pap. 1.25 (ISBN 0-911802-30-4). Free Church Pubns.
Hart, Archibald D. The Success Factor. 160p. 1984. pap. 5.95 (ISBN 0-8007-5138-8, Power Bks). Revell.
Hart, John. The Spirit of the Earth. 1984. pap. 8.95 (ISBN 0-8091-2581-1). Paulist Pr.
Hartley, Fred. Dare to Be Different. 128p. 1980. pap. 5.95 (ISBN 0-8007-5041-1, Power Bks). Revell.
--One Hundred Percent: Beyond Mediocrity. (Illus.). 160p. 1983. pap. 5.95 (ISBN 0-8007-5112-4, Power Bks). Revell.
Harty, Annelle & Harty, Robert. Made to Grow. (Sexuality in Christian Living Ser.). 32p. 1973. 6.95 (ISBN 0-8054-4222-7). Broadman.
Harvey, J. D. Faith Plus - Search for the Holy Life. 1976. pap. 1.75 (ISBN 0-89367-002-2). Light & Life.
Hassall, Phillip. I Cannot Hear You, But I Can Hear God. Mandeville, Sylvia, ed. 144p. 1987. pap. 3.95 (ISBN 0-340-38268-6, Pub. by Hodder & Stoughton UK). David & Charles.
Hatfield, Mark, et al. Confessing Christ & Doing Politics. Skillen, James, ed. LC 80-71233. 100p. (Orig.). 1982. pap. 3.95 (ISBN 0-936456-02-7). Assn Public Justice.
Hathrill, Robert. The Bell Ringer. 1983. 8.95 (ISBN 0-533-05631-4). Vantage.
Hatton, Thomas J. Rabbit Christmas. (Orig.). 1982. pap. 2.95 (ISBN 0-937172-40-5). JLJ Pubs.
Hauerwas, Stanley. Character & the Christian Life: A Study in Theological Ethics. LC 85-5873. (Monograph Series in Religion). 265p. 1985. pap. text ed. 10.95 (ISBN 0-939980-10-X). Trinity U Pr.
Haughey, John C. Holy Use of Money: Personal Finance in Light of Christian Faith. LC 85-29213. 288p. 1986. 16.95 (ISBN 0-385-23448-1). Doubleday.
Haugk, Kenneth C. Christian Caregiving: A Way of Life. LC 84-24341. (Orig.). 1984. pap. 7.95 (ISBN 0-8066-2123-0, 10-1103). Augsburg.
Hausmann, Winifred W. A Guide to Love-Powered Living. LC 85-72282. 192p. (Orig.). 1986. pap. 7.95 (ISBN 0-87516-560-5). De Vorss.
--Your God-Given Potential. LC 77-80458. 1978. 5.95 (ISBN 0-87159-182-0). Unity School.
Havergal, F. R. My King. pap. 2.25 (ISBN 0-685-88388-4). Reiner.
Havergal, Frances R. Kept for the Master's Use. (Large Print Christian Classic Ser.). 1982. 11.95 (ISBN 0-87983-290-8). Keats.
Havergel, Frances. Kept for the Master's Use. 120p. 1986. pap. 4.95 (ISBN 0-89693-279-6). Victor Bks.
Havner, Vance. Lord of What's Left. rev. ed. 124p. 1985. pap. 4.95 (ISBN 0-8010-4286-0). Baker Bk.
--Moments of Decision: Guidelines for the Most Important Choices of Your Life. 128p. 1985. pap. 4.95 (ISBN 0-8010-4287-9). Baker Bk.
--On This Rock I Stand. 160p. 1986. pap. 5.95 (ISBN 0-8010-4296-8). Baker Bk.
--Playing Marbles with Diamonds: And Other Messages for America. 80p. 1985. text ed. 7.95 (ISBN 0-8010-4290-9). Baker Bk.
--Vance Havner Treasury. Hester, Dennis, compiled by. 264p. Date not set. 9.95 (ISBN 0-8010-4315-8). Baker Bk.
--When God Breaks Through: And Other Challenging Talks. 96p. 1987. Repr. price not set. Baker Bk.
Hawkins, O. S. After Revival Comes. LC 81-66090. 1981. pap. 4.95 (ISBN 0-8054-6231-7). Broadman.
--Tracing the Rainbow Through the Rain. LC 85-6610. 1985. 7.95 (ISBN 0-8054-5020-3). Broadman.
Hawkinson, James R., ed. Come, Let Us Praise Him. 1985. pap. 3.95 (ISBN 0-910452-57-1). Covenant.
Hawley, Monroe E. Searching for a Better Way. 1980. pap. 5.50 (ISBN 0-89137-525-2). Quality Pubns.
Hawthorne, Minnie. Here We Go Again Lord. 1982. 4.50 (ISBN 0-8062-1659-X). Carlton.
Hayden, Eric. God's Answer for Fear. LC 85-70873. 1986. pap. 2.95 (ISBN 0-88270-581-4). Bridge Pub.
Hayes, Bernard. Love in Action: Reflections on Christian Service. 120p. (Orig.). pap. 5.95 (ISBN 0-914544-57-8). Living Flame Pr.

Hayes, Gloria L. God Provides. 64p. 1986. 6.95 (ISBN 0-89962-523-1). Todd & Honeywell.

Hayes, Norvel. How to Live & Not Die. (Orig.). 1986. pap. 5.95 (ISBN 0-89274-395-6). Harrison Hse.

Hayford, Jack. Daybreak. 112p. (Orig.). 1987. mass 2.95, (ISBN 0-8423-0524-6). Tyndale.

--Newborn. 96p. 1987. 2.95 (ISBN 0-8423-4677-5). Tyndale.

--The Visitor. 128p. 1986. pap. 4.95 (ISBN 0-8423-7802-2). Tyndale.

--Water Baptism. 96p. (Orig.). cancelled (ISBN 0-8423-7814-6). Tyndale.

Hayford, Jack W. Rebuilding the Real You. 195p. (Orig.). 1986. pap. 7.95 (ISBN 0-8307-1156-2, 5418849). Regal.

Hazelip, Harold. Discipleship. LC 77-89541. (Twentieth Century Sermons Ser.). 11.95 (ISBN 0-89112-309-1, Bibl Res Pr). Abilene Christ U.

He Speaks to You. 2.25 (ISBN 0-8198-3300-2). Dghtrs St Paul.

Hebblethwaite, Brian. The Christian Hope. 248p. (Orig.). 1985. pap. 9.95 (ISBN 0-8028-0054-8). Eerdmans.

Hebert, Yvonne C. Finding Peace in Pain. 108p. (Orig.). 1984. pap. text ed. 3.50 (ISBN 0-914544-53-5). Living Flame Pr.

Heck, Klaus. Before You Cast the Second Stone. 1979. 7.95 (ISBN 0-915948-05-2); pap. 5.95 (ISBN 0-686-52664-3). Bks Distinction.

Heckman, Shirley J. Visions of Peace. LC 83-16522. 75p. (Orig.). 1984. pap. 5.95 (ISBN 0-377-00140-6). Friend Pr.

Hefley, James C. Way Back in the Hills. (Living Bks.). 352p. (Orig.). 1985. 3.95 (ISBN 0-8423-7821-9). Tyndale.

Hegre, T. A. Creative Faith. LC 80-17869. 96p. (Orig.). 1980. pap. 3.95 (ISBN 0-87123-020-8, 210020). Bethany Hse.

Hegstad & Munson. War of the Star Lords. 34p. 1983. pap. 2.50 (ISBN 0-8163-0517-X). Pacific Pr Pub Assn.

Heiges, Donald R. The Christian's Calling. rev. ed. LC 84-47923. 112p. 1984. pap. 4.95 (ISBN 0-8006-1795-9). Fortress.

Heim, Pamela. The Woman God Can Use. LC 85-73070. 176p. 1986. pap. 6.95 (ISBN 0-89636-190-X). Accent Bks.

Heim, S. Mark. Is Christ the Only Way. 160p. 1984. pap. 7.95 (ISBN 0-317-18066-5). Judson.

Helldorfer, Martin C. The Work Trap. LC 80-52059. 96p. 1983. pap. 5.95 (ISBN 0-89571-017-X). Affirmation.

Helldorfer, Martin C. & Polcino, Anna. Relationships: Issues of Emotional Living in an Age of Stress for Clergy & Religious. Sammon, Sean D., ed. LC 83-2706. 144p. (Orig.). 1983. pap. 8.00 (ISBN 0-89571-015-3). Affirmation.

Hellwig, Monika K. Christian Women in a Troubled World: Madeleva Lecture 1984. 60p. (Orig.). 1985. 2.95 (ISBN 0-8091-2713-X). Paulist Pr.

--What Are They Saying about Death & Christian Hope? LC 78-61726. 1978. pap. 3.95 (ISBN 0-8091-2165-4). Paulist Pr.

Helm, Janet. Jesus Changes People. Duckert, Mary, ed. (New Vacation Venture Ser.). leader's guide 3.95; 1.95 (ISBN 0-664-24172-7); resource packet 11.95 (ISBN 0-664-24174-3); New Life Songbook. 0.95 (ISBN 0-664-24171-9). Westminster.

Helwig, Terry. Forgive Me, Lord, I Goofed! (Orig.). 1986. pap. 3.25 (ISBN 0-8054-5035-1). Broadman.

Hembree, Ron. The Speck in Your Brother's Eye: How to Be a More Loving Christian. 192p. 1985. 9.95 (ISBN 0-8007-1426-1). Revell.

Hendee, John. Discipling New Christians with the Spiritual T. E. A. M. Veteran Season. (Spiritual T.E.A.M Ser.). 64p. 1986. pap. 2.95 wkbk. (ISBN 0-87403-153-2, 3246). Standard Pub.

--Discipling New Christians with the Spiritual T. E. A. M. Rookie Season. (Spiritual T.E.A.M. Ser.). 64p. 1986. pap. 2.95 wkbk. (ISBN 0-87403-152-4, 3245). Standard Pub.

--Discipling New Christians with the Spiritual T. E. A. M. Coach's Manual. (Spiritual T.E.A.M. Ser.). 136p. 1986. pap. 5.95 (ISBN 0-87403-151-6, 3244). Standard Pub.

Hendershot, Kathy. Obedience: The Road to Reality. 176p. (Orig.). 1982. pap. 3.50 (ISBN 0-911567-00-3). Christian Mini.

Henderson, E. Harold. Now Abideth Faith. 120p. 1962. pap. 0.50 (ISBN 0-89114-149-9). Baptist Pub Hse.

Hendren, Bob. Chosen for Riches. LC 77-25775. (Journey Bks.). 1978. 3.50 (ISBN 0-8344-0096-0). Sweet.

--Life Without End. LC 80-54164. (Journey Adult Ser.). 144p. 1981. pap. 3.50 (ISBN 0-8344-0118-5). Sweet.

Hendricks, Howard & Hendricks, Jeanne. Footprints: Walking Through the Passages of Life. LC 80-25868. (Illus.). 96p. 1981. pap. 5.95 (ISBN 0-930014-55-3). Multnomah.

Hendrix, John & Householder, Lloyd, eds. The Equipping of Disciples. LC 76-29803. 1977. bds. 9.95 (ISBN 0-8054-3218-3). Broadman.

Henrichsen, Walter. Is It Any of God's Business? A Provocative Look at Faith in the Workplace. LC 86-63651. 204p. (Orig.). 1987. pap. price not set (ISBN 0-89109-138-6). NavPress.

Henrichsen, Walter A. & Jackson, Gayle. A Layman's Guide to Applying the Bible. 224p. (Orig.). 1985. pap. 7.95 (ISBN 0-310-37691-2, 11233P, Pub. by Lamplight); Set pack. pap. 19.95 (ISBN 0-310-37698-X, 11238P, Pub. by Lamplight). Zondervan.

Henry, Carl F. The Christian Mindset in a Secular Society. LC 83-25136. (Critical Concern Ser.). 1984. 9.95 (ISBN 0-88070-041-6); pap. 6.95. Multnomah.

Henry, Carl F., ed. The Biblical Expositor. 1332p. 1986. Repr. text ed. 49.95 (ISBN 0-8010-0890-5). Baker Bk.

Henry, Matthew. The Secret of Communion with God. LC 79-93431. (Shepherd Illustrated Classics Ser.). (Illus.). 144p. 1981. pap. 5.95 (ISBN 0-87983-220-7). Keats.

Henry, Patrick & Stransky, Thomas F. God on Our Minds. LC 81-70593. 176p. 1982. pap. 6.95 (ISBN 0-8006-1600-6, 1-1600). Fortress.

Hensley, J. Clark. Coping with Being Single Again. LC 78-52623. 1978. 7.95 (ISBN 0-8054-5420-9). Broadman.

Hepburn, Daisy. Life with Spice Resource Manual. 1984. 5.95 (ISBN 0-8307-0936-3, 5203006). Regal.

Herbert, Janet. Happy Birthday to You. 32p. 1986. 2.95 (50401, Chariot Bks). Cook.

Hermanson, Renee. Raspberry Kingdom. LC 78-62985. 1978. pap. 4.50 (ISBN 0-8358-0374-0). Upper Room.

Herring, Clyde L. If God Talked Out Loud. LC 76-27479. (Illus.). 1977. pap. 5.50 (ISBN 0-8054-5325-3, 4253-25). Broadman.

--When God & I Talk. LC 80-70917. 1981. pap. 4.95 (ISBN 0-8054-5334-2, 4253-34). Broadman.

Hershey, Terry. Beginning Again: Involvement Guide. 64p. 1986. cancelled (ISBN 0-8407-3084-5). Nelson.

--Beginning Again: Life after a Relationship Ends. 152p. 1986. pap. 7.95 (ISBN 0-8407-3075-6). Nelson.

Hess, Bartlett & Hess, Margaret. Never Say Old. 156p. 1984. pap. 5.95 (ISBN 0-89693-375-X). Victor Bks.

Hession, Roy. Forgotten Factors. 1976. pap. 2.95 (ISBN 0-87508-234-3). Chr Lit.

--Not I but Christ. 1980. pap. 3.95 (ISBN 0-87508-198-3). Chr Lit.

Hestenes, Roberta. Building Christian Community Through Small Groups. pap. 69.95x incl. tapes (ISBN 0-9602638-5-3). Fuller Theol Soc.

Hickey, Marilyn. Fear Free Faith Filled. 176p. 1982. pap. 3.50 (ISBN 0-89274-259-3). Harrison Hse.

Hickingbotham, Ian. Turn Around One Hundred Times. 1985. 21.00x (ISBN 0-7223-1917-7, Pub. by A H Stockwell England). State Mutual Bk.

Hickman, Martha W. When Our Church Building Burned Down. 48p. 1986. 9.95 (ISBN 0-687-45023-3). Abingdon.

Hicks, Darryl E. God Comes to Nashville. LC 79-89583. 1979. pap. 3.50 (ISBN 0-89221-065-6). New Leaf.

Hicks, Robert & Bewes, Richard. The Christian. (Understanding Bible Truth Ser.). (Orig.). 1981. pap. 0.95 (ISBN 0-89840-023-6). Heres Life.

Hicks, Robert H., ed. A Gift More Precious than Gold. (Illus.). 200p. 1985. Repr. 9.95 (ISBN 0-687-14691-7). Abingdon.

Hicks, Roy H. Power of Positive Resistance. 128p. 1983. pap. 2.95 (ISBN 0-89274-294-1). Harrison Hse.

Hightower, James E., Jr., ed. Caring for Folks from Birth to Death. LC 84-20005. 1985. pap. 6.95 (ISBN 0-8054-2415-6). Broadman.

Hill, Edmund. Being Human. 304p. 1984. pap. 14.95 (ISBN 0-225-66358-9, AY8486, HarpR). Har-Row.

Hill, Harold. How to Flip Your Flab-Forever. LC 79-64912. 1979. pap. 2.95 (ISBN 0-88270-377-3). Bridge Pub.

--How to Live Like a King's Kid. LC 73-93002. 1974. pap. 2.95 pocket size (ISBN 0-88270-375-7). Bridge Pub.

Hill, Harold & Harrell, Irene. How to Live in High Victory. LC 77-80293. 1977. pap. 2.95 (ISBN 0-88270-421-4). Bridge Pub.

Hill, Harold & Rogers, Liz. Power to Change: How to Stay Slim, Sober, & Smokeless. (Orig.). 1987. pap. 4.95 (ISBN 0-88270-625-X, P625-X). Bridge Pub.

Hill, Harold, et al. From Goo to You by Way of the Zoo. rev. ed. 224p. 1984. pap. 5.95 (ISBN 0-8007-5174-4, Power Bks). Revell.

Hill, Ruth L. Jeweled Sword. 1987. pap. 5.95 (ISBN 0-89081-565-8). Harvest Hse.

Hilliard, Dick. My Heart Is Happy. LC 79-64822. 1979. pap. 4.95 (ISBN 0-89390-008-7). Resource Pubns.

Hillis, Don W. Stories of Love that Lasts. 80p. 1980. pap. 1.25 (ISBN 0-89323-015-4). Bible Memory.

Hilt, James. How to Have a Better Relationship with Anybody: A Biblical Approach. 1984. pap. 5.95 (ISBN 0-8024-1661-6). Moody.

Hilton, Walter. Toward a Perfect Love: The Spiritual Counsel of Walter Hilton. Jeffrey, David L., ed. LC 85-15470. (Classics of Faith & Devotion Ser.). 1986. 10.95 (ISBN 0-88070-103-X); pap. 7.95 (ISBN 0-88070-176-5). Multnomah.

Hinchey, James F. & Corrado, Dennis, eds. Shepherds Speak: American Bishops Confront the Social & Moral Issues That Challenge Christians Today. 240p. (Orig.). 1986. pap. 11.95 (ISBN 0-8245-0737-1). Crossroad NY.

Hines, Eugene B. Asking the Hard Questions. LC 85-19528. 1986. pap. 4.95 (ISBN 0-8054-5013-0). Broadman.

--Living in the Presence of God. LC 84-24305. 1985. pap. 4.95 (ISBN 0-8054-5229-X). Broadman.

Hirschmann, Maria A. I Am But a Child in Christ: A Basic Guide for Christian Living. LC 77-89331. (Bible Study & Sharing Ser.: No. 1). 192p. (Orig.). 1977. pap. 4.95 (ISBN 0-932878-00-8, HB-00). Hansi.

--I'll Never Walk Alone: Hansi's Journal. LC 73-81015. 170p. (Orig.). 1986. pap. 6.95 (ISBN 0-932878-08-3, HB-009). Hansi.

Hirschmann, Maria A. & Pershing, Betty. God's Word: A Living Rainbow. LC 63-1848. 167p. (Orig.). 1984. pap. 6.95 (ISBN 0-932878-07-5, HB-008). Hansi.

His in the Spirit: Confirmation Text. 1986. 3.75 (ISBN 0-8198-3319-3); tchr's manual 10.00 (ISBN 0-8198-3320-7). Dghtrs St Paul.

Hitt, Russell T. How Christians Grow. 1979. 12.95x (ISBN 0-19-502558-X). Oxford U Pr.

Hitz, Donna. The Triangular Pattern of Life. LC 79-84851. 94p. 1980. 7.95 (ISBN 0-8022-2249-8). Philos Lib.

Hobbs, Carolyn. And He Loved Her. 185p. (Orig.). 1979. pap. 1.95 (ISBN 0-89084-113-6). Bob Jones Univ Pr.

Hobe, Phyllis L. When Love Isn't Easy. 192p. 1986. pap. 3.50 (ISBN 0-553-26055-3). Bantam.

Hocking, David. Are You Spirit-Filled? (Orig.). pap. 5.95 (ISBN 0-89081-493-7). Harvest Hse.

--Pleasing God. 144p. 1985. pap. 5.95 (ISBN 0-89840-101-1). Heres Life.

Hocking, David L. Pleasing God. LC 84-47802. 144p. 1984. Heres Life.

--Who Am I & What Difference Does It Make? LC 85-8810. (Living Theology Ser.). 1985. pap. 7.95 (ISBN 0-88070-102-1). Multnomah.

Hodder, Sharon. The Ultimate Deception. 112p. 1982. pap. 4.95 (ISBN 0-89221-096-6). New Leaf.

Hodges, Doris. Healing Stones. 14th ed. pap. 3.95 (ISBN 0-686-12935-0). Hiawatha Bondurant.

Hoefler, Richard C. Realize & Rejoice. 1981. 4.00 (ISBN 0-89536-468-9, 1803). CSS of Ohio.

Hoekema, Anthony A. The Christian Looks at Himself. 1975. pap. 5.95 (ISBN 0-8028-1595-2). Eerdmans.

--Created in God's Image. 272p. 1986. 19.95 (ISBN 0-8028-3626-7). Eerdmans.

Hoffecker, W. Andrew & Smith, Gary S., eds. Building a Christian World View, Vol. 1: God, Man, & Knowledge. 368p. Date not set. 14.95 (ISBN 0-87552-281-5). Presby & Reformed.

Hoffman, Dominic M. Living Divine Love: Transformation, the Goal of Christian Life. LC 82-11552. 200p. (Orig.). 1982. pap. 7.95 (ISBN 0-8189-0443-7). Alba.

Holdren, Shirley. Why God Gave Me Pain. 128p. 1984. pap. 3.95 (ISBN 0-8294-0469-4). Loyola.

Holland, Leo. Images of God. LC 84-72318. (Illus.). 112p. (Orig.). 1985. pap. 4.95 (ISBN 0-87793-276-X). Ave Maria.

Hollis, Marcia & Hollis, Reginald. The Godswept Heart: Parables of Family Life. (Illus.). 96p. 1983. pap. 5.95 (ISBN 0-8164-2410-1, HarpR). Har-Row.

Holloway, Richard. Beyond Belief: The Christian Encounter with God. LC 81-5438. pap. 43.50 (ISBN 0-317-19824-6, 2023217). Bks Demand UMI.

Holm, Marilyn F. Tell Me Why: A Guide to Children's Questions about Faith & Life. LC 85-7355. 144p. (Orig.). 1985. pap. 6.95 (ISBN 0-8066-2160-5, 10-6230). Augsburg.

Holman, Vernon A. Painful Blessings. LC 85-8042. (Illus.). 45p. (Orig.). 1985. pap. write for info. (ISBN 0-933315-07-4). Taran House Pub.

Holmer, Paul L. Making Christian Sense. LC 83-27373. (Spirituality & the Christian Life Ser.: Vol. 3). 118p. (Orig.). 1984. pap. 7.95 (ISBN 0-664-24614-1). Westminster.

Holmes, Arthur F., et al. The Making of a Christian Mind. LC 84-22476. 160p. (Orig.). 1984. pap. 6.95 (ISBN 0-87784-525-5). Inter-Varsity.

Holmes, Ernest. Give Us This Day. pap. 0.75 (ISBN 0-87516-144-8). De Vorss.

Holmes, Ernest, et al. Light. Kinnear, Willis H., ed. 96p. 1971. pap. 5.50 (ISBN 0-911336-09-5). Sci of Mind.

Holmes, Majorie. Three from Galilee. 240p. 1986. pap. 3.50 (ISBN 0-553-26166-5). Bantam.

Holmes, Marjorie. God & Vitamins. 368p. 1982. pap. 3.50 (ISBN 0-380-56994-9, 68536-1). Avon.

--God & Vitamins. LC 80-911. 360p. 1980. 10.95 (ISBN 0-385-15249-3, Galilee). Doubleday.

--I've Got to Talk to Somebody, God. 15th, anniversary ed. LC 84-28724. 144p. 1985. pap. 5.95 (ISBN 0-385-19751-9, Galilee). Doubleday.

Holmes, Theda. Holiness & Honor of Praise. LC 85-62801. 1986. pap. 3.50 (ISBN 0-88270-599-7). Bridge Pub.

Holmes, Urban T., III. A History of Christian Spirituality: An Analytical Introduction. 176p. 1981. pap. 6.95 (ISBN 0-8164-2343-1, HarpR). Har-Row.

Holmes, Urban T., III & Westerhoff, John H. Christian Believing. (Church's Teaching Ser.: Vol. I). 144p. 1979. 5.95 (ISBN 0-8164-0418-6, HarpR); pap. 3.95 (ISBN 0-8164-2214-1); study guide 1.50 (ISBN 0-8164-2221-4). Har-Row.

Holschbach, Corine. Relatives in Orbit. (Illus.). 64p. 1986. 7.95 (ISBN 0-89962-514-2). Todd & Honeywell.

Holt, Pat. Mommy's Lesson. 32p. 1985. pap. 3.95 (ISBN 0-570-04131-7, 56-1545). Concordia.

Holzbauer, Beth. Love in Action. 1987. Instrs's., 128 pgs. pap. price not set (ISBN 0-87403-043-9, 39968); Student's, 112 pgs. pap. price not set (ISBN 0-87403-044-7, 39967). Standard Pub.

Hong, Edna. The Way of the Sacred Tree. LC 82-72643. 192p. 1983. pap. 10.95 (ISBN 0-8066-1949-X, 10-6958). Augsburg.

Hooker, Morna. A Preface to Paul. 1980. pap. 4.95 (ISBN 0-19-520188-4). Oxford U Pr.

Hooker, Morna D. The Son of Man in Mark. 1967. 12.50 (ISBN 0-7735-0049-9). McGill-Queens U Pr.

Hooks, Margaret Anne. God Cares for Timothy. 1982. 6.95 (ISBN 0-686-36253-5). Rod & Staff.

Hoover, Arlie J. Ideas & Their Consequences. LC 76-3176. (Way of Life Ser: No. 129). 1976. pap. 3.95 (ISBN 0-89112-129-3, Bibl Res Pr). Abilene Christ U.

Hoover, Mab G. God Still Loves My Kitchen Best: Devotions for the Homemaker. 206p. (Orig.). 1977. pap. 3.95 (ISBN 0-310-35612-1, 11270P). Zondervan.

Hopkins, Emma C. For unto Us a Child Is Born. pap. 1.00 (ISBN 0-87516-322-X). De Vorss.

Hopp, Ken. Lawyer Looks at Judgement. (Anchor Ser.). 1984. 5.95 (ISBN 0-8163-0557-9). Pacific Pr Pub Assn.

Hopper, Carol. Daughter of the Sanctuary. 111p. (Orig.). 1984. pap. 3.95 (ISBN 0-88144-022-1, CPS023). Christian Pub.

Hore-Lacy, Ian. Creating Common Wealth. 103p. (Orig.). 1985. pap. 4.95 (ISBN 0-86760-024-1, Pub. by Albatross Bks). ANZ Religious Pubns.

Hornbrook, John & Bakker, Dorothy F. The Miracle of Touching. Keith, Bill, ed. 160p. (Orig.). 1985. pap. 5.95 (ISBN 0-910311-28-5). Huntington Hse Inc.

Horner, Ralph C. From the Altar to the Upper Room. Dayton, Donald W., ed. (The Higher Christian Life Ser.). 301p. 1985. 40.00 (ISBN 0-8240-6423-2). Garland Pub.

Horrell, Benjamin C. Broken Chains. 1972. pap. 2.95 (ISBN 0-87148-106-5). Pathway Pr.

Horst, John L., ed. Instructions to Beginners in the Christian Life. 121p. 1934. pap. 1.95 (ISBN 0-8361-1378-0). Herald Pr.

Horton, Marilee. Free to Stay Home. 177p. 1984. pap. text ed. 5.95 (ISBN 0-8499-3011-1, 3011-1). Word Bks.

Horton, Michael S. Mission Accomplished: What Today's Christian Must Know About God & Salvation. 192p. 1985. pap. 6.95 (ISBN 0-8407-5947-9). Nelson.

Hosmer, Rachel & Jones, Alan. Living in the Spirit. (Church's Teaching Ser.: Vol. 7). 272p. 1979. 5.95 (ISBN 0-8164-0424-0, HarpR); pap. 4.95 (ISBN 0-8164-2220-6); pap. text ed. 1.50 (ISBN 0-8164-2227-3). Har-Row.

Hoster, Helen K. To Love Again: Remarriage for the Christian. (Orig.). 1985. pap. 8.95 (ISBN 0-687-42187-X). Abingdon.

Houselander, Caryll. The Reed of God. 128p. 1978. pap. 3.95 (ISBN 0-88479-013-4). Arena Lettres.

Hover, Margot K. & Breidenbach, Monica E. Christian Family Almanac. 128p. (Orig.). 1980. pap. 9.95 (ISBN 0-697-01740-0). Wm C Brown.

Howard, Richard. Newness of Life. 300p. 1975. 5.95 (ISBN 0-8341-0353-2). Beacon Hill.

Howard, Richard E. So Who's Perfect? 140p. (Orig.). 1985. pap. 5.95 (ISBN 0-8341-1070-9). Beacon Hill.

Howe, Joanne. A Change of Habit. 117p. (Orig.). 1986. 9.95 (ISBN 0-89225-290-1); pap. 6.95 (ISBN 0-89225-292-8). Gospel Advocate.

Howell, John C. Equality & Submission in Marriage. LC 78-67292. 1979. 8.50 (ISBN 0-8054-5632-5). Broadman.

Hoyt, Herman A. Is the United States in Prophecy? 1979. pap. 1.00 (ISBN 0-88469-040-7). BMH Bks.

Hsu, Dorothy. Mending. 1982. pap. 2.95 (ISBN 0-87508-263-7). Chr Lit.

Hudson, R. Lofton. Como Mejorar Sus Relaciores Humanas. De Lerin, O. S. D., tr. 62p. 1984. Repr. of 1982 ed. 1.75 (ISBN 0-311-46037-2). Casa Bautista.

Hudson, Winthrop. Religion in America: An Historical Account of the Development of American Religious Life. 4th ed. 512p. 1987. text ed. write for info. (ISBN 0-02-357280-9). Macmillan.

Huegel, F. J. Ministry of Intercession. LC 76-15861. (Orig.). 1971. pap. 2.95 (ISBN 0-87123-365-7, 200365). Bethany Hse.

Huffard, Evertt W. Deciding to Grow. 1983. pap. 3.95 (ISBN 0-89137-540-6). Quality Pubns.

Huffman, Carolyn & Barrow, Lu Ann. Life Between the Questions. 80p. 1985. 8.95 (ISBN 0-8499-0446-3, 0446-3). Word Bks.

Hufton, Richard A. Philippians: Our High Calling. LC 85-70134. 116p. (Orig.). 1985. pap. 4.00 (ISBN 0-933643-01-2). Grace World Outreach.

--Psalms: A Matchless Treasury. LC 84-82058. 106p. (Orig.). 1984. pap. 4.00 (ISBN 0-933643-02-0). Grace World Outreach.

Hughes, Blaine. Second Man: Monster, Myth, or Minister. 20p. 1976. pap. text ed. 0.95 (ISBN 0-89265-110-5). Randall Hse.

Hughes, R. Kent. Abba Father: The Lord's Pattern for Prayer. LC 85-72920. 128p. 1986. pap. 5.95 (ISBN 0-89107-377-9, Crossway Bks). Good News.

Hughes, Selwyn. The Christian Counselor's Pocket Guide. rev. ed. LC 80-65443. 96p. 1985. pap. 3.50 (ISBN 0-87123-844-6, 200047). Bethany Hse.

--How to Live the Christian Life. 160p. (Orig.). 1982. pap. 6.95 (ISBN 0-8164-2395-4, HarpR). Har-Row.

Hull, William E. The Christian Experience of Salvation. LC 84-20501. (Layman's Library of Christian Doctrine Ser.). 1987. 5.95 (ISBN 0-8054-1639-0). Broadman.

Hulme, William E. Mid-Life Crises. LC 80-11539. (Christian Care Bks.: Vol, 7). 118p. 1980. pap. 7.95 (ISBN 0-664-24324-X). Westminster.

Humbertson, James, ed. Evangelical S. S. Commentary, 1985-1986. text ed. 7.95 (ISBN 0-87148-312-2). Pathway Pr.

Humphrey. What Do You Communicate. 1985. pap. 4.50 (ISBN 0-89349-000-8). Gospel Advocate.

Humphreys, Alice L. Heaven in My Hand. 5.95 (ISBN 0-8042-2352-1). John Knox.

Hunt, Dave. Beyond Seduction. 1987. pap. 7.95 (ISBN 0-89081-558-5). Harvest Hse.

Hunt, Dave & McMahon, T. A. The Seduction of Christianity. LC 84-81211. 242p. 1985. pap. 7.95 (ISBN 0-89081-441-4, 4414). Harvest Hse.

Hunt, Earl G. A Bishop Speaks His Mind. 160p. 1987. 14.95 (ISBN 0-317-54253-2). Abingdon.

Hunt, Gladys. Family Secrets: What You Need to Know to Build a Strong Christian Family. 98p. 1985. pap. 3.95 (ISBN 0-89283-233-9, Pub. by Vine Books). Servant.

--Relationships. (Fisherman Bible Studyguide Ser.). 64p. 1983. saddle stitched 2.95 (ISBN 0-87788-721-7). Shaw Pubs.

Hunt, Sonjia, ed. Youth Leadership Resource Manual. 32p. (Orig.). 1981. pap. text ed. 1.75 (ISBN 0-87148-933-3, 817206). Pathway Pr.

--Youth Leadership Resource Manual, Vol. 2. 54p. (Orig.). 1982. pap. text ed. 2.00 (ISBN 0-87148-934-1). Pathway Pr.

Hunt, Sonjia L. Shaping Faith Through Involvement. 72p. (Orig.). 1981. pap. text ed. 2.50 (ISBN 0-87148-796-9). Pathway Pr.

Hunter, Charles. God's Conditions for Prosperity: How to Earn the Rewards of Christian Living in Tough Times. 110p. 1984. 12.95 (ISBN 0-13-357285-4); pap. 5.95 (ISBN 0-13-357277-3). P-H.

Hunter, Charles & Hunter, Frances. Simple as A, B, C. 1982. pap. 0.75 (ISBN 0-917726-51-0). Hunter Bks.

--This Way Up. 1978. pap. 5.00 (ISBN 0-917726-23-5). Hunter Bks.

--Why Should "I" Speak in Tongues. 1976. pap. 4.95 (ISBN 0-917726-02-2). Hunter Bks.

Hunter, Emily. Como Ser Encantadora (Para Alumna) Mendoza De Mann, Wilma & Mariotti, F. A., trs. Orig. Title: Christian Charm Notebook. (Span., Illus.). 56p. 1984. pap. 2.50 teachers ed. (ISBN 0-311-46054-2); pap. 5.45 student ed., 100 pp. (ISBN 0-311-46055-0). Casa Bautista.

Hunter, Emily & Hunter, Wayne. Man in Demand. Rev. ed. (Illus.). 1986. Repr. of 1975 ed. tchr's ed., 224 pp. 7.95 (ISBN 0-89081-511-9, 5119); student's wkbk. 80 pp 4.95 (ISBN 0-89081-510-0, 5100). Harvest Hse.

Hunter, Frances. It's So Simple. 1978. pap. 3.25 (ISBN 0-87162-130-4). Hunter Bks.

--Possessing the Mind of Christ. 1984. pap. 4.95 (ISBN 0-917726-64-2). Hunter Bks.

Hunter, George G., III. To Spread the Power. 224p. 1987. pap. 9.95 (ISBN 0-687-42259-0). Abingdon.

Hunter, Wayne & Hunter, Emily. Christian Charm Course. Rev. ed. 1986. Repr. of 1967 ed. tchr's ed., 112 pp. 7.95 (ISBN 0-89081-509-7, 5097); student's wkbk., 56 pp 4.95 (ISBN 0-89081-508-9, 5089). Harvest Hse.

--Como Ser un Joven Ideal (Para Alumno) Mariotti, Federico A., tr. Orig. Title: Man in Demand. (Span.). 1980. pap. 6.95 student ed., 80p. (ISBN 0-311-46074-7); pap. 8.75 teacher ed. 1981 (ISBN 0-311-46075-5). Casa Bautista.

Hunting, Gardner. Working with God. 1934. 5.95 (ISBN 0-87159-174-X). Unity School.

Hurnard, Hannah. God's Transmitters. 1975. pap. 2.95 (ISBN 0-8423-1085-1). Tyndale.

--Hearing Heart. 1975. pap. 2.95 (ISBN 0-8423-1405-9). Tyndale.

--Hind's Feet on High Places. 1979. pap. 3.95 (ISBN 0-8423-1429-6). Tyndale.

--Hurnard Gift Set, 8 vols. 1975. 26.50 (ISBN 0-8423-1547-0). Tyndale.

--Mountains of Spices. 1975. pap. 3.50 (ISBN 0-8423-4611-2). Tyndale.

--Walking Among the Unseen. 1977. pap. 3.50 (ISBN 0-8423-7805-7). Tyndale.

Hutches, G. E. Just Passing Through. LC 78-71390. (Stories That Win Ser.). 1979. pap. 1.25 (ISBN 0-8163-0320-7, 10617-9). Pacific Pr Pub Assn.

Huttenlocker, Keith. God, Can I Get to Know You. 1979. pap. 3.95 (ISBN 0-87162-211-4, D3810). Warner Pr.

Hybels, Bill. Caution: Christians under Construction. LC 77-93854. 144p. 1986. pap. 3.95 (ISBN 0-88207-759-7). Victor Bks.

Hyder, O. Quentin. Shape Up. rev. & updated ed. (Illus.). 160p. 1984. pap. 4.95 (ISBN 0-8007-5158-2, Power Bks). Revell.

Hyers, Conrad. The Comic Vision & the Christian Faith: A Celebration of Life & Laughter. LC 81-5221. 96p. (Orig.). 1981. pap. 8.95 (ISBN 0-8298-0440-4). Pilgrim NY.

Idahosa, Benson. Fire in His Bones. (Orig.). 1986. pap. 4.95 (ISBN 0-89274-429-4). Harrison Hse.

Igleheart, Glenn A. Church Members & Nontraditional Religious Groups. LC 85-4226. (Broadman Leadership Ser.). 1985. pap. 5.95 (ISBN 0-8054-6608-8). Broadman.

I'm Still Learning, Lord. 80p. 1986. pap. 5.95 (ISBN 0-8170-1112-9). Judson.

Inge, W. R., et al. Religion & Life: The Foundations of Personal Religion. facs. ed. LC 68-22940. (Essay Index Reprint Ser). 1923. 13.00 (ISBN 0-8369-0819-8). Ayer Co Pubs.

Ingram, Kristen J. Being a Christian Friend. 112p. 1985. pap. 5.95 (ISBN 0-8170-1084-X). Judson.

--Family Worship Through the Year. 80p. 1984. pap. 5.95 (ISBN 0-8170-1052-1). Judson.

Ingram, T. Robert. The World under God's Law. 5th ed. LC 62-16216. 1970. pap. text ed. 3.50 (ISBN 0-686-05040-1). St Thomas.

Inrig, Gary. A Call to Excellence. 132p. 1985. pap. 5.95 (ISBN 0-89693-523-X). Victor Bks.

Inter-Varsity Staff. Grow Your Christian Life. pap. 5.95 (ISBN 0-87784-661-8). Inter-Varsity.

--Rough Edges of the Christian Life. pap. 2.50 (ISBN 0-87784-442-9). Inter-Varsity.

Isler, Betty. I'm Still Here Lord! 1984. pap. 4.95 (ISBN 0-570-03938-X, 12-2873). Concordia.

Israel, Martin. Coming in Glory: Christ's Presence in the World Today. 128p. 1986. pap. 7.95 (ISBN 0-8245-0785-1). Crossroad NY.

--Living Alone. Kelsey, Morton T., intro. by. LC 82-72725. 144p. (Orig.). 1983. pap. 8.95 (ISBN 0-8245-0503-4). Crossroad NY.

--Smouldering Fire. 192p. 1986. pap. 8.95 (ISBN 0-8245-0728-2). Crossroad NY.

Ivins, Dan. God's Surprising Goodness. 128p. 1984. pap. 4.95 (ISBN 0-8170-1044-0). Judson.

--Model for Christian Wholeness. LC 84-9436. 1985. pap. 4.25 (ISBN 0-8054-2252-8). Broadman.

Jabusch, Willard F. Walk Where Jesus Walked: A Pilgrim's Guide with Prayer & Song. LC 86-71224. (Illus.). 200p. (Orig.). 1986. pap. 6.95 (ISBN 0-87793-339-1). Ave Maria.

Jacks, Bob, et al. Your Home: A Lighthouse. rev ed. LC 87-60179. 150p. 1987. pap. 5.95 (ISBN 0-89109-127-0). NavPress.

Jackson, Catherine. The Christian's Secret of a Happy Life for Today. 224p. 1979. pap. 5.95 (ISBN 0-8007-5061-6, Power Bks). Revell.

Jackson, Hulen. Sunshine Through the Shadows. 4.95 (ISBN 0-89315-283-8). Lambert Bk.

Jackson, Neta. A New Way to Live. LC 82-83392. 104p. 1983. pap. 4.95 (ISBN 0-8361-3323-4). Herald Pr.

Jacobson, James R. Soul Talk-How to Rejuvenate Your Life. Ashton, Sylvia, ed. LC 78-54160. 1979. 14.95 (ISBN 0-87949-107-8). Ashley Bks.

Jafolla, Mary-Alice. Simple Truth. 90p. 1982. 5.95 (ISBN 0-87159-146-4). Unity School.

Jameson, Kenneth P. & Wilber, Charles K., eds. Religious Values & Development. (Illus.). 154p. 1981. 44.00 (ISBN 0-08-026107-8). Pergamon.

Jamison-Peterson, Vicki. El Shaddai. 191p. 1983. pap. 4.95 (ISBN 0-88144-055-8). Christian Pub.

--How You Can Have Joy. 130p. 1976. pap. 2.95 (ISBN 0-88144-054-X). Christian Pub.

Jarnagin, Roy C. Christianity & the Narrow Way. 128p. 1982. 7.50 (ISBN 0-682-49832-7). Exposition Pr FL.

Jarrett, Richard B. July Fourth Is Every Day! To Serve, Is to Be Served! (Orig.). 1981. pap. text ed. write for info. Jarrett.

Jay, Ruth J. Learning from God's Wonderful Wildwood. (Learning From...Ser.). (Illus.). 36p. 1982. pap. 3.25 (ISBN 0-934998-13-2). Bethel Pub.

Jefferson. Minister As Shepherd. (Orig.). 1970. pap. 3.25 (ISBN 0-87508-290-4). Chr Lit.

Jennings, Don. A Spiritual Almanac: Guidelines for Better Living Each Month of the Year. 240p. 1984. pap. 5.95 (ISBN 0-13-834748-4). P-H.

Jensen, Margaret. First We Have Coffee. LC 83-48412. 144p. (Orig.). 1983. pap. 5.95 (ISBN 0-89840-050-3). Heres Life.

Jensen, Ronald A. How to Succeed the Biblical Way. 1981. pap. 4.95 (ISBN 0-8423-1541-1). Tyndale.

Jepsen, Dee. Women, the Challenge & the Call: An Agenda for Christian Women in Today's World. (Christian Essentials Ser.). 48p. (Orig.). 1987. pap. 1.95 (ISBN 0-89283-323-8). Servant.

Jeremiah, David. Wisdom of God. 1986. pap. 5.95 (ISBN 0-8010-5220-3). Baker Bk.

Jersild, Paul T. & Johnson, Dale A. Moral Issues & Christian Responses. 3rd ed. 1983. pap. text ed. 25.95 (ISBN 0-03-062464-9). HR&W.

Jesus & Man's Hope: Pittsburgh Festival on the Gospels, April 6-10, 1970, 2 vols. Vols. 1 & 2. 12.00 ea.; Vol. 1. pap. 8.00 (ISBN 0-686-36876-2). Pitts Theolog.

Jewett, Dick. Say Uncle. (Quest Ser.). 32p. 1982. pap. 0.99 (ISBN 0-8163-0489-0). Pacific Pr Pub Assn.

Jobe, Bobbie C. Striving for Holiness. 2.70 (ISBN 0-89137-423-X). Quality Pubns.

Jobe, Bobbie J. God Opens the Doors. (Orig.). 1987. pap. 5.95 (ISBN 0-8054-5041-6). Broadman.

John, Tommy & John, Sally. The Sally & Tommy John Story. 288p. 1985. pap. 3.50 (ISBN 0-425-07304-1). Berkley Pub.

John Paul II, Pope Faith According to St. John of the Cross. Aumann, Jordan, tr. LC 80-82265. Orig. Title: Doctrina de Fide apud S. Joannem a Cruce. 276p. (Orig.). 1981. pap. 13.95 (ISBN 0-89870-010-8). Ignatius Pr.

John-Roger. The Christ Within. LC 77-70405. 1976. pap. 5.00 (ISBN 0-914829-04-1). Baraka Bk.

Johnson, Barbara. Where Does a Mother Go to Resign? LC 79-12686. 160p. 1979. pap. 4.95 (ISBN 0-87123-606-0, 210606). Bethany Hse.

Johnson, Barbara M. Pilgrim on a Bicycle. LC 81-68637. 144p. 1982. write for info. (ISBN 0-86693-001-9). B M Johnson.

Johnson, Carlton. Overcome Any Problem. (Out Ser.). 1985. pap. 1.25 (ISBN 0-8163-0580-3). Pacific Pr Pub Assn.

Johnson, Christopher J. & McGee, Marsha G., eds. Encounters with Eternity. LC 85-17045. (Paperback Ser.). 352p. 1986. 19.95 (ISBN 0-8022-2493-8); pap. 12.95 (ISBN 0-8022-2508-X). Philos Lib.

Johnson, Douglas W. Growing up Christian in the Twenty-First Century. 128p. 1984. pap. 4.95 (ISBN 0-8170-1048-3). Judson.

Johnson, Euteline. Young People's Medicine. 32p. 1986. 5.95 (ISBN 0-89962-522-3). Todd & Honeywell.

Johnson, Keith. Life's Priorities. LC 79-63739. 1979. pap. 3.95 (ISBN 0-89841-000-2). Zoe Pubns.

Johnson, L. D. Images of Eternity. LC 84-4987. 1984. pap. 3.75 (ISBN 0-8054-5342-3). Broadman.

Johnson, Lawrence, ed. The Church Gives Thanks & Remembers. 88p. 1984. pap. 4.95 (ISBN 0-8146-1355-1). Liturgical Pr.

Johnson, Lois W. Either Way, I Win: A Guide for Growth in the Power of Prayer. LC 79-50078. 1979. pap. 4.95 (ISBN 0-8066-1706-3, 10-2040). Augsburg.

Johnson, Marvin L. Signs of the Times. 1983. 6.95 (ISBN 0-8062-2021-X). Carlton.

Johnson, Paul G. Grace: God's Work Ethic. 144p. 1985. pap. 6.95 (ISBN 0-8170-1070-X). Judson.

Johnston, Jon. Christian Excellence. 1985. 9.95 (ISBN 0-8010-5215-7); pap. 6.95 (ISBN 0-8010-5195-9). Baker Bk.

Johnston, Robert K. The Christian at Play. LC 83-16552. Repr. of 1983 ed. 43.50 (2027548). Bks Demand UMI.

Jones, Aaron I. Conquering the Night Season. LC 84-17515. 1985. pap. 4.95 (ISBN 0-8054-2255-2). Broadman.

Jones, Aaron Isaiah. God's Promises to Preachers. LC 81-67128. 1982. 5.50 (ISBN 0-8054-2240-4). Broadman.

Jones, Beneth P. Beauty & the Best: A Handbook of Christian Loveliness. (Illus.). 164p. (Orig.). 1980. pap. 3.95 (ISBN 0-89084-123-3). Bob Jones Univ Pr.

--More Sunshine on the Soapsuds. 110p. (Orig.). 1983. pap. 2.95 (ISBN 0-89084-192-6). Bob Jones Univ Pr.

--Ribbing Him Rightly. (Orig.). 1987. pap. write for info. (ISBN 0-89084-381-3). Bob Jones Univ Pr.

--Sunshine on the Soapsuds. 86p. (Orig.). 1977. pap. 2.95 (ISBN 0-89084-054-7). Bob Jones Univ Pr.

Jones, Bob, Sr. My Friends. (Illus.). 131p. 1983. pap. 3.95 (ISBN 0-89084-230-2). Bob Jones Univ Pr.

Jones, Chris. Y Ahora, Que Hago, Senor? Cabeza, Susana, tr. from Eng. Tr. of What Do I Do Now, Lord? (Span.). 107p. 1978. pap. 2.75 (ISBN 0-89922-123-8). Edit Caribe.

Jones, Cliff. Winning Through Integrity. 160p. 1985. 9.95 (ISBN 0-687-45604-5). Abingdon.

Jones, E. Stanley. Abundant Living. (Festival Bks.). 1976. pap. 4.25 (ISBN 0-687-00689-9). Abingdon.

--Divine Yes. 1976. pap. 1.50 (ISBN 0-89129-154-7). Jove Pubns.

--Victory Through Surrender: Self-Realization Through Self-Surrender. (Festival Ser.). 128p. 1980. pap. 1.50 (ISBN 0-687-43750-4). Abingdon.

--The Way to Power & Poise. (Festival Bks). 1978. pap. 2.25 (ISBN 0-687-44190-0). Abingdon.

Jones, James A. I Never Thought It Would Be This Way. 5.50 (ISBN 0-89137-533-3). Quality Pubns.

Jones, Larry. Practice to Win. 1982. pap. 4.95 (ISBN 0-8423-4887-5). Tyndale.

Jones, Margaret J. The World in My Mirror. LC 79-17730. 1979. 8.75 (ISBN 0-687-46270-3). Abingdon.

Jones, Robert. Limited to Everyone: An Invitation to Christian Faith. 144p. (Orig.). 1982. pap. 7.95 (ISBN 0-8164-2381-4, HarpR). Har-Row.

Jones, Russel A. Guidebook for Victorious Christian Living. 192p. 1983. pap. 5.95 (ISBN 0-8170-1001-7). Judson.

Jones, Russell G. Our God. LC 81-66135. 1981. pap. 4.95 (ISBN 0-89636-069-5). Accent Bks.

Jones, Stephen D. Transforming Discipleship in the Inclusive Church. 160p. 1984. pap. 6.95 (ISBN 0-8170-1049-1). Judson.

Jordan, Bernice C. Los Hechos Epistolas-Vosotros sois Edificio de Dios: 14 Lecciones, Tomo 1. (Pasos De Fe Ser.). (Span.). pap. text ed. 2.50 (ISBN 0-86508-413-0); figuras 8.95 (ISBN 0-86508-414-9). BCM Intl Inc.

Jordan, Jerry M. One More Brown Bag. (Illus.). 128p. 1983. pap. 6.95 (ISBN 0-8298-0645-8). Pilgrim NY.

Jorstad, Erling. Being Religious in America: The Deepening Crises over Public Faith. LC 86-3360. 128p. (Orig.). 1986. pap. 6.95 (ISBN 0-8066-2222-9, 10-0585). Augsburg.

Joseph, Lillian. God's Gift. 112p. (Orig.). 1985. pap. 5.95 (ISBN 0-916829-10-3). Apollo Bks.

Joy, Donald. Rebonding: Preventing & Restoring Damaged Relationships. 192p. 1986. 11.95 (ISBN 0-8499-0519-2, 0519-2). Word Bks.

Joyce, Jon L. When the Angels Go Away. (Orig.). 1980. pap. 3.95 (ISBN 0-937172-14-6). JLJ Pubs.

Joyce, Julian J. Translation. 1979. 9.95 (ISBN 0-89962-010-8). Todd & Honeywell.

Judd, Mary T. Love & Lifestyles. LC 80-54285. (Illus.). 200p. (Orig.). 1981. pap. text ed. 6.80x (ISBN 0-88489-132-1); teacher's guide 9.00x (ISBN 0-88489-134-8). St Mary's.

Judd, Peter A. The Worshiping Community. 177p. 1984. pap. text ed. 9.00 (ISBN 0-8309-0403-4). Herald Hse.

Julien, Tom. Handbook for Young Christians. 1976. pap. 1.00 (ISBN 0-88469-037-7). BMH Bks.

Jungerman, Joan. Share Your Bread. rev. ed. 1.25 (ISBN 0-8091-9313-2). Paulist Pr.

Juvenaly, Arcimndrite, ed. Khristianskaya Zhizn' po Dobrotolijubiju. Tr. of Christian Life According to the Philokalia. 216p. 13.00 (ISBN 0-317-28893-8); pap. 8.00 (ISBN 0-317-28894-6). Holy Trinity.

Kageler, Len & Dale, Daryl. Discipleship for High School Teens. 76p. 1984. wkbk. 5.25 (ISBN 0-87509-351-5). Chr Pubns.

Kaiser, Bill. Who in the World in Christ Are You? 231p. (Orig.). 1983. pap. text ed. 5.50 (ISBN 0-914307-12-6, Dist. by Harrison Hse). Word Faith.

Kalu, Ogbu. Divided People of God. LC 74-81853. 1978. 13.95x (ISBN 0-88357-048-3); pap. 4.95 (ISBN 0-88357-070-X). NOK Pubs.

Kamper, Karl G. & Carson, Karen M. A Call to Awaken, Vol. I. 269p. 1986. text ed. 15.00 (ISBN 0-9616739-1-5). Atonement Ent.

Kane, Herbert T. Christian Missions in Biblical Perspective. 14.95 (ISBN 0-8010-5370-6). Baker Bk.

Kane, J. Herbert. Wanted: World Christians. 204p. 1986. pap. 9.95 (ISBN 0-8010-5474-5). Baker Bk.

Kane, Thomas A. The Healing Touch of Affirmation. LC 76-151154. 126p. 1976. pap. 4.95 (ISBN 0-89571-001-3). Affirmation.

Kantonen, T. A. To Live Is Christ. 1978. pap. 4.50 (ISBN 0-89536-306-2, 2028). CSS of Ohio.

Karo, Nancy & Mickelson, Alvera. La Aventura de Morir. Flores, Jose, tr. from Eng. LC 77-15812. Tr. of Adventure in Dying. (Span.). 197p. 1977. pap. 4.50 (ISBN 0-89922-098-3). Edit Caribe.

Karssen, Gien. Getting the Most Out of Being Single. rev. ed. LC 82-62240. 192p. 1983. pap. 3.95 (ISBN 0-89109-505-5). NavPress.

Kaschmitter, William A. About Happiness. 100p. 1983. pap. 5.00 (ISBN 0-912414-34-0). Lumen Christi.

Kasper, Walter. Introduction to Christian Faith. Smith, David, tr. from Ger. LC 80-82808. 224p. 1981. pap. 4.95 (ISBN 0-8091-2324-X). Paulist Pr.

Kauffman, Donald T. Ask & It Shall Be Given. 48p. 1986. 6.95 (ISBN 0-8378-5095-9). Gibson.

Kauffmann, Joel. The Weight. LC 79-27262. 176p. 1980. pap. 5.95 (ISBN 0-8361-3335-8). Herald Pr.

Kaung, Stephen. Discipled to Christ. Fader, Herbert L., ed. 1976. pap. 2.25 (ISBN 0-935008-17-9). Christian Fellow Pubs.

Kavanaugh, John F. Following Christ in a Consumer Society: The Spirituality of Cultural Resistance. LC 81-38359. 192p. (Orig.). 1981. pap. 6.95 (ISBN 0-88344-090-3). Orbis Bks.

Kaylor, Earl C. Out of the Wilderness: The Brethren & Two Centuries of Life in Central Pennsylvania. (Illus.). 384p. 1981. 12.50 (ISBN 0-8453-4716-0, Cornwall Bks). Assoc Univ Prs.

Kazemi, Hassan. Ten Signs of Faith. Graves, Helen, ed. LC 85-51959. 154p. 1986. 8.95 (ISBN 1-55523-012-1). Winston-Derek.

Keane, Philip S. Christian Ethics & Imagination. 224p. (Orig.). 1984. pap. 9.95 (ISBN 0-8091-2647-8). Paulist Pr.

Kearney, Lawrence. Kingdom Come. 64p. 1980. 15.00x (ISBN 0-8195-2098-5); pap. 7.95 (ISBN 0-8195-1098-X). Wesleyan U Pr.

Keating, Charles J. The Leadership Book. rev. ed. LC 77-99300. 144p. 1982. pap. 4.95 (ISBN 0-8091-2504-8). Paulist Pr.

Keating, John. Strength Under Control: Meekness & Zeal in the Christian Life. (Living As a Christian Ser.). 152p. (Orig.). 1981. pap. 3.50 (ISBN 0-89283-104-9). Servant.

Keck, Saundria. God Made Me. LC 86-17572. (Bible & Me Ser.). 1987. 5.95 (ISBN 0-8054-4173-5). Broadman.

Keefer, Luke, Jr. Everything Necessary: God's Provisions for the Holy Life. 1984. Teacher ed. 64p. 3.95 (ISBN 0-916035-11-5); Student ed. 160p. 4.95 (ISBN 0-916035-12-3). Evangel Indiana.

Keegan, G. Kearnie. Your Next Big Step. LC 60-9533. 1960. gift ed. 8.95 (ISBN 0-8054-5317-2, 4253-17). Broadman.

Keene, Milton H. Patterns for Mature Living. LC 76-27093. Repr. of 1976 ed. 21.30 (ISBN 0-8357-9019-3, 2016389). Bks Demand UMI.

Kelfer, Russell. Self-Control. (Living Studies). 240p. 1985. pap. 5.95 (ISBN 0-8423-5859-5); leader's guide 2.95 (ISBN 0-8423-5860-9). Tyndale.

Keller, John E. Let Go, Let God. LC 85-11048. 128p. 1985. pap. 6.95 (ISBN 0-8066-2162-1, 10-3815). Augsburg.

Keller, Phillip. A Layman Looks at the Love of God. (Orig.). 1982. pap. 4.95 (210314). Bethany Hse.

--Salt for Society. 1986. 5.95 (ISBN 0-8499-3059-6). Word Bks.

Keller, W. Phillip. Lessons from a Sheepdog. 1983. 8.95 (ISBN 0-8499-0335-1). Word Bks.

--Salt for Society. 160p. 1981. 8.95 (ISBN 0-8499-0290-8). Word Bks.

--Walking with God. 160p. 1980. pap. 5.95 (ISBN 0-8007-5187-6). Revell.

Kellermann, Joseph L. Reconciliation with God & Family. 16p. 1981. pap. 0.95 (ISBN 0-89486-146-8). Hazelden.

Kelley, Bennet. Catholic Faith Today. green, flexible bdg. 3.00 (ISBN 0-89942-243-8, 243-04). Catholic Bk Pub.

Kelly, Robert. The Alchemist to Mercury. 230p. 1981. 30.00 (ISBN 0-913028-82-7); pap. 7.95 (ISBN 0-686-69476-7). North Atlantic.

Kelsey, Morton. Christianity As Psychology: The Healing Power of the Christian Message. LC 85-22864. 114p. (Orig.). 1986. pap. 7.95 (ISBN 0-8066-2194-X, 10-1184). Augsburg.

Kelsey, Morton T. Adventure Inward: Christian Growth Through Personal Journal Writing. LC 80-65551. 224p. (Orig.). 1980. pap. 9.95 (ISBN 0-8066-1796-9, 10-0166). Augsburg.

Kendall, R. T. Stand up & Be Counted: Calling for Public Confession of Faith. 128p. (Orig.). 1985. pap. 5.95 (ISBN 0-310-38351-X, 9281P). Zondervan.

Kennedy, Eugene C. The Pain of Being Human. LC 73-83645. 280p. 1974. pap. 4.95 (ISBN 0-385-06888-3, Im). Doubleday.

Kennedy, John W. Torch of the Testimony. (Orig.). 1983. pap. 6.95 (ISBN 0-940232-12-X). Christian Bks.

Kennedy, Margaretta. Considering Marriage? 12p. 1982. pap. 0.15 (ISBN 0-686-36261-6). Faith Pub Hse.

Kennedy, Richard. Now That You're Saved. 1977. pap. 0.95 (ISBN 0-89265-046-X). Randall Hse.

Kenny, James & Kenny, Mary. When Your Marriage Goes Stale. LC 79-51277. (When Bks). (Illus.). 1979. pap. 2.45 (ISBN 0-87029-150-5, 20236-6). Abbey.

Kent, Homer A., Sr. Conquering Frontiers: A History of the Brethren Church. 8.95 (ISBN 0-88469-018-0); pap. 6.95 (ISBN 0-88469-017-2). BMH Bks.

Kenyon, Mel & Christophus, Mike. Burned to Life. LC 76-1060. (Illus.). 1976. pap. 2.95 (ISBN 0-87123-044-5, 200044). Bethany Hse.

Keough, G. Arthur. Infinitely Happy. LC 78-21952. (Horizon Ser.). 1978. pap. 5.95 (ISBN 0-8127-0213-1). Review & Herald.

Kerbs, John G. Answers to Your People Problems. LC 68-25949. (Harvest Ser.). 1978. pap. 4.95 (ISBN 0-8163-0192-1, 01634-5). Pacific Pr Pub Assn.

Kesler, Jay, ed. Parents & Teenagers. 696p. 1984. pap. 16.95 (ISBN 0-88207-817-8). Victor Bks.

Keyes, Elizabeth & Chivington, Paul K. What's Eating You? (Illus.). 1978. pap. 4.50 (ISBN 0-87516-263-0). De Vorss.

Kibildis, Ralph. Turning Road. 112p. (Orig.). 1981. 2.95 (ISBN 0-914544-34-9). Living Flame Pr.

Kiemel, Ann. I Love the Word Impossible. 1978. pock. pap 3.50 (ISBN 0-8423-1578-0). Tyndale.

--It's Incredible. 1977. pap. 2.50 (ISBN 0-8423-1818-6). Tyndale.

Kierkegaard, Soren. The Sickness Unto Death: A Christian Psychological Exposition for Upbuilding & Awakening. Hong, Howard V. & Hong, Edna H., trs. LC 79-3218. (Kierkegaard's Writings Ser.: Vol. XIX). 216p. 1980. 27.50x (ISBN 0-691-07247-7); pap. 9.50x (ISBN 0-691-02028-0). Princeton U Pr.

Kilgo, Edith F. Handbook for Christian Homemakers. 200p. (Orig.). 1982. pap. 5.95 (ISBN 0-8010-5439-7). Baker Bk.

Killinger, John. The Cup & the Waterfall: The Adventure of Living in the Present Moment. LC 82-61421. 1983. pap. 4.95 (ISBN 0-8091-2515-3). Paulist Pr.

Kilpatrick, Paula & Dudley, Cliff. The Ninth Floor. LC 81-80942. 128p. 1981. pap. 4.95 (ISBN 0-89221-085-0). New Leaf.

Kilpatrick, William K. Psychological Seduction: The Failure of Modern Psychology. LC 83-12151. 228p. 1983. pap. 5.95 (ISBN 0-8407-5843-X). Nelson.

Kim, Esther A. If I Perish. 1979. pap. 3.95 (ISBN 0-8024-4003-7). Moody.

Kinard, J. Spencer. A Time for Reflection. 1986. text ed. 9.95 (ISBN 0-87579-049-6). Deseret Bk.

King. No Church Is an Island: Study Guide. 1980. pap. 1.00 (ISBN 0-8298-0389-0). Pilgrim NY.

King, Barbara. Do I Need a Flood? 3.00 (ISBN 0-317-46971-1). CSA Pr.

King, Stephen S. Gods Master Plan. 85p. 1985. pap. 3.95 (ISBN 0-317-52285-X). Christian Pub.

Kinghorn, Kenneth C. Christ Can Make You Fully Human. LC 79-10855. 1979. pap. 4.35 (ISBN 0-687-06930-0). Abingdon.

--Dynamic Discipleship. 160p. 1975. pap. 4.95 (ISBN 0-8010-5357-9). Baker Bk.

Kinneer, Jack. How to Grow in Christ. 1981. pap. 2.95 (ISBN 0-87552-284-X). Presby & Reformed.

Kinsella, Nivard. Unprofitable Servants: Conferences on Humility. 1981. 5.95 (ISBN 0-317-46888-X). Franciscan Herald.

Kinzer, Mark. Living with a Clear Conscience: A Christian Strategy for Overcoming Guilt & Self-Condemnation. (Living As a Christian Ser.). 160p. 1982. pap. 3.50 (ISBN 0-89283-115-4). Servant.

--Self-Image of a Christian: Humility & Self-Esteem. (Living As a Christian Ser.). 106p. (Orig.). 1980. pap. 2.95 (ISBN 0-89283-088-3). Servant.

--Taming the Tongue: Why Christians Should Care about What They Say. (Living as a Christian Ser.). 1982. pap. 2.95 (ISBN 0-89283-165-0). Servant.

Kipp, Maxine. Living Life to the Fullest. LC 79-52997. (Radiant Life Ser.). 160p. 1980. pap. 2.95 (ISBN 0-88243-896-4, 02-0896); teacher's ed 3.95 (ISBN 0-88243-187-0, 32-0187). Gospel Pub.

Kirby, John C. Ephesians, Baptism & Pentecost: An Inquiry into the Structure & Purpose of the Epistle to the Ephesians. 1968. 12.50x (ISBN 0-7735-0051-0). McGill-Queens U Pr.

Kirby, Leo. Should You Become a Brother? 1979. pap. 1.95 (ISBN 0-89243-102-4). Liguori Pubns.

Kirk, J. Andrew. Good News of the Kingdom Coming. LC 84-19293. 164p. 1985. pap. 5.95 (ISBN 0-87784-938-2). Inter-Varsity.

Kirk, Margaret. God Was a Stranger. 1980. pap. 2.75 (ISBN 0-85363-130-1). OMF Bks.

Kirkland, Margie. A Grateful Heart. LC 84-9398. 1984. pap. 3.95 (ISBN 0-8054-5012-2). Broadman.

Kirkley, Robert G. By God, You Can Do It. 1985. 9.95 (ISBN 0-345-32266-5, Pub. by Ballantine Epiphany). Ballantine.

Kleba, Gerald J. The People Parish: A Model of Church Where People Flourish. LC 86-82035. 136p. (Orig.). 1986. pap. 4.95 (ISBN 0-87793-346-4). Ave Maria.

Klein, Chuck. So You Want Solutions. 1979. pap. 4.95 (ISBN 0-8423-6161-8). Tyndale.

Kleiner, Sighard. Serving God First. 1985. 14.95 (ISBN 0-87907-883-9). Cistercian Pubns.

Klewin, Jean & Klewin, Thomas. When the Man You Love Is an Alcoholic. LC 79-51276. (When Bks). (Illus.). 1979. pap. 2.45 (ISBN 0-87029-149-1, 20232-5). Abbey.

Kliewer, Evelyn. Laughter Lives Here. LC 81-70476. 1982. pap. 4.95 (ISBN 0-8054-5203-6). Broadman.

--Please, God, Help Me Get Well in Your Spare Time. LC 79-17683. 128p. 1979. pap. 3.95 (ISBN 0-87123-027-5, 210027). Bethany Hse.

Klug, Ron. Growing in Joy: God's Way to Increase Joy in All of Life. LC 82-72637. 128p. 1983. pap. 5.95 (ISBN 0-8066-1943-0, 10-2902). Augsburg.

Klusmeyer, Joann. What about Me? (Illus.). 1987. 3.95 (ISBN 0-570-03641-0). Concordia.

Knight, A. R. & Schroeder, Gordon H. New Life. rev. ed. 1971. pap. 1.50 (ISBN 0-8170-0120-4); pap. 1.00 spanish ed. (ISBN 0-8170-0696-6). Judson.

Knight, David. His Way: An Everyday Plan for Following Jesus. 1977. pap. 3.50 (ISBN 0-912228-39-3). St Anthony Mess Pr.

--Lift Your Eyes to the Mountain. 8.95 (ISBN 0-87193-137-0); pap. 6.95 (ISBN 0-87193-190-7). Dimension Bks.

Knight, David M. Living the Sacraments: A Call to Conversion. LC 85-60888. 140p. (Orig.). 1985. pap. 6.50 (ISBN 0-87973-815-4, 815). Our Sunday Visitor.

Knight, Walker & Touchton, Ken. Seven Beginnings. LC 75-44496. (Human Torch Ser.: 2nd). (Illus.). 1976. 5.95 (ISBN 0-937170-17-8). Home Mission.

Knoche, Keith. Beyond Knoche's Law. Phillips, ed. (Redwood Ser.). 96p. 1983. pap. 4.95 (ISBN 0-8163-0488-2). Pacific Pr Pub Assn.

--Knoche Writes Again. (Friendship Ser.). 64p. 1983. pap. 4.95 (ISBN 0-8163-0508-0). Pacific Pr Pub Assn.

--Side Trips. (FRD Ser.). 1985. pap. 4.95 (ISBN 0-8163-0596-X). Pacific Pr Pub Assn.

Knorr, Dandi D. When the Answer Is No. 1985. pap. 4.95 (ISBN 0-8054-5801-8). Broadman.

Knowing Yourself. (Benziger Family Life Program Ser.). 4p. 1978. 2.00 (ISBN 0-02-651650-0); tchrs. ed. 4.00 (ISBN 0-02-651660-8); 1.00 (ISBN 0-02-651690-X). Benziger Pub Co.

Koch, Kurt E. Darkness or Light. 80p. 1981. pap. 2.95 (ISBN 0-8254-3048-8). Kregel.

--World Without Chance. LC 72-85598. 96p. 1974. pap. 2.95 (ISBN 0-8254-3012-7). Kregel.

Koehler, George E. Visiting Two-by-Two: Visitor's Guide. LC 86-70579. 72p. (Orig.). 1986. 2.95 (ISBN 0-88177-034-5, DR034B). Discipleship Res.

Koenig, Norma E. Ventures in Leisure-Time Christian Education. (Orig.). 1979. pap. 4.15 (ISBN 0-687-43670-2). Abingdon.

Kohler, Christine. Help Me: I'm Lost. (Growing up Christian Ser.). 24p. (Orig.). 1985. pap. 3.95 (ISBN 0-570-04115-5, 56-1526). Concordia.

--I Help the Handicapped. (Growing Up Christian Ser.). 24p. (Orig.). 1985. pap. 3.95 (ISBN 0-570-04114-7, 56-1525). Concordia.

Kohmescher, Matthew F. Good Morality Is Like Good Cooking... & Other Suggestions for Right Living. 112p. (Orig.). 1987. pap. 4.95 (ISBN 0-8091-2856-X). Paulist Pr.

Kolatch, Alfred J. Sermons for the Seventies. LC 75-164518. 1971. 7.95x (ISBN 0-8246-0122-X). Jonathan David.

Komensky, John A. Labyrinth of the World & the Paradise of the Heart. LC 73-135812. (Eastern Europe Collection Ser). 1970. Repr. of 1901 ed. 22.00 (ISBN 0-405-02754-0). Ayer Co Pubs.

Konieczny, Stanley, ed. The Hands & Feet of Christ. 1987. pap. 1.50 (ISBN 0-8189-0515-8). Alba.

Konig, Adrio. Here Am I! A Christian Reflection on God. LC 82-11377. pap. 62.00 (ISBN 0-317-30148-9, 2025331). Bks Demand UMI.

Koopman, LeRoy. Twenty-Six Vital Issues. (Contemporary Discussion Ser.). 1978. pap. 2.45 (ISBN 0-8010-5398-6). Baker Bk.

Korth, Bob, compiled by. Object Talks on Christian Living. (Illus.). 48p. (Orig.). 1984. pap. 2.95 (ISBN 0-87239-724-6, 2860). Standard Pub.

Koski, Marnie. Personal Talks with Jesus. (Orig.). 1979. pap. 4.95 (ISBN 0-917200-25-X). ESPress.

Kownacki, Mary L. & Clark, Carol. Let Peace Begin With Me: Teacher Manual. 1983. pap. 2.95 (ISBN 0-89622-185-7). Twenty-Third.

Kownacki, Mary Lou & Clark, Carol. Let Peace Begin With Me: Peace Book. 1983. pap. 1.00 (ISBN 0-89622-186-5). Twenty-Third.

Koyama, Kosuke. Three Mile an Hour God. LC 79-24785. 160p. (Orig.). 1980. pap. 3.48 (ISBN 0-88344-473-9). Orbis Bks.

Kraft, Charles H. Communicating the Gospel God's Way. LC 80-53945. 60p. 1980. pap. 2.95x (ISBN 0-87808-742-7). William Carey Lib.

Kramer, William. Here & Hereafter. 1978. pap. 4.95 (ISBN 0-8100-0053-9, 15-0365). Northwest Pub.

Kramer, William A. Living for Christ. rev. ed. LC 72-96585. 1973. 3.25 (ISBN 0-570-03157-5, 12-2542). Concordia.

Krebs, Richard. Alone Again. LC 77-84085. 1978. pap. 5.95 (ISBN 0-8066-1611-3, 10-0240). Augsburg.

Krebs, Robert G. Why We're Here. 1987. 7.95 (ISBN 0-533-07098-8). Vantage.

Kreeft, Peter. For Heaven's Sake. 192p. 1986. 12.95 (ISBN 0-8407-5494-9). Nelson.

Kreider, Alan. The Ethics of Social Holiness: A Way of Living for God's Global Nation. 1987. 14.95 (ISBN 0-310-38390-0). Zondervan.

Kress, Robert. The Difference Jesus Makes. (Synthesis Ser.). 1981. 1.25 (ISBN 0-8199-0372-8). Franciscan Herald.

Krey, Peter C. Lo! the Bridegroom. LC 66-20393. 1966. 3.95 (ISBN 0-686-05043-6). St Thomas.

Krutza, William J. Reaching Out for Life's Best. (Contemporary Discussion Ser.). 96p. (Orig.). 1982. pap. 2.95 (ISBN 0-8010-5444-3). Baker Bk.

Krutza, William J. & DiCicco, Philip P. Facing Your Nation. (Contemporary Discussion Ser.). 1975. pap. 1.95 (ISBN 0-8010-5372-2). Baker Bk.

Kubler-Ross, Elisabeth. Working It Through. (Illus.). 176p. 1987. pap. 5.95 (ISBN 0-02-022000-6, Collier). Macmillan.

Kuhlman, Kathryn. Glimpse into Glory. Buckingham, Jamie, compiled by. LC 79-90558. 1979. pap. 3.50 pocket size (ISBN 0-88270-393-5). Bridge Pub.

Kuhne, Gary W. The Change Factor: The Risks & the Joys. 128p. 1986. pap. 5.95 (ISBN 0-310-27251-3, 12316). Zondervan.

--The Dynamics of Discipleship Training. 1977. pap. 5.95 (ISBN 0-310-26961-X, 12311P). Zondervan.

Kuntz, Arnold G. Serving God Always. 1966. pap. text ed. 2.75 (ISBN 0-570-06645-X, 22-2014); pap. 5.85 manual (ISBN 0-570-06646-8, 22-2015). Concordia.

Kunz, Marilyn & Schell, Catherine. Choose Life. (Neighborhood Bible Studies). 1973. pap. 2.50 (ISBN 0-8423-0460-6). Tyndale.

Kupferle, Mary. God Will See You Through. 1983. 5.95 (ISBN 0-87159-043-3). Unity School.

Kurz, Albert L. Disciple-Maker Workbook. 1981. pap. 10.95 (ISBN 0-8024-2217-9). Moody.

Kushner, Harold S. When Bad Things Happen to Good People. LC 81-40411. 160p. 1981. 11.95 (ISBN 0-8052-3773-9). Schocken.

Kuyper, Neal A. No Matter What, We Still Love You. (Illus.). 40p. (Orig.). 1985. pap. 2.95 (ISBN 0-933350-48-1). Morse Pr.

Kuzma, Kay. Filling Your Loving Cup. Rev. ed. LC 83-60606. 1983. pap. 5.95 (ISBN 0-910529-02-7). Parent Scene.

--Living with God's Kids. LC 83-61552. 1983. pap. 5.95 (ISBN 0-910529-03-5). Parent Scene.

La Farge, Grant. Faith in God & Full Speed Ahead: Fe en Dios y Adelante. tr. LC 84-23948. (Illus.). 160p. (Orig.). 1985. pap. 14.95 (ISBN 0-86534-050-1). Sunstone Pr.

LaHaye, Beverly. The Restless Woman. 176p. 1984. pap. 5.95 (ISBN 0-310-27091-X, 18337P). Zondervan.

LaHaye, Tim. The Coming Peace in the Middle East. 208p. 1984. pap. 6.95 (ISBN 0-310-27031-6, 18341P). Zondervan.

--How to Manage Pressure: Before Pressure Manages You. 240p. 1983. pap. 6.95 (ISBN 0-310-27081-2, 18336P). Zondervan.

Lake, John G. Adventures in God. 131p. 1981. pap. 4.95 (ISBN 0-89274-206-2). Harrison Hse.

Lampson, Adelene. An Open Book to Padre Pio. 160p. 1986. 11.95 (ISBN 0-89962-554-1). Todd & Honeywell.

Lancaster, F. Matthew. Hang Tough. 24p. 1985. pap. 3.95 (ISBN 0-8091-2696-6). Paulist Pr.

Landis, Paul M. Purity in the Christian Home. 1978. 0.95 (ISBN 0-686-25260-8). Rod & Staff.

Landorf, Joyce. I Came to Love You Late. 192p. 1981. pap. 3.50 (ISBN 0-8007-8411-1, Spire Bks). Revell.

--Irregular People. 1982. 9.95 (ISBN 0-8499-0291-6). Word Bks.

--The Richest Lady in Town. 1979. pap. 2.95 (ISBN 0-310-27142-8, 10123P). Zondervan.

Landsman, Michael. Doubling Your Ability Through God. 58p. 1982. pap. 2.25 (ISBN 0-89274-266-6). Harrison Hse.

Lane, Denis. Keeping Body & Soul Together. 1982. pap. 2.25 (ISBN 0-85363-144-1). OMF Bks.

Lane, George A. Christian Spirituality. 88p. 1984. pap. 3.95 (ISBN 0-8294-0450-3). Loyola.

Laney, Lily. Thoughts from Heaven. 128p. 1986. 8.95 (ISBN 0-89962-542-8). Todd & Honeywell.

Langdon, Rohen. Lighthouse of Langdon: Presenting 20th Century Jehovah to Doomsday Man. 207p. 1980. 9.00 (ISBN 0-682-49637-5). Exposition Pr FL.

Langford, Thomas A. Christian Wholeness. LC 78-58011. 1979. pap. 3.50x (ISBN 0-8358-0383-X). Upper Room.

Lanot, Marra P. Passion & Compassion: Mga Tula Sa Ingles at Pilipino. 153p. 1981. pap. 6.50x (ISBN 0-686-32581-8, Pub. by New Day Phillipines). Cellar.

Lapp, Elizabeth. Journal of Tears. 1984. 2.95 (ISBN 0-87813-522-7). Christian Light.

Larkin, Ernest. Silent Presence. 4.95 (ISBN 0-87193-172-9). Dimension Bks.

Larkin, Ernest E. Christ Within Us. 1984. pap. 6.95 (ISBN 0-87193-215-6). Dimension Bks.

Larkin, Francis. Understanding the Heart. rev. ed. LC 80-81066. 127p. 1980. pap. 5.95 (ISBN 0-89870-007-8). Ignatius Pr.

Larsen, John M. Between Us Friends. LC 83-61454. 1983. pap. 7.95 (ISBN 0-89390-050-8). Resource Pubns.

Larsen, Sandy. Choosing: Which Way Do I Go? (Bible Discovery Guide for Campers Ser.). 32p. 1985. pap. 1.50 camper (ISBN 0-87788-115-4); pap. 3.50 counselor (ISBN 0-87788-116-2). Shaw Pubs.

--Everybody Needs the Body. 1984. pap. 3.95 (ISBN 0-88207-594-2). Victor Bks.

--Forgiving: Lightening Your Load. (Bible Discovery Guide). 32p. 1985. pap. 1.50 campers (ISBN 0-87788-279-7); pap. 3.50 counselor (ISBN 0-87788-280-0). Shaw Pubs.

--Running the Race: Keeping the Faith. (Young Fisherman Bible Studyguide Ser.). 64p. (Orig.). 1986. pap. 2.95 (ISBN 0-87788-740-3); tchr's. ed. 4.95 (ISBN 0-87788-741-1). Shaw Pubs.

Larson. No Longer Strangers. 145p. 1985. pap. 5.95 (ISBN 0-8499-3020-0, 3020-0). Word Bks.

Larson, Bruce. My Creator, My Friend. 192p. 1986. 10.95 (ISBN 0-8499-0458-7). Word Bks.

Larson, Jim. Caring Enough to Hear & Be Heard: Leader's Guide. LC 82-403. (Caring Enough Ser.). 1984. pap. 3.95 (ISBN 0-8307-0994-0, 6101948). Regal.

--Growing a Healthy Family. LC 85-28657. 128p. (Orig.). 1986. pap. 6.95 (ISBN 0-8066-2193-1, 10-2901). Augsburg.

--Rights, Wrongs, & In-Betweens: Guiding Our Children to Christian Maturity. LC 83-72121. 144p. (Orig.). 1984. pap. 6.95 (ISBN 0-8066-2065-X, 10-5518). Augsburg.

Larson, Jim & Feldmeth, Joanne. Your Spiritual Gifts Can Help Your Church Grow. 64p. 1985. pap. 3.95 (ISBN 0-8307-1008-6, 6101951). Regal.

Larson, Martin A. The Essene Christian Faith. 273p. 1986. 12.00 (ISBN 0-317-53276-6). Noontide.

Larson, Muriel. Joy Every Morning. (Quiet Time Books). 1979. pap. 3.50 (ISBN 0-8024-4396-6). Moody.

Larson, Ray. A Season of Singleness. LC 83-81762. 128p. (Orig.). 1984. 2.50 (ISBN 0-88243-584-1, 02-0584). Gospel Pub.

Latourelle, Rene. Man & His Problems. O'Connell, Matthew, tr. LC 82-24334. (Fr.). 395p. (Orig.). 1983. pap. 9.95 (ISBN 0-8189-0450-X). Alba.

Lauder, Robert E. Becoming a Christian Person. 140p. (Orig.). 1985. pap. 5.95 (ISBN 0-914544-58-6). Living Flame Pr.

--Loneliness Is for Loving. LC 77-94033. (Illus.). 144p. 1978. pap. 2.95 (ISBN 0-87793-147-X). Ave Maria.

Lauer, Eugene & Mlecko, Joel. A Christian Understanding of the Human Person: Basic Readings. LC 81-8434. 160p. (Orig.). 1982. pap. 7.95 (ISBN 0-8091-2433-5). Paulist Pr.

Lauer, Robert H. Temporal Man: The Meaning & Uses of Social Time. LC 81-11917. 192p. 1981. 34.95 (ISBN 0-03-059719-6). Praeger.

Laurie, Greg. Spiritual Survival in the Last Days. LC 82-81919. Orig. Title: Occupy Till I Come. 144p. (Orig.). 1985. pap. 3.95. Harvest Hse.

Law, Terry. Your Spiritual Weapons. (Illus.). 48p. 1985. pap. 1.95 (ISBN 0-932081-00-2). Victory Hse.

Law, William. Freedom from a Self-Centered Life. Murray, Andrew, ed. LC 77-71426. 144p. 1977. pap. 3.50 (ISBN 0-87123-104-2, 200104). Bethany Hse.

--A Serious Call to a Devout & Holy Life. Meister, John, et al, eds. LC 55-5330. 156p. 1968. pap. 6.95 (ISBN 0-664-24833-0). Westminster.

--A Serious Call to a Devout & Holy Life. LC 82-80470. (Treasures from the Spiritual Classics Ser.). 64p. 1982. pap. 2.95 (ISBN 0-8192-1306-3). Morehouse.

--A Serious Call to Holy Living. Abriged by ed. 96p. 1985. pap. 3.95 (ISBN 0-8423-5861-7). Tyndale.

--Wholly for God. Murray, Andrew, ed. LC 76-6622. 336p. 1976. pap. 4.95 (ISBN 0-87123-602-8, 200602). Bethany Hse.

--William Law: Christian Perfection. Rev. ed. 96p. 1986. pap. 4.95 (ISBN 0-8423-0259-X). Tyndale.

Lawhead, Stephen R. Turn Back the Night: A Christian Response to Popular Culture. LC 84-72005. 192p. (Orig.). 1985. pap. 6.95 (ISBN 0-89107-340-X, Crossway Bks). Good News.

Lawlor, Richard V. Answers to Your Questions. 1980. 5.00 (ISBN 0-8198-0700-1); pap. 4.00 (ISBN 0-8198-0701-X). Dghtrs St Paul.

Lawrence. Practicando la Presencia de Dios. LC 82-50949. Tr. of The Practice of the Presence of God. (Span.). 72p. (Orig.). 1983. pap. 1.35 (ISBN 0-8358-0456-9). Upper Room.

--The Practice of the Presence of God. Helms, Hal H., ed. LC 84-61019. (Living Library Ser.). 161p. (Orig.). 1984. pap. 5.95 (ISBN 0-941478-29-7). Paraclete Pr.

Lawrence, Gene H. Right Human Relations: The Only Way to World Peace. 110p. 1980. pap. 3.00 (ISBN 0-682-49627-8). Exposition Pr FL.

Leach, Ben. Groaning Up. (Uplook Ser.). 32p. 1982. pap. 0.99 (ISBN 0-8163-0513-7). Pacific Pr Pub Assn.

--I Can't Turn Off My Happy. (Uplook Ser.). 32p. 1982. pap. 0.79 (ISBN 0-8163-0515-3). Pacific Pr Pub Assn.

--Riding High. (Uplook Ser.). 32p. 1982. pap. 0.79 (ISBN 0-8163-0514-5). Pacific Pr Pub Assn.

--Worry Free Worry. (Uplook Ser.). 32p. 1982. pap. 0.99 (ISBN 0-8163-0516-1). Pacific Pr Pub Assn.

Leach, Virgil. Attitudes I. 1979. pap. 4.25 (ISBN 0-89137-803-0). Quality Pubns.

--Attitudes II. 1981. pap. 4.25 (ISBN 0-89137-804-9). Quality Pubns.

--Get Behind Me Satan. 1977. 8.75 (ISBN 0-89137-521-X); pap. 5.95 (ISBN 0-89137-520-1). Quality Pubns.

Learning to Be Thankful. 2.98 (ISBN 0-8010-5111-8). Baker Bk.

Learning to Love. 1982. 3.00 (ISBN 0-89858-040-4). Fill the Gap.

LeBar, Mary E. The Best Family of All. 32p. 1977. pap. 3.95 (ISBN 0-88207-251-X). Victor Bks.

Lebuffe, Francis P. Friends Aren't Kept Waiting. 1975. pap. 1.75 (ISBN 0-88479-000-2). Arena Lettres.

--More of My Changeless Friend. 1977. pap. 1.95 (ISBN 0-88479-007-X). Arena Lettres.

Leckey, Dolores R. The Ordinary Way: A Family Spirituality. (Crossroad Paperback Ser.). 192p. 1982. pap. 7.95 (ISBN 0-8245-0442-9). Crossroad NY.

Leclerc, Eloi. People of God in the Night. Lachance, Paul & Schwartz, Paul, trs. (Tau Ser.). 1979. 5.95 (ISBN 0-8199-0768-5). Franciscan Herald.

Lee, G. Avery. The Glorious Company. LC 86-2601. (Orig.). 1986. pap. 3.25 (ISBN 0-8054-1536-X). Broadman.

Lee, Mark W. Who Am I & What Am I Doing Here. 1986. pap. 5.95 (ISBN 0-8010-5643-8). Baker Bk.

Lee, Paul. My Heart a Hiding Place. 1986. pap. 7.95 (ISBN 0-87508-316-1). Chr Lit.

Lee, Peter, et al. Food for Life. LC 77-27693. 1978. pap. 3.95 (ISBN 0-87784-489-5). Inter-Varsity.

Leech, Kenneth. True Prayer: An Invitation to Christian Spirituality. LC 80-8358. 208p. 1986. pap. 7.95 (ISBN 0-06-065232-2, HarpR). Har-Row.

Leen, Jason. The Death of the Prophet. LC 79-18719. (Illus.). 1979. 11.95 (ISBN 0-87961-094-8); pap. 5.95 (ISBN 0-87961-093-X). Naturegraph.

LeFevre, Perry & Schroeder, W. Widick, eds. Pastoral Care & Liberation Praxis: Studies in Personal & Social Transformation. (Studies in Ministry & Parish Life). 112p. 1986. text ed. 18.95x (ISBN 0-913552-31-3); pap. text ed. 8.95x (ISBN 0-913552-32-1). Exploration Pr.

Leih, Virginia. Portrait of a Fulfilled Woman. 1979. pap. 4.95 (ISBN 0-8423-4860-3). Tyndale.

Lelly, Charles. The Beautiful Way of Life. 1980. 4.95 (ISBN 0-87159-010-7). Unity School.

L'Engle, Madeleine. A Circle of Quiet. (The Crosswicks Journal Trilogy). 246p. 1977. pap. 7.95 (ISBN 0-8164-2260-5, HarpR); Three Volume Set. 19.95 (ISBN 0-8164-2617-1). Har-Row.

--The Other Side of the Sun. (Epiphany Bks.). 352p. (Orig.). 1983. pap. 3.50 (ISBN 0-345-30616-3). Ballantine.

--Walking on Water: Reflections on Faith & Art. LC 80-21066. (Wheaton Literary Ser.). 198p. 1980. 10.95 (ISBN 0-87788-918-X); pap. 6.95 (ISBN 0-87788-919-8). Shaw Pubs.

Lensch, Rodney. My Personal Pentecost. 60p. (Orig.). 1972. pap. 1.25 (ISBN 0-89228-025-5). Impact Bks MO.

Leon, Jorge A. Cada Muchacho Necesita un Modelo Vivo. (Span.). 96p. 1983. pap. 4.75 (ISBN 0-311-46087-9). Casa Bautista.

--Psicologia Pastoral de la Iglesia. LC 77-43121. (Span.). 192p. (Orig.). pap. 5.95 (ISBN 0-89922-113-0). Edit Caribe.

Leonard of Taize. Belonging. 172p. 1985. pap. 7.95 (ISBN 0-8298-0565-6). Pilgrim NY.

Lessin, Roy. Spanking: Why? When? How? LC 79-54028. 96p. 1979. pap. 2.95 (ISBN 0-87123-494-7, 200494). Bethany Hse.

Lester, Andrew D. Coping with Your Anger: A Christian Guide. LC 82-24730. 114p. 1983. pap. 6.95 (ISBN 0-664-24471-8). Westminster.

LeTourneau, Richard H. Laws of Success for Christians: There's Only One-Way to Success Both for Today & Forever. LC 85-91034. (LeTourneau One-Way Ser.: Vol. 7). 130p. (Orig.). 1985. pap. 5.95 (ISBN 0-935899-03-0). LeTourneau Pr.

Levick. Breakfast of Champions. 1986. pap. 5.95 (ISBN 0-89225-284-7). Gospel Advocate.

Levine, Samuel. You Take Jesus, I'll Take God. LC 80-82731. 134p. (Orig.). 1980. pap. 4.95 (ISBN 0-9604754-1-9); pap. 4.95 (ISBN 0-9604754-1-9). Hamoroh Pr.

Lewis, C. S. Christian Reflections. 1974. pap. 4.95 (ISBN 0-8028-1430-1). Eerdmans.

--The Joyful Christian: 127 Readings. 256p. 1984. 5.95 (ISBN 0-02-086930-4, Collier). Macmillan.

--Mere Christianity. (Christian Library). 1985. Repr. 6.95 (ISBN 0-916441-18-0). Barbour & Co.

--El Problema del Dolor. Vilela, Ernesto S., tr. from Eng. LC 77-16715. Tr. of The Problem of Pain. (Span.). 156p. 1977. pap. 3.95 (ISBN 0-89922-097-5). Edit Caribe.

--Six by Lewis, 6 vols. 1978. pap. 18.95 (ISBN 0-02-086770-0, Collier). Macmillan.

Lewis, Ernest. Light for the Journey: Living the Ten Commandments. 1985. 10.95. Word Bks.

Lewis, Jim. Finding the Treasure Within You. LC 81-70339. 128p. 1982. pap. 4.75 (ISBN 0-87516-469-2). De Vorss.

L'Heureux, Conrad E. Life Journey & the Old Testament: An Experiential Approach to the Bible & Personal Transformations. 184p. 1986. pap. 8.95 (ISBN 0-8091-2828-4). Paulist Pr.

Liddell, Eric. Disciplines of the Christian Life. 160p. (Orig.). 1985. pap. 6.95 (ISBN 0-687-10810-1). Abingdon.

Lidmus, Susan B. Church Family Ministry: Changing Loneliness to Fellowship in the Church. 1985. pap. 6.95 (ISBN 0-570-03945-2, 12-2878). Concordia.

Liebelt, Gerita G. From Dilemma to Delight. Coffen, Richard W., ed. 96p. (Orig.). 1986. pap. 6.95 (ISBN 0-8280-0298-3). Review & Herald.

Liebersat, Henry. Caught in the Middle. 176p. (Orig.). 1987. pap. 8.95 (ISBN 0-8245-0822-X). Crossroad NY.

Lief, Nina R. The First Year of Life: A Curriculum for Parenting Information. 362p. 21.95 (ISBN 0-686-86720-3). Sadlier.

The Life in the Spirit Seminars Team Manual. rev. ed. 1979. pap. 4.95 (ISBN 0-89283-064-6). Servant.

Ligon, Ernest M. Psychology of Christian Personality. LC 35-22951. 1975. 7.00 (ISBN 0-915744-00-7); pap. 4.00 (ISBN 0-915744-01-5). Character Res.

Limardo, Miguel. Luces Encendidas Para Cada Dia. 376p. 1983. Repr. of 1981 ed. 5.50 (ISBN 0-311-40038-8). Casa Bautista.

Linam, Gail. God's Winter Gifts. (Illus.). 1980. pap. 3.25 (ISBN 0-8054-4158-1, 4142-58). Broadman.

Lindsay, Gordon. Seven Keys to Triumphant Christian Living. 1.25 (ISBN 0-89985-006-5). Christ Nations.

--Should Christians Attend Movies? 0.95 (ISBN 0-89985-007-3). Christ Nations.

--Why Do the Righteous Suffer? (Divine Healing & Health Ser.). 1.50 (ISBN 0-89985-032-4). Christ Nations.

--Why Some Are Not Healed. (Divine Healing & Health Ser.). 1.25 (ISBN 0-89985-033-2). Christ Nations.

Lindsey, Hal. La Liberacion del Planeta Tierra. Tr. of The Liberation of Planet Earth. (Span.). 192p. 1982. pap. 3.95 (ISBN 0-311-13023-2). Casa Bautista.

--The Promise. 208p. 1984. pap. 5.95 (ISBN 0-89081-424-4). Harvest Hse.

--There's a New World Coming: An In-Depth Analysis of the Book of Revelation. updated ed. 288p. 1984. pap. 6.95 (ISBN 0-89081-440-6). Harvest Hse.

Lineberry, John. That We May Have Fellowship: Studies in First John. 112p. 1986. pap. 4.95 (ISBN 0-87227-115-3). Reg Baptist.

Link, Mark. Breakway: Twenty-Eight Steps to a More Reflective Life. LC 67553. 144p. 1980. pap. 3.25 (ISBN 0-89505-050-1). Argus Comm.

--The Seventh Trumpet. LC 78-53943. 1978. 7.95 (ISBN 0-89505-014-5). Argus Comm.

Linn, Dennis & Linn, Matthew. Healing Life's Hurts: Healing Memories Through the Five Stages of Forgiveness. LC 77-14794. 324p. 1978. pap. 5.95 (ISBN 0-8091-2059-3). Paulist Pr.

Linn, Jan G. Christians Must Choose. Lambert, Herbert, ed. LC 85-3731. (Orig.). 1985. pap. 7.95 (ISBN 0-8272-0448-5). CBP.

Lipman, Ed. No Capital Crime. 1975. pap. 2.00x (ISBN 0-915016-04-4). Second Coming.

Littauer, Florence. How to Get along with Difficult People. LC 83-83371. 1984. pap. 4.95 (ISBN 0-89081-429-5). Harvest Hse.

--Personality Plus. (Illus.). 192p. 1982. 5.95 (Power Ed.); pap. 9.95 (ISBN 0-8007-1323-0). Revell.

Litthauer, Florence. It Takes so Little to Be above Average. 192p. 1983. pap. 4.95 (ISBN 0-89081-376-0). Harvest Hse.

Little Lost Lamb. 1.75 (ISBN 0-8198-4415-2). Dghtrs St Paul.

Little, Paul E. The Answer to Life. LC 86-72378. Orig. Title: Faith is for People. 96p. 1987. pap. 4.95 (ISBN 0-89107-429-5, Crossway Bks). Good News.

--How to Give Away Your Faith. LC 66-20710. 1966. pap. 5.95 (ISBN 0-87784-553-0). Inter-Varsity.

Littlepage, Loyd. How to Make Your Dreams Come True. (Illus.). 32p. 1981. pap. 4.50 (ISBN 0-911336-85-0). Sci of Mind.

Llewelyn, Robert. Love Bade Me Welcome. 96p. (Orig.). 1985. pap. 5.95 (ISBN 0-8091-2715-6). Paulist Pr.

Lloyd, Marjorie L. If I Had a Bigger Drum. (Harvest Ser.). 1981. pap. 4.50 (ISBN 0-8163-0399-1). Pacific Pr Pub Assn.

--Why the Cookie Crumbles. (Outreach Ser.). pap. 1.25 (ISBN 0-8163-0400-9). Pacific Pr Pub Assn.

Lloyd-Jones, D. Martyn. Christian Soldier. 12.95 (ISBN 0-8010-5583-0). Baker Bk.

--Life in the Spirit: In Marriage, Home & Work. 372p. 1975. Repr. 12.95 (ISBN 0-8010-5550-4). Baker Bk.

Loader, Bill. What Does It Mean? 64p. (Orig.). 1985. pap. 6.95 (ISBN 0-85819-472-4, Pub. by JBCE). ANZ Religious Pubns.

Loane, Marcus. Grace & the Gentiles. 149p. (Orig.). 1981. pap. text ed. 6.45 (ISBN 0-85151-327-1). Banner of Truth.

Lobo, George V. A Guide to Christian Living: A New Compendium of Moral Theology. 420p. 1984. pap. 16.95 (ISBN 0-87061-092-9). Chr Classics.

Lockerbie, Jeanette. Forgive, Forget & Be Free. rev. ed. 160p. 1984. pap. 5.95 (ISBN 0-89840-068-6). Heres Life.

--More Salt in My Kitchen. LC 80-12357. (Quiet Time Bks.). 1980. pap. 3.50 (ISBN 0-8024-5668-5). Moody.

--Time Out for Coffee. (Quiet Time Bks.). 1978. pap. 3.50 (ISBN 0-8024-8759-9). Moody.

Lockyer, Herbert. Sins of Saints. LC 75-108378. 1970. pap. 5.95 (ISBN 0-87213-532-2). Loizeaux.

Loder, James E. The Transforming Moment: Understanding Convictional Experiences. LC 80-8354. 256p. 1981. 15.45 (ISBN 0-06-065276-4, HarpR). Har-Row.

Loewen, Howard J., ed. One Lord, One Church, One Hope, & One God. (Text-Reader Ser.: No. 2). 369p. 1985. pap. text ed. 12.00x (ISBN 0-936273-08-9). Inst Mennonite.

Lohfink, Gerhard. Jesus & Community: The Social Dimension of Christian Faith. 224p. 1985. pap. 9.95 (ISBN 0-8091-2661-3). Paulist Pr.

Lonergan, Bernard J. F. Understanding & Being: An Introduction & Companion to Insight. Morelli, Elizabeth A. & Morelli, Mark D., eds. (Toronto Studies in Theology: Vol. 5). xii, 368p. 1980. 59.95x (ISBN 0-88946-909-1). E Mellen.

Long, James. What Is Man? Leader's Guide. Chao, Lorna Y., tr. (Basic Doctrine Ser.). 1986. pap. write for info. (ISBN 0-941598-36-5). Living Spring Pubns.

Long, Mildred. Listen to the Silence. (Orig.). 1970. pap. 2.50 (ISBN 0-87516-049-2). De Vorss.

Loomis, Darlene. He Touched Me. (Illus.). 62p. (Orig.). 1977. pap. 3.00 (ISBN 0-686-36275-6). Drain Enterprise.

--Joint Heirs in Christ. (Illus., Orig.). 1977. pap. 2.00 (ISBN 0-686-36277-2). Drain Enterprise.

--On Fire for God. (Illus.). 53p. (Orig.). 1976. 2.00 (ISBN 0-686-36274-8). Drain Enterprise.

--Those Who Won't & Those Who Will. (Illus.). 12p. (Orig.). 1977. pap. 1.00 (ISBN 0-686-36278-0). Drain Enterprise.

Lord Have I Got Problems. (Out Ser.). 1984. 1.25 (ISBN 0-8163-0599-4). Pacific Pr Pub Assn.

The Lord Is My Shepherd. 2.98 (ISBN 0-8010-5113-4). Baker Bk.

Louis Of Granada. Summa of the Christian Life, 3 vols. Aumann, Jordan, tr. from Sp. LC 79-65716. 1979. Set. pap. 24.00 (ISBN 0-89555-121-7). Vol. 1 (ISBN 0-89555-118-7). Vol. 2 (ISBN 0-89555-119-5). Vol. 3 (ISBN 0-89555-120-9). TAN Bks Pubs.

Love, Vicky. Childless Is Not Less. 144p. (Orig.). 1984. pap. 5.95 (ISBN 0-87123-449-1). Bethany Hse.

Lovett, C. S. Dynamic Truths for the Spirit-Filled Life. 1973. pap. 5.95 (ISBN 0-938148-13-3). Personal Christianity.

--The One Hundred Percent Christian. 1970. pap. 4.25 (ISBN 0-938148-07-9). Personal Christianity.

Lowery, Claire. Christian Spirituality for the Eighties. 96p. 1983. pap. 4.50 (ISBN 0-697-01940-3). Wm C Brown.

Lowry, James W. North America Is the Lord's. (Christian Day School Ser.). 1980. 17.05x (ISBN 0-87813-916-8). Christian Light.

Lozano, John M. Life As Parable: Reinterpreting the Religious Life. 208p. (Orig.). 1986. pap. 8.95 (ISBN 0-8091-2825-X). Paulist Pr.

Lubich, Chiara. Journey: Spiritual Insights. Moran, Hugh & Hartnett, William, trs. from Ital. 158p. 1984. pap. 4.95 (ISBN 0-911782-51-6). New City.

--Our Yes to God. Moran, Hugh J., tr. from Ital. LC 81-82064. 112p. (Orig.). 1981. pap. 3.95 (ISBN 0-911782-38-9). New City.

--Servants of All. Moran, Hugh, tr. from It. LC 78-59470. 176p. 1978. pap. 3.50 (ISBN 0-911782-05-2). New City.

--When Did We See You Lord? Moran, Hugh, tr. from Ital. LC 79-88680. Tr. of Gesu Nel Fratello. 134p. 1979. pap. 3.50 (ISBN 0-911782-34-6). New City.

Lucado, Max. On the Anvil. 128p. 1985. pap. 4.95 (ISBN 0-8423-4738-0). Tyndale.

Ludwig, David J. In Good Spirits. LC 82-70944. (Orig.). 1982. pap. 6.95 (ISBN 0-8066-1919-8, 10-3208). Augsburg.

Luebering, Carol & Schmitz, Robert E. Nothing to Fear: Unleashing the Power of the Resurrection. (Illus.). 104p. 1985. pap. text ed. 4.50 (ISBN 0-86716-047-0). St Anthony Mess Pr.

Lueders, Edward. The Clam Lake Papers. (Festival Ser.). 160p. 1982. pap. 3.25 (ISBN 0-687-08580-2). Abingdon.

Lukas, Elisabeth. Meaning in Suffering: Comfort in Crisis Through Logotherapy. Fabry, Joseph, tr. from Ger. Tr. of Auch Dein Leiden hat Sinn. 160p. (Orig.). 1986. pap. 7.95 (ISBN 0-917867-05-X). Inst Logo.

Luke, Helen. The Voice Within: Love & Virtue in the Age of the Spirit. 128p. 1984. pap. 7.95 (ISBN 0-8245-0659-6). Crossroad NY.

Lund, Candida, ed. In Joy & in Sorrow. Large type ed. 164p. 1984. 12.95 (ISBN 0-88347-167-1). Thomas More.

Lund, Carol A. A Journey with Jesus. (Illus.). 214p. (Orig.). 1982. pap. 4.95x (ISBN 0-9608418-0-6). MasterSon Pub.

Lunde, Norman. You Unlimited. LC 65-23608. 1985. pap. 5.95 (ISBN 0-87516-249-5). De Vorss.

Lundstrom, Lowell. Heaven's Answer for the Home. rev. ed. 142p. 1985. pap. 3.50 (ISBN 0-938220-16-0). Whitaker Hse.

Lundy, Richard A. You Can Say That Again: Cultivating New Life in Time-Worn Christian Sayings. LC 80-67556. 72p. 1980. pap. 2.95 (ISBN 0-89505-051-X). Argus Comm.

Luoma, William. God So Loved the World. 1986. pap. 3.95 (6806). CSS of Ohio.

Lutz, Charles P. Farming the Lord's Land: Christian Perspectives on American Agriculture. LC 80-80285. 208p. (Orig.). 1980. pap. 8.95 (ISBN 0-8066-1785-3, 10-2264). Augsburg.

Lutzer, Erwin. Failure: The Back Door to Success. LC 75-16177. 1977. pap. 3.50 (ISBN 0-8024-2516-X). Moody.

Lutzer, Erwin & Van Stone, Doris. Dorie: The Girl Nobody Loved. 1981. pap. 5.95 (ISBN 0-8024-2275-6). Moody.

Lutzer, Erwin W. How to Say No to a Stubborn Habit. LC 79-64039. 143p. 1979. pap. 5.95 (ISBN 0-88207-787-2). Victor Bks.

Lutzer, Erwin W., ed. How in This World Can I Be Holy? (Moody Press Electives Ser.). 1985. pap. text ed. 3.95 (ISBN 0-8024-0730-7); leader's guide 2.50 (ISBN 0-8024-0731-5). Moody.

Luzer, Erwin W. When a Good Man Falls. 132p. 1985. pap. 4.95 (ISBN 0-89693-361-X). Victor Bks.

Lynchard, Danny. Sure to Endure. 43p. 1983. pap. 1.95 (ISBN 0-88144-043-4). Christian Pub.

Lynn, John A. Will the Real You Please Remain Standing! 191p. 1981. pap. 2.95 (ISBN 0-910068-38-0). Am Christian.

--Will the Real You Please Stand Up! 113p. 1980. pap. 2.95 (ISBN 0-910068-28-3). Am Christian.

Lyon, Audley B. Growing Life: Devotionals for the Young in Christ. LC 77-82056. 1970. pap. 5.95 (ISBN 0-930014-07-3). Multnomah.

MacArthur, John. Giving God's Way. 1978. pap. 3.95 (ISBN 0-8423-1034-7). Tyndale.

MacArthur, John F., Jr. Keys to Spiritual Growth. 132p. 1976. pap. 5.95 (ISBN 0-8007-5013-6, Power Bks). Revell.

MacArthur, John, Jr. God's Plan for Giving. (John MacArthur's Bible Studies). 1985. pap. 3.50 (ISBN 0-8024-5107-1). Moody.

Macartney, Clarence E. The Chosen Twelve Plus One. LC 80-17881. (Illus.). 124p. 1980. 39.95 (ISBN 0-930014-43-X); ltd. ed. 200.00 (ISBN 0-930014-52-9); portfolio 24.95. Multnomah.

Macaulay, Susan S. For the Children's Sake: Foundations of Education for Home & School. LC 83-72043. 192p. 1984. pap. 6.95 (ISBN 0-89107-290-X, Crossway Bks). Good News.

McBirnie, William S. The Search for the Twelve Apostles. 1979. pap. 4.50 (ISBN 0-8423-5839-0). Tyndale.

McBride, Alfred. The Kingdom & the Glory. 1977. pap. 1.75 (ISBN 0-88479-003-7). Arena Lettres.

McBride, Richard, et al. Love & Creation. pap. text ed. 2.16 (ISBN 0-317-39314-6); 3.99 (ISBN 0-8215-5842-0); Parent Guidebook 1.98 (ISBN 0-317-39315-4). Sadlier.

McCall, Clark B. Taking Dreams Off Hold. (Out Ser.). 1984. pap. 1.25 (ISBN 0-8163-0551-X). Pacific Pr Pub Assn.

--Tiptoeing Through the Minefield. (Outreach Ser.). 32p. 1982. pap. 1.25 (ISBN 0-8163-0460-2). Pacific Pr Pub Assn.

McCann, Edna. The Heritage Book, 1985. (Illus.). 192p. 1984. 5.95 (ISBN 0-02-582880-0). Macmillan.

McCann Lucas, Jerri. Christianity: A Growing Experience. pap. 4.95 (ISBN 0-89137-429-9). Quality Pubns.

McCarthy, Flor. And the Master Answered. LC 84-72678. (Illus.). 96p. (Orig.). 1985. pap. 4.95 (ISBN 0-87793-279-4). Ave Maria.

McCarty, Michele. Becoming. 1983. pap. 6.95 (ISBN 0-697-01856-3); program manual 10.00 (ISBN 0-697-01857-1); Journal 3.25 (ISBN 0-697-01869-5). Wm C Brown.

--Believing. (Fullness of Life Ser.). 160p. 1980. pap. text ed. 6.95 (ISBN 0-697-01753-2); tchr's manual 8.00 (ISBN 0-697-01754-0). Wm C Brown.

--Belonging. (Fullness of Life Ser.). (YA) 1985. pap. text ed. 7.95 (ISBN 0-697-02068-1); tchr's. ed. 10.00 (ISBN 0-697-02069-X); wkbk. 3.25 (ISBN 0-697-02070-3). Wm C Brown.

--Relating. (Fullness of Life Ser.). 128p. (Orig.). 1979. pap. text ed. 5.50 (ISBN 0-697-01710-9); tchr's manual 8.00 (ISBN 0-697-01711-7). Wm C Brown.

McCauley, George. The Unfinished Image. 462p. (Orig.). 1983. pap. 10.95 (ISBN 0-8215-9903-8). Sadlier.

McClain, Alva J. Freemasonry & Christianity. 1979. pap. 1.00 (ISBN 0-88469-012-1). BMH Bks.

McCleary, Paul & Wogaman, J. Philip. Quality of Life in a Global Society. (Orig.). 1978. pap. 2.50 (ISBN 0-377-00070-1). Friend Pr.

McClellan, Thomas L. Science of Mind Hymnal. 9.50 (ISBN 0-87516-343-2). De Vorss.

McClelland, Bryan L., ed. Fruit of the Vine. LC 85-72071. (Illus.). 392p. (Orig.). 1985. pap. 5.95 (ISBN 0-913342-50-5). Barclay Pr.

McCollister, John C. The Christian Book of Why. 360p. 1986. pap. 7.95 (ISBN 0-8246-0317-6). Jonathan David.

McDermott, Brian O. What Are They Saying about the Grace of Christ? (WATSA Ser.). 1984. pap. 4.95 (ISBN 0-8091-2584-6). Paulist Pr.

McDill, Wayne. Making Friends for Christ. LC 79-55290. 1980. pap. 4.95 (ISBN 0-8054-6224-4). Broadman.

MacDonald, Gail & MacDonald, Gordon. If Those Who Reach Could Touch. 128p. 1985. Repr. of 1984 ed. 5.95 (ISBN 0-8007-5201-5, Power Bks). Revell.

MacDonald, George. Life Essential: The Hope of the Gospel. 2nd ed. Hein, Rolland, ed. LC 74-16732. (Wheaton Literary Ser.). 102p. 1978. pap. 4.95 (ISBN 0-87788-499-4). Shaw Pubs.

--The Musician's Quest. Phillips, Michael, ed. 272p. 1984. pap. 5.95 (ISBN 0-87123-444-0, 210444). Bethany Hse.

MacDonald, Gordon & MacDonald, Gail. Affirmation & Rebuke. (PathFinder Pamphlets Ser.). 32p. (Orig.). 1986. pap. 1.95 (ISBN 0-87784-219-1). Inter-Varsity.

McDonald, Perry & Odell, William. Laws of Christian Living: The Commandments. 170p. (Orig.). 1986. pap. 6.95 (ISBN 0-87973-593-7, 593). Our Sunday Visitor.

MacDonald, William. Lord, Break Me. pap. 1.75 (ISBN 0-937396-24-9). Walterick Pubs.

--There's a Way Back to God. 1986. pap. 2.25 (ISBN 0-937396-42-7). Walterick Pubs.

--Think of Your Future. pap. 1.95 (ISBN 0-937396-44-3). Walterick Pubs.

--True Discipleship. expanded ed. pap. 3.25 (ISBN 0-937396-50-8). Walterick Pubs.

--True Discipleship. pap. 2.50 (ISBN 0-937396-49-4). Walterick Pubs.

MacDougall, Mary K. Happiness Now. 178p. 1971. 5.95 (ISBN 0-87159-053-0). Unity School.

MacDougall, Mary-Katherine. Dear Friend, I Love You. 176p. (Orig.). 1986. pap. 9.95 (ISBN 0-87707-226-4). Now Comns.

McDowell, Josh. The Secret of Loving. 200p. 1985. 11.95 (ISBN 0-86605-157-0). Campus Crusade.

McDowell, Josh & Bellis, Dale. Evidence for Joy. 192p. 1986. pap. 3.50 (ISBN 0-553-26153-3). Bantam.

McDowell, Josh & Stewart, Don. The Creation. LC 83-72898. (Family Handbook of Christian Knowledge Ser.). 178p. 1983. 18.95 (ISBN 0-86605-118-X). Campus Crusade.

McDowell, Mary. Hello, Tomorrow. LC 76-27935. 1977. 5.95 (ISBN 0-87212-069-4). Libra.

Mace, David & Mace, Vera. In the Presence of God: Readings for Christian Marriage. LC 84-26928. 116p. 1985. 8.95 (ISBN 0-664-21261-1). Westminster.

--Letters to a Retired Couple. 160p. 1984. pap. 6.95 (ISBN 0-8170-1005-X). Judson.

--The Sacred Fire Christian Marriage Through the Ages. 1986. 16.95 (ISBN 0-687-36712-3). Abingdon.

McEachern, Alton H. The Lord's Presence. LC 85-29055. 1986. pap. 4.95 (ISBN 0-8054-2314-1). Broadman.

McElrath, William N. Bold Bearers of His Name. 1987. 12.95 (ISBN 0-8054-4339-8). Broadman.

McElvaney, William K. Good News Is Bad News Is Good News. LC 79-22032. 132p. (Orig.). 1980. pap. 5.95 (ISBN 0-88344-157-8). Orbis Bks.

McFadden, Elizabeth S. God's Beloved Rebel. (Daybreak Ser.). 1982. pap. 4.95 (ISBN 0-8163-0442-4). Pacific Pr Pub Assn.

McFadden, Jim. The Fear Factor. (Living As a Christian Ser.). (Orig.). 1983. pap. 3.95 (ISBN 0-89283-159-6). Servant.

McFarland, Ken. Christian Atheist. (Uplook Ser.). 16p. 1982. pap. 0.99 (ISBN 0-8163-0500-5). Pacific Pr Pub Assn.

McFarland, Kenneth. Gospel Showdown. (Outreach Ser.). 32p. 1981. pap. 1.25 (ISBN 0-8163-0435-1). Pacific Pr Pub Assn.

McGinnis, Alan L. La Amistad Factor Decisivo. Orig. Title: The Friendship Factor. (Span.). 204p. 1986. pap. 5.95 (ISBN 0-311-46093-3, Edit Mundo). Casa Bautista.

McGinniss, Alan L. The Friendship Factor: How to Get Closer to the People You Care for. LC 79-50076. 1979. 12.95 (ISBN 0-8066-1710-1, 10-2410); pap. 3.95 (ISBN 0-8066-1711-X, 10-2411). Augsburg.

McGovern, James. To Give the Love of Christ. LC 77-14832. (Emmaus Book). 128p. 1978. pap. 2.95 (ISBN 0-8091-2076-3). Paulist Pr.

McIntyre, Marie. Ears to Hear: Hearts to Praise. (Greeting Book Line Ser.). (Illus.). 48p. (Orig.). 1985. pap. 1.50 (ISBN 0-89622-210-1). Twenty-Third.

McKay, Bobbie. The Unabridged Woman. LC 79-14297. (Orig.). 1979. pap. 5.95 (ISBN 0-8298-0369-6). Pilgrim NY.

McKee, John. The Enemy Within the Gate. LC 74-80023. 1974. 10.00 (ISBN 0-912414-16-2). Lumen Christi.

McKeever, James. Victory in Prayer. 32p. (Orig.). 1985. pap. 1.00 (ISBN 0-86694-103-7). Omega Pubns OR.

McKeever, Jim. Christians Will Go Through the Tribulation. LC 78-55091. (Illus.). 1978. 10.95 (ISBN 0-931608-01-5); pap. 5.95 (ISBN 0-931608-02-3). Omega Pubns OR.

--Only One Word. 1979. 1.00 (ISBN 0-86694-011-1). Omega Pubns OR.

--Why Were You Created. 1980. 1.00 (ISBN 0-86694-083-9). Omega Pubns OR.

MacKenna, Richard. God for Nothing. 186p. 1986. 12.95 (ISBN 0-285-62623-X, Pub. Souvenir Pr Ltd UK). Intl Spec Bk.

McKenney, Tom C. Come & Live. LC 84-242781. (Illus.). 167p. 1982. pap. 5.95 (ISBN 0-934527-01-6). Words Living Minis.

--Come & Live. LC 84-242781. (Illus.). 167p. (Orig.). 1981. pap. 3.95 (ISBN 0-934527-00-8). Words Living Minis.

--Live Free. LC 84-91415. (Illus.). 317p. 1985. 9.95 (ISBN 0-934527-04-0). Words Living Minis.

McKenzie, John L. Source: What the Bible Says about the Problems of Contemporary Life. (Basics of Christian Thought Ser.). 228p. 1984. 14.95 (ISBN 0-88347-172-8). Thomas More.

Mackes, Shy. The Overcoming Power. LC 82-73708. 1983. pap. text ed. 5.00 (ISBN 0-932050-17-4). New Puritan.

Mackey, Bertha. A Saloon Keeper's Daughter Saved. 15p. 1982. pap. 0.15 (ISBN 0-686-36264-0); pap. 0.25 2 copies (ISBN 0-686-37285-9). Faith Pub HSe.

McLelland, Joseph. Trabajo y Justicia. 128p. 1983. Repr. of 1978 ed. 2.50 (ISBN 0-311-46060-7). Casa Bautista.

McLemore, Clinton W. Honest Christianity. LC 84-10450. 116p. (Orig.). 1984. pap. 7.95 (ISBN 0-664-26009-8, Pub. by Bridgebooks). Westminster.

MacLeod, Gavin, et al. Back on Course. (Illus.). 1987. 12.95 (ISBN 0-8007-1533-0). Revell.

McMakin, Jacqueline & Nary, Rhoda. Doorways to Christian Growth. 300p. 1984. pap. 9.95 (ISBN 0-86683-818-X, HarpR). Har-Row.

MacMillan, John A. Encounter with Darkness. LC 80-67656. 116p. 2.25 (ISBN 0-87509-287-X). Chr Pubns.

McMillen, S. I. None of These Diseases. rev. ed. Stern, David E., ed. 192p. 1984. pap. write for info. (ISBN 0-8007-5233-3). Revell.

McMinn, Don. Entering His Presence. LC 86-70743. 1986. pap. 5.95 (ISBN 0-88270-608-X). Bridge Pub.

McMinn, Gordon & Libby, Larry. Choosing to Be Close: Fill Your Life with the Rewards of Relationships. LC 84-3297. 1984. pap. 5.95 (ISBN 0-88070-053-X). Multnomah.

--Taking Charge: The Dynamics of Personal Decision-Making & Self-Management. LC 80-65061. 192p. (Orig.). 1980. pap. 4.95 (ISBN 0-89636-043-1). Accent Bks.

McNeill, Don, et al. Compassion: A Reflection on the Christian Life. LC 83-45045. (Illus.). 160p. 1983. pap. 6.95 (ISBN 0-385-18957-5, Im). Doubleday.

McPhee, John, ed. Manual para la Familia Catolica Hispana de Hoy. Diaz, Olimpia, tr. (Span.). 1980. pap. 1.50 (ISBN 0-89243-123-7, 51900). Liguori Pubns.

McPherson, Aimee S. This Is That: Personal Experiences, Sermons & Writings. Dayton, Daonald W., ed. (The Higher Christian Life Ser.). 685p. 1985. 85.00 (ISBN 0-8240-6428-3). Garland Pub.

Macquarrie, John. Faith of People of God. 191p. 1972. pap. text ed. write for info. (ISBN 0-02-374520-7, Pub. by Scribner). Macmillan.

--In Search of Humanity. rev. ed. 286p. 1985. pap. 11.95 (ISBN 0-8245-0708-8). Crossroad NY.

McReynolds, Janet. Something Supernatural. 103p. 1986. pap. 3.95 (ISBN 0-88144-038-8). Christian Pub.

McWilliams, Warren. When You Walk Through the Fire. (Orig.). 1986. pap. 7.95 (ISBN 0-8054-1621-8). Broadman.

Madden, Myron C. & Madden, Mary B. For Grandparents: Wonders & Worries. LC 80-12778. (Christian Care Bks.: Vol, 9). 118p. 1980. pap. 7.95 (ISBN 0-664-24325-8). Westminster.

Madsen, Norman P. Lord, Teach Us to Live. LC 84-62161. 112p. 1985. pap. 4.95 (ISBN 0-87973-718-2, 718). Our Sunday Visitor.

Maeder, Gary & Williams, Don. The Christian Life: Issues & Answers. LC 76-29258. 208p. 1977. pap. 3.50 (ISBN 0-8307-0470-1, 5404606). Regal.

Maestri, William F. What Do You Seek? LC 85-60887. 170p. (Orig.). 1985. pap. 6.95 (ISBN 0-87973-803-0, 803). Our Sunday Visitor.

Maguire, Daniel C. The Moral Revolution: A Christian Humanist Vision. LC 85-51826. 224p. pap. 12.95 (ISBN 0-86683-520-2, RD 572, HarpR). Har-Row.

Mahan, Asa. Out of Darkness into Light. Dayton, Donald W., ed. (The Higher Christian Life Ser.). 366p. 1985. 45.00 (ISBN 0-8240-6429-1). Garland Pub.

Main, John. Present Christ. 128p. (Orig.). 1986. pap. 7.95 (ISBN 0-8245-0740-1). Crossroad NY.
Mainhood, Beth. Reaching Your World. 118p. 1986. pap. 4.95 (ISBN 0-89109-537-3). NavPress.
Mains, David R. The Truth about the Lie. 128p. 1987. pap. 4.95 (ISBN 0-310-34831-5). Zondervan.
Mains, Karen. Karen! Karen! 1980. 6.95 (ISBN 0-8423-2026-1). Tyndale.
--Making Sunday Special. 192p. 1987. 12.95 (ISBN 0-8499-0612-1). Word Bks.
Mains, Karen B. Open Heart-Open Home. LC 76-1554. 224p. 1976. 5.95 (ISBN 0-89191-111-1). Cook.
--Open Heart-Open Home. 1980. pap. 2.95 (ISBN 0-451-14183-0, AE2641, Sig). NAL.
Maitland, David J. Looking Both Ways: A Theology for Midlife. 240p. 1985. pap. 10.95 (ISBN 0-8042-1127-2). John Knox.
Makrakis, Apostolos. Concerning Our Duties to God. Orthodox Christian Educational Society, ed. 170p. 1958. pap. text ed. 4.50x (ISBN 0-938366-13-0). Orthodox Chr.
Malgo, Wim. Depression & Its Remedy. 1980. 2.95 (ISBN 0-937422-03-7). Midnight Call.
--How to Walk with God. 1980. 1.95 (ISBN 0-937422-02-9). Midnight Call.
--Russia's Last Invasion. 1980. 3.95 (ISBN 0-937422-01-0). Midnight Call.
--There Shall Be Signs from 1948 to 1982. 1980. 2.95 (ISBN 0-937422-00-2). Midnight Call.
Malinski, Mieczyslaw. Our Daily Bread. 142p. 1979. 7.95 (ISBN 0-8245-0363-5). Crossroad NY.
Mallory, James D. & Baldwin, Stanley C. The Kink & I: A Psychiatrist's Guide to Untwisted Living. LC 73-78688. 224p. 1973. pap. 5.95 (ISBN 0-88207-237-4). Victor Bks.
Mallough, Don. Living by Faith: How an Active Faith Can Change Your Life. LC 77-91484. 128p. 1978. pap. 1.50 (ISBN 0-88243-552-3, 02-0552). Gospel Pub.
Maloney, George. Inward Stillness. 6.95 (ISBN 0-87193-062-5). Dimension Bks.
Maloney, George, ed. God's Exploding Love. LC 86-28802. 164p. (Orig.). 1987. pap. 7.95 (ISBN 0-8189-0514-X). Alba.
Maloney, George A. Alone with the Alone. LC 81-70021. (Illus.). 208p. (Orig.). 1982. pap. 4.95 (ISBN 0-87793-243-3). Ave Maria.
--Manna in the Desert. 120p. (Orig.). 1984. pap. 5.95 (ISBN 0-914544-54-3). Living Flame Pr.
--The Silence of Surrendering Love: Body, Soul, Spirit Integration. LC 85-28636. 189p. 1986. pap. 7.95 (ISBN 0-8189-0494-1). Alba.
Maloney, George A., ed. The First Day of Eternity: Resurrection Now. 128p. 1982. 8.95 (ISBN 0-8245-0445-3). Crossroad NY.
Malphurs, J. G. My Hand in His. 1961. 5.00 (ISBN 0-88027-012-8). Firm Foun Pub.
Malz, Betty. Super Natural Living. 1983. pap. 2.50 (ISBN 0-451-12517-7, Sig). NAL.
Mandevile. Good Samaritan. (Ladybird Ser.). 1979. 2.50 (ISBN 0-87508-837-6). Chr Lit.
Mandeville. Lost Sheep. (Ladybird Ser.). 1979. pap. 2.50 (ISBN 0-87508-849-X). Chr Lit.
Mandeville, Sylvia. Amigos de Dios. Gutierrez, Edna L., tr. from Eng. (Serie Apunta Con Tu Dedo). 24p. 1980. pap. 9.95 (ISBN 0-311-38532-X, Edit Mundo). Casa Bautista.
Mandeville, Sylvia & Pierson, Lance. Conoce a Jesus. Gutierrez, Edna L., tr. from Eng. (Pointing Out Bk.). 24p. 1980. pap. 9.95 (ISBN 0-311-38531-1, Edit Mundo). Casa Bautista.
Mandino, Og. The Greatest Miracle in the World. 1977. pap. 3.50 (ISBN 0-553-25914-8). Bantam.
--The Greatest Secret in the World. 1978. pap. 3.50 (ISBN 0-553-26545-8). Bantam.
Mandino, Og & Kaye, Buddy. Gift of Acabar. 1979. pap. 3.50 (ISBN 0-553-26084-7). Bantam.
Maniscalco, Joe. Eight Laws of Health. 1985. pap. 3.95 (ISBN 0-8163-0568-4). Pacific Pr Pub Assn.
Mankin, Jim. Prescription for Troubled Hearts. 1984. pap. 5.95 (ISBN 0-89225-273-1). Gospel Advocate.
Mann, Leonard W. Stars for Your Sky. 1982. pap. 4.95 (ISBN 0-89536-520-0, 1901). CSS of Ohio.
Manning, Brennan. The Gentle Revolutionaries. 5.95 (ISBN 0-87193-012-9). Dimension Bks.
Manske, Ron. A Polish Love Story. LC 79-84322. (Illus.). 1979. pap. 2.50 (ISBN 0-89221-060-5). New Leaf.
Mantle, J. Gregory. Beyond Humiliation. LC 75-6163. 256p. 1975. pap. 4.95 (ISBN 0-87123-040-2). Bethany Hse.
Manuel, David. Like a Mighty River. LC 77-90948. (Illus.). 220p. 1977. 5.95 (ISBN 0-932260-02-0). Rock Harbor.
Manuel, David & Marshall, Peter. In God They Trusted. 60p. (Orig.). 1983. pap. 6.95 (ISBN 0-919463-07-X). Paraclete Pr.
Marcel, Gabriel. Creative Fidelity. (The New Crossroad Paperback Ser.). 304p. 1982. pap. 9.95 (ISBN 0-8245-0446-1). Crossroad NY.
Marheine, Allen H. You Belong. LC 79-21954. (Orig.). 1980. pap. 2.95 (ISBN 0-8298-0380-7). Pilgrim NY.
Marney, Carlyle. The Crucible of Redemption. 64p. 1984. pap. text ed. 5.95 (ISBN 0-913029-04-1). Stevens Bk Pr.
Marrs, Texe W. Rush to Armaggedon. (Living Bk.). 128p. (Orig.). 1987. 3.95 (ISBN 0-8423-5796-3). Tyndale.
Marsh, F. E. Discipler's Manual. new ed. LC 79-2550. 412p. 1980. 12.95 (ISBN 0-8254-3231-6). Kregel.
Marshall, Catherine. The Helper. 1979. pap. 3.95 (ISBN 0-380-45583-8). Avon.
--Meeting God at Every Turn. 224p. 1985. pap. 3.50 (ISBN 0-553-23977-5). Bantam.
--Something More. 1976. pap. 3.50 (ISBN 0-380-00601-4, 60104-4). Avon.
--Something More. 276p. 1976. pap. 3.50 (ISBN 0-8007-8266-6, Spire Bks). Revell.
Marshall, Helen L. Bright Laughter-Warm Tears: Inspirational Thoughts for Mothers. 64p. 1985. pap. 3.95 (ISBN 0-8010-6195-4). Baker Bk.
--Inspirational Resources for Women's Groups. 64p. 1985. pap. 3.95 (ISBN 0-8010-6196-2). Baker Bk.
--Quiet Power: Words of Faith, Hope, & Love. 64p. 1985. pap. 3.95 (ISBN 0-8010-6197-0). Baker Bk.
Marshall, John F. The Long Way Home, the Short Way of Love. (Spirit & Life Ser). 1968. 3.50 (ISBN 0-686-11575-9). Franciscan Inst.
Marshall, Peter & Manuel, David. The Light & the Glory. 352p. 1977. 14.95 (ISBN 0-8007-0886-5); pap. 7.95 (ISBN 0-8007-5054-3, Power Bks). Revell.
Martin, A. N. Living the Christian Life. 32p. 1986. pap. 1.00 (ISBN 0-85151-493-6). Banner of Truth.
Martin, Mrs. Bill. My Special Place. 136p. 1980. pap. 5.95 (ISBN 0-89114-111-1). Baptist Pub Hse.
Martin, Catherine. Building Christian Community. 1.17 (ISBN 0-8091-9311-6). Paulist Pr.
Martin, Elva. Seek Ye First. 1973. pap. 1.65 (ISBN 0-915374-32-3, 32-3). Rapids Christian.
Martin, George. To Pray As Jesus. 1978. pap. 2.50 (ISBN 0-89283-054-9). Servant.
Martin, Grant. Transformed by Thorns. 156p. 1985. pap. 5.95 (ISBN 0-89693-397-0). Victor Bks.
Martin, John R. Ventures in Discipleship. LC 84-19140. 304p. (Orig.). 1984. pap. 12.95 (ISBN 0-8361-3378-1). Herald Pr.
Martin, Maurice. Identity & Faith. LC 81-82655. (Focal Pamphlet Ser.). 104p. (Orig.). 1981. pap. 3.95 (ISBN 0-8361-1979-7). Herald Pr.
Martin, Sara H. Frente Al Cancer, Un Gigante a Mi Lado. (Span.). 96p. 1985. pap. 4.50 (ISBN 0-311-46101-8). Casa Bautista.
Martin, William C. Christians in Conflict. LC 72-88018. (Studies in Religion & Society Ser.). 1972. 14.95x (ISBN 0-913348-01-5); pap. 8.95x (ISBN 0-913348-10-4). Ctr Sci Study.
Martinez, Jose. Novios: Conversemos Sobre Cosas Que Apenas Se Hablan. (Span.). 80p. 1986. pap. 2.95 (ISBN 0-311-46104-2). Casa Bautista.
Martinez, Jose & Trenchard, Ernesto. Escogidos en Cristo. Tr. of Chosen in Christ. (Span.). 320p. 1987. pap. 9.95 (ISBN 0-8254-1737-6). Kregel.
Marty, Martin E. Friendship. LC 80-69243. 180p. 1980. pap. 4.50 (ISBN 0-89505-053-6). Argus Comm.
Massey, Craig. Adjust or Self-Destruct. LC 77-4088. pap. 3.50 (ISBN 0-8024-0136-8). Moody.
Massey, James E. Concerning Christian Unity. 1979. 3.95 (ISBN 0-87162-219-X, D3070). Warner Pr.
Maston, T. B. Consejos a la Juventud. Duffer, H. F., Jr., tr. Orig. Title: Advice to Youth. (Span.). 60p. 1985. pap. 1.55 (ISBN 0-311-46005-4). Casa Bautista.
--The Ethic of the Christian Life. Hogg, Gayle, ed. (Religious Education Ser.). 152p. 1982. kivar 10.75 (ISBN 0-311-72605-4). Casa Bautista.
--Etica de la Vida Cristiana Sus Principios Basicos. Ureta, Floreal, tr. from English. (Span.). 200p. 1981. pap. 6.50 (ISBN 0-311-46076-3). Casa Bautista.
--To Walk As He Walked. LC 85-17173. 1985. pap. 5.95 (ISBN 0-8054-5024-6). Broadman.
--Why Live the Christian Life? LC 79-55292. 1980. pap. 5.95 (ISBN 0-8054-6121-3). Broadman.
Maston, T. B. & Tillman, William A. The Bible & Family Relations. LC 81-67196. 1983. 8.95 (ISBN 0-8054-6124-8). Broadman.
Mather, Cotton. Bonifacius: An Essay Upon the Good. Levin, David, ed. LC 66-14448. pap. 53.80 (2014654). Bks Demand UMI.
--Bonifacius: An Essay...to Do Good. LC 67-18712. 1967. Repr. of 1710 ed. 35.00x (ISBN 0-8201-1032-9). Schol Facsimiles.
Mather, Herbert. Becoming a Giving Church. LC 85-72879. 64p. (Orig.). 1985. pap. 3.50 (ISBN 0-88177-023-X, DR023B). Discipleship Res.
Mathias, Robert. Journey of God's People. 1982. pap. 4.95 (ISBN 0-89536-528-6, 1016). CSS of Ohio.
Mathis, Laura. The Road to Wholeness. 240p. 1986. pap. 6.95 (ISBN 0-8423-5674-6). Tyndale.
Matonti, Charles. Celebrate with Song. LC 81-71237. (Illus.). 144p. (Orig.). 1982. pap. 3.95 (ISBN 0-87793-245-X). Ave Maria.
Matranga, Frances C. One Step at a Time. (Illus.). 1987. pap. 3.95 (ISBN 0-570-03642-9). Concordia.
Matthews, English J. Nature Is Lord. 80p. 1986. 7.95 (ISBN 0-89962-511-8). Todd & Honeywell.
Matthews, R. Arthur. Nascido para a Batalha. Orig. Title: Born for Battle. (Port.). 1986. write for info. (ISBN 0-8297-1606-8). Life Pubs Intl.
Matthews, Robert. The Human Adventure. 1980. pap. 5.95 (ISBN 0-89536-426-3, 0834). CSS of Ohio.
Mattison, Judith. Beginnings: For the Newly Married. LC 79-54114. 96p. 1980. 6.95 (ISBN 0-8066-1753-5, 10-0573). Augsburg.
Mattox, Robert. The Christian Employee. LC 77-20588. 1978. pap. 4.95 (ISBN 0-88270-263-7). Bridge Pub.
Mattson, Lloyd. Build Your Church Through Camping. 48p. (Orig.). 1984. pap. 1.95 (ISBN 0-942684-06-0). Camp Guidepts.
--The Camp Couselor. (Illus.). 192p. 1984. pap. 3.95 (ISBN 0-942684-02-8). Camp Guidepts.
Mauriac, Francois. Souffrances et Bonheur du Chretien. pap. 7.50 (ISBN 0-685-34305-7). French & Eur.
Mauro, Philip. The Last Call to the Godly Remnant. pap. 1.75 (ISBN 0-685-88381-7). Reiner.
--Life in the Word. pap. 1.25 (ISBN 0-87509-101-6). Chr Pubns.
Maves, Paul B. Faith for the Older Years: Making the Most of Life's Second Half. LC 85-13466. 192p. (Orig.). 1986. pap. 9.95 (ISBN 0-8066-2195-8, 10-2181). Augsburg.
Maxwell, C. Mervyn. God Cares, Vol. 1. 1981. pap. 9.95 (ISBN 0-8163-0390-8). Pacific Pr Pub Assn.
Maxwell, Cassandre. Legacy for My Loved Ones. 1984. 12.95 (ISBN 0-317-13919-3). Revell.
Maxwell, Neal A. Notwithstanding My Weakness. LC 81-65352. 129p. 1981. 6.95 (ISBN 0-87747-855-4). Deseret Bk.
--We Talk of Christ, We Rejoice in Christ. LC 84-71873. 180p. 8.95 (ISBN 0-87747-762-0). Deseret Bk.
Maxwell, Patricia. Soldier for Jesus. (Trailblazers Ser.). 1981. pap. 5.95 (ISBN 0-8163-0374-6). Pacific Pr Pub Assn.
May, Gerald. Pilgrimage Home. LC 78-61720. 196p. 1979. pap. 6.95 (ISBN 0-8091-2143-3). Paulist Pr.
--Simply Sane: The Spirituality of Mental Health. (The Crossroad Paperback Ser.). 144p. 1982. pap. 8.95 (ISBN 0-8245-0448-8). Crossroad NY.
Maycock, A. L. Nicholas Ferrar of Little Gidding. LC 80-16684. pap. 63.50 (ISBN 0-8357-9131-9, 2019345). Bks Demand UMI.
Mayhall, Carole. From the Heart of a Woman. LC 76-24066. 108p. 1976. pap. 3.95 (ISBN 0-89109-421-0). NavPress.
--Lord, Teach Me Wisdom. LC 78-78013. 180p. 1979. pap. 5.95 (ISBN 0-89109-432-6). NavPress.
--Words That Hurt, Words That Heal. 112p. Date not set. pap. 3.95 (ISBN 0-89109-178-5). NavPress.
Mayhall, Jack. Discipleship: The Price & the Prize. 156p. 1984. pap. 5.95 (ISBN 0-88207-110-6). Victor Bks.
Mayhue, Richard. Snatched Before the Storm! 1980. pap. 1.00 (ISBN 0-88469-124-1). BMH Bks.
Medeires, Humberto C. Whatever God Wants. 690p. 1984. 6.95 (ISBN 0-8198-8208-9); pap. 5.95 (ISBN 0-8198-8209-7). Dghtrs St Paul.
Megathlin, Earle. Why Doesn't God Do What We Tell Him? 192p. 1984. pap. 10.95 (ISBN 0-8059-2929-0). Dorrance.
Meister, Charles W. The Year of the Lord: A. D. 1844. LC 82-23976. 264p. 1983. lib. bdg. 18.95x (ISBN 0-89950-037-4). McFarland & Co.
Melang, Karen. Jesus: The Servant. (Concept Ser.). (Illus.). 24p. (Orig.). 1986. pap. 3.95 saddlestitched (ISBN 0-570-08532-2, 56-1559). Concordia.
Mellinger, Martha. Little Ones Praise. 1981. 4.35 (ISBN 0-87813-518-9). Christian Light.
Mensendiek, C. William. A Dream Incarnate. (Illus.). 136p. 1987. text ed. 12.95 (ISBN 0-8298-0715-2). Pilgrim NY.
Mensendiek, Mark. Soulwinning: A Way of Life. LC 86-80315. 64p. (Orig.). 1986. pap. 3.50 (ISBN 0-933643-28-4). Grace World Outreach.
Meredith, Don. Becoming One. LC 79-12691. 1979. pap. 5.95 (ISBN 0-8407-5688-7). Nelson.
--Who Says Get Married? How to Be Happy & Single. LC 81-16949. 176p. 1981. pap. 4.95 (ISBN 0-8407-5741-7). Nelson.
Merrill, Dean, ed. Fresh Ideas for Discipleship & Nurture. Shelley, Marshall. (Fresh Ideas Ser.). 190p. 1984. pap. 6.95 (ISBN 0-917463-02-1). Chr Today.
Merrill, Vic. Can You Hear Me God? 96p. 1981. 6.00 (ISBN 0-682-49740-1). Exposition Pr FL.
Merritt, Jeanna. Bread Cast upon the Waters. 25p. (Orig.). 1985. pap. 1.25 (ISBN 0-89265-092-3). Randall Hse.
Messer, Dollas. Operation Discipleship, Level II. 1986. wkbk 12.95 (ISBN 0-317-40165-3). Pathway Pr.
--Operation Discipleship: Being in Christ. 138p. 1984. pap. text ed. 5.95 student manual (ISBN 0-87148-659-8). Pathway Pr.
--Operation Discipleship: Being in Christ. 70p. (Orig.). 1984. pap. text ed. 5.95 tchr's guide (ISBN 0-87148-660-1). Pathway Pr.
Mestinsek, Erma & Mestinsek, Minnie G. Discoveries of the Hidden Things of God. 64p. 1980. 12.50 (ISBN 0-682-49635-9). Exposition Pr FL.
Metcalfe, J. C. Angry Prophet. 1970. pap. 2.25 (ISBN 0-87508-909-7). Chr Lit.
--Bible & the Call of God. 1970. pap. 1.95 (ISBN 0-87508-910-0). Chr Lit.
--Bible & the Spirit Filled Life. 1970. pap. 3.25 (ISBN 0-87508-912-7). Chr Lit.
--Great Deliverance. 1970. pap. 2.25 (ISBN 0-87508-916-X). Chr Lit.
--Great Enemy. 1970. pap. 2.95 (ISBN 0-87508-914-3). Chr Lit.
--Spirit of Calvary. 1970. pap. 3.25 (ISBN 0-87508-921-6). Chr Lit.
--To Be a Christian. 1966. pap. 2.25 (ISBN 0-87508-923-2). Chr Lit.
Meyer, F. B. The Blessed Life. 1979. pap. 0.95 (ISBN 0-87509-052-4). Chr Pubns.
--The Gift of Suffering. LC 79-93432. (Shepherd Illustrated Classics Ser.). (Illus.). 208p. (Orig.). 1980. pap. 5.95 (ISBN 0-87983-211-8). Keats.
--New Testament Men of Faith. LC 79-66338. 1979. pap. 4.95 (ISBN 0-89107-171-7). Good News.
--O Profeta da Esperanca. Orig. Title: The Prophet of Hope. (Port.). 1986. write for info. (ISBN 0-8297-1607-6). Life Pubs Intl.
--Prophet of Hope. 157p. 1983. pap. 3.95 (ISBN 0-317-43398-9). Chr Lit.
--The Secret of Guidance. LC 77-93177. 96p. 1978. pap. 2.95 (ISBN 0-87123-501-3, 200501). Bethany Hse.
--Some Secrets of Christian Living. Allison, Joseph D., ed. 144p. (Orig.). 1985. pap. 4.95 (ISBN 0-310-38721-3, 17076P). Zondervan.
Meyer, Frederick A. Life Is a Trust. (Religious Ser.). 95p. 1986. 8.95 (ISBN 0-935087-09-5). Wright Pub Co.
Miethe, Terry. A Christian's Guide to Faith & Reason. 192p. (Orig.). 1987. pap. 5.95 (ISBN 0-87123-677-X). Bethany Hse.
Milikin. Testing Tongues by the Word. pap. 3.50 (ISBN 0-8054-1918-7). Broadman.
Miller, Barbara & Conn, Charles P. Kathy. (Illus.). 160p. 1981. pap. 2.75 (ISBN 0-8007-8415-4, Spire Bks). Revell.
Miller, C. John. Repentance & Twentieth Century Man. (Orig.). 1980. pap. 2.95 (ISBN 0-87508-334-X). Chr Lit.
Miller, Calvin. Becoming: Yourself in the Making. 1987. 10.95 (ISBN 0-8007-1522-5). Revell.
--A Hunger for Meaning. 2nd ed. LC 83-26490. 180p. 1984. pap. 4.95 (ISBN 0-87784-830-0). Inter-Varsity.
--The Table of Inwardness. LC 84-9134. 132p. (Orig.). 1984. pap. 4.95 (ISBN 0-87784-832-7). Inter-Varsity.
--The Taste of Joy: Recovering the Lost Glow of Discipleship. LC 83-7839. Orig. Title: The Illusive Thing Called Joy. 144p. 1983. pap. 4.95 (ISBN 0-87784-831-9). Inter-Varsity.
Miller, Emmeline S. My Redeemer Lives. 1982. 4.35 (ISBN 0-89536-529-4, 1315). CSS of Ohio.
Miller, Ernest A. Let Your Light So Shine. 218p. (Orig.). 1981. pap. 7.50 (ISBN 0-89216-046-2). Salvation Army.
Miller, Hulda C. The Creche & the Cross. (Illus.). 73p. (Orig.). 1977. pap. 2.00 (ISBN 0-89216-014-4). Salvation Army.
Miller, J. R. The Building of Character. rev. ed. Zodhiates, Joan, ed. 1975. pap. 3.95 (ISBN 0-89957-516-1). AMG Pubs.
--Dying to Live. rev. ed. Zodhiates, Joan, ed. LC 79-51337. Orig. Title: Making the Most of Life. (Illus.). 147p. 1980. pap. 3.95 (ISBN 0-89957-045-3). AMG Pubs.
--Learning to Love. Zodhiates, Joan, ed. Orig. Title: The Lesson of Love. 1977. pap. 3.95 (ISBN 0-89957-521-8). AMG Pubs.
Miller, Judy. Cups Running Over. 1973. cancelled 5.95 (ISBN 0-88027-096-9). Firm Foun Pub.
--Seasons of the Heart. 1984. pap. 5.95 (ISBN 0-89225-272-3). Gospel Advocate.

Miller, Keith. Habitation of Dragons. LC 72-123009. 1983. 6.95 (ISBN 0-8499-2973-3). Word Bks.

Miller, Paul M. Leading the Family of God. LC 81-2267. 215p. 1981. pap. 8.95 (ISBN 0-8361-1950-9). Herald Pr.

Miller, Sheila. Ian & the Gigantic Leafy Obstacle. 1983. pap. 1.50 (ISBN 9971-83-790-0). OMF Bks.

Miller, William A. The Joy of Feeling Good: Eight Keys to a Happy & Abundant Life. LC 86-20574. 192p. (Orig.). (YA) 1986. pap. 4.50 (ISBN 0-8066-2236-9, 10-3601). Augsburg.

--Make Friends with Your Shadow: How to Accept & Use Positively the Negative Side of Your Personality. LC 80-67793. 144p. (Orig.). 1981. pap. 6.95 (ISBN 0-8066-1855-8, 10-4238). Augsburg.

--When Going to Pieces Holds You Together. LC 76-3853. 128p. (Orig.). 1976. pap. 6.95 (ISBN 0-8066-1543-5, 10-7063). Augsburg.

--Why Do Christians Break Down? LC 73-78260. 1973. pap. 6.95 (ISBN 0-8066-1325-4, 10-7140). Augsburg.

Miller, William R. Living As if: How Positive Faith Can Change Your Life. LC 84-13001. 132p. (Orig.). 1985. pap. 7.95 (ISBN 0-664-24635-4). Westminster.

Millheim, John E. Let Rome Speak for Herself. LC 82-16616. 1982. pap. 3.95. Reg Baptist.

Mills, Joann. Making It. 1986. pap. 4.95 (ISBN 0-89137-439-6). Quality Pubns.

Mills, Michael. Dirty Hands, Pure Hearts. 1985. 4.50 (ISBN 0-89536-724-6, 5808). CSS of Ohio.

Milne, Bruce. We Belong Together. LC 78-13882. 1979. pap. 2.95 (ISBN 0-87784-455-0). Inter-Varsity.

Miners, Scott. A Spiritual Approach to Male-Female Relations. LC 83-40326. 220p. (Orig.). 1984. pap. 6.50 (ISBN 0-8356-0583-3, Quest). Theos Pub Hse.

Mitchell, Joan. God's Plan for Us. 1984. 4.95 (ISBN 0-89837-092-2, Pub. by Pflaum Press). Peter Li.

Mitchell, Rod. Bridge Building. 261p. (Orig.). 1981. pap. 21.95 (ISBN 0-85819-357-4, Pub. by JBCE). ANZ Religious Pubns.

Mitchell, Sandi. Why Christians Should Be the Healthiest People in the World. 300p. (Orig.). 1987. pap. 9.95 (ISBN 0-9617419-1-0). But It Really Works Bks.

Mize, Jean. Night of Anguish: Morning of Hope. LC 79-88497. 1979. pap. 2.95 (ISBN 0-87123-398-3, 200398). Bethany Hse.

Moberg, David O. Wholistic Christianity: An Appeal for a Dynamic, Balanced Faith. 228p. 1985. 11.95 (ISBN 0-87178-931-0). Brethren.

Mobley, Mona. Joyful Hospitality. pap. 4.95 (ISBN 0-89137-431-0). Quality Pubns.

Moe, Terry A. Inklings of Grace. 64p. 1981. pap. 3.95 (ISBN 0-8170-0941-8). Judson.

Moffitt, John. The Road to Now. LC 82-4650. 176p. 1982. pap. 7.95 (ISBN 0-8245-0514-X). Crossroad NY.

Mollencott, Virginia R. Godding: Human Responsibility & the Bible. 144p. 1987. 12.95 (ISBN 0-8245-0824-6). Crossroad NY.

Molow, Paul & Molow, Doree. Beyond the Visible: The Triumph Over Yourself...Life & Emotions. 192p. 1981. 10.00 (ISBN 0-682-49739-8). Exposition Pr FL.

Monfalcone, Wesley R. Coping with Abuse in the Family. LC 80-15125. (Christian Care Bks.: Vol. 10). 120p. 1980. pap. 7.95 (ISBN 0-664-24326-6). Westminster.

Monheim, Gabriel. The Bible, Jesus & the Jews. LC 79-89891. 199p. 1980. 12.95 (ISBN 0-8022-2356-7). Philos Lib.

Monk of New Clairvaux. Don't You Belong to Me? LC 79-88985. 180p. 1979. pap. 7.95 (ISBN 0-8091-2217-0). Paulist Pr.

Monson, Thomas S. Be Your Best Self. LC 79-54782. 1979. 7.95 (ISBN 0-87747-787-6). Deseret Bk.

Moody, D. L. The Way to God. 160p. 1983. pap. text ed. 3.50 (ISBN 0-88368-131-5). Whitaker Hse.

Moore, Donald. Improving Your Christian Personality. 61p. 1984. pap. 2.25 (ISBN 0-88144-037-X). Christian Pub.

Moore, George. Radical Love for a Broken World. 175p. (Orig.). 1987. pap. price not set (ISBN 0-89109-139-4). NavPress.

Moore, Joseph. Fastened on God: A Practical Catechtical Program for Teenagers. 88p. (Orig.). 1984. pap. 4.95 (ISBN 0-8091-9566-6). Paulist Pr.

--Monday Morning Jesus. 96p. (Orig.). 1984. pap. 3.95 (ISBN 0-8091-2591-9). Paulist Pr.

Moore, Marvin. When Religion Doesn't Work. Coffen, Richard W., ed. (Better Living Ser.). 32p. (Orig.). 1986. pap. 1.25 (ISBN 0-8280-0314-9). Review & herald.

Moore, Marvin L. Witnesses Through Trial. LC 78-24294. (Orion Ser). 1979. pap. 3.50 (ISBN 0-8127-0216-6). Review & Herald.

Moore, Raymond & Moore, Dorothy. Home-Grown Kids. 253p. 1984. pap. text ed. 7.95 (ISBN 0-8499-3007-3, 3007-3). Word Bks.

Moorehead, Bob. Free at Last. LC 86-71102. 88p. (Orig.). 1986. pap. 3.95 (ISBN 0-89900-212-9). College Pr Pub.

Moormann, Phillip G. The Christian Home Study Handbook 1986. (Illus.). 170p. 1985. pap. 24.95 (ISBN 0-9614323-0-6). G Whitefield Pub.

Moran, Hugh, ed. Words to Live by: Chiara Lubich & Christians from All over the World. Dauphinais, Raymond & Moran, Hugh, trs. from Fr. & Ital. LC 80-82419. 157p. 1980. pap. 4.50 (ISBN 0-911782-08-7). New City.

Moran, Pam. Christian Job Hunter. 224p. (Orig.). 1984. pap. 7.95 (ISBN 0-89283-178-2). Servant.

Morey, Robert. A Christian Handbook for Defending the Faith. 1979. pap. 2.75 (ISBN 0-87552-336-6). Presby & Reformed.

Morgan, Frank, Jr. Keys to Unlock Yourself. LC 84-21418. 1985. pap. 6.95 (ISBN 0-8054-5003-3). Broadman.

Morgan, G. Campbell. Life Problems. (Morgan Library). 1978. pap. 3.95 (ISBN 0-8010-6056-7). Baker Bk.

--Searchlights from the Word. 384p. 1956. 14.95 (ISBN 0-8007-0854-7). Revell.

--The Simple Things of the Christian Life. 1984. pap. 2.25 (ISBN 0-915374-40-4). Rapids Christian.

--The Teaching of Christ. 352p. 1984. 16.95 (ISBN 0-8007-0395-2). Revell.

Morgan, Marabel. The Electric Woman. 224p. 1985. 11.95 (ISBN 0-8499-0497-8, 0497-8). Word Bks.

--The Electric Woman. 1986. 3.95 (ISBN 0-8499-4175-X). Word Bks.

Morgan, Peter. Story Weaving. Lambert, Herbert, ed. LC 86-6079. 128p. (Orig.). 1986. pap. 8.95 (ISBN 0-8272-3423-6). CBP.

Morgan, Trudy J. All My Love, Kate. Woolsey, Raymond H., ed. (Banner Ser.). 96p. (Orig.). 1986. pap. 6.50 (ISBN 0-8280-0318-1). Review & Herald.

Morison, Frank. Quien Movio la Piedra? Ward, Rhode, tr. from Eng. LC 77-11752. Tr. of Who Moved the Stone? (Span.). 206p. 1977. pap. 4.95 (ISBN 0-89922-100-9). Edit Caribe.

Morneau, Robert F. Discovering God's Presence. LC 80-18590. 188p. (Orig.). 1980. pap. 3.95 (ISBN 0-8146-1197-4). Liturgical Pr.

--Trinity Sunday Revisted. LC 79-25097. 96p. 1980. pap. 3.50 (ISBN 0-8146-1084-6). Liturgical Pr.

Morris, Daniel. Beatitude Saints. LC 83-62423. 128p. (Orig.). 1984. pap. 4.95 (ISBN 0-87973-615-1, 615). Our Sunday Visitor.

Morris, George E. Rethinking Congregational Development. LC 84-71366. 144p. (Orig.). 1984. pap. 5.25 (ISBN 0-88177-012-4, DRO12B). Discipleship Res.

Morris, Hazel. My Family. LC 85-24334. (Bible & Me Ser.). (Illus.). 1986. 5.95 (ISBN 0-8054-4164-6). Broadman.

Morris, Henry M. King of Creation. LC 80-80558. 1980. pap. 6.95 (ISBN 0-89051-059-8). Master Bks.

Morrison, Mary. The Journal & the Journey. LC 81-85559. (Pendle Hill Pamphlets Ser.). 32p. (Orig.). 1982. pap. 2.50x (ISBN 0-87574-242-4). Pendle Hill.

Morrison, Mary C. The Way of the Cross. LC 85-60516. 32p. (Orig.). 1985. pap. 2.50x (ISBN 0-87574-260-2). Pendle Hill.

Moses, Sallee. Sallee. 140p. 1985. 5.95 (ISBN 0-89221-120-2). New Leaf.

Moskowitz, Ely. Lord, Make My Days Count. LC 83-2430. 231p. 1983. 14.95 (ISBN 0-8022-2423-7). Philos Lib.

Moss, Michele & Brians, Charlene. Latter Rain. large print ed. 24p. 1984. pap. 5.00 (ISBN 0-914009-03-6). VHI Library.

Mostrom, Donald G. The Dynamics of Intimacy with God. 158p. 1983. pap. 5.95 (ISBN 0-8423-1701-5). Tyndale.

Mother Mary Francis. Walled in Light: St. Colette. 1985. 9.50 (ISBN 0-8199-0889-4). Franciscan Herald.

Moyes, Gordon. Discovering Jesus. (Illus.). 160p. (Orig.). 1984. pap. 9.95 (ISBN 0-86760-005-5, Pub. by Albatross Bks). ANZ Religious Pubns.

Mueller, Charles S. Thank God I Have a Teenager. LC 84-24363. 128p. (Orig.). 1985. pap. 5.95 (ISBN 0-8066-2126-5, 10-6239). Augsburg.

--Words of Faith: A Devotional Dictionary. 160p. (Orig.). 1985. pap. 5.95 (ISBN 0-570-03968-1, 12-3003). Concordia.

Mulder, Alfred E. Happiness Is: An Introduction to Christian Life & Faith. 60p. 1983. pap. 3.25 (ISBN 0-933140-88-6). CRC Pubns.

Mumford, Amy R. It Only Hurts Between Paydays. LC 80-70679. 160p. 1986. pap. 5.95 (ISBN 0-89636-067-9). Accent Bks.

Munger, Robert B. My Heart-Christ's Home. rev. ed. 32p. 1986. pap. 0.75 (ISBN 0-87784-075-X). Inter-Varsity.

Munnik, Len, illus. Nothing to Laugh About. (Illus.). 96p. (Orig.). 1983. pap. 6.95 (ISBN 0-8298-0694-6). Pilgrim NY.

Murdick, Olin J. Achieving Shared Responsibility in the American Church. 14p. 1977. 1.55 (ISBN 0-686-39921-8). Natl Cath Educ.

Murdock, Mike. The Winner's World. (Orig.). 1986. pap. 4.95 (ISBN 0-89274-398-0). Harrison Hse.

Murphey, Cecil. Seven Daily Sins & What to Do about Them. 112p. (Orig.). 1981. pap. 2.95 (ISBN 0-89283-101-4). Servant.

Murphy, Carol. The Examined Life. 1983. pap. 2.50x (ISBN 0-87574-085-5, 085). Pendle Hill.

Murphy, George L. The Trademark of God. 110p. (Orig.). 1986. pap. 6.95 (ISBN 0-8192-1382-9). Morehouse.

Murphy, Joseph. Healing Power of Love. pap. 1.00 (ISBN 0-87516-334-3). De Vorss.

--Love Is Freedom. pap. 1.25 (ISBN 0-87516-337-8). De Vorss.

--Mental Poisons & Their Antidotes. pap. 1.50 (ISBN 0-87516-339-4). De Vorss.

--Within You Is the Power. LC 77-86026. 1978. pap. 6.00 (ISBN 0-87516-247-9). De Vorss.

Murphy-O'Connor, Jerome. What Is Religious Life? A Critical Reappraisal. pap. 4.95 (ISBN 0-89453-074-7). M Glazier.

Murray, Andrew. Abide in Christ. 1968. 4.95 (ISBN 0-87508-371-4); pap. 2.95 (ISBN 0-87508-370-6). Chr Lit.

--Abide in Christ. 1980. pap. 2.95 (ISBN 0-88368-091-2). Whitaker Hse.

--Abide in Christ. (The Christian Library). 1985. Repr. text ed. 6.95 (ISBN 0-916441-10-5). Barbour & Co.

--Absolute Surrender. (Andrew Murray Ser.). pap. 3.50 (ISBN 0-8024-0560-6). Moody.

--Absolute Surrender. 128p. 1981. pap. 3.50 (ISBN 0-88368-093-9). Whitaker Hse.

--The Believer's Absolute Surrender. 150p. 1985. pap. 3.95 (ISBN 0-87123-827-6). Bethany Hse.

--The Believer's Call to Commitment. 110p. 1983. pap. 3.95 (ISBN 0-87123-289-8). Bethany Hse.

--The Believer's Secret of Living Like Christ. 176p. (Orig.). 1985. pap. 3.95 (ISBN 0-87123-445-9). Bethany Hse.

--Believer's Secret of Obedience. LC 82-14603. (Andrew Murray Christian Maturity Library). 88p. 1982. pap. 3.95 (ISBN 0-87123-279-0, 210279). Bethany Hse.

--The Believer's Secret of the Master's Indwelling. rev. ed. 192p. 1986. pap. 3.95 (ISBN 0-87123-653-2, 210653). Bethany Hse.

--Deeper Christian Life. Tucker, Lyman R., ed. 112p. 1986. pap. 5.95 (ISBN 0-310-29791-5, 10365P). Zondervan.

--Like Christ. 240p. 1981. pap. 2.95 (ISBN 0-88368-099-8). Whitaker Hse.

--Living to Please God. 100p. 1985. pap. text ed. 3.50 (ISBN 0-88368-166-8). Whitaker Hse.

--The Master's Indwelling. LC 76-23363. 192p. 1977. pap. 2.95 (ISBN 0-87123-355-X, 200355). Bethany Hse.

--The Ministry of Intercession. 208p. 1982. pap. text ed. 3.50 (ISBN 0-88368-114-5). Whitaker Hse.

--Secret of the Cross. (Secret Ser.). (Orig.). 1980. pap. 1.95 (ISBN 0-87508-389-7). Chr Lit.

--The Spirit of Christ. rev. ed. LC 79-51335. 288p. 1979. pap. 4.95 (ISBN 0-87123-589-7, 210589). Bethany Hse.

--With Christ in the School of Obedience. 108p. 1986. pap. 4.95 (ISBN 0-89693-281-8). Victor Bks.

Murray, Andrew, et al. The Believer's Secret of the Abiding Presence. rev. ed. 144p. 1987. pap. 3.95 (ISBN 0-87123-899-3). Bethany Hse.

Muste, A. J. Saints for This Age. LC 62-21962. (Orig.). 1962. pap. 2.50x (ISBN 0-87574-124-X, 124). Pendle Hill.

Muto, Susan. Approaching the Sacred. 4.95 (ISBN 0-87193-047-1). Dimension Bks.

Muzzy, Ruth & Hughes, R. Kent. The Christian Wedding Planner. 320p. 1984. pap. 9.95 (ISBN 0-8423-0253-0). Tyndale.

Myers, David G. The Inflated Self: Human Illusions & the Bibical Call to Hope. 176p. 1980. 12.95 (ISBN 0-8164-0459-3, HarpR); pap. 5.95 (ISBN 0-8164-2326-1). Har-Row.

Mylander, Charles. Running Red Lights. LC 86-444. 250p. (Orig.). 1986. pap. 6.95 (ISBN 0-8307-1103-1, 5418666). Regal.

Myra, Harold. The New You. 1980. pap. 3.95 (ISBN 0-88207-581-0). Victor Bks.

Nadzo, Stefan C. Take off Your Shoes: A Guide to the Nature of Reality. LC 81-66185. 140p. (Orig.). 1981. pap. 5.95 (ISBN 0-937226-01-7). Eden's Work.

Najarian, Berge. Climbing on Top of Your Troubles. 1984. 6.50 (ISBN 0-8062-2283-2). Carlton.

Nardine, Arlene. In Search of the Yellow Submarine. 222p. 1985. pap. write for info. (ISBN 0-88144-065-5). Christian Pub.

Narramore, Clyde M. La Disciplina en el Hogar. Zorzoli, Ruben O., tr. from Eng. 32p. 1985. Repr. of 1982 ed. 1.50 (ISBN 0-311-46051-8). Casa Bautista.

Nash, Gerald R. Why God Allows Trials & Disappointments. (Uplook Ser.). 31p. 1972. pap. 0.99 (ISBN 0-8163-0082-8, 23618-2). Pacific Pr Pub Assn.

National Association of Catholic Chaplains. Fear Not, I Am with You. 1970. pap. 0.75 (ISBN 0-685-22552-6). Alba.

Natividad, Josephine C. My Oneness with God. 1984. 8.95 (ISBN 0-533-05995-X). Vantage.

Navigators Staff. The Character of the Christian. rev. ed. (Design for Discipleship Ser.: Bk. 4). 49p. 1980. pap. text ed. 1.95 (ISBN 0-934396-19-1). Churches Alive.

--Design for Discipleship, 6 bks. rev. ed. 1980. pap. text ed. 9.35 (ISBN 0-934396-15-9). Churches Alive.

--Foundations for Faith. rev. ed. (Design for Discipleship Ser.: Bk. 5). 1980. pap. text ed. 1.95 (ISBN 0-934396-20-5). Churches Alive.

--Growing in Discipleship. rev. ed. (Design for Discipleship Ser.: Bk. 6). 1980. pap. text ed. 1.95 (ISBN 0-934396-21-3). Churches Alive.

--The Spirit-Filled Christian. rev. ed. (Design for Discipleship Ser.: Bk. 2). 1980. pap. text ed. cancelled (ISBN 0-934396-17-5). Churches Alive.

--Walking with Christ. rev. ed. (Design for Discipleship Ser.: Bk. 3). 1980. pap. text ed. 1.95 (ISBN 0-934396-18-3). Churches Alive.

--Your Life in Christ. rev. ed. (Design for Discipleship Ser.: Bk. 1). 1980. pap. text ed. 1.95 (ISBN 0-934396-16-7). Churches Alive.

Naylor, C. W. Heart Talks. 279p. 1982. pap. 2.50 (ISBN 0-686-36257-8). Faith Pub Hse.

Naylor, Phyllis R. A Triangle Has Four Sides: True-to-Life Stories Show How Teens Deal with Feelings & Problems. LC 83-72123. 128p. (Orig.). (YA) 1984. pap. 3.95 (ISBN 0-8066-2067-6, 10-6700). Augsburg.

Neal, Charles L. Parabolas del Evangelio. 144p. 1983. pap. 2.50 (ISBN 0-311-04338-0). Casa Bautista.

Neale, Robert E. Loneliness, Solitude, & Companionship. LC 83-26065. 132p. (Orig.). 1984. pap. 9.95 (ISBN 0-664-24621-4). Westminster.

Neary, Donal. The Calm Beneath the Storm: Reflections & Prayers for Young People. 80p. 1984. pap. 3.95 (ISBN 0-8294-0470-8). Loyola.

Nee, Watchman. A Balanced Christian Life. Koung, Stephen, tr. 1981. pap. 3.25 (ISBN 0-686-95516-1). Christian Fellow Pubs.

--The Better Covenant. Kaung, Stephen, tr. 1982. 4.75 (ISBN 0-935008-56-X); pap. 3.75 (ISBN 0-935008-55-1). Christian Fellow Pubs.

--Come, Lord Jesus. Kaung, Stephen, tr. 1976. 5.50 (ISBN 0-935008-15-2); pap. 4.25 (ISBN 0-935008-16-0). Christian Fellow Pubs.

--Full of Grace & Truth, Vol. I. Kaung, Stephen, tr. 1980. pap. 3.25 (ISBN 0-935008-49-7). Christian Fellow Pubs.

--The Life that Wins. Fader, Herbert L., ed. Kaung, Stephen, tr. from Chinese. & intro. by. 157p. (Orig.). 1986. 9.00 (ISBN 0-935008-65-9); pap. 4.00 (ISBN 0-935008-66-7). Christian Fellow Pubs.

--Normal Christian Life. 1961-1963. pap. 4.50 (ISBN 0-87508-414-1). Chr Lit.

--The Normal Christian Life. 1977. pap. 4.95 (ISBN 0-8423-4710-0). Tyndale.

--Normal Christian Life Study Guide. Foster, ed. 1978. pap. 2.25 (ISBN 0-87508-418-4). Chr Lit.

--Practical Issues of This Life. Kaung, Stephen, tr. 1975. pap. 3.25 (ISBN 0-935008-29-2). Christian Fellow Pubs.

--Sit, Walk, Stand. 1964. pap. 2.50 (ISBN 0-87508-419-2). Chr Lit.

--The Spirit of the Gospel. Fader, Herbert L., ed. Kaung, Stephen, tr. from Chinese. 100p. (Orig.). 1986. pap. 3.50 (ISBN 0-935008-67-5). Christian Fellow Pubs.

--Spiritual Man. Kaung, Stephen, tr. 1968. 12.50 (ISBN 0-935008-38-1); pap. 7.50 (ISBN 0-935008-39-X). Christian Fellow Pubs.

--Testimony of God. Kaung, Stephen, tr. 1979. pap. 2.75 (ISBN 0-935008-44-6). Christian Fellow Pubs.

--What Shall This Man Do. 1965. pap. 2.95 (ISBN 0-87508-427-3). Chr Lit.

--What Shall This Man Do? 1978. pap. 4.50 (ISBN 0-8423-7910-X). Tyndale.

--Whom Shall I Send? Kaung, Stephen, tr. 1979. pap. 2.25 (ISBN 0-935008-45-4). Christian Fellow Pubs.

Needham, David C. Birthright! Christian, Do You Know Who You Are? LC 79-90682. (Critical Concern Bks.). 293p. 1982. 10.95 (ISBN 0-930014-29-4); pap. 6.95 (ISBN 0-930014-75-8). Multnomah.

Needleman, Jacob & Baker, George, eds. Understanding the New Religions. 1978. (HarpR); pap. 8.95 (ISBN 0-8164-2188-9). Har-Row.

Neff, Pauline. Tough Love: How Parents Can Deal with Drug Abuse. 160p. 1984. pap. 7.50 (ISBN 0-687-42407-0). Abingdon.

Neighbour, Ralph W., Sr. The Searching Heart. 1986. pap. 5.95 (ISBN 0-937931-05-5). Global TN.
--The Shining Light. 1986. pap. 5.95 (ISBN 0-937931-03-9). Global TN.
--Thine Enemy. 1986. pap. 5.95 (ISBN 0-937931-06-3). Global TN.
Nelson, Gertrud M. To Dance with God: Family Ritual & Community Celebration. 176p. 1986. pap. 9.95 (ISBN 0-8091-2812-8). Paulist Pr.
Nelson, James A. How to Enjoy Living. LC 82-70774. 160p. (Orig.). 1982. pap. 4.95 (ISBN 0-89636-087-3). Accent Bks.
Nelson, Stanley A., compiled by. A Journey in Becoming. (Orig.). 1983. pap. 4.95 (ISBN 0-8054-6320-8). Broadman.
Nelson, Steven M. & Starkey, Frank L. Becoming One Flesh. 1979. pap. 2.95 (ISBN 0-89536-354-2, 0229). CSS of Ohio.
Nelson, Thomas. What Christians Believe about the Bible. 183p. 1985. pap. 7.95 (ISBN 0-317-43242-7). Ideals.
Nemeck, Francis K. & Coombs, Marie T. The Way of Spiritual Direction. 1985. pap. 8.95 (ISBN 0-89453-447-5). M Glazier.
Nerney, Catherine. Enrollment in the School of Discipleship. 1.50 (ISBN 0-8091-9331-0). Paulist Pr.
Neville. The Law & the Promise. 156p. 1984. pap. 5.50 (ISBN 0-87516-532-X). De Vorss.
New Harmonia Sacra. 1980. legacy edition 10.00x (ISBN 0-686-91950-5). Park View.
New Life thru Christ. 1981. pap. 0.95 (ISBN 0-89221-055-9). New Leaf.
Newhouse, Flower A. Here Are Your Answers, Vol. III. Boult, Pamela, ed. 222p. 1983. 11.00 (ISBN 0-910378-18-5). Christward.
--Songs of Deliverance. LC 72-94582. 250p. 1972. 9.50 (ISBN 0-910378-08-8). Christward.
Newman, John H. Blessed Art Thou among Women. 1985. 4.95 (ISBN 0-87193-076-5). Dimension Bks.
NFCLC. To Simplify Our Life. 150p. 1982. wkbk. & cassette 10.00x (ISBN 0-913605-04-2). NFCLC.
Nicholas, Charles, illus. God Is My Co-Pilot. LC 78-50959. (Contemporary Motivators Ser.). (Illus.). 1978. pap. text ed. 1.95 (ISBN 0-88301-302-9). Pendulum Pr.
Nichols, Roy. The Greening of the Gospel. 1985. 6.25 (ISBN 0-89536-745-9, 5851). CSS of Ohio.
Nielson, John B. The Towel & the Cross. 118p. (Orig.). 1983. pap. 3.95 (ISBN 0-8341-0847-X). Beacon Hill.
Nielson, Joseph F. You Can Be a Better Parent. (Christian Counseling Aids Ser.). 1977. pap. 0.95 (ISBN 0-8010-6691-3). Baker Bk.
Nieman, Charles. The Life of Excellence. 32p. (Orig.). 1985. wkbk. 4.95 (ISBN 0-914307-37-1). Word Faith.
Niklas, Gerald R. The Making of a Pastoral Person. 159p. (Orig.). 1981. pap. 6.95 (ISBN 0-8189-0409-7). Alba.
Niklaus, Robert, et al, eds. All for Jesus. LC 86-72007. (Illus.). 322p. 1986. 11.95 (ISBN 0-87509-383-3). Chr Pubns.
Nimeth, Albert J. Of Course I Love You. 1973. 5.00 (ISBN 0-8199-0466-X). Franciscan Herald.
--To Listen Is to Heal. 1984. 5.00 (ISBN 0-317-46887-1). Franciscan Herald.
No Greater Love. (Encounter Ser.). 1979. 3.00 (ISBN 0-8198-0588-2); pap. 2.00 (ISBN 0-8198-0589-0). Dghtrs St Paul.
Noble, Ruth A. Wow! God Made Me. 1981. 5.75 (ISBN 0-89536-479-4, 2330). CSS of Ohio.
Nordtvedt, Matilda. Living Beyond Depression. LC 78-58082. 128p. 1978. pap. 3.50 (ISBN 0-87123-339-8, 200339). Bethany Hse.
Norheim, Karen. Mrs. Preacher. 160p. (Orig.). 1985. pap. 3.95 (ISBN 0-89900-204-8). College Pr Pub.
Norick, Sylvester. Outdoor Life in the Menominee Forest. 1979. 7.95 (ISBN 0-8199-0767-7). Franciscan Herald.
Norman, Dwayne, ed. Your Beginning with God. 31p. 1982. pap. 1.95 (ISBN 0-88144-063-9). Christian Pub.
Norman, Louise. God's Power Versus Satan's Power: Christian Life Lessons. (Teaching Bks.). (Illus.). 64p. (Orig.). 1985. pap. text ed. 8.95 (ISBN 0-86508-062-3). BCM Intl Inc.
North, Gary. Backward, Christian Soldiers? 294p. 1984. pap. 4.95 (ISBN 0-930464-01-X). Dominion Pr.
--Honest Money. (The Biblical Blueprint Ser.). Date not set. pap. 6.95 (ISBN 0-8407-3094-2). Nelson.
Noser, A. A. Living with God in My Heart. 1980. 2.50 (ISBN 0-8198-4406-3); pap. 1.50 (ISBN 0-8198-4404-7). Dghtrs St Paul.
Notaro, Thom. Van Til & the Use of Evidence. 1980. pap. 4.50 (ISBN 0-87552-353-6). Presby & Reformed.
Nouwen, Henri J. Clowning in Rome: Reflections on Solitude, Celibacy, Prayer & Contemplation. LC 78-22423. (Illus.). 1979. pap. 4.95 (ISBN 0-385-15129-2, Im). Doubleday.
--Lifesigns: Intimacy, Fecundity, Ecstasy in Christian Perspective. LC 86-4572. (Illus.). 128p. 1986. pap. 11.95 (ISBN 0-385-23627-1). Doubleday.
--Reaching Out: The Three Movements of the Spiritual Life. LC 86-2901. (Illus.). 168p. 1986. pap. 5.95 (ISBN 0-385-23682-4, Im). Doubleday.
Nowlan, Connie W. A Man Who Wouldn't Listen. (Trailblazer Ser.). 1982. pap. 5.95 (ISBN 0-8163-0441-6). Pacific Pr Pub Assn.
Nutt, Grady. Being Me. LC 71-145984. 1971. pap. 3.95 (ISBN 0-8054-6909-5, 4269-09). Broadman.
Nuttall, Geoffrey F. Studies in Christian Enthusiasm. 1983. pap. 2.50x (ISBN 0-87574-041-3, 041). Pendle Hill.
--To the Refreshing of the Children of Light. 1983. pap. 2.50x (ISBN 0-87574-101-0, 101). Pendle Hill.
Nystrom, Carolyn. At the Starting Line: Beginning a New Life. (Young Fisherman Bible Studyguides). 48p. 1985. pap. 2.95 student (ISBN 0-87788-053-0); pap. text ed. 4.95 Tchr's. (ISBN 0-87788-054-9). Shaw Pubs.
--Lord, I Want to Have a Quiet Time: Learning to Study the Bible for Yourself. 156p. 1984. pap. 6.95 (ISBN 0-87788-516-8). Shaw Pubs.
--What Is a Christian? (Children's Bible Basics Ser.). 32p. 1981. 4.95 (ISBN 0-8024-5997-8). Moody.
Oates, Wayne E. Convictions That Give You Confidence. LC 84-5193. (Potentials: Guides for Productive Living Ser.: Vol. 10). 110p. 1984. pap. 7.95 (ISBN 0-664-24529-3). Westminster.
O'Brien, George D. God & the New Haven Railway. LC 86-47554. 144p. 1986. 14.95 (ISBN 0-8070-1010-3). Beacon Pr.
O'Collins, Gerald. The Second Journey. LC 77-99303. 96p. 1978. pap. 3.95 (ISBN 0-8091-2209-X). Paulist Pr.
O'Connor, Francine M. & Boswell, Kathryn. The ABC's of Faith, 2 bks. 1979. Bk. 1. pap. 1.95 (ISBN 0-89243-113-X); Bk. 2. pap. 1.95 (ISBN 0-89243-114-8). Liguori Pubns.
Oden, Thomas C. The Living God. 1986. 29.45 (ISBN 0-317-52383-X, HarpR). Har-Row.
Odhner, Hugo L. The Moral Life. 142p. 1985. Repr. of 1957 ed. write for info. (ISBN 0-910557-08-X). Acad New Church.
O'Donoghue, Noel D. Heaven in Ordinarie. 1979. 14.95 (ISBN 0-87243-085-5). Templegate.
Odor, Harold & Odor, Ruth. Becoming a Christian. (Illus.). 16p. 1985. 0.75 (ISBN 0-87239-901-X, 3301). Standard Pub.
Ogilvie, Lloyd J. Ask Him Anything. (QP Proven-Word Ser.). 244p. 1984. pap. 7.95 (ISBN 0-8499-2982-2). Word Bks.
--Discovering God's Will in Your Life. (Orig.). 1985. pap. 4.95 (ISBN 0-89081-468-6). Harvest Hse.
--L' Ecole des Psaumes. Cosson, Annie L., ed. Rousseau, Marie-Andre, tr. Tr. of Falling into Greatness. (Fr.). 208p. 1985. pap. 3.50 (ISBN 0-8297-0700-X). Life Pubs Intl.
--Radiance of the Inner Splendor. LC 80-51524. 144p. 1980. pap. text ed. 4.95x (ISBN 0-8358-0405-4). Upper Room.
Ogilvie, Lloyd John. Freedom In the Spirit. LC 83-82318. 192p. 1984. pap. 4.95 (ISBN 0-89081-444-9). Harvest Hse.
Ogletree, Thomas W. Hospitality to The Stranger: Dimension of Moral Understanding. LC 84-18763. 176p. 1985. pap. 10.95 (ISBN 0-8006-1839-4, 1-1839). Fortress.
O'Halloran, James. Living Cells: Developing Small Christian Community. LC 83-22076. 132p. (Orig.). 1984. pap. 4.95 (ISBN 0-88344-288-4). Orbis Bks.
Oke, Janette. Love's Abiding Joy. LC 83-15503. 224p. (Orig.). 1983. pap. 4.95 (ISBN 0-87123-401-7, 210401). Bethany Hse.
--Love's Unending Legacy. 224p. (Orig.). 1984. pap. 4.95 (ISBN 0-87123-616-8, 210616). Bethany Hse.
Olbricht, Thomas. The Power to Be. LC 79-67136. (Journey Bks.). 1979. pap. 3.50 (ISBN 0-8344-0108-8). Sweet.
Oldham, Glenna. For He Delights in Me. 1982. gift, padded cover 9.95 (ISBN 0-87162-260-2, D1017). Warner Pr.
Olford, A. Stephen. A Graca de Dar. Orig. Title: The Grace of Giving. (Port.). 1986. write for info. (ISBN 0-8297-1602-5). Life Pubs Intl.
Olford, Stephen. The Grace of Giving. 1986. write for info. (ISBN 0-8297-1263-1). Life Pubs Intl.
Olford, Stephen O. The Secret of Soul-Winning. 1978. pap. 5.95 (ISBN 0-8024-7684-8). Moody.
Olgilvie, Lloyd J. Lloyd John Ogilvie Anthology. 1987. 10.95 (ISBN 0-8307-1189-9, 5419003). Regal.
Oliver, Lucille. Cry for the World. 1981. pap. 3.00 (ISBN 0-8309-0307-0). Herald Hse.
Olson, Chet, ed. Jesus Two: The Life & Wisdom of Jesus. 216p. 1982. 8.95 (ISBN 0-940298-04-X); pap. 5.95 (ISBN 0-940298-03-1). Spiritwarrior Pub.
Olson, Natanael. Como Ganar a Tu Familia Para Cristo. Villarello, Ildefonso, tr. from Eng. 182p. 1983. pap. 1.50 (ISBN 0-311-13801-2). Casa Bautista.
Olson, Richard P. Changing Male Roles in Today's World: A Christian Perspective for Men - & the Women Who Care about Them. 160p. 1982. pap. 5.95 (ISBN 0-8170-0946-9). Judson.
O'Malley, William J. Meeting the Living God. 2nd, rev. ed. 1983. pap. 5.95 (ISBN 0-8091-9565-8). Paulist Pr.
Omartian, Stormie. Greater Health God's Way. 208p. 1984. pap. 5.95 (ISBN 0-917143-00-0). Sparrow Pr CA.
Once upon a Summer. 1987. 5.95 (210413). Bethany Hse.
Oostdyk, Harv. Step One: The Gospel & the Ghetto. 342p. 1983. pap. 8.95 (ISBN 0-89221-094-X). New Leaf.
Oosterhuis, Huub. Times of Life: Prayers & Poems. Smith, N. D., tr. from Dutch. LC 79-89653. 128p. (Orig.). 1980. pap. 4.95 (ISBN 0-8091-2245-6). Paulist Pr.
O'Rourke, Edward. Living Like a King. 1979. 3.95 (ISBN 0-87243-087-1). Templegate.
Orr, C. E. Helps to Holy Living. 64p. pap. 0.40 (ISBN 0-686-29112-3); pap. 1.00 3 copies (ISBN 0-686-29113-1). Faith Pub Hse.
--How to Live a Holy Life. 112p. pap. 0.75 (ISBN 0-686-29120-4). Faith Pub Hse.
Orser, Evelyn. On My Back, Looking Up! Coffen, Richard W., ed. LC 83-13882. (A Banner Bk.). (Illus.). 94p. (Orig.). 1984. pap. 5.95 (ISBN 0-8280-0218-5). Review & Herald.
Ortegel, Adelaide. Banners & Such. LC 86-62616. 1986. pap. 9.95 (ISBN 0-89390-016-8). Resource Pubns.
Orthodox Eastern Church. Service to a Fool for Christ Sake. pap. 0.75 (ISBN 0-686-05663-9). Eastern Orthodox.
Ortiz, Juan C. Cry of the Human Heart. LC 76-24099. 1977. pap. 4.95 (ISBN 0-88419-010-2). Creation Hse.
--The Disciple. LC 74-29650. 144p. 1975. pap. 4.95 (ISBN 0-88419-145-1). Creation Hse.
--Living with Jesus Today. 1982. 4.95 (ISBN 0-88419-187-7). Creation Hse.
Ortiz, Juan Carlos. Jesus en Nuestras Vidas - Hoy. Araujo, Juan S., tr. from Eng. Tr. of Living with Jesus Today. (Span.). 160p. 1987. pap. 4.25 (ISBN 0-88113-157-1). Edit Betania.
Ortiz, Juan Carlos & Buckingham, Jamie. Call to Discipleship. LC 75-7476. 1975. pap. 4.95 (ISBN 0-88270-122-3). Bridge Pub.
Ortland, Anne. Disciplines of the Beautiful Woman. Gift ed. 131p. 1986. Repr. 9.95 (ISBN 0-8499-0551-6). Word Bks.
--Disciplines of the Heart. 1987. 12.95. Word Bks.
Ortlund, Anne. The Acts of Joanna. 160p. 1982. 7.95 (ISBN 0-8499-0283-5). Word Bks.
Ortlund, Raymond & Ortlund, Anne. The Best Half of Life. LC 76-21582. 1976. pap. 3.25 (ISBN 0-8307-0443-4, 5404193). Regal.
Ortlund, Raymond C. Be a New Christian All Your Life. 192p. 1983. 5.95 (ISBN 0-8007-5119-1, Power Bks). Revell.
Osborn, T. L. How to Be Born Again. 160p. pap. 2.95 (ISBN 0-89274-224-0, HH-224). Harrison Hse.
--How to Enjoy Plenty. pap. 2.95 (ISBN 0-89274-222-4, HH-222). Harrison Hse.
--Soulwinning: Out Where the People Are. rev. ed. (Illus.). 218p. (Orig.). 1982. pap. 3.95 (ISBN 0-317-44699-1). Harrison Hse.
Osborne, Cecil G. Amate Siquiera un Poco. Orozco, Julio, tr. from Eng. LC 78-57808. Tr. of The Art of Learning to Love Yourself. (Span.). 182p. 1978. pap. 4.95 (ISBN 0-89922-120-3). Edit Caribe.
--The Art of Getting Along With People. 192p. 1982. pap. 3.95 (ISBN 0-310-30612-4, 10477P). Zondervan.
--The Art of Understanding Yourself. 1986. pap. 4.95 (ISBN 0-310-30592-6, 10472P). Zondervan.
--You're in Charge. pap. write for info (ISBN 0-515-09688-1). Jove Pubns.
O'Shea, Kevin. The Way of Tenderness. LC 78-61728. (Orig.). 1978. pap. 2.95 (ISBN 0-8091-2166-2). Paulist Pr.
Ostrom, William. In God We Live. (Orig.). 1986. pap. 2.50 (ISBN 0-87574-267-X). Pendle Hill.
Our Christian Wedding Guest Book. (Illus.). 48p. 1983. padded cover 8.50 (ISBN 0-8007-1345-1). Revell.
Ouweneel, W. J. What Is Election? pap. 2.25 (ISBN 0-88172-162-X). Believers Bkshelf.
Overton, Basil. Mule Musings. 6.95 (ISBN 0-89137-105-2); pap. 4.25. Quality Pubns.
Owen, Pat H. The Genesis Principle for Parents. 224p. 1985. pap. 6.95 (ISBN 0-8423-0996-9). Tyndale.
Owens, Bill. Health & Healing: God's Way. (Illus.). 124p. (Orig.). Date not set. pap. 5.00 (ISBN 0-936801-01-8). Christ Serv Ctrs.
Packer, J. I. I Want to Be a Christian. 1977. pap. 8.95 (ISBN 0-8423-1842-9). Tyndale.
--Knowing Man. LC 79-52495. 1979. pap. 3.95 (ISBN 0-89107-175-X, Crossway Bks). Good News.
Paddock, Charles L. Going up. LC 53-107000078. (Dest Ser.). 1984. pap. 5.95 (ISBN 0-317-28316-2). Pacific Pr Pub Assn.
Paffard, Michael. The Unattended Moment: Excerpts from Autobiographies with Hints & Guesses. LC 76-368148. 1976. pap. text ed. 3.95x (ISBN 0-8401-1803-1). A R Allenson.
Page, Carole. Carrie: Heartsong Books. 160p. (Orig.). 1984. pap. 2.95 (ISBN 0-87123-441-6). Bethany Hse.
Page, Carole G. Neeley Never Said Good-By. (Sensitive Issues Ser.). (Orig.). 1984. pap. 3.50 (ISBN 0-8024-0342-5). Moody.
Palandro, Michael & Lestarjette, Steve. The Essentials of Christian Relationship. 56p. 1987. pap. text ed. 2.95 (ISBN 0-939079-00-3). Christlife Pubs.
Palau, Luis. Time to Stop Pretending. 156p. 1985. pap. 5.95 (ISBN 0-89693-332-6). Victor Bks.
Palmer, Parker J. The Promise of Paradox. LC 80-68134. 128p. (Orig.). 1980. pap. 3.95 (ISBN 0-87793-210-7). Ave Maria.
Palmer, Phoebe. The Promise of the Father. Dayton, Donald W., ed. (The Higher Christian Life Ser.). 421p. 1985. 50.00 (ISBN 0-8240-6434-8). Garland Pub.
Palms, Roger C. God Guides Your Tomorrows. Rev. ed. LC 86-27688. 96p. 1987. pap. 2.95 (ISBN 0-87784-572-7). Inter Varsity.
Palotta, Joseph L. That Your Joy Might Be Full. 247p. 1981. pap. 6.95 (ISBN 0-9604852-1-X). Revelation Hse.
--True Riches. 319p. (Orig.). 1985. pap. 8.95 (ISBN 0-9604852-2-8). Revelation Hse.
Panos, Chris. Double Agent. 1986. pap. 6.95 (ISBN 0-910311-43-9). Huntington Hse Inc.
Paoli, Arturo. Gather Together in My Name: Reflections on Christianity & Community. Barr, Robert R., tr. LC 86-23806. 144p. (Orig.). 1987. pap. 9.95 (ISBN 0-88344-357-0). Orbis Bks.
Paradise, Valdemar. Preserving One's Own Life. 160p. 1986. 9.95 (ISBN 0-8059-3035-3). Dorrance.
Parent, Neil A., ed. Christian Adulthood. 125p. 1985. pap. 6.95 (ISBN 1-55586-921-1). US Catholic.
--Christian Adulthood 1982. 130p. 1982. pap. 5.95 (ISBN 1-55586-827-4). US Catholic.
--Christian Adulthood 1983. 68p. 1983. pap. 4.95 (ISBN 1-55586-862-2). US Catholic.
--Christian Adulthood 1985-1986. 124p. 1985. pap. 8.95 (ISBN 1-55586-965-3). US Catholic.
Parker, Helen. Light on a Dark Trail. LC 82-71560. 1982. pap. 4.95 (ISBN 0-8054-5430-6). Broadman.
Parker, Margaret. Autobiography of God: Leader's Guide. (Study & Grow Electives). 64p. 1985. pap. 3.95 (ISBN 0-8307-1030-2, 6102058). Regal.
--When You Feel Like a Failure. (Study & Grow Electives). 64p. 1985. pap. 3.95 leader's guide (ISBN 0-8307-1036-1, 6102073). Regal.
Parlette, Ralph. The University of Hard Knocks. 1966. gift ed. 6.95 (ISBN 0-915720-05-1). Brownlow Pub Co.
Parsley, Rod. The Someday Syndrome. 37p. 1986. pap. 2.95 (ISBN 0-88144-069-8). Christian Pub.
Parvey, Constance F., ed. The Community of Women & Men in the Church. LC 82-71831. 288p. (Orig.). 1982. pap. 14.95 (ISBN 0-8006-1644-8, 1-1644). Fortress.
Pass, Gail. Zoe's Book. 224p. 1987. pap. 7.95 (ISBN 0-930044-95-9). Naiad Pr.
Pate, Don. He Shall Be Like a Tree. (Horizon Ser.). 128p. 1981. pap. 5.95 (ISBN 0-8127-0315-4). Review & Herald.
The Patience of God. 4.50 (ISBN 0-8198-5821-8); 3.50 (ISBN 0-8198-5821-8). Dghtrs St Paul.
Patricia & Gyan, Gopi. Oneness, Vol. II. (Orig.). 1980. spiral bdg. 7.95 (ISBN 0-935146-24-5). Morningland.
Patricia, Sri & Gyan, Gopi. Oneness, Vol. I. 1979. pap. 3.95 (ISBN 0-935146-11-3). Morningland.
Patrick, Mary. The Love Commandment: How to Find Its Meaning for Today. Lambert, Herbert, ed. LC 84-7083. 112p. 1984. pap. 6.95 (ISBN 0-8272-2118-5). CBP.
Patzer, Jere. Bored Again Christian. (Quest Ser.). 16p. 1983. pap. 1.25 (ISBN 0-8163-0521-8). Pacific Pr Pub Assn.
Paulsell, William & Kelty, Matthew. Letters from a Hermit. 1978. 7.95 (ISBN 0-87243-086-3). Templegate.
Paulsen, Norman D. Christ Consciousness. 2nd, rev. ed. LC 84-72066. (Illus.). 496p. (Orig.). 1985. 16.95 (ISBN 0-941848-03-5); pap. 10.95 (ISBN 0-941848-04-3). Builders Pub.
Paulson, J. Sig. Here's a Thought. 67p. 1982. pap. 2.00 (ISBN 0-317-20869-1). CSA Pr.

--How to Love Your Neighbor. 184p. 1974. pap. 4.95 (ISBN 0-317-20873-X). CSA Pr.
--Living with Purpose. 142p. 1968. pap. 3.95 (ISBN 0-317-20871-3). CSA Pr.
--The Thirteen Commandments. 154p. 1964. pap. 3.95 (ISBN 0-317-20872-1). CSA Pr.
--Your Power Tube. 166p. 1969. pap. 3.95 (ISBN 0-317-20870-5). CSA Pr.
Pawelzik, Fritz. I Sing Your Praise All the Day Long. (Illus., Orig.). 1967. pap. 1.50 (ISBN 0-377-37221-8). Friend Pr.
Paxson, Ruth. Como Vivir en el Plano Superior. Orig. Title: Life on the Highest Plane. (Span.). 254p. 1984. pap. 4.95 (ISBN 0-8254-1551-9). Kregel.
--Rios De Agua Viva. 96p. 1983. pap. 1.95 (ISBN 0-311-46065-8). Casa Bautista.
Peace, Richard. Pilgrimage: A Workbook on Christian Growth. 1985. pap. 6.95 (ISBN 0-8010-7087-2). Baker Bk.
Peale, John S. Biblical History As the Quest for Maturity. LC 85-5067. (Symposium Ser.: Vol. 15). 120p. 1985. 39.95x (ISBN 0-88946-706-4). E Mellen.
Peale, Norman V. Amazing Results of Positive Thinking. 1982. pap. 2.75 (ISBN 0-449-20304-2, Crest). Fawcett.
--A Guide to Confident Living. 1977. pap. 2.25 (ISBN 0-449-24173-4, Crest). Fawcett.
--Norman Vincent Peale's Treasury of Joy & Enthusiasm. 192p. 1982. pap. 2.50 (ISBN 0-8007-8450-2). Revell.
--The Positive Power of Jesus Christ. 1980. pap. 6.95 1981o. p. (ISBN 0-8423-4875-1); pap. 3.95 (ISBN 0-8423-4914-6). Tyndale.
--Power of the Plus Factor. 1987. 14.95 (ISBN 0-8007-1526-8). Revell.
Peck, M. Scott, et al. What Return Can I Make? The Dimensions of the Christian Experience. LC 85-11945. 96p. 1985. 24.95 (ISBN 0-317-38030-3). S&S.
Pegram, Don R. America: Christian or Pagan. 1982. pap. 1.25 (ISBN 0-89265-082-6). Randall Hse.
--Sheep among Wolves. 1982. pap. 1.25 (ISBN 0-89265-084-2). Randall Hse.
Pegues, Etta B. The Abundant Life. 1971. pap. 2.75 (ISBN 0-88027-081-0). Firm Foun Pub.
Peile, James H. The Reproach of the Gospel: An Inquiry into the Apparent Failure of Christianity As a General Rule of Life & Conduct. 1977. lib. bdg. 59.95 (ISBN 0-8490-2516-8). Gordon Pr.
Pelikan, Jaroslav. The Christian Tradition: A History of the Development of Doctrine, Vol. 3, The Growth of Medieval Theology, 600-1300. LC 78-1501. xxviii, 336p. 1980. pap. 12.95 (ISBN 0-226-65375-7, P896). U of Chicago Pr.
Pellegrino, Cardinal Michael. Give What You Command. flexible bdg 3.00 (ISBN 0-89942-580-1, 580/04). Catholic Bk Pub.
Pemberton, Larry. Called to Care. (Orig.). 1985. pap. text ed. 4.95 (ISBN 0-87148-183-9). Pathway Pr.
Pendleton, Winston K. Do It! Six Steps to Happiness. Lambert, Herbert, ed. LC 86-6112. 96p. (Orig.). 1986. pap. 5.95 (ISBN 0-8272-0613-5). CBP.
Penn, William & Brinton, Anna. No Cross No Crown. 1983. pap. text ed. 2.50x (ISBN 0-87574-030-8, 030). Pendle Hill.
Pennington, M. B. The Manual of Life: The New Testament for Daily Living. 128p. (Orig.). 1985. pap. 4.95 (ISBN 0-8091-2710-5). Paulist Pr.
Penn-Lewis, Jessie. All Things New. 1962. pap. 2.95 (ISBN 0-87508-990-9). Chr Lit.
--Awakening in Wales. 1962. pap. 3.95 (ISBN 0-87508-991-7). Chr Lit.
--Climax of the Risen Life. 1962. pap. 2.95 (ISBN 0-87508-992-5). Chr Lit.
--Communion with God. 1962. pap. 2.95 (ISBN 0-87508-993-3). Chr Lit.
--Cross: Touchstone of Faith. 1962. pap. 2.95 (ISBN 0-87508-994-1). Chr Lit.
--Dying to Live. 1962. pap. 2.25 (ISBN 0-87508-995-X). Chr Lit.
--Life in the Spirit. 1962. pap. 3.95 (ISBN 0-87508-948-8). Chr Lit.
--Opened Heavens. 1962. pap. 2.95 (ISBN 0-87508-996-8). Chr Lit.
--Spiritual Warfare. 1962. pap. 2.95 (ISBN 0-87508-997-6). Chr Lit.
--Thy Hidden Ones. 1962. pap. 4.50 (ISBN 0-87508-998-4). Chr Lit.
--Warfare with Satan. 1962. pap. 4.15 (ISBN 0-87508-999-2). Chr Lit.
Pentecost, J. Dwight. Design for Discipleship. 1977. pap. 4.95 (ISBN 0-310-30861-5, 17011P). Zondervan.
--God's Answers to Man's Problems. (Moody Press Electives Ser.). (Orig.). 1985. pap. text ed. 3.95 (ISBN 0-8024-0702-1); leader's guide 2.50 (ISBN 0-8024-0703-X). Moody.
--Things Which Become Sound Doctrine. 1970. Repr. 5.95 (ISBN 0-310-30901-8, 6504P). Zondervan.
Pepper, Clayton, ed. First Steps in Faith. pap. 2.25 (ISBN 0-89137-206-7). Quality Pubns.
--Introduction to Soul Winning. pap. 2.25 (ISBN 0-89137-204-0). Quality Pubns.
Peppler, Alice S. Single Again--This Time with Children: A Christian Guide for the Single Parent. LC 81-52278. 128p. (Orig.). 1982. pap. 6.95 (ISBN 0-8066-1910-4, 10-5802). Augsburg.
Perersen, William J. C. S. Lewis Had a Wife. 160p. (Orig.). 1985. pap. 2.95 (ISBN 0-8423-0202-6). Tyndale.
Perino, Renato. Call to Holiness: New Frontiers in Spirituality for Today's Religious. LC 85-28621. 160p. (Orig.). 1986. pap. 7.95 (ISBN 0-8189-0475-5). ALBA.
Perkins, John. With Justice for All. LC 80-50262. 216p. 1982. text ed. 10.95 (ISBN 0-8307-0754-9, 5108802); pap. 5.95 (ISBN 0-8307-0934-7, 5418181). Regal.
Perkins, John M. Let Justice Roll Down. LC 74-30172. 224p. 1976. pap. 5.95 (ISBN 0-8307-0345-4, 5404002). Regal.
Perner, Bernard & Perner, Majorie. Mount to the Sky Like Eagles, Vol. 9. (Heritage Ser.). 1986. 10.95 (ISBN 0-911802-64-9). Free Church Pubns.
Perry, Jeff C. Alter Worker's Manual. 2nd ed. 61p. 1982. pap. 3.00 (ISBN 0-933643-07-1). Grace World Outreach.
The Personal Promise Pocketbook. (Pocketpac Ser.). 128p. 1984. deluxe ed. 3.95 leatherette gift (ISBN 0-87788-677-6). Shaw Pubs.
Pesta, Raymond J. The Christian Approach to Successful Selling. LC 81-68890. 92p. 1981. pap. 5.95 (ISBN 0-941280-00-4). Chr Acad Success.
Peters, David B. A Betrayal of Innocence. 160p. 1986. 11.95 (ISBN 0-8499-0502-8, 0502-8). Word Bks.
Petersen, J. Allan. For Families Only. 1981. pap. 2.95 (ISBN 0-8423-0879-2). Tyndale.
Petersen, J. Allan, et al. Two Become One. 1973. pap. 3.95 (ISBN 0-8423-7620-8). Tyndale.
Peterson, Eugene H. Growing up in Christ. pap. 5.50 (ISBN 0-8042-2026-3). John Knox.
Peterson, Levi S. Canyons of Grace. 135p. 1982. pap. 5.95 (ISBN 0-941214-26-5, Orion). Signature Bks.
Petrocelli, Orlando R., ed. The Elbert Hubbard Notebook. rev ed. 192p. 1980. Repr. 10.00 (ISBN 0-89433-144-2). Petrocelli.
Phillips, J. B. The Newborn Christian: 114 Readings. 240p. 1984. 5.95 (ISBN 0-02-088270-X, Collier). Macmillan.
--The Price of Success: An Autobiography. 288p. (Orig.). 1985. pap. 7.95 (ISBN 0-87788-659-8). Shaw Pubs.
Phillips, Keith. The Making of a Disciple. LC 80-24908. 160p. 1983. 2.50 (ISBN 0-8007-8485-5, Spire Bks). Revell.
Phillips, Mike. A Survival Guide for Tough Times. LC 79-4261. 176p. 1979. pap. 3.95 (ISBN 0-87123-498-X, 210498). Bethany Hse.
Picirilli, Robert E. Perseverance. 28p. 1973. pap. 0.95 (ISBN 0-89265-108-3). Randall Hse.
Pictor, Mike. Conversations with Christ. 73p. (Orig.). 1984. pap. 6.95 (ISBN 0-942494-84-9). Coleman Pub.
Pike, Diane K. My Journey into Self Phase One. LC 79-12179. 161p. 1979. pap. 4.95 (ISBN 0-916192-13-X). L P Pubns.
Pillai, K. C. Light Through an Eastern Window. LC 85-51634. 144p. 1986. 4.95 (ISBN 0-910068-63-1). Am Christian.
Pillar in the Twilight. (Encounter Bk.). 3.00 (ISBN 0-8198-0591-2); pap. 2.00 (ISBN 0-8198-0592-0). Dghtrs St Paul.
Pink, A. W. Christian Liberty. pap. 0.50 (ISBN 0-685-88370-1). Reiner.
Pink, Arthur W. Comfort for Christians. (Summit Bks.). 122p. 1976. pap. 2.95 (ISBN 0-8010-7062-7). Baker Bk.
--The Sovereignty of God. pap. 6.95 (ISBN 0-8010-7088-0). Baker Bk.
Pinkston, William S., Jr. With Wings As Eagles. (Illus.). 127p. 1983. pap. 5.95 (ISBN 0-89084-231-0). Bob Jones Univ Pr.
Pinnock, Clark H. Reason Enough: A Case for the Christian Faith. 126p. 1986. pap. 4.95 (ISBN 0-85364-296-6, Pub. by Paternoster UK). Attic Pr.
Pittenger, Norman. Before the Ending of the Day. 110p. 1985. pap. 5.95 (ISBN 0-8192-1365-9). Morehouse.
--The Lure of Divine Love. LC 79-15611. (Orig.). 1979. pap. 6.95 (ISBN 0-8298-0370-X). Pilgrim NY.
Pittenger, Norman W. Passion & Perfection. 1985. pap. 2.00 (ISBN 0-88028-044-1). Forward Movement.
Pittenger, W. Norman. Trying to Be a Christian. LC 72-1567. 128p. 1972. 4.95 (ISBN 0-8298-0237-1). Pilgrim NY.
Pittman, Grace. Hospitality with Confidence. 128p. (Orig.). 1986. pap. 4.95 (ISBN 0-87123-858-6, 210858). Bethany Hse.
Pitts, Audre. Let Me Keep Laughter. 106p. 1986. pap. 3.95 (ISBN 0-8341-1090-3). Beacon Hill.
Pitts, James M., ed. The Way of Faith. 176p. (Orig.). 1985. pap. 8.95 (ISBN 0-913029-10-6). Stevens Bk Pr.
Plaster, David R. Ordinances: What Are They? 1985. pap. 5.95 (ISBN 0-88469-164-0). BMH Bks.
Pocketpac Bks. Promises for the Golden Years. 96p. 1983. pap. 2.50 (ISBN 0-87788-320-3). Shaw Pubs.
Pohle, Myrtle A. Truth Seekers. (Daybreak Ser.). 144p. 1983. pap. 4.95 (ISBN 0-8163-0529-3). Pacific Pr Pub Assn.
Pointer, Lyle. Beginning Anew. (Christian Living Ser.). 32p. (Orig.). 1987. pap. write for info. (ISBN 0-8341-1189-6). Beacon Hill.
--Now That You Are Saved. (Christian Living Ser.). 32p. (Orig.). 1987. pap. 2.50 (ISBN 0-8341-1157-8). Beacon Hill.
--Welcome Back to Jesus. (Christian Living Ser.). 32p. (Orig.). 1987. pap. write for info. (ISBN 0-8341-1190-X). Beacon Hill.
Polek, David & Anderhub, Rita. Advent Begins at Home. 1979. pap. 1.50 (ISBN 0-89243-111-3). Liguori Pubns.
Pollinger, Eileen. Building Christian Discipline. 96p. (Orig.). 1986. pap. 3.95 (ISBN 0-87123-877-2); tchr's guide 4.95 (ISBN 0-87123-878-0). Bethany Hse.
Pollock, Penny. Emily's Tiger. (Orig.). 1984. pap. 1.95 (ISBN 0-8091-6554-6). Paulist Pr.
Polocino, Anna. The Adventure of Affirming: Reflections on Healing & Ministry. LC 86-8005. 111p. (Orig.). 1986. pap. 7.95 (ISBN 0-89571-030-7). Affirmation.
Polston, Don. There Can Be a New You: A Positive Approach to Life. LC 77-84892. 160p. 1980. pap. 3.95 (ISBN 0-89081-099-0, 0990). Harvest Hse.
Polston, Donald H. Where There's a Wall, There's a Way. (Living Books). 224p. 1985. pap. 2.95 (ISBN 0-8423-8204-6). Tyndale.
Pontious, Alfred E. Feed My Sheep. 26p. pap. text ed. 1.95 (ISBN 0-940227-01-0). Liberation Pub.
Pope, Leigh. Dreams & Visions. 96p. (Orig.). 1982. pap. 7.95 (ISBN 0-85819-339-6, Pub. by JBCE). ANZ Religious Pubns.
Pope John Paul II. Light of Christ. 256p. 1987. pap. 9.95 (ISBN 0-8245-0820-3). Crossroad NY.
--Sacred in All Its Forms. 482p. 1984. 7.50 (ISBN 0-8198-6845-0); pap. 6.50 (ISBN 0-8198-6846-9). Dghtrs St Paul.
Pope Pius Tenth. Recipe for Holiness. 125p. 1971. 4.00 (ISBN 0-912414-04-9). Lumen Christi.
Popieluszko, Jerzy. The Way of My Cross: The Masses & Homilies of Father Jerzy Popieluszko. Wren, Michael, tr. from Polish & Fr. 200p. pap. 9.95 (ISBN 0-89526-806-X). Regnery Bks.
Popoff, Peter. Calamities, Catastrophies, & Chaos. Tanner, Don, ed. LC 80-69974. (Illus.). 108p. 1980. pap. 2.50 (ISBN 0-938544-01-2). Faith Messenger.
Porter, Alyene. Papa Was a Preacher. 192p. 1979. 3.50 (ISBN 0-8007-8359-X, Spire Bks). Revell.
Porter, Caryl. To Make All Things New. (Orig.). 1987. 9.95 (ISBN 0-8054-7324-6). Broadman.
Porter, Valerie. Seek Ye First the Kingdom of God. 1984. 6.75 (ISBN 0-8062-2258-1). Carlton.
Postema, Donald H. Space for God: Leader's Guide. 120p. 1983. pap. 3.95 (ISBN 0-933140-47-9). CRC Pubns.
Posterski, Don. Why Am I Afraid to Tell You I'm a Christian? LC 83-12958. 112p. (Orig.). 1983. pap. 2.95 (ISBN 0-87784-847-5). Inter-Varsity.
Potgieter, Pieter. Victory: The Work of the Spirit. 42p. 1984. pap. 1.45 (ISBN 0-85151-430-8). Banner of Truth.
Potterbaum, Charlene. Thanks Lord, I Needed That. 1979. Repr. of 1977 ed. pocket size 2.95 (ISBN 0-88270-411-7, Pub. by Logos). Bridge Pub.
Pounders, Margaret. Laws of Love. LC 79-64898. 1979. 5.95 (ISBN 0-87159-083-2). Unity School.
Pountney, Michael. Getting a Job. LC 84-9039. 160p. (Orig.). 1984. pap. 4.95 (ISBN 0-87784-935-8). Inter-Varsity.
Powell, John. A Reason to Live, a Reason to Die. rev. ed. LC 75-24848. (Illus.). 208p. 1972. pap. 3.95 (ISBN 0-913592-61-7). Argus Comm.
Powell, Larry. I Hear the Rolling Thunder. 1986. 9.25 (ISBN 0-89536-803-X, 6821). CSS of Ohio.
Powell, Paul W. Beyond Conversion. LC 77-80942. 1978. pap. 3.95 (ISBN 0-8054-5260-5). Broadman.
--The Complete Disciple. 120p. 1982. pap. 4.95 (ISBN 0-88207-307-9). Victor Bks.
--Jesus Is for Now! LC 85-4115. 1985. pap. 3.75 (ISBN 0-8054-5006-8). Broadman.
Powell, Terry. Welcome to the Church. (Lay Action Ministry Program Ser.). 96p. 1987. pap. 4.95 (ISBN 0-89191-514-1). Cook.
--Welcome to Your Ministry. (Lay Action Ministry Program Ser.). 96p. 1987. pap. 4.95 (ISBN 0-89191-515-X). Cook.
Power. Heritage Series. 1976. pap. 8.00 (ISBN 0-8298-0313-0). Pilgrim NY.
Power, David & Collins, Mary, eds. Blessing & Power, Vol. 178. (Concilium Ser.). 128p. pap. 6.95 (ISBN 0-567-30058-7, Pub. by T & T Clark Ltd UK). Fortress.
Power, P. B. The I Wills of Christ. 382p. 1984. pap. 5.95 (ISBN 0-85151-429-4). Banner of Truth.
--The I Wills of the Psalms. 395p. 1985. pap. 5.95 (ISBN 0-85151-445-6). Banner of Truth.
Powers, Bruce P. Growing Faith. LC 81-66990. 1982. pap. 5.50 (ISBN 0-8054-3230-2). Broadman.
Powers, Edward A. In Essentials, Unity: An Ecumenical Sampler. (Orig.). 1982. pap. 4.95 (ISBN 0-377-00117-1). Friend Pr.
Powers, Mala. Follow the Year: A Family Celebration of Christian Holidays. LC 85-42791. (Illus.). 128p. 1985. 14.45 (ISBN 0-06-066693-5, HarpR). Har-Row.
Powers, Susan. The Inspirational Series, 12 bks. (Illus.). 1980. 2.95 ea. (Mayflower Bks). Smith Pubs.
Powers, Thomas E. Invitation to a Great Experiment. 3rd ed. LC 74-16887. Orig. Title: First Questions on the Life of the Spirit. (Illus.). 238p. 1986. pap. 8.95 (ISBN 0-914896-33-4). East Ridge Pr.
Practical Christianity. 500p. 1987. 14.95 (ISBN 0-8423-4957-X). Tyndale.
Prange, Erwin C. A Time for Intercession. LC 76-20085. 176p. 1979. pap. 3.95 (ISBN 0-87123-561-7, 210561). Bethany Hse.
Prange, Erwin E. The Gift Is Already Yours. LC 79-55545. 1980. pap. 2.95 (ISBN 0-87123-189-1, 200189). Bethany Hse.
Prather, Hugh. A Book of Games: A Course in Spiritual Play. LC 80-2840. (Illus.). 192p. 1981. pap. 6.95 (ISBN 0-385-14779-1, Dolp). Doubleday.
Pratney, Winkie. Doorways to Discipleship. LC 77-80008. 272p. 1977. pap. 5.95 (ISBN 0-87123-106-9, 210106). Bethany Hse.
--A Handbook for Followers of Jesus. LC 76-44385. 336p. 1976. pap. 6.95 (ISBN 0-87123-378-9, 210378). Bethany Hse.
Premoe, David, ed. Zion, the Growing Symbol. 1980. pap. 6.00 (ISBN 0-8309-0301-1). Herald Hse.
Prentiss, Elizabeth. Stepping Heavenward. pap. 6.95 (ISBN 0-685-99369-8). Reiner.
Prescott, Roger. Hello, My Friend. 1981. 6.75 (ISBN 0-89536-474-3, 0800). CSS of Ohio.
--The Second Mile. 1985. 4.95 (ISBN 0-89536-739-4, 5823). CSS of Ohio.
Price, Eugenia. Leave Yourself Alone. 128p. 1982. pap. 5.95 (ISBN 0-310-31431-3, 16244P). Zondervan.
--No Pat Answers. 144p. 1983. pap. 5.95 (ISBN 0-310-31331-7, 16244P). Zondervan.
--A Woman's Choice: Living Through Your Problems. 192p. 1983. pap. 5.95 (ISBN 0-310-31381-3, 16217P). Zondervan.
Price, Katheryn. Applied Christianity for Today's Christian Woman. 1978. pap. 3.50 (ISBN 0-88027-045-4). Firm Foun Pub.
Price, Nelson L. Called to Splendor. LC 84-17506. 1984. pap. 4.95 (ISBN 0-8054-5007-6). Broadman.
--The Emmanuel Factor. 1987. 8.95 (ISBN 0-8054-5050-5). Broadman.
--Only the Beginning. LC 79-55662. 1980. 7.95 (ISBN 0-8054-5331-8, 4253-31). Broadman.
Prince, Derek. The Grace of Yielding. 1977. pap. 2.50 (ISBN 0-934920-20-6, B-30). Derek Prince.
Proceedings of Holiness Conferences Held at Cincinnati, November 26th, 1877 & at New York, December 17th, 1877. (The Higher Christian Life Ser.). 255p. 1985. lib. bdg. 30.00 (ISBN 0-8240-6438-0). Garland Pub.
Prophet, Mark & Prophet, Elizabeth. Climb the Highest Mountain. LC 72-175101. (Illus.). 516p. 1978. pap. 16.95 (ISBN 0-916766-26-8). Summit Univ.
Protopresbyter Michael Pomazansky. O Zhizni o Vjere o Tzerkvje, 2 vols. Tr. of On Life, Faith & the Church. 650p. 1976. pap. 23.00 (ISBN 0-317-29072-X). Holy Trinity.
Pruitt, Fred. A Great Sacrifice. 31p. 1982. pap. 0.25 (ISBN 0-686-36262-4); pap. 1.00 5 copies (ISBN 0-686-37284-0). Faith Pub Hse.
Pucillo, Gladys, compiled by. God, Grant Me Serenity. 1982. 4.95 (ISBN 0-8378-2030-8). Gibson.
Pulley, Leland E. Reaching Up, Reaching Out. LC 85-90071. (Orig.). 1985. pap. 5.95 (ISBN 0-9611282-1-6). Stewardship Enters.
Punt, Neal. Unconditional Good News: Toward An Understanding of Biblical Universalism. LC 80-10458. pap. 40.80 (ISBN 0-317-20014-3, 2023222). Bks Demand UMI.
Purkiser, W. T. Interpreting Christian Holiness. 70p. (Orig.). 1971. pap. 1.95 (ISBN 0-8341-0221-8). Beacon Hill.
--The Lordship of Jesus. 70p. (Orig.). 1986. pap. 2.95 (ISBN 0-8341-1135-7). Beacon Hill.
Purnell, Dick. Beating the Break-up Habit. 128p. (Orig.). 1983. pap. 5.95 (ISBN 0-89840-059-7). Heres Life.

--The Thirty-One Day Experiment. LC 83-49023. 63p. (Orig.). 1984. pap. 2.95 (ISBN 0-89840-058-9). Heres Life.

Purnell, Douglas. Exploring Your Family Story. (Illus.). 156p. (Orig.). 1983. pap. 9.95 (ISBN 0-85819-415-5, Pub. by JBCE). ANZ Religious Pubns.

Pusey, Merlo. Builders of the Kingdom. LC 81-10005. 1981. 10.95 (ISBN 0-8425-1968-8). Brigham.

Pyatt. Youth Empowerment in the Church. 1983. pap. 5.95 (ISBN 0-8298-0605-9). Pilgrim NY.

Pyron, Bernard. The Great Rebellion: A Biblical Scrutiny of the Popular Culture of 1962-85 & Its Christian Versions. 212p. (Orig.). 1985. pap. text ed. 7.00 (ISBN 0-9615024-0-1). Rebound Pubns.

Quadrupani, R. P. Light & Peace. LC 79-67860. 193p. 1980. pap. 3.50 (ISBN 0-89555-133-0). TAN Bks Pubs.

Quigley, Carol, ed. Turning Points in Religious Life. LC 85-45565. 180p. (Orig.). 1987. pap. 8.95 (ISBN 0-89453-545-5). M Glazier.

Quoist, Michel. Meeting God. 1985. 4.95 (ISBN 0-87193-222-9). Dimension Bks.

Raburn, Terry. Under the Guns in Beirut. LC 80-65308. 160p. 1980. pap. 2.50 (ISBN 0-88243-634-1, 02-0634). Gospel Pub.

Rader, Rosemary. Breaking Boundaries: Male-Female Friendship in Early Christian Communities. (Theological Inquiries Ser.). 144p. 1983. pap. 6.95 (ISBN 0-8091-2506-4). Paulist Pr.

The Radical Bible. 1972. pap. 1.95 (ISBN 0-377-02141-5). Friend Pr.

Ragland, Margaret. Full of Joy. 1980. pap. 5.25 (ISBN 0-89137-415-9). Quality Pubns.

Rahner, Karl. Christian at the Crossroads. Moiser, Jeremy, tr. from Ger. 250p. 1976. 5.95 (ISBN 0-8245-0207-8). Crossroad NY.

--Is Christian Life Possible Today? 1984. pap. 6.95 (ISBN 0-87193-210-5). Dimension Bks.

--The Practice of Faith: A Handbook of Contemporary Spirituality. rev. ed. 336p. 1986. pap. 14.95 (ISBN 0-8245-0779-7). Crossroad NY.

--Words of Faith. 96p. 1986. pap. 5.95 (ISBN 0-8245-0788-6). Crossroad NY.

Rahner, Karl & Weger, Karl-Heinz. Our Christian Faith: Answers for the Future. 208p. (Orig.). 1980. 10.95 (ISBN 0-8245-0361-9); pap. 4.95 (ISBN 0-8245-0362-7). Crossroad NY.

Raines, Robert A. To Kiss the Joy. 160p. 1983. pap. 4.35 (ISBN 0-687-42185-3). Abingdon.

Rainey, Albert. Cosmic Visions. LC 85-90309. 56p. (Orig.). 1986. pap. write for info. (ISBN 0-932971-01-6). Al Rainey Pubns.

Raitt, Jill, et al, eds. Christian Spirituality, Vol. 11. (World Spirituality Ser.: Vol. 17). 528p. 1987. 49.50x (ISBN 0-8245-0765-7). Crossroad NY.

Rajagopal, D., ed. Commentaries on Living: 2nd Series. 1959. 14.95 (ISBN 0-575-00417-7, Pub. by Gollancz England). David & Charles.

--Commentaries on Living: 3rd Series. 1961. 14.95 (ISBN 0-575-00229-8, Pub. by Gollancz England). David & Charles.

Ralph, Margaret. Personas Escogidas de Dios. (Serie Jirafa). Orig. Title: God's Special People. 28p. 1979. 3.95 (ISBN 0-311-38535-4, Edit Mundo). Casa Bautista.

Rambo, Lewis. The Divorcing Christian. 96p. (Orig.). 1983. pap. 5.25 (ISBN 0-687-10994-9). Abingdon.

Ramsey, Russell. God's Joyful Runner: The Story of Eric Liddell. (Orig.). 1987. pap. 9.95 (ISBN 0-88270-624-1, P624-1). Bridge Pub.

Ramshaw-Schmidt, Gail. Letters for God's Name. (Illus.). 1984. pap. 4.95 (ISBN 0-86683-880-5, 7458, HarpR). Har-Row.

Ranaghan, Dorothy. A Day in Thy Courts. LC 84-70866. 144p. (Orig.). 1984. pap. 4.95 (ISBN 0-943780-05-5, 8055). Charismatic Ren Servs.

Ranieri, Ralph F. Christian Living: Ten Basic Virtues. 64p. 1983. pap. 1.50 (ISBN 0-89243-193-8). Liguori Pubns.

Rankin, Peg. Glorify God & Enjoy Him Forever. LC 81-51742. 176p. 1981. pap. 5.95 (ISBN 0-8307-0796-4, 5415209). Regal.

Rathwick, Clyde W. God's Co-Workers: Your Importance to God. 1985. 10.00 (ISBN 0-682-40223-0). Exposition Pr FL.

Ratiu, A. Stolen Church. 192p. 1982. pap. 4.95 (ISBN 0-88264-155-7). Diane Bks.

Rau, Lois. Very Special Day. (Redwood Ser.). 1982. pap. 2.95 (ISBN 0-8163-0447-5). Pacific Pr Pub Assn.

--Very Special Person. (Sunshine Ser.). 1982. pap. 2.95 (ISBN 0-8163-0445-9). Pacific Pr Pub Assn.

--Very Special Planet. (Sunshine Ser.). 1982. pap. 2.95 (ISBN 0-8163-0446-7). Pacific Pr Pub Assn.

--Very Special Promise. (Sunshine Ser.). 1982. pap. 2.95 (ISBN 0-8163-0448-3). Pacific Pr Pub Assn.

Rauch, Gerry. Handling Conflicts: Taking the Tension Out of Difficult Relationships. (Living as a Christian Ser.). 160p. (Orig.). 1985. pap. 3.95 (ISBN 0-89283-187-1). Servant.

Ravenhill, Leonard. Meat for Men. 144p. 1979. pap. 4.95 (ISBN 0-87123-362-2, A-510418). Bethany Hse.

Rawlings, Meridel. Honor Thy Father. Keith, Bill, ed. (Orig.). 1986. pap. 6.95 (ISBN 0-910311-39-0). Huntington Hse Inc.

Ray, Bruce. Withhold Not Correction. 1978. pap. 3.45 (ISBN 0-87552-400-1). Presby & Reformed.

Ray, C. A. La Vida Responsable: Orientacion Biblica Sobre Nuestro Estilo De Vivir. Lopez, Albert C., tr. Orig. Title: Living the Responsible Life. 160p. 1982. Repr. of 1980 ed. 3.75 (ISBN 0-311-46079-8). Casa Bautista.

Ray, Sandy F. Journeying Through a Jungle. LC 79-84787. 1979. 5.50 (ISBN 0-8054-5169-2). Broadman.

Read, David. I Am Persuaded. (The Scholar As Preacher Ser.). 192p. 1961. 12.95 (ISBN 0-567-04430-0, Pub. by T & T Clark Ltd UK). Fortress.

Record of the Convention for the Promotion of Scriptural Holiness Held at Brighton May 29th, to June 7th, 1875. (The Higher Christian Life Ser.). 496p. 1985. lib. bdg. 60.00 (ISBN 0-8240-6439-9). Garland Pub.

Rediger, G. Lloyd. Lord, Don't Let Me Be Bored. LC 85-26379. 132p. 1986. pap. 9.95 (ISBN 0-664-24700-8). Westminster.

Reece, Colleen L. Last Page in the Diary. Wheeler, Gerald, ed. (Banner Ser.). 128p. (Orig.). 1986. pap. 6.50 (ISBN 0-8280-0304-1). Review & Herald.

Reece, Louise. Thank You Lord. (Illus.). 164p. (Orig.). 1983. pap. 3.95x (ISBN 0-9614264-0-3). Lovejoy Pr.

Reed, Bobbie. Making the Most of Single Life. 1980. pap. 3.95 (ISBN 0-570-03809-X, 12-2918). Concordia.

Reed, Gordon K. Living Life By God's Law. 124p. (Orig.). 1984. pap. 6.00 (ISBN 0-317-03221-6). Word Ministries.

Reeder, Rachel. Liturgy: Holy Places. (The Quarterly Journal of the Liturgical Conference: Vol. 3, No. 4). (Illus.). 96p. (Orig.). 1983. pap. text ed. 7.95 (ISBN 0-918208-32-7). Liturgical Conf.

Reeves, R. Daniel & Jenson, Ronald. Always Advancing. LC 83-73182. 196p. (Orig.). 1984. pap. 8.95 (ISBN 0-86605-120-1, 403188). Campus Crusade.

Reichert, Richard. Born in the Spirit of Jesus. (YA) 1985. pap. text ed. 4.50 (ISBN 0-697-02120-3); tchr's. ed. 5.50 (ISBN 0-697-02121-1); spirit masters 10.95 (ISBN 0-697-01727-3). Wm C Brown.

--Confronting Christianity: Adults & Authority. LC 78-53634. 44p. 1978. pap. 9.95 (ISBN 0-88489-102-X). St Marys.

--Confronting Christianity: Faith & Religion. LC 78-53634. 44p. 1978. pap. 9.95 (ISBN 0-88489-100-3). St Marys.

Reid, Garnett. How to Grow in Grace. 1982. pap. 1.50 (ISBN 0-89265-077-X). Randall Hse.

--How to Know God's Will. 1982. pap. 1.50 (ISBN 0-89265-078-8). Randall Hse.

--How to Know You're Saved. 1982. pap. 1.50 (ISBN 0-89265-075-3). Randall Hse.

Reid, Thomas F., et al. Seduction?? A Biblical Response. rev. ed. Biros, Florence K. & Williams, Carole, eds. (Illus.). 1986. pap. 6.95 (ISBN 0-936369-02-7). Son-Rise Pubns.

Reimer, Lawrence D. Living at the Edge of Faith. 96p. 1984. pap. 6.95 (ISBN 0-8170-1023-8). Judson.

Reiser, William. Into the Needle's Eye. LC 83-72741. 144p. (Orig.). 1984. pap. 4.50 (ISBN 0-87793-306-5). Ave Maria.

--An Unlikely Catechism: Some Challenges for the Creedless Catholic. 184p. (Orig.). 1985. pap. 6.95 (ISBN 0-8091-2706-7). Paulist Pr.

Reiss, Walter. Thank God for My Breakdown. 1980. 4.95 (ISBN 0-8100-0114-4, 12N1717). Northwest Pub.

Renirkens, Clement. Love with Your Eyes Open. Lucas, Marc & Lucas, Claudia, trs. from Fr. LC 85-28669. 145p. (Orig.). 1986. pap. 7.95 (ISBN 0-8189-0491-7). Alba.

Rev. Robert Paul Mohan. A Book of Comfort: Thoughts in Late Evening. LC 86-60911. 118p. (Orig.). 1986. pap. 5.95 (ISBN 0-87973-541-4, 541). Our Sunday Visitor.

Rev. William F. Maestri. Living Securely with Insecurity. LC 86-60328. 185p. (Orig.). 1986. pap. 6.95 (ISBN 0-87973-543-0, 543). Our Sunday Visitor.

Rice, Helen S. In the Vineyard of the Lord. (Illus.). 160p. 1979. 12.95 (ISBN 0-8007-1036-3). Revell.

--Loving Promises. (Illus.). 128p. 1975. 12.95 (ISBN 0-8007-0736-2); large-print ed., 176p. 12.95 (ISBN 0-8007-1333-8). Revell.

Rice, Max M. Your Rewards in Heaven. LC 80-68885. 160p. 1981. pap. 4.95 (ISBN 0-89636-063-6). Accent Bks.

Rice, Richard. When Bad Happens to God's People. 1984. pap. 4.95 (ISBN 0-8163-0570-6). Pacific Pr Pub Assn.

Rich in Mercy. 61p. 1980. pap. 3.95 (ISBN 1-55586-734-0). US Catholic.

Rich, Marion K. Where Love is Found. 124p. (Orig.). 1984. pap. 5.95 (ISBN 0-8341-0922-0). Beacon Hill.

Richards, Larry. Love Your Neighbor: A Woman's Workshop on Fellowship. Kobobel, Janet, ed. 144p. 1986. pap. 3.95 (18139). Zondervan.

--Tomorrow Today. 132p. 1986. pap. 4.95 (ISBN 0-89693-505-1). Victor Bks.

Richards, Lawrence & Martin, Gib. Theology of Personal Ministry. 272p. 1981. 17.95 (ISBN 0-310-31970-6, 18137). Zondervan.

Richards, Lawrence O. The Believer's Guidebook from Aspirin to Zoos. 528p. 1983. 9.95 (ISBN 0-310-43470-X, 18163). Zondervan.

--The Christian Man's Promise Book. 1986. pap. 2.50 (ISBN 0-310-43582-X, 18211P). Zondervan.

--How I Can Be Real. (Answers for Youth Ser.). 1980. pap. 4.95 (ISBN 0-310-38971-2, 18207P). Zondervan.

--The Word Parents Handbook. 1983. 9.95 (ISBN 0-8499-0328-9). Word Bks.

Richardson, Frank H. Solo para Muchachos. 112p. 1986. pap. 1.95 (ISBN 0-311-46929-9). Casa Bautista.

Richardson, Jim. Foundations for Living. LC 82-74215. 1983. pap. 9.95 (ISBN 0-911739-13-0). Abbott Loop.

Richardson, John. The Measure of a Man. (Study & Grow Electives). 64p. 1985. pap. 3.95 (ISBN 0-8307-1018-3, 6102023). Regal.

Richardson, Otis D. God in the High Country. 1980. 10.00 (ISBN 0-682-49644-8). Exposition Pr FL.

Ricker, Robert S. & Pitkin, Ron. Soulsearch: Hope for Twenty-First Century Living from Ecclesiastes. rev. ed. LC 85-21594. (Bible Commentary for Laymen Ser.). 168p. 1985. pap. 4.25 (ISBN 0-8307-1100-7, S393118). Regal.

Rickerson, Wayne. Christian Family Activities for Families with Children. LC 82-10385. (Illus.). 96p. (Orig.). 1982. pap. 4.95 (ISBN 0-87239-569-3, 2964). Standard Pub.

Riddle, Donald W. Early Christian Life As Reflected in Its Literature. 256p. 1981. Repr. of 1936 ed. lib. bdg. 40.00 (ISBN 0-8495-4646-X). Arden Lib.

Ridenour, Fritz. How Do You Handle Life? LC 77-140941. 192p. 1976. pap. 3.50 (ISBN 0-8307-0430-2, S104156). Regal.

--How to Be a Christian in an Unchristian World. rev. ed. LC 72-169603. 192p. (Orig.). 1972. pap. 3.50 (ISBN 0-8307-0611-9, S123150). Regal.

--How to Be a Christian Without Being Perfect. LC 86-6479. 250p. (Orig.). 1986. text ed. 12.95 (5111607); pap. text ed. 6.95 (ISBN 0-8307-1106-6, 5418680). Regal.

--How to Be a Christian Without Being Religious. 1971. pap. 5.95 (ISBN 0-8423-1450-4). Tyndale.

--How to Be a Christian Without Being Religious. 2nd ed. LC 72-169603. 176p. 1984. pap. 4.95 (ISBN 0-8307-0982-7, 5418331); Leaders Guide, Doug Van Bronkhorst 3.95 (ISBN 0-8307-0993-2, 6101930). Regal.

--How to Be a Christian Without Being Religious. (Illus.). 166p. 1985. pap. 3.95 (ISBN 0-8307-1026-4, S182104). Regal.

--How to Decide What's Really Important. LC 78-68146. 160p. 1978. 3.50 (ISBN 0-8307-0266-0, S122154). Regal.

--I'm a Good Man, But. LC 75-96702. 1969. pap. 3.50 (ISBN 0-8307-0429-9, S102153). Regal.

Riggs, Ralph M. Living in Christ. LC 67-25874. 1967. pap. 1.50 (ISBN 0-88243-538-8, 02-0538). Gospel Pub.

Rinehart, Stacy & Rinehart, Paula. Choices: Finding God's Way in Dating, Sex, Singleness & Marriage. LC 82-62071. 170p. 1983. pap. 3.95 (ISBN 0-89109-494-6). NavPress.

Riols, Noreen. Eye of the Storm. 176p. 1985. pap. 2.95 (ISBN 0-345-32716-0). Ballantine.

Ripple, Paula. Growing Strong at Broken Places. LC 86-71124. 184p. (Orig.). 1986. pap. 5.95 (ISBN 0-87793-341-3). Ave Maria.

The Rising Generation. 1987. pap. 5.95 (ISBN 0-87579-088-7). Deseret Bk.

Robb, Anita P. Encounter. (Illus.). 153p. (Orig.). 1982. pap. 3.95 (ISBN 0-89216-048-9). Salvation Army.

Robbins, Duffy. Programming to Build Disciples. 64p. 1987. pap. 4.95 (ISBN 0-89693-573-6). Victor Bks.

Roberts, Arthur O. Move over, Elijah. LC 67-24903. 161p. 1967. 3.50 (ISBN 0-913342-11-4). Barclay Pr.

Roberts, Dennis. Well... Excuse Me. LC 80-84233. 48p. (Orig.). 1980. pap. 1.50 (ISBN 0-89081-265-9). Harvest Hse.

Roberts, Frances J. Launch Out! 1964. 2.95 (ISBN 0-932814-21-2). Kings Farspan.

--Learn to Reign. 1963. 2.95 (ISBN 0-932814-22-0). Kings Farspan.

--Listen to the Silence. 1964. 2.95 (ISBN 0-932814-23-9). Kings Farspan.

--Living Water. 1965. 2.95 (ISBN 0-932814-20-4). Kings Farspan.

--Lovest Thou Me? 1967. 2.95 (ISBN 0-932814-19-0). Kings Farspan.

--Sounding of the Trumpet. 1966. 2.95 (ISBN 0-932814-24-7). Kings Farspan.

Roberts, Howard W. The Lasting Words of Jesus. LC 85-12288. 1986. pap. 4.95 (ISBN 0-8054-2257-9). Broadman.

Roberts, Peter. In Search of Early Christian Unity. 1985. 18.00 (ISBN 0-533-05859-7). Vantage.

Roberts, Robert C. The Strengths of a Christian. LC 84-3498. (Spirituality & the Christian Life Ser.: Vol. 2). 118p. 1984. pap. 7.95 (ISBN 0-664-24613-3). Westminster.

Roberts, Roger. Holiness: Every Christian's Calling. LC 85-11330. 1985. pap. 5.95 (ISBN 0-8054-1956-X). Broadman.

Roberts, Roy R. God Has a Better Idea: The Home. pap. 4.95 (ISBN 0-88469-023-7). BMH Bks.

Roberts, Ted. Failing Forward. 1985. pap. 4.95 (ISBN 0-89081-432-5). Harvest Hse.

Robertson, John. Here I Am, God, Where Are You? 1975. pap. 2.50 (ISBN 0-8423-1416-4). Tyndale.

Robertson, John M. Comfort: Prayers & Promises for Times of Sorrow. 1977. pap. 2.95 (ISBN 0-8423-0432-0). Tyndale.

Robertson, Roy. The Timothy Principle. 120p. 1986. pap. 4.95 (ISBN 0-89109-550-0). NavPress.

Robinson, Ras. Free Indeed! (Illus.). 1983. pap. 1.00 (ISBN 0-937778-08-7). Fulness Hse.

--How to Receive God's Anointing. (Illus.). 88p. 1985. pap. text ed. 3.95 (ISBN 0-937778-10-9). Fulness Hse.

Robinson, Ras, ed. The Finest of Fulness. 192p. 1979. pap. 4.00 (ISBN 0-937778-00-1). Fulness Hse.

Robson, Ralph & Billings, Jean. Christian Cross-Cultural Communication. (Mini Bible Studies). (Illus.). 1978. pap. 2.50 instructor (ISBN 0-87239-202-3, 88555); pap. 1.95 student (ISBN 0-87239-198-1, 88551). Standard Pub.

Rockwell, Margaret. Stepping Out, Sharing Christ in Everyday Circumstances. LC 84-47804. 134p. 1984. pap. 5.95 (ISBN 0-89840-072-4). Heres Life.

Roger of Taize. Awakened from Within: Meditations on the Christian Life. LC 86-19615. 144p. 1987. 12.95 (ISBN 0-385-23536-4). Doubleday.

Rogers & Thatcher. The Home Stretch. 160p. 1986. 9.95 (ISBN 0-8499-0344-0). Word Bks.

Rogers, Adrian P. God's Way to Health, Wealth & Wisdom. 1987. 9.95 (ISBN 0-8054-5048-3). Broadman.

Rogers, Barbara. God Rescues His People Activity Book. 72p. (Orig.). 1983. pap. 3.00 (ISBN 0-8361-3338-2). Herald Pr.

Rogers, Charles R. Joy. 1979. pap. 1.00 (ISBN 0-89841-001-0). Zoe Pubns.

Rogers, Dale E. Let Us Love. 1982. 8.95 (ISBN 0-8499-0298-3). Word Bks.

Rogers, Roy, et al. Roy Rogers-Dale Evans: Happy Trails. 1979. 2.50 (ISBN 0-8499-0086-7); 13.95. Word Bks.

Rogness, Alvin N. Book of Comfort. LC 78-66943. 1979. kivar 7.95 (ISBN 0-8066-1677-6, 10-0795). Augsburg.

--Remember the Promise. LC 76-27082. 1978. gift ed. 7.50 (ISBN 0-8066-1619-9, 10-5481). Augsburg.

--Today & Tomorrow. LC 77-84095. 1978. pap. 6.95 (ISBN 0-8066-1621-0, 10-6660). Augsburg.

Roland, Timothy. First Steps. 1984. pap. 1.95 (ISBN 0-88207-450-4). Victor Bks.

Roloff, Marvin L., ed. Education for Christian Living: Strategies for Nurture Based on Biblical & Historical Foundations. LC 86-28756. 224p. (Orig.). 1986. pap. 12.95 (ISBN 0-8066-2238-5, 10-2003). Augsburg.

Romain, Philip S. Growing in Inner Freedom: A Guide for Today. 64p. 1986. pap. 1.95 (ISBN 0-89243-259-4). Liguori Pubns.

Romaine, William. Life, Walk & Triumph of Faith: With an Account of His Life and Work by Peter Toon. 439p. 1970. 14.00 (ISBN 0-227-67744-7). Attic Pr.

Ronk, A. T. A Search for Truth. LC 73-82191. 1973. pap. 1.00x (ISBN 0-934970-04-1). Brethren Ohio.

Room, M. B. Wanted Your Daily Life. 1976. pap. 2.50 (ISBN 0-87508-011-1). Chr Lit.

Roosevelt, Eleanor. You Learn by Living. LC 83-6838. 224p. 1983. pap. 9.95 (ISBN 0-664-24494-7). Westminster.

Rosage, David E. Reconciliation: The Sacramental Path to Peace. 144p. (Orig.). 1984. pap. 5.95 (ISBN 0-914544-56-X). Living Flame Pr.

Rose, Morton F. The Shadow of the Cross. LC 86-9630. (Orig.). 1986. pap. 3.25 (ISBN 0-8054-5030-0). Broadman.

Rose, Tom & Metcalf, Robert. The Coming Victory. (The Coronation Ser.: No. 5). 206p. (Orig.). 1980. pap. 6.95x (ISBN 0-686-28757-6). Chr Stud Ctr.

Roseveare, Helen. Living Holiness. 192p. (Orig.). 1987. pap. 5.95 (ISBN 0-87123-952-3). Bethany Hse.

Rosher, Grace. Beyond the Horizon: Being New Evidence from the Other Side of Life. 154p. 1961. 10.95 (ISBN 0-227-67412-X). Attic Pr.

Ross, Maggie. Fire of Your Life: A Solitude Shared. LC 82-61420. 128p. 1983. pap. 6.95 (ISBN 0-8091-2513-7). Paulist Pr.

Ross, Vicki. Hunger & Discipleship. (Orig.). 1982. pap. 8.00 (ISBN 0-8309-0346-1). Herald Hse.

Rossman, Peter & Noyce, Gaylord. Helping People Care on the Job. 144p. 1985. pap. 5.95. Judson.

Roth, Charles. More Power to You! LC 82-50122. 158p. 1982. 5.95 (ISBN 0-87159-093-X). Unity School.

Rothfuss, Frank. Journey to Jerusalem. 1982. pap. 9.25 (ISBN 0-89536-522-7, 1015). CSS of Ohio.

Roupp, Harold W. One Life Isn't Enough. 3.50 (ISBN 0-910924-44-9). Macalester.

Rowe, Sherlie. Decisions. Vol. 1. pap. 3.95 (ISBN 0-89137-806-5); Vol. 2. pap. 3.95 (ISBN 0-89137-807-3). Quality Pubns.

Rowlands, Gerald. How to Be Alive in the Spirit. (Aglow Cornerstone Ser.). 38p. 1982. pap. 2.50 (ISBN 0-930756-69-X). Aglow Pubns.

Rozentals, Janis. Promise of Eternal Life: Biblical Witness to Christian Hope. LC 86-26456. 112p. (Orig.). 1987. pap. 6.50 (ISBN 0-8066-2254-7, 10-5257). Augsburg.

Rubadeau, Joan. The Little Book of Good: Spiritual Values for Parents & Children. 58p. 1986. pap. 7.00 (ISBN 0-913105-19-8). PAGL Pr.

Ruether, Rosemary R. Disputed Questions: On Being a Christian. LC 81-12718. (Journeys in Faith Ser.). 144p. 1982. 9.95 (ISBN 0-687-10950-7). Abingdon.

Ruhnau, Helena E. Let There Be Light - Words of the Christ. (Illus.). 220p. (Orig.). 1987. pap. text ed. 9.95 (ISBN 0-941036-60-X). Colleasius Pr.

Ruhnke, Robert. For Better & for Ever: Sponsor Couple Program for Christian Marriage Preparation. 1981. pap. 3.95 (ISBN 0-89243-143-1); dialogue packet wkbk. 3.75 (ISBN 0-89243-144-X). Liguori Pubns.

Ruiz, Hugo. Hermanos, Ahora Cartas del Diablo. 64p. 1986. pap. 1.40 (ISBN 0-311-46045-3). Casa Bautista.

Rumble, Dale. Windows of the Soul. (Orig.). 1977. pap. 3.50 (ISBN 0-89350-017-8). Fountain Pr.

Rumble, Leslie & Carty, Charles M. Radio Replies, 3 vols. LC 79-51938. 1979. Set. pap. 27.00 (ISBN 0-89555-159-4). Vol. 1 (ISBN 0-89555-089-X). Vol. 2 (ISBN 0-89555-090-3). Vol. 3 (ISBN 0-89555-091-1). TAN Bks Pubs.

Runk, Wesley. You're God's Masterpiece. 1985. 4.50 (ISBN 0-89536-757-2, 5863). CSS of Ohio.

Runk, Wesley T. Standing Up for Jesus. 1985. 4.50 (ISBN 0-89536-725-4, 5809). CSS of Ohio.

Rupp, Joyce. Fresh Bread & Other Gifts of Spiritual Nourishment. LC 85-70020. 160p. (Orig.). 1985. pap. 4.95 (ISBN 0-87793-283-2). Ave Maria.

Rupprecht, David & Rupprecht, Ruth. Radical Hospitality. 110p. 1983. 7.95 (ISBN 0-87552-421-4); pap. 4.95 (ISBN 0-87552-420-6). Presby & Reformed.

Rusbuldt, Richard E. Hello-Is God There? 64p. 1984. pap. 5.95 (ISBN 0-8170-1043-2). Judson.

Rush, Myron. Burnout. 156p. 1987. pap. 6.95 (ISBN 0-89693-242-7). Victor Bks.

Rushmore, Louis. The Cost of Discipleship. 1986. pap. 4.00 (ISBN 0-89137-563-5). Quality Pubns.

Russell, A. J. God Calling. (Christian Library). 1985. Repr. 6.95 (ISBN 0-916441-22-9). Barbour & Co.

Russell, A. J., ed. God Calling. 208p. 1987. pap. 3.50 (ISBN 0-515-09026-3). Jove Pubns.

Russell, Bert. Hardships & Happy Times. LC 78-75104. (Oral History Ser.: No. 1). 1982. 9.95 (ISBN 0-930344-04-9); pap. 7.95 (ISBN 0-930344-01-4). Lacon Pubs.

Russell, Robert. The Answer Will Come. 91p. 1981. pap. 3.00 (ISBN 0-87516-440-4). De Vorss.

Russell, Robert A. Making the Contact. 90p. 1980. Repr. of 1956 ed. lexitone cover 3.95 (ISBN 0-87516-391-2). De Vorss.

Rust, Brian & McLeish, Barry. The Support-Raising Handbook: A Guide for Christian Workers. LC 84-22448. 156p. (Orig.). 1984. pap. 9.95 (ISBN 0-87784-326-0). Inter-Varsity.

Rust, Henry. Christians As Peacemakers. 54p. (Orig.). 1983. pap. 5.95 (ISBN 0-940754-21-5). Ed Ministries.

Ruyle, Gene. Making a Life: Career, Commitment & the Life Process. 144p. (Orig.). 1983. pap. 7.95 (ISBN 0-8164-2408-X, HarpR). Har-Row.

Ryan, James. Bible Promises for Growing Christians. LC 84-22953. 1985. pap. 2.25 (ISBN 0-8054-5014-9). Broadman.

Ryan, James M. Conversations with God: A Voice That Will Drive You Sane. Lambert, Herbert, ed. LC 84-7620. 96p. 1984. pap. 6.95 (ISBN 0-8272-0444-2). CBP.

Ryan, Pat & Ryan, Rosemary. Lent Begins at Home. 1979. pap. 1.50 (ISBN 0-89243-101-6). Liguori Pubns.

Ryan, Thomas P. Tales of Christian Unity: The Adventures of An Ecumenical Pilgrim. LC 82-60748. 224p. 1983. pap. 9.95 (ISBN 0-8091-2502-1). Paulist Pr.

Ryle, J. C. Five English Reformers. rev. ed. 156p. (Orig.). 1981. pap. text ed. 3.95 (ISBN 0-85151-138-4). Banner of Truth.

--Holiness. (Giant Summit Bks.). pap. 11.95 (ISBN 0-8010-7686-2). Baker Bk.

--No Uncertain Sound: Charges & Addresses. 384p. 1984. pap. 10.95 (ISBN 0-85151-444-8). Banner of Truth.

Ryrie, Charles C. Balancing the Christian Life. 1969. pap. 5.95 (ISBN 0-8024-0452-9). Moody.

--Equilibrio en la Vida Cristiana. Orig. Title: Balancing the Christian Life. (Span.). 208p. 1983. pap. 5.95 (ISBN 0-8254-1628-0). Kregel.

S. P. Publications Editors. What Is the Church? Leader's Guide. Chao, Lorna Y., tr. (Basic Doctrine Ser.). 1986. pap. write for info. (ISBN 0-941598-35-7). Living Spring Pubns.

Sabins, Walter E. With Bible & Spade. (Orig.). 1987. pap. price not set (ISBN 0-89536-897-8, 7883). CSS of Ohio.

Sack, John. The Wolf in Winter: A Story of Francis Assisi. LC 85-60296. 128p. (Orig.). 1985. pap. 4.95 (ISBN 0-8091-6556-2). Paulist Pr.

Sager, Harold G. Rebel for God. 1983. 5.75 (ISBN 0-8062-1868-1). Carlton.

St. Clair, Barry. Giving Away Your Faith. (Moving Toward Maturity Ser.: No. 4). 132p. 1985. pap. 4.95 (ISBN 0-317-16074-5). Victor Bks.

--Growing On. (Moving Toward Maturity Ser.: No. 5). 144p. 1986. pap. 4.95 (ISBN 0-88207-305-2). Victor Bks.

--Making Jesus Lord. 1983. pap. 4.95 (ISBN 0-88207-303-6). Victor Bks.

--Spending Time Alone with God. 144p. 1984. pap. 4.95 (ISBN 0-88207-302-8). Victor Bks.

St. Francis De Sales. Introduction to the Devout Life. rev. ed. Ryan, John K., ed. 1972. pap. 5.50 (ISBN 0-385-03009-6, IM). Doubleday.

St. Romain, Philip. Becoming a New Person: Twelve Steps to Christian Growth. 96p. 1984. pap. 2.95 (ISBN 0-89243-200-4). Liguori Pubns.

--Jesus Alive in Our Lives. LC 85-71676. 104p. (Orig.). 1985. pap. 4.95 (ISBN 0-87793-293-X). Ave Maria.

St. Teresa of Avila. Interior Castle. 1972. pap. 4.50 (ISBN 0-385-03643-4, Im). Doubleday.

Saint John Climacus. Lestvitsa. Tr. of The Ladder. 363p. 18.00 (ISBN 0-317-28895-4); pap. 13.00 (ISBN 0-317-28896-2). Holy Trinity.

Sala, Harold J. Guidelines for Living. (Direction Bks.). 80p. (Orig.). 1982. pap. 2.95 (ISBN 0-8010-8219-6). Baker Bk.

Salem, Luis. El Dios de Nuestros Libertadores. LC 77-165. (Span., Illus.). 172p. (Orig.). 1977. pap. 3.25 (ISBN 0-89922-093-2). Edit Caribe.

Saliba, John A. Religious Cults Today: A Challenge to Christian Families. 48p. 1983. pap. 1.50 (ISBN 0-89243-189-X). Liguori Pubns.

Salin, Mary W. No Other Light. 224p. 1986. 14.95 (ISBN 0-8245-0748-7). Crossroad NY.

Salls, Betty R. My Love Remembers. pap. 1.75 (ISBN 0-686-12740-4). Grace Pub Co.

Salsbury, Barbara G. Just Add Water: How to Use Dehydrated Foods & TVP. 92p. 1972. 5.50 (ISBN 0-88290-011-0). Horizon Utah.

Sampson, William. The Coming of Consolation. (Orig.). 1986. pap. 8.95 (ISBN 0-87061-132-1). Chr Classics.

Sams, Earnell, Jr. The Aorist Participle of Antecedent Action. LC 81-67641. 1982. pap. write for info. (ISBN 0-940068-01-X). Doctrine Christ.

Sanders, J. Oswald. In Pursuit of Maturity. 256p. 1986. pap. text ed. 7.95 (ISBN 0-310-32511-0). Zondervan.

Sanders, Marjorie L. Getting Away. LC 83-70214. 1984. pap. 5.95 (ISBN 0-8054-7523-0). Broadman.

Sanders, Randolph K. & Malony, H. Newton. Speak up! Christian Assertiveness. LC 84-20806. 118p. (Orig.). 1985. pap. 7.95 (ISBN 0-664-24551-X). Westminster.

--Speak up! Christian Assertiveness. 1986. pap. 2.95 (Pub. by Ballantine-Epiphany). Ballantine.

Sanders, Rostelle. When the Working Men Rise & Shine. 1984. 4.95 (ISBN 0-8062-2136-4). Carlton.

Sandford, John & Sandford, Paula. Restoring the Christian Family. LC 79-64977. 336p. 1986. pap. 6.95 (ISBN 0-932081-12-6). Victory Hse.

Sanford, John A. Invisible Partners. LC 79-56604. 139p. (Orig.). 1980. pap. 6.95 (ISBN 0-8091-2277-4). Paulist Pr.

--The Man Who Lost His Shadow. LC 82-62414. 1983. 6.95 (ISBN 0-8091-0337-0). Paulist Pr.

--The Man Who Wrestled with God: Light from the Old Testament on the Psychology of Individuation. LC 80-84829. 128p. 1981. pap. 7.95 (ISBN 0-8091-2367-3). Paulist Pr.

La Santa Eucarista y Otros Servicios. (Span.). 44p. 1983. pap. 1.50 (ISBN 0-935461-05-1). St Alban Pr CA.

Saraydarian, Torkom. Challenge for Discipleship. LC 86-70417. 25.00 (ISBN 0-911794-50-6); pap. 20.00 (ISBN 0-911794-51-4). Aqua Educ.

Sarvin, Margaret M. Hope for Families. 6.95 (ISBN 0-8215-9902-X). Sadlier.

Sattenfield, Charles L. Let's Grow & Make Disciples! 92p. (Orig.). 1980. 2.75 (ISBN 0-88027-080-2). Firm Foun Pub.

Savelle, Jerry. If Satan Can't Steal Your Joy, He Can't Have Your Goods. 160p. 1983. pap. 3.95 (ISBN 0-89274-262-3). Harrison Hse.

--Living in Divine Prosperity. 256p. 1983. pap. 4.95 (ISBN 0-89274-247-X). Harrison Hse.

--Sowing in Famine. 32p. (Orig.). 1982. pap. 1.50 (ISBN 0-686-83911-0). Harrison Hse.

Sawyer, Jane. Why Stay Married? (Outreach Ser.). 1982. pap. 1.25 (ISBN 0-8163-0443-2). Pacific Pr Pub Assn.

Sayler, Mary H. Why Are You Home, Dad? 1983. 4.95 (ISBN 0-8054-4276-6, 4242-76). Broadman.

Scanlan, Michael & Shields, Ann T. And Their Eyes Were Opened. 1976. pap. 3.95 (ISBN 0-89283-035-2). Servant.

Scarborough, Peggy. Hallelujah Anyway, Tim. 1976. pap. 3.95 (ISBN 0-87148-405-6). Pathway Pr.

Schaeffer, Edith. Common Sense Christian Living. LC 83-8263. 272p. 1983. 13.95 (ISBN 0-8407-5280-6). Nelson.

--Diez Pasos a la Vida. Powell, David, tr. from Eng. Orig. Title: Lifelines. (Span.). 192p. 1987. pap. 4.95 (ISBN 0-88113-251-9). Edit Betania.

--The Hidden Art of Homemaking. (Living Studies). 216p. 1985. pap. 6.95 (ISBN 0-8423-1398-2); Leader's Guide 2.95 (ISBN 0-8423-1399-0). Tyndale.

--A Way of Seeing. 256p. 1977. pap. 6.95 (ISBN 0-8007-5036-5, Power Bks). Revell.

Schaeffer, Francis A. The Church at the End of the Twentieth Century: The Church Before the Watching World. 2nd ed. LC 85-71893. 160p. 1985. pap. 6.95 (ISBN 0-89107-368-X, Crossway Bks). Good News.

--How Should We Then Live? LC 83-70956. 288p. 1983. pap. 9.95 (ISBN 0-89107-292-6, Crossway BKs). Good News.

Schall, James V. Christianity & Life. LC 79-89759. 133p. (Orig.). 1981. pap. 7.95 (ISBN 0-89870-004-3). Ignatius Pr.

Schaller, Lyle E. It's a Different World! The Challenge for Today's Pastor. 240p. 1987. pap. 10.95 (ISBN 0-687-19729-5). Abingdon.

Schauer, Ken. Two Fish to You. 65p. 1985. pap. 4.95 (ISBN 0-933350-46-5). Morse Pr.

Schillebeeck, Edward. God among Us. 256p. 1986. pap. 9.95 (ISBN 0-8245-0732-0). Crossroad NY.

Schillebeeckx, Edward. On Christian Faith. 128p. 1987. 12.95 (ISBN 0-8245-0827-0). Crossroad NY.

--Schillebeeckx Reader. Schreiter, Robert, ed. 1987. pap. 16.95 (ISBN 0-8245-0828-9). Crossroad NY.

Schindler, Regine. Hannah at the Manger. (Illus.). 31p. 1983. pap. 9.95 printed binding (ISBN 0-687-16627-6). Abingdon.

--A Miracle for Sarah. Tr. of Und Sara Lacht. (Illus.). 28p. 1985. 7.95 (ISBN 0-687-27044-8). Abingdon.

Schlabach, Chris. Lecciones...la Vida Victoriosa. Orig. Title: Lessons in Victorious Living. (Span.). 1986. write for info. (ISBN 0-8297-0730-1). Life Pubs Intl.

--Lessons in Victorious Living. 160p. (Orig.). 1984. pap. 3.95 (ISBN 0-88368-141-2). Whitaker Hse.

Schlink, Basilea. Blessings of Illness. 1973. pap. 2.50 (ISBN 0-551-00446-0, Pub. by Marshall Morgan & Scott UK). Evang Sisterhood Mary.

--Countdown to World Disaster: Hope & Protection for the Future. 1976. pap. 0.50 (ISBN 3-87209-620-6). Evang Sisterhood Mary.

--Father of Comfort. 128p. 1971. pap. 3.50 (ISBN 0-87123-156-5, 200156). Bethany Hse.

--Hidden in His Hands. LC 79-52346. 96p. 1979. pap. 2.95 (ISBN 0-87123-208-1, 200208). Bethany Hse.

--If I Only Love Jesus. 1973. pap. 0.95 (ISBN 0-551-05288-0). Evang Sisterhood Mary.

--Jesus, My Lord So Hated Today. 1978. pap. 0.50 (ISBN 3-87209-653-2). Evang Sisterhood Mary.

--The Joy of My Heart. 1978. pap. 0.95 (ISBN 3-87209-623-0). Evang Sisterhood Mary.

--More Precious Than Gold. 1978. pap. 4.95 (ISBN 0-88419-178-8). Creation Hse.

--My Father I Trust You. 1976. pap. 1.00 (ISBN 3-87209-617-6). Evang Sisterhood Mary.

--O None Can Be Loved Like Jesus. 1974. pap. 1.00 (ISBN 3-87209-651-6). Evang Sisterhood Mary.

--Repentance: The Joy Filled Life. LC 83-23774. 96p. 1984. pap. 3.95 (ISBN 0-87123-592-7, 210592). Bethany Hse.

Schlink, Mother Basilea. In Our Midst. 1973. pap. 0.95 (ISBN 0-551-05289-9). Evang Sisterhood Mary.

--Realities of Faith. 144p. (Orig.). 1983. pap. 3.95 (ISBN 0-87123-299-5). Bethany Hse.

Schmalenberger, Jerry L. The Good News Way of Life. 1985. 4.75 (ISBN 0-89536-735-1, 5819). CSS of Ohio.

--The Good News Way of Life: Study Book. 1982. pap. 0.50 (ISBN 0-89536-531-6, 0729). CSS of Ohio.

--The Good News Way of Life: Teacher's Guide. 1982. pap. 3.00 (ISBN 0-89536-530-8, 0728). CSS of Ohio.

Schmidt, Dorothy M. Pursuing Life's Adventures. LC 85-40650. 168p. 1985. pap. 5.95 (ISBN 0-938232-84-3, Dist. by Baker & Taylor Co.). Winston-Derek.

Schmidt, J. David. More Graffiti: Devotions for Guys. (Illus.). 128p. 1984. pap. 4.95 (ISBN 0-8007-5142-6, Power Bks). Revell.

Schmidt, Jerry A. Do You Hear What You're Thinking? 1983. pap. 5.95 (ISBN 0-88207-381-8). Victor Bks.

Schmidt, John. Utopia II: An Investigation into the Kingdom of God. (Orig.). 1986. pap. 3.50 (ISBN 0-89540-154-1). Sun Pub.

Schmitt, Abraham. Turn Again to Life. LC 86-33581. 136p. (Orig.). 1987. pap. 8.95 (ISBN 0-8361-3436-2). Herald Pr.

Schmitt, Abraham & Schmitt, Dorothy. When a Congregation Cares. LC 84-19294. 128p. (Orig.). 1984. pap. 6.95 (ISBN 0-8361-3410-9). Herald Pr.

Schneider, Bernard N. The Love of God. 1985. pap. 5.95 (ISBN 0-88469-167-5). BMH Bks.

Schneiders, Sandra M. New Wineskins: Reimagining Religious Life Today. 320p. (Orig.). 1986. pap. 10.95 (ISBN 0-8091-2765-2). Paulist Pr.

Schoenhals, Roger, ed. When Trouble Comes: How to Find God's Help in Difficult Times. (Orig.). 1978. pap. 2.95 (ISBN 0-89367-027-8). Light & Life.

Schramm, John & Schramm, Mary. Things That Make for Peace: A Personal Search for a New Way of Life. LC 76-3861. 96p. (Orig.). 1976. pap. 5.95 (ISBN 0-8066-1537-0, 110-6400). Augsburg.

Schreck, Alan. Catholic & Christian. 240p. (Orig.). 1984. pap. 6.95 (ISBN 0-89283-181-2). Servant.

Schroeder, Theodore W. I Don't Want to Complain, But: Teen Conversations with God. 112p. (Orig.). 1985. pap. 4.95 (ISBN 0-570-03964-9, 12-2999). Concordia.

--Let's Look at This the Right Way: A Guide for Christian Parents in Conflict with Their Teens. 112p. (Orig.). 1986. pap. 4.95 (ISBN 0-570-03987-8, 12-3015). Concordia.

Schuller, Robert. God's Way to the Good Life. (Religion Ser.). 144p. 1987. pap. 2.95 (ISBN 0-553-26803-1). Bantam.

--Tough Times Never Last but Tough People Do! 256p. 1984. pap. 3.95 (ISBN 0-553-24245-8). Bantam.

Schuller, Robert A., ed. Robert Schuller's Life Changers. 192p. 1981. 2.75 (ISBN 0-8007-8476-6, Spire Bks). Revell.

Schuller, Robert H. Power Ideas for a Happy Family. 1987. 8.95 (ISBN 0-8007-1528-4). Revell.

--Reach Out for New Life. 1979. pap. 3.50 (ISBN 0-553-25222-4). Bantam.

--Robert H. Schuller Tells You How to Be an Extraordinary Person in an Ordinary World. Schuller, Robert A., ed. 1987. 16.95 (Large Print Bks). G K Hall.

--Tough Minded Faith for Tender Hearted People. Date not set. 16.95 (ISBN 0-8161-3806-0, Large Print Bks); pap. 9.95 (ISBN 0-8161-3815-X). G K Hall.

--Tough Times Never Last, but Tough People Do! LC 83-4160. (Illus.). 240p. 1983. 12.95 (ISBN 0-8407-5287-3); pap. text ed. 5.95 (ISBN 0-8407-5936-3). Nelson.

--Tough Times Never Last, but Tough People Do! (General Ser.). 1984. lib. bdg. 13.95 (ISBN 0-8161-3677-7, Large Print Bks). G K Hall.

Schultze, Lilli. Shadow of Death. 1981. 3.50 (ISBN 0-87813-516-2). Christian Light.

Schutz, Roger. A Life We Never Dared Hope For. 80p. (Orig.). 1981. pap. 3.95 (ISBN 0-8164-2322-9, HarpR). Har-Row.

--Living Today for God. 80p. (Orig.). 1981. pap. 3.95 (ISBN 0-8164-2323-7, HarpR). Har-Row.

Schwartz, Toby D. Mercy Lord, My Husband's in the Kitchen & Other Equal Opportunity Conversations with God. 96p. 1982. pap. 2.95 (ISBN 0-380-57943-X, 57943-X). Avon.

Schwarz, Hans. What Christians Believe. LC 86-45923. 112p. 1987. pap. 4.95 (ISBN 0-8006-1959-5). Fortress.

Scofield, C. I. The New Life in Christ Jesus. 1975. pap. 1.95 (ISBN 0-915374-41-2, 41-2). Rapids Christian.

Scott, John C. How to Start Your Romance with God. 1987. 7.95. Franciscan Herald.

Scott, Waldron. Bring Forth Justice. LC 80-15992. 304p. 1980. pap. 11.95 (ISBN 0-8028-1848-X). Eerdmans.

Scott, Willard. The Joy of Living. (Epiphany Bks.). 192p. (Orig.). 1983. pap. 2.50 (ISBN 0-345-31073-X). Ballantine.

Scrogin, Michael. Practical Guide to Christian Living. 144p. 1985. pap. 6.95 (ISBN 0-8170-1053-X). Judson.

Scruggs, Julius R. God Is Faithful. 96p. 1985. pap. 6.95 (ISBN 0-8170-1060-2). Judson.

Seagren, Daniel R. To Dad. (Contempo Ser.). 1978. pap. 0.95 (ISBN 0-8010-8113-0). Baker Bk.

Seale, Ervin. Ten Words That Will Change Your Life. 192p. 1972. pap. 6.95 (ISBN 0-911336-38-9). Sci of Mind.

Seashore, Gladys. Jesus & Me. 1975. pap. 2.25 (ISBN 0-911802-37-1). Free Church Pubns.

Seculoff, James. Holy Hour for a New People. LC 76-27491. (Orig.). 1976. pkg. of 10 17.00 (ISBN 0-87973-645-3). Our Sunday Visitor.

Sedgwick, Timothy F. Sacramental Ethics: Paschal Identity & the Christian Life. LC 86-45925. 128p. 1987. pap. text ed. 7.95 (ISBN 0-8006-1965-X, 1-1965). Fortress.

Seerveld, C. Rainbows for the Fallen World. 1980. pap. 9.95x (ISBN 0-919071-01-5). Radix Bks.

Segler, Franklin. Christian Worship: Its Theology & Practice. LC 67-22034. 1975. pap. 8.95 (ISBN 0-8054-2309-5). Broadman.

Sehnert, Keith W. Selfcare-Wellcare. LC 85-15622. 240p. (Orig.). 1985. text ed. 12.95 (ISBN 0-8066-2179-6, 10-5644); pap. 3.95 (ISBN 0-8066-2180-X, 10-5645). Augsburg.

Seivertson, Genevah D. The Christ Highway. LC 81-69023. 184p. 1982. pap. 7.25 (ISBN 0-87516-465-X). De Vorss.

Sekowsky, Jo Anne. Essentials of Our faith: What Christians Believe. (Basic Bible Study Ser.). (Orig.). 1987. pap. 2.95 (ISBN 0-932305-37-7, 521023). Aglow Pubns.

Selness, Craig. When Your Mountain Won't Move. 156p. 1984. pap. 5.95 (ISBN 0-88207-619-1). Victor Bks.

Senior, John. The Death of Christian Culture. 1978. 12.95 (ISBN 0-87000-416-6). Educator Pubns.

Senn, Frank C. Christian Worship & Its Cultural Setting. LC 82-48587. 160p. 1983. pap. 9.95 (ISBN 0-8006-1700-2, 1-1700). Fortress.

Senter, Ruth. Startled by Silence. 160p. 1985. 10.95 (ISBN 0-310-38840-6, 11227). Zondervan.

Serenity. (Pocket Power Ser.). 16p. (Orig.). 1986. pap. 0.50 (ISBN 0-89486-355-X). Hazelden.

Sergio, Lisa. Jesus & Woman: An Exciting Discovery of What He Offered Her. LC 75-4365. 139p. 1980. pap. 4.95 (ISBN 0-914440-44-6). EPM Pubns.

Sernau, Scott. Please Don't Squeeze the Christian. 150p. (Orig.). 1987. pap. 4.95 (ISBN 0-87784-571-9). Inter Varsity.

Sewell, Daisy M. The Home As God Would Have It. 1937. pap. 4.25 (ISBN 0-88027-047-0). Firm Foun Pub.

Sexson, Lynda. Ordinarily Sacred. LC 82-17145. 144p. 1982. 9.95 (ISBN 0-8245-0530-1). Crossroad NY.

Shakarian, Demos. The Happiest People on Earth. 192p. 1979. 2.95 (ISBN 0-8007-8362-X, Spire Bks). Revell.

Sharner, Mariann V. The Holy Spirit Came at 3 AM. 1983. 4.95 (ISBN 0-8062-2156-9). Carlton.

Shaw, Luci. The Sighting. LC 81-9342. (The Wheaton Literary Ser.). (Illus.). 95p. 1981. pap. 5.95 (ISBN 0-87788-768-3). Shaw Pubs.

Shaw, Russell. Does Suffering Make Sense? LC 86-62613. 180p. (Orig.). 1987. pap. 4.95 (ISBN 0-87973-834-0). Our Sunday Visitor.

Shea, John. Stories of Faith. 1980. pap. 9.95 (ISBN 0-88347-112-4). Thomas More.

Shedd, Charlie W. Letters to Philip. (Orig.). 1985. pap. 2.95 (ISBN 0-515-08465-4). Jove Pubns.

Sheen, Fulton J. Life Is Worth Living. 1978. pap. 4.50 (ISBN 0-385-14510-1, Im). Doubleday.

Shelby, Donald J. Meeting the Messiah. LC 79-57363. 96p. (Orig.). 1980. pap. 3.50x (ISBN 0-8358-0398-8). Upper Room.

Sheldon, Charles L. In His Steps. 1980. pap. 3.95 (ISBN 0-88368-090-4). Whitaker Hse.

Sheldon, Charles M. In His Steps. (One Evening Christian Classic Ser.). 1962. pap. 2.95 (ISBN 0-89107-231-4). Good News.

--In His Steps. 1977. large print kivar 8.95 (ISBN 0-310-32797-0, 12561L). Zondervan.

--In His Steps. 1985. pap. 4.95 (ISBN 0-916441-23-7). Barbour & Co.

Shell, Rubel. Heavenly Patters for Happy Homes. 2.50 (ISBN 0-89315-109-2). Lambert Bk.

Shelley, Bruce L. Christian Theology in Plain Language. 256p. 1985. 12.95 (ISBN 0-8499-0381-5, 0381-5). Word Bks.

Shelly, Judith A. Not Just a Job: Serving Christ in Your Work. LC 84-29676. 140p. (Orig.). 1985. pap. 4.95 (ISBN 0-87784-332-5). Inter-Varsity.

Shepard, Annis. The Wrong Kind of Dragon. LC 83-6023. (Illus.). 48p. (Orig.). 1983. pap. 4.50 (ISBN 0-687-46569-9). Abingdon.

Shepherd of My Soul. 1981. 4.95 (ISBN 0-8198-6801-9); pap. 3.50 (ISBN 0-8198-6802-7). Dghtrs St Paul.

Sherrod, Paul. Successful Soul Winning. (Illus.). 1978. 6.95 (ISBN 0-686-14476-7, 1730394523). P Sherrod.

Shideler, Mary M. In Search of the Spirit. 272p. (Orig.). 1985. 11.95 (ISBN 0-345-32107-3, Pub. by Ballantine Epiphany). Ballantine.

Shields, Steven L. No Greater Sacrifice: The Atonement & Redemption of Christ. LC 80-83864. 140p. 1980. 7.95 (ISBN 0-88290-166-4, 1059). Horizon Utah.

Shinn, Roger L. Forced Options. 272p. 1985. pap. 10.95 (ISBN 0-8298-0552-4). Pilgrim NY.

--Forced Options: Social Decisions for the 21st Century. LC 82-47755. (Religious Perspective Ser.). 256p. 1982. 16.30 (ISBN 0-06-067282-X, HarpR). Har-Row.

Shivanandan, Mary. When Your Wife Wants to Work. LC 79-51278. (When Bks). (Illus.). 1980. pap. 2.45 (ISBN 0-87029-151-3, 20237-4). Abbey.

Shlemon, Barbara. Living Each Day by the Power of Faith. 140p. (Orig.). 1986. pap. 4.95 (ISBN 0-89283-289-4). Servant.

Shlemon, Barbara L. Healing the Hidden Self. LC 81-70022. (Illus.). 128p. 1982. pap. 3.50 (ISBN 0-87793-244-1). Ave Maria.

Shockley, Ann A. Say Jesus & Come to Me. 288p. 1986. pap. 8.95 (ISBN 0-930044-98-3). Naiad Pr.

Shoemaker, Mary E. Main Route to Bethlehem. (Orig.). 1981. pap. 4.50 (ISBN 0-937172-26-X). JLJ Pubs.

Short, Ray E. Sex, Dating, & Love: Seventy-Seven Questions Most Often Asked. LC 83-72122. 144p. (Orig.). 1984. pap. 3.95 (ISBN 0-8066-2066-8, 10-5648). Augsburg.

Shriver, Donald W., Jr. The Lord's Prayer: A Way of Life. LC 83-9843. 108p. (Orig.). 1983. pap. 4.95 (ISBN 0-8042-2409-9). John Knox.

Shropshire, Marie. In Touch with God: How God Speaks to a Prayerful Heart. (Orig.). 1985. pap. 4.95 (ISBN 0-89081-447-3). Harvest Hse.

Shuler, J. L. Power for a Finished Work. LC 78-53212. (Stories That Win Ser.). 1978. pap. 0.99 (ISBN 0-8163-0208-1, 16416-0). Pacific Pr Pub Assn.

Siccardi, Mirtha F. Luz Que No Se Apaga. Tr. of The Bright Light. (Span.). 256p. 1983. pap. 4.75 (ISBN 0-8254-1665-5). Kregel.

Sider, Ronald J., ed. Living More Simply. LC 79-3634. (Orig.). 1980. pap. 4.95 (ISBN 0-87784-808-4). Inter-Varsity.

Sikking, Sue. God Always Says Yes. 143p. 1984. pap. 5.95 (ISBN 0-87516-545-1). De Vorss.

Simcox, Carroll. Eternal You. 112p. (Orig.). 1986. pap. 7.95 (ISBN 0-8245-0745-2). Crossroad NY.

Simons, George F. How Big Is a Person? A Book for Loving Out Loud. LC 82-61423. 72p. 1983. 3.95 (ISBN 0-8091-0336-2). Paulist Pr.

Simpson, A. B. The Best of Simpson. Bailey, Keith M., compiled by. 1987. pap. write for info. (ISBN 0-87509-314-0). Chr Pubns.

--Christ in the Tabernacle. LC 85-70720. 150p. 1985. 4.95 (ISBN 0-87509-361-2). Chr Pubns.

--Danger Lines in the Deeper Life. 133p. 1966. pap. 2.00 (ISBN 0-87509-007-9). Chr Pubns.

Simpson, Albert B. The Christ Life. LC 80-69301. 96p. pap. 2.25 (ISBN 0-87509-291-8). Chr Pubns.

--Days of Heaven on Earth. rev. ed. LC 84-70154. 369p. 1984. pap. 7.95 (ISBN 0-87509-346-9). Chr Pubns.

--Larger Christian Life. 3.95 (ISBN 0-87509-025-7); pap. 3.45 mass market (ISBN 0-87509-026-5). Chr Pubns.

--Self Life & the Christ Life. pap. 1.95 (ISBN 0-87509-034-6). Chr Pubns.

Simpson, Douglas J. The Maturing Christian. 1977. pap. 1.50 (ISBN 0-89265-047-8). Randall Hse.

Simpson, F. Dale. Seven Steps along the Way. 1981. pap. 7.45 (ISBN 0-89137-527-9). Quality Pubns.

Simpson, Peggy. Hospitality: In the Spirit of Love. 1980. pap. 4.95 (ISBN 0-89137-416-7). Quality Pubns.

Simpson, Winifred R. Hello, World, You're Mine? (Illus.). 1987. pap. 3.95 (ISBN 0-570-03643-7). Concordia.

Sine, Tom. The Mustard Seed Conspiracy. 1981. 7.95 (ISBN 0-8499-2939-3). Word Bks.

--Taking Discipleship Seriously. 80p. 1985. pap. 4.95 (ISBN 0-8170-1085-8). Judson.

Singer, Mark J. & Shechtman, Stephen A. The Missing Link: Building Quality Time with Teens. 176p. 1985. pap. 7.95 (ISBN 0-687-27078-2). Abingdon.

Singh, Tara. How to Raise a Child of God. 2nd ed. LC 86-82911. (Orig.). 1987. 19.95 (ISBN 1-55531-008-7); pap. 14.95 (ISBN 1-55531-009-5). Life Action Pr.

Sire, J. W. Program for a New Man. pap. 0.75 (ISBN 0-87784-146-2). Inter-Varsity.

Sisson, Richard. Training for Evangelism. 1979. pap. 12.95 (ISBN 0-8024-8792-0). Moody.

Sittser, Jerry. The Adventure: Putting Energy into Your Work with God. LC 85-19695. 236p. 1985. pap. 6.95 (ISBN 0-87784-335-X). Inter-Varsity.

Siudy. Worship. 1980. 5.50 (ISBN 0-8298-0393-9). Pilgrim NY.

Skariah, Matthew. Crispy Christians. LC 85-50245. 184p. (Orig.). 1985. pap. 2.75 (ISBN 0-933495-00-5). World Prayer.

Skinner, John E. The Christian Disciple. LC 83-21772. 92p. (Orig.). 1984. lib. bdg. 20.50 (ISBN 0-8191-3657-3); pap. text ed. 7.75 (ISBN 0-8191-3658-1). U Pr of Amer.

Skinner, Paul H. Self Power. 194p. pap. 7.95 (ISBN 0-942494-44-X). Coleman Pub.

Skoglund, Elizabeth. Growing through Rejection. 1983. pap. 3.95 (ISBN 0-8423-1239-0). Tyndale.

--Safety Zones: Finding Refuge in Times of Turmoil. 220p. 1987. 12.95 (ISBN 0-8499-0555-9). Word Bks.

Skogsbergh, Helga. From These Shores. (Illus.). 1975. pap. 1.50 (ISBN 0-910452-22-9). Covenant.

Slater, Michael. Stretcher Bearers. LC 85-8389. 168p. 1985. pap. write for info. (ISBN 0-8307-1044-2, 5418505). Regal.

Sleeth, Natalie. Adventures for the Soul. 139p. 1987. pap. 5.95 (ISBN 0-916642-30-5, 785). Hope Pub.

Sloat, John W. Lord, Make Us One. 144p. 1986. pap. 7.95 (ISBN 0-8170-1101-3). Judson.

Sloath, Donald E. The Dangers of Growing up in a Christian Home. 224p. 1986. pap. 8.95 (ISBN 0-8407-3064-0). Nelson.

Slocum, Robert. Ordinary Christians in a High-Tech World. 224p. 1986. 10.95 (ISBN 0-8499-0490-0, 0490-0); pap. 9.95 (ISBN 0-8499-3046-4). Word Bks.

Slosser, Bob. Miracle in Darien. LC 79-83791. 1979. 5.95 (ISBN 0-88270-355-2). Bridge Pub.

Slover, Luella, ed. Life after Youth. 1981. pap. 4.50 (ISBN 0-8309-0303-8). Herald Hse.

Smalley, Gary. Joy That Lasts: How to Have an Overflowing Life. 144p. 1986. pap. 11.95 (ISBN 0-310-46290-8, 18254). Zondervan.

--The Key to Your Child's Heart. 160p. 1984. 10.95 (ISBN 0-8499-0433-1, 0433-1). Word Bks.

Smart, Ninian. The Religious Experience of Mankind. 3rd ed. LC 83-20169. (Illus.). 634p. 1984. pap. text ed. 17.95 (ISBN 0-02-412130-4, Pub. by Scribner). Macmillan.

--Teacher & Christian Belief. 208p. 1966. 6.95 (ISBN 0-227-67703-X). Attic Pr.

Smedes, Lewis B. How Can It Be All Right When Everything Is All Wrong. LC 82-47756. 128p. (Orig.). 1982. pap. 6.95 (ISBN 0-06-067409-1, RD398, HarpR). Har-Row.

--Mere Morality: What God Expects from Ordinary People. 292p. 1987. pap. 9.95 (ISBN 0-8028-0257-5). Eerdmans.

Smith. Spiritual Living. 1978. pap. 2.95 (ISBN 0-8423-6410-2). Tyndale.

Smith, Alvin O. There is a Solution. 1983. 5.95 (ISBN 0-8062-1951-3). Carlton.

Smith, Austine. If That Isn't Love. 132p. 1985. pap. 5.95 (ISBN 0-88144-036-1). Christian Pub.

Smith, Charles R. Can You Know God's Will for Your Life? 1979. pap. 1.00 (ISBN 0-88469-044-X). BMH Bks.

--Did Christ Die Only for the Elect? 1979. pap. 1.00 (ISBN 0-88469-025-3). BMH Bks.

--The New "Life after Death" Religion. 1980. pap. 1.00 (ISBN 0-88469-125-X). BMH Bks.

Smith, Edward P. Gerty's Papa's Civil War. Armstrong, William H., ed. (Illus.). 128p. (Orig.). 1984. pap. 7.95 (ISBN 0-8298-0703-9). Pilgrim NY.

Smith, H. Gleanings on the Church. 85p. pap. 4.95 (ISBN 0-88172-150-6). Believers Bkshelf.

Smith, Hannah W. Christian's Secret of a Happy Life. 256p. 1968. o. p. 8.95 (ISBN 0-8007-0044-9); pap. 6.95 (ISBN 0-8007-5004-7, Power Bks); pap. 3.50 (ISBN 0-8007-8007-8, Spire Bks). Revell.

--The Christian's Secret of a Happy Life. 240p. 1983. pap. text ed. 3.50 (ISBN 0-88368-132-3). Whitaker Hse.

--The Christian's Secret of a Happy Life. (Christian Library). 1985. 6.95 (ISBN 0-916441-21-0); pap. 3.95 (ISBN 0-916441-27-X). Barbour & Co.

--The Christian's Secret of a Happy Life. 224p. 1986. pap. 2.50 (ISBN 0-345-33586-4, Pub. by Ballantine Epiphany). Ballantine.

--God of All Comfort. 1956. pap. 4.50 (ISBN 0-8024-0018-3). Moody.

--Living Confidently in God's Love. Orig. Title: Living in the Sunshine the God of All Comfort. 192p. 1984. pap. text ed. 3.50 (ISBN 0-88368-150-1). Whitaker Hse.

Smith, Harold I. You & Your Parents: Strategies for Building an Adult Relationship. 176p. (Orig.). 1987. pap. 8.95 (ISBN 0-8066-2267-9, 10-7407). Augsburg.

Smith, Hattie. Let's Talk it Over God! LC 84-50077. 105p. 1984. 5.95 (ISBN 0-938232-46-0). Winston-Derek.

Smith, James E. First & Second Kings. LC 78-300507. (The Bible Study Textbook Ser.). (Illus.). 1975. 17.50 (ISBN 0-89900-012-6). College Pr Pub.

Smith, Joyce M. Coping with Life & Its Problems. 1976. pap. 2.95 (ISBN 0-8423-0434-7). Tyndale.

--Giants, Lions & Fire. 1981. pap. 2.95 (ISBN 0-8423-1022-3). Tyndale.

--Growing in Faith. 1982. pap. 2.95 (ISBN 0-8423-1227-7). Tyndale.

--A Rejoicing Heart. 1979. pap. 2.95 (ISBN 0-8423-5418-2). Tyndale.

--Walking in the Light. 1980. pap. 2.95 (ISBN 0-8423-7813-8). Tyndale.

Smith, Judy G. Joyful Teaching - Joyful Learning. LC 86-71007. 104p. (Orig.). 1986. pap. 6.95 (ISBN 0-88177-031-0, DR031B). Discipleship Res.

Smith, Louis A. & Barndt, Joseph R. Beyond Brokenness. (Orig.). 1980. pap. 2.95 (ISBN 0-377-00100-7). Friend Pr.

Smith, M. Blaine. One of a Kind: A Biblical View of Self-Acceptance. LC 84-574. 140p. 1984. pap. 3.95 (ISBN 0-87784-921-8). Inter-Varsity.

Smith, Tedra G. How Is Your Public Image? (Orig.). 1977. pap. 2.75 (ISBN 0-89536-096-9, 0823). CSS of Ohio.

Smith, Timothy L. Called unto Holiness, Vol. 1. LC 62-11409. 416p. 1962. 14.95 (ISBN 0-8341-0282-X). Beacon Hill.

Smith, Wilfred C. Religious Diversity. (Crossroad Paperback Ser.). 224p. 1982. pap. 7.95 (ISBN 0-8245-0458-5). Crossroad NY.

Smock, Martha. Listen, Beloved. LC 80-50624. 177p. 1980. 5.95 (ISBN 0-87159-101-4). Unity School.

--Meet It with Faith. 1966. 5.95 (ISBN 0-87159-097-2). Unity School.

--Turning Points. LC 75-41954. 1976. 5.95 (ISBN 0-87159-156-1). Unity School.

Smoke, Jim. Every Single Day. 256p. 1983. 6.95 (ISBN 0-8007-5120-5, Power Bks). Revell.

Smoke, Jim & McAfee, Lisa. Living Beyond Divorce: Working Guide. LC 83-82321. (Orig.). 1985. pap. 5.95 (ISBN 0-89081-407-4); working guide 3.95 (ISBN 0-89081-467-8). Harvest Hse.

Smyres, Roy S. The Thoughts of Chairman Smyres: Chairman, under God, of His Own Life & Thought. vi, 146p. (Orig.). 1986. pap. 8.00 (ISBN 0-9616952-0-X). Smyres Pubns.

Snowden, Rita. Christianity Close to Life. (Crossroad Paperback Ser.). 160p. 1982. pap. 5.95 (ISBN 0-8245-0459-3). Crossroad NY.

Snyder, Chuck. Other Than That I Have No Opinion. 240p. (Orig.). 1985. pap. 5.95 (ISBN 0-8423-4763-1). Tyndale.

Snyder, Helen L. Five Dollar Convention. (Orig.). 1982. pap. 2.95 (ISBN 0-937172-31-6). JLJ Pubs.

--Shall We Take Down the Steeple? (Orig.). 1982. pap. 2.95 (ISBN 0-937172-42-1). JLJ Pubs.

--Why Be Without a Gripe? 1978. pap. 5.00 (ISBN 0-89536-310-0, 2344). CSS of Ohio.

Snyder, John I. The Promise of His Coming. LC 85-52310. 192p. 1986. pap. text ed. 12.50 (ISBN 0-936029-01-3). Western Bk Journ.

Snyder, Pam. A Life Styled by God: A Woman's Workshop on Spiritual Discipline for Weight Control. (Woman's Workshop Ser.). 112p. (Orig.). 1985. pap. 2.95 (ISBN 0-310-42791-6, 11378P). Zondervan.

Soderman, Danuta. A Passion for Living. 1987. 11.95 (ISBN 0-8007-1534-9). Revell.

Soelle, Dorothee. Choosing Life. Kohl, Margaret, tr. from Ger. LC 81-43082. Tr. of Wahlt das Leben. 128p. 1981. 9.95 (ISBN 0-8006-0667-1, 1-667). Fortress.

--The Strength of the Weak: Towards a Christian Feminist Identity. Kimber, Rita & Kimber, Robert, trs. LC 83-27348. 184p. (Orig.). 1984. pap. 9.95 (ISBN 0-664-24623-0). Westminster.

Soelle, Dorothee & Steffensky, Fulbert. Not Just Yes & Amen: Christians with a Cause. LC 84-48708. 96p. 1985. pap. 3.50 (ISBN 0-8006-1828-9, 1-1828). Fortress.

Sokolosky, Valerie. Seasons of Success. 1985. pap. 3.95 (ISBN 0-89274-382-4). Harrison Hse.

Solomon, C. R. Hacia la Felicidad: Como Vivir una Vida Victoriosa y Practicar la Terapia Espiritual. 1983. Repr. of 1979 ed. 3.75 (ISBN 0-311-42060-5). Casa Bautista.

Solomon, Charles. Handbook to Happiness. 1982. pap. 5.95 (ISBN 0-8423-1281-1); leader's guide 2.95 (ISBN 0-8423-1282-X). Tyndale.

Souter, John. Moods. 96p. (Orig.). 1986. 4.95 (ISBN 0-8423-4498-5). Tyndale.

Souter, John C. Growing Stronger-Advanced. 1980. study guide 2.95 (ISBN 0-8423-1234-X). Tyndale.

Sparkman, G. Temp. To Live with Hope. 112p. 1985. pap. 5.95 (ISBN 0-8170-1062-9). Judson.

The Special You. (Benziger Family Life Program Ser.). 6p. 1978. 2.45 (ISBN 0-02-651750-7); tchrs. ed. 4.00 (ISBN 0-02-651760-4); family handbook 1.00 (ISBN 0-02-651790-6). Benziger Pub Co.

Speer, Michael L. A Complete Guide to the Christian's Budget. new ed. LC 74-80341. 160p. 1975. pap. 3.25 (ISBN 0-8054-5227-3). Broadman.

Spirit of Grace. 1979. 2.50 (ISBN 0-681-98059-1); pap. 1.25 (ISBN 0-8198-0598-X). Dghtrs St Paul.

Spray, Pauline E. Coping with Tension. (Direction Bks). 136p. 1981. pap. 2.95 (ISBN 0-8010-8189-0). Baker Bk.

Spray, Russell E. Simple Outlines on the Christian Faith. (Dollar Sermon Library). 1977. pap. 1.95 (ISBN 0-8010-8120-3). Baker Bk.

Springer, Rebecca R. Intra Muros: My Dream of Heaven. LC 78-67820. 1985. pap. 1.75 (ISBN 0-932484-01-8). Book Searchers.

Sproul, R. C. Basic Training: Plain Talk on the Key Truths of the Faith. 176p. (Orig.). 1982. pap. 5.95 (ISBN 0-310-44921-9, 12371P). Zondervan.

--God's Will & the Christian. 96p. 1984. 2.95 (ISBN 0-8423-1096-7). Tyndale.

Spruce, James R. Come, Let Us Worship. 118p. 1986. pap. 3.95 (ISBN 0-8341-1028-8). Beacon Hill.

Spurgeon, C. H. According to Promise. 106p. pap. 2.00 (ISBN 0-89323-003-0, 442). Bible Memory.

--According to Promise. 1979. pap. 2.50 (ISBN 0-686-26192-5). Pilgrim Pubns.

--All of Grace. 1978. pap. 2.25 (ISBN 0-686-00497-3). Pilgrim Pubns.

--Election. 1978. pap. 1.50 (ISBN 0-686-00503-1). Pilgrim Pubns.

Spykman, Gordon. Never On Your Own. 125p. 1983. pap. 4.95 (ISBN 0-933140-85-1); Pt. 1, 48pgs. student manual 1.95 (ISBN 0-933140-86-X); Pt. 2, 48pgs. student manual 1.95 (ISBN 0-933140-87-8). CRC Pubns.

Stadler, Richard H. Living As a Winner. Fischer, William E., ed. (Bible Class Course for Young Adults Ser.). (Illus.). 64p. 1985. pap. 2.95 leaders guide (ISBN 0-938272-23-3); pap. 2.95 students guide (ISBN 0-938272-22-5). WELS Board.

Stafford, Bill. The Adventure of Giving. Griffin, Ted, ed. 128p. (Orig.). 1985. pap. 4.95 (ISBN 0-8423-0036-8). Tyndale.

Stafford, Gilbert W. The Life of Salvation. 1979. pap. 3.95 (ISBN 0-87162-216-5, D5210). Warner Pr.

Stahl, Martha D. By Birth or by Choice. LC 86-33643. 136p. (Orig.). 1987. pap. 5.95 (ISBN 0-8361-3437-0). Herald Pr.

Standiford, Steven & Standiford, Deborah. Sudden Family. 160p. 1986. 9.95 (ISBN 0-8499-0567-2). Word Bks.

Stanford, Miles J. The Complete Green Letters. 368p. 1984. pap. 9.95 (ISBN 0-310-33051-3, 9480, Clarion Class). Zondervan.

Stanley, Phyllis & Yih, Miltinnie. Celebrate the Seasons! 119p. (Orig.). 1986. pap. 4.95 (ISBN 0-89109-116-5). NavPress.

Staten, Ralph. Perseverance in Preservation. 36p. 1975. pap. 0.95 (ISBN 0-89265-109-1). Randall Hse.

Staton, Knofel. Check Your Commitment: Instructor. 160p. 1985. pap. 3.50 (ISBN 0-87239-828-5, 39982). Standard Pub.

--Check Your Commitment: Student. 128p. 1985. pap. 2.95 (ISBN 0-87239-829-3, 39983). Standard Pub.

--Check Your Discipleship. LC 81-9411. 116p. (Orig., Student's & instructor's ed. bnd. together). 1982. pap. 2.25 student ed. (ISBN 0-87239-424-7, 39991); instructor's ed. 2.50 (ISBN 0-87239-423-9, 39990). Standard Pub.

--Check Your Homelife. LC 82-19600. 176p. (Orig.). 1983. pap. 4.95 (ISBN 0-87239-649-5, 39973). Standard Pub.

--Check Your Life in Christ. 160p. pap. 2.95x (ISBN 0-89900-203-X). College Pr Pub.

--Grow, Christian, Grow: Student. LC 77-82120. (New Life Ser.). (Illus.). 1978. pap. 2.25 (ISBN 0-87239-177-9, 39999). Standard Pub.

--What to Do till Jesus Comes. LC 81-14594. 112p. 1983. pap. 2.25 (ISBN 0-87239-481-6, 41016). Standard Pub.

Stauffer, Romaine H. Hidden Riches. 1983. 4.70 (ISBN 0-87813-520-0). Christian Light.

Stearns, Bill. If the World Fits, You're the Wrong Size. 1981. pap. 2.95 (ISBN 0-88207-588-8). SP Pubns.

--If the World Fits, You're the Wrong Size. 1981. pap. 3.95 (ISBN 0-88207-588-8). Victor Bks.

Steere, Douglas. Together in Solitude. LC 82-14918. 160p. 1983. 12.95 (ISBN 0-8245-0531-X). Crossroad NY.

--Together in Solitude. rev. ed. 208p. 1985. pap. 8.95 (ISBN 0-8245-0715-0). Crossroad NY.

Steidl, G. Basics of Assembly Life. pap. 3.75 (ISBN 0-88172-126-3). Believers Bkshelf.

Stein, Jock, ed. Ministers for the Nineteen Eighties. 120p. 1980. pap. 6.00x (ISBN 0-905312-09-0, Pub. by Scot Acad Pr). Longwood Pub Group.

Steinberger, G. In the Footprints of the Lamb. Christensen, Bernard, tr. LC 78-73416. 96p. 1979. pap. 2.95 (ISBN 0-87123-237-5, 200237). Bethany Hse.

Steiner, Susan C. Joining the Army That Sheds No Blood. LC 82-81510. (Christian Peace Shelf Ser.). 176p. (Orig.). 1982. pap. 6.95 (ISBN 0-8361-3305-6). Herald Pr.

Stephan, Eric & Smith, Judith S. What Happy Families Are Doing. LC 81-15151. 131p. 1981. 7.95 (ISBN 0-87747-877-5). Deseret Bk.

Sterk, Andrea & Scazzero, Peter. Christian Character. (Lifebuilder Bible Studies). 60p. (Orig.). 1985. pap. text ed. 2.95 (ISBN 0-8308-1054-4). Inter-Varsity.

--Christian Disciplines: Living the Way God Wants You to Live. (LifeBuilder Bible Studies). 64p. (Orig.). 1986. pap. 2.95 (ISBN 0-8308-1055-2). Inter-Varsity.

Stern, Chaim. Gates of Forgiveness: Selichot. 1980. pap. 1.00 ea. Eng. Ed (ISBN 0-916694-57-7). Hebrew Ed (ISBN 0-916694-74-7). Central Conf.

Stevens, Margaret M. Prosperity Is God's Idea. (Illus.). 1978. pap. 4.50 (ISBN 0-87516-264-9). De Vorss.

Stevens, Velma D. God Is Faithful. LC 86-921. 1986. pap. 3.25 (ISBN 0-8054-5028-9). Broadman.

Stevens, Woodie. How to Fill the Emptiness. (Christian Living Ser.). 32p. (Orig.). 1987. pap. write for info. (ISBN 0-8341-1188-8). Beacon Hill.

Stewart, Avy. The Travelers. (Orig.). 1982. pap. 2.95 (ISBN 0-937172-36-7). JLJ Pubs.

Stewart, Ed & Fishwick, Nina M. Group Talk. LC 85-30142. 162p. (Orig.). 1986. pap. 5.95 (ISBN 0-8307-1139-2, S411103). Regal.

Stewart, Stan & Hubner, Pauline. Talking about Something Important. 128p. (Orig.). 1981. pap. 7.95 (ISBN 0-85819-328-0, Pub. by JBCE). ANZ Religious Pubns.

Stob, George. That I May Know. 128p. 1982. pap. 3.95 (ISBN 0-933140-51-7); pap. 3.95 student wkbk (ISBN 0-933140-52-5). CRC Pubns.

Stobbe, Leslie H. Living with Others. 1986. pap. 4.95 (ISBN 0-8010-8275-7). Baker Bk.

Stoddard, Sandol. God's Little House. (Orig.). 1984. pap. 1.95 (ISBN 0-8091-6553-8). Paulist Pr.

Stoesz, Cheryl & Brandt, Gilbert. Struggle of Love. 110p. (Orig.). 1983. pap. 4.95 (ISBN 0-919797-08-3). Kindred Pr.

Stoesz, Samuel S. Life Is for Growth. 1977. pap. 2.25 (ISBN 0-87509-102-4); leaders guide 1.25 (ISBN 0-87509-169-5). Chr Pubns.

Stoffel, Ernest L. The Dragon Bound: Revelation Speaks to Our Times. 120p. (Orig.). 1981. pap. 5.25 (ISBN 0-8042-0227-3). John Knox.

Stone, H. Lynn. Sing a New Song. LC 81-85596. 123p. (Orig.). 1981. pap. text ed. 3.00 (ISBN 0-87148-798-5). Pathway Pr.

Stone, Hoyt. The Inner Quest. 1980. pap. 6.25 (ISBN 0-87148-435-8). Pathway Pr.

Stone, Hoyt E. Dare to Live Free. 132p. 1984. pap. 4.95 (ISBN 0-88207-617-5). Victor Bks.

--Using Our Gifts. 38p. (Orig.). 1981. pap. text ed. 1.00 (ISBN 0-87148-880-9). Pathway Pr.

Stone, James. How to Become a Star. (How To Ser.). 72p. (Orig.). pap. 2.50 (ISBN 0-934942-38-2). White Wing Pub.

Stoop, David. Self Talk. 160p. 1981. pap. 5.95 (ISBN 0-8007-5074-8, Power Bks). Revell.

Storey, William G. Lest We Forget. 176p. (Orig.). 1985. pap. 4.95 (ISBN 0-8091-2718-0). Paulist Pr.

Storms, Kathleen. Simplicity of Life As Lived in the Everyday. LC 83-16812. 322p. (Orig.). 1984. lib. bdg. 27.75 (ISBN 0-8191-3601-8); pap. text ed. 13.75 (ISBN 0-8191-3602-6). U Pr of Amer.

Story, Grace C. Footprints on the Sands of China. pap. 2.25 (ISBN 0-686-13722-1). Crusade Pubs.

Stott, John. Involvement, Vol. I: Being a Responsible Christian in a Non-Christian Society. (Crucial Questions Ser.). 224p. 1985. 13.95 (ISBN 0-8007-1418-0). Revell.

Stott, John R. Becoming a Christian. pap. 0.75 (ISBN 0-87784-100-4). Inter-Varsity.

--Being a Christian. pap. 0.75 (ISBN 0-87784-101-2). Inter-Varsity.

--One People. LC 84-72468. 127p. pap. 4.95 (ISBN 0-87509-324-8); leader's guide 2.95 (ISBN 0-87509-358-2). Chr Pubns.

--Your Mind Matters. LC 72-94672. 64p. 1973. pap. 3.50 (ISBN 0-87784-441-0). Inter-Varsity.

Stowell, Joseph. Tongue in Check. 132p. pap. 4.95 (ISBN 0-88207-293-5). Victor Bks.

Stowell, Joseph M. Fan the Flame: Living Out Your First Love for Christ. (Orig.). 1986. pap. 5.95 (ISBN 0-8024-2528-3). Moody.

--Through the Fire. 156p. 1985. pap. 5.95 (ISBN 0-89693-601-5). Victor Bks.

Strasheim, Linda & Bence, Evelyn. Something Beautiful. 160p. (Orig.). 1985. pap. 5.95 (ISBN 0-310-29391-X, 10467P). Zondervan.

Straughn, Harold. Five Divorces of a Healthy Marriage. Lambert, Herbert, ed. LC 85-29923. 160p. (Orig.). 1986. pap. 10.95 (ISBN 0-8272-2318-8). CBP.

Strauss, Lehman. Certainties for Today. 1956. pap. 3.25 (ISBN 0-87213-810-0). Loizeaux.

Strauss, Richard. How to Really Know the Will of God. 1982. pap. 5.95 (ISBN 0-8423-1537-3); 2.95 (ISBN 0-8423-1538-1). Tyndale.

--Win the Battle for Your Mind. 132p. 1986. pap. 5.95 (ISBN 0-87213-835-6). Loizeaux.

Strauss, Richard L. Famous Couples of the Bible. Chen, Ruth T., tr. (Chinese.). 1985. pap. write for info. (ISBN 0-941598-29-2). Living Spring Pubns.

Stravinskas, Peter. Essentials of Religious Life Today. (Orig.). pap. price not set (ISBN 0-913382-34-5, 101-34). Prow Bks-Franciscan.

Streib, Betty. Light to Light. 1981. 10.00 (ISBN 0-89536-486-7, 1238). CSS of Ohio.

Stringfellow, Bill. The Ultimate Ripoff. LC 81-49329. 176p. 1981. pap. 3.95 (ISBN 0-939286-00-9). Concerned Pubns.

Strong, June. Where Are We Running? LC 78-26271. (Orion Ser.). 1979. pap. 3.50 (ISBN 0-8127-0207-7). Review & Herald.

Strong, Kendrick. Coping Is Not Enough. LC 86-23260. (Orig.). 1987. text ed. 7.95 (ISBN 0-8054-5042-4). Broadman.

Strubhar, Roy A., compiled by. Sing Unto God. 1972. pap. 1.00x (ISBN 0-87813-108-6). Park View.

Stugard, Christine. Living Bread. (Illus.). 80p. (Orig.). 1983. pap. 4.95 (ISBN 0-88028-023-9). Forward Movement.

Stuhmueller, Carroll C. Biblical Meditations for the Easter Season. LC 80-81030. 256p. 1980. pap. 4.95 (ISBN 0-8091-2283-9). Paulist Pr.

Stump, Gladys S. About God's People, Bk. 4. (Special Ser.). 144p. 1983. pap. 7.95 (ISBN 0-8163-0461-0). Pacific Pr Pub Assn.

--About People for a Special Time. 1981. pap. 7.95 (ISBN 0-8163-0353-3). Pacific Pr Pub Assn.

--About When Satan Tried to Rule, Bk. 2. LC 79-84610. 1980. pap. 7.95 (ISBN 0-8163-0381-9, 01056-1). Pacific Pr Pub Assn.

Subramuniya. I'm All Right, Right Now. pap. 1.00 (ISBN 0-87516-355-6). De Vorss.

--On the Brink of the Absolute. pap. 1.00 (ISBN 0-87516-359-9). De Vorss.

Suenens, Leon J. Nature & Grace: A Vital Unity. (Malines Document Ser.: No. V). (Fr.). 80p. (Orig.). 1986. pap. 5.95 (ISBN 0-89283-303-3). Servant.

Summers, Georgianna. Stress! How Christian Parents Cope. LC 86-71746. 80p. (Orig.). 1986. pap. 5.95 (ISBN 0-88177-032-9, DR032B). Discipleship Res.

Summers, Ray. Digno es el Cordero. Lerin, Alfredo, tr. from Eng. Orig. Title: Worthy is the Lamb. (Span.). 287p. 1981. pap. 4.95 (ISBN 0-311-04305-4). Casa Bautista.

Sumner, Robert L. Powerhouse. 1978. pap. 3.95 (ISBN 0-914012-18-5, Pub. by Bibl Evang Pr). Sword of Lord.

Sumrall, Lester. Take It, It's Yours. 140p. (Orig.). 1986. pap. text ed. 3.95 (ISBN 0-88368-174-9). Whitaker Hse.

Suso, Henry. The Life of the Servant. 144p. 1983. pap. 11.95 (ISBN 0-227-67862-1, Pub. by J Clarke UK). Attic Pr.

Sustar, T. David. A Sure Foundation. LC 80-84008. 124p. (Orig.). 1980. pap. text ed. 3.00 (ISBN 0-87148-795-0); 2.00 (ISBN 0-87148-436-6). Pathway Pr.

Sutton, Hilton. The Devil Ain't What He Used to Be. 78p. (Orig.). 1982. pap. 2.25 (ISBN 0-89274-255-0). Harrison Hse.

Swafford, Z. W. Living for God. (God & Us Ser.). 32p. 1981. pap. 2.00 (ISBN 0-89114-099-9); coloring book 0.69 (ISBN 0-89114-102-2). Baptist Pub Hse.

--Serving God. (God & Us Ser.). 32p. 1981. pap. 2.00 (ISBN 0-89114-097-2); pap. 0.69 coloring bk. (ISBN 0-89114-098-0). Baptist Pub Hse.

Swafford, Mrs. Z. W. Worshiping God. (God & Us Ser.). 32p. 1983. pap. 2.00 (ISBN 0-89114-103-0); coloring book 0.69 (ISBN 0-89114-104-9). Baptist Pub Hse.

Swanson, Richard. Spare Your People! LC 85-73213. 1986. pap. 3.50 (ISBN 0-88270-596-2). Bridge Pub.

Swanson, Steve. What Does God Want Me to Do with My Life? How to Decide about School, Job, Friends, Sex, Marriage. LC 79-50086. 104p. 1979. pap. 3.95 (ISBN 0-8066-1722-5, 10-7046). Augsburg.

Swatos, William. Into Denominationalism. LC 79-53776. (Monograph: No. 2). 1979. pap. 5.50 (ISBN 0-932566-01-4). Soc Sci Stud Rel.

Sweet, Charles F. Champion of the Cross. LC 76-144692. Repr. of 1894 ed. 27.50 (ISBN 0-404-07202-X). AMS Pr.

Sweet, Leonard I. New Life in the Spirit. LC 81-23112. (Library of Living Faith: Vol. 4). 120p. (Orig.). 1982. pap. 5.95 (ISBN 0-664-24414-9). Westminster.

Sweeting, George. The Basics of the Christian Life. rev. ed. (Moody Press Electives Ser.). 1983. pap. 3.95 (ISBN 0-8024-0259-3); Leader's Guide. pap. 2.50 (ISBN 0-8024-0309-3). Moody.

--Catch the Spirit of Love. 120p. 1983. pap. 4.95 (ISBN 0-88207-108-4). Victor Bks.

--Como Iniciar la Vida Cristiana. Orig. Title: How to Begin the Christian Life. (Span.). 1977. pap. 3.50 (ISBN 0-8254-1697-3). Kregel.

--Faith that Works: Study of the Book of James. 1983. pap. 3.95 (ISBN 0-8024-0276-3). Moody.

--How to Begin the Christian Life. LC 75-31674. 128p. 1976. pap. 3.50 (ISBN 0-8024-3626-9). Moody.

Sweeting, George & Sweeting, Donald. Acts of God. (Orig.). 1986. pap. 6.95 (ISBN 0-8024-0497-9). Moody.

Sweeting, George W. You Can Climb Higher: The Christian Persuit of Excellence. 192p. 1985. 10.95 (ISBN 0-8407-5424-8). Nelson.

Swenson, Roger, ed. The Serious Season. LC 86-25876. 116p. (Orig.). 1987. pap. 7.95 (ISBN 0-8189-0512-3). Alba.

Swetmon, Bill. A Giving Heart. 162p. (Orig.). 1986. pap. 3.95 (ISBN 0-89225-288-X). Gospel Advocate.

Swift, Helen C. How Blest You Are: A Living-Room Retreat Based on the Beatitudes. 85p. 1984. pap. 3.50 (ISBN 0-86716-033-0). St Anthony Mess Pr.

Swindoll, Charles. Afirme Sus Valores. Araujo, Juan, tr. from Eng. Orig. Title: Strengthening Your Grip. (Span.). 256p. 1987. pap. 4.95 (ISBN 0-88113-087-7). Edit Betania.

--Strengthening Your Grip. 1986. deluxe ed. 9.95 (ISBN 0-8499-3852-X). Word Bks.

Swindoll, Charles A. Dropping Your Guard. 1986. deluxe ed. 9.95 (ISBN 0-8499-3850-3). Word Bks.

Swindoll, Charles R. Dropping Your Guard. 224p. 1987. pap. 3.50 (ISBN 0-553-26324-2). Bantam.

--Growing Deep in the Christian Life: Returning to Our Roots. LC 86-8661. 1986. 14.95 (ISBN 0-88070-154-4). Multnomah.

--Improving Your Serve: The Art of Unselfish Living. 1981. 10.95 (ISBN 0-8499-0267-3). Word Bks.

--Killing Giants, Pulling Thorns. LC 78-57675. (Illus.). 1978. pap. 9.95 (ISBN 0-930014-25-1). Multnomah.

--Starting over: Fresh Hope for the Road Ahead. LC 82-24636. 1983. pap. 5.95 (ISBN 0-88070-015-7). Multnomah.

--Strenghtening Your Grip. 272p. 1986. pap. 3.50 (ISBN 0-553-25923-7). Bantam.

--Strengthening Your Grip. 236p. 1982. 12.95 (ISBN 0-8499-0312-2). Word Bks.

--Strengthening Your Grip. 1986. 3.50 (ISBN 0-8499-4176-8). Word Bks.

--Three Steps Forward, Two Steps Back. 320p. 1985. pap. 11.95 (ISBN 0-8027-2506-6). Walker & Co.

--You & Your Child. 2nd ed. 1982. pap. 4.95 (ISBN 0-8407-5616-X). Nelson.

Swindoll, Chuck. Compassion: Life Maps. 64p. 1984. 5.95 (ISBN 0-8499-0443-9, 0443-9). Word Bks.

--Victory: Life Maps. 64p. 1984. 5.95 (ISBN 0-8499-0442-0, 0442-0). Word Bks.

Swindoll, Luci. You Bring the Confetti. 160p. 1986. 9.95 (ISBN 0-8499-0527-3). Word Bks.

Swischuk, Leonard. Emergency Radiology of the Acutely Ill or Injured Child. 2nd ed. (Illus.). 656p. 1985. text ed. 78.50 (ISBN 0-683-08049-0). Williams & Wilkins.

Swope, Mary R. Are You Sick & Tired? 176p. (Orig.). 1984. pap. 3.95 (ISBN 0-88368-149-8). Whitaker Hse.

Swor, Chester E. The Best of Chester Swor. LC 81-67202. 1981. pap. 6.95 (ISBN 0-8054-5293-1). Broadman.

Synan, Joseph A. Christian Life in Depth. 3.95 (ISBN 0-911866-60-4); pap. 2.95 (ISBN 0-911866-87-6). Advocate.

Tait, Vera D. Take Command. LC 80-53217. 144p. 1981. 5.95 (ISBN 0-87159-150-2). Unity School.

Talbot, John M. The Fire of God. 144p. 1986. pap. 7.95 (ISBN 0-8245-0789-4). Crossroad NY.

Tan, Paul L. Jesus Is Coming. 1982. pap. 2.95 (ISBN 0-88469-095-4). BMH Bks.

Tapscott, Betty. Set Free. 1978. pap. 4.95 (ISBN 0-917726-24-3). Hunter Bks.

Tari, Mel & Dudley, Cliff. America! Jesus Is Here! LC 76-1058. 1976. 4.95 (ISBN 0-89221-021-4). New Leaf.

--Like a Mighty Wind. 171p. 1978. pap. 4.95 (ISBN 0-89221-123-7). New Leaf.
Tari, Mel & Tari, Noni. Gentle Breeze of Jesus. 125p. pap. 4.95 (ISBN 0-89221-122-9). New Leaf.
Taylor, A., Jr. The Life of My Years. 160p. (Orig.). 1983. pap. 9.95 (ISBN 0-687-21854-3). Abingdon.
Taylor, Charles R. Get All Excited-Jesus is Coming Soon. (Illus.). 108p. (Orig.). 1975. pap. 2.95 (ISBN 0-937682-00-4). Today Bible.
--Pretribulation Rapture & the Bible. (Illus.). 40p. (Orig.). 1980. pap. 1.50 (ISBN 0-937682-03-9). Today Bible.
--Those Who Remain. (Illus.). 104p. (Orig.). 1980. pap. 2.95 (ISBN 0-937682-02-0). Today Bible.
Taylor, Dan. The Myth of Certainty. 128p. 1986. 10.95 (ISBN 0-8499-0547-8). Word Bks.
Taylor, Jack. Much More! LC 72-79179. 160p. 1972. 8.95 (ISBN 0-8054-5523-X). Broadman.
Taylor, Jack R. God's New Creation. 1987. 8.95 (ISBN 0-8054-5046-7). Broadman.
--The Key to Triumphant Living. 208p. 1986. pap. 3.50 (ISBN 0-553-26031-6). Bantam.
--La Llave para una Vida de Triunfo. Guzman, Juan P., tr. from Eng. Orig. Title: The Key to Triumphant Living. 240p. 1982. pap. 6.25 (ISBN 0-311-46095-X, Edit Mundo). Casa Bautista.
Taylor, Jack R. & Hawkins, C. S. When Revival Comes. LC 80-66956. 1980. pap. 5.50 (ISBN 0-8054-6226-0). Broadman.
Taylor, Jeremy. Holy Living & Holy Dying. Hinten, Marvin D., ed. 80p. 1986. pap. 3.95 (ISBN 0-8423-1350-8). Tyndale.
--The Rule & Exercises of Holy Living & the Rule & Exercises of Holy Dying. LC 82-80478. (Treasures from the Spiritual Classics Ser.). 64p. 1982. pap. 2.95 (ISBN 0-8192-1309-8). Morehouse.
Taylor, Julia. Last, Least & Lowest. LC 78-70663. 1979. pap. 2.95 (ISBN 0-89221-058-3). New Leaf.
Taylor, Kenneth N. Giant Steps for Little People. 64p. 1985. 6.95 (ISBN 0-8423-1023-1). Tyndale.
--How to Grow. expanded ed. 192p. Date not set. pap. 7.95. Oliver-Nelson.
--How to Grow: First Steps for New Christians. 176p. 1985. 7.95 (ISBN 0-8407-9038-4). Oliver-Nelson.
Taylor, Richard S. The Disciplined Life. LC 62-7123. 112p. 1974. pap. 3.50 (ISBN 0-87123-098-4, 200098). Bethany Hse.
Taylor, Robert, Jr., ed. Christ in the Home. pap. 5.95 (ISBN 0-89137-314-4). Quality Pubns.
Taylor, Tom. New Life Principles. (Illus.). 1977. tchr's ed. 4.95 (ISBN 0-914936-26-3); wkbk. 1.10 (ISBN 0-914936-30-1). Bible Temple.
Tchividjian, Gigi. Thank You, Lord, for My Home. 1980. Repr. of 1979 ed. 3.95 (ISBN 0-89066-023-9). World Wide Pubs.
Tchividjian, Gigi G. Sincerely. 144p. 1984. 11.95 (ISBN 0-310-44850-6, 18272). Zondervan.
Temple, William. Christian Faith & Life. LC 82-80474. (Treasures from the Spiritual Classics Ser.). 64p. 1982. pap. 2.95 (ISBN 0-8192-1311-X). Morehouse.
Tengbom, M. Help for Families of the Terminally Ill. LC 12-2819. (Trauma Bks.: Ser. 2). 1983. pap. 2.75 ea. (ISBN 0-570-08256-0). Concordia.
Terry, Jack. The Way to Happiness in Your Home: Bible Study on Family Living. 36p. 1982. pap. 3.50 (ISBN 0-939298-06-6). J M Prods.
Testrake, John & Wimbish, Dave. Triumph over Terror on Flight 847. (Illus.). 1987. 14.95 (ISBN 0-8007-1527-6). Revell.
Thatcher, Martha. The Freedom of Obedience. (Christian Character Library). 1986. hdbk. 8.95 (ISBN 0-89109-541-1). NavPress.
Thiele, Margaret. Girl Alive. LC 80-11623. (Orion Ser.). 1980. pap. 3.95 (ISBN 0-8127-0268-9). Review & Herald.
Thielicke, Helmut. Christ & the Meaning of Life. Doberstein, J. W., tr. from Ger. 186p. 1978. Repr. 13.95 (ISBN 0-227-67684-X). Attic Pr.
Thigpen, Thomas P. Come Sing God's Song. (Illus.). 1987. 7.95. Cook.
Thomas, David M., ed. Family Life Ministry. LC 79-53513. (Marriage & Family Living in Depth Bk.). 1979. pap. 2.45 (ISBN 0-87029-157-2, 20243-2). Abbey.
Thomas, Edith L. The Whole World Singing. 1950. 6.95 (ISBN 0-377-30882-X); pap. 4.95 (ISBN 0-377-30881-1). Friend Pr.
Thomas, M. M. Christian Response to the Asian Revolution. 1968. pap. 1.75 (ISBN 0-377-82701-0). Friend Pr.
Thomas, Nancy. Of Deity & Bones. (Illus.). 90p. (Orig.). 1983. pap. 6.95 (ISBN 0-913342-38-6). Barclay Pr.
Thomas, R. B. You Are Gifted. (International Correspondence Program Ser.). (Orig.). 1985. pap. text ed. 6.95 (ISBN 0-87148-935-X). Pathway Pr.
Thomas, Roger W. People Power. LC 80-53675. 96p. (Orig.). 1982. pap. 2.25 (ISBN 0-87239-442-5, 40096). Standard Pub.
Thomas, W. Ian. The Saving Life of Christ. 1961. pap. 3.95 (ISBN 0-310-33262-1, 10908S). Zondervan.
Thomas a Kempis. The Imitation of Christ. Blaiklock, E. M., tr. LC 80-54894. 228p. 1981. pap. 5.95 (ISBN 0-8407-5760-3). Nelson.
--The Imitation of Christ. Helms, Hal M., ed. LC 82-61908. (Living Library Ser.). (Illus.). 280p. (Orig.). 1982. pap. 8.95 (ISBN 0-941478-07-6). Paraclete Pr.
--The Imitation of Christ. 240p. 1983. pap. 4.95 (ISBN 0-310-38441-9, 9283P, Clarion Class). Zondervan.
--Of the Imitation of Christ. 256p. 1981. pap. 2.95 (ISBN 0-88368-094-7). Whitaker Hse.
Thompson, David A. Recovering from Divorce. (Counseling Guides Ser.). 94p. (Orig.). 1982. pap. 5.95 Oversize (ISBN 0-87123-476-9, 210476). Bethany Hse.
Thompson, Jeanie. How to Enter the River. LC 84-62337. 61p. (Orig.). 1985. pap. 6.00 (ISBN 0-930100-18-2). Holy Cow.
Thompson, Ray. Battling with Belief. 79p. (Orig.). 1984. pap. 6.95 (ISBN 0-85819-518-6, Pub. by JBCE). ANZ Religious Pubns.
Thompson, Robert. The Land of Promise. pap. 5.95 (ISBN 0-89728-042-3, 670209). Omega Pubns OR.
Thompson, William D. Listening on Sunday for Sharing on Monday. 64p. 1983. pap. 3.95 (ISBN 0-317-00858-7). Judson.
Thor, Valiant. Outwitting Tomorrow. (Illus.). 64p. (Orig.). pap. 4.50 (ISBN 0-934414-00-9, Co Pub by Intl Evang). Hover.
Thornton, Martin. A Joyful Heart: Meditations for Lent. LC 86-32841. 76p. 1987. pap. 6.95 (ISBN 0-936384-45-X). Cowley Pubns.
The Three D Cookbook. LC 81-52188. 224p. 1982. 14.95 (ISBN 0-941478-01-7). Paraclete Pr.
Tileston, Mary W. Daily Strength for Daily Needs. LC 73-80030. (Large Print Christian Classic Ser.). 1982. 14.95 (ISBN 0-87983-287-8). Keats.
Tillard, J. M. Dilemmas of Modern Religious Life. (Consecrated Life Studies Ser.: Vol. 3). 1984. pap. 5.95 (ISBN 0-89453-446-7). M Glazier.
Tilley, Terrence. Story Theology. (Theology & Life Ser.: Vol. 12). 1985. pap. 10.95 (ISBN 0-89453-464-5). M Glazier.
Tillsley, Bramwell H. Life in the Spirit. 109p. (Orig.). 1986. pap. 4.95 (ISBN 0-86544-037-9). Salv Army Suppl South.
Tilton, Robert. Charting Your Course by the Dream in Your Heart. 178p. (Orig.). 1983. pap. text ed. 5.95 (ISBN 0-914307-11-8, Dist. by Harrison Hse). Word Faith.
--Charting Your Course by the Dream in Your Heart. 150p. (Orig.). 1986. pap. 5.95 (ISBN 0-89274-404-9). Harrison Hse.
--God's Laws of Success. 224p. (Orig.). 1983. pap. text ed. 7.95 (ISBN 0-914307-04-5, Dist. by Harrison Hse). Word Faith.
--Patience & Persistence. (Orig.). 1986. mini bk. 0.75 (ISBN 0-89274-413-8). Harrison Hse.
Timmer, John. They Shall Be My People. LC 83-15380. 200p. 1983. pap. 6.95 (ISBN 0-933140-82-7); pap. 5.95 leader's guide (ISBN 0-933140-83-5). CRC Pubns.
Timmerman, John. A Layman Looks at the Names of Jesus. 1985. pap. 4.95 (ISBN 0-8423-2110-1). Tyndale.
Tingley, Katherine. The Wisdom of the Heart: Katherine Tingley Speaks. Small, W. Emmett, ed. LC 78-65338. 1978. pap. 5.75 (ISBN 0-913004-33-2). Point Loma Pub.
Tinkle, William J. Heredity: A Study in Science & the Bible. LC 67-28034. 1967. 5.50 (ISBN 0-686-05046-0). St Thomas.
Tippit, Sammy. Fire in Your Heart: A Call to Personal Holiness. (Orig.). 1987. pap. 5.95 (ISBN 0-8024-2625-5). Moody.
Tiptaft, William. His People. pap. 0.75 (ISBN 0-685-88377-9). Reiner.
Tobin, Eamon. Help for Making Difficult Decisions. 32p. 1987. pap. 1.50 (ISBN 0-89243-267-5). Liguori Pubns.
--How to Forgive Yourself & Others. 32p. 1983. pap. 1.50 (ISBN 0-89243-197-0). Liguori Pubns.
Toews, Ed. Ministry to Single Adults. pap. 1.95 (ISBN 0-919797-48-2). Herald Pr.
Tolle, James M. Living Without Fear. 1977. 4.95 (ISBN 0-915378-13-2). Tolle Pubns.
Ton, Mary E. Las Llamas No Me Destruyeron. De Gutierrez, Edna L., tr. (Span.). 160p. 1985. pap. 4.95 (ISBN 0-311-46103-4). Casa Bautista.
Tonn, Katie. Expectations, Hopes, Dreams, Fantasies & Desires. (Uplook Ser.). 31p. 1978. pap. 0.99 (ISBN 0-8163-0346-0). Pacific Pr Pub Assn.
Toolan, Suzanne. Keeping Festival. 1979. pap. 4.95 (ISBN 0-89390-011-7). Resource Pubns.
Topete, Eutimio. Recordar Es Vivir. LC 78-71069. 1978. pap. 6.00 (ISBN 0-915808-32-3). Editorial Justa.
Tormey, John. To Love & Be Loved. 1979. pap. 1.95 (ISBN 0-89243-093-1). Liguori Pubns.
Torrey, R. A. The Baptism with the Holy Spirit. 96p. 1972. pap. 2.95 (ISBN 0-87123-029-1). Bethany Hse.
--How to Bring Men to Christ. 128p. 1981. pap. 2.95 (ISBN 0-88368-098-X). Whitaker Hse.
--How to Find Fullness of Power. Orig. Title: How to Obtain Fullness of Power. 112p. 1971. pap. 2.95 (ISBN 0-87123-219-7, 200219). Bethany Hse.
--How to Succeed in the Christian Life. pap. 3.50 (ISBN 0-8024-3659-5). Moody.
--How to Succeed in the Christian Life. 128p. 1984. pap. 3.50 (ISBN 0-88368-143-9). Whitaker Hse.
Torrey, R. A., ed. Get Ready for Forever. 176p. 1984. pap. text ed. 3.50 (ISBN 0-88368-160-9). Whitaker Hse.
Tournier, Paul. The Gift of Feeling. pap. 9.95 (ISBN 0-8042-2071-9). John Knox.
--A Listening Ear: Reflections on Christian Caring. Hudson, Paul, tr. from Fr. Tr. of Vivre a l'ecoute. 144p. 1987. pap. 7.95 (ISBN 0-8066-2266-0, 10-3900). Augsburg.
--The Person Reborn. LC 75-12283. 256p. 1975. (HarpR); pap. 1.95 (ISBN 0-06-068377-5, RD-327). Har-Row.
--To Understand Each Other. 6.95 (ISBN 0-8042-2235-5). John Knox.
Towner, Jason. Forgiveness Is for Giving. pap. 5.95 (ISBN 0-310-70231-3, 14027P). Zondervan.
Tozer, A. W. Paths to Power. 64p. pap. 1.75 (ISBN 0-87509-190-3). Chr Pubns.
--The Set of the Sail. Verploegh, Harry, ed. LC 86-70772. 90p. (Orig.). 1986. pap. 5.95 (ISBN 0-87509-379-5). Chr Pubns.
--Treasury of A. W. Tozer. 1979. 9.95 (ISBN 0-87509-281-0); pap. 4.45 (ISBN 0-87509-176-8). Chr Pubns.
Tozer, Aiden W. Of God & Men. pap. 4.45 (ISBN 0-87509-193-8); 2.95. Chr Pubns.
--Renewed Day by Day. LC 80-69301. 380p. 12.95 (ISBN 0-87509-252-7); pap. 7.95 kivar (ISBN 0-87509-292-6). Chr Pubns.
Tozer, James R. A Shared Adventure. 1985. 5.50 (ISBN 0-89536-736-X, 5820). CSS of Ohio.
Tozer, Tom. On the Road with Jesus. 1980. 3.95 (ISBN 0-89536-415-8, 1526). CSS of Ohio.
Traill, Robert. The Works of Robert Traill, 2 vols. 1975. Set. 28.95 (ISBN 0-85151-393-X). Vol. 1 (ISBN 0-85151-229-1). Vol. 2 (ISBN 0-85151-230-5). Banner of Truth.
Traver, Hope. Love Is for Tomorrow. 271p. 1978. pap. 3.95 (ISBN 0-930756-37-1, 531006). Aglow Pubns.
Trent, John. Growing Together. 156p. 1985. pap. 5.95 (ISBN 0-89693-323-7). Victor Bks.
Trese, Leo J. A Trilogy: More than Many Sparrows, Wisdom Shall Enter & Many Are One, 3 bks. in 1 vol. 271p. 1984. pap. 6.95 (ISBN 971-117-023-X, Pub. by Sinag-Tala Pubs Philippines). Scepter Pubs.
Trilling, Wolfgang. Conversations with Paul. 172p. 1987. 14.95 (ISBN 0-8245-0806-8). Crossroad NY.
Trobisch, Ingrid. On Our Way Rejoicing. LC 64-20195. (Harper Jubilee Book). 256p. 1976. pap. 3.95i (ISBN 0-06-068451-8, HJ-25, HarpR). Har-Row.
Trombley, Charles. Released to Reign. LC 79-90266. 1979. pap. 4.95 (ISBN 0-89221-064-8). New Leaf.
Trotter, Jesse M. Christian Wholeness: Spiritual Direction for Today. LC 81-84718. 80p. (Orig.). 1982. pap. 5.95 (ISBN 0-8192-1294-6). Morehouse.
True Bounds of Christian Freedom. 1978. pap. 5.45 (ISBN 0-85151-083-3). Banner of Truth.
Trumbull, Charles. Victory in Christ. 1970. pap. 2.95 (ISBN 0-87508-533-4). Chr Lit.
Trumbull, H. Clay. The Blood Covenant. 404p. 1975. pap. 5.95 (ISBN 0-89228-029-8). Impact Bks MO.
Tucker, Ronald D. & Hufton, Richard A. Foundations for Christian Growth. 2nd ed. (Illus.). 322p. 1981. incl. 6 cassettes 40.00 (ISBN 0-933643-16-0). Grace World Outreach.
--Foundations for Christian Growth. 3rd ed. LC 85-81911. (Illus.). 322p. 1985. pap. 10.00 (ISBN 0-933643-25-X). Grace World Outreach.
--God's Plan for Christian Service. (Illus.). 418p. 1982. 40.00 (ISBN 0-933643-17-9). Grace World Outreach.
--God's Plan for Christian Service. 2nd ed. LC 86-81343. 300p. 1987. pap. 10.00 (ISBN 0-933643-30-6). Grace World Outreach.
Tugwell, Simon & Hocken, Peter. New Heaven? New Earth? 1977. pap. 5.95 (ISBN 0-87243-072-3). Templegate.
Tula, Jeffries. Singleness of Purpose. LC 85-19525. (Orig.). 1986. pap. 3.25 (ISBN 0-8054-5029-7). Broadman.
Tully, Mary J. No Other God. 96p. 1984. pap. 3.50 (ISBN 0-697-01942-X). Wm C Brown.
--Los Salmos. Marquez, Angelina, tr. 1986. pap. 3.95 (ISBN 0-697-02202-1). Wm C Brown.
Tully, Mary Jo. Blessed Be. 96p. 1982. pap. 3.50 (ISBN 0-697-01822-9). Wm C Brown.
--Church: A Faith Filled People. 96p. 1982. pap. 3.50 (ISBN 0-697-01823-7). Wm C Brown.
Turner, F. Bernadette. God-Centered Therapy. 1968. pap. 4.95 (ISBN 0-8315-0182-0). Speller.
Turner, J. J. God's Way to the Top. 1983. pap. 4.25 (ISBN 0-89137-539-2). Quality Pubns.
--Positive Christian Living. pap. 4.25 (ISBN 0-89137-316-0). Quality Pubns.
--Winning Through Positive Spiritual Attitudes. pap. 4.25 (ISBN 0-89137-318-7). Quality Pubns.
Turning Point II. (Outreach Literature Ser.). 32p. (Orig.). 1986. pap. 0.45 (ISBN 0-932305-42-3, 612002). Aglow Pubns.
Tuttle, Anthony. With God on Our Side. 1978. pap. 2.25 (ISBN 0-89083-324-9). Zebra.
Tuttle, Robert G. Help Me God! It's Hard to Cope. 1984. 4.95 (ISBN 0-89536-698-3, 4881). CSS of Ohio.
Twenty-Fifth Anniversary: Voices from the Heart. Date not set. price not set (ISBN 0-934383-11-1). Pride Prods.
U Thant: Divinity's Smile and Humanity's Cry. pap. 4.95 (ISBN 0-88497-341-7). Aum Pubns.
Underhill, Evelyn. Abba. LC 82-80476. (Treasures from the Spiritual Classics Ser.). 64p. 1982. pap. 2.95 (ISBN 0-8192-1313-6). Morehouse.
--The Fruits of the Spirit. LC 82-80477. (Treasures from the Spiritual Classics Ser.). 64p. 1982. pap. 2.95 (ISBN 0-8192-1314-4). Morehouse.
Unknown Christian. How to Live the Victorious Life. Link, Julie, ed. 112p. 1986. pap. 2.95 (ISBN 0-310-33481-0, 6660P, Clarion Classics). Zondervan.
--The Kneeling Christian. 1979. pap. 2.95 (ISBN 0-310-33492-6, 6657P); large print kivar o.p. 6.95 (ISBN 0-310-33497-7). Zondervan.
Upchurch, T. Howell. How to Hear God. (Illus.). 24p. 1985. pap. text ed. 1.00 (ISBN 0-937778-09-5). Fulness Hse.
Vale, John & Hughes, Robert. Getting Even: Handling Conflict So Both Sides Win. 128p. 1987. pap. 5.95 (ISBN 0-310-35661-X). Zondervan.
Valenti, Tony & Yonan, Grazia P. The Tony Valenti Story. LC 80-83781. 160p. (Orig.). 1981. 2.50 (ISBN 0-88243-752-6, 02-0752). Gospel Pub.
Valenti-Hilliard, Beverly & Hilliard, Richard. Come & Celebrate: More Center Celebrations. LC 85-72456. (Illus.). 184p. (Orig.). 1985. tchr's guidebook 9.95 (ISBN 0-87793-289-1). Ave Maria.
Valentine, Foy. Problemas De Actualidad. Swenson, Ana M., tr. 38p. 1983. Repr. of 1981 ed. 1.50 (ISBN 0-311-46039-9). Casa Bautista.
Valery, Nicole. Prisoner Rejoice. 238p. 1980. pap. 4.95 (ISBN 0-88264-179-4). Diane Bks.
Van Breemen, Peter G. As Bread That Is Broken. 5.95 (ISBN 0-87193-052-8). Dimension Bks.
--Certain As the Dawn. pap. 6.95 (ISBN 0-87193-150-8). Dimension Bks.
Vandeman, George. Stuff of Survival. (Stories That Win Ser.). 1978. pap. 1.25 (ISBN 0-8163-0209-X, 19689-9). Pacific Pr Pub Assn.
Vandeman, Nellie. Not by Bread Alone. (Outreach Ser.). 1981. pap. 1.25 (ISBN 0-8163-0452-1). Pacific Pr Pub Assn.
Vandenbergh, C. W. Sunbursts for the Spirit. LC 79-90313. (Sunbursts for the Spirit Ser.: Vol. 1). (Illus.). 56p. (Orig.). 1979. pap. 3.25 (ISBN 0-935238-02-6). Pine Row.
Vander Lugt, Herbert. Fifty Plus. (Direction Bks.). Orig. Title: The Art of Growing Old. 110p. 1982. pap. 2.95 (ISBN 0-8010-9288-4). Baker Bk.
Van Dyke, Henry. The Other Wise Man. 63p. (Orig.). 1984. pap. 7.95 (ISBN 0-941478-33-5). Paraclete Pr.
Van Eaton, Hugh. Run Devil Run. (Illus.). 1975. pap. 3.95 (ISBN 0-89957-513-7). AMG Pubs.
Van Horn, Bill. A Light for All People. 1981. 3.50 (ISBN 0-89536-469-7, 1215). CSS of Ohio.
Vanier, Jean. Man & Woman He Made Them. 192p. 1985. pap. 6.95 (ISBN 0-8091-2751-2). Paulist Pr.
Van Impe, Jack. First Steps in a New Direction. 32p. 1980. pap. 0.45 (ISBN 0-934803-17-X). J Van Impe.
Van Kaam, Adrian. Looking for Jesus. pap. 4.95 (ISBN 0-87193-146-X); 7.95. Dimension Bks.
--Personality Fulfillment in the Spiritual Life. 4.95 (ISBN 0-87193-043-9). Dimension Bks.
--The Roots of Christian Joy. 1985. 8.95 (ISBN 0-87193-241-5). Dimension Bks.
Van Kaam, Adrian, et al. The Emergent Self, 4 bks. in 1. 1968. cancelled (ISBN 0-87193-165-6). Dimension Bks.

--The Participant Self, 2 vols. in 1. 1985. write for info. (ISBN 0-87193-160-5). Dimension Bks.

Van Note, Gene. A People Called Nazarenes. 120p. 1983. pap. 2.95 (ISBN 0-8341-0894-1). Beacon Hill.

Van Pelt, Nancy L. How to Turn Minuses into Pluses. Coffen, Richard W., ed. (Better Living Ser.). 32p. (Orig.). 1985. pap. 1.25 (ISBN 0-8280-0303-3). Review & Herald.

Van Rys, Janet. Walk with Praise. (Devotional Ser.). (Illus.). 200p. (Orig.). 1986. pap. 4.95 (ISBN 0-9616989-0-X). Jan Van Pubns.

Vanstone, W. H. The Stature of Waiting. 128p. (Orig.). 1983. pap. 8.95 (ISBN 0-8164-2478-0, HarpR). Har-Row.

Van Tatenhove, Frederick C. Ambition: Friend or Enemy? LC 84-5199. (Potentials; Guides for Productive Living Ser.: Vol. 11). 120p. 1984. pap. 7.95 (ISBN 0-664-24530-7). Westminster.

Van Zeller, Hubert. Prayer & the Will of God. 1978. 4.95 (ISBN 0-87243-084-7). Templegate.

--The Trodden Road. 173p. 1982. 4.00 (ISBN 0-8198-7326-8, SP0773); pap. 3.00 (ISBN 0-8198-7327-6). Dghtrs St Paul.

Varga, Andrew C. Main Issues in Bioethics. LC 80-82084. 240p. (Orig.). 1984. pap. 10.95 (ISBN 0-8091-2327-4). Paulist Pr.

Vasquez, Guillermo H. Lo Que los Padres y Maestros Deben Saber Acerca de las Drogas. 128p. 1984. pap. 1.20 (ISBN 0-311-46080-1). Casa Bautista.

Vaught, Laud O. God's Plan for the World, Old Testament Survey. LC 82-62742. (Illus.). 183p. (Orig.). 1983. pap. text ed. 6.95 (ISBN 0-87148-360-2). Pathway Pr.

Venden, Eileen. Higher Ground. (Anch Ser.). 1984. pap. 6.95 (ISBN 0-8163-0562-5). Pacific Pr Pub Assn.

Venden, Morris. From Exodus to Advent. LC 79-22389. (Orion Ser.). 1979. pap. 5.95 (ISBN 0-8127-0255-7). Review & Herald.

--Good News & Bad News: Haru Ser. 1984. pap. 4.95 (ISBN 0-8163-0484-X). Pacific Pr Pub Assn.

Venerable Louis of Granada. The Sinner's Guide. LC 84-51820. 395p. 1985. pap. 8.00 (ISBN 0-89555-254-X). Tan Bks Pubs.

Vernon, Ruth B. Manna in the Morning. 5.75 (ISBN 0-8062-2491-6). Carlton.

Versteeg, Robert. Whose Church Is This Anyway? 1985. 6.95 (ISBN 0-89536-767-X, 5874). CSS of Ohio.

Vicchio, Stephen. A Careful Disorder: Chronicles of Life & Love & Laughter. 300p. (Orig.). 1987. pap. 10.95 (ISBN 0-87061-135-6). Chr Classics.

Vichas, Robert. Annotated Handbook of Biblical Quotations, Verses, & Parables. LC 85-19346. 411p. 1985. 29.95 (ISBN 0-13-037870-4, Busn). P-H.

Vickers, Douglas. A Christian Approach to Economics & the Cultural Condition. 1982. 12.50 (ISBN 0-682-49831-9, University). Exposition Pr FL.

Vikler, Mark. Dialogue with God. LC 86-70744. 1986. pap. 5.95 (ISBN 0-88270-620-9). Bridge Pub.

Von Balthasar, Hans U. Glory of the Lord, Vol. 3. 416p. cancelled (ISBN 0-8245-0699-5). Crossroad NY.

Von Balthasar, Hans Urs. The Christian State of Life. McCarthy, Mary F., tr. from Ger. LC 82-84580. Tr. of Christlicher Stand. 505p. (Orig.). 1984. 24.95 (ISBN 0-89870-022-1). Ignatius Pr.

Von Hildebrand, Dietrich. Liturgy & Personality. LC 85-18388. 182p. 1986. 11.95 (ISBN 0-918477-03-4); pap. 7.95 (ISBN 0-918477-04-2). Sophia Inst Pr.

Von Kuehnelt-Leddihn, Erik. The Timeless Christian. LC 73-10604. 241p. 1976. 4.50 (ISBN 0-685-77519-4). Franciscan Herald.

Von Speyr, Adrienne. The Christian State of Life. McCarthy, Mary F., tr. from Ger. LC 85-81512. Orig. Title: Christlicher Stand. 213p. (Orig.). 1986. pap. 9.95 (ISBN 0-89870-044-2). Ignatius Pr.

Vyvyan, John. A Case Against Jones: Study of Psychical Phenomena. 220p. 1966. 7.50 (ISBN 0-227-67683-1). Attic Pr.

Waddell, Genny & Smith, Agnes. Linda's Song. 136p. (Orig.). 1985. pap. 5.95 (ISBN 0-89265-095-8). Randall Hse.

Wagemaker, Herbert, Jr. Parents & Discipline. LC 80-14624. (Christian Care Bks.: Vol. 12). 120p. 1980. pap. 7.95 (ISBN 0-664-24328-2). Westminster.

Wagner, C. Peter. On the Crest of the Wave: Becoming a World Christian. LC 83-8616. 1983. pap. 5.95 (ISBN 0-8307-0895-2, 5418015). Regal.

Wagner, Clarence M., ed. Heavens Overflow. 73p. pap. 4.00 (ISBN 0-937498-06-8). Tru-Faith.

Wagner, Maurice. La Sensacion de Ser Alguien. Cook, David A., tr. from Eng. LC 77-16714. Tr. of The Sensation of Being Somebody. (Span.). 300p. 1977. pap. 6.50 (ISBN 0-89922-104-1). Edit Caribe.

Waitley, Denis E. The Seeds of Greatness. 224p. 1983. 14.95 (ISBN 0-8007-1361-3); pap. 3.95 (ISBN 0-8007-8560-6). Revell.

Wakefield, John C. Artful Childmaking: Artificial Insemination in Catholic Teaching. LC 78-65765. 205p. 1978. pap. 8.95 (ISBN 0-935372-03-2). Pope john Ctr.

Walchars, John. Resurrection of Value. 176p. (Orig.). 1986. pap. 8.95 (ISBN 0-8245-0746-0). Crossroad NY.

--The Unfinished Mystery. (Orig.). 1978. pap. 5.95 (ISBN 0-8164-2184-6, HarpR). Har-Row.

Waldenfels, Hans. Absolute Nothingness: Foundations for a Buddhist-Christian Dialogue. Heisig, James W., tr. from Ger. LC 80-81442. Orig. Title: Absolutes Nichts. 224p. 1980. pap. 8.95 (ISBN 0-8091-2316-9). Paulist Pr.

Walker, Alan. Life in the Holy Spirit. LC 86-71315. 72p. 1986. pap. 3.95 (ISBN 0-88177-036-1, DR036B). Discipleship Res.

--Your Life Can Be Changed. LC 85-71706. 56p. (Orig.). 1985. pap. 2.95 (ISBN 0-88177-022-1, DR022B). Discipleship Res.

Walker, Gail. Spirits in His Parlor. LC 79-87733. (Destiny Ser.). 1980. pap. 4.95 (ISBN 0-8163-0387-8, 19499-3). Pacific Pr Pub Assn.

Walker, Paul L. The Ministry of Worship. LC 81-84605. 199p. (Orig.). 1981. pap. text ed. 5.95 (ISBN 0-87148-576-1). Pathway Pr.

Walker, Scott. Where the Rivers Flow: Exploring the Sources of Faith Formation. 160p. 1986. 10.95 (ISBN 0-8499-0538-9, 0538-9). Word Bks.

Wall, George B. Looking unto Jesus. 160p. 1986. pap. 7.95 (ISBN 0-8170-1098-X). Judson.

Wallace, Doris. Lamp unto My Feet. LC 83-91018. 49p. 1985. 5.95 (ISBN 0-533-06008-7). Vantage.

Wallace, Joanne. Image of Loveliness. (Illus.). 160p. 1978. pap. 5.95 (ISBN 0-8007-5134-5, Power Bks). Revell.

Wallace, Mary H. My Name Is Christian Woman. LC 85-31575. (Illus., Orig.). 1982. pap. 6.95 (ISBN 0-912315-20-2). Word Aflame.

Wallace, Ralph J. What Does He Mean by "A Little While?". (Orig.). 1981. pap. 5.95 (ISBN 0-937172-30-8). JLJ Pubs.

Walling, Regis. When Pregnancy Is a Problem. LC 79-51280. (When Book Ser.). (Illus.). 1980. pap. 2.45 (ISBN 0-87029-152-1, 20235-8). Abbey.

Wallinga, Robert. Hand in Hand with Jesus: A New Study Guide for Today's Youth. pap. 2.25 (ISBN 0-686-14194-6); tchrs' ed. 0.75 (ISBN 0-686-14195-4). Rose Pub MI.

Wallis, Charles & Wallis, Betty. Our Christian Home & Family: An Illustrated Treasury of Inspirational Quotations, Poems & Prayers. LC 82-47758. (Illus.). 1982. 14.45 (ISBN 0-06-069009-7, HarpR). Har-Row.

Wallis, Jim. Agenda for Biblical People. rev. ed. LC 83-48995. 160p. 1984. pap. 6.95 (ISBN 0-06-069234-0, RD 514, HarpR). Har-Row.

Walpole, Margaret. Walking into the Morning. 48p. 1986. 6.95 (ISBN 0-8378-5093-2). Gibson.

Walpot, Peter. True Surrender & Christian Community of Goods, 1521-1578. 1957. pap. 4.00 (ISBN 0-87486-205-1). Plough.

Walrath, Douglas A. Frameworks: Patterns for Living & Believing Today. 160p. (Orig.). 1987. pap. 8.95 (ISBN 0-8298-0743-8). Pilgrim NY.

Walsh, Brian J. & Middleton, J. Richard. The Transforming Vision: Shaping a Christian World View. LC 84-15646. 240p. (Orig.). 1984. pap. 6.95 (ISBN 0-87784-973-0). Inter-Varsity.

Walsh, John & DiGiacomo, James. Going Together: The Church of Christ. (The Encounter Ser.). (Illus.). 1978. pap. text ed. 4.50 (ISBN 0-03-042771-1, HarpR); resource manual 1.95 (ISBN 0-03-042776-2). Har-Row.

Walsh, P. G. & Walsh, James. Divine Providence & Human Suffering. (Message of the Fathers of the Church Ser.: Vol. 17). 1985. 15.95 (ISBN 0-89453-357-6); pap. 10.95 (ISBN 0-89453-328-2). M Glazier.

Walter, J. A. Need: The New Religion. LC 86-184. 173p. 1986. pap. 6.95 (ISBN 0-87784-948-X). Inter-Varsity.

Walton, Rus. Biblical Principles: Issues of Importance to Godly Christians. 370p. 1984. 4.95 (ISBN 0-317-39815-6). Plymouth Rock Found.

Ward, Carol. The Christian Sourcebook. 1986. 16.95 (ISBN 0-345-32248-7, Pub. by Ballantine Epiphany). Ballantine.

Ward, Elaine. After My House Burned Down. 88p. (Orig.). 1982. pap. 6.95 (ISBN 0-940754-11-8). Ed Ministries.

--Be A Say a Fingerplay. 71p. (Orig.). 1982. pap. 5.95 (ISBN 0-940754-12-6). Ed Ministries.

--Being-in-Creation. 80p. (Orig.). 1983. pap. 9.95 (ISBN 0-940754-14-2). Ed Ministries.

--Feelings Grow Too! 81p. (Orig.). 1981. pap. 9.95 (ISBN 0-940754-07-X). Ed Ministries.

Ward, Frances. Keep the Fruit on the Table. 48p. 1982. pap. 1.75 (ISBN 0-88144-006-X, CPS-006). Christian Pub.

Ward, Patricia A. & Stout, Martha G. Christian Women at Work. 242p. 1984. pap. 6.95 (ISBN 0-310-43701-6). Zondervan.

Ward, Wadene C. Victory Through Word Confessions. 47p. 1985. pap. 1.95 (ISBN 0-88144-040-X). Christian Pub.

Warkentin, Mary J. Lost, but not Forever. 1986. pap. cancelled (ISBN 0-88270-605-5). Bridge Pub.

Warlick, Harold C., Jr. The Rarest of These Is Hope. 1985. 7.50 (ISBN 0-89536-743-2, 5826). CSS of Ohio.

Warr, Gene. The Godly Man. 1978. pap. 3.95 (ISBN 2-01064-105-1, 40121). Word Bks.

Warr, Irma. The Godly Woman. 1978. pap. 5.95 (ISBN 2-01064-201-5, 40123). Word Bks.

Warren, Lindsey D., ed. Headed in the Direction of Heaven. 1980. pap. 2.00 (ISBN 0-934916-28-4). Natl Christian Pr.

Warren, Mary P. Lord, I'm Back Again: Story Devotions for Girls. LC 81-65651. 112p. (Orig.). 1981. pap. 3.95 (ISBN 0-8066-1887-6, 10-4098). Augsburg.

Warren, Max. Creo en la Gran Comision. Sipowicz, Edwin, tr. from Eng. LC 78-54272. (Serie Creo). Tr. of I Believe in the Great Commission. (Span.). 205p. 1978. pap. 5.95 (ISBN 0-89922-112-2). Edit Caribe.

Warren, Richard. Answers to Life's Difficult Questions. 132p. 1985. pap. 4.95 (ISBN 0-89693-395-4). Victor Bks.

Warren, Thomas B. Christians Only & the Only Christians. 89p. 1984. pap. 3.00 (ISBN 0-934916-05-5). Natl Christian Pr.

--Sin, Suffering & God. 1980. pap. 15.00 (ISBN 0-934916-25-X). Natl Christian Pr.

--Three Hundred Thirty-Five Crucial Questions on Christian Unity. 48p. 1984. pap. 1.50 (ISBN 0-934916-06-3). Natl Christian Pr.

--Tract: Questions on Divorce & Remarriage. 1984. 0.60 (ISBN 0-934916-04-7); dozen 6.00; hundred 40.00. Natl Christian Pr.

Warren, Thomas B. & Ballard, L. S. Warren-Ballard Debate. 1979. 9.00 (ISBN 0-934916-39-X). Natl Christian Pr.

Warren, Thomas B. & Elkins, Garland, eds. The Church, the Beautiful Bride of Christ. 1980. pap. 13.00 (ISBN 0-934916-27-6). Natl Christian Pr.

--The Home as God Would Have It & Contemporary Attacks Against It. 1979. pap. 12.00 (ISBN 0-934916-34-9). Natl Christian Pr.

Watchman, Nee. From Faith to Faith. Fader, Herbert L., ed. Kaung, Stephen, tr. 120p. 1984. pap. 3.50 (ISBN 0-935008-62-4). Christian Fellow Pubs.

Waters, Michael. The Faithful. LC 84-4796. (Illus.). 16p. 1984. pap. 4.00 (ISBN 0-918518-31-8). Raccoon Memphis.

Watkins, Janet. Savoring the Sabbath. LC 80-83865. 80p. (Orig.). 1980. pap. 4.95 (ISBN 0-88290-165-6, 1058). Horizon Utah.

Watson. I Believe in the Church. pap. 10.95 (ISBN 0-8028-1788-2). Eerdmans.

Watson, G. D. Coals of Fire. pap. 2.95 (ISBN 0-686-12857-5). Schmul Pub Co.

Watson, Rosemary A. As the Rock Flower Blooms. 1984. pap. 4.95 (ISBN 9971-972-17-4). OMF Bks.

Watt, Gordon. Cross in Faith & Conduct. 1965. pap. 1.95 (ISBN 0-87508-964-X). Chr Lit.

The Way Out. pap. 4.00 (ISBN 0-87516-302-5). De Vorss.

Way, Robert. The Garden of the Beloved. 80p. 1983. pap. 4.95 (ISBN 0-8091-2534-X). Paulist Pr.

The Way to the Kingdom. 2nd ed. 345p. 1972. pap. 6.00 (ISBN 0-87516-164-2). De Vorss.

Waybill, Marjorie. God's Family Activity Book. 64p. (Orig.). 1983. pap. 3.00 (ISBN 0-8361-3336-6). Herald Pr.

We Break Bread in Loving Thanksgiving. 2.85 (ISBN 0-02-649450-7, 64945); tchr's manual 2.52 (ISBN 0-02-649460-4, 64946). Benziger Pub Co.

We Follow Jesus. 2.82 (ISBN 0-02-649490-6, 64949); tchr's manual 2.52 (ISBN 0-02-649500-7, 64950). Benziger Pub Co.

Wead, Douglas. The Compassionate Touch. LC 76-62694. (Illus.). 192p. 1980. pap. 3.50 (ISBN 0-87123-021-6, 200021). Bethany Hse.

Weatherby, W. J., et al. Chariots of Fire & a Christian Message for Today. LC 82-48941. (Quicksilver Bk.). 176p. (Orig.). 1983. pap. 5.95 (ISBN 0-06-069282-0, RD 455, HarpR). Har-Row.

Weatherhead, Leslie D. Leslie D. Weatherhead Library, 8 vols. Set in Slipcase. 17.50 (ISBN 0-687-21373-8). Abingdon.

Weaver, Bertrand. His Cross in Your Life. LC 78-56766. 1978. pap. 2.25 (ISBN 0-8189-1152-2, Pub. by Alba Bks). Alba.

Webb, Barbara O. Devotions for Families with Young Readers. 64p. 1985. pap. 4.95 (ISBN 0-8170-1063-7). Judson.

Webb, William P. Behind the Creed: A Plain Man's Rationale of Faith. LC 84-90201. 115p. 1985. 10.95 (ISBN 0-533-06248-9). Vantage.

Webber, Robert. The Majestic Tapestry: How the Power of Early Christian Tradition Can Enrich Contemporary Faith. 160p. 1986. 12.95 (ISBN 0-8407-5536-8). Nelson.

Weber, Bill. Conquering the Kill-Joys: Positive Living in a Negative World. 160p. 1986. 12.95 (ISBN 0-8499-0439-0, 0439-0). Word Bks.

Weber, Christa. Before the Moon Dies. 1984. pap. 1.50 (ISBN 9971-972-15-8). OMF Bks.

Weber, Gerard P., et al. Act As God's Children. 2nd ed. (The Word Is Life Ser.). 1977. 3.60 (ISBN 0-02-658300-3); tchrs. ed. 8.00 (ISBN 0-02-658310-0); family handbook 1.00 (ISBN 0-02-658350-X). Benziger Pub Co.

--Hear with God's People. 2nd ed. (The Word Is Life Ser.). 1977. 4.00 (ISBN 0-02-658600-2); tchrs. ed. 8.00 (ISBN 0-02-658610-X); family handbook 1.00 (ISBN 0-02-658650-9). Benziger Pub Co.

--Think. 2nd ed. (The Word Is Life Ser.). 1979. 3.60 (ISBN 0-02-658700-9); tchrs. ed. 8.00 (ISBN 0-02-658710-6); family handbook 0.64 (ISBN 0-02-658750-5). Benziger Pub Co.

--Believe with God's Family. 2nd ed. (The Word Is Life Ser.). 1977. 3.92 (ISBN 0-02-658500-6); tchrs. ed. 8.00 (ISBN 0-02-658510-3); family handbook 1.00 (ISBN 0-02-658550-2). Benziger Pub Co.

Wedel, Alton. The Word Today. 1984. 5.25 (ISBN 0-89536-684-3, 4860). CSS of Ohio.

Weems, Ann. Family Faith Stories. LC 85-13771. 142p. 1985. pap. 8.95 (ISBN 0-664-24670-2). Westminster.

--Kneeling in Bethlehem. (Illus.). 96p. (Orig.). 1987. pap. price not set (ISBN 0-664-21323-5). Westminster.

Weersinghe, Sylvia. From Darkness into Light. 1980. pap. 1.95 (ISBN 0-910924-84-8). Macalester.

Weiland. Good News Is Better. (Anch Ser.). 1984. pap. 6.95 (ISBN 0-8163-0592-7). Pacific Pr Pub Assn.

Weillert, Sr. Augustine. Someone Special. (Illus.). 1979. 4.95 (ISBN 0-89962-005-1). Todd & Honeywell.

Welliver, Dotsey. Dotsey's Diary: Her Days & Yours. (Orig.). 1979. pap. text ed. 3.95 (ISBN 0-89367-034-0). Light & Life.

--Smudgkin Elves & Other Lame Excuses. 81p. 1981. pap. 3.95 (ISBN 0-89367-058-8). Light & Life.

Wellman, Don, et al. Dynamics of Discipling. 210p. 1984. spiral bd. 9.95 (ISBN 0-8341-0918-2). Beacon Hill.

Wellman, Pat. You Can Bet the Ranch. 88p. (Orig.). 1986. pap. 4.50 (ISBN 0-8341-1155-1). Beacon Hill.

Wells, Joel. Coping in the Eighties: Eliminating Needless Stress & Guilt. 1986. 10.95 (ISBN 0-88347-201-5); pap. 6.95 (ISBN 0-88347-202-3). Thomas More.

Wells, Robert E. We Are Christians Because... LC 84-28762. 119p. 1985. 7.95 (ISBN 0-87747-639-X). Deseret Bk.

Wells, Tom. Come to Me! 128p. (Orig.). 1986. pap. 3.45 (ISBN 0-85151-471-5). Banner of Truth.

Wenger, Edna K. Happy Life Stories. (Illus.). 1977. 7.50 (ISBN 0-87813-912-5). Christian Light.

Wenger, J. C. Disciples of Jesus. LC 77-86343. (Mennonite Faith Ser.: No. 5). 72p. 1977. pap. 1.50 (ISBN 0-8361-1836-7). Herald Pr.

--The Family of Faith. LC 80-84609. (Mennonite Faith Ser.: No. 10). 72p. 1981. pap. 1.50 (ISBN 0-8361-1951-7). Herald Pr.

--The Way of Peace. LC 77-86349. (Mennonite Faith Ser.: No. 3, Christian Peace Shelf Ser). 72p. 1977. pap. text ed. 1.50 (ISBN 0-8361-1835-9). Herald Pr.

--The Way to a New Life. LC 77-86326. (Mennonite Faith Ser.: No. 2). 72p. 1977. pap. 1.50 (ISBN 0-8361-1834-0). Herald Pr.

Wenger, John P. Because God Loves. LC 76-16245. 56p. 1976. pap. 1.95 (ISBN 0-8361-1339-X). Herald Pr.

Werber, Eva B. In His Presence. 2nd ed. 1970. pap. 3.25 (ISBN 0-87516-102-2). De Vorss.

Wesberry, James P. The Lord's Day. pap. 8.95 (ISBN 0-8054-2264-1). Broadman.

Wesley, John. The Nature of the Kingdom. Weakley, Clare, ed. 288p. 1986. pap. 6.95 (ISBN 0-87123-875-6, 210875). Bethany Hse.

Wesner, Maralene & Miles, E. You Are What You Choose. LC 84-3110. (Orig.). 1984. pap. 4.95 (ISBN 0-8054-5247-8). Broadman.

Wessel, Helen. Christian Marriage, Birth & Nature. rev. ed. LC 85-70830. 325p. Date not set. pap. cancelled (ISBN 0-933082-15-0). Bookmates Intl.

--Natural Childbirth & the Christian Family. 4th, rev. ed. LC 82-48943. (Illus.). 384p. 1985. pap. text ed. 8.95 (ISBN 0-06-069317-7, HarpR). Har-Row.

Westerhoff, John H., III. Living the Faith Community: The Church That Makes a Difference. 1985. pap. cancelled (ISBN 0-317-18159-9). Whitaker Hse.

--Living the Faith Community: The Church That Makes a Difference. 120p. (Orig.). 1985. pap. 6.95 (ISBN 0-86683-870-8, HarpR). Har-Row.

--A Pilgrim People: Learning Through the Church Year. 128p. (Orig.). 1984. pap. 7.95 (ISBN 0-86683-884-8, 7462, HarpR). Har-Row.

Weyland, Jack. If Talent Were Pizza, You'd Be a Supreme. 1986. text ed. 8.95 (ISBN 0-87579-054-2). Deseret Bk.

Whaley, K. A. Basic Bible Doctrines for Victorious Living. 1981. pap. 7.95x (ISBN 0-686-40713-X). Freedom Univ-FSP.

What I Can Give. 2.98 (ISBN 0-8010-5114-2). Baker Bk.

Wheat, Ed. How to Save Your Marriage Alone. 64p. 1983. pap. 2.50 (ISBN 0-310-42522-0, 10267P). Zondervan.

When Things Go Wrong. 2.98 (ISBN 0-8010-5112-6). Baker Bk.

Whitaker, Donald. The Divine Connection: Feel Better & Live Longer. LC 83-82835. 148p. (Orig.). 1983. pap. 4.95 (ISBN 0-910311-06-4). Huntington Hse Inc.

Whitall, Hannah & Smith, Elisabeth E. The Christian's Secret of a Happy Life: Proven Word. 192p. 1985. pap. 5.95 (ISBN 0-8499-2980-6, 2980-6). Word Bks.

Whitcomb, John C. The Early Earth. 1972. pap. 6.95 (ISBN 0-8010-9679-0). Baker Bk.

Whitcomb, John C., Jr. Christ, Our Pattern & Plan. 1979. pap. 1.00 (ISBN 0-88469-031-8). BMH Bks.

White, Anne S. Trial by Fire. 108p. (Orig.). 1975. pap. 3.50 (ISBN 0-89228-045-X). Impact Bks MO.

White, Anne S. & Vanzant, Don. Study Adventure in Trial by Fire. 56p. (Orig.). 1985. pap. 1.95 (ISBN 0-89228-102-2). Impact Bks MO.

White, E. G. From Heaven with Love. 1984. 1.50 (ISBN 0-8163-0553-6). Pacific Pr Pub Assn.

--From Splendor to Shadow. 1984. 1.50 (ISBN 0-8163-0559-5). Pacific Pr Pub Assn.

--From Trials to Triumph. 1984. 1.50 (ISBN 0-8163-0565-X). Pacific Pr Pub Assn.

White, Ellen. The Broad Road. large print ed. 32p. 1985. pap. 5.00 (ISBN 0-914009-47-8). VHI Library.

--Passions. 1985. pap. 6.00 (ISBN 0-914009-55-9). VHI Library.

--Passions among God's People. large print ed. 35p. 1985. pap. 6.00 (ISBN 0-914009-46-X). VHI Library.

White, Ellen G. Cosmic Conflict. 640p. 1983. pap. 0.50 (ISBN 0-8280-0211-8). Pacific Pr Pub Assn.

--From Here to Forever. 436p. 1982. pap. 1.50 (ISBN 0-317-00060-8). Pacific Pr Pub Assn.

--Message from Calvary. (Outreach Ser.). 64p. 1981. pap. 1.25 (ISBN 0-8163-0394-0). Pacific Pr Pub Assn.

--Mind, Character, & Personality: Guidelines to Mental & Spiritual Health, 2 vols. (Christian Home Library). 1978. 8.95 ea. Vol. 1 (ISBN 0-8127-0148-8). Vol. 2 (ISBN 0-8127-0149-6). Review & Herald.

--Steps to Jesus. 128p. 1980. 6.95 (ISBN 0-8127-0316-2); pap. 3.25 (ISBN 0-8127-0318-9). Review & Herald.

--Testimonies to Ministers. 10.95 (ISBN 0-317-28268-9). Pacific pr Pub Assn.

White, James F. Introduction to Christian Worship. LC 79-21073. (Orig.). 1980. pap. 9.50 (ISBN 0-687-19509-8). Abingdon.

White, Jerry. Honesty, Morality, & Conscience. LC 78-61619. 240p. 1979. pap. 5.95 (ISBN 0-89109-431-8). NavPress.

--Power of Commitment. Date not set. pap. price not set. NavPress.

White, Joe. How to Be a Hero to Your Teenager. 144p. (Orig.). 1985. pap. 4.95 (ISBN 0-8423-1495-4). Tyndale.

--The Kingdom of Light. 83p. 1984. pap. 2.50 (ISBN 0-88144-033-7). Christian Pub.

--Who's Number One. 144p. 1986. pap. 4.95 (ISBN 0-8423-8215-1). Tyndale.

White, John. The Fight: A Practical Handbook to Christian Living. LC 76-12297. 230p. (Orig.). 1976. pap. 6.95 (ISBN 0-87784-777-0). Inter-Varsity.

--Parents in Pain. LC 78-24760. 1979. pap. 7.95 (ISBN 0-87784-582-4); study guide 1.95 (ISBN 0-87784-492-5). Inter-Varsity.

--The Race: Discipleship for the Long Run. LC 84-6695. 216p. 1984. pap. 5.95 (ISBN 0-87784-976-5). Inter-Varsity.

Whitehead, Evelyn E. & Whitehead, James D. Christian Life Patterns: The Psychological Challenges & Religious Invitations of Adult Life. LC 81-43442. 288p. 1982. pap. 4.95 (ISBN 0-385-15131-4). Doubleday.

Whittenburg, Ruth S. Time for Everything Under the Sun. LC 79-84856. 1980. 17.50 (ISBN 0-8022-2351-6). Philos Lib.

Who Is a Christian? 24.95 (ISBN 0-87193-188-5). Dimension Bks.

The Whole Person. (Benziger Family Life Program Ser.). 7p. 1978. 2.45 (ISBN 0-02-651800-7); tchrs. ed. 4.00 (ISBN 0-02-651810-4); family handbook 1.00 (ISBN 0-02-651840-6). Benziger Pub Co.

Why Is Life Worth Living? 2.25 (ISBN 0-8198-8211-9). Dghtrs St Paul.

Wicks, Robert J. Christian Introspection: Self-Ministry Through Self-Understanding. LC 83-1932. 128p. 1983. pap. 7.95 (ISBN 0-8245-0583-2). Crossroad NY.

Wieland, Robert J. Gold Tried in the Fire. (Anchor Ser.). 80p. 1983. pap. 6.95 (ISBN 0-8163-0520-X). Pacific Pr Pub Assn.

--In Search of the Cross. LC 78-184590. 120p. 1986. pap. 5.95 (ISBN 0-912145-11-0). MMI Pr.

Wiersbe, Warren. Why Us? When Bad Things Happen to God's People. 160p. 1985. pap. 5.95 (ISBN 0-8007-5208-2, Power Bks). Revell.

Wiersbe, Warren W. Be Encouraged. 156p. 1984. pap. 5.95 (ISBN 0-88207-620-5). Victor Bks.

--Be Free. LC 74-33824. 160p. 1975. pap. 5.95 (ISBN 0-88207-716-3). Victor Bks.

--Be Joyful: A Practical Study of Philippians. LC 74-76328. 130p. 1974. pap. 5.95 (ISBN 0-88207-705-8). Victor Bks.

--Be Mature. LC 78-52558. 176p. 1978. pap. 5.95 (ISBN 0-88207-771-6). Victor Bks.

--Be Real. LC 72-77014. 190p. 1972. pap. 5.95 (ISBN 0-88207-046-0). Victor Bks.

Wierwille, H. E. Uncle Harry: An Autobiography. LC 78-73348. 55p. 1978. 5.95 (ISBN 0-910068-15-1). Am Christian.

Wierwille, Victor P. Christians Should Be Prosperous. 31p. pap. 1.00 (ISBN 0-910068-65-8). Am Christian.

--God's Magnified Word. LC 77-87405. (Studies in Abundant Living: Vol. 4). 276p. 1977. 6.95 (ISBN 0-910068-13-5). Am Christian.

--Life Lines: Quotations of Victor Paul Wierwille. LC 85-52028. 136p. 1985. 5.95 (ISBN 0-910068-64-X). Am Christian.

--Order My Steps in Thy Word. LC 70-176281. (Studies in Abundant Living: Vol. V). 300p. 1985. 6.95 (ISBN 0-910068-59-3). Am Christian.

--The Word's Way. LC 70-176281. (Studies in Abundant Living: Vol. 3). 276p. 1971. 4.95 (ISBN 0-910068-04-6). Am Christian.

Wijngaards, John. Inheriting the Master's Cloak: Creative Biblical Spirituality. LC 85-71535. 192p. (Orig.). 1985. pap. 4.95 (ISBN 0-87793-288-3). Ave Maria.

Wilbur, L. Perry. How to Live Your Faith. 128p. 1984. 12.95 (ISBN 0-13-416850-X); pap. 5.95 (ISBN 0-13-416843-7). P-H.

Wilburn, Stephen S. Kicking Those Habits. 48p. 1985. 4.95 (ISBN 0-8378-5403-2). Gibson.

Wilczak, Paul F., ed. Parenting. LC 78-69758. (Marriage & Family Living in Depth Bk.). 1978. pap. 2.45 (ISBN 0-87029-138-6, 20220-0). Abbey.

--Toward the Extended Christian Family. LC 80-69137. (Marriage & Family Living in Depth Bk.). (Illus.). 80p. 1980. pap. 2.45 (ISBN 0-87029-170-X, 20247-3). Abbey.

Wild, Robert, ed. Journey to the Lonely Christ: The Little Mandate of Catherine de Hueck Doherty. LC 86-17388. 164p. 1987. pap. 7.95 (ISBN 0-8189-0509-3). Alba.

Wilder-Smith, A. E. Why Does God Allow It? LC 80-80283. 1980. pap. 2.95 (ISBN 0-89051-060-1). Master Bks.

Wildmon, Donald. The Home Invaders. 180p. 1985. pap. 6.95 (ISBN 0-89693-521-3). Victor Bks.

Wilhelmsen, Frederick D. Citizen of Rome: Reflections from the Life of a Roman Catholic. 348p. 1980. pap. 6.95 (ISBN 0-89385-005-5). Sugden.

Wilkerson, David. The Christian Maturity Manual. rev. ed. LC 79-169590. 96p. 1977. 3.95 (ISBN 0-8307-0496-5, 5200121). Regal.

--Have You Felt Like Giving up Lately? 160p. 1980. pap. 6.95 (ISBN 0-8007-5042-X, Power Bks). Revell.

--I'm Not Mad at God. 96p. 1967. pap. 2.95 (ISBN 0-87123-245-6, 200245). Bethany Hse.

--Racing Toward Judgment. 160p. 1976. pap. 2.50 (ISBN 0-8007-8276-3, Spire Bks). Revell.

--Victory over Sin & Self. 80p. 1982. pap. 2.95 (ISBN 0-8007-8434-0, Spire Bks). Revell.

--The Vision. 144p. 1974. pap. 3.50 (ISBN 0-8007-8150-3, Spire Bks). Revell.

Wilkerson, Don & Manuel, David. Hell-Bound. LC 78-60735. 199p. 1978. pap. 3.95 (ISBN 0-932260-03-9). Paraclete Pr.

Wilkerson, Rich. Carnal Christians: And Other Words That Don't Go Together. 175p. (Orig.). 1986. pap. 3.50 (ISBN 0-88368-188-9). Whitaker Hse.

--Hold Me While You Let Me Go. LC 82-83838. 196p. (Orig.). 1983. pap. 4.95 (ISBN 0-89081-370-1). Harvest Hse.

Wilkes, Peter. Defeating Anger & Other Dragons of the Soul. (The Dragon Slayer Ser.). 180p. 1987. pap. 5.95 (ISBN 0-87784-517-4). Inter Varsity.

Wilkins, Ronald J. Christian Living: The Challenge of Response. 72p. 1978. pap. 4.20 (ISBN 0-697-01686-2); tchrs. manual 4.50 (ISBN 0-697-01689-7); spirit masters 10.95 (ISBN 0-697-01691-9). Wm C Brown.

--The Emerging Church. rev. ed. (To Live Is Christ Ser). 1981. pap. 5.95 (ISBN 0-697-01760-5); tchr's. manual 4.75 (ISBN 0-697-01761-3); activity cards 7.50 (ISBN 0-697-01899-7); stud. diaries 10.00 (ISBN 0-697-01900-4); spirit masters 9.95 (ISBN 0-697-01898-9). Wm C Brown.

Wilkins, Skip & Dunn, Joseph. The Real Race. 240p. 1987. pap. 6.95 (ISBN 0-8423-5283-X). Tyndale.

Wilkinson, Vernon. After the Bomb: Plight to Utopia. 154p. (Orig.). 1984. pap. 11.95 (ISBN 0-86474-003-4, Pub. by Interface Press). ANZ Religious Pubns.

Willard, Dallas. In Search of Guidance. LC 83-17743. 1983. 10.95 (ISBN 0-8307-0899-5, 5110807). Regal.

--The Spirit of the Disciplines: Understanding How God Changes Lives. 240p. 1986. 13.95 (ISBN 0-06-069441-6, HarpR). Har-Row.

Willcuts, Jack L. Why Friends Are Friends. 90p. (Orig.). 1984. pap. 3.95 (ISBN 0-913342-45-9). Barclay Pr.

Williams, H. A. True Christianity. 1975. 5.95 (ISBN 0-87243-059-6). Templegate.

Williams, Harry A. True Resurrection. 192p. 1983. pap. 7.95 (ISBN 0-87243-115-0). Templegate.

Williams, June A. Strategy of Service. 112p. (Orig.). 1984. pap. 5.95 (ISBN 0-310-45761-0, 12046P). Zondervan.

Williams, Mel & Brittain, Mary A. Christian Education in Family Clusters. 80p. 1982. pap. 6.95 (ISBN 0-8170-0936-1). Judson.

Williams, Pat & Jenkins, Jerry. The Power Within You. LC 82-24825. 180p. 1983. 12.95 (ISBN 0-664-27008-5, A Bridgebooks Publication). Westminster.

Williams, Philip L. The Heart of a Distant Forest. 1985. pap. 3.50 (ISBN 0-345-32365-3). Ballantine.

Williams, Rowan. The Truce of God. 128p. (Orig.). 1983. pap. 3.95 (ISBN 0-8298-0660-1). Pilgrim NY.

Williamson, G. I. Understanding the Times. 1979. pap. 2.95 (ISBN 0-87552-541-5). Presby & Reformed.

Williamson, Peter. How to Become the Person You Were Meant to Be. (Living As Christian Ser.). 112p. (Orig.). 1981. pap. 2.95 (ISBN 0-89283-098-0). Servant.

Willimon, William H. Word, Water, Wine, & Bread. 1980. pap. 5.95 (ISBN 0-8170-0858-6). Judson.

Willis, Elbert. Who Is Responsible for Sickness. 1978. 1.25 (ISBN 0-89858-010-2). Fill the Gap.

Willis, John R. A History of Christian Thought: From Apollinaris to Erasamus, Vol. II. 400p. 1984. 18.00 (ISBN 0-682-49973-0, University). Exposition Pr FL.

Wilner, Herbert. The Quarterback Speaks to His God. 288p. 1987. 17.95 (ISBN 0-933529-04-X); pap. 8.95 (ISBN 0-933529-03-1). Cayuse Pr.

Wilshire, Frances. You. pap. 3.00 (ISBN 0-87516-319-X). De Vorss.

Wilson, Dorothy C. I Will Be a Doctor! LC 83-3862. 160p. (Orig.). 1983. pap. 7.95 (ISBN 0-687-19727-9). Abingdon.

Wilson, Earl D. The Discovered Self. LC 84-28943. 1985. pap. 4.95 (ISBN 0-87784-331-7). Inter-Varsity.

Wilson, J. O. Way Out Is Up. (Redwood Ser.). 1982. pap. 2.95 (ISBN 0-8163-0450-5). Pacific Pr Pub Assn.

Wilson, Ken. Decision to Love: What It Means to Love Others from the Heart. (Living As a Christian Ser.). 77p. (Orig.). 1980. pap. 2.50 (ISBN 0-89283-087-5). Servant.

--God First: What It Means to Love God Above All Things. (Living As a Christian Ser.). 85p. 1980. pap. 2.50 (ISBN 0-89283-089-1). Servant.

--How to Repair the Wrong You've Done. (Living As a Christian Ser.). 80p. 1982. pap. 2.25 (ISBN 0-89283-116-2). Servant.

--Sons & Daughters of God: Our New Identity in Christ. (Living As a Christian Ser.). 80p. (Orig.). 1981. pap. 2.50 (ISBN 0-89283-097-2). Servant.

Wilson, Marion. Adventure of Living God's Will. 48p. 1980. pap. 1.50 (ISBN 0-89114-093-X); tchr's. ed. 1.00 (ISBN 0-89114-094-8). Baptist Pub Hse.

Wilson, Ostis B. Courtship & Marriage. 12p. 1976. pap. 0.15 (ISBN 0-686-36260-8). Faith Pub Hse.

Wilson, Patricia F. Who Put All These Cucumbers in My Garden? LC 83-51398. 144p. (Orig.). 1984. pap. 5.50 (ISBN 0-8358-0475-5). Upper Room.

Wilson, T. W. The Key to Lasting Joy. 192p. 1987. 12.95 (ISBN 0-8499-0534-6). Word Bks.

Wilson, William P. Graca para Crescer. Orig. Title: The Grace to Grow. (Port.). 1986. write for info. (ISBN 0-8297-0743-3). Life Pubs Intl.

Wingeier, Douglas E. Working Out Your Own Beliefs: A Guide for Doing Your Own Theology. LC 79-21097. (Orig.). 1980. pap. 4.95 (ISBN 0-687-46190-1). Abingdon.

Winn, Albert C. A Sense of Mission: Guidance from the Gospel of John. LC 80-28000. 118p. 1981. pap. 6.95 (ISBN 0-664-24365-7). Westminster.

Winston Press Editorial Staff. Joy Six. rev. ed. (Joy Religious Ser.). 1979. pap. 5.87 (ISBN 0-86683-036-7, 665, HarpR); tchr's. ed. 8.95 (ISBN 0-86683-046-4). Har-Row.

Winter, David. Faith under Fire: One Hundred Dynamic Readings from Great Men of the Early Church. LC 77-92353. (Daystar Devotional). Orig. Title: One Hundred Days in the Arena. 112p. 1981. pap. 2.95 (ISBN 0-87788-252-5). Shaw Pubs.

Winter, Terry. Evidence: The Truth about Christianity. rev. ed. LC 79-87769. 1979. pap. 2.25 (ISBN 0-89081-067-2, 2039). Harvest Hse.

Wirt, Sherwood & Beckstrom, Kristen. Topical Encyclopedia of Living Quotations. LC 82-4503. 290p. 1982. pap. 7.95 (ISBN 0-87123-574-9, 210574). Bethany Hse.

Wisdom, or Mind, Will, & Understanding. LC 70-133770. (Tudor Facsimile Texts. Old English Plays Ser.: No. 2). Repr. of 1907 ed. 49.50 (ISBN 0-404-53302-7). AMS Pr.

Wise, Robert, et al. The Church Divided. LC 86-71132. 1986. pap. 5.95 (ISBN 0-88270-622-5). Bridge Pub.

Witmer, Edith. God's Happy Family. (Jewel Bks.). 1986. pap. 1.95. Rod & Staff.

Witte, Kaaren. Angels in Faded Jeans. LC 79-84795. 160p. 1979. pap. 3.95 (ISBN 0-87123-014-3, 210014). Bethany Hse.

Witte, Nancy I., ed. Rising above Strife. pap. 4.95 (ISBN 0-89137-424-8). Quality Pubns.

Wolf, Barbara. Journey in Faith: An Inquirer's Program. rev. ed. 144p. 1982. pap. 5.95 (ISBN 0-8164-2402-0, HarpR). Har-Row.

Wolf, Frederick B. Journey in Faith: Leader's Manual. 80p. (Orig.). 1982. pap. 4.95 (ISBN 0-8164-2400-4, HarpR). Har-Row.

--Journey in Faith: Things to Know. 48p. (Orig.). 1982. pap. 3.50 (ISBN 0-8164-2401-2, HarpR). Har-Row.

Wolf, Frederick B. & Wolf, Barbara B. Exploring Faith & Life: A Journey in Faith for Junior High Student's Reader. 128p. 1983. pap. 5.95 (ISBN 0-8164-2431-4, HarpR). Har-Row.

Wolfe, Fred H. The Divine Pattern. LC 83-70212. 1983. pap. 5.95 (ISBN 0-8054-5244-3). Broadman.

Wolff, Pierre. May I Hate God? LC 78-70815. 80p. 1979. pap. 2.95 (ISBN 0-8091-2180-8). Paulist Pr.

Wolmarans, Theo. Blood Covenant. 175p. (Orig.). 1984. pap. text ed. 5.50 (ISBN 0-914307-26-6). Word Faith.

Wonder: The Book of We. (Infinity Ser.: No. 9). 1972. text ed. 2.50 (ISBN 0-03-004011-6, 243, HarpR); tchr's guide 1.15 (ISBN 0-03-004016-7, 244). Har-Row.

Wonderous Power, Wonderous Love. 250p. 1983. 8.95 (ISBN 0-89066-048-4); pap. 5.95 (ISBN 0-89066-052-2). World Wide Pubs.

Wood, Barry. Questions Christians Ask about Prayer & Intercession. 160p. (Orig.). 1984. pap. 5.95 (ISBN 0-8007-5177-9, Power Bks). Revell.

Wood, George. The Successful Life. Sekowsky, Jo Anne, ed. 64p. 1984. pap. text ed. 3.25 (ISBN 0-930756-82-7, 531017). Aglow Pubns.

Wood, George O. Living Fully: Producing Spiritual Fruit. 1985. pap. 3.95 (ISBN 0-932305-23-7, 531021). Aglow Pubns.

Wood, Herbert G. Christianity & Civilisation. LC 73-17694. 128p. 1973. Repr. of 1943 ed. lib. bdg. 13.00x (ISBN 0-374-98713-0, Octagon). Hippocrene Bks.

Wood, Mike. Pilgrims' Road. 1976. pap. 2.95 (ISBN 0-89390-015-X). Resource Pubns.

Woodbridge, Barry A. A Guidebook for Spiritual Friends. LC 84-51827. 96p. (Orig.). 1985. pap. 4.95 (ISBN 0-8358-0498-4). Upper Room.

Woodrow, Ralph. Women's Adornment: What Does the Bible Really Say? LC 76-17711. (Illus.). 1976. pap. 3.00 (ISBN 0-916938-01-8). R Woodrow.

Woods, Paulette. A Teachable Spirit. 72p. 1984. pap. 3.50 (ISBN 0-8341-0904-2). Beacon Hill.

Woodward, Evelyn. Poets, Prophets & Pragmatists: A New Challenge to Religious Life. LC 86-72375. 248p. (Orig.). 1987. pap. 6.95 (ISBN 0-87793-349-9). Ave Maria.

Woolton, John. The Christian Manual: Or, of the Life & Manners of True Christians. 1851. 21.00 (ISBN 0-384-69210-9). Johnson Repr.

Wooten, Bill D. & Hunt, Sonja. Talk Is Not Enough. LC 83-61814. 112p. (Orig.). 1983. pap. text ed. 4.25 (ISBN 0-87148-849-3); 7.95 (ISBN 0-87148-850-7). Pathway Pr.

Words of Wisdom. 1979. 9.50 (ISBN 0-8198-0605-6). Dghtrs St Paul.

Works of John Flavel, 6 vols. Set. 108.95 (ISBN 0-85151-060-4). Banner of Truth.
Worley, Win. Demolishing the Hosts of Hell: Every Christian's Job. rev. ed. (Orig.). 1980. pap. 5.00 (ISBN 0-685-60693-7). HBC.
Worthington, Lowell. Forty-Five & Satisfied. 1983. pap. 5.50 (ISBN 0-89137-313-6). Quality Pubns.
Wright, A. D. Workshoes for Christ. 1979. pap. 3.75 (ISBN 0-89225-185-9). Gospel Advocate.
Wright, David. Wisdom As a Lifestyle: Building Biblical Life-Codes. 1987. pap. 6.95 (ISBN 0-310-44311-3). Zondervan.
Wright, David & Wright, Jill. Praise with Understanding. 64p. 1983. pap. 3.50 (ISBN 0-85364-355-5, Pub. by Paternoster UK). Attic Pr.
Wright, H. Norman. The Christian Use of Emotional Power. 160p. 1974. pap. 5.95 (ISBN 0-8007-5213-9, Pub. by Power Bk.). Revell.
--Making Peace with Your Past. 1984. 10.95 (ISBN 0-8007-1228-5). Revell.
--Now I Know Why I'm Depressed. 1984. pap. 4.95 (ISBN 0-89081-423-6). Harvest Hse.
Wright, H. Norman & Inmon, Marvin N. Help, We're Having a Baby. LC 79-929649. 192p. 1984. pap. 5.95 (ISBN 0-8307-0997-5, 5418362). Regal.
Wright, Sr. Mary K. God's Unfolding Plan. 2.00 (ISBN 0-87505-307-6, Pub. by Lawrence). Borden.
Wright, Norman. How to Have a Creative Crisis. 176p. 1986. 10.95 (ISBN 0-8499-0540-0). Word Bks.
Wuestefeld, Mary F. To Drink of His Love. Wheeler, Gerald, ed. (Banner Ser.). 128p. (Orig.). 1986. pap. 6.50 (ISBN 0-8280-0312-2). Review & Herald.
Wurmbrand, Judy. Escape From the Grip. 126p. 1985. pap. 4.95 (ISBN 0-88264-153-0). Diane Bks.
Wurmbrand, Richard. My Answer to the Moscow's Bible. pap. 4.95 (ISBN 0-88264-001-1). Diane Bks.
Wyatt, Janice B. Come, Let Us Welcome Jesus. 1980. pap. 3.75 (ISBN 0-89536-411-5, 0375). CSS of Ohio.
Yale, Alfred. My Friend Paul. 1986. pap. 8.25 (ISBN 0-8309-0433-6). Herald Hse.
Yancey, Philip. True Confessions: Owning up to the Secret Everybody Knows. (Christian Essentials Ser.). 48p. (Orig.). 1987. pap. 1.95 (ISBN 0-89283-324-6). Servant.
Yancey, Phillip. Where Is God When It Hurts. 7.95 (ISBN 0-310-35417-X). Zondervan.
Yoder, Elmina & Miller, Lula. Praises We Sing. 1980. 5.45 (ISBN 0-87813-515-4). Christian Light.
Yoder, Mary E. Five Little Andys. (Illus.). 1977. 2.75 (ISBN 0-87813-510-3). Christian Light.
--Story Time with Grandma. 1979. 2.50 (ISBN 0-87813-514-6). Christian Light.
Yoder, Sara. Unto the Hills. 1985. 2.95 (ISBN 0-87813-523-5). Christian Light.
Yohn, Rick. Finding Time. 1986. 6.95 (ISBN 0-8499-3058-8). Word Bks.
Yonggi Cho, Paul. Suffering.... Why Me? LC 86-70741. 1986. pap. 3.50 (ISBN 0-88270-601-2). Bridge Pub.
Yorgason, Blaine M. & Yorgason, Brenton G. Becoming. LC 86-70295. 176p. 1986. 9.95 (ISBN 0-87579-034-8). Deseret Bk.
Youmans, Mary & Youmans, Roger. Testimony of Two. pap. 7.95 (ISBN 0-910924-91-0). Macalester.
Young, David P. The Speed of Love: An Exploration of Christian Faithfulness in a Technological World. 150p. (Orig.). 1986. pap. 6.95 (ISBN 0-377-00159-7). Friend Pr.
Young, Mildred B. Functional Poverty. 1983. pap. 2.50x (ISBN 0-87574-006-5, 006). Pendle Hill.
--What Doth the Lord Require of Thee? 1983. pap. 2.50x (ISBN 0-87574-145-2, 145). Pendle Hill.
Young, Samuel. Working Out What God Works in. (Harvest Ser.). 1981. pap. 4.95 (ISBN 0-8163-0440-8). Pacific Pr Pub Assn.
Yount, William R. Be Opened! LC 76-2238. 240p. 1976. bds. 9.95 (ISBN 0-8054-3216-7). Broadman.
Your Family & You. (Benziger Family Life Program Ser.). 1978. 2.00 (ISBN 0-02-651550-4); tchrs. ed. 4.00 (ISBN 0-02-651560-1); family handbook 1.00 (ISBN 0-02-651590-3). Benziger Pub Co.
Zanca, Kenneth. The Judas Within. (Illus.). 96p. (Orig.). 1978. pap. 2.95 (ISBN 0-914544-25-X). Living Flame Pr.
Zaretsky, Tuvya. Turning to God. 32p. (Orig.). 1984. pap. 0.75 (ISBN 0-87784-064-4). Inter-Varsity.
Zavel, Hubberman. God's Voice. 8.95 (ISBN 0-8062-2496-7). Carlton.
Zeik, Michael, ed. New Christian Communities: Origins, Style, & Survival. LC 76-181995. pap. 4.95 (ISBN 0-87957-002-4). Roth Pub.
Ziglar, Zig. Confessions of a Happy Christian. LC 78-6729. 1978. 12.95 (ISBN 0-88289-196-0). Pelican.
--Confessions of a Happy Christian. 192p. 1986. pap. 3.50 (ISBN 0-553-25551-7). Bantam.
--Nos Veremos en la Cumbre. Rev ed. Fernandez, Sergio, tr. from Eng. Orig. Title: See You at the Top. (Span., Illus.). 352p. 1985. pap. 9.95 (ISBN 0-311-46100-X). Casa Bautista.
Zimney, Connie F. In Praise of Homemaking: Affirming the Choice to be a Mother-at-Home. LC 84-71285. 144p. (Orig.). 1984. pap. 4.95 (ISBN 0-87793-322-7). Ave Maria.
Zook, Mollie B. Dilek. 1983. 3.25 (ISBN 0-87813-521-9). Christian Light.

CHRISTIAN LIFE–ANGLICAN AUTHORS

Downame, John. The Christian Warfare. LC 74-80174. (English Experience Ser.: No. 653). 674p. 1974. Repr. of 1604 ed. 67.00 (ISBN 90-221-0653-5). Walter J Johnson.
Hill, Robert. The Pathway to Prayer & Pietie. LC 74-28864. (English Experience Ser.: No. 744). 1975. Repr. of 1613 ed. 26.50 (ISBN 90-221-0744-2). Walter J Johnson.
Jackson, Abraham. The Pious Prentice, or, the Prentices Piety. LC 74-28866. (English Experience Ser.: No. 746). 1975. Repr. of 1640 ed. 7.00 (ISBN 90-221-0746-9). Walter J Johnson.
Lewis, C. S. The Joyful Christian: One Hundred Readings from the Works of C. S. Lewis. LC 77-21685. 1977. 11.95 (ISBN 0-02-570900-3). Macmillan.
Robinson, Arthur W. The Personal Life of the Christian. 1981. pap. 7.95X (ISBN 0-19-213427-2). Oxford U Pr.
Spurgeon, C. H. Able to the Uttermost. 240p. 1985. pap. 5.95. Pilgrim Pubns.
Taylor, Jeremy. Rule & Exercises of Holy Dying: Means & Instruments of Preparing Ourselves & Others Respectively for a Blessed Death. Kastenbaum, Robert & Thirlwall, Thomas, eds. LC 76-19590. (Death & Dying Ser.). 1977. Repr. of 1819 ed. lib. bdg. 25.50x (ISBN 0-405-09585-6). Ayer Co Pubs.

CHRISTIAN LIFE–BAPTIST AUTHORS

Baldwin, Lindley. The March of Faith: Samuel Morris. 96p. 1969. pap. 2.95 (ISBN 0-87123-360-6, 200360). Bethany Hse.
Ban, Arline J. & Ban, Joseph D. The New Disciple: Church Membership Junior-Junior High. LC 75-35898. 96p. 1976. pap. 1.95 (ISBN 0-8170-0658-3). Judson.
Barnette, Henlee. Your Freedom to Be Whole. LC 84-2381. (Potentials: Guides to Productive Living Ser.: Vol. 7). 118p. 1984. pap. 7.95 (ISBN 0-664-24526-9). Westminster.
Bubeck, Mark I. The Adversary. 1975. pap. 5.95 (ISBN 0-8024-0143-0). Moody.
Davis, R. Dowd. Baptist Distinctives: A Pattern for Service. 64p. (Orig.). 1986. pap. 3.95 (ISBN 0-913029-11-4). Stevens Bk Pr.
Doonan, Gladys. From My Jewel Box. LC 83-4439. 1983p. pap. 3.95 (ISBN 0-87227-092-0). Reg Baptist.
Fawcett, Cheryl. Know & Grow, Vol. 1. LC 82-21567. 1983. pap. 4.95 (ISBN 0-87227-086-6). Reg Baptist.
--Know & Grow, Vol. 2. LC 82-21567. 1983. pap. 4.95 (ISBN 0-87227-090-4). Reg Baptist.
Howard, J. Grant. Trauma of Transparency: A Biblical Approach to Inter-Personal Communication. LC 79-87716. (Critical Concern Bks). 1979. pap. 6.95 (ISBN 0-686-86369-0); study guide 2.95 (ISBN 0-930014-74-X). Multnomah.
Howington, Nolan P. A Royal Priesthood. LC 85-22376. 1986. pap. 4.95 (ISBN 0-8054-1622-6). Broadman.
Kendrick, Ben. A World of Treasure. LC 82-332. 1981. pap. 4.95 (ISBN 0-87227-081-5). Reg Baptist.
Madden, Myron C. Claim Your Heritage. LC 84-7315. (Potentials: Guides for Productive Living Ser.: Vol. 8). 116p. 1984. pap. 7.95 (ISBN 0-664-24531-5). Westminster.
Moore, Winfred. Faith for the Second Mile. LC 86-9535. 1986. 8.95 (ISBN 0-8054-5726-7). Broadman.
Powell, Paul W. Dynamic Discipleship. LC 84-11388. 1984. pap. 5.95 (ISBN 0-8054-5004-1). Broadman.
Tassell, Paul. Pathways to Power: Keys That Open Doors. LC 83-9576. 1983. pap. 3.95 (ISBN 0-87227-093-9). Reg Baptist.
Taylor, Jack R. After the Spirit Comes. LC 73-93908. 1975. 7.95 (ISBN 0-8054-5224-9). Broadman.
Williams, George H. & Mergal, Angel M., eds. Spiritual & Anabaptist Writers. LC 57-5003. (Library of Christian Classics). 418p. 1977. pap. 11.95 (ISBN 0-664-24150-6). Westminster.

CHRISTIAN LIFE–BIBLIOGRAPHY

Chase, Elise, compiled by. Healing Faith: An Annotated Bibliography of Christian Self-Help Books. LC 85-929. (Bibliographies & Indexes in Religious Studies: No. 3). xxxiv, 192p. 1985. lib. bdg. 35.00 (ISBN 0-313-24014-0, DHF/). Greenwood.
Dulles, Avery & Granfield, Patrick. The Church: A Bibliography. (Theology & Biblical Resources Ser: Vol. 1). 1985. 15.00 (ISBN 0-89453-449-1); pap. 8.95 (ISBN 0-89453-470-X). M Glazier.

CHRISTIAN LIFE–BIOGRAPHY

see Christian Biography

CHRISTIAN LIFE–CATHOLIC AUTHORS

Alberione, James. Insights into Religious Life. 1977. 3.00 (ISBN 0-8198-0424-X); pap. 2.00 (ISBN 0-8198-0425-8). Dghtrs St Paul.
--That Christ May Live in Me. 1980. 3.50 (ISBN 0-8198-7300-4); pap. 2.25 (ISBN 0-8198-7301-2). Dghtrs St Paul.
Alcock, John. Mons Perfectionis. LC 74-28823. (English Experience Ser.: No. 706). 1974. Repr. of 1497 ed. 6.00 (ISBN 90-221-0706-X). Walter J Johnson.
Archdiocese of Baltimore Staff. Partners in Catechesis. 96p. 1984. pap. 9.95 (ISBN 0-697-02016-9). Wm C Brown.
Blondel, Maurice. Action: Essay on a Critique of Life & a Science of Practice. Blanchette, Oliva, tr. from Fr. LC 83-401133. 448p. 1984. text ed. 29.95 (ISBN 0-268-00605-9, 85-06057). U of Notre Dame Pr.
Brother Lawrence. Practice of the Presence of God. 64p. pap. 2.75 (ISBN 0-8007-8034-5, Spire Bks). Revell.
Conversations with Monsignor Escriva de Balaguer. 210p. 1977. pap. 5.95 (ISBN 0-933932-05-7). Scepter Pubs.
Crews, Clyde. English Catholic Modernism: Maude Petre's Way of Faith. LC 83-50747. 156p. 1984. text ed. 16.95x (ISBN 0-268-00912-0, 85-09127). U of Notre Dame Pr.
Daly, James J. Road to Peace. facsimile ed. LC 78-107691. (Essay Index Reprint Ser.). 1936. 17.00 (ISBN 0-8369-1495-3). Ayer Co Pubs.
D'Arcy, Martin C. Of God & Man. 1967. pap. 1.25x (ISBN 0-268-00197-9). U of Notre Dame Pr.
Daughters of St Paul. Saint Paul for Every Day of the Year. 1979. 6.00 (ISBN 0-686-63641-4); pap. 4.50 (ISBN 0-8198-0646-3). Dghtrs St Paul.
Delaney, John J., tr. The Practice of the Presence of God. LC 77-70896. 1977. pap. 2.95 (ISBN 0-385-12861-4, Im). Doubleday.
Di Orio, Ralph A. Healing Power of Affirmation. LC 85-4400. 216p. 1986. pap. 6.95 (ISBN 0-385-23592-5, Im). Doubleday.
Donnelly, Dorothy. God & the Apple of His Eye. LC 72-96114. 1973. pap. 2.50 (ISBN 0-913382-05-1, 101-6). Prow Bks-Franciscan.
Duquoc, Christian, ed. Spirituality in Church & World. LC 65-28868. (Concilium Ser.: Vol. 9). 174p. 7.95 (ISBN 0-8091-0139-4). Paulist Pr.
Escriva de Balaguer, Josemaria. The Way. (Foreign language editions avail.). 1965. 9.95 (ISBN 0-933932-00-6). Scepter Pubs.
Freburger, William J. Birthday Blessings. (Greeting Book Line Ser.). 32p. (Orig.). 1985. pap. 1.50 (ISBN 0-89622-242-X). Twenty-Third.
Gallagher, Joseph V. To Be a Catholic. LC 73-137884. 96p. 1970. pap. 1.95 (ISBN 0-8091-5143-X). Paulist Pr.
Garrone, Gabriel-Marie. Poor in Spirit: Awaiting All from God. 1978. pap. 2.95 (ISBN 0-232-51337-6). Living Flame Pr.
Hardon, John A. Religious Life Today. 1977. 3.00 (ISBN 0-8198-0452-5). Dghtrs St Paul.
Harrington, Wilfrid. Christ & Life. 160p. 1976. 7.95 (ISBN 0-8199-0571-2). Franciscan Herald.
Hayes, Edward J., et al. Catholicism & Society. (Catholicism Catechism Ser.). 1982. pap. 5.95 (ISBN 0-913382-26-4, 103-16); tchr's manual 3.00 (ISBN 0-913382-27-2, 103-17). Prow Bks-Franciscan.
Hiesberger, Jean M., ed. Young Adult Living Handbook. LC 79-92005. (Paths of Life Ser.). 126p. 1980. 2.95 (ISBN 0-8091-2259-6). Paulist Pr.
Hinnebusch, Paul. Friendship in the Lord. LC 73-90411. 144p. 1974. pap. 2.75 (ISBN 0-87793-065-1). Ave Maria.
Killgallon, James, et al. Life in Christ. rev. ed. LC 76-26451. 1976. pap. 2.25 (ISBN 0-914070-08-8). ACTA Found.
Kleiner, Sighard. Serving God First. 1985. 14.95 (ISBN 0-87907-883-9). Cistercian Pubns.
Kraft, William F. Achieving Promises: A Spiritual Guide for the Transitions of Life. LC 81-10496. 132p. 1981. pap. 6.95 (ISBN 0-664-24384-3). Westminster.
Leckey, Dolores R. Laity Stirring the Church: Prophetic Questions. LC 86-45213. (Laity Exchange Ser.). 128p. pap. 6.95 (ISBN 0-8006-1659-6, 1-1659). Fortress.
Le Sage, Wilfred. Vision of Renewal. (Orig.). 1967. 4.00 (ISBN 0-8198-0169-0); pap. 3.00 (ISBN 0-8198-0170-4). Dghtrs St Paul.
Lubich, Chiara. Jesus in the Midst: Spiritual Writings. LC 76-18455. 80p. 1976. pap. 2.95 (ISBN 0-911782-26-5). New City.
McNamara, James. The Power of Compassion. 1984. pap. 4.95 (ISBN 0-8091-2567-6). Paulist Pr.
Mauriac, Francois. Anguish & Joy of the Christian Life. (Orig.). pap. 1.25x (ISBN 0-268-00005-0). U of Notre Dame Pr.
Menard, Eusebe. At All Times, in Every Age. 1977. 4.95 (ISBN 0-8199-0663-8). Franciscan Herald.
Montague, George T. Building Christ's Body: The Dynamics of Christian Living According to St. Paul. 1976. 5.50 (ISBN 0-8199-0573-9). Franciscan Herald.
Moran, Peter. Easy Essays. 1977. pap. 6.95 (ISBN 0-8199-0681-6). Franciscan Herald.
Mother Teresa. Heart of Joy: The Transforming Power of Self-Giving. 140p. (Orig.). 1987. pap. 3.95 (ISBN 0-89283-342-4). Servant.
Nimeth, Albert J. Tenderly I Care. 1977. 5.00 (ISBN 0-685-85844-8). Franciscan Herald.
O'Reilly, James. Lay & Religious States of Life. LC 76-43048. 1977. pap. text ed. 0.75 (ISBN 0-685-81233-2). Franciscan Herald.
Parent, Neil, ed. Christian Adulthood Nineteen Eighty-Seven. Date not set. pap. price not set (ISBN 1-55586-106-7). US Catholic.
Philips, Gerard. Achieving Christian Maturity. 4.95 (ISBN 0-685-10957-7, L37990). Franciscan Herald.
Pope John Paul II. Visible Signs of the Gospel. 1980. 4.00 (ISBN 0-8198-8000-0); pap. 2.95 (ISBN 0-8198-8001-9). Dghtrs St Paul.
Priestley, Denise M. Bringing Forth in Hope: Being Creative in a Nuclear Age. 80p. (Orig.). 1983. pap. 4.95 (ISBN 0-8091-2551-X). Paulist Pr.
Reichert, Richard. Growing Within, Changing Without. (New Creation Ser.). 96p. 1985. pap. text ed. 4.05 (ISBN 0-697-01993-4); tchr's. ed. 4.50 (ISBN 0-697-01994-2). Wm C Brown.
--New Creation People. (New Creation Ser.). 96p. 1985. pap. text ed. 4.25 (ISBN 0-697-01997-7); tchr's. ed. 4.50 (ISBN 0-697-01998-5). Wm C Brown.
--On Our Way. (New Creation Ser.). 96p. 1985. pap. text ed. 4.25 (ISBN 0-697-01995-0); tchr's. ed. 4.50 (ISBN 0-697-01996-9). Wm C Brown.
Rivers, Caryl. Virgins. 256p. 1984. 12.95 (ISBN 0-312-84951-6, Pub. by Marek). St Martin.
St. Paul, George A. Here & Hereafter. LC 56-9839. (Loyola Request Reprint Ser.). Repr. of 1963 ed. 59.30 (ISBN 0-8357-9427-X, 2015061). Bks Demand UMI.
Search Institute Staff. There Is a Season. Williams, Dorothy, ed. 1985. program manual 24.95 (ISBN 0-697-02047-9); pap. 4.95 parent book (ISBN 0-697-02046-0); video cassettes avail. Wm C Brown.
Segundo, Juan L. The Community Called Church. Drury, John, tr. from Span. LC 72-85795. (A Theology for Artisans of a New Humanity Ser., Vol. 1). Orig. Title: Esa communidad Lleamasha Iglesia. 181p. 1973. 7.95x (ISBN 0-88344-481-X); pap. 4.95x (ISBN 0-88344-487-9). Orbis Bks.
Sullivan, Peter. Christ: The Answer. (Orig.). pap. 1.95 (ISBN 0-8198-0026-0). Dghtrs St Paul.
Tripole, Martin R. The Jesus Event & Our Response. LC 79-27896. 248p. (Orig.). 1980. pap. 7.95 (ISBN 0-8189-0399-6). Alba.
Urteaga, J. Man the Saint. 218p. 1963. pap. 4.95 (ISBN 0-933932-06-5). Scepter Pubs.
Vanier, Jean. Be Not Afraid. 160p. 1975. pap. 7.95 (ISBN 0-8091-1885-8). Paulist Pr.
Von Hildebrand, Dietrich & Von Hildebrand, Alice. Art of Living. 1965. 3.95 (ISBN 0-685-10959-3, L38009). Franciscan Herald.
Whealon, John F. Living the Catholic Faith Today. LC 75-6801. 1975. 2.50 (ISBN 0-8198-0491-6); pap. 1.50 (ISBN 0-8198-0492-4). Dghtrs St Paul.
Wilkins, Ronald. Focus on Faith in Jesus: Parish Edition. rev. ed. 112p. 1985. pap. text ed. 5.25 (ISBN 0-697-02007-X); tchr's. ed. 12.95 (ISBN 0-697-02009-6). Wm C Brown.
--Focus on Faith in Jesus: School Edition. rev. ed. 192p. 1985. pap. text ed. 6.50 (ISBN 0-697-02006-1); tchr's. ed. 14.95 (ISBN 0-697-02008-8). Wm C Brown.
--Focus on Growth in the Church: Parish Edition. rev. ed. 128p. 1985. pap. text ed. 5.25 (ISBN 0-697-02011-8); tchr's. ed. 12.95 (ISBN 0-697-02013-4). Wm C Brown.
--Focus on Growth in the Church: School Edition. rev. ed. 224p. 1985. pap. text ed. 6.50 (ISBN 0-697-02010-X); tchr's. ed. 14.95 (ISBN 0-697-02012-6). Wm C Brown.
Zamboni, Camillo. He Speaks to You. 1966. pap. 1.25 (ISBN 0-8198-0055-4). Dghtrs St Paul.

CHRISTIAN LIFE–EARLY CHURCH, ca. 30-600

Davies, John G. Daily Life of Early Christians. LC 75-91757. Repr. of 1953 ed. lib. bdg. 22.50x (ISBN 0-8371-2413-1, DAEC). Greenwood.
Lesbaupin, Ivo. Blessed Are the Persecuted: Christian Life in the Roman Empire, A.D. 64-313. Barr, Robert R., tr. from Port. Tr. of A Bem-Aventuranca da Persecucion & La Bienaventuranza de la Persecucion. 112p. (Orig.). 1987. 16.95 (ISBN 0-88344-562-X); pap. 7.95 (ISBN 0-88344-561-1). Orbis Bks.

CHRISTIAN LIFE–LUTHERAN AUTHORS

Deffner, Donald L. Come Closer to Me, God! 1982. pap. 4.95 (ISBN 0-570-03851-0, 12-2806). Concordia.

Jackson, Gregory L. Prophetic Voice for the Kingdom. Paulson, Ross E., ed. LC 86-71907. (Augustana Historical Society Pub. Ser.: No. 35). 239p. 1986. text ed. 19.95 (ISBN 0-910184-35-6). Augustana.

Juel, Donald H. Living a Biblical Faith. LC 82-8652. (Library of Living Faith: Vol. 6). 118p. 1982. pap. 5.95 (ISBN 0-664-24429-7). Westminster.

Rogness, Alvin N. The Jesus Life: A Guide for Young Christians. LC 72-90260. 112p. (Orig.). (YA) 1973. pap. 5.95 (ISBN 0-8066-1307-6, 10-3521). Augsburg.

Thielicke, Helmut. Life Can Begin Again: Sermons on the Sermon on the Mount. Doberstein, John W., tr. from Ger. LC 63-12535. 240p. 1963. pap. 5.95 (ISBN 0-8006-1934-X, 1-1934). Fortress.

CHRISTIAN LIFE–MENNONITE AUTHORS

Driver, John. Community & Commitment. LC 76-41463. 96p. 1976. pap. 3.95 (ISBN 0-8361-1802-2). Herald Pr.

CHRISTIAN LIFE–METHODIST AUTHORS

Dunnam, Maxie D. The Workbook of Living Prayer. 1975. 4.50x (ISBN 0-8358-0323-6). Upper Room.

Ensley, Francis G. Leader's Guide for Use with Persons Can Change, by Francis Gerald Ensley. LC 69-101739. pap. 20.00 (ISBN 0-317-10063-7, 2001430). Bks Demand UMI.

Webb, Lance. Disciplines for Life. 176p. pap. 7.95 (ISBN 0-8358-0539-5, ICN 602777, Dist. by Abingdon Pr). Upper Room.

Wimmer, John R. No Pain, No Gain: Hope for Those Who Struggle. 71p. 1985. 8.95 (ISBN 0-345-32181-2, Epiphany). Ballantine.

CHRISTIAN LIFE–MIDDLE AGES, 600-1500

Butler-Bowdon, W. The Book of Margery Kempe: A Modern Version. 1978. Repr. of 1936 ed. lib. bdg. 25.00 (ISBN 0-8482-3353-0). Norwood Edns.

Erasmus, Desiderius. A Booke Called in Latyn Enchiridian & in Englysshe the Manuell of the Christen Knyght. LC 70-25758. (English Experience Ser.: No. 156). 340p. 1969. Repr. of 1533 ed. 28.00 (ISBN 90-221-0156-8). Walter J Johnson.

CHRISTIAN LIFE–MORMON AUTHORS

Backman, Robert L. Be Master of Yourself. LC 86-2047. 227p. 1986. 9.95 (ISBN 0-87579-033-X). Deseret Bk.

Covey, Stephen R. Spiritual Roots of Human Relations. LC 72-119477. 9.95 (ISBN 0-87747-315-3). Deseret Bk.

Hinckley, Gordon B. Be Thou an Example. LC 81-15109. 144p. 1981. 7.95 (ISBN 0-87747-899-6). Deseret Bk.

Holland, Jeffrey R. However Long & Hard the Road. LC 85-12945. 144p. 1985. 8.95 (ISBN 0-87747-625-X). Deseret Bk.

Kimball, Spencer W. Faith Precedes the Miracle. 9.95 (ISBN 0-87747-490-7). Deseret Bk.

Monson, Thomas S. Conference Classics, Vol. 2. 63p. 1983. 5.95 (ISBN 0-87747-957-7). Deseret Bk.

--Conference Classics, Vol. 3. 64p. 5.95 (ISBN 0-87747-989-5). Deseret Bk.

CHRISTIAN LIFE–ORTHODOX EASTERN AUTHORS

Coniaris, A. M. Eastern Orthodoxy: A Way of Life. 1966. pap. 6.95 (ISBN 0-937032-14-X). Light&Life Pub Co MN.

--Perspectives on Living the Orthodox Faith. 1985. pap. 7.95 (ISBN 0-937032-36-0). Light&Life Pub Co MN.

Harakas, Emily. Through the Year with the Church Fathers. 1985. pap. 8.95 (ISBN 0-937032-37-9). Light&Life Pub Co MN.

Matthew the Poor. Communion of Love. LC 84-10561. 234p. (Orig.). 1984. pap. text ed. 8.95 (ISBN 0-88141-036-5). St Vladimirs.

CHRISTIAN LIFE–PICTURES, ILLUSTRATIONS, ETC.

Sandberg, Craig. Simple Life Coloring Book. 1983. 2.25 (ISBN 0-87813-519-7). Christian Light.

CHRISTIAN LIFE–PRESBYTERIAN AUTHORS

Anderson, Fred R. Singing Psalms of Joy & Praise. LC 86-1550. 78p. (Orig.). 1986. pap. 5.95 ea. (ISBN 0-664-24696-6). Westminster.

Boice, James M. How to Live the Christian Life. LC 81-18839. 128p. 1982. pap. 5.95 (ISBN 0-8024-3666-8). Moody.

Brown, Robert McAfee. Saying Yes & Saying No: On Rendering to God & Caesar. LC 85-29575. 144p. (Orig.). 1986. pap. 7.95 (ISBN 0-664-24695-8). Westminster.

Conn, Harvie M., ed. Reaching the Unreached. (Orig.). 1985. pap. 8.95 (ISBN 0-87552-209-2). Presby & Reformed.

Rassieur, Charles L. Christian Renewal: Living Beyond Burnout. LC 83-26064. (Potentials: Guides for Productive Living: Vol. 5). 120p. (Orig.). 1984. pap. 7.95 (ISBN 0-664-24611-7). Westminster.

Sanderson, John W. The Fruit of the Spirit. 192p. 1985. pap. 3.95 (ISBN 0-87552-431-1). Presby & Reformed.

Young, David P. Twenty-First Century Pioneering: A Scrapbook of the Future. (Illus., Orig.). 1986. pap. 5.95 (ISBN 0-377-00160-0). Friend Pr.

CHRISTIAN LIFE–SEVENTH DAY ADVENTIST

Bothwell, Roger. For the Umpteenth Time. (Outreach Ser.). 16p. 1983. pap. 0.95 (ISBN 0-8163-0538-2). Pacific Pr Pub Assn.

Scott, Hildreth. Alone, Again! (Uplook Ser.). 1976. pap. 0.99 (ISBN 0-8163-0251-0, 01496-9). Pacific Pr Pub Assn.

CHRISTIAN LIFE–STORIES

Adams, Jay E. What to do on Thursday: A Layman's Guide to the Practical Use of the Scriptures. 144p. 1982. pap. 3.95 (ISBN 0-8010-0188-9). Baker Bk.

Anderson, D. Carl. Trial by Death & Fire. LC 80-14446. (Orion Ser.). 160p. 1980. pap. 3.95 (ISBN 0-8127-0292-1). Review & Herald.

Ashton, Leila M. It's Sabbath. (My Church Teaches Ser.). (Illus.). 1978. pap. 1.95 (ISBN 0-8127-0177-1). Review & Herald.

--Today Is Friday. (My Church Teaches Ser.). (Illus.). 1978. pap. 1.954 (ISBN 0-8127-0176-3). Review & Herald.

Gragg, Rod. Bobby Bagley POW. 1978. pap. 3.95 (ISBN 0-89728-022-9, 678434). Omega Pubns OR.

Hunter, Frances. God Is Fabulous. 1978. pap. 3.25 (ISBN 0-87162-115-0). Hunter Bks.

--Hot Line to Heaven. 1978. pap. 3.25 (ISBN 0-87162-117-7). Hunter Bks.

Jackson, Edgar N. The Role of Faith in the Process of Healing. 216p. 1982. pap. 9.95 (ISBN 0-86683-679-9, HarpR). Har-Row.

Klug, Ron & Klug, Lyn, eds. The Christian Family Bedtime Reading Book. LC 82-70952. 128p. pap. 10.95 (ISBN 0-8066-1927-9, 10-1112). Augsburg.

Mings, Lonnie C. The Pure Land. (Orig.). 1979. pap. 4.95 (ISBN 0-8024-5989-7). Moody.

Naylor, Phyllis R. Never Born a Hero. LC 82-70950. 128p. pap. 3.95 (ISBN 0-8066-1925-2, 10-4647). Augsburg.

Nomura, Yushi. Desert Wisdom: Sayings from the Desert Fathers. LC 82-45488. (Illus.). 128p. 1982. 14.95 (ISBN 0-385-18078-0). Doubleday.

Stevens, Margaret M. Stepping Stones for Boys & Girls. (Illus.). 1977. pap. 3.00 (ISBN 0-87516-248-7). De Vorss.

Von Eschen, Jessie M. Pot of Gold. 1983. 7.95 (ISBN 0-8062-2135-6). Carlton.

CHRISTIAN LIFE–STUDY AND TEACHING

Ball, Howard. There Is Help for Your Church. LC 81-65669. 40p. (Orig.). 1981. pap. text ed. 1.50 (ISBN 0-934396-14-0). Churches Alive.

Bright, Bill. Handbook for Christian Maturity. 360p. (Orig.). 1981. pap. 8.95 (ISBN 0-86605-010-8). Campus Crusade.

--Handbook of Concepts for Living. 545p. (Orig.). 1981. pap. 8.95 (ISBN 0-86605-011-6). Campus Crusade.

--How to Be Sure You Are a Christian. (Transferable Concepts Ser.). 63p. 1981. pap. 1.25 (ISBN 0-918956-88-9). Campus Crusade.

--How to Introduce Others to Christ. (Transferable Concepts Ser.). 64p. 1981. pap. 1.25 (ISBN 0-918956-93-5). Campus Crusade.

--How to Love by Faith. (Transferable Concepts Ser.). 64p. 1981. pap. 1.25 (ISBN 0-918956-95-1). Campus Crusade.

DeGolia. Object Lessons Using Common Things. 1954. 3.50 (ISBN 0-88207-026-6). Victor Bks.

Frost, Marie H. Listen to Your Children. LC 80-50320. 144p. (Orig.). 1980. pap. 2.95 (ISBN 0-87239-396-8, 3000). Standard Pub.

Kelly, George A., ed. The Teaching Church in Our Time. 1978. 6.00 (ISBN 0-8198-0523-8); pap. 4.50 (ISBN 0-8198-0524-6). Dghtrs St Paul.

Littauer, Florence. Christian Leader's & Speaker's Seminars. 100p. 1983. incl. lab manual & 12 cassettes 89.95 (ISBN 0-89081-369-8). Harvest Hse.

Maseroni, Robert S. The Gift of Teaching, No. 3. 1983. 0.80 (ISBN 0-89536-627-4, 0735). CSS of Ohio.

Meeter, Merle, et al. English Workbook for Christian Students. 1980. pap. 5.95x (ISBN 0-89051-066-0); tchr.'s guide 2.95x (ISBN 0-686-85807-7). Master Bks.

Navigators. Lessons on Christian Living. (Growing in Christ Ser.). 46p. 1982. pap. text ed. 2.45 (ISBN 0-934396-29-9). Churches Alive.

Navigators Staff. Lessons on Assurance. (Growing in Christ Ser.). 32p. 1982. pap. text ed. 2.45 (ISBN 0-934396-28-0). Churches Alive.

Nee, Watchman. Assembling Together. Kaung, Stephen, tr. (Basic Lesson Ser.: Vol. 3). 1973. 4.50 (ISBN 0-935008-01-2); pap. 3.25 (ISBN 0-935008-02-0). Christian Fellow Pubs.

Nilsen, Mary Y. Our Family Shares Advent: Scripture, Prayer, & Activities for Families. (Illus.). 64p. (Orig.). 1980. pap. 7.95 (ISBN 0-86683-637-3, 8129, HarpR). Har-Row.

Ortlund, Raymond C. Lord, Make My Life Count. LC 75-6188. 144p. 1975. pap. 3.50 (ISBN 0-8307-0348-9, S112175). Regal.

Poetae Christiani Minores, Pt. 1. (Corpus Scriptorum Ecclesiasticorum Latinorum Ser: Vol. 16). 1888. 50.00 (ISBN 0-384-47060-2). Johnson Repr.

Reilly, Mary V. & Wetterer, Margaret K. Voices of Praise. (Illus., Orig.). 1980. pap. 4.95 (ISBN 0-8192-1276-8). Morehouse.

Reilly, Mary V., et al. Wait in Joyful Hope! (Illus., Orig.). 1980. pap. 4.95 (ISBN 0-8192-1275-X). Morehouse.

Savary, Louis M. & Scheihing, Theresa O. Our Treasured Heritage: Teaching Christian Meditation to Children. LC 81-7818. 176p. 1981. 9.95 (ISBN 0-8245-0078-4). Crossroad NY.

Shultz, Leland G. The Bible & the Christian Life. LC 82-82701. (Radiant Life Ser.). 128p. (Orig.). 1984. pap. 2.50 (ISBN 0-88243-857-3, 02-0857); tchr's guide 3.95 (ISBN 0-88243-198-6, 32-0198). Gospel Pub.

Smith, Ken & Smith, Floy. Learning to Be a Family: Leader's Guide. (Orig.). 1985. pap. 3.95 (ISBN 0-934688-17-6). Great Comm Pubns.

Williams, Herman & Greene, Ella L. Attitude Education: A Research Curriculum. LC 75-16677. 1975. pap. 3.00x (ISBN 0-915744-02-3). Character Res.

Young, David S., ed. Study War No More. (Orig.). 1981. pap. 3.95 (ISBN 0-87178-822-5). Brethren.

CHRISTIAN LITERATURE

see also Catholic Literature; Christian Poetry; Christianity and Literature; Christianity in Literature; Devotional Literature

Anderson, Margaret J. The Christian Writer's Handbook. rev. ed. LC 82-48917. 288p. 1983. 9.95 (ISBN 0-06-060195-7, RD/246, HarpR). Har-Row.

Blair, J. W. Coleccion Navidena, No. 1 & 2. 1980. No. 1. pap. 1.75 (ISBN 0-311-08201-7); No. 2. pap. 1.75 (ISBN 0-311-08202-5). Casa Bautista.

Booker, Richard. Intimacy with God. LC 84-70055. 196p. 1983. pap. 5.95 (ISBN 0-88270-552-0). Bridge Pub.

Boudeaux, Michael. Risen Indeed: Lessons of Faith from the U. S. S. R. (Orig.). 1983. pap. text ed. 5.95 (ISBN 0-88141-021-7). St Vladimirs.

Bunyan, John, et al. How They Found Christ: In Their Own Words. Freeman, Bill, ed. LC 83-62268. 66p. (Orig.). 1983. pap. 1.40 (ISBN 0-914271-00-8). NW Christian Pubns.

Campbell, Roger. Lord, I'm Afraid. (Orig.). 1980. pap. 2.50 (ISBN 0-87508-056-1). Chr Lit.

Carlson, Carole. A Light in Babylon. 256p. 1985. 12.95 (ISBN 0-8499-0452-8, 0452-8). Word Bks.

CBA Suppliers Directory, 1987. 1987. 64.95. Chr Bksellers.

Ceynar, Marvin. Writing for the Religious Market. 1986. 2.25 (ISBN 0-89536-804-8, 6822). CSS of Ohio.

Chase, Elise, compiled by. Healing Faith: An Annotated Bibliography of Christian Self-Help Books. LC 85-929. (Bibliographies & Indexes in Religious Studies: No. 3). xxxiv, 192p. 1985. lib. bdg. 35.00 (ISBN 0-313-24014-0, DHF/). Greenwood.

Christian Periodical Index: Annual & Quarterly, 1985. 1985. 32.00 (ISBN 0-318-04217-7). Assn Chr Libs.

Christian Periodical Index: Cumulative, 1982-1984, Vol. 7. 1985. 45.00 (ISBN 0-318-04216-9). Assn Chr Libs.

Christian Periodical Index: Quarterlies, 1984. 10.00 (ISBN 0-318-01672-9). Assn Chr Libs.

Christian Periodical Index: 1979-1981, Cumulated Vol. 35.00 (ISBN 0-318-00379-1). Assn Chr Libs.

Comerchero, Victor, ed. Values in Conflict: Christianity, Marxism, Psychoanalysis & Existentialism. LC 74-111099. 986p. (Orig., Free booklet, "Suggestions for Instructors," available). 1970. pap. text ed. 19.95x (ISBN 0-89197-463-6). Irvington.

Conn, Charles W. Rudder & the Rock. 1976. pap. 4.25 (ISBN 0-87148-733-0). Pathway Pr.

Constant, A. L. Dictionnaire de la Litterature Chretienne, Vol. 7. Migne, J. P., ed. (Nouvelle Encyclopedie Theologique Ser.). (Fr.). 626p. Repr. of 1851 ed. lib. bdg. 80.00x (ISBN 0-89241-257-7). Caratzas.

Darby, J. N. The Collected Writings, 35 vols. Set. 125.00 (ISBN 0-88172-055-0); 4.00 ea. Believers Bkshelf.

Dobbert, John A. If Being a Christian Is So Great, Why Do I Have the Blahs? LC 79-65420. 160p. 1980. pap. 4.95 (ISBN 0-8307-0729-8, 5413206). Regal.

Drummond, Henry. Peace Be with You. (Illus.). 1978. 4.95 (ISBN 0-915720-44-2). Brownlow Pub Co.

Dunn, Ronald. The Faith Crisis. Chao, Lorna Y., tr. (Chinese.). 1985. pap. write for info. (ISBN 0-941598-30-6). Living Spring Pubns.

Durken, Daniel, ed. Blow the Trumpet at the New Moon: A Sisters Today Jubilee. LC 79-27505. xi, 480p. (Orig.). 1980. pap. 3.00 (ISBN 0-8146-1016-1). Liturgical Pr.

Glenn, Paul J. Tour of the Summa. LC 78-66307. 1978. pap. 12.50 (ISBN 0-89555-081-4). TAN Bks Pubs.

Gray, Margaret. The Donkey's Tale. (Illus.). 32p. 1984. casebound 3.95 (ISBN 0-8307-0963-0, 5111209). Regal.

Halverson, Richard C. Somehow Inside of Eternity. LC 80-21687. (Illus., Orig.). 1981. pap. 8.95 (ISBN 0-930014-51-0). Multnomah.

Hendricks, Howard G. Say It with Love. LC 72-77011. 143p. 1972. pap. 5.95 (ISBN 0-88207-050-9). Victor Bks.

Herr, Ethel. An Introduction to Christian Writing. 315p. 1983. pap. 8.95 (ISBN 0-8423-1590-X). Tyndale.

Hobbs, Ruth. The Christian Short Story. 10.95 (ISBN 0-686-32320-3). Rod & Staff.

Horgan, Paul. Under the Sangre de Cristo. (Charlotte Ser.). 90p. 1985. 150.00x (ISBN 0-911292-00-4). Rydal.

Houk, Neil B. Church Bytes Nineteen Eighty-Six. 74p. (Orig.). 1987. pap. 7.95 (ISBN 0-9615086-5-5). Church Bytes.

Hure. Dictionnaire Universel de Philologie Sacree... Suivi du Dictionnaire de Lanque Sainte... par Louis de Wolzoque, 3 vols. in 4. Migne, J. P., ed. (Encyclopedie Theologique Ser.: Vols. 5-7). (Fr.). 2426p. Repr. of 1846 ed. lib. bdg. 309.50x (ISBN 0-89241-232-1). Caratzas.

Hurst, George. An Outline of the History of Christian Literature. 1977. lib. bdg. 69.95 (ISBN 0-8490-2395-5). Gordon Pr.

Jacks, Bob, et al. Your Home, a Lighthouse. LC 85-73824. 142p. (Orig.). 1986. pap. text ed. 4.95 (ISBN 0-934396-41-8). Churches Alive.

Jouhanneaud, P. Dictionnaire d'Anecdotes Chretiennes. Migne, J. P., ed. (Nouvelle Encyclopedie Theologique Ser.: Vol. 10). (Fr.). 610p. Repr. of 1857 ed. lib. bdg. 78.00x (ISBN 0-89241-260-7). Caratzas.

Kavanaugh, Kieran & Rodriguez, Otilio, trs. The Collected Works of St. Teresa of Avila, Vol. 2. LC 75-31305. 560p. 1980. pap. 6.95x (ISBN 0-9600876-6-4). ICS Pubns.

Keesecker, William F., ed. & selected by. A Calvin Reader: Reflections on Living. LC 85-15237. 144p. 1985. pap. 9.95 (ISBN 0-664-24667-2). Westminster.

Kelly, Henry A. The Devil at Baptism: Ritual, Theology, & Drama. LC 85-404. 304p. 1985. text ed. 29.95x (ISBN 0-8014-1806-2). Cornell U Pr.

Kelly, W. Collections of Selected Pamphlets. pap. text ed. 6.95 (ISBN 0-88172-093-3). Believers Bkshelf.

Kelsey, Morton T. The Cross: Meditations on the Last Seven Words of Christ. LC 80-82086. 128p. 1980. pap. 3.95 (ISBN 0-8091-2337-1). Paulist Pr.

McCarthy, David S. Practical Guide for the Christian Writer. 112p. 1983. pap. 5.95 (ISBN 0-8170-0979-5). Judson.

McCarthy, Scott. Creation Liturgy. LC 86-43232. 150p. (Orig.). 1987. pap. 10.95 (ISBN 0-89390-105-9). Resource Pubns.

Martin, Malachi. There Is Still Love. 224p. 1984. 12.95 (ISBN 0-02-580440-5). Macmillan.

Masterpieces of Christian Literature, 2 vols. 1203p. 1963. Set. 60.00x (ISBN 0-89356-150-9). Salem Pr.

Maxwell, Patricia. How to Become a Christian & Stay One. LC 79-4603. (Waymark Ser.). 1979. pap. 2.50 (ISBN 0-8127-0221-2). Review & Herald.

Metropolitan Innocent of Moscow. Indication of the Way Into the Kingdom of Heaven. 48p. (Orig.). 1981. pap. 2.00 (ISBN 0-317-30275-2). Holy Trinity.

Morgan, G. Campbell. Searchlights from the Word. 1984. pap. 11.95 (ISBN 0-8010-6174-1). Baker Bk.

Murray, Andrew. Secret of Fellowship. (Secret Ser.). (Orig.). 1980. pap. 1.95 (ISBN 0-87508-388-9). Chr Lit.

--Secret of Inspiration. (Secret Ser.). (Orig.). 1979. pap. 1.95 (ISBN 0-87508-386-2). Chr Lit.

--Secret of Intercession. (Secret Ser.). (Orig.). 1980. pap. 1.95 (ISBN 0-87508-391-9). Chr Lit.

Nee, Watchman. The Joyful Heart. Chen, Ruth T., tr. (Chinese.). 1985. write for info. (ISBN 0-941598-91-8); pap. write for info. (ISBN 0-941598-24-1). Living Spring Pubns.

Newton, John. Works of John Newton, 6 vols. 1985. Repr. of 1820 ed. Set. 125.00 (ISBN 0-85151-460-X). Banner of Truth.

O'Malley, William J. The Living Word: Scripture & Myth, Vol. 1. LC 80-80534. 180p. (Orig.). 1980. pap. text ed. 4.95 (ISBN 0-8091-9558-5). Paulist Pr.

Perennes, F. Dictionnaire de Lecons et Exemples de Litterature Chretienne en Prose et en Verse, 2 vols. Migne, J. P., ed. (Troisieme et Derniere Encyclopedie Theologique Ser.: Vols. 61-62). (Fr.). 1510p. Repr. of 1864 ed. lib. bdg. 191.50x (ISBN 0-89241-326-3). Caratzas.

Reid, David P. What Are They Saying about the Prophets? LC 80-80869. 112p. (Orig.). 1980. pap. 3.95 (ISBN 0-8091-2304-5). Paulist Pr.

Ricks, Chip & Marsh, Marilyn. How to Write for Christian Magazines. LC 84-23025. 1985. pap. 7.50 (ISBN 0-8054-7910-4). Broadman.

Saint John of Kronstadt. My Life in Christ. Goulaeff, E. E., tr. from Rus. LC 84-81775. 558p. 1984. 25.00 (ISBN 0-88465-018-9); pap. 20.00 (ISBN 0-88465-017-0). Holy Trinity.

Sanders, J. Oswald. Enjoying Intimacy with God. LC 80-21398. 218p. 1980. pap. 5.95 (ISBN 0-8024-2346-9). Moody.

Schlink, Basilea. Dear Brothers & Sisters in Christ: Five Letters of Comfort. 1978. pap. 0.95 (ISBN 3-87209-622-2). Evang Sisterhood Mary.

--What Made Them So Brave? (Illus.). 1978. gift edition 2.25 (ISBN 3-87209-655-9). Evang Sisterhood Mary.

Smith, Gerard. A Trio of Talks. 44p. pap. 4.95 (ISBN 0-87462-440-1). Marquette.

Sommerville, C. John. Popular Religion in Restoration England. LC 77-7618. (University of Florida Social Sciences Monographs: No. 59). 1977. pap. 4.50 (ISBN 0-8130-0564-7). U Presses Fla.

Sonderegger-Kummer, Irene. Transparenz der Wirklichkeit: Edzard Schaper und die innere Spannung in der christlichen Literatur des zwanzigstes Jahrhunderts. (Quellen und Forschungen zur Sprach- und Kulturgeschichte der germanischen Voelker, No. 37). (Ger). 1971. 48.40x (ISBN 3-11-001845-4). De Gruyter.

Spurgeon, Charles. All of Grace. Chen, Ruth T. & Chou, Peter, trs. (Chinese.). 142p. 1984. pap. write for info. (ISBN 0-941598-22-5). Living Spring Pubns.

Taylor, Charles R. When Jesus Comes. (Illus.). 76p. (Orig.). 1985. pap. 4.95 (ISBN 0-937682-08-X). Today Bible.

Thompson, James J., Jr. Christian Classics Revisited. LC 82-84583. 163p. (Orig.). 1983. pap. 8.95 (ISBN 0-89870-028-0). Ignatius Pr.

Treasury of Christian Classics. Bd. with The Greatest Thing in the World; As a Man Thinketh; Acres of Diamonds; The Practice of the Presence of God. (The Christian Library). 241p. 6.95 (ISBN 0-916441-47-4). Barbour & Co.

Wentz, Richard E. More Than You Know. 60p. (Orig.). 1983. pap. 1.25 (ISBN 0-88028-027-1). Forward Movement.

White, William R. Speaking in Stories: Resources for Christian Storytellers. LC 82-70954. 128p. (Orig.). 1982. pap. 6.95 (ISBN 0-8066-1929-5, 10-5886). Augsburg.

Wilson, Ernest C. Like a Miracle. 202p. 1971. 5.95 (ISBN 0-87159-088-3). Unity School.

Zundel, Veronica. Eerdmans' Book of Christian Classics. 125p. 1985. 12.95 (ISBN 0-8028-3612-7). Eerdmans.

CHRISTIAN LITERATURE, EARLY

Bernard of Clairvaux. Treatises I: Apologia, Precept & Dispensation. (Cistercian Fathers Ser.: No. 1). 190p. 7.95 (ISBN 0-87907-101-X). Cistercian Pubns.

Brunet, G. Dictionnaire des Apocryphes, 2 vols. Migne, J. P., ed. (Troisieme et Derniere Encyclopedie Theologique Ser.: Vols. 23-24). (Fr.). 1310p. Repr. of 1858 ed. lib. bdg. 167.50x (ISBN 0-89241-305-0). Caratzas.

Budge, Ernest A., ed. Coptic Martyrdoms, Etc. in the Dialect of Upper Egypt. LC 77-3588. (Coptic Texts: Vol. 4). (Illus.). Repr. of 1914 ed. 60.00 (ISBN 0-404-11554-3). AMS Pr.

--Miscellaneous Coptic Texts in the Dialect of Upper Egypt, 2 vols. LC 77-3587. (Coptic Texts: Vol. 5). (Illus.). Repr. of 1915 ed. 135.00 (ISBN 0-404-11555-1). AMS Pr.

Burghardt, W. J., et al, eds. Egeria, Diary of a Pilgrimage. LC 70-119159. (ACW Ser.: No. 38). 292p. 1970. 14.95 (ISBN 0-8091-0029-0). Paulist Pr.

Cyprian, St. The Lapsed & the Unity of the Church. pap. 2.95 (ISBN 0-686-05646-9). Eastern Orthodox.

Edwards, Richard & Wild, Robert. The Sentences of Sextus. LC 81-13770. (Society of Biblical Literature Texts & Translations Ser.). 1981. pap. text ed. 12.00 (ISBN 0-89130-528-9, 06-02-22). Scholars Pr GA.

Kotter, P. Bonifatius, ed. Die Schriften des Johannes von Damaskos, Vol. 3: Contra imaginum columniatores orationes tres. (Patristische Texte und Studien: Vol. 17). (Ger. & Lat.). xvi, 224p. 1975. 51.20x (ISBN 3-11-005971-1). De Gruyter.

Riddle, Donald W. Early Christian Life As Reflected in Its Literature. 256p. 1981. Repr. of 1936 ed. lib. bdg. 40.00 (ISBN 0-8495-4646-X). Arden Lib.

Rotelle, John E., ed. Augustine's Heritage: Readings from the Augustinian Tradition, 3 vols. Vol. 1. 1.50 (ISBN 0-89942-701-4, 701-04). Vol. 2 (ISBN 0-89942-702-2, 702-04). Vol. 3 (ISBN 0-89942-703-0, 703-04). Catholic Bk Pub.

Staniforth, Maxwell, tr. Early Christian Writings: The Apostolic Fathers. 208p. 1987. 5.95 (ISBN 0-14-044475-0). Penguin.

Tatian. Oratorio ad Graecos & Fragments. Whittaker, Molly, ed. & tr. (Oxford Early Christian Texts). 1982. 27.50x (ISBN 0-19-826809-2). Oxford U Pr.

William of Saint Thierry. Exposition on the Song of Songs. (Cistercian Fathers Ser.: No. 6). 171p. 7.95 (ISBN 0-87907-306-3). Cistercian Pubns.

CHRISTIAN LITERATURE, EARLY (COLLECTIONS)

Here are entered collections of writings of Christian authors to the time of Gregory the Great in the West, and John of Damascus in the East.

see also Apostolic Fathers; Bible–Quotations, Early; Church Orders, Ancient; Fathers of the Church; Jesus Christ–Biography–Apocryphal and Legendary Literature; Jesus Christ–Trial; Liturgies, Early Christian; Martyrologies; Scholia

Ante-Nicene Fathers. Writings of the Ante-Nicene Fathers, 10 vols. Roberts, A. & Donaldson, J., eds. 1951. Set. 179.50 (ISBN 0-8028-8097-5); 17.95 ea. Eerdmans.

Apostolic Fathers. Early Christian Writings. Staniforth, Maxwell, tr. (Gr.). 320p. 1986. 16.95 (ISBN 0-88029-074-9, Pub. by Dorset). Hippocrene Bks.

--Works of Apostolic Fathers, 2 vols. Incl. Vol. 1. Clement, Ignatius, Polycarp, Didache, Barnabas (ISBN 0-674-99027-7); Vol. 2. Shepherd of Hermas, Martyrdom of Polycarp, Epistle to Diognetus (ISBN 0-674-99028-5). (Loeb Classical Library: No. 24-25). 13.95x ea. Harvard U Pr.

Arnold, Eberhard. Early Christians: After the Death of the Apostles. LC 70-115839. (Illus.). 1970. 13.00 (ISBN 0-87486-110-1). Plough.

Austin, R. W., ed. Ibn-Al-Arabi: The Bezels of Wisdom. LC 80-83892. (The Classics of Western Spirituality Ser.). 320p. 1980. 12.95 (ISBN 0-8091-0313-3); pap. 10.95 (ISBN 0-8091-2331-2). Paulist Pr.

Bettenson, Henry, tr. Early Christian Fathers: A Selection from the Writings of the Fathers from St. Clement of Rome to St. Athanasius. 1969. pap. 9.95x (ISBN 0-19-283009-0). Oxford U Pr.

Blumenthal, Uta-Renate, ed. Carolingian Essays: Andrew W. Mellon Lectures in Early Christian Studies. LC 83-14562. 249p. 1983. 25.95x (ISBN 0-8132-0579-4). Cath U Pr.

Budge, Ernest A., tr. The History of the Blessed Virgin Mary & the History of the Likeness of Christ Which the Jews of Tiberius Made to Mock At, 2 vols. LC 73-18848. (Luzac's Semitic Text & Translation Ser.: Nos. 4-5). Repr. of 1899 ed. 45.00 set (ISBN 0-404-11341-9). AMS Pr.

Cureton, William, ed. Spicilegium Syriacum: Containing Remains of Bardesan, Meliton, Ambrose & Mara Bar Serapion, 1855. 1965. 10.00x (ISBN 0-8401-0493-6). A R Allenson.

Dollen, Charles. Jesus Lord. (Orig.). 1964. 3.00 (ISBN 0-8198-0066-X); pap. 2.00 (ISBN 0-8198-0067-8). Dghtrs St Paul.

Let Your Light Shine. 64p. 1983. 3.75 (ISBN 0-317-36762-5). Forum Script.

Lightfoot, J. B. Apostolic Fathers. (Twin Brooks Ser). pap. 7.95 (ISBN 0-8010-5514-8). Baker Bk.

Merton, Thomas. Wisdom of the Desert. LC 59-15021. 1970. 6.50 (ISBN 0-8112-0313-1); pap. 3.95 (ISBN 0-8112-0102-3, NDP295). New Directions.

Migne, Jacques P. Patrologiae Cursus Completus. Incl. Patrologia Latina, 221 vols. pap. write for info.; Patrologia Graeco Latina, 162 vols. pap. write for info.. 1965-71. pap. Adlers Foreign Bks.

Nicene & Post-Nicene Fathers. Writings of the Nicene & Post-Nicene Fathers, 28 vols. Incl. First Series, 14 Vols. 251.30 set (ISBN 0-8028-8114-9); St. Augustine only, 8 Vols. 143.60 set (ISBN 0-8028-8106-8); St. Chrysostom only, 6 Vols. 107.70 set (ISBN 0-8028-8113-0); Second Series, 14 Vols. 251.30 set (ISBN 0-8028-8129-7). 1952-56. Repr. 17.95 ea. Eerdmans.

Richardson, Cyril C., ed. Early Christian Fathers. (Library of Christian Classics: Vol. 1). 1970. pap. 9.95 (ISBN 0-02-088980-1, Collier). Macmillan.

Scriptores Ecclesiastici Minores Saeculorum, Nos. IV, V, VI. (Corpus Scriptorum Ecclesiasticorum Latinorum Ser: Vol. 45). (Lat). 1904. unbound 50.00 (ISBN 0-384-54490-8). Johnson Repr.

Sherrard, Philip & Ware, Kallistos, trs. The Philokalia, Vol. 3. LC 82-202671. 432p. 1984. 29.95 (ISBN 0-571-11726-0). Faber & Faber.

Squire, Aelred, ed. & tr. Fathers Talking: An Anthology. (Studies: No. 93). 1986. 12.95 (ISBN 0-87907-893-6); pap. 6.95 (ISBN 0-87907-993-2). Cistercian Pubns.

Staniforth, Maxwell, tr. Early Christian Writings: The Apostolic Fathers. (Classics Ser.). 240p. 1968. pap. 5.95 (ISBN 0-14-044197-2). Penguin.

Underhill, Evelyn. Meditations Based on the Lord's Prayer. 59.95 (ISBN 0-8490-0601-5). Gordon Pr.

CHRISTIAN LITERATURE, EARLY–BIBLIOGRAPHY

Ferrar, William J. The Early Christian Books. 1919. Repr. 20.00 (ISBN 0-8274-2211-3). R West.

CHRISTIAN LITERATURE, EARLY–HISTORY AND CRITICISM

Augustine, St. St. Augustine: The Greatness of the Soul, Vol. 9. Quasten, J. & Plumpe, J., eds. Colleran, Joseph M., tr. LC 78-62455. (Ancient Christian Writers Ser.). 255p. 1950. 14.95 (ISBN 0-8091-0060-6). Paulist Pr.

Clinton, Henry F. Fasti Romani: The Civil & Literary Chronology of Rome & Constantinople from the Death of Augustus to the Death of Justin the 2nd, 2 Vols. 1965. Repr. of 1850 ed. Set. 105.50 (ISBN 0-8337-0602-0). B Franklin.

Dibelius, Martin. Fresh Approach to the New Testament & Early Christian Literature. LC 78-32096. 1979. Repr. of 1936 ed. lib. bdg. 24.75x (ISBN 0-8371-4219-9, DINT). Greenwood.

Doty, William G. Letters in Primitive Christianity. Via, Dan O., Jr., ed. LC 72-87058. (Guides to Biblical Scholarship: New Testament Ser.). 96p. 1973. pap. 4.50 (ISBN 0-8006-0170-X, 1-170). Fortress.

Ferrar, William J. The Early Christian Books: A Short Introduction to Christian Literature to the Middle of the Second Century. 1979. Repr. of 1919 ed. lib. bdg. 20.00 (ISBN 0-8495-1637-4). Arden Lib.

Glover, Terrot R. Life & Letters in the Fourth Century. LC 68-10923. 1968. Repr. of 1901 ed. 11.00x (ISBN 0-8462-1065-7). Russell.

Goodspeed, Edgar J. History of Early Christian Literature. rev. & enl. ed. Grant, Robert M., ed. LC 66-13871. (Midway Reprint Ser.). 1966. pap. 13.00x (ISBN 0-226-30386-1). U of Chicago Pr.

Hagedorn, Dieter, ed. Der Hiobkommentar Des Arianers Julian. LC 73-75486. (Patristische Texte und Studien, Vol. 14). 410p. 1973. 45.60x (ISBN 3-11-004244-4). De Gruyter.

Hamell, Patrick J. Handbook of Patrology. 1968. pap. 5.95 (ISBN 0-8189-0057-1). Alba.

Hebert, Peter E., ed. Selections from the Latin Fathers. (College Classical Ser.). xvii, 186p. 1982. lib. bdg. 25.00x (ISBN 0-89241-357-3); pap. text ed. 12.50x (ISBN 0-89241-370-0). Caratzas.

Hill, John S. John Milton: Poet, Priest & Prophet: A Study of Divine Vocation in Milton's Poetry & Prose. 233p. 1979. 24.50x (ISBN 0-8476-6124-5). Rowman.

Krueger, Gustav. History of Early Christian Literature in the First Three Centuries. Gillet, Charles R., tr. from Ger. 1969. 26.00 (ISBN 0-8337-1963-7). B Franklin.

McKinnon, James W. Music in Early Christian Literature. (Cambridge Readings in the Literature of Music Ser.). 300p. Date not set. price not set (ISBN 0-521-30497-0). Cambridge U Pr.

McNeill, John T. Books of Faith & Power. facs. ed. LC 75-134112. (Essay Index Reprint Ser). 1947. 18.00 (ISBN 0-8369-1996-3). Ayer Co Pubs.

Martin, Hugh. Great Christian Books. facsimile ed. LC 71-142666. (Essay Index Reprint Ser). Repr. of 1945 ed. 13.00 (ISBN 0-8369-2242-5). Ayer Co Pubs.

Robinson, James M. & Koester, Helmut. Trajectories through Early Christianity. LC 79-141254. 312p. 1971. pap. 9.95 (ISBN 0-8006-1362-7, 1-1362). Fortress.

Rowland, Christopher. The Open Heaven: The Study of Apocalyptic in Judaism & Early Christianity. LC 82-7409. 540p. 1982. 29.50x (ISBN 0-8245-0455-0). Crossroad NY.

Smith, Morton. Clement of Alexandria, & a Secret Gospel of Mark. LC 72-148938. 1973. 30.00x (ISBN 0-674-13490-7). Harvard U Pr.

Smith, Terrence V. Petrine Controversies in Early Christianity: Attitudes Towards Peter in Christian Writings for the First Two Centuries. 259p. (Orig.). 1985. pap. 52.50x (ISBN 3-16-144876-6, Pub. by J C B Mohr BRD). Coronet Bks.

Whittaker, Molly. Jews & Christians: Graeco-Roman Views. (Commentaries on Writings of the Jewish & Christian World 200 B.C. to A.D. 200: Vol. 6). 304p. 1985. 47.50 (ISBN 0-521-24251-7); pap. 18.95 (ISBN 0-521-28556-9). Cambridge U Pr.

Wolfson, Harry A. Philosophy of the Church Fathers: Faith, Trinity, Incarnation. 3rd rev. ed. LC 70-119077. 1970. 32.50x (ISBN 0-674-66551-1). Harvard U Pr.

CHRISTIAN LITERATURE, EARLY–SOURCES

Bell, H. Idris. Fragments of an Unknown Gospel & Other Early Christian Papyri. 59.95 (ISBN 0-8490-0188-9). Gordon Pr.

Hotchkiss, Robert V. A Pseudo-Epiphanius Testimony Book. LC 74-15203. (Society of Biblical Literature. Texts & Translation-Early Christian Literature Ser.). 1974. pap. 8.95 (060204). Scholars Pr GA.

Wiles, Maurice & Santer, M., eds. Documents in Early Christian Thought. LC 74-31807. 304p. 1976. 42.50 (ISBN 0-521-20669-3); pap. 12.95 (ISBN 0-521-09915-3). Cambridge U Pr.

CHRISTIAN LITERATURE FOR CHILDREN

Abrams, Connie. God Is in the Night. (Happy Day Bks.). (Illus.). 24p. 1984. 1.59 (ISBN 0-87239-733-5, 3703). Standard Pub.

Anderson, Debby. God Is with Me. (Happy Day Bks.). (Illus.). 24p. 1984. 1.39 (ISBN 0-87239-734-3, 3704). Standard Pub.

Armstrong, Max & Armstrong, Hylma. A Conscience Is... (I'm Growing Up Ser.). (Illus.). 32p. 1986. casebound 3.95 (ISBN 0-87403-122-2, 3602). Standard Pub.

Aurelio, John R. Story Sunday: Christian Fairy Tales for Children, Parents & Educators. LC 78-51587. 104p. 1978. pap. 3.95 (ISBN 0-8091-2115-8). Paulist Pr.

Beckmann, Beverly. Numbers in God's World. 1983. 5.95 (ISBN 0-570-04083-3, 56-1438). Concordia.

Cachiaras, Dot. God Gives Us Seasons. (Happy Day Bks.). (Illus.). 24p. 1984. 1.59 (ISBN 0-87239-732-7, 3702). Standard Pub.

Carr, Dan. Cheating. (God I Need to Talk to You About...Ser.). (Illus.). 1984. pap. 0.75 (ISBN 0-570-08725-2, 56-1469). Concordia.

--Hurting Others. (God I Need to Talk to You about...Ser.). (Illus.). 1984. pap. 0.75 (ISBN 0-570-08727-9, 56-1471). Concordia.

--Lying. (God I Need to Talk to You About...Ser.). (Illus.). 1984. pap. 0.75 (ISBN 0-570-08732-5, 56-1476). Concordia.

--My Bad Temper. (God I Need to Talk to You About...Ser.). (Illus.). 1984. pap. 0.75 (ISBN 0-570-08730-9, 56-1474). Concordia.

--Paying Attention. (God I Need to Talk to You About...Ser.). (Illus.). 1984. pap. 0.75 (ISBN 0-570-08729-5, 56-1473). Concordia.

--Sharing. (God I Need to Talk to You About...Ser.). (Illus.). 1984. pap. 0.75 (ISBN 0-570-08728-7, 56-1472). Concordia.

--Stealing. (God I Need to Talk to You About...Ser.). (Illus.). 1984. pap. 0.75 (ISBN 0-570-08731-7, 56-1475). Concordia.

--Vandalism. (God I Need to Talk to You About...Ser.). (Illus.). 1984. pap. 0.75 (ISBN 0-570-08726-0, 56-1470). Concordia.

Cowell, Sally. Happy Times with Happy Seeds. (Happy Days Bks.). (Illus.). 24p. 1984. 1.59 (ISBN 0-87239-738-6, 3708). Standard Pub.

Decker, Marjorie A. The Christian Mother Goose Trilogy, 3 Vols. (Illus.). 336p. 1983. PLB 35.50 (ISBN 0-933724-14-4). Decker Pr Inc.

De Jonge, Joanne E. My Listening Ears. LC 85-7372. (My Father's World Ser.). (Illus.). 144p. 1985. pap. 3.95 (ISBN 0-930265-09-2). CRC Pubns.

Dellinger, Annetta E. I Talk to God. LC 84-50287. (Little Happy Day Bks.). (Illus.). 24p. (Orig.). 1984. pap. 0.49 (ISBN 0-87239-802-1, 2162). Standard Pub.

Fiday, Beverly. Jeff's Happy Day. (Happy Day Bks.). (Illus.). 24p. 1984. 1.59 (ISBN 0-87239-740-8, 3710). Standard Pub.

Fletcher, Sarah. Stewardship: Taking Care of God's World. (Illus.). 1984. pap. 3.95 (ISBN 0-570-04106-6, 56-1498). Concordia.

Gambill, Henrietta. How God Gives Us Popcorn. (Happy Days Bks.). (Illus.). 24p. 1984. 1.59 (ISBN 0-87239-739-4, 3709). Standard Pub.

Greene, Carol. Welcome the Stranger. (Illus.). 1984. 7.95 (ISBN 0-570-04105-8, 561497). Concordia.

Greenspan, Alice. What God Gave Me. LC 84-50286. (Little Happy Day Bks.). (Illus.). 24p. (Orig.). 1984. pap. 0.49 (ISBN 0-87239-804-8, 2164). Standard Pub.

Hayes, Sue T. God Made Farm Animals. (Happy Day Bks.). (Illus.). 24p. 1984. 1.59 (ISBN 0-87239-735-1, 3705). Standard Pub.

Hayes, Theresa, compiled by. God Is Everywhere: Fifteen Stories to Help Children Know God. (Illus.). 80p. 1986. 7.95 (ISBN 0-87403-097-8, 3617). Standard Pub.

--God Is On Your Side: Fifteen Stories to Help Young Children Trust God. (Illus.). 80p. 1986. 7.95 (ISBN 0-87403-096-X, 3616). Standard Pub.

Johnsson, Noelene. Today with My Father. Wheeler, Gerald, ed. (Illus.). 384p. 1984. 7.95 (ISBN 0-8280-0240-1). Review & Herald.

Mahany, Patricia. God's Rainbow of Colors. (My Shape Bk.). (Illus.). 12p. 1984. 2.95 (ISBN 0-87239-783-1, 2723). Standard Pub.

--I Love Jesus. (My Shape Bk.). (Illus.). 12p. 1984. 2.95 (ISBN 0-87239-785-8, 2725). Standard Pub.
--My Baby Jesus Book. (My Surprise Book Ser.). (Illus.). 12p. 1984. 4.95 (ISBN 0-87239-800-5, 2732). Standard Pub.
Mahany, Patricia, compiled by. Friends of God. (Story & Color Bks.). (Illus.). 64p. (Orig.). 1984. pap. 2.95 (ISBN 0-87239-795-5, 2371). Standard Pub.
--Good News. (Story & Color Bks.). (Illus.). 64p. (Orig.). 1984. pap. 2.95 (ISBN 0-87239-797-1, 2373). Standard Pub.
Mahany, Patricia S. Clint's "Be Cheerful" Day. (Happy Day Bks.). (Illus.). 24p. 1984. 1.59 (ISBN 0-87239-731-9, 3701). Standard Pub.
Neuberger, Beth. Good News! (Happy Day Bks.). (Illus.). 24p. 1984. 1.59 (ISBN 0-87239-736-X, 3706). Standard Pub.
Oke, Janette. Love's Abiding Joy. 217p. 1985. Large Print. pap. 6.95 (ISBN 0-317-20707-5). Bethany Hse.
--Love's Long Journey. 207p. 1985. Large Print. pap. 6.95 (ISBN 0-317-20714-8). Bethany Hse.
--Love's Unending Legacy. 224p. 1985. Large Print. pap. 6.95 (ISBN 0-87123-855-1). Bethany Hse.
Pearson, Mary R., ed. Fifty-Two Children's Programs. 224p. (Orig.). 1985. pap. 14.95 (ISBN 0-89636-189-6). Accent Bks.
Pettit, Hermon & Wessel, Helen. Beautiful on the Mountain. LC 84-70118. (Illus.). 144p. 1984. 10.95 (ISBN 0-933082-03-7). Bookmates Intl.
--God of the Wilderness. LC 84-70119. (Illus.). 176p. 1984. 10.95 (ISBN 0-933082-04-5). Bookmates Intl.
Stewart, K. K. God Made Me Special. LC 82-62731. (Happy Day Bks.). (Illus.). 24p. 1983. 1.59 (ISBN 0-87239-635-5, 3555). Standard Pub.
Stirrup Associates Inc. All about Love. Phillips, Cheryl M. & Harvey, Bonnie C., eds. LC 84-50915. (Child's Paraphrase Ser.). (Illus.). 32p. 1984. pap. 1.49 (ISBN 0-937420-16-6). Stirrup Assoc.
--Beautiful Attitudes Matthew 5: 3-12. Phillips, Cheryl M. & Harvey, Bonnie C., eds. LC 84-50914. (Child's Paraphrase Ser.). (Illus.). 32p. 1984. pap. 1.49 (ISBN 0-937420-17-4). Stirrup Assoc.
--My Jesus Pocketbook of a Very Special Birth Day. Harvey, Bonnie C. & Phillips, Cheryl M., eds. LC 84-50919. (My Jesus Pocketbook Ser.). (Illus.). 32p. 1984. pap. 0.49 (ISBN 0-937420-15-8). Stirrup Assoc.
--My Jesus Pocketbook of Daniel in the Lion's Den. Harvey, Bonnie C. & Phillips, Cheryl M., eds. LC 84-50916. (My Jesus Pocketbook Ser.). (Illus.). 32p. (Orig.). 1984. pap. text ed. 0.49 (ISBN 0-937420-12-3). Stirrup Assoc.
--My Jesus Pocketbook of the Beginning. Harvey, Bonnie C. & Phillips, Cheryl M., eds. LC 84-50918. (Jesus Pocketbook Ser.). (Illus.). 32p. (Orig.). 1984. pap. 0.49 (ISBN 0-937420-14-X). Stirrup Assoc.
--My Jesus Pocketbook of the Big Little Person: The Story of Zacchaeus. Phillips, Cheryl M. & Harvey, Bonnie C., eds. LC 84-50917. (My Jesus Pocketbook Ser.). (Illus.). 32p. 1984. pap. 0.49 (ISBN 0-937420-13-1). Stirrup Assoc.
Watson, E. Elaine. Jesus Loves Me All the Time. (Happy Day Bks.). (Illus.). 24p. 1984. 1.59 (ISBN 0-87239-741-6, 3711). Standard Pub.

CHRISTIAN MINISTRY

see Clergy–Office

CHRISTIAN PATRON SAINTS

Johnson, Phyllis & Cazelles, Brigitte. Le Vain Siecle Guerpir: A Literary Approach to Sainthood through Old French Hagiography of the Twelfth Century. (Studies in the Romance Languages & Literatures: No.205). 320p. 1979. pap. 19.50x (ISBN 0-8078-9205-X). U of NC Pr.
Nevins, Albert J. A Saint for Your Name: Saints for Boys. LC 79-92504. (Illus.). 120p. (YA) 1980. pap. 5.95 (ISBN 0-87973-320-9, 320). Our Sunday Visitor.
--A Saint for Your Name: Saints for Girls. LC 79-92502. (Illus.). 104p. (YA) 1980. pap. 5.95 (ISBN 0-87973-321-7, 321). Our Sunday Visitor.
O'Brien, Isidore. Francis of Assisi: Mirror Christ. 1978. 6.95 (ISBN 0-8199-0691-3). Franciscan Herald.
Quasten, Johannes. Patrology, 3 vols. 1514p. 1983. Set. pap. 50.00 (ISBN 0-87061-084-8); Vol. 1. pap. 15.00 (ISBN 0-87061-084-8); Vol. 2. pap. 18.00 (ISBN 0-87061-085-6); Vol. 3. pap. 21.00 (ISBN 0-87061-091-0); Set of 4 vols. pap. 85.00. Chr Classics.
Wilson, Stephen, ed. Saints & Their Cults: Studies in Religious Sociology, Folklore & History. LC 82-25296. 416p. 1984. 62.50 (ISBN 0-521-24978-3). Cambridge U Pr.

CHRISTIAN POETRY

see also Carols; Hymns

Alexander, Pat, ed. Eerdmans Book of Christian Poetry. 128p. 1981. 12.95 (ISBN 0-8028-3555-4). Eerdmans.
Anderson, James E. Two Literary Riddles in the Exeter Book: Riddle 1 & the Easter Riddle. LC 85-40471. (Illus.). 288p. 1986. 27.50x (ISBN 0-8061-1947-0). U of Okla Pr.
Barnouw, Adriaan J. Anglo-Saxon Christian Poetry. LC 74-20776. 1974. Repr. of 1914 ed. lib. bdg. 12.50 (ISBN 0-8414-3291-0). Folcroft.
Bloch, Chana. Spelling the Word: George Herbert & the Bible. LC 84-123. 375p. 1985. 37.50x (ISBN 0-520-05121-1). U of Cal Pr.
Brown, Annice H. Thank You, Lord, for Little Things. 3.95 (ISBN 0-8042-2580-X). John Knox.
Cherniss, Michael D. Ingeld & Christ: Heroic Conceptions & Values in Old English Christian Poetry. (Studies in English Literature: No. 74). 267p. 1972. text ed. 29.60x (ISBN 90-2792-335-3). Mouton.
Davie, Donald, ed. The New Oxford Book of Christian Verse. 1982. 27.50x (ISBN 0-19-213426-4). Oxford U Pr.
Downes, David A. Hopkins' Sanctifying Imagination. LC 85-11071. 134p. (Orig.). 1985. lib. bdg. 22.00 (ISBN 0-8191-4755-9); pap. text ed. 8.75 (ISBN 0-8191-4756-7). U Pr of Amer.
Downey, David G. Modern Poets & Christian Teaching: Richard Watson Gilder, Edwin Markham, Edward Rowland Sill. 183p. 1982. Repr. lib. bdg. 40.00 (ISBN 0-89984-013-2). Century Bookbindery.
Francis, Sr. Mary. Variations on a Theme. 1977. 5.00 (ISBN 0-8199-0664-6). Franciscan Herald.
Francis, R. Mabel. Filled with the Spirit-Then What? 1974. 2.50 (ISBN 0-87509-082-6). Chr Pubns.
Harper, Frances E. Idylls of the Bible. LC 75-168245. Repr. of 1901 ed. 11.50 (ISBN 0-404-00058-4). AMS Pr.
Jones, Bob, ed. Rhyme & Reason. (Illus.). 222p. (Orig.). 1981. pap. 9.95 (ISBN 0-89084-142-X). Bob Jones Univ Pr.
Lindskoog, Kathryn. A Child's Garden of Christian Verses. LC 83-9534. 160p. 1983. 6.95 (ISBN 0-8307-0890-1, 5110603). Regal.
Meeter, Merle. Country of the Risen King: Anthology of Christian Poetry. LC 77-87993. 1978. 12.95 (ISBN 0-8010-6042-7). Baker Bk.
Merrill, Thomas F. Epic God-Talk: Paradise Lost & the Grammar of Religious Language. LC 85-29385. 140p. 1986. lib. bdg. 18.95x (ISBN 0-89950-194-X). McFarland & Co.
Perennes, F. Dictionnaire de Lecons et Exemples de Litterature Chretienne en Prose et en Verse, 2 vols. Migne, J. P., ed. (Troisieme et Derniere Encyclopedie Theologique Ser.: Vols. 61-62). (Fr.). 1510p. Repr. of 1864 ed. lib. bdg. 191.50x (ISBN 0-89241-326-3). Caratzas.
Prynne, William. Mount-Orgueil. LC 83-20361. 1984. Repr. of 1641 ed. 40.00x (ISBN 0-8201-1392-1). Schol Facsimiles.
Rice, Helen S. Life Is Forever. (Illus.). 32p. 1974. 8.95 (ISBN 0-8007-0681-1). Revell.
--Somebody Loves You. 128p. 1976. 12.95 (ISBN 0-8007-0818-0); large-print ed. 10.95 (ISBN 0-8007-1120-3). Revell.
Saint Ephrem. The Harp of the Spirit: Eighteen Poems of Saint Ephrem. Brock, Sebastian, tr. LC 84-285. 89p. 1984. Repr. of 1983 ed. lib. bdg. 19.95x (ISBN 0-89370-776-7). Borgo Pr.
Sollov, Jacques. Reborn Again in the Kingdom. LC 81-71382. (The Temple of Love Ser.). (Illus.). 128p. (Orig.). 1982. pap. 10.95 (ISBN 0-941804-04-6). White Eagle Pub.
Summers, Claude J. & Pebworth, Ted-Larry. Bright Shootes of Everlastingnesse: The Seventeenth-Century Religious Lyric. LC 86-16132. 208p. 1987. text ed. 24.00 (ISBN 0-8262-0618-2, 83-36265). U of Mo Pr.
Tennyson, G. B. Victorian Devotional Poetry: The Tractarian Mode. LC 80-14416. 1980. text ed. 18.50x (ISBN 0-674-93586-1). Harvard U Pr.
Tozer, A. W., ed. The Christian Book of Mystical Verse. 1975. Repr. 9.95 (ISBN 0-87509-381-7). Chr Pubns.

CHRISTIAN PRIESTHOOD

see Priesthood

CHRISTIAN REFORMED CHURCH

Boer, Harry R. The Doctrine of Reprobation in the Christian Reformed Church. LC 83-1602. Repr. of 1983 ed. 23.50 (2027537). Bks Demand UMI.
Brink, William P. & DeRidder, Richard R. Manual of Christian Reformed Church Government, 1980. rev. ed. LC 80-24129. 1980. pap. text ed. 7.95 (ISBN 0-933140-19-3). CRC Pubns.
Brinks, Herbert & Heynen, A. James. A Time to Keep: A History of the Christian Reformed Church. text ed. cancelled (ISBN 0-933140-44-4); cancelled leader's guide (ISBN 0-933140-45-2). CRC Pubns.
DeKlerk, Peter & DeRidder, Richard R., eds. Perspectives on the Christian Reformed Church. 1983. 14.95 (ISBN 0-8010-2934-1). Baker Bk.
Goertz, Hans J. Profiles of Radical Reformers. Tr. of Radikale Reformatoren. 228p. 1982. pap. 9.95x (ISBN 0-8361-1250-4). Herald Pr.
Grissen, Lillian V. & Spykman, Gordon J. Men & Women: Partners in Service. 100p. (Orig.). 1981. pap. text ed. 4.50 (ISBN 0-933140-36-3). CRC Pubns.
Liturgical Committee of the Christian Reformed Church. Service Book: Heidelberg Catechism, Pt. No. 5. 64p. (Orig.). 1981. pap. text ed. 2.25 (ISBN 0-933140-35-5). CRC Pubns.
--Service Book: Liturgical Forms for Baptism & the Lord's Supper, Pt. No. 1. 30p. (Orig.). 1981. pap. text ed. 1.50 (ISBN 0-933140-31-2). CRC Pubns.
--Service Book: Liturgical Forms (Non-Sacramental, Pt. No. 2. 30p. (Orig.). 1981. pap. text ed. 1.50 (ISBN 0-933140-32-0). CRC Pubns.
--Service Book: Prayers & Responsive Readings of the Law, Pt. No. 4. 37p. (Orig.). 1981. pap. text ed. 1.50 (ISBN 0-933140-34-7). CRC Pubns.
--Service Book: Service of Word & Sacrament, Pt. No. 3. 64p. (Orig.). 1981. pap. text ed. 1.95 (ISBN 0-933140-33-9). CRC Pubns.
Schaap, James C. CRC Family Portrait: Sketches of Ordinary Christians in a 125-Year-Old Church. LC 82-22625. 287p. (Orig.). 1983. pap. 4.95 (ISBN 0-933140-60-6). CRC Pubns.
VanDyk, Wilbert M. Belonging, An Introduction to the Faith & Life of the Christian Reformed Church. LC 82-1241. (Illus.). 120p. (Orig.). 1982. pap. 4.50 (ISBN 0-933140-43-6). CRC Pubns.

CHRISTIAN SCIENCE

see also Bible–Medicine, Hygiene, etc.; Boston–First Church of Christ, Scientist; Mental Healing

Atkins, Gaius. Modern Religious Cults & Movements. LC 74-126684. Repr. of 1923 ed. 26.50 (ISBN 0-404-00415-6). AMS Pr.
Beals, Ann. Christian Science Treatment. 26p. 1979. pap. 2.00 (ISBN 0-930227-06-9). Pasadena Pr.
--Crisis in the Christian Science Church. 145p. 1978. pap. 6.95 (ISBN 0-930227-08-5). Pasadena Pr.
Beier, Lucinda. Mormans, Jehovah's Witnesses & Christian Scientists. 1985. 13.00x (ISBN 0-7062-3880-X, Pub. by Ward Lock Educ Co Ltd). State Mutual Bk.
Braden, Charles S. Christian Science Today: Power, Policy, Practice. LC 58-11399. 1958. 19.95 (ISBN 0-87074-024-5). SMU Press.
Corey, Arthur. Behind the Scenes with the Metaphysicians. 7.50 (ISBN 0-87516-014-X). De Vorss.
--More Class Notes. pap. 2.50 (ISBN 0-87516-016-6). De Vorss.
Eddy, Mary B. Christian Science. pap. 2.00 (ISBN 0-87516-021-2). De Vorss.
--A Complete Concordance to the Writings of Mary B. Eddy. 33.50 (ISBN 0-87952-092-2). First Church.
--Concordance to Other Writings. 1984. 35.00 (ISBN 0-87952-089-2). First Church.
--Concordance to Science & Health. 1982. 22.50 (ISBN 0-87952-093-0). First Church.
--The First Church of Christ, Scientist, & Miscellany. German Ed. pap. 8.50 (ISBN 0-87952-155-4). First Church.
--The First Church of Christ, Scientist & Miscellany. 1982. pap. 4.50 (ISBN 0-87952-041-8). First Church.
--Manual of the Mother Church, 11 vols. Incl. Vol. 1. Danish. 12.50 (ISBN 0-87952-104-X); Vol. 2. Dutch. 12.50 (ISBN 0-87952-110-4); Vol. 3. French. 12.50 (ISBN 0-87952-118-X); Vol. 4. German. 12.50 (ISBN 0-87952-153-8); Vol. 5. Italian. 12.50 (ISBN 0-87952-181-3); Vol. 6. Norwegian. 12.50 (ISBN 0-87952-196-1); Vol. 7. Portuguese. 12.50 (ISBN 0-87952-206-2); Vol. 8. Spanish. 12.50 (ISBN 0-87952-228-3); Vol. 9. Swedish. 12.50 (ISBN 0-87952-251-8); Vol. 10. Greek. 12.50 (ISBN 0-87952-171-6); Vol. 11. Japanese. 12.50 (ISBN 0-87952-191-0). First Church.
--Manual of the Mother Church, The First Church of Christ, Scientist, in Boston, Massachusetts. standard ed. 9.50 (ISBN 0-87952-061-2); century ed. 11.00 (ISBN 0-87952-063-9); leather 35.00 (ISBN 0-87952-064-7). First Church.
--Miscellaneous Writings, Eighteen Eighty-Three to Eighteen Ninety-Six. 1982. pap. 5.50 (ISBN 0-87952-229-1). First Church.
--The People's Idea of God, Christian Healings No & Yes. pap. 4.50 (ISBN 0-87952-042-6). First Church.
--Prose Works. new type ed. 32.50 (ISBN 0-87952-074-4); brown new type ed. o.p. 70.00 (ISBN 0-87952-076-0); standard ed. 25.00 (ISBN 0-87952-070-1); new type bonded lea. ed. o.p. 47.00 (ISBN 0-87952-075-2). First Church.
--Pulpit & Press. pap. 4.50 (ISBN 0-87952-046-9). First Church.
--Retrospection & Introspection. pap. 4.50 (ISBN 0-87952-044-2). First Church.
--Retrospection & Introspection. French 12.50 (ISBN 0-87952-122-8); German 12.50 (ISBN 0-87952-157-0); Italian 12.50 (ISBN 0-87952-182-1); Portugese 12.50 (ISBN 0-87952-207-0); Spanish 7.50 (ISBN 0-87952-231-3); Swedish 12.50 (ISBN 0-87952-252-6). First Church.
--Rudimental Divine Science & No & Yes. Danish 12.50 (ISBN 0-87952-105-8); German 12.50 (ISBN 0-87952-158-9); Italian 12.50 (ISBN 0-87952-183-X); Portugese 12.50 (ISBN 0-87952-208-9); Swedish 12.50 (ISBN 0-87952-253-4); Spanish 12.50 (ISBN 0-87952-232-1). First Church.
--Rudimental Divine Science: No & Yes. 1976. lib. bdg. 69.95 (ISBN 0-8490-2546-X). Gordon Pr.
--Science & Health with Key to the Scriptures. (Pol.). 25.00 (ISBN 0-87952-200-3). First Church.
--Science & Health with Key to the Scriptures. pap. 10.50 Spanish ed. (ISBN 0-87952-225-9); pap. 10.50 German ed. (ISBN 0-87952-150-3); pap. 10.50 French ed. (ISBN 0-87952-116-3). First Church.
--Science & Health with Key to the Scriptures. Indonesian 25.00 (ISBN 0-87952-175-9); Japanese 25.00 (ISBN 0-87952-190-2). First Church.
--Seven Messages to the Mother Church. pap. 4.50 (ISBN 0-87952-045-0). First Church.
--Unity of Good. Indonesian ed. 12.50 (ISBN 0-87952-177-5); French Ed. 7.50 (ISBN 0-87952-123-6). First Church.
--Unity of Good, Two Sermons. Danish 12.50 (ISBN 0-87952-106-6); Norwegian 12.50 (ISBN 0-87952-197-X); German o.p. 6.00 (ISBN 0-87952-159-7). First Church.
Eustace, Herbert W. Christian Science, Its "Clear, Correct Teaching" & Complete Writings. 2nd ed. 1037p. 1985. 16.00 (ISBN 0-9611156-0-2). Eustace CSB.
--Letter Excerpts, Statements on Christian Science. 36p. 1976. pap. 3.00 (ISBN 0-9611156-1-0). Eustace CSB.
Gottschalk, Stephen. The Emergence of Christian Science in American Religious Life. LC 72-85530. 1974. 20.95 (ISBN 0-520-02308-0); pap. 4.95 (ISBN 0-520-03718-9, CAL 398). U of Cal Pr.
Hoekema, Anthony A. Christian Science. 1974. pap. 2.95 (ISBN 0-8028-1492-1). Eerdmans.
--The Four Major Cults. 1963. 24.95 (ISBN 0-8028-3117-6). Eerdmans.
Jessen, Joel. The Physical, the Mental, the Spiritual. 185p. 1978. pap. 10.00 (ISBN 0-942958-05-5). Kappeler Inst Pub.
Kappeler, Max. Compendium for the Study of Christian Science: No. 1, Introduction. 28p. 1951. pap. 3.50 (ISBN 0-85241-055-7). Kappeler Inst Pub.
--Compendium for the Study of Christian Science: No. 10, Love. 23p. 1953. pap. 3.50 (ISBN 0-85241-064-6). Kappeler Inst Pub.
--Compendium for the Study of Christian Science: No. 2, The Seven Days of Creation. 24p. 1951. pap. 3.50 (ISBN 0-85241-056-5). Kappeler Inst Pub.
--Compendium for the Study of Christian Science: No. 3, The Commandments, the Beatitudes, the Lord's Prayer. 29p. 1951. pap. 3.50 (ISBN 0-85241-057-3). Kappeler Inst Pub.
--Compendium for the Study of Christian Science: No. 4, Mind. 35p. 1951. pap. 3.50 (ISBN 0-85241-058-1). Kappeler Inst Pub.
--Compendium for the Study of Christian Science: No. 5, Spirit. 28p. 1951. pap. 3.50 (ISBN 0-85241-059-X). Kappeler Inst Pub.
--Compendium for the Study of Christian Science: No. 6, Soul. 23p. 1952. pap. 3.50 (ISBN 0-85241-060-3). Kappeler Inst Pub.
--Compendium for the Study of Christian Science: No. 7, Principle. 25p. 1952. pap. 3.50 (ISBN 0-85241-061-1). Kappeler Inst Pub.
--Compendium for the Study of Christian Science: No. 8, Life. 23p. 1952. pap. 3.50 (ISBN 0-85241-062-X). Kappeler Inst Pub.
--Compendium for the Study of Christian Science: No. 9, Truth. 20p. 1953. pap. 3.50 (ISBN 0-85241-063-8). Kappeler Inst Pub.
--The Development of the Christian Science Idea & Practice. LC 73-178890. 78p. 1970. pap. 6.50 (ISBN 0-85241-092-1). Kappeler Inst Pub.
--Epitomes for the Structural Interpretation of the Christian Science Textbook. LC 82-82377. 120p. 1982. write for info. (ISBN 0-942958-06-3). Kappeler Inst Pub.
--First & Second Samuel. Larson, Rory, tr. from Ger. LC 82-80904. (The Bible in the Light of Christian Science Ser.: Vol. IV). Orig. Title: Die Wissenschaft der Bibel. Tr. of Das Buch 1 und 2 Samuel. 200p. 1985. 12.00 (ISBN 0-942958-10-1). Kappeler Inst Pub.
--Introduction to the Science of Christian Science. LC 79-313991. 169p. 1978. 12.00 (ISBN 0-85241-099-9). Kappeler Inst Pub.

--Joshua, Judges. Larson, Rory, tr. from Ger. LC 82-80904. (The Bible in the Light of Christian Science Ser.: Vol. 3). Orig. Title: Die Wissenschaft der Bibel, Das Buch Josua und Das Buch der Richter. 210p. (Orig.). 1983. pap. 12.00 (ISBN 0-942958-07-1). Kappeler Inst Pub.
--Metaphysics & Science in Christian Science. (Orig.). 1985. pap. 3.50 (ISBN 0-942958-11-X). Kappeler Inst Pub.
--The Structure of the Christian Science Textbook: Our Way of Life. LC 58-26857. 206p. 1954. 14.00 (ISBN 0-85241-071-9). Kappeler Inst Pub.
--Why Study Christian Science as a Science? 30p. 1973. pap. 3.50 (ISBN 0-85241-040-9). Kappeler Inst Pub.
Kimball, Edward A. Lectures & Articles on Christian Science. (Illus.). 1976. 12.50 (ISBN 0-911588-01-9); pap. 8.00; leatherette 18.00. N S Wait.
Kirban, Salem. Christian Science. LC 75-124142. (Illus.). 1974. pap. 4.95 (ISBN 0-912582-11-1). Kirban.
McEwan, Elaine. How to Raise a Young Reader. 1987. pap. 5.95. Cook.
Martin, Walter. Christian Science. 32p. 1957. pap. 2.95 (ISBN 0-87123-064-X, 210064). Bethany Hse.
Merritt, Robert E. & Corey, Arthur. Christian Science & Liberty. LC 70-132847. 1970. 5.50 (ISBN 0-87516-060-3). De Vorss.
Roebling, Karl. Christian Science-Kingdom or Cult? 190p. 1984. 12.95 (ISBN 0-942910-09-5). Paragon-Dynapress.
Stanford, Neal. I Do Windows. 48p. 1982. 6.00 (ISBN 0-682-49865-3). Exposition Pr FL.
--Open Windows. 80p. 1984. 8.00 (ISBN 0-682-40172-2). Exposition Pr FL.
Twain, Mark. Christian Science. 196p. 1986. 21.95 (ISBN 0-87975-316-1). Prometheus Bks.
--What Is Man? & Other Philosophical Writings. Baender, Paul, ed. & intro. by. LC 78-104109. (Mark Twain Works: Vol. 19). 1973. 29.00x (ISBN 0-520-01621-1). U of Cal Pr.

CHRISTIAN SCIENCE-HISTORY

Eddy, Mary B. Science & Health with Key to the Scriptures. Indonesian 25.00 (ISBN 0-87952-175-9); Japanese 25.00 (ISBN 0-87952-190-2). First Church.

CHRISTIAN SOCIALISM

see Socialism, Christian

CHRISTIAN SOCIALIST, LONDON

Raven, Charles E. Christian Socialism, Eighteen Forty-Eight to Eighteen Fifty-Four. LC 68-56058. 1968. Repr. of 1920 ed. 35.00x (ISBN 0-678-05148-8). Kelley.

CHRISTIAN SOCIOLOGY

see Sociology, Christian

CHRISTIAN STEWARDSHIP

see Stewardship, Christian

CHRISTIAN SYMBOLISM

see Christian Art and Symbolism

CHRISTIAN THEOLOGIANS

see Theologians

CHRISTIAN UNION

see also Ecumenical Movement

Arsen'ev, Nicolai S. We Beheld His Glory. Ewer, Mary A., tr. LC 76-113545. Repr. of 1936 ed. 18.00 (ISBN 0-404-00407-5). AMS Pr.
Blom, Paul. Ministry of Welcome: A Guide for Ushers & Greeters. 32p. (Orig.). 1980. pap. 2.95 (ISBN 0-8066-1806-X, 10-4442). Augsburg.
Congar, Yves. Diversity & Communion. Tr. of Diversities et Communion. 240p. 1985. pap. text ed. 9.95 (ISBN 0-89622-275-6). Twenty-Third.
Fries, Heinrich & Rahner, Karl. Unity of the Churches: An Actual Possibility. 1985. pap. 6.95 (ISBN 0-8091-2671-0). Paulist Pr.
Miller, Samuel H. & Wright, G. Ernest, eds. Ecumenical Dialogue at Harvard, the Roman Catholic-Protestant Colloquium. LC 64-19583. 1964. 25.00x (ISBN 0-674-23700-5, Belknap Pr). Harvard U Pr.
Nolde, O. Frederick, ed. Toward World-Wide Christianity. LC 70-86049. (Essay & General Literature Index Reprint Ser). 1969. Repr. of 1946 ed. 23.50x (ISBN 0-8046-0581-5, Pub by Kennikat). Assoc Faculty Pr.
Rusch, William G. Ecumenism: A Movement Toward Church Unity. LC 84-48707. 96p. 1985. pap. 6.95 (ISBN 0-8006-1847-5, 1-1847). Fortress.
Sobrino, Jon & Pico, Juan H. Theology of Christian Solidarity. Berryman, Phillip, tr. from Span. LC 84-16533. Orig. Title: Teologia de la Solidaridad Chrisiana. 112p. (Orig.). 1985. pap. 7.95 (ISBN 0-88344-452-6). Orbis Bks.
Steere, Douglas V. Mutual Irradiation: A Quaker View of Ecumenism. LC 73-146680. (Orig.). 1971. pap. 2.50x (ISBN 0-87574-175-4). Pendle Hill.
Thompson, Bert. Non-Denominational Christianity: Is Unity Possible. 29p. (Orig.). 1984. pap. 2.00 (ISBN 0-932859-11-9). Apologetic Pr.
Tully, Mary Jo & Fearon, Mary. Focus on Living. (Light of Faith Ser.). (Orig.). 1981. pap. text ed. 3.85 (ISBN 0-697-01769-9); tchrs.' ed. 12.95 (ISBN 0-697-01770-2); tests 12.95 (ISBN 0-697-01830-X). Wm C Brown.
--Focus on Relating. (Light of Faith Ser.). (Orig.). 1981. pap. text ed. 3.90 (ISBN 0-697-01773-7); avail. tchrs.' ed. 12.95 (ISBN 0-697-01774-5); tests 12.95 (ISBN 0-697-01832-6). Wm C Brown.
Tully, Mary Jo & Hirstein, Sandra J. Focus on Believing. (Light of Faith Ser.). (Orig.). 1981. pap. text ed. 3.85 (ISBN 0-697-01767-2); tchrs.' ed. 12.95 (ISBN 0-697-01768-0); tests 12.95 (ISBN 0-697-01829-6). Wm C Brown.
--Focus on Belonging. (Light of Faith Ser.). (Orig.). 1981. pap. text ed. 3.55 (ISBN 0-697-01765-6); tchrs.' ed. 12.95 (ISBN 0-697-01766-4); tests 12.95 (ISBN 0-697-01828-8). Wm C Brown.
--Focus on Celebrating. (Light of Faith Ser.). (Orig.). 1981. pap. text ed. 3.85 (ISBN 0-697-01771-0); tchr's ed 12.95 (ISBN 0-686-69655-7); tests 12.95 (ISBN 0-697-01831-8). Wm C Brown.
Unite. 1973. 2.94 (ISBN 0-02-649670-4, 64967); tchr's annotated ed. 6.00 (ISBN 0-02-649690-9, 64969); activity bk. 1.74 (ISBN 0-02-640630-6); activity bk. tchr's ed. 2.16 (ISBN 0-02-640750-7, 64075); parents' handbk. 0.75 (ISBN 0-02-649680-1); testing program 0.69 (ISBN 0-02-640840-6, 64084); testing program tchr's manual 0.33 (ISBN 0-02-641090-7, 64109). Benziger Pub Co.
Whitehead, James D. & Whitehead, Evelyn E. Community of Faith: Models & Strategies for Developing Christian Communities. 208p. (Orig.). 1982. pap. 9.95 (ISBN 0-86683-949-6, AY7719, HarpR). Har-Row.
Young, C. A. Historical Documents Advocating Christian Union. (Heritage of a Movement Book Club Ser.). 376p. Repr. of 1904 ed. text ed. 10.95 (ISBN 0-89900-276-5). College Pr Pub.

CHRISTIAN UNION-CATHOLIC CHURCH

Tavard, Georges H. Two Centuries of Ecumenism. LC 78-6449. 1978. Repr. of 1960 ed. lib. bdg. 22.50x (ISBN 0-313-20490-X, TATC). Greenwood.

CHRISTIAN UNION-HISTORY

Black, Donald. Merging Mission & Unity. LC 86-14847. 180p. (Orig.). 1986. pap. 9.95 (ISBN 0-664-24047-X, A Geneva Press Publication). Westminster.
Harmelink, Herman. Ecumenism & the Reformed Church. 1969. pap. 3.95 (ISBN 0-8028-1281-3). Eerdmans.
Lowrey, Mark D. Ecumenism: Striving for Unity amid Diversity. 272p. (Orig.). 1985. pap. text ed. 9.95 (ISBN 0-89622-274-8). Twenty-Third.

CHRISTIAN UNION-ORTHODOX EASTERN CHURCH

Anglican-Orthodox Dialogue. LC 85-1766. 73p. 1986. pap. text ed. 3.95 (ISBN 0-88141-047-0). St Vladimirs.
Dewan, Wilfred F. Catholic Belief & Practice in an Ecumenical Age. (Orig.). 1966. pap. 1.95 (ISBN 0-8091-1510-7, Deus). Paulist Pr.
Helby, Hans. Eastbound Ecumenicism: A Collection of Essays on the World Council of Churches & Eastern Europe. LC 86-9137. 154p. (Orig.). 1986. lib. bdg. 24.50 (ISBN 0-8191-5400-8, Pub. by Interuniversity Inst for Missiological & Ecumenical Res); pap. text ed. 12.25 (ISBN 0-8191-5401-6). U Pr of Amer.
Vatican Council Two. Decree on Ecumenism. Stransky, Thomas, ed. (Orig.). 1965. pap. 1.95 (ISBN 0-8091-5027-1). Paulist Pr.

CHRISTIAN YEAR

see Church Year

CHRISTIANITY

see also Catholicity; Church; Civilization, Christian; Councils and Synods; Deism; Ecumenical Movement; God; Homosexuality and Christianity; Jesus Christ; Jews; Miracles; Missions; Protestantism; Reformation; Socialism, Christian; Sociology, Christian; Theism; Theology; Women in Christianity;
also headings beginning with the word Christian and Church; and names of Christian churches and sects, e.g. Catholic Church, Lutheran Church, Huguenots

Abbott, Lyman. The Evolution of Christianity. vi, 258p. 1985. Repr. of 1919 ed. 34.00 (ISBN 0-318-04538-9, Pub. by Am Repr Serv). Am Biog Serv.
Alexander, John W. What Is Christianity. pap. 0.75 (ISBN 0-87784-133-0). Inter-Varsity.
Allen, J. Catling. Way of the Christian. (The Way Ser.). pap. 5.95 (ISBN 0-7175-0782-3). Dufour.
Anderson, A. L. The Way. 1978. pap. 2.50 (ISBN 0-8100-0006-7, 12N1715). Northwest Pub.
Arch Books Aloud, Sets 42 - 47. LC 59-2142. (Continued Applied Christianity Ser.). 1983. pap. 5.95 ea; two bks & cassette incl. Set no. 42 (ISBN 0-570-08091-6). Set no. 43 (ISBN 0-570-08092-4). Set no. 44 (ISBN 0-570-08093-2). Set no. 45 (ISBN 0-570-08094-0). Set no. 46 (ISBN 0-570-08095-9). Set no. 47 (ISBN 0-570-08096-7). Concordia.
Armerding, Hudson T. A Word to the Wise. 1980. pap. 3.95 (ISBN 0-8423-0099-6). Tyndale.
Assfalg, Julius & Krueger, P. Kleines Woerterbuch Des Christlichen Orients. 1st ed. (Ger.). 1975. 52.00 (ISBN 3-447-01707-4, M-7514, Pub. by Harrassowitz). French & Eur.
Association for Research & Enlightement, Readings Research Dept., compiled by. The Early Christian Epoch. (Library: Vol. 6). (Illus.). 593p. 1976. 10.95 (ISBN 0-87604-089-X). ARE Pr.
Avila, Charles. Ownership: Early Christian Teaching. LC 83-8330. 256p. (Orig.). 1981. pap. 9.95 (ISBN 0-88344-384-8). Orbis Bks.
Ayers, Robert H. Judaism & Christianity: Origins, Developments & Recent Trends. LC 83-3548. (Illus.). 478p. (Orig.). 1983. lib. bdg. 35.75 (ISBN 0-8191-3156-3); pap. text ed. 16.50 (ISBN 0-8191-3157-1). U Pr of Amer.
Bacon, Banjamin W. Non-Resistance: Christian or Pagan. 1918. pap. 19.50x (ISBN 0-686-83649-9). Elliots Bks.
Bacon, Benjamin W. Christianity, Old & New. 1914. 29.50x (ISBN 0-686-83503-4). Elliots Bks.
Barna, George & McKay, William P. Vital Signs: Emerging Social Trends & the Future of American Christianity. LC 84-70658. 160p. (Orig.). 1984. 12.95 (ISBN 0-89107-324-8, Crossway Bks). Good News.
Barrett, Charles D. Understanding the Christian Faith. (Illus.). 1980. text ed. write for info. (ISBN 0-13-935882-X). P-H.
Berdoe, E. Browning & the Christian Faith. LC 79-130244. (Studies in Browning, No. 4). 1970. Repr. of 1896 ed. lib. bdg. 39.95x (ISBN 0-8383-1134-2). Haskell.
Berkhof, Hendrikus. Christian Faith: An Introduction to the Study of the Faith. rev. ed. Woudstra, Sierd, tr. from Dutch. 569p. 1986. 29.95 (ISBN 0-8028-3622-4). Eerdmans.
Biblical Beliefs. 96p. 1982. pap. text ed. 4.95 (ISBN 0-910566-10-0); Perfect bdg. instr's. guide 5.95 (ISBN 0-910566-17-8). Evang Tchr.
Bishop, Tania E. Born of the Spirit. LC 68-13394. 1968. 7.95 (ISBN 0-8022-0134-2). Philos Lib.
Boice, J. Montgomery. God & History. LC 80-24457. (Foundations of the Christian Faith: Vol 4). 292p. (Orig.). 1981. pap. 7.95 (ISBN 0-87784-746-0). Inter-Varsity.
Boice, James M. Foundations of the Christian Faith. 2nd ed. 782p. 24.95 (ISBN 0-87784-991-9). Inter-Varsity.
Boom, Corrie ten. Marching Orders for the End Battle. 1970. pap. 1.95 (ISBN 0-87508-024-3). Chr Lit.
Bowman, George M. Don't Let Go! An Exposition of Hebrews. 170p. 1982. pap. 4.95 (ISBN 0-87552-121-5). Presby & Reformed.
Bowne, Borden P. Studies in Christianity. LC 75-3074. Repr. of 1909 ed. 28.50 (ISBN 0-404-59075-6). AMS Pr.
Braaten, Carl E. & Jenson, Robert W., eds. Christian Dogmatics, 2 vols. LC 83-48007. 1984. Volume 1. 24.95 (ISBN 0-8006-0703-1); Volume 2. 24.95 (ISBN 0-8006-0704-X); Set. 45.95 (ISBN 0-8006-0712-0). Fortress.
Brandt, Frans M. J. The Way to Wholeness: A Guide to Christian Self-Counseling. LC 84-70657. 208p. 1984. pap. 6.95 (ISBN 0-89107-316-7, Crossway Bks). Good News.
Brosse, La. Diccionario del Cristianismo. (Span.). 1104p. 1976. 53.95 (ISBN 84-254-0777-X, S-50202). French & Eur.
Brown, A. The Christian World. LC 83-50692. (Religions of the World Ser.). 1984. PLB 14.96 (ISBN 0-382-06721-5); 10.75 (ISBN 0-382-06929-3). Silver.
Brown, Leslie. The Indian Christians of St. Thomas: An Account of the Ancient Syrian Church of Malabar. LC 81-21766. (Illus.). 330p. 1982. 39.50 (ISBN 0-521-21258-8). Cambridge U Pr.
Brown, Marvin L., Jr. The Wisdom of Christendom. 131p. 1982. pap. 5.95. Edenwood Hse.
Brownlow, Leroy. The Fruit of the Spirit. 1982. gift ed. 6.95 (ISBN 0-915720-59-0). Brownlow Pub Co.
Brunner, Heinrich E. Christianity & Civilisation, 2 vols. in one. LC 77-27182. (Gifford Lectures: 1947-48). Repr. of 1949 ed. 35.00 (ISBN 0-404-60530-3). AMS Pr.
Bryant, David. In the Gap: What It Means to Be a World Christian. LC 84-4880. 280p. 1984. pap. 7.95 (ISBN 0-8307-0952-5, 5418217). Regal.
Butterfield, Herbert. Christianity in European History: The Riddel Memorial Lectures, 1951. 1979. Repr. of 1952 ed. lib. bdg. 15.00 (ISBN 0-8482-3440-5). Norwood Edns.
Caird, Edward. Evolution of Religion, 2 Vols. in 1. LC 1-17697. (Gifford Lectures 1890-1892). 1968. Repr. of 1893 ed. 46.00 (ISBN 0-527-14120-8). Kraus Repr.
Caird, John. The Fundamental Ideas of Christianity, 2 vols. LC 77-27231. (Gifford Lectures: 1892-93, 1895-96). Repr. of 1899 ed. Set. 49.50 (ISBN 0-404-60460-9). AMS Pr.
Carmody, Denise L. & Carmody, John T. Christianity: An Introduction. 288p. 1982. pap. text ed. write for info (ISBN 0-534-01181-0). Wadsworth Pub.
Carmody, John. The Heart of the Christian Matter: An Ecumenical Approach. 304p. (Orig.). 1983. pap. 12.95 (ISBN 0-687-16765-5). Abingdon.
Carnell, Edward J. A Philosophy of the Christian Religion. (Twin Brooks Ser.). 525p. 1981. pap. 10.95 (ISBN 0-8010-2464-1). Baker Bk.
Carr, John & Carr, Adrienne. Experiment in Practical Christianity: Leader's Guide. rev. ed. 96p. 1985. manual 6.95 (ISBN 0-88177-028-0, DRO28B). Discipleship Res.
--Experiment in Practical Christianity: Participant's Guide. 104p. (Orig.). 1985. pap. 6.95 (ISBN 0-88177-027-2, DRO27B). Discipleship Res.
Carus, Paul. The Bride of Christ. 118p. 1908. 15.95 (ISBN 0-87548-218-X). Open Court.
Chai-Shin, Yu. Early Buddhism & Christianity. xv, 241p. 1986. Repr. 17.50 (ISBN 81-208-0050-8, Pub. by Motilal Banarsidass). South Asia Bks.
Chapman, Colin. The Case for Christianity. (Illus.). 313p. 1984. pap. 12.95 (ISBN 0-8028-1984-2). Eerdmans.
Cheve, C. F. Dictionnaire des Bienfaits et Beautes du Christianisme. Migne, J. P., ed. (Troisieme et Derniere Encyclopedie Theologique Ser.: Vol. 9). (Fr.). 732p. Repr. of 1856 ed. lib. bdg. 95.00x (ISBN 0-89241-293-3). Caratzas.
Chick, Jack T. The Next Step. (Illus.). 64p. (Orig.). 1978. pap. 1.95 (ISBN 0-937958-04-2). Chick Pubns.
Chilson, Richard. Way to Christianity: The Pilgrim. 1980. pap. 8.95 (ISBN 0-03-053426-7, HarpR). Har-Row.
Christianica Center Staff. Christianica. LC 74-13005. (Illus.). 1975. 5.95 (ISBN 0-911346-02-3). Christianica.
Clark, Gordon H. Clark Speaks from the Grave. (Trinity Papers: No. 12). 77p. (Orig.). 1986. pap. 3.95 (ISBN 0-940931-12-5). Trinity Found.
Clarke, William N. Immortality. 1920. 29.50x (ISBN 0-686-83578-6). Elliots Bks.
Clebsch, William. Christianity in European History. 1979. pap. 8.95x (ISBN 0-19-502472-9). Oxford U Pr.
Cleobury, F. H. Liberal Christian Orthodoxy. 164p. 1963. 9.50 (ISBN 0-227-67668-8). Attic Pr.
Cobb, John B., Jr. The Structure of Christian Existence. 1979. pap. 6.95 (ISBN 0-8164-2229-X, HarpR). Har-Row.
Cole, C. Donald. Basic Christian Faith. LC 84-72008. 256p. (Orig.). 1985. pap. 6.95 (ISBN 0-89107-338-8, Crossway Bks). Good News.
--Have I Committed the Unpardonable Sin? And Other Questions You Were Afraid to Ask about the Christian Faith. LC 84-71421. 128p. 1984. pap. 5.95 (ISBN 0-89107-317-5, Crossway Bks). Good News.
Conn, Charles W. Like a Mighty Army. 1955. 7.95 (ISBN 0-87148-505-2). Pathway Pr.
Corelli, Marie. The Master Christian. 604p. 1983. Repr. of 1900 ed. lib. bdg. 45.00 (ISBN 0-8495-0961-0). Arden Lib.
Cross, F. L. & Livingstone, Elizabeth A. The Oxford Dictionary of the Christian Church. 1974. 60.00 (ISBN 0-19-211545-6). Oxford U Pr.
Cummins, D. Duane. A Handbook for Today's Disciples in the Christian Church: Disciples of Christ. LC 81-10029. 64p. (Orig.). 1981. pap. 1.95 (ISBN 0-8272-1419-7, 10H1309). CBP.
Curtis, Olin A. The Christian Faith. LC 56-9279. 552p. 1971. 16.95 (ISBN 0-8254-2310-4). Kregel.
Dawson, Christopher. Christianity in East & West. Mulloy, John J., ed. 224p. 1981. pap. text ed. 5.95 (ISBN 0-89385-015-2). Sugden.
De Chateaubriand, Francois R. The Genius of Christianity. LC 75-25532. 1975. Repr. of 1856 ed. 40.00x (ISBN 0-86527-254-9). Fertig.
DeGroat, Florence. This Drama Called Life: An Introduction to Advanced Christianity. (Illus.). 49p. 1984. pap. 6.95 (ISBN 0-942494-89-X). Coleman Pub.
DeMello, Anthony. Sadhana: A Way to God. LC 84-6735. 144p. 1984. pap. 5.50 (ISBN 0-385-19614-8, Im). Doubleday.
De Thomasis, Louis. My Father's Business: Creating a New Future for the People of God. 168p. (Orig.). 1984. pap. 6.95 (ISBN 0-87061-107-0). Chr Classics.
De Young, Garry. The Meaning of Christianity. 96p. 1982. pap. 7.95x (ISBN 0-936128-02-X). tchrs' ed. o. p. 7.95. De Young Pr.

D'Holbach, Paul H. Christianity Unveiled. 69.95 (ISBN 0-87968-068-7). Gordon Pr.

Diehl, William E. Christianity & Real Life. LC 76-7860. 128p. 1976. pap. 4.50 (ISBN 0-8006-1231-0, 1-1231). Fortress.

Dilling, E. The Plot Against Christianity: A Study of the Talmud. 1982. lib. bdg. 69.95 (ISBN 0-87700-359-9). Revisionist Pr.

Dorner, Rita C., ed. From Ashes to Easter. 1979. pap. 9.95 (ISBN 0-918208-99-8). Liturgical Conf.

Douglas, Leonora M., ed. World Christianity: Oceania. pap. 15.00 (ISBN 0-912552-48-4). Missions Adv Res Com Ctr.

Drake, Durant. Problems of Religion: An Introductory Survey. LC 68-19268. Repr. of 1916 ed. lib. bdg. 22.50x (ISBN 0-8371-0062-3, DRPR). Greenwood.

Dugan, Dick. How To Know You'll Live Forever. LC 84-70727. 176p. 1984. pap. 3.95 (ISBN 0-87123-312-6, 200312). Bethany Hse.

Dujarier, Michel. The Rites of Christian Initiation. 244p. 1982. pap. 5.95 (ISBN 0-8215-9328-5). Sadlier.

Dwyer, John C. Son of Man & Son of God: A New Language for Faith. 160p. 1983. pap. 7.95 (ISBN 0-8091-2505-6). Paulist Pr.

Edge, Henry T. Theosophy & Christianity. rev. ed. Small, W. Emmett & Todd, Helen, eds. (Theosophical Manual: No. 12). 80p. 1974. pap. 2.00 (ISBN 0-913004-17-0). Point Loma Pub.

Elder, E. R., ed. The Roots of the Modern Christian Tradition. 1984. 24.95 (ISBN 0-87907-855-3); pap. 10.00. Cistercian Pubns.

Elias, Esther. The Queening of Ceridwen. 1982. 6.95 (ISBN 0-8158-0409-1). Chris Mass.

Erickson, Millard J., ed. Christian Theology, 1 vol. 1986. 39.95 (ISBN 0-8010-3433-7). Baker Bk.

Fackre, Gabriel. The Christian Story. rev. ed. 304p. 1985. pap. 12.95 (ISBN 0-8028-1989-3). Eerdmans.

Farrer, S. Christianity Without the Myths. 39.00x (ISBN 0-317-43636-8, Pub. by Regency pr). State Mutual Bk.

--The Evolution of Christianity Leading to Christianity Without the Myths. 1986. 40.00x (ISBN 0-7212-0740-5, Pub. by Regency Pr). State Mutual Bk.

Fitzgerald, George. Handbook of the Mass. 128p. 1982. pap. 4.95 (ISBN 0-8091-2401-7). Paulist Pr.

Fleming, Bruce C. E. Contextualization of Theology: An Evangelical Assessment. 1981. pap. 5.95 (ISBN 0-87808-431-2). William Carey Lib.

Fox, Robin L. Pagans & Christians. 1987. 35.00 (ISBN 0-394-55495-7). Knopf.

Frank, S. L. God with Us. 1946. 29.50x (ISBN 0-686-83560-3). Elliots Bks.

Frankiel, Sandra S. Christianity: A Way of Salvation. LC 84-48770. 144p. (Orig.). 1985. pap. 6.95 (ISBN 0-06-063015-9, RD 498, HarpR). Har-Row.

Frend, W. H. The Rise of Christianity. LC 83-48909. (Illus.). 1042p. 1984. pap. 24.95 (ISBN 0-8006-1931-5, 1-1931). Fortress.

Gallen, John, ed. Christians at Prayer. LC 76-22407. (Liturgical Studies). 1977. pap. text ed. 5.95 (ISBN 0-268-00719-5). U of Notre Dame Pr.

Garrett, Arthur. The Folk of Christendom. LC 79-92433. 500p. 1981. 49.95 (ISBN 0-8022-2363-X). Philos Lib.

Garver. Our Christian Heritage. (Illus.). 4.50 (ISBN 0-935120-00-9). Christs Mission.

Gascoigne, Bamber. The Christians. (Illus.). 304p. 1986. pap. 15.95 (ISBN 0-224-02863-4, Pub. by Jonathan Cape). Salem Hse Pubs.

Geisler, Norm. False Gods of Our Time. (Orig.). 1985. pap. 5.95 (ISBN 0-89081-494-5). Harvest Hse.

Gibson, Jean. Basic Christian Training. (Believer's Bible Lessons Ser.). 1980. pap. 5.95 (ISBN 0-937396-06-0). Walterick Pubs.

--Survey in Basic Christianity. (Believer's Bible Lessons Ser.). 1979. pap. 5.50 (ISBN 0-937396-41-9). Walterick Pubs.

Gilkey, Langdon. Message & Existence: An Introduction to Christian Theology. 272p. 1980. 12.95 (ISBN 0-8164-0450-X, HarpR); pap. 7.95 (ISBN 0-8164-2023-8). Har-Row.

Glubokovsky, N. N. Blagovjestije Khristikanskoj Slavi v Apokalipsisje. Tr. of The Good News of Christian Glory in the Apocalypse. 116p. 1966. pap. 5.00 (ISBN 0-317-29139-4). Holy Trinity.

Gonzalez, Justo. The Story of Christianity. LC 83-49187. (Reformation to the Present Day Ser.: Vol. II). (Illus.). 448p. (Orig.). 1984. pap. 13.95 kivar cover (ISBN 0-06-063316-6, RD 511, HarpR). Har-Row.

Gonzalez, Justo L. History of Christian Thought, 3 vols. rev. ed. LC 74-109679. 1975. Set. 56.00 (ISBN 0-687-17181-4). Abingdon.

Gougaud, Dom L. Gaelic Pioneers of Christianity: The Work & Influence of Irish Monks & Saints in Continental Europe. Collins, Victor, tr. from Fr. 166p. 1983. lib. bdg. 85.00 (ISBN 0-89984-223-2). Century Bookbindery.

Grainger, Roger. The Language of the Rite. 192p. 1984. pap. 8.95 (ISBN 0-232-51246-9). Chr Classics.

Green, Michael. What Is Christianity? 64p. 1982. 10.95 (ISBN 0-687-44650-3). Abingdon.

Grider, J. Kenneth. Born Again & Growing. 118p. 1982. pap. 3.50 (ISBN 0-8341-0758-9). Beacon Hill.

Groves, Norris A. Christian Devotedness. pap. 1.95 (ISBN 0-937396-63-X). Walterick Pubs.

Grubb, Norman P. Deep Things of God. 1970. pap. 4.95 (ISBN 0-87508-209-2). Chr Lit.

Grundtvig, N. F. What Constitutes Authentic Christianity? Nielsen, Ernest D., ed. & tr. from Ger. LC 84-48728. 128p. 1985. pap. 6.95 (ISBN 0-8006-1844-0, 1-1844). Fortress.

Guinan, Michael D. Gospel Poverty: Witness to the Risen Christ. LC 81-80051. 96p. (Orig.). 1981. pap. 4.95 (ISBN 0-8091-2377-0). Paulist Pr.

Guiness, Os. The Gravedigger File. LC 83-10666. (Illus.). 204p. (Orig.). 1983. pap. 7.95 (ISBN 0-87784-817-3). Inter-Varsity.

Gulledge, Dennis & McWhirter, David. An Index to the Evangelist & the Christian. LC 83-70079. 160p. (Orig.). 1983. pap. 3.95 (ISBN 0-89900-231-5). College Pr Pub.

Hake, Edward. A Touchstone for This Time Present. LC 74-80182. (English Experience Ser.: No. 663). 96p. 1974. Repr. of 1574 ed. 7.00 (ISBN 90-221-0663-2). Walter J Johnson.

Hanson, Anthony & Hanson, Richard. Reasonable Belief: A Funny of the Christian Faith. 1980. pap. 11.95x (ISBN 0-19-213238-5). Oxford U Pr.

Harbin, E. O. The New Fun Encyclopedia: Vol. 1: Games. 256p. (Orig.). 1983. pap. 9.95 (ISBN 0-687-27754-X). Abingdon.

Harkness, Georgia. Understanding the Christian Faith. (Festival Ser.). 192p. 1981. pap. 1.95 (ISBN 0-687-42955-2). Abingdon.

Harnack, Adolf Von. What Is Christianity? 301p. 1980. Repr. of 1901 ed. lib. bdg. 35.50 (ISBN 0-8482-1228-2). Norwood Edns.

Harp, Grace. Handbook of Christian Puppetry. LC 83-73204. 128p. (Orig.). 1984. pap. 5.95 plastic comb bdg. (ISBN 0-89636-125-X). Accent Bks.

Harris, Ralph W. Now What? A Guidebook for the New Christian. 24p. 1964. pap. 0.35 (ISBN 0-88243-558-2, 02-0558). Gospel Pub.

Harvey, J. Glenn. Now That You're a Christian. 127p. (Orig.). 1983. pap. 3.95 (ISBN 0-915059-01-0). Ind Christ Pubns.

Harvey, Van A. The Historian & the Believer: The Morality of Historical Knowledge & Christian Belief. LC 80-27941. 320p. 1981. Westminster.

Harvey, William L. Christianity in Action. 232p. 1954. pap. 1.95 (ISBN 0-88243-487-X, 02-0487). Gospel Pub.

Henry, Antonir Marie & LaBrosse, Olivier De, eds. Dictionnaire de la Foi Chretienne, 2 vols. (Fr.). 792p. 1968. pap. 47.50 (ISBN 0-686-56818-4, M-6596). French & Eur.

Henry, Carl F., et al. Conversations with Carl Henry: Christianity for Today. (Symposium Ser.: No. 18). 204p. 1986. lib. bdg. 49.95 (ISBN 0-88946-709-9). E Mellen.

Herbert, Jerry, ed. America, Christian or Secular? Readings in American Christian History. LC 84-11478. (Orig.). 1984. pap. 10.95 (ISBN 0-88070-067-X). Multnomah.

Herr, William A. This Our Church: The People and Events That Shaped It. (Basics of Christian Thought Ser.). 1986. 17.95 (ISBN 0-88347-193-0). Thomas More.

Hewetson, David & Miller, David. Christianity Made Simple: Belief, Vol. 1. LC 83-10866. 160p. 1983. pap. 4.95 (ISBN 0-87784-811-4). Inter-Varsity.

Hexter, Jack H. The Judaeo Christian Tradition. (Orig.). 1966. pap. text ed. 10.95 scp (ISBN 0-06-042815-5, HarpC). Har-Row.

Hodgson, Peter C. & King, Robert H., eds. Christian Theology: An Introduction to Its Traditions & Tasks. rev. & enl. 2nd ed. LC 84-48720. 432p. 1985. pap. 16.95 (ISBN 0-8006-1848-3, 1-1848). Fortress.

--Readings in Christian Theology. LC 84-48721. 432p. 1985. pap. 19.95 Kivar (ISBN 0-8006-1849-1, 1-1849). Fortress.

Hoffmann, R. Joseph. Marcion: On the Restitution of Christianity. LC 83-9008. (AAR Academy Ser.). 356p. 1984. 16.50 (ISBN 0-89130-638-2, 01 01 46). Scholars Pr GA.

Huck, Gabe, ed. Simple Gifts, Vols. 1&2. 1974. pap. 6.50 (ISBN 0-918208-65-3). Liturgical Conf.

Iacobucci, Albert A. In the Name of Jesus Christ. 129p. 1985. 10.95 (ISBN 0-533-06419-8). Vantage.

Jathanna, Origen V. The Decisiveness of the Christ-Event & the Universality of Christianity in a World of Religious Plurality. (IC-Studies in the Intercultural History of Christianity: Vol. 29). 583p. 1982. pap. 51.60 (ISBN 3-261-04974-X). P Lang Pubs.

Jones, Alan. Exploring Spiritual Direction. 160p. 1982. (HarpR); pap. 7.95 (ISBN 0-8164-2483-7). Har-Row.

Joranson, Philip N. & Butigan, Ken, eds. Cry of the Environment: Rebuilding the Christian Creation Tradition. LC 84-72254. (Illus.). 476p. (Orig.). 1984. pap. 14.95 (ISBN 0-939680-17-3). Bear & Co.

Jorgenson, Dale A. Christianity & Humanism. LC 83-70878. 115p. (Orig.). 1983. pap. 2.95 (ISBN 0-89900-149-1). College Pr Pub.

Joy, Donald M., ed. Moral Development Foundations: Judeo-Christian Alternatives to Piaget-Kohlberg. 240p. (Orig.). 1983. pap. 13.95 (ISBN 0-687-27177-0). Abingdon.

Keating, Charles J. The Heart of the Christian Message. school ed. flexible bdg 1.50 (ISBN 0-89942-246-2, 246-05-SD). Catholic Bk Pub.

Keely, Robin. Eerdmans' Handbook to Christian Belief. (Illus.). 480p. 1982. 24.95 (ISBN 0-8028-3577-5). Eerdmans.

Kelsey, Morton. Christopsychology. 177p. 1984. pap. 9.95 (ISBN 0-8245-0630-8). Crossroad NY.

Kempff, D. Christianity & Scholarship. Date not set. pap. 12.50x cancelled (ISBN 0-86990-687-9). Radix Bks.

Kennedy, D. James. Knowing the Whole Truth: Basic Christianity & What It Means in Your Life. 192p. 1985. 11.95 (ISBN 0-8007-1407-5). Revell.

Keyser, L. D., ed. Un Sistema de Evidencias Christianas. (Span.). 172p. pap. 4.95 (ISBN 0-87148-885-X). Pathway Pr.

Kinnear, Angus. A Table in the Wilderness. 1978. pap. 4.95 (ISBN 0-8423-6900-7). Tyndale.

Kirtanananda Bhaktipada. Christ & Krishna: The Path of Pure Devotion. LC 85-73024. 182p. 1986. 10.95 (ISBN 0-317-43353-9); pap. 6.95 (ISBN 0-317-43354-7). Bhaktipada Bks.

Kreeft, Peter. Yes or No? Straight Answers to Tough Questions about Christianity. 168p. (Orig.). 1984. 5.95 (ISBN 0-89283-217-7). Servant.

Kuhn, Alvin B. Rebirth for Christianity. LC 76-104032. 1970. 6.50 (ISBN 0-8356-0015-7). Theos Pub Hse.

Kyker, Rex, compiled by. I Am Born Again. (Undenominational Christianity Ser.: Vol. 2). 94p. (Orig.). 1983. pap. 2.95 (ISBN 0-88027-110-8). Firm Foun Pub.

LaHaye, Tim. The Battle for the Mind. 224p. 1980. pap. 6.95 (ISBN 0-8007-5043-8, Power Bks). Revell.

Lane, Tony. Harper's Concise Book of Christian Faith. LC 84-47728. (Illus.). 224p. (Orig.). 1984. pap. 9.95 (ISBN 0-06-064921-6, RD 523, HarpR). Har-Row.

Laski, Harold J. Faith, Reason & Civilization: An Essay in Historical Analysis. facsimile ed. LC 74-167375. (Essay Index Reprint Ser). Repr. of 1944 ed. 15.00 (ISBN 0-8369-2662-5). Ayer Co Pubs.

LeGrande, William. Christian Persecution & Genocide. 1982. lib. bdg. 59.95 (ISBN 0-87700-392-0). Revisionist Pr.

Lense, Esther. Light Triumphant. 1978. pap. 3.25 (ISBN 0-89536-301-1, 1253). CSS of Ohio.

Levison, N. The Jewish Background of Christianity: 586 B.C. to A.D. 1. 1977. lib. bdg. 59.95 (ISBN 0-8490-2100-6). Gordon Pr.

Lewis, C. S. Mere Christianity. 1978. pap. 3.95 (Collier). Macmillan.

--Mere Christianity. 180p. 1986. pap. 4.95 (ISBN 0-02-086940-1, Collier). Macmillan.

Linden, Ingemar. The Last Trump. (IC-Studies in the Intercultural History of Christianity: Vol. 17). 372p. 1978. pap. 34.10 (ISBN 3-261-02370-8). P Lang Pubs.

Littlejohn, Ronnie. Exploring Christian Theology. 542p. (Orig.). 1985. lib. bdg. 37.25 (ISBN 0-8191-4459-2); pap. text ed. 19.75 (ISBN 0-8191-4460-6). U Pr of Amer.

Ludlow, William L. What It Means to Be a Christian. 1986. 7.95 (ISBN 0-8158-0434-2). Chris Mass.

Luther, Martin. Luther's Works: Lectures on Romans Glosses & Scholia, Vol. 25. LC 55-9893. (Luther's Works). 1972. 17.95 (ISBN 0-570-06425-2, 15-1767). Concordia.

--Von Christlicher Religion und Christlicher Bildung. (Classics in German Literature & Philosophy Ser). (Ger). 1968. Repr. of 1883 ed. 18.00 (ISBN 0-384-34280-9). Johnson Repr.

McCollister. The Christian Catalogue. LC 77-29136. Date not set. 12.50 (ISBN 0-8246-0226-9). Jonathan David.

McCray, Walter A. How to Stick Together During Times of Tension: Directives for Christian Black Unity. LC 83-70288. 170p. (Orig.). 1983. 11.95 (ISBN 0-933176-04-X); pap. 7.50 (ISBN 0-933176-03-1). Black Light Fellow.

McDowell, Josh & Bellis, Dale. Evidence Growth Guide, Vol. 1: Explaining Misconceptions about Christianity. (Truth Alive Ser.). 80p. (Orig.). 1981. 4.95 (ISBN 0-86605-018-3). Campus Crusade.

McDowell, Josh & Stewart, Don. Answers to Tough Questions. 190p. (Orig.). 1980. pap. 6.95 (ISBN 0-918956-65-X). Campus Crusade.

--Answers to Tough Questions Skeptics Ask About the Christian Faith. LC 80-67432. 190p. 1980. pap. 6.95 (ISBN 0-918956-65-X, 402776). Campus Crusade.

--Reasons. LC 80-67432. (Answers to Tough Questions Ser.: Vol.II). 160p. (Orig.). 1981. pap. 6.95 (ISBN 0-918956-98-6). Campus Crusade.

MacGregor, Geddes. Reincarnation As a Christian Hope. LC 81-8013. (Library of Philosophy & Religion). 174p. 1982. 28.50x (ISBN 0-389-20220-7). B&N Imports.

McKenzie, John L. The Civilization of Christianity. 1986. pap. 9.95 (ISBN 0-88347-208-2). Thomas More.

McKinney, Richard W., ed. Creation, Christ & Culture. 336p. 19.95 (ISBN 0-567-01019-8, Pub. by T & T Clark Ltd UK). Fortress.

Mallock, William H. Studies of Contemporary Superstition. LC 72-333. (Essay Index Reprint Ser.). Repr. of 1895 ed. 20.00 (ISBN 0-8369-2804-0). Ayer Co Pubs.

Maritain, Jacques. Christianity & Democracy. Bd. with Rights of Man & Natural Law. LC 83-80191. 1986. pap. write for info. (ISBN 0-89870-030-2). Ignatius Pr.

Martin, Nancy. Christianity. (Religions of the World Ser.). (Illus.). 48p. 1986. PLB 10.90 (ISBN 0-531-18064-6, Pub. by Bookwright). Watts.

Martin, Walter. Essential Christianity. 1985. pap. 4.95 (ISBN 0-8307-1029-9, 5418458). Regal.

Marty, Martin E. Christianity in the New World: From 1500 to 1800. LC 82-83845. (Illustrated History of the Church Ser.). (Illus.). 127p. 1984. 12.95 (ISBN 0-86683-173-8, 1411, HarpR). Har-Row.

Mather, Cotton. Great Works of Christ in America, 2 vols. 1979. Set. 44.95 (ISBN 0-85151-280-1). Banner of Truth.

Mayo, S. M. The Relevance of the Old Testament for the Christian Faith: Biblical Theology & Interpretive Methodology. 220p. (Orig.). 1982. lib. bdg. 27.75 (ISBN 0-8191-2656-X); pap. text ed. 12.50 (ISBN 0-8191-2657-8). U Pr of Amer.

Mead, G. R. Pistis Sophia: A Gnostic Gospel, Vol. 21. 3rd ed. LC 83-83170. (Spiritual Science Library). 408p. 1984. Repr. of 1921 ed. lib. bdg. 25.00 (ISBN 0-89345-041-3, Spiritual Sci Lib). Garber Comm.

Mead, Sidney. The Old Religion in the Brave New World: Reflections on the Relation Between Christendom & the Republic. LC 76-24588. (Jefferson Memorial Lectures). 1977. 16.95x (ISBN 0-520-03322-1). U of Cal Pr.

Metropolitan Anthony Khrapovitsky. The Christian Faith & War. (Orig.). 1973. pap. 0.50 (ISBN 0-317-30278-7). Holy Trinity.

Metz, Johann B. Faith in History & Society: Toward a Practical Fundamental Theology. 1979. 12.95 (ISBN 0-8245-0305-8). Crossroad NY.

Meyer, John C. Christian Beliefs & Teachings. LC 81-40353. 116p. (Orig.). 1981. lib. bdg. 23.50 (ISBN 0-8191-1757-9); pap. text ed. 9.50 (ISBN 0-8191-1758-7). U Pr of Amer.

Migne, J. P., ed. Dictionnaire de Mystique Chretienne. (Troisieme et Derniere Encyclopedie Theologique Ser.: Vol. 35). (Fr.). 784p. Date not set. Repr. of 1858 ed. lib. bdg. 99.50x (ISBN 0-89241-314-X). Caratzas.

Moberg, David O. Wholistic Christianity: An Appeal for a Dynamic, Balanced Faith. 228p. 1985. 11.95 (ISBN 0-87178-931-0). Brethren.

Monk, Robert C. & Stamey, Joseph. Exploring Christianity: An Introduction. (Illus.). 256p. 1984. text ed. write for info. (ISBN 0-13-296385-X). P-H.

Moore, P. The Arts & Practices of Christianity. 96p. 1985. 20.00x (ISBN 0-7062-4125-8, Pub. by Ward Lock Educ Co Ltd). State Mutual Bk.

Muelder, Walter G. The Ethical Edge of Christian Theology: Forty Years of Communitarian Personalism. LC 83-21935. (Toronto Studies in Theology: Vol. 13). 435p. 1984. 69.95x (ISBN 0-88946-754-4). E Mellen.

Murray, Andrew. The Believer's New Life. LC 83-3006. 208p. 1984. pap. 3.95 (ISBN 0-87123-431-9). Bethany Hse.

Nash, Ronald H. Social Justice & the Christian Church. 175p. 1983. 12.95 (ISBN 0-88062-008-0). Mott Media.

Needleman, Jacob. Lost Christianity: A Journey of Rediscovery. LC 84-48227. 224p. 1985. pap. 6.95 (ISBN 0-06-066102-X, HarpR). Har-Row.

Newhouse, Flower A. Here Are Your Answers, Vol. I. 3rd ed. LC 49-16192. 1948. 9.50 (ISBN 0-910378-01-0). Christward.

--Here Are Your Answers, Vol. II. 2nd ed. LC 76-103410. 1969. 9.50 (ISBN 0-910378-06-1). Christward.

Noll, Mark A., et al, eds. Eerdmans' Handbook to Christianity in America. LC 83-1656. (Illus.). 544p. 1983. 24.95 (ISBN 0-8028-3582-1). Eerdmans.

Norris, Richard A. Understanding the Faith of the Church. (Church's Teaching Ser.: Vol. 4). 288p. 1979. 5.95 (ISBN 0-8164-0421-6, HarpR); pap. 3.95 (ISBN 0-8164-2217-6, Crossroad Bks); user guide .95 (ISBN 0-8164-2224-9). Har-Row.

North, Gary, ed. Tactics of Christian Resistance. LC 83-81783. (Christianity & Civilization Ser.: No. 3). 528p. 1983. pap. 14.95 (ISBN 0-939404-07-9). Geneva Ministr.

Ogden, Schubert M. Christ Without Myth: A Study Based on the Theology of Rudolf Bultmann. LC 79-102841. 1979. pap. 8.95x (ISBN 0-87074-172-1). SMU Press.

Oulton, J. E. & Chadwick, Henry, eds. Alexandrian Christianity. LC 54-10257. (Library of Christian Classics). 472p. 1977. pap. 8.95 (ISBN 0-664-24153-0). Westminster.

Owen, Huw P. Christian Theism: A Study in Its Basic Principles. 184p. 1984. 19.95 (ISBN 0-567-09336-0, Pub. by T&T Clark Ltd Uk). Fortress.

Packer, J. I. & Howard, Thomas. Christianity: The True Humanism. 1985. 9.95 (ISBN 0-8499-0316-5). Word Bks.

Palmer, Parker J. The Company of Strangers: Christians & the Renewal of America's Public Life. 176p. 1983. pap. 7.95 (ISBN 0-8245-0601-4). Crossroad NY.

Pelikan, Jaroslav. The Christian Tradition, Vol. 1. LC 79-142042. 1971. pap. 12.95 (ISBN 0-226-65371-4, P644, Phoen). U of Chicago Pr.

Pennington, M. Basil, et al. The Living Testament: The Essential Writings of Christianity since the Bible. LC 85-42790. 400p. 1985. 22.45 (ISBN 0-06-066499-1, HarpR); pap. 14.95 (ISBN 0-06-066498-3). Har-Row.

Peterson, Michael L. Evil & the Christian God. LC 82-70465. 176p. (Orig.). 1982. pap. 7.95 (ISBN 0-8010-7070-8). Baker Bk.

Picirilli, Robert E. Fundamentals of the Faith. 30p. 1973. pap. 0.95 (ISBN 0-89265-106-7). Randall Hse.

Pink, Arthur W. Practical Christianity. pap. 6.95 (ISBN 0-8010-6990-4). Baker Bk.

Pittenger, Norman. The Pilgrim Church & the Easter People. LC 86-45327. 112p. (Orig.). 1987. pap. 8.95 (ISBN 0-89453-598-6). M Glazier.

Pohier, Jacques & Mieth, Dietmar, eds. One Faith, One Church, Man, Many Moralities, Vol. 150. (Concilium 1981). 128p. (Orig.). 1981. pap. 6.95 (ISBN 0-8164-2350-4, HarpR). Har-Row.

Powell, John S. The Christian Vision: The Truth That Sets Us Free. LC 83-73231. (Illus.). 155p. 1984. pap. 5.95. Argus Comm.

Powell, Larry D. Christianity Is a Verb. 1984. 5.95 (ISBN 0-89536-650-9, 0392). CSS of Ohio.

Powell, Paul W. I Like Being a Christian. LC 82-73370. (Orig.). 1982. pap. 5.50 (ISBN 0-8054-5212-5). Broadman.

Rahner, Karl. Foundations of Christian Faith: An Introduction to the Idea of Christianity. LC 82-4663. 492p. 1982. pap. 16.95 (ISBN 0-8245-0523-9). Crossroad NY.

Rahner, Karl & Weger, Karl-Heinz. Our Christian Faith: Answers for the Future. 208p. (Orig.). 1980. 10.95 (ISBN 0-8245-0361-9); pap. 4.95 (ISBN 0-8245-0362-7). Crossroad NY.

Rashdall, Hastings. Philosophy & Religion: Six Lectures Delivered at Cambridge. Repr. of 1910 ed. lib. bdg. 22.50x (ISBN 0-8371-3025-5, RAPR). Greenwood.

Reisinger, Ernest C. The Carnal Christian: What Should We Think of the Carnal Christian? 75p. 1.20 (ISBN 0-85151-389-1). Banner of Truth.

Rudder, Lena E. White Roots & the Mysteries of God: And the Dead Sea Scrolls. rev. ed. (Illus.). 144p. (Orig.). 1986. write for info. (ISBN 0-937581-01-1). Zarathustrotemo Pr.

Rupp, George. Beyond Existentialism & Zen: Religion in a Pluralistic World. 1979. 14.95x (ISBN 0-19-502462-1). Oxford U Pr.

Rush, Myron D. Management: A Biblical Approach. 1983. pap. 7.95 (ISBN 0-88207-607-8). Victor Bks.

Rutherford, Richard. The Death of a Christian: The Rite of Funerals. (Studies in the Reformed Rites of the Catholic Church: Vol. 7). 1980. pap. 9.95 (ISBN 0-916134-40-7). Pueblo Pub Co.

Rye, Jennifer. The Story of the Christians. (Cambridge Books for Children). (Illus.). 32p. 1987. 7.95 (ISBN 0-521-30118-1); pap. 3.95 (ISBN 0-521-31748-7). Cambridge U Pr.

Ryken, Leland, ed. The Christian Imagination: Essays on Literature & the Arts. LC 80-70154. 344p. (Orig.). 1981. pap. 13.95 (ISBN 0-8010-7702-8). Baker Bk.

St. Hilary Troitsky. Christianity or the Church? 48p. (Orig.). 1985. pap. 2.00 (ISBN 0-317-30269-8). Holy Trinity.

Saint Hilacion Troitsky. Khristianstvo ili Tserkov. Tr. of Christianity or the Church. 64p. pap. 2.00 (ISBN 0-317-28982-9). Holy Trinity.

Sanders, Thomas G. Secular Consciousness & National Conscience: The Church & Political Alternatives in Southern Europe. Spitzer, Manon, ed. LC 77-6457. 144p. 1977. pap. text ed. 6.50 (ISBN 0-910116-90-3). U Field Staff Intl.

Sandmel, Samuel. The Several Israels. 1971. 12.50x. Ktav.

Santmire, H. Paul. The Travail of Nature: The Ambiguous Ecological Promise of Christian Theology. LC 84-47934. 288p. 1985. 16.95 (ISBN 0-8006-1806-8, 1-1806). Fortress.

Schaeffer, Francis A. A Christian Manifesto. LC 81-69737. 192p. 1981. pap. 5.95 (ISBN 0-89107-233-0, Crossway Bks). Good News.

--Mark of the Christian. pap. 2.50 (ISBN 0-87784-434-8). Inter-Varsity.

Schaeffer, Franky. Bad News for Modern Man. LC 84-70082. (Illus.). 192p. (Orig.). 1984. 14.95 (ISBN 0-89107-323-X, Crossway Bks); pap. 7.95 (ISBN 0-89107-311-6). Good News.

Schleiermacher, Friedrich. The Christian Faith. MacKintosh, H. R. & Sterwart, J. S., eds. Tr. of Der Christiliche Glaube. 772p. 1928. 18.95 (ISBN 0-567-02239-0, Pub. by T&T Clark Ltd UK). Fortress.

Scott, Walter. Exposition of the Revelation of Jesus Christ. LC 79-88736. 1979. Repr. 16.95 (ISBN 0-8254-3731-8). Kregel.

Sellner, Edward S. Christian Ministry & the Fifth Step. 32p. 1981. pap. 1.95 (ISBN 0-89486-130-1). Hazelden.

Sharpe, Kevin J. From Science to An Adequate Mythology. (Science, Religion & Society Ser.). 156p. (Orig.). 1984. pap. 11.95 (ISBN 0-86474-000-X, Pub. by Interface Press). ANZ Religious Pubns.

Sheldon, Charles M. In His Steps. 1982. gift ed. 7.95 (ISBN 0-915720-66-3). Brownlow Pub Co.

Sheppard, Joseph B., ed. Christ Church Letters. Repr. of 1877 ed. 27.00 (ISBN 0-384-55120-3). Johnson Repr.

Stedman, Ray C. Authentic Christianity: A Fresh Grip on Life. LC 84-20536. (Authentic Christianity Bks.). 182p. 1985. pap. 6.95 (ISBN 0-88070-072-6). Multnomah.

--Spiritual Warfare: Winning the Daily Battle with Satan. LC 85-2893. (Authentic Christianity Ser.). 145p. 1985. pap. 6.95 (ISBN 0-88070-094-7). Multnomah.

Steficek, Carol. A Future & a Hope. 1985. 2.95 (ISBN 0-89536-940-0, 7560). CSS of Ohio.

Steiner, Rudolf. Christ & the Human Soul. 4th ed. 81p. 1984. pap. 6.50 (ISBN 0-85440-013-3, Pub. by Steinerbooks). Anthroposophic.

--Christianity As Mystical Fact & the Mysteries of Antiquity. write for info. (ISBN 0-910142-04-1). Anthroposophic.

--Exoteric & Esoteric Christianity. 17p. 1983. pap. 3.00 (ISBN 0-919924-20-4). Anthroposophic.

Stone, Charles J. Christianity Before Christ. 1977. lib. bdg. 59.95 (ISBN 0-8490-1616-9). Gordon Pr.

Stott, John R. Basic Christianity. LC 58-13513. (Orig.). pap. 3.95 (ISBN 0-87784-690-1). Inter-Varsity.

Stratman, Chrysostemos. To the Orthodox Christians of the U. S. A. 6p. 1949. pap. 1.00 (ISBN 0-317-30430-5). Holy Trinity.

Strewart, Don. You Be the Judge. 96p. (Orig.). 1983. 2.95 (ISBN 0-89840-055-4). Heres Life.

Stumme, Wayne. Christians & the Many Faces of Marxism. LC 84-10980. 176p. (Orig.). 1984. pap. 8.95 (ISBN 0-8066-2087-0, 10-1195). Augsburg.

Swimme, Brian. The Universe Is a Green Dragon: A Cosmic Creation Story. LC 84-72255. (Illus.). 173p. (Orig.). 1984. pap. 8.95 (ISBN 0-939680-14-9). Bear & Co.

Sykes, Stephen. The Identity of Christianity. LC 83-48907. 256p. 1984. 21.95 (ISBN 0-8006-0720-1, 1-720). Fortress.

Taylor, Blaine, et al. Christianity Without Morals. Cook, Jerry O., ed. 96p. (Orig.). 1982. pap. 7.00 (ISBN 0-914527-16-9). C-Four Res.

Taylor, Kenneth. Is Christianity Credible. pap. 0.75 (ISBN 0-87784-110-1). Inter-Varsity.

Taylor, Richard S. Biblical Authority & Christian Faith. 95p. (Orig.). 1980. pap. 2.95 (ISBN 0-8341-0633-7). Beacon Hill.

Taylor, Thomas. Against the Christians. 119p. 1980. 10.00 (ISBN 0-89005-301-4). Ares.

Teilhard de Chardin, Pierre. Christianity & Evolution. LC 73-12926. 255p. 1974. pap. 6.95 (ISBN 0-15-617740-4, Harv). HarBraceJ.

Theodore Thornton Munger: New England Minister. 1913. 65.00x (ISBN 0-686-83814-9). Elliots Bks.

Thurian, Max. Our Faith: Basic Christian Belief. Chisholm, Emily, tr. from Fr. LC 82-72008. 192p. 1982. 12.95 (ISBN 0-8245-0547-6). Crossroad NY.

Tillich, Paul. A History of Christian Thought. 1972. pap. 11.95 (ISBN 0-671-21426-8, Touchstone Bks). S&S.

Torrance, Thomas F., ed. Belief in Science & in Christian Life. 160p. 1981. pap. 12.00x (ISBN 0-905312-11-2, Pub. by Scot Acad Pr). Longwood Pub Group.

Torrey, Charles G. Apocalypse of John. 1958. 39.50x (ISBN 0-686-83474-7). Elliots Bks.

Tozer, W. Tragedy in the Church. Smith, Gerald, ed. 1978. pap. 3.45 (ISBN 0-87509-215-2). Chr Pubns.

Trace, Arther. Christianity & the Intellectuals. 208p. (Orig.). 1983. pap. 5.95 (ISBN 0-89385-018-7). Sugden.

Van Rheenen, Gailyn. Church Planting in Uganda: A Comparative Study. LC 76-20461. 1976. pap. 4.95 (ISBN 0-87808-314-6). William Carey Lib.

Vila. To the Fountain of Christianity. pap. 3.95 (ISBN 0-935120-02-5). Christs Mission.

Vincellette, Arthur J. Way of Life. 160p. 1983. 7.95 (ISBN 0-89962-312-3). Todd & Honeywell.

Von Balthasar, Hans U. Truth Is Symphonic: Aspects of Christian Pluralism. Harrison, Graham, tr. from Ger. Tr. of Die Warrheit Ist Symphonisch. 192p. 1987. pap. 9.95 (ISBN 0-89870-141-4). Ignatius Pr.

Wallis, Wilson D. Culture Patterns in Christianity. 176p. 1964. 9.50x (ISBN 0-87291-053-9). Coronado Pr.

Ward, William G. The Ideal of a Christian Church Considered in Comparison with Existing Practice. 2nd ed. LC 75-30040. Repr. of 1844 ed. 49.50 (ISBN 0-404-14044-0). AMS Pr.

Weatherhead, Leslie D. The Christian Agnostic. (Festival Books Ser.). 1979. pap. 4.50 (ISBN 0-687-06978-5). Abingdon.

Wegman, Herman A. Christian Worship in East & West. Lathrop, Gordon, tr. from Dutch. 400p. (Orig.). 1985. pap. 19.50 (ISBN 0-916134-71-7). Pueblo Pub Co.

Werning, Waldo J. The Radical Nature of Christianity: Church Growth Eyes Look at the Supernatural Mission of the Christian & the Church. LC 76-8359. 1976. pap. 5.85 (ISBN 0-87808-730-3, Pub. by Mandate Pr). William Carey Lib.

Wilberforce, William. Real Christianity: Contrasted with the Prevailing Religious System. Houston, James M., ed. LC 82-8061. (Classics of Faith & Devotion Ser.). 1982. casebound 10.95 (ISBN 0-930014-90-1). Multnomah.

Wilhelmsson, Lars & Wilhelmsson, Nancy. Vital Christianity Study Guide. (Religion Ser.). 64p. (Orig.). 1982. pap. 2.25 (ISBN 0-941018-08-3). Martin Pr CA.

Wilkins, Ronald J. Understanding Christian Worship: School Edition. (To Live Is Christ Ser.). 216p. 1982. pap. 5.50 (ISBN 0-697-01802-4); tchr's. manual 5.00 (ISBN 0-697-01803-2); kit 32.00 (ISBN 0-697-01676-5); spirit masters 6.50 (ISBN 0-697-01902-0); poster 3.50 (ISBN 0-697-01903-9); activity cards 7.50 (ISBN 0-697-01904-7); progress in prayer 11.50 (ISBN 0-697-01905-5); prayer planning forms 3.00 (ISBN 0-697-01906-3). Wm C Brown.

Wilkinson, Jerry & Richardson, Jim. A Case for Radical Christianity. 1984. pap. 1.75 (ISBN 0-911739-25-4). Abbott Loop.

Will the Real Jesus Christ & Christians Please Stand? (Orig.). 1983. pap. 2.75 (ISBN 0-914335-00-6). Highland.

Winterhalter, Robert. The Odes of Solomon: Original Christianity Revealed. Roche de Coppens, Peter, et al, eds. LC 85-45288. (Spiritual Perspectives Ser.). 240p. (Orig.). 1985. pap. 9.95 (ISBN 0-87542-875-4, L-875). Llewellyn Pubns.

Wood, Barry. Questions New Christians Ask. 160p. 1979. pap. 5.95 (ISBN 0-8007-5044-6, Power Bks). Revell.

Wood, Charles M. The Formation of Christian Understanding: An Essay in Theological Hermeneutics. LC 81-5103. 126p. 1981. pap. 7.95 (ISBN 0-664-24373-8). Westminster.

Ziesler, John. Pauline Christianity. (The Oxford Bible Ser.). (Orig.). 1983. pap. 9.95 (ISBN 0-19-213247-4). Oxford U Pr.

CHRISTIANITY–ADDRESSES, ESSAYS, LECTURES

Alexander, Archibald. Feathers on the Moor. facs. ed. LC 67-22050. (Essay Index Reprint Ser). 1928. 17.00 (ISBN 0-8369-0145-2). Ayer Co Pubs.

Barth, Karl. The Word of God & the Word of Man. Horton, Douglas, tr. 1958. 13.50 (ISBN 0-8446-1599-4). Peter Smith.

Bigelow, John. Toleration, & Other Essays & Studies. facs. ed. LC 78-84298. (Essay Index Reprint Ser). 1927. 14.25 (ISBN 0-8369-1075-3). Ayer Co Pubs.

Booth, Catherine, et al. The Last Days Collection: A Treasury of Articles from Last Days Ministries. (Illus.). 224p. (Orig.). 1986. pap. text ed. 10.95. Pretty Good TX.

Brent, Charles H. Inspiration of Responsibility, & Other Papers. facs. ed. LC 67-22081. (Essay Index Reprint Ser). 1915. 13.00 (ISBN 0-8369-0251-3). Ayer Co Pubs.

Bridges, Horace J. Criticisms of Life. facsimile ed. LC 75-99684. (Essay Index Reprint Ser). 1915. 20.00 (ISBN 0-8369-1342-6). Ayer Co Pubs.

Bryan, William J. In His Image. facsimile ed. LC 73-156618. (Essay Index Reprint Ser). Repr. of 1922 ed. 18.00 (ISBN 0-8369-2270-0). Ayer Co Pubs.

Burkitt, Francis C. Early Christianity Outside the Roman Empire: Two Lectures Delivered at Trinity College, Dublin. LC 82-45806. 1983. Repr. of 1899 ed. 18.00 (ISBN 0-404-62375-1). AMS Pr.

Burnaby, John, ed. Augustine: Later Works. LC 55-5022. (Library of Christian Classics). 356p. 1980. pap. 11.95 (ISBN 0-664-24165-4). Westminster.

De Paul, Vincent. Correspondence, Conferences, Documents, Vol. 1. Law, Helen M., et al, trs. from Fr. & Lat. Kilar, Jacqueline, ed. LC 83-63559. 675p. 1985. 28.00 (ISBN 0-317-27157-1). New City.

Drummond, James. Via, Veritas, Vita: Lectures on "Chrisitianity in Its Most Simple & Intelligible Form". 2nd ed. LC 77-27160. (Hibbert Lectures: 1894). Repr. of 1895 ed. 31.50 (ISBN 0-404-60412-9). AMS Pr.

Evans, Stanley G., ed. Return to Reality: Some Essays on Contemporary Christianity. 1954. 39.50x (ISBN 0-317-07644-2). Elliots Bks.

Everett, Charles C. Theism & the Christian Faith. Hale, Edward, ed. LC 75-3139. Repr. of 1909 ed. 34.00 (ISBN 0-404-59148-5). AMS Pr.

Fellowship of Catholic Scholars. Christian Faith & Freedom: Proceedings. Williams, Paul L., ed. LC 82-81072. 128p. (Orig.). 1982. pap. text ed. 4.50 (ISBN 0-686-97454-9). NE Bks.

Fiske, Charles. Confessions of a Puzzled Parson, & Other Pleas for Reality. facs. ed. LC 68-54345. (Essay Index Reprint Ser). 1968. Repr. of 1928 ed. 18.00 (ISBN 0-8369-0442-7). Ayer Co Pubs.

Harnack, Adolf von. What Is Christianity? LC 86-45209. (Texts in Modern Theology Ser.). Tr. of Das Wesen des Christentums. 320p. 1986. pap. 12.95 (ISBN 0-8006-3201-X, 1-3201). Fortress.

Harnack, Adolph. What Is Christianity. 1958. 17.50 (ISBN 0-8446-2208-7). Peter Smith.

Hebblethwaite, Brian L., ed. The Philosophical Frontiers of Christian Theology: Essays Presented to D. M. Mackinnon. Sutherland, Stewart. LC 81-10132. (Illus.). 230p. 1982. 29.50 (ISBN 0-521-24012-3). Cambridge U Pr.

Hegel, G. W. Three Essays, Seventeen Ninety-Three to Seventeen Ninety-Five: The Tubingen Essay, Berne Fragments, The Life of Jesus. Fuss, Peter & Dobbins, John, eds. LC 83-40599. 192p. 1984. text ed. 18.95x (ISBN 0-268-01854-5, 85-18540). U of Notre Dame Pr.

Hinson, E. Glenn, ed. Understandings of the Church. LC 86-45227. (Sources of Early Christian Thought Ser.). 128p. 1986. pap. 7.95 (ISBN 0-8006-1415-1, 1-1415). Fortress.

Huxley, Thomas H. Science & Christian Tradition. 419p. 1981. Repr. of 1894 ed. lib. bdg. 45.00 (ISBN 0-89984-285-2). Century Bookbindery.

Kerrigan, Anthony & Nozick, Martin, eds. Selected Works of Miguel de Unamuno, Vol. 5: The Agony of Christianity & Essays on Faith. LC 67-22341. (Bollingen Ser.: Vol. 85). 313p. 1974. 34.00x (ISBN 0-691-09933-2). Princeton U Pr.

Lewis, C. S. Mere Christianity. 1964. 10.95 (ISBN 0-02-570610-1); pap. 3.95 (ISBN 0-02-086830-8). Macmillan.

Lloyd-Jones, Martyn. The Cross. 192p. 1986. pap. 6.95 (ISBN 0-89107-382-5, Crossway Bks). Good News.

MacDonald, William. Acts: Studies in Dynamic Christianity. 5.95 (ISBN 0-937396-01-X). Walterick Pubs.

Meyendorff, John. Gregory Palamas, The Triads. (The Classics of Western Spirituality Ser.). 192p. 12.95 (ISBN 0-8091-0328-1); pap. 7.95 (ISBN 0-8091-2447-5). Paulist Pr.

Nacpil, Emerito, ed. The Human & the Holy: Asian Perspectives in Christian Theology. Elwood, Douglas J. 1978. pap. text ed. 10.00x (ISBN 0-686-23912-1, Pub. by New Day Pub). Cellar.

Newman, John H. An Essay in Aid of a Grammar of Assent. Ker, Ian, ed. & intro. by. 480p. 1985. 59.95x (ISBN 0-19-812751-0). Oxford U Pr.

Nygren, Malcolm. The Lord of the Four Seasons. 144p. (Orig.). 1986. pap. 7.95 (ISBN 0-9617890-1-8). Doxology Lane.

Oduyoye, Mercy A. Hearing & Knowing: Theological Reflections on Christianity in Africa. LC 85-29873. 176p. (Orig.). 1986. pap. 9.95 (ISBN 0-88344-258-2). Orbis Bks.

Pacific School Of Religion. Religious Progress on the Pacific Slope: Addresses & Papers at the Celebration of the Semi-Centennial Anniversary of Pacific School of Religion, Berkeley, California. facs. ed. LC 68-22941. (Essay Index Reprint Ser). 1968. Repr. of 1917 ed. 19.00 (ISBN 0-8369-0820-1). Ayer Co Pubs.

Schechter, Solomon. Seminary Addresses & Other Papers. 270p. Date not set. Repr. of 1915 ed. text ed. 62.10x (ISBN 0-576-80119-4, Pub by Gregg Intl Pubs England). Gregg Intl.

Smith, Gerald B., ed. Religious Thought in the Last Quarter-Century. LC 71-107739. (Essay Index Reprint Ser). 1927. 12.00 (ISBN 0-8369-1583-6). Ayer Co Pubs.

Smith, Moody D. Johannine Christianity: Essays on Its Setting, Sources, & Theology. 233p. 1985. 19.95x (ISBN 0-87249-449-7). U of SC Pr.

Stott, John R. & Coote, Robert. Down to Earth: Studies in Christianity & Culture. 2nd ed. (Orig.). 1980. pap. 9.95 (ISBN 0-8028-1827-7). Eerdmans.

Tillman, William M., Jr., ed. Perspectives on Applied Christianity: Essays in Honor of Thomas Buford Maston. (National Association of Baptist Professors of Religion (NABPR) Festschrift Ser.). vi, 108p. 1986. 10.50 (ISBN 0-86554-196-5, MUP-H180). Mercer Univ Pr.

Toon, Peter. Justification & Sanctification. LC 83-70317. (Foundations for Faith Ser.). 160p. 1983. pap. 8.95 (ISBN 0-89107-288-8, Crossway Bks). Good News.

Tozer, A. W. Renewed Day by Day. Smith, Gerald B., ed. 384p. kivar binding 7.95 (ISBN 0-8007-5064-0, Power Bks). Revell.

Tozer, Aiden W. Root of the Righteous. 5.95 (ISBN 0-87509-194-6); pap. 4.45 (ISBN 0-87509-195-4); mass market 3.25 (ISBN 0-87509-224-1). Chr Pubns.

Tracy, James D. Luther & the Modern State in Germany. (Sixteenth Century Essays & Studies: Vol. VII). 110p. 1986. smyth sewn 25.00 (ISBN 0-940474-07-7). Sixteenth Cent.

Von Balthasar, Hans U. Convergences: To the Source of Christian Mystery. Nelson, E. A., tr. from Ger. LC 83-81853. Orig. Title: Einfaltungen: Auf Wegen der Christlichen Einigung. 153p. (Orig.). 1984. pap. 8.95 (ISBN 0-89870-032-9). Ignatius Pr.

Wilson, Theron D. Religion for Tomorrow. LC 62-9776. 148p. 1963. 5.95 (ISBN 0-8022-1897-0). Philos Lib.

Wozniak, Kenneth W. & Grenz, Stanley J., eds. Christian Freedom: Essays in Honor of Vernon C. Grounds. LC 86-24584. (Illus.). 284p. (Orig.). 1987. lib. bdg. 28.50 (ISBN 0-8191-5696-5); pap. text ed. 15.75 (ISBN 0-8191-5697-3). U Pr of Amer.

CHRISTIANITY–APOLOGETIC WORKS

see Apologetics

CHRISTIANITY–BIBLIOGRAPHY

Address Book of Some Assemblies of Christians (Current) 1986. pap. 5.50 (ISBN 0-937396-03-6). Walterick Pubs.

Association of Christian Publishers & Booksellers. Libros Cristianos En Existencia. (Span.). 384p. (Orig.). 1984. write for info. (ISBN 0-943258-01-4). Assn Christian Pub.

Bibliographia Patristica Internationale Patristische Bibliographie: Die Erscheinungen der Jahre 1969 & 1970, Vol. XIV-XV. 1977. 34.40x (ISBN 3-11-007186-X). De Gruyter.

Christian Periodical Index: Annual & Quarterlies. 1980. cancelled. Assn Chr Libs.

Christian Periodical Index, 1976-1978. Cumulated vol. 35.00x (ISBN 0-686-37453-3). Assn Chr Libs.

Gospel Advocate Index. 1985. 49.95 (ISBN 0-89225-280-4). Gospel Advocate.

Kissinger, Warren S. The Lives of Jesus: A History & Bibliography. LC 83-48284. 200p. 1985. lib. bdg. 39.00 (ISBN 0-8240-9035-7). Garland Pub.

Mills, Watson E. Glossolalia: A Bibliography. LC 85-8987. (Studies in the Bible & Early Christianity: Vol. 6). 144p. 1985. 39.95x (ISBN 0-88946-605-X). E Mellen.

O'Toole, James. Guide to the Archives of the Archdiocese of Boston. LC 80-8989. 300p. 1981. lib. bdg. 61.00 (ISBN 0-8240-9359-3). Garland Pub.

Satyaprakash. Christianity: A Select Bibliography. 1986. 18.50x (ISBN 0-8364-1829-8, Pub. by Indian Doc Serv India). South Asia Bks.

Starkey, Edward D. Judaism & Christianity: A Guide to the Reference Literature. (Reference Sources in the Humanities Ser.). 250p. 1987. lib. bdg. 27.50 (ISBN 0-87287-533-4). Libs Unl.

CHRISTIANITY–BIOGRAPHY

see Christian Biography

CHRISTIANITY–CONTROVERSIAL LITERATURE

see also Agnosticism; Atheism; Free Thought; Rationalism; Secularism

Aconcio, Giacomo. Darkness Discovered (Satans Stratagems) LC 78-9490. 1978. Repr. of 1651 ed. 45.00x (ISBN 0-8201-1313-1). Schol Facsimiles.

Ansari, F. R. Islam & Christianity in the Modern World. pap. 14.95 (ISBN 0-686-18577-3). Kazi Pubns.

Bakunin, Michael. God & the State. LC 75-105664. 1970. pap. 3.50 (ISBN 0-486-22483-X). Dover.

Barnes, Harry E. The Twilight of Christianity. 75.00 (ISBN 0-87700-037-9). Revisionist Pr.

Betson, Martin. Here Begynneth a Treatyse to Dyspose Men to Be Vertously Occupyed in Theyr Myndes & Prayers. LC 77-6854. (English Experience Ser.: No. 848). 1977. Repr. of 1500 ed. lib. bdg. 5.00 (ISBN 90-221-0848-1). Walter J Johnson.

Blanshard, Paul. Some of My Best Friends Are Christians. LC 74-744. 200p. 1974. 14.95 (ISBN 0-87548-149-3). Open Court.

Broughton, Hugh. An Epistle to the Learned Nobility of England: Touching Translating the Bible. LC 77-6862. (English Experience Ser.: No. 855). 1977. Repr. of 1597 ed. lib. bdg. 7.00 (ISBN 90-221-0855-4). Walter J Johnson.

Burgess, John H. Christian Pagan: A Naturalistic Survey of Christian History. (Illus.). 1968. 7.00 (ISBN 0-912084-04-9). Mimir.

Burton, Henry. A Tryall of Private Devotions. LC 77-6863. (English Experience Ser.: No. 856). 1977. Repr. of 1628 ed. lib. bdg. 10.50 (ISBN 90-221-0856-2). Walter J Johnson.

Church of Scotland Staff. The First & Second Books of Discipline: Together with Some Acts of the General Assemblies. LC 77-7433. (English Experience Ser.: No. 893). 1977. Repr. of 1621 ed. lib. bdg. 6.00 (ISBN 90-221-0893-7). Walter J Johnson.

Conne, John. Ignatius His Conclave, or His Inthronisation in a Late Election in Hell. LC 77-6876. (English Experience Ser.: No. 868). 1977. Repr. of 1611 ed. lib. bdg. 11.50 (ISBN 90-221-0868-6). Walter J Johnson.

Cresson, Warder. The Key of David: David the True Messiah. Davis, Moshe, ed. LC 77-70671. (America & the Holy Land Ser.). (Illus.). 1977. Repr. of 1852 ed. lib. bdg. 26.50x (ISBN 0-405-10239-9). Ayer Co Pubs.

Ellul, Jacques. The Subversion of Christianity. Bromiley, Geoffrey W., tr. from Fr. 224p. (Orig.). 1986. pap. 9.95 (ISBN 0-8028-0049-1). Eerdmans.

Feuerbach, Ludwig. Essence of Christianity. pap. 7.95x (ISBN 0-06-130011-X, TB11, Torch). Har-Row.

--Essence of Christianity. Eliot, George, tr. 1958. 18.25 (ISBN 0-8446-2055-6). Peter Smith.

Geffre, Claude & Jossua, Jean-Pierre, eds. The Human, Criterion of Christian Existence? (Concilium Ser.: Vol. 155). 128p. (Orig.). 1982. pap. 6.95 (ISBN 0-8164-2386-5, HarpR). Har-Row.

The General Signs & Forerunners of Christ's Comming to Judgment. LC 77-7410. (English Experience Ser.: No. 875). 1977. Repr. of 1620 ed. lib. bdg. 3.50 (ISBN 90-221-0875-9). Walter J Johnson.

Khomiakov, Aleksiei S. L' Eglise Latine et le Protestantisme, Au Point De Vue De l'Eglise d'Orient. LC 80-2362. Repr. of 1872 ed. 49.00 (ISBN 0-404-18908-3). AMS Pr.

Maccoby, Hyam. The Mythmaker: Paul & the Invention of Christianity. LC 85-45680. 256p. 1986. 17.45 (ISBN 0-06-015582-5, HARPT). Har-Row.

MacCollam, Joel A. The Way of Victor Paul Wierwille. 32p. 1978. pap. 0.75 (ISBN 0-87784-162-4). Inter-Varsity.

Molnar, Thomas. Christian Humanism, a Critique of the Secular City & Its Ideology. 1978. 7.95 (ISBN 0-8199-0694-8). Franciscan Herald.

Nietzsche, Friedrich. The Antichrist. LC 70-161338. (Atheist Viewpoint Ser). 60p. 1972. Repr. of 1930 ed. 13.00 (ISBN 0-405-03799-6). Ayer Co Pubs.

Parker, Henry. The Rich & the Poor. LC 77-7419. (English Experience Ser.: No. 882). 1977. Repr. of 1493 ed. lib. bdg. 69.00 (ISBN 90-221-0882-1). Walter J Johnson.

Pinard, C. Dictionnaire des Objections Populaires contre le Dogme, la Morale, la Discipline et L'histoire de Eglise Catholique. Migne, J. P., ed. (Troisieme et Derniere Encyclopedie Theologique Ser.: Vol. 33). (Fr.). 756p. Repr. of 1858 ed. lib. bdg. 96.50x (ISBN 0-89241-312-3). Caratzas.

Powell, Robert. Depopulation Arranged, Convicted & Condemned by the Lawes of God & Man. LC 76-57407. (English Experience Ser.: No. 823). 1977. Repr. of 1636 ed. lib. bdg. 16.00 (ISBN 90-221-0823-6). Walter J Johnson.

Powys, Llewelyn. The Pathetic Fallacy. LC 77-828. 1977. Repr. of 1930 ed. lib. bdg. 25.00 (ISBN 0-8414-6797-8). Folcroft.

Rankin, Oliver S. Jewish Religious Polemic. rev. ed. 1969. 20.00x (ISBN 0-87068-007-2). Ktav.

Robinson, John. A Justification of Separation from the Church of England. LC 77-7427. (English Experience Ser.: No. 888). 1977. Repr. of 1610 ed. lib. bdg. 46.00 (ISBN 90-221-0888-0). Walter J Johnson.

Runes, Dagobert D. Of God, the Devil & the Jews. 1952. 5.00 (ISBN 0-8022-1444-4). Philos Lib.

Sinclair, Upton B. Profits of Religion. LC 73-120566. 1970. Repr. of 1918 ed. 22.50 (ISBN 0-404-06093-5). AMS Pr.

Spurgeon, C. H. The DownGrade Controversy. 1978. pap. 2.75 (ISBN 0-686-00493-0). Pilgrim Pubns.

Wagenseil, Joh. Chr. Tela Ignea Satanae, 2 vols. 1631p. Date not set. Repr. of 1681 ed. text ed. 207.00x (ISBN 0-576-80110-0, Pub by Gregg Intl Pubs England). Gregg Intl.

Walker, Paul L. Is Christianity the Only Way? 1975. pap. 3.95 (ISBN 0-87148-429-3). Pathway Pr.

Wheless, J. Forgery in Christianity. 75.00 (ISBN 0-87968-358-9). Gordon Pr.

Wilken, Robert L. The Christians As the Romans Saw Them. LC 83-12472. 240p. 1984. 22.50x (ISBN 0-300-03066-5); pap. 7.95 (ISBN 0-300-03627-2, Y-575). Yale U Pr.

Zuck, Lowell H., ed. Christianity & Revolution: Radical Christian Testimonies, 1520-1650. LC 74-25355. (Documents in Free Church History Ser.: No. 2). 324p. 1975. 29.95 (ISBN 0-87722-040-9); pap. 12.95 (ISBN 0-87722-044-1). Temple U Pr.

Zwingli, Ulrich. A Short Pathwaye to the Ryghte & True Understanding of the Holye & Sacred Scriptures. Veron, J., tr. LC 77-7443. (English Experience Ser.: No. 901). 1977. Repr. of 1550 ed. lib. bdg. 15.00 (ISBN 90-221-0901-1). Walter J Johnson.

CHRISTIANITY–ESSENCE, GENIUS, NATURE

see also Demythologization

Abbott, Lyman. The Evolution of Christianity. (American Studies Ser.). Repr. of 1892 ed. 24.00 (ISBN 0-384-00075-4). Johnson Repr.

Clymer, R. Swimburne. The Living Christ: Church of Illumination. 58p. 1979. pap. 2.95 (ISBN 0-932785-27-1). Philos Pub.

Farris, Kenna. Christianity Is a Bridge. Date not set. price not set. Port Love Intl.

Ferre, Nels F. Evil & the Christian Faith. facsimile ed. LC 71-134075. (Essay Index Reprints - Reason & the Christian Faith Ser.: Vol. 2). Repr. of 1947 ed. 18.00 (ISBN 0-8369-2393-6). Ayer Co Pubs.

Forman, Charles W. A Faith for the Nations. LC 57-9601. (Layman's Theological Library). 1957. pap. 1.00 (ISBN 0-664-24007-0). Westminster.

Goodrich, Frances C. Third Adam. LC 66-22003. 1967. 5.95 (ISBN 0-8022-0608-5). Philos Lib.

Hall, Marie B. The Christ Principle & True Christianity to Be. (Illus.). 1973. 8.50 (ISBN 0-938760-03-3). Veritat Found.

Harnack, Adolf. What Is Christianity? LC 78-15359. 1978. Repr. lib. bdg. 32.50 (ISBN 0-8414-4869-8). Folcroft.

Koyama, Kosuke. No Handle on the Cross: An Asian Meditation on the Crucified Mind. LC 76-23160. pap. 32.00 (ISBN 0-317-26647-0, 2025120). Bks Demand UMI.

Latourette, Kenneth, ed. Gospel, the Church & the World. LC 76-134107. (Essay Index Reprint Ser). 1946. 18.00 (ISBN 0-8369-1972-6). Ayer Co Pubs.

Lewis, C. S. Mere Christianity. (Illus.). 211p. 1981. 12.95 (ISBN 0-02-570590-3). Macmillan.

Meland, Bernard E. Reawakening of Christian Faith. facsimile ed. LC 72-142670. (Essay Index Reprint Ser). Repr. of 1949 ed. 15.00 (ISBN 0-8369-2663-3). Ayer Co Pubs.

Moody Press Editors. What Christians Believe. 1951. pap. 3.50 (ISBN 0-8024-9378-5). Moody.

Nemeshegyi, Peter. The Meaning of Christianity. 128p. 1982. pap. 3.95 (ISBN 0-8091-2464-5). Paulist Pr.

Park, James. The Existential Christian, No. 1. (Existential Freedom Ser. No. 1). 1970. pap. 1.00x (ISBN 0-89231-001-4). Existential Bks.

--The Existential Christian, No. 2. (Existential Freedom Ser.: No. 2). 1971. pap. 5.00x (ISBN 0-89231-002-2). Existential Bks.

Robinson, John A. Honest to God. LC 63-13819. 144p. 1963. pap. 7.95 (ISBN 0-664-24465-3). Westminster.

Schmaus, Michael. Essence of Christianity. 288p. 1966. pap. 2.50 (ISBN 0-933932-16-2). Scepter Pubs.

Sperry, Willard L. What We Mean by Religion. facsimile ed. LC 78-128316. (Essay Index Reprint Ser.). Repr. of 1940 ed. 17.00 (ISBN 0-8369-2370-7). Ayer Co Pubs.

Thomas, George F., ed. Vitality of the Christian Tradition. facsimile ed. LC 70-134143. (Essay Index Reprint Ser). Repr. of 1944 ed. 22.00 (ISBN 0-8369-2378-2). Ayer Co Pubs.

Troeltsch, Ernst D. Christian Thought, Its History & Application. LC 78-59047. 1985. Repr. of 1923 ed. 23.25 (ISBN 0-88355-719-3). Hyperion Conn.

Waterman, Leroy. The Religion of Jesus: Christianity's Unclaimed Heritage of Prophetic Religion. LC 78-16405. 1978. Repr. of 1952 ed. lib. bdg. 22.50x (ISBN 0-313-20586-8, WARJ). Greenwood.

Weigel, Van B. Ostrich Christianity: Self-Deception in Popular Christianity. LC 85-17981. 254p. (Orig.). 1986. lib. bdg. 25.75 (ISBN 0-8191-4974-8); pap. text ed. 12.75 (ISBN 0-8191-4975-6). U Pr of Amer.

Wilken, Robert L. The Myth of Christian Beginnings. LC 80-11884. 218p. 1980. 17.95 (ISBN 0-268-01347-0); pap. text ed. 6.95 (ISBN 0-268-01348-9). U of Notre Dame Pr.

Wilkins, Ronald J. Christian Faith: The Challenge of the Call. 72p. 1978. pap. 4.20 (ISBN 0-697-01684-6); tchrs.' manual 4.50 (ISBN 0-697-01688-9); spirit masters 10.95 (ISBN 0-697-01690-0). Wm C Brown.

Williams, Trevor. Form & Vitality in the World & God: A Christian Perspective. 1985. 29.95x (ISBN 0-19-826671-5). Oxford U Pr.

Wilson, Herman O. & Womack, Morris M. Pillars of Faith. 6.95 (ISBN 0-8010-9540-9); pap. 4.95 (ISBN 0-8010-9538-7). Baker Bk.

CHRISTIANITY–EVIDENCES

see Apologetics

CHRISTIANITY–HISTORY

see Church History

CHRISTIANITY–MISCELLANEA

Besant, Annie. Esoteric Christianity. 59.95 (ISBN 0-8490-0124-2). Gordon Pr.

Birdsong, Robert E. Fundamentals of Adamic Christianity. (Aquarian Academy Monograph, Series A: Lecture No. 1). 1974. pap. 1.25 (ISBN 0-917108-00-0). Sirius Bks.

Christian Writers Institute Staff. The Successful Writers & Editors Guidebook. LC 76-62692. 1977. 10.95 (ISBN 0-88419-014-5). Creation Hse.

Debor, Jane & Isabel, Linda. Banner Designs for Celebrating Christians. 1984. pap. 5.95 (ISBN 0-570-03931-2, 12-2865). Concordia.

Jacob, Kenneth. Coins & Christianity. 9.50 (ISBN 0-900652-73-X). Numismatic Fine Arts.

Knechtle, Cliffe. Give Me an Answer. LC 86-10549. 132p. (Orig.). 1986. pap. 5.95 (ISBN 0-87784-569-7). Inter-Varsity.

Palms, Roger C. Living on the Mountain. 288p. 1985. 11.95 (ISBN 0-8007-1449-0). Revell.

Torrey, R. A. Preguntas Practicas y Dificiles Contestadas. Orig. Title: Practical & Perplexing Questions Answered. (Span.). 128p. 1980. pap. 3.25 (ISBN 0-8254-1722-8). Kregel.

Van Harn, Roger E. Searchlight. rev. ed. 84p. 1980. pap. 3.25 (ISBN 0-933140-16-9). CRC Pubns.

Wall, James, et al. A Century of the Century. 128p. (Orig.). 1987. pap. 8.95 (ISBN 0-8028-0180-3). Eerdmans.

Woods, Guy N. Questions & Answers, Vol. II. 1986. 16.95 (ISBN 0-89225-277-4). Gospel Advocate.

CHRISTIANITY–ORIGIN

see also Church–Foundation

Bockle, Franz & Beemer, Theo. Dilemmas of Tomorrow's World. LC 78-86974. (Concilium Ser.: No. 45). 188p. 1965. 7.95 (ISBN 0-8091-0030-4). Paulist Pr.

Brown, Schuyler. The Origins of Christianity: A Historical Introduction to the New Testament. (Oxford Bible Ser.). (Orig.). 1984. pap. 8.95 (ISBN 0-19-826202-7). Oxford U Pr.

Bruce, F. F. Jesus & Christian Origins Outside the New Testament. 1974. pap. 5.95 (ISBN 0-8028-1575-8). Eerdmans.

Carus, Paul. The Pleroma: An Essay on the Origin of Christianity. 163p. 1921. pap. 4.95 (ISBN 0-317-40408-3). Open Court.

Charles, R. H., ed. The Book of the Secrets of Enoch. 100p. pap. 11.95 (ISBN 0-88697-010-5). Life Science.

De Chateaubriand, Viscount. The Genius of Christianity, 2 vols. White, Charles I., tr. 245p. 1985. 117.35 (ISBN 0-89901-223-X). Found Class Reprints.

Edwards, O. C. How It All Began: Origins of the Christian Church New Edition with Study Guide. 1978. pap. 6.95 (ISBN 0-8164-2164-1, HarpR). Har-Row.

Gibbon, Edward. The Early Growth of Christianity & the History of the First Christians. (Illus.). 177p. 1986. 135.47 (ISBN 0-89266-557-2). Am Classical Coll Pr.

Halliday, W. R. The Pagan Background of Christianity. 59.95 (ISBN 0-8490-0795-X). Gordon Pr.

Hannay, James B. Symbolism in Relation to Religion. LC 79-118523. (Illus.). 1971. Repr. of 1915 ed. 28.50x (Pub by Kennikat). Assoc Faculty Pr.

Hatch, Edwin. The Influence of Greek Ideas on Christianity. 11.75 (ISBN 0-8446-0683-9). Peter Smith.

Kautsky, Karl. Foundations of Christianity. Hartmann, Jacob W., tr. from Ger. LC 72-81774. 512p. 1972. pap. 15.00 (ISBN 0-85345-262-8, PB-2628). Monthly Rev.

--Foundations of Christianity. Hartmann, Jacob W., tr. from Ger. LC 72-81774. Repr. of 1972 ed. 120.00 (ISBN 0-8357-9441-5, 2016442). Bks Demand UMI.

Lillie, Arthur. Buddha & Buddhism. LC 76-100573. 1975. 11.25x (ISBN 0-89684-372-6). Orient Bk Dist.

Mead, G. R. Fragments of a Faith Forgotten. 2nd ed. 633p. 1906. pap. 43.95 (ISBN 0-88697-011-3). Life Science.

North, Gary. Unconditional Surrender: God's Program for Victory. 2nd ed. LC 82-84385. 280p. 1983. pap. text ed. 9.95 (ISBN 0-939404-06-0). Geneva Ministr.

Oesterley, William O. Jews & Judaism During the Greek Period: The Background of Christianity. LC 74-102580. 1970. Repr. of 1941 ed. 23.00x (ISBN 0-8046-0740-0, Pub. by Kennikat). Assoc Faculty Pr.

Rowland, Christopher. Christian Origins: From Messianic Movement to Christian Religion. LC 85-70241. 448p. (Orig.). 1985. pap. 19.95 (ISBN 0-8066-2173-7, 10-1175). Augsburg.

Steiner, Rudolf. Christianity As Mystical Fact. Tr. of Das Christentum als mystische Tatsache und die Mysterien des Altertums. 195p. 1986. pap. 8.95 (ISBN 0-88010-160-1). Anthroposophic.

CHRISTIANITY–PHILOSOPHY

see also Philosophical Theology; Transcendence of God

Altizer, Thomas J. The Descent into Hell: A Study of the Radical Reversal of the Christain Consciousness. 222p. 1979. pap. 6.95 (ISBN 0-8164-1194-8, HarpR). Har-Row.

Barber, Lucie W. Teaching Christian Values. LC 83-22981. 250p. (Orig.). 1984. pap. 12.95 (ISBN 0-89135-041-1). Religious Educ.

Barrett, J. Edward. Faith in Focus: A Compact Introduction to Christian Theology. LC 81-40167. 130p. (Orig.). 1982. lib. bdg. 24.25 (ISBN 0-8191-1878-8); pap. text ed. 9.50 (ISBN 0-8191-1879-6). U Pr of Amer.

Becon, Thomas. The Principles of Christian Religion. LC 76-57355. (English Experience Ser.: No. 774). 1977. Repr. of 1552 ed. lib. bdg. 14.00 (ISBN 90-221-0774-4). Walter J Johnson.

Biblical Beliefs. 96p. 1982. pap. text ed. 4.95 (ISBN 0-910566-10-0); Perfect bdg. instr's. guide 5.95 (ISBN 0-910566-17-8). Evang Tchr.

Birdsong, Robert E. Adamic Christianity: Questions & Answers, Vol. 1. 1978. pap. 3.75 (ISBN 0-917108-22-1). Sirius Bks.

Blamires, Harry. On Christian Truth. 168p. (Orig.). pap. 4.95 (ISBN 0-89283-130-8). Servant.

Bromiley, G. W., ed. Zwingli & Bullinger. LC 53-1533. (Library of Christian Classics). 360p. 1979. softcover 8.95 (ISBN 0-664-24159-X). Westminster.

Brown, Colin. Philosophy & the Christian Faith. LC 68-58083. (Orig.). 1969. pap. 9.95 (ISBN 0-87784-712-6). Inter-Varsity.

Burbidge, John. Being & Will: An Essay in Philosophical Theology. LC 76-45934. pap. 40.70 (ISBN 0-8357-9484-9, 2013527). Bks Demand UMI.

Calvin, John. Institutes of the Christian Religion, 1536 Edition. Battles, Ford L., tr. from Lat. 464p. 1986. 25.00 (ISBN 0-8028-2319-X). Eerdmans.

Chesterton, G. K. The Everlasting Man. 320p. 1981. Repr. of 1925 ed. lib. bdg. 37.00 (ISBN 0-8495-0855-X). Arden Lib.

Cochrane, Charles N. Christianity & Classical Culture: A Study of Thought & Action from Augustus to Augustine. 1984. 18.00 (ISBN 0-8446-6086-8). Peter Smith.

Conner, T. Doctrina Cristiana. Robleto, Adolfo, tr. Orig. Title: Christian Doctrine. (Span.). 408p. 1981. pap. 7.50 (ISBN 0-311-09012-5). Casa Bautista.

Crouch, Charles E. Principles of New Testament Christianity. 1985. pap. 5.50 (ISBN 0-89137-546-5). Quality Pubns.

Culliton, Joseph T. A Processive World View for Pragmatic Christians. LC 75-3781. 302p. 1975. 13.95 (ISBN 0-8022-2170-X). Philos Lib.

De Voltaire, M. Essays & Criticisms: Containing Letters on the Christian Religion, The Philosophy of History, The Ignorant Philosopher, & the Chinese Catechism. 120p. 1983. Repr. of 1982 ed. lib. bdg. 65.00 (ISBN 0-89987-878-4). Darby Bks.

Eliade, Mircea & Tracy, David, eds. What Is Religion? An Inquiry for Christian Theology, Concilium 136. (New Concilium 1980). 128p. 1980. pap. 5.95 (ISBN 0-8164-2278-8, HarpR). Har-Row.

Evans, C. Stephen. Philosophy of Religion. LC 84-25198. (Contours of Christian Philosophy Ser.). 180p. (Orig.). 1985. pap. 6.95 (ISBN 0-87784-343-0). Inter-Varsity.

Evans, G. Rosemary. Anselm & Talking About God. 1978. 29.95x (ISBN 0-19-826647-2). Oxford U Pr.

Farrer, Austin. Finite & Infinite: A Philosophical Essay. 312p. (Orig.). 1979. pap. 8.95 (ISBN 0-8164-2001-7, HarpR). Har-Row.

Ferguson, Everett. Early Christians Speak. LC 81-68871. 258p. 1981. pap. text ed. 9.95 (ISBN 0-89112-044-0, Bibl Res Pr). Abilene Christ U.

Feuerbach, Ludwig. The Essence of Christianity. Waring, E. Graham & Strothmann, F. W., eds. LC 57-8650. (Milestones of Thought Ser.). 1975. pap. 3.45 (ISBN 0-8044-6145-7). Ungar.

Gaston, Hugh. A Complete Common-Place Book to the Holy Bible; or, a Scriptural Account of the Faith & Practices of Christians: Comprehending a Thorough Arrangement of the Various Texts of Scripture Bearing upon the Doctrines, Duties, & C., of Revealed Religion. 1979. Repr. of 1847 ed. lib. bdg. 15.00 (ISBN 0-8482-4186-X). Norwood Edns.

Gilson, Etienne H. Elements of Christian Philosophy. LC 78-10231. 1978. Repr. of 1960 ed. lib. bdg. 35.00 (ISBN 0-313-20734-8, GIEL). Greenwood.

Gleason, John J., Jr. Consciousness & the Ultimate. LC 80-21397. 192p. (Orig.). 1981. pap. 7.75 (ISBN 0-687-09470-4). Abingdon.

Grau, Joseph A. Morality & the Human Future in the Thought of Teilhard De Chardin: A Critical Study. LC 74-4976. 389p. 1976. 28.50 (ISBN 0-8386-1579-1). Fairleigh Dickinson.

Grisez, Germain. Beyond the New Theism: A Philosophy of Religion. LC 74-27885. 444p. 1975. text ed. 22.95x (ISBN 0-268-00567-2); pap. text ed. 8.95x (ISBN 0-268-00568-0). U of Notre Dame Pr.

Hackett, Stuart C. Reconstruction of the Christian Revelation Claim: A Philosophical & Critical Apologetic. 560p. 1984. pap. 19.95 (ISBN 0-8010-4283-6). Baker Bk.

Hegel, Georg W. The Christian Religion. Lasson, Georg, ed. Hodgson, Peter C., tr. from Ger. LC 79-424. (American Academy of Religion, Texts & Translation Ser.: No. 2). 1979. pap. 10.25_o.s. (ISBN 0-89130-276-X, 010202). Scholars Pr GA.

Hellwig, Monika. Whose Experience Counts in Theological Reflection? LC 82-80331. (Pere Marquette Lecture Ser.). 112p. 1982. 7.95 (ISBN 0-87462-537-8). Marquette.

Hills, A. M. Fundamental Christian Theology. boards 29.95 (ISBN 0-686-27770-8). Schmul Pub Co.

Hodgson, Leonard. Essays in Christian Philosophy. facs. ed. LC 69-17577. (Essay Index Reprint Ser). 1930. 14.00 (ISBN 0-8369-0079-0). Ayer Co Pubs.

Hughes, Gerard J., ed. The Philosophical Assessment of Theology: Essays in Honor of F. C. Copleston. (Orig.). 1987. pap. price not set (ISBN 0-87840-449-X). Georgetown U Pr.

Hunt, Dave. Peace, Prosperity & the Coming Holocaust. LC 82-84069. 224p. 1983. pap. 6.95 (ISBN 0-89081-331-0). Harvest Hse.

Hunter, Charles & Hunter, Frances. Nuggets of Truth. 1975. pap. 3.25 (ISBN 0-917726-01-4). Hunter Bks.

Johnston, William. Christian Mysticism Today. LC 83-48418. 192p. 1984. 12.45i (ISBN 0-06-064202-5, HarpR). Har-Row.

Kalsbeek, L. Contours of a Christian Philosophy. 1975. pap. 9.95x (ISBN 0-88906-000-2). Wedge Pub.

Kelly, J. N. Early Christian Doctrines. rev. ed. LC 58-12933. 1978. pap. 10.95xi (ISBN 0-06-064334-X, RD 233, HarpR). Har-Row.

Kent, John H. The End of the Line? The Development of Christian Theology in the Last Two Centuries. LC 82-7263. 144p. 1982. pap. 6.95 (ISBN 0-8006-1652-9, 1-1652). Fortress.

Kierkegaard, Soren. Concluding Unscientific Postscript. Swenson, D. F. & Lowrie, W., trs. (American-Scandinavian Foundation). 1941. pap. 10.50x (ISBN 0-691-01960-6). Princeton U Pr.

--Fear & Trembling-Repetition, 2 vols. in 1. Hong, Howard V. & Hong, Edna H., eds. Hong, Howard V. & Hong, Edna H., trs. LC 82-9006. (Kierkegaard's Writings Ser.: No. VI). 420p. 1983. 37.00 (ISBN 0-691-07237-X); pap. 7.95 (ISBN 0-691-02026-4). Princeton U Pr.

--Training in Christianity. Lowrie, Walter, tr. (American-Scandinavian Foundation Ser.). 1944. 31.00x (ISBN 0-691-07140-3); pap. 7.95x (ISBN 0-691-01959-2). Princeton U Pr.

McDonald, H. D. The Christian View of Man. LC 81-65471. (Foundations for Faith Ser.). 160p. 1981. pap. 8.95 (ISBN 0-89107-217-9, Crossway Bks). Good News.

McGrath, Alister E. The Making of Modern German Christology: From the Enlightenment to Pannenberg. 240p. 1986. text ed. 34.95x (ISBN 0-631-14512-5). Basil Blackwell.

McInerny, Ralph M., ed. New Themes in Christian Philosophy. LC 68-20439. 1968. 17.95 (ISBN 0-8290-1654-6); pap. text ed. 9.50x (ISBN 0-8290-1606-6). Irvington.

--New Themes in Christian Philosophy. LC 68-20439. 1968. 19.95 (ISBN 0-268-00192-8). U of Notre Dame Pr.

McLean, George F., ed. The Human Person. LC 80-66375. (Proceedings: Vol. 53). 1979. pap. 15.00 (ISBN 0-918090-13-X). Am Cath Philo.

--Immateriality. LC 79-88689. (Proceedings: Vol. 52). 1978. pap. 15.00 (ISBN 0-918090-12-1). Am Cath Philo.

McQuilkin, Robertson. The Great Omission. 96p. 1984. pap. 4.95 (ISBN 0-8010-6167-9). Baker Bk.

Makrakis, Apostolos. The Foundation of Philosophy-a Refutation of Skepticism, the True Jesus Christ, the Science of God & Man; the God of the Christians. Orthodox Christian Educational Society, ed. Lekatsos, Anthony & Cummings, Denver, trs. from Fr. 395p. 1955. 7.50x (ISBN 0-938366-07-6). Orthodox Chr.

--The Orthodox Approach to Philosophy. Orthodox Christian Educational Society, ed. Cummings, Denver, tr. from Hellenic. (The Logos & Holy Spirit in the Unity of Christian Thought Ser.: Vol. 1). 82p. 1977. pap. 3.25x (ISBN 0-938366-06-8). Orthodox Chr.

--The Paramount Doctrines of Orthodoxy-the Tricompositeness of Man, Apology of A. Makrakis & the Trial of A. Makrakis. Orthodox Christian Educational Society, ed. Cummings, Denver, tr. from Hellenic. 904p. 1954. 15.00x (ISBN 0-938366-17-3). Orthodox Chr.

--Philosophy: An Orthodox Christian Understanding. Orthodox Christian Educational Society, ed. Cummings, Denver, tr. from Hellenic. (The Logos & Holy Spirit in the Unity of Christian Thought Ser.: Vol. 5). 279p. 1977. pap. 5.50x (ISBN 0-938366-02-5). Orthodox Chr.

--The Political Philosophy of the Orthodox Church. Orthodox Christian Educational Society, ed. Cummings, Denver, tr. from Hellenic. Orig. Title: The Orthodox Definition of Political Science. 163p. (Orig.). 1965. pap. 4.00x (ISBN 0-938366-11-4). Orthodox Chr.

Maritain, Jacques. Notebooks. Evans, Joseph W., tr. from Fr. LC 83-26743. Tr. of Carnet de Notes. (Illus.). 320p. 1984. 12.95x (ISBN 0-87343-050-6). Magi Bks.

Maritain, Jacques, et al. Wisdom: A Manifesto. 1965. pap. 1.00x (ISBN 0-87343-015-8). Magi Bks.

Masaryk, Thomas G. Masaryk on Thought & Life. LC 78-135840. (Eastern Europe Collection Ser.). 1970. Repr. of 1938 ed. 16.00 (ISBN 0-405-02782-6). Ayer Co Pubs.

Mehl, Roger. Condition of the Christian Philosopher. Kushner, Eva, tr. 221p. 1963. 9.95 (ISBN 0-227-67654-8). Attic Pr.

Niebuhr, Reinhold. Beyond Tragedy: Essays on the Christian Interpretation of History. facsimile ed. LC 76-167397. (Essay Index Reprint Ser). Repr. of 1937 ed. 23.95 (ISBN 0-8369-2437-1). Ayer Co Pubs.

--Beyond Tragedy: Essays on the Christian Interpretation of History. 1937. pap. text ed. 7.95 (ISBN 0-684-16410-8, SL38, ScribT). Scribner.

--Faith & History: A Comparison of Christian & Modern Views of History. (Lib. Rep. Ed.). 1949. 25.00 (ISBN 0-684-15318-1, ScribT). Scribner.

Ouweneel, W. J. What Is the Christian's Hope? 53p. pap. 2.95 (ISBN 0-88172-116-6). Believers Bkshelf.

Pannenberg, Wolfhart. The Idea of God & Human Freedom. LC 73-3165. 224p. 1973. 6.95 (ISBN 0-664-20971-8). Westminster.

Partee, Charles, ed. Calvin & Classical Philosophy 1977. (Studies in the History of Christian Thought: Vol. 14). 30.00 (ISBN 90-04-04839-1). Heinman.

Paul, Leslie A. Meaning of Human Existence. LC 73-148642. 1971. Repr. of 1949 ed. lib. bdg. 22.50x (ISBN 0-8371-6008-1, PAHE). Greenwood.

Pojman, Louis P. The Logic of Subjectivity: Kierkegaard's Philosophy of Religion. LC 83-1053. 174p. 1984. 17.50x (ISBN 0-8173-0166-6). U of Ala Pr.

Rahner, Karl. Theological Investigations, Vol. 22: Humane Society & the Church of Tomorrow. 288p. 1987. 24.50 (ISBN 0-8245-0802-5). Crossroad NY.

Randall, John H. Hellenistic Ways of Deliverance & the Making of the Christian Synthesis. LC 74-137339. 1970. 28.00x (ISBN 0-231-03327-3). Columbia U Pr.

Ratzsch, Del. Philosophy of Science. Evans, C. Stephen, ed. LC 86-178. (Contours of Christian Philosophy Ser.). 128p. (Orig.). 1986. pap. 6.95 (ISBN 0-87784-344-9). Inter-Varsity.

Roper, D. A Christian Philosophy of Culture. Date not set. pap. 3.95x cancelled (ISBN 0-86990-540-6). Radix Bks.

Rosenstock-Huessy, Eugen. I Am an Impure Thinker. 1970. 10.00 (ISBN 0-912148-03-9); pap. 6.95 (ISBN 0-912148-04-7). Argo Bks.

St. Augustine. City of God. Knowles, David, ed. (Classics Ser.). 1984. pap. 12.95 (ISBN 0-14-044426-2). Penguin.

Sayers, Dorothy L. Mind of the Maker. Repr. of 1941 ed. lib. bdg. 22.50x (ISBN 0-8371-3372-6, SAMM). Greenwood.

Schaeffer, Francis. He Is There & He Is Not Silent. 1972. pap. 4.95 (ISBN 0-8423-1413-X). Tyndale.

Schaff, Philip. The Creeds of Christendom, 3 vols. 1983. 75.00 (ISBN 0-8010-8232-3). Baker Bk.

Smedes, Lewis B. Union with Christ: A Biblical View of the New Life in Jesus Christ. rev. ed. Orig. Title: All Things Made New. 208p. 1983. pap. 4.95 (ISBN 0-8028-1963-X). Eerdmans.

Smith, Gerard. Christian Philosophy & Its Future. 144p. 8.95 (ISBN 0-87462-439-8). Marquette.

Smith, Wilbur. Therefore Stand. LC 81-81096. (The Shepherd Illustrated Classics Ser.). (Illus.). 660p. 1982. pap. 9.95 (ISBN 0-87983-260-6). Keats.

Sokolowski, Robert. The God of Faith & Reason: Foundations of Christian Theology. LC 81-19813. 192p. 1982. 15.95 (ISBN 0-268-01006-4); pap. text ed. 6.95 (ISBN 0-268-01007-2). U of Notre Dame Pr.

Teilhard De Chardin, Pierre. Avenir De L'homme. 1959. 21.50 (ISBN 0-685-11021-4). French & Eur.

--Divine Milieu: An Essay on the Interior Life. pap. 6.95 (ISBN 0-06-090487-9, CN487, PL). Har-Row.

--Future of Man. (Orig.). 1969. pap. 7.95 (ISBN 0-06-090496-8, CN496, PL). Har-Row.

--Milieu Divin. (Coll. Livre de vie). 1958. pap. 3.95 (ISBN 0-685-11395-7). French & Eur.

Thomas, George F., ed. Vitality of the Christian Tradition. facsimile ed. LC 70-134143. (Essay Index Reprint Ser). Repr. of 1944 ed. 22.00 (ISBN 0-8369-2378-2). Ayer Co Pubs.

Thompson, James W. The Beginnings of Christian Philosophy: The Epistle to the Hebrews. Vawter, Bruce, ed. LC 81-12295. (Catholic Biblical Quarterly Monograph: Vol. 13). vii, 184p. 1982. 5.50x (ISBN 0-915170-12-4). Catholic Biblical.

Tillich, Paul. Biblical Religion & the Search for Ultimate Reality. LC 55-5149. 1964. pap. 5.00x (ISBN 0-226-80341-4). U of Chicago Pr.

--Protestant Era. abr ed. Adams, James L., tr. 1957. pap. 7.00x (ISBN 0-226-80342-2, P19, Phoen). U of Chicago Pr.

--Theology of Culture. Kimball, Robert C., ed. 1959. pap. 8.95 (ISBN 0-19-500711-5). Oxford U Pr.

Torrance, Thomas F. Divine & Contingent Order. 1981. 29.95x (ISBN 0-19-826658-8). Oxford U Pr.

Trese, Leo. The Faith Explained. rev. ed. 479p. 1984. pap. 7.95 (ISBN 971-117-042-6, Pub. by Sinag-Tala Pubs Philippines). Scepter Pubs.

Troeltsch, Ernst D. Christian Thought, Its History & Application. LC 78-59047. 1985. Repr. of 1923 ed. 23.25 (ISBN 0-88355-719-3). Hyperion Conn.

Underwood, Gary & Underwood, Marylyn. After First Principles. 1984. pap. 4.25 (ISBN 0-89137-710-7). Quality Pubns.

Wallace-Hadrill, D. S. Christian Antioch: A Study of Early Christian Thought in the East. 240p. 1982. 37.50 (ISBN 0-521-23425-5). Cambridge U Pr.

Watson, Philip S. & Lehmann, Helmut T., eds. Luther's Works: Career of the Reformer III, Vol. 33. new ed. LC 55-9893. 1972. 19.95 (ISBN 0-8006-0333-8, 1-333). Fortress.

Wild, John D. Human Freedom & Social Order: An Essay in Christian Philosophy. LC 59-14243. pap. 65.50 (ISBN 0-317-27300-0, 2023468). Bks Demand UMI.

Willis, John R. A History of Christian Thought: From Luther to Marx, Vol. III. LC 76-16237. 1985. 20.00 (ISBN 0-682-40256-7, University). Exposition Pr FL.

Wink, Walter. Unmasking the Powers: The Invisible Forces That Determine Human Existence. LC 85-45480. 224p. 1986. pap. 12.95 (ISBN 0-8006-1902-1, 1-1902). Fortress.

Wolfe, David L. Epistemology. Evans, C. Stephen, ed. (Contours of Christian Philosophy Ser.). 96p. 1982. pap. 5.95 (ISBN 0-87784-340-6). Inter-Varsity.

Yandell, Keith. Christianity & Philosophy. LC 83-14226. (Studies in a Christian World View: Vol. 2). 284p. 1984. pap. 12.95 (ISBN 0-8028-1964-8). Eerdmans.

Young, Warren C. Christian Approach to Philosophy. (Twin Brook Ser.). 1973. pap. 9.95 (ISBN 0-8010-9904-8). Baker Bk.

CHRISTIANITY–POETRY

see Christian Poetry

CHRISTIANITY–POLITY

see Church Polity

CHRISTIANITY–PSYCHOLOGY

Adams, Jay E. Update on Christian Counseling, Vol. 2. 1981. pap. 2.75 (ISBN 0-8010-0180-3). Baker Bk.

Brubaker, J. Omar & Clark, Robert E. Understanding People: Children, Youth, Adults. LC 75-172116. 96p. 1981. pap. text ed. 4.95 (ISBN 0-910566-15-1); Perfect bdg. instr's. guide 5.95 (ISBN 0-910566-25-9). Evang Tchr.

Cohen, Charles. God's Caress: The Psychology of Puritan Religious Experience. 336p. 1986. text ed. 29.95x (ISBN 0-19-503973-4). Oxford U Pr.

Collins, Gary. The Rebuilding of Psychology. 1976. pap. 7.95 (ISBN 0-8423-5315-1). Tyndale.

Collins, Gary R. The Magnificent Mind. 224p. 1985. 9.95 (ISBN 0-8499-0385-8, 0385-8). Word Bks.

Driver, Tom F. Patterns of Grace: Human Experience As Word of God. 214p. 1985. pap. text ed. 9.75 (ISBN 0-8191-4637-4). U Pr of Amer.

Fleck, J. Roland & Carter, John D., eds. Psychology & Christianity: Integrative Readings. LC 81-7911. 400p. (Orig.). 1981. pap. 15.95 (ISBN 0-687-34740-8). Abingdon.

Goldbrunner, Josef. Cure of Mind, Cure of Soul: Depth Psychology & Pastoral Care. 1962. pap. 2.50x (ISBN 0-268-00067-0). U of Notre Dame Pr.

Hammes, John A. Humanistic Psychology: A Christian Interpretation. LC 76-110448. 224p. 1971. 49.50 (ISBN 0-8089-0650-X, 791865). Grune.

Hurding, Roger F. Christian Care & Counseling: A Practical Guide. (Illus.). 128p. (Orig.). 1983. pap. 4.95 (ISBN 0-8192-1321-7). Morehouse.

Koteskey, Ronald L. General Psychology for Christian Counselors. 308p. (Orig.). 1983. pap. 11.95 (ISBN 0-687-14044-7). Abingdon.

McDonagh, John M. Christian Psychology: Toward a New Synthesis. 144p. 1982. 9.95 (ISBN 0-8245-0449-6). Crossroad NY.

Makrakis, Apostolos. Psychology: An Orthodox Christian Perspective. Orthodox Christian Educational Society, ed. Cummings, Denver, tr. from Hellenic. (The Logos & Holy Spirit in the Unity of Christian Thought Ser.: Vol. 2). 151p. 1977. pap. 4.25x (ISBN 0-938366-05-X). Orthodox Chr.

Michael, Chester P. & Norrisey, Marie C. Arise: A Christian Psychology of Love. 162p. (Orig.). 1981. pap. 3.95 (ISBN 0-940136-00-7). Open Door Inc.

Rollins, Wayne G. Jung & the Bible. LC 82-48091. 156p. 1983. pap. 10.95 (ISBN 0-8042-1117-5). John Knox.

Sanford, John A. Kingdom Within: A Study of the Inner Meaning of Jesus' Sayings. LC 77-105548. 1970. Har-Row.

Solignac, Pierre. Christian Neurosis. 256p. 1982. 12.95 (ISBN 0-8245-0108-X). Crossroad NY.

Stein, Murray. Jung's Treatment of Christianity: The Psychotherapy of a Religious Tradition. 2nd ed. LC 85-4739. 194p. 1985. 24.95 (ISBN 0-933029-14-4). Chiron Pubns.

CHRISTIANITY–RENEWAL

see Church Renewal

CHRISTIANITY–UNION BETWEEN CHURCHES

see Christian Union

CHRISTIANITY–EARLY CHURCH, ca. 30-600

Bauer, Walter. Orthodoxy & Heresy in Early Christianity. LC 71-141252. pap. 88.00 (2027876). Bks Demand UMI.

Benko, Stephen. Pagan Rome & the Early Christians. LC 83-48898. 192p. 1985. 20.00x (ISBN 0-253-34286-4). Ind U Pr.

Bouyer, Louis. The Spirituality of the New Testament & the Fathers. (A History of Christian Spirituality Ser.: Vol. 1). 560p. 1982. pap. 13.95 (ISBN 0-8164-2372-5, HarpR). Har-Row.

Bultmann, Rudolf. Primitive Christianity: In Its Contemporary Setting. Fuller, Reginald H., tr. from Ger. LC 80-8043. 256p. 1980. pap. 8.95 (ISBN 0-8006-1408-9, 1-1408). Fortress.

Burkitt, Francis C. Church & Gnosis: A Study of Christian Thought & Speculation in the Second Century. LC 77-84696. (The Morse Lectures: 1931). Repr. of 1932 ed. 26.00 (ISBN 0-404-16104-9). AMS Pr.

Canfield, Leon H. The Early Persecutions of the Christians. LC 68-54259. (Columbia University Studies in the Social Sciences: No. 136). Repr. of 1913 ed. 14.50 (ISBN 0-404-51136-8). AMS Pr.

Chadwick, H., ed. Origen: Contra Celsum. LC 78-73132. 1980. 80.00 (ISBN 0-521-05866-X); pap. 32.50 (ISBN 0-521-29576-9). Cambridge U Pr.

Chadwick, Henry. Early Christian Thoughts & the Classical Tradition: Studies in Justin, Clement & Origan. 182p. 1984. pap. text ed. 13.95x (ISBN 0-19-826673-1). Oxford U Pr.

Clemen, D. D. Primitive Christianity & Its Non-Jewish Sources. 1977. lib. bdg. 59.95 (ISBN 0-8490-2472-2). Gordon Pr.

Cullmann, Oscar. Early Christian Worship. LC 78-6636. 126p. 1978. pap. 6.95 (ISBN 0-664-24220-0). Westminster.

Dengler, Sandy. To Die in the Queen of Cities: A Story of the Christian Courage & Love in the Face of Roman Persecution. 256p. 1986. pap. 6.95 (ISBN 0-8407-5996-7). Nelson.

Gager, John G. Kingdom & Community: The Social World of Early Christianity. 160p. 1975. pap. text ed. write for info. (ISBN 0-13-516203-3). P-H.

Harnack, Adolf. Expansion of Christianity in the First Three Centuries, 2 vols. Moffatt, James, tr. LC 72-4163. (Select Bibliographies Reprint Ser.). 1972. Repr. of 1905 ed. Set. 64.00 (ISBN 0-8369-6882-4). Ayer Co Pubs.

--The Expansion of Christianity in the First Three Centuries, Vol. I. Moffatt, James, ed. LC 72-4163. 494p. Repr. of 1904 ed. 56.00 (ISBN 0-8290-0530-7). Irvington.

Holmberg, Bengt. Paul & Power: The Structure of Authority in the Primitive Church Reflected in the Pauline Epistles. LC 79-8905. 240p. 1980. 3.00 (ISBN 0-8006-0634-5, 1-634). Fortress.

Jehan, L. F. Dictionnaire des Origines du Christianisme. Migne, J. P., ed. (Troisieme et Derniere Encyclopedie Theologique Ser.: Vol. 15). (Fr.). 630p. Repr. of 1856 ed. lib. bdg. 81.00x (ISBN 0-89241-298-4). Caratzas.

John Smith the Platonist. The Excellency & Nobleness of the True Religion. 1984. pap. 4.95 (ISBN 0-916411-35-4, Pub by Alexandrian Pr). Holmes Pub.

Justice, William M. Our Visited Planet. 1978. pap. 4.95 (ISBN 0-918626-03-X). Word Serv.

Knox, W. L. Some Hellenistic Elements in Primitive Christianity. (British Academy, London, Schweich Lectures on Biblical Archaeology Series, 1942). pap. 19.00 (ISBN 0-8115-1284-3). Kraus Repr.

Malherbe, Abraham J. Social Aspects of Early Christianity. 2nd, rev. ed. LC 83-5602. 144p. 1983. pap. 7.95 (ISBN 0-8006-1748-7, 1-1748). Fortress.

Parker, Lois. They of Rome. 128p. 1980. pap. 5.95 (ISBN 0-8127-0308-1). Review & Herald.

Purves, George T. The Testimony of Justin Martyr to Early Christianity. 1977. lib. bdg. 59.95 (ISBN 0-8490-2735-7). Gordon Pr.

Quasten & Plumpe, eds. Epistles of St. Clement of Rome & St. Ignatius of Antioch. Kleist, James A., tr. (Ancient Christian Writers Ser.: No. 1). 1946. 12.95 (ISBN 0-8091-0038-X). Paulist Pr.

Slack, S. B. Early Christianity. 94p. 1914. 0.95 (ISBN 0-317-40436-9). Open Court.

Spence-Jones, H. D. The Early Christians in Rome. 1977. lib. bdg. 56.95 (ISBN 0-8490-1737-8). Gordon Pr.

Thee, Francis C. Julius Africanus & the Early Christian View of Magic. 549p. 1984. lib. bdg. 73.50x (ISBN 3-16-144552-X, Pub. by J C B Mohr BRD). Coronet Bks.

Theissen, Gerd. The Social Setting of Pauline Christianity: Essays on Corinth. Schutz, John H., tr. LC 81-43087. 1982. 19.95 (ISBN 0-8006-0669-8). Fortress.

Thomas, Charles. Christianity in Roman Britain to A. D. 500. (Illus.). 416p. 1981. 40.00x (ISBN 0-520-04392-8). U of Cal Pr.

Tiede, David L. Prophecy & History in Luke-Acts. LC 79-8897. 180p. 1980. 2.00 (ISBN 0-8006-0632-9, 1-632). Fortress.

Tyson, Joseph B. The New Testament & Early Christianity. 480p. 1984. text ed. write for info. (ISBN 0-02-421890-1). Macmillan.

--A Study of Early Christianity. Scott, Kenneth J., ed. (Illus.). 448p. 1973. text ed. write for info. (ISBN 0-02-421900-2). Macmillan.

Weiss, Johannes. Earliest Christianity: A History of the Period A.D. 30-150, 2 vols. Grant, F. C., ed. 24.00 set (ISBN 0-8446-0959-5). Peter Smith.

Workman, Herbert B. Christian Thought to the Reformation. 13.75 (ISBN 0-8369-7127-2, 7961). Ayer Co Pubs.

CHRISTIANITY–MIDDLE AGES, 600-1500

Anderson, Charles S. Augsburg Historical Atlas of Christianity in the Middle Ages & Reformation. LC 67-11723. 1973. pap. 9.95 (ISBN 0-8066-1317-3, 10-0521). Augsburg.

Bellini, Enzo, et al. The Formation of Christian Europe: An Illustrated History of the Church. Drury, John, ed. & tr. (Illus.). 126p. 1980. text ed. 12.95 (ISBN 0-03-056827-7, HarpR). Har-Row.

Bossy, John. Christianity in the West, Fourteen Hundred to Seventeen Hundred. (OPUS). 189p. 1985. 19.95x (ISBN 0-19-219174-8); pap. 7.95 (ISBN 0-19-289162-6). Oxford U Pr.

Corfe, Tom. St. Patrick & Irish Christianity. LC 78-56811. (Cambridge Topic Bks). (Illus.). 1978. PLB 8.95 (ISBN 0-8225-1217-3). Lerner Pubns.

LeClercq, Jean, et al. The Spirituality of the Middle Ages. (A History of Christian Spirituality Ser.: Vol. 2). 616p. 1982. pap. 14.95 (ISBN 0-8164-2373-3, HarpR). Har-Row.

Mellone, Sydney H. Western Christian Thought in the Middle Ages. 1977. lib. bdg. 59.95 (ISBN 0-8490-2816-7). Gordon Pr.

Powicke, Frederick M. The Christian Life in the Middle Ages & Other Essays. LC 78-6723. (Illus.). vi, 176p. Repr. of 1935 ed. lib. bdg. 22.50x (ISBN 0-8371-9304-4, POCL). Greenwood.

Somerville, Robert & Pennington, Kenneth, eds. Law, Church, & Society: Essays in Honor of Stephan Kuttner. LC 76-53199. 1977. 27.95x (ISBN 0-8122-7726-0). U of Pa Pr.

Workman, Herbert B. Christian Thought to the Reformation. 13.75 (ISBN 0-8369-7127-2, 7961). Ayer Co Pubs.

CHRISTIANITY–16TH CENTURY

Bossy, John. Christianity in the West, Fourteen Hundred to Seventeen Hundred. (OPUS). 189p. 1985. 19.95x (ISBN 0-19-219174-8); pap. 7.95 (ISBN 0-19-289162-6). Oxford U Pr.

Dunn, Richard S. Age of Religious Wars, Fifteen Fifty-Nine to Seventeen Fifteen. 2nd ed. (Illus.). 1979. pap. text ed. 7.95x (ISBN 0-393-09021-3). Norton.

Harbison, Elmore H. The Christian Scholar in the Age of the Reformation. LC 83-16511. Repr. of 1983 ed. 46.80 (2027546). Bks Demand UMI.

Tracy, James D. Luther & the Modern State in Germany. (Sixteenth Century Essays & Studies: Vol. VII). 110p. 1986. smyth sewn 25.00 (ISBN 0-940474-07-7). Sixteenth Cent.

Valdes, Alfonso de. Dialogue of Mercury & Charon. Ricapito, Joseph V., tr. from Span. & intro. by. LC 84-48489. 224p. 1986. 25.00x (ISBN 0-253-31700-2). Ind U Pr.

Verkamp, Bernard J. The Indifferent Mean: Adiaphorism in the English Reformation to 1554. Walton, Robert C. & Bebb, Philip N., eds. LC 77-13672. (Studies in the Reformation: Vol. I). 160p. 1978. text ed. 19.95x (ISBN 0-8143-1583-6). Wayne St U Pr.

Workman, Herbert B. Christian Thought to the Reformation. 13.75 (ISBN 0-8369-7127-2, 7961). Ayer Co Pubs.

CHRISTIANITY–17TH CENTURY

Corish, Patrick J. The Catholic Community in the Seventeenth & Eighteenth Centuries. Cosgrove, Art & Collins, Elma, eds. (Helicon History of Ireland). (Illus.). 156p. 1981. 9.95 (ISBN 0-86167-064-7, Pub. by Educ Co Ireland); pap. 6.95 (ISBN 0-86167-063-9). Longwood Pub Group.

Dunn, Richard S. Age of Religious Wars, Fifteen Fifty-Nine to Seventeen Fifteen. 2nd ed. (Illus.). 1979. pap. text ed. 7.95x (ISBN 0-393-09021-3). Norton.

Locke, John. Reasonableness of Christianity & a Discourse of Miracles. Ramsey, I. T., ed. 1958. pap. 6.95x (ISBN 0-8047-0341-8). Stanford U Pr.

Monod, Albert. De Pascal a Chateaubriand: Les Defenseurs Francais de Christianisme de 1670 a 1802. LC 70-170954. (Philosophy Monographs Ser: No. 78). 1916. 32.50 (ISBN 0-8337-4283-3). B Franklin.

CHRISTIANITY–19TH CENTURY

Gifford, Carolyn D. & Dayton, Donald, eds. The American Ideal of the "True Woman" As Reflected in Advice Books to Young Women. Gifford, Carolyn, tr. (Women in American Protestant Religion 1800-1930 Ser.). 431p. 1987. lib. bdg. 60.00 (ISBN 0-8240-0651-8). Garland Pub.

James, Henry, Sr. Moralism & Christianity: Or Man's Experience & Destiny in Three Lectures. LC 72-917. (The Selected Works of Henry James, Sr.: Vol. 4). 192p. 1983. Repr. of 1850 ed. 28.50 (ISBN 0-404-10084-8). AMS Pr.

Kierkegaard, Soren. Attack upon "Christendom". Lowrie, Walter, tr. 1944. pap. 8.50x (ISBN 0-691-01950-9). Princeton U Pr.

Livingston, James C. Matthew Arnold & Christianity: His Religious Prose Writings. 250p. 1986. text ed. 17.95x (ISBN 0-87249-462-4). U of SC Pr.

MacDonell, Robert W. Belle Harris Bennett, Her Life Work. Gifford, Carolyn D. & Dayton, Donald, eds. (Women in American Protestant Religion 1800-1930 Ser.). 297p. 1987. lib. bdg. 40.00 (ISBN 0-8240-0669-0). Garland Pub.

Reardon, Bernard M. Religion in the Age of Romanticism: Studies in Early Nineteenth Century Thought. 320p. 1985. 39.50 (ISBN 0-521-30088-6); pap. 14.95 (ISBN 0-521-31745-2). Cambridge U Pr.

Sexton, Lydia. Autobiography of Lydia Sexton, the Story of Her Life Through a Period of over Seventy-Five Years from 1799 to 1872: Her Early Privations, Adventures, & Reminiscences. Gifford, Carolyn D. & Dayton, Donald, eds. (Women in American Protestant Religion 1800-1930 Ser.). 655p. 1987. lib. bdg. 95.00 (ISBN 0-8240-0673-9). Garland Pub.

Smith, Amanda B. An Autobiography: The Story of the Lord's Dealings with Mrs. Amanda Smith, The Colored Evangelist, Containing an Account of Her Life Work of Faith, & Her Travels in America, England, Ireland, Scotland, India & Africa, as an Independent Missionary. Gifford, Carolyn D. & Dayton, Donald, eds. (Women in American Protestant Religion 1800-1930 Ser.). 506p. 1987. lib. bdg. 70.00 (ISBN 0-8240-0674-7). Garland Pub.

Tolstoy, Leo. The Kingdom of God Is Within You. Garnett, Constance, tr. from Rus. LC 84-10471. xxii, 368p. 1984. 26.95x (ISBN 0-8032-4411-8); pap. 8.50 (ISBN 0-8032-9404-2, BB 897, Bison). U of Nebr Pr.

CHRISTIANITY–20TH CENTURY

see also Death of God Theology

Arsen'ev, Nicolai S. We Beheld His Glory. Ewer, Mary A., tr. LC 76-113545. Repr. of 1936 ed. 18.00 (ISBN 0-404-00407-5). AMS Pr.

Balasuriya, Tissa. Planetary Theology. LC 83-19339. 352p. (Orig.). 1984. pap. 10.95 (ISBN 0-88344-400-3). Orbis Bks.

Barrett, David, ed. World Christian Encyclopedia: A Comparative Survey of Churches & Religions in the Modern World, A. D. 1900 to 2000. (Illus.). 1982. text ed. 165.00x (ISBN 0-19-572435-6). Oxford U Pr.

Barth, Karl. The Word of God & the Word of Man. Horton, Douglas, tr. 1958. 13.50 (ISBN 0-8446-1599-4). Peter Smith.

Bayne, Stephen F. The Optional God. LC 80-80876. 134p. 1980. pap. 6.95 (ISBN 0-8192-1268-7). Morehouse.

Blamires, Harry. The Christian Mind. 1978. pap. 4.95 (ISBN 0-89283-049-2). Servant.

Blewett, George J. The Christian View of the World. 1912. 49.50x (ISBN 0-685-89741-9). Elliots Bks.

Bloesch, Donald G. Crumbling Foundations: Death & Rebirth in an Age of Upheaval. 160p. (Orig.). 1984. pap. text ed. 6.95 (ISBN 0-310-29821-0, 12740P). Zondervan.

Bosanquet, Bernard. What Religion Is. LC 78-12709. 1979. Repr. of 1920 ed. lib. bdg. 22.50x (ISBN 0-313-21202-3, BOWR). Greenwood.

Brunner, Emil. Man in Revolt: A Christian Anthropology. Wyon, Olive, tr. LC 47-2442. 564p. 1979. softcover 9.95 (ISBN 0-664-24245-6). Westminster.

Burton, Ursula & Dolley, Janice. Christian Evolution. 160p. 1984. pap. 9.95 (ISBN 0-85500-204-2). Newcastle Pub.

Bussell, Harold L. Unholy Devotion: Why Cults Lure Christians. 160p. 1983. pap. 5.95 (ISBN 0-310-37251-8, 12388P). Zondervan.

Cardenal, Ernesto. The Gospel in Solentiname, 4 vols. Walsh, Donald D., tr. from Span. LC 76-2681. Orig. Title: El Evangelio en Solentiname. (Orig.). 1982. Vol. 1, 288p. pap. 8.95 (ISBN 0-88344-176-4); Vol. 2, 272p. pap. 8.95 (ISBN 0-88344-175-6); Vol. 3, 320p. pap. 8.95 (ISBN 0-88344-174-8); Vol. 4, 288p. pap. 8.95 (ISBN 0-88344-173-X). Orbis Bks.

Cardwell, Jerry D. A Rumor of Trumpets: The Return of God to Secular Society. 118p. (Orig.). 1985. lib. bdg. 22.00 (ISBN 0-8191-4791-5); pap. text ed. 8.75 (ISBN 0-8191-4792-3). U Pr of Amer.

Carey, Ken. Terra Christa: The Global Spiritual Awakening. Gross, Jim, ed. 256p. (Orig.). 1985. pap. 7.95t (ISBN 0-912949-02-3). Uni-Sun.

Conkin, Paul K. American Christianity in Crisis. LC 81-80738. (Charles Edmondson Historical Lectures Ser.). 48p. (Orig.). 1981. pap. 4.50 (ISBN 0-918954-24-X). Baylor Univ Pr.

Davis, Charles. What Is Living, What Is Dead in Christianity Today. 200p. (Orig.). 1986. 16.95 (ISBN 0-86683-511-3, HarpR). Har-Row.

Dawson, Christopher. Christianity & the New Age. LC 84-29821. 103p. 1985. 10.95 (ISBN 0-918477-02-6); pap. 7.95 (ISBN 0-918477-01-8). Sophia Inst Pr.

Day, Donald & Trohan, Walter. Onward Christian Soldiers Nineteen Twenty to Nineteen Forty-two: Propaganda, Censorship, & One Man's Struggle to Herald the Truth. 1982. lib. bdg. 69.95 (ISBN 0-87700-450-1). Revisionist Pr.

Floyd, Tim. Welcome to the Real World. LC 84-5876. 1984. pap. 5.95 (ISBN 0-8054-5001-7). Broadman.

Gabriel, Ralph H. & Brown, Charles R. Christianity & Modern Thought. 11.00 (ISBN 0-8369-7217-1, 8016). Ayer Co Pubs.

Gallagher, Eric. Christians in Ulster, Nineteen Sixty-Eight to Nineteen Eighty. 1982. 19.95x (ISBN 0-19-213237-7). Oxford U Pr.

Gill, Eric. Christianity & the Machine Age. 59.95 (ISBN 0-87968-864-5). Gordon Pr.

Gritsch, Eric W. Born Againism: Perspectives on a Movement. LC 81-70595. 112p. 1982. pap. 6.95 (ISBN 0-8006-1625-1, 1-1625). Fortress.

Gunton, Colin. Yesterday & Today: Continuites in Christology. 240p. (Orig.). 1983. pap. 7.95 (ISBN 0-8028-1974-5). Eerdmans.

Harakas, S. S. Contemporary Moral Issues Facing the Orthodox Christian. 1982. pap. 6.95 (ISBN 0-937032-24-7). Light&Life Pub Co MN.
Hardon, John A. Christianity in the Twentieth Century. 1978. 5.95 (ISBN 0-8198-0356-1); pap. 2.95 (ISBN 0-8198-0357-X). Dghtrs St Paul.
Hawkin, David. Christ & Modernity: Christian Self-Understanding in a Technological Age. (Studies in Religion: Vol. 17). 200p. 1985. pap. text ed. 12.95x (ISBN 0-88920-193-5, Pub. by Wilfrid Laurier Canada). Humanities.
Horton, Walter M. Realistic Theology. 207p. 1982. Repr. of 1934 ed. lib. bdg. 30.00 (ISBN 0-89760-362-1). Telegraph Bks.
Jerrold, Douglas. Future of Freedom: Notes on Christianity & Politics. facs. ed. LC 68-20311. (Essay Index Reprint Ser). 1938. 18.00 (ISBN 0-8369-0570-9). Ayer Co Pubs.
Jones, E. S., et al. Christian Message for the World Today. facs. ed. LC 77-152163. (Essay Index Reprint Ser). 1934. 17.00 (ISBN 0-8369-2184-4). Ayer Co Pubs.
Keeley, Robin, ed. Christianity in Today's World: An Eerdmans Handbook. (Illus.). 384p. 1985. 29.95 (ISBN 0-8028-3618-6). Eerdmans.
Kurtz, Paul. In Defense of Secular Humanism. LC 83-62188. 273p. 1983. 18.95 (ISBN 0-87975-221-1); pap. 11.95 (ISBN 0-87975-228-9). Prometheus Bks.
Lawrence, M. Therese. Toward a New Christendom. LC 81-84244. (Illus.). 80p. 1982. pap. 5.95 write for info. (ISBN 0-938034-05-7). PAL Pr.
Lewis, C. S. The Screwtape Letters. Bd. with Screwtape Proposes a Toast. 1964-67. 9.95 (ISBN 0-02-571240-3). Macmillan.
--The Screwtape Letters. (Illus.). 144p. 1978. pap. 2.95 (ISBN 0-8007-8336-0, Spire Bks); pap. 4.95 (ISBN 0-8007-5014-4, Power Bks). Revell.
Lutzer, Erwin W. Exploding the Myths That Could Destroy America. (Orig.). 1986. pap. 6.95 (ISBN 0-8024-5692-8). Moody.
Malik, Charles, ed. God & Man in Contemporary Christian Thought. 1970. 16.95x (ISBN 0-8156-6016-2, Am U Beirut). Syracuse U Pr.
Marchant, James. The Reunion of Christendom: A Survey of Present Position. 329p. 1980. Repr. of 1929 ed. lib. bdg. 30.00 (ISBN 0-8495-3771-1). Arden Lib.
Meland, Bernard E. Realities of Faith. 1962. pap. 2.25x (ISBN 0-912182-03-2). Seminary Co-Op.
Menard, Eusebe. At All Times, in Every Age. 1977. 4.95 (ISBN 0-8199-0663-8). Franciscan Herald.
Metz, Johann B. The Emergent Church: The Future of Christianity in a Post-Bourgeois World. 160p. 1981. 10.95 (ISBN 0-8245-0036-9). Crossroad NY.
Miller, Keith. The Dream. 128p. 1985. 8.95 (ISBN 0-8499-0462-5, 0462-5). Word Bks.
Morris, Henry M. Evolution & the Modern Christian. 1967. pap. 2.95 (ISBN 0-87552-337-4). Presby & Reformed.
Muggeridge, Malcolm. The End of Christendom. 1980. pap. 2.95 (ISBN 0-8028-1837-4). Eerdmans.
Naude, C. F. & Solle, Dorothee. Hope for Faith: A Conversation. 48p. (Orig.). 1986. pap. 3.95. Eerdmans.
Niebuhr, H. Richard. Christ & Culture. 17.00 (ISBN 0-8446-2658-9). Peter Smith.
Noll, Mark A., et al. The Search for Christian America. LC 83-71239. 168p. 1983. pap. 6.95 (ISBN 0-89107-285-3, Crossway Bks). Good News.
Oliver, Revilo P. Christianity & the Survival of the West. 1984. lib. bdg. 79.95 (ISBN 0-87700-599-0). Revisionist Pr.
Parrish-Harra, Carol W. Messengers of Hope. 1983. pap. 7.95 (ISBN 0-87613-079-1). New Age.
Randall, Margaret. Christians in the Nicaraguan Revolution. (Illus.). 240p. (Orig.). 1984. 15.95 (ISBN 0-919573-14-2, Pub. by New Star Bks BC); pap. 7.95 (ISBN 0-919573-15-0, Pub. by New Star Bks BC). Left Bank.
Royce, Josiah. Problem of Christianity. LC 68-16716. 1968. 25.00x (ISBN 0-226-73058-1). U of Chicago Pr.
Schaeffer, Francis A. God Who Is There. LC 68-29304. 1968. pap. 7.95 (ISBN 0-87784-711-8). Inter-Varsity.
Scherer, James A. Global Living Here & Now. 1974. pap. 2.25 (ISBN 0-377-00003-5). Friend Pr.
Snyder, Howard A. & Runyon, Daniel V. Foresight: Ten Major Trends That Will Dramatically Affect the Future of Christians & the Church. 176p. 1986. 12.95 (ISBN 0-8407-5531-7). Nelson.
Sperry, Willard L. Signs of These Times: The Ayer Lectures of the Colgate Rochester Divinity School for 1929. facs. ed. LC 68-29247. (Essay Index Reprint Ser). 1968. Repr. of 1929 ed. 15.00 (ISBN 0-8369-0897-X). Ayer Co Pubs.
Stein, Murray. Jung's Treatment of Christianity: The Psychotherapy of a Religious Tradition. 2nd ed. LC 85-4739. 194p. 1985. 24.95 (ISBN 0-933029-14-4). Chiron Pubns.
Sussman, Irving & Sussman, Cornelia. This Train Is Bound for Glory. 1969. 4.95 (ISBN 0-8199-0154-7, L38874). Franciscan Herald.
Trueblood, Elton. Company of the Committed. LC 61-12834. 114p. (Orig.). 1980. pap. 5.95 (ISBN 0-06-068551-4, RD 317, HarpR). Har-Row.
Wainwright, Geoffrey. The Ecumenical Moment: Crisis & Opportunity for the Church. 272p. (Orig.). 1983. pap. 8.95 (ISBN 0-8028-1979-6). Eerdmans.
Wallace, H. A., et al. Christian Bases of World Order. facsimile ed. LC 75-134068. (Essay Index Reprint Ser). (Merrick Lectures, 1943). Repr. of 1943 ed. 19.00 (ISBN 0-8369-2490-8). Ayer Co Pubs.
Wicker, Brian. Toward a Contemporary Christianity. 1967. 21.95 (ISBN 0-268-00282-7). U of Notre Dame Pr.
Wogaman, J. Philip. Faith & Fragmentation: Christianity for a New Age. LC 85-47712. 208p. 1985. pap. 10.95 (ISBN 0-8006-1864-5, 1-1864). Fortress.

CHRISTIANITY–20TH CENTURY–ADDRESSES, ESSAYS, LECTURES

Bockle, Franz. War, Poverty, Freedom: The Christian Response. (Concilium Ser.: Vol. 15). 7.95 (ISBN 0-8091-0154-8). Paulist Pr.
Duquoc, Christian, ed. Spirituality in Church & World. LC 65-28868. (Concilium Ser.: Vol. 9). 174p. 7.95 (ISBN 0-8091-0139-4). Paulist Pr.
Fey, Harold E. & Frakes, Margaret, eds. The Christian Century Reader: Representative Articles, Editorials, & Poems Selected from More Than Fifty Years of the Christian Century. LC 72-331. (Essay Index Reprint Ser.). Repr. of 1962 ed. 24.50 (ISBN 0-8369-2786-9). Ayer Co Pubs.
Merton, Thomas. Seeds of Destruction. 1983. 14.00 (ISBN 0-8446-5988-6). Peter Smith.
Miller, Samuel H. Religion in a Technical Age. LC 68-17628. 1968. 8.95x (ISBN 0-674-75650-9). Harvard U Pr.
Ramsey, A. Michael & Suenens, Leon J. Future of the Christian Church. (Orig.). 1970. pap. 3.95 (ISBN 0-8192-1124-9). Morehouse.
Tillich, Paul. The Future of Religions. Brauer, Jerald C., ed. LC 76-7566. 1976. Repr. of 1966 ed. lib. bdg. 22.50x (ISBN 0-8371-8861-X, TIFR). Greenwood.

CHRISTIANITY AND ANTISEMITISM

Abel, Ernest L. The Roots of Anti-Semitism. LC 73-8286. 264p. 1975. 25.00 (ISBN 0-8386-1406-X). Fairleigh Dickinson.
Braham, Randolph L., ed. The Origins of the Holocaust: Christian Anti-Semitism. (East European Monographs: No. 204). 100p. 1986. 18.00 (ISBN 0-88033-953-5). East Eur Quarterly.
Carr, Joseph J. Christian Heroes of the Holocaust. LC 85-70538. 1985. pap. 3.50 (ISBN 0-88270-582-2). Bridge Pub.
Coffin, Henry S. What Men Are Asking. facs. ed. LC 70-117770. (Essay Index Reprint Ser). 1933. 12.50 (ISBN 0-8369-1791-X). Ayer Co Pubs.
Cohen, Jeremy. The Friars & the Jews: The Evolution of Medieval Anti-Judaism. LC 81-15210. 304p. 1984. pap. 10.95x (ISBN 0-8014-9266-1). Cornell U Pr.
Davies, Alan T., ed. Antisemitism & the Foundations of Christianity. LC 79-65620. 276p. 1979. pap. 8.95 (ISBN 0-8091-2219-7). Paulist Pr.
Glock, Charles Y. & Stark, Rodney. Christian Beliefs & Anti-Semitism. LC 78-31750. (Univ. of California Five-Year Study of Anti-Semitism). 1979. Repr. of 1966 ed. lib. bdg. 24.75x (ISBN 0-313-20969-3, GLCB). Greenwood.
Hay, Malcolm. The Roots of Christian Anti-Semitism. 356p. 10.00 (ISBN 0-686-95112-3). ADL.
Katz, Jacob. Exclusiveness & Tolerance: Studies in Jewish-Gentile Relations in Medieval & Modern Times. LC 80-12181. (Scripta Judaica: No. III). xv, 200p. 1980. Repr. of 1961 ed. lib. bdg. 24.75x (ISBN 0-313-22387-4, KAEX). Greenwood.
Maritain, Jacques. A Christian Looks at the Jewish Question. LC 73-2216. (The Jewish People; History, Religion, Literature Ser.). Repr. of 1939 ed. 17.00 (ISBN 0-405-05280-4). Ayer Co Pubs.
Yaseen, Leonard C. The Jesus Connection: To Triumph over Anti-Semitism. (Illus.). 192p. 1985. pap. 9.95 (ISBN 0-8245-0718-5). Crossroad NY.

CHRISTIANITY AND ATHEISM

see also Communism and Christianity

Akerley, Ben E. The X-Rated Bible. pap. 8.00. Am Atheist.
Dilling, Elizabeth. Plot Against Christianity. 310p. 12.00 (ISBN 0-913022-33-0). Angriff Pr.
Jackson, John G. Christianity Before Christ. 238p. (Orig.). 1985. pap. 7.00 (ISBN 0-910309-20-5). Am Atheist.
MacIntyre, Alasdair & Ricoeur, Paul. The Religious Significance of Atheism. LC 68-28398. (Bampton Lectures in America: No. 18). 98p. 1986. pap. 10.00 (ISBN 0-231-06367-9). Columbia U Pr.
Morey, Robert. The New Atheism & the Erosion of Freedom. 180p. (Orig.). 1986. pap. 5.95 (ISBN 0-87123-889-6, 210889). Bethany Hse.
Perez-Esclarin, Antonio. Atheism & Liberation. Drury, John, tr. from Sp. LC 78-731. Orig. Title: Ateismo Y Liberacion. 205p. (Orig.). 1978. pap. 1.99 (ISBN 0-88344-020-2). Orbis Bks.
Warren, Thomas B. Have Atheists Proved There Is No God? 1974. 8.00 (ISBN 0-934916-33-0). Natl Christian Pr.

CHRISTIANITY AND COMMUNISM

see Communism and Christianity

CHRISTIANITY AND CULTURE

Ackland, Donald F. Broadman Comments: October-December, 1986. 1986. pap. 2.50 (ISBN 0-8054-1499-1). Broadman.
Alcorn, Randy C. Christians in the Wake of the Sexual Revolution: Recovering Our Sexual Sanity. LC 85-4959. (Critical Concern Ser.). 1985. 13.95 (ISBN 0-88070-095-5). Multnomah.
Baer, Mervin J. El Hogar Cristiano. (Span.). pap. 1.75 (ISBN 0-686-32324-6). Rod & Staff.
Brunner, Heinrich E. Christianity & Civilisation, 2 vols. in one. LC 77-27182. (Gifford Lectures: 1947-48). Repr. of 1949 ed. 35.00 (ISBN 0-404-60530-3). AMS Pr.
Burkholder, J. R. & Redekop, Calvin, eds. Kingdom, Cross, & Community. LC 76-29663. 312p. 1976. 14.95 (ISBN 0-317-37847-3). Herald Pr.
Bussell, Harold L. Unholy Devotion: Why Cults Lure Christians. 160p. 1983. pap. 5.95 (ISBN 0-310-37251-8, 12388P). Zondervan.
Cataldo, Peter J., ed. The Dynamic Character of Christian Culture: Essays on Dawsonian Themes. 242p. (Orig.). 1984. lib. bdg. 26.00 (ISBN 0-8191-3959-9, Soc Christ Cult); pap. text ed. 11.75 (ISBN 0-8191-3960-2). U Pr of Amer.
Clapp, Steve. Christian Education As Evangelism. 154p. (Orig.). 1982. pap. 9.00 (ISBN 0-914527-11-8). C-Four Res.
Cochrane, Charles N. Christianity & Classical Culture: A Study of Thought & Action from Augustus to Augustine. 1957. pap. 10.95 (ISBN 0-19-500207-5). Oxford U Pr.
Contemporary Culture & Christianity. (Synthesis Ser). 1978. pap. 1.50 (ISBN 0-8199-0741-3). Franciscan Herald.
Dudley, Roger L. The World Love It or Leave It. (Anchor Ser.). 80p. (Orig.). 1987. pap. 5.95 (ISBN 0-8163-0665-6). Pacific Pr Pub Assn.
Flake, Carol. Redemptorama: Culture, Politics & the New Evangelicalism. (Nonfiction Ser.). 320p. 1985. pap. 7.95 (ISBN 0-14-008265-4). Penguin.
Forell, George W. The Proclemation of the Gospel in a Pluralistic World: Essays on Christianity & Culture. LC 73-79354. pap. 36.00 (2026865). Bks Demand UMI.
Gaebelein, Frank E. The Christian, the Arts, & Truth: Regaining the Vision of Greatness. Lockerbie, D. Bruce, frwd. by. LC 85-9005. (Critical Concern Bks.). 1985. 12.95 (ISBN 0-88070-114-5). Multnomah.
Gallup, George, Jr. & O'Connell, George. Who Do Americans Say That I Am? LC 85-26383. 130p. (Orig.). 1986. pap. 10.95 (ISBN 0-664-24685-0). Westminster.
Gardella, Peter. Innocent Ecstasy: How Christianity Gave America an Ethic of Sexual Pleasure. LC 84-27253. (Illus.). 1985. 17.95 (ISBN 0-19-503612-3). Oxford U Pr.
Gwynne, Walker. The Christian Year; Its Purpose & Its History. LC 74-89269. xiv, 143p. 1972. Repr. of 1917 ed. 43.00x (ISBN 0-8103-3814-9). Gale.
Handy, Robert T. A Christian America: Protestant Hopes & Historical Realities. 2nd & enl. ed. 1983. 27.00x (ISBN 0-19-503386-8); pap. 10.95x (ISBN 0-19-503387-6). Oxford U Pr.
Hart, H. The Challenge of Our Age. LC 68-9843. 1974. pap. 3.25 (ISBN 0-686-11982-7). Wedge Pub.
Hayes, Carlton J. Christianity & Western Civilization. LC 83-5680. vii, 63p. 1983. Repr. of 1954 ed. lib. bdg. 22.50x (ISBN 0-313-23962-2, HACW). Greenwood.
Hopler, Thom. A World of Difference: Following Christ Beyond Your Cultural Walls. LC 81-57818. 192p. (Orig.). 1981. pap. 7.95 (ISBN 0-87784-747-9); pap. 1.95 study guide (ISBN 0-87784-802-5). Inter-Varsity.
Kraft, Charles H. Christianity in Culture. LC 78-13736. 463p. (Orig.). 1979. 14.95 (ISBN 0-88344-075-X). Orbis Bks.
Kraft, Charles H. & Wisley, Thomas N., eds. Readings in Dynamic Indigeneity. LC 79-24160. (Applied Cultural Anthropology Ser). 1979. pap. 12.95x (ISBN 0-87808-739-7). William Carey Lib.
Mayers, Marvin. Christianity Confronts Culture. (Contemporary Evangelical Perspectives Ser.). 10.95 (ISBN 0-310-28891-6, 10230P). Zondervan.
Nida, Eugene A. Religion Across Cultures. LC 68-11733. (Applied Cultural Anthropology Ser). 1979. pap. text ed. 3.95x (ISBN 0-87808-738-9). William Carey Lib.
Niebuhr, H. Richard. Christ & Culture. pap. 7.95x (ISBN 0-06-130003-9, TB3, Torch). Har-Row.
Nietzsche, Friedrich. The Antichrist & Twilight of the Gods. 1974. 100.00 (ISBN 0-87968-210-8). Gordon Pr.
Rupp, George. Culture-Protestantism: German Liberal Theology at the Turn of the Twentieth Century. LC 77-13763. (American Academy of Religion. Studies in Religion: No. 15). 1977. pap. 8.95 (ISBN 0-89130-197-6, 010015). Scholars Pr GA.
Schriner, Chris & Mauck, Sue I. Confident Living: Practical Psychology & the Christian Faith. (Illus.). 101p. (Orig.). 1982. pap. text ed. 6.00 (ISBN 0-914527-17-7). C-Four Res.
Stambaugh, John E. & Balch, David L. The New Testament in Its Social Environment. LC 85-15516. (Library of Early Christianity: Vol. 2). (Illus.). 208p. 1986. 16.95 (ISBN 0-664-21906-3). Westminster.
Tillich, Paul. Theology of Culture. Kimball, Robert C., ed. 1959. pap. 8.95 (ISBN 0-19-500711-5). Oxford U Pr.
Whiteside, Elena. God's Word in Culture. 233p. 1983. pap. 4.95 (ISBN 0-910068-51-8). Am Christian.

CHRISTIANITY AND DEMOCRACY

De Jong, Norman. Christianity & Democracy. 1978. pap. 4.95 (ISBN 0-934532-08-7). Presby & Reformed.
Nash, Ronald H., ed. Social Justice & the Christian Church. 1986. pap. 7.95 (ISBN 0-8010-6746-4). Baker Bk.
Neuhaus, Richard J. The Naked Public Square: Religion & Democracy in America. 280p. 1986. pap. 8.95 (ISBN 0-8028-0080-7). Eerdmans.
Robison, James & Cox, Jim. Save America to Save the World. 1980. pap. 1.95 (ISBN 0-8423-5823-4). Tyndale.
White, Ronald C., Jr., et al, eds. American Christianity: A Case Approach. 208p. (Orig.). 1986. pap. text ed. 11.95 (ISBN 0-8028-0241-9). Eerdmans.

CHRISTIANITY AND ECONOMICS

see also Church and Labor; Communism and Christianity; Socialism, Christian; Sociology, Christian; Stewardship, Christian

Ballou, Adin. Practical Christian Socialism, 2 vols. 655p. 1985. Repr. of 1854 ed. Set. lib. bdg. 69.00 (ISBN 0-932051-86-3, Pub. by Am Repr Serv). Am Biog Serv.
Bennett, John C., et al. Christian Values & Economic Life. facs. ed. LC 71-99624. (Essay Index Reprint Ser.). 1954. 21.50 (ISBN 0-8369-1559-3). Ayer Co Pubs.
Byers, David, ed. Justice in the Marketplace: Collected Statements of the Vatican & the United States Catholic Bishops on Economic Policy, 1891-1984. 554p. 1985. pap. 14.95 (ISBN 1-55586-933-5). US Catholic.
Chafuen, Alejandro A. Christians for Freedom: Late-Scholastic Economics. LC 86-80784. 200p. 1986. pap. 12.95 (ISBN 0-89870-110-4). Ignatius Pr.
Childs, Marquis W. & Cater, Douglass. Ethics in a Business Society. LC 73-7073. 191p. 1973. Repr. of 1954 ed. lib. bdg. 22.50x (ISBN 0-8371-6905-4, CHBS). Greenwood.
Davis, John J. Your Wealth in God's World. 144p. 1984. pap. 4.95 (ISBN 0-87552-219-X). Presby & Reformed.
Ellison, Marvin M. The Center Cannot Hold: The Search for a Global Economy of Justice. LC 82-23795. 330p. (Orig.). 1983. lib. bdg. 31.00 (ISBN 0-8191-2963-1); pap. text ed. 15.50 (ISBN 0-8191-2964-X). U Pr of Amer.
Everett, J. Rutherford. Religion in Economics: A Study of John B. Clark, Richard T. Ely & Simon N. Patten. 1982. Repr. of 1946 ed. lib. bdg. 22.50x (ISBN 0-87991-866-7). Porcupine Pr.
Fanfani, Amintore. Catholicism, Protestantism, & Capitalism. LC 84-40363. 272p. 1984. pap. text ed. 8.95 (ISBN 0-268-00752-7, 85-07527). U of Notre Dame Pr.
Finn, Daniel R. & Pemberton, Prentiss L. Toward a Christian Economic Ethic: Stewardship & Social Power. LC 83-25409. 266p. 1985. pap. 10.95 (ISBN 0-86683-876-7, 7919, HarpR). Har-Row.
Griffiths, Brian. The Creation of Wealth. LC 85-5210. 160p. 1985. pap. 6.95 (ISBN 0-87784-566-2). Inter-Varsity.
Hallam, Arthur F. Christian Capitalism. 182p. (Orig.). 1981. pap. 14.95 (ISBN 0-938770-00-4). Capitalist Pr OH.

Jovah. The Lord's Hidden Message in Money. 1986. 5.75 (ISBN 0-8062-2404-5). Carlton.
Loring, Marion. A Christian View of Economics. 80p. 1983. 5.50 (ISBN 0-682-49903-X). Exposition Pr FL.
Lutz, Charles P., ed. God, Goods & the Common Good: Eleven Perspectives on Economic Justice in Dialog with the Roman Catholic Bishops' Pastoral Letter. 160p. (Orig.). 1987. pap. 9.95 (ISBN 0-8066-2286-5, 10-2563). Augsburg.
McCan, Robert L. World Economy & World Hunger: The Response of the Churches. 119p. 1982. 16.00 (ISBN 0-89093-497-5); pap. 5.00. U Pubns Amer.
McKee, Arnold F. Economics & the Christian Mind. 1987. 10.95 (ISBN 0-533-07175-5). Vantage.
Mullin, Redmond. The Wealth of Christians. LC 84-7262. 256p. (Orig.). 1984. pap. 10.95 (ISBN 0-88344-709-6). Orbis Bks.
Munby, Denys L. God & the Rich Society: A Study of Christians in a World of Abundance. LC 85-21886. v, 218p. 1985. Repr. of 1961 ed. lib. bdg. 39.75x (ISBN 0-313-24925-3, MGRS). Greenwood.
National Conference of Catholic Bishops. Building Economic Justice: The Bishops Pastoral Letter & Tools for Action. 112p. (Orig.). 1986. pap. 7.95 (ISBN 1-55586-122-9). US Catholic.
--Economic Justice for All: Pastoral Letter in Catholic Social Teaching & U. S. Economy. 192p. 1986. pap. 2.95 (ISBN 1-55586-101-6). US Catholic.
Nieman, Charles. God's Plan for Your Financial Success. 230p. (Orig.). 1985. pap. text ed. 6.95 (ISBN 0-914307-34-7). Word Faith.
Obenhaus, Victor. Ethics for an Industrial Age: A Christian Inquiry. LC 73-15317. 338p. 1975. Repr. of 1965 ed. lib. bdg. 22.50x (ISBN 0-8371-7189-X, OBIA). Greenwood.
Oden, Thomas C. Conscience & Dividends: Church & the Multinationals. LC 85-1581. 192p. 1985. 15.00 (ISBN 0-89633-089-3); pap. 9.00 (ISBN 0-89633-090-7). Ethics & Public Policy.
Sappington, Roger E. The Brethren in Industrial America. 512p. 1985. 24.95 (ISBN 0-87178-111-5). Brethren.
Smith, Jackie M. Women, Faith, & Economic Justice. (Illus.). 80p. (Orig.). 1985. pap. 5.95 (ISBN 0-664-24600-1). Westminster.
Sproul, R. C., Jr. Money Matters. 192p. (Orig.). 1985. pap. 5.95 (ISBN 0-8423-4540-X). Tyndale.
Stumme, Wayne. Christians & the Many Faces of Marxism. LC 84-10980. 176p. (Orig.). 1984. pap. 8.95 (ISBN 0-8066-2087-0, 10-1195). Augsburg.
Tawney, Richard H. Religion & the Rise of Capitalism. 12.75 (ISBN 0-8446-1446-7). Peter Smith.
Vickers, Douglas. Economics & Man: Prelude to a Christian Critique. 1976. pap. 6.95 (ISBN 0-934532-27-3). Presby & Reformed.
Viner, Jacob. Religious Thought & Economic Society: Four Chapters of an Unfinished Work. Melitz, Jacques & Winch, Donald, eds. LC 77-93857. 1978. 19.75 (ISBN 0-8223-0398-1). Duke.
Weber, Max. Protestant Ethic & the Spirit of Capitalism. rev. ed. 1977. pap. 8.95 (ISBN 0-684-16489-2, ScribT). Scribner.

CHRISTIANITY AND INTERNATIONAL AFFAIRS

Bolton, J. Andrew. Restoring Persons in World Community. 1986. pap. 9.00 (ISBN 0-8309-0461-1). Herald Hse.
Butterfield, Herbert. International Conflict in the Twentieth Century. LC 74-6777. 123p. 1974. Repr. of 1960 ed. lib. bdg. 65.00 (ISBN 0-8371-7569-0, BUIC). Greenwood.
Byabazaire, Deogratias M. The Contribution of the Christian Churches to the Development of Western Uganda 1894-1974: Theology. (European University Studies: Ser. 23, Vol. 112). 198p. 1979. pap. 21.95 (ISBN 3-261-02553-0). P Lang Pubs.
Canham, Erwin D. Ethics of United States Foreign Relations. LC 66-14031. 101p. 1966. 6.00x (ISBN 0-8262-0044-3). U of Mo Pr.
DH - TE Research Studies. The Vatican & the Third World: Diplomacy & the Future. LC 75-14400. 1975. pap. 3.50 (ISBN 0-686-11971-1). Bks Intl DH-TE.
Epstein, Lawrence J. Zion's Call: Christian Contributions to the Origins & Development of Israel. LC 84-15184. 176p. (Orig.). 1984. lib. bdg. 23.00 (ISBN 0-8191-4185-2); pap. text ed. 11.25 (ISBN 0-8191-4186-0). U Pr of Amer.
Hatfield, Mark, et al. What about the Russians? A Christian Approach to US-Soviet Conflict. Brown, Dale W., ed. 144p. 1984. pap. 6.95 (ISBN 0-87178-751-2). Brethren.
Thomas, Gordon & Morgan-Witts, Max. Averting Armageddon. LC 84-10101. 360p. 1984. 18.95 (ISBN 0-385-18985-0). Doubleday.
Vanderhaar, Gerard A. Christians & Nonviolence in the Nuclear Age: Scripture, the Arms Race & You. 128p. 1982. pap. 5.95 (ISBN 0-89622-162-8). Twenty-Third.
White, John W. Arming for Armageddon. 218p. pap. 5.95 (ISBN 0-88062-109-5). Mott Media.

CHRISTIANITY AND LAW

see Religion and Law

CHRISTIANITY AND LITERATURE

see also Christian Literature; Christianity in Literature

Cary, Norman R. Christian Criticism in the Twentieth Century. (National University Publications Literary Criticism Ser.). 1976. 17.95x (ISBN 0-8046-9104-5, Pub. by Kennikat). Assoc Faculty Pr.
Coursen, Herbert R., Jr. Christian Ritual & the World of Shakespeare's Tragedies. 441p. 1976. 32.50 (ISBN 0-8387-1518-4). Bucknell U Pr.
Edwards, Michael. Towards a Christian Poetics. 260p. 13.95x (ISBN 0-8028-3596-1). Eerdmans.
Gaebelein, Frank E. The Christian, the Arts, & Truth: Regaining the Vision of Greatness. Lockerbie, D. Bruce, frwd. by. LC 85-9005. (Critical Concern Bks.). 1985. 12.95 (ISBN 0-88070-114-5). Multnomah.
Lawrence, Irene. Linguistics & Theology: The Significance of Noam Chomsky for Theological Construction. LC 80-24210. (ATLA Monograph: No. 16). 214p. 1980. 17.50 (ISBN 0-8108-1347-5). Scarecrow.
Mallard, William. The Reflection of Theology in Literature: A Case Study in Theology & Culture. LC 76-14036. (Trinity University Monograph Series in Religion). 271p. 1977. 10.00 (ISBN 0-911536-64-7). Trinity U Pr.
Martin, John D. & Showalter, Lester E. Perspectives of Truth in Literature. (Christian Day School Ser.). 1982. 15.05 (ISBN 0-87813-921-4); tchr's. guide 10.95x (ISBN 0-87813-922-2). Christian Light.
Ryken, Leland. Culture in Christian Perspective: A Door to Understanding & Enjoying the Arts. LC 86-1442. 1986. 13.95 (ISBN 0-88070-115-3). Multnomah.
Sinfield, Alan. Literature in Protestant England: 1560-1660. LC 82-18408. 168p. 1983. text ed. 26.50x (ISBN 0-389-20341-6, 07185). B&N Imports.

CHRISTIANITY AND MEDICINE

see Medicine and Religion

CHRISTIANITY AND OTHER RELIGIONS

see also Paganism

Anderson, Norman. Christianity & World Religions. rev. ed. LC 84-115291. 192p. 1984. pap. 9.95 (ISBN 0-87784-981-1). Inter-Varsity.
Andrews, Samuel J. Christianity & Anti-Christianity in Their Final Conflict. 1982. lib. bdg. 15.00 (ISBN 0-86524-084-1, 9804). Klock & Klock.
Angus, S. The Environment of Early Christianity. 1977. lib. bdg. 59.95 (ISBN 0-8490-1778-5). Gordon Pr.
Angus, Samuel. The Environment of Early Christianity. facsimile ed. LC 75-157322. (Select Bibliographies Reprint Ser). Repr. of 1915 ed. 17.00 (ISBN 0-8369-5781-4). Ayer Co Pubs.
--The Mystery Religions. LC 74-12637. 360p. 1975. pap. 6.95 (ISBN 0-486-23124-0). Dover.
--The Mystery Religions & Christianity. 1977. lib. bdg. 59.95 (ISBN 0-8490-2314-9). Gordon Pr.
--The Religious Quests of the Graeco-Roman World: A Study in the Historical Background of Early Christianity. LC 66-30791. 1929. 18.00 (ISBN 0-8196-0196-9). Biblo.
Ariarajah, Wesley & Thomas, T. K. The Way of Dialogue: Christians & People of Other Faiths. 40p. (Orig.). 1986. pap. 4.50 (ISBN 0-377-00164-3). Friend Pr.
Bavinck, Johan H. The Church Between Temple & Mosque: A Study of the Relationship Between the Christian Faith & Other Religions. LC 66-22946. pap. 51.50 (ISBN 0-317-30133-0, 2025316). Bks Demand UMI.
Bellah, Robert & Greenspahn, Frederick. Uncivil Religion: Interreligious Hostility in America. 256p. 1986. 16.95. Crossroad NY.
Caird, Edward. Evolution of Religion, 2 Vols. in 1. LC 1-17697. (Gifford Lectures 1890-1892). 1968. Repr. of 1893 ed. 46.00 (ISBN 0-527-14120-8). Kraus Repr.
Camps, Arnulf. Partners in Dialogue: Christianity & Other World Religions. Drury, John, tr. from Dutch. LC 82-18798. Tr. of Christendom en godsdidienstein der wereld. 272p. (Orig.). 1983. pap. 10.95 (ISBN 0-88344-378-3). Orbis Bks.
Carmody, Denise L. What Are They Saying about Non-Christian Faith? (WATSA Ser.). 96p. (Orig.). 1982. pap. 4.95 (ISBN 0-8091-2432-7). Paulist Pr.
Carpenter, Edward. Pagan & Christian Creeds. 59.95 (ISBN 0-8490-0794-1). Gordon Pr.
Carpenter, George W. Encounter of the Faiths. (Orig.). 1967. pap. 1.75 (ISBN 0-377-37001-0). Friend Pr.
Case, Shirley J. Experience with the Supernatural in Early Christian Times. LC 75-174851. Repr. of 1929 ed. 26.50 (ISBN 0-405-08345-9, Blom Pubns). Ayer Co Pubs.
Charles, R. H., ed. & The Book of Enoch: Or One Enoch. 2nd ed. 331p. pap. 16.95 (ISBN 0-88697-009-1). Life Science.
Ching, Julia. Confucianism & Christianity. LC 77-75962. 234p. 1978. 16.95x (ISBN 0-87011-303-8). Kodansha.
Clasper, Paul. Eastern Paths & the Christian Way. LC 80-13730. 128p. (Orig.). 1980. pap. 5.95 (ISBN 0-88344-100-4). Orbis Bks.
Copeland, E. L. El Cristianismo y Otras Religiones. Mora, Abdias A., tr. Orig. Title: Christianity & World Religious. (Span., Illus.). 192p. 1981. pap. 3.50 (ISBN 0-311-05760-8, Edit Mundo). Casa Bautista.
Dawe, Donald G. & Carman, John B., eds. Christian Faith in a Religiously Plural World. LC 78-50927. 200p. (Orig.). 1978. pap. 7.95 (ISBN 0-88344-083-0). Orbis Bks.
D'Costa, Gavin. Theology & Religious Pluralism: The Challenge of Other Religions. (Signposts in Theology Ser.). 160p. 1986. text ed. 39.95 (ISBN 0-631-14517-6); pap. text ed. 14.95 (ISBN 0-631-14518-4). Basil Blackwell.
De Mello, Anthony. Sadhana: A Way to God, Christian Exercises in Eastern Form. LC 78-70521. (Study Aids on Jesuit Topics: No. 9). 146p. 1978. pap. 4.95 (ISBN 0-912422-46-7). Inst Jesuit.
Demetrio, Francisco R. Christianity in Context. 134p. 1981. pap. 5.50x (ISBN 0-686-32576-1, Pub. by New Day Phillipines). Cellar.
Elizondo, Virgil & Greinacher, Norbert, eds. Tensions Between the Churches of the First World & the Third World, Vol. 144. (Concilium 1981). 128p. (Orig.). 1981. pap. 6.95 (ISBN 0-8164-2311-3, HarpR). Har-Row.
Fernando, Ajith. The Christian's Attitude Toward World Religions. 160p. (Orig.). 1987. pap. 5.95 (ISBN 0-8423-0292-1). Tyndale.
Ferre, Nels F. The Finality of Faith, & Christianity Among the World Religions. LC 78-11979. 1979. Repr. of 1963 ed. lib. bdg. 22.50x (ISBN 0-313-21182-5, FEFF). Greenwood.
Gregson, Vernon. Lonergan, Spirituality, & the Meeting of Religions. LC 85-3312. (College Theology Society-Studies in Religion: No. 2). 170p. (Orig.). 1985. lib. bdg. 24.50 (ISBN 0-8191-4619-6, Co-Pub by College Theo Soc); pap. text ed. 10.75 (ISBN 0-8191-4620-X). U Pr of Amer.
Griffiths, Bede. The Cosmic Revelation: The Hindu Way to God. 128p. 1983. pap. 7.95 (ISBN 0-87243-119-3). Templegate.
Hick, John & Hebblethwaite, Brian, eds. Christianity & Other Religions: Selected Readings. LC 80-2383. 256p. 1981. pap. 8.95 (ISBN 0-8006-1444-5, 1-1444). Fortress.
Hocking, William E. Living Religions & a World Faith. LC 75-3187. (Hibbert Lectures Ser. 1938). Repr. of 1940 ed. 28.50 (ISBN 0-404-59189-2). AMS Pr.
Hunt, John. Pantheism & Christianity. LC 78-102573. 1970. Repr. of 1884 ed. 25.50 (ISBN 0-8046-0733-8, Pub. by Kennikat). Assoc Faculty Pr.
James, Edwin O. Christian Myth & Ritual: A Historical Study. 11.25 (ISBN 0-8446-2307-5). Peter Smith.
Knitter, Paul F. No Other Name? A Critical Survey of Christian Attitudes Toward the World Religions. LC 84-16491. 304p. (Orig.). 1985. pap. 14.95 (ISBN 0-88344-347-3). Orbis Bks.
Kung, Hans. Do We Know the Others? LC 66-20895. (Concilium Ser.: Vol. 14). 196p. 1966. 7.95 (ISBN 0-8091-0033-9). Paulist Pr.
Kung, Hans & Moltman, Jurgen, eds. Christianity Among World Religions. (Concilium Nineteen Eighty-Six Ser.). 120p. 1986. pap. 6.95 (ISBN 0-567-30063-3, Pub. by T & T Clark Ltd UK). Fortress.
Laing, Gordon. Survivals of Roman Religion. LC 63-10280. (Our Debt to Greece & Rome Ser). 257p. 1963. Repr. of 1930 ed. 25.00x (ISBN 0-8154-0130-2). Cooper Sq.
Legge, Francis. Forerunners & Rivals of Christianity, 2 vols. in 1. 19.00 (ISBN 0-8446-1280-4). Peter Smith.
Legge, James. The Religions of China. LC 78-2685. 1979. Repr. of 1880 ed. lib. bdg. 45.00 (ISBN 0-8495-3313-9). Arden Lib.
Living Non-Christian Religions. 160p. 1984. pap. write for info. (ISBN 0-311-72940-1). Casa Bautista.
Marks, Stanley J. The Two Christs; Or, the Decline & Fall of Christianity. 1983. pap. 14.95 (ISBN 0-938780-03-4). Bur Intl Aff.
Mellen, Philip. Gerhart Hauptman: Religious Syncretism & Eastern Religions. (American University Studies I: Vol. 24). 284p. (Orig.). 1983. pap. text ed. 30.55 (ISBN 0-8204-0060-2). P Lang Pubs.
Miller, Randolph C., ed. Church & Organized Movements. facs. ed. LC 76-134115. (Essay Index Reprint Ser). 1946. 18.00 (ISBN 0-8369-1998-X). Ayer Co Pubs.
Morey, Robert A. Horoscopes & the Christian. 64p. (Orig.). 1981. pap. 2.95 (ISBN 0-87123-202-2, 210202). Bethany Hse.
Murphy, Carol R. Many Religions: One God. LC 66-30689. (Orig.). 1966. pap. 2.50x (ISBN 0-87574-150-9). Pendle Hill.
Neill, Stephen. Christian Faith & Other Faiths. LC 84-19123. 304p. 1984. pap. 9.95 (ISBN 0-87784-337-6). Inter-Varsity.
O'Meara, Dominic J. Neoplatonism & Christian Thought. LC 81-5272. (Neoplatonism: Ancient & Modern Ser.). 270p. 1981. 44.50x (ISBN 0-87395-492-0); pap. 14.95x (ISBN 0-87395-493-9). State U NY Pr.
Oxtoby, Willard G. The Meaning of Other Faiths. LC 83-1090. (Library of Living Faith: Vol. 10). 120p. (Orig.). 1983. pap. 5.95 (ISBN 0-664-24443-2). Westminster.
Paramananda, Swami. Christ & Oriental Ideals. 4th ed. 1968. 4.50 (ISBN 0-911564-14-4). Vedanta Ctr.
Race, Alan. Christians & Religious Pluralism: Patterns in the Christian Theology of Religions. 192p. (Orig.). 1983. pap. 8.95 (ISBN 0-88344-101-2). Orbis Bks.
Reid, Gilbert. A Christian's Appreciation of Other Faiths. 305p. 1921. 22.95 (ISBN 0-87548-219-8). Open Court.
Ridenour, Fritz. So What's the Difference? rev. ed. LC 67-31426. 1979. 5.95 (ISBN 0-8307-0721-2, 5414008). Regal.
Robertson, J. M. Christ & Krishna. 59.95 (ISBN 0-87968-422-4). Gordon Pr.
Robinson, John A. Truth Is Two-Eyed. LC 79-25774. 174p. 1980. pap. 6.95 (ISBN 0-664-24316-9). Westminster.
Saher, P. J. Eastern Wisdom & Western Thought: A Comparative Study in the Modern Philosophy of Religion. LC 72-441621. pap. 73.50 (ISBN 0-317-09011-9, 2012165). Bks Demand UMI.
Sethi, Amarjit S. & Pummer, Reinhard, eds. Comparative Religion. 1979. text ed. 18.95x (ISBN 0-7069-0810-4, Pub. by Vikas India). Advent NY.
Song, Choan-Seng. The Compassionate God. LC 81-16972. 304p. (Orig.). 1982. pap. 12.95 (ISBN 0-88344-095-4). Orbis Bks.
--Third-Eye Theology: Theology in Formation in Asian Settings. LC 79-4208. pap. 72.00 (ISBN 0-317-26666-7, 2025121). Bks Demand UMI.
Sookhdeo, Patrick. Jesus Christ the Only Way: Christian Responsibility in the Multicultural Society. 159p. 1978. pap. 5.95 (ISBN 0-85364-236-2). Attic Pr.
Sookhdeo, Patrick, intro. by. Christianity & Other Faiths. 48p. 1983. pap. 2.95 (ISBN 0-85364-363-6, Pub. by Paternoster UK). Attic Pr.
Steere, Douglas V. Mutual Irradiation: A Quaker View of Ecumenism. LC 73-146680. (Orig.). 1971. pap. 2.50x (ISBN 0-87574-175-4). Pendle Hill.
Swearer, Donald K. Dialogue: The Key to Understanding Other Religions. LC 77-3964. (Biblical Perspectives on Current Issues). 172p. 1977. soft cover 4.95 (ISBN 0-664-24138-7). Westminster.
Taft, Robert. Beyond East & West: Problems in Liturgical Understanding. (NPM Studies in Church Music & Liturgy). 203p. 1934. pap. 11.95 (ISBN 0-912405-13-9). Pastoral Pr.
Thomas, Owen C. Attitudes Toward Other Religions: Some Christian Interpretations. LC 86-4076. 250p. (Orig.). 1986. pap. 11.50 (ISBN 0-8191-5324-9). U Pr of Amer.
Tillich, Paul. Christianity & the Encounter of the World Religions. LC 63-7508. (Bampton Lectures in America: No. 14). pap. 26.80 (ISBN 0-317-42040-2, 2025697). Bks Demand UMI.
Verkuyl, Johannes. Break down the Walls: Christian Cry for Racial Justice. Smedes, Lewis B., ed. LC 72-93620. pap. 41.50 (ISBN 0-317-07869-0, 2012924). Bks Demand UMI.
Watts, Alan W. Beyond Theology: The Art of Godmanship. 1973. pap. 3.95 (ISBN 0-394-71923-9, Vin). Random.
--The Supreme Identity. 1972. pap. 4.95 (ISBN 0-394-71835-6, Vin). Random.
Westermann, Diedrich. Africa & Christianity. LC 74-15102. (Duff Lectures, 1935). Repr. of 1937 ed. 24.50 (ISBN 0-404-12151-9). AMS Pr.
Whittaker, Thomas. Priests, Philosophers & Prophets. LC 77-102589. 1970. Repr. of 1911 ed. 22.50x (ISBN 0-8046-0748-6, Pub. by Kennikat). Assoc Faculty Pr.
Wood, Barry. Questions Non-Christians Ask. 160p. 1980. pap. 5.95 (ISBN 0-8007-5047-0, Power Bks). Revell.
Yamamori, Tetsunao. God's New Envoys: A Bold Strategy for Penetrating "Closed Countries". (Illus.). 1987. 11.95 (ISBN 0-88070-188-9). Multnomah.

CHRISTIANITY AND OTHER RELIGIONS–BUDDHISM

Blyth, R. H. Buddhist Sermons on Christian Texts. 1976. pap. 2.95 (ISBN 0-89346-000-1). Heian Intl.

Callaway, Tucker N. Zen Way - Jesus Way. LC 76-6032. 1976. 11.00 (ISBN 0-8048-1190-3). C E Tuttle.

Carus, Paul. Buddhism & Its Christian Critics. 59.95 (ISBN 0-87968-801-7). Gordon Pr.

--Gospel of Buddha. rev. & enl. ed. LC 17-29837. (Illus.). 331p. 1915. deluxe ed. 24.95 (ISBN 0-87548-226-0); pap. 9.95 (ISBN 0-87548-228-7). Open Court.

Cobb, John B., Jr. Beyond Dialogue: Toward a Mutual Transformation of Christianity & Buddhism. LC 82-8389. 176p. 1982. pap. 8.95 (ISBN 0-8006-1647-2, 1-1647). Fortress.

Dumoulin, Heinrich. Christianity Meets Buddhism. Maraldo, John C., tr. from Ger. LC 73-82783. 212p. 1974. 19.95 (ISBN 0-87548-121-3). Open Court.

Dunne, Carrin. Buddha & Jesus: Conversations. 1975. pap. 4.95 (ISBN 0-87243-057-X). Templegate.

Garbe, Richard. India & Christendom: The Historical Connections Between Their Religions. Robinson, Lydia, tr. from Ger. 321p. 1959. 22.95 (ISBN 0-87548-232-5). Open Court.

Ingram, Paul O. & Streng, Frederick J., eds. Buddhist-Christian Dialogue: Mutual Renewal & Transformation. LC 85-24528. 1986. pap. text ed. 10.00x (ISBN 0-8248-1050-3). UH Pr.

Johnston, William. The Mirror Mind: Spirituality & Transformation. LC 80-8350. 192p. 1984. pap. 6.95 (ISBN 0-06-064206-8, RD 516, HarpR). Har-Row.

--Still Point: Reflections on Zen & Christian Mysticism. LC 75-95713. 1986. pap. 9.00 (ISBN 0-8232-0861-3). Fordham.

Lopez, Donald S., Jr. & Rockefeller, Stephen C., eds. The Christ & the Bodhisattva. (Buddhist Studies). 304p. (Orig.). 1987. 44.50X (ISBN 0-88706-401-9); pap. 14.95X (ISBN 0-88706-402-7). State U NY Pr.

Monier-Williams. Buddhism, in Its Connection with Brahmanism & Hinduism, & in Contrast with Christianity. 2nd ed. LC 78-70101. Repr. of 1890 ed. 57.50 (ISBN 0-404-17349-7). AMS Pr.

O'Connor, Patrick, compiled by. Buddhists Find Christ: The Spiritual Quest of Thirteen Men & Women in Burma, China, Japan, Korea, Sri Lanka, Thailand, Vietnam. 240p. 1975. pap. 2.25 (ISBN 0-8048-1146-6). C E Tuttle.

Peiris, William. The Western Contribution to Buddhism. 372p. 1974. lib. bdg. 79.95 (ISBN 0-87968-550-6). Krishna Pr.

Robinson, John A. Truth Is Two-Eyed. LC 79-25774. 174p. 1980. pap. 6.95 (ISBN 0-664-24316-9). Westminster.

Scott, Archibald. Buddhism & Christianity. LC 78-118547. 1970. Repr. of 1890 ed. 29.50x (ISBN 0-8046-1172-6, Pub. by Kennikat). Assoc Faculty Pr.

Seneviratne, Lionel J. Kharma, Rebirth, God, & Computers. 1987. 6.95 (ISBN 0-533-07145-3). Vantage.

Steiner, Rudolf. Anthroposophy & Christianity. Tr. of Christus und die menschliche Seele, Ueber den sinn deslebens, Theosophische Moral, Anthroposophie und Christentum, German. 26p. (Orig.). 1985. pap. 2.95 (ISBN 0-88010-149-0). Anthroposophic.

Streeter, B. H. The Buddha & the Christ. 59.95 (ISBN 0-87968-799-1). Gordon Pr.

Streeter, Burnett H. Buddha & the Christ. LC 72-102585. 1970. Repr. of 1932 ed. 29.50x (ISBN 0-8046-0745-1, Pub. by Kennikat). Assoc Faculty Pr.

Swearer, Donald K. Dialogue: The Key to Understanding Other Religions. LC 77-3964. (Biblical Perspectives on Current Issues). 172p. 1977. soft cover 4.95 (ISBN 0-664-24138-7). Westminster.

Thelle, Notto R. Buddhism & Christianity in Japan: From Conflict to Dialogue, 1854-1899. (Illus.). 384p. 1987. text ed. 30.00x. UH Pr.

Yu, Chai-Shin. Early Buddhism & Christianity. 1981. 20.00x (ISBN 0-8364-0797-0, Pub. by Motilal Banarsidass). South Asia Bks.

CHRISTIANITY AND OTHER RELIGIONS–GREEK

Bevan, Edwyn R. Hellenism & Christianity. facs. ed. LC 67-26714. (Essay Index Reprint Ser). 1921. 18.00 (ISBN 0-8369-0207-6). Ayer Co Pubs.

Jaeger, Werner. Early Christianity & Greek Paideia. 160p. 1985. pap. text ed. 5.95x (ISBN 0-674-22052-8, Belknap Pr). Harvard U Pr.

Kinneavy, James L. Greek Rhetorical Origins of Christian Faith. 256p. 1986. 29.95x (ISBN 0-19-503735-9). Oxford U Pr.

Newbigin, Lesslie. Foolishness to the Greeks. 176p. (Orig.). 1986. pap. 7.95 (ISBN 0-8028-0176-5). Eerdmans.

Randall, John H. Hellenistic Ways of Deliverance & the Making of the Christian Synthesis. LC 74-137339. 1970. 28.00x (ISBN 0-231-03327-3). Columbia U Pr.

CHRISTIANITY AND OTHER RELIGIONS–HINDUISM

Bassuk, Daniel E. Incarnation in Hinduism & Christianity: The Myth of the God-Man. (Library of Philosophy & Religion Ser.). 256p. 1987. text ed. 35.00 (ISBN 0-391-03452-9). Humanities.

Cave, Sydney. Redemption, Hindu & Christian: The Religious Quest of India. facsimile ed. LC 73-102230. (Select Bibliographies Reprint Ser). 1919. 24.50 (ISBN 0-8369-5115-8). Ayer Co Pubs.

Griffiths, Bede. Christ in India. pap. 8.95 (ISBN 0-87243-134-7). Templegate.

--Vedanta & Christian Faith. LC 73-88179. 85p. 1973. pap. 3.95 (ISBN 0-913922-04-8). Dawn Horse Pr.

Mitra, Kana. Catholicism - Hinduism: Vedantic Investigation of Raimundo Panikkar's Attempt at Bridge Building. 186p. (Orig.). 1987. lib. bdg. 23.00 (ISBN 0-8191-6157-8); pap. text ed. 11.75 (ISBN 0-8191-6158-6). U Pr of Amer.

Nargolkar, V. The Creed of Saint Vinoba. 320p. 1963. pap. 5.00 (ISBN 0-686-96938-3). Greenlf Bks.

Panikkar, Raimundo. The Unknown Christ of Hinduism. LC 81-2886. 208p. (Orig.). 1981. pap. 7.95 (ISBN 0-88344-523-9). Orbis Bks.

Robinson, John A. Truth Is Two-Eyed. LC 79-25774. 174p. 1980. pap. 6.95 (ISBN 0-664-24316-9). Westminster.

CHRISTIANITY AND OTHER RELIGIONS–ISLAM

see also Jesus Christ–Islamic Interpretations; Missions to Muslims

Abdul-Haqq, Adiyah Akbar. Sharing Your Faith with a Muslim. 192p. (Orig.). 1980. pap. 5.95 (ISBN 0-87123-553-6, 210553). Bethany Hse.

Ansari, F. R. Islam & Christianity in the Modern World. pap. 14.95 (ISBN 0-686-18577-3). Kazi Pubns.

Aziz-us-Samad, U. Islam & Christianity. 150p. 1985. write for info. (Pub. by IIFSO Kuwait). New Era Pubns MI.

Basetti-Sami, Giulio. Koran in the Light of Christ. 1977. 8.50 (ISBN 0-8199-0713-8). Franciscan Herald.

Becker, C. H. Christianity & Islam. Chaytor, H. J., tr. LC 74-608. 120p. 1974. Repr. of 1909 ed. lib. bdg. 18.50 (ISBN 0-8337-4816-5). B Franklin.

Biggar, Nigel, et al. Cities of Gods: Faith, Politics & Pluralism in Judaism, Christianity & Islam. LC 85-9879. (Contributions to the Study of Religion Ser.: No. 16). 253p. 1986. lib. bdg. 39.95 (ISBN 0-313-24944-X, BCG/). Greenwood.

Browne, Lawrence E. The Eclipse of Christianity in Asia. 1967. Repr. 27.50x (ISBN 0-86527-049-X). Fertig.

Cragg, Kenneth. Muhammad & the Christian: A Question of Response. 192p. (Orig.). 1984. pap. 8.95 (ISBN 0-88344-349-X). Orbis Bks.

Deedat, A. What the Bible Says about Muhammad? 1.75 (ISBN 0-686-63917-0). Kazi Pubns.

Dretke, James P. A Christian Approach to Muslims: Reflections from West Africa. LC 79-11912. (Islamic Studies). 1979. pap. 3.95 (ISBN 0-87808-432-0). William Carey Lib.

El-Amin, Mustafa. Al-Islam, Christianity, & Freemasonry. 214p. (Orig.). 1985. pap. 6.95 (ISBN 0-933821-05-0). New Mind Prod.

Goldsmith, Martin. Islam & Christian Witness. LC 83-6112. 160p. 1983. pap. 4.95 (ISBN 0-87784-809-2). Inter-Varsity.

Haines, Byron L. & Cooley, Frank L., eds. Christians & Muslims Together: An Exploration by Presbyterians. LC 87-218. 120p. (Orig.). 1987. pap. 7.95 (ISBN 0-664-24061-5). Westminster.

Hourani, Albert. Europe & the Middle East. LC 78-59452. 1980. 33.00x (ISBN 0-520-03742-1). U of Cal Pr.

Joseph, John. Muslim-Christian Relations & Inter-Christian Rivalries in the Middle East: The Case of the Jacobites in an Age of Transition. LC 82-870. 320p. 1983. 49.50x (ISBN 0-87395-600-1); pap. 19.95 (ISBN 0-87395-601-X). State U NY Pr.

McCurry, Don M., ed. The Gospel & Islam: A Compendium. abr. ed. 269p. 1979. pap. 6.95 (ISBN 0-912552-26-3). Missions Adv Res Com Ctr.

Maybaum, Ignay. Trialogue Between Jew, Christian & Muslim. (Littman Library of Jewish Civilization). 192p. 1973. 18.50x (ISBN 0-19-710032-5). Oxford U Pr.

Miller, William M. A Christian Response to Islam. 1976. pap. 4.95 (ISBN 0-87552-335-8). Presby & Reformed.

Nazir-Ali, M. Islam: A Christian Perspective. 160p. (Orig.). 1982. pap. text ed. 9.95 cancelled (ISBN 0-85364-333-4). Attic Pr.

Nazir-Ali, Michael. Islam: A Christian Perspective. LC 84-3615. 186p. 1984. pap. 11.95 (ISBN 0-664-24527-7). Westminster.

Peroncel-Hugoz, Jean-Pierre. The Raft of Mohammed: Social & Human Consequences of the Return to Traditional Religion in the Arab World. 304p. 1987. 18.95 (ISBN 0-913729-31-0). Paragon Hse.

Rashid, M. S. Iqbal's Concept of God. 120p. 1986. pap. text ed. 12.95 (ISBN 0-7103-0004-2). Methuen Inc.

Schuon, Frithjof. Christianity - Islam: Essays on Esoteric Ecumenicism. LC 84-52674. (The Library of Traditional Wisdom). 270p. 1985. pap. 12.00 (ISBN 0-941532-05-4). Wrld Wisdom Bks.

Siegel, Paul N. The Meek & the Militant: Religion & Power Across the World. 260p. 1986. 35.00 (ISBN 0-86232-349-5, Pub. by Zed Pr UK); pap. 12.50 (ISBN 0-86232-350-9, Pub. by Zed Pr UK). Humanities.

Sweetman, James W. Islam & Christian Theology: A Study of the Interpretations of Theological Ideas in the Two Religions, 3 vols. 1980. Set. lib. bdg. 229.95 (ISBN 0-8490-3136-2). Gordon Pr.

Taymiyah, Ibn. A Muslim Theologian's Response to Christianity: A Translation of Ibn Taymiyya's Jawab al-Sahih li-man Baddala din al-Masih. Michel, Thomas F., tr. LC 83-15430. (Studies in Islamic Philosophy & Science). 60.00x (ISBN 0-88206-058-9). Caravan Bks.

Tingle, Donald S. Islam & Christianity. 32p. (Orig.). 1985. pap. 0.75 (ISBN 0-87784-073-3). Inter-Varsity.

Watt, W. Montgomery. Islam & Christianity Today. LC 83-10949. 157p. 1984. 19.95x (ISBN 0-7100-9766-2, Kegan Paul). Methuen Inc.

Ye'or, Bat. The Dhimmi: Jews & Christians under Islam. Maisel, David, et al, trs. from French. LC 84-47749. (Illus.). 444p. 1985. 25.00 (ISBN 0-8386-3233-5); pap. 9.95 (ISBN 0-8386-3262-9). Fairleigh Dickinson.

CHRISTIANITY AND OTHER RELIGIONS–JUDAISM

see also Christianity and Antisemitism; Missions to Jews

Althouse, LaVonne. When Jew & Christian Meet. (Illus.). 1966. pap. 1.50 (ISBN 0-377-36221-2). Friend Pr.

Amber, Lee. Chosen. rev ed. LC 81-51985. 176p. 1981. pap. 3.95 (ISBN 0-88449-079-3, A424025). Vision Hse.

Arno Press Staff. Judaism & Christanity: Selected Accounts, 1892-1962. LC 73-2212. (The Jewish People; History, Religion, Literature Ser.). 22.00 (ISBN 0-405-05276-6). Ayer Co Pubs.

Ayers, Robert H. Judaism & Christianity: Origins, Developments & Recent Trends. LC 83-3548. (Illus.). 478p. (Orig.). 1983. lib. bdg. 35.75 (ISBN 0-8191-3156-3); pap. text ed. 16.50 (ISBN 0-8191-3157-1). U Pr of Amer.

Barrett, Charles K. The Gospel of John & Judaism. Smith, D. M., tr. LC 75-15435. pap. 27.80 (2026897). Bks Demand UMI.

Belcher, Lee & Belcher, Carol. Reaching Our Jewish Friends. (Truthway Ser.). 79p. (Orig.). 1981. pap. text ed. 1.50 (ISBN 0-87148-735-7). Pathway Pr.

Biggar, Nigel, et al. Cities of Gods: Faith, Politics & Pluralism in Judaism, Christianity & Islam. LC 85-9879. (Contributions to the Study of Religion Ser.: No. 16). 253p. 1986. lib. bdg. 39.95 (ISBN 0-313-24944-X, BCG/). Greenwood.

Chrysostom, John. Discourses Against Judaizing Christians. (Fathers of the Church Ser.: Vol. 68). 286p. 1979. 29.95x (ISBN 0-8132-0068-7). Cath U Pr.

Croner, Helga. More Stepping Stones to Jewish Christian Relations. (Stimulus Bk.). 240p. (Orig.). 1985. pap. 7.95 (ISBN 0-8091-2708-3). Paulist Pr.

--Stepping Stones to Further Jewish-Christian Relations: An Unabridged Collection of Christian Documents. 157p. pap. 10.00 (ISBN 0-686-95183-2). ADL.

Croner, Helga, ed. Issues in the Jewish Christian Dialogue. LC 79-88933. 200p. 1979. pap. 7.95 (ISBN 0-8091-2238-3). Paulist Pr.

--Stepping Stones to Further Jewish Relations. 7.95. Paulist Pr.

Croner, Helga & Klenicki, Leon, eds. Issues in the Jewish-Christian Dialogue: Jewish Perspectives on Covenant Mission & Witness. 190p. 7.95 (ISBN 0-686-95172-7). ADL.

Davies, W. D. Christian Origins & Judaism. LC 73-2192. (The Jewish People; History, Religion, Literature Ser.). Repr. of 1962 ed. 22.00 (ISBN 0-405-05258-8). Ayer Co Pubs.

--Jewish & Pauline Studies. LC 82-48620. 432p. 1983. text ed. 29.95 (ISBN 0-8006-0694-9). Fortress.

De Lange, N. R. Origen & the Jews. LC 75-36293. (Oriental Publications Ser.: No. 25). 160p. 1977. 39.50 (ISBN 0-521-20542-5). Cambridge U Pr.

Eckardt, A. R., ed. Your People, My People: The Meeting of Jews & Christians. 212p. 7.95 (ISBN 0-686-95188-3). ADL.

Eckardt, A. Roy. Jews & Christians: The Contemporary Meeting. LC 85-45327. 192p. 1986. 19.95x (ISBN 0-253-33162-5). Ind U Pr.

Endelman, Todd M., ed. Jewish Apostasy in the Modern World. 300p. 1987. 34.50 (ISBN 0-8419-1029-4). Holmes & Meier.

Fairweather, William. The Background of the Gospels. 464p. 1916. 15.95 (ISBN 0-567-02101-7, Pub. by T & T Clark Ltd UK). Fortress.

Fisher, Eugene J. Seminary Education & Christian-Jewish Relationss. 100p. 1983. 4.80 (ISBN 0-318-20615-3). Natl Cath Educ.

Fleischner, Eva. Judaism in German Christian Theology since 1945: Christianity & Israel Considered in Terms of Mission. LC 75-22374. (ATLA Monograph: No. 8). 205p. 1975. 17.50 (ISBN 0-8108-0835-8). Scarecrow.

Friedman, Jerome. The Most Ancient Testimony: Sixteenth-Century Christian-Hebraica in the Age of Renaissance Nostalgia. LC 82-18830. x, 279p. 1983. text ed. 26.95x (ISBN 0-8214-0700-7). Ohio U Pr.

Friedman, Philip. Their Brothers' Keepers: The Christian Heroes & Heroines Who Helped the Oppressed Escaper the Nazi Terror. 232p. Repr. 4.95 (ISBN 0-686-95090-9). ADL.

Fruchtenbaum, Arnold G. Hebrew Christianity: Its Theology, History & Philosophy. Rev. ed. 142p. 1983. pap. 3.50 (ISBN 0-8010-3497-3). Ariel Pr CA.

Goldberg, Louis. Our Jewish Friends. Rev. ed. 1983. pap. text ed. 4.95 (ISBN 0-87213-239-0). Loizeaux.

Grant, Frederick C. Ancient Judaism & the New Testament. LC 77-18848. 1978. Repr. of 1959 ed. lib. bdg. cancelled (ISBN 0-313-20204-4, GRAJ). Greenwood.

Greenspahn, Frederick E., ed. Scripture in the Jewish & Christian Traditions: Authority, Interpretation, Relevance. 240p. 1982. pap. 11.95 (ISBN 0-687-37065-5). Abingdon.

Harshbarger, Luther H. & Mourant, John A. Judaism & Christianity: Perspectives & Traditions. 490p. Date not set. text ed. price not set (ISBN 0-8290-0294-4); pap. text ed. price not set (ISBN 0-8290-0295-2). Irvington.

Holmgren, Frederick. The God Who Cares: A Christian Looks at Judaism. LC 78-52445. (Orig.). 1979. pap. 1.95 (ISBN 0-8042-0588-4). John Knox.

Jacob, Walter. Christianity Through Jewish Eyes. 1974. pap. 9.95x (ISBN 0-685-56220-4). Ktav.

Jocz, Jakob. The Jewish People & Jesus Christ. 1979. pap. 7.95 (ISBN 0-8010-5085-5). Baker Bk.

--The Jewish People & Jesus Christ After Auschwitz. 172p. (Orig.). 1981. pap. 9.95 (ISBN 0-8010-5123-1). Baker Bk.

Kirsch, Paul J. We Christians & Jews. 160p. pap. 3.95 (ISBN 0-686-95187-5). ADL.

--We Christians & Jews. LC 74-26332. pap. 40.00 (2026838). Bks Demand UMI.

Klenicki, Leon & Wigoder, Geoffrey, eds. A Dictionary of the Jewish-Christian Dialogue. (Stimulus Book, Studies in Judaism & Christianity). (Orig.). 1984. pap. 7.95 (ISBN 0-8091-2590-0). Paulist Pr.

Koenig, John. Jews & Christians in Dialogue: New Testament Foundations. LC 79-17583. 188p. 1979. pap. 8.95 (ISBN 0-664-24280-4). Westminster.

Lasker, D. J. Jewish Philosophical Polemics Against Christianity in the Middle Ages. 25.00x (ISBN 0-87068-498-1). Ktav.

Littell, Franklin H. The Crucifixion of the Jews. (Reprints of Scholarly Excellence: No. 12). 160p. 1986. Repr. of 1975 ed. 10.95 (ISBN 0-86554-227-9). Mercer Univ Pr.

Long, J. B., ed. Judaism & the Christian Seminary Curriculum. 166p. pap. 2.95 (ISBN 0-686-95180-8). ADL.

McClain, Alva J. The Jewish Problem. 1979. pap. 1.00 (ISBN 0-88469-014-8). BMH Bks.

Maccoby, Hyman. Judaism on Trial: Jewish-Christian Disputations in the Middle Ages. (Littman Library of Jewish Civilization). 246p. 1982. 34.00x (ISBN 0-19-710046-5). Oxford U Pr.

McNamara, Martin. Palestinian Judaism & the New Testament. (Good News Studies: Vol. 4). 1983. pap. 12.95 (ISBN 0-89453-274-X). M Glazier.

Markish, Shimon. Erasmus & the Jews. Olcott, Anthony, tr. from Rus. LC 85-16454. 1986. lib. bdg. 25.00x (ISBN 0-226-50590-1). U of Chicago Pr.

Marks, Stanley J. & Marks, Ethel M. Judaism Looks at Christianity: 7 BC-1985 C. E. 1985. pap. 19.95; 24.95. Bur Intl Aff.

Maybaum, Ignay. Trialogue Between Jew, Christian & Muslim. (Littman Library of Jewish Civilization). 192p. 1973. 18.50x (ISBN 0-19-710032-5). Oxford U Pr.

Meyer, Ben F. & Sanders, E. P., eds. Jewish & Christian Self-Definition, Vol. 3: Self-Definition in the Greco-Roman World. LC 79-7390. 320p. 1983. 24.95 (ISBN 0-8006-0690-6, 1-690). Fortress.
Mills, Lawrence H. Avesta Eschatology: Compared with the Books of Daniel & Revelations. LC 74-24644. Repr. of 1908 ed. 14.00 (ISBN 0-404-12816-5). AMS Pr.
Morley, John F. Vatican Diplomacy & the Jews During the Holocaust 1939-1943. 320p. 25.00. ADL.
Mussner, Franz. Tractate on the Jews: The Significance of Judaism for the Christian Faith. Swidler, Leonard, tr. from German. LC 83-5699. 352p. 1983. 29.95 (ISBN 0-8006-0707-4, 1-707). Fortress.
Neusner, Jacob. Judaism in the Beginning of Christianity. LC 83-48000. 112p. 1984. pap. 5.95 (ISBN 0-8006-1750-9, 1-1750). Fortress.
--Judaism in the Matrix of Christianity. LC 85-45492. 160p. 1986. pap. 12.95 (ISBN 0-8006-1897-1, 1-1897). Fortress.
--The Religious Study of Judaism: Description, Analysis & Interpretation. LC 85-30411. (Studies in Judaism Ser.: Vol. 1). 188p. (Orig.). 1986. lib. bdg. 22.50 (ISBN 0-8191-5393-1, Pub. by Studies in Judaism); pap. text ed. 9.75 (ISBN 0-8191-5394-X). U Pr of Amer.
--The Religious Study of Judaism: Description, Analysis, Interpretation-The Centrality of Context. LC 85-30411. (Studies in Judaism: Vol. 2). 230p. (Orig.). 1986. lib. bdg. 24.50 (ISBN 0-8191-5450-4, Pub. by Studies in Judaism); pap. text ed. 12.75 (ISBN 0-8191-5451-2). U Pr of Amer.
Neusner, Jacob & Frerichs, Ernest S., eds. To See Ourselves As Others See Us: Christians Jews, "Others" in Late Antiquity. (Scholars Press Studies in the Humanities). (Orig.). 1985. 38.95 (ISBN 0-89130-819-9, 00-01-09); pap. 25.95 (ISBN 0-89130-820-2). Scholars Pr GA.
Newman, Louis I. Jewish Influence on Christian Reform Movements. LC 26-883. (Columbia University. Oriental Studies: No. 23). Repr. of 1925 ed. 45.00 (ISBN 0-404-50513-9). AMS Pr.
Oesterley, William O. The Jewish Background of the Christian Liturgy. 1925. 11.75 (ISBN 0-8446-1329-0). Peter Smith.
--Jews & Judaism During the Greek Period: The Background of Christianity. LC 74-102580. 1970. Repr. of 1941 ed. 23.00x (ISBN 0-8046-0740-0, Pub. by Kennikat). Assoc Faculty Pr.
Pawlikowski, John T. Christ in the Light of the Christian-Jewish Dialogue. LC 81-83186. (Stimulus Bks.). 208p. (Orig.). 1982. pap. 7.95 (ISBN 0-8091-2416-5). Paulist Pr.
--What Are They Saying about Christian-Jewish Relations? LC 79-56135. 144p. (Orig.). 1980. pap. 3.95 (ISBN 0-8091-2239-1). Paulist Pr.
Rhyne, C. Thomas. Faith Establishes the Law. Kee, Howard, ed. LC 81-1794. (Society of Biblical Literature Dissertation Ser.). 1981. pap. 13.50 (ISBN 0-89130-483-5, 06-01-55). Scholars Pr GA.
Rosen, Moishe. Share the New Life with a Jew. LC 76-7627. 1976. pap. 3.95 (ISBN 0-8024-7898-0). Moody.
--Y'shua. 128p. (Orig.). 1983. pap. 3.50 (ISBN 0-8024-9842-6). Moody.
Rosenberg, Stuart E. The Christian Problem: A Jewish View. 304p. 1986. 15.95 (ISBN 0-87052-284-1). Hippocrene Bks.
--Christians & Jews: The Eternal Bond. rev. ed. 200p. 1985. 13.95 (ISBN 0-8044-5800-6). Ungar.
Rousseau, Richard, ed. Christianity & Judaism: The Deepening Dialogue. (Modern Theological Themes: Selections from the Literature Ser.: Vol. 3). (Orig.). 1983. pap. 15.00 (ISBN 0-940866-02-1). Ridge Row.
Rudin, A. James. Israel for Christians. LC 82-7241. 160p. (Orig.). 1983. pap. 8.95 (ISBN 0-8006-1643-X, 1-1643). Fortress.
Rudin, James, et al. Twenty Years of Jewish-Catholic Relations. 336p. (Orig.). 1986. pap. 11.95 (ISBN 0-8091-2762-8). Paulist Pr.
Ruether, Rosemary. Faith & Fratricide: The Theological Roots of Anti-Semitism. 1974. pap. 8.95 (ISBN 0-8164-2263-X, HarpR). Har-Row.
Sanders, E. P. Jesus & Judaism. LC 84-48806. 448p. 1985. 19.95 (ISBN 0-8006-0743-0, 1-743). Fortress.
Sanders, E. P., ed. Jewish & Christian Self-Definition, Vol. 1: The Shaping of Christianity in the Second & Third Centuries. LC 79-7390. 336p. 1980. 5.00 (ISBN 0-8006-0578-0, 1-578). Fortress.
Sanders, E. P., et al, eds. Jewish & Christian Self-Definition, Vol. 2: Aspects of Judaism in the Greco-Roman Period. LC 79-7390. 450p. 1981. 5.00 (ISBN 0-8006-0660-4, 1-660). Fortress.
Sandmel, Samuel. A Jewish Understanding of the New Testament. 1974. 11.95x (ISBN 0-87068-102-8); pap. 9.95x (ISBN 0-87068-262-8). Ktav.
--Judaism & Christian Beginnings. pap. 11.95x (ISBN 0-19-502282-3). Oxford U Pr.
Schaeffer, Edith. Christianity Is Jewish. 1977. pap. 6.95 (ISBN 0-8423-0242-5). Tyndale.
Schiffman, Lawrence H. Who Was Jew: Rabbinic & Halakhic Perspectives on the Jewish-Christian Schism. (Illus.). 140p. 1985. 14.95 (ISBN 0-88125-053-8); pap. 8.95 (ISBN 0-88125-054-6). Ktav.
Schoeps, Hans J. Paul: The Theology of the Apostle in the Light of Jewish Religious History. Knight, Harold, tr. LC 61-10284. 304p. 1979. Repr. of 1961 ed. softcover 7.95 (ISBN 0-664-24273-1). Westminster.
Schoffler, Herbert. Abendland und Altes Testament. pap. 10.00 (ISBN 0-384-54210-7). Johnson Repr.
Siegel, Paul N. The Meek & the Militant: Religion & Power Across the World. 260p. 1986. 35.00 (ISBN 0-86232-349-5, Pub. by Zed Pr UK); pap. 12.50 (ISBN 0-86232-350-9, Pub. by Zed Pr UK). Humanities.
Sigal, Gerald. The Jew & the Christian Missionary: A Jewish Response to Missionary Christianity. 1981. 20.00x (ISBN 0-87068-886-3). Ktav.
Silverman, William B. Judaism & Christianity. LC 68-27330. pap. 5.95x (ISBN 0-87441-016-9). Behrman.
Simon, Marcal. Verus Israel. McKeating, H., tr. 592p. 1985. 57.00x (ISBN 0-19-710035-X). Oxford U Pr.
Simon, Merill. Jerry Falwell & the Jews. LC 83-22266. 172p. 1983. 12.50 (ISBN 0-8246-0300-1). Jonathan David.
Stendahl, Krister. Meanings: The Bible As Document & Guide. LC 83-5601. 240p. 1984. pap. 14.95 (ISBN 0-8006-1752-5, 1-1752). Fortress.
Talmage, Frank. Disputation & Dialogue: Readings in the Jewish Christian Encounter. pap. 14.95x (ISBN 0-87068-284-9). Ktav.
Tebaldus, Massimiliano. Jews, Christians & the Theory of the Soul: New Discoveries in Classical Theology. (Illus.). 138p. 1984. 88.95 (ISBN 0-89266-480-0). Am Classical Coll Pr.
Thoma, Clemens. A Christian Theology of Judaism. Croner, Helga & Frizzell, Lawrence, trs. from Ger. LC 80-82252. (Studies in Judaism & Christianity). 232p. 1980. pap. 7.95 (ISBN 0-8091-2310-X). Paulist Pr.
Thompson, Norma H. & Cole, Bruce, eds. The Future of Jewish-Christian Relations. LC 82-73896. 1982. 10.95 (ISBN 0-915744-27-9); pap. 8.95 (ISBN 0-915744-28-7). Character Res.
Van Buren, Paul M. A Christian Theology of the People Israel. (A Theology of the Jewish-Christian Reality Ser.: Pt. II). 320p. (Orig.). 1983. pap. 26.95 (ISBN 0-8164-0548-4, HarpR). Har-Row.
Von Der Osten-Sacken, Peter. Christian-Jewish Dialogue: Theological Foundations. Kohl, Margaret, tr. from Ger. LC 85-45481. 240p. 1986. 24.95 (ISBN 0-8006-0771-6, 1-771). Fortress.
Weiss-Rosmarin, Trude. Judaism & Christianity: The Differences. 1965. pap. 4.95 (ISBN 0-8246-0044-4). Jonathan David.
Wilde, Robert. The Treatment of the Jews in the Christian Writers of the First Three Centuries, Vol. 81. (Patristic Studies). 255p. 1984. Repr. of 1949 ed. 38.00x (ISBN 0-939738-28-7). Zubal Inc.
Wilken, Robert L., ed. Aspects of Wisdom in Judaism & Early Christianity. LC 74-27888. (University of Notre Dame, Center for the Study of Judaism & Christianity in Antiquity: No. 1). pap. 60.00 (ISBN 0-317-26715-9, 2024365). Bks Demand UMI.
Wilson, Stephen, ed. Anti-Judaism in Early Christianity, Vol. 2: Separation & Polemic. (Studies in Christanity & Judaism: Vol. 2.2). 200p. 1986. pap. text ed. 18.50 (ISBN 0-88920-196-X, Pub. by Wilfrid Laurier Canada). Humanities.
Wood, James E., Jr., ed. Jewish-Christian Relations in Today's World. 164p. pap. 1.95 (ISBN 0-686-95175-1). ADL.
--Jewish-Christian Relations in Today's World. LC 74-185826. 164p. 1971. 8.95 (ISBN 0-918954-09-6); pap. 4.50 (ISBN 0-918954-10-X). Baylor Univ Pr.
Wyschogrod, Michael. The Body of Faith: Judaism As Corporeal Election. 320p. (Orig.). 1983. pap. 24.95 (ISBN 0-8164-0549-2, HarpR). Har-Row.
Zeik, Michael & Siegel, Martin, eds. Root & Branch: The Jewish Christian Dialogue. LC 70-181996. pap. 4.95 (ISBN 0-87957-001-6). Roth Pub.

CHRISTIANITY AND PHILOSOPHY
see Philosophy and Religion

CHRISTIANITY AND POLITICS

Bakole Wa Ilunga. Paths of Liberation: A Third World Spirituality. O'Connell, Matthew J., tr. from Fr. LC 84-5177. Tr. of Chemins de Liberation. 240p. (Orig.). 1984. pap. 12.95 (ISBN 0-88344-401-1). Orbis Bks.
Baralt, Luce L. Huellas del Islam en la Literatura Espanola: De Juan Ruiz a Juan Goytisola. 262p. 1985. 18.00 (ISBN 84-7517-152-4). U of PR Pr.
Belli, Humberto. Breaking Faith: The Sandinista Revolution & Its Impact on Freedom & the Christian Faith in Nicaragua. LC 85-70475. 288p. 1985. pap. 8.95 (ISBN 0-89107-359-0, Crossway Bks). Good News.
Bigler, Robert M. The Politics of German Protestantism: The Rise of the Protestant Church Elite in Prussia, 1815-1848. LC 77-142055. 1972. 38.50x (ISBN 0-520-01881-8). U of Cal Pr.
Bonino, Jose M. Toward a Christian Political Ethics. LC 82-48541. 144p. 1983. pap. 6.95 (ISBN 0-8006-1697-9, 1-1697). Fortress.
Bromley, David G. & Shupe, Anson D., Jr. New Christian Politics. LC 84-6598. xii, 288p. 1984. 23.95 (ISBN 0-86554-115-9, MUP/H108). Mercer Univ Pr.
Candidates Biblical Scoreboard, 1986 California, No. 1. 1.00 (ISBN 0-89921-016-3). Biblical News Serv.
Candidates Biblical Scoreboard, 1986 California, No. 2. 1.00 (ISBN 0-89921-019-8). Biblical News Serv.
Candidates Biblical Scoreboard, 1986 California, No. 3. 1.00 (ISBN 0-89921-020-1). Biblical News Serv.
Candidates Biblical Scoreboard, 1986 National, No. 2. 2.25 (ISBN 0-89921-017-1). Biblical News Serv.
Candidates Biblical Scoreboard, 1986 National, No. 3. 2.25 (ISBN 0-89921-018-X). Biblical News Serv.
Cardwell, Jerry D. A Rumor of Trumpets: The Return of God to Secular Society. 118p. (Orig.). 1985. lib. bdg. 22.00 (ISBN 0-8191-4791-5); pap. text ed. 8.75 (ISBN 0-8191-4792-3). U Pr of Amer.
Carey, George W., ed. Freedom & Virtue: The Conservative Libertarian Debate. LC 84-19637. 164p. (Orig.). 1985. lib. bdg. 25.25 (ISBN 0-8191-4334-0, Co-Pub. by Intercollegiate Studies); pap. text ed. 9.50 (ISBN 0-8191-4335-9, Co-pub. by Intercollegiate Studies). U Pr of Amer.
Carey, George W. & Schall, James V., eds. Essays on Christianity & Political Philosophy. (The ISI Roots of Western Culture Ser.). 144p. (Orig.). 1985. 24.00 (ISBN 0-8191-4275-1, Co-pub. by Intercollegiate Studies); pap. text ed. 8.75 (ISBN 0-8191-4276-X). U Pr of Amer.
Childress, James F. Civil Disobedience & Political Obligation: A Study in Christian Social Ethics. LC 75-158137. (Yale Publication in Religion Ser.: No. 16). pap. 66.50 (ISBN 0-317-09428-9, 2021988). Bks Demand UMI.
Clouse, Robert G., et al, eds. Protest & Politics: Christianity & Contemporary Affairs. 277p. 1968. 5.95 (ISBN 0-87921-000-1). Attic Pr.
Dawson, Christopher H. Beyond Politics. facsimile ed. LC 74-111825. (Essay Index Reprint Ser.). 1939. 14.00 (ISBN 0-8369-1603-4). Ayer Co Pubs.
Dibinga wa Said. The Unification Church Policy on South Africa. (Christian Churches Policies on South Africa Ser.). 14p. (Orig.). 1986. pap. write for info. (ISBN 0-943324-26-2). Omenana.
Eliopoulos, Nicholas C. Oneness of Politics & Religion. 126p. (Orig.). 1970. pap. 3.00x (ISBN 0-9605396-1-1). Eliopoulos.
Fackre, Gabriel. The Religious Right & the Christian Faith. 1982. 8.95 (ISBN 0-8028-3566-X); pap. 4.95 (ISBN 0-8028-1983-4). Eerdmans.
Fierro, Alfredo. The Militant Gospel: A Critical Introduction to Political Theologies. Drury, John, tr. from Span. LC 77-1652. Orig. Title: El Evangelio Beligerente. 459p. (Orig.). 1977. pap. 3.48 (ISBN 0-88344-311-2). Orbis Bks.
Flake, Carol. Redemptorama. LC 82-45356. 288p. 1984. 15.95 (ISBN 0-385-18241-4, Anchor Pr). Doubleday.
--Redemptorama: Culture, Politics & the New Evangelicalism. (Nonfiction Ser.). 320p. 1985. pap. 7.95 (ISBN 0-14-008265-4). Penguin.
Friedrich, Carl J. Transcendent Justice: The Religious Dimensions of Constitutionalism. LC 64-20097. ix, 116p. 1964. 13.75 (ISBN 0-8223-0061-3). Duke.
Grelle, Bruce & Krueger, David A., eds. Christianity & Capitalism: Perspectives on Religion, Liberalism, & the Economy. LC 85-73375. (Studies in Religion & Society Ser.). 189p. 1986. text ed. 25.95x (ISBN 0-913348-23-6); pap. 14.95x (ISBN 0-913348-24-4). Ctr Sci Study.
Griffith, Carol F., ed. Christianity & Politics: Catholic & Protestant Perspectives. LC 81-19412. 124p. 1981. pap. 6.00 (ISBN 0-89633-050-8). Ethics & Public Policy.
Hanna, Mary. Catholics & American Politics. LC 79-11035. 1979. text ed. 16.50x (ISBN 0-674-10325-4). Harvard U Pr.
Hocking, W. E., et al. Church & the New World Mind: The Drake Lectures for 1944. facsimile ed. LC 68-57311. (Essay Index Reprint Ser). Repr. of 1944 ed. 18.00 (ISBN 0-8369-9698-4). Ayer Co Pubs.
Irani, George E. The Papacy & the Middle East: The Role of the Holy See in the Arab-Israeli Conflict, 1962-1984. LC 85-41013. 224p. 1986. text ed. 22.95x (ISBN 0-268-01560-0). U of Notre Dame Pr.
Jerrold, Douglas. Future of Freedom: Notes on Christianity & Politics. facs. ed. LC 68-20311. (Essay Index Reprint Ser). 1938. 18.00 (ISBN 0-8369-0570-9). Ayer Co Pubs.
Jorstad, Erling. The New Christian Right, Nineteen Eighty-One to Nineteen Eighty-Eight: Prospects for the Next Presidential Election. LC 87-1636. (Studies in American Religion: Vol. 25). 280p. 1987. lib. bdg. 49.95 (ISBN 0-88946-669-6). E Mellen.
Kuitert, H. M. Everything Is Politics but Politics Is Not Everything. Bowden, John, tr. from Dutch. 208p. (Orig.). 1986. pap. 8.95 (ISBN 0-8028-0235-4). Eerdmans.
Libanio, J. B. Spiritual Discernment & Politics: Guidelines for Religious Communities. Morrow, Theodore, tr. from Port. LC 82-2257. Orig. Title: Discernment E politica. 144p. (Orig.). 1982. pap. 1.74 (ISBN 0-88344-463-1). Orbis Bks.
McBrien, Richard P. Caesar's Coin: Religion & Politics in America. 320p. 1987. 19.95 (ISBN 0-02-919720-1). Macmillan.
Maritain, Jacques. Christianity & Democracy. Anson, Doris C., tr. from Fr. LC 72-6765. (Essay Index Reprint Ser). 1972. Repr. of 1944 ed. 15.00 (ISBN 0-8369-7243-0). Ayer Co Pubs.
Martin, Richie, ed. Judgment in the Gate. LC 86-70285. (Orig.). 1986. pap. 6.95 (ISBN 0-89107-396-5, Crossway Bks). Good News.
Mawhinney, Brian & Wells, Ronald. Conflict & Christianity in Northern Ireland. LC 75-8948. (Illus.). pap. 31.50 (ISBN 0-317-09250-2, 2012891). Bks Demand UMI.
Messer, Donald E. Christian Ethics & Political Action. 176p. 1984. 8.95 (ISBN 0-8170-1018-1). Judson.
Metz, Johannes B. Faith & the World of Politics. LC 68-31786. (Concilium Ser.: Vol. 36). 191p. 7.95 (ISBN 0-8091-0046-0). Paulist Pr.
Moltmann, Jurgen. On Human Dignity: Political Theology & Ethics. Meeks, M. Douglas, tr. from Ger. LC 83-48913. 240p. 1984. 15.95 (ISBN 0-8006-0715-5, 1-715). Fortress.
Moreau, Jacques. Die Christenverfolgung im roemischen Reich. 2nd ed. 119p. 1971. 9.00 (ISBN 3-1100-2456-X). De Gruyter.
Morris, William D. The Christian Origins of Social Revolt. LC 78-14133. 1979. Repr. of 1949 ed. 19.50 (ISBN 0-88355-805-X). Hyperion Conn.
Mosse, George L. The Holy Pretence. LC 68-14552. 1968. 23.50x (ISBN 0-86527-099-6). Fertig.
Muller, Herbert J. Religion & Freedom in the Modern World. LC 63-20911. 1963. pap. 1.50x (ISBN 0-226-54815-5, P193, Phoen). U of Chicago Pr.
Neuhaus, Richard J., ed. Confession, Conflict, & Community. (The Encounter Ser.: Vol. 3). 128p. (Orig.). 1986. pap. 5.95 (ISBN 0-8028-0203-6). Eerdmans.
Niebuhr, Reinhold. Christianity & Power Politics. LC 69-12421. xi, 226p. 1969. Repr. of 1940 ed. 24.50 (ISBN 0-208-00740-7, Archon). Shoe String.
Palmer, Gordon. By Freedom's Holy Light. 1964. 9.95 (ISBN 0-8159-5110-8). Devin.
Presidential Biblical Scoreboard, 1980. write for info. (ISBN 0-89921-008-2). Biblical News Serv.
Presidential Biblical Scoreboard, 1984, No. 1. 1984. write for info. (ISBN 0-89921-009-0). Biblical News Serv.
Presidential Biblical Scoreboard, 1984, No. 2. write for info. (ISBN 0-89921-010-4). Biblical News Serv.
Presidential Biblical Scoreboard, 1984, No. 3. write for info. (ISBN 0-89921-011-2). Biblical News Serv.
Presidential Biblical Scoreboard, 1984, No. 5. write for info. (ISBN 0-89921-013-9). Biblical News Serv.
Presidential Biblical Scoreboard, 1984, No. 5. write for info. (ISBN 0-89921-014-7). Biblical News Serv.
Reding, Andrew, ed. Christianity & Revolution: Tomas Borge's Theology of Life. LC 86-23788. (Illus.). 160p. (Orig.). 1987. pap. 8.95 (ISBN 0-88344-411-9). Orbis Bks.
Robb, Ed & Robb, Julia. Betrayal of the Church: Apostasy & Renewal in the Mainline Denominations. LC 86-71006. 304p. (Orig.). 1986. pap. 8.95 (ISBN 0-89107-403-1, Crossway Bks). Good News.
Runner, E. H. Scriptural Religion & Political Task. 1974. pap. 2.95 (ISBN 0-686-11989-4). Wedge Pub.

Schaeffer, Franky, ed. Is Capitalism Christian? LC 85-70471. 400p. (Orig.). 1985. pap. 9.95 (ISBN 0-89107-362-0, Crossway Bks). Good News.

Schall, James. Christianity & Politics. 1981. 6.95 (ISBN 0-8198-1406-7); pap. 5.95 (ISBN 0-8198-1407-5). Dghtrs St Paul.

Schall, James V. The Politics of Heaven & Hell: Christian Themes from Classical, Medieval & Modern Political Philosophy. LC 84-7409. 360p. (Orig.). 1984. lib. bdg. 26.00 (ISBN 0-8191-3991-2); pap. text ed. 13.50 (ISBN 0-8191-3992-0). U Pr of Amer.

Skillen, James W. Christians Organizing for Political Service: A Study Guide Based on the Work of the Association for Public Justice. LC 80-66190. 113p. (Orig.). 1982. pap. 3.95 (ISBN 0-936456-01-9). Assn Public Justice.

Solt, Leo F. Saints in Arms. LC 74-153355. (Stanford University. Stanford Studies in History, Economics & Political Science: No. 18). Repr. of 1959 ed. 19.00 (ISBN 0-404-50976-2). AMS Pr.

Stephens, Joseph R., et al. Chartism & Christianity. Thompson, Dorothy, ed. (Chartism, Working-Class Politics in the Industrial Revolution Ser.). 132p. 1987. lib. bdg. 25.00 (ISBN 0-8240-5593-4). Garland Pub.

Stumpf, Samuel E. Democratic Manifesto: The Impact of Dynamic Christianity Upon Public Life & Government. LC 54-4773. 1954. 7.95x (ISBN 0-8265-1039-6). Vanderbilt U Pr.

Thoburn, Robert L. The Christian & Politics. 224p. (Orig.). 1984. pap. text ed. 4.95 (ISBN 0-317-15003-0). Thoburn Pr.

Thompson, Kenneth W. Christian Ethics & the Dilemmas of Foreign Policy. LC 59-15344. pap. 30.40 (ISBN 0-8357-9098-3, 2017937). Bks Demand UMI.

Wallis, Jim. Peacemakers: Christian Voices from the New Abolitionist Movement. LC 82-48940. 160p. (Orig.). 1983. pap. 5.95 (ISBN 0-06-069244-8, CN-4058, HarpR). Har-Row.

Walton, Rus. One Nation under God. 240p. 1987. pap. 9.95 (ISBN 0-8407-3093-4). Nelson.

The War on Christ in America: The Christian Fortress America under Siege Christophobes of the Media & of the Supreme Court in Action Demonic Maladies of the Western Culture, Freud, Marx Skinner & Other Ugly Pagans. 538p. 1985. 22.95 (ISBN 0-930711-01-7); pap. 15.95 (ISBN 0-317-19107-1). Ichthys Bks.

Wilhelmsen, Frederick D. Christianity & Political Philosophy. LC 77-22754. 256p. 1978. 22.00x (ISBN 0-8203-0431-X). U of Ga Pr.

Williams, Edward J. Latin American Christian Democratic Parties. LC 67-13159. Repr. of 1967 ed. 79.00 (2027567). Bks Demand UMI.

Yoder, John H. Christian Witness to the State. 1977. pap. 3.95 (ISBN 0-87303-165-2). Faith & Life.

Zwier, Robert. Born-Again Politics: The New Christian Right in America. (Illus.). 132p. 1982. pap. 4.95 (ISBN 0-87784-828-9). Inter-Varsity.

CHRISTIANITY AND PROGRESS

Bakole Wa Ilunga. Paths of Liberation: A Third World Spirituality. O'Connell, Matthew J., tr. from Fr. LC 84-5177. Tr. of Chemins de Liberation. 240p. (Orig.). 1984. pap. 12.95 (ISBN 0-88344-401-1). Orbis Bks.

Ferrarotti, Franco. A Theology for Nonbelievers: Post-Christian & Post-Marxist Reflections. LC 86-10782. (Studies in Social Thought: Polity & Civil Society). Tr. of Una Teologia per Atei. 208p. 1987. text ed. 21.50x (ISBN 0-8046-9401-X, 9401). Assoc Faculty Pr.

Ruether, Rosemary R. The Radical Kingdom: The Western Experience of Messianic Hope. LC 70-109080. 324p. 1975. pap. 5.95 (ISBN 0-8091-1860-2). Paulist Pr.

Sappington, Roger E. The Brethren in Industrial America. 512p. 1985. 24.95 (ISBN 0-87178-111-5). Brethren.

Wallis, Arthur. The Radical Christian. 160p. 1982. pap. 5.95 (ISBN 0-8007-5081-0, Power Bks). Revell.

CHRISTIANITY AND REVOLUTION

see Revolution (Theology)

CHRISTIANITY AND SCIENCE

see Religion and Science

CHRISTIANITY AND THE WORLD

see Church and the World

CHRISTIANITY AND WAR

see War and Religion

CHRISTIANITY IN LITERATURE

Baldwin, Helene L. Samuel Beckett's Real Silence. LC 80-21465. 184p. 1981. 19.95x (ISBN 0-271-00301-4). Pa St U Pr.

Bloxton, Marian W. Pioneers of Faith. 80p. 1984. pap. 7.95 (ISBN 0-8170-1036-X). Judson.

Boyle, Robert. James Joyce's Pauline Vision: A Catholic Exposition. LC 78-18901. 133p. 1978. 10.95x (ISBN 0-8093-0861-4). S Ill U Pr.

Brooks, Cleanth. Hidden God: Studies in Hemingway, Faulkner, Yeats, Eliot & Warren. (Orig.). 1963. 25.00x (ISBN 0-300-00327-7). Yale U Pr.

Carver, George. The Catholic Tradition in English Literature. 1977. Repr. lib. bdg. 25.00 (ISBN 0-8492-3819-6). R West.

Cavaliero, Glen. Charles Williams, Poet of Theology. LC 82-11420. Repr. of 1983 ed. 52.30 (2027538). Bks Demand UMI.

Chernaik, Warren L. The Poet's Time: Politics & Religion in the Work of Andrew Marvell. LC 82-4395. 250p. 1983. 37.50 (ISBN 0-521-24773-X). Cambridge U Pr.

Ellict, George R. Dramatic Providence in Macbeth: A Study of Shakespeare's Tragic Theme of Humanity & Grace, with a Supplementary Essay on King Lear. LC 70-90501. Repr. of 1960 ed. lib. bdg. 27.50x (ISBN 0-8371-3091-3, ELMA). Greenwood.

Friedrich, Gerhard. In Pursuit of Moby Dick. 1983. pap. 2.50x (ISBN 0-87574-098-7, 098). Pendle Hill.

Hassel, R. Chris, Jr. Renaissance Drama & the English Church Year. LC 78-24233. (Illus.). xii, 215p. 1979. 18.95x (ISBN 0-8032-2304-8). U of Nebr Pr.

Hunter, Robert G. Shakespeare & the Mystery of God's Judgments. LC 75-11449. 224p. 1976. 17.00x (ISBN 0-8203-0388-7). U of Ga Pr.

Jones, Alan H. Independence of Exegesis: The Study of Christianity in the Work of Alfred Loisy, Charles Guignebert, & Maurice Goguel. 313p. 1983. lib. bdg. 75.00x (ISBN 3-16-144451-5, Pub. by J C B Mohr BRD). Coronet Bks.

Knight, G. Wilson. The Christian Renaissance: With Interpretations of Dante, Shakespeare & Goethe & New Discussions of Oscar Wilde & the Gospel of Thomas. LC 81-40252. 366p. 1982. lib. bdg. 32.00 (ISBN 0-8191-1913-X); pap. text ed. 16.50 (ISBN 0-8191-1914-8). U Pr of Amer.

Lewis, C. S. The Visionary Christian: One Hundred Thirty-One Readings from C. S. Lewis, Selected & Edited by Chad Walsh. 256p. 1981. 10.95 (ISBN 0-02-570540-7). Macmillan.

Roberts, Richard. Jesus of Poets & Prophets. LC 74-118546. 1971. Repr. of 1919 ed. 22.50x (ISBN 0-8046-1171-8, Pub. by Kennikat). Assoc Faculty Pr.

Robinson, Fred C. Beowulf & the Appositive Style. LC 84-11889. (Hodges Lecture Ser.). 120p. 1985. text ed. 12.95x (ISBN 0-87049-444-9); pap. 6.95x (ISBN 0-87049-531-3). U of Tenn Pr.

Sammons, Martha C. A Guide Through Narnia. LC 78-26476. (Wheaton Literary Ser.). 164p. 1979. pap. 3.95 (ISBN 0-87788-325-4). Shaw Pubs.

Scott, Nathan A., Jr., ed. Adversity & Grace: Studies in Recent American Literature. LC 68-16717. (Essays in Divinity Ser.: Vol. 4). 1968. 9.50x (ISBN 0-226-74283-0). U of Chicago Pr.

Swardson, Harold R. Poetry & the Fountain of Light: Observations on the Conflict Between Christian & Classical Traditions in Seventeenth-Century Poetry. LC 62-9993. 1962. 4.50x (ISBN 0-8262-0015-X). U of Mo Pr.

White, Helen C. The Tudor Books of Private Devotion. LC 78-21661. (Illus.). 1979. Repr. of 1951 ed. lib. bdg. 24.75x (ISBN 0-313-21063-2, WHTB). Greenwood.

Wilson, Samuel L. The Theology of Modern Literature. LC 76-47565. 1976. Repr. of 1899 ed. lib. bdg. 40.00 (ISBN 0-8414-9484-3). Folcroft.

CHRISTIANS, JEWISH

see Jewish Christians

CHRISTIANS IN AFRICA

Beaver, Robert P. Christianity & African Education: The Papers of a Conference at the University of Chicago. LC 65-25184. pap. 58.30 (ISBN 0-317-09800-4, 2012940). Bks Demand UMI.

Bond, George, et al, eds. African Christianity: Patterns of Religious Continuity. LC 79-51668. (AP Studies in Anthropology Ser.). 1979. 29.95 (ISBN 0-12-113450-4). Acad Pr.

Clarke, Peter B. West Africa & Christianity. 280p. 1986. pap. text ed. 17.95 (ISBN 0-7131-8263-6). E Arnold.

Daneel, M. L. Zionism & Faith-Healing in Rhodesia: Aspects of African Independent Churches. V. A. February Communications, tr. from Dutch. (Illus.). 1970. pap. 6.00x (ISBN 90-2796-278-2). Mouton.

Davies, Horton. Great South African Christians. LC 70-104242. Repr. of 1951 ed. lib. bdg. 22.50x (ISBN 0-8371-3916-3, DAGC). Greenwood.

Eboussi Boulaga, F. Christianity Without Fetishes: An African Critique & Recapture of Christianity. Barr, Robert R., tr. from Fr. LC 84-5807. Tr. of Christianisme sans Fetiche. 256p. (Orig.). 1984. pap. 11.95 (ISBN 0-88344-432-1). Orbis Bks.

Ela, Jean-Marc. African Cry. Barr, Robert R., tr. from Fr. LC 86-12429. Tr. of Le Cri de l'homme Africain. 176p. (Orig.). 1986. pap. 10.95 (ISBN 0-88344-259-0). Orbis Bks.

Forman, Charles W., ed. Christianity in the Non-Western World. facs. ed. LC 71-117792. (Essay Index Reprint Ser). 1967. 17.00 (ISBN 0-8369-1806-1). Ayer Co Pubs.

Hastings, A. A History of African Christianity: 1950-1975. LC 78-16599. (Illus.). 1979. o. p. 49.50 (ISBN 0-521-22212-5); pap. 17.95 (ISBN 0-521-29397-9). Cambridge U Pr.

Hastings, Adrian. African Christianity. 12p. 1977. 9.95 (ISBN 0-8164-0336-8, AY6700, HarpR). Har-Row.

Healey, Joseph G. A Fifth Gospel: The Experience of Black Christian Values. LC 80-25033. (Illus.). 220p. (Orig.). 1981. pap. 3.98 (ISBN 0-88344-013-X). Orbis Bks.

Kraft, Marguerite G. Worldview & Communication of the Gospel. LC 78-10196. (Illus.). 1978. pap. 7.95 (ISBN 0-87808-324-3). William Carey Lib.

Linden, Ian & Linden, Jane. Church & Revolution in Rwanda. LC 76-58329. 295p. 1977. text ed. 39.50x (ISBN 0-8419-0305-0, Africana). Holmes & Meier.

McCracken, J. Politics & Christianity in Malawi 1875-1940. LC 76-27905. (Cambridge Commonwealth Ser.). (Illus.). 1977. 49.50 (ISBN 0-521-21444-0). Cambridge U Pr.

Norman, Edward. Christianity in the Southern Hemisphere: The Churches in Latin America & South Africa. 1981. text ed. 38.95x (ISBN 0-19-821127-9). Oxford U Pr.

Ofori, Patrick E. Christianity in Tropical Africa: A Selective Annotated Bibliography. 461p. 1977. lib. bdg. 48.00 (ISBN 3-262-00002-7). Kraus Intl.

Pope John Paul II. Africa: Apostolic Pilgrimage. 1980. 8.00 (ISBN 0-8198-0708-7); pap. 7.00 (ISBN 0-8198-0709-5). Dghtrs St Paul.

Ranger, T. O. & Weller, John, eds. Themes in the Christian History of Central Africa. 1974. 44.00x (ISBN 0-520-02536-9). U of Cal Pr.

Roberts, Richard. Jesus of Poets & Prophets. LC 74-118546. 1971. Repr. of 1919 ed. 22.50x (ISBN 0-8046-1171-8, Pub. by Kennikat). Assoc Faculty Pr.

Sanneh, Lamin. West African Christianity: The Religious Impact. 304p. (Orig.). 1983. pap. 11.95 (ISBN 0-88344-703-7). Orbis Bks.

Shorter, Aylward. African Christian Theology: Adaptation or Incarnation? LC 77-23325. 180p. (Orig.). 1977. 7.95 (ISBN 0-88344-002-4); pap. 4.95 (ISBN 0-88344-003-2). Orbis Bks.

Swardson, Harold R. Poetry & the Fountain of Light: Observations on the Conflict Between Christian & Classical Traditions in Seventeenth-Century Poetry. LC 62-9993. 1962. 4.50x (ISBN 0-8262-0015-X). U of Mo Pr.

Taber, Charles R., ed. The Church in Africa: Nineteen Seventy Seven. LC 78-14923. 1978. pap. 6.95 (ISBN 0-87808-161-5). William Carey Lib.

Tanner, Ralph E. Transition in African Beliefs: Traditional Religion & Christian Change: A Study in Sukumaland, Tanzania, East Africa. LC 67-21411. pap. 67.50 (ISBN 0-317-26638-1, 2025117). Bks Demand UMI.

Tasie, G. O. Christian Missionary Enterprise in the Niger Delta, 1864-1918. (Studies on Religion in Africa Ser.: No. 3). (Illus.). 1978. text ed. 49.95 (ISBN 90-04-05243-7). Humanities.

CHRISTIANS IN ASIA

Assfalg, Julius & Krueger, P. Kleines Woerterbuch Des Christlichen Orients. 1st ed. (Ger.). 1975. 52.00 (ISBN 3-447-01707-4, M-7514, Pub. by Harrassowitz). French & Eur.

Digan, Parig. Churches in Contestation: Asian Christian Social Protest. LC 83-19338. 224p. (Orig.). 1984. pap. 10.95 (ISBN 0-88344-102-0). Orbis Bks.

Dyrness, W. A. Christian Art in Asia. 1979. pap. text ed. 11.50x (ISBN 0-391-01157-X). Humanities.

Elwood, Douglas J., ed. The Humanities in Christian Higher Education in Asia: Ethical & Religious Perspectives. 1978. pap. 7.50x (ISBN 0-686-23913-X, Pub. by New Day Pub). Cellar.

Forman, Charles W., ed. Christianity in the Non-Western World. facs. ed. LC 71-117792. (Essay Index Reprint Ser). 1967. 17.00 (ISBN 0-8369-1806-1). Ayer Co Pubs.

French, Hajjar. Christiarisme en Orient. 9.00x (ISBN 0-86685-172-0). Intl Bk Ctr.

Lillie, Arthur. Buddha & Buddhism. LC 76-100573. 1975. 11.25x (ISBN 0-89684-372-6). Orient Bk Dist.

Nacpil, Emerito, ed. The Human & the Holy: Asian Perspectives in Christian Theology. Elwood, Douglas J. 1978. pap. text ed. 10.00x (ISBN 0-686-23912-1, Pub. by New Day Pub). Cellar.

Ralli, Augustus. Christians at Mecca. LC 70-118545. 1971. Repr. of 1909 ed. 27.00x (ISBN 0-8046-1170-X, Pub. by Kennikat). Assoc Faculty Pr.

Spidlik, Tomas. The Spirituality of the Christian East: A Systematic Handbook. Gythiel, Anthony P., tr. from Fr. (Cistercian Studies Ser.: No. 79). Tr. of La Spritiualite de l'Orient Chritienne. 1986. 48.95 (ISBN 0-87907-879-0); pap. 17.00 (ISBN 0-87907-979-7). Cistercian Pubns.

CHRISTIANS IN BELIZE

Johnson, Wallace R. A History of Christianity in Belize 1776-1838. (Illus.). 300p. (Orig.). 1985. lib. bdg. 26.00 (ISBN 0-8191-4552-1); pap. text ed. 13.50 (ISBN 0-8191-4553-X). U Pr of Amer.

CHRISTIANS IN CHINA

Adeney, David H. China: The Church's Long March. LC 85-25666. (Worldview Ser.). 238p. 1985. pap. 7.95 (ISBN 0-8307-1096-5, 5418621). Regal.

Barnett, Suzanne W. & Fairbank, John K., eds. Christianity in China: Early Protestant Missionary Writings. (Harvard Studies in American-East Asian Relations: 9). 280p. 1984. text ed. 20.00x (ISBN 0-674-12881-8). Harvard U Pr.

Brown, G. Thompson. Christianity in the People's Republic of China. LC 82-49018. 240p. 1983. pap. 7.25 (ISBN 0-8042-1484-0). John Knox.

--Christianity in the People's Republic of China. rev., 2nd ed. LC 86-45554. 256p. 1986. pap. 9.95 (ISBN 0-8042-1485-9). John Knox.

Covell, Ralph. W. A. P Martin: Pioneer of Progress in China. LC 77-13321. Repr. of 1978 ed. 59.10 (ISBN 0-8357-9133-5, 2012723). Bks Demand UMI.

Demarest, Bruce A. Who Is Jesus. Chen, Ruth T., tr. (Basic Doctrine Ser.: Bk. 1). 1985. pap. write for info. (ISBN 0-941598-26-8). Living Spring Pubns.

Dunn, Ronald. The Faith Crisis. Chao, Lorna Y., tr. (Chinese.). 1985. pap. write for info. (ISBN 0-941598-30-6). Living Spring Pubns.

Flynn, Leslie B. What Is Man. Chao, Lorna Y., tr. (Chinese.). 1985. pap. write for info. (ISBN 0-941598-27-6). Living Spring Pubns.

Gernet, Jacques. China & the Christian Impact: A Conflict of Cultures. LLoyd, Janet, tr. 280p. 1985. 49.50 (ISBN 0-521-26681-5); pap. 17.95 (ISBN 0-521-31319-8). Cambridge U Pr.

Huang, Quentin K. Y. Pilgrim from a Red Land. 1981. 8.00 (ISBN 0-682-49669-3). Exposition Pr FL.

Lawrence, Carl. The Church in China. 176p. (Orig.). 1985. pap. 5.95 (ISBN 0-87123-815-2). Bethany Hse.

Moule, A. C. Christians in China Before the Year 1550. 59.95 (ISBN 0-87968-865-3). Gordon Pr.

Nee, Watchman. The Joyful Heart. Chen, Ruth T., tr. (Chinese.). 1985. write for info. (ISBN 0-941598-91-8); pap. write for info. (ISBN 0-941598-24-1). Living Spring Pubns.

Saucy, Richard L. Is Bible Reliable, Bk. 2. Wong, Ernest, tr. (Basic Doctrine Ser.). (Chinese.). 1985. pap. write for info. (ISBN 0-941598-28-4). Living Spring Pubns.

Shelly, Bruce L. What Is the Church, Bk. 3. Chao, Lorna Y., tr. (Basic Doctrine Ser.). (Chinese.). 1985. pap. write for info. (ISBN 0-941598-25-X). Living Spring Pubns.

Spurgeon, Charles. All of Grace. Chen, Ruth T. & Chou, Peter, trs. (Chinese.). 142p. 1984. pap. write for info. (ISBN 0-941598-22-5). Living Spring Pubns.

Stott, John R. Bible Book for Today. Chan, Silas, tr. (Chinese.). 1985. pap. write for info. (ISBN 0-941598-23-3). Living Spring Pubns.

Strauss, Richard L. Famous Couples of the Bible. Chen, Ruth T., tr. (Chinese.). 1985. pap. write for info. (ISBN 0-941598-29-2). Living Spring Pubns.

Ting, K. H., et al. Chinese Christians Speak Out. (Chinese Spotlight Ser.). (Illus.). 140p. 1984. pap. 3.95 (ISBN 0-8351-1281-0). China Bks.

Wing-hung Lam. Chinese Theology in Construction. LC 81-15483. 320p. 1983. pap. 11.95x (ISBN 0-87808-180-1). William Carey Lib.

Wu, Chao-Kwang. The International Aspect of the Missionary Movement in China. LC 75-41300. (Johns Hopkins University. Studies in Historical & Political Science: Extra Volumes; New Ser.: No. 11). Repr. of 1930 ed. 18.50 (ISBN 0-404-14708-9). AMS Pr.

CHRISTIANS IN EASTERN EUROPE

Canadian Polish Millenium Fund Staff. Poland's Millenium of Christianity. (Eng. & Fr.). 50p. 1966. 1.00 (ISBN 0-940962-29-2). Polish Inst Art & Sci.

Pridham, Geoffrey. Christian Democracy in Western Germany. LC 77-9235. 1978. 27.50x (ISBN 0-312-13396-0). St Martin.

Tec, Nechama. When Light Pierced the Darkness: Christian Rescue of Jews in Nazi-Occupied Poland. (Illus.). 320p. 1986. 19.95 (ISBN 0-19-503643-3). Oxford U Pr.

CHRISTIANS IN INDIA

Faria, S., et al. The Emerging Christian Woman. 292p. 1986. 8.50x (ISBN 0-8364-1810-7, Pub. by Macmillan India). South Asia Bks.

Garbe, Richard. India & Christendom: The Historical Connections Between Their Religions. Robinson, Lydia, tr. from Ger. 321p. 1959. 22.95 (ISBN 0-87548-232-5). Open Court.

Gladstone, J. W. Protestant Christianity & People's Movements in Kerala, 1850-1936. 470p. 1986. 12.50x (ISBN 0-8364-1821-2, Pub. by Somaiya). South Asia Bks.

Godwin, Shiri. Christian Social Thought in India, 1962-77. (Orig.). 1983. pap. 6.00 (ISBN 0-8364-0988-4, Pub. by Christian Lit Soc India). South Asia Bks.

Neill, Stephen. A History of Christianity in India: The Beginnings to 1707. LC 82-23475. 600p. 1984. 85.00 (ISBN 0-521-24351-3). Cambridge U Pr.

Thomas, Abraham V. Christians in Secular India. LC 72-420. 246p. 1973. 20.00 (ISBN 0-8386-1021-8). Fairleigh Dickinson.

CHRISTIANS IN JAPAN

Book, Doyle C. The Threshold Is High: The Brethren in Christ in Japan. Zercher, Ray M. & Pierce, Glen A., eds. (Illus.). xii, 210p. (Orig.). 1986. pap. 7.95 (ISBN 0-916035-15-8). Evangel Indiana.

Cary, Otis. A History of Christianity in Japan: Roman Catholic & Greek Orthodox Missions, 2 vols. LC 75-28972. (Illus.). 1975. Repr. of 1909 ed. boxed 36.95 (ISBN 0-8048-1177-6). C E Tuttle.

Elison, George. Deus Destroyed: The Image of Christianity in Early Modern Japan. LC 72-97833. (East Asian Ser: No. 72). 704p. 1974. 40.00x (ISBN 0-674-19961-8). Harvard U Pr.

Koyama, Kosuke. Mount Fuji & Mount Sinai: A Critique of Idols. LC 84-16556. Orig. Title: Mount Fui & Mount Sinai - A Pilgramage in Theology. 288p. (Orig.). 1985. pap. 12.95 (ISBN 0-88344-353-8). Orbis Bks.

Paske-Smith, Montague, ed. Japanese Traditions of Christianity: Being Some Old Translations from the Japanese, with British Consular Reports of the Persecutions of 1868-1872. (Studies in Japanese History & Civilization). 1979. Repr. of 1930 ed. 17.50 (ISBN 0-89093-257-3). U Pubns Amer.

Phillips, James M. From the Rising of the Sun: Christians & Society in Contemporary Japan. LC 80-24609. 320p. (Orig.). 1981. pap. 14.95 (ISBN 0-88344-145-4). Orbis Bks.

Picken, Stuart D. Christianity & Japan: Meeting, Conflict, Hope. LC 82-48787. (Illus.). 80p. 1983. 18.95 (ISBN 0-87011-571-5). Kodansha.

Scheiner, Irwin. Christian Converts & Social Protest in Meiji Japan. LC 74-94981. (Center for Japanese Studies). 1970. 35.00x (ISBN 0-520-01585-1). U of Cal Pr.

Thelle, Notto R. Buddhism & Christianity in Japan: From Conflict to Dialogue, 1854-1899. (Illus.). 384p. 1987. text ed. 30.00x. UH Pr.

CHRISTIANS IN LATIN AMERICA

Berrigan, Daniel. Steadfastness of the Saints: A Journal of Peace & War in Central & North America. LC 85-5120. 160p. 1985. pap. 7.95 (ISBN 0-88344-447-X). Orbis Bks.

Berryman, Philip. The Religious Roots of Rebellion: Christians in Central American Revolutions. LC 83-19343. 480p. (Orig.). 1984. pap. 19.95 (ISBN 0-88344-105-5). Orbis Bks.

CHRISTIANS IN THE NEAR EAST

Betts, Robert B. Christians in the Arab East. LC 78-8674. 1981. 12.50 (ISBN 0-8042-0796-8). John Knox.

McCurry, Don M., ed. World Christianity: Middle East. LC 79-87790. 156p. 1979. pap. text ed. 12.00 (ISBN 0-912552-27-1). Missions Adv Res Com Ctr.

Reid, Donald M. The Odyssey of Farah Antun: A Syrian Christian's Quest for Secularism. LC 74-80598. (Studies in Middle Eastern History: No. 2). 1975. 25.00x (ISBN 0-88297-009-7). Bibliotheca.

CHRISTIANS IN THE PHILIPPINE ISLANDS

Sitoy, T. Valentino, Jr. A History of Christianity in the Philippines: The Initial Encounter, Vol. 1. (Illus.). 384p. (Orig.). 1985. pap. 18.50x (ISBN 971-10-0254-X, Pub by New Day Philippines). Cellar.

CHRISTIANS IN THE SOVIET UNION

Bailey, Martin. One Thousand Years: Stories from the History of Christianity in the U. S. S. R., 988-1988. 1987. pap. 4.95. Friend Pr.

Chmykhaler, Timothy & Smith, Danny. The Last Christian: Release of the Siberian Seven. 208p. 1985. pap. 7.95 (ISBN 0-310-34021-7, 12411P). Zondervan.

Klibanov, A. I. History of Religious Sectarianism in Russia (1860s-1917) Dunn, Stephen P., ed. LC 81-12180. (Illus.). 380p. 1982. 54.00 (ISBN 0-08-026794-7). Pergamon.

Merlin, Lester. Courage for a Cross: Six Stories About Growing up Christian in the U. S. S. R. 1987. pap. 3.95. Friend Pr.

Talberg, N. D. Istorija Russkoi Tserkvi. Tr. of History of the Russuan Church. 927p. 1959. pap. text ed. 25.00 (ISBN 0-317-30295-7). Holy Trinity.

Voieivkov, N. N. Tserkov', Rus' i Rim. Tr. of The Church, Russia & Rome. 512p. 1983. text ed. 25.00 (ISBN 0-88465-016-2); pap. text ed. 20.00 (ISBN 0-88465-015-4). Holy Trinity.

CHRISTIANS IN TURKEY

Gerostergios, Asterios. St. Photios the Great. LC 80-82285. (Illus.). 125p. 1980. 8.50 (ISBN 0-914744-50-X); pap. 5.50 (ISBN 0-914744-51-8). Inst Byzantine.

CHRISTIANS OF ST. JOHN

see Mandaeans

CHRISTMAS

see also Christmas Decorations; Jesus Christ–Nativity

Aivanhov, Omraam M. Christmas & Easter in the Initiatic Tradition. (Izvor Collection: Vol. 209). (Illus.). 139p. (Orig.). pap. 4.95 (ISBN 2-85566-226-5, Pub. by Prosveta France). Prosveta USA.

Alessi, Vincie, ed. Programs for Advent & Christmas. 1978. pap. 4.95 (ISBN 0-8170-0808-X). Judson.

Alter, Judy & Roach, Joyce G., eds. Texas & Christmas: A Collection of Traditions, Memories & Folklore. LC 83-4717. (Illus.). 86p. 1983. pap. 6.50 (ISBN 0-912646-81-0). Tex Christian.

Arnold, Eberhard, et al. When the Time Was Fulfilled: Talks & Writings on Advent & Christmas. LC 65-17599. 1965. 7.00 (ISBN 0-87486-104-7). Plough.

Arnold, Heini & Blough, Dwight. Christmas Night, O Night of Nights. 1976. pap. 1.25 (ISBN 0-87486-120-9). Plough.

Ashton, John. Righte Merrie Christmasse. LC 68-56543. (Illus.). 1968. Repr. of 1894 ed. 15.00 (ISBN 0-405-08225-8, Pub. by Blom). Ayer Co Pubs.

Auld, William M. Christmas Traditions. LC 68-58167. 1968. Repr. of 1931 ed. 42.00x (ISBN 0-8103-3353-8). Gale.

--Christmas Traditions. 1977. lib. bdg. 59.95 (ISBN 0-8490-1619-3). Gordon Pr.

Austin, E. L. Gift of Christmas. pap. 3.95 (ISBN 0-8010-0149-8). Baker Bk.

Bach, Morcus. Because of Christmas. (Illus.). 192p. 1986. pap. 8.00 (ISBN 0-940581-00-0). Fellowship Spirit.

Bacher, June M. Great Gifts of Christmas Joy. LC 83-70005. 96p. 1983. pap. 4.95 (ISBN 0-8054-5707-0). Broadman.

Baker, Margaret. Discovering Christmas Customs & Folklore: A Guide to Seasonal Rites. 3.25 (ISBN 0-913714-56-9). Legacy Bks.

--Discovering Christmas Customs & Folklore. (Discovering Ser.: No. 32). (Illus.). 56p. (Orig.). 1985. pap. 3.50 (ISBN 0-85263-173-1, Pub. by Shire Pubns England). Seven Hills Bks.

Baldwin, Ed & Baldwin, Stevie. Celebrations of Christmas. LC 85-47331. (A Family Workshop Bk.). 248p. 1985. pap. 12.95 (ISBN 0-8019-7448-8). Chilton.

Barnett, James H. The American Christmas: A Study in National Culture. LC 75-22799. (America in Two Centuries Ser.). 1976. Repr. of 1954 ed. 17.00x (ISBN 0-405-07671-1). Ayer Co Pubs.

Becker, Ralph. The Truth about Christmas. pap. 0.50 (ISBN 0-685-41826-X). Reiner.

Bell, Irving. Christmas in Old New England. LC 80-69858. 54p. 1981. 8.95 (ISBN 0-917780-02-7). April Hill.

Beyer, Douglas. Basic Beliefs of Christians. 64p. 1981. pap. 2.95 (ISBN 0-8170-0896-9). Judson.

Bjorn, Thyra F. Once upon a Christmas Time. 1964. 5.95 (ISBN 0-03-047195-8). H Holt & Co.

Bloom, James M. & Sherer, Michael L. A Festival of Lights. (Orig.). 1986. pap. 2.25 (ISBN 0-89536-833-1, 6847). CSS of Ohio.

Brady, Cyrus T. Little Book for Christmas. facsimile ed. LC 73-167443. (Short Story Index Reprint Ser). (Illus.). Repr. of 1917 ed. 17.00 (ISBN 0-8369-3969-7). Ayer Co Pubs.

Brandling, Redvers. Christmas in the Primary School. (Ward Lock Educational Ser.). 1985. 29.00x (ISBN 0-7062-4068-5, Pub. by Ward Lock Educ Co Ltd). State Mutual Bk.

Bridgman, J. The Christmas Book: Christmas in the Olden Time: Its Customs & Their Origin. 1978. Repr. of 1859 ed. lib. bdg. 27.50 (ISBN 0-8492-3711-4). R West.

Brown, Joan W. Best of Christmas Joys. LC 83-45165. 64p. (Orig.). 1983. pap. 2.95 (ISBN 0-385-19039-5, Galilee). Doubleday.

Buchanan, Annette M. & Martin, Kay A. The Twelve Months of Christmas. Bolt, John, ed. (Illus.). 192p. 1980. pap. 7.95 (ISBN 0-939114-01-1). Partridge Pair.

Campbell, R. J. The Story of Christmas. 1977. lib. bdg. 59.95 (ISBN 0-8490-2677-6). Gordon Pr.

Christmas: A Family Service. 1982. pap. 2.25 (ISBN 0-89536-710-6, 0363). CSS of Ohio.

Christmas Around the World. (Illus.). 169p. 1985. 7.98 (ISBN 1-85079-025-6, Pub. by New Orchard England). Sterling.

Christmas in All the World. LC 79-50087. (Illus.). 1979. pap. 4.95 (ISBN 0-8066-1704-7, 10-11238). Augsburg.

Christmas in Latin America. (Eng.). 1976. pap. 1.00 (ISBN 0-8270-4365-1). OAS.

Christmas Program Resource Book Two. 48p. 1984. pap. 2.50 (ISBN 0-8066-2075-7, 23-1501). Augsburg.

Christmas: The Annual of Christmas Literature & Art, Vol. 54. (Illus.). 64p. 1984. 14.50 (ISBN 0-8066-8965-X, 17-0129); pap. text ed. 6.95 (ISBN 0-8066-8964-1, 17-0128). Augsburg.

Christmas: Voices from the Heart. Date not set. price not set (ISBN 0-934383-10-3). Pride Prods.

Ciappetta, John T. A Christmas Caring, a Christmas Sharing. 32p. 1987. 6.95 (ISBN 0-89962-646-7). Todd & Honeywell.

Conner, Mona. Christmas at Our House. 64p. 1986. 14.45i (ISBN 0-06-015596-5, HarpT). Har-Row.

Cram, Mildred. Born in Time: The Christmas Story. (Illus.). 26p. (Orig.). 1972. pap. 2.50 (ISBN 0-913270-10-5). Sunstone Pr.

Crippen, Thomas G. Christmas & Christmas Lore. LC 69-16067. (Illus.). 256p. 1972. Repr. of 1923 ed. 50.00x (ISBN 0-8103-3029-6). Gale.

--Christmas & Christmas Lore. 1976. lib. bdg. 59.95 (ISBN 0-8490-1617-7). Gordon Pr.

Davidson, Alice J. Christmas Wrapped in Love. 128p. 13.95 (ISBN 0-687-07818-0). Abingdon.

Dawson, William F. Christmas, Its Origin & Associations, Together with Its Historical Events & Festive Celebrations During Nineteen Centuries. LC 68-54857. 1968. Repr. of 1902 ed. 54.00x (ISBN 0-8103-3351-1). Gale.

Day, Mark. Yuletide Lost. 1981. 4.95 (ISBN 0-89536-484-0, 2506). CSS of Ohio.

Dueland, Joy. What Is Christmas? (Illus.). 9p. 1978. pap. 1.50. Phunn Pubs.

Ebel, Holly. Christmas in the Air: A New Fashioned Book for An Old Fashioned Christmas. (Illus.). 96p. (Orig.). 1982. pap. 7.95 (ISBN 0-943786-00-2). HollyDay.

Edington, David W. Christians & the Third World. 160p. 1982. pap. text ed. 7.95 (ISBN 0-85364-286-9). Attic Pr.

Ehlen-Miller, Margaret, et al. The Gift of Time: Family Activities for Advent, Christmas, Epiphany. (Illus.). 1977. pap. 4.95 (ISBN 0-8192-1224-5). Morehouse.

Elspeth. Victorian Christmas: 1876. 1974. pap. 1.50 (ISBN 0-87588-106-8). Hobby Hse.

Flachman, Leonard, ed. Christmas: The Annual of Christmas Literature & Art, Vol. 57. (Illus.). 64p. 1987. text ed. 14.50 (ISBN 0-8066-8971-4, 17-0135); pap. 6.95 (ISBN 0-8066-8970-6, 17-0134). Augsburg.

Frost, Marie H. Our Christmas Handbook, No. 4. (Illus.). 112p. 1986. 7.95 (ISBN 0-87403-081-1, 3044). Standard Pub.

Geller, Norman. It's Not the Jewish Christmas. (Illus.). 20p. 1985. pap. 4.95 (ISBN 0-915753-09-X). N Geller Pub.

Gibbons, Gail. Christmas Time. (Illus.). 32p. 1985. pap. 5.95 (ISBN 0-8234-0575-3). Holiday.

Gober, Lasley F. The Christmas Lover's Handbook. LC 85-13450. (Illus.). 256p. 1985. pap. 12.95 (ISBN 0-932620-53-1). Betterway Pubns.

Golby, J. M. & Purdue, A. W. The Making of the Modern Christmas. LC 86-7083. (Illus.). 144p. 1986. 19.95 (ISBN 0-8203-0879-X). U of GA Pr.

Goodman, Marguerite. Christmas Comes in Assorted Sizes. Ashton, Sylvia, ed. LC 77-80303. 1977. 14.95 (ISBN 0-87949-111-6). Ashley Bks.

Greif, Martin. The St. Nicholas Book. LC 76-5089. (Illus.). 60p. 1976. 5.95 (ISBN 0-87663-554-0). Universe.

Greif, Martin, ed. The Saint Nicholas Book: A Celebration of Christmas Past. 3rd, rev. ed. LC 86-21706. (Illus.). 96p. (Orig.). 1986. pap. 7.95 (ISBN 1-55562-006-X). Main Street.

Hacker, Richard C. The Christmas Pipe: A Collector's Celebration of Pipe Smoking at Yuletide. LC 86-70905. (Illus.). 156p. 1986. 27.95 (ISBN 0-931253-01-2). Autumngold Pub.

Hall, Manly P. Story of Christmas. pap. 2.50 (ISBN 0-89314-379-0). Philos Res.

Halpert, Herbert & Story, G. M., eds. Christmas Mumming in Newfoundland: Essays in Anthropology, Folklore, & History. LC 71-391290. pap. 64.50 (ISBN 0-317-42289-8, 2055819). Bks Demand UMI.

Haugan, Randolph, ed. Christmas, Vol. 47. LC 32-30914. 64p. 1977. 14.50 (ISBN 0-8066-8951-X, 17-0115); pap. 6.95 (ISBN 0-8066-8950-1, 17-0114). Augsburg.

Haugan, Randolph E., ed. Christmas: An American Annual of Christmas Literature & Art, Vol. 48. LC 32-30914. (Illus.). 64p. 1978. 14.50 (ISBN 0-8066-8953-6, 17-0117); pap. 6.95 (ISBN 0-8066-8952-8, 17-0116). Augsburg.

--Christmas: An American Annual of Christmas Literature & Art, Vol. 49. LC 32-30914. (Illus.). 64p. 1979. 14.50 (ISBN 0-8066-8955-2, 17-0119); pap. 6.95 (ISBN 0-8066-8954-4, 17-0118). Augsburg.

Heaton, Rose H. The Perfect Christmas. Repr. of 1932 ed. 20.00 (ISBN 0-686-20659-2). Lib Serv Inc.

Hendricks, William C. & Vogel, Cora. Handbook of Christmas Programs. 1978. pap. 9.95 (ISBN 0-8010-4204-6). Baker Bk.

Hervey, Thomas K. The Book of Christmas. 1977. lib. bdg. 59.95 (ISBN 0-8490-1530-8). Gordon Pr.

Hirth, Mary, compiled by. The Stanley Marcus Collection of Christmas Books. (Illus., Orig.). 1968. pap. 6.00 (ISBN 0-87959-029-7). U of Tex H Ransom Ctr.

Hoard, Laurie. Standard Christmas Program Book, No. 46. 48p. 1985. pap. 1.95 (ISBN 0-87239-850-1, 8646). Standard Pub.

Hoard, Laurie, ed. Christmas Programs for Children. 48p. 1986. pap. 1.95 (ISBN 0-87239-940-0, 8601). Standard Pub.

--Christmas Programs for the Church, No. 19. 64p. 1986. pap. 2.95 (ISBN 0-87239-914-1, 8619). Standard Pub.

Hornung, Clarence P. Old-Fashioned Christmas in Illustration & Decoration. (Orig.). 1970. pap. 5.00 (ISBN 0-486-22367-1). Dover.

Johnston, Patricia C. The Minnesota Christmas Book. LC 85-90344. (Illus.). 96p. 1985. text ed. 27.50 (ISBN 0-942934-08-3). Johnston Pub.

Kapilla, Cleo & Simons, Eleanor. The Joy of Christmas: A Manual for Holiday Survival. LC 83-90104. 96p. (Orig.). 1983. pap. 7.95 (ISBN 0-686-88978-9). K & S.

Kapilla, Cleo, et al. Joy of Christmas. 96p. 1983. pap. 7.95 (ISBN 0-9611466-0-5). Wimmer Bks.

Kellogg, Alice M., ed. How to Celebrate Thanksgiving & Christmas. facs. ed. LC 76-139765. (Granger Index Reprint Ser). 1897. 15.00 (ISBN 0-8369-6219-2). Ayer Co Pubs.

Kemper, Frederick. The Christmas Cycle. 1982. 6.95 (ISBN 0-570-03842-1, 12-2945). Concordia.

Kramer, Robert A. The Colors of Christmas. (Orig.). 1980. pap. 1.75 (ISBN 0-937172-07-3). JLJ Pubs.

Krutch, Joseph W., et al. Wildlife's Christmas Treasury. Rifkin, Natalie S., ed. LC 76-12388. (Illus.). 160p. 1976. 11.95 (ISBN 0-912186-22-4). Natl Wildlife.

Kurtz, Muriel T. Prepare Our Hearts: Advent & Christmas Traditions for Families. 144p. (Orig.). 1986. pap. 6.95 spiral bdg. (ISBN 0-8358-0544-1). Upper Room.

Kyle, Louisa V. Country Woman's Christmas. LC 83-81553. (Illus.). 80p. 1984. 10.95 (ISBN 0-938694-12-X). JCP Corp VA.

Leary, Norma. Christmas on Trial. (Orig.). 1983. pap. 2.95 (ISBN 0-937172-56-1). JLJ Pubs.

--Portraits of Customs & Carols. 1983. pap. 2.95 (ISBN 0-937172-54-5). JLJ Pubs.

--Voices of Christmas. (Orig.). 1983. pap. 3.25 (ISBN 0-937172-55-3). JLJ Pubs.

Lee, Sharon. When the Time Had Fully Come: Christmas Service for Church Schools. 32p. (Orig.). 1984. pap. 0.90 ea. (ISBN 0-8066-2101-X, 23-3010). Augsburg.

Lewis, D. B. & Hexeltine, G. C. A Christmas Book. 1977. Repr. of 1928 ed. lib. bdg. 10.00 (ISBN 0-8495-3204-3). Arden Lib.

Linam, Gail. Celebrate Christmas. 1982. pap. 2.95 (ISBN 0-8054-9305-0, 4293-05). Broadman.

Luccock, Halford E. A Sprig of Holly. new ed. Hartman, Charles S., ed. & intro. by. LC 78-17096. 64p. 1978. text ed. 3.50 (ISBN 0-8298-0354-8). Pilgrim NY.

Luttrell, Susan E. Love Was Born at Christmas. (Orig.). 1981. pap. 3.25 (ISBN 0-89536-483-2, 1234). CSS of Ohio.

McInnes, Celia. An English Christmas: The Traditions, the Observances, the Festivities. LC 86-7553. (Illus.). 104p. 1986. 14.95 (ISBN 0-8050-0043-7). H Holt & Co.

Martin, Marcia O. The Christmas Book. (Illus.). 64p. 1985. 15.95 (ISBN 0-88363-585-2). H L Levin.

Miles, Clement A. Christmas Customs & Traditions: Their History & Significance. LC 76-9183. (Illus.). 1976. pap. 6.50 (ISBN 0-486-23354-5). Dover.

--Christmas Customs & Traditions: Their History & Significance. (Illus.). 15.50 (ISBN 0-8446-5484-1). Peter Smith.

--Christmas in Ritual & Tradition, Christian & Pagan. LC 68-54858. 1968. Repr. of 1912 ed. 37.00x (ISBN 0-8103-3354-6). Gale.

--Christmas in Ritual & Tradition: Christian & Pagan. 1977. lib. bdg. 59.95 (ISBN 0-8490-1618-5). Gordon Pr.

Mueller, Charles S. Christian Family Prepares for Christmas. 1965. laminated bdg. 3.75 (ISBN 0-570-03023-4, 6-1092). Concordia.

Muir, Frank. Christmas Customs & Traditions. LC 77-76504. (Illus.). 1977. 7.95 (ISBN 0-8008-1552-1). Taplinger.

Nast, Thomas. Thomas Nast's Christmas Drawings. (Illus.). 1978. pap. 4.50 (ISBN 0-486-23660-9). Dover.

Navarro, Dawn. The Los Angeles Times Book of Christmas Entertaining. Balsley, Betsy, compiled by. (Illus.). 176p. 1985. 24.95 (ISBN 0-8109-1290-2). Abrams.

Newhouse, Flower A. The Sacred Heart of Christmas. 2nd ed. Bengtson, Athene, ed. LC 78-74956. (Illus.). 1978. pap. 7.00 (ISBN 0-910378-14-2). Christward.

A Nice Place to Live. limited ed. (Illus.). 7.50 (ISBN 0-317-20858-6). Cricketfield Pr.

Nineteen Eighty-Six Take the Crazy out of Christmas Hints & Holiday Planner. 1986. 5.00 (ISBN 0-943786-04-5). Hollyday.

O'Collins, Gerald. The People's Christmas. (Orig.). 1984. pap. 3.50 (ISBN 0-8091-2660-5). Paulist Pr.

Olliver, Jane. Doubleday Christmas Treasury. LC 86-6297. 128p. 1986. 14.95 (ISBN 0-385-23409-0). Doubleday.

O'Neil, Sunny. The Gift of Christmas Past: A Return to Victorian Traditions. LC 81-14961. (Illus.). 146p. 1981. 15.95 (ISBN 0-910050-55-4). AASLH Pr.

Ortega, Pedro R. Christmas in Old Santa Fe. LC 73-90581. (Illus.). 1982. pap. 6.25 (ISBN 0-913270-25-3). Sunstone Pr.

Ortego, Hasa. Christmas Eve on the Big Bayou. 1974. 3.95 (ISBN 0-87511-091-6). Claitors.

Pearson, Derek. We Wish You a Merry Christmas. 1983. 30.00x (ISBN 0-86334-017-2, Pub. by macdonald Pub UK). State Mutual Bk.

Rea, John D. & Rea, Alayna. The Twelve Days of Christmas: The Twelve Stages of a Soul (The Creation of a Universe) 40p. (Orig.). 1987. pap. 4.95 (ISBN 0-938183-04-4). Two Trees Pub.

Reader's Digest Editors. Book of Christmas. LC 73-84158. (Illus.). 304p. 1973. 21.95 (ISBN 0-89577-013-X, Pub. by RD Assn). Random.

Revoir, Trudie W. Christmas Workshop for the Church Family. 96p. 1982. pap. 6.95 (ISBN 0-8170-0963-9). Judson.

Richards, Katharine L. How Christmas Came to the Sunday-Schools: The Observance of Christmas in the Protestant Church Schools of the United States. LC 70-159860. 1971. Repr. of 1934 ed. 40.00x (ISBN 0-8103-3793-2). Gale.

Rogers, John B. The Birth of God: Recovering the Mystery of Christmas. 112p. 1987. pap. 6.95 (ISBN 0-687-03554-6). Abingdon.

Sandys, William. Christmastide: Its History, Festivities & Carols. 69.95 (ISBN 0-87968-867-X). Gordon Pr.

Saturday Evening Post Editors. The Saturday Evening Post Christmas Book. LC 76-24034. (Illus.). 160p. 1976. 14.95 (ISBN 0-89387-001-3, Co-Pub by Sat Eve Post). Curtis Pub Co.

Scentouri Staff. Catering Service Potpourri for Centerpieces, Etc. 16p. 1985. pap. text ed. 3.75 (ISBN 0-318-04421-8, Pub. by Scentouri). Prosperity & Profits.

Schmalenberger, Jerry. Advent & Christmas Saints. 1984. 3.75 (ISBN 0-89536-685-1, 4861). CSS of Ohio.

Seaburg, Carl. Celebrating Christmas. 1983. pap. 12.00 (ISBN 0-933840-17-9). Unitarian Univ.

Seymour, William K. & Smith, John, eds. Happy Christmas. LC 68-26877. 256p. 1979. Repr. of 1968 ed. Westminster.

Shannon, Robert & Shannon, Michael. Celebrating the Birth of Christ. 112p. 1985. pap. 4.95 (ISBN 0-87239-916-8, 3022). Standard Pub.

Sheeley, Jill. Christmas in Aspen. (Illus.). 1982. Repr. write for info (ISBN 0-9609108-0-8). Columbine Pr.

Sloyan, Gerard S. Advent-Christmas. LC 84-18756. (Proclamation 3 C Ser.). 64p. 1985. pap. 3.75 (ISBN 0-8006-4125-6). Fortress.

Smith, Marilyn A. Christmas Programs for Church Groups. (Paperback Program Ser). (Orig.). 1968. pap. 3.95 (ISBN 0-8010-7910-1). Baker Bk.

Smith, Pauline. Christmas. 32p. 1985. pap. 1.50 (ISBN 0-908175-83-3, Pub. by Boolarong Pubn Australia). Intl Spec Bk.

Snyder, Phillip V. The Christmas Tree Book: The History of the Christmas Tree & Antique Christmas Tree Ornaments. LC 76-40224. (Large Format Ser.). (Illus.). 176p. 1977. pap. 10.95 (ISBN 0-14-004518-X). Penguin.

--December Twenty-Fifth: The Joy of Christmas Past. (Illus.). 346p. 1985. 17.95 (ISBN 0-396-08588-1). Dodd.

Sparks, Judy, ed. Christmas Programs for the Church, No. 16. 64p. 1983. pap. 2.95 (ISBN 0-87239-614-2, 8616). Standard Pub.

Spratt, Dora F. Christmas Week at Bigler's Mill: A Sketch in Black & White. LC 72-2171. (Black Heritage Library Collection Ser.). Repr. of 1895 ed. 13.25 (ISBN 0-8369-9065-X). Ayer Co Pubs.

Standard Christmas Program Book, No. 47. Hoard, Laurie, compiled by. 48p. 1986. pap. 1.95 (ISBN 0-87239-935-4, 8647). Standard Pub.

Stricker, William F. Keeping Christmas: An Edwardian-Age Memoir. LC 81-9406. (Illus.). 128p. 1981. 15.00 (ISBN 0-916144-60-7). Stemmer Hse.

Tennant, Eugenia L. American Christmases: From the Puritans to the Victorians. 1975. 10.00 (ISBN 0-682-48358-3, Banner). Exposition Pr FL.

Thomas, Dylan. Child's Christmas in Wales. LC 59-13174. (Illus.). 1969. gift ed. 12.00 (ISBN 0-8112-0391-3). New Directions.

--Child's Christmas in Wales. LC 59-13174. (Illus.). 1959. pap. 3.95 (ISBN 0-8112-0203-8, NDP181). New Directions.

Tille, Alexander. Yule & Christmas. 1977. lib. bdg. 59.95 (ISBN 0-8490-2855-8). Gordon Pr.

Treasured Polish Christmas Customs & Traditions. 8.95 (ISBN 0-685-37594-3). Polanie.

The Twelve Days of Christmas. 12p. 1985. paper wrapped limited ed. 10.00 (ISBN 0-317-38833-9). Walrus Pr.

Vajda, Eduard M. Four Trees of Christmas. 1983. 16.75 (ISBN 0-89536-641-X, 0633). CSS of Ohio.

Vawter, Bruce. Advent-Christmas. LC 84-18756. (Proclamation 3A Ser.). 64p. 1986. pap. 3.75 (ISBN 0-8006-4117-5, 1-4117). Fortress.

Vogel, Cora. Easy to Use Christmas Programs. 144p. 1986. 7.95 (ISBN 0-8010-9302-3). Baker Bk.

Walsh, Colin. The Grown-Up's Xmas Book. 128p. 1986. pap. 7.95 (ISBN 0-907621-44-9, Pub. by Quiller Pr England). Intl Spec Bk.

Warren, Nathan B. Christmas in the Olden Time. LC 76-58002. 1977. Repr. of 1859 ed. lib. bdg. 22.50 (ISBN 0-8414-1656-7). Folcroft.

Weitzel, Lynn. The Christmas Story Revisted. 21p. (Orig.). 1985. pap. 4.95 (ISBN 0-930161-07-6). State of the Art Ltd.

Wernecke, Herbert H. Christmas Customs Around the World. LC 59-9581. 188p. 1979. pap. 7.95 (ISBN 0-664-24258-8). Westminster.

Wernecke, Herbert H., ed. Celebrating Christmas Around the World. LC 62-13232. (Illus.). 256p. 1980. pap. 5.95 (ISBN 0-664-24318-5). Westminster.

Wheatley, Melvin. Christmas Is for Celebrating. 1977. pap. 3.95 (ISBN 0-8358-0366-X). Upper Room.

Whitson, Skip, compiled by. Christmas One Hundred Years Ago. (Sun Historical Ser). (Illus., Orig.). 1976. pap. 3.50 (ISBN 0-89540-036-7, SB-036). Sun Pub.

World Book, Inc. Christmas in Ireland. LC 84-51015. (Round the World Christmas Program Ser.). (Illus.). 80p. 1985. write for info. (ISBN 0-7166-0885-5). World Bk.

World Book, Inc. Editorial Staff. Christmas in Denmark. LC 86-50556. (Round the World Christmas Program Ser.). (Illus.). 80p. 1986. write for info. (ISBN 0-7166-0886-3). World Bk.

Younger, Dory. Christmas International. 1983. pap. 3.75 (ISBN 0-89536-613-4, 0386). CSS of Ohio.

CHRISTMAS–BIBLIOGRAPHY

Grosse, Rudolf. The Christmas Foundation Meeting: Beginning of a New Cosmic Age. Collis, Johanna, tr. from Ger. Tr. of Die Weihnachtstagung als Zeitenwende. 158p. (Orig.). 1984. pap. 14.00 (ISBN 0-919924-23-9, Steiner Bk Ctr). Anthroposophic.

Phillips, Leona. A Christmas Bibliography. 1977. lib. bdg. 69.95 (ISBN 0-8490-1363-1). Gordon Pr.

Samuelson, Sue. Christmas: An Annotated Bibliography of Analytical Scholarship. Dundes, Alan, ed. LC 82-48083. (Garland Folklore Bibliographies Ser.). 200p. 1982. lib. bdg. 31.00 (ISBN 0-8240-9263-5). Garland Pub.

CHRISTMAS–DRAMA

see Christmas Plays

CHRISTMAS–JUVENILE LITERATURE

Anderson, Joan. Christmas on the Prairie. LC 85-4095. (Illus.). 48p. 1985. 13.95 (ISBN 0-89919-307-2, Clarion). Ticknor & Fields.

Anglund, Joan W. Christmas Is a Time of Giving. LC 61-10106. (Illus.). 1961. 7.95 (ISBN 0-15-217863-5, HJ). HarBraceJ.

Banek, Yvette. Christmas Search-a-Picture Puzzles. (Puzzleback Ser.). (Illus.). 64p. (Orig.). 1981. pap. 2.50 (ISBN 0-671-43365-2). Wanderer Bks.

Barth, Edna. A Christmas Feast: Poems, Sayings, Greetings, & Wishes. (Illus.). 176p. 1979. 10.60 (ISBN 0-395-28965-3, Clarion). HM.

--Holly, Reindeer, & Colored Lights: The Story of the Christmas Symbols. LC 71-157731. (Illus.). 96p. 1981. pap. 4.95 (ISBN 0-89919-037-5, Clarion). HM.

--Holly, Reindeer, & Colored Lights: The Story of the Christmas Symbols. LC 71-157731. (Illus.). 96p. 1971. 8.95 (ISBN 0-395-28842-8, Clarion). HM.

Brett, Jan, illus. Twelve Days of Christmas. LC 85-46056. (Illus.). 32p. 1986. PLB 12.95 (ISBN 0-396-08821-X). Dodd.

Brinsmead, Hasba. Christmas at Home. (Illus.). 52p. 1986. 12.95 (ISBN 0-207-14543-1). Salem Hse Pubs.

Brooke, Roger. Santa's Christmas Journey. LC 85-61188. (Illus.). 32p. 1985. 5.95 (ISBN 0-528-82688-3). Macmillan.

Carlson. A Christmas Lullaby. (Arch Bks.). 24p. 1985. pap. 0.99 (ISBN 0-570-06195-4, 59-1296). Concordia.

Carol Time. (Christmas Ser.). 2.95 (ISBN 0-86112-234-8, Pub. by Brimax Bks). Borden.

Carwell, L'Ann. Baby's First Book About Christmas. (Illus.). 1979. 1.25 (ISBN 0-570-08002-9, 56-1327). Concordia.

The Children's Christmas Woodbook. 1986. bds. 8.95 (ISBN 0-8120-5753-8). Barron.

Christian, Mary B. Christmas Reflections. 1980. pap. 3.95 (ISBN 0-570-03494-9, 56-1711). Concordia.

Christmas Book. (The Enchanted World Ser.). (YA) 1986. lib. bdg. 22.60 (ISBN 0-8094-5262-6, Pub. by Time-Life); 16.95 (ISBN 0-8094-5261-8). Silver.

The Christmas Handbook. 1986. 10.95 (ISBN 0-8120-5756-2). Barron.

Christmas: One Hundred Seasonal Favorites. (The Ultimate Ser.). 248p. 1985. 17.95 (ISBN 0-88188-157-0, 00361398). H Leonard Pub Corp.

Christmas Time. (Christmas Ser.). 2.95 (ISBN 0-86112-197-X, Pub. by Brimax Bks). Borden.

Conaway, Judith. Easy-to-Make Christmas Crafts. LC 85-16475. (Illus.). 48p. 1986. PLB 9.49 (ISBN 0-8167-0674-3); pap. text ed. 1.95 (ISBN 0-8167-0675-1). Troll Assocs.

Cooney, Barbara. Christmas. LC 67-18510. (Holiday Ser.). (Illus.). 1967. PLB 12.89i (ISBN 0-690-19201-0, Crowell Jr Bks). HarpJ.

Cuyler, Margery. The All-Around Christmas Book. LC 82-3104. (Illus.). 96p. 1982. 11.95 (ISBN 0-03-060387-0); pap. 4.95 (ISBN 0-03-062183-6). H Holt & Co.

Domanska, Janina, illus. The First Noel. LC 85-27084. (Illus.). 24p. 1986. 11.75 (ISBN 0-688-04324-0); PLB 11.88 (ISBN 0-688-04325-9). Greenwillow.

Eastman, Moira & Poussard, Wendy. The Christmas Book. LC 80-68368. (Illus.). 40p. 1980. 5.95 (ISBN 0-87793-214-X). Ave Maria.

Exley, Richard & Exley, Helen. A Child's View of Christmas. (Illus.). 64p. 1981. 7.50 (ISBN 0-8298-0463-3). Pilgrim NY.

The First Christmas. (Christmas Ser.). 2.95 (ISBN 0-86112-198-8, Pub. by Brimax Bks). Borden.

Gibbons, Gail. Christmas Time. LC 82-1038. (Illus.). 32p. 1982. Reinforced bdg. 12.95 (ISBN 0-8234-0453-6). Holiday.

Giblin, James C. The Truth about Santa Claus. LC 85-47541. (Illus.). 96p. 1985. 11.70 (ISBN 0-690-04483-6, Crowell Jr Bks); PLB 11.89 (ISBN 0-690-04484-4). HarpJ.

Gibson, Roxie C. Hey, God! What Is Christmas. LC 82-60192. (Illus.). 64p. 3.95 (ISBN 0-938232-09-6, 32752). Winston-Derek.

Harris, Leon. Night Before Christmas-in Texas, that Is. (Illus.). 1977. Repr. of 1952 ed. 7.95 (ISBN 0-88289-175-8). Pelican.

Hayes, Sarah. A Bad Start for Santa. (Illus.). 12.95 (ISBN 0-87113-093-9). Atlantic Monthly.

Hill, G. L. The Best Birthday: A Christmas Entertainment for Children. 8.95 (ISBN 0-89190-404-2, Pub. by Am Repr). Amereon Ltd.

Hoffman, Felix. The Story of Christmas. LC 75-6921. (Illus.). 32p. 1975. 6.95 (ISBN 0-689-50031-9, McElderry Bk). Macmillan.

Jaques, Faith. The Christmas Party: A Model Book. (Illus.). 6p. 1986. 8.95 (ISBN 0-399-21393-7, Philomel). Putnam Pub Group.

Jones, Kathy. Celebrate Christmas. (Celebrate Ser.). (Illus.). 144p. 1985. wkbk. 9.95 (ISBN 0-86653-279-X). Good Apple.

Kelley, Emily. Christmas around the World. (On My Own Bks.). (Illus.). 48p. 1986. lib. bdg. 8.95 (ISBN 0-87614-249-8). Carolrhoda Bks.

Kimura, Yuriko. Christmas Present from a Friend. (Illus.). 28p. 1985. Repr. 10.95 (ISBN 0-687-07817-2). Abingdon.

Kurelek, William. A Northern Nativity. (Illus.). 1976. 14.95 (ISBN 0-88776-071-6); pap. 5.95 (ISBN 0-88776-071-6). Tundra Bks.

Lee, Sharon. Joyous Days: A Collection of Advent & Christmas Activities. (The Learning Connections Ser.). 96p. (Orig.). 1984. pap. 7.95 (ISBN 0-86683-833-3, 8443, HarpR). Har-Row.

Moncure, Jane B. The Gift of Christmas. 1985. 5.95 (ISBN 0-89565-083-5, R4914). Standard Pub.

--Our Christmas Book. rev. ed. LC 85-29132. (Special-Day Bks.). (Illus.). 32p. 1986. lib. bdg. 7.45 (ISBN 0-89565-341-9). Childs World.

Odor, Ruth. Christmas Is a Time for Singing. LC 81-86706. (Happy Day Bks.). (Illus.). 24p. (Orig.). 1982. pap. 1.59 (ISBN 0-87239-535-9, 3581). Standard Pub.

Ogilvy, Carol & Tinkham, Trudy. Classy Christmas Concert. 112p. 1986. wkbk. 8.95 (ISBN 0-86653-349-4). Good Apple.

Oxtoby & Sandison. Once upon a Christmas. 1986. 14.95 (ISBN 0-8120-5755-4). Barron.

Patterson, Lillie. Christmas Feasts & Festivals. LC 68-14778. (Holiday Bks.). (Illus.). 64p. 1968. PLB 7.56 (ISBN 0-8116-6562-3). Garrard.

--Christmas in America. LC 69-11077. (Holiday Bks.). (Illus.). 64p. 1969. PLB 7.56 (ISBN 0-8116-6563-1). Garrard.

The Rand McNally Book of Favorite Christmas Stories. (Illus.). 112p. 1985. 8.95 (ISBN 0-528-82678-6). Macmillan.

Reynolds, Joyce. The Search for the True Meaning of Christmas. (Illus.). 1977. pap. text ed. 2.25 (ISBN 0-88243-100-5, 30-0100). Gospel Pub.

Rhodes, John, ed. Christmas: A Celebration. 1986. 15.95 (ISBN 0-571-13752-0). Faber & Faber.

Sader, Kathy. Let Earth Receive Its King: Christmas Service for Children. (Orig.). 1986. pap. 0.90 (ISBN 0-8066-9202-2, 23-1682). Augsburg.

Santa Is Coming. (Christmas Ser.). 2.95 (ISBN 0-86112-229-1, Pub. by Brimax Bks). Borden.

Schlegl, William. Bible Christmas Puzzles. (Illus.). 48p. 1987. pap. 5.95 (ISBN 0-86653-409-1). Good Apple.

Sparks, Judy, ed. Away in a Manger. (Happy Day Bks.). (Illus.). 24p. 1985. 1.59 (ISBN 0-87239-871-4, 3671). Standard Pub.

Stifle, J. M. ABC Book About Christmas. 1981. pap. 3.95 (ISBN 0-570-04053-1, 56-1714). Concordia.

The Story of Christmas for Children. 32p. pap. 2.95 (ISBN 0-89542-454-1). Ideals.

Tudor, Tasha. A Book of Christmas. (Illus.). 1979. 6.95 (ISBN 0-529-05532-5, Philomel). Putnam Pub Group.

--Take Joy: The Tasha Tudor Christmas Book. LC 66-10645. (Illus.). 1980. 14.95 (ISBN 0-399-20766-X, Philomel); PLB 12.99 (ISBN 0-399-61169-X). Putnam Pub Group.

Vesey, A. Merry Christmas, Thomas! (Illus.). 32p. 9.95 (ISBN 0-87113-096-3). Atlantic Monthly.

Weiss, Ellen. Things to Make & Do for Christmas. (Things to Make & Do Bks.). 1980. PLB 8.90 (ISBN 0-531-02293-5, C02); pap. 3.95 (ISBN 0-531-02145-9). Watts.

Ziegler, Sandra, et al. Our Christmas Handbook. LC 80-14587. (Illus.). 112p. (Orig.). 1980. pap. 6.50 (ISBN 0-89565-180-7). Childs World.

CHRISTMAS–MEDITATIONS

Arnold, Eberhard, et al. When the Time Was Fulfilled: Talks & Writings on Advent & Christmas. LC 65-17599. 1965. 7.00 (ISBN 0-87486-104-7). Plough.

Bastin, Marcel, et al. God Day by Day, Vol. 4: Advent & Christmas. 184p. (Orig.). 1985. pap. 8.95 (ISBN 0-8091-2699-0). Paulist Pr.

Batchelor, Mary. Our Family Christmas Book. 96p. 1984. 9.95 (ISBN 0-687-29587-4). Abingdon.

Browne, Muriel. Exalt His Name: A Christmas Program. 1984. pap. 0.95 (ISBN 0-8024-3551-3). Moody.

Christmas Blessings. 16p. 1984. pap. 1.25 (ISBN 0-89542-820-2). Ideals.

Christmas Greeting. 16p. 1984. pap. 1.25 (ISBN 0-89542-819-9). Ideals.

Ehlen-Miller, Margaret, et al. The Gift of Time: Family Activities for Advent, Christmas, Epiphany. (Illus.). 1977. pap. 4.95 (ISBN 0-8192-1224-5). Morehouse.

Glaesner, Kay M. Miracle of Christmas. (Orig.). 1982. pap. 2.95 (ISBN 0-937172-39-1). JLJ Pubs.

Graham, Ruth B. Navidad en Nuestra Familia. Gama, Roberto, tr. from Eng. Orig. Title: Our Christmas Story. (Span., Illus.). 128p. (Orig.). pap. 5.25 (ISBN 0-311-08225-4). Casa Bautista.

Hobe, Phyllis. The Meaning of Christmas. LC 75-12627. 1982. Repr. of 1975 ed. 7.95 (ISBN 0-8054-5118-8). Broadman.

Hopko, Thomas. Winter Pascha. LC 84-27622. 1983. pap. text ed. 6.95 (ISBN 0-88141-025-X). St Vladimirs.

Ikerman, Ruth C. A Heart-Trimmed Christmas: Christmas Inspiration for Your Heart & Home. 112p. (Orig.). 1984. pap. 7.95 (ISBN 0-687-16804-X). Abingdon.

Jacobson, Dick & Naujoks, Bob. ABC for Christmas. 55p. (Orig.). Date not set. pap. 4.95 (ISBN 0-941988-04-X). K Q Assocs.

Miller, Samuel H. What Child Is This? Readings & Prayers for Advent-Christmas. LC 82-5084. (Illus.). 64p. (Orig.). 1982. pap. 3.50 (ISBN 0-8006-1638-3, 1-1638). Fortress.

Ordonez, Francisco. Repertorio de Navidad. 80p. 1986. pap. 1.75 (ISBN 0-311-08211-4). Casa Bautista.

Pennel, Joe E., Jr. The Whisper of Christmas: Reflections for Advent & Christmas. LC 84-50839. 128p. (Orig.). 1984. pap. 4.95 (ISBN 0-8358-0492-5). Upper Room.
Rahner, Karl. Meditations on Hope & Love. LC 77-76614. 1977. pap. 3.95 (ISBN 0-8245-0326-0). Crossroad NY.
Ramm, Charles A. Meditations on the Mystery of Christmas. Lilly, Sr. Catherine M., ed. LC 59-15709. (Illus.). 1959. 6.95 (ISBN 0-87015-092-8). Pacific Bks.
Revoir, Trudie W. Legends & Traditions of Christmas. (Illus.). 112p. 1985. pap. 5.95 (ISBN 0-8170-1082-3). Judson.
Richards, Hubert J. The First Christmas: What Really Happened? (What Really Happened? Ser.). 128p. 1986. pap. 5.95 (ISBN 0-89622-289-6). Twenty-Third.
Schroeder, L. Celebrate-While We Wait. (Illus.). 1977. pap. 4.95 (ISBN 0-570-03052-8, 6-1177). Concordia.
Steiner, Rudolf. Newborn Might & Strength Everlasting: A Christmas Offering. Church, Gilbert, ed. (Illus.). 19p. (Orig.). 1977. pap. 2.00 (ISBN 0-88010-100-8). Anthroposophic.
Tambiah, Stanley J. Culture, Thought, & Social Action: An Anthropological Perspective. (Illus.). 432p. 1985. text ed. 30.00x (ISBN 0-674-17969-2). Harvard U Pr.
Thurman, Howard. The Mood of Christmas. LC 85-16018. 127p. 1985. pap. 9.95 (ISBN 0-913408-90-5). Friends United.
The Treasures of Christmas: The Guideposts Family Christmas Book. 80p. pap. 7.95 (ISBN 0-687-42560-3). Abingdon.
Webb, Wheaton P. The Heart Has Its Seasons: A Sourcebook of Christmas Meditations. LC 82-3898. 96p. (Orig.). 1982. pap. 7.75 (ISBN 0-687-16800-7). Abingdon.

CHRISTMAS–POETRY

see also Carols

Abercrombie, V. T. & Williams, Helen, eds. Christmas in Texas. LC 79-66212. (Illus., Orig.). 1979. pap. 7.95 (ISBN 0-933988-00-1). Brown Rabbit.
Campbell, Vivian, ed. A Christmas Anthology of Poetry & Painting. LC 79-51963. (Granger Poetry Library). 1980. Repr. of 1947 ed. 27.50x (ISBN 0-89609-181-3). Roth Pub Inc.
Christmas: The Annual of Christmas Literature & Arts, Vol. 51. LC 32-30914. (Illus.). 64p. 1981. pap. text ed. 6.95 (ISBN 0-8066-8958-7, 17-0122); 14.50 (ISBN 0-8066-8959-5, 17-0123). Augsburg.
Christmas: The Annual of Christmas Literature & Art, Vol. 52. LC 32-30914. (Illus.). 64p. 1982. pap. text ed. 6.95 (ISBN 0-8066-8960-9, 17-0124); 14.50 (ISBN 0-8066-8961-7, 17-0125). Augsburg.
Elder, Sam. A Christmas Celebration. LC 84-47709. (Illus.). 1984. 5.00 (ISBN 0-06-015359-8, HarpT). Har-Row.
Emurian, Ernest K. Stories of Christmas Carols. (Paperback Program Ser). 1969. pap. 4.95 (ISBN 0-8010-3265-2). Baker Bk.
Foster, Birket, illus. Christmas with the Poets. (Illus.). 1978. Repr. of 1851 ed. 50.00 (ISBN 0-8492-0090-3). R West.
Greif, Martin. The St. Nicholas Book. LC 76-5089. (Illus.). 60p. 1976. 5.95 (ISBN 0-87663-554-0). Universe.
Hayes, Albert & Laughlin, J., eds. A Wreath of Christmas Poems. LC 72-80975. 32p. 1972. pap. 1.95 (ISBN 0-8112-0459-6, NDP347). New Directions.
Knight, William, ed. The Poets on Christmas. Repr. of 1907 ed. lib. bdg. 25.00 (ISBN 0-8495-3016-4). Arden Lib.
Lewis, Wyndham & Heseltine. A Christmas Book: An Anthology for Moderns. 1977. Repr. of 1928 ed. 30.00 (ISBN 0-89984-217-8). Century Bookbindery.
Lohan, Robert & Lohan, Maria, eds. A New Christmas Treasury: With More Stories for Reading Aloud. LC 54-12862. 14.50 (ISBN 0-8044-2536-1, Pub. by Stephen Daye Pr). Ungar.
Moore, Clement C. The Night Before Christmas. (Pictureback Book & Cassette Library Ser.). (Illus.). 32p. 1985. pap. 4.95 incl. cassette (ISBN 0-394-87658-X). Random.
Tibbetts, Laurene J. It's Christmas! Poems & Stories for the Holiday Season. 97p. 1981. write for info. Rector Pub.
Toner, Erwin J. Every Day Is a Christmas Present. 32p. 1967. pap. write for info. (ISBN 0-686-08987-1). Gonzaga U Pr.
Waldo, Beach. Christmas Wonder: An Anthology of Verse & Song. LC 73-79038. pap. 24.00 (2026924). Bks Demand UMI.
Weems, John E., ed. A Texas Christmas, Vol. II. 130p. 1986. 19.95 (ISBN 0-939722-30-5). Presswork.

CHRISTMAS–SONGS AND MUSIC

see Christmas Music

CHRISTMAS BOOKS

see Christmas; Christmas Plays; Christmas Stories; Gift-Books (Annuals, etc.)

Better Homes & Gardens Editors. Better Homes & Gardens Christmas Joys to Craft & Stitch. (Illus.). 80p. 1985. pap. 6.95 (ISBN 0-696-01432-7). BH&G.

CHRISTMAS CARDS

Buday, George. The History of the Christmas Card. LC 74-174012. (Tower Bks.). (Illus.). xxiii, 304p. 1972. Repr. of 1954 ed. 50.00x (ISBN 0-8103-3931-5). Gale.
Family Cirle & Hadda, Ceri, eds. The Family Circle Christmas Treasury. 1986. 19.95 (ISBN 0-933585-02-0). Family Circle Bks.
Menendez, Albert J. Christmas in the White House. LC 83-3629. (Illus.). 128p. 1983. 11.95 (ISBN 0-664-21392-8). Westminster.

CHRISTMAS CAROLS

see Carols

CHRISTMAS COOKERY

Betty Crocker's Christmas Cookbook. (Illus.). 192p. 1982. 14.95 (ISBN 0-307-09820-6, Golden Pr). Western Pub.
Christmas Cookbook. 64p. pap. 3.50 (ISBN 0-89542-602-1). Ideals.
Christmas Gifts From The Kitchen Cookbook. 64p. pap. 3.50 (ISBN 0-89542-635-8). Ideals.
Cutler, Katherine N. & Bogle, Kate C. Crafts for Christmas. (Illus.). 96p. 1975. pap. 1.95 (ISBN 0-688-46663-X). Lothrop.
Cuyler, Margery. The All-Around Christmas Book. LC 82-3104. (Illus.). 96p. 1982. 11.95 (ISBN 0-03-060387-0); pap. 4.95 (ISBN 0-03-062183-6). H Holt & Co.
Elder, Sam. A Christmas Celebration. LC 84-47709. (Illus.). 1984. 5.00 (ISBN 0-06-015359-8, HarpT). Har-Row.
Family Cirle & Hadda, Ceri, eds. The Family Circle Christmas Treasury. 1986. 19.95 (ISBN 0-933585-02-0). Family Circle Bks.
Good Housekeeping Magazine Editors. Good Housekeeping American Family Christmas. (Brownstone Library Book). (Illus.). 168p. 1985. 19.95 (ISBN 0-916410-29-3). A D Bragdon.
Menendez, Albert J. Christmas in the White House. LC 83-3629. (Illus.). 128p. 1983. 11.95 (ISBN 0-664-21392-8). Westminster.
Merrie Christmas Cookbook. 64p. 1955. 5.95 (ISBN 0-88088-429-0). Peter Pauper.
Meyer, Carolyn. Christmas Crafts. LC 74-2608. (Illus.). 160p. 1974. 11.70i (ISBN 0-06-024197-7). HarpJ.
Nickerson, Jill, ed. Country Christmas Entertaining. LC 83-62128. 64p. 1983. pap. 5.95 (ISBN 0-89821-055-0). Reiman Assocs.
Nineteen Eighty-Six Take the Crazy out of Christmas Hints & Holiday Planner. 1986. 5.00 (ISBN 0-943786-04-5). Hollyday.
Sass, Lorna J. Christmas Feasts from History. Atcheson, Jean, ed. LC 81-68835. (Great American Cooking Schools Ser.). (Illus.). 84p. 1981. pap. 5.95 (ISBN 0-941034-01-1). I Chalmers.
Teubner, Christian. Christmas Baking: Traditional Recipes Made Easy. (Illus.). 96p. 1985. 9.95 (ISBN 0-8120-5617-5). Barron.
Vitz, Evelyn B. Continual Feast. LC 84-48629. (Illus.). 356p. 1985. 16.45i (ISBN 0-06-181897-6, HarpT). Har-Row.
Voth, Norma J. Festive Cakes of Christmas. LC 81-2140. (Illus.). 80p. 1981. pap. 3.50 (ISBN 0-8361-1956-8). Herald Pr.
--Festive Cookies of Christmas. LC 81-18258. 104p. (Orig.). 1982. pap. 3.25 (ISBN 0-8361-1983-5). Herald Pr.
Williams, Sara P. National Trust Book of Christmas & Festive Day Recipes. (Illus.). 192p. 1980. 13.95 (ISBN 0-7153-8100-8). David & Charles.

CHRISTMAS DECORATIONS

see also Christmas Trees

Bodger, Lorraine. Christmas Tree Ornaments. LC 84-52753. (Illus.). 168p. 1985. write for info. (ISBN 0-02-496740-8, Pub by Sedgewood Press). Macmillan.
Braga, Meg. Cosas Que Hacer para Navidad. (Editorial Mundo Hispano). (YA) 1981. Repr. of 1980 ed. 3.25 (ISBN 0-311-26607-X). Casa Bautista.
Brenner, Robert. Christmas Past. (Illus.). 256p. 1985. 24.95 (ISBN 0-88740-051-5). Schiffer.
--Christmas Revisited. (Illus.). 206p. 1986. pap. 24.95 (ISBN 0-88740-067-1). Schiffer.
Burkhart, W. Eugene, Jr. Decorating Christmas Trees. (Illus.). 64p. (Orig.). 1985. pap. 8.95 (ISBN 0-9615199-0-8). Burkharts.
Censoni, Bob. Ready-to-Use Christmas Silhouettes. 64p. (Orig.). 1985. pap. 3.50 (ISBN 0-486-24954-9). Dover.
Colonial Williamsburg Staff. Christmas Decorations from Williamsburg's Folk Art Collection: Easy to Follow Instructions for Making 90 Decorations. LC 76-41253. (Illus.). 80p. (Orig.). 1976. pap. 4.95 (ISBN 0-87935-040-7). Williamsburg.
Coskey, Evelyn. Christmas Crafts for Everyone. LC 76-4916. (Illus.). (YA) 1976. 9.95 (ISBN 0-687-07815-6). Abingdon.
Cutler, Katherine N. & Bogle, Kate C. Crafts for Christmas. (Illus.). 96p. 1975. pap. 1.95 (ISBN 0-688-46663-X). Lothrop.
Cuyler, Margery. The All-Around Christmas Book. LC 82-3104. (Illus.). 96p. 1982. 11.95 (ISBN 0-03-060387-0); pap. 4.95 (ISBN 0-03-062183-6). H Holt & Co.
Deems, Betty. Easy-to-Make Felt Ornaments for Christmas & Other Occasions. LC 76-18405. (Dover Needlework Ser). (Illus.). 32p. (Orig.). 1976. pap. 3.50 (ISBN 0-486-23389-8). Dover.
Family Cirle & Hadda, Ceri, eds. The Family Circle Christmas Treasury. 1986. 19.95 (ISBN 0-933585-02-0). Family Circle Bks.
Fitzpatrick, Nancy J., ed. Creative Ideas for Christmas, 1986. (Illus.). 160p. 1986. 17.95 (ISBN 0-8487-0683-8). Oxmoor Hse.
Foose, Sandra L. Scrap Saver's Christmas Stitchery. (Illus.). 160p. 1986. 19.95 (ISBN 0-8487-0646-3). Oxmoor Hse.
Gift of Mistletoe. (Gifts of Gold Ser.). 1972. 5.95 (ISBN 0-88088-618-8). Peter Pauper.
Hornung, Clarence P. Old-Fashioned Christmas in Illustration & Decoration. (Orig.). 1970. pap. 5.00 (ISBN 0-486-22367-1). Dover.
Hornung, Clarence P., ed. An Old-Fashioned Christmas in Illustration & Decoration. (Illus.). 15.75 (ISBN 0-8446-0147-0). Peter Smith.
Johnson, George. Christmas Ornaments, Lights & Decorations. (Illus.). 320p. 1986. 19.95 (ISBN 0-317-52660-X). Collector Bks.
Kirby, Philippa. Christmas Wrappings. LC 86-5617. (Illus.). 72p. 1986. 4.95 (ISBN 1-55584-009-4). Weidenfeld.
Lee, Sharon. Christmas Handbook, No. 3. 112p. 1985. 7.95 (ISBN 0-87239-913-3, 3043). Standard Pub.
Meyer, Carolyn. Christmas Crafts. LC 74-2608. (Illus.). 160p. 1974. 11.70i (ISBN 0-06-024197-7). HarpJ.
Nineteen Eighty-Six Take the Crazy out of Christmas Hints & Holiday Planner. 1986. 5.00 (ISBN 0-943786-04-5). Hollyday.
Oliver, Libby H., et al. Colonial Williamsburg Decorates for Christmas. LC 81-10103. (Illus.). 80p. 1981. 11.95 (ISBN 0-03-060403-6). H Holt & Co.
Parish, Peggy. December Decorations: A Holiday How-to Book. LC 75-14285. (Illus.). 64p. 1975. 9.95 (ISBN 0-02-769920-X). Macmillan.
Pax, Noel. Simply Christmas. (Illus.). 72p. (Orig.). 1980. pap. 3.95 (ISBN 0-8027-7168-8); 5.95 (ISBN 0-8027-0672-X). Walker & Co.
Purdy, Susan. Christmas Gifts for You to Make. LC 76-10160. (Illus.). 1976. PLB 12.89 (ISBN 0-397-31695-X, Lipp Jr Bks); pap. 4.95 o. p. (ISBN 0-397-31696-8). HarpJ.
Reilly, Mary V., et al. Wait in Joyful Hope! (Illus., Orig.). 1980. pap. 4.95 (ISBN 0-8192-1275-X). Morehouse.
Rogers, Maggie & Hawkins, Judith. The Glass Christmas Ornament: Old & New. 2nd, rev. ed. (Illus.). 126p. (Orig.). 1983. pap. 12.95 (ISBN 0-917304-79-9). Timber.
Saltkill, Sue. Christmas Classics. (Illus.). 1985. pap. 6.95 (ISBN 0-943574-32-3). That Patchwork.
Sargent, Lucy. Tincraft for Christmas. (Illus.). 1969. 7.95 (ISBN 0-688-02638-9); pap. 5.95 (ISBN 0-688-07638-6). Morrow.
Scroggins, Clara J. Silver Christmas Ornaments: A Collector's Guide. LC 79-15323. (Illus.). 208p. 1980. 25.00 (ISBN 0-498-02385-0). A S Barnes.
Sheppard, Donna. A Williamsburg Christmas. LC 80-7487. (Illus.). 84p. 1980. 11.95 (ISBN 0-03-057639-3). H Holt & Co.
Sibbett, Ed, Jr. Ready-to-Use Christmas Designs. (Clip Art Ser.). (Illus.). 1979. pap. 3.50 (ISBN 0-486-23900-4). Dover.
Snyder, Phillip V. The Christmas Tree Book: The History of the Christmas Tree & Antique Christmas Tree Ornaments. LC 76-40224. (Large Format Ser.). (Illus.). 176p. 1977. pap. 10.95 (ISBN 0-14-004518-X). Penguin.
Stewart, Linda, ed. Christmas Is Coming! 1986: Holiday Projects for Children & Parents. (Illus.). 128p. 1986. 17.95 (ISBN 0-8487-0688-9). Oxmoor Hse.
Supraner, Robyn. Merry Christmas: Things to Make & Do. LC 80-23884. (Illus.). 48p. 1981. PLB 9.49 (ISBN 0-89375-422-6); pap. 1.95 (ISBN 0-89375-423-4). Troll Assocs.
Whitmyer, Margaret & Whitmyer, Kenn. Christmas Collectibles. (Illus.). 224p. 1986. 19.95 (ISBN 0-317-52666-9). Collector Bks.
Wilson, Erica. Erica Wilson's Christmas World. (Illus.). 160p. 1982. pap. 11.95 (ISBN 0-684-17651-3, ScribT); 17.95 (ISBN 0-684-16672-0). Scribner.
The Wilton Way to Decorate for Christmas. LC 76-16083. 1976. 6.99 (ISBN 0-912696-07-9). Wilton.
Wright, Sandra L. Country Handcrafts Christmas Collection. 34p. 1985. pap. 5.95 (ISBN 0-89821-069-0). Reiman Assocs.

CHRISTMAS MUSIC

see also Carols

Adams, Doug, ed. Dancing Christmas Carols. LC 78-63292. 1978. pap. 7.95 (ISBN 0-89390-006-0). Resource Pubns.
Bartok. Carols & Christmas Songs: Colinde, Vol. 4. (Rumanian Folk Music Ser). 1975. lib. bdg. 131.50 (ISBN 90-247-1737-X, Pub. by Martinus Nijhoff Netherlands). Kluwer Academic.
Beall, Pam & Nipp, Susan. Wee Sing for Christmas. (Illus.). 64p. (Orig.). 1984. pap. 2.25 (ISBN 0-8431-1197-6). Price Stern.
Charlton, Jim & Shulman, Jason. The Family Book of Christmas Songs & Stories. (Illus.). 208p. 1986. pap. 9.95 (ISBN 0-399-51276-4, Perigee). Putnam Pub Group.
Choirs of Angels in Stained Glass. (Illus.). 1985. pap. 5.95 (ISBN 0-8027-7136-X). Walker & Co.
Christmas Recital. (Recital Notebooks Ser.: No. 12). 1967. pap. 2.95 (ISBN 0-8256-8061-1). Music Sales.
Clary, Linda & Harms, Larry. Christmas Music for Little People. Bradley, Richard, ed. (Illus.). 32p. 1985. bk & cassette 9.95 (ISBN 0-89748-160-7). Bradley Pubns.
Clokey, Joseph W. & Kirk, Hazel J. Childe Jesus: A Christmas Cantata for Mixed Voices. pap. 20.00 (ISBN 0-317-09646-X, 2017838). Bks Demand UMI.
De Paola, Tomie. The Friendly Beasts: An Old English Christmas Carol. (Illus.). 32p. 1981. 10.95 (ISBN 0-399-20739-2); pap. 4.95 (ISBN 0-399-20777-5). Putnam Pub Group.
De Vito, Albert. Christmas Songs for Piano. 1968. pap. 2.95 (ISBN 0-934286-53-1). Kenyon.
Ehret, Walter & Evans, George K. International Book of Christmas Carols. LC 80-13105. (Illus.). 352p. 1980. pap. 14.95 (ISBN 0-8289-0378-6). Greene.
Foster, Birket, illus. Christmas with the Poets. (Illus.). 1978. Repr. of 1851 ed. 50.00 (ISBN 0-8492-0090-3). R West.
Gick, Georg J. & Swinger, Marlys. Shepherd's Pipe Songs from the Holy Night: A Christmas Cantata for Children's Voices or Youth Choir. Choral ed. LC 71-85805. (Illus.). 64p. 1969. pap. 2.50 choral ed. (ISBN 0-87486-011-3); cassette 6.00 (ISBN 0-686-66331-4). Plough.
Greenberg, Noah & Smoldon, W. L., eds. Play of Herod: A Twelfth-Century Musical Drama. (Illus.). 1965. pap. 4.25 (ISBN 0-19-385196-2). Oxford U Pr.
Holbrook, David & Postan, Elizabeth, eds. The Apple Tree: Christmas Music from the Cambridge Hymnal. LC 76-12916. 1976. pap. 7.95 o. p. (ISBN 0-521-29116-X). Cambridge U Pr.
Ideals Staff. Book of Christmas Carols. (Illus.). 24p. 1984. pap. 2.95 (ISBN 0-8249-8072-7). Ideals.
Langstaff, John & Langstaff, Nancy, eds. The Christmas Revels Songbook. LC 85-70140. (Illus.). 128p. 1985. cancelled (ISBN 0-87923-586-1); pap. 14.95 (ISBN 0-87923-591-8). Godine.
Loh, ed. A Festival of Asian Christmas Music: Christmas Music from Hongkong, India, Indonesia, Malaysia, Philippines & Taiwan. (Asian Inst. for Liturgy & Music Anthems Ser: No. 2). 68p. (Orig.). 1984. pap. 8.50x (ISBN 971-10-0228-0, Pub. by New Day Philippines). Cellar.
McCabe, Joseph E. Handel's Messiah: A Devotional Commentary. LC 77-25860. 120p. 1978. pap. 5.95 (ISBN 0-664-24192-1). Westminster.
McCaskey, John P. Christmas in Song, Sketch & Story: Nearly Three Hundred Christmas Songs, Hymns & Carols. 1980. lib. bdg. 67.95 (ISBN 0-8490-3175-3). Gordon Pr.
Poffenberger, Nancy. Instant Piano Fun for Christmas. 24p. 1986. pap. text ed. 4.95 (ISBN 0-938293-28-1). Fun Pub OH.
Reed, Will L., ed. Second Treasury of Christmas Music. LC 68-16193. 1968. 12.95 (ISBN 0-87523-165-9). Emerson.
Roseberry, Eric, ed. The Faber Book of Carols & Christmas Songs. 118p. 1983. 8.95 (ISBN 0-571-09249-7); pap. 6.95 (ISBN 0-571-13189-1). Faber & Faber.
Schackel, James. O Come, O Come, Emmanuel. (Candlelight Ser.). 1984. 2.25 (ISBN 0-89536-691-6, 4867). CSS of Ohio.
Simon, Henry A. Treasury of Christmas Songs & Carols. 2nd ed. 1973. 16.95 (ISBN 0-395-17786-3); pap. 9.95 (ISBN 0-395-17785-5). HM.
Waldo, Beach. Christmas Wonder: An Anthology of Verse & Song. LC 73-79038. pap. 24.00 (2026924). Bks Demand UMI.
Willcocks, David, ed. Carols for Christmas. (Illus.). 96p. 1983. 25.00 (ISBN 0-03-064044-X). H Holt & Co.
Willcocks, David & Ruttner, John, eds. Fifty Carols for Christmas & Advent. (Carols for Choirs, Book 2). 1970. 12.00 (ISBN 0-19-353566-1); pap. 7.00 (ISBN 0-19-353565-3). Oxford U Pr.
The World's Best Christmas Carols. rev. ed. 64p. 1987. pap. 2.95 (ISBN 0-87403-212-1, 9848). Standard Pub.

CHRISTMAS PLAYS

see also Crib in Christian Art and Tradition

Berry, Linda. Christmas Plays for Older Children. 1981. saddle wire 2.50 (ISBN 0-8054-9733-1). Broadman.

Christmas Program Resource Book Two. 48p. 1984. pap. 2.50 (ISBN 0-8066-2075-7, 23-1501). Augsburg.

Christmas: The Annual of Christmas Literature & Art, Vol. 54. (Illus.). 64p. 1984. 14.50 (ISBN 0-8066-8965-X, 17-0129); pap. text ed. 6.95 (ISBN 0-8066-8964-1, 17-0128). Augsburg.

DeWitt, Robert H. Arise, Thy Light Is Come. (Orig.). 1957. pap. 1.95 (ISBN 0-8054-9703-X). Broadman.

Dramas Navidenos para Jovenes y Adultos. (Span.). 64p. 1985. pap. 2.25 (ISBN 0-311-08227-0). Casa Bautista.

Dramas Navidenos para Ninos. 32p. (Orig.). 1985. pap. 1.25 (ISBN 0-311-08226-2). Casa Bautista.

Ehlen-Miller, Margaret, et al. The Gift of Time: Family Activities for Advent, Christmas, Epiphany. (Illus.). 1977. pap. 4.95 (ISBN 0-8192-1224-5). Morehouse.

Eisenberg, Helen & Eisenberg, Larry. Programs & Parties for Christmas. 160p. 1980. pap. 4.50 (ISBN 0-8010-3359-4). Baker Bk.

Faust, Harriet. Enough of Christmas. (Orig.). 1980. pap. 2.95 (ISBN 0-937172-08-1). JLJ Pubs.

Funk, Nancy. Two Christmas Plays. 1984. 4.50 (ISBN 0-89536-695-9, 4872). CSS of Ohio.

Gabbott, Mabel J. Have a Very Merry Christmas! Skits for Elementary Schools & Families. LC 80-83034. 56p. (Orig.). 1981. pap. 4.95 (ISBN 0-88290-163-X, 2044). Horizon Utah.

Garbee, Ed & Van Dyke, Henry. Dramas De Navidad. Prince, Soledad G. & Castellon, Guillermo, trs. 1981. pap. 1.50 (ISBN 0-311-08214-9). Casa Bautista.

Glassie, Henry. All Silver & No Brass: An Irish Christmas Mumming. 1983. 9.95 (ISBN 0-8122-1139-1). U of Pa Pr.

Hatton, Thomas J. A Quiet Night: A Play for Christmas. 24p. (Orig.). 1980. pap. text ed. 5.25 (ISBN 0-89536-438-7, 1703). CSS of Ohio.

Henley, Gurden. Joy to You & Me. Sherer, Michael L., ed. (Orig.). 1986. pap. 4.75 (ISBN 0-89536-832-3, 6846). CSS of Ohio.

Long, Edward S. An E. T. Christmas: Two Nativity Dramas. 1985. 3.25 (ISBN 0-89536-763-7, 5870). CSS of Ohio.

--Two Nativity Dramas. 1984. 4.75 (ISBN 0-89536-697-5, 4874). CSS of Ohio.

McGee, Cecil. Dramatic Programs for Christmas. LC 74-93917. 1970. pap. 4.95 (ISBN 0-8054-7507-9). Broadman.

Miller, Sarah W. Christmas Drama for Youth. LC 76-20255. 96p. (Orig.). 1976. pap. 4.50 (ISBN 0-8054-7511-7). Broadman.

Ordonez, Francisco. Del Odio al Amor. 1983. pap. 1.50 (ISBN 0-311-08223-8). Casa Bautista.

Payne, Darwin R. A Christmas Carol: A Playscript. LC 80-18827. (Illus.). 138p. 1981. pap. 4.95 net (ISBN 0-8093-0999-8). S Ill U Pr.

Perez, Belia. Tres Dramas De Navidad. 24p. 1985. pap. 0.80 (ISBN 0-311-08221-1). Casa Bautista.

Picasso, Juan R. Senderos de Navidad. 24p. 1980. pap. 0.80 (ISBN 0-311-08218-1). Casa Bautista.

Pickett, Margaret E. What's Keeping You, Santa? A Christmas Musical Program Package. (Illus.). 74p. (Program package incl. Production Guide with choir arranged songs, cassette tape of songs & thirty slides from book.). 1983. 44.95 (ISBN 0-913939-01-3). TP Assocs.

Pritchard, Gretchen W. Go, Tell It on the Mountain: Three Christmas Pageants for Church Schools. (Illus.). 63p. (Orig.). 1985. pap. 12.50x (ISBN 0-9614022-1-0). Sunday Paper.

Schoer, Karl J., compiled by. Christmas Plays From Oberufer. 3rd ed. Harwood, A. C., tr. & intro. by. 64p. 1973. pap. 3.50 (ISBN 0-85440-279-9, Pub. by Steinerbooks). Anthroposophic.

Shoemaker, Mary E. Meanwhile, Back at the Flock: A Christmas Puppet Play. (Orig.). 1980. pap. 1.85 (ISBN 0-937172-09-X). JLJ Pubs.

Steltz, Nancy. A Christmas Pageant. (Orig.). 1987. pap. price not set (ISBN 0-89536-889-7, 7875). CSS of Ohio.

Urfer, Pamela. Two Christmas Plays. 25p. (Orig.). pap. text ed. 3.95 (ISBN 0-912801-08-5). Creat Arts Dev.

Waldrop, Claracy L. Unto Us. (Orig.). 1957. pap. 1.95 (ISBN 0-8054-9704-8). Broadman.

Watson, E. W. & Blanco, Miquel A. Cuatro Dramas De Navidad. 1984. pap. 0.95 (ISBN 0-311-08224-6). Casa Bautista.

Watson, Elizabeth W. Gift Wrap, Please. (Orig.). 1966. pap. 1.95 (ISBN 0-8054-9710-2). Broadman.

Wells, Edmund E. Christmas Dreaming. (Orig.). pap. 1.50 (ISBN 0-686-30401-2). WOS.

Westberg, Barbara. Christmas Plays. Wallace, Mary H., ed. 40p. (Orig.). 1983. pap. 2.95 (ISBN 0-912315-62-8). Word Aflame.

CHRISTMAS SERMONS

Achtemeier, Paul J. & Mebust, J. Leland. Advent-Christmas. Achtemeier, Elizabeth, et al, eds. LC 79-7377. (Proclamation 2: Aids for Interpreting the Lessons of the Church Year, Ser. B). 64p. (Orig.). 1981. pap. 3.75 (ISBN 0-8006-4060-8, 1-4060). Fortress.

Augustine, St. St. Augustine, Sermons for Christmas & Epiphany. Quasten, J. & Plumpe, J., eds. Lawler, Thomas, tr. LC 78-62464. (Ancient Christian Writers Ser.: No. 15). 250p. 1952. 10.95 (ISBN 0-8091-0137-8). Paulist Pr.

Bass, George. The Cradle, the Cross & the Crown. Sherer, Michael L., ed. (Orig.). 1986. pap. 7.25 (ISBN 0-89536-817-X, 6866). CSS of Ohio.

Boice, James M. The Christ of Christmas. 1983. 9.95 (ISBN 0-8024-0337-9). Moody.

Bringman, Dale. A Star Is Born. (Orig.). 1987. pap. price not set (ISBN 0-89536-881-1, 7867). CSS of Ohio.

Eslinger, Richard. Prepare in the Wilderness. 1984. 5.25 (ISBN 0-89536-680-0, 4856). CSS of Ohio.

Franke, Merle G. It Came upon the Midnight Clear: Christmas Photo Sermon. 1977. pap. 9.50 (ISBN 0-89536-291-0, 0916). CSS of Ohio.

Hagin, Kenneth E. Must Christians Suffer? 1982. pap. 1.50 (ISBN 0-89276-404-X). Hagin Ministries.

Hamilton, M. J. Adam of Dryburgh: Six Christmas Sermons (Introduction & Translation) Hogg, James, ed. (Analecta Cartusiana Ser.: No. 16). (Orig.). 1974. pap. 25.00 (ISBN 3-7052-0018-6, Pub by Salzburg Studies). Longwood Pub Group.

Haskett, William P. Grandpa Haskett Presents: Original New Christmas Stories for the Young & Young-at-Heart. Haskett, M. R., ed. (Illus.). 20p. (Orig.). 1982. pap. 3.00g (ISBN 0-9609724-0-4). Haskett Spec.

Joyce, Jon L. And This Will Be a Sign. (Orig.). 1980. pap. 2.95 (ISBN 0-937172-05-7). JLJ Pubs.

Maurice, Frederick D. Christmas Day & Other Sermons. 410p. 1982. Repr. of 1892 ed. lib. bdg. 50.00 (ISBN 0-89987-595-5). Darby Bks.

Mueller, Daniel. Just Follow the Signs. 1984. 5.00 (ISBN 0-89536-676-2, 4851). CSS of Ohio.

Nehls, H. Michael. The Colors of Christmas. Sherer, Michael L., ed. (Orig.). 1986. pap. 3.95 (ISBN 0-89536-838-2, 6862). CSS of Ohio.

Rest, Friedrich. Our Christian Worship: Advent-Christmas. 1985. 4.75 (ISBN 0-89536-761-0, 5868). CSS of Ohio.

Ridenhour, Thomas E., Sr. Promise of Peace, Call for Justice. Sherer, Michael L., ed. (Orig.). 1986. pap. 6.75 (ISBN 0-89536-822-6, 6831). CSS of Ohio.

Sherer, Mike & Aaseng, Nathan. Night of Wonder: Service-Story for Christmas Eve. 1985. 2.75 (ISBN 0-89536-762-9, 5869). CSS of Ohio.

Sill, Sterling W. Christmas Sermons. LC 73-86165. 184p. 1973. 8.95 (ISBN 0-87747-503-2). Deseret Bk.

Steere, Douglas V. Bethlehem Revisited. LC 65-26995. (Orig.). 1965. pap. 2.50x (ISBN 0-87574-144-4, 144). Pendle Hill.

CHRISTMAS STORIES

Aurelio, John R. Once upon a Christmas Time: Stories for a Family Christmas. (Illus.). 224p. 1986. pap. 8.95 (ISBN 0-8091-2819-5). Paulist Pr.

Bachelder, Louise. Christmas Tidings. 2nd ed. LC 84-60961. (Illus.). 64p. 1984. Repr. of 1969 ed. 5.95 (ISBN 0-88088-088-0, 880880). Peter Pauper.

Benchley, Robert. A Good Old-Fashioned Christmas. (Illus.). 96p. (Orig.). 1981. pap. 7.95 (ISBN 0-938864-02-5). Ipswich Pr.

Blanco, Tomas. The Child's Gifts: A Twelfth Night Tale. LC 75-46530. (Eng. & Span., Illus.). 32p. 1976. 8.95 (ISBN 0-664-32595-5). Westminster.

Bosschere, Jean de & Morris, M. C. Christmas Tales of Flanders. (Illus.). 7.75 (ISBN 0-8446-4516-8). Peter Smith.

Bunsen, Rick, ed. The Golden Christmas Treasury. LC 84-72934. (Illus.). 80p. 1986. 7.95 (ISBN 0-307-15585-4, Pub. by Golden Bks). Western Pub.

Carty, Margaret F. Christmas in Vermont: Three Stories. LC 83-62750. (Illus.). 48p. (Orig.). 1983. pap. 2.95 (ISBN 0-933050-21-6). New Eng Pr VT.

Cavanah, Frances, ed. Favorite Christmas Stories. 1948. 5.95 (ISBN 0-448-02376-8, G&D). Putnam Pub Group.

Charlton, Jim & Shulman, Jason. The Family Book of Christmas Songs & Stories. (Illus.). 208p. 1986. pap. 9.95 (ISBN 0-399-51276-4, Perigee). Putnam Pub Group.

The Christmas Story in Stained Glass. (Illus.). 56p. 1985. pap. 4.95. Walker & Co.

Christmas: The Annual of Christmas Literature & Art, Vol. 54. (Illus.). 64p. 1984. 14.50 (ISBN 0-8066-8965-X, 17-0129); pap. text ed. 6.95 (ISBN 0-8066-8964-1, 17-0128). Augsburg.

Corrin, Sara & Corrin, Stephen, eds. The Faber Book of Christmas Stories. LC 84-13552. (Illus.). 150p. 1984. 9.95 (ISBN 0-571-13348-7). Faber & Faber.

--The Faber Book of Christmas Stories. 9.95 (ISBN 0-317-31393-2). Faber & Faber.

Dickens, Charles. A Christmas Carol: Retold by A. Sweaney. (Oxford Progressive English Readers Ser.). 1975. pap. text ed. 3.75x (ISBN 0-19-580724-3). Oxford U Pr.

Dyke, Van Henry. First Christmas Tree. 76p. 1984. 2.95 (ISBN 0-89783-034-2). Larlin Corp.

Elder, Sam. A Christmas Celebration. LC 84-47709. (Illus.). 1984. 5.00 (ISBN 0-06-015359-8, HarpT). Har-Row.

Erickson, Joyce. In Straw & Story: Christmas Resources for Home & Church. rev. ed. (Illus.). 192p. 1983. pap. 10.95 (ISBN 0-87178-417-3). Brethren.

Fowler, Roe. Christmas Was. 88p. 1982. pap. 6.95 (ISBN 0-686-38093-2). Fig Leaf Pr.

Freeman, James D. Once upon a Christmas. LC 78-53345. (Illus.). 1978. 6.95 (ISBN 0-87159-119-7). Unity School.

Greif, Martin. The St. Nicholas Book. LC 76-5089. (Illus.). 60p. 1976. 5.95 (ISBN 0-87663-554-0). Universe.

Harrison, Shirley. Who Is Father Christmas? (Illus.). 64p. 1983. 7.50 (ISBN 0-7153-8222-5). David & Charles.

Hawkes, Laura M. Favorite Christmas Stories. 64p. 1973. pap. 2.50 (ISBN 0-89036-015-4). Hawkes Pub Inc.

Irving, Washington. Old Christmas. LC 77-8465. (Illus.). 208p. 1977. Repr. of 1875 ed. 10.00 (ISBN 0-912882-30-1). Sleepy Hollow.

Jones, Margaret W. The Christmas Invitation. Easson, Roger R., ed. LC 85-2035. (A Child's Christmas in Memphis Ser.: Vol. 3). (Illus.). 48p. 1985. 9.95 (ISBN 0-918518-42-3). St Luke TN.

Kaaikaula, Becky. The Innkeeper's Wife. (Illus.). 12p. (Orig.). 1983. write for info. (ISBN 0-914599-00-3). Kaaikaula.

Killen, John, ed. The Irish Christmas Book. (Illus.). 132p. (Orig.). 1986. pap. 8.95 (ISBN 0-85640-345-8, Pub. by Blackstaff Pr). Longwood Pub Group.

Knight, Hilary. Christmas Nutshell Library, 4 bks. Incl. Angels & Berries & Candy Canes (ISBN 0-06-023200-5); Christmas Stocking Story (ISBN 0-06-023205-6); Firefly in a Fir Tree (ISBN 0-06-023190-4); The Night Before Christmas. LC 63-18904. 1963. Set. 9.70 (ISBN 0-06-023165-3). HarpJ.

Lederer, William J. A Happy Book of Christmas Stories. (Illus.). 1984. 7.95 (ISBN 0-393-01414-2). Norton.

Lee, Sharon. Christmas Handbook, No. 3. 112p. 1985. 7.95 (ISBN 0-87239-913-3, 3043). Standard Pub.

Lichtfield, Hugh. Preaching the Christmas Story. LC 83-71689. 1984. pap. 5.50 (ISBN 0-8054-2101-7). Broadman.

Livingood, J., et al, eds. Christmas I Remember Best. (Illus., Orig.). write for info. (ISBN 0-910901-00-7); pap. 5.95 (ISBN 0-910901-01-5). Deseret News.

Lohan, Robert & Lohan, Maria, eds. A New Christmas Treasury: With More Stories for Reading Aloud. LC 54-12862. 14.50 (ISBN 0-8044-2536-1, Pub. by Stephen Daye Pr). Ungar.

Lynd, Sylvia. The Christmas Omnibus. 1932. lib. bdg. 15.00 (ISBN 0-8414-5634-8). Folcroft.

MacIver, Kenneth & Thomson, William. An Old New England Christmas. (Illus.). 47p. (Orig.). 1980. pap. 3.00 (ISBN 0-88448-019-4). Harpswell Pr.

Marsh, Carole. The Fortune Cookie Christmas. (Illus.). 50p. (Orig.). 1986. pap. 9.95 (ISBN 0-935326-53-7). Gallopade Pub Group.

Morriss, Frank, ed. A Christmas Celebration: The Wanderer's Christmas Anthology. LC 83-51146. 334p. 1983. 14.95 (ISBN 0-915245-00-0). Wanderer Pr.

Newcombe, Jack, ed. A Christmas Treasury. LC 81-50583. (Illus.). 512p. 1982. 22.95 (ISBN 0-670-22110-4). Viking.

O. Henry. The Gift of the Magi. LC 82-60896. (Illus.). 32p. 1982. 14.95 (ISBN 0-907234-17-8). Picture Bk Studio USA.

Peterson, Carolyn S. & Fenton, Ann D. Christmas Story Programs. (Illus.). 1981. 7.00 (ISBN 0-913545-01-5). Moonlight FL.

Pitcher, Arthur R. Christmas Remembered. 1985. pap. 5.25 (ISBN 0-86544-029-8). Salv Army Suppl South.

Pope John Paul I. The Lesson of the Christmas Donkey. Smith, David & Cunningham, Robert, trs. LC 79-21337. 104p. 1982. 6.95 (ISBN 0-8199-0774-X). Franciscan Herald.

Rayford, Julian Lee. The First Christmas Dinner. (Illus.). 35p. 1947. 7.50 (ISBN 0-940882-03-5). Haunted Bk Shop.

Santa Claus Stories: Broadcast on 1927 from Palais Royal Department Store, Washington DC. 1987. write for info. Interspace Bks.

Saturday Evening Post Editors. The Saturday Evening Post Christmas Stories. LC 80-67058. (Illus.). 144p. 1980. 14.95 (ISBN 0-89387-046-3, Co-Pub by Sat Eve Post). Curtis Pub Co.

Scrocco, Jean L., ed. A Christmas Treasury. LC 84-8798. (Illus.). 48p. 1985. 11.95 (ISBN 0-88101-017-0). Unicorn Pub.

Sheppard, Donna C. Williamsburg Christmas. LC 80-17179. (World of Williamsburg Ser.). (Illus.). 78p. (Orig.). 1980. pap. 6.95 (ISBN 0-87935-054-7). Williamsburg.

Simon, Charlie M. Christmas Every Friday & Other Christmas Stories. Hagen, Lyman B., ed. LC 81-65364. (Illus.). 68p. 1981. 7.95 (ISBN 0-935304-21-5). August Hse.

Smith, Elva S. & Hazeltine, Alice I.compiled by. Christmas in Legend & Story: A Book for Boys & Girls Illustrated from Famous Paintings. LC 72-39390. (Granger Index Reprint Ser.). Repr. of 1915 ed. 18.00 (ISBN 0-8369-6353-9). Ayer Co Pubs.

Tibbetts, Laurene J. It's Christmas! Poems & Stories for the Holiday Season. 97p. 1981. write for info. Rector Pub.

Van Dyke, Henry. The Spirit of Christmas. LC 84-19389. 64p. 1984. pap. 2.95 (ISBN 0-89783-033-4). Larlin Corp.

Weatherford De Ruiz, L. M., compiled by. La Navidad. (Span.). 192p. 1981. pap. 2.75 (ISBN 0-311-08207-6). Casa Bautista.

Weems, John E., ed. A Texas Christmas, Vol. II. 130p. 1986. 19.95 (ISBN 0-939722-30-5). Pressworks.

Williams, Ira, Jr. The Piano Man's Christmas & Other Stories for Christmas. 80p. (Orig.). 1986. pap. 4.95 (ISBN 0-687-30920-4). Abingdon.

CHRISTMAS TREES

see also Christmas Decorations

Benyus, Janine M. Christmas Tree Pests Manual. 107p. 1983. pap. 14.00 (ISBN 0-318-11762-2, S/N 001-001-00589-4). Gov Printing Office.

Burkhart, W. Eugene, Jr. Decorating Christmas Trees. (Illus.). 64p. (Orig.). 1985. pap. 8.95 (ISBN 0-9615199-0-8). Burkharts.

Chapman, Arthur G. & Wray, Robert D. Christmas Trees for Pleasure & Profit. rev. ed. 220p. 1984. pap. text ed. 14.95 (ISBN 0-8135-1074-0). Rutgers U Pr.

Dorrough, Ardith. The Real Christmas Tree. 48p. (Orig.). 1983. pap. 2.50 (ISBN 0-88144-020-5, CPS/020). Christian Pub.

Metcalfe, Edna, compiled by. The Trees of Christmas. LC 79-12288. (Illus.). 1979. pap. 8.75 (ISBN 0-687-42591-3). Abingdon.

Snyder, Phillip V. The Christmas Tree Book: The History of the Christmas Tree & Antique Christmas Tree Ornaments. LC 76-40224. (Large Format Ser.). (Illus.). 176p. 1977. pap. 10.95 (ISBN 0-14-004518-X). Penguin.

CHRISTMAS TREES–JUVENILE LITERATURE

De Paola, Tomie. The Family Christmas Tree Book. LC 80-12081. (Illus.). 32p. 1980. reinforced bdg. 11.95 (ISBN 0-8234-0416-1). Holiday.

CHRISTOLOGY

see Jesus Christ

CHRISTWARD MINISTRY

Newhouse, Flower A. Disciplines of the Holy Quest. 4th ed. LC 59-15553. (Illus.). 1959. 10.50 (ISBN 0-910378-05-3). Christward.

--Drama of Incarnation. 4th ed. 1948. 7.50 (ISBN 0-910378-04-5). Christward.

--Rediscovering the Angels & Natives of Eternity. 7th ed. (Illus.). 11.00 (ISBN 0-910378-02-9). Christward.

CHRONIC DISEASES

Hirsch, Ernest A. Starting Over. 1977. 8.95 (ISBN 0-8158-0350-8). Chris Mass.

CHRONOLOGY, ECCLESIASTICAL

see also Church Calendar

Walton, Robert C. Chronological & Background Charts of Church History. 120p. 1986. pap. text ed. 8.95 (ISBN 0-310-36281-4, 11302P). Zondervan.

CHRONOLOGY, HEBREW

see Chronology, Jewish

CHRONOLOGY, JEWISH

see also Calendar, Jewish

Frank, Edgar. Talmudic & Rabbinical Chronology. 1978. 6.95 (ISBN 0-87306-050-4). Feldheim.

Levi. Jewish Chrononomy. 12.95 (ISBN 0-87306-213-2). Feldheim.

Potok, Chaim. Wanderings: Chaim Potok's History of the Jews. LC 78-54915. 1978. 29.95 (ISBN 0-394-50110-1). Knopf.

Wiesenthal, Simon. Every Day Remembrance Day: A Chronicle of Jewish Martyrdom. (Illus.). 480p. 1987. 19.95 (ISBN 0-8050-0098-4). H Holt & Co.

CHUANG-TZU

Chuang Tsu. Chuang Tsu - Inner Chapters. Gia-Fu Feng, ed. English, Jane, tr. (Giant Ser.). pap. 12.95 (ISBN 0-394-71990-5, V-990, Vin). Random.

CHURCH

see also Christian Union; Christianity; Church Work; Communion of Saints; Ecumenical Movement; Jesus Christ–Mystical Body; Language Question in the Church; Mission of the Church; Priesthood, Universal; Salvation outside the Catholic Church

Adoracion y la Iglesia. (Span.). pap. 1.25 (ISBN 0-686-32316-5). Rod & Staff.

Althoff, Karl F. The Magna Charta of the Christian Church. Grimm, Werner, tr. from Ger. 19p. 1982. pap. 3.00 (ISBN 0-919924-15-8, Pub. by Steiner Book Centre Canada). Anthroposophic.

Artz, Thomas R. God's People: The Now & Future Church. 64p. 1986. pap. 1.95 (ISBN 0-89243-248-9). Liguori Pubns.

Bea, Augustin. Church & Mankind. 6.50 (ISBN 0-8199-0012-5, L38112). Franciscan Herald.

Bilheimer, Robert S. What Must the Church Do? facsimile ed. LC 70-134053. (Essay Index Reprints - Interseminary Ser.: Vol. 5). Repr. of 1947 ed. 17.00 (ISBN 0-8369-2384-7). Ayer Co Pubs.

Boatman, Russell. What the Bible Says about the Church. (What the Bible Says Ser.). text ed. 13.95 (ISBN 0-89900-098-3). College Pr Pub.

Bowen, Francis A. How to Produce a Church Newspaper... & Other Ways Churches Communicate. (Illus.). 1974. 5.00 (ISBN 0-9602830-1-3). F A Bowen.

Brooks, John P. The Divine Church. Dayton, Donald W., ed. (The Higher Christian Life Ser.). 283p. 1985. 35.00 (ISBN 0-8240-6408-9). Garland Pub.

Brown, Robert M. Significance of the Church. LC 56-6172. (Layman's Theological Library). 96p. 1956. pap. 2.45 (ISBN 0-664-24001-1). Westminster.

Buhlmann, Walbert. The Church of the Future: A Model for the Year 2001. Groves, Mary, tr. from Ger. Tr. of Weltkirche-Neue Dimensionen-Model fur das Jahr 2001. 256p. (Orig.). 1986. pap. 10.95 (ISBN 0-88344-253-1). Orbis Bks.

--Courage, Church! Essays in Ecclesial Spirituality. Smith, Mary, tr. from Ital. LC 78-1381. Orig. Title: Corragio Chiesa! 149p. (Orig.). 1978. pap. 2.98 (ISBN 0-88344-068-7). Orbis Bks.

Campbell, R. K. The Church of the Living God. 8.95 (ISBN 0-88172-007-0); pap. 5.95 (ISBN 0-686-13515-6). Believers Bkshelf.

Campolo, Tony. Who Switched Price Tags? How to Make Life Better in Your Work, Family & Church. 224p. 1986. 11.95 (ISBN 0-8499-0491-9). Word Bks.

Carmody, Denise L. & Carmody, John T. Bonded in Christ's Love: Being a Member of the Church. 240p. (Orig.). 1986. pap. 9.95 (ISBN 0-8091-2791-1). Paulist Pr.

Conn, Charles P. & Conn, Charles W. What Is the Church? 1977. pap. 1.99 (ISBN 0-87148-907-4). Pathway Pr.

Dana, H. E. Manual de Eclesiologia. Robleto, Adolfo, tr. Orig. Title: A Manual of Ecclesiology. write for info. (ISBN 0-311-17018-8). Casa Bautista.

Dieter, Melvin E. & Berg, Daniel N., eds. Church. (Wesleyan Theological Perspectives Ser.: Vol. IV). 1984. 14.95 (ISBN 0-87162-406-0, D4853). Warner Pr.

Doohan, Leonard. The Lay-Centered Church: Theology & Spirituality. 204p. 1984. pap. 8.95 (ISBN 0-86683-808-2, AY8403, HarpR). Har-Row.

Driver, John. Community & Commitment. LC 76-41463. 96p. 1976. pap. 3.95 (ISBN 0-8361-1802-2). Herald Pr.

Dulles, Avery. Models of the Church. LC 77-11246. 1987. pap. 4.95 (ISBN 0-385-13368-5, Im). Doubleday.

Dulles, Avery & Granfield, Patrick. The Church: A Bibliography. (Theology & Biblical Resources Ser: Vol. 1). 1985. 15.00 (ISBN 0-89453-449-1); pap. 8.95 (ISBN 0-89453-470-X). M Glazier.

Ellis, Joe. The Church on Target. 128p. 1986. pap. 5.95 (ISBN 0-87403-005-6, 3019). Standard Pub.

Free Church. You & Your Church. 3rd ed. 1978. pap. 1.95. Free Church Pubns.

Fries, Heinrich & Rahner, Karl. Unity of the Churches: An Actual Possibility. Gritsch, E. & Gritsch, R., trs. LC 84-8122. 160p. pap. 6.95 (ISBN 0-8006-1820-3). Fortress.

Fuellenbach, John. Ecclesiastical Office & the Primacy of Rome: An Evaluation of Recent Theological Discussion of First Clement. LC 79-17574. (Catholic University of America. Studies in Christian Antiquity Ser.: No. 20). pap. 72.00 (2029502). Bks Demand UMI.

Getz, Gene A. Measure of a Church. LC 75-17160. (Orig.). 1975. pap. 3.50 (ISBN 0-8307-0398-5, 5014700). Regal.

Griffiths, Michael. God's Forgetful Pilgrims: Recalling the Church to Its Reason for Being. LC 75-16166. Repr. of 1975 ed. 44.00 (2027545). Bks Demand UMI.

Griswold, Roland. The Winning Church. 144p. 1986. pap. 4.95 (ISBN 0-89693-527-2). Victor Bks.

Gritsch, Eric W. & Lehmann, Helmut T., eds. Luther's Works: Church & Ministry I, Vol. 39. LC 55-9893. 1970. 19.95 (ISBN 0-8006-0339-7, 1-339). Fortress.

Harrell, John. To Tell of Gideon: The Art of Storytelling in the Church. 1975. 8.00x (ISBN 0-9615389-4-5); cassette 6.95x (ISBN 0-9615389-5-3). York Hse.

Hinson, E. Glenn. The Integrity of the Church. LC 77-82400. 1978. 8.95 (ISBN 0-8054-1616-1). Broadman.

Hocking, W. E., et al. Church & the New World Mind: The Drake Lectures for 1944. facsimile ed. LC 68-57311. (Essay Index Reprint Ser). Repr. of 1944 ed. 18.00 (ISBN 0-8369-9698-4). Ayer Co Pubs.

Hoffman, Oswald C. God's Joyful People: One in the Spirit. LC 72-96742. 104p. 1973. pap. 2.95 (ISBN 0-570-03152-4, 12-2537). Concordia.

Holland, Daniel W., et al. Using Nonbroadcast Video in the Church. 128p. 1980. pap. 5.95 (ISBN 0-8170-0895-0). Judson.

Holmes, Urban T., III & Westerhoff, John H., III. The Church's Teaching Series, 9 Vols. 1979. Set. 45.45 (ISBN 0-8164-0453-4, HarpR); Set. pap. 24.95 (ISBN 0-8164-2271-0). Har-Row.

Hopewell, James F. Congregation: Stories & Structures. Wheeler, Barbara G., ed. LC 86-45914. 240p. 1987. pap. 14.95 (ISBN 0-8006-1956-0). Fortress.

Hough, Joseph C., Jr. & Cobb, John B., Jr. Christian Identity & Theological Education. (Studies in Religious & Theological Scholarship). 1985. pap. 11.95 (ISBN 0-89130-855-5, 00-08-01). Scholars Pr GA.

Houtepen, Anton. People of God: A Plea for the Church. Bowden, John, tr. from Dutch. Orig. Title: Mensen Van God. 224p. (Orig.). 1985. pap. 10.95 (ISBN 0-88344-402-X). Orbis Bks.

Inrig, Gary. Life in His Body: Discovering Purpose, Form & Freedom in His Church. 182p. 1975. pap. 5.95 (ISBN 0-87788-500-1). Shaw Pubs.

Jacobsen, Wayne. The Naked Church. 208p. (Orig.). 1987. pap. 6.95 (ISBN 0-89081-569-0). Harvest Hse.

Judd, Peter & Lindgren, Bruce. An Introduction to the Saints Church. LC 75-35763. 1976. 14.00 (ISBN 0-8309-0154-X). Herald Hse.

Kilian, Sabbas. Theological Models for the Parish. LC 76-42986. 1977. 5.95 (ISBN 0-8189-0337-6). Alba.

Kiser, Wayne. Getting More Out of Church. 168p. 1986. pap. 5.95 (ISBN 0-89693-530-2). Victor Bks.

Kraeling, Carl H. The Christian Building: Final Report VIII, Part II. LC 43-2669. 32.50 (ISBN 0-685-71744-5). J J Augustin.

Krol, John C. Church: Life Giving Union with Christ. 1978. 7.50 (ISBN 0-8198-0525-4); pap. 5.95 (ISBN 0-8198-0526-2). Dghtrs St Paul.

Kung, Hans. The Church. 600p. 1976. pap. 6.95 (ISBN 0-385-11367-6, Im). Doubleday.

--Structures of the Church. LC 82-4706. 350p. 1982. pap. 12.95 (ISBN 0-8245-0508-5). Crossroad NY.

Lehmann, Helmut T. & Gritsch, Eric W., eds. Luther's Works: Church & Ministry III, Vol. 41. LC 55-9893. 1966. 19.95 (ISBN 0-8006-0341-9, 1-341). Fortress.

Leith, John H. The Church, a Believing Fellowship. LC 80-82192. 192p. 1981. pap. 3.95 (ISBN 0-8042-0518-3). John Knox.

Leonard, Bill J. The Nature of the Church. (Orig.). 1986. 5.95 (ISBN 0-8054-1642-0). Broadman.

Lohmeyer, Ernst. Lord of the Temple: A Study of the Relation Between Cult & Gospel. LC 62-18409. 1961. text ed. 8.50x (ISBN 0-8401-1423-0). A R Allenson.

Lovelace, Richard. Dynamics of Spiritual Life. LC 78-24757. 1979. pap. 11.95 (ISBN 0-87784-626-X). Inter-Varsity.

Lubac, Henri De. The Motherhood of the Church. Englund, Sr. Sergia, tr. from Fr. LC 81-83857. Tr. of Les Eglises particulieres & La maternite de l'eglise. 363p. (Orig.). 1983. pap. 12.95 (ISBN 0-89870-014-0). Ignatius Pr.

Lundy, John P. Monumental Christianity: The Art & Symbolism of the Primitive Church. 1977. lib. bdg. 59.95 (ISBN 0-8490-2278-9). Gordon Pr.

McGavran, Donald. Understanding Church Growth. rev. ed. 488p. (Orig.). 1980. pap. 12.95 (ISBN 0-8028-1849-8). Eerdmans.

Malachuck, Daniel. Stained Glass Religion: Who Needs It. 100p. pap. 4.95 (ISBN 0-89221-127-X, Pub. by SonLife). New Leaf.

Maritain, Jacques. De l'Eglise du Christ. 430p. 1970. 15.95 (ISBN 0-686-56348-4). French & Eur.

Maseroni, Robert S. The Church Will Grow by These. 1983. 5.55 (ISBN 0-317-04044-8, 0060). CSS of Ohio.

Metz, Johann B. Emergent Church. 160p. 1986. pap. 9.95 (ISBN 0-8245-0729-0). Crossroad NY.

Milash, Nikodim. Das Kirchenrecht der Morgenlandischen Kirche. 2nd ed. LC 80-2360. Repr. of 1905 ed. 83.00 (ISBN 0-404-18910-5). AMS Pr.

Miller, Donald G. Nature & Mission of the Church. LC 57-9443. (Orig.). 1957. pap. 5.95 (ISBN 0-8042-3208-3). John Knox.

Miller, Randolph C., ed. Church & Organized Movements. facs. ed. LC 76-134115. (Essay Index Reprint Ser). 1946. 18.00 (ISBN 0-8369-1998-X). Ayer Co Pubs.

Moberg, David A. The Church As a Social Institution. 600p. 1984. pap. 18.95 (ISBN 0-8010-6168-7). Baker Bk.

Moody, J. B. My Church. 325p. 1974. Repr. of 1890 ed. 8.50 (ISBN 0-87921-030-3). Attic Pr.

Morgan, John H., ed. Church Divinity, Nineteen Eighty Five. 109p. (Orig.). 1985. pap. 10.00x (ISBN 0-932269-61-3). Wyndham Hall.

Neighbour, Ralph W., Jr. The Seven Last Words of the Church. LC 79-51937. 1979. pap. 4.95 (ISBN 0-8054-5527-2). Broadman.

Newman, Stewart A. A Free Church Perspective: A Study in Ecclesiology. 113p. (Orig.). 1986. pap. 8.95 (ISBN 0-913029-12-2). Stevens Bk Pr.

Perry, Lloyd M. & Shawchuck, Norman. Revitalizing the Twentieth Century Church. LC 81-16974. Date not set. pap. 7.95 (ISBN 0-8024-7318-0). Moody.

Peters, Stanley J. The Church Unique. 1987. 12.95 (ISBN 0-533-06972-6). Vantage.

Prange, Victor H. Why So Many Churches. 1985. pap. 2.95 (ISBN 0-8100-0188-8, 15N0413). Northwest Pub.

Protopresbyter Michael Pomazansky. O Zhizni o Vjere o Tzerkvje, 2 vols. Tr. of On Life, Faith & the Church. 650p. 1976. pap. 23.00 (ISBN 0-317-29072-X). Holy Trinity.

Provost, James H., ed. Church As Communion. (Permanent Seminar Studies: No. 1). 245p. 1984. pap. 8.00 (ISBN 0-943616-23-9). Canon Law Soc.

--Church As Mission. (Permanent Seminar Studies: No. 2). 288p. 1984. pap. 8.00 (ISBN 0-943616-24-7). Canon Law Soc.

Rahner, Karl. Shape of the Church to Come. 1974. 10.95 (ISBN 0-8245-0372-4). Crossroad NY.

Ratzinger, Joseph & Lehmann, Karl. Living with the Church. Hayes, Zachary, tr. from Ger. LC 78-15509. Orig. Title: Mit der Kirche Leben. 53p. 1978. pap. 1.50 (ISBN 0-8199-0742-1). Franciscan Herald.

Religious Congregations & Health Facilities: Tradition & Transition. LC 84-7692. 100p. (Orig.). 1984. pap. 9.00 (ISBN 0-87125-095-0). Cath Health.

Ridout, Samuel. The Church & Its Order According to Scripture. 1915. pap. 2.75 (ISBN 0-87213-711-2). Loizeaux.

Rife, Carl B. & Bishop, Carolyn. The Church Is You & I. 1984. 1.95 (ISBN 0-89536-658-4, 0394). CSS of Ohio.

Roberts, Donald L. The Perfect Church. LC 79-56331. 95p. (Orig.). 1980. pap. 2.95 (ISBN 0-87509-267-5). Chr Pubns.

Robinson, Darrell W. Total Church Life. LC 85-7900. 1985. 7.95 (ISBN 0-8054-6250-3). Broadman.

Saucy, Robert L. The Church in God's Program. LC 70-175496. (Handbook of Bible Doctrine). 1972. pap. 7.95 (ISBN 0-8024-1544-X). Moody.

Schaller, Lyle E. The Small Church is Different. LC 82-1830. 192p. (Orig.). 1982. pap. 7.95 (ISBN 0-687-38717-5). Abingdon.

Schillebeeckx, Edward, ed. Church & Mankind. LC 65-15249. (Concilium Ser.: Vol. 1). 196p. 1965. 7.95 (ISBN 0-8091-0015-0). Paulist Pr.

Schuller, Robert H. Your Church Has a Fantastic Future. LC 86-11906. 364p. (Orig.). 1986. pap. 7.95 (ISBN 0-8307-1126-0, 5418785). Regal.

Segundo, Juan L. The Community Called Church. Drury, John, tr. from Span. LC 72-85795. (A Theology for Artisans of a New Humanity Ser., Vol. 1). Orig. Title: Esa communidad Lleamasha Iglesia. 181p. 1973. 7.95x (ISBN 0-88344-481-X); pap. 4.95x (ISBN 0-88344-487-9). Orbis Bks.

Silvey, D. O. Lord's Unconquerable Church. 256p. 1972. 4.95 (ISBN 0-89114-052-2); pap. 2.95 (ISBN 0-89114-051-4). Baptist Pub Hse.

Smith, Ebbie C. Balanced Church Growth. LC 84-6456. 1984. pap. 5.95 (ISBN 0-8054-6246-5). Broadman.

Snyder, Howard A. The Community of the King. LC 77-6030. (Illus.). 1977. pap. 7.95 (ISBN 0-87784-752-5). Inter-Varsity.

Snyder, Howard A. & Runyon, Daniel V. Foresight: Ten Major Trends That Will Dramatically Affect the Future of Christians & the Church. 176p. 1986. 12.95 (ISBN 0-8407-5531-7). Nelson.

Stoesz, Samuel J. Understanding My Church. rev. ed. LC 82-73214. 216p. 1983. pap. 5.95 (ISBN 0-87509-325-6); leader's guide 2.95 (ISBN 0-87509-331-0). Chr Pubns.

Surrey, Peter J. The Small Town Church. LC 81-622. (Creative Leadership Ser.). 128p. (Orig.). 1981. pap. 6.95 (ISBN 0-687-38720-5). Abingdon.

Tewes, Robert E., Jr. Conflict in the Church As Seen by a Thirteen Year Old. LC 83-83650. 1983. pap. 17.95 (ISBN 0-915644-24-X). Clayton Pub Hse.

Thompson, Betty. A Chance to Change: Women & Men in the Church. LC 82-71832. pap. 28.00 (2029602). Bks Demand UMI.

Tillapaugh, Frank R. Unleashing the Church. LC 82-9783. 1985. pap. 5.95 (ISBN 0-8307-1024-8, 5418433). Regal.

Tomlinson, M. A. The Glorious Church of God. 1968. pap. 3.50 (ISBN 0-934942-06-4). White Wing Pub.

Troeh, M. Richard & Troeh, Marjorie. The Conferring Church. 1987. pap. 10.00 (ISBN 0-8309-0465-4). Herald Hse.

Trueblood, David E. La Iglesia un Companerismo Incendiario. Velasquez, Roger, tr. from Eng. Orig. Title: The Incendiary Fellowship. (Span.). 114p. 1981. pap. 4.75 (ISBN 0-311-17022-6, Edit Mundo). Casa Bautista.

Visible Community of Love. (Divine Master Ser.). (First Semester). 5.00 (ISBN 0-8198-0003-1); pap. 4.00 (ISBN 0-8198-0004-X); discussion & project manual 0.50 (ISBN 0-8198-0005-8). Dghtrs St Paul.

Wagner, C. Peter. Your Church Can Be Healthy. LC 79-974. (Creative Leadership Ser.). 1979. pap. 7.50 (ISBN 0-687-46870-1). Abingdon.

--Your Church Can Grow. rev. ed. LC 84-8314. 1984. pap. 6.95 (ISBN 0-8307-0978-9, 5418284). Regal.

Walsh, John. Church on Parade. LC 83-62517. 1984. pap. 7.95 (ISBN 0-89390-053-2). Resource Pubns.

Watchman Nee. The Spirit of Wisdom & Revelation. Kaung, Stephen, tr. 1980. pap. 3.25 (ISBN 0-935008-48-9). Christian Fellow Pubs.

Westerhoff, John H., III. Living the Faith Community: The Church That Makes a Difference. 120p. (Orig.). 1985. pap. 6.95 (ISBN 0-86683-870-8, HarpR). Har-Row.

Westerhoff, John H., III & Hughes, Caroline A. On the Threshold of God's Future. 160p. (Orig.). 1986. pap. 7.95 (ISBN 0-06-254781-X, HarpR). Har-Row.

White, Jerry. The Church & the Parachurch: An Uneasy Marriage. LC 83-12125. (Critical Concern Ser.). 1983. 10.95 (ISBN 0-88070-018-1). Multnomah.

Wilson, L. R. The New Testament Church: A Divine Institution. 1970. pap. 2.7500210895x (ISBN 0-88027-035-7). Firm Foun Pub.

Wilson, Robert L. Shaping the Congregation. LC 80-22228. (Into Our Third Century Ser.). 144p. (Orig.). 1981. pap. 3.95 (ISBN 0-687-38334-X). Abingdon.

World Council of Churches, Assembly (6th: 1983: Vancouver, BC) Gathered for Life: Official Report, VI Assembly, World Council of Vancouver of Churches, Vancouver, Canada, 24 July - 10 August 1983. Gill, David, ed. LC 84-141282. Repr. of 1983 ed. 91.30 (2027544). Bks Demand UMI.

Worley, Robert C. A Gathering of Strangers: Understanding the Life of Your Church. rev. & updated ed. LC 83-12343. (Illus.). 122p. 1983. pap. 8.95 (ISBN 0-664-24488-2). Westminster.

Zikmund, Barbara B. Discovering the Church. LC 82-23870. (Library of Living Faith: Vol. 9). 116p. 1983. pap. 5.95 (ISBN 0-664-24441-6). Westminster.

CHURCH–ADDRESSES, ESSAYS, LECTURES

Bowdle, Donald N., ed. The Promise & the Power. 332p. 1980. 14.95 (ISBN 0-87148-706-3). Pathway Pr.

Church, R. W. Occasional Papers, 2 vols. 1973. Repr. of 1897 ed. 20.00 set (ISBN 0-8274-1533-8). R West.

Coe, Ben. Christian Churches at the Crossroads. LC 80-27624. 160p. (Orig.). 1980. pap. 5.95 (ISBN 0-87808-178-X). William Carey Lib.

Hinckley, Gordon B. Be Thou an Example. LC 81-15109. 144p. 1981. 7.95 (ISBN 0-87747-899-6). Deseret Bk.

Latourette, Kenneth, ed. Gospel, the Church & the World. LC 76-134107. (Essay Index Reprint Ser). 1946. 18.00 (ISBN 0-8369-1972-6). Ayer Co Pubs.

MacArthur, John, Jr. The Anatomy of a Church. 2nd ed. (John MacArthur's Bible Studies). 1986. pap. 3.95 (ISBN 0-8024-5132-2). Moody.

Mandeville, Bernard. Free Thoughts on Religion, the Church, & National Happiness. LC 77-17171. 1981. Repr. of 1720 ed. lib. bdg. 60.00x (ISBN 0-8201-1300-X). Schol Facsimiles.

Montgomery, John W. Damned Through the Church. 96p. 1970. 2.95 (ISBN 0-87123-090-9, 200090). Bethany Hse.

Read, Ralph H., ed. Younger Churchmen Look at the Church. facsimile ed. LC 74-156708. (Essay Index Reprint Ser). Repr. of 1935 ed. 21.50 (ISBN 0-8369-2330-8). Ayer Co Pubs.

Wakelyn, Jon L. & Miller, Randall M. Catholics in the Old South: Essays on Church & Culture. LC 83-7893. x, 262p. 1983. 15.95 (ISBN 0-86554-080-2, H74). Mercer Univ Pr.

Walvoord, John F. Church in Prophecy. 6.95 (ISBN 0-310-34051-9, 10969P). Zondervan.

CHURCH–AUTHORITY

see also Liberty of Speech in the Church

Empie, Paul C., et al, eds. Teaching Authority & Infallibility in the Church, No. 6. LC 79-54109. (Lutherans & Catholics in Dialogue). 352p. (Orig.). 1979. pap. 8.95 (ISBN 0-8066-1733-0, 10-6222). Augsburg.

Nuttall, Clayton. The Weeping Church: Confronting the Crisis of Church Polity. LC 85-10760. 1985. pap. 5.95 (ISBN 0-87227-104-8). Reg Baptist.

Swidler, Leonard, ed. Authority in the Church & the Schillebeeckx Case. LC 82-73005. 224p. (Orig.). 1982. pap. 9.95 (ISBN 0-8245-0543-3). Crossroad NY.

Von Campenhausen, Hans. Ecclesiastical Authority & Spiritual Power in the Church of the First Three Centuries. Baker, J. A., tr. 1969. 25.00x (ISBN 0-8047-0665-4). Stanford U Pr.

CHURCH–BIBLICAL TEACHING

Balchin, John F. What the Bible Teaches about the Church. 1979. pap. 3.95 (ISBN 0-8423-7883-9). Tyndale.

Bender, Harold S. These Are My People: The New Testament Church. LC 62-12947. (Conrad Grebel Lecture Ser.). 136p. 1962. pap. 6.95 (ISBN 0-8361-1479-5). Herald Pr.

Carson, D. A., ed. Biblical Interpretation & the Church: The Problem of Contextualization. 232p. 1985. pap. 7.95 (ISBN 0-8407-7501-6). Nelson.

Gallaway, Ira. Drifted Astray: Returning the Church to Witness & Ministry. 160p. (Orig.). 1983. pap. 6.95 (ISBN 0-687-11186-2). Abingdon.

Halton, Thomas. The Church. (Message of the Fathers of the Church Ser.: Vol. 4). 1985. 15.95 (ISBN 0-89453-344-4); pap. 10.95 (ISBN 0-89453-316-9). M Glazier.

Hawkins, O. S. Where Angels Fear to Tread. LC 83-24022. 1984. pap. 4.95 (ISBN 0-8054-5538-8). Broadman.

Hicks, Robert & Bewes, Richard. The Church. (Understanding Bible Truth Ser.). (Orig.). 1981. pap. 0.95 (ISBN 0-89840-018-X). Heres Life.

Lohfink, Gerhard. Jesus & Community: The Social Dimension of Christian Faith. 224p. 1985. pap. 9.95 (ISBN 0-8091-2661-3). Paulist Pr.

North, James B. The Church of the New Testament. (Restoration Booklets Ser.). (Illus., Orig.). 1984. 0.75 (ISBN 0-87239-779-3, 3299). Standard Pub.

Parks, Keith H. First Things First. 2nd rev. ed. 32p. 1981. pap. 2.49 (ISBN 0-88151-012-2). Lay Leadership.

Shelly, Bruce L. What Is the Church, Bk. 3. Chao, Lorna Y., tr. (Basic Doctrine Ser.). (Chinese.). 1985. pap. write for info. (ISBN 0-941598-25-X). Living Spring Pubns.

Stephens, Julius H. The Churches & the Kingdom. LC 78-5676. 1978. Repr. of 1959 ed. lib. bdg. cancelled (ISBN 0-313-20488-8, STCK). Greenwood.

Thomas, Roger. The Perfect Church. LC 81-14544. 96p. (Orig.). 1982. pap. 2.25 (ISBN 0-87239-479-4, 41012). Standard Pub.

CHURCH–FOUNDATION

see also Christianity–Origin; Popes–Primacy

Altheim, Franz & Stiehl, Ruth. Christentum am Roten Meer. Vol. 1, 1971. 153.00x (ISBN 3-11-003790-4); Vol. 2, 1973. 153.00x (ISBN 3-11-003791-2). De Gruyter.

Fiorenza, Francis S. Foundational Theology: Jesus & the Church. 320p. 1984. 22.50 (ISBN 0-8245-0494-1). Crossroad NY.

Lindsay, Gordon. The House the Lord Built. 1.00 (ISBN 0-89985-015-4). Christ Nations.

Rahner, Karl. Foundations of Christian Faith: An Introduction to the Idea of Christianity. LC 82-4663. 492p. 1982. pap. 16.95 (ISBN 0-8245-0523-9). Crossroad NY.

Richards, Michael. Nature & Necessity of Christ's Church. LC 83-2596. 142p. 1983. pap. 7.95 (ISBN 0-8189-0458-5). Alba.

Richardson, Cyril C. The Church Through the Centuries. LC 72-6726. Repr. of 1938 ed. 21.00 (ISBN 0-404-10645-5). AMS Pr.

CHURCH–HISTORY OF DOCTRINES

Bergier, N. S. Dictionnaire de Theologique Dogmatique, Liturgique, Canonique et Disciplinaire, 3 vols. in 4. Migne, J. P., ed. (Encyclopedie Theologique Ser.: Vols. 33-35). (Fr.). 2681p. Repr. of 1851 ed. lib. bdg. 341.00x (ISBN 0-89241-243-7). Caratzas.

Eusebius Pamphili. Ecclesiastical History, Bks. 6-10. (Fathers of the Church Ser: Vol. 29). 325p. 1955. 17.95x (ISBN 0-8132-0029-6). Cath U Pr.

Frend, W. H. Saints & Sinners in the Early Church: Differing & Conflicting Traditions in the First Six Centuries. (Theology & Life Ser.: Vol. 11). 1985. pap. 8.95 (ISBN 0-89453-451-3). M Glazier.

Markus, R. A. Saeculum: History & Society in the Theology of St Augustine. LC 71-87136. 1970. 54.50 (ISBN 0-521-07621-8). Cambridge U Pr.

Morgan, Edmund S. Visible Saints: The History of a Puritan Idea. LC 63-9999. 168p. 1965. pap. 6.95x (ISBN 0-8014-9041-3). Cornell U Pr.

Stanley, David M. Apostolic Church in the New Testament. LC 65-19453. 500p. 1965. 7.95 (ISBN 0-8091-0002-9). Paulist Pr.

Stone, James. The Church of God of Prophecy: History & Polity. 1977. 12.95 (ISBN 0-934942-02-1). White Wing Pub.

Von Campenhausen, Hans. Ecclesiastical Authority & Spiritual Power in the Church of the First Three Centuries. Baker, J. A., tr. 1969. 25.00x (ISBN 0-8047-0665-4). Stanford U Pr.

Wallace, Alston M., Jr. Guides to the Reformed Tradition: The Church. Leith, John H. & Kuykendall, John W., eds. LC 83-49052. 204p. 1984. pap. 10.95 (ISBN 0-8042-3253-9). John Knox.

CHURCH–INFALLIBILITY

see also Catholic Church–Infallibility; Church–Teaching Office; Popes–Infallibility

Chirico, Peter. Infallibility: The Crossroads of Doctrine. (Theology & Life Ser.: Vol. 1). pap. 9.95 (ISBN 0-89453-296-0). M Glazier.

Whitehead, K. D. The Need for the Magisterium of the Church. (Synthesis Ser.). 1979. 0.75 (ISBN 0-8199-0747-2). Franciscan Herald.

CHURCH–JUVENILE LITERATURE

Bennett, Marian. I Go to Church. (My Shape Book Ser.). (Illus.). 10p. 1985. 2.95 (ISBN 0-87239-911-7, 2751). Standard Pub.

Concept Books Series Four, 4 bks. LC 56-1400. 1983. Set. pap. 14.50 (ISBN 0-570-08528-4). Concordia.

Cooper, Harold. Believing Truth about the Church. (Illus.). 122p. 1975. pap. 3.50 (ISBN 0-89114-070-0); P. 64. tchr's ed. 1.00 (ISBN 0-89114-071-9). Baptist Pub Hse.

Hogan, Bernice. The Church Is a Who. LC 78-24087. (Illus.). 1979. 9.95 (ISBN 0-8272-0442-6). CBP.

Johnson, Gordon G. & Putman, Bob. Our Church. LC 83-82990. (Foundation Ser.). (Illus.). 147p. (Orig.). 1984. pap. 2.95 (ISBN 0-935797-06-8). Harvest IL.

Robertson, Everett, ed. Puppet Scripts for Use at Church, No. 2. LC 78-72843. 1980. saddle-wire 6.95 (ISBN 0-8054-7519-2). Broadman.

CHURCH–MISSION

see Mission of the Church

CHURCH–PUBLIC OPINION

Jay, Eric G. The Church: Its Changing Image Through Twenty Centuries. LC 79-92070. pap. 120.50 (2027153). Bks Demand UMI.

CHURCH–REFORM

see Church Renewal

CHURCH–STUDY AND TEACHING

Craig, James D. & Hill, Donald E. One Hundred Series Implementation Outline. 38p. 1980. pap. 9.95 inc. cassettes (ISBN 0-88151-020-3). Lay Leadership.

Ford, LeRoy. Capacitese Como Lider. Blair, Guillermo, tr. Tr. of Developing Skills for Church Leaders. (Span.). 64p. 1986. pap. 3.75 (ISBN 0-311-17023-4, Edit Mundo). Casa Bautista.

CHURCH–TEACHING OFFICE

see also Catechetics; Censorship; Christian Education; Church and Education; Missions; Preaching; Theological Seminaries

Sanks, T. Howland. Authority in the Church: A Study in Changing Paradigms. LC 74-16565. (American Academy of Religion. Dissertation Ser.: No. 2). Repr. of 1974 ed. 37.10 (ISBN 0-8357-9564-0, 2017555). Bks Demand UMI.

Vaillancourt, Jean-Guy. Papal Power: A Study of Vatican Control Over Lay Catholic Elites. 375p. 1980. 24.95x (ISBN 0-520-03733-2). U of Cal Pr.

Whitehead, K. D. The Need for the Magisterium of the Church. (Synthesis Ser.). 1979. 0.75 (ISBN 0-8199-0747-2). Franciscan Herald.

CHURCH–UNITY

Allchin, A. M. The Living Presence of the Past: The Dynamic of Christian Tradition. 192p. (Orig.). 1981. pap. 7.95 (ISBN 0-8164-2334-2, HarpR). Har-Row.

Smyth, Norman & Walker, Williston. Approaches Toward Church Unity. 1919. 34.50x (ISBN 0-686-37862-8). Elliots Bks.

Stauffer, Richard. The Quest for Church Unity: From John Calvin to Isaac d'Huisseau. (Pittsburgh Theological Monographs: No. 19). (Orig.). 1986. pap. 14.00 (ISBN 0-915138-63-8). Pickwick.

CHURCH ADMINISTRATION

see Church Management

CHURCH AND COLLEGE

see also Church and Education; Universities and Colleges–Religion

Bloy, Myron B., Jr., et al. The Recovery of Spirit in Higher Education. Rankin, Robert, ed. 1980. 17.50 (ISBN 0-8164-0469-0, HarpR). Har-Row.

Fisher, Ben C., ed. New Pathways: A Dialogue in Christian Higher Education. LC 80-80255. x, 110p. 1980. pap. 4.95 (ISBN 0-86554-000-4, MUP-P01). Mercer Univ Pr.

Gellhorn, Walter & Greenawalt, R. Kent. Sectarian College & the Public Purse: Fordham: a Case Study. LC 74-111415. 212p. 1970. 10.00 (ISBN 0-379-00456-9). Oceana.

Limbert, Paul M. Denominational Policies in the Support & Supervision of Higher Education. LC 75-176994. (Columbia University. Teachers College. Contributions to Education: No. 378). Repr. of 1929 ed. 22.50 (ISBN 0-404-55378-8). AMS Pr.

Miller, Alexander. Faith & Learning: Christian Faith & Higher Education in Twentieth Century America. LC 77-23142. 1977. Repr. of 1960 ed. lib. bdg. 22.50x (ISBN 0-8371-9458-X, MIFL). Greenwood.

Moots, Philip R. & Gaffney, Edward M. Church & Campus: Legal Issues in Religiously Affiliated Higher Education. LC 79-14002. 1979. pap. text ed. 7.95 (ISBN 0-268-00732-2). U of Notre Dame Pr.

Noffsinger, John S. A Program for Higher Education in the Church of the Brethren. LC 78-177711. (Columbia University. Teachers College. Contributions to Education: No. 172). Repr. of 1925 ed. 22.50 (ISBN 0-404-55172-6). AMS Pr.

Tewksbury, Donald G. Founding of American Colleges & Universities Before the Civil War with Particular Reference to the Religious Influences Bearing upon the College Movement. LC 76-177718. (Columbia University. Teachers College. Contributions to Education Ser.: No. 543). Repr. of 1932 ed. 22.50 (ISBN 0-404-55543-8). AMS Pr.

--Founding of American Colleges & Universities Before the Civil War. LC 79-89246. (American Education: Its Men, Institutions & Ideas, Ser. 1). 1969. Repr. of 1932 ed. 17.00 (ISBN 0-405-01483-X). Ayer Co Pubs.

Wilder, Amos N., ed. Liberal Learning & Religion. LC 77-86072. (Essay & General Literature Index Reprint Ser). 1969. Repr. of 1951 ed. 24.50x (ISBN 0-8046-0595-5, Pub. by Kennikat). Assoc Faculty Pr.

CHURCH AND EDUCATION

see also Church and College; Church Schools; Missions–Educational Work; Religion in the Public Schools; Theology–Study and Teaching also names of particular religious denominations with the subdivision Education, e.g. Catholic Church–Education

Adams, Herbert B. The Church & Popular Education. LC 78-63876. (Johns Hopkins University. Studies in the Social Sciences. Eighteenth Ser. 1900: 8-9). Repr. of 1900 ed. 11.50 (ISBN 0-404-61132-X). AMS Pr.

--The Church & Popular Education. Repr. of 1900 ed. 10.00 (ISBN 0-384-00323-0). Johnson Repr.

--The Church & Popular Education. (The Works of Herbert B. Adams Ser.). 84p. 1985. Repr. of 1900 ed. lib. bdg. 29.00 (ISBN 0-318-03787-4, Pub. by Am Repr Serv). Am Biog Serv.

Beggs, David W. America's Schools & Churches. LC 65-12279. pap. 60.30 (ISBN 0-317-28577-7, 2055190). Bks Demand UMI.

Bell, Sadie. Church, the State, & Education in Virginia. LC 78-89148. (American Education: Its Men, Institutions & Ideas Ser). 1969. Repr. of 1930 ed. 43.00 (ISBN 0-405-01385-X). Ayer Co Pubs.

Blum, Virgil C. Freedom of Choice in Education. LC 77-8086. 1977. Repr. of 1958 ed. lib. bdg. 22.50x (ISBN 0-8371-9677-9, BLFC). Greenwood.

Bossart, Donald E. Creative Conflict in Religious Education & Church Administration. LC 80-12704. 284p. (Orig.). 1980. pap. 12.95 (ISBN 0-89135-048-9). Religious Educ.

Bowes, Betty. Ministry of the Cradle Roll. (Orig.). 1970. pap. 1.95 (ISBN 0-8341-0190-4). Beacon Hill.

Brickman, William W. & Lehrer, Stanley, eds. Religion, Government & Education. LC 77-24684. 1977. Repr. of 1961 ed. lib. bdg. 22.50x (ISBN 0-8371-9749-X, BRRG). Greenwood.

Burron, Arnold, et al. Classrooms in Crisis. LC 85-73068. 196p. (Orig.). 1986. pap. 7.95 (ISBN 0-89636-192-6). Accent Bks.

Byrne, H. W. Improving Church Education. LC 79-10852. 352p. (Orig.). 1979. pap. 12.95 (ISBN 0-89135-017-9). Religious Educ.

Church Educational Ministries. LC 67-27288. 96p. 1980. pap. text ed. 4.95 (ISBN 0-910566-13-5); Perfect bdg. instr's. guide 5.95 (ISBN 0-910566-18-6). Evang Tchr.

Craig, James D., ed. The Care & Feeding of New Converts. 1st ed. 12p. 1981. pap. text ed. 0.49 (ISBN 0-88151-021-1). Lay Leadership.

Crenshaw, Floyd D. & Flanders, John A., eds. Christian Values & the Academic Disciplines. 224p. (Orig.). 1985. lib. bdg. 23.25 (ISBN 0-8191-4306-5); pap. text ed. 11.75 (ISBN 0-8191-4307-3). U Pr of Amer.

Culver, Raymond B. Horace Mann & Religion in the Massachusetts Public Schools. LC 72-89168. (American Education: Its Men, Institutions & Ideas, Ser. 1). 1969. Repr. of 1929 ed. 17.00 (ISBN 0-405-01406-6). Ayer Co Pubs.

De Forest, Grant E. God in the American Schools: Religious Education in a Pluralistic Society. (Illus.). 1979. 49.50 (ISBN 0-89266-181-X). Am Classical Coll Pr.

De Jong, Norman. Christian Approaches to Learning Theory: A Symposium; Major Papers Delivered at the First Annual Conference at Trinity Christian College, November 11-12, 1983. 234p. 1985. 25.00 (ISBN 0-8191-4319-7, Pub. by Trinity Christ Coll). U Pr of Amer.

--Christian Approaches to Learning Theory: A Symposium; Major Papers Delivered at the First Annual Conference at Trinity Christian College, November 11-12, 1983. 234p. (Orig.). 1985. pap. 12.25 (ISBN 0-8191-4320-0, Pub. by Trinity Christ Coll). U Pr of Amer.

Dunn, Frank E. The Ministering Teacher. 112p. 1982. pap. 4.95 (ISBN 0-8170-0958-2). Judson.

Eddleman, H. Leo. Schools & Churches in American Democracy: In Defense of Public Schools. 135p. 1983. pap. 4.00 (ISBN 0-682-40144-7). Exposition Pr FL.

Elder, Rozanne, ed. From Cloister to Classroom: The Spirituality of Western Christendom III. (Cistercian Studies: No. 90). 1986. 26.95 (ISBN 0-87907-890-1); pap. 10.95 (ISBN 0-87907-990-8). Cistercian Pubns.

Elwell, Clarence E. Influence of the Enlightenment on the Catholic Theory of Religious Education in France, 1750-1850. LC 66-27064. 1967. Repr. of 1944 ed. 10.00x (ISBN 0-8462-0980-2). Russell.

Elwood, Douglas J., ed. The Humanities in Christian Higher Education in Asia: Ethical & Religious Perspectives. 1978. pap. 7.50x (ISBN 0-686-23913-X, Pub. by New Day Pub). Cellar.

Fisher, Ben C., ed. New Pathways: A Dialogue in Christian Higher Education. LC 80-80255. x, 110p. 1980. pap. 4.95 (ISBN 0-86554-000-4, MUP-P01). Mercer Univ Pr.

Groome, Thomas H. Christian Religious Education: Sharing Our Story & Vision. LC 81-47847. 320p. 1982. pap. text ed. 12.95 (ISBN 0-06-063494-4, RD 371, HarpR). Har-Row.

Healey, Robert M. Jefferson on Religion in Public Education. LC 73-114422. xi, 294p. 1970. Repr. of 1962 ed. 27.50 (ISBN 0-208-00841-1, Archon). Shoe String.

Hull, J. Studies in Religion & Education. 292p. 1984. 29.00x (ISBN 0-905273-52-4, Falmer Pr); pap. 17.00x (ISBN 0-905273-51-6). Taylor & Francis.

Hunt, Thomas C. & Maxson, Marilyn M., eds. Religion & Morality in American Schooling. LC 81-40154. 297p. (Orig.). 1981. lib. bdg. 25.75 (ISBN 0-8191-1584-3); pap. text ed. 12.50 (ISBN 0-8191-1585-1). U Pr of Amer.

Johnson, F. Ernest, ed. American Education & Religion. LC 68-26192. (Essay & General Literature Index Reprint Ser). 1969. Repr. of 1952 ed. 21.50x (ISBN 0-8046-0220-4, Pub. by Kennikat). Assoc Faculty Pr.

Johnson, Kent L. Paul the Teacher: A Resource for Teachers in the Church. LC 86-17384. 128p. (Orig.). 1986. pap. 6.95 (ISBN 0-8066-2226-1, 10-4905). Augsburg.

Krishnamurti, J. Education & the Signficance of Life. LC 53-10971. 128p. 1981. pap. 6.95 (ISBN 0-06-064876-7, RD 356, HarpR). Har-Row.

Kuhn, Alvin B. The Red Sea Is Your Blood. 66p. 1976. pap. 5.95 (ISBN 0-88697-007-5). Life Science.

McCarthy, Martha M. A Delicate Balance: Church, State & the Schools. LC 83-60797. 184p. 1983. pap. 6.00 (ISBN 0-87367-427-8). Phi Delta Kappa.

Machen, J. Gresham. Education, Christianity & the State. Robbins, John W., ed. & intro. by. (Trinity Papers: No. 19). 150p. (Orig.). 1987. pap. 5.95 (ISBN 0-940931-19-2). Trinity Found.

McLaughlin, Mary M. Intellectual Freedom & Its Limitations in the University of Paris in the Thirteenth & Fourteenth Centuries. Metzger, Walter P., ed. LC 76-55187. (The Academic Profession Ser.). 1977. Repr. lib. bdg. 34.50x (ISBN 0-405-10018-3). Ayer Co Pubs.

McMillan, Richard C., ed. Education, Religion, & the Supreme Court. LC 78-74196. (Special Studies: No. 6). iv, 129p. 1979. pap. 8.95 (ISBN 0-932180-05-1). NABPR.

Makrakis, Apostolos. The Two Contrariant Schools, Concerning the Establishment of a Christian University. Orthodox Christian Educational Society, ed. Cummings, Denver, tr. from Hellenic. 87p. (Orig.). 1949. pap. 2.75x (ISBN 0-938366-27-0). Orthodox Chr.

Miller, Perry, et al. Religion & Freedom of Thought. facs. ed. LC 78-128296. (Essay Index Reprint Ser). 1954. 10.00 (ISBN 0-8369-2199-2). Ayer Co Pubs.

Phenix, Philip H. Religious Concerns in Contemporary Education. LC 59-11329. Repr. of 1959 ed. 29.50 (ISBN 0-8357-9605-1, 2016949). Bks Demand UMI.

Rushdoony, Rousas J. Intellectual Schizophrenia. 1961. pap. 5.50 (ISBN 0-87552-411-7). Presby & Reformed.

Sahas, Daniel. Katechesis. 70p. 1981. pap. 3.00 (ISBN 0-916586-45-6). Holy Cross Orthodox.

Schipani, Daniel S. El Reino de Dios y el Ministerio Educativo de la Iglesia. (Span.). 213p. 1984. pap. 5.50 (ISBN 0-89922-232-3). Edit Caribe.

Sewell, Jesse P., ed. The Church & Her Ideal Educational Situation. Speck, Henry E. 1933. 2.50 (ISBN 0-88027-083-7); pap. 1.50 (ISBN 0-88027-084-5). Firm Foun Pub.

Sha Rocco. The Masculine Cross & Ancient Sex Worship. (Illus.). 65p. 1873. pap. 7.95 (ISBN 0-88697-014-8). Life Science.

Soderholm, Marjorie E. Understanding the Pupil, 3 pts. Incl. Pt. 1. The Pre-School Child; Pt. 2. The Primary & Junior Child; Pt. 3. The Adolescent. pap. 2.50 (ISBN 0-8010-7922-5). pap. Baker Bk.

Sperry, Willard L., et al, eds. Religion in the Post-War World. facsimile ed. LC 76-142698. (Essay Index Reprints - Religion & Education Ser.: Vol. 4). Repr. of 1945 ed. 14.00 (ISBN 0-8369-2202-6). Ayer Co Pubs.

Thayer, Vivian T. Religion in Public Education. LC 78-12385. 1979. Repr. of 1947 ed. lib. bdg. 22.50x (ISBN 0-313-21212-0, THRP). Greenwood.

Thwing, Charles F. Education & Religion. facs. ed. LC 71-105044. (Essay Index Reprint Ser). 1929. 19.00 (ISBN 0-8369-1629-8). Ayer Co Pubs.

Walker, K. R., ed. The Evolution-Creation Controversy Perspectives on Religion, Philosophy, Science & Education: A Handbook. (Paleontological Society Special Publications Ser.). (Illus.). 155p. pap. 6.50 (ISBN 0-931377-00-5). U of Tenn Geo.

Watkins, Morris. Literacy, Bible Reading & Church Growth Through the Ages. LC 78-15315. (Illus.). 1978. pap. 5.95 (ISBN 0-87808-325-1). William Carey Lib.

Westropp, Hodder M. & Staniland, Wake C. Phallism in Ancient Worships: Ancient Symbol Worship. 2nd ed. (Illus.). 111p. pap. 8.95 (ISBN 0-88697-017-2). Life Science.

CHURCH AND EDUCATION IN GREAT BRITAIN

Newsome, David. Godliness & Good Learning: Four Studies on a Victorian Ideal. (Illus.). 1961. 21.00 (ISBN 0-7195-1015-5). Transatl Arts.

CHURCH AND INTERNATIONAL AFFAIRS

see Christianity and International Affairs

CHURCH AND LABOR

see also Christianity and Economics; Church and Social Problems; Work (Theology)

Betten, Neil. Catholic Activism & the Industrial Worker. LC 76-17280. 1976. 10.00 (ISBN 0-8130-0503-5). U Presses Fla.

Catherwood, Fred. On the Job: The Christian Nine to Five. 192p. 1983. pap. 5.95 (ISBN 0-310-37261-5). Zondervan.

Day, Dorothy. Loaves & Fishes: The Story of the Catholic Worker Movement. LC 82-48433. (Illus.). 240p. 1983. pap. 4.95 (ISBN 0-06-061771-3, RD/434, HarpR). Har-Row.

Gladden, Washington T. Working People & Their Employers. LC 75-89734. (American Labor: From Conspiracy to Collective Bargaining Ser., No. 1). 1969. Repr. of 1876 ed. 15.00 (ISBN 0-405-02123-2). Ayer Co Pubs.

Jones, Samuel M. The New Right: A Plea for Fair Play Through a More Just Social Order. LC 75-327. (The Radical Tradition in America Ser.). (Illus.). 479p. 1975. Repr. of 1899 ed. 32.45 (ISBN 0-88355-231-0). Hyperion Conn.

McLean, Edward B. Roman Catholicism & the Right to Work. 186p. (Orig.). 1986. lib. bdg. 25.50 (ISBN 0-8191-5009-6); pap. text ed. 11.25 (ISBN 0-8191-5010-X). U Pr of Amer.

Medhurst, Kenneth N. The Church & Labour in Colombia. LC 82-62254. 320p. 1984. 46.00 (ISBN 0-7190-0969-3, Pub. by Manchester Univ Pr). Longwood Pub Group.

Piehl, Mel. Breaking Bread: The Catholic Worker & the Origin of Catholic Radicalism in America. LC 82-10327. 233p. 1982. 24.95 (ISBN 0-87722-257-6). Temple U Pr.

Pope, Liston. Millhands & Preachers: A Study of Gastonia. (Studies in Religious Education: No. 15). (Illus.). 1965. pap. 11.95x (ISBN 0-300-00182-7). Yale U Pr.

Sullivan, Patrick J. Blue Collar-Roman Collar-White Collar: U. S. Catholic Involvement in Labor Management Controversies, 1960-1980. LC 86-24593. 358p. (Orig.). 1987. lib. bdg. 26.75 (ISBN 0-8191-5704-X); pap. text ed. 16.75 (ISBN 0-8191-5705-8). U Pr of Amer.

--U. S. Catholic Institutions & Labor Unions, 1960-1980. LC 85-20171. 550p. (Orig.). 1986. lib. bdg. 40.50 (ISBN 0-8191-4970-5); pap. text ed. 22.75 (ISBN 0-8191-4971-3). U Pr of Amer.

CHURCH AND RACE RELATIONS

Baum, Gregory B. & Coleman, John, eds. The Church & Racism. (Concilium Ser.: Vol. 151). 128p. (Orig.). 1982. pap. 6.95 (ISBN 0-8164-2382-2, HarpR). Har-Row.

Clark, Henry. The Church & Residential Desegregation. 1965. 16.95x (ISBN 0-8084-0076-2). New Coll U Pr.

Cone, James H. Black Theology & Black Power. LC 70-76462. (Orig.). 1969. pap. 5.95 (ISBN 0-8164-2003-3, SP59, HarpR). Har-Row.

Dorn, Edwin. Rules & Racial Equality. LC 79-64228. 1979. 24.50x (ISBN 0-300-02362-6). Yale U Pr.

Gilmore, J. Herbert. They Chose to Live: The Racial Agony of an American Church. LC 72-75577. pap. 51.50 (ISBN 0-317-07872-0, 2012911). Bks Demand UMI.

Hope, Richard O. Racial Strife in the U. S. Military: Toward the Elimination of Discrimination. LC 79-65932. 144p. 1979. 35.95 (ISBN 0-03-046146-4). Praeger.

Hough, Joseph C., Jr. Black Power & White Protestants: A Christian Response to the New Negro Pluralism. 1968. 18.95x (ISBN 0-19-501178-3). Oxford U Pr.

Jones, Nathan. Sharing the Old, Old Story: Educational Ministry in the Black Community. LC 81-86046. (Illus.). 104p. (Orig.). 1982. pap. 8.95 (ISBN 0-88489-144-5). St Mary's.

Merton, Thomas. Seeds of Destruction. 1983. 14.00 (ISBN 0-8446-5988-6). Peter Smith.

National Conference on Religion & Race. Race: Challenge to Religion. Ahmann, Mathew, ed. LC 78-24276. 1979. Repr. of 1963 ed. lib. bdg. 22.50x (ISBN 0-313-20796-8, NCRA). Greenwood.

Nelson, William S., ed. Christian Way in Race Relations. facs. ed. LC 79-134121. (Essay Index Reprint Ser). 1948. 20.00 (ISBN 0-8369-2004-X). Ayer Co Pubs.

Oldham, Joseph H. Christianity & the Race Problem. LC 73-75534. Repr. of 1924 ed. 19.75x (ISBN 0-8371-1112-9, OLC&, Pub. by Negro U Pr). Greenwood.

Powell, Raphael P. No Black-White Church. 1984. 7.50 (ISBN 0-8062-2295-6). Carlton.

Rader, William. The Church & Racial Hostility: A History of Interpretation of Ephesians. 1978. 71.50x (ISBN 3-16-140112-3). Adlers Foreign Bks.

Radler, William. The Church & Racial Hostility. 282p. 1978. lib. bdg. 45.00x (Pub. by J C B Mohr BRD). Coronet Bks.

Richardson, Neville. The World Council of Churches & Race Relations. (IC-Studies in the Intercultural History of Christianity: Vol. 9). 78p. 1977. pap. 15.65 (ISBN 3-261-01718-X). P Lang Pubs.

CHURCH AND SLAVERY

see Slavery and the Church

CHURCH AND SOCIAL PROBLEMS

see also Christianity and International Affairs; Church and Labor; Church Charities; Civilization, Christian; Judaism and Social Problems; Slavery and the Church; Socialism, Christian; Sociology, Christian

Alberigo, Giuseppe, ed. Where Does the Church Stand, Vol. 146. (Concilium 1981). 128p. (Orig.). 1981. pap. 6.95 (ISBN 0-8164-2313-X, HarpR). Har-Row.

Bland, Salem. New Christianity. LC 72-95815. (Social History of Canada Ser.). 1973. pap. 6.00 (ISBN 0-8020-6179-6). U of Toronto Pr.

Boff, Leonard. Option for the Poor: Challenge to the Reich. Elizondo, Virgil, ed. (Concilium Nineteen Eighty-Six Ser.). 120p. 1986. pap. 6.95 (ISBN 0-567-30067-6, Pub. by T & T Clark Ltd UK). Fortress.

Briggs, Lauren Littauer. What You Can Say When You Don't Know What to Say: Reaching out to Those Who Hurt. 176p. (Orig.). 1985. pap. 4.95 (ISBN 0-89081-465-1). Harvest Hse.

Brinton, Howard H. A Religious Solution to the Social Problem. 1983. pap. 2.50x (ISBN 0-87574-002-2, 002). Pendle Hill.

Camara, Dom H. Desert Is Fertile. 1976. pap. 1.50 (ISBN 0-89129-060-5). Jove Pubns.

Carothers, J. Edward. Living with the Parables: Jesus & the Reign of God. 141p. (Orig.). 1984. pap. 9.95 (ISBN 0-377-00146-5). Friend Pr.

Childs, Marquis W. & Cater, Douglass. Ethics in a Business Society. LC 73-7073. 191p. 1973. Repr. of 1954 ed. lib. bdg. 22.50x (ISBN 0-8371-6905-4, CHBS). Greenwood.

Christian Compassion & Social Concern. 1.75 (ISBN 0-911802-62-2). Free Church Pubns.

Coe, Jolene & Coe, Greg. The Mormon Experience: A Young Couple's Fascinating Journey to Truth. 176p. (Orig.). 1985. pap. 5.95 (ISBN 0-89081-486-4). Harvest Hse.

Collins, Mary J., ed. A Church Divided: Catholics' Attitudes about Family Planning, Abortion, & Teenage Sexuality. (The Bishops Watch Ser.). (Orig.). 1986. pap. 5.00 (ISBN 0-915365-12-X). Cath Free Choice.

Commons, John R. Social Reform & the Church. LC 66-21663. (Illus.). 1967. Repr. of 1894 ed. 22.50x (ISBN 0-678-00286-X). Kelley.

Corson-Finnerty, Adam. No More Plastic Jesus: Global Justice & Christian Lifestyle. LC 76-13174. 223p. (Orig.). 1977. pap. 6.95x (ISBN 0-88344-341-4). Orbis Bks.

Curtis, June. The Gracious Woman: Developing A Servant's Heart Through Hospitality. 176p. (Orig.). 1985. pap. 4.95 (ISBN 0-89081-489-9). Harvest Hse.

Dahlstrom, Daniel O., ed. Realism. (ACPA Proceedings: Vol. 59). 250p. 1985. 15.00 (ISBN 0-918090-19-9). Am Cath Philo.

Day, James M. & Laufer, William, eds. Crimes, Values & Religion. 280p. 1987. text ed. 37.50 (ISBN 0-89391-411-8). Ablex Pub.

De Gruchy, John W. & Villa-Vicencio, Charles, eds. Apartheid Is a Heresy. 208p. (Orig.). 1983. pap. 5.95 (ISBN 0-8028-1972-9). Eerdmans.

Derr, Thomas S. Barriers to Ecumenism: The Holy See & the World Council on Social Questions. LC 82-18761. 112p. (Orig.). 1983. pap. 7.95 (ISBN 0-88344-031-8). Orbis Bks.

Derrick, Christopher. Too Many People? A Problem in Values. LC 85-60469. 116p. (Orig.). 1986. pap. 6.95 (ISBN 0-89870-071-X, 85-60469). Ignatius Pr.

De Santa Ana, Julio, ed. Separation Without Hope? LC 80-12831. 198p. (Orig.). 1980. pap. 2.24 (ISBN 0-88344-456-9). Orbis Bks.

DeSaulniers, Lawrence B. The Response in American Catholic Periodicals to the Crises of the Great Depression, 1930-1935. LC 83-23603. 198p. (Orig.). 1984. lib. bdg. 24.75 (ISBN 0-8191-3786-3); pap. text ed. 11.75 (ISBN 0-8191-3787-1). U Pr of Amer.

Dorr, Donal. Option for the Poor: A Hundred Years of Vatican Social Teaching. 333p. (Orig.). 1983. pap. 11.95 (ISBN 0-88344-365-1). Orbis Bks.

Ellis, Marc. A Year of the Catholic Worker. LC 78-61722. 144p. 1978. pap. 3.50 (ISBN 0-8091-2140-9). Paulist Pr.

Evans, Alice Frazer & Evans, Robert A. Pedagogies for the Non-Poor. LC 86-21831. 272p. (Orig.). 1987. pap. 13.95 (ISBN 0-88344-409-7). Orbis Bks.

Evans, Robert A. & Evans, Alice F. Human Rights: A Dialogue Between the First & Third Worlds. LC 82-18780. 236p. (Orig.). 1983. pap. 9.95 (ISBN 0-88344-194-2). Orbis Bks.

Ezell, Lee. The Cinderella Syndrome: Discovering God's Plan When Your Dreams Don't Come True. 176p. (Orig.). 1985. pap. 4.95 (ISBN 0-89081-475-9). Harvest Hse.

Fey, Harold E. & Frakes, Margaret, eds. The Christian Century Reader: Representative Articles, Editorials, & Poems Selected from More Than Fifty Years of the Christian Century. LC 72-331. (Essay Index Reprint Ser.). Repr. of 1962 ed. 24.50 (ISBN 0-8369-2786-9). Ayer Co Pubs.

Field, David. Marriage Personalities. 192p. (Orig.). 1986. pap. 5.95 (ISBN 0-89081-476-7). Harvest Hse.

Friesen, Duane K. Christian Peacemaking & International Conflict. LC 85-24803. 320p. (Orig.). 1986. pap. 19.95x (ISBN 0-8361-1273-3). Herald Pr.

Grant, Dave. The Great Lover's Manifesto. 160p. (Orig.). 1986. 9.95 (ISBN 0-89081-481-3). Harvest Hse.

Grocott, Allan M. Convicts, Clergymen & Churches. 356p. 1980. 38.00x (ISBN 0-424-00072-5, Pub. by Sydney U Pr Australia). Intl Spec Bk.

Groenhoff, Edwin. Care & Concern of the Churches. LC 81-69760. (Heritage Ser.: Vol. 8). 1984. 8.95 (ISBN 0-911802-59-2). Free Church Pubns.

Hargrove, Eugene C., ed. Religion & Environmental Crisis. LC 86-7019. 248p. 1986. 25.00x (ISBN 0-8203-0845-5); pap. 12.00x (ISBN 0-8203-0846-3). U of GA Pr.

Hauerwas, Stanley. A Community of Character: Toward a Constructive Christian Social Ethic. LC 80-53072. 320p. 1981. pap. text ed. 7.95 (ISBN 0-268-00735-7, NDP 265). U of Notre Dame Pr.

Henderson, George. A Religious Foundation of Human Relations: Beyond Games. LC 76-62510. 1977. 15.95x (ISBN 0-8061-1398-7). U of Okla Pr.

Herron, George D. Between Caesar & Jesus. LC 75-324. (The Radical Tradition in America Ser). 278p. 1975. Repr. of 1899 ed. 23.10 (ISBN 0-88355-227-2). Hyperion Conn.

Herron, Liz. Liz: A Life of Courage. LC 85-60126. 176p. (Orig.). 1986. pap. 4.95 (ISBN 0-89081-472-4, 4724). Harvest Hse.

Hooft, W. A. & Oldham, J. H. The Church & Its Function in Society. 1977. lib. bdg. 59.95 (ISBN 0-8490-1625-8). Gordon Pr.

Hughley, Neal. Trends in Protestant Social Idealism. LC 74-167359. (Essay Index Reprint Ser.). Repr. of 1948 ed. 18.00 (ISBN 0-8369-2771-0). Ayer Co Pubs.

Innes, William C. Social Concern in Calvin's Geneva. (Pittsburgh Theological Monographs: New Series 7). 1983. pap. 22.50 (ISBN 0-915138-33-6). Pickwick.

Jackson, Dave. Dial 911: Peaceful Christians & Urban Violence. LC 81-2541. 160p. 1981. pap. 5.95 (ISBN 0-8361-1952-5). Herald Pr.

Johnson, Daniel. Building with Buses. pap. 2.95 (ISBN 0-8010-5059-6). Baker Bk.

Kavanaugh, John, ed. Quaker Approach to Contemporary Problems. Repr. of 1953 ed. lib. bdg. 22.50x (ISBN 0-8371-4432-9, KAGA). Greenwood.

Ketcherside, W. Carl. A Clean Church. 165p. 1987. pap. 3.95 (ISBN 0-938855-17-4). Gospel Themes Pr.

Kincheloe, Samuel C. Research Memorandum on Religion in the Depression. LC 71-162843. (Studies in the Social Aspects of the Depression). 1971. Repr. of 1937 ed. 17.00 (ISBN 0-405-00846-5). Ayer Co Pubs.

King, David S. No Church Is an Island. LC 79-27113. (Orig.). 1980. pap. 5.95 (ISBN 0-8298-0385-8). Pilgrim NY.

Larue, Gerald A. Euthanasia & Religion: A Survey of the Attitudes of World Religions to the Right-to-Die. LC 84-62806. 155p. 1985. pap. 10.00 (ISBN 0-394-62078-X). Hemlock Soc.

Loomis, Samuel L. Modern Cities & Their Religious Problems. LC 73-112558. (Rise of Urban America). 1970. Repr. of 1887 ed. 23.50 (ISBN 0-405-02464-9). Ayer Co Pubs.

Lubich, Gino & Lazzarin, Piero. Joan Antida Thouret: When God Was the Voice of the Poor. Brody, Joel, tr. from Ital. LC 84-62540. 1985. pap. 5.95 (ISBN 0-911782-47-8). New City.

McCan, Robert L. World Economy & World Hunger: The Response of the Churches. 119p. 1982. 16.00 (ISBN 0-89093-497-5); pap. 5.00. U Pubns Amer.

McMullen, Eleanor & Sonnenfeld, Jean. Go-Groups: Gearing up for Reaching Out. (Orig.). 1977. pap. 2.50 (ISBN 0-377-00060-4). Friend Pr.

Maduro, Otto. Religion & Social Conflicts. Barr, Robert R., tr. from Span. LC 82-3439. Orig. Title: Religion y Lucha de Clase. 192p. (Orig.). 1982. pap. 8.95 (ISBN 0-88344-428-3). Orbis Bks.

Manser, Nancy. Older People Have Choices: Information for Decisions about Health, Home, & Money. 32p. (Orig.). 1984. pap. 3.95 (ISBN 0-8066-2098-6, 10-4741). Augsburg.

Martin. But for the Grace of God.... (Orig.). 1984. pap. 1.00 (ISBN 0-914733-02-8). Desert Min.

Mead, James J. & Balch, Glenn M., Jr. Child Abuse & the Church: A New Mission. (Illus.). 160p. 1987. pap. 9.95 (ISBN 0-937359-10-6). HDL Pubs.

Meehan, Francis X., ed. A Contemporary Social Spirituality. LC 82-2253. 133p. (Orig.). 1982. pap. 6.95 (ISBN 0-88344-022-9). Orbis Bks.

Moser, Mary T. The Evolution of the Option for the Poor in France, 1880-1965. (Illus.). 216p. (Orig.). 1985. lib. bdg. 24.00 (ISBN 0-8191-4814-8); pap. text ed. 11.75 (ISBN 0-8191-4815-6). U Pr of Amer.

Moyser, George, ed. Church & Politics Today. 320p. 1985. pap. 17.95 (ISBN 0-567-29350-5, Pub. by T&T Clark Ltd Uk). Fortress.

Mueller, Franz H. Church & the Social Question. 158p. 1984. 14.95 (ISBN 0-8447-3567-1). Am Enterprise.

Muste, A. J. Of Holy Disobedience. 23p. 1952-1964. pap. 1.25 (ISBN 0-934676-09-7). Greenlf Bks.

Nash, Ronald H. Poverty & Wealth: The Christian Debate over Capitalism. LC 86-70291. 256p. (Orig.). 1986. pap. 8.95 (ISBN 0-89107-402-3, Crossway Bks). Good News.

Nash, Ronald H., ed. Social Justice & the Christian Church. 1986. pap. 7.95 (ISBN 0-8010-6746-4). Baker Bk.

Niebuhr, Reinhold. Christian Realism & Political Problems. LC 75-128062. 1977. Repr. of 1953 ed. 19.50x (ISBN 0-678-02757-9). Kelley.

--The Contribution of Religion to Social Work. LC 74-172444. Repr. of 1932 ed. 5.00 (ISBN 0-404-04708-4). AMS Pr.

Oxnam, Garfield B. Preaching in a Revolutionary Age. facsimile ed. LC 75-142687. (Essay Index Reprint Ser). Repr. of 1944 ed. 18.00 (ISBN 0-8369-2421-5). Ayer Co Pubs.

Phillips, Mike. A Vision for the Church. 110p. 1981. pap. 3.95 (ISBN 0-940652-02-1). Sunrise Bks.

Pierce, Gregory F. Activism that Makes Sense: Congregations & Community Organization. LC 83-82016. (Orig.). 1984. pap. 6.95 (ISBN 0-8091-2600-1). Paulist Pr.

Pinson, William M. Applying the Gospel: Suggestions for Christian Social Action in the Local Church. new ed. LC 75-8374. 160p. 1975. pap. 5.95 (ISBN 0-8054-6306-2). Broadman.

Ruether, Rosemary R. The Radical Kingdom: The Western Experience of Messianic Hope. LC 70-109080. 324p. 1975. pap. 5.95 (ISBN 0-8091-1860-2). Paulist Pr.

Schiblin, Richard. The Bible, the Church, & Social Justice. 64p. 1983. pap. 1.50 (ISBN 0-89243-187-3). Liguori Pubns.

Searle, Mark, ed. Liturgy & Social Justice. LC 80-27011. 102p. 1980. pap. 5.50 (ISBN 0-8146-1209-1). Liturgical Pr.

Sider, Ronald J. Cry Justice: The Bible Speaks on Hunger & Poverty. LC 80-82133. 224p. 1980. pap. 3.95 (ISBN 0-8091-2308-8). Paulist Pr.

Smith, Harold I. Life-Changing Answers to Depression. 192p. (Orig.). 1986. 9.95 (ISBN 0-89081-529-1). Harvest Hse.

Smoke, Jim. Turning Points. 192p. (Orig.). 1985. pap. 5.95 (ISBN 0-89081-484-8). Harvest Hse.

Smoke, Jim & Guest, Lisa. Growing Through Divorce: Working Guide. 96p. (Orig.). 1985. pap. 3.25 (ISBN 0-89081-477-5). Harvest Hse.

Sobrino, Jon. The True Church & the Poor. O'Connell, Mathew J., tr. from Span. LC 84-5661. Orig. Title: Resureccion de la Verdadera Iglesia, Los Pobres Lugar Teologica de la Eclesiologia. 384p. (Orig.). 1984. pap. 13.95 (ISBN 0-88344-513-1). Orbis Bks.

Strauss, Lehman. Demons, Yes - but Thank God for Good Angels. LC 75-38804. 1976. pap. 2.95 (ISBN 0-87213-831-3). Loizeaux.

Tanenbaum, Marc H. Religious Values in an Age of Violence. (Pere Marquette Theology Lectures). 1976. 7.95 (ISBN 0-87462-508-4). Marquette.

Taylor, Jack. One Home under God. LC 73-91609. 8.95 (ISBN 0-8054-5222-2); study guide 1.00 (ISBN 0-8054-5225-7); guide book 5.00 (ISBN 0-8054-5615-5). Broadman.

Troeltsch, Ernst. The Social Teaching of the Christian Churches, 2 vols. 44.00 set (ISBN 0-8446-6134-1). Peter Smith.

Wallace, H. A., et al. Christian Bases of World Order. facsimile ed. LC 75-134068. (Essay Index Reprint Ser). (Merrick Lectures, 1943). Repr. of 1943 ed. 19.00 (ISBN 0-8369-2490-8). Ayer Co Pubs.

Ward, Alfred D. & Clark, John M. Goals of Economic Life. LC 72-167432. (Essay Index Reprint Ser.). Repr. of 1953 ed. 25.00 (ISBN 0-8369-2726-5). Ayer Co Pubs.

Werner, Jayne S. Peasant Politics & Religious Sectarianism: Peasant & Priest in the Cao Dai in Viet Nam. LC 81-52078. (Monograph Ser.: No. 23). 123p. 1981. 10.50x (ISBN 0-938692-07-0). Yale U SE Asia.

White, Ruthe. Today's Woman in Search of Freedom. 176p. (Orig.). 1985. pap. 4.95 (ISBN 0-89081-473-2). Harvest Hse.

Wilbur, Ken. A Sociable God. LC 82-15241. (New Press Ser.). 176p. 1982. 12.95 (ISBN 0-07-070185-7). McGraw.

Wood, James R. Leadership in Voluntary Organizations: The Controversy Over Social Action in Protestant Churches. 155p. 1981. 17.00x (ISBN 0-8135-0920-3). Rutgers U Pr.

Woodruff, George E. From Junk to Jesus & from Crime to Christ. 1983. 6.50 (ISBN 0-8062-1862-2). Carlton.

Wright, H. Norman. The Rights & Wrongs of Anger. 176p. (Orig.). 1985. pap. 4.95 (ISBN 0-89081-457-0). Harvest Hse.

CHURCH AND SOCIAL PROBLEMS–BAPTISTS

Eighmy, John L. Churches in Cultural Captivity: A History of the Social Attitudes of Southern Baptists. LC 70-111047. 1972. 22.50x (ISBN 0-87049-115-6). U of Tenn Pr.

Spain, Rufus B. At Ease in Zion: A Social History of Southern Baptists, 1865-1900. LC 66-10367. 1967. 12.95x (ISBN 0-8265-1096-5). Vanderbilt U Pr.

CHURCH AND SOCIAL PROBLEMS–CATHOLIC CHURCH

see also Catholic Action; Christian Democracy; Socialism and Catholic Church

Au, William A. The Cross, the Flag, & the Bomb: American Catholics Debate War & Peace, 1960-1983. LC 84-25290. (Contributions to the Study of Religion Ser.: No. 12). xviii, 278p. 1985. lib. bdg. 35.00 (ISBN 0-313-24754-4, AUC/). Greenwood.

Betten, Neil. Catholic Activism & the Industrial Worker. LC 76-17280. 1976. 10.00 (ISBN 0-8130-0503-5). U Presses Fla.

Bins, John, ed. Building for Justice: A Guide for Social Concerns Committees. 1.77 (ISBN 0-8091-9309-4). Paulist Pr.

Blanshard, Paul. American Freedom & Catholic Power. LC 84-19141. xii, 402p. 1984. Repr. of 1958 ed. lib. bdg. 47.50x (ISBN 0-313-24620-3, BLAF). Greenwood.

Bronder, Saul E. Social Justice & Church Authority: The Public Life of Archbishop Robert E. Lucey. 215p. 1982. 29.95 (ISBN 0-87722-239-8). Temple U Pr.

Camp, R. L. Papal Ideology of Social Reform: A Study in Historical Development, 1878-1967. 1969. 30.00 (ISBN 9-0040-4317-9). Heinman.

Canadian Christian Movement for Peace Staff. Economic Rights & Human Development. (People Living for Justice Ser.). 240p. 1984. pap. 29.95 (ISBN 0-697-01932-2). Wm C Brown.

--Political & Social Rights & Human Dignity. (People Living for Justice Ser.). 208p. 1984. pap. text ed. 29.95 (ISBN 0-317-19703-7). Wm C Brown.

Curran, Charles E. Directions in Catholic Social Ethics. LC 84-28079. 304p. (Orig.). 1985. pap. text ed. 8.95 (ISBN 0-268-00853-1, 85-08533). U of Notre Dame Pr.

Dear, John. Disarming the Heart, Toward a Vow of Non-Violence. 144p. (Orig.). 1987. pap. 6.95 (ISBN 0-8091-2842-X). Paulist Pr.

Diamant, Alfred. Austrian Catholics & the Social Question, 1918-1933. LC 59-62692. (University of Florida Social Sciences Monographs: No. 2). 1959. pap. 3.50 (ISBN 0-8130-0059-9). U Presses Fla.

Douglass, R. Bruce, et al. The Deeper Meaning of Economic Life: Critical Essays on the U. S. Bishops' Pastoral Letter on the Economy. (Studies in Ethics). Orig. Title: Forging a New Public Philosophy. 296p. 1987. 19.95 (ISBN 0-87840-440-6); pap. 12.95 (ISBN 0-87840-441-4). Georgetown U Pr.

Fanfani, Amintore. Catholicism, Protestantism & Capitalism. LC 78-38251. (The Evolution of Capitalism Ser.). 234p. 1972. Repr. of 1935 ed. 23.50 (ISBN 0-405-04119-5). Ayer Co Pubs.

Fisher, Eugene J. & Polish, Daniel F., eds. Liturgical Foundations of Social Policy in the Catholic & Jewish Traditions. LC 82-40378. 180p. 1983. text ed. 16.95 (ISBN 0-268-01267-9); pap. text ed. 9.95 (ISBN 0-268-01268-7). U of Notre Dame Pr.

Gannon, Thomas M., ed. The Catholic Challenge to the American Economy: Reflections on the Bishops Pastoral Letter on Catholic Social Teaching & the U. S. Economy. 352p. 24.95 (ISBN 0-02-911260-5). Macmillan.

Gleason, Philip. Conservative Reformers: German-American Catholics & the Social Order. 1968. 22.95x (ISBN 0-268-00061-1). U of Notre Dame Pr.

Griese, Orville N. Catholic Identity in Health Care: Principles & Practice. 400p. (Orig.). 1987. pap. 17.95 (ISBN 0-935372-19-9). Pope John Ctr.

Gudorf, Christine E. Catholic Social Teaching on Liberation Themes. LC 80-5382. 394p. 1980. lib. bdg. 29.00 (ISBN 0-8191-1080-9); pap. text ed. 15.50 (ISBN 0-8191-1081-7). U Pr of Amer.

Gunnin, Gerry C. John Wheatley, Catholic Socialism, & Irish Labour in the West of Scotland, 1906-1924. McNeil, William H. & Stansky, Peter, eds. (Modern European History Ser.). 375p. 1987. lib. bdg. 55.00 (ISBN 0-8240-7811-X). Garland Pub.

Harte, Thomas. Papal Social Principles: A Guide & Digest. 12.00 (ISBN 0-8446-1225-1). Peter Smith.

Houck, John W. & Williams, Oliver F., eds. Co-Creation & Capitalism: John Paul II's Laborem Exercens. 318p. (Orig.). 1983. lib. bdg. 30.75 (ISBN 0-8191-3358-2); pap. text ed. 12.50 (ISBN 0-8191-3359-0). U Pr of Amer.

Hughes, Emmet J. Church & the Liberal Society. 1961. pap. 1.95x (ISBN 0-268-00046-8). U of Notre Dame Pr.

Kelly, George A. The Catholic Church & the American Poor. LC 75-16293. 202p. 1976. 5.95 (ISBN 0-8189-0321-X). Alba.

Kennedy, Stanislaus. Who Should Care: The Development of Kilkenny Social Services. (Turoe Press Ser.). 228p. pap. 12.95 (ISBN 0-905223-26-8, Dist. by Scribner). M Boyars Pubs.

Liptak, Dolores. European Immigrants & the Catholic Church in Connecticut: 1870-1920. 1987. 17.50 (ISBN 0-913256-79-X); pap. text ed. 12.95 (ISBN 0-913256-80-3). Ctr Migration.

Lutz, Charles P., ed. God, Goods & the Common Good: Eleven Perspectives on Economic Justice in Dialog with the Roman Catholic Bishops' Pastoral Letter. 160p. (Orig.). 1987. pap. 9.95 (ISBN 0-8066-2286-5, 10-2563). Augsburg.

McNulty, Kenneth K., Sr. Street or Pulpit? The Witness of Activist Monsignor Charles Owen Rice of Pittsburgh. (The Answers Ser.). 288p. (Orig.). 1985. pap. 9.95 (ISBN 0-935025-00-6). Data & Res Tech.

Maritain, Jacques. Christianity & Democracy & The Rights of Man & Natural Law. LC 83-80191. 200p. 1986. pap. 12.95 (ISBN 0-89870-030-2). Ignatius Pr.

--L' Homme et l'Etat. 2nd ed. 212p. 1965. 12.95 (ISBN 0-686-56353-0). French & Eur.

--Man & the State. LC 51-555. 1956. pap. 4.45x (ISBN 0-226-50552-9, P5, Phoen). U of Chicago Pr.

Menczer, Bela, ed. Catholic Political Thought: 1789-1848. 1962. pap. 5.95x (ISBN 0-268-00031-X). U of Notre Dame Pr.

Molnar, Thomas. Politics & the State: The Catholic View. 1980. 7.50 (ISBN 0-317-46875-8). Franciscan Herald.

Musto, Ronald G. The Catholic Peace Tradition. LC 86-12494. 464p. (Orig.). 1986. pap. 21.95 (ISBN 0-88344-263-9). Orbis Bks.

--The Peace Tradition in the Catholic Church: An Annotated Bibliography. LC 86-31950. (Garland Reference Library of Social Science). 500p. 1987. lib. bdg. 67.00 (ISBN 0-8240-8584-1). Garland Pub.

Novak, Michael. Freedom with Justice: Catholic Social Thought & Liberal Institutions. LC 84-47731. 272p. 1984. 17.45 (ISBN 0-06-066317-0, HarpR). Har-Row.

Race, Nation, Person: Total Aspects of the Race Problem. facs. ed. LC 70-128291. (Essay Index Reprint Ser). 1944. 25.50 (ISBN 0-8369-2019-8). Ayer Co Pubs.

Russell, Ralph D., ed. Essays in Reconstruction. LC 68-15835. 1968. Repr. of 1946 ed. 21.50x (ISBN 0-8046-0398-7, Pub. by Kennikat). Assoc Faculty Pr.

Sandover, Oswald D. The Catholic Church, the Peace of the World & the Foreign Policy of the United States. (Illus.). 117p. 1983. 99.45x (ISBN 0-86722-055-4). Inst Econ Pol.

Schultheis, Michael J., et al. Our Best Kept Secret: The Rich Heritage of Catholic Social Teaching. rev. & expanded ed. 75p. (Orig.). 1987. pap. text ed. 4.50 (ISBN 0-934255-03-2). Center Concern.

Sider, Ronald J. Rich Christians in an Age of Hunger: A Biblical Study. LC 76-45106. 254p. 1977. pap. 5.95 (ISBN 0-8091-2015-1). Paulist Pr.

Sturzo, Luigi. Church & State, Two Vols. (Vol. 2, O.P.). 1962. Set. pap. 11.90x (ISBN 0-268-00047-6). U of Notre Dame Pr.

Sullivan, Patrick J. Blue Collar-Roman Collar-White Collar: U. S. Catholic Involvement in Labor Management Controversies, 1960-1980. LC 86-24593. 358p. (Orig.). 1987. lib. bdg. 26.75 (ISBN 0-8191-5704-X); pap. text ed. 16.75 (ISBN 0-8191-5705-8). U Pr of Amer.

Thorning, Joseph F. Builders of the Social Order. facs. ed. LC 68-57340. (Essay Index Reprint Ser.). 1941. 15.00 (ISBN 0-8369-0936-4). Ayer Co Pubs.

To Do the Work of Justice: A Plan of Action for the Catholic Community in the United States. pap. 1.95 (ISBN 1-55586-132-6, B-132). US Catholic.

Westheimer, Karl. Humanity's Contemporary Moral Decay & the Historical Role of the Catholic Church. LC 73-76434. (Illus.). 132p. 1973. 43.40 (ISBN 0-913314-19-6). Am Classical Coll Pr.

Wilkins, Ronald & Grover, Veronica. Achieving Social Justice: A Catholic Perspective. rev. ed. (To Live Is Christ Ser.). (YA) 1987. pap. text ed. write for info. (ISBN 0-697-02126-2); write for info. (ISBN 0-697-02127-0). Wm C Brown.

CHURCH AND SOCIAL PROBLEMS–CHURCH OF ENGLAND

Bright, Laurence & Clements, Simon, eds. The Committed Church. 1966. 39.50x (ISBN 0-317-27423-6). Elliots Bks.

CHURCH AND SOCIAL PROBLEMS–MENNONITES

Mennonite Church General Conference, Board of Christian Service Staff. Church, the State & the Offender. 1963. pap. 0.50 (ISBN 0-87303-200-4). Faith & Life.

CHURCH AND SOCIAL PROBLEMS–METHODIST CHURCH

Jones, Donald G. The Sectional Crisis & Northern Methodism: A Study in Piety, Political Ethics & Civil Religion. LC 78-9978. 349p. 1979. lib. bdg. 22.50 (ISBN 0-8108-1175-8). Scarecrow.

Warner, Wellman J. Wesleyan Movement in the Industrial Revolution. LC 66-24768. 1967. Repr. of 1930 ed. 8.00x (ISBN 0-8462-0960-8). Russell.

CHURCH AND SOCIAL PROBLEMS–GERMANY

Shanahan, William O. German Protestants Face the Social Question: The Conservative Phase, 1815-1871. 1954. 22.95 (ISBN 0-268-00110-3). U of Notre Dame Pr.

CHURCH AND SOCIAL PROBLEMS–GREAT BRITAIN

Bettey, J. H. Church & Community: The Parish Church in English Life. LC 79-14739. (Illus.). 142p. 1979. text ed. 26.50x (ISBN 0-06-490381-8, 06346). B&N Imports.

Schlatter, Richard B. Social Ideas of Religious Leaders, Sixteen Sixty to Sixteen Sixty-Eight. LC 77-120663. 1970. Repr. lib. bdg. 18.50x (ISBN 0-374-97102-1, Octagon). Hippocrene Bks.

Warne, Arthur. Church & Society in Eighteenth Century England. LC 69-16764. (Illus.). 1969. 17.95x (ISBN 0-678-05642-0). Kelley.

Warner, Wellman J. Wesleyan Movement in the Industrial Revolution. LC 66-24768. 1967. Repr. of 1930 ed. 8.00x (ISBN 0-8462-0960-8). Russell.

Wilson, Bryan R. Sects & Society: A Sociological Study of Three Religious Groups in Britain. LC 78-5993. 1978. Repr. of 1961 ed. lib. bdg. 31.00x (ISBN 0-313-20439-X, WISA). Greenwood.

CHURCH AND SOCIAL PROBLEMS–LATIN AMERICA

Beeson, Trevor & Pearce, Jenny, eds. A Vision of Hope: The Churches & Change in Latin America. LC 83-48927. 288p. 1984. pap. 6.95 (ISBN 0-8006-1758-4, 1-1758). Fortress.

McGinnis, James. Solidarity with the People of Nicaragua. LC 84-27202. (Illus.). 192p. (Orig.). 1985. pap. 7.95 (ISBN 0-88344-448-8). Orbis Bks.

Maduro, Otto. Religion & Social Conflicts. Barr, Robert R., tr. from Span. LC 82-3439. Orig. Title: Religion y Lucha de Clase. 192p. (Orig.). 1982. pap. 8.95 (ISBN 0-88344-428-3). Orbis Bks.

Schall, James V. Liberation Theology in Latin America. LC 80-82266. 412p. (Orig.). 1982. pap. 13.95 (ISBN 0-89870-006-X). Ignatius Pr.

Segundo, Juan L. The Hidden Motives of Pastoral Action: Latin American Reflections. Drury, John, tr. from Sp. LC 77-13420. Orig. Title: Accion Pastoral latinoamericana: Sus motivos ocultos. 141p. 1977. 12.95 (ISBN 0-88344-185-3). Orbis Bks.

CHURCH AND SOCIAL PROBLEMS–UNITED STATES

Abell, Aaron I. The Urban Impact on American Protestantism, 1865-1900. x, 275p. 1962. Repr. of 1943 ed. 22.50 (ISBN 0-208-00587-0, Archon). Shoe String.

Barlow, Geoffrey, ed. Vintage Muggeridge: Religion & Society. 200p. (Orig.). 1986. pap. 7.95 (ISBN 0-8028-0181-1). Eerdmans.

Benestad, Brian J. The Pursuit of a Just Social Order: Policy Statements of the U. S. Catholic Bishops, 1966-80. LC 82-18326. 220p. 1982. 12.00 (ISBN 0-89633-060-5); pap. 7.00 (ISBN 0-89633-061-3). Ethics & Public Policy.

Carter, Paul A. The Decline & Revival of the Social Gospel: Social & Political Liberalism in American Protestant Churches, 1920-1940. 2nd ed. LC 70-122413. xxvi, 265p. 1971. Repr. of 1956 ed. 27.50 (ISBN 0-208-01083-1, Archon). Shoe String.

Castelli, Jim, et al. The Abortion Issue in the Political Process: A Briefing for Catholic Legislators. Jackman, Paul, ed. 19p. pap. 3.00 (ISBN 0-915365-08-1). Cath Free Choice.

Cole, Charles C., Jr. Social Ideas of the Northern Evangelists, Eighteen Twenty-Six to Eighteen Sixty. 1966. lib. bdg. 20.50x (ISBN 0-374-91843-0, Octagon). Hippocrene Bks.

Cunningham, W. J. Agony at Galloway: One Church's Struggle with Social Change. LC 79-56698. 1980. 3.95 (ISBN 0-87805-117-1). U Pr of Miss.

Ellingston, Jenefer. We Are the Mainstream. McKenna, Constance, ed. (Illus.). 16p. 1981. pap. 1.00 (ISBN 0-915365-02-2). Cath Free Choice.

Ferrell, Frank, et al. Trevor's Place: The Story of the Boy Who Brings Hope to the Homeless. LC 84-48768. (Illus.). 138p. 1985. 12.45 (ISBN 0-06-062531-7, HarpR). Har-Row.

Freudenberger, C. Dean & Minus, Paul M., Jr. A Christian Responsibility in a Hungry World. LC 75-43764. 1976. pap. 3.25 (ISBN 0-687-07567-X). Abingdon.

Hurst, Jane. The History of Abortion in the Catholic Church. McKenna, Constance, ed. (Illus.). 31p. 1983. pap. 1.00 (ISBN 0-915365-04-9). Cath Free Choice.

Hynes, Kathleen. An Ethical Inquiry. McKenna, Constance & Johnson, Karen, eds. 16p. 1981. pap. 1.00 (ISBN 0-915365-07-3). Cath Free Choice.

Kloetzli, Walter. The Church & the Urban Challenge. LC 61-14757. pap. 23.80 (2027195). Bks Demand UMI.

Lincoln, Eric. Race, Religion, & the Continuing American Dilemma. (American Century Ser.). 304p. 1985. 17.95 (ISBN 0-8090-8016-8). FS&G.

McKenna, Constance, ed. I Support You But I Can't Sign My Name. 20p. 1982. pap. 1.00 (ISBN 0-915365-06-5). Cath Free Choice.

McKenna, Constance, et al, eds. My Conscience Speaks. (Illus.). 48p. 1981. pap. 1.00 (ISBN 0-915365-05-7). Cath Free Choice.

Maguire, Marjorie R. & Maguire, Daniel C. Abortion: A Guide to Making Ethical Choices. Jackman, Paul & Mooney, Anne S., eds. 44p. 1983. pap. 3.00 (ISBN 0-915365-00-6). Cath Free Choice.

Majors, William R. Editorial Wild Oats: Edward Ward Carmack & Tennessee Politics. LC 84-10870. xx, 194p. 1984. 17.50 (ISBN 0-86554-133-7, MUP/H124). Mercer Univ Pr.

Miller, Kenneth R. & Wilson, Mary E. The Church That Cares. LC 85-14786. 96p. 1985. pap. 6.95 (ISBN 0-8170-1087-4). Judson.

Miller, Robert M. American Protestantism & Social Issues, 1919-1939. LC 77-22031. 1977. Repr. of 1958 ed. lib. bdg. 26.75x (ISBN 0-8371-9777-5, MIAM). Greenwood.

On War, Abortion & the Homeless. (Sermon Ser.: No. 1). 18p. 1982. pap. 2.00 (ISBN 0-936384-10-7). Cowley Pubns.

Rees, Seth C. Miracles in the Slums. (The Higher Christian Life Ser.). 301p. 1985. lib. bdg. 40.00 (ISBN 0-8240-6440-2). Garland Pub.

Smith, Timothy L. Revivalism & Social Reform: American Protestantism on the Eve of the Civil War. 11.25 (ISBN 0-8446-2960-X). Peter Smith.

Smith-Perkins, Staunton E. Satan in the Pulpit. (Illus.). 104p. (Orig.). 1982. pap. 4.95 (ISBN 0-943982-00-6, Dis. by Book Carrier). SES Development.

Umbreit, Mark. Crime & Reconciliation. 144p. (Orig.). 1985. pap. 7.95 (ISBN 0-687-09885-8). Abingdon.

CHURCH AND SOCIETY

see Church and the World

CHURCH AND STATE

see also Anti-Clericalism; Christianity and Politics; Church and Education; Church Polity; Church Property; Ecclesiastical Law; Investiture; Liberty of Conscience; Nationalism and Religion; Patronage, Ecclesiastical; Popes–Temporal Power; Religion and State; Religion in the Public Schools; Religious Liberty; Secularization; Taxation, Exemption From

Acton, Lord. Essays on Church & State. 12.00 (ISBN 0-8446-1505-6). Peter Smith.

Adjali, Mia. Of Life & Hope: Toward Effective Witness in Human Rights. (Orig.). 1979. pap. 2.95 (ISBN 0-377-00084-1). Friend Pr.

Barth, Karl. Community, State & Church: Three Essays. 16.75 (ISBN 0-8446-1058-5). Peter Smith.

Bau, Iqnatius. This Ground Is Holy: Church Sanctuary & Central American Refugees. LC 84-60406. 304p. (Orig.). 1985. pap. 9.95 (ISBN 0-8091-2720-2). Paulist Pr.

Baum, Gregory. Constitution on the Church: De Ecclesia. LC 65-17864. 192p. 1965. pap. 2.95 (ISBN 0-8091-1528-X). Paulist Pr.

Bilson, Thomas. The True Difference Between Christian Subjection & Unchristian Rebellion. LC 70-38154. (English Experience Ser.: No. 434). 854p. 1972. Repr. of 1585 ed. 143.00 (ISBN 90-221-0434-6). Walter J Johnson.

Bobango, Gerald J. Religion & Politics: Bishop Valerian Trifa & His Times. (East European Monograph: No. 92). 299p. 1981. 25.00x (ISBN 0-914710-86-9). East Eur Quarterly.

Brother Terence McLaughlin. Catholic School Finance & Church-State Relations. 81p. 1986. 6.60 (ISBN 0-318-20564-5). Natl Cath Educ.

Buzzard, Lynn R. & Brandon, Thomas. Church Discipline & the Courts. (Pressure Point Ser.). 160p. (Orig.). 1987. pap. 6.95 (ISBN 0-8423-0272-7). Tyndale.

Chadwick, Owen. Hensley Henson: A Study in the Friction Between Church & State. 350p. 1983. text ed. 39.95x (ISBN 0-19-825445-8). Oxford U Pr.

Cornwell, Peter. Church & the Nation: The Case for Disestablishment. (Faith & the Future Ser.). 160p. 1984. 24.95x (ISBN 0-631-13223-6); pap. 8.95x (ISBN 0-631-13224-4). Basil Blackwell.

Cosmao, Vincent. Changing the World: An Agenda for the Churches. Drury, John, tr. LC 84-5153. Tr. of Changer le monde-une tache pour l'eglise. 128p. (Orig.). 1984. pap. 7.95 (ISBN 0-88344-107-1). Orbis Bks.

Cox, Harvey. Religion in the Secular City: Toward a Post-Modern Theology. 320p. 1984. 16.95 (ISBN 0-671-45344-0). S&S.

Dante Alighieri. De Monarchia. LC 74-147412. (Library of War & Peace; Proposals for Peace: a History). lib. bdg. 46.00 (ISBN 0-8240-0210-5). Garland Pub.

Dawson, Christopher H. Beyond Politics. facsimile ed. LC 74-111825. (Essay Index Reprint Ser.). 1939. 14.00 (ISBN 0-8369-1603-4). Ayer Co Pubs.

Detweiler, Richard C. Mennonite Statements on Peace. 80p. (Orig.). 1968. pap. 2.95 (ISBN 0-8361-1581-3). Herald Pr.

Gardiner, Stephen. Obedience in Church & State: Three Political Tracts. Janelle, Pierre, ed. LC 68-19272. 1968. Repr. of 1930 ed. lib. bdg. 22.50x (ISBN 0-8371-0081-X, GABW). Greenwood.

Giannella, Donald A., ed. Religion & the Public Order: An Annual Review of Church & State & of Religion, Law, & Society. LC 64-17164. pap. 72.00 (ISBN 0-317-20699-0, 2024114). Bks Demand UMI.

Gladstone, William E. The State in Its Relations with the Church. 1196p. Repr. of 1841 ed. text ed. 62.10x (ISBN 0-576-02192-X, Pub. by Gregg Intl Pubs England). Gregg Intl.

Hammar, Richard R. Pastor, Church & Law. LC 83-80245. 448p. 1983. 16.95 (ISBN 0-88243-580-9, 02-0580). Gospel Pub.

Hauerwas, Stanley. Against the Nations: War & Survival in a Liberal Society. 240p. (Orig.). 1985. 19.95 (ISBN 0-86683-957-7, AY8549, HarpR). Har-Row.

Heering, Gerrit J. Fall of Christianity. LC 77-147670. (Library of War & Peace; Relig. & Ethical Positions on War). 1973. lib. bdg. 46.00 (ISBN 0-8240-0428-0). Garland Pub.

Heyer, Robert, ed. Nuclear Disarmament: Key Statements of Popes, Bishops, Councils & Churches. 1982. pap. 7.95 (ISBN 0-8091-2456-4). Paulist Pr.

Johnson, Alvin W. The Legal Status of Church-State Relationships in the United States with Special Reference to the Public Schools. ix, 332p. 1982. Repr. of 1934 ed. lib. bdg. 30.00x (ISBN 0-8377-0739-0). Rothman.

Kaufman, Donald D. What Belongs to Caeser? LC 70-109939. 128p. 1969. pap. 5.95 (ISBN 0-8361-1621-6). Herald Pr.

Kauper, Paul G. Religion & the Constitution. LC 64-7898. pap. 36.80 (ISBN 0-317-29869-0, 2051881). Bks Demand UMI.

Kelly, Kent. State of North Carolina vs Christian Liberty. 112p. (Orig.). 1978. pap. 2.95 (ISBN 0-9604138-3-9). Calvary Pr.

Kelly, Kent, et al. The Separation of Church & Freedom: A War Manual for Christian Soldiers. LC 80-80341. (Illus.). 308p. 1980. 7.95 (ISBN 0-9604138-0-4). Calvary Pr.

Laski, Harold J. Authority in the Modern State. LC 68-21685. 398p. 1968. Repr. of 1919 ed. 35.00 (ISBN 0-208-00460-2, Archon). Shoe String.

--Studies in the Problem of Sovereignty. 1968. Repr. 29.50x (ISBN 0-86527-191-7). Fertig.

Lasserre, Jean. War & the Gospel. (Christian Peace Shelf Ser.). 243p. 1962. 12.95 (ISBN 0-8361-1475-2). Herald Pr.

Lowry, Charles W. To Pray or Not to Pray: A Handbook for Study of Recent Supreme Court Decisions & American Church-State Doctrine. (Special bicentennial facsimile of enlarged ed). 1978. 7.00 (ISBN 0-685-88420-1, U Pr of Wash). Larlin Corp.

McCarthy, Martha M. A Delicate Balance: Church, State & the Schools. LC 83-60797. 184p. 1983. pap. 6.00 (ISBN 0-87367-427-8). Phi Delta Kappa.

McDonagh, Edna. Church & Politics: From Theology to a Case History of Zimbabwe. LC 80-53070. 200p. 1980. text ed. 14.95 (ISBN 0-268-00734-9); pap. text ed. 5.95 (ISBN 0-268-00736-5). U of Notre Dame Pr.

Machen, J. Gresham. Education, Christianity & the State. Robbins, John W., ed. & intro. by. (Trinity Papers: No. 19). 150p. (Orig.). 1987. pap. 5.95 (ISBN 0-940931-19-2). Trinity Found.

Manning, Leonard F. The Law of Church-State Relations in a Nutshell. LC 80-22991. (Nutshell Ser.). 305p. 1981. pap. text ed. 10.95 (ISBN 0-8299-2113-3). West Pub.

Mechling, Jay, ed. Church, State & Public Policy. 1979. 12.25 (ISBN 0-8447-2159-X); pap. 5.25 (ISBN 0-8447-2160-3). Am Enterprise.

Menendez, Albert J. Church-State Relations: An Annotated Bibliography. LC 75-24894. (Reference Library of Social Science: Vol. 24). 125p. 1976. lib. bdg. 25.00 (ISBN 0-8240-9956-7). Garland Pub.

Metts, Wallis C. Your Faith on Trial. 180p. (Orig.). 1979. pap. 3.95 (ISBN 0-89084-112-8). Bob Jones Univ Pr.

Moltmann, Jurgen, et al. Religion & Political Society. LC 73-18424. (Symposium Ser.: Vol. 1). xi, 209p. 1976. Repr. of 1974 ed. 19.95x (ISBN 0-88946-953-9). E Mellen.

Monahan, Arthur P. John of Paris on Royal & Papal Power: A Translation with Introduction of the de Postestate Regia et Papali of John of Paris. LC 73-16302. (Records of Civilation Ser). 197p. 1974. 27.50x (ISBN 0-231-03690-6). Columbia U Pr.

Morrison, Clinton D. Powers That Be: Earthly Rulers & Demonic Powers in Romans, Chapter 13, 1-7. LC 60-4219. (Studies in Biblical Theology: No. 29). 1960. pap. 10.00x (ISBN 0-8401-3029-5). A R Allenson.

Murray, Albert V. The State & the Church in a Free Society. LC 77-27134. (Hibbert Lectures: 1957). Repr. of 1958 ed. 27.50 (ISBN 0-404-60433-1). AMS Pr.

Nuttall, Clayton L. The Conflict: The Separation of the Church & State. LC 80-21267. 144p. 1980. pap. 4.95 (ISBN 0-87227-076-9, RBP5088). Reg Baptist.

Pfeffer, Leo. Church, State & Freedom, 2 vols. 1987. lib. bdg. 75.00 ea. Vol. 1 (ISBN 0-379-20734-6). Vol. 2 (ISBN 0-379-20735-4). Oceana.

Portes Gil, Emilio. The Conflict Between the Civil Power & the Clergy: Historical & Legal Essay. 1976. lib. bdg. 59.95 (ISBN 0-87968-928-5). Gordon Pr.

Robbins, Thomas & Robertson, Roland, eds. Church-State Relations: Tensions & Transitions. 380p. 1986. 29.95 (ISBN 0-88738-108-1); pap. 14.95 (ISBN 0-88738-651-2). Transaction Bks.

Sanders, Thomas G. Protestant Concepts of Church & State. 19.50 (ISBN 0-8446-6185-6). Peter Smith.

Smith, Sydney D. Grapes of Conflict: The Faith Community & Farm Workers. 160p. 1987. 16.95 (ISBN 0-932727-12-3); pap. 9.95 (ISBN 0-932727-14-X); special ed. 25.00 (ISBN 0-932727-13-1). Hope Pub Hse.

Snyder, Howard. Comunidad del Rey. (Span.). 232p. (Orig.). 1983. pap. 5.50 (ISBN 0-317-00691-6). Edit Caribe.

Sutherland, Arthur E. Church Shall Be Free: A Glance at Eight Centuries of Church & State. LC 65-24000. pap. 15.00 (2017808). Bks Demand UMI.

Swancara, Frank. Separation of Church & State. 346p. pap. 3.00. Truth Seeker.

Tumins, Valerie A. & Vernadsky, George, eds. Patriarch Nikon on Church & State. 812p. 1982. 99.20 (ISBN 90-279-7676-7). Mouton.

Vidler, Alec R. The Orb & the Cross: A Normative Study in the Relations of Church & State, with Reference to Gladstones Early Writings. LC 46-19947. 1945. text ed. 7.50x (ISBN 0-8401-2544-5). A R Allenson.

Walton, Rus. FACS: Fundamentals for American Christians. 372p. 1979. pap. 4.95 (ISBN 0-942516-03-6). Plymouth Rock Found.

--One Nation under God. 240p. 1987. pap. 9.95 (ISBN 0-8407-3093-4). Nelson.

Waring, Luther H. Political Theories of Martin Luther. LC 68-15837. 1968. Repr. of 1910 ed. 21.50x (ISBN 0-8046-0448-5, Pub. by Kennikat). Assoc Faculty Pr.

Weber, Paul J. & Gilbert, Dennis A. Private Churches & Public Money: Church-Government Fiscal Relations. LC 80-1793. (Contributions to the Study of Religion: No. 1). (Illus.). xx, 260p. 1981. lib. bdg. 29.95 (ISBN 0-313-22484-6, WCM/). Greenwood.

Williams, George H. Norman Anonymous of Eleven Hundred A.D. Toward the Identification & Evaluation of the So-Called Anonymous of York. (Harvard Theological Studies). 1951. 24.00 (ISBN 0-527-01018-9). Kraus Repr.

Wood, James E., Jr., ed. Religion, the State, & Education. LC 84-81477. (Institute of Church-State Studies). 151p. 1984. 10.95 (ISBN 0-918954-31-2); pap. 6.95 (ISBN 0-918954-32-0). Baylor Univ Pr.

Wood, James E., Jr., et al. Church & State in Scripture, History, & Constitutional Law. LC 59-21543. (Institute of Church-State Studies). 171p. 1985. pap. 6.95 (ISBN 0-918954-01-0). Baylor Univ Pr.

CHURCH AND STATE–BIBLIOGRAPHY

Kinder, A. Gordon. Spanish Protestants & Reformers in the Sixteenth Century: A Bibliography. (Research Bibliographies & Checklists Ser.: No. 39). 108p. (Orig.). 1983. pap. 11.95 (ISBN 0-7293-0146-X, Pub. by Grant & Cutler). Longwood Pub Group.

CHURCH AND STATE–CATHOLIC CHURCH

see also Church and State in Africa; Church and State in Australia; Church and State in Canada; Church and State in Europe; Church and State in Great Britain; Church and State in Latin America; Church and State in the United States

Benedict, Samuel O. Catholicism & Americanism: The Vision of a Conflict? (Illus.). 147p. 1987. 98.85 (ISBN 0-89266-590-4). Am Classical Coll Pr.

Blantz, Thomas E. A Priest in Public Service: Francis J. Haas & the New Deal. LC 81-40452. 384p. 1982. 25.00 (ISBN 0-268-01547-3). U of Notre Dame Pr.

Bruckberger, R. L. God & Politics. LC 78-190754. (Howard Greenfield Bk.). 1971. 9.95 (ISBN 0-87955-302-2). O'Hara.

Chadwick, Owen. The Popes & European Revolution. (Oxford History of the Christian Church Ser.). 1981. 84.00x (ISBN 0-19-826919-6). Oxford U Pr.

D'Entreves, A. P., ed. Thomas Aquinas: Selected Political Writings. Dawson, J. G., tr. 136p. 1981. 26.50x; pap. 9.95x (ISBN 0-389-20244-4). B&N Imports.

Donoso Cortes, Juan. An Essay on Catholicism, Authority & Order Considered in Their Fundamental Principles. Goddard, Madeleine V., tr. LC 78-59018. 1979. Repr. of 1925 ed. 28.00 (ISBN 0-88355-692-8). Hyperion Conn.

Graham, Robert A. Vatican Diplomacy: A Study of Church & State on the International Plane. LC 59-13870. pap. 113.00 (ISBN 0-317-08423-2, 2015012). Bks Demand UMI.

Hanson, Eric O. The Catholic Church in World Politics. (Illus.). 468p. 1987. 24.95 (ISBN 0-691-07729-0). Princeton U Pr.

McSweeney, William. Roman Catholicism: The Search for Relevance. 1980. 25.00 (ISBN 0-312-68969-1). St Martin.

Maier, Hans. Revolution & Church: The Early History of Christian Democracy, 1789-1901. Schossberger, Emily M., tr. LC 68-27577. 1969. 7.95 (ISBN 0-268-00319-X). U of Notre Dame Pr.

O'Neill, James M. Catholicism & American Freedom. LC 78-21495. 1979. Repr. of 1952 ed. lib. bdg. cancelled (ISBN 0-313-21153-1, ONCA). Greenwood.

Pradera, Victor. The New State. Malley, B., tr. LC 79-180421. Repr. of 1939 ed. 29.50 (ISBN 0-404-56196-9). AMS Pr.

Romero, Sidney J. Religion in the Rebel Ranks. (Illus.). 226p. (Orig.). 1983. lib. bdg. 27.00 (ISBN 0-8191-3327-2); pap. text ed. 12.50 (ISBN 0-8191-3328-0). U Pr of Amer.

Rommen, Heinrich A. State in Catholic Thought: A Treatise in Political Philosophy. Repr. of 1945 ed. lib. bdg. 26.25x (ISBN 0-8371-2437-9, ROCT). Greenwood.

Sturzo, Luigi. Church & State, Two Vols. (Vol. 2, O.P.). 1962. Set. pap. 11.90x (ISBN 0-268-00047-6). U of Notre Dame Pr.

Whyte, John H. Catholics in Western Democracies: A Study in Political Behavior. 1981. 22.50x (ISBN 0-312-12446-5). St Martin.

Yates, Gerard F., ed. Papal Thought on the State: Excerpts from Encyclicals & Other Writings of Recent Popes. LC 58-5745. (Crofts Classics Ser.). 1958. pap. text ed. 1.25x (ISBN 0-88295-064-9). Harlan Davidson.

CHURCH AND STATE–HISTORY

Bellini, Enzo, et al. The Church & the Modern Nations, 1850-1920. Drury, John, ed. & tr. from Ital. (An Illustrated History of the Church). (Illus.). 126p. 1982. 12.95 (ISBN 0-86683-159-2, HarpR). Har-Row.

Birke, Adolf M. & Kluxen, Kurt, eds. Church, State & Society in the Nineteenth Century. (Prince Albert Studies: Vol. 2). 130p. 1984. lib. bdg. 24.00 (ISBN 3-598-21402-2). K G Saur.

Brooke, Christopher N., et al, eds. Church & Government in the Middle Ages: Essays Presented to C. R. Cheney on His 70th Birthday. LC 75-41614. pap. 83.00 (2027285). Bks Demand UMI.

Cameron, James M. Images of Authority: A Consideration of the Concepts of "Regnum" & "Sacerdotium". LC 66-12489. pap. 24.30 (ISBN 0-8357-9261-7, 2016769). Bks Demand UMI.

Cunningham, Agnes. The Early Church & the State. LC 81-70666. (Sources of Early Christian Thought Ser.). 128p. 1982. pap. 7.95 (ISBN 0-8006-1413-5, 1-1413). Fortress.

Eller, Vernard. Christian Anarchy: Jesus' Primacy Over the Powers. 304p. (Orig.). 1987. pap. 13.95 (ISBN 0-8028-0227-3). Eerdmans.

Fox, Edward. The True Differences Between the Regal Power & the Ecclesiastical Power. LC 73-6129. (English Experience Ser.: No. 595). 108p. 1973. Repr. of 1548 ed. 9.50 (ISBN 90-221-0595-4). Walter J Johnson.

Gavin, Frank. Seven Centuries of the Problem of Church & State. 1938. 22.50x (ISBN 0-86527-180-1). Fertig.

Greenslade, Stanley L. Church & State from Constantine to Theodosius. LC 79-8712. 93p. 1981. Repr. of 1954 ed. lib. bdg. 22.50x (ISBN 0-313-20793-3, GRCS). Greenwood.

Healy, Patrick J. The Valerian Persecution: A Study of the Relations Between Church & State in the Third Century A. D. LC 76-185943. xv, 285p. 1972. Repr. of 1905 ed. 21.00 (ISBN 0-8337-4169-1). B Franklin.

Lischer, Richard. Marx & Teilhard: Two Ways to the New Humanity. LC 79-4438. 192p. (Orig.). 1979. pap. 3.48 (ISBN 0-88344-303-1). Orbis Bks.

Monticone, Ronald C. The Catholic Church in Communist Poland, 1945-1985: Forty Years of Church-State Relations. (East European Monographs: No. 205). 256p. 1986. 25.00 (ISBN 0-88033-102-X). East Eur Quarterly.

Morrison, Karl E., ed. The Investiture Controversy: Issues, Ideals & Results. LC 77-15654. (European Problem Studies). 144p. 1976. pap. text ed. 5.95 (ISBN 0-88275-634-6). Krieger.

O'Dwyer, Margaret M. The Papacy in the Age of Napoleon & the Restoration: Pius VII, 1800-1823. 296p. (Orig.). 1985. lib. bdg. 24.00 (ISBN 0-8191-4825-3); pap. text ed. 12.75 (ISBN 0-8191-4826-1). U Pr of Amer.

Petrie, George. Church & State in Early Maryland. LC 78-63810. (Johns Hopkins University. Studies in the Social Sciences. Tenth Ser. 1892: 4). Repr. of 1892 ed. 11.50 (ISBN 0-404-61073-0). AMS Pr.

Runciman, Steven. The Byzantine Theocracy. LC 76-47405. (Weil Lectures Ser.). 1977. 32.50 (ISBN 0-521-21401-7). Cambridge U Pr.

Smith, Arthur L. Church & State in the Middle Ages. new ed. 245p. 1964. 28.50x (ISBN 0-7146-1514-5, F Cass Co). Biblio Dist.

Tierney, Brian. Crisis of Church & State, Ten Fifty to Thirteen Hundred. (Orig.). 1964. pap. 6.50 (ISBN 0-13-193474-0, S102, Spec). P-H.

Wilson, John & Drakeman, Donald, eds. Church & State in American History. 2nd, rev. ed. LC 86-47513. 288p. 1986. pap. 10.95 (ISBN 0-8070-0409-X, BP 728). Beacon Pr.

CHURCH AND STATE IN AFRICA

Boesak, Allan A. & Villa-Vicencio, Charles, eds. When Prayer Makes News. 192p. (Orig.). 1986. pap. 10.95 (ISBN 0-664-24035-6). Westminster.

Villa-Vicencio, Charles, ed. Between Christ & Caesar: Classic & Contemporary Texts on Church & State. 196p. (Orig.). 1986. pap. 16.95 (ISBN 0-8028-0240-0). Eerdmans.

CHURCH AND STATE IN AUSTRALIA

Barrett, John. That Better Country. 1966. 15.50x (ISBN 0-522-83525-2, Pub. by Melbourne U Pr). Intl Spec Bk.

Ely, R. Unto God & Caesar: Religious Issues in the Emerging Commonwealth 1891-1906. 1976. 22.00x (ISBN 0-522-84093-0, Pub. by Melbourne U Pr). Intl Spec Bk.

CHURCH AND STATE IN BAVARIA

Higby, Chester P. Religious Policy of the Bavarian Government During the Napoleonic Period. LC 19-12150. (Columbia University. Studies in the Social Sciences: No. 196). Repr. of 1919 ed. 36.00 (ISBN 0-404-51196-1). AMS Pr.

CHURCH AND STATE IN CANADA

Riddell, Walter A. Rise of Ecclesiastical Control in Quebec. (Columbia University. Studies in the Social Sciences: No. 174). Repr. of 1916 ed. 17.50 (ISBN 0-404-51174-0). AMS Pr.

CHURCH AND STATE IN EUROPE

Here are entered works about the relations of church and state in Europe as a whole, as well as those about specific European countries.

Alexander, Stella. Church & State in Yugoslavia since Nineteen Forty-Five. LC 77-88668. (Soviet & East European Studies). 1979. 52.50 (ISBN 0-521-21942-6). Cambridge U Pr.

Curtiss, John S. The Russian Church & the Soviet State, 1917-1950. 1953. 11.75 (ISBN 0-8446-1141-7). Peter Smith.

Fischel, Jack R. & Pinsker, Sanford, eds. The Churches' Response to the Holocaust. (Holocaust Studies Annual: Vol. II). 200p. 1986. 20.00 (ISBN 0-913283-12-6). Penkevill.

Helmreich, Ernst, ed. Church & State in Europe. LC 78-68021. (Problems in Civilization Ser.). 1979. pap. 6.95x (ISBN 0-88273-405-9). Forum Pr IL.

Locke, Hubert G., ed. The Church Confronts the Nazis: Barmen Then & Now. (Toronto Studies in Theology: Vol. 16). 248p. 1984. 49.95x (ISBN 0-88946-762-5). E Mellen.

O'Dwyer, Margaret M. The Papacy in the Age of Napoleon & the Restoration: Pius VII, 1800-1823. 296p. (Orig.). 1985. lib. bdg. 24.00 (ISBN 0-8191-4825-3); pap. text ed. 12.75 (ISBN 0-8191-4826-1). U Pr of Amer.

CHURCH AND STATE IN FRANCE

Acomb, Evelyn M. French Laic Laws: 1879-1889. LC 67-18747. 1968. Repr. lib. bdg. 21.50 (ISBN 0-374-90038-8, Octagon). Hippocrene Bks.

Bouchard, Constance B. Sword, Miter, & Cloister: Nobility & the Church in Burgundy, 980-1198. LC 86-29158. (Illus.). 416p. 1987. text ed. 41.50x (ISBN 0-8014-1974-3). Cornell U Pr.

Galton, Arthur H. Church & State in France, 1300-1907. LC 70-185939. xxiv, 290p. 1972. Repr. of 1907 ed. lib. bdg. 21.00 (ISBN 0-8337-4124-1). B Franklin.

Hill, Henry B., tr. Political Testament of Cardinal Richelieu: The Significant Chapters & Supporting Selections. (Illus.). 148p. 1961. 15.00x (ISBN 0-299-02420-2); pap. 8.95x (ISBN 0-299-02424-5). U of Wis Pr.

Partin, Malcolm O. Waldeck-Rousseau, Combes, & the Church, 1899-1905: The Politics of Anticlericalism. LC 74-76167. (Duke Historical Publication Ser). 299p. 1969. 23.25 (ISBN 0-8223-0130-X). Duke.

Ravitch, Norman. Sword & Mitre: Government & Episcopate in France & England in the Age of Aristocracy. 1966. text ed. 18.40x (ISBN 0-686-22467-1). Mouton.

Reynolds, Blair. Manner & Method: A Translation of the French Reformed Church's Liturgy. 85p. (Orig.). 1985. pap. 6.95x (ISBN 0-932269-40-0). Wyndham Hall.

Rothrock, George A. The Huguenots: A Biography of a Minority. LC 78-23476. (Illus.). 228p. 1979. 21.95x (ISBN 0-88229-277-3). Nelson-Hall.

Sutton, Michael. Nationalism, Positivism & Catholicism: The Politics of Charles Maurras & French Catholics, 1890-1914. LC 82-4360. (Cambridge Studies in the History & Theory of Politics). 320p. 1983. 47.50 (ISBN 0-521-22868-9). Cambridge U Pr.

Walsh, Henry H. Concordat of 1801. LC 34-12835. (Columbia University. Studies in the Social Sciences: No. 387). Repr. of 1933 ed. 21.00 (ISBN 0-404-51387-5). AMS Pr.

CHURCH AND STATE IN GERMANY

Cochrane, Arthur C. The Church's Confession Under Hitler. 2nd ed. LC 76-57655. (Pittsburgh Reprint Ser.: No. 4). 1977. pap. text ed. 10.75 (ISBN 0-915138-28-X). Pickwick.

Frey, Arthur. Cross & Swastika, the Ordeal of the German Church. McNab, J. Strathearn, tr. LC 78-63668. (Studies in Fascism: Ideology & Practice). 224p. Repr. of 1938 ed. 24.50 (ISBN 0-404-16526-5). AMS Pr.

Helmreich, Ernst. The German Churches Under Hitler: Background, Struggle & Epilogue. LC 78-17737. 617p. 1978. 35.00x (ISBN 0-8143-1603-4). Wayne St U Pr.

Herman, Stewart W. It's Your Souls We Want. LC 72-180406. Repr. of 1943 ed. 29.50 (ISBN 0-404-56130-6). AMS Pr.

King, Christine E. The Nazi State & the New Religions: Five Case Studies in Non-conformity. LC 82-20910. (Studies in Religion & Society: Vol. 4). 332p. 1982. 59.95x (ISBN 0-88946-865-6). E Mellen.

MacFarland, Charles S. The New Church & the New Germany: A Study of Church & State. LC 78-63691. (Studies in Fascism: Ideology & Practice). 224p. Repr. of 1934 ed. 28.00 (ISBN 0-404-16953-8). AMS Pr.

Matheson, Peter, ed. The Third Reich & the Christian Churches. 128p. Date not set. pap. 8.25 (ISBN 0-567-29105-7, Pub. by T & T Clark Ltd UK). Fortress.

Spotts, Frederic. The Churches & Politics in Germany. LC 72-11050. 419p. 1973. 25.00x (ISBN 0-8195-4059-5). Wesleyan U Pr.

Von Ranke, Leopold. Ferdinand I & Maximilian II of Austria. LC 74-153627. Repr. of 1853 ed. 14.50 (ISBN 0-404-09265-9). AMS Pr.

CHURCH AND STATE IN GREAT BRITAIN

Here are entered works dealing not only with church and state in England, Scotland and Ireland, or in any two of them, but also works dealing with England alone.

see also Puritans

Allen, John W. English Political Thought, Sixteen Hundred Three to Sixteen Forty-Four. x, 525p. 1967. Repr. of 1938 ed. 37.50 (ISBN 0-208-00144-1, Archon). Shoe String.

An Answere to a Letter (Saint German, Christopher) LC 73-6097. (English Experience Ser.: No. 566). 1973. Repr. of 1535 ed. 8.00 (ISBN 90-221-0566-0). Walter J Johnson.

The Answeres of Some Brethren of the Ministerie to the Replies Concerning the Late Covenant. LC 74-80155. (English Experience Ser.: No. 636). 1974. Repr. of 1638 ed. 18.50 (ISBN 90-221-0636-5). Walter J Johnson.

Bentley, James. Ritualism & Politics in Victorian Britain. (Oxford Theological Monographs). (Illus.). 1978. 37.00x (ISBN 0-19-826714-2). Oxford U Pr.

Bettey, J. H. Church & Community: The Parish Church in English Life. LC 79-14739. (Illus.). 142p. 1979. text ed. 26.50x (ISBN 0-06-490381-8, 06346). B&N Imports.

Black, J. B. Reign of Elizabeth, Fifteen Fifty-Eight to Sixteen Three. 2nd ed. (Oxford History of England Ser.). 1959. 45.00x (ISBN 0-19-821701-3). Oxford U Pr.

Brooke, C., et al, eds. Church & Government in the Middle Ages. LC 75-41614. (Illus.). 1977. 59.50 (ISBN 0-521-21172-7). Cambridge U Pr.

Bross, Olive J. Church & Parliament: The Reshaping of the Church of England, 1828-1860. LC 59-7423. pap. 30.00 (ISBN 0-317-26542-3, 2023992). Bks Demand UMI.

Buck, Mark. Politics, Finance & the Church in the Reign of Edward II: Walter Stapeldon, Treasurer of England. LC 82-17695. (Cambridge Studies in Medieval Life & Thought 19). 248p. 1983. 52.50 (ISBN 0-521-25025-0). Cambridge U Pr.

Cantor, Norman F. Church, Kingship & Lay Investiture in England, 1089-1135. 1969. lib. bdg. 26.00x (ISBN 0-374-91273-4, Octagon). Hippocrene Bks.

Carleton, George. Jurisdiction Regall, Episcopall, Papall. LC 68-54625. (English Experience Ser.: No. 34). 302p. 1969. Repr. of 1610 ed. 30.00 (ISBN 90-221-0034-0). Walter J Johnson.

Child, Gilbert W. Church & State Under the Tudors. LC 72-183695. 452p. 1974. Repr. of 1890 ed. lib. bdg. 29.50 (ISBN 0-8337-4041-5). B Franklin.

Crowther-Hunt, Norman. Two Early Political Associations: The Quakers & the Dissenting Deputies in the Age of Sir Robert Walpole. LC 78-23805. 1979. Repr. of 1961 ed. lib. bdg. 24.75x (ISBN 0-313-21036-5, HUTW). Greenwood.

Davies, Ebenezer T. Episcopacy & the Royal Supremacy in the Church of England in the XVI Century. LC 78-13202. 1978. Repr. of 1950 ed. lib. bdg. 24.75x (ISBN 0-313-20626-0, DAER). Greenwood.

Dobson, R. B., ed. The Church, Politics & Patronage in the Fifteenth Century. LC 84-15102. 245p. 1985. 25.00 (ISBN 0-312-13481-9). St Martin.

Gasquet, Francis A. Henry the Eighth & the English Monasteries, 2 vols. LC 74-39467. (Select Bibliography Reprint Ser.). 1972. Repr. of 1888 ed. 56.75 (ISBN 0-8369-9905-3). Ayer Co Pubs.

Gottfried, Robert S. Bury St. Edmunds & the Urban Crisis, 1290-1539. LC 81-11984. (Illus.). 324p. 1981. 34.00x (ISBN 0-691-05340-5). Princeton U Pr.

Haller, William. Liberty & Reformation in the Puritan Revolution. LC 54-6482. 410p. 1955. pap. 14.00x (ISBN 0-231-08547-8). Columbia U Pr.

Hooker, Richard. Ecclesiastical Polity, Bk. 8. LC 77-170046. Repr. of 1931 ed. 24.00 (ISBN 0-404-03329-6). AMS Pr.

--Of the Laws of Ecclesiastical Polity, Bks. VI-VIII. Stanwood, P. G., ed. LC 76-24883. (Folger Library Edition of the Works of Richard Hooker). 1980. text ed. 65.00x (ISBN 0-674-63210-9, Belknap). Harvard U Pr.

Klein, Arthur J. Intolerance in the Reign of Elizabeth, Queen of England. LC 67-27614. 1968. Repr. of 1917 ed. 26.50x (ISBN 0-8046-0249-2, Pub. by Kennikat). Assoc Faculty Pr.

Larking, Lambert B., ed. Proceedings Principally in the County of Kent, in Connection with the Parliaments Called in 1640, & Especially with the Committee of Religion Appointed in That Year. (Camden Society, London. Publications, First Series: No. 80a). Repr. of 1862 ed. 37.00 (ISBN 0-404-50180-X). Ams Pr.

--Proceedings, Principally in the County of Kent, in Connection with the Parliaments Called in 1640. Repr. of 1862 ed. 37.00 (ISBN 0-384-31380-9). Johnson Repr.

Nurser, John. The Reign of Conscience: Individual, Church & State in Lord Acton's History of Liberty. McNeill, William H. & Stansky, Peter, eds. (Modern European History Ser.). 225p. 1987. lib. bdg. 40.00 (ISBN 0-8240-7826-8). Garland Pub.

The Protestation of the Generall Assemblie Made in the High Kirk, & at the Mercate Crosse of Glasgow. LC 79-26239. (English Experience Ser.: No. 343). 1971. Repr. of 1638 ed. 7.00 (ISBN 90-221-0525-3). Walter J Johnson.

Ravitch, Norman. Sword & Mitre: Government & Episcopate in France & England in the Age of Aristocracy. 1966. text ed. 18.40x (ISBN 0-686-22467-1). Mouton.

Seaver, Paul S. The Puritan Lectureships: The Politics of Religious Dissent, 1560-1662. LC 71-93497. 1970. 30.00x (ISBN 0-8047-0711-1). Stanford U Pr.

Stanley, Arthur P. Essays Chiefly on Questions of Church & State from 1850 to 1870. 656p. Repr. of 1870 ed. text ed. 74.52x (ISBN 0-576-02173-3). Gregg Intl.

Sykes, Norman. Church & State in England Since the Reformation. 1979. Repr. of 1929 ed. lib. bdg. 12.50 (ISBN 0-8482-6392-8). Norwood Edns.

Tillman, Helene. Die Papstlichen Legaten in England Bis Zur Beendigung der Legation Gualas, 1218. LC 80-2208. 1981. Repr. of 1926 ed. 29.50 (ISBN 0-404-18795-1). AMS Pr.

Wagner, Donald O. Church of England & Social Reform since 1854. LC 77-127438. (Columbia University. Studies in the Social Sciences: No. 325). 12.50 (ISBN 0-404-51325-5). AMS Pr.

Whiting, Charles E. Studies in English Puritanism from the Restoration to the Revolution, 1660-1688. LC 68-56060. 1968. Repr. of 1931 ed. 37.50x (ISBN 0-678-05203-4). Kelley.

CHURCH AND STATE IN GREECE

Hatch, Edwin. The Influence of Greek Ideas & Usages Upon the Christian Church. 384p. 1972. Repr. of 1891 ed. lib. bdg. 21.50 (ISBN 0-8337-1595-X). B Franklin.

CHURCH AND STATE IN GRENADA

Zwerneman, Andrew J. In Bloody Terms: The Betrayal of the Church in Marxist Grenada. LC 85-82316. 113p. (Orig.). 1986. pap. text ed. 6.95 (ISBN 0-937779-00-8). Greenlawn Pr.

CHURCH AND STATE IN GUATEMALA

Holleran, Mary P. Church & State in Guatemala. LC 73-19956. 359p. 1974. Repr. of 1949 ed. lib. bdg. 23.00x (ISBN 0-374-93929-2, Octagon). Hippocrene Bks.

CHURCH AND STATE IN IRELAND

Biggs-Davison, John & Chowdharay-Best, George. The Cross of Saint Patrick: The Catholic Unionist Tradition in Ireland. 1985. 50.80x (ISBN 0-946041-26-1, Pub. by Kensal Pr UK). State Mutual Bk.

Edwards, R. Dudley. Church & State in Tudor Ireland: A History of Penal Laws Against Irish Catholics 1534-1603. LC 76-180608. (Illus.). xliiii, 352p. 1972. Repr. of 1935 ed. 18.00x (ISBN 0-8462-1641-8). Russell.

Miller, David W. Church, State & Nation in Ireland, 1898-1921. LC 72-95453. 1973. 49.95x (ISBN 0-8229-1108-6). U of Pittsburgh Pr.

Titley, E. B. Church, State, & the Control of Schooling in Ireland, 1900-1944. 232p. 1983. 27.50x (ISBN 0-7735-0394-3). McGill-Queens U Pr.

CHURCH AND STATE IN ITALY

Cipolla, Carlo M. Faith, Reason & the Plague in Seventeenth-Century Tuscany. Kittel, Muriel, tr. from Ital. LC 79-2479. (Illus.). 140p. 1980. 17.50x (ISBN 0-8014-1230-7). Cornell U Pr.

--Faith, Reason, & the Plague in Seventeenth-Century Tuscany. 128p. 1981. pap. 4.95 (ISBN 0-393-00045-1). Norton.

A Discovery of the Great Subtiltie & Wonderful Wisdom of the Italians. LC 74-80221. (English Experience Ser.: No. 656). 1974. Repr. of 1591 ed. 10.50 (ISBN 90-221-0656-X). Walter J Johnson.

Halperin, S. William. Separation of Church & State in Italian Thought from Cavour to Mussolini. LC 71-120623. 1970. Repr. lib. bdg. 15.00x (ISBN 0-374-93412-6, Octagon). Hippocrene Bks.

Halperin, Samuel W. Italy & the Vatican at War: A Study of Their Relations from the Outbreak of the Franco-Prussian War to the Death of Pius 9th. LC 68-57606. (Illus.). 1968. Repr. of 1939 ed. lib. bdg. 22.50x (ISBN 0-8371-0461-0, HAIV). Greenwood.

Loud, G. A. Church & Society in the Norman Principality of Capua, 1058-1197. (Historical Monographs). (Illus.). 1985. 42.00x (ISBN 0-19-822931-3). Oxford U Pr.

CHURCH AND STATE IN LATIN AMERICA

Bruneau, Thomas C. The Political Transformation of the Brazilian Catholic Church. LC 73-79318. (Perspective on Development Ser.: Vol. 2). pap. 71.00 (ISBN 0-317-28009-0, 2025579). Bks Demand UMI.

Bruneau, Thomas E. The Church in Brazil: The Politics of Religion. LC 81-16391. (University of Texas at Austin, Institute of Latin American Studies-Latin American Monographs: No. 56). pap. 63.30 (2026564). Bks Demand UMI.

Comblin, Jose. The Church & the National Security State. LC 79-10881. 256p. (Orig.). 1979. pap. 12.95 (ISBN 0-88344-082-2). Orbis Bks.

Espada-Matta, Alberto. Church & State in the Social Context of Latin America. LC 85-90067. 79p. 1986. 7.95 (ISBN 0-533-06592-5). Vantage.

Levine, Daniel H., ed. Churches & Politics in Latin America. LC 79-23827. (Sage Focus Editions: Vol. 14). 288p. 1980. 29.00 (ISBN 0-8039-1298-6); pap. 14.95 (ISBN 0-8039-1299-4). Sage.

Mecham, J. Lloyd. Church & State in Latin America: A History of Politico-Ecclesiastical Relations. rev. ed. xi, 465p. 1969. pap. 7.95x (ISBN 0-8078-4042-4). U. of NC Pr.

Schall, James V. Liberation Theology in Latin America. LC 80-82266. 412p. (Orig.). 1982. pap. 13.95 (ISBN 0-89870-006-X). Ignatius Pr.

Smith, Brian H. The Church & Politics in Chile: Challenges to Modern Catholicism. LC 81-47951. 416p. 1982. 37.00x (ISBN 0-691-07629-4); pap. 13.50x L.P.E. (ISBN 0-691-10119-1). Princeton U Pr.

CHURCH AND STATE IN MEXICO

Bailey, David C. Viva Cristo Rey: The Cristero Rebellion & the Church-State Conflict in Mexico. (Illus.). 360p. 1974. 22.50x (ISBN 0-292-78700-6). U of Tex Pr.

Callcott, Wilfrid H. Church & State in Mexico, 1822-1857. 1965. lib. bdg. 27.00x (ISBN 0-374-91235-1, Octagon). Hippocrene Bks.

CHURCH AND STATE IN NICARAGUA

O'Shaughnessy, Laura & Serra, Luis. The Church & Revolution in Nicaragua. LC 82-92625. (Monographs in International Studies, Latin America Ser.: No. 11). 118p. pap. 11.00x (ISBN 0-89680-126-8, Ohio U Ctr Intl). Ohio U Pr.

CHURCH AND STATE IN NORWAY

Willson, Thomas B. History of the Church & State in Norway: From the 10th to the 16th Century. LC 72-145376. (Illus.). 1971. Repr. of 1903 ed. 49.00x (ISBN 0-403-01280-5). Scholarly.

CHURCH AND STATE IN ROME

Goar, R. J. Cicero & the State Religion. 141p. (Orig.). 1972. pap. text ed. 30.00x (Pub. by A M Hakkert). Coronet Bks.

Setton, Kenneth M. Christian Attitudes Towards the Emperor in the Fourth Century. LC 41-13567. (Columbia University. Studies in Social Sciences: No. 482). Repr. of 1941 ed. 20.00 (ISBN 0-404-51482-0). AMS Pr.

CHURCH AND STATE IN THE SOVIET UNION

Cracraft, James. The Church Reform of Peter the Great. 1971. 27.50x (ISBN 0-8047-0747-2). Stanford U Pr.

Cunningham, James W. A Vanquished Hope: The Movement for Church Renewal in Russia, 1905-1906. LC 81-9077. 384p. 1981. pap. text ed. 10.95 (ISBN 0-913836-70-2). St Vladimirs.

Hecker, Julius F. Religion & Communism. LC 73-842. (Russian Studies: Perspectives on the Revolution Ser.). 302p. 1987. Repr. of 1934 ed. 26.75 (ISBN 0-88355-037-7). Hyperion Conn.

Simon, Gerhard. Church, State & Opposition in U. S. S. R. LC 73-87754. 1974. 37.95x (ISBN 0-520-02612-8). U of Cal Pr.

CHURCH AND STATE IN THE UNITED STATES

Annese, Lucius. The Purpose of Authority? LC 78-72295. (Orig.). 1978. 50.00 (ISBN 0-933402-12-0). Charisma Pr.

Askew, Thomas A., Jr. & Spellman, Peter W. The Churches & the American Experience. 205p. 1984. pap. 9.95 (ISBN 0-8010-0199-4). Baker Bk.

Beggs, David W. America's Schools & Churches. LC 65-12279. pap. 60.30 (ISBN 0-317-28577-7, 2055190). Bks Demand UMI.

Bell, Sadie. Church, the State, & Education in Virginia. LC 78-89148. (American Education: Its Men, Institutions & Ideas Ser). 1969. Repr. of 1930 ed. 43.00 (ISBN 0-405-01385-X). Ayer Co Pubs.

Benedict, Samuel O. Catholicism & Americanism: The Vision of a Conflict? (Illus.). 147p. 1987. 98.85 (ISBN 0-89266-590-4). Am Classical Coll Pr.

Bradley, Gerard V. Church-State Relationships in America. LC 86-27149. (Contributions in Legal Studies). 1987. 29.85 (ISBN 0-313-25494-X, BYC). Greenwood.

Buchanan, Jim. A Guide to Materials about Public Aid to Religious Schools. (Public Administration Ser.: Bibliography P 1621). 1985. pap. 3.75 (ISBN 0-89028-291-9). Vance Biblios.

Buckley, Thomas E. Church & State in Revolutionary Virginia, 1776-1787. LC 77-4283. xii, 217p. 1977. 17.95x (ISBN 0-8139-0692-X). U Pr of Va.

Cobb, Sanford H. Rise of Religious Liberty in America: A History. LC 68-27517. 541p. 1968. Repr. of 1902 ed. 32.50x (ISBN 0-8154-0051-9). Cooper Sq.

--The Rise of Religious Liberty in America: A History. (American Studies). 1970. Repr. of 1902 ed. 30.00 (ISBN 0-384-09445-7). Johnson Repr.

Colombo, Furio. God in America: Religion & Politics in the United States. Jarrat, Kristin, tr. from Ital. LC 84-4278. 208p. 1984. 20.00x (ISBN 0-231-05972-8). Columbia U Pr.

Colwell, Stephen. The Position of Christianity in the United States, in Its Relations with Our Political Institutions, & Specially with Reference to Religious Instruction in the Public Schools. LC 78-38444. (Religion in America, Ser. 2). 180p. 1972. Repr. of 1854 ed. 17.00 (ISBN 0-405-04063-6). Ayer Co Pubs.

Conference of Scientology Ministers. The American Inquisition: U. S. Government Agency Harassment, Religious Persecution & Abuse of Power. 1977. pap. 7.00 (ISBN 0-915598-16-7). Church of Scient Info.

Conway, Flo & Siegelman, Jim. Holy Terror: The Fundamentalist War on America's Freedoms in Religion, Politics, & Our Private Lives. 504p. 1984. pap. 10.95 (ISBN 0-385-29286-4, Delta). Dell.

Cornelison, Isaac J. The Relation of Religion to Civil Government in the United States. LC 75-107409. (Civil Liberties in American History Ser). 1970. Repr. of 1895 ed. lib. bdg. 45.00 (ISBN 0-306-71890-1). Da Capo.

Curran, Francis X. Catholics in Colonial Law. 1963. 2.95 (ISBN 0-8294-0016-8). Loyola.

Curry, Thomas J. The First Freedoms: The Establishment of Freedom of Religion in America. 288p. 1986. text ed. 24.95x (ISBN 0-19-503661-1). Oxford U Pr.

Dawson, Joseph M. America's Way in Church, State & Society. LC 79-15522. 1980. Repr. of 1953 ed. lib. bdg. 22.50x (ISBN 0-313-22006-9, DAAW). Greenwood.

Eckenrode, Hamilton J. Separation of Church & State in Virginia. LC 75-122164. (Civil Liberties in American History Ser). 1971. Repr. of 1910 ed. lib. bdg. 22.50 (ISBN 0-306-71969-X). Da Capo.

Edel, Wilbur. Defenders of the Faith: Religion & Politics from Pilgrim Fathers to Ronald Reagan. LC 87-2367. 280p. 1987. lib. bdg. 38.95 (ISBN 0-275-92662-1, C2662). Praeger.

Evans, Hiram W. The Rising Storm: An Analysis of the Growing Conflict Over the Political Dilemma of Roman Catholics in America. Grob, Gerald, ed. LC 76-46075. (Anti-Movements in America). 1977. lib. bdg. 27.50x (ISBN 0-405-09948-7). Ayer Co Pubs.

Goldberg, George. Church, State & the Constitution. rev. ed. LC 87-4566. 160p. 1987. 14.95 (ISBN 0-89526-794-2). Regnery Bks.

--Reconsecrating America. 160p. 1984. 9.95 (ISBN 0-8028-3607-0). Eerdmans.

Greene, Evarts B. Religion & the State: The Making & Testing of an American Tradition. LC 75-41122. Repr. of 1941 ed. 17.25 (ISBN 0-404-14548-5). AMS Pr.

Hammar, Richard R. Pastor, Church & Law Supplement. LC 85-82192. 208p. (Orig.). 1986. 6.95 (ISBN 0-88243-582-5, 02-0582). Gospel Pub.

Hart, Roderick P. The Political Pulpit. LC 76-12290. 160p. 1977. 7.95 (ISBN 0-911198-44-X). Purdue U Pr.

Hook, Sidney. Religion in a Free Society. LC 67-11242. xii, 120p. 1967. 10.95x (ISBN 0-8032-0077-3). U of Nebr Pr.

Johnson, Alvin W. & Yost, Frank H. Separation of Church & State in the United States. 279p. Repr. of 1948 ed. lib. bdg. 22.50x (ISBN 0-8371-2436-0, JOCS). Greenwood.

Kauper, Paul G. Religion & the Constitution. LC 64-7898. (Edward Douglass White Lectures). 1964. pap. 6.95x (ISBN 0-8071-0114-1). La State U Pr.

Kelley, Dean M. Government Intervention in Religious Affairs, No. 1. LC 82-355. 224p. (Orig.). 1982. 17.95 (ISBN 0-8298-0602-4); pap. 9.95 (ISBN 0-8298-0434-X). Pilgrim NY.

King, James M. Facing the Twentieth Century. Grob, Gerald, ed. LC 76-46085. (Anti-Movements in America Ser.). (Illus.). 1977. Repr. of 1899 ed. lib. bdg. 54.00x (ISBN 0-405-09958-4). Ayer Co Pubs.

Kurland, Philip B. Church & State: The Supreme Court & the First Amendment. 1975. pap. 5.95x (ISBN 0-226-46402-4). U of Chicago Pr.

Lauer, Paul E. Church & State in New England. LC 78-63809. (Johns Hopkins University. Studies in the Social Sciences. Tenth Ser. 1892: 2-3). Repr. of 1892 ed. 11.50 (ISBN 0-404-61072-2). AMS Pr.

Lee, Francis G. Wall of Controversy. 1986. lib. bdg. 6.50 (ISBN 0-89874-828-3). Krieger.

Lowry, Charles W. To Pray or Not to Pray: A Handbook for Study of Recent Supreme Court Decisions & American Church-State Doctrine. 1969. enlarged ed. 6.00 (ISBN 0-87419-013-4, U Pr of Wash). Larlin Corp.

McLoughlin, William G. New England Dissent, 1630-1833: The Baptists & the Separation of Church & State, 2 vols. LC 70-131464. (Center for the Study of the History of Liberty in America Ser). (Illus.). 1971. Set. 80.00x (ISBN 0-674-61175-6). Harvard U Pr.

Mandelker, Ira L. Religion, Society, & Utopia in Nineteenth-Century America. LC 84-47. 200p. 1984. lib. bdg. 22.00x (ISBN 0-87023-436-6). U of Mass Pr.

Miller, William L. & Cureton, Charles T., eds. Supreme Court Decisions on Church & State. 570p. 1986. pap. 11.95x (ISBN 0-935005-08-0). Ibis Pub VA.

Mumford, Stephen D. American Democracy & the Vatican: Population Growth & National Security. LC 84-72500. 268p. (Orig.). 1984. 11.95 (ISBN 0-931779-00-6); pap. 7.95 (ISBN 0-931779-01-4). Humanist Pr.

Noonan, John T. The Believer & the Powers That Are: Cases, History, & Other Data Bearing on the Relation of Religion & Government. LC 86-28440. 1987. 35.00 (ISBN 0-02-923161-2). Macmillan.

Oaks, Dallin H., ed. Wall Between Church & State. LC 63-20897. 1963. pap. 1.95X (ISBN 0-226-61429-8, P137, Phoen). U of Chicago Pr.

O'Neill, James M. Catholicism & American Freedom. LC 78-21495. 1979. Repr. of 1952 ed. lib. bdg. cancelled (ISBN 0-313-21153-1, ONCA). Greenwood.

O'Neill, James Milton. Religion & Education Under the Constitution. LC 72-171389. (Civil Liberties in American History Ser). 338p. 1972. Repr. of 1949 ed. lib. bdg. 39.50 (ISBN 0-306-70228-2). Da Capo.

Petrie, George. Church & State in Early Maryland. LC 78-63810. (Johns Hopkins University. Studies in the Social Sciences. Tenth Ser. 1892: 4). Repr. of 1892 ed. 11.50 (ISBN 0-404-61073-0). AMS Pr.

--Church & State in Early Maryland. 1973. pap. 9.00. Johnson Repr.

Pfeffer, Leo. Creeds in Competition: A Creative Force in American Culture. LC 78-2308. 1978. Repr. of 1958 ed. lib. bdg. 19.00x (ISBN 0-313-20349-0, PFCC). Greenwood.

Press View the FBI Raid. (Illus.). 1977. pap. 3.00 (ISBN 0-915598-17-5). Church of Scient Info.

Prucha, Francis P. Churches & the Indian Schools, 1888-1912. LC 79-12220. (Illus.). xiv, 278p. 1979. 21.50x (ISBN 0-8032-3657-3). U of Nebr Pr.

Reed, Susan M. Church & State in Massachusetts, 1691-1740. (University of Illinois Studies in the Social Sciences: Vol. 3, No. 4). 210p. Repr. of 1914 ed. 15.00 (ISBN 0-384-50110-9). Johnson Repr.

Richardson, Herbert, ed. Constitutional Issues in the Case of Rev. Moon: Amicus Briefs Presented to the United States Supreme Court. (Studies in Religion & Society: Vol. 10). 710p. 1984. 69.95x (ISBN 0-88946-873-7). E Mellen.

Robbins, Edward M. The Christian Church & the Equal Rights Amendment. Graves, Helen, ed. LC 85-40892. 80p. 1986. pap. 6.95 (ISBN 0-938232-95-9, Dist. by Baker & Taylor Co.). Winston-Derek.

Ronsvalle, John & Ronsvalle, Sylvia. Hidden Billions: The Potential of the Church in the U. S. 175p. (Orig.). 1984. pap. 8.00 (ISBN 0-914527-18-5). C-Four Res.

Rouse, John E., Jr., et al, eds. The Political Role of Religion on the U. S. (Special Study Ser.). 300p. 1985. pap. text ed. 24.50x (ISBN 0-8133-7030-2). Westview.

Rowe, H. Edward. The Day They Padlocked the Church. LC 83-80608. 86p. (Orig.). 1983. pap. 3.50 (ISBN 0-910311-05-6). Huntington Hse Inc.

Schaff, Philip. Church & State in the U. S.; or, the American Idea of Religious Liberty & Its... LC 75-38462. (Religion in America, Ser. 2). 188p. 1972. Repr. of 1888 ed. 17.00 (ISBN 0-405-04083-0). Ayer Co Pubs.

Semonche, John E. Religion & Constitutional Government in the United States: A Historical Overview with Sources. (Constitutional Bookshelf Ser.). 250p. (Orig.). 1985. pap. 14.95 (ISBN 0-930095-09-X). Signal Bks.

Shepherd, William C. To Secure the Blessings of Liberty: American Constitutional Law & the New Religious Movements. 128p. 1985. 12.95 (ISBN 0-8245-0664-2); pap. 8.95 (ISBN 0-8245-0670-7). Crossroad NY.

Shuster, George N. Catholic Spirit in Modern English Literature. facs. ed. LC 67-26785. (Essay Index Reprint Ser). 1922. 20.00 (ISBN 0-8369-0878-3). Ayer Co Pubs.

Smith, Rodney K. Public Prayer & the Constitution: A Case Study in Constitutional Interpretation. 320p. 1987. 35.00 (ISBN 0-8420-2260-0). Scholarly Res Inc.

Sorauf, Frank J. The Wall of Separation: The Constitutional Politics of Church & State. LC 75-3476. 420p. 1976. 40.00x (ISBN 0-691-07574-3). Princeton U Pr.

Spykman, Gordon, et al. Society, State, & Schools: A Case for Structural & Confessional Pluralism. 224p. (Orig.). 1981. pap. 9.95 (ISBN 0-8028-1880-3). Eerdmans.

Stokes, Anson & Pfeffer, Leo. Church & State in the United States. rev. ed. LC 73-15318. 660p. 1975. Repr. of 1964 ed. lib. bdg. 47.50x (ISBN 0-8371-7186-5, STCI). Greenwood.

Stone, Ronald H., ed. Reformed Faith & Politics: Essays Prepared for the Advisory Council on Church & Society of the United Presbyterian Church in the U. S. A. & the Council on Theology & Culture of the Presbyterian Church in the U. S. LC 83-10513. 210p. (Orig.). 1983. lib. bdg. 22.00 (ISBN 0-8191-3295-0); pap. text ed. 8.50 (ISBN 0-8191-3296-9). U Pr of Amer.

Strickland, Reba C. Religion & the State in Georgia in the Eighteenth Century. LC 40-4840. (Columbia University Studies in the Social Sciences: No. 460). Repr. of 1939 ed. 18.50 (ISBN 0-404-51460-X). AMS Pr.

Wald, Kenneth D. Religion & Politics in the United States. LC 86-60659. 304p. 1986. 29.95 (ISBN 0-312-67058-3); pap. 10.00 (ISBN 0-312-67056-7). St Martin.

Weeks, Stephen B. Church & State in North Carolina. LC 78-63820. (Johns Hopkins University. Studies in the Social Sciences. Eleventh Ser. 1893: 6). Repr. of 1893 ed. 11.50 (ISBN 0-404-61082-X). AMS Pr.

--Church & State in North Carolina. pap. 9.00. Johnson Repr.

Weiss, Ann E. God & Government: The Separation of Church & State. 160p. 1982. 8.95 (ISBN 0-395-32085-2). HM.

Wilson, John & Drakeman, Donald, eds. Church & State in American History. 2nd, rev. ed. LC 86-47513. 288p. 1986. pap. 10.95 (ISBN 0-8070-0409-X, BP 728). Beacon Pr.

Wilson, John F., ed. Church & State in America: A Bibliographical Guide (The Colonial & Early National Periods). LC 85-31698. 447p. 1986. 49.95 (ISBN 0-313-25236-X, WNC/). Greenwood.

Wise, John. Vindication of the Government of New-England Churches. Miller, Perry, ed. LC 58-5422. Repr. of 1717 ed. 30.00x (ISBN 0-8201-1246-1). Schol Facsimiles.

Zollman, Carl. American Civil Church Law. LC 79-77996. (Columbia University. Studies in the Social Sciences: No. 181). Repr. of 1917 ed. 30.00 (ISBN 0-404-51181-3). AMS Pr.

CHURCH AND THE WORLD

Here are entered works on the position and responsibilities of the Christian church in secular society.

see also Christianity and Economics; Christianity and International Affairs; Christianity and Politics; Church and Social Problems; History (Theology); Kingdom of God; Sociology, Christian

Adeney, Miriam. God's Foreign Policy. LC 83-25343. 152p. (Orig.). 1984. pap. 6.95 (ISBN 0-8028-1968-0). Eerdmans.

Balasuriya, Tissa. Planetary Theology. LC 83-19339. 352p. (Orig.). 1984. pap. 10.95 (ISBN 0-88344-400-3). Orbis Bks.

Baumgartel, Elise J. The Cultures of Prehistoric Egypt, 2 vols. in 1. LC 80-24186. (Illus.). xxiii, 286p. 1981. Repr. of 1955 ed. lib. bdg. 60.00x (ISBN 0-313-22524-9, BACU). Greenwood.

Bea, Augustin. Church & Mankind. 6.50 (ISBN 0-8199-0012-5, L38112). Franciscan Herald.

Beales, D. & Best, G., eds. History, Society & the Churches: Essays in Honour of Owen Chadwick. 335p. 1985. 49.50 (ISBN 0-521-25486-8). Cambridge U Pr.

Beals, Art. Beyond Hunger: A Biblical Mandate for Social Responsibility. LC 85-4912. (Critical Concern Ser.). 1985. 11.95 (ISBN 0-88070-098-X). Multnomah.

Butterfield, Herbert. Writing on Christianity & History. 1979. 19.95x (ISBN 0-19-502454-0). Oxford U Pr.

Cardinale, H. E. Orders of Knighthood, Awards & the Holy See: A Historical Juridical & Practical Compendium. 3rd, rev., enl. ed. 1985. text ed. 55.00x (ISBN 0-905715-26-8). Humanities.

The Church in a Changing Society. 508p. (Orig.). 1979. pap. text ed. 35.00x (ISBN 91-8558-207-7). Coronet Bks.

Church of Christ Staff. What Lack We Yet? Thomas, J. D., ed. LC 74-170920. 319p. 1974. 13.95 (ISBN 0-89112-027-0, Bibl Res Pr). Abilene Christ U.

Clarke, Peter. A Free Church in a Free Society: The Ecclesiology of John England Bishop of Charleston, 1820-1842. 561p. 1983. (Pub. by John England Stud Inc); pap. 15.95x (ISBN 0-87921-073-7). Attic Pr.

Colson, Charles. The Role of the Church in Society. 48p. 1986. 1.95 (ISBN 0-89693-167-6). Victor Bks.

Colson, Charles, et al. Christianity in Conflict: The Struggle for Christian Integrity & Freedom in Secular Culture. Williamson, Peter S. & Perrotta, Kevin, eds. 180p. (Orig.). 1986. pap. 7.95 (ISBN 0-89283-292-4). Servant.

Danielou, Jean. Prayer As a Political Problem. Kirwan, J. R., ed. 1967. 3.50 (ISBN 0-8362-0278-3, Pub. by Sheed). Guild Bks.

Devine, George, ed. A World More Human: A Church More Christian. 204p. 1984. pap. text ed. 9.50 (ISBN 0-8191-3851-7, College Theo Soc). U Pr of Amer.

Dumoulin, Heinrich. Christianity Meets Buddhism. Maraldo, John C., tr. from Ger. LC 73-82783. 212p. 1974. 19.95 (ISBN 0-87548-121-3). Open Court.

Duquoc, Christian, ed. Spirituality in the Secular City. LC 66-30386. (Concilium Ser.: Vol. 19). 192p. 7.95 (ISBN 0-8091-0140-8). Paulist Pr.

El Morya. Encyclical on World Good Will. 1963. 1.50 (ISBN 0-685-79130-0). Summit Univ.

Engel, James F. & Norton, Wilbert H. What's Gone Wrong with the Harvest? 192p. 1975. pap. 7.95 (ISBN 0-310-24161-8, 18417P). Zondervan.

Enroth, Ronald M. & Melton, Gordon J. Why Cults Succeed Where the Church Fails. 128p. 1985. 6.95 (ISBN 0-87178-932-9). Brethren.

Giordani, Igino. Social Message of the Early Church Fathers. 1977. 3.95 (ISBN 0-8198-0469-X); pap. 2.95 (ISBN 0-8198-0470-3). Dghtrs St Paul.

Hargrave, Vessie D. The Church & World Missions. 128p. 1970. 5.25 (ISBN 0-87148-152-9); pap. 4.25 (ISBN 0-87148-153-7). Pathway Pr.

Hessel, Dieter T. Social Ministry. LC 82-6960. 228p. 1982. pap. 10.95 (ISBN 0-664-24422-X). Westminster.

Holmes, Arthur F. Contours of a World View. Henry, Carl F., ed. (Studies in a Christian World View: Vol. 1). 256p. 1983. pap. 8.95 (ISBN 0-8028-1957-5). Eerdmans.

Jasper, Tony. Jesus & the Christian in a Pop Culture. 224p. 1984. 29.00x (ISBN 0-947728-02-3, Pub. by R Royce Ltd Publ England). State Mutual Bk.

Johnston, Robert K. Evangelicals at an Impasse: Biblical Authority in Practice. pap. 3.99 (ISBN 0-8042-2038-7). John Knox.

Krutza, William J. & Dicicco, Philip P. Facing the Issues, No. 1. (Contemporary Discussion Ser.). 1969. pap. 3.50 (ISBN 0-8010-5325-0). Baker Bk.

--Facing the Issues, No. 2. (Contemporary Discussion Ser.). pap. 3.50 (ISBN 0-8010-5326-9). Baker Bk.

--Facing the Issues, No. 3. (Contemporary Discussion Ser.). (Orig.). 1970. pap. 3.50 (ISBN 0-8010-5300-5). Baker Bk.

--Facing the Issues, No. 4. (Contemporary Discussion Ser.). (Orig.). 1971. pap. 3.50 (ISBN 0-8010-5310-2). Baker Bk.

Lefever, Ernest W. Amsterdam to Nairobi: The World Council of Churches & the Third World. 128p. 1985. pap. text ed. 7.50 (ISBN 0-8191-4484-3). U Pr of Amer.

Lundquist, Carl H. Silent Issues of the Church. 156p. 1985. pap. 5.95 (ISBN 0-89693-721-6). Victor Bks.

McCan, Robert L. World Economy & World Hunger: The Response of the Churches. 119p. 1982. 16.00 (ISBN 0-89093-497-5); pap. 5.00. U Pubns Amer.

Marty, Martin E. The Public Church: Mainline-Evangelical-Catholic. 192p. 1981. 10.95 (ISBN 0-8245-0019-9). Crossroad NY.

Merton, Thomas. Contemplation in a World of Action. 400p. 1973. pap. 5.50 (ISBN 0-385-02550-5, Im). Doubleday.

Metz, Johannes B. Theology of the World. 1969. pap. 3.95 (ISBN 0-8245-0396-1). Crossroad NY.

Miller, Kenneth R. & Wilson, Mary E. The Church That Cares. LC 85-14786. 96p. 1985. pap. 6.95 (ISBN 0-8170-1087-4). Judson.

Morano, Roy W. The Protestant Challenge to Corporate America: Issues of Social Responsibility. Farmer, Richard, ed. LC 84-8514. (Research for Business Decisions Ser.: No. 69). 256p. 1984. 44.95 (ISBN 0-8357-1592-2). UMI Res Pr.

Nash, Ronald H., ed. Social Justice & the Christian Church. 1986. pap. 7.95 (ISBN 0-8010-6746-4). Baker Bk.

Pastoral Constitution on the Church in the Modern World (Gaudium et Spes) 138p. 1965. pap. 3.95 (ISBN 1-55586-015-X). US Catholic.

Pettitt, Walter R. The Evangelism Ministry of the Local Church. 119p. 1969. 5.25 (ISBN 0-87148-276-2); pap. 4.25 (ISBN 0-87148-277-0). Pathway Pr.

Phan, Peter C. Social Thought. (Message of the Fathers of the Church Ser.: Vol. 20). 15.95 (ISBN 0-89453-360-6); pap. 9.95 (ISBN 0-89453-331-2). M Glazier.

Robbins, John W. War & Peace: A Christian Foreign Policy. (Trinity Papers: No. 1). 250p. (Orig.). 1987. pap. 8.95 (ISBN 0-940931-21-4). Trinity Found.

Rose, Larry L., et al. An Urban World. LC 84-12649. 1984. pap. 8.95 (ISBN 0-8054-6339-9). Broadman.

Safranski, Scott R. Managing God's Organization: The Catholic Church in Society. Farmer, Richard, ed. LC 85-16540. (Research for Business Decisions: No. 79). 200p. 1985. 44.95 (ISBN 0-8357-1669-4). UMI Res Pr.

Scherer, James A. Global Living Here & Now. 1974. pap. 2.25 (ISBN 0-377-00003-5). Friend Pr.

Snyder, Howard A. Liberating the Church: The Ecology of Church & Kingdom. 280p. (Orig.). 1982. pap. 8.95 (ISBN 0-87784-385-6); cloth 12.95 (ISBN 0-87784-894-7). Inter-Varsity.

Spong, John S. Into the Whirlwind: The Future of the Church. 224p. 1983. 9.95 (ISBN 0-86683-899-6, HarpR). Har-Row.

Toton, Suzanne C. World Hunger: The Responsibility of Christian Education. LC 81-16906. 224p. (Orig.). 1982. pap. 7.95 (ISBN 0-88344-716-9). Orbis Bks.

Tozer, A. W. Gems from Tozer. 96p. 1979. pap. 2.45 (ISBN 0-87509-163-6). Chr Pubns.

Verkuyl, Johannes. Break down the Walls: Christian Cry for Racial Justice. Smedes, Lewis B., ed. LC 72-93620. pap. 41.50 (ISBN 0-317-07869-0, 2012924). Bks Demand UMI.

Webber, Robert E. The Church in the World. 368p. (Orig.). 1986. pap. text ed. 11.95 (ISBN 0-310-36601-1, 12213P). Zondervan.

Webster, John C. & Webster, Ellen L., eds. The Church & Women in the Third World. LC 84-26967. 168p. (Orig.). 1985. pap. 11.95 (ISBN 0-664-24601-X). Westminster.

Westerhoff, John H., III. Living the Faith Community: The Church That Makes a Difference. 1985. pap. cancelled (ISBN 0-317-18159-9). Whitaker Hse.

Westheimer, Karl. Humanity's Contemporary Moral Decay & the Historical Role of the Catholic Church. LC 73-76434. (Illus.). 132p. 1973. 43.40 (ISBN 0-913314-19-6). Am Classical Coll Pr.

Williams, George H. The Law of Nations & the Book of Nature. Franklin, R. W., ed. LC 84-72274. (New Essays in Christian Humanism: Vol. 1). (Illus.). 60p. (Orig.). 1985. pap. 4.95x (ISBN 0-9613867-0-3). St Johns Univ Christ Hum.

Wood, Herbert G. Christianity & Civilisation. LC 73-17694. 128p. 1973. Repr. of 1943 ed. lib. bdg. 13.00x (ISBN 0-374-98713-0, Octagon). Hippocrene Bks.

CHURCH AND WAR

see War and Religion

CHURCH ANNIVERSARIES

Johnson, Alvin D. Celebrating Your Church Anniversary. LC 68-28077. 1968. pap. 3.95 (ISBN 0-8170-0408-4). Judson.

CHURCH ANTIQUITIES

see Christian Antiquities

CHURCH ARCHITECTURE

see also Abbeys; Architecture, Cistercian; Architecture, Gothic; Cathedrals; Chapels; Church Decoration and Ornament; Vaults

Abrams, Barbara C. Estates of Grace: The Architectural Heritage of Religious Structures in Rye, N. Y. Morison, Susan A., intro. by. (Illus.). 20p. (Orig.). 1986. pap. text ed. 4.00 (ISBN 0-9615327-1-8). Rye Hist Soc.

Architectural Record Magazine Staff. Religious Buildings. 1980. 43.50 (ISBN 0-07-002342-5). McGraw.

Child, Mark. Discovering Church Architecture. (Discovering Ser.: No. 214). (Illus., Orig.). 1984. pap. 3.50 (ISBN 0-85263-328-9, Pub. by Shire Pubns England). Seven Hills Bks.

Downs, Barry. Sacred Places: Religious Architecture of the 18th & 19th Centuries in British Columbia. LC 81-670050. (Illus.). 160p. 1980. 29.95 (ISBN 0-295-95774-3, Pub. by Douglas & McIntyre Canada). U of Wash Pr.

Durantis, Gulielmus. Symbolism of Churches & Church Ornaments: A Translation of the First Book of the Rationale Divinorum Officiorum. Neale, John M. & Webb, Benjamin, eds. Repr. of 1843 ed. 28.00 (ISBN 0-404-04653-3). AMS Pr.

Gunter, Christopher L. The Intelligent Understanding of Sculptures & Mosaics in the Early Church. (Illus.). 138p. 1982. 75.45 (ISBN 0-86650-037-5). Gloucester Art.

Heath, Sidney. The Romance of Symbolism & Its Relation to Church Ornament & Architecture. LC 70-174054. (Illus.). 1976. Repr. of 1909 ed. 40.00x (ISBN 0-8103-4302-9). Gale.

Holly, Henry H. Church Architecture. 1980. lib. bdg. 75.00 (ISBN 0-8490-3141-9). Gordon Pr.

Leask, Harold G. Irish Churches & Monastic Buildings, 3 Vols. Vol. I: First Phases & Romanesque, 173p. 16.95 (ISBN 0-85221-016-7); Vol. II: Gothic to A.D. 1400, 162p. 16.95 (ISBN 0-85221-011-6). Dufour.

Macaulay, David. Cathedral. (Illus.). 1981. pap. 6.95 (ISBN 0-395-31668-5); prepack of 10 59.50 (ISBN 0-395-31766-5). HM.

Martin, W. W. Manual of Ecclesiastical Architecture. 1977. lib. bdg. 75.00 (ISBN 0-8490-2206-1). Gordon Pr.

Marvel, Thomas S. & Moreno, Maria L. La Arquitectura de los Templos Parroquiales de Puerto Rico - Architecture of Parish Churches in Puerto Rico. bilingual ed. LC 81-10291. (Illus.). 1984. pap. 10.00 (ISBN 0-8477-2114-0). U of PR Pr.

Norton, Charles E. Historical Studies of Church-Building in the Middle Ages: Venice, Siena, Florence. LC 78-15869. 1978. Repr. of 1880 ed. lib. bdg. 35.00 (ISBN 0-89341-361-5). Longwood Pub Group.

Payne, Suzzy C. & Murwin, Susan A. Creative American Quilting Inspired by the Bible. (Illus.). 192p. 1982. 18.95 (ISBN 0-8007-1402-4). Revell.

Smith, T. Roger & Slater, John. Architecture, Classic & Early Christian. 1980. Repr. of 1893 ed. lib. bdg. 35.00 (ISBN 0-89341-364-X). Longwood Pub Group.

Sovik, Edward A. Architecture for Worship. LC 73-78254. (Illus.). 112p. (Orig.). 1973. pap. 5.95 (ISBN 0-8066-1320-3, 10-0425). Augsburg.

Stell, C. Hallelujah: Recording Chapels & Meeting Houses. (Illus.). 48p. 1985. pap. text ed. 7.95 (ISBN 0-906780-49-7, Pub. by Council British Archaeology). Humanities.

Vance, Mary. Monographs on Church Architecture, 2 vols. (Architecture Ser.: Bibliography A1209). 249p. 1984. Set. pap. 20.00 (ISBN 0-89028-019-3). Vance Biblios.

Vosko, Richard S. Through the Eye of a Rose Window: A Perspective on the Environment for Worship. 1981. pap. text ed. 7.95 (ISBN 0-89390-028-1). Resource Pubns.

Ward, Clarence. Mediaeval Church Vaulting. LC 72-177847. Repr. of 1915 ed. 19.50 (ISBN 0-404-06836-7). AMS Pr.

Withers, Frederick C. Church Architecture. 1980. lib. bdg. 64.95 (ISBN 0-8490-3198-2). Gordon Pr.

CHURCH ARCHITECTURE–DESIGNS AND PLANS

Davies, J. G. Temples, Churches & Mosques: A Guide to the Appreciation of Religious Architecture. LC 82-13130. (Illus.). 256p. 1982. 27.50 (ISBN 0-8298-0634-2). Pilgrim NY.

Hayes, Bartlett. Tradition Becomes Innovation: Modern Religious Architecture in America. LC 82-18581. (Illus.). 176p. 1982. 27.50 (ISBN 0-8298-0635-0); pap. 12.95 (ISBN 0-8298-0624-5). Pilgrim NY.

Ray, David R. Small Churches Are the Right Size. LC 82-11256. 224p. (Orig.). 1982. pap. 7.95 (ISBN 0-8298-0620-2). Pilgrim NY.

Sweeney, Patrick & Crewe, Sarah. Visionary Spires: The Most Beatiful Churches That Never Were. LC 85-43038. (Illus.). 144p. 1985. 25.00 (ISBN 0-8478-0660-X). Rizzoli Intl.

CHURCH ARCHITECTURE–DETAILS

Evans, E. P. Animal Symbolism in Ecclesiastical Architecture. 59.95 (ISBN 0-87968-638-3). Gordon Pr.

CHURCH ARCHITECTURE–HISTORY

Bouyer, Louis. Liturgy & Architecture. 1967. 6.95x (ISBN 0-268-00159-6). U of Notre Dame Pr.

Curcic, Slobodan. Gracanica: King Milutin's Church & Its Place in Late Byzantine Architecture. LC 79-11984. (Illus.). 1980. 34.95x (ISBN 0-271-00218-2). Pa St U Pr.

Gimpel, Jean. The Cathedral Builders. Waugh, Teresa, tr. LC 84-47572. (Illus.). 192p. 1984. pap. 8.95 (ISBN 0-06-091158-1, CN 1158, PL). Har-Row.

Liscombe, Rhodri W. The Church Architecture of Robert Mills. (Illus.). 160p. 1985. 30.00 (ISBN 0-89308-542-1). Southern Hist Pr.

Otto, Christian F. Space into Light: The Churches of Balthasar Neumann. (Illus.). 1979. 55.00x (ISBN 0-262-15019-0). MIT Pr.

Short, Ernest H. The House of God: A History of Religious Architecture & Symbolism. 75.00 (ISBN 0-8490-0374-1). Gordon Pr.

CHURCH ARCHITECTURE–EUROPE

Here are entered works about church architecture in Europe as a whole, as well as those about specific European countries.

Buxton, David. The Wooden Churches of Eastern Europe: An Introductory Survey. (Illus.). 384p. 1982. 90.00 (ISBN 0-521-23786-6). Cambridge U Pr.

Hardy, Paul E. & Bishop of Exeter. A Guide to the Preservation of Medieval Cathedrals & Churches. LC 82-14257. (Illus.). 160p. 1983. pap. text ed. 16.95 (ISBN 0-582-30514-4, Construction Press). Longman.

Roggenkamp. Stave Churches in Norway. 17.95 (ISBN 0-85440-205-5). Anthroposophic.

CHURCH ARCHITECTURE–FRANCE

Adams, Henry B. Mont-Saint-Michel & Chartres. LC 82-14018. 408p. 1982. 25.00 (ISBN 0-89783-019-9). Larlin Corp.

Jantzen, Hans. High Gothic. LC 83-43099. (Illus.). 196p. 1984. 25.00x (ISBN 0-691-04026-5); pap. 7.95x (ISBN 0-691-00372-6). Princeton U Pr.

Martene, Edmond & Durand, Ursin. Voyage Litteraire de Deux Benedictins de la Congregation de Saint-Maur, 2 vols. 1042p. Repr. of 1717 ed. text ed. 207.00x (ISBN 0-576-99707-2, Pub. by Gregg Intl Pubs England). Gregg Intl.

Sieur de Moleon. Voyages Liturgiques de France. 694p. Repr. of 1718 ed. text ed. 165.60x (ISBN 0-576-99713-7, Pub. by Gregg Intl Pubs England). Gregg Intl.

Stoddard, Whitney S. Art & Architecture in Medieval France. (Icon Editions Ser.). Orig. Title: Monastery & Cathedral in Medieval France. (Illus.). 436p. 1972. pap. 14.95xi (ISBN 0-06-430022-6, IN-22, HarpT). Har-Row.

--Monastery & Cathedral in France: Medieval Architecture, Sculpture, Stained Glass, Manuscripts, the Art of the Church Treasuries. LC 66-23923. 412p. 1966. 35.00x (ISBN 0-8195-3071-9). Wesleyan U Pr.

CHURCH ARCHITECTURE–GREAT BRITAIN

Bond, Francis. An Introduction to English Church Architecture: From the 11th to the 16th Century. LC 77-94546. 1979. Repr. of 1908 ed. lib. bdg. 25.00 (ISBN 0-89341-225-2). Longwood Pub Group.

Braun, Hugh. Parish Churches: Their Architectural Development in England. 1970. 12.50 (ISBN 0-571-09045-1). Transatl Arts.

Butler, L. A. & Morris, R. K., eds. The Anglo-Saxon Church: Papers on History, Architecture, & Archaeology in Honor of Dr. H. M. Taylor. (Research Report Ser.: No. 60). (Illus.). 240p. 1986. pap. 45.00x (ISBN 0-906780-54-3, Pub. by Council British Archaelogy). Humanities.

Clinch, George. Old English Churches: Their Architecture, Furniture, Decorations & Monuments. 1977. lib. bdg. 59.95 (ISBN 0-8490-2368-8). Gordon Pr.

--Old English Churches: Their Architecture, Furniture, Decoration & Monuments. LC 77-94552. 1978. Repr. of 1900 ed. lib. bdg. 30.00 (ISBN 0-89341-221-X). Longwood Pub Group.

Coulton, George G. Art & the Reformation. LC 69-15789. (Illus.). xxii, 662p. 1969. Repr. of 1928 ed. 45.00 (ISBN 0-208-00738-5, Archon). Shoe String.

Cox, J. Charles. The English Parish Church. (Illus.). 1977. Repr. of 1914 ed. 25.00x (ISBN 0-7158-1174-6). Charles River Bks.

Kemp, Brian. English Church Monuments. 240p. 1980. 45.00 (ISBN 0-7134-1735-8, Pub. by Batsford England). David & Charles.

McAleer, J. Phillip. The Romanesque Church Facade in Britain. LC 83-48699. (Theses from the Courtauld Institute of Art Ser.). (Illus.). 785p. 1984. lib. bdg. 80.00 (ISBN 0-8240-5979-4). Garland Pub.

Moore, Charles H. The Mediaeval Church Architecture of England. facsimile ed. LC 74-37900. (Select Bibliographies Reprint Ser). Repr. of 1912 ed. 29.00 (ISBN 0-8369-6738-0). Ayer Co Pubs.

Platt, Colin. The Abbeys & Priories of Medieval England. LC 84-80387. (Illus.). xvii, 270p. 1984. 32.50 (ISBN 0-8232-1117-7); pap. 19.95 (ISBN 0-8232-1118-5). Fordham.

Spence, Keith & McVeigh, Shaun. Cathedrals & Abbeys of England & Wales. (Blue Guides Ser.). (Illus.). 1984. 29.95 (ISBN 0-393-01664-1); pap. 16.95 (ISBN 0-393-30071-4). Norton.

CHURCH ARCHITECTURE–ITALY

Johnson, Eugene J. S. Andrea in Mantua: The Building. LC 74-30085. (Illus.). 220p. 1975. 42.50x (ISBN 0-271-01186-6). Pa St U Pr.

Lewis, Douglas. The Late Baroque Churches of Venice. LC 78-94704. (Outstanding Dissertations in the Fine Arts Ser.). 1979. lib. bdg. 63.00 (ISBN 0-8240-3236-5). Garland Pub.

Norton, Charles E. Historical Studies of Church-Building in the Middle Ages. LC 78-95072. (Select Bibliographies Reprint Ser.). 1902. 32.00 (ISBN 0-8369-5072-0). Ayer Co Pubs.

--Historical Studies of Church Building in the Middle Ages: Venice, Sienna, Florence. 1977. lib. bdg. 39.95 (ISBN 0-8490-1962-1). Gordon Pr.

Smith, Christine. The Baptistery of Pisa. LC 77-94715. (Outstanding Dissertations in the Fine Arts Ser.). (Illus.). 432p. 1978. lib. bdg. 53.00 (ISBN 0-8240-3249-7). Garland Pub.

Wittkower, Rudolf. Gothic Vs. Classic: Architectural Projects in Seventeenth-Century Italy. LC 73-79607. (Illus.). 192p. 1974. 12.50 (ISBN 0-8076-0704-5); pap. 4.95 (ISBN 0-8076-0705-3). Braziller.

CHURCH ARCHITECTURE–MEXICO

The Open-Air Churches of Sixteenth-Century Mexico: Atrios, Posas, Open Chapels, & Other Studies. LC 63-17205. pap. 160.00 (ISBN 0-317-10003-3, 2003001). Bks Demand UMI.

CHURCH ARCHITECTURE–PALESTINE

Mader, Andreas E. Altchristliche Basiliken und Lokaltraditionen in Sudjudaa. pap. 19.00 (ISBN 0-384-35000-3). Johnson Repr.

CHURCH ARCHITECTURE–SPAIN

Cram, R. A. Folio. 1932. 22.00 (ISBN 0-527-01687-X). Kraus Repr.

Frischauer, A. S. Altspanischer Kirchenbau. (Studien zur spaetantiken Kunstgeschichte, Vol. 3). (Illus.). x, 100p. 1978. Repr. of 1930 ed. 58.80x (ISBN 3-11-005703-4). De Gruyter.

Street, George E. Gothic Architecture in Spain, 2 Vols. King, Georgiana G., ed. LC 68-56490. (Illus.). 1968. Repr. of 1914 ed. Set. 55.00 (ISBN 0-405-09008-0); 27.50 ea. Vol. 1 (ISBN 0-405-09009-9). Vol. 2 (ISBN 0-405-09010-2). Ayer Co Pubs.

Whittlesey, A. Minor Ecclesiastical, Domestic & Garden Architecture of Southern Spain. 1976. lib. bdg. 75.00 (ISBN 0-8490-2259-2). Gordon Pr.

CHURCH ARCHITECTURE–UNITED STATES

Andrew, Laurel B. The Early Temples of the Mormons: The Architecture of the Millennial Kingdom in the American West. LC 77-23971. (Illus.). 1978. 29.50 (ISBN 0-87395-358-4). State U NY Pr.

Mutrux, Robert. Great New England Churches: Sixty-Five Houses of Worship That Changed Our Lives. LC 81-80425. (Illus.). 288p. (Orig.). 1981. pap. 14.95 (ISBN 0-87106-950-4). Globe Pequot.

Pogzeba, Wolfgang & Overbeck, Joy. Ranchos De Taos: San Francisco De Asis Church. LC 81-82257. (Illus.). 68p. (Orig.). 1981. pap. 7.95 (ISBN 0-913504-66-1). Lowell Pr.

Robison, R. Warren. Louisiana Church Architecture. LC 84-70619. (USL Architecture Ser.: No. 2). 90p. 1984. 19.95 (ISBN 0-940984-20-2). U of SW LA Ctr LA Studies.

Upjohn, Everard M. Richard Upjohn, Architect & Churchman. LC 68-26119. (Architecture & Decorative Art Ser). (Illus.). 1968. Repr. of 1939 ed. lib. bdg. 45.00 (ISBN 0-306-71043-9). Da Capo.

Young, Mary E. & Attoe, Wayne. Places of Worship-Milwaukee. (Publications in Architecture & Urban Planning Ser.). (Illus.). viii, 112p. 1977. 10.00 (ISBN 0-938744-46-1, R77-1). U of Wis Ctr Arch Urban.

CHURCH ATTENDANCE

see also Public Worship

Gentle, Jimmie & Richard, Dwight Peter. Programmed Guide to Increasing Church Attendance. 1980. 10.75 (ISBN 0-89536-446-8, 1641). CSS of Ohio.

Henderson, Robert T. Beating the Church Going Blahs. LC 86-21338. 132p. 1986. pap. 5.95 (ISBN 0-87784-516-6). Inter Varsity.

Hunter, George, 3rd. The Contagious Congregation: Frontiers in Evangelism & Church Growth. LC 78-12322. 1979. pap. 6.95 (ISBN 0-687-09490-9). Abingdon.

Irwin, Kevin W. Sunday Worship. 1983. pap. 14.95 (ISBN 0-916134-52-0). Pueblo Pub Co.

Lawson, LeRoy. The Family of God: The Meaning of Church Membership. LC 80-53497. 64p. (Orig.). 1981. pap. 1.50 (ISBN 0-87239-432-8, 39970). Standard Pub.

Mains, David. Making Church More Enjoyable. (Chapel Talks Ser.). 64p. 0.95 (ISBN 0-89191-256-8, 52563). Cook.
Maney, Thomas. Basic Communities: A Practical Guide for Renewing Neighborhood Churches. 96p. (Orig.). 1984. pap. 5.95 (ISBN 0-86683-857-0, 8411, HarpR). Har-Row.
Perry, Earl & Perry, Wilma. Puppets Go to Church. 85p. 1975. pap. 2.50 (ISBN 0-8341-0385-0). Beacon Hill.
Roberts, Donald L. The Practicing Church. LC 1-67318. 100p. (Orig.). 1981. pap. 2.95 (ISBN 0-87509-303-5). Chr Pubns.

CHURCH BELLS
see Bells

CHURCH BIOGRAPHY
see Christian Biography

CHURCH BUILDINGS
see Church Architecture; Churches

CHURCH BULLETINS
De Jong, Benjamin R. Uncle Ben's Instant Clip Quotes. 128p. 1985. pap. 5.95 (ISBN 0-8010-2954-6). Baker Bk.
Eisenberg, Helen & Eisenberg, Larry. More Bulletin Boards-ers. 1984. 5.25 (ISBN 0-89536-704-1, 4887). CSS of Ohio.
Jackson, Phil. Ready to Use Cartoons for Church Publications. 160p. 1987. pap. price not set (ISBN 0-8010-5221-1). Baker Bk.
Knight, George W. Church Bulletin Bits 3. 128p. 1987. pap. 4.95 (ISBN 0-8010-5479-6). Baker Bk.
--Clip Art Features for Church Newsletters. 1984. pap. 4.50 (ISBN 0-8010-5465-6). Baker Bk.
--Clip-Art Features for Church Newsletters, No. 2. (Illus.). 96p. 1986. pap. 4.95 (ISBN 0-8010-5471-0). Baker Bk.
Knight, George W., compiled By. Church Bulletin Bits, No. 2. 144p. (Orig.). 1980. pap. 4.50 (ISBN 0-8010-5424-9). Baker Bk.
--Clip-Art Sentence Sermons for Church Publications. 96p. 1986. pap. 3.95 (ISBN 0-8010-5475-3). Baker Bk.
--Instant Cartoons for Church Newsletters, No. 1. 4.95 (ISBN 0-8010-5451-6). Baker Bk.
--Instant Cartoons for Church Newsletters, No. 3. 1986. pap. 4.95 (ISBN 0-8010-5473-7). Baker Bk.
Lambert, Gussie. Bulletin Builders. 3.95 (ISBN 0-89315-024-X). Lambert Bk.
McKenzie, E. C. Quips & Quotes for Church Bulletins. (Direction Bks). 1978. pap. 2.95 (ISBN 0-8010-6059-1). Baker Bk.

CHURCH CALENDAR
see also Chronology, Ecclesiastical; Church Year; Fasts and Feasts; Saints–Calendar
Buckland, Patricia B. Advent to Pentecost-A History of the Church Year. 1979. pap. 4.95 (ISBN 0-8192-1251-2). Morehouse.
Bushong, Ann B. A Guide to the Lectionary. 1978. pap. 5.95 (ISBN 0-8164-2156-0, HarpR). Har-Row.
Cronin, Gaynell B. Holy Days & Holidays: Prayer Celebrations with Children. rev. ed. 112p. 1985. pap. 7.95 (ISBN 0-86683-226-2, HarpR). Har-Row.
Foley, Leonard. Saint of the Day: A Life & Lesson for Each of the 173 Saints of the New Missal, Vol. 2. (Illus.). 160p. 1975. pap. 3.50 (ISBN 0-912228-20-2). St Anthony Mess Pr.
Henel, Heinrich. Studien Zum Altenglischen Computus. 1934. pap. 8.00 (ISBN 0-384-22300-1). Johnson Repr.
Makris, Kallistos. The God-Inspired Orthodox Julian Calendar VS. the False Gregorian Papal Calendar. Vlesmas, Jerry, tr. from Hellenic. 118p. (Orig.). 1971. pap. 3.25x (ISBN 0-938366-36-X). Orthodox Chr.
Neufelder, Jerome. The Church Year in Prayer. LC 84-62162. 200p. (Orig.). 1985. pap. 7.95 (ISBN 0-87973-729-8, 729). Our Sunday Visitor.
Nineteen Eighty-Eight Liturgical Calendar & Ordo. (Liturgical Calendar & Ordo Ser.). 120p. (Orig.). 1987. pap. 7.50 (ISBN 1-55586-141-5). US Catholic.
Nordtvedt, Matilda & Steinkuehler, Pearl. Programs for Special Occasions. (Orig.). 1984. pap. 4.95 (ISBN 0-8024-1218-1). Moody.
O'Malley, John. Fifth Week. LC 75-43583. 1976. 2.95 (ISBN 0-8294-0248-9). Loyola.
Porter, H. Boone. Keeping the Church Year. 1978. pap. 5.95 (ISBN 0-8164-2161-7, HarpR). Har-Row.
Sakkas, Basil Priest. The Calendar Question. 96p. (Orig.). 1973. pap. 4.00 (ISBN 0-317-30294-9). Holy Trinity.

CHURCH CAMPS
Dieleman, Dale. Our Life & Times. 1985. pap. 5.95 (ISBN 0-8010-2951-1). Baker Bk.
Genne, Elizabeth & Genne, William. Church Family Camps & Conferences. LC 78-24395. 1979. pap. 2.95 (ISBN 0-8170-0818-7). Judson.
Larsen, Sandy. Sticking Together: Friendships for Life. (Bible Discovery Guides for Teen Campers Ser.). 32p. (Orig.). (YA) 1987. pap. 1.50 camper (ISBN 0-87788-787-X); pap. 1.50 counselor (ISBN 0-87788-788-8). Shaw Pubs.
Mattson, Lloyd. Build Your Church Through Camping. 48p. (Orig.). 1984. pap. 1.95 (ISBN 0-942684-06-0). Camp Guidepts.
--The Camp Couselor. (Illus.). 192p. 1984. pap. 3.95 (ISBN 0-942684-02-8). Camp Guidepts.
Mattson, Lloyd & Graendorf, Werner. Introduction to Christian Camping. Rev. ed. (Illus.). pap. 7.95 (ISBN 0-942684-07-9). Camp Guidepts.
Mattson, Lloyd, ed. God's Good Earth. (Illus.). 224p. (Orig.). 1985. pap. 25.00 (ISBN 0-942684-09-5). Camp Guidepts.

CHURCH CHARITIES
see also subdivision Charities under names of religions, religious denominations, etc., e.g. Catholic Church–Charities
Durnbaugh, Donald F., ed. Every Need Supplied: Mutual Aid & Christian Community in Free Churches, 1525-1675. LC 73-94279. (Documents in Free Church History Ser.: No. 1). (Illus.). 258p. 1974. 19.95 (ISBN 0-87722-031-X). Temple U Pr.
Prelinger, Catherine M. Charity, Challenge, & Change: Religious Dimensions of the Mid-Nineteenth Century Women's Movement in Germany. LC 86-19432. (Contributions in Women's Studies Ser.: No. 75). 225p. 1987. lib. bdg. 29.95 (ISBN 0-313-25401-X, PCY). Greenwood.
Rohrer, Norman. Open Arms. 256p. (Orig.). 1987. pap. 6.95 (ISBN 0-8423-4754-2). Tyndale.

CHURCH CHRONOLOGY
see Chronology, Ecclesiastical

CHURCH COLLEGES
see also Church and College
Christian College Coalition Staff. A Guide to Christian Colleges 1984-85. rev. ed. 160p. 1984. pap. 12.95 (ISBN 0-8028-0010-6). Eerdmans.
Patton, Leslie K. The Purpose of Church-Related Colleges. LC 78-177145. (Columbia University. Studies in the Social Sciences: No. 783). Repr. of 1940 ed. 22.50 (ISBN 0-404-55783-X). AMS Pr.

CHURCH COMMITTEES
see also Parish Councils
Fransen, Paul. Effective Church Councils: Leadership Styles & Decision Making in the Church. (Administration Series for Churches). 56p. (Orig.). 1985. pap. 3.95 (ISBN 0-8066-2198-2, 10-2023). Augsburg.
Troeh, M. Richard & Troeh, Marjorie. The Conferring Church. 1987. pap. 10.00 (ISBN 0-8309-0465-4). Herald Hse.

CHURCH COSTUME
see Church Vestments

CHURCH COUNCILS
see Councils and Synods

CHURCH COURTS
see Ecclesiastical Courts

CHURCH DECORATION AND ORNAMENT
see also Altarpieces; Altars; Christian Art and Symbolism; Church Furniture; Flower Arrangement in Churches; Glass Painting and Staining; Mosaics; Mural Painting and Decoration
Cahn, Walter. The Romanesque Wooden Doors of Auvergne. LC 74-15391. (College Art Association Monograph Ser.: Vol. 30). (Illus.). 225p. 1985. Repr. of 1974 ed. 30.00x (ISBN 0-271-00400-2). Pa St U Pr.
Clinch, George. Old English Churches: Their Architecture, Furniture, Decorations & Monuments. 1977. lib. bdg. 59.95 (ISBN 0-8490-2368-8). Gordon Pr.
Durantis, Gulielmus. The Symbolism of Churches & Church Ornaments. 1980. lib. bdg. 64.95 (ISBN 0-8490-3166-4). Gordon Pr.
Grant, Sandy. Celebrate the Church. 80p. 1987. pap. 5.95 (ISBN 1-55513-826-8). Cook.
--Share the Gospel. 80p. 1987. pap. 5.95 (ISBN 1-55513-825-X). Cook.
Heath, Sidney. The Romance of Symbolism & Its Relation to Church Ornament & Architecture. LC 70-174054. (Illus.). 1976. Repr. of 1909 ed. 40.00x (ISBN 0-8103-4302-9). Gale.
Lauckner, Edie. Signs of Celebration. 1978. 3.50 (ISBN 0-570-03770-0, 12-2706). Concordia.
Milroy, M. E., ed. Church Lace: Being Eight Ecclesiastical Patterns in Pillow Lace. (Illus.). 121p. 1981. Repr. of 1920 ed. 42.00x (ISBN 0-8103-3014-8). Gale.
Randall, Gerald. Church Furnishing & Decoration in England & Wales. LC 80-11125. (Illus.). 240p. 1980. text ed. 42.50x (ISBN 0-8419-0602-5). Holmes & Meier.
Smith, John C. Church Woodcarvings: A West Country Study. LC 79-77874. (Illus.). 1969. 17.95x (ISBN 0-678-05533-5). Kelley.
Snyder, Bernadette M. & Terry, Hazelmai M. Decorations for Forty-Four Parish Celebrations: Enhancing Worship Experiences Tastefully & Simply. (Illus., Orig.). 1982. pap. 9.95 (ISBN 0-89622-167-9). Twenty-Third.
Symbol Patterns: Ideas for Banners, Posters, Bulletin Boards. 40p. (Orig.). 1981. pap. 4.95 (ISBN 0-8066-1897-3, 10-6173). Augsburg.
Wildridge, Thomas T. Grotesque in Church Art. LC 68-30633. 1969. Repr. of 1899 ed. 35.00x (ISBN 0-8103-3077-6). Gale.

CHURCH DISCIPLINE
see also Absolution; Asceticism; Celibacy; Church Orders, Ancient; Confession; Ecclesiastical Courts; Indulgences; Inquisition; Marriage, Mixed; Penance; Purgatory; Visitations, Ecclesiastical; also subdivision Discipline under names of religions, religious denominations, etc., e.g. Catholic Church–Discipline
Adams, Jay E. Godliness Through Discipline. 1972. pap. 0.95 (ISBN 0-87552-021-9). Presby & Reformed.
--Handbook of Church Discipline. (Jay Adams Library). 144p. 1986. pap. 6.95 (ISBN 0-310-51191-7). Zondervan.
Addington, Gordon. Discipline. 0.75 (ISBN 0-911802-51-7). Free Church Pubns.
Baker, Don. Beyond Forgiveness: The Healing Touch of Church Discipline. LC 84-3417. 1984. 8.95 (ISBN 0-88070-054-8). Multnomah.
Buzzard, Lynn R. & Brandon, Thomas. Church Discipline & the Courts. (Pressure Point Ser.). 160p. (Orig.). 1987. pap. 6.95 (ISBN 0-8423-0272-7). Tyndale.
Cocoris, G. Michael. An Outline for Discipling. rev. ed. 9p. 1984. pap. 1.00 (ISBN 0-935729-10-0). Church Open Door.
Foster, Richard J. Celebration of Discipline Study Guide. LC 77-20444. 96p. (Orig.). 1983. pap. 5.95 (ISBN 0-06-062833-2, RD/390, HarpR). Har-Row.
Gage, Ken & Gage, Joy. Restoring Fellowship: Judgement & Church Discipline. (Orig.). 1984. pap. 4.50 (ISBN 0-8024-4440-7). Moody.
Gates, Rebecca L. The Beauty of a Disciplined Life. 96p. 1987. pap. 4.95 (ISBN 0-89693-248-6). Victor Bks.
Gotwald, William K. Ecclesiastical Censure at the End of the Fifteenth Century. LC 78-64124. (Johns Hopkins University. Studies in the Social Sciences. Forty-Fifth Ser. 1927: 3). Repr. of 1927 ed. 13.50 (ISBN 0-404-61238-5). AMS Pr.
Jeschke, Marlin. Discipling the Brother. rev. ed. LC 72-2052. 190p. 1979. pap. 2.95 (ISBN 0-8361-1897-9). Herald Pr.
Laney, J. Carl. A Guide to Church Discipline. 160p. 1985. 8.95 (ISBN 0-87123-834-9, 230834). Bethany Hse.
Marshall, Nathaniel. Penitential Discipline of the Primitive Church. LC 74-172846. (Library of Anglo-Catholic Theology: No. 13). Repr. of 1844 ed. 27.50 (ISBN 0-404-52105-3). AMS Pr.
Orsy, Ladislas. The Lord of Confusion. 5.00 (ISBN 0-87193-064-1). Dimension Bks.
Rausch, Robert A. Creative Discipline. Brooks, Frances, ed. 1986. pap. 5.95 (ISBN 0-939697-05-X). Graded Pr.
Thomassin, L. Dictionnaire de Discipline Ecclesiastique, 2 vols. Migne, J. P., ed. (Troisieme et Derniere Encyclopedie Theologique Ser.: Vols. 25-26). (Fr.). 1466p. Repr. of 1856 ed. lib. bdg. 186.00x (ISBN 0-89241-306-9). Caratzas.
Tomczak, Larry. God, the Rod, & Your Child's Bod. LC 81-23507. 128p. 1982. pap. 5.95 (ISBN 0-8007-5082-9, Power Bks). Revell.
White, John & Blue, Ken. Healing the Wounded. LC 85-2358. 240p. (Orig.). 1985. 11.95 (ISBN 0-87784-939-0); pap. 6.95 (ISBN 0-87784-533-6). Inter-Varsity.
Wiersbe, Warren W. Be Diligent. 156p. 1987. pap. 5.95 (ISBN 0-89693-356-3). Victor Bks.
Wray, Daniel E. Biblical Church Discipline. 25p. 1978. pap. 1.20 (ISBN 0-85151-269-0). Banner of Truth.

CHURCH ENTERTAINMENTS
Alessi, Vincie, ed. Programs for Advent & Christmas, Vol. 2. 64p. 1981. pap. 4.95 (ISBN 0-8170-0930-2). Judson.
Barragar, Pam. Spiritual Growth Through Creative Drama. 128p. 1981. pap. 5.95 (ISBN 0-8170-0923-X). Judson.
Bolding, Amy. Please Plan a Program. (Paperback Program Ser). (Orig.). 1971. pap. 3.95 (ISBN 0-8010-0527-2). Baker Bk.
Clemens, Frances & Tully, Robert, eds. Recreation & the Local Church. LC 57-18412. pap. 47.80 (ISBN 0-317-28391-X, 2022409). Bks Demand UMI.
Harvey, Adell & Gonzalez, Mari. Sacred Chow. 176p. 1987. pap. 9.95 (ISBN 0-687-36713-1). Abingdon.
Landorf, Joyce. Let's Have a Banquet: Or will One Dollar & thirtysix cents be Enough. 1968. pap. 4.95 (ISBN 0-310-27131-2, 9994P). Zondervan.
Parade of Plays for Your Church. 96p. pap. 5.95 (ISBN 0-317-47009-4, 33274, Chariot Bks). Cook.
Shotwell, Malcolm G. Creative Programs for the Church Year. 96p. 1986. pap. 7.95 (ISBN 0-8170-1102-1). Judson.
Wade, Mildred. Socials for All Occasions. LC 79-55492. (Orig.). 1980. pap. 4.95 (ISBN 0-8054-7518-4). Broadman.

CHURCH FACILITIES
Bowman, Ray, ed. Church Building Sourcebook Two. 264p. 1982. 3-ring vinyl notebook 39.95 (ISBN 0-8341-0759-7). Beacon Hill.
Hoff, B. J. Baby's First Days: Enrollment Certificate. (Certificate Booklets Ser.). (Illus.). 16p. 1982. pap. 0.95 self-cover (ISBN 0-87239-530-8, 1182). Standard Pub.
Rickard, Marvin G. Let It Grow: Your Church Can Chart a New Course. LC 84-22733. 1985. pap. 5.95 (ISBN 0-88070-074-2). Multnomah.

CHURCH FATHERS
see Fathers of the Church

CHURCH FESTIVALS
see Fasts and Feasts

CHURCH FINANCE
see also Church Charities; Church Property; Church Work–Forms, Blanks, etc.; Churchwardens' Accounts; Stewardship, Christian; Taxation, Exemption From; Tithes also subdivision Finance under Church denominations and under special topics, e.g. Church of England–Finance
Abingdon Clergy Income Tax Guide, 1985. 80p. (Orig.). 1986. pap. 5.95 (ISBN 0-687-00363-6). Abingdon.
Accounting Principles & Reporting Practices for Churches & Church Related Organizations. 64p. 1983. pap. 21.95 (ISBN 1-55586-855-X). US Catholic.
Church Finance Record System Manual. 7.95 (ISBN 0-8054-3103-9). Broadman.
Cleary, Patrick. The Church & Usury. 1979. lib. bdg. 59.95 (ISBN 0-8490-2884-1). Gordon Pr.
Economic Indicators & the GPID: An Attempt to Bring Economics Back into the Church Without Losing the Faith. 27p. 1980. pap. 5.00 (ISBN 92-808-0134-1, TUNU068, UNU). Bernan-Unipub.
Ellis, Loudell O. Church Treasurer's Handbook. LC 77-10433. 1978. 6.95 (ISBN 0-8170-0762-8). Judson.
Harrison, Frederick. Practical Church Financing. 128p. 1970. pap. 5.95 (ISBN 0-912522-58-5). Aero Medical.
Hartley, Loyde H. Understanding Church Finances: The Economics of the Local Church. LC 83-23769. 192p. (Orig.). 1984. pap. 10.95 (ISBN 0-8298-0708-X). Pilgrim NY.
Heyd, Tom. Accounting Systems for Churches. (Administration Series for Churches). 64p. 1984. pap. 3.95 (ISBN 0-8066-2032-3, 10-0126). Augsburg.
Holck, Manfred, Jr. Annual Budgeting: Developing & Using an Annual Budget Effectively. 1977. pap. 3.95 (ISBN 0-8066-1549-4, 10-0360). Augsburg.
--Church Finance in a Complex Economy. 138p. (Orig.). 1983. pap. 6.95 (ISBN 0-687-08156-4). Abingdon.
--Money & Your Church. LC 74-75979. (Illus.). 189p. 1974. 7.95 (ISBN 0-87983-080-8). Keats.
Johnson, Douglas W. Let's Be Realistic about Your Church Budget. 112p. 1984. pap. 3.95 (ISBN 0-8170-1025-4). Judson.
Knudsen, Raymond B. New Models for Financing the Local Church. 2nd ed. 157p. 1985. pap. 8.95 (ISBN 0-8192-1369-1). Morehouse.
McKeever, Jim. Almighty & the Dollar Workbook. 1980. 23.95. Omega Pubns OR.
McLeod, Thomas E. The Work of the Church Treasurer. 80p. 1981. pap. 6.95 (ISBN 0-8170-0908-6). Judson.
Meitler, Neal D. & La Porte, Linda M. Standard Accounting System for Lutheran Congregations. 1981. 4.95 (ISBN 0-8100-0129-2, 21N2001). Northwest Pub.
Moriarty, Daniel P. How to Raise Money at Church Without Sales or Bingo. 1977. pap. 4.00 (ISBN 0-933968-00-0). D Moriarty.
Rickard, Marvin G. Let It Grow: Your Church Can Chart a New Course. LC 84-22733. 1985. pap. 5.95 (ISBN 0-88070-074-2). Multnomah.
Walker, Joe E. Money in the Church. LC 81-20583. (Into Our Third Century Ser.). (Orig.). 1982. pap. 3.95 (ISBN 0-687-27160-6). Abingdon.

CHURCH FINANCE–EARLY CHURCH, ca. 30-600
Nickle, Keith. Collection: A Study in Paul's Strategy. LC 66-72379. (Studies in Biblical Theology: No. 48). 1966. pap. 10.00x (ISBN 0-8401-3048-1). A R Allenson.

CHURCH FURNITURE
see also Altarpieces; Altars
Clinch, George. Old English Churches: Their Architecture, Furniture, Decorations & Monuments. 1977. lib. bdg. 59.95 (ISBN 0-8490-2368-8). Gordon Pr.
Howkins, Christopher. Discovering Church Furniture. (Discovering Ser.: No. 69). (Illus.). 80p. 1983. pap. 3.50 (ISBN 0-85263-496-X, Pub. by Shire Pubns England). Seven Hills Bks.

CHURCH GOVERNMENT
see Church Polity

CHURCH GROUP WORK
see also Church Meetings; Prayer Groups; Young People's Meetings (Church Work)
Bolding, Amy. Stimulating Devotions for Church Groups. 144p. 1986. pap. 4.95 (ISBN 0-8010-0921-9). Baker Bk.

Campbell, Viola D. Recreation Cristiana. (Span., Illus.). 160p. 1986. pap. 4.25 (ISBN 0-311-11037-1). Casa Bautista.

Cho, Paul Y. & Hostetler, Harold. Successful Home Cell Groups. LC 81-80025. 1981. pap. 5.95 (ISBN 0-88270-513-X, Pub. by Logos). Bridge Pub.

Churches Alive, Inc. Staff. Caring. rev. ed. LC 81-66927. 60p. 1981. pap. text ed. 3.95 (ISBN 0-934396-23-X). Churches Alive.

Denning, Dennis. We Are One in the Lord: Developing Caring Groups in the Church. LC 81-14958. 96p. (Orig.). 1982. pap. 5.50 (ISBN 0-687-44281-8). Abingdon.

Dibbert, Michael T., et al. Growth Groups: A Key to Christian Fellowship & Spiritual Maturity in the Church. 160p. (Orig.). 1985. pap. 5.95 (ISBN 0-310-23121-3, 11673P). Zondervan.

Gibson, Ruth E. In Search of Young Parents. 120p. (Orig.). 1984. pap. 4.95 (ISBN 0-8341-0911-5). Beacon Hill.

Harsin, L. D. Our Caring Fellowship. 1983. pap. 8.50 (ISBN 0-8309-0373-9). Herald Hse.

Hastings, Gerald L. Publish Good News: A Resource Guide for Self-Publishing Church Groups. (Illus.). 80p. (Orig.). 1986. pap. 6.50 (ISBN 0-937641-01-4). Stone Canyon Pr.

Hayes, Edward L. The Focused Life. 96p. 1986. 4.95 (ISBN 0-8010-4297-6). Baker Bk.

Hurston, Zora N. The Sanctified Church. 107p. 1983. pap. 6.95 (ISBN 0-913666-44-0). Turtle Isl Foun.

Lange, Martin & Iblacker, Reinhold, eds. Witnesses of Hope: The Persecution of Christians in Latin America. Jerman, William E., tr. from Ger. LC 81-38378. Orig. Title: Christenverfolgung in SudAmerica: Zeugen du Hoffnung. Tr. of Christenverfalgung in Sudamerica: Zeugen der Hoffreung. 176p. (Orig.). 1981. pap. 6.95 (ISBN 0-88344-759-2). Orbis Bks.

Lavin, Ronald J. You Can Grow in a Small Group. 144p. 1976. pap. 5.75 (ISBN 0-89536-273-2, 2500). CSS of Ohio.

McKinley, John. Group Development Through Participation Training: A Trainers Resource for Team Building. LC 78-71870. 162p. (Orig.). 1980. pap. text ed. 9.95 (ISBN 0-8091-2247-2); participant's bk. 2.50 (ISBN 0-8091-2299-5). Paulist Pr.

Mallison, John. Building Small Groups in the Christian Community. (Abridged Small Group Ser.). (Illus.). 238p. (Orig.). 1978. pap. 7.95 (ISBN 0-909202-05-2, Pub. by Renewal Pubns). ANZ Religious Pubns.

--Creative Ideas for Small Group in the Christian Community. (Abridged Small Group Ser.). 250p. (Orig.). 1978. pap. 7.95 (ISBN 0-909202-06-0, Pub. by Renewal Pubns). ANZ Religious Pubns.

Metz, Rene & Schlick, Jean, eds. Informal Groups in the Church: Papers of the Second Cerdic Colloquium, Strasbourg, May 13-15, 1971. O'Connell, Matthew J., tr. LC 75-25591. (Pittsburgh Theological Monographs: No. 7). 1975. pap. 5.25 (ISBN 0-915138-08-5). Pickwick.

Moody, Timothy E. Devotional Talks on Christian Commitment. (Devotional Resources for Adults Ser.). 96p. 1986. 4.95 (ISBN 0-8010-6203-9). Baker Bk.

Nilsen, Mary Y. Tending the Family Tree: A Family-Centered, Bible-Based Experience for Church Groups. 80p. (Orig.). 1982. pap. 7.95 (ISBN 0-86683-169-X, HarpR). Har-Row.

Olsen, Charles M. Cultivating Religious Growth Groups. LC 83-27328. (The Pastor's Handbook Ser.: Vol. 3). 118p. (Orig.). 1984. pap. 7.95 (ISBN 0-664-24617-6). Westminster.

Olsen, Mary P. For the Greater Glory: A Church Needlepoint Handbook. (Illus.). 192p. 1980. 17.50 (ISBN 0-8164-0476-3, HarpR). Har-Row.

Rice, Wayne & Yaconelli, Mike. Right-on Ideas for Youth Groups. (Illus.). 96p. 1973. pap. 6.95 (ISBN 0-310-34951-6, 10796P). Zondervan.

Searle, Mark, ed. Parish: A Place for Worship. LC 81-13655. 192p. (Orig.). 1981. pap. 5.95 (ISBN 0-8146-1236-9). Liturgical Pr.

Smith, Donald P. Congregations Alive. LC 81-1371. 198p. 1981. pap. 10.95 (ISBN 0-664-24370-3). Westminster.

Walsh, Albert J. Reflections on Death & Grief. 96p. 1986. 4.50 (ISBN 0-8010-9673-1). Baker Bk.

CHURCH GROWTH

Anderson, Andy. Effective Methods of Church Growth. LC 85-6620. 1985. pap. 5.95 (ISBN 0-8054-3237-X). Broadman.

Bartel, Floyd. A New Look at Church Growth. LC 79-53523. 1979. pap. 2.95 (ISBN 0-87303-027-3). Faith & Life.

Chaney, Charles L. & Lewis, Ron S. Design for Church Growth. LC 77-87364. 1978. pap. 6.95 (ISBN 0-8054-6218-X). Broadman.

--Manual for Design for Church Growth. 1978. pap. text ed. 2.50 (ISBN 0-8054-6219-8). Broadman.

Conn, Harvie M. Theological Perspectives on Church Growth. 1976. pap. 4.95 (ISBN 0-87552-150-9). Presby & Reformed.

Dudley, Roger L. & Cummings, Des, Jr. Adventures in Church Growth. Wheeler, Gerald, ed. LC 83-16089. (Illus.). 160p. (Orig.). 1983. pap. 8.95 (ISBN 0-8280-0228-2). Review & Herald.

Elliott, Ralph H. Church Growth That Counts. 128p. 1982. pap. 5.95 (ISBN 0-8170-0943-4). Judson.

Exman, Gary. Get Ready... Get Set... Grow! Sherer, Michael L., ed. (Orig.). 1987. pap. 8.75 (ISBN 0-89536-865-X, 7824). CSS of Ohio.

Hall, Robert B. Church Growth for Episcopalians. 1982. pap. 4.95 (ISBN 0-686-37069-4). Episcopal Ctr.

Hoge, Dean R. & Roozen, David A., eds. Understanding Church Growth & Decline, 1950-78. LC 79-4166. (Illus.). 1979. pap. 9.95 (ISBN 0-8298-0358-0). Pilgrim NY.

Hohensee, Donald W. Church Growth in Burundi. LC 76-54342. 1977. pap. 4.95 (ISBN 0-87808-316-2). William Carey Lib.

Jenson, Ron & Stevens, Jim. Dynamics of Church Growth. 280p. 1981. pap. 8.95 (ISBN 0-8010-5161-4). Baker Bk.

Krahn, John & Foster, Betty J. Ministry Ideabank III. (Orig.). 1987. pap. price not set (ISBN 0-89536-895-1, 7881). CSS of Ohio.

Kraus, Norman C. Missions, Evangelism, & Church Growth. LC 80-10922. (Mennonite Central Committee Story Ser.). 176p. 1980. pap. 6.95 (ISBN 0-8361-1925-8). Herald Pr.

McGavran, Donald. Understanding Church Growth. rev. ed. 488p. (Orig.). 1980. pap. 12.95 (ISBN 0-8028-1849-8). Eerdmans.

McGavran, Donald & Arn, Winfield. Back to Basics in Church Growth. 1981. pap. 5.95 (ISBN 0-8423-0116-X). Tyndale.

McGavran, Donald & Hunter, George G., III. Church Growth: Strategies That Work. LC 79-26962. (Creative Leadership Ser.). (Orig.). 1980. pap. 6.95 (ISBN 0-687-08160-2). Abingdon.

McGavran, Donald A. Church Growth & Group Conversion. new ed. LC 73-80163. 128p. 1973. pap. 3.95 (ISBN 0-87808-712-5). William Carey Lib.

McGavran, Donald A. & Arn, Winfield C. Ten Steps for Church Growth. LC 76-62950. 1977. pap. 6.95 (ISBN 0-06-065352-3, RD 215, HarpR). Har-Row.

McGavran, Donald A., ed. Church Growth Bulletin: Second Consolidated Volume (Sept. 1969 -July 1975) LC 77-5192. 1977. pap. 7.95x (ISBN 0-87808-702-8). William Carey Lib.

Miles, Delos. Church Growth - A Mighty River. LC 80-67352. 1981. pap. 6.50 (ISBN 0-8054-6227-9). Broadman.

Miranda, Juan C. Church Growth Manual. Lamigueiro, Fernando, ed. Orig. Title: Manual De Iglecrecimiento. 192p. 1985. pap. 4.50 (ISBN 0-8297-0707-7). Life Pubs Intl.

North, Ira. Balance, A Tried & Tested Formula for Church Growth. 1983. pap. 5.95 (ISBN 0-89225-270-7). Gospel Advocate.

Peters, George. A Theology of Church Growth. 368p. 1981. pap. 10.95 (ISBN 0-310-43101-8, 11285P). Zondervan.

Planning for Church Growth: A Comprehensive Guide: Developing a Total Program for Ministry. 299p. (Orig.). 1983. wkbk. 150.00 (ISBN 0-914307-42-8). Word Faith.

Powell, Paul W. The Nuts & Bolts of Church Growth. LC 81-68926. 1982. pap. 5.95 (ISBN 0-8054-2542-X). Broadman.

Shenk, Wilbert R. Exploring Church Growth. 336p. 1983. pap. 10.95 (ISBN 0-8028-1962-1). Eerdmans.

Shenk, Wilbert R., ed. The Challenge of Church Growth. (Mennonite Missionary Studies: Pt. 1). 112p. 1973. pap. 4.95 (ISBN 0-8361-1200-8). Herald Pr.

Sherer, Michael L., ed. Excellence in Ministry. (Orig.). 1987. pap. 8.75 (ISBN 0-89536-866-8, 7825). CSS of Ohio.

Sisemore, John T. Church Growth Through the Sunday School. LC 82-70870. (Orig.). 1983. pap. 6.50 (ISBN 0-8054-6237-6). Broadman.

Smith, Ebbie C. Balanced Church Growth. LC 84-6456. 1984. pap. 5.95 (ISBN 0-8054-6246-5). Broadman.

Swanson, Allen J. Mending the Nets: Taiwan Church Growth & Loss in the 1980's. LC 86-47704. 320p. 1986. pap. 7.95 (ISBN 0-87808-207-7, WCL 207-7). William Carey Lib.

Towns, Elmer L. & Vaughan, John. The Complete Book of Church Growth. 1981. 14.95 (ISBN 0-8423-0408-8). Tyndale.

Turner, J. J. Leadership & Church Growth. pap. 2.75 (ISBN 0-89315-137-8). Lambert Bk.

Wagner, C. Peter. Church Growth & the Whole Gospel: A Biblical Mandate. LC 81-47433. 224p. 1981. 13.00 (ISBN 0-06-068942-0, HarpR). Har-Row.

--Leading Your Church to Growth. LC 83-19272. 224p. 1984. pap. 6.95 (ISBN 0-8307-0922-3, 5418091). Regal.

Wagner, Peter C. Strategies for Church Growth. 1987. 12.95 (ISBN 0-8307-1245-3, 5111756). Regal.

Watkins, Morris. Literacy, Bible Reading & Church Growth Through the Ages. LC 78-15315. (Illus.). 1978. pap. 5.95 (ISBN 0-87808-325-1). William Carey Lib.

Werning, Waldo J. Vision & Strategy for Church Growth. 2nd ed. 1983. pap. 4.50 (ISBN 0-8010-9658-8). Baker Bk.

Yamamori, Tetsunao. Church Growth in Japan. LC 74-4009. (Illus.). 184p. (Orig.). 1974. pap. 4.95 (ISBN 0-87808-412-6). William Carey Lib.

Yamamori, Tetsunao & Lawson, E. Leroy. Introducing Church Growth. LC 74-24577. (New Life Books). (Illus.). 256p. 1974. 7.95 (ISBN 0-87239-000-4, 40002). Standard Pub.

Zunkel, C. W. Church Growth under Fire. LC 86-31814. 256p. (Orig.). 1987. pap. 8.95 (ISBN 0-317-52328-7). Herald Pr.

CHURCH HISTORY

This heading is subdivided first according to subject matter, e.g. Church History–Philosophy, and second, chronologically, according to the period of history covered.

see also Abbeys; Church and State; Convents and Nunneries; Councils and Synods; Creeds; Dioceses; Ecclesiastical Geography; Episcopacy; Fathers of the Church; Inquisition; Language Question in the Church; Miracles; Missions; Monasticism and Religious Orders; Papacy; Persecution; Popes; Protestant Churches; Protestantism; Reformation; Religious Thought; Revivals; Sects; Sisterhoods;

also subdivision Church History under names of countries; names of denominations, sects, churches, councils, etc.; headings beginning with the word Christian

Abbott, Lyman. The Evolution of Christianity. vi, 258p. 1985. Repr. of 1919 ed. 34.00 (ISBN 0-318-04538-9, Pub. by Am Repr Serv). Am Biog Serv.

Acton. Essays on Freedom & Power. 13.25 (ISBN 0-8446-0000-8). Peter Smith.

Addison, William G. The Renewed Church of the United Brethren, 1722-1930. (Church Historical Society London Ser.: No. 9). Repr. of 1932 ed. 40.00 (ISBN 0-8115-3133-3). Kraus Repr.

Aland, Kurt. A History of Christianity, Vol. 2: From the Reformation to the Present. Schaaf, James L., tr. from Ger. LC 85-47913. 608p. 1986. 29.95 (ISBN 0-8006-0759-7, 1-759). Fortress.

Anderson, Dave. More Funny Things on the Way to Church. Wilcox, Tim, ed. (Continued Applied Christianity Ser.). 1983. pap. 4.50 (ISBN 0-570-03893-6, 12-2975). Concordia.

Atiya, Aziz S. History of Eastern Christianity. LC 67-31393. pap. 125.00 (ISBN 0-317-42117-4, 2025944). Bks Demand UMI.

Atkins, Gaius G. Pilgrims of the Lonely Road. facs. ed. LC 67-28741. (Essay Index Reprint Ser). 1913. 18.00 (ISBN 0-8369-0162-2). Ayer Co Pubs.

Aubert, Roger. Christian Centuries: Church in a Secularized Society, Vol. 5. LC 78-53496. 820p. 1978. 22.95 (ISBN 0-8091-0244-7). Paulist Pr.

Aubert, Roger, ed. Historical Investigations. LC 66-29260. (Concilium Ser.: Vol. 17). 196p. 1966. 7.95 (ISBN 0-8091-0063-0). Paulist Pr.

--Historical Problems of Church Renewal. LC 65-26792. (Concilium Ser.: Vol. 7). 196p. 1965. 7.95 (ISBN 0-8091-0064-9). Paulist Pr.

Austin, Bill R. Austin's Topical History of Christianity. 527p. 1983. 14.95 (ISBN 0-8423-0096-1). Tyndale.

Avis, Paul, ed. A History of Christian Theology, Vol. 1: The Science of Theology. 336p. (Orig.). 1986. pap. 14.95 (ISBN 0-8028-0195-1). Eerdmans.

Ayer, Joseph C. Sourcebook of Ancient Church History. LC 70-113536. Repr. of 1913 ed. lib. bdg. 64.50 (ISBN 0-404-00436-9). AMS Pr.

Azhar, A. Christianity in History. 12.50 (ISBN 0-686-18580-3). Kazi Pubns.

Backman, Milton V., Jr. The Heavens Resound: A History of the Latter-Day Saints in Ohio 1830-1838. LC 83-12882. (Illus.). 480p. 1983. 14.95 (ISBN 0-87747-973-9). Deseret Bk.

Bainton, Roland H. The Church of Our Fathers. (Illus.). 222p. 1978. pap. text ed. write for info. (ISBN 0-02-305450-6, Pub. by Scribner). Macmillan.

--Early Christianity. LC 83-25150. 188p. 1984. pap. text ed. 7.50 (ISBN 0-89874-735-X). Krieger.

Bainton, Ronald H. The Church of Our Fathers. 1984. 16.75 (ISBN 0-8446-6120-1). Peter Smith.

Baker, Archibald G., ed. Short History of Christianity. LC 40-34185. (Midway Reprints Ser.). 1983. Repr. of 1940 ed. 11.00x (ISBN 0-226-03527-1). U of Chicago Pr.

Baker, Derek. Religious Motivation: Biographical & Sociological Problems for the Church Historian. (Studies in Church History: Vol. 15). 516p. 1978. 45.00x (ISBN 0-631-19250-6). Basil Blackwell.

--Renaissance & Renewal in Christian History. (Studies in Church History: Vol. 14). 428p. 1977. 45.00x (ISBN 0-631-17780-9). Basil Blackwell.

Baker, R. A. Compendio de la Historia Cristiana. Almanza, Francisco G., tr. Orig. Title: A Summary of Christian History. (Span.). 372p. 1985. pap. 9.50 (ISBN 0-311-15032-2). Casa Bautista.

Baker, Robert A. Summary of Christian History. (Illus.). 1959. 16.95 (ISBN 0-8054-6502-2). Broadman.

Barry, Colman J., ed. Readings in Church History, 3 vols. in 1. 1985. pap. 50.00 (ISBN 0-87061-104-6). Chr Classics.

Bauer, Walter. Orthodoxy & Heresy in Earliest Christianity. Kraft, Robert A. & Krodel, Gerhard, eds. LC 71-141252. 360p. 1979. pap. 2.50 (ISBN 0-8006-1363-5, 1-1363). Fortress.

Bausch, William J. Pilgrim Church. LC 73-6608. 560p. 1980. pap. 9.95 (ISBN 0-89622-140-7). Twenty-Third.

Beales, D. & Best, G., eds. History, Society & the Churches: Essays in Honour of Owen Chadwick. 335p. 1985. 49.50 (ISBN 0-521-25486-8). Cambridge U Pr.

Belloc, Hilaire. Great Heresies. facs. ed. LC 68-16908. (Essay Index Reprint Ser). 1938. 18.00 (ISBN 0-8369-0189-4). Ayer Co Pubs.

Berkhof, Louis. The History of Christian Doctrine. 1978. 14.95 (ISBN 0-85151-005-1). Banner of Truth.

Betten, Francis S. From Many Centuries: A Collection of Historical Papers. facs. ed. LC 68-16910. (Essay Index Reprint Ser). 1968. Repr. of 1938 ed. 18.00 (ISBN 0-8369-0206-8). Ayer Co Pubs.

Bettey, J. H. Church & Community: The Parish Church in English Life. LC 79-14739. (Illus.). 142p. 1979. text ed. 26.50x (ISBN 0-06-490381-8, 06346). B&N Imports.

Bevan, Edwyn R. Christianity. LC 80-24452. (The Home University Library of Modern Knowledge Ser.: No. 157). 255p. 1981. Repr. of 1948 ed. lib. bdg. 25.00x (ISBN 0-313-22681-4, BECY). Greenwood.

Bickerman, Elias. Studies in Jewish & Christian History, Pt. 3. (Arbeiten zur Geschichte des antiken Judentums und des Urchritentums Ser.: Band 9). xvi, 392p. 1986. 93.50 (ISBN 90-04-07480-5, Pub. by E J Brill). Heinman.

Binyon, Pamela M. The Concepts of Spirit & Demon: A Study in the Use of Different Languages Describing the Same Phenomena. (IC-Studies in the International History of Christianity: Vol. 8). 132p. 1977. pap. 19.60 (ISBN 3-261-01787-2). P Lang Pubs.

Boever, Richard A. Cameos of Church History. 64p. 1986. pap. 1.95 (ISBN 0-89243-249-7). Liguori Pubns.

Booty, John E. The Church in History. (Church's Teaching Ser.: Vol. 3). 320p. 1979. 5.95 (ISBN 0-8164-0420-8, HarpR); pap. 3.95 (ISBN 0-8164-2216-8); user guide 0.95 (ISBN 0-8164-2223-0). Har-Row.

Bowman, Rufus D. Church of the Brethren & the War, 1788-1914. LC 75-147667. (Library of War & Peace; Relig. & Ethical Positions on War). 1972. 46.00 (ISBN 0-8240-0425-6). Garland Pub.

Boys, Don. Pilgrims, Puritans & Patriots: Our Christian Heritage. 1983. pap. 9.00x (ISBN 0-686-40717-2). Freedom Univ-FSP.

Brauer, Jerald C., ed. The Impact of the Church Upon Its Culture: Reappraisals of the History of Christianity. Breen, Quirinus & Drake, George A. LC 67-30155. (Essays in Divinity: Vol. 2). pap. 101.50 (ISBN 0-317-26159-2, 2024085). Bks Demand UMI.

Bruce, F. F. The Spreading Flame: The Rise & Progress of Christianity from Its Beginnings to the Conversion of the English. 432p. 1980. pap. 14.95 (ISBN 0-8028-1805-6). Eerdmans.

Buchholz, Peter, ed. Bibliographie Zur alteuropaeischen Religionsgeschichte, Vol. 1: Nineteen Fifty-Four Bis Nineteen Sixty-Four Literatur zu den antiken Rand-und Nachfolgekulturen im aussermediterranen Europa unter besonderer Beruecksichtigung der nichtchristlichen Religionen. (Arbeitem zur Fruehmittelalterforschung, Vol. 2). (Ger). 1967. 26.80x (ISBN 3-11-000373-2). De Gruyter.

Cairns, Earle E. Christianity Through the Centuries. 544p. 1981. 19.95 (ISBN 0-310-38360-9, 9377P). Zondervan.

Campbell, R. K. Prophetic History of Christendom. 6.95 (ISBN 0-88172-012-7). Believers Bkshelf.

Carroll, Warren H. The Founding of Christendom. (History of Christendom Ser.: Vol. 1). 605p. 1985. 24.95 (ISBN 0-931888-21-2); pap. 12.95 (ISBN 0-931888-21-2). Christendom Pubns.

Chesnut, Glenn F. The First Christian Histories: Eusebius, Socrates, Sozomen, Theodoret, & Evagrius. 2nd, rev. ed. xiv, 296p. 1986. 34.95 (ISBN 0-86554-164-7, MUP/H154); pap. 19.95 (ISBN 0-86554-203-1, MUP-P22). Mercer Univ Pr.

Church History, Vols. 1-37. 1977. Repr. of 1932 ed. Set. lib. bdg. 1572.50 (ISBN 0-685-77256-X); lib. bdg. 42.50 ea. AMS Pr.

The Church of Stiled the Great 1881-1981: The Heart of Little Italy. LC 81-67378. (Illus.). 136p. 1982. 25.00 (ISBN 0-9607014-0-0). Church St Leo.

Clouse, Robert, et al. Church in History Series, 6 bks. 1980. pap. 27.95 set (ISBN 0-570-06277-2, 12-2780). Concordia.

Cocoris, G. Michael. Seventy Years on Hope Street: A History of the Church of the Open Door 1915-1985. (Illus.). 151p. 1985. text ed. 35.00 (ISBN 0-935729-09-7). Church Open Door.

--Seventy Years on Hope Street: A History of the Church of the Open Door 1915-1985. (Illus.). 151p. 1985. deluxe ed. 195.95 (ISBN 0-935729-30-5). Church Open Door.

Comby, Jean. How to Understand Church History. 208p. 1985. pap. 10.95 (ISBN 0-8245-0722-3). Crossroad NY.

Conn, Charles. Our First One Hundred Years. (Church Training Course Ser.). 1986. cloth 5.75 (ISBN 0-87148-668-7); pap. 4.75 (ISBN 0-87148-669-5). Pathway Pr.

Contos, Leonidas C. Two Thousand & One the Church in Crisis. 60p. 1981. pap. 2.95 (ISBN 0-916586-46-4). Holy Cross Orthodox.

Countryman, L. Wm. The Rich Christian in the Church of the Early Empire: Contradictions & Accomodations. LC 80-81884. (Texts & Studies in Religion: Vol. 7). viii, 248p. 1980. 49.95x (ISBN 0-88946-970-9). E Mellen.

Coustant, Pierre. Epistolae Romanorum Pontificum. 942p. Repr. of 1721 ed. text ed. 207.00x (ISBN 0-576-99106-6, Pub. by Gregg Intl Pubs England). Gregg Intl.

Cowan, Henry. Landmarks of Church History to the Reformation. new rev. & enl. ed. LC 70-144590. Repr. of 1896 ed. 17.00 (ISBN 0-404-01787-8). AMS Pr.

Cox, George W. Latin & Teutonic Christendom: An Historical Sketch. LC 77-94557. 1979. Repr. of 1870 ed. lib. bdg. 30.00 (ISBN 0-89341-259-7). Longwood Pub Group.

Coyle, Alcuin & Bonner, Dismas. The Church Under Tension. 1976. pap. 2.95 (ISBN 0-685-77495-3). Franciscan Herald.

Crews, Clyde F. An American Holy Land: A History of the Archdiocese of Louisville. 360p. 1987. 29.95 (ISBN 0-89453-622-2). M Glazier.

Cushman, Joseph D., Jr. Sound of Bells: The Episcopal Church in South Florida, 1892-1969. LC 75-30946. (Illus.). 1976. 15.00 (ISBN 0-8130-0518-3). U Presses Fla.

Daneel, M. L. Old & New in Southern Shona, Independent Churches, Vol. 1: Background & Rise of the Major Movements. (Change & Continuity in Africa Ser). 1971. text ed. 29.60x (ISBN 0-686-22598-8). Mouton.

Davidson, Henry M. Good Christian Men. facsimile ed. LC 70-142616. (Essay Index Reprint Ser). Repr. of 1940 ed. 19.00 (ISBN 0-8369-2390-1). Ayer Co Pubs.

Davies, Horton. The English Free Churches. 2nd. ed. LC 85-7684. vii, 208p. 1985. Repr. of 1963 ed. lib. bdg. 37.50x (ISBN 0-313-20838-7, DAEF). Greenwood.

Davies, Horton, ed. Studies of the Church in History: Essays Honoring Robert S. Paul on His Sixty-Fifth Birthday, Vol. X. (Pittsburgh Theological Monographs. New Series: No. 5). 276p. (Orig.). 1983. pap. 16.95 (ISBN 0-686-45571-1). Pickwick.

Dawes, Walter A. Christianity Four Thousand Years Before Jesus. Dawes, Kathleen A., ed. (Illus.). 63p. (Orig.). 1982. pap. 4.95 (ISBN 0-938792-17-2). New Capernaum.

Dekar, Paul R. & Ban, Joseph D., eds. In the Great Tradition. 240p. 1982. 25.00 (ISBN 0-8170-0972-8). Judson.

De Lacey, D. R. Expansion of Christianity. (Discovering the Bible Ser.). pap. 8.95 (ISBN 0-7175-1163-4). Dufour.

Desseaux, Jacques. Twenty Centuries of Ecumenism. 1984. pap. 4.95 (ISBN 0-8091-2617-6). Paulist Pr.

Dollinger, John J. The First Age of Christianity & the Church. 1977. lib. bdg. 59.95 (ISBN 0-8490-1840-4). Gordon Pr.

Dowley, Tim. Eerdmans' Handbook to the History of Christianity. LC 77-5616. 1977. 24.95 (ISBN 0-8028-3450-7). Eerdmans.

Drane, John. The Early Christians: Life in the First Years of the Church, an Illustrated Documentary. LC 81-47835. (Illus.). 144p. (Orig.). 1982. pap. 9.95 (ISBN 0-06-062067-6, RD 378, HarpR). Har-Row.

Dunney, Joseph A. Church History in the Light of the Saints. LC 74-2196. (Essay Index Reprint Ser.). Repr. of 1944 ed. 25.00 (ISBN 0-518-10162-2). Ayer Co Pubs.

Dupin, Louis E. Nouvelle Bibliotheque des Auteurs Ecclesiastiques du Premier au 173 Siecle, 36 vols, Ser. I. 18798p. Date not set. Repr. of 1723 ed. text ed. 3720.00 (ISBN 0-576-72786-5, Pub. by Gregg Intl Pubs England). Gregg Intl.

Durand, Eugene. The Biggest Little Church in the World. Wheeler, Gerald, ed. (Better Living Ser.). 32p. (Orig.). 1986. pap. 1.25 (ISBN 0-8280-0320-3). Review & Herald.

Dwyer, John C. Church History: Twenty Centuries of Catholic Christianity. 424p. (Orig.). 1985. pap. 9.95 (ISBN 0-8091-2686-9). Paulist Pr.

Eliade, Mircea & Kitagawa, Joseph, eds. The History of Religions: Essays in Methodology. LC 59-11621. 1973. pap. 3.50 (ISBN 0-226-20395-6, P549, Phoen). U of Chicago Pr.

Elizondo, Virgilio P. La Morenita: Evangelizadora de las Americas. (Span.). 96p. 1981. pap. 2.50 (ISBN 0-89243-145-8). Liguori Pubns.

Ellis, John T., ed. Documents of American Catholic History, 3 vols. LC 86-80801. 1200p. 1987. Set. 65.00; 25.00 ea. Vol. 1: 1494-1865 (ISBN 0-89453-611-7). Vol. 2: 1866-1966 (ISBN 0-89453-612-5). Vol. 3: 1967-1986 (ISBN 0-89453-588-9). M Glazier.

Eusebius. History of the Church (From Christ to Constantine) Williamson, G. A., tr. 1985. Repr. of 1965 ed. 16.95 (ISBN 0-317-19661-8, Pub. by Dorset Pr). Hippocrene Bks.

Eusebius Pamphili. Ecclesiastical History: Books 1-5. LC 65-27501. (Fathers of the Church Ser: Vol. 19). 347p. 1953. 18.95x (ISBN 0-8132-0019-9). Cath U Pr.

Evans, G. R. & Singer, C. C. The Church & the Sword. 2nd ed. LC 82-50234. 1983. pap. text ed. 5.00 (ISBN 0-932050-20-4). New Puritan.

Ewing, Upton C. The Essene Christ. LC 61-10608. (Illus.). 456p. 1977. pap. 12.95 (ISBN 0-8022-0461-9). Philos Lib.

Farmer, William R. & Moule, C. F., eds. Christian History & Interpretation: Studies Presented to John Knox. LC 67-15306. pap. 116.00 (ISBN 0-317-08479-8, 2022449). Bks Demand UMI.

Fenton, Geoffrey, tr. A Form of Christian Policy Gathered Out of French. 504p. Repr. of 1574 ed. 50.00 (ISBN 0-384-15483-2). Johnson Repr.

Ferguson, Everett. Backgrounds of Early Christianity. 464p. (Orig.). 1987. pap. 22.95 (ISBN 0-8028-0292-3). Eerdmans.

--Early Christians Speak. LC 81-68871. 258p. 1981. pap. text ed. 9.95 (ISBN 0-89112-044-0, Bibl Res Pr). Abilene Christ U.

--The New Testament Church. LC 68-55790. (Way of Life Ser: No. 108). 1968. pap. 3.95 (ISBN 0-89112-108-0, Bibl Res Pr). Abilene Christ U.

Finn, Edward E. These Are My Rites: A Brief History of the Eastern Rites of Christianity. LC 79-24937. (Illus.). 104p. 1980. pap. 4.95 (ISBN 0-8146-1058-7). Liturgical Pr.

Fisher, George P. History of the Christian Church. LC 75-41094. 48.50 (ISBN 0-404-14662-7). AMS Pr.

Flood, Bob. The Story of Moody Church. (Orig.). 1985. pap. 5.95 (ISBN 0-8024-0539-8). Moody.

Foxe, John. Acts & Monuments, 8 Vols. Cattley, S. R. & Townsend, George, eds. LC 79-168132. Repr. of 1849 ed. Set. 400.00 (ISBN 0-404-02590-0). AMS Pr.

Frankforter, A. Daniel. A History of the Christian Movement: The Development of Christian Institutions. LC 77-8071. 332p. 1978. text ed. 22.95x (ISBN 0-88229-292-7); pap. 11.95x (ISBN 0-88229-568-3). Nelson-Hall.

Gaebelein, Arno C. The Conflict of the Ages. x ed. (Illus.). 171p. pap. 5.50 (ISBN 0-9609260-1-1). Exhorters.

Garrett, Clarke. Spirit Possession & Popular Religion: From the Camisards to the Shakers. LC 86-46284. 288p. 1987. text ed. 29.50x (ISBN 0-8018-3486-4). Johns Hopkins.

Gaustad, Edwin S. Dissent in American Religion. (Chicago History of American Religion Ser). 1973. 12.95x (ISBN 0-226-28436-0). U of Chicago Pr.

General Conference Youth Department. Church Heritage: A Course in Church History. pap. 2.50 (ISBN 0-686-82636-1). Review & Herald.

Gibbon, Edward. History of Christianity. 59.95 (ISBN 0-8490-0319-9). Gordon Pr.

Gillum, Perry. History of Christianity. (Whole Man Whole World Bible Lessons Ser.). 140p. (Orig.). 1984. pap. 3.95 (ISBN 0-934942-48-X); text ed. 2.95 (ISBN 0-934942-49-8); tchr's. ed. 2.95 (ISBN 0-934942-47-1). White Wing Pub.

Glisson, Jerry & Taylor, Jack R. The Church in a Storm. LC 82-74208. (Orig.). 1983. pap. 5.95 (ISBN 0-8054-5522-1). Broadman.

Godwin, William. St. Leon: A Tale of the Sixteenth Century. LC 74-162884. (Illus.). Repr. of 1835 ed. 32.50 (ISBN 0-404-54405-3). AMS Pr.

Gonzalez, Justo L. La Era de las Tinieblas. (Y Hasta Lo Ultimo de la Tierra: una Historia Ilustrada del Christianismo Ser.: Tomo III). (Span., Illus.). 199p. (Orig.). 1978. pap. 5.95 (ISBN 0-89922-128-9). Edit Caribe.

--La Era de los Altos Ideales. (Y Hasta Lo Ultimo de la Tierra: una Historia Ilustrada Del Cristianismo Ser.: Tomo IV). (Span., Illus.). 197p. (Orig.). 1979. pap. 5.95 (ISBN 0-89922-135-1). Edit Caribe.

--La Era de los Conquistadores. (Y Hasta Lo Ultimo de la Tierra: una Historia Ilustrada del Cristianismo: Tomo VII). (Span., Illus.). 218p. (Orig.). 1981. pap. 5.95 (ISBN 0-89922-162-9). Edit Caribe.

--La Era de los Dogmas y las Dudas. (Y hasta lo ultimo de la tierra Ser.: Tomo No. 8). (Illus.). 224p. (Orig.). 1983. pap. 5.95 (ISBN 0-89922-171-8). Edit Caribe.

--La Era de los Gigantes. (Y Hasta Lo Ultimo de la Tierra: una Historia Ilustrada del Cristianismo Ser.: Tomo II). (Span., Illus.). 184p. (Orig.). 1978. pap. 5.95 (ISBN 0-89922-117-3). Edit Caribe.

--La Era de los Martires. (Y Hasta Lo Ultimo de la Tierra: una Historia Ilustrada del Christianismo Ser.: Tomo I). (Span., Illus.). 189p. (Orig.). 1978. pap. 5.95 (ISBN 0-89922-109-2). Edit Caribe.

--La Era de los Reformadores. (Y Hasta Lo Ultimo de la Tierra: una Historia Ilustrada del Cristianismo Ser.: Tomo VI). (Span., Illus.). 219p. (Orig.). 1980. pap. 5.95 (ISBN 0-89922-154-8). Edit Caribe.

--La Era de los Suenos Frustrados. (Y Hasta Lo Ultimo de la Tierra: una Historia Ilustrada del Cristianismo Ser.: Tomo V). (Span., Illus.). 182p. (Orig.). 1979. pap. 5.95 (ISBN 0-89922-139-4). Edit Caribe.

--A History of Christian Thought. rev. ed. 1987. Set. 59.95 (ISBN 0-687-17185-7). Abingdon.

--Luces Bajo el Almud. LC 77-11753. (Span.). 76p. (Orig.). 1977. pap. 2.50 (ISBN 0-89922-102-5). Edit Caribe.

--The Story of Christianity, Volume 1: The Early Church to the Reformation. LC 83-48430. (Illus.). 448p. (Orig.). 1983. pap. 13.95 (ISBN 0-317-01107-3, RD 510, HarpR). Har-Row.

Gonzalez, Justo, Sr. Historia de un Milagro. (Span.). 166p. 1984. pap. 3.95 (ISBN 0-89922-144-0). Edit Caribe.

Gorman, G. E. & Gorman, Lyn. Theological & Religious Reference Materials: Systematic Theology & Church History. LC 83-22759. (Bibliographies & Indexes in Religious Studies: No. 2). xiv, 401p. 1985. lib. bdg. 47.50 (ISBN 0-313-24779-X, GOS/). Greenwood.

Gorman, Michael J. Abortion & the Early Church: Christian, Jewish, & Pagan Attitudes. 120p. (Orig.). 1982. pap. 4.95 (ISBN 0-87784-397-X). Inter-Varsity.

Grimm, Hans. Tradition & History of the Early Churches of Christ in Central Europe. pap. 1.00 (ISBN 0-88027-095-0). Firm Foun Pub.

Guide for Writing the History of a Church. LC 70-87728. pap. 2.95 (ISBN 0-8054-3504-2). Broadman.

Hagin, Kenneth E. The Coming Restoration. 1985. mini bk. 0.50 (ISBN 0-89276-267-5). Hagin Ministries.

Halverson, Richard C. The Timelessness of Jesus Christ. LC 82-80008. 1982. 8.95 (ISBN 0-8307-0838-3, 5109902). Regal.

Handy, Robert T. A History of the Churches in the United States & Canada. 1977. 29.95x (ISBN 0-19-826910-2). Oxford U Pr.

--A History of the Churches in the United States & Canada. 1977. pap. 8.95 (ISBN 0-19-502531-8). Oxford U Pr.

Hawkins, Elza M. From Now to Pentecost: A Mirrored View of Development in Christianity. 260p. (Orig.). 1982. pap. 11.00 (ISBN 971-10-0038-5, Pub. by New Day Philippines). Cellar.

Hefele, Karl J. A History of the Councils of the Church from the Original Documents, 5 vols. Clark, William R., ed. & tr. from Ger. LC 79-39294. Repr. of 1896 ed. Set. 172.50 (ISBN 0-404-03260-5); 34.50 ea.; Vol. 1. (ISBN 0-404-03261-3); Vol. 2. (ISBN 0-404-03262-1); Vol. 3. (ISBN 0-404-03263-X); Vol. 4. (ISBN 0-404-03264-8); Vol. 5. (ISBN 0-404-03265-6). AMS Pr.

Hempel, Charles J. True Organization of the New Church. LC 40-30032. Repr. of 1848 ed. 31.50 (ISBN 0-404-08464-8). AMS Pr.

Heritage Village Church & Missionary Fellowship, Inc. Staff. People That Love. Boulton, Roger H., ed. (Illus.). 128p. (Orig.). 1986. text ed. write for info. (ISBN 0-912275-05-7); pap. text ed. write for info. (ISBN 0-912275-06-5). PTL Enterprises.

The History of the Church, 10 Vols. 920p. 1980. complete set 595.00x (ISBN 0-8245-0318-X). Crossroad NY.

Hoffmann, R. Joseph, ed. The Origins of Christianity: A Critical Introduction. 326p. (Orig.). 1985. pap. 15.95 (ISBN 0-87975-308-0). Prometheus Bks.

Holfelder, Hans H. Tentatio et Consolatio: Studien zu Bugenhagens Interpretatio in Librum Psalmorum. LC 73-80563. (Arbeiten Zur Kirchengeschichte, Vol. 46). (Ger.). 132p. 1974. 35.60 (ISBN 3-11-004327-0). De Gruyter.

Holmes, T. Scott. The Origin & Development of the Christian Church in Gaul During the First Six Centuries of the Christian Era. 1977. lib. bdg. 59.95 (ISBN 0-8490-2382-3). Gordon Pr.

Hood, John C. Icelandic Church Saga. LC 79-8720. (Illus.). xii, 241p. 1981. Repr. of 1946 ed. lib. bdg. 27.50x (ISBN 0-313-22194-4, HOIC). Greenwood.

Hotema, Hilton. Secret of Regeneration. Orig. Title: The Science of Human Regeneration (Postgraduate Orthopathy) (Illus.). 900p. 1963. pap. 59.95 (ISBN 0-88697-019-9). Life Science.

Houghton, S. M. Sketches from Church History. Murray, Iain, ed. (Illus.). 256p. (Orig.). 1981. pap. 12.45 (ISBN 0-85151-317-4). Banner of Truth.

Howlett, William J. Old St. Thomas' at Poplar Neck, Bardstown, Kentucky. (Illus.). 200p. 1971. pap. 3.25 (ISBN 0-913228-02-8). R J Liederbach.

Hugh The Chantor. The History of the Church of York, Ten Sixty Six-Eleven Twenty Seven. Johnson, Charles, ed. (Oxford Medieval Texts Ser.). 1984. 22.00x (ISBN 0-19-822213-0). Oxford U Pr.

Hurlbut, Jesse L. Story of the Christian Church. rev. ed. 192p. 1986. 11.95 (ISBN 0-310-26510-X, 6527). Zondervan.

Ioseliani, Platon. A Short History of the Georgian Church. 208p. 1983. pap. 6.00 (ISBN 0-317-30451-8). Holy Trinity.

Jacobs, James P. Rome, Judea & Christianity: The Crucifixion. 300p. 1987. pap. 7.95 (ISBN 0-9617280-0-0). James Pr Inc.

Jay, Eric G. The Church: Its Changing Image Through Twenty Centuries. LC 79-92070. pap. 120.50 (2027153). Bks Demand UMI.

Jedin, Hubert & Dolan, John P., eds. The Church Between Revolution & Restoration. (History of the Church: Vol. 7). 1980. 59.50x (ISBN 0-8245-0004-0). Crossroad NY.

--The Church in the Age of Absolutism & Enlightenment. (History of the Church: Vol. 6). 1981. 59.50x (ISBN 0-8245-0010-5). Crossroad NY.

--The Church in the Age of Liberalism. (History of the Church: Vol. 8). 1981. 59.50x (ISBN 0-8245-0011-3). Crossroad NY.

--From the Apostolic Community to Constantine. (History of the Church: Vol. 1). 1980. 59.50x (ISBN 0-8245-0314-7). Crossroad NY.

Johnson, Paul. A History of Christianity. LC 76-9002. 560p. 1976. pap. 11.95 (ISBN 0-689-70591-3, 252). Atheneum.

Jones, William. The History of the Christian Church, or Jones' Church History, 2 vols. 1983. Repr. of 1826 ed. 42.50 set (ISBN 0-317-01250-9). Church History.

Jordan, James B., ed. The Reconstruction of the Church. LC 86-80570. (Christianity & Civilization Ser.: No. 4). xiv, 338p. (Orig.). 1986. pap. 12.95 (ISBN 0-939404-11-7). Geneva Ministr.

Kannengiesser, Charles, ed. Early Christian Spirituality. Bright, Pamela, tr. from Lat. & Gr. LC 86-45226. (Sources of Early Christian Thought). 144p. 1986. pap. 7.95 (ISBN 0-8006-1416-X). Fortress.

Kater, John. Christians on the Right: The Moral Majority in Perspective. 176p. (Orig.). 1982. pap. 8.95 (ISBN 0-8164-2379-2, HarpR). Har-Row.

Kelly, J. N. Early Christian Doctrines. rev. ed. LC 58-12933. 1978. pap. 10.95xi (ISBN 0-06-064334-X, RD 233, HarpR). Har-Row.

Ketcherside, Carl. Which Church. pap. 0.50 (ISBN 0-686-70363-4). Reiner.

Kidwell, R. J. & DeWelt, Don. Ecclesiastes; Song of Solomon. LC 78-301088. (The Bible Study Textbook Ser.). 1977. 14.30 (ISBN 0-89900-019-3). College Pr Pub.

Kuiper, B. K. The Church in History. pap. 12.95x (ISBN 0-8028-1777-7); tchrs.' manual 6.95x (ISBN 0-8028-1314-3). Eerdmans.

Lapple, Alfred. A Concise History of the Catholic Church. (Orig.). 1985. pap. 4.95 (ISBN 0-8091-9567-4). Paulist Pr.

Larson, Martin A. The Story of Christian Origins. LC 76-40842. 1977. 12.50 (ISBN 0-88331-090-2). J J Binns.

Latham, William I. The Last Outpost of Texas: A History of First Baptist Church, El Paso, Texas--The First Fifty Years. 1987. 20.00 (ISBN 0-930208-21-8). Mangan Bks.

Latourette, Kenneth S. Christianity Through the Ages. (Orig.). pap. 8.95 (ISBN 0-06-065011-7, CB1, HarpR). Har-Row.

--Christianity Through the Ages. 16.75 (ISBN 0-8446-2434-9). Peter Smith.

--Historia del Cristianismo, Tomo II. Quarles, Jaime C. & Quarles, Lemuel C., trs. (Desde el Siglo XVI Hasta el Siglo XX). Orig. Title: A History of the Expansion of Christianity. 968p. 1983. pap. 17.95 (ISBN 0-311-15012-8). Casa Bautista.

--Historia del Cristianismo, Tomo I. Quarles, Jaime C. & Quarles, Lemuel C., trs. from Eng. (Illus.). 819p. 1984. pap. 17.95 (ISBN 0-311-15010-1). Casa Bautista.

--A History of Christianity. rev. ed. Incl. Vol. 1. Beginnings to 1500. 758p. pap. 11.00 (ISBN 0-06-064952-6, RD-93); Vol. 2. Reformation to the Present. 922p. pap. 13.95 (ISBN 0-06-064953-4, RD-94). LC 74-25692. 1975. pap. (HarpR). Har-Row.

--A History of Christianity, 2 vols. Date not set. Vol. I. 13.95 (ISBN 0-317-52393-7, RD 93, HarpR); Vol. II. 13.95 (ISBN 0-317-52394-5, RD 94, HarpR). Har-Row.

Lawson, LeRoy. The New Testament Church Then & Now Workbook. 48p. 1983. pap. 1.75 (ISBN 0-87239-609-6, 88586). Standard Pub.

LeClercq, Jean, et al. A History of Christian Spirituality, 3 vols. 1982. Set. pap. 45.00 slip-cased (ISBN 0-8164-2369-5, HarpR). Har-Row.

Leo Baeck Institute Staff. Leo Baeck Institute Yearbook XXXI. 1987. 35.00 (ISBN 0-436-25545-6, Pub. by Secker & Warburg UK). David & Charles.

Leonard, Bill J. Early American Christianity. LC 83-71489. 1984. pap. 10.95 (ISBN 0-8054-6578-2). Broadman.

Levy, Leonard. Blasphemy in Massachusetts: Freedom of Conscience & the Abner Kneeland Case. LC 70-16634. 592p. 1973. lib. bdg. 65.00 (ISBN 0-306-70221-5). Da Capo.

Littell, Franklin H. Macmillan Atlas History of Christianity. LC 75-22113. (Illus.). 176p. 1976. 24.95 (ISBN 0-02-573140-8, 57314). Macmillan.

Livingston, James C. Modern Christian Thought: From the Enlightenment to Vatican Two. 1971. text ed. write for info. (ISBN 0-02-371420-4). Macmillan.

Loades, David M., ed. The End of Strife. 233p. 1984. 17.95 (ISBN 0-567-09347-6, PUb. by T&T Clark Ltd UK). Fortress.

Lohse, Eduard. The First Christians: Their Beginnings, Writings, & Beliefs. LC 82-7454. 128p. (Orig.). 1983. pap. 6.95 (ISBN 0-8006-1646-4, 1-1646). Fortress.

Lonigan, Paul R. Early Irish Church: From the Beginnings to the Two Doves. 2nd ed. (Illus.). 100p. 1986. pap. 15.99x (ISBN 0-9614753-1-5). Celt Heritage Pr.

McAllister, Lester G. & Tucker, William E. Journey in Faith: A History of the Christian Church. LC 75-11738. 512p. 1975. 14.95 (ISBN 0-8272-1703-X). CBP.

McBride, Alfred & Praem, O. The Story of the Church: Peak Moments from Pentecost to the Year 2000. (Illus.). 168p. 1984. pap. text ed. 7.95 (ISBN 0-86716-029-2). St Anthony Mess Pr.

McCabe, Joseph. The Church Defies Modern Life. 31p. pap. cancelled (ISBN 0-911826-75-0). Am Atheist.

--The Church, the Enemy of the Workers. 32p. 1942. cancelled (ISBN 0-911826-74-2). Am Atheist.

--History's Greatest Liars. 176p. (YA) 1985. pap. 5.00. Am Atheist.

McClain, S. C. Highlights in Church History. 9th ed. (Illus.). 66p. 1983. pap. 2.95 (ISBN 0-912315-06-7). Word Aflame.

MacDonald, William. Christ Loved the Church. pap. 2.95 (ISBN 0-937396-09-5). Walterick Pubs.

MacGregor, Geddes. Reincarnation in Christianity. LC 77-20925. (Orig.). 1978. 9.75 (ISBN 0-8356-0504-3). Theos Pub Hse.

Mack, Burton L. A Myth of Innocence: Mark & Christian Origins. LC 86-45906. (Foundations and Facets Ser.). 448p. 1987. text ed. 9.95 (ISBN 0-8006-2113-1). Fortress.

McKenna, Megan & Ducote, Darryl. Beginnings of the Church. LC 78-71533. (Followers of the Way Ser.: Vol. 6). 1980. 22.50 (ISBN 0-8091-9547-X); cassette 7.50 (ISBN 0-8091-7671-8). Paulist Pr.

Maier, Paul L. First Christians: Pentecost & the Spread of Christianity. LC 75-36751. (Illus.). 160p. 1976. 11.00 (ISBN 0-06-065399-X, HarpR). Har-Row.

--First Christmas, First Easter, First Christians, 3 Bks. (Illus.). 128p. 1982. Boxed Set. pap. 11.00 ea. (ISBN 0-06-065395-7, RD 381, HarpR). Har-Row.

Malgo, Wim. In the Beginning Was the End. pap. 4.95 (ISBN 0-937422-33-9). Midnight Call.

--The Rapture & Its Mystery. pap. 1.95 (ISBN 0-937422-13-4). Midnight Call.

--The Sword of the Lord. pap. 2.95 (ISBN 0-937422-24-X). Midnight Call.

Maner, Robert E. Making the Small Church Grow. 101p. 1982. pap. 2.95 (ISBN 0-8341-0741-4). Beacon Hill.

Manschreck, Clyde L. A History of Christianity in the World: From Persecution to Uncertainty. 2nd ed. (Illus.). 352p. 1985. text ed. 28.67 (ISBN 0-13-389354-5). P-H.

Manschreck, Clyde L., ed. A History of Christianity: Volume II, Readings in the History of the Church from the Reformation to the Present. 576p. 1981. pap. 23.95 (ISBN 0-8010-6124-5). Baker Bk.

Maritain, Jacques. De l'Eglise du Christ. 430p. 1970. 15.95 (ISBN 0-686-56348-4). French & Eur.

Marks, Stanley J. The Two Christs; Or, the Decline & Fall of Christianity. 1983. pap. 14.95 (ISBN 0-938780-03-4). Bur Intl Aff.

Marstin, Ronald. Beyond Our Tribal Gods: The Maturing of Faith. LC 79-4354. 160p. (Orig.). 1979. pap. 5.95 (ISBN 0-88344-030-X). Orbis Bks.

Marty, Martin E. A Short History of Christianity. LC 80-8042. 384p. 1980. pap. 9.95 (ISBN 0-8006-1427-5, 1-1427). Fortress.

Mathews, Thomas F. Early Churches of Constantinople: Architecture & Liturgy. LC 78-111972. (Illus.). 1971. 29.95x (ISBN 0-271-00108-9). Pa St U Pr.

Mead, Frank S. Ten Decisive Battles of Christianity. LC 72-117823. (Essay Index Reprint Ser). 1937. 15.00 (ISBN 0-8369-1812-6). Ayer Co Pubs.

Meeks, Wayne A., ed. Library of Early Christianity. 200p. 1987. 18.95. Westminster.

Mews, Stuart, ed. Religion & National Identity. (Studies in Church History: Vol. 18). 500p. 1982. 45.00x (ISBN 0-631-18060-5). Basil Blackwell.

Middleton, Christopher. The Historie of Heaven. LC 76-57400. (English Experience Ser.: No. 816). 1977. Repr. of 1596 ed. lib. bdg. 5.00 (ISBN 90-221-0777-9). Walter J Johnson.

Milburn, Robert L. Early Christian Interpretations of History. LC 79-21671. 1980. Repr. of 1954 ed. lib. bdg. 22.50x (ISBN 0-313-22157-X, MIEA). Greenwood.

Miller, T., ed. The Old English Version of Bede's Ecclesiastical History, Pt. II, No. 1. (EETS OS Ser.: Vol. 110). Repr. of 1898 ed. 21.00 (ISBN 0-8115-3368-9). Kraus Repr.

Mommsen, A. Athenae Christianae. (Illus.). 177p. 1977. 12.50 (ISBN 0-89005-216-6). Ares.

Montgomery, John W. History & Christianity. 128p. 1986. pap. 3.95 (ISBN 0-87123-890-X, 210890). Bethany Hse.

Morland, Samuel. History of the Evangelical Churches of the Valleys of Piemont. 1983. 32.00 (ISBN 0-686-42929-X). Church History.

Morris, Bryon T. A Charge to Keep. 1971. 4.00 (ISBN 0-87012-092-1). McClain.

Munson, Gorham B. Twelve Decisive Battles of the Mind: The Story of Propaganda During the Christian Era, with Abridged Versions of Texts That Have Shaped History. LC 72-167388. (Essay Index Reprint Ser.). Repr. of 1942 ed. 18.00 (ISBN 0-8369-2705-2). Ayer Co Pubs.

Murray, Andrew. State of the Church. 1983. pap. 2.95 (ISBN 0-87508-407-9). Chr Lit.

Nash, Ronald H. Christian Faith & Historical Understanding. 176p. 1984. pap. 5.95 (ISBN 0-310-45121-3, 12379P). Zondervan.

Neale, John M. Essays on Liturgiology & Church History. LC 70-173070. Repr. of 1863 ed. 32.50 (ISBN 0-404-04667-3). AMS Pr.

Neander, Johann A. General History of the Christian Religion & Church, 9 vols. rev. ed. Torrey, Joseph, tr. from Ger. Repr. of 1858 ed. Set. lib. bdg. 495.00 (ISBN 0-404-09590-9); lib. bdg. 55.00 ea. AMS Pr.

Neill, Stephen. The Pelican History of the Church: A History of the Christian Missions, Vol. 6. 512p. 1987. pap. 6.95 (ISBN 0-14-022736-9, Pelican). Penguin.

Newman, Albert H. A Manual of Church History, 2 vols. 1977. Set. lib. bdg. 250.00 (ISBN 0-8490-2205-3). Gordon Pr.

Newman, Louis I. Jewish Influence on Christian Reform Movements. LC 26-883. (Columbia University. Oriental Studies: No. 23). Repr. of 1925 ed. 45.00 (ISBN 0-404-50513-9). AMS Pr.

Nibley, Hugh. The World & the Profits: Mormanism & Earlt Christianity. 1987. 10.95 (ISBN 0-87579-078-X). Deseret Bk.

North, Gary, ed. Tactics of Christian Resistance. LC 83-81783. (Christianity & Civilization Ser.: No. 3). 528p. 1983. pap. 14.95 (ISBN 0-939404-07-9). Geneva Ministr.

Nystrom, Carolyn. Romans: Christianity on Trial. (Young Fisherman Bible Studyguide Ser.). (Illus.). 124p. 1980. pap. 4.95 tchr's ed. (ISBN 0-87788-899-X); student ed. 3.95 (ISBN 0-87788-898-1). Shaw Pubs.

O'Donnell, J. D. A Survey of Church History. 1973. pap. 4.95 (ISBN 0-89265-009-5). Randall Hse.

Ordericus Vitalis. Ecclesiastical History of England & Normandy, 4 Vols. Forrester, T., tr. LC 68-57872. (Bohn's Antiquarian Library Ser). Repr. of 1856 ed. Set. 115.00 (ISBN 0-404-50040-4). AMS Pr.

Paget, Wilkes M. Poverty, Revolution & the Church. 142p. (Orig.). 1982. pap. text ed. 10.95 (ISBN 0-85364-285-0). Attic Pr.

Pannenberg, Wolfhart. The Church. Crim, Keith, tr. LC 82-23768. 176p. 1983. pap. 10.95 (ISBN 0-664-24460-2). Westminster.

Paulus Orosius. Seven Books of History Against the Pagans. LC 64-8670. (Fathers of the Church Ser: Vol. 50). 414p. 1964. 22.95x (ISBN 0-8132-0050-4). Cath U Pr.

Pennington, M. Basil, et al. The Living Testament: The Essential Writings of Christianity since the Bible. LC 85-42790. 400p. 1985. 22.45 (ISBN 0-06-066499-1, HarpR); pap. 14.95 (ISBN 0-06-066498-3). Har-Row.

Peters, George. A Theology of Church Growth. 368p. 1981. pap. 10.95 (ISBN 0-310-43101-8, 11285P). Zondervan.

Peterson, Eugene. Traveling Light. LC 82-15314. 204p. (Orig.). 1982. pap. 5.25 (ISBN 0-87784-377-5). Inter-Varsity.

Petry, Ray C., ed. A History of Christianity: Volume I, Readings in the History of the Early & Medieval Church. 576p. 1981. pap. 23.95 (ISBN 0-8010-7064-3). Baker Bk.

Phillips, Charles S. The New Commandment: An Inquiry into the Social Precept & Practice of the Ancient Church. (Church Historical Society London Ser.: No. 4). Repr. of 1930 ed. 40.00 (ISBN 0-8115-3128-7). Kraus Repr.

Pickering, Ernest. Biblical Separation: The Struggle for a Pure Church. LC 78-26840. 1979. 6.95 (ISBN 0-87227-069-6). Reg Baptist.

Pierre, Dom & Morice, Hyacinthe. Histoire Ecclesiastique et Civile de Bretagne, 2 vols. 752p. Date not set. Repr. of 1756 ed. text ed. 310.50x (ISBN 0-576-78866-X, Pub. by Gregg Intl Pubs England). Gregg Intl.

Pope, Robert G., ed. The Notebook of the Reverand John Fiske: 1644 to 1675. LC 74-81447. 256p. 1974. 17.50 (ISBN 0-88389-052-6). Essex Inst.

Porter, Larry. Illustrated Stories from Church History, 16 vols. Cheesman, Paul R., ed. (Illus.). write for info (ISBN 0-911712-21-6). Promised Land.

Praeder, Susan M. Miracle Stories in Christian Antiquity. LC 86-45909. 288p. 1987. pap. 22.95 (ISBN 0-8006-2115-8, 1-2115). Fortress.

Preston, Daniel. The Church Triumphant. pap. 4.95 (ISBN 0-934942-30-7). White Wing Pub.

Prudentius. Poems, Vol. 1. LC 63-5499. (Fathers of the Church Ser: Vol. 43). 343p. 1962. 16.95x (ISBN 0-8132-0043-1). Cath U Pr.

Pruitt, Fred. Past, Present & Future of the Church. 72p. pap. 0.60 (ISBN 0-686-29133-6). Faith Pub Hse.

Renwick, A. M. & Harman, A. M. The Story of the Church. 2nd. enl. ed. 272p. (Orig.). 1985. pap. 8.95 (ISBN 0-8028-0092-0). Eerdmans.

Riggle, H. M. The Christian Church: Its Rise & Progress. 488p. 5.00 (ISBN 0-686-29144-1). Faith Pub Hse.

Roberts, B. H. Outlines of Ecclesiastical History. LC 79-9744. 1979. 7.95 (ISBN 0-87747-748-5). Deseret Bk.

Roberts, Frank. To All Generations, a Study of Church History. 276p. (Orig.). 1981. pap. text ed. 10.95 (ISBN 0-933140-17-7); leader's guide 7.95 (ISBN 0-933140-18-5). CRC Pubns.

Rudin, A. James. Israel for Christians. LC 82-7241. 160p. (Orig.). 1983. pap. 8.95 (ISBN 0-8006-1643-X, 1-1643). Fortress.

Russell, D. S. From Early Judaism to Early Church. LC 85-31776. 1986. pap. 5.95 (ISBN 0-8006-1921-8). Fortress.

Schaff, Philip. History of the Christian Church, 8 vols. Incl. Vol. 1. Apostolic Christianity. 17.95 (ISBN 0-8028-8047-9); Vol. 2. Ante-Nicene. 100-325. 17.95 (ISBN 0-8028-8048-7); Vol. 3. Nicene & Post-Nicene. 311-600. 17.95 (ISBN 0-8028-8049-5); Vol. 4. Medieval Christianity. 590-1073. 17.95 (ISBN 0-8028-8050-9); Vol. 5. Middle Ages. 1049-1294. 17.95 (ISBN 0-8028-8051-7); Vol. 6. Middle Ages. 1295-1517. 17.95 (ISBN 0-8028-8052-5); Vol. 7. German Reformation. 17.95 (ISBN 0-8028-8053-3); Vol. 8. Swiss Reformation. 17.95 (ISBN 0-8028-8054-1). 1960. Repr. 17.95 ea.; 143.60 (ISBN 0-8028-8046-0). Eerdmans.

Schaller, Lyle E. Looking in the Mirror: Self-Appraisal in the Local Church. 208p. 1984. pap. 9.50 (ISBN 0-687-22635-X). Abingdon.

Shelly, Bruce. Church History in Plain Language. 512p. 1982. pap. 12.95 (ISBN 0-8499-2906-7). Word Bks.

Sider, Ronald J. Rich Christians in an Age of Hunger: A Biblical Study. 2nd, rev. ed. LC 84-4549. (Illus.). 257p. 1984. pap. 7.95 (ISBN 0-87784-977-3). Inter-Varsity.

Siegel, Paul N. The Meek & the Militant: Religion & Power Across the World. 260p. 1986. 35.00 (ISBN 0-86232-349-5, Pub. by Zed Pr UK); pap. 12.50 (ISBN 0-86232-350-9, Pub. by Zed Pr UK). Humanities.

Sisemore, John T. Church Growth Through the Sunday School. LC 82-70870. (Orig.). 1983. pap. 6.50 (ISBN 0-8054-6237-6). Broadman.

Sitoy, T. Valentino, Jr. A History of Christianity in the Philippines: The Initial Encounter, Vol. 1. (Illus.). 384p. (Orig.). 1985. pap. 18.50x (ISBN 971-10-0254-X, Pub by New Day Philippines). Cellar.

Smith, H. Shelton, et al. American Christianity: An Historical Interpretation with Representative Documents. lib. rep. ed. 1960. Vol. I. 45.00x (ISBN 0-684-15744-6, ScribT); Vol. II. 45.00x (ISBN 0-684-15745-4). Scribner.

Spittler, Russell P. The Church. LC 77-83982. (Radiant Life Ser.). 126p. 1977. pap. 2.50 (ISBN 0-88243-910-3, 02-0910); tchr's. ed. 3.95 (ISBN 0-88243-180-3, 32-0180). Gospel Pub.

Sprunger, Keith. Dutch Puritanism. (Studies in the History of Christian Thought: Vol. 31). 485p. 1982. text ed. 90.00x (ISBN 90-04-06793-0, Pub. by E J Brill Holland). Humanities.

Stambaugh, John E. & Balch, David L. The New Testament in Its Social Environment. LC 85-15516. (Library of Early Christianity: Vol. 2). (Illus.). 208p. 1986. 16.95 (ISBN 0-664-21906-3). Westminster.

Stedman, Ray C. Solomon's Secret: Enjoying Life, God's Good Gift. LC 85-8967. (Authentic Christianity Bks.). 1985. pap. 6.95 (ISBN 0-88070-076-9). Multnomah.

Steiner, Rudolf. From Buddha to Christ. Church, Gilbert, ed. Tr. of Das Esoterische Christentum & die geistige Fuehrung der Menschheit. 103p. 1987. pap. 5.95 (ISBN 0-88010-178-4). Anthroposophic.

Strothmann, Werner. Johannes von Apamea. (Patristische Texte und Studien 11). 1972. 48.40x (ISBN 3-11-002457-8). De Gruyter.

Stupperich, Martin. Osiander in Preussen (1549-1552) (Arbeiten Zur Kirchengeschichte, Vol. 44). 402p. 1973. 30.80x (ISBN 3-11-004221-5). De Gruyter.

Suenens, Leon J. Open the Frontiers. 1981. 8.95 (ISBN 0-8164-0489-5, HarpR). Har-Row.

Talberg, N. D. Istorija Kristijanskoj Tserkvi. Tr. of History of the Christian Church. 494p. 1964. pap. text ed. 20.00 (ISBN 0-317-30289-2); pap. 15.00 (ISBN 0-317-30290-6). Holy Trinity.

--Istorija Russkoi Tserkvi. Tr. of History of the Russuan Church. 927p. 1959. pap. text ed. 25.00 (ISBN 0-317-30295-7). Holy Trinity.

Taylor, John V. The Growth of the Church in Buganda: An Attempt at Understanding. LC 78-26702. (Illus.). 1979. Repr. of 1958 ed. lib. bdg. 24.75x (ISBN 0-313-20802-6, TAGC). Greenwood.

Tefler, William. The Treasure of Sao Roque. (Church Historical Society London N. S. Ser.: No. 14). Repr. of 1932 ed. 40.00 (ISBN 0-8115-3137-6). Kraus Repr.

Tewinkel, Joseph M. Built upon the Cornerstone. LC 80-65148. (Illus.). 178p. (Orig.). 1980. 3.95 (ISBN 0-87509-280-2); Leader's Guide. 2.95 (ISBN 0-87509-286-1). Chr Pubns.

Tillesley, Richard. Animadversions Upon M. Seldens History of Tithes & His Review Thereof. LC 77-7435. (English Experience Ser.: No. 896). 1977. Repr. of 1619 ed. lib. bdg. 26.50 (ISBN 90-221-0896-1). Walter J Johnson.

Toynbee, Arnold J. Christianity & Civilization. 1983. pap. 2.50x (ISBN 0-87574-039-1, 039). Pendle Hill.

Turner, Victor & Turner, Edith. Image & Pilgrimage in Christian Culture. LC 77-25442. (Lectures on the History of Religions Ser.). 1978. 25.00x (ISBN 0-231-04286-8). Columbia U Pr.

Tvedtnes, John. The Church of the Old Testament. rev. ed. LC 80-18595. 111p. 1980. 6.95 (ISBN 0-87747-827-9). Deseret Bk.

Van Der Bent, A. J. God So Loves the World: The Immaturity of World Christianity. LC 79-4470. 160p. (Orig.). 1979. pap. 2.98 (ISBN 0-88344-159-4). Orbis Bks.

Van Engen. The Growth of the True Church. (Amsterdam Studies in Theology: Vol. III). 545p. 1981. pap. text ed. 55.00x (ISBN 90-6203-783-6, Pub. by Rodopi Holland). Humanities.

Vernon, Louise A. Ink on His Fingers. LC 73-171105. (Illus.). 128p. 1972. 4.95 (ISBN 0-8361-1660-7); pap. 4.50 (ISBN 0-8361-1673-9). Herald Pr.

Vigeveno, Henk S. Thirteen Men Who Changed the World. LC 86-3209. (Illus.). 154p. 1986. pap. 5.95 (ISBN 0-8307-1150-3, 5418817) (ISBN 0-8307-1174-0, 6102292). Regal.

Von Funk, Franz X. Manual of Church History, 2 Vols. Cappadelta, Luigi, tr. LC 78-168077. 1910. Set. 67.50 (ISBN 0-404-02646-X). AMS Pr.

Vos, Howard F. Breve Historia de la Iglesia. Orig. Title: An Introduction to Church History. (Span.). 160p. 1987. pap. 3.95 (ISBN 0-8254-1824-0). Kregel.

--An Introduction to Church History. (Orig.). 1984. pap. 7.95 (ISBN 0-8024-0315-8). Moody.

Walker, Sheila S. The Religious Revolution in the Ivory Coast: The Prophet Harris & the Harris Church. LC 81-13010. (Studies in Religion). xvii, 206p. 1983. 29.95x (ISBN 0-8078-1503-9). U of NC Pr.

Walker, Williston. A History of the Christian Church. 4th ed. 1985. text ed. write for info. (ISBN 0-02-423870-8, Pub. by Scribner). Macmillan.

--A History of the Christian Church. 3rd, rev. ed. Handy, Robert T., rev. by. 601p. 1970. text ed. write for info. (ISBN 0-02-424300-0, Pub. by Scribner). Macmillan.

Walton, Robert C. Chronological & Background Charts of Church History. 120p. 1986. pap. text ed. 8.95 (ISBN 0-310-36281-4, 11302P). Zondervan.

Wantland, William C. Foundations of the Faith. LC 82-61889. 176p. (Orig.). 1983. pap. 7.95 (ISBN 0-8192-1320-9). Morehouse.

Weisser, Thomas H. After the Way Called Heresy. (Illus.). 131p. pap. 5.95 (ISBN 0-9610710-0-1). Tom Weisser.

Whaley, Joachim. Religious Toleration & Social Change in Hamburg, 1529-1819. (Cambridge Studies in Early Modern History). 290p. 1985. 49.50 (ISBN 0-521-26189-9). Cambridge U Pr.

White, R. E. Christian Ethics: The Historical Development. pap. 11.95 (ISBN 0-8042-0791-7). John Knox.

Wiersbe, David & Wiersbe, Warren. Making Sense of the Ministry. 128p. (Orig.). 1983. pap. 5.95 (ISBN 0-8024-0164-3). Moody.

Wilbur, Ruth E. & Wilbur, C. Keith. Bid Us God Speed: The History of the Edwards Church, Northhampton, Massachusetts 1833-1983. LC 82-22347. (Illus.). 120p. 1983. 12.95 (ISBN 0-914016-93-8). Phoenix Pub.

Wiles, Maurice. The Christian Fathers. 1982. pap. 6.95x (ISBN 0-19-520260-0). Oxford U Pr.

Wilken, Robert L. The Myth of Christian Beginnings. LC 80-11884. 218p. 1980. 17.95 (ISBN 0-268-01347-0); pap. text ed. 6.95 (ISBN 0-268-01348-9). U of Notre Dame Pr.

Willey, Basil. Christianity, Past & Present. LC 78-65632. 1980. Repr. of 1952 ed. 16.50 (ISBN 0-88355-877-7). Hyperion Conn.

Wilson, Michael L. Outline of Bible History & Major Christian Movements. 1974. pap. 4.95 (ISBN 0-88027-014-4). Firm Foun Pub.

Wright, Christopher. The Christian Church. (Today's World Ser.). (Illus.). 72p. 1982. 16.95 (ISBN 0-7134-4279-4, Pub. by Batsford England). David & Charles.

CHURCH HISTORY–BIBLIOGRAPHY

Dupin, Louis E. Bibliotheque Des Auteurs Ecclesiastiques Du 18e Siecle, 5 vols, Ser. 4. 2100p. Date not set. Repr. of 1736 ed. text ed. 517.50x (ISBN 0-576-72789-X, Pub. by Gregg Intl Pubs England). Gregg Intl.

--Bibliotheque Des Auteurs Separes De la Communion De L'Eglise Romaine Du 16e et 17e Siecles, 5 vols, Ser. III. 1910p. Date not set. Repr. of 1719 ed. text ed. 517.50x (ISBN 0-576-72788-1, Pub. by Gregg Intl Pubs England). Gregg Intl.

Gliozzo, Charles A. Bibliography of Ecclesiastical History of the French Revolution. LC 73-154506. (Bibliographia Tripotamopolitana: No. 6). 1972. 8.00x (ISBN 0-931222-05-2). Pitts Theolog.

Pfaff, Richard W. Medieval Latin Liturgy: A Select Bibliography. (Toronto Medieval Bibliographies Ser.). 128p. 1982. pap. 12.50 (ISBN 0-8020-6488-4). U of Toronto Pr.

Ussher, J., ed. Britannicarum Ecclesiarum Antiquitates. 788p. Date not set. Repr. of 1687 ed. text ed. 165.60x (ISBN 0-576-72233-2, Pub. by Gregg Intl Pubs England). Gregg Intl.

CHURCH HISTORY–CHRONOLOGY

see Chronology, Ecclesiastical

CHURCH HISTORY–DICTIONARIES

Boissonet, V. D. Dictionnaire Dogmatique, Moral, Historique, Canonique, Liturgique et Disciplinaire des Decrets des Diverse Congregations Romaines. Migne, J. P., ed. (Nouvelle Encyclopedie Theologique Ser.: Vol. 26). (Fr.). 646p. Repr. of 1852 ed. lib. bdg. 82.50x (ISBN 0-89241-269-0). Caratzas.

Brauer, Jerald C., ed. Westminster Dictionary of Church History. LC 69-11071. 900p. 1971. 27.50 (ISBN 0-664-21285-9). Westminster.

Grosse, E. Dictionnaire d'Antiphilosophisme ou Refutation des Erreurs du 18e Siecle. Migne, J. P., ed. (Troisieme et Derniere Encyclopedie Theologique Ser.: Vol. 18). (Fr.). 770p. Repr. of 1856 ed. lib. bdg. 97.50x (ISBN 0-89241-301-8). Caratzas.

Guerin, L. F. Dictionnaire de l'Histoire Universelle de l'Eglise, 6 vols. Migne, J. P., ed. (Troisieme et Derniere Encyclopedie Theologique Ser.: Vols. 51-56). (Fr.). 4187p. Repr. of 1873 ed. lib. bdg. 532.50x (ISBN 0-89241-322-0). Caratzas.

McClintock, John & Strong, James. Cyclopaedia of Biblical, Theological, & Ecclesiastical Literature: Cyclopaedia of Biblical Literature, Vol. 1-10. 250.00 (ISBN 0-405-00020-0, 11917). Ayer Co Pubs.

CHURCH HISTORY–HISTORIOGRAPHY

Chadwick, Owen. Catholicism & History. LC 77-77740. 1978. 24.95 (ISBN 0-521-21708-3). Cambridge U Pr.

Downing, Francis G. Church & Jesus. LC 78-3050. (Studies in Biblical Theology, 2nd Ser.: No. 10). 1968. pap. 10.00x (ISBN 0-8401-3060-0). A R Allenson.

CHURCH HISTORY–JUVENILE LITERATURE

Bellini, Enzo, et al. The First Christians: An Illustrated History of the Church. Drury, John, ed. & tr. from Ital. (Illus.). 126p. 1980. 12.95 (ISBN 0-03-056823-4, HarpR). Har-Row.

Hurlbut, Jesse L. Story of the Christian Church. rev. ed. 192p. 1986. 11.95 (ISBN 0-310-26510-X, 6527). Zondervan.

Kepes, Joanne L. Church History. 1981. 9.95 (ISBN 0-89837-070-1, Pub. by Pflaum Pr). Peter Li.

Norwood, Frederick A. & Carr, Jo. Young Reader's Book of Church History. LC 81-20505. (Illus.). 176p. 1982. 11.95 (ISBN 0-687-46827-2). Abingdon.

Vozdvizhensky, P. Moja pervaja Svjashchennaja Istorija, dlja detjej. Tr. of My First Sacred History, for Children. (Illus.). 101p. 1968. pap. 4.00 (ISBN 0-317-30407-0). Holy Trinity.

CHURCH HISTORY–PHILOSOPHY

Hayes, Norvel. From Heaven Come God's Weapons for the Church. 1979. pap. 0.75 (ISBN 0-89274-366-2). Harrison Hse.

Penter, John. Circumstantial Evidence. 144p. 1981. 11.95 (ISBN 0-939762-00-5). Faraday.

CHURCH HISTORY–PRIMITIVE AND EARLY CHURCH, ca. 30-600

see also Alexandrian School, Christian; Apostles; Apostolic Fathers; Catacombs; Church Orders, Ancient; Fathers of the Church; Jewish Christians; Montanism; Neoplatonism

Aland, Kurt. A History of Christianity, Vol. 1: From the Beginnings to the Threshold of the Reformation. Schaaf, James L., tr. LC 84-47913. 464p. 24.95 (ISBN 0-8006-0725-2, 1-725). Fortress.

Angus, Samuel. The Religious Quests of the Graeco-Roman World: A Study in the Historical Background of Early Christianity. LC 66-30791. 1929. 18.00 (ISBN 0-8196-0196-9). Biblo.

Ayer, Joseph C. Sourcebook of Ancient Church History. LC 70-113536. Repr. of 1913 ed. lib. bdg. 64.50 (ISBN 0-404-00436-9). AMS Pr.

Barnes, Arthur S. Christianity at Rome in the Apostolic Age. LC 72-114462. (Illus.). 1971. Repr. of 1938 ed. lib. bdg. 55.00x (ISBN 0-8371-4760-3, BACR). Greenwood.

Barnes, Timothy. Constantine & Eusebius. LC 81-4248. (Illus.). 448p. 1981. text ed. 37.50x (ISBN 0-674-16530-6). Harvard U Pr.

Bartlet, James V. Church Life & Church Order During the First Four Centuries. Cadoux, Cecil J., ed. 1980. lib. bdg. 59.95 (ISBN 0-8490-3147-8). Gordon Pr.

Baur, Ferdinand C. The Church History of the First Three Centuries, 2 vols. Menzies, A., ed. 1980. lib. bdg. 199.75 (ISBN 0-8490-3146-X). Gordon Pr.

Bellini, Enzo, et al. The Church Established, 180-381. Drury, John, ed. & tr. from Ital. (An Illustrated History of the Church). (Illus.). 126p. 12.95 (ISBN 0-03-056824-2, HarpR). Har-Row.

--The End of the Ancient World, Three Hundred Eighty-One to Six Hundred. Drury, John, ed. & tr. from Ital. (Illustrated History of the Church). (Illus.). 126p. 1982. 12.95 (ISBN 0-03-056826-9, HarpR). Har-Row.

Bienert, Wolfgang. Dionysius Von Alexandrien Zur Frage Des Originismus. (Patristische Texte und Studien, 21). 1978. 35.20x (ISBN 3-11-007442-7). De Gruyter.

Bienert, Wolfgang A. Allegoria und Anagoge bei Didymos dem Blinden von Alexandria. (Patristische Texte und Studien Ser.: Vol. 13). xii, 188p. 1972. 23.20x (ISBN 3-11-003715-7). De Gruyter.

Bigg, Charles. The Church's Task Under the Roman Empire. 1977. lib. bdg. 59.95 (ISBN 0-8490-1629-0). Gordon Pr.

Bowra, C. M. Palladas & Christianity. 1959. pap. 2.25 (ISBN 0-85672-641-9, Pub. by British Acad). Longwood Pub Group.

Bray, Gerald. Creeds, Councils & Christ. LC 83-26443. 220p. 1984. pap. 6.95 (ISBN 0-87784-969-2). Inter-Varsity.

Bright, William. Age of the Fathers, 2 Vols. LC 77-113564. Repr. of 1903 ed. Set. 85.00 (ISBN 0-404-01077-6). Vol. 1 (ISBN 0-404-01078-4). Vol. 2 (ISBN 0-404-01079-2). AMS Pr.

Brooks, Keith L. Acts, Adventures of the Early Church. (Teach Yourself the Bible Ser). 1961. pap. 2.75 (ISBN 0-8024-0125-2). Moody.

--Colossians & Philemon. (Teach Yourself the Bible Ser.). 81p. (Orig.). 1961. pap. 2.75 (ISBN 0-8024-1525-3). Moody.

Bruce, F. F. Peter, Stephen, James & John: Studies in Non-Pauline Christianity. (Orig.). 1980. 8.95 (ISBN 0-8028-3532-5). Eerdmans.

Burkitt, Francis C. Early Christianity Outside the Roman Empire: Two Lectures Delivered at Trinity College, Dublin. LC 82-45806. 1983. Repr. of 1899 ed. 18.00 (ISBN 0-404-62375-1). AMS Pr.

Burns, J. Patout, ed. Theological Anthropology. LC 81-43080. (Sources of Early Christian Thought Ser.). 1981. pap. 7.95 (ISBN 0-8006-1412-7). Fortress.

Cadoux, C. John. The Early Christian Attitude to War: A Contribution to the History of Christian Ethics. 304p. 1982. pap. 9.95 (ISBN 0-8164-2416-0, HarpR). Har-Row.

Cary, Margaret M. Are Your Meetings Held in the Life. 1983. pap. 2.50x (ISBN 0-87574-037-5, 037). Pendle Hill.

Chadwick, Henry. Early Church, Pelican History of the Church, Vol. 1. (Orig.). 1968. pap. 5.95 (ISBN 0-14-020502-0, Pelican). Penguin.

Chapman, H. John. Studies on the Early Papacy. LC 76-118517. 1971. Repr. of 1928 ed. 23.00x (ISBN 0-8046-1139-4, Pub. by Kennikat). Assoc Faculty Pr.

Clarke, C. P. Church History from Nero to Constantine. 1977. lib. bdg. 59.95 (ISBN 0-8490-1626-6). Gordon Pr.

Cochrane, Charles N. Christianity & Classical Culture: A Study of Thought & Action from Augustus to Augustine. 1957. pap. 10.95 (ISBN 0-19-500207-5). Oxford U Pr.

Coleman, Christopher B. Constantine the Great & Christianity. LC 70-155636. (Columbia University Studies in the Social Sciences: No. 146). Repr. of 1914 ed. 18.50 (ISBN 0-404-51146-5). AMS Pr.

Coleman, Robert E. The Master Plan of Discipleship. 9.95; pap. 5.95. Revell.

Colledge, M. A. The Parthian Period. (Iconography of Religions XIV Ser.: No. 3). (Illus.). xiv, 47p. 1986. pap. 34.25 (ISBN 90-04-07115-6, Pub. by E J Brill). Heinman.

Conzelmann, Hans. History of Primitive Christianity. Steely, John E., tr. from Ger. LC 72-8818. Orig. Title: Geschichte Des Unchristentums. 192p. 1973. pap. 8.95 (ISBN 0-687-17252-7). Abingdon.

Cunningham, Agnes. The Early Church & the State. LC 81-70666. (Sources of Early Christian Thought Ser.). 128p. 1982. pap. 7.95 (ISBN 0-8006-1413-5, 1-1413). Fortress.

Danielou, Jean & Marrou, Henri. Christian Centuries, Vol. 1: First Six Hundred Years. LC 78-55069. (Illus.). 610p. 1969. 22.95 (ISBN 0-8091-0275-7). Paulist Pr.

Davies, J. G. The Early Christian Church. (Twin Brooks Ser.). 1980. pap. 9.95 (ISBN 0-8010-2906-6). Baker Bk.

Davies, John G. The Early Christian Church. LC 75-3989. (Illus.). 314p. 1976. Repr. of 1965 ed. lib. bdg. 24.00x (ISBN 0-8371-7696-4, DAECC). Greenwood.

Davies, W. D. Christian Origins & Judaism. LC 73-2192. (The Jewish People; History, Religion, Literature Ser.). Repr. of 1962 ed. 22.00 (ISBN 0-405-05258-8). Ayer Co Pubs.

Deanesly, Margaret. The Pre-Conquest Church in England. 2nd ed. (Ecclesiastical History of England Ser.). 376p. 1963. text ed. 30.00x (ISBN 0-06-491638-3). B&N Imports.

Dobschutz, Ernst Von. Christian Life in the Primitive Church. 1977. lib. bdg. 59.95 (ISBN 0-8490-1615-0). Gordon Pr.

Edmundson, George. The Church in Rome in the First Century. 1976. lib. bdg. 59.95 (ISBN 0-8490-1627-4). Gordon Pr.

Edwards, Gene. The Early Church. 1974. pap. text ed. 5.95 (ISBN 0-940232-02-2). Christian Bks.

Eusebeius. The History of the Church: From Christ to Constantine. Williamson, G. A., tr. from Latin. LC 75-22726. Orig. Title: Historia Ecclesiastica. 432p. 1975. pap. 12.95 (ISBN 0-8066-1509-5, 10-3045). Augsburg.

Eusebius. Ecclesiastical History. (Twin Brooks Ser). pap. 11.95 (ISBN 0-8010-3306-3). Baker Bk.

--The History of the Church from Christ to Constantine. Williamson, G. A., tr. (Classics Ser.). 1981. pap. 5.95 (ISBN 0-14-044138-7). Penguin.

Eusebius Pamphili. Ecclesiastical History, 2 Vols. (Loeb Classical Library: No. 153, 265). 13.95x ea. Vol. 1 (ISBN 0-674-99169-9). Vol. 2 (ISBN 0-674-99293-8). Harvard U Pr.

Fiorenza, Elizabeth S., ed. Aspects of Religious Propaganda in Judaism & Early Christianity. LC 74-27890. (University of Notre Dame. Center for the Study of Judaism & Christianity in Antiquity Ser: No. 2). pap. 51.30 (2029308). Bks Demand UMI.

Firth, John B. Constantine the Great: The Reorganization of the Empire & the Triumph of the Church. facsimile ed. LC 77-152983. (Select Bibliographies Reprint Ser). Repr. of 1904 ed. 27.50 (ISBN 0-8369-5735-0). Ayer Co Pubs.

Fowler, Henry T. The History & Literature of the New Testament. LC 78-12516. 1979. Repr. of 1925 ed. lib. bdg. cancelled (ISBN 0-313-21188-4, FOHL). Greenwood.

Frend, W. H. The Early Church. LC 81-43085. 1982. pap. 11.95 (ISBN 0-8006-1615-4). Fortress.

--The Rise of the Monophysite Movement: Chapters in the History of the Church in the Fifth & Sixth Centuries. LC 72-75302. (Illus.). 400p. 1972. 74.50 (ISBN 0-521-08130-0). Cambridge U Pr.

Gibbon, Edward. The Early Growth of Christianity & the History of the First Christians. (Illus.). 177p. 1986. 137.45 (ISBN 0-89266-557-2). Am Classical Coll Pr.

--History of Christianity. LC 79-169227. (Atheist Viewpoint Ser.). (Illus.). 912p. 1972. Repr. of 1883 ed. 51.00 (ISBN 0-405-03796-1). Ayer Co Pubs.

Gilles, Anthony E. People of the Creed: The Story Behind the Early Church. (The People Ser.: Vol. 3). (Illus., Orig.). 1985. pap. text ed. 5.95 (ISBN 0-86716-046-2). St Anthony Mess Pr.

Goodenough, Erwin R. Church in the Roman Empire. LC 77-122754. 1970. Repr. of 1931 ed. lib. bdg. 23.50x (ISBN 0-8154-0337-2). Cooper Sq.

Grant, Robert M. Gods & the One God. LC 85-11443. (Library of Early Christianity: Vol. 1). 212p. 1986. 16.95 (ISBN 0-664-21905-5). Westminster.

Greenslade, Stanley L. Church & State from Constantine to Theodosius. LC 79-8712. 93p. 1981. Repr. of 1954 ed. lib. bdg. 22.50x (ISBN 0-313-20793-3, GRCS). Greenwood.

Gregorius, Saint Les Livres des Miracles & Autres Opuscules, 4 Vols. 1863. Set. 149.00 (ISBN 0-384-19888-0); 38.00 ea.; pap. 32.00 ea.; Set. pap. 125.00 (ISBN 0-384-19889-9). Johnson Repr.

Gryson, R. Le Receuil Arien de Verone. 1983. 46.00 (ISBN 90-247-2705-7, Pub. by Martinus Nijhoff Netherlands). Kluwer Academic.

Guenther, Heinz O. The Footprints of Jesus' Twelve in Early Christian Traditions: A Study in the Meaning of Religious Symbolism. LC 84-48032. (American University Studies VII (Theology & Religion): Vol. 7). 156p. 1984. text ed. 20.90 (ISBN 0-8204-0164-1). P Lang Pubs.

Guthrie, Donald. The Apostles. 432p. 1981. pap. 12.95 (ISBN 0-310-25421-3, 12235P). Zondervan.

Gwatkin, Henry M. Early Church History to A. D. 313, 2 vols. 1977. lib. bdg. 200.00 (ISBN 0-8490-1738-6). Gordon Pr.

--Early Church History to A.D. 313, 2 Vols. LC 77-168216. Repr. of 1909 ed. 52.50 (ISBN 0-404-02966-3). AMS Pr.

Hackett, John. A History of the Orthodox Church of Cyprus from the Coming of the Apostles Paul & Barnabas to the Commencement of the British Occupation (A.D. 45-A.D. 1878) Together with Some Account of the Latin & Other Churches Existing in the Island. LC 79-185941. (Illus.). 760p. 1972. Repr. of 1901 ed. lib. bdg. 35.50 (ISBN 0-8337-1515-1). B Franklin.

Hatch, Edwin. The Influence of Greek Ideas & Usages Upon the Christian Church. 384p. 1972. Repr. of 1891 ed. lib. bdg. 21.50 (ISBN 0-8337-1595-X). B Franklin.

--The Organization of the Early Christian Churches: Eight Lectures Delivered Before the University of Oxford in the Year 1880 on the Foundation of the Late Rev. John Bampton, M. A., Canon of Salisbury. LC 77-183696. (Research & Source Works Ser). 222p. 1972. Repr. of 1881 ed. lib. bdg. 18.50 (ISBN 0-8337-4163-2). B Franklin.

Hedrick, Dr. Charles W., Sr. & Hodgson, Robert, Jr. Nag Hammadi, Gnosticism & Early Christianity. 296p. 1986. pap. 14.95 (ISBN 0-913573-16-7). Hendrickson MA.

Helgeland, John & Daly, Robert J. Christians & the Military: The Early Experience. Burns, J. Patout, ed. LC 84-48718. 112p. 1985. pap. 5.95 (ISBN 0-8006-1836-X, 1-1836). Fortress.

Hengel, Martin. Property & Riches in the Early Church: Aspects of a Social History of Early Christianity. Bowden, John, tr. from Ger. LC 75-305658. pap. 26.00 (2026856). Bks Demand UMI.

Hertling, Ludwig. Communio: Church & Papacy in Early Christianity. Wicks, Jared, tr. from Ger. LC 75-38777. (Orig.). 1972. pap. 2.95 (ISBN 0-8294-0212-8). Loyola.

Hickey, Anne E. Women of the Roman Aristocracy As Christian Monastics. Miles, Margaret R., ed. LC 86-19242. (Studies in Religion: No. 1). 159p. 1986. 39.95 (ISBN 0-8357-1757-7). UMI Res Pr.

Hinson, E. Glenn, ed. & tr. Understanding of the Church: Sources of Early Christian Thought. pap. 6.95 (ISBN 0-317-52518-2). Fortress.

Hofler, Karl A., ed. Geschichtschreiber der Husitischen Bewegung in Bohmen, Vols. 2, 6, 7. (Ger). pap. 65.00 ea. vol. 2, 6; pap. 23.00 vol. 7 (ISBN 0-384-23810-6). Johnson Repr.

Huttman, Maude A. Establishment of Christianity & the Proscription of Paganism. LC 15-703. (Columbia University. Studies in the Social Sciences: No. 147). Repr. of 1914 ed. 18.50 (ISBN 0-404-51147-3). AMS Pr.

Ide, Arthur F. Martyrdom of Women in the Early Christian Church. LC 85-14741. (Illus.). 100p. 1985. pap. 6.95 (ISBN 0-934667-00-4). Tangelwuld.

Jedin, Hubert & Dolan, John P., eds. The Imperial Church from Constantine to the Early Middle Ages. (History of the Church: Vol. 2). 1980. 59.50x (ISBN 0-8245-0315-5). Crossroad NY.

Jehan, L. F. Dictionnaire des Origines du Christianisme. Migne, J. P., ed. (Troisieme et Derniere Encyclopedie Theologique Ser.: Vol. 15). (Fr.). 630p. Repr. of 1856 ed. lib. bdg. 81.00x (ISBN 0-89241-298-4). Caratzas.

Joachim Pillai, C. A. Early Missionary Preaching: A Study of Luke's Report in Acts 13. 1979. 8.00 (ISBN 0-682-49403-8, University). Exposition Pr FL.

Jones, Clifford M. New Testament Illustrations. (Cambridge Bible Commentary on the New English Bible, New Testament Ser.). 27.95 (ISBN 0-521-05446-X); pap. 12.95x (ISBN 0-521-09376-7, 376). Cambridge U Pr.

Kenyon, Frederic G. The Bible & Modern Scholarship. LC 78-9892. 1979. Repr. of 1948 ed. lib. bdg. 22.50x (ISBN 0-313-21009-8, KEBI). Greenwood.

Kidd, Beresford J. A History of the Church to A.D. 461, 3 vols. LC 75-41165. Repr. of 1922 ed. Set. 135.00 (ISBN 0-404-15010-1). AMS Pr.

Kirsch, Johann P. Roemischen Titelkirchen Im Altertum. 1918. 19.00 (ISBN 0-384-29614-9). Johnson Repr.

Kydd, Dr. Ronald A. Charismatic Gifts in the Early Church. 172p. 1984. pap. 4.95 (ISBN 0-913573-09-4). Hendrickson MA.

Lanslots, D. I. The Primitive Church. LC 79-67862. 295p. 1980. pap. 5.50 (ISBN 0-89555-134-9). TAN Bks Pubs.

Lawson, LeRoy. The New Testament Church Then & Now. LC 81-50631. 160p. (Orig.). 1981. pap. 3.95 (ISBN 0-87239-443-3, 88585). Standard Pub.

Lebreton, Jules & Zeiller, Jacques. History of the Primitive Church. 80.00 (ISBN 0-8490-0361-X). Gordon Pr.

Leigh-Bennett, Ernest. Handbook of Early Christian Fathers. 59.95 (ISBN 0-8490-0276-1). Gordon Pr.

Lindsell, Harold. The Armageddon Spectre. LC 84-72012. 142p. (Orig.). 1984. pap. 5.95 (ISBN 0-89107-329-9, Crossway Bks). Good News.

McCullough, W. Stewart. A Short History of Syriac Christianity to the Rise of Islam. LC 80-29297. (Scholars Press Polebridge Bks.). 1981. 21.95 (ISBN 0-89130-454-1, 00-03-04). Scholars Pr GA.

March, W. Eugene, ed. Texts & Testaments: Critical Essays on the Bible & Early Church Fathers. LC 79-92585. 321p. 1980. 15.00 (ISBN 0-911536-80-9). Trinity U Pr.

Massey, Gerald. Gnostic & Historic Christianity. 1985. pap. 5.95 (ISBN 0-916411-51-6). Sure Fire.

Mattingly, Harold. Christianity in the Roman Empire. 1967. pap. 4.95x (ISBN 0-393-00397-3, Norton Lib). Norton.

Mills, Michael. Dirty Hands, Pure Hearts. 1985. 4.50 (ISBN 0-89536-724-6, 5808). CSS of Ohio.

Milman, Henry H. History of Christianity from the Birth of Christ to the Abolition of Paganism in the Roman Empire, 3 Vols. new & rev. ed. LC 78-172733. Repr. of 1863 ed. Set. 125.00 (ISBN 0-404-04350-X). AMS Pr.

Moore, E. A. The Early Church in the Middle East. 55p. 1985. 19.00x (ISBN 0-317-39058-9, Pub. by Luzac & Co Ltd). State Mutual Bk.

Neusner, Jacob. Judaism, Christianity & Zoroastrianism in Talmudic Babylonia. (Studies in Judaism). 240p. (Orig.). 1987. lib. bdg. 26.50 (ISBN 0-8191-5727-9, Pub. by Studies in Judaism); pap. text ed. 13.50 (ISBN 0-8191-5728-7). U Pr of Amer.

Neusner, Jacob & Frerichs, Ernest S., eds. To See Ourselves As Others See Us: Christians Jews, "Others" in Late Antiquity. (Scholars Press Studies in the Humanities). (Orig.). 1985. 38.95 (ISBN 0-89130-819-9, 00-01-09); pap. 25.95 (ISBN 0-89130-820-2). Scholars Pr GA.

Nickelsburg, George W. & MacRal, George W., eds. Christians Among Jews & Gentiles: Essays in Honor of Krister Stendahl. pap. 19.95 (ISBN 0-317-52516-6). Fortress.

Parham, Charles F. & Parham, Sarah E. The Life of Charles F. Parham, Founder of the Apostolic Faith Movement. (The Higher Christian Life Ser.). 468p. 1985. lib. bdg. 60.00 (ISBN 0-8240-6436-4). Garland Pub.

Pfleiderer, Otto. Primitive Christianity, 4 vols. Morrison, W. D., ed. Montgomery, W., tr. LC 65-22085. (Library of Religious & Philosophical Thought). 1966. Repr. of 1906 ed. lib. bdg. 150.00x (ISBN 0-678-09954-5, Reference Bk Pubs). Kelley.

Phillips, Charles S. New Commandment: An Inquiry into the Social Precept & Practice of the Ancient Church. LC 31-31370. (Church Historical Society Ser.: No. 4). 1930. 10.00x (ISBN 0-8401-5004-0). A R Allenson.

Ramsay, W. M. The Church in the Roman Empire Before A. D. 170. LC 77-6997. 1977. Repr. of 1904 ed. 50.00 (ISBN 0-89341-216-3). Longwood Pub Group.

--Pauline & Other Studies in Early Christian History. 1977. lib. bdg. 59.95 (ISBN 0-8490-2416-1). Gordon Pr.

Raven, Charles. Apollinarianism: An Essay on the Christology of the Early Church. LC 77-84706. Repr. of 1923 ed. 38.00 (ISBN 0-404-16113-8). AMS Pr.

Richardson, P. & Granskou, D., eds. Anti-Judaism in Early Christianity: Vol. 1, Paul & the Gospels. 240p. 1984. pap. text ed. 17.95x (ISBN 0-88920-167-6, Pub. by Wilfrid Laurier Canada). Humanities.

Saint Victor Of Vita. Historia Persecutionis Africanae Provinciae. (Corpus Scriptorum Ecclesiasticorum Latinorum Ser.: Vol. 7). 1881. 30.00 (ISBN 0-384-64540-2). Johnson Repr.

Schell, William G. Biblical Trace of the Church. 173p. pap. 1.50 (ISBN 0-686-29103-4). Faith Pub Hse.

Sevestre, A. Dictionnaire de Patrologie, 4 vols. in 5. Migne, J. P., ed. (Nouvelle Encyclopedie Theologique Ser.: Vols. 20-23b). (Fr.). 3830p. Repr. of 1859 ed. lib. bdg. 485.00x (ISBN 0-89241-267-4). Caratzas.

Shotwell, James T. & Loomis, Louis R., eds. See of Peter. 1965. lib. bdg. 49.00x (ISBN 0-374-97391-1, Octagon). Hippocrene Bks.

Simon, Marcal. Verus Israel. McKeating, H., tr. 592p. 1985. 57.00x (ISBN 0-19-710035-X). Oxford U Pr.

Smith, Michael K. The Church Under Siege. LC 76-12304. (Illus.). 1976. pap. 5.95 (ISBN 0-87784-855-6). Inter-Varsity.

Sordi, Marta. The Christians & the Roman Empire. Bedini, Annabel, tr. LC 86-40081. 224p. 1986. 22.50x (ISBN 0-8061-2011-8). U of Okla Pr.

Stowers, Stanley K. Letter Writing in Greco-Roman Antiquity. LC 86-9082. (Library of Early Christianity: Vol. 5). 192p. 1986. 18.95 (ISBN 0-664-21909-8). Westminster.

Streeter, B. H. The Primitive Church: Studies in the Origin of the Christian Ministry. 1977. lib. bdg. 59.95 (ISBN 0-8490-2473-0). Gordon Pr.

Strzygowski, Josef. Early Church Art in Northern Europe. LC 77-73725. (Illus.). 1980. Repr. of 1928 ed. lib. bdg. 30.00 (ISBN 0-87817-246-7). Hacker.

Swartley, Willard M., ed. Essays on War & Peace: Bible & Early Church. (Occasional Papers Ser.: No. 9). 154p. 1986. pap. text ed. 6.50 (ISBN 0-936273-09-7). Inst Mennonite.

Taylor, John W. The Coming of the Saints: Imaginations & Studies in Early Church History & Tradition. 1977. lib. bdg. 59.95 (ISBN 0-8490-1647-9). Gordon Pr.

Theissen, Gerd. Sociology of Early Palestinian Christianity. Bowden, John, tr. from Ger. LC 77-15248. Tr. of Soziologie der Jesusbewegung. 144p. 1978. pap. 5.95 (ISBN 0-8006-1330-9, 1-1330). Fortress.

Trigg, Joseph W. Origen: The Bible & Philosophy in the Third Century Church. (Illus.). 280p. 1983. pap. 16.95 (ISBN 0-8042-0945-6). John Knox.

Trimingham, J. Spencer. Christianity among the Arabs in Pre-Islamic Times. (Arab Background Ser.). (Illus.). 1979. text ed. 30.00x (ISBN 0-582-78081-0). Longman.

The Triumph of the Meek: Why Early Christianity Succeeded. LC 86-45030. (Illus.). 256p. 1986. 17.95 (ISBN 0-06-069254-5, HarpR). Har-Row.

Volz, Carl A. Faith & Practice in the Early Church. LC 82-72654. 224p. 1983. pap. 11.95 (ISBN 0-8066-1961-9, 10-2177). Augsburg.

Wallace-Hadrill, J. M. The Frankish Church. LC 83-13051. (Oxford History of the Chri). 1983. 59.95x (ISBN 0-19-826906-4). Oxford U Pr.

Wand, J. W. C. History of the Early Church from A.D. 500. 4th ed. 300p. 1975. pap. 11.95x (ISBN 0-416-18110-4, NO. 2572). Methuen Inc.

Weber, Hans R. The Militant Ministry: People & Pastors of the Early Church. LC 64-12990. (The Knubel-Miller Lectures for 1963). pap. 30.00 (2027186). Bks Demand UMI.

Westbury-Jones, John. Roman & Christian Imperialism. LC 78-118555. 1971. Repr. of 1939 ed. 28.00x (ISBN 0-8046-1180-7, Pub. by Kennikat). Assoc Faculty Pr.

Wilde, Robert. The Treatment of the Jews in the Christian Writers of the First Three Centuries, Vol. 81. (Patristic Studies). 255p. 1984. Repr. of 1949 ed. 38.00x (ISBN 0-939738-28-7). Zubal Inc.

Winslow, Donald F. The Dynamics of Salvation: A Study in Gregory of Nazianzus. LC 79-89897. (Patristic Mongraph: No. 7). 1979. pap. 8.50 (ISBN 0-915646-06-4). Phila Patristic.

Winslow, Donald F., ed. Disciplina Nostra: Essays in Memory of Robert F. Evans. LC 79-89556. (Patristic Monograph: No. 6). (Orig.). 1979. pap. 8.50 (ISBN 0-915646-05-6). Phila Patristic.

Ydur, Rudy. Key to Inerrancy. 1980. pap. 3.00 (ISBN 0-930592-05-0). Lumeli Pr.

CHURCH HISTORY–PRIMITIVE AND EARLY CHURCH, ca. 30-600–FICTION

Boyer, John W. & Kirshner, Julius, eds. University of Chicago Readings in Western Civilization: The Church in the Roman Empire, Vol. 3. LC 85-16328. 1986. lib. bdg. 20.00x (ISBN 0-226-06938-9); pap. text ed. 7.95x (ISBN 0-226-06939-7). U of Chicago Pr.

Kee, Howard C. Miracle in the Early Christian World: A Study in Sociohistorical Method. LC 83-40004. 304p. 1983. 30.00x (ISBN 0-300-03008-8); pap. 9.95 (ISBN 0-300-03632-9, Y-570). Yale U Pr.

Sienkiewicz, Henryk. Quo Vadis. (Classics Ser). 1968. pap. 2.50 (ISBN 0-8049-0188-0, CL-188). Airmont.

Spears, W. H., Jr. Constantine's Triumph: A Tale of the Era of the Martyrs. LC 63-19710. 1964. 3.95 (ISBN 0-9600106-1-0). Spears.

CHURCH HISTORY–MIDDLE AGES, 600-1500

see also Albigenses; Crusades; Inquisition; Monasticism and Religious Orders–Middle Ages, 600-1500; Mysticism–Middle Ages, 600-1500; Papacy; Patarines; Popes–Temporal Power; Reformation–Early Movements; Schism, the Great Western, 1378-1417; Waldenses

Aland, Kurt. A History of Christianity, Vol. 1: From the Beginnings to the Threshold of the Reformation. Schaaf, James L., tr. LC 84-47913. 464p. 24.95 (ISBN 0-8006-0725-2, 1-725). Fortress.

Allies, Mary H. Three Catholic Reformers of the Fifteenth Century. facsimile ed. LC 73-38755. (Essay Index Reprint Ser). Repr. of 1878 ed. 13.00 (ISBN 0-8369-2633-1). Ayer Co Pubs.

Bainton, Roland H. The Medieval Church. LC 78-11433. (Anvil Ser.). 192p. 1979. pap. 7.50 (ISBN 0-88275-786-5). Krieger.

Baker, Derek, ed. Medieval Women. (Studies in Church History: Subsidia 1). (Illus.). 412p. 1979. 45.00x (ISBN 0-631-19260-3). Basil Blackwell.

--Medieval Women. (Studies in Church History: Subsidia 1). 412p. 1981. pap. 9.95x (ISBN 0-631-12539-6). Basil Blackwell.

Baldwin, Marshall W. The Mediaeval Church. (Development of Western Civilization Ser). 124p. (Orig.). 1953. pap. 4.95x (ISBN 0-8014-9842-2). Cornell U Pr.

--The Mediaeval Church. LC 82-2992. (The Development of Western Civilization Ser.). xii, 124p. 1982. Repr. of 1953 ed. lib. bdg. 22.50x (ISBN 0-313-23554-6, BAME). Greenwood.

Baldwin, Summerfield. Organization of Medieval Christianity. 1986. 11.25 (ISBN 0-8446-1051-8). Peter Smith.

Bellini, Enzo. The Middle Ages, 900-1300. Drury, John, ed. & tr. from Ital. (An Illustrated History of the Church). 126p. 12.95 (ISBN 0-03-056828-5, HarpR). Har-Row.

Bellini, Enzo, et al. The Church in the Age of Humanism, 1300-1500. Drury, John, ed. & tr. (An Illustrated History of the Church). 126p. 12.95 (ISBN 0-03-056829-3, HarpR). Har-Row.

Brehier, Louis. La Querelle des Images Huitieme-Neuvieme Siecle. 1969. 14.00 (ISBN 0-8337-0362-5). B Franklin.

Buck, Mark. Politics, Finance & the Church in the Reign of Edward II: Walter Stapeldon, Treasurer of England. LC 82-17695. (Cambridge Studies in Medieval Life & Thought 19). 248p. 1983. 52.50 (ISBN 0-521-25025-0). Cambridge U Pr.

Bullough, Vern & Brundage, James, eds. Sexual Practices & the Medieval Church. LC 80-85227. 289p. 1984. pap. 15.95 (ISBN 0-87975-268-8). Prometheus Bks.

Bynum, Caroline W. Jesus As Mother: Studies in the Spirituality of the High Middle Ages. LC 81-13137. (Center for Medieval & Renaissance Studies. UCLA Publications: No. 16). 280p. 1982. pap. text ed. 7.95 (ISBN 0-520-05222-6, CAL 697). U of Cal Pr.

Cannon, William R. History of Christianity in the Middle Ages. (Twin Brooks Ser.). 1983. pap. 9.95 (ISBN 0-8010-2492-7). Baker Bk.

Cheney, Mary G. Roger, Bishop of Worcestor Eleven Sixty Four to Eleven Seventy Nine: An English Bishop of the Age of Becket. (Oxford Historical Monographs). (Illus.). 1980. 63.00x (ISBN 0-19-821879-6). Oxford U Pr.

Chibnall, Marjorie, ed. The Ecclesiastical History of Orderic Vitalis, Vol. 1. (Oxford Medieval Texts Ser.). (Illus.). 1981. 98.00x (ISBN 0-19-822243-2). Oxford U Pr.

Cohn, Norman. Pursuit of the Millennium. rev ed. 1970. pap. 11.95 (ISBN 0-19-500456-6). Oxford U Pr.

Cowie, Frederick J. Giants of Medieval Church. 175p. Date not set. pap. 7.95 (ISBN 0-87973-586-4, 586). Our Sunday Visitor.

Damian, Peter. Book of Gomorrah: An Eleventh-Century Treatise Against Clerical Homosexual Practices. Payer, Pierre J., tr. 120p. 1982. pap. text ed. 10.50x (ISBN 0-88920-123-4, Pub. by Wilfrid Laurier Canada). Humanities.

Deanesly, Margaret. History of the Medieval Church, Five Ninety to Fifteen Hundred. 9th ed. 1969. pap. 12.50x (ISBN 0-416-18100-7, NO. 2163). Methuen Inc.

Dobson, R. B., ed. The Church, Politics & Patronage in the Fifteenth Century. LC 84-15102. 245p. 1985. 25.00 (ISBN 0-312-13481-9). St Martin.

Doellinger, Johann J. Beitrage Zur Sektengenchichte des Mittelalter, 2 vols in 1. LC 91-26634. (Social Science Ser). (Ger). 1970. Repr. of 1890 ed. Set. lib. bdg. 57.50 (ISBN 0-8337-0880-5). B Franklin.

Elder, Rozanne, ed. From Cloister to Classroom: The Spirituality of Western Christendom III. (Cistercian Studies: No. 90). 1986. 26.95 (ISBN 0-87907-890-1); pap. 10.95 (ISBN 0-87907-990-8). Cistercian Pubns.

Eusebius. The History of the Church from Christ to Constantine. Williamson, G. A., tr. (Classics Ser.). 1981. pap. 5.95 (ISBN 0-14-044138-7). Penguin.

Evans, G. Rosemary. Anselm & a New Generation. 1980. 32.50x (ISBN 0-19-826651-0). Oxford U Pr.

Ferguson, Everett. Church History, Early & Medieval. 2nd ed. (Way of Life Ser: No. 106). (Orig.). 1966. pap. 3.95 (ISBN 0-89112-106-4, Bibl Res Pr). Abilene Christ U.

Fine, John V. The Bosnian Church: A Study of the Bosnian Church & Its Place in State & Society from the 13th to 15th Centuries. (East European Monographs: No. 10). 447p. 1975. 30.00x (ISBN 0-914710-03-6). East Eur Quarterly.

Fischer, Maximiliano, ed. Codex Traditionum Ecclesiae Collegiatae Claustroneoburgensis Continens Donationes, Fundationes Commutationesque Hanc Ecclesiam Attinentes Ab Anno Domin: MCCLX Usque Circiter MCCLX. Repr. of 1851 ed. 23.00 (ISBN 0-384-29873-7). Johnson Repr.

Fletcher, R. A. The Episcopate in the Kingdom of Leon in the Twelfth Century. (Historical Monographs). (Illus.). 1978. 42.00x (ISBN 0-19-821869-9). Oxford U Pr.

Flick, Alexander C. Decline of the Medieval Church, 2 vols. (Bibliography & Reference Ser.: No. 133). 1968. Repr. of 1930 ed. Set. 48.00 (ISBN 0-8337-1158-X). B Franklin.

--Rise of the Medieval Church & Its Influence on the Civilization of Western Europe from the 1st to the 13th Century. 636p. 1973. Repr. of 1909 ed. lib. bdg. 33.50 (ISBN 0-8337-1159-8). B Franklin.

Gabel, Leona C. Benefit of Clergy in England in the Later Middle Ages. 1969. lib. bdg. 17.00x (ISBN 0-374-92964-5, Octagon). Hippocrene Bks.

Garnier, H. L' Idee du Juste Prix Chez les Theologiens et Cannonistes du Moyen Age. LC 79-122228. (Fr.). 164p. 1973. Repr. of 1900 ed. lib. bdg. 20.50 (ISBN 0-8337-1286-1). B Franklin.

Gill, Joseph. The Council of Florence. LC 78-63345. (The Crusades & Military Orders: Second Ser.). (Illus.). 480p. Repr. of 1959 ed. 37.50 (ISBN 0-404-17016-1). AMS Pr.

Haureau, Barthelemy. Bernard Delicieux et l'Inquisition Albigeoise, 1300-1320. LC 78-63180. (Heresies of the Early Christian & Medieval Era: Second Ser.). Repr. of 1877 ed. 31.00 (ISBN 0-404-16223-1). AMS Pr.

Hillgarth, J. N., ed. Christianity & Paganism, Three Hundred Fifty to Seven Hundred Fifty: The Conversion of Western Europe. rev. ed. LC 85-1154. (Middle Ages Ser.). 160p. 1986. lib. bdg. 25.00 (ISBN 0-8122-7993-X); pap. 10.95 (ISBN 0-8122-1213-4). U of Pa Pr.

Howorth, Henry H. Golden Days of the Early English Church from the Arrival of Theodore to the Death of Bede, 3 Vols. LC 79-153612. Repr. of 1917 ed. Set. 75.00 (ISBN 0-404-09470-8); 25.00 ea. Vol. 1 (ISBN 0-404-09471-6). Vol. 2 (ISBN 0-404-09472-4). Vol. 3 (ISBN 0-404-09473-2). AMS Pr.

Hugh The Chantor. The History of the Church of York, Ten Sixty Six-Eleven Twenty Seven. Johnson, Charles, ed. (Oxford Medieval Texts Ser.). 1984. 22.00x (ISBN 0-19-822213-0). Oxford U Pr.

Johannes Canaparius. Das Leben Des Bischofs Adalbert Von Prag. Hueffer, Hermann, tr. xiv, 54p. (Ger.). pap. 8.00 (ISBN 0-384-31946-7). Johnson Repr.

Kieckhefer, Richard. Unquiet Souls: Fourteenth Century Saints & Their Religious Milieu. LC 84-210. (Illus.). viii, 238p. 1987. pap. 10.95 (ISBN 0-226-43510-5). U of Chicago Pr.

Knowles, David & Obolensky, Dimitri. Christian Centuries, Vol. 2: Middle Ages. LC 63-22123. 628p. 1969. 22.95 (ISBN 0-8091-0276-5). Paulist Pr.

Loud, G. A. Church & Society in the Norman Principality of Capua, 1058-1197. (Historical Monographs). (Illus.). 1985. 42.00x (ISBN 0-19-822931-3). Oxford U Pr.

Lytle, Guy F., ed. Reform & Authority in the Medieval & Reformation Church. LC 79-17380. pap. 87.80 (2029496). Bks Demand UMI.

MacCulloch, J. Arnott. Medieval Faith & Fable. 1978. Repr. of 1932 ed. lib. bdg. 47.50 (ISBN 0-8492-1662-1). R West.

Maitland, S. R. Dark Ages: Essays Illustrating the State of Religion & Literature in the Ninth, Tenth, Eleventh & Twelfth Centuries, 2 vols. LC 68-8242. 1969. Repr. of 1889 ed. 40.00 (ISBN 0-8046-0297-2, Pub. by Kennikat). Assoc Faculty Pr.

Oakley, Francis. The Western Church in the Later Middle Ages. LC 79-7621. 352p. 1985. 32.50x (ISBN 0-8014-1208-0); pap. text ed. 9.95x (ISBN 0-8014-9347-1). Cornell U Pr.

O'Brien, John M. Medieval Church. (Quality Paperback: No. 227). 120p. (Orig.). 1968. pap. 2.95 (ISBN 0-8226-0227-X). Littlefield.

Pargoire, Jules. Eglise Byzantine De 527 a 847. 1971. Repr. of 1905 ed. lib. bdg. 26.00 (ISBN 0-8337-2672-2). B Franklin.

Russell, Jeffrey. History of Medieval Christianity. LC 68-9743. 1968. pap. 8.95x (ISBN 0-88295-761-9). Harlan Davidson.

Russell, Jeffrey B. Dissent & Reform in the Early Middle Ages. LC 78-63178. (Heresies of the Early Christian & Medieval Era: Second Ser.). 344p. Repr. of 1965 ed. 36.00 (ISBN 0-404-16196-0). AMS Pr.

Sheedy, Charles E. The Eucharistic Controversy of the Eleventh Century Against the Background of Pre-Scholastic Theology. LC 78-63179. (Heresies of the Early Christian & Medieval Era: Second Ser.). Repr. of 1947 ed. 30.00 (ISBN 0-404-16197-9). AMS Pr.

Smith, Jonathan R. The First Crusade & the Idea of Crusading. LC 86-1608. (Middle Ages Ser.). 224p. 1986. text ed. 29.95x (ISBN 0-8122-8026-1). U of Pa Pr.

Smith, Michael K. The Church Under Siege. LC 76-12304. (Illus.). 1976. pap. 5.95 (ISBN 0-87784-855-6). Inter-Varsity.

Somerville, Robert. Pope Alexander III & the Council of Tours (1163) A Study of Ecclesiastical Politics & Institutions in the Twelfth Century. (Center for Medieval & Renaissance Studies, UCLA: Publications No. 12). 1978. 24.50x (ISBN 0-520-03184-9). U of Cal Pr.

Somerville, Robert, ed. Scotia Pontificia: Papal Letters to Scotland Before the Pontificate of Innocent III, 1198 to 1216. 1981. 65.00x (ISBN 0-19-822433-8). Oxford U Pr.

Volz, Carl A. Church of the Middle Ages. LC 72-99217. (Church in History Ser). 1978. pap. 4.95 (ISBN 0-570-06270-5, 12-2725). Concordia.

Weinstein, Donald & Bell, Rudolph M. Saints & Society: The Two Worlds of Western Christendom, 1000 to 1700. LC 82-7972. (Illus.). xii, 314p. 1986. 25.00x (ISBN 0-226-89055-4); pap. 11.95 (ISBN 0-226-89056-2). U of Chicago Pr.

Weske, Dorothy B. Convocation of the Clergy: A Study of Antecedents & Its Rise, with Special Emphasis upon Its Growth & Activities in the Thirteenth & Fourteenth Centuries. (Church Historical Society London N. S. Ser.: No. 23). Repr. of 1937 ed. 60.00 (ISBN 0-8115-3147-3). Kraus Repr.

Williams, John. The Holy Table, Name & Thing, More Patiently, Properly, & Literally Used Under the New Treatment, Than That of an Altar. LC 79-84146. (English Experience Ser.: No.962). 244p. 1979. Repr. of 1637 ed. lib. bdg. 22.00 (ISBN 90-221-0962-3). Walter J Johnson.

Zeibig, Hartmann, ed. Urkundenbuch Des Stiftes Klosterneuburg Bis Zum Ende Des Vierzehnten Jahrhunderts. (Ger). Repr. of 1857 ed. 62.00 (ISBN 0-384-29875-3). Johnson Repr.

CHURCH HISTORY–MIDDLE AGES, 600-1500–HISTORIOGRAPHY

Jedin, Hubert & Dolan, John P., eds. From the High Middle Ages to the Eve of the Reformation. (History of the Church: Vol. 4). 1980. 59.50x (ISBN 0-8245-0317-1). Crossroad NY.

Southerm, R. W. Western Society & the Church in the Middle Ages. (History of the Church). (Orig.). 1970. pap. 5.95 (ISBN 0-14-020503-9, Pelican). Penguin.

CHURCH HISTORY–REFORMATION, 1517-1648

see Reformation

CHURCH HISTORY–SOURCES

see also Christian Literature, Early

Articles Agreed on in the National Synode of the Reformed Churches of France. LC 76-57381. (English Experience Ser.: No. 799). 1977. Repr. of 1623 ed. lib. bdg. 5.00 (ISBN 90-221-0799-X). Walter J Johnson.

Broughton, Richard. English Protestants Plea. LC 76-57380. (English Experience Ser.: No. 798). 1977. Repr. of 1621 ed. lib. bdg. 9.50 (ISBN 90-221-0798-1). Walter J Johnson.

Bucer, Martin. A Briefe Treatise Concerning the Burnynge of Bucer & Phagius at Cambridge. LC 76-57362. (English Experience Ser.: No. 780). 1977. Repr. of 1562 ed. lib. bdg. 14.00 (ISBN 90-221-0780-9). Walter J Johnson.

Burton, Henry. An Apology of Appeale: Also, an Epistle to the True Hearted Nobility. LC 76-57364. (English Experience Ser.: No. 782). 1977. Repr. of 1636 ed. lib. bdg. 5.00 (ISBN 90-221-0782-5). Walter J Johnson.

--For God & the King. LC 76-57365. (English Experience Ser.: No. 783). 1977. lib. bdg. 17.50 (ISBN 90-221-0783-3). Walter J Johnson.

Downing, Francis G. Church & Jesus. LC 78-3050. (Studies in Biblical Theology, 2nd Ser.: No. 10). 1968. pap. 10.00x (ISBN 0-8401-3060-0). A R Allenson.

Draxe, Thomas. Bibliotheca Scholastica Instructissima: Or a Treasure of Ancient Adagies. LC 76-57378. (English Experience Ser.: No. 796). 1977. Repr. lib. bdg. 24.00 (ISBN 90-221-0796-5). Walter J Johnson.

Erasmus. Enchiridion Militis Christiani. O'Donnell, Anne M., ed. (Early English Text Society Ser.). (Illus.). 1981. text ed. 47.00x (ISBN 0-19-722284-6). Oxford U Pr.

Heylin, Peter. A Briefe & Moderate Answer to H. Burton. LC 76-57389. (English Experience Ser.: No. 806). 1977. Repr. of 1637 ed. lib. bdg. 22.00 (ISBN 90-221-0806-6). Walter J Johnson.

Nilles, Nicolaus. Kalendarium Manuale Utriusque Ecclesiae Orientalis & Occidentalis. (Fr.). 1509p. Date not set. Repr. of 1897 ed. text ed. 310.50x (ISBN 0-576-99195-3, Pub by Gregg Intl Pubs England). Gregg Intl.

Powell, Gabriel. The Catholikes Supplication Unto the King's Majestie, for Toleration of Catholike Religion in England. LC 76-57406. (English Experience Ser.: No. 822). 1977. lib. bdg. 6.00 (ISBN 90-221-0822-8). Walter J Johnson.

Sibthorpe, Robert. Apostolike Obedience: A Sermon. LC 76-57418. (English Experience Ser.: No. 831). 1977. Repr. of 1627 ed. lib. bdg. 6.00 (ISBN 90-221-0831-7). Walter J Johnson.

CHURCH HISTORY–MODERN PERIOD, 1500-

see also Counter-Reformation; Evangelical Revival; Missions–History; Protestantism–History; Reformation; Sects

Adams, Doug. Meeting House to Camp Meeting: Toward a History of American Free Church Worship from 1620-1835. 160p. (Orig.). 1981. pap. text ed. 6.95 (ISBN 0-941500-26-8). Sharing Co.

Backman, Milton V., Jr. Christian Churches of American Origins & Beliefs. rev. ed. 278p. 1983. pap. text ed. write for info. (ISBN 0-02-305090-X, Pub. by Scribner). Macmillan.

Bayley, P. French Pulpit Oratory: Fifteen Ninety-Eight to Sixteen Fifty. LC 79-50175. 1980. 57.50 (ISBN 0-521-22765-8). Cambridge U Pr.

Bellini, Enzo, et al. The Church in Revolutionary Times. Drury, John, ed. & tr. from Ital. (An Illustrated History of the Church). (Illus.). 126p. 1981. 12.95 (ISBN 0-86683-158-4, HarpR). Har-Row.

Boles, John B. Religion in Antebellum Kentucky. LC 76-4434. (Kentucky Bicentennial Bookshelf Ser.). 160p. 1976. 6.95 (ISBN 0-8131-0227-8). U Pr of Ky.

Burnet, Bishop. History of His Own Times. 409p. 1980. Repr. lib. bdg. 12.50 (ISBN 0-89987-056-2). Darby Bks.

Clouse, Robert. Church in an Age of Orthodoxy & Enlightenment. 1980. pap. 4.95 (ISBN 0-570-06273-X, 12-2746). Concordia.

Collett, Barry. Italian Benedictine Scholars & the Reformation: The Congregation of Santa Giustina of Padua. (Historical Monographs). 300p. 1985. 48.00x (ISBN 0-19-822934-8). Oxford U Pr.

Cragg, Gerald R. Church & the Age of Reason. (History of the Church: Vol. 4). (Orig.). 1961. pap. 5.95 (ISBN 0-14-020505-5, Pelican). Penguin.

D'Aubigne, Merle. History of the Reformation. (Religious Heritage Reprint Library). 1976. Repr. 18.95 (ISBN 0-8010-2859-0). Baker Bk.

Dobson, R. B., ed. The Church, Politics & Patronage in the Fifteenth Century. LC 84-15102. 245p. 1985. 25.00 (ISBN 0-312-13481-9). St Martin.

Ferguson, Everett. Church History, Reformation & Modern. (Way of Life Ser: No. 107). 1967. pap. 3.95 (ISBN 0-89112-107-2, Bibl Res Pr). Abilene Christ U.

Foster, Marshall E. & Swanson, Mary E. The American Covenant: The Untold Story. rev. ed. (Illus.). 186p. (Orig.). 1982. limited, signed 19.95; pap. text ed. 9.95 (ISBN 0-941370-00-3). Mayflower Inst.

Grannis, Chandler B., et al. Century of a Modern Church. LC 83-4800. (Illus.). 120p. (Orig.). 1983. pap. 5.00 (ISBN 0-9610366-0-5). Union Cong Church.

Guy, B. Domestic Correspondance of Dominique-Marie Varlet: Bishop of Babylon 1678-1742. (Studies in the History of Christian Thought: No. 36). ix, 150p. 1986. 22.00 (ISBN 90-04-07671-9, Pub. by E J Brill). Heinman.

Henry VII. Answere Made by the Kynges Hyghnes to the Petitions of the Rebelles in Yorkshire. LC 77-7417. (English Experience Ser.: No. 872). 1977. Repr. of 1536 ed. lib. bdg. 3.50 (ISBN 90-221-0872-4). Walter J Johnson.

Jedin, Hubert & Dolan, John P., eds. The Church in the Age of Feudalism. (History of the Church: Vol. 3). 1980. 59.50x (ISBN 0-8245-0316-3). Crossroad NY.

--The Church in the Modern Age. (History of the Church: Vol. 10). 1980. 59.50x (ISBN 0-8245-0013-X). Crossroad NY.

Kamen, Henry. Inquisition & Society in Spain in the Sixteenth & Seventeenth Centuries. LC 85-10804. (Illus.). 320p. 1985. 27.50x (ISBN 0-253-33015-7); pap. 10.95x (ISBN 0-253-22775-5). Ind U Pr.

Knipping, John B. Iconography of the Counter Reformation in the Netherlands: Heaven on Earth, 2 vols. LC 73-85234. (Illus.). 539p. 1974. Set. text ed. 195.00x (Pub. by B De Graaf Netherlands). Coronet Bks.

Peers, Edgar A. The Church in Spain, Seventeen Thirty-Seven to Nineteen Thirty-Seven. 1980. lib. bdg. 44.95 (ISBN 0-8490-3149-4). Gordon Pr.

Rogers, Francis M. The Quest for Eastern Christians: Travels & Rumor in the Age of Discovery. LC 62-18138. pap. 58.30 (ISBN 0-317-41750-9, 2055901). Bks Demand UMI.

Thompson, Bard. Renaissance & Reformation. (Texts & Studies in Religion). (Orig.). write for info. (ISBN 0-88946-915-6). E Mellen.

Vidler, Alec I. Church in an Age of Revolution. rev. ed. (History of the Church: Vol. 5). (Orig.). 1962. pap. 5.95 (ISBN 0-14-020506-3, Pelican). Penguin.

CHURCH HISTORY–18TH CENTURY

see also Evangelical Revival

Burnet, Bishop. History of His Own Times. 409p. 1980. Repr. lib. bdg. 12.50 (ISBN 0-89987-056-2). Darby Bks.

Coalter, Milton J., Jr. Gilbert Tennent, Son of Thunder: A Case Study of Continental Pietism's Impact on the First Great Awakening in the Middle Colonies. LC 86-9967. (Contributions to the Study of Religion: No. 18). 247p. 1986. 35.00 (ISBN 0-313-25514-8, CGI/). Greenwood.

Grosse, E. Dictionnaire d'Antiphilosophisme ou Refutation des Erreurs du 18e Siecle. Migne, J. P., ed. (Troisieme et Derniere Encyclopedie Theologique Ser.: Vol. 18). (Fr.). 770p. Repr. of 1856 ed. lib. bdg. 97.50x (ISBN 0-89241-301-8). Caratzas.

Noll, Mark A. Christians & the American Revolution. LC 77-23354. pap. 48.80 (ISBN 0-8357-9125-4, 2016042). Bks Demand UMI.

Ressler, Martin E., et al. Lancaster County Churches in the Revolutionary War Era. Harrison, Matthew W., Jr., ed. LC 76-21210. (Illus.). 96p. 1976. pap. 3.50 (ISBN 0-915010-11-9, Co-Pub by Lancaster County Bicentennial Committee). Sutter House.

Watson, John. The Scot of the Eighteenth Century. LC 76-47571. 1976. Repr. of 1907 ed. lib. bdg. 39.50 (ISBN 0-8414-9459-2). Folcroft.

CHURCH HISTORY–19TH CENTURY

Conn, Charles W. Like a Mighty Army. rev. ed. LC 77-82067. 1977. 12.95 (ISBN 0-87148-510-9). Pathway Pr.

Fishburn, Janet F. The Fatherhood of God & the Victorian Family: The Social Gospel in America. LC 81-43090. 220p. 1982. 4.95 (ISBN 0-8006-0671-X). Fortress.

Goen, C. C. Broken Churches, Broken Nation: Denominational Schism & the Coming of the American Civil War. 208p. 1985. 17.95 (ISBN 0-86554-166-3, MUP-H156). Mercer Univ Pr.

Gribbin, William. The Churches Militant: The War of 1812 & American Religion. LC 72-91313. pap. 55.00 (ISBN 0-317-29581-0, 2022000). Bks Demand UMI.

Jedin, Hubert & Dolan, John P., eds. The Church in the Industrial Age. (History of the Church: Vol. 9). 1981. 59.50x (ISBN 0-8245-0012-1). Crossroad NY.

Latourette, Kenneth S. Christianity in a Revolutionary Age, 5 vols. 1973. Repr. of 1958 ed. Set. lib. bdg. 160.50x (ISBN 0-8371-5700-5, LACH). Greenwood.

Martin, Roger H. Evangelicals United: Ecumenical Stirrings in Pre-Victorian Britain, 1795-1830. LC 82-10784. (Studies in Evangelicalism: No. 4). 244p. 1983. 19.00 (ISBN 0-8108-1586-9). Scarecrow.

Norman, Edward. The English Catholic Church in the Nineteenth Century. 1984. pap. 13.95x (ISBN 0-19-822955-0). Oxford U Pr.

Partin, Malcolm O. Waldeck-Rousseau, Combes, & the Church: The Politics of Anticlericalism, 1899-1905. LC 74-76167. pap. 77.80 (ISBN 0-317-20441-6, 2023432). Bks Demand UMI.

Prelinger, Catherine M. Charity, Challenge, & Change: Religious Dimensions of the Mid-Nineteenth Century Women's Movement in Germany. LC 86-19432. (Contributions in Women's Studies Ser.: No. 75). 225p. 1987. lib. bdg. 29.95 (ISBN 0-313-25401-X, PCY). Greenwood.

Reardon, Bernard M. Religious Thought in the Victorian Age: A Survey from Coleridge to Gore. (Illus.). 512p. 1980. pap. text ed. 15.95x (ISBN 0-582-49126-6). Longman.

Riplinger, Thomas. An American Vision of the Church: The Church in American Protestant Theology 1937-1967, Vol. 76. (European University Studies: Ser. 23). vi, 320p. 1977. pap. 33.95 (ISBN 3-261-02093-8). P Lang Pubs.

CHURCH HISTORY–20TH CENTURY

Cardwell, Jerry D. A Rumor of Trumpets: The Return of God to Secular Society. 118p. (Orig.). 1985. lib. bdg. 22.00 (ISBN 0-8191-4791-5); pap. text ed. 8.75 (ISBN 0-8191-4792-3). U Pr of Amer.

Chaney, Charles. Church Planting in America at the End of the Twentieth Century. 128p. 1982. pap. 6.95 (ISBN 0-8423-0279-4). Tyndale.

Conn, Charles W. Like a Mighty Army. rev. ed. LC 77-82067. 1977. 12.95 (ISBN 0-87148-510-9). Pathway Pr.

Cunningham, James. A Vanquished Hope: The Church in Russia on the Eve of the Revolution. 1981. pap. 40.00x (Pub. by Mowbrays Pub Div). State Mutual Bk.

Davies, Tom & Hodder, John. Stained Glass Hours: Modern Pilgrimage. (Illus.). 161p. 1985. 29.95 (ISBN 0-450-06053-5, New Eng Lib). David & Charles.

D'Mar Shimun, Surma. Assyrian Church Customs & the Murder of Mar Shimun. Wigram, W. A., ed. (Illus.). 128p. 1983. pap. 5.00 (ISBN 0-931428-02-5). Vehicle Edns.

Fishburn, Janet F. The Fatherhood of God & the Victorian Family: The Social Gospel in America. LC 81-43090. 220p. 1982. 4.95 (ISBN 0-8006-0671-X). Fortress.

Gordon, Frank J. Growing in Grace. (Illus.). 111p. (Orig.). 1981. pap. 6.00 (ISBN 0-686-34382-4). G Lutheran Foun.

Gurian, Waldemar. Hitler & the Christians. Peeler, E. F., tr. LC 78-63675. (Studies in Fascism: Ideology & Practice). 184p. Repr. of 1936 ed. 22.00 (ISBN 0-404-16937-6). AMS Pr.

Hitchcock, James. The New Enthusiasts: And What They Are Doing to the Catholic Church. 168p. 1982. pap. 9.95 (ISBN 0-88347-150-7). Thomas More.

Kent, Peter. The Pope & the Duce. 1981. 26.00 (ISBN 0-312-63024-7). St Martin.

Latourette, Kenneth S. Christianity in a Revolutionary Age, 5 vols. 1973. Repr. of 1958 ed. Set. lib. bdg. 160.50x (ISBN 0-8371-5700-5, LACH). Greenwood.

MacEoin, Gary. Memoirs & Memories. 308p. (Orig.). 1986. pap. 9.95 (ISBN 0-89622-317-5). Twenty-Third.

Partin, Malcolm O. Waldeck-Rousseau, Combes, & the Church: The Politics of Anticlericalism, 1899-1905. LC 74-76167. pap. 77.80 (ISBN 0-317-20441-6, 2023432). Bks Demand UMI.

Premoli, Orazio M. Contemporary Church History. 1977. lib. bdg. 59.95 (ISBN 0-8490-1669-X). Gordon Pr.

Ramientos, Nene. Contemporary Christian Issues. 71p. 1982. pap. 4.00 (ISBN 971-10-0013-X, Pub. by New Day Philippines). Cellar.

Simpson, F. Dale. Leading the First Century Church in the Space Age. 1972. 8.75 (ISBN 0-89137-003-X); pap. 5.95. Quality Pubns.

Taylor, Blaine. John Wesley: A Blueprint for Church Renewal. 221p. (Orig.). 1984. pap. 10.00 (ISBN 0-914527-19-3). C-Four Res.

Welsby, Paul A. The History of the Church of England, 1945-80. 1984. 29.95x (ISBN 0-19-213231-8). Oxford U Pr.

CHURCH LAW

see Ecclesiastical Law

CHURCH LEADERSHIP

see Christian Leadership

CHURCH LIBRARIES

see Libraries, Church

CHURCH MANAGEMENT

see also Advertising–Churches; Church Finance; Parish Councils

Adams, Arthur M. Effective Leadership for Today's Church. LC 77-27547. 202p. 1978. pap. 6.95 (ISBN 0-664-24196-4). Westminster.

Adams, Walter H. Church Administration: A Handbook for Church Leaders. 1979. pap. 2.95 (ISBN 0-88027-001-2). Firm Foun Pub.

Anderson, James D. & Jones, Ezra E. The Management of Ministry. LC 76-62942. 1978. 13.45 (ISBN 0-06-060235-X, HarpR). Har-Row.

Bedell, Kenneth. Using Personal Computers in the Church. 112p. 1982. pap. 5.95 (ISBN 0-8170-0948-5). Judson.

Borsch, Frederick H. & Napier, Davie. Advent-Christmas. Achtemeier, Elizabeth, et al, eds. LC 79-7377. (Proclamation 2: Aids for Interpreting the Lessons of the Church Year, Ser. A). 64p. (Orig.). 1980. pap. 3.75 (ISBN 0-8006-4091-8, 1-4091). Fortress.

Bowen, Van S. A Vestry Member's Guide. rev. ed. 80p. 1983. pap. 3.95 (ISBN 0-8164-2464-0, HarpR). Har-Row.

Brown, Lowell & Haystead, Wes. The Church Computer Manual. 160p. (Orig.). 1985. pap. 12.95 (ISBN 0-8423-0271-9). Tyndale.

Brown, Pat. Locating & Preserving Your Church's Records. Deweese, Charles W., ed. (Resource Kit for Your Church's History Ser.). 8p. 1984. 0.50 (ISBN 0-939804-15-8). Hist Comm S Baptist.

Callahan, Kennon L. Twelve Keys to an Effective Church. LC 83-47718. 1983. pap. 13.45 (ISBN 0-06-061297-5, HarpR). Har-Row.

Carroll, Jackson W., et al, eds. Handbook for Congregational Studies. 192p. (Orig.). 1986. pap. 16.95 (ISBN 0-687-16562-8). Abingdon.

Chandler, Robert, et al. The Church Handbook: A Creative Guide for Churches. Gardner, Anna Marie, ed. 224p. (Orig.). 1986. pap. text ed. 16.95 (ISBN 0-9616767-0-1). David Pub MN.

Church Finance Record System Manual. 7.95 (ISBN 0-8054-3103-9). Broadman.

Colson, Howard P. & Rigdon, Raymond M. Understanding Your Church's Curriculum. rev. ed. LC 80-67351. 1981. pap. 5.95 (ISBN 0-8054-3201-9). Broadman.

Conn, Charles W. A Balanced Church. 1983. pap. 6.95 (ISBN 0-87148-017-4). Pathway Pr.

Cook, J. Keith. The First Parish: A Pastor's Survival Manual. LC 83-6940. 154p. (Orig.). 1983. pap. 8.95 (ISBN 0-664-24442-4). Westminster.

Crockett, W. David. Promotion & Publicity for Churches. LC 74-80382. 48p. (Orig.). 1974. pap. 3.95 (ISBN 0-8192-1181-8). Morehouse.

Davis, Warren B. & Cromie, Richard M. The Future Is Now. 110p. (Orig.). 1984. pap. 6.00 (ISBN 0-914733-03-6). Desert Min.

A Day in the Life of a DRE. 36p. 1977. 3.60 (ISBN 0-318-20612-9). Natl Cath Educ.

Derrick, Christopher. Church Authority & Intellectual Freedom. LC 81-80209. 113p. (Orig.). 1981. pap. 7.95 (ISBN 0-89870-011-6). Ignatius Pr.

Deweese, Charles W., ed. Resource Kit for Your Church's History. 1984. 11.95 (ISBN 0-939804-12-3). Hist Comm S Baptist.

Dixon, Gregory L. Noteworthy: A Believer's Companion. 116p. 1986. 9.95 (ISBN 0-9616294-0-1). Joi Prod Enter.

Donovan, Suzanne & Bannon, William J. Volunteers & Ministry: A Manual for Developing Parish Volunteers. LC 82-62963. 112p. 1983. pap. 6.95 (ISBN 0-8091-2545-5). Paulist Pr.

Fegan, W. R. Becoming a Church Member. 1979. pap. 3.50 (ISBN 0-89536-389-5, 0232). CSS of Ohio.

Frey, Conrad I. Handbook for Church Officers & Boards. 1985. pap. 1.50 (ISBN 0-8100-0187-X, 15N0414). Northwest Pub.

Gardiner, M. James. Program Evaluation in Church Organization. LC 77-80070. (Management Ser.). (Illus.). 1977. pap. 4.50 (ISBN 0-89305-017-2). Anna Pub.

Green, Hollis. Why Churches Die. 224p. (Orig.). 1972. pap. 5.95 (ISBN 0-87123-642-7, 210642). Bethany Hse.

Harbin, J. William. When a Pastor Search Committee Comes... or Doesn't. LC 85-13541. 1985. pap. 4.95 (ISBN 0-8054-2545-4). Broadman.

Hendrix, Olan. Management for the Christian Leader. 1986. text ed. 8.95 (ISBN 0-8010-4313-1). Baker Bk.

Hogue, C. B. I Want My Church to Grow. LC 77-85280. 1977. 7.95 (ISBN 0-8054-6217-1). Broadman.

Holck, Manfred, Jr. Clergy Desk Book. 288p. (Orig.). 1985. pap. 19.95 (ISBN 0-687-08656-6). Abingdon.

Houk, Neil B. Church Bytes Software Guide: For Church Administration & Finances. 110p. (Orig.). 1986. pap. 10.95 (ISBN 0-9615086-3-9). Church Bytes.

Johnson, William R. The Pastor & the Personal Computer: Information Management for Ministers. 224p. (Orig.). 1985. pap. 10.50 (ISBN 0-687-30134-3). Abingdon.

Kilinski, Kenneth & Wolfert, Jerry. Organization & Leadership in the Local Church. 14.95 (ISBN 0-310-26810-9, 18132). Zondervan.

Kittlaus, Paul & Leas, Speed. Church Fights: Managing Conflict in the Local Church. LC 73-6790. 184p. 1973. pap. 9.95 (ISBN 0-664-24974-4). Westminster.

Knudsen, Raymond B. Models for Ministry: Creative Administration in the Local Church. (Orig.). 1978. pap. 5.95 (ISBN 0-377-00082-5). Friend Pr.

Kung, Hans & Moltman, Jurgen, eds. Who Has the Say in the Church, Vol. 148. (Concilium 1981). 128p. (Orig.). 1981. pap. 6.95 (ISBN 0-8164-2348-2, HarpR). Har-Row.

Leas, Speed B. Time Management. LC 78-8628. (Creative Leadership Ser.). 1978. pap. 5.95 (ISBN 0-687-42120-9). Abingdon.

Lee, Harris W. Theology of Administration: A Bibical Basis for Organizing the Congregation. LC 81-147067. 40p. 1981. pap. 3.95 (ISBN 0-8066-1875-2, 10-6290). Augsburg.

Lindgren, Alvin J. Foundations for Purposeful Church Administration. LC 65-16459. 1965. 13.95 (ISBN 0-687-13339-4). Abingdon.

McCarty, Doran C. Working with People. (Orig.). 1987. pap. 5.95 (ISBN 0-8054-3241-8). Broadman.

McIntosh, Duncan & Rusbuldt, Richard E. Planning Growth in Your Church. 224p. 1983. pap. 16.95 (ISBN 0-8170-1007-6). Judson.

McLeod, Thomas E. The Work of the Church Treasurer. 80p. 1981. pap. 6.95 (ISBN 0-8170-0908-6). Judson.

McMichael, Betty. The Church Librarian's Handbook. 288p. 1984. pap. 9.95 (ISBN 0-8010-6166-0). Baker Bk.

Massey, Floyd, Jr. & McKinney, Samuel B. Church Administration in the Black Perspective. LC 76-9804. 176p. 1976. pap. 7.95 (ISBN 0-8170-0710-5). Judson.

Miranda, Juan C. Church Growth Manual. Lamigueiro, Fernando, ed. Orig. Title: Manual De Iglecrecimiento. 192p. 1985. pap. 4.50 (ISBN 0-8297-0707-7). Life Pubs Intl.

Neuhaus, Richard J. Freedom for Ministry: A Critical Affirmation of the Church & Its Mission. LC 78-3352. 256p. 1984. pap. 7.95 (ISBN 0-06-066095-3, RD 505, HarpR). Har-Row.

Northcutt, David L. Financial Management for Clergy. 192p. 1984. pap. 6.95 (ISBN 0-8010-6740-5). Baker Bk.

Olsen, Frank H. Church Staff Support: Cultivating & Maintaining Staff Relationships. (Administration for Churches Ser.). 40p. (Orig.). 1982. pap. 3.95 (ISBN 0-8066-1964-3, 10-1370). Augsburg.

Otto, A. S., ed. Chairman's Chat-Life Lines. 120p. 1981. vinyl 24.95 (ISBN 0-912132-11-6). Dominion Pr.

Pattison, E. Mansell. Pastor & Parish: A Systems Approach. Clinebell, Howard J. & Stone, Howard W., eds. LC 76-62619. (Creative Pastoral Care & Counseling Ser.). 96p. 1977. pap. 0.50 (ISBN 0-8006-0559-4, 1-559). Fortress.

Powell, Paul W. Go-Givers in a Go-Getter World. 1986. pap. 5.95 (ISBN 0-8054-2546-2). Broadman.

Robinson, Darrell W. Total Church Life. LC 85-7900. 1985. 7.95 (ISBN 0-8054-6250-3). Broadman.

Rogers, Kristine M. & Rogers, Bruce A. Paths to Transformation: A Study of the General Agencies of the United Methodist Church. LC 81-17565. (Into Our Third Century Ser.). 96p. (Orig.). 1982. pap. 3.50 (ISBN 0-687-30094-0). Abingdon.

Rueter, Alvin. Personnel Management in the Church: Developing Personnel Policies & Practices. (Church Administration Ser.). 56p. (Orig.). 1984. pap. 3.95 (ISBN 0-8066-2072-2, 10-4920). Augsburg.

Rusbuldt, Richard E., et al. Local Church Planning Manual. 1977. pap. 14.95 (ISBN 0-8170-0753-9). Judson.

--Medidas Principales en la Planificacion de la Iglesia Local: Key Steps in Local Church Planning. Rodriguez, Oscar E., tr. from Eng. (Span.). 134p. 1981. pap. 5.95 (ISBN 0-8170-0933-7). Judson.

Schaller, Lyle E. Effective Church Planning. LC 78-26462. 1979. 6.95 (ISBN 0-687-11530-2). Abingdon.

--The Middle-Sized Church: Problems & Prescriptions. 160p. (Orig.). 1985. pap. 6.95 (ISBN 0-687-26948-2). Abingdon.

--The Multiple Staff & the Larger Church. LC 79-20796. 1980. pap. 6.95 (ISBN 0-687-27297-1). Abingdon.

Schuller, Robert H. Your Church Has a Fantastic Future! A Possibility Thinker's Guide to a Successful Church. rev. ed. LC 86-11906. (Illus.). 336p. 1986. pap. 14.95 (ISBN 0-8307-1180-5, 5111659). Regal.

Secretary's Guide to Church Office Management. 128p. (Orig.). 1985. pap. 9.95 (ISBN 0-687-37131-7). Abingdon.

Shawchuck, Norman & Lindgren, Alvin J. Management for Your Church: How to Realize Your Church's Potential Through a Systems Approach. (Illus.). 160p. 1985. pap. 8.95 (ISBN 0-938180-14-2). Org Resources Pr.

Stoesz, Samuel. Church & Membership Awareness. rev. ed. pap. 2.95 (ISBN 0-87509-332-9). Chr Pubns.

Sumners, Bill. Displaying & Exhibiting Your Church's History. Deweese, Charles W., ed. (Resource Kit for Your Church's History Ser.). 1984. 0.50 (ISBN 0-939804-22-0). Hist Comm S Baptist.

Sumrall, Velma & Germany, Lucille. Telling the Story of the Local Church: The Who, What, When, Where & Why of Communication. (Orig.). 1979. pap. 5.00 (ISBN 0-8164-2193-5, HarpR); wkbk. avail. (ISBN 0-685-59466-1). Har-Row.

Thistlethwaite, Susan B. Metaphors for the Contemporary Church. 192p. (Orig.). 1983. pap. 8.95 (ISBN 0-8298-0692-X). Pilgrim NY.

Thulin, Richard L. The Lesser Festivals 1: Saints' Days & Special Occasions. Achtemeier, Elizabeth, et al, eds. LC 79-7377. (Proclamation 2: Aids for Interpreting the Lessons of the Church Year). 64p. (Orig.). 1980. pap. 3.75 (ISBN 0-8006-1393-7, 1-1393). Fortress.

Tibbetts, Orlando L. The Work of the Church Trustee. 1979. pap. 4.95 (ISBN 0-8170-0825-X). Judson.

Tidwell, Charles A. Church Administration-Effective Leadership for Ministry. LC 85-6620. 1985. pap. 8.95 (ISBN 0-8054-3113-6). Broadman.

Total Environmental Action, Inc. The Energy-Efficient Church. Hoffman, Douglas, ed. LC 79-10432. (Illus.). 1979. pap. 4.95 (ISBN 0-8298-0362-9). Pilgrim NY.

Townsend, L., et al, eds. Parade of Plays II. 96p. 1986. pap. 5.95 (ISBN 0-89191-323-8). Cook.

Trotti, John B. The Lesser Festivals 2: Saints' Days & Special Occasions. Achtemeier, Elizabeth, et al, eds. LC 79-7377. (Proclamation 2: Aids for Interpreting Thee Lessons of the Church Year). 64p. (Orig.). 1980. pap. 3.75 (ISBN 0-8006-1394-5, 1-1394). Fortress.

Tucker, Grayson L., Jr. A Church Planning Questionnaire: Manual & Discoveries from 100 Churches. 161p. (Orig.). 1983. pap. text ed. 8.50 (ISBN 0-9610706-0-9). G L Tucker.

Wade, Larry. Local Church Administration. (Illus.). 122p. 1978. pap. 8.95 (ISBN 0-914936-32-8). Bible Temple.

Walrath, Douglas A. Leading Churches Through Change. LC 79-4456. (Creative Leadership Ser.). 1979. pap. 6.95 (ISBN 0-687-21270-7). Abingdon.

--New Possibilities for Small Churches. 120p. (Orig.). 1983. pap. 7.95 (ISBN 0-8298-0668-7). Pilgrim NY.

Walz, Edgar. How to Manage Your Church. 192p. 1986. pap. 8.95 (ISBN 0-570-04434-0). Concordia.

Waymire, Bob & Wagner, C. Peter. The Church Growth Survey Handbook. 3rd. rev. ed. 4.15 (ISBN 0-318-20599-8). Overseas Crusade.

Wedel, Leonard E. Church Staff Administration: Practical Approaches. LC 78-51490. 1978. 10.95 (ISBN 0-8054-3105-5). Broadman.

Williams, Barbara. Public Relations Handbook for Your Church. 112p. 1985. pap. 5.95 (ISBN 0-8170-1050-5). Judson.

Williams, George M. Improving Parish Management: Working Smarter, Not Harder. 112p. pap. 9.95 (ISBN 0-89622-176-8). Twenty-Third.

Zunkel, C. Wayne. Strategies for Growing Your Church. 112p. 1986. pap. 12.95 (ISBN 0-89191-344-0). Cook.

CHURCH MEETINGS

Anderson, Philip A. Church Meetings That Matter. enl. ed. 128p. 1987. pap. 5.95 (ISBN 0-8298-0752-7). Pilgrim NY.

Bible Temple Staff. The Home Fellowship Meetings. rev. ed. 1975. 6.95 (ISBN 0-914936-14-X). Bible Temple.

Book of Minutes: Nineteen Hundred Six to Nineteen Seventeen. (Vol. 1). 304p. 1978. 7.95 (ISBN 0-87148-103-0). Pathway Pr.

Brians, Pearl. My First SDA Camp Meeting. large print ed. 44p. 1985. pap. 6.00 (ISBN 0-914009-27-3). VHI Library.

Genne, Elizabeth & Genne, William. Church Family Camps & Conferences. LC 78-24395. 1979. pap. 2.95 (ISBN 0-8170-0818-7). Judson.

Merrill, R. Dale. The Church Business Meeting. LC 68-28075. 1968. pap. 2.95 (ISBN 0-8170-0409-2). Judson.

Minutes of the General Assembly of the Church of God, 1978. 114p. 1979. 4.75 (ISBN 0-87148-572-9); pap. 1.00 (ISBN 0-87148-573-7). Pathway Pr.

Tauler, John. Spiritual Conferences. Colledge, Eric & Jane, M., trs. LC 78-74568. 1979. pap. 7.00 (ISBN 0-89555-082-2). TAN Bks Pubs.

CHURCH MEMBERSHIP

see also Baptism; Church Discipline; Confirmation; Covenants (Church Polity); Lord's Supper

Advisory Committee. The Community of Women & Men in the Church: A Study Program. (Orig.). 1978. pap. 1.95 (ISBN 0-377-00092-2). Friend Pr.

Braden, Suzanne G. The First Year: Incorporating New Members. (Pathways to Church Growth Ser.). 80p. (Orig.). Date not set. pap. 5.95 (ISBN 0-88177-046-9, DR046B). Discipleship Res.

Clark, Wayne C. The Meaning of Church Membership. pap. 4.50 (ISBN 0-8170-0103-4). Judson.

Conn, Harvie M. Theological Perspectives on Church Growth. 1976. pap. 4.95 (ISBN 0-87552-150-9). Presby & Reformed.

Dudley, Carl S. Where Have All Our People Gone? New Choices for Old Churches. LC 79-525. (Illus.). 1979. pap. 6.95 (ISBN 0-8298-0359-9). Pilgrim NY.

Edwards, Gene. How to Have a Soul Winning Church. 1963. pap. 3.95 (ISBN 0-88243-524-8, 02-0524). Gospel Pub.

Elliott, Ralph H. Church Growth That Counts. 128p. 1982. pap. 5.95 (ISBN 0-8170-0943-4). Judson.

Free Church. You & Your Church. 3rd ed. 1978. pap. 1.95. Free Church Pubns.

Glock, Charles Y. & Stark, Rodney. Northern California Church Member Study, 1963. LC 79-63206. 1979. codebk. write for info. (ISBN 0-89138-980-6). ICPSR.

Harre, Alan F. Close the Back Door. 1984. pap. 6.50 (ISBN 0-570-03932-0, 12-2867). Concordia.

Hoge, Dean R. & Roozen, David A., eds. Understanding Church Growth & Decline, 1950-78. LC 79-4166. (Illus.). 1979. pap. 9.95 (ISBN 0-8298-0358-0). Pilgrim NY.

Hoyer, Robert. He Calls Me by My Name: A Pre-Membership Course for Adults. LC 77-74385. 1977. pap. text ed. 4.75 (ISBN 0-915644-09-6). Clayton Pub Hse.

Igleheart, Glenn A. Church Members & Nontraditional Religious Groups. LC 85-4226. (Broadman Leadership Ser.). 1985. pap. 5.95 (ISBN 0-8054-6608-8). Broadman.

Johnson, Douglas W., et al. Churches & Church Membership in the United States, 1971. LC 73-94224. 256p. 1974. pap. 15.00x (ISBN 0-914422-01-4). Glenmary Res Ctr.

Krahn, John H. Reaching the Inactive Member. 1982. 5.25 (ISBN 0-89536-570-7, 1815). CSS of Ohio.

LaSuer, Donald F. & Sells, L. Ray. Bonds of Belonging: Pathways to Discipleship for Church Members. LC 86-72150. 88p. (Orig.). 1986. pap. 5.95 (ISBN 0-88177-038-8, DR038B). Discipleship Res.

Lewis, Douglass. Resolving Church Conflicts: A Case Study Approach for Local Congregations. LC 80-8347. 192p. (Orig.). 1981. pap. 7.95 (ISBN 0-06-065244-6, RD 342, HarpR). Har-Row.

Miller, Herb. How to Build a Magnetic Church. 128p. 1987. pap. 7.95 (ISBN 0-687-17762-6). Abingdon.

Mylander, Charles. Secrets for Growing Churches. LC 79-1764. 1979. pap. 4.95i (ISBN 0-06-066055-4, RD 302, HarpR). Har-Row.

Newman, William M. & Halvorson, Peter L. Patterns in Pluralism: A Portrait of American Religion, 1952-1971. LC 79-55177. 1980. pap. 6.50 (ISBN 0-914422-10-3). Glenmary Res Ctr.

Pope, Robert G. Half-Way Covenant: Church Membership in Puritan New England. Repr. of 1969 ed. 63.30 (ISBN 0-8357-9500-4, 2011473). Bks Demand UMI.

Powell, Paul W. Go-Givers in a Go-Getter World. 1986. pap. 5.95 (ISBN 0-8054-2546-2). Broadman.

Powell, Terry. Welcome to the Church. (Lay Action Ministry Program Ser.). 96p. 1987. pap. 4.95 (ISBN 0-89191-514-1). Cook.

--Welcome to Your Ministry. (Lay Action Ministry Program Ser.). 96p. 1987. pap. 4.95 (ISBN 0-89191-515-X). Cook.

Schaller, Lyle E. Assimilating New Members. LC 77-18037. (The Creative Leadership Ser.). 1978. pap. 7.50 (ISBN 0-687-01938-9). Abingdon.

--Growing Plans: Strategies to Increase Your Church's Membership. 176p. 1983. pap. 7.95 (ISBN 0-687-15962-8). Abingdon.

Schmalenberger, Jerry L. Why Belong to the Church? 1971. 3.50 (ISBN 0-89536-261-9). CSS of Ohio.

Silvey, D. O. Welcome, New Church Member. 20p. 1964. pap. 0.60 (ISBN 0-89114-112-X). Baptist Pub Hse.

Stoesz, Samuel. Church & Membership Awareness. rev. ed. pap. 2.95 (ISBN 0-87509-332-9). Chr Pubns.
Stoesz, Samuel J. Church & Membership Awareness. pap. 2.95 (ISBN 0-87509-066-4); leaders guide 0.95 (ISBN 0-87509-067-2). Chr Pubns.
Sweetser, Thomas P. The Catholic Parish: Shifting Membership in a Changing Church. LC 74-84543. (Studies in Religion & Society). 1974. 15.95x (ISBN 0-913348-06-6); pap. 8.95x (ISBN 0-913348-13-9). Ctr Sci Study.
Wagner, C. Peter. Leading Your Church to Growth. LC 83-19272. 224p. 1984. pap. 6.95 (ISBN 0-8307-0922-3, 5418091). Regal.
Williams, Jerome O. Definite Decisions for New Church Members. pap. 1.25 (ISBN 0-8054-9402-2). Broadman.
Wray, Daniel E. The Importance of the Local Church. 15p. (Orig.). 1981. pap. 1.00 (ISBN 0-85151-330-1). Banner of Truth.
Yamamori, Tetsunao & Lawson, E. Leroy. Introducing Church Growth. LC 74-24577. (New Life Books). (Illus.). 256p. 1974. 7.95 (ISBN 0-87239-000-4, 40002). Standard Pub.
Zunkel, C. Wayne. Growing the Small Church: A Guide for Church Leaders. 109p. 1982. tchr's. ed. 12.95 (ISBN 0-89191-952-X). Cook.
--Growing the Small Church: A Guide for Church Members. 120p. 1984. pap. text ed. 2.95 (ISBN 0-89191-951-1). Cook.

CHURCH MUSIC

see also Carols; Choirs (Music); Choral Music; Christmas Music; Conducting, Choral; Easter Music; Hymns; Liturgies; Music in Churches; Organ Music; Psalmody; Religion and Music; Sequences (Liturgy)

Are, Thomas L. Faithsong: A New Look at the Ministry of Music. LC 81-4789. 96p. 1981. pap. 6.95 (ISBN 0-664-24375-4). Westminster.
Arnold, Denis. Monteverdi Church Music. LC 81-71298. (BBC Music Guides Ser.). 64p. (Orig.). 1983. pap. 4.95 (ISBN 0-295-95923-1). U of Wash Pr.
Atkins, Ivor A. The Early Occupants of the Office of Organist & Master of the Choristers of the Cathedral Church of Christ & the Blessed Virgin Mary, Worcester. LC 74-27329. Repr. of 1913 ed. 24.50 (ISBN 0-404-12855-6). AMS Pr.
Baker, Clara B. Sing & Be Happy: Songs for the Young Child. LC 80-13421. (Illus.). 96p. 1980. pap. 7.95 spiral (ISBN 0-687-38547-4). Abingdon.
Baker, Paul. Contemporary Christian Music: Where It Came from, Where It Is, Where It Is Going. rev. ed. 1985. pap. 8.95 (ISBN 0-89107-343-4, Crossway Bks). Good News.
Bandel, Betty. Sing the Lord's Song in a Strange Land: The Life of Justin Morgan. LC 78-73309. 264p. 1981. 24.50 (ISBN 0-8386-2411-1). Fairleigh Dickinson.
Barbour, James M. The Church Music of William Billings. 167p. Repr. of 1960 ed. lib. bdg. 29.00 (Pub. by Am Repr Serv). Am Biog Serv.
Barrett, William A. English Church Composers: The Great Musicians. facsimile ed. LC 70-102224. (Select Bibliographies Reprint Ser). 1882. 19.00 (ISBN 0-8369-5109-3). Ayer Co Pubs.
Benham, Hugh. Latin Church Music in England, Fourteen Sixty to Fifteen Seventy-Five. (Music Reprint Ser.: 1980). (Illus.). 1980. Repr. of 1977 ed. lib. bdg. 35.00 (ISBN 0-306-76025-8). Da Capo.
Bennett, Marian, ed. Songs for Preschool Children. LC 80-25091. 96p. (Orig.). 1981. pap. 7.95 (ISBN 0-87239-429-8, 5754). Standard Pub.
Berglund, Robert. A Philosophy of Church Music. (Orig.). 1985. pap. 9.95 (ISBN 0-8024-0279-8). Moody.
Beutner, Ed. Biblical Ballads. (Illus.). 1985. 4.95 (ISBN 0-911346-09-0). Christianica.
Bordes, Charles, ed. Anthologie Des Maitres Religieux Primirties Des XV, XVI & XVII Siecles, 6 vols. (Music Ser.). 1981. Repr. of 1893 ed. Set. lib. bdg. 250.00 (ISBN 0-306-76089-4); Vol. 1; IV, 184 Pp. lib. bdg. 47.50 (ISBN 0-306-76114-9); Vol. 2; VIII, 194 Pp. lib. bdg. 47.50 (ISBN 0-306-76115-7); Vol. 3; IV, 184 Pp. lib. bdg. 47.50 (ISBN 0-306-76116-5); Vol. 4; IV, 190 Pp. lib. bdg. 47.50 (ISBN 0-306-76117-3); Vol. 5; II, 190 Pp. lib. bdg. 47.50 (ISBN 0-306-76118-1); Vol. 6; II, 202 Pp. lib. bdg. 47.50 (ISBN 0-306-76119-X). Da Capo.
Boyd, Jack. Leading the Lord's Singing. 1981. pap. 5.95 (ISBN 0-89137-603-8). Quality Pubns.
Buck, P. C., ed. John Taverner: Part 1. (Tudor Church Music Ser.: Vol. 1). 1963. Repr. of 1923 ed. write for info. (ISBN 0-8450-1851-5). Broude.
--John Taverner: Part 2. (Tudor Church Music Ser.: Vol. 3). 1963. Repr. of 1924 ed. 85.00x (ISBN 0-8450-1853-1). Broude.
--Orlando Gibbons. (Tudor Church Music Ser.: Vol. 4). 1963. Repr. of 1925 ed. 85.00x (ISBN 0-8450-1854-X). Broude.
Buck, P. C., et al, eds. Robert White. (Tudor Church Music Ser.: Vol. 5). 1963. Repr. of 1926 ed. 85.00x (ISBN 0-8450-1855-8). Broude.
Burgus, Jackie. God Given Territory. 96p. 1986. pap. 2.95 (ISBN 0-938612-13-1). Revival Press.
Butler, Charles. Principles of Musik, in Singing & Setting. LC 68-13273. (Music Ser.). 1970. Repr. of 1636 ed. lib. bdg. 23.50 (ISBN 0-306-70939-2). Da Capo.
--The Principles of Musik, in Singing & Setting. LC 74-25439. (English Experience Ser.: No. 284). 136p. 1971. Repr. of 1636 ed. 14.00 (ISBN 90-221-0284-X). Walter J Johnson.
Byrd, William, et al. Gradualia, Bks.1 & 2. Buck, P. C., ed. (Tudor Church Music: Vol. 7). 1963. Repr. of 1927 ed. 85.00x (ISBN 0-8450-1857-4). Broude.
--Masses, Cantiones, Motets. Buck, P. C., ed. (Tudor Church Music Ser.: Vol. 9). 1963. Repr. of 1928 ed. write for info. (ISBN 0-8450-1859-0). Broude.
Carus, Paul. Sacred Tunes for the Consecration of Life. 48p. 1899. 0.95 (ISBN 0-317-40427-X). Open Court.
Christian, Chris. How to Get Started in Christian Music. Styll, John, ed. 167p. 1986. 12.95 (ISBN 0-9616817-0-5). Home Sweet Home.
Clawson, Sharalee S. I Feel My Saviour's Love: Themes from LDS Children's Songs in Counted Cross-Stitch. 9p. 1986. pap. 5.00 (ISBN 0-88290-277-6). Horizon Utah.
Crockett, Richard H. & Horsch, James E., eds. Jesus Life Songbook. 134p. 1975. pap. 3.95 (ISBN 0-8361-2785-4). Herald Pr.
Cumnock, Frances, ed. Catalog of the Salem Congregation Music. (Illus.). 682p. 31.50 (ISBN 0-8078-1398-2). Moravian Music.
Cundick, Robert, ed. A First Album for Church Organists. (Illus.). 64p. 1967. pap. 7.95 (ISBN 0-8258-0227-X, 0-4655). Fischer Inc NY.
Dean & Acuff. The S.D.N. Theory of Music. pap. 1.95 (ISBN 0-88027-058-6). Firm Foun Pub.
D'Ortigue, J. L. Dictionnaire Liturgique, Historique, et Theorique de Plain Chante de Musique Religieuse. Migne, J. P., ed. (Nouvelle Encyclopedie Theologique Ser.: Vol. 29). (Fr.). 782p. Date not set. Repr. of 1860 ed. lib. bdg. 99.00x (ISBN 0-89241-272-0). Caratzas.
Ellsworth, Donald P. Christian Music in Contemporary Witness: Historical Antecedents & Contemporary Practices. LC 79-52359. 1980. 7.95 (ISBN 0-8010-3338-1). Baker Bk.
English Sacred Lyrics. 1978. Repr. of 1884 ed. lib. bdg. 30.00 (ISBN 0-8492-0061-X). R West.
Espina, Noni. Vocal Solos for Christian Churches: A Descriptive Reference of Solo Music for the Church Year. 3rd ed. LC 84-51398. 256p. 25.00 (ISBN 0-8108-1730-6). Scarecrow.
Fellowes, Edmund H. Appendix with Supplementary Notes. (Tudor Church Music Ser.). 1963. Repr. of 1948 ed. 50.00x (ISBN 0-8450-1861-2). Broude.
--English Cathedral Music. 5th, rev. ed. Westrup, J. A., ed. LC 80-24400. (Illus.). xi, 283p. 1981. Repr. of 1973 ed. lib. bdg. 27.50x (ISBN 0-313-22643-1, FEEC). Greenwood.
Fortunato, Connie. Children's Music Ministry. 222p. 1981. pap. 6.95 (ISBN 0-89191-341-6). Cook.
Fredrickson, Carl, ed. Church Soloists Favorites, 2 bks. (Illus.). 1963. Bk. 1, High Voice, 64p. pap. 6.95 (ISBN 0-8258-0228-8, RB-65); Bk. 2, Low Voice, 85p. pap. 6.95 (ISBN 0-8258-0229-6, RB-66). Fischer Inc NY.
Gardner, Johann V. Dostojino Jest', 8-mi glasov, znamennago rospjeva. Tr. of It is Truly Meet, Eight Tones, Znamenny Chant. 1967. pap. 3.00 (ISBN 0-317-30397-X). Holy Trinity.
Gastoue, Amedee. Musique et Liturgie: Le Graduel et l'Antiphonaire Romains; Histoire et Description. LC 70-178577. (Fr.). Repr. of 1913 ed. 32.50 (ISBN 0-404-56608-1). AMS Pr.
Gatens, William J. Victorian Cathedral Music in Theory & Practice. 300p. 1986. 39.50 (ISBN 0-521-26808-7). Cambridge U Pr.
Gould, Nathaniel D. Church Music in America. 1980. lib. bdg. 59.75 (ISBN 0-8490-3192-3). Gordon Pr.
--Church Music in America, Comprising Its History & Its Peculiarities at Different Periods. LC 78-144620. Repr. of 1853 ed. 19.25 (ISBN 0-404-02888-8). AMS Pr.
Goulder, Michael D. The Song of Fourteen Songs. (JSOT Supplement Ser.: No. 36). viii, 94p. 1986. text ed. 18.00x (ISBN 0-905774-86-8, Pub. by JSOT Pr England); pap. text ed. 7.50x (ISBN 0-905774-87-6). Eisenbrauns.
Hannum, Harold E. Let the People Sing. Davis, Tom, ed. 112p. 1981. pap. 7.95 (ISBN 0-8280-0029-8). Review & Herald.
Hastings, Thomas. Dissertation on Musical Taste. LC 68-16237. (Music Ser.). 228p. 1974. Repr. of 1822 ed. lib. bdg. 35.00 (ISBN 0-306-71085-4). Da Capo.
--Dissertation on Musical Taste. LC 6-18360. (American Studies). 1968. Repr. of 1853 ed. 24.00 (ISBN 0-384-21750-8). Johnson Repr.
Holy Song Book: Collection Of Unification Church Songs. 2nd rev. ed. (Illus.). 60p. 1972. pap. 5.50 (ISBN 0-910621-19-5). HSA Pubns.
Hood, George. History of Music in New England, with Biographical Sketches of Reformers & Psalmists. (American Studies). 1970. Repr. of 1846 ed. 24.00 (ISBN 0-384-24140-9). Johnson Repr.
Hunt, T. W. Music in Missions: Discipling Through Music. LC 86-28333. (Orig.). 1987. pap. 9.95 (ISBN 0-8054-6343-7). Broadman.
Hunter, Stanley A., ed. Music & Religion. LC 72-1615. Repr. of 1930 ed. 19.00 (ISBN 0-404-08316-1). AMS Pr.
Hustad, Donald P. Jubilate!(Church Music in the Evangelical Tradition) LC 80-85185. 368p. 1981. 17.95 (ISBN 0-916642-17-8). Hope Pub.
Johansson, Calvin M. Music & Ministry: A Biblical Counterpoint. 152p. 1984. pap. 6.95 (ISBN 0-913573-07-8). Hendrickson MA.
Johnson, Gary L. Son Songs for Christian Folk, 2 vols. Incl. Vol. I. pap. 1.25 (ISBN 0-87123-509-9, 280509); Vol. II. pap. 1.50 (ISBN 0-87123-532-3, 280532). 1975. pap. Bethany Hse.
Johnson, Lawrence J. The Mystery of Faith: The Ministers of Music. 128p. (Orig.). 1983. pap. 5.95 (ISBN 0-9602378-9-5). Pastoral Pr.
Kroeger, Karl & Crawford, Richard, eds. The Complete Works of William Billings, Vol. III: The Psalm-Singer's Amusement, the Suffolk Harmony, & Independent Publications. (Illus.). 456p. 1986. text ed. 50.00x (ISBN 0-8139-1130-3, Pub. by American Musicological Society-Colonial Society MA). U Pr of Va.
Lancaster, Reid. Rejoice & Sing. 1984. pap. 2.95 (ISBN 0-8344-0126-6). Sweet.
Lawrence, Joy & Ferguson, John. A Musician's Guide to Church Music. LC 80-27567. 280p. 1981. 16.95 (ISBN 0-8298-0424-2). Pilgrim NY.
Le Huray, Peter, ed. The Treasury of English Church Music 1545-1650. 250p. 1982. 47.50 (ISBN 0-521-24889-2); pap. 19.95 (ISBN 0-521-28405-8). Cambridge U Pr.
Lloyd, Frederick E., ed. Lloyd's Church Musicians Directory. LC 72-1733. Repr. of 1910 ed. 14.75 (ISBN 0-404-08319-6). AMS Pr.
Lovelace, Austin C. & Rice, William C. Music & Worship in the Church. rev. ed. LC 76-13524. pap. 64.00 (ISBN 0-317-09866-7, 2020266). Bks Demand UMI.
McCabe, Joseph E. Handel's Messiah: A Devotional Commentary. LC 77-25860. 120p. 1978. pap. 5.95 (ISBN 0-664-24192-1). Westminster.
MacDougall, Hamilton C. Early New England Psalmody: An Historical Appreciation, 1620-1820. LC 79-87398. (Music Reprint Ser.). 1969. Repr. of 1940 ed. lib. bdg. 29.50 (ISBN 0-306-71542-2). Da Capo.
McKenna, Edward J. The Ministry of Musicians. 40p. (Orig.). 1983. pap. 1.25 (ISBN 0-8146-1295-4). Liturgical Pr.
Mason, Lowell. Musical Letters from Abroad. 2nd ed. LC 67-13035. (Music Ser). 1967. Repr. of 1854 ed. lib. bdg. 37.50 (ISBN 0-306-70940-6). Da Capo.
Mitchell, Robert H. Ministry & Music. LC 77-20815. 164p. 1978. pap. 8.95 (ISBN 0-664-24186-7). Westminster.
Montgomery, Charles, ed. The Handbook for the Ultimate Church Musician. Montgomery, Jane. 1985. pap. 3.95 (ISBN 0-916043-04-5). Light Hearted Pub Co.
The Music Locator. Orig. Title: MusiCatalog. 584p. 1987. pap. 89.95 (ISBN 0-89390-098-2). Resource Pubns.
National Society of Colonial Dames of America. Church Music & Musical Life in Pennsylvania in the Eighteenth Century, 3 vols. in 4 pts. LC 79-38037. (Illus.). Repr. of 1926 ed. Set. 150.00 (ISBN 0-404-08090-1). AMS Pr.
Noble, E. Myron. The Gospel of Music: A Key to Understanding a Major Chord of Ministry. LC 85-63559. 159p. (Orig.). 1986. pap. 4.95 (ISBN 0-9616056-1-8). Mid Atl Reg Pr.
Nordon, Hugo, tr. Chorale Harmonization in the Church Modes. 1974. pap. 3.75 (ISBN 0-8008-1516-5, Crescendo). Taplinger.
Obikhod Tserkovnago Penija. Tr. of Obikhod of Sacred Music. 167p. 1959. 20.00 (ISBN 0-317-30405-4). Holy Trinity.
Osbeck, Kenneth W. Ministry of Music. LC 61-14865. 192p. 1975. pap. 5.95x (ISBN 0-8254-3410-6). Kregel.
--My Music Workbook. 144p. 1982. pap. 5.95x (ISBN 0-8254-3415-7). Kregel.
Peck, Richard. Rock: Making Musical Choices. 174p. (Orig.). 1985. pap. 4.95 (ISBN 0-89084-297-3). Bob Jones Univ Pr.
Perennes, F. Dictionnaire de Noels et de Cantiques. Migne, J. P., ed. (Troisieme et Derniere Encyclopedie Theologique Ser.: Vol. 63). (Fr.). 720p. Repr. of 1867 ed. lib. bdg. 91.50x (ISBN 0-89241-327-1). Caratzas.
Phelps, Austin, et al. Hymns & Choirs. LC 78-144671. Repr. of 1860 ed. 29.50 (ISBN 0-404-07207-0). AMS Pr.
Porte, Jacques. Encyclopedie Des Musiques Sacrees, 3 vols. (Fr.). 1978. Set. 95.00 (ISBN 0-686-57145-2, M-6202). French & Eur.
Powell, Paul. Wherever He Leads I'll Go: The Story of B. B. McKinney. 50p. (Orig.). 1974. pap. 2.00 (ISBN 0-914520-04-0). Insight Pr.
Pratt, Waldo S. Music of the French Psalter of 1562. LC 40-4909. Repr. of 1939 ed. 15.00 (ISBN 0-404-05119-7). AMS Pr.
--Musical Ministries in the Church. LC 74-24193. Repr. of 1923 ed. 18.75 (ISBN 0-404-13095-X). AMS Pr.
Pugh, Nathanael. Music: Does It Really Matter? 2nd ed. Wallace, Mary H., ed. (Illus.). 79p. 1984. pap. 2.50 (ISBN 0-912315-73-3). Word Aflame.
Rain in the Desert Music Book. 5.95 (ISBN 0-8198-0727-3). Dghtrs St Paul.
Rau, Albert G. & David, Hans T. Catalogue of Music by American Moravians, 1742-1842. LC 76-134283. Repr. of 1938 ed. 14.00 (ISBN 0-404-07206-2). AMS Pr.
The Recording Locator. Orig. Title: MusiCatalog. 858p. 1986. pap. 160.00 (ISBN 0-89390-098-2). Resource Pubns.
Resource Publications, Inc. Staff. MusiCatalog. Cunningham, W. P., ed. 1978. pap. 54.90x (ISBN 0-89390-013-3). Resource Pubns.
Rhys, Stephen & Palmer, King. ABC of Church Music. LC 73-83175. 1969. 7.50 (ISBN 0-8008-0010-9, Crescendo). Taplinger.
Routley, Erik & Young, Carlton R. Music Leadership in the Church. 136p. 1985. pap. text ed. 6.95 (ISBN 0-916642-24-0). Agape IL.
Ryken, Leland. Culture in Christian Perspective: A Door to Understanding & Enjoying the Arts. LC 86-1442. 1986. 13.95 (ISBN 0-88070-115-3). Multnomah.
Schalk, Carl. The Pastor & the Church Musicians: Thoughts on Aspects of a Common Ministry. 12p. (Orig.). 1984. pap. 1.50 (ISBN 0-570-01330-5, 99-1256). Concordia.
Schield, Dean C. More Effective Choir Ministry: A Manual for Church Musicians. LC 86-42932. 32p. (Orig.). 1986. pap. 4.00 (ISBN 0-937021-02-4). Sagamore Bks MI.
Schlink, Basilea. Songs & Prayers of Victory. 1978. pap. 1.50 (ISBN 3-87209-652-4). Evang Sisterhood Mary.
Schneider, Kent E. The Creative Musician in the Church. 1976. pap. 8.95 (ISBN 0-89390-014-1). Resource Pubns.
Seipt, A. A. Schwenkfelder Hymnology. LC 77-134414. Repr. of 1909 ed. 14.50 (ISBN 0-404-09908-4). AMS Pr.
Silva, Owen F., tr. Mission Music of California. Bienbar, Arthur, ed. LC 77-16531. (Music Reprint Ser.). (Illus.). 1978. Repr. of 1941 ed. lib. bdg. 39.50 (ISBN 0-306-77524-7). Da Capo.
The Singing Church. 623p. 1985. 7.95x (ISBN 0-916642-25-9). Hope Pub.
Smith, Carolyn. Rebirth of Music: Training Course. 76p. 1985. pap. 4.95 (ISBN 0-938612-10-7). Revival Press.
Sounds of Joy & Praise: Accompaniment. write for info. (ISBN 0-8198-6873-6). Dghtrs St Paul.
Sounds of Joy & Praise: Singers Edition. 0.50 (ISBN 0-8198-6872-8). Dghtrs St Paul.
Stevens, Denis. Tudor Church Music. LC 73-4335. (Music Reprint Ser.). 144p. 1973. Repr. of 1955 ed. lib. bdg. 25.00 (ISBN 0-306-70579-6). Da Capo.
Swan, M. L. The New Harp of Columbia. Horn, Dorothy D., et al, eds. LC 78-5504. (Tennesseana Editions Ser.). (Facsimile of 1867 Ed.). 1978. 18.95x (ISBN 0-87049-251-9). U of Tenn Pr.
Tallis, Thomas, et al. Thomas Tallis. Buck, P. C., ed. (Tudor Church Music Ser.: Vol. 6). 1963. Repr. of 1928 ed. write for info. (ISBN 0-8450-1856-6). Broude.
Temperley, Nicholas. The Music of the English Parish Church, Vol. 1. LC 77-84811. (Cambridge Studies in Music). 1983. pap. 23.95 (ISBN 0-521-27457-5). Cambridge U Pr.
Tippett, Sir Michael. Music of the Angels. (Eulenburg Music Ser.). 1982. pap. text ed. 19.50 (ISBN 0-903873-60-5). Da Capo.
Tomkins, Thomas. Services, Pt. 1. Buck, P. C., ed. (Tudor Music Ser.: Vol.8). 1963. Repr. of 1928 ed. 85.00x (ISBN 0-8450-1858-2). Broude.
Voznesensky, J. Obshchjedostupnija Chtenija o Tserkovnom Penijі. Tr. of Popular Readings in Church Singing. 48p. 1969. pap. 2.00 (ISBN 0-317-30383-X). Holy Trinity.
Warburton, Ernest, ed. Miscellaneous Church Music. (John Christian Bach, 1735-1782 The Collected Works Ser.). 75.00 (ISBN 0-8240-6073-3). Garland Pub.
Warren, Jean, compiled by. Piggyback Songs in Praise of God. (Piggyback Songs Ser.). (Illus.). 80p. (Orig.). 1986. pap. 6.95 (ISBN 0-911019-10-3). Warren Pub Hse.

Wienandt, Elwyn A., ed. Opinions on Church Music: Comments & Reports from Four & a Half Centuries. LC 74-75229. 214p. 1974. 14.00 (ISBN 0-918954-12-6). Baylor Univ Pr.

Willis, Richard S. Our Church Music. LC 72-1662. Repr. of 1856 ed. 11.50 (ISBN 0-404-08336-6). AMS Pr.

Winter, Miriam T. Why Sing? Toward a Theology of Catholic Church Music. 346p. (Orig.). 1984. pap. 11.95 (ISBN 0-912405-07-4). Pastoral Pr.

Wohlgemuth, Paul W. Rethinking Church Music. rev. ed. LC 80-85254. 112p. 1981. pap. 5.95 (ISBN 0-916642-15-1). Hope Pub.

Wyeth, John. Wyeth's Repository of Sacred Music, 1 & 2 pts. LC 64-18989. (Music Reprint Ser.). 148p. 1964. Repr. of 1820 ed. Pt. 1. 25.00 (ISBN 0-306-70903-1); Pt. 2. 25.00 (ISBN 0-686-85854-9). Da Capo.

CHURCH MUSIC–BIBLIOGRAPHY

A Guide to Music for the Church Year. 4th ed. 1974. 4.95 (ISBN 0-8066-0930-3, 11-9195). Augsburg.

Laster, James, compiled by. Catalogue of Choral Music Arranged in Biblical Order. LC 82-16745. 269p. 1983. 27.50 (ISBN 0-8108-1592-3). Scarecrow.

Laster, James H., compiled by. Catalogue of Vocal Solos & Duets Arranged in Biblical Order. LC 84-14187. 212p. 1984. 17.50 (ISBN 0-8108-1748-9). Scarecrow.

Metcalf, Frank J. American Psalmody. 2nd ed. LC 68-13274. (Music Reprint Ser.). (Illus.). 1968. Repr. of 1917 ed. lib. bdg. 19.50 (ISBN 0-306-71132-X). Da Capo.

Rau, Albert G. & David, Hans T. Catalogue of Music by American Moravians, 1742-1842. LC 76-134283. Repr. of 1938 ed. 14.00 (ISBN 0-404-07206-2). AMS Pr.

Von Ende, Richard C. Church Music: An International Bibliography. LC 79-23697. 473p. 1980. lib. bdg. 30.00 (ISBN 0-8108-1271-1). Scarecrow.

--Church Music: An International Bibliography. LC 79-23697. pap. 118.30 (ISBN 0-317-52049-0, 2027497). Bks Demand UMI.

Warrington, James. Short Titles of Books Relating to or Illustrating the History & Practice of Psalmody in the U. S., 1620-1820. LC 77-178095. (American Classics in History & Social Science Ser.: No. 218). 102p. 1972. Repr. of 1898 ed. lib. bdg. 19.00 (ISBN 0-8337-5357-6). B Franklin.

CHURCH MUSIC–CATHOLIC CHURCH

see also Catholic Church–Liturgy and Ritual; Chants (Plain, Gregorian, etc.)

Baxter, James H. An Old St. Andrews Music Book. facsimile ed. LC 70-178515. (Medieval Studies Ser.). Repr. of 1931 ed. 34.50 (ISBN 0-404-56525-5). AMS Pr.

Brokering, Herb & Brokering, Lois. Love Songs: Musical Activities for Christian Celebration. 36p. (Orig.). 1981. pap. 3.95 (ISBN 0-942562-01-1). Brokering Pr.

Dreves, Guido M., ed. Cantiones Bohemicae. 1886. 60.00 (ISBN 0-384-12860-2). Johnson Repr.

--Cantiones et Muteti, 3 vols. (Illus.). 1895-1904. 60.00 ea. (ISBN 0-384-12865-3). Johnson Repr.

--Hymnodia Hiberica: Liturgische Reimofficien, Aus Spanischen Brevieren. (Illus.). 1894. 60.00 (ISBN 0-384-12915-3). Johnson Repr.

Fellerer, Karl G. The History of Catholic Church Music. Brunner, Francis A., tr. LC 78-21637. 1979. Repr. of 1951 ed. lib. bdg. 22.50x (ISBN 0-313-21147-7, FECC). Greenwood.

Gelineau, Joseph. Learning to Celebrate: The Mass & Its Music. 1985. pap. 6.95 (ISBN 0-317-38557-7). Pastoral Pr.

Hammerich, Angul. Mediaeval Musical Relics of Denmark. LC 74-24104. Repr. of 1912 ed. 24.50 (ISBN 0-404-12952-8). AMS Pr.

Kurtzman, Jeffrey. Essays on the Monteverdi Mass & Vespers of 1610. LC 78-66039. (Rice University Studies: Vol. 64, No.4). (Illus.). 182p. 1979. pap. 10.00x (ISBN 0-89263-238-0). Rice Univ.

Nemmers, Erwin E. Twenty Centuries of Catholic Church Music. LC 78-17248. 1978. Repr. of 1949 ed. lib. bdg. 22.50x (ISBN 0-313-20542-6, NETW). Greenwood.

Proske, Karl, ed. Musica Divina Selectus Novus Missarum, 10 vols in 8. 1973. Repr. of 1855 ed. 545.00 (ISBN 0-384-48055-1). Johnson Repr.

Roche, Jerome. North Italian Church Music in the Age of Monteverdi. (Illus.). 1984. 45.00x (ISBN 0-19-316118-4). Oxford U Pr.

Stevenson, Robert. Spanish Cathedral Music in the Golden Age. LC 76-1013. (Illus.). 523p. 1976. Repr. of 1961 ed. lib. bdg. 39.50x (ISBN 0-8371-8744-3, STSP). Greenwood.

Tomasello, Andrew. Music & Ritual at Papal Avignon, 1309-1403. Buelow, George, ed. LC 83-18296. (Studies in Musicology: No. 75). 314p. 1983. 49.95 (ISBN 0-8357-1493-4). UMI Res Pr.

Warburton, Thomas. Josquin Des Prez's "Missa Pange Lingua". An Edition, with Notes for Performance & Commentary. LC 76-22703. (Early Musical Masterworks--Critical Editions & Commentaries). ix, 63p. 1977. 21.00x (ISBN 0-8078-1296-X). U of NC Pr.

Winter, Dina S. & Richards, Theodora. Toward Freedom in Singing. 1986. pap. 4.50 (ISBN 0-916786-84-6). St George Bk Serv.

CHURCH MUSIC–CHORUSES AND CHOIR BOOKS

see Choruses, Sacred; Sacred Vocal Music; Service Books (Music)

CHURCH MUSIC–CHURCH OF ENGLAND

see also Church of England–Liturgy and Ritual

Buck, P. C. & Fellowes, E. H., eds. Tudor Church Music. Incl. Vol. 1. John Taverner - Part One (ISBN 0-8450-1851-5); Vol. 2. William Byrd - English Church Music, Part One (ISBN 0-8450-1852-3); Vol. 3. John Tavernen - Part Two (ISBN 0-8450-1853-1); Vol. 4. Orlando Gibbons (ISBN 0-8450-1854-X); Vol. 5. Robert White (ISBN 0-8450-1855-8); Vol. 6. Tallis, Thomas (ISBN 0-8450-1856-6); Vol. 7. Byrd, William (ISBN 0-8450-1857-4); Vol. 8. Thomas Tomkins (ISBN 0-8450-1858-2); Vol. 9 (ISBN 0-8450-1859-0); Vol. 10. Aston, Hugh & Marbeck, John. (ISBN 0-8450-1860-4). 1963. Repr. of 1922 ed. 750.00x set (ISBN 0-8450-1850-7); 85.00x ea.; appendix 50.00x (ISBN 0-8450-1861-2). Broude.

Foster, Myles B. Anthems & Anthem Composers. LC 76-125047. (Music Ser.). 1970. Repr. of 1901 ed. lib. bdg. 32.50 (ISBN 0-306-70012-3). Da Capo.

Temperley, Nicholas. The Music of the English Parish Church, 2 vols. LC 77-84811. (Cambridge Studies in Music). (Illus.). 1980. Vol. 1. 100.00 (ISBN 0-521-22045-9); Vol. 2. 52.50 (ISBN 0-521-22046-7). Cambridge U Pr.

CHURCH MUSIC–CHURCH OF JESUS CHRIST OF LATTER-DAY SAINTS

Swan, Howard. Music in the Southwest, 1825-1950. LC 77-5421. (Music Reprint Ser.). 1977. Repr. of 1952 ed. lib. bdg. 39.50 (ISBN 0-306-77418-6). Da Capo.

CHURCH MUSIC–DISCOGRAPHY

Freeman, Robert N. Franz Schneider (Seventeen Thirty-Seven to Eighteen Twelve) A Thematic Catalogue of His Works. LC 79-15260. (Thematic Catalogues Ser.: No. 5). 1979. lib. bdg. 24.00x (ISBN 0-918728-13-4). Pendragon NY.

CHURCH MUSIC–GREEK CHURCH

see Church Music–Orthodox Eastern Church

CHURCH MUSIC–HISTORY AND CRITICISM

Brown, Carleton. Religious Lyrics of the Thirteenth, Fourteenth, & Fifteenth Centuries, 3 vols. 300.00 (ISBN 0-8490-0942-1). Gordon Pr.

Dickinson, E. Music in the History of the Western Church. LC 68-25286. (Studies in Music, No. 42). 1969. Repr. of 1902 ed. lib. bdg. 49.95x (ISBN 0-8383-0301-3). Haskell.

Dickinson, Edward. Music in the History of the Western Church. LC 77-127454. Repr. of 1902 ed. 14.50 (ISBN 0-404-02127-1). AMS Pr.

--Music in the History of the Western Church, with an Introduction in Religious Music Among the Primitive & Ancient Peoples. LC 69-13884. Repr. of 1902 ed. lib. bdg. 22.50x (ISBN 0-8371-1062-9, DIMW). Greenwood.

--Music in the History of the Western Church, with an Introduction in Religious Music Among the Primitive & Ancient Peoples. 1977. Repr. 19.00 (ISBN 0-403-08194-7). Scholarly.

Ellinwood, Leonard. History of American Church Music. LC 69-12683. (Music Reprint Ser.). 1970. Repr. of 1953 ed. lib. bdg. 32.50 (ISBN 0-306-71233-4). Da Capo.

Fortune, Nigel & Lewis, Anthony, eds. New Oxford History of Music, Vol. 5: Opera & Church Music 1630-1750. (Illus.). 1975. 49.95x (ISBN 0-19-316305-5). Oxford U Pr.

Gavaert, Francois A. Les Origines du Chant Litturgique de l'Eglise Latin. 93p. Repr. of 1890 ed. lib. bdg. 30.00x (Pub. by G. Olms BRD). Coronet Bks.

Hammerich, Angul. Mediaeval Musical Relics of Denmark. LC 74-24104. Repr. of 1912 ed. 24.50 (ISBN 0-404-12952-8). AMS Pr.

Hastings, Robert J. Glorious Is Thy Name! LC 85-26948. 1986. 7.95 (ISBN 0-8054-7230-4). Broadman.

Hutchings, Arthur. Church Music in the Nineteenth Century. (Studies in Church Music). 1977. Repr. of 1967 ed. lib. bdg. 22.50x (ISBN 0-8371-9695-7, HUCMN). Greenwood.

Lutkin, Peter C. Music in the Church. LC 72-135722. Repr. of 1910 ed. 21.45 (ISBN 0-404-04069-1). AMS Pr.

MacDougall, Hamilton C. Early New England Psalmody: An Historical Appreciation, 1620-1820. LC 79-87398. (Music Reprint Ser.). 1969. Repr. of 1940 ed. lib. bdg. 29.50 (ISBN 0-306-71542-2). Da Capo.

Mealy, Norman & Rock, Judith. Music, Dance & Religion: The Performing Arts in Worship. (Illus.). 192p. 1985. 15.95 (ISBN 0-13-607219-4); pap. 8.95 (ISBN 0-13-607201-1). P-H.

Parry, W. H. Three Centuries of English Church Music. 1977. lib. bdg. 59.95 (ISBN 0-8490-2745-4). Gordon Pr.

Routley, Erik. Church Music & the Christian Faith. LC 78-110219. 156p. 1978. pap. 7.95 (ISBN 0-916642-10-0). Agape IL.

Temperley, Nicholas. The Music of the English Parish Church, 2 vols. LC 77-84811. (Cambridge Studies in Music). (Illus.). 1980. Vol. 1. 100.00 (ISBN 0-521-22045-9); Vol. 2. 52.50 (ISBN 0-521-22046-7). Cambridge U Pr.

CHURCH MUSIC–LUTHERAN CHURCH

Schalk, Carl. Music in Lutheran Worship. 16p. (Orig.). 1983. pap. 1.25 (ISBN 0-570-01323-2, 99-1253). Concordia.

CHURCH MUSIC–MORAVIAN CHURCH

David, Hans T. Music of the Moravians in America from the Archives of the Moravian Church at Bethlehem Pa, 2 vols. Incl. Vol. 1. Ten Sacred Songs. Dencke, J., et al.; Vol. 2. Six Quintets. Peter, John F. write to C. F. Peters Corp., NY for prices (ISBN 0-685-22862-2). NY Pub Lib.

CHURCH MUSIC–ORTHODOX EASTERN CHURCH

Conomos, Dimitri E. The Late Byzantine & Slavonic Communion Cycle: Liturgy & Music. LC 84-12176. (Dumbarton Oaks Studies: Vol. 21). (Illus.). 222p. 1985. 25.00x (ISBN 0-88402-134-3). Dumbarton Oaks.

Gardner, Johann V. Aljeksjej Theodorovich L'vov-director Imperatorskoj pridvornoj pevcheskoj kapelli i dukhovnij kompozitor. Tr. of Alexei Feodorovitch Lvov-Director of the Emperors Court Capella & Composer of Sacred Music. 90p. 1970. pap. 3.00 (ISBN 0-317-30387-2). Holy Trinity.

Mancuso, Laurence. Liturgical Music: Dogmatica & Other Selections, Vol. II. (New Skete). 107p. (Orig.). 1978. pap. 15.00 (ISBN 0-9607924-2-2). Monks of New Skete.

--Liturgical Music: Selection for Vespers, Matins, & Liturgy, Vol. I. (New Skete). 172p. (Orig.). 1975. 18.00x (ISBN 0-9607924-0-6); pap. 15.00x (ISBN 0-9607924-1-4). Monks of New Skete.

Tillyard, Henry J. Byzantine Music & Hymnography. LC 74-24242. Repr. of 1923 ed. 11.50 (ISBN 0-404-13116-6). AMS Pr.

Wellesz, Egon. History of Byzantine Music & Hymnography. 2nd ed. 1961. 49.95x (ISBN 0-19-816111-5). Oxford U Pr.

CHURCH MUSIC–PROTESTANT CHURCHES

Alford, Delton L. Music in the Pentecostal Church. 113p. 1969. 5.25 (ISBN 0-87148-561-3); pap. 4.25 (ISBN 0-87148-562-1). Pathway Pr.

Bach, Johann C. Music for Vespers II. (Johann Christian Bach: The Collected Works). 400p. 1985. lib. bdg. 85.00 (ISBN 0-8240-6072-5). Garland Pub.

Davison, Archibald. Protestant Church Music in America. 59.95 (ISBN 0-8490-0905-7). Gordon Pr.

Dean, Talmage W. Twentieth-Century Protestant Church Music in America. (Orig.). 1987. text ed. 14.95 (ISBN 0-8054-6813-7). Broadman.

Etherington, Charles L. Protestant Worship Music: Its History & Practice. LC 77-15990. (Illus.). 1978. Repr. of 1962 ed. lib. bdg. 35.00x (ISBN 0-313-20024-6, ETPW). Greenwood.

Ferguson, Everett. A Cappella Music in the Public Worksip of the Church. LC 72-76963. (Way of Life Ser: No. 125). 1972. pap. text ed. 3.95 (ISBN 0-89112-125-0, Bibl Res Pr). Abilene Christ U.

Mapson, J. Wendell, Jr. The Ministry of Music in the Black Church. 1984. pap. 5.95 (ISBN 0-8170-1057-2). Judson.

Stevenson, Robert M. Patterns of Protestant Church Music. LC 53-8271. viii, 219p. 1953. 20.50 (ISBN 0-8223-0168-7). Duke.

--Patterns of Protestant Church Music. LC 53-8271. pap. 56.80 (ISBN 0-317-26858-9, 2023455). Bks Demand UMI.

CHURCH MUSIC–SERVICE BOOKS

see Service Books (Music)

CHURCH OF CHRIST

Black, Garth. The Holy Spirit. rev. ed. (Way of Life Ser: No. 102). 1967. pap. 3.95 (ISBN 0-89112-102-1, Bibl Res Pr). Abilene Christ U.

Boles, H. Leo. Eldership of the Churches of Christ. 1978. pap. 1.50 (ISBN 0-89225-179-4). Gospel Advocate.

Clark, Vynomma. So You're a Woman. LC 70-180790. 4.95 (ISBN 0-89112-050-5, Bibl Res Pr). Abilene Christ U.

Clevenger, Ernest, Jr. Directory Alabama Churches of Christ, 1976. (Illus.). 1976. pap. 2.00 (ISBN 0-88428-039-X). Parchment Pr.

Davis, William H. Science & Christian Faith. LC 68-21524. (Way of Life Ser: No. 104). 1968. pap. 3.95 (ISBN 0-89112-104-8, Bibl Res Pr). Abilene Christ U.

Eckstein, Stephen D., Jr. A History of Churches of Christ in Texas, 1824-1950. 1963. 6.95 (ISBN 0-88027-098-5); 4.95. Firm Foun Pub.

Lemmons, Reuel. The King & His Kingdom. Thomas, J. D., ed. LC 68-59307. (Twentieth Century Sermons Ser). 1968. 11.95 (ISBN 0-89112-301-6, Bibl Res Pr). Abilene Christ U.

Pack, Frank & Meador, Prentice A., Jr. Preaching to Modern Man. Thomas, J. D., ed. LC 73-75928. 1969. 10.95 (ISBN 0-89112-060-2, Bibl Res Pr). Abilene Christ U.

Pullias, Athens C. Sermons of Athens Clay Pullias. Thomas, J. D., ed. (Great Preachers Ser). 1962. 11.95 (ISBN 0-89112-203-6, Bibl Res Pr). Abilene Christ U.

Schubert, Joe D. Marriage, Divorce & Purity. (Way of Life Ser: No. 101). 1966. pap. 3.95 (ISBN 0-89112-101-3, Bibl Res Pr). Abilene Christ U.

Thomas, J. D. Self-Study Guide to Galatians & Romans. rev. ed. (Way of Life Ser: No. 122). Orig. Title: Self-Study Guide to Romans. (Orig.). 1971. pap. text ed. 3.95 (ISBN 0-89112-122-6, Bibl Res Pr). Abilene Christ U.

--Self-Study Guide to the Corinthian Letters. (Way of Life Ser: No. 123). (Orig.). 1972. pap. text ed. 3.95 (ISBN 0-89112-123-4, Bibl Res Pr). Abilene Christ U.

Thomas, J. D., ed. Sermons of Batsell Barrett Baxter. (Great Preachers Ser). 1960. 11.95 (ISBN 0-89112-201-X, Bibl Res Pr). Abilene Christ U.

--Sermons of Frank Pack. (Great Preachers Ser). 1963. 11.95 (ISBN 0-89112-205-2, Bibl Res Pr). Abilene Christ U.

--Sermons of George W. Bailey. (Great Preachers Ser). 1961. 11.95 (ISBN 0-89112-202-8, Bibl Res Pr). Abilene Christ U.

--Sermons of Gus Nichols. (Great Preachers Ser). 1966. 11.95 (ISBN 0-89112-209-5, Bibl Res Pr). Abilene Christ U.

--Sermons of John H. Banister. (Great Preachers Ser). 1965. 11.95 (ISBN 0-89112-208-7, Bibl Res Pr). Abilene Christ U.

--Sermons of M. Norvel Young. (Great Preachers Ser). 1963. 11.95 (ISBN 0-89112-204-4, Bibl Res Pr). Abilene Christ U.

--Sermons of William S. Banowsky. (Great Preachers Ser). 1967. 11.95 (ISBN 0-89112-211-7, Bibl Res Pr). Abilene Christ U.

Thomas, J. D., et al. Sorrow & Joy. 1963. 11.95 (ISBN 0-89112-025-4, Bibl Res Pr). Abilene Christ U.

--Spiritual Power: Great Single Sermons. LC 74-170920. 1972. 13.95 (ISBN 0-89112-026-2, Bibl Res Pr). Abilene Christ U.

Tucker, Johnny, et al. Like a Meteor Across the Horizon: The Jesse B. Ferguson Story & History of the Church of Christ in Nashville. (Illus., Orig.). 1978. pap. 2.95 (ISBN 0-686-26617-X). Tucker Pubns.

Warren, Thomas B. The Bible Only Makes Christians Only & the Only Christians. 220p. 1986. pap. 11.00 (ISBN 0-934916-09-8). Natl Christian Pr.

Where the Saints Meet, Nineteen Eight-Four. 1979. pap. text ed. 10.00 (ISBN 0-686-25231-4). Firm Foun Pub.

Willis, John Thomas. Insights from the Psalms, Vol. 1. LC 73-93946. (Way of Life Ser: No. 131). 1974. pap. text ed. 3.95 (ISBN 0-89112-131-5, Bibl Res Pr). Abilene Christ U.

CHURCH OF CHRIST OF LATTER-DAY SAINTS

see Church of Jesus Christ of Latter-Day Saints; Mormons and Mormonism

CHURCH OF ENGLAND

see also Anglo-Catholicism; Church and State in Great Britain; Dissenters, Religious–England; Episcopacy; Oxford Movement; Puritans

Baker, Jan. The Church of England. 1978. pap. 3.35 (ISBN 0-08-021408-8). Pergamon.

Bale, John. Select Works of John Bale, Bishop of Ossory. 51.00 (ISBN 0-384-03135-8). Johnson Repr.

Bancroft, Richard. A Survey of the Pretended Holy Dicipline. LC 78-38148. (English Experience Ser.: No. 428). 472p. 1972. Repr. of 1593 ed. 67.00 (ISBN 90-221-0428-1). Walter J Johnson.

Barrow, Isaac. Theological Works of Isaac Barrow, 9 Vols. Napier, Alexander, ed. LC 72-161751. Repr. of 1859 ed. Set. lib. bdg. 215.00 (ISBN 0-404-00670-1); lib. bdg. 25.00 ea. AMS Pr.

Becon, Thomas. The Early Works of Thomas Becon, Chaplain to Archbishop Cranmer. Repr. of 1843 ed. 41.00 (ISBN 0-384-03725-9). Johnson Repr.

Bell, G. K. The English Church. 10.00 (ISBN 0-8414-1634-6). Folcroft.

Beveridge, William. Complete Works, 12 vols. LC 72-39437. (Library of Anglo-Catholic Theology: No. 2). Repr. of 1848 ed. Set. 360.00 (ISBN 0-404-52040-5). AMS Pr.

Borsch, Frederick H., ed. Anglicanism & the Bible. LC 83-62717. (Anglican Studies). (Orig.). 1984. pap. 8.95 (ISBN 0-8192-1337-3). Morehouse.

Bouyer, Louis. Orthodox Spirituality & Protestant & Anglican Spirituality. (A History of Christian Spirituality Ser.: Vol. 3). 232p. 1982. pap. 9.95 (ISBN 0-8164-2374-1, HarpR). Har-Row.

Bradford, John. Writings of John Bradford...Martyr, 1555, 2 Vols. Repr. of 1853 ed. Set. 92.00 (ISBN 0-384-05440-4). Johnson Repr.

Brandreth, Henry R. Episcopi Vagantes & the Anglican Church. 80p. Date not set. lib. bdg. 19.95x (ISBN 0-89370-558-6). Borgo Pr.

Brewer, Clifton H. A History of Religious Education in the Episcopal Church to Eighteen Thirty-Five. 1924. 14.50x (ISBN 0-686-51401-7). Elliots Bks.

Bryant, M. D., ed. The Future of Anglican Theology. LC 84-8983. (Toronto Studies in Theology: Vol. 17). 208p. 1984. 49.95x (ISBN 0-88946-763-3). E Mellen.

Butler, L. A. & Morris, R. K., eds. The Anglo-Saxon Church: Papers on History, Architecture, & Archaeology in Honor of Dr. H. M. Taylor. (Research Report Ser.: No. 60). (Illus.). 240p. 1986. pap. 45.00x (ISBN 0-906780-54-3, Pub. by Council British Archaelogy). Humanities.

Cheney, Christopher R. Episcopal Visitation of Monasteries in the Thirteenth Century. 2nd, rev. ed. xxxi, 192p. 1983. lib. bdg. 25.00x (ISBN 0-87991-638-9). Porcupine Pr.

Chillingworth, William. Works of William Chillingworth, 3 Vols. Repr. of 1838 ed. Set. lib. bdg. 95.00 (ISBN 0-404-01570-0). Vol. 1 (ISBN 0-404-01571-9). Vol. 3 (ISBN 0-404-01572-7). Vol. 4 (ISBN 0-404-01573-5). AMS Pr.

Connell, Joan. The Roman Catholic Church in England 1780-1850: A Study in Internal Politics. 215p. 1984. 14.00 (ISBN 0-87169-158-2). Am Philos.

Coverdale, Myles. Remains of Myles Coverdale, Bishop of Exeter. 1846. 51.00 (ISBN 0-384-09950-5). Johnson Repr.

Crakanthorp, Richard. Defensio Ecclesiae Anglicanae. LC 72-1027. (Library of Anglo-Catholic Theology: No. 6). Repr. of 1847 ed. 27.50 (ISBN 0-404-52087-1). AMS Pr.

Edwards, David L. What Anglicans Believe. 128p. 1975. pap. 1.90 (ISBN 0-88028-003-4, 503). Forward Movement.

Fifty letije Arkjierejsksgo Sluzhenie Mitropolita Anastasia. Tr. of Fifty Anniversary of Episcopal Service of Metropolitan Anastassy. 259p. 1956. pap. 10.00 (ISBN 0-317-29032-0). Holy Trinity.

Greenham, Richard. The Works, Examined, Corrected & Published: By H. Holland. LC 72-5999. (English Experience Ser.: No. 524). 496p. 1973. Repr. of 1599 ed. 70.00 (ISBN 90-221-0524-5). Walter J Johnson.

Hall, Joseph. Works of Bishop Joseph Hall, 10 Vols. Wynter, P., ed. LC 76-86830. Repr. of 1863 ed. Set. 375.00 (ISBN 0-404-03070-X); 37.50 ea. AMS Pr.

Harvey, George L., ed. Church & the Twentieth Century. facs. ed. LC 67-26747. (Essay Index Reprint Ser). 1936. 21.50 (ISBN 0-8369-0517-2). Ayer Co Pubs.

Holloway, Richard, et al. The Anglican Tradition. Holloway, Richard, ed. LC 83-62541. 132p. (Orig.). 1984. pap. 6.95 (ISBN 0-8192-1338-1). Morehouse.

Holmes, Urban T., III. Turning to Christ: A Theology of Renewal & Evangelization. 240p. (Orig.). 1981. pap. 8.95 (ISBN 0-8164-2289-3, HarpR). Har-Row.

Holmes, Urban T., 3rd. What Is Anglicanism? LC 81-84715. 112p. (Orig.). 1982. pap. 5.95 (ISBN 0-8192-1295-4). Morehouse.

Hooper, John. The Early Writings of John Hooper. 1843. 51.00 (ISBN 0-384-24210-3). Johnson Repr.

--The Later Writings of Bishop Hooper. 1852. 55.00 (ISBN 0-384-24211-1). Johnson Repr.

Huelin, Gordon, ed. Old Catholics & Anglicans: 1931-81. (Illus.). 1983. text ed. 27.50x (ISBN 0-19-920129-3). Oxford U Pr.

Jewel, John. An Apology of the Church of England. Booty, John E., ed. (Paperbacks Ser). 1978. pap. 7.90x (ISBN 0-918016-63-0). Folger Bks.

--Works, 4 Vols. 1845-1850. Set. 204.00 (ISBN 0-384-27217-7). Johnson Repr.

Lewis, C. S. The Joyful Christian: One Hundred Readings from the Works of C. S. Lewis. LC 77-21685. 1977. 11.95 (ISBN 0-02-570900-3). Macmillan.

Lincoln, English: Lincoln Diocese Documents. (EETS, OS Ser.: No. 149). Repr. of 1914 ed. 28.00 (ISBN 0-527-00145-7). Kraus Repr.

Marshall, Michael E. The Anglican Church Today & Tomorrow. LC 83-62718. 176p. (Orig.). 1984. pap. 7.95 (ISBN 0-8192-1341-1). Morehouse.

Parker Society-London. Parker Society Publications, 55 Vols. Repr. of 1841 ed. Set. 2200.00 (ISBN 0-384-44880-1). Johnson Repr.

Pilkington, James. Works of James Pilkington, Lord Bishop of Durham. 1842. Repr. of 1842 ed. 55.00 (ISBN 0-384-46530-7). Johnson Repr.

Ridley, Nicholas. Works of Nicholas Ridley, D.D., Sometime Lord Bishop of London, Martyr, 1555. Repr. of 1841 ed. 41.00 (ISBN 0-384-50840-5). Johnson Repr.

Sisson, C. H. Anglican Essays. 142p. 1983. 20.00 (ISBN 0-85635-456-2). Carcanet.

Smyth, Norman. Story of Church Unity: The Lambeth Conference of Anglican Bishops & the Congregational-Episcopal Approaches. 1923. 29.50x (ISBN 0-686-83788-6). Elliots Bks.

Taylor, John, ed. Believing in the Church: Doctrine Commission of the Church of England. LC 82-80254. 320p. (Orig.). 1982. Repr. of 1981 ed. 17.95 (ISBN 0-8192-1301-2). Morehouse.

Vanuken, Sheldon. A Severe Mercy. 1979. pap. 3.95 (ISBN 0-553-25155-4). Bantam.

Wall, John N., Jr. A New Dictionary for Episcopalians. 168p. (Orig.). 1985. pap. 7.95 (ISBN 0-86683-787-6, HarpR). Har-Row.

Wand, J. W. What the Church of England Stands For. LC 76-106700. 131p. 1972. Repr. of 1951 ed. lib. bdg. 22.50x (ISBN 0-8371-3382-3, WACE). Greenwood.

Whitelock, Dorothy & Brett, Martin. Council & Synods with Other Documents Relating to the English Church, Vol. 1: A. D. 871-1204, 2 Vols. 1981. text ed. 139.00x (ISBN 0-19-822394-3). Oxford U Pr.

CHURCH OF ENGLAND–BIOGRAPHY

see also Church of England–Clergy

Lawton, George. Within the Rock of Ages: Life & Work of Augustus Moretague Toplady. 249p. 1983. 25.00 (ISBN 0-227-67836-2). Attic Pr.

Mackay, Henry F. Followers in the Way. LC 71-93359. (Essay Index Reprint Ser). 1934. 17.00 (ISBN 0-8369-1304-3). Ayer Co Pubs.

Morse-Boycott, Desmond L. Lead, Kindly Light. LC 70-107728. (Essay Index Reprint Ser). 1933. 16.00 (ISBN 0-8369-1529-1). Ayer Co Pubs.

Peart-Binns, John S. Defender of the Church of England: A Biography of R. R. Williams, Bishop of Leicester. 172p. 1984. 30.00x (ISBN 0-317-43628-7, Pub. by Amate Pr. Ltd.). State Mutual Bk.

Pfatteicher, Carl F. John Redford: Organist & Almoner of St. Paul's Cathedral in the Reign of Henry VIII. LC 74-24184. Repr. of 1934 ed. 24.00 (ISBN 0-404-13088-7). AMS Pr.

Smith, Martin L., ed. Benson of Cowley. 153p. 1983. pap. 8.00 (ISBN 0-936384-12-3). Cowley Pubns.

CHURCH OF ENGLAND–BISHOPS

Church of England Staff. Articles to Be Inquired of, in the First Metropoliticall Visitation of the Most Reverend Father Richarde...Archbishop of Canterbury. LC 74-28851. (English Experience Ser.: No. 732). 1975. Repr. of 1605 ed. 3.50 (ISBN 90-221-0732-9). Walter J Johnson.

Peart-Binns, John S. Defender of the Church of England: A Biography of R. R. Williams, Bishop of Leicester. 172p. 1984. 30.00x (ISBN 0-317-43628-7, Pub. by Amate Pr. Ltd.). State Mutual Bk.

Pruter, Karl. Directory of Autocephalous Anglican, Catholic, & Orthodox Bishops. 3rd ed. LC 86-34289. 53p. 1986. lib. bdg. 19.95x (ISBN 0-89370-528-4). Borgo Pr.

CHURCH OF ENGLAND–BOOK OF COMMON PRAYER

The Book of Common Prayer. 1928 ed. write for info. Oxford U Pr.

The Book of Common Prayer. fac: ed. 1976. 15.00 (ISBN 0-8164-5088-9, HarpR). Har-Row.

The Book of Common Prayer & Books Connected with Its Origin & Growth. 2nd ed. 1985. 30.00 (ISBN 0-317-13412-4). Boston Public Lib.

Book of Common Prayer with the Additions & Deviations Proposed in 1928. 10.95x (ISBN 0-19-141202-3). Oxford U Pr.

Church of England Staff. The Durham Book: Being the First Draft of the Revision of the Book of Common Prayer in 1661. Cuming, G. J., ed. LC 79-12674. 1979. Repr. of 1961 ed. lib. bdg. cancelled (ISBN 0-313-21481-6, CEBC). Greenwood.

Cuming, Geoffrey. A History of Anglican Liturgy. (Illus.). 450p. 1980. Repr. of 1969 ed. text ed. 55.00x (ISBN 0-333-30661-9). Humanities.

Episcopal Church. Prayer Book Guide to Christian Education. 224p. 1983. pap. 9.95 (ISBN 0-8164-2422-5, HarpR). Har-Row.

Hassel, R. Chris, Jr. Renaissance Drama & the English Church Year. LC 78-24233. (Illus.). xii, 215p. 1979. 18.95x (ISBN 0-8032-2304-8). U of Nebr Pr.

Jacobson, W. Fragmentary Illustrations of the History of the Book of Common Prayer. 122p. Repr. of 1874 ed. text ed. 33.12x (ISBN 0-576-99146-5, Pub. by Gregg Intl Pubs England). Gregg Intl.

Maurice, Frederick D. The Prayer Book & the Lord's Prayer. 416p. 1977. Repr. of 1880 ed. 12.50 (ISBN 0-87921-038-9). Attic Pr.

Neill, Stephen, et al. When Will Ye Be Wise? Kilmister, C. A., ed. 208p. (Orig.). 1984. pap. 6.95. St Thomas.

Noble, Richmond. Shakespeare's Biblical Knowledge & Use of the Book of Common Prayer. 1970. lib. bdg. 20.00x (ISBN 0-374-96115-8, Octagon). Hippocrene Bks.

Pocock, Nicholas, ed. Troubles Connected with the Prayer Book of 1549. 1884. 27.00 (ISBN 0-384-47030-0). Johnson Repr.

Pullan, Leighton. The History of the Book of Common Prayer. 330p. 1981. Repr. of 1901 ed. lib. bdg. 35.00 (ISBN 0-8492-2167-6). R West.

CHURCH OF ENGLAND–CATECHISMS AND CREEDS

Norwell, Alexander. Catechism Written in Latin Together with the Same Catechism Translated into English. Repr. of 1853 ed. 25.00 (ISBN 0-384-42090-7). Johnson Repr.

CHURCH OF ENGLAND–CLERGY

see also Anglican Orders; Apostolic Succession; Episcopacy

Anstruther, Godfrey. The Seminary Priests: A Dictionary of the Secular Clery of England & Wales, 1558 to 1800, Vols. 1-4. Incl. Vol. 1. Elizabethan 1558-1603. 1969. text ed. 21.50x (ISBN 0-8401-0071-X); Vol. 2. Early Stuarts 1603-1659. 1975. text ed. 21.50x (ISBN 0-8401-0072-8); Vol. 3. 1660-1715. 1976. text ed. 27.50x (ISBN 0-8401-0073-6); Vol. 4. 1716-1800. 1977. text ed. 27.50x (ISBN 0-8401-0074-4). LC 76-441910. A R Allenson.

Carlyle, Alexander. Autobiography of the Rev. Dr. Alexander Carlyle: Containing Memorials of Men & Events of His Time. Burton, John H., ed. LC 78-67649. Repr. of 1860 ed. 44.50 (ISBN 0-404-17179-6). AMS Pr.

Lehman, Edward C., Jr. English Church Members' Responses to Women Clergy: A Sociological Analysis. LC 86-28547. (Studies in Religion & Society). 224p. 1987. text ed. 49.95 (ISBN 0-88946-858-3). E Mellen.

Mason, Thomas. Serving God & Mammon: William Juxon, 1582-1663. LC 83-40507. (Illus.). 208p. 1985. 29.50 (ISBN 0-87413-251-7). U Delaware Pr.

Shaw, George P. Patriarch & Patriot: William Grant Broughton 1788-1853: Colonial Statesman & Ecclesiastic. 1978. 28.50x (ISBN 0-522-84122-8, Pub. by Melbourne U Pr). Intl Spec Bk.

CHURCH OF ENGLAND–CLERGY–CORRESPONDENCE, REMINISCENSES, ETC.

Cartwright, Thomas. A Briefe Apologie Against M. Sutcliffe. LC 78-25890. (English Experience Ser.: No. 237). 28p. 1970. Repr. of 1596 ed. 7.00 (ISBN 90-221-0237-8). Walter J Johnson.

Jones, Girault M. That Reminds Me. (Illus.). xiv, 211p. (Orig.). 1984. pap. write for info. (ISBN 0-918769-08-6). Univ South.

Maurice, Frederick D. Toward the Recovery of Unity. Porter, John F. & Wolf, William J., eds. LC 64-12942. 1964. text ed. 10.00x (ISBN 0-8401-1596-2). A R Allenson.

CHURCH OF ENGLAND–CONSTITUTION

see Church of England–Government

CHURCH OF ENGLAND–DOCTRINAL AND CONTROVERSIAL WORKS

The Answeres of Some Brethren of the Ministerie to the Replies Concerning the Late Covenant. LC 74-80155. (English Experience Ser.: No. 636). 1974. Repr. of 1638 ed. 18.50 (ISBN 90-221-0636-5). Walter J Johnson.

Becon, Thomas. The Catechism of Thomas Becon. Repr. of 1884 ed. 55.00 (ISBN 0-384-03715-1). Johnson Repr.

--Prayers & Others Pieces of Thomas Becon, Chaplain to Archbishop Cranmer. Repr. of 1844 ed. 55.00 (ISBN 0-384-03730-5). Johnson Repr.

Bell, Thomas. The Anatomie of Popish Tyrannie. LC 74-28833. (English Experience Ser.: No. 714). 1975. Repr. of 1603 ed. 16.00 (ISBN 90-221-0714-0). Walter J Johnson.

Calderwood, David. A Solution of Doctor Resolutus, His Resolutions for Kneeling. LC 79-84093. (English Experience Ser.: No. 913). 60p. 1979. Repr. of 1619 ed. lib. bdg. 8.00 (ISBN 90-221-0913-5). Walter J Johnson.

Cartwright, Thomas. The Christian Letter of Certaine English Protestants Unto Mr. R. Hooker. LC 72-180. (English Experience Ser.: No. 202). 50p. 1969. Repr. of 1599 ed. 8.00 (ISBN 90-221-0202-5). Walter J Johnson.

The Confession of the Fayth of Certayne English People, Living in Exile in the Lowe Contreyes. LC 72-208. (English Experience Ser.: No. 346). 58p. Repr. of 1602 ed. 9.50 (ISBN 90-221-0346-3). Walter J Johnson.

Crowley, Richard. The Way to Wealth, Wherein Is Plainly Taught a Remedy for Sedicion. LC 74-28843. (English Experience Ser.: No. 724). 1975. Repr. of 1550 ed. 3.50 (ISBN 90-221-0724-8). Walter J Johnson.

Hooker, Richard. Of the Lawes of Ecclesiasticall Politie, 2 pts. LC 76-171765. (English Experience Ser.: No. 390). 500p. 1971. Repr. of 1594 ed. 46.00 (ISBN 90-221-0390-0). Walter J Johnson.

--Works of That Learned & Judicious Divine Mr. Richard Hooker with an Account of His Life & Death by Isaac Walton, 3 vols. 7th ed. LC 76-125020. (Research & Source Works Ser.: No. 546). 1970. Repr. of 1888 ed. 103.00 (ISBN 0-8337-1731-6). B Franklin.

Jewel, John. An Apologie or Answer in Defence of the Church of England. Bacon, Ann, tr. LC 72-38204. (English Experience Ser.: No. 470). 140p. 1972. Repr. of 1562 ed. 20.00 (ISBN 90-221-0470-2). Walter J Johnson.

McAdoo, Henry R. The Unity of Anglicanism: Catholic & Reformed. 48p. 1983. pap. 4.95 (ISBN 0-8192-1324-1). Morehouse.

Melanchthon. The Confessyon of the Fayth of the Germaynes in the Councell, 2 pts. LC 76-57351. (English Experience Ser.: No. 771). 1977. Repr. of 1536 ed. Set. lib. bdg. 39.00 (ISBN 90-221-0771-X). Walter J Johnson.

Montagu, Richard. Appello Caesarem: A Just Appeale from Two Unjust Informers. LC 75-38210. (English Experience Ser.: No. 475). 348p. 1972. Repr. of 1625 ed. 49.00 (ISBN 90-221-0475-3). Walter J Johnson.

--A Gagg for the New Gospell? No: A New Gagg for an Old Goose. LC 74-28872. (English Experience Ser.: No. 751). 1975. Repr. of 1624 ed. 26.00 (ISBN 90-221-0751-5). Walter J Johnson.

Newman, John H., et al, eds. Tracts for the Times, 6 Vols. 1833-1841. Set. lib. bdg. 295.00 (ISBN 0-404-19560-1). Vol. 1 (ISBN 0-404-04711-4). Vol. 2 (ISBN 0-404-04712-2). Vol. 3 (ISBN 0-404-04713-0). Vol. 4 (ISBN 0-404-04714-9). Vol. 5 (ISBN 0-404-04715-7). Vol. 6 (ISBN 0-404-04716-5). AMS Pr.

Rogers, Thomas. The Catholic Doctrine of the Church of England. Repr. of 1854 ed. 31.00 (ISBN 0-384-51710-2). Johnson Repr.

Rowell, Geoffrey. The Vision Glorious: Themes & Personalities of the Catholic Revival in Anglicanism. 280p. 1983. text ed. 27.00x (ISBN 0-19-826443-7). Oxford U Pr.

Smith, David M. English Episcopal Acta I: Lincoln 1067-1185. (English Episcopal Acta Ser.). (Illus.). 312p. 1980. 67.50 (ISBN 0-85672-645-1, Pub. by British Acad). Longwood Pub Group.

Some, Robert. A Godly Treatise Containing & Deciding Certaine Questions. LC 74-80231. (English Experience Ser.: No. 696). 204p. 1974. Repr. of 1588 ed. 20.00 (ISBN 90-221-0696-9). Walter J Johnson.

Southgate, Wyndham M. John Jewel & the Problem of Doctrinal Authority. LC 62-9430. (Historical Monographs: No. 49). (Illus.). 1962. 16.50x (ISBN 0-674-47750-2). Harvard U Pr.

Staniloae, Dumitru. Theology & the Church. Barringer, Robert, tr. from Romanian. LC 80-19313. 240p. 1980. pap. 7.95 (ISBN 0-913836-69-9). St Vladimirs.

Teixeira, Jose. The Spanish Pilgrime, or: An Admirable Discovery of a Romish Catholike. LC 72-6033. (English Experience Ser.: No. 560). 148p. 1973. Repr. of 1625 ed. 15.00 (ISBN 90-221-0560-1). Walter J Johnson.

Tyndale, William. Doctrinal Treatises, an Introduction to Different Portions of the Holy Scriptures. Repr. of 1848 ed. 51.00 (ISBN 0-384-62250-X). Johnson Repr.

Whittingham, William. A Briefe Discourse of the Troubles Begonne at Franckford. LC 71-38228. (English Experience Ser.: No. 492). 210p. 1972. Repr. of 1574 ed. 13.00 (ISBN 90-221-0492-3). Walter J Johnson.

CHURCH OF ENGLAND–GOVERNMENT

Fenner, Dudley. A Counter-Poyson..., to the Objections & Reproaches, Wherewith the Aunswerer to the Abstract, Would Disgrace the Holy Discipline of Christ. LC 74-28854. (English Experience Ser.: No. 735). 1975. Repr. of 1584 ed. 10.50 (ISBN 90-221-0735-3). Walter J Johnson.

Hall, Joseph. An Humble Remonstrance to the High Court of Parliament. LC 72-203. (English Experience Ser.: No. 255). 44p. 1970. Repr. of 1640 ed. 8.00 (ISBN 90-221-0255-6). Walter J Johnson.

Jacob, Henry. An Attestation of Many Learned, Godly, & Famous Divines...Justifying...That the Church Government Ought to Be Always with the Peoples Free Consent. LC 74-28868. (English Experience Ser.: No. 747). 1975. Repr. of 1613 ed. 16.00 (ISBN 90-221-0747-7). Walter J Johnson.

Jewel, John. An Apology of the Church of England. Booty, John E., ed. (Paperbacks Ser). 1978. pap. 7.90x (ISBN 0-918016-63-0). Folger Bks.

Johnson, John. Collection of the Laws & Canons of the Church of England: Theological Works, 4 Vols. LC 72-1032. (Library of Anglo-Catholic Theology: No. 10). Repr. of 1851 ed. Set. 115.00 (ISBN 0-404-52110-X). AMS Pr.

Kemp, Eric W. Counsel & Consent. LC 62-3455. (Bampton Lectures). 1961. 15.00x (ISBN 0-8401-1317-X). A R Allenson.

Maitland, Frederic W. Roman Canon Law in the Church of England. 1969. Repr. of 1898 ed. 21.00 (ISBN 0-8337-2186-0). B Franklin.

Makower, Felix. The Constitutional History & the Constitutions of the Church of England. LC 61-2869. (Research & Source Works Ser.). Tr. of Die Verfassung der Kirche Von England. 556p. 1972. Repr. of 1895 ed. lib. bdg. 32.00 (ISBN 0-8337-2195-X). B Franklin.

Overall, John. Convocation Book of 1606. LC 77-173482. (Library of Anglo-Catholic Theology: No. 15). Repr. of 1844 ed. 27.50 (ISBN 0-404-52107-X). AMS Pr.

Rodes, Robert E., Jr. Ecclesiastical Admininstration in Medieval England: The Anglo-Saxons to the Reformation. LC 73-22584. 1977. text ed. 19.95x (ISBN 0-268-00903-1). U of Notre Dame Pr.

Shaw, William A. A History of the English Church During the Civil Wars & under the Commonwealth, 1640-1660. LC 78-184708. 1974. Repr. of 1900 ed. lib. bdg. 57.50 (ISBN 0-8337-4389-9). B Franklin.

Sutcliffe, Matthew. A Treatise of Ecclesiastical Discipline. LC 73-7082. (English Experience Ser.: No. 626). 1973. Repr. of 1590 ed. 21.00 (ISBN 90-221-0626-8). Walter J Johnson.

CHURCH OF ENGLAND–HISTORY

Abbey, Charles J. The English Church & Its Bishops, 1700-1800, 2 Vols. LC 77-130230. Repr. of 1887 ed. Set. 74.50 (ISBN 0-404-00290-0). AMS Pr.

Ames, William. A Fresh Suit Against Human Ceremonies in God's Worship. 886p. Repr. of 1633 ed. text ed. 82.80x (ISBN 0-576-99734-X, Pub. by Gregg Intl Pubs England). Gregg Intl.

Baker, Derek, ed. The Church in Town & Countryside: Papers Read at the Seventeenth Summer Meeting & the Eighteenth Winter Meeting of the Ecclesiastical History Society. (Studies in Church History: Vol. 16). 502p. 1979. 45.00 (ISBN 0-631-11421-1). Basil Blackwell.

Barlow, Frank. The English Church, Ten Sixty-Six to Eleven Fifty-Four: A History of the Anglo-Norman Church. (Illus.). 1979. text ed. 40.00x (ISBN 0-582-50236-5). Longman.

Bede the Venerable. History of the English Church & People. Sherley-Price, Leo, tr. 400p. 1985. 16.95 (ISBN 0-88029-042-0, Pub. by Dorset Pr). Hippocrene Bks.

Brooks, Nicholas. The Early History of the Church at Canterbury. (Studies in the Early History of Britain). 237p. 1983. text ed. 60.00x (ISBN 0-7185-1182-4, Leicester). Humanities.

Bross, Olive J. Church & Parliament: The Reshaping of the Church of England, 1828-1860. LC 59-7423. pap. 30.00 (ISBN 0-317-26542-3, 2023992). Bks Demand UMI.

Cartwright, Thomas. Diary. 1843. 19.00 (ISBN 0-384-07815-X). Johnson Repr.

--Diary of Dr. Thomas Cartwright, Bishop of Chester October 1687. (Camden Society, London. Publications. First Ser.: No. 22). Repr. of 1843 ed. 19.00 (ISBN 0-404-50122-2). AMS Pr.

Cheney, C. R. & Jones, Bridgette A., eds. English Episcopal Acta: Canterbury, 1193-1205, 2 vols, Vols. I & II. (Episcopal Acta). 1984. Set. 165.00x (ISBN 0-19-726022-5). Oxford U Pr.

Cox, Jeffrey. The English Churches in a Secular Society: Lambeth, 1870-1930. (Illus.). 1982. 45.00x (ISBN 0-19-503019-2). Oxford U Pr.

Crowther, M. A. Church Embattled: Religious Controversy in Mid-Victorian England. LC 70-19499. (Library of Politics & Society Ser.). 272p. 1970. 29.50 (ISBN 0-208-01091-2, Archon). Shoe String.

Davie, Donald. A Gathered Church: The Literature of the English Dissenting Interest, 1700-1930. (The Clark Lectures 1976). 1978. 17.50x (ISBN 0-19-519999-5). Oxford U Pr.

Davies, Ebenezer T. Episcopacy & the Royal Supremacy in the Church of England in the XVI Century. LC 78-13202. 1978. Repr. of 1950 ed. lib. bdg. 24.75x (ISBN 0-313-20626-0, DAER). Greenwood.

Deanesly, Margaret. The Pre-Conquest Church in England. 2nd ed. (Ecclesiastical History of England Ser.). 376p. 1963. text ed. 30.00x (ISBN 0-06-491638-3). B&N Imports.

Dickinson, J. C. The Later Middle Ages: From the Norman Conquest to the Eve of the Reformation. (Ecclesiastical History of England Ser.). 487p. 1979. text ed. 30.00x (ISBN 0-06-491678-2). B&N Imports.

Distad, N. Merrill. Guessing at Truth: The Life of Julius Charles Hare 1795-1855. LC 78-11625. xiv, 258p. 1979. 23.50x (ISBN 0-915762-07-2). Patmos Pr.

Gallyon, Margaret. The Early Church in Eastern England. 1979. 30.00x (ISBN 0-900963-19-0, Pub. by Terence Dalton England). State Mutual Bk.

Hart, A. Tindal. The Parson & the Publican. 1984. 9.50 (ISBN 0-533-05730-2). Vantage.

Haselmayer, Louis A. Medieval English Episcopal Registers. (Church Historical Society, London, New Ser.: No. 33). pap. 16.00 (ISBN 0-8115-3157-0). Kraus Repr.

Hutton, William H. English Church from the Accession of Charles First to the Death of Anne, 1625-1714. LC 4-4381. (History of the English Church Ser.: No. 6). Repr. of 1903 ed. 29.50 (ISBN 0-404-50756-5). AMS Pr.

Jagger, Peter J. Clouded Witness: Initiation in the Church of England in the Mid-Victorian Period 1850-1875. (Pittsburgh Theological Monographs New Ser.: No. 1). vii, 221p. (Orig.). 1982. pap. 12.00 (ISBN 0-915138-51-4). Pickwick.

Kemp, Eric W. Counsel & Consent. LC 62-3455. (Bampton Lectures). 1961. 15.00x (ISBN 0-8401-1317-X). A R Allenson.

Lawrence. The English Church & the Papacy in the Middle Ages. LC 65-12529. 265p. 1984. pap. 10.00 (ISBN 0-8232-0646-7). Fordham.

Lingard, John. History & Antiquities of the Anglo-Saxon Church, 2 vols. LC 77-6976. 1977. Repr. of 1845 ed. lib. bdg. 70.00 (ISBN 0-89341-212-0). Longwood Pub Group.

Manning, Bernard L. Making of Modern English Religion. LC 70-161528. 1929. text ed. 6.00x (ISBN 0-8401-1558-X). A R Allenson.

Manwaring, Randle. From Controversy to Co-Existence: Evangelicals in the Church of England, 1914-1980. 240p. 1985. 34.50 (ISBN 0-521-30380-X). Cambridge U Pr.

Marrin, Albert. The Last Crusade: The Church of England in the First World War. LC 72-97471. xv, 303p. 1973. 19.75 (ISBN 0-8223-0298-5). Duke.

Miller, E. C., Jr. Toward a Fuller Vision: Orthodoxy & the Anglican Experience. LC 84-61015. 188p. (Orig.). 1984. pap. 7.95 (ISBN 0-8192-1351-9). Morehouse.

Moorman, John R. Church Life in England in the Thirteenth Century. LC 76-29401. Repr. of 1945 ed. 32.50 (ISBN 0-404-15352-6). AMS Pr.

Morgan, R. W. St. Paul in Britain. LC 83-73168. 128p. 1984. pap. 4.50 (ISBN 0-934666-12-1). Artisan Sales.

Nennius. Nennius's "History of the Brittons". Wade-Evans, A. W., tr. Bd. with The Annals of Britons of Court Pedigree of Hywel the Good. (Church Historical Society, London, N. S.: No. 34). pap. 23.00 (ISBN 0-317-15134-7). Kraus Repr.

Norman, Edward. The English Catholic Church in the Nineteenth Century. 1984. pap. 13.95x (ISBN 0-19-822955-0). Oxford U Pr.

O'Day, Rosemary & Heal, Felicity, eds. Princes & Paupers in the English Church: 1500-1800. 294p. 1981. 28.50x (ISBN 0-389-20200-2, 06982). B&N Imports.

Pantin, W. A. The English Church in the Fourteenth Century. (Medieval Academy Reprints for Teaching Ser.). 1980. pap. 6.50 (ISBN 0-8020-6411-6). U of Toronto Pr.

Philpot, J. H. The Seceders. pap. 2.95 (ISBN 0-85151-132-5). Banner of Truth.

Raban, S. Mortmain Legislation & the English Church, 1279-1500. LC 81-21685. (Cambridge Studies in Medieval Life & Thought: No. 17). (Illus.). 244p. 1982. 47.50 (ISBN 0-521-24233-9). Cambridge U Pr.

Rodes, Robert E., Jr. Ecclesiastical Admininstration in Medieval England: The Anglo-Saxons to the Reformation. LC 73-22584. 1977. text ed. 19.95x (ISBN 0-268-00903-1). U of Notre Dame Pr.

Sampson, H. Grant. The Anglican Tradition in Eighteenth Century Verse. (De Proprietatibus Litterarum, Ser. Practica: No. 33). 1971. pap. text ed. 27.20x (ISBN 90-2791-907-0). Mouton.

Shaw, William A. A History of the English Church During the Civil Wars & under the Commonwealth, 1640-1660. LC 78-184708. 1974. Repr. of 1900 ed. lib. bdg. 57.50 (ISBN 0-8337-4389-9). B Franklin.

Stevenson, Joseph. The Church Histories of England. 59.95 (ISBN 0-87968-869-6). Gordon Pr.

Strype, John. Historical Collections of the Life & Acts of John Aylmer, Bishop of London, in the Reign of Queen Elizabeth. LC 74-979. 244p. 1974. Repr. of 1821 ed. lib. bdg. 22.50 (ISBN 0-8337-4427-5). B Franklin.

Tyack, George S. Lore & Legend of the English Church. 1979. Repr. of 1899 ed. lib. bdg. 50.00 (ISBN 0-8495-5135-8). Arden Lib.

Vogel, Arthur A., et al. Theology in Anglicanism. LC 84-60624. (Anglican Studies). 160p. (Orig.). 1984. pap. 8.95 (ISBN 0-8192-1344-6). Morehouse.

Wagner, Donald O. Church of England & Social Reform since 1854. LC 77-127438. (Columbia University. Studies in the Social Sciences: No. 325). 12.50 (ISBN 0-404-51325-5). AMS Pr.

Wakeman, Henry O. Introduction to the History of the Church of England, from the Earliest Times to the Present Day. 7th ed. LC 77-137302. Repr. of 1908 ed. 32.50 (ISBN 0-404-06802-2). AMS Pr.

Ware, Sedley L. The Elizabethan Parish in Its Ecclesiastical & Financial Aspects. LC 78-63927. (Johns Hopkins University. Studies in the Social Sciences. Twenty-Sixth Ser. 1908: 7-8). Repr. of 1908 ed. 14.50 (ISBN 0-404-61177-X). AMS Pr.

Warre-Cornish, Francis. English Church in the Nineteenth Century, 2 Vols. LC 75-148325. (History of the English Church Ser.: No. 8). Repr. of 1910 ed. Set. 59.00 (ISBN 0-404-50760-3); 29.50 ea. Vol. 1 (ISBN 0-404-50758-1). Vol. 2 (ISBN 0-404-50759-X). AMS Pr.

Watson, Edward W. The Church of England. LC 80-22643. (Home University Library of Modern Knowledge: No. 90). 192p. 1981. Repr. of 1961 ed. lib. bdg. 25.00x (ISBN 0-313-22683-0, WAEN). Greenwood.

Welsby, Paul A. The History of the Church of England, 1945-80. 1984. 29.95x (ISBN 0-19-213231-8). Oxford U Pr.

CHURCH OF ENGLAND–LITURGY AND RITUAL

see also Church of England–Book of Common Prayer

Book of Common Prayer & Administration of the Sacraments: According to the Use of the Church of England. 11.95x (ISBN 0-19-130601-0). Oxford U Pr.

Laud, William. A Speech Delivered in the Starr-Chamber, at the Censure of J. Bastwick. LC 79-171771. (English Experience Ser.: No. 396). 92p. 1971. Repr. of 1637 ed. 14.00 (ISBN 90-221-0396-X). Walter J Johnson.

Maskell, William. Ancient Liturgy of the Church of England. 3rd ed. LC 71-172848. Repr. of 1882 ed. 29.50 (ISBN 0-404-04196-5). AMS Pr.

--The Ancient Liturgy of the Church of England. 1977. lib. bdg. 59.95 (ISBN 0-8490-1425-5). Gordon Pr.

--Monumenta Ritualia Ecclestiae Anglicanae, 3 vols. 1710p. 1882. text ed. 186.30x (ISBN 0-576-99784-6, Pub. by Gregg Intl Pub England). Gregg Intl.

CHURCH OF ENGLAND–MISSIONS

Gibson, Alan G. Eight Years in Kaffraria, 1882-1890. LC 79-82052. (Illus.). Repr. of 1891 ed. cancelled (ISBN 0-8371-1573-6, GIK&, Pub. by Negro U Pr). Greenwood.

Ritchie, Carson I. Frontier Parish: An Account of the Society for the Propagation of the Gospel & the Anglican Church in America, Drawn from the Records of the Bishop of London. LC 75-3564. 210p. 1976. 18.50 (ISBN 0-8386-1735-2). Fairleigh Dickinson.

Shenk, Wilbert R. The Church in Mission. LC 84-81231. (Mennonite Faith Ser.: Vol. 15). 1984. pap. 1.50 (ISBN 0-8361-3377-3). Herald Pr.

Tucker, Alfred R. Eighteen Years in Uganda & East Africa. LC 77-106884. Repr. of 1911 ed. cancelled (ISBN 0-8371-3280-0, TUU&, Pub. by Negro U Pr). Greenwood.

CHURCH OF ENGLAND–PRAYER BOOKS AND DEVOTIONS

Keeling, William. Liturgiae Britannicae. 498p. Repr. of 1851 ed. text ed. 74.52x (ISBN 0-576-99718-8, Pub. by Gregg Intl Pubs England). Gregg Intl.

CHURCH OF ENGLAND–RELATIONS

Aveling, J. C., et al. Rome & The Anglicans: Historical & Doctrinal Aspects of Anglican-Roman Catholic Relations. Haase, Wolfgang, ed. 301p. 1982. 81.50 (ISBN 3-11-008267-5). De Gruyter.

McAdoo, Henry R. The Unity of Anglicanism: Catholic & Reformed. 48p. 1983. pap. 4.95 (ISBN 0-8192-1324-1). Morehouse.

Spoer, Hans H. Aid for Churchmen, Episcopal & Orthodox. LC 71-79152. Repr. of 1930 ed. 12.50 (ISBN 0-404-06197-4). AMS Pr.

CHURCH OF ENGLAND IN AMERICA

Bolton, Charles S. Southern Anglicanism: The Church of England in Colonial South Carolina. LC 81-6669. (Contributions to the Study of Religion: No. 5). (Illus.). 248p. 1982. lib. bdg. 29.95 (ISBN 0-313-23090-0, BOS/). Greenwood.

Cross, Arthur L. The Anglican Episcopate & the American Colonies. ix, 368p. 1964. Repr. of 1902 ed. 32.50 (ISBN 0-208-00420-3, Archon). Shoe String.

Davidson, Elizabeth H. Establishment of the English Church in Continental American Colonies. (Duke University. Trinity College Historical Society. Historical Papers: No. 20). Repr. of 1936 ed. 24.50 (ISBN 0-404-51770-6). AMS Pr.

Eckenrode, Hamilton J. Separation of Church & State in Virginia. LC 75-122164. (Civil Liberties in American History Ser). 1971. Repr. of 1910 ed. lib. bdg. 22.50 (ISBN 0-306-71969-X). Da Capo.

Ingle, E. Parish Institutions of Maryland, with Illustrations from Parish Records. 1973. pap. 9.00 (ISBN 0-384-25740-2). Johnson Repr.

Laugher, Charles T. Thomas Bray's Grand Design: Libraries of the Church of England in America, 1695-1785. LC 73-16332. (ACRL Publications in Librarianship Ser.: No. 35). pap. 31.30 (ISBN 0-317-29444-X, 2024224). Bks Demand UMI.

Mayhew, Jonathan. Observations on the Charter & Conduct of the Society for the Propagation of the Gospel in Foreign Parts; Designed to Show Their Non-Conformity to Each Other. LC 72-38456. (Religion in America, Ser. 2). 180p. 1972. Repr. of 1763 ed. 15.00 (ISBN 0-405-04077-6). Ayer Co Pubs.

Mills, Frederick V., Sr. Bishops by Ballot: An Eighteenth-Century Ecclesiastical Revolution. 1978. 19.95x (ISBN 0-19-502411-7). Oxford U Pr.

Perry, William S. Historical Collections Relating to the American Colonial Church, 5 Pts. in 4 Vols. LC 75-99948. Repr. of 1878 ed. Set. 245.00 (ISBN 0-404-05070-0). Vol. 1 (ISBN 0-404-05071-9). Vol. 2 (ISBN 0-404-05072-7). Vol. 3 (ISBN 0-404-05073-5). Vol. 4 (ISBN 0-404-05074-3). AMS Pr.

Sellar, Robert. Tragedy of Quebec. LC 72-1429. (Select Bibliographies Reprint Ser.). 1972. Repr. of 1907 ed. 17.25 (ISBN 0-8369-6836-0). Ayer Co Pubs.

Woodmason, Charles. Carolina Backcountry on the Eve of the Revolution: The Journal & Other Writings of Charles Woodmason, Anglican Itinerant. Hooker, Richard J., ed. (Institute of Early American History & Culture Ser.). xxxix, 305p. 1953. 25.00x (ISBN 0-8078-0643-9). U of NC Pr.

CHURCH OF GOD

Here are entered works on the various religious bodies using the words church of god in their name.

Callen, Barry L., ed. First Century: Church of God Reformation Movement, 2 vols. 1977. Set. 19.95 set. Vol. I (ISBN 0-87162-200-9, D1386). Vol. II (ISBN 0-87162-220-3, D1387). Warner Pr.

Ensenanzas, Disciplina y Gobierna de la Iglesia de Dios. (Span.). 137p. 1980. pap. 3.95 (ISBN 0-87148-304-1). Pathway Pr.

Hughes, Ray H., ed. Distintivos de la Iglesia de Dios. (Span.). 116p. 1970. pap. 5.95 (ISBN 0-87148-256-8). Pathway Pr.

Minutes of the General Assembly of the Church of God 1980. 107p. 1981. pap. 1.50 (ISBN 0-87148-575-3). Pathway Pr.

Minutes of the General Assembly of the Church of God: 1982. 1983. text ed. 6.95 (ISBN 0-87148-577-X); pap. 5.95 (ISBN 0-87148-578-8). Pathway Pr.

Newell, Arlo. The Church of God As Revealed in Scripture. 1983. pap. 1.95 (ISBN 0-87162-269-6, D4775). Warner Pr.

Pettitt, Bryce. Worldwide Church of God. (Truthway Ser.). 26p. (Orig.). 1981. pap. text ed. 1.25 (ISBN 0-87148-916-3). Pathway Pr.

Smith, John W. Brief History of the Church of God Reformation Movement. 1976. pap. 3.95 (ISBN 0-87162-188-6, D2350). Warner Pr.

--I Will Build My Church. 1985. pap. 3.95 (ISBN 0-87162-411-7, D4320). Warner Pr.

Williams, Lima L. Walking in Missionary Shoes. 1986. pap. 14.95 (ISBN 0-87162-417-6, D8750). Warner Pr.

CHURCH OF IRELAND

Akenson, Donald H. The Church of Ireland: Ecclesiastical Reform & Revolution, 1880-1885. LC 76-151565. pap. 81.40 (ISBN 0-317-08435-6, 2013197). Bks Demand UMI.

Warre-Cornish, Francis. English Church in the Nineteenth Century, 2 Vols. LC 75-148325. (History of the English Church Ser.: No. 8). Repr. of 1910 ed. Set. 59.00 (ISBN 0-404-50760-3); 29.50 ea. Vol. 1 (ISBN 0-404-50758-1). Vol. 2 (ISBN 0-404-50759-X). AMS Pr.

CHURCH OF JESUS CHRIST OF LATTER-DAY SAINTS

see also Reorganized Church of Jesus Christ of Latter-Day Saints

Allred, Gordon T. God the Father. 1979. 8.95 (ISBN 0-87747-746-9). Deseret Bk.

Arrington, Leonard J. Great Basin Kingdom: An Economic History of the Latter-Day Saints, 1830-1900. LC 58-12961. (Illus.). xx, 550p. 1966. pap. 13.95 (ISBN 0-8032-5006-1, BB 342, Bison). U of Nebr Pr.

Arrington, Leonard J., ed. The Presidents of the Church. LC 85-31117. 468p. 1986. 15.95 (ISBN 0-87579-026-7). Deseret Bk.

Backman, Milton V., Jr. The Heavens Resound: A History of the Latter-Day Saints in Ohio 1830-1838. LC 83-12882. (Illus.). 480p. 1983. 14.95 (ISBN 0-87747-973-9). Deseret Bk.

Barrington, George. Use Even Me. 1983. pap. 10.00 (ISBN 0-8309-0375-5). Herald Hse.

Batchelor, Walter D. Gateway to Survival Is Storage. 128p. 1974. pap. 3.95 (ISBN 0-89036-127-4). Hawkes Pub Inc.

Bell, T. H., et al, eds. Excellence. LC 84-71872. 140p. 1984. 8.95 (ISBN 0-87747-776-0). Deseret Bk.
Bennion, Lowell L. I Believe. LC 83-70024. 87p. 1983. 5.95 (ISBN 0-87747-954-2). Deseret Bk.
Britsch, R. Lanier. Unto the Islands of the Sea: A History of the Latter-day Saints in the Pacific. LC 85-27463. (Illus.). 599p. 1986. 16.95 (ISBN 0-87747-754-X). Deseret Bk.
Broderick, Carlfred. One Flesh, One Heart: Putting Celestial Love into Your Temple Marriage. LC 85-29329. 101p. 1986. 8.95 (ISBN 0-87579-010-0). Deseret Bk.
Burgess, Allan K. How to Understand & Enjoy the Scriptures. LC 85-29212. (Illus.). 80p. 1986. 5.95 (ISBN 0-87579-030-5). Deseret Bk.
Christensen, Joe J. & Christensen, Barbara K. Making Your Home a Missionary Training Center. 140p. 1985. 7.95 (ISBN 0-87747-589-X). Deseret Bk.
Christensen, Leon N. The Little Book: Why I Am a Mormon. 1976. 12.00 (ISBN 0-8283-1606-6). Branden Pub Co.
Corrill, John. Brief History of the Church of Christ of Latter Day Saints. 48p. (Orig.). 1983. pap. 1.95 (ISBN 0-942284-05-4). Restoration Re.
Crowther, Duane S. Come unto Christ. LC 70-173393. (Scripture Guide Ser.). 240p. 1971. pap. 5.95 (ISBN 0-88290-007-2). Horizon Utah.
--God & His Church. LC 76-173392. (Scripture Guide Ser.). 244p. 1971. pap. 5.95 (ISBN 0-88290-006-4). Horizon Utah.
--The Plan of Salvation & the Future in Prophecy. LC 72-173391. (Scripture Guide Ser.). 228p. 1971. pap. 5.95 (ISBN 0-88290-005-6). Horizon Utah.
Edwards, F. Henry. The History of the Reorganized Church of Jesus Christ of Latter Day Saints, Vols. 6 & 7. Incl. Vol. 6. 1903-1914. 1970 (ISBN 0-8309-0030-6); Vol. 7. 1915-1925. 1973 (ISBN 0-8309-0075-6). 22.50 ea. Herald Hse.
England, Kathleen. Why We Are Baptized. LC 78-19180. (Illus.). 1978. 5.95 (ISBN 0-87747-893-7). Deseret Bk.
Flanders, Robert B. Nauvoo: Kingdom on the Mississippi. LC 65-19110. (Illus.). 374p. 1975. pap. 8.95 (ISBN 0-252-00561-9). U of Ill Pr.
Gibbons, Francis M. David O. McKay: Apostle to the World, Prophet of God. LC 86-4564. (Illus.). 455p. 1986. 13.95 (ISBN 0-87579-036-4). Deseret Bk.
God, Family, Country: Our Three Great Loyalties. Ezra Taft Benson. LC 74-84477. 437p. 1974. 11.95 (ISBN 0-87747-541-5). Deseret Bk.
Grant, J. M. J. M. Grant's Rigdon. 16p. (Orig.). 1984. pap. 1.95 (ISBN 0-942284-06-2). Restoration Re.
Hawkes, John D. Doctrine & Covenants & Pearl of Great Price Digest. 1977. pap. text ed. 4.95 (ISBN 0-89036-100-2). Hawkes Pub Inc.
Jacobs, Barbara & Jacobs, Briant. Missions for Marrieds. LC 83-70189. 136p. 1983. 6.95 (ISBN 0-87747-953-4). Deseret Bk.
Jenson, Andrew. Church Chronology: A Record of Important Events Pertaining to the History of the Church of Jesus Christ of the Latter-Day Saints (Mormons, 2 vols. 1980. lib. bdg. 200.00 (ISBN 0-8490-3139-7). Gordon Pr.
Judd, Peter A. & Cole, Clifford A. Distinctives: Yesterday & Today. 168p. 1983. pap. 10.50 (ISBN 0-8309-0378-X). Herald Hse.
Kenney, Scott G. & Smith, Hyrum, III. From Prophet to Son. LC 81-15173. 132p. 1981. 6.95 (ISBN 0-87747-885-6). Deseret Bk.
Kimball, Spencer W. Faith Precedes the Miracle. 9.95 (ISBN 0-87747-490-7). Deseret Bk.
Kimball, Spencer W., et al. Woman. LC 79-64908. 1979. 8.95 (ISBN 0-87747-758-2). Deseret Bk.
Lythgoe, Dennis L. A Marriage of Equals. 160p. 1985. 8.95 (ISBN 0-87747-700-0). Deseret Bk.
McConkie, Bruce R. A New Witness for the Articles of Faith. LC 85-12888. 735p. 1985. 17.95 (ISBN 0-87747-872-4). Deseret Bk.
Monson, Thomas S. Conference Classics, Vol. 2. 63p. 1983. 5.95 (ISBN 0-87747-957-7). Deseret Bk.
--Conference Classics, Vol. 3. 64p. 5.95 (ISBN 0-87747-989-5). Deseret Bk.
Nibley, Hugh. Old Testament & Related Studies. LC 85-27544. (Collected Works of Hugh Nibley Ser.). 304p. 1986. 15.95 (ISBN 0-87579-032-1). Deseret Bk.
Packer, Boyd K. Our Father's Plan. LC 84-72516. (Illus.). 64p. 1984. 8.95 (ISBN 0-87747-523-7). Deseret Bk.
Palmer, Spencer W. The Expanding Church. LC 78-26082. 1979. 6.95 (ISBN 0-87747-732-9). Deseret Bk.
Random Sampler: Helpful Hints for Latter-day Living from the Ensign. LC 86-1465. 220p. 1986. 7.95 (ISBN 0-87747-977-1). Deseret Bk.
Rich, Russell R. Ensign to the Nations: A History of the LDS Church from 1846 to 1972. LC 72-91730. (Illus.). 680p. 1972. pap. 9.95 (ISBN 0-8425-0671-3). Brigham.
Sarre, Winifred. Perce Judd: Man of Peace. (Illus.). 176p. 1983. pap. 10.00 (ISBN 0-8309-0377-1). Herald Hse.
Shipps, Jan, et al. After One Hundred Fifty Years: The Latter-Day Saints in Sesquicentennial Perspective. Alexander, Thomas G. & Embry, Jessie L., eds. (Charles Redd Monographs in Western History: No. 13). (Illus.). 207p. (Orig.). 1983. pap. 6.95 (ISBN 0-941214-08-7, Dist. by Signature Bks). C Redd Ctr.
Topical Guide to the Scriptures of the Church of Jesus Christ of Latter-Day Saints. 1977. pap. 2.95 (ISBN 0-87747-764-7). Deseret Bk.
Woods, Ron. You're in Control: A Guide for Latter-Day Saint Youth. (YA) 1986. 8.95 (ISBN 0-87579-046-1). Deseret Bk.
Yorgason, Blaine M. & Yorgason, Brenton G. The Loftier Way. LC 85-70919. 143p. 1985. 8.95 (ISBN 0-87747-785-X). Deseret Bk.

CHURCH OF SCOTLAND

see also Presbyterian Church; Presbyterianism

Calderwood, David. The True History of the Church of Scotland: From the Beginnings of the Reform to the End of the Reign of King James VI, 8 vols. Thomson, Thomas, ed. LC 83-45577. Date not set. Repr. of 1842 ed. Set. 525.00 (ISBN 0-404-19894-5). AMS Pr.
The Confession of Faith Professit, & Belevit, Be the Protestantes Within the Realme of Scotland. LC 72-6029. (English Experience Ser.: No. 555). 1972. Repr. of 1561 ed. 7.00 (ISBN 90-221-0555-5). Walter J Johnson.
Hetherington, William M., ed. Lectures on the Revival of Religion by Ministers of the Church of Scotland. (Revival Library). xxvi, 444p. 1980. Repr. of 1840 ed. lib. bdg. 15.95 (ISBN 0-940033-15-1). R O Roberts.
Mechie, Stewart. The Church & Scottish Social Development, 1780-1870. LC 75-3740. 181p. 1975. Repr. of 1960 ed. lib. bdg. 22.50x (ISBN 0-8371-8060-0, MECS). Greenwood.
Melville, James. Diary. LC 70-172723. (Bannatyne Club, Edinburgh. Publications: No. 34). Repr. of 1829 ed. 32.50 (ISBN 0-404-52740-X). AMS Pr.
The Protestation of the Generall Assemblie Made in the High Kirk, & at the Mercate Crosse of Glasgow. LC 79-26239. (English Experience Ser.: No. 343). 1971. Repr. of 1638 ed. 7.00 (ISBN 90-221-0525-3). Walter J Johnson.
Rothes, John L. Relation of Proceedings Concerning the Affairs of the Kirk of Scotland. LC 79-174966. (Bannatyne Club, Edinburgh. Publications: No. 37). Repr. of 1830 ed. 28.00 (ISBN 0-404-52743-4). AMS Pr.
Row, John & Row, William. Historie of the Kirk of Scotland, 2 Vols. LC 70-174969. (Maitland Club. Glasgow. Publications: No. 55). Repr. of 1842 ed. Set. 57.50 (ISBN 0-404-53039-7). AMS Pr.
Spottiswood, John. History of the Church of Scotland, 3 Vols. Russell, Michael & Napier, Mark, eds. LC 76-176004. (Bannatyne Club, Edinburgh. Publications: No. 93). Repr. of 1851 ed. Set. 145.00 (ISBN 0-404-52840-6). AMS Pr.
Thomson, Thomas, ed. Acts & Proceedings of the General Assemblies of the Kirk of Scotland, 3 Vols. LC 72-1053. 1839-45. Set. 125.00 (ISBN 0-404-52820-1). AMS Pr.
Wodrow, Robert. Collections Upon the Lives of the Reformers & Most Eminent Ministers of the Church of Scotland, 2 Vols. in 3 Pts. LC 70-178317. (Maitland Club, Glasgow. Publications: No. 32). Repr. of 1848 ed. Set. 105.00 (ISBN 0-404-52993-3). AMS Pr.

CHURCH OF THE NEW JERUSALEM

see New Jerusalem Church

CHURCH OFFICERS

see also Church Secretaries; Church Ushers; Deacons; Elders (Church Officers); Installation Service (Church Officers)

Asquith, Glenn H. Church Officers at Work. pap. 4.95 (ISBN 0-8170-0048-8). Judson.
Berghoef, Gerard & DeKoster, Lester. The Deacon's Handbook. 269p. 15.95 (ISBN 0-934874-01-8). Chr Lib Pr.
--The Elders Handbook. LC 79-54143. 303p. 1979. 15.95 (ISBN 0-934874-00-X). Chr Lib Pr.
Faulkner, Brooks R. Forced Termination. LC 86-6122. (Orig.). 1986. pap. 4.95 (ISBN 0-8054-5435-7). Broadman.
Grenell, Zelotes & Goss, Agnes G. The Work of the Clerk. 1967. pap. 3.95 (ISBN 0-8170-0383-5). Judson.
Johnson, L. T. The Serving Church. 2nd ed. LC 83-80609. (Enabling Ser.). (Illus.). 104p. (Orig.). 1984. pap. 5.95 (ISBN 0-935797-01-7). Harvest IL.
Perry, Charles E., Jr. Why Christians Burn Out. LC 82-2098. 168p. 1982. pap. 4.95 (ISBN 0-8407-5800-6). Nelson.
Shearn, Carol R. The Church Office Handbook: A Basic Guide to Keeping Order. 288p. pap. 12.95 (ISBN 0-8192-1391-8). Morehouse.
Ward, Mae Y. The Seeking Heart: Prayer Journal of Mae Yoho Ward. Ward, Don, ed. LC 84-23836. 144p. (Orig.). 1985. pap. 7.95 (ISBN 0-8272-3420-1). CBP.
Wiebe, Ronald W. & Rowlison, Bruce A. Let's Talk about Church Staff Relationships. 64p. 1983. pap. 3.95 (ISBN 0-938462-12-1). Green Leaf CA.

CHURCH ORDERS, ANCIENT

see also Canon Law; Liturgies, Early Christian

Schermann, Theodor. Die Allgemeine Kirchenordnung Fruehchristliche Liturgien und Kirchliche Uberlieferung, 3 pts. Repr. of 1914 ed. Set. 55.00 (ISBN 0-384-53740-5). Johnson Repr.

CHURCH ORNAMENT

see Church Decoration and Ornament

CHURCH POLITY

see also Cardinals; Church and State; Church Discipline; Church Finance; Church Membership; Church Officers; Church Orders, Ancient; Church Property; Clergy; Congregationalism; Covenants (Church Polity); Dioceses; Ecclesiastical Law; Episcopacy; Investiture; Laity; Liberty of Conscience; Methodism; Patronage, Ecclesiastical; Presbyterianism; Puritans; Sunday
also subdivision Government under church denominations, e.g. Church of England–Government

Baker, Derek, ed. Church Society & Politics. (Studies in Church History Ser.: Vol. 12). 440p. 1976. 45.00x (ISBN 0-631-16970-9). Basil Blackwell.
Booty, John E. & Hooker, Richard, eds. Of the Laws of Ecclesiastical Polity: Attack & Response, Vol. IV. (The Folger Library Edition of the Works of Richard Hooker). (Illus.). 320p. 1981. text ed. 45.00 (ISBN 0-674-63216-8). Harvard U Pr.
Bouchard, Constance B. Spirituality & Administration: The Role of the Bishop in Twelfth-Century Auxerre. LC 78-55889. 1979. 11.00x (ISBN 0-910956-79-0, SAM5); pap. 5.00x (ISBN 0-910956-67-7). Medieval Acad.
Elizondo, Virgil & Greinacher, Norbert, eds. Tensions Between the Churches of the First World & the Third World, Vol. 144. (Concilium 1981). 128p. (Orig.). 1981. pap. 6.95 (ISBN 0-8164-2311-3, HarpR). Har-Row.
Ferrarotti, Franco. A Theology for Nonbelievers: Post-Christian & Post-Marxist Reflections. LC 86-10782. (Studies in Social Thought: Polity & Civil Society). Tr. of Una Teologia per Atei. 208p. 1987. text ed. 21.50x (ISBN 0-8046-9401-X, 9401). Assoc Faculty Pr.
Fries, Heinrich & Rahner, Karl. Unity of the Churches: An Actual Possibility. Gritsch, E. & Gritsch, R., trs. LC 84-8122. 160p. pap. 6.95 (ISBN 0-8006-1820-3). Fortress.
Gause, R. H. Church of God Polity: With Supplement. 1958. 9.95 (ISBN 0-87148-158-8). Pathway Pr.
Grant, Peter. The Power of Intecession. 108p. (Orig.). 1984. pap. 4.95 (ISBN 0-89283-132-4). Servant.
Griffiss, James E. Church, Ministry & Unity: A Divine Commission. 118p. 1984. 24.95x (ISBN 0-631-13185-X); pap. 8.95x (ISBN 0-631-13227-9). Basil Blackwell.
Hatch, Edwin. The Organization of the Early Christian Churches: Eight Lectures Delivered Before the University of Oxford in the Year 1880 on the Foundation of the Late Rev. John Bampton, M. A., Canon of Salisbury. LC 77-183696. (Research & Source Works Ser). 222p. 1972. Repr. of 1881 ed. lib. bdg. 18.50 (ISBN 0-8337-4163-2). B Franklin.
Hooker, Richard. Ecclesiastical Polity, Bk. 8. LC 77-170046. Repr. of 1931 ed. 24.00 (ISBN 0-404-03329-6). AMS Pr.
--Of the Laws of Ecclesiastical Polity, Bks. VI-VIII. Stanwood, P. G., ed. LC 76-24883. (Folger Library Edition of the Works of Richard Hooker). 1980. text ed. 65.00x (ISBN 0-674-63210-9, Belknap). Harvard U Pr.
--Of the Laws of Ecclesiastical Polity: Preface & Books I-V, 2 vols. Hill, W. Speed, ed. (Folger Library Edition of the Works of Richard Hooker). 1977. Set. 85.00x (ISBN 0-674-63205-2, Belknap Pr). Harvard U Pr.
--Works of That Learned & Judicious Divine Mr. Richard Hooker with an Account of His Life & Death by Isaac Walton, 3 vols. 7th ed. LC 76-125020. (Research & Source Works Ser.: No. 546). 1970. Repr. of 1888 ed. 103.00 (ISBN 0-8337-1731-6). B Franklin.
Jacob, Henry. An Attestation of Many Learned, Godly, & Famous Divines...Justifying...That the Church Government Ought to Be Always with the Peoples Free Consent. LC 74-28868. (English Experience Ser.: No. 747). 1975. Repr. of 1613 ed. 16.00 (ISBN 90-221-0747-7). Walter J Johnson.
Kittlaus, Paul & Leas, Speed. Church Fights: Managing Conflict in the Local Church. LC 73-6790. 184p. 1973. pap. 9.95 (ISBN 0-664-24974-4). Westminster.
Lemon, Robert. God's People & Church Government. 64p. (Orig.). 1983. pap. 2.25 (ISBN 0-89274-282-8). Harrison Hse.
Lewis, Douglass. Resolving Church Conflicts: A Case Study Approach for Local Congregations. LC 80-8347. 192p. (Orig.). 1981. pap. 7.95 (ISBN 0-06-065244-6, RD 342, HarpR). Har-Row.
Lightfoot, J. B. The Christian Ministry. LC 83-62042. 120p. 1983. pap. 8.95 (ISBN 0-8192-1331-4). Morehouse.
Nuttall, Clayton. The Weeping Church: Confronting the Crisis of Church Polity. LC 85-10760. 1985. pap. 5.95 (ISBN 0-87227-104-8). Reg Baptist.
Overall, John. Convocation Book of 1606. LC 77-173482. (Library of Anglo-Catholic Theology: No. 15). Repr. of 1844 ed. 27.50 (ISBN 0-404-52107-X). AMS Pr.
Paget, Francis. An Introduction to the Fifth Book of Hooker's Treatise of the Laws of Ecclesiastical Polity. 265p. 1981. Repr. of 1899 ed. lib. bdg. 85.00 (ISBN 0-8495-4402-5). Arden Lib.
Picirilli, Robert E. Church Government & Ordinances. 1973. pap. 0.95 (ISBN 0-89265-102-4). Randall Hse.
Prinzing, Fred W. Handling Church Tensions Creatively. LC 86-80687. 216p. (Orig.). 1986. pap. 4.95 (ISBN 0-935797-23-8). Harvest IL.
Sheeran, Michael J. Beyond Majority Rule: Voteless Decisions in the Religious Society of Friends. (Illus.). 153p. (Orig.). 1983. pap. 4.95 (ISBN 0-941308-04-9). Religious Soc Friends.
Steele, David A. Images of Leadership & Authority for the Church: Biblical Principles & Secular Models. LC 86-24589. 206p. (Orig.). 1987. lib. bdg. 23.50 (ISBN 0-8191-5710-4); pap. text ed. 13.25 (ISBN 0-8191-5711-2). U Pr of Amer.
Swidler, Leonard, ed. Authority in the Church & the Schillebeeckx Case. LC 82-73005. 224p. (Orig.). 1982. pap. 9.95 (ISBN 0-8245-0543-3). Crossroad NY.

CHURCH PROPERTY

see also Convents and Nunneries; Monasteries; Patronage, Ecclesiastical; Secularization

Dignan, Patrick J. A History of the Legal Incorporation of Catholic Church Property in the United States (1784-1932) LC 73-3569. (Catholic University of America. Studies in American Church History: No. 14). Repr. of 1933 ed. 31.00 (ISBN 0-404-57764-4). AMS Pr.
Oaks, Dallin H. Trust Doctrines in Church Controversies. LC 83-25058. xiv, 125p. 1984. 13.95x (ISBN 0-86554-104-3, MUP/H96). Mercer Univ Pr.

CHURCH PROPERTY–MAINTENANCE AND REPAIR

Taylor, Robert C. Building Maintenance for Churches. (Illus.). 136p. 1982. 13.95 (ISBN 0-9608714-0-3). Carrol Gate Pr.

CHURCH PROPERTY–TAXATION

see also Taxation, Exemption from

Clotfelter, Charles T. & Salamon, Lester M. The Federal Government & the Nonprofit Sector: The Impact of the 1981 Tax Act on Individual Charitable Giving. LC 82-113321. cancelled. Urban Inst.
Treusch, Paul E. & Sugarman, Norman A. Tax Exempt Charitable Organizations. 2nd ed. LC 83-70067. 726p. 1983. text ed. 95.00 (ISBN 0-8318-0429-7, B429). Am Law Inst.

CHURCH REFORM

see Church Renewal

CHURCH RENEWAL

see also Counter-Reformation; Mission of the Church; Reformation–Early Movements

Adams, Jay E. Ready to Restore. 1981. pap. 3.50 (ISBN 0-87552-070-7). Presby & Reformed.
Akenson, Donald H. The Church of Ireland: Ecclesiastical Reform & Revolution, 1880-1885. LC 76-151565. pap. 81.40 (ISBN 0-317-08435-6, 2013197). Bks Demand UMI.
Aubert, Roger, ed. Progress & Decline in the History of Church Renewal. LC 67-30136. (Concilium Ser.: Vol. 27). 191p. 1967. 7.95 (ISBN 0-8091-0119-X). Paulist Pr.
Avis, Paul D. The Church in the Theology of the Reformers. Toon, Peter & Martin, Ralph, eds. LC 80-16186. (New Foundations Theological Library). 256p. 1981. 6.49 (ISBN 0-8042-3708-5); pap. 2.99 (ISBN 0-8042-3728-X). John Knox.
Barnhart, David R. The Church's Desperate Need for Revival. 163p. (Orig.). 1986. pap. 8.95 (ISBN 0-9617377-0-0). Abiding Word Pubns.
Bellini, Enzo, et al. Protestant & Catholic Reform. Drury, John, ed. & tr. from Ital. (An Illustrated History of the Church). (Illus.). 124p. (Orig.). 1981. 12.95 (ISBN 0-03-056831-5, HarpR). Har-Row.
Cathey, Bill V. A New Day in Church Revivals. LC 83-70645. 1984. pap. 7.95 (ISBN 0-8054-6244-9). Broadman.
Coleman, Robert E. Dry Bones Can Live Again. pap. 4.95 (ISBN 0-8007-5154-X, Power Bks). Revell.

Crandall, Ronald & Sells, Ray. There's New Life in the Small Congregation: Why It Happens & How. LC 83-71697. 120p. (Orig.). 1983. pap. 7.50 (ISBN 0-88177-001-9, DR001B). Discipleship Res.

De Thomasis, Louis. My Father's Business: Creating a New Future for the People of God. 168p. (Orig.). 1984. pap. 6.95 (ISBN 0-87061-107-0). Chr Classics.

De Vito, Michael J. The New York Review, 1905-1908. LC 77-75637. (Monograph Ser.: No. 34). (Illus.). 1977. 13.95x (ISBN 0-930060-14-8). US Cath Hist.

Faase, Thomas P. Making the Jesuits More Modern. LC 81-40388. (Illus.). 478p. (Orig.). 1981. lib. bdg. 31.50 o. p. (ISBN 0-8191-1761-7); pap. text ed. 18.75 (ISBN 0-8191-1762-5). U Pr of Amer.

Gerard, Francois C. The Future of the Church: The Theology of Renewal of Willem Adolf Visser't Hooft. LC 74-26564. (Pittsburgh Theological Monographs: No. 2). 1974. pap. 6.00 (ISBN 0-915138-01-8). Pickwick.

Hall, Douglas J. Has the Church a Future? LC 79-29647. 192p. 1980. pap. 8.95 (ISBN 0-664-24308-8). Westminster.

Haney, David. Renueva Mi Iglesia. Martinez, Jose Luis, ed. Kratzig, Guillermo, tr. Orig. Title: Renew My Church. (Span.). 104p. 1983. pap. 3.75 (ISBN 0-311-17025-0). Casa Bautista.

Hocken, Peter. Streams of Renewal. 288p. (Orig.). 1986. pap. 11.95 (ISBN 0-932085-03-2). Word Among Us.

Holmes, Urban T., III. Turning to Christ: A Theology of Renewal & Evangelization. 240p. (Orig.). 1981. pap. 8.95 (ISBN 0-8164-2289-3, HarpR). Har-Row.

Huttenlocker, Keith. Becoming the Family of God: A Handbook for Developing Creative Relationships in the Church. 128p. 1986. pap. 6.95 (ISBN 0-310-75211-6). Zondervan.

Ingram, T. Robert. New Liturgy, Old Heresy. LC 81-52116. (Orig.). 1981. pap. 4.50 (ISBN 0-686-75087-X). St Thomas.

Kinghorn, Kenneth C. Fresh Wind of the Spirit. 128p. 1986. pap. 6.95 (ISBN 0-310-75221-3, 17033P). Zondervan.

Lienhard, Marc. Luther: Witness to Jesus Christ: Stages & Themes of the Reformer's Christology. Robertson, Edwin H., tr. LC 81-52285. 432p. 1982. text ed. 24.95 (ISBN 0-8066-1917-1, 10-4149). Augsburg.

Lovelace, Richard. Dynamics of Spiritual Life. LC 78-24757. 1979. pap. 11.95 (ISBN 0-87784-626-X). Inter-Varsity.

McGavran, Donald A. Church Growth & Group Conversion. new ed. LC 73-80163. 128p. 1973. pap. 3.95 (ISBN 0-87808-712-5). William Carey Lib.

McGavran, Donald A. & Arn, Winfield C. How to Grow a Church. LC 73-80207. 192p. (Orig.). 1973. pap. 6.95 (ISBN 0-8307-0238-5, 5406706). Regal.

McLoughlin, William G. Revivals, Awakening, & Reform: An Essay on Religion & Social Change in America, 1607 to 1977. LC 77-27830. xvi, 240p. 1980. pap. 9.00x (ISBN 0-226-56092-9, P891, Phoen). U of Chicago Pr.

MacNair, Donald J. The Living Church: A Guide for Revitalization. (Illus.). 167p. (Orig.). 1980. pap. 4.95 (ISBN 0-934688-00-1). Great Comm Pubns.

Meeting the Challenge of Change: A Sixty-Year History of the St. Stephens Baptist Church, Kansas City, Mo. 15.00 (ISBN 0-685-02662-0). Univ Place.

Miller, C. John. Outgrowing the Ingrown Church. 176p. 1986. pap. 7.95 (ISBN 0-310-28411-2). Zondervan.

Moore, Robert L., ed. Sources of Vitality in American Church Life. LC 78-71065. (Studies in Ministry & Parish Life). 1978. text ed. 13.95x (ISBN 0-913552-14-3). Exploration Pr.

Neighbour, Ralph W., Jr. La Iglesia del Futuro. Martinez, Jose L., tr. from Eng. Orig. Title: Future Church. 256p. 1983. pap. 7.95 (ISBN 0-311-17024-2). Casa Bautista.

Newsome, Robert R. The Ministering Parish: Methods & Procedures for the Pastoral Organization. LC 81-85381. 128p. (Orig.). 1982. pap. 8.95 (ISBN 0-8091-2435-1). Paulist Pr.

Popoff, Peter. Twenty-Seven Things the Church Must Go Through Before the Great Tribulation. Tanner, Don, ed. LC 81-68675. (Illus.). 50p. 1981. pap. 1.00 (ISBN 0-938544-08-X). Faith Messenger.

Purkiser. The Church in a Changing World. pap. 1.00 (ISBN 0-686-12910-5). Schmul Pub Co.

Raines, Robert A. New Life in the Church. rev. ed. LC 61-5267. (Harper's Ministers Paperback Library). 192p. 1980. pap. 4.50i (ISBN 0-06-066773-7, RD 309, HarpR). Har-Row.

Reynolds, Blair. Manner & Method: A Translation of the French Reformed Church's Liturgy. 85p. (Orig.). 1985. pap. 6.95x (ISBN 0-932269-40-0). Wyndham Hall.

Schaller, Lyle E. Activating the Passive Church: Diagnosis & Treatment. LC 81-3460. 160p. (Orig.). 1981. pap. 6.95 (ISBN 0-687-00716-X). Abingdon.

Shepherd, J. W. Church, Falling Away & Restoration. 8.95 (ISBN 0-89225-065-8). Gospel Advocate.

Snyder, Howard A. Liberating the Church: The Ecology of Church & Kingdom. 280p. (Orig.). 1982. pap. 8.95 (ISBN 0-87784-385-6); cloth 12.95 (ISBN 0-87784-894-7). Inter-Varsity.

--The Problem of Wineskins: Church Renewal in Technological Age. LC 74-31842. (Illus.). 216p. 1975. pap. text ed. 6.95 (ISBN 0-87784-769-X). Inter-Varsity.

Steinke, Frank F. Greater Works Shall Ye Do. 101p. (Orig.). 1980. pap. 2.25 (ISBN 0-686-73996-5). Impact Bks Mo.

Thompson, James. Strategy for Survival. LC 79-67274. (Journey Bks). 144p. 1980. pap. 3.50 (ISBN 0-8344-0113-4). Sweet.

Tilberg, Cedric W. Revolution Underway: An Aging Church in an Aging Society. LC 84-8122. 128p. 1984. pap. 5.95 (ISBN 0-8006-1817-3). Fortress.

Tucker, Robert & Waitley, Denis. Winning the Innovation Game. 256p. 1986. 15.95 (ISBN 0-8007-1494-6). Revell.

Van Der Post, Laurens. Patterns of Renewal. LC 62-15859. (Orig.). 1962. pap. 2.50x (ISBN 0-87574-121-5). Pendle Hill.

Westerhoff, John H., III. Inner Growth-Outer Change: An Educational Guide to Church Renewal. (Orig.). pap. 4.95 (ISBN 0-8164-2213-3, HarpR). Har-Row.

CHURCH RENEWAL–CATHOLIC CHURCH

Archdiocese of Newark, Office of Pastoral Renewal Staff. Renew, Leadership Book. 1980. write for info. (ISBN 0-8091-9195-4). Paulist Pr.

--Renew, Parish Book. 1980. write for info. (ISBN 0-8091-9191-1). Paulist Pr.

--Renew, Participant Book: Empowerment by the Spirit. 1980. write for info. (ISBN 0-8091-9194-6). Paulist Pr.

--Renew, Participant Book: Our Response. 1980. write for info. (ISBN 0-8091-9193-8). Paulist Pr.

--Renew, Participant Book: The Lord's Call. 1980. write for info. (ISBN 0-8091-9192-X). Paulist Pr.

--Renew, Pastoral Staff Book. 1980. write for info. (ISBN 0-8091-9196-2). Paulist Pr.

Flanagan, Donal. Evolving Church. 1966. 4.95 (ISBN 0-8189-0047-4). Alba.

Hofinger, Johannes. Pastoral Life in the Power of the Spirit. LC 81-1439. (Illus.). 215p. 1982. pap. 6.95 (ISBN 0-8189-0427-5). Alba.

Ollard, Sidney. The Anglo-Catholic Revival. 59.95 (ISBN 0-87968-634-0). Gordon Pr.

Packer, James I. God in Our Midst: Seeking & Receiving Ongoing Revival. (Christian Essentials Ser.). 48p. (Orig.). 1987. pap. 1.95 (ISBN 0-89283-327-0). Servant.

Sussman, Irving & Sussman, Cornelia. This Train Is Bound for Glory. 1969. 4.95 (ISBN 0-8199-0154-7, L38874). Franciscan Herald.

Tracy, David, et al, eds. Towards Vatican III: The Work That Has to Be Done. 1978. 14.95x (ISBN 0-8245-0397-X); pap. 5.95 (ISBN 0-8245-0398-8). Crossroad NY.

Vidler, Alexander R. The Modernist Movement in the Roman Church. 69.95 (ISBN 0-8490-0889-1). Gordon Pr.

Weigand, John. We Are the Church: The Manual. 80p. (Orig.). 1986. pap. 2.50 (ISBN 0-941850-17-X). Sunday Pubns.

Weigand, John J. We Are the Church: The Book. 128p. (Orig.). 1986. pap. 12.95 (ISBN 0-941850-16-1). Sunday Pubns.

CHURCH SCHOOLS

see also Vacation Schools, Religious; Week-Day Church Schools;

also subdivision Education under names of religious denominations, e.g. Lutheran Church–Education

Adcock, Joy. Building Your Christian Day School, Bk. 1: Policies & Procedures. 60p. 1985. pap. text ed. 3.95 (ISBN 0-931097-07-X). Sentinel Pub.

--Building Your Christian Day School, Bk. 2: Handwork & Curriculum. 410p. 1985. pap. text ed. 14.95 (ISBN 0-931097-08-8). Sentinel Pub.

Bailey, Ron & Bailey, Betty. Team Teaching Children in Bible Class. 1972. 4.95 (ISBN 0-931097-05-3). Sentinel Pub.

Buchanan, Jim. A Guide to Materials about Public Aid to Religious Schools. (Public Administration Ser.: Bibliography P 1621). 1985. pap. 3.75 (ISBN 0-89028-291-9). Vance Biblios.

Burba, Linda J. & Burba, Keith V. T-R-A-I-N up the Children. 111p. 1985. pap. 4.50 (ISBN 0-8341-1062-8). Beacon Hill.

Calderon, Wilfredo, ed. Dinamicas de la Escuela Dominical. (Span.). 108p. 1973. pap. 3.25 (ISBN 0-87148-255-X). Pathway Pr.

Current Issues in Catholic Higher Education. Incl. Vol. 1, No. 1. Registration-Draft-National Service. 40p. 1980. 2.40 (ISBN 0-686-39990-0); Vol. 1, No. 2. Peace & Justice. 40p. 1981. 2.40 (ISBN 0-686-39991-9); Vol. 2, No. 1. 50p. 1981. 2.40 (ISBN 0-686-39994-3); Vol. 2, No. 2. Campus as Context. 48p. 1982. 2.40 (ISBN 0-686-39995-1); Vol. 3, No. 1. 40p. 1982. 3.60. Natl Cath Educ.

Deuink, James W. Christian School Finance. (Illus.). 160p. 1985. pap. 6.60 (ISBN 0-89084-304-X). Bob Jones Univ Pr.

--The Ministry of the Christian School Guidance Counselor. (Illus.). 175p. (Orig.). 1984. pap. 6.60 (ISBN 0-89084-273-6). Bob Jones Univ Pr.

Deuink, James W., ed. Some Light on Christian Education. (Illus.). 195p. (Orig.). 1984. pap. 4.95 (ISBN 0-89084-262-0). Bob Jones Univ Pr.

Gleaves, Les. Building Your Bible School. 1986. 4.95 (ISBN 0-931097-10-X). Sentinel Pub.

Holmes, Arthur F. The Idea of a Christian College. 1975. pap. 5.95 (ISBN 0-8028-1592-8). Eerdmans.

Jones, Bob. Cornbread & Caviar. (Illus.). 236p. 1985. 12.95 (ISBN 0-89084-305-8); pap. 8.95 (ISBN 0-89084-306-6). Bob Jones Univ Pr.

Lee, Sharon. When the Time Had Fully Come: Christmas Service for Church Schools. 32p. (Orig.). 1984. pap. 0.90 ea. (ISBN 0-8066-2101-X, 23-3010). Augsburg.

O'Keefe, Bernadette. Faith, Culture & the Dual System: A Comparative Study of Church & County Schools. 200p. 1986. 27.00x (ISBN 1-85000-110-3, Falmer Pr); pap. 15.00x (ISBN 1-85000-111-1, Falmer Pr). Taylor & Francis.

Phillips, Harold R. & Firth, Robert E., eds. Cases in Denominational Administration: A Management Casebook for Decision-Making. vi, 314p. 1978. pap. text ed. 4.95 (ISBN 0-943872-75-8). Andrews Univ Pr.

Piarist Fathers. Constitutions of the Order of the Pious Schools. Cudinach, Salvidor, ed. & tr. from Lat. LC 85-60915. Tr. of Constitutiones Ordinis Scholarum Piarum. 110p. Date not set. price not set (ISBN 0-9614908-0-2). Piarist Father.

Sandell, Mary. Building an Effective Church School. 1986. pap. 10.00 (ISBN 0-8309-0441-7). Herald Hse.

Sherrill, Lewis J. Presbyterian Parochial Schools, 1846-1870. LC 74-89234. (American Education: Its Men, Institutions & Ideas, Ser. 1). 1969. Repr. of 1932 ed. 11.50 (ISBN 0-405-01471-6). Ayer Co Pubs.

Smith, Judy G. Celebrating Special Days in the Church School Year. Zapel, Arthur L., ed. LC 81-83441. (Illus.). 125p. (Orig.). 1981. pap. text ed. 8.95 (ISBN 0-916260-14-3). Meriwether Pub.

Twomley, Dale E. Parochiaid & the Courts. (Andrews University Monographs, Studies in Education: Vol. 2). x, 165p. 1979. 3.95 (ISBN 0-943872-51-0). Andrews Univ Pr.

Ulrich, Robert J. The Bennett Law of 1889: Education & Politics in Wisconsin. Cordasco, Francesco, ed. LC 80-902. (American Ethnic Groups Ser.). 1981. lib. bdg. 55.00x (ISBN 0-405-13462-2). Ayer Co Pubs.

Watkins, Dawn L. The Medallion. (English Skills for Christian Schools Ser.). (Illus.). 223p. (Orig.). 1985. pap. 5.95 (ISBN 0-89084-282-5). Bob Jones Univ Pr.

Wells, Guy F. Parish Education in Colonial Virginia. LC 73-177649. Repr. of 1923 ed. 22.50 (ISBN 0-404-55138-6). AMS Pr.

CHURCH SECRETARIES

Secretary's Guide to Church Office Management. 128p. (Orig.). 1985. pap. 9.95 (ISBN 0-687-37131-7). Abingdon.

CHURCH SLAVIC LANGUAGE

Gamanovitch, Hieromonk A. Grammatika Tserkovno-Slavjanskago Jazika. Tr. of Church Slavonic Grammer. 264p. 1984. pap. text ed. 9.00 (ISBN 0-317-30313-9). Holy Trinity.

Lunt, Horace G. Old Church Slavonic Grammar. rev. ed. (Slavistic Printings & Reprintings Ser: No. 3). 1974. text ed. 54.00x (ISBN 90-2793-362-6). Mouton.

Picchio, Riccardo & Goldblatt, Harvey, eds. Aspects of the Slavic Language Question: Vol. 1, Church Slavonic-South Slavic-West Slavic. (Yale Russian & East European Publications Ser.: No. 4-a). 416p. 1984. 35.00 (ISBN 0-936586-03-6). Yale Russian.

Trager, G. L. Old Church Slavonic Kiev Fragment. (LM). 1933. pap. 16.00 (ISBN 0-527-00817-6). Kraus Repr.

CHURCH SLAVIC LITERATURE

Kantor, Marvin, ed. Medieval Slavic Lives of Saints & Princes. (Michigan Slavic Translations: No. 5). 1983. 15.00 (ISBN 0-930042-44-1). Mich Slavic Pubns.

Picchio, Riccardo & Goldblatt, Harvey, eds. Aspects of the Slavic Language Question: Church Slavonic-South Slavic-West Slavic, Vol. 1. (Yale Russian & East European Publications Ser.: No. 4a). 416p. 1984. 35.00 (ISBN 0-936586-03-6). Slavica.

CHURCH SOCIABLES

see Church Entertainments

CHURCH STAFF

see Church Officers

CHURCH STATISTICS

see also Church Work–Forms, Blanks, etc.; Ecclesiastical Geography

Dabbs, Jack A. & Breitenkamp, Edward C. Records of Salem Lutheran Church, Brenham, Texas 1850-1940. LC 86-72575. (Illus.). 501p. 1986. 35.00 (ISBN 0-911494-10-3). Dabbs.

First Book of Records of the First Church in Pepperrellborough: Now Saco, Maine. 78p. 1985. pap. 7.75 (ISBN 0-935207-25-2). DanBury Hse Bks.

Historical Records Survey, WPA Staff. Inventory of the Roman Catholic Church Records of New Hampshire. 19p. 1985. pap. 3.50 (ISBN 0-935207-18-X). DanBury Hse Bks.

Munnick, Harriet D., compiled by. Catholic Church Records of the Pacific Northwest: Roseburg & Portland. LC 85-63221. (Illus.). 440p. 1986. 25.00 (ISBN 0-8323-0447-6). Binford-Metropolitan.

Orange County Genealogical Committee Members & Hovemeyer, Gretchen A., eds. Early Records of the St. James Episcopal Church of Goshen, New York: Baptisms, Marriages, & Funerals, 1799-1911. 140p. (Orig.). 1985. pap. 20.00 (ISBN 0-9604116-4-X). Orange County Genealog.

Oseney Abbey. The English Register of Oseney Abbey: Parts 1 & 2. (EETS, OS Ser.: No. 133, 144). 1907-1913. Repr. of 1907 ed. 22.00 (ISBN 0-527-00130-9). Kraus Repr.

Weiser, Frederick S., ed. Maryland German Church Records, Vol. 1: Christ Reformed Church, Middletown. LC 86-61245. (Maryland German Church Records Ser.). 108p. (Orig.). 1986. pap. 15.00x (ISBN 0-913281-03-4). Noodle Doosey.

--Maryland German Church Records, Vol. 2: Zion Lutheran Church, Middletown. Zahn, Charles T., tr. LC 86-62419. (Orig.). 1986. pap. 15.00x (ISBN 0-913281-04-2). Noodle-Doosey.

Weiser, Frederick S., ed. & tr. Maryland German Church Records, Vol. 3: Monocacy Lutheran Congregation & Evangelical Lutheran Church - Baptisms 1742-1779. LC 86-63901. (Orig.). 1987. pap. 20.00x (ISBN 0-913281-05-0). Noodle-Doosey.

Weiser, Frederick S., ed. Maryland German Church Records, Vol. 5: Evangelical Reformed Church 1746-1789, Frederick. Hinke, William J., tr. (Maryland German Church Records Ser.). (Orig.). 1987. pap. 20.00x (ISBN 0-913281-07-7). Noodle Doosey.

CHURCH UNITY

see Christian Union

CHURCH USHERS

Blom, Paul. Ministry of Welcome: A Guide for Ushers & Greeters. 32p. (Orig.). 1980. pap. 2.95 (ISBN 0-8066-1806-X, 10-4442). Augsburg.

Clark, Thomas L. A Guide for the Church Usher. LC 83-26211. 1984. pap. 5.50 (ISBN 0-8054-3517-4). Broadman.

--A Yearly Planning Guide for the Church Usher. 1986. pap. 3.95 (ISBN 0-8054-9407-3). Broadman.

Clevenger, Ernest A., Jr. The Art of Greeting & Seating: The Church Usher's Guide. (Illus.). 16p. 1983. pap. 0.95 (ISBN 0-88428-000-4). Parchment Pr.

Enlow, David R. Church Usher: Servant of God. LC 80-66769. 64p. (Orig.). 1980. pap. 1.95 (ISBN 0-87509-284-5). Chr Pubns.

Garrett, Willis O. Church Ushers' Manual. 64p. pap. 2.50 (ISBN 0-8007-8456-1, Spire Bks.). Revell.

Johnson, Alvin D. The Work of the Usher. (Orig.). pap. 3.95 (ISBN 0-8170-0356-8). Judson.

Johnson, Kenneth M. Church Ushers: Embodiment of the Gospel. LC 81-21022. 64p. (Orig.). 1982. pap. 3.95 (ISBN 0-8298-0493-5). Pilgrim NY.

Lang, Paul H. Church Ushering. rev. ed. 1957. pap. 1.25 (ISBN 0-570-03522-8, 14-1141). Concordia.

Parrott, Leslie. Usher's Manual. 1969. pap. 2.95 (ISBN 0-310-30651-5, 10513P). Zondervan.

CHURCH VACATION SCHOOLS

see Vacation Schools, Religious

CHURCH VESTMENTS

Chrysostomos, Archimandrite. Orthodox Liturgical Vesture: An Historical Treatment. 76p. 1981. 6.95 (ISBN 0-916586-43-X); pap. 3.95 (ISBN 0-916586-44-8). Holy Cross Orthodox.

Hall, Linda B. Making Eucharistic Vestments on a Limited Budget. 2nd ed. Barrett, James E., ed. (Illus.). 48p. 1985. pap. text ed. 8.50 (ISBN 0-942466-07-1). Hymnary Pr.

Jerde, Rebecca. Fabric Applique for Worship: Patterns & Guide for Sewing Banners, Vestments, & Paraments. LC 83-133006. 80p. 1983. pap. 8.95 (ISBN 0-8066-1965-1, 10-2153). Augsburg.

Mayo, Janet. A History of Ecclesiastical Dress. (Illus.). 196p. 1984. text ed. 39.50x (ISBN 0-8419-0983-0). Holmes & Meier.

Piepkorn, Arthur Carl. The Survival of the Historic Vestments in the Lutheran Church after Fifteen Fifty-Five. 120p. 1956. write for info. Concordia Schl Grad Studies.

Scott, Stephen. Why Do They Dress That Way? LC 86-81058. (People's Place Booklet Ser.: No. 7). (Illus.). 160p. (Orig.). 1986. pap. 5.50 (ISBN 0-934672-18-0). Good Bks PA.

CHURCH WARDENS' ACCOUNTS

see Churchwardens' Accounts

CHURCH WORK

see also Christian Leadership; Church and Social Problems; Church Group Work; Church Management; Church Officers; Church Secretaries; Church Ushers; City Churches; City Clergy; City Missions; Evangelistic Work; Parish Houses; Pastoral Counseling; Pastoral Psychology; Public Relations–Churches; Revivals; Rural Churches; Suburban Churches; Sunday-Schools; Telephone in Church Work; Visitations (Church Work); Women in Church Work

Adams, Jay E. Journal of Pastoral Practice, Vol. IV, No. 3. pap. 5.00 (ISBN 0-8010-0170-6). Baker Bk.

--Journal of Pastoral Practice, Vol. IV, No. 4. pap. 5.00 (ISBN 0-8010-0177-3). Baker Bk.

Amberson, Talmadge R. Reaching Out to People. LC 79-55435. 1979. pap. 5.95 (ISBN 0-8054-6321-6). Broadman.

Andersen, Richard. Positive Power of Christian Partnership. 1982. pap. 1.95 (ISBN 0-570-03844-8, 12-2947). Concordia.

Anderson, James D. & Jones, Ezra E. Ministry of the Laity. LC 84-48211. 224p. 1985. 14.45 (ISBN 0-06-060194-9, HarpR). Har-Row.

Anderson, Robert. The Gospel & Its Ministry. LC 78-9539. (Sir Robert Anderson Library). 224p. 1978. pap. 4.95 (ISBN 0-8254-2126-8). Kregel.

Backmen, Richard J. & Nerheim, Steven J. Toward a Healing Ministry: Exploring & Implementing a Congregational Ministry. 72p. (Orig.). 1985. pap. 5.95 (ISBN 0-8066-2176-1, 12-2022). Augsburg.

Ballard, Monroe & Ballard, JoeAnn. Serving in the City: Nurturing the Poor to Independence. 88p. 1986. 3 ring binder 10.95 (ISBN 0-8341-1125-X, S-350). Beacon Hill.

Barbeau, Clayton C. Delivering the Male: Out of the Tough-Guy Trap into a Better Marriage. 120p. (Orig.). 1982. pap. 6.95 (ISBN 0-86683-642-X, HarpR). Har-Row.

Barr, Browne. High Flying Geese: Unexpected Reflections on the Church & Its Ministry. (Illus.). 96p. (Orig.). 1983. pap. 6.95 (ISBN 0-86683-900-3, HarpR). Har-Row.

Barrett, James E. The Hymnary II: A Table For Service Planning. 2nd ed. Barrett, James E., ed. 96p. 1987. pap. text ed. 13.95 (ISBN 0-942466-11-X); 16.50 (ISBN 0-942466-12-8). Hymnary Pr.

Barrett, Lois. Building the House Church. LC 86-14324. 176p. (Orig.). 1986. pap. 8.95 (ISBN 0-8361-3415-X). Herald Pr.

Bavarel, Michel. New Communities, New Ministries: The Church Resurgent in Africa, Asia, & Latin America. Martin, Francis, tr. from Fr. LC 82-22318. Orig. Title: Chretienes Du Bout Du Monde. 122p. (Orig.). 1983. pap. 5.95 (ISBN 0-88344-337-6). Orbis Bks.

Beierle, Herbert L., ed. Ministers Manual. 1978. 10.00 (ISBN 0-940480-03-4). U of Healing.

Belasic, David & Schmidt, Paul. The Penguin Principles. 1986. 5.95 (ISBN 0-89536-799-8, 6817). CSS of Ohio.

Bell, Buddy. Ministry of Helps Study Course. 40p. (Orig.). 1983. pap. 1.95 (ISBN 0-89274-292-5). Harrison Hse.

Berry, Jo. The Priscilla Principle: Making Your Life a Ministry. 256p. 1984. pap. 6.95 (ISBN 0-310-42631-6, 11218P). Zondervan.

Berry, Leonidas H. I Wouldn't Take Nothin' for My Journey: Two Centuries of an American Minister's Family. 1981. 14.95 (ISBN 0-686-95206-5). Johnson Chi.

Bicket, Zenas J. We Hold These Truths. LC 78-56133. (Workers Training Book of the Year). (Illus.). 128p. 1978. pap. 1.50 (ISBN 0-88243-631-7, 02-0631). Gospel Pub.

Bishop, David S. Effective Communication. LC 76-58043. 1977. 5.25 (ISBN 0-87148-285-1); pap. text ed. 4.25 (ISBN 0-87148-286-X). Pathway Pr.

Blessings & Consecrations: A Book of Occasional Services. 64p. 1984. pap. 3.95 (ISBN 0-687-03626-7). Abingdon.

Bloom, Dorothy. Church Doors Open Outward: A Practical Guide to Beginning Community Ministry. 80p. 1987. pap. 6.95 (ISBN 0-8170-1117-X). Judson.

Blumenberg, Rick. The Prayer Support System: A Plan to Strengthen the Local Church. LC 86-42933. 40p. (Orig.). 1986. pap. 4.00 (ISBN 0-937021-04-0). Sagamore Bks MI.

Boys, Mary C., ed. Ministry & Education in Conversation. LC 80-53204. 160p. (Orig.). 1981. pap. 6.95 (ISBN 0-88489-126-7). St Mary's.

Brant, Roxanne. Ministering to the Lord. 80p. (Orig.). 1973. pap. 3.95 (ISBN 0-89228-031-X). Impact Bks MO.

Brown, Pat. Locating & Preserving Your Church's Records. Deweese, Charles W., ed. (Resource Kit for Your Church's History Ser.). 8p. 1984. 0.50 (ISBN 0-939804-15-8). Hist Comm S Baptist.

Brueggemann, Walter, et al. To Act Justly, Love Tenderly, Walk Humbly: An Agenda for Ministers. 88p. 1986. pap. 3.95 (ISBN 0-8091-2760-1). Paulist Pr.

Bubna, Donald & Ricketts, Sarah. Building People Through a Caring, Sharing Fellowship. 1982. pap. 5.95 (ISBN 0-8423-0187-9); leader's guide o. p. 2.95 (ISBN 0-8423-0188-7). Tyndale.

Burrows, William R. New Ministries: The Global Context. LC 80-17261. 192p. (Orig.). 1980. pap. 7.95 (ISBN 0-88344-329-5). Orbis Bks.

Byers, David M. & Quinn, Bernard. Readings for Town & Country Church Workers: An Annotated Bibliography. LC 74-77445. 120p. 1974. pap. 2.00x (ISBN 0-914422-00-6). Glenmary Res Ctr.

Campbell, Anne. Girls in the Gang. (Illus.). 284p. 1984. 16.95 (ISBN 0-631-13374-7). Basil Blackwell.

Campbell, Thomas C. & Reierson, Gary B. The Gift of Adminstration. LC 80-24594. 138p. 1981. pap. 6.95 (ISBN 0-664-24357-6). Westminster.

Carney, Russell & Moss, Jim. Building Your Youth Ministry. 1986. 4.95 (ISBN 0-931097-09-6). Sentinel Pub.

Chilson, Richard W. A Lenten Pilgrimage-Dying & Rising in the Lord: A Manual for Ministry in the Lenten Catechumenate. (Orig.). 1984. pap. 8.95 (ISBN 0-8091-2589-7); handbook 4.95 (ISBN 0-8091-2569-2). Paulist Pr.

Christ-Church Work Book. 1987. 5.95 (240550). Bethany Hse.

Claerbaut, David. Urban Ministry. 224p. 1984. pap. 7.95 (ISBN 0-310-45961-3, 12605P). Zondervan.

Clasper, Paul D. The Yogi, the Commissar & the Third World Church. 92p. (Orig.). 1982. pap. 5.00 (ISBN 0-686-37580-7, Pub. by New Day Philippines). Cellar.

Clowney, Edmund. Called to the Ministry. 1976. pap. 3.50 (ISBN 0-87552-144-4). Presby & Reformed.

Cook, R. Franklin & Weber, Steve. The Greening: The Story of Nazarene Compassionate Ministries. 104p. (Orig.). 1986. pap. 3.95 (ISBN 0-8341-1130-6). Beacon Hill.

Cooney, Randy. Reaching, Touching, Teaching: How to Run Successful Days of Retreat. 1986. pap. 15.95 (ISBN 0-697-02199-8). Wm C Brown.

Craig, James D. & Hill, Donald E., eds. How to Start a Home Cell Ministry. 1st ed. 32p. 1981. pap. 7.95 includes cassettes (ISBN 0-88151-019-X). Lay Leadership.

Dale, Robert D. Surviving Difficult Church Members. 128p. (Orig.). 1984. pap. 6.95 (ISBN 0-687-40763-X). Abingdon.

Damp, Margaret M. Finding Fulfillment in the Manse. 115p. 1978. pap. 2.95 (ISBN 0-8341-0544-6). Beacon Hill.

Davidson, James. Mobilizing Social Movement Organization: The Formation, Institionalization & Effectiveness of Economical Urban Ministries. (Monograph: No. 6). 1985. pap. 8.00 (ISBN 0-932566-05-7). Soc Sci Stud Rel.

Davis, Gerald C., ed. Setting Free the Ministry of the People of God. 120p. (Orig.). 1984. pap. 1.75 (ISBN 0-88028-038-7). Forward Movement.

Davis, Lawrence B. Immigrants, Baptists & the Protestant Mind in America. LC 72-81264. pap. 60.00 (ISBN 0-8357-9682-5, 2019040). Bks Demand UMI.

De Blase, Betty E. Survivor of a Tarnished Ministry. 176p. (Orig.). 1983. pap. text ed. 6.95 (ISBN 0-913621-00-5). Truth CA.

Deweese, Charles W., ed. Resource Kit for Your Church's History. 1984. 11.95 (ISBN 0-939804-12-3). Hist Comm S Baptist.

DiMauro, Joseph & Tumulty, Sharon A. Together: A Process for Parish Family Ministry. 1985. Envisioning. pap. 2.50 (ISBN 0-697-02024-X); Listening. pap. 3.50 (ISBN 0-697-02025-8); Responding. pap. 3.50 (ISBN 0-697-02026-6); Enabling. pap. 3.50 (ISBN 0-697-02027-4); Administering. pap. 3.50 (ISBN 0-697-02028-2); Administrator manual. 20.00 (ISBN 0-697-02023-1). Wm C Brown.

Dudley, Carl S., ed. Building Effective Ministry: Theory & Practice in the Local Church. LC 82-48411. 256p. 1983. pap. 8.95 (ISBN 0-06-062102-8, RD-418, HarpR). Har-Row.

Dunn, Frank E. The Ministering Teacher. 112p. 1982. pap. 4.95 (ISBN 0-8170-0958-2). Judson.

Eakin, Mary M. Scuffy Sandals: A Guide for Church Visitation in the Community. LC 81-15824. 96p. (Orig.). 1982. pap. 5.95 (ISBN 0-8298-0490-0). Pilgrim NY.

Elizondo, Virgil & Greinacher, Norbert, eds. Religion & Churches in Eastern Europe. (Concilium Ser.: Vol. 154). 128p. (Orig.). 1982. pap. 6.95 (ISBN 0-8164-2385-7, HarpR). Har-Row.

Fabella, Virginia & Torres, Sergio, eds. Irruption of the Third World: Challenge to Theology. LC 82-18851. 304p. (Orig.). 1983. pap. 10.95 (ISBN 0-88344-216-7). Orbis Bks.

Faulkner, Brooks R. Burnout in Ministry. LC 81-67752. 1981. pap. 5.95 (ISBN 0-8054-2414-8). Broadman.

Fletcher, William M. El Segundo de los Grandes Mandamientos. Carrodeguas, Angel, ed. Romanenghi de Powell, Elsie R., tr. from Eng. Tr. of The Second Greatest Commandment. (Span.). 192p. Date not set. pap. text ed. 2.95 (ISBN 0-8297-0722-0). Life Pubs Intl.

Foster, Arthur L., ed. The House Church Evolving. LC 76-4198. (Studies in Ministry & Parish Life). 126p. 1976. 13.95x (ISBN 0-913552-04-6); pap. 6.95x (ISBN 0-913552-05-4). Exploration Pr.

Garlow, James L. LITE Manual. 177p. 1982. pap. 6.95 spiral binding (ISBN 0-8341-0883-6, S-2000); Leader's Guide 14.95. Beacon Hill.

Gerber, Bobbie. Shelter: A Work of Ministry. 160p. 1983. pap. 8.95 (ISBN 0-8164-2622-8, HarpR). Har-Row.

Gibbs, M. Christians with Secular Power. LC 80-8048. (Laity Exchange). 144p. (Orig.). 1981. pap. 5.95 (ISBN 0-8006-1389-9, 1-1389). Fortress.

Griffiths, Michael. Get Your Church Involved in Missions. 1972. pap. 1.00 (ISBN 9971-83-784-6). OMF Bks.

Gura, Carol. Ministering to Young Adults. (Illus.). 200p. 1987. spiralbound 28.95 (ISBN 0-88489-179-8). St Mary's.

Hack, John. How to Operate a Cassette Tape Ministry. LC 81-66822. 1981. pap. 4.25 (ISBN 0-8054-3429-1). Broadman.

Hagin, Kenneth E. The Gifts & Calling of God. 1986. pap. 0.50 (ISBN 0-89276-268-3). Hagin Ministries.

--Ministering to the Oppressed. 2nd ed. 1983. pap. 1.00 (ISBN 0-89276-027-3). Hagin Ministries.

--The Ministry of a Prophet. 1968. pap. 1.00 (ISBN 0-89276-009-5). Hagin Ministries.

--La Oracion Que Prevalece. (Span.). 1986. pap. 2.50 (ISBN 0-89276-186-5). Hagin Ministries.

--Sign of the Times. 1986. pap. 0.50 (ISBN 0-89276-269-1). Hagin Ministries.

Hagin, Kenneth E. & Hagin, Kenneth, Jr. Ministering to Your Family. 1986. pap. 1.50 (ISBN 0-89276-407-4). Hagin Ministries.

Hagin, Kenneth, Jr. The Life of Obedience. 1986. pap. 1.00 (ISBN 0-89276-720-0). Hagin Ministries.

Hall, George F. The Missionary Spirit in the Augustana Church. LC 84-72945. (Publications Ser.: No. 32). 166p. 1985. 7.50 (ISBN 0-910184-32-1). Augustana.

Hamilton, Michael. God's Plan for the Church-Growth! LC 81-82021. (Radiant Life Ser.). 128p. (Orig.). 1981. 2.50 (ISBN 0-88243-885-9, 02-0885); teacher's ed. 3.95 (ISBN 0-88243-194-3, 32-0194). Gospel Pub.

Hammond, Phillip E. The Role of Ideology in Church Participation. Zuckerman, Harriet & Merton, Robert K., eds. LC 79-9003. (Dissertations on Sociology Ser.). 1980. lib. bdg. 27.50x (ISBN 0-405-12972-6). Ayer Co Pubs.

Haney, David. El Ministerio de Todo Creyente. Martinez, Jose Luis, ed. Kratzig, Guillermo, tr. 200p. 1984. pap. 4.75 (ISBN 0-311-09099-0). Casa Bautista.

Hart, Lee. Adult Ministries in the Church & the World. LC 76-773. 1976. 11.00 (ISBN 0-8309-0160-4). Herald Hse.

Hater, Robert J. The Ministry Explosion. 96p. (Orig.). 1979. pap. 3.25 (ISBN 0-697-01709-5). Wm C Brown.

Henkelmann, Ervin F. & Carter, Stephen J. How to Develop a Team Ministry & Make It Work. 1985. pap. 8.95 (ISBN 0-570-03946-0, 12-2879). Concordia.

Heritage Village Church Presents the Ministry of Jim & Tammy Bakker. Date not set. price not set. PTL Enterprises.

Hibbert, Albert. Smith Wigglesworth: The Secret of His Power. 112p. 1982. pap. 4.95 (ISBN 0-89274-211-9, HH-211). Harrison Hse.

Hickman, Hoyt. A Primer for Church Worship. 112p. (Orig.). 1984. pap. 7.95 (ISBN 0-687-34033-0). Abingdon.

Hill, C. R., Jr. Between Two Worlds: An Approach to Ministry. LC 76-4276. 1976. 3.50 (ISBN 0-89937-007-1). Ctr Res Soc Chg.

Hillock, Wilfred M. Involved. LC 77-78102. (Anvil Ser.). 1977. pap. 8.95 (ISBN 0-8127-0140-2). Review & Herald.

Holmes, George. Toward an Effective Pulpit Ministry. LC 72-152056. 1971. 4.00 (ISBN 0-88243-610-4, 02-0610). Gospel Pub.

Hopewell, James F., et al. Ministry & Mission: Theological Reflections for the Life of the Church. Taylor, Barbara B., ed. 192p. (Orig.). 1985. pap. 9.95x (ISBN 0-935311-00-9). Post Horn Pr.

Hoyer, Jeff. Life-Changing Learning for Adults. (C. E. Ministries Ser.). 96p. (Orig.). 1984. pap. 3.50 (ISBN 0-89367-097-9). Light & Life.

Hudnut, Robert K. This People, This Parish. 192p. 1986. pap. 7.95 (ISBN 0-310-38241-6, 12329P). Zondervan.

Hufton, Richard A. The Pastor's Handbook. 47p. (Orig.). 1984. pap. 3.00 (ISBN 0-933643-05-5). Grace World Outreach.

Hughes, Alfred C. Preparing for Church Ministry: A Practical Guide to Spiritual Formation. 6.95 (ISBN 0-87193-167-2). Dimension Bks.

Jackson, Neil E., Jr. Motivational Ideas for Changing Lives. LC 81-68366. 1982. pap. 4.95 (ISBN 0-8054-5647-3). Broadman.

Johnson, Daniel L. Starting Right, Staying Strong: A Guide to Effective Ministry. LC 82-22383. 108p. (Orig.). 1983. pap. 5.95 (ISBN 0-8298-0648-2). Pilgrim NY.

Johnson, Douglas W. The Care & Feeding of Volunteers. LC 78-8295. (Creative Leadership Ser.). 1978. pap. 7.25 (ISBN 0-687-04669-6). Abingdon.

Jones, Nathan. Sharing the Old, Old Story: Educational Ministry in the Black Community. LC 81-86046. (Illus.). 104p. (Orig.). 1982. pap. 8.95 (ISBN 0-88489-144-5). St Mary's.

Kadel, Thomas E., ed. Growth in Ministry. LC 79-8902. 176p. 1980. pap. 6.95 (ISBN 0-8006-1383-X, 1-1383). Fortress.

Kane, J. Herbert. Wanted: World Christians. 204p. 1986. pap. 9.95 (ISBN 0-8010-5474-5). Baker Bk.

Kaung, Stephen. Discipled to Christ. Hsu, Lily, tr. from Eng. (Chinese.). 1984. pap. write for info. (ISBN 0-941598-13-6). Living Spring Pubns.

Kelsey, Morton. Prophetic Ministry. 224p. 1984. pap. 9.95 (ISBN 0-8245-0631-6). Crossroad NY.

Killinger, John. Steeple People & the World: Planning for Mission Through the Church. (Orig.). 1977. pap. 2.50 (ISBN 0-377-00059-0). Friend Pr.

Knutson, Gerhard. Ministry to Inactives: A Manual for Establishing a Listening Witness to Inactive Members. 40p. (Orig.). 1983. pap. 3.95 (ISBN 0-8066-1729-2, 10-4443). Augsburg.

Korth, Robert E., compiled by. Special Ministries for Caring Churches. 128p. 1986. pap. 5.95 (ISBN 0-87403-145-1, 3183). Standard Pub.

Krahn, John & Foster, Betty J. Ministry Ideabank No. 2. 1986. 7.50 (ISBN 0-89536-801-3, 6819). CSS of Ohio.

Krahn, John H. & Foster, Betty J. Ministry Ideabank. 136p. (Orig.). 1981. pap. text ed. 6.75 (ISBN 0-89536-488-3, 1314). CSS of Ohio.

Krupp, Nate. You Can Be a Soul Winner, Here's How! LC 78-64961. 176p. 1978. pap. 3.95 (ISBN 0-89221-050-8). New Leaf.

Kwatera, Michael. The Liturgical Ministry of the Deacon. (Ministry Ser.). 96p. 1985. pap. 1.95 (ISBN 0-8146-1386-1). Liturgical Pr.

Laing, Joseph & McClung, Grant. Effective Communications Instructor's Manual. 1977. pap. 5.25 (ISBN 0-87148-289-4). Pathway Pr.

Landsman, Michael. Supportive Ministries. 1981. pap. 1.95 (ISBN 0-89274-181-3). Harrison Hse.

Lawyer, John & Katz, Neil. Communication Skills for Ministry. 176p. 1983. pap. text ed. 17.95 (ISBN 0-8403-2987-3, 40371201). Kendall-Hunt.

Lee, Stephen. Grace: Living on the Friendship of God. (Orig.). 1987. pap. 3.25 (ISBN 0-8054-5437-3). Broadman.

LeFeber, Larry. Building a Young Adult Ministry. 1980. pap. 5.95 (ISBN 0-8170-0848-9). Judson.

Lewis, V. H. The Church Winning Souls. 83p. 1983. pap. 2.95 (ISBN 0-8341-0893-3). Beacon Hill.

Lienhard, Joseph T. Ministry. (Message of the Fathers of the Church Ser.: Vol. 8). 15.00 (ISBN 0-89453-348-7); pap. 7.95 (ISBN 0-89453-320-7). M Glazier.

Lore-Kelly, Christin. Caring Community: A Design for Ministry. 1984. 12.95 (ISBN 0-8294-0423-6). Loyola.

Lovett, C. S. Census Manual. 1961. pap. 1.00 (ISBN 0-938148-18-4). Personal Christianity.

--Visitation Made Easy. 1959. pap. 2.95 (ISBN 0-938148-15-X). Personal Christianity.

Lovorn, Tom & Lovorn, Janie. Building a Caring Church. 104p. 1986. pap. 8.95 (ISBN 0-89693-150-1). Victor Bks.

McDonough, Reginald M. Working with Volunteer Leaders in the Church. LC 75-16579. 140p. 1976. pap. 6.50 (ISBN 0-8054-3214-0). Broadman.

McKee, William. How to Reach Out to Inactive Catholics: A Practical Parish Program. 40p. 1982. pap. 6.95 (ISBN 0-89243-155-5). Liguori Pubns.

Macquarrie, John. Theology, Church & Ministry. 224p. 1986. 16.95 (ISBN 0-8245-0787-8). Crossroad NY.

Malony, H. Newton. Church Organization Development: Perspectives & Resources. LC 86-81285. (Orig.). 1986. pap. 10.00 (ISBN 0-9609928-2-0). Integ Pr.

Maney, Thomas. Basic Communities: A Practical Guide for Renewing Neighborhood Churches. 96p. (Orig.). 1984. pap. 5.95 (ISBN 0-86683-857-0, 8411, HarpR). Har-Row.

Marty, Martin E. Being Good & Doing Good. LC 84-47929. (Lead Bks.). 128p. 1984. pap. 4.95 (ISBN 0-8006-1603-0). Fortress.

Maseroni, Robert S. The Gift of Ministry & Service, No. 2. 1983. 0.80 (ISBN 0-89536-626-6, 0734). CSS of Ohio.

Matthews, Elwood. A Maturing Ministry. 1981. pap. 3.50 (ISBN 0-934942-22-6). White Wing Pub.

Menking, Stanley J. Helping Laity Help Others. LC 83-26061. (The Pastor's Handbook Ser.: Vol. 2). 114p. (Orig.). 1984. pap. 7.95 (ISBN 0-664-24615-X). Westminster.

Meyners, Robert & Wooster, Claire. Solomon's Sword: Clarifying Values in the Church. LC 77-9391. Repr. of 1977 ed. 27.40 (ISBN 0-8357-9028-2, 2016408). Bks Demand UMI.

Miller, Kenneth R. & Wilson, Mary E. The Church That Cares. LC 85-14786. 96p. 1985. pap. 6.95 (ISBN 0-8170-1087-4). Judson.

Miller, Kevin, ed. Inside the Church: Finding Your Place Within God's Family. (Senior High Pacesetter Ser.). 64p. 1986. pap. 7.95 (ISBN 0-89191-325-4). Cook.

Miller, Paul M. Peer Counseling in the Church. LC 78-9299. 168p. 1978. pap. 7.95 (ISBN 0-8361-1854-5). Herald Pr.

The Minister's Manual. rev. ed. 1970. Repr. of 1960 ed. 5.95 (ISBN 0-916035-04-2). Evangel Indiana.

Mitchell, Kenneth R. & Anderson, Herbert. All Our Losses, All Our Griefs: Resources for Pastoral Care. LC 83-19851. 180p. (Orig.). 1983. pap. 8.95 (ISBN 0-664-24493-9). Westminster.

Mitchell, Robert H. Ministry & Music. LC 77-20815. 164p. 1978. pap. 8.95 (ISBN 0-664-24186-7). Westminster.

Mother Teresa of Calcutta & Spink, Kathryn. I Need Souls Like You Sharing in the Work of Charity Through Prayer & Suffering. LC 83-48984. 128p. 1984. 10.45 (ISBN 0-06-068236-1, HarpR). Har-Row.

Mottweiler, Jack. Adults As Learners. (C. E. Ministries Ser.). 95p. (Orig.). 1984. pap. 3.50 (ISBN 0-89367-098-7). Light & Life.

Mouw, Richard J. Called to Holy Worldliness. Gibbs, Mark, ed. LC 80-8047. (Laity Exchange). 160p. (Orig.). 1980. pap. 5.95 (ISBN 0-8006-1397-X, 1-1397). Fortress.

Mulholland, Kenneth. Adventures in Training the Ministry. 1976. pap. 5.95 (ISBN 0-87552-340-4). Presby & Reformed.

National Conference of Religious Vocation Directors. Ministries for the Lord: A Resource Guide & Directory of Catholic Church Vocations for Men, 1985. 128p. (Orig.). 1985. pap. 4.95 (ISBN 0-8091-2724-5). Paulist Pr.

Neal, Emily G. Healing Ministry. 176p. 1985. pap. 7.95 (ISBN 0-8245-0688-X). Crossroad NY.

Nee, Watchman. The Church & the Work, 3 vols. Kaung, Stephen, tr. (Chinese.). 550p. 1982. 27.00 (ISBN 0-935008-57-8); pap. text ed. 15.00 (ISBN 0-935008-58-6). Christian Fellow Pubs.

--The Ministry of God's Word. Kaung, Stephen, tr. 1971. 5.50 (ISBN 0-935008-27-6); pap. 4.25 (ISBN 0-935008-28-4). Christian Fellow Pubs.

New Parish Ministries. 400p. 1983. pap. 17.50 (ISBN 0-86683-742-6, HarpR). Har-Row.

NFCLC. The Cry of the People: Workshops for Christian Service. 318p. (Orig.). 1980. pap. 10.00 (ISBN 0-913605-06-9). NFCLC.

Ng, David. See It! Do It! Your Faith in Action. (Orig.). 1972. pap. 2.50 (ISBN 0-377-02401-5). Friend Pr.

Niebuhr, H. Richard. The Purpose of the Church & Its Ministry. LC 76-62925. (Orig.). 1977. pap. 3.00i (ISBN 0-06-066174-7, RD 211, HarpR). Har-Row.

Niebuhr, H. Richard & Williams, Daniel D., eds. The Ministry in Historical Perspectives. rev. ed. LC 80-8899. (Ministers Paperback Library). 384p. 1983. pap. 8.95 (ISBN 0-06-066232-8, RD 354, HarpR). Har-Row.

Oduyoye, Modupe. Sons of the Gods & Daughters of Men: An Afro-Asiatic Interpretation of Genesis 1-11. LC 83-6308. 126p. (Orig.). 1983. pap. 12.95 (ISBN 0-88344-467-4). Orbis Bks.

Olson, Richard P. & Pia-Terry, Carole D. Ministry with Remarried Persons. 160p. 1984. pap. 6.95 (ISBN 0-8170-0990-6). Judson.

O'Neill, Dennis. Lazarus Interlude: A Story of God's Healing Love in a Moment of Ministry. LC 83-60438. 80p. (Orig.). 1983. pap. 2.95 (ISBN 0-87793-271-9). Ave Maria.

Oosterhouse, Kenneth, et al. Born of a Glorious Thunder: Real Life Accounts of Foreign Christian Work. Kortenhoeven, Helen, tr. 304p. (Orig.). 1986. pap. 6.95. West Indies Pub.

Otto, A. S., ed. Invisible Ministry Annual Reports. 60p. 1985. vinyl 19.95 (ISBN 0-912132-12-4). Dominion Pr.

Palmer, John M. Equipping for Ministry. LC 85-80220. 88p. (Orig.). 1985. pap. cancelled (ISBN 0-88243-802-6, 02-0802). Gospel Pub.

Pennock, Michael. Your Church & You. LC 83-70053. (Illus.). 288p. (Orig.). 1983. pap. 5.50 student text (ISBN 0-87793-268-9); tchr's. ed. 3.50 (ISBN 0-87793-269-7). Ave Maria.

Perkins, Pheme. Ministering in the Pauline Churches: Partners for Christ. LC 82-60849. 1982. pap. 4.95 (ISBN 0-8091-2473-4). Paulist Pr.

Peterson, Eugene H. Working the Angles: A Trigonometry for Pastoral Work. 266p. (Orig.). 1987. pap. 7.95 (ISBN 0-8028-0265-6). Eerdmans.

Pitt, Theodore K. Premarital Counseling Handbook for Ministers. 192p. 1985. pap. 9.95 (ISBN 0-8170-1071-8). Judson.

Powell, Paul W. How to Make Your Church Hum. LC 76-47791. 1977. pap. 3.95 (ISBN 0-8054-2528-4). Broadman.

Powers, Betty & Mall, E. Jane. Church Office Handbook for Ministers. 80p. 1983. pap. 3.95 (ISBN 0-8170-1011-4). Judson.

Pragman, James H. Traditions of Ministry. LC 12-2982. (Continued Applied Christianity Ser.). 1983. pap. 15.95 (ISBN 0-570-03900-2, 12-2982). Concordia.

Preston, Daniel D. The Life & Work of the Minister. 1968. 5.95 (ISBN 0-934942-11-0). White Wing Pub.

Ray, Charles. Marvelous Ministry. 100p. 1985. pap. 2.95. Pilgrim Pubns.

Reichert, Richard. Adult Education Ministry: A Parish Manual. 1986. pap. 5.95 (ISBN 0-697-02206-4). Wm C Brown.

Resources for Women's Ministries. (Women's Ministries Commission Ser.). 1975. 4.00 (ISBN 0-8309-0258-9). Herald Hse.

Reynolds, Brian & Northeast Center for Youth Ministry Staff. A Chance to Serve: Peer Minister's Handbook. (Illus.). 75p. (Orig.). 1983. pap. 4.95 (ISBN 0-88489-154-2); pap. 9.95 leader's manual (ISBN 0-88489-153-4). St Mary's.

Richards, Larry. Personal Ministry Handbook. 224p. 1986. pap. 9.95 (ISBN 0-8010-7736-2). Baker Bk.

Rodd, Cyril S., ed. The Pastor's Problems. 168p. pap. 11.65 Canada (ISBN 0-317-31449-1); pap. 8.95 (ISBN 0-317-31450-5, 30-29117-1902). Fortress.

Rossman, Peter & Noyce, Gaylord. Helping People Care on the Job. 144p. 1985. pap. 5.95. Judson.

Rouse, Jerry L. Church Building: The Ministry of Leadership in the Body of Christ. 0.75 (ISBN 0-911802-57-6). Free Church Pubns.

Rusbuldt, Richard E. Basic Leader Skills: Handbook for Church Leaders. 64p. 1981. pap. 5.95 (ISBN 0-8170-0920-5). Judson.

Sammon, Sean D. Growing Pains in Ministry. LC 83-9991. 240p. 1983. 12.95 (ISBN 0-89571-027-7); study guide, 77p 3.95 (ISBN 0-89571-029-3). Affirmation.

Sample, Tex. Blue-Collar Ministry. 192p. 1984. pap. 9.95 (ISBN 0-8170-1029-7). Judson.

Sawyer, David. R. Work of the Church: Getting the Job Done in Boards & Committees. 128p. 1987. pap. 6.95 (ISBN 0-8170-1116-1). Judson.

Schillebeeckx, Edward. Ministry. 160p. 1981. 12.95 (ISBN 0-8245-0030-X). Crossroad NY.

--Ministry. Bowden, John, tr. 176p. 1984. pap. 9.95 (ISBN 0-8245-0638-3). Crossroad NY.

Schirer, Marshall E. & Forehand, Mary A. Cooperative Ministry: Hope for Small Churches. 96p. 1984. pap. 3.95 (ISBN 0-8170-1030-0). Judson.

Scholer, David M., ed. Perspectives in Churchmanship: Essays in Honor of Robert G. Torbet. (Festschriften Ser.: No. 3). vi, 108p. 1986. write for info. (ISBN 0-86554-268-6, MUP/H231). NABPR.

Schreck, Harley & Barrett, David, eds. Unreached Peoples '86: Clarifying the Task. pap. write for info. (ISBN 0-912552-58-1). Missions Adv Res Com Ctr.

Seraydarian, Patricia M. The Church Secretary's Handbook. 159p. 1982. pap. 5.95 (ISBN 0-8423-0281-6). Tyndale.

Shim, Steve S. Korean Immigrant Churches Today in Southern California. LC 76-24724. 1977. soft bdg. 11.00 (ISBN 0-88247-426-X). R & E Pubs.

Sider, Ronald J., ed. Evangelicals & Development: Toward a Theology of Social Change. LC 82-6970. (Contemporary Issues in Social Ethics Ser.). 122p. 1982. pap. 6.95 (ISBN 0-664-24445-9). Westminster.

Simma, Maria. My Personal Experiences with the Poor Souls. Helena, M., tr. from Ger. 1978. 6.95 (ISBN 0-8199-0744-8). Franciscan Herald.

Simon, Arthur. Bread for the World. rev. ed. LC 84-238017. 219p. 1985. pap. 4.95 (ISBN 0-8091-2670-2). Paulist Pr.

Simpson, Charles. The Challenge to Care: A Fresh Look at How Pastors & Lay Leaders Relate to the People of God. 196p. 1986. pap. 5.95 (ISBN 0-89283-269-X, Pub. by Vine Books). Servant.

Southard, Samuel. Training Church Members for Pastoral Care. 96p. 1982. pap. 4.95 (ISBN 0-8170-0944-2). Judson.

Spurgeon, C. H. All Round Ministry. 1978. pap. 7.45 (ISBN 0-85151-181-3). Banner of Truth.

Starkes, M. Thomas. The Dual Ministry. 1986. pap. 3.95 (ISBN 0-937931-01-2). Global TN.

Steindam, Harold. Pastor at Work. (Illus.). 128p. 1985. pap. 7.95 (ISBN 0-8298-0562-1). Pilgrim NY.

Stewart, Ed, ed. Teaching Adults Through Discussion. 32p. 1978. pap. 1.50 (ISBN 0-8307-0508-2, 9970401). Regal.

Stone, J. David. Creative Movement Ministry, Vol. I. Brooks, Frances, ed. (Orig.). 1986. pap. 5.95 (ISBN 0-939697-04-1). Graded Pr.

Strang, Stephen, et al, eds. Solving the Ministry's Toughest Problems, 2 vols. 432p. 1984. Vol. I. 24.95 (ISBN 0-930525-00-0); Vol. II. write for info. (ISBN 0-930525-01-9). Strang Comms Co.

Stubbe, Arlon. The Phantom Church. 1986. 7.95 (ISBN 0-89536-802-1, 6820). CSS of Ohio.

Stubblefield, Jerry M. A Church Ministering to Adults. LC 86-2299. (Orig.). 1986. pap. 9.95 (ISBN 0-8054-3235-3). Broadman.

Sumners, Bill. Displaying & Exhibiting Your Church's History. Deweese, Charles W., ed. (Resource Kit for Your Church's History Ser.). 1984. 0.50 (ISBN 0-939804-22-0). Hist Comm S Baptist.

Thurmann, Joyce V. New Wineskins: A Study of the House Church Movement, Vol. 30. (IC-Studien zur Interkulturellen Geschichte). 109p. 1982. pap. 14.20 (ISBN 3-8204-7172-3). P Lang Pubs.

Tibbetts, Orlando L. How to Keep Useful Church Records. 96p. 1983. pap. 3.95 (ISBN 0-317-00687-8). Judson.

Tillapaugh, Frank R. The Church Unleashed: Getting God's People Out Where the Needs Are. LC 82-9783. 224p. 1982. pap. 5.95 (ISBN 0-8307-0823-5, 5416300). Regal.

To Build & Be Church, Lay Ministry Resource Packet. 73p. 1979. pap. 6.50 (ISBN 1-55586-621-2). US Catholic.

Trevino, Alejandro. El Predicador: Platicas a Mis Estudiantes. 155p. 1984. pap. 2.95 (ISBN 0-311-42016-8). Casa Bautista.

Troeltsch, Ernst. The Social Teaching of the Christian Churches, 2 vols. Wyon, Olive, tr. LC 81-10443. 1981. Vol. 1, 446p. pap. 17.00X (ISBN 0-226-81298-7); Vol. II, 569p. pap. 17.00 (ISBN 0-226-81299-5). U of Chicago Pr.

Underwood, B. E. Spiritual Gifts-Ministries & Manifestations. pap. 6.95 (ISBN 0-911866-03-5). Advocate.

A Vision of Youth Ministry: Bilingual Edition. (Eng. & Span.). 48p. 1986. pap. text ed. 2.95 (ISBN 1-55586-107-5). US Catholic.

Wagner, C. P., ed. Church Growth: The State of the Art. 288p. 1986. pap. 9.95 (ISBN 0-8423-0287-5). Tyndale.

Walker, Paul L. The Ministry of the Church & Pastor. 107p. 1965. 5.25 (ISBN 0-87148-556-7); pap. 4.25 (ISBN 0-87148-557-5). Pathway Pr.

Warren, Thomas B. Lectures on Church Co-Operation & Orphan Homes. 1958. pap. 7.00 (ISBN 0-934916-48-9). Natl Christian Pr.

Weber, Herbert. The Parish Help Book: A Guide to Social Ministry in the Parish. LC 83-71894. 112p. 1983. pap. 3.95 (ISBN 0-87793-304-9). Ave Maria.

Weidman, Mavis. Junior Worker's Handbook. pap. 1.95 (ISBN 0-87509-098-2). Chr Pubns.

Westing, Harold J. Multiple Church-Staff Handbook. LC 85-9811. (Illus.). 208p. (Orig.). 1985. pap. 10.95 (ISBN 0-8254-4031-9). Kregel.

Wierwille, Victor P. The New Dynamic Church. LC 70-176281. (Studies in Abundant Living: Vol. 2). 242p. 1971. 6.95 (ISBN 0-910068-03-8). Am Christian.

Wilson, Marlene. How to Mobilize Church Volunteers. LC 83-70506. 160p. (Orig.). 1983. pap. 8.95 (ISBN 0-8066-2012-9, 10-3175). Augsburg.

Wilson, Samuel & Siewert, John. Mission Handbook. 13th ed. write for info. (ISBN 0-912552-55-7). Missions Adv Res Com Ctr.

Wittlinger, Carlton O. Quest for Piety & Obedience: The Story of the Brethren in Christ. LC 77-94894. 1978. 12.95 (ISBN 0-916035-05-0). Evangel Indiana.

Woodburn, et al. Complete Set of God's People at Work in the Parish Series, 11 bks. 1979. pap. 12.50 set (ISBN 0-570-08036-3, 12-2775). Concordia.

Yoder, Perry & Yoder, Elizabeth. New Men-New Roles. 1977. pap. 2.00 (ISBN 0-87303-001-X). Faith & Life.

CHURCH WORK–DATA PROCESSING

Bedell, Kenneth. Using Personal Computers in the Church. 112p. 1982. pap. 5.95 (ISBN 0-8170-0948-5). Judson.

Bedell, Kenneth & Rossman, Parker. Computers: New Opportunities for Personalized Ministry. 128p. 1984. pap. 4.95 (ISBN 0-8170-1039-4). Judson.

Brown, Lowell & Haystead, Wes. The Church Computer Manual. 160p. (Orig.). 1985. pap. 12.95 (ISBN 0-8423-0271-9). Tyndale.

Dilday, Russell H., Jr. Personal Computer: A New Tool for Ministers. LC 84-20360. 1985. pap. 8.95 (ISBN 0-8054-3111-X). Broadman.

Emswiler, James P. Using a Computer in Church Ministry. 1986. pap. 6.95 (ISBN 0-87193-248-2). Dimension Bks.

Houk, Neil B. Church Bytes Software Guide: For Church Administration & Finances. 110p. (Orig.). 1986. pap. 10.95 (ISBN 0-9615086-3-9). Church Bytes.

--Church Bytes: 1985. 60p. (Orig.). 1986. pap. 5.95 (ISBN 0-9615086-1-2). Church Bytes.

--Pastor Goode & His Marvelous Micro. 59p. (Orig.). 1984. pap. 5.95 (ISBN 0-9615086-0-4). Church Bytes.

Iles, Robert H. & Callison, William L. Selecting Computers for Ministry. LC 84-62333. (Illus.). 160p. (Orig.). 1985. pap. 13.95 (ISBN 0-932489-00-1). New Begin Co.

Johnson, William R. The Pastor & the Personal Computer: Information Management for Ministers. 224p. (Orig.). 1985. pap. 10.50 (ISBN 0-687-30134-3). Abingdon.

--Selecting the Church Computer. 160p. (Orig.). 1984. pap. 8.95 (ISBN 0-687-37135-X). Abingdon.

Pastor Goode & His Marvelous Micro. rev. ed. 1986. pap. 6.95 (ISBN 0-9615086-4-7). Church Bytes.

Sargent, Richard B. & Benson, John E. Computers in the Church: Practical Assistance in Making the Computer Decision. (Administration Series for Churches). 112p. (Orig.). 1986. pap. 10.95 (ISBN 0-8066-2231-8, 10-1625). Augsburg.

CHURCH WORK–FORMS, BLANKS, ETC.

Abell, Aaron I. The Urban Impact on American Protestantism, 1865-1900. x, 275p. 1962. Repr. of 1943 ed. 22.50 (ISBN 0-208-00587-0, Archon). Shoe String.

Bower, William C., ed. Church at Work in the Modern World. facs. ed. LC 67-26717. (Essay Index Reprint Ser). 1935. 18.00 (ISBN 0-8369-0231-9). Ayer Co Pubs.

Dobbins, Gaines S. Ministering Church. LC 60-9530. 1960. 9.95 (ISBN 0-8054-2505-5). Broadman.

Gockel, Herman W. What Jesus Means to Me. 1956. 4.95 (ISBN 0-570-03021-8, 6-1008). Concordia.

Pastor's Wedding & Funeral Record. LC 68-12321. 1968. 11.95 (ISBN 0-8054-2306-0). Broadman.

Paulson, Wayne. Parish Secretary's Handbook. 192p. (Orig.). 1983. pap. 12.95 (ISBN 0-8066-1898-1, 10-4868). Augsburg.

CHURCH WORK, RURAL

see Rural Churches

CHURCH WORK AS A PROFESSION

Baker, Benjamin S. Feeding the Sheep. LC 85-15139. 1985. pap. 5.95 (ISBN 0-8054-2544-6). Broadman.

Harbaugh, Gary L. Pastor As Person. LC 84-24259. 176p. (Orig.). 1984. pap. 9.95 (ISBN 0-8066-2115-X, 10-4889). Augsburg.

Little, Sara. To Set One's Heart: Belief & Teaching in the Church. LC 82-49020. 160p. 1983. pap. 8.95 (ISBN 0-8042-1442-5). John Knox.

MacArthur, John, Jr. Exposing False Spiritual Leaders. (John MacArthur's Bible Studies). (Orig.). 1986. pap. 3.95 (ISBN 0-8024-5345-7). Moody.

Mixon, Jerry W. Off the Main Road. LC 85-19065. 1985. 5.95 (ISBN 0-8054-5015-7). Broadman.

Nelson, John O. Opportunities in Religious Service. (VGM Career Bks.). (Illus.). 160p. 1983. 9.95 (ISBN 0-8442-6600-0, 6600-0, Passport Bks); pap. 7.95 (ISBN 0-8442-6601-9, 6601-9). Natl Textbk.

Wolseley, Roland E. Careers in Religious Communications. 264p. 1977. pap. 6.95 (ISBN 0-8361-1823-5). Herald Pr.

CHURCH WORK WITH ADULTS

see Church Work

CHURCH WORK WITH ALCOHOLICS

Cairns, Thomas H. Preparing Your Church for Ministry to Alcoholics & Their Families. 136p. 1986. 19.75x (ISBN 0-398-05230-1). C C Thomas.

Drews, Toby R. Getting Them Sober, Vol. 3. LC 85-73330. 1986. pap. 3.95 (ISBN 0-88270-610-1). Bridge Pub.

Dunn, Jerry G. God Is for the Alcoholic. Tr. of Deus e a Favor do Alcoolatra. 1986. write for info. (ISBN 0-8297-1610-6). Life Pubs Intl.

Fichter, Joseph H. The Rehabilitation of Clergy Alcoholics: Ardent Spirits Subdued. LC 80-28447. 203p. 1982. 26.95 (ISBN 0-89885-009-6). Human Sci Pr.

Jack, S. Spiritual Reflections for the Recovering Alcoholic. LC 84-18590. (Illus.). 90p. 1985. pap. 5.95 (ISBN 0-8189-0477-1). Alba.

Keller, John E. Ministering to Alcoholics. rev. ed. LC 66-22560. 1966. pap. 8.95 (ISBN 0-8066-0922-2, 10-4439). Augsburg.

Lord, Luther & Lord, Eileen. How to Communicate in Sobriety. LC 77-94793. (Illus.). 120p. (Orig.). 1978. pap. 5.95 (ISBN 0-89486-046-1). Hazelden.

Marsh, Jack. You Can Help the Alcoholic: A Christian Plan for Intervention. LC 82-74499. 88p. (Orig.). 1983. pap. 2.95 (ISBN 0-87793-270-0). Ave Maria.

Martin. But for the Grace of God.... (Orig.). 1984. pap. 1.00 (ISBN 0-914733-02-8). Desert Min.

CHURCH WORK WITH CHILDREN

see also Church Camps

Forliti, John E. Program Planning for Youth Ministry. LC 75-143. 1975. pap. 4.50 (ISBN 0-88489-061-9). St Marys.

Heusser, D-B & Heusser, Phyllis. Children As Partners in the Church. LC 85-9934. 64p. 1985. pap. 3.95 (ISBN 0-8170-1054-8). Judson.

I Believe in God. 52p. 1975. 3.60 (ISBN 0-686-29267-7). Natl Cath Educ.

Isham, Linda. On Behalf of Children. LC 74-17842. 48p. (Orig.). 1975. pap. 1.95 (ISBN 0-8170-0666-4). Judson.

Lang, June & Carl, Angela. Twenty-Six Children's Church Programs: Getting to Know Jesus. (Illus.). 112p. 1983. pap. 7.95 (ISBN 0-87239-608-8, 3378). Standard Pub.

Lester, Andrew D. Pastoral Care with Children in Crisis. LC 84-21901. 144p. (Orig.). 1985. pap. 9.95 (ISBN 0-664-24598-6). Westminster.

Lindner, Eileen W., et al. When Churches Mind the Children: A Study of Day Care in Local Parishes. LC 83-22545. 192p. (Orig.). 1983. pap. 10.00 (ISBN 0-931114-23-3). High-Scope.

O'Neal, Debbie. Handbook for Church Nurseries. 32p. (Orig.). 1985. pap. 2.95 (ISBN 0-8066-2174-5, 10-2944). Augsburg.

Pearson, Mary R., ed. Fifty-Two Children's Programs. 224p. (Orig.). 1985. pap. 14.95 (ISBN 0-89636-189-6). Accent Bks.

Quinley, Ernest & Quinley, Rachel. Let's Have Church, Children, No. 2. 1981. pap. 7.95 (ISBN 0-87148-513-3). Pathway Pr.

Sewell, Jesse P. & Speck, Henry E., eds. The Church & the Children. 1935. 1.50 (ISBN 0-88027-104-3). Firm Foun Pub.

Sundquist, Ralph R., Jr. Whom God Chooses: The Child in the Church. rev. ed. 94p. 1973. pap. 1.65 (ISBN 0-664-71004-2, Pub. by Geneva Pr). Westminster.

Wight, Maxine C. A Story About Light. LC 79-14691. 1979. 1.99 (ISBN 0-8309-0236-8). Herald Hse.

CHURCH WORK WITH CRIMINALS

see also Church Work with Juvenile Delinquents

Singer, Phillip B. In Prison You Came to Me. (Looking Up Ser.). 24p. (Orig.). 1984. pap. 1.25 (ISBN 0-8298-0473-0). Pilgrim NY.

Umphrey, Don. The Meanest Man in Texas. LC 84-3383. 288p. 1984. pap. 6.95 (ISBN 0-8407-5870-7). Nelson.

Wallace, Tay. Prison Ministry Training Manual. (Illus.). 44p. (Orig.). 1981. pap. 3.00 (ISBN 0-933643-08-X). Grace World Outreach.

CHURCH WORK WITH DIVORCED PEOPLE

Richards, Sue & Hagemeyer, Stanley. Ministry to the Divorced: Guidance, Structure & Organization That Promote Healing in the Church. 112p. 1986. text ed. 6.95 (ISBN 0-310-20051-2, 9604P). Zondervan.

CHURCH WORK WITH EXCEPTIONAL CHILDREN

Schuster, Clara S., ed. Jesus Loves Me, Too. 160p. (Orig.). 1985. pap. 6.95 (ISBN 0-8341-1074-1). Beacon Hill.

CHURCH WORK WITH FAMILIES

Durka, Gloria & Smith, Joanmarie. Family Ministry. 216p. (Orig.). 1980. pap. 7.95 (ISBN 0-86683-762-0, HarpR). Har-Row.

Guernsey, Dennis B. A New Design for Family Ministry. LC 82-72793. 126p. 1982. pap. 6.95 (ISBN 0-89191-650-4). Cook.

Hinkle, Joseph & Cook, Melva. How to Minister to Families in Your Church. LC 77-82925. 1978. 8.50 (ISBN 0-8054-3224-8). Broadman.

Leonard, Joe, Jr., ed. Church Family Gatherings. 1978. pap. 6.95 (ISBN 0-8170-0809-8). Judson.

Middlebrook, J. D. & Summers, Larry. The Church & Family. LC 80-66326. 128p. 1980. pap. 1.95 (ISBN 0-88243-482-9, 02-0482). Gospel Pub.

Money, Royce. Ministering to Families. 300p. 1987. pap. 10.95 (ISBN 0-915547-92-9). Abilene Christ U.

Monkers, Peter R. Ministry with the Divorced. 128p. 1985. pap. text ed. 7.95 (ISBN 0-8298-0566-4). Pilgrim NY.

Rickerson, Wayne. Newly Married. (Family Ministry Ser.). 96p. 1986. pap. 19.95 (ISBN 0-89191-967-8). Cook.

--Strengthening the Family. 128p. 1987. pap. 5.95 (ISBN 0-87403-206-7, 3186). Standard Pub.

Saxton, et al, eds. The Changing Family: Views from Theology & Social Sciences in the Light of the Aspostolic Exhortation "Familiaris Consortio". 224p. 1984. 12.95 (ISBN 0-8294-0458-9). Loyola.

Schervish, Paul, et al. Families, the Economy & the Church: A Book of Readings & Discussion Guide. Brigham, Frederick & Preister, Steven, eds. 144p. (Orig.). 1987. pap. 5.95 (ISBN 1-55586-136-9). US Catholic.

Wilson, Earl D. Empty Nest: Life after the Kids Leave Home. (Family Ministry Ser.). 96p. 1986. pap. 19.95 (ISBN 0-89191-969-4). Cook.

CHURCH WORK WITH JUVENILE DELINQUENTS

Wilkerson, David, et al. Cross & the Switchblade. 160p. pap. 2.95 (ISBN 0-8007-8009-4, Spire Bks). Revell.

CHURCH WORK WITH MIGRANT LABOR

National Conference of Catholic Bishops Staff. Together, a New People: Pastoral Statement on Migrants & Refugees. 40p. (Orig.). 1987. pap. 3.95 (ISBN 1-55586-147-4). US Catholic.

CHURCH WORK WITH MINORITIES

The Hispanic Presence: Challenge & Commitment. 73p. 1983. pap. 2.25 (ISBN 1-55586-891-6). US Catholic.

CHURCH WORK WITH REFUGEES

Fein, Helen. Congregational Sponsorship of Indochinese Refugees in the United States, 1979-1981: Helping Beyond Borders: A Study of Collective Altruism. LC 85-45952. 168p. 1987. 26.50x (ISBN 0-8386-3279-3). Fairleigh Dickinson.

CHURCH WORK WITH SINGLE PEOPLE

Bontrager, Frances. Church & the Single Person. (Family Life Ser). 32p. (Orig.). 1969. pap. 1.00 (ISBN 0-8361-1575-9). Herald Pr.

Cahill, Linda, et al. Successful Single Adult Ministry. 144p. 1987. pap. price not set (ISBN 0-87403-229-6, 3219). Standard Pub.

Claussen, Russell, ed. The Church's Growing Edge: Single Adults. 1981. pap. 4.95 (ISBN 0-8298-0429-3). Pilgrim NY.

Craig, Floyd. How to Communicate with Single Adults. 1978. pap. 11.95 (ISBN 0-8054-3510-7). Broadman.

Crawford, Dan R. Single Adults: Resource & Recipients for Revival. LC 85-7889. 1985. pap. 5.95 (ISBN 0-8054-3236-1). Broadman.

Hertzler, Lois S. Prayers for the Newly Single. 32p. 1981. pap. 1.95 (ISBN 0-8170-0914-0). Judson.

Johnson, Douglas W. The Challenge of Single Adult Ministry. 112p. 1982. pap. 5.95 (ISBN 0-8170-0939-6). Judson.

Meredith, Don. Who Says Get Married? How to Be Happy & Single. LC 81-16949. 176p. 1981. pap. 4.95 (ISBN 0-8407-5741-7). Nelson.

Planning for Single Young Adult Ministry: Directions for Ministerial Outreach. 65p. 1981. pap. 4.95 (ISBN 1-55586-738-3). US Catholic.

Van Note, Gene. Ministering to Single Adults. 109p. 1978. pap. 2.95 (ISBN 0-8341-0556-X). Beacon Hill.

Wood, Britton. Single Adults Want to Be the Church, Too. LC 77-78411. 1977. 9.50 (ISBN 0-8054-3221-3). Broadman.

CHURCH WORK WITH STUDENTS

Evans, John Whitney. The Newman Movement. 264p. 1980. 16.95 (ISBN 0-268-01453-1). U of Notre Dame Pr.

Foster, Charles R. The Ministry of the Volunteer Teacher. 96p. 1986. pap. 6.95 (ISBN 0-687-27040-5). Abingdon.

Jones, Jeffrey D. & Potts, Kenneth C. Organizing a Youth Ministry to Fit Your Needs. 64p. 1983. pap. 3.95 (ISBN 0-8170-1004-1). Judson.

Le Sourd, Howard M. The University Work of the United Lutheran Church in America: A Study of the Work Among Lutheran Students at Non-Lutheran Institutions. LC 70-176990. (Columbia University. Teachers College. Contributions to Education: No. 377). Repr. of 1929 ed. 17.50 (ISBN 0-404-55377-X). AMS Pr.

National Conference of Catholic Bishops. Empowered by the Spirit: Campus Ministry Faces the Future. 56p. 1986. pap. 2.95 (ISBN 1-55586-981-5). US Catholic.

Plake, David C. & Plake, Roberta S. The Ministry of Teaching. LC 82-81509. (Workers Training Ser.). 128p. (Orig.). 1982. pap. 2.50 (ISBN 0-88243-567-1, 02-0567). Gospel Pub.

Rice, Wayne. Junior High Ministry. 220p. 1987. text ed. 12.95 (ISBN 0-310-34970-2). Zondervan.

Schroeder, Phil, ed. Ministry with the Community College: A Lutheran Perspective. (Illus.). 75p. 1982. pap. text ed. 2.75 (ISBN 0-9609438-0-3). Luth Coun IL.

CHURCH WORK WITH THE AGED

Bauerle, Richard E. I, the Prophet. 1981. pap. 6.95 (ISBN 0-570-03835-9, 12YY2800). Concordia.

Becker, Arthur H. Ministry with Older Persons: A Guide for Clergy & Congregations. LC 86-1101. 228p. (Orig.). 1986. pap. 12.95 (ISBN 0-8066-2196-6, 10-4444). Augsburg.

Clements, William M., ed. Ministry with the Aging: Designs-Challenges-Foundations. LC 80-7739. 1983. pap. 9.95 (ISBN 0-06-061497-8, RD/452, HarpR). Har-Row.

Douglas, J. D. & Van der Maas, E., eds. The New Zondervan Pictorial Bible Dictionary. rev. ed. 1000p. 1987. price not set. Zondervan.

Episcopal Society for Ministry on Aging, compiled by. Affirmative Aging: A Resource for Ministry. 192p. (Orig.). 1986. pap. 8.95 (ISBN 0-86683-786-8, HarpR). Har-Row.

Faber, Heije. Striking Sails: A Pastoral View of Growing Older in Our Society. Mitchell, Kenneth R., tr. 160p. 1984. pap. 10.95 (ISBN 0-687-39941-6). Abingdon.

Hendrickson, Michael C., ed. The Role of the Church in Aging: Implications for Policy & Action. LC 85-17564. (Journal of Religion & Aging: Vol. 2, Nos. 1-2). 178p. 1986. text ed. 29.95 (ISBN 0-86656-482-9, B482); pap. text ed. 19.95 (ISBN 0-86656-483-7, B483). Haworth Pr.

Kerr, Horace L. How to Minister to Senior Adults in Your Church. LC 77-80944. 1980. 8.50 (ISBN 0-8054-3222-1). Broadman.

Lyon, K. Brynolf. Toward a Practical Theology of Aging. LC 85-47720. (Theology & Pastoral Care Ser.). 128p. 1986. pap. 7.95 (ISBN 0-8006-1735-5). Fortress.

McClellan, Robert W. & Usher, Carolyn E. Claiming a Frontier: Ministry & Older People. LC 77-85413. 1977. 10.00x (ISBN 0-88474-040-4, 05741-X). Lexington Bks.

Manser, Nancy. Older People Have Choices: Information for Decisions about Health, Home, & Money. 32p. (Orig.). 1984. pap. 3.95 (ISBN 0-8066-2098-6, 10-4741). Augsburg.

Otte, Elmer & Bergmann, Mark. Engaging the Aging in Ministry. LC 12-2798. 1981. pap. 6.95 (ISBN 0-570-03833-2). Concordia.

Rendahl, J. Stanley. Working with Older Adults. LC 84-80708. (Equipping Ser.). (Illus., Orig.). 1984. pap. 5.95 (ISBN 0-935797-08-4). Harvest IL.

Schenk, Fredrick J. & Anderson, James V. Aging Together, Serving Together: A Guide to Congregational Planning for the Aging. LC 10-185. 40p. (Orig.). 1982. pap. 3.50 (ISBN 0-8066-1963-5, 10-0185). Augsburg.

Taylor, Blaine. The Church's Ministry with Older Adults. 144p. 1987. pap. 10.95 (ISBN 0-687-08382-6). Abingdon.

Tobin, Sheldon S., et al. Enabling the Elderly: Religious Institutions Within the Community Service System. (Aging Ser.). 154p. (Orig.). 1986. 34.50x (ISBN 0-88706-334-9); pap. 10.95x (ISBN 0-88706-335-7). State U NY Pr.

CHURCH WORK WITH THE BEREAVED

see also Funeral Service

Detrich, Richard L. & Steele, Nicola. How to Recover from Grief. 128p. 1983. pap. 7.95 (ISBN 0-8170-0989-2). Judson.

Irion, Paul E. The Funeral: Vestige or Value? Kastenaum, Robert, ed. LC 76-19578. (Death & Dying Ser.). 1977. Repr. lib. bdg. 22.00x (ISBN 0-405-09575-9). Ayer Co Pubs.

Miller, Roger F. What Can I Say? Lambert, Herbert, ed. 96p. (Orig.). 1987. pap. 4.95 (ISBN 0-8272-4220-4). CBP.

Murphey, Cecil. Comforting Those Who Grieve. LC 78-71052. 64p. 1979. pap. 1.00 (ISBN 0-8042-1099-3). John Knox.

Shelley, Bruce L. Christian Theology in Plain Language. 256p. 1985. 12.95 (ISBN 0-8499-0381-5, 0381-5). Word Bks.

Tanner, Ira J. Healing the Pain of Everyday Loss. 188p. 1980. pap. 4.95 (ISBN 0-03-057849-3, HarpR). Har-Row.

Williams, Philip W. When a Loved One Dies. LC 75-22713. 96p. 1976. pap. 5.95 (ISBN 0-8066-1520-6, 10-7056). Augsburg.

CHURCH WORK WITH THE HANDICAPPED

Colston, Lowell G. Pastoral Care with Handicapped Persons. Clinebell, Howard J. & Stone, Howard W., eds. LC 77-15229. (Creative Pastoral Care & Counseling Ser). 96p. (Orig.). 1978. pap. 4.50 (ISBN 0-8006-0560-8, 1-560). Fortress.

Hogan, Griff, ed. The Church & Disabled Persons. 128p. 1983. pap. 8.95 (ISBN 0-87243-123-1). Templegate.

Ikeler, Bernard. Parenting Your Disabled Child. LC 86-9118. 138p. (Orig.). 1986. pap. 8.95 (ISBN 0-664-24044-5). Westminster.

Kern, Walter. Pastoral Ministry with Disabled Persons. LC 84-24619. 248p. 1985. pap. 6.95 (ISBN 0-8189-0472-0). Alba.

Ohsberg, H. Oliver. Church & Persons with Handicaps. LC 82-80342. 128p. 1982. pap. 7.95 (ISBN 0-8361-1996-7). Herald Pr.

Wilke, Harold H. Creating the Caring Congregation: Guidelines for Ministering with the Handicapped. LC 79-28626. (Orig.). 1980. pap. 6.50 (ISBN 0-687-09815-7). Abingdon.

CHURCH WORK WITH THE MENTALLY HANDICAPPED

Oosterveen, Gerald & Cook, Bruce L. Serving Mentally Impaired People. 52p. 1983. pap. 5.95 (ISBN 0-89191-764-0). Cook.

Vanier, Jean. The Challenge of l'Arche. (Illus.). 286p. 1982. pap. 9.95 (ISBN 0-89088-072-7, HarpR). Har-Row.

CHURCH WORK WITH THE MENTALLY ILL

De Blassie, Richard R. & Anderson, John. Helping the Troubled. 179p. 1981. pap. 3.95 (ISBN 0-8189-1163-8). Alba.

Oates, Wayne E. The Religious Care of the Psychiatric Patient. LC 78-18454. 252p. 1978. 13.95 (ISBN 0-664-21365-0). Westminster.

CHURCH WORK WITH THE SICK

see also Pastoral Medicine

Bayley, Robert G. The Healing Ministry of the Local Church. 32p. 1983. 1.95 (ISBN 0-934421-03-X). Presby Renewal Pubns.

Catholic Health Association Staff. The Ministry of Healing: Readings in the Catholic Health Care Ministry. LC 81-12201. 120p. 1981. pap. 7.50 (ISBN 0-686-85771-2). Cath Health.

Douglas, J. D. & Van der Maas, E., eds. The New Zondervan Pictorial Bible Dictionary. rev. ed. 1000p. 1987. price not set. Zondervan.

Elser, Otto, ed. The Ministry of Health & Healing. 1986. pap. 7.50 (ISBN 0-8309-0451-4). Herald Hse.

Faber, Heije. Pastoral Care in the Modern Hospital. De Waal, Hugo, tr. LC 70-168632. 160p. 1972. 10.95 (ISBN 0-664-20922-X). Westminster.

Fichter, Joseph H. Healing Ministries: Conversations on the Spiritual Dimensions of Health Care. 224p. 1986. pap. 9.95 (ISBN 0-8091-2807-1). Paulist Pr.

Freeman, Joanna M. How to Minister in Nursing Homes. 40p. 1983. pap. text ed. 3.95 (ISBN 0-87148-410-2). Pathway Pr.

Granberg-Michaelson, Karin. In the Land of the Living: Health Care & the Church. 1984. pap. 4.95 (ISBN 0-310-27491-5, 6897P). Zondervan.

Holst, Lawrence. Hospital Ministry. 256p. 1987. pap. 10.95 (ISBN 0-8245-0819-X). Crossroad NY.

Lauterbach, William A. Prayers for the Sickroom. 1953. 1.10 (ISBN 0-570-03524-4, 14-1236). Concordia.

McGeehan, Jude J. Ministry to the Sick & Dying. (Synthesis Ser.). 1981. 1.75 (ISBN 0-8199-0836-3). Franciscan Herald.

Niklas, Gerals R. & Stefanics, Charlotte. Ministry to the Sick. LC 82-4083. 143p. (Orig.). 1982. pap. 7.95 (ISBN 0-8189-0429-1). Alba.

Religious Congregations & Health Care Facilities: Commitment & Collaboration. LC 81-18064. 100p. 1982. pap. 6.00 (ISBN 0-87125-073-X). Cath Health.

Shockey, Richard W. Training for Hospital Visitation: A Three-Week Course for Laypersons. LC 86-42930. 40p. (Orig.). 1986. pap. 4.00 (ISBN 0-937021-01-6). Sagamore Bks MI.

Wallace, Tay. Ministering to the Sick. 60p. (Orig.). 1981. pap. 3.00 (ISBN 0-933643-06-3). Grace World Outreach.

CHURCH WORK WITH YOUNG ADULTS

Koteskey, Ronald L. Understanding Adolescence. 168p. 1987. pap. 5.95 (ISBN 0-89693-249-4). Victor Bks.

Planning for Single Young Adult Ministry: Directions for Ministerial Outreach. 65p. 1981. pap. 4.95 (ISBN 1-55586-738-3). US Catholic.

Reed, Bobbie. Single on Sunday: A Manual for Successful Single Adult Ministries. 1979. pap. 5.95 (ISBN 0-570-03781-6, 12-2735). Concordia.

Sewell, Jesse P. & Speck, Henry E., eds. The Church & the Young People. 1935. 1.50 (ISBN 0-88027-105-1). Firm Foun Pub.

Smith, Glenn C. Evangelizing Youth. 352p. (Orig.). 1985. pap. 12.95 (ISBN 0-8423-0791-5). Tyndale.
Warren, Michael. Youth & the Future of the Church: Ministry with Youth & Young Adults. 156p. 1985. pap. 8.95 (ISBN 0-86683-917-8, 7915, Winston-Seabury). Har-Row.
Watson, Stanley J. Youth Ministry in the Church. LC 78-73597. 1978. pap. 2.50 (ISBN 0-8054-3228-0, 4232-28). Broadman.

CHURCH WORK WITH YOUTH

see also Church Camps; Church Work with Juvenile Delinquents; Coffee House Ministry; Young People's Meetings (Church Work)

Ban, Arline J. & Ban, Joseph D. The New Disciple, Leader's Guide. 48p. 1976. pap. 1.50 (ISBN 0-8170-0706-7). Judson.
Barr, Debbie. Caught in the Crossfire. 288p. (Orig.). 1985. pap. 8.95 (ISBN 0-310-28561-5, 12083P). Zondervan.
Benson, Dennis C. Creative Worship in Youth Ministry. LC 85-24735. (Illus.). 249p. (Orig.). 1985. pap. 11.95 (ISBN 0-931529-05-0). Group Bks.
Bimler, Richard. Seventy-Seven Ways of Involving Youth in the Church. (Illus.). 1976. pap. 4.50 (ISBN 0-570-03737-9, 12-2641). Concordia.
Borthwick, Paul. Any Old Time, Bk. 5. 80p. 1986. pap. 6.95 (ISBN 0-89693-187-0). Victor Bks.
Brown, Carolyn C. Youth Ministries: Thinking Big With Small Groups. 96p. 1984. pap. 7.95 (ISBN 0-687-47203-2). Abingdon.
Burns, Jim & Yaconelli, Mike. High School Ministry. 368p. 1986. 16.95 (ISBN 0-310-34920-6, 10826). Zondervan.
Burns, Ridge & Campbell, Pam. Create in Me a Youth Ministry. 204p. 1986. pap. 11.95 (ISBN 0-89693-636-8). Victor Bks.
Carney, Glandion. Creative Urban Youth Ministries. 74p. 1984. pap. 6.95 (ISBN 0-89191-846-9). Cook.
Cavin, Thomas F. Champion of Youth: Daniel A. Lord, S. J. 1977. 6.50 (ISBN 0-8198-0398-7); pap. text ed. 5.00 (ISBN 0-8198-0399-5). Dghtrs St Paul.
Christie, Les. Unsung Heroes: How to Recruit & Train Volunteers. 176p. 1987. text ed. 12.95 (ISBN 0-310-35150-2). Zondervan.
Colkmire, Lance. Reasoning with Juniors for Christs Sake. 1982. pap. 5.95 (ISBN 0-87148-736-5). Pathway Pr.
Dale, Daryl. Youth Worker's Manual. 95p. 1985. pap. write for info. (ISBN 0-87509-350-7). Chr Pubns.
Dausey, Gary. The Youth Leader's Sourcebook. 320p. 1983. 15.95 (ISBN 0-310-29310-3, 11633). Zondervan.
Dieleman, Dale. Our Life & Times. 1985. pap. 5.95 (ISBN 0-8010-2951-1). Baker Bk.
Dieleman, Dale, compiled by. Taking Charge. (Good Things for Youth Leaders Ser.). pap. 3.45 (ISBN 0-8010-2911-2). Baker Bk.
Dockrey, Karen. Getting to Know God: Study Guide. LC 86-8272. (Orig.). 1986. pap. 3.25 (ISBN 0-8054-3240-X). Broadman.
Donaldson, Joseph C., et al. How To Manual for Volunteer Youth Leaders. LC 86-80688. (Equipping Ser.). (Illus.). 136p. (Orig.). 1986. pap. 6.96 (ISBN 0-935797-22-X). Harvest IL.
Doyle, Aileen A. Youth Retreats: Creating Sacred Space for Young People. (Illus.). 107p. 1986. spiral bdg. 12.95 (ISBN 0-88489-177-1). St Mary's.
Duckworth, John, et al, eds. The Battle. (Pacesetter Ser.). 64p. 1987. tchr's. ed. 7.95. Cook.
--The Bible. (Pacesetter Ser.). 64p. 1987. tchr's. ed. 7.95 (ISBN 0-318-21517-9). Cook.
--The Family. (Pacesetter Ser.). 64p. 1987. tchr's. ed. 7.95. Cook.
--Give It Away! (Pacesetter Ser.). 64p. 1987. tchr's. ed. 7.95. Cook.
--Identity Search. (Pacesetter Ser.). 64p. 1987. tchr's. ed. 7.95. Cook.
--Rites of Passage. (Pacesetter Ser.). 64p. 1987. tchr's. ed. 7.95. Cook.
Edwards, Maria. Total Youth Ministry: A Handbook for Parishes. LC 76-29885. 1976. pap. 4.50 (ISBN 0-88489-085-6). St Mary's.
Eitzen, Ruth. Fun to Do All Year Through. 32p. 1982. pap. 2.95 (ISBN 0-8170-0969-8). Judson.
Evans, David M. Shaping the Church's Ministry with Youth. (Orig.). pap. 2.95 (ISBN 0-8170-0342-8). Judson.
Fortunato, Connie. Children's Music Ministry. 222p. 1981. pap. 6.95 (ISBN 0-89191-341-6). Cook.
Gibson, Ruth E. In Search of Young Parents. 120p. (Orig.). 1984. pap. 4.95 (ISBN 0-8341-0911-5). Beacon Hill.
Hancock, Jim, ed. Resource Directory for Youth Workers 1986. rev. ed. 128p. pap. 9.95 (ISBN 0-310-35161-8, 10785P). Zondervan.
Hansen, Cindy S., ed. Group Magazine's Best Youth Group Programs, Vol. 1. LC 86-313. (Illus.). 224p. 1986. 17.95 (ISBN 0-931529-11-5). Group Bks.
Hennig, David, ed. Good Stuff, Vol. 2. 160p. 1986. wkbk. 9.95 (ISBN 0-87403-014-5, 3407). Standard Pub.
Hershey, Terry. Young Adult Ministry. LC 86-3103. 276p. (Orig.). 1986. pap. 12.95 (ISBN 0-931529-08-5). Group Bks.
Irwin, Paul B. The Care & Counseling of Youth in the Church. Clinebell, Howard J. & Stone, Howard W., eds. LC 74-26334. (Creative Pastoral Care & Counseling Ser.). 96p. 1975. pap. 4.50 (ISBN 0-8006-0552-7, 1-552). Fortress.
Jacobson, Lyle. Home & Church: Ministering to Youth. 32p. 1977. pap. 1.50 (ISBN 0-8307-0501-5, 977208). Regal.
Jones, Dale. Youth Ministries Ideas III. 1986. pap. 6.00 (ISBN 0-8309-0470-0). Herald Hse.
Kamstra, Douglas, compiled by. Good Times Game Book: Good Things for Youth Leaders. 1981. pap. 5.95 (ISBN 0-8010-7705-2). Baker Bk.
Keefauver, Larry. Friends & Faith: How to Use Friendship Evangelism In Youth Ministry. LC 86-7577. 156p. (Orig.). 1986. pap. 9.95 (ISBN 0-931529-10-7). Group Bks.
Koffarnus, Richard, et al. Good Stuff, No. 3. (Illus.). 160p. 1986. wkbk. 9.95 (ISBN 0-87403-066-8, 3411). Standard Pub.
Leonard, Larry & McCormick, Jack, eds. Youth Program Hour Idea Book. 156p. 1985. pap. 6.95 (ISBN 0-8341-0949-2). Beacon Hill.
Ludwig, Glenn E. Building an Effective Youth Ministry. LC 79-12282. (Creative Leadership Ser.). 1979. pap. 6.95 (ISBN 0-687-03992-4). Abingdon.
McCane, Bryon R. & VanLoon, Preston C. Building a Faith to Live By: Programs for Youth (Foundation for Discipleship) 128p. 1987. pap. 9.95 (ISBN 0-8170-1107-2). Judson.
Madsen, Erik C. Youth Ministry & Wilderness Camping. 160p. 1982. pap. 7.95 (ISBN 0-8170-0962-0). Judson.
Markell, David. Expanded Ministry to Youth: Program Guidelines. (C. E. Ministries Ser.). 1977. pap. 3.50 (ISBN 0-89367-021-9). Light & Life.
Meier, Paul D. & Burnett, Linda. Unwanted Generation. 1981. 7.95 (ISBN 0-8010-6101-6). Baker Bk.
Ng, David. Youth in the Community of Disciples. 80p. 1984. pap. 3.95 (ISBN 0-8170-1015-7). Judson.
Noon, Scott. Building a Fort in the Family Tree. 1984. 3.50 (ISBN 0-89536-703-3, 4884). CSS of Ohio.
Nordyke, Spencer & Nordyke, Cyndy. Essentials of Basic Youth Ministry. 49p. (Orig.). 1984. wkbk. 4.95 (ISBN 0-914307-21-5). Word Faith.
O'Hara, Jim & Walle, Grace. Collage; A Resource Book for Christian Youth Groups. 86p. (Orig.). 1976. pap. 4.00 (ISBN 0-9608124-5-8). Marianist Com Ctr.
Oldham, Bruce, ed. Footprints: Following Jesus for Junior Highers. 170p. (Orig.). 1983. pap. 4.50 (ISBN 0-8341-0863-1). Beacon Hill.
Pearson, Darrell. Parents As Partners in Youth Ministry. 64p. 1985. 5.95 (ISBN 0-89693-322-9). Victor Bks.
Peters, Dan, et al. Rock's Hidden Persuader: The Truth about Back Masking. 128p. 1985. pap. 3.95 (ISBN 0-87123-857-8, 200857). Bethany Hse.
Pollock, Shirley. Building Teen Excitement: A Youth Worker's Guide. LC 85-11256. 80p. (Orig.). 1985. pap. 8.95 (ISBN 0-687-03993-2). Abingdon.
Rice, Wayne. Great Ideas for Small Youth Groups. 256p. (Orig.). 1985. pap. 7.95 (ISBN 0-310-34891-9, 10823P). Zondervan.
--Junior High Ministry. 220p. 1987. text ed. 12.95 (ISBN 0-310-34970-2). Zondervan.
--The Youth Specialties Clip Art Book. 240p. (Orig.). 1985. pap. 14.95 (ISBN 0-310-34911-7, 10824P). Zondervan.
Rice, Wayne & Yaconelli, Mike. Far Out Ideas for Young Groups. 96p. 1975. pap. 6.95 (ISBN 0-310-34941-9, 10797P). Zondervan.
--Incredible Ideas for Youth Groups. 160p. (Orig.). 1982. pap. 7.95 (ISBN 0-310-45231-7, 11370P). Zondervan.
--Play It: Team Games for Groups. 256p. 1986. pap. 10.95 (ISBN 0-310-35191-X, 10799). Zondervan.
Rice, Wayne, ed. Ideas, 39 vols. (Ideas Library). (Illus.). 52p. (Orig.). pap. 7.95 ea.; Set. pap. 140.00 (ISBN 0-910125-00-7); index o.p. 6.95 (ISBN 0-910125-01-5). Youth Special.
Richie, David S. Memories & Meditations of a Workcamper. LC 73-84213. 36p. (Orig.). 1973. pap. 2.50x (ISBN 0-87574-190-8, 189). Pendle Hill.
Roberto, John, ed. Creative Communication & Community Building. LC 81-83635. (Creative Resources for Youth Ministry Ser.: Vol. 1). (Illus.). 108p. (Orig.). 1981. pap. 8.95 (ISBN 0-88489-135-6). St Mary's.
--Creative Learning Experiences. LC 81-83636. (Creative Resources for Youth Ministry Ser.: Vol. 2). (Illus.). 144p. (Orig.). 1981. pap. 8.95 (ISBN 0-88489-136-4). St Mary's.
--Creative Projects & Worship Experiences. LC 81-86367. (Creative Resources for Youth Ministry Ser.: Vol. 3). (Illus.). 80p. (Orig.). 1981. pap. 8.95 (ISBN 0-88489-137-2). St Mary's.
Rydberg, Denny. Building Community in Youth Groups. LC 85-17645. (Illus.). 177p. (Orig.). 1985. pap. 11.95 (ISBN 0-931529-06-9). Group Bks.
St. Clair, Barry. Joy Explosion. 128p. 1986. pap. 9.95 (ISBN 0-88207-306-0). Victor Bks.
Sawyer, Kieran. The Jesus Difference: And Other Youth Ministry Activities. LC 86-72571. 168p. (Orig.). 1987. spiral binding 8.95 (ISBN 0-87793-353-7). Ave Maria.
Schultz, Joani, et al. Youth Ministry Cargo. LC 86-14836. (Illus.). 410p. (Orig.). 1986. 18.95 (ISBN 0-931529-14-X). Group Bks.
Schultz, Thom & Schultz, Joani. Involving Youth in Youth Ministry. 200p. (Orig.). 1987. pap. 9.95 (ISBN 0-931529-20-4). Group Bks.
Shellenberger, Susie. There's Sheep in My Mirror. 108p. 1985. pap. 4.50 (ISBN 0-8341-1054-7). Beacon Hill.
Sparks, Lee, ed. The Youth Worker's Personal Management Handbook. LC 84-73152. 264p. 1985. 16.95 (ISBN 0-931529-03-4). Group Bks.
Stevens, Douglas. Called to Care. (YA) 1985. 12.95 (ISBN 0-310-28461-9, 11366, Pub. by Youth Spec). Zondervan.
Stewart, Ed, ed. Outreach to Youth. 1978. pap. 1.50 (ISBN 0-8307-0503-1, 9770402). Regal.
Stone, J. David. Spiritual Growth in Youth Ministry. LC 85-12623. 213p. 1985. 12.95 (ISBN 0-931529-04-2). Group Bks.
Stone, J. David, ed. The Complete Youth Ministries Handbook, Vol. 1. 256p. (Orig.). 1980. pap. 14.95 (ISBN 0-687-09340-6). Abingdon.
Underwood, Jon & Roadcup, David, eds. Methods for Youth Ministry. 272p. 1986. pap. 7.95 (ISBN 0-87239-991-5, 88589). Standard Pub.
Veerman, David R. Any Old Time, Bk. 6. 1986. pap. 6.95 (ISBN 0-89693-510-8). Victor Bks.
--Any Old Times, Bk. 1. 80p. 1984. pap. 6.95 (ISBN 0-88207-595-0). Victor Bks.
Warren, Michael. Youth & the Future of the Church: Ministry with Youth & Young Adults. 160p. 1982. 10.95 (ISBN 0-8164-0513-1, HarpR). Har-Row.
--Youth & the Future of the Church: Ministry with Youth & Young Adults. 156p. 1985. pap. 8.95 (ISBN 0-86683-917-8, 7915, Winston-Seabury). Har-Row.
Warrick, Keith, et al. Catholic High School Ministry. (Illus.). 224p. 1986. loose-leaf bdg. 34.95 (ISBN 0-88489-173-9). St Mary's.
Wensing, Michael G. Ministering to Youth: A Guide for Parents, Teachers & Youth Workers. 120p. (Orig.). 1982. pap. 4.95 (ISBN 0-8189-0444-5). Alba.
Yaconelli, Mike & Rice, Wayne. Creative Socials & Specials Events. 192p. 1986. pap. 7.95 (ISBN 0-310-35131-6, 10827P). Zondervan.
Youth Ministry Ideabook. 1986. 5.95 (ISBN 0-89536-797-1, 6815). CSS of Ohio.

CHURCH YEAR

see also Christmas; Church Calendar; Easter; Fasts and Feasts; Good Friday; Holy Week; Lent; Pentecost Festival

Adam, Adolf. The Liturgical Year: Its History & Its Meaning after the Reform of the Liturgy. O'Connell, Matthew J., tr. from Ger. 1981. pap. 16.60 (ISBN 0-916134-47-4). Pueblo Pub Co.
Alexander, Charles. Church's Year. (Illus.). 1950. 3.00x (ISBN 0-19-273007-X). Oxford U Pr.
Bradner, John. Symbols of Church Seasons & Days. (Illus.). 1977. pap. 6.95 (ISBN 0-8192-1228-8). Morehouse.
Brewster, Harold P. Saints & Festivals of the Christian Church. LC 73-159869. (Illus.). xiv, 558p. 1975. Repr. of 1904 ed. 48.00x (ISBN 0-8103-3992-7). Gale.
Brueggemann, Walter. Advent-Christmas: Series B. LC 84-6020. (Proclamation 3: Aids for Interpreting the Lessons of the Church Year Ser.). 64p. 1984. pap. 3.75 (ISBN 0-8006-4101-9). Fortress.
Buckland, Patricia B. Advent to Pentecost-A History of the Church Year. 1979. pap. 4.95 (ISBN 0-8192-1251-2). Morehouse.
Deems, Edward M., ed. Holy-Days & Holidays: A Treasury of Historical Material, Sermons in Full & in Brief, Suggestive Thoughts & Poetry, Relating to Holy Days & Holidays. LC 68-17940. 1968. Repr. of 1902 ed. 65.00x (ISBN 0-8103-3352-X). Gale.
Gwynne, Walker. The Christian Year; Its Purpose & Its History. LC 74-89269. xiv, 143p. 1972. Repr. of 1917 ed. 43.00x (ISBN 0-8103-3814-9). Gale.
Heline, Corinne. Star Gates. 7.95 (ISBN 0-933963-09-2). New Age.
Hessel, Dieter T., ed. Social Themes of the Christian Year: A Commentary on the Lectionary. LC 83-1504. 284p. (Orig.). 1983. pap. 10.95 (ISBN 0-664-24472-6, A Geneva Press Publication). Westminster.
Hickman, Hoyt L., et al, eds. Handbook of the Christian Year. 304p. (Orig.). 1986. pap. 16.95 (ISBN 0-687-16575-X). Abingdon.
Isaac Of Stella. Isaac of Stella: Sermons on the Christian Year, Vol. 1. McCaffrey, Hugh, tr. LC 78-868. (Cistercian Fathers Ser.: No. 11). 1979. 15.95 (ISBN 0-87907-611-9). Cistercian Pubns.
Keble, John. Concordance to the Christian Year. 1871. 28.00 (ISBN 0-384-28985-1). Johnson Repr.
Keck, Leander E. & Hobbie, Francis W. Pentecost One. LC 79-7377. (Proclamation 2: Aids for Interpreting the Lessons of the Church Year, Series B). 64p. 1982. pap. 3.75 (ISBN 0-8006-4089-6, 1-4089). Fortress.
Motte, Ganzague. Homilies for Sundays of the Year: Cycle A. 1974. 7.50 (ISBN 0-8199-0535-6). Franciscan Herald.
Murphy, Arlene W. The Liturgical Year in Puzzles. 1982. 9.95 (Pub. by Pflaum Pr). Peter Li.
Talley, Thomas J. Origins of the Liturgical Year. 300p. (Orig.). 1986. pap. 17.50 (ISBN 0-916134-75-X). Pueblo Pub Co.

CHURCH YEAR–MEDITATIONS

Doty, William L. One Season Following Another: A Cycle of Faith. LC 68-54394. 141p. 1968. 4.50 (ISBN 0-8199-0152-0, L38573). Franciscan Herald.
Dubay, Thomas. Dawn of a Consecration. 1964. 4.00 (ISBN 0-8198-0034-1). Dghtrs St Paul.
Goossens, Mathias, ed. With the Church. 6.95 (ISBN 0-8199-0148-2, L39000). Franciscan Herald.
Keble, John. The Christian Year: Thoughts in Verse for the Sundays & Holidays Throughout the Year. LC 70-167019. (Illus.). 291p. 1975. Repr. of 1896 ed. 43.00x (ISBN 0-8103-4095-X). Gale.
L'Engle, Madeleine. The Irrational Season. (The Crosswicks Journal Trilogy). 224p. 1977. 12.95 (ISBN 0-8164-0324-4, HarpR); pap. 7.95 (ISBN 0-8164-2261-3); Three Volume Set 19.95 (ISBN 0-8164-2617-1). Har-Row.
--The Irrational Season. 430p. 1985. pap. 13.95 large print ed. (ISBN 0-8027-2476-0). Walker & Co.

CHURCH YEAR SERMONS

Fichtner, Joseph. Proclaim His Word: Homiletic Themes for Sundays & Holy Days - Cycle C, Vol. 1. new ed. LC 73-5726. 238p. (Orig.). 1973. pap. 3.95 (ISBN 0-8189-0274-4). Alba.

CHURCHES

see also Baptisteries; Cathedrals; Chapels; Christian Patron Saints; Church Architecture; Church Decoration and Ornament; City Churches; Parish Houses; Parishes
also names of individual churches; subdivision Churches under names of cities

Adams, Jennifer A. The Solar Church. Hoffman, Douglas R., ed. LC 82-11281. 288p. (Orig.). 1982. pap. 9.95 (ISBN 0-8298-0482-X). Pilgrim NY.
Addyman, Peter & Morris, Richard, eds. The Archaeological Study of Churches. LC 77-365546. (Council for British Archaeology Research Report Ser.: No. 13). (Illus.). pap. 24.00 (ISBN 0-317-09531-5, 2014021). Bks Demand UMI.
Clowney, Paul & Clowney, Tessa. Exploring Churches. LC 82-210857. pap. 23.50 (ISBN 0-317-30134-9, 2025317). Bks Demand UMI.
Dimier. Recueil de Plans d'Eglises Cisterciennes, 2 tomes. Set. 100.75 (ISBN 0-685-34012-0). French & Eur.
Dudley, Carl S. Making the Small Church Effective. LC 78-2221. 1983. pap. 7.95 (ISBN 0-687-23044-6). Abingdon.
Durantis, Gulielmus. The Symbolism of Churches & Church Ornaments. 1980. lib. bdg. 64.95 (ISBN 0-8490-3166-4). Gordon Pr.
Hardy, Paul E. & Bishop of Exeter. A Guide to the Preservation of Medieval Cathedrals & Churches. LC 82-14257. (Illus.). 160p. 1983. pap. text ed. 16.95 (ISBN 0-582-30514-4, Construction Press). Longman.
Harries, John. Discovering Churches. (Discovering Ser.: No. 137). 1984. pap. 4.50 (ISBN 0-85263-471-4, Pub. by Shire Pubns England). Seven Hills Bks.
Jaberg, Gene & Wargo, Louis G., Jr. The Video Pencil: Cable Communications for Church & Community. LC 80-7951. 156p. 1980. lib. bdg. 24.00 (ISBN 0-8191-1085-X); pap. text ed. 9.75 (ISBN 0-8191-1086-8). U Pr of Amer.
Johnston, Jon & Sullivan, Bill M., eds. The Smaller Church in a Super Church Era. 152p. 1983. pap. 5.95 (ISBN 0-8341-0895-X). Beacon Hill.
Jones, Ezra E. Strategies for New Churches. LC 75-36731. 1979. pap. 7.95 (ISBN 0-06-064184-3, RD 276, HarpR). Har-Row.

Kidd, Beresford J. The Churches of Eastern Christendom from Four Hundred Fifty-One A.D. to the Present Time, 2 vols. 1980. Set. lib. bdg. 195.00 (ISBN 0-8490-3196-6). Gordon Pr.

Kightly, Charles. A Traveller's Guide to Places of Worship. 1986. 14.95 (ISBN 0-918678-18-8). Historical Times.

Lehman, James H. Thank God for New Churches! Church Planting: Source of New Life. 108p. (Orig.). 1984. pap. 6.95 (ISBN 0-87178-840-3). Brethren.

McBride, Esther B. Open Church: History of an Idea. LC 83-91256. (Illus.). 112p. 1983. pap. 10.50 (ISBN 0-9613017-0-8). Esther McBride.

Mirsky, Jeannette. Houses of God. LC 76-1536. 1976. pap. 25.00x (ISBN 0-226-53184-8, P690, Phoen). U of Chicago Pr.

Mitchell, Robert B. Heritage & Horizons: A History of the Open Bible Standard Churches. LC 81-18884. (Illus., Orig.). 1982. 6.95 (ISBN 0-9608160-0-3); pap. 4.95 (ISBN 0-9608160-1-1). Open Bible.

Norton, Charles E. Historical Studies of Church-Building in the Middle Ages: Venice, Siena, Florence. LC 78-15869. 1978. Repr. of 1880 ed. lib. bdg. 35.00 (ISBN 0-89341-361-5). Longwood Pub Group.

Randall, Robert L. Pastors & Parishes. LC 86-27176. 184p. 1987. text ed. 29.95 (ISBN 0-89885-348-6). Human Sci Pr.

Redford, F. J. Planting New Churches. LC 78-55694. 1979. 8.50 (ISBN 0-8054-6314-3). Broadman.

Robinson, Robert. Ecclesiastical Researches. 1984. Repr. of 1792 ed. 37.00 (ISBN 0-317-11349-6). Church History.

The Seven Churches. 36p. (Orig.). pap. 0.95 (ISBN 0-937408-20-4). GMI Pubns Inc.

Simpson, A. B. Spirit Filled Church in Action. 112p. 1975. 2.00 (ISBN 0-87509-037-0). Chr Pubns.

Smith, Roland A. Before You Build Your Church. LC 76-73134. 1979. pap. 2.50 (ISBN 0-8054-3511-5). Broadman.

Vaughan, John N. The Large Church. 1985. pap. 7.95 (ISBN 0-8010-9298-1). Baker Bk.

--The World's Twenty Largest Churches. 1984. pap. 12.95 (ISBN 0-8010-9297-3). Baker Bk.

Williams, John. Living Churches: A Reconsideration of Their Basis of Life & Leadership. 144p. 1975. pap. 4.95 (ISBN 0-85364-122-6). Attic Pr.

CHURCHES–LIBRARIES
see Libraries, Church

CHURCHES–MANAGEMENT
see Church Management

CHURCHES–STATISTICAL METHODS
see Church Statistics

CHURCHES–AFRICA

Taylor, John V. The Growth of the Church in Buganda: An Attempt at Understanding. LC 78-26702. (Illus.). 1979. Repr. of 1958 ed. lib. bdg. 24.75x (ISBN 0-313-20802-6, TAGC). Greenwood.

West, Martin. Bishops & Prophets in a Black City: African Independent Churches in Soweto, Johannesburg. 1977. text ed. 16.50x (ISBN 0-8426-1590-3). Verry.

CHURCHES–ASIA

Forman, Charles W. The Island Churches of the South Pacific: Emergence in the Twentieth Century. LC 81-18666. 304p. (Orig.). 1982. pap. 17.50 (ISBN 0-88344-218-3). Orbis Bks.

Hinton, Keith. Growing Churches: Singapore Style. 1985. pap. 4.95 (ISBN 9971-972-24-7). OMF Bks.

The Laodecian Church. 28p. (Orig.). 1982. pap. 0.95 (ISBN 0-937408-17-4). GMI Pubns Inc.

CHURCHES–EUROPE

Cross, Samuel H. Mediaeval Russian Churches. 1949. 10.00x (ISBN 0-910956-27-8). Medieval Acad.

Dictionnaire des Eglises de France, 5 tomes. Incl. Tome I. Histoire Generale des Eglises de France; Tome II. Region Centre et Sud-Est; Tome III. Region Sud-Ouest; Tome IV. Region ouest de Paris, Paris et ses environs, Bretagne, Normandie; Tome V. Nord, Est, Belgique, Luxembourg, Suisse. 91.95 ea. French & Eur.

Elizondo, Virgil & Greinacher, Norbert, eds. Religion & Churches in Eastern Europe. (Concilium Ser.: Vol. 154). 128p. (Orig.). 1982. pap. 6.95 (ISBN 0-8164-2385-7, HarpR). Har-Row.

Florisoone, Michel. Dictionnaire des Cathedrales de France. (Fr.). 256p. 1971. pap. 6.95 (ISBN 0-686-56834-6, M-6612). French & Eur.

Heiligenkreuz. Austria (Cistercian Abbey) Urkunden Des Cistercienser-Stiftes Heiligenkreuz Im Wiener Walde, 2 vols. 1856-1859. Vol. 11. pap. 23.00 (ISBN 0-384-22083-5); Vol. 16. pap. 62.00 (ISBN 0-685-27596-5). Johnson Repr.

CHURCHES–GREAT BRITAIN

Addison, William. Local Styles of the English Parish Church. (Illus.). 192p. 1982. text ed. 35.00x (ISBN 0-8419-6401-7). Holmes & Meier.

Addy, Sidney O. Church & Manor: A Study in English Economic History. LC 70-107902. (Illus.). 1970. Repr. of 1913 ed. 37.50x (ISBN 0-678-00632-6). Kelley.

Andrews, William, ed. Antiquities & Curiosities of the Church: Folklore & Historical Traditions About English Churches. LC 77-87673. Repr. of 1897 ed. 20.00 (ISBN 0-404-16465-X). AMS Pr.

Betjeman, John. American's Guide to English Parish Churches. (Illus.). 1959. 20.00 (ISBN 0-8392-1004-3). Astor-Honor.

Bill, E. G., compiled by. The Queen Anne Churches: A Catalogue of the Papers in Lambeth Palace Library of the Commission for Building Fifty New Churches in London & Westminster, 1711-1759. 280p. 1979. 53.00x (ISBN 0-7201-0919-1). Mansell.

Bonney, T. G., et al. Abbeys & Churches of England & Wales. LC 77-23529. 1977. Repr. of 1890 ed. lib. bdg. 40.00 (ISBN 0-89341-203-1). Longwood Pub Group.

Bottomley, Frank. The Church Explorer's Guide to England, Scotland, & Wales. 1978. pap. 4.95 (ISBN 0-7182-1187-1, Pub. by Kaye & Ward). David & Charles.

Brabbs, Derry. English Country Churches. 160p. 1985. 25.00 (ISBN 0-670-80736-2). Viking.

Chatfield, Mark. Churches the Victorians Forgot. (Illus.). 1979. 15.00 (ISBN 0-903485-76-1, Pub. by Moorland Pub Co England). Eastview.

Clarke, Basil. The Building of the Eighteenth Century Church. LC 66-37309. (Illus.). 1963. text ed. 20.00x (ISBN 0-8401-0404-9). A R Allenson.

Foster, Richard. Discovering English Churches: A Beginner's Guide to the Story of the Parish Church from Before the Conquest to the Gothic Revival. (Illus.). 1982. 30.00x (ISBN 0-19-520366-6). Oxford U Pr.

Hubbuck, Rodney. Portsea Island Churches. 1969. 39.00x (ISBN 0-317-43678-3, Pub. by City of Portsmouth). State Mutual Bk.

Knowles, David & Hadcock, R. Neville. Medieval Religious Houses, England & Wales. LC 72-181783. pap. 147.00 (ISBN 0-317-08419-4, 2016312). Bks Demand UMI.

Littlehales, H., ed. St. Mary at Hill Church: The Medieval Records of a London City Church A.D. 1420-1559, Pts. 1 & 2. (EETS, OS Ser.: Nos. 125, 128). Repr. of 1905 ed. Set. 77.00 (ISBN 0-527-00121-X). Kraus Repr.

London. St. Bartholomew's Priory. The Book of the Foundation of St. Bartholomew's Church in London. (EETS, OS Ser.: No. 163). 1923. pap. 12.00 (ISBN 0-527-00160-0). Kraus Repr.

Magilton, J. R. The Church of St. Helen on the Walls, Aldwark, York. (Archaeology of York Ser.: Vol. 10). 64p. 1980. pap. text ed. 15.00x (ISBN 0-900312-98-X, Pub. by Coun Brit Archaeology). Humanities.

Pevsner, Nikolaus & Metcalf, Priscilla. The Cathedrals of England: Midland, Eastern & Northern England, Vol. 2. 400p. 1985. 40.00 (ISBN 0-670-80125-9). Viking.

--The Cathedrals of England: Southern England, Vol. 1. 384p. 1985. 40.00 (ISBN 0-670-80124-0). Viking.

Platt, Colin. Parish Churches of Medieval England. 1981. 34.95 (ISBN 0-436-37553-2, Pub. by Secker & Warburg UK); pap. 16.95 (ISBN 0-436-37554-0, Pub. by Secker & Warburg UK). David & Charles.

Randall, Gerald. Church Furnishing & Decoration in England & Wales. LC 80-11125. (Illus.). 240p. 1980. text ed. 42.50x (ISBN 0-8419-0602-5). Holmes & Meier.

Soden, R. W. A Guide to Welsh Parish Churches. 149p. 1985. 40.50x (ISBN 0-86383-082-X, Pub. by Gomer Pr). State Mutual Bk.

Thomas, Peggy. Redland Park Recorded. 240p. 1986. pap. 30.00x (ISBN 0-947939-03-2, Pub. by Elmcrest Uk). State Mutual Bk.

Walters, Henry B. London Churches at the Reformation: With an Account of Their Contents. (Church Historical Society London N. S. Ser.: No. 37). Repr. of 1939 ed. 95.00 (ISBN 0-8115-3160-0). Kraus Repr.

Young, Elizabeth & Young, Wayland. London's Churches: A Visitor's Companion. (Illus.). 252p. (Orig.). 1986. pap. 14.95 (ISBN 0-88162-212-5). Salem Hse Pubs.

CHURCHES–ITALY

Blunt, Anthony. Guide to Baroque Rome. LC 82-47546. (Icon Editions). (Illus.). 256p. 1982. 34.50i (ISBN 0-06-430395-0, HarpT). Har-Row.

Brewyn, William. A Fifteenth Century Guidebook to the Principal Churches of Rome. Woodruff, C. Eveleigh, tr. LC 78-63451. (The Crusades & Military Orders: Second Ser.). Repr. of 1933 ed. 17.00 (ISBN 0-404-16374-2). AMS Pr.

CHURCHES–PALESTINE

Crowfoot, J. W. Early Churches in Palestine. (British Academy, London, Schweich Lectures on Biblical Archaeology Series, 1937). pap. 28.00 (ISBN 0-8115-1279-7). Kraus Repr.

Mader, Andreas E. Altchristliche Basiliken und Lokaltraditionen in Sudjudaa. pap. 19.00 (ISBN 0-384-35000-3). Johnson Repr.

CHURCHES–PORTUGAL

De Azevedo, Carlos. Churches of Portugal. LC 85-50365. (Illus.). 196p. 1985. 35.00 (ISBN 0-935748-66-0). Scala Books.

CHURCHES–ROMANIA

Fletcher, John. The Painted Churches of Romania: A Visitor's Impressions. (Illus.). 52p. 1971. 22.95 (ISBN 0-88010-062-1, Pub. by Steinerbooks). Anthroposophic.

CHURCHES–UNITED STATES

Backman, Milton V., Jr. Christian Churches of America. rev. ed. 288p. 1984. 17.95 (ISBN 0-684-17992-X, P656, ScribT); pap. 12.95 (ISBN 0-684-17995-4). Scribner.

Broadus, Boyce. History of First Baptist Church Russellville. 1967. 10.00 (ISBN 0-317-13830-8); pap. 7.00. Banner Pr AL.

Chase, Elizabeth, ed. Pioneer Churches of Florida. LC 77-72276. (Illus.). 74p. 1977. pap. 6.00 (ISBN 0-913122-11-4). Mickler Hse.

Davis, Vernon P. & Rawlings, James S. The Colonial Churches of Virginia, Maryland, & North Carolina. 1985. pap. 25.00 (ISBN 0-87517-057-9). Dietz.

Espenschied, Steven. Historical Review: St. Paul's Family Parish, North Canton, Ohio, Pt. II. LC 85-29277. 240p. (Orig.). 1986. 14.95 (ISBN 0-938936-52-2). Daring Bks.

Helmbold, F. Wilbur, ed. Seventy-Five Years, Central Park Baptist Church, Birmingham, Alabama, 1910-1985. (Illus., Orig.). 1985. 25.00 (ISBN 0-87121-447-4). Banner Pr AL.

Ingle, Edward. Parish Institutions of Maryland. LC 78-63736. (Johns Hopkins University. Studies in Social Sciences. First Ser. 1882-1883: 6). Repr. of 1883 ed. 11.50 (ISBN 0-404-61006-4). AMS Pr.

Johnson County Historical Society Staff. A History of Johnson County Churches. Morgan, John, ed. 176p. 1986. 20.00 (ISBN 0-916369-06-4). Magnolia Pr.

Johnson, Mayme H. A Treasury of Tennessee Churches. (Illus.). 160p. 1986. 29.95 (ISBN 0-939298-60-0, 600). J M Prods.

Kennedy, Roger. American Churches. (Illus.). 296p. 1982. 50.00 (ISBN 0-8245-0539-5). Crossroad NY.

Lambert, Eleanor R. In the Palm of His Hand: 1838 to 1984. LC 85-9036. (Illus.). 200p. 1985. 14.98 (ISBN 0-935304-92-4). August Hse.

Langley, Florence. With Prayer & Psalm: The History of Wilmot, New Hampshire Churches. LC 81-5116. 80p. 1981. 7.95x (ISBN 0-914016-77-6). Phoenix Pub.

Mays, Benjamin E. & Nicholson, Joseph W. Negro's Church. LC 70-83430. (Religion in America, Ser. 1). 1969. Repr. of 1933 ed. 25.50 (ISBN 0-405-00255-6). Ayer Co Pubs.

Nothstein, Ira O., ed. & tr. The Planting of the Swedish Church in America: Graduation Dissertation of Tobias Eric Biorck. LC 43-18182. (Augustana College Library Publication Ser.: No. 19). 39p. 1943. pap. 3.00x (ISBN 0-910182-14-0). Augustana Coll.

Pearson, Esther. Early Churches of Washington State. LC 79-57216. (Illus.). 182p. 1980. 27.50 (ISBN 0-295-95713-1). U of Wash Pr.

The Philadelphia Church. 27p. (Orig.). pap. 0.95 (ISBN 0-937408-19-0). GMI Pubns Inc.

Roberts, Anne F. & Cockrell, Marcia W., eds. Historic Albany: Its Churches & Synagogues. (Illus.). 415p. (Orig.). 1986. pap. 15.00 (ISBN 0-941237-00-1). Libr Commns Servs.

Sampson, Gloria. Historic Churches & Temples of Georgia. (Illus.). 144p. 1987. 24.95 (ISBN 0-86554-242-2, MUP-H212). Mercer Univ Pr.

Schumacher, Claire W. This Is Our St. Rose Church in Proctor Minnesota. (Illus.). 100p. 1976. pap. 3.00 (ISBN 0-917378-02-4). Schumacher Pubns.

Stineman, William F. & Porter, Jack W. Saint John the Evangelist Church, Indianapolis, Indiana: A Photographic Essay of the Oldest Catholic Church in Indianapolis & Marion County. LC 85-63564. (Illus.). 80p. 1986. 39.95 (ISBN 0-9616134-0-8). ST John Evang.

Three Hundred & Fiftieth Anniversary Book Committee of Old North Church. Under the Golden Cod: A Shared History of the Old North Church & the Town of Marblehead, Massachusetts. LC 84-7821. (Illus.). 160p. 1984. 17.95 (ISBN 0-914659-05-7). Phoenix Pub.

Wallington, Nellie U. Historic Churches of America. LC 77-85628. 1977. Repr. of 1907 ed. lib. bdg. 25.00 (ISBN 0-89341-227-9). Longwood Pub Group.

Wilkinson, Theodore S. Churches at the Testing Point: A Study in Rural Michigan. (World Council of Churches Studies in Mission). 1970. pap. 3.95 (ISBN 0-377-82021-0). Friend Pr.

Wilson, Mabel P., et al. Some Early Alabama Churches. 316p. 1973. 14.95x (ISBN 0-88428-029-2). Parchment Pr.

Wise, John. Vindication of the Government of New-England Churches. Miller, Perry, ed. LC 58-5422. Repr. of 1717 ed. 30.00x (ISBN 0-8201-1246-1). Schol Facsimiles.

CHURCHES, AFRO-AMERICAN
see Afro-American Churches

CHURCHES, CITY
see City Churches

CHURCHES, RURAL
see Rural Churches

CHURCHES, SUBURBAN
see Suburban Churches

CHURCHES OF CHRIST

Paregien, Stanley. The Day Jesus Died. 1970. 3.00 (ISBN 0-88027-004-7). Firm Foun Pub.

Thomas, J. D. We Be Brethen. 1958. 13.95 (ISBN 0-89112-001-7, Bibl Res Pr). Abilene Christ U.

CHURCHWARDENS' ACCOUNTS

Accounting Principles & Reporting Practices for Churches & Church Related Organizations. 64p. 1983. pap. 21.95 (ISBN 1-55586-855-X). US Catholic.

Ludlow England Parish. Churchwardens' Accounts of the Town of Ludlow in Shropshire from 1540 to the End of the Reign of Queen Elizabeth. Repr. of 1869 ed. 19.00 (ISBN 0-384-34130-6). Johnson Repr.

Wright, Thomas, ed. Churchwardens' Accounts of the Town of Ludlow in Shropshire. (Camden Society, London. Publications, First Ser.: No. 102). Repr. of 1869 ed. 19.00 (ISBN 0-404-50202-4, A17-1267). AMS Pr.

CISTERCIANS
see also Benedictines; Trappists

Adams, Daniel J. Thomas Merton's Shared Contemplation: A Protestant Perspective. Doyle, Teresa A., ed. (Cistercian Studies: No. 62). 1979. 8.00 (ISBN 0-87907-862-6). Cistercian Pubns.

Aelred Of Rievaulx. Dialogue on the Soul. (Cistercian Fathers Ser.: No. 22). Orig. Title: De Anima. 1981. 10.95 (ISBN 0-87907-222-9). Cistercian Pubns.

--The Mirror of Charity. Connor, Elizabeth, tr. from Latin. (Cistercian Fathers Ser.: No. 17). Orig. Title: Speculum Caritatis. Date not set. pns (ISBN 0-87907-217-2); pap. pns (ISBN 0-87907-717-4). Cistercian Pubns.

Ambrose Wathan: Silence. LC 74-188556. (Cistercian Studies: No. 22). 10.95 (ISBN 0-87907-822-7). Cistercian Pubns.

Anderson, John D. & Kennan, Elizabeth T., trs. Bernard of Clairvaux: Consideration: Advice to a Pope. LC 75-27953. (Cistercian Fathers Ser.: No. 37). 1976. 5.00 (ISBN 0-87907-137-0). Cistercian Pubns.

Barakat, Robert. Cistercian Sign Language. LC 70-152476. (Cistercian Studies: No. 11). 1976. 14.95 (ISBN 0-87907-811-1). Cistercian Pubns.

Bernard of Clairvaux. Treatises I: Apologia, Precept & Dispensation. (Cistercian Fathers Ser.: No. 1). 190p. 7.95 (ISBN 0-87907-101-X). Cistercian Pubns.

The Chimaera of His Age. 146p. pap. 8.95 (ISBN 0-87907-863-4). Cistercian Pubns.

The Cistercian Heritage, Vol. 4: Roche, Salley. (Orig.). 1978. pap. 16.00 (ISBN 3-7052-0263-4, Pub. by Salzburg Studies). Longwood Pub Group.

Colledge, Edmund & Walsh, James. Guigo II: The Ladder of Monks & Twelve Meditations. 14.95; pap. 6.00 (ISBN 0-87907-948-7). Cistercian Pubns.

Farmer, David H. Saint Hugh of Lincoln. (Cistercian Studies: No. 87). xi, 114p. 1987. pap. 7.95 (ISBN 0-87907-887-1). Cistercian Pubns.

Hausherr, I. Penthos. 24.95 (ISBN 0-87907-853-7); pap. 7.95 (ISBN 0-87907-953-3). Cistercian Pubns.

Idung Of Prufening. Cistercians & Cluniacs: The Case for Citeaux. O'Sullivan, Jeremiah F. & Leahey, Joseph, trs. LC 77-9289. 1977. 12.95 (ISBN 0-87907-633-X). Cistercian Pubns.

Krailsheimer, A. J., ed. The Letters of Armand Jean de Rance Abbot & Reformer of La Trappe, 2 vols. Vol. I. 25.00; Vol. II. 25.00. Cistercian Pubns.

Lekai, Louis J. The Cistercians: Ideals & Reality. LC 77-3692. (Illus.). 534p. 1977. 28.50x (ISBN 0-87338-201-3). Kent St. U Pr.

Lillich, Meredith P., ed. Studies in Cistercian Art & Architecture, II. (Cistercian Studies: No. 69). (Illus.). pap. 14.95 (ISBN 0-87907-869-3). Cistercian Pubns.

--Studies in Cistercian Art & Architecture, III. (Cistercian Studies: No. 89). (Orig.). 1987. pap. write for info. (ISBN 0-87907-889-8). Cistercian Pubns.

McGuire, Brian P. The Cistercians in Denmark: Their Attitudes, Roles, & Functions in Medieval Society. (Cistercian Studies: No. 35). 1982. 35.00 (ISBN 0-87907-835-9). Cistercian Pubns.

Manrique, Angel. Annales Cistercienses, 4 vols. 3196p. Date not set. Repr. of 1659 ed. text ed. 662.40x (ISBN 0-576-72863-2, Pub. by Gregg Intl Pubs England). Gregg Intl.

Noble Piety & Reformed Monasticism. 166p. pap. 8.95 (ISBN 0-87907-864-2). Cistercian Pubns.

O'Dwyer, Barry W., tr. from Lat. Letters from Ireland, 1228-1229. (Cistercian Fathers Ser.: No. 28). Orig. Title: Registrum epistolarum Stephani de Lexinton abbatis de Stannlegia et de Saviagnaco. 1982. 24.95 (ISBN 0-87907-428-0). Cistercian Pubns.
Parry, David. Households of God. (Cistercian Studies: No. 39). (Orig.). 1980. pap. 7.95 (ISBN 0-87907-939-8). Cistercian Pubns.
Pennington, Basil. O Holy Mountain: Journal of a Retreat on Mount Athos. pap. 6.95 (ISBN 0-89453-382-7). M Glazier.
Pennington, M. Basil, ed. The Cistercian Spirit: A Symposium in Memory of Thomas Merton. (Cistercian Studies: No. 3). xvi, 286p. 1973. Repr. of 1972 ed. 7.95 (ISBN 0-87907-803-0). Cistercian Pubns.
Perigo, Grace, tr. Letters of Adam of Perseigne. LC 76-15486. (Cistercian Father Ser.: No. 21). 1976. 11.95 (ISBN 0-87907-621-6). Cistercian Pubns.
The Sayings of the Desert Fathers. (Cistercian Studies: No. 59). pap. 7.95 (ISBN 0-87907-859-6). Cistercian Pubns.
Sommerfeldt, J. R., ed. Studies in Medieval Cistercian History, Vol. 2. (Studies Ser.: No. 24). 1977. pap. 10.95 (ISBN 0-87907-824-3). Cistercian Pubns.
Sommerfeldt, John R., ed. Cistercian Ideals & Reality. LC 78-16615. (Cistercian Studies: No. 60). 1978. pap. 8.95 (ISBN 0-87907-860-X). Cistercian Pubns.
Theodoret. A History of the Monks of Syria. Price, R. M., tr. from Gr. (Cistercian Studies: No. 88). 1986. 26.95x (ISBN 0-87907-888-X); pap. 10.00x (ISBN 0-87907-988-6). Cistercian Pubns.
Vandenbroucke, Francis. Why Monks? LC 75-182090. (Cistercian Studies: Vol. 17). 1972. 4.00 (ISBN 0-87907-817-0). Cistercian Pub.
William of Saint Thierry. Exposition on the Song of Songs. (Cistercian Fathers Ser.: No. 6). 171p. 7.95 (ISBN 0-87907-306-3). Cistercian Pubns.
Zwetl, Austria (Cistercian Monastery) Das Stiftungen-Buch der Cistercienser-Klosters Zwetl. xvi, 736p. Repr. of 1851 ed. 62.00 (ISBN 0-384-71300-9). Johnson Repr.

CISTERCIANS–HISTORY

Berman, Constance H. Medieval Agriculture, the Southern French Countryside & the Early Cistercians: A Study of Forty-Three Monasteries. LC 84-71079. (Transaction Ser.: Vol. 76, Pt. 5). 179p. 1986. 18.00 (ISBN 0-87169-765-3). Am Philos.
Bernard of Clairvaux. The Life & Death of Saint Malachy the Irishman. (Cistercian Fathers Ser.: No. 10). 170p. 7.95. Cistercian Pubns.
Carville, Geraldine. Norman Splendour: Duiske Abbey, Graignamanagh. (Illus.). 120p. 1979. 11.25 (ISBN 0-85640-171-4, Pub. by Blackstaff Pr). Longwood Pub Group.
--The Occupation of Celtic Sites in Medieval Ireland by the Canons Regular of St Augustine & the Cistercians. (Cistercian Studies Ser.: Nbr. 56). (Illus.). 1983. 13.95 (ISBN 0-87907-856-1). Cistercian Pubns.
Elder, E. R., ed. Heaven on Earth: Studies in Medieval Cistercian History, IX. (Cistercian Studies: No. 68). (Orig.). 1982. pap. 7.95 (ISBN 0-87907-868-5). Cistercian Pubns.
Elder, E. Rozanne, et al, eds. Cistercians in the Late Middle Ages: Studies in Medieval Cistercian History. (Cistercian Studies: No. VI). 161p. (Orig.). 1981. pap. 8.95 (ISBN 0-87907-865-0). Cistercian Pubns.
Goad & Nail: Studies in Medieval Cistercian History X. (Cistercian Studies: No. 84). pap. 14.95 (ISBN 0-87907-984-3). Cistercian Pubns.
Goldfrank, D. Rule of Iosif of Volokolamsk. (Cistercian Studies: No. 36). pap. 14.95 (ISBN 0-87907-836-7). Cistercian Pubns.
Hogg, James. The Yorkshire Cistercian Heritage: Introduction. (Orig.). 1985. pap. 16.00 (ISBN 3-7052-0260-X, Pub. by Salzburg Studies). Longwood Pub Group.
--The Yorkshire Cistercian Heritage, Vol. 2: Rievaulx, Jervaulx, Byland. (Orig.). 1978. pap. 16.00 (ISBN 3-7052-0261-8, Pub. by Salzburg Studies). Longwood Pub Group.
--The Yorkshire Cistercian Heritage, Vol. 3: Fountains, Kirstall, Meaux. (Orig.). 1978. pap. 16.00 (ISBN 3-7052-0262-6, Pub. by Salzburg Studies). Longwood Pub Group.
King, Peter. Cistercian Finances in the Fourteenth Century. 24.95 (ISBN 0-87907-885-5). Cistercian Pubns.
Lekai, Louis J. Nicolas Cotheret's Annals of Citeaux, Outlined from the Original French. (Cistercian Studies Ser.: 57). 1983. pap. 13.95 (ISBN 0-87907-857-X). Cistercian Pubns.
Lillich, Meredith, et al, eds. Studies in Cistercian Art & Architecture, I. (Cistercian Studies: No. 66). (Illus., Orig.). 1982. pap. 12.95 (ISBN 0-87907-866-9). Cistercian Pubns.
Lillich, Meredith P., ed. Studies in Cistercian Art & Architecture, III. (Cistercian Studies: No. 89). (Orig.). 1987. pap. write for info. (ISBN 0-87907-889-8). Cistercian Pubns.
Louf, Andre. The Cistercian Way. (Cistercian Studies: No. 76). pap. 7.95 (ISBN 0-87907-976-2). Cistercian Pubns.
Merton, Thomas. The Last of the Fathers: Saint Bernard of Clairvaux & the Encyclical Letter, Doctor Mellifluus. LC 81-4105. 128p. 1981. pap. 4.95 (ISBN 0-15-649438-8, Harv). HarBraceJ.
Morson, John. Christ the Way: The Christology of Guerric of Igny. (Cistercian Studies: N0.25). 1978. 11.95 (ISBN 0-87907-825-1). Cistercian Pubns.
O'Callahan, J. F., ed. Studies in Cistercian Medieval History: Presented to Jeremiah F. O'Sullivan. LC 77-152486. (Cistercian Studies: No. 13). 1971. 7.95 (ISBN 0-87907-813-8). Cistercian Pubns.
Pachomian Koinonia II: Chronicles & Rules. (Cistercian Studies: No. 46). 239p. 1981. pap. 10.00 (ISBN 0-87907-946-0). Cistercian Pubns.
Sommerdfeldt, John R., ed. Simplicity & Ordinariness: Studies in Medieval Cistercian History, Vol. IV. (Cistercian Studies: No. 61). (Orig.). 1980. pap. text ed. 8.95 (ISBN 0-87907-861-8). Cistercian Pubns.

CITIES AND TOWNS–RELIGIOUS LIFE

Hawkins, Peter S., ed. Civitas: Christian Ideas of the City. (Scholars Press Studies in the Humanities). 143p. 1986. 20.95 (ISBN 0-89130-987-X, 00-01-10). Scholars Pr GA.
Ostrom, Karl A. & Shriver, Donald W., Jr. Is There Hope for the City? LC 77-22187. (Biblical Perspectives on Current Issues). 204p. 1977. softcover 4.95 (ISBN 0-664-24147-6). Westminster.
Rose, Larry L. & Hadaway, C. Kirk, eds. The Urban Challenge. LC 82-71026. 1982. pap. 5.95 (ISBN 0-8054-6238-4). Broadman.
Schroeder, W. Widick, et al. Suburban Religion: Churches & Synagogues in the American Experience. LC 74-82113. (Studies in Religion & Society). 1974. 19.95x (ISBN 0-913348-05-8); pap. 10.95x (ISBN 0-913348-11-2). Ctr Sci Study.
Skiba, Richard J. The Faithful City: A Biblical Study. 68p. 1976. 1.25 (ISBN 0-8199-0704-9). Franciscan Herald.

CITY CHURCHES

see also City Clergy; City Missions; Suburban Churches

Abell, Aaron I. The Urban Impact on American Protestantism, 1865-1900. x, 275p. 1962. Repr. of 1943 ed. 22.50 (ISBN 0-208-00587-0, Archon). Shoe String.
Bakke, Raymond. The Urban Christian. 160p. 1987. pap. 6.95 (ISBN 0-87784-523-9). Inter-Varsity.
Bennett, G. Willis. Effective Urban Church Ministry. LC 83-70370. 1983. pap. 5.95 (ISBN 0-8054-5526-4). Broadman.
Bilhartz, Terry D. Urban Religion & the Second Great Awakening. LC 83-49455. 240p. 1986. 27.50x (ISBN 0-8386-3227-0). Fairleigh Dickinson.
Cross, Robert D., ed. The Church & the City: 1865-1910. LC 66-17273. 1967. 49.50x (ISBN 0-672-50994-6). Irvington.
Davidson, James. Mobilizing Social Movement Organization: The Formation, Institionalization & Effectiveness of Economical Urban Ministries. (Monograph: No. 6). 1985. pap. 8.00 (ISBN 0-932566-05-7). Soc Sci Stud Rel.
Ducey, Michael H. Sunday Morning: Aspects of Urban Ritual. LC 76-25342. 1977. 17.00 (ISBN 0-02-907640-4). Free Pr.
Fichter, Joseph H. Dynamics of a City Church. 26.50 (ISBN 0-405-10829-X, 11836). Ayer Co Pubs.
--Social Relations in the Urban Parish. LC 54-11207. pap. 68.00 (ISBN 0-317-07856-9, 2020061). Bks Demand UMI.
Greenway, Roger S. Discipling the City. LC 78-67165. 1979. pap. 9.95 (ISBN 0-8010-3727-1). Baker Bk.
Harris, James H. Black Ministers & Laity in the Urban Church: An Analysis of Political & Social Expectations. LC 86-28151. (Illus.). 146p. 1987. lib. bdg. 23.50 (ISBN 0-8191-5823-2); pap. text ed. 9.75 (ISBN 0-8191-5824-0). U Pr of Amer.
Kloetzli, Walter. The Church & the Urban Challenge. LC 61-14757. pap. 23.80 (2027195). Bks Demand UMI.
Lane, George A. Chicago Churches & Synagogues. iv, 236p. 1981. 25.00 (ISBN 0-8294-0373-6). Loyola.
Rosenbaum, Larry. You Shall Be My Witnesses: How to Reach Your City for Christ. LC 86-90426. 144p. (Orig.). 1986. pap. 5.00 (ISBN 0-938573-00-4). SOS Minist Pr.
Tonna, Benjamin. Gospel for the Cities. Jerman, William E., tr. from It. LC 81-18807. Orig. Title: Un Vangelo per le Citta. Tr. of Un Vangelo per le Citta. 224p. (Orig.). 1982. pap. 10.95 (ISBN 0-88344-155-1). Orbis Bks.

CITY CLERGY

Ellison, Craig. The Urban Mission: Essays on the Building of a Comprehensive Model for Evangelical Urban Ministry. LC 82-23764. 230p. 1983. pap. text ed. 12.50 (ISBN 0-8191-2968-2). U Pr of Amer.
Greenway, Roger S. Discipling the City. LC 78-67165. 1979. pap. 9.95 (ISBN 0-8010-3727-1). Baker Bk.
Rosenbaum, Larry. You Shall Be My Witnesses: How to Reach Your City for Christ. LC 86-90426. 144p. (Orig.). 1986. pap. 5.00 (ISBN 0-938573-00-4). SOS Minist Pr.
Younger, George D. From New Creation to Urban Crisis: A History of Action Training Ministries, 1962-1975. LC 86-70421. (Studies in Religion & Society). 260p. 1987. text ed. 25.95x (ISBN 0-913348-25-2). Ctr Sci Study.

CITY MISSIONS

Ballard, Monroe & Ballard, JoeAnn. Serving in the City: Nurturing the Poor to Independence. 88p. 1986. 3 ring binder 10.95 (ISBN 0-8341-1125-X, S-350). Beacon Hill.
Ellis, Marc. A Year of the Catholic Worker. LC 78-61722. 144p. 1978. pap. 3.50 (ISBN 0-8091-2140-9). Paulist Pr.
Ellison, Craig. The Urban Mission: Essays on the Building of a Comprehensive Model for Evangelical Urban Ministry. LC 82-23764. 230p. 1983. pap. text ed. 12.50 (ISBN 0-8191-2968-2). U Pr of Amer.
Greenway, Roger S. Apostles to the City: Biblical Strategies for Urban Missions. 1978. pap. 4.95 (ISBN 0-8010-3724-7). Baker Bk.
Loomis, Samuel L. Modern Cities & Their Religious Problems. LC 73-112558. (Rise of Urban America). 1970. Repr. of 1887 ed. 23.50 (ISBN 0-405-02464-9). Ayer Co Pubs.
Rees, Seth C. Miracles in the Slums. (The Higher Christian Life Ser.). 301p. 1985. lib. bdg. 40.00 (ISBN 0-8240-6440-2). Garland Pub.

CIUDAD RODRIGO, SPAIN–CATHEDRAL

Quinn, R. M. Fernando Gallego & the Retablo of Ciudad Rodrigo. LC 60-15915. (Span. & Eng., Illus.). 117p. 1961. 8.50x (ISBN 0-8165-0034-7). U of Ariz Pr.

CIVIL RIGHTS

see also Natural Law; Religious Liberty

Adjali, Mia. Of Life & Hope: Toward Effective Witness in Human Rights. (Orig.). 1979. pap. 2.95 (ISBN 0-377-00084-1). Friend Pr.
Ballou, Adin. Christian Non-Resistance. LC 70-121104. (Civil Liberties in American History Ser). 1970. Repr. of 1910 ed. lib. bdg. 35.00 (ISBN 0-306-71980-0). Da Capo.
Billings, Peggy. Paradox & Promise in Human Rights. (Orig.). 1979. pap. 2.95 (ISBN 0-377-00083-3). Friend Pr.
Blakely, W. A., ed. American State Papers Bearing on Sunday Legislation. LC 79-122165. (Civil Liberties in American History Ser.). 1970. Repr. of 1911 ed. lib. bdg. 95.00 (ISBN 0-306-71973-8). Da Capo.
Cohn, Haim H. Human Rights in Jewish Law. LC 83-14846. 266p. 1984. 25.00x (ISBN 0-88125-036-8). Ktav.
Council of Europe Staff, ed. Collected Edition of the "Travaux Preparatoires of the European Convention on Human Rights". Vol. V Legal Committee-Ad Hoc Joint Committee-Committee of Ministers-Consultative Assembly 23 June - 28 August 1950. 356p. 1979. lib. bdg. 131.60 (ISBN 90-247-1970-4). Kluwer Academic.
Cushman, Robert F. Cases in Civil Liberties. 3rd ed. 1979. 18.95. P-H.
Dorsen, Norman & Law, Sylvia. Emerson, Haber & Dorsen's Political & Civil Rights in the United States, Vol. 2. 4th ed. 1979. text ed. 34.00 student ed. (ISBN 0-316-19049-7); lawyers ed. 55.00 (ISBN 0-316-23627-6). Little.
Evans, Robert A. & Evans, Alice F. Human Rights: A Dialogue Between the First & Third Worlds. LC 82-18780. 236p. (Orig.). 1983. pap. 9.95 (ISBN 0-88344-194-2). Orbis Bks.
Hevener, Natalie K., ed. Dynamics of Human Rights in United States Foreign Policy. LC 79-66435. 375p. 1981. pap. 14.95x. Transaction Bks.
Ingram, T. Robert. What's Wrong with Human Rights. LC 78-68732. (Orig.). 1979. pap. 3.50 (ISBN 0-686-24267-X). St Thomas.
Kommers, Donald P. & Loescher, Gilburt D., eds. Human Rights & American Foreign Policy. LC 78-62966. 1979. pap. text ed. 9.95 (ISBN 0-268-01075-7). U of Notre Dame Pr.
Koop, C. Everett & Schaeffer, Francis A. Whatever Happened to the Human Race? LC 83-70955. 168p. 1983. pap. 7.95 (ISBN 0-89107-291-8, Crossway Bks). Good News.
Kraemer, Paul E. Awakening from the American Dream: The Human Rights Movement in the U. S. Assessed During a Crucial Decade, 1960-1970. LC 73-78045. (Studies in Religion & Society Ser.). 1973. pap. 8.95x (ISBN 0-913348-09-0). Ctr Sci Study.
Laqueur, Walter & Rubin, Barry, eds. The Human Rights Reader. (Orig.). 1979. pap. 9.95 (ISBN 0-452-00853-0, F661, Mer). NAL.
--The Human Rights Reader. 384p. 1979. 29.95 (ISBN 0-87722-170-7). Temple U Pr.
Larson, E. Richard & McDonald, Laughlin. The Rights of Racial Minorities. 1979. pap. 1.95 (ISBN 0-380-75077-5, 75077-5, Discus). Avon.
Maguire, Daniel C. A New American Justice: A Moral Proposal for the Reconciliation of Personal Freedom & Social Justice. 218p. 1982. pap. 9.95 (ISBN 0-86683-636-5, HarpR). Har-Row.
Meltzer, Milton. The Human Rights Book. LC 79-13017. 272p. 1979. 11.95 (ISBN 0-374-33514-1). FS&G.
Moltmann, Jurgen. On Human Dignity: Political Theology & Ethics. Meeks, M. Douglas, tr. from Ger. LC 83-48913. 240p. 1984. 15.95 (ISBN 0-8006-0715-5, 1-715). Fortress.
Montgomery, John W. Human Rights & Human Dignity: An Apologetic for the Transcendent Perspective. 192p. 1986. pap. 10.95 (ISBN 0-310-28571-2, 18392P). Zondervan.
Mower, A. Glenn, Jr. The United States, the United Nations, & Human Rights: The Eleanor Roosevelt & Jimmy Carter Eras. LC 78-22134. (Studies in Human Rights Ser.: No. 4). xii, 215p. 1979. lib. bdg. 29.95 (ISBN 0-313-21090-X, MUH/). Greenwood.
Navasky, Victor. Naming Names. LC 80-15044. 468p. 1980. 15.95 (ISBN 0-670-50393-2). Viking.
Oddo, Gilbert L. Freedom & Equality: Civil Liberties & the Supreme Court. LC 78-25592. 1979. pap. text ed. write for info. (ISBN 0-673-16262-1). Scott F.
O'Mahoney, Patrick J. The Fantasy of Human Rights. 192p. 1978. pap. 4.95 (ISBN 0-85597-256-4). Attic Pr.
Pollock, Ervin H. Human Rights: Amintaphil, Vol. 1. LC 70-173834. xviii, 419p. 1971. lib. bdg. 37.50 (ISBN 0-930342-65-8). W S Hein.
Reddy, T. J. Poems in One Part Harmony. 60p. 1980. pap. 4.00 (ISBN 0-932112-07-2). Carolina Wren.
Riga, Peter J. Human Rights as Human & Christian Realities. LC 81-69244. (New Studies on Law & Society). 165p. (Orig.). 1982. 26.00x (ISBN 0-86733-016-3, 5016). Assoc Faculty Pr.
Rohrer, Daniel M. Freedom of Speech & Human Rights: An International Perspective. 1979. pap. text ed. 12.95 (ISBN 0-8403-1987-8, 40198701). Kendall-Hunt.
Rudman, Jack. Senior Field Representative (Human Rights) (Career Examination Ser.: C-2563). (Cloth bdg. avail. on request). pap. 14.00 (ISBN 0-8373-2563-3). Natl Learning.
Said, Abdul. Human Rights & World Order. LC 78-62438. 170p. 1978. pap. 5.95 (ISBN 0-87855-718-0). Transaction Bks.
Sidorsky, David, et al, eds. Essays on Human Rights: Contemporary Issues & Jewish Perspectives. LC 78-1170. 416p. 1978. 12.00 (ISBN 0-8276-0107-7, 420). Jewish Pubns.
Swidler, Arlene, ed. Human Rights in Religious Traditions. LC 82-15014. 128p. (Orig.). 1982. pap. 8.95 (ISBN 0-8298-0633-4). Pilgrim NY.
Swidler, Leonard, ed. Religious Liberty & Human Rights in Nations & in Religions. 255p. (Orig.). 1986. pap. 9.95 (ISBN 0-931214-06-8). Ecumenical Phila.
Thompson, Kenneth W., ed. The Moral Imperatives of Human Rights: A World Survey. LC 79-3736. 1980. text ed. 25.00 (ISBN 0-8191-0920-7); pap. text ed. 9.75 (ISBN 0-8191-0921-5). U Pr of Amer.
United States Foreign Policy & Human Rights: Principles, Priorities & Practice. 1979. pap. 3.00 (ISBN 0-934654-22-0). UNA-USA.
Veenhoven, ed. Case Studies on Human Rights & Fundamental Freedoms. Incl. Vol. 1. 1975 (ISBN 90-247-1780-9); Vol. 2. 1975; Vol. 3. 1976 (ISBN 90-247-1955-0); Vol. 4. 1976; Vol. 5. 1976. lib. bdg. 52.50 ea. (Pub. by Martinus Nijhoff Netherlands). Kluwer Academic.

CIVILIZATION–PHILOSOPHY

see also Philosophical Anthropology

Barfield, Owen. Saving the Appearances: A Study in Idolatry. LC 65-23538. 190p. 1965. pap. 4.95 (ISBN 0-15-679490-X, Harv). HarBraceJ.
Berdiaer, Nicolaii. The Realm of Spirit & the Realm of Caesar. Luurie, Donald A., tr. from Rus. LC 74-1554. 182p. 1975. Repr. of 1953 ed. lib. bdg. 55.00x (ISBN 0-8371-7395-7, BESC). Greenwood.
Conference on Science, Philosophy & Religion in Their Relation to the Democratic Way of Life, 6th. Approaches to Group Understanding: Proceedings. Repr. of 1947 ed. 24.00 (ISBN 0-527-00653-X). Kraus Repr.
Conference on Science-Philosophy & Religion in Their Relation to the Democratic Way of Life - 4th. Approaches to World Peace: Proceedings. 1944. 70.00 (ISBN 0-527-00651-3). Kraus Repr.
Conference on Science-Philosophy & Religion in Their Religion to the Democratic Way of Life, New York. Ethics & Bigness: Proceedings. 1962. 41.00 (ISBN 0-527-00664-5). Kraus Repr.

Conference on Science-Philosophy & Religion in Their Relation to the Democratic Way of Life, 11th. Foundations of World Organization: A Political & Cultural Appraisal: Proceeding. 37.00 (ISBN 0-527-00658-0). Kraus Repr.
Conference on Science-Philosophy & Religion in Their Relation to the Democratic Way of Live, 12th, New York. Freedom & Authority in Our Time: Proceeding. 1953. 51.00 (ISBN 0-527-00659-9). Kraus Repr.
Conference on Science-Philosophy & Religion in Their Relation to the Democratic Way of Life - 9th. Goals for American Education: Proceedings. 1950. 28.00 (ISBN 0-527-00656-4). Kraus Repr.
Conference on Science, Philosophy & Religion in Their Relation to the Democratic Way of Life, 3rd. Science, Philosophy, & Religion: Proceedings. 1943. 37.00 (ISBN 0-527-00650-5). Kraus Repr.
Conference on Science, Philosophy & Religion in Their Relation to the Democratic Way of Life, 2nd. Science, Philosophy, & Religion: Proceedings. 1942. 37.00 (ISBN 0-527-00649-1). Kraus Repr.
Conference on Science, Philosophy & Religion & Their Relation to the Democratic Way of Life, 1st. Science, Philosophy, & Religion: Proceedings. 1941. 37.00 (ISBN 0-527-00648-3). Kraus Repr.
Conference on Science-Philosphy & Religion in Their Relation to the Democratic Way of Life - 5th. Approaches to National Unity: Proceedings. 1945. 70.00 (ISBN 0-527-00652-1). Kraus Repr.
Dixon, W. Macneile. The Human Situation. 75.00 (ISBN 0-87968-062-8). Gordon Pr.
Lewisohn, Ludwig. Permanent Horizon. LC 73-117818. (Essay Index Reprint Ser). 1934. 19.00 (ISBN 0-8369-1811-8). Ayer Co Pubs.
Oliver, Peter. Saints of Chaos. facs. ed. LC 67-23255. (Essay Index Reprint Ser). 1934. 17.00 (ISBN 0-8369-0752-3). Ayer Co Pubs.
Wilson, Colin. Religion & the Rebel. LC 74-9134. 338p. 1974. Repr. of 1957 ed. lib. bdg. 27.50x (ISBN 0-8371-7596-8, WIRA). Greenwood.

CIVILIZATION, ANCIENT

Burton, O. E. Study in Creative History. LC 71-105821. (Classics Ser). 1971. Repr. of 1932 ed. 26.00x (ISBN 0-8046-1197-1, Pub. by Kennikat). Assoc Faculty Pr.
Dawson, Christopher. The Age of the Gods. LC 68-9653. (Illus., Maps, Tabs). 1971. Repr. of 1928 ed. 35.00x (ISBN 0-86527-001-5). Fertig.
Glover, Terrot R. Springs of Hellas. LC 74-122878. (Essay & General Literature Index Reprint Ser). 1971. Repr. of 1945 ed. 21.00x (ISBN 0-8046-1333-8, Pub. by Kennikat). Assoc Faculty Pr.
Gordon, Cyrus H. Common Background of Greek & Hebrew Civilizations. (Illus.). 1965. pap. 7.95 (ISBN 0-393-00293-4, Norton Lib). Norton.
Wilder, Alexander. The Peculiar Mystical Rites of Ancient Peoples. (Illus.). 269p. 1984. 117.85x (ISBN 0-89266-451-7). AM Classical Coll Pr.
Yereance, Robert A. Strangers, All Strangers. LC 79-27016. 1981. 14.95 (ISBN 0-87949-151-5). Ashley Bks.

CIVILIZATION, CHRISTIAN

see also Christianity and Culture; Church and Social Problems

Belloc, Hilaire. The Crisis of Civilization. LC 73-114465. 245p. 1973. Repr. of 1937 ed. lib. bdg. 22.50x (ISBN 0-8371-4761-1, BECC). Greenwood.
Dawson, Christopher H. Medieval Essays. facs. ed. LC 68-58785. (Essay Index Reprint Ser). 1954. 18.00 (ISBN 0-8369-0070-7). Ayer Co Pubs.
--Progress & Religion, an Historical Enquiry. LC 79-104266. Repr. of 1929 ed. lib. bdg. 27.50x (ISBN 0-8371-3917-1, DAPR). Greenwood.
Ferrero, Guglielmo. Peace & War. facs. ed. Pritchard, B., tr. LC 69-18927. (Essay Index Reprint Ser). 1933. 18.00 (ISBN 0-8369-0041-3). Ayer Co Pubs.
Heering, Gerrit J. Fall of Christianity. LC 77-147670. (Library of War & Peace; Relig. & Ethical Positions on War). 1973. lib. bdg. 46.00 (ISBN 0-8240-0428-0). Garland Pub.
Hoffman, Ross. Tradition & Progress, & Other Historical Essays in Culture, Religion & Politics. LC 68-26213. 1968. Repr. of 1938 ed. 23.50x (ISBN 0-8046-0211-5, Pub by Kennikat). Assoc Faculty Pr.
Jerrold, Douglas. Future of Freedom: Notes on Christianity & Politics. facs. ed. LC 68-20311. (Essay Index Reprint Ser). 1938. 18.00 (ISBN 0-8369-0570-9). Ayer Co Pubs.
Littell, Franklin H. Macmillan Atlas History of Christianity. LC 75-22113. (Illus.). 176p. 1976. 24.95 (ISBN 0-02-573140-8, 57314). Macmillan.
Major, Henry D. Civilization & Religious Values. LC 77-27137. (Hibbert Lectures: 1946). Repr. of 1948 ed. 20.00 (ISBN 0-404-60431-5). AMS Pr.
Mead, Frank S. Ten Decisive Battles of Christianity. LC 72-117823. (Essay Index Reprint Ser). 1937. 15.00 (ISBN 0-8369-1812-6). Ayer Co Pubs.
Peters, Edward, ed. Monks, Bishops, & Pagans: Christian Culture in Gaul & Italy. Incl. Selections from the Minor Writings. Gregory Of Tours. McDermott, William C., ed. LC 74-33702. (Middle Ages Ser.). 252p. 1975. (Pa Paperbks); pap. text ed. 10.95x (ISBN 0-8122-1069-7). U of Pa Pr.
Thomas, George F., ed. Vitality of the Christian Tradition. facsimile ed. LC 70-134143. (Essay Index Reprint Ser). Repr. of 1944 ed. 22.00 (ISBN 0-8369-2378-2). Ayer Co Pubs.
Walsh, Chad. Early Christians of the Twenty-First Century. LC 78-138136. 188p. 1972. Repr. of 1950 ed. lib. bdg. 22.50x (ISBN 0-8371-5709-9, WACH). Greenwood.

CIVILIZATION, HINDU

Bharati, Agehananda. Hindu Views & Ways & the Hindu-Muslim Interface. 1981. 8.00x (ISBN 0-8364-0772-5, Pub. by Munshiram). South Asia Bks.
Brown, W. Norman. Man in the Universe: Some Cultural Continuities in Indian Thought. LC 66-12648. (Rabindranath Tagore Memorial Lectures). 1966. 24.00x (ISBN 0-520-00185-0). U of Cal Pr.
Embree, Ainslie, ed. Alberuni's India. abr. ed. Sachau, Edward C., tr. 1971. pap. 2.75x (ISBN 0-393-00568-2, Norton Lib). Norton.
Ghurye, G. S. Vedic India. 1979. 46.00 (ISBN 0-89684-061-1, Pub. by Motilal Banarsidass India). Orient Bk Dist.
Jyotir Maya Nanda, Swami. Mysticism of Hindu Gods & Goddesses. (Illus.). 1974. pap. 3.99 (ISBN 0-934664-08-0). Yoga Res Foun.
Majumdar, R. C. Kambuja-Desa; or, an Ancient Hindu Colony in Cambodia. LC 80-18307. 178p. 1980. Repr. of 1944 ed. text ed. 19.95 (ISBN 0-915980-28-2). ISHI PA.
Sastri, S. Subrahmanya. Samgraha-Cudamani of Govinda. 4.75 (ISBN 0-8356-7354-5). Theos Pub Hse.
Splendours of the Vijayanagara. 1981. 30.00x (ISBN 0-8364-0792-X, Pub. by Marg India). South Asia Bks.
Venkatasubbiah, A. Vedic Studies, Vol. 2. 5.25 (ISBN 0-8356-7447-9). Theos Pub Hse.

CIVILIZATION, ISLAMIC

Abel, Armand, et al. Unity & Variety in Muslim Civilization. Von Grunebaum, Gustave E., ed. LC 55-11191. (Comparative Studies of Cultures & Civilizations: No. 7). pap. 99.30 (ISBN 0-317-11328-3, 2013614). Bks Demand UMI.
Ansari, M. A., tr. from Persian. Man & His Destiny. Tr. of Insan wa Sarnawisht. 124p. 1985. pap. 5.00 (ISBN 0-941724-39-5). Islamic Seminary.
Arberry, Arthur J. Aspects of Islamic Civilization As Depicted in the Original Texts. LC 77-673. 1977. Repr. of 1964 ed. lib. bdg. 29.25x (ISBN 0-8371-9494-6, ARAI). Greenwood.
--Aspects of Islamic Civilization as Depicted in the Original Text. 1967. pap. 9.95 (ISBN 0-472-06130-5, 130, AA). U of Mich Pr.
Arnold, Thomas W. Painting in Islam. (Illus.). 16.25 (ISBN 0-8446-1553-6). Peter Smith.
Ayati, Ibrahim. A Probe into the History of Ashura. Tr. of Barasi Tarkh-i-Ashura. 234p. 1985. pap. 9.00 (ISBN 0-941724-41-7). Islamic Seminary.
Baig, M. A. Wisdom of Islamic Civilization. 9.95 (ISBN 0-317-01595-8). Kazi Pubns.
Bammate, Haidar. Muslim Contribution to Civilization. Date not set. 2.50 (ISBN 0-89259-029-7). Am Trust Pubns.
Batra, Ravi. Muslim Civilization & the Crisis in Iran. 218p. 1980. pap. 2.00 (ISBN 0-686-95468-8). Ananda Marga.
Beg, M. A. S. Fine Arts in Islamic Civilisation. 7.95 (ISBN 0-686-83581-6). Kazi Pubns.
Christopher, John B. The Islamic Tradition. (Major Traditions in World Civilization Ser.). 1972. pap. text ed. 11.95 scp (ISBN 0-06-041283-6, HarpC). Har-Row.
Crosby, Everett U., et al. Medieval Studies: A Bibliographical Guide. LC 83-48259. (Reference Library of the Humanities: Vol. 427). 1156p. 1985. 109.00 (ISBN 0-8240-9107-8). Garland Pub.
Ede, David, et al. Guide to Islam. 265p. 1983. lib. bdg. 59.50 (ISBN 0-8161-7905-0, Hall Reference). G K Hall.
Faris, Nabih A., ed. The Arab Heritage. LC 79-2856. 279p. 1981. Repr. of 1944 ed. 30.00 (ISBN 0-8305-0030-8). Hyperion Conn.
Ferber, Stanley, ed. Islam & the Medieval West. (Illus.). 1979. pap. 29.50x (ISBN 0-87395-802-0). State U NY Pr.
Hartmann, Angelika. An-Nasir Li-Din Allah (1180-1225) Politik, Religion, Kultur in der Spaeten Abbasidenzeit. (Studien Zur Sprache, Geschichte und Kultur Des Islamischen Orients, N. F.: Vol. 8). 1975. 88.00x (ISBN 3-11-004179-0). De Gruyter.
Heyd, Uriel, ed. Studies in Islamic History & Civilization. (Scripta Hierosolymitana Ser.: Vol. 9). pap. 60.00 (ISBN 0-317-08597-2, 2051596). Bks Demand UMI.
Hitti, Philip K. Islam & the West: A Historical Cultural Survey. LC 78-10793. (Anvil Ser.). 192p. 1979. pap. 7.50 (ISBN 0-88275-787-3). Krieger.
Iqbal, A. Contemporary Muslim World: A Brief Note on Current Muslim World. 27.50 (ISBN 0-317-46090-0). Kazi Pubns.
--Culture of Islam. 1981. 16.50 (ISBN 0-686-97867-6). Kazi Pubns.
Irving, T. B. Tide of Islam. 7.95 (ISBN 0-686-83887-4). Kazi Pubns.
McNeill, William H. & Waldman, Marilyn Robinson, eds. The Islamic World. LC 83-18246. xviii, 468p. 1984. pap. 15.00x (ISBN 0-226-56155-0). U of Chicago Pr.
Martin, Richard C. Islam: A Cultural Perspective. (Illus.). 192p. 1982. pap. text ed. 17.00 (ISBN 0-13-506345-0). P-H.
Musallam, Basim F. Sex & Society in Islam: Birth Control Before the Nineteenth Century. (Cambridge Studies in Islamic Civilization). 176p. 1986. pap. 12.95 (ISBN 0-521-33858-1). Cambridge U Pr.
Mutahhari, Ayatullah M. Social & Historical Change: An Islamic Perspective. Algar, Hamid, ed. Campbell, R., tr. from Persian. (Contemporary Islamic Thought, Persian Ser.). 156p. 1986. 18.95 (ISBN 0-933782-18-7); pap. 7.95 (ISBN 0-933782-19-5). Mizan Pr.
Naipaul, V. S. Among the Believers: An Islamic Journey. LC 81-47503. 512p. 1981. 15.00 (ISBN 0-394-50969-2). Knopf.
Nasn, S. H. Islamic Life & Thought. 232p. 1981. 35.00x (ISBN 0-317-39093-7, Pub. by Luzac & Co Ltd). State Mutual Bk.
Rauf, A. Story of Islamic Culture. 1981. 2.50 (ISBN 0-686-97868-4). Kazi Pubns.
Richards, D. S. Islamic Civilization, Nine Fifty - Eleven Fifty. 284p. 1983. 50.00x (ISBN 0-317-39090-2, Pub. by Luzac & Co Ltd). State Mutual Bk.
Sardar, Ziauddin. The Future of Muslim Civilisation. 224p. 1979. 25.00 (ISBN 0-85664-800-0, Pub. by Croom Helm Ltd). Methuen Inc.
Schacht, Joseph & Bosworth, C. E., eds. The Legacy of Islam. 2nd ed. (Legacy Ser). (Illus.). 1974. text ed. 29.95x (ISBN 0-19-821913-X). Oxford U Pr.
Siddiqui, M. I. Why Islam Forbids Free Mixing of Men & Women. 19.95. Kazi Pubns.
Smith, Wilfred C. Islam in Modern History. 1957. 37.00 (ISBN 0-691-03030-8); pap. 10.50x (ISBN 0-691-01991-6). Princeton U Pr.
--On Understanding Islam. (Religion & Reason Ser.: No. 19). 352p. 1984. 55.50 (ISBN 90-279-3448-7); pap. 19.95 (ISBN 3-11-010020-7). Mouton.
Some Aspects of Islamic Culture. 3.00 (ISBN 0-686-83584-0). Kazi Pubns.
Yapp, Malcolm. Ibn Sina & the Muslim World. Killingray, Margaret & O'Connor, Edmund, eds. (World History Ser.). (Illus.). 1980. lib. bdg. 6.95 (ISBN 0-89908-037-5); pap. text ed. 2.45 (ISBN 0-89908-012-X). Greenhaven.

CIVILIZATION, JEWISH

see Jews–Civilization

CIVILIZATION, MEDIEVAL

see also Art, Medieval; Middle Ages; Monasticism and Religious Orders; Renaissance; Science, Medieval

Best Radio Plays of 1984. (Methuen Modern Plays Ser.). 172p. 1985. 22.00 (ISBN 0-413-58430-5, 9650). Methuen Inc.
Crump, C. G. & Jacob, E. F., eds. Legacy of the Middle Ages. (Legacy Ser.). (Illus.). 1926. 32.50x (ISBN 0-19-821907-5). Oxford U Pr.
Dawson, Christopher H. Medieval Essays. facs. ed. LC 68-58785. (Essay Index Reprint Ser). 1954. 18.00 (ISBN 0-8369-0070-7). Ayer Co Pubs.
Durant, Will. Age of Faith. (Story of Civilization: Vol. 4). (Illus.). 1950. 32.95 (ISBN 0-671-01200-2). S&S.
Ferber, Stanley, ed. Islam & the Medieval West. (Illus.). 1979. pap. 29.50x (ISBN 0-87395-802-0). State U NY Pr.
Geanakoplos, Deno J. Western Medieval Civilization. 1979. text ed. 23.95 (ISBN 0-669-00868-0). Heath.
Hamilton, Bernard. Medieval Inquisition: Foundations of Medieval History. LC 80-27997. 110p. (Orig.). 1981. 24.50x (ISBN 0-8419-0718-8); pap. text ed. 14.95x (ISBN 0-8419-0695-5). Holmes & Meier.
Henisch, Bridget Ann. Fast & Feast: Food in Medieval Society. LC 76-15677. (Illus.). 1977. pap. 12.50x (ISBN 0-271-00424-X). Pa St U Pr.
Huizinga, J. Waning of the Middle Ages. LC 54-4529. pap. 5.95 (ISBN 0-385-09288-1, A42, Anch). Doubleday.
Lloyd, Roger B. Golden Middle Age. LC 75-90654. (Essay Index Reprint Ser). 1939. 18.00 (ISBN 0-8369-1208-X). Ayer Co Pubs.
MacCulloch, J. Arnott. Medieval Faith & Fable. 1978. Repr. of 1932 ed. lib. bdg. 47.50 (ISBN 0-8492-1662-1). R West.
McGarry, Daniel D. Medieval History & Civilization. (Illus.). 896p. 1976. text ed. write for info. (ISBN 0-02-379100-4). Macmillan.
Patschovsky, Alexander. Die Anfaenge einer staendigen Inquisition in Boehmen: Ein Prager Inquisitoren-Handbuch aus der ersten Haelfte des 14 Jahrhunderts. (Beitraege zur Geschichte und Quellenkunde des Mittelalters, Vol. 3). (Illus.). xviii, 319p. 1975. 39.60x (ISBN 3-11-004404-8). De Gruyter.
Rand, Edward K. Founders of the Middle Ages. 1928. pap. 7.95 (ISBN 0-486-20369-7). Dover.
Sellery, G. C. & Krey, A. C. Medieval Foundations of Western Civilization. LC 68-24116. (World History Ser., No. 48). (Illus.). 1968. Repr. 74.95x (ISBN 0-8383-0926-7). Haskell.
Szarmach, Paul E., ed. Aspects of Jewish Culture in the Middle Ages: Papers from the Eighth Annual CEMERS Conference. 230p. 10.00 (ISBN 0-87395-165-4, Pub. by SUNY Pr). Medieval & Renaissance NY.
White, Lynn, Jr. Medieval Religion & Technology: Collected Essays. LC 77-83113. (Center for Medieval & Renaissance Studies, UCLA: Publication: No. 13). 1978. pap. 11.95x (ISBN 0-520-05896-8, CAMPUS 371). U of Cal Pr.
Wood, Charles T. The Quest for Eternity: Manners & Morals in the Age of Chivalry. LC 82-40476. (Illus.). 172p. 1983. pap. 8.00x (ISBN 0-87451-259-X). U Pr of New Eng.

CIVILIZATION, MUSLIM

see Civilization, Islamic

CIVILIZATION, OCCIDENTAL–ORIENTAL INFLUENCES

see East and West

CIVILIZATION, ORIENTAL–OCCIDENTAL INFLUENCES

see East and West

CIVILIZATION, SEMITIC

see also Jews–Civilization

Schaeffer, Henry. The Social Legislation of the Primitive Semites. LC 70-174369. Repr. of 1915 ed. 16.00 (ISBN 0-405-08929-5). Ayer Co Pubs.
Van der Toorn, K. Sin & Sanction in Israel & Mesopotamia: A Comparative Study. (Studia Semitica Neerlandica: No. 22). 213p. 1985. pap. 20.00 (ISBN 90-232-2166-4, Pub. by Van Gorcum Holland). Longwood Pub Group.
Wevers, John W. & Redford, D. B., eds. Essays on the Ancient Semitic World. LC 76-23038. (Toronto Semitic Texts & Studies). pap. 33.30 (2026403). Bks Demand UMI.

CIVILIZATION, VEDIC

see Civilization, Hindu

CIVILIZATION AND SCIENCE

see Science and Civilization

CLAP, THOMAS, 1703-1767

Tucker, Louis L. Puritan Protagonist: President Thomas Clap of Yale College. xviii, 283p. 1962. 25.00x (ISBN 0-8078-0841-5). U of NC Pr.

CLARA OF ASSISI, SAINT, d. 1253

Seraphim, Mary. Clare: Her Light & Her Song. 44p. 1983. 18.00 (ISBN 0-8199-0870-3). Franciscan Herald.

CLARES, POOR

see Poor Clares

CLARISSES

see Poor Clares

CLASSICAL ANTIQUITIES

see also Classical Philology; Mythology, Classical also subdivision Antiquities under names of countries, e.g. Greece–Antiquities

Cook, Arthur B. Zeus: A Study of Ancient Religion, 2 vols. Incl. Vol. 1. Zeus, God of the Bright Sky. LC 64-25839. (Illus.). 885p. Repr. of 1914 ed. 50.00x (ISBN 0-8196-0148-9); Vol. 2. Zeus, God of the Dark Sky: Thunder & Lightning, 2 pts. LC 64-25839. Repr. of 1925 ed. 100.00xset (ISBN 0-8196-0156-X); Vol. 2, Pt. 1. Text & Notes. xliii, 858p; Vol. 2, Pt. 2. Appendixes & Index. (Illus.). 539p. Biblo.
Frantz, Alison. The Church of the Holy Apostles. LC 76-356003. (Athenian Agora Ser: Vol. 20). (Illus.). xiii, 45p. 1972. 15.00x (ISBN 0-87661-220-6). Am Sch Athens.
Schous, Gerald P. The Extramural Sanctuary of Demeter & Persephone at Cyrene, Libya, Final Reports: Volume II: The East Greek, Island, & Laconian Pottery. White, Donald, ed. (University Museum Monograph: No. 56). (Illus.). xxi, 121p. 1986. 45.00 (ISBN 0-934718-55-5). Univ Mus of U PA.

CLASSICAL ARCHAEOLOGY

see Classical Antiquities

CLASSICAL MYTHOLOGY

see Mythology, Classical

CLASSICAL PHILOLOGY

Here are entered treatises on the theory, methods and history of classical scholarship.

see also Classical Antiquities; Greek Literature (Collections); Hellenism; Humanism

Jones, L. W., ed. Classical & Mediaeval Studies in Honor of Edward Kennard Rand, Presented upon the Completion of His Fortieth Year of Teaching. facs. ed. LC 68-57312. (Essay Index Reprint Ser). 1938. 21.50 (ISBN 0-8369-0312-9). Ayer Co Pubs.

CLASSIFICATION–BOOKS–RELIGION

Kersten, Dorothy B. Classifying Church or Synagogue Library Materials. LC 77-16476. (Guide Ser.: No. 7). 1977. pap. 3.95x (ISBN 0-915324-13-X); pap. 3.00 members. CSLA.

--Subject Headings for Church or Synagogue Libraries. rev. ed. LC 78-818. (Guide Ser.: No. 8). 1984. pap. 4.95 (ISBN 0-915324-14-8); pap. 3.95 members. CSLA.

Larrabee, James, ed. Religion, BL-BX. LC 85-6863. (LC Cumulative Classification Ser.). 1000p. 1985. loose-leaf set 105.00 (ISBN 0-933949-11-1); vol. 1 0.00 (ISBN 0-933949-12-X); vol. 2 0.00 (ISBN 0-933949-13-8); fiche set 0.00 (ISBN 0-933949-15-4); fiche vol. 1 0.00 (ISBN 0-933949-16-2); fiche vol. 2 0.00 (ISBN 0-933949-17-0). Livia Pr.

CLASSIFICATION, LIBRARY OF CONGRESS

Larrabee, James, ed. Religion, BL-BX. LC 85-6863. (LC Cumulative Classification Ser.). 1000p. 1985. loose-leaf set 105.00 (ISBN 0-933949-11-1); vol. 1 0.00 (ISBN 0-933949-12-X); vol. 2 0.00 (ISBN 0-933949-13-8); fiche set 0.00 (ISBN 0-933949-15-4); fiche vol. 1 0.00 (ISBN 0-933949-16-2); fiche vol. 2 0.00 (ISBN 0-933949-17-0). Livia Pr.

CLAUDEL, PAUL, 1868-1955

Berchan, Richard. Inner Stage: An Essay on the Conflict of Vocations in the Early Works of Paul Claudel. 1966. 3.50 (ISBN 0-87013-097-8). Mich St U Pr.

Cattaui, Georges & Madaule, Jacques, eds. Entretiens Sur Paul Claudel: Decades Du Centre Culturel International De Cerisy-la-Salle. (Nouvelle Series: No. 11). 1968. pap. 14.00x (ISBN 90-2796-249-9). Mouton.

Chaigne, Louis. Paul Claudel: The Man & the Mystic. LC 78-5951. 1978. Repr. of 1961 ed. lib. bdg. 24.75x (ISBN 0-313-20465-9, CHCL). Greenwood.

Chiari, Joseph. Poetic Drama of Paul Claudel. LC 71-90365. 1969. Repr. of 1954 ed. 15.00x (ISBN 0-87752-018-6). Gordian.

Claudel, Paul. Correspondance avec Andre Gide: 1899-1926. 1949. pap. 7.95 (ISBN 0-686-51967-1). French & Eur.

--Correspondance avec Andre Suares: 1904-1938. 1951. pap. 5.95 (ISBN 0-686-51968-X). French & Eur.

--Correspondance avec Francis Jammes et Gabriel Frizeau: 1897-1938. 1952. pap. 7.95 (ISBN 0-686-51969-8). French & Eur.

Guillemin. Le Converti Paul Claudel. 25.95 (ISBN 0-685-37276-6). French & Eur.

Heppenstall, Rayner. Double Image: Mutations of Christian Mythology in the Works of Four French Catholic Writers of Today & Yesterday. LC 72-93063. 1969. Repr. of 1947 ed. 23.00 (ISBN 0-8046-0676-5, Pub. by Kennikat). Assoc Faculty Pr.

Watson, Harold M. Claudel's Immortal Heroes: A Choice of Deaths. LC 73-160572. 1971. 25.00 (ISBN 0-8135-0695-6). Rutgers U Pr.

CLAY, JOHN, 1796-1856

Clay, Walter L. Prison Chaplain: Memoirs of the Rev. John Clay with Selections from His Reports & Correspondence & a Sketch of Prison Discipline in England. LC 69-16232. (Criminology, Law Enforcement, & Social Problems Ser.: No. 90). (Index added). 1969. Repr. of 1861 ed. 25.00 (ISBN 0-87585-090-1). Patterson Smith.

CLEMENS, TITUS FLAVIUS, ALEXANDRINUS

Barnard, P. M., ed. The Biblical Text of Clement of Alexandria in the Four Gospels & the Acts of the Apostles. (Texts & Studies Ser.: No. 1, Vol. 5, Pt. 5). pap. 13.00 (ISBN 0-8115-1700-4). Kraus Repr.

Bigg, Charles. Christian Platonists of Alexandria: Eight Lectures. LC 75-123764. Repr. of 1886 ed. 27.50 (ISBN 0-404-00799-6). AMS Pr.

Clark, Elizabeth A. Clement's Use of Aristotle: The Aristotelian Contribution of Clement of Alexandria's Refutation of Gnosticism. LC 77-93913. (Texts & Studies in Religion: Vol. 1). vii, 192p. 1981. Repr. of 1977 ed. text ed. 49.95x (ISBN 0-88946-984-9). E Mellen.

Wyrwa, Dietmar. Die Christliche Platonaneigunug in den Stromateis des Clemens von Alexandrien. (Ger.). 364p. 1983. 33.60 (ISBN 3-11-008903-3). De Gruyter.

CLERGY

see also Bishops; Celibacy; Chaplains; Church Vestments; City Churches; City Clergy; Deacons; Elders (Church Officers); Monasticism and Religious Orders; Ordination; Pastoral Theology; Patronage, Ecclesiastical; Priests; Rabbis; Theologians; Vows; Women Clergy

also subdivision Clergy under church denominations, e.g. Church of England–Clergy

Anderson, Dave & Wilcox, Tim. A Funny Thing Happened on the Way to Church. 1981. pap. 4.50 (ISBN 0-570-03834-0, 12YY2799). Concordia.

Bair, Ray & Bair, Lillian. God's Managers. 48p. 1981. pap. 4.00 (ISBN 0-8361-3406-0). Herald Pr.

Barber, Cyril J. The Minister's Library, Vol. I. 1985. 19.95 (ISBN 0-8024-5296-5). Moody.

Baxter, Richard. The Reformed Pastor: A Pattern for Personal Growth & Ministry. rev. ed. Houston, James M., ed. LC 82-18825. (Classics of Faith & Devotion Ser.). 150p. 1983. 10.95 (ISBN 0-88070-003-3). Multnomah.

Benson, Dennis C. & Wolfe, Bill. The Basic Encyclopedia for Youth Ministry. LC 81-81967. (Illus.). 352p. 1981. 16.95 (ISBN 0-936664-04-5). Group Bks.

Bergendoff, Conrad. The Augustana Ministerium: A Study of the Careers of the 2504 Pastors of the Augustana Evangelical Lutheran Synod-Church 1850-1962. LC 80-66400. (Augustana Historical Society Ser.: No. 28). 246p. 1980. 15.00 (ISBN 0-910184-28-3). Augustana.

Bigler, Robert M. The Politics of German Protestantism: The Rise of the Protestant Church Elite in Prussia, 1815-1848. LC 77-142055. 1972. 38.50x (ISBN 0-520-01881-8). U of Cal Pr.

Bissonnette, Georges. Moscow Was My Parish. LC 78-16489. 1978. Repr. of 1956 ed. lib. bdg. 22.50x (ISBN 0-313-20594-9, BIMM). Greenwood.

Blizzard, Samuel. The Protestant Parish Minister: A Behavioral Science Interpretation. LC 85-50402. (SSSR Monography: No. 5). 1985. pap. 8.00 (ISBN 0-932566-04-9). Soc Sci Stud Rel.

Briggs, George S. The Cognizance. 48p. 1984. 7.95 (ISBN 0-533-06100-8). Vantage.

Brister, C. W. Take Care. LC 76-51022. 1979. pap. 3.95 (ISBN 0-8054-5578-7). Broadman.

Brose, E. F. Twenty New Ways to Get the Minister Out of Moneyraising. 1976. 2.50 (ISBN 0-941500-18-7). Sharing Co.

Brown, Jack & Armbrister, David. The Life & Works of Charles Harmon. 136p. 1986. 16.95; pap. 12.95. Commonwealth Pr.

Brown, Raymond E. Priest & Bishop. LC 78-139594. 96p. 1970. pap. 4.95 (ISBN 0-8091-1661-8). Paulist Pr.

Burg, B. R. Richard Mather of Dorchester. LC 75-41987. 224p. 1976. 21.00x (ISBN 0-8131-1343-1). U Pr of Ky.

Buxton, Clyne. Minister's Service Manual. text ed. 8.95 (ISBN 0-87148-584-2). Pathway Pr.

Caldwell, Louise. Timothy: Young Pastor. (BibLearn Ser..). (Illus.). 1978. 5.95 (ISBN 0-8054-4239-1, 4242-39). Broadman.

Caltagirone, Carmen L. The Catechist as a Minister. LC 82-1605. 116p. (Orig.). 1982. pap. 4.95 (ISBN 0-8189-0430-5). Alba.

Carter, Bill. Each One a Minister. LC 86-71722. 72p. (Orig.). 1986. pap. 4.95 (ISBN 0-88177-037-X, DR037B). Discipleship Res.

Child, Frank S. Colonial Parson of New England. LC 74-19532. 1974. Repr. of 1896 ed. 35.00x (ISBN 0-8103-3667-7). Gale.

Clapp, Steve. Ministerial Competency Report. (Practice of Ministry Ser.). 123p. (Orig.). 1982. pap. 8.00 (ISBN 0-914527-10-X). C-Four Res.

Clifford, Richard J. & Rockwell, Hays H. Holy Week. Achtemeier, Elizabeth, ed. LC 79-7377. (Proclamation 2, Ser. C). 1980. pap. 3.75 (ISBN 0-8006-4088-8, 1-4088). Fortress.

Coffin, William S. Living the Truth in a World of Illusions. LC 84-48766. 160p. 1985. 12.45 (ISBN 0-06-061512-5, HarpR). Har-Row.

Collins, Gary. Helping People Grow. LC 79-6402. (Orig.). 1980. pap. 8.95 (ISBN 0-88449-069-6, A424068). Vision Hse.

Cook, J. Keith. The First Parish: A Pastor's Survival Manual. LC 83-6940. 154p. (Orig.). 1983. pap. 8.95 (ISBN 0-664-24442-4). Westminster.

Cooke, Bernard. Ministry to Word & Sacraments: History & Theology. LC 75-36459. 688p. 1980. pap. 16.95 (ISBN 0-8006-1440-2, 1-1440). Fortress.

Cox, James W., ed. The Ministers Manual for Nineteen Eighty-Six. LC 25-21658. 352p. 1985. 14.45 (ISBN 0-06-061595-8, HarpR). Har-Row.

Crew, P. Mack. Calvinist Preaching & Iconoclasm in the Netherlands, 1544-1569. LC 77-77013. (Studies in Early Modern History). 1978. 37.50 (ISBN 0-521-21739-3). Cambridge U Pr.

Davidson, Clarissa S. God's Man: The Story of Pastor Niemoeller. LC 78-21065. 1979. Repr. of 1959 ed. lib. bdg. 22.50x (ISBN 0-313-21065-9, DAGM). Greenwood.

Delfeld, Paula. The Indian Priest: Philip B. Gordon, 1885-1948. 1977. 5.95 (ISBN 0-8199-0650-6). Franciscan Herald.

De Nogent, Guibert. The Autobiography of Guibert, Abbot of Nogent-Sous-Coucy. Bland, C. C., tr. from Lat. LC 79-11248. 1980. Repr. of 1926 ed. lib. bdg. 24.75x (ISBN 0-313-21460-3, GUAU). Greenwood.

Ditchfield, P. H. The Old-Time Parson. 342p. 1980. Repr. of 1908 ed. lib. bdg. 35.00 (ISBN 0-89760-130-0). Telegraph Bks.

Dittes, James E. Minister on the Spot. LC 79-114051. 1970. pap. 3.95 (ISBN 0-8298-0155-3). Pilgrim NY.

Eck, John. Enchiridion of Commonplaces of John Eck. (Twin Brooks Ser.). pap. 9.95 (ISBN 0-8010-3352-7). Baker Bk.

Eliot, George. Scenes of Clerical Life. Lodge, David, ed. (English Library). (Orig.). 1973. pap. 4.95 (ISBN 0-14-043087-3). Penguin.

Elson, Edward. Wide Was His Parish. 320p. 1986. 12.95 (ISBN 0-8423-8205-4). Tyndale.

Etheridge, Myrna L. Spring Wind of the Silent Administrator. 80p. (Orig.). Date not set. pap. 4.00 (ISBN 0-937417-02-5). Etheridge Minist.

Finn, Virginia S. Pilgrim in the Parish: Spirituality for Lay Ministers. 208p. (Orig.). 1986. pap. 8.95 (ISBN 0-8091-2742-3). Paulist Pr.

Foley, N. Nadine, intro. by. Preaching & the Non-Ordained: An Interdisciplinary Study. 1983. pap. 6.95 (ISBN 0-8146-1291-1). Liturgical Pr.

Francis Asbury: God's Circuit Rider. Date not set. pap. 6.95 (ISBN 0-8010-5641-1). Baker Bk.

Free Church. Ministers Service Manual. 1981. 5.95 (ISBN 0-911802-48-7). Free Church Pubns.

Gates, Larry W. Dwelling in Scullerland. LC 85-40200. 105p. (Orig.). 1985. pap. text ed. 8.95 (ISBN 0-938232-68-1). Winston-Derek.

Gaudiose, Dorothy. Prophet of the People: A Biography of Padre Pio. LC 74-7123. 1977. pap. 5.95 (ISBN 0-8189-0351-1). Alba.

Glatfelter, Charles H. Pastors & People: German Lutheran & Reformed Churches in the Pennsylvania Field, 1717-1793. LC 80-83400. (Penn. German Ser.: Vol. 13). (Illus.). 1979. 30.00 (ISBN 0-911122-40-0). Penn German Soc.

Goodenough, Simon. The Country Parson. (Illus.). 192p. 1983. 19.95 (ISBN 0-7153-8238-1). David & Charles.

Grant, F. W. Nicolaitanism, the Rise & Growth of the Clergy. Daniel, R. P., ed. pap. 2.95 (ISBN 0-88172-139-5). Believers Bkshelf.

Grein, Janny. Called, Appointed, Annointed. 95p. (Orig.). 1985. pap. 4.00 (ISBN 0-89274-354-9). Harrison Hse.

Grindall, Irene V. Teaching Gifts. LC 85-71784. 64p. (Orig.). 1985. pap. 3.50 (ISBN 0-88177-020-5, DR020B). Discipleship Res.

Gritsch, Eric W. & Lehmann, Helmut T., eds. Luther's Works: Church & Ministry I, Vol. 39. LC 55-9893. 1970. 19.95 (ISBN 0-8006-0339-7, 1-339). Fortress.

Hagin, Kenneth E. Godliness Is Profitable. 1982. pap. 0.50 mini bk. (ISBN 0-89276-256-X). Hagin Ministries.

--The Ministry Gifts Study Guide. 1981. pap. 10.00 spiral bdg. (ISBN 0-89276-092-3). Hagin Ministries.

Hall, David D. The Faithful Shepherd: A History of the New England Ministry in the Seventeenth Century. 320p. 1974. pap. 3.45x (ISBN 0-393-00719-7, Norton Lib). Norton.

--The Faithful Shepherd: A History of the New England Ministry in the Seventeenth Century. LC 72-81326. (Institute for Early American History & Culture Ser.). xvi, 301p. 1972. 27.50x (ISBN 0-8078-1193-9). U of NC Pr.

Hamill, James E. Pastor to Pastor. LC 85-60248. 192p. 1985. 5.50 (ISBN 0-88243-600-7, 02-0600). Gospel Pub.

Harvey, H. El Pastor. Trevino, Alejandro, tr. Orig. Title: The Pastor. (Span.). 232p. 1984. pap. 3.95 (ISBN 0-311-42025-7). Casa Bautista.

Hathaway, Richard D. Sylvester Judd's New England. LC 81-17854. (Illus.). 362p. 1982. 24.95x (ISBN 0-271-00307-3). Pa St U Pr.

Hocking, David. Be a Leader People Follow. LC 78-67854. 192p. 1979. pap. 5.95 (ISBN 0-8307-0680-1, 5411718). Regal.

Horowitz, David. Pastor Charles Taze Russell. LC 85-20511. 159p. 1986. 15.95 (ISBN 0-8022-2503-9); pap. 9.95 (ISBN 0-8022-2504-7). Philos Lib.

Huron, Rod. Christian Minister's Manual. (Illus.). 256p. (Orig.). 1984. skivertex 12.95 (ISBN 0-87239-753-X, 3028); sewn 19.95 (ISBN 0-87239-592-8, 3029). Standard Pub.

Hutchinson, Duane. Pastor Pete. (Illus.). pap. write for info (ISBN 0-934988-05-6). Foun Bks.

Iverson, Dick & Grant, Ray. Team Ministry. (Illus.). 143p. 1984. pap. 8.95 (ISBN 0-914936-61-1). Bible Temple.

Jones, Edgar D. Lincoln & the Preachers. (Biography Index Reprint Ser). 1948. 21.00 (ISBN 0-8369-8018-2). Ayer Co Pubs.

Jones, Terry L. & Nixon, David L. Venom in My Veins: The Terry Jones Story. 88p. (Orig.). 1985. pap. 3.95 (ISBN 0-8341-1078-4). Beacon Hill.

Juel, Donald H. & Buttrick, David. Pentecost 2. Achtemeier, Elizabeth, et al, eds. LC 79-7377. (Proclamation 2: Aids for Interpreting the Lessons of the Church Year, Ser. C). 64p. 1980. pap. 3.75 (ISBN 0-8006-4083-7, 1-4083). Fortress.

Kemper, Robert G. What Every Church Member Should Know about Clergy. 180p. 1985. pap. 7.95 (ISBN 0-8298-0728-4). Pilgrim NY.

Kennedy, Nell. Dream Your Way to Success. LC 79-93290. 1980. pap. 4.95 (ISBN 0-88270-407-9). Bridge Pub.

Ketcherside, C. Clergy System. pap. 0.50 (ISBN 0-686-64390-9). Reiner.

Kring, Walter D. Henry Whitney Bellows. 1979. pap. 7.95 (ISBN 0-933840-03-9). Unitarian Univ.

Laity, Edward. Priesthood, Old & New. 1980. 2.25 (ISBN 0-86544-012-3). Salv Army Suppl South.

Lehmann, Helmut T. & Gritsch, Eric W., eds. Luther's Works: Church & Ministry III, Vol. 41. LC 55-9893. 1966. 19.95 (ISBN 0-8006-0341-9, 1-341). Fortress.

Lewis, Jack. Leadership Questions Confronting the Church. 1985. pap. 5.95 (ISBN 0-89225-275-8). Gospel Advocate.

Lindsay, Gordon. John Alexander Dowie: A Life of Tragedies & Triumphs. 1980. 4.95 (ISBN 0-89985-985-2). Christ Nations.

Lippy, Charles H. Seasonable Revolutionary: The Mind of Charles Chauncy. LC 81-9560. 176p. 1981. text ed. 19.95x (ISBN 0-88229-625-6). Nelson-Hall.

McCarthy, Doran C. The Inner Heart of Ministry. LC 85-15152. (Orig.). 1985. pap. 3.25 (ISBN 0-8054-6942-7). Broadman.

McConnell, Theodore A. Finding a Pastor: The Search Committee Handbook. 72p. (Orig.). 1985. pap. 4.95 (ISBN 0-86683-493-1, HarpR). Har-Row.

McKinty, Neil. In the Stillness Dancing: The Life of Father John Main. 192p. 1987. 14.95 (ISBN 0-8245-0799-1). Crossroad NY.

McNeil, Jesse Jai. Minister's Service Book. 212p. 1982. 7.95 (ISBN 0-8028-3580-5). Eerdmans.

Malony, H. Newton. Integration Musings: Thoughts on Being A Christian Professional. LC 86-81512. (Orig.). 1986. pap. 12.95 (ISBN 0-9609928-3-9). Integ Pr.

Manni, Alvin S. Brother Peter Ferraris. (Illus.). 1974. pap. 4.95 (ISBN 0-89944-027-4). Don Bosco Multimedia.

Martin, Dorothy. Faith at Work. (Peggy Ser.: No. 9). 1985. pap. 3.50 (ISBN 0-8024-8309-7). Moody.

Martin, Roger A. John J. Zubly: Colonial Georgia Minister. 25.00 (ISBN 0-405-14095-9). Ayer Co Pubs.

Miller, Robert M. How Shall They Hear Without a Preacher: The Life of Ernest Fremont Tittle. LC 74-149031. xii, 524p. 1971. 35.00 (ISBN 0-8078-1173-4). U of NC Pr.

Mother Martha. Papa Nicholas Planas. Holy Transfiguration Monastery, ed. & tr. from Greek. (Orig.). 1981. pap. 5.50x (ISBN 0-913026-18-2). St Nectarios.

Moxcey, Mary E. Some Qualities Associated with Success in the Christian Ministry. LC 76-177095. (Columbia University. Teachers College. Contributions to Education: No. 122). Repr. of 1922 ed. 22.50 (ISBN 0-404-55122-X). AMS Pr.

Murray, Frank S. The Sublimity of Faith. LC 81-81770. (Illus.). 952p. 1982. 25.00 (ISBN 0-910840-20-2). Kingdom.

Narvaez, Jorge. Father Meroto. 160p. pap. text ed. 6.95 (ISBN 0-936123-03-6). NY Circus Pubns.

Nelson, Virgil & Nelson, Lynn. Catalog of Creative Ministries. 144p. 1983. pap. 9.95 (ISBN 0-8170-1017-3). Judson.

Nickel, Margaret C. Dream of Spring. 256p. 1987. 12.95 (ISBN 0-89962-589-4). Todd & Honeywell.

Norton, John. Abel Being Dead, Yet Speaketh. LC 78-8184. 1978. Repr. of 1658 ed. 30.00x (ISBN 0-8201-1310-7). Schol Facsimiles.

Oxnam, Garfield B. Preaching in a Revolutionary Age. facsimile ed. LC 75-142687. (Essay Index Reprint Ser). Repr. of 1944 ed. 18.00 (ISBN 0-8369-2421-5). Ayer Co Pubs.

Patsavos, L. J. & Charles, G. J. The Role of the Priest & the Apostolate of the Laity. Vaporis, N. M., ed. (Clergy Seminar Lectures Ser.). 63p. (Orig.). 1983. pap. 3.00 (ISBN 0-916586-57-X). Holy Cross Orthodox.

Peabody, Larry. Secular Work Is Full Time Service. 1974. pap. 2.95 (ISBN 0-87508-448-6). Chr Lit.

Pearlman, Myer. The Minister's Service Book. 4.95 (ISBN 0-88243-551-5, 02-0551). Gospel Pub.

Perry, Charles E., Jr. Why Christians Burn Out. LC 82-2098. 168p. 1982. pap. 4.95 (ISBN 0-8407-5800-6). Nelson.

Peterson, Eugene H. Five Smooth Stones for Pastoral Work. LC 79-87751. 1980. pap. 9.95 (ISBN 0-8042-1103-5). John Knox.

Pugh, J. T. For Preachers Only. LC 86-10976. 192p. (Orig.). 1971. pap. 5.95 (ISBN 0-912315-35-0). Word Aflame.

Rallings, E. M. & Pratto, David J. Two-Clergy Marriages: A Special Case of Dual Careers. 126p. (Orig.). 1985. 24.00 (ISBN 0-8191-4343-X); pap. text ed. 9.50 (ISBN 0-8191-4344-8). U Pr of Amer.

Ramsden, William E. Ministries Through Non-Parish Institutions. LC 80-22294. (Into Our Third Century Ser.). 96p. (Orig.). 1981. pap. 4.95 (ISBN 0-687-27037-5). Abingdon.

Randall, Robert L. Pastors & Parishes. LC 86-27176. 184p. 1987. text ed. 29.95 (ISBN 0-89885-348-6). Human Sci Pr.

Rassieur, Charles L. Stress Management for Ministers. LC 81-16458. 168p. 1982. pap. 8.95 (ISBN 0-664-24397-5). Westminster.

Rediger, G. Lloyd. Coping with Clergy Burnout. 112p. 1982. pap. 5.95 (ISBN 0-8170-0956-6). Judson.

Reverend Elhanan Winchester: Biography & Letters. LC 72-38464. (Religion in America, Ser. 2). 358p. 1972. Repr. of 1972 ed. 26.50 (ISBN 0-405-04090-3). Ayer Co Pubs.

Ridout, Lionel J. Renegade, Outcast & Maverick: Three Pioneer California Clergy 1847-1893. 1973. 7.95x (ISBN 0-916304-10-8). SDSU Press.

Riggs, Ralph M. The Spirit-Filled Pastor's Guide. 1948. pap. 5.95 (ISBN 0-88243-588-4, 02-0588). Gospel Pub.

Rinaldi, Peter M. In Verdant Pastures: From a Pastor's Diary. LC 85-72837. 228p. (Orig.). 1985. pap. 7.95 (ISBN 0-89944-202-1). Don Bosco Multimedia.

Robinson, Joseph A. Gilbert Crispin, Abbot of Westminster: A Study of the Abby Under Norman Rule. LC 80-2211. Repr. of 1911 ed. 37.50 (ISBN 0-404-18785-4). AMS Pr.

Robinson, Stewart M. And We Mutually Pledge. LC 64-17287. pap. 3.25 (ISBN 0-912806-19-2). Long Hse.

Rogers, James A. Richard Furman: Life & Legacy. (Illus.). xxxii, 336p. 1985. 24.95 (ISBN 0-86554-151-5, MUP/H142). Mercer Univ Pr.

St. Francis De Sales. Introduction to the Devout Life. rev. ed. Ryan, John K., ed. 1972. pap. 5.50 (ISBN 0-385-03009-6, IM). Doubleday.

Sammon, Sean D. Growing Pains in Ministry. LC 83-9991. 240p. (Orig.). 1983. pap. 8.00 (ISBN 0-89571-016-1). Affirmation.

Sanford, John A. Ministry Burnout. 144p. 1982. 5.95 (ISBN 0-8091-2465-3). Paulist Pr.

Schalk, Carl. The Pastor & the Church Musicians: Thoughts on Aspects of a Common Ministry. 12p. (Orig.). 1984. pap. 1.50 (ISBN 0-570-01330-5, 99-1256). Concordia.

Scott, Donald M. From Office to Profession: The New England Ministry, 1750-1850. LC 77-20304. 1978. 21.00x (ISBN 0-8122-7737-6). U of Pa Pr.

Shelp, Earl E. & Sunderland, Ronald H., eds. The Pastor As Priest. (Pastoral Ministry Ser.). 160p. (Orig.). 1987. pap. 9.95 (ISBN 0-8298-0751-9). Pilgrim NY.

Sherman, R. J. Pastor of the Range. (Illus.). 224p. 1985. 13.00 (ISBN 0-682-40225-7). Exposition Pr FL.

Sherman, Ruth W., ed. Peleg Burroughs's Journal, 1778-1798: The Tiverton R. I. Years of the Humbly Bold Baptist Minister. LC 80-39673. (Illus.). xxvi, 404p. 1981. 19.00x (ISBN 0-9604144-0-1). RI Genealogical.

Sidney, Edwin. The Life of the Rev. Rowland Hill, A. M. 1978. Repr. of 1834 ed. lib. bdg. 25.00 (ISBN 0-8495-4870-5). Arden Lib.

Sisemore, John T. The Ministry of Visitation. LC 54-2969. 1954. 1.25 (ISBN 0-88243-550-7, 02-0550). Gospel Pub.

Sprague, William B. Annals of the American Pulpit - Or, Commemorative Notices of Distinguished American Clergymen of Various Denominations, from the Early Settlement of the Country to the Close of the Year 1855, with Historical Introductions, 9 Vols. LC 75-83442. (Religion in America Ser). 1969. Repr. of 1857 ed. Set. 300.00 (ISBN 0-405-00267-X). Ayer Co Pubs.

Stafford, William S. Domesticating the Clergy: The Inception of the Reformation in Strasbourg 1522-1524. LC 76-15567. (American Academy of Religion, Dissertation Ser.). 1976. pap. 9.95 (ISBN 0-89130-109-7, 010117). Scholars Pr GA.

Stone, Sam E. The Christian Minister. LC 79-63601. (Bible College Textbooks Ser.). 256p. (Orig.). 1980. pap. text ed. 6.95 (ISBN 0-87239-348-8, 88580). Standard Pub.

Stuhr, Walter M., Jr. The Public Style: A Study of the Community Participation of Protestant Ministers. LC 72-89687. (Studies in Religion & Society Ser.). 1972. 14.95x (ISBN 0-913348-12-0); pap. 8.95x (ISBN 0-913348-02-3). Ctr Sci Study.

Synan, Joseph A. A Good Minister of Jesus Christ. pap. 1.50 (ISBN 0-911866-81-7). Advocate.

Tracy, David & Cobb, John B., Jr. Talking about God: Doing Theology in the Context of Modern Pluralism. 144p. 1983. 6.95 (ISBN 0-8164-2458-6, HarpR). Har-Row.

Trenchard, Ernesto. Consejos para Jovenes Predicadores. (Span.). 100p. 1957. pap. 3.25 (ISBN 0-8254-1726-0). Kregel.

Updike, L. Wayne. Ministry to the Bereaved. 1986. pap. 6.00 (ISBN 0-8309-0450-6). Herald Hse.

Walker, Mary J. The F. Stanley Story. Lyon, Jene, ed. (Illus.). 98p. 1985. lib. bdg. 25.00 (ISBN 0-89016-082-1). Lightning Tree.

Walsh, J. J. Our American Cardinals. 59.95 (ISBN 0-8490-0782-8). Gordon Pr.

Warlick, Harold C., Jr. How to Be a Minister & a Human Being. 128p. 1982. pap. 7.95 (ISBN 0-8170-0961-2). Judson.

Wayland, Francis & Wayland, H. L. A Memoir of the Life & Labors of Francis Wayland, D. D., L. L. D. LC 76-38465. (Religion in America, Ser. 2). 818p. 1972. Repr. of 1867 ed. 52.00 (ISBN 0-405-04092-X). Ayer Co Pubs.

Weatherspool, W. W. Those Days. 1981. 5.95 (ISBN 0-8062-1835-5). Carlton.

Weis, Frederick L. The Colonial Clergy of Maryland, Delaware & Georgia. LC 77-93959. 104p. 1978. Repr. of 1950 ed. 10.00 (ISBN 0-8063-0800-1). Genealog Pub.

Wemp, C. Sumner. Guide to Practical Pastoring. LC 82-12562. 1982. 15.95 (ISBN 0-8407-5271-7). Nelson.

Wolhorn, Herman. Emmet Fox's Golden Keys to Successful Living. LC 76-62930. 1977. 10.84 (ISBN 0-06-069670-2, HarpR). Har-Row.

Youngs, J. William T., Jr. God's Messengers: Religious Leadership in Colonial New England, 1700-1750. LC 76-8544. 192p. 1976. 19.50x (ISBN 0-8018-1799-4). Johns Hopkins.

CLERGY–APPOINTMENT, CALL AND ELECTION

see also Missionaries–Appointment, Call, and Election; Vocation (In Religious Orders, Congregations, etc.)

Academy of Religion & Mental Health Staff. Psychological Testing for Ministerial Selection: Proceedings of the Seventh Academy Symposium. Bier, W. C., ed. LC 73-79568. 1970. 25.00 (ISBN 0-8232-0850-8). Fordham.

Byers, David, ed. Vocations & Church Leadership. 96p. (Orig.). 1986. pap. 5.95 (ISBN 1-55586-108-3). US Catholic.

Carroll, Jackson & Wilson, Robert. Too Many Pastors? The State of the Clergy Job Market. LC 80-16037. 1980. pap. 6.95 (ISBN 0-8298-0405-6). Pilgrim NY.

Constable, G. & Smith, B., eds. Libellus De Diversis Ordinibus et Professionibus Qui Sunt in Aecclesia: Orders & Callings of the Church. (Oxford Medieval Texts Ser). 1972. 45.00x (ISBN 0-19-822218-1). Oxford u Pr.

Cornwall Collective Staff. Your Daughters Shall Prophesy: Feminist Alternatives in Theological Education. LC 80-14891. 155p. 1980. pap. 6.95 (ISBN 0-8298-0404-8). Pilgrim NY.

Cox, James W., ed. The Ministers Manual for 1987. 1986. 14.45 (ISBN 0-317-52366-X, HarpR). Har-Row.

English, E. Schuyler. Ordained of the Lord: H. A. Ironside. LC 76-13873. (Illus.). 1976. pap. 4.95 (ISBN 0-87213-143-2). Loizeaux.

Enyart, David K. Applying for Your Church. LC 84-71852. 72p. (Orig.). pap. 2.95 (ISBN 0-89900-192-0). College Pr Pub.

Forrest, Tom, ed. Be Holy: God's First Call to Priests Today. Orig. Title: A Call to Holiness: World Retreat for Priests. (Illus.). 132p. 1987. pap. 5.95 (ISBN 0-937779-04-0). Greenlawn Pr.

Harbin, J. William. When a Pastor Search Committee Comes... or Doesn't. LC 85-13541. 1985. pap. 4.95 (ISBN 0-8054-2545-4). Broadman.

Hill, Leonard E. Your Work on the Pulpit Committee. LC 70-93916. 1970. pap. 3.25 (ISBN 0-8054-3502-6). Broadman.

Hooper, Robert E. A Call to Remember. 1978. pap. 5.00 (ISBN 0-89225-183-2). Gospel Advocate.

Hulme, William. Managing Stress in Ministry. LC 84-48221. 160p. 1985. 13.45 (ISBN 0-06-064077-4, HarpR). Har-Row.

Kemper, Robert G. Beginning a New Pastorate. LC 77-18055. (Creative Leadership Ser.). 1978. pap. 6.95 (ISBN 0-687-02750-0). Abingdon.

McAllister, Robert J. Living the Vows. Date not set. 19.45 (ISBN 0-317-52397-X, HarpR). Har-Row.

Mather, Cotton. Manuductio Administerium, Directions for a Candidate of the Ministry. LC 75-41190. Repr. of 1938 ed. 17.25 (ISBN 0-404-14685-6). AMS Pr.

Oden, Thomas. Becoming a Minister. 256p. 1987. 17.95 (ISBN 0-8245-0825-4). Crossroad NY.

Weske, Dorothy B. Convocation of the Clergy: A Study of Antecedents & Its Rise, with Special Emphasis upon Its Growth & Activities in the Thirteenth & Fourteenth Centuries. (Church Historical Society London N. S. Ser.: No. 23). Repr. of 1937 ed. 60.00 (ISBN 0-8115-3147-3). Kraus Repr.

CLERGY–CORRESPONDENCE, REMINISCENCES, ETC.

see also subdivision Clergy–Correspondence, Reminiscences, etc. under particular denominations, e.g. Catholic Church–Clergy–Correspondence, Reminiscences, etc.

Bacon, Samuel. Memoir of the Life & Character of the Rev. Samuel Bacon. facs. ed. Ashmun, Jehudi, ed. (Black Heritage Library Collection). 1822. 20.25 (ISBN 0-8369-8781-0). Ayer Co Pubs.

Barbee, A. H. Behind the Iron Curtain: The Story of John Visser. 75p. 1985. pap. 2.95 (ISBN 0-89084-280-9). Bob Jones Univ Pr.

Bernanos, Georges. The Diary of a Country Priest: Thomas More Books to Live Ser. Morris, Pamela, tr. (Fr.). 1983. 14.95 (ISBN 0-88347-155-8). Thomas More.

Bertolucci, John & Lilly, Fred. On Fire with the Spirit. 140p. (Orig.). 1984. pap. 4.95 (ISBN 0-89283-193-6). Servant.

Bissonnette, Georges. Moscow Was My Parish. LC 78-16489. 1978. Repr. of 1956 ed. lib. bdg. 22.50x (ISBN 0-313-20594-9, BIMM). Greenwood.

Bonhoeffer, Dietrich. Letters & Papers from Prison. enl. ed. 1972. pap. 7.95 (ISBN 0-02-083920-0, Collier). Macmillan.

Brace, Beverly W. The Humboldt Years, 1930-39. 1977. pap. 4.50 (ISBN 0-686-19169-2). B W Brace.

Brostrom, Kenneth N., ed. Archpriest Avvakum: The Life Written by Himself. (Michigan Slavic Translations Ser.: No. 4). 1979. 20.00 (ISBN 0-930042-33-6); pap. 10.00 (ISBN 0-930042-37-9). Mich Slavic Pubns.

Burgess, W. J. Brother Burgess. (Illus.). 121p. 1975. 3.50 (ISBN 0-89114-069-7); pap. 1.50 (ISBN 0-89114-068-9). Baptist Pub Hse.

Caccamo, Domenico. Eretici Italiani in Moravia, Polonia, Transilvania (1558-1611) LC 72-3474. (Corpus Reformatorum Italicorum & Biblioteca Ser.). (Lat. & Ital., Illus.). 286p. 1970. pap. 17.50 (ISBN 0-87580-511-6). N Ill U Pr.

Caponetto, Salvatore, ed. Benedetto Da Mantova: Il Beneficio Di Cristo. LC 72-3471. (Corpus Reformatorum Italicorum & Biblioteca Ser.). (Lat. & Ital., Illus.). 558p. 1972. 40.00 (ISBN 0-87580-035-1). N Ill U Pr.

Cleobury, F. H. From Clerk to Cleric. 64p. 1977. pap. 1.95 (ISBN 0-227-67825-7). Attic Pr.

Cole, Myron C. Myron Here. LC 82-61064. (Illus.). 260p. (Orig.). 1983. pap. 5.00 (ISBN 0-935356-04-5). Mills Pub Co.

Conn, Charles P. Fathercare: What It Means to Be Gods Child. 128p. 1984. pap. 2.95 (ISBN 0-425-08460-4); pap. 3.95 (ISBN 0-8128-8184-2). Berkley Pub.

Crider, Virginia. Cry of the Northland. (Northland Ser). 1973. pap. 2.50 (ISBN 0-87813-505-7). Christian Light.

Ferrer, Cornelio M. Pastor to the Rural Philippines: an Autobiography. 1974. wrps. 2.50x (ISBN 0-686-18697-4). Cellar.

Finney, Charles G. The Autobiography of Charles G. Finney. Wessel, Helen S., ed. LC 77-2813. 1977. pap. 5.95 (ISBN 0-87123-010-0). Bethany Hse.

Fontaine, Jacob, III & Burd, Gene. Jacob Fontaine: From Slavery to the Greatness of the Pulpit, Press, & Public Service. 96p. 1984. pap. 6.95 (ISBN 0-89015-438-4). Eakin Pr.

Ginzburg, Carlo, ed. I Costituti Di Don Pietro Manelfi. LC 72-3473. (Corpus Reformatorum Italicorum & Biblioteca Ser.). (Illus.). 101p. 1970. pap. 10.00 (ISBN 0-87580-510-8). N Ill U Pr.

Harper, Tommie F. From the Plow to the Pulpit. Neeld, Elizabeth H., ed. LC 86-9656. (Illus.). 360p. (Orig.). 1986. pap. 9.95 (ISBN 0-937897-77-9). Centerpoint Pr.

Harris, Murray J. Easter in Durham: Bishop Jenkins & the Resurrection of Jesus. 32p. 1986. pap. 1.95 (ISBN 0-85364-419-5, Pub. by Paternoster UK). Attic Pr.

Henson, Josiah. Father Henson's Story of His Own Life. 212p. 1973. Repr. of 1855 ed. 16.95 (ISBN 0-87928-037-9). Corner Hse.

--Father Henson's Story of His Own Life. (Illus.). 224p. 1986. pap. text ed. 6.95x (ISBN 0-8290-1902-2). Irvington.

Holcomb, Brent H., ed. Journal of the Rev. Godfrey Drehr, Eighteen Nineteen to Eighteen Fifty-One. 104p. 1978. 15.00 (ISBN 0-89308-060-8). Southern Hist Pr.

Huang, Quentin K. Y. Pilgrim from a Red Land. 1981. 8.00 (ISBN 0-682-49669-3). Exposition Pr FL.

Hudnut, William H., III & Keene, Judy. Minister-Mayor. LC 86-32512. 192p. 1987. 12.95 (ISBN 0-664-21321-9). Westminster.

Kaye, J. Patrick. Call Me Monsignor. LC 74-78032. (Illus.). 1974. pap. 5.00 (ISBN 0-87423-008-X). Westburg.

Kinzie, Frederick E. & Kinzie, Vera D. Strength Through Struggle. Stewart, James, ed. & intro. by. LC 86-1645. (Illus.). 350p. (Orig.). 1986. pap. 6.95 (ISBN 0-912315-98-9). Word Aflame.

Knight, R. Gaveston. Miracles Among You. 100p. 1985. 13.50x (ISBN 0-85088-379-2, Pub. by Gomer Pr). State Mutual Bk.

Lee, Luther. Autobiography of the Rev. Luther Lee. Dayton, Donald W., ed. (The Higher Christian Life Ser.). 345p. 1985. 45.00 (ISBN 0-8240-6426-7). Garland Pub.

Lindsay, Gordon. God's Twentieth Century Barnabas: The Gordon Lindsay Story. Christ for the Nations, ed. 284p. (Orig.). 1982. pap. 3.95 (ISBN 0-89985-002-2, 104). Christ Nations.

Nelson, Wesley W. Crying for My Mother: The Intimate Life of a Clergyman. 120p. 1975. pap. 4.00 (ISBN 0-910452-26-1). Covenant.

Nicholson, Dan. From Hippie to Happy. (Orig.). 1984. pap. write for info. (ISBN 0-88144-026-4, CPS026). Christian Pub.

Niebuhr, Reinhold. Leaves from the Notebook of a Tamed Cynic. LC 79-2992. (Harper's Ministers Paperback Library). 224p. 1980. pap. 5.95i (ISBN 0-06-066231-X, RD 311, HarpR). Har-Row.

Niemoller, Martin. Exile in the Fatherland: Martin Niemoller's Letters from Moabit Prison. Locke, Hubert G., ed. Kaemke, Ernst, tr. 212p. (Orig.). 1986. pap. 9.95 (ISBN 0-8028-0188-9). Eerdmans.

Nouwen, Henri J. Love in Fearful Land: A Guatemalan Story. LC 85-71913. (Illus.). 120p. (Orig.). 1985. pap. 5.95 (ISBN 0-87793-294-8). Ave Maria.

Opie, Robert. Rev'rund, Get Your Gun. LC 77-78851. 1978. pap. 3.50 (ISBN 0-88419-141-9). Creation Hse.

Pankey, William R. Edge of Paradise: Fifty Years in the Pulpit. 1972. 7.00 (ISBN 0-87012-111-1). McClain.

Perez, J. Guillent. A Case of Conscience. 370p. (Orig.). 1985. pap. 12.95 (ISBN 0-9607590-2-6). Action Life Pubns.

Perkins, Paul. Forgotten Is the Name. 1985. 7.95 (ISBN 0-89536-938-9, 7556). CSS of Ohio.

Pope, Robert H. Incidental Grace. 176p. 1985. pap. 6.95 (ISBN 0-310-34651-7, 12743P). Zondervan.

Pruitt, Fred & Pruitt, Lawrence. God's Gracious Dealings. (Illus.). 496p. 5.00 (ISBN 0-686-29110-7). Faith Pub Hse.

Raines, Robert. Going Home. LC 84-23210. 154p. 1985. pap. 6.95 (ISBN 0-8245-0692-8). Crossroad NY.

Read, Opie. Confessions of a Negro Preacher. LC 73-18597. Repr. of 1928 ed. 21.50 (ISBN 0-404-11408-3). AMS Pr.

Rotondo, Antonio, ed. Camillo Renato: Opere, Documenti E Testimonianze. LC 72-3454. (Corpus Reformatorum Italicorum & Biblioteca Ser.). (Lat. & Ital., Illus.). 353p. 1968. 25.00 (ISBN 0-87580-034-3). N Ill U Pr.

Sharp, John K. Old Priest Remembers, Eighteen Ninety-Two to Nineteen Seventy-Eight. 2nd ed. 1978. 10.00 (ISBN 0-682-49183-7). Exposition Pr FL.

Shimada, Shigeo. A Stone Cried Out. 208p. 1986. pap. 7.95 (ISBN 0-8170-1111-0). Judson.

Shutts, Mark. Walking to Jesus: Scenes from My Journey. LC 84-91288. (Illus.). 80p. (Orig.). 1984. pap. 3.98 (ISBN 0-9614077-1-9). Shutts Minist.

Skane, Edward R. God's Man-Satan's Trap. 180p. Repr. of 1984 ed. 12.95 (ISBN 0-917655-00-1). Dane Bks.

Smith, John C. From Colonialism to World Community: The Church's Pilgrimage. LC 82-12138. 334p. 1982. pap. 8.95 (ISBN 0-664-24452-1, Pub. by Geneva Press). Westminster.

Still, William. Letters of Still. (Religious Ser.). 192p. (Orig.). 1984. pap. 5.95x (ISBN 0-85151-378-6). Banner of Truth.

Trobisch, Ingrid. On Our Way Rejoicing. 240p. (Orig.). 1986. pap. 6.95 (ISBN 0-8423-4745-3). Tyndale.

Truman, Ruth. Spaghetti from the Chandelier: And Other Humorous Adventures of a Minister's Family. 160p. 1984. pap. 7.95 (ISBN 0-687-39146-6). Abingdon.

Utley, Uldine. Why I Am a Preacher: A Plain Answer to an Oft-Repeated Question. Gifford, Carolyn D. & Dayton, Donald, eds. (Women in American Protestant Religion 1800-1930 Ser.). 152p. 1987. lib. bdg. 25.00 (ISBN 0-8240-0680-1). Garland Pub.

Velichkovsky, Paisius. Blessed Paisius Velichkovsky: His Life & Writings. 1973. 12.00x (ISBN 0-686-05406-7). Eastern Orthodox.

Wise, Robert. The Pastors' Barracks. 192p. 1986. pap. 11.95 (ISBN 0-89693-157-9). Victor Bks.

CLERGY–LEGAL STATUS, LAWS, ETC.

Malony, H. Newton. Clergy Malpractice. Needham, Thomas L. & Southaud, Samuel, eds. LC 85-31466. 192p. (Orig.). 1986. pap. 12.95 (ISBN 0-664-24591-9). Westminster.

CLERGY–MAJOR ORDERS

see Bishops; Clergy

CLERGY–MALPRACTICE

McMenamin, Robert W. Clergy Malpractice. LC 86-81075. 209p. 1986. lib. bdg. 27.50 (ISBN 0-89941-483-4). W S Hein.

Malony, H. Newton. Clergy Malpractice. Needham, Thomas L. & Southaud, Samuel, eds. LC 85-31466. 192p. (Orig.). 1986. pap. 12.95 (ISBN 0-664-24591-9). Westminster.

Metts, Walley. Faith Brokers: Professional Christians & Their Un-Godly Gains. 1986. pap. 5.95 (ISBN 0-937931-00-4). Global TN.

CLERGY–OFFICE

Bedell, Kenneth & Rossman, Parker. Computers: New Opportunities for Personalized Ministry. 128p. 1984. pap. 4.95 (ISBN 0-8170-1039-4). Judson.

Bergendoff, Conrad & Lehman, Helmut H., eds. Luther's Works: Church & Ministry II, Vol. 40. LC 55-9893. 1958. 19.95 (ISBN 0-8006-0340-0, 1-340). Fortress.

Bicket, Zenas J. The Effective Pastor. LC 74-80729. 185p. 1973. 3.95 (ISBN 0-88243-512-4, 02-0512). Gospel Pub.

Bridges, Charles. The Christian Ministry. 1980. 13.95 (ISBN 0-85151-087-6). Banner of Truth.

Coffin, Henry S. In a Day of Social Rebuilding: Lectures on the Ministry of the Church. 1919. 29.50x (ISBN 0-686-51402-5). Elliots Bks.

Crandall, Robert. Ministry to Persons: Organization & Administration. (Illus.). 96p. (Orig.). 1981. pap. 3.50 (ISBN 0-89367-070-7). Light & Life.

Doohan, Helen. The Minister of God: Effective & Fulfilled. LC 86-14099. 127p. (Orig.). 1986. pap. 6.95 (ISBN 0-8189-0507-7). Alba.

Durham, John I., ed. Southeastern Studies: Toward A.D. 2000. LC 77-80400. (Emerging Directions in Christian Ministry Ser.: Vol. 1). viii, 146p. 1981. 8.95 (ISBN 0-86554-026-8, MUP-H004). Mercer Univ Pr.

Estes, D. Timothy. A Humanizing Ministry. LC 84-15669. 160p. 1984. pap. 7.95 (ISBN 0-8361-3365-X). Herald Pr.

Fenhagen, James C. Ministry & Solitude: The Ministry of Laity & Clergy in Church & Society. 128p. 1981. 9.95 (ISBN 0-8164-0498-4, HarpR). Har-Row.

Feucht, O. E. Everyone a Minister. 160p. pap. 2.95 (ISBN 0-570-03184-2, 12-2587). Concordia.

Fleming, Austin. Yours Is a Share: The Call of Liturgical Ministry. 1985. pap. 4.95 (ISBN 0-317-38558-5). Pastoral Pr.

Fukuyama, Yoshio. The Ministry in Transition: A Case Study of Theological Education. LC 72-1395. 200p. 1973. 22.50x (ISBN 0-271-01129-7). Pa St U Pr.

Garlow, James. Partners in Ministry. (Illus.). 195p. (Orig.). 1981. pap. 4.95 (ISBN 0-8341-0693-0). Beacon Hill.

Glasse, James D. Profession: Minister. LC 68-17447. Repr. of 1968 ed. 33.50 (ISBN 0-8357-9021-5, 2011670). Bks Demand UMI.

Gritsch, Eric W. & Lehmann, Helmut T., eds. Luther's Works: Church & Ministry I, Vol. 39. LC 55-9893. 1970. 19.95 (ISBN 0-8006-0339-7, 1-339). Fortress.

Kemp, Charles F. Reflections: Fifty Years of Pastoral Ministry. (Orig.). pap. 9.95 (ISBN 0-937689-04-1). Chisum Pub.

Lehmann, Helmut T. & Gritsch, Eric W., eds. Luther's Works: Church & Ministry III, Vol. 41. LC 55-9893. 1966. 19.95 (ISBN 0-8006-0341-9, 1-341). Fortress.

Leigh, Ronald W. Effective Christian Ministry. 256p. 1984. pap. 6.95 (ISBN 0-8423-0733-8); leader's guide 2.95 (ISBN 0-8423-0734-6). Tyndale.

Lightfoot, J. B. The Christian Ministry. LC 83-62042. 120p. 1983. pap. 8.95 (ISBN 0-8192-1331-4). Morehouse.

Lyon, William. A Pew for One, Please. LC 76-41976. 1977. 6.95 (ISBN 0-8164-0374-0, HarpR). Har-Row.

McElvaney, William K. The People of God in Ministry. LC 80-26077. 176p. (Orig.). 1981. pap. 7.75 (ISBN 0-687-30660-4). Abingdon.

Madsen, Keith. Fallen Images: Experiencing Divorce in the Ministry. 128p. 1985. pap. 5.95 (ISBN 0-8170-1076-9). Judson.

Mapson, J. Wendell, Jr. The Ministry of Music in the Black Church. 1984. pap. 5.95 (ISBN 0-8170-1057-2). Judson.

Murphy, Judith K. Sharing Care: The Christian Ministry of Respite Care. (Illus.). 64p. (Orig.). 1986. pap. 3.95 (ISBN 0-8298-0575-3). Pilgrim NY.

Neuhaus, Richard J. Freedom for Ministry: A Critical Affirmation of the Church & Its Mission. LC 78-3352. 256p. 1984. pap. 7.95 (ISBN 0-06-066095-3, RD 505, HarpR). Har-Row.

Ng, David. Developing Leaders for Youth Ministry. 64p. 1984. pap. 5.95 (ISBN 0-8170-1032-7). Judson.

Peck, George & Hoffman, John S., eds. The Laity in Ministry. 176p. 1984. pap. 7.95 (ISBN 0-8170-1041-6). Judson.

Pittenger, Norman. The Ministry of All Christians. 96p. 1983. pap. 5.95 (ISBN 0-8192-1323-3). Morehouse.

Pruyser, Paul W. The Minister As Diagnostician: Personal Problems in Pastoral Perspective. LC 76-8922. 144p. 1976. pap. 7.95 (ISBN 0-664-24123-9). Westminster.

Sample, Tex. Blue-Collar Ministry. 192p. 1984. pap. 9.95 (ISBN 0-8170-1029-7). Judson.

Segler, Franklin M. Theology of Church & Ministry. LC 60-14146. 1960. bds. 11.95 (ISBN 0-8054-2506-3). Broadman.

Shaffer, Floyd & Sewall, Penne. Clown Ministry. LC 84-80322. 112p. (Orig.). 1984. pap. 7.95 (ISBN 0-936664-18-5). Group Bks.

Shearn, Carol R. The Church Office Handbook: A Basic Guide to Keeping Order. 288p. pap. 12.95 (ISBN 0-8192-1391-8). Morehouse.

Slover, Luella H., ed. Ministry with the Confined. (Orig.). 1981. pap. 4.50 (ISBN 0-8309-0318-6). Herald Hse.

Smart, James D. The Rebirth of Ministry: A Study of the Biblical Character of the Church's Ministry. LC 60-6189. 192p. 1978. pap. 4.95 (ISBN 0-664-24206-5). Westminster.

Smith, Gregory F. The Ministry of Ushers. 32p. (Orig.). 1980. pap. 1.25 (ISBN 0-8146-1207-5). Liturgical Pr.

Spurgeon, C. H. An All-Round Ministry. 1983. pap. 4.95 (ISBN 0-686-09107-8). Pilgrim Pubns.

--The Pastor in Prayer. 3.75 (ISBN 0-686-09092-6). Pilgrim Pubns.

Steele, David A. Images of Leadership & Authority for the Church: Biblical Principles & Secular Models. LC 86-24589. 206p. (Orig.). 1987. lib. bdg. 23.50 (ISBN 0-8191-5710-4); pap. text ed. 13.25 (ISBN 0-8191-5711-2). U Pr of Amer.

Wallace, James. The Ministry of Lectors. 48p. 1981. softcover 1.25 (ISBN 0-8146-1229-6). Liturgical Pr.

Walsh, John. Evangelization & Justice: New Insights for Christian Ministry. LC 82-6279. 128p. (Orig.). 1982. pap. 6.95 (ISBN 0-88344-109-8). Orbis Bks.

Whitehead, James D. & Whitehead, Evelyn E. Method in Ministry: Theological Reflection & Christian Ministry. 224p. 1980. (HarpR); pap. 9.95 (ISBN 0-86683-459-1). Har-Row.

Williamson, Gerald M. Pastor Search Committee Planbook. LC 81-68923. 1982. pap. 5.50 (ISBN 0-8054-3515-8). Broadman.

--Pastor Search Committee Primer. LC 81-68924. 1982. pap. 3.50 (ISBN 0-8054-3516-6). Broadman.

Wood, Miriam. Those Happy Golden Years. 1980. 6.95 (ISBN 0-8280-0062-X, 20380-2). Review & Herald.

CLERGY–RELIGIOUS LIFE

see also Retreats; Spiritual Direction

Berg, Kay K. & Rogers, Donald B. Teachable Moments. LC 85-71827. 52p. (Orig.). 1985. pap. 3.95 (ISBN 0-88177-019-1, DR019B). Discipleship Res.

Campbell, Donald K., ed. Walvoord: A Tribute. LC 81-16888. 396p. 1982. 15.95 (ISBN 0-8024-9227-4). Moody.

Gumbley, Walter. Parish Priests among the Saints. facs. ed. LC 76-148214. (Biography Index Reprint Ser.). 1947. 15.00 (ISBN 0-8369-8061-1). Ayer Co Pubs.

Huber, J. William, et al. Fear: Issues of Emotional Living in an Age of Stress for Clergy & Religious. Kraus, Marie, ed. LC 86-3533. 141p. 1986. pap. 8.00 (ISBN 0-89571-028-5). Affirmation.

Loetscher, Lefferts A. Facing the Enlightenment & Pietism: Archibald Alexander & the Founding of Princeton Theological Seminary. LC 82-11995. (Contributions to the Study of Religion Ser.: No. 8). x, 303p. 1983. lib. bdg. 35.00 (ISBN 0-313-23677-1, LOE/). Greenwood.

Madden, Edward H. & Hamilton, James E. Freedom & Grace: The Life of Asa Mahan. LC 82-5724. (Studies in Evangelicalism: No. 3). 287p. 1982. 19.00 (ISBN 0-8108-1555-9). Scarecrow.

Moremen, William M. Developing Spiritually & Professionally. LC 84-5194. (The Pastor's Handbooks: Vol. 5). 120p. 1984. pap. 7.95 (ISBN 0-664-24604-4). Westminster.

O'Meara, Thomas F. Theology of Ministry. LC 82-60588. 1983. pap. 11.95 (ISBN 0-8091-2487-4). Paulist Pr.

Perez, J. Guillent. A Case of Conscience. 370p. (Orig.). 1985. pap. 12.95 (ISBN 0-9607590-2-6). Action Life Pubns.

Robinson, Arthur W. The Personal Life of the Christian. 1981. pap. 7.95X (ISBN 0-19-213427-2). Oxford U Pr.

CLERGY–SALARIES, PENSIONS, ETC.

Akin, Herbert L. Clergy Compensation & Financial Planning Workbook. (Illus.). 100p. 1982. wkbk. 6.95 (ISBN 0-938736-05-1). Life Enrich.

Morgan, Darold H. Personal Finances for Ministers. LC 85-17443. (Broadman Leadership Ser.). 1985. pap. 5.95 (ISBN 0-8054-6405-0). Broadman.

Worth, B. J. Income Tax Law for Ministers & Religious Workers: 1986 Edition for 1985 Returns. 64p. 1984. pap. 4.95 (ISBN 0-8010-9671-5, 9671-5). Baker Bk.

--Income Tax Law for Ministers & Religious Workers: 1987 Edition for Preparing 1986 Returns. 96p. 1987. pap. 4.95 (ISBN 0-8010-9676-6). Baker Bk.

CLERGY–GERMANY

Bonhoeffer, Dietrich. Letters & Papers from Prison. enl. ed. 1972. pap. 7.95 (ISBN 0-02-083920-0, Collier). Macmillan.

CLERGY–GREAT BRITAIN

Anstruther, Godfrey. The Seminary Priests: A Dictionary of the Secular Clergy of England & Wales, 1558-1850, 4 vols. Incl. Vol. 1. Elizabethan, 1558-1603. 1968 (ISBN 0-87921-059-1); Vol. 2. Early Stuarts, 1603-1659. 1975 (ISBN 0-85597-082-0); Vol. 3 Paperback. 660-1715. 1976 (ISBN 0-85597-116-9); Vol. 4 Paperback. 1716-1800. 1977 (ISBN 0-85597-118-5). text ed. 18.50x ea. Attic Pr.

Begbie, Harold. Painted Windows. LC 77-108696. (Essay & General Literature Index Reprint Ser). 1970. Repr. of 1922 ed. 23.50x (ISBN 0-8046-0918-7, Pub. by Kennikat). Assoc Faculty Pr.

Coleridge, John T. A Memoir of the Rev. John Keble, 2 vols. in 1. 2nd rev. ed. LC 75-30019. Repr. of 1869 ed. 38.50 (ISBN 0-404-14024-6). AMS Pr.

Collinson, Patrick. Archbishop Grindal, 1519-1589: The Struggle for a Reformed Church in England. LC 78-65474. 1979. 46.00x (ISBN 0-520-03831-2). U of Cal Pr.

Colloms, Brenda. Victorian Country Parsons. LC 77-82027. (Illus.). 284p. 1978. 21.50x (ISBN 0-8032-0981-9). U of Nebr Pr.

Cutts, Edward L. Parish Priests & Their People in the Middle Ages in England. LC 74-107457. Repr. of 1898 ed. 32.50 (ISBN 0-404-01898-X). Ams Pr.

Davies, Horton. Like Angels from a Cloud: The English Metaphysical Preachers 1588-1645. 500p. 1986. 30.00 (ISBN 0-87328-088-1). Huntington Lib.

Davison, William T. Mystics & Poets. LC 77-924. 1977. lib. bdg. 25.00 (ISBN 0-8414-3680-0). Folcroft.

Distad, N. Merrill. Guessing at Truth: The Life of Julius Charles Hare 1795-1855. LC 78-11625. xiv, 258p. 1979. 23.50x (ISBN 0-915762-07-2). Patmos Pr.

Gabel, Leona C. Benefit of Clergy in England in the Later Middle Ages. 1969. lib. bdg. 17.00x (ISBN 0-374-92964-5, Octagon). Hippocrene Bks.

Haig, Alan. The Victorian Clergy. 380p. 1984. 33.00 (ISBN 0-7099-1230-7, Pub. by Croom Helm Ltd). Methuen Inc.

Hart, A. Tindal. The Country Priest in English History. 1959. Repr. 30.00 (ISBN 0-8274-2107-9). R West.

Heeney, Brian. A Different Kind of Gentleman: Parish Clergy As Professional Men in Early & Mid-Victorian England. LC 76-17329. (Studies in British History & Culture: Vol. 5). (Illus.). xii, 169p. 1976. 21.50 (ISBN 0-208-01605-8, Archon). Shoe String.

Jowett, John H. Best of John Henry Jowett. Kennedy, Gerald, ed. LC 79-179729. (Biography Index Reprint Ser.). Repr. of 1948 ed. 16.00 (ISBN 0-8369-8097-2). Ayer Co Pubs.

Kilvert, Francis. Kilvert's Diary 1870-1879. LC 86-80573. 288p. 1986. 24.95 (ISBN 0-87923-637-X). Godine.

Link, Eugene P. Labor-Religion Prophet: The Times & Life of Harry F. Ward. (Academy of Independent Scholars Retrospections Ser.). 270p. 1984. 22.00x (ISBN 0-86531-621-X). Westview.

Macfarlane, Alan. The Family Life of Ralph Josselin: An Essay in Historical Anthropology. (Illus.). 1977. pap. 7.95 (ISBN 0-393-00849-5, Norton Lib). Norton.

Toon, Peter. J. C. Ryle: A Self-Portrait. 1975. 4.95 (ISBN 0-685-52822-7). Reiner.

CLERGY–IRAN

Algar, Hamid. Religion & State in Iran, 1785-1906: The Role of the 'Ulama in the Qajar Period. LC 72-79959. (Near Eastern Center, UCLA; Ca. Library Reprint Ser.: No. 106). 1980. 34.50x (ISBN 0-520-04100-3). U of Cal Pr.

CLERGY–SCOTLAND

Blakey, Ronald S. The Man in the Manse, Eighteen Hundred to Nineteen Hundred. 160p. 1979. 10.00x (ISBN 0-905312-05-8, Pub. by Scot Acad Pr). Longwood Pub Group.

Bonar, Andrew. Andrew Bonar Life & Diary. 535p. 1984. Repr. of 1893 ed. 14.95 (ISBN 0-85151-432-4). Banner of Truth.

Brown, Stewart J. Thomas Chalmers & Godly Commonwealth in Scotland. (Illus.). 1982. 55.00x (ISBN 0-19-213114-1). Oxford U Pr.

CLERGY–SOVIET UNION

Elchaninov, Alexander. The Diary of a Russian Priest. 2nd ed. Ware, Kallistos T., ed. LC 82-16795. (Illus.). 225p. (Orig.). 1982. pap. 8.95 (ISBN 0-88141-000-4). St Vladimirs.

Freeze, Gregory L. The Parish Clergy in Nineteenth-Century Russia: Crisis, Reform, Counter-Reform. LC 82-61361. 552p. 1983. 52.50x (ISBN 0-691-05381-2). Princeton U Pr.

--The Russian Levites: Parish Clergy in the Eighteenth Century. (Russian Research Center Studies: 78). 1977. 22.50x (ISBN 0-674-78175-9). Harvard U Pr.

Gagarin, Jean X. Russian Clergy. LC 70-131035. Repr. of 1872 ed. 21.00 (ISBN 0-404-02666-4). AMS Pr.

CLERGY, AFRO-AMERICAN

see Afro-American Clergy

CLERGY, CITY

see City Clergy

CLERGY, PRIVILEGE OF

see Privilegium Fori

CLERGY, TRAINING OF

see also Theology–Study and Teaching

Bolinder, Garth, et al. What Every Pastor Needs to Know about Music, Youth, & Education. (Leadership Library). 192p. 1986. 9.95 (ISBN 0-917463-09-9). Chr Today.

Chandler, Mary. The Pastoral Associate & the Lay Pastor. 72p. 1986. pap. 3.95 (ISBN 0-8146-1470-1). Liturgical Pr.

Charry, Dana. Mental Health Skills for Clergy. 160p. 1981. 10.95 (ISBN 0-8170-0886-1). Judson.

Fukuyama, Yoshio. The Ministry in Transition: A Case Study of Theological Education. LC 72-1395. 200p. 1973. 22.50x (ISBN 0-271-01129-7). Pa St U Pr.

Grubbs, Jerry C. Continuing Education: A Hedge Against Boredom in Ministry. LC 86-42931. 40p. (Orig.). 1986. pap. 4.00 (ISBN 0-937021-03-2). Sagamore Bks MI.

Pickthorn, William E., compiled by. Ministers Manual Ser, 3 vols. Incl. Vol. 1, Services for Special Occasions (ISBN 0-88243-547-7, 02-0547); Vol. 2, Services for Weddings & Funerals (ISBN 0-88243-548-5, 02-0548); Vol. 3, Services for Ministers & Workers (ISBN 0-88243-549-3, 02-0549). LC 65-13222. 1965. Set. 13.95 (ISBN 0-88243-544-2, 02-0544); 4.95 ea. Gospel Pub.

CLERGY IN LITERATURE

Lang, Edgar A. Ludwig Tieck's Early Concept of Catholic Clergy & Church. LC 74-140044. (Catholic University Studies in German Ser.: No. 8). Repr. of 1936 ed. 28.00 (ISBN 0-404-50228-8). AMS Pr.

CLERGYMEN'S FAMILIES

see also Clergymen's Wives

Bailey, Robert & Bailey, Mary Frances. Coping with Stress in the Minister's Home. LC 79-51135. 1979. 6.95 (ISBN 0-8054-5266-4). Broadman.

Bradsher, Frances. The Preacher Had Ten Kids. 1980. pap. 3.50 (ISBN 0-8423-4886-7). Tyndale.

Madsen, Keith. Fallen Images: Experiencing Divorce in the Ministry. 128p. 1985. pap. 5.95 (ISBN 0-8170-1076-9). Judson.

Merrill, Dean. Clergy Couples in Crisis. (Leadership Library). 216p. 1985. 9.95 (ISBN 0-917463-06-4). Chr Today.

Olsson, Karl A. A Family of Faith. 157p. 1975. cloth 5.45 (ISBN 0-910452-24-5). Covenant.

CLERGYMEN'S WIVES

see also Clergymen's Families

Bess, Mary E. Tips for Ministers & Mates. 1987. pap. 5.95 (ISBN 0-8054-6943-5). Broadman.

Biros, Florence K. With the Ups Comes the Downs. (Illus.). 104p. (Orig.). 1986. pap. 2.95 (ISBN 0-936369-01-9). Son-Rise Pubns.

Coble, Betty J. The Private Life of the Minister's Wife. LC 81-65385. 1981. pap. 5.95 (ISBN 0-8054-6935-4). Broadman.

Damp, Margaret M. Finding Fulfillment in the Manse. 115p. 1978. pap. 2.95 (ISBN 0-8341-0544-6). Beacon Hill.

MacDonald, Gail. High Call, High Privilege. 1981. pap. 6.95 (ISBN 0-8423-1424-5). Tyndale.

Montgomery, Shirley E. A Growth Guide for Ministers' Wives. LC 83-71066. 1984. pap. 6.95 (ISBN 0-8054-2708-2). Broadman.

Nelson, Martha. This Call We Share. LC 76-29804. 1977. 8.50 (ISBN 0-8054-2701-5). Broadman.

Phillips, Gloria & Harrell, Irene B. A Heart Set Free. (Orig.). 1985. pap. 5.00 (ISBN 0-915541-02-5); study guide: Spiritual Warfare 5.00 (ISBN 0-915541-16-5); answer bk. avail. (ISBN 0-915541-17-3). Star Bks Inc.

Ray, Charles. Mrs. C. H. Spurgeon. 1979. pap. 2.50 (ISBN 0-686-09102-7). Pilgrim Pubns.

Ross, Charlotte. Who Is the Minister's Wife? A Search for Personal Fulfillment. LC 79-24027. 132p. 1980. pap. 6.95 (ISBN 0-664-24302-9). Westminster.
Senter, Ruth. So You're the Pastor's Wife. 1979. pap. 4.95 (ISBN 0-310-38821-X). Zondervan.
Sinclair, Donna M. The Pastor's Wife Today. LC 80-26076. (Creative Leadership Ser.). 128p. (Orig.). 1981. pap. 5.95 (ISBN 0-687-30269-2). Abingdon.
Spray, Pauline. Confessions of a Preacher's Wife. 174p. (Orig.). 1986. pap. 4.95 (ISBN 0-8341-0939-5). Beacon Hill.
Sweet, Leonard. The Minister's Wife: Her Role in Nineteenth Century American Evangelicalism. 323p. 1983. text ed. 29.95 (ISBN 0-87722-283-5). Temple U Pr.
Taylor, Alice. How to Be a Minister's Wife & Love It. 1968. pap. 3.95 (ISBN 0-310-33131-5, 10877P). Zondervan.
White, Ruthe. What Every Pastor's Wife Should Know. 176p. (Orig.). 1986. pap. 5.95 (ISBN 0-8423-7932-0). Tyndale.
Winning Ways for Minister's Wives. (Orig.). 1987. pap. 6.95 (ISBN 0-8054-2710-4). Broadman.
Wurmbrand, Sabina. The Pastor's Wife. 1979. pap. 4.95 (ISBN 0-88264-000-3). Diane Bks.
Young, Muriel. My Life as a Maine-iac. Hunting, Constance, ed. (Illus.). 150p. 1984. pap. 6.95 (ISBN 0-913006-30-0). Puckerbrush.

CLERICAL CELIBACY
see Celibacy

CLERICAL MEDICINE
see Pastoral Medicine

CLERICAL PSYCHOLOGY
see Pastoral Psychology

CLIFFORD, JOHN, 1836-1923
Byrt, G. W. John Clifford: A Fighting Free Churchman. 192p. 1947. Repr. 2.95 (ISBN 0-87921-011-7). Attic Pr.

CLOISTERS
see Convents and Nunneries; Monasteries

CLOTILDA, SAINT, 747-545
Kurth, Godefried J. Saint Clotilda. Crawford, M. V., tr. LC 72-171634. Repr. of 1906 ed. 7.00 (ISBN 0-404-03788-7). AMS Pr.

CLOUD OF UNKNOWING
Englert, Robert W. Scattering & Oneing: A Study of Conflict in the Works of the Author of the Cloud of Unknowing. Hogg, James, ed. (Analecta Cartusiana Ser.: No. 105). 184p. (Orig.). 1983. pap. 25.00 (ISBN 0-317-42594-3, Pub. by Salzburg Studies). Longwood Pub Group.
Johnston, William. The Mysticism of the Cloud of Unknowing: A Modern Interpretation. LC 74-30738. (Religious Experience Ser.: Vol. 8). pap. 74.30 (2052172). Bks Demand UMI.
Llewelyn, Robert, ed. Daily Readings from the Cloud of Unknowing. (Daily Readings Ser.). 1986. pap. 4.95 (ISBN 0-87243-149-5). Templegate.

CLUNIACS
see also Benedictines
Hunt, Noreen, ed. Cluniac Monasticism in the Central Middle Ages. x, 248p. 1971. 25.00 (ISBN 0-208-01247-8, Archon). Shoe String.
Idung Of Prufening. Cistercians & Cluniacs: The Case for Citeaux. O'Sullivan, Jeremiah F. & Leahey, Joseph, trs. LC 77-9289. 1977. 12.95 (ISBN 0-87907-633-X). Cistercian Pubns.
Rosenwein, Barbara H. Rhinoceros Bound: Cluny in the Tenth Century. LC 81-43525. (Middle Ages Ser.). 192p. 1982. 24.00x (ISBN 0-8122-7830-5). U of Pa Pr.

CLUNY, FRANCE (BENEDICTINE ABBEY)
Hunt, Noreen. Cluny under Saint Hugh, Ten Forty-Nine to Eleven Hundred Nine. 1st ed. LC 68-11411. pap. 60.00 (ISBN 0-317-29696-5, 2022064). Bks Demand UMI.
Rosenwein, Barbara H. Rhinoceros Bound: Cluny in the Tenth Century. LC 81-43525. (Middle Ages Ser.). 192p. 1982. 24.00x (ISBN 0-8122-7830-5). U of Pa Pr.

COFFEE HOUSE MINISTRY
Dieleman, Dale. Our Life & Times. 1985. pap. 5.95 (ISBN 0-8010-2951-1). Baker Bk.
Shellenberger, Susie. There's Sheep in My Mirror. 108p. 1985. pap. 4.50 (ISBN 0-8341-1054-7). Beacon Hill.

COFFMAN, JOHN SAMUEL, 1848-1899
Coffman, Barbara F. His Name Was John: The Life Story of John S. Coffman, an Early Mennonite Leader. LC 64-18732. (Illus.). 352p. 1964. 12.95 (ISBN 0-8361-1486-8). Herald Pr.

COHEN, HERMANN, 1842-1918
Dietrich, Wendell S. Cohen & Troeltsch: Ethical Monotheistic Religion & Theory of Culture. (Brown Judaic Studies). 1986. text ed. 23.95 (ISBN 1-55540-017-5, 14-01-20); pap. 18.95 (ISBN 1-55540-018-3). Scholars Pr GA.

COLEGIO DE SAN PABLO
Martin, Luis. Intellectual Conquest of Peru: The Jesuit College of San Pablo, 1568-1767. LC 67-26159. (Orig.). 1968. 25.00 (ISBN 0-8232-0785-4). Fordham.

COLET, JOHN 1467?-1519
Dark, Sidney. Five Deans. facsimile ed. LC 71-93332. (Essay Index Reprint Ser.). 1928. 18.00 (ISBN 0-8369-1285-3). Ayer Co Pubs.
--Five Deans: John Colet, John Donne, Jonathan Swift, Arthur Penrhyn Stanley & William Ralph Inge. LC 70-86011. (Essay & General Literature Index Reprint Ser.). 1969. Repr. of 1928 ed. 22.50x (ISBN 0-8046-0555-6, Pub. by Kennikat). Assoc Faculty Pr.
Jayne, Sears R. John Colet & Marsilio Ficino. LC 80-17262. (Illus.). 172p. 1980. Repr. of 1963 ed. lib. bdg. 24.75x (ISBN 0-313-22606-7, JACF). Greenwood.
Lupton, Joseph H. Life of John Colet. 1887. 20.50 (ISBN 0-8337-4243-4). B Franklin.
Miles, Leland. John Colet & the Platonic Tradition. LC 60-16716. 258p. 1961. 11.95 (ISBN 0-87548-005-5); pap. 6.95 (ISBN 0-87548-006-3). Open Court.

COLLECTIVE SETTLEMENTS–ISRAEL
Lilker, Shalom. Kibbutz Judaism: A New Tradition in the Making. LC 80-70886. (Norwood Editions, Kibbutz, Cooperative Societies, & Alternative Social Policy Bk.: Vol. 7). 240p. 1982. 14.95 (ISBN 0-8453-4740-3, Cornwall Bks). Assoc Univ Prs.
Shaham, Nathan. The Other Side of the Wall: Three Novellas. Gold, Leonard, tr. from Hebrew. 256p. 1983. 13.95 (ISBN 0-8276-0223-5, 607). Jewish Pubns.

COLLEGE AND CHURCH
see Church and College

COLLEGE STUDENTS–RELIGIOUS LIFE
Becker, Verne, et al. Questions? Answers! (Campus Life Ser.). 158p. 1986. pap. 5.95 (ISBN 0-8423-5117-5). Tyndale.
Caldwell, Louis O. Good Morning, Lord: Devotions for College Students. (Good Morning Lord Ser.). 1971. 4.95 (ISBN 0-8010-2324-6). Baker Bk.
Gesch, Roy G. Help, I'm in College. LC 70-77282. 1969. pap. 3.50 (ISBN 0-570-03100-1, 12-2663). Concordia.
Hoge, Dean R. Commitment on Campus: Changes in Religion & Values Over Five Decades. LC 74-7236. (Illus.). 240p. 1974. 10.00 (ISBN 0-664-20706-5). Westminster.
Kitay, P. M. Radicalism & Conservatism Toward Conventional Religion: A Psychological Study Based on a Group of Jewish College Students. LC 72-176953. (Columbia University. Teachers College. Contributions to Education: No. 919). Repr. of 1947 ed. 22.50 (ISBN 0-404-55919-0). AMS Pr.
Murphy, David, ed. What I Believe: Catholic College Students Discuss Their Faith. 164p. 1985. 11.95 (ISBN 0-88347-181-7). Thomas More.
Rupp, Richard H. Getting Through College. LC 84-60726. 223p. 1984. pap. 9.95 (ISBN 0-8091-2627-3). Paulist Pr.
Schimmels, Cliff. The First Three Years of School: A Survivor's Guide. 160p. (Orig.). 1984. pap. 5.95 (ISBN 0-8007-5175-2, Power Bks). Revell.
Short, Stephen N. Pentecost: The Christian Student Movement from Howard University. (Illus., Orig.). 1987. pap. 6.95 (ISBN 0-9616056-2-6). Mid Atl Reg Pr.
Toohey, William. Life after Birth: Spirituality for College Students. 112p. 1980. pap. 4.95 (ISBN 0-8164-2290-7, HarpR). Har-Row.

COLLEGIALITY OF BISHOPS
see Episcopacy

COLLIER, JOHN, 1708-1786
Haworth, Peter. English Hymns & Ballads. 1927. lib. bdg. 16.50 (ISBN 0-8414-4975-9). Folcroft.

COLMAN, BENJAMIN, 1673-1747
Sadowy, Chester P. Benjamin Colman's "Some of the Glories of Our Lord & Saviour Jesus Christ," Exhibited in Twenty Sacramental Discourses (1928) 1979. lib. bdg. 35.00 (ISBN 0-8482-6210-7). Norwood Edns.
Turell, Ebenezer. The Life & Character of the Reverend Benjamin Colman, D. D. LC 72-4539. 256p. 1972. Repr. of 1749 ed. 40.00x (ISBN 0-8201-1104-X). Schol Facsimiles.

COLONIA BARON DE HIRSCH, ARGENTINE REPUBLIC
Winsberg, Morton D. Colonia Baron Hirsch: A Jewish Agricultural Colony in Argentina. LC 64-63523. (University of Florida Social Sciences Monographs: No. 19). 1963. pap. 3.50 (ISBN 0-8130-0259-1). U Presses Fla.

COLUMBAN, SAINT, 543-615
Fischer, Edward. Japan Journey: The Columban Fathers in Nippon. LC 84-14228. 208p. 1984. pap. 9.95 (ISBN 0-8245-0656-1). Crossroad NY.
O'Fiaich, Tomas. St. Columbanus in His Own Words. pap. 4.95 (ISBN 0-686-05661-2). Eastern Orthodox.

COMBER, THOMAS J., 1852-1887
Myers, John B. Thomas J. Comber, Missionary Pioneer to the Congo. LC 74-98739. (Illus.). Repr. of 1888 ed. lib. bdg. cancelled (ISBN 0-8371-2769-6, MYC&, Pub. by Negro U Pr). Greenwood.

COMBONI, DANIELE, BP., 1831-1881
Mondini, A. G. Africa or Death. (Illus.). 1964. 5.00 (ISBN 0-8198-0007-4). Dghtrs St Paul.

COMENIUS, JOHANN AMOS, 1592-1670
Anastasas, Florence H. And They Called Him Amos: The Story of John Amos Comenius-a Woodcut in Words. LC 73-86540. 1973. 10.00 (ISBN 0-682-47814-8, University). Exposition Pr FL.
Jakubec, Jan. Johannes Amos Comenius. LC 70-135811. (Eastern Europe Collection Ser). 1970. Repr. of 1928 ed. 12.00 (ISBN 0-405-02753-2). Ayer Co Pubs.
Keatinge, M. W. The Great Didactic of John Amos Comenius. (Educational Ser.). 1896. Repr. 40.00 (ISBN 0-8482-4764-7). Norwood Edns.
Keatinge, M. W., ed. The Great Didactic of John Maos Comenius. 316p. 1981. Repr. of 1907 ed. lib. bdg. 50.00 (ISBN 0-89984-304-2). Century Bookbindery.
Laurie, Simon S. John Amos Comenius, Bishop of the Moravians, His Life & Educational Works. LC 72-10020. (Illus.). 272p. 1973. Repr. of 1893 ed. 21.00 (ISBN 0-8337-2028-7). B Franklin.
Monroe, Will S. Comenius & the Beginnings of Educational Reform. LC 78-135824. (Eastern Europe Collection Ser). 1970. Repr. of 1900 ed. 13.50 (ISBN 0-405-02765-6). Ayer Co Pubs.
Young, Robert F. Comenius in England: The Visit of Jan Amos Komensky Comenius, Czech Philosopher & Educationalist, to London in 1641-1642. LC 70-135838. (Eastern Europe Collection Ser). 1970. Repr. of 1932 ed. 12.00 (ISBN 0-405-02780-X). Ayer Co Pubs.

COMIC BOOKS, STRIPS, ETC.
De Goscinny, Rene. The Mansion of the Gods. (Asterix Ser.). (Illus.). 1976. 7.95x (ISBN 0-340-17719-5); pap. 4.95x (ISBN 2-2050-6916-0). Intl Learn Syst.
Salajan, Ioanna. Zen Comics. LC 74-35679. 88p. 1974. pap. 4.95 (ISBN 0-8048-1120-2). C E Tuttle.

COMIC STRIPS
see Comic Books, Strips, etc.

COMMANDMENTS (JUDAISM)
Appel, Gersion. A Philosophy of Mizvot. pap. 11.95x (ISBN 0-87068-250-4). Ktav.
Maimonides. Commandments, 2 Vols. Set. 35.00x (ISBN 0-685-01042-2); pap. 25.00. Bloch.
Sperling, Abraham I. Reasons for Jewish Customs & Traditions. Matts, Abraham, tr. LC 68-31711. cancelled. (ISBN 0-8197-0184-X); pap. cancelled (ISBN 0-8197-0008-8). Bloch.

COMMANDMENTS, TEN
Barclay, William. The Ten Commandments for Today. LC 83-6103. 208p. (Orig.). 1983. pap. 7.95 (ISBN 0-06-060417-4, RD 476, HarpR). Har-Row.
Barnum, Priscilla H., ed. Dives & Pauper, Vol. I, Pt. 2. (Early English Text Society Original Ser.). (Illus.). 1980. 32.50x (ISBN 0-19-722282-X). Oxford U Pr.
Blidstein, Gerald. Honor Thy Father & Mother. 15.00x (ISBN 0-87068-251-2); pap. 9.95. Ktav.
Brockbank, Bernard P. Commandments & Promises of God. LC 82-23629. 667p. 1983. 15.95 (ISBN 0-87747-889-9). Deseret Bk.
Brokke, Harold J. Ten Steps to the Good Life. LC 75-44926. 160p. 1976. pap. 1.95 (ISBN 0-87123-332-0, 200332). Bethany Hse.
Coffman, James B. The Ten Commandments Yesterday & Today. pap. 4.50 (ISBN 0-88027-094-2). Firm Foun Pub.
Connolly, Finbarr & Burns, Peter. The Ten Commandments & Today's Christian. 48p. 1985. pap. 1.50 (ISBN 0-89243-233-0). Liguori Pubns.
Daughters of St. Paul. Brief Summary of the Ten Commandments. 1976. pap. text ed. 1.75 (ISBN 0-8198-0386-3). Dghtrs St Paul.
Davidman, Joy. Smoke on the Mountain: An Interpretation of the Ten Commandments. LC 85-7622. 144p. 1985. pap. 7.95 (ISBN 0-664-24680-X). Westminster.
Dives & Pauper (1493) LC 73-17391. 1973. Repr. of 1493 ed. lib. bdg. 90.00x (ISBN 0-8201-1111-2). Schol Facsimiles.
Drew, George. The Ten Commandments in Today's World. 48p. (Orig.). 1979. pap. 6.95 (ISBN 0-940754-00-2). Ed Ministries.
Forell, George W. Ethics of Decision: An Introduction to Christian Ethics. LC 55-7767. 176p. 1955. pap. 4.50 (ISBN 0-8006-1770-3, 1-1770). Fortress.
Fox, Emmet. The Ten Commandments. LC 53-8369. 1953. 12.45 (ISBN 0-06-062990-8, HarpR). Har-Row.
Gnuse, Robert. You Shall Not Steal: Community & Property in the Biblical Tradition. LC 85-4810. 176p. (Orig.). 1985. pap. 9.95 (ISBN 0-88344-799-1). Orbis Bks.
Godsey, John D. Preface to Bonhoeffer: The Man & Two of His Shorter Writings. LC 79-7378. 80p. 1979. pap. 3.50 (ISBN 0-8006-1367-8, 1-1367). Fortress.
Harrelson, Walter. The Ten Commandments & Human Rights. Brueggemann, Walter & Donahue, John R., eds. LC 77-15234. (Overtures to Biblical Theology Ser.). 240p. 1980. pap. 10.95 (ISBN 0-8006-1527-1, 1-1527). Fortress.
Hooper, John. The Early Writings of John Hooper. 1843. 51.00 (ISBN 0-384-24210-3). Johnson Repr.
Hybels, Bill. Laws That Liberate. 132p. 1985. pap. 4.95 (ISBN 0-89693-394-6). Victor Bks.
Ianucci, R. J. Treatment of the Capital Sins. LC 70-140024. (Catholic University Studies in German: No. 17). Repr. of 1942 ed. 21.00 (ISBN 0-404-50237-7). AMS Pr.
Kappeler, Max. Compendium for the Study of Christian Science: No. 3, The Commandments, the Beatitudes, the Lord's Prayer. 29p. 1951. pap. 3.50 (ISBN 0-85241-057-3). Kappeler Inst Pub.
Lasserre, Jean. War & the Gospel. (Christian Peace Shelf Ser.). 243p. 1962. 12.95 (ISBN 0-8361-1475-2). Herald Pr.
Lewis, Ernest. Light for the Journey: Living the Ten Commandments. 1985. 10.95. Word Bks.
Lewis, Jim. The Ten Commandments: Then & Now. LC 84-50912. 95p. (Orig.). 1984. pap. 5.95 (ISBN 0-942482-07-7). Unity Church Denver.
Lewis, Joseph. The Ten Commandments. 644p. cancelled (ISBN 0-911826-36-X). Am Atheist.
Lochman, Jan M. Signposts to Freedom: The Ten Commandments of Christian Ethics. Lewis, David, tr. LC 81-52283. 192p. (Orig.). 1982. pap. 10.95 (ISBN 0-8066-1915-5, 10-5767). Augsburg.
McAllaster, Elva. When a Father Is Hard to Honor. 126p. (Orig.). 1984. pap. 6.95 (ISBN 0-87178-930-2). Brethren.
Miller, Carol E. The Ten Commandments: Youth & Adult Student. 1971. pap. 0.85 (ISBN 0-915374-45-5). Rapids Christian.
Morgan, G. Campbell. Ten Commandments. (Morgan Library). 1974. pap. 3.95 (ISBN 0-8010-5954-2). Baker Bk.
Noerdlinger, Henry S. Moses & Egypt: The Documentation to the Motion Picture "the Ten Commandments". LC 56-12886. 202p. 1956. pap. 1.95 (ISBN 0-88474-007-2). U of S Cal Pr.
Overduin, Daniel. Reflections on the Ten Commandments. 1980. pap. 1.95 (ISBN 0-570-03813-8, 12-2781). Concordia.
Packer, J. I. The Ten Commandments. 1982. pap. 3.95 (ISBN 0-8423-7004-8); leader's guide 2.95 (ISBN 0-8423-7005-6). Tyndale.
Palmer, Earl F. Old Law New Life: Ten Commandments & New Testament Faith. 128p. (Orig.). 1984. pap. 7.95 (ISBN 0-687-28744-8). Abingdon.
Pink, Arthur W. Ten Commandments. pap. 2.50 (ISBN 0-685-00740-5). Reiner.
Prokop, Phyllis S. The Positive Power of the Ten Commandments. LC 86-31043. (Orig.). 1987. 7.95 (ISBN 0-8054-5037-8). Broadman.
Richard, H. M. Skeptic & the Ten Commandmants. (Uplook Ser.). 1981. pap. 0.99 (ISBN 0-686-79998-4). Pacific Pr Pub Assn.
Roland, Michael L. Sabbath at Sea. (Destiny II Ser.). 108p. 1984. pap. 6.50 (ISBN 0-8163-0547-1). Pacific Pr Pub Assn.
Rosales, Antonio. A Study of a Sixteenth-Century Tagalog Manuscript on the Ten Commandments: Its Significance & Implications. (Illus.). 166p. 1985. text ed. 16.00x (ISBN 0-8248-0971-8). UH Pr.
Schaeffer, Edith. Lifelines: God's Frame Work For Christian Living. LC 83-71240. 224p. (Orig.). 1982. (Crossway Bks); pap. 6.95 (ISBN 0-89107-294-2). Good News.
Schuller, Robert H. God's Way to the Good Life. LC 74-18978. (Pivot Family Reader Ser). 128p. 1974. pap. 1.75 (ISBN 0-87983-098-0). Keats.
Steiner, Rudolf. The Ten Commandments & the Sermon on the Mount. Solomon, Frieda, tr. from Ger. 44p. 1978. pap. 2.00 (ISBN 0-910142-79-3). Anthroposophic.
Sueltz, Arthur F. New Directions from the Ten Commandments. LC 75-36744. 128p. (Orig.). 1976. pap. 3.95i (ISBN 0-06-067760-0, RD145, HarpR). Har-Row.
Teaching the Ten Commandments. 20p. 1982. pap. 7.55 (ISBN 0-88479-035-5). Arena Lettres.
Watson, Thomas. The Ten Commandments. 245p. pap. 8.45 (ISBN 0-85151-146-5). Banner of Truth.
Williams, Barbara M. Freddie & the Ten Commandments. 3rd ed. 1978. 0.95 (ISBN 0-686-05835-6). Crusade Pubs.

COMMANDMENTS, TEN–JUVENILE LITERATURE
Cone, Molly. Who Knows Ten: Children's Tales of the Ten Commandments. LC 65-24639. (Illus.). 1968. text ed. 6.00 (ISBN 0-8074-0080-7, 102551); record o.p. 5.95 (ISBN 0-8074-0081-5, 102552). UAHC.

Curley, Maureen. The Ten Commandments. (Children of the Kingdom Activities Ser.). 1976. 9.95 (ISBN 0-89837-015-9, Pub. by Pflaum Pr). Peter Li.
Lovasik, Lawrence G. The Ten Commandments. (Saint Joseph Picture Bks.). (Illus.). flexible bdg. 0.95 (ISBN 0-89942-287-X, 287). Catholic Bk Pub.
O'Connor, Francine & Boswell, Kathryn. ABC's of Faith, Bk. 3. (Illus.). 32p. (Orig.). 1980. pap. 1.95 (ISBN 0-89243-125-3). Liguori Pubns.
Truitt, G. A. The Ten Commandments: Learning about God's Law. LC 56-1398. (Concept Bks.: Series 4). 1983. pap. 3.95 (ISBN 0-570-08527-6). Concordia.

COMMANDMENTS, TEN–SERMONS

Calvin, John. John Calvin's Sermons on the Ten Commandments. Farley, Benjamin W., ed. 544p. 1980. 12.95 (ISBN 0-8010-2443-9). Baker Bk.
Earles, Brent D. Perfect "10". 112p. 1986. 5.95 (ISBN 0-8010-3431-0). Baker Bk.
Erdahl, Lowell. Ten for Our Time. 1986. 5.50 (ISBN 0-89536-786-6, 6804). CSS of Ohio.

COMMITMENT

Duffy, Regis. Real Presence: Worship, Sacraments, & Commitment. LC 81-47877. 192p. 1982. pap. 8.95 (ISBN 0-06-062105-2, RD 383, HarpR). Har-Row.
Engstrom, Ted & Larson, Robert C. A Time for Commitment. 112p. 1987. padded gift ed. 9.95 (ISBN 0-310-51010-4); pap. 4.95 (ISBN 0-310-51011-2). Zondervan.
Staton, Knofel. Check Your Commitment: Instructor. 160p. 1985. pap. 3.50 (ISBN 0-87239-828-5, 39982). Standard Pub.
--Check Your Commitment: Student. 128p. 1985. pap. 2.95 (ISBN 0-87239-829-3, 39983). Standard Pub.
White, Jerry. The Power of Commitment. (Christian Character Library). 176p. 1985. 8.95 (ISBN 0-89109-532-2). NavPress.

COMMUNICATION (THEOLOGY)

see also Church Group Work; Evangelistic Work; Mass Media in Religion

Adams, Jay E. Communicating with Twentieth Century Man. 41p. 1979. pap. 1.95 (ISBN 0-87552-008-1). Presby & Reformed.
Arnold, Eberhard. The Inner Land, Vol. 5: The Living Word. LC 75-33241. 1975. 3.50 (ISBN 0-87486-157-8). Plough.
Blamires, Harry. Words Made Flesh: God Speaks to Us in the Ordinary Things of Life. 173p. (Orig.). 1985. pap. 6.95 (ISBN 0-89283-235-5). Servant.
Bolding, Amy. Simple Welcome Speeches & Other Helps. (Pocket Pulpit Library). 1973. pap. 4.50 (ISBN 0-8010-0612-0). Baker Bk.
Buckingham, Jamie. The Last Word. LC 78-56932. 1978. pap. 4.95 (ISBN 0-88270-303-X). Bridge Pub.
Buerlein, Homer K. How to Preach More Powerful Sermons. LC 85-26378. 140p. (Orig.). 1986. pap. 10.95 (ISBN 0-664-24683-4). Westminster.
Cox, James W. Preaching: A Comprehensive Approach to the Design & Delivery of Sermons. LC 84-48214. 320p. 1985. 18.45 (ISBN 0-06-061600-8, HarpR). Har-Row.
Craig, Floyd A. Christian Communicator's Handbook. rev. ed. LC 77-80946. 1977. pap. 8.95 (ISBN 0-8054-3508-5). Broadman.
Cummings. Men in the Sunlight of the Word. pap. 5.95 (ISBN 0-686-27771-6). Schmul Pub Co.
Dunkin, Steve. Church Advertising: A Practical Guide. LC 81-17562. (Creative Leadership Ser.). 128p. (Orig.). 1982. pap. 6.95 (ISBN 0-687-08140-8). Abingdon.
Erickson, Kenneth A. The Power of Communication. 112p. (Orig.). 1986. pap. 4.95 (ISBN 0-570-04435-9). Concordia.
Fischer, Edward. Everybody Steals from God: Communication as Worship. LC 77-3711. 1977. text ed. 10.95x (ISBN 0-268-00904-X). U of Notre Dame Pr.
Hughes, Ray H. Pentecostal Preaching. LC 81-84606. 159p. (Orig.). 1981. pap. text ed. 5.95 (ISBN 0-87148-711-X). Pathway Pr.
Kreckel, Marga. Communicative Acts & Shared Knowledge in Natural Discourse. LC 81-66392. 1981. 68.00 (ISBN 0-12-426180-9). Acad Pr.
Lawless, Agnes & Goodboy, Eadie. The Word: God's Manual for Maturity. (Bible Study Enrichment Ser.). 64p. (Orig.). 1980. pap. 2.95 (ISBN 0-930756-59-2, 522004). Aglow Pubns.
Loewen, Jacob A. Culture & Human Values: Christian Intervention in Anthropological Perspective. Smalley, William A., ed. LC 75-12653. (Applied Cultural Anthropology Ser.). 443p. (Orig.). 1975. pap. 10.95x (ISBN 0-87808-722-2). William Carey Lib.
Main, John. Word into Silence. LC 80-84660. 96p. 1981. pap. 4.95 (ISBN 0-8091-2369-X). Paulist Pr.
Nichols, Sue. Words on Target: For Better Christian Communication. LC 63-16410. (Illus., Orig.). 1963. pap. 5.50 (ISBN 0-8042-1476-X). John Knox.
Reese, James M. Experiencing the Good News: The New Testament as Communication. (Good News Studies Ser.: Vol. 10). 1984. pap. 9.95 (ISBN 0-89453-448-3). M Glazier.
Schwarz, Hans. Divine Communication: Word & Sacrament in Biblical, Historical & Contemporary Perspective. LC 84-48732. 176p. 1985. pap. 10.95 (ISBN 0-8006-1846-7, 1-1846). Fortress.
Skudlarek, William. The Word in Worship. LC 80-25525. (Abingdon Preacher's Library). 128p. (Orig.). 1981. pap. 6.95 (ISBN 0-687-46131-6). Abingdon.
Sogaard, Viggo B. Everything You Need to Know for a Cassette Ministry. LC 74-20915. 224p. 1975. pap. 7.95 (ISBN 0-87123-125-5, 210125). Bethany Hse.
Stauderman, Albert P. Let Me Illustrate: Stories & Quotations for Christian Communicators. LC 83-70511. 192p. (Orig.). 1983. pap. 9.95 (ISBN 0-8066-2017-X, 10-3817). Augsburg.

COMMUNION

see Lord's Supper

COMMUNION OF SAINTS

Benko, Stephen. Meaning of Sanctorum Communio. LC 64-55292. (Studies in Historical Theology: No. 3). 1964. pap. 10.00x (ISBN 0-8401-0178-3). A R Allenson.
Provost, James H., ed. Church As Communion. (Permanent Seminar Studies: No. 1). 245p. 1984. pap. 8.00 (ISBN 0-943616-23-9). Canon Law Soc.

COMMUNION SERMONS

Alexander, J. W. God is Love: Communion Addresses. 368p. 1985. pap. 5.95 (ISBN 0-85151-459-6). Banner of Truth.
Lybrand, R. E., Jr. Holy Communion Is... Sherer, Michael L., ed. (Orig.). 1987. pap. 6.50 (ISBN 0-89536-853-6, 7812). CSS of Ohio.
Maclaren, Alexander, et al. Communion Meditations & Outlines. (Pocket Pulpit Library). 1979. pap. 4.50 (ISBN 0-8010-6199-7). Baker Bk.
Weenink, Allen J. Sounds of Stillness. 1984. 3.95 (ISBN 0-89536-686-X, 4862). CSS of Ohio.

COMMUNISM AND CHRISTIANITY

Alexander, Stella. Church & State in Yugoslavia since Nineteen Forty-Five. LC 77-88668. (Soviet & East European Studies). 1979. 52.50 (ISBN 0-521-21942-6). Cambridge U Pr.
Bales, James. Two Worlds: Christianity & Communism. pap. 2.25 (ISBN 0-686-80419-8). Lambert Bk.
Brown, William M. Communism & Christianism. 252p. lib. bdg. 24.95 (ISBN 0-88286-046-1); pap. 4.00 (ISBN 0-88286-045-3). C H Kerr.
Burbick, Leslie. The Church's Strange Bedfellows. 1986. 6.95 (ISBN 0-8062-2408-8). Carlton.
Coste, Rene. Marxist Analysis & Christian Faith. Couture, Roger A., et al, trs. from Fr. LC 85-3119. Tr. of Analyse Marxiste et foi Chretienne. 256p. (Orig.). 1985. pap. 11.95 (ISBN 0-88344-342-2). Orbis Bks.
Dean, Thomas. Post-Theistic Thinking: The Marxist-Christian Dialogue in Radical Perspective. LC 74-83202. 300p. 1975. 29.95 (ISBN 0-87722-037-9). Temple U Pr.
Elliot, Delber H. Doom of the Dictators. LC 59-14581. pap. 23.00 (ISBN 0-317-07875-5, 2012820). Bks Demand UMI.
Feibleman, James K. Christianity, Communism & the Ideal Society: A Philosophical Approach to Modern Politics. LC 75-3140. Repr. of 1937 ed. 38.00 (ISBN 0-404-59149-3). AMS Pr.
Fierro, Alfredo. The Militant Gospel: A Critical Introduction to Political Theologies. Drury, John, tr. from Span. LC 77-1652. Orig. Title: El Evangelio Beligerente. 459p. (Orig.). 1977. pap. 3.48 (ISBN 0-88344-311-2). Orbis Bks.
Gonzalez-Ruiz, Jose-Maria. The New Creation: Marxist & Christian? O'Connell, Mathew J., tr. from Spanish. LC 76-10226. Orig. Title: Marximo y Cristianismo Frente Al Hombre Nuevo. 160p. (Orig.). 1976. 1.74 (ISBN 0-88344-327-9). Orbis Bks.
Heit, Edmund. The Soviets Are Coming. LC 80-18836. 160p. 1980. pap. 2.95 (ISBN 0-88243-585-X, 02-0585). Gospel Pub.
Jones, E. Stanley. Cristo y el Comunismo. Gattinoni, C. T., tr. from Eng. Orig. Title: Christ's Alternative to Communism. (Span.). 96p. 1981. pap. 2.10 (ISBN 0-311-05040-9, Edit Mundo). Casa Bautista.
Lawrence, John. The Hammer & the Cross. LC 86-4025. 208p. 1986. text ed. 15.00x (ISBN 0-87663-470-6). Universe.
Lloyd, Roger B. Revolutionary Religion: Christianity, Fascism, & Communism. LC 78-63686. (Studies in Fascism: Ideology & Practice). Repr. of 1938 ed. 24.50 (ISBN 0-404-16903-1). AMS Pr.
Lochman, Jan M. Encountering Marx: Bonds & Barriers between Christians & Marxists. Robertson, Edwin H., tr. LC 76-55827. pap. 39.00 (2026917). Bks Demand UMI.
Lyon, David. Karl Marx: A Christian Assessment of His Life & Thought. LC 81-8268. 192p. (Orig.). 1981. pap. 5.95 (ISBN 0-87784-879-3). Inter-Varsity.
McGovern, Arthur. Marxism: An American Christian Perspective. LC 79-27257. 352p. (Orig.). 1980. pap. 12.95 (ISBN 0-88344-301-5). Orbis Bks.
MacIntyre, Alasdair. Marxism & Christianity. LC 83-40600. 143p. 1984. pap. text ed. 6.95 (ISBN 0-268-01358-6, 85-13590). U of Notre Dame Pr.
Miranda, Jose. Communism in the Bible. Barr, Robert R., tr. from Span. LC 81-16936. Orig. Title: Comunismo En la Biblia. 96p. (Orig.). 1982. pap. 6.95 (ISBN 0-88344-014-8). Orbis Bks.
Miranda, Jose P. Marx & the Bible: A Critique of the Philosophy of Oppression. Eagleson, John, tr. from Span. LC 73-89053. Orig. Title: Marx y la Biblia: Critica a la filosofia de la opresion. Tr. of Marx y la Biblia. 360p. (Orig.). 1974. pap. 8.95x (ISBN 0-88344-307-4). Orbis Bks.
Parsons, Howard L. Christianity Today in the U. S. S. R. LC 86-27320. 216p. (Orig.). 1987. pap. 6.95 (ISBN 0-7178-0651-0). Intl Pubs CO.
Piediscalzi, Nicolas & Thobaben, Robert G., eds. Three Worlds of Christian Marxist Encounters. LC 84-48724. 240p. 1985. pap. 14.95 (ISBN 0-8006-1840-8, 1-1840). Fortress.
Powell, David E. Antireligious Propaganda in the Soviet Union: A Study of Mass Persuasion. LC 74-34127. 206p. 1975. pap. 8.95x (ISBN 0-262-66042-3). MIT Pr.
Tischner, Josef. Marxism & Christianity: The Quarrel & the Dialogue in Poland. (Orig.). 1987. 9.95 (ISBN 0-87840-419-8). Georgetown U Pr.
Turner, Denys. Marxism & Christianity. LC 82-22713. 268p. 1983. text ed. 27.50x (ISBN 0-389-20351-3). B&N Imports.
Vander Stelt, John C., ed. The Challenge of Marxist & Neo-Marxist Ideologies for Christian Scholarship. 280p. 1982. pap. 12.95 (ISBN 0-932914-07-1). Dordt Coll Pr.
Wurmbrand, Richard. In God's Underground. Orig. Title: Christ in the Communist Prisons. 1973. pap. text ed. 3.95 (ISBN 0-88264-003-8). Diane Bks.
--Marx & Satan. 143p. 1986. pap. 5.95 (ISBN 0-89107-379-5, Crossway Bks). Good News.

COMMUNISM AND RELIGION

see also Christianity and Economics; Communism and Christianity; Socialism and Catholic Church

Aptheker, Herbert. The Urgency of Marxist - Christian Dialogue. LC 73-109081. 1976. Repr. of 1970 ed. 24.00 (ISBN 0-527-03002-3). Kraus Repr.
Bales, J. D. Communism & the Reality of Moral Law. 1969. pap. 3.75 (ISBN 0-934532-01-X). Presby & Reformed.
Berdyaev, Nicolas. Origin of Russian Communism. 1960. pap. 8.95 (ISBN 0-472-06034-1, 34, AA). U of Mich Pr.
Communism: A Critique & Counter Proposal. 1975. pap. 2.00 (ISBN 0-686-13413-3). Unification Church.
Crawford, Matsu. My Head Is Bloody But Unbowed. 111p. (Orig.). 1983. pap. 5.00 (ISBN 0-9612862-0-2). R E F Typesetting Pub.
D'Arcy, Martin C. Communism & Christianity. 1957. 10.00 (ISBN 0-8159-5208-2). Devin.
De George, R. T. & Scanlan, J. P., eds. Marxism & Religion in Eastern Europe. LC 75-33051. (Sovietica Ser: No. 36). 180p. 1976. lib. bdg. 39.50 (ISBN 90-277-0636-0, Pub. by Reidel Holland). Kluwer Academic.
Dunn, Dennis J., ed. Religion & Communist Society: Selected Papers from the Second World Congress for Soviet & East European Studies. 165p. (Orig.). 1983. pap. 14.00 (ISBN 0-933884-29-X). Berkeley Slavic.
Gwynne, H. A., intro. by. The Cause of World Unrest. 1978. pap. 5.00x (ISBN 0-911038-40-X). Noontide.
Holzman, Michael. Lukac's Road to God: The Early Criticism Against Its Pre-Marxist Background. (Current Continental Research Ser.: No. 208). 196p. (Orig.). 1985. lib. bdg. 25.00 (ISBN 0-8191-4719-2); pap. text ed. 11.25 (ISBN 0-8191-4720-6). U Pr of Amer.
Lash, Nicholas. A Matter of Hope: A Theologian's Reflections on the Thought of Karl Marx. LC 82-1980. 312p. 1982. text ed. 19.95 (ISBN 0-268-01352-7). U of Notre Dame Pr.
Lewis, John, et al, eds. Christianity & the Social Revolution. facsimile ed. LC 79-37892. (Select Bibliographies Reprint Ser). Repr. of 1935 ed. 25.00 (ISBN 0-8369-6729-1). Ayer Co Pubs.
Piety, James. Chicago Historical Geographic Guide. (Illus.). 125p. (Orig.). 1983. pap. text ed. 6.80 wkbk. (ISBN 0-87563-290-4). Stipes.
Reed, Douglas. Behind the Scene. (Pt. 2 of Far & Wide). 1976. pap. 3.50x (ISBN 0-911038-41-8). Noontide.
Salluste, A. Marxism & Judaism. 1982. lib. bdg. 69.95 (ISBN 0-87700-329-7). Revisionist Pr.
Thrower, James. Marxist-Leninist 'Scientific Atheism' & the Study of Religion & Atheism in the U. S. S. R. (Ger.). 500p. 1983. 78.00 (ISBN 90-279-3060-0). Mouton.
Trotsky, Leon. Leon Trotsky on the Jewish Question. pap. 0.95 (ISBN 0-87348-157-7). Path Pr NY.
Vardys, V. Stanley. The Catholic Church, Dissent & Nationality in Soviet Lithuania. (East European Monographs: No. 43). 336p. 1978. 30.00x (ISBN 0-914710-36-2). East Eur Quarterly.

COMMUNITY CHURCHES

Adams, Jay E. Four Weeks with God & Your Neighbor. pap. 2.50 (ISBN 0-8010-0140-4). Baker Bk.
De Azevedo, Marcello C. Basic Ecclesiastical Communities. Drury, John, tr. 1987. write for info. (ISBN 0-87840-430-9); pap. write for info. (ISBN 0-87840-448-1). Georgetown U Pr.
Hoover, Dwight W. Henry James, Sr. & the Religion of the Community. LC 68-57113. pap. 38.00 (ISBN 0-317-08994-3, 2012947). Bks Demand UMI.

COMPANY FOR THE PROPAGATION OF THE GOSPEL IN NEW ENGLAND AND PARTS ADJACENT, LONDON

Rose-Troup, Frances. Massachusetts Bay Company & Its Predecessors. LC 68-56574. 1973. Repr. of 1930 ed. 22.50x (ISBN 0-678-00871-X). Kelley.

COMPARATIVE PHILOSOPHY

see Philosophy, Comparative

COMPARATIVE RELIGION

see Christianity and Other Religions; Religions

COMPUTERS–MORAL AND RELIGIOUS ASPECTS

Davis, Dennis M. & Clapp, Steve. The Third Wave & the Local Church. 175p. (Orig.). 1983. pap. 8.00 (ISBN 0-914527-54-1). C-Four Res.
Johnson, Douglas W. Computer Ethics: A Guide for the New Age. 128p. (Orig.). 1984. pap. 6.95 (ISBN 0-87178-155-7). Brethren.

COMPUTUS

see Calendar

CONCILIAR THEORY

see also Councils and Synods

Black, Antony. Council & Commune: The Conciliar Movement & the Fifteenth-Century Heritage. LC 79-89220. x, 253p. 1979. 25.95x (ISBN 0-915762-08-0). Patmos Pr.

CONCORDANCES

see also Bible–Concordances

Howard-Hill, T. H. Literary Concordances: A Complete Handbook for the Preparation of Manual & Computer Concordances. 1979. text ed. 18.00 (ISBN 0-08-023021-0). Pergamon.
McEvoy, Helena M. Concordance to Progress & Poverty. 729p. 1959. 1.00 (ISBN 0-911312-11-0). Schalkenbach.
Mignani, Rigo, et al, eds. Concordance To Juan Ruiz Libro De Buen Amor. LC 76-46390. 328p. 1977. 55.50 (ISBN 0-87395-322-3). State U NY Pr.
Van Zijl, J. B. A Concordance to the Targum of Isaiah. LC 78-25832. (Society of Biblical Literature. Aramaic Studies: No. 3). Repr. of 1979 ed. 53.80 (ISBN 0-8357-9569-1, 2017542). Bks Demand UMI.

CONDUCT OF LIFE

see also Altruism; Business Ethics; Charity; Christian Life; Encouragement; Ethics; Family Life Education; Forgiveness; Friendship; Interpersonal Relations; Justice; Kindness; Love; Obedience; Patriotism; Pride and Vanity; Right and Wrong; Self-Control; Self-Respect; Simplicity; Spiritual Life; Success; Temperance; Virtue and Virtues; Worry

also subdivision Conduct of Life under names of classes of persons, e.g. Youth–Conduct of Life

Adelsperger, Charlotte. When Your Child Hurts. LC 81-68639. 1985. pap. 5.95 (ISBN 0-8066-2161-3, 10-7088). Augsburg.
Allen, Roger & Rose, Ron. Common Sense Discipline. LC 86-61522. 1986. 12.95 (ISBN 0-8344-0135-5, BA110H). Sweet.
Altman, Nat. Ahimsa: Dynamic Compassion. LC 80-51548. 150p. (Orig.). 1981. pap. 4.95 (ISBN 0-8356-0537-X, Quest). Theos Pub Hse.
Ames, David A. & Gracey, Colin B. Good Genes? Emerging Values for Science, Religion & Society. (Illus.). 136p. 1984. pap. 3.60 (ISBN 0-88028-034-4). Forward Movement.
Ames, William. Conscience with the Power & Cases Thereof. LC 74-28826. (English Experience Ser.: No. 708). 1975. Repr. of 1639 ed. 35.00 (ISBN 9-0221-0708-6). Walter J Johnson.
Austin, Lou. You Are Greater Than You Know. 7.50 (ISBN 0-934538-16-6); pap. 4.50 (ISBN 0-934538-11-5). Partnership Foundation.
Baba, Meher, et al. Meher Baba Journal, Vol. 1, No. 11. Patterson, Elizabeth, ed. (No. 11). (Illus.). 66p. 1974. pap. 2.50x (ISBN 0-913078-18-2). Sheriar Pr.

Bach, Marcus. The Power of Total Living. 1978. pap. 2.50 (ISBN 0-449-23747-8, Crest). Fawcett.
Backman, Robert L. Be Master of Yourself. LC 86-2047. 227p. 1986. 9.95 (ISBN 0-87579-033-X). Deseret Bk.
Banas, Jackie. I Love Me, the Only Diet There Is: A Manual. (Orig.). 1986. spiral bdg. 7.00 (ISBN 0-9614014-3-5). Know Him Pr.
Barber, Bill. A Second Hand Life: Discussions with Bill Barber. 144p. (Orig.). 1986. pap. 8.95 (ISBN 0-87418-025-2, 163). Coleman Pub.
Barnes, Emilie. More Hours in My Day. (Orig.). 1982. pap. 5.95 (ISBN 0-89081-355-8). Harvest Hse.
Bass, Charles D. Banishing Fear from Your Life. LC 85-23943. 168p. 1986. 14.95 (ISBN 0-385-23331-0). Doubleday.
Baxter, Batsell B. & Hazelip, Harold. Anchors in Troubled Waters. Abr. ed. LC 82-50267. (Journey Adult Ser.). 126p. 1981. pap. text ed. 4.95 (ISBN 0-8344-0120-7). Sweet.
Benson, Dan. The Total Man. 1977. pap. 3.95 (ISBN 0-8423-7289-X). Tyndale.
Bernstein, Joanne. Loss & How to Cope with It. 160p. 1981. pap. 4.95 (ISBN 0-395-30012-6, Clarion). HM.
Bishop Ian Shervill. Going It - With God. 4th ed. 94p. 1985. 4.95 (ISBN 0-908175-37-X, Pub. by Boolarong Pubn Australia). Intl Spec Bk.
Black, Daniel. Never A Day Too Much. (Orig.). 1985. pap. text ed. 4.95 (ISBN 0-87148-631-8). Pathway Pr.
Blair, Caroline G. Prayers for Mothers. 1980. pap. 1.95 (ISBN 0-8170-0864-0). Judson.
Briscoe, Stuart D. God's Way to Live Successfully. 144p. 1986. pap. 2.95 (ISBN 0-8007-8582-7, Spire Bks). Revell.
Brister, C. W. Caring for the Caregivers. LC 85-3793. 1985. pap. 8.95 (ISBN 0-8054-5537-X). Broadman.
Brown, John. Worship Celebrations for Youth. 1980. pap. 4.95 (ISBN 0-8170-0866-7). Judson.
Brown, Marion R. Putting Life Back Together. 96p. 1986. 5.95 (ISBN 0-87159-132-4). Unity School.
Buber, Martin. The Way of Man. 44p. 1985. pap. 3.50 (ISBN 0-8065-0024-7). Citadel Pr.
Buerger, Jane. Growing As Jesus Grew. LC 80-17187. (Illus.). 32p. 1980. PLB 5.95 (ISBN 0-89565-173-4). Childs World.
Burns, Jim & Webster, Doug. Commitment to Growth: Experiencing the Fruit of the Spirit. 64p. (Orig.). 1985. wkbk. 3.95 (ISBN 0-89081-480-5). Harvest Hse.
Caldwell, Louis. After the Tassel Is Moved. (Ultra Bks Ser.). 1968. 4.95 (ISBN 0-8010-2332-7). Baker Bk.
Caldwell, Louis O. Another Tassel Is Moved: Guidelines for College Graduates. (Ultra Books Ser). 1970. 4.95 (ISBN 0-8010-2343-2). Baker Bk.
--Something Good for Those Who Feel Bad: Positive Solutions for Negative Emotions. 96p. 1985. pap. 6.95 (ISBN 0-8010-2505-2). Baker Bk.
--You Can Overcome Your Fears, Phobias, & Worries. 1985. pap. 1.25 (ISBN 0-8010-2506-0). Baker Bk.
Camara, Dom H. Questions for Living. Barr, Robert R., tr. from Fr. Tr. of Des Questions pour Vivre. (Illus.). 112p. (Orig.). 1987. pap. 7.95 (ISBN 0-88344-558-1). Orbis Bks.
Campbell, Roger. Staying Positive in a Negative World. 132p. 1984. pap. 4.95 (ISBN 0-89693-377-6). Victor Bks.
Campbell, Ross & Gray, Randall. How to Keep Going When the Storms Keep Coming. 288p. (Orig.). 1986. pap. 6.95 (ISBN 0-8423-1376-1). Tyndale.
Carlisle, Thomas J. Journey with Jonah. rev. ed. 96p. 1984. pap. 1.95 (ISBN 0-88028-035-2). Forward Movement.
Chamberlain, Jonathan M. Eliminate Your SDBS: Self-Defeating Behaviors. LC 77-27634. (Illus.). 1978. pap. 7.95 (ISBN 0-8425-0998-4). Brigham.
Chastain, Jane. Concerned Women Can Make a Difference. 1987. pap. 7.95 (ISBN 0-8307-1185-6, 5418968). Regal.
Chaudhuri, Haridas. Mastering the Problems of Living. new ed. LC 75-4172. 222p. 1975. pap. 2.75 (ISBN 0-8356-0463-2, Quest). Theos Pub Hse.
Christopher. Scott. new ed. (Orig.). 1978. pap. 3.95 (ISBN 0-87243-078-2). Templegate.
Coakley, Mary L. How to Live Life to the Fullest: A Handbook for Seasoned Citizens. LC 83-63167. 168p. 1984. pap. 4.95 (ISBN 0-87973-628-3, 628). Our Sunday Visitor.
Coffin, Glenyce. Run to Win: Training for the Overcoming Life. (Cornerstone Ser.). 40p. 1984. pap. 2.50 (ISBN 0-930756-87-8, 533010). Aglow Pubns.
Cottrell, Stan. To Run & Not Be Weary. (Illus.). 192p. 1985. 12.95 (ISBN 0-8007-1444-X). Revell.
Covey, Stephen R. How to Succeed with People. 151p. 1971. 6.95 (ISBN 0-87747-439-7). Deseret Bk.
Crockett, William J. Life: Voices from the Heart. 15p. 1985. pap. 3.00 (ISBN 0-934383-05-7). Pride Prods.
--My Quest: Voices from the Heart. 15p. 1985. pap. 3.00 (ISBN 0-934383-32-4). Pride Prods.
Curtis, Helene & Dudley, Cliff. All That I Have. LC 77-81394. 1979. pap. 2.95 (ISBN 0-89221-044-3). New Leaf.
Dahlstrom, J. & Ryel, D. Promises to Keep: Reading & Writing about Values. 1977. pap. text ed. write for info (ISBN 0-13-731059-5). P-H.
Daly, Cahal. Morals, Law & Life. 228p. 1966. 5.95 (ISBN 0-933932-08-1). Scepter Pubs.
Daniels, Madeline M. Living Your Religion in the Real World. LC 84-18209. 192p. 14.95 (ISBN 0-13-539016-8); pap. 6.95 (ISBN 0-13-539008-7). P-H.
Davis, Roy E. My Personal Fulfillment Plan Workbook. 32p. 1984. pap. 3.95 (ISBN 0-317-20868-3). CSA Pr.
De Benedittis, Suzanne M. Teaching Faith & Morals. 200p. (Orig.). 1981. pap. 8.95 (ISBN 0-86683-621-7, HaprsR). Har-Row.
Duckworth, Robin. This Is the Word of the Lord: Year B., the Year of the Mark. 1981. pap. 9.95 (ISBN 0-19-826662-6). Oxford U Pr.
Durham, Ken. Speaking from the Heart. LC 86-61523. 1986. 10.95 (ISBN 0-8344-0136-3, BA120H). Sweet.
Earles, Brent D. Bouncing Back. (Life Enrichment Ser.). 144p. Date not set. pap. 5.95 (ISBN 0-8010-3435-3). Baker Bk.
--You're Worth It! But Do You Believe It? 112p. 1985. pap. 5.95 (ISBN 0-8010-3427-2). Baker Bk.
Edwards, LaVell. Achieving. 77p. 1985. 7.95 (ISBN 0-934126-79-8). Randall Bk Co.
Eisenman, Tom. On My Own. (Family Ministry Ser.). (Illus.). 54p. 1985. pap. text ed. 19.95 (ISBN 0-89191-978-3). Cook.
Ewin, R. E. Cooperation & Human Values: A Study of Moral Reasoning. 1981. 22.50 (ISBN 0-312-16956-6). St Martin.
Farina, Richard. Been Down So Long It Looks Like up to Me. 1983. pap. 6.95 (ISBN 0-14-006536-9). Penguin.
Faulkner, Paul. Making Things Right, When Things Go Wrong. LC 86-61405. 1986. 11.95 (ISBN 0-8344-0137-1, BA130H). Sweet.
Fillmore, Charles. Dynamics for Living. 1967. 5.95 (ISBN 0-87159-025-5). Unity School.
Fillmore, Lowell. Health, Wealth & Happiness. 1964. 5.95 (ISBN 0-87159-055-7). Unity School.
Fillmore, Myrtle. How to Let God Help You. 1956. 5.95 (ISBN 0-87159-057-3). Unity School.
Firestone, Robert & Catlett, Joyce. The Truth: A Psychological Curse. 234p. 1981. 13.95 (ISBN 0-02-538380-9). Macmillan.
Forlines, F. Leroy. The Doctrine of Perseverance. 2nd ed. 24p. 1987. pap. price not set. Randall Hse.
Foth, Margaret. Life Is Too Short. 144p. (Orig.). 1985. pap. 5.95 (ISBN 0-310-42681-2, 12779P). Zondervan.
Fox, Emmet. Diagrams for Living: The Bible Unveiled. LC 69-10475. 1968. 12.45 (ISBN 0-06-062851-0, HarpR). Har-Row.
Franasiak, Edwin J., ed. Belonging: Issues of Emotional Living in an Age of Stress for Clergy & Religious. LC 79-11482. 127p. 1979. pap. 4.95 (ISBN 0-89571-007-2). Affirmation.
Fuller, Clifford. Let's Try This Way. pap. 1.00 (ISBN 0-87516-196-0). De Vorss.
Galloway. Twelve Ways to Develop a Positive Attitude. 1975. pap. 1.95 (ISBN 0-8423-7550-3). Tyndale.
Geddes, Jim. The Better Half of Life. (Orig.). 1987. pap. 7.95 (ISBN 0-8054-5732-1). Broadman.
Goldsmith, Joel S. Living Now. Sinkler, Lorraine, ed. 192p. 1984. pap. 5.95 (ISBN 0-8065-0911-2). Citadel Pr.
Gore, Charles. The Philosophy of the Good Life. LC 77-27197. (Gifford Lectures: 1929-30). Repr. of 1930 ed. 24.00 (ISBN 0-404-60484-6). AMS Pr.
Hadfield, J. A. Psychology & Morals. 245p. 1980. Repr. of 1926 ed. lib. bdg. 30.00 (ISBN 0-8492-5282-2). R West.
Hall, Theodore. The Mysterious Fundamental Option. (Synthesis Ser.). 1979. 0.75 (ISBN 0-8199-0746-4). Franciscan Herald.
Hamilton, Iva. The Story of Albert J. (Illus., Orig.). 1985. pap. 6.95 (ISBN 0-87418-028-7, 162). Coleman Pub.
Harbaugh, Gary L. The Faith-Hardy Christian: How to Face the Challenges of Life with Confidence. LC 86-7966. (Christian Growth Ser.). 128p. 1986. pap. 6.95 (ISBN 0-8066-2212-1, 10-2184). Augsburg.
Hardisty, Margaret. Forever My Love. LC 74-32644. 1979. pap. 3.25 (ISBN 0-89081-140-7, 1407). Harvest Hse.
Harker, Herbert. Turn Home Again. 245p. 1984. 6.95 (ISBN 0-934126-57-7). Randall Bk Co.
Hausmann, Winifred W. A Guide to Love-Powered Living. LC 85-72282. 192p. (Orig.). 1986. pap. 7.95 (ISBN 0-87516-560-5). De Vorss.
--How to Live Life Victoriously. 160p. 1982. 5.95 (ISBN 0-87159-060-3). Unity School.
Hepburn, Daisy. Get Up & Grow. LC 84-3361. (Life with Spice Bible Study Ser.). 64p. 1984. 2.95 (ISBN 0-8307-0942-8, 6101800). Regal.
Heubach, Paul. Living with Suffering. Coffen, Richard W., ed. (Better Living Ser.). 32p. (Orig.). 1986. pap. 1.25 (ISBN 0-8280-0322-X). Review & Herald.
Hilt, James. Melhor Relacionamento com. Orig. Title: How to Have a Better Relationship with Anybody. (Port.). 1986. write for info. (ISBN 0-8297-0542-2). Life Pubs Intl.
Hinckley, Lawrence. Bridge to a Better Life: An Introduction to New Thought. 1978. pap. 2.25 (ISBN 0-87516-255-X). De Vorss.
Hindson, Edward & Byrd, Walter. When the Road Gets Tough. 160p. 1986. 9.95 (ISBN 0-8007-1495-4). Revell.
Holm, Marilyn F. Tell Me Why: A Guide to Children's Questions about Faith & Life. LC 85-7355. 144p. (Orig.). 1985. pap. 6.95 (ISBN 0-8066-2160-5, 10-6230). Augsburg.
Holt, Pat. Mommy's Lesson. 32p. 1985. pap. 3.95 (ISBN 0-570-04131-7, 56-1545). Concordia.
Hong, Edna. Forgiveness Is a Work As Well As a Grace. LC 84-6470. 128p. (Orig.). 1984. pap. 5.95 (ISBN 0-8066-2081-1, 10-2356). Augsburg.
Hoppe, Leslie. Being Poor: A Biblical Study. (Theology & Life Ser.). 240p. 1987. pap. 9.95 (ISBN 0-89453-620-6). M Glazier.
Hora, Thomas. Right Usefulness. 35p. 1987. pap. 4.00 (ISBN 0-913105-12-0). PAGL Pr.
--What God Wants. 35p. 1987. pap. 4.00 (ISBN 0-913105-11-2). PAGL Pr.
Howard, Richard E. So Who's Perfect? 140p. (Orig.). 1985. pap. 5.95 (ISBN 0-8341-1070-9). Beacon Hill.
Hsi, Chu. The Philosophy of Human Nature. 1976. lib. bdg. 59.95 (ISBN 0-8490-2432-3). Gordon Pr.
Hume, David. An Enquiry Concerning the Principles of Morals. Schneewind, J. B., ed. LC 82-11679. (HPC Philosophical Classics Ser.). 132p. 1983. lib. bdg. 15.00 (ISBN 0-915145-46-4); pap. text ed. 3.45 (ISBN 0-915145-45-6). Hackett Pub.
Institute for Religious & Social Studies. Integrity & Compromise: Problems of Public & Private Conscience. facsimile ed. MacIver, R. M., ed. LC 76-167367. (Essay Index Reprints - Religion & Civilization Ser). Repr. of 1957 ed. 15.00 (ISBN 0-8369-2656-0). Ayer Co Pubs.
Jackson, Neil E., Jr. Beyond All Expectations. (Orig.). 1987. pap. 6.95 (ISBN 0-8054-5044-0). Broadman.
James, Henry, Sr. Morality & the Perfect Life. LC 72-918. (The Selected Works of Henry James, Sr.: Vol. 5). 88p. 1983. Repr. of 1906 ed. 18.00 (ISBN 0-404-10085-6). AMS Pr.
Jiggetts, Robert C., Jr. Beyond Circumstances. (Illus.). 96p. (Orig.). 1986. pap. 9.95 (ISBN 1-55630-016-6). Brentwood Comm.
Jones, Cliff. Winning Through Integrity. 160p. 1985. 9.95 (ISBN 0-687-45604-5). Abingdon.
Kennedy, D. James. Learning to Live with the People You Love. 200p. (Orig.). 1987. pap. text ed. 3.95 (ISBN 0-88368-190-0). Whitaker Hse.
Kiemel, Ann. Hi, I'm Ann. (Direction Bks). pap. 2.50 (ISBN 0-8010-5346-3). Baker Bk.
Kinzer, Mark. Living with a Clear Conscience: A Christian Strategy for Overcoming Guilt & Self-Condemnation. (Living As a Christian Ser.). 160p. 1982. pap. 3.50 (ISBN 0-89283-115-4). Servant.
Knight, Margaret. Morals Without Religion. 124p. 1981. 25.00x (ISBN 0-686-97044-6, Pub. by Dobson Bks England). State Mutual Bk.
Krishnamurti, Jiddu. Think on These Things. 1970. pap. 4.95 (ISBN 0-06-080192-1, P192, PL). Har-Row.
--You Are the World. 160p. 1973. pap. 4.95 (ISBN 0-06-080303-7, P303, PL). Har-Row.
Krutza, William J. & DiCicco, Philip P. Facing Your Nation. (Contemporary Discussion Ser.). 1975. pap. 1.95 (ISBN 0-8010-5372-2). Baker Bk.
Kubler-Ross, Elisabeth. Working It Through. (Illus.). 176p. 1987. pap. 5.95 (ISBN 0-02-022000-6, Collier). Macmillan.
Kuntzleman, Charles T. The Well Family Book. 256p. 1985. 13.95 (ISBN 0-89840-092-9). Heres Life.
Ladd, George T. Philosophy of Conduct: A Treatise of the Facts, Principles, & Ideals of Ethics. LC 75-3222. Repr. of 1902 ed. 46.50 (ISBN 0-404-59218-X). AMS Pr.
Lance, Fran & King, Pat. Tell Your Secret. 128p. 1986. pap. 5.95 (ISBN 0-89221-142-3). New Leaf.
Lee, Clay F. Jesus Never Said Everyone Was Lovable. 112p. 1987. pap. 6.95 (ISBN 0-687-19980-8). Abingdon.
Leichtman, Robert R. & Japikse, Carl. The Art of Living, Vol. IV. LC 83-703086. (Illus.). 280p. (Orig.). 1984. pap. 6.95 (ISBN 0-89804-035-3). Ariel OH.
Lewis, H. Spencer. Self Mastery & Fate with the Cycles of Life. LC 55-16785. (Illus.). 253p. 1986. pap. 8.95 (ISBN 0-912057-45-9, G-657). AMORC.
Lindskoog, Kathryn. A Partir del Eden. Orozco, Julio, tr. from Eng. LC 77-73843. Tr. of Up from Eden. (Span.). 144p. 1977. pap. 3.50 (ISBN 0-89922-092-4). Edit Caribe.
Linthorst, Jan & Rubadeau, Joan. Handbook for Building a Beautiful Homelife. 1987. pap. 12.00 (ISBN 0-913105-20-1). PAGL Pr.
Loomis, Darlene. Growing Together with Guys, Gals & Animal Pals. (Illus., Orig.). 1977. pap. 2.00 (ISBN 0-686-36276-4). Drain Enterprise.
Lubich, Chiara. Stars & Tears. LC 85-72399. 153p. 1986. pap. 5.25 (ISBN 0-911782-54-0). New City.
Luccock, Halford E. & Rauschenbusch, Walter. Living a Thousand Lives. LC 82-9091. 80p. (Orig.). 1982. pap. 5.95 (ISBN 0-8298-0622-9). Pilgrim NY.
Lynch, Richard. Know Thyself. 1967. 5.95 (ISBN 0-87159-077-8). Unity School.
McCall, Clark B. Putting up with Your Put Downs. (Uplook Ser.). 1978. pap. 0.79 (ISBN 0-8163-0093-3, 16970-6). Pacific Pr Pub Assn.
McClelland, W. Robert. Chance to Dance: Risking a Spiritually Mature Life. Lambert, Herbert, ed. LC 85-18987. 128p. (Orig.). 1986. pap. 8.95 (ISBN 0-8272-0449-3). CBP.
McCullough, Mamie. I Can, You Can Too! 224p. 1986. 14.95 (ISBN 0-8407-3068-3). Nelson.
McDowell, Josh. His Image...My Image: Biblical Principles for Improving Your Self Image. 180p. 1985. pap. 6.95 (ISBN 0-89840-103-8). Heres Life.
Mandelbaum, Bernard. Choose Life. 1972. pap. 5.95 (ISBN 0-8197-0006-1). Bloch.
Mandino, Og. The Greatest Gift in the World. LC 76-43508. (Illus.). 128p. 1976. 8.95 (ISBN 0-8119-0274-9). Fell.
Marquis, Anthony J. A Lifetime. 48p. 1986. 5.95 (ISBN 0-89962-521-5). Todd & Honeywell.
Martin, Laurence. Discover Life. LC 75-18373. 80p. 1975. pap. 1.95 (ISBN 0-8361-1779-4). Herald Pr.
Maxwell, John. Your Attitude: Key to Success. 156p. 1985. pap. 5.95 (ISBN 0-89840-102-X). Heres Life.
Mayhall, Carole. Words That Hurt, Words That Heal. 112p. 1986. hdbk. 8.95 (ISBN 0-89109-543-8). NavPress.
Meador, Prentice A., Jr. Who Rules Your Life? LC 79-64089. (Journey Bks.). 1979. pap. 3.50 (ISBN 0-8344-0107-X). Sweet.
Meiburg, Albert L. Sound Body Sound Mind. LC 84-10356. (Potentials: Guides for Productive Living Ser.: Vol. 9). 112p. 1984. pap. 7.95 (ISBN 0-664-24532-3). Westminster.
Miller, Kevin, ed. Help: Coping with Crisis. (Senior High Pacesetter Ser.). 64p. 1986. pap. 7.95 (ISBN 0-89191-282-7). Cook.
--Life Choices: Tackling the Biggest Decisions You'll Ever Make. (Senior High Pacesetter Ser.). 64p. 1986. pap. 7.95 (ISBN 0-89191-327-0). Cook.
Mills, Michael. Dirty Hands, Pure Hearts. 1985. 4.50 (ISBN 0-89536-724-6, 5808). CSS of Ohio.
Moncure, Jane B. Growing Strong Inside. LC 85-10341. (A New Values Ser.). (Illus.). 32p. 1985. PLB 7.45 (ISBN 0-89565-333-8). Childs World.
Moody, D. L. Heaven: How to Get There. 112p. 1982. pap. text ed. 3.50 (ISBN 0-88368-115-3). Whitaker Hse.
Morrell, Gloria G. Lying...Not a Very Fun Thing. 1986. pap. 3.95 (ISBN 0-8054-4338-X). Broadman.
--Sally's Calendar Book. 1986. pap. 3.95 (ISBN 0-8054-4337-1). Broadman.
Mosher, Ralph, ed. Moral Education: A First Generation of Research & Development. LC 80-18607. 426p. 1980. 42.95 (ISBN 0-03-053961-7). Praeger.
Muck, Terry C. When to Take a Risk, No. 9. 192p. 1987. 9.95 (ISBN 0-8499-0615-6). Word Bks.
Mullen, Tom. Laughing Out Loud & Other Religious Experiences. 1983. 8.95 (ISBN 0-8499-0329-7). Word Bks.
Murray, Andrew. Living the New Life. 256p. 1982. pap. text ed. 3.50 (ISBN 0-88368-108-0). Whitaker Hse.
Nachman of Breslov. Rabbi Nachman's Stories. Kaplan, Aryeh, tr. from Hebrew. LC 83-70201. Tr. of Sippurey Ma'asioth. 552p. 1983. 15.00 (ISBN 0-930213-02-5). Breslov Res Inst.
--Rabbi Nachman's Tikkun: The Comprehensive Remedy. Greenbaum, Avraham, tr. from Hebrew. 240p. 1984. 10.00 (ISBN 0-930213-06-8). Breslov Res Inst.

--Rabbi Nachman's Wisdom. Rosenfeld, Zvi A., ed. Kaplan, Aryeh, tr. from Hebrew. Tr. of Shevachay HaRan-Sichos HaRan. (Illus.). 510p. 1984. 14.00 (ISBN 0-930213-00-9); pap. 11.00 (ISBN 0-930213-01-7). Breslov Res Inst.

--Les Contes. Regnot, Franz, tr. from Yiddish. Tr. of Sippurey Ma'asioth. (Fr.). 180p. (Orig.). 1981. pap. 7.00 (ISBN 0-930213-22-X). Breslov Res Inst.

--The Gems of Rabbi Nachman. Rosenfeld, Tzvi A., ed. Kaplan, Ayreh, tr. from Hebrew. (Illus.). 186p. (Orig.). 1980. pap. 2.00 (ISBN 0-930213-10-6). Breslov Res Inst.

--Hitbodedouth: Ou La Porte du Ciel. Besancon, Its'hak, adapted by. (Fr.). 110p. (Orig.). 1982. pap. 2.00 (ISBN 0-930213-27-0). Breslov Res Inst.

Nachman of Breslov & Nathan of Breslov. Azamra (I Will Sing) Greenbaum, Avraham, tr. from Hebrew. 64p. (Orig.). 1984. pap. 1.50 (ISBN 0-930213-11-4). Breslov Res INst.

--Courage! Tr. of Meshivat Nefesh. 119p. (Orig.). 1983. pap. 3.00 (ISBN 0-930213-23-8). Breslov Res Inst.

--Restore My Soul. Greenbaum, Avraham, tr. from Hebrew. Tr. of Meshivat Nefesh. 128p. (Orig.). 1980. pap. 3.00 (ISBN 0-930213-13-0). Breslov Res Inst.

Nathan of Breslov. Advice. Greenbaum, Avraham, tr. from Hebrew. LC 83-70202. Tr. of Likutey Etzot. 522p. 1983. 13.00 (ISBN 0-930213-04-1). Breslov Res Inst.

Nearing, Helen & Nearing, Scott. Living the Good Life: How to Live Sanely & Simply in a Troubled World. LC 73-127820. (Illus.). 1971. pap. 5.25 (ISBN 0-8052-0300-1). Schocken.

Norris, John. Treatises Upon Several Subjects. Wellek, Rene, ed. LC 75-11244. (British Philosophers & Theologians of the 17th & 18th Centuries Ser.). 1978. Repr. of 1698 ed. lib. bdg. 51.00 (ISBN 0-8240-1796-X). Garland Pub.

Oates, Wayne E., ed. Potentials: (Guides for Productive Living Ser.). 1984. pap. 7.95 ea. Westminster.

Odhner, Hugo L. The Moral Life. 142p. 1985. Repr. of 1957 ed. write for info. (ISBN 0-910557-08-X). Acad New Church.

Palms. First Things First. 1983. 5.95 (ISBN 0-88207-290-0). Victor Bks.

Passamaneck, Marge. People Are Different, People Are the Same. 1983. pap. 3.10 (ISBN 0-89536-615-0, 1629). CSS of Ohio.

Paulson, J. Sig. Living with Purpose. 142p. 1968. pap. 3.95 (ISBN 0-317-20871-3). CSA Pr.

Peale, Norman V. Inspiring Messages for Daily Living. 1981. pap. 2.50 (ISBN 0-449-92383-5, Crest). Fawcett.

--The New Art of Living. 160p. 1977. pap. 2.50 (ISBN 0-449-23938-1, Crest). Fawcett.

--Sin, Sex & Self-Control. 1978. pap. 2.50 (ISBN 0-449-23921-7, Crest). Fawcett.

--Stay Alive All Your Life. 256p. 1978. pap. 2.25 (ISBN 0-449-23513-0, Crest). Fawcett.

Pearl, Cyril. The Girl with the Swansdown Seat: Aspects of Mid-Victorian Morality. 6.95 (ISBN 0-686-85784-4, Pub. by Quartet England). Charles River Bks.

Pendleton, Winston K. Do It! Six Steps to Happiness. Lambert, Herbert, ed. LC 86-6112. 96p. (Orig.). 1986. pap. 5.95 (ISBN 0-8272-0613-5). CBP.

Petersen, J. Allan. The Art of Being a Man. 1974. pap. 1.25 (ISBN 0-8423-0085-6). Tyndale.

--The Myth of the Greener Grass. 1983. 8.95 (ISBN 0-8423-4656-2); pap. 6.95 (ISBN 0-8423-4651-1). Tyndale.

Pilch, John J. Wellness Spirituality. 112p. 1985. pap. 7.95 (ISBN 0-8245-0710-X). Crossroad NY.

Pirola, Teresa. Empowered People. 48p. (Orig.). 1985. pap. text ed. 1.95 (ISBN 0-911905-26-X). Past & Mat Rene Ctr.

Pitts, Audre. Let Me Keep Laughter. 106p. 1986. pap. 3.95 (ISBN 0-8341-1090-3). Beacon Hill.

Polston, Don. Living Without Losing. LC 75-27142. 1976. pap. 5.95 (ISBN 0-89081-015-X). Harvest Hse.

Ponder, Catherine. The Millionaire from Nazareth. (The Millionaires of the Bible Ser.). 1979. pap. 6.95 (ISBN 0-87516-370-X). De Vorss.

Pontifical Council for the Family. Family Hope for the World. 71p. pap. 3.50 (ISBN 0-317-46615-1). New City.

Pontifical Council for the Laity. A Festival of Hope. 179p. pap. 6.00 (ISBN 0-317-46617-8). New City.

Powell. Stand Tough. 1983. 3.95 (ISBN 0-88207-592-6). Victor Bks.

Powell, John. Fully Human, Fully Alive. LC 76-41586. 1976. pap. 3.95 (ISBN 0-913592-77-3). Argus Comm.

Preston, Mary Jane. Getting Your House in Order. 130p. 1986. pap. 8.95 (ISBN 0-941478-48-3). Paraclete Pr.

Purgraski. Sorting Life Out. LC 60-9573. 1978. 24.00x (ISBN 0-930004-00-0); free student packet, 36 pgs. C E M Comp.

Rajneesh, Bhagwan Shree. Don't Look Before You Leap. Rajneesh Foundation International, ed. LC 83-3282. (Initiation Talks Ser.). 480p. (Orig.). 1983. pap. 4.95 (ISBN 0-88050-554-0). Chidvilas Found.

Rector, Connie. Sustaining. 79p. 1985. 7.95 (ISBN 0-934126-59-3). Randall Bk Co.

Roberts, Oral. Your Road to Recovery. 224p. 1986. 12.95 (ISBN 0-8407-9058-9). Oliver-Nelson.

Rossignol, Elaine. You Are What You Swallow. LC 86-83406. 220p. (Orig.). 1987. pap. 9.95 (ISBN 0-89896-240-4). Larksdale.

Russell, Robert A. You Too Can Be Prosperous. 162p. 1975. pap. 3.95 (ISBN 0-87516-205-3). De Vorss.

Sailes, Samuel. Self-Help. Bull, George & Joseph, Keith, eds. 240p. 1986. pap. 6.95 (ISBN 0-14-009100-9). Penguin.

Sand, Faith A. The Travels of Faith. LC 85-17751. (Illus.). 152p. (Orig.). 1986. pap. 4.95 (ISBN 0-932727-03-4). Hope Pub Hse.

Sanderlin, David. Putting on the New Self: A Guide to Personal Development & Community Living. 1986. pap. 12.95 (ISBN 0-87061-125-9). Chr Classics.

Sapp, Gary L., ed. Handbook of Moral Development. 296p. 1986. pap. 14.95 (ISBN 0-89135-054-3). Religious Educ.

Satchidananda, S., ed. Living Yoga. (Psychic Studies). 336p. 1977. 30.95 (ISBN 0-677-05230-8). Gordon & Breach.

Schaefer, Christopher & Voors, Tijno. Vision in Action: The Art of Taking & Shaping Initiatives. 199p. (Orig.). 1986. pap. text ed. 12.95 (ISBN 0-88010-150-4). Anthroposophic.

Schuller, Arvella. The Positive Family. 1983. pap. 2.75 (ISBN 0-8007-8474-X, Spire Bks). Revell.

Schuller, Robert H. Self-Love. 160p. 1975. pap. 2.95 (ISBN 0-8007-8195-3, Spire Bks). Revell.

--You Can Become the Person You Want to Be. 160p. 1976. pap. 2.95 (ISBN 0-8007-8235-6, Spire Bks). Revell.

Schutz, Susan P. Creeds to Live By, Dreams to Follow. LC 86-7318. (Illus.). 64p. (Orig.). 1987. pap. 4.95 (ISBN 0-88396-248-9). Blue Mtn Pr Co.

Sears, Buddy. Purpose: A Little Gift in the Adventure of Life. 169p. (Orig.). 1986. pap. 6.95 (ISBN 0-87418-023-6, 160). Coleman Pub.

Sehnert, Keith W. Selfcare-Wellcare. LC 85-15622. 240p. (Orig.). 1985. text ed. 12.95 (ISBN 0-8066-2179-6, 10-5644); pap. 3.95 (ISBN 0-8066-2180-X, 10-5645). Augsburg.

Shedd, Charlie W. Letters to Philip. (Orig.). 1985. pap. 2.95 (ISBN 0-515-08465-4). Jove Pubns.

Shinn, Florence S. The Secret Door to Success. 1978. pap. 2.50 (ISBN 0-87516-258-4). De Vorss.

Sinetar, Marsha. Do What You Love, the Money Will Follow. 1987. pap. 9.95. Paulist Pr.

Sire, James W. The Universe Next Door: A Basic World View Catalog. LC 75-32129. 240p. (Orig.). 1976. pap. 7.95 (ISBN 0-87784-772-X). Inter-Varsity.

Smith, Donald. How to Cure Yourself of Positive Thinking. LC 77-70191. 1977. 7.95 (ISBN 0-912458-80-1). E A Seemann.

Smith, F. LaGard. Insights for Today: The Wisdom of the Proverbs. LC 85-80483. 1985. leather 19.95 (ISBN 0-89081-499-6). Harvest Hse.

Smoke, Jim & McAfee, Lisa. Living Beyond Divorce: Working Guide. LC 83-82321. (Orig.). 1985. pap. 5.95 (ISBN 0-89081-407-4); working guide 3.95 (ISBN 0-89081-467-8). Harvest Hse.

Smyly, Glenn A. & Smyly, Barbara J. All in the Name of Love. 116p. 1986. 17.95 (ISBN 0-9616707-0-3); pap. 9.95 (ISBN 0-9616707-1-1). Alivening Pubns.

Snelling, George. Allow Divine Energy to Help You. 181p. pap. 4.95 (ISBN 0-934142-03-3). Vancento Pub.

Speas, Ralph. How to Deal with How You Feel. LC 80-65316. 1980. pap. 4.50 (ISBN 0-8054-5278-8). Broadman.

Spurgeon, C. H. Around the Wicket Gate. 1973. pap. 2.50 (ISBN 0-686-09098-5). Pilgrim Pubns.

--Words of Cheer for Daily Life. 1978. pap. 2.50 (ISBN 0-686-09101-9). Pilgrim Pubns.

--Words of Warning for Daily Life. 1980. pap. 2.50 (ISBN 0-686-09100-0). Pilgrim Pubns.

--Words of Wisdom for Daily Life. pap. 2.50 (ISBN 0-686-09099-3). Pilgrim Pubns.

Stanley, Charles F. Confronting Casual Christianity. LC 85-7764. 1985. 7.95 (ISBN 0-8054-5022-X). Broadman.

Stapleton, Ruth C. & Cochran, Robert. How Do You Face Disappointments? LC 77-78468. (Lifeline Ser.). 1977. pap. 0.95 (ISBN 0-88419-136-2). Creation Hse.

Stearns, Bill. If the World Fits, You're the Wrong Size. 1981. pap. 3.95 (ISBN 0-88207-588-8). Victor Bks.

Steele, James. Bible Solutions to Problems of Daily Living. 132p. 1983. 10.95 (ISBN 0-13-078022-7); pap. 4.95 (ISBN 0-13-078014-6). P-H.

Stein, Harry. Ethics & Other Liabilities: Trying to Live Right in an Amoral World. 176p. 1983. pap. 4.95 (ISBN 0-312-26544-1). St Martin.

Steinberg, David. Welcome Brothers: Poems of a Changing Man's Consciousness. (Illus.). 1976. pap. 3.00 (ISBN 0-914906-04-6). Red Alder.

Stephens, Don. Trial by Trial: Destiny of a Believer. LC 85-80485. 176p. (Orig.). 1985. pap. 6.95 (ISBN 0-89081-498-8). Harvest Hse.

Stevens, R. David. Five Steps to Freedom. 60p. 1980. pap. 2.25 (ISBN 0-87516-400-5). De Vorss.

Stobbe, Leslie H. Living with Others. 1986. pap. 4.95 (ISBN 0-8010-8275-7). Baker Bk.

Stoddard, Andrea. How to Bind & Loose in Spiritual Conflict. 56p. (Orig.). 1986. 3.95 (ISBN 0-936371-00-5). Spirit Faith.

Stott, John R. The Message of the Semon on the Mount. LC 84-27763. (Bible Speaks Today Ser.). 1978. pap. 6.95 (ISBN 0-87784-296-5). Inter-Varsity.

Swischuk, Leonard. Emergency Radiology of the Acutely Ill or Injured Child. 2nd ed. (Illus.). 656p. 1985. text ed. 78.50 (ISBN 0-683-08049-0). Williams & Wilkins.

Taylor, Kenneth N. How to Grow: Expanded Edition. 192p. Date not set. pap. 7.95 (ISBN 0-317-47452-9). Oliver-Nelson.

Thomas, Arthur G. Abundance Is Your Right. LC 77-76207. 1987. pap. 6.95 (ISBN 0-941992-10-1). Los Arboles Pub.

Tollett, T. O., compiled by. Best Gifts. 1971. pap. 1.00 (ISBN 0-89114-062-X). Baptist Pub Hse.

--Way of the Wise. 64p. 1970. pap. 1.00 (ISBN 0-89114-061-1). Baptist Pub Hse.

Trungpa, Chogyam. Shambhala: The Sacred Path of the Warrior. LC 83-20401. (Illus.). 199p. 1984. pap. 7.95 (ISBN 0-87773-264-7). Shambhala Pubns.

--Shambhala: The Sacred Path of the Warriors. 176p. 1986. pap. 3.95 (ISBN 0-553-26172-X). Bantam.

Vail, James G. Science & the Business of Living. 1983. pap. 2.50x (ISBN 0-87574-070-7, 070). Pendle Hill.

Vander Goot, Mary. A Life Planning Guide for Women. 128p. 1982. pap. 9.95x (ISBN 0-88946-512-6). E Mellen.

Vannier, Maryhelen. Have the Time of Your Life! 1986. pap. 6.50 (ISBN 0-687-16657-8). Abingdon.

Van Vuuren, Nancy. Work & Career. LC 83-12338. (Choices: Guides for Today's Woman: Vol. 2). 116p. (Orig.). 1983. pap. 6.95 (ISBN 0-664-24539-0). Westminster.

Walker, Paul. How to Keep Your Joy. 192p. 1987. 12.95 (ISBN 0-8407-9076-7). Oliver-Nelson.

Walker, Paul L. & Conn, Charles P. Who Am I? LC 74-82934. 1974. pap. 1.99 (ISBN 0-87148-905-8). Pathway Pr.

Warren, Norman. What's the Point? Reynolds, A., ed. 80p. 1987. pap. 2.50 (ISBN 0-7459-1224-9). Lion USA.

Webber, Robert E. The Moral Majority: Right or Wrong. 190p. 1981. 9.95. Cornerstone.

Weil, Simone. Two Moral Essays: Human Personality & on Human Obligations. Repr. 2.50x (ISBN 0-686-79299-8). Pendle Hill.

White, Ernest. The Art of Human Relations. LC 85-5953. 1985. pap. 6.95 (ISBN 0-8054-5008-4). Broadman.

Wiersbe. Be Wise. 1983. 5.95 (ISBN 0-88207-384-2). Victor Bks.

Wiersbe, Warren W. Be Alert! 168p. 1984. pap. 5.95 (ISBN 0-89693-380-6). Victor Bks.

Williams, Shirley & Zalaquett, Jose. The Moral Dimensions of International Conduct. Devereux, James, ed. (The Jesuit Community Lectures Ser.: 1982). 128p. (Orig.). pap. 5.95 (ISBN 0-87840-406-6). Georgetown U Pr.

Wood, Ernest. Taking Charge of Your Life. rev. ed. LC 84-40512. 136p. 1985. pap. 4.75 (ISBN 0-8356-0594-9). Theos Pub Hse.

Wright, Linda R. Staying on Top When Things Go Wrong. 120p. 1983. pap. 2.95 (ISBN 0-8423-6623-7). Tyndale.

Yerman, Ron. Religion: Innocent or Guilty. LC 85-90019. 180p. 1985. 11.95 (ISBN 0-533-06540-2). Vantage.

Yogananda, Paramahansa. Man's Eternal Quest. LC 75-17183. (Illus.). 503p. 1982. 9.95 (ISBN 0-87612-233-0); Italian ed. 10.00x (ISBN 0-87612-237-3). Self Realization.

Yohn, Rick. Living Securely in an Unstable World: God's Solution to Man's Dilemma. LC 85-4895. (Living Theology Ser.). 1985. pap. 8.95 (ISBN 0-88070-082-3). Multnomah.

Young, Mildred B. A Standard of Living. 1983. pap. 2.50x (ISBN 0-87574-012-X, 012). Pendle Hill.

CONDUCT OF LIFE–EARLY WORKS TO 1900

Feltham, Owen. Resolves, a Duple Century. 3rd ed. LC 74-28853. (English Experience Ser.: No. 734). 1975. Repr. of 1628 ed. 35.00 (ISBN 90-221-0734-5). Walter J Johnson.

Fenton, Geoffrey. A Forme of Christian Pollicie. LC 78-38180. (English Experience Ser.: No. 454). 424p. 1972. Repr. of 1574 ed. 42.00 (ISBN 90-221-0454-0). Walter J Johnson.

Seneca. Moral Letters, 3 vols. (Loeb Classical Library: No. 75-77). 12.50x (ISBN 0-686-76874-4). Vol. 1 (ISBN 0-674-99084-6). Vol. 2 (ISBN 0-674-99085-4). Vol. 3 (ISBN 0-674-99086-2). Harvard U Pr.

CONDUCT OF LIFE–QUOTATIONS, MAXIMS, ETC.

Ball, Judy. Listenings. (Orig.). 1987. pap. 7.00 (ISBN 0-915541-12-2). Star Bks Inc.

Bates, Raymond. Wilt Thou Be Made Whole? (Orig.). Date not set. pap. 5.00 (ISBN 0-915541-08-4). Star Bks Inc.

Carroll, Carroll. Carroll's First Book of Proverbs or Life Is a Fortune Cookie. (Illus.). 80p. 1981. pap. 4.95 (ISBN 0-87786-004-1). Gold Penny.

Dant, Penny. Springs of Joy. (Orig.). 1987. pap. 7.00 (ISBN 0-915541-11-4). Star Bks Inc.

Parrish, Katharine W. Dustmop Devotionals. (Orig.). 1986. pap. 7.00 (ISBN 0-915541-09-2). Star Bks Inc.

CONDUCTING, CHORAL

see also Choirs (Music); Choral Singing

Decker, Harold A. & Herford, Julius, eds. Choral Conducting: A Symposium. LC 72-94347. (Illus.). 320p. 1973. 34.00 (ISBN 0-13-133355-0). P-H.

Ehmann, Wilhelm. Choral Directing. Wiebe, George D., tr. 1968. 15.95 (ISBN 0-8066-0832-3, 11-9130). Augsburg.

Moe, Daniel. Problems in Conducting. rev. ed. 1968. pap. 4.50 (ISBN 0-8066-0834-X, 11-9369). Augsburg.

CONFESSION

see also Absolution; Penance; Penitentials; Sin

Archpriest Michael Bogoslovsky. Prigotovlenije k Ispovjedi i Blagogvejnomy Prithashcheniju Svjatikh Khristvikh Tajin. Tr. of Preporation for Confession & the Receiving of the Holy Mysteries. 169p. pap. 8.00 (ISBN 0-317-29105-X). Holy Trinity.

Baur, Benedict. Frequent Confession. 224p. 1980. 7.00 (ISBN 0-906127-20-3). Lumen Christi.

Belgic Confession Translation Committee. Service Book, Part Six: Belgic Confession. 45p. (Orig.). 1984. pap. 1.25 (ISBN 0-933140-92-4). CRC Pubns.

Burr, Anna R. Religious Confessions & Confessants. 1977. lib. bdg. 59.95 (ISBN 0-8490-2511-7). Gordon Pr.

Capps, Charles. Developing Faith in Your Confession. 1986. mini bk. 0.75 (ISBN 0-89274-412-X). Harrison Hse.

Champlin, Joseph M. Together in Peace: Penitents Edition. 104p. (Orig.). 1975. pap. 1.50 (ISBN 0-87793-095-3). Ave Maria.

--Together in Peace: Priests Edition. (Illus.). 272p. 1975. pap. 3.95 (ISBN 0-87793-094-5). Ave Maria.

Chiniquy, Charles. The Priest, the Woman, & the Confessional. 144p. 1979. pap. 4.50 (ISBN 0-937958-03-4). Chick Pubns.

Conser, Walter H., Jr. Church & Confession: Conservative Theologians in Germany, England, & America, 1815-1866. LC 84-18990. viii, 360p. 1984. 28.95 (ISBN 0-86554-119-1, MUP/H109). Mercer Univ Pr.

Donoghue, Quentin & Shapiro, Linda. Bless Me, Father, for I Have Sinned: Catholics Speak Out about Confession. LC 84-81332. 303p. 1984. 17.95 (ISBN 0-917657-02-0). D I Fine.

--Bless Me Father, for I Have Sinned: Catholics Speak Out about Confession. LC 84-81332. 303p. 1985. pap. 8.95 (ISBN 0-917657-44-6). D I Fine.

Ecumenical Creeds & Reformed Confessions. 1979. pap. text ed. 3.75 (ISBN 0-933140-02-9). CRC Pubns.

Erasmus, Desiderius. A Lytle Treatise of the Maner & Forme of Confession. LC 79-39487. (English Experience Ser.: No. 553). (Illus.). 232p. 1973. Repr. of 1535 ed. 16.00 (ISBN 90-221-0553-9). Walter J Johnson.

Heron, Alasdair I., ed. The Westminster Confession in the Church Today: Church of Scotland Panel on Doctrine. 1982. 9.95x (ISBN 0-7152-0497-1). Outlook.

Jean-Mesmy, Claude. Conscience & Confession. Malachy, Carroll, tr. LC 65-22643. 239p. 1965. 4.95 (ISBN 0-8199-0013-3, L38877). Franciscan Herald.

Khrapovitsky, Antony. Confession. Birchall, Christopher, tr. from Rus. LC 74-29537. 100p. (Orig.). 1975. pap. 3.00 (ISBN 0-88465-005-7). Holy Trinity.

Knight, David. Confession Can Change Your Life. (Illus.). 64p. (Orig.). 1985. pap. text ed. 2.50 (ISBN 0-86716-041-1). St Anthony Mess Pr.

Koehler, Walter J. Counseling & Confession. 1982. pap. 7.50 (ISBN 0-570-03849-9, 12-2804). Concordia.

Lea, Henry C. History of Auricular Confession & Indulgences in the Latin Church, 3 Vols. LC 68-19287. 1968. Repr. of 1896 ed. lib. bdg. 67.25x (ISBN 0-8371-0140-9, LEHC). Greenwood.

Mildenberger, Friedrich. Theology of the Lutheran Confessions. Lueker, Erwin, tr. LC 85-47727. 272p. 1986. 19.95 (ISBN 0-8006-0749-X). Fortress.

Murray, Andrew. Confession: The Road to Forgiveness. Orig. Title: Have Mercy Upon Me. 160p. 1983. pap. text ed. 3.50 (ISBN 0-88368-134-X). Whitaker Hse.

Nee, Watchman. The Good Confession. Kaung, Stephen, tr. (Basic Lesson Ser.: Vol. 2). 1973. 4.25 (ISBN 0-935008-05-5); pap. 2.75 (ISBN 0-935008-06-3). Christian Fellow Pubs.

Plantinga, Cornelius, Jr. A Place to Stand: A Reformed Study of Creeds & Confessions. LC 79-371. (Illus.). 1979. pap. text ed. 8.95 (ISBN 0-933140-01-0). CRC Pubns.

Rogge, O. John. Why Men Confess. LC 74-22067. (Quality Paperbacks Ser.). iv, 298p. 1975. pap. 5.95 (ISBN 0-306-80006-3). Da Capo.

Sasse, Herman. We Confess, Vol. 1: Jesus Christ. Nagel, Norman, tr. 1984. pap. 10.95 (ISBN 0-570-03941-X, 12-2877). Concordia.

Smith, Martin L. Reconciliation: Preparing for Confession in the Episcopal Church. LC 85-21271. 121p. (Orig.). 1985. pap. 8.95 (ISBN 0-936384-30-1). Cowley Pubns.

CONFESSION–JUVENILE LITERATURE

Harrison House Staff. Confessions for Kids. (Illus.). 29p. (Orig.). 1984. pap. 0.75 (ISBN 0-89274-322-0). Harrison Hse.

CONFESSIONS OF FAITH

see Creeds

CONFIRMATION

see also Church Membership; Sacraments

Cully, Kendig B., ed. Confirmation Re-Examined. LC 82-81428. 144p. (Orig.). 1982. pap. 7.95 (ISBN 0-8192-1304-7). Morehouse.

Daughters of St. Paul. Brief Review for Confirmation. 1973. pap. 0.75 (ISBN 0-8198-0250-6). Dghtrs St Paul.

Haggerty, Brian A. & Walters, Thomas P. We Receive the Spirit of Jesus (Confirmation Program) wkbk. 3.50 (ISBN 0-8091-9532-1); parent's notes 2.45 (ISBN 0-8091-9533-X); celebration's bk. 9.95 (ISBN 0-8091-9531-3); director's manual 7.50 (ISBN 0-8091-9530-5). Paulist Pr.

Haggerty, Brian A., et al. We Share New Life (Baptism Program) Reflections & Activities for Families. 2.95 (ISBN 0-8091-9183-0); Activities for Children. 2.75 (ISBN 0-8091-9182-2); director's manual 7.95 (ISBN 0-8091-9181-4); celebrations bk. 4.95 (ISBN 0-8091-9184-9). Paulist Pr.

Haugan, Randolph E. My Confirmation Book. (Illus.). 1942. pap. 2.50 ea. (ISBN 0-8066-0078-0, 10-4631). Augsburg.

Jungkuntz, Theodore R. Confirmation & the Charismata. LC 83-10450. 126p. (Orig.). 1983. lib. bdg. 24.00 (ISBN 0-8191-3344-2); pap. text ed. 8.75 (ISBN 0-8191-3345-0). U Pr of Amer.

Kramer, William A. Living for Christ. rev. ed. LC 72-96585. 1973. 3.25 (ISBN 0-570-03157-5, 12-2542). Concordia.

Lynch, Kilian F. The Sacrament of Confirmation in the Early - Middle Scholastic Period: Texts, Vol. 1. (Theology Ser). 1957. 17.00 (ISBN 0-686-11589-9). Franciscan Inst.

Moore, Joseph. Choice: Confirmation Journal. 96p. 1986. pap. text ed. 3.50 (ISBN 0-8091-9569-0). Paulist Pr.

Rahner, Karl. Confirmation. 1.50 (ISBN 0-87193-123-0). Dimension Bks.

Remember Your Confirmation. 1977. pap. 2.10 (ISBN 0-570-03751-4, 12-2655). Concordia.

Sherer, Mike. Growing in Grace. 1986. 5.50 (ISBN 0-89536-798-X, 6816). CSS of Ohio.

Walsh, Chad. Knock & Enter. (Orig.). 1953. pap. 4.95 (ISBN 0-8192-1076-5). Morehouse.

CONFIRMATION–CATHOLIC CHURCH

see also First Communion

Coleman, Bill & Coleman, Patty. My Confirmation Journal. 95p. 1979. pap. 3.95 (ISBN 0-89622-114-8). Twenty-Third.

Montgomery, Mary & Montgomery, Herb. Live This Gift: A Program for Confirmation Preparation. 1975. student guide 3.25 (ISBN 0-03-014266-0, 127, HarpR); parent guide 1.95 (ISBN 0-03-014271-7, 128); tchr's. guide 4.35 (ISBN 0-03-014276-8, 129). Har-Row.

Weber, Gerard P., et al. We Grow in God's Family: Preparation for Confirmation. (Illus., Orig.). 1968. pap. 2.32 (ISBN 0-02-649060-9, 64906); pap. 1.50 tchr's. manual (ISBN 0-02-649070-6, 64907). Benziger Pub Co.

CONFIRMATION–INSTRUCTION AND STUDY

Keller, Paul F. Studies in Lutheran Doctrine. LC 60-15574. (YA) 1959. pap. 5.50 (ISBN 0-570-03517-1, 14-1265); correction & profile chart 0.40 (ISBN 0-570-03526-0, 14-1267); tests 0.45 (ISBN 0-570-03525-2, 14-1266). Concordia.

Reichert, Richard. Born in the Spirit of Jesus. 84p. (Orig.). 1980. pap. text ed. 3.20 (ISBN 0-697-01725-7); tchr's manual 4.00 (ISBN 0-697-01726-5); spirit masters 10.95. Wm C Brown.

Rife, Carl B. Confirmation Resources. 1982. pap. 5.25 tchr's. guide (ISBN 0-89536-537-5, 0356). CSS of Ohio.

Thiry, Joan & Burbach, Marilyn. Confirmation Is Saying Yes to God. duplicating masterbook 12.95 (ISBN 0-89837-071-X, Pub. by Pflaum Pr). Peter Li.

CONFUCIANISM

see also Neo-Confucianism

Armstrong, Robert C. Light from the East. Studies in Japanese Confucianism. lib. bdg. 79.95 (ISBN 0-87968-134-9). Krishna Pr.

Chen, Liu F. The Confucian Way: A New & Systematic Study of the Four Books. Liu, Shih S., tr. 620p. 1986. text ed. 59.95 (ISBN 0-7103-0171-5). Methuen Inc.

Ching, Julia. Confucianism & Christianity. LC 77-75962. 234p. 1978. 16.95x (ISBN 0-87011-303-8). Kodansha.

Ch'u Chai & Chai, Winberg. Confucianism. LC 73-3977. 1974. pap. text ed. 5.50 (ISBN 0-8120-0303-9). Barron.

Douglas, R. Confucianism & Taoism. 59.95 (ISBN 0-87968-930-7). Gordon Pr.

Dubs, Homer H. Hsuntze, the Moulder of Ancient Confucianism. 339p. Repr. of 1927 ed. text ed. 22.50x (ISBN 0-89644-006-0, Pub. by Chinese Matl Ctr). Coronet Bks.

Gardner, Daniel K. Chu Hsi & the Ta-hsueh: Neo-Confucian Reflection on the Confucian Canon. (Harvard East Asian Monographs: No. 118). 300p. 1985. text ed. 20.00x (ISBN 0-674-13065-0, Pub. by Coun East Asian Stud). Harvard U Pr.

Giles, Herbert A. Confucianism & Its Rivals. LC 77-27155. (Hibbert Lectures: 1914). Repr. of 1915 ed. 30.00 (ISBN 0-404-60416-1). AMS Pr.

Hall, David L. & Ames, Roger T. Thinking Through Confucius. (Systematic Philosophy Ser.). 320p. 1987. 39.50X (ISBN 0-88706-376-4); pap. 12.95x (ISBN 0-88706-377-2). State U NY Pr.

Hartman, Charles. Han Yu & the T'ang Search for Unity. LC 85-16885. 448p. 1986. text ed. 50.00 (ISBN 0-691-06665-5). Princeton U Pr.

Lee, Don Y. An Outline of Confucianism. LC 85-80477. 113p. 1984. 29.50x (ISBN 0-939758-10-5). Eastern Pr.

Louie, Kamm. Critiques of Confucius in Contemporary China. LC 80-214. 210p. 1980. 27.50 (ISBN 0-312-17645-7). St Martin.

Mencius. Works of Mencius. Legge, James, tr. 15.75 (ISBN 0-8446-0331-7). Peter Smith.

Taylor, R. L. The Way of Heaven: An Introduction to the Confucian Religious Lufe. (Iconography of Religions XII Ser.: No. 3). (Illus.). xi, 37p. 1986. pap. 29.50 (ISBN 90-04-07423-6, Pub. by E J Brill). Heinman.

Tsung-Hsi, Huang. The Records of Ming Scholars. Ching, Julia & Fang, Chaoying, eds. LC 86-27257. 688p. 1987. text ed. 27.00x (ISBN 0-8248-1028-7). UH Pr.

Wei-Ming, Tu. Humanity & Self-Cultivation Essays in Confucian Thought. 1980. text ed. 30.00 (ISBN 0-89581-600-8, Asian Humanities). Asian Human Pr.

Wright, Arthur F., ed. Confucianism & Chinese Civilization. LC 75-6317. 364p. 1964. 27.50x (ISBN 0-8047-0890-8); pap. 10.95 (ISBN 0-8047-0891-6, SP138). Stanford U Pr.

CONFUCIUS AND CONFUCIANISM

Beck, L. A. The Story of Confucius & of the Other Great Chinese Mystics, 3 vols. (Illus.). 241p. 1986. Set. 187.75 (ISBN 0-89901-274-4). Found Class Reprints.

Chai, Ch'U & Chai, Winberg, eds. Li Chi: Book of Rites, 2 Vols. 1966. 25.00 (ISBN 0-8216-0107-5). Univ Bks.

Chen, Huan-Chang. The Economic Principles of Confucius & His School, 2 vols. lib. bdg. 250.00 set (ISBN 0-87968-080-6). Krishna Pr.

Ch'u Chai & Chai, Winberg. Confucianism. LC 73-3977. 1974. pap. text ed. 5.50 (ISBN 0-8120-0303-9). Barron.

Confucius. The Analects of Confucius. (Illus.). 149p. 1986. 88.85 (ISBN 0-89266-538-6). Am Classical Coll Pr.

--Confucian Analects, the Great Learning & the Doctrine of the Mean. Legge, James, ed. 1893. pap. 7.95 (ISBN 0-486-22746-4). Dover.

--The Great Learning & the Doctrine of the Mean. (Illus.). 151p. 1986. 88.85 (ISBN 0-89266-539-4). Am Classical Coll Pr.

--The Most Compelling Sayings by Confucius. Lynall, Leonard D., tr. (Most Meaningful Classics in World Culture Ser.). (Illus.). 166p. 1983. 83.45 (ISBN 0-89266-387-1). Am Classical Coll Pr.

--The Wisdom of Confucius. (Illus.). 131p. 1982. 63.45 (ISBN 0-89266-359-6). Am Classical Coll Pr.

--Wisdom of Confucius. 1965. 5.95 (ISBN 0-88088-100-3). Peter Pauper.

--The Wisdom of Confucius. Yutang, Lin, ed. & tr. LC 38-27366. 290p. 1938. 5.95 (ISBN 0-394-60426-1). Modern Lib.

Covell, Ralph R. Confucius, the Buddha, & Christ: A History of the Gospel in Chinese. LC 86-8615. 304p. (Orig.). 1986. pap. 14.95 (ISBN 0-88344-267-1, CIP). Orbis Bks.

Creel, Herrlee G. Confucius, the Man & the Myth. LC 72-7816. 363p. 1973. Repr. of 1949 ed. lib. bdg. 23.00x (ISBN 0-8371-6531-8, CRCO). Greenwood.

Doerblin, Alfred. The Living Thoughts of Confucius. 182p. 1983. Repr. of 1940 ed. lib. bdg. 25.00 (ISBN 0-89987-173-9). Darby Bks.

Dow, T. I. Confucianism vs. Marxism. 200p. 1977. pap. text ed. 12.50 (ISBN 0-8191-0183-4). U Pr of Amer.

Eber, Irene. Confucianism: The Dynamics of Tradition. 264p. 1986. text ed. 27.50x (ISBN 0-02-908780-5). Macmillan.

Feiring, Evelyn B. Concatenation: Enoch's Prophecy Fulfilling! Hebrew-Christian Metaphysics Supported by Modern Science. LC 72-96989. 5.00x (ISBN 0-9603386-0-8); pap. 2.00x (ISBN 0-9603386-1-6). Rocky Mtn Bks.

Fingarette, Herbert. Confucius: The Secular As Sacred. 160p. 1972. pap. 6.95x (ISBN 0-06-131682-2, TB1682, Torch). Har-Row.

Fontenay, Charles L. The Keyen of Fu Tze: The Wise Sayings of Confucious. 1977. 5.95 (ISBN 0-900306-50-5, Pub. by Coombe Springs Pr). Claymont Comm.

Giles, H. A. Confucianism & Its Rivals. lib. bdg. 79.95 (ISBN 0-87968-520-4). Krishna Pr.

Hall, David L. & Ames, Roger T. Thinking Through Confucius. (Systematic Philosophy Ser.). 320p. 1987. 39.50X (ISBN 0-88706-376-4); pap. 12.95x (ISBN 0-88706-377-2). State U NY Pr.

Johnson, Spencer. The Value of Honesty: The Story of Confucius. LC 78-4351. (ValueTales Ser.). (Illus.). 1979. 7.95 (ISBN 0-916392-36-8, Dist. by Oak Tree Pubns). Value Comm.

Johnston, Reginald F. Confucianism & Modern China. LC 79-2830. (Illus.). 272p. 1986. Repr. of 1934 ed. 24.50 (ISBN 0-8305-0007-3). Hyperion Conn.

Kenney, Edward H. A Confucian Notebook. LC 79-2828. 89p. 1986. Repr. of 1950 ed. 15.00 (ISBN 0-8305-0008-1). Hyperion Conn.

Lidin, Olof. The Life of Ogyu Sorai: A Tokugawa Philosopher. (Scandinavian Institute of Asian Studies Monograph Ser.: No. 19). 250p. 1982. pap. text ed. 18.95x (ISBN 0-7007-0068-4, Pub. by Curzon Pr England). Apt Bks.

Liu, Wu-Chi. A Short History of Confucian Philosophy. LC 78-20480. 1983. Repr. of 1955 ed. 20.50 (ISBN 0-88355-857-2). Hyperion Conn.

Liu Wu-Chi. Confucius, His Life & Time. LC 73-138159. 189p. 1972. Repr. of 1955 ed. lib. bdg. 22.50x (ISBN 0-8371-5616-5, LICO). Greenwood.

Louie, Kamm. Critiques of Confucius in Contemporary China. LC 80-214. 210p. 1980. 27.50 (ISBN 0-312-17645-7). St Martin.

Nivison, David S. & Wright, Arthur F., eds. Confucianism in Action. LC 59-7433. 1959. 30.00x (ISBN 0-8047-0554-2). Stanford U Pr.

Paley, Alan L. Confucius: Ancient Chinese Philosopher. Rahmas, D. Steve, ed. (Outstanding Personalities Ser.: No. 59). 32p. (Orig.). 1973. lib. bdg. 3.50 incl. catalog cards (ISBN 0-87157-559-0); pap. 1.95 vinyl laminated covers (ISBN 0-87157-059-9). SamHar Pr.

Palmer, Spencer J. Confucian Rituals in Korea. (Religions of Asia Ser.). (Illus.). 270p. 1984. 30.00 (ISBN 0-89581-457-9). Asian Human Pr.

Rowland-Entwistle, Theodore. Confucius & Ancient China. (Life & Times Ser.). (Illus.). 64p. 1987. lib. bdg. 11.40 (ISBN 0-531-18101-4, Pub. by Bookwright Pr). Watts.

Rule, Paul A. K'ung-Tzu or Confuscius? The Jesuit Interpretation of Confucianism. 292p. (Orig.). 1987. pap. text ed. 18.95x (ISBN 0-86861-913-2). Allen Unwin.

Sunoo, Harold H. China of Confucius: A Critical Interpretation. LC 85-7639. (Illus.). 208p. 1985. lib. bdg. 28.95 (ISBN 0-912617-00-4); pap. 12.95 (ISBN 0-912617-01-2). Heritage Res Hse.

Wang Kung-Hsing. Chinese Mind. LC 68-23336. 1968. Repr. of 1946 ed. lib. bdg. 22.50x (ISBN 0-8371-0260-X, WACM). Greenwood.

Weber, Max. Religion of China. 1968. 14.95 (ISBN 0-02-934440-9); text ed. 14.95 (ISBN 0-02-934450-6). Free Pr.

Williams, Wells S. China, Chinese Philosophers & Confucianism. (Illus.). 137p. 1982. Repr. of 1883 ed. 73.45 (ISBN 0-89901-059-8). Found Class Reprints.

Wilson, Epiphanius, ed. The Wisdom of Confucius. 15.95 (ISBN 0-89190-545-6, Pub. by Am Repr). Amereon Ltd.

Wisdom of Confucius. LC 68-56192. 1968. 5.00 (ISBN 0-8022-0853-3). Philos Lib.

Wright, Arthur F., ed. The Confucian Persuasion. LC 60-8561. 1960. 30.00x (ISBN 0-8047-0018-4). Stanford U Pr.

Wright, Arthur F. & Twitchett, Denis, eds. Confucian Personalities. LC 62-16950. (Illus.). 1962. 30.00x (ISBN 0-8047-0044-3). Stanford U Pr.

CONGREGATIONAL CHRISTIAN CHURCHES

Walker, Randi J., ed. Kept by Grace: A Centennial History of First Congregational Church of Pasadena. 128p. (Orig.). 1986. text ed. 8.95 (ISBN 0-932727-10-7). Hope Pub Hse.

CONGREGATIONAL CHURCHES

see also United Church of Christ

Barlow, T. Ed. Congregational House Churches. (Orig.). 1978. pap. 1.50 (ISBN 0-8309-0214-7). Herald Hse.

Burg, B. R. Richard Mather of Dorchester. LC 75-41987. 224p. 1976. 21.00x (ISBN 0-8131-1343-1). U Pr of Ky.

De Rosa Villarosa, Carlantonio. Memorie Degli Scrittori Filippini o Siano Della Congregazione Dell' Oratorio de S. Filippo Neri, 2 vols. 1380p. Date not set. Repr. of 1842 ed. text ed. 74.52x (ISBN 0-576-72217-0, Pub. by Gregg Intl Pubs England). Gregg Intl.

Dexter, Henry M. The Congregationalism of the Last Three Hundred Years As Seen in Its Literature. 1072p. Date not set. Repr. of 1879 ed. text ed. 99.36x (Pub. by Gregg Intl Pubs England). Gregg Intl.

Edwards, Jonathan. Selected Writings of Jonathan Edwards. Simonson, Harold P., ed. LC 78-115064. (Milestones of Thought Ser.). 1970. pap. 7.95 (ISBN 0-8044-6132-5). Ungar.

Fleming, Sanford. Children & Puritanism: The Place of Children in the Life & Thought of the New England Churches, 1620-1847. LC 70-89178. (American Education: Its Men, Institutions & Ideas Ser). 1969. Repr. of 1933 ed. 15.00 (ISBN 0-405-01416-3). Ayer Co Pubs.

Fraser, James W. Pedagogue for God's Kingdom: Lyman Beecher & the Second Great Awakening. LC 85-17794. 248p. 1985. lib. bdg. 27.50 (ISBN 0-8191-4905-5); pap. text ed. 12.75 (ISBN 0-8191-4906-3). U Pr of Amer.

Hostetter, B. David. Psalms & Prayers for Congregational Participation: Series A. 1983. 7.75 (ISBN 0-89536-639-8, 1633). CSS of Ohio.

Kopf, Carl H. Windows on Life. facs. ed. LC 70-76908. (Essay Index Reprint Ser). 1941. 17.50 (ISBN 0-8369-1041-9). Ayer Co Pubs.

Lippy, Charles H. Seasonable Revolutionary: The Mind of Charles Chauncy. LC 81-9560. 176p. 1981. text ed. 19.95x (ISBN 0-88229-625-6). Nelson-Hall.

Norton, John. Abel Being Dead, Yet Speaketh. LC 78-8184. 1978. Repr. of 1658 ed. 30.00x (ISBN 0-8201-1310-7). Schol Facsimiles.

Oberholzer, Emil, Jr. Delinquent Saints: Disciplinary Action in the Early Congregational Churches of Massachusetts. LC 70-76660. (Columbia University. Studies in the Social Sciences: No. 590). Repr. of 1956 ed. 14.50 (ISBN 0-404-51590-8). AMS Pr.

Oliver, Egbert S. Saints & Sinners: The Planting of New England Congregationalism in Portland, Oregon, 1851-1876. Pierce, Joe E., ed. (Illus.). 250p. 1987. pap. 4.95 (ISBN 0-913244-66-X). Hapi Pr.

Pruter, Hugo R. The Theology of Congregationalism. LC 85-12844. 100p. 1985. Repr. lib. bdg. 19.95x (ISBN 0-89370-597-7). Borgo Pr.

Shepard, Thomas. Works, 3 vols. Albro, John A., ed. LC 49-1393. Repr. of 1853 ed. Set. 85.00 (ISBN 0-404-05990-2). Vol. 1 (ISBN 0-404-05991-0). Vol. 2 (ISBN 0-404-05992-9). Vol. 3 (ISBN 0-404-05993-7). AMS Pr.

Smyth, Norman. Story of Church Unity: The Lambeth Conference of Anglican Bishops & the Congregational-Episcopal Approaches. 1923. 29.50x (ISBN 0-686-83788-6). Elliots Bks.

Townsend, Charles D., ed. The History of the Third Congregational Church of Middleborough, Known Today As North Congregational Church, United Church of Christ, North Middleboro, Massachusetts: Includes S. Hopkins Emery's Church History Reprinted from 1876 Edition. (Illus.). 300p. 1982. 22.50 (ISBN 0-9607906-0-8). ACETO Bookmen.

Walker, Randi J., ed. Kept by Grace: A Centennial History of First Congregational Church of Pasadena. 128p. (Orig.). 1986. text ed. 8.95 (ISBN 0-932727-10-7). Hope Pub Hse.

Walker, Williston. Ten New England Leaders. LC 76-83445. (Religion in America Ser). 1969. Repr. of 1901 ed. 28.00 (ISBN 0-405-00278-5). Ayer Co Pubs.

Walker, Williston, ed. Creeds & Platforms of Congregationalism. LC 60-14698. 1960. 10.95 (ISBN 0-8298-0034-4). Pilgrim NY.

Willard, Samuel. Compleat Body of Divinity. (American Studies). Repr. of 1726 ed. 62.00 (ISBN 0-384-68533-1). Johnson Repr.

Wise, John. Churches Quarrel Espoused, 1713. LC 66-10006. 1966. 35.00x (ISBN 0-8201-1052-3). Schol Facsimiles.

Youngs, J. William T., Jr. God's Messengers: Religious Leadership in Colonial New England, 1700-1750. LC 76-8544. 192p. 1976. 19.50x (ISBN 0-8018-1799-4). Johns Hopkins.

Zaccaria, Joseph S. Facing Change: Strategies for Problem Solving in the Congregation. LC 84-18552. 112p. (Orig.). 1984. pap. 5.95 (ISBN 0-8066-2097-8, 10-2156). Augsburg.

CONGREGATIONAL CHURCHES–SERMONS

Bushnell, Horace. God in Christ. LC 76-39568. Repr. of 1849 ed. 25.00 (ISBN 0-404-01245-0). AMS Pr.

Cotton, John. God's Mercie Mixed with His Justice. LC 58-5651. 1977. Repr. of 1641 ed. 30.00x (ISBN 0-8201-1242-9). Schol Facsimiles.

Finney, Charles G. Charles G. Finney Memorial Library, 8 vols. 1975. Set. pap. 31.50 (ISBN 0-8254-2623-5). Kregel.

--Guilt of Sin. LC 65-25845. (Charles G. Finney Memorial Library). 124p. 1975. pap. 4.50 (ISBN 0-8254-2616-2). Kregel.

--Prevailing Prayer. LC 65-25846. (Charles G. Finney Memorial Library). 1975. pap. 3.50 (ISBN 0-8254-2603-0). Kregel.

--So Great Salvation. LC 65-25844. (Charles G. Finney Memorial Library). 128p. 1975. pap. 4.50 (ISBN 0-8254-2621-9). Kregel.

--True & False Repentance. LC 66-10576. (Charles G. Finney Memorial Library). 122p. 1975. pap. 4.50 (ISBN 0-8254-2617-0). Kregel.

--True Saints. LC 66-24880. (Charles G. Finney Memorial Library). 120p. 1975. pap. 4.50 (ISBN 0-8254-2622-7). Kregel.

--True Submission. LC 66-24881. (Charles G. Finney Memorial Library). 128p. 1975. pap. 4.50 (ISBN 0-8254-2618-9). Kregel.

--Victory Over the World. LC 66-24879. (Charles G. Finney Memorial Library). 124p. 1975. pap. 4.50 (ISBN 0-8254-2619-7). Kregel.

Herron, George D. Social Meanings of Religious Experiences. (American Studies Ser.). 1969. Repr. of 1896 ed. 18.00 (ISBN 0-384-22660-4). Johnson Repr.

Lloyd-Jones, D. Martyn. Spiritual Depression: Its Causes & Cure. 1965. pap. 5.95 (ISBN 0-8028-1387-9). Eerdmans.

March, Daniel. Night Scenes in the Bible. LC 77-189204. 348p. 1977. 12.95 (ISBN 0-8254-3211-1). Kregel.

Mather, Cotton. Day of Humiliation: Times of Affliction & Disaster. LC 68-24211. 1970. 55.00x (ISBN 0-8201-1067-1). Schol Facsimiles.

CONGREGATIONALISM

see also Antinomianism; Brownists; Calvinism; Covenants (Church Polity); Dissenters, Religious; New England Theology; Presbyterianism; Puritans; Unitarianism

Andrew, John A., III. Rebuilding the Christian Commonwealth: New England Congregationalists & Foreign Missions, 1800-1830. LC 75-38214. 240p. 1976. 22.00x (ISBN 0-8131-1333-4). U Pr of Ky.

Boissonet, V. D. Dictionnaire Dogmatique, Moral, Historique, Canonique, Liturgique et Disciplinaire des Decrets des Diverse Congregations Romaines. Migne, J. P., ed. (Nouvelle Encyclopedie Theologique Ser.: Vol. 26). (Fr.). 646p. Repr. of 1852 ed. lib. bdg. 82.50x (ISBN 0-89241-269-0). Caratzas.

Dexter, Henry M. Congregationalism of the Last Three Hundred Years As Seen in Its Literature, 2 Vols. LC 65-58213. (Research & Source Ser.: No. 519). 1970. Repr. of 1880 ed. Set. lib. bdg. 53.00 (ISBN 0-8337-0851-1). B Franklin.

Everist, Norma J. Education Ministry in the Congregation: Eight Ways We Learn from One Another. LC 83-70515. 240p. (Orig.). 1983. pap. 11.95 (ISBN 0-8066-2021-8, 10-2006). Augsburg.

Martin, Ralph P. The Spirit & the Congregation: Studies in I Corinthians 12-15. 160p. (Orig.). 1984. 11.95 (ISBN 0-8028-3608-9). Eerdmans.

Pruter, Hugo R. Neo-Congregationalism. LC 85-13416. 90p. 1985. Repr. lib. bdg. 19.95x (ISBN 0-89370-598-5). Borgo Pr.

--The Theology of Congregationalism. LC 85-12844. 100p. 1985. Repr. lib. bdg. 19.95x (ISBN 0-89370-597-7). Borgo Pr.

Spinks, Bryan D. Freedom or Order? The Eucharistic Liturgy in English Congregationalism 1645-1980. (Pittsburgh Theological Monographs: New Ser. 8). (Orig.). 1984. pap. 22.50 (ISBN 0-915138-33-6). Pickwick.

Stanley, A. Knighton. The Children Is Crying. LC 78-26544. 1979. 8.95 (ISBN 0-8298-0347-5). Pilgrim NY.

CONNECTICUT–CHURCH HISTORY

Greene, M. Louise. Development of Religious Liberty in Connecticut. facs. ed. LC 79-126235. (Select Bibliographies Reprint Ser). 1905. 26.50 (ISBN 0-8369-5461-0). Ayer Co Pubs.

--Development of Religious Liberty in Connecticut. LC 74-99858. (Civil Liberties in American History Ser). 1970. Repr. of 1905 ed. lib. bdg. 59.50 (ISBN 0-306-71861-8). Da Capo.

Keller, Charles R. The Second Great Awakening in Connecticut. LC 68-26923. ix, 275p. 1968. Repr. of 1942 ed. 25.00 (ISBN 0-208-00662-1, Archon). Shoe String.

Larned, E. D. Church Records of Killingly, Connecticut. 56p. 1984. pap. 5.95 (ISBN 0-912606-22-3). Hunterdon Hse.

CONSCIENCE

see also Casuistry; Free Will and Determinism; Guilt; Liberty of Conscience

Amato, Joseph A., II. Guilt & Gratitude: A Study of the Origins of Contemporary Conscience. LC 81-6991. (Contributions in Philosophy Ser.: No. 20). xxv, 218p. 1982. lib. bdg. 29.95 (ISBN 0-313-22946-5, AGG/). Greenwood.

Ames, William. Conscience with the Power & Cases Thereof. LC 74-28826. (English Experience Ser.: No. 708). 1975. Repr. of 1639 ed. 35.00 (ISBN 9-0221-0708-6). Walter J Johnson.

Arnold, Eberhard. The Inner Land, Vol. 2: The Struggle of the Conscience. LC 75-1335. 1975. 3.50 (ISBN 0-87486-154-3). Plough.

Burke, Cormac. Conscience & Freedom. 159p. (Orig.). 1977. pap. 4.95x (ISBN 0-933932-39-1). Scepter Pubs.

Carmody, John. Reexamining Conscience. 144p. (Orig.). 1982. pap. 8.95 (ISBN 0-8164-2405-5, HarpR). Har-Row.

Clagett, John Y. Christian Conscience. LC 84-9824. 1984. pap. 3.95 (ISBN 0-87227-097-1). Reg Baptist.

Conn, Walter E. Conscience: Development & Self-Transcendence. LC 80-24043. 230p. (Orig.). 1981. pap. 12.95 (ISBN 0-89135-025-X). Religious Educ.

Daughters of St. Paul. The Conscience Game. 1966. 2.00 (ISBN 0-8198-0231-X). Dghtrs St Paul.

Davies, Horton M. Catching the Conscience. LC 84-71181. 169p. (Orig.). 1984. pap. 7.50 (ISBN 0-936384-21-2). Cowley Pubns.

Donnelly, John & Lyons, Leonard, eds. Conscience. new ed. LC 72-6720. 249p. (Orig.). 1973. pap. 4.95 (ISBN 0-8189-0259-0). Alba.

Durstewitz, Claire W. Conscience Plays. 1982. pap. 4.95 (ISBN 0-89536-527-8, 0340). CSS of Ohio.

Graham, John W. Conscription & Conscience: A History 1916-1919. LC 78-81509. 1969. Repr. of 1922 ed. 35.00x (ISBN 0-678-00507-9). Kelley.

Johnson, Ronald C., et al, eds. Conscience, Contract, & Social Reality: Theory & Research in Behavioral Science. LC 77-166108. 1972. 39.50x (ISBN 0-8290-0382-7); pap. text ed. 19.95x (ISBN 0-8290-0381-9). Irvington.

Kroy, M. The Conscience: A Structural Theory. 244p. 1974. text ed. 49.00x (ISBN 0-7065-1462-9, Pub. by Keter Pub Jerusalem). Coronet Bks.

Miller, Donald E. The Wing-Footed Wanderer: Conscience & Transcendence. LC 77-1503. Repr. of 1977 ed. 45.60 (ISBN 0-8357-9032-0, 2016421). Bks Demand UMI.

Nash, Gerald R. You & Your Conscience. (Outreach Ser.). 1981. pap. 1.25 (ISBN 0-8163-0428-9). Pacific Pr Pub Assn.

Perkins, William. The Whole Treatise of the Cases of Conscience. LC 74-38218. (English Experience Ser.: No. 482). 690p. 1972. Repr. of 1606 ed. 43.00 (ISBN 90-221-0482-6). Walter J Johnson.

Pontas, J. Dictionnaire de Cas de Conscience ou Decisions, 2 vols. Migne, J. P., ed. (Encyclopedie Theologique Ser.: Vols. 18-19). (Fr.). 1326p. Repr. of 1847 ed. lib. bdg. 169.00x (ISBN 0-89241-238-0). Caratzas.

Rose, E. Cases of Conscience. LC 74-76947. 272p. 1975. 44.50 (ISBN 0-521-20462-3). Cambridge U Pr.

Solomon, Robert C. In the Spirit of Hegel: A Study of G. W. F. Hegel's "Phenomenology of Spirit". (Illus.). 1983. 32.50x (ISBN 0-19-503169-5); pap. 14.95x (ISBN 0-19-503650-6). Oxford U Pr.

Toon, Peter. Your Conscience As Your Guide. LC 83-62870. 102p. (Orig.). 1984. pap. 5.95 (ISBN 0-8192-1339-X). Morehouse.

CONSCIOUSNESS

see also Belief and Doubt; Personality; Self

Adlam, Diana, et al, eds. Ideology & Consciousness, No. 5. 1979. pap. text ed. 6.95x (ISBN 0-391-01189-8). Humanities.

Aron, Elaine & Aron, Arthur. The Maharishi Effect: A Revolution Through Meditation. 235p. (Orig.). 1986. pap. 9.95 (ISBN 0-913299-26-X, Dist. by NAL). Stillpoint.

Barfield, Owen. History, Guilt, & Habit. LC 79-65333. 104p. 1981. pap. 9.95 (ISBN 0-8195-6064-2). Wesleyan U Pr.

Besant, Annie. Study in Consciousness. 6th ed. 1972. 7.50 (ISBN 0-8356-7287-5). Theos Pub Hse.

Burke, Maurice R. The Evolution of the Human Mind: The Passage from Self to Cosmic Consciousness. (Physic Research Library Bks.). (Illus.). 137p. 1981. Repr. of 1905 ed. 69.85 (ISBN 0-89901-033-4). Found Class Reprints.

Chaudhuri, Haridas. Evolution of Integral Consciousness. LC 77-4219. 1977. pap. 4.25 (ISBN 0-8356-0494-2, Quest). Theos Pub Hse.

Davis, Roy E. Conscious Immortality. 150p. 1978. pap. 2.95 (ISBN 0-87707-216-7). CSA Pr.

De Langre, Jacques. Food Consciousness for Spiritual Development. LC 80-84993. (Illus., Orig.). 1986. pap. 6.00 (ISBN 0-916508-05-6). Happiness Pr.

Eastcott, Michal J. I: The Story of the Self. LC 80-51552. (Illus.). 201p. (Orig.). 1980. pap. 5.50 (ISBN 0-8356-0541-8, Quest). Theos Pub Hse.

Ey, Henri. Consciousness: A Phenomenological Study of Being Conscious & Becoming Conscious. Flodstrom, John H., tr. LC 76-26429. (Studies in Phenomenology & Existential Philosophy Ser.). (Illus.). 448p. 1978. 29.50x (ISBN 0-253-31408-9). Ind U Pr.

Faber, M. D. Culture & Consciousness: The Social Meaning of Altered Awareness. LC 80-36683. 296p. 1981. text ed. 34.95 (ISBN 0-87705-505-X); professional 32.95. Human Sci Pr.

Gardner, Edward L. The Play of Consciousness in the Web of the Universe. LC 86-30006. (Illus.). 224p. 1987. pap. 7.25 (ISBN 0-8356-0236-2). Theos Pub Hse.

Globus, Gordon, et al, eds. Consciousness & the Brain: A Scientific & Philosophical Inquiry. LC 75-44478. (Illus.). 378p. 1976. 45.00x (ISBN 0-306-30878-9, Plenum Pr). Plenum Pub.

Goldsmith, Joel S. Consciousness Is What I Am. Sinkler, Lorraine, ed. LC 76-9967. 160p. 1976. 11.45 (ISBN 0-06-063173-2, HarpR). Har-Row.

Hall, Brian. The Development of Consciousness: A Confluent Theory of Values. LC 75-34843. 288p. 1976. 9.95 (ISBN 0-8091-0201-3); pap. 8.95 (ISBN 0-8091-1894-7). Paulist Pr.

Holt, Edwin B. The Concept of Consciousness. LC 73-2969. (Classics in Psychology Ser.). Repr. of 1914 ed. 23.50 (ISBN 0-405-05141-7). Ayer Co Pubs.

Hulsmann, Carl. Awakening of Consciousness. (Illus.). 192p. 1982. 18.00 (ISBN 0-86164-151-5, Pub. by Momenta Publishing Ltd. U. K.). Hunter Hse.

Keyes, Ken, Jr. Handbook to Higher Consciousness. 5th ed. LC 73-83071. 240p. 1975. pap. 4.95 (ISBN 0-9600688-8-0). Living Love.

Kushner, Lawrence. The River of Light: Spirituality, Judaism, & the Evolution of Consciousness. LC 80-7738. 192p. (Orig.). 1981. pap. 7.95 (ISBN 0-06-064902-X, RD 370, HarpR). Har-Row.

Lawrence, D. H. Fantasia & Psychoanalysis & the Unconscious. 1978. pap. 6.95 (ISBN 0-14-003303-3). Penguin.

Marcel, Gabriel. Being & Having: An Existentialist Diary. 11.25 (ISBN 0-8446-2528-0). Peter Smith.

Muktananda, Swami. Play of Consciousness. LC 78-15841. (Illus.). 1979. pap. 7.64 (ISBN 0-06-066044-9, RD 223, HarpR). Har-Row.

--Play of Consciousness. LC 78-62769. 322p. 1978. 9.95 (ISBN 0-914602-36-5); pap. 6.95 (ISBN 0-914602-37-3). SYDA Found.

Navickas. Consciousness & Reality. 1976. pap. 37.00 (ISBN 90-247-1775-2, Pub. by Martinus Nijhoff Netherlands). Kluwer Academic.

Neumann, Erich. Origins & History of Consciousness. Hull, R. F., tr. (Bollingen Ser.: Vol. 42). (Illus.). 1954. pap. 9.95 (ISBN 0-691-01761-1). Princeton U Pr.

The New Consciousness Sourcebook, No. 5. LC 84-15040. 256p. 1985. Repr. of 1982 ed. lib. bdg. 19.95x (ISBN 0-89370-887-9). Borgo Pr.

Obayashi, Hiroshi. Agape & History: A Theological Essay on Historical Consciousness. LC 80-1683. 356p. (Orig.). 1981. pap. text ed. 15.25 (ISBN 0-8191-1713-7). U Pr of Amer.

Orr, Leonard & Ray, Sondra. Rebirthing in the New Age. LC 76-53337. 1978. pap. 9.95 (ISBN 0-89087-134-5). Celestial Arts.

Satprem. Mother or the New Species. LC 83-4370. Orig. Title: Mere Ou L'espece Nouvelle. 530p. 1983. pap. 8.95 (ISBN 0-938710-03-6). Inst Evolutionary.

Schultheis, Rob. Bone Games: One Man's Search for the Ultimate Athletic High. LC 84-42622. 240p. 1985. 15.95 (ISBN 0-394-53967-2). Random.

Schwartz, Gary E. & Shapiro, David, eds. Consciousness & Self-Regulation: Advances in Research & Theory. Incl. Vol. 1. 422p. 1976. 35.00x (ISBN 0-306-33601-4); Vol. 2. 470p. 1978. 35.00x (ISBN 0-306-33602-2). LC 76-8907. (Illus., Plenum Pr). Plenum Pub.

Stuart, Friend. Adventures in Consciousness. 1962. pap. 6.95 (ISBN 0-912132-00-0). Dominion Pr.

Tart, Charles T. Waking up. LC 86-11844. 300p. 1986. 17.95 (ISBN 0-87773-374-0, Pub. by New Sci Lib-Shambhala). Shambhala Pubns.

Toolan, David. Facing West from California's Shores: A Jesuit's Journey in the Consciousness Movement. 352p. 1987. 19.95 (ISBN 0-8245-0805-X). Crossroad NY.

Unger, Carl. The Language of the Consciousness Soul. 1983. 25.00 (ISBN 0-916786-56-0). St George Bk Serv.

Wilber, Ken. The Spectrum of Consciousness. LC 76-39690. (Illus.). 1977. 12.00 (ISBN 0-8356-0495-0). Theos Pub Hse.

Zinberg, Norman E., ed. Alternate States of Consciousness. LC 76-46722. 1977. 14.95 (ISBN 0-02-935770-5); pap. text ed. 7.95 (ISBN 0-02-935930-9). Free Pr.

CONSECRATION OF BISHOPS

see also Bishops; Investiture

Jenkins, Claude. Bishop Barlow's Consecration & Archbishop Parker's Register: With Some New Documents. (Church Historical Society London New Ser.: No. 17). Repr. of 1935 ed. 20.00 (ISBN 0-8115-3140-6). Kraus Repr.

CONSECRATION SERVICES

see Dedication Services

CONSERVATIVE JUDAISM

Cohen, Boaz. Law & Tradition in Judaism. 1959. 12.50x (ISBN 0-87068-023-4). Ktav.

Gordis, Robert. Understanding Conservative Judaism. 15.00x (ISBN 0-87068-680-1). Ktav.

Morgan, Roger & Silvestri, Stefano. Moderates & Conservatives in Western Europe. LC 83-5662. 288p. 1983. 27.50 (ISBN 0-8386-3201-7). Fairleigh Dickinson.

Shargel, Baila R. Practical Dreamer: Israel Friedlaender & the Shaping of American Judaism. (Illus.). 1985. text ed. 20.00 (ISBN 0-87334-025-6, Pub. by Jewish Theol Seminary). Ktav.

Siegel, S., ed. Conservative Judaism & Jewish Law. 20.00x (ISBN 0-87068-428-0); pap. 9.95. Ktav.

Sklare, Marshall. Conservative Judaism: An American Religious Movement. cancelled. Transaction Bks.

--Conservative Judaism: An American Religious Movement. (Illus.). 336p. 1985. pap. text ed. 12.75 (ISBN 0-8191-4480-0, Co-Pub. by Ctr Jewish Comm Studies). U Pr of Amer.

CONSOLATION

see also Joy and Sorrow; Peace of Mind

Allen, Charles L. When You Lose a Loved One. 64p. 1959. 7.95 (ISBN 0-8007-0347-2). Revell.

Allen, Charles L. & Rice, Helen S. When You Lose a Loved One-Life Is Forever. 128p. 1979. pap. 5.95 (ISBN 0-8007-5031-4, Power Bks). Revell.

Berner, Carl W. Why Me, Lord? Meaning & Comfort in Times of Trouble. LC 73-78267. 112p. (Orig.). 1973. pap. 5.95 (ISBN 0-8066-1331-9, 10-7172). Augsburg.

Booz, Gretchen & Holmes, Reed M. Kendra. LC 79-12285. 1979. 2.00 (ISBN 0-8309-0234-1). Herald Hse.

Burton, Clea M. & Burton, Alma P. For They Shall Be Comforted. 5.95 (ISBN 0-87747-091-X). Deseret Bk.

Cardano, Girolamo. Cardanus Comforte. Bedingfield, T., ed. LC 77-6565. (English Experience Ser.: No. 82). 204p. 1969. Repr. of 1576 ed. 25.00 (ISBN 90-221-0082-0). Walter J Johnson.

Carter, James E. Facing the Final Foe. LC 85-19517. 1986. pap. 2.25 (ISBN 0-8054-5433-0). Broadman.

Erdahl, Lowell O. The Lonely House: Strength for Times of Loss. LC 77-1907. Repr. of 1977 ed. 21.30 (ISBN 0-8357-9015-0, 2016377). Bks Demand UMI.

Greenberg, Sidney S., ed. Treasury of Comfort. pap. 5.00 (ISBN 0-87980-167-0). Wilshire.

Grollman, Earl A. Living When a Loved One Has Died. LC 76-48508. (Illus.). 1977. pap. 6.95 (ISBN 0-8070-2741-3, BP560). Beacon Pr.

Grollman, Earl A., ed. What Helped Me When My Loved One Died. LC 80-68166. 168p. 1982. pap. 7.95 (ISBN 0-8070-3229-8, BP 626). Beacon Pr.

Hobe, Phyllis, ed. The Wonder of Comfort. LC 82-8322. (Small Wonders Ser.). (Illus.). 108p. (Orig.). 1982. pap. 4.95 (ISBN 0-664-26003-9, A Bridgebooks Publication). Westminster.

Holmes, Marjorie. To Help You Through the Hurting. 176p. 1985. pap. 8.95 (ISBN 0-8027-2508-2). Walker & Co.

Jackson, Edgar N. When Someone Dies. Hulme, William E., ed. LC 76-154488. (Pocket Counsel Bks). 58p. (Orig.). 1971. pap. 2.50 (ISBN 0-8006-1103-9, 1-1103). Fortress.

Kreis, Bernardine & Pattie, Alice. Up from Grief. 292p. 1984. pap. 9.95 large print ed. (ISBN 0-8027-2486-8). Walker & Co.

Lee, Laurel. To Comfort You. Phillips, Cheryl M. & Harvey, Bonnie C., eds. (Illus.). 32p. (Orig.). 1984. pap. 0.98 (ISBN 0-937420-11-5). Stirrup Assoc.

Lester, Andrew D. It Hurts So Bad, Lord! LC 75-42860. 1976. 5.95 (ISBN 0-8054-5238-9). Broadman.

Lewis, C. S. A Grief Observed. 160p. 1976. pap. 3.50 (ISBN 0-553-25614-9). Bantam.

--A Grief Observed. 64p. (Orig.). 1966. pap. 3.95 (ISBN 0-571-06624-0). Faber & Faber.

--Grief Observed. 1963. 6.95 (ISBN 0-8164-0137-3, HarpR). Har-Row.

--A Grief Observed. 120p. 1985. pap. 5.95 large print ed. (ISBN 0-8027-2470-1). Walker & Co.

Miller, J. R. Words of Comfort. (Illus.). 1976. 5.95 (ISBN 0-89957-518-8); pap. 2.95 (ISBN 0-89957-517-X). AMG Pubs.

More, Thomas. A Fruteful & Pleasaunt Worke of the Beste State of a Publyque Weale & the Newe Yle Called Utopia. Robynson, R., tr. LC 75-26096. (English Experience Ser.: No. 108). 1969. Repr. of 1551 ed. 21.00 (ISBN 90-221-0108-8). Walter J Johnson.

More, St. Thomas. A Dialogue of Comfort Against Tribulation. (The Complete Works of St. Thomas More Ser.: No. 12). 1976. 77.00x (ISBN 0-300-01609-3). Yale U Pr.

Oates, Wayne E. Your Particular Grief. LC 81-3328. 114p. 1981. pap. 6.95 (ISBN 0-664-24376-2). Westminster.

Petroff, Elizabeth. Consolation of the Blessed. (Illus.). 224p. 1980. 12.95 (ISBN 0-686-32835-3). Alta Gaia Bks.

Pink, Arthur W. Comfort for Christians. pap. 3.95 (ISBN 0-685-19825-1). Reiner.

Saleska, E. J. Let Not Your Heart Be Troubled. 1945. 0.95 (ISBN 0-570-03676-3, 74-1001). Concordia.

Shelley, Bruce L. Christian Theology in Plain Language. 256p. 1985. 12.95 (ISBN 0-8499-0381-5, 0381-5). Word Bks.

Southwell, Robert. An Epistle of Comfort. Waugh, Margaret, ed. LC 66-22384. 1966. 3.95 (ISBN 0-8294-0072-9). Loyola.

Spiro, Jack D. Time to Mourn: Judaism and the Psychology of Bereavement. 1968. 8.95 (ISBN 0-8197-0185-8). Bloch.

Strauss, Lehman. Certainties for Today. 1956. pap. 3.25 (ISBN 0-87213-810-0). Loizeaux.

Taber, Gladys. Another Path. LC 63-17678. 1963. 12.45i (ISBN 0-397-00260-2). Har-Row.

Westberg, Granger E. Good Grief. LC 78-21233. 64p. (Orig.). 1962. pap. 1.95 (ISBN 0-8006-1114-4, 1-1114); pap. 3.95 large print ed. (ISBN 0-8006-1361-9, 1-1361). Fortress.

Wiersbe, Warren. Five Secrets of Living. 1978. pap. 2.95 (ISBN 0-8423-0870-9). Tyndale.

Wisloff, Fredrik. On Our Father's Knee: Devotions for Times of Illness. LC 72-90264. 144p. 1973. pap. 5.95 (ISBN 0-8066-1309-2, 10-4765). Augsburg.

Words of Comfort. (Words of... Ser.). (Illus.). 48p. 1983. 3.95 (ISBN 0-8407-5331-4). Nelson.

CONSTANCE, COUNCIL OF, 1414-1418

McGowan, John P. Pierre d'Ailly & the Council of Constance. 110p. 1984. Repr. of 1936 ed. 22.00x (ISBN 0-939738-34-1). Zubal Inc.

CONSTANTINE, DONATION OF

see Donation of Constantine

CONSTANTINE 1ST, THE GREAT, EMPEROR OF ROME, d. 337

Barnes, Timothy. Constantine & Eusebius. LC 81-4248. (Illus.). 448p. 1981. text ed. 37.50x (ISBN 0-674-16530-6). Harvard U Pr.

Baumstark, Anton. Die Modestianischen und Die Konstantinischen Bauten Am Heiligen Grabe Zu Jerusalem. Repr. of 1915 ed. 15.00 (ISBN 0-384-03585-X). Johnson Repr.

Baynes, N. H. Constantine the Great & the Christian Church. (Raleigh Lectures on History). 1977. Repr. of 1929 ed. 4.50 (ISBN 0-85672-000-3, Pub. by British Acad). Longwood Pub Group.

Baynes, Norman H. Constantine the Great & the Christian Church. 1974. lib. bdg. 59.95 (ISBN 0-87968-934-X). Gordon Pr.

--Constantine the Great & the Christian Church. LC 74-34500. (World History Ser., No. 48). 1972. Repr. of 1930 ed. lib. bdg. 75.00x (ISBN 0-8383-0131-2). Haskell.

Coleman, Christopher B. Constantine the Great & Christianity. LC 70-155636. (Columbia University Studies in the Social Sciences: No. 146). Repr. of 1914 ed. 18.50 (ISBN 0-404-51146-5). AMS Pr.

Doerries, Hermann. Constantine & Religious Liberty. 1960. 39.50x (ISBN 0-686-51363-0). Elliots Bks.

Eadie, John W., ed. The Conversion of Constantine. LC 76-25480. (European American Studies). 120p. 1977. pap. text ed. 5.95 (ISBN 0-88275-453-X). Krieger.

Firth, John B. Constantine the Great: The Reorganization of the Empire & the Triumph of the Church. facsimile ed. LC 77-152983. (Select Bibliographies Reprint Ser). Repr. of 1904 ed. 27.50 (ISBN 0-8369-5735-0). Ayer Co Pubs.

Huttman, Maude A. Establishment of Christianity & the Proscription of Paganism. LC 15-703. (Columbia University. Studies in the Social Sciences: No. 147). Repr. of 1914 ed. 18.50 (ISBN 0-404-51147-3). AMS Pr.

Keresztes, Paul. Constantine: A Great Christian Monarch & Apostle. (London Studies in Classical Philology Ser.). 218p. 1981. pap. text ed. 28.50x (ISBN 90-70265-03-6, Pub. by Gieben Holland). Humanities.

Killingray, Margaret. Constantine. Yapp, Malcolm, et al, eds. (World History Ser.). (Illus.). 32p. 1980. lib. bdg. 6.95 (ISBN 0-89908-040-5); pap. text ed. 2.45 (ISBN 0-89908-015-4). Greenhaven.

Nicephorus. Nicephori Archiepiscopi Constantinopolitani Opuscula Historica. De Boor, Carl G., ed. LC 75-7311. (Roman History Ser.). (Gr.). 1975. Repr. 25.50x (ISBN 0-405-07193-0). Ayer Co Pubs.

Preger, Theodorus, ed. Scriptores Originum Constantino-Politanarum. LC 75-7335. (Roman History Ser.). (Gr.). 1975. Repr. 32.00x (ISBN 0-405-07054-3). Ayer Co Pubs.

CONTEMPLATION

see also Devotion; Meditation

Borst, James. Contemplative Prayer: A Guide for Today's Catholic. 1979. pap. 1.50 (ISBN 0-89243-106-7). Liguori Pubns.

Jager, Willigis. The Way to Contemplation: Encountering God Today. O'connell, Matthew J., tr. 1987. pap. 7.95. Paulist Pr.

Keating, Thomas. The Heart of the World: An Introduction to Contemplative Christianity. 96p. 1981. 8.95 (ISBN 0-8245-0014-8). Crossroad NY.

Lefebvre, Dom G. God Present. 1979. pap. 3.95 (ISBN 0-03-053436-4, HarpR). Har-Row.

Lull, Ramon, pseud. The Art of Contemplation. Peers, Allison, tr. 1976. lib. bdg. 69.95 (ISBN 0-8490-1451-4). Gordon Pr.

Lyman, Frederick C. Posture of Contemplation. LC 68-54973. 123p. 1969. 5.00 (ISBN 0-8022-2258-7). Philos Lib.

Maloney, George. Jesus, Set Me Free! Inner Freedom Through Contemplation. 4.95 (ISBN 0-87193-096-X). Dimension Bks.

Maloney, George A. Journey into Contemplation. 144p. (Orig.). 1983. pap. 3.95 (ISBN 0-914544-51-9). Living Flame Pr.

Merton, Thomas. What Is Contemplation? 80p. 1981. pap. 4.95 (ISBN 0-87243-103-7). Templegate.

Murphy, Carol. Nurturing Contemplation. 1983. pap. 2.50x (ISBN 0-87574-252-1, 252). Pendle Hill.

Roberts, Bernadette. The Experience of No-Self: A Contemplative Journey. LC 84-5500. 204p. 1984. pap. 9.95 (ISBN 0-87773-289-2, 72693-6). Shambhala Pubns.

Rossetti, Stephen J. I Am Awake: A Guide to the Contemplative Life. 1987. pap. 3.95. Paulist Pr.

Twitchell, Paul. Eckankar: Illuminated Way Letters 1966-1971. 272p. 1975. 5.95 (ISBN 0-914766-25-2). IWP Pub.

Walker, Susan, ed. Speaking of Silence: Christians & Buddhists on the Contemplative Way. 1987. pap. 14.95. Paulist Pr.

Walsh, James, tr. A Letter of Private Direction. 1979. pap. 5.95 (ISBN 0-87243-083-9). Templegate.

CONTEMPT OF THE WORLD

see Asceticism

CONTRARIETY IN RELIGION, FOLK-LORE, ETC.)

see Polarity (In Religion, Folk-Lore, etc.)

CONTRITION

see Penance; Repentance

CONVENTS AND NUNNERIES

see also Abbeys; Monasteries; Monasticism and Religious Orders for Women; Priories; Secularization

Eckenstein, Lina. Woman Under Monasticism: Chapters on Saint-Lore & Convent Life Between A. D. 500 & A. D. 1500. LC 63-11028. 1963. Repr. of 1896 ed. 10.00x (ISBN 0-8462-0363-4). Russell.

Moorman, John R. Medieval Franciscan Houses. Marcel, George, ed. (History Ser.: No. 4). 1983. 40.00 (ISBN 0-318-00515-8). Franciscan Inst.

Sanchez, Julio. The Community of the Holy Spirit: A Movement of Change in a Covent of Nuns in Puerto Rico. 190p. (Orig.). 1984. lib. bdg. 25.25 (ISBN 0-8191-3367-1); pap. text ed. 11.75 (ISBN 0-8191-3368-X). U Pr of Amer.

CONVERSION

see also Christianity–Psychology; Converts; Grace (Theology); Repentance; Salvation

Atkins, Susan & Slosser, Bob. Child of Satan, Child of God. LC 77-81947. 1977. (Pub. by Logos); pap. 2.95 (ISBN 0-88270-276-9). Bridge Pub.

Barbernitz, Patricia. RCIA Team Manual: How to Implement the Rite of Christian Initiation of Adults in Your Parish. 88p. 1986. pap. 7.95 (ISBN 0-8091-2814-4). Paulist Pr.

Barnhart, Joe E. & Barnhart, Mary A. The New Birth: A Naturalist View of Religious Conversion. LC 81-9557. xiv, 174p. 1981. 15.50 (ISBN 0-86554-009-8, MUP-H11). Mercer Univ Pr.

Brancaforte, Benito. Guzman de Alfarache: Conversion o Proceso de Degradacion? vi, 230p. 1980. 11.00x (ISBN 0-942260-14-7). Hispanic Seminary.

Chesterton, G. K. & More, Thomas. Orthodoxy. (Books to Live Ser.). 1985. Repr. of 1908 ed. 10.95 (ISBN 0-88347-184-1). Thomas More.

Cheve, C. F. Dictionnaire des Conversions. Migne, J. P., ed. (Nouvelle Encyclopedie Theologique Ser.: Vol. 33). (Fr.). 836p. Repr. of 1852 ed. lib. bdg. 106.00x (ISBN 0-89241-275-5). Caratzas.

Colson, Charles. Born Again. (Illus.). 352p. 1977. Movie ed. pap. 3.95 (ISBN 0-8007-8290-9, Spire Bks); (Spire Bks). Revell.

Conn, Walter E. Conversion: Perspectives on Personal & Social Transformation. LC 78-19079. 1978. pap. 10.95 (ISBN 0-8189-0368-6). Alba.

Doran, Robert M. Psychic Conversion & Theological Foundations: Toward a Reorientation of the Human Sciences. LC 81-9360. (American Academy of Religion Studies in Religion Ser.). 1981. pap. 9.95 (ISBN 0-89130-522-X, 01-00-25). Scholars Pr GA.

Duffy, Regis, et al. Initiation & Conversion. Johnson, Lawrence, ed. 96p. 1985. pap. 4.95 (ISBN 0-8146-1431-0). Liturgical Pr.

Duggan, Robert, ed. Conversion & the Catechumenate. 1984. pap. 7.95 (ISBN 0-8091-2614-1). Paulist Pr.

Erickson, Gary D. The Conversion Experience: A Biblical Study of the Blood, Water & Spirit. Bernard, David, ed. (Illus.). 160p. (Orig.). 1987. pap. 5.95 (ISBN 0-932581-13-7). Word Aflame.

Fichter, Joseph H. Autobiographies of Conversion. LC 87-1634. (Studies in Religion & Society: Vol. 17). 232p. 1987. 49.95 (ISBN 0-88946-857-5). E Mellen.

Griffin, Emilie. Turning: Reflections on the Experience of Conversion. LC 79-6652. 224p. 1982. 8.95 (ISBN 0-385-15823-8, Im); pap. 4.50 (ISBN 0-385-17892-1). Doubleday.

Harris, Irving. He Touched Me: Conversion Stories of Norman Vincent Peale, Bruce Larson, Ernest Gordon, Bill Wilson, & Others. 144p. (Orig.). pap. 8.95 (ISBN 0-687-16680-2). Abingdon.

Helm, Paul. The Beginnings: Word & Spirit in Conversion. 133p. (Orig.). 1986. pap. 4.95 (ISBN 0-85151-470-7). Banner of Truth.

Hooker, Thomas. The Soules Preparation for Christ: Or, a Treatise of Contrition. LC 78-291. (American Puritan Writings Ser.). (Illus.). 256p. 1981. Repr. of 1638 ed. 67.50 (ISBN 0-404-60815-9). AMS Pr.

Ingle, Clifford, ed. Children & Conversion. LC 79-113212. 160p. 1975. pap. 4.95 (ISBN 0-8054-2514-4). Broadman.

James, William. Varieties of Religious Experience. LC 37-27013. 1936. 6.95 (ISBN 0-394-60463-6). Modern Lib.

--Varieties of Religious Experience. pap. 4.50 (ISBN 0-451-62486-6, ME2069, Ment). NAL.

--The Varieties of Religious Experience. (The Works of William James). (Illus.). 728p. 1985. text ed. 45.00x (ISBN 0-674-93225-0). Harvard U Pr.

Kasdorf, Hans. Christian Conversion in Context. LC 80-12871. 208p. 1980. pap. 9.95 (ISBN 0-8361-1926-6). Herald Pr.

Kerr, Hugh T. & Mulder, John M., eds. Conversions. 288p. 1983. 12.95 (ISBN 0-8028-3587-2). Eerdmans.

Kerr, Hugh T. & Mulder, John T., eds. Conversions. 384p. 1985. pap. 7.95 (ISBN 0-8028-0016-5). Eerdmans.

Kourdakov, Sergei. Persecutor. (Illus.). 256p. 1974. pap. 3.50 (ISBN 0-8007-8177-5, Spire Bks). Revell.

Laun, Hellmut. How I Met God: An Unusual Conversion. Smith, David, tr. 163p. 1983. 10.50 (ISBN 0-8199-0871-1). Franciscan Herald.

Malgo, Wim. Seven Signs of a Born Again Person. 1.45 (ISBN 0-937422-14-2). Midnight Call.

Omrcanin, Ivo. Forced Conversions of Croatians to the Serbian Faith in History. 92p. (Orig.). 1985. pap. 6.00 (ISBN 0-9613814-1-8). Samizdat.

Packard, Russell C. Come, Journey with Me: A Personal Story of Conversion & Ordination. LC 84-24356. 208p. (Orig.). 1984. pap. 8.00 (ISBN 0-89571-021-8). Affirmation.

Photiou, Paul. My Conversion to Christ. Orthodox Christian Educational Society, ed. (Gr., Orig.). 1970. Repr. of 1952 ed. 0.50x (ISBN 0-938366-41-6). Orthodox Chr.

Robleto, Adolfo. Catecismo Biblico y Doctrinal Para el Nuevo Creyente. 164p. 1985. pap. 1.95 (ISBN 0-311-09088-5). Casa Bautista.

Rubenstein, Hymie. It's Getting Gooder & Gooder. (Orig.). 1976. pap. 4.95 (ISBN 0-89350-006-2). Fountain Pr.

Seashore, Gladys. The New Me. 1972. pap. 1.75 (ISBN 0-911802-31-2). Free Church Pubns.

Sheen, Fulton J. Peace of Soul. 1954. pap. 4.95 (ISBN 0-385-02871-7, D8, Im). Doubleday.

Spurgeon, C. H. Conversion & Experiences After Conversion. 1977. pap. 1.50 (ISBN 0-686-17969-2). Pilgrim Pubns.

Thompson, James J. Fleeing the Whore of Babylon: A Modern Conversion Story. 1986. pap. 9.95 (ISBN 0-87061-130-5). Chr Classics.

Wallis, Jim. Call to Conversion: Recovering the Gospel for These Times. LC 80-8901. 208p. 1983. pap. 9.95 (ISBN 0-686-92025-2, RD414, HarpR). Har-Row.

Weinandy, Thomas. Receiving the Promise: The Spirit's Work of Conversion. 128p. 1985. pap. 3.95 (ISBN 0-932085-01-6). Word Among Us.

Wenger, J. C., ed. They Met God: A Number of Conversion Accounts & Personal Testimonies of God's Presence & Leading in the Lives of Children. LC 64-15344. pap. 48.00 (ISBN 0-317-26611-X, 2025422). Bks Demand UMI.

CONVERT MAKING

see Evangelistic Work

CONVERTS

see also Buddhist converts, etc. for works on converts to religions other than Christianity

Ashley, Meg. Meg. LC 83-1332. 128p. 1983. pap. text ed. 2.95 (ISBN 0-88449-101-3, A324581). Vision Hse.

Baily, Keith M. Care of Converts. 95p. (Orig.). 1979. pap. 1.50 (ISBN 0-87509-156-3); leader's guide 0.75 (ISBN 0-87509-157-1). Chr Pubns.

Brown, Rebecca. He Came to Set the Captives Free. 288p. (Orig.). 1986. pap. 7.50 (ISBN 0-937958-25-5). Chick Pubns.

Cheve, C. F. Dictionnaire des Conversions. Migne, J. P., ed. (Nouvelle Encyclopedie Theologique Ser.: Vol. 33). (Fr.). 836p. Repr. of 1852 ed. lib. bdg. 106.00x (ISBN 0-89241-275-5). Caratzas.

Childress, Harvey. My Triumphant Life. 1978. pap. 2.25 (ISBN 0-88027-087-X). Firm Foun Pub.

Clark. Instructions to Christian Converts. pap. 1.95 (ISBN 0-686-12883-4). Schmul Pub Co.

Cobin, Martin. From Convincement to Conversion. LC 64-17424. (Orig.). 1964. pap. 2.50x (ISBN 0-87574-134-7). Pendle Hill.

Down, Goldie. Saga of an Ordinary Man. (Dest Two Ser.). 1984. pap. 4.95 (ISBN 0-8163-0554-4). Pacific Pr Pub Assn.

Fackler, Mark. Ride the Hot Wind. LC 77-78850. 1978. pap. 2.95 (ISBN 0-88419-126-5). Creation Hse.

Griffiths, Michael. Encouraging New Christians. pap. 0.75 (ISBN 0-87784-106-3). Inter-Varsity.

Hester, Glenn & Nygren, Bruce. Child of Rage. LC 81-9490. 192p. 1981. pap. 5.95 (ISBN 0-8407-5810-3). Nelson.

Jarrard, Dan. The Calling. Wheeler, Gerald, ed. 96p. 1987. pap. price not set (ISBN 0-8280-0382-3). Review & Herald.

Lewis, C. S. Surprised by Joy: The Shape of My Early Life. LC 56-5329. 248p. 1956. 12.95 (ISBN 0-15-187011-X). HarBraceJ.

--Surprised by Joy: The Shape of My Early Life. LC 56-5329. 1966. pap. 4.95 (ISBN 0-15-687011-8, Harv). HarBraceJ.

Lovett, C. S. Operation Manhunt Made Easy. 1961. 2.95 (ISBN 0-938148-17-6). Personal Christianity.

--Soul-Winning Made Easy. 1978. pap. 4.25 (ISBN 0-938148-10-9). Personal Christianity.

--What to Do When Your Friends Reject Christ. 1966. pap. 4.25 (ISBN 0-938148-06-0). Personal Christianity.

Martin, Ralph. Why Be a Christian. 48p. (Orig.). 1987. pap. 1.95 (ISBN 0-89283-336-X). Servant.

Mayson, Barry & Marco, Tony. Fallen Angel: Hell's Angel to Heaven's Saint. LC 81-43539. (Illus.). 312p. 1982. 15.95 (ISBN 0-385-17934-0); pap. write for info. (ISBN 0-385-19626-1). Doubleday.

Pepper, Clayton, ed. Keeping Converts & Restoring the Erring. pap. 2.25 (ISBN 0-89137-205-9). Quality Pubns.

Price, Eugenia. The Burden Is Light. 272p. 1985. pap. 11.95 (ISBN 0-8027-2514-7). Walker & Co.

Underwood, Gary & Underwood, Marylyn. First Principles: Topical Studies for New Converts. 1978. 4.95 (ISBN 0-89137-709-3). Quality Pubns.

Venden, Morris L. Defeated Demons. (Uplook Ser.). 16p. 1982. pap. 0.99 (ISBN 0-8163-0487-4). Pacific Pr Pub Assn.
Whitcomb, Paul. Confession of a Roman Catholic. 55p. 1985. pap. 1.25 (ISBN 0-89555-281-7). Tan Bks Pubs.
Winters, William, ed. Conservacion de Convertidos. (Span.). 120p. 1980. pap. 3.95 (ISBN 0-87148-182-0). Pathway Pr.
Winters, William E. Convert Conservation. 120p. pap. 4.25 (ISBN 0-87148-161-8). Pathway Pr.

CONVERTS, CATHOLIC

Blunt, Hugh F. Great Penitents. facs. ed. LC 67-30198. (Essay Index Reprint Ser). 1921. 17.00 (ISBN 0-8369-0220-3). Ayer Co Pubs.
Burton, Katherine K. In No Strange Land. facsimile ed. LC 72-99619. (Essay Index Reprint Ser). 1942. 19.50 (ISBN 0-8369-1551-8). Ayer Co Pubs.
Day, Dorothy. From Union Square to Rome. 17.00 (ISBN 0-405-10815-X). Ayer Co Pubs.
Forrest, M. D. Chats with Converts: Complete Explanation of Catholic Belief. 31st ed. LC 78-56979. 1978. pap. 5.00 (ISBN 0-89555-069-5). TAN Bks Pubs.
Gower, Joseph F. & Leliaert, Richard M., eds. The Brownson-Hecker Correspondence. LC 76-20160. 1979. text ed. 25.00x (ISBN 0-268-00656-3). U of Notre Dame Pr.
Hope, Alexander. Are You Thinking of Becoming a Catholic? (Illus.). 90p. 1974. 47.35 (ISBN 0-913314-39-0). Am Classical Coll Pr.
Kenny, John. Now That You Are a Catholic. rev. & enl. ed. LC 73-80417. 108p. (Orig.). 1986. pap. 3.95 (ISBN 0-8091-1743-6). Paulist Pr.
Killgallon, James J. Becoming Catholic, Even If You Happen to Be One. LC 79-89875. 1980. pap. 4.50 (ISBN 0-914070-13-4). ACTA Found.
Lunn, Arnold H. Roman Converts. facs. ed. LC 67-22102. (Essay Index Reprint Ser). 1923. 18.00 (ISBN 0-8369-0636-5). Ayer Co Pubs.
Peil, William. The Big Way. 1983. 1.00 (ISBN 0-89536-952-4, 7503). CSS of Ohio.
Powell, Walter. The Intimate Notebook of a Recent Convert to Catholicism: The Confessions of an Anguished Soul. (Illus.). 1977. 41.45 (ISBN 0-89266-079-1). Am Classical Coll Pr.
Sargent, Daniel. Four Independents. facs. ed. LC 68-55856. (Essay Index Reprint Ser.). 1935. 18.00 (ISBN 0-8369-0850-3). Ayer Co Pubs.
Wu, John C. Beyond East & West. 388p. 1980. 5.95 (ISBN 0-89955-182-3, Pub. by Mei Ya China). Intl Spec Bk.

CONVERTS FROM JUDAISM

Endelman, Todd M., ed. Jewish Apostasy in the Modern World. 300p. 1987. 34.50 (ISBN 0-8419-1029-4). Holmes & Meier.
Levy, Rosalie M. What Think You of Christ. 1962. 1.50 (ISBN 0-8198-0172-0). Dghtrs St Paul.
Markell, Jan. Gone the Golden Dream. LC 79-16718. 176p. 1979. pap. 4.95 (ISBN 0-87123-049-6, 210049). Bethany Hse.
Oesterreicher, John M. Five in Search of Wisdom. abr. ed. Orig. Title: Walls Are Crumbling: Seven Jewish Philosophers Discover Christ. 1967. pap. 2.25x (ISBN 0-268-00100-6). U of Notre Dame Pr.
--Walls Are Crumbling. (Illus.). 10.00 (ISBN 0-8159-7201-6). Devin.
Schlamm, J. Vera & Friedman, Bob. Pursued. rev. ed. LC 86-600. 189p. 1986. pap. 3.95 (ISBN 0-8307-1146-5, 5018631). Regal.
Simon, Raphael. The Glory of Thy People. 1986. pap. 6.95 (ISBN 0-932506-47-X). St Bedes Pubns.
Van Hattenberg, Ludwig. The Conversion of the Jews. (Intimate Life of Man Library). (Illus.). 1979. 49.85 (ISBN 0-89266-191-7). Am Classical Coll Pr.
Zvi. LC 78-56149. 1978. pap. 3.95 (ISBN 0-915540-23-1). Friends Israel-Spearhead Pr.

CONVICTION

see Belief and Doubt; Truth

COOK-BOOKS

see Cookery

COOKERY

see also Christmas Cookery; Food

Blue, Lionel & Rose, June. A Taste of Heaven: Adventures in Food & Faith. new ed. (Orig.). 1978. pap. 4.50 (ISBN 0-87243-077-4). Templegate.
Buchanan, Annette M. & Martin, Kay A. The Twelve Months of Christmas. Bolt, John, ed. (Illus.). 192p. 1980. pap. 7.95 (ISBN 0-939114-01-1). Partridge Pair.
Capon, Robert F. The Supper of the Lamb: A Culinary Reflection. LC 78-14937. 271p. 1979. pap. 3.95 (ISBN 0-15-686893-8, Harv). HarBracej.
Carr, Francis A. Shaker Your Plate: Of Shaker Cooks & Cooking. LC 85-51982. (Illus.). 156p. (Orig.). 1985. pap. 10.95 (ISBN 0-915836-02-5). Shaker Pr ME.
Cook, Bill J. Saints & Sinners. 64p. 1981. pap. 3.95 (ISBN 0-938400-05-3). Donahoe Pubs.
Cookbook Committee of Holy Trinity Episcopal Church, ed. Not by Bread Alone. (Illus.). 304p. 1985. pap. 11.95 (ISBN 0-9615284-0-0). Holy Episcopal.
Donald, G. H. Cooking for Your Children Cookbook. 17.50 (ISBN 0-87559-125-6). Shalom.
Greig, Doris W. We Didn't Know They Were Angels. Beckwith, Mary, ed. 300p. (Orig.). 1987. pap. 7.95 (ISBN 0-8307-1145-7, 5418802). Regal.
Gustafson, Dana, ed. Food from Afar. spiral 3.95 (ISBN 0-686-12747-1). Grace Pub Co.
Kinard, Malvina & Crisler, Janet. Loaves & Fishes: Foods from Bible Times. LC 75-19544. (Illus.). 224p. 1975. pap. 4.95 (ISBN 0-87983-173-1). Keats.
Kreitzman, Sue. Comfort Food: Ninety-Five Recipes to Nourish the Soul As Well As the Body. 96p. 1985. pap. 6.95 (ISBN 0-517-55939-0, Harmony). Crown.
Longacre, Doris. More-with-Less Cookbook. LC 75-23563. 320p. 1976. pap. 9.95 (ISBN 0-8361-1786-7). Herald Pr.
Showalter, Mary E. Favorite Family Recipes. 128p. 1972. pap. 2.95 (ISBN 0-8361-1682-8). Herald Pr.
Solomon, Charmaine & Huxley, Dee. Love & a Wooden Spoon. LC 83-25446. 168p. 1985. pap. 10.00 (ISBN 0-385-19387-4). Doubleday.
Thackeray, Helen & Brown, Beth. Mormon Family Cookbook. LC 82-73085. (Illus.). 180p. 1982. 12.95 (ISBN 0-87747-930-5). Deseret Bk.
Voth, Norma J. Festive Cakes of Christmas. LC 81-2140. (Illus.). 80p. 1981. pap. 3.50 (ISBN 0-8361-1956-8). Herald Pr.

COOKERY, JEWISH

see also Jews–Dietary Laws

Blau, Esther & Deitsch, Cyrel, eds. Spice & Spirit of Kosher-Passover Cooking. LC 77-72116. (Lubavitch Women's Organization Ser.). 1981. 7.95 (ISBN 0-317-14690-4). Lubavitch Women.
David, Suzy, ed. The Sephardic Kosher Kitchen. LC 84-8150. (Illus.). 228p. 1985. 14.95 (ISBN 0-8246-0303-6). Jonathan David.
Leonard, Leah W. Jewish Cookery. (International Cook Book Ser.). 512p. 1949. 10.95 (ISBN 0-517-09758-3). Crown.
Nathan, Joan. The Children's Jewish Holiday Kitchen. LC 86-22016. (Illus.). 144p. 1987. plastic comb. 10.95 (ISBN 0-8052-0827-5). Schocken.
Rousso, Nira. The Passover Gourmet. (Illus.). 192p. 1987. 19.95 (ISBN 0-915361-66-3, Dist. by Watts). Adama Pubs Inc.
Yeshivat Aish HaTorah Woman's Organization. Kosher for Pessach Cookbook. 1982. spiral bd. 5.95 (ISBN 0-87306-223-X). Feldheim.

COOKERY, YOGA

Devi, Indra. Yoga for Americans. 1971. pap. 2.25 (ISBN 0-451-09869-2, E9869, Sig). NAL.
Himalayan International Institute. The Yoga Way Cookbook: Natural Vegetarian Recipes. rev. ed. LC 80-81994. (Illus.). 249p. 1980. spiral bdg. 9.95 (ISBN 0-89389-067-7). Himalayan Pubs.
Zorba the Buddha Rajneesh Restaurants & Staff. Zorba the Buddha Rajneesh Cookbook. Swami Premdharma & Ma Dhyan Yogini, eds. LC 84-61260. 240p. (Orig.). 1984. pap. 4.95 (ISBN 0-918963-00-1). Rajneesh Neo-Sannyas Intl.

COPTIC CHURCH

see also Ethiopic Church

Abdel-Massih, Ernest. The Life & Miracles of Pope Kirillos VI. 139p. (Orig.). 1982. pap. text ed. 3.00 (ISBN 0-932098-20-7). St Mark Coptic Orthodox.
Butcher, Edith L. The Story of the Church of Egypt, 2 vols. LC 75-41459. Repr. of 1897 ed. Set. 87.50 (ISBN 0-404-56231-0). AMS Pr.
Coptic Church Staff. Coptic Morning Service for the Lord's Day. Crichton-Stuart, John P., tr. LC 72-39871. Repr. of 1908 ed. 17.25 (ISBN 0-404-01247-7). AMS Pr.
Guirguis, Fouad. The Difficult Years of Survival. LC 83-90921. 89p. 1985. 7.95 (ISBN 0-533-05937-2). Vantage.
Leeder, S. H. Modern Sons of the Pharaohs. LC 73-6288. (The Middle East Ser.). Repr. of 1918 ed. 29.00 (ISBN 0-405-05346-0). Ayer Co Pubs.
Robinson, Forbes, tr. Coptic Apocryphal Gospels. (Texts & Studies: No. 1, Vol. 4-Pt. 2). pap. 19.00 (ISBN 0-8115-1693-8). Kraus Repr.

COPTIC LITERATURE–TRANSLATIONS

Abdel-Massih, Ernest T., et al, trs. from Coptic. The Divine Liturgy of St. Basil the Great. 257p. 1982. pap. 7.00 (ISBN 0-932098-19-3). St Mark Coptic Orthodox.
Budge, Ernest A. Coptic Texts Edited with Introductions & English Translations, 5 vols. Repr. of 1915 ed. 345.00 set (ISBN 0-404-11550-0); write for info. AMS Pr.
Bullard, Roger A., ed. The Hypostasis of the Archons: The Coptic Text with Translation & Commentary. (Patristische Texte und Studien Ser.: Vol. 10). (Coptic & Eng). 1970. 27.50x (ISBN 3-11-006356-5). De Gruyter.
Haase, Felix A. Die Koptischen Quellen Zum Konzil Von Nicaa. 12.00 (ISBN 0-384-20630-1). Johnson Repr.
Peters, Melvin K. A Critical Edition of the Coptic (Bohairic) Pentateuch, Vol. 5. LC 83-3260. (SBL Septuagint & Cognate Studies). 126p. 1983. pap. 11.95 (ISBN 0-89130-617-X, 06 04 15). Scholars Pr GA.

COPTS

Abdel-Massih, Ernest. The Life & Miracles of Pope Kirillos VI. 139p. (Orig.). 1982. pap. text ed. 3.00 (ISBN 0-932098-20-7). St Mark Coptic Orthodox.
Carter, Barbara L. The Copts in Egyptian Politics 1918 - 1952. 256p. 1985. 43.00 (ISBN 0-7099-3417-3, Pub. by Croom Helm Ltd). Methuen Inc.
Leeder, S. H. Modern Sons of the Pharaohs. LC 73-6288. (The Middle East Ser.). Repr. of 1918 ed. 29.00 (ISBN 0-405-05346-0). Ayer Co Pubs.
Mikhail, Kyriakos. Copts & Moslems under British Control. LC 70-118537. 1971. Repr. of 1911 ed. 24.00x (ISBN 0-8046-1160-2, Pub. by Kennikat). Assoc Faculty Pr.
Wallis-Budge, E. A., tr. The Bandlet of Righteousness: An Ethiopian Book of the Dead. (Coptic.). 1984. pap. 3.95 (ISBN 0-916411-23-0, Near Eastern). Holmes Pub.

CORINTH, GREECE–ANTIQUITIES

Amyx, D. A. & Lawrence, Patricia. Archaic Corinthian Pottery & the Anaploga Well. LC 75-4551. (Corinth Ser.: Vol. 7, Pt. 2). (Illus.). 1976. 35.00x (ISBN 0-87661-072-6, NK4647). Am Sch Athens.

CORONADO ISLANDS

Chavez, Angelico. Coronado's Friars: The Franciscans in the Coronado Expedition. (Monograph Ser.). (Illus.). 1968. 10.00 (ISBN 0-88382-058-7). AAFH.

CORPORAL WORKS OF MERCY

Daughters of St. Paul. Seven Spiritual Works of Mercy. 1979. 1.75 (ISBN 0-8198-6805-1); pap. 1.00 (ISBN 0-8198-6806-X). Dghtrs St Paul.

CORPORATIONS, RELIGIOUS

see also Sects

Oaks, Dallin H. Trust Doctrines in Church Controversies. LC 83-25058. xiv, 125p. 1984. 13.95x (ISBN 0-86554-104-3, MUP/H96). Mercer Univ Pr.
Zollman, Carl. American Civil Church Law. LC 79-77996. (Columbia University. Studies in the Social Sciences: No. 181). Repr. of 1917 ed. 30.00 (ISBN 0-404-51181-3). AMS Pr.

CORPUS CHRISTI FESTIVAL

Fisher, Lizette A. Mystic Vision in the Grail Legend & in the Divine Comedy. LC 79-168029. Repr. of 1917 ed. 16.50 (ISBN 0-404-02389-4). AMS Pr.
Kolve, V. A. Play Called Corpus Christi. LC 66-15301. 1966. 27.50x (ISBN 0-8047-0277-2); pap. 8.95 (ISBN 0-8047-0278-0, SP126). Stanford U Pr.

CORRESPONDENCE

see Letters

CORTES, HERNANDO, 1485-1547

Braden, Charles S. Religious Aspects of the Conquest of Mexico. LC 74-181914. Repr. of 1930 ed. 37.50 (ISBN 0-404-00925-5). AMS Pr.
Gomara, Francisco Lopez de. Cortes: The Life of the Conqueror of Mexico by His Secretary, Francisco Lopez de Gomara. Simpson, Lesley B., ed. & tr. LC 64-13474. 1964. pap. 5.95 (ISBN 0-520-00493-0, CAL 126). U of Cal Pr.
Hernan Cortes. (Span.). 10.95 (ISBN 84-241-5408-8). E Torres & Sons.
Isabel la Catolica. (Span.). 9.50 (ISBN 84-241-5417-7). E Torres & Sons.
Wagner, H. R. Rise of Fernando Cortes. (Cortes Society). 1944. 51.00 (ISBN 0-527-19733-5). Kraus Repr.

CORTES, HERNANDO, 1485-1547–BIBLIOGRAPHY

Valle, Rafael H. Bibliografia De Hernan Cortes. LC 75-133935. (Bibliography & Reference Ser.: No. 386). 1971. Repr. lib. bdg. 21.00 (ISBN 0-8337-3610-8). B Franklin.

CORTES, HERNANDO, 1485-1547–JUVENILE LITERATURE

Wilkes, John. Hernan Cortes: Conquistador in Mexico. LC 76-22436. (Cambridge Topic Bks). (Illus.). 1977. PLB 8.95 (ISBN 0-8225-1205-X). Lerner Pubns.

COSMAS, SAINT

Ligeti, Louis. Proceedings of the Cosma de Koros Memorial Symposium. 586p. 1978. 142.50x (ISBN 0-569-08468-7, Pub. by Collets (UK)). State Mutual Bk.
--Tibetan & Buddhist Studies Commemorating the 200th Anniversary of the Birth of Alexander Csoma de Koros, 2 vols. 388p. 1984. 350.00x (ISBN 0-569-08826-7, Pub. by Collets (UK)). State Mutual Bk.

COSMIC HARMONY

see Harmony of the Spheres

COSMOGONY

see also Creation

Brandall, William S. The Secret of the Universe: New Discoveries on God, Man & the Eternity of Life. (Illus.). 119p. 1985. 127.45 (ISBN 0-89266-535-1). Am Classical Coll Pr.
Burnet, Thomas. Sacred Theory of the Earth. LC 65-10027. (Centaur Classics Ser.). (Illus.). 414p. 1965. 22.50x (ISBN 0-8093-0186-5). S Ill U Pr.
Enuma Elish. The Seven Tablets of Creation, 2 vols. LC 73-18850. (Luzac's Semitic Text & Translation Ser.: Nos. 12 & 13). (Illus.). Repr. of 1902 ed. Set. 45.00 (ISBN 0-404-11344-3). AMS Pr.
Foster, Fred B. & Foster, Linda. Guardian I: The Answers. 224p. 1984. pap. 9.95 (ISBN 0-9613762-0-1). F B Foster Pubns.
Heidel, Alexander. Babylonian Genesis. 2nd ed. LC 51-822. 1963. 6.00x (ISBN 0-226-32399-4, P133, Phoen). U of Chicago Pr.
Hoyle, Fred. The Cosmogony of the Solar System. LC 78-21286. (Illus.). 168p. 1979. 17.95x (ISBN 0-89490-023-4). Enslow Pubs.
Norman, Ernest L. Cosmic Continuum. 2nd ed. (Illus.). 1960. 7.95 (ISBN 0-932642-17-9). Unarius Pubns.
Whitcomb, John C., Jr. The Origin of the Solar System. 1979. pap. 1.75 (ISBN 0-317-53170-0). BMH Bks.

COSMOGONY, BIBLICAL

see Creation

COSMOLOGY

see also Creation; Harmony of the Spheres; Philosophy; Religion and Astronautics; Theosophy

Bahadur, K. P. The Wisdom of Saankhya. LC 78-901698. (The Wisdom of India Ser.: Vol. 2). 222p. 1977. 9.25 (ISBN 0-89684-469-2). Orient Bk Dist.
Balian, R. & Adouse, J. Physical Cosmology. (Les Houches Summer School Ser.: Vol. 32). 668p. 1980. 115.00 (ISBN 0-444-85433-9). Elsevier.
Beckett, L. C. Movement & Emptiness. 1969. pap. 1.45 (ISBN 0-8356-0414-4, Quest). Theos Pub Hse.
Beesley, Ronald P. The Creative Ethers. 1978. pap. 3.95 (ISBN 0-87516-268-1). De Vorss.
Caillat, Collette. Jain Cosmology. (Illus.). 192p. 1982. 55.00 (ISBN 0-517-54662-0, Harmony). Crown.
Chelvam, Reginald T. Einstein Was Wrong: Or the Scroll Theory of Cosmology & of Matter. LC 82-71689. (Illus.). 268p. (Orig.). 1982. pap. 19.95 (ISBN 0-943796-00-8). Penso Pubns.
Collin, Rodney. The Theory of Celestial Influence: Man, The Universe, & Cosmic Mystery. LC 83-20286. (Illus.). 392p. (Orig.). 1984. pap. 10.95 (ISBN 0-87773-267-1, 72391-0). Shambhala Pubns.
--The Theory of Eternal Life. LC 83-20288. (Illus.). 132p. (Orig.). 1984. pap. 5.95 (ISBN 0-87773-273-6, 72399-6). Shambhala Pubns.
Davies, P. C. The Accidental Universe. LC 81-21592. (Illus.). 160p. 1982. 23.95 (ISBN 0-521-24212-6); pap. 11.95 (ISBN 0-521-28692-1). Cambridge U Pr.
Dewey, Barbara. The Creating Cosmos. LC 85-70369. 128p. 1985. 16.95 (ISBN 0-933123-00-0). Bartholomew Bks.
Dodson, E. O. The Phenomenon of Man Revisited: A Biological Viewpoint on Teilhard de Chardin. LC 83-20959. (Illus.). 288p. 1984. 26.50x (ISBN 0-231-05850-0). Columbia U Pr.
Douglas, Mary. Natural Symbols: Explorations in Cosmology. 1982. pap. 5.95 (ISBN 0-394-71105-X). Pantheon.
Gross, Darwin. The Key to the Universe. 75p. (Orig.). 1986. pap. 3.00 (ISBN 0-931689-08-2). SOS Pub OR.
Hatcher, John S. The Purpose of Physical Reality: The Kingdom of Names. Fisher, Betty J. & Hill, Richard A., eds. 250p. 1987. pap. 12.00 (ISBN 0-87743-208-2). Baha'i.
Horigan, James E. Chance or Design? LC 79-83605. 242p. 1979. 13.95 (ISBN 0-8022-2238-2). Philos Lib.
Kranich, Ernst M. Planetary Influences Upon Plants: Cosmological Botany. 184p. (Orig.). pap. 12.50 (ISBN 0-938250-20-5). Anthroposophic.
Kundakunda Acharya. Building of the Cosmos; Or, Panchastikayasara (the Five Cosmic Constituents) Chakravartinayanan, A., ed. LC 73-3837. (No. 3). Repr. of 1920 ed. 25.00 (ISBN 0-404-57703-2). AMS Pr.
Laird, John. Theism & Cosmology. facs. ed. LC 74-84317. (Essay Index Reprint Ser). 1942. 21.50 (ISBN 0-8369-1147-4). Ayer Co Pubs.
Merleau-Ponty, Jacques & Morando, Bruno. The Rebirth of Cosmology. LC 82-60404. (Illus.). xvi, 302p. 1982. pap. text ed. 9.95x (ISBN 0-8214-0606-X). Ohio U Pr.
Middleton, John, ed. Myth & Cosmos: Readings in Mythology & Symbolism. LC 75-43817. (Texas Press Sourcebooks in Anthropology: No. 5). 382p. 1976. pap. 9.95x (ISBN 0-292-75030-7). U of Tex Pr.
Miller, Jeanine. The Vision of Cosmic Order in the Vedas. 320p. 1985. 39.95x (ISBN 0-7102-0369-1). Methuen Inc.

Munitz, Milton K. Space, Time & Creation: Philosophical Aspects of Scientific Cosmology. 2nd ed. 11.75 (ISBN 0-8446-5908-8). Peter Smith.

Norman, Ruth E. History of the Universe, Vol. 2. (Illus.). 450p. 1982. 9.95x (ISBN 0-932642-72-1). Unarius Pubns.

Novak, David & Samuelson, Norbert, eds. Creation & the End of Days - Judaism & Scientific Cosmology: Proceedings of the 1984 Meeting of the Academy for Jewish Philosophy. LC 86-19062. 336p. (Orig.). 1986. 26.75 (ISBN 0-8191-5524-1, Pub. by Studies in Judaism); pap. text ed. 14.50 (ISBN 0-8191-5525-X, Pub. by Studies in Judaism). U Pr of Amer.

Rajneesh, Bhagwan S. The Beginning of the Beginning. 3rd ed. Parimal, Ma P., ed. vi, 113p. (Orig.). 1982. pap. 2.95x (ISBN 0-7069-2123-2, Pub. by Vikas India). Advent NY.

Rosenzweig, Franz. The Star of Redemption. Hallo, William W., tr. from Ger. LC 84-40833. 464p. 1985. text ed. 30.00 (ISBN 0-268-01717-4, 85-17179); pap. text ed. 12.95 (ISBN 0-268-01718-2, 85-17187). U of Notre Dame Pr.

Schindler, David L., ed. Beyond Mechanism: The Universe in Recent Physics & Catholic Thought. 166p. (Orig.). 1986. lib. bdg. 22.75 (ISBN 0-8191-5357-5, Pub. by Communio Intl Cth Review); pap. text ed. 10.75 (ISBN 0-8191-5358-3). U Pr of Amer.

Sherburne, Donald W., ed. A Key to Whitehead's "Process & Reality". LC 81-11661. 264p. 1981. pap. 10.00x (ISBN 0-226-75293-3). U of Chicago Pr.

Shetter, Janette. Rhythms of the Ecosystem. LC 76-26392. (Illus., Orig.). 1976. pap. 2.50x (ISBN 0-87574-208-4). Pendle Hill.

Spencer, H. S. The Mysteries of God in the Universe: Including the Reincarnation & Karma in the Gathas, the Bible, & Koran, 2 vols. Repr. of 1967 ed. Set. text ed. 35.00x. Coronet Bks.

Steiner, Rudolf. Philosophy, Cosmology & Religion: Ten Lectures. Easton, Stewart C., et al, eds. 180p. (Orig.). 1984. 16.00 (ISBN 0-88010-109-1); pap. 9.95 (ISBN 0-88010-110-5). Anthroposophic.

Szekely, Edmond B. The Cosmotherapy of the Essenes. (Illus.). 64p. 1975. pap. 3.50 (ISBN 0-89564-012-0). IBS Intl.

--The Discovery of the Essene Gospel of Peace: The Essenes & the Vatican. (Illus.). 96p. 1977. pap. 4.80 (ISBN 0-89564-004-X). IBS Intl.

Teilhard De Chardin, Pierre. Hymn of the Universe. LC 65-10375. 1969. pap. 6.95x (ISBN 0-06-131910-4, TB1910, Torch). Har-Row.

--Hymne De L'univers. 1966. 13.95 (ISBN 0-685-11240-3). French & Eur.

--Phenomene Humain. (Coll. Points). 1955. pap. 6.25 (ISBN 0-685-11491-0). French & Eur.

--Phenomenon of Man. pap. 7.95 (ISBN 0-06-090495-X, CN495, PL). Har-Row.

Terzian, Yervant & Bilson, Elizabeth, eds. Cosmology & Astrophysics: Essays in Honor of Thomas Gold on His 60th Birthday. (Illus.). 168p. 1982. 27.50x (ISBN 0-8014-1497-0). Cornell U Pr.

Tillyard, Eustace M. Elizabethan World Picture. 1959. pap. 3.16 (ISBN 0-394-70162-3, Vin). Random.

Tracy, David & Lash, Nicholas. Cosmology & Theology. (Concilium 1983: Vol. 166). 128p. (Orig.). 1983. pap. 6.95 (ISBN 0-8164-2446-2, HarpR). Har-Row.

Urton, Gary. At the Crossroads of the Earth & the Sky: An Andean Cosmology. (Latin American Monograph Ser.: No. 55). (Illus.). 268p. 1981. text ed. 30.00x (ISBN 0-292-70349-X). U of Tex Pr.

Van Pelt, G. Hierarchies: The Cosmic Ladder of Life. Small, W. Emmett & Todd, Helen, eds. (Theosophical Manual: No. 9). 1975. pap. 2.00 (ISBN 0-913004-23-5). Point Loma Pub.

Vollert, Cyril, et al, trs. Saint Thomas, Sieger De Brabant, St. Bonaventure: On the Eternity of the World. (Medieval Philosophical Texts in Translation: No. 16). 1965. pap. 7.95 (ISBN 0-87462-216-6). Marquette.

Von Del Chamberlain. When Stars Came Down to Earth: Cosmology of the Skidi Pawnee Indians of North America. LC 82-16390. (Ballena Press Anthropological Papers: No. 26). (Illus.). 260p. (Orig.). 1982. pap. 17.95 (ISBN 0-87919-098-1). Ballena Pr.

Wagoner, R. & Goldsmith, D. Cosmic Horizons: Understanding the Universe. 250p. 1982. 22.95 (ISBN 0-7167-1417-5); pap. 12.95 (ISBN 0-7167-1418-3). W H Freeman.

Wesner, R. The Wesner Conjectures. LC 82-21421. 128p. 1985. pap. 4.95 (ISBN 0-88437-070-4). Psych Dimensions.

Willcox, P. J. Modern Cosmology: A Survey in Four Lectures. LC 82-90241. (Illus.). 96p. 1982. pap. 4.50 (ISBN 0-9608436-0-4). P J Willcox.

Yourgrau, Wolfgang & Breck, Allen D., eds. Cosmology, History, & Theology. LC 76-54269. (Illus.). 416p. 1977. 69.50x (ISBN 0-306-30940-8, Plenum Pr). Plenum Pub.

COSMOLOGY–CURIOSA AND MISCELLANEA

Eliade, Mircea. Myth of the Eternal Return. Trask, Willard R., tr. (Bollingen Ser.: Vol. 46). 1954. 24.00 (ISBN 0-691-09798-4); pap. 8.50 (ISBN 0-691-01777-8). Princeton U Pr.

COSMOLOGY–HISTORY

Duhem, Pierre. Medieval Cosmology: Theories of Infinity, Place, Time, Void, & the Plurality of Worlds. Ariew, Roger, ed. LC 85-8115. 642p. 1986. lib. bdg. 35.00x (ISBN 0-226-16922-7). U of Chicago Pr.

Henderson, John B. The Development & Decline of Chinese Cosmology. LC 84-4000. (Neo-Confucian Studies). 280p. 1984. 36.00 (ISBN 0-231-05772-5); pap. cancelled (ISBN 0-231-05773-3). Columbia U Pr.

Wildiers, N. Max. The Theologian & His Universe: Theology & Cosmology from the Middle Ages to the Present. 320p. (Orig.). 1982. 21.95 (ISBN 0-8164-0533-6, HarpR). Har-Row.

COSMOLOGY–JUVENILE LITERATURE

Jenkins, Peggy. Climbing the Rainbow. 92p. pap. 5.95 (ISBN 0-942494-48-2). Coleman Pub.

Myring. First Guide to the Universe. (Let's Find Out About Ser.). 1982. 10.95 (ISBN 0-86020-611-4, Usborne-Hayes). EDC.

Whitcomb, John C. & DeYoung, Donald B. The Moon: Its Creation, Form & Significance. 7.95 (ISBN 0-88469-102-0). BMH Bks.

COTTON, JOHN, 1584-1652

Emerson, Everett H. John Cotton. (Twayne's United States Authors Ser). 1965. pap. 8.95x (ISBN 0-8084-0180-7, T80, Twayne). New Coll U Pr.

Norton, John. Abel Being Dead, Yet Speaketh. LC 78-8184. 1978. Repr. of 1658 ed. 30.00x (ISBN 0-8201-1310-7). Schol Facsimiles.

COUGHLIN, CHARLES EDWARD, 1891-

Tull, Charles J. Father Coughlin & the New Deal. LC 65-11680. (Illus.). 1965. 10.95x (ISBN 0-8156-0043-7). Syracuse U Pr.

COUNCIL OF CONSTANCE, 1414-1418

see Constance, Council of, 1414-1418

COUNCIL OF TRENT, 1545-1563

see Trent, Council of 1545-1563

COUNCILS AND SYNODS

see also Conciliar Theory; Popes; Popes–Primacy

Albergio, Giuseppe & Provost, James, eds. The Extraordinary Synod Nineteen Eighty-Five: An Evaluation. (Concilium Nineteen Eighty-Six Ser.). 120p. 1986. pap. 6.95 (ISBN 0-567-30068-4, Pub. by T & T Clark Ltd UK). Fortress.

Bogolepov, Alexander. Church Reforms in Russia, 1905-1918. 59p. 1966. pap. 1.95 (ISBN 0-913836-01-X). St Vladimirs.

Duffy, John, ed. Synodicon Vetus. Parker, John. LC 79-52935. (Dumbarton Oaks Texts: Vol. 5). 209p. 1979. 35.00x (ISBN 0-88402-088-6). Dumbarton Oaks.

Graebner, Alan. Uncertain Saints. LC 75-1573. (Contributions in American History: No. 42). 320p. 1975. lib. bdg. 29.95 (ISBN 0-8371-7963-7, GUS/). Greenwood.

McDonald, William J. The General Council: Special Studies in Doctrinal & Historical Background. LC 62-20329. pap. 48.00 (ISBN 0-317-07854-2, 2005223). Bks Demand UMI.

Meiring, Bernard J. Educational Aspects of the Legislation of the Councils of Baltimore, 1829-1884. 25.50 (ISBN 0-405-10844-3, 11821). Ayer Co Pubs.

Orthodox Eastern Church. Synod of Sixteen Seventy-Two: Acts & Decrees of the Jerusalem Synod Held Under Dositheus, Containing the Confession Published Name of Cyril Lukaris. Robertson, J. N., tr. LC 78-81769. 1969. Repr. of 1899 ed. 18.50 (ISBN 0-404-03567-1). AMS Pr.

Peltier, A. C. Dictionnaire Universel et Complet des Conciles, 2 vols. Migne, J. P., ed. (Encyclopedie Theologique Ser.: Vols. 13-14). (Fr.). 1378p. Repr. of 1846 ed. lib. bdg. 175.00x (ISBN 0-89241-236-4). Caratzas.

Poussin, J. C. & Garnier, J. C. Dictionnaire de la Tradition Pontificale, Patristique et Conciliaire, 2 vols. Migne, J. P., ed. (Troisieme et Derniere Encyclopedie Theologique Ser.: Vol. 12-13). (Fr.). 1464p. Repr. of 1855 ed. lib. bdg. 186.00x (ISBN 0-89241-296-8). Caratzas.

Schuppert, Mildred. Digest & Index of the Minutes of General Synod, 1958-1977. pap. 10.95 (ISBN 0-8028-1774-2). Eerdmans.

Whitelock, Dorothy & Brett, Martin. Council & Synods with Other Documents Relating to the English Church, Vol. 1: A. D. 871-1204, 2 Vols. 1981. text ed. 139.00x (ISBN 0-19-822394-3). Oxford U Pr.

COUNCILS AND SYNODS, ECUMENICAL

see also names of Councils and Synods, e.g. Vatican Council, 2nd.

Derr, Thomas S. Barriers to Ecumenism: The Holy See & the World Council on Social Questions. LC 82-18761. 112p. (Orig.). 1983. pap. 7.95 (ISBN 0-88344-031-8). Orbis Bks.

DuBose, William P. The Ecumenical Councils. 1977. lib. bdg. 59.95 (ISBN 0-8490-1751-3). Gordon Pr.

Extraordinary Synod Nineteen Eighty-Five. 2.50 (ISBN 0-8198-2315-5). Dghtrs St Paul.

Lyles, Jean C. A Practical Vision of Christian Unity. LC 81-15032. (Into Our Third Century Ser.). 96p. (Orig.). 1982. pap. 3.95 (ISBN 0-687-33330-X). Abingdon.

McDonald, William J., ed. The General Council: Special Studies in Doctrinal & Historical Background. LC 78-10099. 1979. Repr. of 1962 ed. lib. bdg. cancelled (ISBN 0-313-20753-4, MCGC). Greenwood.

Schieffer, Rudolphus. Acta Conciliorum Oecumenicorum Tomus 4, Volumen 3: Index Generalis Tomorum 1-4, Pars 1; Indices Codicum et. LC 74-79318. 579p. 1974. 136.00x (ISBN 3-11-004449-8). De Gruyter.

Sjem' Vsjeljenskikh Soborov. Tr. of The Seven Ecumenical Councils. 143p. 1968. pap. 5.00 (ISBN 0-317-30292-2). Holy Trinity.

Slaatte, Howard A. The Seven Ecumenical Councils. LC 80-5755. 55p. 1980. pap. text ed. 7.25 (ISBN 0-8191-1204-6). U Pr of Amer.

COUNCILS AND SYNODS, PARISH

see Parish Councils

COUNSELING

see also Marriage Counseling; Pastoral Counseling

Adams, Jay E. Christian Counselor's Wordbook: A Primer of Nouthetic Counseling. 90p. 1981. pap. 1.95 (ISBN 0-87552-069-3). Presby & Reformed.

--Counseling & the Five Points of Calvinism. 1981. pap. 0.75 (ISBN 0-87552-072-3). Presby & Reformed.

--How to Help People Change. (Jay Adams Library). 208p. 1986. pap. 7.95 (ISBN 0-310-51181-X). Zondervan.

--Language of Counseling. 90p. 1981. pap. 2.45 (ISBN 0-87552-009-X). Presby & Reformed.

--Update on Christian Counseling, Vol. II. 1981. pap. 2.75 (ISBN 0-87552-071-5). Presby & Reformed.

--What about Nouthetic Counseling? The Question & Answer Book. 1977. pap. 2.50 (ISBN 0-8010-0114-5). Baker Bk.

Aultman, Donald S. Guiding Youth. 1977. pap. 3.95 (ISBN 0-87148-358-0). Pathway Pr.

Caldwell, Louis O. You Can Find Help Through Counseling: Christain Counseling Aids. 1983. pap. 0.95 (ISBN 0-8010-2484-6). Baker Bk.

Christian Broadcasting Network Staff, ed. The Christian Counselor's Handbook. 240p. 1987. pap. 8.95 (ISBN 0-8423-0255-7). Tyndale.

DeBardeleben, Martha G. Fear's Answer: A Case History in Nouthetic Counseling. 1981. pap. 3.75 (ISBN 0-87552-236-X). Presby & Reformed.

Fontes, M. E. Existentialism & Its Implications for Counseling. pap. 0.75 (ISBN 0-8199-0382-5, L38138). Franciscan Herald.

Goldsmith, Earl A. Counseling with Confidence. 155p. 1984. pap. 5.95 (ISBN 0-916945-01-4). V I Pr.

Headington, Bonnie J. Communication in the Counseling Relationship. LC 78-9026. 1979. cloth 16.50x (ISBN 0-910328-23-4); pap. 11.00x (ISBN 0-910328-24-2). Carroll Pr.

Hendricks, Gay & Weinhold, Barry. Transpersonal Approaches to Counseling & Psychotherapy. 199p. 1982. pap. text ed. 12.95 (ISBN 0-89108-112-7). Love Pub Co.

Jackins, Harvey. Is Death Necessary? 1970. pap. 0.50 (ISBN 0-911214-22-4). Rational Isl.

Koteskey, Ronald L. General Psychology for Christian Counselors. 308p. (Orig.). 1983. pap. 11.95 (ISBN 0-687-14044-7). Abingdon.

Kuhne, Gary W. The Dynamics of Discipleship Training. 1977. pap. 5.95 (ISBN 0-310-26961-X, 12311P). Zondervan.

Long, Tic, ed. Resource Directory for Youth Workers, 1985. 128p. (Orig.). 1985. pap. 8.95 (ISBN 0-687-36167-2). Abingdon.

Martin, Grant. Counseling in Cases of Family Violence & Abuse. 192p. 1987. 12.95 (ISBN 0-8499-0587-7). Word Bks.

Miller, Paul M. Peer Counseling in the Church. LC 78-9299. 168p. 1978. pap. 7.95 (ISBN 0-8361-1854-5). Herald Pr.

Moses, A. Elfin & Hawkins, Robert O., Jr. Counseling Lesbian Women & Gay Men: A Life-Issues Approach. 263p. 1982. pap. text ed. 19.95 (ISBN 0-675-20599-9). Merrill.

Quesnell, John Q. The Message of Christ & the Counselor. (Synthesis Ser). 1975. 2.00 (ISBN 0-8199-0534-8). Franciscan Herald.

Seamands, David A. Healing of Memories. 156p. 1985. text ed. 11.95 (ISBN 0-89693-532-9); pap. 6.95 (ISBN 0-89693-169-2). Victor Bks.

Skoglund, Elizabeth. Can I Talk to You? 1977. pap. 3.25 (ISBN 0-8307-0557-0, 5407508). Regal.

Taulman, James E. Encouragers: The Sunday School Worker's Counseling Ministry. LC 85-19523. 1986. pap. 4.95 (ISBN 0-8054-3712-6). Broadman.

Welter, Paul. When Your Friend Needs You. abr. ed. (Pocket Guides Ser.). 96p. 1986. mass 1.95 (ISBN 0-8423-7998-3). Tyndale.

Worthington, Everett L., Jr. When Someone Asks for Help: A Practical Guide to Counseling. LC 82-81. (Illus.). 239p. (Orig.). 1982. pap. 7.95 (ISBN 0-87784-375-9). Inter-Varsity.

COUNSELING, PASTORAL

see Pastoral Counseling

COUNSELING, RABBINICAL

see Pastoral Counseling (Judaism)

COUNTER-REFORMATION

see also Church History–Modern Period, 1500-; Jesuits; Reformation; Trent, Council of 1545-1563

Bireley, Robert S. J. Religion & Politics in the Age of the Counterreformation: Emperor Ferdinand II, William Lamormaini, S.J., & the Formation of Imperial Policy. LC 80-27334. xiii, 311p. 1981. 30.00x (ISBN 0-8078-1470-9). U of NC Pr.

Clancy, Thomas H. Papist Pamphleteers. LC 64-14078. (Jesuit Studies). 1964. 4.95 (ISBN 0-8294-0013-3). Loyola.

Davidson, Nicholas S. The Counter-Reformation. 96p. 1987. pap. text ed. 7.95 (ISBN 0-631-14888-4). Basil Blackwell.

Dickens, A. G. The Counter-Reformation. (Library of World Civilization). (Illus.). 1979. pap. 7.95x (ISBN 0-393-95086-7). Norton.

Evennett, H. Outram. Spirit of the Counter-Reformation. LC 68-11282. 1970. pap. 4.95x (ISBN 0-268-00425-0). U of Notre Dame Pr.

Gleason, Elisabeth G. Reform Thought in Sixteenth Century Italy. Massey, James A., ed. LC 81-5648. (American Academy of Religion Texts & Translations Ser.). 1981. pap. text ed. 10.95 (ISBN 0-89130-498-3, 01-02-04). Scholars Pr GA.

The History of the Church, 10 Vols. 920p. 1980. complete set 595.00x (ISBN 0-8245-0318-X). Crossroad NY.

Jedin, Hubert & Dolan, John, eds. Reformation & Counter-Reformation. 1980. 59.50x (ISBN 0-686-95526-9). Crossroad NY.

Kidd, Beresford J. The Counter-Reformation, Fifteen Fifty to Sixteen Hundred. LC 79-8713. 270p. 1980. Repr. of 1933 ed. lib. bdg. 24.75x (ISBN 0-313-22193-6, KICR). Greenwood.

Knipping, John B. Iconography of the Counter Reformation in the Netherlands: Heaven on Earth, 2 vols. LC 73-85234. (Illus.). 539p. 1974. Set. text ed. 195.00x (Pub. by B De Graaf Netherlands). Coronet Bks.

Lindsay, Thomas M. A History of the Reformation, 2 vols. facsimile ed. LC 72-37893. (Select Bibliographies Reprint Ser). Repr. of 1907 ed. Set. 54.00 (ISBN 0-8369-6730-5). Ayer Co Pubs.

O'Connell, M. R. Thomas Stapleton & the Counter Reformation. 1964. 49.50x (ISBN 0-685-69850-5). Elliots Bks.

Pullapilly, Cyriac K. Caesar Baronius: Courtier-Reformation Historian. 1975. 21.95x (ISBN 0-268-00501-X). U of Notre Dame Pr.

Ridley, Francis A. The Jesuits: A Study in Counter-Reformation. LC 83-45595. Date not set. Repr. of 1938 ed. 35.00 (ISBN 0-404-19888-0). AMS Pr.

Von Velsen, Dorothee. Gegenreformation in den Fürstentumern Liegnitz-Brirg-Wohlau, Ihre Vorgeschichte und Ihre Staatsrechtlichen Grundlagen. (Ger.). 34.00 (ISBN 0-384-64224-1); pap. 28.00 (ISBN 0-384-64223-3). Johnson Repr.

Wright, A. D. The Counter-Reformation: Catholic Europe & the Non-Christian World. LC 82-3210. 334p. 1984. pap. 12.95 (ISBN 0-312-17022-X). St Martin.

COUNTRY CHURCHES

see Rural Churches

COURTENAY, WILLIAM, ABP. OF CANTERBURY, 1342-1396

Dahmus, Joseph. William Courtenay: Archbishop of Canterbury, 1381-1396. LC 66-18194. 1966. 28.75x (ISBN 0-271-73121-4). Pa St U Pr.

COURTS, ECCLESIASTICAL

see Ecclesiastical Courts

COVENANTS

Foster, W. The Church Before Covenants. 1975. 12.50x (ISBN 0-7073-0184-X, Pub. by Scot Acad Pr). Longwood Pub Group.

Goode, Francis. The Better Covenant. 408p. 1986. 14.95 (ISBN 0-8254-2726-6). Kregel.

Zinkand, John M. Covenants: God's Claims. 120p. (Orig.). 1984. pap. 5.95 (ISBN 0-932914-10-1). Dordt Coll Pr.

COVENANTS (CHURCH POLITY)

Behm, Douglas R. The New Covenant's Power. 1983. 3.50 (ISBN 0-89536-600-2, 1412). CSS of Ohio.

Murray, Andrew. The Believer's New Covenant. LC 83-21408. 128p. 1983. pap. 3.95 (ISBN 0-87123-406-8, 210406). Bethany Hse.

Pope, Robert G. Half-Way Covenant: Church Membership in Puritan New England. Repr. of 1969 ed. 63.30 (ISBN 0-8357-9500-4, 2011473). Bks Demand UMI.

COVENANTS (THEOLOGY)

see also Dispensationalism; Grace (Theology); Salvation; Typology (Theology)

Allis, Oswald T. Prophecy & the Church. 1945. pap. 5.95 (ISBN 0-87552-104-5). Presby & Reformed.

Booker, Richard. The Miracle of the Scarlet Thread. LC 80-84802. (Orig.). 1981. pap. 4.95 (ISBN 0-88270-499-0). Bridge Pub.

Cameron, W. J. Covenant People. 3.00 (ISBN 0-685-08801-4). Destiny.

Christenson, Larry. The Covenant. (Trinity Bible Ser.). 144p. 1973. pap. 5.95 spiral wkbk. (ISBN 0-87123-551-X, 240551). Bethany Hse.

Clements, Ronald E. Abraham & David: Genesis 15 & Its Meaning for Israelite Tradition. LC 67-8569. (Studies in Biblical Theology, 2nd Ser.: No. 5). 1967. pap. 10.00x (ISBN 0-8401-3055-4). A R Allenson.

Cowen, Deborah, ed. The Year of Grace of the Lord. 254p. (Orig.). 1980. pap. 8.95 (ISBN 0-913836-68-0). St Vladimirs.

Guinan, Michael D. Covenant in the Old Testament. (Biblical Booklets Ser). 68p. 1975. pap. 1.25 (ISBN 0-8199-0520-8). Franciscan Herald.

Hagin, Kenneth E. A Better Covenant. 1981. pap. 0.50 mini bk. (ISBN 0-89276-251-9). Hagin Ministries.

Hesselgrave, David J. Counseling Cross-Culturally. 1984. 14.95p (ISBN 0-8010-4282-8). Baker Bk.

Hillers, Delbert R. Covenant: The History of a Biblical Idea. LC 69-13539. (Seminars in the History of Ideas Ser: No. 3). 206p. (Orig.). 1969. pap. 4.95x (ISBN 0-8018-1011-6). Johns Hopkins.

Ironside, H. A. Wrongly Dividing the Word of Truth. pap. 1.25 (ISBN 0-87213-392-3). Loizeaux.

Kuyvenhoven, Andrew. Partnership, A Study of the Covenant. 80p. 1983. pap. 2.50 (ISBN 0-933140-89-4). CRC Pubns.

Larsen, Paul E. The Mission of a Covenant. 1985. pap. 6.95 (ISBN 0-910452-61-X). Covenant.

Morris, Danny. Discovering Our Family Covenants. LC 81-51299. 1981. pap. 2.95x (ISBN 0-8358-0419-4). Upper Room.

Murray, Andrew. Covenants & Blessings. 176p. 1984. pap. text ed. 3.50 (ISBN 0-88368-136-6). Whitaker Hse.

--Two Covenants. 1974. pap. 3.50 (ISBN 0-87508-396-X). Chr Lit.

Neilands, David L. Studies in the Covenant of Grace. 1981. pap. 5.75 (ISBN 0-87552-365-X). Presby & Reformed.

Pink, Arthur W. The Divine Covenants: God's Seven Covenant Engagements with Man. 317p. 1984. pap. 7.95 (ISBN 0-8010-7082-1). Baker Bk.

Rogness, Alvin N. Remember the Promise. LC 76-27082. 1977. kivar 2.95 (ISBN 0-8066-1567-2, 10-5480). Augsburg.

Schumacher, Evelyn A. Covenant Love: Reflections on the Biblical Covenant Theme. (Orig.). 1981. pap. 2.95 (ISBN 0-914544-38-1). Living Flame Pr.

Smith, Mont. What the Bible Says about the Covenant. 2nd ed. LC 81-65516. (What the Bible Says Ser.). 472p. 1981. 13.95 (ISBN 0-89900-083-5). College Pr Pub.

Sperry Symposium, ed. Hearken, O Ye People. 297p. 1984. 9.95 (ISBN 0-934126-56-9). Randall Bk Co.

Stoever, William K. A Faire & Easie Way to Heaven: Covenant Theology & Antinomianism in Early Massachusetts. LC 77-14851. 251p. 1978. 22.00x (ISBN 0-8195-5024-8). Wesleyan U Pr.

Talbot, Louis T. God's Plan of the Ages. 1936. pap. 8.95 (ISBN 0-8028-1194-9). Eerdmans.

Von Rohr, John. The Covenant of Grace in Puritan Thought. (American Academy of Religion Studies in Religion). 240p. 1987. 18.95 (01-00-45); pap. 13.95. Scholars Pr Ga.

CRANMER, THOMAS, ABP. OF CANTERBURY, 1489-1556

Belloc, Hilaire. Cranmer. LC 72-4495. (English Biography Ser., No. 31). 1972. Repr. of 1931 ed. lib. bdg. 55.95x (ISBN 0-8383-1610-7). Haskell.

Hughes, Philip E., ed. & intro. by. Faith & Works: Cranmer & Hooker on Justification. 128p. (Orig.). 1982. pap. 7.95 (ISBN 0-8192-1315-2). Morehouse.

Nichols, John G., ed. Narrative of the Days of the Reformation, Chiefly from the Manuscripts of John Foxe the Martyrologist. Repr. of 1859 ed. 37.00 (ISBN 0-384-41460-5). Johnson Repr.

--Narrative of the Days of the Reformation. (Camden Society, London. Publications, First Ser.: No. 77). Repr. of 1859 ed. 37.00 (ISBN 0-404-50177-X). AMS Pr.

Pollard, Albert F. Thomas Cranmer & the English Reformation, 1849-1556. LC 83-45587. Date not set. Repr. of 1927 ed. 42.50 (ISBN 0-404-19905-4). AMS Pr.

Ridley, Jasper. Thomas Cranner. 450p. 1983. Repr. of 1962 ed. lib. bdg. 65.00 (ISBN 0-89987-737-0). Darby Bks.

Smyth, Charles H. Cranmer & the Reformation under Edward VI. Repr. of 1926 ed. lib. bdg. 22.50x (ISBN 0-8371-4025-0, SMCR). Greenwood.

CRASHAW, RICHARD, 1613?-1649

Bennett, Joan. Five Metaphysical Poets: Donne, Herbert, Vaughan, Crashaw, Marvell. 1964. 32.50 (ISBN 0-521-04156-2); pap. 9.95 (ISBN 0-521-09238-8). Cambridge U Pr.

Foy, Thomas. Richard Crashaw Poet & Saint. LC 74-9797. 1933. lib. bdg. 10.00 (ISBN 0-8414-4204-5). Folcroft.

Shepherd, R. A. The Religious Poems of Richard Crashaw with an Introductory Study. 1979. Repr. of 1914 ed. lib. bdg. 35.00 (ISBN 0-8495-4942-6). Arden Lib.

White, Helen C. The Metaphysical Poets: A Study in Religious Experience. LC 83-45866. 1936. 39.50 (ISBN 0-404-20285-3, PR549). AMS Pr.

Willey, Basil. Richard Crashaw. LC 76-26647. 1949. lib. bdg. 12.50 (ISBN 0-8414-9386-3). Folcroft.

Williams, George W. Image & Symbol in the Sacred Poetry of Richard Crashaw. 2nd edition ed. LC 63-12394. x, 152p. 1967. 21.95x (ISBN 0-87249-087-4). U of SC Pr.

CREATION

see also Cosmology; Deluge; Evolution; God; Jesus Christ–Primacy

Ackerman, Paul D. It's a Young World after All. 128p. 1986. pap. 6.95 (ISBN 0-8010-0204-4). Baker Bk.

Alderink, Larry J. Creation & Salvation in Ancient Orphism. LC 81-5772. (APA American Classical Studies Ser.). 1981. pap. 10.00 (ISBN 0-89130-502-5, 400408). Scholars Pr GA.

Allen, Eula. Creation Trilogy, 3 vols. rev. ed. Incl. Vol. 1. Before the Beginning. 1966 (ISBN 0-87604-054-7); Vol. 2. The River of Time. 1965 (ISBN 0-87604-055-5); Vol. 3. You Are Forever. 1966 (ISBN 0-87604-056-3). (Illus.). pap. 10.95 set (ISBN 0-87604-125-X); pap. 3.95 ea. ARE Pr.

Anderson, Bernhard W., ed. Creation in the Old Testament. LC 83-48910. (Issues in Religion & Theology Ser.). 192p. 1984. pap. 7.95 (ISBN 0-8006-1768-1, 1-768). Fortress.

Aw, S. E. Chemical Evolution. LC 81-70575. 1982. pap. 9.95 (ISBN 0-89051-082-2). Master Bks.

Banks, William D. The Heavens Declare... (Illus.). 288p. (Orig.). 1985. pap. 6.95 (ISBN 0-89228-101-4). Impact Bks MO.

Blavatsky, Helena P. The Secret Doctrine, 3 vols. 7th ed. De Zirkoff, Boris, ed. (Illus.). 1980. 45.00 ea. (ISBN 0-8356-7525-4). Theos Pub Hse.

Bonhoeffer, Dietrich. Creation & Fall. Bd. with Temptation. 1965. pap. 4.95 (ISBN 0-02-083890-5). Macmillan.

--Creation & Fall: Temptation. 1983. 13.00 (ISBN 0-8446-5962-2). Peter Smith.

Boodin, John E. God & Creation, 2 vols. LC 75-3058. Repr. of 1934 ed. 67.50 set (ISBN 0-404-59057-8). AMS Pr.

Brandall, William S. The Secret of the Universe: New Discoveries on God, Man & the Eternity of Life. (Illus.). 119p. 1985. 127.45 (ISBN 0-89266-535-1). Am Classical Coll Pr.

Brown, Dovid. Mysteries of the Creation. (Illus.). 400p. 1987. 19.99 (ISBN 0-939833-24-7). Mosdos Pubs.

Brunner, Emil. The Christian Doctrine of Creation & Redemption. Wyon, Olive, tr. LC 50-6821. (Dogmatic Ser.: Vol. 2). 396p. 1979. pap. 10.95 (ISBN 0-664-24248-0). Westminster.

Capon, Robert F. The Third Peacock. 108p. (Orig.). 1986. pap. 7.50 (ISBN 0-86683-497-4, HarpR). Har-Row.

Carpenter, Edward. The Art of Creation. 1978. Repr. of 1904 ed. lib. bdg. 45.00 (ISBN 0-8495-0814-2). Arden Lib.

Chittick, Donald E. The Controversy: Roots of the Creation-Evolution Conflict. LC 84-22670. (Critical Concern Ser.). 1984. 13.95 (ISBN 0-88070-019-X); pap. 9.95. Multnomah.

Clark, Harold. The New Creationism. LC 79-22250. (Horizon Ser.). 1980. pap. 9.95 (ISBN 0-8127-0247-6). Review & Herald.

Cohen, I. L. Darwin Was Wrong: A Study in Probabilities. Murphy, G., ed. LC 84-22613. (Illus.). 225p. 1985. 16.95 (ISBN 0-910891-02-8). New Research.

Cushing, Frank H. Outlines of Zuni Creation Myths. LC 74-7947. Repr. of 1896 ed. 20.00 (ISBN 0-404-11834-8). AMS Pr.

Dankenbring, William F. The First Genesis: A New Case for Creation. LC 75-10841. (Illus.). 408p. 1975. 8.95 (ISBN 0-685-54180-0). Triumph Pub.

--The First Genesis: The Saga of Creation Versus Evolution. new ed. LC 79-65131. (Illus.). 1979. 12.00 (ISBN 0-917182-14-6). Triumph Pub.

Davidson, Herbert. Proofs for Eternity, Creation, & the Existence of God in Medieval Islamic & Jewish Philosophy. (Studies in Northeast Culture & Society: Vol. 7). 500p. 1985. write for info. (ISBN 0-89003-180-0); pap. 62.00x (ISBN 0-89003-181-9). Undena Pubns.

Dewey, Barbara. The Creating Cosmos. LC 85-70369. 128p. 1985. 16.95 (ISBN 0-933123-00-0). Bartholomew Bks.

Dobracyynski, J. Before the Earth Arose. 1981. 8.95 (ISBN 0-317-46868-5). Franciscan Herald.

Dow, T. W. Truth of Creation. LC 67-31148. (Illus.). 1968. 5.00 (ISBN 0-910340-04-8). Celestial Pr.

Driver, Tom F. Patterns of Grace: Human Experience As Word of God. 214p. 1985. pap. text ed. 9.75 (ISBN 0-8191-4637-4). U Pr of Amer.

Dunne, John. How God Created. pap. 2.00 (ISBN 0-268-00120-0). U of Notre Dame Pr.

Edman, David. Once upon an Eternity. LC 83-62515. 108p. 1984. pap. 6.95 (ISBN 0-89390-052-4). Resource Pubns.

Enuma Elish. The Seven Tablets of Creation, 2 vols. LC 73-18850. (Luzac's Semitic Text & Translation Ser.: Nos. 12 & 13). (Illus.). Repr. of 1902 ed. Set. 45.00 (ISBN 0-404-11344-3). AMS Pr.

Erickson, Lonni R. Creation vs. Evolution: A Comparison. 30p. write for info. Scandia Pubs.

Flamming, Peter J. God & Creation. LC 85-6647. (Layman's Liberty of Christian Doctrine Ser.). 1985. 5.95 (ISBN 0-8054-1635-8). Broadman.

Follette, Marcel la. Creationism, Science, & the Law: Arkansas Case Documents & Commentaries. LC 82-21646. 232p. (Orig.). 1983. pap. 11.95x (ISBN 0-262-62041-3). MIT Pr.

Foster, Ann T. Theodore Roethke's Meditative Sequences: Contemplation & the Creative Process. LC 85-3041. (Studies in Art & Religious Interpretation: Vol. 4). 210p. 1985. 49.95x (ISBN 0-88946-555-X). E Mellen.

Francuch, Peter D. Four Concepts of the Spiritual Structure of Creation. LC 82-62630. 119p. 1983. pap. 3.95 (ISBN 0-939386-05-4). TMH Pub.

Friedman, Irving. The Book of Creation. 64p. 1977. pap. 2.95 (ISBN 0-87728-289-7). Weiser.

Frye, Roland M., ed. Is God a Creationist? Religious Arguments Against Creation-Science. 256p. 1983. 15.95 (ISBN 0-684-17993-8, ScribT). Scribner.

Gange, Robert. Origins & Destiny: A Scientist Examines God's Handiwork. 192p. 1986. 12.95 (ISBN 0-8499-0447-1, 0447-1). Word Bks.

Gilkey, Langdon. Creationism on Trial: Evolution & God at Little Rock. LC 85-50256. 301p. (Orig.). 1985. pap. 12.95 (ISBN 0-86683-780-9, HarpR). Har-Row.

--Maker of Heaven & Earth: The Christian Doctrine of Creation in the Light of Modern Knowledge. 392p. 1986. pap. text ed. 14.75 (ISBN 0-8191-4976-4). U Pr of Amer.

Gish, Duane T. Up with Creation! Acts, Facts, Impacts, Vol. 3. LC 78-55612. (Illus.). 1978. pap. 6.95 (ISBN 0-89051-048-2). Master Bks.

Godfrey, Laurie R., ed. Scientists Confront Creationism. 352p. 1984. pap. 8.95 (ISBN 0-393-30154-0). Norton.

Gold, E. J. Creation Story Verbatim. 278p. (Orig.). 1986. pap. 11.95 (ISBN 0-89556-047-X). Gateways Bks & Tapes.

Good, Mrs. Marvin. How God Made the World. 1978. pap. 1.95 (ISBN 0-686-24050-2). Rod & Staff.

Hanson, Robert W., ed. Science & Creation: Geological, Theological & Educational Perspectives. LC 83-50822. (AAAS Ser. on Issues in Science & Technology). 288p. 1985. text ed. 24.95x (ISBN 0-02-949870-8). Macmillan.

Hayes, Zachary. What Are They Saying about Creation? LC 80-80870. 128p. 1980. pap. 3.95 (ISBN 0-8091-2286-3). Paulist Pr.

Heidel, Alexander. Babylonian Genesis. 2nd ed. LC 51-822. 1963. 6.00x (ISBN 0-226-32399-4, P133, Phoen). U of Chicago Pr.

Hessel, Dieter T., ed. For Creation's Sake: Preaching, Ecology, & Justice. LC 85-816. 144p. 1985. pap. 8.95 (ISBN 0-664-24637-0, A Geneva Press Publication). Westminster.

Horigan, James E. Chance or Design? LC 79-83605. 242p. 1979. 13.95 (ISBN 0-8022-2238-2). Philos Lib.

Hyers, Conrad. The Meaning of Creations. LC 84-47795. 212p. pap. 11.95 (ISBN 0-8042-0125-0). John Knox.

In the Beginning: The Story of Creation. (Illus.). 1986. 9.95 (ISBN 0-915720-22-1). Brownlow Pub Co.

James, Henry, Sr. Christianity the Logic of Creation. LC 72-921. (The Selected Works of Henry James, Sr.: Vol. 1). 272p. 1983. Repr. of 1857 ed. 30.00 (ISBN 0-404-10081-3); Set, 10 vols. 295.00. AMS Pr.

--Substance & Shadow: Or, Morality & Religion in Their Relation to Life, an Essay upon the Physics of Creation. LC 72-915. (The Selected Works of Henry James, Sr.: Vol. 8). 552p. 1983. Repr. of 1863 ed. 49.50 (ISBN 0-404-10088-0). AMS Pr.

Jastrow, Robert. God & the Astronomers. (Illus.). 1978. 9.95 (ISBN 0-393-85000-5). Norton.

Johnstone, Parker L. Origin of the Universe, Life, Then Religion. 235p. 7.95 (ISBN 0-917802-20-9). Theoscience Found.

Kalechofsky, Roberta. The Sixth Day of Creation: A Discourse on Post Biblical, Post Modern Thought. (Illus.). 24p. 1986. 10.00 (ISBN 0-916288-20-X). Micah Pubns.

Kang, C. H. & Nelson, Ethel. The Discovery of Genesis. 1979. pap. 4.95 (ISBN 0-570-03792-1, 12-2755). Concordia.

Kappeler, Max. Compendium for the Study of Christian Science: No. 2, The Seven Days of Creation. 24p. 1951. pap. 3.50 (ISBN 0-85241-056-5). Kappeler Inst Pub.

Katter, Reuben L. History of Creation & Origin of the Species: A Scientific Theological Viewpoint (How the Universe Came into Being) 3rd ed. 480p. 1984. 16.95 (ISBN 0-911806-01-6, C13374); pap. 11.95 (ISBN 0-911806-00-8). Theotes.

--A Paradisical Universe for Man: Man's Preparation for Sharing. 2nd ed. 200p. 1984. pap. 5.95 (ISBN 0-911806-03-2). Theotes.

Kistler, Don, ed. God's Numbers in Creation, Vol. 1. 1986. pap. 4.95 (ISBN 0-940532-03-4). AOG.

Kitcher, Philip. Abusing Science: The Case Against Creationism. (Illus.). 224p. 1982. 22.50x (ISBN 0-262-11085-7); pap. 7.95 (ISBN 0-262-61037-X). MIT Pr.

Klaaren, Eugene M. Religious Origins of Modern Science: Belief in Creation in Seventeenth-Century Thought. LC 85-17804. 256p. 1985. pap. text ed. 12.75 (ISBN 0-8191-4922-5). U Pr of Amer.

Klotz, John. Studies in Creation: A General Introduction to the Creation-Evolution Debate. 224p. (Orig.). 1985. pap. 9.95 (ISBN 0-570-03969-X, 12-3004). Concordia.

Kwak, Chung H., ed. Principle of Creation. (Home Study Course Ser.). 60p. 1980. pap. 4.00. HSA Pubns.

Lammerts, Walter E. Why Not Creation? (Illus.). 388p. (Orig.). 1970. pap. 6.95 (ISBN 0-8010-5528-8). Creation Research.

Larson, Edward J. Trial & Error: The American Controversy over Creation & Evolution. LC 85-7144. 232p. 1985. 17.95 (ISBN 0-19-503666-2). Oxford U Pr.

L'Engle, Madeleine. And It Was Good: Reflections on Beginnings. LC 83-8518. 219p. 1983. 11.95 (ISBN 0-87788-046-8). Shaw Pubs.

Levitt, Zola. Creation: A Scientist's Choice. 1981. pap. 4.95 (ISBN 0-89051-074-1). Master Bks.

Lindsay, Gordon. The Creation. (Old Testament Ser.). 1.25 (ISBN 0-89985-123-1). Christ Nations.

Lockerbie, D. Bruce. The Cosmic Center: The Supremacy of Christ in a Secular Wasteland. LC 85-18741. (Critical Concern Bks.). 1986. Repr. of 1977 ed. 11.95 (ISBN 0-88070-132-3). Multnomah.

Long, Charles H. Alpha: The Myths of Creation. LC 82-21532. (AAR-SP Classics in Religious Studies). 320p. 1982. Repr. of 1963 ed. 13.50x (ISBN 0-89130-604-8, 01-05-04). Scholars Pr GA.

Maatman, Russell. The Unity in Creation. 143p. (Orig.). 1978. pap. 4.95 (ISBN 0-932914-00-4). Dordt Coll Pr.

McDaniel, Timothy R. The Creational Theory of Man & of the Universe. (Illus.). 141p. 1980. deluxe ed. 88.85 (ISBN 0-89266-242-5). Am Classical Coll Pr.

McGowan, Chris. In the Beginning: A Scientist Shows Why the Creationists Are Wrong. LC 83-62997. (Illus.). 208p. 1984. pap. 12.95 (ISBN 0-87975-240-8). Prometheus Bks.

McGowen, Charles H. In Six Days. 108p. 1986. pap. 3.95 (ISBN 0-936369-03-5). Son-Rise Pubns.

McMullin, Ernan, ed. Evolution & Creation. LC 84-40818. (University of Notre Dame Studies in the Philosophy of Religion: Vol. 4). 307p. 1987. pap. 12.95 (ISBN 0-268-00918-X). U of Notre Dame Pr.

Maravillas De la Creacion. Orig. Title: Wonders of Creation. 124p. 1979. 18.95 (ISBN 0-311-09092-3, Edit Mundo). Casa Bautista.

May, Gerhard. Schoepfung aus dem Nichts: Die Entstehung der Lehre von der Creatio Ex Nihilo. (Arbeiten zur Kirchengeschichte: Vol. 48). 1978. 34.40 (ISBN 3-11-007204-1). De Gruyter.

Mihaly, Eugene. A Song to Creation: A Dialogue with a Text. LC 75-35761. pap. 27.00 (ISBN 0-317-42034-8, 2025694). Bks Demand UMI.
Moltman, Jurgen. God in Creation: A New Theology of Creation & the Spirit of God. LC 85-42785. 384p. 1985. 25.45 (ISBN 0-06-065899-1, HarpR). Har-Row.
Montagu, Ashley, ed. Science & Creationism. LC 82-14173. 434p. 1984. 24.95 (ISBN 0-19-503252-7); pap. 11.95x (ISBN 0-19-503253-5). Oxford U Pr.
Montenat, C. & Plateaux, L. How to Read Creation & Evolution. 144p. 1985. pap. 10.95 (ISBN 0-8245-0721-5). Crossroad NY.
Moore, John N. Questions & Answers on Creation-Evolution. 128p. 1976. pap. 3.95 (ISBN 0-8010-5997-6). Baker Bk.
Morris & Rohrer. Decade of Creation: Acts-Facts-Impacts, Vol. 4. LC 80-67426. 320p. 1980. pap. 7.95 (ISBN 0-89051-069-5). Master Bks.
Morris, H. Creation & Its Critics. LC 82-84483. 32p. 1982. 1.00 (ISBN 0-89051-091-1). Master Bks.
Morris, Henry. Biblical Cosmology & Modern Science. 1970. pap. 4.50 (ISBN 0-87552-349-8). Presby & Reformed.
Morris, Henry M. Creation & the Modern Christian. 298p. 1985. pap. 8.95 (ISBN 0-89051-111-X). Master Bks.
--Many Infallible Proofs. LC 74-81484. 384p. 1974. pap. 8.95 (ISBN 0-89051-005-9). Master Bks.
--Men of Science, Men of God. (Illus.). 1982. pap. 2.95 (ISBN 0-89051-080-6). Master Bks.
--The Remarkable Birth of Planet Earth. 124p. 1973. pap. 2.50 (ISBN 0-89051-000-8). Master Bks.
--The Scientific Case for Creation. LC 77-78019. (Illus.). 1977. pap. 2.95 (ISBN 0-89051-037-7). Master Bks.
--What is Creation Science. LC 82-70114. (Illus.). 1982. pap. 8.95 (ISBN 0-89051-081-4). Master Bks.
Morris, Henry M. & Gish, Duane T. The Battle for Creation: Acts, Facts, Impacts, Vol. 2. LC 74-75429. (Illus.). 1976. pap. 5.95 (ISBN 0-89051-020-2). Master Bks.
Morris, Henry M., et al, eds. Creation: The Cutting Edge-Acts, Facts, Impacts, Vol. 5. 240p. 1982. pap. 7.95 (ISBN 0-89051-088-1). Master Bks.
--Scientific Creationism. LC 74-14160. 1974. pap. 8.95 (ISBN 0-89051-003-2). Master Bks.
Morton, John. Redeeming Creation: A Christian World Evolving. (Illus.). 84p. (Orig.). 1984. pap. 9.95 (ISBN 0-318-20036-8, Pub. by Zealandia Pubns). ANZ Religious Pubns.
National Research Council. Science & Creationism: A View from the National Academy of Sciences. 28p. 1984. pap. 4.00 (ISBN 0-309-03440-X). Natl Acad Pr.
Nee, Watchman. The Mystery of Creation. Kaung, Stephen, tr. 1981. pap. 3.10 (ISBN 0-935008-52-7). Christian Fellow Pubs.
Nelkin, Dorothy. The Creation Controversy: Science or Scripture in the Schools. 256p. 1982. 16.95 (ISBN 0-393-01635-8). Norton.
--The Creation Controversy: Science or Scripture in the Schools? LC 83-45954. 242p. 1984. pap. 9.95x (ISBN 0-8070-3155-0, BP 675). Beacon Pr.
Neville, Robert C. God the Creator: On the Transcendence & Presence of God. LC 68-13128. (Illus.). 1968. 12.50x (ISBN 0-226-57641-8). U of Chicago Pr.
Newell, Norman D. Creation & Evolution: Myth or Reality? LC 81-21767. (Convergence Ser.). 232p. 1982. 24.00x (ISBN 0-231-05348-7). Columbia U Pr.
Niditch, Susan. Chaos to Cosmos: Studies in Biblical Patterns of Creation. (Scholars Press Studies in the Humanities: No. 6). 1985. 13.95 (ISBN 0-89130-762-1, 00 01 06); pap. 9.25 (ISBN 0-89130-763-X). Scholars Pr GA.
Novak, David & Samuelson, Norbert, eds. Creation & the End of Days - Judaism & Scientific Cosmology: Proceedings of the 1984 Meeting of the Academy for Jewish Philosophy. LC 86-19062. 336p. (Orig.). 1986. 26.75 (ISBN 0-8191-5524-1, Pub. by Studies in Judaism); pap. text ed. 14.50 (ISBN 0-8191-5525-X, Pub. by Studies in Judaism). U Pr of Amer.
O'Brien, Joan & Major, Wilfred. In the Beginning: Creation Myths from Ancient Mesopotamia, Israel, & Greece. LC 81-21311. (American Academy of Religion Academy Ser.). 1982. pap. 8.25 (ISBN 0-89130-559-9, 010311A). Scholars Pr GA.
Onslow-Ford, Gordon. Creation. (Illus.). 123p. 1978. text ed. 30.00 (ISBN 0-9612760-0-2). Bishop Pine.
Ouweneel, W. J. Creation or Evolution-What Is the Truth? 58p. pap. 3.95 (ISBN 0-88172-145-X). Believers Bkshelf.
Parker, Gary E. From Evolution to Creation: A Personal Testimony. LC 77-78020. 1978. pap. 1.00 (ISBN 0-89051-035-0). Master Bks.
Patten, Donald W., ed. Symposium on Creation, No. 4. pap. 3.95 (ISBN 0-8010-6925-4). Baker Bk.
Pavlu, Ricki. Evolution: When Fact Became Fiction. LC 86-13144. (Illus.). 184p. (Orig.). 1986. pap. 6.95 (ISBN 0-932581-51-X). Word Aflame.
Peacocke, Arthur R. Creation & the World of Science. LC 79-40267. 408p. 1985. Repr. text ed. 9.95 (ISBN 0-268-00755-1, 85-07550, Dist. by Har-Row). U of Notre Dame Pr.
Pink, A. W. La Soberania De Dios. 3.50 (ISBN 0-85151-416-2). Banner of Truth.
Porter, H. Boone. The Song of Creation: Selections from the First Article. 120p. (Orig.). 1986. pap. 6.95 (ISBN 0-936384-34-4). Cowley Pubns.
Puhalo, Lazar. Creation & Fall. 36p. (Orig.). 1986. pap. text ed. 4.00 (ISBN 0-913026-97-2). Synaxis Pr.
Rev. William Kramer. Evolution & Creation: A Catholic Understanding. LC 86-60907. 168p. (Orig.). 1986. pap. 6.95 (ISBN 0-87973-511-2, 511). Our Sunday Visitor.
Ryrie, Charles. We Believe in Creation. 62p. 1976. pap. 0.50 (ISBN 0-937396-54-0). Walterick Pubs.
Schmitz, Kenneth L. The Gift: Creation. (Aquinas Lecture Ser.). 160p. 1982. 12.95 (ISBN 0-87462-149-6). Marquette.
Seidman, Bradley. Absent at the Creation. LC 83-90254. 1984. 10.95 (ISBN 0-87212-175-5). Libra.
Siegfried. Beginning to Beginning. LC 84-90251. 65p. 1985. 6.95 (ISBN 0-533-06286-1). Vantage.
Skeem, Kenneth A. In the Beginning... Skeem, Jeanette L., ed. LC 81-68054. (Illus.). 256p. 1981. 12.00 (ISBN 0-9606782-0-4). Behemoth Pub.
Soelle, Dorothee & Cloyes, Shirley A. To Work & to Love: A Theology of Creation. LC 84-47936. 160p. 1984. pap. 7.95 (ISBN 0-8006-1782-7). Fortress.
Staub, Jacob. The Creation of the World According to Gersonides. LC 81-13523. (Brown Judiac Studies). 1982. pap. 20.00 (ISBN 0-89130-526-2, 14-00-24). Scholars Pr GA.
Steiner, Rudolf. The Evolution of the Earth & the Influence of the Stars. Hahn, Gladys, tr. from Ger. Tr. of Die Schoepfung der Welt und des Menschen Erdenleben und Sternenwirken. (Illus.). 200p. 1987. 20.00 (ISBN 0-88010-181-4); pap. 10.95 (ISBN 0-88010-180-6). Anthroposophic.
Stevenson, Warren. Divine Analogy: A Study of the Creation Motif in Blake & Coleridge. Hogg, James, ed. (Romantic Reassessment Ser.). 403p. (Orig.). 1972. pap. 15.00 (ISBN 0-317-40044-4, Pub. by Salzburg Studies). Longwood Pub Group.
Stewardship of Creation: Basic Resource Guide. 96p. pap. 6.45 (ISBN 0-664-24489-0). Westminster.
Stewardship of Creation: Guide for Older Youth. 32p. Pack of 10. pap. 31.50 (ISBN 0-664-24492-0). Westminster.
Stewardship of Creation: Guide for Younger Youth. 32p. Pack of 10. pap. 31.50 (ISBN 0-664-24491-2). Westminster.
Stewardship of Creation: Introductory Kit. Set of Four Guides. pap. 14.50 (ISBN 0-664-24560-9). Westminster.
Stokes, William L. The Genesis Answer: A Scientist's Testament of Divine Creation. 1984. pap. 14.95 (ISBN 0-317-03128-7). P-H.
Storer, Ronald. Creation & the Character of God. 204p. 1986. 39.00X (ISBN 0-7223-1973-8, Pub. by A H Stockwell England). State Mutual BK.
Strickling, James E., Jr. Origins: Today's Science, Tomorrow's Myth. 1986. 11.95 (ISBN 0-317-40170-X). Vantage.
Szekely, Edmond B. The Essene Book of Creation. (Illus.). 86p. 1975. pap. 4.50 (ISBN 0-89564-005-8). IBS Intl.
--The Essene Code of Life. (Illus.). 44p. 1978. pap. 3.50 (ISBN 0-89564-013-9). IBS Intl.
Tarneja, Sukh R. Nature, Spirituality & Science. 240p. 1980. text ed. 27.50x (ISBN 0-7069-1203-9, Pub by Vikas India). Advent NY.
Taylor, James. The Andrew Project. LC 85-42826. (Illus.). 108p. (Orig.). 1985. pap. 4.95 (ISBN 0-8042-0461-6). John Knox.
Teilhard De Chardin, Pierre. Hymn of the Universe. LC 65-10375. 1969. pap. 6.95x (ISBN 0-06-131910-4, TB1910, Torch). Har-Row.
--Hymne De L'univers. 1966. 13.95 (ISBN 0-685-11240-3). French & Eur.
Thompson, Bert. The Scientific Case for Creation. (That You May Believe Ser.). 47p. (Orig.). 1985. pap. 1.50 (ISBN 0-932859-03-8). Apologetic Pr.
Tomoko, Terrie K. The Wonderful Story of God's Creation. 1978. plastic bdg. 2.50 (ISBN 0-8198-0375-8); pap. 1.75 (ISBN 0-8198-0376-6). Dghtrs St Paul.
Torrance, Thomas F. The Ground & Grammar of Theology. LC 79-21429. 180p. 1980. 13.95x (ISBN 0-8139-0819-1). U Pr of Va.
Tracy, David & Lash, Nicholas. Cosmology & Theology. (Concilium 1983: Vol. 166). 128p. (Orig.). 1983. pap. 6.95 (ISBN 0-8164-2446-2, HarpR). Har-Row.
Twenty-One Scientists Who Believe in Creation. LC 77-81165. (Illus.). 1977. pap. 1.00 (ISBN 0-89051-038-5). Master Bks.
Vandeman, George. Tying Down the Sun. LC 78-61749. (Stories That Win Ser.). 1978. pap. 1.25 (ISBN 0-8163-0211-1, 20990-8). Pacific Pr Pub Assn.
Van Over, Raymond. Sun Songs: Creation Myths from Around the World. (Orig.). 1980. pap. 2.95 (ISBN 0-452-00730-5, Mer). NAL.
Van Till, Howard J. The Fourth Day: What the Bible & the Heavens Are Telling Us about the Creation. LC 85-29400. (Illus.). 286p. (Orig.). 1986. pap. 9.95 (ISBN 0-8028-0178-1). Eerdmans.
Walker, K. R., ed. The Evolution-Creation Controversy Perspectives on Religion, Philosophy, Science & Education: A Handbook. (Paleontological Society Special Publications Ser.). (Illus.). 155p. pap. 6.50 (ISBN 0-931377-00-5). U of Tenn Geo.
Walker, Paul L. Understanding the Bible & Science. LC 75-25343. (Illus.). 1976. pap. 1.99 (ISBN 0-87148-878-7). Pathway Pr.
Wesner, R. The Wesner Conjectures. LC 82-21421. 128p. 1985. pap. 4.95 (ISBN 0-88437-070-4). Psych Dimensions.
Whitcomb, John C. Origin of the Solar System. (Biblical & Theological Studies). pap. 2.50 (ISBN 0-8010-9590-5). Baker Bk.
Wilder-Smith, A. E. Creation of Life. LC 78-133984. 269p. 1981. pap. 8.95 (ISBN 0-89051-070-9). Master Bks.
Youngblood, Ronald, ed. The Genesis Debate: Persistent Questions about Creation & the Flood. 240p. 1986. pap. 12.95 (ISBN 0-8407-7517-2). Nelson.
Zimmerman, Gene. Why Do Mullet Jump? And Other Puzzles & Possibilities of God's Creation. 128p. (Orig.). 1986. pap. 6.95 (ISBN 0-935311-01-7). Post Horn Pr.

CREATION–EARLY WORKS TO 1800

Burnet, Thomas. Sacred Theory of the Earth. LC 65-10027. (Centaur Classics Ser.). (Illus.). 414p. 1965. 22.50x (ISBN 0-8093-0186-5). S Ill U Pr.
Whiston, William. A New Theory of the Earth: Its Original, to the Consummation of All Things Wherein the Creation of the World in Six Days. Albritton, Claude C., Jr., ed. LC 77-6545. (History of Geology Ser.). 1978. lib. bdg. 37.50x (ISBN 0-405-10463-4). Ayer Co Pubs.

CREATION–JUVENILE LITERATURE

Aronow, Sara. Seven Days of Creation. (Bible Stories in Rhymes Ser.: Vol. 1). (Illus.). 32p. 1985. 4.95 (ISBN 0-87203-119-5). Hermon.
Caffrey, Stephanie & Kenslea, Timothy. How the World Began. (Rainbow Books (Bible Story Books for Children)). 16p. 1978. pap. 1.00 (ISBN 0-8192-1233-4). Morehouse.
Dakenbing, William F. The Creation Book. LC 75-39840. (Illus.). 70p. 1976. 5.95 (ISBN 0-685-68397-4); pap. 3.95 (ISBN 0-685-68398-2). Triumph Pub.
Davidson, Alice J. The Story of Creation. (The Alice in Bibleland Storybooks). (Illus.). 32p. 1984. 4.95 (ISBN 0-8378-5066-5). Gibson.
Ebert, Barbara. God's World. 1985. pap. 0.98 (ISBN 0-317-30757-6, 2695). Standard Pub.
Gambill, Henrietta D. Seven Special Days. (Happy Day Bks.). (Illus.). 32p. 1987. 1.59 (ISBN 0-87403-281-4, 3781). Standard Pub.
God's World, Our World. (Little Books to Treasure). (Illus.). 32p. 1985. 1.95 (ISBN 0-225-66389-9, HarpR). Har-Row.
Hilliard, Dick & Valenti-Hilliard, Beverly. Surprises. (Center Celebration Ser.). (Illus.). 60p. (Orig.). 1981. pap. text ed. 3.95 (ISBN 0-89390-031-1). Resource Pubns.
Kasuya, Masahiro. The Beginning of the World. LC 81-3582. (Illus.). 1982. 8.95g (ISBN 0-687-02765-9). Abingdon.
McNeil. How Things Began. (Books of the World). 1975. 8.95 (ISBN 0-86020-027-2, Usborne-Hayes); PLB 12.96 (ISBN 0-88110-114-1); pap. 5.95 (ISBN 0-86020-199-6). EDC.
Mahany, Patricia, ed. God Made Kids Classroom Coloring Book. (Classroom Activities Bks.). (Illus.). 96p. (Orig.). 1982. pap. 2.95 (ISBN 0-87239-500-6, 2331). Standard Pub.
Metten, Patricia. The Power of Creativity. LC 81-50863. (Power Tales Ser.). pap. write for info. (ISBN 0-911712-89-5). Promised Land.
Miyoshi, Sekiya. Oldest Story in the World. Jensh, Barbara L., ed. LC 69-18145. (Illus.). 5.95 (ISBN 0-8170-0436-X). Judson.
Noe, Tom. The Sixth Day. LC 79-55296. (Illus.). 80p. (Orig.). 1979. pap. 2.95 (ISBN 0-87793-190-9). Ave Maria.
Stonecipher, Judy. Creation: For Kids & Other People Too. LC 82-62362. (Accent Discoveries Ser.). (Illus.). 64p. (Orig.). 1982. gift book 4.50 (ISBN 0-89636-095-4). Accent Bks.
Taylor, Kenneth N. What High School Students Should Know about Creation. (YA) 1983. pap. 2.50 (ISBN 0-8423-7872-3). Tyndale.
Ulmer. Adam's Story. LC 59-1292. (Arch Bks.). 24p. (Orig.). 1985. pap. 0.99 (ISBN 0-570-06191-1). Concordia.
Wangerin, Walter, Jr. In the Beginning...There Was No Sky. 36p. 1986. 10.95 (ISBN 0-8407-6671-8). Nelson.
Waskow, Arthur, et al. Before There Was a Before. LC 84-11177. (Illus.). 80p. 1984. 8.95 (ISBN 0-915361-08-6, 09404-9, Dist. by Watts). Adama Pubs Inc.

CREATION IN ART

De Civrieux, Marc. Watunna: An Orinoco Creation Cycle. Guss, David, ed. LC 80-82440. (Illus.). 216p. 1980. 20.00 (ISBN 0-86547-002-2); pap. 12.50 (ISBN 0-86547-003-0). N Point Pr.
Rehwinkel, Alfred M. The Wonders of Creation. LC 74-8416. 288p. 1973. pap. 7.95 (ISBN 0-87123-649-4, 210649). Bethany Hse.

CREATIVE ACTIVITIES AND SEATWORK

Abbott, Grace, ed. Ideas for Use with Two's & Three's. 176p. (Orig.). 1985. pap. 7.95 (ISBN 0-8341-1056-3). Beacon Hill.
Adcock, Mabel & Blackwell, Elsie. Creative Activities. (Illus.). 1984. 4.95 (ISBN 0-87162-011-1, D3195). Warner Pr.
Beall, Pamela C. & Nipp, Susan H. Wee Color Wee Sing for Christmas. (Wee Sing Ser.). (Illus.). 48p. 1986. pap. 1.95 (ISBN 0-8431-1781-8); book & cassette 6.95 (ISBN 0-8431-1782-6). Price Stern.
--Wee Sing Bible Songs. (Illus.). 64p. 1986. pap. 2.25 (ISBN 0-8431-1566-1); book & cassette 8.95 (ISBN 0-8431-1780-X). Price Stern.
Carson, Patti & Dellosa, Janet. Christmas Readiness Activities. (Stick-Out-Your-Neck Ser.). (Illus.). 32p. 1983. pap. 1.98 (ISBN 0-88724-049-6, CD-8025). Carson-Dellos.
--Christmas Reading & Activity Book. (Stick-Out-Your-Neck Ser.). (Illus.). 32p. 1983. pap. 1.98 (ISBN 0-88724-038-0, CD-8029). Carson-Dellos.
--Easter Preschool-K Practice. (Stick-Out-Your-Neck Ser.). (Illus.). 32p. 1984. pap. 1.98 (ISBN 0-88724-017-8, CD-8032). Carson-Dellos.
--Easter Primary Reading & Art Activities. (Stick-Out-Your-Neck Ser.). (Illus.). 32p. 1984. pap. 1.98 (ISBN 0-88724-027-5, CD-8042). Carson-Dellos.
Fine, Helen. G'Dee's Book of Holiday Fun. (Illus.). 1961. pap. 3.00 (ISBN 0-685-20737-4, 121701). UAHC.
Franklin, M. & Dotts, Maryann J. Clues to Creativity, Vol. 2: J-P. (Orig.). 1975. pap. 4.95 (ISBN 0-377-00041-8). Friend Pr.
--Clues to Creativity, Vol. 3: R-Z. (Orig.). 1976. pap. 4.95 (ISBN 0-377-00042-6). Friend Pr.
Lehman, Carolyn. God's Wonderful World: Thirteen Pupil Activities, Bk. 2. (God's Wonderful World Ser.). (Illus.). 32p. 1985. 1.50 (ISBN 0-87239-838-2, 3318). Standard Pub.
Ludwig, Nancy. Christmas Puppets Plays & Art Project Puppets. (Stick-Out-Your-Neck Ser.). (Illus.). 32p. 1983. pap. 1.98 (ISBN 0-88724-045-3, CD-8021). Carson-Dellos.
Mathson, Patricia. Creative Learning Activities for Religious Education: A Catalog of Teaching Ideas for Church, School, & Home. (Illus.). 192p. 1984. pap. 8.95 (ISBN 0-13-189838-8). P-H.
Powers, Bruce P. Church Administration Handbook. LC 84-29249. 1985. pap. 9.95 (ISBN 0-8054-3112-8). Broadman.
Sharon, Ruth. Arts & Crafts the Year Round, 2 Vols. (Illus.). 1965. Set. 29.00x (ISBN 0-8381-0213-1). United Syn Bk.
Vesey, Susan. Spring Activity Book. Alexander, P., ed. (Illus.). 32p. 1987. pap. 3.95 (ISBN 0-7459-1015-7). Lion USA.

CREEDS

see also Apostles' Creed; Athanasian Creed; Catechisms; Covenants (Church Polity); Nicene Creed;
also subdivision Catechisms and Creeds under names of religions, religious denominations, etc. e.g. Catholic Church–Catechisms and Creeds

Ainsworth, Henry. A True Confession of the Faith, Which Wee Falsley Called Brownists, Doo Hold. LC 78-26338. (English Experience Ser.: No. 158). 24p. 1969. Repr. of 1956 ed. 7.00 (ISBN 90-221-0158-4). Walter J Johnson.
The Confession of the Fayth of Certayne English People, Living in Exile in the Lowe Contreyes. LC 72-208. (English Experience Ser.: No. 346). 58p. Repr. of 1602 ed. 9.50 (ISBN 90-221-0346-3). Walter J Johnson.
Creed. 20p. 1980. pap. 7.55 (ISBN 0-88479-026-6). Arena Lettres.

Eakin, Frank E., Jr. We Believe in One God: Creed & Scripture. LC 85-51755. 165p. 1985. pap. text ed. 21.95 (ISBN 0-932269-64-8). Wyndham Hall.

Eberts, Harry W., Jr. We Believe: A Study of the Book of Confessions for Church Officers. LC 87-2097. 120p. (Orig.). 1987. pap. price not set (ISBN 0-664-24063-1, A Geneva Press Publication). Westminster.

Ecumenical Creeds & Reformed Confessions. 1979. pap. text ed. 3.75 (ISBN 0-933140-02-9). CRC Pubns.

Hellwig, Monika. The Christian Creeds. 112p. 1973. pap. 1.95 (ISBN 0-8278-9057-5, Pub. by Pflaum Pr). Peter Li.

Heyer, Friedrich. Konfessionskunde. 1977. 39.20 (ISBN 3-11-006651-3). De Gruyter.

Hodge, A. A. Confession of Faith. 1978. 13.95 (ISBN 0-85151-275-5). Banner of Truth.

Hunter, George G., III. And Every Tongue Confess. LC 83-73224. 56p. (Orig.). 1983. pap. 4.50 (ISBN 0-88177-004-3, DR004B). Discipleship Res.

Illustrated Articles of Faith. write for info. (ISBN 0-911712-18-6). Promised Land.

Leith, John H., ed. Creeds of the Churches: A Reader in Christian Doctrine from the Bible to the Present. 3rd ed. LC 82-48029. 1982. pap. 10.95 (ISBN 0-8042-0526-4). John Knox.

Plantinga, Cornelius, Jr. A Place to Stand: A Reformed Study of Creeds & Confessions. LC 79-371. (Illus.). 1979. pap. text ed. 8.95 (ISBN 0-933140-01-0). CRC Pubns.

Routley, Erik. Creeds & Confessions: The Reformation & Its Modern Ecumenical Implications. LC 63-3127. (Studies in Theology: No. 62). 1962. text ed. 8.50x (ISBN 0-8401-6062-3). A R Allenson.

Swanston, Hamish F. A Language for Madness: The Abuse & the Use of Christian Creeds. 154p. 1976. pap. text ed. 12.50 (ISBN 90-232-1426-9, Pub. by Van Gorcum Holland). Longwood Pub Group.

Van Til, Cornelius. My Credo. 1971. pap. 3.50 (ISBN 0-87552-490-7). Presby & Reformed.

CREEDS–HISTORY AND CRITICISM

Bell, H. I. Cults & Creeds in Graeco-Roman Egypt. 1975. pap. 7.50 (ISBN 0-89005-088-0). Ares.

Bray, Gerald. Creeds, Councils & Christ. LC 83-26443. 220p. 1984. pap. 6.95 (ISBN 0-87784-969-2). Inter-Varsity.

Kelly, J. N. Early Christian Creeds. 3rd ed. 446p. 1981. text ed. 16.95 (ISBN 0-582-49219-X). Longman.

Overduin, Daniel. Reflections on the Creed. 1980. pap. 1.95 (ISBN 0-570-03814-6, 12-2782). Concordia.

Williamson, G. I. Westminster Confession of Faith. pap. 6.95 (ISBN 0-8010-9591-3). Baker Bk.

CREIGHTON, MANDELL, BP. OF LONDON, 1843-1901

Shaw, William A. Bibliography of the Historical Works of Dr. Creighton, Dr. Stubbs, Dr. S. R. Gardiner, & the Late Lord Acton. 1969. 17.50 (ISBN 0-8337-3242-0). B Franklin.

CREMATION

see also Funeral Rites and Ceremonies

Fraser, James W. Cremation: Is It Christian? 1965. pap. 1.50 (ISBN 0-87213-180-7). Loizeaux.

CREVECOEUR, MICHEL GUILLAUME JEAN DE, CALLED ST. JOHN DE CREVECOEUR, 1735-1813

Allen & Asselineau. Biography of Crevecoeur. 1987. write for info (ISBN 0-670-81345-1). Viking.

Mitchell, Julia P. Saint Jean De Crevecoeur. LC 71-181959. Repr. of 1916 ed. 20.00 (ISBN 0-404-04347-X). AMS Pr.

CRIB IN CHRISTIAN ART AND TRADITION

Swarzenski, Hanns. An Eighteenth Century Creche. LC 66-25450. (Illus.). 1966. pap. 2.00 (ISBN 0-87846-142-6, Pub. by Mus Fine Arts Boston). C E Tuttle.

CRISIS THEOLOGY

see Dialectical Theology

CROMWELL, OLIVER, 1599-1658

Abbot, Wilbur C. Bibliography of Oliver Cromwell. 1929. Repr. 65.00 (ISBN 0-8482-7261-7). Norwood Edns.

Barker, Ernest. Oliver Cromwell & the English People. facsimile ed. LC 72-37329. (Select Bibliographies Reprint Ser). Repr. of 1937 ed. 12.00 (ISBN 0-8369-6674-0). Ayer Co Pubs.

Buchan, John. Oliver Cromwell. 1957. 25.00 (ISBN 0-8274-3062-0). R West.

Cocks, H. Lovell. The Religious Life of Oliver Cromwell. LC 61-47823. 1961. text ed. 6.00x (ISBN 0-8401-0443-X). A R Allenson.

Gardiner, Samuel R. Cromwell's Place in History. LC 76-94270. (Select Bibliographies Reprint Ser). 1897. 15.00 (ISBN 0-8369-5044-5). Ayer Co Pubs.

--Oliver Cromwell. 1977. Repr. of 1909 ed. 25.00x (ISBN 0-7158-1181-9). Charles River Bks.

Harrison, Frederic. Oliver Cromwell. 228p. 1980. Repr. of 1915 ed. lib. bdg. 25.00 (ISBN 0-8495-2293-5). Arden Lib.

--Oliver Cromwell. LC 78-39196. (Select Bibliographies Reprint Ser.). Repr. of 1888 ed. 18.00 (ISBN 0-8369-6798-4). Ayer Co Pubs.

--Oliver Cromwell. 1973. Repr. of 1888 ed. lib. bdg. 25.00 (ISBN 0-8414-5006-4). Folcroft.

Hillis, Newell D. Great Men As Prophets of a New Era. facs. ed. LC 68-16939. (Essay Index Reprint Ser). 1968. Repr. of 1922 ed. 15.00 (ISBN 0-8369-0541-5). Ayer Co Pubs.

Johnstone, Hilda. Oliver Cromwell & His Times. 92p. 1981. Repr. lib. bdg. 20.00 (ISBN 0-89987-430-4). Darby Bks.

Morley, John. Oliver Cromwell. 1977. Repr. of 1900 ed. lib. bdg. 25.00 (ISBN 0-8492-1850-0). R West.

New, John F., ed. Oliver Cromwell: Pretender, Puritan, Statesman, Paradox? LC 76-23190. (European Prob. Studies Ser.). 128p. 1977. pap. text ed. 5.95 (ISBN 0-88275-457-2). Krieger.

Picton, J. Allanson. Oliver Cromwell: The Man & His Mission. 1978. Repr. of 1883 ed. lib. bdg. 40.00 (ISBN 0-8482-2126-5). Norwood Edns.

Waldman, Milton. Some English Dictators. LC 77-112820. 1970. Repr. of 1940 ed. 24.50x (ISBN 0-8046-1087-8, Pub.by Kennikat). Assoc Faculty Pr.

CROMWELL, THOMAS, EARL OF ESSEX, 1485?-1540

Elton, G. R. Policy & Police: The Enforcement of the Reformation in the Age of Thomas Cromwell. 458p. 1985. pap. 14.95 (ISBN 0-521-31309-0). Cambridge U Pr.

Elton, Geoffrey R. Reform & Renewal, Thomas Cromwell & the Common Weal. (Wiles Lectures, 1972). 230p. 1973. pap. 11.95 (ISBN 0-521-09809-2). Cambridge U Pr.

CROSS

see Holy Cross

CROSS-WORD PUZZLES

see Crossword Puzzles

CROSSES

see also Christian Art and Symbolism; Symbolism

Baldwin, Stanley C. When Death Means Life: Choosing the Way of the Cross. (Living Theology Ser.). 1986. pap. 6.95 (ISBN 0-88070-161-7). Multnomah.

Benson, George W. The Cross: Its History & Symbolism. LC 73-88643. 1976. Repr. of 1934 ed. lib. bdg. 25.00 (ISBN 0-87817-149-5). Hacker.

Chalmers, Patrick. Ancient Sculptured Monuments of the County of Angus. LC 72-1052. (Bannatyne Club, Edinburgh. Publications: No. 88). Repr. of 1848 ed. 145.00 (ISBN 0-404-52818-X). AMS Pr.

Hill, Thomas D. & Farrell, Robert T. The Anglo-Saxon Cross. (Yale Studies in English: Nos. 23 & 50). iv, 282p. 1976. Repr. of 1904 ed. 27.50 (ISBN 0-208-01555-8, Archon). Shoe String.

Langdon, Arthur G. Old Cornish Crosses. 1977. lib. bdg. 134.95 (ISBN 0-8490-2367-X). Gordon Pr.

Napier, Arthur S., ed. History of the Holy Rood-Tree. (EETS, OS Ser.: No. 103). Repr. of 1894 ed. 12.00 (ISBN 0-527-00104-X). Kraus Repr.

Porter, Arthur K. Crosses & Culture of Ireland. LC 68-56480. (Illus.). 1969. Repr. of 1931 ed. 33.00 (ISBN 0-405-08860-4, Pub. by Blom). Ayer Co Pubs.

CROSSWORD PUZZLES

Kayne, Joseph D. Pencils & Sticks: Scripture Word-Searches for LDS Families. 32p. (Orig.). 1983. pap. 3.95 (ISBN 0-88290-218-0). Horizon Utah.

CROWLAND ABBEY

Ingulf, Abbot. Ingulph's Chronicle of the Abbey of Croyland. Riley, H. T., tr. LC 68-55553. (Bohn's Antiquarian Library Ser). Repr. of 1854 ed. 34.50 (ISBN 0-404-50018-8). AMS Pr.

CRUCIFIXION OF CHRIST

see Jesus Christ–Crucifixion

CRUSADES

Here are entered works on the crusades in general. Specific crusades are listed chronologically at the end of this entry.

see also Jerusalem–History–Latin Kingdom, 1099-1244; Templars

Archer, T. A. The Crusades. 1894. 15.00 (ISBN 0-8482-7265-X). Norwood Edns.

Archer, Thomas A. & Kingsford, Charles L. The Crusades: The Story of the Latin Kingdom of Jerusalem. LC 76-29833. Repr. of 1900 ed. 39.50 (ISBN 0-404-15409-3). AMS Pr.

Atiya, Aziz S. The Crusade of Nicopolis. LC 76-29829. (Illus.). Repr. of 1934 ed. 29.50 (ISBN 0-404-15410-7). AMS Pr.

Barker, Ernest. The Crusades. facsimile ed. LC 76-160956. (Select Bibliographies Reprint Ser). Repr. of 1923 ed. 12.00 (ISBN 0-8369-5823-3). Ayer Co Pubs.

Bercovici, Konrad. The Crusades. 1979. Repr. of 1929 ed. lib. bdg. 25.00 (ISBN 0-8482-3439-1). Norwood Edns.

Burns, Robert I. Diplomatarium of the Crusader Kingdom of Valencia: The Registered Charters of Its Conqueror, Jaume I, 1257-1276. Volume I: Society & Documentation in Crusader Valencia. LC 84-17828. (Illus.). 288p. 1985. text ed. 40.00x (ISBN 0-691-05435-5). Princeton U Pr.

Christiansen, Eric. The Northern Crusades: The Baltic & the Catholic Frontier, 1100-1525. (Illus.). xxii, 265p. 1981. 25.00 (ISBN 0-8166-0994-2); pap. 10.95x (ISBN 0-8166-1018-5). U of Minn Pr.

Conroy, Michael R. Crusaders. 1975. 19.95 (ISBN 0-915626-02-0). Yellow Jacket.

Cowdrey, H. E. Popes, Monks & Crusaders. (No. 27). 400p. 1983. 40.00 (ISBN 0-907628-34-6). Hambledon Press.

Cox, George W. The Crusades. Repr. 12.00 (ISBN 0-8482-3560-6). Norwood Edns.

D'Ault-Dumesnil, G. E. Dictionnaire Historique, Geographique et Biographique des Croisades. Migne, J. P., ed. (Nouvelle Encyclopedie Theologique Ser.: Vol. 18). (Fr.). 619p. Repr. of 1852 ed. lib. bdg. 79.00x (ISBN 0-89241-265-8). Caratzas.

De Lion, Gwoffrey, et al. Chronicles of the Crusades. Giles, John A. & Johnes, Thomas, trs. LC 73-84862. (Bohn's Antiquarian Library Ser.). Repr. of 1848 ed. 41.50 (ISBN 0-404-50014-5). AMS Pr.

De Villehardouin, Geoffrey & De Joinville, Jean. Chronicles of the Crusades. Shaw, Margaret R., tr. (Classics Ser.). (Orig.). 1963. pap. 5.95 (ISBN 0-14-044124-7). Penguin.

De Villehardouin, Geoffroi & Joinville. Memoirs of the Crusades. LC 83-1515. (Everyman's Library: History: No. 333). xli, 340p. 1983. Repr. of 1908 ed. lib. bdg. 45.00x (ISBN 0-313-23856-1, VIME). Greenwood.

Donovan, Joseph P. Pelagius & the Fifth Crusade. LC 76-29822. Repr. of 1950 ed. 29.00 (ISBN 0-404-15416-6). AMS Pr.

Enlart, Camille. Les Monuments des Croises dans le Royaume de Jerusalem, 4 vols. LC 78-63336. (The Crusades & Military Orders: Second Ser.). Repr. of 1927 ed. Set. 495.00 (ISBN 0-404-17050-1). AMS Pr.

Erdmann, Carl. The Origin of the Idea of Crusade. Baldwin, Marshall W. & Goffart, Walter, trs. from Ger. 1977. 55.50x (ISBN 0-691-05251-4). Princeton U Pr.

Finucane, Ronald C. Soldiers of the Faith: Crusaders & Moslems at War. (Illus.). 256p. 1984. 19.95 (ISBN 0-312-74256-8). St Martin.

Forbes-Boyd, Eric. In Crusader Greece. (Illus.). 10.00 (ISBN 0-87556-091-1). Saifer.

Gabrieli, Francesco, ed. Arab Historians of the Crusades. LC 68-23783. 1978. 40.00x (ISBN 0-520-03616-6); pap. 9.95 (ISBN 0-520-05224-2, CAL 699). U of Cal Pr.

Gruhn, Albert. Die Byzantinische Politik Zur der Zeit Kreuzzuege. 1904. 12.50 (ISBN 0-8337-1479-1). B Franklin.

Guilelmus. Godeffroy of Boloyne; or, the Siege & Conquest of Jerusalem. Colvin, Mary N., ed. (EETS, ES Ser.: No. 64). Repr. of 1893 ed. 29.00 (ISBN 0-527-00269-0). Kraus Repr.

Kedar, Benjamin Z. Crusade & Mission. LC 84-3403. (Illus.). 256p. 1984. text ed. 26.50x (ISBN 0-691-05424-X). Princeton U Pr.

Lamb, Harold. The Crusades: Iron Men & Saints. 368p. 1983. Repr. of 1930 ed. lib. bdg. 36.50 (ISBN 0-89987-527-0). Darby Bks.

Ludlow, James M. The Age of the Crusades. 1977. lib. bdg. 59.95 (ISBN 0-8490-1405-0). Gordon Pr.

Maalouf, Amin. The Crusades Through Arab Eyes. 312p. 1985. 16.95 (ISBN 0-8052-4004-7). Schocken.

--The Crusades Through Arab Eyes. LC 85-8367. 312p. 1987. pap. 8.95 (ISBN 0-8052-0833-X). Schocken.

Mayer, Hans E. The Crusades. Gillingham, John, tr. from Ger. (Illus.). 1972. pap. text ed. 12.95x (ISBN 0-19-873016-0). Oxford U Pr.

Michaud, Joseph F. Bibliotheque des croisades, 4 vols. LC 76-29846. (Fr.). Repr. of 1829 ed. Set. 149.50 (ISBN 0-404-15450-6). AMS Pr.

--History of the Crusades, 3 Vols. Robson, W., tr. LC 72-172729. Repr. of 1852 ed. 110.00 (ISBN 0-404-04320-8). AMS Pr.

Miller, William. Essays on the Latin Orient. LC 78-63360. (The Crusades & Military Orders: Second Ser.). Repr. of 1921 ed. 54.50 (ISBN 0-404-17024-2). AMS Pr.

Munro, Dana C. The Kingdom of the Crusaders. LC 65-20472. 1966. Repr. of 1935 ed. 22.50x (ISBN 0-8046-0326-X, Pub. by Kennikat). Assoc Faculty Pr.

Myers, Geoffrey M., et al, eds. Les Chetifs. LC 79-2565. (Old French Crusade Cycle Ser.: Vol. V). xxxvi, 352p. 1981. text ed. 35.00 (ISBN 0-8173-0023-6). U of Ala Pr.

Nicholson, Robert L. Joscelyn I, Prince of Edessa. LC 78-63352. (The Crusades & Military Orders: Second Ser.). 120p. Repr. of 1954 ed. 21.50 (ISBN 0-404-17025-0). AMS Pr.

Ordericus Vitalis. Ecclesiastical History of England & Normandy, 4 Vols. Forrester, T., tr. LC 68-57872. (Bohn's Antiquarian Library Ser). Repr. of 1856 ed. Set. 115.00 (ISBN 0-404-50040-4). AMS Pr.

Ordericus, Vitalis. Historiae Ecclesiasticae Libri Tredecim, 5 Vols. Le Prevost, A., ed. Set. 240.00 (ISBN 0-384-43511-4); Set. pap. 210.00 (ISBN 0-384-43512-2). Johnson Repr.

Paetow, Louis J., ed. Crusades & Other Historical Essays, Presented to Dana C. Munro by His Former Students. facs. ed. LC 68-14902. (Essay Index Reprint Ser). 1928. 21.50 (ISBN 0-8369-0354-4). Ayer Co Pubs.

Peters, Edward, ed. Christian Society & the Crusades, 1198-1229: Sources in Translation, Including the Capture of Damietta. LC 78-163385. (Middle Ages Ser). 1971. 21.00x (ISBN 0-8122-7644-2); pap. 9.95x (ISBN 0-8122-1024-7, Pa Paperbks). U of Pa Pr.

Pissard, Hippolyte. La Guerre Sainte en Pays Chretien. LC 78-63357. (The Crusades & Military Orders: Second Ser.). Repr. of 1912 ed. 23.50 (ISBN 0-404-17027-7). AMS Pr.

Prawer, Joshua. Crusader Institutions. (Illus.). 1980. 89.00x (ISBN 0-19-822536-9). Oxford U Pr.

Recueil des Historiens des Croisades: Lois, 2 vols. (Fr.). Repr. of 1906 ed. text ed. 258.76x ea. vol. (ISBN 0-576-78858-9, Pub. by Gregg Intl Pubs England). Gregg Intl.

Recueil des Historiens des Croisades: Documents Armeniens, 2 vols. (Fr.). Repr. of 1906 ed. text ed. 310.50x ea. vol. (ISBN 0-576-78860-0, Pub. by Gregg Intl Pubs England). Gregg Intl.

Recueil des Historiens des Croisades: Historiens Grecs, 2 vols. (Fr.). Repr. of 1906 ed. text ed. 207.00x ea. vol. (ISBN 0-576-78859-7, Pub. by Gregg Intl Pubs England). Gregg Intl.

Recueil des Historiens des Croisades: Historiens Occidentaux, 6 vols. (Fr.). Repr. of 1906 ed. text ed. 258.76x ea. vol. (ISBN 0-576-78857-0, Pub. by Gregg Intl Pubs England). Gregg Intl.

Riley-Smith, Louise & Riley-Smith, Jonathan. The Crusades: Idea & Reality, 1095-1274. (Documents in Medieval History). 208p. 1981. pap. text ed. 17.95 (ISBN 0-7131-6348-8). E Arnold.

Setton, Kenneth M., ed. History of the Crusades, 5 vols. Incl. Vol. 1. The First Hundred Years. Baldwin, Marshall W., ed. (Illus.). 740p. 1969. Repr. of 1955 ed (ISBN 0-299-04831-4); Vol. 2. The Later Crusades, 1189 to 1311. 2nd ed. Wolff, Robert L. & Hazard, Harry W., eds. (Illus.). 896p. Repr. of 1962 ed (ISBN 0-299-04841-1); Vol. 3. The Fourteenth & Fifteenth Centuries. Hazard, Harry W. & Setton, Kenneth M., eds. (Illus.). 836p. 1975 (ISBN 0-299-06670-3); Vol. 4. The Art & Architecture of the Crusader States. Hazard, Harry W. & Setton, Kenneth M., eds. (Illus.). 444p. 1977 (ISBN 0-299-06820-X); Vol. 5. The Impact of the Crusades on the Near East. Setton, Kenneth M. & Zacour, Norman P., eds. (Illus.). 512p. 1985 (ISBN 0-299-09140-6). LC 68-9837. 40.00x ea. U of Wis Pr.

Siberry, Elizabeth. Criticism of Crusading, Ten Ninety-Five to Twelve Seventy-Four. 1985. 37.00x (ISBN 0-19-821953-9). Oxford U Pr.

Smail, R. C. Crusading Warfare, 1097-1193: A Contribution to Medieval Military History. LC 67-26956. (Cambridge Studies in Medieval Life & Thought Ser: No. 3). 1967. pap. 16.95 (ISBN 0-521-09730-4). Cambridge U Pr.

Smith, Jonathan R. The First Crusade & the Idea of Crusading. LC 86-1608. (Middle Ages Ser.). 224p. 1986. text ed. 29.95x (ISBN 0-8122-8026-1). U of Pa Pr.

Stevenson, W. B. Crusaders in the East. 16.00x (ISBN 0-86685-035-X). Intl Bk Ctr.

Throop, Palmer A. Criticism of the Crusade: A Study of Public Opinion & Crusade Propaganda. LC 75-26530. (Perspectives in European Hist.: No. 12). xv, 291p. 1975. Repr. of 1940 ed. lib. bdg. 27.50x (ISBN 0-87991-618-4). Porcupine Pr.

Vertot, Rene A. The History of the Knights Hospitallers of St. John of Jerusalem, 5 vols. LC 78-63372. (The Crusades & Military Orders: Second Ser.). Repr. of 1757 ed. Set. 200.00 (ISBN 0-404-17040-4). AMS Pr.

Villehardouin, Joinville. Chronicles of the Crusades. Shaw, M. R., tr. from Fr. 258p. 1985. 14.95 (ISBN 0-88029-037-4, Pub. by Dorset Pr). Hippocrene Bks.

Villey, Michel. La Croisade: Essai sur la Formation d'une Theorie Juridique. LC 78-63373. (Crusades Ser.). Repr. of 1942 ed. 30.00 (ISBN 0-404-17046-3). AMS Pr.

Vincent, Hughes. Jerusalem, 2 vols. in 4. LC 78-63368. (The Crusades & Military Orders: Second Ser.). Repr. of 1926 ed. Set. 495.00 (ISBN 0-404-17060-9). AMS Pr.

CRUSADES–BIBLIOGRAPHY

Atiya, Aziz S. The Crusade: Historiography & Bibliography. LC 75-22640. 1976. lib. bdg. 22.50x (ISBN 0-8371-8364-2, ATTC). Greenwood.

CRUSADES–JUVENILE LITERATURE

Williams, Ann. The Crusades. Reeves, Marjorie, ed. (Then & There Ser.). (Illus.). 95p. (YA) 1975. pap. text ed. 4.75 (ISBN 0-582-20441-0). Longman.

CRUSADES–FIRST, 1096-1099

Chazan, Robert. European Jewry & the First Crusade. 1987. 37.50. U of Cal Pr.

David, Charles W. Robert Curthose, Duke of Normandy. LC 78-63356. (The Crusades & Military Orders: Second Ser.). (Illus.). 296p. Repr. of 1920 ed. 32.50 (ISBN 0-404-17007-2). AMS Pr.

Eidelberg, Shlomo, ed. Jews & the Crusaders: The Hebrew Chronicles of the First & Second Crusades. (Illus.). 200p. 1977. 24.95x (ISBN 0-299-07060-3). U of Wis Pr.

Foucher De Chartres. Chronicle of the First Crusade. McGinty, Martha E., tr. LC 76-29823. Repr. of 1941 ed. 22.50 (ISBN 0-404-15417-4). AMS Pr.

Heraclius. Here Begynneth the Boke Intituled Eracles & Also Godefrey of Boloyne. Caxton, William, tr. LC 73-6140. (English Experience Ser.: No. 604). 1973. Repr. of 1481 ed. 52.00 (ISBN 90-221-0604-7). Walter J Johnson.

Hill, John H. & Hill, Laurita L. Peter Tudebode: Historia De Hierosolymitano Itinere. LC 74-78091. (Memoirs Ser.: Vol. 101). 1974. 6.50 (ISBN 0-87169-101-9). Am Philos.

Ibn Al-Qalanisi. The Damascus Chronicle of the Crusades. Gibb, H. A., tr. LC 78-63342. (The Crusades & Military Orders: Second Ser.). Repr. of 1967 ed. 32.50 (ISBN 0-404-17019-6). AMS Pr.

Krey, A. C. The First Crusade: Accounts of Eye-Witnesses & Participants. 11.75 (ISBN 0-8446-1272-3). Peter Smith.

Nichol, Jon. The First & Third Crusades. (Resource Units: Middle Ages, 1066-1485 Ser.). (Illus.). 24p. 1974. pap. text ed. 12.95 10 copies & tchr's guide (ISBN 0-582-39377-9). Longman.

Peters, Edward, ed. First Crusade: The Chronicle of Fulcher of Chartres & Other Source Materials. LC 74-163384. (Middle Ages Ser.). 1971. 21.00x (ISBN 0-8122-7643-4); pap. text ed. 9.95x (ISBN 0-8122-1017-4, Pa Paperbks). U of Pa Pr.

Rousset, Paul. Les Origines et les caracteres de la premiere croisade. LC 76-29837. (Fr.). Repr. of 1945 ed. 25.00 (ISBN 0-404-15428-X). AMS Pr.

Smith, Jonathan R. The First Crusade & the Idea of Crusading. LC 86-1608. (Middle Ages Ser.). 224p. 1986. text ed. 29.95x (ISBN 0-8122-8026-1). U of Pa Pr.

CRUSADES–SECOND, 1147-1149

Eidelberg, Shlomo, ed. Jews & the Crusaders: The Hebrew Chronicles of the First & Second Crusades. (Illus.). 200p. 1977. 24.95x (ISBN 0-299-07060-3). U of Wis Pr.

Odo of Deuil. De Profectione Ludovici VII in Orientem: The Journey of Louis the Seventh to the East. Berry, Virginia G., ed. & tr. 1965. pap. 6.95x (ISBN 0-393-09662-9). Norton.

CRUSADES–THIRD, 1189-1192

Archer, Thomas A. The Crusade of Richard I, 1189-92. LC 76-29828. Repr. of 1889 ed. 65.00 (ISBN 0-404-15408-5). AMS Pr.

Hubert, Morton J. & La Monte, John L. Crusade of Richard Lion-Heart, by Ambroise. (Illus.). 1969. lib. bdg. 40.00x (ISBN 0-374-94009-6, Octagon). Hippocrene Bks.

Nichol, Jon. The First & Third Crusades. (Resource Units: Middle Ages, 1066-1485 Ser.). (Illus.). 24p. 1974. pap. text ed. 12.95 10 copies & tchr's guide (ISBN 0-582-39377-9). Longman.

CRUSADES–FOURTH, 1202-1204

De Villehardouin, Geoffroi. De la Conqueste de Constantinoble. Paris, Paulin, ed. 1965. 39.00 (ISBN 0-685-92799-7); pap. 33.00 (ISBN 0-384-64581-X). Johnson Repr.

De Villehardouin, Geoffroy. Conqueste de Constantinople. White, Julian E., Jr., ed. LC 68-16196. (Medieval French Literature Ser). (Fr., Orig.). 1968. pap. text ed. 5.95x (ISBN 0-89197-102-5). Irvington.

Godfrey, John. Twelve Hundred & Four-the Unholy Crusade. (Illus.). 1980. 39.95x (ISBN 0-19-215834-1). Oxford U Pr.

Miller, William. The Latins in the Levant: A History of Frankish Greece. LC 75-41193. Repr. of 1908 ed. 57.50 (ISBN 0-404-14689-9). AMS Pr.

Queller, Donald E. The Fourth Crusade. LC 77-81454. (Middle Ages Ser). 1977. pap. 10.95x (ISBN 0-8122-1098-0). U of Pa Pr.

Recueil des Historiens des Croisades: Historiens Orientaux, 4 vols. (Fr.). Repr. of 1906 ed. text ed. 258.76x ea. vol. (ISBN 0-576-78861-9, Pub. by Gregg Intl Pubs England). Gregg Intl.

CRUSADES–LATER, 13TH, 14TH, AND 15TH CENTURIES

Argenti, Philip P. The Occupation of Chios by the Genoese & Their Administration of the Island, 1346-1566, 3 vols. LC 78-63339. (The Crusades & Military Orders: Second Ser.). Repr. of 1958 ed. Set. 120.00 (ISBN 0-404-17000-5); 40.00 ea. AMS Pr.

Delaville Le Roulx, Joseph. La France en Orient au XIVe Siecle, 2 vols. LC 78-63335. (The Crusades & Military Orders: Second Ser.). Repr. of 1886 ed. Set. 37.50 (ISBN 0-404-17020-X). AMS Pr.

Housley, Norman. The Avignon Papacy & the Crusades, Thirteen Five to Thirteen Seventy-Eight. 450p. 1986. 55.00x (ISBN 0-19-821957-1). Oxford U Pr.

--The Italian Crusade: The Papal-Angevin Alliance & the Crusades Against Christian Lay Powers, 1254-1343. (Illus.). 1982. 47.50x (ISBN 0-19-821925-3). Oxford U Pr.

Machairas, Leontios. Recital Concerning the Sweet Land of Cyprus, 2 vols. Dawkins, R. M., ed. LC 78-63351. (The Crusades & Military Orders: Second Ser.). Repr. of 1932 ed. Set. 92.50 (ISBN 0-404-17030-7). AMS Pr.

Purcell, M. Papal Crusading Policy, Twelve Hundred Forty-Four to Twelve Hundred Ninety-One. 1975. 40.00 (ISBN 90-04-04317-9). Heinman.

Simonde De Sismondi, Jean C. History of the Crusades Against the Albigenses in the Thirteenth Century. LC 72-178564. Repr. of 1826 ed. 30.00 (ISBN 0-404-56672-3). AMS Pr.

CUBA–RELIGION

Cabrera, Lydia. La Regla Kimbisa del Santo Cristo del Buen Viaje. 2nd ed. (Coleccion del Chichereku en el Exilio Ser.). (Span.). 85p. 1986. pap. 6.95 (ISBN 0-89729-396-7). Ediciones.

Clark, Juan. Religious Repression in Cuba. 115p. (Orig.). 1986. pap. 8.95 (ISBN 0-935501-04-5). U Miami N-S Ctr.

--La Represion Religiosa en Cuba. (Span.). 124p. (Orig.). Date not set. pap. cancelled (ISBN 0-917049-05-5). Saeta.

Fernandez, Manuel. Religion y Revolucion en Cuba. (Realidades Ser.). (Span., Illus.). 250p. 1984. pap. 14.95 (ISBN 0-917049-00-4). Saeta.

CULT

see also Ritual

Hadfield, P. Traits of Divine Kingship in Africa. LC 78-32120. 1979. Repr. of 1949 ed. lib. bdg. 22.50x (ISBN 0-8371-5189-9, HDK&, Pub. by Negro U Pr). Greenwood.

Melton, J. Gordon & Moore, Robert L. The Cult Experience: Responding to the New Religious Pluralism. LC 82-16136. 160p. (Orig.). 1982. pap. 8.95 (ISBN 0-8298-0619-9). Pilgrim NY.

CULTS

Here are entered works on groups or movements whose system of religious beliefs or practices differs significantly from the major world religions and which are often gathered around a specific diety or person. Works on the major world religions are entered under Religions. Works on religious groups whose adherents recognize special teachings or practices which fall within the normative bounds of the major world religions are entered under Sects.

see also Nativistic Movements; Sects

Beckford, James A. Cult Controversies: The Societal Response to the New Religious Movements. 336p. 1985. 39.95 (ISBN 0-422-79630-1, 9592, Pub. by Tavistock England); pap. 13.95 (ISBN 0-422-79640-9, 9593, Pub. by Tavistock England). Methuen Inc.

Begg, Ean. The Cult of the Black Virgin. (Illus.). 288p. (Orig.). 1985. pap. 11.95 (ISBN 1-85063-022-4, Ark Paperbks). Methuen Inc.

Bennett, F. M. Religious Cults Associated with the Amazons. v, 79p. 1985. Repr. of 1912 ed. lib. bdg. 25.00x (ISBN 0-89241-204-6). Caratzas.

Boa, Kenneth. Cults, World Religions, & You. 1977. pap. 6.95 (ISBN 0-88207-752-X). Victor Bks.

Bromley, David & Shupe, Anson. A Documentary History of the Anti-Cult Movement. LC 84-25560. (Studies in American Religion: Vol. 13). 420p. 1985. 69.95x_cancelled (ISBN 0-88946-656-4). E Mellen.

--Strange Gods: The Great American Cult Scare. LC 81-65763. 192p. 1982. 21.95x (ISBN 0-8070-3256-5); pap. 8.95 (ISBN 0-8070-1109-6, BP641). Beacon Pr.

Burrell, Maurice C. The Challenge of the Cults. (Direction Bks.). 160p. (Orig.). 1982. pap. 3.95 (ISBN 0-8010-0816-6). Baker Bk.

Burstein, A. Religion, Cults & the Law. 2nd ed. (Legal Almanac Ser.: No. 23). 128p. 1980. 6.95 (ISBN 0-379-11133-0). Oceana.

Bussell, Harold L. Unholy Devotion: Why Cults Lure Christians. 160p. 1983. pap. 5.95 (ISBN 0-310-37251-8, 12388P). Zondervan.

Carroll, Michael P. The Cult of the Virgin Mary: Psychological Origins. LC 85-43273. (Illus.). 325p. 1986. 25.00 (ISBN 0-691-09420-9). Princeton U Pr.

Cocoris, G. Michael. Cults: Deception or Denomination. 53p. (Orig.). 1984. pap. text ed. 1.00 (ISBN 0-935729-11-9). Church Open Door.

Cushman, Rudolf E. Peculiar Forms of Ancient Religious Cults. (Illus.). 1980. deluxe ed. 67.50 (ISBN 0-89266-234-4). Am Classical Coll Pr.

Daly, Lloyd W. Iohannis Philoponi: De Vocabulis Quae Diversum Significatum Exhibent Secundum Differentiam Accentus. LC 81-72156. (Memoirs Ser.: Vol. 151). 1983. 20.00 (ISBN 0-87169-151-5). Am Philos.

Dieckmann, Ed, Jr. The Secret of Jonestown: The Reason Why. 176p. (Orig.). 1982. pap. 6.00 (ISBN 0-939482-02-9). Noontide.

Eisenberg, Gary. Smashing the Idols: A Jewish Inquiry into the Cults. 325p. 1987. 25.00 (ISBN 0-87668-974-8). Aronson.

Elkins, Chris. Heavenly Deception. 1981. pap. 9.95 incl. cassette (ISBN 0-8423-1403-2). Tyndale.

Ellwood, Robert S. Alternative Altars: Unconventional & Eastern Spirituality in America. LC 78-15089. (Chicago History of American Religion Ser.). 1979. lib. bdg. 12.95x (ISBN 0-226-20618-1); pap. 5.50x (ISBN 0-226-20620-3). U of Chicago Pr.

Enroth, Ronald. The Lure of the Cults. rev. ed. 130p. 1987. pap. 5.95 (ISBN 0-87784-994-3). Inter-Varsity.

Enroth, Ronald, et al. A Guide to Cults & New Religions. LC 83-44. 200p. (Orig.). 1983. pap. 6.95 (ISBN 0-87784-837-8). Inter-Varsity.

Enroth, Ronald M. & Melton, Gordon J. Why Cults Succeed Where the Church Fails. 128p. 1985. 6.95 (ISBN 0-87178-932-9). Brethren.

Evans, Elizabeth C. The Cults of the Sabine Territory. LC 39-25699. (American Academy in Rome. Papers & Monographs: Vol. 11). pap. 71.00 (2026727). Bks Demand UMI.

Evenhouse, Bill. Reasons One, Sects & Cults with Non-Christian Roots. 120p. (Orig.). 1981. pap. text ed. 4.10 (ISBN 0-933140-23-1); tchr's manual, 61 pgs. 4.10 (ISBN 0-933140-24-X). CRC Pubns.

Greenberg, Martin H. & Waugh, Charles G., eds. Cults! An Anthology of Secret Societies, Sects, & the Supernatural. 368p. 1983. 17.95 (ISBN 0-8253-0159-9). Beaufort Bks NY.

Hale, Annie R. These Cults. 1981. 8.95 (ISBN 0-686-76751-9). B of A.

Halperin, D. A. Psychodynamic Perspectives on Religion, Sect & Cult. 416p. 1983. pap. text ed. 46.50 (ISBN 0-7236-7029-3). PSG Pub Co.

Heider, George C. The Cult of Molek: A Reassessment. (JSOT Supplement Ser.: No. 43). xiv, 446p. 1986. text ed. 28.50x (ISBN 1-85075-019-X, Pub. by JSOT Pr England); pap. text ed. 13.50x (ISBN 1-85075-018-1). Eisenbrauns.

Hexham, Irving & Poewe, Karla. Understanding Cults & New Religions. 192p. (Orig.). 1986. pap. 8.95 (ISBN 0-8028-0170-6). Eerdmans.

Hunt, Dave. The Cult Explosion. LC 80-80458. 240p. 1980. pap. 6.95 (ISBN 0-89081-241-1). Harvest Hse.

Keiser, Thomas W. & Keiser, Jacqueline L. The Anatomy of Illusion: Religious Cults & Destructive Persuasion. (Illus.). 160p. 1987. 25.25 (ISBN 0-398-05295-6). C C Thomas.

Langley, Myrtle, et al. A Book of Beliefs. Alexander, P., ed. 192p. 1987. pap. 12.95 (ISBN 0-85648-504-7). Lion USA.

Larson, Bob. Larson's Book of Cults. 1982. 9.95 (ISBN 0-8423-2104-7). Tyndale.

Lewis, David A. Dark Angels of Light. LC 84-61915. 100p. (Orig.). 1985. pap. 5.95 (ISBN 0-89221-117-2). New Leaf.

Lewis, Gordon. Confronting the Cults. pap. 6.50 (ISBN 0-8010-5560-1). Baker Bk.

Lewis, I. M. Religion in Context: Cults & Charisma. (Essays in Social Anthropology Ser.). (Illus.). 160p. 1986. 37.50 (ISBN 0-521-30616-7); pap. 9.95 (ISBN 0-521-31596-4). Cambridge U Pr.

McDowell, Josh & Stewart, Don. Understanding the Cults. LC 81-81850. (Handbook of Today's Religion Ser.). 199p. 1982. pap. 6.95 (ISBN 0-86605-090-6, 402826). Heres Life.

MacMunn, George. The Religions & Hidden Cults of India. (Illus.). xii, 244p. 1983. text ed. 30.00x (ISBN 0-86590-107-4). Apt Bks.

Martin, Walter. The Kingdom of the Cults. rev. ed. 450p. 1985. 14.95 (ISBN 0-87123-796-2, 230796). Bethany Hse.

--The New Cults. LC 80-52210. (Orig.). 1980. pap. 8.95 (ISBN 0-88449-016-5, A424378). Vision Hse.

Martin, Walter R. Walter Martin's Cults Reference Bible. LC 81-52881. 1248p. 1981. 19.99 (ISBN 0-88449-075-0, VH301). Vision Hse.

Melton, J. Gordon. Biographical Dictionary of American Cult & Sect Leaders. LC 83-48226. (Library of Social Sciences). 534p. 1986. lib. bdg. 39.95 (ISBN 0-8240-9037-3). Garland Pub.

Milne, Hugh. Bhagwan: The God That Failed. (Illus.). 320p. 1987. pap. 10.95 (ISBN 0-312-00106-1, Pub. by Thomas Dunne Bks). St Martin.

Mitchell, Nathan. Cult & Controversy: The Worship of the Eucharist Outside Mass. Kavanagh, Aidan, ed. (Studies in the Reformed Rites of the Catholic Church: Vol. IV). 460p. (Orig.). 1982. pap. 14.95 (ISBN 0-916134-50-4). Pueblo Pub Co.

Mosatche, Harriet S. Searching: Practices & Beliefs of the Religious Cults & Human Potential Movements. LC 83-4829. (Illus.). 437p. 1984. 14.95 (ISBN 0-87396-092-0). Stravon.

Nandi, R. N. Religious Institutions & Cults in the Deccan. 1973. 8.50 (ISBN 0-8426-0564-9). Orient Bk Dist.

Obeyesekere, Gananath. The Cult of the Goddess Pattini. LC 83-5884. (Illus.). 629p. 1984. lib. bdg. 42.50x (ISBN 0-226-61602-9). U of Chicago Pr.

O'Neil, Kevin R. What to Tell Your Children about Cults. 52p. (Orig.). 1982. pap. 9.95 (ISBN 0-86627-001-9). Crises Res Pr.

Pavlos, Andrew J. The Cult Experience. LC 81-13175. (Contributions to the Study of Religion: No. 6). xvi, 209p. 1982. lib. bdg. 29.95 (ISBN 0-313-23164-8, PEX/). Greenwood.

Persinger, Michael A., et al. TM & Cult Mania. 208p. 1980. 10.95 (ISBN 0-8158-0392-3). Chris Mass.

Petersen, Bill. Those Curious New Cults in the Eighties. rev. ed. LC 72-93700. 1982. pap. text ed. 3.95 (ISBN 0-87983-317-3). Keats.

Peterson, Roy M. The Cults of Campania. LC 23-13673. (American Academy in Rome, Papers & Monographs: Vol. 1). pap. 103.30 (2026716). Bks Demand UMI.

Porter, Jack N. Handbook of Cults, Sects, & Self-Realization Groups. 95p. (Orig.). 1982. pap. 6.95 (ISBN 0-932270-03-4). Spencer Pr.

Pritchett, W. Douglas. The Children of God-Family of Love: An Annotated Bibliography. Melton, J. Gordon, ed. LC 83-48223. (Sects & Cults in America: Bibliographical Guides Ser.). 250p. 1984. lib. bdg. 33.00 (ISBN 0-8240-9043-8). Garland Pub.

Rajneesh, Bhagwan Shree. The Mustard Seed. rev. ed. Prabhu, Swami Krishna, ed. LC 84-43009. (Jesus Ser.). 560p. 1984. pap. 5.95 (ISBN 0-88050-595-8). Chidvilas Found.

Robbins, Thomas, et al, eds. Cults, Culture & the Law: Perspectives on New Religious Movements. (American Academy of Religion Studies in Religion: No. 36). 1985. 18.95 (ISBN 0-89130-832-6, 01 00 36); pap. 13.50 (ISBN 0-89130-833-4). Scholars Pr GA.

Robertson, Irvine G. What the Cults Believe. rev. ed. 1966. pap. 5.95 (ISBN 0-8024-9411-0). Moody.

Rogers, John T. Communicating Christ to the Cults. LC 83-4421. 1983. pap. 3.95 (ISBN 0-87227-091-2). Reg Baptist.

Rudin, A. James & Rudin, Marcia R. Prison or Paradise? The New Religious Cults? LC 80-10210. 168p. 1980. 4.95 (ISBN 0-8006-1937-4, 1-1937). Fortress.

Saliba, John A. Religious Cults Today: A Challenge to Christian Families. 48p. 1983. pap. 1.50 (ISBN 0-89243-189-X). Liguori Pubns.

Scott, Gini G. Cult & Countercult: A Study of a Spiritual Growth Group & a Witchcraft Order. LC 79-54057. (Contributions in Sociology: No. 38). (Illus.). 1980. lib. bdg. 29.95x (ISBN 0-313-22074-3, SCC/). Greenwood.

Sheehan, John. Religion & Cult. 240p. pap. 6.95 (ISBN 0-87462-446-0). Marquette.

Sheils, W. J. & Wood, Diana, eds. Voluntary Religion, Vol. 23. 544p. 1987. text ed. 49.95 (ISBN 0-631-15054-4). Basil Blackwell.

Shupe, Anson D., Jr. Six Perspectives on New Religions: A Case Study Approach. LC 81-9464. (Studies in Religion & Society: Vol. 1). 246p. 1981. 49.95x (ISBN 0-88946-983-0). E Mellen.

Sire, James W. Scripture Twisting: Twenty Ways the Cults Misread the Bible. LC 80-19309. 216p. (Orig.). 1980. pap. 6.95 (ISBN 0-87784-611-1). Inter-Varsity.

Stankes, M. Thomas. Confronting Cults, Old & New. pap. 6.95 (ISBN 0-317-12202-9). AMG Pubs.

Stark, Rodney, ed. Religious Movements: Genesis, Exodus, & Numbers. LC 85-9539. (Sociology of Religion Ser.). 369p. 1986. 24.95 (ISBN 0-913757-43-8, Pub by New Era Bks); pap. 12.95 (ISBN 0-913757-44-6, Pub. by New Era Bks). Paragon Hse.

Streiker, Lowell D. Cults: The Continuing Threat. 144p. 1983. pap. 3.95 (ISBN 0-687-10069-0). Abingdon.

Verdier, Paul A. Brainwashing & the Cults. 3.00 (ISBN 0-87980-357-6). Borden.

Wallis, Roy. The Elementary Forms of the New Religious Life. LC 83-11092. (International Library of Sociology). 171p. 1984. 26.95x (ISBN 0-7100-9890-1). Methuen Inc.

Whalen, William J. Strange Gods: Contemporary Religious Cults in America. LC 80-81451. 1981. pap. 4.95 (ISBN 0-87973-666-6, 666). Our Sunday Visitor.
Williams, J. L. Victor Paul Wierwille & the Way International. LC 79-22007. 1979. pap. 3.95 (ISBN 0-8024-9233-9). Moody.
Wooden, Kenneth, ed. The Children of Jonestown. (Paperbacks Ser.). 1980. pap. 5.95 (ISBN 0-07-071641-2). McGraw.

CULTS, MESSIANIC
see Nativistic Movements

CULTS, PROPHETISTIC
see Nativistic Movements

CULTURE AND CHRISTIANITY
see Christianity and Culture

CULTURE AND RELIGION
see Religion and Culture

CULTUS
see also Emperor Worship; Kings and Rulers (In Religion, Folk-Lore, Etc.); Liturgics; Ritual; Saints–Cultus; Shrines
also subdivision Cultus under names of individual saints, e.g. Mary, Virgin–Cultus
Di Nola, Alfonso, ed. Prayers of Man. 1960. 27.95 (ISBN 0-8392-1152-X). Astor-Honor.
Durkheim, Emile. Elementary Forms of the Religious Life. Swain, Joseph W., tr. 1965. pap. text ed. 14.95 (ISBN 0-02-908010-X). Free Pr.
Kaihong. The Cult Phenomenon: Its Recognition, Evaluation & Control. 100p. (Orig.). 1987. pap. text ed. 19.00. Kaihong.
Parrinder, Geoffrey. Worship in the World's Religions. 2nd ed. (Quality Paperback: No. 316). 239p. 1976. pap. 4.95 (ISBN 0-8226-0316-0). Littlefield.
Simon, Pierre J. & Simon-Barouh, Ida. Hau Bong: Un Culte Vietnamien De Possession Transplante En France. (Cahiers De L'homme, Nouvelle Serie: No. 13). (Illus.). 1973. pap. 9.20x (ISBN 90-2797-185-4). Mouton.
Willetts, R. F. Cretan Cults & Festivals. LC 79-16739. 1980. Repr. of 1962 ed. lib. bdg. 32.50x (ISBN 0-313-22050-6, WICU). Greenwood.

CULTUS, DISPARITY OF
see Marriage, Mixed

CULTUS, EGYPTIAN
Vidman, Ladislav. Isis und Sarapis bei den Griechen und Roemern: Epigraphische Studien zur Verbreitung und zu den Traegern des aegyptischen Kultes. (Religionsgeschichtliche Versuche und Vorarbeiten, No. 29). (Ger). 1970. 26.00x (ISBN 3-11-006392-1). De Gruyter.

CULTUS, GREEK
see also Delphian Oracle; Eleusinian Mysteries; Oracles
Anderson, Florence M. Religious Cults Associated with the Amazons. LC 73-158253. Repr. of 1912 ed. 16.00 (ISBN 0-404-00749-X). AMS Pr.
Cook, Arthur B. Zeus: A Study of Ancient Religion, 2 vols. Incl. Vol. 1. Zeus, God of the Bright Sky. LC 64-25839. (Illus.). 885p. Repr. of 1914 ed. 50.00x (ISBN 0-8196-0148-9); Vol. 2. Zeus, God of the Dark Sky: Thunder & Lightning, 2 pts. LC 64-25839. Repr. of 1925 ed. 100.00xset (ISBN 0-8196-0156-X); Vol. 2, Pt. 1. Text & Notes. xliii, 858p; Vol. 2, Pt. 2. Appendixes & Index. (Illus.). 539p. Biblo.
Edelstein, Emma J. & Edelstein, Ludwig. Asclepius: A Collection & Interpretation of the Testimonies, 2 vols. in 1. facsimile ed. LC 75-10635. (Ancient Religion & Mythology Ser.). (Eng. & Gr.). 1976. Repr. of 1945 ed. 57.50x (ISBN 0-405-07009-8). Ayer Co Pubs.
Farnell, Lewis R. The Cults of the Greek States, 5 vols. Incl. Vol. 1. Cronos, Zeus, Hera, Athena. 50.00 (ISBN 0-89241-029-9); Vol. 2. Artemis, Aphrodite. 50.00 (ISBN 0-89241-030-2); Vol. 3. Cults of the Mother of the Gods, Raeh, Cybele. 50.00 (ISBN 0-89241-031-0); Vol. 4. Poseidon, Apollo. 60.00 (ISBN 0-89241-032-9); Vol. 5. Hermes, Dionysos, Hestia Hephaistos, Ares, the Minor Cults. 60.00 (ISBN 0-89241-033-7). (Illus.). 1977. Repr. 250.00x set (ISBN 0-89241-049-3). Caratzas.
Hamilton, Edith. Greek Way. (YA) 1948. 19.95 (ISBN 0-393-04162-X). Norton.
--The Greek Way. 1983. pap. 3.95 (ISBN 0-393-00230-6). Norton.
Harrison, Jane E. Prolegomena to the Study of Greek Religion. facsimile ed. LC 75-10639. (Ancient Religion & Mythology Ser.). (Illus.). 1976. Repr. of 1922 ed. 57.50x (ISBN 0-405-07018-7). Ayer Co Pubs.

CULTUS, HINDU
see also Mandala
Obeyesekere, Gananath. Medusa's Hair: An Essay on Personal Symbols & Religious Experiences. LC 80-27372. (Illus.). 252p. 1981. lib. bdg. 22.50x (ISBN 0-226-61600-2). U of Chicago Pr.
Sarkar, Benoy K. Folk-Element in Hindu Culture: A Contribution to Socio-Religious Studies in Hindu Folk Institutions. LC 72-907790. 332p. 1972. Repr. of 1917 ed. 24.00 (ISBN 0-89684-387-4). Orient Bk Dist.

CULTUS, JEWISH
see also Ark of the Covenant; Jews–Liturgy and Ritual; Judaism; Tabernacle
Bailey, Cyril. Phases in the Religion of Ancient Rome. LC 75-114460. 340p. 1972. Repr. of 1932 ed. lib. bdg. 22.50x (ISBN 0-8371-4759-X, BARA). Greenwood.
Vaughan, P. H. Meaning of Bama in the Old Testament. LC 73-89004. (Society for Old Testament Study Monographs: No. 3). (Illus.). 96p. 1974. 29.95 (ISBN 0-521-20425-9). Cambridge U Pr.

CULTUS, SEMITIC
Hooke, S. H. The Origins of Early Semitic Ritual. (British Academy, London, Schweich Lectures on Biblical Archeology Series, 1935). pap. 19.00 (ISBN 0-8115-1277-0). Kraus Repr.

CULTUS, ROMAN
Burriss, Eli E. Taboo, Magic, Spirits: A Study of Primitive Elements in Roman Religion. LC 72-114489. x, 250p. Repr. of 1931 ed. lib. bdg. 22.50x (ISBN 0-8371-4724-7, BUTA). Greenwood.
Scott, Kenneth. The Imperial Cult Under the Flavians. facsimile ed. LC 75-10655. (Ancient Religion & Mythology Ser.). 1976. Repr. of 1936 ed. 17.00x (ISBN 0-405-07263-5). Ayer Co Pubs.
Taylor, Lily R. The Divinity of the Roman Emperor. LC 75-7348. (Roman History Ser.). (Illus.). 1975. Repr. 29.00x (ISBN 0-405-07068-3). Ayer Co Pubs.
Weinstock, Stefan. Divus Julius. 1971. 74.00x (ISBN 0-19-814287-0). Oxford U Pr.

CUMBERLAND PRESBYTERIAN CHURCH IN TEXAS
Brackenridge, R. Douglas. Voice in the Wilderness: A History of the Cumberland Presbyterian Church in Texas. LC 68-20136. (Illus.). 192p. 1968. 4.00 (ISBN 0-911536-03-5). Trinity U Pr.

CURE OF SOULS
see Pastoral Counseling; Pastoral Theology

CURSING AND BLESSING
see Blessing and Cursing

CUTHBERT, SAINT
Bede the Venerable. Ecclesiastical History of the English Nation & Other Writings. Stevens, John, tr. 1978. Repr. of 1910 ed. 12.95x (ISBN 0-460-00479-4, Evman). Biblio Dist.
Colgrave, Bertram, ed. Two Lives of Saint Cuthbert. 388p. 1985. 44.50 (ISBN 0-521-30925-5); pap. 16.95 (ISBN 0-521-31385-6). Cambridge U Pr.
Forbes-Leith, W., tr. from Latin. Life of Saint Cuthbert. pap. 6.95 (ISBN 0-317-52092-X). Eastern Orthodox.

CYNEWULF
Anderson, Earl R. Cynewulf: Structure, Style, & Theme in His Poetry. LC 81-65464. 248p. 1983. 32.50 (ISBN 0-8386-3091-X). Fairleigh Dickinson.
Cynewulf. Christ of Cynewulf: A Poem in Three Parts, the Advent, the Ascension, & the Last Judgment. facsimile ed. Cook, Albert S., ed. LC 74-114906. (Select Bibliographies Reprint Ser). 1900. 25.50 (ISBN 0-8369-5310-X). Ayer Co Pubs.
Das, S. K. Cynewulf & the Cynewulf Canon. 59.95 (ISBN 0-87968-987-0). Gordon Pr.
Das Satyendra Kimar. Cynewulf & the Cynewulf Canon. LC 73-17006. 1942. lib. bdg. 27.50 (ISBN 0-8414-7701-9). Folcroft.
Holt, Lucius H. Elene of Cynewulf. LC 75-11897. (Yale Studies in English Ser: Vol. 21). 1904. lib. bdg. 12.50 (ISBN 0-8414-4851-5). Folcroft.
Holt, Lucius H., ed. The Elene of Cynewulf. 1904. 20.00 (ISBN 0-8274-2235-0). R West.
Kennedy, C. W., tr. Cynewulf's Poems. 11.25 (ISBN 0-8446-1143-3). Peter Smith.
Schaar, Claes. Critical Studies in Cynewulf Group. LC 67-30824. (Beowulf & the Literature of the Anglo Saxons Ser., No. 2). 1969. Repr. of 1949 ed. lib. bdg. 75.00x (ISBN 0-8383-0740-X). Haskell.
Simons, Richard. Cynewulfs Wortshatz. 1899. 65.00 (ISBN 0-8274-2126-5). R West.
Sisam, Kenneth. Cynewulf & His Poetry. LC 75-1103. Repr. of 1933 ed. lib. bdg. 12.50 (ISBN 0-8414-7838-4). Folcroft.
Smithson, George A. Old English Christian Epic. LC 75-128192. 128p. 1971. Repr. of 1910 ed. 12.50x (ISBN 0-87753-050-5). Phaeton.

CYPRIANUS, SAINT, BP. OF CARTHAGE
Faulkner, John A. Cyprian: The Churchman. 1977. lib. bdg. 59.95 (ISBN 0-8490-1698-3). Gordon Pr.
Laurance, John D. Priest as Type of Christ: The Leader of the Eucharist in Salvation History According to Cyprian of Carthage. LC 84-47539. (American University Studies VII (Theology & Religion): Vol. 5). 245p. (Orig.). 1984. 37.25 (ISBN 0-8204-0117-X). P Lang Pubs.
Pontus, St. Life of St. Cyprian. pap. 1.50 (ISBN 0-686-05651-5). Eastern Orthodox.

CYRILLUS, SAINT, OF THESSALONICA, 827-869
The Apostles of the Slavs. 56p. 1985. pap. 3.95 (ISBN 1-55586-972-6). US Catholic.
Dvornik, Francis. Legendes de Constantin et de methode vues de Byzance. (Russian Ser: No. 12). 1969. Repr. of 1933 ed. 35.00 (ISBN 0-87569-009-2). Academic Intl.

D

DAHOMEYANS
Herskovits, Melville J. & Herskovits, Frances S. Outline of Dahomean Religious Belief. LC 34-5259. (American Anthro. Association Memoirs). 1933. 11.00 (ISBN 0-527-00540-1). Kraus Repr.

DAILY READINGS (SPIRITUAL EXERCISES)
see Devotional Calendars

DAILY VACATION BIBLE SCHOOLS
see Vacation Schools, Religious

DAMIEN DE VEUSTER, JOSEPH (FATHER DAMIEN), 1840-1889
Caudwell, Irene. Damien of Molokai, Eighteen Forty to Eighteen Eighty-Nine. 1979. Repr. of 1932 ed. lib. bdg. 20.00 (ISBN 0-8492-4041-7). R West.
Christopher, Kenneth. Damien & the Island of Sickness: A Story About Damien. new ed. (Stories About Christian Heroes Ser.). (Illus.). 1979. pap. 1.95 (ISBN 0-86683-768-X, HarpR). Har-Row.
Daughters of St Paul. Father Damien of Molokai. 1979. pap. 0.95 (ISBN 0-8198-0640-4). Dghtrs St Paul.
Daws, Gavan. Holy Man: Father Damien of Molokai. 328p. 1984. pap. 8.95 (ISBN 0-8248-0920-3). UH Pr.
Dutton, Charles J. The Samaritans of Molokai. facsimile ed. (Select Bibliographies Reprint Ser). Repr. of 1932 ed. 23.50 (ISBN 0-8369-5733-4). Ayer Co Pubs.
Englebert, Omer. Hero of Molokai. (Illus.). 1977. 4.00 (ISBN 0-8198-0057-0); pap. 3.00 (ISBN 0-8198-0058-9). Dghtrs St Paul.
Farrow, John. Damien the Leper. 1954. pap. 3.95 (ISBN 0-385-02918-7, D3, Im). Doubleday.
Neimark, Anne E. Damien, the Leper Priest. LC 80-15141. 160p. 1980. 11.25 (ISBN 0-688-22246-3); PLB 11.88 (ISBN 0-688-32246-8). Morrow.

DANCE OF DEATH
Kurtz, L. P. The Dance of Death & the Macabre Spirit in European Literature. 79.95 (ISBN 0-87968-188-8). Gordon Pr.
Warren, F., ed. Dance of Death. (EETS, OS: No. 181). Repr. of 1931 ed. 10.00 (ISBN 0-527-00178-3). Kraus Repr.
Warthin, Alfred S. The Physician of the Dance of Death: A Historical Study of the Evolution of the Dance of Death Mythus in Art. Kastenbaum, Robert, ed. LC 76-19592. (Death & Dying Ser.). (Illus.). 1977. Repr. of 1931 ed. lib. bdg. 17.00x (ISBN 0-405-09587-2). Ayer Co Pubs.
Whyte, Florence. The Dance of Death in Spain & Catalonia. Kastenbaum, Robert, ed. LC 76-19594. (Death & Dying Ser.). 1977. Repr. of 1931 ed. lib. bdg. 19.00x (ISBN 0-405-09588-0). Ayer Co Pubs.
--The Dance of Death in Spain & Catalonia. 1977. lib. bdg. 69.95 (ISBN 0-8490-1699-1). Gordon Pr.

DANCING (IN RELIGION, FOLK-LORE, ETC.)
see also Indians of North America–Dances
Adams, Doug. Appropriating Australian Folk Dances into Sacred Dance. 1987. pap. 3.00 (ISBN 0-941500-45-4). Sharing Co.
--Congregational Dancing in Christian Worship. rev. ed. 1984. 4.95 (ISBN 0-941500-02-0). Sharing Co.
--Involving the People in Dancing Worship: Historic & Contemporary Patterns. 1975. 2.00 (ISBN 0-941500-11-X). Sharing Co.
Adams, Doug & Rock, Judith. Biblical Criteria in Modern Dance: Modern Dance As a Prophetic Form. 1979. 2.50 (ISBN 0-941500-01-2). Sharing Co.
Backman, Eugene L. Religious Dances in the Christian & in Popular Medicine. Classen, E., ed. LC 77-8069. 1977. Repr. of 1952 ed. 32.00x (ISBN 0-8371-9678-7, BARD). Greenwood.
Bellamak, Lu. Non-Judgemental Sacred Dance: Simple Ways to Pray Through Dance. 1984. 3.00 (ISBN 0-941500-14-4). Sharing Co.
Blogg, Martin. Dance & the Christian Faith. (Illus.). 283p. 1987. pap. 17.95 (ISBN 0-340-35173-X, Pub. by Hodder & Stoughton UK). David & Charles.
Buck, Dorothy. The Dance of Life. (Patterns of World Spirituality Ser.). 160p. (Orig.). 1987. pap. 8.95 (ISBN 0-913757-52-7, Pub. by New Era Bks). Paragon Hse.
Deitering, Carolyn. The Liturgy As Dance & the Liturgical Dancer. (Illus.). 144p. 1984. pap. 8.95 (ISBN 0-8245-0654-5). Crossroad NY.
De Sola, Carla. The Spirit Moves: A Handbook of Dance & Prayer. Adams, Doug, ed. & intro. by. LC 77-89743. (Illus.). 152p. 1986. pap. 9.95 (ISBN 0-941500-38-1). Sharing Co.
Fallon, Dennis J. & Wolbers, Mary J., eds. Religion & Dance. LC 83-189712. (Focus on Dance Ser.: No. 10). pap. 24.00 (2029558). Bks Demand UMI.
Fantin, Mario. Mani Rimdu-Nepal: The Buddhist Dance Drama of Tengpoche (1976) (Illus.). 1978. 40.00. Heinman.
Fisher, Constance. Dancing Festivals of the Church Year. Adams, Doug, ed. (Illus.). 120p. (Orig.). 1986. pap. 8.95 (ISBN 0-941500-42-X). Sharing Co.
Fisher, Constance & Adams, Doug. Dancing with Early Christians. (Illus.). 176p. 1983. pap. 6.95 (ISBN 0-941500-30-6). Sharing Co.
Fisher, Constance L. Music & Dance: In the Worship Program of the Church. (Orig.). 1981. pap. 2.50 (ISBN 0-941500-20-9). Sharing Co.
Gagne, Ronald, et al. Introducing Dance in Christian Worship. (Illus.). 184p. 1984. pap. 7.95 (ISBN 0-912405-04-X). Pastoral Pr.
Hoeckmann, Olaf. Dance in Hebrew Poetry. Adams, Doug, ed. 1987. pap. 3.00 (ISBN 0-941500-44-6). Sharing Co.
Huff, Joan. Celebrating Pentecost Through Dance. Adams, Doug, ed. (Orig.). 1986. pap. 3.00 (ISBN 0-941500-41-1). Sharing Co.
Kirk, Martha A. Mexican & Native American Dances in Christian Worship & Education. Adams, Doug, ed. (Orig.). 1981. pap. 3.00 (ISBN 0-941500-22-5). Sharing Co.
MacLeod, Marian B. Dancing Through Pentecost: Dance Language for Worship from Pentecost to Thanksgiving. Adams, Doug, ed. (Orig.). 1981. pap. 3.00 (ISBN 0-941500-23-3). Sharing Co.
Miller, James. Measures of Wisdom: The Cosmic Dance in Classical & Christian Antiquity. 672p. 1986. 60.00 (ISBN 0-8020-2553-6). U of Toronto Pr.
Nebesky-Wojkowitz, Rene De. Tibetan Religious Dances. Furer-Haimendorf, Christoph Von, ed. (Religion & Society: No. 2). 1976. text ed. 36.00x (ISBN 90-279-7621-X). Mouton.
Neilan, Ruth E. American Military Movement Relating Sacred Dance. Adams, Doug, ed. & intro. by. (Orig.). 1985. pap. 3.00 (ISBN 0-941500-37-3). Sharing Co.
Reed, Carlynn. And We Have Danced: The History of the Sacred Dance Guild, 1958-1978. Adams, Doug, ed. 1978. 5.95 (ISBN 0-941500-00-4). Sharing Co.
Roberts, Debbie. Rejoice: A Biblical Study of the Dance. 98p. 1982. pap. 3.95 (ISBN 0-938612-02-6). Revival Press.
Rock, Judith. Theology in the Shape of Dance: Using Dance in Worship & Theological Process. 1977. 2.50 (ISBN 0-941500-16-0). Sharing Co.
Sautter, Cynthia D. Irish Dance & Spirituality: Relating Folkdance & Faith. Adams, Doug, ed. (Orig.). 1986. pap. text ed. 3.00 (ISBN 0-941500-39-X). Sharing Co.
Seaton, Linda K. Scriptural Choreography: Biblical Dance Forms in Shaping Contemporary Worship. 1979. 2.50 (ISBN 0-941500-15-2). Sharing Co.
Stone, Martha. At the Sign of Midnight: The Concheros Dance Cult of Mexico. LC 73-76303. (Illus.). 262p. 1975. pap. 7.45x (ISBN 0-8165-0507-1). U of Ariz Pr.
Taussig, Hal. Dancing the New Testament: A Guide to Texts. 1977. 2.00 (ISBN 0-941500-06-3). Sharing Co.
--The Lady of the Dance: A Movement Approach to the Biblical Figures of Wisdom in Worship & Education. (Orig.). 1981. pap. 2.50 (ISBN 0-941500-24-1). Sharing Co.
--New Categories for Dancing: The Old Testament. (Orig.). 1981. pap. 2.50 (ISBN 0-941500-25-X). Sharing Co.
Taylor, Margaret. Considerations for Starting & Stretching a Sacred Dance Choir. 1978. 2.75 (ISBN 0-941500-03-9). Sharing Co.
Taylor, Margaret F. Look up & Live: Dance in Prayer & Meditation. Adams, Doug, ed. 96p. 1980. 4.95 (ISBN 0-941500-12-8). Sharing Co.
--A Time to Dance: Symbolic Movement in Worship. Adams, Doug, ed. 192p. 1980. 5.95 (ISBN 0-941500-17-9). Sharing Co.
Trolin, Clifford. Movement in Prayer in a Hasidic Mode. 1979. 2.50 (ISBN 0-941500-13-6). Sharing Co.
Van Zile, Judy. The Japanese Bon Dance in Hawaii. (Illus.). 96p. 1982. pap. 5.95 (ISBN 0-916630-27-7). Pr Pacifica.

Winton-Henry, Cynthia. Dancing God's People into the Year Two Thousand: A Critical Look at Dance Performance in the Church. Adams, Doug, ed. & intro. by. (Orig.). 1985. pap. 3.00 (ISBN 0-941500-36-5). Sharing Co.

DANIEL, THE PROPHET

Anderson, R. A. Unfolding Daniel. LC 75-16526. (Dimension Ser.). 192p. 1975. pap. 6.95 (ISBN 0-8163-0180-8, 21390-0). Pacific Pr Pub Assn.

Carballosa, Evis L. Daniel y el Reino Mesianico. Orig. Title: Daniel & the Messianic Kingdom. 320p. 1979. pap. 7.95 (ISBN 0-8254-1101-7). Kregel.

Connelly, Douglas. Daniel: Spiritual Living in a Secular World. (LifeBuilder Bible Studies). 64p. (Orig.). 1986. pap. 2.95 (ISBN 0-8308-1031-5). Inter-Varsity.

DeHaan, M. R. Daniel the Prophet. 340p. 1983. pap. 8.95 (ISBN 0-310-23321-6). Zondervan.

Gammie, John G. Daniel. (Preaching Guides Ser.). 116p. 1983. pap. 5.95 (ISBN 0-8042-3224-5). John Knox.

McClain, Alva J. Daniel's Prophecy of the Seventy Weeks. pap. 3.95 (ISBN 0-310-29011-2, 10177P). Zondervan.

Pusey, Edward B. Daniel the Prophet. 1978. 19.50 (ISBN 0-86524-103-1, 2701). Klock & Klock.

DANIEL, THE PROPHET–DRAMA

Greenberg, Noah & Auden, W. H., eds. Play of Daniel, a Thirteenth-Century Musical Drama. (Illus.). 1959. pap. 5.95 (ISBN 0-19-385195-4). Oxford U Pr.

DANIEL, THE PROPHET–JUVENILE LITERATURE

Barrett, Ethel. Daniel. LC 79-65230. (Bible Biography Ser.). 128p. 1979. pap. 1.95 (ISBN 0-8307-0761-1, 5810306). Regal.

Diamond, Lucy. Story of Daniel. (Ladybird Ser). (Illus.). 1958. bds. 2.50 (ISBN 0-87508-866-X). Chr Lit.

Heath, Lou. Daniel: Faithful Captive. (Biblearn Ser.). (Illus.). 1977. bds. 5.95 (ISBN 0-8054-4231-6, 4242-31). Broadman.

Latourette, Jane & Mathews. Daniel in the Lions' Den. (Arch Bks.: Set 3). 1966. laminated bdg. 0.99 (ISBN 0-570-06018-4, 59-1127). Concordia.

Scheck, Joann. Three Men Who Walked in Fire. (Arch Bks: Set 4). 1967. laminated bdg. 0.99 (ISBN 0-570-06026-5, 59-1137). Concordia.

Shimoni, S. Legends of Daniel. (Biblical Ser.). (Illus.). 1975. 3.00 (ISBN 0-914080-14-8). Shulsinger Sales.

Storr, Catherine, as told by. The Trials of Daniel. (People of the Bible Ser.). (Illus.). 32p. 1985. PLB 10.65 (ISBN 0-8172-2040-2). Raintree Pubs.

DANISH MYTHOLOGY

see Mythology, Norse

DANSE MACABRE

see Dance of Death

DANTE ALIGHIERI, 1265-1321

Barnes, C. L. Parallels in Dante & Milton. LC 74-3180. 1917. lib. bdg. 12.50 (ISBN 0-8414-9926-8). Folcroft.

Charity, Alan. Events & Their Afterlife: The Dialectics of Christian Typology in the Bible & Dante. 300p. Date not set. pap. price not set (ISBN 0-521-34923-0). Cambridge U Pr.

Collins, James. Pilgrim in Love: An Introduction to Dante & His Spirituality. 312p. 1984. 12.95 (ISBN 0-8294-0453-8). Loyola.

Fisher, Lizette A. Mystic Vision in the Grail Legend & in the Divine Comedy. LC 79-168029. Repr. of 1917 ed. 16.50 (ISBN 0-404-02389-4). AMS Pr.

Gardner, E. G. Dante & the Mystics: A Study of the Mystical Aspect of the Divina Commedia. LC 68-24952. (Studies in Italian Literature, No. 46). 1969. Repr. of 1913 ed. lib. bdg. 49.95x (ISBN 0-8383-0271-8). Haskell.

Gladden, Washington. Witnesses of the Light. facs. ed. LC 77-84307. (Essay Index Reprint Ser). 1903. 17.75 (ISBN 0-8369-1081-8). Ayer Co Pubs.

Gurteen, S. Humphreys. Epic of the Fall of Man. LC 65-15879. (Studies in Comparative Literature, No. 35). 1969. Repr. of 1896 ed. lib. bdg. 75.00x (ISBN 0-8383-0561-X). Haskell.

Harris, W. T. The Mythology of Plato & Dante & the Future Life. (The Essential Library of the Great Philosophers). (Illus.). 107p. 1983. Repr. of 1896 ed. 71.85 (ISBN 0-89901-091-1). Found Class Reprints.

Herford, C. H. Dante & Milton. 1924. lib. bdg. 10.00 (ISBN 0-8414-5044-7). Folcroft.

Hillis, Newell D. Great Men As Prophets of a New Era. facs. ed. LC 68-16939. (Essay Index Reprint Ser). 1968. Repr. of 1922 ed. 15.00 (ISBN 0-8369-0541-5). Ayer Co Pubs.

Holloway, Julia B. THe Pilgrim & the Book: A Study of Dante, Langland & Chaucer. (American University Studies IV- English Language & Literature: Vol. 42). 343p. 1987. text ed. 30.75 (ISBN 0-8204-0345-8). P Lang Pubs.

Kennard, Joseph S. Friar in Fiction, Sincerity in Art, & Other Essays. facs. ed. LC 68-20313. (Essay Index Reprint Ser). 1923. 20.00 (ISBN 0-8369-0588-1). Ayer Co Pubs.

Kirkpatrick, R. Dante's Paradiso & the Limitations of Modern Criticism. LC 77-80839. 1978. 39.50 (ISBN 0-521-21785-7). Cambridge U Pr.

Moore, Edward. Studies in Dante, First Series: Scriptures & Classical Authors in Dante. LC 68-57627. (Illus.). 1969. Repr. of 1896 ed. lib. bdg. 22.50x (ISBN 0-8371-0909-4, MODF). Greenwood.

--Studies in Dante, Second Series: Miscellaneous Essays. LC 68-57628. (Illus.). 1969. Repr. of 1899 ed. lib. bdg. 22.50x (ISBN 0-8371-0908-6, MOSD). Greenwood.

--Studies in Dante, Third Series: Miscellaneous Essays. LC 68-57629. (Illus.). 1969. Repr. of 1903 ed. lib. bdg. 22.50x (ISBN 0-8371-0917-5, MODT). Greenwood.

Mordell, Albert. Dante & Other Waning Classics. LC 68-8219. 1969. Repr. of 1915 ed. 18.50x (ISBN 0-8046-0322-7, Pub. by Kennikat). Assoc Faculty Pr.

Wicksteed, Philip H. Dante & Aquinas. LC 79-153489. (Studies in Dante, No. 9). 1971. Repr. of 1913 ed. lib. bdg. 49.95x (ISBN 0-8383-1240-3). Haskell.

DARK AGES

see Middle Ages

DARRELL, JOHN

Rickert, Corinne H. Case of John Darrell: Minister & Exorcist. LC 62-62828. (University of Florida Humanities Monographs: No. 9). 1962. pap. 3.50 (ISBN 0-8130-0197-8). U Presses Fla.

DATE ETIQUETTE

see Dating (Social Customs)

DATING (SOCIAL CUSTOMS)

Butler, John. Christian Ways to Date, Go Steady, & Break up. (Mini Bible Studies). (Illus.). 1978. pap. 2.95 (ISBN 0-87239-986-9, 39949). Standard Pub.

Christie, Les. Dating & Waiting: A Chrisitan View of Love, Sex, & Dating. LC 83-1232. (Illus.). 80p. (Orig.). 1983. pap. 2.95 (ISBN 0-87239-643-6, 39972). Standard Pub.

Daniel, R. P. Dating, Marriage, Sex & Divorce. 75p. pap. 3.95 (ISBN 0-88172-147-6). Believers Bkshelf.

Diorio, MaryAnn L. Dating Etiquette for Christian Teens. (Illus.). 48p. (Orig.). 1984. pap. 3.95 (ISBN 0-930037-00-6). Daystar Comm.

Dockrey, Karen. Dating: Making Your Own Choices. LC 86-30985. (Orig.). (YA) 1987. pap. 4.95 (ISBN 0-8054-5345-8). Broadman.

Earles, Brent D. The Dating Maze. pap. 3.95 (ISBN 0-8010-3424-8). Baker Bk.

Hartley, Fred. Update. 160p. 1982. pap. 2.95 (ISBN 0-8007-8431-6, Spire Bks). Revell.

Huggett, Joyce. Dating, Sex & Friendship. LC 85-19734. 204p. 1985. pap. 5.95 (ISBN 0-87784-406-2). Inter-Varsity.

Laurie, Greg. God's Design for Christian Dating. 2nd ed. LC 82-83836. 96p. (YA) 1983. pap. 2.25 (ISBN 0-89081-373-6). Harvest Hse.

Pugh, Nathanael. Dating Tips. Wallace, Mary H., ed. (Illus.). 120p. 1983. pap. 4.95 (ISBN 0-912315-00-8). Word Aflame.

Rinehart, Stacy & Rinehart, Paula. Choices: Finding God's Way in Dating, Sex, Singleness & Marriage. LC 82-62071. 170p. 1983. pap. 3.95 (ISBN 0-89109-494-6). NavPress.

Scalf, Cherie & Waters, Kenneth. Dating & Relating. 160p. 1982. pap. 7.95 (ISBN 0-8499-2890-7). Word Bks.

Short, Ray E. Sex, Dating, & Love: Seventy-Seven Questions Most Often Asked. LC 83-72122. 144p. (Orig.). 1984. pap. 3.95 (ISBN 0-8066-2066-8, 10-5648). Augsburg.

Wright, Norman & Inmon, Marvin. Guidebook to Dating, Waiting & Choosing a Mate. LC 78-26913. 1978. pap. 4.95 (ISBN 0-89081-150-4). Harvest Hse.

DAUGHTERS OF SAINT PAUL

Daughters of St. Paul. Communicators for Christ. 1973. 5.00 (ISBN 0-8198-0249-2). Dghtrs St Paul.

--Woman of Faith. (Illus.). 1965. 3.00 (ISBN 0-8198-0179-8). Dghtrs St Paul.

DAVID, KING OF ISRAEL

Alexander, Joyce & Alexander, Dorsey, illus. David: Psalm Twenty-Four. (Illus., Calligraphy & Illus.). 1970. pap. 5.00 (ISBN 0-912020-17-2). Turtles Quill.

Andre, G. David, the Man after God's Own Heart. (Let's Discuss It Ser.). pap. 2.50 (ISBN 0-88172-134-4). Believers Bkshelf.

Brueggemann, Walter. David's Truth: In Israel's Imagination & Memory. LC 85-47717. 128p. 1985. pap. 5.95 (ISBN 0-8006-1865-3). Fortress.

Castleman, Robbie. David: Man after God's Own Heart, 2 vols. (Fisherman Bible Studyguide). 1981. saddle stitched 2.95 ea. Vol. 1, 70p (ISBN 0-87788-164-2). Vol. 2, 63p (ISBN 0-87788-165-0). Shaw Pubs.

Corvin, R. O. David & His Mighty Men. facs. ed. LC 74-136646. (Biography Index Reprint Ser.). 1950. 17.00 (ISBN 0-8369-8041-7). Ayer Co Pubs.

David the Anointed: Leader's Guide. (Orig.). 1984. pap. text ed. 3.95 (ISBN 0-934688-10-9). Great Comm Pubns.

Dorr, Roberta. David & Bathsheba. 1982. pap. 4.95 (ISBN 0-8423-0618-8). Tyndale.

Hollyer, Belinda. David & Goliath. LC 84-50452. (Bible Stories Ser.). (Illus.). 24p. 1984. 5.45 (ISBN 0-382-06940-4); PLB 6.96 (ISBN 0-382-06791-6). Silver.

Keller, W. Phillip. David I: The Time of Saul's Tyranny. 256p. 1985. 10.95 (ISBN 0-8499-0470-6, 0470-6). Word Bks.

--David II: The Shepherd King. 224p. 1986. 11.95 (ISBN 0-8499-0559-1). Word Bks.

Krummacher, Frederick W. David, King of Israel. 548p. 1983. lib. bdg. 20.50 (ISBN 0-86524-142-2, 8404). Klock & Klock.

Lindsay, Gordon. David Comes into the Kingdom. (Old Testament Ser.). 1.25 (ISBN 0-89985-142-8). Christ Nations.

--David Reaping the Whirlwind. (Old Testament Ser.). 1.25 (ISBN 0-89985-143-6). Christ Nations.

--The Early Life of David. (Old Testament Ser.). 1.25 (ISBN 0-89985-141-X). Christ Nations.

--The Last Days of David & His Contemporaries. (Old Testament Ser.). 1.25 (ISBN 0-89985-144-4). Christ Nations.

McCord, David. A Loser, a Winner, & a Wise-Guy: Saul, David & Solomon. LC 79-67438. 96p. 1980. pap. 2.25 (ISBN 0-87239-380-1, 40084). Standard Pub.

Meyer, F. B. David. 1970. pap. 4.50 (ISBN 0-87508-342-0). Chr Lit.

Petersen, Mark E. Three Kings of Israel. LC 80-36697. 179p. 1980. 6.95 (ISBN 0-87747-829-5). Deseret Bk.

Pink, Arthur W. The Life of David, 2 vols. in one. (Giant Summit Ser.). 768p. 1981. pap. 14.95 (ISBN 0-8010-7061-9). Baker Bk.

--Life of David. 14.95 (ISBN 0-685-19837-5). Reiner.

Redpath, Alan. Making of a Man of God: Studies in the Life of David. 256p. 1962. 12.95 (ISBN 0-8007-0189-5). Revell.

Small, Dwight H. No Rival Love. 201p. (Orig.). 1985. pap. 4.95 (ISBN 0-87508-495-8). Chr Lit.

Spurgen, C. H. Treasury of David, 7 vols. 1983. Set. 75.00 (ISBN 0-686-40818-7). Pilgrim Pubns.

Weisfeld, Israel H., ed. David the King. LC 83-62421. 290p. 20.00x (ISBN 0-8197-0493-8). Bloch.

Young, H. Edwin. David: After God's Own Heart. (Orig.). 1984. pap. 4.25 (ISBN 0-8054-1531-9). Broadman.

DAVID, KING OF ISRAEL–JUVENILE LITERATURE

Barrett, Ethel. David: The Giant-Slayer. LC 82-80009. (Bible Biography Ser.). 128p. 1982. pap. 2.50 (ISBN 0-8307-0770-0, 5811007). Regal.

Brin, Ruth F. David & Goliath. (Foreign Lands Bks). (Illus.). 32p. 1977. PLB 5.95 (ISBN 0-8225-0365-4). Lerner Pubns.

Daughters of St. Paul. David. 0.75 (ISBN 0-8198-1800-3). Dghtrs St Paul.

Freehof, Lillian S. Stories of King David. (Illus.). 1952. 5.95 (ISBN 0-8276-0162-X, 263). Jewish Pubns.

Hollaway, Lee. David: Shepherd, Musician, & King. (BibLearn Ser.). (Illus.). 1977. bds. 5.95 (ISBN 0-8054-4230-8, 4242-30). Broadman.

McMillan, Mary. King David. (Color, Cut & Paste Ser.). (Illus.). 48p. 1987. pap. 5.95 (ISBN 0-86653-392-3). Good Apple.

Storr, Catherine, as told by. King David. (People of the Bible Ser.). (Illus.). 32p. 1985. PLB 10.65 (ISBN 0-8172-2042-9). Raintree Pubs.

Warren, Mary P. & Mathews. Boy with a Sling. LC 65-15143. (Arch Bks: Set 2). 1965. pap. 0.99 (ISBN 0-570-06012-5, 59-1116). Concordia.

DAY, DOROTHY, 1897-1980

Day, Dorothy. The Long Loneliness: An Autobiography. LC 81-4727. (Illus.). 1981. pap. 7.95 (ISBN 0-06-061751-9, RD363, HarpR). Har-Row.

Miller, William D. All Is Grace: The Spirituality of Dorothy Day. LC 86-1228. 216p. 1987. 14.95 (ISBN 0-385-23429-5). Doubleday.

--Dorothy Day: A Biography. LC 81-47428. (Illus.). 1984. pap. 10.95 (ISBN 0-06-065749-9, RD 501, HarpR). Har-Row.

DAY OF ATONEMENT (JEWISH HOLIDAY

see Yom Kippur

DAY OF JUDGMENT

see Judgment Day

DAYS

see also Fasts and Feasts; Holidays; Sunday also names of special day, e.g. Christmas

Chambers, Robert, ed. Book of Days: A Miscellany of Popular Antiquities in Connection with the Calendar, Including Anecdote, Biography & History, Curiosities of Literature, & Oddities of Human Life & Character, 2 Vols. LC 67-13009. (Illus.). 1967. Repr. of 1862 ed. 125.00x (ISBN 0-8103-3002-4). Gale.

DEACONESSES

see also Deacons

Ludlow, John M. Woman's Work in the Church. LC 75-33300. 1976. Repr. of 1866 ed. 14.95 (ISBN 0-89201-007-X). Zenger Pub.

DEACONS

see also Church Officers

Barnett, James M. The Diaconate: A Full & Equal Order. 256p. (Orig.). 1981. pap. 9.95 (ISBN 0-8164-2331-8, HarpR). Har-Row.

Brockman, Norbert. Ordained to Service: A Theology of the Permanent Diaconate. 1976. 7.50 (ISBN 0-682-48561-6, University). Exposition Pr FL.

Deweese, Charles W. The Emerging Role of Deacons. LC 79-50337. 1980. pap. 3.75 (ISBN 0-8054-3512-3). Broadman.

Diaconado Permanente en los Estados Unidos: Directivas para Su Formacion y Ministerio. (Span.). 56p. 1986. pap. 4.95 (ISBN 1-55586-131-8). US Catholic.

Dresselhaus, Richard L. The Deacon & His Ministry. LC 77-73518. 1977. pap. 2.25, 2.00 for 6 or more (ISBN 0-88243-493-4, 02-0493). Gospel Pub.

Echlin, Edward P. Deacon in the Church. LC 75-158571. 1971. 4.95 (ISBN 0-8189-0213-2). Alba.

Foshee, Howard B. Now That You're a Deacon. LC 74-79488. 128p. 1975. 7.95 (ISBN 0-8054-3506-9). Broadman.

Hiebert, Waldo & Kopp, Herb. Deacons & Their Ministry. (Orig.). 1981. pap. 1.95 (ISBN 0-937364-02-9). Kindred Pr.

Johnson, L. T. The Serving Church. 2nd ed. LC 83-80609. (Enabling Ser.). (Illus.). 104p. (Orig.). 1984. pap. 5.95 (ISBN 0-935797-01-7). Harvest IL.

Kleiber, Kenneth & Lemire, Deacon H. Deacons: Permanent or Passing? 70p. 1982. 6.95 (ISBN 0-911519-02-5). Richelieu Court.

Landregan, Steve. Reflections on Deacon Spirituality. (Orig.). Date not set. pap. price not set (ISBN 1-55586-150-4). US Catholic.

Liptak, David Q. & Sheridan, Philip A. The New Code: Laity & Deacons. 128p. (Orig.). 1986. pap. 7.95 (ISBN 0-941850-20-X). Sunday Pubns.

Nelson, Martha. On Being a Deacon's Wife. LC 72-96150. 96p. 1973. 7.95 (ISBN 0-8054-3505-0). Broadman.

Nichols, Harold. The Work of the Deacon & Deaconess. (Orig.). pap. 4.95 (ISBN 0-8170-0328-2). Judson.

O'Donnell, J. D. Handbook for Deacons. 1973. pap. 3.95 (ISBN 0-89265-011-7). Randall Hse.

Permanent Deacons in the United States: Guidelines on Their Formation & Ministry. rev. ed. 60p. 1985. pap. 3.95 (ISBN 1-55586-974-2). US Catholic.

Plater, Ormonde. The Deacon in the Liturgy. (Illus.). 60p. (Orig.). 1981. pap. 6.00 (ISBN 0-9605798-0-X). Natl Ctr Diaconate.

Shaw, Russell. Permanent Deacons. rev. ed. 40p. 1986. pap. 1.95 (ISBN 1-55586-989-0). US Catholic.

Thomas, Donald F. The Deacon in a Changing Church. LC 69-16388. 1969. pap. 4.95 (ISBN 0-8170-0414-9). Judson.

Wilks, Karl G. Deacons: Servants of the Church Christ Built & Spiritual Gifts. LC 86-90143. (Bible Teaching on Church Government & Management Ser.). 66p. (Orig.). 1986. pap. 6.00 (ISBN 0-9616912-0-4). K G Wilks.

DEAD (IN RELIGION, FOLK-LORE, ETC.)

see also Ancestor Worship

Ellis, Hilda R. Road to Hell: A Study of the Conception of the Dead in Old Norse Literature. LC 68-23286. (Illus.). 1968. Repr. of 1943 ed. lib. bdg. 22.50x (ISBN 0-8371-0070-4, ELRH). Greenwood.

Frazer, James G. The Fear of the Dead in Primitive Religion, 3 vols. in one. Kastenaum, Robert, ed. LC 76-19571. (Death & Dying Ser.). 1977. Repr. of 1936 ed. lib. bdg. 57.50x (ISBN 0-405-09566-X). Ayer Co Pubs.

Hamilton, Gavin & Fernandez, David. Donde Estan los Muertes? Orig. Title: Where Are the Dead? (Span.). 64p. 1983. pap. 2.25 (ISBN 0-8254-1301-X). Kregel.

Heisler, Hermann. Our Relationship to Those Who Have Died. 1976. pap. 2.50 (ISBN 0-916786-03-X). St George Bk Serv.

DEAD, PRAYERS FOR THE

see Prayers for the Dead

DEAD SEA SCROLLS

see also Essenes; Qumran Community

Allegro, J. M. Dead Sea Scrolls. 1956. pap. 4.95 (ISBN 0-14-020376-1, Pelican). Penguin.

Allegro, John. The Dead Sea Scrolls & the Christian Myth. LC 83-63566. (Illus.). 248p. 1984. 19.95 (ISBN 0-87975-241-6). Prometheus Bks.

Baillet, Maurice, ed. Qumran Grotte Four, No. III. (Discoveries in the Judean Desert Ser.: Vol. 7). (Illus.). 1982. 140.00x (ISBN 0-19-826321-X). Oxford U Pr.

Black, Matthew. The Scrolls & Christian Origins: Studies in the Jewish Background of the New Testament. LC 83-11519. (Brown Judaic Studies). 232p. 1983. pap. 14.00 (ISBN 0-89130-639-0, 14 00 48). Scholars Pr GA.

Bogue, Robert H. The Dawn of Christianity. 1985. 15.00 (ISBN 0-533-06545-3). Vantage.

Brownlee, William H. The Midrash Pesher of Habakkuk. LC 76-30560. (Society of Biblical Literature Monograph). 220p. 1979. pap. 9.95 (ISBN 0-89130-147-X, 06 00 24). Scholars Pr GA.

Bruce, F. F. Second Thoughts on the Dead Sea Scrolls. 157p. 1986. pap. 7.95 (ISBN 0-85364-017-3, Pub. by Paternoster UK). Attic Pr.

Charlesworth, James H. The Discovery of a Dead Sea Scroll: It's Importance in the History of Jesus Research. 41p. 1985. pap. 6.00 (ISBN 0-318-18993-3, 85-1). Intl Ctr Arid & Semi-Arid.

Cross, Frank M. The Ancient Library of Qumran & Modern Biblical Studies. LC 76-29736. (The Haskell Lectures, 1956-57). (Illus.). 1976. Repr. of 1958 ed. lib. bdg. 22.50x (ISBN 0-8371-9281-1, CRAL). Greenwood.

Danielou, Jean. The Dead Sea Scrolls & Primitive Christianity. Attanasio, Salvator, tr. from Fr. LC 78-21516. 1979. Repr. of 1958 ed. lib. bdg. 22.50x (ISBN 0-313-21144-2, DADE). Greenwood.

Davies, A. Meaning of the Dead Sea Scrolls. pap. 2.95 (ISBN 0-451-62447-5, ME2097, Ment). NAL.

De Vaux, R. Archaeology & the Dead Sea Scrolls. 2nd & rev. ed. (Schweich Lectures on Biblical Archaeology). (Illus.). 142p. 1977. 13.50 (ISBN 0-85672-725-3, Pub. by British Acad). Longwood Pub Group.

De Vaux, R. & Milik, J. T. Discoveries in the Judaean Desert: Qumran Grotte 4-11, Vol. 6. (Illus.). 1977. text ed. 52.00x (ISBN 0-19-826317-1). Oxford U Pr.

Dobson Books Ltd., ed. The Sacred Bridge: Supplementary Volume. 256p. 1981. 75.00x (ISBN 0-234-77038-4, Pub. by Dobson Bks England). State Mutual Bk.

Dupont-Sommer, A. The Essene Writings from Qumran. Vermes, G., tr. 13.50 (ISBN 0-8446-2012-2). Peter Smith.

Ewing, Upton C. Prophet of the Dead Sea Scrolls. 148p. pap. 6.95 (ISBN 0-317-07628-0). Edenite.

Fitzmyer, Joseph A. The Dead Sea Scrolls: Major Publications & Tools for Study. LC 75-5987. (Society of Biblical Literature. Sources for Biblical Study Ser.). xiv, 171p. 1975. pap. 10.50 (ISBN 0-88414-053-9, 060308). Scholars Pr GA.

Garnett, Paul. Salvation & Atonement in the Qumran Scrolls. 160p. 1977. pap. 24.00x (Pub. by J C B Mohr BRD). Coronet Bks.

Gaster, Theodor H. The Dead Sea Scriptures. 2nd ed. LC 76-2840. 1976. pap. 7.95 (ISBN 0-385-08859-0, Anchor Pr). Doubleday.

Hillers, Delbert R. Micah. LC 83-48002. (Hermenaia Ser.). 192p. 1983. 17.95 (ISBN 0-8006-6012-9, 20-6012). Fortress.

Kittel, Bonnie P. The Hymns of Qumran: Translation & Commentary. Kittel, Bonnie, tr. LC 80-11616. 1981. pap. 13.50 (ISBN 0-89130-397-9, 06 01 50). Scholars Pr GA.

LaSor, William S. The Dead Sea Scrolls & the New Testament. 280p. 1972. pap. 5.95 (ISBN 0-8028-1114-0). Eerdmans.

McClelland, Kate M. The Mouth of Witnesses: Biblical Exegesis & the Dead Sea Scrolls. LC 76-48407. 1978. 10.00 (ISBN 0-916620-09-3). Portals Pr.

Mansoor, Menahem. The Dead Sea Scrolls. 2nd ed. 300p. 1983. pap. 8.95 (ISBN 0-8010-6152-0). Baker Bk.

Newton, Michael. The Concept of Purity at Quaram & in the Letters of Paul. (Society of New Testament Studies Monograph: No. 53). 180p. 1985. 32.50 (ISBN 0-521-26583-5). Cambridge U Pr.

Nickelsburg, George W. Jewish Literature Between the Bible & the Mishnah: A Historical & Literary Introduction. LC 80-16176. 352p. 1981. 19.95 (ISBN 0-8006-0649-3, 1-649). Fortress.

Pfeiffer, Charles F. Dead Sea Scrolls & the Bible. rev. & enl. ed. (Baker Studies in Biblical Archaeology). (Illus.). 1969. pap. 5.95 (ISBN 0-8010-6898-3). Baker Bk.

Pinnock, Clark H. Reason Enough: A Case for the Christian Faith. 126p. 1986. pap. 4.95 (ISBN 0-85364-296-6, Pub. by Paternoster UK). Attic Pr.

Qimron, Elisha. The Hebrew of the Dead Sea Scrolls. (Harvard Semitic Ser.: No. 29). 1986. text ed. 13.95 (ISBN 0-89130-989-6, 04-04-29). Scholars Pr GA.

Rabin, Chaim. Qumran Studies. LC 76-40116. (Scripta Judaica: No. 2). 1976. Repr. of 1957 ed. lib. bdg. 22.50x (ISBN 0-8371-9060-6, RAQS). Greenwood.

Roth, Cecil. Dead Sea Scrolls: A New Historical Approach. 1966. pap. 3.95x (ISBN 0-393-00303-5, Norton Lib). Norton.

Rudder, Lena E. White Roots & the Mysteries of God: About the Dead Sea Scrolls. (Illus.). 144p. (Orig.). 1986. pap. write for info. (ISBN 0-937581-00-3). Zarathustrotemo Pr.

--White Roots & the Mysteries of God: And the Dead Sea Scrolls. rev. ed. (Illus.). 144p. (Orig.). 1986. write for info. (ISBN 0-937581-01-1). Zarathustrotemo Pr.

Schiffman, Lawrence. Sectarian Laws in the Dead Sea Scrolls: Courts, Testimony & the Penal Code. LC 82-837. (Brown Judaic Studies). 294p. 1983. pap. 27.50 (ISBN 0-89130-569-6). Scholars Pr GA.

Schubert, Kurt. Dead Sea Community: Its Origin & Teachings. Doberstein, John W., tr. LC 73-15245. 178p. 1974. Repr. of 1959 ed. lib. bdg. 22.50x (ISBN 0-8371-7169-5, SCDS). Greenwood.

Schuller, Eileen M. Non-Canonical Psalms from Qumran: A Pseudepigraphic Collection. (Harvard Semitic Studies). 1987. 23.95 (ISBN 0-89130-943-8, 04-04-28). Scholars Pr GA.

Siegel, Jonathan P. The Severus Scroll & 1Q1SA. LC 75-28372. (Society of Biblical Literature, Masoretic Studies). 1975. pap. 8.95 (ISBN 0-89130-028-7, 060502). Scholars Pr GA.

Szekely, Edmond B. The Teachings of the Essenes from Enoch to the Dead Sea Scrolls. (Illus.). 112p. 1981. pap. 4.80 (ISBN 0-89564-006-6). IBS Intl.

Trever, John C. Scrolls from Qumran Cave I: The Great Isaiah Scroll the Order of the Community, the Pesher to Habakkuk (color) 163p. 1972. text ed. 30.00x (ISBN 0-89757-002-2, Am Sch Orient Res); pap. 6.00x. Eisenbrauns.

--Scrolls from Qumran Cave I: The Great Isaiah Scroll the Order of the Community, the Pesher to Habakkuk. 82p. 1974. pap. text ed. 6.00x (ISBN 0-89757-001-4). Am Sch Orient Res.

Vermes, Geza. The Dead Sea Scrolls: Qumran in Perspective. LC 80-2382. 240p. 1981. pap. 8.95 (ISBN 0-8006-1435-6, 1-1435). Fortress.

--Jesus & the World of Judaism. LC 83-16535. 224p. 1984. pap. 10.95 (ISBN 0-8006-1784-3, 1-1784). Fortress.

Werner, Eric. The Sacred Bridge. 640p. 1981. 60.00x (ISBN 0-234-77352-9, Pub. by Dobson Bks England). State Mutual Bk.

Wilson, Edmund. Dead Sea Scrolls 1947-1969. 1969. 22.50x (ISBN 0-19-500665-8). Oxford U Pr.

--Israel & the Dead Sea Scrolls. 416p. 1978. pap. 9.25 (ISBN 0-374-51341-4). FS&G.

Yusseff, M. A. The Dead Sea Scrolls, The Gospel of Barnabas & the New Testament. LC 85-73210. 154p. (Orig.). 1986. pap. 8.00 (ISBN 0-89259-061-0). Am Trust Pubns.

DEADLY SINS

see also Pride and Vanity

Capps, Donald. Deadly Sins & Saving Virtues. LC 85-45912. 176p. 1987. pap. text ed. 10.95 (ISBN 0-8006-1948-X, 1-1948). Fortress.

Ianucci, R. J. Treatment of the Capital Sins. LC 70-140024. (Catholic University Studies in German: No. 17). Repr. of 1942 ed. 21.00 (ISBN 0-404-50237-7). AMS Pr.

Joyce, Jon L. The Seven Deadly Sins. 1973. pap. 3.50 (ISBN 0-89536-210-4, 1912). CSS of Ohio.

Shoemaker, Stephen H. The Jekyll & Hyde Syndrome. (Orig.). 1987. text ed. 9.95 (ISBN 0-8054-1538-6). Broadman.

Sunday Times, London. Seven Deadly Sins. LC 75-117848. (Essay Index Reprint Ser). 1962. 14.00 (ISBN 0-8369-1722-7). Ayer Co Pubs.

DEATH

see also Children and Death; Future Life; Future Punishment; Heaven; Hell; Immortalism; Martyrdom; Terminal Care

Abrahamsson, Hans. The Origin of Death: Studies in African Mythology. Kastenbaum, Robert, ed. LC 76-19555. (Death and Dying Ser.). 1977. Repr. of 1951 ed. lib. bdg. 23.50x (ISBN 0-405-09551-1). Ayer Co Pubs.

Alden, Henry M. A Study of Death: Works of Henry Mills Alden. (Works of Henry Mills Alden Ser.). vii, 335p. 1985. Repr. of 1895 ed. 39.00 (Pub. by Am Repr Serv). Am Biog Serv.

Aries, Philippe. Western Attitudes Toward Death: From the Middle Ages to the Present. Ranum, Patricia, tr. from Fr. LC 73-19340. (Symposia in Comparative History Ser). (Illus.). 122p. 1974. pap. 4.95x (ISBN 0-8018-1762-5). Johns Hopkins.

Austin, Mary. Experiences Facing Death. Kastenbaum, Robert, ed. LC 76-19557. (Death and Dying Ser.). 1977. Repr. of 1931 ed. lib. bdg. 23.50x (ISBN 0-405-09553-8). Ayer Co Pubs.

Bailey, Lloyd R., Sr. Biblical Perspectives on Death, No. 5. Brueggemann, Walter & Donahue, John R., eds. LC 78-145661. (Overtures to Biblical Theology Ser.). 180p. 1978. pap. 8.95 (ISBN 0-8006-1530-1, 1-1530). Fortress.

Bardi, Panos D. History of Thanatology: Philosophical, Religious, Psychological, & Sociological Ideas Concerning Death from Primitive Times to the Present. LC 81-43026. 102p. (Orig.). 1981. lib. bdg. 21.00 (ISBN 0-8191-1648-3); pap. text ed. 8.25 (ISBN 0-8191-1649-1). U Pr of Amer.

Beauchamp, Thom & Perlin, Seymour. Ethical Issues in Death & Dying. 1978. pap. write for info. (ISBN 0-13-290114-5). P-H.

Becker, Ernest. The Denial of Death. LC 73-1860. 1973. 19.95 (ISBN 0-02-902150-2); pap. 8.95 (ISBN 0-02-902380-7). Free Pr.

Bendit, Laurence J. Mirror of Life & Death. 1965. pap. 1.35 (ISBN 0-8356-0411-X, Quest). Theos Pub Hse.

Boerstler, Richard W. Letting Go: A Holistic & Meditative Approach to Living & Dying. LC 81-71653. (Illus.). 112p. (Orig.). 1982. pap. 3.95 (ISBN 0-9607928-0-5). Assocs Thanatology.

Boros, Ladislaus. The Mystery of Death. 216p. 1973. pap. 3.95 (ISBN 0-8245-0330-9). Crossroad NY.

Brunson, Madelon. Dying, Death & Grief. 1978. pap. 4.50 (ISBN 0-8309-0223-6). Herald Hse.

Congdon, Howard K. The Pursuit of Death. LC 76-44308. Repr. of 1977 ed. 36.30 (ISBN 0-8357-9022-3, 2016395). Bks Demand UMI.

Croskery, Beverly F. Death Education: Attitudes of Teachers, School Board Members & Clergy. LC 78-68458. 1979. perfect bdg. 9.95 (ISBN 0-88247-559-2). R & E Pubs.

Culver, Sylvia A. Keep the River Flowing. 92p. 1979. pap. 2.50 (ISBN 0-8341-0592-6). Beacon Hill.

Dehejia, Vidya. Living & Dying: An Inquiry into the Enigma of Death & After-Life. 1979. 8.95x (ISBN 0-7069-0815-5, Pub. by Vikas India). Advent NY.

Dunne, John S. The City of the Gods: A Study in Myth & Mortality. LC 78-2588. 1978. Repr. of 1965 ed. text ed. 7.95 (ISBN 0-268-00725-X). U of Notre Dame Pr.

--Time & Myth. LC 74-32289. 128p. 1975. pap. 4.95 (ISBN 0-268-01828-6). U of Notre Dame Pr.

Feifel, Herman. New Meanings of Death. (Illus.). 1977. 25.00 (ISBN 0-07-020350-4); pap. 18.95 (ISBN 0-07-020349-0). McGraw.

Francis, J. R. The Encyclopedia of Death. large type ed. (Illus.). pap. 7.00 (ISBN 0-910122-47-4). Amherst Pr.

Frazel, J. G. The Fear of the Dead in Primitive Religion. LC 66-15215. 1933. 10.00 (ISBN 0-8196-0167-5). Biblo.

Gerber, Irwin, et al, eds. Perspectives on Bereavement. (Thanatology Ser.). 1978. 14.95x (ISBN 0-8422-7304-2); pap. text ed. 7.95x (ISBN 0-8290-1878-6). Irvington.

Grof, Stanislav & Grof, Christina. Beyond Death: The Gates of Consiousness. (Art & Imagination Ser.). (Illus.). 1980. pap. 10.95 (ISBN 0-500-81019-2). Thames Hudson.

Grollman, Earl A., ed. Concerning Death: A Practical Guide for the Living. LC 73-17117. 384p. 1974. pap. 9.95 (ISBN 0-8070-2765-0, BP484). Beacon Pr.

--Explaining Death to Children. LC 67-4891. 1969. pap. 8.95 (ISBN 0-8070-2385-X, BP317). Beacon Pr.

Gruman, Gerald J. A History of Ideas about the Prolongation of Life: The Evolution of Prolongevity Hypotheses to 1800. Kastenbaum, Robert, ed. LC 76-19574. (Death & Dying Ser.). (Illus.). 1977. Repr. of 1966 ed. lib. bdg. 17.00x (ISBN 0-405-09572-4). Ayer Co Pubs.

Guthmann, Robert F., Jr. & Womack, Sharon K. Death, Dying & Grief: A Bibliography. LC 77-82084. 1978. pap. text ed. 5.50 (ISBN 0-918626-01-3, Pied Publications). Word Serv.

Hall, Manly P. Death to Rebirth. pap. 4.95 (ISBN 0-89314-395-2). Philos Res.

Heidel, Alexander. Gilgamesh Epic & Old Testament Parallels. 2nd ed. LC 49-5734. 1963. 8.95 (ISBN 0-226-32398-6, P136, Phoen). U of Chicago Pr.

Hocking, William E. The Meaning of Immortality in Human Experience, Including Thoughts on Death & Life. rev. ed. 263p. 1973. Repr. of 1957 ed. lib. bdg. 27.50x (ISBN 0-8371-6621-7, HOMI). Greenwood.

Huntington, R. & Metcalf, P. Celebrations of Death. LC 79-478. (Illus.). 1979. 39.50 (ISBN 0-521-22531-0); pap. 10.95x (ISBN 0-521-29540-8). Cambridge U Pr.

Irion, Clyde. Profit & Loss of Dying. 4.95 (ISBN 0-87516-030-1). De Vorss.

Ironside, H. A. Death & Afterwards. pap. 1.50 (ISBN 0-87213-346-X). Loizeaux.

Islam, K. M. Spectacle of Death. pap. 16.50 (ISBN 0-686-63915-4). Kazi Pubns.

Jyotir Maya Nanda, Swami. Death & Reincarnation. (Illus.). 1970. 6.99 (ISBN 0-934664-04-8). Yoga Res Foun.

Kastenbaum, Robert, ed. Death As a Speculative Theme in Religious, Scientific, & Social Thought: An Original Anthology. LC 76-19566. (Death & Dying Ser.). 1977. Repr. of 1976 ed. lib. bdg. 29.00x (ISBN 0-405-09562-7). Ayer Co Pubs.

Kreeft, Peter J. Love Is Stronger Than Death. LC 78-15839. 1979. 8.95 (ISBN 0-06-064774-4, HarpR). Har-Row.

Landorf, Joyce. Mourning Song. 192p. 1974. 10.95 (ISBN 0-8007-0680-3). Revell.

Landsberg, Paul-Louis. The Experience of Death: The Moral Problem of Suicide. Kastenaum, Robert, ed. LC 76-19579. (Death & Dying Ser.). 1977. Repr. of 1953 ed. lib. bdg. 19.00x (ISBN 0-405-09576-7). Ayer Co Pubs.

Lee, Jung Y. Death & Beyond in the Eastern Perspective. new ed. LC 73-85065. 112p. 1974. 24.50x (ISBN 0-677-05010-0). Gordon & Breach.

Leone, Bruno, et al, eds. Death-Dying, 1985 Annual. (Opposing Viewpoints SOURCES Ser.). 115p. 1985. pap. text ed. 9.95 (ISBN 0-89908-511-3). Greenhaven.

Liguori, St. Alphonsus. How to Face Death Without Fear. 1976. pap. 1.95 (ISBN 0-89243-029-X, 28376). Liguori Pubns.

Lindsay, Gordon. Death & the Hereafter. (Sorcery & Spirit World Ser.). 1.25 (ISBN 0-89985-096-0). Christ Nations.

Lodo, Venerable L. Bardo Teachings: The Way of Death & Rebirth. Clark, Nancy & Parke, Caroline M., eds. LC 82-21372. (Illus.). 76p. 1982. pap. text ed. 5.95 (ISBN 0-910165-00-9). KDK Pubns.

Marryat, Florence. There Is No Death. 69.95 (ISBN 0-8490-1192-2). Gordon Pr.

Mayer, Gladys. Behind the Veils of Death & Sleep. 1973. lib. bdg. 79.95 (ISBN 0-87968-541-7). Krishna Pr.

Montell, William L. Ghosts along the Cumberland: Deathlore in the Kentucky Foothills. LC 74-32241. (Illus.). 272p. 1975. 22.50x (ISBN 0-87049-165-2). U of Tenn Pr.

Morey, Robert A. Death & the Afterlife. 250p. 1984. pap. 11.95 (ISBN 0-87123-433-5). Bethany Hse.

Morgan, Ernest. Dealing Creatively with Death: A Manual of Death Education & Simple Burial. 10th ed. 1984. pap. 6.50. Continent Assn Funeral.

Murphy, Carol R. The Valley of the Shadow. LC 72-80095. 24p. (Orig.). 1972. pap. 2.50x (ISBN 0-87574-184-3). Pendle Hill.

Phipps, William E. Death: Confronting the Reality. LC 86-45405. 204p. (Orig.). 1987. pap. 11.95 (ISBN 0-8042-0487-X). John Knox.

Richards, Hubert J. Death & After: What Will Really Happen? (What Really Happened? Ser.). 1987. pap. 5.95 (ISBN 0-89622-288-8). Twenty-Third.

Ritchie, George G. & Sherrill, Elizabeth. Return from Tomorrow. 128p. 1981. pap. 2.95 (ISBN 0-8007-8412-X, Spire Bks). Revell.

Rosenthal, Ted. How Could I Not Be Among You? LC 73-80922. (Illus.). 80p. 1987. pap. 9.95 (ISBN 0-89255-117-8). Persea Bks.

Smith, Bradford. Dear Gift of Life: A Man's Encounter with Death. LC 65-24496. (Orig.). 1965. pap. 2.50x (ISBN 0-87574-142-8). Pendle Hill.

Spurgeon, C. H. Death. 1978. pap. 1.95 (ISBN 0-686-23024-8). Pilgrim Pubns.

Stannard, David E. The Puritan Way of Death: A Study in Religion, Culture & Social Change. LC 76-42647. (Illus.). 1977. 19.95x (ISBN 0-19-502226-2). Oxford U Pr.

Thompson, Mervin E. When Death Touches Your Life: Practical Help in Preparing for Death. 224p. 1986. 11.95 (ISBN 0-933173-02-4). Prince Peace Pub.

Tormey, John C. Life Beyond Death. 64p. 1981. pap. 1.50 (ISBN 0-89243-151-2). Liguori Pubns.

Towns, Jim. A Family Guide to Death & Dying. 192p. (Orig.). 1987. pap. 5.95 (ISBN 0-8423-0830-X). Tyndale.

Tromp, Nicholas J. Primitive Conceptions of Death & the Nether World in the Old Testament. (Biblica et Orientalia: Vol. 21). 1969. pap. 18.00 (ISBN 88-7653-321-4). Loyola.

Vernon, Glenn M. A Time to Die. 1977. 9.50 (ISBN 0-8191-0126-5). U Pr of Amer.

Weir, Robert F. Ethical Issues in Death & Dying. LC 77-24707. 1977. 38.00x (ISBN 0-231-04306-6); pap. 16.00x (ISBN 0-231-04307-4). Columbia U Pr.

Whyte, Florence. The Dance of Death in Spain & Catalonia. Kastenbaum, Robert, ed. LC 76-19594. (Death & Dying Ser.). 1977. Repr. of 1931 ed. lib. bdg. 19.00x (ISBN 0-405-09588-0). Ayer Co Pubs.

Wilczak, Paul F. When a Family Loses a Loved One. LC 81-68846. (WHEN Bk. Ser.). 96p. (Orig.). 1981. pap. 2.45 (ISBN 0-87029-179-3, 20272-1). Abbey.
Wright, Leoline L. After Death, What? rev. ed. Small, W. Emmett & Todd, Helen, eds. (Theosophical Manual: No. 5). 96p. 1974. pap. 2.50 (ISBN 0-913004-15-4). Point Loma Pub.
Zandee, Jan. Death As an Enemy According to Ancient Egyptian Conceptions. Kastenbaum, Robert, ed. LC 76-19597. (Death & Dying Ser.). 1977. Repr. of 1960 ed. lib. bdg. 37.50x (ISBN 0-405-09591-0). Ayer Co Pubs.

DEATH–BIBLIOGRAPHY

Fulton, Robert. Death, Grief & Bereavement: A Bibliography, 1845-1975. Kastenbaum, Robert, ed. LC 76-19572. (Death and Dying Ser.). 1976. PLB 27.50 (ISBN 0-405-09570-8). Ayer Co Pubs.
Kutscher, Austin H. & Kutscher, M. L., eds. Bibliography of Books on Death, Bereavement, Loss & Grief, Supplement, 1935-1971. 170p. 1970. pap. 9.95 (ISBN 0-930194-79-9). Ctr Thanatology.
Kutscher, Martin L., et al, eds. A Comprehensive Bibliography of the Thanatology Literature. LC 75-5627. 285p. 1976. 14.00 (ISBN 0-8422-7274-7). Irvington.
O'Connor, Sr. M. Catharine. Art of Dying Well. Repr. of 1942 ed. 15.00 (ISBN 0-404-04811-0). AMS Pr.
Simpson, M. A. Dying, Death, & Grief: A Critically Annotated Bibliography & Source Book of Thanatology & Terminal Care. LC 78-27273. 300p. 1979. 35.00x (ISBN 0-306-40147-9, Plenum Pr). Plenum Pub.

DEATH–JUVENILE LITERATURE

Koch, Ron. Goodbye, Grandpa. LC 74-14183. 96p. 1975. pap. 4.95 (ISBN 0-8066-1465-X, 10-2816). Augsburg.
Nystrom, Carolyn. What Happens When We Die? (Children's Bible Basics Ser.). 32p. 1981. 4.95 (ISBN 0-8024-5995-1). Moody.

DEATH–MEDITATIONS

Alberione, James. Last Things. (Orig.). 1965. 4.50 (ISBN 0-8198-0072-4). Dghtrs St Paul.
Armstrong, O. V., compiled by. Comfort for Those Who Mourn. LC 77-17182. pap. 20.00 (ISBN 0-8357-9003-7, 2016353). Bks Demand UMI.
Arya, Usharbudh. Meditation & the Art of Dying. 196p. pap. 7.95 (ISBN 0-89389-056-1). Himalayan Pubs.
Biegert. When Death has Touched Your Life. 1981. pap. 1.25 (ISBN 0-8298-0455-2). Pilgrim NY.
Budge, E. A. The Book of the Dead. (Illus.). 992p. 1985. pap. 9.95 (ISBN 1-85063-020-8, Ark Paperbks). Methuen Inc.
Carlson, Neal. To Die is Gain. (Solace Ser.). 1983. pap. 1.50 (ISBN 0-8010-2487-0). Baker Bk.
Champlin, Joseph M. Together by Your Side: A Book for Comforting the Sick & Dying. LC 79-51016. 80p. 1979. pap. 1.95 (ISBN 0-87793-180-1). Ave Maria.
Chervin, Ronda. Victory over Death. LC 85-8213. (Orig.). 1985. pap. 3.95 (ISBN 0-932506-43-7). St Bedes Pubns.
Goffstein, M. B. Your Lone Journey. LC 86-45107. (Illus.). 32p. 12.45 (ISBN 0-06-015659-7, HarpT). Har-Row.
Hoeller, Stephen. The Gnostic Jung & the Seven Sermons to the Dead. LC 82-50220. 282p. (Orig.). 1982. 13.95 (ISBN 0-8356-0573-6). Theos Pub Hse.
Johnson, L. D. The Morning after Death. LC 77-99255. 1978. 7.50 (ISBN 0-8054-2412-1). Broadman.
Luebering, Carol. To Comfort All Who Mourn: A Parish Handbook for Ministry to the Grieving. (Illus.). 96p. 1985. pap. 4.95 (ISBN 0-86716-045-4). St Anthony Mess Pr.
Noll, Peter. On Death & Dying. 1987. price not set (ISBN 0-670-80703-6). Viking.
Richardson, John R. What Happens After Death? Some Musing on -- Is God Through with a Person After Death? LC 81-52115. 1981. 6.95 (ISBN 0-686-79843-0). St Thomas.
Strauss, Lehman. When Loved Ones Are Taken in Death. pap. 2.50 (ISBN 0-310-33102-1, 6340P). Zondervan.
Swami Muktananda. Does Death Really Exist? LC 81-50161. 64p. 1983. pap. 3.95 (ISBN 0-914602-56-X). SYDA Found.
Westberg, Granger. Ante la Perdida de un Ser Querido. Rodriguez, Jorge A., tr. 32p. 1985. Repr. of 1984 ed. 1.50 (ISBN 0-311-46081-X). Casa Bautista.

DEATH–RELIGIOUS AND MORAL ASPECTS

Amato, Joseph. Ethics, Living or Dead? xii, 132p. 1982. 10.50 (ISBN 0-9614119-0-2, Co-Pub Portals Press). V Amati.
Amato, Joseph A. Death Book: Terrors, Consolations, Contradictions & Paradoxes. 1985. 13.95 (ISBN 0-9614119-1-0, Co-Pub Ellis Press). V Amati.
Anderson, Ray S. Theology, Death & Dying. LC 85-30806. 192p. 1986. 34.95 (ISBN 0-631-14846-9); pap. 8.95 (ISBN 0-631-14847-7). Basil Blackwell.
Ars Moriendi, That Is to Saye the Craft for to Deye for the Helthe of Mannes Sowle. LC 74-80159. (English Experience Ser.: No. 639). 1974. Repr. of 1491 ed. 3.50 (ISBN 90-221-0639-X). Walter J Johnson.
Badham, Paul & Badham, Linda. Death & Immortality in the Religions of the World. 256p. 1987. 22.95 (ISBN 0-913757-54-3, Pub. by New Era Bks); pap. 12.95 (ISBN 0-913757-67-5, Pub. by New Era Bks). Paragon Hse.
Bailey, Lloyd R., Sr. Biblical Perspectives on Death, No. 5. Brueggemann, Walter & Donahue, John R., eds. LC 78-145661. (Overtures to Biblical Theology Ser.). 180p. 1978. pap. 8.95 (ISBN 0-8006-1530-1, 1-1530). Fortress.
Baker, C. J. Beyond Death. 1977. 2.50 (ISBN 0-87813-953-2). Christian Light.
Bane, Bernard M. On the Impact of Morality in Our Times. 113p. 1985. pap. 5.00 (ISBN 0-317-20545-5). BMB Pub Co.
Bardi, Panos D. History of Thanatology: Philosophical, Religious, Psychological, & Sociological Ideas Concerning Death from Primitive Times to the Present. LC 81-43026. 102p. (Orig.). 1981. lib. bdg. 21.00 (ISBN 0-8191-1648-3); pap. text ed. 8.25 (ISBN 0-8191-1649-1). U Pr of Amer.
Bell, Martin. Nenshu & the Tiger: Parables of Life & Death. 112p. 1982. pap. 5.95 (ISBN 0-8164-2356-3, HarpR). Har-Row.
Benton, Josephine M. A Door Ajar: Facing Death Without Fear. LC 65-16442. 1979. pap. 4.45 (ISBN 0-8298-0366-1). Pilgrim NY.
Billnitzer, Harold. It's Your Death, Make the Most of It. LC 79-88402. 1979. pap. 7.95 (ISBN 0-933350-27-9). wkbk. 0.90 (ISBN 0-933350-28-7). Morse Pr.
Billon, B. M. Death's an End & a Beginning Without. 1981. 15.00x (ISBN 0-7223-1388-8, Pub. by A H Stockwell England). State Mutual Bk.
Carter, James E. Facing the Final Foe. LC 85-19517. 1986. pap. 2.25 (ISBN 0-8054-5433-0). Broadman.
Caxton, W., tr. Here Begynneth a Lityll Treatise Spekynge of the Arte & Crafte to Knowe Well to Dye. LC 72-169. (English Experience Ser.: No. 221). 28p. Repr. of 1490 ed. 14.00 (ISBN 90-221-0221-1). Walter J Johnson.
Chirban, John T., ed. Coping with Death & Dying: An Interdisciplinary Approach. 108p. 1986. lib. bdg. 22.00 (ISBN 0-8191-4984-5); pap. text ed. 8.75 (ISBN 0-8191-4985-3). U Pr of Amer.
Comper, Frances M. M. & Kastenbaum, Robert, eds. The Book of the Craft of Dying & Other Early English Tracts Concerning Death. LC 76-19564. (Death & Dying Ser.). 1977. Repr. of 1917 ed. lib. bdg. 19.00x (ISBN 0-405-09560-0). Ayer Co Pubs.
Cyprian, Saint A Christian Preparation for Death. pap. 1.50 (ISBN 0-686-25548-8). Eastern Orthodox.
Cyprian, St. On Mortality. pap. 1.50 (ISBN 0-686-05658-2). Eastern Orthodox.
Da Free John. Easy Death: Talks & Essays on the Inherent & Ultimate Transcendence of Death & Everything Else. 450p. pap. 10.95 (ISBN 0-913922-57-9). Dawn Horse Pr.
Dodd, Robert V. Helping Children Cope with Death. LC 84-6713. 56p. (Orig.). 1984. pap. 1.95 (ISBN 0-8361-3368-4). Herald Pr.
Doebler, Bettie A. The Quickening Seed: Death in the Sermons of John. (Elizabethan & Renaissance Studies). 297p. (Orig.). 1974. pap. 15.00 (ISBN 3-7052-0678-8, Pub. by Salzburg Studies). Longwood Pub Group.
Drummond, William. Flowres of Sion: To Which Is Adjoyned His Cypresse Grove. LC 73-6124. (English Experience Ser.: No. 590). 80p. 1973. Repr. of 1623 ed. 8.00 (ISBN 90-221-0590-3). Walter J Johnson.
Erasmus, Desiderius. Preparation to Deathe: A Boke As Devout As Eloquent. LC 74-28852. (English Experience Ser.: No. 733). 1975. Repr. of 1538 ed. 6.00 (ISBN 90-221-0762-0). Walter J Johnson.
Frazel, J. G. The Fear of the Dead in Primitive Religion. LC 66-15215. 1933. 10.00 (ISBN 0-8196-0167-5). Biblo.
Garland, Robert. The Greek Way of Death. LC 85-470. (Illus.). 208p. 1985. text ed. 22.50x (ISBN 0-8014-1823-2). Cornell U Pr.
Gerber, Samuel. Learning to Die. Dyck, Peter, tr. from Ger. LC 84-10809. 104p. (Orig.). 1984. pap. 5.95 (ISBN 0-8361-3369-2). Herald Pr.
Gualtieri, Antonio R. The Vulture & the Bull: Religious Responses to Death. 194p. (Orig.). 1984. lib. bdg. 26.00 (ISBN 0-8191-3963-7); pap. text ed. 11.75 (ISBN 0-8191-3964-5). U Pr of Amer.
Hall, Manly P. Death & After. pap. 2.50 (ISBN 0-89314-312-X). Philos Res.
--From Death to Rebirth. pap. 3.50 (ISBN 0-89314-316-2). Philos Res.
Hill, Brennan. The Near-Death Experience: A Christian Approach. 66p. 1981. pap. 3.50 (ISBN 0-697-01756-7). Wm C Brown.
Hill, Dick. Death & Dying. 4.25 (ISBN 0-89137-532-5). Quality Pubns.
Hill, Robert. The Pathway to Prayer & Pietie. LC 74-28864. (English Experience Ser.: No. 744). 1975. Repr. of 1613 ed. 26.50 (ISBN 90-221-0744-2). Walter J Johnson.
Holck, Frederick H., ed. Death & Eastern Thought: Understanding Death in Eastern Religions & Philosophies. LC 74-10650. pap. 49.10 (ISBN 0-8357-9004-5, 2015656). Bks Demand UMI.
Houston, Victor. One Step Between Death & Me. (Illus.). 68p. (Orig.). 1986. pap. 9.95 (ISBN 1-55630-019-0). Brentwood Comm.
Humphreys, S. C. & King, H., eds. Mortality & Immortality: The Anthropology & Archaeology of Death. LC 81-67910. (Research Seminars in Archaeology Ser.). 1982. 54.50 (ISBN 0-12-361550-X). Acad Pr.
Huyck, Donna. With Death at My Back. (Uplook Ser.). pap. 0.99 (ISBN 0-8163-0427-0). Pacific Pr Pub Assn.
Jebb, Philip, intro. by. By Death Parted: The Stories of Six Widows. 1986. pap. 5.95 (ISBN 0-932506-45-3). St Bedes Pubns.
Justice, William G., Jr. When Your Patient Dies. LC 83-15064. 60p. 1983. pap. 7.50 (ISBN 0-87125-091-8). Cath Health.
Kinast, Robert L. When a Person Dies: Pastoral Theology in Death Experiences. LC 84-11431. 160p. (Orig.). 1984. pap. 9.95 (ISBN 0-8245-0657-X). Crossroad NY.
Kniazev, V. V. Zhizn' dlja vsjekh i smert' za vsjekh. Tr. of Life is for All & Death is for All. 1971. pap. 1.00 (ISBN 0-317-30338-4). Holy Trinity.
Koop, C. E. To Live or Die: Facing Decisions at the End of Life. (Christian Essentials Ser.). 48p. 1987. pap. 1.95 (ISBN 0-89283-322-X). Servant.
Kopp, Ruth & Sorenson, Stephen. When Someone You Love Is Dying: A Handbook for Counselors & Those Who Care. 2nd ed. 240p. 1985. pap. 8.95 (ISBN 0-310-41601-9, 11165P). Zondervan.
Leone, Bruno, et al, eds. Death-Dying. (Opposing Viewpoints SOURCES Ser.). 375p. 1984. text ed. 39.95 (ISBN 0-89908-515-6). Greenhaven.
Liguori, Alphonsus. Preparation for Death. abr. ed. 1982. pap. 5.00 (ISBN 0-89555-174-8). TAN Bks Pubs.
Lovett, C. S. Death: Graduation to Glory. 1974. pap. 4.25 (ISBN 0-938148-20-6). Personal Christianity.
Lyman, Mary E. Death & the Christian Answer. 1983. pap. 2.50x (ISBN 0-87574-107-X, 107). Pendle Hill.
McGill, Arthur. Death & Life: An American Theology. Wilson, Charles A. & Anderson, Per M., eds. LC 86-45215. 112p. 1987. pap. 7.95 (ISBN 0-8006-1927-7, 1-1927). Fortress.
Miller, Randolph C. Live until You Die. LC 73-8657. 144p. 1973. 5.95 (ISBN 0-8298-0253-3). Pilgrim NY.
Montagu, Henry. Contemplatio Mortis et Immortalitatis. LC 72-218. (English Experience Ser.: No. 337). 148p. 1971. Repr. of 1631 ed. 11.50 (ISBN 90-221-0337-4). Walter J Johnson.
Moraczewski, Albert S. & Showalter, J. Stuart. Determination of Death: Theological, Medical, Ethical & Legal Issues. LC 82-1127. 32p. (Orig.). 1982. pap. 3.00 (ISBN 0-87125-072-1). Cath Health.
Motter, Alton M., ed. Preaching about Death: Eighteen Sermons Dealing with the Experience of Death from the Christian Perspective. LC 74-26336. pap. 23.50 (2026862). Bks Demand UMI.
Mumford, Amy Ross. It Hurts to Lose a Special Person. (Accent Expressions Ser.). (Illus.). 24p. (Orig.). 1982. gift book 4.95 (ISBN 0-89636-093-8). Accent Bks.
Nevins, Albert J. Life after Death. LC 83-61888. 136p. (Orig.). 1983. pap. 5.95 (ISBN 0-87973-612-7, 612). Our Sunday Visitor.
The New Technologies of Birth & Death: Medical, Legal & Moral Dimensions. LC 80-83425. xvi, 196p. (Orig.). 1980. pap. 8.95 (ISBN 0-935372-07-5). Pope John Ctr.
Nouwen, Henri J. In Memoriam. LC 79-56690. 64p. 1980. pap. 2.50 (ISBN 0-87793-197-6). Ave Maria.
Ochs, Carol. An Ascent to Joy: Transforming Deadness of Spirit. LC 85-41019. 160p. 1986. text ed. 12.95x (ISBN 0-268-00615-6). U of Notre Dame Pr.
Office of Worship for the Presbyterian Church (U. S. A.) & the Cumberland Presbyterian Church. The Funeral: A Service of Witness to the Resurrection. (Supplemental Liturgical Resource Ser.: 4). 120p. (Orig.). 1986. pap. write for info. (ISBN 0-664-24034-8). Westminster.
Owen, John. Death of Death. 1983. pap. 7.95 (ISBN 0-85151-382-4). Banner of Truth.
Parrish-Harra, Carol W. A New Age Handbook on Death & Dying: Death Is Life Too. LC 81-70369. 160p. 1982. pap. 5.95 (ISBN 0-87516-470-6). De Vorss.
Partridge, Jeannette. Losing a Loved One. 3.50 (ISBN 0-913420-86-7). Olympus Pub Co.
Poss, Sylvia. Towards Death with Dignity: Caring for Dying People. 1981. 33.75x (ISBN 0-317-05777-4, Pub. by Natl Soc Work). State Mutual Bk.
Provonsha, Jack. Is Death for Real? (Outreach Ser.). 1981. pap. 3.95 (ISBN 0-8163-0406-8). Pacific Pr Pub Assn.
Quezada, Adolfo. Good-Bye, My Son, Hello. LC 84-72629. 64p. (Orig.). 1985. pap. 2.95 (ISBN 0-87029-196-3). Abbey.
Rahner, Karl & Thusing, Wilhelm. A New Christology. 256p. 1980. 12.95 (ISBN 0-8245-0333-3). Crossroad NY.
Riemer, Jack, ed. Jewish Reflections on Death. LC 74-18242. 192p. 1976. pap. 5.95 (ISBN 0-8052-0516-0). Schocken.
Rosage, David E. Living Here & Hereafter. (Christian Dying, Death & Resurection Ser.). 128p. (Orig.). 1982. pap. 2.95 (ISBN 0-914544-44-6). Living Flame Pr.
Ruegg, Lawrence. When Someone You Love Dies. 1984. 0.95 (ISBN 0-89536-659-2, 2355). CSS of Ohio.
Schmalenberg, Erich. Das Todesverstaendnis bei Simone de Beauvoir: Eine Theologische Untersuchung. LC 72-77421. (Theologische Bibliothek Toepelmann, No. 25). 1972. 20.80x (ISBN 3-11-004036-0). De Gruyter.
Soulen, Richard N. Care for the Dying. LC 74-19968. 120p. 1975. pap. 6.50 (ISBN 0-8042-1098-5). John Knox.
Watson, Jeffrey A. Looking Beyond. 132p. 1986. pap. 4.95 (ISBN 0-89693-155-2). Victor Bks.
Weatherhead, Leslie D. Life Begins at Death. (Festival Ser.). 112p. 1981. pap. 2.25 (ISBN 0-687-21806-3). Abingdon.
Weir, Robert F., ed. Ethical Issues in Death & Dying. 2nd ed. 425p. 1986. 40.00x (ISBN 0-231-06222-2); pap. 16.00x (ISBN 0-231-06223-0). Columbia U Pr.
Wernecke, Herbert. When Loved Ones Are Called Home. (Ultra Bks Ser). pap. 1.95 (ISBN 0-8010-9513-1). Baker Bk.
Westphal, Merold. God, Guilt & Death: An Existential Phenomenology of Religion. LC 83-48525. (Studies in Phenomenology & Existential Philosophy). 320p. 1987. 27.50x (ISBN 0-253-32586-2); pap. 9.95 (ISBN 0-253-32586-2). Ind U Pr.
Winkler, Gershon. Dybbuk. (Illus.). 1981. 13.95 (ISBN 0-910818-38-X); pap. 9.95 (ISBN 0-910818-37-1). Judaica Pr.

DEATH–SOCIAL ASPECTS

Flumiani, C. M. The Philosophy of Life & the Philosophy of Death. 89p. 1987. pap. 8.50 (ISBN 0-86650-223-8). Gloucester Art.
Ogg, Elizabeth. Facing Death & Loss. LC 85-51126. 106p. 1985. pap. 19.00 (ISBN 0-87762-423-2). Technomic.
Rohr, Janelle, ed. Death & Dying. 2nd, rev. ed. (Opposing Viewpoints Ser.). (Illus.). 1987. 12.95 (ISBN 0-317-53944-2); pap. 6.95. Greenhaven.
Weir, Robert F., ed. Ethical Issues in Death & Dying. 2nd ed. 425p. 1986. 40.00x (ISBN 0-231-06222-2); pap. 16.00x (ISBN 0-231-06223-0). Columbia U Pr.

DEATH AND CHILDREN

see Children and Death

DEATH OF CHILDREN

see Children–Death and Future State

DEATH OF GOD THEOLOGY

see also Secularization (Theology)

Larson, Martin A. The Essence-Christian Faith. 273p. 10.95 (ISBN 0-318-19483-X). Truth Seeker.
Metz, Johannes B., ed. Is God Dead? LC 66-25679. (Concilium Ser.: Vol. 16). 189p. 7.95 (ISBN 0-8091-0078-9). Paulist Pr.
Taylor, Mark C. Erring: A Post Modern A-Theology. LC 84-88. xiv, 220p. 1987. pap. 9.95 (ISBN 0-226-79142-0). U of Chicago Pr.
Vahanian, Gabriel. No Other God. LC 66-28591. (Orig.). 1966. pap. 2.50 (ISBN 0-8076-0389-9). Braziller.
Wellwarth, George E. Modern Drama & the Death of God. LC 86-40064. 192p. 1986. text ed. 25.75x (ISBN 0-299-10850-3). U of Wis Pr.

DEATHS, REGISTERS OF

see Registers of Births, Deaths, Marriages, Etc.

DECCAN, INDIA–HISTORY

Nandi, R. N. Religious Institutions & Cults in the Deccan. 1973. 8.50 (ISBN 0-8426-0564-9). Orient Bk Dist.

DECENNALIA

see Roman Emperors

DECISION-MAKING

Brock, Horace, ed. Game Theory, Social Choice, & Ethics. 1979. lib. bdg. 31.50 (ISBN 0-686-26826-1, Pub. by Reidel Holland). Kluwer Academic.

Johnson, Luke T. Decision Making in the Church: A Biblical Model. LC 82-17675. 112p. 1983. pap. 6.95 (ISBN 0-8006-1694-4). Fortress.

Meador, Prentice A., Jr. Who Rules Your Life? LC 79-64089. (Journey Bks.). 1979. pap. 3.50 (ISBN 0-8344-0107-X). Sweet.

Richards, Lawrence O. How I Can Make Decisions. (Answers for Youth Ser.). 1980. pap. 4.95 (ISBN 0-310-38981-X, 18208P). Zondervan.

DECISION-MAKING (ETHICS)

Arnold, John D. & Tompkins, Bert. How to Make the Right Decisions. 1986. pap. 5.95 (ISBN 0-8010-0209-5). Baker Bk.

Asher, Joseph. Moral Choices: A Religious Perspective. 50p. (Orig.). 1984. pap. write for info. (ISBN 0-936434-14-7, Pub. by Zellerbach Fam Fund). SF Study Ctr.

Brinton, Howard H. Reaching Decisions. 1983. pap. 2.50x (ISBN 0-87574-065-0, 065). Pendle Hill.

Everding, H. Edward, Jr. & Wilbanks, Dana M. Decision Making & the Bible. LC 75-11656. 160p. 1975. pap. 5.95 (ISBN 0-8170-0668-0). Judson.

Larsen, Sandy & Larsen, Dale. Choices: Picking Your Way Through the Ethical Jungle. (Young Fisherman Bible Studyguide). (Illus.). 61p. (Orig.). (YA) 1983. saddle-stitched student ed. 2.95 (ISBN 0-87788-113-8); tchr's. ed. 4.95 (ISBN 0-87788-114-6). Shaw Pubs.

LeMaire, H. Paul. Personal Decisions. LC 81-43668. 220p. (Orig.). 1982. lib. bdg. 28.25 (ISBN 0-8191-2329-3); pap. text ed. 11.75 (ISBN 0-8191-2330-7). U Pr of Amer.

McCasland. Free to Choose. 1983. 3.95 (ISBN 0-88207-593-4). Victor Bks.

McCormick, Richard A. & Ramsey, Paul, eds. Doing Evil to Achieve Good: Moral Choice in Conflict Situations. 274p. 1985. pap. text ed. 11.75 (ISBN 0-8191-4586-6). U Pr of Amer.

Meyners, Robert & Wooster, Claire. Solomon's Sword: Clarifying Values in the Church. LC 77-9391. Repr. of 1977 ed. 27.40 (ISBN 0-8357-9028-2, 2016408). Bks Demand UMI.

Price, Eugenia. A Woman's Choice: Living Through Your Problems. 192p. 1983. pap. 5.95 (ISBN 0-310-31381-3, 16217P). Zondervan.

Richards, Lawrence O. How I Can Make Decisions. (Answers for Youth Ser.). 1980. pap. 4.95 (ISBN 0-310-38981-X, 18208P). Zondervan.

Rush, Vincent E. The Responsible Christian: A Guide for Moral Decision Making According to Classical Tradition. 288p. 1984. 9.95 (ISBN 0-8294-0448-1). Loyola.

DECLAMATION

see Recitations

DEDICATION, FEAST OF

see Hanukkah (Feast of Lights)

DEDICATION SERVICES

Holck, Manfred, Jr., compiled by. Dedication Services for Every Occasion. 96p. 1984. pap. 5.95 (ISBN 0-8170-1033-5). Judson.

DEISM

see also Atheism; Christianity; Cosmology; Free Thought; God; Positivism; Rationalism; Theism

Gildon, Charles. The Deist's Manual; or a Rational Enquiry into the Christian Religion. Wellek, Rene, ed. LC 75-11220. (British Philosophers & Theologians of the 17th & 18th Centuries Ser.: Vol. 23). 1976. Repr. of 1705 ed. lib. bdg. 51.00 (ISBN 0-8240-1774-9). Garland Pub.

Middleton, Conyers. A Free Enquiry into the Miraculous Powers, Which Are Supposed to Have Subsisted in the Christian Church. Wellek, Rene, ed. LC 75-11235. (British Philosophers & Theologians of the 17th & 18th Centuries: Vol. 36). 1976. Repr. of 1749 ed. lib. bdg. 51.00 (ISBN 0-8240-1788-9). Garland Pub.

Morgan, Thomas. The Moral Philosopher in a Dialogue Between Philalethes, a Christian Deist, & Theophanes, a Christian Jew. LC 75-11239. (British Philosophers & Theologians of the 17th & 18th Centuries Ser.: Vol. 39). 463p. 1977. Repr. of 1737 ed. lib. bdg. 51.00 (ISBN 0-8240-1791-9). Garland Pub.

Pike, Edgar R. Slayers of Superstition. LC 78-102581. 1970. Repr. of 1931 ed. 16.50x (ISBN 0-8046-0741-9, Pub.by Kennikat). Assoc Faculty Pr.

Sullivan, Robert E. John Toland & the Deist Controversy: A Study in Adaptations. LC 81-7137. (Harvard Historical Studies: 101). (Illus.). 384p. 1982. text ed. 27.50x (ISBN 0-674-48050-3). Harvard U Pr.

Waring, E. Graham, ed. Deism & Natural Religion: A Source Book. LC 66-28139. (Milestones of Thought Ser.). pap. 4.95 (ISBN 0-8044-6968-7). Ungar.

DEJECTION

see Depression, Mental

DELPHIAN ORACLE

Amandry, Pierre. La Mantique Apollinienne a Delphes: Essai Sur le Fonctionnement De L'Oracle. facsimile ed. LC 75-10627. (Ancient Religion & Mythology Ser.). (Fr., Illus.). 1976. Repr. of 1950 ed. 23.50x (ISBN 0-405-07003-9). Ayer Co Pubs.

Dempsey, T. Delphic Oracle: Its Early History, Influence & Fall. LC 69-13234. Repr. of 1918 ed. 15.00 (ISBN 0-405-08442-0). Ayer Co Pubs.

DELUGE

Bloomfield, Arthur. The Changing Climate. LC 77-80427. 128p. 1977. pap. 2.50 (ISBN 0-87123-060-7, 200060). Bethany Hse.

Clay, Albert T. A Hebrew Deluge Story in Cuneiform. LC 78-63549. (Yale Oriental Ser. Researches: No. 5, Pt. 3). Repr. of 1922 ed. 20.00 (ISBN 0-404-60275-4). AMS Pr.

Custance, Arthur C. Doorway Papers: Flood; Local or Global, Vol. 9. 312p. 1985. pap. text ed. 9.95 (ISBN 0-310-23041-1, 10667P). Zondervan.

Donnelly, Ignatius. Atlantis: The Antediluvian World. lib. bdg. 100.00 (ISBN 0-87968-055-5). Krishna Pr.

Heidel, Alexander. Gilgamesh Epic & Old Testament Parallels. 2nd ed. LC 49-5734. 1963. 8.95 (ISBN 0-226-32398-6, P136, Phoen). U of Chicago Pr.

King, Barbara. What Is a Flood? 61p. 1981. pap. 3.00 (ISBN 0-317-20874-8). CSA Pr.

Nelson, Byron C. Deluge Story in Stone. (Illus.). 1968. Repr. of 1931 ed. 5.95 (ISBN 0-87123-095-X, 210095). Bethany Hse.

Rehwinkel, Alfred M. Flood. 2nd ed. (Orig.). (YA) 1951-1957. pap. 9.95 (ISBN 0-570-03183-4, 12-2103). Concordia.

Warren, Erasmus. Geologia: Discourse Concerning the Earth Before the Deluge, Wherein the Form & Properties Ascribed to It. LC 77-6546. (History of Geology Ser.). (Illus.). 1978. Repr. of 1690 ed. lib. bdg. 34.50x (ISBN 0-405-10470-7). Ayer Co Pubs.

Wheeler, Gerald W. Deluge. LC 78-8404. (Flame Ser.). 1978. pap. 0.99 (ISBN 0-8127-0191-7). Review & Herald.

Whitcomb, John C. World That Perished. pap. 5.95 (ISBN 0-8010-9537-9). Baker Bk.

--The World That Perished. pap. 4.95 (ISBN 0-88469-059-8). BMH Bks.

Whitcomb, John C. & Morris, Henry M. The Genesis Flood. pap. 8.95 (ISBN 0-8010-9501-8). Baker Bk.

--The Genesis Flood. pap. 8.95 (ISBN 0-88469-067-9). BMH Bks.

Whitcomb, John C., Jr. & Morris, H. M. Genesis Flood. 1960. pap. 8.95 (ISBN 0-87552-338-2). Presby & Reformed.

DELUSIONS

see Impostors and Imposture; Superstition; Witchcraft

DEMONIAC POSSESSION

see also Satanism

Crapanzano, Vincent & Garrison, Vivian, eds. Case Studies in Spirit Possession. LC 76-26653. (Contemporary Religious Movements Ser.). pap. 118.30 (ISBN 0-317-08510-7, 2055396). Bks Demand UMI.

Cristiani, Leon. Evidence of Satan in the Modern World. Rowland, Cynthia, tr. from Fr. (Eng.). 1977. pap. 5.50 (ISBN 0-89555-032-6). TAN Bks Pubs.

Fiore, Edith. Unquiet Dead: A Psychologist Works with Spirit Possession. LC 86-29096. 192p. 1987. 15.95 (ISBN 0-385-23904-1, Dolp). Doubleday.

Jay, Carroll E. Gretchen, I Am. 1979. pap. 2.25 (ISBN 0-380-42820-2, 42820-2). Avon.

Montgomery, John W. Demon Possession. LC 75-19313. 1976. pap. 9.95 (ISBN 0-87123-102-6, 210102). Bethany Hse.

Oesterreich, T. K. Possession: Demoniacal & Other. 400p. 1974. pap. 4.95 (ISBN 0-8065-0436-6). Citadel Pr.

Oesterreich, Traugott K. Possession. 1966. 10.00 (ISBN 0-8216-0138-5). Univ Bks.

Sanchez-Perez, J. M. Engrammes of the Universe: Extra-Cerebral Memory, Reincarnation & Demonic Possession. 1980. 8.50 (ISBN 0-682-49474-7). Exposition Pr FL.

Walker, D. P. Unclean Spirits: Possession & Exorcism in France & England in the Late 16th & Early 17th Centuries. LC 80-22649. 1981. 18.95x (ISBN 0-8122-7797-X). U of Pa Pr.

DEMONOLOGY

see also Apparitions; Devil; Evil Eye; Exorcism; Satanism; Superman; Superstition; Witchcraft

Bayley, Robert G. Deliver Us from the Evil One. 36p. 1987. pap. 2.95 (ISBN 0-934421-09-9). Presby Renewal Pubns.

Bubeck, Mark I. The Adversary. 1975. pap. 5.95 (ISBN 0-8024-0143-0). Moody.

Carus, Paul. History of the Devil & the Idea of Evil. (Illus.). 496p. 1974. pap. 14.95 (ISBN 0-87548-307-0). Open Court.

Conway, Moncure D. Demonology & Devil-Lore, 2 vols. Set. 250.00 (ISBN 0-8490-0017-3). Gordon Pr.

Deacon, John & Walker, John. Dialogicall Discourses of Spirits & Devils, Declaring Their Proper Essence. LC 76-57377. (English Experience Ser.: No. 795). 1977. Repr. of 1601 ed. lib. bdg. 37.00 (ISBN 90-221-0795-7). Walter J Johnson.

De Menil, Dominique, intro. by. Constant Companions: An Exhibition of Mythological Animals, Demons, & Monsters. (Illus.). 1964. pap. 6.00 (ISBN 0-914412-19-1). Inst for the Arts.

Ferguson, Everett. Demonology of the Early Christian World. LC 84-16681. (Symposium Ser.: Vol. 12). 190p. 1984. 19.95 (ISBN 0-88946-703-X). E Mellen.

Gilpin, R. Biblical Demonology: A Treatise on Satan's Temptations. 1982. lib. bdg. 20.00 (ISBN 0-86524-093-0, 9805). Klock & Klock.

Hagin, Kenneth E. Bible Answers to Man's Questions on Demons. 1983. pap. 1.00 (ISBN 0-89276-028-1). Hagin Ministries.

--Demons & How to Deal With Them. 2nd ed. 1983. pap. 1.00 (ISBN 0-89276-026-5). Hagin Ministries.

--The Origin & Operation of Demons. 2nd ed. 1983. pap. 1.00 (ISBN 0-89276-025-7). Hagin Ministries.

Hall, Frederic T. The Pedigree of the Devil. LC 76-173108. (Illus.). Repr. of 1883 ed. 27.50 (ISBN 0-405-08594-X, Blom Pubns). Ayer Co Pubs.

Hayes, Norvel. Number One Way to Fight the Devil. 1978. pap. 0.75 (ISBN 0-89274-094-9, HH-094). Harrison Hse.

James First King Of England. Daemonologie, in Forme of a Dialogue. (English Experience Ser.: No. 94). 1969. Repr. of 1597 ed. 13.00 (ISBN 90-221-0094-4). Walter J Johnson.

Jung, Leo. Fallen Angels in Jewish & Christian & Mohammedan Literature. 1926. 25.00x (ISBN 0-87068-236-9). Ktav.

Kapferer, Bruce. A Celebration of Demons: Exorcism & the Aesthetics of Healing in Sri Lanka. LC 81-48677. (Midland Bks: No. 304). (Illus.). 312p. 1983. 32.50x (ISBN 0-253-31326-0); pap. 18.50x (ISBN 0-253-20304-X). Ind U Pr.

Khristianskoje Uchenijr o Zlikh Dukhakh. Tr. of The Christian Teaching on Evil Spirits. 30p. pap. 2.00 (ISBN 0-317-29008-8). Holy Trinity.

Kiessling, Nicolas. The Incubus in English Literature: Provenance & Progeny. (Illus.). 1977. pap. 12.95 (ISBN 0-87422-006-8). Wash St U Pr.

Kirban, Salem. Six Hundred Sixty-Six: Pictoral Format. 1980. pap. 4.95 (ISBN 0-912582-33-2). Kirban.

Knowles, Victor. What the Bible Says about Angels & Demons. LC 86-71104. (What the Bible Says Ser.). 405p. 1986. 13.95 (ISBN 0-89900-252-8). College Pr Pub.

Lehner, Ernst & Lehner, Johanna. Picture Book of Devils, Demons & Witchcraft. (Illus.). 15.50 (ISBN 0-8446-5830-8). Peter Smith.

Lindsay, Gordon. Origin of Demons & the Orders, Vol. 5. (Sorcery & Spirit World Ser.). 0.95 (ISBN 0-89985-088-X). Christ Nations.

Milner, Max, ed. Entretiens Sur L'homme et le Diable. (Decades Du Centre Culturel International De Cerisy-la Salle, Nouvelle Ser.: No. 1). 1965. pap. 14.00x (ISBN 90-2796-012-7). Mouton.

Newport, John P. Demons, Demons, Demons. LC 78-189503. 1977. pap. 3.95 (ISBN 0-8054-5577-9). Broadman.

Nugent, Christopher. Masks of Satan: The Demonic in History. 216p. 1984. 22.50 (ISBN 0-89860-128-2, Sheed & Ward). Eastview.

Parry, Michel, ed. The Devil's Children: Tales of Demons & Exorcists. LC 74-21721. 212p. 1975. 7.95 (ISBN 0-8008-2188-2). Taplinger.

Patterson, Ray. House Beautiful. (Illus.). 118p. 1987. pap. 3.95 (ISBN 0-936369-05-1). Son-Rise Pubns.

Popoff, Peter. Demons At Your Doorstep. Tanner, Don, ed. LC 82-82842. (Illus.). 56p. 1982. pap. 1.50 (ISBN 0-938544-13-6). Faith Messenger.

Prince, Derek. Expelling Demons. 1969. pap. 0.25 (ISBN 0-934920-18-4, B70). Derek Prince.

Rhodes, H. T. The Satanic Mass. 256p. 1974. 7.95 (ISBN 0-8065-0405-6). Citadel Pr.

Russell, Jeffrey B. Lucifer: The Devil in the Middle Ages. LC 84-45153. (Illus.). 360p. 1986. pap. text ed. 12.95x (ISBN 0-8014-9429-X). Cornell U Pr.

Scanlan, Michael & Cirner, Randall J. Deliverance from Evil Spirits: A Weapon for Spiritual Warfare. 125p. (Orig.). 1980. pap. 4.95 (ISBN 0-89283-091-3). Servant.

Schneweis, Emil. Angels & Demons According to Lactantius. LC 79-8121. (Satanism Ser.). 192p. Repr. of 1944 ed. 26.00 (ISBN 0-404-18433-2). AMS Pr.

Scott, Walter. Demonology & Witchcraft. 1970. 7.95 (ISBN 0-8065-0213-4). Citadel Pr.

--Letters on Demonology & Witchcraft. 1887. Repr. 25.00 (ISBN 0-8274-2850-2). R West.

Sinistrari, Ludovico M. Demoniality. LC 72-83751. Repr. of 1927 ed. lib. bdg. 22.00 (ISBN 0-405-08976-7, Pub. by Blom). Ayer Co Pubs.

Spalding, T. A. Elizabeth Demonology. 1880. lib. bdg. 27.50 (ISBN 0-8414-1620-6). Folcroft.

Stambaugh, Ria, ed. Teufelbuecher in Auswahl, 3 vols. (Ausgaben Deutscher Literatur des 15. bis 18. Jahrh). (Ger). Vol. 1, 1970. write for info (ISBN 3-11-006388-3); Vol. 2, 1972. 112.00x (ISBN 3-11-003924-9); Vol. 3, 1973. 141.00x (ISBN 3-11-004127-8). De Gruyter.

Summers, Montague. History of Witchcraft & Demonology. (Illus.). 370p. 1973. pap. 8.95 (ISBN 0-7100-7613-4). Methuen Inc.

--Malleus Maleficarum. 288p. 1971. pap. 7.50 (ISBN 0-486-22802-9). Dover.

Summers, Montague, ed. & tr. Malleus Maleficarum. LC 68-57193. 1969. Repr. of 1928 ed. 27.50 (ISBN 0-405-09016-1, Pub. by Blom). Ayer Co Pubs.

Sumrall, Lester. One Hundred & One Questions & Answers on Demon Powers. 145p. (Orig.). 1983. pap. 3.25 (ISBN 0-89274-261-5). Harrison Hse.

Taylor, Jack R. Victory over the Devil. LC 72-96149. 128p. 1973. pap. 4.95 (ISBN 0-8054-5131-5). Broadman.

Thompson, Reginald C. The Devils & Evil Spirits of Babylonia, 2 vols. LC 73-18855. (Luzac's Semitic Text & Translation Ser.: Nos. 14-15). (Illus.). Repr. of 1904 ed. 47.50 set (ISBN 0-404-11353-2). AMS Pr.

Wedeck, Harry E. Triumph of Satan. 160p. 1974. pap. 2.95 (ISBN 0-8065-0422-6). Citadel Pr.

White, Hugh W. Demonism Verified & Analyzed. 69.95 (ISBN 0-8490-0016-5). Gordon Pr.

DEMYTHOLOGIZATION

Here are entered works dealing with a method of New Testament interpretation proposed first by Rudolf Bultmann. To demythologize is to translate the Mythological discourse of the New Testament into existential (or anthropological) terminology.

see also Communication (Theology); Myth

Bultmann, Rudolf. The New Testament & Mythology & Other Basic Writings. Ogden, Schubert M., ed. & tr. LC 84-47921. 192p. 1984. 12.95 (ISBN 0-8006-0727-9). Fortress.

Jones, Geraint V. Christology & Myth in the New Testament. LC 56-4228. 1956. A R Allenson.

DENOMINATIONAL SCHOOLS

see Church Schools

DENOMINATIONS, RELIGIOUS

see Religions; Sects;

also particuliar denominations and sects

DEONTOLOGY

see Ethics

DEPRAVITY

see Sin, Original

DEPRESSION, MENTAL

Fairchild, Roy W. Finding Hope Again: A Pastor's Guide to Counseling Depressed Persons. LC 79-2988. 160p. 1980. 9.45 (ISBN 0-06-062325-X, HarpR). Har-Row.

Geddes, Jim. The Bright Side of Depression. LC 85-17123. (Orig.). 1985. pap. 5.95 (ISBN 0-8054-5016-5). Broadman.

Green, Richard J. Dissolving Depression & Finding Peace. pap. 2.50 (ISBN 0-87516-278-9). De Vorss.

Hart, Archibald. Counseling the Depressed. 224p. 1987. 12.95 (ISBN 0-8499-0582-6). Word Bks.

LaHaye, Tim. How to Win Over Depression. 224p. 1974. pap. text ed. 6.95 (ISBN 0-310-26981-4, 18072P); pap. 3.95 (ISBN 0-310-26982-2, 18082P). Zondervan.

--Ten Steps to Victory over Depression. 1974. pap. 1.50 (ISBN 0-310-27002-2, 18074P). Zondervan.

Minirth, Frank B. & Skipper, States. One Hundred Ways to Live a Happy & Successful Life. (Direction Bks.). 1979. pap. 4.95 (ISBN 0-8010-6213-6). Baker Bk.

Mower, Richard K. Overcoming Depression. LC 85-29228. 160p. 1986. 8.95 (ISBN 0-87579-025-9). Deseret Bk.

Smith, Harold I. Life-Changing Answers to Depression. 192p. (Orig.). 1986. 9.95 (ISBN 0-89081-529-1). Harvest Hse.

Weapons of Our Warfare: Help for Troubled Minds. (Illus.). 144p. 1987. pap. 3.95 (ISBN 0-936369-06-X). Son-Rise Pubns.

Wright, H. Norman. Now I Know Why I'm Depressed. 1984. pap. 4.95 (ISBN 0-89081-423-6). Harvest Hse.

Wright, Norman. Living with Your Emotions: Self-Image & Depression. LC 79-83661. 1979. 7.95 (ISBN 0-89081-193-8); avail. tchr's guide. Harvest Hse.

DEPRESSIVE PSYCHOSES

see Depression, Mental

DESCARTES, RENE, 1596-1650

Balz, Albert G. Descartes & the Modern Mind. xiv, 492p. 1967. Repr. of 1952 ed. 37.50 (ISBN 0-208-00023-2, Archon). Shoe String.

Blom, John J. Descartes: His Moral Philosophy & Psychology. LC 78-55241. 1978. 35.00 (ISBN 0-8147-0999-0). NYU Pr.

Cottingham, John, ed. & tr. Descartes' Conversation with Burman. 1974. 11.95x (ISBN 0-19-824671-4). Oxford U Pr.
Curley, E. M. Descartes Against the Skeptics. LC 77-14366. 1978. 17.50x (ISBN 0-674-19826-3). Harvard U Pr.
Descartes, Rene. Oeuvres et Lettres: Avec: Discours de la Methode. 1424p. 1937. 42.95 (ISBN 0-686-55676-3). French & Eur.
Gysi, Lydia. Platonism & Cartesianism in the Philosophy of Ralph Cudworth. 163p. 1962. 14.35 (ISBN 3-261-00648-X). P Lang Pubs.
Koyre, Alexandre. Essai Sur l'Idee de Dieu et les Preuves de Son Existence Chez Descartes. Doney, Willis, ed. (The Philosophy of Descartes Ser.). (Fr.). 250p. 1987. lib. bdg. 40.00 (ISBN 0-8240-4665-X). Garland Pub.
Laberthonniere. Etudes sur Descartes, 2 tomes. Set. 29.90 (ISBN 0-685-34226-3). French & Eur.
Mahaffy, John P. Descartes. facs. ed. LC 71-94277. (Select Bibliographies Reprint Ser.). 1902. 19.00 (ISBN 0-8369-5051-8). Ayer Co Pubs.
Maritain, Jacques. Three Reformers: Luther-Descartes-Rousseau. Repr. of 1950 ed. lib. bdg. 22.50x (ISBN 0-8371-2825-0, MATR). Greenwood.
Mellone, Sydney H. The Dawn of Modern Thought: Descartes, Spinoza, Leibniz, with Introductory Note by W. D. Ross. LC 72-85001. 124p. 1973. Repr. of 1930 ed. 10.00x (ISBN 0-8462-1686-8). Russell.
Valery, Paul. Descartes. 133p. 1980. Repr. lib. bdg. 15.00 (ISBN 0-89984-477-4). Century Bookbindery.
Vartanian, Aram. Diderot & Descartes: A Study of Scientific Naturalism in the Enlightment. LC 75-18406. (History of Ideas Series: No. 6). 336p. 1975. Repr. of 1953 ed. lib. bdg. 22.50x (ISBN 0-8371-8337-5, VADD). Greenwood.

DESERTS (IN RELIGION, FOLK-LORE, ETC.)

see also Wilderness (Theology)

Cummings, Charles. Spirituality & the Desert Experience. 1976. cancelled (ISBN 0-87193-166-4). Dimension Bks.
Nouwen, Henri J. The Way of the Heart: Desert Spirituality & Contemporary Ministry. 96p. 1981. 8.95 (ISBN 0-86683-913-5, AY7443, HarpR). Har-Row.
Self, Carolyn S. & Self, William L. Confessions of a Nomad: A Devotional Guide. LC 83-61913. 168p. 1983. 1.98 (ISBN 0-931948-47-9). Peachtree Pubs.

DES MARQUETS, ANN

Seiler, Sr. M. Hilarine. Anne De Marquets, Poetesse Religieuse De Seizieme Siecle. LC 75-94200. (Catholic University of America. Studies in Romance Languages & Literatures: No. 4). (Fr). Repr. of 1931 ed. 21.00 (ISBN 0-404-50304-7). AMS Pr.

DESPAIR

see also Hope

McCloskey, Pat. When You Are Angry with God. 1987. pap. 4.95. Paulist Pr.

DESTINY

see Fate and Fatalism

DESTITUTION

see Poverty

DESTRUCTION OF THE JEWS (1939-1945)

see Holocaust, Jewish (1939-1945)

DETERMINISM AND INDETERMINISM

see Free Will and Determinism

DEVELOPING COUNTRIES–RELIGION

Kirk, J. Andrew. Theology & the Third World Church. LC 83-8560. (Outreach & Identity: Evangelical Theological Monographs). 64p. (Orig.). 1983. pap. 2.95 (ISBN 0-87784-892-0). Inter-Varsity.

DEVIL

see also Demonology; Satanism

Anshen, Ruth N. Anatomy of Evil. Orig. Title: The Reality of the Devil. (Illus.). 224p. 1985. pap. 8.95 (ISBN 0-918825-15-6, Dist. by Kampmann & Co.). Moyer Bell Limited.
Aranza, Jacob. More Rock, Country & Backward Masking. 1985. pap. 5.95 (ISBN 0-910311-30-7). Huntington Hse Inc.
Ashton, J. The Devil in Britain & America. 75.00 (ISBN 0-87968-450-X). Gordon Pr.
Ashton, John. The Devil in Britain & America. LC 80-19692. 363p. 1980. Repr. of 1972 ed. lib. bdg. 19.95x (ISBN 0-89370-608-6). Borgo Pr.
Belisle, Bertrand. The Myths of Satan. 64p. 1982. 6.95 (ISBN 0-89962-284-4). Todd & Honeywell.
Bounds, E. M. Satan: His Personality, Power & Overthrow. (Direction Bks). 1972. pap. 2.95 (ISBN 0-8010-0586-8). Baker Bk.
--Winning the Invisible War. 160p. 1984. pap. 3.50 (ISBN 0-88368-145-5). Whitaker Hse.
Breese, David. Satan's Ten Most Believable Lies. 2nd ed. 1987. pap. 6.95 (ISBN 0-8024-7675-9). Moody.
Bubeck, Mark I. The Adversary. 1975. pap. 5.95 (ISBN 0-8024-0143-0). Moody.
Carr, Joseph. The Lucifer Connection. 1986. pap. 6.96 (ISBN 0-910311-42-0). Huntington Hse Inc.
Chafer, Lewis S. Satan. 1977. pap. 5.95 (ISBN 0-310-22361-X, 6308P). Zondervan.
Christiani, Leon. Evidence of Satan in the Modern World. 1975. pap. 1.50 (ISBN 0-380-00413-5, 25122). Avon.
Cobbe, F. P. The Devil: His Origin, Greatness & Decline. 59.95 (ISBN 0-8490-0022-X). Gordon Pr.
Cohen, Daniel. Dealing with the Devil. LC 79-14692. (Illus.). 1979. 11.95 (ISBN 0-396-07700-5). Dodd.
Cristiani, Leon. Evidence of Satan in the Modern World. Rowland, Cynthia, tr. from Fr. (Eng.). 1977. pap. 5.50 (ISBN 0-89555-032-6). TAN Bks Pubs.
Delaporte. The Devil: Does He Exist & What Does He Do? 212p. 1982. pap. 4.00 (ISBN 0-89555-173-X). TAN Bks Pubs.
Downame, John. The Christian Warfare. LC 74-80174. (English Experience Ser.: No. 653). 674p. 1974. Repr. of 1604 ed. 67.00 (ISBN 90-221-0653-5). Walter J Johnson.
Farschman, Marc W. Setting the Captives Free! A Practical Guide to Breaking the Power of Satan over Your Life. LC 85-61138. 146p. (Orig.). 1985. pap. 4.95 (ISBN 0-934285-00-4). New Life Faith.
Finnegan, Robert E. Christ & Satan: A Critical Edition. 169p. 1977. pap. text ed. 15.95x (ISBN 0-88920-041-6, Pub. by Wilfrid Laurier Canada); pap. text ed. 10.50 (ISBN 0-88920-040-8). Humanities.
Hagin, Kenneth, Jr. Showdown with the Devil. 1983. pap. 0.50 mini bk. (ISBN 0-89276-715-4). Hagin Ministries.
Hall, Frederic T. The Pedigree of the Devil. LC 76-173108. (Illus.). Repr. of 1883 ed. 27.50 (ISBN 0-405-08594-X, Blom Pubns). Ayer Co Pubs.
Jewett, Edward H. Diabolology: The Person & Kingdom of Satan. 1977. lib. bdg. 59.95 (ISBN 0-8490-1715-7). Gordon Pr.
Kater, John. The Letter of John to James. (Illus.). 64p. (Orig.). 1981. pap. 3.95 (ISBN 0-8164-2344-X, HarpR). Har-Row.
Kirban, Salem. Satan's Music Exposed. 1980. pap. 5.95 (ISBN 0-912582-35-9). Kirban.
Langton, Edward. Satan, A Portrait: A Study of the Character of Satan Through All the Ages. LC 74-2434. 1973. lib. bdg. 35.00 (ISBN 0-8414-5716-6). Folcroft.
--Satan, a Portrait: A Study of the Character of Satan Through All the Ages. 1976. lib. bdg. 59.95 (ISBN 0-8490-2568-0). Gordon Pr.
Lehner, Ernst & Lehner, Johanna. Picture Book of Devils, Demons, & Witchcraft. LC 72-137002. 1972. pap. 6.50 (ISBN 0-486-22751-0). Dover.
--Picture Book of Devils, Demons & Witchcraft. (Illus.). 15.50 (ISBN 0-8446-5830-8). Peter Smith.
Lindsay, Gordon. Satan, Fallen Angels & Demons. (Satan Ser.: Vol. 2). pap. 1.25 (ISBN 0-89985-954-2). Christ Nations.
--Satan, Rebellion & Fall, 3 vols. (Sorcery & Spirit World Ser.: Vol. 3). 1.25 ea. (ISBN 0-89985-953-4). Christ Nations.
--Satan's Demon Manifestations & Delusions. (Satan Ser.: Vol. 3). pap. 1.25 (ISBN 0-89985-955-0). Christ Nations.
Lindsey, Hal. Satan Is Alive & Well on Planet Earth. 256p. 1985. pap. 3.95 (ISBN 0-553-24406-X). Bantam.
Lindsey, Hal & Carlson, C. C. Satan Is Alive & Well on Planet Earth. 256p. (Orig.). 1974. pap. 4.95 (ISBN 0-310-27792-2, 18195P00687079X). Zondervan.
Nurbakhsh, Iavad. The Great Satan "EBLIS". Graham, Terry, et al, trs. 1986. pap. 6.00x (ISBN 0-933546-23-8). KhaniQahi-Nimatullahi-Sufi.
Penn-Lewis, Jessie & Roberts, Evan. War on the Saints. 9th ed. 1986. Repr. of 1912 ed. 10.50 (ISBN 0-913926-02-7). T E Lowe.
Pentecost, J. Dwight. Your Adversary the Devil. 192p. 1976. pap. 6.95 (ISBN 0-310-30911-5, 17010P). Zondervan.
Popoff, Peter. Six Things Satan Uses to Rob You of God's Abundant Blessings. Tanner, Don, ed. LC 81-86521. (Illus.). 96p. 1982. pap. 2.00 (ISBN 0-938544-11-X). Faith Messenger.
Rhodes, H. T. The Satanic Mass. 256p. 1974. 7.95 (ISBN 0-8065-0405-6). Citadel Pr.
Rice, George E. Christ in Colision. (Harvest Ser.). 112p. 1982. pap. 4.95 (ISBN 0-8163-0473-4). Pacific Pr Pub Assn.
Rudwin, Maximilian. The Devil in Legend & Literature. LC 73-85284. (Illus.). 365p. 1973. 22.95 (ISBN 0-87548-247-3); pap. 9.95 (ISBN 0-87548-248-1). Open Court.
Rudwin, Maximilian J. Devil in Legend & Literature. LC 71-111780. (Illus.). Repr. of 1931 ed. 14.50 (ISBN 0-404-05451-X). AMS Pr.
Russell, Jeffrey B. The Devil: Perceptions of Evil from Antiquity to Primitive Christianity. LC 77-3126. (Illus.). 288p. 1977. 27.50x (ISBN 0-8014-0938-1). Cornell U Pr.
--Lucifer: The Devil in the Middle Ages. LC 84-45153. (Illus.). 360p. 1986. pap. text ed. 12.95x (ISBN 0-8014-9429-X). Cornell U Pr.
--Mephistopheles: The Devil in the Modern World. LC 86-47648. (Illus.). 352p. 1986. text ed. 24.95x (ISBN 0-8014-1808-9). Cornell U Pr.
Sanders, J. Oswald. Satan Is No Myth. LC 74-15358. 1983. pap. 5.95 (ISBN 0-8024-7525-6). Moody.
Showers, Renald E. What on Earth Is God Doing? Satan's Conflict with God. LC 73-81551. 1973. pap. 3.95 (ISBN 0-87213-784-8). Loizeaux.
Spurgeon, C. H. Satan. 1978. pap. 1.95 (ISBN 0-686-23026-4). Pilgrim Pubns.
Steiner, Moses J. Satan in the Woods. LC 78-54567. 1978. 10.95 (ISBN 0-88400-057-5). Shengold.
Stowell, Joseph M. Kingdom Conflict. 156p. 1984. pap. 5.95 (ISBN 0-89693-376-8). Victor Bks.
Taylor, Jack R. Victory over the Devil. LC 72-96149. 128p. 1973. pap. 4.95 (ISBN 0-8054-5131-5). Broadman.
Tremmel, William C. Dark Side. Lambert, Herbert, ed. 160p. (Orig.). 1987. pap. 9.95 (ISBN 0-8272-0614-3). CBP.
Unger, Merrill F. Demons in the World Today. 1980. pap. 6.95 (ISBN 0-8423-0661-7). Tyndale.
Usher, Charles H. Satan: A Defeated Foe. 1964. pap. 1.95 (ISBN 0-87508-546-6). Chr Lit.
Voarhis, B. D. Satan Exposed. 1975. pap. 2.25 (ISBN 0-87148-785-3). Pathway Pr.
Wall, J. C. Devils. 59.95 (ISBN 0-8490-0025-4). Gordon Pr.
Wiersbe, Warren W. The Strategy of Satan. 1979. 3.95 (ISBN 0-8423-6665-2). Tyndale.

DEVIL IN LITERATURE

Anstice, R. H. Satan of Milton. LC 72-191957. 1910. lib. bdg. 10.00 (ISBN 0-8414-0289-2). Folcroft.
Hamilton, G. Rostrevor. Hero or Fool. LC 70-98995. (Studies in Milton, No. 22). 1970. pap. 19.95x (ISBN 0-8383-0038-3). Haskell.
--Hero or Fool: A Study of Milton's Satan. LC 74-16136. 1944. lib. bdg. 17.50 (ISBN 0-8414-4860-4). Folcroft.
Jurjevich, Ratibor-Ray. The Contemporary Faces of Satan. 437p. 1985. 21.95 (ISBN 0-930711-00-9); pap. 14.95 (ISBN 0-317-19630-8). Ichthys Bks.
Kelly, Henry A. The Devil at Baptism: Ritual, Theology, & Drama. LC 85-404. 304p. 1985. text ed. 29.95x (ISBN 0-8014-1806-2). Cornell U Pr.
Masson, David. Three Devils: Luther's, Milton's & Goethe's. LC 72-193946. 1874. lib. bdg. 20.00 (ISBN 0-8414-6495-2). Folcroft.
Milner, Max, ed. Entretiens Sur L'homme et le Diable. (Decades Du Centre Culturel International De Cerisy-la Salle, Nouvelle Ser.: No. 1). 1965. pap. 14.00x (ISBN 90-2796-012-7). Mouton.
Rudwin, Maximilian. The Devil in Legend & Literature. LC 73-85284. (Illus.). 365p. 1973. 22.95 (ISBN 0-87548-247-3); pap. 9.95 (ISBN 0-87548-248-1). Open Court.
Rudwin, Maximilian J. Devil in Legend & Literature. LC 71-111780. (Illus.). Repr. of 1931 ed. 14.50 (ISBN 0-404-05451-X). AMS Pr.
Russell, Jeffrey B. Lucifer: The Devil in the Middle Ages. LC 84-45153. (Illus.). 384p. 1984. 24.95x (ISBN 0-8014-1503-9). Cornell U Pr.
Tremmel, William C. Dark Side. Lambert, Herbert, ed. 160p. (Orig.). 1987. pap. 9.95 (ISBN 0-8272-0614-3). CBP.
Woodhull, Marianna. Epic of Paradise Lost. LC 72-194899. 1907. lib. bdg. 12.50 (ISBN 0-8414-9501-7). Folcroft.
--Epic of Paradise Lost: Twelve Essays. LC 68-57833. 386p. 1968. Repr. of 1907 ed. 32.50x (ISBN 0-87752-124-7). Gordian.

DEVOTION

see also Contemplation; Devotional Exercises; Prayer; Worship

Blitchington, Evelyn. The Family Devotions Idea Book. LC 82-4252. 139p. (Orig.). 1982. pap. 4.95 (ISBN 0-87123-254-5, 210254). Bethany Hse.
De Montfort, Louis. True Devotion. LC 63-12679. 1973. 3.50 (ISBN 0-8198-0517-3); pap. 2.50. Dghtrs St Paul.
Hagin, Kenneth E. Don't Blame God. 1979. pap. 0.50 mini bk. (ISBN 0-89276-056-7). Hagin Ministries.
--How to Write Your Own Ticket with God. 1979. mini bk. .50 (ISBN 0-89276-055-9). Hagin Ministries.
--Plead Your Case. 1979. pap. 0.50 mini bk. (ISBN 0-89276-058-3). Hagin Ministries.
--Words. 1979. pap. 0.50 mini bk. (ISBN 0-89276-057-5). Hagin Ministries.
--You Can Have What You Say. 1978. mini bk. 0.50 (ISBN 0-89276-054-0). Hagin Ministries.
Mueller, Charles S. Words of Faith: A Devotional Dictionary. 160p. (Orig.). 1985. pap. 5.95 (ISBN 0-570-03968-1, 12-3003). Concordia.
Palmer, Phobe. Entire Devotion to God. 2.95 (ISBN 0-686-27774-0). Schmul Pub Co.
Townsend, Ralph. Faith, Prayer & Devotion. (Faith & the Future Ser.). 123p. 1984. cloth 24.95x (ISBN 0-631-13189-2); pap. 8.95x (ISBN 0-631-13232-5). Basil Blackwell.

DEVOTIONAL CALENDARS

Alberione, James. Saint & Thought for Every Day. 1976. 4.50 (ISBN 0-8198-0471-1); pap. 3.50 (ISBN 0-8198-6800-0). Dghtrs St Paul.
Appleton, George. The Quiet Heart: Prayers & Meditations for Each Day of the Year. LC 84-6019. 480p. 1984. pap. 7.95 (ISBN 0-8006-1789-4). Fortress.
Aridas, Christopher. Soundings: A Thematic Guide for Daily Scripture Prayer. LC 83-16509. 224p. 1984. pap. 4.50 (ISBN 0-385-19157-X, Im). Doubleday.
Arnold, Emmy, ed. Inner Words for Every Day of the Year. LC 77-164915. 1963. 3.50 (ISBN 0-87486-101-2). Plough.
Bastin, Marcel, et al. God Day by Day, Vol. 2: Ordinary Time: Matthew. 576p. (Orig.). 1984. pap. 14.95 (ISBN 0-8091-2643-5). Paulist Pr.
--God Day by Day, Vol. 4: Advent & Christmas. 184p. (Orig.). 1985. pap. 8.95 (ISBN 0-8091-2699-0). Paulist Pr.
Baxter, J. Sidlow. Awake My Heart. 13.95 (ISBN 0-310-20590-5, 6729). Zondervan.
Bodo, Murray. Through the Year with Francis of Assisi: Daily Meditations from His Words & Life. LC 87-4158. (Illus.). 240p. 1987. pap. 7.95 (ISBN 0-385-23823-1, Im). Doubleday.
Broderick, Robert C. Days of Praise. 1977. 5.50 (ISBN 0-8199-0653-0). Franciscan Herald.
Bryant, Al. Time Out. pap. 2.95 (ISBN 0-310-22122-6). Zondervan.
Carmack, Rita J. Image to Image, Vol. II. 155p. 1986. pap. 5.00 (ISBN 0-937093-00-9). Jewel Pr.
Case, Charles C. Talking Trees & Singing Whales. Woolsey, Raymond H., ed. (Devotional Ser.). 365p. 1985. 7.95 (ISBN 0-8280-0285-1). Review & Herald.
Chambers, Oswald. Daily Thoughts for Disciples. 1976. 10.95 (ISBN 0-310-22400-4). Zondervan.
--Still Higher for His Highest. LC 75-120048. 1970. Repr. of 1970 ed. 8.95 (ISBN 0-310-22410-1, 6494); large print 6.95 (ISBN 0-310-22417-9, 12565L). Zondervan.
Christian Center Staff. Bible Birthday Book. 1983. 5.95t (ISBN 0-911346-06-6). Christianica.
Compton, LaNell. Looking Forward to a New Day. 1984. 7.95 (ISBN 0-8158-0418-0). Chris Mass.
Cook, Bob. Today with the King. 408p. 1985. 12.95 (ISBN 0-89693-364-4). Victor Bks.
Cowman, Mrs. Charles E. Streams in the Desert, Vol. 1. 9.95 (ISBN 0-310-22520-5, 6901, Pub. by Cowman). Zondervan.
--Streams in the Desert, Vol. 2. 1986. 9.95 (ISBN 0-310-22430-6, 6902, Pub. by Cowman). Zondervan.
Crussell, Leah A., ed. Three Hundred Sixty-Five Devotions, 1986-1987. 1986. pocket ed. 3.95 (ISBN 0-87403-003-X, 3087); pap. 5.95 (ISBN 0-87403-004-8, 4087). Standard Pub.
Daily Light on the Daily Path. 9.95 (ISBN 0-310-23060-8, 18011); pap. 5.95 (ISBN 0-310-23061-6, 18012P). Zondervan.
Day by Day. 365p. (Orig.). 1986. pap. 5.95 (ISBN 0-86683-536-9, HarpR). Har-Row.
De Haan, Richard W. & Bosch, Henry G., eds. Our Daily Bread Favorites. 384p. 1971. 10.95 (ISBN 0-310-23590-1). Zondervan.
De Pree, Gordon & De Pree, Gladis. Blade of Grass. LC 65-19504. 1971. pap. 4.95 (ISBN 0-310-23641-X). Zondervan.
Doward, Jan S. The Moment to Decide. Woolsey, Raymond H., ed. (Daily Devotional Ser.). 384p. 1984. 7.95 (ISBN 0-8280-0234-7). Review & Herald.
Draper, Edythe. Living Light. Incl. Large Print Edition. 1976. kivar 8.95 (ISBN 0-8423-2652-9). 1972. leatherette o.p. 8.95 (ISBN 0-8423-2651-0). Tyndale.
Gockel, Herman W. Daily Walk with God. 1982. 15.95 (ISBN 0-570-03298-9, 15-2171); pap. 10.95 (ISBN 0-570-03855-3, 12YY2810). Concordia.
Goodyear, Imogene, ed. Daily Bread, 1987. 1986. pap. 8.00 (ISBN 0-8309-0435-2). Herald Hse.
Hanson, Virginia. Gifts of the Lotus. LC 74-5130. 192p. (Orig.). 1974. pap. 3.50 (ISBN 0-8356-0450-0, Quest). Theos Pub Hse.
Hills, Desmond B. Light for My Life. Van Dolson, Bobbie J., ed. 384p. 1981. 7.95 (ISBN 0-8280-0041-7). Review & Herald.
Huxhold, Harry N. Family Altar. rev. ed. 1964. 12.95 (ISBN 0-570-03071-4, 6-1085). Concordia.
Jacobs, Joy. They Were Women Like Me: Women of the New Testament in Devotions for Today. 216p. 1985. 14.95 (ISBN 0-13-917048-0); pap. 7.95 (ISBN 0-13-917030-8). P-H.

Journeying Through the Days 1987. 272p. (Orig.). 1986. pap. 10.95 (ISBN 0-8358-0541-7). Upper Room.

Killinger, John. A Devotional Guide to the Gospels: Three Hundred Sixty-Six Meditations. 588p. 1984. Repr. 14.95 (ISBN 0-8499-3008-1, 3008-1). Word Bks.

MacDonald, George. Diary of an Old Soul. LC 65-12143. 132p. 1965. pap. 6.95 (ISBN 0-8066-1503-6, 10-1895). Augsburg.

Magers, Mary A. Holy Horoscopes...for Those under the Sign of the Cross. LC 85-50451. 112p. 1985. 6.95 (ISBN 0-938232-74-6). Winston-Derek.

More, Thomas. A Book for All Seasons. Reynolds, E. E., ed. 1978. 8.95 (ISBN 0-87243-079-0). Templegate.

Mother Teresa. Jesus, the Word to Be Spoken: A Daily Devotional. 1987. 9.95 (ISBN 0-8027-2574-0). Walker & Co.

Murray, Andrew. Every Day with Andrew Murray. rev. ed. Tr. of God's Best Secret. 208p. 1986. pap. 3.95 (ISBN 0-89283-302-5, Pub. by Vine Books). Servant.

--God's Best Secrets. 1986. pap. 9.95 (ISBN 0-310-29711-7, 10391P). Zondervan.

My Living Counselor: Daily Readings form the Living Bible. LC 76-43126. (Illus.). 736p. 1976. kivar bdg. 4.95 (ISBN 0-87788-573-7). Shaw Pubs.

Raskas, Bernard S. Heart of Wisdom-One. 1962. 8.50 (ISBN 0-8381-2102-0). United Syn Bk.

--Heart of Wisdom-Two. 1979. 9.50 (ISBN 0-8381-2104-7). United Syn Bk.

Rogness, Alvin N. The Word for Every Day: Three Hundred & Sixty-Five Devotional Reading. LC 81-65650. 376p. 1981. kivar 12.95 (ISBN 0-8066-1886-8, 10-7284). Augsburg.

Russell, Arthur J., ed. God at Eventide. 1950. 9.95 (ISBN 0-396-03183-8). Dodd.

--God Calling: A Devotional Diary. 10.95 (ISBN 0-396-02621-4). Dodd.

Schneider, Yvonne. Life's Candle Light. 82p. pap. 5.95 (ISBN 0-942494-29-6). Coleman Pub.

Schuller, Robert H. Daily Power Thoughts. LC 77-68012. 1978. 9.95 (ISBN 0-89081-131-8); pap. 6.95 (ISBN 0-89081-123-7). Harvest Hse.

Sheen, Fulton. Through the Year with Fulton Sheen: Inspiration Selections for Each Day of the Year. 213p. 1985. pap. 6.95 (ISBN 0-89283-236-3). Servant.

Sprague, Betty. The Little Blank Book. (Illus.). 64p. 1982. pap. 5.95 (ISBN 0-942494-24-5). Coleman Pub.

Spurgeon, Charles H. Daily Help. 1959. 4.95 (ISBN 0-399-12825-5, G&D). Putnam Pub Group.

Stamm, Millie. Meditation Moments for Women. 1967. pap. 7.95 (ISBN 0-310-32981-7). Zondervan.

Tileston, Mary W. Daily Strength for Daily Needs. 1942. 7.70i (ISBN 0-316-84592-2). Little.

Tileston, Mary W., ed. Daily Strength for Daily Needs. 1959. 4.95 (ISBN 0-399-12826-3, G&D). Putnam Pub Group.

Van Pelt, Nancy L. The Compleat Tween. Coffen, Richard W., ed. 96p. (Orig.). 1986. pap. 5.95 (ISBN 0-8280-0288-6). Review & Herald.

Watson, David. How to Find God. LC 76-43125. 157p. 1976. pap. 1.95 (ISBN 0-87788-390-4). Shaw Pubs.

White, Anne S. Healing Devotions. LC 75-5218. 138p. 1975. pap. 3.95 (ISBN 0-8192-1192-3). Morehouse.

Wolf, Carol. Women's Devotional Talks for Special Occasions. 64p. (Orig.). 1984. pap. 3.95 (ISBN 0-87239-745-9, 2976). Standard Pub.

Wurmbrand, Richard. Reaching Toward the Heights. 1979. pap. 7.95x (ISBN 0-88264-142-5). Diane Bks.

DEVOTIONAL EXERCISES

see also Church Music; Devotional Calendars; Hymns; Liturgies; Lord's Prayer; Lord's Supper; Meditations; Prayer

also subdivision Prayer-books and Devotions under particular denominations

Ammerman, Leila T. Inspiring Devotional Programs for Women's Groups. (Paperback Program Ser). 1971. pap. 3.50 (ISBN 0-8010-0015-7). Baker Bk.

Andersen, Richard. Devotions for Church School Teachers. LC 76-2158. 64p. 1976. pap. 2.25 (ISBN 0-570-03722-0, 12-2624). Concordia.

Anderson, Evelyn M. Good Morning, Lord: Devotions for Women. (Good Morning Lord Ser.). 1971. 4.95 (ISBN 0-8010-0023-8). Baker Bk.

Andrewes, Lancelot. Private Devotions of Lancelot Andrewes. Brightman, F. E., tr. & intro. by. 15.25 (ISBN 0-8446-1534-X). Peter Smith.

Arthur, Kay. How Can I Live. 528p. (Orig.). 1981. pap. 7.95 (ISBN 0-8007-5077-2, Power Bks). Revell.

Association for Research & Enlightenment, Readings Research Dept., compiled by. Daily Living. (Library: Vol. 12). 241p. 1981. 10.95 (ISBN 0-87604-133-0). ARE Pr.

Aven, Russell E. Devotions for Laymen...by a Layman. LC 81-67751. 1982. pap. 6.50 (ISBN 0-8054-5185-4). Broadman.

Bailey, Robert W. The Joy of Discipleship. LC 81-69402. 1982. pap. 5.95 (ISBN 0-8054-5188-9). Broadman.

Beyerle, Edith M., compiled by. Daily Meditations, 4 vols. 120p. Vol. 2. pap. 0.50 (ISBN 0-87509-075-3); Vol. 3. pap. 0.50 (ISBN 0-87509-076-1); Vol. 4. pap. 0.50 (ISBN 0-87509-077-X). Chr Pubns.

Biddle, Perry H., Jr. The Goodness of Marriage: A Devotional Book for Newlyweds. LC 84-50840. 144p. 1984. 6.95 (ISBN 0-8358-0490-9). Upper Room.

Billheimer, Paul. Don't Waste Your Sorrows. 1977. pap. 4.95 (ISBN 0-87508-007-3). Chr Lit.

Bimler, Rich & Brokering, Herb. Lord, I Want to Celebrate. 1980. pap. 2.95 (ISBN 0-570-03069-2, 06-1185). Concordia.

Bolding, Amy. Dynamic Fingertip Devotions. (Paperback Program Ser.). 1977. pap. 3.95 (ISBN 0-8010-0708-9). Baker Bk.

--Please Give a Devotion. 1963. 3.95 (ISBN 0-8010-0819-0). Baker Bk.

--Please Give a Devotion for All Occasions. 1967. pap. 4.45 (ISBN 0-8010-0519-1). Baker Bk.

--Stimulating Devotions for Church Groups. 144p. 1986. pap. 4.95 (ISBN 0-8010-0921-9). Baker Bk.

Bridget. The Magnificent Prayers of Saint Bridget of Sweden. (Illus.). 19p. 1983. pap. 1.00 (ISBN 0-89555-220-5). TAN Bks Pubs.

Brokering, Herbert. I Opener. LC 74-4912. (YA) 1974. pap. 2.50 (ISBN 0-570-06472-4, 12-2584). Concordia.

Bryant, Al, ed. New Every Morning: Three Hundred Sixty-Six Daily Meditations from Your Favorite Christian Writers. 224p. 1985. 9.95 (ISBN 0-8499-0507-9, 0507-9). Word Bks.

Bundschuh, Rick. Glow in the Dark. LC 86-31350. (Illus.). 148p. (Orig.). pap. 4.25 (ISBN 0-8307-1091-4, S182323). Regal.

Carmack, Rita J. Image to Image, Vol. 1. 146p. 1985. pap. 5.00 (ISBN 0-88144-047-7). Jewel Pr.

Carstens, Christopher & Mahedy, William. Right Here, Right Now: Spiritual Exercises for Busy Christians. 1985. 9.95 (ISBN 0-345-31801-3, Pub. by Ballantine Epiphany). Ballantine.

--Right Here, Right Now: Spiritual Exercises for Busy Christians. 1987. pap. 2.95 (ISBN 0-345-34018-3, Pub. by Ballantine Epiphany). Ballantine.

Caulfield, Sean. Under the Broom Tree. LC 82-60593. 80p. 1983. pap. 4.95 (ISBN 0-8091-2493-9). Paulist Pr.

Chadwick. Twenty-Five Mornings & Evenings. pap. 3.95 (ISBN 0-686-12924-5). Schmul Pub Co.

Chambers, Oswald. Daily Thoughts for Disciples. 208p. 1985. 8.95 (ISBN 0-310-30470-9). Zondervan.

--Servant As His Lord. 1973. pap. 2.95 (ISBN 0-87508-137-1). Chr Lit.

Chapian, Marie. Am I the Only One Here with Faded Genes? (Teen Devotionals Ser.). (Illus.). 192p. 1987. pap. 5.95 (ISBN 0-87123-945-0). Bethany Hse.

Chautard, Jean-Baptiste. The Soul of the Apostolate. 1977. pap. 6.00 (ISBN 0-89555-031-8). TAN Bks Pubs.

Chinmoy, Sri. Songs of the Soul. 96p. (Orig.). 1983. pap. 5.00 (ISBN 0-88497-738-2). Aum Pubns.

Clanton, Bruce. Family Adventures. LC 80-51060. 1980. pap. 4.95 (ISBN 0-89390-018-4). Resource Pubns.

Cooper, Davis. Daily Devotions for Newlyweds. LC 81-67204. 1983. 8.95 (ISBN 0-8054-5646-5). Broadman.

Coppolino, Joseph, compiled by. A Book of Devotions. 68p. (Orig.). 1986. pap. 1.75 (ISBN 0-8189-0502-6). Alba.

Cowman, Charles E. & Serrano, Antonio. Manantiales en el Desierto. Orig. Title: Stream in the Desert. 1986. pap. 4.95 (ISBN 0-311-40028-0, Edit Mundo). Casa Bautista.

Cowman, Mrs. Charles E. Streams in the Desert, Vol. 2. large print ed. 384p. 1976. 9.95 (ISBN 0-310-22537-X, 12557L). Zondervan.

Crum, Mary A. A Giggle Goes a Long Way. 96p. 1986. 4.95 (ISBN 0-8010-2510-9). Baker Bk.

Cully, Iris V. We Give Thanks. (Illus., Orig.). 1976. pap. text ed. 1.95x (ISBN 0-8192-4070-2); tchr's. ed. 4.50x (ISBN 0-8192-4069-9); guidebk. for parents 1.95x (ISBN 0-8192-4071-0). Morehouse.

DelBene, Ron & Montgomery, Herb. Alone with God: A Place for Your Time Together. 120p. (Orig.). 1984. pap. 4.95 (ISBN 0-86683-856-2, 8434, HarpR). Har-Row.

De Mello, Anthony. Sadhana: A Way to God, Christian Exercises in Eastern Form. LC 78-70521. (Study Aids on Jesuit Topics: No. 9). 146p. 1978. pap. 4.95 (ISBN 0-912422-46-7). Inst Jesuit.

Denny, Randal E. Personal Devotions. (Christian Living Ser.). 32p. (Orig.). 1987. pap. write for info. (ISBN 0-8341-1186-1). Beacon Hill.

Duckworth, John, et al, eds. The Battle. (Pacesetter Ser.). 64p. 1987. tchr's. ed. 7.95. Cook.

Edwards, Deborah. Opening Devotions for Womens Groups. 96p. 1985. pap. 4.95 (ISBN 0-8010-3428-0). Baker Bk.

Fair, Harold L. Class Devotions, 1986-1987: For Use with the 1986-1987 International Lesson Annual. 128p. (Orig.). 1986. pap. 6.50 (ISBN 0-687-08626-4). Abingdon.

--Class Devotions, 1987-1988. 128p. 1987. pap. 6.50 (ISBN 0-687-08627-2). Abingdon.

Finney, Charles. Principles of Devotion. rev. ed. Parkhurst, Louis, ed. 288p. 1987. pap. 6.95 (ISBN 0-87123-873-X). Bethany Hse.

Foley, Leonard. Signs of Love: The Sacraments of Christ. (Illus.). 1976. pap. 1.95 (ISBN 0-912228-32-6). St Anthony Mess Pr.

Fosdick, Harry E. The Meaning of Prayer. LC 76-50560. 1976. Repr. of 1946 ed. lib. bdg. 18.50 (ISBN 0-8414-4159-6). Folcroft.

French, Curtis. Winning Words: Devotions for Athletes. LC 77-75467. 1983. pap. 5.95 (ISBN 0-8499-2805-2). Word Bks.

Fritz, Patricia. Te Alabamos Senor: We Praise You O Lord. Sarre, Alicia, tr. from Span. 112p. 1984. pap. 3.95 (ISBN 0-8091-2641-9). Paulist Pr.

Goldsmith, Joel S. The Letters. 299p. 1980. pap. 5.95 (ISBN 0-87516-386-6). De Vorss.

Graham, Billy. Unto the Hills: A Devotional Treasury from Billy Graham. 384p. 1986. 14.95 (ISBN 0-8499-0603-2). Word Bks.

Grubb, Norman P. Who Am I? 1975. pap. 2.95 (ISBN 0-87508-227-0). Chr Lit.

Gust, Dodie. As I Take Christ: Daily Prayer & Reflection with Paul. LC 86-72439. 136p. (Orig.). 1987. pap. 4.95 (ISBN 0-87793-352-9). Ave Maria.

Hall, Carolyn. Does God Give Interviews? 56p. 1985. 7.95 (ISBN 0-533-06644-1). Vantage.

Hall, Manly P. Is Each Individual Born with a Purpose? pap. 2.50 (ISBN 0-89314-325-1). Philos Res.

--Lone Traveler. pap. 2.50 (ISBN 0-89314-329-4). Philos Res.

--White Bird of Tao. pap. 4.00 (ISBN 0-89314-371-5). Philos Res.

--Wisdom Beyond the Mind. pap. 2.50 (ISBN 0-89314-372-3). Philos Res.

Hall, Terry. Finally, Family Devotions That Work. (Orig.). 1986. pap. 5.95 (ISBN 0-8024-2538-0). Moody.

Havergal, F. R. Morning Bells. pap. 2.25 (ISBN 0-685-88387-6). Reiner.

--Royal Bounty. pap. 1.95 (ISBN 0-685-88391-4). Reiner.

Havergal, Frances R. Opened Treasures. LC 62-21063. 1962. 7.95 (ISBN 0-87213-320-6). Loizeaux.

Havner, Vance. Consider Jesus. 104p. 1987. pap. 4.95 (ISBN 0-8010-4306-9). Baker Bk.

Hayes, Edward L. The Focused Life. 96p. 1986. 4.95 (ISBN 0-8010-4297-6). Baker Bk.

Hembree, Ron. Good Morning, Lord: Devotions for New Christians. (Good Morning, Lord Ser.). 96p. 1983. 4.95 (ISBN 0-8010-4271-2). Baker Bk.

--Good Morning, Lord: More Five Minute Devotions. (Good Morning, Lord Ser.). 64p. 1977. Repr. 3.95 (ISBN 0-8010-4178-3). Baker Bk.

Henry Duke Of Lancaster. Livre de Seyntz Medicines. Arnould, E. J., ed. 1967. Repr. of 1940 ed. 19.00 (ISBN 0-384-22400-8). Johnson Repr.

Hicks, Robert F. The Gift of Goodness. Jenkins, Simon, ed. (The Gift of... Ser.). (Illus.). 24p. 1984. pap. 1.25 (ISBN 0-687-14698-4). Abingdon.

Hilton, Walter. The Stairway of Perfection. LC 78-60288. 1979. pap. 4.95 (ISBN 0-385-14059-2, Im). Doubleday.

Hufstader, Anselm. God's Time Is the Best Time. (Ways of Prayer Ser.: Vol. 11). 8.95 (ISBN 0-89453-386-X); pap. 4.95 (ISBN 0-89453-385-1). M Glazier.

Jennings, Don. A Spiritual Almanac: Guidelines for Better Living Each Month of the Year. 240p. 1984. pap. 5.95 (ISBN 0-13-834748-4). P-H.

Jones, E. Stanley. In Christ. (Festival Bks.). 1980. pap. 2.25 (ISBN 0-687-18786-9). Abingdon.

Journeying Through the Days, 1986. 1985. spiral bdg. 10.95 (ISBN 0-8358-0523-9, Dist. by Abingdon Press). Upper Room.

King, J. Norman. Experiencing God All Ways & Every Day. 160p. (Orig.). 1982. pap. 7.95 (ISBN 0-86683-632-2, HarpR). Har-Row.

Knight, David. To Follow His Way: A Parish Renewal Program. 112p. (Orig.). 1980. pap. 3.95 (ISBN 0-912228-70-9). St Anthony Mess Pr.

Knight, David M. Make Me A Sabbath of Your Heart. 6.95 (ISBN 0-87193-191-5). Dimension Bks.

Lapp, Rhonda S. Devotionals for Nurses. (Ultra Bks.). 4.95 (ISBN 0-8010-5539-3). Baker Bk.

Lloyd-Jones, D. Martyn. First Book of Daily Readings. 1970. pap. 6.95 (ISBN 0-8028-1354-2). Eerdmans.

Loeks, Mary F. The Glorious Names of God. 1986. pap. 3.95 (ISBN 0-8010-5629-2). Baker Bk.

McCarroll, Tolbert. Notes from the Song of Life. rev. ed. LC 77-7135. (Illus.). 144p. (Orig.). 1986. pap. 6.95. Celestial Arts.

McCarthy, David. Devotions from a Stamp Album. 104p. 1983. pap. 4.95 (ISBN 0-8010-6156-3). Baker Bk.

McCumber, William. Take a Bible Break. 115p. 1986. pap. 3.95 (ISBN 0-8341-1080-6). Beacon Hill.

McDaniel, Audrey. Hope for Every Heart. LC 85-29110. 1986. 5.50 (ISBN 0-8054-5031-9). Broadman.

Maloney, George A. Singers of the New Song: A Mystical Interpretation of the Song of Songs. LC 85-71639. 176p. (Orig.). 1985. pap. 4.95 (ISBN 0-87793-292-1). Ave Maria.

Martin, Paul. Good Night, Lord. 64p. 1974. 1.95 (ISBN 0-8341-0241-2). Beacon Hill.

Miller. Devotional Dramas for Christmas. LC 72-79175. 1.95 (ISBN 0-8054-7510-9). Broadman.

Mohr, David & Schwartz, Faye. From Birth to Death. 1983. 2.50 (ISBN 0-89536-599-5, 0604). CSS of Ohio.

Monsma, Hester, compiled by. Devotions for Boys & Girls. (Devotions for Daily Living Ser.). 30p. 1982. pap. 1.50 (ISBN 0-8010-2924-4). Baker Bk.

--Devotions for Those Who Are Recovering. (Devotions for Daily Living Ser.). 30p. 1982. pap. 1.25 (ISBN 0-8010-2919-8). Baker Bk.

--Devotions for Today's Teens. (Devotions for Daily Living Ser.). 30p. 1982. pap. 1.25 (ISBN 0-8010-2923-6). Baker Bk.

Moody, Timothy E. Devotional Talks on Christian Commitment. (Devotional Resources for Adults Ser.). 96p. 1986. 4.95 (ISBN 0-8010-6203-9). Baker Bk.

Morris, Henry M. Days of Praise. (Illus.). 388p. (Orig.). 1986. pap. 9.95 (ISBN 0-89051-116-0). Master Bks.

Murphey. Devotions for Travelers. 1.95 (ISBN 0-318-18171-1). WCTU.

Murray, Andrew. Aids to Devotions. 1961. pap. 2.95 (ISBN 0-87508-378-1). Chr Lit.

--Daily Thoughts on Holiness. 1977. 6.95 (ISBN 0-87508-369-2). Chr Lit.

--Let Us Draw Nigh. 1962. pap. 2.95 (ISBN 0-87508-379-X). Chr Lit.

--Secret of Adoration. (Secret Ser.). (Orig.). 1979. pap. 1.95 (ISBN 0-87508-384-6). Chr Lit.

Nee, Watchman. Joyful Heart. 1977. pap. 3.95 (ISBN 0-87508-417-6). Chr Lit.

Nelson, Edward W. Que Mi Pueblo Adore. Mussiett, Salomon C., tr. from Eng. Tr. of Music & Worship. (Span.). 184p. 1986. pap. 5.00 (ISBN 0-311-17029-3). Casa Bautista.

O'Connor, Elizabeth. Our Many Selves. LC 78-124699. 1971. pap. 4.95 (ISBN 0-06-066336-7, RD-36, HarpR). Har-Row.

Palmer, Bernard & Palmer, Marjorie. Light a Small Candle. LC 82-84439. 1982. 10.95 (ISBN 0-911802-54-1). Free Church Pubns.

Parker, Clayton A. My Will Be Done. 201p. 1982. pap. 3.00 (ISBN 0-686-86578-2, 0-9606438). C A Parker Pubns.

Patterson, Ward. Under His Wings. LC 86-70646. 160p. 1986. pap. 6.95 (ISBN 0-89636-216-7). Accent Bks.

Pennington, M. Basil. Daily We Follow Him: Learning Discipleship from Peter. LC 86-20157. 160p. 1987. pap. 4.95 (ISBN 0-385-23535-6, Im). Doubleday.

Pratt, Louis. Sing Praises to His Name. Sherer, Michael L., ed. (Orig.). 1986. pap. 6.75 (ISBN 0-89536-831-5, 6845). CSS of Ohio.

Quoist, Michel. Living Words. 5.95 (ISBN 0-87193-196-6). Dimension Bks.

Reid, David R. Devotions for Growing Christians. 256p. (Orig.). 1986. pap. 4.95 (ISBN 0-87213-701-5). Loizeaux.

Rey, Greta. Good Morning, Lord: Devotions for Young Teens. (Good Morning, Lord Ser.). 96p. 1983. 4.95 (ISBN 0-8010-7719-2). Baker Bk.

Rogahn, Kenneth W. Begin with Prayer: Prayers & Devotional Outlines for Church Meetings. 112p. 1985. 6.95 (ISBN 0-570-03962-2, 15-2178). Concordia.

Rouse, Richard & Rouse, Susan. The Last Week. 1985. 1.00 (ISBN 0-89536-726-2, 5810). CSS of Ohio.

Russell, A. J. A Treasury of Devotion. 432p. 1986. 16.95 (ISBN 0-396-08885-6). Dodd.

Russell, Arthur J., ed. God at Eventide. 156p. 1974. pap. 2.75 (ISBN 0-8007-8154-6, Spire Bks). Revell.

Seaman, Joanna S. Thirty Days to Victorious Living: A Devotional Workbook. 84p. (Orig.). 1986. pap. write for info. (ISBN 0-939113-00-7). Ansley Pubns.

Shibley, David & Shibley, Naomi. More Special Times with God. LC 84-3485. 168p. 1984. 5.95 (ISBN 0-8407-5363-2). Nelson.

Simmons, Patricia A. Between You & Me, God. LC 74-79486. 1974. pap. 5.95 (ISBN 0-8054-4412-2, 4244-12). Broadman.

Sivewright, Gary. Following. 32p. 1986. pap. 1.50 (ISBN 0-8341-1127-6). Beacon Hill.

Smith, Bailey E. Nothing but the Blood. (Orig.). 1987. pap. 6.95 (ISBN 0-8054-1537-8). Broadman.

Smith, Hannah W. Daily Devotions from the Christian's Secret of a Happy Life. Hill, Robert C., ed. 288p. (Orig.). 1984. pap. 5.95 (ISBN 0-8007-5139-6, Power Bks). Revell.

Smith, Harold I. More Than "I Do". Devotions for the Engaged Couple. 1983p. (Orig.). 1983. pap. 2.95 (ISBN 0-8341-0805-4). Beacon Hill.

Smith, Harold I., compiled by. The Quotable Bresee. 280p. (Orig.). 1983. pap. 5.95 (ISBN 0-8341-0835-6). Beacon Hill.

Snyder, Bernadette. Hoorays & Hosannas. LC 80-66937. (Illus.). 56p. (Orig.). 1980. pap. 3.95 (ISBN 0-87793-205-0). Ave Maria.

Spencer, Duane. Ephesians for the Family: A Daily Devotional Commentary. 336p. 1984. 12.95 (ISBN 0-8059-2942-8). Dorrance.

Spurgeon, Charles H. Morning & Evening. 774p. Date not set. 13.95 (ISBN 0-917006-26-7). Hendrickson MA.

Stone, James. How to Have Powerful Daily Devotions. (How To Ser.). 81p. (Orig.). 1983. pap. 2.50 (ISBN 0-934942-33-1). White Wing Pub.

Taylor, Bonnie. Devotions for New Mothers. 128p. 1987. 10.95 (ISBN 0-8170-1081-5); pap. 6.95 (ISBN 0-8170-1115-3). Judson.

Ten Boom, Corrie. Cada Nuevo Dia. Clifford, Alejandro, tr. from Eng. Tr. of Each New Day. 224p. 1983. pap. 4.50 (ISBN 0-311-40043-4, Edit Mundo). Casa Bautista.

Thornton, Edward E., ed. A Love That Heals. LC 83-21083. 1984. pap. 3.75 (ISBN 0-8054-5105-6). Broadman.

Vandermey, Mary A. Sparkling Devotions for Women's Groups. 144p. 1985. pap. 4.95 (ISBN 0-8010-9300-7). Baker Bk.

Vonk, Idalee. Thirty-Six Devotionals for Women's Groups. LC 81-52993. 112p. (Orig.). 1982. pap. 3.95 (ISBN 0-87239-493-X, 3216). Standard Pub.

Walsh, Albert J. Reflections on Death & Grief. 96p. 1986. 4.50 (ISBN 0-8010-9673-1). Baker Bk.

Ward, Ruth. Devotions: A Family Affair. (Directory Bks.). 64p. 1981. pap. 2.45 (ISBN 0-8010-9632-4). Baker Bk.

Watkins, James N. Devotional Pursuits: Truth & Trivia. 96p. (Orig.). 1986. pap. 3.95 (ISBN 0-8341-1139-X). Beacon Hill.

Weatherhead, Leslie D. Leslie D. Weatherhead Library, 8 vols. Set in Slipcase. 17.50 (ISBN 0-687-21373-8). Abingdon.

Weisheit, Eldon. God's Love for God's Children: Story Devotion for Family Time. LC 86-3397. (Illus.). 256p. (Orig.). 1986. kivar paper 9.95 (ISBN 0-8066-2213-X, 10-2680). Augsburg.

--God's Word in a Child's World: Messages & Guidelines for Sharing the Gospel with Children. LC 86-3442. 128p. (Orig.). 1986. pap. 6.95 (ISBN 0-8066-2214-8, 10-2745). Augsburg.

Wesley, John. Devotions & Prayers of John Wesley. (Devotional Classics). 1977. pap. 2.95 (ISBN 0-8010-9597-2). Baker Bk.

Wiersbe, Warren W. A Time to Be Renewed. Adair, James, ed. 400p. 1986. pap. 12.95 (ISBN 0-89693-391-1). Victor Bks.

Wiersbe, Warren W. & Wiersbe, David W. Devotional Talks for People Who Do God's Business. 96p. 1986. pap. 5.95 (ISBN 0-8010-9675-8). Baker Bk.

The Wonderful Names of Our Wonderful Lord. LC 79-50205. 1979. Repr. deluxe ed. 8.95 (ISBN 0-88270-365-X). Bridge Pub.

Wood, Robert. Thirty Days Are Not Enough: More Images for Meditative Journaling. 112p. (Orig.). 1983. pap. 3.75 (ISBN 0-8358-0445-3). Upper Room.

Yates, Elizabeth. A Book of Hours. 128p. 1985. pap. 4.95 large print ed. (ISBN 0-8027-2484-1). Walker & Co.

DEVOTIONAL LITERATURE

see also Religious Literature; also subdivision Devotional Literature under specific subjects, e.g. Jesus christ–devotional Literature

Adams, Jay E. Time Is at Hand. 1970. pap. 3.50 (ISBN 0-87552-060-X). Presby & Reformed.

Adams, Jay E. & Thompson, Lyle A. Predicar Al Corazon-Bosquejos Selectos. Carrodeguas, Angel A., tr. from English. (Span.). 175p. 1986. pap. 2.95 (ISBN 0-8297-0699-2). Life Pubs Intl.

Adams, Judith. Against the Gates of Hell. 152p. pap. 2.50 (ISBN 0-87509-232-2). Chr Pubns.

Alberione, James. Call to Total Consecration. 1974. 3.00 (ISBN 0-8198-0312-X); pap. 2.00 (ISBN 0-8198-0313-8). Dghtrs St Paul.

--Month with Saint Paul. 1952. pap. 2.25 (ISBN 0-8198-0104-6). Dghtrs St Paul.

Alberione, James J. Personality & Configuration with Christ. (Orig.). 3.50 (ISBN 0-8198-0120-8); pap. 2.50 (ISBN 0-8198-0121-6). Dghtrs St Paul.

Allen, Charles L. God's Psychiatry. 1984. pap. 2.95 (ISBN 0-515-08234-1). Jove Pubns.

Allen, R. Praise: A Matter of Life & Breath. Chan, Silas, tr. (Chinese.). 204p. 1982. pap. write for info. (ISBN 0-941598-04-7). Living Spring Pubns.

Allen, R. Earl. Good Morning, Lord: Devotions for Hospital Patients. 96p. 1975. 4.95 (ISBN 0-8010-0079-3). Baker Bk.

Allen, Ronald B. & Borror, Gordon. Worship: Rediscovering the Missing Jewel. (Critical Concern Bks.). 1987. pap. 7.95 (ISBN 0-88070-140-4). Multnomah.

Allison, Joseph D. The Devotional Resource Guide: Selecting the Best in Classic & Contemporary Christian Literature. 176p. 1986. pap. 8.95 (ISBN 0-8407-5950-9). Nelson.

Anderson, Debby. God Gives Me a Smile. LC 85-71985. (Illus.). 24p. 1985. comb bdg. 3.95 (ISBN 0-89191-669-5, 56697). Cook.

--God Is the Greatest. LC 85-71986. (Illus.). 24p. 1985. comb bdg. 3.95 (ISBN 0-89191-673-3, 56739). Cook.

Anderson, Robert. Forgotten Truths. LC 80-17526. (Sir Robert Anderson Library). 166p. 1980. pap. 4.50 (ISBN 0-8254-2130-6). Kregel.

Arbour, Basil. The Final Gift: A New Way of the Cross. (Illus.). 64p. 1981. pap. 2.95 (ISBN 0-86683-647-0, HarpR). Har-Row.

Armstrog, William H. Minister Heal Thyself. 64p. (Orig.). 1985. pap. 4.95 (ISBN 0-8298-0551-6). Pilgrim NY.

Arnold, Eberhard. The Inner Land, Vol. 1: The Inner Life. LC 74-18434. 1975. postpaid 3.50 (ISBN 0-87486-153-5). Plough.

Arnold, Edwin, tr. from Sanskrit. Song Celestial: Bhagavad-Gita. 176p. 1985. Repr. 3.50 (ISBN 0-87612-210-1). Self Realization.

Asbury, Francis. Heart & Church. pap. 4.95 (ISBN 0-686-23583-5). Schmul Pub Co.

Ashcraft, Morris. The Will of God. LC 80-65714. 1980. pap. 4.95 (ISBN 0-8054-1620-X). Broadman.

Augsburger, David. The Freedom of Forgiveness. 128p. 1973. pap. 3.50 (ISBN 0-8024-2875-4). Moody.

Aultman, Donald S. Learning Christian Leadership. 1960. 4.95 (ISBN 0-87148-501-X). Pathway Pr.

Bach, Marcus. Make It an Adventure. LC 75-32232. 206p. 1975. pap. 6.95 (ISBN 0-918936-01-2). Astara.

--The Will to Believe. 186p. 1973. pap. 7.50 (ISBN 0-911336-46-X). Sci of Mind.

Backman, Pat & Geiger, Lura J. Braided Streams: Leader's Guide. 128p. (Orig.). 1986. pap. 12.95 spiral bound (ISBN 0-931055-09-1). LuraMedia.

Baillie, John. A Diary of Readings. 400p. 1986. pap. 4.95 (ISBN 0-02-048360-0, Collier). Macmillan.

Baker, H. A. Visions Beyond the Veil. 1973. pap. 3.95 (ISBN 0-88368-019-X). Whitaker Hse.

Baldree, J. Martin. Sunday School Growth. 1971. 5.25 (ISBN 0-87148-761-6); pap. 4.25 (ISBN 0-87148-762-4). Pathway Pr.

Bankson, Marjory Z. Seasons of Friendship: Naomi & Ruth As a Pattern. Broucek, Marcia, ed. 200p. (Orig.). 1987. pap. 9.95 (ISBN 0-931055-41-5). LuraMedia.

Bardsley, Herbert J. Reconstructions of Early Christian Documents. 1977. lib. bdg. 59.95 (ISBN 0-8490-2504-4). Gordon Pr.

Baring-Gould, Sabine. Eastern Orthodox Saints. pap. 0.95 (ISBN 0-686-01292-5). Eastern Orthodox.

Barrus, David F. The Way to the Sun: A Guide to Celestial Living. 104p. 1972. 5.95 (ISBN 0-88290-008-0). Horizon Utah.

Barton, Ralph. God's Country. 59.95 (ISBN 0-8490-0242-7). Gordon Pr.

Basham, Don. Lead Us Not into Temptation. (Quality Paper Ser.). 1986. pap. 6.95 (ISBN 0-8007-9082-0, Chosen Bks). Revell.

Bassett, Paul M. Keep the Wonder. 61p. 1979. pap. 1.95 (ISBN 0-8341-0608-6). Beacon Hill.

Bawa Muhaiyaddeen, M. R. A Book of God's Love. LC 81-4503. (Illus.). 126p. 1981. 7.95 (ISBN 0-914390-19-8). Fellowship Pr PA.

Beatty, David. He That Wins Souls Is Wise. 1982. pap. 0.75 (ISBN 0-88144-005-1, CPS-005). Christian Pub.

Beckmann, Beverly. Seasons in God's World. (In God's World Ser.). (Illus.). 24p. 1985. 5.95 (ISBN 0-570-04127-9, 56-1538). Concordia.

Benton, John. Do You Know Where Your Children Are? 160p. 1983. pap. 2.95 (ISBN 0-8007-8480-4). Revell.

Bernard, David. Essentials of Oneness Theology. (Illus.). 32p. (Orig.). 1985. pap. 2.25 (ISBN 0-912315-89-X). Word Aflame.

Bernstein, Matt. This Messiah Fellow. 1985. 6.75 (ISBN 0-8062-2344-8). Carlton.

Bieber, Richard. Rebirth of the Congregation. 1973. pap. 1.25 (ISBN 0-87508-012-X). Chr Lit.

Bird, Christopher. The Divining Hand. 1985. pap. 15.00 (ISBN 0-87613-090-2). New Age.

Bishop, Joseph P. Soul Mending: Letters to Friends in Crisis. 160p. 1986. pap. 8.95 (ISBN 0-8192-1379-9). Morehouse.

Blackmore, R. W., tr. Duties of Parish Priests in the Russian Orthodox Church. Repr. of 1845 ed. 15.00 (ISBN 0-686-01291-7). Eastern Orthodox.

Blalock, Jack E., Jr. It's All There If You Want It: And Here Is the Map. LC 80-69519. 200p. (Orig.). 1981. 12.95 (ISBN 0-9605156-0-7); pap. 10.95 (ISBN 0-9605156-1-5). J Blalock.

Blanchard, John. Aceptado Por Dios. 2.95 (ISBN 0-85151-406-5). Banner of Truth.

Blay, Cecil J. It Is Written. 120p. 1973. text ed. 4.00 (ISBN 0-910424-62-4). Concordant.

Bock, Fred & Leech, Bryan J., eds. Hymns for the Family of God. 1976. 7.95 (ISBN 0-89477-000-4, Dist. by Alexandria House); looseleaf 6.95 (ISBN 0-89477-002-0); pap. 7.95 (ISBN 0-89477-001-2). Paragon Benson.

Bodo, Murray. Francis: The Journey & the Dream. (Illus.). 1972. pap. 2.95 (ISBN 0-912228-07-5). St Anthony Mess Pr.

Boehme, Jacob. Signature of All Things: & Other Writings. 307p. 1969. pap. 12.95 (ISBN 0-227-67733-1). Attic Pr.

Bokser, Ben-Zion. The Gifts of Life & Love. 193p. 1975. 7.00 (ISBN 0-88482-894-8). Hebrew Pub.

Bolding, Amy. I'll Be Glad to Give a Devotion. (Paperback Program Ser). 1978. pap. 3.95 (ISBN 0-8010-0709-7). Baker Bk.

--Inspiring Devotions for Church Groups. 144p. 1985. pap. 4.95 (ISBN 0-8010-0889-1). Baker Bk.

--Please Give a Devotion for Church Groups. (Paperback Program Ser.). pap. 3.95 (ISBN 0-8010-0623-6). Baker Bk.

Booker, Richard. Intimacy with God. LC 84-70055. 196p. 1983. pap. 5.95 (ISBN 0-88270-552-0). Bridge Pub.

Boom. This Day is the Lord's Day. 2.75 (ISBN 0-318-18182-7). WCTU.

Boom, Corrie ten. Amor, Asombroso Amor. Orig. Title: Amazing Love. 112p. 1980. pap. 2.25 (ISBN 0-311-40035-3, Edit Mundo). Casa Bautista.

Boone, Jerome. Let There Be Praise. (International Correspondence Program Ser.). 226p. (Orig.). pap. 6.95 (ISBN 0-87148-524-9). Pathway Pr.

Bowdle, Donald W. Redemption Accomplished & Applied. 1972. 5.25 (ISBN 0-87148-726-8); pap. 4.25 (ISBN 0-87148-727-6). Pathway Pr.

Brand, Paul & Yancey, Philip. A Imagen de Dios. Delgado, Ady, tr. Tr. of In His Image. 272p. 1987. pap. 4.95 (ISBN 0-88113-128-8). Edit Betania.

Braun, John A. By His Grace. 1983. pap. 7.95 (ISBN 0-8100-0161-6, 06N0560). Northwest Pub.

Bremer, Maura. And Send the Sun Tomorrow: A Journal of My Father's Last Days. 1979. pap. 2.95 (ISBN 0-03-049396-X, HarpR). Har-Row.

Bridges, Jerry. The Practice of Godliness. (Christian Character Library). 272p. 1985. hdbk. 8.95 (ISBN 0-89109-466-0). NavPress.

--The Pursuit of Holiness. (Christian Character Library). 158p. 1985. hdbk. 8.95 (ISBN 0-89109-467-9). NavPress.

Bridges, Ron. Falling in Love with the Lord. 1987. price not set (ISBN 0-89109-143-2). NavPress.

Brooks, Thomas. Precious Remedies Against Satan's Devices. 253p. 1984. pap. 5.95x (ISBN 0-85151-002-7). Banner of Truth.

Brownlow, Leroy. Give Us This Day: A Devotional Guide for Daily Living. 1986. 7.95 (ISBN 0-915720-23-X). Brownlow Pub Co.

Brubaker, Pamela. She Hath Done What She Could. 224p. (Orig.). 1985. pap. 7.95 (ISBN 0-87178-942-6). Brethren.

Bryant, Al, compiled by. A Pocket Treasury of Devotional Verse. 160p. (Orig.). 1980. pap. 3.50 (ISBN 0-87123-466-1, 200466). Bethany Hse.

Bugg, Charles B. Things My Children Are Teaching Me. LC 81-70409. 1982. pap. 3.95 (ISBN 0-8054-5650-3). Broadman.

Buls, Alfred M. Devotions for New Parents. (Orig.). (YA) 1972. pap. 1.50 (ISBN 0-570-03675-5, 74-1010). Concordia.

Bunyan, John. House of God. pap. 0.95 (ISBN 0-685-19834-0). Reiner.

--Light for Them That Sit in Darkness. pap. 3.50 (ISBN 0-685-19838-3). Reiner.

Burke, Albert L. He That Hath an Ear. 101p. (Orig.). 1982. pap. 3.50 (ISBN 0-9608662-0-5). Eleventh Hour.

Calvin, John. Knowledge of God the Creator. 2.50 (ISBN 0-686-23485-5). Rose Pub MI.

Camara, Dom H. Into Your Hands, Lord. 80p. 1987. text ed. 9.95 (ISBN 0-940989-06-9). Meyer Stone Bks.

Carey, Floyd D. & Byrd, James F., eds. Manna: A Book of Table Devotions. 1973. pap. 3.95 (ISBN 0-87148-564-8). Pathway Pr.

Carey, Floyd D., Jr. Teen-Agers' Treasure Chest. 100p. 1963. pap. 1.25 (ISBN 0-87148-830-2). Pathway Pr.

Carey, Howard R. Journey into Light & Joy. LC 79-53905. (Illus.). 180p. 1979. pap. 4.50 (ISBN 0-87516-380-7). De Vorss.

Carlson, Betty. No One's Perfect. LC 76-17669. 1976. pap. 4.95 (ISBN 0-89107-143-1). Good News.

Carmichael, Amy. Figures of the True. 1968. pap. 1.50 (ISBN 0-87508-065-0). Chr Lit.

--Whispers of His Power. 256p. 1985. pap. 6.95 (ISBN 0-8007-5206-6, Power Bks). Revell.

Carney, Mary L. There's an Angel in My Locker. 112p. (Orig.). 1985. pap. 4.95 (ISBN 0-310-28471-6, 11341P). Zondervan.

Carothers, J. Edward. Caring for the World. (Orig.). 1978. pap. 4.95 (ISBN 0-377-00078-7). Friend Pr.

Carroll. Learning God's Word, 3 bks. 1971. Bk. 1. pap. 1.75 (ISBN 0-87148-502-8); Bk. 2. pap. 1.35 (ISBN 0-87148-503-6); Bk. 3. pap. 1.35 (ISBN 0-87148-504-4). Pathway Pr.

Cary, Joyce. Except the Lord. LC 85-10601. (Second Trilogy Ser.: Bk. 2). 288p. 1985. pap. 7.95 (ISBN 0-8112-0965-2, NDP607). New Directions.

Castle, Tony, ed. The New Book of Christian Quotations. LC 82-25253. 272p. 1983. pap. 9.95 (ISBN 0-8245-0551-4). Crossroad NY.

Catoir, John T. Enjoy the Lord. 1979. pap. 2.95 (ISBN 0-88479-023-1). Arena Lettres.

Chambers, Oswald. Devotions for a Deeper Life. Black, Glenn D., ed. 320p. 1986. 10.95 (ISBN 0-310-38710-8, 17070). Zondervan.

--Place of Help. 1973. pap. 2.95 (ISBN 0-87508-139-8). Chr Lit.

Chatham, Joe. Eternal Security Obtained after Completing a Faithful Course. 1978. pap. 1.50 (ISBN 0-934942-05-6). White Wing Pub.

Chinmoy, Sri. Beyond Within. 525p. 1985. pap. 10.95 (ISBN 0-88497-115-5). Aum Pubns.

--Eternity's Breadth. 116p. 1975. pap. 5.00 (ISBN 0-88497-235-6). Aum Pubns.

--Flower-Flames. 208p. 1985. pap. 10.00 (ISBN 0-88497-829-X). Aum Pubns.

--Inner & Outer Peace. 113p. (Orig.). 1984. pap. 5.95 (ISBN 0-88497-769-2). Aum Pubns.

--My Lord's Secrets Revealed. 102p. text ed. 10.00 (ISBN 0-88497-793-5); pap. 5.00 (ISBN 0-317-46895-2). Aum Pubns.

--O My Pilot Beloved. 54p. (Orig.). 1980. pap. 2.00 (ISBN 0-88497-502-9). Aum Pubns.

--One Lives, One Dies. 81p. 1974. pap. 2.00 (ISBN 0-88497-072-8). Aum Pubns.

--The Summits of God Life: Samadhi & Siddhi. LC 80-65397. 145p. 1984. pap. 3.95 (ISBN 0-88497-145-7). Aum Pubns.

Christensen, James L. Communion Reflections & Prayers. Lambert, Herbert, ed. LC 84-29361. 64p. (Orig.). 1985. pap. 4.95 (ISBN 0-8272-0446-9). CBP.

Christian Readings, 6 vols. Incl. Vol. 1. Easter to 17th Sunday, Year II. red bdg. 4.00 (ISBN 0-89942-601-8, 601/04); Vol. 2. 17th Sunday to Advent, Year II. green bdg. 4.00 (ISBN 0-89942-602-6, 602/04); Vol. 3. Advent to Easter, Year I. purple bdg. 4.00 (ISBN 0-89942-603-4, 603/04); Vol. 4. Easter to 17th Sunday, Year I. tan bdg. 4.00 (ISBN 0-89942-604-2, 604/04); Vol. 5. 17th Sunday to Advent, Year I. brown bdg. 4.00 (ISBN 0-89942-605-0, 605/04); Vol. 6. Advent to Easter, Year II. blue bdg. 4.00 (ISBN 0-89942-606-9, 606/04). Catholic Bk Pub.

Clark, Glenn. Come Follow Me. 4.95 (ISBN 0-910924-04-X). Macalester.

--Divine Plan. pap. 0.50 (ISBN 0-910924-05-8). Macalester.

--Fishers of Men. pap. 1.95 (ISBN 0-910924-62-7). Macalester.

--From Crime to Christ. pap. 2.50 (ISBN 0-910924-61-9). Macalester.

--I Will Lift up Mine Eyes. LC 77-7830. (Illus.). 208p. 1984. pap. 7.95 (ISBN 0-06-061394-7, RD 518, HarpR). Har-Row.

--Song of Souls of Men. pap. 0.95 (ISBN 0-910924-14-7). Macalester.

--Under the Shelter of His Wings. pap. 0.20 (ISBN 0-910924-50-3). Macalester.

--What Would Jesus Do? pap. 7.95 (ISBN 0-910924-20-1). Macalester.

Clarkson, Margaret. Destined for Glory: The Meaning of Suffering. 144p. 1983. pap. 4.95 (ISBN 0-8028-1953-2). Eerdmans.

Clason, George. The Richest Man in Babylon. 160p. 1985. pap. 3.50 (ISBN 0-553-25345-X). Bantam.

Claypool, John R. Opening Blind Eyes. 144p. (Orig.). 1987. pap. 7.95 (ISBN 0-940989-05-0). Meyer Stone Bks.

Clement Of Alexandria. Christ the Educator. LC 66-20313. (Fathers of the Church Ser.: Vol. 23). 309p. 1954. 16.95x (ISBN 0-8132-0023-7). Cath U Pr.

Cleveland, E. E. The Exodus. Wheeler, Gerald, ed. 1985. write for info. (ISBN 0-8280-0299-1). Review & Herald.

--Milk & Honey. Wheeler, Gerald, ed. 1985. write for info. (ISBN 0-8280-0301-7). Review & Herald.

--One More River. Wheeler, Gerald, ed. 1985. write for info. (ISBN 0-8280-0300-9). Review & Herald.

Clevenger & Hill, eds. Jesus of the Bible. 1973. pap. 1.50 (ISBN 0-88428-007-1, 101). Parchment Pr.

Coleman, William L. Listen to the Animals. LC 79-11312. 128p. 1979. pap. 4.95 (ISBN 0-87123-341-X, 210341). Bethany Hse.

Collins, Vincent P. Me, Myself & You. rev. ed. LC 74-17734. 1974. pap. 2.95 (ISBN 0-87029-001-0, 20033-7). Abbey.

Compton, W. H. Special Day Sermons. 1972. 3.25 (ISBN 0-87148-752-7). Pathway Pr.

Conant, Newton. Changed by Beholding Him. 1972. pap. 2.95 (ISBN 0-87508-147-9). Chr Lit.

Confucius. The Analects. Lau, D. C., tr. 1979. pap. 4.95 (ISBN 0-14-044348-7). Penguin.

Conn, Charles W. A Certain Journey. 152p. 1965. 4.25 (ISBN 0-87148-000-X); pap. 3.25 (ISBN 0-87148-001-8). Pathway Pr.

--The Evangel Reader. 1958. 3.25 (ISBN 0-87148-275-4). Pathway Pr.

--Why Men Go Back. 1983. 6.95 (ISBN 0-87148-902-3); pap. 5.95 (ISBN 0-87148-917-1). Pathway Pr.

Contemplation of Sinners. LC 75-315474. (English Experience Ser.: No. 645). 200p. 1974. Repr. of 1499 ed. 17.50 (ISBN 90-221-0645-4). Walter J Johnson.

Conway, Charles A., Jr. The Vita Christi of Ludolph of Saxony & Late Medieval Devotion Centered on the Incarnation: A Descriptive Analysis. Hogg, James, ed. (Analecta Cartusiana Ser.: No. 34). 153p. (Orig.). 1976. pap. 25.00 (ISBN 3-7052-0036-4, Pub. by Salzburg Studies). Longwood Pub Group.

Cook, Lyndon W. & Cannon, Donald Q. A New Light Breaks Forth. pap. 7.95 (ISBN 0-89036-148-7). Hawkes Pub Inc.

Coolidge, Edna M. Celestial Gems Books, Vol. 1. rev. ed. LC 73-88209. 150p. 10.00 (ISBN 0-914154-00-1). Celestial Gems.

--Celestial Gems Books, Vols. 2-3. LC 73-88209. (Illus.). 48p. 1972. spiral bdg. 10.00 ea. Vol. 2 (ISBN 0-914154-01-X). Celestial Gems.

--Celestial Gems Books, Vol. 4. LC 73-88209. 65p. 1974. spiral bdg. 10.00 (ISBN 0-914154-03-6). Celestial Gems.

--Celestial Gems Books, Vols. 5-6. LC 73-88209. (Illus.). 150p. 1975. 10.00 ea.; Vol. 5. (ISBN 0-914154-05-2). Celestial Gems.

Corelli, Marie. Barabbas. pap. 5.95 (ISBN 0-910122-00-8). Amherst Pr.

Cornwall, Judson. Let Us Draw Near. LC 77-24832. 1977. pap. 4.95 (ISBN 0-88270-226-2, Pub. by Logos). Bridge Pub.

Cornwell, Malcolm. Arise & Renew. 96p. 1986. pap. 5.95 (ISBN 0-8146-1441-8). Liturgical Pr.

Coughlin, Kevin. Finding God in Everyday Life. LC 80-84506. 64p. (Orig.). 1981. pap. 2.95 (ISBN 0-8091-2351-7). Paulist Pr.

Cowman, Charles E. Streams in the Desert Sampler. 128p. 1983. pap. 3.95 (ISBN 0-310-37651-3, 6881P). Zondervan.

Cowman, Mrs. Charles E. Mountain Trailways for Youth: Devotions for Young People. 1979. pap. 6.95 (ISBN 0-310-37641-6, 6880P). Zondervan.

--Streams in the Desert. 1974. large print kiver 9.95 (ISBN 0-310-22527-2, 12555L). Zondervan.

Cowman, Mrs. Charles E., ed. Springs in the Valley. 2nd ed. 384p. 1980. pap. 4.95 (ISBN 0-310-22511-6, 6806P). Zondervan.

Cox, Carol M. Jubilee Time: Celebrating Gods Grace & Justice. 112p. (Orig.). 1984. pap. 8.25 (ISBN 0-687-20609-X). Abingdon.

Coyle, Neva, compiled by. Scriptures for Living Free. 58p. (Orig.). 1982. pap. 5.95 (ISBN 0-87123-576-5, 210576). Bethany Hse.

Crawford, C. C. The Eternal Spirit: His Person & Powers. (The Bible Study Textbook Ser.). 1973. 14.30 (ISBN 0-89900-050-9). College Pr Pub.

Crom, Scott. On Being Real. LC 67-29811. (Orig.). 1967. pap. 2.50x (ISBN 0-87574-155-X, 155). Pendle Hill.

Crosby, Michael H. Thank God Ahead of Time: The Life & Spirituality of Solanus Casey. 1985. 9.50 (ISBN 0-8199-0879-7). Franciscan Herald.

Cross, James A. The Glorious Gospel. 1956. 4.25 (ISBN 0-87148-350-5). Pathway Pr.

Cross, Luther S. Growing in Faith: Devotions for Parent-Child Interaction. 32p. (Orig.). 1984. pap. 2.95 (ISBN 0-8066-2070-6, 23-1606). Augsburg.

Cruden, Alexander. Cruden's Unabridged Concordance. LC 54-11084. 17.95 (ISBN 0-8054-1123-2). Broadman.

Cruz, Nicky. Run Baby Run: The Story of a Gang-Lord Turned Crusader. LC 68-23446. 240p. 1968. pap. 3.50 (ISBN 0-912106-58-1, Pub. by Logos). Bridge Pub.

Curtiss, Harriette & Homer, F. The Truth about Evolution & the Bible. 1928. 5.50 (ISBN 0-87516-308-4). De Vorss.

Daily Bread Cookbook. LC 82-83956. 1975. pap. 6.95 (ISBN 0-916035-00-X, BE-141). Evangel Indiana.

Daily Devotional Bible Commentary, 4 vols. LC 76-46492. 1982. Repr. of 1974 ed. 39.95 (ISBN 0-8054-1228-X). Broadman.

Daily Devotional Bible Commentary: Genesis--Job, Vol. 1. LC 79-46492. 1982. Repr. of 1974 ed. 10.95 (ISBN 0-8054-1224-7). Broadman.

Daily Devotional Bible Commentary: Matthew--Acts, Vol. 3. LC 76-46441. 1982. Repr. of 1974 ed. 10.95 (ISBN 0-8054-1226-3). Broadman.

Daily Devotional Bible Commentary: Romans--Revelation, Vol. 4. LC 76-46442. 1982. Repr. of 1974 ed. 10.95 (ISBN 0-8054-1227-1). Broadman.

Daily Light. deluxe ed. 384p. 1985. 12.95 (ISBN 0-8407-5480-9). Nelson.

Daily Light on the Daily Path. large print ed. 384p. 1975. kivar 9.95 (ISBN 0-310-23067-5, 18011L). Zondervan.

Daughters of St. Paul, ed. One Family under God. (Divine Master Ser.). (Orig.). 1968. 3.00 (ISBN 0-8198-0109-7); pap. 2.00 (ISBN 0-8198-0110-0). Dghtrs St Paul.

Davidson, Alice J. Reflections of Love. (Illus.). 128p. 1982. 12.95 (ISBN 0-8007-1327-3). Revell.

Davidson, C. T. Upon This Rock, 3 vols. 692p. 1973. Vol. 1. 11.95 (ISBN 0-934942-16-1); Vol. 2. 14.95 (ISBN 0-934942-17-X); Vol. 3. 13.95 (ISBN 0-934942-18-8). White Wing Pub.

Davis, John J. The Perfect Shepherd: Studies in the Twenty-Third Psalm. pap. 5.50 (ISBN 0-88469-110-1). BMH Bks.

Davis, Ron L. & Denney, James D. A Time for Compassion. (Crucial Questions Ser.). 224p. 1986. 13.95 (ISBN 0-8007-1492-X). Revell.

Davis, Susan. I Choose to Belong. (My Church Teaches Ser.). 1979. pap. 1.65 (ISBN 0-8127-0237-9). Review & Herald.

Day, Hughes W. Beside Still Waters. 418p. 1979. 9.95 (ISBN 0-8341-0599-3). Beacon Hill.

Day, Ralph E. Our Church of God Faith for Children. 1961. pap. 1.25 (ISBN 0-87148-652-0). Pathway Pr.

--Our Church of God Faith: For Young People & Adults. 1959. pap. 1.95 (ISBN 0-87148-651-2). Pathway Pr.

Dayton, Donald W., ed. The Devotional Writings of Robert Pearsall Smith & Hannah Whitall Smith. (The Higher Christian Life Ser.). 477p. 1985. lib. bdg. 60.00 (ISBN 0-8240-6444-5). Garland Pub.

Dayton, Edward R. God's Purpose - Man's Plans. 64p. 1982. pap. 5.95 (ISBN 0-912552-11-5). Missions Adv Res Com Ctr.

--That Everyone May Hear: Workbook. pap. 5.75 (ISBN 0-912552-53-0). Missions Adv Res Com Ctr.

Deal, William S. Christian's Daily Manna. 0.95 (ISBN 0-686-13721-3). Crusade Pubs.

DeBlassie, Paul, III. Inner Calm: A Christian Answer to Modern Stress. LC 84-52377. 128p. 1985. pap. 3.95 (ISBN 0-89243-229-2). Liguori Pubns.

Deck, Gladys E. Bits of Solace, Guidance & Consolation. 97p. 1984. 7.50 (ISBN 0-913382-30-2, 101-30). Prow Bks-Franciscan.

DeHaan, Dan. The God You Can Know. (Moody Press Electives Ser.). 1985. pap. text ed. 3.95 (ISBN 0-8024-0697-1); leader's guide 2.50 (ISBN 0-8024-0698-X). Moody.

Delano, Lucile. Charles de Lannoy: Victor of Pavia. 144p. 1983. 9.75 (ISBN 0-8158-0442-3). Chris Mass.

Dellinger, Annetta. Chuckles & Challenges. 96p. 1986. pap. 4.95 (ISBN 0-8010-2960-0). Baker Bk.

De Pons, Beatriz. Crecer Contigo. 80p. 1978. pap. 2.50 (ISBN 0-311-40037-X). Casa Bautista.

De Purucker, G. Clothed with the Sun: The Mystery-Tale of Jesus the Avatara. rev. ed. Small, Emmett & Todd, Helen, eds. Orig. Title: The Story of Jesus. (Illus.). 56p. 1972. pap. 1.00 (ISBN 0-913004-06-5). Point Loma Pub.

De Robeck, Nesta. Praise the Lord. 1967. 4.50 (ISBN 0-8199-0086-9, L38643). Franciscan Herald.

De Sales, Saint Francoise. Treatise on the Love of God. Mackey, Henry B., tr. LC 71-156190. xiiv, 555p. Repr. of 1942 ed. lib. bdg. 31.75x (ISBN 0-8371-6139-8, FRLG). Greenwood.

De Waters, Lillian. The Word Made Flesh. (Practical Demonstration Ser.). pap. 0.95 (ISBN 0-686-05718-X). L De Waters.

Dick, Louise L., ed. Clips from Tom M. Olson: Nuggets from the Writings of Tom M. Olson Provide the Only-Way to View Events. LC 86-90141. (One-Way Ser.: Vol. 10). 251p. (Orig.). 1986. pap. 6.95 (ISBN 0-935899-06-5). LeTourneau Pr.

Dietrich, Martin O. & Lehmann, Helmut T., eds. Luther's Works: Devotional Writings I, Vol. 42. LC 55-9893. (Prog. Bk.). 1969. 19.95 (ISBN 0-8006-0342-7, 1-342). Fortress.

Dilke, Emilia F. Book of the Spiritual Life. LC 70-37689. (Illus., With a memoir of the author by the Rt. Hon. Sir Charles W. Dilke). Repr. of 1905 ed. 26.00 (ISBN 0-404-56743-6). AMS Pr.

Dittmer, Bernice. Let There Be Light... Date not set. 40.00 (ISBN 0-930208-23-4). Mangan Bks.

Doherty, Catherine De Hueck. Urodivoi: Fools for Good. LC 82-23530. 112p. 1983. 9.95 (ISBN 0-8245-0553-0). Crossroad NY.

Dollen, Charles. Ready or Not. LC 67-29164. 1969. 3.00 (ISBN 0-8198-0130-5). Dghtrs St Paul.

Donders, Joseph G. Liberation, the Jesus Mode: Reflections on the Gospels for the B-Cycle. LC 87-5700. 228p. (Orig.). 1987. pap. 10.95 (ISBN 0-88344-553-0). Orbis Bks.

Donovan, Robert O. Her Door of Faith. LC 79-172385. (Illus.). 112p. 1971. pap. 2.95 (ISBN 0-913748-02-1). Orovan Bks.

Dougherty, Flavian, ed. The Deprived, the Disabled & the Fullness of Life. 1984. pap. 4.95 (ISBN 0-89453-442-4). M Glazier.

Douma, George. Encouragement. pap. 0.45 (ISBN 0-686-23477-4). Rose Pub MI.

--My Doctrine Book. pap. 2.25 (ISBN 0-686-23469-3). Rose Pub MI.

--Together with God. pap. 0.45 (ISBN 0-686-23478-2). Rose Pub MI.

Dowd, John C. You Cannot Hold Back the Dawn. LC 74-75619. 1974. 4.95 (ISBN 0-8198-0320-0); pap. 3.95 (ISBN 0-8198-0321-9). Dghtrs St Paul.

Dox, Victor L. What the World Needs. LC 67-31068. 3.50 (ISBN 0-8198-0328-6); pap. 2.50 (ISBN 0-8198-0329-4). Dghtrs St Paul.

Drakeford, John W. Growing Old-Feeling Young. LC 84-21341. 1985. pap. 7.95 (ISBN 0-8054-5009-2). Broadman.

Drescher, Sandra. Just Between God & Me. 1977. girls o.p. 9.95 (ISBN 0-310-23940-0); boys gift ed. o.p. 9.95 (ISBN 0-310-23950-8, 18111B); pap. 4.95 (ISBN 0-310-23941-9, 18111P). Zondervan.

Duck, Ruth C. Flames of the Spirit. (Orig.). 1985. pap. 6.95 (ISBN 0-8298-0537-0). Pilgrim NY.

Duckworth, Marion. Becoming Complete: Embracing Your Biblical Image. LC 85-10465. 1985. pap. 5.95 (ISBN 0-88070-099-8). Multnomah.

Dumitriu, Petru. To the Unknown God. Kirkup, James, tr. from Fr. LC 82-5722. 256p. 1982. pap. 11.95 (ISBN 0-8164-2424-1, HarpR). Har-Row.

Eastman, Dick. No Easy Road: Inspirational Thoughts on Prayer. new ed. (Direction Bks.). 1973. pap. 2.50 (ISBN 0-8010-3259-8). Baker Bk.

Eddy, Mary B. Unity of Good, Rudimental Divine Science. pap. 4.50 (ISBN 0-87952-043-4). First Church.

Edgar, Carlson M. The Classic Christian Faith: Chapel Meditations Based on Luther's Small Catechism. LC 59-9093. pap. 42.80 (2026912). Bks Demand UMI.

Edman, V. E. & Laidlaw, R. A. The Fullness of the Spirit. 36p. pap. 0.95 (ISBN 0-87509-083-4). Chr Pubns.

Edwards, Bruce & Fudge, Edward. A Journey Toward Jesus. 1.50 (ISBN 0-686-12687-4). E Fudge.

Edwards, Jonathan. The Works of Jonathan Edwards, 2 vols. 1979. Set. 66.95 (ISBN 0-85151-397-2); Vol. 1. 36.95 (ISBN 0-85151-216-X); Vol. 2. 36.95 (ISBN 0-85151-217-8). Banner of Truth.

Effendi, Shoghi. The Advent of Divine Justice. rev. ed. LC 84-436. x, 104p. 1984. 14.95 (ISBN 0-87743-195-7); pap. 8.95 (ISBN 0-87743-196-5). Baha'i.

Eight Keys to Spiritual & Physical Health. 96p. 1982. pap. 3.95 (ISBN 0-89221-092-3, Pub. by SonLife). New Leaf.

Eker, Dorothy. Reflections of Him. LC 75-393402. 1976. 4.95 (ISBN 0-87212-053-8). Libra.

Elder, John. A Goodly Heritage - Pioneers for God: Devotional Readings. Armajani, Yahya, tr. from Farsi. LC 83-62806. viii, 141p. (Orig.). 1983. pap. 3.50 (ISBN 0-9608440-1-5). Nur Pubns.

Elliot, Norman K. God Really Loves You. 0.50, 3 for 1.00 (ISBN 0-910924-25-2). Macalester.

Erdman, V. R. Signs of Christ's Second Coming. 29p. pap. 0.95 (ISBN 0-87509-130-X). Chr Pubns.

Eshbaugh, Howard. Hear the Good News. 1984. 3.50 (ISBN 0-89536-656-8, 0805). CSS of Ohio.

Esposito, Donna J., ed. Printed Circuit Board Basics. 92p. (Orig.). 1986. 14.95 (ISBN 0-931463-00-9). PMS Indus.

Estrada, Jose R. Dias Sin Gloria. (Span.). 64p. 1982. pap. 1.95 (ISBN 0-311-08213-0, Edit Mundo). Casa Bautista.

Etling, Harold H. Emmanuel, God with Us: Studies in Matthew. pap. 4.95 (ISBN 0-88469-107-1). BMH Bks.

Eyer, Mary S. Reflection of a Soul. 83p. 1986. 7.95 (ISBN 0-934126-66-6). Randall Bk Co.

Eyer, Richard C. Devotions of Hope. 1984. 1.95 (ISBN 0-89536-653-3, 0418). CSS of Ohio.

Fackenheim, Emil L. God's Presence in History. 1972. pap. 5.95x (ISBN 0-06-131690-3, TB1690, Torch). Har-Row.

Fankhauser, Jerry. Everybody Is Your Teacher. 58p. 1986. pap. 7.00 (ISBN 0-9617006-2-9). J Fankhauser.

Feider, Paul A. The Journey to Inner Peace. LC 84-71863. 112p. (Orig.). 1984. pap. 3.95 (ISBN 0-87793-275-1). Ave Maria.

Fenelon. Let Go! 1973. pap. 3.50 (ISBN 0-88368-010-6). Whitaker Hse.

Fenelon, Francois D. Spiritual Letters to Women. LC 80-82327. (Shepherd Illustrated Classics Ser.). 1980. pap. 5.95 (ISBN 0-87983-233-9). Keats.

Field, John. A Godly Exhortation. Incl. Sermon Preached at Pawles Crosse, 3 November 1577. White, Thomas. Repr. of 1578 ed. Repr. of 1583 ed. 28.00 (ISBN 0-384-15680-0). Johnson Repr.

Fields, Mary E. Foundations of Truth. LC 80-67931. 275p. 1980. 10.00 (ISBN 0-87516-423-4). De Vorss.

Fields, Rick, et al. Chop Wood, Carry Water: A Guide to Finding Spiritual Fulfillment in Everyday Life. LC 84-23942. 304p. 1984. pap. 11.95 (ISBN 0-87477-209-5). J P Tarcher.

Finegold, Julius J. & Thetford, William N., eds. Choose Once Again. LC 76-20363. (Illus.). 112p. 1981. 6.95 (ISBN 0-89087-413-1). Celestial Arts.

Finley, Tom. The World Is Not Enough. Parrish, Annette, ed. LC 86-22049. 252p. (Orig.). (YA) 1986. pap. 4.25 (ISBN 0-8307-1151-1, S183329). Regal.

Fleece, Isabel. Not by Accident. 1987. pap. 1.95 (ISBN 0-317-54045-9). Moody.

Fontaine, Patrick. Little Talks About Life. 1956. 4.50 (ISBN 0-8198-0082-1). Dghtrs St Paul.

Friedrich, Elizabeth. The Story of God's Love. 144p. 1985. 9.95 (ISBN 0-570-04122-8, 56-1533). Concordia.

Frost, Gerhard E. Bless My Growing: For Parents, Teachers, & Others Who Learn. LC 74-77680. (Illus.). 96p. 1975. pap. 5.95 (ISBN 0-8066-1431-5, 10-0770). Augsburg.

Frost, Robert C. Aglow with the Spirit: How to Receive the Baptism in the Holy Spirit. 1965. pap. 2.95 (ISBN 0-912106-64-6). Bridge Pub.

Fudge, Edward. Gold from the Gospels. pap. 2.00 (ISBN 0-686-12679-3). E Fudge.

Fullam, Everett L. How to Walk with God. 192p. 1987. pap. 8.95 (ISBN 0-8407-9514-9). Oliver-Nelson.

Garvie, A. E. Studies in the Inner Life of Jesus. 1977. lib. bdg. 69.95 (ISBN 0-8490-2705-5). Gordon Pr.

Gealy, Fred D., et al. Companion to the Hymnal. 1970. 19.95 (ISBN 0-687-09259-0). Abingdon.

Gee, Donald. The Fruit of the Spirit. 80p. 1975. pap. 1.95 (ISBN 0-88243-501-9, 02-0501, Radiant Bks). Gospel Pub.

--This Is the Way. (Radiant Bks.). Orig. Title: Studies in Guidance. 64p. 1975. pap. 0.95 (ISBN 0-88243-630-9, 02-0630). Gospel Pub.

--A Word to the Wise. (Radiant Bks.). Orig. Title: Proverbs for Pentecost. 80p. 1975. pap. 0.95 (ISBN 0-88243-632-5, 02-0632). Gospel Pub.

Gesch, Roy. Made for Each Other: Devotions for Newly Married Couples. 112p. 1987. pap. 4.95 (ISBN 0-570-04453-7, 12-3059). Concordia.

Gesswein, Armin R. With One Accord in One Place. 93p. (Orig.). 1978. pap. 1.75 (ISBN 0-87509-161-X). Chr Pubns.

Getz, Gene A. Bajo Presion. Tr. of When the Pressure Is On. (Span.). 1986. pap. 3.25 (ISBN 0-8297-0898-7). Life Pubs Intl.

Gillies, George & Gillies, Harriet. Scriptural Outline of the Baptism of the Holy Spirit. 32p. 1972. pap. 1.50 (ISBN 0-88368-062-9). Whitaker Hse.

Glinsky, Vladimir. Confessionary Questions: A Preparation for the Sacrament of Penitence with Text of the Office. pap. 0.25 (ISBN 0-686-05391-5). Eastern Orthodox.

Gockel, Herman W. My Hand in His. rev. ed. LC 60-15577. 1975. pap. 6.50 (12-2613). Concordia.

Goetz, Joseph. Mirrors of God. 1984. pap. 4.95 (ISBN 0-86716-031-4). St Anthony Mess Pr.

Goldsmith, Joel S. I Am the Vine. 1972. pap. 1.00 (ISBN 0-87516-138-3). De Vorss.
--Love & Gratitude. 1972. pap. 1.75 (ISBN 0-87516-139-1). De Vorss.
--Truth. 1972. pap. 1.00 (ISBN 0-87516-141-3). De Vorss.
Gonzales, F. Jose. He Reigns from the Cross. Lemon, tr. 1962. 3.00 (ISBN 0-8198-0054-6). Dghtrs St Paul.
Gordon, Arthur. Through Many Windows. 192p. 1985. pap. 6.95 (ISBN 0-8007-5207-4, Power Bks). Revell.
Goulooze, William. Comfort for the Sorrowing. pap. 0.45 (ISBN 0-686-23474-X). Rose Pub MI.
--The Shepherd's Care. pap. 0.45 (ISBN 0-686-23475-8). Rose Pub MI.
Grams, Betty J. Women of Grace. LC 77-93409. 128p. 1978. pap. 3.95 (ISBN 0-88243-751-8, 02-0751, Radiant Books); tchr's. ed 3.95 (ISBN 0-88243-336-9, 02-0336). Gospel Pub.
Gratton, Carolyn. Trusting: Theory & Practice. LC 82-9760. 256p. 1983. pap. 9.95 (ISBN 0-8245-0548-4). Crossroad NY.
Green, Thomas H. Opening to God. (Religion Ser.). 128p. 1987. pap. 2.95 (ISBN 0-553-26666-7). Bantam.
Griffiths, Michael. God Is Great, God Is Good: I'd Believe Him If I Could. LC 86-62368. Orig. Title: Down to Earth God. 170p. 1987. pap. 4.50 (ISBN 0-89109-468-7). NavPress.
Grimley, Mildred H. Mattie Loves All. (Illus.). 22p. 1985. 5.95 (ISBN 0-87178-552-8). Brethren.
Groom, Olive. Yasmin Meets a Yak. 1973. pap. 1.95 (ISBN 0-87508-806-6). Chr Lit.
Groomer, Vera. Kind Kristy. (Come Unto Me Library). 1979. pap. 1.65 (ISBN 0-8127-0209-3). Review & Herald.
Guthrie, Lula. The Sunshine Basket. (Illus.). 1986. pap. 1.95 (ISBN 0-89265-112-1). Randall Hse.
Haas, Wayne. Your Crocodile Is Ready. 1984. 6.25 (ISBN 0-89536-620-7, 4888). CSS of Ohio.
Hagin, Kenneth E. How You Can Be Led by the Spirit of God. 1978. pap. 3.50 (ISBN 0-89276-500-3). Hagin Ministries.
Hall, Roger L., ed. The Happy Journey: Thirty-Five Shaker Spirituals Compiled by Miss Clara Endicott Sears. LC 81-69875. (Illus.). 60p. (Orig.). 1982. 8.00 (ISBN 0-941632-00-8). Fruitlands Mus.
Halverstadt, Robert. God's Word for Your Healing. 1982. pap. 1.95 (ISBN 0-88144-003-5, CPS-003). Christian Pub.
--God's Word for Your Prosperity. 1982. pap. 1.95 (ISBN 0-88144-002-7, CPS-002). Christian Pub.
--Your New Birth. 1982. pap. 0.75 (ISBN 0-88144-001-9, CPS-001). Christian Pub.
Hammel, W. W. So Great Salvation. 1972. pap. 2.95 (ISBN 0-87148-751-9). Pathway Pr.
Hammes, John A. Ascend to Your Father: An Introduction to Marian Meditation. (Orig.). 1987. pap. 5.95 (ISBN 0-913382-36-1, 101-36). Prow Bks-Franciscan.
Haney, Thomas R. Reach Out & Touch. 1980. pap. 3.95 (ISBN 0-88479-027-4). Arena Lettres.
Haring, Bernard. Eucharistic Devotion: New Meanings for a Timeless Tradition. 48p. 1987. pap. 1.95 (ISBN 0-89243-261-6). Liguori Pubns.
Harper, Albert F. God Speaks Through His Word. 432p. 1985. pap. 11.95 (ISBN 0-8341-1067-9). Beacon Hill.
Harper, Steve. Devotional Life in the Wesleyan Tradition. 80p. (Orig.). 1983. pap. 3.95 (ISBN 0-8358-0467-4). Upper Room.
Hart, S. L. Lifetime of Love. LC 67-29163. 1969. 6.50 (ISBN 0-8198-0076-7); pap. 5.50 (ISBN 0-8198-4426-8). Dghtrs St Paul.
Hartman, Jane E. Hoku & the Precious Stones. 1985. pap. 4.95 (ISBN 0-87613-087-2). New Age.
Harvey, J. Glenn. How to Go to Heaven. 104p. (Orig.). 1982. pap. 2.95 (ISBN 0-915059-00-2). Ind Christ Pubns.
--Therefore. (Orig.). 1984. pap. 3.95 (ISBN 0-915059-02-9). Ind Christ Pubns.
Havner, Vance. Best of Vance Havner. (Best Ser.). pap. 3.95 (ISBN 0-8010-4234-8). Baker Bk.
--Day by Day: With Vance Havner. 272p. 1984. pap. 5.95 (ISBN 0-8010-4279-8). Baker Bk.
--Pleasant Paths. (Direction Bks.). 96p. 1983. pap. 2.95 (ISBN 0-8010-4268-2). Baker Bk.
Hayden, Eric W. Letting the Lion Loose. 1984. pap. 3.95 (ISBN 0-907927-05-X). Pilgrim Pubns.
Hecht, Michael. Have You Ever Asked Yourself These Questions. LC 75-163738. 267p. 1971. 7.95 (ISBN 0-88400-034-6). Shengold.
Heline, Corinne. Sacred Science of Numbers. 33p. pap. 4.00 (ISBN 0-87613-027-9). New Age.
Helms, Hal M. With the Lord Today, 4 vols. (Orig.). 1985. Set. 14.95 set (ISBN 0-941478-39-4). Paraclete Pr.
Hendricks, William C. Good Morning, Lord: Devotions for Boys. (Good Morning Lord Ser.). 1974. 4.95 (ISBN 0-8010-4100-7). Baker Bk.
Henrichsen, Walter. Apres le Sacrifice. Orig. Title: After the Sacrifice. (Fr.). 1986. write for info. (ISBN 0-8297-0524-4). Life Pubs Intl.
Henry, Ed. In Remembrance. 1978. pap. 1.50 (ISBN 0-89900-113-0). College Pr Pub.
Henry, James. Prescriptions from the Beloved Physician. 108p. 1972. pap. 1.00 (ISBN 0-89114-055-7). Baptist Pub Hse.
Henson, Paul F. Teach the Word. 1972. 5.25 (ISBN 0-87148-826-4); pap. 4.25 (ISBN 0-87148-827-2). Pathway Pr.
Hocquard, Gaston. Les Meditations du Bienheureux de Guigues de Saint Romain: Cinquieme Prieur de Chartreuse (1109-1136) Hogg, James, ed. (Analecta Cartusiana Ser.: No. 112). 311p. (Orig.). 1984. pap. 25.00 (ISBN 0-317-42589-7, Pub. by Salzburg Studies). Longwood Pub Group.
Hodges, Doris. Healing Stones. 14th ed. pap. 3.95 (ISBN 0-686-12935-0). Hiawatha Bondurant.
Hodson, Geoffrey. The Hidden Wisdom in the Holy Bible, Vol. 3. 1971. 7.95 (ISBN 0-8356-7493-2). Theos Pub Hse.
Hoffs, Harry. God Giveth Strength. pap. 0.45 (ISBN 0-686-23472-3). Rose Pub MI.
Hogan, Jan. Gladdys Makes Peace. (Illus.). 22p. 1985. 5.95 (ISBN 0-87178-313-4). Brethren.
Hogg, James. The Speculum Devotorum of an Anonymous Carhusian of Sheen: From the manuscripts Cambridge University Library (Gg. I.6 & Foyle Vol.2) (Analecta Carusiana Ser.: No. 12). (Eng.). 173p. (Orig.). 1973. pap. 25.00 (ISBN 3-7052-0013-5, Pub by Salzburg Studies). Longwood Pub Group.
--The Speculum Devotorum of an Anonymous Carthusian of Sheen: Introduction. (Analceta Cartusiana Ser.: No. 11). (Orig.). 1985. pap. 25.00 (ISBN 3-7052-0012-7, Pub by Salzburg Studies). Longwood Pub Group.
Hogg, james, ed. The Speculum Devotorum of an Anonymous Carhusian of Sheen: From the Manuscripts Cambridge University Library (Gg. I.6 & Foyle Vol.3, Pt. 2) (Analecta Carusiana Ser.: No. 13). (Eng.). 174p. (Orig.). 1974. pap. 25.00 (ISBN 3-7052-0014-3, Pub by Salzburg Studies). Longwood Pub Group.
Holmes, Ernest & Barker, Raymond C. Richer Living. 372p. 1973. pap. 9.50 (ISBN 0-911336-48-6). Sci of Mind.
Holmes, Marjorie. Lord, Let Me Love. 288p. 1981. pap. 3.95 (ISBN 0-553-25859-1). Bantam.
--To Help You Through the Hurting. LC 81-43571. (Illus.). 160p. 1983. 9.95 (ISBN 0-385-17842-5). Doubleday.
Hoover, Mab G. Lord, Please Zip Up My Armor. 112p. 1986. pap. 3.95 (ISBN 0-310-35642-3). Zondervan.
Horton, Harold. The Gifts of the Spirit. 208p. 1975. pap. 2.50 (ISBN 0-88243-504-3, 02-0504, Radiant Bks). Gospel Pub.
Horton, Wade H. Glossolalia Phenomenon. 1966. 7.95 (ISBN 0-87148-351-3). Pathway Pr.
--Pentecost Yesterday & Today. 1972. 7.25 (ISBN 0-87148-676-8). Pathway Pr.
--Trinitarian Concept of God. 1964. pap. 1.95 (ISBN 0-87148-833-7). Pathway Pr.
Hospital Strength. pap. 0.45 (ISBN 0-686-23471-5). Rose Pub MI.
Houselander, Caryll. Lift up Your Hearts. 1979. pap. 2.25 (ISBN 0-88479-020-7). Arena Lettres.
How to Rule the World, or Seek First the Kingdom of God. 1984. write for info. Kingdom God.
Howard, Virginia. The Messenger. 1971. pap. 3.95 (ISBN 0-910122-31-8). Amherst Pr.
Hubbard, David. Beyond Futility. 2nd ed. Semarians, Beer-Shiba, tr. (Chinese.). 106p. 1982. pap. write for info (ISBN 0-941598-02-0). Living Spring Pubns.
Huber, Georges. My Angel Will Go Before You. Adams, Michael, tr. from Fr. Tr. of Mon Ange Marchera Devant Toi. 135p. 1983. pap. 9.95. Chr Classics.
Huggett, Joyce. Approaching Easter. Reynolds, A., ed. 96p. 1987. pap. 6.95 (ISBN 0-7459-1120-X). Lion USA.
Hughes, John J. Proclaiming the Good News: Homilies for the "C" Cycle, No. 724. 1985. 14.95 (ISBN 0-87973-724-7). Our Sunday Visitor.
Hughes, Ray H. & Woodard, Bernice Stout. Planning for Sunday School Progress. 5.25 (ISBN 0-87148-682-2). Pathway Pr.
Hunter, Frances. How to Talk to God Every Day of the Year: A Book of Devotions for Twelve Positive Months. 240p. 1984. 14.95 (ISBN 0-13-435248-3); pap. 6.95 (ISBN 0-13-435230-0). P-H.
Hunter, JoAnn H. & Freund, John. Mirror of God's Love. 64p. 1984. pap. 2.50 (ISBN 0-916134-60-1). Pueblo Pub Co.
Icons in the Eastern Orthodox Church, a Brief Theological Introduction: Jeremiah, Patriarch of Constantinople & St. John of Damascus. pap. 0.50 (ISBN 0-686-01294-1). Eastern Orthodox.
Inter-Varsity Staff. Quiet Time. pap. 1.95 (ISBN 0-87784-250-7). Inter Varsity.
International Congress of Psychology, 10th: Copenhagen, 1932 (Papers Read) Repr. 53.00 (ISBN 0-8115-3551-7). Kraus Repr.
Irland, Nancy B. Little Talks with Jesus. Wheeler, Gerald, ed. 1985. 9.95 (ISBN 0-8280-0251-7). Review & Herald.
Ironside, H. A. Eternal Security of the Believer. pap. 1.50 (ISBN 0-87213-347-8). Loizeaux.
--Not Wrath: But Rapture. pap. 1.50 (ISBN 0-87213-380-X). Loizeaux.
Irwin, Elvin. O Plano de Deus para a Familia. Orig. Title: Living on God's Family Plan. (Port.). 1986. write for info. (ISBN 0-8297-0708-5). Life Pubs Intl.
Isaac, Reid. Conversations with the Crucified. 128p. (Orig.). 1982. pap. 6.95 (ISBN 0-8164-2417-9, HarpR). Har-Row.
Isaac, Stephen. Songs from the House of Pilgrimage. LC 77-169595. 1971. 9.50 (ISBN 0-8283-1334-2). Christward.
Jabay, Earl. The God-Players. LC 69-11637. 155p. 1970. pap. 5.95 (ISBN 0-310-26541-X, 9939P). Zondervan.
Jacks, Bob, et al. Your Home, a Lighthouse. LC 85-73824. 142p. (Orig.). 1986. pap. text ed. 4.95 (ISBN 0-934396-41-8). Churches Alive.
Jacobs, Mildred Spires. Come unto Me. (Illus.). 56p. (Orig.). 1982. pap. 2.95 (ISBN 0-9609612-0-8). Enrich Enter.
Jarrett, R. H. It Works. 31st ed. 1976. pap. 1.00 (ISBN 0-87516-323-8). De Vorss.
Jay, Ruth J. Learning from God's Animals. (Illus.). 36p. (Orig.). 1981. pap. 3.25 (ISBN 0-934998-04-3). Bethel Pub.
--Learning from God's Birds. (Illus.). 34p. (Orig.). 1981. pap. 3.25 (ISBN 0-934998-05-1). Bethel Pub.
Johnson, Elliot. The Point After: Advice from God's Athletes. 128p. 1987. pap. 5.95 (ISBN 0-310-26171-6, 12416P). Zondervan.
Johnson, Lissa H. Something to Live For. 1986. 5.95 (ISBN 0-8007-5228-7). Revell.
Jones, Dennis M. And Then There Was Peace. (Orig.). 1987. pap. 3.00 (ISBN 0-941992-08-X). Los Arboles Pub.
Jones, E. Stanley. The Way: Three Hundred Sixty-Four Adventures in Daily Living. 368p. (Orig.). 1984. pap. 4.35 (ISBN 0-687-44099-8). Abingdon.
Jones, Gladys V. The Flowering Tree. 316p. 1984. pap. 8.95 (ISBN 0-87516-527-3). De Vorss.
Jordan, Bernice C. Los Hechos Epistolas-Vosotros sois Edificio de Dios: 14 Lecciones, Tomo 1. (Pasos De Fe Ser.). (Span.). pap. text ed. 2.50 (ISBN 0-86508-413-0); figuras 8.95 (ISBN 0-86508-414-9). BCM Intl Inc.
Judd, Wayne. Kissing, Hugging, &... LC 79-20362. (Nugget Ser.). 1979. pap. 0.79 (ISBN 0-8127-0249-2). Review & Herald.
Kaplan, David & Kaplan, Marcia. Smiles. (Inspirational Ser.). (Illus.). 100p. 1982. pap. 4.95 (ISBN 0-939944-05-7). M & L Sales.
Kaplan, Mordecai M., et al, eds. The Faith of America. LC 51-14109. 328p. 1951. pap. 4.95 (ISBN 0-935457-33-X). Reconstructionist Pr.
Karssen, Gien. The Man Who Was Different. 1987. price not set (ISBN 0-89109-136-X). NavPress.
Kasper, Walter. God of Jesus Christ. 1984. 24.50x (ISBN 0-8245-0629-4). Crossroad NY.
Kauffeld, Eugene P. Divine Footprints. 1983. pap. 9.95 (ISBN 0-8100-0148-9, 15N0382). Northwest Pub.
Kelly, Thomas R. A Testament of Devotion. 1941. 12.45 (ISBN 0-06-064370-6, HarpR). Har-Row.
Kelsey, Morton T. Companions on the Inner Way: The Art of Spiritual Guidance. LC 82-23541. 250p. 1983. 17.50 (ISBN 0-8245-0585-9); pap. 9.95 (ISBN 0-8245-0560-3). Crossroad NY.
Kennedy, D. James. Truths That Transform. 160p. 1974. power bks. 5.95 (ISBN 0-8007-5148-5). Revell.
Kennedy, Eugene C. The Joy of Being Human: Reflections for Every Day of the Year. 360p. 1976. pap. 5.95 (ISBN 0-385-00943-7, Im). Doubleday.
Kent, Homer A., Jr. Treasures of Wisdom: Studies in Colossians & Philemon. pap. 5.95 (ISBN 0-88469-062-8). BMH Bks.
Kenyon, Don J. The Double Mind. 95p. 1981. pap. 2.25 (ISBN 0-87509-288-8). Chr Pubns.
Kern, Alma. You Are Special. (Illus.). 144p. (Orig.). 1985. pap. 5.00 (ISBN 0-9614955-0-2, 2050). Lutheran Womens.
Kim, Chi-ha. The Gold-Crowned Jesus & Other Writings. Kim, Chong Sun & Killen, Shelly, eds. LC 77-17522. pap. 44.50 (ISBN 0-317-26644-6, 2025119). Bks Demand UMI.
Kirban, Doreen & Kirban, Diane. Stranger in Tomorrow's Land. 1970. 4.95 (ISBN 0-912582-40-5). Kirban.
Kirban, Salem. Guide to Survival. 1979. pap. 6.95 (ISBN 0-912582-24-3). Kirban.
--How to Be Sure of Crowns in Heaven. 1980. pap. 5.95 (ISBN 0-912582-34-0). Kirban.
--Plain Truth About the Plain Truth. (Illus.). 1972. pap. 4.95 (ISBN 0-912582-12-X). Kirban.
--Questions Frequently Asked Me on Prophecy. (Illus.). 1981. pap. 4.95 (ISBN 0-912582-01-4). Kirban.
Knight, Cecil B. Keeping the Sunday School Alive. 1959. 5.25 (ISBN 0-87148-475-7). Pathway Pr.
Korfker, Dena. Good Morning, Lord: Devotions for Children. (Good Morning Lord Ser.). 1973. 4.95 (ISBN 0-8010-5328-5). Baker Bk.
Kotter, Bonnie. Thank God for the Crumbs. Wheeler, Gerald, ed. (Banner Bks.). 96p. (Orig.). 1986. pap. 6.50 (ISBN 0-8280-0315-7). Review & Herald.
Kranzler, George. Face of Faith. 1972. 15.00x (ISBN 0-685-38401-2). Ktav.
Kroll, Woodrow M. Early in the Morning. 128p. 1986. 4.95 (ISBN 0-87213-474-1). Loizeaux.
Kung, Hans. Do We Know the Others? LC 66-20895. (Concilium Ser.: Vol. 14). 196p. 1966. 7.95 (ISBN 0-8091-0033-9). Paulist Pr.
Kunz, Marilyn & Schell, Catherine. Four Men of God, Neighborhood Bible Study. 1972. pap. 2.95 (ISBN 0-8423-0900-4). Tyndale.
Kupferle, Mary L. God Never Fails. 141p. 1983. pap. 4.95 (ISBN 0-87516-513-3). De Vorss.
Kurl, Shreeprakash, tr. The Devotional Poems of Mirabai. (Writers Workshop Saffronbird Ser.). 87p. 1975. 15.00 (ISBN 0-88253-722-9); pap. 6.75 (ISBN 0-89253-539-3). Ind-US Inc.
Lancaster, John. The Spirit-Filled Church. LC 75-22584. 112p. 1975. pap. 1.25 (ISBN 0-88243-601-5, 02-0601, Radiant Bks). Gospel Pub.
Lane, William L. Call to Commitment: Responding to the Message of Hebrews. LC 85-15597. 192p. 1985. pap. 8.95 (ISBN 0-8407-5948-7). Nelson.
Lang, J. David. Your Phone's Ringing, No. 2. (Illus.). 64p. 1985. pap. 2.50 (ISBN 0-87239-898-6, 2828). Standard Pub.
Larson, Jim. Walking in God's Light. LC 84-9963. 1984. pap. 3.95 (ISBN 0-8307-0953-3, S181216). Regal.
Laurence, Richard. The Book of Enoch the Prophet. 2nd ed. Laurence, Richard, tr. from Old Ethiopic. LC 72-95273. (Secret Doctrine Reference Ser). 220p. 1972. Repr. of 1883 ed. 11.00 (ISBN 0-913510-01-7). Wizards.
Lauterbach, William. Es Will Abend Werden. Kujath, Mentor, ed. 1978. pap. 2.25 (ISBN 0-8100-0101-2, 26-0511). Northwest Pub.
Law, William. Power of the Spirit. Hunt, D., ed. 1971. pap. 2.95 (ISBN 0-87508-247-5). Chr Lit.
--A Serious Call to a Devout & Holy Life. 1967. Repr. of 1906 ed. 12.95x (ISBN 0-460-00091-8, Evman). Biblio Dist.
Leary, James. Hear O Israel. 1980. pap. 3.95 (ISBN 0-88479-029-0). Arena Lettres.
Lemmons, Reuel & Bannister, John. Unto Us a Child is Born. Kyker, Rex, compiled by. 126p. (Orig.). 1982. pap. 2.95 (ISBN 0-88027-109-4). Firm Foun Pub.
Lemons, Frank W. Looking Beyond. 78p. 1969. 3.95 (ISBN 0-87148-506-0); pap. 2.95 (ISBN 0-87148-507-9). Pathway Pr.
--Perennial Pentecost. 1971. pap. 2.95 (ISBN 0-87148-679-2). Pathway Pr.
--Profiles of Faith. 1971. pap. 2.95 (ISBN 0-87148-683-0). Pathway Pr.
Lerin, Alfredo, compiled by. Quinientas Ilustraciones. (Span.). 324p. 1984. pap. 5.95 (ISBN 0-311-42037-0). Casa Bautista.
Leroy, Douglas. I Didn't Know That. 1973. pap. 3.95 (ISBN 0-87148-425-0). Pathway Pr.
Lewis, C. S. Pilgrim's Regress. 224p. 1981. pap. 3.50 (ISBN 0-553-26063-4). Bantam.
Liddy, Richard. In Gods Gentle Arms. 1979. pap. 2.95 (ISBN 0-88479-022-3). Arena Lettres.
Light, Mary. God's Guidance at Dawn. pap. 1.00 (ISBN 0-910924-68-6). Macalester.
--Joy of the Lord. pap. 0.50 (ISBN 0-910924-67-8). Macalester.
--Rays of Light. pap. 1.00 (ISBN 0-910924-59-7). Macalester.
--Rejoice & Be Exceeding Glad. pap. 1.00 (ISBN 0-910924-60-0). Macalester.
--Signs & Wonders. 1968. pap. 1.00 (ISBN 0-910924-66-X). Macalester.
Lind, Miriam S. No Crying He Makes. LC 78-181580. 96p. 1972. pap. 1.50 (ISBN 0-8361-1321-7). Herald Pr.
Littleton, Mark. A Place to Stand: When Life Throws You Off Balance. (Christian Living Ser.). 1986. pap. 6.95 (ISBN 0-88070-141-2). Multnomah.
Lloyd-Jones, Martyn D. De la Angoisse a la Foi. Tr. of From Fear to Faith. (Fr.). 1986. pap. 1.70 (ISBN 0-8297-0694-1). Life Pubs Intl.
Lockerbie, Jeanette. A Cup of Sugar, Neighbor. (Quiet Time Bks.). 128p. 1974. pap. 3.50 (ISBN 0-8024-1681-0). Moody.

Loder, Ted. No One But Us: Personal Reflections on Public Sanctuary. LC 86-7516. 224p. (Orig.). 1986. pap. 9.95 (ISBN 0-931055-09-1). LuraMedia.
--Sand in the Cloud: Voices of Old Testament Witnesses. Broucek, Marcia, ed. 180p. (Orig.). 1987. pap. 9.95 (ISBN 0-931055-42-3). LuraMedia.
The Lord Is My Shepherd. (Illus.). 48p. 1982. Repr. 7.95 (ISBN 0-86683-687-X, AY8288, HarpR). Har-Row.
The Lord's Prayer: St. Cyprian. pap. 1.95 (ISBN 0-686-01296-8). Eastern Orthodox.
Lubich, Chiara. Unity & Jesus Forsaken. LC 85-72397. 105p. 1985. pap. 4.95 (ISBN 0-911782-53-2). New City.
--When Our Love Is Charity. LC 72-85632. 82p. 1972. pap. 2.95 (ISBN 0-911782-02-8). New City.
Lummis, Charles F. My Friend Will. 1972. 3.50 (ISBN 0-87516-161-8). De Vorss.
Luther, Martin. Bondage of the Will. Packer, J. I. & Johnston, O. R., trs. 322p. 1970. 13.95 (ISBN 0-8007-0028-7). Revell.
Luz Diaria Para el Camino Diario. 284p. 1984. pap. 5.50 (ISBN 0-311-40045-0). Casa Bautista.
Maassen, Pierce. Heavenly Comfort. pap. 0.45 (ISBN 0-686-23473-1). Rose Pub MI.
Macarius, Staretz. Russian Letters of Direction. LC 75-1064. 115p. 1975. pap. 4.95 (ISBN 0-913836-23-0). St Vladimirs.
MacArthur, John, Jr. Comfort for Troubled Hearts. (John MacArthur's Bible Studies). (Orig.). 1986. pap. 3.95 (ISBN 0-8024-5342-2). Moody.
MacDonald, George. George MacDonald: An Anthology. Lewis, C. S., ed. 192p. 1986. pap. 6.95 (ISBN 0-02-022640-3, Collier). Macmillan.
McDonnell, Rea. Prayer Pilgrimage with Paul. 112p. 1986. pap. 4.95 (ISBN 0-8091-2746-6). Paulist Pr.
Macquarrie, John. The Faith of the People of God: A Lay Theology. LC 72-1224. 188p. 1973. pap. 7.95 (ISBN 0-684-13060-2, ScribT). Scribner.
Mallis, W. Way of the Wind. (YA) 1971. pap. 1.50 (ISBN 0-87508-326-9). Chr Lit.
Man Chong Fung, tr. Be Perfect. 2nd ed. (Chinese.). 160p. 1982. pap. write for info (ISBN 0-941598-03-9). Living Spring Pubns.
Mandino, Og. The God Memorandum. new ed. LC 80-81145. 112p. 1980. 6.95 (ISBN 0-8119-0337-0). Fell.
--The Greatest Salesman in the World. 128p. 1974. pap. 3.50 (ISBN 0-553-26880-5). Bantam.
Mantle, J. Gregory. Better Things from Above. 1971. pap. 3.00 (ISBN 0-87509-051-6). Chr Pubns.
Mara. Tracings. LC 80-67934. (Earth Song Ser.). 84p. 1980. pap. 4.95 (ISBN 0-9605170-0-6). Earth-Song.
Marshall, Catherine. To Live Again. 1976. pap. 3.95 (ISBN 0-380-01586-2). Avon.
Marshall, Helen L. Quiet Power: Words of Faith, Hope, & Love. 64p. 1985. pap. 3.95 (ISBN 0-8010-6197-0). Baker Bk.
Marshall, I. Howard. Biblical Inspiration. 128p. 1983. pap. 5.95 (ISBN 0-8028-1959-1). Eerdmans.
Martin, Paul. Good Morning, Lord: More Devotions for Teens. (Good Morning Lord Ser.). 1973. 4.95 (ISBN 0-8010-5915-1). Baker Bk.
Massie, Robert. His Image... My Image: Leader's Guide. 86p. 1986. pap. 1.95 (ISBN 0-86605-159-7). Campus Crusade.
Maughon, Martha. Why Am I Crying? 1983. pap. 5.95 (ISBN 0-310-37671-8, 11221P). Zondervan.
Maxwell, John. Think on These Things. 128p. 1979. pap. 2.95 (ISBN 0-8341-0600-0). Beacon Hill.
Medeiros, Huberto C. Thy Kingdom Come. 1980. 3.00 (ISBN 0-8198-7307-1); pap. 1.95 (ISBN 0-8198-7308-X). Dghtrs St Paul.
Metcalfe, J. C. God the Spirit. 1972. pap. 1.50 (ISBN 0-87508-917-8). Chr Lit.
Meyers, Carol L. & O'Connor, M., eds. The Word of the Lord Shall Go Forth: Essays in Honor of David Noel Freedman in Celebration of His Sixtieth Birthday. (American Schools of Oriental Research, Special Volume Ser.: No. 1). 1983. text ed. 35.00x (ISBN 0-931464-19-6). Eisenbrauns.
Michael, Arnold. Blessed among Women. 1985. pap. 8.95 (ISBN 0-87613-091-0). New Age.
Miller, Randolph C. Living with Anxiety. LC 75-168525. 190p. 1971. 5.95 (ISBN 0-8298-0206-1). Pilgrim NY.
Mills, Dick. He Spoke & I Was Strengthened. 1973. pap. 2.95 (ISBN 0-88368-026-2). Whitaker Hse.
Miner, Ernest. Living Thoughts. (Book of Inspirational Thoughts Ser.). 84p. 1985. 7.95 (ISBN 0-935087-00-1). Wright Pub Co.
Mischke, Bernard C. & Mischke, Fritz. Pray Today's Gospel: Reflections on the Day's Good News. LC 80-14186. 358p. (Orig.). 1980. pap. 9.95 (ISBN 0-8189-0403-8). Alba.
Mitchell, John G. Fellowship: A Devotional Study of the Epistles of John. LC 84-193801. (Orig.). 1974. pap. text ed. 6.95 (ISBN 0-930014-06-5). Multnomah.
Moldstad, Joslyn W. Few Minutes with Jesus. 1984. pap. 5.95 (ISBN 0-8100-0189-6, 06N0565). Northwest Pub.
Moore, Marvin. Sacrifice. LC 78-21712. (Flame Ser.). 1979. pap. 0.99 (ISBN 0-8127-0214-X). Review & Herald.
Morantte, M. P. God Is in the Heart: Poetical & Symbolical Essays. (Illus.). 78p. (Orig.). 1982. pap. 4.75 (ISBN 971-10-0040-7, Pub. by New Day Philippines). Cellar.
More, St. Thomas. The Confutation of Tyndale's Answer, 3 pts. Schuster, Louis A., et al, eds. LC 63-7949. (Complete Works of St. Thomas More Ser.: No. 8). 1836p. 1973. Set. 155.00x (ISBN 0-300-01302-7). Yale U Pr.
Morgan, G. Campbell. Discipleship. (Morgan Library). 1973. pap. 3.45 (ISBN 0-8010-5920-8). Baker Bk.
Muller, Richard A. A Dictionary of Latin & Greek Theological Terms. 1985. 14.95 (ISBN 0-8010-6185-7). Baker Bk.
Munce, R. H. Ruth. 117p. 1971. spral bdg 3.95x (ISBN 0-914674-00-5). Freelandia.
Mundfrom, Gerald F. My Experience with Clinical Depression. rev. ed. (Illus.). 184p. 1986. pap. 5.50x (ISBN 0-9615494-1-6). Mercy & Truth.
Murphy, Chuck & Murphy, Anne. When the Saints Go Marching Out. 1987. pap. 5.95 (Chosen Bks). Revell.
Murphy, Elspeth C. God Hears Me When I Pray. (Hardcover Psalm Books for Children). (Illus.). 96p. 1985. 7.95 (ISBN 0-89191-645-8, 56457). Cook.
--God Helps Me Everyday. (Hardcover Psalm Books for Children). (Illus.). 96p. 1985. 7.95 (ISBN 0-89191-642-3, 56424). Cook.
Murray, Andrew. The Believer's Secret of Waiting on God. 169p. 1986. pap. 3.95 (ISBN 0-87123-886-1). Bethany Hse.
--Daily Secrets of Christian Living. LC 77-17187. 400p. 1978. pap. 7.95 (ISBN 0-87123-500-5, 210500). Bethany Hse.
--Jesus Himself. 27p. 1966. pap. 0.95 (ISBN 0-87509-096-6). Chr Pubns.
--Waiting on God. 160p. 1981. pap. 3.50 (ISBN 0-88368-101-3). Whitaker Hse.
My God, My Life. 71p. pap. 5.95 (ISBN 0-9616007-0-5). M F Turner Pub.
Myers, Rawley. Jesus Is Here: Devotions to the Sacred Heart & Precious Blood. LC 85-63066. 144p. (Orig.). 1986. pap. 5.95 (ISBN 0-87973-520-1, XXX 520). Our Sunday Visitor.
Nee, Watchman. Conhecimento Espiritual. Orig. Title: Spiritual Knowledge. (Port.). 1986. write for info. (ISBN 0-8297-0781-6). Life Pubs Intl.
--Conocimiento Espiritual. Orig. Title: Spiritual Knowledge. (Span.). 1986. write for info. (ISBN 0-8297-0782-4). Life Pubs Intl.
--The Joyful Heart. 1977. pap. 4.50 (ISBN 0-8423-1975-1). Tyndale.
Nee, Watchmans. Love Not the World. 1977. pap. 3.50 (ISBN 0-8423-3850-0). Tyndale.
Neel, Peg. How to Pray According to God's Word. 72p. 1982. pap. 2.25 (ISBN 0-88144-004-3, CPS-004). Christian Pub.
Neighbour, Ralph W., Jr. The Touch of the Spirit. LC 72-84243. 1977. pap. 4.25 (ISBN 0-8054-5158-7). Broadman.
Nelson, F. Burton. The Story of the People of God. (Illus.). 436p. 1971. pap. 5.50 (ISBN 0-910452-17-2). Covenant.
Nelson, Wesley W. Liberation. 1974. pap. 2.95 (ISBN 0-910452-19-9). Covenant.
Nestorian Church. Liturgy & Ritual: The Liturgy of the Holy Apostles Adai & Mari. LC 79-131032. Repr. of 1893 ed. 14.50 (ISBN 0-404-03997-9). AMS Pr.
Never Alone. pap. 0.45 (ISBN 0-686-23470-7). Rose Pub MI.
Nineteen Eighty-Eighty-One Collection of Fellowship Readings. 105p. 7.50 (ISBN 0-318-03276-7, 142802). ASHMM.
Nineteen Eighty-Three Annual Conference Proceedings. 160p. 25.00 (ISBN 0-318-03308-9, 142805). ASHMM.
Nineteen Eighty-Three Collection of Fellowship Readings. 95p. 18.00 (ISBN 0-318-03298-8, 142804). ASHMM.
Nineteen Eighty-Two Collection of Fellowship Readings. 127p. 10.00 (ISBN 0-318-03296-1, 142803). ASHMM.
Norden, John. Progress of Piety. Repr. of 1847 ed. 21.00 (ISBN 0-384-41910-0). Johnson Repr.
Nyvall, David. My Father's Testament. 1974. pap. 5.95 (ISBN 0-910452-20-2). Covenant.
O'Connor, Elizabeth. Search for Silence. rev. ed. Broucek, Marcia, ed. LC 86-114. 192p. 1986. pap. 8.95 (ISBN 0-931055-08-3). LuraMedia.
Ogilvie, Lloyd J. Ask Him Anything. (QP Proven-Word Ser.). 244p. 1984. pap. 7.95 (ISBN 0-8499-2982-2). Word Bks.
--A Sarca Ainda Arde. Orig. Title: The Bush Is Still Burning. (Port.). 1986. write for info. (ISBN 0-8297-1093-0). Life Pubs Intl.
--La Zarza Sique Ardiendo. Orig. Title: The Bush Is Still Burning. (Span.). 1986. write for info. (ISBN 0-8297-1094-9). Life Pubs Intl.
O. Henry, et al. Inspiration Three, Vol. 5: Three Famous Classics in One Book. LC 73-80032. (Pivot Family Reader Ser.). 1973. pap. 1.25 (ISBN 0-87983-045-X). Keats.
Opatz, Patrica G. The Pleasure of God's Company. 96p. 1985. pap. 3.95 (ISBN 0-8146-1437-X). Liturgical Pr.
Ortlund, Raymond C. Lord, Make My Life a Miracle! LC 73-89714. (Orig.). 1974. pap. 3.50 (ISBN 0-8307-0284-9, 5011701); study guide 1.59 (ISBN 0-8307-0626-7, 6101305). Regal.
Oursler, Fulton. The Greatest Story Ever Told. 1981. pap. 2.95 (ISBN 0-671-44742-4). PB.
Owens, Virginia S. And the Trees Clap Their Hands: Faith, Perception & the New Physics. 148p. 1983. pap. 6.95 (ISBN 0-8028-1949-4). Eerdmans.
Palmer, Phoebe. The Devotional Writings of Phoebe Palmer. Dayton, Donald W., ed. (The Higher Christian Life Ser.). 640p. 1985. 80.00 (ISBN 0-8240-6431-3). Garland Pub.
Panning, Armin J. The Life of Christ. 1971. pap. 2.50 (ISBN 0-8100-0018-0, 09-0932). Northwest Pub.
Parkhurst, Genevieve. Glorious Victory Thru Healing Memories. 4.95 (ISBN 0-910924-55-4). Macalester.
--Take a Walk with Jesus. pap. 0.40 ea. 3 for 1.00 (ISBN 0-910924-31-7). Macalester.
Paulk, Earl P. Sunday School Evangelism. 1958. 4.95 (ISBN 0-87148-759-4). Pathway Pr.
Payne, Richard, ed. Letters to Young People: A World Spiritual Legacy for Our Future Earth. (Patterns of World Spirituality Ser.). 240p. pap. 9.95 (ISBN 0-913757-72-1). Paragon Hse.
Pearlman, Myer. Let's Meet the Holy Spirit. (Radiant Bks.). 64p. 1975. pap. 0.95 (ISBN 0-88243-565-5, 02-0565). Gospel Pub.
Peguy, Charles. Notre Seigneur. pap. 2.50 (ISBN 0-685-37032-1). French & Eur.
The Perpetual Help Story. A Redemptorist Publication. 64p. 1977. pap. 1.95 (ISBN 0-89243-066-4, 29230). Liguori Pubns.
Petty, James & Petty, Frances. That Door with the Lock. 1973. pap. 2.95 (ISBN 0-88428-023-3, 314). Parchment Pr.
Pfarr, Anthony J. Seek His Face. LC 73-86211. 1973. 4.95 (ISBN 0-8198-0353-7); pap. 3.95 (ISBN 0-8198-0354-5). Dghtrs St Paul.
Phillips, Allen. Nuggets for Happiness. 1959. 2.95 (ISBN 0-87148-625-3). Pathway Pr.
Pink, A. W. Profiting from the Word. 1977. pap. 3.45 (ISBN 0-85151-032-9). Banner of Truth.
Pink, Arthur W. Comfort for Christians. (Summit Bks.). 122p. 1976. pap. 2.95 (ISBN 0-8010-7062-7). Baker Bk.
Poling, David, compiled by. Inspiration Three, Vol. 3: Three Famous Classics in One Book - Wisdom of Luther, Calvin & Wesley. LC 73-80032. (Pivot Family Reader Ser). 1973. pap. 1.25 (ISBN 0-87983-043-3). Keats.
Pollard, T. E. Fullness of Humanity: Christ's Humanness & Ours. 128p. 1982. text ed. 19.95x (ISBN 0-907459-10-2, Pub. by Almond Pr England); pap. text ed. 9.95x (ISBN 0-907459-11-0, Pub. by Almond Pr England). Eisenbrauns.
Ponder, Catherine. Dynamic Laws of Healing. 1972. pap. 6.95 (ISBN 0-87516-156-1). De Vorss.
Popley, H. A., ed. & tr. The Sacred Kural. 2nd. ed. Orig. Title: The Tamil Veda of Tiruvalluvar. 159p. pap. 2.80 (ISBN 0-88253-386-X). Ind-US Inc.
Precious Bible Promises: From the King James Version. 384p. 1984. 16.95 (ISBN 0-8407-5354-3). Nelson.
Precious Bible Promises: From the New American Bible. 384p. 1985. 17.95 (ISBN 0-8407-5456-6). Nelson.
Preston, John. Breastplate of Faith & Love. Facs. ed. 241p. 1979. Repr. of 1630 ed. 22.95 (ISBN 0-85151-289-5). Banner of Truth.
Price, Eugenia. Early Will I Seek Thee. 160p. pap. 2.95 (ISBN 0-8007-8584-3, Spire Bks). Revell.
The Promised Ones Are Alive & Well on Planet Earth. 1986. write for info. Port Love Intl.
Prophet, Elizabeth C., ed. Pearls of Wisdom 1976, Vol. 19. LC 76-52850. 13.95 (ISBN 0-916766-24-1). Summit Univ.
Pruitt, Robert J. The Death of the Third Nature. 1975. pap. 1.95 (ISBN 0-934942-04-8). White Wing Pub.
--The Kingdom of God & the Church of God. 1977. pap. 1.95 (ISBN 0-934942-09-9). White Wing Pub.
Prynne, William. Mount-Orgueil. LC 83-20361. 1984. Repr. of 1641 ed. 40.00x (ISBN 0-8201-1392-1). Schol Facsimiles.
Puryear, Herbert B. Reflections on the Path. 224p. 1986. pap. 3.50 (ISBN 0-553-25659-9). Bantam.
Putnam, Roy C. In It to Win It. 1973. pap. 2.95 (ISBN 0-87508-440-0). Chr Lit.
Pylant, Agnes D. Threescore & Ten-Wow. LC 70-151621. 1971. pap. 2.75 (ISBN 0-8054-5213-3). Broadman.
Quenon, Paul. Carved in Stone. (Illus.). 40p. 1979. pap. 2.50 (ISBN 0-87793-195-X). Ave Maria.
Quiros, T. E. Por Sendas Biblicas. (Span.). 162p. 1985. pap. 3.25 (ISBN 0-311-08753-1). Casa Bautista.
Quoist, Michael. Prayers. 1975. pap. 5.95 (ISBN 0-380-00406-2, 60244-X). Avon.
Raines, Robert. A Faithing Oak. 128p. 1984. pap. 6.95 (ISBN 0-8245-0636-7). Crossroad NY.
Rankin, Peg. Yet Will I Trust Him. LC 79-91705. 160p. 1980. 5.95 (ISBN 0-8307-0741-7, 5412005). Regal.
Ransom, Ralph. Steps on the Stairway. LC 81-66408. 96p. 1981. 8.95 (ISBN 0-8119-0424-5). Fell.
Rector, Hartman, Jr. Already to Harvest. 91p. 1985. 7.95 (ISBN 0-934126-67-4); pap. 4.95 (ISBN 0-934126-73-9). Randall Bk Co.
Reddin, Opal. Have It His Way. LC 78-73143. 128p. 1980. pap. 1.95 (ISBN 0-88243-717-8, 02-0717); tchr's ed 2.95 (ISBN 0-88243-332-6, 02-0332). Gospel Pub.
Redpath, Alan. Making of a Man of God: Studies in the Life of David. 256p. 1962. 12.95 (ISBN 0-8007-0189-5). Revell.
Rest, Friedrich. Fourteen Messages of Hope. (Pulpit Library). 96p. 1985. pap. 3.95 (ISBN 0-8010-7733-8). Baker Bk.
Richards, Larry. When It Hurts Too Much to Wait: Understanding God's Timing. 160p. 1985. 9.95 (ISBN 0-8499-0489-7, 0489-7). Word Bks.
Richards, Lawrence O. The Believer's Praise Book. 1986. pap. 2.50 (ISBN 0-310-43512-9, 18204P). Zondervan.
Richardson, Don. Peace Child. LC 75-26356. (Illus.). 288p. 1975. Repr. of 1974 ed. digest 6.95 (ISBN 0-8307-0415-9, 5403006). Regal.
Ridout, Samuel. Lectures on the Tabernacle. (Illus.). 1973. Repr. of 1914 ed. 13.95 (ISBN 0-87213-715-5); chart only 0.15 (ISBN 0-87213-716-3). Loizeaux.
Roberts, Frances J. Come Away, My Beloved. 1970. 9.95 (ISBN 0-932814-01-8); pap. 6.95 (ISBN 0-932814-02-6). Kings Farspan.
--Dialogues with God. 1968. 6.95 (ISBN 0-932814-07-7); pap. 4.95 (ISBN 0-932814-08-5). Kings Farspan.
--On the Highroad of Surrender. 1973. 6.95 (ISBN 0-932814-14-X); pap. 4.95 (ISBN 0-932814-15-8). Kings Farspan.
--Progress of Another Pilgrim. 1970. 6.95 (ISBN 0-932814-10-7); pap. 4.95 (ISBN 0-932814-11-5). Kings Farspan.
--When the Latch Is Lifted. 1970. 3.95 (ISBN 0-932814-18-2). Kings Farspan.
Rodriguez, Cookie. Please Make Me Cry! 1974. pap. 2.95 (ISBN 0-88368-042-4). Whitaker Hse.
Rogers, Joyce. The Wise Woman. LC 80-68538. 1981. 8.95 (ISBN 0-8054-5289-3). Broadman.
Rogers, W. R. You Can Give a Chalk Talk. LC 80-65775. 1981. saddlewire 5.25 (ISBN 0-8054-6931-1). Broadman.
Rogness, Michael. The Hand That Holds Me. LC 84-14447. 112p. (Orig.). 1984. pap. 5.95 (ISBN 0-8066-2093-5, 10-2943). Augsburg.
Roper, Gayle G. Mother's World. (Ultra Bks Ser). 96p. 1975. 3.50 (ISBN 0-8010-7631-5). Baker Bk.
Rosage, David E. The Bread of Life. (Orig.). 1979. pap. 2.50 (ISBN 0-89283-067-0). Servant.
Rosenstock-Huessy, Eugen. Multiformity of Man. 1973. pap. 3.50 (ISBN 0-912148-06-3). Argo Bks.
Rowland, May. Dare to Believe. 1961. 5.95 (ISBN 0-87159-024-7). Unity School.
Rudolph, Erwin, ed. William Law on Christian Perfection. 146p. 1981. pap. 3.95 (ISBN 0-87123-117-4, 210117). Bethany Hse.
Russell, A. J. God Calling. (The Christian Library). 249p. 1986. Repr. leatherette 3.95 (ISBN 0-916441-45-8). Barbour & Co.
Russell, A. J., ed. God Calling. 192p. 1972. pap. 3.50 (ISBN 0-8007-8096-5, Spire Bks). Revell.
Russell, Robert A. You Try It. 1953. pap. 5.50 (ISBN 0-87516-326-2). De Vorss.
Rutledge, Don & Furlow, Elaine S. The Human Touch. LC 75-2365. (Human Touch Ser.). (Illus.). 1975. 5.95 (ISBN 0-937170-13-5). Home Mission.
Ryan, James. Bible Promises for Growing Christians. LC 84-22953. 1985. pap. 2.25 (ISBN 0-8054-5014-9). Broadman.
Ryle, John C. Old Paths: Being Plain Statements on Some of the Weightier Matters of Christianity. 553p. 1977. 12.95 (ISBN 0-227-67821-4). Attic Pr.

Ryrie, Charles C. Dispensationalism Today. LC 65-14611. 211p. 1973. pap. 6.95 (ISBN 0-8024-2256-X). Moody.

Samuel, Vinay & Sugden, Chris, eds. Sharing Jesus in the "Two Thirds" World. 432p. (Orig.). 1984. pap. 10.95 (ISBN 0-8028-1997-4). Eerdmans.

Sanders, J. Oswald. Enjoying Intimacy with God. LC 80-21398. 218p. 1980. pap. 5.95 (ISBN 0-8024-2346-9). Moody.

Sanford, Agnes. Behold Your God. 5.95 (ISBN 0-910924-35-X); pap. 4.50 (ISBN 0-910924-63-5). Macalester.

Sangster, Margaret E. Fairest Girlhood. 224p. 1987. pap. 5.95 (ISBN 0-310-34471-9). Zondervan.

Sasser, Nancy L. Around the Advent Wreath: Devotions for Families Using the Advent Wreath. 40p. (Orig.). 1984. pap. 2.95 (ISBN 0-8066-2074-9, 23-1064). Augsburg.

Sayers, Stanley. Lord Went with Them. pap. 2.50 (ISBN 0-89315-143-2). Lambert Bk.

Schievella, Pasqual S. Hey! Is That You, God? Crystal, Richard O., ed. Date not set. 16.95. Sebastian LI.

Schillebeeckx, Edward. God among Us: The Gospel Proclaimed. LC 82-23575. 278p. 1983. 12.95 (ISBN 0-8245-0575-1). Crossroad NY.

Schlink, Basilea. Let Me Stand at Your Side. 1975. 2.95 (ISBN 3-87209-614-1). Evang Sisterhood Mary.

--My All for Him. 160p. 1971. pap. 3.95 (ISBN 0-87123-370-3, 200370). Bethany Hse.

--Ruled by the Spirit. 144p. 1970. pap. 3.50 (ISBN 0-87123-483-1, 200483). Bethany Hse.

--You Will Never Be the Same. 192p. 1972. pap. 3.50 (ISBN 0-87123-661-3, 200661). Bethany Hse.

Schmemann, Alexander. For the Life of the World: Sacraments & Orthodoxy. 151p. 1973. pap. 5.95 (ISBN 0-913836-08-7). St Vladimirs.

Schneider, Claire. Inspirations Unlimited. 48p. (Orig.). 1985. pap. 4.95 (ISBN 0-9601982-2-9). Greenwood Hse.

Schroeder, Janet E. Dialogue with the Other: Martin Buber & the Quaker Experience. LC 73-92486. 32p. (Orig.). 1973. pap. 2.50x (ISBN 0-87574-192-4). Pendle Hill.

Scott-Maxwell, Florida. The Measure of My Days. 1979. pap. 5.95 (ISBN 0-14-005164-3). Penguin.

Scragg, Walter R. Such Bright Hopes. Woolsey, Raymond, ed. 377p. 1987. price not set (ISBN 0-8280-0389-0). Review & Herald.

Sheed, F. J. Map of Life. 1979. pap. 2.95 (ISBN 0-88479-017-7). Arena Lettres.

Sheen, Fulton J. God Love You. LC 80-23085. 224p. 1981. pap. 4.50 (ISBN 0-385-17486-1, Im). Doubleday.

--Lift up Your Heart. 280p. 1975. pap. 4.50 (ISBN 0-385-09001-3, Im). Doubleday.

--Rejoice. LC 84-45271. (Illus.). 80p. 1984. pap. 8.95 (ISBN 0-385-19164-2, Im). Doubleday.

--The World's First Love. 240p. 1976. 4.50 (ISBN 0-385-11559-8, Im). Doubleday.

Shull, Russell. Letters to Eva in Heaven. 3.95 (ISBN 0-910924-51-1). Macalester.

Simpson, A. B. Is Life Worth Living? 30p. pap. 0.95 (ISBN 0-87509-045-1). Chr Pubns.

Simpson, Albert B. Divine Emblems. pap. 2.95 (ISBN 0-87509-009-5). Chr Pubns.

Sinclair, Keith V., compiled by. French Devotional Texts of the Middle Ages: A Bibliographic Manuscript Guide. LC 79-7587. 1979. lib. bdg. 49.95x (ISBN 0-313-20649-X, SFT/). Greenwood.

Sinclair, Keith V., ed. French Devotional Texts of the Middle Ages: A Bibliographic Manuscript Guide, First Supplement. LC 82-11773. xvi, 234p. 1982. lib. bdg. 65.00 (ISBN 0-313-23664-X, SIF/). Greenwood.

Slay, James L. Rescue the Perishing. 1961. 6.95 (ISBN 0-87148-729-2). Pathway Pr.

--This We Believe. 1963. pap. 4.95 (ISBN 0-87148-832-9). Pathway Pr.

Smiley, Emma. Bread of Life. 1972. pap. 1.00 (ISBN 0-87516-157-X). De Vorss.

--Search for Certainty. 1972. pap. 2.50 (ISBN 0-87516-159-6). De Vorss.

Smith, Chuck. Answers for Today, Vol. II. (Answers for Today Ser.). 80p. (Orig.). 1986. pap. write for info. (ISBN 0-936728-28-0). Word for Today.

Smith, Hannah W. God Is Enough. Dieter, Melvin & Dieter, Hallie, eds. 320p. 1986. 10.95 (ISBN 0-310-46260-6). Zondervan.

Smith, Henry J. Time of the End. (International Correspondence Program Ser.). 159p. (Orig.). pap. 6.95 (ISBN 0-87148-853-1). Pathway Pr.

Smith, Jim L. He Arose. 1973. pap. 1.75 (ISBN 0-88428-026-8, 317). Parchment Pr.

Speer, Robert E. Five Minutes a Day. LC 43-16427. 384p. 1977. softcover 3.95 (ISBN 0-664-24139-5). Westminster.

Speyr, Adrienne von. Handmaid of the Lord. LC 85-60468. Tr. of Magd des Herrn. 178p. 1985. 9.95 (ISBN 0-89870-042-6). Ignatius Pr.

Sprague, Betty W. The Inner Voice Speaks. 59p. pap. 7.95 (ISBN 0-942494-30-X). Coleman Pub.

Spurgeon, C. H. The Comforter. 1978. pap. 0.95 (ISBN 0-686-26194-1). Pilgrim Pubns.

--Go in Peace. 1978. pap. 0.50 (ISBN 0-685-36795-9). Reiner.

--John Ploughman's Pictures. 1974. pap. 2.50 (ISBN 0-686-10526-5). Pilgrim Pubns.

--Saint & His Savior. Date not set. pap. write for info. Pilgrim Pubns.

Spurgeon, Charles H. Spurgeon's Devotional Bible. 1974. Repr. 19.95 (ISBN 0-8010-8043-6). Baker Bk.

Stalker, D. M. Genesis One to Twelve. 0.50x (ISBN 0-685-33497-X). Outlook.

Stanley, Charles. How to Listen to God. 160p. 1985. 10.95 (ISBN 0-8407-9041-4). Oliver-Nelson.

Stanley, W. P. The Student. 1957. 4.95 (ISBN 0-87148-756-X). Pathway Pr.

Stapleton, Ruth. Power Through Release. pap. 0.50 (ISBN 0-910924-39-2); 3 for 1.00 (ISBN 0-685-04195-6). Macalester.

Staton, Knofel. Check Your Life in Christ. 160p. pap. 2.95x (ISBN 0-89900-203-X). College Pr Pub.

Steele. Gospel of the Comforter. pap. 5.95 (ISBN 0-686-12870-2). Schmul Pub Co.

--Half Hours with St. John. pap. 5.95 (ISBN 0-686-12871-0). Schmul Pub Co.

--Half Hours with St. Paul. pap. 5.95 (ISBN 0-686-12872-9). Schmul Pub Co.

Steere, Douglas V. On Being Present Where You Are. LC 67-12913. (Orig.). 1967. pap. 2.50x (ISBN 0-87574-151-7, 151). Pendle Hill.

--On Speaking out of the Silence: Vocal Ministry. LC 72-182983. 24p. (Orig.). 1972. pap. 2.50x (ISBN 0-87574-182-7). Pendle Hill.

Stewart, Leon. Too Late. pap. 5.95 (ISBN 0-911866-66-3). Advocate.

Stone, Hal. Embracing Heaven & Earth: A Personal Odyssey. LC 84-72044. 179p. 1985. pap. 8.95 (ISBN 0-87516-547-8). De Vorss.

Strauss, Lehman. First Person. LC 67-20931. 1967. 7.95 (ISBN 0-87213-815-1). Loizeaux.

Struzzo, John A., et al. Suffering: Issues of Emotional Living in an Age of Stress for Clergy & Religious. Gilmartin, Richard J., ed. LC 84-9334. 144p. 1984. pap. 8.00 (ISBN 0-89571-020-X). Affirmation.

Stuart, Friend. Twenty Years of Tidings. 180p. 1986. vinyl 29.95 (ISBN 0-912132-10-8). Dominion Pr.

Subramuniya. The Lotus of the Heart. (On the Path Ser.). (Illus.). 72p. 1972. pap. 2.00 (ISBN 0-87516-352-1). De Vorss.

Swami Krishnananda: In Conversation. 1983. 30.00x (ISBN 0-7069-2346-4, Pub. by Vikas India). Advent NY.

Swedenborg, Emanuel. The Spiritual World Laid Open. lib. bdg. 79.95 (ISBN 0-87968-561-1). Krishna Pr.

Swenson, Keith M. The Blessings Cup: A Guide to Family Devotions for Lent. 32p. (Orig.). 1984. pap. 2.75 (ISBN 0-8066-2033-1, 23-1120). Augsburg.

Swindoll, Charles R. Come Before Winter & Share my Hope. LC 85-11590. 352p. 1985. 14.95 (ISBN 0-88070-110-2). Multnomah.

Taege, Marlys. Women Through the Bible: Devotions for Women's Groups. 160p. 1987. pap. 5.95 (ISBN 0-570-04460-X, 12-3064). Concordia.

Tanksley, Perry. Love from the Living Bible. 1976. 4.95 (ISBN 0-686-17793-2). Allgood Bks.

--These Things I've Loved. 5.95 (ISBN 0-686-21184-7). Allgood Bks.

--We're in This Thing Together. 1974. 4.50 (ISBN 0-8007-0664-1). Allgood Bks.

Tannehill, Robert C. The Sword of His Mouth. Beardslee, William A., ed. LC 75-18948. (Semeia Studies). 236p. 1976. pap. 7.95 (ISBN 0-8006-1501-8, 1-1501). Fortress.

Taylor, James. An Everyday God. 116p. (Orig.). 1983. pap. 5.95 (ISBN 0-8358-0470-4). Upper Room.

Taylor, Kenneth N. Devotions for the Children's Hour. pap. 3.95 (ISBN 0-8024-0061-2). Moody.

Taylor, Michael J. The Sacraments As Encasement: Jesus Is with Us. 80p. 1986. pap. 4.95 (ISBN 0-8146-1469-8). Liturgical Pr.

Telushkin, Joseph. Uncommon Sense: The World's Fullest Compendium of Wisdom. 1986. 14.95 (ISBN 0-933503-48-2). Shapolsky Pubs.

Ten Boom, Corrie & Buckingham, Jamie. Tramp for the Lord. (Illus.). 192p. 1974. pap. 6.95 (ISBN 0-8007-0769-9). Revell.

Terry, Lindsay. Good Morning, Lord: Devotions from Famous Hymn Stories. (Good Morning Lord Ser.). 1974. 3.95 (ISBN 0-8010-8882-8). Baker Bk.

Thom, Robert. New Wine Is Better. 1974. pap. 2.95 (ISBN 0-88368-036-X). Whitaker Hse.

Thomas a Kempis. Imitation of Christ. new, rev. ed. Fitzpatrick, Clare L., ed. (Illus., Large Type). maroon, colored edges 4.95 (ISBN 0-89942-320-5, 320/00). Catholic Bk Pub.

Thornton, Martin. Spiritual Direction. LC 83-73658. 145p. (Orig.). 1984. pap. 6.95 (ISBN 0-936384-17-4). Cowley Pubns.

Thurman, Howard. Deep Is the Hunger. LC 73-16023. 212p. 1973. pap. 6.95 (ISBN 0-913408-10-7). Friends United.

--Disciplines of the Spirit. LC 77-88388. 1977. pap. 6.95 (ISBN 0-913408-35-2). Friends United.

--Meditations of the Heart. LC 76-18287. 216p. 1976. pap. 6.95 (ISBN 0-913408-25-5). Friends United.

To Come & See. 1985. 10.00 (ISBN 0-8199-0879-7). Franciscan Herald.

Todd, Floyd & Todd, Pauline. Good Morning, Lord: Devotions for Campers. (Good Morning Lord Ser.). 1973. 3.95 (ISBN 0-8010-8792-9). Baker Bk.

Tomlinson, M. A. God's Church in the Plan of the Ages. 1974. pap. 2.95 (ISBN 0-934942-07-2). White Wing Pub.

--Let the Church Counsel Together. 1978. pap. 3.25 (ISBN 0-934942-10-2). White Wing Pub.

Torrey, R. A. The Baptism with the Holy Spirit. 96p. 1972. pap. 2.95 (ISBN 0-87123-029-1). Bethany Hse.

--How to Find Fullness of Power. Orig. Title: How to Obtain Fullness of Power. 112p. 1971. pap. 2.95 (ISBN 0-87123-219-7, 200219). Bethany Hse.

Townsend, Zella. Whisperings in the Silence. 1972. pap. 2.00 (ISBN 0-87516-121-9). De Vorss.

Tracy, Wesley. When Adam Clarke Preached, People Listened. 238p. (Orig.). 1981. pap. 4.95 (ISBN 0-8341-0714-7). Beacon Hill.

Traill, Robert. The Works of Robert Traill, 2 vols. 1975. Set. 28.95 (ISBN 0-85151-393-X). Vol. 1 (ISBN 0-85151-229-1). Vol. 2 (ISBN 0-85151-230-5). Banner of Truth.

Trombley, Charles. Kicked Out of the Kingdom. 1974. pap. 2.95 (ISBN 0-88368-044-0). Whitaker Hse.

Tucker, Austin B. My Lord Knows the Way. (Illus.). 80p. (Orig.). 1982. pap. 1.50 (ISBN 0-89323-036-7). Bible Memory.

Tullis, Dawn. Teach Us to Pray. 2.25 (ISBN 0-686-13717-5). Crusade Pubs.

Turnbull, Ralph G. At the Lord's Table: Twenty Communion Meditations. (Pocket Pulpit Library). 142p. 1985. pap. 4.95 (ISBN 0-8010-8821-6). Baker Bk.

Turner, George A. Witnesses of the Way. 176p. (Orig.). 1981. pap. 3.95 (ISBN 0-8341-0692-2). Beacon Hill.

Tutu, Desmond M. Hope & Suffering: Sermons & Speeches. 189p. (Orig.). 1984. pap. 6.95 (ISBN 0-8028-0085-8). Eerdmans.

Unity School of Christianity, ed. Works & Wonders. LC 78-68931. 1979. 5.95 (ISBN 0-87159-175-8). Unity School.

VanderArk, Nelle. Devotionals for Teachers. (Ultra Bks Ser.). 80p. 1975. 5.95 (ISBN 0-8010-9263-9). Baker Bk.

Vanier, Jean. I Walk with Jesus. 208p. (Orig.). 1986. pap. 7.95 (ISBN 0-8091-2786-5). Paulist Pr.

Van McNeal, Henry. Beyond Fulfilment: The Spiritual Message of Henry Van McNeal, Vol. 1. 180p. (Orig.). 1986. pap. 9.95 (ISBN 0-916641-27-9). Natl Academy Songwriters.

Van Zeller, Hubert. Leave Your Life Alone. 6.95 (ISBN 0-87243-043-X). Templegate.

--Other Kingdom. 3.95 (ISBN 0-87243-032-4). Templegate.

Verheylezoon, Louis. Devotion to the Sacred Heart: Objects, Ends, Practice, Motives. LC 78-74569. 1979. pap. 8.50 (ISBN 0-89555-083-0). TAN Bks Pubs.

Verwer, George. Pseudo Discipleship. (YA) 1970. pap. 1.50 (ISBN 0-87508-548-2). Chr Lit.

Vick, Edward. Speaking Well of God. LC 79-9336. (Anvil Ser.). 1979. pap. 8.95 (ISBN 0-8127-0245-X). Review & Herald.

Vines, Jerry. Fire in the Pulpit. LC 77-78155. 1977. 7.95 (ISBN 0-8054-5159-5). Broadman.

Vis, Jean A. We Are the Lord's. 3.50 (ISBN 0-686-23479-0). Rose Pub MI.

Vos, Nelvin. Seven Days a Week: Faith in Action. LC 84-47937. 144p. 1985. pap. 5.95 (ISBN 0-8006-1658-8, 1-1658). Fortress.

Walking with God. 8.95 (ISBN 0-318-18183-5). WCTU.

Wallace, Joyce. A Closer Walk. LC 82-99994. 128p. 1982. pap. 4.00 (ISBN 0-686-38098-3). Foun Christ Serv.

Wallis, Arthur. Into Battle. 1973. pap. 2.95 (ISBN 0-87508-560-1). Chr Lit.

Walsh, James, tr. A Letter of Private Direction. 1979. pap. 5.95 (ISBN 0-87243-083-9). Templegate.

Walters, Richard P. Forgive & Be Free: Healing the Wounds of Past & Present. 144p. 1983. pap. 5.95 (ISBN 0-310-42611-1, 12339P). Zondervan.

Ward, Frances. Keep the Fruit on the Table. 48p. 1982. pap. 1.75 (ISBN 0-88144-006-X, CPS-006). Christian Pub.

Ward, Horace. Power for Living. (International Correspondence Program Ser.). (Orig.). 1986. pap. text ed. 6.95 (ISBN 0-87148-718-7). Pathway Pr.

Watson, David. Grow & Flourish: A Daily Guide to Personal Renewal. Watson, Jean, ed. (General). 392p. 1983. pap. 6.95 (ISBN 0-87788-327-0). Shaw Pubs.

Watts, Alan W. Behold the Spirit. 288p. 1972. pap. 4.95 (ISBN 0-394-71761-9, Vin). Random.

Watts, Dorothy E. Stepping Stones. Woolsey, Raymond, ed. (Morning Watch Ser.). 384p. 1987. text ed. price not set (ISBN 0-8280-0384-X). Review & Herald.

Weatherhead, Leslie D. The Transforming Friendship. (Festival Books). 1977. pap. 1.25 (ISBN 0-687-42510-7). Abingdon.

Weekley, James. Recycled Hallelujahs. 1982. pap. 4.95 (ISBN 0-89536-532-4, 1814). CSS of Ohio.

Welch, Reuben. We Really Do Need Each Other. 112p. 1982. pap. 4.95 (ISBN 0-310-70221-6, 14012P). Zondervan.

Welter, Jean T. L' Exemplum dans la Litterature Religieuse et Didactique du Moyen Age. LC 70-178558. (Fr.). Repr. of 1927 ed. 45.00 (ISBN 0-404-56688-X). AMS Pr.

Wheat, Ed. Amor que no se Apaga. 1984. 4.25 (ISBN 0-88113-010-9). Edit Betania.

Wheless. By the Sweat of My Brow. 2.50 (ISBN 0-685-02583-7). Outlook.

White, Ellen G. The Great Controversy. 1950. 5.95 (ISBN 0-8163-0035-6, 07886-5); deluxe ed. 9.95 (ISBN 0-8163-0036-4, 07882-4); pap. 1.45 (ISBN 0-8163-0037-2, 07887-3). Pacific Pr Pub Assn.

--Reflecting Christ. Woolsey, Raymond H., ed. (Devotional Ser.). 384p. 1985. 7.95 (ISBN 0-8280-0305-X). Review & Herald.

--Thoughts from the Mount of Blessing. LC 56-7170. 172p. 1956. 6.95 (ISBN 0-8163-0047-X, 20401-6). Pacific Pr Pub Assn.

White Eagle. The Gentle Brother. 1968. 3.95 (ISBN 0-85487-002-4). De Vorss.

--The Path of the Soul. 1959. 5.95 (ISBN 0-85487-020-2). De Vorss.

--The Quiet Mind. 1972. 3.95 (ISBN 0-85487-009-1). De Vorss.

Whiteside, Elena S. The Way: Living in Love. LC 72-89132. Devin.

Whyte, H. A. Power of the Blood. 1973. pap. 3.50 (ISBN 0-88368-027-0). Whitaker Hse.

Wicks, Robert J. Christian Introspection: Self-Ministry Through Self-Understanding. LC 83-1932. 128p. 1983. pap. 7.95 (ISBN 0-8245-0583-2). Crossroad NY.

Wierwille, Victor P. Are the Dead Alive Now? LC 82-70237. 108p. 1982. 6.95 (ISBN 0-910068-40-2). Am Christian.

--The Bible Tells Me So. LC 70-176281. (Studies in Abundant Living: Vol. 1). 202p. 1971. 6.95 (ISBN 0-910068-10-0). Am Christian.

Wilkerson, David. Promises to Live by. LC 72-86208. 96p. (Orig.). 1972. pap. 2.50 (ISBN 0-8307-0197-4, 5007305). Regal.

Williams, Sally. Aunt Sally: Or, the Cross, the Way of Freedom. facs. ed. LC 75-89438. (Black Heritage Library Collection Ser.). 1858. 14.25 (ISBN 0-8369-8692-X). Ayer Co Pubs.

Williamson, G. I. Westminster Confession of Faith: A Study Manual. 1964. pap. 5.50 (ISBN 0-87552-538-5). Presby & Reformed.

Willis, Elbert. Being Fully Persuaded. 1977. 1.25 (ISBN 0-89858-017-X). Fill the Gap.

--Divine Guidance. 350p. 1982. write for info. Fill the Gap.

--How Can I Be Healed. 1978. 1.25 (ISBN 0-89858-013-7). Fill the Gap.

--An Interceding Faith. 1978. 1.25 (ISBN 0-89858-018-8). Fill the Gap.

--Overcoming Discouragement. 1976. 1.25 (ISBN 0-89858-000-5). Fill the Gap.

--Overcoming Worry. 1976. 1.25 (ISBN 0-89858-001-3). Fill the Gap.

--Those Who Move with God. 1977. 1.25 (ISBN 0-89858-006-4). Fill the Gap.

--Victory over the Impossible. 1978. 1.25 (ISBN 0-89858-008-0). Fill the Gap.

Wilson, Guy H. That Ye May Know. 2.50 (ISBN 0-910924-47-3). Macalester.

Wirt, Sherwood E., ed. Spiritual Awakening: Classic Writings of the Eighteenth Century to Inspire the Twentieth Century Reader. LC 86-70283. 256p. (Orig.). 1986. pap. 8.95 (ISBN 0-89107-394-9, Crossway Bks). Good News.

Wolff, Pierre. May I Hate God? LC 78-70815. 80p. 1979. pap. 2.95 (ISBN 0-8091-2180-8). Paulist Pr.

Wood, Ernest. The Glorious Presence. LC 74-1045. pap. 2.75 (ISBN 0-8356-0446-2, Quest). Theos Pub Hse.

Works of John Flavel, 6 vols. Set. 108.95 (ISBN 0-85151-060-4). Banner of Truth.

Wuellner, Flora S. Prayer, Stress & Our Inner Wounds. 94p. (Orig.). 1985. pap. 4.95 (ISBN 0-8358-0501-8). Upper Room.

Wulf, Dick. Conozcase y Consagrese. Orig. Title: Find Yourself, Give Yourself. (Span.). 1986. write for info. (ISBN 0-8297-0688-7). Life Pubs Intl.
--De la Decouverte au Don de Soi. Orig. Title: Find Yourself, Give Yourself. (Fr.). 1986. write for info. (ISBN 0-8297-0687-9). Life Pubs Intl.
Yoder, C. F. God's Means of Grace. 12.50 (ISBN 0-88469-111-X). BMH Bks.
Zamboni, Camillo. He Speaks to You. 1966. pap. 1.25 (ISBN 0-8198-0055-4). Dghtrs St Paul.
Zanca, Kenneth. Reasons for Rejoicing: Readings in Christian Hope. (Orig.). 1976. pap. 2.95 (ISBN 0-914544-12-8). Living Flame Pr.
Zimmerman, Thomas F., et al. He Is Worthy. LC 77-92881. 64p. 1978. pap. 0.50 (ISBN 0-88243-523-X, 02-0523, Radiant Books). Gospel Pub.

DEVOTIONAL LITERATURE (SELECTIONS: EXTRACTS, ETC.)

Baker, Frank, ed. Heart of True Spirituality: John Wesley's Own Choice, Vol. 2: Selections from Thomas a Kempis, et. al. 1985. pap. 4.95 (ISBN 0-317-46009-9). Zondervan.
Barcus, Nancy B. Help Me, God, I'm a Working Mother! 64p. 1982. pap. 3.95 (ISBN 0-8170-0954-X). Judson.
Baxter, J. Sidlow. Daily Wings. 384p. 1983. pap. 10.95 (ISBN 0-310-20751-7). Zondervan.
Bolding, Amy. Easy Devotions to Give. (Paperback Program Ser.). 96p. (Orig.). 1981. pap. 3.95 (ISBN 0-8010-0794-1). Baker Bk.
Brother Lawrence. Daily Readings with Brother Lawrence. Llewelyn, Robert, ed. (Daily Readings Ser.). 1986. pap. 4.95 (ISBN 0-87243-144-4). Templegate.
Bryant, Al. A Pocket Treasury of Daily Devotions. LC 77-82183. 112p. 1978. pap. 3.50 (ISBN 0-87123-464-5, 200464). Bethany Hse.
Byrum, Isabel. The Pilot's Voice. (Illus.). 146p. pap. 1.50 (ISBN 0-686-29159-X). Faith Pub Hse.
Canclini, Santiago. Alzare Mis Ojos. (Span.). 316p. 1984. pap. 7.95 (ISBN 0-311-40047-7). Casa Bautista.
Chrysostomos, Archimandrite. The Ancient Fathers of the Church: Translated Narratives from the Evertinos on Passions & Perfection in Christ. (Illus.). 118p. 1980. 7.95 (ISBN 0-916586-77-4); pap. 4.95 (ISBN 0-686-69869-X). Hellenic Coll Pr.
Coleman, William L. Singing Penguins & Puffed-up Toads. 125p. 1981. pap. 4.95 (ISBN 0-87123-554-4, 210554). Bethany Hse.
Cravey, Charles E. Diamonds in the Rough. 64p. (Orig.). 1986. pap. 4.00 (ISBN 0-938645-00-5). Upper Rm Pub.
Daily Light on the Daily Path: From the New International Version. large print ed. 384p. 1983. pap. 9.95 (ISBN 0-310-23117-5, 18027L). Zondervan.
De Caussode, Jean Pierre. Daily Readings with Jean-Pierre de Caussade. LLewelyn, Robert, ed. (Daily Readings Ser.). 1986. pap. 4.95 (ISBN 0-87243-145-2). Templegate.
Dudley-Smith, Timothy. Someone Who Beckons. LC 78-18548. 1978. pap. 3.95 (ISBN 0-87784-731-2). Inter-Varsity.
Eck, Margaret. Lest We Forget. 72p. pap. 0.75 (ISBN 0-686-29125-5); pap. 2.00 3 copies (ISBN 0-686-29126-3). Faith Pub Hse.
Fant, Clyde, compiled by. The Best of Open Windows. LC 81-67201. 1981. 7.95 (ISBN 0-8054-5290-7). Broadman.
Hale, Mabel. Stories of Home Folks. 160p. pap. 1.50 (ISBN 0-686-29143-3). Faith Pub Hse.
Havner, Vance. The Vance Havner Devotional Treasury: Daily Meditations for a Year. (Direction Books). 192p. 1981. pap. 4.50 (ISBN 0-8010-4257-7). Baker Bk.
Hoover, Mab G. God Even Likes My Pantry: Devotions for Dieters. 128p. 1983. pap. 3.95 (ISBN 0-310-47012-9, 11269P). Zondervan.
Jones, E. Stanley. The Word Became Flesh. (Festival Bks). 1979. pap. 3.25 (ISBN 0-687-46128-6). Abingdon.
Julian of Norwich. Daily Readings with Julian of Norwich, 2 vols. LLewelyn, Robert, ed. (Daily Reading Ser.). 1986. pap. 4.95 ea. Vol. 1 (ISBN 0-87243-142-8). Vol. 2 (ISBN 0-87243-143-6). Templegate.
Klug, Ronald. Following Christ: Prayers from Imitation of Christ. LC 80-25260. (Illus.). 63p. 1981. pap. 3.95 (ISBN 0-570-03826-X, 12-2791). Concordia.
Lenzkes, Susan. A Silver Pen for Cloudy Days. 144p. 1987. pap. 7.95 (ISBN 0-310-43671-0). Zondervan.
Llewelyn, Robert, ed. Daily Readings from the Cloud of Unknowing. (Daily Readings Ser.). 1986. pap. 4.95 (ISBN 0-87243-149-5). Templegate.
Lockerbie, Jeanette. A Plate of Hot Toast. (Quiet Time Bks.). 128p. (Orig.). 1971. pap. 3.50 (ISBN 0-8024-6625-7). Moody.
McDaniel, Audrey. Greatest of These Is Love. LC 64-23538. (Illus.). 1972. 6.95 (ISBN 0-8378-1713-7). Gibson.
Moody, Dwight L. & Turnbull, Ralph G., eds. The Best of Dwight L. Moody. (Best Ser.). 1979. pap. 6.95 (ISBN 0-8010-6216-0). Baker Bk.
Moran, Patrick R., ed. Day by Day: With My Daily Visitor. LC 79-92536. 200p. (Orig.). 1980. pap. 5.95 (ISBN 0-87973-530-9, 530). Our Sunday Visitor.
More, St. Thomas. The Tower Works: Devotional Writings. Haupt, Garry E., ed. Miller, Clarence, tr. from Lat. LC 78-16995. (Selected Works of St. Thomas More). (Illus.). 368p. 1980. text ed. 42.00x (ISBN 0-300-02265-4). Yale U Pr.
Mueller, Charles S. Words of Faith: A Devotional Dictionary. 160p. (Orig.). 1985. pap. 5.95 (ISBN 0-570-03968-1, 12-3003). Concordia.
Murray, Andrew. Believer's Daily Renewal. LC 81-6143. 125p. 1981. pap. 3.95 (ISBN 0-87123-147-6, 210147). Bethany Hse.
Orr, C. E. Food for Lambs. 168p. pap. 1.50 (ISBN 0-686-29109-3). Faith Pub Hse.
--Heavenly Life for Earthly Living. 60p. pap. 0.40 (ISBN 0-686-29111-5); pap. 1.00 3 copies (ISBN 0-686-34362-X). Faith Pub Hse.
--Odors from Golden Vials. 78p. pap. 0.60 (ISBN 0-686-29131-X). Faith Pub Hse.
Palms, Roger C. Living on the Mountain. 288p. 1985. 11.95 (ISBN 0-8007-1449-0). Revell.
Petty, Jo. An Apple a Day: Treasured Selections from Apples of Gold. 1979. 6.95 (ISBN 0-8378-5025-8). Gibson.
Rahner, Karl. Prayers & Meditations: An Anthology of the Spiritual Writings of Karl Rahner. Griffiths, John, ed. 128p. 1980. pap. 4.95 (ISBN 0-8245-0053-9). Crossroad NY.
Rendall, K. Norline. Just a Taste of Honey. (Quiet Time Bks.). 1975. pap. 3.50 (ISBN 0-8024-4494-6). Moody.
Riggle, H. M. The Kingdom of God & the One Thousand Years Reign. 160p. pap. 1.50 (ISBN 0-686-29153-0). Faith Pub Hse.
St. Francis de Sales. Daily Readings with St. Francis de Sales. LLewelyn, Robert, ed. (Daily Readings Ser.). 1986. pap. 4.95 (ISBN 0-87243-147-9). Templegate.
St. John of the Cross. Daily Readings with St. John of the Cross. Llewelyn, Robert, ed. (Daily Readings Ser.). 1986. pap. 4.95 (ISBN 0-87243-148-7). Templegate.
St. Teresa of Avila. Daily Readings with St. Teresa of Avila. LLewelyn, Robert, ed. (Daily Readings Ser.). 1986. pap. 4.95 (ISBN 0-87243-146-0). Templegate.
Schmidt, J. David. More Graffiti: Devotions for Girls. (Illus.). 128p. (Orig.). 1984. pap. 4.95 (ISBN 0-8007-5143-4, Power Bks). Revell.
Shaw, Jean. Second Cup of Coffee: Proverbs for Today's Woman. 192p. (Orig.). 1981. pap. 3.95 (ISBN 0-310-43542-0, 9609P). Zondervan.
Shedd, Charlie. Devotions for Dieters. 1983. 8.95 (ISBN 0-8499-0330-0). Word Bks.
Spurgeon, Charles H. Morning & Evening. 736p. 1980. Repr. 13.95 (ISBN 0-310-32940-X, 10873); large print kivar 11.95 (ISBN 0-310-32927-2). Zondervan.
Teasley, D. O. Rays of Hope. 95p. pap. 0.75 (ISBN 0-686-29137-9). Faith Pub Hse.
Tengbom, Mildred. Does Anybody Care How I Feel? LC 81-3808. 122p. 1981. pap. 4.95 (ISBN 0-87123-142-5, 210142). Bethany Hse.
Wiersbe, Warren W., ed. Giant Steps. 496p. 1981. 15.95 (ISBN 0-8010-9648-0). Baker Bk.
Williams, Effie. The Man of His Counsel. 112p. pap. 1.00 (ISBN 0-686-29156-5). Faith Pub Hse.
Willis, John T. The Wisdom Literature: Job, Proverbs, Ecclesiastes. LC 81-69494. (Way of Life Ser.: No. 145). 1982. pap. 3.95 (ISBN 0-89112-145-5, Biblo Res Pr). Abilene Christ U.
Zahn, Gordon. In Solitary Witness. rev. ed. 1986. pap. 10.95 (ISBN 0-87243-141-X). Templegate.

DEVOTIONAL LITERATURE–HISTORY AND CRITICISM

Hagedorn, Maria. Reformation und Spanische Andachtsliteratur. 1934. 12.00 (ISBN 0-384-20770-7). Johnson Repr.
Peers, Edgar A. Behind That Wall. facs. ed. LC 72-90672. (Essay Index Reprint Ser). 1948. 15.00 (ISBN 0-8369-1210-1). Ayer Co Pubs.
St. John Of The Cross. The Poems of St. John of the Cross. Barnstone, Willis, tr. & intro. by. LC 68-14597. (Eng. & Span.). 144p. 1972. pap. 4.95 (ISBN 0-8112-0449-9, NDP341). New Directions.
Tennyson, G. B. Victorian Devotional Poetry: The Tractarian Mode. LC 80-14416. 1980. text ed. 18.50x (ISBN 0-674-93586-1). Harvard U Pr.
White, Helen C. The Tudor Books of Private Devotion. LC 78-21661. (Illus.). 1979. Repr. of 1951 ed. lib. bdg. 24.75x (ISBN 0-313-21063-2, WHTB). Greenwood.
--Tudor Books of Saints & Martyrs. LC 63-13741. 318p. pap. 73.00 (ISBN 0-317-07866-6, 2004164). Bks Demand UMI.

DEVOTIONAL LITERATURE, JEWISH

see Jewish Devotional Literature

DEVOTIONAL THEOLOGY

see Devotional Exercises; Devotional Literature; Meditations; Prayers;
also subdivision Prayer-Books and Devotions under names of Christian denominations, religious orders, classes of persons, etc.

DEVOTIONAL YEARBOOKS

see Devotional Calendars

DEVOTIONS

see Devotional Exercises

DE VRIES, PETER

Bowden, J. H. Peter De Vries. (United States Authors Ser.). 1983. lib. bdg. 16.95 (ISBN 0-8057-7388-6, Twayne). G K Hall.

DHARMA

Dharma for All. 264p. 1987. pap. 3.50 (Pub. by Ramakrishna Math Madras India). Vedanta Pr.
Lodo, Venerable Larma. The Quintessence of the Animate & Inanimate: A Discourse on the Holy Dharma. Clark, Nancy & Parke, Caroline, eds. LC 85-2290. (Illus.). 238p. 1985. pap. 11.95 (ISBN 0-910165-01-7). KDK Pubns.
Macy, Joanna. Dharma & Development. rev. ed. LC 85-256. (KP Monograph: No. 2). 119p. 1985. pap. 8.75 (ISBN 0-931816-53-X). Kumarian Pr.
Master Hua, Tripitaka. Great Compassion Dharma Transmission Verses of the 42 Hands & Eyes. Buddhist Text Translation Society, tr. from Chinese. (Illus.). 100p. (Orig.). 1983. pap. 16.00 (ISBN 0-88139-002-X). Buddhist Text.
Piatigorsky, Alexander. The Buddhist Philosophy of Thought: Essays in Interpretation. LC 82-3987. 240p. 1984. text ed. 24.50x (ISBN 0-389-20266-5, 07084). B&N Imports.
Ramakrishna: The Power & the Glory. 303p. (Orig.). 1987. pap. 3.50 (ISBN 0-87481-544-4, Pub. by Ramakrishna Math Madras India). Vedanta Pr.
Tripitaka Master Hua. The Ten Dharma Realms Are Not Beyond a Single Thought. Buddhist Text Translation Society, tr. from Chinese. (Eng., Illus.). 72p. (Orig.). 1976. pap. 4.00 (ISBN 0-917512-12-X). Buddhist Text.
Tripitaka Master Hua, commentary by. Dharma Flower Sutra, Vol. III. Buddhist Text Translation Society, tr. from Chinese. (Illus.). 183p. (Orig.). 1979. pap. 8.00 (ISBN 0-917512-26-X). Buddhist Text.
--Dharma Flower Sutra, Vol. X. Buddhist Text Translation Society Staff, tr. from Chinese. 150p. (Orig.). pap. 7.50 (ISBN 0-917512-34-0). Buddhist Text.
Trungpa, Chogyam. Glimpses of Abhidharma. LC 86-31409. (Dragon Ser.). 100p. 1987. pap. 9.95 (ISBN 0-87773-282-5). Shambhala Pubns.

DHYANA (MEDITATION)

see Meditation (Buddhism)

DHYANA (SECT)

see Zen Buddhism

DIACONATE

see Deacons

DIAKONIA (THEOLOGY)

see Service (Theology)

DIALECTIC

see also Transcendence of God

Buckley, Michael J. Motion & Motion's God: Thematic Variations in Aristotle, Cicero, Newton, & Hegel. LC 73-132234. 1971. 30.50 (ISBN 0-691-07124-1). Princeton U Pr.
Diem, Hermann. Kierkegaard's Dialectic of Existence. Knight, Harold, tr. from German. LC 77-18886. 1978. Repr. of 1959 ed. lib. bdg. 22.50x (ISBN 0-313-20220-6, DIKD). Greenwood.
Reymond, Robert. Brunner's Dialectic. 1967. pap. 0.75 (ISBN 0-87552-404-4). Presby & Reformed.

DIALECTIC (RELIGION)

see Dialectical Theology; Polarity (In Religion, Folk-Lore, etc.)

DIALECTICAL THEOLOGY

McConnachie, John. Barthian Theology. LC 72-2493. (Select Bibliography Reprint Ser). 1972. Repr. of 1933 ed. 19.00 (ISBN 0-8369-6861-1). Ayer Co Pubs.
Szekely, Edmond B. The Dialectical Method of Thinking. (Illus.). 40p. 1973. pap. 2.95 (ISBN 0-89564-063-5). IBS Intl.

DIANETICS

The Background & Ceremonies of the Church of Scientology of California, World Wide: From the Works of L. Ron Hubbard. 1972. 62.17 (ISBN 0-88404-054-2). Bridge Pubns Inc.
Baybak, Michael. Viewpoints. 32p. 1976. pap. 6.00 (ISBN 0-915598-09-4). Church of Scient Info.
Breaching the Wall: Of Separation Between Church & State, Excessive Entanglement & the IRS. pap. 4.00 (ISBN 0-915598-39-6). Church of Scient Info.
The Care & Maintenance of the Fourth Amendment: The Owner's Manual. pap. 6.00 (ISBN 0-915598-30-2). Church of Scient Info.
The Character of Government: An Examination of U. S. Government Agencies' Crimes. pap. 9.00 (ISBN 0-905931-10-6). Church of Scient Info.
Church of Scientology Information Service Staff. The Indispensability of Scientology Press, Vol. 1, Pt. 5. 1976. pap. 2.60 (ISBN 0-915598-10-8). Church of Scient Info.
Church of Scientology Information Service Staff & Hubbard, L. Ron. Success with Scientology. 112p. 1976. pap. 8.00 (ISBN 0-915598-01-9). Church of Scient Info.
Church of Scientology Press: Volume 1, Issue 6. (Illus.). 1976. pap. 2.60 (ISBN 0-915598-13-2). Church of Scient Info.
Church of Scientology Press: Volume 1, Issue 7. (Illus.). 1977. pap. 2.60 (ISBN 0-915598-15-9). Church of Scient Info.
Church of Scientology-Religious Nature & Community Activities. (Illus.). 1976. pap. 7.00 (ISBN 0-915598-12-4). Church of Scient Info.
Conference of Scientology Ministers. The American Inquisition: U. S. Government Agency Harassment, Religious Persecution & Abuse of Power. 1977. pap. 7.00 (ISBN 0-915598-16-7). Church of Scient Info.
Dianetic Information Group. pap. 4.00 (ISBN 0-686-74640-6). Church of Scient Info.
The Dossier Disease: The Truth About Government Agency False Files. pap. 6.00 (ISBN 0-915598-27-2). Church of Scient Info.
Evidence on Religious Bona Fides & Status of the Church of Scientology. 1974. pap. 8.00 (ISBN 0-915598-02-7). Church of Scient Info.
Freedom Reports: The Internal Revenue Service. pap. 5.00 (ISBN 0-915598-40-X). Church of Scient Info.
Garrison, Omar V. The Hidden Story of Scientology. 8.50 (ISBN 0-8065-0440-4). Church of Scient Info.
--Playing Dirty: The Secret War Against Beliefs. 13.95 (ISBN 0-931116-04-X). Church of Scient Info.
--Playing Dirty: The Secret War Against Beliefs. LC 80-51315. (Illus.). 288p. 1980. 10.50 (ISBN 0-931116-04-X); pap. 4.95 (ISBN 0-931116-05-8). Ralston-Pilot.
--The Secret World of Interpol. 13.95 (ISBN 0-686-74638-4). Church of Scient Info.
The Guardian Office of the Church of Scientology. pap. 7.00 (ISBN 0-915598-25-6). Church of Scient Info.
Hubbard, L. Ron. Advanced Procedure & Axioms. 1951. 30.00 (ISBN 0-88404-021-6). Bridge Pubns Inc.
--Advanced Procedures & Axioms. 31.00 (ISBN 0-686-30782-8). Church Scient NY.
--All about Radiation. 20.00 (ISBN 0-686-30790-9). Church Scient NY.
--Axioms & Logics. 5.00 (ISBN 0-686-30793-3). Church Scient NY.
--Axioms & Logics. 1958. pap. 6.97 (ISBN 0-88404-066-6). Bridge Pubns Inc.
--Background & Ceremonies of the Church of Scientology. 40.00 (ISBN 0-686-30794-1). Church Scient NY.
--The Book Introducing the E-Meter. 8.75 (ISBN 0-686-30797-6). Church Scient NY.
--The Book of E-Meter Drills. 8.75 (ISBN 0-686-30796-8). Church Scient NY.
--Child Dianetics. 20.00 (ISBN 0-686-30781-X). Church Scient NY.
--Control & Mechanics of S. C. S. (Start, Change, Stop) 1951. pap. 9.67 (ISBN 0-88404-067-4). Bridge Pubns Inc.
--Control & the Mechanics of SCS. 8.75 (ISBN 0-686-30792-5). Church Scient NY.
--The Creation of Human Ability. 31.00 (ISBN 0-686-13922-4). Church Scient NY.
--The Creation of Human Ability: A Handbook for Scientologists. 292p. 1954. 36.44 (ISBN 0-88404-011-9). Bridge Pubns Inc.
--Dianetica: la Ciencia Moderna De Salud Mental. spanish ed. 1976. pap. 3.95 (ISBN 0-88404-086-0). Bridge Pubns Inc.
--Dianetics. 1977. pap. 2.00 (ISBN 0-685-76384-6). Church of Scient Info.
--Dianetics & Scientology Technical Dictionary. 50.00 (ISBN 0-686-30803-4). Church Scient NY.
--Dianetics & Scientology Technical Dictionary. 1975. 79.32 (ISBN 0-88404-037-2). Bridge Pubns Inc.
--Dianetics: Evolution of a Science. 20.00 (ISBN 0-686-30777-1). Church Scient NY.
--Dianetics Fifty-Five. 20.00 (ISBN 0-686-13920-8). Church Scient NY.
--Dianetics Fifty-Five. 168p. 1955. 36.44 (ISBN 0-88404-003-8). Bridge Pubns Inc.
--Dianetics: The Evolution of a Science. 110p. 1950. 21.44 (ISBN 0-88404-017-8). Bridge Pubns Inc.
--Dianetics: The Modern Science of Mental Health. 20.00 (ISBN 0-686-30776-3). Church Scient NY.
--Dianetics: The Modern Science of Mental Health. 483p. 1950. 32.16 (ISBN 0-88404-000-3). Bridge Pubns Inc.
--Dianetics, the Original Thesis. 20.00 (ISBN 0-686-13917-8). Church Scient NY.
--Dianetics: The Original Thesis. 157p. 1951. 21.44 (ISBN 0-88404-002-X). Bridge Pubns Inc.

--Dianetics Today. 76.00 (ISBN 0-686-30802-6). Church Scient NY.
--Dianetics Today. 1975. 120.04 (ISBN 0-88404-036-4). Bridge Pubns Inc.
--E-Meter Essentials. 8.75 (ISBN 0-686-30795-X). Church Scient NY.
--Fundamentals of Thought. 20.00 (ISBN 0-686-13919-4). Church Scient NY.
--Group Auditor's Handbook. 50.00 (ISBN 0-686-30787-9). Church Scient NY.
--Handbook for Preclears. 20.00 (ISBN 0-686-30783-6). Church Scient NY.
--Handbook for Preclears. (Illus.). 192p. 1951. 38.59 (ISBN 0-88404-016-X). Bridge Pubns Inc.
--Have You Lived Before This Life? 20.00 (ISBN 0-686-13921-6). Church Scient NY.
--How to Live Though an Executive: Communications Manual. 132p. 1953. 32.16 (ISBN 0-88404-010-0). Bridge Pubns Inc.
--How to Live Through an Executive. 20.00 (ISBN 0-686-30786-0). Church Scient NY.
--Hymn of Asia. 40.00 (ISBN 0-686-30801-8). Church Scient NY.
--Introduction to Scientology Ethics. 20.00 (ISBN 0-686-13916-X). Church Scient NY.
--Introduction to Scientology Ethics. 74p. 1968. 32.16 (ISBN 0-88404-015-1). Bridge Pubns Inc.
--The Management Series. (Vol. I). 100.00 (ISBN 0-686-30799-2). Church Scient NY.
--Mission into Time. 20.00 (ISBN 0-686-13923-2). Church Scient NY.
--Modern Management Technology Defined. 94.00 (ISBN 0-686-30806-9). Church Scient NY.
--Modern Management Technology Defined. 1977. text ed. 107.18 (ISBN 0-88404-040-2). Bridge Pubns Inc.
--Notes on the Lectures. 31.00 (ISBN 0-686-30778-X). Church Scient NY.
--Notes on the Lectures of L. Ron Hubbard. (Illus.). 160p. 1951. 36.44 (ISBN 0-88404-005-4). Bridge Pubns Inc.
--The Organization Executive Course. 840.00 (ISBN 0-686-30798-4). Church Scient NY.
--The Organization Executive Course: An Encyclopedia of Scientology Policy (1950-1951, 1953-1974, 7 vols. Incl. Vol. 0. Basic Staff Volume of the Organization Executive Course (ISBN 0-88404-025-9); Vol. 1. Hubbard Communications Office Division One of the Organization Executive Course (ISBN 0-88404-026-7); Vol. 2. Hubbard Communications Office Dissemination Division Two of the Organization Executive Course (ISBN 0-88404-027-5); Vol. 3. Treasury Division Three of the Organization Executive Course (ISBN 0-88404-028-3); Vol. 4. Technical Division Four of the Organization Executive Course (ISBN 0-88404-029-1); Vol. 5. Qualifications Division Five of the Organization Executive Course (ISBN 0-88404-030-5); Vol. 6. Distribution Division Six of the Organization Executive Course. 1971 (ISBN 0-88404-031-3); Vol. 7. Executive Division Seven: The Executive's Handbook of the Organization Executive Course (ISBN 0-88404-032-1). 1974. 836.00 set (ISBN 0-88404-033-X); 107.18 ea. Bridge Pubns Inc.
--The Phoenix Lectures. 31.00 (ISBN 0-686-13925-9). Church Scient NY.
--The Problems of Work. 20.00 (ISBN 0-686-30789-5). Church Scient NY.
--The Problems of Work: Scientology Applied to the Work-a-Day World. 106p. 1956. 21.44 (ISBN 0-88404-007-0). Bridge Pubns Inc.
--Research & Discovery Series, 8 vols. Set. write for info. (ISBN 0-686-30030-0); Vol. 1, June 1950. 100.00 (ISBN 0-686-30031-9); Vol. 2, July 1950. 100.00 (ISBN 0-686-30032-7); Vol. 3. 100.00; Vol. 4. 100.00. Church Scient NY.
--Science of Survival. 31.00 (ISBN 0-686-30779-8). Church Scient NY.
--Science of Survival: Prediction of Human Behavior. LC 51-5566. (Illus.). 550p. 1951. 47.16 (ISBN 0-88404-001-1). Bridge Pubns Inc.
--Scientology: A History of Man. 31.00 (ISBN 0-686-30784-4). Church Scient NY.
--Scientology: A History of Man. 1952. 13.00 (ISBN 0-88404-024-0). Bridge Pubns Inc.
--Scientology: A New Slant on Life. 20.00 (ISBN 0-686-13918-6). Church Scient NY.
--Scientology: A New Slant on Life. 160p. 1965. 21.44 (ISBN 0-88404-013-5). Bridge Pubns Inc.
--Scientology: Clear Procedure. 8.75 (ISBN 0-686-30791-7). Church Scient NY.
--Scientology: Clear Procedure Issue One. 1957. pap. 9.50 (ISBN 0-88404-069-0). Bridge Pubns Inc.
--Scientology Eight to Eight Thousand Eight. 152p. 1953. 32.16 (ISBN 0-88404-008-9). Bridge Pubns Inc.
--Scientology: Eight to Eights. 31.00 (ISBN 0-686-30785-2). Church Scient NY.
--Scientology Eight to Eighty: The Discovery & Increase of Life Energy in the Genus Homo Sapiens. 1952. 27.85 (ISBN 0-88404-020-8). Bridge Pubns Inc.
--Scientology: The Fundamentals of Thought. 20.00 (ISBN 0-686-30788-7). Church Scient NY.
--Scientology: The Fundamentals of Thought. 128p. 1956. 21.44 (ISBN 0-88404-018-6). Bridge Pubns Inc.
--Scientology Zero-Eight, the Book of Basics. 31.00 (ISBN 0-686-30808-5). Church Scient NY.
--Scientology Zero to Eight: The Book of Basics. 159p. 1950. 32.16 (ISBN 0-88404-009-7). Bridge Pubns Inc.
--Scientology: 8-8008. 31.00 (ISBN 0-686-13924-0). Church Scient NY.
--Self Analysis. 20.00 (ISBN 0-686-30780-1). Church Scient NY.
--Self Analysis. 254p. 1983. pap. 8.95 (ISBN 0-88404-109-3). Bridge Pubns Inc.
--The Volunteer Minister's Handbook. 76.00 (ISBN 0-686-30805-0). Church Scient NY.
--Volunteer Minister's Handbook. 1976. 124.33 (ISBN 0-88404-039-9). Bridge Pubns Inc.
--What Is Scientology? 50.00 (ISBN 0-686-30807-7). Church Scient NY.
Hubbard, L. Ron, intro. by. Child Dianetics. 1951. 38.59 (ISBN 0-88404-022-4). Bridge Pubns Inc.
Hubbard, Mary Sue. Marriage Hats. 1970. pap. 12.87 (ISBN 0-88404-068-2). Bridge Pubns Inc.
In Behalf of Spiritual Freedom. pap. 10.00 (ISBN 0-915598-26-4). Church of Scient Info.
Information Ser. Scientology: A Religion Helping Others. (Illus.). 1978. pap. 4.00 (ISBN 0-915598-21-3). Church of Scient Info.
Information Service. The Spies Among Us: Agents Provocateurs. 1978. pap. 3.00 (ISBN 0-915598-19-1). Church of Scient Info.
The International Conference for World Peace & Social Reform & Human Rights Prayer Day--1976: Proceedings. (Illus.). 1976. pap. 11.50 (ISBN 0-915598-14-0). Church of Scient Info.
The Justice Department & Abuse of the Judicial System. pap. 3.00 (ISBN 0-915598-22-1). Church of Scient Info.
The Management Series Volume 1: Data, Public Relations, Personnel, Organizing, Finance, Executive, Establishment Officer. 578p. 1974. 120.04 (ISBN 87-7336-107-0). Bridge Pubns Inc.
The Membership: Interpol Dossier, Pt. Two. pap. 5.75 (ISBN 0-905931-00-9). Church of Scient Info.
The Mind Control Papers, Vol. I. pap. 6.00 (ISBN 0-915598-35-3). Church of Scient Info.
Oosthuizen, G. C. The Church of Scientology Religious Philosophy, Religion, & Church. pap. 4.00 (ISBN 0-686-74641-4). Church of Scient Info.
Scientology & Dianetics. (Illus.). 1971. pap. 4.00 (ISBN 0-915598-03-5). Church of Scient Info.
Scientology Documenting the Truth. pap. 7.00 (ISBN 0-915598-24-8). Church of Scient Info.
Towards Peace on Earth: The Church of Scientology. pap. 4.00 (ISBN 0-686-74643-0). Church of Scient Info.
Wallis, Roy. The Road to Total Freedom. LC 76-27273. 1977. 32.00x (ISBN 0-231-04200-0). Columbia U Pr.
What Is Scientology? Taken from the Works of L. Ron Hubbard. 1978. 47.16 (ISBN 0-88404-061-5). Bridge Pubns Inc.
Whitehead, Harriet. Renunciation & Reformulation: A Study of Conversion in an American Sect. LC 86-16211. (Anthropology of Contemporary Issues Ser.). (Illus.). 304p. 1987. text ed. 32.50x (ISBN 0-8014-1849-6). Cornell U Pr.
With Malice Toward Some: A Documented Sampling of U. S. Government Conspiracy-Infiltration-Manipulation 1950-1979. pap. 7.00 (ISBN 0-686-74642-2). Church of Scient Info.

DIASPORA
see Israel and the Diaspora

DIDACHE
Burghardt, W. J., et al, eds. The Didache, the Epistle of Barnabas, the Epistle & Martyrdom of St. Polycarp, the Fragments of Papias, the Epistle of Diognetus. LC 78-62453. (ACW Ser.: No. 6). 241p. 1948. 13.95 (ISBN 0-8091-0247-1). Paulist Pr.
Vokes, Frederick E. The Riddle of the Didache: Fact or Fiction, Heresy or Catholicism? (Church Historical Society London N. S.: No. 32). Repr. of 1938 ed. 40.00 (ISBN 0-8115-3156-2). Kraus Repr.

DIETARY LAWS, JEWISH
see Jews–Dietary Laws

DINKA (NILOTIC TRIBE)
Lienhardt, Godfrey. Divinity & Experience: The Religion of the Dinka. 1961. 45.00x (ISBN 0-19-823119-9). Oxford U Pr.

DIOCESAN SCHOOLS
see Church Schools

DIOCESES
see also Bishops; Cathedrals
Building the Local Church, Shared Responsibiity in Diocesan Pastoral Councils. 88p. 1984. pap. 6.95 (ISBN 1-55586-907-6). US Catholic.
Faherty, William B. Dream by the River. rev. ed. (Illus.). 1981. Repr. of 1973 ed. 4.95 (ISBN 0-933150-21-0). River City MO.
Leckey, Dolores R., ed. Journeying Together: Proceedings of Three Regional Convocations on Shared Responsibility in America. 48p. 1986. pap. 4.95 (ISBN 1-55586-975-0). US Catholic.

DIONYSIUS
Danielou, Alain. Shiva & Dionysus. 250p. (Orig.). 1984. pap. 8.95 (ISBN 0-89281-057-2). Inner Tradit.
Ebel, Henry. After Dionysus: An Essay on Where We Are Now. LC 70-156321. 136p. 1972. 15.00 (ISBN 0-8386-7958-7). Fairleigh Dickinson.
Linforth, Ivan M. The Arts of Orpheus. LC 72-9296. (The Philosophy of Plato & Aristotle Ser.). Repr. of 1941 ed. 24.50 (ISBN 0-405-04847-5). Ayer Co Pubs.
Otto, Walter F. Dionysus: Myth & Cult. Palmer, Robert B., tr. from Ger. LC 86-13742. (Dunquin Ser.: No. 14). xxi, 243p. 1981. pap. 13.00 (ISBN 0-88214-214-3). Spring Pubns.
Roberts, W. Rhys. Dionysius of Halicarnassus, on Literary Composition & Dionysius of Halicarnassus: The Three Literary Letters (EP. AD Ammaeum I, EP. AD Popeium, EP. AD Ammaeum II, 2 vols. Taran, Leonardo, ed. (Ancient Greek Literature Ser.). 616p. 1987. lib. bdg. 90.00 (ISBN 0-8240-7766-0). Garland Pub.

DIONYSIUS AREOPAGITA, PSEUDO.
Durantel, J. Saint Thomas et le Pseudo-Denis. (Medieval Studies Ser.). (Fr.). Repr. of 1919 ed. lib. bdg. 45.00x (ISBN 0-697-00036-2). Irvington.

DIONYSIUS 1ST, OF TELL-MAHRE, PATRIARCH OF THE JACOBITES, d. 845
Campbell, Thomas L., tr. from Gr. Dionysius the Pseudo-Areopagite: The Ecclesiastical Hierarchy. LC 81-40140. 236p. (Orig.). 1981. lib. bdg. 27.50 (ISBN 0-8191-1798-6); pap. text ed. 12.50 (ISBN 0-8191-1799-4). U Pr of Amer.

DIRECTION, SPIRITUAL
see Spiritual Direction

DIRECTORS OF RELIGIOUS EDUCATION
see also Sunday-School Superintendents
Aylmer, G. E. & Cant, R. C., eds. A History of York Minster. (Illus.). 1977. 32.50x (ISBN 0-19-817199-4). Oxford U Pr.
Dunning, James B. Ministries: Sharing God's Gifts. LC 80-52058. (Illus.). 136p. (Orig.). 1980. pap. 5.95 (ISBN 0-88489-123-2). St Marys.
Guiles, Cecil R. Ministering to Youth. 1973. 5.25 (ISBN 0-87148-551-6); pap. 4.25 (ISBN 0-87148-552-4); instrs. guide 4.95 (ISBN 0-87148-834-5). Pathway Pr.
Harris, Maria, ed. The DRE Reader: A Sourcebook in Education & Ministry. LC 80-52059. 192p. (Orig.). 1980. pap. 6.95 (ISBN 0-88489-124-0). St Marys.
Polen, O. W. The Sunday School Teacher. 1956. pap. 5.25 (ISBN 0-87148-765-9). Pathway Pr.

DISABILITIES, POLITICAL (GREAT BRITAIN)
see Catholic Emancipation; Dissenters, Religious–England

DISCIPLES, TWELVE
see Apostles

DISCIPLES OF CHRIST
Barclay, William. The Master's Men. (Festival Books). 1976. pap. 3.25 (ISBN 0-687-23732-7). Abingdon.
Becoming a Disciple of Christ: A Monk of Marmion Abbey. 5.95 (ISBN 0-87193-195-8). Dimension Bks.
Boice, James M. Christ's Call to Discipleship. 1986. text ed. 9.95 (ISBN 0-8024-1397-8). Moody.
Borsh, Frederick H. Power in Weakness: New Hearing for Gospel Stories of Healing & Discipleship. LC 82-15997. 160p. 1983. pap. 8.95 (ISBN 0-8006-1703-7, 1-1703). Fortress.
Campbell, Alexander. The Christian System. LC 73-83412. (Religion in America Ser). 1969. Repr. of 1871 ed. 20.00 (ISBN 0-405-00233-5). Ayer Co Pubs.
Churches Alive, Inc. Staff. Growing as a Disciple Conference Notebook. rev. ed. 85p. 1983. pap. write for info. (ISBN 0-934396-37-X). Churches Alive.
Coleman, William. Peter. LC 81-85894. 160p. (Orig.). 1982. pap. 4.95 (ISBN 0-89081-305-1). Harvest Hse.
Cummins, D. Duane. Un Manual para los Discipulos de Hoy. Delgado, Conchita & Sanchez, Zayda N., trs. from Eng. LC 83-15489. Tr. of A Handbook for Today's Disciples. (Span., Illus.). 64p. (Orig.). 1983. pap. 2.25 (ISBN 0-8272-2316-1). CBP.
Eims, Leroy. The Lost Art of Disciple Making. pap. 6.95 (ISBN 0-310-37281-X, 9233P). Zondervan.
Featherstone, Vaughn J. The Disciple of Christ. LC 84-71706. 100p. 7.95 (ISBN 0-87747-910-0). Deseret Bk.
Flynn, Leslie. The Twelve. 156p. 1982. pap. 5.95 (ISBN 0-88207-310-9). Victor Bks.
Hayden, Amos S. Early History of the Disciples in the Western Reserve, Ohio; with Biographical Sketches of the Principal Agents in Their Religious Movement. LC 76-38449. (Religion in America, Ser. 2). 480p. 1972. Repr. of 1875 ed. 32.00 (ISBN 0-405-04068-7). Ayer Co Pubs.
Henrichsen, Walter A. Disciples Are Made-Not Born. LC 74-79162. 160p. 1974. pap. 4.50 (ISBN 0-88207-706-6). Victor Bks.
John-Roger. Disciples of Christ. 1976. pap. 5.00 (ISBN 0-914829-07-6). Baraka Bk.
Johnson, H. Eugene. The Christian Church Plea. LC 75-12012. (New Life Bks). 96p. 1975. pap. 2.95 (ISBN 0-87239-053-5, 40028). Standard Pub.
Mahoney, Robert. Two Disciples at the Tomb. (Theologie und Wirklichkeit: Vol. 6). 344p. 1974. pap. 29.75 (ISBN 3-261-00943-8). P Lang Pubs.
Moloney, F. J. Disciples & Prophets. 240p. 1981. 12.95 (ISBN 0-8245-0049-0). Crossroad NY.
Osborn, Ronald E. The Faith We Affirm. LC 79-21079. 1979. pap. 3.50 (ISBN 0-8272-1009-4). CBP.
Richesin, L. Dale & Bouchard, Larry D., eds. Interpreting Disciples: Practical Theology in the Disciples of Christ. LC 86-30072. 295p. (Orig.). 1987. pap. text ed. 14.95x (ISBN 0-87565-072-4). Tex Christian.
Segovia, Fernando F., ed. Discipleship in the New Testament. LC 85-47730. 240p. 1985. pap. 16.95 (ISBN 0-8006-1873-4, 1-1873). Fortress.
Stone, Barton W. The Biography of Eld. Barton Warren Stone, Written by Himself: With Additions & Reflections. LC 79-38463. (Religion in America, Ser. 2). 476p. 1972. Repr. of 1847 ed. 27.00 (ISBN 0-405-04089-X). Ayer Co Pubs.
Thomson, E. Roberts. Baptists & Disciples of Christ. 195p. 1948. pap. 2.95 (ISBN 0-87921-004-4). Attic Pr.
Torrey, Charles G. Apocalypse of John. 1958. 39.50x (ISBN 0-686-83474-7). Elliots Bks.

DISCIPLES OF CHRIST–HISTORY
Ford, Harold W. A History of the Restoration Plea. 2nd ed. 1967. pap. 3.95 (ISBN 0-89900-110-6). College Pr Pub.

DISCIPLES OF CHRIST–HYMNS
Heaton, Charles H., ed. Hymnbook for Christian Worship. LC 69-14339. 1970. Red. 7.95x (ISBN 0-8272-8020-3). Blue. 7.95x (ISBN 0-8272-8021-1); Beige. 7.95x (ISBN 0-8272-8024-6); 19.50x (ISBN 0-8272-8023-8); 8.95x (ISBN 0-8272-8022-X); brown gift 8.50x (ISBN 0-8272-8027-0). CBP.

DISCIPLES OF CHRIST–LITURGY AND RITUAL
McWhirter, David. Millenial Harbinger - Index. LC 81-65031. (Millenial Harbinger Ser.). 776p. 1981. 19.95 (ISBN 0-89900-228-5). College Pr Pub.

DISCIPLES OF CHRIST–SERMONS
Ross, Bob L. Acts Two: Thirty-Eight. 1976. 2.25 (ISBN 0-686-09114-0). Pilgrim Pubns.
--Campbellism: Its History & Heresies. 1981. 2.90 (ISBN 0-686-09113-2). Pilgrim Pubns.

DISCIPLES OF SAINT JOHN
see Mandaeans

DISCIPLESHIP
see Christian Life

DISCIPLINE, ECCLESIASTICAL
see Church Discipline

DISCUSSION IN RELIGIOUS EDUCATION
Howe, Reuel L. Miracle of Dialogue. 1963. pap. 6.95 (ISBN 0-86683-886-4, SP9, HarpR). Har-Row.
Krutza, William J. & DiCicco, Philip P. Facing the Issues, No. 4. (Contemporary Discussion Ser.). (Orig.). 1971. pap. 3.50 (ISBN 0-8010-5310-2). Baker Bk.

DISPARITY OF CULTUS
see Marriage, Mixed

DISPENSATIONALISM
Cox, William E. An Examination of Dispensationalism. 1963. pap. 2.75 (ISBN 0-87552-153-3). Presby & Reformed.
Eade, Alfred T. Expanded Panorama Bible Study Course. (Illus.). 192p. 12.95 (ISBN 0-8007-0086-4). Revell.
Fuller, Daniel P. Gospel & Law: Contrast or Continuum? the Hermeneutics of Dispensationalism & Covenant Theology. (Orig.). 1980. pap. 8.95 (ISBN 0-8028-1808-0). Eerdmans.
Gerstner, John H. A Primer on Dispensationalism. 1982. pap. 1.75 (ISBN 0-87552-273-4). Presby & Reformed.
Ryrie, Charles C. Dispensacionalismo, Hoy. Orig. Title: Dispensationalism Today. (Span.). 256p. 1974. pap. 4.75 (ISBN 0-8254-1627-2). Kregel.
--Dispensationalism Today. LC 65-14611. 211p. 1973. pap. 6.95 (ISBN 0-8024-2256-X). Moody.

DISSENTERS, RELIGIOUS
see also Congregationalism; Methodism; Presbyterianism
Claussen, Martin P. & Claussen, Evelyn B. The Voice of Christian & Jewish Dissenters in America: U. S. Internal Revenue Service Hearings, December 1978. xv, 591p. 1982. pap. 25.00. Piedmont.
Gaustad, Edwin S. Dissent in American Religion. LC 73-77131. xii, 184p. 1975. pap. 3.95x (ISBN 0-226-28437-9, P637, Phoen). U of Chicago Pr.
Goricheva, Tatiana. Talking about God Is Dangerous: The Diary of a Russian Dissident. 144p. 1987. 11.95 (ISBN 0-8245-0798-3). Crossroad NY.
Johnson, John R. Liturgy for the Free Church. LC 86-18782. 176p. 1986. lib. bdg. 19.95x (ISBN 0-89370-527-6). Borgo Pr.
Kiraly, Bela K., ed. Tolerance & Movements of Religious Dissent in Eastern Europe. (East European Monographs: No. 13). 227p. 1976. 20.00x (ISBN 0-914710-06-0). East Eur Quarterly.
McIlwaine, Henry R. The Struggle of Protestant Dissenters for Religious Toleration in Virginia. LC 78-63830. (Johns Hopkins University. Studies in the Social Sciences. Twelfth Ser. 1894: 4). Repr. of 1894 ed. 11.50 (ISBN 0-404-61090-0). AMS Pr.
McLoughlin, William G. New England Dissent, 1630-1833: The Baptists & the Separation of Church & State, 2 vols. LC 70-131464. (Center for the Study of the History of Liberty in America Ser). (Illus.). 1971. Set. 80.00x (ISBN 0-674-61175-6). Harvard U Pr.
Moore, R. I. The Origins of European Dissent. 338p. 1985. pap. 12.95x (ISBN 0-631-14404-8). Basil Blackwell.
Ozment, Steven E. Mysticism & Dissent: Religious Ideology & Social Protest in the Sixteenth Century. LC 72-91316. 272p. 1973. 33.00x (ISBN 0-300-01576-3). Yale U Pr.
Platon. Present State of the Greek Church in Russia. LC 75-131031. Repr. of 1815 ed. 21.50 (ISBN 0-404-05059-X). AMS Pr.
Randall, Emilius O. History of the Zoar Society. 3rd ed. LC 75-134427. 1972. Repr. of 1904 ed. 14.50 (ISBN 0-404-08467-2). AMS Pr.
Sangster, Paul. A History of the Free Churches. (Illus.). 224p. 1984. 29.95 (ISBN 0-434-41330-5, Pub. by W Heinemann Ltd). David & Charles.
Sellers, Ian. Nineteenth Century Nonconformity. (Foundations of Modern History Ser.). 110p. 1977. pap. text ed. 14.50x (ISBN 0-8419-5802-5). Holmes & Meier.
Watts, Michael R. The Dissenters: From the Reformation to the French Revolution. 568p. 1986. pap. 19.95x (ISBN 0-19-822956-9). Oxford U Pr.

DISSENTERS, RELIGIOUS–ENGLAND
Crowther-Hunt, Norman. Two Early Political Associations: The Quakers & the Dissenting Deputies in the Age of Sir Robert Walpole. LC 78-23805. 1979. Repr. of 1961 ed. lib. bdg. 24.75x (ISBN 0-313-21036-5, HUTW). Greenwood.
Davie, Donald. A Gathered Church: The Literature of the English Dissenting Interest, 1700-1930. (The Clark Lectures 1976). 1978. 17.50x (ISBN 0-19-519999-5). Oxford U Pr.
Davies, Horton. The English Free Churches. 2nd. ed. LC 85-7684. vii, 208p. 1985. Repr. of 1963 ed. lib. bdg. 37.50x (ISBN 0-313-20838-7, DAEF). Greenwood.
Furneaux, Philip. The Palladium of Conscience. LC 74-122161. (Civil Liberties in American History Ser). 267p. 1974. Repr. of 1773 ed. lib. bdg. 35.00 (ISBN 0-306-71972-X). Da Capo.
Kendall, Ritchie D. The Drama of Dissent: The Radical Poetics of Nonconformity, 1380-1590. LC 86-1289. (Studies in Religion). 286p. 1986. 27.50x (ISBN 0-8078-1700-7). U of NC Pr.
Koss, Stephen. Nonconformity in Modern British Politics. LC 75-8646. 272p. 1975. 26.00 (ISBN 0-208-01553-1, Archon). Shoe String.
Lee, Philip J., Jr. Against the Protestant Gnostics. 288p. 1987. 18.95 (ISBN 0-19-504067-8). Oxford U Pr.
Rose, Elliot. Cases of Conscience: Alternatives Open to Recusants & Puritans under Elizabeth I & James I. LC 74-76947. pap. 68.50 (2027243). Bks Demand UMI.
Thompson, David M., ed. Nonconformity in the Nineteenth Century. (The Birth of Modern Britain Ser.). 1972. pap. 9.95x (ISBN 0-7100-7275-9). Methuen Inc.
Whiting, Charles E. Studies in English Puritanism from the Restoration to the Revolution, 1660-1688. LC 68-56060. 1968. Repr. of 1931 ed. 37.50x (ISBN 0-678-05203-4). Kelley.

DIVES AND LAZARUS
Bunyan, John. Groans of a Lost Soul. LC 68-6571. 1967. pap. 3.25 (ISBN 0-685-19830-8). Reiner.

DIVINE GLORY
see Glory of God

DIVINE HEALING
see Christian Science; Miracles

DIVINE IMMANENCE
see Immanence of God

DIVINE RIGHT OF KINGS
see also Emperor Worship; Kings and Rulers (In Religion, Folk-Lore, etc.)
Figgis, John N. The Divine Right of Kings. 14.00 (ISBN 0-8446-0621-9). Peter Smith.
Gee, Edward. The Divine Right & Original of the Civil Magistrate from God. LC 75-31092. Repr. of 1658 ed. 30.00 (ISBN 0-404-13510-2). AMS Pr.
Paul, Robert A. The Tibetan Symbolic World: Psychoanalytic Explorations. LC 81-16505. (Chicago Originals Ser.). (Illus.). 360p. 1982. lib. bdg. 14.00x (ISBN 0-226-64987-3). U of Chicago Pr.
Tyndale, William. The Obedience of a Christen Man & How Christe Rulers Ought to Governe. LC 77-7436. (English Experience Ser.: No. 897). 1977. Repr. of 1528 ed. lib. bdg. 24.00 (ISBN 90-221-0897-X). Walter J Johnson.

DIVINE SCIENCE CHURCH–DOCTRINAL AND CONTROVERSIAL WORKS
Baum, Mrs. C. L. Studies in Divine Science. 1964. 6.50 (ISBN 0-686-24362-5). Divine Sci Fed.
Brooks, Louise. Early History of Divine Science. 1963. 5.95 (ISBN 0-686-24363-3). Divine Sci Fed.
James, Fannie B. Truth & Health. 1970. 8.95 (ISBN 0-686-24356-0). Divine Sci Fed.
James, Fannie B., compiled by. Divine Science: Its Principle & Practice. 1957. pap. 7.50 (ISBN 0-686-24361-7). Divine Sci Fed.
Selected Bible Readings. 1962. pap. 2.95 (ISBN 0-686-24354-4); spiral bdg. 3.95 (ISBN 0-686-24355-2); Fabrikoid 4.95 (ISBN 0-686-28567-0). Divine Sci Fed.
Zagat, Helen. Faith & Works. 1955. 6.95 (ISBN 0-686-24360-9). Divine Sci Fed.

DIVINE TRANSCENDENCE
see Transcendence of God

DIVINITY OF CHRIST
see Jesus Christ–Divinity

DIVORCE
see also Divorcees; Marriage–Annulment; Remarriage
Arnold, William V. When Your Parents Divorce, Vol. 1. LC 79-20055. (Christian Care Bks.). 118p. 1980. pap. 7.95 (ISBN 0-664-24294-4). Westminster.
Arnold, William V., et al. Divorce: Prevention or Survival. LC 77-22066. 128p. 1977. pap. 5.95 (ISBN 0-664-24142-5). Westminster.
Billnitzer, Harold. Before You Divorce. 1978. pap. 0.95 (ISBN 0-933350-12-0). Morse Pr.
Bontrager, G. Edwin. Divorce & the Faithful Church. LC 78-4671. 224p. 1978. 12.95 (ISBN 0-8361-1850-2); pap. 8.95 (ISBN 0-8361-1851-0). Herald Pr.
Bouma, Mary La G. Divorce in the Parsonage. LC 79-16157. 160p. 1979. pap. 3.95 (ISBN 0-87123-109-3, 210109). Bethany Hse.
Bunny, Edmund. Of Divorce for Adulterie & Marrying Againe: That There Is No Sufficient Warrant So to Do. (English Experience Ser.: No. 781). 1977. Repr. of 1612 ed. lib. bdg. 20.00 (ISBN 90-221-0781-7). Walter J Johnson.
Burkhart, Wanda. Submitting To A Sinning Husband. 64p. 1984. pap. 2.95 (ISBN 0-88144-042-6). Christian Pub.
Bustanoby, Andre. But I Didn't Want a Divorce. 1978. o. p. 5.95 (ISBN 0-310-22170-6, 9207P); pap. 5.95 (ISBN 0-310-22171-4). Zondervan.
Carter, Velma T. & Leavenworth, Lynn J. Caught in the Middle: Children of Divorce. 176p. 1985. pap. 6.95 (ISBN 0-8170-1037-8). Judson.
Catoir, John. Catholics & Broken Marriage. LC 78-74434. 72p. 1979. pap. 1.95 (ISBN 0-87793-176-3). Ave Maria.
Cerling, Charles. The Divorced Christian. 1984. 9.95 (ISBN 0-8010-2495-1); pap. 5.95 (ISBN 0-8010-2486-2). Baker Bk.
Connally, Andrew M. & Hicks, Olan. Connally-Hicks Debate on Divorce & Remarriage. 1979. pap. 13.00 (ISBN 0-934916-31-4). Natl Christian Pr.
Cottle, Thomas J. Divorce & the Jewish Child. 28p. 1981. pap. 2.50 (ISBN 0-87495-034-1). Am Jewish Comm.
Crook, Roger H. An Open Book to the Christian Divorcee. LC 73-87064. pap. 4.95 (ISBN 0-8054-5217-6). Broadman.
Daniel, R. P. Dating, Marriage, Sex & Divorce. 75p. pap. 3.95 (ISBN 0-88172-147-6). Believers Bkshelf.
De Margerie, Bertrand. Remarried Divorcees & Eucharistic Communion. 1980. pap. 1.95 (ISBN 0-8198-6401-3). Dghtrs St Paul.
Duty, Guy. Divorce & Remarriage. LC 96-2485. 160p. 1983. 8.95 (ISBN 0-87123-097-6, 230097). Bethany Hse.
--Divorcio y Nuevo Matrimonio. 176p. 1975. 2.95 (ISBN 0-88113-060-5). Edit Betania.
Elliot, Elisabeth. What God Has Joined. 32p. 1983. Repr. 1.50 (ISBN 0-89107-276-4). Good News.
Ellisen, Stanley A. Divorce & Remarriage in the Church. 1977. pap. 5.95 (ISBN 0-310-35561-3, 11256P). Zondervan.
Erasmus, Desiderius. The Censure & Judgement of Erasmus: Whyther Dyuorsemente Stondeth with the Lawe of God. Lesse, N., tr. LC 76-38177. (English Experience Ser.: No. 452). 160p. 1972. Repr. of 1550 ed. 15.00 (ISBN 90-221-0452-4). Walter J Johnson.
Feeney, James H. Divorce & Marriage. 1980. pap. 1.75 (ISBN 0-911739-06-8). Abbott Loop.
Friedman, Natalie & Rogers, Theresa F. The Jewish Community & Children of Divorce: A Pilot Study of Perceptions & Responses. 32p. 1983. pap. 2.00 (ISBN 0-87495-051-1). Am Jewish Comm.
Garber, Marjorie, ed. Cannibals, Witches, & Divorce: Estranging the Renaissance. LC 86-45472. (Selected Papers from the English Institute, 1985 New Ser.: No. 11). 256p. 1987. text ed. 19.50x (ISBN 0-8018-3405-8). Johns Hopkins.
Hertzler, Lois S. Prayers for the Newly Single. 32p. 1981. pap. 1.95 (ISBN 0-8170-0914-0). Judson.
Hickey, Marilyn. Divorce Is Not the Answer. LC 75-32006. 1979. pap. 4.95 (ISBN 0-89221-009-5). New Leaf.
Joiner, E. Earl. A Christian Considers Divorce & Remarriage. LC 81-70411. 1983. pap. 5.95 (ISBN 0-8054-5427-6). Broadman.
Judd, Wayne. Breaking up. (Uplook Ser.). 1978. pap. 0.99 (ISBN 0-8163-0194-8, 12466). Pacific Pr Pub Assn.
Kelly, Kevin T. Divorce & Second Marriage: Facing the Challenge. 112p. 1983. pap. 6.95 (ISBN 0-8164-2471-3, HarpR). Har-Row.
Laney, J. Carl. The Divorce Myth. LC 81-7690. 152p. 1981. 8.95 (ISBN 0-87123-144-1, 230144). Bethany Hse.
Lannan, Paul A. & Spaniol, LeRoy J. Getting Unstuck: Moving on after Divorce. (Orig.). 1984. pap. 5.95 (ISBN 0-8091-2580-3). Paulist Pr.
MacArthur, John, Jr. On Divorce. (John MacArthur's Bible Studies). 1985. pap. 3.50 (ISBN 0-8024-5111-X). Moody.
Madsen, Keith. Fallen Images: Experiencing Divorce in the Ministry. 128p. 1985. pap. 5.95 (ISBN 0-8170-1076-9). Judson.
Paige, Roger. Dealing with Divorce. 1979. pap. 4.50 (ISBN 0-8309-0240-6). Herald Hse.
Payne, Dorothy. Life after Divorce. (Looking Up Ser.). 24p. (Orig.). 1982. pap. 1.25 booklet (ISBN 0-8298-0610-5). Pilgrim NY.
Peppler, Alice S. Divorced & Christian. LC 74-4505. 96p. 1974. pap. 3.75 (ISBN 0-570-03189-3, 12-2591). Concordia.
Pothen, S. Divorce: Its Causes & Consequences in Hindu Society. 320p. 1986. text ed. 35.00x (ISBN 0-7069-2932-2, Pub. by Vikas India). Advent NY.
Rambo, Lewis. The Divorcing Christian. 96p. (Orig.). 1983. pap. 5.25 (ISBN 0-687-10994-9). Abingdon.
Smoke, Jim & McAfee, Lisa. Living Beyond Divorce: Working Guide. LC 83-82321. (Orig.). 1985. pap. 5.95 (ISBN 0-89081-407-4); working guide 3.95 (ISBN 0-89081-467-8). Harvest Hse.
Steele & Ryrie. Meant to Last. 1983. 5.95 (ISBN 0-686-46323-4). Victor Bks.
Sweatte, Appolles T. Marriage, Divorce, & the Believer. LC 85-91361. 53p. 1986. 6.95. Vantage.
Telford, Dr. Andrew. Miscarriage of Marriage. pap. 1.45 (ISBN 0-686-12750-1). Grace Pub Co.
Thomas, J. D. Divorce & Remarriage. (Way of Life Ser.: No.159). 1977. pap. 3.95 (ISBN 0-89112-159-5, Bibl Res Pr). Abilene Christ U.
Thompson, John & Thompson, Patti. Dance of the Broken Heart: A Family Love Story. 1986. 11.95 (ISBN 0-687-10080-1). Abingdon.
Wallerstein, Judith S. & Kelly, Joan B. Surviving the Breakup: How Children & Parents Cope with Divorce. 1982. pap. 9.95x (ISBN 0-465-08339-0, TB-5094). Basic.
Warren, Thomas B. Three Hundred Charts You Can Use in Preaching, Teaching & Studying on Divorce & Remarriage. 1978. pap. 11.00looseleaf (ISBN 0-934916-29-2). Natl Christian Pr.
--Tract: Questions on Divorce & Remarriage. 1984. 0.60 (ISBN 0-934916-04-7); dozen 6.00; hundred 40.00. Natl Christian Pr.
Warren, Thomas B. & Fuqua, E. C. Divorce & Remarriage: Are Non-Christians Amenable to the Law of Christ? 1977. pap. 6.00 (ISBN 0-934916-30-6). Natl Christian Pr.
Winters, Mary S. Divorce Law: A Concise Guide for Clergy & Laity. 32p. (Orig.). 1986. pap. 1.95 (ISBN 0-8298-0740-3). Pilgrim NY.
Wright, Norman. Answer to Divorce. LC 76-52831. (Answer Ser.). 1977. pap. 1.95 (ISBN 0-89081-033-8, 0338). Harvest Hse.
Young, James J. Divorcing, Believing, Belonging. 240p. (Orig.). 1984. pap. 7.95 (ISBN 0-8091-2634-6). Paulist Pr.
--When You're Divorced & Catholic. LC 80-69090. (When Bk). 96p. 1980. pap. 2.45 (ISBN 0-87029-172-6, 20265-5). Abbey.

DIVORCE–BIBLICAL TEACHING
Ashenhurst, Harry J. Divorce & Beyond. 1984. pap. 7.75 (ISBN 0-8309-0385-2). Herald Hse.
Baca, Joyce. Divorce: Making It a Growth Experience. LC 85-13067. 136p. 1985. 8.95 (ISBN 0-87747-835-X). Deseret Bk.
Billheimer, Paul E. Love Covers. LC 83-15823. 174p. (Orig.). 1983. pap. 4.95 (ISBN 0-87123-400-9, 210400). Bethany Hse.
Brunsman, Barry. New Hope for Divorced Catholics: A Concerned Pastor Offers Alternatives to Annulment. LC 85-42770. 128p. 1986. 12.95 (ISBN 0-06-061147-2, HarpR). Har-Row.
Efird, James M. Marriage & Divorce: What the Bible Says. (Contemporary Christian Concerns Ser.). 96p. (Orig.). 1985. pap. 4.95 (ISBN 0-687-23619-3). Abingdon.
Laney, J. Carl. The Divorce Myth. pap. 5.95 (ISBN 0-87123-892-6, 210892). Bethany Hse.
Martin, Norma & Levitt, Zola. Divorce, a Christian Dilemma. LC 76-45939. 168p. 1977. pap. 1.95 (ISBN 0-8361-1808-1). Herald Pr.
Miller, J. R. Come Ye Apart. 4.95 (ISBN 0-317-12209-6). AMG Pubs.
Morgan, Richard L. Is There Life after Divorce in the Church? LC 85-42825. 200p. 1985. pap. 12.95 (ISBN 0-8042-1123-X). John Knox.
Olsen, V. N. The New Testament Logia on Divorce: A Study of their Interpretation from Erasmus to Milton. 167p. (Orig.). 1971. pap. 40.00x (Pub. by J. C. B. Mohr BRD). Coronet Bks.
Thompson, William E. Devotions for Divorcing. LC 85-42827. 96p. 1985. pap. 6.95 (ISBN 0-8042-2525-7). John Knox.
Vickers, Rod. A New Day. 47p. 1984. pap. 0.95 (ISBN 0-88144-032-9). Christian Pub.
White, Ellen. Forbidden Marriages & Divorce. large print ed. 27p. 1985. pap. 5.00 (ISBN 0-914009-38-9). VHI Library.
Williams, John. For Every Cause? A Biblical Study of Divorce. 96p. 1982. pap. 3.25 (ISBN 0-87213-953-0). Loizeaux.
Willis, Gladys J. The Penalty of Eve: John Milton & Divorce. LC 83-49352. (American University Studies IV (English Language & Literature): Vol. 6). 164p. (Orig.). 1985. text ed. 21.55 (ISBN 0-8204-0094-7). P Lang Pubs.
Woodrow, Ralph. Divorce & Remarriage: What Does the Bible Really Say? LC 82-99960. (Illus.). 1982. pap. 4.95 (ISBN 0-916938-06-9). R Woodrow.
Zodhiates, Spiros. May I Divorce & Remarry. write for info. (ISBN 0-89957-600-1). AMG Pubs.
--What about Divorce. 7.95 (ISBN 0-89957-574-9). AMG Pubs.

DIVORCE–JUVENILE LITERATURE
Mumford, Amy R. Help Me Understand. (Accent Expressions Ser.). 24p. (Orig.). 1984. pap. 4.95 (ISBN 0-89636-142-X). Accent Bks.
What Would You Do? A Child's Book about Divorce. (Youth Publications). 3.50. Borden.

DIVORCE–RELIGIOUS ASPECTS–CHRISTIANITY
Carroll, Anne Kristin. Together Forever. 256p. (Orig.). 1982. pap. 7.95 (ISBN 0-310-45021-7, 6885P). Zondervan.
Heth, William A. & Wenham, Gordon J. Jesus & Divorce: The Problem with the Evangelical Consensus. 288p. 1985. pap. 7.95 (ISBN 0-8407-5962-2). Nelson.
Laney, J. Carl. The Divorce Myth. pap. 5.95 (ISBN 0-87123-892-6, 210892). Bethany Hse.
Shepard, Andrea J. Sing a New Song. 96p. (Orig.). 1986. pap. 4.95 (ISBN 0-310-34302-X, 12352P). Zondervan.
Sigal, Phillip. The Halakah of Jesus of Nazareth According to the Gospel of Matthew. 282p. (Orig.). 1986. lib. bdg. 23.75 (ISBN 0-8191-5210-2); pap. text ed. 13.25 (ISBN 0-8191-5211-0). U Pr of Amer.
Smith, Harold I. I Wish Someone Understood My Divorce: A Practical Cope-Book. LC 86-28874. 160p. (Orig.). 1987. pap. 7.95 (ISBN 0-8066-2246-6, 10-3194). Augsburg.
Stewart, Ken. Divorce & Remarriage. 141p. (Orig.). 1984. pap. 4.95 (ISBN 0-89274-343-3). Harrison Hse.
Tracy, Jim. Divorce & Remarriage. (Illus.). 80p. (Orig.). 1986. pap. 9.95 (ISBN 1-55630-008-5). Brentwood Comm.

DIVORCE (CANON LAW)
see also Marriage–Annulment (Canon Law)
Mackin, Theodore. Divorce & Remarriage. (Marriage in the Catholic Church Ser.: Vol. II). 688p. (Orig.). 1984. pap. 19.95 (ISBN 0-8091-2585-4). Paulist Pr.
Twomey, Gerald S. When Catholics Marry Again: A Guide for the Divorced, Their Families & Those Who Minister to Them. 194p. (Orig.). 1982. pap. 7.95 (ISBN 0-86683-633-0, HarpR). Har-Row.

Young, James J. Divorce Ministry & the Marriage Tribunal. LC 82-60851. 1982. pap. 5.95 (ISBN 0-8091-2477-7). Paulist Pr.

DIVORCE (JEWISH LAW)

Cottle, Thomas J. Divorce & the Jewish Child. 28p. 1981. pap. 2.50 (ISBN 0-87495-034-1). Am Jewish Comm.

Fried, Jacob L. Jews & Divorce. 1968. 12.50x (ISBN 0-87068-049-8). Ktav.

Friedman, Nathalie & Rogers, Theresa F. The Divorced Parent & the Jewish Community. LC 85-61859. 58p. (Orig.). 1985. pap. 5.00 (ISBN 0-87495-074-0). Am Jewish Comm.

Haut, Irwin H. Divorce in Jewish Law & Life. (Studies in Jewish Jurisprudence Ser.: Vol. 5). 160p. 1983. 12.50 (ISBN 0-87203-110-1); pap. 9.75 (ISBN 0-87203-114-4). Hermon.

Riskin, Shlomo. The Wife's Role in Initiating Divorce in Jewish Law & the Agunah Problem: A Halakhic Solution. 1987. 17.95 (ISBN 0-88125-122-4); pap. 11.95 (ISBN 0-88125-132-1). Ktav.

Sigal, Phillip. The Halakah of Jesus of Nazareth According to the Gospel of Matthew. 282p. (Orig.). 1986. lib. bdg. 23.75 (ISBN 0-8191-5210-2); pap. text ed. 13.25 (ISBN 0-8191-5211-0). U Pr of Amer.

DIVORCEES

see also Single-Parent Family

Streeter, Carole S. Finding Your Place after Divorce: How Women Can Find Healing. 144p. 1986. pap. 5.95 (ISBN 0-310-41691-4, 10816P). Zondervan.

Thompson, Mervin E. Starting over Single: Life & Hope after the Death of a Marriage. 160p. 1985. 10.95 (ISBN 0-933173-00-8). Prince Peace Pub.

DOCTRINAL ANTHROPOLOGY

see Man (Theology)

DOCTRINAL DEVELOPMENT

see Dogma, Development of

DOCTRINAL THEOLOGY

see Theology, Doctrinal

DOCTRINE, CHRISTIAN (CATHOLIC CHURCH)

see Catechetics–Catholic Church

DOCTRINES

see Dogma; Theology, Doctrinal

DOCUMENTS, PAPAL

see Papal Documents

DOGMA

see also Apostasy; Theology, Doctrinal

Bavinck, Herman. Doctrine of God. (Twin Brooks Ser.). 1977. pap. 13.95 (ISBN 0-8010-0723-2). Baker Bk.

Braaten, Carl E. & Jenson, Robert W., eds. Christian Dogmatics, 2 vols. LC 83-48007. 1984. Volume 1. 24.95 (ISBN 0-8006-0703-1); Volume 2. 24.95 (ISBN 0-8006-0704-X); Set. 45.95 (ISBN 0-8006-0712-0). Fortress.

Dulles, Avery. The Survival of Dogma: Faith, Authority & Dogma in a Changing World. (Crossroad Paperback Ser.). 240p. 1982. pap. 7.95 (ISBN 0-8245-0427-5). Crossroad NY.

Grabbe, George. Dogmat Tserkvi v Sovrjemjennom Mire. Tr. of The Dogma of the Church in the Modern World. 1975. pap. 1.50 (ISBN 0-317-30381-3). Holy Trinity.

Lenin, V. I. Against Dogmatism & Sectarianism. 215p. 1978. 4.95 (ISBN 0-8285-0066-5, Pub. by Progress Pubs USSR). Imported Pubns.

Lindbeck, George A. The Nature of Doctrine: Religion & Theology in a Postliberal Age. LC 83-27332. 142p. 1984. 16.95 (ISBN 0-664-21829-6); pap. 9.95 (ISBN 0-664-24618-4). Westminster.

Ommen, Thomas B. The Hermeneutic of Dogma. LC 75-29493. (American Academy of Religion. Dissertation Ser.). 1975. pap. 9.95 (ISBN 0-89130-039-2, 010111). Scholars Pr GA.

Pieper, Francis. Christian Dogmatics, 4 Vols. Engelder, Theodore, et al, trs. 1950-1957. Vol. 1. 18.95 (ISBN 0-570-06712-X, 15-1001); Vol. 2. 18.95 (ISBN 0-570-06713-8, 15-1002); Vol. 3. 18.95 (ISBN 0-570-06714-6, 15-1003); Vol. 4. 25.95 (ISBN 0-570-06711-1, 15-1000); Set. 69.95 (ISBN 0-570-06715-4, 15-1852). Concordia.

Ratzinger, Joseph C. Dogma & Preaching. O'Connell, Matthew J., tr. 1983. 9.95 (ISBN 0-8199-0819-3). Franciscan Herald.

Reik, Theodor. Dogma & Compulsion. LC 72-9369. 332p. 1973. Repr. of 1951 ed. lib. bdg. 45.00x (ISBN 0-8371-6577-6, REDC). Greenwood.

Reiser, William E. What Are They Saying about Dogma? LC 78-58955. 1978. pap. 3.95 (ISBN 0-8091-2127-1). Paulist Pr.

Tixeront, J. History of Dogmas, 3 vols. Panico, Edward J., ed. (Orig.). 1984. pap. 50.00 (ISBN 0-87061-093-7). Chr Classics.

Wicksteed, Philip H. The Reactions Between Dogma & Philosophy Illustrated from the Works of St. Thomas Aquinas. LC 77-27153. (Hibbert Lectures: 1916). Repr. of 1920 ed. 57.50 (ISBN 0-404-60418-8). AMS Pr.

DOGMA, DEVELOPMENT OF

see also Theology, Doctrinal–History

Hanson, R. P. The Continuity of Christian Doctrine. 112p. 1981. 9.95 (ISBN 0-8164-0504-2, HarpR). Har-Row.

Hefling, Charles. Why Doctrines? LC 82-83553. 196p. (Orig.). 1984. pap. 8.00 (ISBN 0-936384-09-3). Cowley Pubns.

Pelikan, Jaroslav. The Christian Tradition: a History of the Development of Doctrine, Vol. 2: The Spirit of Eastern Christendom, 600-1700. LC 79-142042. xxv, 432p. 1974. 25.00x (ISBN 0-226-65372-2). U of Chicago Pr.

--Development of Christian Doctrine: Some Historical Prolegomena. LC 69-14864. (St. Thomas More Lectures Ser.: No. 3). 174p. 1969. 18.50x (ISBN 0-300-01082-6). Yale U Pr.

Wiles, Maurice F. Making of Christian Doctrine. 1967. 32.50 (ISBN 0-521-06803-7). Cambridge U Pr.

DOGMATIC THEOLOGY

see Theology, Doctrinal

DOGONS (AFRICAN PEOPLE)

Griaule, Marcel. Conversations with Ogotemmeli: An Introduction to Dogon Religious Ideas. (Illus.). 1975. pap. 8.95x (ISBN 0-19-519821-2). Oxford U Pr.

--Conversations with Ogotemmeli: An Introduction to Dogon Religious Ideas. LC 65-3614. pap. 62.00 (ISBN 0-317-28624-2, 2055384). Bks Demand UMI.

DOGS (IN RELIGION, FOLK-LORE, ETC.)

Kretschmar, Freda. Hundestammvater und Kerberos, 2 vols. Repr. of 1938 ed. Set. 37.00 (ISBN 0-384-30430-3). Johnson Repr.

DOLET, ETIENNE, 1508-1546

Dawson, John C. Toulouse in the Renaissance: The Floral Games, University & Student Life: Etienne Dolet. (Columbia University. Studies in Romance Philology & Literature: No. 33). Repr. of 1923 ed. 18.50 (ISBN 0-404-50633-X). AMS Pr.

DOMINGO DE GUZMAN, SAINT, 1170-1221

Domingo De Guzman, Saint The Life of St. Dominie in Old French Verse. Manning, Warren F., ed. (Harv Studies in Romance Languages). 1944. 32.00 (ISBN 0-527-01118-5). Kraus Repr.

Dorcy, Mary J. Saint Dominic. LC 82-50978. 173p. 1982. pap. 5.00 (ISBN 0-89555-195-0). TAN Bks Pubs.

DOMINICANS

Bennett, Ralph F. Early Dominicans: Studies in 13th-Century Dominican History. LC 71-139903. 1971. Repr. of 1937 ed. 12.00x (ISBN 0-8462-1531-4). Russell.

Dorcy, Mary J. St. Dominic's Family. LC 83-70219. 631p. 1983. pap. 20.00 (ISBN 0-89555-208-6). TAN Bks Pubs.

Jordan of Saxony. Jordan of Saxony: On the Beginnings of the Order of Preachers. Tugwell, Simon, ed. & tr. (Dominican Sources: New Editions in English). 35p. 1982. pap. 4.00 (ISBN 0-9511202-0-4). Parable.

Meigs, Peveril. Dominican Mission Frontier of Lower California. pap. 25.00 (ISBN 0-384-38005-0). Johnson Repr.

Robinson, David. Apostle of Culture: Emerson As Preacher & Lecturer. LC 81-16228. 200p. 1982. 21.00x (ISBN 0-8122-7824-0). U of Pa Pr.

St. Thomas Aquinas. Summa Theologica, 5 vols. 3057p. 1982. 225.00 (ISBN 0-87061-063-5); pap. 150.00 (ISBN 0-87061-069-4). Chr Classics.

Tugwell, Simon, ed. Early Dominicans, Selected Writings. (The Classics of Western Spirituality Ser.). 400p. 1982. 14.95 (ISBN 0-8091-0325-7); pap. 10.95 (ISBN 0-8091-2414-9). Paulist Pr.

DONATION OF CONSTANTINE

Coleman, Christopher B. Constantine the Great & Christianity. LC 70-155636. (Columbia University Studies in the Social Sciences: No. 146). Repr. of 1914 ed. 18.50 (ISBN 0-404-51146-5). AMS Pr.

Constantine I. A Treatise of the Donation of Gyfts & Endowment of Possessyons Gyven & Graunted Unto Sylvester Pope of Rome by Constantyne Emperour of Rome. Marshall, William, tr. LC 79-84096. (English Experience Ser.: No. 916). (Eng.). 152p. 1979. Repr. of 1534 ed. lib. bdg. 24.00 (ISBN 90-221-0916-X). Walter J Johnson.

DONATIONS

see Endowments; Gifts

DONATISTS

Augustinus, Saint Scripta Contra Donatistas, 3 Vols, Pts. 3. (Corpus Scriptorum Ecclesiasticorum Latinorum Ser: Vols. 51, 52, 53). Set. 130.00 (ISBN 0-384-02553-6). Johnson Repr.

Benedict, David. History of the Donatists. 1985. Repr. of 1875 ed. 15.00 (ISBN 0-317-31641-9). Church History.

Frend, W. H. The Donatist Church: A Movement of Protest in Roman North Africa. 384p. 1985. 42.00x (ISBN 0-19-826408-9). Oxford U Pr.

DONNE, JOHN, 1573-1631

Campbell, Oscar J., et al. Studies in Shakespeare, Milton & Donne. McCartney, Eugene S., ed. LC 78-93244. (University of Michigan Publications: Vol. 1). 235p. 1970. Repr. of 1925 ed. 20.00x (ISBN 0-87753-020-3). Phaeton.

Carey, John. John Donne: Life, Mind & Art. 1981. 25.00x (ISBN 0-19-520242-2). Oxford U Pr.

Carrithers, Gale H. Donne at Sermons: A Christian Existential World. LC 74-171183. 1972. 49.50 (ISBN 0-87395-122-0). State U NY Pr.

Cathcart, Dwight. Doubting Conscience: Donne & the Poetry of Moral Argument. LC 74-78985. 1975. 10.00x (ISBN 0-472-08198-5). U of Mich Pr.

Dark, Sidney. Five Deans. facsimile ed. LC 71-93332. (Essay Index Reprint Ser.). 1928. 18.00 (ISBN 0-8369-1285-3). Ayer Co Pubs.

--Five Deans: John Colet, John Donne, Jonathan Swift, Arthur Penrhyn Stanley & William Ralph Inge. LC 70-86011. (Essay & General Literature Index Reprint Ser.). 1969. Repr. of 1928 ed. 22.50x (ISBN 0-8046-0555-6, Pub. by Kennikat). Assoc Faculty Pr.

Donne, John. Devotions upon Emergent Occasions. Bd. with Death's Duel. 1959. pap. 7.95 (ISBN 0-472-06030-9, 30, AA). U of Mich Pr.

--The Sermons of John Donne: In Ten Volumes. Simpson, Evelyn M. & Potter, George R., eds. LC 52-7179. 4365p. 1984. lib. bdg. 450.00x set (ISBN 0-520-05255-2). U of Cal Pr.

Grant, Patrick. The Transformation of Sin: Studies in Donne, Herbert, Vaughan & Traherne. LC 73-93174. 308p. 1974. 20.00x (ISBN 0-87023-158-8). U of Mass Pr.

Grierson, Herbert. Criticism & Creation. LC 73-733. 1949. lib. bdg. 17.50 (ISBN 0-8414-1603-6). Folcroft.

Hardy, Evelyn. Donne, a Spirit in Conflict. LC 72-187484. 1942. lib. bdg. 35.00 (ISBN 0-8414-4993-7). Folcroft.

Husain, I. Dogmatic & Mystical Theology of Donne. LC 70-119088. (Studies in Philosophy, No. 40). 1970. Repr. of 1938 ed. lib. bdg. 39.95x (ISBN 0-8383-1084-2). Haskell.

Husain, Itra. Dogmatic & Mystical Theology of John Donne. LC 75-43972. 1938. lib. bdg. 17.50 (ISBN 0-8414-4747-0). Folcroft.

Husain, Itrat. Dogmatic & Mystical Theology of John Donne. Repr. of 1938 ed. lib. bdg. 22.50x (ISBN 0-8371-4243-1, HUJD). Greenwood.

Jackson, Robert. John Donne's Christian Vocation. 1970. 19.95 (ISBN 0-8101-0289-7). Northwestern U Pr.

Jessopp, Augustus. John Donne: Sometime Dean of St. Paul's AD 1621-1631. LC 71-39284. (English Biography Ser. 31). 238p. 1972. Repr. of 1897 ed. lib. bdg. 49.95x (ISBN 0-8383-1395-7). Haskell.

Martz, Louis L. John Donne in Meditation: The Anniversaries. LC 70-99172. (English Literature Ser., No. 33). 1970. Repr. of 1947 ed. lib. bdg. 39.95x (ISBN 0-8383-0335-8). Haskell.

Matsuura, Kaichi. Study of Donne's Imagery: A Revelation of His Outlook on the World & His Vision of a Christian Monarchy. LC 72-7223. Repr. of 1953 ed. lib. bdg. 25.00 (ISBN 0-8414-0270-1). Folcroft.

Mueller, William R. John Donne: Preacher. 1977. Repr. of 1962 ed. lib. bdg. 19.50x (ISBN 0-374-95988-9, Octagon). Hippocrene Bks.

Reeves, Troy D. An Annotated Index to the Sermons of John Donne: Index to Proper Names, Vol. II. Hogg, James, ed. (Elizabethan & Renaissance Studies). 148p. (Orig.). 1980. pap. 15.00 (ISBN 0-317-40117-3, Pub by Salzburg Studies). Longwood Pub Group.

--An Annotated Index to the Sermons of John Donne: Index to the Scriptures, Vol. I. Hogg, James, ed. (Elizabethan & Renaissance Studies). 229p. (Orig.). 1979. pap. 15.00 (ISBN 0-317-40114-9, Pub by Salzburgh Studies). Longwood Pub Group.

--An Annotated Index to the Sermons of John Donne: Index to Topics, Vol. III. Hogg, James, ed. (Elizabethan & Renaissance Studies). 226p. (Orig.). 1981. pap. 15.00 (ISBN 0-317-40118-1, Pub by Salzburg Studies). Longwood Pub Group.

Rowe, Frederick A. I Launch at Paradise: A Consideration of John Donne, Poet & Preacher. LC 65-84641. 1964. 10.00x (ISBN 0-8401-2055-9). A R Allenson.

--I Launch at Paradise: A Consideration of John Donne Poet & Preacher. 253p. 1983. lib. bdg. 40.00 (ISBN 0-89984-841-9). Century Bookbindery.

Schleiner, Winfried. The Imagery of John Donne's Sermons. LC 70-91655. Repr. of 1970 ed. 66.00 (2027523). Bks Demand UMI.

Sherwood, Terry G. Fulfilling the Circle: A Study of John Donne's Thought. 231p. 1984. 27.50x (ISBN 0-8020-5621-0). U of Toronto Pr.

Sloane, Thomas O. Donne, Milton, & the End of Humanist Rhetoric. LC 83-24315. 1985. 38.50x (ISBN 0-520-05212-9). U of Cal Pr.

Spencer, Theodore, ed. A Garland for John Donne 1631-1931. 11.25 (ISBN 0-8446-1418-1). Peter Smith.

White, Helen C. The Metaphysical Poets: A Study in Religious Experience. LC 83-45866. 1936. 39.50 (ISBN 0-404-20285-3, PR549). AMS Pr.

DONNE, JOHN, 1573-1631–BIBLIOGRAPHY

White, William. John Donne Since 1900: A Bibliography of Periodical Articles. LC 77-25861. 1942. lib. bdg. 17.50 (ISBN 0-8414-9557-2). Folcroft.

DOOMSDAY

see Judgment Day

DORT, SYNOD OF, 1618-1619

Girod, Gordon H. The Deeper Faith: An Exposition of the Canons of Dort. 1978. pap. 1.95 (ISBN 0-8010-3725-5). Baker Bk.

The Judgement of the Synode at Dort Touching Conradus Vortius. (English Experience Ser.: No. 678). 1974. Repr. of 1619 ed. 10.50 (ISBN 90-221-0678-0). Walter J Johnson.

McComish, William A. The Epigones: A Study of the Theology of the Synod of Dort, with Special Reference to Giovanni Diodati. (Princeton Theological Monograph Ser.: No. 13). (Orig.). 1987. pap. price not set (ISBN 0-915138-62-X). Pickwick.

DOSTOEVSKII, FEDOR MIKHAILOVICH, 1821-1881

Dirscherl, Denis. Dostoevsky & the Catholic Church. 179p. 1986. 12.95 (ISBN 0-8294-0502-X). Loyola.

Gibson, Boyce. Religion of Dostoevsky. 214p. 6.95 (ISBN 0-664-20989-0). Brown Bk.

Gide, Andre P. Dostoevsky. LC 78-14443. 1979. Repr. of 1961 ed. lib. bdg. 22.50x (ISBN 0-313-21178-7, GIDO). Greenwood.

Goldstein, David I. Dostoyevsky & the Jews. (University of Texas Press Slavic Ser.: No. 3). 256p. 1981. 20.00x (ISBN 0-292-71528-5). U of Tex Pr.

Hingley, Ronald. Dostoevsky: His Life & Work. 1978. 5.95 (ISBN 0-684-15916-3, ScribT); encore ed. 5.95 (ISBN 0-684-17232-1). Scribner.

Kostovski, Ilya. Goethe & Dostoyevsky: Two Devils, Two Geniuses, a Study of the Demonic in Their Work. 1974. lib. bdg. 69.95 (ISBN 0-87700-215-0). Revisionist Pr.

Leatherbarrow, William J. Feodor Dostoevsky. (World Authors Ser.). 15.95 (ISBN 0-8057-6480-1, Twayne). G K Hall.

Lloyd, J. A. Fyodor Dostoevsky. 1978. Repr. of 1946 ed. lib. bdg. 25.00 (ISBN 0-8495-3228-0). Arden Lib.

--Fyodor Dostoevsky. LC 78-164532. 1971. Repr. of 1947 ed. 24.50x (ISBN 0-8154-0401-8). Cooper Sq.

--Fyodor Dostyevsky. 1973. lib. bdg. 20.00 (ISBN 0-8414-5871-5). Folcroft.

Mochulsky, Konstantin. Dostoevsky: His Life & Work. Minihan, Michael A., tr. 1967. pap. 14.50x (ISBN 0-691-01299-7). Princeton U Pr.

Seduro, Vladimir. Dostoevsky in Russian & World Theatre. 1977. 17.50 (ISBN 0-8158-0347-8). Chris Mass.

DOUBT

see Belief and Doubt

DRAMA, LITURGICAL

see Liturgical Drama

DRAMA, MEDIEVAL

see also Liturgical Drama; Moralities; Mysteries and Miracle-Plays;

also Drama of various countries, e.g. English Drama–history and criticism

Allen, John, ed. Three Medieval Plays: The Coventry Nativity Play, Everyman, Master Pierre Pathelin. 1968. pap. 3.50x (ISBN 0-87830-529-7). Theatre Arts.

Axton, Richard. European Drama of the Early Middle Ages. LC 74-24680. 1975. 19.95x (ISBN 0-8229-3301-2). U of Pittsburgh Pr.

Bevington, David. Medieval Drama. 1975. text ed. 34.95 (ISBN 0-395-13915-5). HM.

Cargill, Oscar. Drama & Liturgy. LC 73-86272. 1969. Repr. of 1930 ed. lib. bdg. 17.00x (ISBN 0-374-91292-0, Octagon). Hippocrene Bks.

Collins, Fletcher, Jr., ed. Medieval Church Music-Dramas: A Repertory of Complete Plays. LC 75-33896. Repr. of 1976 ed. 128.50 (ISBN 0-8357-9809-7, 2013180). Bks Demand UMI.

Lesker, G. A., ed. Three Late Medieval Morality Plays: Mankind, Everyman & Mundis et Infans. (New Mermaids Ser.). 1984. pap. text ed. 6.95x (ISBN 0-393-90054-1). Norton.

Loomis, Roger S. & Wells, Henry W., eds. Representative Medieval & Tudor Plays. LC 77-111109. (Play Anthology Reprint Ser). 1942. 22.50 (ISBN 0-8369-8202-9). Ayer Co Pubs.

Mill, Anna J. Medieval Plays in Scotland. LC 68-56497. 1969. Repr. of 1927 ed. 24.50 (ISBN 0-405-08789-6, Pub. by Blom). Ayer Co Pubs.

Nagler, A. M. The Medieval Religious Stage: Shapes & Phantoms. LC 75-43328. (Illus.). 1976. 22.00x (ISBN 0-300-01986-6). Yale U Pr.

Parker, Elizabeth C. The Descent from the Cross: Its Relation to the Extra-Liturgical Depositio Drama. LC 77-94713. (Outstanding Dissertations in the Fine Arts Ser.). 1978. lib. bdg. 41.00 (ISBN 0-8240-3245-4). Garland Pub.

Sticca, Sandro, ed. The Medieval Drama. LC 78-152517. (Illus.). 154p. 1972. 39.50 (ISBN 0-87395-085-2). State U NY Pr.

Stratman, Carl J. Bibliography of Medieval Drama. LC 78-163141. 1047p. 1972. 100.00 (ISBN 0-8044-3272-4). Ungar.

DRAMA, RELIGIOUS

see Religious Drama

DREYFUS, ALFRED, 1859-1935

Bredin, Jean-Denis. The Affair: The Case of Alfred Dreyfus. Mehlman, Jeffrey, tr. from Fr. Tr. of L'Affaire. (Illus.). 1987. pap. 12.95 (ISBN 0-8076-1175-1). Braziller.

DRINKING AND YOUTH

see Alcohol and Youth

DRUG ABUSE

see also Alcoholism

Aranza, Jacob. More Rock, Country & Backward Masking. 1985. pap. 5.95 (ISBN 0-910311-30-7). Huntington Hse Inc.

Cassel, Russell N. Drug Abuse Education. 1970. 8.95 (ISBN 0-8158-0245-5). Chris Mass.

Conscious Contact. 24p. (Orig.). 1985. pap. 0.95 (ISBN 0-89486-323-1). Hazelden.

Hill, Harold, et al. The Impossible Takes a Little Longer. 224p. 1985. pap. 6.95 (ISBN 0-8007-5192-2). Revell.

Jackson, Sue B. Hooked on Prescription Drugs. Wallace, Mary H., ed. 112p. (Orig.). 1981. pap. 2.95 (ISBN 0-912315-33-4). Word Aflame.

Justus, Adalu & Marlin, Ira J. My Son, My Mother: Indestructible Chain of Love. LC 86-3884. 200p. (Orig.). 1986. pap. 7.95 (ISBN 0-937109-00-2). Silo Pubs.

Mann, George A. Recovery of Reality: Overcoming Chemical Dependency. LC 78-19496. (Illus.). 1979. 14.45 (ISBN 0-06-250560-2, HarpR). Har-Row.

Manning, William O. & Vinton, Jean, eds. Harmfully Involved: Updated for the Eighties. 168p. (Orig.). 1978. pap. 10.95 (ISBN 0-89486-056-9). Hazelden.

Mehl, Duane. No More for the Road: One Man's Journey from Chemical Dependency to Freedom. LC 75-22721. 144p. 1976. pap. 7.95 (ISBN 0-8066-1515-X, 10-4665). Augsburg.

Neff, Pauline. Tough Love: How Parents Can Deal with Drug Abuse. 160p. 1984. pap. 7.50 (ISBN 0-687-42407-0). Abingdon.

Rehrer, Ronald. Now What Do I Do? 1982. pap. 4.95 (ISBN 0-570-03854-5, 12-2809). Concordia.

Sztorc, Mary V. Student's Values in Drugs & Drug Abuse. 1976. pap. 2.00 (ISBN 0-87507-000-0). Cath Lib Assn.

DRUG ADDICTION

see Drug Abuse

DRUG HABIT

see Drug Abuse

DRUGS AND YOUTH

CSAA. You, Your Child & Drugs. 1971. pap. 1.75 (ISBN 0-87183-238-0). Jewish Bd Family.

Griffin, LaDean. Escape the Drug Scene. pap. 3.95 (ISBN 0-89036-141-X). Hawkes Pub Inc.

Perez, Guillermo H. Lo Que los Jovenes Deben Saber Acerca de las Drogas. 80p. 1983. pap. 1.10 (ISBN 0-311-46070-4). Casa Bautista.

DRUIDS AND DRUIDISM

see also Folk-Lore of Trees; Mythology, Celtic

Bonwick, James. Irish Druids & Old Irish Religions. LC 75-36830. (Occult Ser.). 1976. Repr. of 1894 ed. 25.50x (ISBN 0-405-07942-7). Ayer Co Pubs.

Capt, E. Raymond. Stonehenge & Druidism. rev. ed. LC 79-54773. (Illus.). 96p. 1979. pap. 3.00 (ISBN 0-934666-04-0). Artisan Sales.

Davies, Edward. Celtic Researches, on the Origin, Traditions & Language, of the Ancient Britons. Feldman, Burton & Richardson, Robert D., eds. LC 78-60902. (Myth & Romanticism Ser.: Vol. 8). (Illus.). 1979. lib. bdg. 80.00 (ISBN 0-8240-3557-7). Garland Pub.

Higgins, Godfrey. Celtic Druids. 40.00 (ISBN 0-89314-412-6). Philos Res.

Kendrick, Thomas D. Druids. (Illus.). 227p. 1966. Repr. of 1927 ed. 32.50x (ISBN 0-7146-1485-8, BHA-01485, F Cass Co). Biblio Dist.

Owen, A. L. The Famous Druids: A Survey of Three Centuries of English Literature in the Druids. LC 78-13614. (Illus.). 1979. Repr. of 1962 ed. lib. bdg. 22.50x (ISBN 0-313-20629-5, OWFD). Greenwood.

Rowlands, Henry. Mona Antiqua Restaurata. Feldman, Burton & Richardson, Robert D., eds. LC 78-60894. (Myth & Romanticism Ser.: Vol. 21). 399p. 1979. lib. bdg. 80.00 (ISBN 0-8240-3570-4). Garland Pub.

Rutherford, Ward. The Druids: Magicians of the West. 176p. 1984. pap. 7.95 (ISBN 0-85030-346-X). Newcastle Pub.

--The Druids: Magicians of the West. LC 86-18803. 176p. 1986. lib. bdg. 19.95x (ISBN 0-8095-7007-6). Borgo Pr.

Sharkey, John. Celtic Mysteries: Art & Imagination Ser. (Illus.). 1987. pap. text ed. 10.95 (ISBN 0-500-81009-5). Thames Hudson.

Steiner, Rudolf. Man in the Past, the Present, & the Future: The Sun-Initiation of the Druid Priest & His Moon-Science. Goddard, E., tr. from Ger. 82p. 1982. pap. 5.00 (ISBN 0-85440-403-1, Pub by Steinerbooks). Anthroposophic.

Toland, John. A Collection of Several Pieces, 2 vols. Wellek, Rene, ed. LC 75-11258. (British Philosophers & Theologians of the 17th & 18th Centuries: Vol. 57). 1976. Repr. of 1726 ed. Set. lib. bdg. 101.00 (ISBN 0-8240-1808-7). Garland Pub.

DRUNKENNESS

see Alcoholics; Alcoholism; Temperance

DRUSES

Alamuddin, Nura S. & Starr, Paul D. Crucial Bonds: Marriage Among the Lebanese Druze. LC 78-10465. 1980. 25.00x (ISBN 0-88206-024-4). Caravan Bks.

Churchill, Charles H. The Druzes & the Maronites Under the Turkish Rule from 1840 to 1860. LC 73-6273. (The Middle East Ser.). Repr. of 1862 ed. 20.00 (ISBN 0-405-05329-0). Ayer Co Pubs.

Hitti, Philip K. Origins of the Druze People & Religion, with Extracts from Their Sacred Writings. LC 30-27674. (Columbia University. Oriental Studies: No. 28). Repr. of 1928 ed. 19.00 (ISBN 0-404-50518-X). AMS Pr.

DRYDEN, JOHN, 1631-1700

Atkins, G. Douglas. The Faith of John Dryden: Change & Continuity. LC 80-12890. 208p. 1980. 19.00x (ISBN 0-8131-1401-2). U Pr of Ky.

Ferry, Anne D. Milton & the Miltonic Dryden. LC 68-25608. 1968. 16.50x (ISBN 0-674-57576-8). Harvard U Pr.

Garnett, R. The Age of Dryden. 1977. Repr. of 1909 ed. lib. bdg. 17.50 (ISBN 0-8495-1902-0). Arden Lib.

Garnett, Richard. The Age of Dryden. facsimile ed. LC 70-164601. (Select Bibliographies Reprint Ser). Repr. of 1895 ed. 20.00 (ISBN 0-8369-5885-3). Ayer Co Pubs.

--The Age of Dryden. 1973. Repr. of 1895 ed. 17.50 (ISBN 0-8274-1280-0). R West.

Lowell, James R. Among My Books. LC 75-126666. 1970. 11.50 (ISBN 0-404-04039-X). AMS Pr.

McHenry, Robert, ed. Contexts: Absalom & Achitophel. LC 84-24160. (Contexts Ser.: No. 3). (Illus.). xiv, 296p. 1986. lib. bdg. 29.50 (ISBN 0-208-01845-X, Archon Bks). Shoe String.

Myers, Robert M. Handel, Dryden & Milton. 1956. lib. bdg. 32.50 (ISBN 0-8414-6129-5). Folcroft.

Scott, Sir Walter. The Life of John Dryden. Kreissman, Bernard, ed. LC 63-8121. xx, 471p. 1963. pap. 5.95x (ISBN 0-8032-5177-7, BB 157, Bison). U of Nebr Pr.

DUALISM

see also Idealism; Mind and Body; Monism; Soul

Bakan, David. Duality of Human Existence: Isolation & Communion in Western Man. (Illus.). 1971. pap. 4.95x (ISBN 0-8070-2969-6, BP395). Beacon Pr.

Beierle, Herbert L. Dualism. 1979. 10.00 (ISBN 0-940480-06-9). U of Healing.

Lovejoy, Arthur O. Revolt Against Dualism. 2nd ed. (Paul Carus Lecture Ser.). 420p. 1960. 21.95 (ISBN 0-87548-106-X); pap. 8.95 (ISBN 0-87548-107-8). Open Court.

Mitchell, Roy. The Exile of the Soul. Davenport, John L., ed. LC 83-62528. 338p. 1984. 18.95 (ISBN 0-87975-232-7); pap. 9.95 (ISBN 0-87975-233-5). Prometheus Bks.

Runciman, Steven. The Medieval Manichee: A Study of the Christian Dualist Heresy. LC 82-4123. 224p. 1982. 39.50 (ISBN 0-521-06166-0); pap. 13.95 (ISBN 0-521-28926-2). Cambridge U Pr.

Yolton, John W. Metaphysical Analysis. LC 68-88650. pap. 58.30 (ISBN 0-317-08857-2, 2014464). Bks Demand UMI.

DULIA

see Saints–Cultus

DUNS, JOANNES, SCOTUS, 1265?-1308?

Bettoni, Efrem. Duns Scotus: The Basic Principles of His Philosophy. Bonansea, Berbardine, ed. LC 78-14031. 1979. Repr. of 1961 ed. lib. bdg. 35.00x (ISBN 0-313-21142-6, BEDS). Greenwood.

Currey, Cecil B. Reason & Revelation: John Duns Scotus on Natural Theology. LC 77-9614. (Synthesis Ser.). 1977. pap. 0.75 (ISBN 0-8199-0717-0). Franciscan Herald.

John Duns Scotus: Reason & Revelation. (Franciscan Educational Conferences Ser). 1976. pap. 0.75 (ISBN 0-685-77549-6). Franciscan Herald.

Ryan, John K. John Duns Scotus, Twelve Sixty Five-Nineteen Sixty Five. Bonansea, Bernardine M., ed. LC 61-66336. (Studies in Philosophy & the History of Philosophy Ser.: Vol. 3). pap. 98.00 (ISBN 0-317-08040-7, 2022584). Bks Demand UMI.

DUNSTAN, SAINT, ABP. OF CANTERBURY, d. 988

Stubbs, William. Historical Introduction to the Rolls Series. LC 77-158211. Repr. of 1902 ed. 11.50 (ISBN 0-404-06302-0). AMS Pr.

DURKHEIM, EMILE, 1858-1917

Pickering, W. S. Durkheim's Sociology of Religion: Themes & Theories. 576p. 1984. 45.00x (ISBN 0-7100-9298-9). Methuen Inc.

Thompson, Kenneth. Emile Durkheim. LC 81-20294. (Key Sociologists Ser.). 120p. 1982. pap. 4.95x (ISBN 0-85312-419-1, NO. 3674, Pub. by Tavistock England). Methuen Inc.

DYING PATIENT

see Terminal Care

E

EARLY CHRISTIAN LITERATURE

see Christian Literature, Early

EARLY CHRISTIAN LITURGIES

see Liturgies, Early Christian

EAST AND WEST

see also Philosophy, Comparative

Coomaraswamy, Ananda K. Am I My Brother's Keeper? facs. ed. LC 67-23196. (Essay Index Reprint Ser.). 1947. 12.00 (ISBN 0-8369-0335-8). Ayer Co Pubs.

Copleston, Frederick. Religion & the One: Philosophies East & West. LC 81-5372. (Gifford Lectures, 1980 Ser.). 320p. 1981. 24.50x (ISBN 0-8245-0092-X). Crossroad NY.

Hitti, Philip K. Islam & the West: A Historical Cultural Survey. LC 78-10793. (Anvil Ser.). 192p. 1979. pap. 7.50 (ISBN 0-88275-787-3). Krieger.

Watts, Alan W. The Meaning of Happiness: The Quest for Freedom of the Spirit in Modern Psychology & the Wisdom of the East. 1979. pap. 6.95 (ISBN 0-06-090676-6, CN 676, PL). Har-Row.

EAST INDIAN PHILOSOPHY

see Philosophy, Indic

EASTER

see also Jesus Christ–Resurrection; Paschal Mystery

Aivanhov, Omraam M. Christmas & Easter in the Initiatic Tradition. (Izvor Collection: Vol. 209). (Illus.). 139p. (Orig.). pap. 4.95 (ISBN 2-85566-226-5, Pub. by Prosveta France). Prosveta USA.

Alessi, Vincie. Programs for Lent & Easter, Vol. 2. 64p. 1983. pap. 5.95 (ISBN 0-8170-1016-5). Judson.

Alessi, Vincie, ed. Programs for Lent & Easter. 1979. pap. 3.95 (ISBN 0-8170-0861-6). Judson.

Bainton, Roland. The Martin Luther Easter Book. LC 82-15996. 88p. 1983. pap. 3.95 (ISBN 0-8006-1685-5). Fortress.

Barth, Edna. Lilies, Rabbits, & Painted Eggs: The Story of the Easter Symbols. LC 74-79033. (Illus.). 1970. 8.95 (ISBN 0-395-28844-4, Clarion). HM.

Becker, Ralph. Lent, Good Friday & Easter. pap. 0.50 (ISBN 0-685-41825-1). Reiner.

Berger, Gilda. Easter & Other Spring Holidays. (First Bks.). (Illus.). 72p. 1983. PLB 9.90 (ISBN 0-531-04547-1). Watts.

The Book of Easter. LC 76-159894. Repr. of 1911 ed. 51.00x (ISBN 0-8103-3401-1). Gale.

Burgess, Beverly C. Is Easter Just for Bunnies? (Illus.). 30p. (Orig.). 1985. pap. 1.98 (ISBN 0-89274-310-7). Harrison Hse.

Corwin, Judith H. Easter Fun. LC 84-9122. (Messner Holiday Library). (Illus.). 64p. 1984. PLB 9.29 (ISBN 0-671-50798-2); pap. 5.95 (ISBN 0-671-53108-5). Messner.

Davis, Nancy M., et al. April & Easter. (Davis Teaching Units Ser.: Vol. 1, No. 8). (Illus.). 45p. (Orig.). 1986. pap. 5.95 (ISBN 0-937103-10-1). DaNa Pubns.

Dietz, Sarah S. Easter Activity Book. (Stick-Out-Your Neck Ser.). (Illus.). 32p. 1984. pap. 1.98 (ISBN 0-88724-067-4, CD-8051). Carson-Dellos.

Easter. (Illus.). 64p. 1984. 19.95 (ISBN 0-86683-826-0, 8465, HarpR); pap. 9.95 (ISBN 0-86683-811-2, 8343). Har-Row.

Easter: Voices from the Heart. Date not set. price not set (ISBN 0-934383-15-4). Pride Prods.

Ehlen-Miller, Margaret, et al. A Time of Hope: Family Celebrations & Activities for Lent & Easter. (Illus., Orig.). 1979. pap. 4.95 (ISBN 0-8192-1247-4). Morehouse.

Ellebracht, Mary P. Easter Passage: The RCIA Experience. 204p. 1983. pap. 11.95 (ISBN 0-86683-693-4, HarpR). Har-Row.

Fisher, Aileen. Easter. LC 67-23666. (Holiday Ser.). (Illus.). 1968. PLB 12.89 (ISBN 0-690-25236-6, Crowell Jr Bks). HarpJ.

Fittro, Pat, compiled by. Easter Programs for the Church, No. 11. (Illus.). 64p. 1987. pap. 3.50 (ISBN 0-87403-283-0, 8723). Standard Pub.

--Standard Easter Program Book, No. 37. 48p. 1986. pap. 1.95 (ISBN 0-87403-083-8, 8707). Standard Pub.

Geisler, Ruth. The Christian Family Prepares for Easter. 96p. (Orig.). 1985. pap. 6.95 (ISBN 0-570-03977-0, 12-2893). Concordia.

Greene, Carol. Kiri & the First Easter. (Arch Bks: Set 9). (Illus.). 32p. 1972. pap. 0.99 (ISBN 0-570-06064-8, 59-1182). Concordia.

Griggs, Patricia & Griggs, Donald. Teaching & Celebrating Lent-Easter. (Griggs Educational Resources Ser.). 1980. pap. 6.95 (ISBN 0-687-41081-9). Abingdon.

Hoard, Laurie, compiled by. Easter Programs for the Church, No. 8. 64p. (Orig.). 1984. pap. 2.95 (ISBN 0-87239-767-X, 8720). Standard Pub.

--Easter Programs for the Church, No. 9. 64p. 1985. pap. 2.95 (ISBN 0-87239-845-5, 8721). Standard Pub.

--Easter Programs for the Church, No. 10. 64p. 1986. pap. 2.95 (ISBN 0-87403-082-X, 8722). Standard Pub.

Hoard, Laurie, ed. Standard Easter Program Book, No. 35. 48p. (Orig.). 1984. pap. 1.95 (ISBN 0-87239-768-8, 8705). Standard Pub.

Hoard, Laurie, compiled by. Standard Easter Program Book, No. 36. 48p. 1985. pap. 1.95 (ISBN 0-87239-870-6, 8706). Standard Pub.

Hunter, Leona W. The Easter Bunny Book: A Celebration of the Easter Season. LC 85-23216. (Illus.). 96p. (Orig.). 1986. pap. 8.95 (ISBN 0-915590-84-0). Main Street.

Ideal Editors. Ideals Easter. 1985. pap. 3.50 (ISBN 0-8249-1041-9). Ideals.

Krentz, Edgar. Easter. LC 84-18756. (Proclamation 3, Ser. B). 64p. 1985. pap. 3.75 (ISBN 0-8006-4105-1, 1-4105). Fortress.

Krentz, Edgar & Vogel, Arthur A. Easter. Achtemeier, Elizabeth, et al, eds. LC 79-7377. (Proclamation 2: Aids for Interpreting the Lessons of the Church Year, Ser. C). 64p. 1980. pap. 3.75 (ISBN 0-8006-4080-2, 1-4080). Fortress.

Lawrence, Jane. Easter Joy. 1983. 0.50 (ISBN 0-89536-594-4, 0501). CSS of Ohio.

Linam, Gail. Celebrate Easter. LC 84-12692. 1985. pap. 2.95 (ISBN 0-8054-9306-9). Broadman.

MacRae, George W. & Price, Charles P. Easter. LC 79-7377. 64p. 1982. pap. 3.75 (ISBN 0-8006-4087-X, 1-4087). Fortress.

O'Dea, Barbara. Of Fast & Festival: Celebrating Lent & Easter. 1982. pap. 3.95 (ISBN 0-8091-2426-2). Paulist Pr.

Patterson, Lillie. Easter. LC 66-10150. (Holiday Bks.). (Illus.). 1966. PLB 7.56 (ISBN 0-8116-6559-3). Garrard.

Perry, Charles A. The Resurrection Promise: An Interpretation of the Easter Narratives. 152p. (Orig.). 1987. pap. 8.95 (ISBN 0-8028-0249-4). Eerdmans.

Quillin, Roger T. Meeting Christ in Handel's Messiah: Lent & Easter Messages Based on Handel's Texts & Music. 96p. 1984. pap. 4.95 (ISBN 0-8066-2118-4, 10-4318). Augsburg.

Ratzinger, Joseph. Journey Towards Easter. 160p. 1987. 12.95 (ISBN 0-8245-0803-3). Crossroad NY.

Reeder, Rachel, ed. Liturgy: Easter's Fifty Days. (Journal of The Liturgical Conference: Vol. 3, No. 1). (Illus.). 72p. 1982. pap. text ed. 7.95 (ISBN 0-918208-29-7). Liturgical Conf.

Reilly, Barbara. Children's Bulletin Sundays of Easter. 1979. pap. 7.55 (ISBN 0-88479-008-8). Arena Lettres.

Richards, Hubert J. The First Easter: What Really Happened? (What Really Happened? Ser.). 144p. 1986. pap. 5.95 (ISBN 0-89622-282-9). Twenty-Third.

Riley, Kelly. Celebrate Easter. (Celebrate Ser.). (Illus.). 144p. 1987. pap. 9.95 (ISBN 0-86653-385-0). Good Apple.

Saffen, Wayne. The Second Season: Lent, Easter, Ascension. LC 72-87064. pap. 24.00 (2026827). Bks Demand UMI.

Seagren, Daniel R. Easter Is a Time. (Contempo Ser.). pap. 0.95 (ISBN 0-8010-8140-8). Baker Bk.

Shoemaker, Mary E. Easter: A Promise Kept. (Orig.). 1981. pap. 1.75 (ISBN 0-937172-19-7). JLJ Pubs.

Stochl, Susan, ed. Easter People, Grade 5: Gather. (Easter People Ser.). (Illus.). 1979. pap. text ed. 5.65 (ISBN 0-03-050761-8, HarpR); tchr's manual 7.60 (ISBN 0-03-050771-5); wkbk. 3.90 (ISBN 0-03-050776-6); parent bk. 2.25 (ISBN 0-03-050766-9). Har-Row.

Stochl, Susan, et al, eds. Easter People, Grade 3: Journey. (Easter People Ser). (Illus.). 1977. pap. text ed. 3.34 (ISBN 0-03-020396-1, 169, HarpR); tchr's. ed. 7.60 (ISBN 0-03-020406-2, 171); parent wkbk. 2.25 (ISBN 0-03-020401-1, 172); activity pack 3.90 (ISBN 0-03-020411-9, 170). Har-Row.

Tickle, Phyllis A. Final Sanity: Essays on Lent & Easter. 128p. (Orig.). 1987. pap. 6.95 (ISBN 0-8358-0545-X). Upper Room.
Von Balthasar, Hans U. Life out of Death: Meditations on the Easter Mystery. LC 84-48704. 64p. 1985. pap. 3.50 (ISBN 0-8006-1821-1, 1-1821). Fortress.
Voth, Norma J. Festive Breads of Easter. LC 79-23702. (Illus.). 80p. 1980. pap. 3.50 (ISBN 0-8361-1917-7). Herald Pr.
Warren, Ramona, et al. Easter Handbook. LC 85-24322. (Holiday Handbooks Ser.). (Illus.). 96p. 1986. lib. bdg. 12.95 (ISBN 0-89565-306-0). Childs World.
Wharton, James. Easter. LC 84-18756. (Proclamation 3 A). 64p. 1987. pap. 3.75 (ISBN 0-8006-4121-3, 1-4121). Fortress.
Wiersum, Beverly. The Story of Easter for Children. Kuse, James A., ed. (Illus.). 1979. pap. 2.95 (ISBN 0-89542-452-5). Ideals.
Young, Karl. The Dramatic Associations of the Easter Sepulchre. 1977. lib. bdg. 59.95 (ISBN 0-8490-1732-7). Gordon Pr.

EASTER–DRAMA
see also Drama, Medieval; Mysteries and Miracle-Plays
Joyce, Jon L. Easter Plays. (Orig.). 1983. pap. 2.95 (ISBN 0-937172-48-0). JLJ Pubs.
Miller, Sarah W. Devotional Dramas for Easter. (Orig.). 1967. pap. 1.95 (ISBN 0-8054-9715-3). Broadman.
--I Saw Him. (Orig.). 1964. pap. 1.95 (ISBN 0-8054-9708-0). Broadman.

EASTER–PRAYER-BOOKS AND DEVOTIONS
Bastin, Marcel, et al. God Day by Day, Vol. 1: Lent & the Easter Season. 320p. (Orig.). 1984. pap. 10.95 (ISBN 0-8091-2642-7). Paulist Pr.
Berger & Hollerweger, eds. Celebrating the Easter Vigil. O'Connell, Matthew J., tr. (Ger.). 160p. 1983. pap. 9.95 (ISBN 0-916134-56-3). Pueblo Pub Co.
Hobbie, F. Wellford. Easter. LC 84-18756. (Proclamation Three C Ser.). 64p. 1986. pap. 3.75 (ISBN 0-8006-4129-9, 1-4129). Fortress.
Hohenstein, Herbert E. Upper Room to Garden Tomb: Messages for Lent & Easter on the Passion Narrative in Mark. LC 84-21735. 80p. (Orig.). 1984. pap. 4.95 (ISBN 0-8066-2117-6, 10-6840). Augsburg.
Lawrence, Emeric. Risen & with You Always: Daily Meditations for the Easter Season Masses. 140p. 1986. pap. 5.95 (ISBN 0-8146-1448-5). Liturgical Pr.
O'Neal, Debbie T. An Easter People: Family Devotional Activities for Lent & Easter. 32p. (Orig.). 1986. pap. 3.95 (ISBN 0-8066-2255-5, 10-1990). Augsburg.
Sheen, Fulton J. Cross-Ways: A Book of Inspiration. LC 83-45272. (Illus.). 80p. 1984. pap. 7.95 (ISBN 0-385-19205-3, Im). Doubleday.

EASTER–SERMONS
Beringer, Robert. The Easter People. 1984. 4.75 (ISBN 0-89536-682-7, 4858). CSS of Ohio.
Budd, Leonard H. & Talbott, Roger G. Resurrection Promises. Sherer, Michael L., ed. (Orig.). 1987. pap. 6.25 (ISBN 0-89536-850-1, 7809). CSS of Ohio.
Erickson, Craig D. Under the Shadow of Your Wings. Sherer, Michael L., ed. (Orig.). 1987. pap. 6.75 (ISBN 0-89536-844-7, 7803). CSS of Ohio.
Gray, G. Franklin & Woods, Charles A. Welcome, Blessed Morning! Sherer, Michael L., ed. (Orig.). 1987. pap. 3.50 (ISBN 0-89536-849-8, 7808). CSS of Ohio.
Hegele, Paul. When Messiah Comes. Sherer, Michael L., ed. (Orig.). 1986. pap. 6.25 (ISBN 0-89536-823-4, 6832). CSS of Ohio.
Jensen, Richard. The Crucified Ruler. (Orig.). 1987. pap. price not set (ISBN 0-89536-870-6, 7856). CSS of Ohio.
Kalas, J. Ellsworth. A Pilgrimage. Sherer, Michael L., ed. (Orig.). 1987. pap. 3.95 (ISBN 0-89536-845-5, 7804). CSS of Ohio.
McCabe, Kendall K. The Path of the Phoenix. Sherer, Michael L., ed. (Orig.). 1986. pap. 7.25 (ISBN 0-89536-818-8, 6827). CSS of Ohio.
Puffenberger, Allen. Words for the Weary. (Orig.). 1987. pap. price not set (ISBN 0-89536-875-7, 7861). CSS of Ohio.
Shannon, Robert & Shannon, Michael. Celebrating the Resurrection. (Illus.). 112p. (Orig.). 1984. pap. 5.95 (ISBN 0-87239-754-8, 3021). Standard Pub.
Spira, Andreas & Klock, Christoph. The Easter Sermons of Gregory of Nyssa: A Translation & Commentary. LC 81-84108. (Patristic Monograph Ser.: No. 9). 384p. 1981. pap. 11.00 (ISBN 0-915646-08-0). Phila Patristic.
Steimle, Edmund A. God the Stranger: Reflections About Resurrection. LC 78-14674. 80p. 1979. pap. 4.95 (ISBN 0-8006-1354-6, 1-1354). Fortress.
Steinke, Peter L. Preaching the Theology of the Cross: Sermons & Worship Ideas for Lent & Easter. LC 82-72638. 128p. (Orig.). 1983. pap. 6.95 (ISBN 0-8066-1944-9, 10-5144). Augsburg.
Vawter, Bruce & Carl, William J., III. Easter. LC 79-7377. (Proclamation 2: Aids for Interpreting the Lessons of the Church Year, Ser. A). 64p. (Orig.). 1981. pap. 3.75 (ISBN 0-8006-4095-0, 1-4095). Fortress.

EASTER–SONGS AND MUSIC
see Easter Music

EASTER–STORIES
see Easter Stories

EASTER CAROLS
see Carols

EASTER MUSIC
see also Carols
Reed, Will L., ed. Treasury of Easter Music & Music for Passiontide. 1963. 12.95 (ISBN 0-87523-142-X). Emerson.

EASTER STORIES
Charette, Beverly. Deluxe Story of Easter for Children. (Illus.). 48p. 1985. 5.95 (ISBN 0-8249-8076-X). Ideals.
Harper, Wilhelmina, ed. Easter Chimes: Stories for Easter & the Spring. (Illus.). 1967. 8.95 (ISBN 0-525-29037-0). Dutton.
Himmel, Roger J. & Manoni, Mary H. The Big Easter Egg Hunt. LC 72-739482. (The Adventures of the Lollipop Dragon Ser.). (Illus.). 1978. pap. text ed. 25.95 (ISBN 0-89290-039-3). Soc for Visual.
Molan, Chris, illus. The First Easter: Retold by Catherine Storr. (People of the Bible Ser.). (Illus.). 32p. 1984. 10.65 (ISBN 0-8172-1987-0, Raintree Childrens Books Belitha Press Ltd. - London). Raintree Pubs.

EASTERN CHURCHES
see also Orthodox Eastern Church
Arseniev, Nicholas. Mysticism & the Eastern Church. 173p. 1979. pap. 7.95 (ISBN 0-913836-55-9). St Vladimirs.
Arseniew, Nicholas. Mysticism & the Eastern Church. 1977. lib. bdg. 59.95. Gordon Pr.
Atiya, Aziz S. History of Eastern Christianity. LC 80-232. 1980. Repr. lib. bdg. 52.00 (ISBN 0-527-03703-6). Kraus Repr.
Brehier, Louis. L' Eglise et l'Orient au moyen age: Les croisades. 2nd ed. LC 76-29834. (Fr.). Repr. of 1907 ed. 39.50 (ISBN 0-404-15413-1). AMS Pr.
Clarke, Boden & Burgess, Mary. Eastern Churches Review: An Index to Volumes One Through Ten, 1966-1978. LC 80-2550. (Borgo Reference Library: Vol. 6). 96p. 1987. lib. bdg. 19.95x (ISBN 0-89370-812-7); pap. text ed. 9.95x (ISBN 0-89370-912-3). Borgo Pr.
Danielou, Jean, ed. From Glory to Glory: Texts from Gregory of Nyssa's Mystical Writings. LC 79-38. 304p. 1979. pap. 9.95 (ISBN 0-913836-54-0). St Vladimirs.
Emhardt, William C. Eastern Church in the Western World. LC 74-131039. Repr. of 1928 ed. 15.75 (ISBN 0-404-02329-0). AMS Pr.
Fortescue, Adrian. Lesser Eastern Churches. LC 79-168124. Repr. of 1913 ed. 31.50 (ISBN 0-404-02517-X). AMS Pr.
Kucharek, Casimir. Our Faith. Vinck, Jose D., ed. LC 82-73784. 350p. 1983. 17.75 (ISBN 0-911726-43-8). Alleluia Pr.
Lossky, Vladimir. The Mystical Theology of the Eastern Church. LC 76-25448. Orig. Title: Essai sur la theologie mystique de L'eglise d'orient. 252p. 1976. pap. 8.95 (ISBN 0-913836-31-1). St Vladimirs.
Meyendorff, John. Christ in Eastern Christian Thought. LC 75-31977. Orig. Title: Le Christ Dans la Theologie Byzantine. 248p. 1975. pap. 10.95 (ISBN 0-913836-27-3). St Vladimirs.
Velimirovic, Milos, ed. Studies in Eastern Chant, Vol. IV. 248p. 1979. pap. text ed. 10.95 (ISBN 0-913836-57-5). St Vladimirs.
Ware, Kallistos T. Orthodox Way. 196p. 1979. pap. 4.95 (ISBN 0-913836-58-3). St Vladimirs.

EASTERN CHURCHES–LITURGY AND RITUAL
Gardner, Johann V. Bogosluzhebnoje Penije Russkoj Pravoslavnoj Tserkvi: Istorija, Vol. 2. LC 77-77086. Tr. of Liturgical Chant of the Russian Orthodox Church; History. (Illus.). 1981. text ed. 30.00 (ISBN 0-88465-010-3); pap. text ed. 25.00 (ISBN 0-317-30384-8). Holy Trinity.
St. Germanus of Constantinople. On the Divine Liturgy. Meyendorff, Paul, tr. from Gr. LC 84-27615. 107p. 1984. pap. text ed. 4.95 (ISBN 0-88141-038-1). St Vladimirs.

EASTERN ORTHODOX CHURCH
see Orthodox Eastern Church

EASTERN SCHISM
see Schism–Eastern and Western Church

EBNER VON ESCHENBACH, MARIE, FREIFRAU, 1830-1916
Doyle, Sr. Rosa. Catholic Atmosphere in Marie Von Ebner Eschenbach: Its Use As a Literary Device. LC 70-140040. (Catholic University Studies in German Ser.: No. 6). Repr. of 1936 ed. 18.00 (ISBN 0-404-50226-1). AMS Pr.

ECCLESIASTICAL ANTIQUITIES
see Christian Antiquities

ECCLESIASTICAL ARCHITECTURE
see Church Architecture

ECCLESIASTICAL ART
see Christian Art and Symbolism

ECCLESIASTICAL BIOGRAPHY
see Christian Biography

ECCLESIASTICAL CORPORATIONS
see Corporations, Religious

ECCLESIASTICAL COSTUME
see Church Vestments

ECCLESIASTICAL COURTS
see also Church Discipline; Privilegium Fori
Houlbrooke, Ralph. Church Courts & the People During the English Reformation Fifteen Twenty to Fifteen Seventy. (Oxford Historical Monographs). 1979. 36.00x (ISBN 0-19-821876-1). Oxford U Pr.
Phillimore, Robert. The Principal Ecclesiastical Judgments Delivered in the Court of Arches 1867 to 1875. xiii, 420p. 1981. Repr. of 1876 ed. lib. bdg. 35.00x (ISBN 0-8377-2504-6). Rothman.
Williams, Paul L., ed. Issues in the Wake of Vatican II: Proceedings of the Eighth Convention of the Fellowship of Catholic Scholars. 128p. (Orig.). 1985. pap. 6.95 (ISBN 0-937374-02-4). NE Bks.

ECCLESIASTICAL DECORATION AND ORNAMENT
see Church Decoration and Ornament

ECCLESIASTICAL DISCIPLINE
see Church Discipline

ECCLESIASTICAL DIVISIONS
see Ecclesiastical Geography

ECCLESIASTICAL FASTS AND FEASTS
see Fasts and Feasts

ECCLESIASTICAL FURNITURE
see Church Furniture

ECCLESIASTICAL GEOGRAPHY
see also Bible–Geography; Church Statistics; Dioceses
Benoist De Matougues, L. Dictionnaire de Geographie Sacree et Ecclesiastique, 3 vols. Migne, J. P., ed. (Encyclopedie Theologique Ser.: Vols. 28-30). (Fr.). 1886p. Repr. of 1854 ed. lib. bdg. 240.50x (ISBN 0-89241-241-0). Caratzas.
Littell, Franklin H. Macmillan Atlas History of Christianity. LC 75-22113. (Illus.). 176p. 1976. 24.95 (ISBN 0-02-573140-8, 57314). Macmillan.

ECCLESIASTICAL HISTORY
see Church History

ECCLESIASTICAL INSTITUTIONS
see Religious and Ecclesiastical Institutions

ECCLESIASTICAL LAW
see also Canon Law; Church Property; Corporations, Religious; Ecclesiastical Courts; Sunday Legislation; Tithes
also subdivision Government under denominations, e.g. Church of England–Government
Andre. Dictionnaire Alphabetique, Theorique et Pratique de Droit Civil Ecclesiastique, 2 vols. Migne, J. P., ed. (Troisieme et Derniere Encyclopedie Theologique Ser.: Vols. 64-65). (Fr.). 1332p. Repr. of 1873 ed. lib. bdg. 170.00x (ISBN 0-89241-328-X). Caratzas.
Bentley, James. Ritualism & Politics in Victorian Britain. (Oxford Theological Monographs). (Illus.). 1978. 37.00x (ISBN 0-19-826714-2). Oxford U Pr.
Blakely, W. A., ed. American State Papers Bearing on Sunday Legislation. LC 79-122165. (Civil Liberties in American History Ser.). 1970. Repr. of 1911 ed. lib. bdg. 95.00 (ISBN 0-306-71973-8). Da Capo.
Box, Hubert S. The Principles of Canon Law. LC 86-3163. 1986. Repr. of 1949 ed. 32.75x (ISBN 0-313-25204-1, BPRC/). Greenwood.
Carleton, George. Jurisdiction Regall, Episcopall, Papall. LC 68-54625. (English Experience Ser.: No. 34). 302p. 1969. Repr. of 1610 ed. 30.00 (ISBN 90-221-0034-0). Walter J Johnson.
Church of England Staff. A Booke of Certaine Canons, Concernynge Some Parte of the Discipline of the Churche of England. LC 70-26475. (English Experience Ser.: No. 312). 1971. Repr. of 1571 ed. 7.00 (ISBN 9-0221-0312-9). Walter J Johnson.
Cyprian. De Lapsis & de Eccìesiae Catholicae Unitate. Benevot, Maurice, ed. (Oxford Early Christian Texts Ser.). 1971. 32.50x (ISBN 0-19-826804-1). Oxford U Pr.
Doddridge, John. A Compleat Parson: Or, a Description of Advowsons. LC 73-6119. (English Experience Ser.: No. 586). 95p. 1973. Repr. of 1630 ed. 10.50 (ISBN 90-221-0586-5). Walter J Johnson.
Gabel, Leona C. Benefit of Clergy in England in the Later Middle Ages. 1969. lib. bdg. 17.00x (ISBN 0-374-92964-5, Octagon). Hippocrene Bks.
General Demands Concerning the Late Covenent: Together with the Answers. LC 74-80156. (English Experience Ser.: No. 635). 1974. Repr. of 1638 ed. 6.00 (ISBN 90-221-0635-7). Walter J Johnson.
Hooker, Richard. Ecclesiastical Polity, Bk. 8. LC 77-170046. Repr. of 1931 ed. 24.00 (ISBN 0-404-03329-6). AMS Pr.
--Works of That Learned & Judicious Divine Mr. Richard Hooker with an Account of His Life & Death by Isaac Walton, 3 vols. 7th ed. LC 76-125020. (Research & Source Works Ser.: No. 546). 1970. Repr. of 1888 ed. 103.00 (ISBN 0-8337-1731-6). B Franklin.
Huels, John. One Table, Many Laws: Essays on Catholic Eucharistic Discipline. 112p. 1986. pap. 5.95 (ISBN 0-8146-1465-5). Liturgical Pr.
Mitzner, D. T., et al. Constitutional Problems in Church-State Relations: A Symposium. LC 75-155825. (Symposia on Law & Society Ser). 1971. Repr. of 1966 ed. lib. bdg. 19.50 (ISBN 0-306-70131-6). Da Capo.
Muller, Alexander V., ed. & tr. from Russian. The Spiritual Regulation of Peter the Great. LC 74-4590. (Publications on Russia & Eastern Europe of the School of International Studies: No. 3). 188p. 1972. 16.50x (ISBN 0-295-95237-7); pap. 6.95x (ISBN 0-295-95282-2). U of Wash Pr.
Oaks, Dallin H., ed. Wall Between Church & State. LC 63-20897. 1963. pap. 1.95X (ISBN 0-226-61429-8, P137, Phoen). U of Chicago Pr.
Ogle, Arthur. Canon Law in Mediaeval England: An Examination of William Lyndwood's Provinciale. LC 78-156390. (Research & Source Works Ser.: No. 731). 1971. Repr. of 1912 ed. lib. bdg. 20.50 (ISBN 0-8337-2603-X). B Franklin.
Piarist Fathers. Constitutions of the Order of the Pious Schools. Cudinach, Salvidor, ed. & tr. from Lat. LC 85-60915. Tr. of Constitutiones Ordinis Scholarum Piarum. 110p. Date not set. price not set (ISBN 0-9614908-0-2). Piarist Father.
Prompsault, J. H. Dictionnaire Raisonne de Droit et de Jurisprudence en Matiere Civile Ecclesiastique, 3 vols. Migne, J. P., ed. (Encyclopedie Theologique Ser.: Vols. 36-38). (Fr.). 1948p. Repr. of 1849 ed. lib. bdg. 248.00x (ISBN 0-89241-244-5). Caratzas.
Torpey, William G. Judicial Doctrines of Religious Rights in America. LC 78-132289. (Civil Liberties in American History Ser). 1970. Repr. of 1948 ed. lib. bdg. 42.50 (ISBN 0-306-70067-0). Da Capo.
Williams, Paul L., ed. The Church & the Law: The Seventh Proceedings of the Fellowship of Catholic Scholars. 128p. (Orig.). 1985. pap. 6.95 (ISBN 0-937374-01-6). NE Bks.
Zollman, Carl. American Civil Church Law. LC 79-77996. (Columbia University. Studies in the Social Sciences: No. 181). Repr. of 1917 ed. 30.00 (ISBN 0-404-51181-3). AMS Pr.

ECCLESIASTICAL OFFICE
see Clergy–Office

ECCLESIASTICAL PATRONAGE
see Patronage, Ecclesiastical

ECCLESIASTICAL RITES AND CEREMONIES
see Liturgies; Rites and Ceremonies; Sacraments

ECCLESIASTICAL STATISTICS
see Church Statistics

ECCLESIASTICAL THEOLOGY
see Church

ECCLESIASTICAL TRIBUNALS
see Ecclesiastical Courts

ECCLESIASTICAL VESTMENTS
see Church Vestments

ECCLESIASTICAL VISITATIONS
see Visitations, Ecclesiastical

ECCLESIASTICAL YEAR
see Church Year

ECKHART, JOHANNES, 1260-1327
Clark, James M. Great German Mystics: Eckhart, Tauler & Suso. LC 73-81493. 1970. Repr. of 1949 ed. 15.00x (ISBN 0-8462-1351-6). Russell.
Eckhart, Meister. Meister Eckhart: Mystic & Philosopher. Schurmann, Reiner, tr. LC 76-26416. (Studies in Phenomenology & Existential Philosophy Ser.). 320p. 1978. 22.50x (ISBN 0-253-35183-9). Ind U Pr.
Fahrner, R. Wortsinn und Wortschoepfung Bei Meister Eckehart. pap. 9.00 (ISBN 0-384-15090-X). Johnson Repr.
Jostes, Franz, ed. Meister Eckhart und seine Juenger: Ungedruckte Texte zur Geschichte der deutschen Mystik. (Deutsche Neudrucke Texte des Mittelalters Ser.). (Ger.). 216p. 1972. 17.40 (ISBN 3-11-004356-4). De Gruyter.
Pfeiffer, Franz. Meister Eckhart, 2 vols. 1977. lib. bdg. 250.00 (ISBN 0-8490-2222-3). Gordon Pr.

ECONOMICS–MORAL AND RELIGIOUS ASPECTS
Danner, Peter L. An Ethics for the Affluent. LC 80-5528. 424p. 1980. lib. bdg. 31.25 (ISBN 0-8191-1163-5); pap. text ed. 15.25 (ISBN 0-8191-1164-3). U Pr of Amer.
Finn, James, ed. Global Economics & Religion. 277p. 1983. 26.95 (ISBN 0-87855-477-7). Transaction Bks.

George, Denise. The Christian As a Consumer. LC 83-26062. (Potentials: Guides for Productive Living Ser.,: Vol. 3). 114p. (Orig.). 1984. pap. 7.95 (ISBN 0-664-24518-8). Westminster.
McKeever, Jim. Financial Guidance. 400p. 1980. 10.95 (ISBN 0-931608-09-0); pap. 7.95 (ISBN 0-931608-10-4). Omega Pubns OR.
Powellson, Jack. Holistic Economics & Social Protest. 1983. pap. 2.50x (ISBN 0-87574-250-5, 250). Pendle Hill.
Rose, Tom. Economics: Principles & Policy from a Christian Perspective. 2nd ed. LC 85-72235. (Illus.). 380p. 1985. text ed. 18.95 (ISBN 0-9612198-5-8); instrs' manual 7.00 (ISBN 0-9612198-1-5). A E P.
Skurski, Roger. New Directions in Economic Justice. LC 83-1254. 304p. 1983. text ed. 20.95x (ISBN 0-268-01460-4, 85-14606); pap. text ed. 10.95x (ISBN 0-268-01461-2, 85-14614). U of Notre Dame Pr.
Solowsky, Alan S. God & the American Corporation. (International Council for Excellence in Management Library). (Illus.). 1980. deluxe ed. 69.95 (ISBN 0-89266-266-2). Am Classical Coll Pr.
Sombart, Werner. Jews & Modern Capitalism. LC 81-16152. (Social Science Classics Ser.). 475p. 1982. pap. 19.95 (ISBN 0-87855-837-3). Transaction Bks.

ECONOMICS AND CHRISTIANITY
see Christianity and Economics

ECSTASY
see also Enthusiasm; Trance
Holm, Nils G., ed. Religious Ecstasy. (Scripta Instituti Donnerain Aboensis: No. XI). 306p. 1982. pap. text ed. 25.00x (ISBN 91-22-00574-9, Pub. by Almqvist & Wiksell Sweden). Humanities.
Laski, Marghanita. Ecstasy: A Study of Some Secular & Religious Experiences. LC 68-55635. (Illus.). 1968. Repr. of 1962 ed. bds. 27.50x (ISBN 0-8371-0529-3, LAEC). Greenwood.

ECUMENICAL COUNCILS AND SYNODS
see Councils and Synods, Ecumenical

ECUMENICAL MOVEMENT
see also Christian Union
Bell, George K. The Kingship of Christ: The Story of the World Council of Churches. LC 78-10482. 1979. Repr. of 1954 ed. lib. bdg. 22.50x (ISBN 0-313-21121-3, BEKC). Greenwood.
Breslauer, S. Daniel. The Ecumenical Perspective & the Modernization of Jewish Religion: A Study in the Relationship Between Theology & Myth. 1978. pap. 9.00 (ISBN 0-89130-236-0, 140005). Scholars Pr GA.
Browning, Robert L. & Reed, Roy A. The Sacraments in Religious Education & Liturgy: An Ecumenical Model. LC 84-27536. 313p. (Orig.). 1985. pap. 14.95 (ISBN 0-89135-044-6). Religious Educ.
Cushman, Robert E. Faith Seeking Understanding: Essays Theological & Critical. LC 80-69402. xvi, 373p. 1981. 30.25 (ISBN 0-8223-0444-9). Duke.
Desseaux, Jacques. Twenty Centuries of Ecumenism. 1984. pap. 4.95 (ISBN 0-8091-2617-6). Paulist Pr.
Geffre, Claude & Jossua, Jean-Pierre. Indifference to Religion. (Concilium 1983: Vol. 165). 128p. (Orig.). 1983. pap. 6.95 (ISBN 0-8164-2445-4, HarpR). Har-Row.
Lowrey, Mark D. Ecumenism: Striving for Unity amid Diversity. 272p. (Orig.). 1985. pap. text ed. 9.95 (ISBN 0-89622-274-8). Twenty-Third.
Martin, Roger H. Evangelicals United: Ecumenical Stirrings in Pre-Victorian Britain, 1795-1830. LC 82-10784. (Studies in Evangelicalism: No. 4). 244p. 1983. 19.00 (ISBN 0-8108-1586-9). Scarecrow.
Morrison, Charles C. Unfinished Reformation. facs. ed. LC 68-20322. (Essay Index Reprint Ser). 1953. 17.50 (ISBN 0-8369-0723-X). Ayer Co Pubs.
Newbigin, Lesslie. Unfinished Agenda: An Autobiography. (Illus.). 280p. (Orig.). 1985. pap. 11.95 (ISBN 0-8028-0091-2). Eerdmans.
Rusch, William G. Ecumenism: A Movement Toward Church Unity. LC 84-48707. 96p. 1985. pap. 6.95 (ISBN 0-8006-1847-5, 1-1847). Fortress.
Samartha, S. J. Courage for Dialogue: Ecumenical Issues in Inter-Religious Relationships. LC 81-16936. 172p. (Orig.). 1982. pap. 4.48 (ISBN 0-88344-094-6). Orbis Bks.
Sansoucie, Larry A. The Ecumenical Lectionary. 111p. (Orig.). 1986. pap. 9.95 (ISBN 0-937505-04-8). Glyndwr Resc.
Schellman, James M. Ecumenical Services of Prayer: Consultation on Common Texts. 80p. 1983. pap. 1.95 (ISBN 0-8091-5180-4). Paulist Pr.
Schuon, Frithjof. Christianity - Islam: Essays on Esoteric Ecumenicism. LC 84-52674. (The Library of Traditional Wisdom). 270p. 1985. pap. 12.00 (ISBN 0-941532-05-4). Wrld Wisdom Bks.
Smith, John C. From Colonialism to World Community: The Church's Pilgrimage. LC 82-12138. 334p. 1982. pap. 8.95 (ISBN 0-664-24452-1, Pub. by Geneva Press). Westminster.
Smyth, Norman. Story of Church Unity: The Lambeth Conference of Anglican Bishops & the Congregational-Episcopal Approaches. 1923. 29.50x (ISBN 0-686-83788-6). Elliots Bks.
Spasskii, A. Isotoriia Dogmaticheskikh Divhenii v Epokhu Vselenskikh Soborov. 656p. Repr. of 1914 ed. text ed. 74.52x (ISBN 0-576-99173-2, Pub. by Gregg Intl Pubs England). Gregg Intl.
Tavard, Georges H. Two Centuries of Ecumenism. LC 78-6449. 1978. Repr. of 1960 ed. lib. bdg. 22.50x (ISBN 0-313-20490-X, TATC). Greenwood.
Tsirpanlis, C. N. Ecumenical Consensus on the Church, the Sacraments, the Minstry & Reunion. 37p. 1980. pap. 1.50 (ISBN 0-686-36333-7). EO Pr.
Wasserzug, Dr. G. The Terrifying Goal of the Ecumenical Movement. 1.45 (ISBN 0-937422-77-0). Midnight Call.
World Council of Churches, Geneva. Classified Catalog of the Ecumenical Movement: First Supplement. 1981. lib. bdg. 105.00 (ISBN 0-8161-0360-7, Hall Library). G K Hall.
World Council of Churches, Geneva, Switzerland. Classified Catalog of the Ecumenical Movement, 2 vols. 1972. lib. bdg. 198.00 (ISBN 0-8161-0925-7, Hall Library). G K Hall.

ECUMENICAL MOVEMENT–CATHOLIC CHURCH
see Christian Union–Catholic Church

ECUMENICAL MOVEMENT–ORTHODOX EASTERN CHURCH
see Christian Union–Orthodox Eastern Church

EDDAS
MacCulloch, John A. Eddic Mythology. LC 63-19087. (Mythology of All Races Ser.: Vol. 2). (Illus.). Repr. of 1932 ed. 30.00x (ISBN 0-8154-0143-4). Cooper Sq.
Sturluson, S. Prose Edda. Brodeur, A. G., tr. 1916. 12.50x (ISBN 0-89067-000-5). Am Scandinavian.

EDDY, MARY (BAKER),
Carpenter, Gilbert C., Sr. & Carpenter, Gilbert C., Jr. Mary Baker Eddy: Her Spiritual Footsteps. 290p. 1985. pap. 20.00 (ISBN 0-930227-02-6). Pasadena Pr.
Corey, Arthur. Behind the Scenes with the Metaphysicians. 7.50 (ISBN 0-87516-014-X). De Vorss.
Dakin, Edwin F. Mrs. Eddy: The Biography of a Virginal Mind. 13.25 (ISBN 0-8446-0570-0). Peter Smith.
Dickey, Adam H. Memoirs of Mary Baker Eddy. 51p. 1985. pap. 6.00 (ISBN 0-930227-04-2). Pasadena Pr.
Eddy, Mary B. & Carpenter, Gilbert C., eds. Watches, Prayers, Arguments. 100p. 1985. pap. 12.00 (ISBN 0-930227-01-8). Pasadena Pr.

EDICT OF NANTES
Baird, Henry M. The Huguenots & the Revocation of the Edict of Nantes, 2 vols. LC 76-161752. Repr. of 1895 ed. Set. 74.50 (ISBN 0-404-08003-0). AMS Pr.
Maugis, Edquard. Histoire du Parlement De Paris De l'Avenement Des Rois Valois a la Mort D'Henri Quatre, 3 Vols. 1967. Repr. of 1913 ed. 92.50 (ISBN 0-8337-2304-9). B Franklin.
Stankiewicz, W. J. Politics & Religion in Seventeenth-Century France. LC 76-2075. 269p. 1976. Repr. of 1960 ed. lib. bdg. 22.50x (ISBN 0-8371-8770-2, STPR). Greenwood.

EDMUND, SAINT, KING OF EAST ANGLIA, 841-870
Aelfric. Lives of Three English Saints. Needham, G. I., ed. (Old English Ser.). 1966. pap. text ed. 9.95x (ISBN 0-89197-564-0). Irvington.

EDUCATION, CHARACTER
see Moral Education

EDUCATION, CHRISTIAN
see Religious Education

EDUCATION, ETHICAL
see Moral Education; Religious Education

EDUCATION, MORAL
see Moral Education

EDUCATION, RELIGIOUS
see Religious Education

EDUCATION, THEOLOGICAL
see Religious Education; Theology–Study and Teaching

EDUCATION AND CHURCH
see Church and College; Church and Education

EDUCATION AND RELIGION
see Church and Education

EDUCATIONAL MISSIONS
see Missions–Educational Work

EDWARD 2ND, KING OF ENGLAND, 1284-1327
Buck, Mark. Politics, Finance & the Church in the Reign of Edward II: Walter Stapeldon, Treasurer of England. LC 82-17695. (Cambridge Studies in Medieval Life & Thought 19). 248p. 1983. 52.50 (ISBN 0-521-25025-0). Cambridge U Pr.
Furnivall, F. J. Adam Davy's Five Dreams about Edward 2nd. Incl. The Life of St. Alexius; Solomon's Book of Wisdom; St. Jeremies Fifteen Tokens Before Doomsday; The Lamentacion of Souls. (EETS, OS Ser.: No. 69). Repr. of 1878 ed. 10.00 (ISBN 0-527-00068-X). Kraus Repr.

EDWARDS, JONATHAN, 1703-1758
Allen, Alexander. Jonathan Edwards: Seventeen Three to Seventeen Fifty-Eight. lib. bdg. 23.50 (ISBN 0-8337-3926-3). B Franklin.
Cherry, Conrad, et al. Jonathan Edwards: His Life & Influence. Angoff, Charles, ed. LC 74-4516. (Leverton Lecture Series II). 65p. 1975. 9.50 (ISBN 0-8386-1571-6). Fairleigh Dickinson.
Cooey, Paula M. Jonathan Edwards on Nature & Destiny: A Systematic Analysis. LC 85-21499. (Studies in American Religion: Vol. 16). 296p. 1985. lib. bdg. 49.95x (ISBN 0-88946-660-2). E Mellen.
Davidson, Edward H. Jonathan Edwards: The Narrative of a Puritan Mind. LC 68-7254. pap. 43.80 (ISBN 0-317-07848-8, 2005489). Bks Demand UMI.
Edwards, Jonathan. The Great Awakening. Goen, C. C., ed. LC 75-179472. (Works of Johathan Edwards Ser.: Vol. 4). 1972. 50.00x (ISBN 0-300-01437-6). Yale U Pr.
--The Life & Character of the Late Reverend, Learned, & Pious Mr. Jonathan Edwards, President of the College in New Jersey. LC 75-31090. Repr. of 1804 ed. 28.50 (ISBN 0-404-13508-0). AMS Pr.
Faust, Clarence H. & Johnson, Thomas H. Jonathan Edwards. 1981. Repr. of 1935 ed. lib. bdg. 40.00 (ISBN 0-89760-234-X). Telegraph Bks.
Fiering, Norman. Jonathan Edward's Moral Thought & Its British Context. LC 80-26755. (Institute of Early American History & Culture Ser.). xi, 391p. 1981. 32.50x (ISBN 0-8078-1473-3). U of NC Pr.
Griffin, Edward M. Jonathan Edwards. (Pamphlets on American Writers Ser: No. 97). (Orig.). 1971. pap. 1.25x (ISBN 0-8166-0601-3, MPAW97). U of Minn Pr.
Johnson, Thomas H. Printed Writings of Jonathan Edwards 1703-1758: A Bibliography. 1970. Repr. of 1940 ed. text ed. 21.50 (ISBN 0-8337-1854-1). B Franklin.
Kuklick, Bruce. Jonathan Edwards Jr. Works, 2 vols. (American Religious Thought of the 18th & 19th Centuries Ser.). 1114p. 1987. Set. lib. bdg. 145.00 (ISBN 0-8240-6953-6). Garland Pub.
McGiffert, Arhtur C. Jonathan Edwards. LC 75-3134. (Philosophy of American Ser.). Repr. of 1932 ed. 28.00 (ISBN 0-404-59143-4). AMS Pr.
Macphail, Andrew. Essays in Puritanism: Jonathan Edwards, John Winthrop, Margaret Fuller, Walt Whitman, John Wesley. LC 68-26205. 1969. Repr. of 1905 ed. 22.50x (ISBN 0-8046-0286-7, Pub. by Kennikat). Assoc Faculty Pr.
Manspeaker, Nancy. Jonathan Edwards, Seventeen Fifty-Six to Nineteen Seventy-Eight: Bibliographical Synopses. LC 81-9491. (Studies in American Religion: Vol. 3). (Illus.). xviii, 278p. 1981. 49.95x (ISBN 0-88946-907-5). E Mellen.
Miller, Perry. Jonathan Edwards. LC 72-7877. (American Men of Letters Ser.). (Illus.). 348p. 1973. Repr. of 1949 ed. lib. bdg. 25.00x (ISBN 0-8371-6551-2, MIJE). Greenwood.
--Jonathan Edwards. LC 81-4496. (New England Writers Ser.). 384p. 1981. pap. text ed. 11.95x (ISBN 0-87023-328-9). U of Mass Pr.
Parkes, Henry B. Jonathan Edwards, the Fiery Puritan. LC 75-3135. Repr. of 1930 ed. 30.00 (ISBN 0-404-59144-2). AMS Pr.
Pfisterer, Karl D. The Prism of Scripture: Studies on History & Historicity in the Work of Jonathan Edwards, Vol. 1. (Anglo-American Forum Ser.: Vol. 1). 381p. 1975. pap. 31.55 (ISBN 3-261-00965-9). P Lang Pubs.
Scheick, William J. The Writings of Jonathan Edwards: Theme, Motif, & Style. LC 75-18689. 192p. 1975. 14.50x (ISBN 0-89096-004-6). Tex A&M Univ Pr.
Storms, C. Samuel. Tragedy in Eden: Original Sin in the Theology of Jonathan Edwards. LC 85-17866. 328p. 1986. lib. bdg. 27.25 (ISBN 0-8191-4936-5); pap. text ed. 12.75 (ISBN 0-8191-4937-3). U Pr of Amer.
Tracy, Patricia. Jonathan Edwards, Pastor: Religion & Society in Eighteenth-Century Northampton. (American Century Ser.). 288p. 1980. 14.95 (ISBN 0-8090-6195-3); pap. 5.95 (ISBN 0-8090-0149-7). Hill & Wang.
Van Doren, Carl. Benjamin Franklin & Jonathan Edwards. 1979. Repr. of 1920 ed. lib. bdg. 20.00 (ISBN 0-8495-5525-6). Arden Lib.
Wilson-Kastner, Patricia. Coherence in a Fragmented World: Jonathan Edwards' Theology of the Holy Spirit. LC 78-62667. 1978. pap. text ed. 8.50 (ISBN 0-8191-0587-2). U Pr of Amer.
Wolf, Carl J., ed. Jonathan Edwards on Evangelism. LC 81-2266. xii, 137p. 1981. Repr. of 1958 ed. lib. bdg. 22.50x (ISBN 0-8371-6588-1, EDOE). Greenwood.

EFFICIENCY, PERSONAL
see Success

EFFIGIES, SEPULCHRAL
see Sepulchral Monuments

EGO (PSYCHOLOGY)
see also Identity (Psychology)
Hirschfield, Jerry. My Ego, Higher Self & I. 281p. (Orig.). 1986. pap. 11.95 (ISBN 0-87418-014-7, 151). Coleman Pub.

EGYPT–ANTIQUITIES
Arnold, Dieter. The Temple of Mentuhotep at Dier El Bahari. (Publications of the Metropolitan Museum of Art Egyptian Expedition: Vol. XXI). (Illus.). 1979. 60.00 (ISBN 0-87099-163-9). Metro Mus Art.
Budge, E. A. Mummy. 2nd ed. LC 64-13391. (Illus.). 1894. 25.00 (ISBN 0-8196-0139-X). Biblo.
Erman, Adolf. Life in Ancient Egypt. Tirard, H. M., tr. (Illus.). pap. 8.50 (ISBN 0-486-22632-8). Dover.
Erman, Adolph. Life in Ancient Egypt. LC 68-56523. (Illus.). Repr. of 1894 ed. 25.00 (ISBN 0-405-08488-9, Blom Pubns). Ayer Co Pubs.
--Life in Ancient Egypt. 16.75 (ISBN 0-8446-0090-3). Peter Smith.
Frith, Francis. Egypt & the Holy Land in Historic Photographs. White, Jon. E., selected by. 16.50 (ISBN 0-8446-5887-1). Peter Smith.
Lamy, Lucie. Egyptian Mysteries: New Light on Ancient Spiritual Knowledge. Purce, Jill, ed. LC 81-66806. (The Illustrated Library of Sacred Imagination Ser.). (Illus.). 96p. 1981. pap. 9.95 (ISBN 0-8245-0055-5). Crossroad NY.
Lefebvre, G., ed. Inscriptiones Graecae Aegypti, No. 5: Christian Inscriptions. xlii, 173p. 1978. 30.00 (ISBN 0-89005-248-4). Ares.
Mace, Arthur C. & Winlock, Herbert E. The Tomb of Senebtisi at Lisht: Metropolitan Museum of Art Egyptian Expedition Publications, Vol. 1. LC 73-168408. (Metropolitan Museum of Art Publications in Reprint). (Illus.). 228p. 1972. Repr. of 1916 ed. 32.00 (ISBN 0-405-02241-7). Ayer Co Pubs.
The Monastery of Epiphanius at Thebes, 2 bks in one, Pt. 1. Incl. The Archaeological Material. Winlock, H. E; The Literary Material. Crum, W. E. (Metropolitan Museum of Art Egyptian Expedition Publications Ser., Vol. 3). 1972. Repr. of 1926 ed. 40.00 (ISBN 0-405-02250-6). Ayer Co Pubs.
The Monastery of Epiphanius at Thebes, 2 bks in one, Pt. 2. Incl. Coptic Ostraca & Papyri. Crum, W. E; Greek Ostraca & Papyri. White, H. G. (Metropolitan Museum of Art Egyptian Expedition Publication Ser., Vol. 4). 1972. Repr. of 1926 ed. 45.00 (ISBN 0-405-02251-4). Ayer Co Pubs.
Murray, Margaret A. Egyptian Temples. LC 75-41203. Repr. of 1931 ed. 27.50 (ISBN 0-404-14719-4). AMS Pr.
Pearson, Birger A. & Goehring, James E., eds. The Roots of Egyptian Christianity. LC 85-47736. (Studies in Antiquity & Christianity). 336p. 1986. 39.95 (ISBN 0-8006-3100-5, 1-3100). Fortress.
Porter, Bertha & Moss, Rosalind. Theban Temples, Vol. 2. rev ed. (Topographical Bibliography of Ancient Egyptian Hieroglyphic Texts, Reliefs & Paintings Ser.). 586p. 1972. text ed. 60.00 (ISBN 0-900416-18-1, Pub. by Aris & Phillips UK). Humanities.
--Upper Egypt Chief Temples, Six. (Topographical Bibliography of Ancient Egyptian Hieroglyphic Texts, Reliefs & Paintings Ser.: Vol. 6). 264p. 1939. text ed. 38.50 (ISBN 0-900416-30-0, Pub. by Aris & Phillips UK). Humanities.
Portner, Balthasar. Die Agyptischen Totenstelen Als Zeugen Des Sozialen und Religiosen Lebens Ihrer Zeit. pap. 8.00 (ISBN 0-384-47040-8). Johnson Repr.
Van Siclen, Charles C., III. The Chapel of Sesostris III at Uronarti. 58p. 1982. pap. text ed. 10.00x (ISBN 0-933175-02-7). Van Siclen Bks.
--Wall Scenes from the Tomb of Amenhotep (Huy) Governor of Bahria Oasis. (Illus.). ii, 46p. 1981. pap. text ed. 11.00x (ISBN 0-933175-00-0). Van Siclen Bks.
Walters, C. C. Monastic Archaeology in Egypt. 354p. 1974. text ed. 38.50x (ISBN 0-85668-008-7, Pub. by Aris & Phillips UK). Humanities.

Ward, William. Index of Egyptian Administrative & Religious Titles of the Middle Kingdom. 244p. 1983. text ed. 60.00x (ISBN 0-8156-6065-0, Am U Beirut). Syracuse U Pr.
Weeks, Kent R. The Classic Christian Townsite at Arminna West. (Pubns of the Penn-Yale Expedition to Egypt: No. 3). (Illus.). xv, 88p. 1967. 21.00x (ISBN 0-686-17769-X). Univ Mus of U PA.
Weigall, Arthur. Tutankhamen & Other Essays. LC 73-115210. 1971. Repr. of 1924 ed. 24.50x (ISBN 0-8046-1103-3, Pub by Kennikat). Assoc Faculty Pr.
White, Hugh G. & Hauser, Walter. The Monasteries of the Wadi 'n Natrun: Metropolitan Museum of Art Egyptian Expedition Publications, 3 vols. Incl. Vol. 1. New Coptic Texts from the Monastery of Saint Macarius. (Illus.). 308p. Repr. of 1926 ed. 42.00 (ISBN 0-405-02243-3); Vol. 2. the History of the Monasteries of Nitria & of Scetis. Hauser, Walter. (Illus.). Repr. of 1932 ed. 57.50 (ISBN 0-405-02244-1); Vol. 3. Hauser, Walter. (Illus.). 480p. Repr. of 1933 ed. 57.50 (ISBN 0-405-02245-X). LC 77-168409. (Metropolitan Museum of Art Publications in Reprint). (Illus.). 1340p. 172.00 set (ISBN 0-405-02242-5). Ayer Co Pubs.
Winlock, Herbert E. Bas-Reliefs from the Temple of Rameses One at Abydos, 2 vols in 1. Incl. The Temple of Rameses One at Abydos. LC 72-2519. (Metropolitan Museum of Art Publications in Reprint). (Illus.). 1972. Repr. of 1937 ed. 20.00 (ISBN 0-685-32631-4). Ayer Co Pubs.

EGYPT–CIVILIZATION

Baines, J. Fecundity Figures: Egyptian Personification & the Iconology of a Genre. (Illus.). 200p. 1983. 60.00 (ISBN 0-85668-087-7, Pub. by Aris & Phillips UK). Humanities.
Baines, John. Fecundity Figures: Egyptian Personification & the Iconology of a Genre. (Egyptology Ser.). (Illus.). 400p. (Orig.). 1985. pap. 59.00 (ISBN 0-86516-122-4). Bolchazy-Carducci.
Bryce, Glendon E. A Legacy of Wisdom: The Egyptian Contribution to the Wisdom of Israel. LC 74-4984. 336p. 1979. 24.50 (ISBN 0-8387-1576-1). Bucknell U Pr.
Glanville, Stephen R. The Legacy of Egypt. LC 76-44448. (Illus.). 1976. Repr. of 1942 ed. lib. bdg. 34.00x (ISBN 0-8371-9092-4, GLLE). Greenwood.
Harris, J. R., ed. Legacy of Egypt. 2nd ed. (Legacy Ser.). (Illus.). 1971. 35.00x (ISBN 0-19-821912-1). Oxford U Pr.
Kamil, Jill. The Ancient Egyptians: How They Lived & Worked. LC 76-42175. 1977. 12.95 (ISBN 0-8023-1267-5). Dufour.
Noerdlinger, Henry S. Moses & Egypt: The Documentation to the Motion Picture "the Ten Commandments". LC 56-12886. 202p. 1956. pap. 1.95 (ISBN 0-88474-007-2). U of S Cal Pr.
Smith, Grafton E. Ancient Egyptians & the Origin of Civilization. facs. ed. LC 79-133534. (Select Bibliographies Reprint Ser.). 1923. 17.00 (ISBN 0-8369-5566-8). Ayer Co Pubs.
Trigger, B. G., et al. Ancient Egypt: A Social History. LC 82-22196. 450p. 1983. 57.50 (ISBN 0-521-24080-8); pap. 19.95 (ISBN 0-521-28427-9). Cambridge U Pr.
White, J. Manchip. Ancient Egypt: Its Culture & History. LC 75-115748. 1970. pap. 4.95 (ISBN 0-486-22548-8). Dover.
--Ancient Egypt: Its Culture & History. (Illus.). 14.50 (ISBN 0-8446-0336-8). Peter Smith.
Wilson, John A. Culture of Ancient Egypt. LC 56-4923. (Illus.). 1956. pap. 7.95 (ISBN 0-226-90152-1, P11, Phoen). U of Chicago Pr.

EGYPT–HISTORY–TO 640

Baikie, James. A History of Egypt: From the Earliest Times to the End of the Eighteenth Dynasty, 2 vols. facsimile ed. LC 79-157323. (Select Bibliographies Reprint Ser.). Repr. of 1929 ed. Set. 66.00 (ISBN 0-8369-5782-2). Ayer Co Pubs.
Budge, E. Wallis. The Dwellers on the Nile: The Life, History, Religion, & Literature of the Ancient Egyptians. (Illus.). 326p. 1977. pap. 5.95 (ISBN 0-486-23501-7). Dover.
Cooper, William R. Archaic Dictionary. LC 73-76018. 688p. 1969. Repr. of 1876 ed. 75.00x (ISBN 0-8103-3885-8). Gale.
Rawlinson, George. The Story of Ancient Egypt. 1887. Repr. 50.00 (ISBN 0-8482-5897-5). Norwood Edns.
Schmidt, John D. Ramesses II: A Chronological Structure of His Reign. LC 72-6558. (Near Eastern Studies). Repr. of 1973 ed. 56.00 (ISBN 0-8357-9282-X, 2011503). Bks Demand UMI.
White, J. Manchip. Ancient Egypt: Its Culture & History. (Illus.). 14.50 (ISBN 0-8446-0336-8). Peter Smith.

EGYPT–HISTORY–640-1882

Dye, William M. Moslem Egypt & Christian Abyssinia. LC 78-97365. Repr. of 1880 ed. 23.00x (ISBN 0-8371-2432-8, DYM&, Pub. by Negro U Pr). Greenwood.
Winter, Michael. Society & Religion in Early Ottoman Egypt. LC 81-3042. 350p. 1981. 39.95 (ISBN 0-87855-351-7). Transaction Bks.

EGYPT–RELIGION

Adolf, Erman. Die Religion der Aegypter. (Illus.). 1978. Repr. of 1934 ed. 19.20x (ISBN 3-11-005187-7). De Gruyter.
Allen, George, tr. Book of the Dead; or, Going Forth by Day: Ideas of the Ancient Egyptians Concerning the Hereafter As Expressed in Their Own Terms. LC 74-10338. (Studies in Ancient Oriental Civilization Ser: No. 37). 1974. pap. text ed. 20.00x (ISBN 0-226-62410-2). U of Chicago Pr.
Anan Isho, compiled by. The Wit & Wisdom of the Christian Fathers of Egypt: The Syrian Version of the Apophthegmata Patrum. Wallis Budge, Ernest A., tr. LC 80-2354. Repr. of 1934 ed. 53.50 (ISBN 0-404-18900-8). AMS Pr.
Armstrong, A. H., ed. Classical Mediterranean Spirituality. (World Spirituality Ser.). 499p. 1986. 49.50x (ISBN 0-8245-0764-9). Crossroad NY.
Baines, John. Fecundity Figures: Egyptian Personification & the Iconology of a Genre. (Egyptology Ser.). (Illus.). 400p. (Orig.). 1985. pap. 59.00 (ISBN 0-86516-122-4). Bolchazy-Carducci.
Bonnet, Hans. Reallexikon der aegyptischen Religionsgeschichte. 2nd ed. (Ger., Illus.). 1981. 71.20x (ISBN 3-11-003365-8). De Gruyter.
Breasted, James H. Development of Religion & Thought in Ancient Egypt. LC 58-7111. 406p. 1972. pap. 12.95x (ISBN 0-8122-1045-X, Pa Paperbks). U of Pa Pr.
Budge, E. A. Ancient Egyptian Theology. 1985. pap. 5.95 (ISBN 0-916411-91-5). Holmes Pub.
--Egyptian Heaven & Hell. 1980. lib. bdg. 59.95 (ISBN 0-8490-3203-2). Gordon Pr.
Budge, E. Wallis. Egyptian Magic. 1971. pap. 4.00 (ISBN 0-486-22681-6). Dover.
--Egyptian Religion. (Illus.). 1979. pap. 6.95 (ISBN 0-7100-0134-7). Methuen Inc.
--From Fetish to God in Ancient Egypt. LC 72-82206. (Illus.). Repr. of 1934 ed. 33.00 (ISBN 0-405-08317-3, Blom Pubns). Ayer Co Pubs.
Budge, Ernest A. The Egyptian Heaven & Hell. (Illus.). 200p. 1974. lib. bdg. 16.95 (ISBN 0-87548-311-9); pap. 5.95 (ISBN 0-87548-298-8). Open Court.
Cerny, Jaroslav. Ancient Egyptian Religion. LC 78-9931. 1979. Repr. of 1957 ed. lib. bdg. 50.00x (ISBN 0-313-21104-3, CEAE). Greenwood.
David, A. Rosalie. The Ancient Egyptians: Religious Beliefs & Practices. (Religious Beliefs & Practices Ser.). 250p. 1982. 26.00x (ISBN 0-7100-0877-5); pap. 10.00 (ISBN 0-7100-0878-3). Methuen Inc.
Erman, Adolf. A Handbook of Egyptian Religions. LC 76-27517. (Illus.). 1976. Repr. of 1907 ed. lib. bdg. 30.00 (ISBN 0-89341-032-2). Longwood Pub Group.
Frankfort, Henri. Ancient Egyptian Religion: An Interpretation. pap. 7.95x (ISBN 0-06-130077-2, TB77, Torch). Har-Row.
--Ancient Egyptian Religion: An Interpretation. 16.00 (ISBN 0-8446-2084-X). Peter Smith.
--Kingship & the Gods: A Study of Ancient Near Eastern Religion As the Integration of Society & Nature. LC 48-5158. 1978. pap. 12.95 (ISBN 0-226-26011-9, P766, Phoen). U of Chicago Pr.
Frith, Francis. Egypt & the Holy Land in Historic Photographs. White, Jon. E., selected by. 16.50 (ISBN 0-8446-5887-1). Peter Smith.
Hornung, Erik & Baines, John, trs. from Ger. Conceptions of God in Ancient Egypt: The One & the Many. LC 82-71602. (Illus.). 296p. 1982. 29.95x (ISBN 0-8014-1223-4). Cornell U Pr.
Lamy, Lucie. Egyptian Mysteries: New Light on Ancient Spiritual Knowledge. Purce, Jill, ed. LC 81-66806. (The Illustrated Library of Sacred Imagination Ser.). (Illus.). 96p. 1981. pap. 9.95 (ISBN 0-8245-0055-5). Crossroad NY.
Lesko, Leonard H. Index of the Spells on Egyptian Middle Kingdom Coffins & Related Documents. LC 79-66500. (Orig.). 1979. pap. text ed. 6.00x (ISBN 0-930548-02-7). B C Scribe.
McPherson, Joseph W. The Moulids of Egypt: Egyptian Saints-Days. LC 77-87654. Repr. of 1941 ed. 28.50 (ISBN 0-404-16408-0). AMS Pr.
Meinardus, Otto. The Holy Family in Egypt: In the Steps of the Tradition. 1987. pap. 10.00 (ISBN 977-424-129-0, Pub. by Am Univ Cairo Pr). Columbia U Pr.
Morenz, Siegfried. Egyptian Religion. LC 73-8407. 395p. 1973. 39.95x (ISBN 0-8014-0782-6). Cornell U Pr.
Murray, Margaret A. Egyptian Religious Poetry. Cranmer-Byng, J. L., ed. LC 79-8714. (The Wisdom of the East Ser.). 120p. 1980. Repr. of 1949 ed. lib. bdg. 22.50x (ISBN 0-313-21012-8, MUER). Greenwood.
Nikopol, Georg R. The Artistic & Mystical Significance of Indian & Egyptian Temples. (Illus.). 187p. 1984. 137.45 (ISBN 0-86650-131-2). Gloucester Art.
Otto, Walter G. Priester und Tempel Im Hellenistischen Agypten: Ein Beitrag Zur Kulturgeschichte Des Hellenismus, 2 vols. in 1. facsimile ed. LC 75-10645. (Ancient Religion & Mythology Ser.). (Ger.). 1976. Repr. 62.00x (ISBN 0-405-07278-3). Ayer Co Pubs.
Petrie, William F. Religion & Conscience in Ancient Egypt. LC 72-83176. Repr. of 1898 ed. 24.50 (ISBN 0-405-08854-X). Ayer Co Pubs.
Portner, Balthasar. Die Agyptischen Totenstelen Als Zeugen Des Sozialen und Religiosen Lebens Ihrer Zeit. pap. 8.00 (ISBN 0-384-47040-8). Johnson Repr.
Reed, Bika. Rebel in the Soul. LC 78-15791. (Illus.). 1979. pap. 9.95 (ISBN 0-89281-004-1). Inner Tradit.
Renouf, Peter L. Lectures on the Origin & Growth of Religion as Illustrated by the Religion of Ancient Egypt. 2nd ed. LC 77-27171. (Hibbert Lectures: 1879). Repr. of 1884 ed. 30.00 (ISBN 0-404-60401-3). AMS Pr.
Sauneron, Serge. The Priests of Ancient Egypt. LC 59-10792. (Illus.). 192p. 1980. pap. 3.50 (ISBN 0-394-17410-0, B433, BC). Grove.
Sayce, Archibald H. The Religions of Ancient Egypt & Babylonia. LC 77-27223. (Gifford Lectures: 1902). Repr. of 1903 ed. 46.50 (ISBN 0-404-60457-9). AMS Pr.
Schermann, Theodor. Agyptische Abendmahlsliturgien Des Ersten Jahrtausends. Repr. of 1912 ed. 19.00 (ISBN 0-384-53730-8). Johnson Repr.
Schuler, G. H., ed. Egypt & Nuclear Technology: The Peace Divident. (Significant Issues Ser.: Vol. V, No. 9). 24p. (Orig.). 1983. pap. text ed. 6.95 (ISBN 0-8191-5924-7, Pub. by CSIS). U Pr of Amer.
Schwaller de Lubicz, R. A. Nature-Word. Lawlor, Deborah & Lawlor, Robert, trs. from Fr. LC 82-81069. 160p. 1982. pap. 8.95 (ISBN 0-89281-036-X). Inner Tradit.
Seligman, Charles G. Egypt & Negro Africa: Study in Divine Kingship. LC 74-15088. (Frazer Lecture: 1933). (Illus.). Repr. of 1934 ed. 21.50 (ISBN 0-404-12138-1). AMS Pr.
Vidman, Ladislav. Isis und Sarapis bei den Griechen und Roemern: Epigraphische Studien zur Verbreitung und zu den Traegern des aegyptischen Kultes. (Religionsgeschichtliche Versuche und Vorarbeiten, No. 29). (Ger). 1970. 26.00x (ISBN 3-11-006392-1). De Gruyter.
Winter, Michael. Society & Religion in Early Ottoman Egypt. LC 81-3042. 350p. 1981. 39.95 (ISBN 0-87855-351-7). Transaction Bks.
Zimmermann, Friedrich. Die Agyptische Religion Nach der Darstellung der Kirchenschriftsteller und Die Agyptischen Denkmale. 15.00 (ISBN 0-384-71000-X). Johnson Repr.

EGYPTIAN LANGUAGE–INSCRIPTIONS

Lefebvre, G., ed. Inscriptiones Graecae Aegypti, No. 5: Christian Inscriptions. xlii, 173p. 1978. 30.00 (ISBN 0-89005-248-4). Ares.
Reed, Bika. Rebel in the Soul. LC 78-15791. (Illus.). 1979. pap. 9.95 (ISBN 0-89281-004-1). Inner Tradit.
Sayce, A. H., ed. Records of the Past: Being English Translations of the Ancient Monuments of Egypt & Western Asia, 6 vols. in 2. LC 72-83175. Repr. of 1888 ed. Set. 71.00 (ISBN 0-405-08918-X); 35.75 ea. Vol. 1 (ISBN 0-405-08919-8). Vol. 2 (ISBN 0-405-08922-8). Ayer Co Pubs.
Seele, Keith C. Tomb of Tjanefer at Thebes. LC 59-14285. (Oriental Institute Pubns. Ser: No. 86). (Illus.). 1959. 22.00x (ISBN 0-226-62187-1, OIP86). U of Chicago Pr.

EGYPTIAN LANGUAGE–PAPYRI

Book of the Dead Staff. The Chapters of Coming Forth by Day, 3 vols. LC 73-18833. Repr. of 1910 ed. 49.50 set (ISBN 0-404-11303-6). AMS Pr.

EGYPTIAN MYTHOLOGY

see Mythology, Egyptian

EGYPTIAN PAPYRI

see Egyptian Language–Papyri

EGYPTIAN STUDIES

see Egyptology

EGYPTOLOGY

Budge, E. Wallis. The Dwellers on the Nile: The Life, History, Religion, & Literature of the Ancient Egyptians. (Illus.). 326p. 1977. pap. 5.95 (ISBN 0-486-23501-7). Dover.
Institut Dominicain d'Etudes Orientales du Caire. Melanes: French-Arabic Text, Vol. 14. 1980. 30.00x (ISBN 0-86685-284-0). Intl Bk Ctr.
--Melanges: Tables Generales Tomes 1-13 (1954-1977) (Fr. & Arabic.). 1980. 10.00x (ISBN 0-86685-283-2). Intl Bk Ctr.
Lehner, Mark. The Egyptian Heritage: Based on the Edgar Cayce Readings. 136p. 1974. pap. 5.95 (ISBN 0-87604-071-7). ARE Pr.
Lurker, Manfred. Gods & Symbols of Ancient Egypt: An Illustrated Dictionary. Clayton, Peter A., rev. by. (Illus.). 142p. 1984. pap. 9.95f (ISBN 0-500-27253-0). Thames Hudson.
Schwaller De Lubicz, Isha. Her-Bak Egyptian Initiate. Fraser, Ronald, tr. from Fr. (Illus.). 400p. 1982. pap. 9.95 (ISBN 0-89281-002-5). Inner Tradit.

EIKONS

see Icons

ELDERS (CHURCH OFFICERS)

Buck, Carlton C. Communion Thoughts & Prayers. new ed. LC 76-46943. 1977. 5.95 (ISBN 0-8272-0440-X). CBP.
Eyres, Lawrence. The Elders of the Church. 1975. pap. 2.50 (ISBN 0-87552-258-0). Presby & Reformed.
MacNair, Donald J. The Challenge of the Eldership: A Handbook for the Elders of the Church. (Orig.). 1984. pap. text ed. 1.95 (ISBN 0-934688-12-5). Great Comm Pubns.
Strauch, Alexander. Biblical Eldership: A Study Guide. 100p. (Orig.). 1987. pap. price not set (ISBN 0-936083-01-8). Lewis Roth.
Taylor, Robert, Jr. Elder & His Work. 7.95 (ISBN 0-89315-041-X); pap. 4.95 (ISBN 0-89315-042-8). Lambert Bk.
Wright, Paul S. The Presbyterian Elder. rev. ed. 64p. (Orig.). 1986. pap. 4.95 saddle stapled (ISBN 0-664-24014-3). Westminster.

ELECTION (THEOLOGY)

see also Jews–Election, Doctrine Of; Perseverance (Theology); Predestination

Baker, Alvin L. Berkouwer's Doctrine of Election: Balance or Imbalance? 1981. pap. 5.95 (ISBN 0-87552-119-3). Presby & Reformed.
Hausmann, William J. Karl Barth's Doctrine of Election. LC 74-81812. 1969. 5.95 (ISBN 0-8022-2281-1). Philos Lib.
Jewett, Paul K. Election & Predestination. 184p. (Orig.). 1985. pap. 8.95 (ISBN 0-8028-0090-4). Eerdmans.
King, William. An Essay on the Origin of Evil. Bd. with Dissertations Concerning the Fundamental Principle & Immediate Criterion of Virtue. LC 75-11228. (British Philosophers & Theologians of the 17th & 18th Centuries Ser.). 391p. 1978. lib. bdg. 51.00 (ISBN 0-8240-1782-X). Garland Pub.
Nettleton, David. Chosen to Salvation: Select Thoughts on the Doctrine of Election. LC 83-11062. 1983. pap. 5.95 (ISBN 0-87227-094-7). Reg Baptist.
Shank, Robert. Elect in the Son: A Study of the Doctrine of Election. LC 74-114957. 256p. 1970. 7.95 (ISBN 0-911620-02-8). Westcott.
Shariati, Ali. Selection & Election. Ghasemy, Ali A., tr. from Persian. 12p. 1980. pap. 0.75 (ISBN 0-941722-13-9). Book-Dist-Ctr.
Storms, Samuel C. Chosen For Life. 160p. 1987. pap. 6.95 (ISBN 0-8010-8270-6). Baker Bk.

ELECTION OF ISRAEL

see Jews–Election, Doctrine Of

ELEUSINIAN MYSTERIES

Clinton, Kevin. The Sacred Officials of the Eleusinian Mysteries. LC 73-79573. (Transaction Ser.: Vol. 64, Pt. 3). (Illus.). 1974. pap. 16.00 (ISBN 0-87169-643-6). Am Philos.
Kerenyi, Carl. Archetypal Images in Greek Religion, 5 vols. Manheim, R., tr. Incl. Vol. 1. Prometheus: Archetypal Image of Human Existence. 1963; Vol. 2. Dionysos: Archetypal Image of Industructible Life. 1975; Vol. 3. Asklepios: Archetypal Image of the Physician's Existence. 1959. 37.00x (ISBN 0-691-09703-8); Vol. 4. Eleusis: Archetypal Image of Mother & Daughter. 1967; Vol. 5. Zeus & Hera-Archetypal Image of Father, Husband & Wife. Holme, tr. 1975. (Bollingen Ser.: Vol. 65). Princeton U Pr.

ELEUSIS

Clinton, Kevin. The Sacred Officials of the Eleusinian Mysteries. LC 73-79573. (Transaction Ser.: Vol. 64, Pt. 3). (Illus.). 1974. pap. 16.00 (ISBN 0-87169-643-6). Am Philos.
Foucart, Paul F. Les Mysteres d'Eleusis. facsimile ed. LC 75-10636. (Ancient Religion & Mythology Ser.). (Fr.). 1976. Repr. of 1914 ed. 37.50x (ISBN 0-405-07013-6). Ayer Co Pubs.
Kerenyi, Carl. Archetypal Images in Greek Religion, 5 vols. Manheim, R., tr. Incl. Vol. 1. Prometheus: Archetypal Image of Human Existence. 1963; Vol. 2. Dionysos: Archetypal Image of Industructible Life. 1975; Vol. 3. Asklepios: Archetypal Image of the Physician's Existence. 1959. 37.00x (ISBN 0-691-09703-8); Vol. 4. Eleusis: Archetypal Image of Mother & Daughter. 1967; Vol. 5. Zeus & Hera-Archetypal Image of Father, Husband & Wife. Holme, tr. 1975. (Bollingen Ser.: Vol. 65). Princeton U Pr.

ELIJAH, THE PROPHET

Castleman, Robbie. Elijah: Obedience in a Threatening World. (Fisherman Bible Studyguide Ser.). 64p. (Orig.). 1986. pap. 2.95 (ISBN 0-87788-218-5). Shaw Pubs.

Edersheim, Alfred. Practical Truths from Elisha. LC 82-18702. 368p. 1983. 14.95 (ISBN 0-8254-2511-5). Kregel.

Hendricks, Howard G. Taking a Stand: What God Can Do Through Ordinary You. LC 83-8241. 1983. pap. 4.95 (ISBN 0-88070-025-4). Multnomah.

Katz, Menke. A Chair for Elijah. LC 85-61563. (Illus.). 104p. 1985. 9.95 (ISBN 0-912292-78-4); pap. 6.95 (ISBN 0-912292-77-6). The Smith.

Keller, Phillip. Elijah: Prophet of Power. 160p. 1980. 8.95 (ISBN 0-8499-0266-5). Word Bks.

Lee, G. Avery. Elijah: Yahweh Is My God. (Orig.). 1987. pap. 5.50 (ISBN 0-8054-1539-4). Broadman.

Lindsay, Gordon. Elijah: The Man Who Did Not Die. (Old Testament Ser.). 1.25 (ISBN 0-89985-149-5). Christ Nations.

--Elijah: The Whirlwind Prophet. (Old Testament Ser.). 1.25 (ISBN 0-89985-148-7). Christ Nations.

Meyer, F. B. Elijah. 1972. pap. 4.50 (ISBN 0-87508-343-9). Chr Lit.

Pink, A. W. The Life of Elijah. 1976. pap. 5.95 (ISBN 0-85151-041-8). Banner of Truth.

--La Vida de Elias. (Span.). 360p. 1984. pap. 4.95 (ISBN 0-85151-424-3). Banner of Truth.

Stephens, William H. Elijah. 1979. pap. 3.95 (ISBN 0-8423-4023-8). Tyndale.

Stone, Michael E. & Strugnell, John. The Books of Elijah, Pts. 1 & 2. LC 79-15153. (Pseudepigrapha Ser.: No. 8). 1979. 13.50 (ISBN 0-89130-315-4, 060218); pap. 8.95 o.s. (ISBN 0-89130-316-2). Scholars Pr GA.

Wiener, Aharon. The Prophet Elijah in the Development of Judaism. (Littman Library of Jewish Civilization). 250p. 1978. 24.00x (ISBN 0-19-710010-4). Oxford U Pr.

Wood, Leon J. Elijah: Prophet of God. 1968. 2.95 (ISBN 0-87227-020-3). Reg Baptist.

ELIJAH, THE PROPHET–JUVENILE LITERATURE

Entz, Angeline J. Elijah: Brave Prophet. (BibLearn Ser.). (Illus.). 1978. 5.95 (ISBN 0-8054-4244-8, 4242-44). Broadman.

Shimoni, S. Legends of Elijah. (Biblical Ser.). (Illus.). 1975. 3.00 (ISBN 0-914080-13-X). Shulsinger Sales.

ELIOT, JOHN, 1604-1690

Francis, Convers. Life of John Eliot: The Apostle to the Indians. 1972. Repr. of 1854 ed. lib. bdg. 29.00 (ISBN 0-8422-8049-9). Irvington.

ELISHA BEN ABUYAH, 2ND CENTURY–FICTION

Steinberg, Milton. As a Driven Leaf. LC 75-32237. 1939. pap. 7.95x (ISBN 0-87441-074-6). Behrman.

ELISHA THE PROPHET

Kolbrek, Loyal. The Day God Made It Rain. (Arch Books Series Fourteen). 1977. pap. 0.99 (ISBN 0-570-06108-3, 59-1226). Concordia.

Lindsay, Gordon. Elisha-Prophet of the Supernatural. (Old Testament Ser.). 1.25 (ISBN 0-89985-151-7). Christ Nations.

--Elisha-The Man Who Received the Double Portion. (Old Testament Ser.). 1.25 (ISBN 0-89985-150-9). Christ Nations.

ELLSKWATAWA, SHAWNEE PROPHET, 1775-1834

Drake, Benjamin. Life of Tecumseh & of His Brother the Prophet: With a Historical Sketch of the Shawanoe Indians. LC 78-90173. (Mass Violence in America Ser). Repr. of 1841 ed. 14.00 (ISBN 0-405-01307-8). Ayer Co Pubs.

ELPHINSTONE, WILLIAM, BP. OF ABERDEEN, 1431-1514

Boece, Hector. Hectoris Boetii Murthlacensium Et Aberdonensium Episcoporum Vitae, Iterum in Lucem Editae. LC 76-39462. (Bannatyne Club, Edinburgh. Publications: No. 11). Repr. of 1825 ed. 20.00 (ISBN 0-404-52711-6). AMS Pr.

Gardyne, Alexander. A Theatre of Scottish Worthies, & the Lyf, Doings & Deathe of William Elphinston, Bishop of Aberdee. Repr. of 1878 ed. 40.00 (ISBN 0-384-17655-0). Johnson Repr.

EMANCIPATION, CATHOLIC

see Catholic Emancipation

EMBLEMS

see also Christian Art and Symbolism; Symbolism

Boudard, J. B. Iconologie. LC 75-27888. (Renaissance & the Gods Ser.: Vol. 43). (Illus.). 1976. Repr. of 1766 ed. lib. bdg. 80.00 (ISBN 0-8240-2092-8). Garland Pub.

Diehl, Huston. An Index of Icons in English Emblem Books, 1500-1700. LC 85-40950. (Illus.). 288p. 1986. 35.00x (ISBN 0-8061-1989-6). U of Okla Pr.

Drake, Maurice. Saints & Their Emblems. (Illus.). 1971. Repr. of 1916 ed. lib. bdg. 24.50 (ISBN 0-8337-0902-X). B Franklin.

Peacham, Henry. Minerva Britanna, or a Garden of Heroical Devises. LC 73-171783. (English Experience Ser.: No. 407). 232p. 1971. Repr. of 1612 ed. 33.50 (ISBN 90-221-0407-9). Walter J Johnson.

Ripa, Cesare. Iconologia. LC 75-27865. (Renaissance & the Gods Ser.: Vol. 21). (Illus.). 581p. 1976. Repr. of 1611 ed. lib. bdg. 88.00 (ISBN 0-8240-2070-7). Garland Pub.

Stiebner, Erhardt D. & Urban, Dieter. Signs & Emblems. LC 83-14793. (Illus.). 352p. 1984. 17.95 (ISBN 0-442-28059-9). Van Nos Reinhold.

EMERSON, RALPH WALDO, 1803-1882

Alcott, Amos B. Ralph Waldo Emerson. LC 68-24930. (American Biography Ser., No. 32). 1969. Repr. of 1881 ed. lib. bdg. 49.95x (ISBN 0-8383-0908-9). Haskell.

Allen, Fay W. Waldo Emerson. (Illus.). 782p. 1982. pap. 10.95 (ISBN 0-14-006278-5). Penguin.

Allen, Gay W. Waldo Emerson: A Biography. LC 81-65275. (Illus.). 696p. 1981. 25.00 (ISBN 0-670-74866-8). Viking.

Baildon, Henry B. Ralph Waldo Emerson: Man & Teacher. LC 72-14362. Repr. of 1884 ed. lib. bdg. 10.00 (ISBN 0-8414-1340-1). Folcroft.

Bishop, Jonathan. Emerson on the Soul. LC 80-2527. Repr. of 1964 ed. 29.50 (ISBN 0-404-19251-3). AMS Pr.

Bolton, Sarah K. Ralph Waldo Emerson. LC 73-15752. 1973. lib. bdg. 10.00 (ISBN 0-8414-3304-6). Folcroft.

Brooks, Van Wyck. Emerson & Others. LC 73-3132. 250p. 1973. Repr. lib. bdg. 20.50x (ISBN 0-374-90998-9, Octagon). Hippocrene Bks.

--The Life of Emerson. LC 80-2528. Repr. of 1932 ed. 37.00 (ISBN 0-404-19252-1). AMS Pr.

Choate, Joseph H. Ralph Waldo Emerson. 1978. Repr. of 1903 ed. lib. bdg. 8.50 (ISBN 0-8495-0818-5). Arden Lib.

--Ralph Waldo Emerson. LC 73-4034. 1973. lib. bdg. 7.50 (ISBN 0-8414-1831-4). Folcroft.

Christy, Arthur. Orient in American Transcendentalism: A Study of Emerson, Thoreau & Alcott. 1963. lib. bdg. 26.00x (ISBN 0-374-91539-3, Octagon). Hippocrene Bks.

Collins, Robert E. Theodore Parker: American Transcendentalist: A Critical Essay & a Collection of His Writings. LC 73-9593. 277p. 1973. 17.50 (ISBN 0-8108-0641-X). Scarecrow.

Cooke, George W. Ralph Waldo Emerson. LC 74-8996. 1882. lib. bdg. 30.00 (ISBN 0-8414-3367-4). Folcroft.

Dillaway, Newton. Gospel of Emerson. 1968. Repr. 5.95 (ISBN 0-87159-046-8). Unity School.

Dugard, Marie. Ralph Waldo Emerson: Sa Vie et Son Oeuvre. LC 76-100530. (Illus.). Repr. of 1907 ed. 37.50 (ISBN 0-404-02215-4). AMS Pr.

--Ralph Waldo Emerson: Sa Vie et Son Oeuvre. 1973. 16.45 (ISBN 0-8274-0066-7). R West.

Firkins, Oscar W. Ralph Waldo Emerson. LC 80-2532. Repr. of 1915 ed. 44.50 (ISBN 0-404-19258-0). AMS Pr.

Garnett, Richard. Life of Emerson. LC 73-21630. (American Biography Ser., No. 32). 1974. lib. bdg. 49.95x (ISBN 0-8383-1775-8). Haskell.

--Life of Ralph Waldo Emerson. LC 73-12352. 1972. Repr. of 1888 ed. lib. bdg. 12.50 (ISBN 0-8414-4404-8). Folcroft.

Gordon, John D. Ralph Waldo Emerson Eighteen Hundred Three to Eighteen Eighty-Two. LC 73-16267. 1973. lib. bdg. 10.00 (ISBN 0-8414-4481-1). Folcroft.

Goren, Leyla. Elements of Brahmanism in the Transcendentalism of Emerson. LC 80-2534. Repr. of 1959 ed. 18.50 (ISBN 0-404-19260-2). AMS Pr.

Guernsey, Alfred H. Ralph Waldo Emerson. 1978. Repr. of 1901 ed. lib. bdg. 30.00 (ISBN 0-8492-0969-2). R West.

Hale, Edward E. Ralph Waldo Emerson. LC 72-8439. 1972. Repr. of 1902 ed. lib. bdg. 20.00 (ISBN 0-8414-0295-7). Folcroft.

Harris, Kenneth M. Carlyle & Emerson: Their Long Debate. LC 77-28036. 1978. 14.00x (ISBN 0-674-09755-6). Harvard U Pr.

Haskins, David G. Ralph Waldo Emerson. LC 76-122656. 1971. Repr. of 1887 ed. 26.50x (ISBN 0-8046-1305-2, Pub. by Kennikat). Assoc Faculty Pr.

Hill, J. Arthur. Emerson & His Philosophy. LC 72-192678. 1919. lib. bdg. 15.00 (ISBN 0-8414-0783-5). Folcroft.

Holmes, John H. The Enduring Significance of Emerson's Divinity School Address. LC 73-9537. 1938. Repr. lib. bdg. 8.50 (ISBN 0-8414-2073-4). Folcroft.

Hopkins, Vivian C. Spires of Forms: A Study of Emerson's Aesthetic Theory. LC 80-2537. Repr. of 1951 ed. 33.50 (ISBN 0-404-19263-7). AMS Pr.

Hubbard, Stanley. Nietzche und Emerson. LC 80-2538. Repr. of 1958 ed. 25.50 (ISBN 0-404-19264-5). AMS Pr.

Husband, Thomas F. Emerson. A Lecture. LC 77-23227. 1977. Repr. of 1892 ed. lib. bdg. 8.50 (ISBN 0-8414-4947-3). Folcroft.

Hutch, Richard A. Emerson's Optics: Biographical Process & the Dawn of Religious Leadership. 380p. (Orig.). 1983. lib. bdg. 34.25 (ISBN 0-8191-3005-2); pap. text ed. 17.75 (ISBN 0-8191-3006-0). U Pr of Amer.

Kennedy, William S. Clues to Emerson's Mystic Verse. (Studies in Emerson, No. 12). 1970. pap. 39.95x (ISBN 0-8383-0048-0). Haskell.

Loewenberg, Robert J. An American Idol: Emerson & the "Jewish Idea". LC 84-7206. 148p. (Orig.). 1984. lib. bdg. 20.75 (ISBN 0-8191-3955-6); pap. text ed. 9.25 (ISBN 0-8191-3956-4). U Pr of Amer.

Loving, Jerome. Emerson, Whitman, & the American Muse. LC 82-1868. xii, 220p. 1982. 22.00 (ISBN 0-8078-1523-3). U of NC Pr.

Michaud, Regis. Emerson, the Enraptured Yankee. Boas, George, tr. LC 74-5374. Repr. of 1930 ed. 30.00 (ISBN 0-404-11538-1). AMS Pr.

Paramananda, Swami. Emerson & Vedanta. 2nd ed. 1985. pap. 3.50 (ISBN 0-911564-13-6). Vedanta Ctr.

Perris, George H. Emerson. 1973. Repr. of 1910 ed. 25.00 (ISBN 0-8274-0995-8). R West.

Perry, Bliss. Emerson Today. LC 69-19220. 140p. 1969. Repr. of 1931 ed. 18.00 (ISBN 0-208-00798-9, Archon). Shoe String.

Pochmann, Henry A. New England Transcendentalism & St. Louis Hegelianism. LC 68-55163. (Studies in Comparative Literature, No. 35). 1969. Repr. of 1948 ed. lib. bdg. 39.95x (ISBN 0-8383-0610-1). Haskell.

Radicalism in Religion, Philosophy, & Social Life: Four Papers from the Boston Courier for 1858. LC 72-1804. (Black Heritage Library Collection Ser.). Repr. of 1858 ed. 10.50 (ISBN 0-8369-9052-8). Ayer Co Pubs.

Reaver, J. Russell. Emerson As Mythmaker. LC 54-8431. 1954. pap. 4.00 (ISBN 0-8130-0195-1). U Presses Fla.

Robinson, David. Apostle of Culture: Emerson As Preacher & Lecturer. LC 81-16228. 200p. 1982. 21.00x (ISBN 0-8122-7824-0). U of Pa Pr.

Sanborn, Franklin B. Ralph Waldo Emerson. LC 72-7220. Repr. of 1901 ed. lib. bdg. 15.00 (ISBN 0-8414-0262-0). Folcroft.

Sanborn, Franklin B., ed. Genius & Character of Emerson. LC 72-122663. 1971. Repr. of 1885 ed. 27.50x (ISBN 0-8046-1312-5, Pub. by Kennikat). Assoc Faculty Pr.

Searle, January, pseud. Emerson: His Life & Writings. LC 76-40142. 1973. lib. bdg. 10.00 (ISBN 0-8414-7813-9). Folcroft.

Snider, Denton J. A Biography of Ralph Waldo Emerson: Set Forth As His Life Essay. LC 77-9617. 1977. Repr. of 1921 ed. lib. bdg. 40.00 (ISBN 0-8414-7671-3). Folcroft.

--The Life of Emerson. 1973. Repr. of 1921 ed. 30.00 (ISBN 0-8274-0462-X). R West.

Staebler, Warren. Ralph Waldo Emerson. (World Leaders Ser.). 1973. lib. bdg. 12.50 (ISBN 0-8057-3674-3, Twayne). G K Hall.

Stoehr, Taylor. Nay-Saying in Concord: Emerson, Alcott & Thoreau. LC 78-25580. 179p. 1979. 21.50 (ISBN 0-208-01767-4, Archon). Shoe String.

Woodberry, George. Ralph Waldo Emerson. LC 68-24947. (American Biography Ser., No. 32). 1969. Repr. of 1907 ed. lib. bdg. 49.95x (ISBN 0-8383-0262-9). Haskell.

Woodberry, George E. Ralph Waldo Emerson. 1973. lib. bdg. 12.75 (ISBN 0-8414-9790-7). Folcroft.

Zink, Harriet R. Emerson's Use of the Bible. 75p. 1980. Repr. of 1935 ed. lib. bdg. 15.00 (ISBN 0-8495-6206-6). Arden Lib.

--Emerson's Use of the Bible. LC 77-7882. 1977. lib. bdg. 20.00 (ISBN 0-8414-9805-9). Folcroft.

EMERSON, RALPH WALDO, 1803-1882–BIBLIOGRAPHY

Cooke, George W. Bibliography of Ralph Waldo Emerson. 1908. 32.00 (ISBN 0-527-19250-3). Kraus Repr.

EMOTIONS

see also Anxiety; Belief and Doubt; Fear; Grief; Joy and Sorrow; Love; Pain; Prejudices and Antipathies; Temperament; Worry

Albin, Rochelle S. Emotions. LC 83-10187. (Choices: Guides for Today's Woman: Vol. 1). 120p. 1983. pap. 6.95 (ISBN 0-664-24540-4). Westminster.

Baars, Conrad W. Feeling & Healing Your Emotions. LC 79-53629. 1979. pap. 5.95 (ISBN 0-88270-384-6, Pub. by Logos). Bridge Pub.

Belcher, Jim, Jr. The Inspirations of God & the Emotions of Life. 64p. 1987. 6.95 (ISBN 0-89962-588-6). Todd & Honeywell.

Burgess, Andrew J. Passion, Knowing How, & Understanding: An Essay on the Concept of Faith. LC 75-31550. (American Academy of Religion. Dissertation Ser.). 1975. pap. 9.95 (ISBN 0-89130-044-9, 010109). Scholars Pr GA.

Chisholm, Alex & Chisholm, Sarah. Emotions: Can You Trust Them? Leader's Guide. 48p. 1984. pap. 3.95 (ISBN 0-8307-0992-4, 6101926). Regal.

Dobson, James. Emotions: Can You Trust Them? LC 79-91703. 144p. 1980. text ed. 7.95 (ISBN 0-8307-0730-1, 5109108). Regal.

Drane, James. Your Emotional Life & What You Can Do about It. 204p. 1984. 9.95 (ISBN 0-88347-157-4). Thomas More.

Edwards, Jonathan. Religious Affections. Smith, John E., ed. LC 59-12702. (Works of Jonathan Edwards Ser.: Vol. 2). (Illus.). 1959. 50.00x (ISBN 0-300-00966-6). Yale U Pr.

Franasiak, Edwin J., ed. Belonging: Issues of Emotional Living in an Age of Stress for Clergy & Religious. LC 79-11482. 127p. 1979. pap. 4.95 (ISBN 0-89571-007-2). Affirmation.

Furst, Jeffrey, ed. Edgar Cayce's Story of Attitudes & Emotions. 1983. pap. 3.50 (ISBN 0-425-08194-X). Berkley Pub.

Ghezzi, Bert. Facing Your Feelings: How to Get Your Emotions to Work for You. (Living as a Christian Ser.). 112p. 1983. pap. 2.95 (ISBN 0-89283-133-2). Servant.

Hutcheson, Francis. Essay on the Nature & Conduct of the Passions & Affections, 1742. 3rd ed. LC 76-81361. (History of Psychology Ser.). 1969. Repr. of 1742 ed. 50.00x (ISBN 0-8201-1058-2). Schol Facsimiles.

I Have Many Feelings: With Scriptural Encouragement. (Little Shape Bks.). (Illus.). 22p. 1984. 2.50 (ISBN 0-89954-240-9). Antioch Pub Co.

King, William. An Essay on the Origin of Evil. Bd. with Dissertations Concerning the Fundamental Principle & Immediate Criterion of Virtue. LC 75-11228. (British Philosophers & Theologians of the 17th & 18th Centuries Ser.). 391p. 1978. lib. bdg. 51.00 (ISBN 0-8240-1782-X). Garland Pub.

Langer, Susanne K. Mind: An Essay on Human Feeling. Incl. Vol. I. Mind. (Illus.). 512p. 1967. 34.50x (ISBN 0-8018-0360-8); pap. 11.95 (ISBN 0-8018-1150-3); Vol. II. 412p. 1973. 28.50x (ISBN 0-8018-1428-6); pap. 9.95 (ISBN 0-8018-1607-6); Vol. III. 264p. Set of 3 vols. 26.50 (ISBN 0-8018-2756-6); pap. 8.95 (ISBN 0-8018-2511-3); pap. 28.85x (ISBN 0-8018-2555-5). LC 66-26686. Johns Hopkins.

Lutzer, Erwin. Managing Your Emotions. 180p. 1983. pap. 5.95 (ISBN 0-88207-386-9). Victor Bks.

Neblett, William. The Role of Feelings in Morals. LC 81-40105. 114p. (Orig.). 1981. lib. bdg. 24.75 (ISBN 0-8191-1752-8); pap. text ed. 9.75 (ISBN 0-8191-1753-6). U Pr of Amer.

Poujol, F. A. Dictionnaire des Facultes Intellectuelles et Affectives de l'ame ou l'on Traite des Passions, des Vertus, des Vices, des Defauts. Migne, J. P., ed. (Encyclopedie Theologique Ser.: Vol. 39). (Fr.). 560p. Repr. of 1849 ed. lib. bdg. 72.00x (ISBN 0-89241-245-3). Caratzas.

Roberts, Robert C. Spirituality & Human Emotion. 134p. 1983. pap. 5.95 (ISBN 0-8028-1939-7). Eerdmans.

Seamands, David A. Healing for Damaged Emotions. 1981. pap. 5.95 (ISBN 0-88207-228-5). Victor Bks.

Smith, Joyce M. Understanding Your Emotions. 1977. pap. 2.95 (ISBN 0-8423-7770-0). Tyndale.

Solomon, Robert C. The Passions. xxv, 448p. 1983. text ed. 22.95x (ISBN 0-268-01551-1); pap. text ed. 9.95x (ISBN 0-268-01552-X). U of Notre Dame Pr.

Stroud, Marion. Please Tell Me How You Feel. LC 83-22410. 160p. 1984. pap. 4.95 (ISBN 0-87123-427-0, 210427). Bethany Hse.

Tengbom, Mildred. I Wish I Felt Good All the Time. 160p. (Orig.). 1983. pap. 4.95 (ISBN 0-87123-281-2, 210281). Bethany Hse.

Thurston, Mark. How to Change Attitudes & Emotions. Orig. Title: A Course in Practical Spirituality. 147p. 1986. wkbk., text, 4 cassettes 29.95 (ISBN 0-87604-181-0). ARE Pr.

Villafranca, Anthony L. The Theory of Sin & the Equilibrium Between the Emotional & the Rational in Man. (Illus.). 104p. 1986. 88.50 (ISBN 0-89266-568-8). Am Classical Coll Pr.

Westermarck, Edward. The Theory of the Moral Emotions. (Illus.). 161p. 1984. 89.75x (ISBN 0-89266-464-9). Am Classical Coll Pr.

White, Ellen. Passions. 1985. pap. 6.00 (ISBN 0-914009-55-9). VHI Library.

--Passions among God's People. large print ed. 35p. 1985. pap. 6.00 (ISBN 0-914009-46-X). VHI Library.

Wright, Norman. Living with Your Emotions: Self-Image & Depression. LC 79-83661. 1979. 7.95 (ISBN 0-89081-193-8); avail. tchr's guide. Harvest Hse.

EMPEROR WORSHIP

Morrison, Clinton D. Powers That Be: Earthly Rulers & Demonic Powers in Romans, Chapter 13, 1-7. LC 60-4219. (Studies in Biblical Theology: No. 29). 1960. pap. 10.00x (ISBN 0-8401-3029-5). A R Allenson.

Scott, Kenneth. The Imperial Cult Under the Flavians. facsimile ed. LC 75-10655. (Ancient Religion & Mythology Ser.). 1976. Repr. of 1936 ed. 17.00x (ISBN 0-405-07263-5). Ayer Co Pubs.

Taylor, Lily R. The Divinity of the Roman Emperor. LC 75-7348. (Roman History Ser.). (Illus.). 1975. Repr. 29.00x (ISBN 0-405-07068-3). Ayer Co Pubs.

Weinstock, Stefan. Divus Julius. 1971. 74.00x (ISBN 0-19-814287-0). Oxford U Pr.

EMPIRICAL THEOLOGY

Dean, William. American Religious Empiricism. (Religious Studies). 126p. (Orig.). 1986. 34.50x (ISBN 0-88706-280-6); pap. 10.95 (ISBN 0-88706-281-4). State U NY Pr.

Meland, Bernard E. Future of Empirical Theology. Braver, J. C., ed. LC 78-83980. (Essays in Divinty Ser: Vol. 7). 1969. 20.00x (ISBN 0-226-51955-4). U of Chicago Pr.

EMPIRICISM

see also Empirical Theology

Dennehy, Raymond. Reason & Dignity. LC 81-40364. 152p. 1982. lib. bdg. 25.00 (ISBN 0-8191-1898-2); pap. text ed. 9.75 (ISBN 0-8191-1899-0). U Pr of Amer.

Sextus Empiricus. Scepticism, Man & God: Selections from the Major Writings Of Sextus Empiricus. Hallie, Philip P., ed. Etheridge, Sanford G., tr. LC 64-22377. pap. 62.00 (ISBN 0-317-08988-9, 2001959). Bks Demand UMI.

Smith, John E. Religion & Empiricism. (Aquinas Lecture Ser.). 1967. 7.95 (ISBN 0-87462-132-1). Marquette.

ENCOURAGEMENT

Adelsperger, Charlotte. Effective Encouragement. (Illus.). 64p. 1986. pap. 2.95 (ISBN 0-87403-077-3, 3197). Standard Pub.

Doering, Jeanne. Your Power of Encouragement. (Moody Press Electives Ser.). (Orig.). 1985. pap. text ed. 3.95 (ISBN 0-8024-0687-4); leader's guide 2.50 (ISBN 0-8024-0688-2). Moody.

Taulman, James E. Encouragers: The Sunday School Worker's Counseling Ministry. LC 85-19523. 1986. pap. 4.95 (ISBN 0-8054-3712-6). Broadman.

Words of Encouragement. (Words of... Ser.). (Illus.). 48p. 1983. 3.95 (ISBN 0-8407-5332-2). Nelson.

ENCYCLICALS, PAPAL

The Addresses of His Holiness Pope John Paul II to the United States Bishops During Their Ad Limina Visits: Ad Limina Addresses. 60p. 1983. pap. 4.95 (ISBN 1-55586-926-2). US Catholic.

Daughters of St. Paul, ed. Dimensions of the Priesthood. new ed. 1973. 5.75 (ISBN 0-8198-0253-0); pap. 4.50 (ISBN 0-8198-0254-9). Dghtrs St Paul.

Monks Of Solesmes, ed. Liturgy: One Hundred Sixty-Nine Pronouncements from Benedict Fourteenth to John Twenty-Third. 5.00 (ISBN 0-8198-0083-X). Dghtrs St Paul.

Pope Pius Twelfth. Directives to Lay Apostles: Eighty-Six Pronouncements. Monks Of Solesmes, ed. 1964. 4.00 (ISBN 0-8198-0035-X); pap. 3.00 (ISBN 0-8198-0036-8). Dghtrs St Paul.

Von Hildebrand, Dietrich. Encyclical Humanae Vitae: A Sign of Contradiction. (Orig.). 1969. pap. 2.00 (ISBN 0-685-10965-8). Franciscan Herald.

END OF THE WORLD

see also Antichrist; Judgment Day

Barrett, James W., ed. End of 'The World' facs. ed. LC 72-117866. (Select Bibliographies Reprint Ser). 1931. 24.50 (ISBN 0-8369-5319-3). Ayer Co Pubs.

Cohen, Daniel. Waiting for the Apocalypse: Doomsday Deferred. rev. ed. LC 83-62189. (Illus.). 260p. 1983. pap. 10.95 (ISBN 0-87975-223-8). Prometheus Bks.

Cribb, C. C. Armageddon-Dead Ahead. LC 77-70212. pap. 2.95 (ISBN 0-932046-03-7). Manhattan Ltd NC.

--Man's Earth-Lease Is About to Expire. LC 77-70210. pap. 2.95 (ISBN 0-932046-01-0). Manhattan Ltd NC.

Crowley, Dale. Soon Coming of Our Lord. 1958. pap. 2.95 (ISBN 0-87213-091-6). Loizeaux.

Davies, Kirk. Earth's Final Hours. 330p. (Orig.). 1982. pap. 9.95 (ISBN 0-9609174-0-3). Pacific Inst.

De Haan, M. R. Days of Noah. 5.95 (ISBN 0-310-23331-3, 9512P). Zondervan.

De Haan, Martin R. Coming Events in Prophecy. 5.95 (ISBN 0-310-23301-1). Zondervan.

Douglas, C. E. When All Hell Breaks Loose. 1974. pap. 4.95 (ISBN 0-9601124-0-5). Tusayan Gospel.

English, E. Schuyler. The Rapture. 1954. pap. 5.95 (ISBN 0-87213-144-0). Loizeaux.

Hayes, Zachary. What Are They Saying about the End of the World? (WATSA Ser.). 80p. (Orig.). 1983. pap. 4.95 (ISBN 0-8091-2550-1). Paulist Pr.

LaHaye, Tim. Beginning of the End. 1981. pap. 3.50 mass market (ISBN 0-8423-0114-3). Tyndale.

Lerner, Robert E. The Powers of Prophecy: The Cedar of Lebanon Vision from the Mongol Onslaught to the Dawn of the Enlightenment. LC 82-4824. 256p. 1983. text ed. 38.50x (ISBN 0-520-04461-4). U of Cal Pr.

Lovett, C. S. Latest Word on the Last Days. (Illus., Orig.). 1980. pap. 6.95 (ISBN 0-938148-00-1). Personal Christianity.

Malgo, Wim. Shadows of Armageddon. 4.95 (ISBN 0-937422-15-0). Midnight Call.

Miller, Calvin. The Finale. LC 78-70810. (Illus.). 1979. pap. 5.95 (ISBN 0-87784-627-8). Inter-Varsity.

Ryrie, Charles C. The Final Countdown. 120p. 1982. pap. 4.95 (ISBN 0-88207-347-8). Victor Bks.

Schlink, Basilea. Patmos: When the Heavens Opened. LC 76-24522. 1976. pap. 1.95 (ISBN 0-88419-012-9). Creation Hse.

Talbot, Louis T. God's Plan of the Ages. 1936. pap. 8.95 (ISBN 0-8028-1194-9). Eerdmans.

Thomas, Leslie G. Truth, the Millennium, & the Battle of Armageddon. 1979. pap. 2.50 (ISBN 0-89225-188-3). Gospel Advocate.

Van Doren, Mark. How Praise a World That May Not Last. 1977. pap. 6.95 handset, handbound (ISBN 0-89016-039-2). Lightning Tree.

Welch, Adam C. Visions of the End: A Study in Daniel & Revelation. 260p. 1958. Repr. of 1922 ed. 10.95 (ISBN 0-227-67631-9). Attic Pr.

Wilson, Everett L. Jesus & the End-Time. 1977. pap. 3.95 (ISBN 0-910452-32-6). Covenant.

ENDLESS PUNISHMENT

see Future Punishment; Hell

ENDOWMENTS

Here are entered general works on endowed institutions, endowment funds and donations to such funds. Works on the legal structure of endowments are entered under the heading Charitable Uses, trusts and Foundations.

see also Charities

Butler, Francis J. & Farrell, Catherine E. Foundation Guide for Religious Grant Seekers. 2nd, rev., updated ed. LC 84-10593. (Handbook Ser.). 150p. 1984. pap. 11.95 (ISBN 0-89130-756-7, 00 15 02). Scholars Pr GA.

Stough, Richard H. Bequests, Endowments, & Special Gifts. (Orig.). 1981. pap. 1.75 (ISBN 0-937172-27-8). JLJ Pubs.

ENGLAND, JOHN, BP., 1786-1842

Carey, Patrick. An Immigrant Bishop: John England's Adaptation of Irish Catholicism to American Republicanism. LC 79-63860. (USCHS Monograph: Vol. 36). (Illus.). ix, 236p. 1982. 14.95x (ISBN 0-930060-16-4). US Cath Hist.

Guilday, Peter K. Life & Times of John England. LC 70-83422. (Religion in America, Ser. 1). 1969. Repr. of 1927 ed. 54.00 (ISBN 0-405-00247-5). Ayer Co Pubs.

ENGLAND-ANTIQUITIES

Hope, Robert C. Legendary Lore of the Holy Wells of England. LC 68-21775. (Illus.). 1968. Repr. of 1893 ed. 35.00x (ISBN 0-8103-3445-3). Gale.

ENGLAND, CHURCH OF

see Church of England

ENGLISH DRAMA (COLLECTIONS)-TO 1500

Bevington, David M., ed. The Macro Plays. LC 72-3905. 1972. 50.00 (ISBN 0-384-34920-X). Johnson Repr.

Block, K. S., ed. Ludus Coventriae, Or, the Place Called Corpus Christi. (Early English Text Society Ser.). 1922. 26.00x (ISBN 0-19-722560-8). Oxford U Pr.

Cawley, A. C., ed. Everyman & Medieval Miracle Plays. 10.95x (ISBN 0-460-10381-4, Evman). Biblio Dist.

Eccles, Mark, ed. Macro Plays: The Castle of Perseverance, Wisdom, Mankind. (Early English Text Society Ser.). 1969. 17.95x (ISBN 0-19-722265-X). Oxford U Pr.

Franklin, Alexander. Seven Miracle Plays. 1963. pap. 8.95x (ISBN 0-19-831391-8). Oxford U Pr.

Hopper, Vincent F. & Lahey, Gerald B., eds. Medieval Mysteries, Moralities & Interludes. LC 61-18362. 1962. pap. text ed. 5.95 (ISBN 0-8120-0135-4). Barron.

Manly, John M. Specimens of the Pre-Shakespearean Drama, 2 Vols. LC 67-18432. 1897. 20.00 (ISBN 0-8196-0200-0). Biblo.

Rose, Martial, ed. Wakefield Mystery Plays. 1969. pap. 10.95x (ISBN 0-393-00483-X, Norton Lib). Norton.

Smith, Lucy T., ed. York Plays: The Plays Performed on the Day of Corpus Christi in the 14th, 15th, & 16th Centuries. LC 63-15180. (Illus.). 1963. Repr. of 1885 ed. 21.00x (ISBN 0-8462-0313-8). Russell.

ENGLISH DRAMA-HISTORY AND CRITICISM-TO 1500

Collier, Richard. Poetry & Drama in the York Corpus Christi Play. LC 77-21348. 303p. 1977. 27.50 (ISBN 0-208-01611-2, Archon). Shoe String.

Craig, Hardin. English Religious Drama of the Middle Ages. LC 78-6893. 1978. Repr. of 1968 ed. lib. bdg. 37.50x (ISBN 0-313-20496-9, CRER). Greenwood.

Davidson, Charles. Studies in the English Mystery Plays. LC 68-752. (Studies in Drama, No. 39). 1969. Repr. of 1892 ed. lib. bdg. 49.95x (ISBN 0-8383-0536-9). Haskell.

Gardiner, Harold C. Mysteries' End: An Investigation of the Last Days of the Medieval Religious Stage. LC 67-26652. (Yale Studies in English Ser.: No. 103). xiv, 139p. 1967. Repr. of 1946 ed. 21.50 (ISBN 0-208-00385-1, Archon). Shoe String.

Gardner, John C. The Construction of the Wakefield Cycle. LC 74-5191. (Literary Structures Ser.). 173p. 1974. 8.95x (ISBN 0-8093-0668-9). S Ill U Pr.

Hone, William. Ancient Mysteries Described. LC 67-23905. (Illus.). 1969. Repr. of 1823 ed. 35.00x (ISBN 0-8103-3444-5). Gale.

Lumiansky, R. M. & Mills, David. The Chester Mystery Cycle: Essays & Documents. LC 82-1838. viii, 339p. 1983. 40.00x (ISBN 0-8078-1522-5); essay "Music in the Cycle" by Richard Rastall incl. U of NC Pr.

Nelson, Alan H. The Medieval English Stage: Corpus Christi Pageants & Plays. LC 73-85247. (Patterns of Literary Criticism Ser). 288p. 1974. 21.00x (ISBN 0-226-57173-4). U of Chicago Pr.

Neuss, Paula, ed. Aspects of Early English Drama. LC 83-21331. (Illus.). 176p. 1985. Repr. of 1983 ed. 42.50x (ISBN 0-389-20428-5, 07314). B&N Imports.

Prosser, Eleanor. Drama & Religion in the English Mystery Plays: A Re-Evaluation. 1961. 18.50x (ISBN 0-8047-0060-5). Stanford U Pr.

Whiting, B. J. Proverbs in the Earlier English Drama. LC 70-86290. 1969. Repr. of 1938 ed. lib. bdg. 34.50x (ISBN 0-374-98513-8, Octagon). Hippocrene Bks.

ENGLISH LITERATURE-CATHOLIC AUTHORS

Boulger, James D. The Calvinistic Temper in English Poetry. (De Proprietatibus Litterarum, Ser. Major: No. 21). 1980. text ed. 71.00x (ISBN 90-279-7575-2). Mouton.

Braybrooke, Patrick. Some Catholic Novelists. facs. ed. LC 67-22078. (Essay Index Reprint Ser.). 1931. 19.00 (ISBN 0-8369-1323-X). Ayer Co Pubs.

Gross, Raphael H., ed. Century of the Catholic Essay. facs. ed. LC 76-134087. (Essay Index Reprint Ser.). 1946. 19.00 (ISBN 0-8369-2190-9). Ayer Co Pubs.

Mary Louise, Sr., ed. Over the Bent World. LC 73-105031. (Essay Index Reprint Ser.). 1939. 40.00 (ISBN 0-8369-1676-X). Ayer Co Pubs.

ENGLISH LITERATURE-CATHOLIC AUTHORS-HISTORY AND CRITICISM

Boulger, James D. The Calvinistic Temper in English Poetry. (De Proprietatibus Litterarum, Ser. Major: No. 21). 1980. text ed. 71.00x (ISBN 90-279-7575-2). Mouton.

Braybrooke, Patrick. Some Victorian & Georgian Catholics. facs. ed. LC 67-22080. (Essay Index Reprint Ser.). 1932. 18.00 (ISBN 0-8369-1325-6). Ayer Co Pubs.

Colby, Elbridge. English Catholic Poets, Chaucer to Dryden. facs. ed. LC 67-28733. (Essay Index Reprint Ser.). 1936. 18.00 (ISBN 0-8369-0321-8). Ayer Co Pubs.

Hutton, Edward. Catholicism & English Literature. LC 76-26671. 1942. lib. bdg. 30.00 (ISBN 0-8414-4926-0). Folcroft.

ENGLISH LITERATURE-TRANSLATIONS FROM ORIENTAL LITERATURE

Pritchard, James B., ed. Ancient Near East in Pictures with Supplement. 2nd ed. Incl. Ancient Near Eastern Texts Relating to the Old Testament with Supplement. 3rd ed. Set. text ed. 60.50x ea. (ISBN 0-691-03503-2, 035032T); pictures 66.25x (032024T). 1969. deluxe ed. 68.50x ea. (ISBN 0-691-03502-4); Set. 126.75x (ISBN 0-686-66606-2). Princeton U Pr.

ENGLISH POETRY (COLLECTIONS)

see also American Poetry (Collections)

Emerson, Ralph Waldo, ed. Parnassus. facsimile ed. LC 73-116400. (Granger Index Reprint Ser). 1874. 25.50 (ISBN 0-8369-6141-2). Ayer Co Pubs.

Reeves, Una G. Writing Verse As a Hobby. 1962. 6.95 (ISBN 0-8158-0172-6). Chris Mass.

ENGLISH POETRY (COLLECTIONS)-20TH CENTURY

Catholic Anthology: Nineteen Fourteen to Nineteen Fifteen. LC 78-64009. (Des Imagistes: Literature of the Imagist Movement). Repr. of 1915 ed. 15.00 (ISBN 0-404-17083-8). AMS Pr.

ENGLISH POETRY-TRANSLATIONS FROM ANGLO-SAXON

Anderson, James E. Two Literary Riddles in the Exeter Book: Riddle 1 & the Easter Riddle. LC 85-40471. (Illus.). 288p. 1986. 27.50x (ISBN 0-8061-1947-0). U of Okla Pr.

Kennedy, Charles W., tr. Early English Christian Poetry. 1963. pap. 5.95 (ISBN 0-19-500246-6). Oxford U Pr.

ENLIGHTENMENT

Beierle, Herbert L. Illumination: Handbook of Ascended Masters. 1978. 20.00 (ISBN 0-940480-02-6). U of Healing.

Bernard, Paul P. Jesuits & Jacobins: Enlightenment & Enlightened Despotism in Austria. LC 78-151997. 207p. 1971. 19.95 (ISBN 0-252-00180-X). U of Ill Pr.

Bobroff, Alvin & Krishnamurti, U. G. Mystique of Enlightenment. 190p. 1985. pap. 9.95 (ISBN 0-87418-020-1, 156). Coleman Pub.

Bredvold, Louis I. The Brave New World of the Enlightenment. LC 61-10987. pap. 43.00 (ISBN 0-317-08088-1, 2051585). Bks Demand UMI.

Commager, Henry S. The Empire of Reason: How Europe Imagined & America Realized the Enlightenment. 1984. 17.25 (ISBN 0-8446-6088-4). Peter Smith.

Cragg, Gerald R. Church & the Age of Reason. (History of the Church: Vol. 4). (Orig.). 1961. pap. 5.95 (ISBN 0-14-020505-5, Pelican). Penguin.

Crocker, Lester G. An Age of Crisis: Man & World in Eighteenth Century French Thought. LC 59-14233. (Goucher College Ser.). Repr. of 1959 ed. 129.00 (ISBN 0-8357-9260-9, 2011983). Bks Demand UMI.

Dass, Ram. The Only Dance There Is. LC 73-14054. 295p. 1974. pap. 6.95 (ISBN 0-385-08413-7, Anch). Doubleday.

Frankel, Charles. Faith of Reason. LC 71-86277. 1969. Repr. of 1948 ed. lib. bdg. 17.00x (ISBN 0-374-92850-9, Octagon). Hippocrene Bks.

Gay, Peter. The Enlightenment: An Interpretation-the Rise of Modern Paganism, Vol. 1. 1977. pap. 10.95x (ISBN 0-393-00870-3, N870, Norton Lib). Norton.

Harari, Josue V. Scenarios of the Imaginary: Theorizing the French Englightenment. LC 86-24247. 240p. 1987. text ed. 24.95x (ISBN 0-8014-1842-9). Cornell U Pr.

Hunt, Margaret & Jacob, Margaret, eds. Women & the Enlightenment. LC 84-590. (Women & History: No. 9). 93p. 1984. text ed. 24.95 (ISBN 0-86656-190-0). Haworth Pr.

John, Da F. Enlightenment & the Transformation of Man. LC 83-72730. 1983. pap. 7.95 (ISBN 0-913922-83-8). Dawn Horse Pr.

Manuel, Frank E. The Changing of the Gods. LC 82-40475. 216p. 1983. 20.00x (ISBN 0-87451-254-9). U Pr of New Eng.

Matsuo, Hosaku. The Logic of Unity: The Discovery of Zero & Emptiness in Prajanaparamita Thought. Inada, Kenneth K., tr. (Buddhist studies). 144p. 1987. 29.50 (ISBN 0-88706-391-8); pap. 9.95 (ISBN 0-88706-392-6). State U NY Pr.

Muktananda, Swami. En Busca del Ser. LC 81-50917. 140p. 1981. pap. 4.95 (ISBN 0-914602-71-3). SYDA Found.

--En Compania de un Siddha. LC 81-84263. 1981. pap. 5.95. SYDA Found.

--La Relacion Perfecta. LC 81-84261. 218p. 1982. pap. 6.95 (ISBN 0-914602-84-5). SYDA Found.

Perkins, J. A. The Concept of the Self in the French Enlightenment. 162p. (Orig.). 1969. pap. text ed. 24.50x (Pub. by Droz Switzerland). Coronet Bks.

Sher, Richard B. Church & University in the Scottish Enlightenment: The Moderate Literati of Edinburgh. LC 85-17911. (Illus.). 1985. text ed. 47.50x (ISBN 0-691-05445-2). Princeton U Pr.

Smothermon, Ron. Winning Through Enlightenment. 2nd ed. 226p. 1982. pap. 9.95 (ISBN 0-932654-01-0). Context Pubns.

Stone, Barbara. The Open Moment. 400p. (Orig.). 1985. pap. 11.95 (ISBN 0-87418-021-X, 158). Coleman Pub.

Swami Virajananda. Toward the Goal Supreme. LC 73-87782. 155p. 1973. pap. 3.50 (ISBN 0-87481-029-9). Vedanta Pr.

Wessell, Leonard P. G.E Lessing's Theology: A Reinterpretation, a Study in the Problematic Nature of the Enlightenment. 1977. 20.00x (ISBN 90-279-7801-8). Mouton.

ENOCH

Knibb, M. A., ed. The Ethiopic Book of Enoch, 2 vols. 1978. 84.00x set (ISBN 0-19-826163-2). Oxford U Pr.

Lawrence, Richard, tr. The Book of Enoch. LC 80-65736. 96p. 1980. pap. 4.00 (ISBN 0-934666-06-7). Artisan Sales.

Lindsay, Gordon. Enoch & Noah, Patriarchs of the Deluge. (Old Testament Ser.). 1.25 (ISBN 0-89985-125-8). Christ Nations.

Nibley, Hugh. Enoch the Prophet. 1986. text ed. 15.95 (ISBN 0-87579-047-X). Deseret Bk.

Prophet, Elizabeth C. Forbidden Mysteries of Enoch. LC 82-62445. (Illus.). 504p. 1983. pap. 12.95 (ISBN 0-916766-60-8). Summit Univ.

VanderKam, James C. Enoch & the Growth of an Apocalyptic Tradition. LC 83-10134. (Catholic Biblical Quarterly Monographs: No. 16). 217p. 1984. pap. 6.50 (ISBN 0-915170-15-9). Catholic Bibl Assn.

ENTHUSIASM

Casaubon, Meric. Treatise Concerning Enthusiasme. LC 77-119864. 1970. Repr. of 1656 ed. 45.00x (ISBN 0-8201-1077-9). Schol Facsimiles.

Knox, Ronald A. Enthusiasm. 630p. 1983. pap. 14.95 (ISBN 0-87061-080-5). Chr Classics.

Lee, Umphrey. Historical Backgrounds of Early Methodist Enthusiasm. LC 31-18047. (Columbia University. Studies in the Social Sciences: No. 339). Repr. of 1931 ed. 17.50 (ISBN 0-404-51339-5). AMS Pr.

Peale, Norman V. Enthusiasm Makes the Difference. 1978. pap. 2.50 (ISBN 0-449-23698-6, Crest). Fawcett.

ENVY

Ulanov, Barry & Ulanov, Ann. Cinderella & Her Sisters: The Envied & the Envying. LC 83-10463. 186p. 1983. pap. 9.95 (ISBN 0-664-24482-3). Westminster.

EPHRATA COMMUNITY

Jacoby, John E. Two Mystic Communities in America. LC 75-326. (The Radical Tradition in America Ser). 104p. 1975. Repr. of 1931 ed. 15.00 (ISBN 0-88355-230-2). Hyperion Conn.

Sachse, Julius F. Music of the Ephrata Cloister. LC 77-134386. (Communal Societies Ser.). Repr. of 1903 ed. 15.00 (ISBN 0-404-05500-1). AMS Pr.

Wust, Klaus. The Saint-Adventurers of the Virginia Frontier. LC 76-48566. (Illus.). 1977. 8.50 (ISBN 0-917968-29-8). Shenandoah Hist.

Zerfass, Samuel G. Souvenir Book of the Ephrata Cloister: Complete History from Its Settlement in 1728 to the Present Time. LC 72-2960. Repr. of 1921 ed. 14.25 (ISBN 0-404-10724-9). AMS Pr.

EPIPHANY

see also Magi

Augustine, St. St. Augustine, Sermons for Christmas & Epiphany. Quasten, J. & Plumpe, J., eds. Lawler, Thomas, tr. LC 78-62464. (Ancient Christian Writers Ser.: No. 15). 250p. 1952. 10.95 (ISBN 0-8091-0137-8). Paulist Pr.

Bass, George. The Cradle, the Cross & the Crown. Sherer, Michael L., ed. (Orig.). 1986. pap. 7.25 (ISBN 0-89536-817-X, 6866). CSS of Ohio.

Bershadsky, Luba & Millington, Ada. I Know His Touch. 240p. 1985. pap. 2.95 (ISBN 0-345-32164-2). Ballantine.

Burgess, Joseph A. & Winn, Albert C. Epiphany. Achtemeier, Elizabeth, et al, eds. LC 79-7377. (Proclamation 2: Aids for Interpreting the Lessons of the Church Year, Series A). 64p. (Orig.). 1980. pap. 3.75 (ISBN 0-8006-4092-6, 1-4092). Fortress.

Buttrick, David. Epiphany. LC 84-18756. (Proclamation 3 C Ser.). 64p. 1985. pap. 3.75 (ISBN 0-8006-4126-4). Fortress.

Carlston, Charles. Epiphany. Achtemeier, Elizabeth, ed. LC 84-6012. (Proclamation 3: Aids for Interpreting the Lessons of the Church Year Series B). 64p. 1984. pap. 3.75 (ISBN 0-8006-4102-7). Fortress.

Dorsett, Lyle W. And God Came In: The Extraordinary Story of Joy Davidman; Her Life & Marriage to C. S. Lewis. (Illus.). 192p. 1984. pap. 2.95 (ISBN 0-345-31787-4). Ballantine.

Eslinger, Richard. Prepare in the Wilderness. 1984. 5.25 (ISBN 0-89536-680-0, 4856). CSS of Ohio.

Gauchat, Dorothy & Lyons, Arthur. All God's Children. 224p. 1985. pap. 2.50 (ISBN 0-345-31988-5). Ballantine.

Hopko, Thomas. Winter Pascha. LC 84-27622. 1983. pap. text ed. 6.95 (ISBN 0-88141-025-X). St Vladimirs.

Micks, Marianne H. Epiphany. LC 84-18756. (Proclamation 3A Ser.). 64p. 1986. pap. 3.75 (ISBN 0-8006-4118-3). Fortress.

Mueller, Daniel. Just Follow the Signs. 1984. 5.00 (ISBN 0-89536-676-2, 4851). CSS of Ohio.

Pervo, Richard I. & Carl, William J., III. Epiphany. Achtemeier, Elizabeth, et al, eds. LC 79-7377. (Proclamation 2: Aids for Interpreting the Lessons of the Church Year, Series C). 64p. 1979. pap. 3.75 (ISBN 0-8006-4085-3, 1-4085). Fortress.

Ridenhour, Thomas E., Sr. Promise of Peace, Call for Justice. Sherer, Michael L., ed. (Orig.). 1986. pap. 6.75 (ISBN 0-89536-822-6, 6831). CSS of Ohio.

Saunders, Ernest W. & Craddock, Fred B. Epiphany. Achtemeier, Elizabeth, et al, eds. LC 79-7377. (Proclamation 2: Aids for Interpreting the Lessons of the Church Year, Series B). 64p. 1981. pap. 3.75 (ISBN 0-8006-4069-1, 1-4069). Fortress.

EPISCOPACY

see also Anglican Orders; Apostolic Succession; Bishops; Dioceses; Methodism

Batterson, Herman G. Sketchbook of the American Episcopate, During One Hundred Years, 1783-1883. 1980. Repr. cancelled (ISBN 0-87921-047-8). Attic Pr.

Booty, John E. The Servant Church: Diaconal Ministry & the Episcopal Church. LC 82-81429. (Orig.). 1982. pap. 7.95 (ISBN 0-8192-1316-0). Morehouse.

--What Makes Us Episcopalians? 48p. 1982. pap. 3.50 (ISBN 0-8192-1302-0, 82-80468). Morehouse.

Cross, Arthur L. The Anglican Episcopate & the American Colonies. ix, 368p. 1964. Repr. of 1902 ed. 32.50 (ISBN 0-208-00420-3, Archon). Shoe String.

EPISCOPAL CHURCH

see Church of England; Church of Ireland; Protestant Episcopal Church in the U. S. A.

Sumner, David E. The Episcopal Church's History: 1945-1985. 1987. 24.95. Morehouse.

EPISCOPALIANS

Bragg, George F., Jr. History of the Afro-American Group of the Episcopal Church. (Basic Afro-American Reprint Library). (Illus.). Repr. of 1922 ed. 17.00 (ISBN 0-384-05495-1). Johnson Repr.

Douglass, William. Sermons Preached in the African Protestant Episcopal Church of St. Thomas' Philadelphia. facs. ed. LC 79-157366. (Black Heritage Library Collection Ser). 1854. 20.00 (ISBN 0-8369-8804-3). Ayer Co Pubs.

Hall, Robert B. Church Growth for Episcopalians. 1982. pap. 4.95 (ISBN 0-686-37069-4). Episcopal Ctr.

Hoskins, Charles L. Black Episcopalians in Georgia: Strife, Struggle & Salvation. (Illus.). 168p. 1980. 8.00 (ISBN 0-686-31304-6). St Matthew's.

Whalen, William J. Reaching Out to the Episcopalians with Heart & Mind. (Reaching Out to...Ser.). 32p. 1984. pap. 1.50 (ISBN 0-89243-210-1). Liguori Pubns.

EPITAPHS

see also Sepulchral Monuments

Bourasse, J. J. Dictionnaire d'Epigraphie Chretienne, 2 vols. Migne, J. P., ed. (Nouvelle Encyclopedie Theologique Ser.: Vols. 30-31). (Fr.). 1262p. Repr. of 1852 ed. lib. bdg. 161.00x (ISBN 0-89241-273-9). Caratzas.

Dingley, Thomas. History from Marble, 2 Vols. LC 70-164834. (Camden Society, London. Publications, First Ser.: Nos. 94 & 97). Repr. of 1868 ed. Set. 74.00 (ISBN 0-404-50210-5). AMS Pr.

Jones, Philipa. Selected Garlands. 160p. 1986. pap. 30.00x (ISBN 0-947939-02-4, Pub. by Elmcrest UK). State Mutual Bk.

Kippax, John R. Churchyard Literature: A Choice Collection of American Epitaphs. 213p. 1978. Repr. of 1876 ed. 16.95 (ISBN 0-87928-087-5). Corner Hse.

EQUALITY

Bailey, Deloros S. God's Country U. S. A. 1982. 17.95 (ISBN 0-913730-04-1). Robinson Pr.

Carens, Joseph H. Equality, Moral Incentives, & the Market. LC 80-36774. (Illus.). 264p. 1981. lib. bdg. 19.00x (ISBN 0-226-09269-0). U of Chicago Pr.

Davenport, R. Edward. Free to Share. LC 82-62743. 183p. (Orig.). 1983. pap. text ed. 6.95 (ISBN 0-87148-337-8). Pathway Pr.

Greene, William B. Transcendentalism; bd. with Equality. LC 81-8972. (Repr. of 1849 eds.). 1981. 35.00x (ISBN 0-8201-1366-2). Schol Facsimiles.

Mooney, Christopher F. Inequality & the American Conscience: Justice Through the Judicial System. (Woodstock Studies). 144p. 1983. pap. 6.95 (ISBN 0-8091-2500-5). Paulist Pr.

Siriwardena, R., ed. Equality & the Religious Traditions of Asia. 300p. 1987. 29.95 (ISBN 0-312-00401-X). St Martin.

ERASMUS, DESIDERIUS, d. 1536

Allen, P. S. Erasmus' Services to Learning. 1974. lib. bdg. 59.95 (ISBN 0-8490-0123-4). Gordon Pr.

--Erasmus' Services to Learning. (Studies in Philosophy: No. 40). 1972. pap. 39.95x (ISBN 0-8383-0111-8). Haskell.

Amey, Peter, et al. Luther, Erasmus & Loyola. Yapp, Malcolm, et al, eds. (World History Ser.). (Illus.). 1980. lib. bdg. 6.95 (ISBN 0-89908-043-X); pap. text ed. 2.45 (ISBN 0-89908-018-9). Greenhaven.

Bainton, Roland. Erasmus of Christendom. (Crossroad Paperback Ser.). 320p. 1982. pap. 12.95 (ISBN 0-8245-0415-1). Crossroad NY.

Bainton, Roland H. Erasmus of Christendom. LC 68-27788. (Illus.). 1969. 20.00 (ISBN 0-684-15380-7, ScribT). Scribner.

Barber, James D. Erasmus: A Play on Words. LC 81-40002. 80p. (Orig.). 1982. lib. bdg. 23.50 (ISBN 0-8191-1868-0); pap. text ed. 5.75 (ISBN 0-8191-1869-9). U Pr of Amer.

Boyle, Marjorie O. Christening Pagan Mysteries: Erasmus in Pursuit of Wisdom. (Erasmus Studies). 168p. 1981. 22.50x (ISBN 0-8020-5525-7). U of Toronto Pr.

--Erasmus on Language & Method in Theology. LC 77-2606. (Erasmus Studies: No. 2). pap. 70.30 (ISBN 0-317-26938-0, 2023596). Bks Demand UMI.

--Rhetoric & Reform: Erasmus' Civil Dispute with Luther. (Harvard Historical Monographs: No. 71). 240p. 1983. text ed. 24.00x (ISBN 0-674-76870-1). Harvard U Pr.

Capey, Ernest F. Erasmus. 1902. 25.00 (ISBN 0-8274-2284-9). R West.

DeMolen, Richard L., ed. Erasmus. LC 73-89992. (Documents of Modern History Ser.). 208p. 1974. 18.95 (ISBN 0-312-25795-3). St Martin.

--Erasmus of Rotterdam: A Quincentennial Symposium. LC 76-125264. 151p. 1971. text ed. 29.00x (ISBN 0-8290-0170-0). Irvington.

Devereux, E. J. Renaissance English Translations of Erasmus: A Bibliography to 1700. (Erasmus Ser.). 256p. 1983. 35.00x (ISBN 0-8020-2411-4). U of Toronto Pr.

Elliott-Binns, Leonard E., ed. Erasmus the Reformer: A Study in Restatement. LC 83-45655. Date not set. Repr. of 1923 ed. 24.50 (ISBN 0-404-19805-8). AMS Pr.

Emerton, E. Erasmus of Rotterdam. 59.95 (ISBN 0-8490-0122-6). Gordon Pr.

Emerton, Ephraim. Desiderius Erasmus of Rotterdam. 1900. 35.00 (ISBN 0-8274-2167-2). R West.

Erasmus, Desiderius. The Correspondence of Erasmus, Letters, 1501-1514, Vol. 2. Corrigan, Beatrice, ed. LC 72-47422. (Collected Works of Erasmus: Vol. 2). (Illus.). 1975. 75.00x (ISBN 0-8020-1983-8). U of Toronto Pr.

--The Correspondence of Erasmus, Vol. 1: Letters 1-141: 1484-1500. Corrigan, Beatrice, ed. LC 72-97422. (Collected Works of Erasmus: Vol. 1). (Illus.). 1974. 75.00x (ISBN 0-8020-1981-1). U of Toronto Pr.

--Correspondence of Erasmus, Vol. 3: Letters 298-445 (1514-1516) Mynors. Mynors, R. A. & Thomson, D. F., trs. LC 72-97422. (Collected Works of Erasmus: Vol. 3). (Illus.). 1976. 75.00x (ISBN 0-8020-2202-2). U of Toronto Pr.

--The Correspondence of Erasmus, Vol. 4: Letters 446-593. Mynors, R. A. & Thomson, D. F., trs. LC 72-97422. (Collected Works of Erasmus: Vol. 4). 1977. 75.00x (ISBN 0-8020-5366-1). U of Toronto Pr.

--The Correspondence of Erasmus, Vol. 5: Letters 594-841 (July 1517 - April 1518) Mynors, R. A. & Thomson, D. F., trs. LC 78-6904. (Collected Works of Erasmus: Vol. 5). 1979. 75.00x (ISBN 0-8020-5429-3). U of Toronto Pr.

--The Correspondence of Erasmus, Vol. 6: Letters 842-992 (May 1518 - June 1519) Mynors, R. A. & Thomson, D. F., trs. (Collected Works of Erasmus: Vol. 6). 1981. 75.00x (ISBN 0-8020-5500-1). U of Toronto Pr.

--Paraphrases on Romans & Galatians. Sider, Robert D., ed. Payne, John B., et al, trs. (Collected Works of Erasmus Ser.: Vol. 42). 232p. 1984. 29.50x (ISBN 0-8020-2510-2). U of Toronto Pr.

Froude, J. A. The Life & Letters of Erasmus & the Unknown Historical Significance of the Protestant Reformation, 2 vols. (Illus.). 157p. 1984. 147.55x set (ISBN 0-89266-469-X). Am Classical Coll Pr.

Froude, James A. A Comparative Analysis of the Philosophies of Erasmus & Luther. (Illus.). 133p. 1981. Repr. of 1868 ed. 69.85 (ISBN 0-89901-038-5). Found Class Reprints.

--Life & Letters of Erasmus. LC 70-155628. Repr. of 1895 ed. 24.50 (ISBN 0-404-02627-3). AMS Pr.

Himelick, Raymond, tr. Erasmus & the Seamless Coat of Jesus. LC 70-151515. 232p. 1971. 6.25 (ISBN 0-911198-29-6). Purdue U Pr.

Huizinga, Johan. Erasmus & the Age of Reformation: With a Selection from the Letters of Erasmus. LC 84-42547. (Illus.). 312p. 1984. text ed. 32.50x (ISBN 0-691-05421-5); pap. 8.95 (ISBN 0-691-00801-9). Princeton U Pr.

Jebb, Richard C. Erasmus. (Select Bibliographies Reprint Ser). 1890. 12.00 (ISBN 0-8369-5289-8). Ayer Co Pubs.

Luther, Martin. Bondage of the Will. Packer, J. I. & Johnston, O. R., trs. 322p. 1970. 13.95 (ISBN 0-8007-0028-7). Revell.

Mangan, John J. Life, Character & Influence of Desiderius Erasmus of Rotterdam, 2 Vols. LC 73-147113. Repr. of 1927 ed. 78.50 (ISBN 0-404-04178-7). AMS Pr.

Mansfield, Bruce. Phoenix of His Age: Interpretations of Erasmus, Fifteen Fifty to Seventeen Fifty. LC 79-14960. (Erasmus Studies). (Illus.). 1979. 30.00x (ISBN 0-8020-5457-9). U of Toronto Pr.

Margolin, Jean-Claude. Neuf Annees De Bibliographie Erasmienne (1962-1970) 1977. 85.00x (ISBN 0-8020-2276-6). U of Toronto Pr.

Markish, Shimon. Erasmus & the Jews. Olcott, Anthony, tr. from Rus. LC 85-16454. 1986. lib. bdg. 25.00x (ISBN 0-226-50590-1). U of Chicago Pr.

Mestwerdt, Paul. Die Anfaenge Des Erasmus: Humanismus und Devotio Moderna. 34.00 (ISBN 0-384-38351-3); pap. 28.00 (ISBN 0-384-38350-5). Johnson Repr.

Murray, Robert H. Erasmus & Luther: Their Attitude to Toleration. LC 83-45659. (The Zodiac Club Ser.). Date not set. Repr. of 1920 ed. 57.50 (ISBN 0-404-19809-0). AMS Pr.

Olin, John C. Christian Humanism & the Reformation: Selected Writings of Erasmus. 2nd ed. LC 65-10218. (Illus.). xiv, 202p. 1975. pap. 9.00 (ISBN 0-8232-0988-1). Fordham.

--Six Essays on Erasmus & a Translation of Erasmus' Letter to Carondelet 1523. LC 76-18467. (Illus.). xiv, 125p. 1977. 17.50 (ISBN 0-8232-1023-5); pap. 8.00 (ISBN 0-8232-1024-3). Fordham.

Pennington, Arthur R. The Life & Character of Erasmus. 1977. lib. bdg. 59.95 (ISBN 0-8490-2159-6). Gordon Pr.

Rabil, Albert. Erasmus & the New Testament: The Mind of a Christian Humanist. LC 71-184768. (Trinity University Monograph Series in Religion: Vol. 1). pap. 51.50 (ISBN 0-317-08044-X, 2022565). Bks Demand UMI.

Reynolds, Ernest E. Thomas More & Erasmus. LC 65-26739. x, 260p. 1966. 25.00 (ISBN 0-8232-0670-X). Fordham.

Siirala, Aarne. Divine Humanness. Kantonen, T. A., tr. LC 70-99460. pap. 48.00 (2026964). Bks Demand UMI.

Smith, P. Key to the Colloquies of Erasmus. (Harvard Theological Studies). 1927. pap. 15.00 (ISBN 0-527-01013-8). Kraus Repr.

Stupperich, Robert. Erasmus Von Rotterdam und Seine Welt. 1977. 19.20x (ISBN 3-11-007085-5). De Gruyter.

Tracy, James D. The Politics of Erasmus: A Pacifist Intellectual & His Political Milieu. LC 77-20697. (Erasmus Studies). 1978. 22.50x (ISBN 0-8020-5393-9). U of Toronto Pr.

Woodward, William H., ed. Desiderius Erasmus Concerning the Aim & Method of Education. LC 64-18613. (Classics in Education Ser.). (Orig.). 1964. pap. text ed. 5.00x (ISBN 0-8077-2347-9). Tchrs Coll.

Zweig, Stefan. Erasmus. 1934. 35.00 (ISBN 0-8274-2283-0). R West.

EREMITES

see Carthusians; Hermits

ERIKSON, ERIK HOMBURGER, 1902-

Capps, Donald, et al. Encounter with Erikson: Historical Interpretation & Religious Biography. LC 76-44434. (American Academy of Religion, Formative Contemporary Thinkers Ser.: No. 2). 1977. pap. 13.50 (010402). Scholars Pr GA.

Evans, Richard I. Dialogue with Erik Erikson: And Reactions from Ernest Jones. LC 81-15379. 188p. 1981. 33.95 (ISBN 0-03-059923-7). Praeger.

Knowles, Richard T. Human Development & Human Possibility: Erikson in the Light of Heidegger. LC 85-20498. (Illus.). 224p. (Orig.). 1986. lib. bdg. 26.00 (ISBN 0-8191-4992-6); pap. text ed. 12.25 (ISBN 0-8191-4993-4). U Pr of Amer.

Tribe, Carol. Profile of Three Theories: Erikson, Maslow, Piaget. 120p. 1982. pap. text ed. 8.95 (ISBN 0-8403-2800-1). Kendall-Hunt.

Wright, J. Eugene, Jr. Erikson: Identity & Religion. 240p. (Orig.). 1982. pap. 9.95 (ISBN 0-8164-2362-8, HarpR). Har-Row.

ERKEWALD, SAINT–LEGEND

Peterson, Clifford, ed. Saint Erkenwald. new ed. LC 76-53197. (Haney Foundation Ser). 1977. 16.00x (ISBN 0-8122-7723-6). U of Pa Pr.

ESCHATOLOGY

see also Antichrist; Apocalyptic Literature; Beatific Vision; Death; Demythologization; Dispensationalism; End of the World; Future Life; Future Punishment; Heaven; Hell; Immortality; Judgment Day; Kingdom of God; Millennium; Nirvana; Paradise; Purgatory; Resurrection; Second Advent; Time (Theology)

Alberione, James. Last Things. (Orig.). 1965. 4.50 (ISBN 0-8198-0072-4). Dghtrs St Paul.

Berdiaev, Nikolai A. The Beginning & the End. French, R. M., tr. from Russian. LC 76-6083. 1976. Repr. of 1952 ed. lib. bdg. 35.00x (ISBN 0-8371-8837-7, BEBE). Greenwood.

Boatman, Russel. What the Bible Says about End Time. 3rd ed. LC 79-56542. (What the Bible Says Ser.). 1980. 13.95 (ISBN 0-89900-075-4). College Pr Pub.

Boettner, Loraine. Immortality. 1956. 4.50 (ISBN 0-87552-127-4). Presby & Reformed.

Bratt, John H. Final Curtain. (Contemporary Discussion Ser.). 1978. pap. 1.95 (ISBN 0-8010-0748-8). Baker Bk.

Brunner, Heinrich E. Eternal Hope. Knight, Harold, tr. LC 72-6930. 232p. 1973. Repr. of 1954 ed. lib. bdg. 22.50x (ISBN 0-8371-6508-3, BREH). Greenwood.

Brunt, John C. Promise & Present: Adventist Eschatology & Ethics. Coffen, Richard W., ed. 96p. 1987. pap. 5.95 (ISBN 0-8280-0386-6). Review & Herald.

Bryant, M. Darrol & Dayton, Donald W., eds. Coming Kingdom: Essays in American Millennialism & Eschatology. LC 83-82211. xii, 258p. 1984. text ed. 15.95 o. p. (ISBN 0-913757-01-2, Pub. by New Era Bks); pap. text ed. 11.95 (ISBN 0-913757-00-4, Pub. by New Era Bks). Paragon Hse.

Davis, John J. Christ's Victorious Kingdom. 144p. 1987. pap. 6.95 (ISBN 0-8010-2970-8). Baker Bk.

Dienstag, Jacob I. Eschatology in Maimonidean Thought: Messianism, Resurrection, & the World to Come-Jacob I. LC 82-17303. cxx, 281p. 1982. 59.50x (ISBN 0-87068-706-9). Ktav.

Ewert, David. And Then Comes the End. LC 79-28410. 216p. 1980. pap. 7.95 (ISBN 0-8361-1921-5). Herald Pr.

Fisher, Clay C. New Concepts of Bible Mysteries & Eschatologies. LC 76-96074. 1969. pap. 2.50 (ISBN 0-686-00510-4). C C Fisher.

Gundry, Robert H. The Church & the Tribulation. 224p. 1973. pap. 7.95 (ISBN 0-310-25401-9, 18097P). Zondervan.

Hoyt, Herman A. The End Times. pap. 6.95 (ISBN 0-88469-077-6). BMH Bks.

Hummel, Leonard C. Time Is Running Out: It's Much Later Than You Think. 26p. (Orig.). 1986. pap. 1.95 (ISBN 0-940853-00-0). Power Word Pubns.

Ironside, H. A. & Ottman, F. Studies in Biblical Eschatology. 426p. 1983. lib. bdg. 16.00 Smythe Sewn (ISBN 0-86524-143-0, 9806). Klock & Klock.

Ladd, George E. The Last Things. 1978. pap. 3.95 (ISBN 0-8028-1727-0). Eerdmans.

Lindsay, Gordon. The Great Tribulation. (End of the Age Ser.: Vol. 4). 1.50 (ISBN 0-89985-070-7). Christ Nations.

--The Great White Throne. (End of the Age Ser.: Vol. 9). 1.25 (ISBN 0-89985-075-8). Christ Nations.

--It's Sooner Than You Think. (Prophecy Ser.). 1.25 (ISBN 0-89985-057-X). Christ Nations.

--The Rapture. (Prophecy Ser.). 1.50 (ISBN 0-89985-063-4). Christ Nations.

--Will Christians Go Through the Great Tribulation? (Prophecy Ser.). 1.50 (ISBN 0-89985-065-0). Christ Nations.

--The World Two Thousand A.D. (Prophecy Ser.). 2.50 (ISBN 0-89985-064-2). Christ Nations.

MacDonald, Charles. Church & World in the Plan of God: Aspects of History & Eschatology in the Thought of Pere Yves Congar. (Regensburger Studien zur Theologie: Vol. 27). 178p. 1981. 22.75 (ISBN 3-8204-5945-6). P Lang Pubs.

Mattill, A. J., Jr. Luke & the Last Things. 1979. pap. 8.95 (ISBN 0-915948-03-6). Bks Distinction.

Miller, Alvin. Weird Eschatology: An Alternative View of the Second Coming. LC 86-80018. (Illus.). 52p. (Orig.). 1986. pap. 3.00 (ISBN 0-9616435-0-1). Last Things.

Mills, Lawrence H. Avesta Eschatology: Compared with the Books of Daniel & Revelations. LC 74-24644. Repr. of 1908 ed. 14.00 (ISBN 0-404-12816-5). AMS Pr.

Pelikan, Jaroslav J. The Shape of Death: Life, Death, & Immortality in the Early Fathers. LC 78-6030. 1978. Repr. of 1961 ed. lib. bdg. 22.50x (ISBN 0-313-20458-6, PESD). Greenwood.

Pentecost, J. Dwight. Things to Come. 1958. 18.95 (ISBN 0-310-30890-9, 6355, Pub by Dunhan). Zondervan.

Phan, Peter C. Culture & Eschatology: The Iconographical Vision of Paul Evdokimov. LC 83-48751. (American University Studies VII (Theology & Religion): Vol. 1). 345p. 1984. text ed. 36.50 (ISBN 0-8204-0040-8). P Lang Pubs.

Pohle, Joseph. Eschatology. LC 72-109823. 1971. Repr. of 1917 ed. lib. bdg. 22.50x (ISBN 0-8371-4314-4, POES). Greenwood.

Schillebeeckx, Edward & Willems, Boniface, eds. Problem of Eschatology. LC 79-76195. (Concilium Ser.: Vol. 41). 175p. 1969. 7.95 (ISBN 0-8091-0117-3). Paulist Pr.

Sikking, Robert P. A Matter of Life & Death. 1978. pap. 4.95 (ISBN 0-87516-256-8). De Vorss.

Slaatte, Howard A. Time & Its End: A Comparative Existential Interpretation of Time & Eschatology. LC 80-7814. 298p. 1980. pap. text ed. 13.25 (ISBN 0-8191-1070-1). U Pr of Amer.

Smith, Chuck. The Tribulation & the Church. 64p. (Orig.). 1980. pap. 1.50 (ISBN 0-936728-01-9). Word for Today.

Smith, Jane I. & Haddad, Yvonne Y. Islamic Understanding of Death & Resurrection. LC 80-21303. 270p. 1981. 49.50x (ISBN 0-87395-506-4); pap. 19.95 (ISBN 0-87395-507-2). State U NY Pr.

Smith, Jane I., ed. The Precious Pearl: A Translation from the Arabic. LC 79-140. (Studies in World Religions: No. 1). 1979. 15.00 (ISBN 0-89130-278-6, 030001); pap. 8.95 05539067x (ISBN 0-89130-305-7). Scholars Pr GA.

Summers, Ray. Life Beyond. LC 83-20874. 1973. pap. 8.95 (ISBN 0-8054-1608-0). Broadman.

Wainwright, Geoffrey. Eucharist & Eschatology. 1981. 21.95x (ISBN 0-19-520248-1); pap. text ed. 8.95 (ISBN 0-19-520249-X). Oxford U Pr.

Wenham, David. The Rediscovery of Jesus' Eschatological Discourse: Studies in the History of Gospel Traditions. (Gospel Perspectives Ser.: Vol. IV). 406p. 1984. text ed. 24.50x (ISBN 0-905774-72-8, Pub. by JSOT Pr England); pap. text ed. 13.50x (ISBN 0-905774-73-6, Pub. by JSOT England). Eisenbrauns.

Wilcox, Llewellyn A. Now Is the Time. rev. ed. 1966. 8.95 (ISBN 0-911080-06-6). Outdoor Pict.

Wilmore, Gayraud S. Last Things First. LC 81-23136. (Library of Living Faith.: Vol. 3). 118p. (Orig.). 1982. pap. 5.95 (ISBN 0-664-24412-2). Westminster.

Zacharias, Paul B. Insights into the Beyond. LC 76-6756. pap. 1.00 (ISBN 0-87785-156-5). Swedenborg.

ESCHATOLOGY–BIBLICAL TEACHING

Burnett, Fred W. The Testament of Jesus-Sophia: A Redaction-Critical Study of the Eschatological Discourse in Matthew. LC 80-67211. 491p. (Orig.). 1981. lib. bdg. 35.75 (ISBN 0-8191-1743-9); pap. text ed. 19.75 (ISBN 0-8191-1744-7). U Pr of Amer.

Campbell, Roderick. Israel & the New Covenant. LC 82-142978. 364p. 1982. Repr. of 1954 ed. 12.95 (ISBN 0-939404-01-X). Geneva Ministr.

Cox, William E. Biblical Studies in Final Things. 1967. pap. 5.95 (ISBN 0-87552-152-5). Presby & Reformed.

Dankenbring, William F. The Last Days. LC 77-79265. 1977. 11.95 (ISBN 0-917182-05-7). Triumph Pub.

Gowan, Donald E. Eschatology in the Old Testament. LC 85-4550. 160p. 1985. pap. 9.95 (ISBN 0-8006-1906-4, 1-1906). Fortress.

Hiers, Richard H. The Historical Jesus & the Kingdom of God: Present & Future in the Message & Ministry of Jesus. LC 73-2623. (University of Florida Humanities Monographs: No. 38). 1973. pap. 3.50 (ISBN 0-8130-0386-5). U Presses Fla.

Hoyt, Herman A. The End Times. pap. 6.95 (ISBN 0-88469-077-6). BMH Bks.

Plueger, Aaron L. Things to Come for Planet Earth. 1977. pap. 3.95 (ISBN 0-570-03762-X, 12-2691). Concordia.

Portillo, Carlos E. That Unknown Day. LC 85-52117. (Illus.). 400p. (Orig.). 1986. 14.95 (ISBN 0-937365-00-9); pap. 9.95 (ISBN 0-937365-01-7). WCP Pubns.

Sauer, Val J., Jr. The Eschatology Handbook: The Bible Speaks to Us about Endtimes. (Illus.). 180p. (Orig.). 1981. pap. 3.99 (ISBN 0-8042-0066-1). John Knox.

Wilder, Amos N. Eschatology & Ethics in the Teaching of Jesus. LC 78-16425. 1978. Repr. of 1950 ed. lib. bdg. 27.50 (ISBN 0-313-20585-X, WIEE). Greenwood.

Wood, Leon J. The Bible & Future Events. (Contemporary Evangelical Perspectives Ser.). 224p. 1973. kivar 6.95 (ISBN 0-310-34701-7, 10231P). Zondervan.

ESCHATOLOGY, EGYPTIAN

Budge, Ernest A. The Egyptian Heaven & Hell, 3 vols. LC 73-18844. (Illus.). Repr. of 1906 ed. Set. 57.50 (ISBN 0-404-11326-5). AMS Pr.

Zandee, Jan. Death As an Enemy According to Ancient Egyptian Conceptions. Kastenbaum, Robert, ed. LC 76-19597. (Death & Dying Ser.). 1977. Repr. of 1960 ed. lib. bdg. 37.50x (ISBN 0-405-09591-0). Ayer Co Pubs.

ESCHATOLOGY, JEWISH

Cedar Rapids Community School District Staff. Improving Spelling Performance: Student Edition Block IV. 136p. 1981. pap. text ed. 2.55 (ISBN 0-8403-2419-7). Kendall-Hunt.

Fischer, Ulrich. Eschatologie & Jenseitserwartung Im Hellenistischen Diasporajudentum. (Beiheft 44 Zur Zeitschrift Fuer Die Alttestamentliche Wissenschaft). 1978. 29.20x (ISBN 3-11-007595-4). De Gruyter.

ESSENES

see also Dead Sea Scrolls; Qumran Community; Zealots (Jewish Party)

Chaney, Robert G. The Essenes & Their Ancient Mysteries. (Adventures in Esoteric Learning Ser.). 1968. pap. 4.25 (ISBN 0-918936-14-4). Astara.

Dupont-Sommer, A. The Essene Writings from Qumran. Vermes, G., tr. 13.50 (ISBN 0-8446-2012-2). Peter Smith.

Jones, Allen H. Essenes: The Elect of Israel & the Priests of Artemis. (Illus.). 146p. (Orig.). 1985. lib. bdg. 23.50 (ISBN 0-8191-4744-3); pap. text ed. 9.50 (ISBN 0-8191-4745-1). U Pr of Amer.

Larson, Martin A. The Essene-Christian Faith. LC 79-83606. 297p. 1980. 10.95 (ISBN 0-8022-2241-2). Philos Lib.

--The Essene-Christian Faith. 273p. 10.95. Truth Seeker.

Parry, Danaan. The Essene Book of Days 1987. 400p. (Orig.). 1986. pap. 12.95 (ISBN 0-913319-02-3). Sunstone Pubns.

Savoy, Gene. The Millennium Edition of the Essaei Document: Secrets of an Eternal Race. Revised ed. LC 83-83221. Orig. Title: The Essaei Document. (Illus.). xii, 140p. 1983. text ed. 39.50 (ISBN 0-936202-07-6). Intl Comm Christ.

Szekely, Edmond B. The Cosmotherapy of the Essenes. (Illus.). 64p. 1975. pap. 3.50 (ISBN 0-89564-012-0). IBS Intl.

--The Discovery of the Essene Gospel of Peace: The Essenes & the Vatican. (Illus.). 96p. 1977. pap. 4.80 (ISBN 0-89564-004-X). IBS Intl.

--The Essene Book of Asha: Journey to the Cosmic Ocean. (Illus.). 140p. 1976. pap. 7.50 (ISBN 0-89564-008-2). IBS Intl.

--The Essene Book of Creation. (Illus.). 86p. 1975. pap. 4.50 (ISBN 0-89564-005-8). IBS Intl.

--The Essene Code of Life. (Illus.). 44p. 1978. pap. 3.50 (ISBN 0-89564-013-9). IBS Intl.

--The Essene Communions with the Infinite. (Illus.). 64p. 1979. pap. 3.95 (ISBN 0-89564-009-0). IBS Intl.

--The Essene Gospel of Peace, Bk. 1. (Illus.). 72p. 1981. pap. 1.00 (ISBN 0-89564-000-7). IBS Intl.

--The Essene Gospel of Peace, Bk. 2. (Illus.). 132p. 1981. pap. 5.80 (ISBN 0-89564-001-5). IBS Intl.

--The Essene Gospel of Peace, Bk. 3: Lost Scrolls of the Essene Brotherhood. (Illus.). 144p. 1981. pap. 5.60 (ISBN 0-89564-002-3). IBS Intl.

--The Essene Gospel of Peace, Bk. 4: Teachings of the Elect. (Illus.). 40p. 1981. pap. 4.50 (ISBN 0-89564-003-1). IBS Intl.

--The Essene Jesus. (Illus.). 72p. 1977. pap. 4.50 (ISBN 0-89564-007-4). IBS Intl.

--The Essene Origins of Christianity. (Illus.). 184p. 1981. pap. 8.50 (ISBN 0-89564-015-5). IBS Intl.

--The Essene Science of Life. (Illus.). 64p. 1976. pap. 3.50 (ISBN 0-89564-010-4). IBS Intl.

--The Essene Teachings of Zarathurstra. (Illus.). 32p. 1974. pap. 2.95 (ISBN 0-89564-016-3). IBS Intl.

--The Essene Way: Biogenic Living. (Illus.). 200p. 1981. pap. 8.80 (ISBN 0-89564-019-8). IBS Intl.

--The Essene Way: World Pictures & Cosmic Symbols. (Illus.). 40p. 1978. pap. 1.80 (ISBN 0-89564-050-3). IBS Intl.

--The Essenes, by Josephus & His Contemporaries. (Illus.). 32p. 1981. pap. 2.95 (ISBN 0-89564-014-7). IBS Intl.

--The Fiery Chariots. (Illus.). 96p. 1971. pap. 4.80 (ISBN 0-89564-017-1). IBS Intl.

--The First Essene. (Illus.). 240p. 1981. pap. 9.50 (ISBN 0-89564-018-X). IBS Intl.

--I Came Back Tomorrow. (Illus.). 32p. 1976. pap. 3.50 (ISBN 0-89564-073-2). IBS Intl.

--The Teachings of the Essenes from Enoch to the Dead Sea Scrolls. (Illus.). 112p. 1981. pap. 4.80 (ISBN 0-89564-006-6). IBS Intl.

ESTABLISHED CHURCH OF IRELAND

see Church of Ireland

ESTHER, FEAST OF

see Purim (Feast of Esther)

ESTHER, QUEEN OF PERSIA

Baldwin, Joyce G. Esther. Wiseman, D. J., ed. LC 84-15670. (Tyndale Old Testament Commentaries Ser.). 122p. 1984. 12.95 (ISBN 0-87784-964-1); pap. 6.95 (ISBN 0-87784-262-0). Inter-Varsity.

Bankson, Marjory Z. Braided Streams: Esther & a Woman's Way of Growing. LC 85-50203. (Illus.). 184p. (Orig.). 1985. pap. 8.95 (ISBN 0-931055-05-9). LuraMedia.

Kaplan, Aryeh, tr. The Book of Esther. 268p. 8.95 (ISBN 0-686-27543-8); pap. 6.45 (ISBN 0-940118-21-1). Maznaim.

Smith, Joyce M. Esther, a Woman of Courage. 1981. pap. 2.95 (ISBN 0-8423-0729-X). Tyndale.

Tompkins, Iverna M. If It Please the King. 183p. (Orig.). 1983. pap. 5.00 (ISBN 0-9611260-1-9). I Tompkins.

ESTHER, QUEEN OF PERSIA–DRAMA

Aberg, Gilbert S. Esther: A Play. LC 69-17410. (Illus.). 163p. 1969. 4.50 (ISBN 0-87601-001-X). Carnation.

Lynn, Claire. Esther, Queen of Persia. 63p. 1981. pap. 1.50 (ISBN 0-89323-019-7). Bible Memory.

ESTHER, QUEEN OF PERSIA–JUVENILE LITERATURE

Weil, Lisl. Esther. LC 79-22543. (Illus.). 48p. 1980. 9.95 (ISBN 0-689-30761-6, Childrens Bk). Macmillan.

ESTONIAN MYTHOLOGY

see Mythology, Finno-Ugrian

ETERNAL LIFE

see Future Life

ETERNAL PUNISHMENT

see Future Punishment; Hell

ETERNITY

Here are entered works of the philosophical concept of eternity, Eschatological works are entered under the heading Future Life.

see also Future Life; Time (Theology)

Davidson, Herbert. Proofs for Eternity, Creation, & the Existence of God in Medieval Islamic & Jewish Philosophy. (Studies in Northeast Culture & Society: Vol. 7). 500p. 1985. write for info. (ISBN 0-89003-180-0); pap. 62.00x (ISBN 0-89003-181-9). Undena Pubns.

Gram, Robert L. An Enemy Disguised: Unmasking the Illusion of Meaningful Death. 224p. 1985. 10.95 (ISBN 0-8407-5942-8). Nelson.

Meek, George W. After We Die, What Then? rev. ed. LC 79-909. (Illus.). 216p. 1987. pap. 8.95 (ISBN 0-89804-099-X). Ariel OH.

Sauer, Erich. De Eternidad a Eternidad. Orig. Title: From Eternity to Eternity. (Span.). 1977. pap. 4.95 (ISBN 0-8254-1653-1). Kregel.

Zagrebelny, P. From the Point of View of Eternity. 231p. 1978. pap. 4.45 (ISBN 0-8285-1076-8, Pub. by Progress Pubs USSR). Imported Pubns.

ETHICAL CULTURE MOVEMENT

Alder, Felix. Creed & Deed: A Series of Discourses. LC 76-38430. (Religion in America Ser: 2). 254p. 1972. Repr. of 1877 ed. 17.00 (ISBN 0-405-04051-2). Ayer Co Pubs.

Bridges, Horace J., ed. Aspects of Ethical Religion: Essays in Honor of Felix Adler on the Fiftieth Anniversary of His Founding of the Ethical Movement. facs. ed. LC 68-29190. (Essay Index Reprint Ser). 1968. Repr. of 1926 ed. 20.00 (ISBN 0-8369-0161-4). Ayer Co Pubs.

Kraut, Benny. From Reform Judaism to Ethical Culture: The Religious Evolution of Felix Adler. LC 79-14441. (Monographs: No. 5). 285p. 1979. 16.50x (ISBN 0-87820-404-0). Ktav.

ETHICAL EDUCATION

see Moral Education; Religious Education

ETHICAL THEOLOGY

see Christian Ethics

ETHICS

see also Altruism; Asceticism; Business Ethics; Casuistry; Charity; Chastity; Christian Ethics; Christian Life; Conduct of Life; Conscience; Decision-Making (Ethics); Divorce; Free Will and Determinism; Friendship; Good and Evil; Guilt; Happiness; Hedonism; Joy and Sorrow; Judgment (Ethics); Justice; Kindness; Literature and Morals; Love; Medical Ethics; Moral Education; Natural Law; Obedience; Patriotism; Peace; Political Ethics; Pride and Vanity; Religious Ethics; Right and Wrong; Science and Ethics; Secularism; Self-Realization; Self-Respect; Sexual Ethics; Simplicity; Sin; Sins

also subdivision Moral and Religious Aspects under specific subjects

Abelard, Peter. Ethics. Luscombe, D. E., ed. (Oxford Medieval Texts Ser). 1971. 54.00X (ISBN 0-19-822217-3). Oxford U Pr.

Adams, Elie M. Ethical Naturalism & the Modern World-View. LC 73-3019. 229p. 1973. Repr. of 1960 ed. lib. bdg. 45.00 (ISBN 0-8371-6820-1, ADEN). Greenwood.

Adams, Robert M. The Virtue of Faith & Other Essays in Philosophical Theology. 256p. 1987. 29.95 (ISBN 0-19-504145-3); pap. 12.95 (ISBN 0-19-504146-1). Oxford U Pr.

American Catholic Philosophical Association Staff. Ethics & Other Knowledge: Proceedings, Vol. 31. 1957. 18.00 (ISBN 0-384-14760-7). Johnson Repr.

Anandamurti, Shrii S. A Guide to Human Conduct. LC 80-70792. 55p. 1981. pap. 3.00 (ISBN 0-88476-010-3). Ananda Marga.

Anderson, Thomas C. The Foundation & Structure of Sartrean Ethics. LC 79-11762. x, 186p. 1979. 22.50x (ISBN 0-7006-0191-0). U Pr of KS.

Anscombe, G. E. Collected Philosophical Papers: Ethics, Religion & Politics, Vol. 3. LC 81-4315. 192p. 1981. 27.50x (ISBN 0-8166-1082-7); pap. 10.95x (ISBN 0-8166-1083-5). U of Minn Pr.

Aristotle. The Nicomachean Ethics. Apostle, Hippocrates G., tr. LC 75-5871. (Synthese Historical Library: No. 13). 372p. 1975. lib. bdg. 71.00 (ISBN 90-277-0569-0, Pub. by Reidel Holland). Kluwer Academic.

Bahm, Archie J. Ethics: The Science of Oughtness. LC 80-66406. 260p. 1980. 15.00 (ISBN 0-911714-12-X). Bahm.

Baldwin, William. Treatise of Morall Philosophie. rev. ed. LC 67-10126. 1967. Repr. of 1620 ed. 50.00x (ISBN 0-8201-1003-5). Schol Facsimiles.

Barrow, Robin. Moral Philosophy for Education. (Unwin Education Books). 1975. pap. text ed. 9.95x (ISBN 0-04-370060-8). Allen Unwin.

Barth, Karl. Ethics. 1981. 34.95 (ISBN 0-8164-0484-4, HarpR). Har-Row.

Battaglia, Anthony. Toward a Reformulation of Natural Law. 1981. 14.95 (ISBN 0-8164-0490-9, HarpR). Har-Row.

Battin, Margaret P. & Maris, Ronald, eds. Suicide & Ethics. (Special Issue S Ser.: Vol. 13, No. 3). 112p. 1984. pap. 9.95. Guilford Pr.

Baum, Robert J. Ethical Arguments for Analysis. 2nd ed. LC 76-1952. 1976. pap. text ed. 19.95 (ISBN 0-03-089646-0, HoltC). HR&W.

--Ethical Arguments for Analysis: Brief Edition. 2nd ed. LC 78-10770. 1979. pap. text ed. 15.95 (ISBN 0-03-045011-X, HoltC). HR&W.

Bayles, Michael D. Professional Ethics. 176p. 1981. pap. text ed. write for info. (ISBN 0-534-00998-0). Wadsworth Pub.

Beauchamp, Tom L. & Pinkard, Terry P., eds. Ethics & Public Policy: Introduction to Ethics. (Illus.). 416p. 1983. pap. write for info. (ISBN 0-13-290957-X). P-H.

Beck, R. N. & Orr, J. B. Ethical Choice: A Case Study Approach. LC 70-122282. 1970. pap. text ed. 10.95 (ISBN 0-02-902060-3). Free Pr.

Bennett, John G. The Foundations of Moral Philosophy, Vol. 2. (Dramatic Universe Ser.). 12.95 (ISBN 0-900306-42-4, Pub. by Coombe Springs Pr). Claymont Comm.

Bergson, Henri. The Two Sources of Morality & Religion. LC 74-10373. 308p. 1974. Repr. of 1935 ed. lib. bdg. 25.00x (ISBN 0-8371-7679-4, BETS). Greenwood.

Bierman, A. K. Life & Morals: An Introduction to Ethics. 596p. 1980. pap. text ed. 14.95 (ISBN 0-15-550725-7, HC). HarBraceJ.

Blum, Lawrence. Friendship, Altruism & Morality. (International Library of Philosophy). 256p. 1980. 24.95x (ISBN 0-7100-0582-2); pap. 9.95x (ISBN 0-7100-9332-2). Methuen Inc.

Bond, E. J. Reason & Value. LC 82-4564. (Cambridge Studies in Philosophy). 220p. 1983. 32.50 (ISBN 0-521-24571-0); pap. 11.95 (ISBN 0-521-27079-0). Cambridge U Pr.

Boulding, Kenneth E. Beyond Economics: Essays on Society, Religion, & Ethics. 1970. pap. 4.95 (ISBN 0-472-06167-4, 167, AA). U of Mich Pr.

Bowne, Borden P. The Principles of Ethics. LC 75-3073. (Philosophy in America Ser.). Repr. of 1892 ed. 28.00 (ISBN 0-404-59074-8). AMS Pr.

Boyce, William D. & Jensen, Larry C. Moral Reasoning: A Psychological-Philosophical Integration. LC 78-5935. xii, 291p. 1978. 22.50x (ISBN 0-8032-0982-7). U of Nebr Pr.

Brandt, Richard B. A Theory of the Good & the Right. 1979. 32.00x (ISBN 0-19-824550-5); pap. 15.95x (ISBN 0-19-824744-3). Oxford U Pr.

Brennan, John M. The Open Texture of Moral Concepts. LC 74-31826. 171p. 1977. text ed. 26.50x (ISBN 0-06-490656-6, 06364). B&N Imports.

Broad, C. D. Five Types of Ethical Theory. 8th ed. (International Library of Philosophy & Scientific Method). 1930. text ed. 35.00x (ISBN 0-7100-3080-0). Humanities.

Bruce, Alexander B. The Moral Order of the World in Ancient & Modern Thought. LC 77-527224. (Gifford Lectures: 1898). Repr. of 1899 ed. 40.00 (ISBN 0-404-60456-0). AMS Pr.

Cabanis, Pierre J. On the Relations Between the Physical & Moral Aspects of Man, Vol. I. Saidi, Margaret D., tr. LC 80-21694. pap. 112.00 (ISBN 0-317-08229-9, 2019949). Bks Demand UMI.

Calkins, Mary W. The Good Man & the Good: An Introduction to Ethics. LC 75-3093. Repr. of 1918 ed. 24.50 (ISBN 0-404-59090-X). AMS Pr.

Callahan, Daniel, ed. The Teaching of Ethics in Higher Education: A Report by the Hastings Center. LC 80-10294. (The Teaching of Ethics Ser.). 103p. 1980. pap. 5.00 xerox form only (ISBN 0-916558-09-6). Hastings Ctr.

Callahan, Daniel & Bok, Sissela, eds. Ethics Teaching in Higher Education. LC 80-24002. (Hastings Center Monograph Ser.). 332p. 1980. 29.50x (ISBN 0-306-40522-9). Plenum Pub.

Campbell, Keith. A Stoic Philosophy of Life. LC 86-13351. 216p. (Orig.). 1986. lib. bdg. 22.50 (ISBN 0-8191-5529-2); pap. text ed. 12.25 (ISBN 0-8191-5530-6). U Pr of Amer.

Caplan, Arthur L. & Callahan, Daniel, eds. Ethics in Hard Times. LC 81-17728. (The Hastings Center Series in Ethics). 312p. 1981. text ed. 29.50 (ISBN 0-306-40790-6, Plenum Pr). Plenum Pub.

Carritt, E. F. The Theory of Morals: An Introduction to Ethical Philosophy. 144p. 1982. Repr. of 1928 ed. lib. bdg. 30.00 (ISBN 0-89984-118-X). Century Bookbindery.

Carritt, Edgar F. The Theory of Morals. LC 73-3021. 144p. 1974. Repr. of 1928 ed. lib. bdg. 22.50 (ISBN 0-8371-6827-9, CATM). Greenwood.

Carter, Curtis I. & Flew, Anthony, eds. Skepticism & Moral Principles: Modern Ethics in Review. 14.95 (ISBN 0-89044-017-4); pap. 8.95. Precedent Pub.

Carter, Curtis L., ed. Skepticism & Moral Principles: Modern Ethics in Review. LC 73-79477. (Studies in Ethics & Society Ser.: Vol. 1). 1973. 9.95 (ISBN 0-89044-017-4); pap. 4.95 (ISBN 0-89044-018-2). New Univ Pr.

Carter, Robert E. Dimensions of Moral Education. 254p. 1984. pap. 11.95 (ISBN 0-8020-6540-6). U of Toronto Pr.

Carus, Paul. The Ethical Problem: Three Lectures on Ethics As a Science. 2nd enl ed. LC 75-3103. Repr. of 1899 ed. 25.50 (ISBN 0-404-59100-0). AMS Pr.

Cecil, Andrew R., et al. Conflict & Harmony. (Andrew R. Cecil Lectures on Moral Values in a Free Society: Vol. III). 228p. 1982. text ed. 14.50x (ISBN 0-292-71081-X, Pub. by U of Tex. at Dallas). U of Tex Pr.

Chiari, Joseph. Reflections on Life & Death. LC 77-4054. 141p. 1977. 12.50x (ISBN 0-87752-212-X). Gordian.

Clouser, K. Danner. Teaching Bioethics: Strategies, Problems & Resources. LC 80-10492. (The Teaching of Ethics Ser.: Vol. IV). 77p. 1980. pap. 4.00 (ISBN 0-916558-07-X). Hastings Ctr.

Colton, Ann R. Ethical ESP. LC 78-149600. 367p. 1971. 11.50 (ISBN 0-917187-03-2). A R C Pub.

Cooper, Neil. The Diversity of Moral Thinking. (CLLP Ser.). (Illus.). 1981. text ed. 45.00x (ISBN 0-19-824423-1). Oxford U Pr.

Cua, A. S. Dimensions of Moral Creativity: Paradigms, Principles, & Ideals. LC 77-16169. 1978. 22.50x (ISBN 0-271-00540-8). Pa St U Pr.

Danner, Peter L. An Ethics for the Affluent. LC 80-5528. 424p. 1980. lib. bdg. 31.25 (ISBN 0-8191-1163-5); pap. text ed. 15.25 (ISBN 0-8191-1164-3). U Pr of Amer.

Dawson, M. M. The Ethics of Socrates. LC 74-30274. (Studies in Philosophy, No. 40). 1974. lib. bdg. 75.00x (ISBN 0-8383-2042-2). Haskell.

DeBurgh, W. G. From Morality to Religion. LC 70-102568. 1970. Repr. of 1938 ed. 31.50x (ISBN 0-8046-0728-1, Pub. by Kennikat). Assoc Faculty Pr.

De Burgh, W. G. From Morality to Religion. 352p. 1985. Repr. of 1938 ed. lib. bdg. 85.00 (ISBN 0-89984-042-6). Century Bookbindery.

DePalma, David J. & Foley, Jeanne M. Moral Development: Current Theory & Research. LC 75-14211. 206p. 1975. text ed. 24.95x (ISBN 0-89859-116-3). L Erlbaum Assocs.

De Purucker, G. The Path of Compassion: Time-honored Principles of Spiritual & Ethical Conduct. 84p. 1986. pap. 4.00 (ISBN 0-911500-69-3). Theos U Pr.

Dewey, John. Outlines of a Critical Theory of Ethics. LC 71-92299. Repr. of 1957 ed. lib. bdg. 22.50x (ISBN 0-8371-2707-6, DETE). Greenwood.

Dewey, Robert E. & Hurlbutt, Robert H. Introduction to Ethics. 1977. write for info. (ISBN 0-02-329480-9, 32948). Macmillan.

Dorsey, John M. Psychology of Ethics. 261p. 1974. 18.95 (ISBN 0-8143-1639-5). Wayne St U Pr.

Dunn, Robert. The Possibility of Weakness of Will. LC 85-24784. 192p. 1986. lib. bdg. 25.00 (ISBN 0-915145-99-5); pap. 14.50 (ISBN 0-915145-98-7). Hackett Pub.

Eby, Louise S. Quest for Moral Law. facsimile ed. LC 78-37849. (Essay Index Reprint Ser). Repr. of 1944 ed. 20.00 (ISBN 0-8369-2588-2). Ayer Co Pubs.

Edwards, Steven A. Interior Acts: Teleology, Justice, & Friendship in the Religious Ethics of Thomas Aquinas. LC 85-29530. 184p. (Orig.). 1986. lib. bdg. 24.75 (ISBN 0-8191-5212-9); pap. text ed. 11.75 (ISBN 0-8191-5213-7). U Pr of Amer.

Elliot, John H. A Home for the Homeless: A Sociological Exegesis of 1 Peter, Its Solution & Strategy. LC 80-2394. 320p. 1981. 24.95 (ISBN 0-8006-0659-0, 1-659). Fortress.

Evans, William A. Management Ethics: An Intercultural Perspective. (Dimensions in International Business Ser.). 256p. 1981. lib. bdg. 15.00 (ISBN 0-89838-055-3). Kluwer-Nijhoff.

Ewing, Alfred C. The Definition of Good. LC 78-59021. 1979. Repr. of 1947 ed. 20.25 (ISBN 0-88355-695-2). Hyperion Conn.

--Ethics. 1965. pap. text ed. 9.95 (ISBN 0-02-910030-5). Free Pr.

Facione, Peter A., et al. Values & Society: An Introduction to Ethics & Social Philosophy. 1978. pap. text ed. write for info (ISBN 0-13-940338-8). P-H.

Ferguson, Adam. Principles of Moral & Political Science, 2 Vols. LC 71-147970. Repr. of 1792 ed. Set. 85.00 (ISBN 0-404-08222-X). AMS Pr.

--Principles of Moral & Political Science, 2 vols. Wellek, Rene, ed. LC 75-11218. (British Philosophers & Theologians of the 17th & 18th Centuries Ser.: Vol. 21). 1978. Repr. of 1792 ed. Set. lib. bdg. 101.00 (ISBN 0-8240-1772-2). Garland Pub.

Feuer, Lewis S. Psychoanalysis & Ethics. LC 73-1433. 134p. 1973. Repr. of 1955 ed. lib. bdg. 45.00x (ISBN 0-8371-6795-7, FEPE). Greenwood.

Fisk, Milton. Ethics & Society: A Marxist Interpretation of Value. LC 79-3513. 1980. 20.00x (ISBN 0-8147-2564-3). NYU Pr.

Fitzgerald, John & White, Michael. The Tabula of Cebes. LC 82-19118. (SBL Texts & Translations). 236p. 1983. pap. 14.25 (ISBN 0-89130-601-3, 06 02 24). Scholars Pr GA.

Fitzgibbon, John F. Ethics: Fundamental Principles of Moral Philosophy. LC 83-1178. 92p. (Orig.). 1983. lib. bdg. 22.25 (ISBN 0-8191-3064-8); pap. text ed. 8.75 (ISBN 0-8191-3065-6). U Pr of Amer.

Flumiani, C. M. The Philosophy of Life & the Philosophy of Death. 89p. 1987. pap. 8.50 (ISBN 0-86650-223-8). Gloucester Art.

Foot, Philippa, ed. Theories of Ethics. (Oxford Readings in Philosophy Ser.). 1967. pap. 8.95x (ISBN 0-19-875005-6). Oxford U Pr.

Foot, Philippa R. Virtues & Vices, & Other Essays in Moral Philosophy. LC 78-54794. 1979. 32.50x (ISBN 0-520-03686-7); pap. 5.95 (ISBN 0-520-04396-0, CAL 494). U of Cal Pr.

Fortenbaugh, William. Quellen zur Ethik Theophrasts. 380p. 1983. 48.00x (ISBN 90-6032-218-5, Pub by B R Gruener Amsterdam). Benjamins North Am.

Fotion, N. Moral Situations. LC 68-31034. 135p. 1968. 8.00x (ISBN 0-87338-076-2); pap. 4.95x (ISBN 0-87338-077-0). Kent St U Pr.

Frankena, William K. Ethics. 2nd ed. (Foundations of Philosophy Ser.). 144p. 1973. pap. text ed. write for info. (ISBN 0-13-290478-0). P-H.

--Thinking about Morality. (Michigan Faculty Ser.). 112p. 1980. pap. 4.95 (ISBN 0-472-06316-2). U of Mich Pr.

Frankena, William K. & Granrose, John T. Introductory Readings in Ethics. 496p. 1974. text ed. write for info. (ISBN 0-13-502112-X). P-H.

French, Peter. The Scope of Morality. 1980. 25.00 (ISBN 0-8166-0837-7); pap. 9.95 (ISBN 0-8166-0900-4). U of Minn Pr.

French, Peter A. Ethics in Government. 176p. 1983. pap. write for info. (ISBN 0-13-290908-1). P-H.

French, Peter A., et al, eds. Studies in Ethical Theory. (Midwest Studies in Philosophy: Vol. 3). 1980. 25.00x (ISBN 0-8166-0968-3); pap. 12.95 (ISBN 0-8166-0971-3). U of Minn Pr.

Fried, Charles. An Anatomy of Values: Problems of Personal & Social Choice. LC 78-111483. 1970. 18.50x (ISBN 0-674-03151-2). Harvard U Pr.

Gale, Rodney. The Natural Path to Genuine Lasting Happiness. 1976. 6.50 (ISBN 0-533-02131-6). H R Gale.

Gewirth, Alan. Reason & Morality. LC 77-13911. 1978. pap. text ed. 9.95x (ISBN 0-226-28876-5). U of Chicago Pr.

Goldman, Alan H. The Moral Foundations of Professional Ethics. LC 80-11696. (Philosophy & Society Ser.). 305p. 1980. 28.95x (ISBN 0-8476-6274-8); pap. 11.95x (ISBN 0-8476-6285-3). Rowman.

Goldstein, Eleanor C., ed. Ethics, Vol. 1 (incl. 1979 & 1981 Supplement) (Social Issues Resources Ser.). 1982. 70.00 (ISBN 0-89777-026-9). Soc Issues.

Gow, Kathleen M. Yes, Virginia, There Is Right & Wrong. 255p. 1985. 12.95 (ISBN 0-8423-8558-4); pap. 6.95 (ISBN 0-8423-8561-4). Tyndale.

Grassian, Victor. Moral Reasoning: Ethical Theory & Some Contemporary Moral Problems. 400p. 1981. pap. text ed. write for info. (ISBN 0-13-600759-7). P-H.

Green, Thomas H. Prolegomena to Ethics. 5th ed. Bradley, A. C., ed. LC 32-3225. 1968. Repr. of 1929 ed. 42.00 (ISBN 0-527-35800-2). Kraus Repr.

Grisez, Germain & Shaw, Russell. Beyond the New Morality: The Responsibilities of Freedom. rev. ed. LC 80-18293. 240p. 1980. text ed. 14.95 (ISBN 0-268-00663-6); pap. 6.95 (ISBN 0-268-00665-2). U of Notre Dame Pr.

--A Grisez Reader for Beyond the New Morality. Casey, Joseph H., ed. LC 81-43481. 218p. (Orig.). 1982. lib. bdg. 29.00 (ISBN 0-8191-2243-2); pap. text ed. 11.50 (ISBN 0-8191-2244-0). U Pr of Amer.

Gronlund, Laurence. Our Destiny: The Influence of Socialism on Morals & Religion; an Essay on Ethics. LC 75-321. (The Radical Tradition in America Ser.). 170p. 1975. Repr. of 1890 ed. 19.25 (ISBN 0-88355-225-6). Hyperion Conn.

Gula, Richard M. What Are They Saying about Moral Norms? LC 81-83188. 128p. (Orig.). 1982. pap. 4.95 (ISBN 0-8091-2412-2). Paulist Pr.

Gustafson, James M. Ethics from a Theocentric Perspective: Theology & Ethics, Vol. 1. LC 81-11603. 284p. 1981. 27.50x (ISBN 0-226-31110-4). U of Chicago Pr.

--Ethics from a Theocentric Perspective: Theology & Ethics, Vol. 1. LC 81-11603. xiv, 346p. 1983. pap. 12.00x (ISBN 0-226-31111-2). U of Chicago Pr.

--Ethics from a Theocentric Perspective, Vol. 2: Ethics & Theology. LC 81-11603. 370p. 1984. lib. bdg. 25.00x (ISBN 0-226-31112-0). U of Chicago Pr.

Hampshire, Stuart. Morality & Conflict. 176p. 1987. pap. text ed. 9.50x (ISBN 0-674-58732-4). Harvard U Pr.

Hardie, W. F. Aristotle's Ethical Theory. 2nd ed. 1981. pap. 29.95x (ISBN 0-19-824633-1). Oxford U Pr.

Hare, R. M. Essays on the Moral Concepts. LC 70-187322. (New Studies in Practical Philosophy). 150p. 1972. 18.50x (ISBN 0-520-02231-9). U of Cal Pr.

--Moral Thinking: Its Levels, Methods, & Point. 1981. 27.00x (ISBN 0-19-824659-5); pap. 9.95x (ISBN 0-19-824660-9). Oxford U Pr.

Hare, Richard M. Freedom & Reason. (Oxford Paperbacks Ser.: No. 92). 1965. pap. text ed. 8.95x (ISBN 0-19-881092-X). Oxford U Pr.

Harman, Gilbert. The Nature of Morality: An Introduction to Ethics. 1977. pap. text ed. 10.95x (ISBN 0-19-502143-6). Oxford U Pr.

Harris. Applying Moral Theories. 1985. pap. text ed. write for info. (ISBN 0-534-05898-1). Wadsworth Pub.

Harris, Alan. Teaching Morality & Religion. 104p. 1975. 14.95x (ISBN 0-8464-1274-8). Beekman Pubs.

Harrod, Howard L. The Human Center: Moral Agency in the Social World. LC 80-2392. 160p. 1981. 3.50 (ISBN 0-8006-0657-4, 1-657). Fortress.

Hartmann, Heinz. Psychoanalysis & Moral Values. LC 58-9230. (The New York Psychoanalytic Institute Freud Anniversary Lecture Ser.). 121p. 1960. text ed. 17.50 (ISBN 0-8236-5240-8). Intl Univs Pr.

Hauerwas, Stanley & MacIntyre, Alasdair, eds. Revisions: Changing Perspectives in Moral Philosophy. (Revisions Ser.). 320p. 1983. text ed. 24.95 (ISBN 0-268-01614-3); pap. text ed. 9.95 (ISBN 0-268-01617-8). U of Notre Dame Pr.

Haughey, John. Personal Values in Public Policy. LC 79-84401. (Woodstock Studies: No. 3). 288p. (Orig.). 1979. pap. 6.95 (ISBN 0-8091-2201-4). Paulist Pr.

Hegel, G. W. Philosophy of Right. Knox, T. M., tr. 1942. 37.50x (ISBN 0-19-824128-3); pap. 10.95x (ISBN 0-19-500276-8). Oxford U Pr.

Hester, Joseph P. & Killian, Don R. Cartoons for Thinking: Issues in Ethics & Values. (Illus.). 1984. 9.95 (ISBN 0-89824-007-7). Trillium Pr.

Heyd, David. Supererogation: Its Status in Ethical Theory. LC 81-15476. (Cambridge Studies in Philosophy). 180p. 1982. 37.50 (ISBN 0-521-23935-4). Cambridge U Pr.

Hilpinen, Risto, ed. New Studies in Deontic Logic: Norms, Actions & the Foundations of Ethics. 272p. 1981. 39.50 (ISBN 90-277-1278-6, Pub. by Reidel Holland). Kluwer Academic.

Hoffman, John C. Ethical Confrontation in Counseling. LC 78-11799. 1979. lib. bdg. 10.50x (ISBN 0-226-34785-0). U of Chicago Pr.

Hospers, John. Human Conduct: Problems of Ethics. 2nd ed. 481p. 1982. pap. text ed. 15.95 (ISBN 0-15-540094-0, HC). HarBraceJ.

Howie, John. Perspectives for Moral Decisions. LC 80-6102. 192p. 1981. lib. bdg. 25.00 (ISBN 0-8191-1375-1); pap. text ed. 11.25 (ISBN 0-8191-1376-X). U Pr of Amer.

Hughes, Gerard. Authority in Morals. 160p. (Orig.). 1984. pap. 6.95 (ISBN 0-87840-410-4). Georgetown U Pr.

Hume, David. Enquiries Concerning Human Understanding & Concerning the Principles of Morals. 3rd ed. Nidditch, P. H., ed. 1975. pap. text ed. 10.95x (ISBN 0-19-824536-X). Oxford U Pr.

--Enquiry Concerning the Principles of Morals. 2nd ed. 200p. 1966. 15.95 (ISBN 0-87548-017-9); pap. 4.95 (ISBN 0-87548-018-7). Open Court.

--Inquiry Concerning the Principles of Morals: With a Supplement, a Dialogue. Hendel, Charles W., ed. 1957. pap. 7.20 scp (ISBN 0-672-60236-9, LLA62). Bobbs.

--Moral & Political Philosophy. Aiken, Henry D., ed. (Library of Classics Ser.: No. 3). 1975. pap. text ed. 8.95x (ISBN 0-02-846170-3). Hafner.

Hutcheson, Francis. Essay on the Nature & Conduct of the Passions & Affections, 1742. 3rd ed. LC 76-81361. (History of Psychology Ser.). 1969. Repr. of 1742 ed. 50.00x (ISBN 0-8201-1058-2). Schol Facsimiles.

Huxley, Thomas H. Evolution & Ethics, & Other Essays. LC 70-8391. 334p. 1897. Repr. 49.00x (ISBN 0-403-00041-6). Scholarly.

Ibn-Gabirol, Solomon B. Improvement of the Moral Qualities: An Ethical Treatise of the Eleventh Century. Wise, Stephen S., ed. LC 2-8360. (Columbia University. Oriental Studies: No. 1). Repr. of 1902 ed. 17.25 (ISBN 0-404-50491-4). AMS Pr.

Iyer, Raghavan. The Moral & Political Thought of Mahatma Gandi. (Illus.). xviii, 478p. pap. 17.50 (ISBN 0-88695-002-3). Concord Grove.

Jaffa, Harry V. Thomism & Aristotelianism: A Study of the Commentary by Thomas Aquinas on the Nicomachean Ethics. LC 78-21520. 1979. Repr. of 1952 ed. lib. bdg. 29.75x (ISBN 0-313-21149-3, JATA). Greenwood.

Jensen, Larry C. & Hughston, Karen M. Responsibility & Morality: Helping Children Become Responsible & Morally Mature. LC 79-10727. (Illus.). 1979. pap. 7.95x (ISBN 0-8425-1679-4). Brigham.

Jones, D. Gareth. Brave New People: Ethical Issues at the Commencement of Life. LC 85-4582. 232p. 1985. pap. 8.95 (ISBN 0-8028-0070-X). Eerdmans.

Jones, Donald G., ed. Business, Religion & Ethics: Inquiry & Encounter. LC 82-14479. 288p. 1982. 25.00 (ISBN 0-89946-164-6); pap. text ed. 12.95 (ISBN 0-89946-166-2). Oelgeschlager.

Kainz, Howard P. Ethica Dialectica. x, 145p. 1980. lib. bdg. 34.00 (ISBN 90-247-2078-8, Pub. by Martinus Nijhoff Netherlands). Kluwer Academic.

Kant, Immanuel. Foundations of the Metaphysics of Morals. Beck, Lewis W., tr. Bd. with What Is Enlightenment. LC 59-11679. 1959. pap. 4.79 scp (ISBN 0-672-60312-8, LLA113). Bobbs.

--Foundations of the Metaphysics of Morals: Text & Critical Essays. Wolff, Robert P., ed. LC 68-9841. (Text & Critical Essays Ser.). 1969. pap. 10.28 scp (ISBN 0-672-61114-7, TC1). Bobbs.

--Fundamental Principles of the Metaphysic of Ethics. Manthey-Zorn, Otto, tr. (Century Philosophy Ser.). 1966. pap. text ed. 7.95x (ISBN 0-89197-185-8). Irvington.

--Fundamental Principles of the Metaphysics of Morals. Abbott, Thomas K., tr. 1949. pap. 4.24 scp (ISBN 0-672-60177-X, LLA16). Bobbs.

--Grounding for the Metaphysics of Morals. Ellington, James W., tr. from Ger. LC 80-28839. (HPC Philosophical Classics Ser.). 80p. 1981. lib. bdg. 16.50 (ISBN 0-915145-01-4); pap. text ed. 3.45 (ISBN 0-915145-00-6). Hackett Pub.

--Groundwork of the Metaphysics of Morals. Paton, H. J., tr. Orig. Title: Moral Law. pap. 6.95x (ISBN 0-06-131159-6, TB1159, Torch). Har-Row.

--Lectures on Ethics. 11.25 (ISBN 0-8446-2348-2). Peter Smith.

--Metaphysical Elements of Justice: Part I of the Metaphysics of Morals. Ladd, John, tr. (Orig.). 1965. pap. 7.20 scp (ISBN 0-672-60250-4, LLA72). Bobbs.

Kaplan, Morton A. Justice, Human Nature, & Political Obligation. LC 76-8145. 1976. 18.95 (ISBN 0-02-916890-2). Free Pr.

Katz, Lilian G. & Ward, Evangeline H. Ethical Behavior in Early Childhood Education. LC 78-57538. 26p. 1978. pap. text ed. 2.00 (ISBN 0-912674-61-X, NAEYC #112). Natl Assn Child Ed.

Kiefer, Howard E. & Munitz, Milton K., eds. Ethics & Social Justice. (Contemporary Philosophic Thought: Vol. 4). 1970. 49.50 (ISBN 0-87395-054-2). State U NY Pr.

Knight, Margaret. Morals Without Religion. 124p. 1981. 25.00x (ISBN 0-686-97044-6, Pub. by Dobson Bks England). State Mutual Bk.

Koenig, Thomas R., ed. An Introduction to Ethics: A Philosophical Orientation. 187p. 1974. pap. text ed. 8.95x (ISBN 0-8422-0444-X). Irvington.

Kolnai, Aurel. Ethics, Value, & Reality: Selected Papers of Aurel Kolnai. LC 77-83145. 280p. 1978. 25.00 (ISBN 0-915144-39-5); pap. text ed. 15.00 cancelled (ISBN 0-915144-40-9). Hackett Pub.

Kruschwitz & Roberts. Virtues: Contemporary Essay of Moral Character. King, Ken, ed. (Orig.). 1986. write for info. (ISBN 0-534-06720-4). Wadsworth Pub.

Kuhmerker, Lisa, et al, eds. Evaluating Moral Development. LC 80-68348. (Orig.). 1980. 9.95 (ISBN 0-915744-24-4); pap. 6.95 (ISBN 0-915744-21-X). Character Res.

Kurtz, Paul, ed. Moral Problems in Contemporary Society: Essays in Humanistic Ethics. 2nd ed. 301p. 1973. pap. 10.95 (ISBN 0-87975-022-7). Prometheus Bks.

Labacqz, Karen. Professional Ethics: Power & Paradox. 192p. (Orig.). 1985. pap. 11.95 (ISBN 0-687-34325-9). Abingdon.

LaCroix, W. L. Meaning & Reason in Ethics. rev. ed. LC 79-52963. 1979. pap. text ed. 8.75 (ISBN 0-8191-0786-7). U Pr of Amer.

Ladd, George T. Philosophy of Conduct: A Treatise of the Facts, Principles, & Ideals of Ethics. LC 75-3222. Repr. of 1902 ed. 46.50 (ISBN 0-404-59218-X). AMS Pr.

Laird, John. Enquiry into Moral Notions. LC 76-114045. Repr. of 1936 ed. 22.50 (ISBN 0-404-03802-6). AMS Pr.

Lamont, William D. Introduction to Green's Moral Philosophy. LC 78-20478. 1980. Repr. of 1934 ed. 21.45 (ISBN 0-88355-855-6). Hyperion Conn.

Lande, Nathaniel & Slade, Afton. Stages: Understanding How You Make Your Moral Decisions. LC 78-195000. 1979. 10.00 (ISBN 0-06-250510-6, HarpR). Har-Row.

Larsen, Sandy & Larsen, Dale. Choices: Picking Your Way Through the Ethical Jungle. (Young Fisherman Bible Studyguide). (Illus.). 61p. (Orig.). (YA) 1983. saddle-stitched student ed. 2.95 (ISBN 0-87788-113-8); tchr's. ed. 4.95 (ISBN 0-87788-114-6). Shaw Pubs.

Leiser, Burton M. Liberty, Justice, & Morals: Contemporary Value Conflicts. 2nd ed. (Illus.). 1979. text ed. write for info. (ISBN 0-02-369510-2). Macmillan.

LeMaire, H. Paul. Personal Decisions. LC 81-43668. 220p. (Orig.). 1982. lib. bdg. 28.25 (ISBN 0-8191-2329-3); pap. text ed. 11.75 (ISBN 0-8191-2330-7). U Pr of Amer.

Lewis, Clarence I. Values & Imperatives: Studies in Ethics. Lange, John, ed. LC 69-13181. 1969. 17.50x (ISBN 0-8047-0687-5). Stanford U Pr.

Lutzer, Erwin W. The Necessity of Ethical Absolutes: (CFUC) 112p. (Orig.). 1981. pap. 6.95 (ISBN 0-310-35791-8, 12659P). Zondervan.

Lynchburg College Faculty Staff, ed. Faith & Morals. LC 81-71948. (Classical Selections on Great Issues, Symposium Readings Ser.: Vol. 4). 472p. 1982. lib. bdg. 24.00 (ISBN 0-8191-2301-3); pap. text ed. 9.25 (ISBN 0-8191-2302-1). U Pr of Amer.

Macbeath, Alexander. Experiments in Living: A Study of the Nature & Foundation of Ethics or Morals in the Light of Recent Work in Social Anthropology. LC 77-27180. (Gifford Lectures: 1948-49). Repr. of 1952 ed. 28.00 (ISBN 0-404-60503-6). AMS Pr.

McCosh, James. Our Moral Nature. LC 75-3260. Repr. of 1892 ed. 18.00 (ISBN 0-404-59247-3). AMS Pr.

Mackie, J. L. Ethics: Inventing Right & Wrong. 1977. pap. 6.95 (ISBN 0-14-021957-9, Pelican). Penguin.

McLean, George F., ed. Ethical Wisdom East &-or West. LC 78-106891. (Proceedings of the American Catholic Philosophical Association: Vol. 51). 1977. pap. 15.00 (ISBN 0-918090-11-3). Am Cath Philo.

Maguire, Daniel C. The Moral Choice. 1979. pap. 12.95 (ISBN 0-86683-771-X, AY8112, HarpR). Har-Row.

--The Moral Revolution. 224p. (Orig.). 1986. pap. 12.95 (ISBN 0-06-254539-6, HarpR). Har-Row.

Mahoney, John. Bioethics & Belief. 128p. 1984. pap. 8.95 (ISBN 0-7220-1319-1). Chr Classics.

Malinowski, Bronislaw. The Foundations of Faith & Morals. LC 74-20949. 1974. Repr. of 1936 ed. lib. bdg. 20.50 (ISBN 0-8414-5965-7). Folcroft.

Mandelbaum, Maurice. The Phenomenology of Moral Experience. 336p. 1969. pap. 8.95x (ISBN 0-8018-1095-7). Johns Hopkins.

Mathews, Donald G. Slavery & Methodism: A Chapter in American Morality, 1780-1845. LC 78-13249. 1978. Repr. of 1965 ed. lib. bdg. 27.75 (ISBN 0-313-21045-4, MASAM). Greenwood.

Mazzini, Giuseppe. The Morality & the Immorality of the Human Race. (Illus.). 144p. Repr. of 1862 ed. 127.45 (ISBN 0-89901-115-2). Found Class Reprints.

Melden, A. I. Ethical Theories: A Book of Readings with Revisions. 2nd ed. 1967. text ed. write for info. (ISBN 0-13-290122-6). P-H.

Mishan, E. J. Making the World Safe for Pornography. LC 73-83001. 262p. 1973. 1.95 (ISBN 0-912050-41-1, Library Pr). Open Court.

Mooney, Tom. The Early History of a Purpose Machine. 1976. 5.95 (ISBN 0-9601240-1-2); pap. 2.95 (ISBN 0-9601240-2-0). Mooney.

Moore, F. C. T. The Psychological Basis of Morality: An Essay on Value & Desire. LC 77-22632. (Library of Philosophy & Religion Ser). 106p. 1978. text ed. 28.50x (ISBN 0-06-494933-8). B&N Imports.

Moore, George E. Ethics. 1967. pap. 5.95x (ISBN 0-19-500354-3). Oxford U Pr.

--Principia Ethica. 1959. 37.50 (ISBN 0-521-05753-1); pap. 12.95 (ISBN 0-521-09114-4). Cambridge U Pr.

Morris, Herbert. On Guilt & Innocence: Essays in Legal Philosophy & Moral Psychology. 1976. pap. 3.95 (ISBN 0-520-03944-0, 434). U of Cal Pr.

Murphy, Carol. Holy Morality. LC 71-110286. (Orig.). 1970. pap. 2.50x (ISBN 0-87574-169-X). Pendle Hill.

Nagel, T. Mortal Questions. LC 78-58797. 1979. 32.50 (ISBN 0-521-22360-1); pap. 10.95 (ISBN 0-521-29460-6). Cambridge U Pr.

Nelson, Leonard. System of Ethics. 1956. 49.50x (ISBN 0-685-69846-7). Elliots Bks.

New York Academy Of Medicine. Ministry & Medicine in Human Relations. facs. ed. Galdston, Iago, ed. LC 77-142682. (Essay Index Reprint Ser). 1955. 17.00 (ISBN 0-8369-2120-8). Ayer Co Pubs.

Nielsen, Kai. Ethics Without God. (Skeptic's Bookshelf Ser.). 112p. 1973. pap. 9.95 (ISBN 0-87975-019-7). Prometheus Bks.

Nietzsche, Friedrich. Daybreak: Thoughts on the Prejudices of Morality. Hollingdale, R. J., tr. LC 81-18017. (Texts in German Philosophy). 220p. 1982. 22.95 (ISBN 0-521-24396-3); pap. 9.95 (ISBN 0-521-28662-X). Cambridge U Pr.

--On the Genealogy of Morals. Kaufman, Walter, tr. Bd. with Ecce Homo. 1967. pap. 4.76 (ISBN 0-394-70401-0, Vin). Random.

Nolan, Richard T. & Kirkpatrick, Frank G. Living Issues in Ethics. 400p. 1982. pap. text ed. write for info. (ISBN 0-534-01140-3). Wadsworth Pub.

Norton, David L. Personal Destinies: A Philosophy of Ethical Individualism. 1976. 47.50x (ISBN 0-691-07215-9); pap. 10.95x (ISBN 0-691-01975-4). Princeton U Pr.

Olson, Robert G. Ethics: A Short Introduction. 1977. pap. text ed. 6.50 (ISBN 0-394-32033-6, RanC). Random.

O'Reilly, Sean. Bioethics & the Limits of Science. 176p. (Orig.). 1980. pap. 9.95 (ISBN 0-931888-02-6, Chris. Coll. Pr.). Christendom Pubns.

Outka, Gene. Agape: An Ethical Analysis. LC 78-88070. (Publications in Religion Ser.: No. 17). 336p. 1972. 33.00x (ISBN 0-300-01384-1); pap. 8.95x (ISBN 0-300-02122-4). Yale U Pr.

Paley, William. The Principles of Moral & Political Philosophy. Wellek, Rene, ed. LC 75-11246. (British Philosophers & Theologians of the 17th & 18th Centuries Ser.: Vol. 45). 1977. Repr. of 1785 ed. lib. bdg. 51.00 (ISBN 0-8240-1797-8). Garland Pub.

Pannenberg, Wolfhart. Ethics. Crim, Keith, tr. from Ger. LC 81-13051. Orig. Title: Ethik und Ekklesiologie. 222p. 1981. pap. 10.95 (ISBN 0-664-24392-4). Westminster.

Parker, De Witt. Human Values: An Interpretation of Ethics Based on a Study of Values. LC 75-3305. Repr. of 1931 ed. 42.50 (ISBN 0-404-59290-2). AMS Pr.

Perry, Thomas D. Moral Reasoning & Truth: An Essay in Philosophy & Jurisprudence. 1976. 38.00x (ISBN 0-19-824532-7). Oxford U Pr.

Porter, Burton F. The Good Life: Alternatives in Ethics. (Illus.). 1980. pap. text ed. write for info. (ISBN 0-02-396120-1). Macmillan.

Price, Richard. Review of the Principal Questions in Morals. LC 73-179398. 516p. 1974. Repr. of 1787 ed. lib. bdg. 32.50 (ISBN 0-8337-2831-8). B Franklin.

Prichard, Harold A. Moral Obligation & Duty & Interest: Essays & Lectures. (Oxford Paperbacks Ser). (Orig.). 1968. pap. 4.95x (ISBN 0-19-881151-9). Oxford U Pr.

Priest, James E. Governmental & Judicial Ethics in the Bible & Rabbinic Literature. LC 79-23423. 312p. 1980. 17.95x (ISBN 0-87068-697-6). Pepperdine U Pr.

Prior, Arthur N. Logic & the Basis of Ethics. 1949. 17.95x (ISBN 0-19-824157-7). Oxford U Pr.

--Papers in Logic & Ethics. Geach, P. T. & Kenny, A. J., eds. LC 76-9376. 238p. 1976. 15.00x (ISBN 0-87023-213-4). U of Mass Pr.

Purcell, Royal. Ethics, Morality, & Mores. 177p. (Orig.). 1986. pap. 9.95 (ISBN 0-933189-01-X). Purcell Pub.

Purtill, Richard. Thinking about Ethics. 160p. 1976. pap. text ed. write for info. (ISBN 0-13-917716-7). P-H.

Quinn, Philip L. Divine Commands & Moral Requirements. (Clarendon Library of Logic & Philosophy). 1978. text ed. 36.00x (ISBN 0-19-824413-4). Oxford U Pr.

Rand, Benjamin, ed. The Classical Moralists: Selections Illustrating Ethics from Socrates to Martineau. 16.50 (ISBN 0-8446-1374-6). Peter Smith.

Raphael, D. D. Moral Philosophy. (Oxford Paperbacks University Ser.). (Orig.). 1981. pap. text ed. 8.95x (ISBN 0-19-289136-7). Oxford U Pr.

Raphael, D. D., ed. British Moralists, Sixteen Fifty to Eighteen Hundred, 2 vols. 1969. Set. pap. 18.95x (ISBN 0-19-875010-2). Oxford U Pr.

Raphael, David D. Moral Judgment. LC 77-28440. 1978. Repr. of 1955 ed. lib. bdg. 22.25x (ISBN 0-313-20246-X, RAMJ). Greenwood.

Reamer, Frederic G. Ethical Dilemmas in Social Service. LC 81-18071. 304p. 1982. 22.50x (ISBN 0-231-05188-3). Columbia U Pr.

Regan, Tom, ed. Matters of Life & Death: New Introductory Essays in Moral Philosophy. 368p. 1980. 32.95 (ISBN 0-87722-181-2). Temple U Pr.

Regan, Tom & Van DeVeer, Donald, eds. And Justice for All: New Introductory Essays in Ethics & Public Policy. LC 81-23446. (Philosophy & Society Ser.). 320p. 1982. 34.00x (ISBN 0-8476-7059-7); pap. 12.50x (ISBN 0-8476-7060-0). Rowman.

Richardson, J. & Co. Staff. Moral Philosophy, Vol. 9. 1982. 62.50x (ISBN 0-317-54279-6, Pub. by J Richardson UK); pap. 47.50x (ISBN 0-317-54280-X, Pub. by J Richardson UK). State Mutual Bk.

Robert, Charles, ed. Manipulated Man: The Power of Man Over Man, Its Risks & Its Limits. European Studies. Strasbourg, September 24-29, 1973. Frank, C. P., tr. LC 77-24330. (Pittsburgh Theological Monographs: No. 16). 1977. pap. 8.00 (ISBN 0-915138-21-2). Pickwick.

Rosen, Bernard & Caplan, Arthur L. Ethics in the Undergraduate Curriculum. LC 80-12351. (The Teaching of Ethics Ser.). 67p. 1980. pap. 4.00 (ISBN 0-916558-13-4). Hastings Ctr.

Ross, Sir William D. Kant's Ethical Theory: A Commentary on the Grundlegung zur Metaphysik der Sitten. LC 78-6730. 1978. Repr. of 1954 ed. lib. bdg. 22.50x (ISBN 0-8371-9059-2, ROKE). Greenwood.

Rotenstreich, Nathan. Practice & Realization. 1979. lib. bdg. 29.00 (ISBN 90-247-2112-1, Pub. by Martinus Nijhoff Netherlands). Kluwer Academic.

Russell, Bertrand. Human Society in Ethics & Politics. 1954. text ed. 18.50x (ISBN 0-04-172004-0). Allen Unwin.

Rynkiewich, Michael A. & Spradley, James P. Ethics & Anthropology. LC 81-3698. 198p. 1981. Repr. of 1976 ed. lib. bdg. 14.50 (ISBN 0-89874-349-4). Krieger.

Sabini, Jon & Silver, Maury. Moralities of Everyday Life. 1982. 22.50x (ISBN 0-19-503016-8); pap. 8.95 (ISBN 0-19-503017-6). Oxford U Pr.

Scheler, Max. Formalism in Ethics & Non-Formal Ethics of Values: A New Attempt Toward the Foundation of an Ethical Personalism. Frings, Manfred S. & Funk, Roger L., trs. from Ger. LC 72-97416. (Studies in Phenomenology & Existential Philosophy). Orig. Title: Der Formalismus der Ethik und die Materiale Wertethik. 750p. 1973. text ed. 29.95 (ISBN 0-8101-0415-6); 14.95 (ISBN 0-8101-0620-5). Northwestern U Pr.

Schneider, Herbert W. Morals for Mankind. LC 60-14882. 96p. 1960. 5.00x (ISBN 0-8262-0006-0). U of Mo Pr.

Schopenhauer, Arthur. On the Basis of Morality. Payne, E. F., tr. LC 65-26525. (Orig.). 1965. pap. write for info. (ISBN 0-02-392400-4, LLA203). Macmillan.

Schweitzer, Albert. Essence of Faith. pap. 0.95 (ISBN 0-685-19400-0, 127, WL). Citadel Pr.

Selby-Bigge, L. A., ed. British Moralists: Being Selections from Writers Principally of the Eighteenth Century, 2 vols. in 1. LC 64-20242. 1964. 74.50 (ISBN 0-672-51067-7); pap. text ed. 17.95x (ISBN 0-8290-1894-8). Irvington.

Sellers, James H. & Milam, Edward E. Accounting Student Perceptions of Business & Professional Ethics. 50p. (Orig.). 1981. pap. 4.50 (ISBN 0-938004-00-X). U MS Bus Econ.

Shannon, Thomas & Manfra, Jo Ann. Law & Bioethics: Selected Cases. LC 81-80876. 448p. (Orig.). 1981. pap. 14.95 (ISBN 0-8091-2353-3). Paulist Pr.

Sharp, Frank C. Ethics. LC 75-3365. Repr. of 1928 ed. 45.50 (ISBN 0-404-59362-3). AMS Pr.

Sheriff, John K. The Good-Natured Man: The Evolution of a Moral Ideal, 1660-1800. LC 81-14758. 144p. 1982. text ed. 13.50 (ISBN 0-8173-0097-X). U of Ala Pr.

Shirts, R. Garry. Where Do You Draw the Line. 1977. 29.00 (ISBN 0-686-10238-X). Simile II.

Sidgwick, Henry. The Methods of Ethics. LC 81-85772. (Philosophical Classics Ser.). 568p. 1981. 30.00 (ISBN 0-915145-29-4); pap. 12.50 (ISBN 0-915145-28-6). Hackett Pub.

Silcock, Thomas H. Words & Testimonies. LC 72-80097. (Orig.). 1972. pap. 2.50x (ISBN 0-87574-186-X). Pendle Hill.

Singer, Marcus G. Generalization in Ethics: An Essay in the Logic of Ethics with the Rudiments of a System of Moral Philosophy. LC 70-152539. (With a new introduction). 1971. Repr. of 1961 ed. 11.00x (ISBN 0-8462-1612-4). Russell.

Smith, Adam. The Theory of Moral Sentiments. (Glasgow Edition of the Works & Correspondence of Adam Smith Ser.). (Illus.). 1976. 54.00x (ISBN 0-19-828189-7). Oxford U Pr.

Smith, Steven A. Satisfaction of Interest & the Concept of Morality. LC 73-8305. 165p. 1975. 18.00 (ISBN 0-8387-1383-1). Bucknell U Pr.

Sneath, E. Hershey, ed. Evolution of Ethics. 1927. 49.50x (ISBN 0-685-69867-X). Elliots Bks.

Spencer, Herbert. The Principles of Ethics, 2 vols. LC 77-71453. 550p. 1980. Set. pap. 8.00 (ISBN 0-913966-34-7, Liberty Clas); Vol. I. pap. (ISBN 0-913966-77-0); Vol. II. pap. (ISBN 0-913966-75-4). Liberty Fund.

--The Principles of Ethics, 2 vols. LC 77-71453. 1978. Repr. Set. 20.00 (ISBN 0-913966-33-9, Liberty Clas); Vol. I. (ISBN 0-913966-76-2); Vol. II. (ISBN 0-913966-74-6). Liberty Fund.

Spinoza, B. De. Ethics & on the Improvement of the Understanding. 1974. 7.95x (ISBN 0-02-852650-3). Hafner.

Spinoza, Baruch. The Ethics & Selected Letters. Feldman, Seymour, intro. by. Shirley, Samuel, tr. from Lat. & Heb. LC 81-7199. 268p. 1982. lib. bdg. 19.50 (ISBN 0-915145-18-9); pap. text ed. 4.95 (ISBN 0-915145-19-7). Hackett Pub.

--The Ethics of Spinoza. 1976. pap. 4.95 (ISBN 0-8065-0536-2). Citadel Pr.

Spong, John & Haines, Denise. Beyond Moralism. 204p. (Orig.). 1986. pap. 9.95 (ISBN 0-86683-514-8, HarpR). Har-Row.

Stace, Walter T. Concept of Morals. 11.25 (ISBN 0-8446-2990-1). Peter Smith.

Stevens, Edward. The Morals Game. LC 74-18855. 216p. 1975. pap. 5.95 (ISBN 0-8091-1852-1). Paulist Pr.

Stevenson, Charles. Ethics & Language. LC 75-41263. Repr. of 1944 ed. 22.50 (ISBN 0-404-14806-9). AMS Pr.

Stewart, Dugald. Outlines of the Moral Philosophy. LC 75-11255. (British Philosophers & Theologians of the 17th & 18th Centuries: Vol. 54). 322p. 1976. Repr. of 1793 ed. lib. bdg. 51.00 (ISBN 0-8240-1805-2). Garland Pub.

Stout, Jeffrey. Flight from Authority: Religion, Morality & the Quest for Autonomy. LC 81-2340. (Revisions Ser.: Vol. 1). 307p. 1987. pap. text ed. 12.95x (ISBN 0-268-00971-6, Dist. by Har-Row). U of Notre Dame Pr.

Stromberg, Peter L., et al. The Teaching of Ethics in the Military. LC 81-86583. (The Teaching of Ethics in Higher Education Ser.: Vol. XII). 85p. (Orig.). 1982. pap. 5.00 (ISBN 0-916558-16-9). Hastings Ctr.

Struhl, Paula R. & Struhl, Karsten J., eds. Ethics in Perspective: A Reader. 3rd ed. 1980. pap. text ed. 13.00 (ISBN 0-394-32354-8, RanC). Random.

Taylor, A. E. The Faith of the Moralist: Gifford Lectures Delivered in the University of St. Andrews, 1926-1928, 2 vols. 1977. Repr. of 1932 ed. Set. lib. bdg. 50.00 (ISBN 0-8482-2663-1). Norwood Edns.

Taylor, Alfred E. Faith of a Moralist, 2 Vols. in 1. LC 37-23815. (Gifford Lectures 1926-1928). 1968. Repr. of 1937 ed. 41.00 (ISBN 0-527-89062-6). Kraus Repr.

Thiroux, Jacques P. Ethics: Theory & Practice. 2nd ed. 392p. 1980. pap. text ed. write for info. (ISBN 0-02-470220-X). Macmillan.

Thorpe, W. H. The Origins & Rise of Ethology. 186p. 1979. 35.95 (ISBN 0-03-053251-5). Praeger.

Tredennick, Hugh, ed. The Ethics of Aristotle: The Nicomachean Ethics. rev ed. Thomson, J. A., tr. 1955. pap. 5.95 (ISBN 0-14-044055-0). Penguin.

Trotsky, Leon, et al. Their Morals & Ours. new ed. House, ed. LC 73-82168. 96p. 1974. 14.00 (ISBN 0-87348-318-9); pap. 4.95 (ISBN 0-87348-319-7). Path Pr NY.

Tsanoff, R. A. The Moral Ideals of Our Civilization. 1977. lib. bdg. write for info. (ISBN 0-8490-2279-7). Gordon Pr.

Tucker, Abraham. The Light of Nature Pursued, 7 vols. Wellek, Rene, ed. LC 75-11262. (British Philosophers & Theologians of the 17th & 18th Centuries: Vol. 60). 4075p. 1984. Repr. of 1805 ed. Set. lib. bdg. 355.00 (ISBN 0-8240-1811-7). Garland Pub.

Ulanov, Ann & Ulanov, Barry. Religion & the Unconscious. LC 75-16302. 288p. 1975. 13.95 (ISBN 0-664-20799-5). Westminster.

--Religion & the Unconscious. 2nd ed. LC 75-16302. 288p. 1985. pap. 14.95 (ISBN 0-664-24657-5). Westminster.

Veatch, Henry B. For an Ontology of Morals: A Critique of Contemporary Ethical Theory. 1971. 14.95 (ISBN 0-8101-0352-4). Northwestern U Pr.

--Rational Man: A Modern Interpretation of Aristotelian Ethics. LC 62-16161. (Midland Bks.: No. 71). 228p. 1962. pap. 8.95x (ISBN 0-253-20071-7). Ind U Pr.

Walten, Maximilian G. & Fuller, Thomas, eds. Holy State & the Profane State, 2 Vols. LC 70-168072. Repr. of 1938 ed. 55.00 (ISBN 0-404-02637-0). AMS Pr.

Warnock, Mary. Ethics since Nineteen Hundred. 3rd ed. 1978. pap. 4.95x (ISBN 0-19-289108-1). Oxford U Pr.

Warwick, Donald P. The Teaching of Ethics & the Social Sciences. LC 80-10154. (The Teaching of Ethics Ser.). 69p. 1980. pap. 4.00 (ISBN 0-916558-11-8). Hastings Ctr.

Waterman, Leroy. Religion Faces the World Crisis. 1943. 3.75x (ISBN 0-685-21800-7). Wahr.

Wayland, Francis. Elements of Moral Science. Blau, Joseph L., ed. LC 63-19149. (The John Harvard Library). 1963. 27.50x (ISBN 0-674-24600-4). Harvard U Pr.

Weiss, Paul. Man's Freedom. LC 67-23318. (Arcturus Books Paperbacks). 335p. 1967. pap. 8.95x (ISBN 0-8093-0277-2). S Ill U Pr.

Weiss, Paul & Weiss, Jonathan. Right & Wrong: A Philosophical Dialogue Between Father & Son. LC 73-12702. (Arcturus Books Paperbacks). 222p. 1974. pap. 5.95x (ISBN 0-8093-0658-1). S Ill U Pr.

Wellman, Carl. Challenge & Response: Justification in Ethics. LC 73-132478. 309p. 1971. 15.00x (ISBN 0-8093-0490-2). S Ill U Pr.

Westermarck, Edvard A. Ethical Relativity. Repr. of 1932 ed. lib. bdg. 22.50x (ISBN 0-8371-4366-7, WEER). Greenwood.

Westermarck, Edward. The Origin & Development of the Moral Ideas, 2 vols. facsimile ed. LC 74-37359. (Select Bibliographies Reprint Ser.). Repr. of 1908 ed. Set. 81.50 (ISBN 0-8369-6706-2). Ayer Co Pubs.

Westermarck, Edward A. The Origin & Development of the Moral Ideas, 2 vols. 2nd ed. (Landmarks in Anthropology Ser). 1621p. Repr. 115.00 (ISBN 0-384-66958-1). Johnson Repr.

White, Morton. What Is & What Ought to Be Done: An Essay on Ethics & Epistemology. 1981. 14.95x (ISBN 0-19-502916-X). Oxford U Pr.

Williams, Bernard. Ethics & the Limits of Philosophy. 248p. 1985. 17.50 (ISBN 0-674-26857-1). Harvard U Pr.

--Morality: An Introduction to Ethics. LC 70-172503. 1972. pap. 5.95x (ISBN 0-06-131632-6, TB1632, Torch). Har-Row.

Williams, Gardner. Humanistic Ethics. 1951. 6.00 (ISBN 0-8022-1886-5). Philos Lib.

Witherspoon, John. An Annotated Edition of Lectures on Moral Philosophy. Scott, Jack, ed. LC 80-24404. 213p. 1981. 27.50 (ISBN 0-87413-164-2). U Delaware Pr.

Wolter, Allan B., ed. Duns Scotus on the Will & Morality. 1986. 54.95 (ISBN 0-8132-0622-7). Cath U Pr.

Wren, Thomas E. Agency & Urgency: The Origin of Moral Obligation. 169p. 1974. 9.95 (ISBN 0-913750-06-9). Precedent Pub.

Zink, Sidney. Concepts of Ethics. 1969. 18.95 (ISBN 0-312-16100-X). St Martin.

ETHICS–ADDRESSES, ESSAYS, LECTURES

Aiken, Henry D. Reason & Conduct: New Bearings in Moral Philosophy. LC 77-26079. 1978. Repr. of 1962 ed. lib. bdg. 28.50 (ISBN 0-313-20083-1, AIRD). Greenwood.

Alder, Felix. Creed & Deed: A Series of Discourses. LC 76-38430. (Religion in America Ser: 2). 254p. 1972. Repr. of 1877 ed. 17.00 (ISBN 0-405-04051-2). Ayer Co Pubs.

Beattie, James. Elements of Moral Science, 2 vols. Wellek, Rene, ed. LC 75-11195. (British Philosophers & Theologians of the 17th & 18th Centuries: Vol. 2). 1976. Repr. of 1793 ed. Set. lib. bdg. 101.00 (ISBN 0-8240-1751-X); lib. bdg. write for info. Garland Pub.

Blaguy, John. The Foundation of Moral Goodness, 2 vols. in 1. Wellek, Rene, ed. LC 75-11194. (British Philosophers & Theologians of the 17th & 18th Centuries Ser.: Vol. 1). 1976. Repr. of 1729 ed. lib. bdg. 51.00 (ISBN 0-8240-1750-1). Garland Pub.

Brock, Horace, ed. Game Theory, Social Choice, & Ethics. 1979. lib. bdg. 31.50 (ISBN 0-686-26826-1, Pub. by Reidel Holland). Kluwer Academic.

Burton, Asa. Essays on Some of the First Principles of Metaphysicks, Ethicks, & Theology. LC 73-4839. (History of Psychology Ser.). 432p. 1973. Repr. of 1824 ed. lib. bdg. 60.00x (ISBN 0-8201-1114-7). Schol Facsimiles.

Dobrin, Arthur. Little Heroes. (Ethical Humanist Society Monograph: No. 1). (Illus.). 1977. pap. 2.50x (ISBN 0-89304-200-5, CCC111). Cross Cult.

Feltham, Owen. Resolves, a Duple Century. 3rd ed. LC 74-28853. (English Experience Ser.: No. 734). 1975. Repr. of 1628 ed. 35.00 (ISBN 90-221-0734-5). Walter J Johnson.

Hardin, Garrett. Prometean Ethics: Living with Death, Competition, & Triage. LC 79-56592. (The Jesse & John Danz Lecture Ser.). 92p. 1980. 10.00x (ISBN 0-295-95717-4). U of Wash Pr.

Henry, Caleb S. Moral & Philosophical Essays. LC 75-3178. Repr. of 1839 ed. 10.50 (ISBN 0-404-59181-7). AMS Pr.

Hopkins, Mark. Lectures on Moral Science. LC 75-3197. Repr. of 1862 ed. 37.50 (ISBN 0-404-59198-1). AMS Pr.

James, William. Essays in Religion & Morality. LC 81-7040. (Illus.). 376p. text ed. 25.00x (ISBN 0-674-26735-4). Harvard U Pr.

Kant, Immanuel. Lectures on Ethics. Infield, Louis, tr. from Ger. LC 80-22092. 272p. 1980. pap. text ed. 6.95 (ISBN 0-915144-26-3). Hackett Pub.

Levine, Maurice. Psychiatry & Ethics. LC 72-18354. 384p. 1972. 12.50 (ISBN 0-8076-0642-1). Braziller.

Lumby, Joseph R. Ratis Raving, & Other Moral & Religious Pieces. (EETS, OS Ser.: No. 43). Repr. of 1870 ed. 12.00 (ISBN 0-527-00038-8). Kraus Repr.

Melden, A. I., ed. Essays in Moral Philosophy. LC 58-10483. 288p. 1966. 15.00x (ISBN 0-295-73774-3); pap. 4.95x (ISBN 0-295-74049-3, WP20). U of Wash Pr.

Midgley, Mary. Heart & Mind: Varieties of Moral Experience. 1981. 20.00x (ISBN 0-312-36588-8). St Martin.

Mill, John S. Essays on Ethics, Religion & Society. Robson, J. M., ed. (Collected Works of John Stuart Hill Ser.: Vol. 10). pap. 160.00 (ISBN 0-317-41695-2, 2055827). Bks Demand UMI.

Mitchell, Basil. Morality-Religious & Secular: The Dilemma of the Traditional Conscience. 1980. 29.95x (ISBN 0-19-824537-8). Oxford U Pr.

Reid, Charles. Choice & Action: An Introduction to Ethics. 1981. pap. text ed. write for info. (ISBN 0-02-399180-1). Macmillan.

Stein, Harry. Ethics & Other Liabilities. 160p. 1982. 10.95 (ISBN 0-312-26557-3). St Martin.

Swinburne, Richard. The Evolution of the Soul. 320p. 1986. 45.00x (ISBN 0-19-824915-2). Oxford U Pr.

Taylor, Richard. Ethics, Faith, & Reason. 128p. 1985. pap. text ed. 15.00 (ISBN 0-13-290552-3). P-H.

Winch, Peter. Ethics & Action. (Studies in Ethics & the Philosophy of Religion). 240p. 1972. 20.00x (ISBN 0-7100-7438-7). Methuen Inc.

Witherspoon, John. Lectures on Moral Philosophy. Collins, Varnum L., ed. LC 75-3424. Repr. of 1912 ed. 12.00 (ISBN 0-404-59420-4). AMS Pr.

ETHICS–DICTIONARIES

Ferm, Vergilius, ed. Encyclopedia of Morals. LC 70-90504. Repr. of 1956 ed. lib. bdg. 40.00x (ISBN 0-8371-2138-8, FEEM). Greenwood.

Mathews, Shailer & Smith, Gerald B., eds. Dictionary of Religion & Ethics. LC 70-145713. 1971. Repr. of 1921 ed. 51.00x (ISBN 0-8103-3196-9). Gale.

ETHICS–HISTORY

Behrendt, Leo. Ethical Teaching of Hugo of Trimberg. LC 77-140042. (Catholic University of America. Studies in German: No. 1). Repr. of 1926 ed. 18.00 (ISBN 0-404-50221-0). AMS Pr.

Callahan, Daniel & Engelhardt, H. Tristram, Jr., eds. The Roots of Ethics. (The Hasting Center Series in Ethics). 464p. 1981. 35.00 (ISBN 0-306-40796-5, Plenum Pr). Plenum Pub.

Crocker, Lester G. An Age of Crisis: Man & World in Eighteenth Century French Thought. LC 59-14233. (Goucher College Ser.). Repr. of 1959 ed. 129.00 (ISBN 0-8357-9260-9, 2011983). Bks Demand UMI.

Feldman, Fred. Introductory Ethics. 1978. text ed. write for info. (ISBN 0-13-501783-1). P-H.

Fiering, Norman. Moral Philosophy at Seventeenth-Century Harvard: A Discipline in Transition. LC 80-18282. (Institute of Early American History & Culture Ser.). xiii, 323p. 1981. 27.50x (ISBN 0-8078-1459-8). U of NC Pr.

Hale, Edward E. Ralph Waldo Emerson. LC 72-8439. 1972. Repr. of 1902 ed. lib. bdg. 20.00 (ISBN 0-8414-0295-7). Folcroft.

Markun, Leo. Mrs. Grundy: A History of Four Centuries of Morals Intended to Illuminate Present Problems in Great Britain & the United States. 1930. 69.00 (ISBN 0-403-00130-7). Scholarly.

Meeks, Wayne A. The Moral World of the First Christians. LC 86-5504. (Library of Early Christianity: Vol. 6). 180p. 1986. 18.95 (ISBN 0-664-21910-1). Westminster.

Meyer, Donald H. The Instructed Conscience: The Shaping of the American National Ethic. LC 76-175512. (Illus.). 1972. 18.95x (ISBN 0-8122-7651-5); pap. 9.95x (ISBN 0-8122-1066-2). U of Pa Pr.

Navia, Luis E. & Kelly, Eugene, eds. Ethics & the Search for Values. LC 80-82123. 530p. 1980. pap. text ed. 17.95 (ISBN 0-87975-139-8). Prometheus Bks.

Norman, Richard. The Moral Philosophers: An Introduction to Ethics. 1983. 29.95x (ISBN 0-19-875060-9); pap. 10.95x (ISBN 0-19-875059-5). Oxford U Pr.

Robertson, Archibald. Morals in World History. LC 74-6354. (World History Ser., No. 48). 1974. lib. bdg. 49.95x (ISBN 0-8383-1918-1). Haskell.

Rogers, Arthur K. Morals in Review. LC 72-126697. Repr. of 1927 ed. 31.50 (ISBN 0-404-05379-3). AMS Pr.

Stroh, Guy W. American Ethical Thought. LC 79-891. 336p. 1979. 23.95x (ISBN 0-88229-356-7). Nelson-Hall.

Tsanoff, Radoslav A. Moral Ideals of Our Civilization. facsimile ed. LC 70-38738. (Essay Index Reprint Ser). Repr. of 1942 ed. 36.50 (ISBN 0-8369-2675-7). Ayer Co Pubs.

Westermarck, Edvard A. Ethical Relativity. Repr. of 1932 ed. lib. bdg. 22.50x (ISBN 0-8371-4366-7, WEER). Greenwood.

Westermarck, Edward. The Origin & Development of the Moral Ideas, 2 vols. facsimile ed. LC 74-37359. (Select Bibliographies Reprint Ser.). Repr. of 1908 ed. Set. 81.50 (ISBN 0-8369-6706-2). Ayer Co Pubs.

Westermarck, Edward A. The Origin & Development of the Moral Ideas, 2 vols. 2nd ed. (Landmarks in Anthropology Ser). 1621p. Repr. 115.00 (ISBN 0-384-66958-1). Johnson Repr.

ETHICS–JUVENILE LITERATURE

Curley, Ed. Morals, Value, & Motivation: Ethics for Today. 1978. 9.95 (ISBN 0-89837-039-6, Pub. by Pflaum Pr). Peter Li.

Phillips, Cara L. Doing Right Makes Me Happy. Mahany, Patricia, ed. LC 82-80028. (Happy Day Bks.). (Illus.). 24p. (Orig.). 1982. pap. 1.59 (ISBN 0-87239-536-7, 3582). Standard Pub.

ETHICS, BRITISH

Schneewind, J. B. Sidgwick's Ethics & Victorian Moral Philosophy. 1977. 49.95x (ISBN 0-19-824552-1). Oxford U Pr.

ETHICS, BUDDHIST

see Buddhist Ethics

ETHICS, CHINESE

Chuang Tzu. Chuang Tzu: Mystic, Moralist, & Social Reformer. 2nd rev. ed. Giles, Herbert A., tr. LC 70-38059. (BCL Ser.: No. II). Repr. of 1926 ed. 44.50 (ISBN 0-404-56915-3). AMS Pr.

Confucius. Sayings of Confucius. Ware, James R., tr. (Orig.). pap. 2.95 (ISBN 0-451-62168-9, Ment). NAL.

Hu, Shih. The Development of the Logical Method in Ancient China. lib. bdg. 79.95 (ISBN 0-87968-524-7). Krishna Pr.

Liang Chi-Chao. History of Chinese Political Thought. LC 70-100526. Repr. of 1930 ed. 17.50 (ISBN 0-404-03985-5). AMS Pr.

Ssu Shu. Chinese Classical Work Commonly Called the Four Books, 1828. Collie, David, ed. LC 75-122487. 1970. Repr. of 1828 ed. 50.00x (ISBN 0-8201-1079-5). Schol Facsimiles.

Wilson, Richard W., et al, eds. Moral Behavior in Chinese Society. LC 81-4581. 232p. 1981. 35.95 (ISBN 0-03-056922-2). Praeger.

ETHICS, CHRISTIAN

see Christian Ethics

ETHICS, GREEK

Aristotle. Athenian Constitution. Bd. with Eudemian Ethics, Bks 1-3, 7 & 8; Virtues & Vices. (Loeb Classical Library: No. 285). 13.95x (ISBN 0-674-99315-2). Harvard U Pr.

--Ethics. Warrington, John, tr. 1975. Repr. of 1963 ed. 12.95x (ISBN 0-460-00547-2, Evman). Biblio Dist.

--Nicomachean Ethics. Ostwald, Martin, tr. LC 62-15690. (Orig.). 1962. pap. 6.65 scp (ISBN 0-672-60256-3, LLA75). Bobbs.

--Nicomachean Ethics. (Loeb Classical Library: No. 73). 13.95x (ISBN 0-674-99081-1). Harvard U Pr.

Bourke, Vernon J. Saint Thomas & the Greek Moralists. (Aquinas Lecture). 1947. 7.95 (ISBN 0-87462-111-9). Marquette.

Depew, David J., ed. The Greeks & the Good Life. 280p. lib. bdg. 25.00 (ISBN 0-937622-00-1); pap. text ed. 7.95 (ISBN 0-937622-01-X). CSU Fullerton.

Earp, Frank R. Way of the Greeks. LC 75-136393. Repr. of 1929 ed. 21.50 (ISBN 0-404-02234-0). AMS Pr.

Epictetus. The Most Meaningful Writings by Epictetus. Roswell, Steve C., tr. (The Most Meaningful Classics in World Culture Ser.). (Illus.). 1979. 49.75 (ISBN 0-89266-183-6). Am Classical Coll Pr.

Epicurus. Epicurus's Morals. Digby, John, tr. LC 74-158299. Tr. of Le Morale d'Epicure. Repr. of 1712 ed. 28.00 (ISBN 0-404-54114-3). AMS Pr.

Malherbe, Abraham J. Moral Exhortation, a Greco-Roman Sourcebook. LC 86-5499. (Library of Early Christianity: Vol. 4). 180p. 1986. 18.95 (ISBN 0-664-21908-X). Westminster.

North, Helen. From Myth to Icon: Reflections of Greek Ethical Doctrine in Literature & Art. LC 79-7619. (Cornell Studies in Classical Philology). (Illus.). 288p. 1979. 29.95x (ISBN 0-8014-1135-1). Cornell U Pr.

Oakeley, Hilda D., ed. Greek Ethical Thought from Homer to the Stoics. LC 79-173804. (Library of Greek Thought: No. 5). Repr. of 1925 ed. 10.00 (ISBN 0-404-07804-4). AMS Pr.

Pearson, Lionel. Popular Ethics in Ancient Greece. 1962. 20.00x (ISBN 0-8047-0102-4). Stanford U Pr.

Schwartz, Eduard. Ethik der Griechen. facsimile ed. Richter, Will, ed. LC 75-13293. (History of Ideas in Ancient Greece Ser.). (Ger.). 1976. Repr. of 1951 ed. 17.00x (ISBN 0-405-07337-2). Ayer Co Pubs.

Symonds, John A. Problem in Greek Ethics. LC 71-163126. (Studies in Philosophy, No. 40). 1971. lib. bdg. 31.95x (ISBN 0-8383-1253-5). Haskell.

--Studies in Sexual Inversion. LC 72-9683. Repr. of 1928 ed. 32.50 (ISBN 0-404-57503-X). AMS Pr.

ETHICS, HINDU

see Hindu Ethics

ETHICS, HUMANISTIC

see Humanistic Ethics

ETHICS, ISLAMIC

see Islamic Ethics

ETHICS, JAPANESE

see also Bushido

Ninomiya, Sontoku. Sage Ninomiya's Evening Talks. Yamagata, Isoh, tr. Repr. of 1953 ed. lib. bdg. 22.50x (ISBN 0-8371-3134-0, NIEV). Greenwood.

ETHICS, JEWISH

see also Jewish Way of Life

Abraham Ben Moses Ben Maimon. High Ways to Perfection of Abraham Maimonides. Rosenblatt, Samuel, tr. LC 74-158221. (Columbia University Oriental Studies: No. 27). 1927. 19.00 (ISBN 0-404-50517-1); Suppl., 1982. 35.00; Supp., 1983. 43.50. AMS Pr.

Aronson, David. Jewish Way of Life. 1957. 5.00x (ISBN 0-8381-1107-6). United Syn Bk.

Berachya. The Ethical Treatises of Berachya, Son of Rabbi Natronai Ha-Nakdan. LC 73-2187. (The Jewish People; History, Religion, Literature Ser.). Repr. of 1902 ed. 37.50 (ISBN 0-405-05253-7). Ayer Co Pubs.

Birnbaum, Philip, ed. The New Treasury of Judaism. 1977. 15.00 (ISBN 0-88482-410-1, Sanhedrin Pr); pap. 9.95 (ISBN 0-88482-411-X, Sanhedrin Pr). Hebrew Pub.

Bloch, Abraham P. A Book of Jewish Ethical Concepts. 1984. 20.00 (ISBN 0-88125-039-2). Ktav.

Borowitz, Eugene B. Choosing a Sex Ethic: A Jewish Inquiry. LC 73-79123. 1970. pap. 5.95 (ISBN 0-8052-0276-5). Schocken.

Breslauer, S. Daniel. A New Jewish Ethics. LC 83-23659. (Symposium Ser.: Vol. 9). 136p. 1983. lib. bdg. 19.95x (ISBN 0-88946-700-5). E Mellen.

Breslauer, S. Daniel, compiled by. Contemporary Jewish Ethics: A Bibliographical Survey. LC 85-9895. (Bibliographies & Indexes in Religious Studies: No. 6). xi, 213p. 1985. lib. bdg. 37.50 (ISBN 0-313-24594-0, BCJ/). Greenwood.

--Modern Jewish Morality: A Bibliographical Survey. LC 86-12145. 249p. 1986. 39.95 (ISBN 0-313-24700-5, BJM/). Greenwood.

Building Jewish Ethical Character. 319p. 6.00 (ISBN 0-914131-08-7, I20). Torah Umesorah.

Cohen, S. J., ed. The Holy Letter: A Study in Medieval Jewish Sexual Morality. pap. 7.95x (ISBN 0-87068-490-6). Ktav.

Dan, Joseph. Jewish Mysticism & Jewish Ethics. LC 85-40358. 158p. 1986. 20.00x (ISBN 0-295-96265-8). U of Wash Pr.

Dessler, E. E. Strive for the Truth: The World of Rav Dessler. Carmell, Aryeh, tr. from Hebrew. Tr. of Michtav M'Eliyahu. 1978. 9.95 (ISBN 0-87306-139-X); pap. 7.95 (ISBN 0-87306-177-2). Feldheim.

Eckman, Lester. Jewish Tradition & Corporate Morality. LC 85-63013. 96p. 1986. 10.95. Shengold.

Fox, Marvin, ed. Modern Jewish Ethics: Theory & Practice. LC 74-28395. 274p. 1975. 14.50 (ISBN 0-8142-0192-X). Ohio St U Pr.

Friedman, Murray. Solving Ethical Problems. 0.50 (ISBN 0-914131-58-3, I38). Torah Umesorah.

Gordis, Robert. Judaic Ethics for a Lawless World. 185p. 1986. 20.00. Ktav.

Greenberg, S. The Ethical in the Jewish & American Heritage. (Moreshet Ser: No. 4). 25.00x (ISBN 0-87334-002-7, Pub. by Jewish Theol Seminary). Ktav.

Haas, Peter, ed. Biblical Hermeneutics in Jewish Moral Discourse. (Semeia Ser.: No. 34). pap. 9.95 (06 20 34). Scholars Pr GA.

Hayyim, Hafetz, pseud. Ahavath Chesed: The Love of Kindness As Required by G-D. 2nd & rev. ed. Oschry, Leonard, tr. from Hebrew. Orig. Title: Ahavath Hesed. 1976. 9.95 (ISBN 0-87306-110-1). Feldheim.

Herring, Basil F. Jewish Ethics & Halakhah for Our Time. 1984. 15.00 (ISBN 0-88125-044-9); pap. 9.95 (ISBN 0-88125-045-7). Ktav.

Herzog, Isaac. Judaism-Law & Ethics. 227p. 1974. 9.95 (ISBN 0-900689-73-0). Soncino Pr.

Ibn-Gabirol, Solomon B. Improvement of the Moral Qualities: An Ethical Treatise of the Eleventh Century. Wise, Stephen S., ed. LC 2-8360. (Columbia University. Oriental Studies: No. 1). Repr. of 1902 ed. 17.25 (ISBN 0-404-50491-4). AMS Pr.

Jacobs, Louis. Jewish Ethics, Philosophy & Mysticism. LC 71-80005. (Chain of Tradition Ser). 1969. pap. 5.95x (ISBN 0-87441-012-6). Behrman.

--Jewish Values. LC 75-103241. 10.95x (ISBN 0-87677-001-4). Hartmore.

Kaplan, Aryeh. Ethics of the Talmud. 2nd ed. 336p. 1981. pap. 2.95 (ISBN 0-940118-31-9). Maznaim.

Kellner, Menachem M., ed. Contemporary Jewish Ethics. new ed. (Sanhedrin Jewish Studies). 1978. (Sanhedrin Pr); pap. 11.95x (ISBN 0-88482-920-0, Sanhedrin Pr). Hebrew Pub.

Levine, Aaron. Free Enterprise & Jewish Law: Aspects of Jewish Business Ethics. 1979. 20.00 (ISBN 0-87068-702-6). Ktav.

Maimonides, Moses & Judah, trs. Fathers According to Rabbi Nathan Goldin. (Judaica Ser.: No. 10). 1955. 26.50x (ISBN 0-300-00497-4). Yale U Pr.

Markowitz, Sidney L. What You Should Know about Jewish Religion, History, Ethics, & Culture. 226p. 1973. pap. 5.95 (ISBN 0-8065-0028-X). Citadel Pr.

Meier, Levi, ed. Jewish Values in Bioethics. 195p. 1986. text ed. 26.95 (ISBN 0-89885-299-4). Human Sci Pr.

Mishnah: Pirkay Avot-Ethics of the Fathers. (Home Study Program Ser.: No. 401). 7.00 (ISBN 0-686-96126-9). United Syn Bk.

Montefiore, C. G. & Loewe, H., eds. A Rabbinic Anthology. LC 73-91340. 1970. pap. 16.95 (ISBN 0-8052-0442-3). Schocken.

Moses Ben Maimon. Eight Chapters of Maimonides on Ethics. (Columbia University. Oriental Studies: No. 7). Repr. of 1912 ed. 24.50 (ISBN 0-404-50497-3). AMS Pr.

Pakuda, Bahya I. The Book of Direction to the Duties of the Heart. Mansoor, Menahem, et al, trs. from Arabic. (Littman Library of Jewish Civilization). 1973. 43.00x (ISBN 0-19-710020-1). Oxford U Pr.

Priest, Ames. Governmental & Judicial Ethics in the Bible & Rabbinic Literature. 1980. 20.00x (ISBN 0-87068-697-6). Ktav.

Riemer, Jack & Stampfer, Nathaniel, eds. Ethical Wills: A Jewish Tradition. LC 82-19160. 192p. 1983. 16.95 (ISBN 0-8052-3839-5). Schocken.

Rosner, Fred. Modern Medicine & Jewish Ethics. LC 86-2910. 1986. text ed. 22.50 (ISBN 0-88125-091-0); pap. text ed. 14.95 (ISBN 0-88125-102-X). Ktav.

Rosner, Fred, et al. Jewish Bioethics. 1979. (Sanhedrin Pr); pap. 11.95 (ISBN 0-88482-935-9, Sanhedrin Pr). Hebrew Pub.

Saldarini, Anthony J. Scholastic Rabbinism: A Literary Study of the Fathers According to Rabbi Nathan. LC 81-13564. (Brown Judaic Studies). 1982. pap. text ed. 12.00 (ISBN 0-89130-523-8, 14-00-14). Scholars Pr GA.

Silver, Daniel J. Judaism & Ethics. 1970. 20.00x (ISBN 0-87068-010-2). Ktav.

Sobel, Ronald & Wallach, Sidney. Justice, Justice, Shalt Thou Pursue. 10.00x (ISBN 0-87068-458-2). Ktav.

Spero, Moshe. Handbook of Psychotherapy & Jewish Ethics. 1986. 19.95 (ISBN 0-87306-406-2). Feldheim.

Ury, Zalman F. Bridging the Gap Between Ethical Theory & Conduct. 0.75 (ISBN 0-914131-07-9, I35). Torah Umesorah.

Vorspan, Albert. Great Jewish Debates & Dilemmas: Perspectives on Moral Issues in Conflict in the 80's. LC 80-21057. 240p. 1980. pap. text ed. 5.95 (ISBN 0-8074-0049-1). UAHC.

ETHICS, JEWISH–JUVENILE LITERATURE

Fine, Helen. At Camp Kee Tov: Ethics for Jewish Juniors. (Illus.). text ed. 6.95 (ISBN 0-8074-0128-5, 121711). UAHC.

ETHICS, MEDICAL

see Medical Ethics

ETHICS, MODERN–20TH CENTURY

Hoffmann, Stanley. Duties Beyond Borders: On the Limits & Possibilities of Ethical International Politics. LC 81-2401. 288p. 1981. 22.00x (ISBN 0-8156-0167-0); pap. 10.95x (ISBN 0-8156-0168-9). Syracuse U Pr.

Singer, Peter. Practical Ethics. LC 79-52328. 1980. 37.50 (ISBN 0-521-22920-0); pap. 10.95 (ISBN 0-521-29720-6). Cambridge U Pr.

Stein, Harry. Ethics & Other Liabilities: Trying to Live Right in an Amoral World. 176p. 1983. pap. 4.95 (ISBN 0-312-26544-1). St Martin.

Warnock, G. J. Object of Morality. 1971. pap. 10.95x (ISBN 0-416-29900-8, NO. 2575). Methuen Inc.

ETHICS, MUSLIM

see Islamic Ethics

ETHICS, POLITICAL

see Political Ethics

ETHICS, PRACTICAL

see Conduct of Life; Ethics

ETHICS, PRIMITIVE

Marett, R. R. Faith, Hope & Charity in Primitive Religion. LC 72-80150. Repr. of 1932 ed. 22.00 (ISBN 0-405-08780-2, Pub. by Blom). Ayer Co Pubs.

ETHICS, SEXUAL

see Sexual Ethics

ETHICS AND LAW

see Law and Ethics

ETHICS AND RELIGION

see Religion and Ethics

ETHICS AND SCIENCE

see Science and Ethics

ETHICS AND TECHNOLOGY

see Technology and Ethics

ETHICS OF WEALTH

see Wealth, Ethics Of

ETHIOPIC CHURCH

Bonk, Jon. Ethiopian Orthodox Church. LC 84-10547. (ATLA Bibliography Ser.: No. 11). 132p. 1984. 15.00 (ISBN 0-8108-1710-1). Scarecrow.

Cowley, Roger W. The Traditional Interpretation of the Apocalypse of St. John in the Ethiopian Orthodox Church. LC 82-19834. (University of Cambridge Oriental Publications Ser.: No. 33). 480p. 1983. 77.50 (ISBN 0-521-24561-3). Cambridge U Pr.

ETHNIC REVIVALS

see Nativistic Movements

ETHOLOGY

see Ethics

EUCHARIST

see Lord's Supper

EUCKEN, RUDOLF CHRISTOF, 1846-1926

Slosson, Edwin E. Six Major Prophets. facsimile ed. LC 71-167421. (Essay Index Reprint Ser). Repr. of 1917 ed. 23.00 (ISBN 0-8369-2571-8). Ayer Co Pubs.

EUROPE–HISTORY–476-1492

see also Middle Ages–History

Barraclough, Geoffrey. The Crucible of Europe: The Ninth & Tenth Centuries in European History. LC 75-21934. (Illus.). 180p. 1976. 36.50x (ISBN 0-520-03105-9); pap. 6.95 (ISBN 0-520-03118-0, CAL 326). U of Cal Pr.

Brown, R. Allen. The Origins of Modern Europe: The Medieval Heritage of Western Civilization. LC 72-11597. 1973. pap. 7.95x (ISBN 0-88295-705-8). Harlan Davidson.

Cantor, Norman F. & Werthman, Michael S., eds. Renaissance, Reformation, & Absolutism: 1450 to 1650. 2nd ed. LC 72-76355. (Structure of European History Ser.: Vol. 3). 319p. 1972. pap. text ed. 7.95x (ISBN 0-88295-712-0). Harlan Davidson.

Duby, Georges. The Age of the Cathedrals: Art & Society, 980-1420. Levieux, Eleanor & Thompson, Barbara, trs. LC 80-22769. (Illus.). vi, 312p. 1981. 26.00x (ISBN 0-226-16769-0); pap. 11.95 (ISBN 0-226-16770-4). U of Chicago Pr.

Henningsen, Gustav & Tedeschi, John, eds. The Inquisition in Early Modern Europe: Studies on Sources & Methods. 254p. 1986. 27.50 (ISBN 0-87580-102-1). N Ill U Pr.

Hoyt, Robert S. & Chodorow, Stanley. Europe in the Middle Ages. 3rd ed. (Illus.). 707p. 1976. text ed. 25.95 (ISBN 0-15-524712-3, HC). HarBraceJ.

Little, Lester K. Religious Poverty & the Profit Economy in Medieval Europe. LC 78-58630. 278p. (Orig.). 1983. pap. 10.95x (ISBN 0-8014-9247-5). Cornell U Pr.

McGarry, Daniel D. Medieval History & Civilization. (Illus.). 896p. 1976. text ed. write for info. (ISBN 0-02-379100-4). Macmillan.

Pirenne, Henri. Mohammed & Charlemagne. (B & N Paperback Ser.). 239p. (Orig.). 1983. pap. 9.95x (ISBN 0-389-20134-0, 06641, 444). B&N Imports.

Powell, James M. Anatomy of a Crusade, Twelve Thirteen to Twelve Twenty-One. (Middle Ages Ser.). (Illus.). 336p. 1986. text ed. 34.95x (ISBN 0-8122-8025-3). U of Pa Pr.

Tout, Thomas F. The Empire & the Papacy, Nine Eighteen to Twelve Seventy-Three. 8th ed. LC 80-18865. (Periods of European History: Period II). (Illus.). vii, 526p. 1980. Repr. of 1965 ed. lib. bdg. 42.50x (ISBN 0-313-22372-6, TOEP). Greenwood.

EUROPE–HISTORY–1492-1648

Cantor, Norman F. & Werthman, Michael S., eds. Renaissance, Reformation, & Absolutism: 1450 to 1650. 2nd ed. LC 72-76355. (Structure of European History Ser.: Vol. 3). 319p. 1972. pap. text ed. 7.95x (ISBN 0-88295-712-0). Harlan Davidson.

Green, Vivian H. Renaissance & Reformation. 2nd ed. (Illus.). 1974. pap. text ed. 16.95 (ISBN 0-312-67305-1). St Martin.

McGrath, Alister E. The Intellectual Origins of the European Reformation. 272p. 1987. text ed. 39.95 (ISBN 0-631-15144-3). Basil Blackwell.

Malament, Barbara C., ed. After the Reformation: Essays in Honor of J. H. Hexter. LC 79-5254. 256p. 1980. 36.95x (ISBN 0-8122-7774-0). U of Pa Pr.

EUROPE–RELIGION

Ahrendts, Juergen, ed. Bibliographie zur alteuropaeischen Religionsgeschichte II, 1965-1969: Eine interdisziplinaere Auswahl von Literatur zu den Rand-und Nachfolgekulturen der Antike in Europa unter besonderer Beruecksichtigung der nichtchristlichen Religionen. LC 68-86477. (Arbeiten Zur Fruehmittelalterforschung: Vol. 5). xxvi, 591p. 1974. 59.20x (ISBN 3-11-003398-4). De Gruyter.

Bellini, Enzo, et al. The Formation of Christian Europe: An Illustrated History of the Church. Drury, John, ed. & tr. (Illus.). 126p. 1980. text ed. 12.95 (ISBN 0-03-056827-7, HarpR). Har-Row.

Berger, Suzanne, ed. Religion in West European Politics. (Illus.). 200p. 1982. text ed. 29.50x (ISBN 0-7146-3218-X, F Cass Co). Biblio Dist.

Butterfield, Herbert. Christianity in European History: The Riddel Memorial Lectures, 1951. 1979. Repr. of 1952 ed. lib. bdg. 15.00 (ISBN 0-8482-3440-5). Norwood Edns.

Davidson, H. Ellis. Gods & Myths of Northern Europe. (Orig.). 1965. pap. 5.95 (ISBN 0-14-020670-1, Pelican). Penguin.

Hillgarth, J. N., ed. Christianity & Paganism, Three Hundred Fifty to Seven Hundred Fifty: The Conversion of Western Europe. rev. ed. LC 85-1154. (Middle Ages Ser.). 160p. 1986. lib. bdg. 25.00 (ISBN 0-8122-7993-X); pap. 10.95 (ISBN 0-8122-1213-4). U of Pa Pr.

Kaplan, Steven L., ed. Understanding Popular Culture: Europe from the Middle Ages to the Nineteenth Century. LC 84-1001. (New Babylon, Studies in the Social Sciences: No. 40). viii, 311p. 1984. 64.75x (ISBN 3-11-009600-5). Mouton.

Ling, Trevor. Karl Marx & Religion: In Europe & India. LC 79-55947. 168p. 1980. text ed. 28.50x (ISBN 0-06-494294-5). B&N Imports.

McLeod, Hugh. Religion & the People of Western Europe, 1789-1970. (Oxford Paperbacks University Ser.). 1981. 17.95x (ISBN 0-19-215832-5); pap. 8.95x (ISBN 0-19-289101-4). Oxford U Pr.

Mullett, Michael. Radical Religious Movements in Early Modern Europe. (Early Modern Europe Today Ser.). 208p. 1980. text ed. 9.95 (ISBN 0-04-901028-X). Allen Unwin.

Salisbury, Joyce E. Iberian Popular Religion, Six Hundred B. C. to Seven Hundred A. D. Celts, Romans & Visigoths. (Texts & Studies in Religion: Vol. 20). 340p. 1985. 59.95x (ISBN 0-88946-809-5). E Mellen.

Spitz, Lewis W. The Protestant Reformation, Fifteen Seventeen to Fifteen Fifty-Nine: The Rise of Modern Europe. LC 83-48805. (Illus.). 448p. 1986. pap. 8.95 (ISBN 0-06-091277-4, PL 1277, PL). Har-Row.

Stahl, Paul H. Household, Village, & Village Confederation in Southeastern Europe. (East European Monographs: No. 200). 252p. 1986. 25.00 (ISBN 0-88033-094-5). East Eur Quarterly.

Tout, Thomas F. The Empire & the Papacy, Nine Eighteen to Twelve Seventy-Three. 8th ed. LC 80-18865. (Periods of European History: Period II). (Illus.). vii, 526p. 1980. Repr. of 1965 ed. lib. bdg. 42.50x (ISBN 0-313-22372-6, TOEP). Greenwood.

Van Belzen, J. A. & Van Der Lans, J. M., eds. Proceedings of the Third Symposium on the Psychology of Religion in Europe: Current Issues in the Psychology of Religion. (Amsterdam Studies in Theology Ser.). 292p. 1986. pap. text ed. 65.00 (ISBN 90-6203-758-5, Pub. by Rodopi Holland). Humanities.

Will, James E. Must Walls Divide? The Creative Witness of the Churches in Europe. (Orig.). 1981. pap. 3.75 (ISBN 0-377-00106-6). Friend Pr.

EUROPE, EASTERN–RELIGION

Ascher, A., et al, eds. The Mutual Effects of the Islamic & Judeo-Christian Worlds: The East European Pattern. LC 77-90629. (Studies on Society in Change: No. 3). 1979. write for info (ISBN 0-930888-00-6). Brooklyn Coll Pr.

Eliade, Mircea. Zalmoxis: The Vanishing God. LC 72-76487. (Comparative Studies in the Religions & Folklore of Dacia & Eastern Europe). x, 260p. 1986. pap. text ed. 16.00x (ISBN 0-226-20385-9, Midway Reprint). U of Chicago Pr.

Ramet, Pedro, ed. Religion & Nationalism in Soviet & East European Politics. (Policy Studies). v, 282p. 1985. text ed. 35.00 (ISBN 0-8223-0608-5). Duke.

Shuster, George N. Religion Behind the Iron Curtain. LC 78-13547. 1978. Repr. of 1954 ed. lib. bdg. 22.50x (ISBN 0-313-20634-1, SHRB). Greenwood.

EUSEBIUS PAMPHILI, BISHOP OF CAESAREA

Drake, H. A. In Praise of Constantine: A Historical Study & New Translation of Eusebius' Tricennial Orations. LC 75-62009. (UC Publications in Classical Studies: Vol. 15; California Library Reprint Ser.: No. 93). 1976. Repr. of 1975 ed. 22.50x (ISBN 0-520-03694-8). U of Cal Pr.

Grant, Robert M. Eusebius As Church Historian. 1980. 36.00x (ISBN 0-19-826441-0). Oxford U Pr.

Mosshammer, Alden A. The Chronicle of Eusebius & Greek Chronographic Tradition. LC 76-1029. 366p. 1979. 29.50 (ISBN 0-8387-1939-2). Bucknell U Pr.

EUTHALIUS, BP. OF SULCA

Robinson, J. A. Euthaliana, Studies of Euthalius: Codex H of the Pauline Epistles & the Armenian Version. (Texts & Studies Ser.: No. 1, Vol. 3, Pt. 3). pap. 19.00 (ISBN 0-8115-1690-3). Kraus Repr.

EUTHANASIA

Erdahl, Lowell O. Pro-Life, Pro-Peace: Life Affirming Alternatives to Abortion, War, Mercy Killing, & the Death Penalty. LC 86-3552. 160p. (Orig.). 1986. pap. 8.95 (ISBN 0-8066-2209-1, 10-5240). Augsburg.

Gula, Richard S. What Are They Saying about Euthenasia? (W. A. T. S. A. Ser.). 192p. (Orig.). 1986. pap. 5.95 (ISBN 0-8091-2766-0). Paulist Pr.

Hensley, Jeffrey, ed. The Zero People. 310p. 1983. pap. 7.95 (ISBN 0-89283-126-X). Servant.

Koop, C. Everett & Schaeffer, Francis A. Whatever Happened to the Human Race? LC 83-70955. 168p. 1983. pap. 7.95 (ISBN 0-89107-291-8, Crossway Bks). Good News.

Larue, Gerald A. Euthanasia & Religion: A Survey of the Attitudes of World Religions to the Right-to-Die. LC 84-62806. 155p. 1985. pap. 10.00 (ISBN 0-394-62078-X). Hemlock Soc.

McMillan, Richard C., et al. Euthanasia & the Newborn: Conflicts Regarding Saving Lives. LC 86-33835. (Philosophy & Medicine Ser.: Vol. 24). 1987. 39.50 (ISBN 9-02-772299-4). Kluwer Academic.

Maestri, William. Choose Life & Not Death: A Primer on Abortion, Euthanasia, & Suicide. LC 85-28687. 9.95 (ISBN 0-8189-0490-9). Alba.

Poss, Sylvia. Towards Death with Dignity: Caring for Dying People. 1981. 33.75x (ISBN 0-317-05777-4, Pub. by Natl Soc Work). State Mutual Bk.

Range, Cornelius. Heal Me or Kill Me! LC 85-71350. 1985. pap. 5.95 (ISBN 0-88270-592-X). Bridge Pub.

Shannon, Thomas A. & Faso, Charles N. Let Them Go Free: A Family Prayer Service & Guidelines for the Withdrawal of Life Support Systems. 1987. pap. 2.95. Paulist Pr.

Wertenbaker, Lael T. Death of a Man. LC 73-16889. 192p. 1974. pap. 7.95x (ISBN 0-8070-2763-4, BP482). Beacon Pr.

EVANGELICAL ALLIANCE MISSION

Jordan, Phillip D. The Evangelical Alliance for the United States of America, 1847-1900: Ecumenism, Identity & the Religion of the Republic. LC 82-24953. (Studies in American Religion: Vol. 7). 288p. 1983. 49.95x (ISBN 0-88946-650-5). E Mellen.

EVANGELICAL AND REFORMED CHURCH

see also United Church of Christ

Davis, John J. Evangelical Ethics: Issues Facing the Church Today. 304p. 1985. 13.95 (ISBN 0-87552-222-X). Presby & Reformed.

Morland, Samuel. History of the Evangelical Churches of the Valleys of Piemont. 1983. 32.00 (ISBN 0-686-42929-X). Church History.

Weiser, Frederick S., ed. Maryland German Church Records, Vol. 5: Evangelical Reformed Church 1746-1789, Frederick. Hinke, William J., tr. (Maryland German Church Records Ser.). (Orig.). 1987. pap. 20.00x (ISBN 0-913281-07-7). Noodle Doosey.

--Maryland German Church Records, Vol. 6: Evangelical Reformed Church 1790-1835, Frederick. Hinke, William J., tr. (Maryland German Church Records Ser.). (Orig.). 1987. pap. 20.00x (ISBN 0-913281-08-5). Noodle Doosey.

--Maryland German Church Records, Vol. 7: St. Mary's Lutheran Church 1783-1863, St. Mary's Reformed Church 1812-1866, & Jerusalem Lutheran Church 1799-1859. (Maryland German Church Records Ser.). (Orig.). 1987. pap. 15.00x (ISBN 0-913281-09-3). Noodle Doosey.

Wright, David F., ed. Essays in Evangelical Social Ethics. 192p. 1982. 18.95 (ISBN 0-85364-288-5); pap. text ed. 9.50 (ISBN 0-85364-290-7). Attic Pr.

EVANGELICAL COUNSELS

see also Chastity; Monastic and Religious Life; Monastic and Religious Life of Women; Obedience; Poverty; Poverty (Virtue)

Davis, John J. Demons, Exorcism & the Evangelical. 1979. pap. 1.00 (ISBN 0-88469-043-1). BMH Bks.

EVANGELICAL COVENANT CHURCH OF AMERICA

Anderson, Glenn P., ed. Covenant Roots: Sources & Affirmations. Jansson, Fred O., et al, trs. from Swedish. 238p. (Orig.). 1980. pap. 6.95 (ISBN 0-910452-46-6). Covenant.

Frisk, Donald C. Covenant Affirmations: This We Believe. 196p. (Orig.). 1981. pap. 6.95 (ISBN 0-910452-48-2). Covenant.

Hawkinson, Eric G. Images in Covenant Beginnings. (Illus.). 1968. 3.95 (ISBN 0-910452-04-0). Covenant.

Klassen, Randolph J. Reaching Out in Love. 144p. (Orig.). 1981. pap. 5.95 (ISBN 0-910452-47-4). Covenant.

Olsson, Karl A. By One Spirit. (Illus.). 1962. pap. 9.95x (ISBN 0-910452-10-5). Covenant.

EVANGELICAL COVENANT CHURCH OF AMERICA–SERMONS

Johnson, Gustaf F. Hearts Aflame. 1970. 4.50 (ISBN 0-910452-06-7). Covenant.

EVANGELICAL FREE CHURCH OF AMERICA

Olson, Arnold T. The Significance of Silence. LC 80-70698. (Heritage Ser.: Vol. 2). 208p. 1981. 8.95 (ISBN 0-911802-49-5). Free Church Pubns.

--Stumbling Toward Maturity. LC 81-66943. (Heritage Ser.: Vol. 3). 208p. 1981. 8.95 (ISBN 0-911802-50-9). Free Church Pubns.

--This We Believe. 2nd ed. LC 61-18801. 1965. Repr. of 1961 ed. 6.95 (ISBN 0-911802-01-0). Free Church Pubns.

Olson, Arnold T., ed. The Search for Identity. LC 80-66030. (Heritage Ser.: Vol. 1). 160p. 1980. 8.95 (ISBN 0-911802-46-0). Free Church Pubns.

Thompson, Roy A. The Dynamic of the Printed Page in Evangelical Free Church History. LC 82-69760. (Heritage Ser.: Vol. 4). 176p. 1981. 8.95 (ISBN 0-911802-53-3). Free Church Pubns.

EVANGELICAL LUTHERAN CHURCH

Hull, Bill. Revitalizing the Church. 1986. pap. cancelled (ISBN 0-89109-539-X). NavPress.

Jacobs, Henry E. A History of the Evangelical Lutheran Church in the United States. LC 83-45644. Date not set. Repr. of 1893 ed. 54.50 (ISBN 0-404-19853-8). AMS Pr.

Schmid, Heinrich. Doctrinal Theology of the Evangelical Lutheran Church. LC 66-13052. 1961. 25.95 (ISBN 0-8066-0107-8, 10-1930). Augsburg.

EVANGELICAL LUTHERAN SYNOD OF MISSOURI, OHIO, AND OTHER STATES

Brokering, Herbert F., ed. Luthers Prayers. Kistler, Charles E., tr. LC 67-25366. 1967. lea. bdg. 7.95 (ISBN 0-8066-0721-1, 10-4231). Augsburg.

Danker, Frederick W. No Room in the Brotherhood: The Preus-Otten Purge of Missouri. LC 77-74386. (Illus.). 1977. text ed. 12.95 (ISBN 0-915644-10-X). Clayton Pub Hse.

Eisenberg, C. G. History of the First Dakota-District of the Evangelical-Lutheran Synod of Iowa & Other States. Richter, Anton H., tr. from Ger. LC 82-17645. 268p. (Orig.). 1983. lib. bdg. 29.25 (ISBN 0-8191-2798-1); pap. text ed. 13.75 (ISBN 0-8191-2799-X). U Pr of Amer.

Gockel, Herman W. & Saleska, Edward J., eds. Child's Garden of Prayer. (Illus.). 1981. pap. 1.50 (ISBN 0-570-03412-4, 56-1016). Concordia.

Huxhold, Harry N. Family Altar. rev. ed. 1964. 12.95 (ISBN 0-570-03071-4, 6-1085). Concordia.

Little Folded Hands. rev. ed. LC 59-12074. 1959. 3.50 (ISBN 0-570-03417-5, 56-1038); pap. 1.85 laminated (ISBN 0-570-03416-7, 56-1037). Concordia.

Marquart, Kurt E. Anatomy of an Explosion: A Theological Analysis of the Missouri Synod Conflict. 1978. pap. 3.95 (ISBN 0-8010-6049-4). Baker Bk.

Meyer, Carl S., ed. Moving Frontiers. 524p. 1986. pap. 12.95 (ISBN 0-570-04461-8). Concordia.

Nelson, Ruth Y. God's Song in My Heart: Daily Devotions. LC 56-11912. 432p. 1957. 8.95 (ISBN 0-8006-0254-4, 1-254). Fortress.

Wiencke, Gustav K. & Lehman, Helmut T., eds. Luther's Works: Devotional Writings II, Vol. 43. LC 55-9893. 1968. 19.95 (ISBN 0-8006-0343-5, 1-343). Fortress.

EVANGELICAL RELIGION

see Evangelicalism

EVANGELICAL REVIVAL

see also Evangelicalism; Great Awakening; Methodism

Bradley, Joshua. Accounts of Religious Revivals in Many Parts of the United States from 1815 to 1818: Collected from Numerous Publications & Letters from Persons of Piety & Correct Information. (Reival Library). 300p. lib. bdg. 11.95 (ISBN 0-940033-13-5). R O Roberts.

Carwardine, Richard. Transatlantic Revivalism: Popular Evangelicalism in Britain & America, 1790-1865. LC 77-94740. (Contributions in American History Ser.: No. 75). 1978. lib. bdg. 35.00 (ISBN 0-313-20308-3, CTR/). Greenwood.

Christian Life Staff. America's Great Revivals. 1970. pap. 3.50 (ISBN 0-87123-003-8). Bethany Hse.

Dolan, Jay P. Catholic Revivalism: The American Experience, 1830-1900. LC 77-89755. 1979. pap. text ed. 4.95x (ISBN 0-268-00729-2). U of Notre Dame Pr.

Gill, Frederick C. The Romantic Movement & Methodism: A Study of English Romanticism & the Evangelical Revival. 1978. Repr. of 1937 ed. lib. bdg. 25.00 (ISBN 0-8492-4910-4). R West.

Hand-book on Revival. 4.95 (ISBN 0-686-27778-3). Schmul Pub Co.

Moore, Martin. Boston Revival, Eighteen Forty-Two: A Brief History of the Evangelical Churches of Boston, Together with a More Particular Account of the Revival of 1842. (Revival Library). (Illus.). 148p. 1980. Repr. of 1842 ed. lib. bdg. 9.95. R O Roberts.

Pratney, Winkie. Revival: Principles to Change the World. 320p. (Orig.). 1983. pap. 3.95 (ISBN 0-88368-124-2). Whitaker Hse.

Ravenhill, Leonard. America Is Too Young to Die. LC 79-19229. 128p. 1979. pap. 4.95 (ISBN 0-87123-013-5, 210013). Bethany Hse.

--Revival God's Way. 128p. (Orig.). 1983. pap. 7.95 (210620). Bethany Hse.

--Revival Praying. 176p. 1962. pap. 4.95 (ISBN 0-87123-482-3, 210482). Bethany Hse.

--Why Revival Tarries. 176p. 1979. pap. 4.95 (ISBN 0-87123-607-9, 210607). Bethany Hse.

Reid, William, ed. Authentic Records of Revival, Now in Progress in the United Kingdom. (Revival Library). viii, 478p. 1980. Repr. of 1860 ed. lib. bdg. 15.95 (ISBN 0-940033-17-8). R O Roberts.

EVANGELICAL UNITED BRETHREN CHURCH

Krueger, Kenneth W., ed. The History of the Evangelical United Brethren Church. LC 79-14738. (Illus.). 1979. 17.95 (ISBN 0-687-17206-3). Abingdon.

Washburn, Paul. An Unfinished Church: A Brief History of the Union of the Evangelical United Brethern Church & the Methodist Church. 176p. 14.95 (ISBN 0-687-01378-X). Abingdon.

EVANGELICALISM

see also Evangelical Revival; Fundamentalism; Keswick Movement; Pietism

Abraham, William J. The Coming Great Revival: Recovering the Full Evangelical Tradition. LC 84-47710. 160p. 1984. 12.45 (ISBN 0-06-060035-7, HarpR). Har-Row.

Aldrich, Joseph C. Life-style Evangelism: Crossing Traditional Boundaries to Reach the Unbelieving World. LC 80-27615. (Critical Concern Bks.). 1981. 10.95 (ISBN 0-930014-46-4). Multnomah.

--Life-Style Evangelism: Study Guide. 1983. pap. 2.95 (ISBN 0-88070-020-3). Multnomah.

Altschuler, Glenn C. & Saltzgaber, Jan M. Revivalism, Social Conscience, & Community in the Burned-Over District: The Trial of Rhoda Bement. (Illus.). 184p. 1983. 27.95x (ISBN 0-8014-1541-1); pap. 8.95x (ISBN 0-8014-9246-7). Cornell U Pr.

Anderson, Gerald H., ed. Witnessing to the Kingdom: Melbourne & Beyond. LC 82-3530. 176p. (Orig.). 1982. pap. 7.95 (ISBN 0-88344-708-8). Orbis Bks.

Armstrong, James A. From the Underside: Evangelism from a Third World Vantage Point. LC 81-9509. 112p. (Orig.). 1981. pap. 4.95 (ISBN 0-88344-146-2). Orbis Bks.

Armstrong, Richard S. The Pastor-Evangelist in Worship. LC 85-26380. 216p. (Orig.). 1986. pap. 9.95 (ISBN 0-664-24693-1). Westminster.

Augsburger, Myon S. Evangelism As Discipling. LC 82-83387. (Mennonite Faith Ser.: Vol. 12). 80p. 1983. pap. 1.50 (ISBN 0-8361-3322-6). Herald Pr.

Augsburger, Myron S. Evangelizacion y Discipulado. Rindzinski, Milka, tr. from Eng. LC 84-80159. (Mennonite Faith Ser.: No. 12). 72p. (Orig.). 1984. pap. 1.50x (ISBN 0-8361-1267-9). Herald Pr.

Baggett, Lee. Utilice Su Casa para Evangelizar. 32p. 1984. Repr. of 1983 ed. 1.50 (ISBN 0-311-13832-2). Casa Bautista.

Bailey, David T. Shadow on the Church: Southwestern Evangelical Religion & the Issue of Slavery, 1783-1860. LC 84-45795. 264p. 1985. text ed. 26.95x (ISBN 0-8014-1763-5). Cornell U Pr.

Bales, James. Evangelism: Every Member, Every Day. pap. 2.50 (ISBN 0-89315-038-X). Lambert Bk.

Barth, Karl. Evangelical Theology: An Introduction. Foley, Grover, tr. LC 79-16735. Tr. of Einfuhrung in Die Evangelische Theologie. 1979. pap. 9.95 (ISBN 0-8028-1819-6). Eerdmans.

Bisagno, John R. How to Build an Evangelistic Church. LC 78-178055. 1972. 8.50 (ISBN 0-8054-2524-1). Broadman.

Black, R. L. Discerning the Body. 98p. (Orig.). 1984. pap. 3.95 (ISBN 0-934942-42-0, 1264). White Wing Pub.

Branson, Mark L., ed. The Reader's Guide to the Best Evangelical Books. LC 82-48205. 208p. (Orig.). 1982. pap. 5.95 (ISBN 0-06-061046-8, RD-388, HarpR). Har-Row.

Brengle, Samuel L. Helps to Holiness. 1978. pap. 3.95 (ISBN 0-86544-003-4). Salv Army Suppl South.

Brestin, Dee. Finders Keepers: Introducing Your Friends to Christ & Helping Them Grow. LC 83-8522. 180p. 1985. 8.95 (ISBN 0-87788-265-7); pap. 5.95 (ISBN 0-87788-267-3). Shaw Pubs.

Cassidy, Michael. Bursting the Wineskins: Spiritual Odyssey of a Peacemaker. 280p. 1983. pap. 6.95 (ISBN 0-87788-094-8). Shaw Pubs.

Clapp, Steve. Christian Education As Evangelism. 154p. (Orig.). 1982. pap. 9.00 (ISBN 0-914527-11-8). C-Four Res.

Clouse, Robert G., et al, eds. Protest & Politics: Christianity & Contemporary Affairs. 277p. 1968. 5.95 (ISBN 0-87921-000-1). Attic Pr.

Coleman, Richard J. Issues of Theological Conflict: Evangelicals & Liberals. Rev. ed. LC 79-19494. pap. 74.00 (ISBN 0-317-19816-5, 2023209). Bks Demand UMI.

Coleman, Robert E. The Heartbeat of Evangelism. 32p. 1985. pap. 1.95 (ISBN 0-89109-400-8). NavPress.

--The Master Plan of Evangelism. 128p. 1978. pap. 5.95 (ISBN 0-8007-5007-1, Power Bks); pap. 2.50 (ISBN 0-8007-8303-4, Spire Bks). Revell.

Compton, Alan. Comunicacion Cristiana. 168p. 1985. Repr. of 1982 ed. 4.15 (ISBN 0-311-13833-0). Casa Bautista.

Crawford, Dan R. Evangelife: A Guide to Life-Style Evangelism. LC 84-1805. 1984. pap. 4.95 (ISBN 0-8054-6247-3). Broadman.

Curry, Dean C., ed. Evangelicals & the Bishops' Pastoral Letter. LC 84-4005. 254p. (Orig.). 1984. pap. 10.95 (ISBN 0-8028-1985-0). Eerdmans.

Davis, Earl C. Christ at the Door. LC 84-27441. 1985. pap. 5.95 (ISBN 0-8054-6249-X). Broadman.

Davis, John J. Foundations of Evangelical Theology: A Contextualized Approach. 232p. 1984. pap. 9.95 (ISBN 0-8010-2937-6). Baker Bk.

Dayton, Ed & Wilson, Samuel. The Future of World Evangelization: The Lausanne Movement. 1984. 7.95 (ISBN 0-912552-42-5). Missions Adv Res Com Ctr.

DeWitt, David. Beyond the Basics. 1983. pap. 5.95 (ISBN 0-8024-0178-3). Moody.

Eisenman, Tom. Everyday Evangelism. 180p. (Orig.). 1987. pap. 5.95 (ISBN 0-87784-997-8). Inter-Varsity.

Evangelical Catechism. LC 82-70953. 416p. (Orig.). 1982. pap. 5.95 (ISBN 0-8066-1928-7, 10-2099). Augsburg.

Evangelical Teacher Training Association. Training When Meeting. 32p. 1981. pap. text ed. 2.95 (ISBN 0-910566-33-X); planbook 3.95 (ISBN 0-910566-34-8). Evang Tchr.

Fetterhoff, Dean. Dynamics of Evangelism. pap. 1.00 (ISBN 0-88469-019-9). BMH Bks.

Fischer, John. The Olive Tree Connection: Sharing Israel's Messiah. LC 83-12645. 192p. (Orig.). 1983. pap. 8.95 (ISBN 0-87784-848-3). Inter-Varsity.

Flake, Carol. Redemptorama: Culture, Politics & the New Evangelicalism. (Nonfiction Ser.). 320p. 1985. pap. 7.95 (ISBN 0-14-008265-4). Penguin.

Forster, Roger & Marston, Paul. That's a Good Question. 2nd ed. Sun, Hugo S. & Chan, Silas, trs. (Chinese.). 204p. 1982. pap. write for info (ISBN 0-941598-01-2). Living Spring Pubns.

Fowler, Robert B. A New Engagement: Evangelical Political Thought, 1966-1976. 298p. (Orig.). 1983. pap. 13.95 (ISBN 0-8028-1929-X). Eerdmans.

--A New Engagement: Evangelical Political Thought, 1966-1976. LC 82-11389. Repr. of 1982 ed. 77.00 (2027453). Bks Demand UMI.

Frank, Douglas W. Less Than Conquerors. 336p. (Orig.). 1986. pap. 14.95 (ISBN 0-8028-0228-1). Eerdmans.

Fuller, David O., ed. A Treasury of Evangelical Writings. LC 61-9768. 472p. 1974. pap. 11.95 (ISBN 0-8254-2613-8). Kregel.

Garrett, James L., Jr. & Hinson, E. Glenn. Are Southern Baptists "Evangelicals"? LC 82-18870. 247p. 1983. 14.95 (ISBN 0-86554-033-0, MUP-H44). Mercer Univ Pr.

Gier, Nicholas F. God, Reason & the Evangelicals: The Case Against Evangelical Rationalism. 404p. (Orig.). 1987. lib. bdg. 34.50 (ISBN 0-8191-5812-7); pap. text ed. 19.75 (ISBN 0-8191-5813-5). U Pr of Amer.

Graham, Billy, Center Staff, ed. An Evangelical Agenda: Nineteen Eighty-Four & Beyond. LC 79-15889. 1979. pap. 5.95 (ISBN 0-87808-171-2). William Carey Lib.

Green, Michael. Evangelism in the Early Church. 1970. pap. 7.95 (ISBN 0-8028-1612-6). Eerdmans.

--Evangelism: Now & Then. 150p. 1982. pap. 3.50 (ISBN 0-87784-394-5). Inter-Varsity.

Greinacher, Norbert, ed. Evangelization in the World Today. (Concilium Ser.: Vol. 114). 1979. pap. 6.95 (ISBN 0-8245-0274-4). Crossroad NY.

Gulledge, Dennis & McWhirter, David. An Index to the Evangelist & the Christian. LC 83-70079. 160p. (Orig.). 1983. pap. 3.95 (ISBN 0-89900-231-5). College Pr Pub.

Gurganus, Gene. The Great Omission: Fruit That Remains. (Illus.). 104p. 1983. pap. 3.95 (ISBN 0-89084-191-8). Bob Jones Univ Pr.

Hagstrom, Jane. The Young Witness: Evangelism to & by Children & Youth. LC 23-3036. 56p. (Orig.). 1986. pap. 4.95 (ISBN 0-8066-2233-4). Augsburg.

Hannah, John, ed. Inerrancy & the Church. (Orig.). 1984. pap. 14.95 (ISBN 0-8024-0327-1). Moody.

Hardesty, Nancy A. Women Called to Witness: Evangelical Feminism in the Nineteenth Century. LC 83-45959. 176p. (Orig.). 1984. pap. 8.95 (ISBN 0-687-45959-1). Abingdon.

Harrell, David E., Jr., ed. Varieties of Southern Evangelicalism. LC 81-11312. xii, 114p. 1981. 9.95 (ISBN 0-86554-015-2, MUP-H18). Mercer Univ Pr.

Hassey, Janette. No Time for Silence: Evangelical Women in Public Ministry Around the Turn of the Century. 176p. 1986. pap. 7.95 (ISBN 0-310-29451-7, 12786P). Zondervan.

Henderson, Robert T. Joy to the World: An Introduction to Kingdom Evangelism. LC 80-14597. 207p. (Orig.). 1980. pap. 6.50 (ISBN 0-8042-2096-4). John Knox.

Henry, Carl F. & Hancock, Robert L., eds. The Ministry of Development in Evangelical Perspective: A Symposium on the Social & Spiritual Mandate. LC 78-27821. 1979. pap. 4.95 (ISBN 0-87808-164-X). William Carey Lib.

Hillis, Don W. Evangelical Idolatry. (Illus.). 95p. (Orig.). 1983. pap. 2.75 (ISBN 0-89323-040-5). Bible Memory.

Hinkle, Joseph W., et al. Oikos: A Practical Approach to Family Evangelism. LC 81-69328. 1982. pap. 4.95 (ISBN 0-8054-6234-1). Broadman.

Hinson, E. Glenn. The Evangelization of the Roman Empire: Identity & Adaptability. LC 81-11266. viii, 332p. 1981. 22.00 (ISBN 0-86554-244-9, MUP-P36). Mercer Univ Pr.

Hodge, A. A. Evangelical Theology. 1976. pap. 6.95 (ISBN 0-85151-236-4). Banner of Truth.

Hodges, Zane C. El Evangelio Bajo Sito: Un Estudio Sobre la Fe y las Obras. Whitehouse, Thomas, tr. 128p. (Orig.). 1985. pap. 4.95 (ISBN 0-9607576-4-3). Redencion Viva.

Holash, Lisa. Evangelization. 80p. 1984. pap. 3.50 (ISBN 0-697-01868-7). Wm C Brown.

Hollinger, Dennis P. Individualism & Social Ethics: An Evangelical Syncretism. 284p. 1984. lib. bdg. 28.50 (ISBN 0-8191-3580-1); pap. text ed. 13.50 (ISBN 0-8191-3581-X). U Pr of Amer.

Howard, David. Why World Evangelism. pap. 0.75 (ISBN 0-87784-141-1). Inter-Varsity.

Humbertson, James E., ed. Evangelical Sunday School Lesson Commentary, 1981-1982. 448p. text ed. 3.65 (ISBN 0-87148-297-5). Pathway Pr.

Humphreys, Fisher. Nineteenth Century Evangelical Theology. LC 83-71439. (Orig.). 1984. pap. 10.95 (ISBN 0-8054-6579-0). Broadman.

Hunter, James D. American Evangelicalism: Conservative Religion & the Quandary of Modernity. LC 82-317. 166p. 1983. 27.50x (ISBN 0-8135-0960-2); pap. 9.95x (ISBN 0-8135-0985-8). Rutgers U Pr.

--Evangelicalism: The Coming Generation. LC 86-16022. (Illus.). 320p. 1987. lib. bdg. 19.95 (ISBN 0-226-36082-2). U of Chicago Pr.

Huston, Sterling. Crusade Evangelism & the Local Church. 215p. 1984. pap. 5.95 (ISBN 0-89066-047-6). World Wide Pubs.

Hutcheson, Richard G., Jr. Mainline Churches & the Evangelicals. LC 80-84648. 192p. (Orig.). 1981. pap. 9.95 (ISBN 0-8042-1502-2). John Knox.

Hutchinson, William R. Errand to the World: American Protestant Thought & Foreign Missions. 216p. 1987. lib. bdg. 24.95x (ISBN 0-226-36257-4). U of Chicago Pr.

Jay, Elisabeth. The Evangelical & Oxford Movements. LC 82-9605. (Cambridge English Prose Texts Ser.). 232p. 1983. 34.50 (ISBN 0-521-24403-X); pap. 13.95 (ISBN 0-521-28669-7). Cambridge U Pr.

--The Religion of the Heart: Anglican Evangelicalism & the Nineteenth-Century Novel. 1979. 49.00x (ISBN 0-19-812092-3). Oxford U Pr.

Johnson, Ben C. An Evangelism Primer: Practical Principles for Congregations. LC 82-49021. 120p. 1983. pap. 5.95 (ISBN 0-8042-2039-5). John Knox.

Jorstad, Erling. Evangelicals in the White House: The Cultural Maturation of Born-Again Christianity, 1960-1981. LC 81-9674. (Studies in American Religion: Vol. 4). 171p. 1981. 39.95x (ISBN 0-88946-982-2). E Mellen.

Kane, J. Herbert. A Concise History of the Christian World Mission. 2nd ed. 1978. 7.95 (ISBN 0-8010-5395-1). Baker Bk.

Kempf, Charles. Revival & Local Church Evangelism. (Orig.). 1987. pap. price not set (ISBN 0-89084-369-4). Bob Jones Univ Pr.

Kennedy, D. James & Moore, T. M. Chain Reaction: Changing the World from Where You Are. LC 85-6458. 160p. 1985. 9.95 (ISBN 0-8499-0486-2, 0486-2). Word Bks.

Koop, Allen V. American Evangelical Missionaries in France, 1945-1975. (Illus.). 220p. (Orig.). 1986. lib. bdg. 27.00 (ISBN 0-8191-5204-8); pap. text ed. 13.50 (ISBN 0-8191-5205-6). U Pr of Amer.

Kraus, C. Norman, ed. Evangelicalism & Anabaptism. LC 79-12663. 192p. 1979. pap. 5.95 (ISBN 0-8361-1892-8). Herald Pr.

Kuiper, R. B. God Centered Evangelism. 1978. pap. 5.45 (ISBN 0-85151-110-4). Banner of Truth.

Lapsanski, Duane. Evangelical Perfection: An Historical Examination of the Concept in the Early Franciscan Sources. (Theology Ser.). 1977. 15.00 (ISBN 0-686-27933-6). Franciscan Inst.

Leavell, Landrum P. & Bryson, Harold. Evangelism: Christ's Imperative Commission. rev. ed. LC 78-59983. 1979. 10.95 (ISBN 0-8054-2534-9). Broadman.

Le Roy. Evangelismo en Accion. Pierson, Carlos C., tr. 144p. 1979. 4.95 (ISBN 0-311-13831-4). Casa Bautista.

Lightner, Robert P. Evangelical Theology. 1984. 15.95 (ISBN 0-8010-5628-4). Baker Bk.

--Neoevangelicalism Today. LC 78-11426. (Illus.). 1979. pap. 3.95 (ISBN 0-87227-067-X). Reg Baptist.

Loud, Grover C. Evangelized America. facsimile ed. LC 70-169770. (Select Bibliographies Reprint Ser). Repr. of 1928 ed. 27.50 (ISBN 0-8369-5990-6). Ayer Co Pubs.

Loveland, Anne C. Southern Evangelicals & the Social Order, 1800-1860. LC 80-11200. 354p. 1980. 32.50x (ISBN 0-8071-0690-9); pap. 9.95x (ISBN 0-8071-0783-2). La State U Pr.

McCulloh, Gerald O. Ministerial Education in the American Methodist Movement. LC 80-69028. (An Informed Ministry Ser.: 200 Years of American Methodist Thought). 342p. (Orig.). 1980. pap. 3.95 (ISBN 0-938162-00-4). United Meth Educ.

McGavran, Donald. The Bridges of God. rev. ed. 1981. pap. 5.95 (ISBN 0-377-45071-5). Friend Pr.

McKenna, David L. Contemporary Issues for Evangelical Christians. (Contemporary Discussion Ser). 1978. pap. 1.95 (ISBN 0-8010-6053-2). Baker Bk.

McKinney, Joseph C. Living in the Power of Pentecost. 112p. (Orig.). 1987. pap. 4.95 (ISBN 0-89283-311-4). Servant.

McLoughlin, William G. American Evangelicals, 1800-1900: An Anthology. 12.00 (ISBN 0-8446-0793-2). Peter Smith.

Manwaring, Randle. From Controversy to Co-Existence: Evangelicals in the Church of England, 1914-1980. 240p. 1985. 34.50 (ISBN 0-521-30380-X). Cambridge U Pr.

Marsden, George, ed. Evangelicalism & Modern America. 212p. (Orig.). 1984. pap. 8.95 (ISBN 0-8028-1993-1). Eerdmans.

Marsden, George M. Fundamentalism & American Culture: The Shaping of Twentieth-Century Evangelicalism, 1870-1925. 1980. pap. 9.95 (ISBN 0-19-503083-4). Oxford U Pr.

Martin, Roger H. Evangelicals United: Ecumenical Stirrings in Pre-Victorian Britain, 1795-1830. LC 82-10784. (Studies in Evangelicalism: No. 4). 244p. 1983. 19.00 (ISBN 0-8108-1586-9). Scarecrow.

Mayers, Ronald B. Evangelical Perspectives: Toward a Biblical Balance. LC 86-28966. 204p. (Orig.). 1987. lib. bdg. 24.50 (ISBN 0-8191-6062-8); pap. text ed. 12.75 (ISBN 0-8191-6063-6). U Pr of Amer.

Merrill, Dean & Shelley, Marshall, eds. Fresh Ideas for Preaching, Worship & Evangelism. (Fresh Ideas Ser.). 155p. 1984. pap. 6.95 (ISBN 0-917463-00-5). Chr Today.

Miles, Delos. Introduction to Evangelism. LC 82-73078. 1983. 19.95 (ISBN 0-8054-6239-2). Broadman.

--Master Principles of Evangelism. LC 81-66291. 1982. pap. 3.95 (ISBN 0-8054-6232-5). Broadman.

Miller, C. J. Evangelism & Your Church. 1980. pap. 2.95 (ISBN 0-87552-290-4). Presby & Reformed.

Miller, Herbert. Evangelism's open Secrets. 2nd ed. LC 77-23468. 112p. 1985. pap. 6.95 (ISBN 0-8272-0805-7). CBP.

Mullin, Robert B. Episcopal Vision-American Reality: High Church Theology & Social Thought in Evangelical America. 1986. 20.00 (ISBN 0-300-03487-3). Yale U Pr.

Nash, Ronald H. Evangelicals in America: Who They Are, What They Believe. 128p. 1987. pap. 7.95 (ISBN 0-687-12177-9). Abingdon.

Neighbour, Ralph. Contacto en el Espiritu. Martinez, Jose L., ed. Kratzig, Guillermo, tr. (Span.). 120p. 1983. pap. 2.50 (ISBN 0-311-09098-2). Casa Bautista.

Neuhaus, Richard J. & Cromartie, Michael, eds. Confronting This World: Evangelicals, Fundamentalists, & Politics. (Orig.). 1986. text ed. 22.00 (ISBN 0-89633-107-5); pap. text ed. 14.00 (ISBN 0-89633-108-3). Ethics & Public Policy.

Newsome, David H. Wilberforces & Henry Manning: The Parting of Friends. LC 67-2. (Illus.). 1966. 30.00x (ISBN 0-674-95280-4, Belknap Pr). Harvard U Pr.

Nicholls, Bruce & Kantzer, Kenneth. In Word & Deed. 224p. 1986. pap. 10.95 (ISBN 0-8028-1965-6). Eerdmans.

O'Donovan, Oliver. Resurrection & Moral Order: An Outline for an Evangelical Ethics. 320p. 1986. 18.95 (ISBN 0-8028-3610-0). Eerdmans.

Parks, Keith H. Fishers of Men. 3rd rev. ed. 196p. 1981. pap. text ed. 17.00 (ISBN 0-88151-014-9). Lay Leadership.

--Fishers of Men: Home Study Guide. 3rd rev. ed. 64p. 1981. 8.00 (ISBN 0-88151-015-7). Lay Leadership.

Pippert, Rebecca & Siemens, Ruth. Evangelism. (Lifebuilder Bible Studies). 64p. (Orig.). 1985. pap. text ed. 2.95 (ISBN 0-8308-1050-1). Inter-Varsity.

Pippert, Rebecca M. Out of the Saltshaker: Evangelism As a Way of Life. LC 79-1995. 1979. pap. 6.95 (ISBN 0-87784-735-5); study guide 2.95 (ISBN 0-87784-532-8). Inter-Varsity.

Pope Paul VI. On Evangelization in the Modern World. 1976. pap. text ed. 0.40 (ISBN 0-8198-0409-6). Dghtrs St Paul.

Prince, Matthew. Winning Through Caring: The Handbook on Friendship Evangelism. 96p. (Orig.). 1981. pap. 3.95 (ISBN 0-8010-7065-1). Baker Bk.

Quebedeaux, Richard & Sawatsky, Rodney, eds. Evangelical-Unification Dialogue. LC 79-89421. (Conference Ser.: No. 3). 374p. (Orig.). 1979. pap. text ed. 7.95 (ISBN 0-932894-02-X, Pub. by New Era Bks). Paragon Hse.

Ramm, Bernard L. After Fundamentalism: The Future of Evangelical Theology. LC 82-47792. 226p. 1984. text ed. 14.37i (ISBN 0-06-066791-5, RD 473, HarpR); pap. 9.95 (HarpR). Har-Row.

Reisinger, Ernest C. Today's Evangelism: It's Message & Methods. 1982. pap. 4.95 (ISBN 0-87552-417-6). Presby & Reformed.

Reynolds, Ralph V. All Things to All Men. Wallace, Mary H., ed. 128p. 1983. pap. 4.95 (ISBN 0-912315-01-6). Word Aflame.

Richards, Elton P., Jr. Outreach Preaching: The Role of Preaching in Evangelism. 56p. (Orig.). 1986. pap. 4.25 (ISBN 0-8066-2232-6, 10-4859). Augsburg.

Ritchie, John. Five Hundred Evangelistic Sermon Outlines. LC 86-27200. 128p. 1987. pap. 4.95 (ISBN 0-8254-3619-2). Kregel.

Rowlison, Bruce A. Creative Hospitality As a Means of Evangelism. rev. ed. LC 81-84182. (Illus.). 144p. 1982. pap. 5.95 (ISBN 0-938462-03-2). Green Leaf CA.

Samuel, D. N., ed. The Evangelical Succession. 144p. 1979. pap. 5.95 (ISBN 0-227-67834-6). Attic Pr.

Schaeffer, Francis A. The Great Evangelical Disaster. LC 83-73125. 192p. 1984. 14.95 (ISBN 0-89107-309-4, Crossway Bks); pap. 7.95 (ISBN 0-89107-308-6). Good News.

Schaeffer, Franky. Addicted to Mediocrity. LC 80-85325. (Illus.). 128p. 1981. pap. 5.95 (ISBN 0-89107-214-4, Crossway Bks). Good News.

Schaffer, James & Todd, Colleen. Christian Wives: Women Behind the Evangelists. LC 87-5291. (Illus.). 168p. 1987. 12.95 (ISBN 0-385-23581-X, Dolp). Doubleday.

Schmithals, Walter. Einleitung in die Drei Ersten Evangelien. 512p. 1985. 23.20x (ISBN 3-11-010263-3). De Gruyter.

Schultz, Samuel J. Deuteronomio: El Evangelio del Amor (Comentario Biblico Portavoz) Orig. Title: Deuteronomy (Everyman's Bible Commentary) (Span.). 122p. 1979. pap. 3.50 (ISBN 0-8254-1658-2). Kregel.

Sider, Ronald J., ed. Evangelicals & Development: Toward a Theology of Social Change. LC 82-6970. (Contemporary Issues in Social Ethics Ser.). 122p. 1982. pap. 6.95 (ISBN 0-664-24445-9). Westminster.

Smalley, Stephen S. John: Evangelist & Interpreter. 285p. 1983. cancelled; pap. 10.95 (ISBN 0-85364-345-8). Attic Pr.

Smith, Bailey E. Real Evangelism. LC 77-92283. 1978. 8.95 (ISBN 0-8054-6220-1). Broadman.

--Real Revival Preaching. LC 81-66667. 1982. 8.50 (ISBN 0-8054-6235-X). Broadman.

South African Evangelicals. Evangelical Witness in South Africa: An Evangelical Critique of Evangelical Theology & Practice. 46p. (Orig.). 1987. pap. 3.95 (ISBN 0-8028-0291-5). Eerdmans.

Southard, Samuel. Pastoral Evangelism. LC 80-82196. 192p. 1981. pap. 4.50 (ISBN 0-8042-2037-9). John Knox.

Sparagna, Aniceto. Personal Evangelism among Roman Catholics. (Orig.). 1978. pap. 3.95 (ISBN 0-89900-122-X). College Pr Pub.

Stott, John R. & Meeking, Basil, eds. The Evangelical-Roman Catholic Dialogue on Mission, 1977-1984. 80p. (Orig.). 1986. pap. 4.95 (ISBN 0-8028-0184-6). Eerdmans.

Strand, Robert J. Evangelism: The Unfinished Task. LC 81-80303. (Workers Training Ser.). 128p. (Orig.). 1981. pap. 2.25 (ISBN 0-88243-513-2, 02-0513). Gospel Pub.

Stranges, Frank E. Heaven. 16p. (Orig.). 1985. pap. text ed. 2.00 (ISBN 0-933470-03-7). Intl Evang.

--Mystery Man of Darkness No. 666. 16p. 1985. pap. text ed. 2.00 (ISBN 0-933470-05-3). Intl Evang.

--Pre-Eternal Rest. 12p. 1985. pap. text ed. 2.00 (ISBN 0-933470-07-X). Intl Evang.

--The Secret Place of the Most High. 12p. 1985. pap. text ed. 2.00 (ISBN 0-933470-09-6). Intl Evang.

--The Star of Bethlehem. 20p. (Orig.). 1985. pap. text ed. 2.00 (ISBN 0-933470-06-1). Intl Evang.

--The White Planet. 24p. 1985. pap. text ed. 2.00 (ISBN 0-933470-04-5). Intl Evang.

Sumner, Robert L. Biblical,Evangelism in Action. 1966. pap. 6.50 (ISBN 0-914012-29-0, Pub. by Bibl Evang Pr). Sword of Lord.

--Evangelism: The Church on Fire! 220p. 1960. 3.25 (ISBN 0-87398-211-8, Pub. by Bibl Evang Pr). Sword of Lord.

--Hell Is No Joke. 1959. pap. 3.25 (ISBN 0-914012-28-2, Pub.by Bibl Evang Pr). Sword of Lord.

Sweazey, George E. The Church As Evangelist. LC 77-20452. 272p. 1984. pap. 7.95 (ISBN 0-06-067777-5, RD 502, HarpR). Har-Row.

Sweet, Leonard I., ed. The Evangelical Tradition in America. LC 84-6723. x, 320p. 1984. 25.95 (ISBN 0-86554-092-6, MUP/H84). Mercer Univ Pr.

Tanenbaum, Marc H. & Wilson, Marvin R., eds. Evangelicals & Jews in an Age of Pluralism. 272p. 1984. pap. 9.95 (ISBN 0-8010-8871-2). Baker Bk.

Thielicke, Helmut. The Evangelical Faith: The Doctrine of God & of Christ, Vol. 2. Bromiley, Geoffrey W., ed. LC 74-7010. pap. 123.30 (ISBN 0-317-30163-2, 2025345). Bks Demand UMI.

--The Evangelical Faith, Vol. 1: Prolegomena: The Relation of Theology to Modern Thought-Forms. Bromiley, Geoffrey W., tr. 420p. Date not set. 24.95 (ISBN 0-567-02354-0, Pub. by T & T Clark Ltd UK). Fortress.

--The Evangelical Faith, Vol. 2: The Doctrine of God & Christ. Bromiley, Geoffrey W., tr. 476p. Date not set. 24.95 (ISBN 0-567-02355-9, Pub. by T & T Clark Ltd UK). Fortress.

--The Evangelical Faith, Vol. 3: Theology of the Spirit. Bromiley, Geoffrey W., tr. 480p. Date not set. 24.95 (ISBN 0-8028-2344-0, Pub. by T & T Clark Ltd UK). Fortress.

Thompson, W. Oscar, Jr. & Thompson, Carolyn. Concentric Circles of Concern. LC 81-67488. 1981. 7.95 (ISBN 0-8054-6233-3). Broadman.

Toon, Peter & Martin, Peter, eds. Evangelical Theology, Eighteen Thirty-Three to Eighteen Fifty-Six: A Response to Tractarianism. LC 79-16701. (New Foundations Theological Library Ser.). 254p. 3.25 (ISBN 0-8042-3703-4). John Knox.

Torrance, T. F. Reality & Evangelical Theology. LC 81-19811. 174p. 1982. pap. 8.95 (ISBN 0-664-24401-7). Westminster.

Tozer, A. W. Worship: The Missing Jewel of the Evangelical Church. 30p. 1979. bklet 0.95 (ISBN 0-87509-219-5). Chr Pubns.

Trigg, Joseph W. & Sachs, William L. Of One Body: Renewal Movements in the Church. LC 86-2788. 168p. (Orig.). 1986. pap. 9.95 (ISBN 0-8042-0677-5). John Knox.

Tristano, Richard. What Southern Catholics Need to Know about Evangelical Religion. 1984. pap. 3.00x (ISBN 0-914422-14-6). Glenmary Res Ctr.

Tucker, Roanld D. Evangelism. (Illus.). 40p. (Orig.). 1983. pap. 2.00 (ISBN 0-933643-13-6). Grace World Outreach.

Watson, David. Creo en la Evangelizacion. Schwieters, Elsa S., tr. from Eng. (Serie Creo). Tr. of I Believe in Evangelism. (Span.). 235p. 1979. pap. 5.95 (ISBN 0-89922-133-5). Edit Caribe.

Webber, Robert. Celebrating Our Faith: Evangelism Through Worship. 1986. 10.95 (ISBN 0-06-069286-3, HarpR). Har-Row.

Winter, Ralph D. & Hawthorne, Steven C., eds. Perspectives on the World Christian Movement: A Reader. LC 81-69924. (Illus.). 864p. (Orig.). 1981. pap. 14.95x (ISBN 0-87808-189-5). William Carey Lib.

Wright, David F., ed. Essays in Evangelical Social Ethics. LC 82-62581. 192p. (Orig.). 1983. pap. 8.95 (ISBN 0-8192-1326-8). Morehouse.

Zimbelman, Ernie, ed. Human Sexuality & Evangelical Christians. (Illus.). 394p. (Orig.). 1985. lib. bdg. 31.50 (ISBN 0-8191-4477-0); pap. text ed. 16.75 (ISBN 0-8191-4478-9). U Pr of Amer.

Zodhiates, Spiros. Christianity: Not Just a Religion. (Illus.). 1979. pap. 1.75 (ISBN 0-89957-523-4). AMG Pubs.

EVANGELISTIC SERMONS

Apostolon, Billy. Evangelistic Sermon Outlines. (Sermon Outline Ser.). pap. 2.50 (ISBN 0-8010-0144-7). Baker Bk.

Bolick, James H. Sermon Outlines for Revival Preaching. (Pulpit Library). 106p. 1986. pap. 2.95 (ISBN 0-8010-0922-7). Baker Bk.

Carter, James E. Help for the Evangelistic Preacher. LC 83-70371. 1985. pap. 6.50 (ISBN 0-8054-6243-0). Broadman.

Finney, Charles G. Charles G. Finney Memorial Library, 8 vols. 1975. Set. pap. 31.50 (ISBN 0-8254-2623-5). Kregel.

--Guilt of Sin. LC 65-25845. (Charles G. Finney Memorial Library). 124p. 1975. pap. 4.50 (ISBN 0-8254-2616-2). Kregel.

--Prevailing Prayer. LC 65-25846. (Charles G. Finney Memorial Library). 1975. pap. 3.50 (ISBN 0-8254-2603-0). Kregel.

--So Great Salvation. LC 65-25844. (Charles G. Finney Memorial Library). 128p. 1975. pap. 4.50 (ISBN 0-8254-2621-9). Kregel.

--True & False Repentance. LC 66-10576. (Charles G. Finney Memorial Library). 122p. 1975. pap. 4.50 (ISBN 0-8254-2617-0). Kregel.

--True Saints. LC 66-24880. (Charles G. Finney Memorial Library). 120p. 1975. pap. 4.50 (ISBN 0-8254-2622-7). Kregel.

--True Submission. LC 66-24881. (Charles G. Finney Memorial Library). 128p. 1975. pap. 4.50 (ISBN 0-8254-2618-9). Kregel.

--Victory Over the World. LC 66-24879. (Charles G. Finney Memorial Library). 124p. 1975. pap. 4.50 (ISBN 0-8254-2619-7). Kregel.

Henry, Jim. Heartwarmers. LC 77-79094. 1977. 5.95 (ISBN 0-8054-5156-0). Broadman.

Joyce, Jon L. Evangelists Speak. (Orig.). 1983. pap. 2.95 (ISBN 0-937172-50-2). JLJ Pubs.

Keiningham, C. W. Outlines for Evangelistic Preaching. 80p. 1984. pap. 2.95 (ISBN 0-8010-5461-3). Baker Bk.

Macfarlan, Duncan. The Revivals of the Eighteenth Century, Particulary at Cambuslang: With Three Sermons by the Rev. George Whitefield. (Revival Library). (Illus.). 263p. 1980. Repr. of 1847 ed. lib. bdg. 12.95 (ISBN 0-940033-14-3). R O Roberts.

Moody, D. L. Way to God. pap. 3.95 (ISBN 0-8024-9231-2). Moody.

Skinner, Tom. Words of Revolution: A Call Involvement in the Real Revolution. 44p. 1971. pap. 4.25 (ISBN 0-85364-113-7). Attic Pr.

Spurgeon, C. H. New Park Street Pulpit Index. 1976. pap. 1.50 (ISBN 0-686-16848-8). Pilgrim Pubns.

Spurgeon, C H. New Park Street Pulpit 1855-1860, 6 vols. 1981. Set. 60.00 (ISBN 0-686-16847-X). Pilgrim Pubns.

Spurgeon, Charles H. Sermons on Revival: Kelvedon. Cook, Charles T., ed. 256p. 1977. Repr. of 1958 ed. limp bk. 5.95 (ISBN 0-551-05575-8). Attic Pr.

Torrey, R. A. Revival Addresses. 282p. 1974. Repr. of 1903 ed. 10.95 (ISBN 0-227-67808-7). Attic Pr.

Urshan, Nathaniel A. & Becton, Cleveland M. Harvestime Pulpit Series, Vol. III. Wallace, Mary H., ed. (Illus.). 406p. (Orig.). 1985. pap. 14.95 (ISBN 0-912315-83-0). Word Aflame.

Warner, Wayne E., ed. Revival! (Illus.). 163p. (Orig.). 1978. pap. 4.95 (ISBN 0-89274-303-4). Harrison Hse.

Wood, Charles R., ed. Evangelistic Sermon Outlines. 64p. (Orig.). 1975. pap. 2.95 (ISBN 0-8254-4004-1). Kregel.

--Revival Sermon Outlines. 64p. 1975. pap. 2.95 (ISBN 0-8254-4005-X). Kregel.

EVANGELISTIC WORK

see also Camp-Meetings; Church Growth; Coffee House Ministry; Communication (Theology); Conversion; Jesus Christ–Evangelistic Methods; Missions; Revivals; Salvation Army

Aldrich, Joseph C. Life-Style Evangelism: Crossing Traditional Boundaries to Reach the Unbelieving World. LC 80-27615. (Critical Concern Ser.). 246p. 1983. pap. 6.95 (ISBN 0-88070-023-8). Multnomah.

Anderson, Gerald H. & Stransky, Thomas F., eds. Mission Trends: Faith Meets Faith, No. 5. (Mission Trends Ser.). 320p. (Orig.). 1981. pap. 3.95 (ISBN 0-8028-1821-8). Eerdmans.

Arias, Mortimer. Announcing the Reign of God: Evangelization & the Subversive Memory of Jesus. LC 83-5696. 176p. 1984. pap. 8.95 (ISBN 0-8006-1712-6, 1-1712). Fortress.

Armstrong, Richard S. The Pastor As Evangelist. LC 84-10359. 202p. 1984. pap. 9.95 (ISBN 0-664-24556-0). Westminster.

--Service Evangelism. LC 78-26701. 198p. 1979. pap. 8.95 (ISBN 0-664-24252-9). Westminster.

Balda, Wesley. Heirs of the Same Promise: Using Acts As a Study Guide for Evangelizing Ethnic America. 1984. 3.95 (ISBN 0-912552-44-1). Missions Adv Res Com Ctr.

Barreiro, Alvaro. Basic Ecclesial Communities: The Evangelization of the Poor. Campbell, Barbara, tr. from Portuguese. LC 81-16898. Orig. Title: Comunidades Eclesiais De Base E Evangelizacao Dos Pobres. 96p. (Orig.). 1982. pap. 5.95 (ISBN 0-88344-026-1). Orbis Bks.

Beidelman, T. O. Colonial Evangelism: A Socio-Historical Study of an East African Mission at the Grassroots. LC 81-47771. (Midland Bks. Ser.: No. 278). (Illus.). 296p. 1982. 29.95x (ISBN 0-253-31386-4); pap. 12.50x (ISBN 0-253-20278-7). Ind U Pr.

Beller, Dan. Progress Through Pioneer Evangelism. pap. 2.00 (ISBN 0-911866-80-9). Advocate.

Berlucchi, Jim. Person to Person: How to Be Effective in Evangelism. 144p. (Orig.). 1984. pap. 3.50 (ISBN 0-89283-164-2). Servant.

Bisagno, John R. Power of Positive Evangelism: How to Hold a Revival. LC 68-26912. 1968. pap. 3.95 (ISBN 0-8054-2503-9). Broadman.

Boom, Corrie ten. Plenty for Everyone. 1967. pap. 2.95 (ISBN 0-87508-023-5). Chr Lit.

Boschman, LaMar. The Prophetic Song. (Orig.). 1986. pap. 3.95 (ISBN 0-938612-12-3). Revival Press.

Chafer, Lewis S. True Evangelism. pap. 5.95 (ISBN 0-310-22381-4, 6312P). Zondervan.

Chick, Jack T. The Last Call. (Illus.). 64p. (Orig.). 1963. pap. 1.95 (ISBN 0-937958-06-9). Chick Pubns.

--La Ultima Llamada. (Span., Illus.). 64p. (Orig.). 1972. pap. 1.95 (ISBN 0-937958-02-6). Chick Pubns.

Chironna, Mark. The Elisha Principle. 54p. (Orig.). 1985. pap. 2.95 (ISBN 0-938612-11-5). Revival Press.

Cocoris, G. Michael. Evangelism: A Biblical Approach. (Orig.). 1984. pap. 6.95 (ISBN 0-8024-2396-5). Moody.

--Making Evangelism Personal, Pt. 1. 56p. (Orig.). 1984. pap. text ed. 1.00 (ISBN 0-935729-16-X). Church Open Door.

--Making Evangelism Personal, Pt. 2. 41p. (Orig.). 1984. pap. text ed. 1.00 (ISBN 0-935729-17-8). Church Open Door.

Coleman, Robert E. Evangelism in Perspective. LC 75-31306. 3.95 (ISBN 0-87509-080-X); pap. 2.00 (ISBN 0-87509-081-8). Chr Pubns.

Conn, Harvie. Evangelism: Doing Justice & Preaching Grace. 112p. (Orig.). 1982. pap. 4.95 (ISBN 0-310-45311-9, 11646P). Zondervan.

Dalaba, Oliver V. That None Be Lost. LC 77-74553. (Workers' Training Ser.). 128p. 1977. 1.25 (ISBN 0-88243-621-X, 02-621). Gospel Pub.

Dale, Robert D. Evangelizing the Hard-to-Reach. LC 85-24262. (Broadman Leadership Ser.). 1986. pap. 4.95 (ISBN 0-8054-6251-1). Broadman.

Daughters of St. Paul. Where the Gospel Meets the World. 1977. 6.95 (ISBN 0-8198-0482-7); pap. 5.00 (ISBN 0-8198-0483-5). Dghtrs St Paul.

Davenport, R. Edward. Person to Person Evangelism. new ed. LC 77-23716. 1978. pap. 2.95 (ISBN 0-87148-691-1). Pathway Pr.

Dhavamony, Mariasusai, ed. Evangelization, Dialogue & Development. (Documenta Missionalia Ser.: No. 5). 1972. pap. 20.00 (ISBN 0-8294-0323-X, Pub. by Gregorian U Pr). Loyola.

Downey, Murray W. Art of Soul Winning. 1957. pap. 5.95 (ISBN 0-8010-2820-5). Baker Bk.

Dresselhaus, Richard L. Teaching for Decision. LC 73-75502. 124p. 1973. pap. 1.25 (ISBN 0-88243-616-3, 02-0616). Gospel Pub.

Drummond, Lewis. Leading Your Church in Evangelism. LC 75-30135. 168p. 1976. pap. 5.50 (ISBN 0-8054-6210-4). Broadman.

Edwards, Jonathan. Religious Affections. 382p. 1986. pap. 9.45 (ISBN 0-85151-485-5). Banner of Truth.

Evans, Eifion. Daniel Rowland & the Great Evangelical Awakening in Wales. 383p. 1985. 22.95 (ISBN 0-85151-446-4). Banner of Truth.

Finney, Charles G. How to Experience Revival. 143p. 1984. pap. text ed. 3.50 (ISBN 0-88368-140-4). Whitaker Hse.

--Principles of Union with Christ. Parkhurst, Louis G., ed. 128p. 1985. pap. 4.95 (ISBN 0-87123-447-5, 210447). Bethany Hse.

Fish, Roy J. Every Member Evangelism for Today. rev. ed. LC 75-12289. 128p. 1976. pap. 6.95 (ISBN 0-06-061551-6, RD125, HarpR). Har-Row.

Ford, Leighton. Good News Is for Sharing. LC 77-78496. 1977. 6.95 (ISBN 0-89191-083-2). Cook.

Foust, Paul. Reborn to Multiply. LC 73-9110. 1973. pap. 2.75 (ISBN 0-570-03170-2, 12-2573). Concordia.

Fox, H. Eddie & Morris, George E. Faith-Sharing. 144p. 1987. pap. 7.95 (ISBN 0-310-38381-1). Zondervan.

Galilea, Segundo. The Beatitudes: To Evangelize as Jesus Did. Barr, Robert R., tr. from Span. LC 83-19342. Tr. of La Mision Segun Las Bienaventuranzas. 128p. (Orig.). 1984. pap. 5.95 (ISBN 0-88344-344-9). Orbis Bks.

Graham, Billy. Billy Graham Christian Worker's Handbook. 240p. 1982. write for info. (ISBN 0-89066-042-5); pap. 7.95. World Wide Pub.

Greenleaf, Simon. The Testimony of the Evangelists. 640p. 1984. Repr. of 1874 ed. 19.95 (ISBN 0-8010-3803-0). Baker Bk.

Grossinger, Richard. Early Field Notes from the All-American Revival Church. 1973. pap. 3.50 (ISBN 0-913028-19-3). North Atlantic.

Gunn, George S. This Gospel of the Kingdom: Dilemmas in Evangelism. 167p. 1964. 5.95 (ISBN 0-227-67660-2). Attic Pr.

Gurganus, George P., ed. Guidelines for World Evangelism. 1977. 11.95 (ISBN 0-89112-040-8, Bibl Res Pr). Abilene Christ U.

Hagin, Kenneth, Jr. Man's Impossibility, God's Possibility. 1978. pap. 2.50 (ISBN 0-89276-700-6). Hagin Ministries.

Haiven, Judith. Faith, Hope, No Charity: An Inside Look at the Born Again Movement in Canada & the United States. (Illus.). 221p. 1984. lib. bdg. 14.95 (ISBN 0-919573-32-0); pap. 7.95 (ISBN 0-919573-33-9). Left Bank.

Hall, Robert B. Sharing Your Faith. 1981. pap. 4.95 (ISBN 0-686-14949-1). Episcopal Ctr.

Harper, Howard. Evangelism in My Parish. 1972. pap. 3.00 (ISBN 0-686-14947-5). Episcopal Ctr.

Heck, Joel D. Make Disciples. 1984. pap. 6.50 (ISBN 0-570-03934-7, 12-2869). Concordia.

Hedley, Leslie W. The Day Japan Bombed Pearl Harbor & Other Stories. 148p. 1984. pap. 7.95 (ISBN 0-933515-03-0). Exile Pr.

Hetherington, William M., ed. Lectures on the Revival of Religion by Ministers of the Church of Scotland. (Revival Library). xxvi, 444p. 1980. Repr. of 1840 ed. lib. bdg. 15.95 (ISBN 0-940033-15-1). R O Roberts.

Hill, Richard O. Training Evangelism Callers. 64p. (Orig.). 1986. Leader Guide. pap. 4.95 (ISBN 0-8066-2227-X, 23-1960); Caller Manual. pap. 3.50 (ISBN 0-8066-2228-8, 23-1961). Augsburg.

Hinson, William H. A Place to Dig In. 1987. 10.95t (ISBN 0-687-31549-2). Abingdon.

Hofinger, Johannes. Pastoral Life in the Power of the Spirit. LC 81-1439. (Illus.). 215p. 1982. pap. 6.95 (ISBN 0-8189-0427-5). Alba.

Holmes, Urban T., III. Turning to Christ: A Theology of Renewal & Evangelization. 240p. (Orig.). 1981. pap. 8.95 (ISBN 0-8164-2289-3, HarpR). Har-Row.

Holton, Susan & Jones, David L. Spirit Aflame: Luis Palau's Mission to London. 258p. 1985. 7.95 (ISBN 0-8010-4293-3). Baker Bk.

Hostetler, John A. An Invitation to Faith. 40p. (Orig.). 1957. pap. 1.00 (ISBN 0-8361-1381-0). Herald Pr.

Hughes, Richard & Serig, Joseph A., eds. Evangelism: The Ministry of the Church. 1981. pap. 12.00 (ISBN 0-8309-0304-6). Herald Hse.

Johnson, Ben C. Rethinking Evangelism: A Theological Approach. LC 86-26787. 142p. (Orig.). 1987. pap. 9.95 (ISBN 0-664-24060-7). Westminster.

Jonathan Edwards: On Revival. 1984. pap. 5.45 (ISBN 0-85151-431-6). Banner of Truth.

Kolb, Robert A. Speaking the Gospel Today: A Theology for Evangelism. 1984. 16.95 (ISBN 0-570-04205-4, 15-2173). Concordia.

Kromminga, Carl. Bringing God's News to Neighbors. 1976. pap. 4.50 (ISBN 0-87552-314-5). Presby & Reformed.

Kuhne, Gary W. The Dynamics of Personal Follow-up. 192p. 1976. pap. 5.95 (ISBN 0-310-26951-2, 12310P). Zondervan.

Lesick, Lawrence T. The Lane Rebels: Evangelicalism & Antislavery in Antebellum America. LC 80-24123. (Studies in Evangelicalism: No. 2). 287p. 1980. 21.00 (ISBN 0-8108-1372-6). Scarecrow.

Lischer, Richard. Speaking of Jesus: Finding the Words for Witness. LC 81-70556. 144p. 1982. pap. 6.95 (ISBN 0-8006-1631-6, 1-1631). Fortress.

Lyke, James P. What We Have Seen & Heard: A Pastoral Letter on Evangelization from the Black Bishops of the United States. 40p. (Orig.). 1984. pap. text ed. 1.95 (ISBN 0-86716-040-3). St Anthony Mess Pr.

McIntosh, Duncan. The Everyday Evangelist. 64p. 1984. pap. 2.95 (ISBN 0-8170-1042-4). Judson.

MacMullen, Ramsay. Christianizing the Roman Empire: A.D. 100-400. LC 84-3694. 200p. 1984. 22.50x (ISBN 0-300-03216-1); pap. 7.95 (ISBN 0-300-03642-6, Y-571). Yale U Pr.

Malik, Charles. The Two Tasks. 37p. 1980. pap. 1.95 (ISBN 0-89107-212-8, Crossway Bks). Good News.

Mallison, John, ed. Youth Outreach & Evangelism: Youth Work Guides Ser. (Illus.). 104p. (Orig.). 1975. pap. 5.95 (ISBN 0-85819-108-3, Pub. by JBCE). ANZ Religious Pubns.

Maxwell, Mervyn. Tell It to the World. LC 76-6619. 1976. 6.95 (ISBN 0-8163-0217-0, 20077-4). Pacific Pr Pub Assn.

Miles, Delos. Evangelism & Social Involvement. LC 86-2660. 1986. 9.95 (ISBN 0-8054-6248-1). Broadman.

Miller, Herbert S. Christian Worker's Manual. pap. 4.00 (ISBN 0-87509-065-6). Chr Pubns.

Moore, Wayland B. New Testament Follow-Up. (Orig.). 1963. pap. 3.95 (ISBN 0-8028-1136-1). Eerdmans.

Neville, Joyce. How to Share Your Faith Without Being Offensive. 160p. (Orig.). 1983. pap. 6.95 (ISBN 0-8164-2228-1, HarpR). Har-Row.

Nicholas, Tim & Touchton, Ken. More Than Just Talk. Furlow, Elaine S., ed. (Human Touch Photo-Text Ser.). (Illus.). 1977. 6.95g (ISBN 0-937170-16-X). Home Mission.

Orsen, Dennis. Focus for Evangelism: The Evangelical Implications of Ministry. 48p. (Orig.). 1985. pap. 3.95 (ISBN 0-8066-2199-0, 23-1601). Augsburg.

Packer, James I. Evangelism & the Sovereignty of God. LC 67-28875. 1961. pap. 3.95 (ISBN 0-87784-680-4). Inter-Varsity.

Peace, Richard. Small Group Evangelism. rev. ed. 225p. 1983. pap. 6.95 (ISBN 0-87784-329-5). Inter-Varsity.

Pepper, Clayton, ed. Total Evangelism. pap. 2.25 (ISBN 0-89137-203-2). Quality Pubns.

Petersen, Jim. Evangelism for Our Generation. 216p. 1985. pap. 5.95 (ISBN 0-89109-476-8). NavPress.

Pinson, William M., Jr. Ready to Minister. LC 84-3052. (Broadman Leadership Ser.). 1984. pap. 4.95 (ISBN 0-8054-3109-8). Broadman.

Pope Paul Sixth. On Evangelization in the Modern World. 70p. 1975. pap. 2.95 (ISBN 1-55586-129-6). US Catholic.

Price, Wendell W. Contemporary Problems of Evangelism. LC 76-12941. 1976. 3.95 (ISBN 0-87509-070-2); pap. 2.00 (ISBN 0-87509-071-0). Chr Pubns.

Quick, Daniel L. & Noton, Thomas A. Cry from the Mountain. 159p. 1986. pap. 5.95 (ISBN 0-89066-064-6). World Wide Pubs.

Ravenhill, Leonard. Sodom Had No Bible. 208p. 1979. pap. 4.95 (ISBN 0-87123-496-3, 210496). Bethany Hse.

Robinson, Darrell W. Total Church Life. LC 85-7900. 1985. 7.95 (ISBN 0-8054-6250-3). Broadman.

Roozen, David A. & McKinney, Wiliam. Varieties of Religious Presence: Mission in Public Life. 400p. (Orig.). 1984. pap. 12.95 (ISBN 0-8298-0724-1). Pilgrim NY.

Rudnick, Milton L. Speaking the Gospel Through the Ages: A History of Evangelism. 1984. 24.95 (ISBN 0-570-04204-6, 15-2172). Concordia.

Rusbuldt, Richard E. Evangelism on Purpose. 48p. 1980. pap. 2.95 (ISBN 0-8170-0894-2). Judson.

Scarborough, Lee R. With Christ after the Lost. rev. ed. Head, E. D., ed. 1953. 12.95 (ISBN 0-8054-6203-1). Broadman.

Schmidt, Henry J., ed. Witnesses to a Third Way. 160p. (Orig.). 1986. pap. 5.95 (ISBN 0-87178-940-X). Brethren.

Schmidt, Walter. Lay Evangelism Calling: Participants Manual. 1986. 4.50 (ISBN 0-89536-805-6, 6825); training manual 2.95 (ISBN 0-89536-800-5, 6818). CSS of Ohio.

Schmidt, Walter A. Recruiting Evangelism Callers: Enlisting & Coordinating Workers. 64p. (Orig.). 1984. pap. 3.95 (ISBN 0-8066-2069-2, 23-1830). Augsburg.

Schweer, G. William. Personal Evangelism for Today. LC 83-70003. 1984. 10.95 (ISBN 0-8054-6241-4). Broadman.

Sisson, Richard. Training for Evangelism. 1979. pap. 12.95 (ISBN 0-8024-8792-0). Moody.

Sisson, Richard, et al. Preparese Para Evangelizar: Un Programa De Evangelizacion Personal. Powell, David & Ditmore, Esteban, trs. Tr. of Training for Evangelism - A Program for Personal Evangelism. (Span.). 224p. (Orig.). 1984. pap. 5.95. Casa Bautista.

Small, Jacquelyn. Transformers-The Therapists of the Future. 272p. 1984. pap. 11.95 (ISBN 0-87516-529-X). De Vorss.

Smith, Amanda. Autobiography. LC 71-99407. 1969. Repr. of 1893 ed. lib. bdg. 25.00 (ISBN 0-8411-0080-2). Metro Bks.

Smith, Glen C. Evangelizing Adults. 404p. (Orig.). 1985. pap. 12.95 (ISBN 0-8423-0793-1). Tyndale.

Sproul, R. C. Chosen by God. 1986. 10.95 (ISBN 0-8423-0282-4). Tyndale.

Spurgeon, Charles H. The Soulwinner. (Orig.). 1963. pap. 4.95 (ISBN 0-8028-8081-9). Eerdmans.

Stewart, Marjorie. Women in Neighborhood Evangelism. LC 77-93410. 128p. 1978. pap. 1.50 (ISBN 0-88243-723-2, 02-0723, Radiant Books). Gospel Pub.

Sumner, Robert L. After the Revival-What? 1980. pap. 3.95 (ISBN 0-914012-22-3, Pub. by Bibl Evang Pr). Sword of Lord.

Torrey, A. How to Work for Christ. 512p. 1901. 15.95 (ISBN 0-8007-0144-5). Revell.

Torrey, R. A. How to Bring Men to Christ. LC 76-57111. 128p. 1977. pap. 2.95 (ISBN 0-87123-230-8, 200230). Bethany Hse.

Torrey, R. A., ed. How to Witness to Anyone: Guidelines for Effective Evangelism. 1985. pap. text ed. 3.50 (ISBN 0-88368-170-6). Whitaker Hse.

Torrey, Reuben A. KJV Vest Pocket Companion. pap. 1.95 (ISBN 0-310-33321-0, 12151P). Zondervan.

--Personal Work. 180p. 1956. 10.95 (ISBN 0-8007-0251-4). Revell.

Towns, Elmer L. Evangelize Thru Christian Education. LC 78-97811. 96p. 1970. pap. text ed. 4.95 (ISBN 0-910566-08-9); Perfect bdg. instr's. guide 5.95 (ISBN 0-910566-30-5). Evang Tchr.

Tyler, Bennet. New England Revivals, As They Existed at the Close of the Eighteenth & the Beginning of the Nineteenth Centuries Compiled Principally from Narratives First Pub. in the Conn. Evangelical Magazine Revival Library. 378p. 1980. Repr. of 1846 ed. lib. bdg. 12.95 (ISBN 0-940033-18-6). R O Roberts.

Unreached Peoples '80. LC 79-57522. 383p. 1980. 7.95 (ISBN 0-912552-50-6). Missions Adv Res Com Ctr.

Unreached Peoples '82. LC 81-69100. 435p. 7.95 (ISBN 0-912552-52-2). Missions Adv Res Com Ctr.

Vaudrey, Stephen J. How to Win Your Family to Christ. 1985. 13.95 (ISBN 0-317-18081-9); pap. 6.95 (ISBN 0-317-18082-7). P-H.

Wallinga, Robert. God's Church in Today's World 1. pap. 2.25 (ISBN 0-686-14196-2). Rose Pub MI.

--God's Church in Today's World 2. pap. 2.25 (ISBN 0-686-14197-0). Rose Pub MI.

Watson, David. I Believe in Evangelism. (I Believe Ser). 1977. pap. 5.95 (ISBN 0-8028-1687-8). Eerdmans.

Whitesell, Faris D. Sixty-Five Ways to Give Evangelistic Invitations. LC 84-11269. 128p. 1984. pap. 5.95 (ISBN 0-8254-4021-1). Kregel.

Williams, Theodore, ed. Together in Mission. 90p. (Orig.). 1983. pap. 2.00. World Evang Fellow.

Wilson, Samuel & Aeschliman, Gordon. The Hidden Half: Discovering the World of Unreached Peoples. 1984. 5.50 (ISBN 0-912552-43-3). World Vision Intl.

Wimber, John & Springer, Kevin. Power Evangelism. 224p. 1986. 13.45 (ISBN 0-06-069532-3). Har-Row.

Wiseman, Neil B., ed. Evangelism: One Hundred Thirty-Nine Ideas & Quotes. 110p. (Orig.). 1983. pap. 3.50 (ISBN 0-8341-0889-5). Beacon Hill.

Woods, C. Stacey. Growth of a Work of God. LC 77-6553. 1978. pap. 4.95 (ISBN 0-87784-741-X). Inter-Varsity.

The Work of an Evangelist. 888p. 1984. 19.95 (ISBN 0-89066-049-2). World Wide Pubs.

Youngman, Bernard R. Spreading the Gospel. (Background to the Bible Ser.). pap. 8.95 (ISBN 0-7175-0420-4). Dufour.

EVANGELISTS

Altschuler, Glenn C. & Saltzgaber, Jan M. Revivalism, Social Conscience, & Community in the Burned-Over District: The Trial of Rhoda Bement. (Illus.). 184p. 1983. 27.95x (ISBN 0-8014-1541-1); pap. 8.95x (ISBN 0-8014-9246-7). Cornell U Pr.

Bonar, Andrew. The Life of R. M. M'Cheyne. 1978. pap. 3.45 (ISBN 0-85151-085-X). Banner of Truth.

Bonar, Andrew A. Memoir & Remains of R. M. M'cheyne. 1978. 16.95 (ISBN 0-85151-084-1). Banner of Truth.

Brians, Pearl. Adventist Evangelist's Diary. large print ed. 1985. pap. 4.00 (ISBN 0-914009-25-7). VHI Library.

Catherwood, Christopher. Five Evangelical Leaders. 240p. 1985. pap. 7.95 (ISBN 0-87788-274-6); 12.95 (ISBN 0-87788-257-6). Shaw Pubs.

Cole, Charles C., Jr. Social Ideas of the Northern Evangelists, Eighteen Twenty-Six to Eighteen Sixty. 1966. lib. bdg. 20.50x (ISBN 0-374-91843-0, Octagon). Hippocrene Bks.

Cornwell, Patricia D. A Time for Remembering: The Ruth Bell Graham Story. LC 82-48922. (Illus.). 320p. 1983. 13.45 (ISBN 0-06-061685-7, HarpR). Har-Row.

Finney, Charles G. The Autobiography of Charles G. Finney. Wessel, Helen S., ed. LC 77-2813. 1977. pap. 5.95 (ISBN 0-87123-010-0). Bethany Hse.

--Reflections on Revival. LC 78-26527. 160p. 1979. pap. 4.95 (ISBN 0-87123-157-3, 210157). Bethany Hse.

Fuller, Elizabeth. The Touch of Grace. (Illus.). 256p. 1986. 14.95 (ISBN 0-396-08667-5). Dodd.

Green, John L. Pioneer Evangelists of the Church of God in the Pacific Northwest. 164p. pap. 2.00 (ISBN 0-686-29135-2). Faith Pub Hse.

Johnson, Thomas C. The Life of Robert Lewis Dabney. 1977. 16.95 (ISBN 0-85151-253-4). Banner of Truth.

Johnston, Robert K. Evangelicals at an Impasse: Biblical Authority in Practice. pap. 3.99 (ISBN 0-8042-2038-7). John Knox.

Jordan, Mickey & Harrell, Irene B. Let Yesterday Go. LC 84-51995. 285p. 1984. pap. 6.00 (ISBN 0-915541-01-7). Star Bks Inc.

Joyce, Jon L. Profiles of Our Heritage. (Orig.). 1983. pap. 3.00 (ISBN 0-937172-51-0). JLJ Pubs.

McDonald, William & Searless, John E. The Life of the Rev. John S. Inskip. Dayton, Donald W., ed. (The Higher Christian Life Ser.). 374p. 1985. 45.00 (ISBN 0-8240-6424-0). Garland Pub.

Madden, Edward H. & Hamilton, James E. Freedom & Grace: The Life of Asa Mahan. LC 82-5724. (Studies in Evangelicalism: No. 3). 287p. 1982. 19.00 (ISBN 0-8108-1555-9). Scarecrow.

Nelson, E. Clifford, ed. A Pioneer Churchman: J. W. C. Dietrichson in Wisconsin, 1844-1850. Rosholt, Malcolm & Kaasa, Harris, trs. from Norwegian. 1973. lib. bdg. 11.50 (ISBN 0-8057-5443-1, Twayne). G K Hall.

Norton, John. The Orthodox Evangelist. LC 78-280. (American Puritan Writings Ser.: No. 11). Repr. of 1654 ed. 67.50 (ISBN 0-404-60811-6). AMS Pr.

Pratt, Josiah, ed. Thought of the Evangelical Leaders: John Newton, Thomas Scott, Charles Simeon, Etc. 1978. 18.95 (ISBN 0-85151-270-4). Banner of Truth.

Roberts, Kenneth J. The Evangelizers. Waters, Anna M., ed. (Illus.). 100p. (Orig.). 1984. pap. text ed. 3.50 (ISBN 0-9610984-2-2). PAX Tapes.

Ryle, J. C. The Upper Room. 1983. pap. 9.95 (ISBN 0-85151-017-5). Banner of Truth.

Shaw, Joseph M. Pulpit under the Sky: A Life of Hans Nielson Hauge. LC 78-12391. 1979. Repr. of 1955 ed. lib. bdg. 24.75x (ISBN 0-313-21123-X, SHPU). Greenwood.

Snider, Joel P. The Cotton Patch Gospel: The Proclamation of Clarence Jordan. LC 85-6224. 112p. (Orig.). 1985. lib. bdg. 22.00 (ISBN 0-8191-4680-3); pap. text ed. 9.50 (ISBN 0-8191-4681-1). U Pr of Amer.

Stanley, David. Life with Elvis. (Illus.). 1986. 12.95 (ISBN 0-8007-1490-3). Revell.

Stebbins, George C. Reminiscences & Gospel Hymn Stories. LC 74-144689. Repr. of 1924 ed. 24.50 (ISBN 0-404-07203-8). AMS Pr.

Streett, R. Alan. The Effective Invitation. 1984. pap. 6.95 (ISBN 0-8007-5170-1, Power Bks). Revell.

Toon, Peter. John Charles Ryle, Evangelical Bishop. 5.95 (ISBN 0-685-88379-5). Reiner.

Tyler, Bennet & Bonar, Andrew. The Life & Labours of Asahel Nettleton. 1975. 10.95 (ISBN 0-85151-208-9). Banner of Truth.

Vassady, Bela. Limping along: Confessions of a Pilgrim Theologian. 248p. (Orig.). 1985. pap. 13.95 (ISBN 0-8028-0095-5). Eerdmans.

Wagler, Elizabeth. Evangelist in Chains. 8.95 (ISBN 0-318-00390-2). Rod & Staff.

Walker, Luisa J. Dynamic Evangelism. 1986. write for info. (ISBN 0-8297-0737-9). Life Pubs Intl.

Warner, Wayne E. & Warner, Wayne E. The Woman Evangelist: The Life & Times of Charismatic Evangelist Maria B. Woodworth-Etter. LC 86-11854. (Studies in Evangelicalism: No. 8). (Illus.). 354p. 1986. 32.50 (ISBN 0-8108-1912-0). Scarecrow.

Webber, Robert E. Evangelicals on the Canterbury Trail: Why Evangelicals Are Attracted to the Liturgical Church. 160p. 1985. 13.95 (ISBN 0-8499-0402-1, 04021). Word Bks.

Winter, Rebecca J. The Night Cometh: Two Wealthy Evangelicals Face the Nation. LC 77-87594. 1977. pap. 2.95 (ISBN 0-87808-429-0). William Carey Lib.

Zodhiates, Spiros. Who Is Worth Following. 1982. pap. 4.95 (ISBN 0-89957-514-5). AMG Pubs.

EVANGELISTS (BIBLE)

Craig, James D. Fishers of Men: Group Leader Guide. 3rd rev. ed. 116p. 1981. 4.00 (ISBN 0-88151-016-5). Lay Leadership.

Graham, Billy. A Biblical Standard for Evangelists. LC 84-51639. 144p. 1984. pap. 5.95 (ISBN 0-89066-057-3). World Wide Pubs.

Parks, Keith H. You Are Welcome. 2nd rev. ed. 32p. 1981. pap. 2.49 (ISBN 0-88151-013-0). Lay Leadership.

EVANS, WILLIAM BACON

Brinton, Anna C. The Wit & Wisdom of William Bacon Evans. 1966. pap. 2.50x (ISBN 0-87574-146-0, 146). Pendle Hill.

EVE (BIBLICAL CHARACTER)

Carlisle, Thomas J. Eve & after: Old Testament Woman in Portrait. 160p. (Orig.). 1984. pap. 5.95 (ISBN 0-8028-1970-2). Eerdmans.

Pagels, Elaine. Adam, Eve & the Serpent. 1987. 17.95 (ISBN 0-394-52140-4). Random.

Phillips, J. A. Eve: The History of an Idea. LC 83-48424. (Illus.). 192p. 1984. 12.45 (ISBN 0-06-066552-1, HarpR). Har-Row.

Phillips, John A. Eve: The History of an Idea. LC 83-48424. (Illus.). 224p. 1985. pap. 7.95 (ISBN 0-06-250670-6, HarpR). Har-Row.

Reed, Gwendolyn. Adam & Eve. LC 68-27712. (Illus.). 1968. PLB 11.88 (ISBN 0-688-51256-9). Lothrop.

Vinck, Catherine D. A Book of Eve. 1979. text ed. 5.00 (ISBN 0-911726-40-3); stereo record & text incl. Alleluia Pr.

EVERLASTING PUNISHMENT

see Future Punishment; Hell

EVIDENCES OF CHRISTIANITY

see Apologetics

EVIL

see Good and Evil

EVIL, NON-RESISTANCE TO

see also Pacifism

Ballou, Adin. Christian Non-Resistance. LC 70-121104. (Civil Liberties in American History Ser). 1970. Repr. of 1910 ed. lib. bdg. 35.00 (ISBN 0-306-71980-0). Da Capo.

--Christian Non-Resistance in All Its Important Bearings, Illustrated & Defended. LC 76-137527. (Peace Movement in America Ser). 240p. 1972. Repr. of 1846 ed. lib. bdg. 18.95x (ISBN 0-89198-054-7). Ozer.

Darrow, Clarence S. Resist Not Evil. LC 77-137538. (Peace Movement in America Ser). 179p. 1972. Repr. of 1903 ed. lib. bdg. 14.95x (ISBN 0-89198-065-2). Ozer.

Darrow, Clarence S. & Lewis, Arthur M. Marx Versus Tolstoy: A Debate. LC 73-137537. (Peace Movement in America Ser). 124p. 1972. Repr. of 1911 ed. lib. bdg. 12.95x (ISBN 0-89198-066-0). Ozer.

Holmes, John H. New Wars for Old. LC 71-147623. (Library of War & Peace; Non-Resis. & Non-Vio.). 1972. lib. bdg. 46.00 (ISBN 0-8240-0398-5). Garland Pub.

Tolstoy, Leo. The Kingdom of God Is Within You. Garnett, Constance, tr. from Rus. LC 84-10471. xxii, 368p. 1984. 26.95x (ISBN 0-8032-4411-8); pap. 8.50 (ISBN 0-8032-9404-2, BB 897, Bison). U of Nebr Pr.

Villard, Fanny G., ed. William Lloyd Garrison on Nonresistance Together with a Personal Sketch by His Daughter and a Tribute by Leo Tolstoi. LC 74-137556. (Peace Movement in America Ser). xii, 79p. 1972. Repr. of 1924 ed. lib. bdg. 11.95x (ISBN 0-89198-087-3). Ozer.

EVIL EYE

see also Superstition; Witchcraft

Elworthy, Frederick T. The Evil Eye: An Account of This Ancient & Widespread Superstition. (Illus.). 1986. pap. 7.95 (ISBN 0-517-55971-4, Julian). Crown.

Maloney, Clarence, ed. The Evil Eye. LC 76-16861. (Illus.). 334p. 1976. 30.00 (ISBN 0-231-04006-7); pap. 14.50. Columbia U Pr.

Rosenbaum, Brenda. How to Avoid the Evil Eye: Five Thousand Years of Jewish Superstition. (Illus.). 96p. 1985. pap. 5.95 (ISBN 0-312-39584-1). St Martin.

EVIL IN LITERATURE

Bandy, Melanie. Mind Forg'd Manacles: Evil in the Poetry of Blake & Shelley. LC 80-18779. (Illus.). 210p. 1981. text ed. 19.95 (ISBN 0-8173-0046-5). U of Ala Pr.

Houston, John P. Demonic Imagination: Style & Theme in French Romantic Poetry. LC 69-15051. xi, 177p. 20.00x (ISBN 0-8071-0306-3). La State U Pr.

Tatlow, Anthony. The Mask of Evil. (European University Studies: Series 18, Comparative Literature, Vol. 12). 1977. 52.20 (ISBN 3-261-02905-6). P Lang Pubs.

Whitney, Barry L. Evil & the Process God: The Problem of Evil in Charles Hartshorne's Thought. LC 84-25505. (Toronto Studies in Theology: Vol. 19). 247p. 1985. 49.95x (ISBN 0-88946-760-9). E Mellen.

EVIL SPIRITS

see Demonology

EVOLUTION

see also Creation; Holism; Life–Origin; Man–Origin

Barborka, Geoffrey. The Peopling of the Earth. LC 75-4243. (Illus.). 240p. 1975. 10.00 (ISBN 0-8356-0221-4). Theos Pub Hse.

Bart-Williams, P. J. Evolution & the Word of God. LC 83-91501. 87p. 1985. 8.95 (ISBN 0-533-06080-X). Vantage.

Bergson, Henri. Creative Evolution. Mitxhell, Arthur, tr. LC 83-19859. 460p. 1984. pap. text ed. 13.50 (ISBN 0-8191-3553-4). U Pr of Amer.

Berry, R. J. Neo-Darwinism. (Studies in Biology: No. 144). 72p. 1982. pap. text ed. 9.95 (ISBN 0-7131-2849-6). E Arnold.

Birx, H. James. Pierre Teilhard De Chardin's Philosophy of Evolution. 192p. 1972. 21.50x (ISBN 0-398-02466-9). C C Thomas.

Bliss, Richard. Origins: Two Models. Gish, Duane T. & Moore, John N., eds. LC 76-20178. (Illus.). 1976. 5.95 (ISBN 0-89051-027-X); tchr's. guide avail. Master Bks.

Bowden, Malcolm. Rise of the Evolution Fraud. 1982. pap. 8.95 (ISBN 0-89051-085-7). Master Bks.

Brown, Frank B. The Evolution of Darwin's Religious Views. (Special Studies: No. 10). 72p. pap. text ed. 7.95 (ISBN 0-86554-239-2, MUP/M12). NABPR.

Cameron, Nigel. Evolution & the Authority of the Bible. 128p. 1983. pap. 6.95 (ISBN 0-85364-326-1, Pub. by Paternoster UK). Attic Pr.

Cohen, I. L. Darwin Was Wrong: A Study in Probabilities. Murphy, G., ed. LC 84-22613. (Illus.). 225p. 1985. 16.95 (ISBN 0-910891-02-8). New Research.

Commission For Christian Literature, ed. Is Evolutionism the Answer. (Truth Unchanging Series). (Illus.). 1968. pap. 2.50 (ISBN 0-8100-0023-7, 12-0331). Northwest Pub.

The Creation-Evolution Controversy. 1976. 15.95 (ISBN 0-918112-01-X); pap. 8.95 kivar (ISBN 0-918112-02-8). Inquiry Pr.

Culliton, Joseph T. A Processive World View for Pragmatic Christians. LC 75-3781. 302p. 1975. 13.95 (ISBN 0-8022-2170-X). Philos Lib.

Curtiss, Harriette & Homer, F. The Truth about Evolution & the Bible. 1928. 5.50 (ISBN 0-87516-308-4). De Vorss.

Dankenbring, William F. The First Genesis: A New Case for Creation. LC 75-10841. (Illus.). 408p. 1975. 8.95 (ISBN 0-685-54180-0). Triumph Pub.

--The First Genesis: The Saga of Creation Versus Evolution. new ed. LC 79-65131. (Illus.). 1979. 12.00 (ISBN 0-917182-14-6). Triumph Pub.

Davidheiser, Bolton. Evolution & Christian Faith. 1969. pap. 10.95 (ISBN 0-87552-251-3). Presby & Reformed.

Davis, Willard O. Evolution & Revelation. 6.95 (ISBN 0-88027-097-7). Firm Foun Pub.

Dodson, E. O. The Phenomenon of Man Revisited: A Biological Viewpoint on Teilhard de Chardin. LC 83-20959. (Illus.). 288p. 1984. 26.50x (ISBN 0-231-05850-0). Columbia U Pr.

Durant, John, ed. Darwinism & Divinity: Essays on Evolution & Religious Belief. 224p. 1986. pap. text ed. 14.95 (ISBN 0-631-15101-X). Basil Blackwell.

Edge, Henry T. Evolution: Who & What Is Man. Small, W. Emmett & Todd, Helen, eds. (Theosophical Manual: No. 6). 78p. 1975. pap. 2.00 (ISBN 0-913004-22-7, 913004-22). Point Loma Pub.

Eisen, Sydney & Lightman, Bernard V. Victorian Science & Religion: A Bibliography of Works on Ideas & Institutions with Emphasis on Evolution, Belief & Unbelief, Published from 1900 to 1975. LC 82-24497. xix, 696p. 1984. lib. bdg. 49.50 (ISBN 0-208-02010-1, Archon Bks). Shoe String.

Erickson, Lonni R. Creation vs. Evolution: A Comparison. 30p. write for info. Scandia Pubs.

Evolution: Material or Spiritual? 25p. 1986. 3.50 (ISBN 0-942958-08-X). Kappeler Inst Pub.

Field, A. N. The Evolution Hoax Exposed. 1971. pap. 3.00 (ISBN 0-89555-049-0). TAN Bks Pubs.

Follette, Marcel la. Creationism, Science, & the Law: Arkansas Case Documents & Commentaries. LC 82-21646. 232p. (Orig.). 1983. pap. 11.95x (ISBN 0-262-62041-3). MIT Pr.

Forlines, Leroy. Evolution. 1973. pap. 0.95 (ISBN 0-89265-105-9). Randall Hse.

Frye, Roland M. Is God a Creationist? The Religious Case Against Creation Science. 256p. 1983. pap. text ed. write for info. (ISBN 0-02-339560-5, Pub. by Scribner). Macmillan.

Geisler, Norman L. Creator in the Courtroom "Scopes II". 1987. pap. 5.95 (ISBN 0-8010-3814-6). Baker Bk.
Geisler, Norman L. & Anderson, J. Kerby. Origin Science. 1987. pap. 8.95 (ISBN 0-8010-3808-1). Baker Bk.
Glick, Thomas, compiled by. Darwinism in Texas. LC 72-185614. (Illus.). 38p. 1972. 7.00 (ISBN 0-87959-032-7). U of Tex H Ransom Ctr.
Haeckel, Ernst. Riddle of the Universe at the Close of the 19th Century. LC 6403. 1900. 18.00x (ISBN 0-403-00117-X). Scholarly.
Ham, Ken. The Lie: Evolution. 188p. 1987. 10.95 (ISBN 0-89051-117-9). Master Bks.
Heinze, Thomas F. Creation vs. Evolution Handbook. (Direction Books). 1973. pap. 3.50 (ISBN 0-8010-4002-7). Baker Bk.
Horigan, James E. Chance or Design? LC 79-83605. 242p. 1979. 13.95 (ISBN 0-8022-2238-2). Philos Lib.
Huse, Scott M. Collapse of Evolution. 192p. 1986. pap. 7.95 (ISBN 0-8010-4310-7). Baker Bk.
Huxley, Thomas H. Evolution & Ethics, & Other Essays. LC 70-8391. 334p. 1897. Repr. 49.00x (ISBN 0-403-00041-6). Scholarly.
Hyers, Conrad. The Meaning of Creations. LC 84-47795. 212p. pap. 11.95 (ISBN 0-8042-0125-0). John Knox.
Jackson, Wayne. The Mythology of Modern Geology: A Refutation of Evolution's Most Influential Argument. 45p. (Orig.). 1980. pap. 1.95 (ISBN 0-932859-13-5). Apologetic Pr.
Jasson, Wilbur A. Beyond Evolution. LC 84-52700. (Illus.). 141p. 1986. 14.95 (ISBN 0-9614464-0-4); pap. 8.95 (ISBN 0-9614464-1-2). Sarasota Sci.
Kitcher, Philip. Abusing Science: The Case Against Creationism. (Illus.). 224p. 1982. 22.50x (ISBN 0-262-11085-7); pap. 7.95 (ISBN 0-262-61037-X). MIT Pr.
Klotz, John. Studies in Creation: A General Introduction to the Creation-Evolution Debate. 224p. (Orig.). 1985. pap. 9.95 (ISBN 0-570-03969-X, 12-3004). Concordia.
Klotz, John W. Genes, Genesis & Evolution. rev. ed. 1970. pap. 17.95 (ISBN 0-570-03212-1, 12-2637). Concordia.
Larson, Edward J. Trial & Error: The American Controversy over Creation & Evolution. LC 85-7144. 232p. 1985. 17.95 (ISBN 0-19-503666-2). Oxford U Pr.
Lau, Dicksen T. The New Religion & Relativity. LC 83-62038. 138p. (Orig.). 1983. pap. 5.95 (ISBN 0-9612000-0-6). Magnolia Bks.
Le Conte, Joseph. Evolution: Its Nature Its Evidences, - Its Relation to Religious Thought. 2nd ed. 1897. 29.00 (ISBN 0-527-55700-5). Kraus Repr.
Lindsay, Gordon. Evolution-The Incredible Hoax. 1.50 (ISBN 0-89985-115-0). Christ Nations.
Livingstone, David N. Darwin's Forgotten Defenders: The Encounter Between Evangelical Theology & Evolutionary Thought. 144p. (Orig.). 1987. pap. 9.95 (ISBN 0-8028-0260-5). Eerdmans.
Maatman, Russell. The Bible, Natural Science, & Evolution. (Orig.). 1980. pap. 4.95 (ISBN 0-932914-03-9). Dordt Coll Pr.
McMullin, Ernan, ed. Evolution & Creation. LC 84-40818. (University of Notre Dame Studies in the Philosophy of Religion: Vol. 4). 307p. 1987. pap. 12.95 (ISBN 0-268-00918-X). U of Notre Dame Pr.
McWilliams, Donald A. Myth of Evolution. LC 73-88018. 1973. 3.95x (ISBN 0-916434-08-7). Plycon Pr.
Mauro, Philip. Evolution. pap. 2.25 (ISBN 0-685-88374-4). Reiner.
--The World & Its God. 95p. 1981. pap. 2.95 (ISBN 0-89084-151-9). Bob Jones Univ Pr.
Maxwell, Mary. Human Evolution: A Philosophical Anthropology. 288p. 1984. 38.00x (ISBN 0-231-05946-9, King's Crown Paperbacks); pap. 18.00x (ISBN 0-231-05947-7). Columbia U Pr.
Midgley, Mary. Evolution As a Religion: Strange Hopes & Stranger Fears. 192p. 1986. text ed. 33.00 (ISBN 0-416-39650-X, 9512); pap. text ed. 12.95 (ISBN 0-416-39660-7, 9513). Methuen Inc.
Millikan, Robert A. Evolution in Science & Religion. 1979. Repr. of 1929 ed. lib. bdg. 17.50 (ISBN 0-8495-3846-7). Arden Lib.
--Evolution in Science & Religion. 1935. 15.50x (ISBN 0-686-51381-9). Elliots Bks.
Montenat, C. & Plateaux, L. How to Read Creation & Evolution. 144p. 1985. pap. 10.95 (ISBN 0-8245-0721-5). Crossroad NY.
Moore, J. R. The Post Darwinian Controversies. LC 77-94372. 1979. 57.50 (ISBN 0-521-21989-2); pap. 24.95 (ISBN 0-521-28517-8). Cambridge U Pr.
Moore, John N. Should Evolution Be Taught? 1977. pap. 1.00 (ISBN 0-89051-043-1). Master Bks.
Morris, H. Creation & Its Critics. LC 82-84483. 32p. 1982. 1.00 (ISBN 0-89051-091-1). Master Bks.
Morris, Henry M. Evolution & the Modern Christian. pap. 3.95 (ISBN 0-8010-5881-3). Baker Bk.
--The Troubled Waters of Evolution. 2nd ed. LC 82-15254. (Illus.). 225p. 1975. pap. 6.95 (ISBN 0-89051-087-3). Master Bks.
--Twilight of Evolution. LC 76-2265. 1963. pap. 4.95 (ISBN 0-8010-5862-7). Baker Bk.
National Research Council. Science & Creationism: A View from the National Academy of Sciences. 28p. 1984. pap. 4.00 (ISBN 0-309-03440-X). Natl Acad Pr.
Nelkin, Dorothy. The Creation Controversy: Science or Scripture in the Schools? LC 83-45954. 242p. 1984. pap. 9.95x (ISBN 0-8070-3155-0, BP 675). Beacon Pr.
Newell, Norman D. Creation & Evolution: Myth or Reality? LC 81-21767. (Convergence Ser.). 232p. 1982. 24.00x (ISBN 0-231-05348-7). Columbia U Pr.
Pavlu, Ricki. Evolution: When Fact Became Fiction. LC 86-13144. (Illus.). 184p. (Orig.). 1986. pap. 6.95 (ISBN 0-932581-51-X). Word Aflame.
Plummer, L. Gordon. From Atom to Kosmos: A Theosophical Study in Evolution. (Illus.). 134p. Date not set. price not set (ISBN 0-913004-49-9). Point Loma Pub.
Poppelbaum, Hermann. New Light on Heredity & Evolution. Macbeth, Norman, tr. 1977. pap. 6.95 (ISBN 0-916786-15-3). St George Bk Serv.
Rev. William Kramer. Evolution & Creation: A Catholic Understanding. LC 86-60907. 168p. (Orig.). 1986. pap. 6.95 (ISBN 0-87973-511-2, 511). Our Sunday Visitor.
Roszak, Theodore. Unfinished Animal. 1977. pap. 5.95 (ISBN 0-06-090537-9, CN 537, PL). Harper Row.
Steiner, Rudolf. Aspects of Human Evolution. Stebbing, Rita, tr. 1986. 20.00 (ISBN 0-88010-251-9); pap. 9.95 (ISBN 0-88010-252-7). Anthroposophic.
--The Evolution of the Earth & the Influence of the Stars. Hahn, Gladys, tr. from Ger. Tr. of Die Schoepfung der Welt und des Menschen Erdenleben und Sternenwirken. (Illus.). 200p. 1987. 20.00 (ISBN 0-88010-181-4); pap. 10.95 (ISBN 0-88010-180-6). Anthroposophic.
--Man's Being, His Destiny & World Evolution. 3rd ed. McArthur, Erna & Riggins, William, trs. from Ger. 123p. (Orig.). 1984. pap. 7.95 (ISBN 0-88010-090-7). Anthroposophic.
Strickling, James E., Jr. Origins: Today's Science, Tomorrow's Myth. 1986. 11.95 (ISBN 0-317-40170-X). Vantage.
Teilhard De Chardin, Pierre. Avenir De L'homme. 1959. 21.50 (ISBN 0-685-11021-4). French & Eur.
--Phenomene Humain. (Coll. Points). 1955. pap. 6.25 (ISBN 0-685-11491-0). French & Eur.
Thomas, J. D. Evolution & Antiquity. 2nd ed. (Way of Life Ser: No. 120). Orig. Title: Doctrine of Evolution & the Antiquity of Man. (Orig.). 1959. pap. 3.95 (ISBN 0-89112-120-X, Bibl Res Pr). Abilene Christ U.
Thompson, Bert. The History of Evolutionary Thought. 192p. (Orig.). 1981. pap. 3.50 (ISBN 0-932859-10-0). Apologetic Pr.
--Theistic Evolution. 235p. (Orig.). 1977. pap. 5.50 (ISBN 0-932859-08-9). Apologetic Pr.
Tobias, Michael. After Eden: History, Ecology, & Conscience. LC 83-73257. 376p. (Orig.). 1985. pap. 14.95 (ISBN 0-932238-28-9, Pub. by Avant Bks). Slawson Comm.
Van Gogh, Anna. Promise Me Life: Evolution & Creation As a Dynamic Unity. (Illus.). 424p. (Orig.). Date not set. PLB price not set (ISBN 0-913829-34-X); pap. price not set (ISBN 0-913829-35-8). Lucy Mary Bks.
Walker, K. R., ed. The Evolution-Creation Controversy Perspectives on Religion, Philosophy, Science & Education: A Handbook. (Paleontological Society Special Publications Ser.). (Illus.). 155p. pap. 6.50 (ISBN 0-931377-00-5). U of Tenn Geo.
Wilson, David B., ed. Did the Devil Make Darwin Do It? Modern Perspectives on the Creation-Evolution Controversy. (Illus.). 242p. 1983. pap. 13.95 (ISBN 0-8138-0434-5). Iowa St U Pr.
Zetterberg, J. Peter. Evolution Versus Creationism: The Public Education Controversy. LC 82-18795. 528p. 1983. lib. bdg. 41.00 (ISBN 0-89774-061-0). Oryx Pr.
Zimmerman, Dean R. Evolution: A Golden Calf. 232p. (Orig.). 1976. pap. 3.95 (ISBN 0-89036-059-6). Hawkes Pub Inc.

EVOLUTION–ADDRESSES, ESSAYS, LECTURES

Gordon, Cyrus H. Before the Bible. LC 72-10828. (Essay Index Reprint Ser.). 1973. Repr. of 1962 ed. 24.00 (ISBN 0-8369-7219-8). Ayer Co Pubs.
Hardin, Garrett, ed. Population, Evolution, & Birth Control: A Collage of Controversial Ideas. 2nd ed. LC 69-16921. (Biology Ser.). (Illus.). 386p. 1969. pap. text ed. 13.95x (ISBN 0-7167-0670-9). W H Freeman.
Metz, Johannes B., ed. Evolving World & Theology. LC 67-25695. (Concilium Ser.: Vol. 26). 91p. 1967. 7.95 (ISBN 0-8091-0042-8). Paulist Pr.
Montagu, Ashley, ed. Science & Creationism. LC 82-14173. 434p. 1984. 24.95 (ISBN 0-19-503252-7); pap. 11.95x (ISBN 0-19-503253-5). Oxford U Pr.

EVOLUTION–HISTORY

Claiborne, Robert. God or Beast: Evolution & Human Nature. (Illus.). 1974. 7.95 (ISBN 0-393-06399-2). Norton.
Nelkin, Dorothy. The Creation Controversy: Science or Scripture in the Schools. 256p. 1982. 16.95 (ISBN 0-393-01635-8). Norton.
Pitman, Michael. Adam & Evolution. 269p. 1986. pap. 12.95 (ISBN 0-8010-7092-9). Baker Bk.

EX-NUNS

see also Nuns

Hollingsworth, Gerelyn. Ex-Nuns: Women Who Have Left the Convent. LC 84-43207. 136p. 1985. lib. bdg. 16.95x (ISBN 0-89950-156-7). McFarland & Co.
Upton, Elizabeth. Secrets of a Nun: My Own Story. LC 84-14828. 264p. 1985. 16.95 (ISBN 0-688-04187-6). Morrow.
Walter, Alice E. Katharine Luther, Liberated Nun. LC 81-65305. (Illus., Orig.). 1981. pap. text ed. 3.95 (ISBN 0-915644-22-3). Clayton Pub Hse.

EXCAVATIONS (ARCHAEOLOGY)

Dever, William G. & Darrel, Lance H. A Manual of Field Excavation. 1979. 15.00x (ISBN 0-87820-303-6). Ktav.
Lapp, Nancy L., ed. The Tale of the Tell: Archaeological Studies by Paul W. Lapp. LC 75-5861. (Pittsburgh Theological Monographs: No. 5). 1975. pap. text ed. 9.25 (ISBN 0-915138-05-0). Pickwick.
Macalister, Robert A. A Century of Excavation in Palestine. Davis, Moshe, ed. LC 77-70720. (America & the Holy Land Ser.). (Illus.). 1977. Repr. of 1925 ed. lib. bdg. 32.00x (ISBN 0-405-10265-8). Ayer Co Pubs.
Vos, Howard. Archaeology in Bible Lands. LC 77-2981. (Illus.). 1977. 11.95 (ISBN 0-8024-0289-5). Moody.

EXECRATION

see Blessing and Cursing

EXEMPLA

see also Fables; Homiletical Illustrations; Legends; Parables

Gaster, Moses. Exempla of the Rabbis. rev. ed. 1968. 25.00x (ISBN 0-87068-055-2). Ktav.
Jacobus De Vitriaco. Exempla, or Illustrative Stories from the Sermones Vulgares of Jacques De Vitry. Crane, Thomas F., ed. 1971. Repr. of 1890 ed. lib. bdg. 23.50 (ISBN 0-8337-0715-9). B Franklin.

EXERCISES, SPIRITUAL

see Spiritual Exercises

EXISTENTIALISM

see also Demythologization; Situation Ethics

Buri, Fritz. Theology of Existence. Oliver, Harold H, tr. 128p. 1965. 3.95 (ISBN 0-87921-001-X). Attic Pr.
Comerchero, Victor, ed. Values in Conflict: Christianity, Marxism, Psychoanalysis & Existentialism. LC 74-111099. 986p. (Orig., Free booklet, "Suggestions for Instructors," available). 1970. pap. text ed. 19.95x (ISBN 0-89197-463-6). Irvington.
Diem, Hermann. Kierkegaard's Dialectic of Existence. Knight, Harold, tr. from German. LC 77-18886. 1978. Repr. of 1959 ed. lib. bdg. 22.50x (ISBN 0-313-20220-6, DIKD). Greenwood.
Earle, William, et al, eds. Christianity & Existentialism. (Studies in Phenomenology & Existential Philosophy). 1963. pap. 7.95 (ISBN 0-8101-0084-3). Northwestern U Pr.
Evans, C. Stephen. Existentialism: The Philosophy of Despair & the Quest for Hope. LC 83-11198. (Orig.). 1984. pap. 6.95 (ISBN 0-310-43741-5, 11198P). Zondervan.
Fontes, M. E. Existentialism & Its Implications for Counseling. pap. 0.75 (ISBN 0-8199-0382-5, L38138). Franciscan Herald.
Grene, Marjorie. Introduction to Existentialism. LC 84-2725. (Midway Ser.). x, 150p. 1984. pap. text ed. 7.00x (ISBN 0-226-30823-5). U of Chicago Pr.
Herberg, Will, ed. Four Existentialist Theologians. LC 75-17472. 346p. 1975. Repr. of 1958 ed. lib. bdg. 29.75x (ISBN 0-8371-8303-0, HEFE). Greenwood.
Kaufmann, Walter. Existentialism, Religion & Death. 1976. pap. 4.95 (ISBN 0-452-00648-1, F648, Mer). NAL.
Kingston, Frederick T. French Existentialism, a Christian Critique. LC 61-925. pap. 59.30 (ISBN 0-317-08761-4, 2014272). Bks Demand UMI.
Lescoe, Francis J. Existentialism: With or Without God. LC 74-1427. 1976. pap. 10.95 (ISBN 0-8189-0340-6). Alba.
Macquarrie, John. An Existentialist Theology: A Comparison of Heidegger & Bultmann. LC 79-4604. 1979. Repr. of 1955 ed. lib. bdg. 22.50x (ISBN 0-313-20795-X, MAAE). Greenwood.
Magnus, Bernd. Nietzsche's Existential Imperative. LC 77-9864. (Studies in Phenomenology & Existential Philosophy Ser.). 256p. 1978. 20.00x (ISBN 0-253-34062-4). Ind U Pr.
Mihalich, Joseph C. Existentialism & Thomism. (Orig.). pap. 0.95 (ISBN 0-685-19401-9, 77, WL). Citadel Pr.
--Existentialism & Thomism. (Quality Paperback: No. 170). 91p. 1969. pap. 3.95 (ISBN 0-8226-0170-2). Littlefield.
Park, James. The Existential Christian, No. 1. (Existential Freedom Ser. No. 1). 1970. pap. 1.00x (ISBN 0-89231-001-4). Existential Bks.
--The Existential Christian, No. 2. (Existential Freedom Ser.: No. 2). 1971. pap. 5.00x (ISBN 0-89231-002-2). Existential Bks.
Rupp, George. Beyond Existentialism & Zen: Religion in a Pluralistic World. 1979. 14.95x (ISBN 0-19-502462-1). Oxford U Pr.
Sanborn, Patricia F. Existentialism. 192p. 1984. text ed. 22.00x (ISBN 0-8290-1015-7); pap. text ed. 9.95x (ISBN 0-8290-1016-5). Irvington.
Slatte, Howard A. The Paradox of Existentialist Theology: The Dialectics of a Faith-Subsumed Reason-in-Existence. LC 81-43508. 272p. 1982. lib. bdg. 29.00 (ISBN 0-8191-2187-8); pap. text ed. 13.25 (ISBN 0-8191-2188-6). U Pr of Amer.
Stack, George J. Kierkegaard's Existential Ethics. LC 75-16344. (Studies in Humanities: No. 16). 240p. 1977. 15.00 (ISBN 0-8173-6624-5); pap. 5.50 (ISBN 0-8173-6626-1). U of Ala Pr.
Tillich, Paul. Courage to Be. (Terry Lectures Ser.). 1952. pap. 6.95 (ISBN 0-300-00241-6, Y11). Yale U Pr.
Van Kaam, Adrian. The Art of Existential Counseling. 6.95 (ISBN 0-87193-044-7). Dimension Bks.

EXISTENTIALISM IN LITERATURE

Ruotolo, Lucio P. Six Existential Heroes: The Politics of Faith. LC 72-86386. 192p. 1973. 12.50x (ISBN 0-674-81025-2). Harvard U Pr.

EXODUS, THE

Fields, Wilbur. Exploring Exodus. LC 78-301089. (The Bible Study Textbook Ser.). (Illus.). 1977. 18.95 (ISBN 0-89900-006-1). College Pr Pub.
Goldberg, Michael. Jews & Christians, Getting Our Stories Straight: The Exodus & the Passion...Resurrection. 240p. (Orig.). 1985. pap. 12.95 (ISBN 0-687-20330-9). Abingdon.
Greenberg, Moshe. Understanding Exodus. 214p. 1969. pap. 9.95x (ISBN 0-87441-265-X). Behrman.
Jacobson, Howard. The Exagoge of Ezekiel. LC 82-4410. 240p. 1983. 49.50 (ISBN 0-521-24580-X). Cambridge U Pr.
Kappeler, Max. Exodus. LC 82-80905. (Bible in the Light of Christian Science Ser.: Vol. II). 90p. (Orig.). 1982. pap. 6.00 (ISBN 0-942958-01-2). Kappeler Inst Pub.
Palmer, Edward H. The Desert of the Exodus: Journeys on Foot in the Wilderness of the Forty Years Wanderings, 2 vols. in one. Davis, Moshe, ed. (America & the Holy Land Ser.). (Illus.). lib. bdg. 51.00x (ISBN 0-405-10276-3). Ayer Co Pubs.
Sarna, Nahum M. Exploring Exodus: The Heritage of Biblical Israel. LC 85-18445. 288p. 1987. pap. 8.95 (ISBN 0-8052-0830-5). Schocken.
Synge, Ursula. The People & the Promise. LC 74-10661. 192p. 1974. 12.95 (ISBN 0-87599-208-0). S G Phillips.

EXORCISM

see also Blessing and Cursing; Demonology; Witchcraft

Davis, Winston. Dojo: Magic & Exorcism in Modern Japan. LC 79-64219. (Illus.). xx, 324p. 1980. 27.50x (ISBN 0-8047-1053-8); pap. 9.95 (ISBN 0-8047-1131-3, SP-7). Stanford U Pr.
Deacon, John & Walker, John. Dialogicall Discourses of Spirits & Devils, Declaring Their Proper Essence. LC 76-57377. (English Experience Ser.: No. 795). 1977. Repr. of 1601 ed. lib. bdg. 37.00 (ISBN 90-221-0795-7). Walter J Johnson.
Dolger, Franz J. Der Exorzismus Im Altchristlichen Taufritual. 1909. pap. 15.00 (ISBN 0-384-12090-3). Johnson Repr.
Farley, G. M. & Pelton, Robert W. Satan Unmasked: Principles & Practice of Christian Exorcism. LC 78-70632. (Illus.). 1979. 7.50 (ISBN 0-916620-24-7). Portals Pr.
Kapferer, Bruce. A Celebration of Demons: Exorcism & the Aesthetics of Healing in Sri Lanka. LC 81-48677. (Midland Bks: No. 304). (Illus.). 312p. 1983. 32.50x (ISBN 0-253-31326-0); pap. 18.50x (ISBN 0-253-20304-X). Ind U Pr.
Lindsay, Gordon. Ministry of Casting Out Demons, Vol. 7. (Sorcery & Spirit World Ser.). 1.25 (ISBN 0-89985-090-1). Christ Nations.
Manual of Exorcism: Useful for Priests & Ministers of the Church. LC 74-84092. 141p. 1975. pap. 2.95 (ISBN 0-913456-73-X, Pub. by Hispanic Soc). Interbk Inc.

Martin, Malachi. Hostage to the Devil: The Possession of Exorcism of Five Living Americans. LC 86-46207. 488p. 1987. pap. 8.95 (ISBN 0-06-097103-7, PL 7103, PL). Har-Row.

Nauman, Elmo, Jr. Exorcism Through the Ages. (Illus.). 256p. 1974. pap. 3.95 (ISBN 0-8065-0450-1). Citadel Pr.

Pelton, Robert W. The Devil & Karen Kingston: The Incredible Three-Day Exorcism That Brought Miraculous Deliverance to a Totally Demonized Young Girl. LC 76-12148. (Illus.). 1976. 7.50 (ISBN 0-916620-10-7). Portals Pr.

Rickert, Corinne H. Case of John Darrell: Minister & Exorcist. LC 62-62828. (University of Florida Humanities Monographs: No. 9). 1962. pap. 3.50 (ISBN 0-8130-0197-8). U Presses Fla.

Walker, D. P. Unclean Spirits: Possession & Exorcism in France & England in the Late 16th & Early 17th Centuries. LC 80-22649. 1981. 18.95x (ISBN 0-8122-7797-X). U of Pa Pr.

White, Nelson & White, Anne. The Complete Exorcist. LC 83-50160. (Exorcism from Scratch Ser.). (Illus.). 75p. (Orig.). 1983. pap. 15.00 (ISBN 0-939856-33-6). Tech Group.

Worley, Win. Battling the Hosts of Hell: Diary of an Exorcist. rev. ed. 1980. pap. 5.00 (ISBN 0-9601276-1-5). HBC.

--Conquering the Hosts of Hell: An Open Triumph. 1977. pap. 5.00 (ISBN 0-685-88034-6). HBC.

EXPERIENCE (RELIGION)

see also Inner Light

Armstrong, Karen, ed. Tongues of Fire: An Anthology of Religious & Poetic Experience. 444p. 1986. 19.95 (ISBN 0-670-80878-4). Viking.

Batson, C. Daniel, et al. Commitment Without Ideology. LC 72-13000. 1973. 6.95 (ISBN 0-8298-0245-2). Pilgrim NY.

Baum, Gregory. Journeys: The Impact of Personal Experience on Religious Thought. LC 75-31401. pap. 52.90 (ISBN 0-8357-9486-5, 2013525). Bks Demand UMI.

Bouquet, Alan C. Religious Experience: Its Nature, Types, & Validity. LC 75-40997. 140p. 1976. Repr. of 1968 ed. lib. bdg. 22.50x (ISBN 0-8371-8714-1, BORL). Greenwood.

Brakenhelm, C. R. Problems of Religious Experience. 158p. 1985. pap. 23.50x (ISBN 91-554-1657-8, Pub. by Almqvist & Wiksell). Coronet Bks.

Carmody, John T. & Carmody, Denise L. Interpreting the Religious Experience: A Worldview. 240p. Date not set. text ed. price not set (ISBN 0-13-475609-6). P-H.

Clare, Frances. Wow God. 189p. pap. 4.95 (ISBN 0-89221-131-8). New Leaf.

Clark, Walter H., et al. Religious Experience: Its Nature & Function in the Human Psyche. (Illus.). 168p. 1973. 13.00x (ISBN 0-398-02550-9). C C Thomas.

Davis, J., ed. Religious Organization & Religious Experience. (ASA Monograph). 1982. 42.00 (ISBN 0-12-206580-8). Acad Pr.

Dunn, James D. Jesus & the Spirit: A Study of the Religious & Charismatic Experience of Jesus & the First Christians as Reflected in the New Testament. LC 75-9802. 528p. 1979. pap. 15.95 (ISBN 0-664-24290-1). Westminster.

Galloway, Dale. You Can Win with Love. LC 76-15129. 176p. 1980. pap. 2.95 (ISBN 0-89081-233-0). Harvest Hse.

Garvey, John. The Prematurely Saved. 1986. pap. 8.95 (ISBN 0-87243-150-9). Templegate.

Goodenough, Erwin R. The Psychology of Religious Experiences. (Brown Classics in Judaica Ser.). 214p. 1986. pap. text ed. 10.75 (ISBN 0-8191-4489-4). U Pr of Amer.

Hicks, Roy. Another Look at the Rapture. 120p. (Orig.). 1982. pap. 3.95 (ISBN 0-89274-246-1). Harrison Hse.

James, William. The Varieties of Religious Experience. (The Works of William James). (Illus.). 728p. 1985. text ed. 45.00x (ISBN 0-674-93225-0). Harvard U Pr.

Klein, Anne. Knowledge & Liberation. LC 86-1784. 283p. (Orig.). 1986. 27.50 (ISBN 0-937938-24-6); pap. 15.95 (ISBN 0-937938-23-8). Snow Lion.

Levinson, Henry S. & Levering, Ralph. The Religious Investigations of William James. LC 80-26109. (Studies in Religion). xii, 316p. 1981. 27.50x (ISBN 0-8078-1468-7). U of NC Pr.

McCarthy, David S. That Unforgettable Encounter. 108p. (Orig.). 1983. pap. 2.95 (ISBN 0-8341-0834-8). Beacon Hill.

McClelland, W. Robertt. God Our Loving Enemy. LC 81-12680. 160p. 1982. pap. 7.75 (ISBN 0-687-15220-8). Abingdon.

MacMurray, John. The Structure of Religious Experience. LC 73-122406. xi, 77p. 1971. Repr. of 1936 ed. 15.00 (ISBN 0-208-00958-2, Archon). Shoe String.

Martin, Sydney. Living with Fire. 120p. (Orig.). 1983. pap. 3.95 (ISBN 0-8341-0845-3). Beacon Hill.

Matthews, John. The Grail: Quest for the Eternal. Purce, Jill, ed. LC 81-66807. (The Illustrated Library of Sacred Imagination). (Illus.). 110p. 1981. pap. 9.95 (ISBN 0-8245-0035-0). Crossroad NY.

Meissner, W. W. Psychoanalysis & Religious Experience. LC 83-51296. 272p. 1986. pap. 9.95x (ISBN 0-300-03751-1, Y-599). Yale U Pr.

A Message from Heaven & Things to Think about. LC 76-18436. 1976. 2.95 (ISBN 0-686-16284-6). W R Inman.

Nature of Religious Experience: Essays in Honor of Douglas Clyde Macintosh. facsimile ed. LC 78-152202. (Essay Index Reprint Ser). Repr. of 1937 ed. 16.00 (ISBN 0-8369-2286-7). Ayer Co Pubs.

Pettersson, T. Retention of Religious Experiences. (Illus.). 158p. (Orig.). 1975. pap. text ed. 18.50x (Pub. Almqvist & Wiksell). Coronet Bks.

Proudfoot, Wayne. Religious Experience. LC 84-23928. 1985. 30.00x (ISBN 0-520-05143-2). U of Cal Pr.

Soelle, Dorothee. Death by Bread Alone: Texts & Reflections on Religious Experience. Scheidt, David L., tr. from Ger. LC 77-78643. 168p. 1978. 2.00 (ISBN 0-8006-0514-4, 1-514). Fortress.

Tari, Mel & Dudley, Cliff. Like a Mighty Wind. 171p. 1978. pap. 4.95 (ISBN 0-89221-123-7). New Leaf.

Tari, Mel & Tari, Noni. Gentle Breeze of Jesus. 125p. pap. 4.95 (ISBN 0-89221-122-9). New Leaf.

Temple, William. Religious Experience & Other Essays & Addresses. Baker, A. E., ed. 270p. 1959. 10.95 (ISBN 0-227-67579-7). Attic Pr.

Thomas, Jesse J. The Youniverse: Gestalt Therapy, Non-Western Religions & the Present Age. LC 77-89164. (Illus.). 1978. 8.95 (ISBN 0-930626-00-1); pap. 4.95 (ISBN 0-930626-01-X). Psych & Consul Assocs.

Thurman, Howard. The Creative Encounter. LC 72-12773. 155p. 1972. pap. 6.95 (ISBN 0-913408-07-7). Friends United.

Titon, Jeff T. Powerhouse for God: Sacred Speech, Chant & Song in an Appalachian Baptist Church. (American Folklore Recordings Ser.). 26p. 1982. pap. 20.00x incl. records (ISBN 0-8078-4084-X). U of NC Pr.

Trueblood, D. E. Trustworthiness of Religious Experience. LC 78-24656. 1979. pap. 2.45 (ISBN 0-913408-45-X). Friends United.

Tuckwell, James H. Religion & Reality. LC 77-118552. 1971. Repr. of 1915 ed. 25.00x (ISBN 0-8046-1177-7, Pub. by Kennikat). Assoc Faculty Pr.

Turner, John E. Essentials in the Development of Religion. LC 70-102587. 1970. Repr. of 1934 ed. 24.50x (ISBN 0-8046-0747-8, Pub. by Kennikat). Assoc Faculty Pr.

Wach, Joachim. Types of Religious Experience: Christian & Non-Christian. LC 51-9885. 275p. 1972. pap. 2.45x (ISBN 0-226-86710-2, P482, Phoen). U of Chicago Pr.

Watson, John. The Interpretation of Religious Experience, 2 vols. LC 77-27216. (Gifford Lectures: 1910-12). Repr. of 1912 ed. Set. 67.50 (ISBN 0-404-60510-9). AMS Pr.

Weiss, Paul. God We Seek. LC 64-13476. 267p. 1964. 10.95x (ISBN 0-8093-0133-4). S Ill U Pr.

--God We Seek. LC 72-11838. (Arcturus Books Paperbacks). 268p. 1973. pap. 7.95x (ISBN 0-8093-0628-X). S Ill U Pr.

White, Sharon. The Man Who Talked With Angels. 226p. (Orig.). 1982. pap. 5.95 (ISBN 0-89221-088-5, Pub. by SonLife). New Leaf.

EXPERIENCE (RELIGION) AND HALLUCONGENIC DRUGS

see Hallucinogenic Drugs and Religious Experience

EXTERMINATION, JEWISH (1939-1945)

see Holocaust, Jewish (1939-1945)

EXTREME UNCTION

Roccapriore, Maria. Anointing the Sick. LC 80-65722. (Illus.). 144p. (Orig.). 1980. pap. 2.95 (ISBN 0-8189-1160-3, 160, Pub. by Alba Bks). Alba.

EYB, ALBRECHT VON, 1420-1475

Hiller, Joseph A. Albrecht Von Eyb, Medieval Moralist. LC 70-140027. (Catholic University Studies in German Ser.: No. 13). 1970. Repr. of 1939 ed. 25.00 (ISBN 0-404-50233-4). AMS Pr.

EYCK, HUBERT VAN, 1366-1426

Brockwell, Maurice W. Van Eyck Problem. LC 78-138101. (Illus.). 1971. Repr. of 1954 ed. lib. bdg. 22.50x (ISBN 0-8371-5677-7, BRVE). Greenwood.

EYCK, JAN VAN, 1386-1440

Purtle, Carol J. The Marian Paintings of Jan Van Eyck. LC 81-47943. (Illus.). 288p. 1982. 52.50x (ISBN 0-691-03989-5). Princeton U Pr.

EZEKIEL, THE PROPHET

Carley, Keith W. Ezekiel Among the Prophets: A Study of Ezekiel's Place in Prophetic Tradition. (Studies in Biblical Theology, 2nd Ser.: No. 31). 1975. pap. text ed. 10.00x (ISBN 0-8401-3081-3). A R Allenson.

Fudge, Edward. Ezekiel: Prophet of Jehovah's Glory. 1.00 (ISBN 0-686-12692-0). E Fudge.

Gaebelein, Arno C. Ezekiel. LC 72-88419. 9.95 (ISBN 0-87213-217-X). Loizeaux.

Jacobson, Howard. The Exagoge of Ezekiel. LC 82-4410. 240p. 1983. 49.50 (ISBN 0-521-24580-X). Cambridge U Pr.

Job, John. Watchman in Babylon: A Study Guide to Ezekiel. 112p. (Orig.). pap. 4.95 (ISBN 0-85364-339-3). Attic Pr.

Siegman, Edward F. Ezechiel. (Bible Ser.). pap. 1.00 ea.; Pt. 1. pap. (ISBN 0-8091-5045-X); Pt. 2. pap. (ISBN 0-8091-5046-8). Paulist Pr.

Torrey, Charles C. Pseudo-Ezekiel & the Original Prophecy. LC 78-63562. (Yale Oriental Ser. Researches: No. 18). Repr. of 1930 ed. 15.00 (ISBN 0-404-60288-6). AMS Pr.

EZRA, THE PROPHET

Lindsay, Gordon. Ezra & Nehemiah & the Return from Babylon. (Old Testament Ser.). 1.25 (ISBN 0-89985-154-1). Christ Nations.

Lipshitz, Abe. The Commentary of Abraham Ibn Ezra on Hosea. 190p. 1987. 19.95 (ISBN 0-87203-127-6). Hermon.

Torrey, Charles C. Ezra Studies. rev. ed. 1970. 29.50x (ISBN 0-87068-014-5). Ktav.

F

FABLES

see also Folk-Lore; Parables

Clark, Glenn. God's Voice in the Folklore. 4.95 (ISBN 0-910924-06-6). Macalester.

Donze, Sr. M. Terese. The Kingdom Lost & Found: A Fable for Everyone. LC 82-71983. (Illus.). 64p. (Orig.). 1982. pap. 3.95 (ISBN 0-87793-253-0). Ave Maria.

FABRI, FELIX, 1441-1502

Prescott, Hilda F. Once to Sinai. LC 78-63358. (The Crusades & Military Orders: Second Ser.). Repr. of 1957 ed. 27.00 (ISBN 0-404-17028-5). AMS Pr.

FAITH

see also Apostasy; Atheism; Faith and Reason; Hope; Salvation; Sanctification; Skepticism; Trust in God; Truth

Akehurst, John. The Faith Within You: The Essence & Meaning of the Christian Faith. 141p. (Orig.). 1984. pap. 10.95 (ISBN 0-85819-469-4, Pub. by JBCE). ANZ Religious Pubns.

Alberione, James. A Time for Faith. 1978. 4.00 (ISBN 0-8198-0371-5); pap. 3.00 (ISBN 0-8198-0372-3). Dghtrs St Paul.

Al-Ghazzali. Foundations of the Articles of Faith. 1969. 7.50x (ISBN 0-87902-058-X). Orientalia.

Allen. Faith, Hope & Love. 5.95 (ISBN 0-318-18178-9). WCTU.

Allen, Charles. My Lord & My God. 48p. 1985. 6.95 (ISBN 0-8378-5083-5). Gibson.

Al-Muzaffar, Muhammed R. The Faith of Shi'a Islam. 89p. (Orig.). 1986. pap. text ed. 8.95 (ISBN 0-7103-0157-X). Methuen Inc.

Anderson, C. Alan. The Problem Is God: The Selection & Care of Your Personal God. LC 84-50108. (Illus.). 304p. (Orig.). 1985. pap. 9.95 (ISBN 0-913299-02-2). Stillpoint.

Andrews, James E. & Burgess, Joseph A. An Invitation to Action: The Lutheran-Reformed Dialogue, Ser. III, 1981-1983; A Study of Ministry, Sacraments & Recognition. LC 84-47885. 144p. 1984. pap. 2.00 (ISBN 0-8006-1818-1, 1-1818). Fortress.

Angell, James W. Accept No Imitations: Finding a Genuine Faith in a Counterfeit World. 144p. 1984. pap. 8.75 (ISBN 0-687-00692-9). Abingdon.

Ansari, F. R. Foundations of Faith. pap. 1.50 (ISBN 0-686-18472-6). Kazi Pubns.

Arnold, E. Pearls of Faith. 319p. 1984. 60.00x (ISBN 0-317-39177-1, Pub. by Luzac & Co Ltd). State Mutual Bk.

Arthur, Kay. How Can I Be Blessed? 256p. (Orig.). 1984. pap. 6.95 (ISBN 0-317-06624-2, Power Bks). Revell.

Asquith, Glenn H. Mature Faith: A Spiritual Pilgrimage. LC 84-12890. 120p. (Orig.). 1984. pap. 6.95 (ISBN 0-8361-3366-8). Herald Pr.

Bachman, John W. Faith That Makes a Difference. LC 83-70508. 128p. (Orig.). 1983. pap. 6.95 (ISBN 0-8066-2014-5, 10-2193). Augsburg.

Baker, Albert E. Prophets for a Day of Judgment. facsimile ed. LC 72-90605. (Essay Index Reprint Ser). 1944. 17.00 (ISBN 0-8369-1390-6). Ayer Co Pubs.

Barlow, Philip L., ed. A Thoughtful Faith: Essays on Belief by Mormon Scholars. LC 86-71882. 275p. 1986. 14.95 (ISBN 0-939651-00-9). Canon Pr.

Barnes, Peter. Milk of the World. 80p. (Orig.). 1985. pap. 2.95 (ISBN 0-85151-434-0). Banner of Truth.

Barnidge, Thomas & Grow, Douglas. The Jim Hart Story. LC 77-12538. (Illus.). 1977. 6.95 (ISBN 0-8272-1705-6); pap. 4.95 (ISBN 0-8272-1704-8). CBP.

Barrett, J. Edward. Faith in Focus: A Compact Introduction to Christian Theology. LC 81-40167. 130p. (Orig.). 1982. lib. bdg. 24.25 (ISBN 0-8191-1878-8); pap. text ed. 9.50 (ISBN 0-8191-1879-6). U Pr of Amer.

Bauer, Fred. Just a Touch of Nearness. 48p. 1985. 6.95 (ISBN 0-8378-5082-7). Gibson.

Beachey, Duane. Faith in a Nuclear Age. LC 82-11785. (Christian Peace Shelf Ser.). 136p. (Orig.). 1983. pap. 6.95 (ISBN 0-8361-3308-0). Herald Pr.

Beard, Charles A. Written History As an Act of Faith. 1960. pap. 3.00 (ISBN 0-87404-084-1). Tex Western.

Beck, Nestor. Doctrine of Faith. 1987. pap. 15.95 (ISBN 0-570-04469-3). Concordia.

Bennett, Jane. Unthinking Faith & Enlightenment: Nature & Politics in a Post-Hegelian Era. 192p. 1987. 30.00 (ISBN 0-8147-1095-6). NYU Pr.

Benton, John. Coming to Faith in Christ. 15p. 1977. pap. 0.80 (ISBN 0-85151-252-6). Banner of Truth.

Bethune, Joanna. The Power of Faith Exemplified in the Life & Writings of the Late Mrs. Isabella Graham. De Swarte, Carolyn G. & Dayton, Donald, eds. (Women in American Protestant Religion Series 1800-1930). 440p. 1987. lib. bdg. 65.00 (ISBN 0-8240-0659-3). Garland Pub.

Bilheimer, Robert S., ed. Faith & Ferment: An Interdisciplinary Study of Christian Beliefs & Practices. LC 83-70512. 352p. (Orig.). 1983. pap. 15.95 (ISBN 0-8066-2018-8, 10-2168). Augsburg.

Bin-Nun, Aaron. The Language of Faith. LC 78-65723. 1979. 8.95 (ISBN 0-88400-061-3). Shengold.

Bjorge, James R. Forty Ways to Fortify Your Faith. LC 83-72115. 128p. (Orig.). 1984. pap. 5.95 (ISBN 0-8066-2059-5, 10-2358). Augsburg.

Bloxton, Marian W. Pioneers of Faith. 80p. 1984. pap. 7.95 (ISBN 0-8170-1036-X). Judson.

Boesak, Allan. The Finger of God: Sermons on Faith & Socio-Political Responsibility. Randall, Peter, tr. from Afrikaans. LC 81-16943. Tr. of Die Vinger Van God. 112p. (Orig.). 1982. pap. 5.95 (ISBN 0-88344-135-7). Orbis Bks.

Boff, Leonardo & Elizondo, Virgil, eds. La Iglesia Popular: Between Fear & Hope, Vol. 176. (Concilium Ser.). 128p. 1984. pap. 6.95 (ISBN 0-567-30056-0, Pub. by T & T Clark Ltd UK). Fortress.

Bormann, Eugenie. Glauben und Aberglauben. LC 84-70173. 120p. 23.00x (ISBN 0-938100-32-7). Camden Hse.

Boros, Ladislaus. The Closeness of God. 1978. pap. 3.95 (ISBN 0-8245-0210-8). Crossroad NY.

Bothwell, Sr. Mary D. We Believe. (Christ Our Life Ser.). (Illus.). 1981. pap. text ed. 4.20 (ISBN 0-8294-0367-1); tchr's ed. 12.95 (ISBN 0-8294-0368-X). Loyola.

Boyd, James E. Faith Is Sort of Like This. (Illus.). 64p. (Orig.). 1986. pap. 9.95 (ISBN 1-55630-012-3). Brentwood Comm.

Boyd, R. Vernon. Undying Dedication. 1985. pap. 5.95 (ISBN 0-89225-281-2). Gospel Advocate.

Bradshaw, Charles E. Profile of Faith. 9.95 (ISBN 0-911866-01-9). Advocate.

Bradshaw, Charles O. Faith Development: The Lifelong Process. (Complete Teacher Training Meeting Ser.). 48p. 1985. pap. text ed. 9.95 (ISBN 0-89191-761-6). Cook.

Bregman, Lucy. Through the Landscape of Faith. LC 85-26381. 120p. (Orig.). 1986. pap. 9.95 (ISBN 0-664-24704-0). Westminster.

Breybach, Breyten. Endpapers: Political Essay. 1986. 16.95 (ISBN 0-374-14829-5). FS&G.

Bright, Bill. How to Love by Faith. (Transferable Concepts Ser.). 64p. 1981. pap. 1.25 (ISBN 0-918956-95-1). Campus Crusade.

Briscoe, Jill. Faith Enough to Finish. 108p. 1987. pap. 4.95 (ISBN 0-89693-238-9). Victor Bks.

Brown, Joan W. Never Alone. 48p. 1985. 6.95 (ISBN 0-8378-5084-3). Gibson.

Brown, John. I've Got Mixed-Up Feelings, God. 64p. 1984. pap. 3.95 (ISBN 0-8170-1035-1). Judson.

Brown, Robert M. Is Faith Obsolete? LC 74-13420. 160p. 1979. pap. 3.95 (ISBN 0-664-24230-8). Westminster.

Brown, Willis M. How I Got Faith. 199p. 2.00 (ISBN 0-686-29117-4). Faith Pub Hse.

Brueggemann, Walter. In Man We Trust: The Neglected Side of Biblical Faith. LC 72-1761. 144p. 1984. pap. 7.95 (ISBN 0-8042-0198-6). John Knox.

Brunner, Emil. The Christian Doctrine of the Church, Faith, & the Consummation. LC 50-6821. (Dogmatic Ser., Vol. 3). 472p. 1978. softcover o.s.i. 9.95 (ISBN 0-664-24218-9). Westminster.

Brynteson, Paul & Brynteson, Donna. Fitness & Faith. 224p. 1985. pap. 7.95 (ISBN 0-8407-5920-7). Nelson.

Bultmann, Rudolf. Faith & Understanding. Funk, Robert W., ed. Smith, Louise P., tr. LC 86-45901. 352p. 1987. pap. 12.95 (ISBN 0-8006-3202-8). Fortress.

Bunson, Maggie. Faith in Paradise. 1977. 8.00 (ISBN 0-8198-0414-2). Dghtrs St Paul.

--Founding of Faith. 1977. 6.00 (ISBN 0-8198-0412-6); pap. 5.00 (ISBN 0-8198-0413-4). Dghtrs St Paul.

Burgess, Andrew J. Passion, Knowing How, & Understanding: An Essay on the Concept of Faith. LC 75-31550. (American Academy of Religion. Dissertation Ser.). 1975. pap. 9.95 (ISBN 0-89130-044-9, 010109). Scholars Pr GA.

Burgess, Beverly C. God Are You Really Real? (Illus.). 30p. (Orig.). 1985. pap. 1.98 (ISBN 0-89274-309-3). Harrison Hse.

Burke, Dennis. Knowing God Intimately. 1985. pap. 2.95 (ISBN 0-89274-349-2). Harrison Hse.

Burrell, Jill & Burrell, Maurice. Arctic Mission. 1974. 1.60 (ISBN 0-08-017621-6). Pergamon.

Cabestrero, Teofilo, ed. Faith: Conversations with Contemporary Theologians. Walsh, Donald D., tr. from Span. LC 80-1431. Orig. Title: Coversationes sobre la fe. 192p. (Orig.). 1980. pap. 3.98 (ISBN 0-88344-126-8). Orbis Bks.

Capps, Charles. Can Your Faith Fail? 1978. pap. 1.75 (ISBN 0-89274-105-8). Harrison Hse.

--How to Have Faith in Your Faith. 1986. pap. 3.95 (ISBN 0-89274-415-4). Harrison Hse.

--Righteousness Which Is of Faith. (Orig.). 1986. mini bk. 0.75 (ISBN 0-89274-411-1). Harrison Hse.

Carballosa, Evis L. Santiago: Una Fe en Accion. Orig. Title: James: Faith in Action. (Span.). 352p. (Orig.). 1986. pap. 10.95 (ISBN 0-8254-1112-2). Kregel.

Carnes, Ralph & Carnes, Valerie. The Road to Damascus. 336p. 1986. 16.95 (ISBN 0-312-68517-3, Thomas Dunne Bks). St Martin.

Cassie, Dhyan. So Who's Perfect! LC 84-12948. 248p. (Orig.). 1984. pap. 12.95 (ISBN 0-8361-3372-2). Herald Pr.

Chittister, Joan D. & Marty, Martin E. Faith & Ferment: An Interdisciplinary Study of Christian Beliefs & Practices. Bilheimer, Robert S., ed. 352p. 1983. pap. 15.95 (ISBN 0-8146-1289-X). Liturgical Pr.

Cho, Paul Y. The Leap of Faith. 120p. 1984. pap. 2.95 (ISBN 0-88270-574-1). Bridge Pub.

Clark, Gordon H. Faith & Saving Faith. (Trinity Papers: No. 5). 118p. (Orig.). 1983. pap. 5.95 (ISBN 0-940931-05-2). Trinity Found.

Cobble, James F. Faith & Crisis in the Stages of Life. 128p. 1985. pap. 6.95 (ISBN 0-913573-17-5). Hendrickson MA.

Cole, C. Donald. Basic Christian Faith. LC 84-72008. 256p. (Orig.). 1985. pap. 6.95 (ISBN 0-89107-338-8, Crossway Bks). Good News.

Collingwood, Guillermo. Las Dos Naturalezas del Creyente. 2nd ed. Bennett, Gordon H., ed. Bautista, Sara, tr. from Eng. (La Serie Diamante). Tr. of The Believer's Two Natures. (Span., Illus.). 52p. 1982. pap. 0.85 (ISBN 0-942504-03-8). Overcomer Pr.

Cook, Gene R. Living by the Power of Faith. 120p. 1985. 8.95 (ISBN 0-87747-745-0). Deseret Bk.

Cook, Michael L. The Jesus of Faith: A Study in Christology. LC 80-84510. 192p. (Orig.). pap. 6.95 (ISBN 0-8091-2349-5). Paulist Pr.

Cook, Robert. Ahora que Creo. Orig. Title: Now That I Believe. (Span.). 128p. 1984. pap. 3.25 (ISBN 0-8254-1137-8). Kregel.

Cooke, Bernard. Formation of Faith. LC 65-27619. (Pastoral Ser). 1965. pap. 2.00 (ISBN 0-8294-0014-1). Loyola.

Cookson, Catherine. The Glass Virgin. 352p. 1981. pap. 3.95 (ISBN 0-552-08849-8). Bantam.

Cope, Lamar. Faith for a New Day. Lambert, Herbert, ed. 128p. (Orig.). 1986. pap. 8.95 (ISBN 0-8272-1013-2). CBP.

Corrigan, John T. Archives: The Light of Faith. (Catholic Library Association Studies in Librarianship: No. 4). 1980. 4.00 (ISBN 0-87507-008-6). Cath Lib Assn.

Crawford, C. C. What the Bible Says about Faith. LC 82-72621. (What the Bible Says Ser.). 380p. 1982. cancelled (ISBN 0-89900-089-4). College Pr Pub.

Crockett, Maline. More Stories to See & Share. (Illus.). 64p. 1981. pap. 3.95 (ISBN 0-87747-886-4). Deseret Bk.

Crockett, William J. Faith: Voices from the Heart. 15p. Date not set. pap. 3.00 (ISBN 0-934383-31-6). Pride Prods.

Crooks, Mrs. Boyd. Our Faith Speaks. 62p. 1962. pap. 0.35 (ISBN 0-89114-147-2). Baptist Pub Hse.

Crowley, Mary C. A Pocketful of Hope. 352p. 1981. 12.50 (ISBN 0-8007-1272-2). Revell.

D'Arcy, Martin C. The Nature of Belief. facsimile ed. (Select Bibliographies Reprint Ser). Repr. of 1931 ed. 21.00 (ISBN 0-8369-5930-2). Ayer Co Pubs.

D'Arcy, Paula. Where the Wind Begins: Stories of Hurting People Who Said Yes to Life. 144p. 1985. pap. 5.95 (ISBN 0-87788-925-2). Shaw Pubs.

Daud, Abraham I. The Exalted Faith. Weiss, Gershon, ed. Samuelson, Norbert, tr. LC 83-49341. (Hebrew.). 408p. 1986. 75.00x (ISBN 0-8386-3185-1). Fairleigh Dickinson.

Daughters of St. Paul. Everyman's Challenge. LC 73-89938. 1974. 5.00 (ISBN 0-8198-0294-8). Dghtrs St Paul.

--Faces of Courage. (Illus.). 1974. 5.00 (ISBN 0-8198-0292-1); pap. 4.00 (ISBN 0-8198-0293-X). Dghtrs St Paul.

--Faith We Live By. LC 68-59044. (Divine Master Ser., Vol. 3). (Illus.). 1969. 7.50 (ISBN 0-8198-0039-2); pap. 6.00 (ISBN 0-8198-0040-6); discussion & project manual 0.60 (ISBN 0-8198-0041-4). Dghtrs St Paul.

Daujat, Jean. The Faith Applied. 1963. 5.95x (ISBN 0-933932-22-7). Scepter Pubs.

Davidson, Alice J. Reflections of Love. (Illus.). 128p. 1982. 12.95 (ISBN 0-8007-1327-3). Revell.

Davis, Stephen. Faith, Skepticism & Evidence: An Essay in Religious Epistemology. 233p. 1978. 20.00 (ISBN 0-8387-2039-0). Bucknell U Pr.

Day, N. R. David's Faithfulness. 85p. (Orig.). 1979. pap. 6.95 (ISBN 0-940754-02-9). Ed Ministries.

Day, N. Raymond. Energizing Your Faith. 56p. (Orig.). 1985. pap. 5.95 (ISBN 0-940754-28-2). Ed Ministries.

Dayton, Ed. Faith That Goes Further: Facing the Contradictions of Life. LC 84-14693. 1984. pap. 5.95 (ISBN 0-88070-062-9). Multnomah.

Deal, William S. Faith, Facts & Feelings. 3rd ed. 1978. pap. 0.95 (ISBN 0-686-05527-6). Crusade Pubs.

De Beer, Francis. We Saw Brother Francis. 1983. 12.00 (ISBN 0-8199-0803-7). Franciscan Herald.

De Benedittis, Suzanne M. Teaching Faith & Morals. 200p. (Orig.). 1981. pap. 8.95 (ISBN 0-86683-621-7, HaprsR). Har-Row.

Deerfield, William. Stretching Your Faith. 48p. 1985. 4.95 (ISBN 0-8378-5401-6). Gibson.

De la Barca, Pedro C. Celos Aun Del Aire Matan. Stroud, Matthew D., tr. LC 80-54543. (Span. & Eng., Illus.). 219p. 1981. 15.00 (ISBN 0-911536-90-6); pap. 10.00 (ISBN 0-939980-01-0). Trinity U Pr.

De la Cruz Aymes, Maria & Buckley, Francis J. Fe y Cultura: Manual de Direccion. 112p. (Orig.). 1986. pap. 8.95 (ISBN 0-8091-2749-0); apuntes 5.95; leader's manual 8.95 (ISBN 0-8091-2748-2). Paulist Pr.

De Lubac, Henri. Christian Faith. Arnandez, Richard, tr. from Fr. LC 84-80903. Orig. Title: La Foi Chretienne. 353p. (Orig.). 1986. pap. 12.95 (ISBN 0-89870-053-1). Ignatius Pr.

DeWitt, John R. What Is the Reformed Faith? (Orig.). 1981. pap. text ed. 1.45 (ISBN 0-85151-326-3). Banner of Truth.

DiCarlo, Joseph, Jr. Following Christ. (Faith & Life Ser.). (Illus.). 142p. (Orig.). 1985. pap. 6.20 (ISBN 0-89870-065-5). Ignatius Pr.

Digiacomo, James, et al. The Longest Step: Searching for God. (The Encounter Ser.). (Illus.). 1977. pap. text ed. 4.50 (ISBN 0-86683-180-0, 315, HarpR); resource manual 1.95 (ISBN 0-86683-181-9, 316). Har-Row.

--Meet the Lord: Encounters with Jesus. (The Encounter Ser.). 1977. pap. 3.98 (ISBN 0-03-021281-2, 317, HarpR); resource manual 1.95 (ISBN 0-03-021866-7, 318). Har-Row.

Doherty, Catherine D. Doubts, Loneliness & Rejection. LC 81-19115. (Illus.). 93p. 1982. pap. 4.50 (ISBN 0-8189-0419-4). Alba.

Drane, John W. Old Testament Faith. LC 86-45075. (Illus.). 224p. (Orig.). 1986. pap. 10.95 (ISBN 0-06-062064-1, HarpR). Har-Row.

Droege, Thomas A. Faith Passages & Patterns. LC 82-48544. (Lead Bks.). 128p. 1983. pap. 4.95 (ISBN 0-8006-1602-2, 1-1602). Fortress.

Dubay, Thomas. Faith & Certitude. LC 84-80910. 266p. (Orig.). 1985. pap. 9.95 (ISBN 0-89870-054-X). Ignatius Pr.

Duckworth, John, et al, eds. Give It Away! (Pacesetter Ser.). 64p. 1987. tchr's. ed. 7.95. Cook.

Dufresne, Ed. Faithfulness. 57p. 1981. pap. 0.75 (ISBN 0-89274-378-6). Harrison Hse.

Dykstra, Craig & Parks, Sharon, eds. Faith Development & Fowler. 322p. (Orig.). 1986. pap. 14.95 (ISBN 0-89135-056-X). Religious Educ.

Eareckson, Joni & Musser, Joe. Joni. (Illus.). 256p. 1980. pap. 3.95 (ISBN 0-310-23982-6, 12009P). Zondervan.

Ebeling, Gerhard. The Nature of Faith. Smith, Ronald G., ed. LC 62-7194. pap. 47.80 (2026871). Bks Demand UMI.

Edwards, Jonathan. Religious Affections. Houston, James M., ed. LC 84-14863. (Classics of Faith & Devotion Ser.). 1984. 11.95 (ISBN 0-88070-064-5). Multnomah.

Eidsmoe, John. God & Caesar: Christian Faith & Political Action. LC 84-71423. 226p. 1984. (Crossway Bks); pap. 7.95 (ISBN 0-89107-313-2). Good News.

Elbert, John A. Newman's Concept of Faith. 59.95 (ISBN 0-8490-0729-1). Gordon Pr.

Elizondo, Virgil & Greinacher, Norbert, eds. The Transmission of Faith to the Next Generation, Vol. 174. (Concilium Ser.). 128p. pap. 6.95 (ISBN 0-567-30054-4, Pub. by T & T Clark Ltd UK). Fortress.

Elwood, Douglas. Faith Encounters Ideology: Christian Discernment & Social Change. xvi, 318p. (Orig.). 1985. pap. 16.00 (ISBN 971-10-0201-9, Pub. by New Day Philippines). Cellar.

England, Kathy. What Is Faith? (Illus.). 27p. 1981. pap. 4.95 (ISBN 0-87747-876-7). Deseret Bk.

Engstrom, Barbie. Faith to See: Reflections & Photographs. LC 74-25540. (Illus.). 64p. 1979. pap. 3.00 (ISBN 0-932210-00-7). Kurios Found.

Evans, C. Stephens. The Quest for Faith. LC 86-7436. 144p. (Orig.). 1986. pap. 4.95 (ISBN 0-87784-511-5). Inter-Varsity.

Evans, Donald. Faith, Authenticity, & Morality. 1980. 30.00x (ISBN 0-8020-5424-2). U of Toronto Pr.

Evely, Louis. Faith of a Modern Man. 1.95 (ISBN 0-317-06468-1). Dimension Bks.

The Faith Builder. 2.95 (ISBN 0-686-12914-8). Schmul Pub Co.

Faith Development in the Adult Life Cycle. 1983. 10.95 (ISBN 0-8215-9899-6). Sadlier.

Faith's Cooperating Powers. 1979. 1.25 (ISBN 0-89858-028-5). Fill the Gap.

Faith's Definition. 1981. 1.25 (ISBN 0-89858-019-6). Fill the Gap.

Faith's Destroyers. 1981. 1.25 (ISBN 0-89858-020-X). Fill the Gap.

Faith's Prayer Sequence. 1979. 1.25 (ISBN 0-89858-029-3). Fill the Gap.

Faith's Steadfastness. 1981. 1.25 (ISBN 0-89858-021-8). Fill the Gap.

Faris, N. A. Foundation of Articles of Faith. 9.50 (ISBN 0-686-18607-9). Kazi Pubns.

Fellowship of Catholic Scholars. Christian Faith & Freedom: Proceedings. Williams, Paul L., ed. LC 82-81072. 128p. (Orig.). 1982. pap. text ed. 4.50 (ISBN 0-686-97454-9). NE Bks.

Fenhagen, James C. Invitation to Holiness. LC 85-42774. 128p. 1985. 12.45 (ISBN 0-06-062351-9, HarpR). Har-Row.

Fenocketti, Mary M. Learning from Little Ones: Insights from the Gospel. 48p. 1984. pap. 1.95 (ISBN 0-89243-203-9). Liguori Pubns.

Ferguson, Franklin C. A Pilgrimage in Faith: An Introduction to the Episcopal Church. rev. ed. LC 75-5220. 180p. (Orig.). 1979. pap. 6.95 (ISBN 0-8192-1277-6). Morehouse.

Ferre, Nels F. The Finality of Faith, & Christianity Among the World Religions. LC 78-11979. 1979. Repr. of 1963 ed. lib. bdg. 22.50x (ISBN 0-313-21182-5, FEFF). Greenwood.

Fichte, Johann G. The Vocation of Man. Smith, William, tr. LC 56-44104. 1956. pap. 5.99 scp (ISBN 0-672-60220-2, LLA50). Bobbs.

--Vocation of Man. Smith, William, tr. from Ger. 190p. 1965. 12.95 (ISBN 0-87548-074-8); pap. 5.95 (ISBN 0-87548-075-6). Open Court.

Fillmore, Myrtle. Come Dejar Que Dios Te Ayude. Tr. of How to Let God Help You. 1984. 5.95 (ISBN 0-87159-019-0). Unity School.

Fishelis, Avraham. Bastion of Faith. 3rd ed. 256p. 1980. 9.00 (ISBN 0-9605560-1-X). A Fishelis.

Fisher, Eugene. Faith Without Prejudice: Rebuilding Christian Attitudes Toward Judaism. LC 77-83550. 196p. 1977. pap. 3.95 (ISBN 0-8091-2064-X). Paulist Pr.

Fisher, Kathleen R. & Hart, Thomas N. Christian Foundations: An Introduction to Faith in Our Time. 240p. 1986. pap. 9.95 (ISBN 0-8091-2817-9). Paulist Pr.

Flesseman-Van Leer, E. A Faith for Today. Steely, John E., tr. LC 79-56514. (Special Studies Ser.: No. 7). vii, 148p. 1980. pap. 6.95 (ISBN 0-932180-06-X). NABPR.

Flood, Robert. Faith for All Generations. LC 86-70628. Orig. Title: Up with America. 96p. 1986. pap. 4.95 (ISBN 0-89636-214-0). Accent Bks.

Foley, Leonard. Believing in Jesus: A Popular Overview of the Catholic Faith. (Illus.). 185p. (Orig.). 1981. pap. text ed. 5.95 (ISBN 0-912228-79-2). St Anthony Mess Pr.

Footprints: An Affirmation of Faith. (Illus.). 24p. (Orig.). 1984. pap. 1.95 (ISBN 0-89954-285-9). Antioch Pub Co.

Forde, Gerhard O. Justification by Faith: A Matter of Death & Life. LC 81-70663. 112p. 1982. pap. 5.95 (ISBN 0-8006-1634-0, 1-1634). Fortress.

Fosdick, Harry E. The Meaning of Faith. (Festival Bks). 352p. 1982. pap. 3.95 (ISBN 0-687-23959-1). Abingdon.

Franzblau, Abraham N. Religious Belief & Character among Jewish Adolescents. LC 78-176783. (Columbia University. Teachers College. Contributions to Education: No. 634). Repr. of 1934 ed. 22.50 (ISBN 0-404-55634-5). AMS Pr.

Fry, Mae. Faith Is the Victory. (Orig.). 1986. pap. 1.95 (ISBN 0-89265-098-2). Randall Hse.

Gabhart, Herbert C. Meeting the Challenge. 1984. 6.95 (ISBN 0-8054-5340-7, 4253-40). Broadman.

Galilea, Segundo. The Way of Living Faith. 12.45 (ISBN 0-317-52400-3, HarpR). Har-Row.

Gandhi, M. K. My Religion. Kumarappa, B., ed. 178p. (Orig.). 1983. pap. 5.00 (ISBN 0-934676-54-2). Greenlf Bks.

Garrotto, Alfred J. Christ in Our Lives. (Orig.). 1980. pap. text ed. 4.95 (ISBN 0-03-056979-6, HarpR). Har-Row.

Getz, Gene A. Believing God When You Are Tempted to Doubt: The Measure of a Christian; Studies in James I. LC 84-27543. 160p. pap. 5.95 (ISBN 0-8307-1021-3, 5418416). Regal.

Gift of Infallibility. 5.00 (ISBN 0-8198-3042-9); 4.00 (ISBN 0-8198-3041-0). Dghtrs St Paul.

Goodwin, Thomas. Justifying Faith. 593p. 1985. 15.95 (ISBN 0-85151-447-2). Banner of Truth.

Gordis, Robert. Faith for Moderns. 2nd rev. ed. LC 76-136424. 1971. pap. 8.95x (ISBN 0-8197-0001-0, 10001). Bloch.

Graham, Henry G. What Faith Really Means. LC 82-74243. 94p. 1982. pap. 2.00 (ISBN 0-89555-204-3). TAN Bks Pubs.

Greeley, Andrew M. The Great Mysteries: An Essential Catechism. 192p. (Orig.). 1976. pap. 8.95x (ISBN 0-8164-0309-0, AY7823, HarpR). Har-Row.

Griffith, Gwilym O. Interpreters of Reality: Lao-Tse, Heraclitus & the Christian Faith. 1977. lib. bdg. 59.95 (ISBN 0-8490-2065-4). Gordon Pr.

Groenhoff, Edwin L. It's Your Choice. 1975. pap. 1.75 (ISBN 0-911802-38-X). Free Church Pubns.

Grubb, Norman P. Law of Faith. 1969. pap. 3.95 (ISBN 0-87508-223-8). Chr Lit.

Gutting, Gary. Religious Belief & Religious Skepticism. LC 82-50287. 192p. 1982. text ed. 15.95 (ISBN 0-268-01613-5). U of Notre Dame Pr.

--Religious Belief & Religious Skepticism. LC 82-50287. xi, 192p. 1983. pap. text ed. 9.95x (ISBN 0-268-01618-6, 85-16189). U of Notre Dame Pr.

Hagin, Kenneth. His Name Shall Be Called Wonderful. 1983. pap. 0.50 mini bk. (ISBN 0-89276-260-8). Hagin Ministries.

--Obedience in Finances. 1983. pap. 0.50 mini bk. (ISBN 0-89276-259-4). Hagin Ministries.

--Understanding the Anointing. 1983. pap. 3.50 (ISBN 0-89276-507-0). Hagin Ministries.

Hagin, Kenneth E. La Autoridad Del Creyente. 2nd ed. (Span.). 1982. pap. 1.00 (ISBN 0-89276-106-7). Hagin Ministries.

--Como Desatar Su Fe. 2nd ed. (Span.). 1982. pap. 1.00 (ISBN 0-89276-107-5). Hagin Ministries.

--Como Retener Su Sanidad. (Span.). 1983. pap. 0.50 mini bk. (ISBN 0-89276-159-8). Hagin Ministries.

--Los Dones Del Ministerio. 1983. study guide 10.00 (ISBN 0-89276-192-X). Hagin Ministries.

--En El. (Span.). 1983. pap. 0.50 mini bk. (ISBN 0-89276-152-0). Hagin Ministries.

--Exceedingly Growing Faith. 1983. pap. 3.50 (ISBN 0-89276-506-2). Hagin Ministries.

--Faith Food for Autumn. 2nd ed. (Illus.). 1978. pap. 1.95 (ISBN 0-89276-040-0). Hagin Ministries.

--Faith Food for Spring. 2nd ed. (Illus.). 1978. pap. 1.95 (ISBN 0-89276-042-7). Hagin Ministries.

--Faith Food for Summer. 2nd ed. (Illus.). 1978. pap. 1.95 (ISBN 0-89276-043-5). Hagin Ministries.

--Faith Food for Winter. 2nd ed. (Illus.). 1977. pap. 1.95 (ISBN 0-89276-041-9). Hagin Ministries.

--La Fe, Lo Que Es. 2nd ed. (Span.). 1982. pap. 1.00 (ISBN 0-89276-102-4). Hagin Ministries.

--Having Faith in Your Faith. 1981. pap. 0.50 mini bk. (ISBN 0-89276-252-7). Hagin Ministries.

--How to Turn Your Faith Loose. 2nd ed. 1983. pap. 1.00 (ISBN 0-89276-007-9). Hagin Ministries.

--How to Walk in Love. 1983. pap. 0.50 mini bk. (ISBN 0-89276-262-4). Hagin Ministries.

--How You Can Know the Will of God. 2nd ed. 1983. pap. 1.00 (ISBN 0-89276-019-2). Hagin Ministries.

--I Believe in Visions. 2nd ed. 1984. pap. 3.50 (ISBN 0-89276-508-9). Hagin Ministries.

--Man on Three Dimensions. 1973. pap. 1.00 (ISBN 0-89276-020-6). Hagin Ministries.

--La Medicina De Dios. (Span.). 1982. pap. 0.50 mini bk. (ISBN 0-89276-153-9). Hagin Ministries.
--New Thresholds of Faith. 2nd ed. 1972. pap. 2.50 (ISBN 0-89276-070-2). Hagin Ministries.
--No Culpe a Dios! (Span.). 1983. pap. 0.50 mini bk. (ISBN 0-89276-156-3). Hagin Ministries.
--El Nuevo Nacimiento. (Span.). 1983. pap. 0.50 mini bk. (ISBN 0-89276-150-4). Hagin Ministries.
--Palabras. (Span.). 1983. pap. 0.50 mini bk. (ISBN 0-89276-157-1). Hagin Ministries.
--El Pensar Bien y Mal. 2nd ed. (Span.). 1983. pap. 1.00 (ISBN 0-89276-104-0). Hagin Ministries.
--El Porque De Las Lenguas. (Span.). 1983. pap. 0.50 (ISBN 0-89276-151-2). Hagin Ministries.
--Prayer Secrets. 2nd ed. 1983. pap. 1.00 (ISBN 0-89276-005-2). Hagin Ministries.
--The Present-Day Ministry of Jesus Christ. 2nd ed. 1983. pap. 1.00 (ISBN 0-89276-014-1). Hagin Ministries.
--The Real Faith. 1970. pap. 1.00 (ISBN 0-89276-017-6). Hagin Ministries.
--Redeemed from Poverty, Sickness, & Death. 1966. pap. 1.00 (ISBN 0-89276-001-X). Hagin Ministries.
--Redimido De La Pobreza, La Enfermedad, La Muerte. 2nd ed. 1982. pap. 1.00 (ISBN 0-89276-101-6). Hagin Ministries.
--Right & Wrong Thinking. 2nd ed. 1966. pap. 1.00 (ISBN 0-89276-004-4). Hagin Ministries.
--Seven Vital Steps to Receiving the Holy Spirit. 2nd ed. 1980. pap. 1.00 (ISBN 0-89276-003-6). Hagin Ministries.
--Siete Pasos Para Recibir El Espiritu Santo. 2nd ed. 1983. pap. 1.00 (ISBN 0-89276-103-2). Hagin Ministries.
--Three Big Words. 1983. pap. 0.50 mini bk. (ISBN 0-89276-258-6). Hagin Ministries.
--Usted Puede Tener lo Que Diga. (Span.). 1983. pap. 0.50 mini bk. (ISBN 0-89276-154-7). Hagin Ministries.
--What Faith Is. 2nd ed. 1966. pap. 1.00 (ISBN 0-89276-002-8). Hagin Ministries.
Hagin, Kenneth, Jr. The Answer for Oppression. 1983. pap. 0.50 mini bk. (ISBN 0-89276-717-0). Hagin Ministries.
--Blueprint for Building Strong Faith. 1980. pap. 0.50 mini bk. (ISBN 0-89276-704-9). Hagin Ministries.
--Faith Takes Back What the Devil's Stolen. 1982. pap. 0.50 mini bk (ISBN 0-89276-709-X). Hagin Ministries.
--Faith Worketh by Love. 1979. pap. 0.50 mini bk. (ISBN 0-89276-703-0). Hagin Ministries.
--La Fe Obra Por El Amor. (Span.). 1983. pap. 0.50 mini bk. (ISBN 0-89276-173-3). Hagin Ministries.
--Get Acquainted with God. 1983. pap. 0.50 mini bk. (ISBN 0-89276-714-6). Hagin Ministries.
--Las Imposibilidades Del Hombre-Posibilidades Para Dios. (Span.). 1983. pap. 2.50 (ISBN 0-89276-170-9). Hagin Ministries.
--Siete Impedimentos Para Recibir Sanidad. (Span.). 1983. pap. 0.50 mini bk. (ISBN 0-89276-175-X). Hagin Ministries.
--El Tiempo Pasada De La Palabra De Dios. (Span.). 1983. pap. 0.50 mini bk. (ISBN 0-89276-176-8). Hagin Ministries.
--Unforgiveness. 1983. pap. 0.50 (ISBN 0-89276-716-2). Hagin Ministries.
Hakeda, Yoshito S., tr. The Awakening of Faith, Attributed to Asvaghosha. LC 67-13778. 128p. 1974. 24.00x (ISBN 0-231-03025-8); pap. 10.00x (ISBN 0-231-08336-X). Columbia U Pr.
Hakenewerth, Quentin. The Prayer of Faith. 76p. (Orig.). 1969. pap. 1.75 (ISBN 0-9608124-3-1). Marianist Com Ctr.
Hamann, Henry P. Justification by Faith in Modern Theology. 114p. 1957. write for info. Concordia Schl Grad Studies.
Hampsch, John H. & Kelly, Clint. Faith: Key to the Heart of God. LC 84-62433. (Keyhole Ser.: No. 1). 102p. (Orig.). 1985. pap. 6.95 (ISBN 0-9613575-1-7). Perf Pr.
Handford, Elisabeth R. Yo? Obedecer a Mi Marido? Orig. Title: Me? Obey Him? Tr. of Me? Obey Him. (Span.). 128p. 1984. pap. 3.25 (ISBN 0-8254-1302-8). Kregel.
Hanks, Geoffrey. Children of Naples. 1974. 1.60 (ISBN 0-08-017619-4). Pergamon.
Hansburg, Mary E. Myth, Faith & Hermeneutics. 85p. (Orig.). 1985. pap. 6.95x (ISBN 0-932269-23-0). Wyndham Hall.
Happold, F. C. Religious Faith & Twentieth Century Man. 192p. 1981. 6.95 (ISBN 0-8245-0046-6). Crossroad NY.
Harbaugh, Gary L. The Faith-Hardy Christian: How to Face the Challenges of Life with Confidence. LC 86-7966. (Christian Growth Ser.). 128p. 1986. pap. 6.95 (ISBN 0-8066-2212-1, 10-2184). Augsburg.
Hatch, W. H. Pauline Idea of Faith in Its Relation to Jewish & Hellenistic Religion. (Harvard Theological Studies). 1917. 11.00 (ISBN 0-527-01002-2). Kraus Repr.
Hateley, B. J. Telling Your Story, Exploring Your Faith. Lambert, Herbert, ed. LC 85-13307. 120p. (Orig.). 1985. pap. 8.95 (ISBN 0-8272-3626-3). CBP.
Haughey, John C. The Faith That Does Justice: Examining the Christian Sources for Social Change. LC 77-74578. 312p. (Orig.). 1977. pap. 8.95 (ISBN 0-8091-2026-7). Paulist Pr.
Hayes, Norvel. God's Boot Camp. 30p. (Orig.). 1979. pap. 1.50 (ISBN 0-89274-277-1). Harrison Hse.
--How to Protect Your Faith. 70p. (Orig.). 1983. pap. 3.95 (ISBN 0-89274-279-8). Harrison Hse.
Hayford, Jack W. Daybreak: Walking Daily in Christ's Presence. LC 84-80749. (Orig.). 1984. pap. 2.95 (ISBN 0-916847-05-5). Living Way.
--Spirit-Filled: Anointed by Christ the King. LC 84-80747. (Orig.). 1984. pap. 2.95 (ISBN 0-916847-04-7). Living Way.
--Stepping Up in Faith. LC 84-80748. (Orig.). 1984. pap. 2.95 (ISBN 0-916847-02-0). Living Way.
Heil, Ruth. My Child Within. LC 82-83901. 128p. 1983. pap. 5.95 (ISBN 0-89107-268-3). Good News.
Heinecken, Martin J. We Believe & Teach. Rast, Harold W., ed. LC 80-16363. (A Lead Book). 128p. (Orig.). 1980. pap. 3.95 (ISBN 0-8006-1387-2, 1-1387). Fortress.
Heinzmann, Josef. Faith is Friendship. 146p. 1983. pap. 6.95 (ISBN 0-8189-0451-8). Alba.
Helm, Paul. The Divine Revelation. LC 82-72325. (Foundations for Faith Ser.). 144p. (Orig.). 1982. pap. 8.95 (ISBN 0-89107-258-6, Crossway Bks). Good News.
Henry, Patrick & Stransky, Thomas F. God on Our Minds. LC 81-70593. 176p. 1982. pap. 6.95 (ISBN 0-8006-1600-6, 1-1600). Fortress.
Hickman, Martha W. The Growing Season. LC 80-68983. 128p. (Orig.). 1980. pap. 4.50x (ISBN 0-8358-0411-9). Upper Room.
Hicks, Roy H. Use It or Lose It: The Word of Faith. (Orig.). 1976. pap. 2.95 (ISBN 0-89274-002-7). Harrison Hse.
Hines, Eugene B. Asking the Hard Questions. LC 85-19528. 1986. pap. 4.95 (ISBN 0-8054-5013-0). Broadman.
Hodges, Zane C. The Gospel under Siege: A Study on Faith & Works. 124p. (Orig.). 1981. pap. 4.95 (ISBN 0-9607576-0-0). Redencion Viva.
Holloway, Richard. Beyond Belief: The Christian Encounter with God. LC 81-5438. pap. 43.50 (ISBN 0-317-19824-6, 2023217). Bks Demand UMI.
Holmes, Dana. Your Faith Account. 48p. (Orig.). 1983. pap. 0.95 (ISBN 0-88144-019-1, CPS/019). Christian Pub.
Holmes, Marjorie. I've Got to Talk to Somebody. 144p. 1984. pap. 2.95 (ISBN 0-8007-8080-9, Spire Bks). Revell.
Hoover, Arlie J. Fallacies of Unbelief. LC 75-36313. (Way of Life Ser: No. 128). 94p. 1976. pap. 3.95 (ISBN 0-89112-128-5, Bibl Res Pr). Abilene Christ U.
Horden, William. Experience & Faith. LC 82-72653. 160p. 1983. pap. 9.95 (ISBN 0-8066-1960-0, 10-2133). Augsburg.
Huber, Jane P. A Singing Faith. LC 86-753277. 144p. (Orig.). 1987. pap. 7.95 (ISBN 0-664-24055-0); spiral bound 10.95 (ISBN 0-664-24056-9). Westminster.
Hughes, Selwyn. The Introvert's Guide to Spontaneous Witnessing. LC 83-22390. 192p. 1984. pap. 5.95 (ISBN 0-87123-428-9, 210428). Bethany Hse.
Hutton, Richard H. Essays on Some of the Modern Guides to English Thought in Matters of Faith. LC 72-8580. (Essay Index Reprint Ser.). 1972. Repr. of 1887 ed. 23.50 (ISBN 0-8369-7319-4). Ayer Co Pubs.
Inge, William R. Faith & Its Psychology. LC 10-654. (Studies in Theology Ser.: No. 12). 1909. text ed. 8.50x (ISBN 0-8401-6012-7). A R Allenson.
Interfaith Consultative Group, Board for Mission & Unity, Church of England. Towards a Theology for Inter-Faith Dialogue. (Lambeth Study Bks.). 56p. 1986. pap. 2.25 (ISBN 0-88028-058-1). Forward Movement.
Jackson, W. Barbara. Faith & Freedom: A Study of Western Society. LC 72-8239. 308p. 1974. Repr. of 1954 ed. lib. bdg. 22.50x (ISBN 0-8371-6542-3, JAFF). Greenwood.
Jackson, Wayne. Fortify Your Faith. 74p. (Orig.). 1974. pap. text ed. 2.50 (ISBN 0-932859-09-7). Apologetic Pr.
Jensen, Margaret. Lena. LC 84-62381. 150p. (Orig.). 1985. pap. text ed. 9.95 (ISBN 0-89840-074-0). Heres Life.
Johnson, Luke T. Sharing Possessions: Mandate & Symbol of Faith. Brueggemann, Walter & Donahue, John R., eds. LC 80-2390. (Overtures to Biblical Theology Ser.: No. 9). 176p. (Orig.). 1981. pap. 8.95 (ISBN 0-8006-1534-4, 1-1534). Fortress.
Johnsson, William G. Blessed Assurance. Coffen, Richard W., ed. 144p. (Orig.). 1985. pap. 5.95 (ISBN 0-8280-0313-0). Review & Herald.
Jones, Gary. Patience Never Fails. 45p. 1985. pap. 0.95 (ISBN 0-88144-048-5). Christian Pub.
Joseph Cardinal Ratzinger. Seeking God's Face. 1982. 6.95 (ISBN 0-317-46880-4). Franciscan Herald.
Jung, Leo, ed. Faith. 212p. 1968. 8.50 (ISBN 0-900689-01-3). Soncino Pr.
Juvenaly, Archimandrite, ed. Khristijanskaja Zhizn' po Dobrotoljubiju: Izbrannija Mjesta iz Tborenji Svjatikh Otsoff i Utchitjeljej Tserkvi. Tr. of Christian Life by the Philokalia; Selected Passages from the Writings of the Holy Fathers. (Rus.). 216p. (Orig.). 1972. 13.00x (ISBN 0-88465-031-6); pap. 8.00x (ISBN 0-88465-032-4). Holy Trinity.
Kaiser, Christopher B. The Doctrine of God. LC 82-72324. (Foundations for Faith Ser.). 160p. 1982. pap. 8.95 (ISBN 0-89107-259-4, Crossway Bks). Good News.
Kapp, Ardeth G. I Walk by Faith. 1987. 9.95 (ISBN 0-87579-072-0). Deseret Bk.
Kasper, Walter. Faith & the Future. LC 82-12720. 192p. 1982. 12.95 (ISBN 0-8245-0504-2). Crossroad NY.
Kauffman, Karen, compiled by. With Faith All Things Are Possible. (Illus.). 1983. 8.00 (ISBN 0-8378-1802-8). Gibson.
Kaufman, Gordon D. Relativism, Knowledge, & Faith. LC 59-11620. pap. 38.80 (2026778). Bks Demand UMI.
Kazee, Buell H. Faith is the Victory. 1983. pap. 4.95 (ISBN 0-8423-0844-X). Tyndale.
Keck, Leander. New Testament Experience of Faith. 2nd ed. LC 76-46491. 160p. 1985. pap. 6.95 (ISBN 0-8272-2508-3). CBP.
Keidel, Levi. Caught in the Crossfire. LC 79-10910. 256p. 1979. pap. 7.95 (ISBN 0-8361-1888-X). Herald Pr.
Kelly, Geffrey B. Liberating Faith: Bonhoeffer's Message for Today. LC 84-15863. 208p. (Orig.). 1984. pap. 11.95 (ISBN 0-8066-2092-7, 10-3832). Augsburg.
Kemp, Raymond. A Journey in Faith. pap. 5.95 (ISBN 0-8215-9329-3). Sadlier.
Kennedy, D. James. Why I Believe. 1980. 6.95 (ISBN 0-8499-2943-1). Word Bks.
Kenny, Anthony. Faith & Reason. LC 82-22187. (Bampton Lectures in America Ser.). 100p. 1983. 21.50 (ISBN 0-231-05488-2). Columbia U Pr.
Khrapovitsky, Antony. Moral Idea of the Main Dogmas of the Faith. Novakshonoff, Varlaam & Puhalo, Lazar, trs. from Rus. 170p. (Orig.). 1984. pap. text ed. 8.00 (ISBN 0-911523-01-4). Synaxis Pr.
Kimball, Spencer W., et al, eds. Faith. LC 83-72343. 119p. 1983. 8.95 (ISBN 0-87747-980-1). Deseret Bk.
Knox, Lloyd H., ed. A Faith to Grow by. 1977. pap. 2.95 (ISBN 0-89367-009-X). Light & Life.
Krolikowski, Walter, ed. Faith & Justice. 174p. 1982. pap. text ed. 6.95 (ISBN 0-8294-0397-3). Loyola.
Kroner, Richard. Culture & Faith. LC 51-7837. pap. 73.50 (ISBN 0-317-09283-9, 2016993). Bks Demand UMI.
--The Primacy of Faith. LC 77-27184. (Gifford Lectures: 1939-40). Repr. of 1943 ed. 26.25 (ISBN 0-404-60497-8). AMS Pr.
Kuasten, J. & Plumpe, J., eds. St. Augustine, Faith, Hope & Charity. Arand, Louis A., tr. LC 78-62450. (Ancient Christian Writers Ser.: No. 3). 165p. 1947. 10.95 (ISBN 0-8091-0045-2). Paulist Pr.
Lackey, Donald L. Faith, the Ultimate Power. LC 81-52786. 144p. (Orig.). 1981. pap. 4.95x (ISBN 0-941116-00-X, 711A). Univ Pubns.
Laidlaw, Robert A. The Reason Why. 48p. 1975. pap. 1.95 (ISBN 0-310-27112-6, 18243P). Zondervan.
Lamb, Bob. The Blood of Jesus: A Foundation for Faith. 1983. pap. 1.95 (ISBN 0-910709-07-6). PTL Repro.
Larson, Christian D. Leave It to God. pap. 1.00 (ISBN 0-87516-191-X). De Vorss.
Lawhead, Steve & Lawhead, Alice. Judge for Yourself. 160p. 1985. pap. 3.95 (ISBN 0-88207-597-7). Victor Bks.
Leroy, Douglas. We Believe. (Illus.). 56p. 1975. pap. 3.95 (ISBN 0-87148-906-6). Pathway Pr.
Lewis, Margie M. & Lewis, Gregg. The Hurting Parent. 160p. (Orig.). 1980. pap. 5.95 (ISBN 0-310-41731-7, 11222P). Zondervan.
Lidiard, Victoria. Christianity: Faith, Love & Healing. LC 84-90145. 80p. 1985. 5.95 (ISBN 0-533-06204-7). Vantage.
Life: A Gift of God. 7.00 (ISBN 0-8198-4441-1). Dghtrs St Paul.
Lindsey, Hal. Combat Faith. 256p. (Orig.). 1986. pap. 7.95 (ISBN 0-553-34342-4). Bantam.
Lings, Martin. Ancient Beliefs & Modern Superstitions. (Unwin Paperbacks). 1980. pap. 4.50 (ISBN 0-04-200034-3). Allen Unwin.
Liptak, David Q. Questions about Your Faith, Bk. IV. pap. 3.95 (ISBN 0-941850-09-9). Sunday Pubns.
Littauer, Florence. Personality Plus. (Illus.). 192p. 1982. 5.95 (Power Ed.); pap. 9.95 (ISBN 0-8007-1323-0). Revell.
Little, Paul. Know What You Believe. 192p. 1985. pap. 2.95 (ISBN 0-89693-526-4). Victor Bks.
Little, Paul E. Know Why You Believe. 160p. 1984. pap. 2.95 (ISBN 0-89693-717-8). Victor Bks.
Louis C.O. Newman's Vision of Faith. LC 86-81425. 210p. 1986. pap. 10.95 (ISBN 0-89870-113-9). Ignatius Pr.
Love Covenant. 3.25 (ISBN 0-8198-4432-2); 2.25 (ISBN 0-8198-4433-0). Dghtrs St Paul.
Lovett, C. S. The Thrill of Faith. 1960. pap. 2.95 (ISBN 0-938148-21-4). Personal Christianity.
Lovette, Roger. A Faith of Our Own. LC 75-27086. 144p. 1976. 6.95 (ISBN 0-8298-0299-1). Pilgrim NY.
Lown, Albert J. Portraits of Faith. 155p. (Orig.). 1981. pap. 3.95 (ISBN 0-8341-0695-7). Beacon Hill.
Lustiger, Jean-Marie. Dare to Believe: Addresses, Sermons, Interviews, 1981-1984. Marana, Nelly, tr. 260p. 1986. 14.95 (ISBN 0-8245-0778-9). Crossroad NY.
MacArthur, John, Jr. Justification by Faith. (John MacArthur's Bible Studies). 1985. pap. 4.95 (ISBN 0-8024-5120-9). Moody.
McCurley, Foster R. Ancient Myths & Biblical Faith. LC 82-48589. 208p. 1983. pap. 12.95 (ISBN 0-8006-1696-0, 1-1696). Fortress.
McIntire, Russell. Live Your Faith! LC 78-25579. 167p. 1979. 6.95 (ISBN 0-88289-217-7). Pelican.
McKenna, Megan & Ducote, Darryl. Old Testament Journeys in Faith. LC 78-71528. (Followers of the Way Ser.: Vol. 1). 1979. 22.50 (ISBN 0-8091-9542-9); 7.50 (ISBN 0-8091-7666-1). Paulist Pr.
Mackey, James P. The Problems of Religious Faith. 344p. 1975. 12.95 (ISBN 0-8199-0454-6). Franciscan Herald.
McMillan, Robert M. Faith Without Fantasy. LC 80-66541. 1981. 4.50 (ISBN 0-8054-5285-0). Broadman.
McPherson, John. The Westminster Confession of Faith. (Handbooks for Bible Classes & Private Students). 182p. 1882. pap. 6.95 (ISBN 0-567-28143-4, Pub. by T & T Clark Ltd Uk). Fortress.
MacRae, George W. Faith in the Word: The Fourth Gospel. (Biblical Booklets Ser). 1975. pap. 1.25 (ISBN 0-8199-0515-1). Franciscan Herald.
Madauss, Martyria. The Shield of Faith. 1974. gift edition 0.95 (ISBN 3-87209-659-1). Evang Sisterhood Mary.
Magno, Joseph A. & LaMotte, Victor S. The Christian, the Atheist, & Freedom. LC 74-165170. 99p. 1975. 7.95 (ISBN 0-913750-08-5). Precedent Pub.
Magubane, Peter. Soweto: The Fruit of Fear. 1986. pap. 14.95 (ISBN 0-8028-0248-6). Eerdmans.
Makarim, Sami N. Druze Faith. LC 73-19819. 1974. 25.00x (ISBN 0-88206-003-1). Caravan Bks.
Marcel, Gabriel. Being & Having: An Existentialist Diary. 11.25 (ISBN 0-8446-2528-0). Peter Smith.
--Mystery of Being, Vol. II: Faith & Reality. 198p. 1984. pap. text ed. 7.75 (ISBN 0-8191-3311-6). U Pr of Amer.
Marie, Patricia. Night Cries. 1981. 4.75 (ISBN 0-8062-1794-4). Carlton.
Martin, John B. & Martin, Catherine. Works of Mercy. 1.17 (ISBN 0-8091-9337-X). Paulist Pr.
Massey, Craig. Ajustarse o Autodestruirse. Orig. Title: Adjust or Self-Destruct. (Span.). 144p. 1983. pap. 3.50 (ISBN 0-8254-1470-9). Kregel.
Means, James. A Tearful Celebration: Courage in Crisis. LC 85-343. 1985. pap. 5.95 (ISBN 0-88070-078-5). Multnomah.
Melanchthon, Philipp. The Justification of Man by Faith Only. Lesse, Nicholas, tr. LC 79-84123. (English Experience Ser.: No. 942). 204p. 1979. Repr. of 1548 ed. lib. bdg. 15.00 (ISBN 90-221-0942-9). Walter J Johnson.
Melnikov, F. E. Otkuda Proizoshla Vijera v Boga. Tr. of Where did Faith in God Come from? 48p. 1938. pap. 2.00 (ISBN 0-317-29132-7). Holy Trinity.
Merrell, James L. Finding Faith in the Headlines. Lambert, Herbert, ed. LC 85-481. (Orig.). 1985. pap. 7.95 (ISBN 0-8272-1012-4). CBP.
Mesle, C. Robert. Fire in My Bones: Reflection on Faith. 1984. pap. 14.00 (ISBN 0-8309-0387-9). Herald Hse.
Metz, Johann B. Faith in History & Society: Toward a Practical Fundamental Theology. 1979. 12.95 (ISBN 0-8245-0305-8). Crossroad NY.
Metz, Johannes-Baptist & Schillebeeckx, Edward, eds. The Teaching Authority of the Believers. (Concilium Ser.). 128p. 1985. pap. 6.95 (Pub. by T & T Clark Ltd UK). Fortress.
Miller, Kevin, ed. Faith Questions: Seeking God's Answers to Our Toughest Questions. (Senior High Pacesetter Ser.). 64p. 1986. pap. 7.95 (ISBN 0-89191-329-7). Cook.

Miller, William R. Living As if: How Positive Faith Can Change Your Life. LC 84-13001. 132p. (Orig.). 1985. pap. 7.95 (ISBN 0-664-24635-4). Westminster.

Mills, Dick. Word in Season, Vol. 1. (Orig.). 1986. pap. 6.95 (ISBN 0-89274-418-9). Harrison Hse.

Mitchell, Basil. The Justification of Religious Belief. (Orig.). 1981. pap. 7.95x (ISBN 0-19-520124-8). Oxford U Pr.

Mitchell, Hubert. Putting Your Faith on the Line. (Orig.). 1981. pap. 5.95 (ISBN 0-89840-027-9). Heres Life.

Mitchell, Joan. Me, Believing. (Infinity Ser.: No. 8). 1972. text ed. 2.50 (ISBN 0-03-004061-2, 241, HarpR). Har-Row.

Mohler, James A. Dimensions of Faith. LC 69-13120. (Orig.). 1969. pap. 2.80 (ISBN 0-8294-0100-8). Loyola.

Mooney, Christopher F., ed. Presence & Absence of God. LC 68-8748. 1969. 20.00 (ISBN 0-8232-0810-9). Fordham.

Moore, Florence. To Know the Unknown. 1984. 5.75 (ISBN 0-8062-2340-5). Carlton.

Moreno, Francisco Jose. Between Faith & Reason: An Approach to Individual & Social Psychology. LC 76-56926. 1977. 20.00x (ISBN 0-8147-5416-3). NYU Pr.

Morris, George E. & Fox, H. E. Faith Sharing: Dynamic Christian Witnessing By Invitation. LC 86-71913. 176p. (Orig.). 1986. pap. 6.95 ea. (ISBN 0-88177-039-6, DR039B). Discipleship Res.

Morse, Charles & Morse, Ann. Whobody There? 1977. pap. 4.95x (ISBN 0-8358-0350-3). Upper Room.

Mounce, William D. Profiles in Faith. LC 84-9961. 1984. pap. 3.95 (ISBN 0-8307-0984-3, S382102). Regal.

Mueller, Virginia. What Is Faith? (A Happy Day Book). (Illus.). 24p. (Orig.). 1980. 1.59 (ISBN 0-87239-411-5, 3643). Standard Pub.

Murphy, Joseph. Magic of Faith. pap. 1.50 (ISBN 0-87516-291-6). De Vorss.

Murray, Andrew. Secret of the Faith Life. (Secret Ser.). (Orig.). 1979. pap. 1.95 (ISBN 0-87508-387-0). Chr Lit.

Mutahhari, Morteza. Man & Faith. Abri, Amir F. & Talebinejad, Mohammad, trs. from Arabic. LC 82-60360. 64p. 1985. pap. 3.95 (ISBN 0-940368-48-X). Tahrike Tarsile Quran.

Nash, Gerald R. When Faith Meets the Impossible. (Outreach Ser.). pap. 1.25 (ISBN 0-686-78874-5). Pacific Pr Pub Assn.

Naude, C. F. & Solle, Dorothee. Hope for Faith: A Conversation. 1986. pap. 3.95 (ISBN 0-8028-0191-9). Eerdmans.

Needleman, Jacob. Lost Christianity: A Journey of Rediscovery. LC 84-48227. 224p. 1985. pap. 6.95 (ISBN 0-06-066102-X, HarpR). Har-Row.

Neighbour, Ralph W., Sr. A Voice from Heaven. 1986. pap. 5.95 (ISBN 0-937931-04-7). Global TN.

Nelson, C. Ellis. Don't Let Your Conscience Be Your Guide. LC 77-94430. 120p. 1978. pap. 2.95 (ISBN 0-8091-2099-2). Paulist Pr.

--Where Faith Begins. pap. 8.95 (ISBN 0-8042-1471-9). John Knox.

Nelson, Wesley W. God's Friends: Called to Believe & Belong. 1985. 15.95 (ISBN 0-910452-59-8); pastor's guide 19.95. Covenant.

Neusner, Jacob. Understanding Seeking Faith: Essays on the Case of Judaism Vol. 1: Dabates on Method Reports of Results. (Brown University Ser.). 158p. 1986. 25.95 (ISBN 1-55540-053-1, 14-01-16). Scholars Pr GA.

Neville. Your Faith Is Your Fortune. pap. 5.50 (ISBN 0-87516-078-6). De Vorss.

Newman, John H. A Reason for the Hope Within: Sermons on the Theory of Religious Belief. 368p. 1985. pap. 14.95 (ISBN 0-87193-219-9). Dimension Bks.

--The Theological Papers of John Henry Newman: On Faith & Certainty, Vol. 1. Holmes, Derek, ed. 1976. 22.50x (ISBN 0-19-920071-8). Oxford U Pr.

Nuzum, C. The Life of Faith. 96p. 1956. pap. 1.95 (ISBN 0-88243-539-6, 02-0539). Gospel Pub.

O'Connor, Francine & Boswell, Kathryn. ABC'S of Faith, Bk. 5. (Illus.). 32p. 1982. pap. 1.95 (ISBN 0-89243-165-2). Liguori Pubns.

--ABC's of Faith, Bk. 6. (Illus.). 32p. 1984. pap. 1.95 (ISBN 0-89243-214-4). Liguori Pubns.

Oda, Stephanie C. Reaching for Joy. 48p. 1985. 4.95 (ISBN 0-8378-5402-4). Gibson.

Odor, Harold & Odor, Ruth. Sharing Your Faith. (Illus.). 16p. 1985. 0.75 (ISBN 0-87239-902-8, 3302). Standard Pub.

Olan, Levi A. Prophetic Faith & the Secular Age. LC 82-2903. 168p. 1982. 15.00x (ISBN 0-87068-888-X). Ktav.

Olsson, Karl A. Into One Body... by the Cross, Vol. 1. 1985. pap. 8.95 (ISBN 0-910452-62-8). Covenant.

O'Malley, William J. The Roots of Unbelief: In Defense of Everything. LC 75-34840. 96p. 1976. pap. 2.95 (ISBN 0-8091-1915-3). Paulist Pr.

Osborn, T. L. Faith Speaks. 1982. pap. 2.95 (ISBN 0-89274-226-7, HH-226). Harrison Hse.

Osborne, Cecil G. The Joy of Understanding Your Faith. 192p. (Orig.). 1983. pap. 7.75 (ISBN 0-687-20594-8). Abingdon.

Ost, Steve. How to Increase Your Faith. (Cornerstone Ser.). 32p. 1981. pap. 2.00 (ISBN 0-930756-61-4, 533003). Aglow Pubns.

Owen, Jackie & Laemmlen, Ann. Articles of Faith Learning Book. (Illus.). 64p. 1982. Bk. I. pap. 3.95 (ISBN 0-87747-878-3); Bk. II, 80pgs. pap. 3.95 (ISBN 0-87747-915-1); Bk. III, 80pgs. pap. 3.95 (ISBN 0-87747-922-4). Deseret Bk.

Owen, R. J. Trial of Faith. 1.60 (ISBN 0-08-017609-7). Pergamon.

Palmer, Earl. In Search of a Faith That Works. LC 85-18421. (In Search of Ser.). 140p. 1985. write for info. (ISBN 0-8307-0889-8, 5110509). Regal.

Palmer, Earl F. Old Law New Life: Ten Commandments & New Testament Faith. 128p. (Orig.). 1984. pap. 7.95 (ISBN 0-687-28744-8). Abingdon.

Papadopoulos, Gerasimos. Orthodoxy, Faith & Life: Christ & the Church. 151p. 1981. 10.95 (ISBN 0-916586-48-0); pap. 5.95 (ISBN 0-916586-47-2). Holy Cross Orthodox.

Patterson, David. Faith & Philosophy. LC 81-43469. 162p. (Orig.). 1982. pap. text ed. 10.50 (ISBN 0-8191-2651-9). U Pr of Amer.

Peachment, Brian. An Aeroplane or a Grave. 1974. pap. 1.85 (ISBN 0-08-017841-3). Pergamon.

--Devil's Island. 1974. pap. 1.60 (ISBN 0-08-017613-5). Pergamon.

--Down among the Dead Men. 1974. pap. 1.60 (ISBN 0-08-017615-1). Pergamon.

Pedraz, Juan L. I Wish I Could Believe. Attanasio, Salvatore, tr. from Span. LC 82-20606. 201p. (Orig.). 1983. pap. 7.95 (ISBN 0-8189-0445-3). Alba.

The Pilgrim's Staff or Daily Steps Heavenward by the Pathway of Faith. 1979. Repr. of 1897 ed. lib. bdg. 20.00 (ISBN 0-8495-4332-0). Arden Lib.

Pittenger, Norman. Before the Ending of the Day. 110p. 1985. pap. 5.95 (ISBN 0-8192-1365-9). Morehouse.

Pittenger, William N. Christian Faith & the Question of History. LC 73-79353. pap. 39.00 (2026910). Bks Demand UMI.

Pitts, James M., ed. The Way of Faith. 176p. (Orig.). 1985. pap. 8.95 (ISBN 0-913029-10-6). Stevens Bk Pr.

Plantinga, Alvin & Wolterstorff, Nicholas, eds. Faith & Rationality: Reason & Belief in God. LC 83-14843. 336p. 1984. 24.95x (ISBN 0-268-00964-3, 85-09648); pap. text ed. 11.95x (ISBN 0-268-00965-1, 85-09655). U of Notre Dame Pr.

Portugal: Message of Fatima. 3.50 (ISBN 0-8198-5809-9); 2.50 (ISBN 0-8198-5810-2). Dghtrs St Paul.

Pragai, Michael J. Faith & Fulfillment: Christians & the Return to the Promised Land. (Illus.). 326p. 1985. 24.00x (ISBN 0-85303-210-6, Vallentine Mitchell England); pap. 12.50x (ISBN 0-85303-211-4). Biblio Dist.

Price, Charles P. A Matter of Faith. LC 83-50559. 80p. 1983. pap. 5.95 (ISBN 0-8192-1335-7). Morehouse.

Price, Charles S. Real Faith: One of the Classic Faith-Builders. 1972. pap. 4.95 (ISBN 0-88270-000-6). Bridge Pub.

Price, Eugenia. No Pat Answers. 144p. 1983. pap. 5.95 (ISBN 0-310-31331-7, 16244P). Zondervan.

Price, Frederick. Como Obra la Fe. 111p. 1980. pap. 2.95 (ISBN 0-89274-157-0). Harrison Hse.

Price, Frederick K. Faith, Foolishness, or Presumption. 160p. (Orig.). 1979. pap. 4.95 (ISBN 0-89274-103-1). Harrison Hse.

--How Faith Works. 128p. (Orig.). 1979. pap. 3.95 (ISBN 0-89274-001-9). Harrison Hse.

--How to Obtain Strong Faith: Six Principles. 184p. pap. 4.95 (ISBN 0-89274-042-6). Harrison Hse.

--Now Faith Is. 32p. 1984. pap. 0.75 (ISBN 0-89274-302-6). Harrison Hse.

Price, Theron D. Revelation & Faith: Theological Reflections on the Knowing & Doing of Faith. 192p. 1987. 29.95 (ISBN 0-86554-260-0, MUP H-221); pap. 14.95 (ISBN 0-86554-261-9, MUP P-45). Mercer Univ Pr.

Prince, Derek. Faith to Live by. 1977. pap. 5.95 (ISBN 0-934920-25-7, B-29). Derek Prince.

--Foundation for Faith. (Foundation Ser.: Bk. I). 1965-66. pap. 2.95 (ISBN 0-934920-00-1, B-10). Derek Prince.

Protopresbyter Michael Pomazansky. O Zhizni o Vjere o Tzerkvje, 2 vols. Tr. of On Life, Faith & the Church. 650p. 1976. pap. 23.00 (ISBN 0-317-29072-X). Holy Trinity.

Pruitt, Raymond M. Fundamentals of the Faith. 1981. 16.95 (ISBN 0-934942-21-8). White Wing Pub.

Puccetti, Patricia I. Credo: I Believe: Activity Book. 46p. (Orig.). 1985. pap. 2.50 (ISBN 0-89870-082-5). Ignatius Pr.

Purnell, Dick. Faith: A Thirty-One-Day Experiment. 60p. (Orig.). 1985. pap. 2.95 (ISBN 0-89840-076-7). Heres Life.

Radhakrishnan, Sarvepalli. Recovery of Faith. Repr. of 1955 ed. lib. bdg. 22.50x (ISBN 0-8371-0197-2, RARF). Greenwood.

Rahner, Karl. The Practice of Faith: A Handbook of Contemporary Spirituality. rev. ed. 336p. 1986. pap. 14.95 (ISBN 0-8245-0779-7). Crossroad NY.

Ratzinger, Joseph. The Feast of Faith. Harrison, Graham, tr. from Ger. LC 85-82175. Orig. Title: Das Fest des Glaubens. 175p. (Orig.). 1986. pap. 8.95 (ISBN 0-89870-056-6). Ignatius Pr.

Redpath, Alan. Victorious Christian Faith. 192p. 9.95 (ISBN 0-8007-1208-0). Revell.

Reeve, Pamela. Faith Is. 1970. pap. 4.95 (ISBN 0-930014-05-7). Multnomah.

Requirements for Faithfulness. 1981. 1.25 (ISBN 0-89858-030-7). Fill the Gap.

Richardson, W. Christian Doctrine: The Faith... Once Delivered. LC 82-25598. (Bible College Textbooks Ser.). 448p. (Orig.). 1983. pap. 9.95 (ISBN 0-87239-610-X, 88588). Standard Pub.

Ripley, Francis J. This Is the Faith. 317p. 1973. pap. 5.95 (ISBN 0-903348-02-0). Lumen Christi.

Robinson, Wayne. Questions Are the Answer. LC 80-36780. 110p. 1980. pap. 5.95 (ISBN 0-8298-0409-9). Pilgrim NY.

Ronald Reagan: In God I Trust. 1984. pap. 3.95 (ISBN 0-8423-5704-1). Tyndale.

Ross, Bob L. Salvation by Grace Through Faith in Contrast to the Restorationist Doctrine. 1979. pap. 1.00 (ISBN 0-686-35836-8). Pilgrim Pubns.

Routley, Erik. Church Music & the Christian Faith. LC 78-110219. 1979. 7.95 (ISBN 0-916642-11-9, Agape). Hope Pub.

Roy, Paul S. Building Christian Communities for Justice. LC 81-80050. 188p. (Orig.). 1981. pap. 9.95 (ISBN 0-8091-2380-0). Paulist Pr.

Russell, Robert A. God Works Through Faith. 1957. pap. 3.95 (ISBN 0-87516-325-4). De Vorss.

Ryrie, Charles C. Las Bases de la Fe Premilenial. Orig. Title: The Basis of the Premillennial Faith. (Span.). 224p. 1984. pap. 3.95 (ISBN 0-8254-1626-4). Kregel.

St. Clair, Barry. Giving Away Your Faith. (Moving Toward Maturity Ser.: No. 4). 132p. 1985. pap. 4.95 (ISBN 0-317-16074-5). Victor Bks.

St. Romain, Philip. Faith & Doubt Today. LC 85-82033. 128p. (Orig.). 1986. pap. 3.25 (ISBN 0-89243-245-4). Liguori Pubns.

Samuel, Leith. Share Your Faith. (Contemporary Discussion Ser.). 104p. 1981. pap. 2.95 (ISBN 0-8010-8187-4). Baker Bk.

--There Is an Answer. pap. 2.50 (ISBN 0-87508-469-9). Chr Lit.

Sanders, J. Oswald. Effective Faith. Orig. Title: Mighty Faith. 1980. pap. 1.00 (ISBN 9971-83-833-8). OMF Bks.

Savelle, Jerry. Energizing Your Faith. 64p. 1984. pap. 2.25 (ISBN 0-89274-285-2, HH-285). Harrison Hse.

Sawyer, Kieran. Confirming Faith. LC 82-71984. (Illus.). 208p. (Orig.). 1982. pap. text ed. 9.75 directors manual (ISBN 0-87793-251-4). Ave Maria.

--Confirming Faith: Participant Book. LC 82-71984. (Illus.). 96p. (Orig.). 1982. pap. text ed. 3.75 (ISBN 0-87793-252-2). Ave Maria.

Schillebeeckx, Edward. On Christian Faith: The Spiritual, Ethical & Political Dimensions. 1987. 12.95. Crossroad NY.

Schroeder, David. Faith Refined by Fire. LC 85-80428. (Faith & Life Bible Studies). 143p. (Orig.). 1985. pap. 4.95 (ISBN 0-87303-103-2). Faith & Life.

Schuller, Robert H. Tough-Minded Faith for Tender-Hearted People. LC 83-22144. 384p. 1984. 14.95 (ISBN 0-8407-5358-6). Nelson.

Scwarz, Hans. Responsible Faith: Christian Theology in the Light of 20th-Century Questions. LC 85-26657. 448p. 1986. text ed. 23.95 (ISBN 0-8066-2188-5, 10-5483). Augsburg.

Seilhamer, Frank S. Adventure in Faith. 1983. 7.95 (ISBN 0-89536-675-4, 0125). CSS of Ohio.

Sell, Charles. The House on the Rock. 168p. 1987. pap. 5.95 (ISBN 0-89693-048-3). Victor Bks.

Selness, Craig. When Your Mountain Won't Move. 156p. 1984. pap. 5.95 (ISBN 0-88207-619-1). Victor Bks.

Set Apart for Service. 4.00 (ISBN 0-8198-6832-9); 3.00 (ISBN 0-8198-6833-7). Dghtrs St Paul.

Shaw, Judy. Little Faith Builders. 30p. (Orig.). 1983. pap. 0.75 (ISBN 0-89274-290-9). Harrison Hse.

Sheets, John R. To Believe Is to Exist. 1986. pap. 14.95 (ISBN 0-87193-247-4). Dimension Bks.

Sheldon, Charles. In His Steps. pap. 5.95, 250p. (ISBN 0-8007-5011-X, Power Bks); pap. 3.50, 192p. (ISBN 0-8007-8022-1, Spire Bks). Revell.

Shepherd, Victor A. The Nature & Function of Faith in the Theology of John Calvin. LC 82-24899. vii, 248p. 1983. pap. 17.45 (ISBN 0-86554-066-7, P07). Mercer Univ Pr.

Short, Robert L. Something to Believe in. LC 75-36754. (Illus.). 1977. pap. 5.95i (ISBN 0-06-067381-8, RD 169, HarpR). Har-Row.

Simmons, Billy E. A Functioning Faith. 144p. 1983. pap. 4.00 (ISBN 0-914520-18-0). Insight Pr.

--Resplendent Themes. 70p. 1983. pap. 4.00 (ISBN 0-914520-19-9). Insight Pr.

Skinner, John E. The Meaning of Authority. LC 82-25098. 88p. (Orig.). 1983. lib. bdg. 22.00 (ISBN 0-8191-3044-3, Co-pub. by Episcopal Div Sch); pap. text ed. 8.50 (ISBN 0-8191-3045-1). U Pr of Amer.

Slay, James L., ed. Esto Creemos. (Span.). 156p. 1963. pap. 4.95 (ISBN 0-87148-309-2). Pathway Pr.

Smart, James D. The Cultural Subversion of the Biblical Faith: Life in the 20th Century under the Sign of the Cross. LC 77-22063. 126p. 1977. pap. 5.95 (ISBN 0-664-24148-4). Westminster.

Smith, Chuck. The Gospel According to Grace. 176p. 1981. pap. 3.95 (ISBN 0-936728-12-4). Word for Today.

Smith, Hannah W. Christian's Secret of a Happy Life. 256p. 1968. o. p. 8.95 (ISBN 0-8007-0044-9); pap. 6.95 (ISBN 0-8007-5004-7, Power Bks); pap. 3.50 (ISBN 0-8007-8007-8, Spire Bks). Revell.

Smith, Joseph. Lectures on Faith. LC 84-73495. 96p. 1985. 6.95 (ISBN 0-87747-897-X). Deseret Bk.

Smith, Kent D. Faith: Reflections on Experience, Theology & Fiction. 114p. (Orig.). 1984. lib. bdg. 22.00 (ISBN 0-8191-3634-4); pap. text ed. 9.25 (ISBN 0-8191-3635-2). U Pr of Amer.

Smith, Wilfred C. Belief & History. LC 75-50587. 138p. 1977. pap. 7.95x (ISBN 0-8139-1086-2). U Pr of Va.

--Faith & Belief. LC 78-63601. 1979. 35.50x (ISBN 0-691-07232-9). Princeton U Pr.

--Faith & Belief. 360p. 1987. pap. 12.50 (ISBN 0-691-02040-X). Princeton U Pr.

Smock, Martha. Este Es el Tiempo para la Fe. Tr. of Now Is the Time for Faith. 1984. 5.95 (ISBN 0-87159-033-6). Unity School.

Sockey, Daria. Our Heavenly Father. (Faith & Life Ser.: Bk. 1). (Illus.). 125p. 1987. pap. text ed. 4.95; activity book 2.50. Ignatius Pr.

Sockey, Daria M. Credo: I Believe. Puccetti, Patricia I., ed. (Faith & Life Ser.). (Illus.). 132p. 1985. pap. 6.20 (ISBN 0-89870-081-7). Ignatius Pr.

Sovenson, Lois B. What Does It Mean to Believe in Jesus. (Cornerstone Ser.). 32p. 1981. pap. 2.00 (ISBN 0-930756-64-9, 533004). Aglow Pubns.

Sponheim, Paul R. God: The Question & the Quest. LC 85-47737. 224p. 1986. 19.95 (ISBN 0-8006-0756-2). Fortress.

Sproul, R. C. Reason to Believe. 160p. 1982. pap. 5.95 (ISBN 0-310-44911-1, 12370P). Zondervan.

Spurgeon, C. H. Sin of Unbelief. 1977. pap. 0.95 (ISBN 0-686-23224-0). Pilgrim Pubns.

Spurgeon, Charles H. Faith's Checkbook. pap. 3.95 (ISBN 0-8024-0014-0). Moody.

Steidl, G. S. By Faith. 48p. pap. 3.25 (ISBN 0-88172-127-1). Believers Bkshelf.

Stevens, Velma D. God Is Faithful. LC 86-921. 1986. pap. 3.25 (ISBN 0-8054-5028-9). Broadman.

Stewart, Ken. Do's & Don'ts for an Overnight Stay in the Lion's Den. 31p. write for info. (ISBN 0-89274-043-4). Harrison Hse.

--Doubt: The Enemy of Faith. 32p. (Orig.). 1984. pap. 1.95 (ISBN 0-89274-034-5). Harrison Hse.

Sumrall, Lester. Faith to Change the World. 173p. (Orig.). 1983. pap. 4.95 (ISBN 0-89274-306-9, HH-306). Harrison Hse.

Surath, Sri. To God Through Faith: From Christ to Sri Ramakrishna. 1978. pap. 3.00 (ISBN 0-685-58452-6). Ranney Pubns.

Sutherland, Stewart R. God, Jesus & Belief: The Legacy of Theism. 160p. 1984. 29.95x (ISBN 0-631-13548-0); pap. 12.95 (ISBN 0-631-13591-X). Basil Blackwell.

Swafford, Mrs. Z. W. This We Believe. (Illus.). 109p. (Orig.). 1983. pap. 2.50 (ISBN 0-89114-115-4). Baptist Pub Hse.

Sykes, Reverend William G. Visions of Faith: An Anthology of Reflections. 544p. 1986. 19.95 (ISBN 0-920792-25-1). Eden Pr.

Talec, Pierre. Jesus & the Hunger for Things Unknown. Neugroschel, Joachim, tr. from Fr. Orig. Title: Les Choses de la Foi. 250p. 1982. 12.95 (ISBN 0-8164-0510-7, HarpR). Har-Row.

Theissen, Gerd. Biblical Faith: An Evolutionary Approach. Bowden, John, tr. LC 84-21072. 224p. 1985. pap. 8.95 (ISBN 0-8006-1842-4, 1-1842). Fortress.

Thielicke, Helmut. Faith the Great Adventure. LC 84-48716. 160p. 1985. pap. 8.95 (ISBN 0-8006-1833-5, 1-1833). Fortress.

Tillich, Paul. Dynamics of Faith. pap. 6.95x (ISBN 0-06-130042-X, TB42, Torch). Har-Row.
Tilton, Robert. God's Laws of Success. 1986. pap. 6.95 (ISBN 0-89274-405-7). Harrison Hse.
Towns, Elmer & Falwell, Jerry. Stepping Out on Faith. 192p. 1984. pap. 6.95 (ISBN 0-8423-6626-1). Tyndale.
Towns, Elmer L. What the Faith Is All About. LC 83-70235. 480p. 1983. pap. 9.95 (ISBN 0-8423-7870-7); leader's guide 2.95 (ISBN 0-8423-7869-3). Tyndale.
Townsend, Ralph. Faith, Prayer & Devotion. (Faith & the Future Ser.). 123p. 1984. cloth 24.95x (ISBN 0-631-13189-2); pap. 8.95x (ISBN 0-631-13232-5). Basil Blackwell.
Trese, Leo. The Faith Explained. rev. ed. 479p. 1984. pap. 7.95 (ISBN 971-117-042-6, Pub. by Sinag-Tala Pubs Philippines). Scepter Pubs.
Troki, Isaac. Faith Strengthened. Mocatta, Moses, tr. from Hebrew. LC 74-136768. 320p. 1975. pap. 9.75 (ISBN 0-87203-022-9). Hermon.
Tucker, Roanld D. Faith. (Illus.). 56p. 1983. pap. 2.00 (ISBN 0-933643-14-4). Grace World Outreach.
Tuttle, Robert G. Help Me God! It's Hard to Cope. 1984. 4.95 (ISBN 0-89536-698-3, 4881). CSS of Ohio.
Ujka, Mary. The Cross Gives Me Courage. LC 83-60743. 132p. (Orig.). 1983. pap. 5.95 (ISBN 0-87973-618-6, 618). Our Sunday Visitor.
Upham, Thomas C. The Life of Faith. (The Higher Christian Life Ser.). 480p. 1985. lib. bdg. 60.00 (ISBN 0-8240-6447-X). Garland Pub.
Upton, Charles B. Lectures on the Bases of Religious Belief. 2nd ed. LC 77-27161. (Hibbert Lectures: 1893). Repr. of 1897 ed. 39.50 (ISBN 0-404-60411-0). AMS Pr.
Vander Kolk, Justin. To Set Things Right: The Bible Speaks on Faith & Justice. 48p. 1971. pap. 1.25 (ISBN 0-377-02001-X). Friend Pr.
Van Til, Cornelius. Why I Believe in God. 1948. pap. 0.75 (ISBN 0-87552-496-6). Presby & Reformed.
Vickers, Douglas. Now That You Have Believed: An Exploration of the Life & Walk of Faith. 1981. 10.00 (ISBN 0-682-49830-0). Exposition Pr FL.
Vos, Nelvin. Seven Days a Week: Faith in Action. LC 84-47937. 144p. 1985. pap. 5.95 (ISBN 0-8006-1658-8, 1-1658). Fortress.
Wagar, W. Warren, ed. The Secular Mind: Transformations of Faith in Modern Europe. LC 81-20019. 275p. 1982. text ed. 42.50x (ISBN 0-8419-0766-8). Holmes & Meier.
Wagner, Clarence M. Invisible & Invincible. 78p. 1982. pap. 4.00 (ISBN 0-937498-05-X). Tru-Faith.
Wahlie, Jim. The God Kind of Faith for Total Prosperity. 61p. 1986. pap. 3.95 (ISBN 0-88144-049-3). Christian Pub.
Waltz, Alan K. To Proclaim the Faith. 144p. 1983. pap. 3.95 (ISBN 0-687-42252-3). Abingdon.
Wangerin, Walter, Jr. The Orphean Passages: The Drama of Faith. 305p. 1986. 16.95 (ISBN 0-06-069256-1). Har-Row.
Watchman, Nee. From Faith to Faith. Fader, Herbert L., ed. Kaung, Stephen, tr. 120p. 1984. pap. 3.50 (ISBN 0-935008-62-4). Christian Fellow Pubs.
Watts, Alan W. Does It Matter. LC 72-89988. 1971. pap. 3.95 (ISBN 0-394-71665-5, Vin). Random.
Wedderspoon, William M. God & the Procurator, Some Questions Asked. 176p. 1986. 9.95 (ISBN 0-8059-3020-5). Dorrance.
Weissinger, Muir. The Failure of Faith: An Investigation into Totalitarianism, Irrationality & Faith. LC 83-8171. 219p. 1983. 32.00 (ISBN 0-86187-284-3, Pub. by Frances Pinter). Longwood Pub Group.
Wells, David F. God the Evangelist: How the Holy Spirit Works to Bring Men & Women to Faith. 144p. (Orig.). 1987. pap. 6.95 (ISBN 0-8028-0271-0). Eerdmans.
Wells, Tom. Faith the Gift of God. 156p. 1983. pap. 3.95 (ISBN 0-85151-361-1). Banner of Truth.
--Moral Basis of Faith. 28p. (Orig.). 1986. pap. 1.45 (ISBN 0-85151-469-3). Banner of Truth.
Wenger, J. C. El Libro Llamado la Biblia. Rindzinski, Milka, tr. from Eng. LC 84-80158. (Mennonite Faith Ser.: No. 8). 72p. (Orig.). 1984. pap. 1.50 (ISBN 0-8361-1268-7). Herald Pr.
Westerhoff, John H., III. Will Our Children Have Faith? 144p. 1983. pap. 6.95 (ISBN 0-8164-2435-7, AY7452, HarpR). Har-Row.
Westra, Rinny. The Faith of A Radical. 80p. (Orig.). 1984. pap. 8.95 (ISBN 0-86474-001-8, Pub. by Interface Press). ANZ Religious Pubns.
Weyland, Jack. First Day Forever & the Other Stories for LDS Youth. LC 80-82455. 120p. 1980. 7.95 (ISBN 0-88290-136-2, 2037). Horizon Utah.
Wigglesworth, Smith. Ever Increasing Faith. rev. ed. 176p. 1971. pap. 1.95 (ISBN 0-88243-494-2, 02-0494). Gospel Pub.
--Faith That Prevails. 64p. 1966. pap. 1.75 (ISBN 0-88243-711-9, 02-0711). Gospel Pub.
Wilbur, L. Perry. How to Live Your Faith. 128p. 1984. 12.95 (ISBN 0-13-416850-X); pap. 5.95 (ISBN 0-13-416843-7). P-H.
Wilburn, Stephen S. Resting in the Lord. 48p. 1985. 4.95 (ISBN 0-8378-5404-0). Gibson.
William of St. Thierry. The Mirror of Faith. Elder, E. Rozanne, ed. Davis, Thomas X., tr. from Lat. LC 78-12897. (Cistercian Fathers Ser.). (Illus.). 1979. 12.95 (ISBN 0-87907-315-2). Cistercian Pubns.
Williamson, Clark M. Has God Rejected His People? LC 81-12847. 192p. (Orig.). 1982. pap. 8.75 (ISBN 0-687-16649-7). Abingdon.
Willimon, William H. Sighing for Eden: Sin, Evil & the Christian Faith. 208p. 1985. pap. 8.95 (ISBN 0-687-38447-8). Abingdon.
Wilson-Kastner, Patricia. Faith, Feminism & the Christ. LC 83-5688. 160p. 1983. pap. 8.95 (ISBN 0-8006-1746-0). Fortress.
Wirt, Sherwood E. Faith's Heroes. LC 78-71943. 1979. pap. 3.95 (ISBN 0-89107-162-8, Crossway Bks). Good News.
Wolf, Barbara & Wolf, Frederick B. Exploring Faith & Life: A Journey in Faith for Junior High - Manual for Clergy & Leaders. 64p. (Orig.). 1983. pap. 3.95 (ISBN 0-8164-2437-3, HarpR). Har-Row.
--Exploring Faith & Life: A Journey in Faith for Junior High - Manual for Sponsors. 32p. (Orig.). 1983. pap. 2.95 (ISBN 0-8164-2436-5, HarpR). Har-Row.
Wolf, Frederick B. & Wolf, Barbara B. Exploring Faith & Life: A Journey in Faith for Junior High Student's Reader. 128p. 1983. pap. 5.95 (ISBN 0-8164-2431-4, HarpR). Har-Row.
Wolff, Robert L. Gains & Losses. (Victorian Fiction Ser.). Orig. Title: Faith & Doubt in Victorian England. 1977. lib. bdg. 33.00 (ISBN 0-8240-1617-3). Garland Pub.
Woodson, William. Standing for Their Faith. 1979. 8.95 (ISBN 0-317-39803-2). Gospel Advocate.
Words of Faith. (Words of... Ser.). (Illus.). 48p. 1983. 3.95 (ISBN 0-8407-5333-0). Nelson.
Wurmbrand, Richard. Victorious Faith. 1979. pap. 3.95 (ISBN 0-88264-120-4). Diane Bks.
Yasko, Bill & Yasko, Dot. Building Your Faith. 76p. (Orig.). 1984. pap. text ed. 4.95 (ISBN 0-931097-01-0). Sentinel Pub.
Youngblood, Ronald F. Faith of Our Fathers. LC 75-23514. 1976. pap. 3.50 (ISBN 0-8307-0370-5, S302101). Regal.
Zodhiates, Spiros. The Work of Faith. (Trilogy Ser.: Vol. 2). (Illus.). pap. 6.95 (ISBN 0-89957-545-5). AMG Pubs.

FAITH, CONFESSIONS OF
see Creeds

FAITH AND JUSTIFICATION
see Justification

FAITH AND REASON
see also Philosophy and Religion; Religion and Science

Augsburger, Myron S. When Reason Fails. 112p. 1985. pap. 4.95 (ISBN 0-8423-7999-1). Tyndale.
Bambrough, Renford. Reason, Truth & God. (Library Reprints Ser.). 174p. 1979. 45.00x (ISBN 0-416-72530-9, NO. 2823). Methuen Inc.
Campolo, Anthony. A Reasonable Faith. 208p. 1985. 8.95 (ISBN 0-8499-3040-5, 3040-5). Word Bks.
Carstens, R. W. Notes on Humanity: Faith, Reason, Certainty. 142p. (Orig.). 1985. pap. text ed. 8.50 (ISBN 0-8191-4885-7). U Pr of Amer.
Colton, C. E. The Faithfulness of Faith. LC 85-9845. 1985. pap. 4.95 (ISBN 0-8054-1534-3). Broadman.
Crowley, Mary C. You Can Too. 176p. 1980. pap. 5.95 (ISBN 0-8007-5028-4, Power Bks). Revell.
Dahlstrom, Daniel O., ed. Practical Reasoning: ACPA Proceedings, 1984, Vol. 58. 250p. 1985. pap. 12.00 (ISBN 0-918090-18-0). Am Cath Philo.
Farah, Charles, Jr. From the Pinnacle of the Temple. LC 79-89218. 1979. pap. 4.95 (ISBN 0-88270-462-1). Bridge Pub.
Ferre, Nels F. Faith & Reason. facsimile ed. LC 78-142626. (Essay Index Reprints - Reason & the Christian Faith Ser.: Vol. 1). Repr. of 1946 ed. 19.00 (ISBN 0-8369-2392-8). Ayer Co Pubs.
Flewelling, Ralph T. The Reason in Faith. LC 75-3148. Repr. of 1924 ed. 24.00 (ISBN 0-404-59155-8). AMS Pr.
Hayner, Jerry. Yes, God Can. LC 84-4153. 1985. 6.95 (ISBN 0-8054-2258-7). Broadman.
Hegel, G. W. Faith & Knowledge: The Reflective Philosophy of Subjectivity. Harris, H. S. & Cerf, Walter, eds. Harris, H. S. & Cerf, Walter., trs. from Ger. LC 76-10250. 1977. 39.50 (ISBN 0-87395-338-X). State U NY Pr.
LeNoir, C. P. Dictionnaire des Droits et de la Raison. Migne, J. P., ed. (Troisieme et Derniere Encyclopedie Theologique Ser.: Vol. 57). (Fr.). 952p. Repr. of 1860 ed. lib. bdg. 120.00x (ISBN 0-89241-323-9). Caratzas.
--Dictionnaire des Harmonies de la Raison et de la Foi. Migne, J. P., ed. (Troisieme et Derniere Encyclopedie Theologique Ser.: Vol. 19). (Fr.). 876p. Repr. of 1856 ed. lib. bdg. 110.50x (ISBN 0-89241-302-6). Caratzas.
Miethe, Terry. A Christian's Guide to Faith & Reason. 192p. (Orig.). 1987. pap. 5.95 (ISBN 0-87123-677-X). Bethany Hse.
Moltmann, Jurgen. Experiences of God. Kohl, Margaret, tr. from Ger. LC 80-8046. 96p. 1980. pap. 4.25 (ISBN 0-8006-1406-2, 1-1406). Fortress.
Parker, Francis H. Reason & Faith Revisited. (Aquinas Lecture 1971). 7.95 (ISBN 0-87462-136-4). Marquette.
Pieper, Josef. Belief & Faith: A Philosophical Tract. Winston, Richard & Winston, Clara, trs. from German. LC 75-31841. 106p. 1976. Repr. of 1963 ed. lib. bdg. 22.50x (ISBN 0-8371-8490-8, PIBF). Greenwood.
Redwood, John. Reason, Ridicule & Religion. 1976. 16.50x (ISBN 0-674-74953-7). Harvard U Pr.
Sokolowski, Robert. The God of Faith & Reason: Foundations of Christian Theology. LC 81-19813. 192p. 1982. 15.95 (ISBN 0-268-01006-4); pap. text ed. 6.95 (ISBN 0-268-01007-2). U of Notre Dame Pr.
Stott, John R. Your Mind Matters. LC 72-94672. 64p. 1973. pap. 3.50 (ISBN 0-87784-441-0). Inter-Varsity.
Swinburne, Richard. Faith & Reason. 1981. pap. 10.95X (ISBN 0-19-824725-7). Oxford U Pr.
Thompson, Conrad M. Mender of Broken Hearts: How Christ Gives Us Courage to Live. LC 81-52270. 128p. (Orig.). 1982. pap. 5.95 (ISBN 0-8066-1902-3, 10-4343). Augsburg.
Towns, Elmer L. Say-It-Faith. 1983. pap. 5.95 (ISBN 0-8423-5825-0). Tyndale.
White, Ellen G. Selected Messages, Vol. III. 1980. Christian Home Library Ed. 8.95 (ISBN 0-8280-0055-7, 19275-7); Shield Ser. Ed. 4.95 (ISBN 0-8280-0056-5, 19276-5); Special Ed. pap. 4.50 (ISBN 0-8280-0057-3, 19277-3). Review & Herald.
--Selected Messages, 3 vols. 1980. Set. pap. 11.95 (ISBN 0-8280-0059-X, 19269-0). Review & Herald.

FAITH CURE
see Spiritual Healing

FAITH HEALING
see Spiritual Healing

FALASHAS

Ashkenazi, Michael & Weingrod, Alex. Ethiopian Jews & Israel. 188p. 1987. 24.95 (ISBN 0-88738-133-2). Transaction Bks.
Kessler, David. The Falashas. (Illus.). 205p. 1985. pap. 7.95 (ISBN 0-8052-0791-0). Schocken.
Leslau, Wolf, tr. Falasha Anthology. (Judaica Ser.: No. 6). (Illus.). 1951. 26.00x (ISBN 0-300-00681-0). Yale U Pr.
Messing, Simon D. The Story of the Falashas: "Black Jews" of Ethiopia. (Illus.). 134p. 1982. pap. 7.50 (ISBN 0-9615946-9-1). Messing Pub.
Parfitt, Tudor. Operation Moses: The Untold Story of the Secret Exodus of the Falasha Jews from Ethiopia. LC 85-40240. (Illus.). 192p. 1986. 16.95 (ISBN 0-8128-3059-8). Stein & Day.

FALL OF MAN
see also Good and Evil; Paradise; Sin; Sin, Original

Bonhoeffer, Dietrich. Creation & Fall. Bd. with Temptation. 1965. pap. 4.95 (ISBN 0-02-083890-5). Macmillan.
--Creation & Fall: Temptation. 1983. 13.00 (ISBN 0-8446-5962-2). Peter Smith.
Gurteen, S. Humphreys. Epic of the Fall of Man. LC 65-15879. (Studies in Comparative Literature, No. 35). 1969. Repr. of 1896 ed. lib. bdg. 75.00x (ISBN 0-8383-0561-X). Haskell.
Haines, Victor Y. The Fortunate Fall of Sir Gawain: The Typology of Sir Gawain & the Green Knight. LC 80-5847. (Illus.). 240p. (Orig.). 1982. PLB 29.00 (ISBN 0-8191-2437-0); pap. text ed. 12.75 (ISBN 0-8191-2438-9). U Pr of Amer.
Melzer, Sara E. Discourses of the Fall: A Study of Pascal's Pensees. LC 85-24519. 128p. 1986. text ed. 22.95x (ISBN 0-520-05540-3). U of Cal Pr.
Puhalo, Lazar. Creation & Fall. 36p. (Orig.). 1986. pap. text ed. 4.00 (ISBN 0-913026-97-2). Synaxis Pr.
Williams, Norman P. The Ideas of the Fall & of Original Sin: A Historical & Critical Study. LC 79-8125. Repr. of 1927 ed. 49.00 (ISBN 0-404-18439-1). AMS Pr.
Woodhull, Marianna. Epic of Paradise Lost. LC 72-194899. 1907. lib. bdg. 12.50 (ISBN 0-8414-9501-7). Folcroft.
--Epic of Paradise Lost: Twelve Essays. LC 68-57833. 386p. 1968. Repr. of 1907 ed. 32.50x (ISBN 0-87752-124-7). Gordian.

FAMILY
see also Church Work with Families; Divorce; Family Life Education; Fathers; Grandparents; Marriage; Mothers; Parent and Child; Single-Parent Family; Widows

Anway, Carol. Family Enrichment Book. 1979. pap. 8.00 (ISBN 0-8309-0247-3). Herald Hse.
Blitchington, Evelyn. The Family Devotions Idea Book. LC 82-4252. 139p. (Orig.). 1982. pap. 4.95 (ISBN 0-87123-254-5, 210254). Bethany Hse.
Boulding, Elise. The Family As a Way into the Future. 1983. pap. 2.50x (ISBN 0-87574-222-X, 222). Pendle Hill.
Bullinger, Heinrich. The Christian State of Matrimonye. Coverdale, Myles, tr. LC 74-80167. (English Experience Ser.: No. 646). 168p. 1974. Repr. of 1541 ed. 11.50 (ISBN 90-221-0646-2). Walter J Johnson.
Demos, John. Little Commonwealth: Family Life in Plymouth Colony. (Illus.). 1970. pap. 6.95x (ISBN 0-19-501355-7). Oxford U Pr.
Denton, Wallace & Denton, Juanita H. Creative Couples: The Growth Factor in Marriage. LC 82-17439. 154p. 1983. pap. 8.95 (ISBN 0-664-24453-X). Westminster.
Dyer, William G. Creating Closer Families: Principles of Positive Family Interaction. LC 75-20169. (Illus.). 144p. 1975. pap. 6.95 (ISBN 0-8425-0726-4). Brigham.
God, Family, Country: Our Three Great Loyalties. Ezra Taft Benson. LC 74-84477. 437p. 1974. 11.95 (ISBN 0-87747-541-5). Deseret Bk.
Hiesberger, Jean M., ed. Healing Family Hurts. LC 79-90991. (Paths of Life Ser.). 128p. (Orig.). 1979. pap. 2.95 (ISBN 0-8091-2266-9). Paulist Pr.
Howell, Mary. Helping Ourselves: Families & the Human Network. LC 75-5291. 1975. pap. 6.95x (ISBN 0-8070-2759-6, BP551). Beacon Pr.
James, Gene G., ed. The Family & the Unification Church. LC 83-80638. (Conference Ser.: No. 17). 1983. 14.95 (ISBN 0-932894-19-4, Pub. by New Era Bks); pap. text ed. 10.95 (ISBN 0-932894-17-8). Paragon Hse.
Kaplan, Benjamin. Jew & His Family. LC 67-21376. 1967. 25.00x (ISBN 0-8071-0545-7). La State U Pr.
Kesler, Jay. Family Forum. 1984. 12.95 (ISBN 0-88207-820-8). Victor Bks.
Konopka, Coles, et al. Function of Rebellion: Is Youth Creating New Family Values? LC 66-17843. 1968. pap. 2.85 (ISBN 0-686-25738-3). Jewish Bd Family.
Linzer, Norman. The Jewish Family: Authority & Tradition in Modern Perspectives. 217p. 1984. 34.95 (ISBN 0-89885-149-1); pap. 14.95 (ISBN 0-89885-191-2). Human Sci Pr.
Money, Royce. Building Stronger Families. LC 83-51300. 156p. 1984. pap. 5.95 (ISBN 0-88207-244-7). Victor Bks.
Monfalcone, Wesley R. Coping with Abuse in the Family. LC 80-15125. (Christian Care Bks.: Vol. 10). 120p. 1980. pap. 7.95 (ISBN 0-664-24326-6). Westminster.
Neff, Pauline. Tough Love: How Parents Can Deal with Drug Abuse. 160p. 1984. pap. 7.50 (ISBN 0-687-42407-0). Abingdon.
Peck, Jane C. Self & Family. LC 84-13166. (Choices: Guides for Today's Woman Ser.: Vol. 11). 118p. 1984. pap. 6.95 (ISBN 0-664-24547-1). Westminster.
Perersen, William J. C. S. Lewis Had a Wife. 160p. (Orig.). 1985. pap. 2.95 (ISBN 0-8423-0202-6). Tyndale.
Pipe, Virginia E. Live & Learn with Your Teenager. LC 85-18451. (Family Life Ser.). 160p. 1985. pap. 6.95 (ISBN 0-8170-1069-6). Judson.
Reilly, Terry & Reilly, Mimi. Noches Para la Familia. Movimiento Familiar Cristiano De Miami, tr. LC 81-65209. (Span., Illus.). 64p. 1981. pap. 2.95 (ISBN 0-87029-175-0, 20249-9). Abbey.
Robison, James. Attack on the Family. 1980. pap. 2.95 (ISBN 0-8423-0092-9). Tyndale.
Ross, Aileen D. The Hindu Family in Its Urban Setting. LC 62-2801. pap. 84.80 (ISBN 0-317-09747-4, 2014388). Bks Demand UMI.
Rowatt, G. Wade, Jr. & Rowatt, Mary Jo. The Two-Career Marriage. LC 79-28408. (Christian Care Bks.: Vol. 5). 120p. 1980. pap. 7.95 (ISBN 0-664-24298-7). Westminster.
Sapone, Edith. To You Mom. (Illus.). 1961. 3.00 (ISBN 0-8198-0162-3); pap. 2.00 (ISBN 0-8198-0163-1). Dghtrs St Paul.
Shorter, Edward. The Making of the Modern Family. LC 75-7266. (Illus.). 1975. pap. 13.50x (ISBN 0-465-09722-7, TB-5042). Basic.
Shoulson, Abraham B., ed. Marriage & Family Life: A Jewish View. 19.95x (ISBN 0-8084-0378-8). New Coll U Pr.
Slater, Philip. Footholds: Understanding the Shifting Family & Sexual Tensions in Our Culture. LC 77-12124. 1978. 13.95x (ISBN 0-8070-4160-2). Beacon Pr.

Smalley, Gary & Trent, John. The Blessing: Giving & Gaining Family Approval. 224p. 1986. pap. text ed. 14.95 (ISBN 0-8407-3066-7). Nelson.
Thompson, David A. A Premarital Guide for Couples & Their Counselors. 80p. 1979. pap. 4.95 (ISBN 0-87123-465-3, 210465). Bethany Hse.
Van Regenmorter, John & Van Regenmorter, Sylvia. Dear God, Why Can't We Have a Baby? 1986. 6.95 (ISBN 0-8010-9301-5). Baker Bk.
White, Joe. How to Be a Hero to Your Teenager. 144p. (Orig.). 1985. pap. 4.95 (ISBN 0-8423-1495-4). Tyndale.
Wright, H. Norman & Johnson, Rex. Characteristics of a Caring Home Growthbook. 80p. (Orig.). 1983. 4.95 (ISBN 0-88449-048-3, A424608). Vision Hse.
Your Family & You. (Benziger Family Life Program Ser.). 1978. 2.00 (ISBN 0-02-651550-4); tchrs. ed. 4.00 (ISBN 0-02-651560-1); family handbook 1.00 (ISBN 0-02-651590-3). Benziger Pub Co.

FAMILY–BIBLICAL TEACHING

Balch, David. Let Wives Be Submissive: The Domestic Code in 1 Peter. LC 80-21203. (Society of Biblical Literature Monograph). 196p. 1981. pap. 21.00 (ISBN 0-89130-429-0). Scholars Pr GA.
Grunlan, Stephen A. Marriage & the Family: A Christian Perspective. 384p. 1984. pap. 10.95 (ISBN 0-310-36341-1, 11282P). Zondervan.
Hamilton, Alastair. The Family of Love. 185p. 1981. text ed. 29.95 (ISBN 0-227-67845-1). Attic Pr.
Harbour, Brian L. Famous Couples of the Bible. LC 78-60053. 1979. pap. 4.95 (ISBN 0-8054-5630-9). Broadman.
Kennedy, D. James. Learning to Live with the People You Love. 200p. (Orig.). 1987. pap. text ed. 3.95 (ISBN 0-88368-190-0). Whitaker Hse.
Lewis, Margie M. & Lewis, Gregg. The Hurting Parent. 160p. (Orig.). 1980. pap. 5.95 (ISBN 0-310-41731-7, 11222P). Zondervan.
Mack, Wayne. Homework Manual for Biblical Counseling: Family & Marital Problems, Vol. 2. 1980. pap. 3.95 (ISBN 0-87552-357-9). Presby & Reformed.
Narramore, Bruce. Parenting with Love & Limits. 312p. 1987. pap. 9.95 (ISBN 0-310-30541-1). Zondervan.
Norris, Bill & Norris, Judy, eds. What the Bible Says about Families. (What the Bible Says Ser.). 425p. (Orig.). text ed. 13.95 (ISBN 0-89900-099-1). College Pr Pub.
Robison, James. Attack on the Family. 1980. pap. 2.95 (ISBN 0-8423-0092-9). Tyndale.
Strauss, Richard L. Famous Couples of the Bible. Chen, Ruth T., tr. (Chinese.). 1985. pap. write for info. (ISBN 0-941598-29-2). Living Spring Pubns.
Sutton, Ray R. Who Owns the Family. (The Biblical Blueprint ser.). 1986. pap. 6.95 (ISBN 0-8407-3097-7). Nelson.
Werth, Alvin, compiled by. Papal Pronouncements on Marriage & the Family: From Leo XIII to Pius XII (1878-1954) LC 82-6265. xxi, 189p. 1982. Repr. of 1955 ed. lib. bdg. 27.50x (ISBN 0-313-22521-4, WEPA). Greenwood.

FAMILY–PRAYER-BOOKS AND DEVOTIONS

Brandt, Leslie & Brandt, Edith. Growing Together: Prayers for Married People. LC 75-2830. 96p. (Orig.). 1975. pap. 5.95 (ISBN 0-8066-1476-5, 10-2903). Augsburg.
Brusius, Ron & Noettl, Margaret. Family Evening Activity Devotions. pap. 4.95 (ISBN 0-570-03803-0, 12-2912). Concordia.
Bryant, Al. Love Songs: Daily Meditations for Married Couples. 8.95 (ISBN 0-8499-3036-7). Word Bks.
Dellinger, Annetta. Happy Talk. 1982. pap. 5.95 (ISBN 0-570-03859-6, 12-2953). Concordia.
Hammond, Heather. Preparing for God's Gift: Devotions for Families Using the Advent Wreath. 40p. (Orig.). 1986. pap. 2.50 (ISBN 0-8066-2260-1, 23-1809). Augsburg.
Henshaw, Paul & Weemhoff, Harold. Worship in Our Family. LC 81-52045. 84p. 1981. pap. 4.95x (ISBN 0-8358-0421-6). Upper Room.
Huxhold, Harry N. Family Altar. rev. ed. 1964. 12.95 (ISBN 0-570-03071-4, 6-1085). Concordia.
Ingram, Kristen J. Family Worship Through the Year. 80p. 1984. pap. 5.95 (ISBN 0-8170-1052-1). Judson.
Jahsmann, Allan H. & Simon, Martin P. Little Visits with God. 1957. 9.50 (ISBN 0-570-03016-1, 6-1055); pap. 6.95 (ISBN 0-570-03032-3, 6-1158). Concordia.
--More Little Visits with God. 1961. 9.50 (ISBN 0-570-03017-X, 6-1080); pap. 6.95 (ISBN 0-570-03033-1, 6-1159). Concordia.
Jurries, Ginger & Mulder, Karen. Fun Ideas for Family Devotions (with Activity Pages) LC 81-50347. (Illus.). 176p. (Orig.). 1981. pap. 6.50 (ISBN 0-87239-415-8, 2968). Standard Pub.
Martin, Paul. Family Fare. 79p. 1976. pap. 1.25 (ISBN 0-8341-0403-2). Beacon Hill.
O'Neal, Debbie T. An Easter People: Family Devotional Activities for Lent & Easter. 32p. (Orig.). 1986. pap. 3.95 (ISBN 0-8066-2255-5, 10-1990). Augsburg.
Reilly, Terry & Reilly, Mimi. Family Nights: Advent-Christmas. 1977. pap. 1.45 (ISBN 0-87029-135-1, 20161-6). Abbey.
--Family Nights: Lent-Easter. 1977. pap. 1.45 (ISBN 0-87029-130-0, 20158-2). Abbey.
--Family Nights: Summer-Vacation. 1977. pap. 1.45 (ISBN 0-87029-134-3, 20160-8). Abbey.
Robertson, John M. Roots & Wings: Prayers & Promises for Parents. 84p. 1983. pap. 2.50 (ISBN 0-8423-5712-2). Tyndale.
Seifert, Lois. Our Family Night In: Workbook of Covenant Living. LC 80-54803. 200p. (Orig.). pap. 4.95x (ISBN 0-8358-0420-8). Upper Room.
Spiess, Margaret B. Gather Me Together, Lord: And Other Prayers for Mothers. 96p. 1982. 4.95 (ISBN 0-8010-8229-3). Baker Bk.
Toelke, Otto W. In the Presence of God. rev. ed. LC 61-18225. 1962. 4.95 (ISBN 0-570-03019-6, 6-1152). Concordia.
Webb, Barbara O. Devotions for Families: Building Blocks of Christian Life. LC 75-22162. 48p. 1976. pap. 1.95 (ISBN 0-8170-0680-X). Judson.

FAMILY–RELIGIOUS LIFE

see also Religious Education–Home Training

Adams, Anne. Brittany: Child of Joy. LC 86-24477. (Orig.). 1987. pap. 7.95 (ISBN 0-8054-5038-6). Broadman.
Anderson, Joan W. Dear World: Don't Spin So Fast, I'm Having Trouble Hanging On. LC 82-73131. 160p. 1982. pap. 4.95 (ISBN 0-87029-188-2, 20280-4). Abbey.
Anderson, Ray S. & Guernsey, Dennis B. On Being Family: Essays on a Social Theology of the Family. 192p. (Orig.). 1986. pap. 9.95 (ISBN 0-8028-1990-7). Eerdmans.
Baer, Mervin. The Christian Home. 1976. 1.95 (ISBN 0-686-11147-8). Rod & Staff.
Banks, J. A. Victorian Values: Secularism & the Smaller Family. 288p. 1981. 26.95x (ISBN 0-7100-0807-4). Methuen Inc.
Bateman, Helen R. Roots & Wings. LC 83-1868. (Illus.). 160p. 1983. 7.95 (ISBN 0-87747-950-X). Deseret Bk.
Bender, Ross T. Christians in Families. LC 82-6058. (Conrad Grebel Lecture Ser.). 184p. (Orig.). pap. 8.95 (ISBN 0-8361-3301-3). Herald Pr.
Bomgren, Marilyn J. Godparents, Why? 1981. 2.50 (ISBN 0-89536-473-5, 0717). CSS of Ohio.
Bowman, Thea, Sr., ed. Families: Black & Catholic, Catholic & Black, Readings, Resources & Family Activities. 160p. 1985. pap. 14.95 (ISBN 1-55586-890-8). US Catholic.
Brandt, Patricia & Jackson, Dave. Just Me & the Kids. (Family Ministry Ser.). (Illus.). 54p. 1985. pap. text ed. 19.95 (ISBN 0-89191-750-0). Cook.
Brock, Raymond T. The Christ-Centered Family. LC 76-46036. (Radiant Life Ser.). 128p. 1977. pap. 2.50 (ISBN 0-88243-903-0, 02-0903); teacher's ed 3.95 (ISBN 0-88243-173-0, 32-0173). Gospel Pub.
Buth, Lenore. The Employed Wife. 176p. (Orig.). 1986. pap. 5.95 (ISBN 0-570-04436-7). Concordia.
Cardozo, Arlene R. Jewish Family Celebrations: Shabbat, Festivals & Traditional Ceremonies. LC 82-5566. (Illus.). 288p. 1982. 17.50 (ISBN 0-312-44231-9). St Martin.
Carroll, Anne Kristin. Together Forever. 256p. (Orig.). 1982. pap. 7.95 (ISBN 0-310-45021-7, 6885P). Zondervan.
Castle, Tony. Celebrations for the Family. 126p. (Orig.). 1986. pap. 5.95 (ISBN 0-89283-270-3). Servant.
Catoir, John. Family Matters. Thomas, Joseph R., ed. & intro. by. 180p. (Orig.). 1984. pap. 5.00 (ISBN 0-317-46547-3). Chrstphrs NY.
Chartier, Jan & Chartier, Myron. Nurturing Faith in the Family. (Family Life Ser.). 160p. 1986. pap. 6.95 (ISBN 0-8170-1093-9). Judson.
Chartier, Janet A. & Chartier, Myron R. Caring Together: Faith, Hope, & Love in Your Family. LC 86-3460. 132p. (Orig.). 1986. pap. 8.95 (ISBN 0-664-24019-4). Westminster.
Chemnitz, Martin. Justification: The Chief Article of Christian Doctrine. Preus, J. A., tr. 200p. 1986. 16.95 (ISBN 0-570-04227-5, 15-2186). Concordia.
Christenson, Larry. La Familia Cristiana. 238p. 1972. 3.95 (ISBN 0-88113-080-X). Edit Betania.
--Family Pocket Promise Book. LC 83-72175. 128p. (Orig.). 1983. pap. 2.95 (ISBN 0-87123-303-7, 200303). Bethany Hse.
Christopherson, Victor A. Child Rearing In Today's Christian Family. (Family Life Ser.). 176p. 1985. pap. 6.95 (ISBN 0-8170-1065-3). Judson.
Clark, Glenn. Beatitudes of Married Life. pap. 0.20 (ISBN 0-910924-02-3). Macalester.
Cocoris, G. Michael. Formulas for Family Living. 46p. (Orig.). 1983. pap. text ed. 1.00 (ISBN 0-935729-28-3). Church Open Door.
Coleman, William L. Today I Feel Loved! LC 82-4184. 128p. (Orig.). 1982. pap. 4.95 (ISBN 0-87123-566-8, 210566). Bethany Hse.
Colligan, John, et al. The Extended Catholic Family: Rediscovering Our Catholic Identity Through Intimate Relationships with Fellow Catholics. LC 83-62198. 110p. (Orig.). 1983. pap. text ed. 4.95 (ISBN 0-911905-06-5). Past & Mat Rene Ctr.
Compton, Al. Armonia Familiar. 32p. 1981. pap. 1.30 (ISBN 0-311-46078-X). Casa Bautista.
Connolly, Paul H. Building Family: An Act of Faith. LC 82-74073. 96p. 1982. pap. 4.95 (ISBN 0-87029-186-6, 20277-0). Abbey.
Cowles, C. S. Family Journey into Joy. 168p. 1982. pap. 3.95 (ISBN 0-8341-0803-8). Beacon Hill.
Curran, Dolores. Family Prayer. rev. ed. 136p. (Orig.). 1983. pap. text ed. 5.95 (ISBN 0-86716-014-4). St Anthony Mess Pr.
D'Antonio, William V. & Aldous, Joan, eds. Families & Religions: Conflict & Change in Modern Society. 320p. 1983. 29.00 (ISBN 0-8039-2075-X); pap. 14.50 (ISBN 0-8039-2468-2). Sage.
Daughters of St. Paul. Teenagers Today. 1981. 4.00 (ISBN 0-8198-7303-9); pap. 3.00 (ISBN 0-8198-7304-7). Dghtrs St Paul.
Deal, William S. Plain Talks on Parenting. 1984. pap. 3.95 (ISBN 0-318-18715-9). Crusade Pubs.
Deck, Gladys E. Meet the Holy Family. 139p. 1978. 7.50 (ISBN 0-913382-24-8, 101-24). Prow Bks-Franciscan.
De Gidio, Sandra. Re-Treat Your Family to Lent. 50p. (Orig.). 1983. pap. text ed. 1.95 (ISBN 0-86716-022-5). St Anthony Mess Pr.
DeHoyos, Genieve. Stewardship, the Divine Order. LC 81-82055. 200p. 1982. 6.95 (ISBN 0-88290-191-5, 1065). Horizon Utah.
Dillon, Valerie V., ed. A Positive Vision for Family Life: A Resource Guide for Pope John Paul II's Apostolic Exhortation Familiaris Consortio. 56p. 1985. pap. 3.95 (ISBN 1-55586-938-6). US Catholic.
Dobson, Edward. What the Bible Really Says about Marriage, Divorce & Remarriage. 160p. 1986. 9.95 (ISBN 0-8007-1493-8). Revell.
Drescher, John M. If I Were Starting My Family Again. LC 78-13278. (Festival Ser.). (Illus.). 1979. pap. 2.95 (ISBN 0-687-18674-9). Abingdon.
Durka, Gloria & Smith, Joanmarie. Family Ministry. 216p. (Orig.). 1980. pap. 7.95 (ISBN 0-86683-762-0, HarpR). Har-Row.
Edwards, Judson. With Love from Dad. 208p. 1986. pap. 5.95 (ISBN 0-89081-501-1). Harvest Hse.
Elders of Bible Temple & Iverson, Dick. Restoring the Family. 3rd ed. 143p. Date not set. pap. price not set. Bible Temple.
Family: Center of Love. 6.00 (ISBN 0-8198-2608-1); 5.00 (ISBN 0-8198-2609-X). Dghtrs St Paul.
Ferguson, Larry & Jackson, Dave. The Freedom Years. (Family Ministry Ser.). (Illus.). 54p. 1985. pap. text ed. 19.95 (ISBN 0-89191-966-X). Cook.
Finley, Mitch & Finley, Kathy. Christian Families in the Real World. 1984. pap. 8.95 (ISBN 0-88347-192-2). Thomas More.
Fisher, Robert. The Family & the Church. LC 77-99163. 1978. 5.25 (ISBN 0-87148-334-3); pap. 4.25 (ISBN 0-87148-335-1). Pathway Pr.
Fitzpatrick, Kathryn. Commandments: Twenty-Eight Family Times to Respond in Love. (Familytime - Faithtime: A Home-Based Approach to Religious Education Ser.). (Illus.). 52p. (Orig.). 1982. pap. text ed. 3.50 (ISBN 0-86716-013-6). St Anthony Mess Pr.
--Creed: Twenty-Nine Family Times to Explore Belief, 3 Vols. (Family Time - Faith Time: A Home-Based Approach to Religious Education Ser.). (Illus.). 70p. (Orig.). 1982. pap. text ed. 3.50 (ISBN 0-86716-012-8). St Anthony Mess Pr.
--Family Time, Faith Time, 3 Vols. (Illus.). 307p. (Orig.). 1982. Set. pap. text ed. 8.95 (ISBN 0-86716-030-6). St Anthony Mess Pr.
--Sacraments: Twenty-Eight Family Times to Celebrate Life. (Family Time - Faith Time: A Home-Based Approach to Religious Education Ser.). (Illus.). 70p. (Orig.). 1982. pap. 3.50 (ISBN 0-86716-010-1). St Anthony Mess Pr.
Forliti, John E. Reverence for Life & Family Program: Parent-Teacher Resource. 1981. pap. 4.50 176 pp (ISBN 0-697-01789-3); tchr. training tape 9.95 (ISBN 0-697-01837-7). Wm C Brown.
Furutan, A. Mothers, Fathers, & Children: Practical Advice to Parents. 280p. pap. 8.95 (ISBN 0-85398-095-0). G Ronald Pub.
Gallagher, Maureen, ed. Christian Parenting Handbook. 2.95 (ISBN 0-8091-2262-6). Paulist Pr.
Gaulke, Earl H. You Can Have a Family Where Everybody Wins. LC 75-23574. 104p. 1975. pap. 3.50 (ISBN 0-570-03723-9, 12-2625). Concordia.
Gibson, Dennis L. Live, Grow & Be Free: A Guide to Self-Parenting. LC 82-82412. 136p. 1982. pap. 5.95 (ISBN 0-89840-030-9). Here's Life.
Grams, Betty J. Families Can Be Happy. LC 81-82420. 128p. (Orig.). 1981. pap. 2.50 (ISBN 0-88243-759-3, 02-0759); tchr's ed 3.95 (ISBN 0-88243-334-2, 02-0334). Gospel Pub.
Grinstead, Wayne. The Ross Hannas: Living, Laughing, Loving. LC 86-6807. (Meet the Missionary Ser.). 1986. 5.50 (ISBN 0-8054-4325-8). Broadman.
Guernsey, Dennis B. The Family Covenant: Students Manual. 113p. 1984. pap. text ed. 3.95 (ISBN 0-89191-843-4). Cook.
Hall, Ruthann. That's Life. 1974. pap. 2.25 (ISBN 0-89265-020-6). Randall Hse.
Hanks, Darla & Bascom, Arlene. To Parents, with Love: Practical Pointers for Family Success. 341p. 1978. 10.95 (ISBN 0-88290-090-0). Horizon Utah.
Hansel, Tim. What Kids Need Most in a Dad. LC 83-22902. 192p. 1984. 10.95 (ISBN 0-8007-1390-7). Revell.
Hartley, Jan. Sharing Faith at Home. (SPAN Ser.). (Illus.). 31p. (Orig.). 1983. pap. 3.95 (ISBN 0-85819-450-3, Pub. by JBCE). ANZ Religious Pubns.
Hazelip, Harold. Happiness in the Home: Guidelines for Spouses & Parents. 120p. 1985. pap. 3.95 (ISBN 0-8010-4294-1). Baker Bk.
Hendricks, Howard G. Heaven Help the Home! LC 73-78689. 143p. 1973. pap. 5.95 (ISBN 0-88207-240-4). Victor Bks.
Herr, Ethel. Growing up Is a Family Affair. LC 78-17581. 1978. pap. 5.95 (ISBN 0-8024-3359-6). Moody.
Hess, Edith & Blass, Jacqueline. Peter & Susie Find a Family. Tr. of Peter & Susi Finden eine Familie. (Illus.). 28p. 1985. Repr. of 1981 ed. 10.95 (ISBN 0-687-30848-8). Abingdon.
Heynen, Ralph. Christian Home. (Contemporary Discussion Ser.). (Orig.). 1974. pap. 1.25 (ISBN 0-8010-4109-0). Baker Bk.
Hickey, Marilyn. God's Covenant for Your Family. 140p. (Orig.). 1982. pap. 4.95 (ISBN 0-89274-245-3). Harrison Hse.
Hinkle, Joseph W., et al. Oikos: A Practical Approach to Family Evangelism. LC 81-69328. 1982. pap. 4.95 (ISBN 0-8054-6234-1). Broadman.
Hogan, Richard M. & Levoir, John M. Covenant of Love: Pope John Paul II on Sexuality, Marriage & Family in the Modern World. LC 84-18666. 264p. 1985. 15.95 (ISBN 0-385-19540-0). Doubleday.
Honea, Charla, compiled by. Family Rituals. LC 81-52861. (Illus., Orig.). 1981. pap. 3.95x (ISBN 0-8358-0433-X). Upper Room.
Hoover, Mab G. God Still Loves My Kitchen. 208p. (Orig.). 1981. pap. 3.95 (ISBN 0-310-35622-9, 11271P). Zondervan.
Howell, John C. Equality & Submission in Marriage. LC 78-67292. 1979. 8.50 (ISBN 0-8054-5632-5). Broadman.
Hoyer, George W. The Lord Be with You. LC 77-85172. (Child of God Ser.: Vol. 1). 1977. pap. text ed. 4.95 (ISBN 0-915644-11-8). Clayton Pub Hse.
Hunt, Gladys. Family Secrets: What You Need to Know to Build a Strong Christian Family. 98p. 1985. pap. 3.95 (ISBN 0-89283-233-9, Pub. by Vine Books). Servant.
Iatesta, Robert. Fathers: A Fresh Start for the Christian Family. 238p. (Orig.). 1980. pap. 5.95 (ISBN 0-89283-083-2). Servant.
Ingram, Kristen J. Family Worship Through the Year. 80p. 1984. pap. 5.95 (ISBN 0-8170-1052-1). Judson.
Javernick, Ellen. Celebrate the Christian Family. (Celebrate Ser.). (Illus.). 144p. 1987. pap. 9.95 (ISBN 0-86653-391-5, SS844). Good Apple.
Kobobel, Janet. The Family Covenant: Leaders Manual. 35p. 1984. tchr's ed. 10.95 (ISBN 0-89191-892-2). Cook.
Kuntzleman, Charles T. The Well Family Book. 256p. 1985. 13.95 (ISBN 0-89840-092-9). Heres Life.
LaHaye, Tim. The Battle for the Family. (Illus.). 256p. 1981. power ed. 6.95 (ISBN 0-8007-5117-5). Revell.
Lanstrom, Edith. Christian Parent Burnout. LC 12-2979. (Continued Applied Christianity Ser.). 1983. pap. 2.95 (ISBN 0-570-03897-9). Concordia.
Larson, Jim. Growing a Healthy Family. LC 85-28657. 128p. (Orig.). 1986. pap. 6.95 (ISBN 0-8066-2193-1, 10-2901). Augsburg.

--Teaching Christian Values in the Family. (Illus.). 48p. 1982. pap. text ed. 29.95 (ISBN 0-89191-649-0). Cook.

Larson, John. A Church Guide for Strengthening Families: Strategies, Models, Programs, & Resources. LC 86-7965. 128p. (Orig.). 1986. pap. 8.95 (ISBN 0-8066-2217-2, 10-1320). Augsburg.

Larson, Roland & Larson, Doris. Values & Faith: Value Clarifying Exercises for Family & Church Groups. (Illus.). 260p. 1976. pap. 6.95 (ISBN 0-86683-673-X, HarpR). Har-Row.

Lasch, Christopher. Haven in a Heartless World: The Family Besieged. LC 77-75246. 1979. pap. 7.95x (ISBN 0-465-02884-5, TB-5047). Basic.

Law, Peter. Portrait of My Father: The Wonder of Knowing God. LC 85-15458. (Living Theology Ser.). 1985. pap. 7.95 (ISBN 0-88070-107-2). Multnomah.

Lee, Mark & Grant, James M. This Family Business. LC 82-73873. 150p. 1984. pap. 6.45 (ISBN 0-87509-328-0); pap. 2.95 (ISBN 0-87509-356-6). Chr Pubns.

Leonard, Joe, Jr. Planning Family Ministry: A Guide for the Teaching Church. 64p. 1982. pap. 3.95 (ISBN 0-8170-0971-X). Judson.

Lovett, C. S. Unequally Yoked Wives. 1968. pap. 5.45 (ISBN 0-938148-22-2). Personal Christianity.

Luebering, Carol. The Forgiving Family: First Steps to Reconciliation. 84p. (Orig.). 1983. pap. text ed. 2.50 (ISBN 0-86716-027-6). St Anthony Mess Pr.

Lybrand, R. E., Jr. Home Is a Four-Letter Word. 1985. 5.95 (ISBN 0-89536-719-X, 5803). CSS of Ohio.

MacArthur, John. The Family. 1982. pap. 5.95 (ISBN 0-8024-2524-0). Moody.

McCarthy, Donald G., ed. The Family Today & Tomorrow: The Church Addresses Her Future. 291p. 1985. pap. 17.95 (ISBN 0-935372-17-2). Pope John Ctr.

McDannell, Colleen. The Christian Home in Victorian America, 1840-1900. LC 85-42947. (Religion in North America Ser.). (Illus.). 224p. 1986. 25.00x (ISBN 0-253-31376-7). Ind U Pr.

McGinnis, Alan L. La Amistad Factor Decisivo. Orig. Title: The Friendship Factor. (Span.). 204p. 1986. pap. 5.95 (ISBN 0-311-46093-3, Edit Mundo). Casa Bautista.

McGinnis, Kathleen & McGinnis, James. Parenting for Peace & Justice. LC 81-3917. 143p. (Orig.). 1981. pap. 7.95 (ISBN 0-88344-376-7). Orbis Bks.

McGuiness, Thomas. Family Renewal in the Home. LC 83-63006. 83p. (Orig.). 1984. pap. text ed. 4.95 (ISBN 0-911905-17-0). Past & Mat Rene Ctr.

McRoberts, Darlene. Family Fare: Christian Activities for Every Season of the Year. LC 81-65642. (Illus.). 80p. (Orig.). 1981. pap. 5.95 (ISBN 0-8066-1878-7, 10-2247). Augsburg.

Malcolm, Kari T. Building Your Family to Last. 180p. (Orig.). 1987. pap. 6.95 (ISBN 0-87784-984-6). Inter-Varsity.

Martin, Ralph. Husbands, Wives, Parents, Children. rev. ed. 1983. pap. 6.95 (ISBN 0-89283-149-9). Servant.

Martin, Thomas M. Christian Family Values. 128p. 1984. pap. 7.95 (ISBN 0-8091-2579-X). Paulist Pr.

Mason, Rosalie. Beginners' Guide to Family Preparedness. LC 77-79750. (Illus.). 160p. 1977. pap. 6.95 (ISBN 0-88290-082-X). Horizon Utah.

Meier, Paul & Meier, Richard. Family Foundations. 96p. (Orig.). 1981. 8.95 (ISBN 0-8010-6117-2). Baker Bk.

Milburn, Joyce. Helping Your Children Love Each Other. LC 83-15505. 160p. (Orig.). 1983. pap. 4.95 (ISBN 0-87123-307-X, 210307). Bethany Hse.

Miller, John F. The Art of Parenting in a Changing Society. 1979. 8.95 (ISBN 0-8199-0761-8). Franciscan Herald.

Montgomery, Mary. Home Is Where the Start Is: Ideas to Help Families Grow in Love & Faith. 132p. (Orig.). 1985. pap. 6.95 (ISBN 0-86683-868-6, HarpR). Har-Row.

Morningstar, Jim. Family Awakening in Body, Mind, & Spirit. 60p. 1984. pap. 6.00 (ISBN 0-9604856-1-9). Transform Inc.

Narramore, Bruce S. Parenting with Love & Limits. 176p. 1982. pap. 5.95 (ISBN 0-310-30351-6, 11240P). Zondervan.

National Conference of Catholic Bishops, United States Catholic Conference. A Vision & Strategy: The Plan of Pastoral Action for Family Ministry. (Illus., Orig.). 1978. pap. 3.75 (ISBN 1-55586-961-0). US Catholic.

Nieman, Charles. Gods Plan for the Family. 58p. (Orig.). 1985. 4.95 (ISBN 0-914307-49-5). Word Faith.

Nilsen, Mary Y. Tending the Family Tree: A Family-Centered, Bible-Based Experience for Church Groups. 80p. (Orig.). 1982. pap. 7.95 (ISBN 0-86683-169-X, HarpR). Har-Row.

O'Brien, Joachim. Parish Family Life & Social Action. LC 77-3573. 1977. pap. 1.50 (ISBN 0-8199-0673-5). Franciscan Herald.

On the Family. 93p. 1981. pap. 3.95 (ISBN 1-55586-833-9). US Catholic.

Orr, Bill & Lutzer, Erwin. If I Could Change My Mom & Dad. 128p. 1983. pap. 3.50 (ISBN 0-8024-0174-0). Moody.

Orso, Kathryn W. Parenthood: A Commitment in Faith. LC 75-5219. 64p. (Orig.). 1975. pap. text ed. 2.95 (ISBN 0-8192-1198-2); tchr's ed. 3.75 (ISBN 0-8192-1204-0); wkbk. 3.95 (ISBN 0-8192-1199-0). Morehouse.

Otto, Donna. All in Good Time. 240p. 1985. 12.95 (ISBN 0-8407-5963-0). Nelson.

Overly, Fay. Missing: A Family's Triumph in the Tragedy No Parent Ever Wants to Face. LC 84-72590. 210p. (Orig.). 1985. pap. 6.95 (ISBN 0-89636-151-9). Accent Bks.

Petersen, Evelyn & Petersen, J. Allan. For Women Only. pap. 7.95, 1974 (ISBN 0-8423-0896-2); pap. 3.95 1982 (ISBN 0-8423-0897-0). Tyndale.

Petersen, J. Allan. For Men Only. 1982. pap. 3.95 (ISBN 0-8423-0892-X). Tyndale.

Peterson, Eugene H. Growing up in Christ. pap. 5.50 (ISBN 0-8042-2026-3). John Knox.

Pitts, David. How in the World Do I Get Along With My Parents? 40p. 1982. pap. 0.95 (ISBN 0-88144-046-9). Christian Pub.

Popoff, Peter. America's Family Crisis. Tanner, Don, ed. LC 82-82843. 80p. 1982. pap. 2.00 (ISBN 0-938544-15-2). Faith Messenger.

Quesnell, John G. Holy Terrors & Holy Parents. 228p. 1976. 7.95 (ISBN 0-8199-0561-5). Franciscan Herald.

Rediscovery of the Family & Other Lectures: Sister Marie Hilda Memorial Lectures 1954-1973. 112p. 1981. pap. 12.00 (ISBN 0-08-025754-2). Pergamon.

Reed, Bobbie. Christian Family Activities for One-Parent Families. LC 82-5704. (Illus.). 96p. (Orig.). 1982. pap. 4.95 (ISBN 0-87239-571-5, 2966). Standard Pub.

Rickerson, Wayne. Christian Family Activities for Families with Children. LC 82-10385. (Illus.). 96p. (Orig.). 1982. pap. 4.95 (ISBN 0-87239-569-3, 2964). Standard Pub.

--Christian Family Activities for Families with Preschoolers. LC 82-5583. (Illus.). 96p. (Orig.). 1982. pap. 4.95 (ISBN 0-87239-568-5, 2963). Standard Pub.

--Christian Family Activities for Families with Teens. LC 82-5833. (Illus.). 96p. (Orig.). 1982. pap. 4.95 (ISBN 0-87239-570-7, 2965). Standard Pub.

--Family Fun Times: Activities That Bind Marriages, Build Families, & Develop Christian Leaders. 80p. Date not set. pap. 7.95 (ISBN 0-87403-207-5, 3187). Standard Pub.

Rodriguez, P. Pedro. Matrimono y Familia Cristiana. LC 84-7000069. 116p. 1984. pap. 2.95 (ISBN 0-915388-20-0). Buckley Pubns.

Ross, Bette M. Our Special Child. rev. ed. 256p. 1984. pap. 8.95 (ISBN 0-8007-1230-7). Revell.

Rouse, Richard & Rouse, Susan. The Last Week. 1985. 1.00 (ISBN 0-89536-726-2, 5810). CSS of Ohio.

Sandford, John & Sandford, Paula. Restoring the Christian Family. LC 79-64977. 336p. 1986. pap. 6.95 (ISBN 0-932081-12-6). Victory Hse.

Sawyers, Lindell, ed. Faith & Families. 208p. (Orig.). 1986. pap. 12.95 (ISBN 0-664-24038-0). Westminster.

Saxton, et al, eds. The Changing Family: Views from Theology & Social Sciences in the Light of the Aspostolic Exhortation "Familiaris Consortio". 224p. 1984. 12.95 (ISBN 0-8294-0458-9). Loyola.

Schaeffer, Edith. The Hidden Art of Homemaking. (Living Studies). 216p. 1985. pap. 6.95 (ISBN 0-8423-1398-2); Leader's Guide 2.95 (ISBN 0-8423-1399-0). Tyndale.

--What Is a Family? 256p. 1982. pap. 7.95 (ISBN 0-8007-5088-8, Power Bks). Revell.

Schmitt, Abraham & Schmitt, Dorothy. Renewing Family Life. LC 84-22504. (Orig.). 1985. pap. 6.95 (ISBN 0-8361-3384-6). Herald Pr.

Schroeder, L. Celebrate-While We Wait. (Illus.). 1977. pap. 4.95 (ISBN 0-570-03052-8, 6-1177). Concordia.

Schuller, Robert. Power Ideas for a Happy Family. 1982. pap. 1.95 (ISBN 0-515-06499-8). Jove Pubns.

Sears, William. Christian Parenting & Child Care. 544p. 1985. 19.95 (ISBN 0-8407-5422-1). Nelson.

Sell, Charles M. Family Ministry: Family Life Through the Church. 272p. 15.95 (ISBN 0-310-42580-8, 12335). Zondervan.

Semja Pravoslavnago Khristjanina. Tr. of The Family of an Orthodox Christian. 569p. 1958. Repr. 15.00 (ISBN 0-317-30248-5). Holy Trinity.

Shedd, Charlie & Shedd, Martha. Bible Study Together: Making Marriage Last. 144p. 1987. pap. 5.95 (ISBN 0-310-42381-3). Zondervan.

--Praying Together: Making Marriage Last. 128p. 1987. pap. 5.95 (ISBN 0-310-43291-X). Zondervan.

Sheek, G. William. The Word on Families: A Biblical Guide to Family Well-Being. Schaller, Lyle E., ed. 160p. (Orig.). 1985. pap. 7.50 (ISBN 0-687-46135-9). Abingdon.

Smalley, Gary & Scott, Steve. For Better or for Best. 160p. 1982. pap. 5.95 (ISBN 0-310-44871-9, 18246P). Zondervan.

--If Only He Knew: A Valuable Guide to Knowing, Understanding, & Loving Your Wife. 144p. 1982. pap. 5.95 (ISBN 0-310-44881-6, 18247P). Zondervan.

Smith, Chuck. Family Relationships. 48p. (Orig.). 1980. pap. 0.95 (ISBN 0-936728-04-3). Word for Today.

Smith, Wallace C. The Church in the Life of the Black Family. (Family Life Ser.). 160p. 1985. pap. 8.50 (ISBN 0-8170-1040-8). Judson.

Sparks, Merla J. Creative Christian Home. pap. 1.95 (ISBN 0-8010-8050-9). Baker Bk.

Stephens, John F. Spirit Filled Family, No. 11. 48p. (Orig.). 1980. pap. 1.95 (ISBN 0-89841-008-8). Zoe Pubns.

Stine, Alan. Love Power: New Dimensions for Building Strong Families. LC 78-70360. 1978. 8.95 (ISBN 0-88290-105-2). Horizon Utah.

Summers, Georgianna. Stress! How Christian Parents Cope. LC 86-71746. 80p. (Orig.). 1986. pap. 5.95 (ISBN 0-88177-032-9, DR032B). Discipleship Res.

Sutton, Ray R. Who Owns the Family. (The Biblical Blueprint ser.). 1986. pap. 6.95 (ISBN 0-8407-3097-7). Nelson.

Taylor, Guillermo D. La Familia Autenticamente Cristiana. Tr. of The Authentic Christian Family. (Span.). 240p. 1983. pap. 4.50 (ISBN 0-8254-1702-3). Kregel.

Thomas, David M. When God Is at Home with Your Family. LC 78-73019. (When Bk.). (Illus.). 1978. pap. 2.45 (ISBN 0-87029-146-7, 20231-7). Abbey.

Thomas, David M., ed. Family Life Ministry. LC 79-53513. (Marriage & Family Living in Depth Bk.). 1979. pap. 2.45 (ISBN 0-87029-157-2, 20243-2). Abbey.

--God, Religion, & Family Life. LC 79-53512. (Marriage & Family Living in Depth Book Ser.). 1979. pap. 2.45 (ISBN 0-87029-156-4, 20242-4). Abbey.

--Prayer in the Home. LC 81-69503. (Marriage & Family Living in Depth Bk.). 1981. pap. 2.45 (ISBN 0-87029-180-7, 20250-7). Abbey.

Thomas, John L. The American Catholic Family. LC 80-15221. (Illus.). xii, 471p. 1980. Repr. of 1956 ed. lib. bdg. 37.50x (ISBN 0-313-22473-0, THAC). Greenwood.

Thompson, James. Our Life Together. LC 77-79338. (Journey Bks.). 1977. pap. 3.50 (ISBN 0-8344-0095-2). Sweet.

Tournier, Paul. The Gift of Feeling. pap. 9.95 (ISBN 0-8042-2071-9). John Knox.

Tychsen, Laurie. Too Many People? Answers & Hope for the Human Family. 46p. (Orig.). 1986. pap. 3.25 (ISBN 0-937779-03-2). Greenlawn Pr.

Van Pelt, Nancy L. From This Day Forward: Blueprint for Family Happiness. Coffen, Richard W., ed. 128p. (Orig.). 1985. pap. 1.95 (ISBN 0-8280-0280-0). Review & Herald.

Vasi, Dianne. It Shouldn't Hurt to Be a Child. Coffen, Richard W., ed. (Better Living Ser.). 32p. (Orig.). 1985. pap. 0.99 (ISBN 0-8280-0310-6). Review & Herald.

Vaudrey, Stephen J. How to Win Your Family to Christ. 1985. 13.95 (ISBN 0-317-18081-9); pap. 6.95 (ISBN 0-317-18082-7). P-H.

Vaught, Laud O. Focus on the Christian Family. 1976. pap. 3.95 (ISBN 0-87148-332-7). Pathway Pr.

Voigt, Tracy. The Relatives. (Orig.). 1982. pap. write for info. T Voigt.

Walsh, David. Getting in Touch with Yourself-&-Your Parents. 1982. pap. 4.25 (ISBN 0-86716-009-8). St Anthony Mess Pr.

Webb, Barbara O. Families Sharing God. 48p. 1981. pap. 3.50 (ISBN 0-8170-0900-0). Judson.

Welliver, Dotsey. Laughing Together: The Value of Humor in Family Life. Eller, David, ed. 128p. (Orig.). 1986. pap. 6.95 (ISBN 0-87178-226-X). Brethren.

Wessel, Helen. Natural Childbirth & the Christian Family. 4th, rev. ed. LC 82-48943. (Illus.). 384p. 1985. pap. text ed. 8.95 (ISBN 0-06-069317-7, HarpR). Har-Row.

Wheeler, Bonnie G. Meet the Overcomers: The Story of a Special Family. (Orig.). 1984. pap. 5.95 (ISBN 0-8024-0440-5). Moody.

White, Mary. Growing Together: Building Your Family's Spiritual Life. 2nd ed. 144p. 1985. pap. 4.95 (ISBN 0-89109-484-9). NavPress.

Wilczak, Paul F., ed. Healing in the Family. LC 79-53515. (Marriage & Family Living in Depth Bk.). 1979. pap. 2.45 (ISBN 0-87029-158-0, 20244-0). Abbey.

Wilson, Prue. My Father Took Me to the Circus: Religious Life from Within. 144p. 1985. pap. 5.95 (ISBN 0-87193-218-0). Dimension Bks.

Yates, John W. For the Life of the Family: Family Life Action Groups or Starting & Using FLAG in Your Church. 256p. 1987. pap. 9.95. Morehouse.

Your Family: Leader's Guide. (Electives Ser.). 1983. pap. 2.50 (ISBN 0-8024-0307-7). Moody.

Zanzucchi, Annamaria. My Child & God: Religious Education in the Family. Hartman, Thomas, ed. Sczesniak, Lenny, tr. LC 78-52599. 100p. 1978. pap. 2.95 (ISBN 0-911782-31-1). New City.

Zuck, Roy B. & Getz, Gene A. Adult Education in the Church. LC 79-123154. 1970. pap. 15.95 (ISBN 0-8024-0468-5). Moody.

FAMILY LIFE EDUCATION

see also Counseling; Finance, Personal; Home Economics; Interpersonal Relations; Marriage Counseling; Sex Instruction

Barcus, Nancy B. The Family Takes a Child. 96p. 1983. pap. 5.95 (ISBN 0-8170-0998-1). Judson.

Compton, Al. Armonia Familiar. 32p. 1981. pap. 1.30 (ISBN 0-311-46078-X). Casa Bautista.

Cooper, Darien B. You Can Be the Wife of a Happy Husband. LC 74-77450. 156p. 1974. pap. 5.95 (ISBN 0-88207-711-2). Victor Bks.

DeHaan, Richard W. The Secret of a Happy Home. (Direction Bks.). 88p. 1982. pap. 2.95 (ISBN 0-8010-2916-3). Baker Bk.

Dobson, James. Esto Es Ser Hombre: Conversaciones Francas Con los Hombres y Sus Esposas. Almanza, Francisco, tr. from Eng. Orig. Title: Straight Talk to Men & Wives. 240p. 1986. pap. 7.50 (ISBN 0-311-46096-8, Edit Mundo). Casa Bautista.

Duckworth, John, et al, eds. The Family. (Pacesetter Ser.). 64p. 1987. tchr's. ed. 7.95. Cook.

The Encyclopedia of Christian Parenting. 540p. 1982. 16.95 (ISBN 0-8007-1276-5). Revell.

Johnson, Rex. Communication: Key to Your Parents. LC 78-61874. 1978. pap. 3.95 (ISBN 0-89081-157-1). Harvest Hse.

Mace, David R. Getting Ready for Marriage. 128p. 1985. pap. 5.95 (ISBN 0-687-14136-2). Abingdon.

National Council of Jewish Women. Family Life Education Program Idea Guide. (Illus.). 37p. 1985. pap. text ed. 3.00 (ISBN 0-941840-21-2). NCJW.

Petersen, J. Allan, compiled by. The Marriage Affair. 1971. pap. 9.95 (ISBN 0-8423-4171-4). Tyndale.

Rediscovery of the Family & Other Lectures: Sister Marie Hilda Memorial Lectures 1954-1973. 112p. 1981. pap. 12.00 (ISBN 0-08-025754-2). Pergamon.

Ripple, Paula. The Pain & the Possibility. LC 78-67745. 144p. 1978. pap. 2.95 (ISBN 0-87793-162-3). Ave Maria.

Schneid, Hayyim, ed. The Family. LC 73-11760. (Popular Judaica Library). (Illus.). 120p. 1974. pap. 3.95 (ISBN 0-8276-0029-1, 341). Jewish Pubns.

Trobisch, Walter. I Loved a Girl. LC 75-12281. 128p. 1975. pap. 6.95 (ISBN 0-06-068443-7, RD 352, HarpR). Har-Row.

Weems, Ann. Family Faith Stories. LC 85-13771. 142p. 1985. pap. 8.95 (ISBN 0-664-24670-2). Westminster.

Williams, Pat & Williams, Jill. Keep the Fire Glowing: How a Loving Marriage Builds a Loving Family. 160p. 1986. 9.95 (ISBN 0-317-46133-8). Revell.

Wright, Norman. An Answer to Parent-Teen Relationships. (Orig.). pap. 1.95 (ISBN 0-89081-075-3). Harvest Hse.

--An Answer to Submission & Decision Making. pap. 1.95 (ISBN 0-89081-078-8). Harvest Hse.

Wright, Norman & Inmon, Marvin. Guidebook to Dating, Waiting & Choosing a Mate. LC 78-26913. 1978. pap. 4.95 (ISBN 0-89081-150-4). Harvest Hse.

Wright, Norman & Johnson, Rex. Communication: Key to Your Teens. LC 78-61872. 1978. pap. 3.95 (ISBN 0-89081-158-X). Harvest Hse.

FAMILY PLANNING

see Birth Control

FAMILY WORSHIP

see Family–Prayer-Books and Devotions; Family–Religious Life

FANATICISM

see also Asceticism; Enthusiasm

Ahmed, K. Fanaticism, Intolerance & Islam. pap. 1.00 (ISBN 0-686-18491-2). Kazi Pubns.

Billingsley, Lloyd. Religion's Rebel Son: Fanaticism in Our Time. LC 86-16311. 1986. 11.95 (ISBN 0-88070-139-0). Multnomah.

Hoffer, Eric. True Believer. 1966. pap. 3.95 (ISBN 0-06-080071-2, P71, PL). Har-Row.

Matthews, Ronald. English Messiahs: Studies of Six English Religious Pretenders, 1656-1927. LC 76-172553. Repr. of 1936 ed. 12.75 (ISBN 0-405-18187-6, Pub. by Blom). Ayer Co Pubs.

Rudin, Josef. Fanaticism. LC 69-14813. (Ger). 1969. Repr. of 1965 ed. 17.95 (ISBN 0-268-00318-1). U of Notre Dame Pr.

FANTASY

Cordovano, Steven & Sechi, Stephan M. The Compleat Alchemist. (The Compleat Fantasy Ser.). (Illus.). 45p. 1983. pap. text ed. 7.95 (ISBN 0-9610770-0-X, 4801). Bard Games.

Cox, Harvey. Feast of Fools: A Theological Essay on Festivity & Fantasy. LC 75-75914. (William Belden Noble Lectures Ser). 1969. 15.00x (ISBN 0-674-29525-0). Harvard U Pr.

Leeming, David A. Flights: Readings in Magic, Mysticism, Fantasy & Myth. 388p. (Orig.). 1974. pap. text ed. 11.95 (ISBN 0-15-527556-9, HC). HarBraceJ.

FAST DAYS

see Fasts and Feasts

FASTING

see also Fasts and Feasts

Anderson, Andy. Fasting Changed My Life. LC 77-82404. 1977. pap. 3.95 (ISBN 0-8054-5259-1). Broadman.

Brianchaninov, Ignatius. Fasting. pap. 0.25 (ISBN 0-686-05642-6). Eastern Orthodox.

Chatham, Romara. Fasting. LC 85-73212. 1986. pap. cancelled (ISBN 0-88270-604-7). Bridge pub.

Cott, Allan. Fasting: The Ultimate Diet. 160p. 1986. pap. 3.50 (ISBN 0-553-25967-9). Bantam.

DeWelt, Don & Baird, John. What the Bible Says about Fasting. LC 79-57087. (What the Bible Says Ser.). 1984. 13.95 (ISBN 0-89900-077-0). College Pr Pub.

Faris, N. A. The Mysteries of Fasting. pap. 3.75 (ISBN 0-686-18615-X). Kazi Pubns.

Fulton, Alvenia M. The Fasting Primer. 2nd & rev. ed. Williams, James C., ed. LC 78-60661. 1978. pap. 5.95 (ISBN 0-931564-04-2). JBR Pub.

Hagin, Kenneth E. A Commonsense Guide to Fasting. 1981. pap. 1.50 (ISBN 0-89276-403-1). Hagin Ministries.

International Partners in Prayer. Fasting: A Reference. 25p. Date not set. pap. text ed. 2.00 (ISBN 0-917593-07-3, Pub. by Intl Partners). Prosperity & Profits.

Lindsay, Gordon. Prayer & Fasting. (School of Prayer Ser.). 1.75 (ISBN 0-89985-076-6). Christ Nations.

--Prayer That Moves Mountains. (School of Prayer Ser.). 2.50 (ISBN 0-89985-078-2). Christ Nations.

Massey, James E. Spiritual Disciplines: Growth Through the Practice of Prayer, Fasting, Dialogue, & Worship. rev. ed. Allison, Joseph D., ed. 112p. 1985. pap. 4.95 (ISBN 0-310-37151-1, 12410P). Zondervan.

Prince, Derek. How to Fast Successfully. 1976. pap. 2.50 (ISBN 0-934920-19-2, B-28). Derek Prince.

--Shaping History Through Prayer & Fasting. 1973. 9.95 (ISBN 0-934920-23-0, B-24); pap. 5.95 (ISBN 0-686-12766-8, B-25). Derek Prince.

Ryan, Thomas. Fasting Rediscovered: A Guide to Health & Wholeness for Your Body-Spirit. LC 80-81581. 160p. (Orig.). 1981. pap. 6.95 (ISBN 0-8091-2323-1). Paulist Pr.

Smith, D. Fasting. 1973. 3.95 (ISBN 0-87508-516-4); pap. 2.95 (ISBN 0-87508-515-6). Chr Lit.

Szekely, Edmond B. The Essene Science of Fasting & the Art of Sobriety. (Illus.). 48p. 1981. pap. 3.50 (ISBN 0-89564-011-2). IBS Intl.

Wimmer, Joseph F. Fasting in the New Testament. LC 81-83183. 160p. (Orig.). 1982. pap. 8.95 (ISBN 0-8091-2420-3). Paulist Pr.

FASTS AND FEASTS

Here are entered works on religious fasts and feasts in general and on Christian fasts and feasts. see also Agape; Christmas; Church Year; Easter; Epiphany; Good Friday; Holidays; Lent; Pentecost Festival; Sacred Meals; Thanksgiving Day

Bludau, August. Die Pilgerreise der Aetheria. pap. 22.00 (ISBN 0-384-04760-2). Johnson Repr.

Bynum, Caroline W. Holy Feast & Holy Fast: The Religious Significance of Food to Medieval Women. LC 85-28896. 300p. 1986. 29.95 (ISBN 0-520-05722-8). U of Cal Pr.

Cass-Beggs, Barbara. A Musical Calender of Festivals: Folk Songs of Feast-Days & Holidays from Around the World. (Ward Lock Educational Ser.). 1985. 25.00x (ISBN 0-7062-4226-2, Pub. by Ward Lock Educ Co Ltd). State Mutual Bk.

Chambers, Robert, ed. Book of Days: A Miscellany of Popular Antiquities in Connection with the Calendar, Including Anecdote, Biography & History, Curiosities of Literature, & Oddities of Human Life & Character, 2 Vols. LC 67-13009. (Illus.). 1967. Repr. of 1862 ed. 125.00x (ISBN 0-8103-3002-4). Gale.

Cronin, Gaynell & Cronin, Jim. Celebrations. 1980. pap. 7.55 (ISBN 0-88479-031-2). Arena Lettres.

Curley, Ed. Church Feasts & Celebrations. 1983. 9.95 (ISBN 0-89837-085-X, Pub. by Pflaum Pr). Peter Li.

Deems, Edward M., ed. Holy-Days & Holidays: A Treasury of Historical Material, Sermons in Full & in Brief, Suggestive Thoughts & Poetry, Relating to Holy Days & Holidays. LC 68-17940. 1968. Repr. of 1902 ed. 65.00x (ISBN 0-8103-3352-X). Gale.

Falwell, Jerry. Fasting. 1981. pap. 2.50 (ISBN 0-8423-0849-0). Tyndale.

Fisher, Constance. Dancing Festivals of the Church Year. Adams, Doug, ed. (Illus.). 120p. (Orig.). 1986. pap. 8.95 (ISBN 0-941500-42-X). Sharing Co.

Gaster, Theodor H. Festivals of the Jewish Year: A Modern Interpretation & Guide. 1971. pap. 7.95 (ISBN 0-688-06008-0). Morrow.

Hatch, Jane M., ed. American Book of Days. LC 78-16239. 1212p. 1978. 73.00 (ISBN 0-8242-0593-6). Wilson.

Hazlitt, William C. Faiths & Folklore of the British Isles, 2 Vols. LC 64-18758. 1905. Set. 44.00 (ISBN 0-405-08604-0, Blom Pubns); 22.00 ea. Vol. 1 (ISBN 0-405-08605-9). Vol. 2 (ISBN 0-405-08606-7). Ayer Co Pubs.

Kelly, Armandine. Stories for Seasonal Festivals. LC 86-62627. 100p. (Orig.). 1987. pap. 7.95 (ISBN 0-89390-096-6). Resource Pubns.

Marcus, Leah S. The Politics of Mirth: Jonson, Herrick, Milton, Marvell, & the Defense of Old Holiday Pastimes. LC 86-7133. (Illus.). 328p. 1986. lib. bdg. 29.00x (ISBN 0-226-50451-4). U of Chicago Pr.

Monks of New Skete Staff. Entry of the Theotokos. Reverend Laurence Mancuso, tr. from Gr. & Church Slavonic. (Liturgical Music Series I: Great Feasts: Vol. 5). 40p. 1986. pap. text ed. 12.00 (ISBN 0-935129-06-5). Monks of New Skete.

--Great & Holy Pascha. Reverend Laurence Mancuso, tr. from Gr. & Church Slavonic. (Liturgical Music Series I: Great Feasts: Vol. 6). 60p. (Orig.). 1986. pap. text ed. 15.00 (ISBN 0-935129-07-3). Monks of New Skete.

Nieting, Lorenz. Lesser Festivals 4: Saints' Days & Special Occasions. Achtemeier, Elizabeth, et al, eds. LC 79-7377. (Proclamation Two Ser.: Aids for Interpreting the Lessons of the Church Year). 64p. (Orig.). 1981. pap. 3.75 (ISBN 0-8006-1396-1, 1-1396). Fortress.

Palmer, Martin. Faiths & Festivals. (Ward Lock Educational Ser.). 25.00x (ISBN 0-7062-4293-9, Pub. by Ward Lock Educ Co Ltd). State Mutual Bk.

Reid, Richard & Crum, Milton, Jr. Lesser Festivals 3: Saints' Days & Special Occasions. Achtemeier, Elizabeth, et al, eds. LC 79-7377. (Proclamation 2: Aids for Interpreting the Lessons of the Church Year). 64p. (Orig.). 1981. pap. 3.75 (ISBN 0-8006-1395-3, 1-1395). Fortress.

Reilly, Mary V. & Wetterer, Margaret K. From Thy Bounty: Holiday Foods Around from the World. (Illus.). 44p. (Orig.). 1982. pap. 4.95 (ISBN 0-8192-1299-7). Morehouse.

--The Seeds of Paradise: A Garland of Holiday Projects. (Illus.). 44p. (Orig.). 1982. pap. 4.95 (ISBN 0-8192-1298-9). Morehouse.

Ritchie, John. Feasts of Jehovah. LC 82-182. 80p. 1982. pap. 3.95 (ISBN 0-8254-3613-3). Kregel.

Zimmerman, Martha. Celebrate the Feasts: Of the Old Testament in Your Own Home or Church. 186p. 1981. pap. 5.95 (ISBN 0-87123-228-6). Bethany Hse.

FASTS AND FEASTS-CATHOLIC CHURCH

Escriva de Balaguer, Josemaria. Christ Is Passing by. LC 74-78783. 276p. (Foreign language editions avail). 1977. pap. 6.95 (ISBN 0-933932-04-9). Scepter Pubs.

Holy Days in the United States, Histoy, Theology, Celebration. 104p. 1984. pap. 8.95 (ISBN 0-317-46230-X). US Catholic.

Reeder, Rachel, ed. Liturgy: Feasts & Fasting. (The Quarterly Journal of the Liturgical Conference: Vol. 2, No. 1 of Liturgy). (Illus.). 80p. (Orig.). 1981. pap. text ed. 7.95 (ISBN 0-918208-25-4). Liturgical Conf.

FASTS AND FEASTS-JUDAISM

see also names of individual fasts and feast, e.g. sukkoth

Adler, David A. A Picture Book of Jewish Holidays. LC 81-2765. (Illus.). 32p. 1981. reinforced bdg. 12.95 (ISBN 0-8234-0396-3). Holiday.

Agnon, Y. Days of Awe: A Treasury of Tradition, Legends & Learned Commentaries Concerning Rosh Hashanah, Yom Kippur & the Days Between. LC 48-8316. 1965. pap. 8.95 (ISBN 0-8052-0100-9). Schocken.

Bloch, A. P. The Biblical & Historical Background of the Jewish Holy Days. 1978. 20.00x (ISBN 0-87068-338-1); pap. 11.95. Ktav.

Brinn, Ruth E. Let's Celebrate: Fifty-Seven Jewish Holiday Crafts for Young Children. (Illus.). 72p. 1977. pap. 4.95 (ISBN 0-930494-02-4). Kar Ben.

Cardozo, Arlene R. Jewish Family Celebrations: Shabbat, Festivals & Traditional Ceremonies. LC 82-5566. (Illus.). 288p. 1982. 17.50 (ISBN 0-312-44231-9). St Martin.

Cashman, Greer F. Jewish Days & Holidays. LC 79-66167. (Illus.). 64p. 1979. Repr. of 1976 ed. 10.95 (ISBN 0-89961-000-5). SBS Pub.

Cashman, Greer F. & Frankel, Alona. Jewish Days & Holidays. LC 86-70789. (Illus.). 61p. 1986. 9.95 (ISBN 0-915361-58-2, Dist. by Watts). Adama Pubs Inc.

Chanover, Hyman & Zusman, Evelyn. A Book of Prayer for Junior Congregations: Sabbath & Festivals. (Eng. & Hebrew.). 256p. 4.50x (ISBN 0-8381-0174-7, 10-174). United Syn Bk.

Cycle of the Jewish Year. 1982. 6.00 (ISBN 0-686-76502-8). Feldheim.

Drucker, Malka. Sukkot: A Time to Rejoice. LC 82-80814. (A Jewish Holidays Bk.). (Illus.). 96p. 1982. Reinforced bdg. 10.95 (ISBN 0-8234-0466-8). Holiday.

Eisenberg, Azriel & Robinson, Jessie B. My Jewish Holidays. 208p. 3.95x (ISBN 0-8381-0176-3, 10-176). United Syn Bk.

Elias, Joseph. The Haggadah. (The Art Scroll Mesorah Ser.). 224p. 1977. 10.95 (ISBN 0-89906-150-8); pap. 7.95 (ISBN 0-89906-151-6). Mesorah Pubns.

Fuchs, Daniel. Israel's Holy Days: In Type & in Prophecy. LC 85-13172. 96p. 1985. pap. 3.95 (ISBN 0-87213-198-X). Loizeaux.

Gilbert, Arthur & Tarcov, Oscar. Your Neighbor Celebrates. 38p. 0.75 (ISBN 0-686-74967-7). ADL.

Goldman, Alex J. A Handbook for the Jewish Family: Understanding & Enjoying the Sabbath & Other Holidays. LC 58-12938. (Illus.). 1983. Repr. of 1958 ed. 14.95 (ISBN 0-8197-0085-1). Bloch.

Goodman, Robert. A Teacher's Guide to Jewish Holidays. LC 83-70197. 224p. 1983. pap. text ed. 15.00 (ISBN 0-86705-036-5). AIRE.

The Gospel in the Feasts of Israel. 1954. pap. 2.95 (ISBN 0-915540-00-2). Friends Israel-Spearhead Pr.

Greenfeld, Howard. Chanukah, Passover, Rosh Hashanah, Yom Kippur. 1982. boxed set 20.00 (ISBN 0-03-057626-1). H Holt & Co.

Houtsma, Roger V. Understanding the Feasts of the Lord, God's Time Clock for the Ages. 195p. (Orig.). 1986. pap. 6.95 (ISBN 0-9617623-0-6). World Outreach.

Jewish Holidays. pap. 1.19 (9059). Garrard.

Kanter, Shamai. Rabban Gamaliel II: The Legal Traditions. LC 80-12229. (Brown Judaic Studies: No. 8). 15.00x (ISBN 0-89130-403-7, 14 00 08); pap. 10.50x (ISBN 0-89130-404-5). Scholars Pr GA.

Kaplan, Aryeh. The Story of Tisha B'Av. 160p. (Orig.). 1981. pap. 2.95 (ISBN 0-940118-32-7). Maznaim.

Knobel, Peter, ed. Gates of the Seasons: A Guide to the Jewish Year. 200p. 1983. pap. text ed. 9.95 (ISBN 0-916694-92-5). Central Conf.

Kozodoy, Ruth. The Book of Jewish Holidays. Rossel, Seymour, ed. (Illus.). 192p. (Orig.). 1981. pap. text ed. 5.95x (ISBN 0-87441-334-6); tchr's. guide with duplicating masters by Moshe Ben-Aharon 3.25x (ISBN 0-87441-367-2). Behrman.

Kripke, Dorothy K. Lets Talk about the Jewish Holidays. 1982. pap. 5.95 (ISBN 0-8246-0267-6). Jonathan David.

Machzorim-Rosh Hashana & Yom Kippur. 1982. 9.00 (ISBN 0-686-76540-0). Feldheim.

Margolis, Isidor & Markowitz, Sidney L. Jewish Holidays & Festivals. (Orig.). 1962. pap. 3.95 (ISBN 0-8065-0285-1). Citadel Pr.

Renberg, Dalia H. The Complete Family Guide to Jewish Holidays. (Illus.). 256p. 1984. pap. 15.95 (ISBN 0-531-09408-1). Watts.

--The Complete Family Guide to Jewish Holidays. LC 84-11008. (Illus.). 1985. pap. 15.95 (ISBN 0-915361-09-4, 09408-1, Dist. by Watts). Adama Pubs Inc.

Roth, Cecil. Soncino Haggadah. 4.95x (ISBN 0-685-01039-2). Bloch.

Saypol, Judyth R. & Wikler, Madeline. My Very Own Megillah. (Illus.). 32p. 1977. pap. 2.95 (ISBN 0-930494-01-6). Kar Ben.

--My Very Own Sukkot Book. LC 83-26738. (Illus.). 40p. 1980. pap. 2.95 (ISBN 0-930494-09-1). Kar Ben.

Schauss, Hayyim. Jewish Festivals: From Their Beginnings to Our Own Day. rev. ed. (Illus.). (YA) 1969. 8.00 (ISBN 0-8074-0095-5, 383202); course syll. 1.25 (ISBN 0-686-66555-4, 247330). UAHC.

--The Jewish Festivals: History & Observance. LC 62-13140. 1973. pap. 7.50 (ISBN 0-8052-0413-X). Schocken.

Scherman, Nosson. The Haggadah Treasury. (The Art Scroll Mesorah Ser.). 200p. 1978. 10.95 (ISBN 0-89906-200-8); pap. 7.95 (ISBN 0-89906-201-6). Mesorah Pubns.

Scherman, Nosson, tr. The Family Haggadah. (Artscroll Mesorah Ser.). 96p. (Orig.). 1981. pap. 2.75 (ISBN 0-89906-178-8). Mesorah Pubns.

Shepherd, Coulson. Jewish Holy Days: Their Prophetic & Christian Significance. LC 61-16660. 1961. pap. 3.25 (ISBN 0-87213-780-5). Loizeaux.

Silverman, Morris, ed. Passover Haggadah. pap. 4.95 (ISBN 0-87677-029-4). Hartmore.

Simon, Norma. Tu Bishvat. (Festival Series of Picture Story Books). (Illus.). 1961. plastic cover 4.50 (ISBN 0-8381-0709-5). United Syn Bk.

Sperling, Abraham I. Reasons for Jewish Customs & Traditions. Matts, Abraham, tr. LC 68-31711. cancelled. (ISBN 0-8197-0184-X); pap. cancelled (ISBN 0-8197-0008-8). Bloch.

Stern, Chaim, ed. Gates of Repentance. 1978. 16.00 (ISBN 0-916694-38-0); pulpit ed. 20.00 (ISBN 0-916694-40-2); Hebrew ed. 15.00 (ISBN 0-916694-39-9); Hebrew pulpit ed. 20.00 (ISBN 0-686-77334-9). Central Conf.

Strassfeld, Michael. Jewish Holidays. LC 84-48196. (Illus.). 1985. 24.45i (ISBN 0-06-015406-3, HarpT); pap. 15.95 (ISBN 0-06-091225-1). Har-Row.

Waskow, Arthur I. Seasons of Our Joy: A Handbook of Jewish Festivals. 1986. 17.95 (ISBN 0-671-61865-2). Summit Bks.

Wolfson, Ron. The Art of Jewish Living: The Sabbath Seder. (Illus.). 1985. pap. 9.95 (ISBN 0-935665-00-5); tchr's. ed 4.95 (ISBN 0-935665-01-3); cassette tape 3.00 (ISBN 0-935665-02-1). Fed Jewish Mens Clubs.

Zevin, Shlomo Y. The Festivals in Halachah, Vol. II. Kaploon, Uri, ed. Fox-Ashrei, Meir, tr. from Hebrew. (Artscroll Judica Classics Ser.). 336p. 1981. 14.95 (ISBN 0-89906-908-8); pap. 11.95 (ISBN 0-89906-909-6). Mesorah Pubns.

FASTS AND FEASTS-JUDAISM-JUVENILE LITERATURE

Cedarbaum, Sophia. A First Book of Jewish Holidays. LC 85-105348. (Illus.). 80p. 1984. pap. text ed. 6.00 (ISBN 0-8074-0274-5, 301500). UAHC.

Cohen, Barbara. First Fast. (Illus.). 32p. 1987. 7.95 (ISBN 0-8074-0354-7). UAHC.

Corwin, Judith H. Jewish Holiday Fun. 1987. 4.95. Wanderer Bks.

Drucker, Malka. Shabbat: A Peaceful Island (a Jewish Holidays Book) LC 83-7900. (Illus.). 96p. 1983. reinforced bdg. 11.95 (ISBN 0-8234-0500-1). Holiday.

Englander, Lois, et al. The Jewish Holiday Do-Book. new ed. 1977. 9.95x (ISBN 0-685-76976-3). Bloch.

Epstein, Morris. All about Jewish Holidays & Customs. rev. ed. 1969. pap. 7.95x (ISBN 0-87068-500-7). Ktav.

--My Holiday Story Book. rev. ed. 1958. pap. 4.50x (ISBN 0-87068-368-3). Ktav.

Fine, Helen. G'Dee. (Illus.). 1958. text ed. 4.50 (ISBN 0-8074-0137-4, 123702). UAHC.

--G'Dee's Book of Holiday Fun. (Illus.). 1961. pap. 3.00 (ISBN 0-685-20737-4, 121701). UAHC.

Gamoran, Mamie G. Fun Ways to Holidays. 1951. pap. 2.00 (ISBN 0-8074-0136-6, 321400). UAHC.

Garvey, Robert. First Book of Jewish Holidays. (Illus.). 1954. pap. 4.50x (ISBN 0-87068-362-4). Ktav.

Geller, Norman. Color Me Happy: It's Rosh Hashannah & Yom Kippur. (Illus.). 36p. 1986. pap. 2.50 (ISBN 0-915753-10-3). N Geller Pub.

Gersh, Harry. When a Jew Celebrates. LC 70-116678. (Jewish Values Ser.). (Illus.). 256p. 1971. pap. text ed. 6.95x (ISBN 0-87441-091-6). Behrman.

Greenfeld, Howard. Rosh Hashanah & Yom Kippur. LC 79-4818. (Illus.). 1979. 6.95 (ISBN 0-03-044756-9). H Holt & Co.

Jaffe, Leonard. The Pitzel Holiday Book. (Illus.). 1962. 7.95x (ISBN 0-87068-359-4). Ktav.

Mack, Grace C. My Special Book of Jewish Celebrations. (Illus.). 36p. (Orig.). 1984. pap. 8.95 (ISBN 0-9602338-4-9). Rockdale Ridge.

Schaffer, Patricia. Chag Sameach! A Jewish Holiday Book for Children. (Illus.). 28p. (Orig.). 1985. pap. 4.95 (ISBN 0-935079-16-5). Tabor Sarah Bks.

Schlein, Miriam. Our Holidays. (Illus.). 128p. 1983. pap. text ed. 4.95x (ISBN 0-87441-382-6). Behrman.

FATE AND FATALISM

see also Free Will and Determinism; Predestination

Bryans, J. Lonsdale. The Curve of Fate: From Man-Ape to the Man-God. 1977. lib. bdg. 59.95 (ISBN 0-8490-1696-7). Gordon Pr.

Cather, Willa. Obscure Destinies. LC 74-5323. 1974. pap. 4.95 (ISBN 0-394-71179-3, V-179, Vin). Random.

Curtiss, H. A. & Curtiss, F. H. The Key to the Universe. 391p. 1981. pap. 21.00 (ISBN 0-89540-069-3, SB-069). Sun Pub.

Deacon, Richard. Napoleon's Book of Fate. Orig. Title: The Book of Fate: Its Origins & Uses. 1977. 10.00 (ISBN 0-8065-0564-8); pap. 4.95 (ISBN 0-8065-0577-X). Citadel Pr.

Elliott, Albert P. Fatalism in the Works of Thomas Hardy. LC 74-10791. 1972. lib. bdg. 17.50 (ISBN 0-8414-3950-8). Folcroft.

Fortes, Meyer. Oedipus & Job in West African Religion. 1980. Repr. of 1959 ed. lib. bdg. 15.50x (ISBN 0-374-92820-7, Octagon). Hippocrene Bks.

Fortes, Meyer & Horton, Robin. Oedipus & Job in West African Religion. LC 83-7587. (Cambridge Studies in Social Anthropology: No. 48). 128p. 1984. 32.50 (ISBN 0-521-26208-9); pap. 9.95 (ISBN 0-521-27719-1). Cambridge U Pr.

Hughes, Richard. Theology & the Cain Complex. LC 81-43698. 148p. (Orig.). 1982. lib. bdg. 24.75 (ISBN 0-8191-2357-9); pap. text ed. 9.50 (ISBN 0-8191-2358-7). U Pr of Amer.

Man's Origin, Man's Destiny. 1987. 9.95 (210356). Bethany Hse.

Owens, Joseph. Human Destiny: Some Problems for Catholic Philosophy. LC 82-21496. 126p. 1985. 16.95 (ISBN 0-8132-0604-9); pap. 7.95 (ISBN 0-8132-0605-7). Cath U Pr.

Schopenhauer, Arthur. Free Will & Fatalism. (Illus.). 131p. 1985. 97.85 (ISBN 0-89266-508-4). Am Classical Coll Pr.

Socrates & Plato. The Psychology of Fate & of Free Will. (Illus.). 121p. 1983. 75.85 (ISBN 0-89920-067-2). Am Inst Psych.

Steiner, Rudolf. Man's Being, His Destiny & World Evolution. 3rd ed. McArthur, Erna & Riggins, William, trs. from Ger. 123p. (Orig.). 1984. pap. 7.95 (ISBN 0-88010-090-7). Anthroposophic.

FATHER AND CHILD

Hansel, Tim. What Kids Need Most in a Dad. LC 83-22902. 192p. 1984. 10.95 (ISBN 0-8007-1390-7). Revell.

Sifford, Darrell. Father & Son. LC 82-11063. 270p. 1982. 9.95 (ISBN 0-664-27004-2, A Bridgebooks Publication). Westminster.

Stein, Edward V., ed. Fathering: Fact or Fable? LC 76-56840. Repr. of 1977 ed. 47.50 (ISBN 0-8357-9007-X, 2016357). Bks Demand UMI.

Webb, Jim, et al. Effective Father Action Guide. 1979. 3.95 (ISBN 0-8423-0688-9). Tyndale.

FATHER DIVINE

Hoshor, John. God in a Rolls Royce. facsimile ed. LC 70-170698. (Black Heritage Library Collection). Repr. of 1936 ed. 15.00 (ISBN 0-8369-8888-4). Ayer Co Pubs.

Weisbrot, Robert. Father Divine. LC 84-45084. (Illus.). 241p. 1984. pap. 10.95x (ISBN 0-8070-0901-6, BP684). Beacon Pr.

FATHERS

see also Grandparents

Fulton, Ginger A. When I'm a Daddy. 1985. pap. 2.95 (ISBN 0-8024-0387-5). Moody.

Goldsmith, Michael, et al. Today's Father: A Guide to Understanding, Enjoying & Making Things for the Growing Family. (Winston Family Handbooks). 96p. (Orig.). 1984. pap. 9.95 (ISBN 0-86683-849-X, AY8494, HarpR). Har-Row.

Grant, Wilson W. The Caring Father. LC 82-72990. (Orig.). 1983. pap. 5.95 (ISBN 0-8054-5654-6). Broadman.

Haffey, Richard. Thank You, Dad. (Greeting Book Line Ser.). 24p. (Orig.). 1986. pap. 1.50 (ISBN 0-89622-305-1). Twenty-Third.

Kitzinger, Sheila. Giving Birth: The Parents' Emotions in Childbirth. LC 77-2518. (Orig.). 1978. pap. 4.95 (ISBN 0-8052-0573-X). Schocken.

Law, Peter. Portrait of My Father: The Wonder of Knowing God. LC 85-15458. (Living Theology Ser.). 1985. pap. 7.95 (ISBN 0-88070-107-2). Multnomah.

MacDonald, Gordon. The Effective Father. 1977. pap. 6.95 (ISBN 0-8423-0680-3). Tyndale.

Preston, William H., ed. Fathers Are Special. LC 76-39715. (Illus.). 1977. 8.95 (ISBN 0-8054-5622-8, 4256-22). Broadman.

Purdy, J. David. Dads Are Special, Too. 96p. 1985. pap. 3.95 (ISBN 0-8423-0503-3). Tyndale.

Robinson, James & Cox, Jimmie. In Search of a Father. 1979. pap. 1.95 (ISBN 0-8423-1634-5). Tyndale.

Stanley, Charles F. A Man's Touch. LC 77-80948. 120p. 1977. pap. 3.95 (ISBN 0-88207-753-8). Victor Bks.

Stanley, Hugh P. The Challenge of Fatherhood. LC 82-73132. 96p. (Orig.). 1982. pap. 2.45 (ISBN 0-87029-185-8, 20279-6). Abbey.

FATHERS, APOSTOLIC

see Apostolic Fathers

FATHERS OF THE CHURCH

Here are entered works on the life and thought of the Fathers of the Church, a term that embraces the leaders of the early church to the time of Gregory the Great in the West and John of Damascus in the east. Works on their writing are entered under the heading Christian Literature, Early.

see also Apostolic Fathers; Persecution

Bettenson, Henry, ed. & tr. The Later Christian Fathers: A Selection from the Writings of the Fathers from St. Cyril of Jerusalem to St. Leo the Great. 1972. pap. 8.95x (ISBN 0-19-283012-0). Oxford U Pr.

Campbell, James. Greek Fathers. LC 63-10279. (Our Debt to Greece & Rome Ser.). 167p. 1963. Repr. of 1930 ed. 18.50x (ISBN 0-8154-0046-2). Cooper Sq.

Chrysostomos, Bishop. Repentance. (Themes in Orthodox Patristic Psychology Ser.: Vol. III). 75p. (Orig.). 1986. pap. 5.00 (ISBN 0-911165-09-6). Ctr Trad Orthodox.

Cruttwell, Charles T. Literary History of Early Christianity, 2 Vols. LC 76-129369. Repr. of 1893 ed. 65.00 (ISBN 0-404-01877-7). AMS Pr.

Cyprian, St. Life & Works of St. Cyprian of Carthage, 4 vols. Vols. 1, 2, & 4. pap. 1.50 ea.; Vol. 3. pap. 2.95 (ISBN 0-686-05649-3); pap. 6.95 set (ISBN 0-686-05650-7). Eastern Orthodox.

Father Andrew. The Life & Letters of Father Andrew. LC 82-80473. (Treasures from the Spiritual Classics Ser.). 64p. 1982. pap. 2.95 (ISBN 0-8192-1310-1). Morehouse.

Giordani, Igino. Social Message of the Early Church Fathers. 1977. 3.95 (ISBN 0-8198-0469-X); pap. 2.95 (ISBN 0-8198-0470-3). Dghtrs St Paul.

Greer, Rowan. The Captain of Our Salvation: A Study in the Patristic Exegesis of Hebrews. 325p. 1973. lib. bdg. 52.00x (Pub. by J C B Mohr BRD). Coronet Bks.

Gregorius, Saint Les Livres des Miracles & Autres Opuscules, 4 Vols. 1863. Set. 149.00 (ISBN 0-384-19888-0); 38.00 ea.; pap. 32.00 ea.; Set. pap. 125.00 (ISBN 0-384-19889-9). Johnson Repr.

James, E., tr. & illus. Gregory of Tours-Life of the Fathers. (Translated Texts for Historians-Latin Ser.: No. I). (Illus.). 174p. 1985. pap. text ed. 15.00x (ISBN 0-85323-115-X, Pub. by Liverpool U Pr). Humanities.

Leigh-Bennett, Ernest. Handbook of the Early Church Fathers. 1980. lib. bdg. 75.00 (ISBN 0-8490-3107-9). Gordon Pr.

Mackay, Henry F. Followers in the Way. LC 71-93359. (Essay Index Reprint Ser). 1934. 17.00 (ISBN 0-8369-1304-3). Ayer Co Pubs.

Osiek, Carolyn. Rich & Poor in the Shepherd of Hermas: An Exegetical-Social Investigation. Vawter, Bruce, ed. LC 83-7385. (Catholic Biblical Quarterly Monographs: No. 15). xi, 184p. (Orig.). 1983. pap. 6.00x (ISBN 0-915170-14-0). Catholic Biblical.

Pelikan, Jaroslav J. The Shape of Death: Life, Death, & Immortality in the Early Fathers. LC 78-6030. 1978. Repr. of 1961 ed. lib. bdg. 22.50x (ISBN 0-313-20458-6, PESD). Greenwood.

Pennington, Basil. The Last of the Fathers. LC 82-24098. 1983. pap. 14.95 (ISBN 0-932506-24-0). St Bedes Pubns.

Plummer, Alfred. The Church of the Early Fathers. 1892. 15.00 (ISBN 0-8414-9261-1). Folcroft.

Quasten, Johannes & Di Berardino, Angelo, eds. Patrology, Vol. IV: The Golden Age of Latin Patristic Literature. Solari, Placid, tr. 1986. 48.00 (ISBN 0-87061-126-7); pap. 39.95 (ISBN 0-87061-127-5); Set of 4 vols. pap. 85.00. Chr Classics.

Sider, Robert D. The Gospel & Its Proclamation. (Message of the Fathers of the Church Ser.: Vol. 10). 15.95 (ISBN 0-89453-350-9); pap. 9.95 (ISBN 0-89453-321-5). M Glazier.

Stinger, Charles L. Humanism & the Church Fathers: Ambrogio Traversari (1386-1439) & the Revival of Patristic Theology in the Early Italian Renaissance. LC 76-21699. 1977. 49.50x (ISBN 0-87395-304-5). State U NY Pr.

Studia Patristica XVIII: Papers of the 1983 Oxford International Patristics Conference, Vol. 1. pap. 40.00 (ISBN 0-87907-350-0). Cistercian Pubns.

Von Campenhausen, Hans. The Fathers of the Latin Church. Hoffmann, Manfred, tr. LC 76-75260. 1964. 32.50x (ISBN 0-8047-0685-9). Stanford U Pr.

FATHERS OF THE CHURCH–BIOBIOGRAPHY

Gregory, St. Life of St. Macrina. 1974. pap. 2.95 (ISBN 0-686-10202-9). Eastern Orthodox.

Hamell, Patrick J. Handbook of Patrology. 1968. pap. 5.95 (ISBN 0-8189-0057-1). Alba.

Schneemelcher, Wilhelm, ed. Bibliographia Patristica: Internationale Patristische Bibliographie. Incl. Vol. 1. Erscheinungen des Jahres 1956. xxviii, 103p. 1959. 13.80x (ISBN 3-11-001248-0); Vol. 2. Erscheinungen des Jahres 1957. xxx, 115p. 1959. 13.80 (ISBN 3-11-001249-9); Vol. 3. Erscheinungen des Jahres 1958. xxxi, 119p. 1960. 13.80x (ISBN 3-11-001250-2); Vol. 4. Erscheinungen des Jahres 1959. xxxiii, 126p. 1961. 9.20x (ISBN 3-11-001251-0); Vol. 5. Erscheinungen des Jahres 1960. xxxiii, 114p. 1962. 9.20x (ISBN 3-11-001252-9); Vol. 6. Erscheinungen des Jahres 1961. xxxiii, 98p. 1963. 9.20x (ISBN 3-11-001253-7); Vol. 7. Erscheinungen des Jahres 1962. xxxiv, 108p. 1964. 9.20x (ISBN 3-11-001254-5); Vol. 8. Erscheinungen des Jahres 1963. xxxiv, 120p. 1966. 12.00x (ISBN 3-11-001255-3); Vol. 9. Erscheinungen des Jahres 1964. xxxiv, 157p. 1967. 12.00x (ISBN 3-11-001256-1); Vol. 10. Erscheinungen Des Jahres 1965. xxxiv, 127p. 1969. 12.00x (ISBN 3-11-001257-X); Vol. 11. Erscheinungen Des Jahres 1966. 1971. 28.80x (ISBN 3-11-003531-6); Vols. 12 & 13. Erscheinungen Des Jahres 1967-68. 1975. 28.80x (ISBN 3-11-004631-8). De Gruyter.

FATHERS OF THE CHURCH–BIBLIOGRAPHY

Krueger, Gustav. History of Early Christian Literature in the First Three Centuries. Gillet, Charles R., tr. from Ger. 1969. 26.00 (ISBN 0-8337-1963-7). B Franklin.

FATHERS OF THE CHURCH–DICTIONARIES

Goodspeed, Edgar J. Index Patristicus, Sive Clavis Patrum Apostolicorum Operum. LC 60-52358. 1960. 18.00x (ISBN 0-8401-0863-X). A R Allenson.

Hebert, Peter E., ed. Selections from the Latin Fathers. (College Classical Ser.). xvii, 186p. 1982. lib. bdg. 25.00x (ISBN 0-89241-357-3); pap. text ed. 12.50x (ISBN 0-89241-370-0). Caratzas.

Smith, William & Wace, Henry, eds. Dictionary of Christian Biography, Literature, Sects & Doctrines: Being a Continuation of the Dictionary of the Bible, 4 Vols. LC 12-3122. 1968. Repr. of 1877 ed. Set. 375.00 (ISBN 0-527-84200-1). Kraus Repr.

FATIMA, NOSSA SENHORA DA

Dacruz, J. More about Fatima. De Oca, V. Montes, tr. from Port. Tr. of Prodige Prow de Fatima. 1979. pap. 1.00 (ISBN 0-913382-16-7, 102-95). Prow Bks-Franciscan.

McMillin, John & Glenn, Jim. Twelve Minutes over Fatima. 1986. 10.95 (ISBN 0-533-06492-9). Vantage.

Our Lady of Fatima's Peace Plan from Heaven. 32p. 1983. pap. 0.40 (ISBN 0-89555-217-5). TAN Bks Pubs.

Pelletier, Joseph A. Sun Danced at Fatima. rev. ed. LC 83-45046. (Illus.). 240p. 1983. pap. 6.95 (ISBN 0-385-18965-6, Im). Doubleday.

Walsh, William Thomas. Our Lady of Fatima. pap. 4.50 (ISBN 0-385-02869-5, D1, Im). Doubleday.

FATIMA, PORTUGAL (SHRINE)

Alonso, Joaquin M. The Secret of Fatima Fact & Legend. Dominican Nuns of the Perpetual Rosary, tr. from Span. LC 79-13182. (Illus.). 1979. 8.95 (ISBN 0-911218-14-9); pap. 3.95 (ISBN 0-911218-15-7). Ravengate Pr.

Cappa, Alphonse. Fatima: Cove of Wonders. 1980. 4.50 (ISBN 0-8198-0569-6); pap. 3.25 (ISBN 0-8198-0570-X). Dghtrs St Paul.

Carroll, Warren H. Nineteen Seventeen: Red Banners, White Mantle. 168p. (Orig.). 1981. pap. 4.95 (ISBN 0-931888-05-0). Christendom Pubns.

Culligan, Emmett. Fatima Secret. 1975. pap. 1.50 (ISBN 0-89555-052-0). TAN Bks Pubs.

Di Marchi, John. Fatima from the Beginning. (Illus.). 1980. pap. 5.95 (ISBN 0-911218-16-5). Ravengate Pr.

Fox, Robert J. Fatima Today. (Illus.). 263p. (Orig.). pap. 6.95 (ISBN 0-931888-11-5). Christendom Pubns.

Johnston, Francis. Fatima: The Great Sign. 152p. 1980. 4.95 (ISBN 0-911988-37-8). AMI Pr.

--Fatima: The Great Sign. LC 80-54423. 1980. Repr. of 1979 ed. 5.00 (ISBN 0-89555-163-2). Tan Bks Pubs.

McMillin, John & Glenn, Jim. Twelve Minutes over Fatima. 1986. 10.95 (ISBN 0-533-06492-9). Vantage.

Oliveira, Joseph De. Jacinta, Flower of Fatima. 192p. 1972. pap. 3.95 (ISBN 0-911988-45-9). AMI Pr.

Rengers, Christopher. The Youngest Prophet: The Life of Jacinta Marto, Fatima Visionary. LC 85-30789. 144p. (Orig.). 1986. pap. 5.95 (ISBN 0-8189-0496-8). Alba.

FATIMITES

Lewis, Bernard. The Origins of Isma'ilism: A Study of the Historical Background of the Fatimid Caliphate. LC 74-180357. Repr. of 1940 ed. 22.50 (ISBN 0-404-56289-2). AMS Pr.

FEAR

see also Anxiety; Peace of Mind

Allison, C. FitzSimons. Fear, Love, & Worship. pap. 4.95 (ISBN 0-8164-2020-3, SP17, HarpR). Har-Row.

Angell, James W. Learning to Manage Our Fears. LC 81-1878. 128p. 1981. 7.75 (ISBN 0-687-21329-0). Abingdon.

Buckley, Michael. Why Are You Afraid. pap. 5.95 (ISBN 0-87061-060-0). Chr Classics.

Gaspard, Perry A. Freedom from Fear. 1980. pap. 2.00 (ISBN 0-931867-06-1). Abundant Life Pubns.

Gossett, Don. How to Conquer Fear. Orig. Title: How You Can Rise Above Fear. 160p. 1981. pap. 2.95 (ISBN 0-88368-092-0). Whitaker Hse.

Hauck, Paul A. Overcoming Worry & Fear. LC 74-20629. 112p. 1975. pap. 6.95 (ISBN 0-664-24811-X). Westminster.

Hayden, Eric. God's Answer for Fear. LC 85-70873. 1986. pap. 2.95 (ISBN 0-88270-581-4). Bridge Pub.

Huber, J. William, et al. Fear: Issues of Emotional Living in an Age of Stress for Clergy & Religious. Kraus, Marie, ed. LC 86-3533. 141p. 1986. pap. 8.00 (ISBN 0-89571-028-5). Affirmation.

Kirkpatrick, Jean. Fear & Worry: Our Common Enemies. 14p. 1982. pap. 1.50 (ISBN 0-686-19760-7). WFS.

Living Beyond Worry & Anger. LC 79-83659. 1979. 7.95 (ISBN 0-89081-194-6). Harvest Hse.

McFadden, Jim. The Fear Factor. (Living As a Christian Ser.). (Orig.). 1983. pap. 3.95 (ISBN 0-89283-159-6). Servant.

Murphy, Joseph. Supreme Mastery of Fear. pap. 0.75 (ISBN 0-87516-340-8). De Vorss.

Price, Nelson L. Farewell to Fear. (Orig.). 1983. pap. 5.95 (ISBN 0-8054-5533-7). Broadman.

Pugh, Nathanael. Running Free: Conquering Fear & Shyness. Wallace, Mary H., ed. 96p. (Orig.). 1984. pap. 4.50 (ISBN 0-912315-69-5). Word Aflame.

Tolle, James M. Living Without Fear. 1977. 4.95 (ISBN 0-915378-13-2). Tolle Pubns.

Wright, Norm. Healing of Fears. LC 81-83238. 176p. (Orig.). 1982. pap. 4.95 (ISBN 0-89081-302-7). Harvest Hse.

FEAR OF GOD

Bunyan, John. Fear of God. pap. 3.95 (ISBN 0-685-19828-6). Reiner.

Burke, Dennis. Understanding the Fear of the Lord. 1982. pap. 2.25 (ISBN 0-89274-265-8, HH-265). Harrison Hse.

FEAST OF DEDICATION

see Hanukkah (Feast of Lights)

FEAST OF ESTHER

see Purim (Feast of Esther)

FEAST OF LIGHTS

see Hanukkah (Feast of Lights)

FEAST OF TABERNACLES

see Sukkoth

FEAST OF THE MACCABEES

see Hanukkah (Feast of Lights)

FEAST OF WEEKS

see Shavu'oth (Feast of Weeks)

FEASTS

see Fasts and Feasts

FEDERAL THEOLOGY

see Covenants (Theology)

FEELINGS

see Emotions

FEMININITY OF GOD

Craighead, Meinrad. The Mother's Songs: Images of God the Mother. LC 85-50408. 96p. (Orig.). 1985. pap. 9.95 (ISBN 0-8091-2716-4). Paulist Pr.

FENELON, FRANCOIS DE SALIGNAC DE LA MOTHE, ABP., 1651-1715

Davis, James H., Jr. Fenelon. (World Authors Ser.). 1979. lib. bdg. 15.95 (ISBN 0-8057-6384-8, Twayne). G K Hall.

De Salignac de la Mothe-Fenelon, Francoise. Along the Royal Way. Helms, Hal M., ed. LC 83-61406. (Living Library Ser.). 152p. (Orig.). 1984. pap. 5.95 (ISBN 0-941478-20-3). Paraclete Pr.

St. Cyres, Viscount. Francois de Fenelon. LC 72-113319. 1970. Repr. of 1901 ed. 25.50x (ISBN 0-8046-0998-5, Pub. by Kennikat). Assoc Faculty Pr.

FENJAS

see Falashas

FERNANDO 5TH, EL CATOLICO, KING OF SPAIN, 1452-1516

McKendrick, Melveena. Ferdinand & Isabella. LC 68-14974. (Horizon Caravel Bks.). 1544p. (YA) 1968. PLB 15.89 (ISBN 0-06-024165-9). HarpJ.

FERRARA–HISTORY

Gardner, Edmund G. Dukes & Poets of Ferrara: A Story in the Poetry, Religion & Politics of Fifteenth & Early Sixteenth Centuries. LC 78-145033. xiv, 578p. 1972. Repr. of 1904 ed. 39.00x (ISBN 0-403-00776-3). Scholarly.

FESTIVAL OF HANUKKAH

see Hanukkah (Feast of Lights)

FESTSCHRIFTEN–BIBLIOGRAPHY

Marcus, J. R. & Bilgray, A., eds. Index to Jewish Festschriften. Repr. of 1937 ed. 29.00 (ISBN 0-527-61300-2). Kraus Repr.

FETISHISM

see also Animism; Idols and Images; Nature Worship; Voodooism

Farrow, Stephen S. Faith, Fancies & Fetish or Yoruba Paganism. LC 76-98718. (Illus.). Repr. of 1926 ed. 22.50x (ISBN 0-8371-2759-9, FFF&, Pub. by Negro U Pr). Greenwood.

Nassau, Robert H. Fetishism in West Africa: Forty Years' Observation of Native Customs & Superstitions. LC 69-18995. (Illus.). Repr. of 1904 ed. 22.50x (ISBN 0-8371-0977-9, NAF&, Pub. by Negro U Pr). Greenwood.

FIFTH MONARCHY MEN

Brown, Louise F. Political Activities of the Baptists & the Fifth Monarchy Men in England During the Interregnum. 1964. Repr. of 1911 ed. 20.50 (ISBN 0-8337-0399-4). B Franklin.

FINANCE, CHURCH

see Church Finance

FINANCE, PERSONAL

Bruso, Dick. Bible Promises, Help & Hope for Your Finances. 156p. (Orig.). 1985. pap. 2.95 (ISBN 0-89840-075-9). Heres Life.

Burkett, Larry. The Financial Planning Workbook. LC 82-7877. (Christian Financial Concepts Ser.). 1982. pap. 6.95 (ISBN 0-8024-2546-1). Moody.

--How to Manage Your Money. LC 82-7904. (Christian Financial Concepts Ser.). 1982. pap. 7.95 (ISBN 0-8024-2547-X). Moody.

--Using Your Money Wisely: Guidelines from Scripture. 1986. pap. 7.95 (ISBN 0-8024-3425-8). Moody.

Fries, Michael, et al. A Christian Guide to Prosperity. 2nd ed. Frank, Diane, ed. LC 83-46178. (Illus.). 523p. 1984. pap. 9.95 (ISBN 0-9611910-5-8). Comm Res.

Haughey, John C. Holy Use of Money: Personal Finance in Light of Christian Faith. LC 85-29213. 288p. 1986. 16.95 (ISBN 0-385-23448-1). Doubleday.

MacGregor, Malcolm & Baldwin, Stanley C. Your Money Matters. LC 75-56123. 176p. 1977. pap. 4.95 (ISBN 0-87123-662-1, 210662). Bethany Hse.

Morgan, Darold H. Personal Finances for Ministers. LC 85-17443. (Broadman Leadership Ser.). 1985. pap. 5.95 (ISBN 0-8054-6405-0). Broadman.

Mumford, Amy R. It Only Hurts Between Paydays. LC 80-70679. 160p. 1986. pap. 5.95 (ISBN 0-89636-067-9). Accent Bks.

Wilson, Ken. Your Money & Your Life: Practical Guidance for Earning, Managing & Giving Money. (Living as a Christian Ser.). 96p. (Orig.). 1983. pap. 2.95 (ISBN 0-89283-171-5). Servant.

FINCH, ROBERT, 1783-1830

Nitchie, Elizabeth. Reverend Colonel Finch. LC 40-33650. Repr. of 1940 ed. 12.50 (ISBN 0-404-04777-7). AMS Pr.

FINLEY, ROBERT, 1772-1817

Brown, Isaac V. Biography of the Reverend Robert Finley. LC 73-82178. (Anti-Slavery Crusade in America Ser). 1969. Repr. of 1857 ed. 18.00 (ISBN 0-405-00617-9). Ayer Co Pubs.

FINNEY, CHARLES GRANDISON, 1792-1875

Drummond, Lewis. The Life & Ministry of Charles Finney. 272p. 1985. pap. 5.95 (ISBN 0-87123-818-7, 210818). Bethany Hse.

Edman, V. Raymond. Finney Lives On. 256p. 1970. pap. 4.95 (ISBN 0-87123-150-6, 210150). Bethany Hse.

Finney, Charles G. The Autobiography of Charles G. Finney. Wessel, Helen S., ed. LC 77-2813. 1977. pap. 5.95 (ISBN 0-87123-010-0). Bethany Hse.

--Charles G. Finney: An Autobiography. 480p. 16.95 (ISBN 0-8007-0095-3). Revell.

Hardman, Keith J. Charles Grandison Finney, Seventeen Ninety-Two to Eighteen Seventy-Five: Revivalist & Reformer. (Illus.). 536p. 1987. text ed. 45.00x (ISBN 0-8156-2397-6). Syracuse U Pr.

Miller, Basil. Charles Finney. 144p. 1983. pap. 2.95 (ISBN 0-88113-034-6). Edit Betania.

--Charles G. Finney. 144p. 1969. pap. 3.50 (ISBN 0-87123-061-5, 200061). Bethany Hse.

Weddle, David L. The Law As Gospel: Revival & Reform in the Theology of Charles G. Finney. LC 85-8303. (Studies in Evangelicalism: No. 6). 293p. 1985. 23.50 (ISBN 0-8108-1819-1). Scarecrow.

FINNISH MYTHOLOGY

see Mythology, Finno-Ugrian

FINNO-UGRIAN MYTHOLOGY

see Mythology, Finno-Ugrian

FIRE (IN RELIGION, FOLK-LORE, ETC.)

Furley, William D. Studies in the Use of Fire in the Ancient Greek Religion. rev. ed. Connor, W. R., ed. LC 80-2650. (Monographs in Clasical Studies). (Illus.). 1981. lib. bdg. 29.00 (ISBN 0-405-14037-1). Ayer Co Pubs.

FIRST COMMUNION

Avramis, Tom. Preparing to Receive Holy Communion. 1986. pap. 1.95 (ISBN 0-937032-43-3). Light&Life Pub Co MN.

Grimbol, William R. The Communion Clown Circle. 1985. 3.25 (ISBN 0-89536-734-3, 5818). CSS of Ohio.

Heeg, Aloysius J. Jesus & I. pap. text ed. 1.00 (ISBN 0-8294-0214-4). Loyola.

McIntyre, Marie. Eucharist: Our Communal Celebration. LC 76-25620. (Illus., Orig.). 1978. pap. 2.95 (ISBN 0-89622-077-X). Twenty-Third.

The New Saint Joseph First Communion Cathechism. rev. ed. (Official Baltimore Catechism Ser.). (Illus.). 1.60 (ISBN 0-89942-240-3, 240/05). Catholic Bk Pub.

Schrieber, Angela. Our First Communion: A Growing-up Moment. Fischer, Carl, ed. 1986. dupl. masterbk 9.95 (ISBN 0-89837-107-4). Peter Li.

Thiry, Joan & Burbach, Marilyn. Eucharist Is for Sharing. 1977. duplicating masterbook 12.95 (ISBN 0-89837-051-5, Pub. by Pflaum Pr). Peter Li.

Your Child's First Communion: A Look at Your Dreams. 32p. (Orig.). 1984. pap. 1.35 (ISBN 0-86716-035-7). St Anthony Mess Pr.

FISH (IN RELIGION, FOLK-LORE, ETC.)

Titcomb, Margaret. Native Use of Fish in Hawaii. 2nd ed. 185p. 1972. pap. 4.50 (ISBN 0-8248-0592-5). UH Pr.

Trevelyan, Marie. Folk-Lore & Folk-Stories of Wales. (Folklore Ser). 35.00 (ISBN 0-8482-2749-2). Norwood Edns.

FITZRALPH, RICHARD, ABP. OF ARMAGH, d. 1360

Walsh, Katherine. A Fourteenth-Century Scholar & Primate: Richard FitzRalph in Oxford, Avignon, & Armagh. (Illus.). 1981. 65.00x (ISBN 0-19-822637-3). Oxford U Pr.

FLAGET, BENEDICT JOSEPH, BP., 1763-1850

Spalding, Martin J. Sketches of the Life, Times, -Character of Right Reverend Benedict Joseph Flaget, First Bishop of Louisville. LC 71-83441. (Religion in America, Ser. 1). 1969. Repr. of 1852 ed. 21.00 (ISBN 0-405-00266-1). Ayer Co Pubs.

FLEURY, ANDRE HERCULE DE, CARDINAL, 1653-1743

Wilson, Arthur M. French Foreign Policy During the Administration of Cardinal Fleury: 1726-1743; a Study in Diplomacy & Commercial Development. LC 70-138193. 433p. 1972. Repr. of 1936 ed. lib. bdg. 22.50x (ISBN 0-8371-5333-6, WIFP). Greenwood.

FLINT, TIMOTHY, 1780-1840

Kirkpatrick, John E. Timothy Flint: Pioneer, Missionary, Author, Editor, 1780-1840. LC 68-56780. (Research & Source Works Ser: No. 267). 1968. Repr. of 1911 ed. 21.50 (ISBN 0-8337-1930-0). B Franklin.

FLOOD, BIBLICAL

see Deluge

FLORENCE–CHURCHES

Luchs, Allison. Cestello: A Cistercian Church of the Florentine Renaissance. LC 76-23642. (Outstanding Dissertations in the Fine Arts - 2nd Series - 15th Century). (Illus.). 1977. Repr. lib. bdg. 76.00 (ISBN 0-8240-2706-X). Garland Pub.

Trachtenberg, Marvin. The Campanile of Florence Cathedral: Giotto's Tower. LC 70-124532. (Illus.). 458p. 1971. 135.00 (ISBN 0-8147-8151-9). NYU Pr.

FLOWER ARRANGEMENT IN CHURCHES

Moffitt, Oleta S. Arranging Flowers for the Church. rev. ed. 1977. pap. 1.95 (ISBN 0-8006-1837-8, 1-1837). Fortress.

Taylor, Jean. Flowers in Church. 161p. 1985. pap. 10.95 (ISBN 0-8192-1361-6). Morehouse.

FOCOLARE MOVEMENT

Lorit, Sergius C. & Grimaldi, Nuzzo. Focolare: After Thirty Years: Insights into the Life of the Focolare Movement. LC 76-18456. (Illus.). 268p. 1976. pap. 4.50 (ISBN 0-911782-27-3). New City.

Lubich, Chiara. May They All Be One: Origins & Life of the Focolare Movement. LC 71-77438. 1977. pap. 2.50 cancelled (ISBN 0-911782-28-1). New City.

FOGGARA

see Falashas

FOLK LITERATURE

see also Legends; Proverbs

Armistead, Samuel G. & Silverman, Joseph H. Folk-Literature of the Sephardic Jews, Vol. 1. The Judeo-Spanish Ballad Chapbooks of Yacob Abraham Yona. LC 71-78565. 1971. 60.00x (ISBN 0-520-01648-3). U of Cal Pr.

Kelly, Eamon. Bless Me Father. 1977. pap. 6.95 (ISBN 0-85342-489-6, Pub. by Mercier Pr Ireland). Irish Bks Media.

FOLK LITERATURE–THEMES, MOTIVES

Cook, Arthur B. Zeus: A Study of Ancient Religion, 2 vols. Incl. Vol. 1. Zeus, God of the Bright Sky. LC 64-25839. (Illus.). 885p. Repr. of 1914 ed. 50.00x (ISBN 0-8196-0148-9); Vol. 2. Zeus, God of the Dark Sky: Thunder & Lightning, 2 pts. LC 64-25839. Repr. of 1925 ed. 100.00xset (ISBN 0-8196-0156-X); Vol. 2, Pt. 1. Text & Notes. xliii, 858p; Vol. 2, Pt. 2. Appendixes & Index. (Illus.). 539p. Biblo.

FOLK-LORE

see also Animism; Devil; Evil Eye; Fables; Grail; Incantations; Legends; Marriage Customs and Rites; Myth; Mythology; Proverbs; Story-Telling; Superstition; Witchcraft

Baring-Gould, Sabine. Curious Myths of the Middle Ages. 69.95 (ISBN 0-87968-261-2). Gordon Pr.

Bendix, Regina. Progress & Nostalgia: Silvester-Klausen in Urnasch, Switzerland. LC 84-28128. (UC Publications in Folklore & Mythology: Vol. 33). 1985. 21.00 (ISBN 0-520-09959-1). U of Cal Pr.

Blinkenberg, C. The Thunderweapon in Religion & Folklore. 1977. lib. bdg. 59.95 (ISBN 0-8490-2749-7). Gordon Pr.

Bulfinch, Thomas. Bulfinch's Mythology. 2nd rev. ed. LC 69-11314. (Illus.). 1970. 16.45i (ISBN 0-690-57260-3). T Y Crowell.

Chaplin, Dorothea. Mythological Bonds Between East & West. 1976. lib. bdg. 59.95 (ISBN 0-8490-2325-4). Gordon Pr.

Cox, G. W. An Introduction to the Science of Comparative Mythology & Folklore. 69.95 (ISBN 0-8490-0420-9). Gordon Pr.

Cox, George W. An Introduction to the Science of Comparative Mythology & Folklore. 1976. lib. bdg. 59.95 (ISBN 0-8490-2071-9). Gordon Pr.

Farrer, Claire R., ed. Women & Folklore: Images & Genres. (Illus.). 100p. 1986. pap. text ed. 6.95x (ISBN 0-88133-227-5). Waveland Pr.

Gaster, Moses. Studies & Texts in Folklore, Magic, Medieval Romance, Hebrew Apocrypha & Samaritan Archaeology, 3 Vols. rev. ed. 1970. Set. 45.00x (ISBN 0-87068-056-0). Ktav.

Gruffydd, W. J. Folklore & Myth in the Mabinogion. LC 75-34083. 1958. lib. bdg. 15.00 (ISBN 0-8414-4522-2). Folcroft.

Gubernatis, Angelo De. Zoological Mythology, 2 Vols. LC 68-58904. 1968. Repr. of 1872 ed. Set. 56.00x (ISBN 0-8103-3527-1). Gale.

Hartland, Edwin S. Mythology & Folktales: Their Relation & Interpretation. LC 75-144519. (Popular Studies in Mythology, Romance & Folklore: No. 7). Repr. of 1900 ed. 5.50 (ISBN 0-404-53507-0). AMS Pr.

Jung, Carl G. & Kerenyi, Carl. Essays on a Science of Mythology: The Myths of the Divine Child & the Mysteries of Eleusis. rev. ed. (Bollingen Ser.: Vol. 22). 1963. pap. 6.95 (ISBN 0-691-01756-5). Princeton U Pr.

Kellett, Ernst E. Story of Myths. (Folklore & Society Ser). 1969. Repr. of 1927 ed. 20.00 (ISBN 0-384-29025-6). Johnson Repr.

Lang, Andrew. Custom & Myth. 2nd rev. ed. LC 68-59267. Repr. of 1885 ed. 11.00 (ISBN 0-404-03817-4). AMS Pr.

Owen, Mary A. Voodoo Tales As Told among the Negroes of the Southwest. facs. ed. LC 70-149874. (Black Heritage Library Collection). (Illus.). 1893. 17.00 (ISBN 0-8369-8754-3). Ayer Co Pubs.

Popular Studies in Mythology, Romance & Folklore, 15 vols. Repr. of 1908 ed. write for info. (ISBN 0-404-53500-3). AMS Pr.

Porteous, A. Forest Folklore, Mythology & Romance. 1977. lib. bdg. 59.95 (ISBN 0-8490-1858-7). Gordon Pr.

Raglan, FitzRoy. The Hero: A Study in Tradition, Myth, & Drama. LC 75-23424. 296p. 1975. Repr. of 1956 ed. lib. bdg. 45.00x (ISBN 0-8371-8138-0, RATH). Greenwood.

Richardson, Alan. Gate of Moon: Mythical & Magical Doorways to the Otherworld. 160p. 1984. pap. 9.95 (ISBN 0-85030-365-6). Newcastle Pub.

Schneiderman, Leo. The Psychology of Myth, Folklore & Religion. LC 81-9471. 232p. 1981. text ed. 21.95x (ISBN 0-88229-659-0); pap. text ed. 10.95x (ISBN 0-88229-783-X). Nelson-Hall.

Schwab, Gustav. Gods & Heroes. LC 47-873. 1977. pap. 9.95 (ISBN 0-394-73402-5). Pantheon.

Schwarzbaum, Haim. Studies in Jewish & World Folklore. (Fabula Supplement Ser., No. B 3). 1968. 97.50x (ISBN 3-11-000393-7). De Gruyter.

Thompson, C. J. Hand of Destiny: The Folk-Lore & Superstition of Everyday Life. LC 70-125600. 1970. Repr. of 1932 ed. 46.00x (ISBN 0-8103-3419-4). Gale.

Tilton, Rafael. The Immortal Dragon of Sylene & Other Faith Tales. (Illus.). 128p. 1982. 9.95 (ISBN 0-86683-656-X, HarpR). Har-Row.

FOLK-LORE–DICTIONARIES

Bonnerjea, Biren. Dictionary of Superstitions & Mythology. LC 69-17755. 1969. Repr. of 1927 ed. 43.00x (ISBN 0-8103-3572-7). Gale.

Jobes, Gertrude. Dictionary of Mythology, Folklore & Symbols, 3 Vols. LC 61-860. 1759p. 1961. Vols. 1 & 2. 70.00 (ISBN 0-8108-0034-9); Vol. 3 index, 482 pgs. 35.00 (ISBN 0-8108-1697-0). Scarecrow.

Leach, ed. Funk & Wagnalls Standard Dictionary of Folklore, Mythology & Legend. LC 72-78268. (Funk & W Bk.). 23.00i (ISBN 0-308-40090-9). T Y Crowell.

Leach, Maria & Fried, Jerome, eds. Funk & Wagnall's Standard Dictionary of Folklore, Mythology, & Legends. 1984. pap. 29.95 (ISBN 0-06-250511-4, HarpR). Har-Row.

Radford, Edwin & Radford, Mona A. Encyclopedia of Superstitions. Repr. of 1949 ed. lib. bdg. 45.00x (ISBN 0-8371-2115-9, RASU). Greenwood.

FOLK-LORE, AFRICAN

Alhaji Obaba Abdullahi Muhammad. Three Little Africans. (Illus.). 36p. (Orig.). 1978. pap. 2.50 (ISBN 0-916157-00-8). African Islam Miss Pubns.

Farrow, Stephen S. Faith, Fancies & Fetish or Yoruba Paganism. LC 76-98718. (Illus.). Repr. of 1926 ed. 22.50x (ISBN 0-8371-2759-9, FFF&, Pub. by Negro U Pr). Greenwood.

Gbadamosi, Bakare & Beier, Ulli. Not Even God Is Ripe Enough. (African Writers Ser.). 1968. pap. text ed. 4.00x (ISBN 0-435-90048-X). Heinemann Ed.

Helser, Albert D. Education of Primitive People. LC 75-97403. Repr. of 1934 ed. cancelled (ISBN 0-8371-2651-7, HPP&, Pub. by Negro U Pr). Greenwood.

FOLK-LORE, CHINESE

Ho Ting-Jui. A Comparative Study of Myths & Legends of Formosan Aborigines. (Asian Folklore & Social Life Monograph: No. 18). 1972. 17.00 (ISBN 0-89986-020-6). Oriental Bk Store.

Levy, Howard S., tr. from Chinese. China's Dirtiest Trickster: Folklore About Hsu Wen-ch'ang (1521-1593) (Sino-Japanese Folklore Translations Ser.: No. 1). (Illus.). 68p. 1974. 15.00 (ISBN 0-686-05428-8). Oriental BK Store.

Li Lin-Tsan. Studies in Mo-So Tribal Stories. (Asian Folklore & Social Life Monograph: No. 3). (Chinese.). 1970. 17.00 (ISBN 0-89986-006-0). Oriental Bk Store.

Mackenzie, Donald A. The Myths of China & Japan. LC 77-6878. 1977. Repr. of 1923 ed. lib. bdg. 45.00 (ISBN 0-89341-149-3). Longwood Pub Group.

Nowak, Margaret & Durrant, Stephen. The Tale of the Nisan Shamaness: A Manchu Folk Epic. LC 76-49171. (Publications on Asia of the School of International Studies: No. 31). 192p. 1977. 15.00x (ISBN 0-295-95548-1). U of Wash Pr.

Palmer, Martin, tr. from Chinese. T'ung Shu. LC 85-2520. (Illus.). 240p. 1986. pap. 7.95 (ISBN 0-87773-346-5, 74221-4, Dist. by Random). Shambhala Pubns.

Ryuzo, Nagao. Chinese Folklore: Belief & Marriage. (Asian Folklore & Social Life Monograph: No. 14). (Japanese.). 1938. 14.00 (ISBN 0-89986-035-4). Oriental Bk Store.

FOLK-LORE, GREEK

Edwards, R. B. Kadmos the Phoenician: A Study in Greek Legends & the Mycenaean Age. xiv, 258p. 1979. pap. text ed. 67.50x (Pub. by A. M. Hakkert). Coronet Bks.

Hyde, Walter W. Greek Religion & Its Survivals. LC 63-10268. (Our Debt to Greece & Rome Ser). 1963. Repr. of 1930 ed. 18.50x (ISBN 0-8154-0117-5). Cooper Sq.

FOLK-LORE, HAITIAN

Metraux, Alfred. Voodoo in Haiti. LC 77-185327. (Illus.). 1972. pap. 8.95 (ISBN 0-8052-0341-9). Schocken.

FOLK-LORE, HAWAIIAN

Emerson, Nathaniel B. Unwritten Literature of Hawaii: The Sacred Songs of the Hula. LC 65-12971. (Illus.). 1965. pap. 6.75 (ISBN 0-8048-1067-2). C E Tuttle.

Westervelt, William D., ed. Hawaiian Legends of Ghosts & Ghost-Gods. LC 63-22543. (Illus.). 1963. 7.25 (ISBN 0-8048-0238-6). C E Tuttle.

FOLK-LORE, INDIAN

Here are entered works on the folk-lore of the American Indians; Collections of Indan tales, legends, or myths are entered under Indians of North America–Legends; Indians of South America–Legends; etc.

see also Totems

Boatright, Mody C., ed. The Sky Is My Tipi. LC 49-1690. (Texas Folklore Society Publications: No. 22). (Illus.). 1966. Repr. of 1949 ed. 13.95 (ISBN 0-87074-010-5). SMU Press.

Brinton, D. G. Myths of the New World: A Treatise on the Symbolism & Mythology of the Red Race of America. LC 68-24972. (American History & Americana Ser., No. 47). 1969. Repr. of 1876 ed. lib. bdg. 75.00x (ISBN 0-8383-0918-6). Haskell.

Brinton, Daniel G. The Myths of the New World. LC 71-144901. 331p. 1972. Repr. of 1876 ed. 10.00 (ISBN 0-403-00839-5). Scholarly.
--Myths of the New World: A Treatise on the Symbolism & Mythology of the Red Race of America. 2nd ed. LC 69-13839. 1969. Repr. of 1876 ed. lib. bdg. 22.50x (ISBN 0-8371-2040-3, BRMN). Greenwood.
Bullchild, Percy. The Sun Came Down: The History of the World as My Blackfeet Elders Told It. LC 85-42771. (Illus.). 384p. 1985. 22.45 (ISBN 0-06-250107-0, HarpR). Har-Row.
Curtin, Jeremiah. Creation Myths of Primitive America. 1980. 31.00 (ISBN 0-405-13697-8, 1710). Ayer Co Pubs.
Erodes, Richard & Ortiz, Alfonso. American Indian Myth & Legends. LC 84-42669. (Illus.). 504p. 1984. 19.45 (ISBN 0-394-50796-7). Pantheon.
Gossen, Gary. Chamulas in the World of the Sun: Time & Space in a Maya Oral Tradition. (Illus.). 382p. 1984. pap. text ed. 10.95x (ISBN 0-88133-091-4). Waveland Pr.
Harris, Lorie K. Tlingit Tales: Potlach & Totem Pole. (Illus.). 64p. 11.95 (ISBN 0-87961-152-9); pap. 5.95 (ISBN 0-87961-153-7). Naturegraph.
Indian Lore. (Illus.). 90p. 1959. pap. 1.00x (ISBN 0-8395-3358-6, 3358). BSA.
Jacobs, Melville. Content & Style of an Oral Literature: Clackamas Chinook Myths & Tales. LC 58-5617. 1959. 17.50x (ISBN 0-226-38973-1). U of Chicago Pr.
Levi-Strauss, Claude. From Honey to Ashes. (Science of Mythology Ser.). 1980. Repr. of 1973 ed. lib. bdg. 34.50x (ISBN 0-374-94952-2, Octagon). Hippocrene Bks.
Mooney, James. Myths of the Cherokee. LC 70-108513. (American Indian History Sers). 1970. Repr. of 1900 ed. 89.00 (ISBN 0-403-00221-4). Scholarly.
Rossman, Douglas A. Where Legends Live. (Illus.). 48p. (Orig.). 1986. pap. 5.00x (ISBN 0-935741-10-0). Cherokee Pubns.
Roth, Walter E. An Inquiry into the Animism & Folklore of the Guiana Indians. LC 16-9897. (Landmarks in Anthropology Ser). Repr. of 1915 ed. 23.00 (ISBN 0-384-52130-4). Johnson Repr.
Spencer, Katherine. Reflections of Social Life in the Navaho Origin Myth. LC 76-43850. (Univ. of New Mexico. Publications in Anthropology: No. 3). 1983. Repr. of 1947 ed. 20.00 (ISBN 0-404-15705-X). AMS Pr.
Swanton, John R. Haida Texts & Myths: Skidegate Dialect. LC 5-41613. (Landmarks in Anthropology Ser). Repr. of 1905 ed. 34.00 (ISBN 0-384-59020-9). Johnson Repr.
Von Del Chamberlain. When Stars Came Down to Earth: Cosmology of the Skidi Pawnee Indians of North America. LC 82-16390. (Ballena Press Anthropological Papers: No. 26). (Illus.). 260p. (Orig.). 1982. pap. 17.95 (ISBN 0-87919-098-1). Ballena Pr.
Wood, Marion. Spirits, Heroes & Hunters from North American Indian Mythology. LC 81-14572. (World Mythologies Ser.). (Illus.). 156p. 1982. 16.95 (ISBN 0-8052-3792-5). Schocken.

FOLK-LORE, INDIC

Gauba, Om P. Sandarbh-MulAK Shabd-Kosh: Hindi-English-Hindi Dictionary of Phrase & Fable Including Symbolic & Idiomatic Expressions. viii, 258p. 1986. text ed. 35.00x (ISBN 81-7018-363-4, Pub. by B. R. Pub Corp Delhi). Apt Bks.
Narayan, R. K. The Ramayana of R. K. Narayan: A Shortened Modern Prose Version of the Indian Epic, Suggested by the Tamil Version of Kamban. LC 79-189514. (Illus.). 192p. 1972. 13.95 (ISBN 0-670-58950-0). Viking.

FOLK-LORE, IRISH

Curtin, Jeremiah. Myths & Folk-Lore of Ireland. 1976. Repr. 18.00x (ISBN 0-7158-1090-1). Charles River Bks.
--Myths & Folk Tales of Ireland. LC 69-18206. 256p. 1975. pap. 4.50 (ISBN 0-486-22430-9). Dover.
Kelly, Eamon. Bless Me Father. 1977. pap. 6.95 (ISBN 0-85342-489-6, Pub. by Mercier Pr Ireland). Irish Bks Media.
Neeson, Eoin. The First Book of Irish Myths & Legends. 128p. 1982. pap. 5.95 (ISBN 0-85342-130-7, Pub. by Mercier Pr Ireland). Irish Bks Media.
--The Second Book of Irish Myths & Legends. 128p. 1981. pap. 5.95 (ISBN 0-85342-131-5, Pub. by Mercier Pr Ireland). Irish Bks Media.

FOLK-LORE, JAPANESE

Chiba, Reiko. Seven Lucky Gods of Japan. LC 65-25467. (Illus.). 1966. 12.95 (ISBN 0-8048-0521-0). C E Tuttle.
Hearn, Lafcadio. In Ghostly Japan. LC 79-138068. (Illus.). (YA) 1971. pap. 5.25 (ISBN 0-8048-0965-8). C E Tuttle.
--Kokoro: Hints & Echoes of Japanese Inner Life. LC 79-184814. 1972. pap. 6.50 (ISBN 0-8048-1035-4). C E Tuttle.
--Kokoro: Hints & Echoes of Japanese Inner Life. Repr. of 1896 ed. lib. bdg. 22.50x (ISBN 0-8371-1633-3, HEKO). Greenwood.
Mackenzie, Donald A. The Myths of China & Japan. LC 77-6878. 1977. Repr. of 1923 ed. lib. bdg. 45.00 (ISBN 0-89341-149-3). Longwood Pub Group.
Varley, H. Paul, tr. from Japanese. A Chronicle of Gods & Sovereigns: Jinno Shotoki of Kitabatake Chikafusa. LC 80-10430. (Translations from Oriental Classics Ser.). 1980. 32.00x (ISBN 0-231-04940-4). Columbia U Pr.

FOLK-LORE, JEWISH

Aunt Naomi, pseud. Jewish Fairy Tales & Legends. 16.95 (ISBN 0-89190-314-3, Pub. by Am Repr). Amereon ltd.
Ausubel, Nathan, ed. Treasury of Jewish Folklore. 1948. 14.95 (ISBN 0-517-50293-3). Crown.
Braude, William G. & Kapstein, Israel J., trs. from Heb. Tanna Debe Eliyyahu. LC 80-10805. Tr. of The Lore of the School of Elijah. 660p. 1980. 27.50 (ISBN 0-8276-0174-3, 455). Jewish Pubns.
Cahan, Judah L. Shtudies Vegn Yidisher Folksshafung. Weinreich, ed. 1952. 5.00 (ISBN 0-914512-05-6). Yivo Inst.
Eichhorn, David M., ed. Joys of Jewish Folklore. LC 80-13936. 534p. 1981. 16.95 (ISBN 0-8246-0254-4). Jonathan David.
Friedlander, Gerald. Jewish Fairy Tales & Stories. LC 78-67711. (The Folktale). (Illus.). Repr. of 1919 ed. 20.00 (ISBN 0-404-16088-3). AMS Pr.
Gorion, Micha J. bin & Gorion, Emanuel bin, eds. Mimekor Yisrael: Classical Jewish Folktales, 3 vols. Lask, I. M., tr. from Heb. LC 74-15713. 1666p. 1976. 100.00 (ISBN 0-253-15330-1). Ind U Pr.
Haggart, James A. Stories of Lost Israel in Folklore. LC 80-65735. 144p. 1981. pap. 5.00 (ISBN 0-934666-08-3). Artisan Sales.
Hausdorff, David M. A Book of Jewish Curiosities. LC 55-11366. 1979. pap. 5.95 (ISBN 0-8197-0466-0). Bloch.
Haut, Irwin H. The Talmud As Law Or Literature: An Analysis of David W. Halivni's Mekorot Umasorot. x, 83p. pap. 6.95 (ISBN 0-87203-107-1). Hermon.
Higgens, Elford. Hebrew Idolatry & Superstition. 1971. Repr. of 1893 ed. 19.50x (ISBN 0-8046-1150-5, Pub. by Kennikat). Assoc Faculty Pr.
Jung, Leo. Love & Life. LC 79-87873. 84p. 1979. 7.50 (ISBN 0-8022-2355-9). Philos Lib.
Levin, Meyer. Classic Hassidic Tales. (Illus.). 10.00 (ISBN 0-8446-5216-4). Peter Smith.
Neusner, Jacob. The Peripatetic Saying: The Problem of the Thrice-Told Tale in the Canon of Talmudic Literature. (Brown Judaic Studies: No. 89). 208p. 1985. 18.95 (ISBN 0-89130-830-X, 14 00 89); pap. 15.95 (ISBN 0-89130-831-8). Scholars Pr GA.
Noy, Dov. Studies in Jewish Folklore. 1981. 25.00x (ISBN 0-915938-02-2). Ktav.
Omer, Devorah. Once There Was a Hassid. (Illus.). 28p. 1987. 9.95 (ISBN 0-915361-73-6, Dist. by Watts). Adama Pubs Inc.
Patai, Raphael, et al. Studies in Biblical & Jewish Folklore. LC 72-6871. (Studies in Comparitive Literature: No. 35). 1972. Repr. of 1960 ed. lib. bdg. 49.95x (ISBN 0-8383-1665-4). Haskell.
Rabbi Alon I. Tolwin. Taryag: The Six Hundred Thirteenth Mitzvos. 106p. 1983. pap. 5.95 (ISBN 0-87306-378-3). Feldheim.
Rappoport, Angelo S. Folklore of the Jews. LC 71-167125. Repr. of 1937 ed. 40.00x (ISBN 0-8103-3864-5). Gale.
Ruthen, Gerald C., retold by. Daniel & the Silver Flute: An Old Hassidic Tale. (Illus.). 32p. 11.95. United Synagogue.
Sanua, Victor D., ed. Fields of Offerings: Studies in Honor of Raphael Patai. LC 82-21072. (Illus.). 352p. 1983. 28.50 (ISBN 0-8386-3171-1). Fairleigh Dickinson.
Scheiber, Alexander. Essays on Jewish Folklore & Comparative Literature. (Illus.). 456p. 1985. 55.00x (ISBN 963-05-3944-6, Pub. by Akademiai Kiado Hungary). Humanities.
Schram, Peninnah. Jewish Stories One Generation Tells Another. 350p. 1987. 30.00 (ISBN 0-87668-967-5). Aronson.
Schwarzbaum, Haim. Studies in Jewish & World Folklore. (Fabula Supplement Ser., No. B 3). 1968. 97.50x (ISBN 3-11-000393-7). De Gruyter.
Simon, Solomon. Adventures of Simple Shmerl. (Illus.). 1942. 4.95 (ISBN 0-87441-127-0). Behrman.
Stern, Stephen. The Sephardic Jewish Community of Los Angeles: A Study in Folklore & Ethnic Identity. Dorson, Richard M., ed. LC 80-734. (Folklore of the World Ser.). 1980. lib. bdg. 40.00x (ISBN 0-405-13324-3). Ayer Co Pubs.
Strauss, Ruby G., ed. If Grandma Had Wheels: Jewish Folk Sayings. LC 85-7466. (Illus.). 64p. 1985. 8.95 (ISBN 0-689-31156-7, Childrens Bk). Macmillan.
Thompson, Reginald C. Semitic Magic: Its Origins & Development. LC 73-18858. Repr. of 1908 ed. 24.50 (ISBN 0-404-11361-3). AMS Pr.
Weinreich, Uriel, ed. The Field of Yiddish: Studies in Yiddish Language, Folklore, & Literature. LC 54-12380. 317p. 1954. Repr. 12.50 (ISBN 0-936368-02-0). Lexik Hse.
Winkler, Gershon. The Golem of Prague. (Illus.). 1980. pap. 9.95 (ISBN 0-910818-25-8). Judaica Pr.
Yassif, Eli. Jewish Folklore: An Annotated Bibliography. LC 83-48282. 500p. 1985. lib. bdg. 65.00 (ISBN 0-8240-9039-X). Garland Pub.

FOLK-LORE, LATIN AMERICAN

Roth, Walter E. An Inquiry into the Animism & Folklore of the Guiana Indians. LC 16-9897. (Landmarks in Anthropology Ser). Repr. of 1915 ed. 23.00 (ISBN 0-384-52130-4). Johnson Repr.

FOLK-LORE, MALAYAN

Skeat, Walter W. Malay Magic: Being an Introduction to the Folklore & Popular Religion of the Malay Peninsula. LC 70-174437. (Illus.). 1973. Repr. of 1900 ed. lib. bdg. 28.00 (ISBN 0-405-08980-5). Ayer Co Pubs.

FOLK-LORE, MEDICAL

see Folk Medicine

FOLK-LORE, NORWEGIAN

Hveberg, H. Norweigian of Gods & Giants. 4th ed. (Tanum of Norway Tokens Ser). 86p. pap. 12.75x (ISBN 82-518-0083-8, N430). Vanous.
Schach, Paul, tr. from Old Norse. The Saga of Tristram & Isond. LC 73-76351. (Illus.). xxiv, 148p. 1973. 14.95x (ISBN 0-8032-0832-4); pap. 3.95x (ISBN 0-8032-5847-X, BB 608, Bison). U of Nebr Pr.

FOLK-LORE, PALESTINE

Hanauer, James E. Folk-Lore of the Holy Land: Moslem, Christian & Jewish. LC 77-22030. 1977. Repr. of 1935 ed. lib. bdg. 25.00 (ISBN 0-8414-4955-4). Folcroft.
--Folklore of the Holy Land. 280p. 1980. Repr. of 1935 ed. lib. bdg. 35.00 (ISBN 0-8492-5272-5). R West.

FOLK-LORE OF BIRTH

see Birth (In Religion, Folk-Lore, etc.)

FOLK-LORE OF DANCING

see Dancing (In Religion, Folk-Lore, etc.)

FOLK-LORE OF DAYS

see Days

FOLK-LORE OF DOGS

see Dogs (In Religion, Folk-Lore, etc.)

FOLK-LORE OF FIRE

see Fire (In Religion, Folk-Lore, etc.)

FOLK-LORE OF FISHES

see Fish (In Religion, Folk-Lore, etc.)

FOLK-LORE OF INITIATIONS

see Initiations (In Religion, Folk-Lore, etc.)

FOLK-LORE OF PLANTS

see Folk-Lore of Trees

FOLK-LORE OF POLARITY

see Polarity (In Religion, Folk-Lore, etc.)

FOLK-LORE OF SERPENTS

see Serpents (In Religion, Folk-Lore, Etc.)

FOLK-LORE OF THE DEAD

see Dead (In Religion, Folk-Lore, etc.)

FOLK-LORE OF THE SUN

see Sun (In Religion, Folk-Lore, etc.)

FOLK-LORE OF TREES

see also Christmas Trees

Philpot, J. H. The Sacred Tree: The Tree in Religion & Myth. 1977. lib. bdg. 69.95 (ISBN 0-8490-2553-2). Gordon Pr.

FOLK MEDICINE

Camp, John. Magic, Myth & Medicine. LC 73-18793. 200p. 1974. 8.50 (ISBN 0-8008-5046-7). Taplinger.
Fabrega, Horacio, Jr. & Silver, Daniel B. Illness & Shamanistic Curing in Zinacantan: An Ethnomedical Analysis. LC 73-80621. 304p. 1973. 22.50x (ISBN 0-8047-0844-4). Stanford U Pr.

FOLK-TALES

see Folk Literature; Folk-Lore; Legends

FOOD

see also Cookery; Nutrition; Vegetarianism

Meigs, Anna S. Food, Sex & Pollution: A New Guinea Religion. 195p. 1984. text ed. 22.50 (ISBN 0-8135-0968-8). Rutgers U Pr.

FOOD–HISTORY

Galavaris, George. Bread & the Liturgy: The Symbolism of Early Christian & Byzantine Bread Stamps. LC 75-98120. pap. 63.30 (ISBN 0-317-07859-3, 2015361). Bks Demand UMI.
Henisch, Bridget Ann. Fast & Feast: Food in Medieval Society. LC 76-15677. (Illus.). 1977. pap. 12.50x (ISBN 0-271-00424-X). Pa St U Pr.
Kinard, Malvina & Crisler, Janet. Loaves & Fishes: Foods from Bible Times. LC 75-19544. (Illus.). 224p. 1975. pap. 4.95 (ISBN 0-87983-173-1). Keats.

FOREIGN MISSIONS

see Missions, Foreign

FOREORDINATION

see Predestination

FORGIVENESS

Beals, Ivan A. What It Means to Forgive. (Christian Living Ser.). 32p. (Orig.). 1987. pap. write for info. (ISBN 0-8341-1185-3). Beacon Hill.
Bergan, Jacqueline & Schwan, S. Marie. Forgiveness: A Guide for Prayer. (Take & Receive Ser.). 200p. (Orig.). 1985. pap. 6.95 (ISBN 0-88489-169-0). St Mary's.
Floristan, Casiano & DuQuoc, Christian, eds. Forgiveness. (Concilium Nineteen Eighty-Six Ser.). 120p. 1986. pap. 6.95 (ISBN 0-567-30064-1, Pub. by T & T Clark Ltd UK). Fortress.
Kuhlewind, Georg. Forgiving. St. Goar, Maria, tr. from Ger. Miller, John, ed. (Illus.). 24p. (Orig.). 1985. pap. 3.50 (ISBN 0-932776-09-4). Adonis Pr.
Larsen, Sandy. Forgiving: Lightening Your Load. (Bible Discovery Guide). 32p. 1985. pap. 1.50 campers (ISBN 0-87788-279-7); pap. 3.50 counselor (ISBN 0-87788-280-0). Shaw Pubs.
Larsen, Sandy & Larsen, Dale. Forgiveness: No Guilt, No Grudges. (Young Fisherman Bible Studyguides). (Illus.). 80p. 1984. pap. 2.95 student ed. (ISBN 0-87788-277-0); tchr's. ed. 4.95 (ISBN 0-87788-278-9). Shaw Pubs.
Parker, Margaret. Love, Acceptance & Forgiveness: Leader's Guide. LC 79-63763. 128p. 1984. pap. 3.95 (ISBN 0-8307-0989-4, 6101895). Regal.
Patton, John. Is Human Forgiveness Possible? A Pastoral Care Perspective. 192p. (Orig.). 1985. pap. 10.95 (ISBN 0-687-19704-X). Abingdon.
Sekowsky, JoAnne. Forgiveness-A Two-Way Street. LC 53-3011. (Cornerstone Ser.). 40p. 1985. pap. 2.75 (ISBN 0-930756-95-9). Aglow Pubns.
Singh, Tara. Love Holds No Grievances: The Ending of Attack. 2nd ed. LC 86-14834. 1986. 8.95 (ISBN 1-55531-120-2); pap. 4.95 (ISBN 1-55531-007-9). Life Action Pr.

FORGIVENESS OF SIN

see also Absolution; Confession; Penance; Repentance

Aridas, Chris. Reconciliation: Celebrating God's Healing Forgiveness. LC 87-5344. 160p. 1987. pap. 3.95 (ISBN 0-385-24022-8, Im). Doubleday.
Augsburger, David. Caring Enough to Forgive Caring Enough Not to Forgive. LC 81-80913. 160p. (Orig.). 1981. pap. 5.95 (ISBN 0-8361-1965-7). Herald Pr.
--Caring Enough to Forgive: Caring Enough to Not Forgive. LC 80-50545. 176p. 1981. pap. 5.95 (ISBN 0-8307-0749-2, 5413702). Regal.
--Perdonar para Ser Libre. Orig. Title: Freedom of Forgiveness. (Span.). 160p. 1977. pap. 3.50 (ISBN 0-8254-1046-0). Kregel.
Bangley, Bernard. Forgiving Yourself. 96p. (Orig.). 1986. pap. 4.95 (ISBN 0-87788-281-9). Shaw Pubs.
Benko, Stephen. Meaning of Sanctorum Communio. LC 64-55292. (Studies in Historical Theology: No. 3). 1964. pap. 10.00x (ISBN 0-8401-0178-3). A R Allenson.
Bright, Bill. How to Experience God's Love & Forgiveness. (Transferable Concepts Ser.). 63p. 1981. pap. 1.25 (ISBN 0-918956-89-7). Campus Crusade.
Cornwall, Judson. Let Us Enjoy Forgiveness. LC 78-8306. 159p. 1978. pap. 4.95 (ISBN 0-8007-5090-X). Bridge Pub.
Donnelly, Doris. Learning to Forgive. (Festival Ser.). 144p. 1982. pap. 4.95 (ISBN 0-687-21324-X). Abingdon.
--Putting Forgiveness into Practice. LC 82-71967. 192p. 1982. 5.95 (ISBN 0-89505-087-0). Argus Comm.
Howard, Barbara. The Journey of Forgiveness. 1986. pap. 7.50 (ISBN 0-8309-0463-8). Herald Hse.
Kilpack, Gilbert. Ninth Hour. 1983. pap. 2.50x (ISBN 0-87574-063-4, 063). Pendle Hill.
Koplik, William & Brady, Joan. Celebrating Forgiveness. LC 81-51994. 96p. 1981. pap. 9.95 (ISBN 0-89622-137-7). Twenty-Third.
McDonald, H. D. Forgiveness & Atonement. 1984. 5.95p (ISBN 0-8010-6165-2). Baker Bk.
Mackintosh, Carlos H. El Perdon de los Pecados. 2nd ed. Bennett, Gordon H., ed. Bautista, Sara, tr. from Eng. (La Serie Diamante). Tr. of The Forgiveness of Sins. (Span.). 36p. 1982. pap. 0.85 (ISBN 0-942504-02-X). Overcomer Pr.
Morrissey, Kirkie. A Woman's Workshop on Forgiveness. (Woman's Workshop Ser.). 160p. 1982. pap. 3.95 (ISBN 0-310-44931-6, 16245P). Zondervan.
Ogilvie, Lloyd J. Loved & Forgiven. LC 76-29889. 160p. 1977. pap. 3.50 (ISBN 0-8307-0442-6, S313103). Regal.
Wapnick, Kenneth. Forgiveness & Jesus: The Meeting Place of a Course in Miracles & Christianity. 3rd ed. 340p. 1985. pap. 16.00 (ISBN 0-933291-01-9). Foun Miracles.
Williams, Charles. The Forgiveness of Sins. 128p. 1984. pap. 3.95 (ISBN 0-8028-0032-7). Eerdmans.

FORSYTH, PETER TAYLOR, 1848-1921

Miller, Donald G., et al. P. T. Forsyth: The Man, the Preacher's Theologian & Prophet for the Twentieth Century. (Pittsburgh Theological Monograph Ser.: No. 36). 1981. pap. 18.00 (ISBN 0-915138-48-4). Pickwick.

Pitt, Clifford S. Church, Ministry & Sacraments: A Critical Evaluation of the Thought of Peter Taylor Forsyth. LC 82-24817. 360p. (Orig.). 1983. lib. bdg. 31.25 (ISBN 0-8191-3027-3); pap. text ed. 15.75 (ISBN 0-8191-3028-1). U Pr of Amer.

FORTUNA, GODDESS

Patch, Howard R. The Tradition of the Goddess Fortuna in Medieval Philosophy & Literature. Repr. of 1922 ed. lib. bdg. 15.00 (ISBN 0-8414-6751-X). Folcroft.

--The Tradition of the Goddess Fortuna in Roman Literature & in the Transitional Period. LC 76-41188. 1976. Repr. of 1922 ed. lib. bdg. 15.50 (ISBN 0-8414-6753-6). Folcroft.

--The Tradition of the Goddess Fortuna in Roman Literature & in the Transitional Period. 1980. Repr. of 1912 ed. 15.00 (ISBN 0-8482-5593-3). Norwood Edns.

FOSDICK, HARRY EMERSON, 1878-1964

Fosdick, Harry E. A Pilgrimage to Palestine. Davis, Moshe, ed. LC 77-70688. (America & the Holy Land Ser.). 1977. Repr. of 1927 ed. lib. bdg. 30.00x (ISBN 0-405-10247-X). Ayer Co Pubs.

Miller, Robert M. Harry Emerson Fosdick: Preacher, Pastor, Prophet. LC 84-7168. (Illus.). 608p. 1985. 34.50x (ISBN 0-19-503512-7). Oxford U Pr.

FOX, GEORGE, 1624-1691

Brinton, Howard H. Religion of George Fox: As Revealed in His Epistles. LC 68-57978. (Orig.). 1968. pap. 2.50x (ISBN 0-87574-161-4). Pendle Hill.

Fogelklou-Norlind, Emilia. Atonement of George Fox. Mather, Eleanore P., ed. LC 75-84675. (Orig.). 1969. pap. 2.50x (ISBN 0-87574-166-5). Pendle Hill.

Fox, George. George Fox's Book of Miracles. Cadbury, Henry J., ed. LC 73-735. 161p. 1973. Repr. of 1948 ed. lib. bdg. 16.50x (ISBN 0-374-92825-8, Octagon). Hippocrene Bks.

Gwyn, Douglas. Apocalypse of the Word: The Life & Message of George Fox (1624-1690) 240p. (Orig.). 1986. pap. 14.95 (ISBN 0-913408-91-3). Friends United.

Jones, Rufus M. The Journal of George Fox. 576p. 1976. pap. 8.50 (ISBN 0-913408-24-7). Friends United.

Vernon, Louise A. Key to the Prison. LC 86-11054. (Illus.). 144p. 1968. 4.50 (ISBN 0-8361-1813-8). Herald Pr.

FOXE, JOHN, 1516-1587

Foxe, John. The English Sermons of John Foxe. LC 77-29100. 1978. Repr. of 1578 ed. 60.00x (ISBN 0-8201-1267-4). Schol Facsimiles.

Mozley, James F. John Foxe & His Book. LC 76-120651. 1970. Repr. of 1940 ed. lib. bdg. 18.50x (ISBN 0-374-95977-3, Octagon). Hippocrene Bks.

Olsen, V. Norskov. John Foxe & the Elizabethan Church. 1973. 38.50x (ISBN 0-520-02075-8). U of Cal Pr.

FRANCE–CHURCH HISTORY

Aulard, Alphonse. Christianity & the French Revolution. 1966. 27.50x (ISBN 0-86527-025-2). Fertig.

Birks, Walter & Gilbert, R. A. The Treasure of Montsegur. (Crucible Ser.). 176p. 1987. pap. 9.95 (ISBN 0-85030-424-5). Inner Tradit.

Chamier, Adrian C., ed. Les Actes des Colloques des Eglises Francaises et des Synodes: (Huguenot Society, Vols. 204) Bd. with Register of the Protestant Church at Guisnes. Minet, William, ed. Repr. of 1891 ed; Registre Des Baptesmes, Mariages & Mortz. Marett, Humphrey, ed. Repr. of 1890 ed. 93.00 (ISBN 0-8115-1643-1). Kraus Repr.

The Church in France, Eighteen Forty-Eight to Nineteen Hundred Seven. (Church Historical Society London Ser.: No. 19). pap. 31.00 (ISBN 0-8115-3142-2). Kraus Repr.

Delisle, Leopold V., ed. Rouleaux Des Morts Du IXe Au XVe Siecle. 1866. 43.00 (ISBN 0-384-11361-3); pap. 37.00 (ISBN 0-384-11360-5). Johnson Repr.

De Sainte Marthe, Denis. Gallia Christiana, 16 vols. 12462p. Repr. of 1715 ed. text ed. 1863.00x (ISBN 0-576-78556-3, Pub. by Gregg Intl Pubs England). Gregg Intl.

Galpern, A. N. The Religions of the People in Sixteenth Century Champagne. (Historical Studies: No. 92). 1976. 22.50x (ISBN 0-674-75836-6). Harvard U Pr.

Gregorius, Saint Histoire Ecclesiastique Des Francs, 4 vols. 1967. 154.00 (ISBN 0-384-19875-9); pap. 130.00 (ISBN 0-384-19874-0). Johnson Repr.

--Zehn Bucher Frankischer Geschichte, 3 vols. 4th ed. Hellmann, S., ed. Von Geisebrecht, Wilhel M, tr. 1911-1913. 34.00 ea. (ISBN 0-384-19908-9). Johnson Repr.

Haag. La France Protestante: Biographies Historiques, 12 tomes. Set. 113.75 (ISBN 0-685-36098-9). French & Eur.

Histoire du Catholicisme en France, 3 tomes. Incl. Tome I. Des origines a la chretiente medievale (du IIe a la fin du XIIe siecle) Palanque & Delaruelle. 7.50 (ISBN 0-685-36063-6); Tome II. Sous les Rois Tres Chretiens (Du XIIIe au XVIIIe Siecle) Delaruelle & Latreilla. 8.50 (ISBN 0-685-36064-4); Tome III. La Periode Contemporaine (du XVIIIe Siecle a nos Jours) Latreille & Remona. 9.50 (ISBN 0-685-36065-2). French & Eur.

La Gorce, Pierre F. Histoire Religieuse de la Revolution francaise, 5 Vols. LC 71-88239. (Fr.). Repr. of 1923 ed. Set. 235.50 (ISBN 0-404-03810-7); 47.00 ea. Vol. 1 (ISBN 0-404-03811-5). Vol. 2 (ISBN 0-404-03812-3). Vol. 3 (ISBN 0-404-03813-1). Vol. 4 (ISBN 0-404-03814-X). Vol. 5 (ISBN 0-404-03815-8). AMS Pr.

McManners, John. The French Revolution & the Church. LC 82-15532. x, 161p. 1982. Repr. of 1969 ed. lib. bdg. 22.50x (ISBN 0-313-23074-9, MCFR). Greenwood.

Martene, Edmond & Durand, Ursin. Voyage Litteraire de Deux Benedictins de la Congregation de Saint-Maur, 2 vols. 1042p. Repr. of 1717 ed. text ed. 207.00x (ISBN 0-576-99707-2, Pub. by Gregg Intl Pubs England). Gregg Intl.

Matthew, Donald. The Norman Monasteries & Their English Possessions. LC 78-26293. (Oxford Historical Ser.). 1979. Repr. of 1962 ed. lib. bdg. 24.75x (ISBN 0-313-20847-6, MANM). Greenwood.

Mention, Leon. Documents Relatifs aux Rapports du Clerge avec la Royaute de 1682 a 1789, 2 vols. in 1. (Fr.). 461p. Repr. of 1893 ed. lib. bdg. 67.50x. Coronet Bks.

Mitchell, Allan. Victors & Vanquished: The German Influences on Army & Church in France after 1870. LC 83-25917. xiv, 169p. 1984. 32.00x (ISBN 0-8078-1603-5). U of NC Pr.

Neale, J. E. The Age of Catherine de Medici. 272p. 1978. pap. 6.50 (ISBN 0-224-60566-6, Pub. by Jonathan Cape). Salem Hse Pubs.

Palm, Franklin C. Politics & Religion in Sixteenth-Century France: A Study of the Career of Henry of Montmorency-Damville, Uncrowned King of the South. 13.25 (ISBN 0-8446-0835-1). Peter Smith.

Perrens, Francois T. Libertins en France au Dix-Septieme Siecle. LC 72-168701. (Fr.). 428p. 1973. Repr. of 1896 ed. lib. bdg. 29.00 (ISBN 0-8337-2728-1). B Franklin.

Phillips, Charles S. The Church in France, Seventeen Eighty-Seven to Eighteen Forty-Eight. (Church Historical Society London Ser.: No. 19A). Repr. of 1934 ed. 40.00 (ISBN 0-8115-3143-0). Kraus Repr.

Poncet, Rene. Les Privileges des Clercs Au Moyen-Age. (Fr.). 230p. Repr. of 1901 ed. lib. bdg. 42.50x. Coronet Bks.

Robinet, Jean F. Le Mouvement religieux a Paris pendant la Revolution: 1789-1801, 2 vols. LC 70-174331. (Collection de documents relatifs a l'histoire de Paris pendant la Revolution francaise). Repr. of 1898 ed. Set. 169.00 (ISBN 0-404-52567-9); 84.50 ea. Vol. 1 (ISBN 0-404-52568-7). Vol. 2 (ISBN 0-404-52569-5). AMS Pr.

Schwartz, Hillel. The French Prophets: The History of a Millenarian Group in Eighteenth-Century England. LC 78-65459. (Illus.). 1980. 42.00x (ISBN 0-520-03815-0). U of Cal Pr.

Seguy, J. Les Assemblees Anabaptistes-Mennonites de France. 1977. 64.00x (ISBN 90-279-7524-8). Mouton.

Stoddard, Whitney S. The Facade of Saint-Gilles-du-Gard: Its Influence on French Sculpture. LC 72-3696. (Illus.). 341p. 1973. pap. 17.50 (ISBN 0-8195-6068-5). Wesleyan U Pr.

Tackett, T. Priest & Parish in Eighteenth-Century France. 1977. 38.00 (ISBN 0-691-05243-3). Princeton U Pr.

Tackett, Timothy. Priest & Parish in Eighteenth-Century France. LC 76-29801. 368p. 1986. 19.50x (ISBN 0-691-10199-X). Princeton U Pr.

Vast, Henri. Le Cardinal de Bessarion 1405-1472: Etude sun la Chretiente et la Renaissance vers le Milieu du XVe Siecle. (Fr.). 487p. Repr. of 1878 ed. lib. bdg. 57.50x. Coronet Bks.

Wakefield, Walter L. Heresy, Crusade, & Inquisition in Southern France, 1100-1250. 1974. 40.00x (ISBN 0-520-02380-3). U of Cal Pr.

FRANCESCO D'ASSISI, SAINT, 1182-1226

Armstrong, Edward A. St. Francis, Nature Mystic: The Derivation & Significance of the Nature Stories in the Franciscan Legend. LC 74-149949. (Hermeneutics: Studies in the History of Religions). 1973. pap. 5.95 (ISBN 0-520-03040-0, CAL 314). U of Cal Pr.

Bodo, Murray. Through the Year with Francis of Assisi: Daily Meditations from His Words & Life. LC 87-4158. (Illus.). 240p. 1987. pap. 7.95 (ISBN 0-385-23823-1, Im). Doubleday.

--Way of St. Francis: The Challenge of Franciscan Spirituality for Everyone. LC 83-14066. 192p. 1984. 12.95 (ISBN 0-385-19073-5). Doubleday.

Boff, Leonardo. Saint Francis: A Model for Human Liberation. 192p. 1984. pap. 9.95 (ISBN 0-8245-0671-5). Crossroad NY.

Brown, Raphael. The Roots of St. Francis. 9.50 (ISBN 0-686-45828-1). Franciscan Herald.

--True Joy from Assisi. 276p. 1978. 8.95 (ISBN 0-8199-0688-3). Franciscan Herald.

Carretto, Carlo. I, Francis. Barr, Robert R., tr. from Ital. LC 81-16913. Orig. Title: Io Francesco. 144p. (Orig.). 1982. pap. 6.95 (ISBN 0-88344-200-0). Orbis Bks.

Celano, Thomas. St. Francis of Assisi. 1963. pap. 10.50 (ISBN 0-8199-0098-2). Franciscan Herald.

Chesterton, G. K. St. Francis of Assisi. 1979. Repr. lib. bdg. 25.00 (ISBN 0-8495-0933-5). Arden Lib.

--Saint Francis of Assisi. LC 57-1230. 1957. pap. 3.95 (ISBN 0-385-02900-4, Im). Doubleday.

Christiani, Leon. St. Francis of Assisi. LC 74-79802. 1975. 4.95 (ISBN 0-8198-0494-0). Dghtrs St Paul.

Clissold, Stephen, compiled by. The Wisdom of St. Francis & His Companions. LC 78-27504. (Wisdom Books). 1979. pap. 4.95 (ISBN 0-8112-0721-8, NDP477). New Directions.

Coulton, G. G. Two Saints: St. Bernard & St. Francis. 1923. lib. bdg. 15.00 (ISBN 0-8414-3513-8). Folcroft.

Cunningham, Lawrence. Saint Francis of Assisi. LC 81-47419. (Illus.). 128p. 1981. 5.00 (ISBN 0-06-061651-2, HarpR). Har-Row.

Doyle, Eric. Saint Francis & the Song of Brotherhood. 1981. pap. 5.95 (ISBN 0-8164-2300-8, HarpR). Har-Row.

Easwaran, Eknath. Love Never Faileth: The Inspiration of St. Francis, St. Augustine, St. Paul & Mother Teresa. (Illus.). 208p. (Orig.). 1985. 15.00 (ISBN 0-915132-31-1); pap. 8.00 (ISBN 0-915132-32-X). Nilgiri Pr.

Egan, Maurice F. The Life of St. Francis & the Soul of Modern Man. (Illus.). 131p. 1983. 88.85 (ISBN 0-89266-427-4). Am Classical Coll Pr.

Englebert, Omer. Saint Francis of Assisi: A Biography. abr. ed. 1979. pap. 3.95 (ISBN 0-89283-071-9). Servant.

Erikson, Joan M. Saint Francis & His Four Ladies. LC 71-127178. (Illus.). 1970. 6.95 (ISBN 0-393-05427-6). Norton.

Felder, Hilaron. The Ideals of St. Francis of Assisi. 1983. 12.50 (ISBN 0-8199-0845-2). Franciscan Herald.

Flood, David & Matura, Thadee. The Birth of a Movement. LaChance, Paul & Schwartz, Paul, trs. 168p. 1975. 6.95 (ISBN 0-8199-0567-4). Franciscan Herald.

Floristan, Casiano & Duquoc, Christian. Francis of Assisi Today, Vol. 149. (Concilium 1981). 128p. (Orig.). 1981. pap. 6.95 (ISBN 0-8164-2349-0, HarpR). Har-Row.

Fortini, Arnaldo. Francis of Assisi. Moak, Helen, tr. 900p. 1980. 39.50x (ISBN 0-8245-0003-2). Crossroad NY.

Garner, Robert H. The Way of St. Francis. 1984. 6.95 (ISBN 0-8062-1605-0). Carlton.

Green, Julien. God's Fool: The Life of Francis of Assisi. LC 84-48771. 256p. 1985. 16.95 (ISBN 0-06-063462-6, HarpR). Har-Row.

Habig, M. A. Francis of Assisi: Writer. 1981. 2.00 (ISBN 0-8199-0844-4). Franciscan Herald.

Habig, Marion A., ed. English Omnibus of Sources: St. Francis of Assisi. new ed. 1977. 30.00 (ISBN 0-8199-0658-1). Franciscan Herald.

--St. Francis of Assisi: Omnibus of Sources of the Life of St.Francis. Brown, Raphael & Fahy, B., trs. (Illus.). 1828p. 1975. 35.00 (ISBN 0-8199-0440-6). Franciscan Herald.

Hardick, Lothar, et al. The Admonitions of St. Francis of Assisi. Smith, David, tr. 399p. 1983. 12.50 (ISBN 0-8199-0869-X). Franciscan Herald.

Hegener, Mark. Poverello: St. Francis of Assisi. pap. 2.00 (ISBN 0-8199-0358-2). Franciscan Herald.

Jessey, Cornelia. The Prayer of Cosa: Praying in the Way of Francis of Assisi. (Orig.). 1985. pap. 5.95 (ISBN 0-86683-936-4, AY8512, HarpR). Har-Row.

Jorgensen, Johannes. Saint Francis of Assisi. pap. 4.95 (ISBN 0-385-02875-X, D22, Im). Doubleday.

Kazantzakis, Nikos. Saint Francis. 1963. Translation 1971. pap. 9.95 (ISBN 0-671-21247-8, Touchstone Bks). S&S.

Line, Francis R. & Line, Helen E. Man with a Song. 1978. 8.95 (ISBN 0-8199-0756-1). Franciscan Herald.

Matura, Thaddee. The Gospel Life of Francis of Assisi Today. 1980. 6.95 (ISBN 0-317-46873-1). Franciscan Herald.

Mayer-Skumanz, Lene. The Story of Brother Francis. Bomer, Hildegard, tr. from Ger. LC 83-71779. (Illus.). 48p. (Orig.). 1983. pap. 6.95 (ISBN 0-87793-307-3). Ave Maria.

Meiss, Millard. Giotto & Assisi. LC 60-9443. (Walter W. S. Cook Alumni Lecture Ser.: 1959). pap. 20.00 (ISBN 0-317-09361-4, 2050841). Bks Demand UMI.

Meyer, James. Social Ideals of St. Francis. 2.75 (ISBN 0-8199-0296-9, L38825). Franciscan Herald.

--Words of St. Francis. Rev. ed. 1982. 6.00 (ISBN 0-8199-0833-9). Franciscan Herald.

Moorman, John R. H. St. Francis of Assisi. 1986. 4.95 (ISBN 0-8199-0904-1). Franciscan Herald.

Nicholson, D. H. The Mysticism of St. Francis of Assissi. 1977. lib. bdg. 59.95 (ISBN 0-8490-2319-X). Gordon Pr.

O'Brien, Isidore. Francis of Assisi: Mirror Christ. 1978. 6.95 (ISBN 0-8199-0691-3). Franciscan Herald.

Petry, Ray C. Francis of Assisi. LC 41-25932. Repr. of 1941 ed. 11.50 (ISBN 0-404-05017-4). AMS Pr.

Podles, Mary S. & Porter, Vicki. A Guide to God's Minstrel: St. Francis of Assisi. Strohecker, Carol, ed. (Illus.). 24p. (Orig.). 1982. pap. 1.50 (ISBN 0-911886-23-0). Walters Art.

Raymond, Ernest. In the Steps of St. Francis. 380p. 1975. pap. 4.95 (ISBN 0-8199-0557-7). Franciscan Herald.

Reynolds, E. E. The Life of Saint Francis of Assisi. 128p. 1983. pap. 5.95 (ISBN 0-87061-081-3). Chr Classics.

Sabatier, Paul. Life of St. Francis of Assisi. 1977. lib. bdg. 59.95 (ISBN 0-8490-2167-7). Gordon Pr.

Sabatini, Rafael. Heroic Lives. facs. ed. LC 70-99648. (Essay Index Reprint Ser.). 1934. 19.50 (ISBN 0-8369-2071-6). Ayer Co Pubs.

St. Francis of Assisi & Nature. cancelled (ISBN 0-8199-0882-7). Franciscan Herald.

St. Francis: Poet of Creation. 1985. 7.50 (ISBN 0-8199-0877-0). Franciscan Herald.

Sheehan, Maurice W., ed. St. Francis of Assisi: Essays in Commemoration, 1982. 10.00. Franciscan Inst.

Sheehan, Thomas, ed. The Knight-Errant of Assisi. Little, B., tr. Repr. 7.00. Franciscan Inst.

Subercaseaux, Pedro E. Life of Saint Francis. 1977. buckram 25.00 (ISBN 0-8199-0615-8). Franciscan Herald.

Timmermans, Felix. The Perfect Joy of St. Francis. 280p. 1974. pap. 4.95 (ISBN 0-385-02378-2, Im). Doubleday.

Van Corstanje, Auspicius. Covenant with God's Poor. 3.95 (ISBN 0-8199-0014-1). Franciscan Herald.

Van Doornik, N. Francis of Assisi: A Prophet for Our Time. 1978. 8.95 (ISBN 0-8199-0695-6). Franciscan Herald.

Van Moorselaar, Corinne. Francis & the Animals. Hegener, Mark, ed. Smith, David, tr. LC 77-7391. (Dutch., Illus.). 1977. 3.50x (ISBN 0-685-81231-6). Franciscan Herald.

Von Galli, Mario. Living Our Future: St. Francis of Assisi & the Church Tomorrow. new ed. (Illus.). 239p. 1976. pap. 4.95 (ISBN 0-8199-0439-2). Franciscan Herald.

Vorreux, Damien. First Encounter with Francis of Assisi. Schwartz, Paul & Lachance, Paul, trs. from Fr. 1979. pap. 6.95 (ISBN 0-8199-0698-0). Franciscan Herald.

Works of the Seraphic Father St. Francis of Assisi: Translated by a Religious of the Order. 269p. 1982. Repr. of 1890 ed. lib. bdg. 40.00 (ISBN 0-89984-015-9). Century Bookbindery.

FRANCESCO D'ASSISI, SAINT, 1182-1226–ART

Fortini, Arnaldo. Francis of Assisi. Moak, Helen, tr. 900p. 1980. 39.50x (ISBN 0-8245-0003-2). Crossroad NY.

Tintori, Leonetto & Meiss, Millard. The Painting of the Life of St. Francis in Assisi, with Notes on the Arena Chapel. LC 62-10308. pap. 55.50 (ISBN 0-317-10175-7, 2050842). Bks Demand UMI.

FRANCESCO D'ASSISI, SAINT, 1182-1226–FICTION

Brown, Raphael, tr. Little Flower of St. Francis. 1971. pap. 5.50 (ISBN 0-385-07544-8, Im). Doubleday.

FRANCESCO D'ASSISI, SAINT, 1182-1226–JUVENILE LITERATURE

Bawden, Nina. St. Francis of Assisi. LC 82-13105. (Illus.). 32p. 1983. PLB 10.88 (ISBN 0-688-01653-7). Lothrop.

De Paola, Tomie. Francis: The Poor Man of Assisi. LC 81-6984. (Illus.). 48p. 1982. reinforced 14.95 (ISBN 0-8234-0435-8). Holiday.

FRANCIS OF PAOLA, SAINT, 1416-1507

Gasnick, Roy. Francis: Brother of the Universe. (Illus.). 1.00. Paulist Pr.

FRANCISCAN RECOLLETS

see Recollets (Franciscan)

FRANCISCAN SISTERS

Flood, David. Franciscan Women. 64p. 1976. pap. 0.95 (ISBN 0-8199-0593-3). Franciscan Herald.

Mary in the Franciscan Order: Proceedings Third National Meeting of Franciscan Teaching Sisterhoods, Vol. 3. 1955. 4.00 (ISBN 0-686-11578-3). Franciscan Inst.

FRANCISCANS

see also Recollets (Franciscan)

Antonio, Joannes A. Bibliotheca Universa Franciscana, 3 vols. 1640p. Date not set. Repr. of 1733 ed. text ed. 496.80x (ISBN 0-576-72343-6, Pub. by Gregg Intl Pubs England). Gregg Intl.

Bodo, Murray. The Way of St. Francis: The Challenge of Franciscan Spirituality for Everyone. LC 83-14066. 1985. 6.95 (ISBN 0-385-19913-9, Im). Doubleday.

Boehner, Philotheus. Conferences for Franciscan Religious. (Spirit & Life Ser). 1966. 2.00 (ISBN 0-686-11571-6). Franciscan Inst.

Ciampi, Luke. Watering the Seed. 1977. 5.95 (ISBN 0-685-71934-0). Franciscan Herald.

De Aspurz-Iriarte, Lazaro. The Franciscan Calling. Kelly, Sr. Marie, tr. 300p. 1975. 6.95 (ISBN 0-8199-0538-0). Franciscan Herald.

Debevec, et al, eds. United States Documents in the Propaganda Fide Archives, Vol. 9. 1982. 40.00 (ISBN 0-88382-210-5). AAFH.

Douie, Decima L. The Nature & the Effect of the Heresy of the Fraticelli. LC 77-84715. Repr. of 1932 ed. 36.50 (ISBN 0-404-16121-9). AMS Pr.

Esser, Cajetan. Origins of the Order of Friars Minor. (Orig.). 1970. 12.50 (ISBN 0-8199-0414-7). Franciscan Herald.

Fleming, John V. An Introduction to the Franciscan Literature of the Middle Ages. 274p. 1977. 10.95 (ISBN 0-8199-0651-4). Franciscan Herald.

Flood, David & Matura, Thadee. The Birth of a Movement. LaChance, Paul & Schwartz, Paul, trs. 168p. 1975. 6.95 (ISBN 0-8199-0567-4). Franciscan Herald.

Franciscan Essay I. 128p. 1912. text ed. 33.12x (ISBN 0-576-99220-8, Pub. by Gregg Intl Pubs England). Gregg Intl.

Franciscan Essays II. 103p. 1932. text ed. 33.12x (ISBN 0-576-99222-4, Pub. by Gregg Intl Pubs England). Gregg Intl.

Gasnick, Roy M., compiled By. The Francis Book: A Celebration of the Universal Saint. (Illus.). 320p. 1980. (Collier); pap. 15.95 (ISBN 0-02-003200-5). Macmillan.

Habig, Marion A., ed. Vitam Alere, Franciscan Readings. (Tau Ser.). 1979. 5.95 (ISBN 0-8199-0769-3). Franciscan Herald.

Harkins, Conrad L., ed. Franciscan Studies. (Annual review). 16.00 (ISBN 0-686-12038-8). Franciscan Inst.

Iriarte, Lazaro. History of the Franciscan Order. 1983. 25.00 (ISBN 0-8199-0831-2). Franciscan Herald.

Jeffrey, David L. The Early English Lyric & Franciscan Spirituality. LC 74-78478. (Illus.). xvi, 306p. 1975. 24.50x (ISBN 0-8032-0845-6). U of Nebr Pr.

Kiemen, Mathias, et al, eds. United States Documents in the Propaganda Fide Archives, Vol. 10. 1984. 40.00 (ISBN 0-88382-211-3). AAFH.

Kingsford, C. L. Collectanea Franciscana II. 169p. Repr. of 1922 ed. text ed. 33.12x (ISBN 0-576-99210-0, Pub. by Gregg Intl Pubs England). Gregg Intl.

Lapsanski, Duane V. The First Franciscans & the Gospel. 1976. 6.95 (ISBN 0-8199-0568-2). Franciscan Herald.

Little, A. G., et al. Collectanea Franciscana I. 170p. 1914. text ed. 41.40x (ISBN 0-576-99205-4, Pub. by Gregg Intl Pubs England). Gregg Intl.

Marshall, John F. Conferences on the Our Father. (Spirit & Life Ser). 1967. 2.00 (ISBN 0-686-11573-2). Franciscan Inst.

Moorman, John R. Medieval Franciscan Houses. Marcel, George, ed. (History Ser.: No. 4). 1983. 40.00 (ISBN 0-318-00515-8). Franciscan Inst.

Mrozinski, Ronald. Franciscan Prayer Life. 1983. 12.50 (ISBN 0-8199-0795-2). Franciscan Herald.

Muller, Francis J. De Paroecia Domui Religiosae Commissa. 1956. 3.50 (ISBN 0-686-11580-5). Franciscan Inst.

Musser, Benjamin F. Franciscan Poets. facs. ed. LC 67-26768. (Essay Index Reprint Ser). 1933. 17.25 (ISBN 0-8369-0732-9). Ayer Co Pubs.

Muzzey, D. S. The Spiritual Franciscans. 59.95 (ISBN 0-8490-1113-2). Gordon Pr.

Nota, John H. Max Scheler: The Man & His Works. 1983. 12.00 (ISBN 0-8199-0852-5). Franciscan Herald.

O'Neill, Daniel. Troubadour for the Lord: The Story of John Michael Talbot. 192p. 1983. 9.95 (ISBN 0-8245-0567-0). Crossroad NY.

Ozanam, Frederick. Franciscan Poets of the Thirteenth Century. LC 68-26288. 1969. Repr. of 1914 ed. 24.50x (ISBN 0-8046-0342-1). Assoc Faculty Pr.

Pohlmann, Constantin. Francis, a Way: The Franciscan Alternative. Smith, Davie, tr. 1988. cancelled 12.50 (ISBN 0-8199-0865-7). Franciscan Herald.

Religious in the Nineteen Eighty-Three Code. 1985. 5.50 (ISBN 0-8199-0884-3). Franciscan Herald.

Romb, Anselm. Franciscan Charism. LC 79-91837. 122p. 1969. 3.00 (ISBN 0-8199-0477-5); pap. 1.95 (ISBN 0-685-77516-X). Franciscan Herald.

Salimbene Di Adam. From Saint Francis to Dante: Translations from the Chronicle of the Franciscan Salimbene (1221-88) Coulton, G. G., ed. & tr. from It. LC 68-10910. 462p. 1972. pap. 10.95x (ISBN 0-8122-1053-0, Pa Paperbks). U of Pa Pr.

Van Corstanje, Auspicius. Covenant with God's Poor. 3.95 (ISBN 0-8199-0014-1). Franciscan Herald.

Wolter, Allan B. Living in God's Love. 172p. 1958. pap. 1.75 (ISBN 0-8199-0059-1, L38375). Franciscan Herald.

FRANCISCANS–BIBLIOGRAPHY

Adams, Eleanor B. Bio-Bibliography of Franciscan Authors in Colonial Central America. (Bibliographical Ser.). 1953. 10.00 (ISBN 0-88382-101-X). AAFH.

FRANCISCANS–MISSIONS

Bacigalupo, Leonard F. The American Franciscan Missions in Central America. LC 80-68205. 483p. (Orig.). 1980. 19.50 (ISBN 0-933402-20-1); pap. 9.95 (ISBN 0-933402-21-X). Charisma Pr.

Dawson, Christopher. Mission to Asia. (Medieval Academy Reprints for Teaching Ser.). 228p. 1981. pap. 6.95 (ISBN 0-8020-6436-1). U of Toronto Pr.

Habig, Marion A. In Journeyings Often: Franciscan Pioneers in the Orient. (Spirit & Life Ser). 1953. 6.50 (ISBN 0-686-11564-3). Franciscan Inst.

--Spanish Texas Pilgrimage: The Old Franciscan Missions & Other Spanish Settlements of Texas, 1632-1821. 1985. 12.50 (ISBN 0-8199-0883-5). Franciscan Herald.

O'Rourke, Thomas P. The Franciscan Missions in Texas (1690-1793) LC 73-3559. (Catholic University of America. Studies in American Church History: No. 5). Repr. of 1927 ed. 19.50 (ISBN 0-404-57755-5). AMS Pr.

Willeke, Bernard H. Imperial Government & Catholic Missions in China During the Years 1784-1785. (Missiology Ser). 1948. 3.50 (ISBN 0-686-11584-8). Franciscan Inst.

FRANCISCANS–PRAYER-BOOKS AND DEVOTIONS

Boehner, Philotheus. Walter Burleigh De Puritate Artis Logicae Tractus Langios. Incl. Tractatus Brevior. (Text Ser). 1955. 6.00 (ISBN 0-686-17965-X). Franciscan Inst.

Jaki, Stanley L. The Keys of the Kingdom: A Tool's Witness to Truth. (Illus.). 1986. 9.95 (ISBN 0-8199-0898-3). Franciscan Herald.

FRANCISCANS–SECOND ORDER

see Poor Clares

FRANCISCANS–THIRD ORDER

Esser, Cajetan. Origins of the Order of Friars Minor. (Orig.). 1970. 12.50 (ISBN 0-8199-0414-7). Franciscan Herald.

Wolter, Allan B. The Book of Life: An Explanation of the Rule of the Third Order Regular of Saint Francis. (Spirit & Life Ser). 1954. pap. 2.50 (ISBN 0-686-11566-X). Franciscan Inst.

FRANCISCANS IN AMERICA

Griffen, William B. Indian Assimilation in the Franciscan Area of Nueva Vizcaya. LC 78-14546. (Anthropological Papers: No. 33). 122p. 1979. pap. 10.95x (ISBN 0-8165-0584-5). U of Ariz Pr.

Morales, Francisco, ed. Franciscan Presence in the Americas. (Misc. Ser.). 1984. 40.00 (ISBN 0-88382-258-X). AAFH.

Phelan, John L. The Millennial Kingdom of the Franciscans in the New World. 2nd rev ed. 1970. 35.95x (ISBN 0-520-01404-9). U of Cal Pr.

FRANCISCANS IN CHINA

Dawson, Christopher H., ed. The Mongol Mission. LC 78-63334. (The Crusades & Military Orders: Second Ser.). Repr. of 1955 ed. 33.00 (ISBN 0-404-17008-0). AMS Pr.

FRANCISCANS IN ENGLAND

A Fifteenth Century Courtesy Book & Two Franciscan Rules: EETS OS Ser, Vol. 148. Repr. of 1914 ed. 15.00 (ISBN 0-8115-3372-7). Kraus Repr.

FRANCISCANS IN THE UNITED STATES

Bolton, Herbert E. Fray Juan Crespi, Missionary Explorer on the Pacific Coast, 1769-1774. LC 78-158616. Repr. of 1927 ed. 29.50 (ISBN 0-404-01838-6). AMS Pr.

Geiger, Maynard. Franciscan Missionaries in Hispanic California 1769-1848: A Biographical Dictionary. LC 74-79607. Repr. of 1969 ed. 60.50 (ISBN 0-8357-9191-2, 2015007). Bks Demand UMI.

Morales, Francisco. Ethnic & Social Background of the Franciscan Friars in Seventeenth Century Mexico. (Monograph Ser.). 1973. 20.00 (ISBN 0-88382-060-9). AAFH.

Zarate Salmeron, Geronimo. Relaciones. LC 66-27660. 122p. 1982. lib. bdg. 29.95x (ISBN 0-89370-728-7). Borgo Pr.

FRANCISCO XAVIER, SAINT, 1506-1552

Daughters of St. Paul. Flame in the Night. 1967. 3.00 (ISBN 0-8198-0234-4); pap. 2.00 (ISBN 0-8198-2610-3). Dghtrs St Paul.

Gowen, Herbert H. Five Foreigners in Japan. facs. ed. LC 67-28735. (Essay Index Reprint Ser). 1936. 20.00 (ISBN 0-8369-0491-5). Ayer Co Pubs.

Schurhammer. Indonesia & India, Fifteen Forty-Five to Fifteen Forty-Nine. 726p. (Orig.). 1980. 40.00 (ISBN 0-8294-0356-6). Loyola.

Schurhammer, Georg. Francis Xavier, His Life, His Times. Costelloe, M. Joseph, tr. Incl. Vol. 1. Europe, 1506-1541. (Illus.). xxxii, 791p. 1973. 35.00 (ISBN 0-8294-0354-X); Vol. 2. India, 1541-1545. (Illus.). xvi, 759p. 1977. 35.00 (ISBN 0-8294-0355-8); Vol. 3. Indonesia & India, 1545-1549. xiv, 726p. 1980. 40.00 (ISBN 0-8294-0356-6); Vol. 4. Japan, India & China, 1549-1552. xii, 713p. 1982. 45.00 (ISBN 0-8294-0357-4). LC 72-88247. (Illus.). Jesuit Hist.

FRANCK, FREDERICH, 1909-

Franck, Frederick. Art As a Way: A Return to the Spiritual Roots. LC 81-7853. (Illus.). 160p. (Orig.). 1981. pap. 9.95 (ISBN 0-8245-0076-8). Crossroad NY.

--Zen of Seeing. 1973. pap. 8.95 (ISBN 0-394-71968-9, V968, Vin). Random.

FRANCOIS DE SALES, SAINT, BISHOP OF GENEVA, 1567-1622

Bregy, Katherine. The Story of Saint Francis de Sales: Patron of Catholic Writers. 108p. 1982. Repr. of 1958 ed. lib. bdg. 35.00 (ISBN 0-89984-015-9). Century Bookbindery.

Rivet, Mother Mary M. Influence of the Spanish Mystics on the Works of Saint Francis De Sales. LC 79-115355. (Catholic University of America. Studies in Romance Languages & Literatures: No. 22). Repr. of 1941 ed. 20.00 (ISBN 0-404-50322-5). AMS Pr.

Streebing, Cecilian. Devout Humanism as a Style. LC 70-128930. (Catholic University. Romance Literature: No. 50). Repr. of 1954 ed. 23.80 (ISBN 0-404-50350-0). AMS Pr.

FRANKS

Gregorius, Saint Histoire Ecclesiastique Des Francs, 4 vols. 1967. 154.00 (ISBN 0-384-19875-9); pap. 130.00 (ISBN 0-384-19874-0). Johnson Repr.

Gregory - Bishop of Tours. History of the Franks. Brehaut, Ernest, tr. (Columbia University Records of Civilization Ser). 1969. pap. 7.95x (ISBN 0-393-09845-1, NortonC). Norton.

Gregory of Tours. The History of the Franks: Gregory of Tours. Thorpe, Lewis, tr. 720p. 1976. pap. 6.95 (ISBN 0-14-044295-2). Penguin.

FRANSON, FREDRIK, 1852-1908

Torjesen, Edward P. Fredrik Franson: Model for Worldwide Evangelism. LC 82-17892. 128p. (Orig.). 1983. pap. 4.95 (ISBN 0-87808-191-7). William Carey Lib.

FREE AGENCY

see Free Will and Determinism

FREE CHURCHES

see Dissenters, Religious

FREE METHODIST CHURCH

Bastian, Donald N. Belonging! Adventures in Church Membership. 1978. pap. 4.95 (ISBN 0-89367-044-8). Light & Life.

Marston, Leslie R. From Age to Age a Living Witness. 1960. 10.95 (ISBN 0-685-14209-4). Light & Life.

FREE THOUGHT

see also Bible–Evidences, Authority, Etc.; Rationalism; Religious Liberty; Skepticism

Besant, Annie. The Freethinker's Textbook: Christianity, Its Evidences, Its Origin, Its Morality, Its History, Pt. 2. 3rd ed. LC 77-169205. (Atheist Viewpoint Ser). 288p. 1972. Repr. 21.00 (ISBN 0-405-03803-8). Ayer Co Pubs.

Lewis, Joseph. Atheism & Other Addresses. LC 72-161333. (Atheist Viewpoint Ser). (Illus.). 510p. 1972. Repr. of 1960 ed. 32.00 (ISBN 0-405-03800-3). Ayer Co Pubs.

Powys, Llewelyn. Rats in the Sacristy. facs. ed. LC 67-30226. (Essay Index Reprint Ser). 1937. 17.00 (ISBN 0-8369-0798-1). Ayer Co Pubs.

Russell, Bertrand. Why I Am Not a Christian & Other Essays on Religion & Related Subjects. 1967. pap. 6.95 (ISBN 0-671-20323-1, Touchstone Bks). S&S.

Stein, Gordon. Freethought in the United Kingdom & the Commonwealth: A Descriptive Bibliography. LC 80-1792. xxiii, 193p. 1981. lib. bdg. 39.95 (ISBN 0-313-20869-7, SFU/). Greenwood.

Swancara, Frank. Obstruction of Justice by Religion: A Treatise on Religious Barbarities of the Common Law, & a Review of Judicial Oppressions of the Non-Religious in the U. S. LC 70-139581. (Civil Liberties in American History Ser). (Illus.). 1971. Repr. of 1936 ed. lib. bdg. 32.50 (ISBN 0-306-71964-9). Da Capo.

FREE WILL AND DETERMINISM

see also Decision-Making (Ethics); Freedom (Theology); God–Will; Pelagianism

Aivanhov, Omraam M. Man Master of His Destiny. (Izvor Collection Ser.: Vol. 202). 194p. 1982. pap. 4.95 (ISBN 0-911857-01-X). Prosveta USA.

Edwards, Jonathan. A Dissertation Concerning Liberty & Necessity. LC 73-21786. 1974. Repr. of 1797 ed. lib. bdg. 22.50 (ISBN 0-8337-1003-6). B Franklin.

--Freedom of the Will. Kaufman, Arnold S. & Frankena, William K., eds. LC 82-18742. 300p. 1982. pap. text ed. 14.95x (ISBN 0-8290-1264-8). Irvington.

--Freedom of the Will. Ramsey, Paul, ed. (Works of Jonathan Edwards Ser.: Vol. 1). (Illus.). 1957. 50.00x (ISBN 0-300-00848-1). Yale U Pr.

Gerstner, John H. A Primer on Free Will. 1982. pap. 1.50 (ISBN 0-87552-272-6). Presby & Reformed.

Goodenough, Daniel W. Providence & Free Will in Human Actions. 132p. 1986. pap. 5.95 (ISBN 0-915221-63-2). Swedenborg Sci Assn.

Heschel, Abraham J. The Insecurity of Freedom: Essays on Human Existence. LC 66-16293. 320p. 1985. pap. 7.95 (ISBN 0-8052-0361-3). Schocken.

Kane, R. Free Will & Values. (Series in Philosophy). 328p. 1985. 44.50 (ISBN 0-88706-101-X); pap. 18.95 (ISBN 0-88706-102-8). State U NY Pr.

Kashap, S. Paul. Spinoza & Moral Freedom. (SUNY Series in Philosophy). 130p. 1987. text ed. 32.50x (ISBN 0-88706-529-5); pap. 10.95x. State U NY Pr.

Kenny, Anthony. Freewill & Responsibility: Four Lectures. 1978. 15.00x (ISBN 0-7100-8998-8). Methuen Inc.

Luther, Martin. Bondage of the Will. Packer, J. I. & Johnston, O. R., trs. 322p. 1970. 13.95 (ISBN 0-8007-0028-7). Revell.

--Christian Liberty. Grimm, Harold J., ed. Lambert, W. A., tr. from Ger. 1943. pap. 1.50 (ISBN 0-8006-0182-3, 1-182). Fortress.

McTaggart, John. Some Dogmas of Religion. LC 7-7484. 1968. Repr. of 1906 ed. 23.00 (ISBN 0-527-60000-8). Kraus Repr.

Maritain, Jacques. Freedom & the Modern World. O'Sullivan, Richard, tr. LC 77-150414. 231p. 1971. Repr. of 1936 ed. 15.00x (ISBN 0-87752-147-6). Gordian.

Price, Richard. A Free Discussion of the Doctrine of Materialism and Philosophical Necessity, 1778. Wellek, Rene, ed. LC 75-11247. (British Philosophers & Theologians of the 17th & 18th Centuries Ser.). 1978. lib. bdg. 51.00 (ISBN 0-8240-1798-6). Garland Pub.

Rice, Richard. God's Foreknowledge & Man's Free Will. 128p. (Orig.). 1985. pap. 4.95 (ISBN 0-87123-845-4, 210845). Bethany Hse.

Rupp, E. Gordon & Watson, Philip S., eds. Luther & Erasmus: Free Will & Salvation. LC 76-79870. (Library of Christian Classics). 356p. 1978. softcover 10.95 (ISBN 0-664-24158-1). Westminster.

St. Augustine. The Theory of Free Will. (Illus.). 117p. 1984. 66.55 (ISBN 0-89266-466-5). Am Classical Coll Pr.

Saint Augustine. On Free Choice of the Will. Benjamin, A. S. & Hackstaff, L. H., trs. LC 63-16932. (Orig.). 1964. pap. 7.20 scp (ISBN 0-672-60368-3, LLAS150). Bobbs.

Schopenhauer, Arthur. Free Will & Fatalism. (Illus.). 131p. 1985. 97.85 (ISBN 0-89266-508-4). Am Classical Coll Pr.

Schuller, Robert H. Discover Freedom. (Orig.). 1978. pap. 1.25 (ISBN 0-89081-155-5). Harvest Hse.

Socrates & Plato. The Psychology of Fate & of Free Will. (Illus.). 121p. 1983. 75.85 (ISBN 0-89920-067-2). Am Inst Psych.

Steiner, Rudolf. Philosophy of Freedom. Wilson, Michael, tr. from Ger. 226p. 1973. pap. 7.95 (ISBN 0-910142-52-1). Anthroposophic.

Venden, Morris L. Salvation by Faith & Your Will. LC 78-7597. (Horizon Ser.). 1978. pap. 5.95 (ISBN 0-8127-0190-9). Review & Herald.

Wolter, Allan B., ed. Duns Scotus on the Will & Morality. 1986. 54.95 (ISBN 0-8132-0622-7). Cath U Pr.

FREEDOM (THEOLOGY)

Brown, Delwin. To Set at Liberty: Christian Faith & Human Freedom. LC 80-21783. 144p. (Orig.). 1981. pap. 6.95 (ISBN 0-88344-501-8). Orbis Bks.

Flew, Antony. God, Freedom & Immortality: A Critical Analysis. LC 84-42543. 183p. 1984. pap. text ed. 10.95 (ISBN 0-87975-251-3). Prometheus Bks.

Hawkinson, James R., ed. Bound to Be Free. 150p. 1975. 6.95 (ISBN 0-910452-40-7); pap. 5.45 (ISBN 0-910452-25-3). Covenant.

Hummel, Charles. Becoming Free. pap. 0.75 (ISBN 0-87784-137-3). Inter-Varsity.

Jeeves, Malcolm A., et al. Free to Be Different. American ed. LC 84-10525. Repr. of 1985 ed. 40.80 (2027547). Bks Demand UMI.

Johann, Robert O., ed. Freedom & Value. LC 76-13969. xii, 186p. 1976. pap. 9.00 (ISBN 0-8232-1011-1). Fordham.

Jones, Amos, Jr. Paul's Message of Freedom: What Does It Mean to the Black Church? 256p. 1984. 12.95 (ISBN 0-8170-0840-3). Judson.

Kappen, Sebastian. Jesus & Freedom. LC 76-25927. 186p. (Orig.). 1977. 4.48 (ISBN 0-88344-232-9). Orbis Bks.

Kasemann, Ernst. Jesus Means Freedom. Clarke, Frank, tr. from Ger. LC 75-94357. 168p. (Orig.). 1972. pap. 6.50 (ISBN 0-8006-1235-3, 1-1235). Fortress.

McLean, George F., ed. Freedom. LC 77-153528. (Proceedings of the American Catholic Philosophical Association: Vol. 50). 1976. pap. 15.00 (ISBN 0-918090-10-5). Am Cath Philo.

Martin, Everett D. Liberty. 307p. 1981. Repr. of 1930 ed. lib. bdg. 20.00 (ISBN 0-8495-3828-9). Arden Lib.

Palmer, Otto. Rudolf Steiner on His Book, The Philosophy of Freedom. Spock, Marjorie, tr. from Ger. 1975. 4.50 (ISBN 0-910142-68-8). Anthroposophic.

Paoli, Arturo. Freedom to Be Free. Quinn, Charles U., tr. from It. LC 72-93340. Tr. of Dialogo Della Liberazione. 320p. (Orig.). 1973. pap. 2.48 (ISBN 0-88344-143-8). Orbis Bks.

Perry, Ralph B. The Free Man & the Soldier. facsimile ed. LC 73-24250. (Select Bibliographies Reprint Ser.). Repr. of 1916 ed. 16.00 (ISBN 0-8369-5438-6). Ayer Co Pubs.

Ruether, Rosemary. Liberation Theology: Human Hope Confronts Christian History & American Power. LC 72-92263. Repr. of 1972 ed. 50.50 (ISBN 0-8357-9487-3, 2015212). Bks Demand UMI.

Russell, Letty M. Human Liberation in a Feminist Perspective: A Theology. LC 74-10613. 214p. 1974. pap. 8.95 (ISBN 0-664-24991-4). Westminster.

Schwanktfeld, Kurt W. The Hegel-Kierkegaard Cosmology of the Spirit. (Illus.). 103p. 1984. 87.85 (ISBN 0-89266-497-5). Am Classical Coll Pr.

Shaw, Graham. The Cost of Authority: Manipulation & Freedom in the New Testament. LC 82-48545. 320p. 1983. pap. 16.95 (ISBN 0-8006-1707-X). Fortress.

Smith, Gerard. Freedom in Molina. 1966. 2.25 (ISBN 0-8294-0070-2). Loyola.

Steiger, Brad. In My Soul I Am Free. 206p. 1968. pap. 5.95 (ISBN 0-88155-003-5). IWP Pub.

Topel, John. The Way to Peace: Liberation Through the Bible. LC 78-9148. 208p. (Orig.). 1979. pap. 7.95 (ISBN 0-88344-704-5). Orbis Bks.

Trungpa, Chogyam. The Myth of Freedom & the Way of Meditation. LC 75-40264. (Illus.). 176p. (Orig.). 1976. pap. 7.95 (ISBN 0-87773-084-9). Shambhala Pubns.

Woodhouse, A. S., ed. & intro. by. Puritanism & Liberty: Being the Army Debates (1647-9) from the Clarke Manuscripts with Supplementary Documents. 634p. 1986. pap. 11.95x (ISBN 0-460-01057-3, Pub. by Evman England). Biblio Dist.

Wright, Elliott. Go Free. 128p. (Orig.). 1973. pap. 1.75 (ISBN 0-377-03011-2). Friend Pr.

FREEDOM OF RELIGION

see Religious Liberty

FREEDOM OF SPEECH IN THE CHURCH

see Liberty of Speech in the Church

FREEDOM OF THE WILL

see Free Will and Determinism

FREEDOM OF WORSHIP

see Religious Liberty

FREEMASONS

Bailey, Foster. The Spirit of Masonry. rev. ed. 143p. 1979. pap. 6.00 (ISBN 0-85330-135-2). Lucis.

Bede, Elbert. The Landmarks of Freemasonry. 56p. 1980. pap. text ed. 3.00 (ISBN 0-88053-020-0). Macoy Pub.

Blackmer, Rollin C. The Lodge & the Craft. 295p. 1976. text ed. 7.95 s.p. (ISBN 0-88053-043-X). Macoy Pub.

Blakemore, Louis B. Masonic Lodge Methods. 320p. 1981. Repr. of 1953 ed. text ed. 11.50 (ISBN 0-88053-027-8, M-76). Macoy Pub.

Blanchard, J. Standard Freemasonry. 9.00x (ISBN 0-685-22116-4). Wehman.

Cahill, E. Freemasonry & the Anti-Christian Movement. 59.95 (ISBN 0-8490-0195-1). Gordon Pr.

Cass. Negro Freemasonry & Segregation. 11.00 (ISBN 0-685-19494-9). Powner.

Cass, D. A. Negro Freemasonry. 11.00x (ISBN 0-685-22057-5). Wehman.

Chase, Jackson H. Cryptic Masonry. 94p. Repr. of 1981 ed. s.p. soft cover 4.75 (ISBN 0-88053-014-6). Macoy Pub.

Clymer, R. Swinburne. Mysticism of Masonry. 1924. 4.95 (ISBN 0-686-00820-0). Philos Pub.

Coil, Henry W. Coil's Masonic Encyclopedia. LC 60-53289. 749p. cloth w/slipcase 31.50 (ISBN 0-88053-054-5). Macoy Pub.

--A Comprehensive View of Freemasonry. (Illus.). 1985. Repr. of 1954 ed. text ed. 12.50 (ISBN 0-88053-053-7). Macoy Pub.

De Poncins, Leon. Freemasonry & the Vatican. 1982. lib. bdg. 69.95 (ISBN 0-87700-351-3). Revisionist Pr.

Diccionario Enciclopedico de la Masoneria. (Span.). 40.95 (ISBN 0-686-56654-8, S-14860). French & Eur.

Dillon, George E. Freemasonry Unmasked. Fuhley, Denis, pref. by. 114p. 1984. pap. 6.00 (ISBN 0-89562-095-2). Sons Lib.

El-Amin, Mustafa. Al-Islam, Christianity, & Freemasonry. 214p. (Orig.). 1985. pap. 6.95 (ISBN 0-933821-05-0). New Mind Prod.

Garver, William L. Brother of the Third Degree. 14.95 (ISBN 0-87505-089-1). Borden.

Hall, Manly P. Freemasonry of the Ancient Egyptians. 10.50 (ISBN 0-89314-803-2). Philos Res.

--Lost Keys of Freemasonry. 8.95 (ISBN 0-89314-500-9). Philos Res.

--The Lost Keys of Freemasonry: Or, the Secret of Hiram Abiff. rev. and enl. ed. 190p. 1981. Repr. text ed. 8.95 (ISBN 0-88053-044-8). Macoy Pub.

--Masonic Orders of Fraternity. 5.95 (ISBN 0-89314-536-X). Philos Res.

Hammond, William E. What Masonry Means. 1978. Repr. of 1939 ed. 5.50 (ISBN 0-88053-051-0, M-311). Macoy Pub.

Haywood, H. L., ed. The Great Teachings of Masonry. rev. enl. ed. 200p. 1971. Repr. of 1921 ed. text ed. 8.75 (ISBN 0-88053-041-3, M-90). Macoy Pub.

--How to Become a Masonic Lodge Officer. 228p. 1983. Repr. of 1958 ed. soft cover 7.50 (ISBN 0-88053-028-6, M-77). Macoy Pub.

Knight, Stephen. The Brotherhood: The Secret World of the Freemasons. LC 84-45208. 336p. 1984. 17.95 (ISBN 0-8128-2994-8). Stein & Day.

McClain, Alva J. Freemasonry & Christianity. 1979. pap. 1.00 (ISBN 0-88469-012-1). BMH Bks.

Mackey, Albert G. Jurisprudence of Freemasonry. 12.00 (ISBN 0-685-19480-9). Powner.

--Mackey's Jurisprudence of Freemasonry. 1985. Repr. 12.75 (ISBN 0-88053-026-X). Macoy Pub.

Macoy, Robert. Worshipful Master's Assistant. rev/ ed. 302p. 1980. Repr. s.p. hardcover 11.95 (ISBN 0-88053-008-1). Macoy Pub.

Makrakis, Apostolos. Freemasonry Known by the Masonic Diploma. Cummings, Denver, tr. 135p. (Orig.). 1956. pap. 4.50 (ISBN 0-938366-42-4). Orthodox Chr.

Masonic Quiz: Ask Me Another, Brother. 12.00 (ISBN 0-685-19487-6). Powner.

Mellor, Allec. Dictionnaire de la Franc-Maconnerie et des Francs-Macons. (Fr.). 400p. 1971. 27.50 (ISBN 0-686-57043-X, M-6403). French & Eur.

More Light. 8.50 (ISBN 0-685-19492-2). Powner.

Morgan, William. Freemasonry Exposed. 8.50 (ISBN 0-685-19475-2). Powner.

Morris, Robert. Freemasonry in the Holy Land: Handmarks of Hiram's Builders. Davis, Moshe, ed. LC 77-70731. (America & the Holy Land Ser.). (Illus.). 1977. Repr. of 1872 ed. lib. bdg. 46.50x (ISBN 0-405-10270-4). Ayer Co Pubs.

Morris, Woodrow W. The Greatest of These: Quotations on Fundamental Truths of Charity - The Teaching of Freemasonry. (Illus.). 132p. 1985. 8.75 (ISBN 0-88053-080-4). Macoy Pub.

Nettl, Paul. Mozart & Masonry. LC 78-114564. (Music Ser.). 1970. Repr. of 1957 ed. lib. bdg. 25.00 (ISBN 0-306-71922-3). Da Capo.

Newton, Joseph F. The Men's House: Masonic Papers & Addresses. 253p. 1969. text ed. 5.00 (ISBN 0-88053-037-5, M-86). Macoy Pub.

Petersen, William. Masonic Quiz. 12.00x (ISBN 0-685-22032-X). Wehman.

Pocket Lexicon of Freemasonry. 3.50 (ISBN 0-685-19495-7). Powner.

Pollard, Stewart M. Tied to Masonic Apron Strings. Cook, Lewis C., ed. 1979. pap. 4.50 (ISBN 0-88053-059-6, M-322). Macoy Pub.

Pott, Constance M. Francis Bacon & His Secret Society. LC 71-174282. Repr. of 1891 ed. 32.50 (ISBN 0-404-05096-4). AMS Pr.

Roberts, Allen E. How to Conduct a Leadership Seminar. 11p. 1970. pap. 1.00 (ISBN 0-88053-013-8). Macoy Pub.

Robison, John. Proofs of a Conspiracy. 1967. pap. 4.95 (ISBN 0-88279-121-4). Western Islands.

Ronayne. Freemasonry Handbook. 9.00x (ISBN 0-685-21949-6). Wehman.

Ronayne, Edmond. Blue Lodge & Chapter. 1947. 11.00 (ISBN 0-685-19465-5). Powner.

--Chapter Degrees. 8.50 (ISBN 0-685-19469-8). Powner.

--Mah Hah Bone. 11.00 (ISBN 0-685-19485-X). Powner.

--Master's Carpet. 9.00 (ISBN 0-685-19490-6). Powner.

Shepherd, Silas H., et al. Little Masonic Library, 5 vols. 1977. Repr. cloth 35.00 set (ISBN 0-88053-005-7, M-5). Macoy Pub.

Simons, George E. The Standard Masonic Monitor. 248p. 1984. pap. 7.50 enlarged type (ISBN 0-88053-010-3). Macoy Pub.

Upton, William H. Negro Masonry. LC 70-144696. Repr. of 1902 ed. 16.00 (ISBN 0-404-00218-8). AMS Pr.

Voorhis, H. V., compiled by. Facts for Freemasons. 258p. 1979. text ed. 9.50 (ISBN 0-88053-016-2, M-65). Macoy Pub.

Wathen, James F. Is the Order of St. John Masonic? 84p. 1973. pap. 3.50 (ISBN 0-89555-250-7). TAN Bks Pubs.

Willets, Walter E. Master's Book of Short Speeches. rev. ed. 65p. 1984. Repr. s.p. soft cover 2.95 (ISBN 0-88053-050-2). Macoy Pub.

Wilson-Ludlam, Mae. The Power Trio. 152p. 1981. Repr. of 1976 ed. soft cover 6.95 (ISBN 0-88053-765-5). Macoy Pub.

Worthy Matron's Year Book. 1985. Repr. s.p. hardcover, looseleaf 10.00 (ISBN 0-88053-333-1). Macoy Pub.

Wright, Dudley. Roman Catholicism & Freemasonry. 1977. lib. bdg. 69.95 (ISBN 0-8490-2531-1). Gordon Pr.

Yarker, John. Speculative Freemasonary. 1987. pap. 3.95 (ISBN 0-916411-66-4, Pub. by Sure Fire). Holmes Pub.

FREEMASONS–HISTORY

Coil, Henry W. Freemasonry Through Six Centuries, 2 vols. 600p. 1976. Repr. of 1966 ed. text ed. 23.50 slipcase (ISBN 0-88053-034-0). Macoy Pub.

Cooper & Oakley. Masonry & Medieval Mysticism. pap. 9.25 (ISBN 0-8356-5301-3). Theos Pub Hse.

--Masonry & Medieval Mysticism. 12.95 (ISBN 0-8356-5309-9). Theos Pub Hse.

Darrah, D. D. History & Evolution of Freemasonry. 12.00x (ISBN 0-685-21969-0). Wehman.

Darrah, Delmore D. History & Evolution of Freemasonry. (Illus.). 1951. 12.00 (ISBN 0-685-19479-5). Powner.

Grimshaw, William H. Official History of Free Masonry among the Colored People in North America. LC 74-91257. (Illus.). Repr. of 1903 ed. 22.50x (ISBN 0-8371-2051-9, GRF&, Pub. by Negro U Pr). Greenwood.

--Official History of Freemasonry among the Colored People in North America. facs. ed. LC 74-157370. (Black Heritage Library Collection). 1903. 22.50 (ISBN 0-8369-8808-6). Ayer Co Pubs.

Gwynne, H. A., intro. by. The Cause of World Unrest. 1978. pap. 5.00x (ISBN 0-911038-40-X). Noontide.

Haywood, H. L., ed. The Newly Made Mason: What He & Every Mason Should Know about Masonry. 5th ed. (Illus.). 256p. 1978. Repr. of 1973 ed. text ed. 12.50 (ISBN 0-88053-030-8, M-80). Macoy Pub.

Headings, Mildred J. French Freemasonry under the Third Republic. LC 78-64206. (Johns Hopkins University. Studies in the Social Sciences. Sixty-Sixth Ser. 1948: 1). Repr. of 1949 ed. 26.00 (ISBN 0-404-61311-X). AMS Pr.

Katz, Jacob. Jews & Freemasons in Europe, 1723-1939. Oschry, Leonard, tr. from Heb. LC 71-115475. 1970. 22.50x (ISBN 0-674-47480-5). Harvard U Pr.

Lipson, Dorothy Ann. Freemasonry in Federalist Connecticut, 1789-1835. 1977. 40.00 (ISBN 0-691-04646-8). Princeton U Pr.

Macbride, A. S. Speculative Masonry Its Mission, Its Evolution & Its Landmarks. 264p. 1971. Repr. of 1924 ed. text ed. 6.00 (ISBN 0-88053-040-5, M-89). Macoy Pub.

McCabe, Joseph. History of Free Masonry. 31p. pap. cancelled (ISBN 0-911826-73-4). Am Atheist.

Newton, Joseph F. The Builders: A Story & Study of Freemasonry. 9th printing ed. (Illus.). 345p. 1985. Repr. 11.95 (ISBN 0-88053-045-6). Macoy Pub.

--Short Talks on Masonry. 255p. 1979. Repr. of 1969 ed. text ed. 6.95 (ISBN 0-88053-036-7, M-85). Macoy Pub.

Van der Veur, Paul W. Freemasonry in Indonesia from Radermacher to Soekanto, 1762-1961. LC 76-620040. (Papers in International Studies: Southeast Asia Ser.: No. 40). (Illus.). 1976. pap. 4.00x (ISBN 0-89680-026-1, 82-90413, Ohio U Ctr Intl). Ohio U Pr.

FREEMASONS–KNIGHTS TEMPLARS

see also Templars

Blanchard, J. Knight Templarism. rev. ed. 9.50x (ISBN 0-685-22013-3). Wehman.

Cook, E. H. Knight Templarism. 9.50 (ISBN 0-685-19481-7). Powner.

Macoy, Robert. Christmas, Easter, Ascension & Burial Services for Knights Templar. rev. ed. 112p. 1978. pap. 4.00 (ISBN 0-88053-011-1). Macoy Pub.

FREEMASONS–MONITORS

see Freemasons–Rituals

FREEMASONS–RITUALS

Blue Lodge Enlightenment. 8.50 (ISBN 0-685-19466-3). Powner.

Brunke, Ottillie S. Chapter Ceremonies & Poems. 60p. pap. text ed. 2.50 (ISBN 0-88053-305-6, S-192). Macoy Pub.

Ceremonies, Heroines of Jericho. 3.50 (ISBN 0-685-19468-X). Powner.

Cook, E. A. Scottish Rite Masonry, 2 vols. Set. 20.00x (ISBN 0-685-22097-4). Wehman.

Duncan, M. C. Masonic Ritual. rev. ed. 12.50x (ISBN 0-685-22033-8). Wehman.

Duncan, Malcolm. Masonic Ritual & Monitor, 2 Pts. 1946. 8.50 ea.; 1 vol. ed. 12.50 (ISBN 0-685-19489-2). Powner.

Duncan, Malcolm C. Duncan's Masonic Ritual & Monitor. new ed. 288p. 1976. 10.95 (ISBN 0-679-50979-8); pap. 5.95. McKay.

Heroines of Jerico Ritual. 3.50 (ISBN 0-685-19478-7). Powner.

Lester. Look to the East. 8.95x (ISBN 0-685-22017-6). Wehman.

Lester, Ralph P. Look to the East. 8.50 (ISBN 0-685-19484-1). Powner.

Lodge of Sorrows. pap. 1.75 (ISBN 0-685-19483-3). Powner.

Masonic Burial Service. 3.00 (ISBN 0-685-19486-8). Powner.

Maxwell, Geraldine Boldt. Royal Matron's Treasury of Addresses & Ceremonies, No. 2. 1975. pap. 2.00 29 selections (ISBN 0-88053-320-X). Macoy Pub.

Ronayne, E. Ma-Ha-Bone: Ritual. 11.00x (ISBN 0-685-22019-2). Wehman.

Ronayne, Edmond. Handbook of Freemasonry. 9.00 (ISBN 0-685-19476-0). Powner.

Scottish Rite Masonry, 2 vols. Set. 20.00 (ISBN 0-685-19498-1). Powner.

Simons, George E. Standard Monitor. 7.50 (ISBN 0-685-19502-3). Powner.

Standard Freemasonry. (Illus.). 9.00 (ISBN 0-685-19501-5). Powner.

Welcomes & Ceremonies for the Year's Program. 34p. 1985. Repr. s.p. soft cover 1.25 (ISBN 0-88053-332-3). Macoy Pub.

Worshipful Master's Assistant. 10.00 (ISBN 0-685-19506-6). Powner.

FREEMASONS–SYMBOLISM

Buck, Jirah D. Symbolism of Freemasonry. 12.00 (ISBN 0-685-19503-1). Powner.

Claudy, Carl H., ed. Foreign Countries: A Gateway to the Interpretation & Development of Certain Symbols of Freemasonry. 160p. 1971. Repr. of 1925 ed. text ed. 6.00 (ISBN 0-88053-039-1, M-88). Macoy Pub.

Mackey, A. G. Symbolism of Freemansonry. 12.00x (ISBN 0-685-22122-9). Wehman.

Mackey, Albert G. Symbolism of Freemasonry. 12.00 (ISBN 0-685-19504-X). Powner.

Percival, Harold W. Masonry & Its Symbols, in Light of "Thinking & Destiny". LC 52-2237. 1979. pap. 3.95 (ISBN 0-911650-07-5). Word Foun.

Roberts, Allen E. The Craft & Its Symbols. 5th printing ed. LC 73-89493. (Illus.). 92p. 1985. Repr. text ed. 7.50 (ISBN 0-88053-058-8). Macoy Pub.

Steinmetz, George H. The Royal Arch: Its Hidden Meaning. (Illus.). 145p. 1979. Repr. of 1946 ed. text ed. 9.50 (M-302). Macoy Pub.

FREEMASONS–TEMPLARS

see Freemasons–Knights Templars

FREEMASONS AND CATHOLIC CHURCH

see also Anti-Clericalism

DePoncins, Leon V. Freemasonry & the Vatican. 59.95 (ISBN 0-8490-0196-X). Gordon Pr.

Thornton, Mary C. The Church & Freemasonry in Brazil, 1872-1875. LC 73-2647. 287p. 1973. Repr. of 1948 ed. lib. bdg. 22.50x (ISBN 0-8371-6816-3, THCF). Greenwood.

FRESCO PAINTING

see Mural Painting and Decoration

FRIARS

see also Carmelites; Dominicans; Franciscans; Monasticism and Religious Orders

Fish, Simon. A Supplicacyon for the Beggers. LC 72-5989. (English Experience Ser.: No. 515). 16p. 1973. Repr. of 1529 ed. 6.00 (ISBN 90-221-0515-6). Walter J Johnson.

Hoad, Harold. Grey Friars. 1979. 6.95 (ISBN 0-8199-0779-0). Franciscan Herald.

Kennard, Joseph S. Friar in Fiction, Sincerity in Art, & Other Essays. facs. ed. LC 68-20313. (Essay Index Reprint Ser). 1923. 20.00 (ISBN 0-8369-0588-1). Ayer Co Pubs.

Leutenegger, Benedict, tr. Life of Fray Antonio Margil De Jesus. (Illus.). 1967. 10.00 (ISBN 0-88382-254-7). AAFH.

Little, A. G. Introduction of the Observant Friars into England. 1925. pap. 2.25 (ISBN 0-85672-686-9, Pub. by British Acad). Longwood Pub Group.

FRIARS, BLACK
see Dominicans

FRIARS, GRAY
see Franciscans

FRIARS MINOR
see Franciscans

FRIARS PREACHERS
see Dominicans

FRIENDS, SOCIETY OF
see also Inner Light

Adede, Rose. Joel Litu: African Quaker. LC 82-81325. 32p. 1982. pap. 2.50x (ISBN 0-87574-243-2). Pendle Hill.

Alexander, Horace. Quakerism in India. 1983. pap. 2.50x (ISBN 0-87574-031-6, 031). Pendle Hill.

Applegarth, Albert C. Quakers in Pennsylvania. LC 78-63813. (Johns Hopkins University. Studies in the Social Sciences. Tenth Ser. 1892: 8-9). Repr. of 1892 ed. 11.50 (ISBN 0-404-61076-5). AMS Pr.

--Quakers in Pennsylvania. pap. 9.00 (ISBN 0-384-01765-7). Johnson Repr.

Bartoo, Glenn. Decisions by Consensus: A Study of the Quaker Method. (Studies in Quakerism: No. 4). 48p. (Orig.). 1978. pap. 2.00 (ISBN 0-89670-003-8). Progresiv Pub.

Battey, Thomas C. The Life & Adventures of a Quaker among the Indians. 339p. 1972. Repr. of 1875 ed. 20.00 (ISBN 0-87928-025-5). Corner Hse.

Benfey, Theodor. Friends & the World of Nature. LC 80-82941. 28p. (Orig.). 1980. pap. 2.50x (ISBN 0-87574-233-5). Pendle Hill.

Benson, Lewis. Catholic Quakerism: A Vision for All Men. 108p. 1968. pap. text ed. 2.50 (ISBN 0-941308-03-0). Religious Soc Friends.

Blom, Dorothea. Encounters with Art. 1983. pap. 2.50x (ISBN 0-87574-128-2, 128). Pendle Hill.

Boardman, Elizabeth J. The Phoenix Trip: Notes on a Quaker Mission to Haiphong. LC 84-72319. (Illus.). 192p. 1985. pap. 9.95 (ISBN 0-914064-22-3). Celo Pr.

Boulding, Kenneth. New Nations for Old. 1983. pap. 2.50x (ISBN 0-87574-017-0, 017). Pendle Hill.

Boulding, Kenneth E. The Evolutionary Potential of Quakerism. 1983. pap. 2.50x (ISBN 0-87574-136-3, 136). Pendle Hill.

Braithwaite, William C. The Beginnings of Quakerism. (Illus.). 562p. 1981. Repr. of 1923 ed. lib. bdg. 65.00 (ISBN 0-8495-0625-5). Arden Lib.

Brinton, Anna, ed. Then & Now. facs. ed. LC 72-128214. (Essay Index Reprint Ser). 1960. 21.50 (ISBN 0-8369-1905-X). Ayer Co Pubs.

Brinton, Howard. Ethical Mysticism in the Society of Friends. LC 67-31429. (Orig.). 1983. pap. 2.50x (ISBN 0-87574-156-8). Pendle Hill.

Brinton, Howard H. Guide to Quaker Practice. LC 43-11899. (Orig.). 1943. pap. 2.50x (ISBN 0-87574-020-0). Pendle Hill.

--How They Became Friends. LC 61-12670. (Orig.). 1961. pap. 2.50x (ISBN 0-87574-114-2, 114). Pendle Hill.

--Meeting House & Farm House. LC 72-80096. (Orig.). 1972. pap. 2.50x (ISBN 0-87574-185-1). Pendle Hill.

--The Nature of Quakerism. 1983. pap. 2.50x (ISBN 0-87574-047-2, 047). Pendle Hill.

--Prophetic Ministry. 1983. pap. 2.50x (ISBN 0-87574-054-5, 054). Pendle Hill.

--Quaker Doctrine of Inward Peace. LC 64-23230. (Orig.). 1948. pap. 2.50x (ISBN 0-87574-044-8). Pendle Hill.

--Quaker Journals: Varieties of Religious Experience among Friends. LC 78-188399. (Illus., Orig.). 1983. 7.00 (ISBN 0-87574-952-6). Pendle Hill.

--Quakerism & Other Religions. 1983. pap. 2.50x (ISBN 0-87574-093-6, 093). Pendle Hill.

--Reaching Decisions. 1983. pap. 2.50x (ISBN 0-87574-065-0, 065). Pendle Hill.

--The Society of Friends. 1983. pap. 2.50x (ISBN 0-87574-048-0, 048). Pendle Hill.

--Sources of the Quaker Peace Testimony. 1983. pap. 2.50x (ISBN 0-87574-027-8, 027). Pendle Hill.

Bristol, James E. Stand Fast in Liberty. 1983. pap. 2.50x (ISBN 0-87574-119-3, 119). Pendle Hill.

Bronner, Edwin B. Quakerism & Christianity. LC 67-18689. (Orig.). 1967. pap. 2.50x (ISBN 0-87574-152-5, 152). Pendle Hill.

Cadbury, Henry J. The Character of a Quaker. 1983. pap. 2.50x (ISBN 0-87574-103-7, 103). Pendle Hill.

Carroll, Kenneth. Quakerism on the Eastern Shore. LC 70-112986. (Illus.). 328p. 1970. 15.00x (ISBN 0-938420-15-1). Md Hist.

Cartland, Fernando G. Southern Heroes, or the Friends in Wartime. Bd. with Conscript Quakers. Foster, Ethan. (Library of War & Peace; Conscrip. & Cons. Object.). 1972. lib. bdg. 42.00 (ISBN 0-8240-0424-8). Garland Pub.

Collier, Howard E. The Quaker Meeting. 1983. pap. 2.50x (ISBN 0-87574-026-X, 026). Pendle Hill.

Crom, Scott. Quaker Worship & Techniques of Meditation. 1983. pap. 2.50x (ISBN 0-87574-195-9, 195). Pendle Hill.

Domino, Ruth. Search. 1983. pap. 2.50x (ISBN 0-87574-052-9, 052). Pendle Hill.

Doncaster, Hugh L. The Quaker Message: A Personal Affirmation. 1983. pap. 2.50x (ISBN 0-87574-181-9, 181). Pendle Hill.

Eishenberg, Fritz. Artist on the Witness Stand. LC 84-61828. (Orig.). 1984. pap. 2.50x (ISBN 0-87574-257-2). Pendle Hill.

Ferguson, Henry. Essays in American History. LC 68-26266. 1969. Repr. of 1894 ed. 21.50x (ISBN 0-8046-0144-5, Pub. by Kennikat). Assoc Faculty Pr.

Fisher, Sidney G. Quaker Colonies. 1919. 8.50x (ISBN 0-686-83720-7). Elliots Bks.

Fowler, Albert. Two Trends in Modern Quaker Thought. 1983. pap. 2.50x (ISBN 0-87574-112-6, 112). Pendle Hill.

Gorman, George. The Society of Friends. 1978. pap. 3.15 (ISBN 0-08-021412-6). Pergamon.

Gray, Elizabeth J. Contributions of the Quakers. 1983. pap. 2.50x (ISBN 0-87574-034-0, 034). Pendle Hill.

Gummere, Amelia M. Quaker: A Study in Costume. LC 68-56494. (Illus.). 1968. Repr. of 1901 ed. 20.00 (ISBN 0-405-08585-0, Blom Pubns). Ayer Co Pubs.

Hancock, Thomas. Principles of Peace: Exemplified by the Conduct of the Society of Friends in Ireland, 1798. LC 70-147620. (Library of War & Peace; Non-Resis. & Non-Vio.). lib. bdg. 46.00 (ISBN 0-8240-0377-2). Garland Pub.

Hartman, Grover L. Militarism for America. 1983. pap. 2.50x (ISBN 0-87574-025-1, 025). Pendle Hill.

Hay, Hope. The Quakers. 1985. 13.00x (ISBN 0-7062-4025-1, Pub. by Ward Lock Educ Co Ltd). State Mutual Bk.

Heard, Gerald. A Quaker Mutation. 1983. pap. 2.50x (ISBN 0-87574-007-3, 007). Pendle Hill.

Hilty, Hiram. Toward Freedom for All: North Carolina Quakers & Slavery. 120p. 1984. pap. 9.95 (ISBN 0-913408-83-2). Friends United.

Hintz, Howard W. Quaker Influence in American Literature. Repr. of 1940 ed. lib. bdg. 18.75 (ISBN 0-8371-3945-7, HIGA). Greenwood.

Hobart, John H. Can Quakerism Speak to the Times? 1983. pap. 2.50x (ISBN 0-87574-078-2, 078). Pendle Hill.

Hodge, Susan W. The Elfreth Book of Letters. ltd. ed. (Illus.). 320p. (Orig.). 1985. text ed. 50.00 leather & Bucksam (ISBN 0-8122-7982-4); pap. 9.95 (ISBN 0-8122-1208-8). U of Pa Pr.

Hutchinson, Dorothy. From Where They Sit. 1983. pap. 2.50x (ISBN 0-87574-084-7, 084). Pendle Hill.

--Unless One Is Born Anew. LC 65-26994. (Orig.). 1965. pap. 2.50x (ISBN 0-87574-143-6, 143). Pendle Hill.

Ives, Kenneth, et al. Black Quakers: Brief Biographies. (Studies in Quakerism: 12). (Illus.). 118p. (Orig.). 1986. pap. 8.00 (ISBN 0-89670-015-1). Progresiv Pub.

Ives, Kenneth H. Nurturing Spiritual Development: Stages, Structure, Style. (Studies in Quakerism: No. 8). 60p. (Orig.). 1982. pap. 4.00 (ISBN 0-89670-011-9). Progresiv Pub.

James, Sydney V. People among Peoples: Quaker Benevolence in Eighteenth Century America. LC 62-20248. (Center for the Study of the History of Liberty in America Ser). 1963. 27.50x (ISBN 0-674-66050-1). Harvard U Pr.

Jones, Rufus M. The Faith & Practice of the Quakers. 181p. 1980. pap. 3.95 (ISBN 0-913408-57-3). Friends United.

--Rethinking Quaker Principles. 1983. pap. 2.50x (ISBN 0-87574-008-1, 008). Pendle Hill.

Jorns, Auguste. Quakers As Pioneers in Social Work. LC 68-8232. 1969. Repr. of 1931 ed. 26.50x (ISBN 0-8046-0244-1, Pub. by Kennikat). Assoc Faculty Pr.

--Quakers As Pioneers in Social Work. Brown, Thomas K., tr. LC 69-14934. (Criminology, Law Enforcement, & Social Problems Ser.: No. 27). 1969. Repr. of 1931 ed. 8.50x (ISBN 0-87585-027-8). Patterson Smith.

Kavanaugh, John, ed. Quaker Approach to Contemporary Problems. Repr. of 1953 ed. lib. bdg. 22.50x (ISBN 0-8371-4432-9, KAGA). Greenwood.

Kenworthy, Leonard S. Quakerism: A Study Guide on the Religious Society of Friends. LC 81-80656. 224p. 1981. pap. 5.00 (ISBN 0-932970-21-4). Prinit Pr.

Kenworthy, Leonard S., ed. Friends Face the World: Some Continuing & Current Quaker Concerns. 220p. 1987. pap. 6.95 (ISBN 0-913408-97-2). Friends United.

Lacey, Paul. Quakers & the Use of Power. LC 81-85558. (Pendle Hill Pamphlets Ser.). 32p. (Orig.). 1982. pap. 2.50x (ISBN 0-87574-241-6, 241). Pendle Hill.

Lachmund, Margarethe. With Thine Adversary in the Way: A Quaker Witness for Reconciliation. Kite, Florence, tr. LC 79-91957. (Orig.). pap. 2.50x (ISBN 0-87574-228-9). Pendle Hill.

Laughlin, Sceva B., ed. Beyond Dilemmas. LC 79-86035. (Essay & General Literature Index Reprint Ser). 1969. Repr. of 1937 ed. 25.50x (ISBN 0-8046-0567-X, Pub. by Kennikat). Assoc Faculty Pr.

Lucas, Sidney. The Quaker Message. 1983. pap. 2.50x (ISBN 0-87574-040-5, 040). Pendle Hill.

Mather, Eleanore P. Anna Brinton: A Study in Quaker Character. LC 74-152086. (Illus., Orig.). 1971. pap. 2.50x (ISBN 0-87574-176-2). Pendle Hill.

--Barclay in Brief. 1983. pap. 2.50x (ISBN 0-87574-028-6, 028). Pendle Hill.

Maurer, Herrymon, ed. Pendle Hill Reader. facsimile ed. LC 74-142668. (Essay Index Reprint Ser). Repr. of 1950 ed. 18.00 (ISBN 0-8369-2415-0). Ayer Co Pubs.

Murphy, Carol R. The Roots of Pendle Hill. LC 78-1768. (Orig.). pap. 2.50x (ISBN 0-87574-223-8). Pendle Hill.

Nevaskar, Balwant S. Capitalists Without Capitalism: The Jains of India & the Quakers of the West. LC 72-98709. (Contributions in Sociology: No. 6). 1971. lib. bdg. 29.95 (ISBN 0-8371-3297-5, NCA/). Greenwood.

Newby, James R. Reflections from the Light of Christ: 5 Quaker Classics. LC 80-7477. 126p. 1980. 7.95 (ISBN 0-913408-55-7). Friends United.

Newman, Daisy. A Procession of Friends. 484p. 1980. pap. 11.95 (ISBN 0-913408-59-X). Friends United.

Peck, George. Simplicity: A Rich Quaker's View. LC 72-97851. (Orig.). 1973. pap. 2.50x (ISBN 0-87574-189-4). Pendle Hill.

Pickard, Bertram. Peacemakers' Dilemma. 1983. pap. 2.50x (ISBN 0-87574-016-2, 016). Pendle Hill.

Poley, Irvin C. & Poley, Ruth V. Quaker Anecdotes. 1983. pap. 2.50x (ISBN 0-87574-033-2, 033). Pendle Hill.

Proud, Robert. The History of Pennsylvania, 2 Vols. LC 66-25101. 1967. Repr. of 1797 ed. 20.00 ea. Vol. 1 (ISBN 0-87152-031-1). Vol. 2 (ISBN 0-87152-032-X). Set. 40.00 (ISBN 0-87152-305-1). Reprint.

Punshon, John. Alternative Christianity. 1982. pap. 2.50x (ISBN 0-87574-245-9, 245). Pendle Hill.

--Encounter with Silence: Reflections from the Quaker Tradition. 156p. (Orig.). 1987. pap. 6.95 (ISBN 0-913408-96-4). Friends United.

The Quaker Struggle for the Rights of Women. pap. 0.70 (ISBN 0-686-95360-6). Am Fr Serv Comm.

Rawlins, Winifred. The Inner Islands. 1983. pap. 2.50x (ISBN 0-87574-073-1, 073). Pendle Hill.

Ruopp, Phillips. Private Testimony & Public Policy. 1983. pap. 2.50x (ISBN 0-87574-105-3, 105). Pendle Hill.

Schuckman, Roy. Puerto Rican Neighbor. 1983. pap. 2.50x (ISBN 0-87574-075-8, 075). Pendle Hill.

Sheeran, Michael J. Beyond Majority Rule: Voteless Decisions in the Religious Society of Friends. (Illus.). 153p. (Orig.). 1983. pap. 4.95 (ISBN 0-941308-04-9). Religious Soc Friends.

Steere, Douglas V. Community & Worship. 1983. pap. 2.50x (ISBN 0-87574-010-3, 010). Pendle Hill.

--The Hardest Journey. 1983. pap. 2.50x (ISBN 0-87574-163-0, 163). Pendle Hill.

--Prayer & Worship. LC 78-70480. 1978. pap. 3.95 (ISBN 0-913408-44-1). Friends United.

Steere, Douglas V., ed. Quaker Spirituality: Selected Writings. (Classics of Western Spirituality Ser.). 384p. 1984. 12.95 (ISBN 0-8091-0335-4); pap. 9.95 (ISBN 0-8091-2510-2). Paulist Pr.

Stephen, Caroline. Quaker Strongholds. Ogilvie, Mary G., ed. LC 51-4625. 32p. (Orig.). 1951. pap. 2.50x (ISBN 0-87574-059-6, 059). Pendle Hill.

Taylor, Richard. Friends & the Racial Crisis. LC 70-129552. (Orig.). pap. 2.50x (ISBN 0-87574-172-X). Pendle Hill.

Tonge, Mildred. A Sense of Living. 1983. pap. 2.50x (ISBN 0-87574-079-0, 079). Pendle Hill.

Weeks, Stephen B. Southern Quakers & Slavery: A Study in Institutional History. LC 78-64260. (Johns Hopkins University. Studies in the Social Sciences. Extra Volumes: 15). Repr. of 1896 ed. 31.00 (ISBN 0-404-61363-2). AMS Pr.

White, Miles. Early Quaker Records in Virginia. LC 76-46154. 64p. 1985. pap. 5.00 (ISBN 0-317-31654-0). Genealog Pub.

Whitney, Norman J. Experiments in Community. 1983. pap. 2.50x (ISBN 0-87574-149-5, 149). Pendle Hill.

Wood, Raquel & Banerji, Ranan. Non-Christian Quakers: Their Faith & Message. Ives, Kenneth, ed. (Studies in Quakerism Ser.: No. 9). 59p. (Orig.). 1983. pap. 4.00 (ISBN 0-89670-012-7). Progresiv Pub.

Woody, Thomas. Quaker Education in the Colony & State of New Jersey. LC 76-89256. (American Education: Its Men, Institutions & Ideas, Ser. 1). 1969. Repr. of 1923 ed. 32.00 (ISBN 0-405-01494-5). Ayer Co Pubs.

Woolman, John. The Journal of John Woolman. 256p. 1972. pap. 5.95 (ISBN 0-8065-0294-0). Citadel Pr.

--Journal of John Woolman & a Plea for the Poor. 17.00 (ISBN 0-8446-0297-3). Peter Smith.

--Worship. 1983. pap. 2.50x (ISBN 0-87574-051-0, 051). Pendle Hill.

Wright, Luella M. Literary Life of the Early Friends, 1650-1725. LC 32-25426. Repr. of 1932 ed. 19.50 (ISBN 0-404-07046-9). AMS Pr.

Yarrow, C. H. Quaker Experiences in International Conciliation. LC 78-7415. 1978. 25.00x (ISBN 0-300-02260-3). Yale U Pr.

Yates, Elizabeth. Gifts of the True Love. (Illus.). 1983. pap. 2.50x (ISBN 0-87574-100-2, 100). Pendle Hill.

Young, Mildred B. The Candle, the Lantern, the Daylight. LC 61-15103. (Orig.). 1961. pap. 2.50x (ISBN 0-87574-116-9). Pendle Hill.

Yungblut, John. Quakerism of the Future: Mystical, Prophetic & Evangelical. LC 74-81830. (Orig.). 1974. pap. 2.50x (ISBN 0-87574-194-0). Pendle Hill.

--Speaking As One Friend to Another. (Orig.). 1983. pap. 2.50x (ISBN 0-87574-249-1, 249). Pendle Hill.

FRIENDS, SOCIETY OF–AMERICAN FRIENDS SERVICE COMMITTEE

Nixon, E. Anna. A Century of Planting: A History of the American Friends Mission in India. LC 85-72070. (Illus.). 493p. (Orig.). 1985. 16.95x (ISBN 0-913342-55-6); pap. 11.95 (ISBN 0-913342-54-8). Barclay Pr.

Robson, Walter. An English View of American Quakerism: The Journal of Walter Robson 1842-1929 Written During the Fall of 1877, While Traveling Among American Friends. Bronner, Edwin B., ed. LC 71-107345. (American Philosophical Society Memoirs Ser.: Vol. 79). pap. 43.80 (ISBN 0-317-27898-3, 2025135). Bks Demand UMI.

FRIENDS, SOCIETY OF–BIBLIOGRAPHY

Swarthmore College. Catalog of the Friends Historical Library Book & Serial Collections, 6 vols. 1982. Set. lib. bdg. 655.00 (ISBN 0-8161-0376-3, Hall Library). G K Hall.

FRIENDS, SOCIETY OF–BIOGRAPHY

Best, Mary A. Rebel Saints. facs. ed. LC 68-55839. (Essay Index Reprint Ser). 1925. 18.00 (ISBN 0-8369-0205-X). Ayer Co Pubs.

Blom, Dorothea. Life Journey of a Quaker Artist. LC 80-80916. 32p. (Orig.). 1980. 2.50x (ISBN 0-87574-232-7). Pendle Hill.

Chalkley, Thomas. The Journal of Thomas Chalkley. LC 75-31088. (Incl. a collection of author's works). Repr. of 1808 ed. 45.00 (ISBN 0-404-13506-4). AMS Pr.

Dalglish, Doris N. People Called Quakers. facsimile ed. LC 78-90628. (Essay Index Reprint Ser). 1938. 15.00 (ISBN 0-8369-1254-3). Ayer Co Pubs.

Friedman, Maurice. The Covenant of Peace. 1983. pap. 2.50x (ISBN 0-87574-110-X, 110). Pendle Hill.

Fuchs, Emil. Christ in Catastrophe. 1983. pap. 2.50x (ISBN 0-87574-049-9, 049). Pendle Hill.

Halle, Anna S. Thoughts Are Free: A Quaker Youth in Nazi Germany. LC 85-61843. (Orig.). 1985. pap. 2.50 (ISBN 0-87574-265-3). Pendle Hill.

Hixon, Robert. Lawrie Tatum: Indian Agent. LC 81-81684. 28p. 1981. pap. 2.50x (ISBN 0-87574-238-6, 238). Pendle Hill.

Ives, Kenneth, et al. Black Quakers: Brief Biographies. (Studies in Quakerism: 12). (Illus.). 118p. (Orig.). 1986. pap. 8.00 (ISBN 0-89670-015-1). Progresiv Pub.

Kenworthy, Leonard. Living in a Larger World: The Life of Murray S. Kenworthy. (Illus.). 120p. (Orig.). 1987. pap. 8.95 (ISBN 0-913408-93-X). Friends United.

McNichols, Donald. Portrait of a Quaker. LC 80-66654. (Illus.). 180p. 1980. 12.50 (ISBN 0-913342-24-6). Barclay Pr.

Murphy, Carol. The Faith of An Ex-Agnostic. 1983. pap. 2.50x (ISBN 0-87574-046-4, 046). Pendle Hill.

Penington, Isaac. The Inward Journey of Isaac Penington. Leach, Robert J., ed. LC 44-280. (Orig.). 1944. pap. 2.50x (ISBN 0-87574-029-4). Pendle Hill.

Raistrick, Arthur. Quakers in Science & Industry. LC 68-18641. (Illus.). 1968. Repr. of 1950 ed. 35.00x (ISBN 0-678-05622-6). Kelley.

Reynolds, Reginald. John Woolman & the Twentieth Century. 1983. pap. 2.50x (ISBN 0-87574-096-0, 096). Pendle Hill.
Smuck, Harold. Friends in East Africa. 120p. (Orig.). 1987. pap. 8.95 (ISBN 0-913408-92-1). Friends United.
Szittya, Ruth O. That's My Brother. LC 82-70603. (Illus.). 32p. (Orig.). 1982. pap. 3.95 (ISBN 0-913408-74-3). Friends United.

FRIENDS, SOCIETY OF–DOCTRINAL AND CONTROVERSIAL WORKS

Brinton, Howard. Light & Life in the Fourth Gospel. LC 76-128679. (Orig.). 1971. pap. 2.50x (ISBN 0-87574-179-7). Pendle Hill.
Brinton, Howard H. Evolution & the Inward Light. LC 77-137101. (Orig.). 1970. pap. 2.50x (ISBN 0-87574-173-8). Pendle Hill.
Broyn, Severyn. Quaker Testimonies & Economic Alternatives. LC 80-80915. 35p. pap. 2.50x (ISBN 0-87574-231-9). Pendle Hill.
Fox, George. The Works of George Fox, Vols. 1-8. Incl. Vols. 1 & 2. A Journal or Historical Account of the Life, Travels, Sufferings, Christian Experiences & Labour of Love in the Work of the Ministry, of That Ancient, Eminent, & Faithful Servant of Jesus Christ, George Fox. LC 75-16194. Vol. 1 (ISBN 0-404-09351-5). Vol. 2 (ISBN 0-404-09352-3); Vol. 3. The Great Mystery of the Great Whore Unfolded. LC 75-16195. 616p (ISBN 0-404-09353-1); Vols. 4-6. Gospel Truth Demonstrated, in a Collection of Doctrinal Books, Given Forth by That Faithful Minister of Jesus Christ, George Fox. LC 75-16199. Vol. 4 (ISBN 0-404-09354-X). Vol. 5 (ISBN 0-404-09355-8). Vol. 6 (ISBN 0-404-09356-6); Vols. 7 & 8. A Collection of Many Select & Christian Epistles, Letters & Testimonies. LC 75-16207. Vol. 7 (ISBN 0-404-09357-4). Vol. 8 (ISBN 0-404-09358-2). Repr. of 1831 ed. Set. 320.00 (ISBN 0-404-09350-7); 40.00 ea. AMS Pr.
Silcock, Thomas H. Words & Testimonies. LC 72-80097. (Orig.). 1972. pap. 2.50x (ISBN 0-87574-186-X). Pendle Hill.
Thurman, Howard. The Search for Common Ground. 108p. 1986. pap. 7.95 (ISBN 0-913408-94-8). Friends United.
Weisser, Thomas H. Anti-Trinitarianism of Early Quakers. 39p. 2.00 (ISBN 0-317-40412-1). Tom Weisser.
Wilson, Dan. An Opening Way. LC 61-11637. (Orig.). 1961. pap. 2.50x (ISBN 0-87574-113-4, 113). Pendle Hill.

FRIENDS, SOCIETY OF–EDUCATION

Brinton, Howard. The Pendle Hill Idea. LC 50-11234. (Orig.). 1950. pap. 2.50x (ISBN 0-87574-055-3). Pendle Hill.
Brinton, Howard H. Quaker Education in Theory & Practice. rev. ed. LC 58-12843. (Orig.). 1940. pap. 15.00x (ISBN 0-87574-009-X). Pendle Hill.
Heath, Douglas. Why a Friends School. LC 75-81158. (Orig.). 1969. pap. 2.50x (ISBN 0-87574-164-9). Pendle Hill.
Heath, Douglas H. The Peculiar Mission of a Friends School. LC 79-84919. 1979. pap. 2.50x (ISBN 0-87574-225-4). Pendle Hill.
Homan, Walter J. Children & Quakerism. LC 70-169387. (Family in America Ser). 180p. 1972. Repr. of 1939 ed. 14.00 (ISBN 0-405-03864-X). Ayer Co Pubs.
Loukes, Harold. Friends & Their Children: A Study in Quaker Education. LC 79-12928. 1979. Repr. of 1958 ed. lib. bdg. 22.50x (ISBN 0-313-21150-7, LOFT). Greenwood.
Stewart, W. A. Quakers & Education. LC 76-115330. 1971. Repr. of 1953 ed. 32.50x (ISBN 0-8046-1121-1, Pub. by Kennikat). Assoc Faculty Pr.
Woody, Thomas. Early Quaker Education in Pennsylvania. LC 77-177623. (Columbia University. Teachers College. Contributions to Education Ser.: No. 105). Repr. of 1920 ed. 22.50 (ISBN 0-404-55105-X). AMS Pr.
--Early Quaker Education in Pennsylvania. LC 72-89255. (American Education: Its Men, Institutions & Ideas, Ser. 1). 1969. Repr. of 1920 ed. 17.50 (ISBN 0-405-01493-7). Ayer Co Pubs.

FRIENDS, SOCIETY OF–FICTION, JUVENILE

Vernon, Louise A. Key to the Prison. LC 86-11054. (Illus.). 144p. 1968. 4.50 (ISBN 0-8361-1813-8). Herald Pr.

FRIENDS, SOCIETY OF–HISTORY

Bacon, Margaret H. The Quiet Rebels: The Story of the Quakers in America. 250p. 1985. lib. bdg. 24.95 (ISBN 0-86571-058-9); pap. 8.95 (ISBN 0-86571-057-0). New Soc Pubs.
Barbour, Hugh. The Quakers in Puritan England. LC 85-6963. 300p. 1985. pap. 14.95 (ISBN 0-913408-87-5). Friends United.
Bauman, Richard. Let Your Words Be Few: Symbolism of Speaking & Silence Among Seventeenth Century Quakers. LC 83-1982. (Cambridge Studies in Oral & Literate Culture Ser.: No. 8). 208p. 1984. 34.50 (ISBN 0-521-25506-6); pap. 10.95 (ISBN 0-521-27514-8). Cambridge U Pr.
Benjamin, Philip S. The Philadelphia Quakers in the Industrial Age, 1865-1920. LC 75-22967. 309p. 1976. 19.95 (ISBN 0-87722-086-7). Temple U Pr.
Best, Mary A. Rebel Saints. facs. ed. LC 68-55839. (Essay Index Reprint Ser). 1925. 18.00 (ISBN 0-8369-0205-X). Ayer Co Pubs.
Bowden, James. The History of the Society of Friends in America, 2 vols. in 1. LC 73-38440. (Religion in America, Ser. 2). 870p. 1972. Repr. of 1854 ed. 58.50 (ISBN 0-405-04061-X). Ayer Co Pubs.
Brinton, Anna. Toward Undiscovered Ends. 1983. pap. 5.00x (ISBN 0-87574-062-6, 062). Pendle Hill.
Brinton, Howard H. Friends for Three Hundred Years. LC 52-5424. (Orig.). 1965. pap. 4.00 (ISBN 0-87574-903-8). Pendle Hill.
Brock, Peter. Pioneers of a Peaceable Kingdom: The Quaker Peace Testimony from the Colonial Era to the First World War. 1970. pap. 12.95x (ISBN 0-691-00573-7). Princeton U Pr.
Cadbury, Henry J. Quaker Relief During the Siege of Boston. 1983. pap. 2.50x (ISBN 0-686-43965-1, 004). Pendle Hill.
Chu, Jonathan M. Neighbors, Friends, or Madmen: The Puritan Adjustment to Quakerism in Seventeenth-Century Massachusetts Bay. LC 84-29035. (Contributions to the Study of Religion Ser.: No. 14). xiii, 207p. 1985. lib. bdg. 29.95 (ISBN 0-313-24809-5, CNE/). Greenwood.
Cox, Gray. Bearing Witness: Quaker Process & a Culture of Peace. LC 85-61133. 32p. (Orig.). 1985. pap. 2.50x (ISBN 0-87574-262-9). Pendle Hill.
Elkinton, Russell J. & Clark, Robert A. The Quaker Heritage in Medicine. (Illus.). 1978. pap. 3.95 (ISBN 0-910286-68-X). Boxwood.
Foulds, Elfrida V. Let Your Lives Speak. 1983. pap. 2.50x (ISBN 0-87574-071-5, 071). Pendle Hill.
Gorman, George. The Society of Friends. 1978. pap. 3.15 (ISBN 0-08-021412-6). Pergamon.
Hallowell, Richard P. The Quaker Invasion of Massachusetts. 13.50 (ISBN 0-8369-7139-6, 7972). Ayer Co Pubs.
Hirst, Margaret E. The Quakers in Peace & War: An Account of Their Peace Principles & Practice. LC 73-137545. (Peace Movement in America Ser). 560p. 1972. Repr. of 1923 ed. lib. bdg. 32.95x (ISBN 0-89198-073-3). Ozer.
Ingle, H. Larry. Quakers in Conflict: The Hicksite Reformation. LC 86-1528. 330p. 1986. text ed. 29.95x (ISBN 0-87049-501-1). U of Tenn Pr.
Jones, Rufus M. The Later Periods of Quakerism, 2 vols. LC 74-109758. 1921. Repr. Set. lib. bdg. 95.00x (ISBN 0-8371-4248-2, JOQU). Greenwood.
Lloyd, Arnold. Quaker Social History: Sixteen Sixty-Nine to Seventeen Thirty-Eight. LC 79-4398. 1979. Repr. of 1950 ed. lib. bdg. 22.50x (ISBN 0-313-20943-X, LLQU). Greenwood.
Marietta, Jack D. The Reformation of American Quakerism, 1748-1783. LC 83-23502. 352p. 1984. 28.95 (ISBN 0-8122-7922-0). U of Pa Pr.
Milner, Clyde A., II. With Good Intentions: Quaker Work among the Pawnees, Otos, & Omahas in the 1870's. LC 81-16238. (Illus.). xvi, 246p. 1982. 21.50x (ISBN 0-8032-3066-4). U of Nebr Pr.
Minear, Mark. Richmond Eighteen Eighty-Seven: A Quaker Drama Unfolds. 150p. 1987. pap. 5.95 (ISBN 0-913408-98-0). Friends United.
Oats, William N. A Question of Survival: Quakers in Australia in the Nineteenth Century. LC 84-2351. (Illus.). 409p. 1985. text ed. 35.00x (ISBN 0-7022-1708-5). U of Queensland Pr.
Penn, William. The Rise & Progress of the People Called Quakers. 1977. pap. 2.95 (ISBN 0-913408-32-8). Friends United.
Pringle, Cyrus. Civil War Diary of Cyrus Pringle: Record of Quaker Conscience. LC 62-18328. Orig. Title: Record of a Quaker Conscience. (Orig.). 1962. pap. 2.50x (ISBN 0-87574-122-3, 122). Pendle Hill.
Rauman, Richard. For the Reputation of Truth: Politics, Religion, & Conflict Among the Pennsylvanian Quakers, 1750-1800. LC 79-143626. pap. 70.00 (ISBN 0-317-39712-5, 2025828). Bks Demand UMI.
Reynolds, Reginald. The Wisdom of John Woolman: With a Selection from His Writings As a Guide to the Seekers of Today. LC 79-8724. xii, 178p. 1981. Repr. of 1948 ed. lib. bdg. 22.50x (ISBN 0-313-22190-1, REJW). Greenwood.
Russell, Elbert. History of Quakerism. LC 79-53169. 612p. 1980. pap. 14.95 (ISBN 0-913408-52-2). Friends United.
Seadle, Michael. Quakers in Nazi Germany. (Studies in Quakerism: No. 5). 44p. (Orig.). 1978. pap. 2.00 (ISBN 0-89670-006-2). Progresiv Pub.
Smith, Hannah W. The Unselfishness of God & How I Discovered It. (The Higher Christian Life Ser.). 312p. 1985. lib. bdg. 40.00 (ISBN 0-8240-6443-7). Garland Pub.
Soderlund, Jean R. Quakers & Slavery: A Divided Spirit. LC 85-42707. (Illus.). 240p. 1985. text ed. 27.50x (ISBN 0-691-04732-4). Princeton U Pr.
Tjossem, Wilmer L. Quaker Sloopers: From the Fjords to the Prairies. LC 84-80195. 80p. 1984. pap. 8.95 (ISBN 0-913408-85-9). Friends United.
Tolles, Frederick. Quakers & the Atlantic Culture. 1980. Repr. of 1960 ed. lib. bdg. 16.00x (ISBN 0-374-97949-9, Octagon). Hippocrene Bks.
Tolles, Frederick B. Meeting House & Counting House. (Illus.). 1963. pap. 8.95 (ISBN 0-393-00211-X, Norton Lib). Norton.
Trueblood, D. Elton. People Called Quakers. LC 66-15046. 1971. pap. 9.95 (ISBN 0-913408-02-6). Friends United.
Vipont, Elfrida. The Story of Quakerism. rev. ed. LC 77-71638. (Illus.). 1977. pap. 9.95 (ISBN 0-913408-31-X). Friends United.
Weisser, Thomas H. Anti-Trinitarianism of Early Quakers. 39p. 2.00 (ISBN 0-317-40412-1). Tom Weisser.
Wilson, Roger. Relief & Reconstruction. 1983. pap. 2.50x (ISBN 0-87574-022-7, 022). Pendle Hill.
Worrall, Arthur J. Quakers in the Colonial Northeast. LC 79-63086. 248p. 1980. 20.00x (ISBN 0-87451-174-7). U Pr of New Eng.

FRIENDS, SOCIETY OF–SERMONS

Jones, Rufus M. Thou Dost Open up My Life. LC 63-11819. (Orig.). 1963. pap. 2.50x (ISBN 0-87574-127-4). Pendle Hill.

FRIENDS, SOCIETY OF–GREAT BRITAIN

Bittle, Willliam G. James Nayler: The Quaker Indicted by Parliament. 248p. (Orig.). 1987. pap. 14.95x (ISBN 1-85072-015-0). Friends United.
Crowther-Hunt, Norman. Two Early Political Associations: The Quakers & the Dissenting Deputies in the Age of Sir Robert Walpole. LC 78-23805. 1979. Repr. of 1961 ed. lib. bdg. 24.75x (ISBN 0-313-21036-5, HUTW). Greenwood.
Foulds, Elfrida V. The Candle of the Lord. pap. 2.50x (ISBN 0-87574-248-3, 248). Pendle Hill.
Pratt, David H. English Quakers & the First Industrial Revolution: A Study of the Quaker Community in Four Industrial Counties; York, Warwick, & Gloucester, 1750-1830. LC 84-46009. (British Economic History Ser.). 236p. 1985. lib. bdg. 28.00 (ISBN 0-8240-6689-8). Garland Pub.
Raistrick, Arthur. Quakers in Science & Industry. LC 68-18641. (Illus.). 1968. Repr. of 1950 ed. 35.00x (ISBN 0-678-05622-6). Kelley.
Reay, Barry. The Quakers & the English Revolution. LC 84-22355. 200p. 1985. 22.50 (ISBN 0-312-65808-7). St Martin.
Wright, Luella M. Literary Life of the Early Friends, 1650-1725. LC 32-25426. Repr. of 1932 ed. 19.50 (ISBN 0-404-07046-9). AMS Pr.

FRIENDS OF GOD (GOTTESFREUNDE)

Seesholtz, Anna G. Friends of God: Practical Mystics of the Fourteenth Century. 1970. Repr. of 1934 ed. 14.50 (ISBN 0-404-05697-0). AMS Pr.

FRIENDSHIP

see also Love

Anderson, Debby. Being a Friend Means... (Sparkler Bks.). (Illus.). 32p. 1986. plastic comb bndg. 2.95 (ISBN 0-89191-932-5, 59329, Chariot Bks). Cook.
Beilenson, Nick, ed. Gift of Friendship. LC 86-63857. (Illus.). 64p. 1987. 5.95 (ISBN 0-88088-216-6). Peter Pauper.
Bowman, Jayne, compiled by. The World of Friendship. (Illus.). 1983. 8.00 (ISBN 0-8378-1801-X). Gibson.
Briscoe, Jill. Thank You for Being a Friend. 192p. (Orig.). 1981. pap. 5.95 (ISBN 0-310-21851-9, 9261P). Zondervan.
Bustanoby, Andre. Just Friends? 160p. (Orig.). 1985. pap. 6.95 (ISBN 0-310-45431-X, 9254P). Zondervan.
Coleman, William. Friends Forever. 160p. (Orig.). 1987. pap. 5.95 (ISBN 0-87123-959-0). Bethany Hse.
Crockett, William J. Friendship: Voices from the Heart. 15p. 1985. pap. 3.00 (ISBN 0-934383-04-9). Pride Prods.
Daniels, Althea. The Friendship Factor Study Guide. 32p. (Orig.). 1984. pap. 0.95 (ISBN 0-8066-2079-X, 10-2413). Augsburg.
Dockrey, Karen. Friends: Finding & Keeping Them. LC 85-12783. 1985. pap. 4.50 (ISBN 0-8054-5343-1). Broadman.
Engstrom, Ted W. & Larson, Robert C. The Fine Art of Friendship. 176p. 1985. 9.95 (ISBN 0-8407-5419-1). Nelson.
Francis, Mary. But I Have Called You Friends. 1974. 4.95 (ISBN 0-8199-0500-3). Franciscan Herald.
Griffin, Em. Making Friends & Making Them Count. LC 87-2619. (Illus.). 220p. (Orig.). 1987. pap. 7.95 (ISBN 0-87784-996-X). Inter-Varsity.
Grosso, Stephan. Harry, My Friend. LC 85-82391. 80p. 1986. pap. 2.95 (ISBN 0-89243-247-0). Liguori Pubns.
Heinzmann, Josef. Faith is Friendship. 146p. 1983. pap. 6.95 (ISBN 0-8189-0451-8). Alba.
Hill, Elsie Isensce & Dudley, Cliff. Abused But Chosen. LC 83-61439. 144p. 1983. 4.95 (ISBN 0-89221-106-7). New Leaf.
Hinnebusch, Paul. Friendship in the Lord. LC 73-90411. 144p. 1974. pap. 2.75 (ISBN 0-87793-065-1). Ave Maria.
Howell, Clinton T., ed. Better Than Gold. (Illus.). 200p. 1984. 12.95 (ISBN 0-8407-5388-8). Nelson.
Iannaci, Tina. For a Special Friend. (Greeting Book Line Ser.). 24p. (Orig.). 1986. pap. 1.50 (ISBN 0-89622-303-5). Twenty-Third.
Ingram, Kristen J. Being a Christian Friend. 112p. 1985. pap. 5.95 (ISBN 0-8170-1084-X). Judson.
Inrig, Gary. Quality Friendship. LC 81-38379. 192p. (Orig.). 1981. pap. 5.95 (ISBN 0-8024-2891-6). Moody.
Kiesling, Christopher. Celibacy, Prayer & Friendship: A Making-Sense-Out-of-Life Approach. LC 77-25084. 1978. pap. 7.95 (ISBN 0-8189-0365-1). Alba.
Larsen, Sandy. Sticking Together: Friendships for Life. (Bible Discovery Guides for Teen Campers Ser.). 32p. (Orig.). (YA) 1987. pap. 1.50 camper (ISBN 0-87788-787-X); pap. 1.50 counselor (ISBN 0-87788-788-8). Shaw Pubs.
Meilaender, Gilbert C. Friendship: A Study in Theological Ethics. LC 81-50459. 118p. 1981. text ed. 10.95 (ISBN 0-268-00956-2). U of Notre Dame Pr.
Miller, Kevin, ed. Friends: Becoming a Friend Finder & Keeper. (Senior High Pacesetter Ser.). 64p. 1986. pap. 7.95 (ISBN 0-89191-343-2). Cook.
Naylor, Phyllis R. Getting Along with Your Friends. LC 79-22999. (Illus.). 1980. 8.75g (ISBN 0-687-14122-2). Abingdon.
Ogilvie, Lloyd J. The Beauty of Friendship. LC 80-80463. 1980. pap. 5.95 (ISBN 0-89081-243-8). Harvest Hse.
Ripple, Paula. Called to Be Friends. LC 80-67402. 160p. (Orig.). 1980. pap. 3.95 (ISBN 0-87793-212-3). Ave Maria.
Scholem, Gershom. Walter Benjamin: The Story of a Friendship. Zohn, Harry, tr. from Ger. LC 81-11790. (Illus.). 240p. 1981. 13.95 (ISBN 0-8276-0197-2). Jewish Pubns.
Sternberg, Patricia. Be My Friend: The Art of Good Relationships. LC 83-10254. 192p. 1983. pap. 8.95 (ISBN 0-664-26007-1, A Bridgebooks Publication). Westminster.
Stone, J. David & Keefauver, Larry. Friend to Friend: How You Can Help a Friend Through a Problem. LC 83-80942. (Illus.). 80p. (Orig.). 1983. pap. 5.95 (ISBN 0-936664-11-8). Group Bks.
Welter, Paul. How to Help a Friend. 1983. pap. 8.95 (ISBN 0-8423-1505-5); 2.95 (ISBN 0-8423-1504-7). Tyndale.
Willcuts, Jack L. Why Friends Are Friends. 90p. (Orig.). 1984. pap. 3.95 (ISBN 0-913342-45-9). Barclay Pr.
Words of Friendship. (Words of... Ser.). (Illus.). 48p. 1983. 3.95 (ISBN 0-8407-5334-9). Nelson.

FULAH EMPIRE

Hiskett, Mervyn. The Sword of Truth: The Life & Times of the Shehu Usuman Dan Fodio. (Illus.). 1973. pap. 3.00x (ISBN 0-19-501647-5). Oxford U Pr.

FULGENTIUS, FABIUS PLANCIADES

Friebel, Otto. Fulgentius, der Mythograph und Bischof. pap. 15.00 (ISBN 0-384-16880-9). Johnson Repr.

FULGENTIUS, SAINT, BP. OF RUSPA, 468-533

Friebel, Otto. Fulgentius, der Mythograph und Bischof. pap. 15.00 (ISBN 0-384-16880-9). Johnson Repr.

FULLER, THOMAS, 1608-1661

Houghton, Walter E., Jr. Formation of Thomas Fuller's Holy & Profane States. (Harvard Studies in English: Vol. 19). 1969. Repr. of 1938 ed. 23.00 (ISBN 0-384-24390-8). Johnson Repr.
Jessop, Augustus. Wise Words & Quaint Counsels of Thomas Fuller: Selected & Arranged with a Short Sketch of the Author's Life. 1979. Repr. of 1892 ed. lib. bdg. 45.00 (ISBN 0-8492-5602-X). R West.

FUNDAMENTAL THEOLOGY

see Apologetics

FUNDAMENTALISM

see also Evangelicalism; Modernism; Modernist-Fundamentalist Controversy

Beale, David O. In Pursuit of Purity: A History of American Fundamentalism since 1850. 1986. 15.95 (ISBN 0-89084-351-1); pap. 12.95 (ISBN 0-89084-350-3). Bob Jones Univ Pr.
Bridges, Horace J. God of Fundamentalism & Others Studies. facs. ed. LC 79-86733. (Essay Index Reprint Ser.). 1925. 19.00 (ISBN 0-8369-1249-7). Ayer Co Pubs.

Caplan, Lionel, ed. Studies in Religious Fundamentalism. 240p. 1987. 39.50 (ISBN 0-88706-518-X); pap. 14.95 (ISBN 0-88706-519-8). State U NY Pr.
Clabaugh, Gary K. Thunder on the Right: The Protestant Fundamentalists. LC 74-9551. 283p. 1974. 19.95x (ISBN 0-88229-108-4). Nelson-Hall.
Cole, Stewart G. History of Fundamentalism. LC 70-138107. 1971. Repr. of 1931 ed. lib. bdg. 22.50x (ISBN 0-8371-5683-1, COHF). Greenwood.
Daschbach, Edwin. Interpreting Scripture: A Catholic Response to Fundamentalism. 144p. 1985. pap. 6.95 (ISBN 0-697-02110-6). Wm C Brown.
Dobson, Ed, et al. The Fundamentalist Phenomenon: The Resurgence of Conservative Christianity. 2nd ed. pap. 7.95 (ISBN 0-8010-2958-9). Baker Bk.
Gasper, Louis. The Fundamentalist Movement. (Twin Brooks Ser.). 181p. (Orig.). 1981. pap. 6.95 (ISBN 0-8010-3769-7). Baker Bk.
Gilles, Anthony E. Fundamentalism: What Every Catholic Needs to Know. (Illus.). 72p. (Orig.). 1985. pap. text ed. 3.75 (ISBN 0-86716-043-8). St Anthony Mess Pr.
Hill, Samuel S. & Owen, Dennis E. The New Religious-Political Right in America. LC 81-20661. 160p. 1982. 10.95 (ISBN 0-687-27867-8). Abingdon.
Ide, Arthur F. Unholy Rollers: The Selling of Jesus. LC 85-19883. (Illus.). 120p. 1985. pap. 5.95 (ISBN 0-935175-01-6). Lib Arts Pr.
Malachy, Yona. American Fundamentalism & Israel: The Relation of Fundamentalist Churches to Zionism & the State of Israel. 178p. 1978. pap. text ed. 10.50x (Pub. by Magnes Pr Israel). Humanities.
Neuhaus, Richard J. & Cromartie, Michael, eds. Confronting This World: Evangelicals, Fundamentalists, & Politics. (Orig.). 1986. text ed. 22.00 (ISBN 0-89633-107-5); pap. text ed. 14.00 (ISBN 0-89633-108-3). Ethics & Public Policy.
Packer, James I. Fundamentalism & the Word of God. 1958. pap. 6.95 (ISBN 0-8028-1147-7). Eerdmans.
Rausch, David A. Zionism Within Early American Fundamentalism, 1878-1918: A Convergence of Two Traditions. LC 79-66371. (Texts & Studies in Religion: Vol. 4). viii, 386p. 1980. 59.95x (ISBN 0-88946-875-3). E Mellen.
Selvidge, Marla J., ed. Fundamentalism Today: What Makes It So Attractive? 144p. (Orig.). 1984. pap. 7.95 (ISBN 0-87178-297-9). Brethren.
Streiker, Lowell D. The Gospel Time Bomb. 200p. 20.95 (ISBN 0-87975-259-9). Prometheus Bks.
Trigg, Joseph W. & Sachs, William L. Of One Body: Renewal Movements in the Church. LC 86-2788. 168p. (Orig.). 1986. pap. 9.95 (ISBN 0-8042-0677-5). John Knox.

FUNERAL MUSIC

Gregory Nazianzen, St. & Ambrose, St. Funeral Orations. LC 67-28586. (Fathers of the Church Ser: Vol. 22). 344p. 1953. 18.95x (ISBN 0-8132-0022-9). Cath U Pr.
Leaver, Robin A. Music in the Service of the Church: The Funeral Sermon for Heinrich Schuetz. 68p. (Orig.). 1985. pap. 6.75 (ISBN 0-570-01331-3, 99-1261). Concordia.

FUNERAL RITES AND CEREMONIES

see also Ancestor Worship; Cremation; Funeral Service; Mourning Customs

Bendann, Effie. Death Customs: An Analytical Study of Burial Rites. 1971. 37.00x (ISBN 0-8103-3733-9). Gale.
--Death Customs: An Analytical Study of Burial Rites. 59.95 (ISBN 0-8490-0010-6). Gordon Pr.
Bernardin, Joseph B. Burial Services: Revised & Updated. 1980. casebound 14.95 (ISBN 0-8192-1267-9). Morehouse.
Bloch, Maurice & Parry, Jonathan, eds. Death & the Regeneration of Life. LC 82-9467. 256p. 1982. 34.50 (ISBN 0-521-24875-2); pap. 11.95 (ISBN 0-521-27037-5). Cambridge U Pr.
Book of the Dead Staff. The Chapters of Coming Forth by Day, 3 vols. LC 73-18833. Repr. of 1910 ed. 49.50 set (ISBN 0-404-11303-6). AMS Pr.
Bowman, LeRoy E. The American Funeral: A Study in Guilt, Extravagance, & Sublimity. LC 72-14083. 181p. 1973. Repr. of 1959 ed. lib. bdg. 22.50x (ISBN 0-8371-6749-3, BOFU). Greenwood.
Budge, E. A. Mummy. 2nd ed. LC 64-13391. (Illus.). 1894. 25.00 (ISBN 0-8196-0139-X). Biblo.
Budge, E. Wallis. The Liturgy of Funerary Offerings: The Egyptian Texts with English Translations. LC 72-83744. (Illus.). Repr. of 1909 ed. 22.00 (ISBN 0-405-08322-X, Blom Pubns). Ayer Co Pubs.
Ch'en Kou-Chun. Studies in Marriage & Funerals of Taiwan Aborigines. (Asian Folklore & Social Life Monograph: No. 4). (Chinese.). 1970. 14.00 (ISBN 0-89986-007-9). Oriental Bk Store.
Continental Assocation of Funeral & Memorial Societies, Inc & Memorial Society Association of Canadacompiled by. Handbook for Funeral & Memorial Societies. Fleming, Peggy, ed. LC 72-7963. 1976. pap. 3.50 (ISBN 0-686-18088-7). Continent Assn Funeral.
Cumont, Franz. Recherches sur le Symbolisme Funeraire des Romains. facsimile ed. LC 75-10632. (Ancient Religion & Mythology Ser.). (Fr., Illus.). 1976. Repr. of 1942 ed. 57.50x (ISBN 0-405-07007-1). Ayer Co Pubs.
Curl, James S. The Victorian Celebration of Death: The Architecture & Planning of the 19th-Century Necropolis. LC 70-184048. 222p. 1972. 35.00x (ISBN 0-8103-2000-2). Gale.
Ellis, Hilda R. Road to Hell: A Study of the Conception of the Dead in Old Norse Literature. LC 68-23286. (Illus.). 1968. Repr. of 1943 ed. lib. bdg. 22.50x (ISBN 0-8371-0070-4, ELRH). Greenwood.
Fleming, Stuart, et al. The Egyptian Mummy: Secrets & Science. (University Museum Handbook Ser.: No. 1). (Illus.). x, 93p. (Orig.). 1980. pap. 10.00x (ISBN 0-934718-38-5). Univ Mus of U Pa.
Funeral Liturgy Planning Guide. 1984. pap. 1.00 (ISBN 0-8146-1362-4). Liturgical Pr.
Giesey, R. E. The Royal Funeral Ceremony in Renaissance France. viii, 240p. (Orig.). 1960. pap. text ed. 40.00x (Pub. by Droz Switzerland). Coronet Bks.
Goody, Jack. Death, Property, & the Ancestors: A Study of the Mortuary Customs of the LoDagaa of West Africa. (Illus.). 1962. 32.50x (ISBN 0-8047-0068-0). Stanford U Pr.
Gorer, Geoffrey. Death, Grief, & Mourning. Kastenbaum, Robert, ed. LC 76-19573. (Death & Dying Ser.). (Illus.). 1977. Repr. of 1965 ed. lib. bdg. 24.50x (ISBN 0-405-09571-6). Ayer Co Pubs.
Huntington, R. & Metcalf, P. Celebrations of Death. LC 79-478. (Illus.). 1979. 39.50 (ISBN 0-521-22531-0); pap. 10.95x (ISBN 0-521-29540-8). Cambridge U Pr.
International Committee on English in the Liturgy, tr. Rite of Funerals. blue cloth 8.50 (ISBN 0-89942-350-7, 350/22). Catholic Bk Pub.
Metcalf, Peter. A Borneo Journey into Death: Berawan Eschatology from Its Rituals. LC 82-8460. (Symbol & Culture Ser.). (Illus.). 304p. 1982. 26.00x (ISBN 0-8122-7849-6). U of Pa Pr.
Poovey, W. A., ed. Planning a Christian Funeral: A Minister's Guide. LC 78-52198. 1978. pap. 7.95 (ISBN 0-8066-1668-7, 10-4990). Augsburg.
Rosenblatt, Paul C., et al. Grief & Mourning in Cross-Cultural Perspective. LC 76-29270. (Comparative Studies Ser.). 242p. 1976. pap. 7.00x (ISBN 0-87536-334-2). HRAFP.
Rutherford, Richard. The Death of a Christian: The Rite of Funerals. (Studies in the Reformed Rites of the Catholic Church: Vol. 7). 1980. pap. 9.95 (ISBN 0-916134-40-7). Pueblo Pub Co.
Toynbee, J. M. Death & Burial in the Roman World. Scullard, H. H., ed. LC 77-120603. (Aspects of Greek & Roman Life Ser). (Illus.). 336p. 1971. 35.00x (ISBN 0-8014-0593-9). Cornell U Pr.
Wagner, Johannes, ed. Reforming the Rites of Death. LC 68-20845. (Concilium Ser.: Vol. 32). 189p. 7.95. Paulist Pr.

FUNERAL SERMONS

Allen, R. Earl. Funeral Source Book. (Preaching Helps Ser.). (Orig.). 1984. pap. 3.50 (ISBN 0-8010-0076-9). Baker Bk.
Bansemer, Richard. Day Full of Grace. Sherer, Michael, ed. (Orig.). 1987. pap. 5.95 (ISBN 0-89536-854-4, 7813). CSS of Ohio.
Bedwell, B. L. Sermons for Funeral Occasions. 1960. pap. 2.00 (ISBN 0-88027-029-2). Firm Foun Pub.
D'Alembert, Jean. Eulogies. 59.95 (ISBN 0-8490-0137-4). Gordon Pr.
Doyle, Charles H. Fifty Funeral Homilies. 110p. 1984. pap. 10.00 spiral bdg. (ISBN 0-87061-094-5). Chr Classics.
Ford, Herschel W. Simple Sermons for Funeral Services. 54p. 1985. pap. 2.95 (ISBN 0-8010-3514-7). Baker Bk.
In Sure & Certain Hope: Funeral Messages Anthology. 1986. 6.25 (ISBN 0-89536-785-8, 6803). CSS of Ohio.
Meyer, F. B., et al. Funeral Sermons & Outlines. (Pulpit Library). 1984. pap. 3.50 (ISBN 0-8010-5873-2). Baker Bk.
Wood, Charles R., ed. Sermon Outlines for Funeral Services. 64p. 1970. pap. 2.95 (ISBN 0-8254-4007-6). Kregel.

FUNERAL SERVICE

see also Funeral Rites and Ceremonies

Champlin, Joseph M. Through Death to Life. LC 78-74436. 88p. 1979. pap. 1.95 (ISBN 0-87793-175-5). Ave Maria.
Irion, Paul E. The Funeral: Vestige or Value? Kastenaum, Robert, ed. LC 76-19578. (Death & Dying Ser.). 1977. Repr. lib. bdg. 22.00x (ISBN 0-405-09575-9). Ayer Co Pubs.
Lamont, Corliss. Humanist Funeral Service. 3rd ed. LC 77-76001. 48p. 1977. pap. 6.95 (ISBN 0-87975-090-1). Prometheus Bks.
Martin, Edward A. Psychology of Funeral Service. 6th ed. text ed. 12.50 (ISBN 0-686-20530-8). E A Martin.
Office of Worship for the Presbyterian Church (U. S. A.) & the Cumberland Presbyterian Church. The Funeral: A Service of Witness to the Resurrection. (Supplemental Liturgical Resource Ser.: 4). 120p. (Orig.). 1986. pap. write for info. (ISBN 0-664-24034-8). Westminster.
Order of Christian Funerals: General Introduction & Pastoral Notes. (Liturgy Documentary Ser.: No. 8). 72p. (Orig.). Date not set. pap. 5.95 (ISBN 1-55586-990-4). US Catholic.
Rest, Friedrich. Funeral Handbook. 144p. 1982. 9.95 (ISBN 0-8170-0929-9). Judson.
Wagner, Johannes, ed. Reforming the Rites of Death. LC 68-20845. (Concilium Ser.: Vol. 32). 189p. 7.95. Paulist Pr.

FUNK, JOHN FRETZ, BP. 1835-1930

Wenger, J. C. Bless the Lord, O My Soul. LC 64-23575. (Illus.). 264p. 1964. 9.95 (ISBN 0-8361-1497-3). Herald Pr.

FUNNIES

see Comic Books, Strips, etc.

FUTURE LIFE

see also Children–Death and Future State; Eschatology; Eternity; Future Punishment; Immortality; Resurrection; Soul

Alger, William R. Destiny of the Soul: Critical History of the Doctrine of a Future Life, 2 Vols. 10th ed. LC 68-19263. 1968. Repr. of 1880 ed. Set. lib. bdg. 43.25x (ISBN 0-8371-0003-8, ALDS). Greenwood.
Almeder, Robert. Beyond Death: Evidence for Life after Death. 176p. 1987. 24.50x (ISBN 0-398-05327-8). C C Thomas.
Bachelder, Robert S. Between Dying & Birth. 1983. 5.95 (ISBN 0-89536-623-1, 0236). CSS of Ohio.
Badham, Paul & Badham, Linda. Immortality or Extinction? LC 81-17595. (Library of Philosophy & Religion). 156p. 1982. text ed. 28.50x (ISBN 0-389-20251-7, 07055). B&N Imports.
Barker, A. Trevor, ed. Mahatma Letters to A. P. Sinnett. 3rd ed. 1972. 11.50 (ISBN 0-8356-7013-9). Theos Pub Hse.
Bender, Philip. New Heaven on a New Earth. LC 85-81579. (Faith & Life Bible Studies). 106p. (Orig.). 1985. pap. 4.95 (ISBN 0-87303-106-7). Faith & Life.
Benson, Elizabeth P., ed. Death & the Afterlife in Pre-Columbian America: A Conference at Dumbarton Oaks, October 27, 1973. LC 74-22694. (Illus.). 196p. 1975. 15.00x (ISBN 0-88402-062-2). Dumbarton Oaks.
Bo Yin Ra. The Book on Life Beyond. Reichenbach, Bodo A., tr. from Ger. LC 78-51633. 1978. pap. 5.00 (ISBN 0-915034-02-6). Kober Pr.
Brody, Harry. As Once to Birth I Went, Now I Am Taken Back. 1981. 2.00 (ISBN 0-936814-07-1). New Collage.
Brown, Theo. The Fate of the Dead: A Study in Folk-Eschatology in the West Country After the Reformation. (Folklore Society Mistletoe Ser.). 118p. 1979. 26.50x (ISBN 0-8476-6214-4). Rowman.
Brown, Walton J. Home at Last. (Discovery Ser.). 96p. pap. 5.95 (ISBN 0-317-01321-1). Review & Herald.
Budge, E. A. The Book of the Dead. (Illus.). 992p. 1985. pap. 9.95 (ISBN 1-85063-020-8, Ark Paperbks). Methuen Inc.
Budge, Ernest A. Egyptian Ideas of the Future Life. LC 73-18839. Repr. of 1899 ed. 14.00 (ISBN 0-404-11330-3). AMS Pr.
Case, Charles J. Beyond Time: Ideas of the Great Philosophers on Eternal Existence & Immortality. LC 85-17864. 144p. (Orig.). 1985. lib. bdg. 20.75 (ISBN 0-8191-4933-0); pap. text ed. 8.25 (ISBN 0-8191-4934-9). U Pr of Amer.
Cayce, Edgar & Cayce, Hugh L. God's Other Door & the Continuity of Life. 1976. pap. 2.95 (ISBN 0-87604-007-5). ARE Pr.
Contreras, Edgar. Y Despues de la Muerte, Que? Orig. Title: After Death, What. (Span.). 1988. pap. 4.95 (ISBN 0-8254-1130-0). Kregel.
Cooke, Grace & Cooke, Ivan. The Return of Arthur Conan Doyle. (Illus.). 1963. 9.95 (ISBN 0-85487-037-7). De Vorss.
Cournand, Andre & Levy, Maurice. Shaping the Future: Gaston Berger & the Concept of Prospective. LC 72-78388. (Current Topics of Contemporary Thought Ser.). 314p. 1973. 72.75 (ISBN 0-677-12550-X). Gordon & Breach.
Cribb, C. C. From Now till Eternity. LC 76-21571. 12.95 (ISBN 0-932046-00-2). Manhattan Ltd NC.
--The Horrified & the Glorified. LC 77-70214. pap. 2.95 (ISBN 0-932046-05-3). Manhattan Ltd NC.
Deal, William S. After Death, What? 1977. 1.75 (ISBN 0-686-19329-6). Crusade Pubs.
Dehejia, Vidya. Living & Dying: An Inquiry into the Enigma of Death & After-Life. 1979. 8.95x (ISBN 0-7069-0815-5, Pub. by Vikas India). Advent NY.
DeWolf, L. Harold. Eternal Life: Why We Believe. LC 79-21670. 112p. 1980. pap. 6.95 (ISBN 0-664-24288-X). Westminster.
Eby, Richard E. Tell Them I Am Coming. 1980. pap. 5.95 (ISBN 0-8007-5045-4, Power Bks). Revell.
Ellis, Hilda R. Road to Hell: A Study of the Conception of the Dead in Old Norse Literature. LC 68-23286. (Illus.). 1968. Repr. of 1943 ed. lib. bdg. 22.50x (ISBN 0-8371-0070-4, ELRH). Greenwood.
Fortman, Edmund J. Everlasting Life: Towards a Theology of the Future Life. LC 85-30720. 369p. (Orig.). 1986. pap. 9.95 (ISBN 0-8189-0495-X). Alba.
Greg, William R. Enigmas of Life. LC 72-323. (Essay Index Reprint Ser.). Repr. of 1879 ed. 21.00 (ISBN 0-8369-2794-X). Ayer Co Pubs.
A Guide for the Still Perplexed: Heaven, Bk. I. 65p. (Orig.). 1986. pap. 4.95 (ISBN 0-940733-00-5). Dimona Pr.
Harris, W. T. The Mythology of Plato & Dante & the Future Life. (The Essential Library of the Great Philosophers). (Illus.). 107p. 1983. Repr. of 1896 ed. 71.85 (ISBN 0-89901-091-1). Found Class Reprints.
Hellwig, Monika K. What Are They Saying about Death & Christian Hope? LC 78-61726. 1978. pap. 3.95 (ISBN 0-8091-2165-4). Paulist Pr.
Hendriksen, William. Bible on the Life Hereafter. (Direction Books). 1971. pap. 6.95 (ISBN 0-8010-4022-1). Baker Bk.
Hick, John H. Death & Eternal Life. LC 76-9965. 496p. 1980. pap. text ed. 11.95 (ISBN 0-06-063904-0, RD 332, HarpR). Har-Row.
Hillis, Don. Heaven is Out of This World. (Illus.). 47p. 1982. pap. 2.00 (ISBN 0-89323-032-4). Bible Memory.
Horgan, Paul. Memories of the Future. 216p. 1966. 4.95 (ISBN 0-374-20756-9). FS&G.
Howells, William D., et al. In After Days: Thoughts on Future Life. Kastenaum, Robert, ed. LC 76-19576. (Death & Dying Ser.). (Illus.). 1977. Repr. of 1910 ed. lib. bdg. 24.50x (ISBN 0-405-09574-0). Ayer Co Pubs.
Hudson, Thomas. A Scientific Demonstration of the Future Life. 1979. pap. 2.50 (ISBN 0-89083-464-4). Zebra.
Hughes, Ray H. The Order of Future Events. 1970. pap. 3.50 (ISBN 0-87148-650-4). Pathway Pr.
Johnstone, Parker L. Life, Death & Hereafter. LC 76-21518. 1976. cloth 7.95 (ISBN 0-917802-00-4). Theoscience Found.
Kirk, Joseph E. Death, Resurrection, Immortality. 111p. 1977. 4.00 (ISBN 0-910424-66-7); pap. 3.00 (ISBN 0-910424-67-5). Concordant.
Kung, Hans. Eternal Life: Life after Death as a Medical, Philosophical, & Theological Problem. Quinn, Edward, tr. LC 82-45112. 271p. 1984. 15.95 (ISBN 0-385-18207-4). Doubleday.
LaHaye, Tim. Life in the Afterlife. Tyndale.
La Perchia, Alex. A Spiritual Guide to Eternal Life. LC 77-75258. 89p. 1977. 6.95 (ISBN 0-8022-2203-X). Philos Lib.
Leadbeater. Life after Death. 4.50 (ISBN 0-8356-7148-8). Theos Pub Hse.
Leedy, Kay. Life Never Ends. 141p. pap. 7.95 (ISBN 0-942494-41-5). Coleman Pub.
LeGoff, Jacques. The Birth of Purgatory. Goldhammer, Arthur, tr. LC 83-1108. (Illus.). x, 430p. 1986. pap. 13.95 (ISBN 0-226-47083-0). U of Chicago Pr.
Lindsay, Gordon. Death & the Hereafter. (Sorcery & Spirit World Ser.). 1.25 (ISBN 0-89985-096-0). Christ Nations.
--Life after Death. (Sorcery & Spirit World Ser.). 3.00 (ISBN 0-89985-083-9). Christ Nations.
--Paradise-Abode of the Righteous Dead. (Sorcery & Spirit World Ser.). 1.25 (ISBN 0-89985-085-5). Christ Nations.
--Scenes Beyond the Grave. (Sorcery & Spirit World Ser.). 2.95 (ISBN 0-89985-091-X). Christ Nations.
Lorimer, David. Survival: Body, Mind & Death in the Light of Psychic Experience. 288p. (Orig.). 1984. pap. 12.95 (ISBN 0-7102-0003-X). Methuen Inc.
Lummis, Charles F. My Friend Will. 1972. 3.50 (ISBN 0-87516-161-8). De Vorss.
Maloney, George A. The Everlasting Now. LC 79-57550. 224p. (Orig.). 1980. pap. 3.95 (ISBN 0-87793-201-8). Ave Maria.
Mann, Stella T. Beyond the Darkness. 1972. pap. 2.95 (ISBN 0-87516-054-9). De Vorss.
Mathis, Mary E. A Scriptural Treasury of Eternal Life. 1981. pap. 0.40 (ISBN 0-570-08357-5, 12-2937). Concordia.

Meek, George W. After We Die, What Then? LC 79-90909. (Life's Energy Fields Ser.: Vol. 3). (Illus., Orig.). 1980. 8.95 (ISBN 0-935436-00-6). Metascience.
--After We Die, What Then? rev. ed. LC 79-909. (Illus.). 216p. 1987. pap. 8.95 (ISBN 0-89804-099-X). Ariel OH.
Moore, Marvin. Where Is Bobby Now? (Flame Ser.). 1976. pap. 0.99 (ISBN 0-8127-0106-2). Review & Herald.
Nikhilananda, Swami. Man in Search of Immortality. LC 68-101793. 112p. 4.95 (ISBN 0-911206-12-4). Ramakrishna.
Norman, Ruth E. Your Encounter with Life, Death & Immortality. (Illus.). 1978. pap. 2.00 (ISBN 0-932642-43-8). Unarius Pubns.
Osis, Karlis & Haraldsson, Erlendur. At the Hour of Death. 1985. pap. 3.95 (ISBN 0-380-49486-8, 49486-8, Discus). Avon.
Phillips, John. Exploring the Future. LC 82-557. 400p. 1983. 14.95 (ISBN 0-8407-5275-X). Nelson.
The Philosophy of Life & the Philosophy of Death: Considerations & Anticipations of the Future Universe & of Man's Existence in It. 2nd ed. (Illus.). 1977. 47.25 (ISBN 0-89266-058-9). Am Classical Coll Pr.
Pittenger, Norman. After Death-Life in God. 96p. 1980. 4.95 (ISBN 0-8164-0108-X, HarpR). Har-Row.
Porrath, Samuel. Life Beyond the Final Curtain. 250p. text ed. 17.95 (ISBN 0-88125-083-X). Ktav.
Quadrupani, R. P. Light & Peace. LC 79-67860. 193p. 1980. pap. 3.50 (ISBN 0-89555-133-0). TAN Bks Pubs.
Randolph, Paschal B. After Death: The Immortality of Man. 272p. 1970. write for info. (ISBN 0-932785-00-X). Philos Pub.
Rice, Max M. Your Rewards in Heaven. LC 80-68885. 160p. 1981. pap. 4.95 (ISBN 0-89636-063-6). Accent Bks.
Richards, Hubert J. Death & After: What Will Really Happen? (What Really Happened? Ser.). 1987. pap. 5.95 (ISBN 0-89622-288-8). Twenty-Third.
Riggle, H. M. Beyond the Tomb. 288p. 4.00 (ISBN 0-686-29100-X). Faith Pub Hse.
Rogo, D. Scott. Man Does Survive Death. 1977. pap. 3.95 (ISBN 0-8065-0582-6). Citadel Pr.
Rossier, H. Que Pasa Despues de la Muerte? 2nd ed. Bennett, Gordon H., ed. Bautista, Sara, tr. from Eng. (La Serie Diamante). Tr. of What Happens After Death? (Span., Illus.). 36p. 1982. pap. 0.85 (ISBN 0-942504-07-0). Overcomer Pr.
St. Johns, A. R. No Good-byes: My Search Into Life Beyond Death. 1981. 10.95 (ISBN 0-07-054450-6). McGraw.
Salomon, Michel. Future Life. 384p. 1983. 19.95 (ISBN 0-02-606770-6). Macmillan.
Schwarz, Hans. Beyond the Gates of Death: A Biblical Examination of Evidence for Life After Death. LC 80-67805. 136p. 1981. pap. 6.95 (ISBN 0-8066-1868-X, 10-0647). Augsburg.
Seymour, Richard. The Gift of God. pap. 1.50 (ISBN 0-686-12746-3). Grace Pub Co.
Shank, Robert. God's Tomorrow: The Life Beyond Death. (Orig.). 1975. pap. 1.95 (ISBN 0-911620-03-6). Westcott.
Shell, Joy. The Ministry of Angels. 1977. pap. 3.95 (ISBN 0-8065-0586-9). Citadel Pr.
Sherman, Harold. You Live after Death. 176p. 1987. pap. 2.95 (GM). Fawcett.
Smith, Charles R. The New "Life after Death" Religion. 1980. pap. 1.00 (ISBN 0-88469-125-X). BMH Bks.
Spong, John S. The Easter Moment. 176p. 1980. 9.95 (ISBN 0-8164-0133-0, HarpR). Har-Row.
Steiner, Rudolf. Life Between Death & Rebirth. Querido, R. M., tr. from Ger. LC 68-57429. 308p. (Orig.). 1975. pap. 9.95 (ISBN 0-910142-62-9). Anthroposophic.
Studer, Gerald C. After Death, What? LC 75-38074. 160p. 1976. pap. 1.95 (ISBN 0-8361-1792-1). Herald Pr.
Swain, Jasper. From My World to Yours: A Young Man's Account of the Afterlife. Langley, Noel, ed. LC 76-52573. 103p. 1984. pap. 7.95 (ISBN 0-8027-7257-9). Walker & Co.
Swedenborg, Emanuel. Heaven & Hell. large print ed. LC 81-52785. 800p. 8.25 (ISBN 0-87785-130-1). Swedenborg.
--Heaven & Hell. LC 77-93044. cancelled (ISBN 0-87785-167-0); student ed. 12.00 (ISBN 0-87785-066-6); pap. 5.95 (ISBN 0-87785-153-0). Swedenborg.
Tormey, John C. Life Beyond Death. 64p. 1981. pap. 1.50 (ISBN 0-89243-151-2). Liguori Pubns.
Urwin, J. & Robinson, S. J. The Christian State after Death Before Resurrection. pap. 2.25 (ISBN 0-88172-164-6). Believers Bkshelf.
Van de Walle, A. R. From Darkness to the Dawn: How Belief in the Afterlife Affects Living. Tr. of Tot het aanbreken van de dageraad. 272p. 1985. pap. text ed. 10.95 (ISBN 0-89622-272-1). Twenty-Third.
Van Dusen, Wilson. The Presence of Other Worlds. LC 73-18684. 240p. pap. 5.95 (ISBN 0-87785-166-2). Swedenborg.
Van Impe, Jack. The Eighties, the Antichrist & Your Startling Future. 87p. 1982. pap. 1.95 (ISBN 0-934803-12-9). J Van Impe.
--Escape the Second Death. 60p. 1985. pap. 1.95 (ISBN 0-934803-38-2). J Van Impe.
Von Speyr, Adrienne. The Gates of Eternal Life. Sharp, Corona, tr. from Ger. LC 82-84582. Tr. of Die Pforten des Ewigen Lebens. 140p. (Orig.). 1984. pap. 7.95 (ISBN 0-89870-025-6). Ignatius Pr.
Wheeler, Penny. The Beginning. Phillips, ed. (Daybreak Ser.). 112p. 1982. pap. 3.95 (ISBN 0-8163-0478-5). Pacific Pr Pub Assn.
Zodhiates, Spiros. Life after Death!? Zodhiates, Spiros, tr. from Greek. Orig. Title: What Happens After Death? (Illus.). 1977. pap. 3.95 (ISBN 0-89957-525-0). AMG Pubs.

FUTURE LIFE–BIBLIOGRAPHY

Alger, William R. Destiny of the Soul: Critical History of the Doctrine of a Future Life, 2 Vols. 10th ed. LC 68-19263. 1968. Repr. of 1880 ed. Set. lib. bdg. 43.25x (ISBN 0-8371-0003-8, ALDS). Greenwood.

FUTURE LIFE–CASE STUDIES

Marsh, Michael. A Matter of Personal Survival. LC 84-40514. (Illus.). 209p. (Orig.). 1985. pap. 7.50 (ISBN 0-8356-0596-5). Theos Pub Hse.
Rawlings, Maurice. Beyond Death's Door. 1979. pap. 3.50 (ISBN 0-553-25204-6). Bantam.
Ritchie, George G. & Sherrill, Elizabeth. Return from Tomorrow. 128p. 1981. pap. 2.95 (ISBN 0-8007-8412-X, Spire Bks). Revell.

FUTURE PUNISHMENT

see also Future Life; Hell; Purgatory; Universalism

Blodgett, Ralph. Hell: Will the Wicked Burn Forever? (Outreach Ser.). 1981. pap. 0.99 (ISBN 0-8163-0375-4). Pacific Pr Pub Assn.
Bunyan, John. Groans of a Lost Soul. LC 68-6571. 1967. pap. 3.25 (ISBN 0-685-19830-8). Reiner.
Pink, Arthur W. Eternal Punishment. pap. 0.75 (ISBN 0-685-00734-0). Reiner.
Shedd, W. G. The Doctrine of Endless Punishment. 1980. 8.25 (ISBN 0-86524-019-1, 9803). Klock & Klock.

G

GABRIEL RICHARD, FATHER

Maxwell, Charles H. Adventures of Gabriel in His Search for God. 1933. Repr. 12.50 (ISBN 0-8274-1821-3). R West.

GAELS

see Celts

GALATIANS

see also Celts

Stott, John R. The Message of Galatians. pap. 6.95 (ISBN 0-87784-288-4). Inter-Varsity.

GALILEO (GALILEO GALILEI), 1564-1642

Fahie, J. J. Galileo: His Life & Work. (Illus.). Repr. of 1903 ed. lib. bdg. 57.00x (ISBN 0-697-00003-6). Irvington.
Galileo: Arabic. (MacDonald Educational Ser.). (Illus.). 3.50x (ISBN 0-86685-249-2). Intl Bk Ctr.
Gebler, Karl Von. Galileo Galilei & the Roman Curia from Authentic Sources. Sturge, Jane, tr. LC 76-1124. 1977. Repr. of 1897 ed. lib. bdg. 28.50x (ISBN 0-915172-11-9). Richwood Pub.
Langford, Jerome J. Galileo, Science & the Church. rev. ed. 1971. pap. 7.95x (ISBN 0-472-06173-9, 173, AA). U of Mich Pr.
Lijegren, Sten. Studies in Milton. LC 67-30816. (Studies in Milton, No. 22). 1969. Repr. of 1918 ed. lib. bdg. 75.00x (ISBN 0-8383-0718-3). Haskell.
Liljegren, Sten B. Studies in Milton. 1918. lib. bdg. 20.00 (ISBN 0-8414-5707-7). Folcroft.
Santillana, Giorgio. The Crime of Galileo. LC 55-7400. (Midway Reprint Ser). (Illus.). xvi, 339p. 1955. pap. 14.00x (ISBN 0-226-73481-1). U of Chicago Pr.

GAMES

see also Bible Games and Puzzles

Baumgartner, Keith A. & Schiff, Marty. The Armageddon: Color & Game Book. (Illus.). 28p. 1984. pap. 2.95 (ISBN 0-916343-02-2). J R Simon.
Braidfoot, Larry. Gambling: A Deadly Game. LC 85-19066. (Orig.). 1985. pap. 4.95 (ISBN 0-8054-5664-3). Broadman.
Brown, Marice C. Amen, Brother Ben: A Mississippi Collection of Children's Rhymes. LC 78-32017. 1979. pap. text ed. 5.00 (ISBN 0-87805-094-9). U Pr of Miss.
Hohenstein, Mary, compiled by. Games. LC 80-23047. 298p. (Orig.). 1980. pap. 6.95 (ISBN 0-87123-191-3, 210191). Bethany Hse.
Millen, Nina. Children's Festivals from Many Lands. 1964. pap. 4.95 (ISBN 0-377-44501-0). Friend Pr.
--Children's Games from Many Lands. 1965. pap. 5.95 (ISBN 0-377-45011-1). Friend Pr.
Rice, Wayne, et al. Fun-N-Games. 1977. pap. 6.95 (ISBN 0-310-35001-8, 10798P). Zondervan.
Schaupp, Jack. Creating & Playing Games with Students. (Orig.). 1981. pap. 6.50 (ISBN 0-687-09809-2). Abingdon.
Seagrist, Edward M. More Word Search Puzzles. (Quiz & Puzzle Bks.). 80p. 1986. pap. 3.95 (ISBN 0-8010-8263-3). Baker Bk.
Wade, Mildred. Games for Fun. LC 77-76616. 1977. pap. 3.95 (ISBN 0-8054-7513-3). Broadman.

GANDAVYUHA

Fontein, J. Pilgrimage of Sudhana. 1967. text ed. 35.60x (ISBN 90-2796-387-8). Mouton.

GANDHI, MOHANDAS KARAMCHAND, 1869-1948

Afaque, Khan M. Gandhian Approach to Communal Harmony: A Critical Study. 140p. 1986. 11.00 (ISBN 81-202-0163-9, Pub. by Ajanta). South Asia Bks.
Alexander, Horace. Gandhi Remembered. LC 71-84674. (Orig.). 1969. pap. 2.50x (ISBN 0-87574-165-7). Pendle Hill.
Bakshi, S. R. Gandhi & Khilafat. 1985. 18.00x (ISBN 0-8364-1491-8, Pub. by Gitanjali Prakashan). South Asia Bks.
Barker, A. Trevor, compiled by. The Mahatma Letters to A. P. Sinnett. facsimile of 1926, 2nd ed. LC 75-10574. 1975. 12.00 (ISBN 0-911500-20-0); pap. 7.00 (ISBN 0-911500-21-9). Theos U Pr.
Chatterjee, Margaret. Gandhi's Religious Thought. LC 83-5841. 224p. 1984. text ed. 19.95x (ISBN 0-268-01009-9, 85-10091). U of Notre Dame Pr.
--Gandhi's Religious Thought. LC 83-5841. 208p. 1986. pap. 9.95 (ISBN 0-268-01011-0). U of Notre Dame Pr.
Desai, Mahadev. A Righteous Struggle. 105p. 1983. pap. 1.25 (ISBN 0-934676-34-8). Greenlf Bks.
Dhar, Niranjan. Aurobindo, Gandhi & Roy: A Yogi, a Mahatma & a Rationalist. 1986. 13.50x (ISBN 0-8364-1578-7, Pub. by Minerva India). South Asia Bks.
Douglass, James W. Lightning East to West: Jesus, Gandhi & the Nuclear Age. 112p. 1983. pap. 6.95 (ISBN 0-8245-0587-5). Crossroad NY.
Iyer, Raghavan. The Moral & Political Thought of Mahatma Gandi. (Illus.). xviii, 478p. pap. 17.50 (ISBN 0-88695-002-3). Concord Grove.
Jesudasan, Ignatius. A Gandhian Theology of Liberation. LC 83-19486. 192p. (Orig.). 1984. pap. 10.95 (ISBN 0-88344-154-3). Orbis Bks.
Jones, E. Stanley. Ghandi: Portrayal of a Friend. 192p. 1983. pap. 3.25 (ISBN 0-687-13999-6). Abingdon.
McLaughlin, Elizabeth T. Ruskin & Gandhi. LC 72-3260. 202p. 1974. 20.00 (ISBN 0-8387-1086-7). Bucknell U Pr.
Pyarelal, et al. Gandhian Thought & Contemporary Society. Mathur, J. S., ed. 285p. 1983. 18.00 (ISBN 0-934676-31-3). Greenlf Bks.
Rao, K. L. Mahatma Gandhi & Comparative Religion. 1979. 15.00x (ISBN 0-89684-034-4). South Asia Bks.
Roy-Chaudhury, P. C. Gandhi & His Contemporaries. 336p. 1972. 25.00x (ISBN 0-89684-394-7). Orient Bk Dist.

GANGES RIVER

Darian, Steven G. The Ganges in Myth & History. LC 77-21374. (Illus.). 236p. 1978. text ed. 12.00x (ISBN 0-8248-0509-7). UH Pr.

GASPE, DISTRICT, QUEBEC–DESCRIPTION AND TRAVEL

Le Clercq, Chretien. New Relation of Gaspesia: With the Customs & Religion of the Gaspesian Indian. Ganong, William F., ed. LC 68-28600. 1968. Repr. of 1910 ed. lib. bdg. 33.75x (ISBN 0-8371-5044-2, LERG). Greenwood.

GAUL–HISTORY

Pirenne, Henri. Mohammed & Charlemagne. (B & N Paperback Ser.). 239p. (Orig.). 1983. pap. 9.95x (ISBN 0-389-20134-0, 06641, 444). B&N Imports.

GAUTAMA BUDDHA

Arnold, Edwin. The Light of Asia: The Life & Teaching of Gautama Buddha. xi, 238p. 1977. 5.00 (ISBN 0-938998-17-X). Theosophy.
Aryasura. The Marvelous Companion: Life Stories of the Buddha. (Illus.). 250p. 1983. 25.00 (ISBN 0-913546-88-7). Dharma Pub.
Asvaghosa. The Buddhacharita or Acts of the Buddha, 2 vols. in 1. Johnson, E. H., ed. & tr. Repr. of 1936 ed. text ed. 25.00x. Coronet Bks.
Auboyer, J. Buddha: A Pictorial History of His Life & Legacy. (Illus.). 272p. 1987. 40.00 (ISBN 0-8334-1000-8, Freedeeds Bks). Garber Comm.
Auboyer, Jeannine. Buddha: A Pictorial History of His Life & Legacy. Marans, Nelly, tr. from Fr. LC 83-10140. (Illus.). 272p. 1983. 100.00 (ISBN 0-8245-0588-3). Crossroad NY.
Brewster, Earl H., compiled by. The Life of Gotama Buddha (Compiled Exclusively from the Pali Canon) LC 78-72380. Repr. of 1926 ed. 27.50 (ISBN 0-404-17229-6). AMS Pr.
Bucke, Richard M. Buddha, Mohammed, Bacon, Whitman & Others & the Theory of Cosmic Consciousness, 2 vols. (Illus.). 291p. 1986. Set. 237.50 (ISBN 0-89901-269-8). Found Class Reprints.
Buddhist Sutra. How One Thousand Buddhas Became Enlightened, 3 Vols. 1986. Set. cancelled (ISBN 0-89800-136-6). Dharma Pub.
Byles, Marie B. Footprints of Gautama the Buddha. LC 68-5855. (Illus.). 1967. pap. 5.95 (ISBN 0-8356-0399-7, Quest). Theos Pub Hse.
Carus, Paul. The Gospel of Buddha. 59.95 (ISBN 0-8490-0252-4). Gordon Pr.
Coomaraswamy, Ananda K. Buddha & the Gospel of Buddhism. (Illus.). 1975. text ed. 17.00x. Coronet Bks.
Csoma, Sandor K. The Life & Teachings of Buddha. LC 78-72399. Repr. of 1957 ed. 21.50 (ISBN 0-404-17258-X). AMS Pr.
Davids, C. Rhys. Gotama, the Man. LC 78-72409. Repr. of 1928 ed. 25.00 (ISBN 0-404-17273-3). AMS Pr.
Davids, C. Rhys, intro. by. Stories of the Buddha. LC 78-72444. Repr. of 1929 ed. 30.00 (ISBN 0-404-17316-0). AMS Pr.
Davids, T. Rhys. Buddhism: Being a Sketch of the Life & Teachings of Guatama, the Buddha. LC 78-72417. Repr. of 1877 ed. 28.00 (ISBN 0-404-17278-4). AMS Pr.
Easwaran, Eknath, tr. from Pali. The Dhammapada. 1986. 13.95 (ISBN 0-915132-38-9); pap. 6.95 (ISBN 0-915132-37-0). Nilgiri Pr.
Foucher, Alfred C. The Life of the Buddha. Boas, Simone B., tr. LC 72-6195. 272p. 1972. Repr. of 1963 ed. lib. bdg. 22.50x (ISBN 0-8371-6476-1, FOLB). Greenwood.
Gautama. Gautama: The Nyaya Philosophy. Junankar, N. S., tr. from Sanskrit. 1978. 25.50 (ISBN 0-89684-002-6, Pub. by Motilal Banarsidass India). Orient Bk Dist.
Herold, A. Ferdinand. Life of Buddha: According to the Legend of Ancient India. LC 55-12748. 1954. pap. 6.95 (ISBN 0-8048-0382-X). C E Tuttle.
Holmes, Edmond. The Creed of Buddha. LC 72-9918. 260p. 1973. Repr. of 1957 ed. lib. bdg. 22.50x (ISBN 0-8371-6606-3, HOCB). Greenwood.
Ikeda, Daisaku. The Living Buddha: An Interpretive Biography. LC 75-40446. (Illus.). 164p. 1975. 7.95 (ISBN 0-8348-0117-5). Weatherhill.
Kalupahana, David J. & Kalupahana, Indrani. The Way of Siddhartha: A Life of the Buddha. 242p. 1987. pap. text ed. 11.75 (ISBN 0-8191-6066-0). U Pr of Amer.
Kazantzakis, Nikos. Buddha. Friar, Kimon & Dallas-Damis, Athena, trs. from Greek. LC 81-71164. 172p. (Orig.). 1983. pap. 11.95 (ISBN 0-932238-14-9, Pub. by Avant Bks.). Slawson Comm.
Krom, N. J., ed. The Life of Buddha on the Stupa of Barabudur, According to the Lalitavistara-Text. LC 78-72460. Repr. of 1926 ed. 30.00 (ISBN 0-404-17328-4). AMS Pr.
Moore, K. R. Saying of Buddha. 159p. 1982. 15.95x. Coronet Bks.
Muni Shri Nagraj Ji. The Contemporaneity & the Chronology of Mahavira & Buddha. 188p. 1975. 4.00 (ISBN 0-88065-163-6, Pub. by Messers Today & Tomorrows Printers & Publishers India). Scholarly Pubns.
Nakamura, Hajime. Gotama Buddha. LC 77-8589. 1977. 8.95x (ISBN 0-914910-05-1); pap. 6.95x (ISBN 0-914910-06-X). Buddhist Bks.
Oldenber. Buddha: His Life, Doctrine, Order. 1971. 28.00 (ISBN 0-89684-493-5). Orient Bk Dist.
Oldenberg, Hermann. Buddha: His Life, His Doctrine & His Order. 59.95 (ISBN 0-87968-800-9). Gordon Pr.
Parrinder, Geoffrey. The Wisdom of the Early Buddhists. LC 77-7945. (New Directions Wisdon Ser.). 1977. pap. 4.95 (ISBN 0-8112-0667-X, NDP444). New Directions.
Pye, Michael. The Buddha. 148p. 1979. 18.00 (ISBN 0-7156-1302-2, Pub. by Duckworth London); pap. 8.95 (ISBN 0-7156-1387-1). Longwood Pub Group.
Rady, Martyn C. Medieval Buda. 1985. 32.00 (ISBN 0-88033-074-0). East Eur Quarterly.
Rajneesh, Bhagwan Shree. The Diamond Sutra. Pratima, Ma Yoga, ed. LC 82-185071. (Buddha Ser.). (Illus.). 492p. (Orig.). 1979. 19.50 (ISBN 0-88050-043-3). Chidvilas Found.
--The Discipline of Transcendence, 4 vols. Vandana, Ma Ananda & Pratima, Ma Yoga, eds. LC 78-906087. (Buddha Ser.). (Illus., Orig.). 1978. Vol. I, 324 pgs. 16.50 ea. (ISBN 0-88050-045-X). Vol. II, 348 pgs (ISBN 0-88050-046-8). Vol. III, 320 pgs (ISBN 0-88050-047-6). Vol. IV, 376 pgs (ISBN 0-88050-048-4). Chidvilas Found.

Rawding, F. W. The Buddha. LC 78-56789. (Cambridge Topic Bks). (Illus.). PLB 8.95 (ISBN 0-8225-1212-2). Lerner Pubns.
Rockhill, William W., ed. The Life of Buddha & the Early History of His Order. 285p. Repr. of 1884 ed. text ed. 19.50x (ISBN 0-89563-149-0, Pub. by Chinese Matl Ctr). Coronet Bks.
Saunders, Kenneth J. Gotama Buddha: A Biography. LC 78-70119. Repr. of 1922 ed. 18.00 (ISBN 0-404-17376-4). AMS Pr.
Swearer, Donald K. Wat Haripunjaya: A Study of the Royal Temple of the Buddha's Relic, Lamphun, Thailand. LC 75-33802. (American Academy of Religion. Studies in Religion). 1976. pap. 9.95 (ISBN 0-89130-052-X, 010010). Scholars Pr GA.
Syama-Sankara, Hara C. Buddha & His Sayings. LC 78-70128. Repr. of 1914 ed. 18.00 (ISBN 0-404-17387-X). AMS Pr.
Szekely, Edmond B. The Living Buddha. (Illus.). 70p. 1977. pap. 4.50 (ISBN 0-89564-059-7). IBS Intl.

GAY LIB
see Gay Liberation Movement

GAY LIBERATION MOVEMENT
Edwards, George R. Gay-Lesbian Liberation: A Biblical Perspective. 144p. (Orig.). 1984. pap. 9.95 (ISBN 0-8298-0725-X). Pilgrim NY.
Johnson, Paul R. Gays & Fundamentalism. (Illus.). 56p. (Orig.). 1983. pap. 2.95 (ISBN 0-910097-02-X). Paul R Johnson.
--Gays & the Bible. (Illus.). 52p. (Orig.). 1983. pap. 2.95 (ISBN 0-910097-00-3). Paul R Johnson.
--Gays & the Church. (Illus.). 48p. (Orig.). 1983. pap. 2.95 (ISBN 0-910097-04-6). Paul R Johnson.
Kelly, George A. The Political Struggle of Active Homosexuals to Gain Social Acceptance. 106p. 1975. pap. 1.50 (ISBN 0-8199-0365-5). Franciscan Herald.

GAYAL
Simoons, Frederick J. & Simoons, Elizabeth S. Ceremonial Ox of India: The Mithan in Nature, Culture, & History. LC 68-9023. (Illus.). 340p. 1968. 40.00x (ISBN 0-299-04980-9). U of Wis Pr.

GEMS (IN RELIGION, FOLK-LORE, ETC.)
Carley, Ken. Gems & Stones: Scientific Properties & Aspects of Twenty Two-A Comparative Study Based upon the Edgar Cayce Psychic Readings. rev. ed. 1979. pap. 4.95 (ISBN 0-87604-110-1). ARE Pr.
Evans, Joan. Magical Jewels of the Middle Ages & the Renaissance Particularly in England. LC 75-26288. (Illus.). 288p. 1976. pap. 5.95 (ISBN 0-486-23367-7). Dover.
Kunz, George. The Curious Lore of Precious Stones. (Illus.). 14.50 (ISBN 0-8446-0173-X). Peter Smith.
Kunz, George F. Curious Lore of Precious Stones. 1970. pap. 7.95 (ISBN 0-486-22227-6). Dover.
Lorusso, Julia & Glick, Joel. Stratagems. 108p. (Orig.). 1985. pap. 7.95 (ISBN 0-914732-15-3). Bro Life Inc.
Mella, Dorothee I. Stone Power II: The Legendary & Practical Use of Gems & Stones. Orig. Title: Stone Power, The Legendary & Practical Use of Gems & Stones. (Illus.). 164p. (Orig.). 1986. pap. 11.95 (ISBN 0-914732-18-8). Bro Life Inc.
Richardson, Wally G. & Huett, Lenora. The Spiritual Value of Gem Stones. LC 79-54728. 168p. 1980. pap. 6.50 (ISBN 0-87516-383-1). De Vorss.

GENERAL JUDGMENT
see Judgment Day

GENESIS (MIDDLE HIGH GERMAN POEM)
Weller, Alfred. Die Fruhmittelhochdeutsche Wiener Genesis. 27.00 (ISBN 0-384-66731-7); pap. 22.00 (ISBN 0-384-66730-9). Johnson Repr.

GENIZAH
Ginzberg, L. & Davidson, I. Genizah Studies in Memory of Solomon Schechter, 3 vols. Incl. Vol. 1. Midrash & Haggadah. Ginzberg, L. 1969. Repr. of 1928 ed. 17.50 (ISBN 0-87203-015-6); Vol. 2. Geonic & Early Karaitic Halakah. Ginzberg, L. Repr. of 1929 ed. 17.50 (ISBN 0-87203-016-4); Vol. 3. Liturgical & Secular Poetry. Davidson, I. Repr. of 1928 ed. 17.50 (ISBN 0-87203-017-2). LC 73-76172. Hermon.
Gottheil, Richard J., ed. Fragments from the Cairo Genizah in the Freer Collection. Repr. of 1927 ed. 37.00 (ISBN 0-384-38813-2). Johnson Repr.
Morag, Shelomo. Vocalised Talmudic Manuscripts in the Cambridge Genizah Collections: Taylor-Schnechter Old Series, Vol. 1. (Cambridge University Library Genizan Ser.: No. 4). 60p. Date not set. Vol. I: Taylor-Schechter Old Series. price not set (ISBN 0-521-26863-X). Cambridge U Pr.

GENTILE, GIOVANNI, 1875-1944
Holmes, Roger W. The Idealism of Giovanni Gentile. LC 78-63683. (Studies in Fascism: Ideology & Practice). Repr. of 1937 ed. 29.50 (ISBN 0-404-16948-1). AMS Pr.
Romanell, Patrick. Croce Versus Gentile: A Dialogue on Contemporary Italian Philosophy. LC 78-63709. (Studies in Fascism: Ideology & Practice). (Illus.). 80p. Repr. of 1947 ed. 18.00 (ISBN 0-404-16979-1). AMS Pr.
Smith, William A. Giovanni Gentile on the Existence of God. Matczak, S. A., ed. & intro. by. LC 70-111087. (Philosophical Questions Ser.: No. 7). 1970. 18.00 (ISBN 0-912116-04-8). Learned Pubns.

GEOGRAPHY, ECCLESIASTICAL
see Ecclesiastical Geography

GEOGRAPHY AND RELIGION
see Religion and Geography

GEOLOGY AND RELIGION
see Religion and Science

GEORGE, SAINT, d. 303
Budge, Ernest A., tr. George of Lydda, the Patron Saint of England. LC 77-87668. (Luzac's Semitic Texts & Translations: No. 20). (Eng. & Ethiopic., Illus.). Repr. of 1930 ed. 55.00 (ISBN 0-404-11348-6). AMS Pr.
Fox, David. Saint George: The Saint with Three Faces. (Illus.). 188p. 1986. 42.00 (ISBN 0-946041-13-X). Salem Hse Pubs.

GERMAINE COUSIN, SAINT, 1579-1601
Cantoni, Louise. St. Germaine. rev. ed. 1973. 1.75 (ISBN 0-8198-0262-X). Dghtrs St Paul.

GERMAN HYMNS
see Hymns, German

GERMAN REFORMED CHURCH (U. S.)
see Reformed Church in the United States

GERMANIC MYTHOLOGY
see Mythology, Germanic

GERMANIC TRIBES-RELIGION
see also Mythology, Germanic; Mythology, Norse
De La Saussaye, P. Chantepie. The Religion of the Teutons. LC 76-27519. 1976. Repr. of 1902 ed. lib. bdg. 50.00 (ISBN 0-89341-030-6). Longwood Pub Group.
Dumezil, Georges. Gods of the Ancient Northmen. Haugen, Einar, ed. & tr. (Center for the Study of Comparative Folklore & Mythology, UCLA Ser.: No. 3). 1974. 34.00x (ISBN 0-520-02044-8); pap. 8.95 (ISBN 0-520-03507-0, CAL 371). U of Cal Pr.

GERMANY-CHURCH HISTORY
Bonifacius, Saint Winfrid. Briefe des Heiligen Bonifatius. pap. 23.00 (ISBN 0-384-05025-5). Johnson Repr.
Entscheidungen in Kirchensachen Seit 1946, Vol. 13. 1978. 79.20 (ISBN 3-11-007625-X). De Gruyter.
Heyen, Franz J., ed. Germania Sacra: Die Bistuemer der Kirchenprovinz Trier: Das Erzbistum Trier, 1. das Stift St. Paulin Vor Trier. (Germania Sacra: Historisch-Statistische Beschreibung der Kirche Des Alten Reiches, N. F. 6). xiv, 855p. 1972. pap. 88.00 (ISBN 3-11-002273-7). De Gruyter.
King, Christine E. The Nazi State & the New Religions: Five Case Studies in Non-conformity. LC 82-20910. (Studies in Religion & Society: Vol. 4). 332p. 1982. 59.95x (ISBN 0-88946-865-6). E Mellen.
Otto, Von St. Blasien. Die Chronik Des Otto Von St. Blasien. Kohl, Horst, tr. (Ger). pap. 10.00 (ISBN 0-384-43970-5). Johnson Repr.
Otto Bishop of Freising. Der Chronik des Bischofs Otto, Von Freising, Sechstes und Siebentes Buch. Kohl, H., tr. (Ger.). pap. 10.00 (ISBN 0-384-43965-9). Johnson Repr.
Schutz, Wilhelm W. Pens under the Swastika. LC 70-118415. 1971. Repr. of 1946 ed. 19.95x (ISBN 0-8046-1192-0, Pub. by Kennikat). Assoc Faculty Pr.
Scribner, R. The German Reformation. LC 85-19732. (Studies in European History). 88p. 1986. pap. text ed. 7.95x (ISBN 0-391-03362-X). Humanities.

GERMANY-RELIGION
Arsen'ev, Nicolai S. We Beheld His Glory. Ewer, Mary A., tr. LC 76-113545. Repr. of 1936 ed. 18.00 (ISBN 0-404-00407-5). AMS Pr.
Cochrane, Arthur C. The Church's Confession Under Hitler. 2nd ed. LC 76-57655. (Pittsburgh Reprint Ser.: No. 4). 1977. pap. text ed. 10.75 (ISBN 0-915138-28-X). Pickwick.
Erickson, Robert P. Theologians under Hitler. LC 84-40731. 256p. 1987. pap. 8.95 (ISBN 0-300-03889-5, Y-618). Yale U Pr.
Faulhaber. Judaism, Christianity & Germany. Smith, George D., tr. from Ger. 116p. 1981. Repr. of 1934 ed. lib. bdg. 30.00 (ISBN 0-89987-263-8). Darby Bks.
Frey, Arthur. Cross & Swastika, the Ordeal of the German Church. McNab, J. Strathearn, tr. LC 78-63668. (Studies in Fascism: Ideology & Practice). 224p. Repr. of 1938 ed. 24.50 (ISBN 0-404-16526-5). AMS Pr.
Heine, Heinrich. Religion & Philosophy in Germany. Snodgrass, John, tr. from Ger. 210p. (Orig.). 1986. 29.50x (ISBN 0-88706-282-2); pap. 9.95 (ISBN 0-88706-283-0). State U NY Pr.
Herman, Stewart W. It's Your Souls We Want. LC 72-180406. Repr. of 1943 ed. 29.50 (ISBN 0-404-56130-6). AMS Pr.
Hollerbach, Marion. Das Religionsgespraech Als Mittel Der Konfessionellen Und Politischen Auseinandersetzung Im Deutschland Des 16. Jahrhunderts. (European University Studies: No. 3, Vol. 165). (Ger.). 1982. 36.85 (ISBN 3-8204-7015-8). P Lang Pubs.
Krausen, Edgard. Germania Sacra, New Series II: Bistuemer der Kirchenprovinz Salzburg. 1977. 62.40x (ISBN 3-11-006826-5). De Gruyter.
Liberles, Robert. Religious Conflict in Social Context: The Resurgence of Orthodox Judaism in Frankfurt Am Main, 1838-1877. LC 84-27981. (Contributions to the Study of Religion Ser.: No. 13). xvi, 297p. 1985. lib. bdg. 29.95 (ISBN 0-313-24806-0, LRX/). Greenwood.
Liebersohn, Harry. Religion & Industrial Society: The Protestant Social Congress in Wilhelmine Germany. LC 86-71421. (Transaction Ser.: Vol. 76, Pt. 6). 1986. 15.00 (ISBN 0-87169-766-1). Am Philos.
Loader, Jamer A. Polar Structures in the Book of Qohelet. (Beihefte aur Zeitschrift fuer die alttestamentliche Wissenschaft). 150p. 1979. text ed. 32.75x (ISBN 3-11-007636-5). De Gruyter.
McGrath, Alister E. The Making of Modern German Christology: From the Enlightenment to Pannenberg. 240p. 1986. text ed. 34.95x (ISBN 0-631-14512-5). Basil Blackwell.
Pois, Robert A. National Socialism & the Religion of Nature. LC 85-27615. 208p. 1986. 27.50 (ISBN 0-312-55958-5). St Martin.
Power, Michael. Religion in the Reich. LC 78-63706. (Studies in Fascism: Ideology & Practice). 1979. Repr. of 1939 ed. 28.00 (ISBN 0-404-16976-7). AMS Pr.
Smith, Clifford N. Nineteenth-Century Emigration of "Old Lutherans" from Eastern Germany (Mainly Pomerania & Lower Silesia) to Australia, Canada, & the United States. (German-American Genealogical Research Monograph: No. 7). 1979. pap. 14.00 (ISBN 0-915162-06-7). Westland Pubns.
Sykes, S. W., ed. England & Germany: Studies in Theological Diplomacy. (IC-Studies in the Intercultural History of Christianity: Vol. 25). 170p. 1981. pap. 22.15 (ISBN 3-8204-5854-9). P Lang Pubs.
Trillhaas, Wolfgang. Schleiermachers Predigt. 2nd ed. (Theologische Bibliothek Toepelmann, Vol. 28). 1975. 20.80x (ISBN 3-11-005739-5). De Gruyter.
Viehmeyer, L. Allen. Tumultuous Years - Schwenkfelder Chronicles Fifteen Eighty to Seventeen Fifty: The Reports of Martin John, Jr. & Balthazar Hoffmann. 157p. (Orig.). 1980. pap. write for info. (ISBN 0-935980-00-8). Schwenkfelder Lib.
Whaley, Joachim. Religious Toleration & Social Change in Hamburg, 1529-1819. (Cambridge Studies in Early Modern History). 290p. 1985. 49.50 (ISBN 0-521-26189-9). Cambridge U Pr.

GHANA-RELIGION
Appiah-Kubi, Kofi. Man Cures, God Heals: Religion & Medical Practice Among the Akans of Ghana. LC 81-65019. (Illus.). 188p. 1981. text ed. 18.95x (ISBN 0-86598-011-X). Allanheld.
--Man Cures, God Heals: Religion & Medical Practice Among the Akans of Ghana. (Orig.). 1981. pap. 10.95 (ISBN 0-377-00114-7). Friend Pr.
Bartels, Francis L. The Roots of Ghana Methodism. LC 64-21525. pap. 95.50 (ISBN 0-317-08427-5, 2050799). Bks Demand UMI.
Field, Margaret J. Religion & Medicine of the Ga People. LC 76-44718. 1977. Repr. of 1937 ed. 37.50 (ISBN 0-404-15923-0). AMS Pr.
Maier, D. J. E. Priests & Power: The Case of the Dente Shrine in Nineteenth-Century Ghana. LC 82-48582. (Illus.). 272p. 1983. 22.50X (ISBN 0-253-34602-9). Ind U Pr.
Wyllie, Robert W. Spiritism in Ghana: A Study of New Religious Movements. Cherry, Conrad, ed. LC 79-20486. (Studies in Religion: No. 21). 139p. 14.00 (ISBN 0-89130-355-3, 01-00-21); pap. 9.95 (ISBN 0-89130-356-1). Scholars Pr GA.

GHOSE, AUROBINDO, 1872-1950
Chaudhuri, Haridas. Being, Evolution & Immortality. rev. ed. LC 74-4821. Orig. Title: Philosophy of Integralism. 224p. 1974. pap. 6.95 (ISBN 0-8356-0449-7, Quest). Theos Pub Hse.
Donnelly, Morwenna. Founding the Life Divine: An Introduction to the Integral Yoga of Sri Aurobindo. LC 74-2430. 250p. 1976. pap. 7.95 (ISBN 0-913922-13-7). Dawn Horse Pr.
O'Connor, June. The Quest for Political & Spiritual Liberation: A Study in the Thought of Sri Aurobindo Ghose. LC 75-5249. 153p. 1976. 16.50 (ISBN 0-8386-1734-4). Fairleigh Dickinson.

GHOST DANCE
Barney, Garold D. Mormons, Indians & the Ghost Dance Religion of 1890. LC 85-29509. (Illus.). 258p. (Orig.). 1986. lib. bdg. 28.00 (ISBN 0-8191-5227-7); pap. text ed. 13.50 (ISBN 0-8191-5228-5). U Pr of Amer.
Ghost Dance Religion: Smohalla. facs. ed. (Shorey Historical Soc). 40p. pap. 3.95 (ISBN 0-8466-0002-1, S2). Shorey.
Ghost Dancers in the West: The Sioux at Pine Ridge & Wounded Knee in 1891. 1976. pap. 1.00 (ISBN 0-916552-08-X). Acoma Bks.
Lesser, Alexander. Pawnee Ghost Dance Hand Game. LC 79-82340. (Columbia Univ. Contributions to Anthropology Ser.: Vol. 16). 1969. Repr. of 1933 ed. 37.00 (ISBN 0-404-50566-X). AMS Pr.
Mooney, James. Ghost-Dance Religion & the Sioux Outbreak of 1890. Wallace, Anthony F., ed. LC 64-24971. (Orig.). 1965. pap. 14.00 (ISBN 0-226-53517-7, P176, Phoen). U of Chicago Pr.
--Ghost Dance Religion: Shakers of Puget Sound - Extracts. facsimile ed. (Shorey Indian Ser.). 21p. pap. 3.50 (ISBN 0-8466-0003-X, S3). Shorey.

GIBBON, EDWARD, 1737-1794
Blunden, Edmund. Edward Gibbon & His Age. 1978. Repr. of 1935 ed. lib. bdg. 12.50 (ISBN 0-8495-0448-1). Arden Lib.
Blunden, Edmund C. Edward Gibbon & His Age. LC 74-14702. 1974. Repr. of 1935 ed. lib. bdg. 7.50 (ISBN 0-8414-3287-2). Folcroft.
Gibbon, Edward. Autobiography. (World's Classics Ser., No. 139). 16.95 (ISBN 0-19-250139-9). Oxford U Pr.
McCloy, Shelby T. Gibbon's Antagonism to Christianity. 1933. 23.50 (ISBN 0-8337-2311-1). B Franklin.

GIBRAN, KAHLIL, 1883-1931
Bushrui, Suheil. Gibran of Lebanon. 12.00x (ISBN 0-86685-008-2). Intl Bk Ctr.
Daoudi, M. S. The Meaning of Kahlil Gibran. 160p. 1982. 9.95 (ISBN 0-8065-0804-3). Citadel Pr.
--The Meaning of Kahlil Gibran. 140p. 1984. pap. 5.95 (ISBN 0-8065-0929-5). Citadel Pr.
Ghougassian, Joseph P. Kahlil Gibran: Wings of Thought. LC 73-77402. (Illus.). 255p. 1973. 7.50 (ISBN 0-8022-2115-7). Philos Lib.
Hilu, Virginia, ed. Beloved Prophet: The Love Letters of Kahlil Gibran & Mary Haskell & Her Private Journal. 1972. 18.95 (ISBN 0-394-43298-3). Knopf.
Kahlil Gibran: Collection of His Famous Works. (Arabic.). 25.00x (ISBN 0-86685-149-6). Intl Bk Ctr.
Mutlak, Suheil. In Memory of Kahil Gibran. (Arabic.). 1982. 14.00x (ISBN 0-86685-295-6). Intl Bk Ctr.
Naimy, Nadeem. The Lebanese Prophets of New York. 112p. 1985. text ed. 18.00x (ISBN 0-8156-6073-1, Am U Beirut). Syracuse U Pr.
Young, Barbara. This Man from Lebanon. (Illus.). (YA) 1950. 18.95 (ISBN 0-394-44848-0). Knopf.

GIDE, ANDRE PAUL GUILLAUME, 1869-1951
Claudel, Paul. Correspondance avec Andre Gide: 1899-1926. 1949. pap. 7.95 (ISBN 0-686-51967-1). French & Eur.
Guerard, Albert J. Andre Gide. rev. ed. LC 74-88805. 1969. 20.00x (ISBN 0-674-03525-9). Harvard U Pr.
Nersoyan, H. J. Andre Gide: The Theism of an Atheist. LC 69-17717. 1969. 19.95x (ISBN 0-8156-2135-3). Syracuse U Pr.
O'Brien, Justin. Portrait of Andre Gide. 390p. 1976. Repr. of 1953 ed. lib. bdg. 29.00x (ISBN 0-374-96139-5, Octagon). Hippocrene Bks.
Pierre-Quint, Leon. Andre Gide. Richardson, Dorothy, tr. 1934. 30.00 (ISBN 0-8274-1865-5). R West.
Rossi, Vinio. Andre Gide. LC 68-54458. (Columbia Essays on Modern Writers Ser.: No. 35). (Orig.). 1968. pap. 3.00 (ISBN 0-231-02960-8). Columbia U Pr.
Weinberg, Kurt. On Gide's Promethee: Private Myth & Public Mystification. LC 70-173760. (Princeton Essays in Literature Ser.). 144p. 1972. 22.50x (ISBN 0-691-06222-6). Princeton U Pr.

GIDEON, JUDGE OF ISRAEL
Andre, G. Gideon, Samson & Other Judges of Israel. (Let's Discuss It Ser.). pap. 1.95 (ISBN 0-88172-132-8). Believers Bkshelf.
Keller, W. Phillip. Mighty Man of Valor. 128p. 1979. pap. 4.95 (ISBN 0-8007-5072-1, Power Bks). Revell.
Lindsay, Gordon. Gideon & the Early Judges. (Old Testament Ser.). 1.25 (ISBN 0-89985-135-5). Christ Nations.
Omer, Devorah. The Gideonites. 256p. 1968. 3.50 (ISBN 0-88482-750-X). Hebrew Pub.

GIFT-BOOKS (ANNUALS, ETC.)
Flachman, Leonard. Christmas: The Annual of Christmas Literature & Art, Vol. 55. 64p. 1985. text ed. 14.50 (ISBN 0-8066-8967-6, 17-0131); pap. text ed. 6.95 (ISBN 0-8066-8966-8, 17-0130). Augsburg.
Haugan, Randolph E., ed. Christmas: An American Annual of Christmas Literature & Art, Vol. 46. LC 32-30914. 64p. 1976. 14.50 (ISBN 0-8066-8948-X, 17-0113); pap. 6.95 (ISBN 0-8066-8947-1, 17-0112). Augsburg.

Hoff, B. J. Baby's First Days: Enrollment Certificate. (Certificate Booklets Ser.). (Illus.). 16p. 1982. pap. 0.95 self-cover (ISBN 0-87239-530-8, 1182). Standard Pub.
Our Christian Wedding. (Illus.). 48p. 1982. padded cover boxed 12.95 (ISBN 0-8007-1309-5). Revell.

GIFT OF TONGUES
see Glossolalia

GIFTS
Stough, Richard H. Bequests, Endowments, & Special Gifts. (Orig.). 1981. pap. 1.75 (ISBN 0-937172-27-8). JLJ Pubs.
Tournier, Paul. The Meaning of Gifts. LC 63-19122. 1976. 5.95 (ISBN 0-8042-2124-3); pap. 1.25 (ISBN 0-8042-3604-6). John Knox.

GIFTS, SPIRITUAL
see also Fear of God; Glossolalia; Prophecy (Christianity)
Almirudus, Hiram, ed. Los Dones del Espiritu. (Span.). 88p. 1978. pap. 2.75 (ISBN 0-87148-520-6). Pathway Pr.
Baldwin, Lindley. The March of Faith: Samuel Morris. 96p. 1969. pap. 2.95 (ISBN 0-87123-360-6, 200360). Bethany Hse.
Baxter, Ronald E. Gifts of the Spirit. LC 83-14963. 280p. (Orig.). 1983. pap. 8.95 (ISBN 0-8254-2243-4). Kregel.
Bennett, Dennis & Bennett, Rita. The Holy Spirit & You: The Text Book of the Charismatic Renewal. LC 71-140673. 224p. 1971. pap. 5.95 (ISBN 0-912106-14-X). Bridge Pub.
Bryant, Charles. Rediscovering the Charismata: Building up the Body of Christ Through Spiritual Gifts. 192p. 1986. 11.95 (ISBN 0-8499-0539-7). Word Bks.
Carter, Howard. Questions & Answers on Spiritual Gifts. 127p. 1976. pocket bk. 2.95 (ISBN 0-89274-007-8). Harrison Hse.
--Spiritual Gifts & Their Operation. 96p. 1968. pap. 1.95 (ISBN 0-88243-593-0, 02-0593). Gospel Pub.
Clowers, Don. The Power of God's Character. 230p. (Orig.). 1983. pap. text ed. 5.50 (ISBN 0-914307-14-2, Dist. by Harrison Hse). Word Faith.
Colligan, John, et al. A Guide for Using Charisms in the Parish. LC 83-62985. 63p. (Orig.). 1983. pap. text ed. 2.95 (ISBN 0-911905-10-3). Past & Mat Rene Ctr.
Criswell, W. A. The Baptism, Filling & Gifts of the Holy Spirit. 192p. 1973. pap. 4.95 (ISBN 0-310-22751-8, 18351P). Zondervan.
Edgar, Thomas R. Miraculous Gifts: Are They for Today? 384p. 1983. 11.95 (ISBN 0-87213-133-5). Loizeaux.
Fearon, Mary & Hirstein, Sandra J. Celebrating the Gift of Forgiveness. 64p. 1982. pap. 3.50 (ISBN 0-697-01792-3); program manual 6.95 (ISBN 0-697-01793-1). Wm C Brown.
Gangel, Kenneth O. Unwrap Your Spiritual Gifts. 120p. 1983. pap. 4.95 (ISBN 0-88207-102-5). Victor Bks.
Gee, Donald. Concerning Spiritual Gifts. rev. ed. LC 80-83784. 144p. 1972. pap. 2.95 (ISBN 0-88243-486-1, 02-0486). Gospel Pub.
--Spiritual Gifts in the Work of the Ministry Today. 102p. 1963. pap. 1.25 (ISBN 0-88243-592-2, 02-0592). Gospel Pub.
Gobbell, Phyllis C. Like a Promise. LC 83-71490. 1983. 8.95 (ISBN 0-8054-7319-X). Broadman.
Goetchius, Eugene V. & Price, Charles P. The Gifts of God. LC 84-60627. 128p. (Orig.). 1984. pap. 4.95 (ISBN 0-8192-1349-7). Morehouse.
Hagin, Kenneth E. Concerning Spiritual Gifts. 2nd ed. 1974. pap. 2.50 (ISBN 0-89276-072-9). Hagin Ministries.
Harrison, Doyle & Landsman, Michael. Mercy: The Gift Before & Beyond Faith. 64p. (Orig.). 1984. pap. 2.25 (ISBN 0-89274-305-0). Harrison Hse.
Horton, Harold. The Gifts of the Spirit. 208p. 1975. pap. 2.50 (ISBN 0-88243-504-3, 02-0504, Radiant Bks). Gospel Pub.
Jones, R. Wayne. Using Spiritual Gifts. LC 83-70642. 1985. pap. 4.95 (ISBN 0-8054-6940-0). Broadman.
Kinghorn, Kenneth C. Discovering Your Spiritual Gifts: A Personal Inventory Method. 1981. pap. 2.95 (ISBN 0-310-75061-X, 17029P). Zondervan.
--Gifts of the Spirit. LC 75-22268. 128p. 1976. pap. 5.95 (ISBN 0-687-14695-X). Abingdon.
Lindsay, Gordon. Gifts of the Spirit, 4 vols. 2.50 ea. Vol. 1 (ISBN 0-89985-195-9). Vol. 2 (ISBN 0-89985-196-7). Vol. 3 (ISBN 0-89985-197-5). Vol. 4 (ISBN 0-89985-199-1). Christ Nations.
Lloyd-Jones, Martyn. The Sovereign Spirit: Discerning His Gifts. 160p. 1986. pap. 7.95 (ISBN 0-87788-697-0). Shaw Pubs.
McConkie, Joseph F. Seeking the Spirit. LC 78-13372. 122p. 1985. pap. 4.95 (ISBN 0-87747-818-X). Deseret Bk.
MacGorman, J. W. The Gifts of the Spirit. LC 75-55191. 1980. pap. 3.95 (ISBN 0-8054-1385-5). Broadman.
McRae, William. The Dynamics of Spiritual Gifts. 144p. 1983. pap. 4.95 (ISBN 0-310-29091-0). Zondervan.
McRae, William J. The Dynamics of Spiritual Gifts. 160p. 1976. pap. 2.95 (ISBN 0-310-29092-9). Zondervan.
Mallone, George, et al. Those Controversial Gifts. LC 83-8. 168p. (Orig.). 1983. pap. 5.95 (ISBN 0-87784-823-8). Inter-Varsity.
Nee, Watchman. Full of Grace & Truth, Vol. II. Kaung, Stephen, tr. 1981. pap. 3.25 (ISBN 0-935008-51-9). Christian Fellow Pubs.
Neighbour, Ralph W. This Gift Is Mine. LC 73-93907. 1974. 5.50 (ISBN 0-8054-5223-0). Broadman.
Offner, Hazel. The Fruit of the Spirit. (LifeGuide Bible Studies). 64p. 1987. pap. 2.95. Inter-Varsity.
Prophet Pearl. Weight Group Therapist: Spiritual Gifts. large type ed. 32p. 1984. pap. 6.00 (ISBN 0-914009-16-8). VHI Library.
Rowlands, Gerald. The Holy Spirit & His Gifts. Sekowsky, Jo Anne, ed. (Aglow Basic Bible Study Ser.). 64p. 1984. pap. 2.95 (ISBN 0-930756-83-5, 521017). Aglow Pubns.
Sanders, J. Oswald. Holy Spirit & His Gifts. (Contemporary Evangelical Perspectives Ser). kivar 5.95 (ISBN 0-310-32481-5, 6520P). Zondervan.
Sanford, Agness. The Healing Gifts of the Spirit. LC 83-48998. 240p. 1984. pap. 6.95 (ISBN 0-06-067052-5, RD 519, HarpR). Har-Row.
Schramm, Mary R. Gifts of Grace. LC 82-70946. 1982. pap. 5.95 (ISBN 0-8066-1921-X, 10-2551). Augsburg.
Shalm, George. Spiritual Gifts. 131p. 1983. pap. 4.95 (ISBN 0-912315-04-0). Word Aflame.
Tollett, T. O., compiled by. Best Gifts. 1971. pap. 1.00 (ISBN 0-89114-062-X). Baptist Pub Hse.
Underwood, B. E. Spiritual Gifts-Ministries & Manifestations. pap. 6.95 (ISBN 0-911866-03-5). Advocate.
Unger, Merrill F. The Baptism & Gifts of the Holy Spirit. LC 74-2931. 192p. 1974. pap. text ed. 6.95 (ISBN 0-8024-0467-7). Moody.
Winward, Stephen F. Fruit of the Spirit. 208p. (Orig.). 1984. pap. 4.95 (ISBN 0-8028-0003-3). Eerdmans.

GILGAMESH
Heidel, Alexander. Gilgamesh Epic & Old Testament Parallels. 2nd ed. LC 49-5734. 1963. 8.95 (ISBN 0-226-32398-6, P136, Phoen). U of Chicago Pr.

GILL, ERIC, 1882-1940
Attwater, Donald, ed. Modern Christian Revolutionaries. facsimile ed. LC 76-156608. (Essay Index Reprint Ser). Repr. of 1947 ed. 23.00 (ISBN 0-8369-2304-9). Ayer Co Pubs.
Yorke, Malcolm. Eric Gill: Man of Flesh & Spirit. LC 81-71073. (Illus.). 304p. 1985. pap. 14.95 (ISBN 0-87663-883-3). Universe.
--Eric Gill: Man of Flesh & Sprit. LC 81-71073. (Illus.). 256p. 1982. 27.50x (ISBN 0-87663-387-4). Universe.

GIOTTO DI BONDONE, 1266?-1337
Meiss, Millard. Giotto & Assisi. (Illus.). 12.50 (ISBN 0-912158-42-5). Hennessey.
--Giotto & Assisi. LC 60-9443. (Walter W. S. Cook Alumni Lecture Ser.: 1959). pap. 20.00 (ISBN 0-317-09361-4, 2050841). Bks Demand UMI.
Stubblebine, James, ed. Giotto: The Arena Chapel Frescoes. LC 67-17689. (Critical Studies in Art History Ser). (Illus.). 1969. pap. text ed. 7.95x (ISBN 0-393-09858-3, NortonC). Norton.
Trachtenberg, Marvin. The Campanile of Florence Cathedral: Giotto's Tower. LC 70-124532. (Illus.). 458p. 1971. 135.00 (ISBN 0-8147-8151-9). NYU Pr.

GIRLS–RELIGIOUS LIFE
Johnson, Lois. Just a Minute, Lord: Prayers for Girls. LC 73-78265. (Illus.). 96p. (Orig.). 1973. pap. 3.95 (ISBN 0-8066-1329-7, 10-3605). Augsburg.
Thiele, Margaret. Girl Alive. LC 80-11623. (Orion Ser.). 1980. pap. 3.95 (ISBN 0-8127-0268-9). Review & Herald.

GIRLS IN THE BIBLE
see Children in the Bible

GLADNESS
see Happiness

GLASS, STAINED
see Glass Painting and Staining

GLASS PAINTING AND STAINING
Brisac, Catherine. Thousand Years of Stained Glass. LC 85-4506. 200p. 1986. 40.00 (ISBN 0-385-23184-9). Doubleday.
Caviness, Madeline E. & Husband, Timothy. Corpus Vitrearum: Studies on Medieval Stained Glass. (Occasional Papers: No. 1). (Illus.). 160p. 1985. 35.00 (ISBN 0-87099-391-7). Metro Mus Art.
Caviness, Madeline H. The Early Stained Glass of Canterbury Cathedral: 1175-1220. (Illus.). 1978. text ed. 68.50x (ISBN 0-691-03927-5). Princeton U Pr.
Frueh, Erne & Frueh, Florence. Chicago Stained Glass. (Illus.). 160p. 1983. 19.95 (ISBN 0-8294-0435-X). Loyola.
Grodecki, Louis & Brisac, Catherine. Gothic Stained Glass: 1200-1300. Boehm, Barbara D., tr. from Fr. LC 85-71277. (Illus.). 288p. 1985. text ed. 75.00x (ISBN 0-8014-1809-7). Cornell U Pr.
Irimie, Cornel & Focsa, Marcela. Romanian Icons Painted on Glass. (Illus.). 1971. 75.00 (ISBN 0-393-04309-6). Norton.
Lillich, Meredith P. The Stained Glass of Saint-Pere de Chartres. LC 77-13926. (Illus.). 1978. 50.00x (ISBN 0-8195-5023-X). Wesleyan U Pr.
Stephany, Konrad. Ludwig Schaffrath, Stained Glass & Mosaic. LC 77-79948. 1977. write for info. (ISBN 0-686-05497-0). C & R Loo.

GLASTONBURY ABBEY
Capt, E. Raymond. The Traditions of Glastonbury. LC 82-72525. (Illus.). 128p. (Orig.). 1983. pap. 5.00 (ISBN 0-934666-10-5). Artisan Sales.
Maltwood, K. E. A Guide to Glastonbury's Temple of the Stars. 128p. 1983. pap. 11.95 (ISBN 0-227-67867-2, Pub. by J Clarke UK). Attic Pr.

GLORIFICATION (THEOLOGY)
see Glory of God

GLORY, DIVINE
see Glory of God

GLORY OF GOD
see also Theophanies
Abrahams, Israel & Buchler, Adolf. The Foundations of Jewish Life: Three Studies. LC 73-2197. (The Jewish People; History, Religion, Literature Ser.). 38.50 (ISBN 0-405-05263-4). Ayer Co Pubs.
Bomely, Steven. Glory to God: A Candlelight Service for Christmas. 1983. pap. 2.75 (ISBN 0-89536-625-8, 0733). CSS of Ohio.
Brown, Gerda. Carismas de Dios. (Span., Illus.). 589p. (Orig.). 1983. pap. 8.95 (ISBN 0-939868-98-9). Chr Intl Pubs.
Pendleton, Nathaniel D. The Glorification: Sermons & Papers. 2nd ed. 221p. 1985. Repr. of 1941 ed. 7.00 (ISBN 0-910557-10-1). Acad New Church.
Smith, W. R. Glorifying God. rev. ed. (Way of Life Ser.: No. 134). 1979. 3.95 (ISBN 0-89112-134-X, Bibl Res Pr). Abilene Christ U.
Warch, William A. How to Use Your Twelve Gifts from God. LC 76-41588. 112p. 1983. pap. 5.95 (ISBN 0-87516-530-3). De Vorss.

GLOSSOLALIA
see also Pentecostal Churches
Banks, William. Questions You Have Always Wanted to Ask about Tongues, but... (Illus.). 1979. pap. 2.25 (ISBN 0-89957-526-9). AMG Pubs.
Barnett, Donald L. & McGregor, Jeffrey P. Speaking in Other Tongues: A Scholarly Defense. 840p. 1986. 25.00 (ISBN 0-934287-23-6). Comm Chapel Pubns.
Basham, Don. Handbook on Tongues, Interpretation & Prophecy. (Handbk. Ser.: No. 2). 1971. pap. 2.95 (ISBN 0-88368-004-1). Whitaker Hse.
Bauman, Lewis. The Tongues Movement. 1979. pap. 1.00 (ISBN 0-88469-047-4). BMH Bks.
Baxter, Ronald E. The Charismatic Gift of Tongues. LC 81-17182. 162p. 1982. pap. 7.95 (ISBN 0-8254-2225-6). Kregel.
Black, R. L. Holy Ghost & Speaking in Tongues. 180p. (Orig.). 1983. pap. 4.95 (ISBN 0-934942-35-8, 1869). White Wing Pub.
Bouterse, Wesley. Scriptural Light on Speaking in Tongues. 1980. pap. 1.25 (ISBN 0-86544-010-7). Salv Army Suppl South.
Burgess, W. J. Glossolalia. 64p. 1968. pap. 1.00 (ISBN 0-89114-053-0). Baptist Pub Hse.
Christenson, Larry. Speaking in Tongues. LC 97-5595. 1968. pap. 3.95 (ISBN 0-87123-518-8, 200518). Bethany Hse.
Cook, Bob. Speaking in Tongues: Is That All There Is? (Discovery Bks.). (Illus.). 48p. (YA) 1982. pap. text ed. 1.50 (ISBN 0-88243-932-4, 02-0932); tchr's ed. 3.95 (02-0935). Gospel Pub.
Edgar, Thomas R. Miraculous Gifts: Are They for Today? 384p. 1983. 11.95 (ISBN 0-87213-133-5). Loizeaux.
Gromacki, Robert G. Modern Tongues Movement. pap. 4.95 (ISBN 0-8010-3708-5). Baker Bk.
--Modern Tongues Movement. 1967. pap. 4.95 (ISBN 0-87552-304-8). Presby & Reformed.
Gustafson, Robert R. Authors of Confusion. pap. 1.45 (ISBN 0-686-12743-9). Grace Pub Co.
Harris, Ralph W. Spoken by the Spirit. LC 73-87106. 128p. 1973. pap. 2.50 (ISBN 0-88243-725-9, 02-0725). Gospel Pub.
Hayes, Norvel. The Gift of Tongues & Interpretation. 1980. pap. 0.75 (ISBN 0-89274-374-3). Harrison Hse.
Heijkoop, H. L. Faith Healing & Speaking in Tongues. 40p. pap. 2.95 (ISBN 0-88172-083-6). Believers Bkshelf.
Horton, Stanley M. Tongues & Prophecy. (Charismatic Bks.). 32p. 1972. pap. 0.69 (ISBN 0-88243-917-0, 02-0917). Gospel Pub.
Humphreys, Fisher & Tolbert, Malcolm. Speaking in Tongues. LC 73-86749. 94p. (Orig.). 1973. pap. 3.00 (ISBN 0-914520-05-9). Insight Pr.
Kelsey, Morton. Tongue Speaking: The History & Meaning of the Charismatic Experience. 256p. 1981. pap. 8.95 (ISBN 0-8245-0073-3). Crossroad NY.
Lightner, Robert P. Speaking in Tongues & Divine Healing. LC 65-5805. 1978. pap. 1.95 (ISBN 0-87227-059-9). Reg Baptist.
Malony, H. Newton & Lovekin, A. Adams. Glossolalia: Behavioral Science Perspectives on Speaking in Tongues. 320p. 1985. 29.95x (ISBN 0-19-503569-0). Oxford U Pr.
Martin, Ira J. Glossolalia, the Gift of Tongues. 75p. 1970. pap. 2.25 (ISBN 0-87148-352-1). Pathway Pr.
Mauro, Philip. Speaking in Tongues. 1978. pap. 0.50 (ISBN 0-685-36793-2). Reiner.
Mills, Watson E. A Theological-Exegetical Approach to Glossolalia. 192p. (Orig.). 1985. lib. bdg. 25.00 (ISBN 0-8191-4526-2); pap. text ed. 10.75 (ISBN 0-8191-4527-0). U Pr of Amer.
Mills, Watson E., ed. Speaking in Tongues: A Guide to Research on Glossolalia. 552p. (Orig.). 1986. pap. 24.95 (ISBN 0-8028-0183-8). Eerdmans.
Montague, George T. The Spirit & His Gifts. LC 74-77425. 72p. (Orig.). 1974. pap. 1.95 (ISBN 0-8091-1829-7, Deus). Paulist Pr.
Pegram, Don R. Why We Do Not Speak in Tongues. 1982. pap. 1.25 (ISBN 0-89265-086-9). Randall Hse.
Picirilli, Robert. What the Bible Says about Tongues. 1981. pap. 0.95 (ISBN 0-89265-071-0). Randall Hse.
Schwab, Richard C. Let the Bible Speak...About Tongues. LC 85-8098. (Illus.). 144p. (Orig.). 1985. pap. 6.95 (ISBN 0-8254-3753-9). Kregel.
Sherrill, John. They Speak with Other Tongues. 144p. 1966. pap. 3.50 (ISBN 0-8007-8041-8, Spire Bks). Revell.
Smith, Charles R. Tongues in Biblical Perspective. pap. 4.95 (ISBN 0-88469-005-9). BMH Bks.
Turner, William H. Pentecost & Tongues. pap. 3.50 (ISBN 0-911866-83-3). Advocate.
Unger, Merrill F. New Testament Teaching on Tongues. LC 70-165057. 1971. pap. 5.95 (ISBN 0-8254-3900-0). Kregel.
Welborn, Don. On the Subject of Tongues: From the New Testament. 56p. pap. 0.50 (ISBN 0-937396-48-6). Walterick Pubs.
Why Should I Speak in Tongues? 1984. pap. 0.95 (ISBN 0-930756-85-1, 541012). Aglow Pubns.
Zeller, George W. God's Gift of Tongues: The Nature, Purpose, & Duration of Tongues As Taught in the Bible. LC 78-100. (Orig.). 1978. pap. 2.50 (ISBN 0-87213-985-9). Loizeaux.
Zodhiates, Spiros. Tongues!? (I Corinthians Ser.). (Illus.). 1974. pap. 6.95 (ISBN 0-89957-512-9). AMG Pubs.

GNOMES (MAXIMS)
see Aphorisms and Apothegms; Proverbs

GNOSTICISM
see also Mandaeans
Buckley, Jorunn J. Female Fault & Fulfilment in Gnosticism. LC 85-29020. (Studies in Religion). xvi, 180p. 1986. 32.50x (ISBN 0-8078-1696-5). U of NC Pr.
Doellinger, Johann J. Beitrage Zur Sektengenchichte des Mittelalter, 2 vols in 1. LC 91-26634. (Social Science Ser). (Ger). 1970. Repr. of 1890 ed. Set. lib. bdg. 57.50 (ISBN 0-8337-0880-5). B Franklin.
Doresse, Jean. The Secret Books of the Egyptian Gnostics. (Illus.). 446p. 1986. pap. 14.95 (ISBN 0-89281-107-2). Inner Tradit.
Fossum, Jarl E. The Name of God & the Angel of the Lord: Samaritan & Jewish Concepts of Intermeditation & the Origin of Gnosticism. 400p. 1985. lib. bdg. 54.00x (ISBN 3-16-144789-1, Pub. by J C B Mohr BRD). Coronet Bks.
Grant, Robert M., ed. Gnosticism: A Source Book of Heretical Writings from the Early Christian Period. LC 77-85274. Repr. of 1961 ed. 32.50 (ISBN 0-404-16108-1). AMS Pr.
Green, Henry A. The Economic & Social Origins of Gnosticism. (SBL Dissertation). 1985. 26.95 (ISBN 0-89130-842-3, 06-01-77); pap. 17.95 (ISBN 0-89130-843-1). Scholars Pr GA.
Hedrick, Dr. Charles W., Sr. & Hodgson, Robert, Jr. Nag Hammadi, Gnosticism & Early Christianity. 296p. 1986. pap. 14.95 (ISBN 0-913573-16-7). Hendrickson MA.
Ichazo, Oscar. Hypergnostic Questions & Concomitant Association for Discharging the Past. LC 86-70565. 90p. 1986. ring-binder 35.00 (ISBN 0-916554-13-9). Arica Inst Pr.
Jackson, Howard. The Lion Becomes Man: The Gnostic Leontomorphic Creator & the Creator & the Platonic Tradition. (SBL Dissertation Ser.). 1985. 17.95 (ISBN 0-89130-872-5, 06-01-81); pap. 11.95 (ISBN 0-89130-873-3). Scholars Pr GA.
Jonas, Hans. Gnostic Religion. 1958. pap. 10.95x (ISBN 0-8070-5799-1, BP259). Beacon Pr.

--Gnostic Religion: The Message of the Alien God & the Beginnings of Christianity. 2nd, rev. ed. 18.00 (ISBN 0-8446-2339-3). Peter Smith.

King, C. W. The Gnostics & Their Remains. LC 73-76092. (Secret Doctrine Reference Ser.). (Illus.). 500p. 1982. Repr. of 1887 ed. 21.00 (ISBN 0-913510-34-3). Wizards.

Kraeling, Carl H. Anthropos & Son of Man. LC 27-23162. (Columbia University. Oriental Studies: No. 25). Repr. of 1927 ed. 18.50 (ISBN 0-404-50515-5). AMS Pr.

Layton, Bentley. The Gnostic Scriptures: A New Translation with Annotations. LC 85-25234. (Illus.). 800p. 1987. 35.00 (ISBN 0-385-17447-0). Doubleday.

MacGregor, Geddes. Gnosis. LC 78-64908. 1979. pap. 10.75 (ISBN 0-8356-0522-1). Theos Pub Hse.

Mansel, Henry L. The Gnostic Heresies of the First & Second Centuries. Lightfoot, J. B., ed. LC 78-63170. (Heresies of the Early Christian & Medieval Era: Second Ser.). Repr. of 1875 ed. 42.00 (ISBN 0-404-16185-5). AMS Pr.

Massey, Gerald. Gnostic & Historic Christianity. 1985. pap. 5.95 (ISBN 0-916411-51-6). Sure Fire.

Meyer, Marvin W., tr. The Secret Teachings of Jesus: Four Gnostic Gospels. LC 84-42528. 224p. 1984. 15.45 (ISBN 0-394-52959-6). Random.

Pagels, Elaine. The Gnostic Gospels. LC 79-4764. 1979. 14.95 (ISBN 0-394-50278-7). Random.

Perkins, Pheme. The Gnostic Dialogue: The Early Church & Crisis of Gnosticism. LC 80-81441. (Theological Inquiries Ser.). 256p. 1980. pap. 7.95 (ISBN 0-8091-2320-7). Paulist Pr.

Quispel, Gilles & Scholem, Gershom. Jewish & Gnostic Man. LC 85-26137. (Eranos Lectures Ser.: No. 3). 46p. (Orig.). 1986. pap. 7.50 (ISBN 0-88214-403-0). Spring Pubns.

Raschke, Carl A. The Interruption of Eternity: Modern Gnosticism & the Origins of the New Religious Consciousness. LC 79-16460. 280p. 1980. 21.95x (ISBN 0-88229-374-5). Nelson-Hall.

Robinson, James M. The Nag Hammadi Library. 1978. 23.03i (ISBN 0-06-066929-2, HarpR); pap. 11.95 (CN4008). Har-Row.

Rudolph, Kurt. Gnosis: The Nature & History of Gnosticism. LC 81-47437. 411p. 1982. 28.45 (ISBN 0-06-067017-7, HarpR); pap. 14.95 (ISBN 0-06-067018-5, PL 4122). Har-Row.

Segal, Robert A. The Poimandres As Myth: Scholarly Theory & Gnostic Meaning. (Religion & Reason Ser.: No. 33). 216p. 1986. lib. bdg. 58.00x (ISBN 0-89925-146-3). Mouton.

Voegelin, Eric. Science, Politics & Gnosticism. LC 68-14367. 128p. 4.95 (ISBN 0-89526-964-3). Regnery Bks.

Walker, Benjamin. Gnosticism: Its History & Influence. 224p. 1984. pap. 9.95 (ISBN 0-85030-324-9). Newcastle Pub.

--Gnosticism: Its History & Influence. LC 86-34294. 320p. 1986. lib. bdg. 24.95x (ISBN 0-8095-7019-X). Borgo Pr.

Wilson, Robert M. The Gnostic Problem. LC 78-63175. (Heresies of the Early Christian & Medieval Era: Second Ser.). Repr. of 1958 ed. 32.00 (ISBN 0-404-16193-6). AMS Pr.

GOD

see also Agnosticism; Anthropomorphism; Atheism; Beatific Vision; Christianity; Creation; Deism; Fear of God; Free Thought; Glory of God; Goddesses; Holy Spirit; Jesus Christ; Metaphysics; Monotheism; Myth; Mythology; Natural Theology; Ontology; Pantheism; Providence and Government of God; Rationalism; Religion; Theism; Theodicy; Theology; Trinities; Trinity; Trust in God

Adams, James E. Liberacion: El Evangelo de Dios. 1980. pap. 2.95 (ISBN 0-85151-417-0). Banner of Truth.

Adams, Jay E. Godliness Through Discipline. 1977. pap. 1.25 (ISBN 0-8010-0057-2). Baker Bk.

Adams, Kenneth. Foolishness of God. 1981. pap. 5.95 (ISBN 0-87508-036-7). Chr Lit.

Adler, Mortimer J. How to Think About God: A Guide for the Twentieth-Century Pagan. 1980. 10.95 (ISBN 0-02-500540-5). Macmillan.

Alexander, S. Space, Time & Deity: The Gifford Lectures at Glasgow 1916-1918, 2 Vols. Set. 32.00 (ISBN 0-8446-1521-8). Peter Smith.

Allan, John. Shopping for a God. 218p. 1987. pap. price not set (ISBN 0-8010-0212-5). Baker Bk.

Allen, Grant. The Evolution of the Idea of God. 1977. lib. bdg. 59.95 (ISBN 0-8490-1796-3). Gordon Pr.

Allred, Gordon T. God the Father. 1979. 8.95 (ISBN 0-87747-746-9). Deseret Bk.

Anderson, Robert. The Silence of God. LC 78-9528. (Sir Robert Anderson Library). 232p. 1978. pap. 5.95 (ISBN 0-8254-2128-4). Kregel.

Angeles, Peter, ed. Critiques of God. pap. 7.00 (ISBN 0-87980-349-5). Wilshire.

Angeles, Peter A. The Problem of God: A Short Introduction. rev. ed. LC 73-85469. 156p. 1981. pap. text ed. 11.95 (ISBN 0-87975-216-5). Prometheus Bks.

Anselm Of Canterbury. Anselm of Canterbury: Why God Became Man. Hopkins, Jasper & Richardson, Herbert, eds. 105p. 1980. soft cover 7.95x (ISBN 0-88946-009-4). E Mellen.

Araya, Victorio. God of the Poor. Barr, Robert R., tr. from Span. 224p. (Orig.). 1987. 19.95 (ISBN 0-88344-566-2); pap. 9.95 (ISBN 0-88344-565-4). Orbis Bks.

Arya, Usharbudh. God. 162p. (Orig.). pap. 7.95 (ISBN 0-89389-060-X). Himalayan Pubs.

Association for Research & Enlightement, Readings Research Dept., compiled by. The Expanded Search for God: Pts. 1 & 2. (Library: Vol.16 & 17). Pt. 1 499pgs. 11/1983. 12.95 (ISBN 0-87604-153-5); Pt. 2 662pgs. 12/1983. 14.95 (ISBN 0-87604-154-3). ARE Pr.

Association for Research & Enlightenment, Inc. Virginia Beach, Va. Study Groups, et al, eds. Search for God: Nineteen Forty-Two to Nineteen Fifty, 2 Bks. 1942-1950. 4.95 ea. Bk. 1 (ISBN 0-87604-000-8). Bk. 2 (ISBN 0-87604-001-6). ARE Pr.

Baha'u'llah, the Bab & Abdu'l-Baha. Communion with God. large-type ed. 1976. pap. 1.50 (ISBN 0-87743-110-8, 315-011). Baha'i.

Bambrough, Renford. Reason, Truth & God. (Library Reprints Ser.). 174p. 1979. 45.00x (ISBN 0-416-72530-9, NO. 2823). Methuen Inc.

Bassler, Jouette M. Divine Impartiality: Paul & a Theological Axiom. Baird, William, ed. LC 81-1367. (Society of Biblical Literature Dissertation Ser.). 1981. pap. text ed. 13.50 (ISBN 0-89130-475-4, 0-06-01-59). Scholars Pr GA.

Beasley-Murray, George R. The Coming of God. 64p. 1983. pap. 3.95 (ISBN 0-85364-350-4, Pub. by Paternoster UK). Attic Pr.

Becker, Siegbert W. Foolishness of God. 1982. 8.95 (ISBN 0-8100-0155-1, 15N0383). Northwest Pub.

Belleggia, Sr. Concetta. God & the Problem of Evil. 1980. 3.75 (ISBN 0-8198-3007-0); pap. 2.50 (ISBN 0-8198-3008-9). Dghtrs St Paul.

Bernard, David K. The Oneness of God. Wallace, Mary K., ed. LC 86-19051. 326p. (Orig.). 1983. pap. 6.95 (ISBN 0-912315-12-1). Word Aflame.

Berry, Roger L. God's World-His Story. (Christian Day School Ser.). 1976. 18.80x (ISBN 0-87813-911-7); tchr's guide 19.65x (ISBN 0-87813-914-1). Christian Light.

Bisagno, John. God Is. 1981. 4.95 (ISBN 0-88207-345-1). Victor Bks.

Blair, Joe. When Bad Things Happen, God Still Loves. LC 85-13240. 1986. pap. 4.95 (ISBN 0-8054-5010-6). Broadman.

Boas, George. The Mind's Road to God: Bonaventura. 1953. pap. text ed. write for info. (ISBN 0-02-311250-6). Macmillan.

Bonaventura. The Problem of God & the Emotional Equilibrium of Man. (Illus.). 78p. 1984. pap. 23.75 (ISBN 0-89266-490-8). Am Classical Coll Pr.

Boudreaux, Florentin. God Our Father. LC 65-36485. pap. 55.00 (ISBN 0-317-10042-4, 2001664). Bks Demand UMI.

Bouyer, Louis. The Church of God. Quinn, Charles U., tr. 1983. 25.00 (ISBN 0-686-45823-0). Franciscan Herald.

Bowker, John. The Religious Imagination & the Sense of God. 1978. text ed. 32.50x (ISBN 0-19-826646-4). Oxford U Pr.

Braaten, Carl E. The Whole Counsel of God. LC 73-88345. pap. 44.00 (2026840). Bks Demand UMI.

Brightman, Edgar S. The Problem of God. LC 75-3085. (Philosophy in America Ser.). Repr. of 1930 ed. 27.50 (ISBN 0-404-59084-5). AMS Pr.

Brightman, Edgare S. The Problem of God. 1979. Repr. of 1930 ed. lib. bdg. 30.00 (ISBN 0-8482-7365-6). Norwood Edns.

Briscoe, Stuart. Taking God Seriously. 192p. 1986. 10.95 (ISBN 0-8499-0523-0, 0523-0). Word Bks.

Brizee, Robert. Where in the World Is God? God's Presence in Every Moment of Our Lives. 160p. 1987. pap. 6.95 (ISBN 0-8358-0556-5). Upper Room.

Brother Lawrence. The God-Illuminated Cook: The Practice of the Presence of God. Dawes, Robin, ed. LC 74-84399. (Illus.). 144p. 1975. pap. 2.50 (ISBN 0-914896-00-8, Strength). East Ridge Pr.

--God-Illuminated Cook: The Practice of the Presence of God. (East Ridge Press Ser.). (Illus.). 142p. 1980. pap. 4.50 (ISBN 0-89345-217-3). Garber Comm.

Brumback, Carl. God in Three Persons. 192p. 1959. pap. 4.95 (ISBN 0-87148-354-8). Pathway Pr.

Bryant, M. Darrol & Mataragnon, Rita H., eds. The Many Faces of Religion & Society. LC 84-26539. (God Ser.). 208p. (Orig.). 1985. 21.95 (ISBN 0-913757-20-9, Pub. by New Era Bks.); pap. 12.95 (ISBN 0-913757-21-7, Pub. by New Era Bks). Paragon Hse.

Bryson, Harold T. The Reality of Hell & the Goodness of God. LC 83-51674. 192p. 1984. pap. 4.95 (ISBN 0-8423-5279-1). Tyndale.

Calvin, John. Concerning the Eternal Predestination of God. Reid, J. K., tr. 1961. pap. 13.95 (ISBN 0-227-67438-3). Attic Pr.

Centre, Michael. In Search of God-the Solar Connection. LC 78-73706. (Illus.). 1978. 9.95x (ISBN 0-932876-00-5); pap. 5.95 (ISBN 0-932876-01-3). Centre Ent.

Clarke, Bowman & Long, Eugene T., eds. God & Temporality. (God Ser.). 320p. (Orig.). 1986. pap. 12.95 (ISBN 0-913757-10-1, Pub. by New Era Bks). Paragon Hse.

Clemens, David A. God Encountered, Vol. 1. LC 79-52420. (Steps to Maturity Ser.). 1973. tchrs'. manual 17.95x (ISBN 0-86508-002-X); student's manual 15.95x (ISBN 0-86508-001-1); visuals packett 4.95x (ISBN 0-86508-007-0). BCM Intl Inc.

Cochran, Louis. The Fool of God. (Heritage of a Movement Book Club Ser.). 416p. Repr. of 1958 ed. 11.95 (ISBN 0-89900-275-7). College Pr Pub.

Cohen, I. L. Urim & Thumim: The Secret of God. Murphy, G., ed. LC 82-24578. (Illus.). 280p. 1983. 16.95 (ISBN 0-910891-00-1). New Research.

Collins, James D. God in Modern Philosophy. LC 77-25963. 1978. Repr. of 1959 ed. lib. bdg. 32.75x (ISBN 0-313-20079-3, COGM). Greenwood.

Compton, Arthur H. Man's Destiny in Eternity. LC 75-117821. (Essay Index Reprint Ser). 1949. 19.00 (ISBN 0-8369-1762-6). Ayer Co Pubs.

Corlett, D. Shelby. God in the Present Tense. 176p. 1974. 1.95 (ISBN 0-8341-0248-X). Beacon Hill.

Cox, Willis F. Conversations about God from the Journal of Willis F. Cox. LC 85-91148. (Illus., Orig.). 1985. 11.95 (ISBN 0-9610758-2-1); pap. 6.95 (ISBN 0-9610758-3-X); pap. text ed. 6.95 (ISBN 0-9610758-1-3). W F Cox.

Craighead, Meinrad. The Mother's Songs: Images of God the Mother. LC 85-50408. 96p. (Orig.). 1985. pap. 9.95 (ISBN 0-8091-2716-4). Paulist Pr.

Creswell, Mike. Your God, My God. Pennington, Celeste, ed. (Human Touch-Photo Text Ser.). 172p. 1980. 7.95 (ISBN 0-937170-22-4). Home Mission.

Daughters of St. Paul. God or Nothing? 222p. 1985. 4.00 (ISBN 0-8198-3039-9); pap. 3.00 (ISBN 0-8198-3040-2). Dghtrs St Paul.

Davidson, Herbert. Proofs for Eternity, Creation, & the Existence of God in Medieval Islamic & Jewish Philosophy. (Studies in Northeast Culture & Society: Vol. 7). 500p. 1985. write for info. (ISBN 0-89003-180-0); pap. 62.00x (ISBN 0-89003-181-9). Undena Pubns.

Dean, William & Axel, Larry E., eds. The Size of God: The Theology of Bernard Loomer in Context. 96p. 1987. 16.95 (ISBN 0-86554-255-4, MUP H-223). Mercer Univ Pr.

De Nicolas, Antonio T. & Moutsopolous, Evanghelos, eds. God: Experience or Origin? (God Ser.). 256p. (Orig.). 1986. 21.95 (ISBN 0-913757-24-1, Pub. by New Era Bks); pap. 12.95 (ISBN 0-913757-25-X, Pub. by New Era Bks). Paragon Hse.

Doherty, Catherine D. Molchanie: The Silence of God. 112p. 1982. 8.95 (ISBN 0-8245-0407-0). Crossroad NY.

Doherty, Catherine de Hueck. Molchanie: The Silence of God. 128p. 1984. pap. 7.95 (ISBN 0-8245-0672-3). Crossroad NY.

Donceel, Joseph F. The Searching Mind: An Introduction to a Philosophy of God. LC 79-18166. 1979. text ed. 6.95 (ISBN 0-268-01700-X). U of Notre Dame Pr.

Duerlinger, James P., ed. Ultimate Reality & Spiritual Discipline. (God Ser.). 240p. (Orig.). 1984. text ed. 21.95 (ISBN 0-913757-09-8, Pub. by New Era Bks); pap. text ed. 12.95 (ISBN 0-913757-08-X, Pub. by New Era Bks). Paragon Hse.

Dugan, LeRoy. Help Yourself to a Healthier Mind. 112p. (Orig.). 1980. 5.95 (ISBN 0-87123-205-7, 210205). Bethany Hse.

Dumery, Henry. The Problem of God in Philosophy of Religion: A Critical Examination of the Category of the Absolute & the Scheme of Transcendence. Courtney, Charles, tr. (Studies in Phenomenology & Existential Philosophy). 135p. 1964. 14.95 (ISBN 0-8101-0083-5); pap. 8.95 (ISBN 0-8101-0606-X). Northwestern U Pr.

Durrant, Michael. The Logical Status of God. LC 72-93886. (New Studies in the Philosophy of Religion). 132p. 1973. 18.95 (ISBN 0-312-49455-6). St Martin.

Eaton, Jeffrey C., ed. For God & Clarity: New Essays in Honor of Austin Farrer. Loades, Ann. (Pittsburgh Theological Monographs New Series: No. 4). 206p. 1983. pap. 12.00 (ISBN 0-915138-52-2). Pickwick.

Edwards, Denis. Human Experience of God. 1984. pap. 7.95 (ISBN 0-8091-2559-5). Paulist Pr.

Edwards, F. Henry. God Our Help. 1981. pap. 11.00 (ISBN 0-8309-0310-0). Herald Hse.

Eisner, Will. A Contract with God. 136p. 1985. signed ed. o.p. 25.00 (ISBN 0-87816-017-5); pap. 7.95 (ISBN 0-87816-018-3). Kitchen Sink.

Elder, John. Belief in God in the Twentieth Century. LC 82-81671. 70p. 1982. pap. 3.25 (ISBN 0-9608440-0-7). Nur Pubns.

Emilsen, William W. & Irvine, A. D., eds. Remodelling God. 125p. (Orig.). 1983. pap. 7.95 (ISBN 0-85819-418-X, Pub. by JBCE). ANZ Religious Pubns.

Erickson, Millard J., ed. Readings In Christian Theology. 1973. pap. 12.95 (ISBN 0-8010-3305-5). Baker Bk.

Faber, Frederick W. The Creator & Creature. LC 78-66301. 1978. pap. 9.50 (ISBN 0-89555-076-8). TAN Bks Pubs.

Father Benedict, ed. Wondrous Is God in His Saints. LC 85-63506. (Illus.). 190p. (Orig.). 1985. pap. 6.95 (ISBN 0-936649-00-3). St Anthony Orthodox.

Ferre, Frederick P. & Mataragnon, Rita H., eds. God & Global Justice: Religion & Poverty in an Unequal World. LC 84-26538. (God Ser.). 224p. (Orig.). 1985. text ed. 21.95 (ISBN 0-913757-36-5, Pub. by New Era Bks.); pap. text ed. 12.95 (ISBN 0-913757-37-3, Pub. by New Era Bks.). Paragon Hse.

Ferre, Nels. The Christian Understanding of God. LC 78-12234. 1979. Repr. of 1951 ed. lib. bdg. 22.50x (ISBN 0-313-21183-3, FECU). Greenwood.

Flamming, Peter J. God & Creation. LC 85-6647. (Layman's Liberty of Christian Doctrine Ser.). 1985. 5.95 (ISBN 0-8054-1635-8). Broadman.

Freddoso, Alfred J., ed. The Existence & Nature of God. LC 83-47521. (Notre Dame Studies in Philosophy of Religion). 190p. 1984. 16.95x (ISBN 0-268-00910-4, 85-09119); pap. text ed. 9.95x (ISBN 0-268-00911-2). U of Notre Dame Pr.

Frost, Robert. Our Heavenly Father. LC 77-95191. 1978. pap. 3.95 (ISBN 0-88270-266-1). Bridge Pub.

Gee, Donald. Is It God? (Charismatic Bks.). 30p. 1972. pap. 0.69 (ISBN 0-88243-916-2, 02-0916). Gospel Pub.

Gill, Jerry H. On Knowing God. LC 81-10481. 174p. 1981. pap. 9.95 (ISBN 0-664-24380-0). Westminster.

Goblet D'Alviella, Eugene F. Lectures on the Origin & Growth of the Conception of God as Illustrated by Anthropology & History. Wicksteed, P. H., tr. LC 77-27163. (Hibbert Lectures: 1887). Repr. of 1892 ed. 34.00 (ISBN 0-404-60409-9). AMS Pr.

Goldsmith, Joel S. Conscious Union with God. 1977. pap. text ed. 5.95 (ISBN 0-8065-0578-8). Citadel Pr.

Goswami, Shrivatsa & Shinn, Larry, eds. In Search of the Divine: Some Unexpected Consequences of Interfaith Dialogue. (God Ser.). 240p. (Orig.). 1987. text ed. 22.95 (ISBN 0-913757-28-4, Pub. by New Era Bks.); pap. text ed. 12.95 (ISBN 0-913757-29-2, Pub. by New Era Bks). Paragon Hse.

Graham, Billy. Paz con Dios. Muntz, Carrie, tr. from Eng. Orig. Title: Peace with God. 272p. 1981. pap. 3.75 (ISBN 0-311-43037-6). Casa Bautista.

Gray, Donald. Finding God among Us. 2nd ed. LC 77-89322. 1977. pap. 3.95 (ISBN 0-88489-090-2). St Mary's.

Guest, Dean. Discovering the Word of God. 64p. (Orig.). 1980. pap. 1.95 (ISBN 0-89841-011-8). Zoe Pubns.

Habel, Norman C. Vahweh vs. Baal. 128p. 1964. write for info. Concordia Schl Grad Studies.

Halverstadt, Robert. God's Word for Your Healing. 1982. pap. 1.95 (ISBN 0-88144-003-5, CPS-003). Christian Pub.

--God's Word for Your Prosperity. 1982. pap. 1.95 (ISBN 0-88144-002-7, CPS-002). Christian Pub.

Hamilton, Elizabeth. I Stay in the Church. 183p. 1973. 4.95 (ISBN 0-85478-053-X). Attic Pr.

Hancock, James & Elliott, Hugh. The Herons Handbook. LC 84-47576. (Illus.). 288p. 1984. 24.45i (ISBN 0-06-015331-8, HarpT). Har-Row.

Hartshorne, Charles. The Divine Relativity: A Social Conception of God. LC 48-7802. (The Terry Lectures Ser.). 184p. 1982. pap. 7.95x (ISBN 0-300-02880-6, Y-430). Yale U Pr.

--Omnipotence & Other Theological Mistakes. LC 83-6588. 144p. 1983. 34.50 (ISBN 0-87395-770-9); pap. 9.95x (ISBN 0-87395-771-7). State U NY Pr.

Hartshorne, Charles & Reese, William L. Philosophers Speak of God. LC 53-10041. (Midway Reprint Ser.). 1976. 24.00x (ISBN 0-226-31862-1). U of Chicago Pr.

Haughton, Rosemary. The Passionate God. LC 81-80049. 352p. 1981. pap. 9.95 (ISBN 0-8091-2383-5). Paulist Pr.

Heijke, Joseph. St. Augustine's Comments on Imago Dei. 3.00 (ISBN 0-686-23375-1). Classical Folia.

Henry, Carl F. God, Revelation & Authority: God Who Speaks & Shows, Vols. 3, 4, 5 & 6. 1979. Vol. 3. 24.95 (ISBN 0-8499-0091-3); Vol. 4. 24.95 (ISBN 0-8499-0126-X); Vol. 5. 24.95 (ISBN 0-8499-0320-3); Vol. 6. 24.95 (ISBN 0-8499-0333-5). Word Bks.

Henry, Patrick & Stransky, Thomas F. God on Our Minds. LC 81-70593. 176p. 1982. pap. 6.95 (ISBN 0-8006-1600-6, 1-1600). Fortress.

--God on Our Minds. LC 81-70593. 176p. 1982. pap. 6.95 (ISBN 0-8146-1249-0). Liturgical Pr.

Hicks, Robert & Bewes, Richard. God. (Understanding Bible Truth Ser.). (Orig.). 1981. pap. 0.95 (ISBN 0-89840-024-4). Heres Life.

Holland, Thomas W. God & Jesus: Nothing More Than Four-Letter Words. 1987. 6.95 (ISBN 0-533-07206-9). Vantage.

Holmes, Arthur F. All Truth is God's Truth. LC 83-18411. 148p. 1983. pap. 4.95 (ISBN 0-87784-818-1). Inter-Varsity.

Howard, Leslie G. The Expansion of God. LC 81-4521. 464p. (Orig.). 1981. pap. 3.74 (ISBN 0-88344-121-7). Orbis Bks.

Huffmon, H. B., et al, eds. The Quest for the Kingdom of God: Essays in Honor of George E. Mendenhall. 1983. text ed. 20.00x (ISBN 0-931464-15-3). Eisenbrauns.

Humphreys, Fisher. La Naturaleza de Dios. Canclini, Arnoldo, tr. from Eng. (Biblioteca de Doctrina Cristiana). Tr. of The Nature of God. (Span.). 144p. (Orig.). 1987. pap. 5.95 (ISBN 0-311-09114-8). Casa Bautista.

Hutchinson, Roger. Works. 1842. 31.00 (ISBN 0-384-25120-X). Johnson Repr.

Ilon. The Supremacy of God. LC 80-66408. 1980. pap. 4.50 (ISBN 0-9600958-6-1). Birth Day.

Ingrams, Richard. God's Apology. (Illus.). 192p. 1986. pap. 13.95 (ISBN 0-241-11746-1, Pub. by Hamish Hamilton England). David & Charles.

Jarrett, Richard B. Gods Rainbowed Week. (Orig.). 1982. pap. text ed. 5.00 (ISBN 0-9606884-1-2). Jarrett.

Johann, Robert O. Pragmatic Meaning of God. (Aquinas Lecture). 1966. 7.95 (ISBN 0-87462-131-3). Marquette.

Johnstone, Parker L. Is God a Separate Being? LC 76-706635. 1977. cloth 7.95 (ISBN 0-917802-01-2). Theoscience Found.

Joyce, George H. Principles of Natural Theology. LC 79-170829. Repr. of 1923 ed. 37.45 (ISBN 0-404-03609-0). AMS Pr.

Kahn, Lothar, ed. God: What People Have Said about Him. 320p. 1980. 9.95 (ISBN 0-8246-0251-X). Jonathan David.

Kappeler, Max. The Seven Synonyms for God. Lee, Kathleen, tr. from Ger. LC 83-83266. Tr. of Die sieben Synonyme fur Gott. 400p. 35.00 (ISBN 0-942958-09-8). Kappeler Inst Pub.

Kaspar, Walter. God of Jesus Christ. rev. ed. 450p. 1986. text ed. 14.95 (ISBN 0-8245-0777-0). Crossroad NY.

Kasper, Walter. God's Time for Mankind. 93p. 1983. 8.00 (ISBN 0-8199-0812-6). Franciscan Herald.

Kaufman, Gordon D. God the Problem. LC 70-174543. 1972. 17.50x (ISBN 0-674-35525-3); pap. 8.95x (ISBN 0-674-35526-1). Harvard U Pr.

--The Theological Imagination: Constructing the Concept of God. LC 81-12960. 310p. 1981. pap. 13.95 (ISBN 0-664-24393-2). Westminster.

Kistler, Don, ed. God's Numbers in Creation, Vol. 1. 1986. pap. 4.95 (ISBN 0-940532-03-4). AOG.

Koushiafes, Nicholas J. God. LC 81-90329. (Illus.). 300p. 1982. 25.00 (ISBN 0-9607228-0-7). Gods Universe.

Kramer, William A. God's People. LC 75-16790. 1975. lib. bdg. 7.25 (ISBN 0-8100-0010-5, 06N552). Northwest Pub.

Krol, John C. God-the Cornerstone of Our Life. 1978. 5.50 (ISBN 0-8198-0531-9); pap. 3.95 (ISBN 0-8198-0532-7). Dghtrs St Paul.

Krol, Cardinal John. To Insure Peace Acknowledge God. 1978. 5.50 (ISBN 0-8198-0561-0); pap. 3.95 (ISBN 0-8198-0562-9). Dghtrs St Paul.

Kropf, Richard W. Evil & Evolution. LC 81-72041. 224p. 1983. 27.50 (ISBN 0-8386-3157-6). Fairleigh Dickinson.

Kuhlman, Kathryn. Nothing Is Impossible with God. (Orig.). 1976. pap. 1.75 (ISBN 0-89129-084-2). Jove Pubns.

Kung, Hans. Does God Exist? An Answer for Today. LC 81-40072. 864p. 1981. pap. 10.95 (ISBN 0-394-74737-2, Vin). Random.

Kupferle, Mary L. God Never Fails. 141p. 1983. pap. 4.95 (ISBN 0-87516-513-3). De Vorss.

Laird, Carobeth. Encounter with an Angry God. 1977. pap. 2.25 (ISBN 0-345-28464-X). Ballantine.

Larimore, John. The Creator of This World & the Universe. LC 78-54161. 1979. 13.95 (ISBN 0-87949-115-9). Ashley Bks.

Lawrence. Practice of the Presence of God. 128p. 1981. pap. 6.95 (ISBN 0-87243-129-0). Templegate.

Lawrence, Brother. The Practice of the Presence of God. Blaiklock, E. M., tr. 96p. 1982. pap. 4.95 (ISBN 0-8407-5803-0). Nelson.

--The Practice of the Presence of God. 96p. 1982. pap. 3.50 (ISBN 0-88368-105-6). Whitaker Hse.

Lee, Jung Y. The Theology of Change: A Christian Concept of God in an Eastern Perspective. LC 78-16745. 155p. (Orig.). 1979. pap. 5.95 (ISBN 0-88344-492-5). Orbis Bks.

Leuba, J. H. The Belief in God & Immortality, a Psychological, Anthropological & Statistical Study. LC 17-54. Repr. of 1916 ed. 29.00 (ISBN 0-527-56600-4). Kraus Repr.

Lloyd-Jones, D. Martyn. God's Ultimate Purpose. (Illus.). 12.95 (ISBN 0-8010-5591-1). Baker Bk.

Loomis, Farnsworth W. God Within. (Illus.). 1968. 5.95 (ISBN 0-8079-0122-9). October.

Lossky, Vladimir. In the Image & Likeness of God. LC 76-383878. 232p. 1974. pap. 9.95 (ISBN 0-913836-13-3). St Vladimirs.

--The Vision of God. 139p. 1963. 7.95 (ISBN 0-913836-19-2). St Vladimirs.

Loudy, Adlai. God's Eonian Purpose. text ed. 7.00 (ISBN 0-910424-56-X). Concordant.

McFague, Sallie. Metaphorical Theology: Models of God in Religious Language. LC 82-7246. 240p. 1982. pap. 11.95 (ISBN 0-8006-1687-1, 1-1687). Fortress.

McGinty, Park. Interpretation & Dionysos: Method in the Study of a God. (Religon & Reason Ser.: No. 16). 1978. 37.50x (ISBN 90-279-7844-1). Mouton.

Machlachlan, Lewis. God Face to Face. 160p. 1968. pap. 2.95 (ISBN 0-227-67728-5). Attic Pr.

Maclean, Angus H. The Idea of God in Protestant Religious Education. LC 75-177033. (Columbia University. Teachers College. Contributions to Education: No. 410). Repr. of 1930 ed. 22.50 (ISBN 0-404-55410-5). AMS Pr.

MacMaster, Eve. God's Family. LC 81-6551. (Story Bible Ser.: No. 1). (Illus.). 168p. 1981. pap. 5.95 (ISBN 0-8361-1964-9). Herald Pr.

McNeely, Kenneth. What Do We Really Know about God? LC 86-91364. 1987. 12.00 (ISBN 0-87212-201-8). Libra.

McTaggart, John. Some Dogmas of Religion. LC 7-7484. 1968. Repr. of 1906 ed. 23.00 (ISBN 0-527-60000-8). Kraus Repr.

Mains, David & Mains, Karen. The God Hunt: A Discovery Book for Men & Women. 1984. spiral wkbk. 4.95 (ISBN 0-89191-813-2, 58131). Cook.

Marsh, F. E. Living God's Way. LC 80-8073. 230p. (Reprint of The Spiritual Life). 1981. pap. 7.95 (ISBN 0-8254-3233-2). Kregel.

Martell, Dwane K. The Enigma of God & Man's Proclivity to Evil. (Institute for Religious Research Library). (Illus.). 77p. 1983. 47.75 (ISBN 0-89920-049-4). Am Inst Psych.

Matczak, Sebastian A., ed. God in Contemporary Thought: A Philosophical Perspective. LC 75-31391. (Philosophical Questions Ser.: No. 10). 1977. 65.00x (ISBN 0-912116-12-9). Learned Pubns.

Mathias, Willis D. Ideas of God & Conduct. LC 71-177059. (Columbia University. Teachers College. Contributions to Education: No. 874). Repr. of 1943 ed. 22.50 (ISBN 0-404-55874-7). AMS Pr.

Mays, Benjamin E. Negro's God As Reflected in His Literature. LC 69-16578. (Illus.). Repr. of 1938 ed. 24.75x (ISBN 0-8371-1139-0, MAG&, Pub. by Negro U Pr). Greenwood.

Meynell, Hugo A. The Intelligible Universe: A Cosmological Argument. LC 81-19065. 164p. 1982. 28.50x (ISBN 0-389-20253-3, 07057). B&N Imports.

Moltmann-Wendel, Elisabeth & Moltmann, Jurgen. Humanity in God. (Illus.). 160p. 1983. pap. 8.95 (ISBN 0-8298-0670-9). Pilgrim NY.

Moncure, Jane B. How Beautiful God's Gifts. Buerger, Jane, ed. LC 80-15434. (Illus.). 32p. 1980. 5.95 (ISBN 0-89565-172-6, 4923). Standard Pub.

Montstuart, John W. The Theory of the Physical Spirit & the Nature of God. (Illus.). 129p. 1987. 98.85 (ISBN 0-89266-591-2). Am Classical Coll Pr.

Moody, Dwight L. El Camino Hacia Dios. Orig. Title: The Way to God. (Span.). 128p. 1983. pap. 3.25 (ISBN 0-8254-1490-3). Kregel.

Mooney, Christopher F., ed. Presence & Absence of God. LC 68-8748. 1969. 20.00 (ISBN 0-8232-0810-9). Fordham.

Moscow Synod. Staff, ed. Preobrazhenije Gospodnje. Tr. of The Rransfiguration of the Lord. 128p. pap. 6.00 (ISBN 0-317-29169-6). Holy Trinity.

Mulford, Elisha. The Republic of God: An Institute of Theology. LC 75-3291. Repr. of 1881 ed. 18.00 (ISBN 0-404-59277-5). AMS Pr.

Mullet, Rosa M. God's Marvelous Work, Bk. 2. 1981. write for info. (ISBN 0-686-25256-X); tchr's. ed. avail. (ISBN 0-686-25257-8). Rod & Staff.

Murphree, Jon T. A Loving God & a Suffering World. LC 81-11759. 144p. (Orig.). 1981. pap. 4.50 (ISBN 0-87784-877-7). Inter-Varsity.

Murray, Andrew. Secret of Power from on High. (Secret Ser.). (Orig.). 1980. pap. 1.95 (ISBN 0-87508-392-7). Chr Lit.

Nash, Ronald. Concept of God. 1983. (cep) 5.95 (ISBN 0-310-45141-8, 12381P). Zondervan.

Newell, Theron A. My Friend God: This Amazing Universe! Who Made It? LC 82-73698. (Illus.). 92p. 1983. 9.95 (ISBN 0-9610080-0-8). Dentan Pr.

Nicholas Of Cusa. The Vision of God. Satter, Emma G., tr. LC 60-9104. pap. 3.95x (ISBN 0-8044-6594-0). Ungar.

O'Donnell, John J. Trinity & Temporality. (Oxford Theological Monographs). 1983. 32.50x (ISBN 0-19-826722-3). Oxford U Pr.

Ogilvie, Lloyd J. Autobiography of God. LC 78-53355. 324p. 1981. pap. 7.95 (ISBN 0-8307-0791-3, 5415106). Regal.

Ott, Heinrich. God. LC 73-5350. 128p. 1974. pap. 5.95 (ISBN 0-8042-0590-6). John Knox.

Our Father, Friend of Little Children Coloring Book. 1973. 2.50 (ISBN 0-89536-177-9, 1515). CSS of Ohio.

Packer, J. I. Knowing God. LC 73-81573. 1973. pap. 7.95 (ISBN 0-87784-770-3). Inter-Varsity.

Pettazzoni, Rattaele. The All Knowing God: Researches into the Early Religion & Cultlure. Bolle, Kees W., ed. LC 77-79150. (Mythology Ser.). (Illus.). 1978. Repr. of 1956 ed. lib. bdg. 40.00x (ISBN 0-405-10559-2). Ayer Co Pubs.

Phillips, John B. Your God Is Too Small. pap. 3.95 (ISBN 0-02-088540-7, Collier). Macmillan.

Pink, Arthur W. Gleanings in the Godhead. LC 75-15760. 256p. pap. 10.95 (ISBN 0-8024-3003-1). Moody.

Princehouse, Nona T. The Creator & the Creature. (Illus.). 96p. 1986. 9.95 (ISBN 0-89962-530-4). Todd & Honeywell.

Protopresbyter Michael Pomazansky. Bog Nash na Njbesi i na zjemli. Tr. of Our God is in Heaven & on Earth. 140p. 1985. pap. 5.00 (ISBN 0-317-29087-8). Holy Trinity.

Purdy, Alexander. The Reality of God: Thoughts on the Death of God Controversy. LC 67-23314. (Orig.). pap. 2.50x (ISBN 0-87574-154-1). Pendle Hill.

Qamar, J. God's Existence & Contemporary Science. pap. 1.00 (ISBN 0-686-18452-1). Kazi Pubns.

Reeves, Kenneth V. The Godhead. Rev. ed. Wallace, Mary H., ed. 1984. pap. 4.50 (ISBN 0-912315-64-4). Word Aflame.

Reichenbach, Bruce R. The Cosmological Argument: A Reassessment. (Illus.). 160p. 1972. 16.00x (ISBN 0-398-02387-5). C C Thomas.

Richardson, James. The God Who Shows Up. LC 81-47889. 55p. (Orig.). 1981. pap. 3.00 (ISBN 0-914520-16-4). Insight Pr.

Robertson, C. Alton. Is God Still Here: Q-Book No. 15. (Orig.). 1968. pap. 0.75 (ISBN 0-377-86371-8). Friend Pr.

Robinson, John A. Exploration into God. LC 67-26529. 1967. 4.95 (ISBN 0-8047-0322-1). Stanford U Pr.

--The Human Face of God. LC 73-78. 282p. 1979. softcover 5.95 (ISBN 0-664-24241-3). Westminster.

Rollins, Marion J. The God of the Old Testament in Relation to War. LC 72-176551. (Columbia University. Teachers College. Contributions to Education Ser.: No. 263). Repr. of 1927 ed. 22.50 (ISBN 0-404-55263-3). AMS Pr.

Rosenthal, Stanley. One God or Three? 1978. pap. text ed. 2.25 (ISBN 0-87508-464-8). Chr Lit.

Roth, John & Sontag, Fredrick E., eds. The Defense of God. LC 84-25592. (God Ser.). 196p. (Orig.). 1985. text ed. 21.95 (ISBN 0-913757-26-8, Pub. by New Era Bks); pap. text ed. 12.95 (ISBN 0-913757-27-6, Pub. by New Era Bks). Paragon Hse.

Sadtler, Barbara. The Echo is of God. 96p. (Orig.). 1986. pap. 1.90 (ISBN 0-88028-052-2). Forward Movement.

St. Thomas Aquinas. Summa Contra Gentiles, 4 bks. Incl. Bk. 1. God. Pegis, Anton C., tr. 317p. pap. 7.45x (ISBN 0-268-01678-X); Bk. 2. Creation. Anderson, James F., tr. 351p. text ed. 16.95 (ISBN 0-268-01679-8); pap. 7.45 (ISBN 0-268-01680-1); Bk. 3. Providence, 2 bks. in 1. Bourke, Vernon J., tr. 560p. text ed. 35.00x (ISBN 0-268-01681-X); pap. 15.00x (ISBN 0-268-01682-8); Bk. 4. Salvation. O'Neil, Charles J., tr. 360p. text ed. 16.95 (ISBN 0-268-01683-6); pap. 8.95x (ISBN 0-268-01684-4). LC 75-19883. 1975. Set. pap. 35.00. U of Notre Dame Pr.

Scharlemann, Robert P., ed. Naming God. (The Contemporary Discussion Ser.). 224p. (Orig.). 1986. 21.95 (ISBN 0-913757-22-5, Pub. by New Era Bks.); pap. 12.95 (ISBN 0-913757-23-3, Pub. by New Era Bks). Paragon Hse.

Schlink, Basilea. God Laments & Our Response. Tr. of Gott Klagt und Unsere Antwort. 64p. 1981. 0.50 (ISBN 3-87209-625-7). Evang Sisterhood Mary.

Seth, Pattison A. Idea of God in the Light of Recent Philosophy: Gifford Lectures Delivered in the University of Aberdeen, 1912 & 1913. 2nd ed. rev. ed. Repr. of 1920 ed. 29.00 (ISBN 0-527-81500-4). Kraus Repr.

Shannon, Foster H. God Is Light. LC 80-83606. (Illus.). 240p. (Orig.). 1981. pap. 6.95 (ISBN 0-938462-00-8). Green Leaf CA.

Shea, John. Stories of God: An Unauthorized Biography. 1978. pap. 8.95 (ISBN 0-88347-085-3). Thomas More.

Sherer, Michael L. And God Said... Yes! 1983. 5.75 (ISBN 0-89536-634-7, 0123). CSS of Ohio.

Showers, Renald E. What on Earth Is God Doing? Satan's Conflict with God: Study Guide. 48p. 1983. pap. 3.50 (ISBN 0-87213-785-6). Loizeaux.

Smith, Joyce M. A Rejoicing Heart. 1979. pap. 2.95 (ISBN 0-8423-5418-2). Tyndale.

Solovyev, Vladimir. God, Man & the Church. Attwater, Donald, tr. from Rus. 192p. 1975. 10.95 (ISBN 0-227-67690-4). Attic Pr.

--Lectures in Godmanhood. 214p. 1981. 37.00x (ISBN 0-234-77047-3, Pub. by Dobson Bks England). State Mutual Bk.

Sontag, Frederick & Bryant, Darrol, eds. God, the Contemporary Discussion. LC 82-70771. 419p. (Orig.). 1982. pap. 13.95 (ISBN 0-318-03629-0). Rose Sharon Pr.

Sontag, Frederick & Bryant, M. Darrol, eds. God: The Contemporary Discussion. LC 82-70771. (Conference Ser.: No. 12). vi, 419p. (Orig.). 1982. pap. text ed. 12.95 (ISBN 0-932894-12-7, Pub. by New Era Bks). Paragon Hse.

Stark, Claude. God of All. 1982. 20.00 (ISBN 0-89007-000-8); pap. 6.00 (ISBN 0-89007-102-0). Branden Pub Co.

Staton, Knofel. How to Know the Will of God. LC 78-62707. 96p. (Orig.). 1979. pap. 2.95 (ISBN 0-87239-985-0, 39948). Standard Pub.

Steeman, T. What's Wrong with God. McNamee, Fantan, ed. (Synthesis Ser.). pap. 0.75 (ISBN 0-8199-0391-4). Franciscan Herald.

Steiner, Robert A. The Truth Shall Make You Free: An Inquiry into the Legend of God. LC 80-80646. (Illus.). 56p. (Orig.). 1980. pap. 3.95 (ISBN 0-9604044-0-6). Penseur Pr.

Steuer, Alexel D. & McClendon, James W., Jr., eds. Is God God? LC 81-1927. 288p. (Orig.). 1981. pap. 10.95 (ISBN 0-687-19703-1). Abingdon.

Stowell, Joseph M. Kingdom Conflict. 156p. 1984. pap. 5.95 (ISBN 0-89693-376-8). Victor Bks.

Sutherland, Stewart R. God, Jesus & Belief: The Legacy of Theism. 160p. 1984. 29.95x (ISBN 0-631-13548-0); pap. 12.95 (ISBN 0-631-13591-X). Basil Blackwell.

Sweeney, Terrance A. God &... Thirty Interviews. 240p. 1985. pap. 8.95 (ISBN 0-86683-804-X, 8404, HarpR). Har-Row.

Swinburne, Richard. The Existence of God. 1979. 42.00x (ISBN 0-19-824611-0); pap. 10.95x (ISBN 0-19-824778-8). Oxford U Pr.

Thomas, Owen C. God's Activity in the World: The Contemporary Debate. LC 82-19148. (AAR Studies in Religion). 248p. 1983. pap. 8.50 (ISBN 0-89130-602-1, 01 00 31). Scholars Pr GA.

Thompson, Bert. Theistic Evolution. pap. 5.50 (ISBN 0-89315-300-1). Lambert Bk.

Tozer, A. W. La Busqueda de Dios. Bruchez, Dardo, tr. 130p. (Orig.). 1979. pap. 2.75 (ISBN 0-87509-162-8); pap. 2.00 mass mkt. (ISBN 0-87509-159-8). Chr Pubns.

Tracey, David. Analogical Imagination. 496p. 1985. pap. 14.95 (ISBN 0-8245-0694-4). Crossroad NY.

Tracy, Thomas F. God, Action & Embodiment. 208p. (Orig.). 1984. pap. 11.95 (ISBN 0-8028-1999-0). Eerdmans.

Treash, Gordon. Kant: Einzig Mogliche Beweisgrund. LC 77-86227. Tr. of The One Possible Basis for a Demonstration of the Existence of God. 1978. 20.00 (ISBN 0-913870-37-4). Abaris Bks.

Turner, J. E. The Revelation of Deity. Repr. of 1931 ed. 20.00 (ISBN 0-527-91170-4). Kraus Repr.

Turner, J. J. & Myers, Edwards. Doctrine of the Godhead. pap. 5.50 (ISBN 0-89137-553-8). Quality Pubns.

Varghese, Roy A., ed. The Intellectuals Speak Out About God. 1984. pap. 7.95 (ISBN 0-89526-827-2). Regnery Bks.

Varillon, Francois. The Humility & Suffering of God. Marans, Nelly, ed. LC 83-2724. 202p. (Orig.). 1983. pap. 8.95 (ISBN 0-8189-0448-8). Alba.

Verheijen, J. A. Het Hoogste Wezen Bij De Manggaraiers. Repr. of 1951 ed. 46.00 (ISBN 0-384-64290-X). Johnson Repr.

Vinoi, Lawrence. God & Man: The Essential Knowledge Which Everyone, but Absolutely Everyone Ought to Possess About Human Nature & the Nature of God & How the Two Are Related. (Essential Knowledge Ser. Books). (Illus.). 1978. plastic spiral bdg. 44.75 (ISBN 0-89266-118-6). Am Classical Coll Pr.

Voillaume, Rene. The Living God. 1971. 5.95 (ISBN 0-87193-169-9). Dimension Bks.

Wainwright, Geoffrey. Doxology: The Praise of God in Worship, Doctrine & Life: A Systematic Theology. 1980. 35.00x (ISBN 0-19-520192-2); pap. 12.95 (ISBN 0-19-520433-6). Oxford U Pr.

Warburton, John. Mercies of a Covenant God. pap. 6.95 (ISBN 0-686-66520-1). Reiner.

Warren, Mervyn A. God Made Known. Wheeler, Gerald, ed. LC 83-17677. (Illus.). 94p. (Orig.). 1983. pap. 5.95 (ISBN 0-8280-0230-4). Review & Herald.

Warren, Thomas B. & Matson, Wallace I. Warren-Matson Debate on the Existence of God. LC 78-64546. 1979. 14.00 (ISBN 0-934916-41-1); pap. 11.00 (ISBN 0-934916-45-4). Natl Christian Pr.

Warren, Thomas B. & Flew, A. G. N., eds. Warren-Flew Debate on the Existence of God. 1977. 14.00 (ISBN 0-934916-40-3). Natl Christian Pr.

Webb, Clement C. Divine Personality & Human Life: Being the Gifford Lectures Delivered in the University of Aberdeen in the Years 1918 & 1919, Second Course. facsimile ed. LC 77-37917. (Select Bibliographies Reprint Ser.). Repr. of 1920 ed. 21.00 (ISBN 0-8369-6754-2). Ayer Co Pubs.

--God & Personality: Being the Gifford Lectures Delivered in the University of Aberdeen in the Years 1918 & 1919. facsimile ed. LC 76-164632. (Select Bibliographies Reprint Ser.). Repr. of 1919 ed. 20.00 (ISBN 0-8369-5916-7). Ayer Co Pubs.

White, David M. The Search for God. 448p. 1983. 24.95 (ISBN 0-02-627110-9). Macmillan.

Wilder-Smith, A. E. He Who Thinks Has to Believe. 91p. 1982. pap. 2.95 (ISBN 0-87123-259-6, 200259). Bethany Hse.

Wilmot, Laurence. Whitehead & God: Prolegomena to Theological Reconstruction. 200p. 1979. text ed. 17.25x (ISBN 0-88920-070-X, Pub. by Wilfrid Laurier Canada). Humanities.

Wise, Charles C., Jr. Thus Saith the Lord: The Autobiography of God. LC 84-60414. 293p. (Orig.). 1984. pap. 7.95 (ISBN 0-917023-07-2). Magian Pr.

Yogananda, Paramahansa. Man's Eternal Quest. LC 75-17183. (Illus.). 503p. 1982. 9.95 (ISBN 0-87612-233-0); Italian ed. 10.00x (ISBN 0-87612-237-3). Self Realization.

Yohn, Rick. What Every Christian Should Know about God: A Study Manual. LC 76-20396. 80p. 1976. 3.95 (ISBN 0-89081-054-0). Harvest Hse.

Young, Henry J. God & Human Freedom: A Festschrift in Honor of Howard Thurman. 200p. 1982. text ed. 13.95 (ISBN 0-913408-81-6). Friends United.

Zubiri, Xavier. Nature, History, God. Fowler, Thomas B., Jr., tr. from Span. LC 80-1355. 441p. 1981. lib. bdg. 31.25; pap. text ed. 17.75. U Pr of Amer.

GOD–ANGER

see God–Wrath

GOD–ART

see also Gods in Art; Jesus Christ–Art

Baldwin, Louis. Portraits of God: Word Pictures of the Deity from the Earliest Times Through Today. LC 85-43571. 192p. 1986. lib. bdg. 18.95x (ISBN 0-89950-198-2). McFarland & Co.

Hamilton, James D. The Faces of God. 100p. 1985. pap. 3.95 (ISBN 0-8341-0940-9). Beacon Hill.

Stucki, Margaret E. War on Light: The Destruction of the Image of God in Man Through Modern Art. 1975. 15.00 (ISBN 0-686-23419-7). Birds' Meadow Pub.

GOD–ATTRIBUTES

see also Providence and Government of God

The Attributes of God. (Orig.). 1987. pap. 1.95 (ISBN 0-8024-0737-4). Moody.

Charnock, Stephen. Existence & Attributes of God, 2 vols. 1979. Repr. 29.95 set (ISBN 0-8010-2437-4). Baker Bk.

Derham, William. Physico-Theology: A Demonstration of the Being & Attributes of God, from His Works of Creation. Egerton, Frank N., 3rd, ed. LC 77-74212. (History of Ecology Ser.). 1978. Repr. of 1716 ed. lib. bdg. 37.50 (ISBN 0-405-10383-2). Ayer Co Pubs.

Farnell, Lewis R. The Attributes of God. LC 77-27205. (Gifford Lectures Ser.: 1924-25). 296p. Repr. of 1925 ed. 34.50 (ISBN 0-404-60475-7). AMS Pr.

Fox, Douglas A. What Do You Think about God. 96p. 1985. pap. 4.95 (ISBN 0-8170-1077-7). Judson.

Henry, Carl F. God, Revelation & Authority: God Who Speaks & Shows, Vols. 3, 4, 5 & 6. 1979. Vol. 3. 24.95 (ISBN 0-8499-0091-3); Vol. 4. 24.95 (ISBN 0-8499-0126-X); Vol. 5. 24.95 (ISBN 0-8499-0320-3); Vol. 6. 24.95 (ISBN 0-8499-0333-5). Word Bks.

Knudsen, Harald. Gottesbeweise im Deutschen Idealismus: Die modaltheoretische Begruendung des Absoluten, dargestellt an Kant, Hegel und Weisse. (Theologische Bibliothek Toepelmann 23). vi, 280p. 1972. 31.60x (ISBN 3-11-003787-4). De Gruyter.

Maloney, George S. A Theology of Uncreated Energies of God. (Pere Marquette Lecture Ser.). 1978. 7.95 (ISBN 0-87462-516-5). Marquette.

Ochs, Carol. Behind the Sex of God: Toward a New Consciousness - Transcending Matriarchy & Patriarchy. LC 76-48519. 1977. pap. 8.95x (ISBN 0-8070-1113-4, Pub. by Ariadne Bks, BPA12). Beacon Pr.

Ost, Steve. The Lord's Balance. 32p. 1979. pap. 0.95 (ISBN 0-930756-43-6, 541007). Aglow Pubns.

Pink, A. W. Los Atributos de Dios. 2.95 (ISBN 0-686-12561-4). Banner of Truth.

Plantinga, Alvin. Does God Have a Nature? LC 80-65585. (Aquinas Lecture Ser.). 1980. 7.95 (ISBN 0-87462-145-3). Marquette.

Scharlemann, Robert P. The Being of God: Theology & the Experience of Truth. 224p. 1981. 14.95 (ISBN 0-8164-0494-1, HarpR). Har-Row.

Schillebeeckx, Edward & Metz, Johannes B. God & Father, Vol. 143. (Concilium 1981). 128p. (Orig.). 1981. pap. 6.95 (ISBN 0-8164-2310-5, HarpR). Har-Row.

Scragg, Walter R. Directions: A Look at the Paths of Life. LC 77-78101. (Horizon Ser.). 1977. pap. 5.95 (ISBN 0-8127-0136-4). Review & Herald.

Strauss, Lehman. First Person. LC 67-20931. 1967. 7.95 (ISBN 0-87213-815-1). Loizeaux.

Strauss, Richard L. The Joy of Knowing God. 305p. 1984. pap. 8.95 (ISBN 0-87213-834-8). Loizeaux.

Swain, Joseph R. What Does God Do All Day? 1977. 7.00 (ISBN 0-682-48919-0, Testament). Exposition Pr FL.

Swinburne, Richard. The Coherence of Theism. (Clarendon Library of Logic & Philosophy). 1977. 42.00x (ISBN 0-19-824410-X). Oxford U Pr.

Synan, J. A. The Trinity, or the Tri-Personal Being of God. pap. 2.95 (ISBN 0-911866-00-0). Advocate.

Tozer, A. W. The Knowledge of the Holy. LC 75-12279. 128p. 1978. pap. 6.95 (ISBN 0-06-068412-7, RD 291, HarpR). Har-Row.

Walters, Julie & De Leu, Barbara. God Is Like: Three Parables for Little Children. (Illus.). 96p. 1974. pap. 1.95 (ISBN 0-87793-073-2). Ave Maria.

GOD–BIBLICAL TEACHING

Cottrell, Jack. What the Bible Says about God the Creator. (What the Bible Says Ser.). 1983. 13.95 (ISBN 0-89900-094-0). College Pr Pub.

Cottvell, Jack. What the Bible Says about God the Ruler. (What the Bible Says about Ser.). 465p. 13.95 (ISBN 0-89900-094-0). College Pr Pub.

Crenshaw, James L. Hymnic Affirmation of Divine Justice. LC 75-22349. (Society of Biblical Literature. Dissertation Ser.: No. 24). Repr. of 1975 ed. 36.10 (ISBN 0-8357-9571-3, 2017523). Bks Demand UMI.

De Dietrich, Suzanne. The Witnessing Community: The Biblical Record of God's Purpose. LC 58-5020. 180p. 1978. pap. 3.95 (ISBN 0-664-24199-9). Westminster.

God's Financial Partner: A Bible Course on God, Money & You. write for info. (ISBN 0-9607644-0-2). Financial.

Gray, John. The Biblical Doctrine of the Reign of God. 414p. 29.95 (ISBN 0-567-09300-X, Pub. by T & T Clark Ltd UK). Fortress.

Hamerton-Kelly, Robert. God the Father: Theology & Patriarchy in the Teaching of Jesus, No. 4. Brueggemann, Walter & Donahue, John R., eds. LC 78-54551. (Overtures to Biblical Theology Ser.). 144p. 1979. pap. 8.95 (ISBN 0-8006-1528-X, 1-1528). Fortress.

Henry, Carl F. God, Revelation & Authority: God Who Speaks & Shows, Vols. 1 & 2. Incl. Vol. 1 (ISBN 0-87680-477-6, 80477); Vol. 2 (ISBN 0-87680-485-7, 80485). LC 76-15936. 1976. 22.95 ea. Word Bks.

Holbrook, Clyde A. The Iconoclastic Deity: Biblical Images of God. 240p. 1984. 29.50 (ISBN 0-8387-5069-9). Bucknell U Pr.

Humphreys, Fisher. The Nature of God. LC 84-20037. (Layman's Library of Christian Doctrine Ser.). 1985. 5.95 (ISBN 0-8054-1634-X). Broadman.

Ishee, John A. What Every Person Should Know About God: Bible Study for New Christians. 36p. 1982. pap. 3.50 (ISBN 0-939298-05-8). J M Prods.

Jenson, Robert W. The Triune Identity: God According to the Gospel. LC 81-43091. 1982. 16.95 (ISBN 0-8006-0672-8). Fortress.

--The Triune Identity: God According to the Gospel. LC 81-43091. pap. 51.80 (2029621). Bks Demand UMI.

Lawson, LeRoy. God's Word A. D. LC 83-348. 112p. (Orig.). 1984. pap. 2.95 (ISBN 0-87239-668-1, 41022). Standard Pub.

McCaffrey, James. Thirsting for God in Scripture. 96p. 1984. pap. 2.95 (ISBN 0-914544-55-1). Living Flame Pr.

McDowell, Josh & Bellis, Dale. Evidence Growth Guide, Vol. 2: Uniqueness of the Bible. 80p. (Orig.). 1981. 4.95 (ISBN 0-86605-019-1). Campus Crusade.

Nystrom, Carolyn. Behold Your Christ: A Woman's Workshop on Jesus. (Woman's Workshop Ser.). 128p. (Orig.). 1985. pap. 3.95 (ISBN 0-310-41981-6, 11284P). Zondervan.

Parke-Taylor, G. H. Yahweh: The Divine Name in the Bible. 134p. 1975. text ed. 14.95x (ISBN 0-88920-014-9, Pub. by Wilfrid Laurier Canada). Humanities.

Splitter, Russell P. God the Father. LC 76-20888. (Radiant Life Ser.). 128p. 1976. pap. 2.50 (ISBN 0-88243-898-0, 02-0898, Radiant Bks); teacher's ed 3.95 (ISBN 0-88243-170-6, 32-0170). Gospel Pub.

Wade, John W. God's Word B. C. LC 83-349. (Orig.). 1983. pap. 2.95 (ISBN 0-87239-667-3, 41020). Standard Pub.

Williamson, Denise J. Bible Readings on God's Creation. (Bible Readings Ser.). 112p. (Orig.). 1987. pap. 3.95 (ISBN 0-8066-2277-6, 10-0696). Augsburg.

Zimmerli, Walther. I Am Yahweh. Brueggemann, Walter, ed. Scott, Doug, tr. from German. LC 81-85326. 160p. 1982. 15.95 (ISBN 0-8042-0519-1). John Knox.

GOD–COMPARATIVE STUDIES

Roberts, Brigham H. Mormon Doctrine of Deity: The Roberts-Van der Donckt Discussion. 296p. 1975. 9.95 (ISBN 0-88290-058-7). Horizon Utah.

Spencer, H. S. The Mysteries of God in the Universe: Including the Reincarnation & Karma in the Gathas, the Bible, & Koran, 2 vols. Repr. of 1967 ed. Set. text ed. 35.00x. Coronet Bks.

GOD–FEAR

see Fear of God

GOD–GLORY

see Glory of God

GOD–HISTORY OF DOCTRINES

Brandewie, Ernest. Wilhelm Schmidt & the Origin of the Idea of God. 352p. (Orig.). 1983. lib. bdg. 30.00 (ISBN 0-8191-3363-9); pap. text ed. 15.50 (ISBN 0-8191-3364-7). U Pr of Amer.

Empson, William. Milton's God. LC 78-14409. 1978. Repr. of 1961 ed. lib. bdg. 27.50x (ISBN 0-313-21021-7, EMMG). Greenwood.

Hick, John H. Existence of God. 305p. 1964. pap. 4.95 (ISBN 0-02-085450-1, Collier). Macmillan.

Jones, Kenneth E. The Word of God. 1980. pap. 3.95 (ISBN 0-87162-224-6, D9205). Warner Pr.

King, J. Norman. The God of Forgiveness & Healing in the Theology of Karl Rahner. LC 81-40932. 100p. (Orig.). 1982. lib. bdg. 24.00 (ISBN 0-8191-2237-8); pap. text ed. 8.25 (ISBN 0-8191-2238-6). U Pr of Amer.

Kung, Hans. Does God Exist? An Answer for Today. LC 81-40072. 864p. 1981. pap. 10.95 (ISBN 0-394-74737-2, Vin). Random.

Lossky, Vladimir. The Vision of God. 139p. 1963. 7.95 (ISBN 0-913836-19-2). St Vladimirs.

Murray, John C. Problem of God: Yesterday & Today. (St. Thomas More Lectures Ser.: No. 1). (Orig.). 1964. pap. 5.95x (ISBN 0-300-00171-1, Y138). Yale U Pr.

Patterson, Robert L. The Conception of God in the Philosophy of Thomas Aquinas. 508p. 1977. Repr. of 1935 ed. lib. bdg. 30.00 (ISBN 0-915172-27-5). Richwood Pub.

Taylor, Mark L. God Is Love: A Study in the Theology of Karl Rahner. (AAR-Academy Ser.). 1986. 24.95 (ISBN 0-89130-925-X, 01-01-50); pap. 18.25 (ISBN 0-89130-926-8). Scholars Pr GA.

Winchell, Paul. God Two Thousand: Religion Without the Bible. LC 82-71878. 329p. 1982. 20.00 (ISBN 0-9608772-0-7). April Enterp.

GOD–IMMANENCE

see Immanence of God

GOD–JUVENILE LITERATURE

Anderson, Debby. God Loves Even Me. (Happy Day Bks.). (Illus.). 24p. 1985. 1.59 (ISBN 0-87239-873-0, 3673). Standard Pub.

Bennett, Marian. God Made Chickens. (Happy Day Bks.). (Illus.). 24p. 1985. 1.59 (ISBN 0-87239-874-9, 3674). Standard Pub.

--Thank You, God. (My Surprise Book Ser.). (Illus.). 10p. 1985. 4.95 (ISBN 0-87239-906-0, 2730). Standard Pub.

Bennett, Marian, ed. God Made Me. (My Shape Book Ser.). (Illus.). 10p. 1985. 2.95 (ISBN 0-87239-908-7, 2748). Standard Pub.

Boyer, Linda. God Made Me. LC 81-50677. (A Happy Day Bks.). (Illus.). 24p. (Orig.). 1981. pap. 1.59 (ISBN 0-87239-464-6, 3597). Standard Pub.

Brooks, Sandra. I Can Pray to God. LC 82-80031. (Happy Day Bks.). (Illus.). 24p. (Orig.). 1982. pap. 1.59 (ISBN 0-87239-540-5, 3586). Standard Pub.

Cachiaras, Dot. God Created Me Too! (Happy Day Bks.). (Illus.). 32p. 1987. 1.59 (ISBN 0-87403-274-1, 3774). Standard Pub.

Cone, Molly. About God. (Shema Storybooks: No. 4). (Illus.). 64p. 1973. pap. 5.00 (ISBN 0-8074-0126-9, 101084). UAHC.

Davis, Jennie. Praise Him, Praise Him! 1982. pap. text ed. 4.95 (ISBN 0-89693-208-7, Sonflower Bks). SP Pubns.

Dean, Bessie. Aprendamos el Plan de Dios. Balderas, Eduardo, tr. from Eng. LC 80-82256. (Books for LDS Children Ser.). Orig. Title: Let's Learn God's Plan. (Span., Illus.). 64p. (Orig.). 1980. pap. text ed. 3.95 (ISBN 0-88290-135-4). Horizon Utah.

Fitzgerald, Annie. Dear God, Let's Play. LC 83-70495. 16p. (Orig.). 1983. pap. 1.50 (ISBN 0-8066-2001-3, 10-1852). Augsburg.

--Dear God, Thanks for Thinking up Love. LC 83-70499. 16p. 1983. pap. 1.50 (ISBN 0-8066-2005-6, 10-1853). Augsburg.

--Dear God, Thanks for Your Help. LC 83-70496. 16p. 1983. pap. 1.50 (ISBN 0-8066-2002-1, 10-1854). Augsburg.

--Dear God, We Just Love Christmas. LC 83-70494. 16p. (Orig.). 1983. pap. 1.50 (ISBN 0-8066-2000-5, 10-1855). Augsburg.

--Dear God, Where Do You Live? LC 83-70497. 16p. 1983. pap. 1.50 (ISBN 0-8066-2003-X, 10-1856). Augsburg.

--Dear God, Your World Is Wonderful. LC 83-70498. 16p. 1983. pap. 1.50 (ISBN 0-8066-2004-8, 10-1857). Augsburg.

Ford, Lauren. Little Book about God. LC 81-43749. (Illus.). 48p. 1985. 9.95 (ISBN 0-385-17691-0). Doubleday.

Frost, Marie H. I Thank God. (First Happy Day Bks.). (Illus.). 20p. 1986. casebound 1.29 (ISBN 0-87403-134-6, 2004). Standard Pub.

Fulton, Ginger A. God Made Me Special Even Before I Was Born. (Illus., Orig.). 1986. pap. 2.95 (ISBN 0-8024-3011-2). Moody.

Gallagher, Maureen. God's Love for Us. 1983. 3.95 (ISBN 0-89837-090-6, Pub. by Pflaum Pr); 3.95 (ISBN 0-89837-091-4). Peter Li.

Gibson, Roxie C. Hey, God! Hurry! LC 82-60193. (Illus.). 52p. 1982. 3.95 (ISBN 0-938232-08-8, 32534). Winston-Derek.

--Hey, God! Listen! LC 82-60195. (Illus.). 68p. 1982. 3.95 (ISBN 0-938232-06-1, 32466). Winston-Derek.

--Hey, God! What Is America? LC 81-71025. (Illus.). 52p. 1982. 3.95 (ISBN 0-938232-05-3, 32795). Winston-Derek.

--Hey, God! What Is Christmas. LC 82-60192. (Illus.). 64p. 3.95 (ISBN 0-938232-09-6, 32752). Winston-Derek.

--Hey, God! Where are You? LC 82-60194. (Illus.). 64p. 1982. 3.95 (ISBN 0-938232-07-X, 32485). Winston-Derek.

God Made Animals. (Baby's First Cloth Bks.). 6p. 1.98 (ISBN 0-8307-0814-6, 5608003). Regal.

God Made Food. (Baby's First Cloth Bks.). 6p. 1981. 1.98 (ISBN 0-8307-0815-4, 5608017). Regal.

God Made Me. (Baby's First Cloth Bks.). 6p. 1981. 1.98 (ISBN 0-8307-0816-2, 5608021). Regal.

God Made Our World. (Baby's First Cloth Bks.). 6p. 1982. 1.98 (ISBN 0-8307-0817-0, 5608036). Regal.

Groth, Lynn. God Cares for Me. (A Cradle Roll Program Ser.). 8p. (Orig.). pap. 1.25 (ISBN 0-938272-75-6). Wels Board.

Hein, Lucille E. Thank You, God. (Illus.). 32p. 1981. pap. 3.50 (ISBN 0-8170-0912-4). Judson.

Hughes, Barbara & Dwiggins, Gwen. God Loves Seasons. (God Loves...Coloring Book Ser.). (Illus.). 0.75t (ISBN 0-8091-6563-5). Paulist Pr.

Humble, Linda. Tell Me about God. LC 81-86703. (Happy Day Bks.). (Illus.). 24p. (Orig.). 1982. pap. 1.59 (ISBN 0-87239-544-8, 3590). Standard Pub.
Hutson, Joan. I Think...I Know: A Poster Book about God. (Illus.). 32p. (Orig.). 1979. pap. 1.95 (ISBN 0-87793-186-0). Ave Maria.
Kepes, Joanne L. God's Wonderful World & Me. 1982. 9.95 (ISBN 0-89837-086-8, Pub. by Pflaum Pr). Peter Li.
--Our Father. 1982. 9.95 (ISBN 0-89837-060-4, Pub. by Pflaum Pr). Peter Li.
Larson, Nora E. The Alphabet of God. LC 81-66071. (Illus.). 56p. (Orig.). 1981. pap. 4.00 (ISBN 0-87516-450-1). De Vorss.
Mains, Karen & Mains, David. The God Hunt: A Discovery Book for Boys & Girls. LC 84-14204. (Illus.). 1984. Spiral 3.95 (ISBN 0-89191-886-8, 58867). Cook.
Marshall, Catherine. God Loves You. 1973. pap. 0.95 (ISBN 0-380-01221-9, 14712). Avon.
Mitchell, Joan. Our God Gives Life. 1984. 9.95 (ISBN 0-89837-098-1, Pub. by Pflaum Press). Peter Li.
Mock, Dorothy. Thank You, God, for Water. (Happy Day Bks.). (Illus.). 24p. 1985. 1.59 (ISBN 0-87239-880-3, 3680). Standard Pub.
Moskin, Marietta. In Search of God. LC 79-10493. (Illus.). 160p. 1979. 10.95 (ISBN 0-689-30719-5). Atheneum.
Murphy, Campbell. David & I Talk to God. 1983. pap. 2.95 each (ISBN 0-686-45018-3). Cook.
Murphy, Elspeth. Everybody, Shout Hallelujah! (David & I Talk to God Ser.). (Illus.). 24p. 1981. pap. 2.50 (ISBN 0-89191-369-6, 53694). Cook.
--God Cares When I Do Something Stupid. (God's Word in My Heart Ser.). (Illus.). 24p. 1984. pap. 2.95 (ISBN 0-89191-792-6). Cook.
--God Cares When I Need to Talk to Somebody. (God's Word in My Heart Ser.). (Illus.). 24p. 1984. pap. 2.95 (ISBN 0-89191-887-6). Cook.
--God Cares When Somebody Hurts Me. (God's Word in My Heart Ser.). (Illus.). 24p. 1984. pap. 2.95 (ISBN 0-89191-790-X). Cook.
--Sometimes I Get Lonely. LC 80-70251. (David & I Talk to God Ser.). (Illus.). 24p. 1981. pap. 2.95 (ISBN 0-89191-367-X, 53678). Cook.
Murphy, Elspeth C. I'm Listening, God: Psalm 19. (David & I Talk to God Ser.). (Illus.). 1983. misc. format 2.50 (ISBN 0-89191-583-4). Cook.
--Make Way for the King: Psalm 145 & 24. (David & I Talk to God Ser.). (Illus.). 1983. 2.95 (ISBN 0-89191-581-8). Cook.
--Sometimes Everything Feels Just Right. (David & I Talk to God Ser.). (Illus.). 1987. pap. 2.95 (ISBN 1-55513-038-0, Chariot Bks). Cook.
Nystrom, Carolyn. Who Is God? (Children's Bible Basics Ser.). 32p. 1980. pap. 4.95 (ISBN 0-8024-5992-7). Moody.
Patterson, Yvonne. God Made Fish. (Happy Day Bks.). (Illus.). 24p. 1986. 1.59 (ISBN 0-87403-026-9, 3486). Standard Pub.
Peterson, Lorraine. If God Loves Me, Why Can't I Get My Locker Open? LC 80-27014. 141p. (Orig.). 1980. pap. 4.95 (ISBN 0-87123-251-0, 210251). Bethany Hse.
--Why Isn't God Giving Cash Prizes? (Devotionals for Teens Ser.: No. 3). (Illus.). 160p. 1982. pap. 4.95 (ISBN 0-87123-626-5, 210626). Bethany Hse.
Richards, Lawrence O. How I Can Experience God. (Answers for Youth Ser.). 1980. pap. 4.95 (ISBN 0-310-38991-7, 18209P). Zondervan.
Rohwer, Lee O. What Is God Like? (Illus.). 64p. (Orig.). 1986. pap. 5.95 (ISBN 0-9617788-0-6). Damon Pub.
Shibley, David & Shibley, Naomi. Special Times with God. LC 81-14116. 160p. 1981. 5.95 (ISBN 0-8407-5780-8). Nelson.
Stuckey, Debra. God Made Everything. (God's Creature Ser.). (Illus.). 4.95 (ISBN 0-570-04109-0, 56-1484). Concordia.
--God Made Me. (God's Creature Ser.). (Illus.). 1985. 4.95 (ISBN 0-570-04108-2, 56-1483). Concordia.
Stuckey, Debra K. God Made Families. (God's Creature Ser.). (Illus.). 24p. 1986. 4.95 (ISBN 0-570-04118-X). Concordia.
Sullivan, Jessie. This Is God Speaking: Twenty-Six Lessons for Children's Church. LC 81-18476. (Illus.). 112p. (Orig.). 1982. pap. 7.95 (ISBN 0-87239-496-4, 3371). Standard Pub.
Swafford, Mrs. A. W. Knowing God. rev. ed. (God & Us Ser.). Tr. of God & Us. 32p. 1980. tchrs' ed. 2.00 (ISBN 0-89114-090-5). Baptist Pub Hse.
Tester, Sylvia R. & Miller, Marge, eds. I Read about God's Love. rev. ed. (Illus.). 128p. 1983. text ed. 7.95 (ISBN 0-87239-661-4, 2951). Standard Pub.
Thiry, Joan. Sharing His Life. 1981. 3.75 (ISBN 0-89837-056-6, Pub. by Pflaum Pr); pap. 1.50 (ISBN 0-89837-084-1). Peter Li.
--Sharing His Love. 1981. 3.75 (ISBN 0-89837-066-3, Pub. by Pflaum Pr). Peter Li.
Tucker, James A. & Tucker, Priscilla. Glimpses of God's Love. Woolsey, Raymond H., ed. LC 83-61683. (Junior-Youth Devotional Ser.: 1984). 386p. 1983. 7.95 (ISBN 0-8280-0216-9). Review & Herald.
Watson, Elaine. God Knows Everything. (Happy Day Bks.). (Illus.). 24p. 1986. 1.59 (ISBN 0-87403-025-0, 3485). Standard Pub.
Watson, Elizabeth E. God Knows You. LC 81-50678. (A Happy Day Bks.). (Illus.). 24p. (Orig.). 1981. pap. 1.59 (ISBN 0-87239-463-8, 3596). Standard Pub.
--God Made the Sea, the Sand & Me. (Illus.). 1979. 4.95 (ISBN 0-8054-4254-5, 4242-54). Broadman.
--Where Are You, God? (Illus.). 1977. bds. 5.50 (ISBN 0-8054-4235-9, 4242-35). Broadman.
Wolf, Jill. I Know God Loves Me. (Illus.). 24p. 1984. pap. 1.95 (ISBN 0-89954-288-3). Antioch Pub Co.
Wright, Beverly W. God Made Everything. LC 82-80029. (Happy Day Bks.). (Illus.). 24p. (Orig.). 1982. pap. 1.59 (ISBN 0-87239-537-5, 3583). Standard Pub.
Ziegler, Sandy. Friends. Buerger, Jane, ed. 112p. 1980. 5.95 (ISBN 0-89565-174-2, 4931). Standard Pub.

GOD–KNOWABLENESS

Anderson, Robert. El Silencio de Dios. Orig. Title: The Silence of God. (Span.). 192p. 1981. pap. 3.95 (ISBN 0-8254-1022-3). Kregel.
Arnold, Eberhard. The Inner Land, Vol. 3: The Experience of God. LC 75-9720. 1975. 3.50 (ISBN 0-87486-155-1). Plough.
Barth, Karl. The Knowledge of God & the Service of God According to the Teaching of the Reformation: Recalling the Scottish Confession of 1560. LC 77-27187. (Gifford Lectures: 1937-38). Repr. of 1939 ed. 30.00 (ISBN 0-404-60495-1). AMS Pr.
Bryden, W. W. The Christian's Knowledge of God. 278p. 1960. 6.95 (ISBN 0-227-67434-0). Attic Pr.
Burrell, David B. Knowing the Unknowable God: Ibn-Sina, Maimonides, Aquinas. LC 85-40600. 160p. 1986. text ed. 15.95x (ISBN 0-268-01225-3, 85-12253). U of Notre Dame Pr.
--Knowing the Unknowable God: Ibn-Sina, Maimonides, Aquinas. 130p. 1986. pap. text ed. 8.95x (ISBN 0-268-01226-1, Dist. by Har-Row). U of Notre Dame Pr.
Charnock, Stephen. Knowledge of God. 598p. 1985. 15.95 (ISBN 0-85151-448-0). Banner of Truth.
Christensen, Chuck & Christensen, Winnie. How to Listen When God Speaks. LC 78-73294. 79p. 1979. pap. 2.95 (ISBN 0-87788-355-6). Shaw Pubs.
Dockrey, Karen. Getting to Know God. LC 84-1702. (Orig.). 1984. pap. 4.50 (ISBN 0-8054-5341-5, 4253-41). Broadman.
Dunne, John S. A Search for God in Time & Memory. LC 76-20165. 1977. text ed. 15.95x (ISBN 0-268-01689-5); pap. 6.95 (ISBN 0-268-01673-9). U of Notre Dame Pr.
Duro, Peter A. & Duro, Carol J. You Don't Know My God. LC 85-81388. 238p. (Orig.). 1985. pap. 5.95 (ISBN 0-9615955-0-7). Emmanuel Christian.
Eddy, George S. Man Discovers God. facs. ed. LC 68-24849. (Essay Index Reprint Ser). 1968. Repr. of 1942 ed. 18.00 (ISBN 0-8369-0401-X). Ayer Co Pubs.
Eugene, P. Marie. I Want to See God - I Am a Daughter of the Church, 2 vols. in 1. 1216p. 1986. pap. 39.95 (ISBN 0-87061-134-8). Chr Classics.
Fitti, Charles J. Between God & Man. LC 78-50527. 49p. 1978. 10.00 (ISBN 0-8022-2225-0). Philos Lib.
Gabriel. Divine Intimacy, Vol. 1. 12.95 (ISBN 0-87193-194-X). Dimension Bks.
Gilson, Etienne. God & Philosophy. (Powell Lectures Ser.). 1941. pap. 6.95x (ISBN 0-300-00097-9, Y8). Yale U Pr.
Gwatkin, Henry M. The Knowledge of God & Its Historical Development, 2 vols. LC 77-27219. (Gifford Lectures: 1904-05). 1978. Repr. of 1906 ed. Set. 49.50 (ISBN 0-404-60490-0). AMS Pr.
Hardy, Daniel W. & Ford, David F. Praising & Knowing God. LC 84-25756. 226p. (Orig.). 1985. pap. 12.95 (ISBN 0-664-24624-9). Westminster.
Hartshorne, Charles. The Logic of Perfection & Other Essays in Neoclassical Metaphysics. LC 61-11286. 351p. 1973. pap. 8.95 (ISBN 0-87548-037-3). Open Court.
Howard, Richard. Where on Earth Is God? 144p. 1983. pap. 3.95 (ISBN 0-8341-0823-2). Beacon Hill.
Langston, Douglas C. God's Willing Knowledge: The Influence of Scotus' Analysis of Omniscience. LC 85-31956. 151p. 1986. 18.95x (ISBN 0-271-00429-0). PA St U Pr.
Larranaga, Ignacio & Diercksmeier, John. Sensing Your Hidden Presence: Toward Intimacy With God. LC 87-5232. 264p. 1987. pap. 7.95 (ISBN 0-385-24021-X, Im). Doubleday.
McClelland, W. Robertt. God Our Loving Enemy. LC 81-12680. 160p. 1982. pap. 7.75 (ISBN 0-687-15220-8). Abingdon.
McCloskey, Pat. When You Are Angry with God. 1987. pap. 4.95. Paulist Pr.
Maritain, Jacques. Approaches to God. O'Reilly, Peter, tr. from Fr. LC 78-16555. 1978. Repr. of 1954 ed. lib. bdg. 32.50x (ISBN 0-313-20606-6, MATG). Greenwood.
Moore, Hastings & Moore, Gary W., eds. The Neighborhood of IS, Approaches to the Inner Solitude, A Thematic Anthology: Plotinus, Dionysius the Areopagite, The Cloud of Unknowing, The Book of Privy Counseling, Meister Eckhart. 108p. (Orig.). 1984. pap. text ed. 9.50 (ISBN 0-8191-3972-6). U Pr of Amer.
Nemeck, Francis K. Receptivity. 135p. 1985. 10.00 (ISBN 0-533-06057-5). Vantage.
Neville, Robert C. God the Creator: On the Transcendence & Presence of God. LC 68-13128. (Illus.). 1968. 12.50x (ISBN 0-226-57641-8). U of Chicago Pr.
O'Connor, William R. Natural Desire for God: Aquinas Lectures. 1948. 7.95 (ISBN 0-87462-113-5). Marquette.
Packer, James I., pref. by. Knowing God: Study Guide. 1975. pap. 2.95 (ISBN 0-87784-413-5). Inter-Varsity.
Price, Eugenia. What Is God Like? 192p. 1982. pap. 5.95 (ISBN 0-310-31441-0, 16242P). Zondervan.
Rouner, Leroy S. Knowing Religiously. LC 85-8689. (Boston University Studies in Philosophy & Religion: Vol. 7). 240p. 1985. text ed. 22.95x (ISBN 0-268-01224-5, 85-12246, Dist. by Har-Row). U of Notre Dame Pr.
Stafford, Tim. Knowing the Face of God. 256p. Date not set. pap. 8.95 (ISBN 0-310-32851-9). Zondervan.
Steiner, Rudolf. The Change in the Path to Supersensible Knowledge. 22p. 1982. pap. 3.00 (ISBN 0-919924-18-2, Pub. by Steiner Book Centre Canada). Anthroposophic.
Synan, J. A. The Trinity, or the Tri-Personal Being of God. pap. 2.95 (ISBN 0-911866-00-0). Advocate.
White, Ellen G. Can We Know God? (Uplook Ser.). 1970. pap. 0.99 (ISBN 0-8163-0067-4, 03035-3). Pacific Pr Pub Assn.
William of St. Thierry: The Enigma of Faith, Vol. 3. LC 74-4465. (Cistercian Fathers Ser.: No. 9). 1974. 7.95 (ISBN 0-87907-309-8). Cistercian Pubns.

GOD–LOVE

Here are entered works on God's love toward man. Works on the love and worship which man accords to God are entered under the heading God–Worship and Love.

Ames, Ruth M. God's Plenty. 288p. 1984. 12.95 (ISBN 0-8294-0426-0). Loyola.
Aridas, Chris. Reconciliation: Celebrating God's Healing Forgiveness. LC 87-5344. 160p. 1987. pap. 3.95 (ISBN 0-385-24022-8, Im). Doubleday.
Bernard of Clairvaux & William of St. Thierry. The Love of God. Houston, James M., ed. LC 83-10533. (Classics of Faith & Devotion). Orig. Title: Life & Works of St. Bernard. 1983. 11.95 (ISBN 0-88070-017-3). Multnomah.
Bothwell, Sr. Mary. God Guides Us. (Christ Our Life Ser). (Illus.). 1981. pap. text ed. 4.60 (ISBN 0-8294-0365-5); tchr's ed. 12.95 (ISBN 0-8294-0366-3). Loyola.
Boylan, M. Eugene. This Tremendous Lover. 396p. 1987. pap. 7.95 (ISBN 0-87061-138-0). Chr Classics.
Brown, John. I've Got Mixed-Up Feelings, God. 64p. 1984. pap. 3.95 (ISBN 0-8170-1035-1). Judson.
Carter, Edward. Response to God's Love: A View of the Spiritual Life. 184p. 1984. 9.95 (ISBN 0-317-14585-1). Loyola.
Castro, Carol C. Welcoming God's Forgiveness. 120p. 1978. pap. text ed. 3.95 (ISBN 0-697-01681-1); leader's guide 4.50 (ISBN 0-697-01682-X); classroom tchr's guide .75 (ISBN 0-697-01907-1); adult resource book, pack/10,10.25 1.05 (ISBN 0-697-01685-4). Wm C Brown.
Chapian, Marie. Love & Be Loved. 192p. 1983. pap. 6.95 (ISBN 0-8007-5092-6, Power Bks). Revell.
Christenson, Evelyn. Gaining Through Losing. LC 80-51630. 180p. 1981. 5.95 (ISBN 0-88207-795-3); pap. 5.95 (ISBN 0-88207-344-3). Victor Bks.
Compton-Burnett, Ivy. A God & His Gifts. 1963. 15.95 (ISBN 0-575-02578-6, Pub by Gollancz England). David & Charles.
Cooper, Douglas. Living God's Love. LC 74-27171. (Redwood Ser.). 1975. pap. 4.95 (ISBN 0-8163-0176-X, 12523-7). Pacific Pr Pub Assn.
De La Touche, Louise M. The Sacred Heart & the Priesthood. LC 79-90487. 1979. pap. 5.00 (ISBN 0-89555-128-4). TAN Bks Pubs.
Demaray, Donald E. & Bro. Lawrence, eds. The Practice of the Presence of God. (Devotional Classics Ser). 64p. 1975. pap. 2.45 (ISBN 0-8010-2844-2). Baker Bk.
De Waters, Lillian. The Finished Kingdom. 5.95 (ISBN 0-686-05716-3). L De Waters.
--God & Oneself. pap. 3.00 (ISBN 0-686-05705-8). L De Waters.
--God Is All. pap. 0.95 (ISBN 0-686-05711-2). L De Waters.
Diemer, J. Nature & Miracle. 1977. pap. 1.95 (ISBN 0-88906-015-0). Wedge Pub.
Dobson, Theodore. Inner Healing: God's Great Assurance. LC 78-65129. 216p. 1978. pap. 7.95 (ISBN 0-8091-2161-1). Paulist Pr.
Douty, Norman. Loving Kindness of the Sovereign God. pap. 0.50 (ISBN 0-685-88383-3). Reiner.
Evans, W. Glyn. Beloved Adversary: Our Complex Relationship with a Loving God. Link, Julie A., ed. 96p. 1985. pap. 5.95 (ISBN 0-310-29371-5, 10462P). Zondervan.
Farrell, Edward. The Father Is Very Fond of Me. 6.95 (ISBN 0-87193-029-3). Dimension Bks.
Finney, Charles G. God's Love for a Sinning World. LC 66-19200. (Charles G. Finney Memorial Library). 122p. 1975. pap. 4.50 (ISBN 0-8254-2620-0). Kregel.
Glaphre. When the Pieces Don't Fit... God Makes the Difference. 176p. 1984. pap. 5.95 (ISBN 0-310-45341-0, 12239P). Zondervan.
God Loves His People. (Christ Our Life Ser.). 1982. text ed. 4.60 (ISBN 0-8294-0398-1); tchrs. ed 9.95 (ISBN 0-8294-0399-X). Loyola.
Haas, Lois J. Tell Me about God: 12 Lessons, Vol. 1. (Tiny Steps of Faith Ser.). 1966. complete kit 12.95 (ISBN 0-86508-011-9); text only 2.95 (ISBN 0-86508-012-7); color & action book 0.90 (ISBN 0-86508-013-5). BCM Intl Inc.
Hagin, Kenneth E. El Shaddai. 1980. pap. 1.50 (ISBN 0-89276-401-5). Hagin Ministries.
Hayes, Norvel. The Unopened Gift. cancelled (ISBN 0-89841-002-9). Zoe Pubns.
Hess, Nancy B. By the Grace of God. 1979. 12.50 (ISBN 0-87813-207-4). Park View.
Hick, John H. Evil & the God of Love. rev. ed. LC 76-62953. 1977. pap. 6.95 (ISBN 0-06-063902-4, RD219, HarpR). Har-Row.
Hughes, Hugh P. The Philanthropy of God: Described & Illustrated in a Series of Sermons. 1978. Repr. of 1892 ed. lib. bdg. 12.50 (ISBN 0-8482-4402-8). Norwood Edns.
Hykes, Susan S. The Leading Edge of Now: The Living Love of God. 24p. (Orig.). 1982. pap. 3.00 (ISBN 0-9608894-0-X). S S Hykes.
Ivins, Dan. God's Surprising Goodness. 128p. 1984. pap. 4.95 (ISBN 0-8170-1044-0). Judson.
Johnson, Lois W. Falling Apart or Coming Together: How You Can Experience the Faithfulness of God. LC 83-72112. 128p. (Orig.). 1984. pap. 5.95 (ISBN 0-8066-2056-0, 10-2208). Augsburg.
Johnsson, William G. Blessed Assurance. Coffen, Richard W., ed. 144p. (Orig.). 1985. pap. 5.95 (ISBN 0-8280-0313-0). Review & Herald.
Julian of Norwich. Revelations of Divine Love. Roberts, Roger L., ed. LC 82-80471. (Treasures from the Spiritual Classics Ser.). 64p. 1982. pap. 2.95 (ISBN 0-8192-1308-X). Morehouse.
Keller, Phillip. A Layman Looks at the Love of God. 122p. 1984. pap. 7.95 (ISBN 0-87123-618-4). Bethany Hse.
Knoche, Philip B. Has God Given You up? (Uplook Ser). 1970. pap. 0.99 (ISBN 0-8163-0257-X, 08165-3). Pacific Pr Pub Assn.
Koenig, John. Charismata: God's Gift for God's People. LC 77-12700. (Biblical Perspectives on Current Issues). 214p. 1978. softcover 5.95 (ISBN 0-664-24176-X). Westminster.
Landorf, Joyce. His Stubborn Love. pap. 2.95 (ISBN 0-310-27122-3, 9991P). Zondervan.
Larsen, Norma C. His Everlasting Love: Stories of the Father's Help to His Children. LC 77-79752. 173p. 1977. 8.95 (ISBN 0-88290-083-8). Horizon Utah.
Lewis, Tommy & Harrell, Irene B. Isn't It Amazin'? A Book about the Love of God. 184p. (Orig.). 1983. pap. 6.00 (ISBN 0-915541-00-9). Star Bks Inc.
Lovasik, Lawrence G. God Loves Us All. (Saint Joseph Picture Bks.). (Illus.). flexible bdg. 0.95 (ISBN 0-89942-282-9, 282). Catholic Bk Pub.
Maloney, George. Inward Stillness. 6.95 (ISBN 0-87193-062-5). Dimension Bks.
Manning, Joseph F. The Miracle of Agape Love. 160p. 1977. pap. 2.95 (ISBN 0-88368-079-3). Whitaker Hse.
Miller, Kevin, ed. How Big Is God? Discovering Our Creator's Love & Power. (Senior High Pacesetter Ser.). 64p. 1986. pap. 7.95 (ISBN 0-89191-328-9). Cook.
Mullet, Rosa M. God's Marvelous Work, Bk. 1. 1980. Repr. of 1975 ed. write for info. (ISBN 0-686-11149-4); tchr's. ed. avail. (ISBN 0-686-11150-8). Rod & Staff.
O'Shea, Kevin. The Way of Tenderness. LC 78-61728. (Orig.). 1978. pap. 2.95 (ISBN 0-8091-2166-2). Paulist Pr.
Otis, George, Jr. The God They Never Knew. 244p. 1982. pap. 5.95 (ISBN 0-915134-84-5). Mott Media.

Packer, James I. Your Father Loves You: Daily Insights for Knowing God. Watson, Jean, ed. & compiled by. 392p. 1986. pap. 9.95 (ISBN 0-87788-975-9). Shaw Pubs.
Rice, Helen S. Love. (Illus.). 128p. 1980. 12.95 (ISBN 0-8007-1072-X). Revell.
Rich in Mercy. 61p. 1980. pap. 3.95 (ISBN 1-55586-734-0). US Catholic.
Rolle, Richard. The Fire of Love. Wolters, Clifton, tr. (Classics Ser.). 192p. 1972. pap. 4.95 (ISBN 0-14-044256-1). Penguin.
Schlink, Basilea. I Want to Console You. 72p. 1981. pap. 1.50 (ISBN 3-87209-626-5). Evang Sisterhood Mary.
Schmitt, Abraham. Before I Wake: Listening to God in Your Dreams. 160p. 1984. pap. 7.95 (ISBN 0-687-02605-9). Abingdon.
Sica, Joseph F. God So Loved the World. LC 81-40441. 120p. (Orig.). 1981. lib. bdg. 21.00 o. p. (ISBN 0-8191-1677-7); pap. text ed. 9.25 (ISBN 0-8191-1678-5). U Pr of Amer.
Sikking, Sue. God Always Says Yes. 143p. 1984. pap. 5.95 (ISBN 0-87516-545-1). De Vorss.
Solomon, Charles R. The Rejection Syndrome. 144p. 1982. pap. 5.95 (ISBN 0-8423-5417-4). Tyndale.
Thompson, D. E. God's Abundant Supply. (Illus., Orig.). 1984. pap. 4.95 (ISBN 0-912315-75-X). Word Aflame.
Thorndike, Ruth M. God's Everlasting Arms of Love. 1977. 6.50 (ISBN 0-682-48736-8). Exposition Pr FL.
Thornsberry, Grover. God Flows Within You. 152p. pap. 7.95 (ISBN 0-942494-39-3). Coleman Pub.
Tonn, Katie. Try God, You'll Like Him. (Uplook Ser.). 1975. pap. 0.99 (ISBN 0-8163-0178-6, 20340-6). Pacific Pr Pub Assn.
Tucker, James A. & Tucker, Priscilla. Glimpses of God's Love. Woolsey, Raymond H., ed. LC 83-61683. (Junior-Youth Devotional Ser.: 1984). 386p. 1983. 7.95 (ISBN 0-8280-0216-9). Review & Herald.
Urteaga, J. God & Children. 241p. 1965. pap. 4.95x (ISBN 0-933932-07-3). Scepter Pubs.
Wall, Betty J. Going Through God. 277p. pap. 7.95 (ISBN 0-942494-36-9). Coleman Pub.
Warren, Thomas B. Our God: A "Sun & Shield" for Troubled Hearts. 1963. 10.00 (ISBN 0-934916-38-1). Natl Christian Pr.
Weber, Gerard P., et al. Grow in God's Love. 2nd ed. 1977. 2.64 (ISBN 0-02-658200-7); tchrs. ed. 8.00 (ISBN 0-02-658210-4); family handbook 1.00 (ISBN 0-02-658250-3). Benziger Pub Co.
Wild, Robert. Who I Will Be: Is There Joy & Suffering in God? 5.95 (ISBN 0-87193-089-7). Dimension Bks.
Williams, Charles. He Came Down from Heaven. 160p. 1984. pap. 3.95 (ISBN 0-8028-0033-5). Eerdmans.
Wilson, Lois. Like a Mighty River. (Illus.). 125p. (Orig.). 1981. pap. 6.95 (ISBN 0-919599-01-X). Wood Lake Pr.
Wilson, Patricia. Have You Met My Divine Uncle George? 96p. (Orig.). pap. 5.95 (ISBN 0-8358-0529-8, Dist. by Abingdon Pr). Upper Room.
Worcester, Vern. From God with Love. pap. cancelled (ISBN 0-89900-106-8). College Pr Pub.
Wuestefeld, Mary F. To Drink of His Love. Wheeler, Gerald, ed. (Banner Ser.). 128p. (Orig.). 1986. pap. 6.50 (ISBN 0-8280-0312-2). Review & Herald.
Zeuner, Milton L. Universal Majesty. (Illus.). 80p. 1984. 6.00 (ISBN 0-682-40159-5, Chart). Exposition Pr FL.

GOD–MISCELLANEA

Baumgartner, Anne S. Ye Gods! 192p. 1984. 14.95 (ISBN 0-8184-0349-7). Lyle Stuart.
Bloesch, Donald G. Battle for the Trinity: The Debate over Inclusive God-Language. 1985. 8.95 (ISBN 0-89283-230-4, Pub. by Vine Books). Servant.
Dowsett, Dick. Is God Really Fair? 1985. pap. 3.95 (ISBN 0-8024-3277-8). Moody.
Kendrick, Rosalyn. Does God Have a Body? 1979. pap. 4.95 (ISBN 0-8192-1257-1). Morehouse.
Palau, Luis. My Response. 1985. pap. 3.95 (ISBN 0-8024-8782-3). Moody.
Parrott, Bob W. God's Sense of Humor. LC 82-9142. 221p. 1984. 17.50 (ISBN 0-8022-2421-0). Philos Lib.
Pitts, V. Peter, ed. Children's Pictures of God. LC 79-56298. (Illus.). 1979. pap. 3.95 (ISBN 0-915744-20-1). Character Res.
St. John, Patricia. Twice Freed: The Story of Onesimus, a Runaway Slave. (Orig.). 1985. pap. 3.95 (ISBN 0-8024-8848-X). Moody.
Stewart, Don. One Hundred & Three Questions People Ask about God. 188p. 1987. pap. 5.95 (ISBN 0-8423-4747-X). Tyndale.
Vander Lugt, Herbert. God's Plan in All the Ages: The Kingdom & Redemption from Genesis to Revelation. 208p. 1980. pap. 4.95 (ISBN 0-310-42181-0, 10227P). Zondervan.

GOD–NAME

Arthur, Kay. Lord, I Want to Know You. 192p. (Orig.). 1984. pap. 6.95 (ISBN 0-8007-5159-0, Power Bks). Revell.
Hick, John. God Has Many Names. LC 82-1959. 140p. 1982. pap. 8.95 (ISBN 0-664-24419-X). Westminster.
Hickey, Marilyn. God in You, to You, & for You. 199p. (Orig.). 1983. pap. text ed. 4.95 (ISBN 0-914307-13-4, Dist. by Harrison Hse). Word Faith.
Jukes, Andrew. Names of God in Holy Scripture. LC 67-28843. 1976. pap. 7.95 (ISBN 0-8254-2958-7). Kregel.
Lockyer, Herbert. All the Divine Names & Titles in the Bible. 352p. 1975. 15.95 (ISBN 0-310-28040-0, 10077). Zondervan.
Scharlemann, Robert P., ed. Naming God. (The Contemporary Discussion Ser.). 224p. (Orig.). 1986. 21.95 (ISBN 0-913757-22-5, Pub. by New Era Bks.); pap. 12.95 (ISBN 0-913757-23-3, Pub. by New Era Bks). Paragon Hse.
Stone, Nathan. Names of God. 1944. pap. 3.50 (ISBN 0-8024-5854-8). Moody.
Strauss, Lehman. First Person. LC 67-20931. 1967. 7.95 (ISBN 0-87213-815-1). Loizeaux.
Vandana. Nama Japa: Prayer of the Name in the Hindu & Christian Traditions. 1985. pap. 10.00 (ISBN 0-8364-1509-4, Pub. by Bharatiya Vidya Bhavan). South Asia Bks.
William of St. Thierry: The Enigma of Faith, Vol. 3. LC 74-4465. (Cistercian Fathers Ser.: No. 9). 1974. 7.95 (ISBN 0-87907-309-8). Cistercian Pubns.

GOD–OMNIPOTENCE

Caffarel, Henri. Being Present to God: Letters on Prayer. LC 83-15459. 202p. 1983. pap. 6.95 (ISBN 0-8189-0462-3). Alba.
Coffman, Carl. Unto a Perfect Man. 4th ed. 209p. 1982. pap. 8.95 (ISBN 0-943872-83-9). Andrews Univ Pr.
Crenshaw, James L. & Sandmel, Samuel. The Divine Helmsman: Studies on God's Control of Human Events. 1979. 35.00x (ISBN 0-87068-700-X). Ktav.
Erb, Paul. El Alfa & la Omega. 230p. 1968. pap. 3.30x (ISBN 0-8361-1111-7). Herald Pr.
Kenny, Anthony. The God of the Philosophers. 1979. 26.00x (ISBN 0-19-824594-7). Oxford U Pr.
Krakovsky, Levi. The Omnipotent Light Revealed: Wisdom of the Kabbalah. 4.00 (ISBN 0-686-13335-8). Yesod Pubs.
Kvanvig, Jonathan L. The Possibility of an All-Knowing God. LC 86-6465. 224p. 1986. 27.50 (ISBN 0-312-63195-2). St Martin.
Maquarrie, John. In Search of Deity. 288p. 14.95 (ISBN 0-8245-0682-0). Crossroad NY.
Pink, A. W. La Soberania De Dios. 3.50 (ISBN 0-85151-416-2). Banner of Truth.
--The Sovereignty of God. 1976. pap. 3.95 (ISBN 0-85151-133-3). Banner of Truth.
Spurgeon, C. H. Immutability of God. 1977. pap. 0.95 (ISBN 0-686-23221-6). Pilgrim Pubns.
Starkes, M. Thomas. God's Commissioned People. LC 84-4968. 1984. pap. 12.95 (ISBN 0-8054-6338-0). Broadman.
Tousley, Pershing. The Master Sculptor. LC 81-7189. 1981. pap. 10.00 (ISBN 0-8309-0316-X). Herald Hse.
Wilcox, L. D. Power from on High. 1.50 (ISBN 0-686-27776-7). Schmul Pub Co.

GOD–PERMISSIVE WILL

see Theodicy

GOD–PROMISES

Achtemeier, Paul J. & Achtemeier, Elizabeth. The Old Testament Roots of Our Faith. LC 78-14659. 160p. 1979. pap. 5.95 (ISBN 0-8006-1348-1, 1-1348). Fortress.
Bale, John. Chief Promises of God. LC 70-133635. (Tudor Facsimile Texts. Old English Plays: No. 21). Repr. of 1908 ed. 49.50 (ISBN 0-404-53321-3). AMS Pr.
Branson, Robert. God's Word in Man's Language. 83p. (Orig.). 1980. pap. 2.75 (ISBN 0-8341-0659-0). Beacon Hill.
Bulle, Florence. God Wants You Rich: And Other Enticing Doctrines. 223p. (Orig.). 1983. pap. 5.95 (ISBN 0-87123-264-2, 210264). Bethany Hse.
Deffner, Donald. You Promised Me God. LC 12-2792. (Illus.). 1981. pap. 4.95 (ISBN 0-570-03827-8). Concordia.
Lilly, Gene. God Is Calling His People to Forgiveness. 1977. pap. 3.95 (ISBN 0-917726-15-4). Hunter Bks.
Murphey, Cecil. But God Has Promised. LC 76-16283. 1976. pap. 2.95 (ISBN 0-88419-002-1). Creation Hse.
Nederhood, Joel. Promises, Promises, Promises. LC 79-18889. (Orig.). 1979. pap. text ed. 4.50 (ISBN 0-933140-09-6). CRC Pubns.
Promesas Personales de la Biblia. (Span.). 128p. 1982. pap. 2.50 (ISBN 0-87788-692-X). Shaw Pubs.
Richardson, Valeria, ed. God's Promises for Today's Believer. 100p. (Orig.). 1986. write for info. (ISBN 0-88368-162-5). Whitaker Hse.
Vaughn, Nancy R. & Sloan, Johnny W. Where Is the Rainbow? LC 84-52691. (Illus.). 144p. (Orig.). 1985. pap. 5.95 (ISBN 0-318-04447-1). Vaughn Pub KY.

GOD–PROOF

Barth, Karl. Anselm: Fides Quaerens Intellectum. Robertson, Ian W., tr. from Ger. LC 76-10795. (Pittsburgh Reprint Ser.: No. 2). 1985. text ed. 15.00 (ISBN 0-915138-75-1). Pickwick.
Bonansea, Bernardino M. God & Atheism: A Philosophical Approach to the Problem of God. LC 78-12064. 378p. 1979. 19.95x (ISBN 0-8132-0549-2). Cath U Pr.
Brady, Jules M. A Philosopher's Search for the Infinite. 96p. 1983. 10.00 (ISBN 0-8022-2410-5). Philos Lib.
Brown, Vinson. Tracking the Glorious Lord: Vital Scientific Proofs of the Existence of God. (Paperback Ser.). 96p. (Orig.). 1987. pap. 5.95 (ISBN 0-8022-2519-5). Philos Lib.
Buckley, Michael J. Motion & Motion's God: Thematic Variations in Aristotle, Cicero, Newton, & Hegel. LC 73-132234. 1971. 30.50 (ISBN 0-691-07124-1). Princeton U Pr.
Caes, Charles J. Introduction to the Arguments for God. LC 82-82548. 1983. 8.95 (ISBN 0-87212-162-3). Libra.
Charnock, Stephen. Existence & Attributes of God, 2 vols. 1979. Repr. 29.95 set (ISBN 0-8010-2437-4). Baker Bk.
Chrysostom, John. On the Incomprehensible Nature of God. Harkins, Paul W., tr. from Greek. LC 83-1984. (Fathers of the Church Ser.: No. 72). 357p. 1984. 29.95x (ISBN 0-8132-0072-5). Cath U Pr.
Detacuden, Nam U. The Simplest Explanation of God Ever Explained. 230p. 1983. 13.50 (ISBN 0-682-49951-X). Exposition Pr FL.
Dore, Clement. Theism. 1984. lib. bdg. 34.50 (ISBN 0-318-00886-6, Pub. by Reidel Holland). Kluwer Academic.
Drew, George E. What Kind of God Is God? 65p. (Orig.). 1986. pap. 6.95 (ISBN 0-940754-33-9). Ed Ministries.
Gilson, Etienne. God & Philosophy. (Powell Lectures Ser.). 1941. pap. 6.95x (ISBN 0-300-00097-9, Y8). Yale U Pr.
Hartshorne, Charles. Anselm's Discovery: A Re-Examination of the Ontological Proof for God's Existence. LC 65-20278. 349p. 1973. 23.95 (ISBN 0-87548-216-3); pap. 11.95 (ISBN 0-87548-217-1). Open Court.
Haught, John F. What Is God? How to Think about the Divine. 160p. (Orig.). 1986. pap. 7.95 (ISBN 0-8091-2754-7). Paulist Pr.
Hick, John H. Existence of God. 305p. 1964. pap. 4.95 (ISBN 0-02-085450-1, Collier). Macmillan.
John, Da F. God Is Not a Gentleman & I Am That One. LC 83-73178. 1983. 6.95 (ISBN 0-913922-85-4). Dawn Horse Pr.
Johnstone, Parker L. Who, or What, Is God? 212p. 1984. 7.95 (ISBN 0-917802-12-8). Theoscience Found.
Laird, John. Theism & Cosmology. facs. ed. LC 74-84317. (Essay Index Reprint Ser). 1942. 21.50 (ISBN 0-8369-1147-4). Ayer Co Pubs.
McLean, George F., ed. The Existence of God. LC 73-161203. (Proceedings of the American Catholic Philosophical Association: Vol. 46). 1972. pap. 15.00 (ISBN 0-918090-06-7). Am Cath Philo.
Mahin, Mark. The New Scientific Case for God's Existence. LC 84-62349. 137p. (Orig.). 1985. pap. 8.95 (ISBN 0-931959-01-2). Mindlifter Pr.
Philaretos, S. D. The Idea of the Being. Orthodox Christian Educational Society, ed. Cummings, D., tr. from Hellenic. 287p. 1963. 5.75x (ISBN 0-938366-09-2). Orthodox Chr.
Ross, Robert R. N. The Non-Existence of God: Linguistic Paradox in Tillich's Thought. LC 78-65486. (Toronto Studies in Theology: Vol. 1). xiv, 216p. 1978. 39.95x (ISBN 0-88946-905-9). E Mellen.
Smith, John E. Experience & God. LC 68-18566. 1974. pap. 6.95 (ISBN 0-19-501847-8). Oxford U Pr.
Visser 't Hooft, W. A. The Fatherhood of God in an Age of Emancipation. LC 82-13403. 176p. 1983. pap. 7.95 (ISBN 0-664-24462-9). Westminster.

GOD–PROOF, EMPIRICAL

Buber, Martin, et al. I & Thou. Kaufman, Walter & Smith, S. G., trs. LC 72-123845. (Hudson River Edition). 1970. 20.00 (ISBN 0-684-15575-3, ScribT); pap. 6.95 (ISBN 0-684-71725-5, ScribT). Scribner.
Marshall, Peter & Manuel, David. From Sea to Shining Sea. 448p. 1985. 14.95 (ISBN 0-8007-1451-2). Revell.
Rasmussen, Royal. How New Evidence of God Can Bring You Joy. (Illus.). 228p. 1986. 14.95 (ISBN 0-936223-01-4). Sunshine Pr.
Reeves, Kenneth V. The Supreme Godhead. Wallace, Mary H., ed. (Illus.). 100p. (Orig.). 1984. pap. 5.50 (ISBN 0-912315-74-1). Word Aflame.

GOD–PROVIDENCE AND GOVERNMENT

see Providence and Government of God

GOD–WILL

Boas, George. Vox Populi: Essays in the History of an Idea. LC 69-13538. (Seminars in the History of Ideas Ser.). (Illus.). pap. 77.00 (ISBN 0-317-41626-X, 2025833). Bks Demand UMI.
Bray, Gerald L. Holiness & the Will of God: Perspectives on the Theology of Tertullian. LC 79-5211. (New Foundations Theological Library). (Peter Toon & Ralph Martin series editors). 1980. 3.25 (ISBN 0-8042-3705-0). John Knox.
Coleman, Charles G. Divine Guidance: That Voice Behind You. LC 77-6796. 1977. pap. 2.50 (ISBN 0-87213-087-8). Loizeaux.
Copeland, Gloria. God's Will Is Prosperity. pap. 2.95 (ISBN 0-89274-090-6, HH-090). Harrison Hse.
Drexelius, Jeremias. Heliotropium: Conformity of the Human Will to the Divine. LC 84-51597. 416p. 1985. pap. 8.50 (ISBN 0-89555-245-0). Tan Bks Pubs.
Friesen, Garry & Maxson, J. Robin. Decision Making & the Will of God: A Biblical Alternative to the Traditional View. LC 80-24592. (Critical Concern Ser.). 252p. 1983. pap. 9.95 (ISBN 0-88070-024-6); study guide 2.95 (ISBN 0-88070-021-1). Multnomah.
Hook, Martha. A Woman's Workshop on Faith. (A Woman's Workshop Ser.). 1977. leaders 3.95 (ISBN 0-310-26231-3, 11681P); students 2.95 (ISBN 0-310-26241-0, 11682P). Zondervan.
Howard, J. Grant, Jr. Knowing God's Will & Doing It! 116p. 1983. pap. 4.95 (ISBN 0-310-26281-X, 9986P). Zondervan.
Katterjohn, Arthur & Fackler, Mark. Lord, When? LC 76-16284. 1976. pap. 1.50 (ISBN 0-88419-003-X). Creation Hse.
Libanio, J. B. Spiritual Discernment & Politics: Guidelines for Religious Communities. Morrow, Theodore, tr. from Port. LC 82-2257. Orig. Title: Discernment E politica. 144p. (Orig.). 1982. pap. 1.74 (ISBN 0-88344-463-1). Orbis Bks.
Lindsay, Gordon. How to Find the Perfect Will of God. 1.25 (ISBN 0-89985-003-0). Christ Nations.
Little, Paul. Affirming the Will of God. pap. 0.75 (ISBN 0-87784-139-X). Inter-Varsity.
Macarthur, John, Jr. Found God's Will. 1977. pap. 1.95 (ISBN 0-88207-503-9). Victor Bks.
McKeever, Jim. How You Can Know the Will of God. 24p. 1982. 1.00 (ISBN 0-86694-095-2). Omega Pubns OR.
Moon, Sun M. The Way of God's Will. 418p. (Orig.). Date not set. pap. 6.95 (ISBN 0-910621-31-4). HSA Pubns.
Murray, Andrew. Not My Will. Schoolland, Marian, tr. 1977. pap. 2.95 (ISBN 0-310-29722-2, 10381P). Zondervan.
--Secret of Power from on High. (Secret Ser.). (Orig.). 1980. pap. 1.95 (ISBN 0-87508-392-7). Chr Lit.
Rosenthal, Joan. Lord Is My Strength. 1976. pap. 1.25 (ISBN 0-89129-086-9). Jove Pubns.
St. Alphonsus de Liguori. Uniformity with God's Will. 1977. pap. 1.00 (ISBN 0-89555-019-9). TAN Bks Pubs.
Shields, Ann. Yielding to the Power of God: The Importance of Surrender, Abandonment, & Obedience to God's Will. 48p. (Orig.). 1987. pap. 1.95 (ISBN 0-89283-348-3). Servant.
Smith, M. Blaine. Knowing God's Will. LC 78-24756. 1979. pap. 4.95 (ISBN 0-87784-610-3). Inter-Varsity.
Sproul, R. C. God's Will & the Christian. 96p. 1984. 2.95 (ISBN 0-8423-1096-7). Tyndale.
Stark, Tom & Stark, Joan. Guidance & God's Will. (Fisherman Bible Studyguide). 60p. 1978. saddle stitch 2.50 (ISBN 0-87788-324-6). Shaw Pubs.
Weatherhead, Leslie D. The Will of God. (Festival Books). 1976. pap. 2.95 (ISBN 0-687-45600-2). Abingdon.
Weising, Gwen. Guidance-Knowing the Will of God. (Workbook Ser.). 72p. 1985. pap. 4.95 (ISBN 0-930756-99-1, 581006). Aglow Pubns.

GOD–WILL, PERMISSIVE

see Theodicy

GOD–WISDOM

Allan, John. The Kingdom of God. pap. 2.50 (ISBN 0-87516-286-X). De Vorss.
Doyle, Alfreda C. The Creator or Almighty Always Has an Answer. Date not set. 7.95 (Pub. by Biblio Pr GA); pap. text ed. 2.95 (ISBN 0-939476-23-1, Pub. by Biblio Pr GA). Prosperity & Profits.
Duff, Clarence W. God's Higher Ways. 1978. pap. 7.50 (ISBN 0-87552-257-2). Presby & Reformed.
Fortuna, James L., Jr. The Unsearchable Wisdom of God: A Study of Providence in Richardson's Pamela. LC 80-14919. (University of Florida Humanities Monographs: No. 49). vii, 130p. 1980. pap. 6.50 (ISBN 0-8130-0676-7). U Presses Fla.

Hayes, Norvel. The Unopened Gift. cancelled (ISBN 0-89841-002-9). Zoe Pubns.

Prabhavananda, Swami. Bhagavatam, Srimad: The Wisdom of God. 1979. pap. 5.95 (ISBN 0-87481-490-1). Vedanta Pr.

Taylor, Jack R. God's Miraculous Plan of Economy. LC 75-27411. 168p. 1975. 8.95 (ISBN 0-8054-5565-5). Broadman.

GOD–WORSHIP AND LOVE

see also Bhakti; Fear of God

Anderson, C. Alan. The Problem Is God: The Selection & Care of Your Personal God. LC 84-50108. (Illus.). 304p. (Orig.). 1985. pap. 9.95 (ISBN 0-913299-02-2). Stillpoint.

Anthony of Sourozh. God & Man. 2nd ed. 125p. 1983. pap. text ed. 4.95 (ISBN 0-88141-024-1). St Vladimirs.

Azcar. How to Talk Directly with God. 51p. 1977. pap. 1.95 (ISBN 0-931865-05-0). Psychegenics.

Baba, Meher, ed. God to Man & Man to God. 287p. 1984. 8.95 (ISBN 0-913078-27-1); pap. 6.95 (ISBN 0-913078-21-2). Sheriar Pr.

Beierle, Herbert L. How Much of God I Express Is How Much I Profess. 1982. 1.00 (ISBN 0-686-35834-1). U of Healing.

Beltz, Oliver S., ed. Te Decet Laus: To Thee Belongeth Praise. Revised ed. (Illus.). viii, 223p. 1982. 9.95 (ISBN 0-943872-84-7). Andrews Univ Pr.

Billheimer, Paul E. Destined for the Throne. LC 83-15151. 140p. (Orig.). 1983. pap. 4.95 (ISBN 0-87123-309-6, 210309). Bethany Hse.

Bothwell, Sr. Mary D. We Worship. (Christ Our Life Ser.). (Illus.). 1982. text ed. 4.20 (ISBN 0-8294-0391-4); tchrs. ed. 12.95 (ISBN 0-8294-0392-2). Loyola.

Breault, Joseph. Seeking Purity of Heart: The Gift of Ourselves to God. (Illus.). 96p. (Orig.). 1975. pap. 3.95 (ISBN 0-914544-07-1). Living Flame Pr.

Bridges, Jerry. L' Exercice de la Piete. Cosson, Annie L., ed. Claeys, Monique, tr. Tr. of The Practice of Godliness. (Fr.). 240p. 1985. pap. text ed. 2.50 (ISBN 0-8297-1458-8). Life Pubs Intl.

Carson, Alex. Confidence in God in Times of Danger. pap. 2.75 (ISBN 0-685-88371-X). Reiner.

Chapian, Marie. Love & Be Loved. 192p. 1983. pap. 6.95 (ISBN 0-8007-5092-6, Power Bks). Revell.

Coniaris, A. M. Making God Real in the Orthodox Christian Home. 1977. pap. 5.95 (ISBN 0-937032-07-7). Light&Life Pub Co MN.

Contemporary Testimony Committee of the Christian Reformed Church. Our World Belongs to God: A Contemporary Testimony (Study Version) 1984. pap. 1.00 (ISBN 0-933140-91-6). CRC Pubns.

Cornwall, Judson. Let Us Worship. LC 82-74089. 1983. pap. 4.95 (ISBN 0-88270-542-3). Bridge Pub.

Davis, Clara. The Move of God: Azusa Street to Now. 80p. (Orig.). 1983. pap. 2.95 (ISBN 0-88144-016-7, CPS-016). Christian Pub.

Dayringer, Richard. God Cares for You. LC 83-70210. (Orig.). 1984. pap. 5.95 (ISBN 0-8054-5232-X). Broadman.

De Jong, James. Into His Presence: Perspectives on Reformed Worship. 1985. pap. 7.95 (ISBN 0-933140-99-1); pap. text ed. 3.95 leader's guide (ISBN 0-930265-08-4). CRC Pubns.

De Robeck, Nesta. Praise the Lord. 1967. 4.50 (ISBN 0-8199-0086-9, L38643). Franciscan Herald.

Doyle, Eric. The Disciple & the Master: St. Bonaventure's Sermons on St. Francis of Assisi. 220p. 1983. 15.00 (ISBN 0-8199-0842-8). Franciscan Herald.

Godsey, John D. Preface to Bonhoeffer: The Man & Two of His Shorter Writings. LC 79-7378. 80p. 1979. pap. 3.50 (ISBN 0-8006-1367-8, 1-1367). Fortress.

Grant, Junior. I Have Seen the Lord. 48p. 1982. 5.95 (ISBN 0-8059-2845-6). Dorrance.

Gruen, Ernest J. Touching the Heart of God. (Orig.). 1986. pap. 3.95 (ISBN 0-88368-175-7). Whitaker Hse.

Habig, Marion A. My God & My All. 1977. 4.50 (ISBN 0-685-77278-0). Franciscan Herald.

Hagin, Kenneth E. In Him. 1975. pap. 0.50 mini bk. (ISBN 0-89276-052-4). Hagin Ministries.

--The New Birth. 1975. pap. 0.50 mini bk. (ISBN 0-89276-050-8). Hagin Ministries.

--Turning Hopeless Situations Around. 1981. pap. 1.00 (ISBN 0-89276-022-2). Hagin Ministries.

--Why Do People Fall under the Power? 1981. pap. 0.50 mini bk (ISBN 0-89276-254-3). Hagin Ministries.

--Why Tongues? 1975. pap. 0.50 mini bk (ISBN 0-89276-051-6). Hagin Ministries.

--ZOE: The God-Kind of Life. 1981. pap. 2.50 (ISBN 0-89276-402-3). Hagin Ministries.

Hagin, Kenneth, Jr. Itching Ears. 1982. pap. 0.50 mini bk. (ISBN 0-89276-711-1). Hagin Ministries.

--The Prison Door Is Open: What Are You Still Doing Inside? 1982. pap. 0.50 mini bk (ISBN 0-89276-710-3). Hagin Ministries.

--Where Do We Go from Here? 1982. pap. 0.50 mini bk (ISBN 0-89276-712-X). Hagin Ministries.

Hardy, Daniel W. & Ford, David F. Praising & Knowing God. LC 84-25756. 226p. (Orig.). 1985. pap. 12.95 (ISBN 0-664-24624-9). Westminster.

Hieronymus, Lynn. What the Bible Says about Worship. (What the Bible Says Ser.). 300p. 1984. 13.95 (ISBN 0-89900-097-5). College Pr Pub.

Huff, Sr. M. Cyria. The Sonnet-No Me Mueve, Mi Dios-Its Theme in Spanish Tradition. LC 73-94177. (Catholic University of America Studies in Romance Languages & Literatures Ser: No. 33). Repr. of 1948 ed. 20.00 (ISBN 0-404-50333-0). AMS Pr.

Hunter, Frances. Praise the Lord Anyway. 1978. pap. 3.25 (ISBN 0-87162-131-2). Hunter Bks.

Ingles, David. Worshipping the Father in Spirit & in Truth. 40p. (Orig.). 1986. wkbk. 4.95 (ISBN 0-914307-63-0). Word Faith.

Kakimoto, Kozo. God, You Are Always With Us. 28p. 9.95 (ISBN 0-687-15303-4). Abingdon.

Levitt, Zola & McCall, Tom. Raptured. LC 75-15481. 1975. pap. 4.95 (ISBN 0-89081-014-1). Harvest Hse.

Lussier, Ernest. Adore the Lord: Adoration Viewed Through the Old Testament. LC 78-20783. 1979. 6.95 (ISBN 0-8189-0380-5). Alba.

--Jesus Christ Is Lord: Adoration Viewed Through the New Testament. LC 79-15581. 1980. 7.95 (ISBN 0-8189-0382-1). Alba.

McCumber, W. E. Holy God-Holy People. 124p. 1982. pap. 3.95 (ISBN 0-8341-0779-1). Beacon Hill.

MacDonald, William. God's Answers to Man's Questions. pap. 1.95 (ISBN 0-937396-16-8). Walterick Pubs.

Marshall, John F. By the Light of His Lamp. (Spirit & Life Ser). 1967. 2.00 (ISBN 0-686-11574-0). Franciscan Inst.

Martin, Ralph P. The Worship of God: Some Theological, Pastoral & Practical Reflections. 237p. (Orig.). 1982. pap. 10.95 (ISBN 0-8028-1934-6). Eerdmans.

Mir Valiuddin. Love of God. LC 85-27481. 216p. 1985. Repr. lib. bdg. 19.95x (ISBN 0-89370-577-2). Borgo Pr.

Myers, William F. The Brightness of His Presence: Theological Dissertation. LC 82-90351. 64p. 1982. 6.95 (ISBN 0-87948-049-1). Beatty.

Nee, Watchman. Do All to the Glory of God. Kaung, Stephen, tr. (Basic Lesson Ser.: Vol. 5). 1974. 5.50 (ISBN 0-935008-03-9); pap. 4.25 (ISBN 0-935008-04-7). Christian Fellow Pubs.

Pratt, Louis. Worship the Lord. 1983. 4.35 (ISBN 0-89536-580-4, 2332). CSS of Ohio.

Price, Frederick K. Thank God for Everything. 31p. pap. 0.75 mini-bk. (ISBN 0-89274-056-6). Harrison Hse.

Ramsey, Evelyn. Show Me, Lord. 178p. 1982. pap. 4.95 (ISBN 0-8341-0781-3). Beacon Hill.

St. Francis de Sales. Treatise on the Love of God, 2 vols. Ryan, John K., tr. 1975. Set. pap. 10.00 (ISBN 0-89555-064-4); Vol. 1. pap. (ISBN 0-89555-062-8, 166-l); Vol. 2. pap. (ISBN 0-89555-063-6). TAN Bks Pubs.

Salls, Betty R. Greatest of These-Love. pap. 1.75 (ISBN 0-686-12744-7). Grace Pub Co.

Schlink, Mother Basilea. I Found the Key to the Heart of God. LC 75-23920. 416p. 1975. pap. 5.95 (ISBN 0-87123-239-1, 200239). Bethany Hse.

Smith, W. Have You Considered Him? pap. 0.75 (ISBN 0-87784-108-X). Inter-Varsity.

Stafford, Tim. Knowing the Face of God: The Search for a Personal Relationship with God. 256p. 1986. text ed. 12.95 (ISBN 0-310-32850-0, 10836). Zondervan.

Stone, James. How to Worship God. 60p. (Orig.). 1982. pap. 1.95 (ISBN 0-934942-32-3). White Wing Pub.

Stuckey, Debra. God Made Me. (God's Creature Ser.). (Illus.). 1985. 4.95 (ISBN 0-570-04108-2, 56-1483). Concordia.

Thou Shalt Call His Name. (Illus.). 102p. 1975. pap. 2.50 (ISBN 0-915952-00-9). Lord's Line.

Tozer, Aiden W. Pursuit of God. LC 82-70768. 128p. 1982. 4.95 (ISBN 0-87509-191-1); pap. 3.95 (ISBN 0-87509-192-X); 3.25 (ISBN 0-87509-223-3); legacy ed. 5.95 (ISBN 0-87509-366-3). Chr Pubns.

Trombley, Charles. Praise Faith in Action. (Orig.). 1976. pap. 3.95 (ISBN 0-89350-009-7). Fountain Pr.

Wannamaker, Bruce. God's Care Is Everywhere. LC 82-7244. (Illus.). 32p. 1982. PLB 4.95 (ISBN 0-89693-202-8). Dandelion Hse.

Weber, Gerard P., et al. Live in God's World. 2nd ed. (The Word Is Life Ser.). 1977. 2.64 (ISBN 0-02-658100-0); tchrs. ed. 8.00 (ISBN 0-02-658110-8); family handbook 1.00 (ISBN 0-02-658150-7). Benziger Pub Co.

Weil, Simone. Waiting for God. pap. 5.95 (ISBN 0-06-090295-7, CN295, PL). Har-Row.

Welch, Reuben. We Really Do Need Each Other. 112p. 1982. pap. 4.95 (ISBN 0-310-70221-6, 14012P). Zondervan.

Willimon, William H. The Gospel for the Person Who Has Everything. 1978. pap. 4.95 (ISBN 0-8170-0758-X). Judson.

Wolter, Allan B. Living in God's Love. 172p. 1958. pap. 1.75 (ISBN 0-8199-0059-1, L38375). Franciscan Herald.

GOD–WRATH

Kelderman, Duane. When a Good God Lets Bad Things Happen. 1983. 3.25 (ISBN 0-89536-583-9, 2333). CSS of Ohio.

Vatai, Laszlo. Az Isten Szornyetege: Ady Iiraja. 2nd ed. LC 77-89126. (Hungarian.). 390p. 1977. 15.00 (ISBN 0-911050-45-0). Occidental.

GOD (BRAHMANISM)

see God (Hinduism)

GOD (GREEK RELIGION)

Caird, Edward. Evolution of Theology in the Greek Philosophers, the Gifford Lectures, 1900-1902, 2 Vols. 1968. 39.00x (ISBN 0-403-00116-1). Scholarly.

Hack, Roy K. God in Greek Philosophy to the Time of Socrates. 1970. Repr. of 1931 ed. lib. bdg. 12.50 (ISBN 0-8337-1514-3). B Franklin.

GOD (HINDUISM)

Bhaktivedanta, Swami A. C. Krsna: The Supreme Personality of Godhead, 3 vols. LC 74-118081. (Illus.). 1970. Vol. 1. pap. 12.95 (ISBN 0-89213-136-5). Bhaktivedanta.

Pandurangarao, Malyala. Hanumaan Chaaleesa. (Illus.). 16p. (Orig.). 1984. pap. 2.00x (ISBN 0-317-07665-5). Sri Shirdi Sai.

GOD (ISLAM)

Ali ibn Isma'il, A. H., et al. Al ibanah 'an usul addiyanah. Klein, W. C., tr. (American Oriental Ser.: Vol. 19). 1940. 18.00 (ISBN 0-527-02693-X). Kraus Repr.

Duncan, David D. The World of Allah. 1982. 40.00 (ISBN 0-395-32504-8). HM.

Friedlander, Ira. The Ninety-Nine Names of Allah. (Orig.). 1978. pap. 6.95 (ISBN 0-06-090621-9, CN 621, PL). Har-Row.

Geffre, Claude & Jossua, Jean-Pierre, eds. Monotheism, Vol. 177. (Concilium Ser.). 128p. pap. 6.95 (ISBN 0-567-30057-9, Pub. by T & T Clark Ltd UK). Fortress.

Ghazi, A. Messenger of Allah, Vol. II. 1981. 4.50 (ISBN 0-686-97851-X). Kazi Pubns.

Mutahhery, Murtaza. Monotheistic Point of View. 70p. 1984. pap. 3.95 (ISBN 0-940368-39-0). Tahrike Tarsile Quran.

Siddiqui, M. I. Rights of Allah & Human Rights. 1981. 15.95 (ISBN 0-686-97876-5). Kazi Pubns.

Ullah, Mohammad Z. The Islamic Concept of God. 100p. (Orig.). 1984. 26.95x (ISBN 0-7103-0076-X, Kegan Paul). Methuen Inc.

--The Islamic Concept of God. 116p. 1985. pap. 9.95 (ISBN 0-7103-0127-8, Kegan Paul). Methuen Inc.

GOD (JUDAISM)

Bibago, Abraham. Derek Emunah: The Path of Faith. 204p. 1521. text ed. 49.68x (ISBN 0-576-80102-X, Pub. by Gregg Intl Pubs England). Gregg Intl.

Sonsino, Rifat & Syme, Daniel B. Finding God. 1986. 7.95 (ISBN 0-8074-0312-1, 571200). UAHC.

GOD, FEAR OF

see Fear of God

GOD, GLORY OF

see Glory of God

GOD AND MAN, MYSTICAL UNION OF

see Mystical Union

GOD IN LITERATURE

Berryman, Charles. From Wilderness to Wasteland: The Trial of the Puritan God in the American Imagination. (National University Publications, Literary Criticism Ser.). 1979. 21.50x (ISBN 0-8046-9235-1, Pub. by Kennikat). Assoc Faculty Pr.

Daiches, David. God & the Poets. 232p. 1986. pap. 15.95x (ISBN 0-19-812862-2). Oxford U Pr.

Hamilton, William. Melville & the Gods. (Scholars Press Studies in the Humanities: No. 7). 1985. pap. 13.25 (ISBN 0-89130-741-9, 00 01 07). Scholars Pr GA.

Madigan, Mary F. The Passio Domini Theme in the Works of Richard Rolle: His Personal Contribution in Its Religeous Cultural, & Literary Context. Hogg, James, ed. (Elizabethan & Renaissance Studies). 347p. (Orig.). 1978. pap. 15.00 (ISBN 3-7052-0723-7, Pub. by Salzburg Studies). Longwood Pub Group.

Merrill, Thomas F. Epic God-Talk: Paradise Lost & the Grammar of Religious Language. LC 85-29385. 140p. 1986. lib. bdg. 18.95x (ISBN 0-89950-194-X). McFarland & Co.

Miller, J. Hillis. The Disappearance of God: Five Nineteenth Century Writers. 392p. 1976. text ed. 22.50x (ISBN 0-674-21101-4, Belknap Pr). Harvard U Pr.

GOD IS DEAD THEOLOGY

see Death of God Theology

GOD TRANSCENDENCE

see Transcendence of God

GODDESSES

see also Mother-Goddesses

Berger, Pamela. The Goddess Obscured: Transformation of the Grain Protectress from Goddess to Saint. LC 85-47524. (Illus.). 250p. 1986. 19.95 (ISBN 0-8070-6722-9). Beacon Pr.

Bookidis, Nancy & Stroud, Ronald. Demeter & Persephone in Ancient Corinth. (Corinth Notes Ser.: No. 2). (Illus.). 32p. (Orig.). 1987. pap. 3.00. Am Sch Athens.

De Armas, Frederick A. The Return of Astraea: An Astral-Imperial Myth in Calderon. LC 86-7758. (Studies in Romance Languages: No. 32). 272p. 1986. 27.00 (ISBN 0-8131-1570-1). U Pr of Ky.

Maier, Walter A., III. Aserah: Extrabiblical Evidence. (Harvard Semitic Monographs). 274p. 1987. 21.95 (ISBN 1-55540-046-9, 04-00-37). Scholars Pr GA.

Olsen, Carl. Book of the Goddess. 264p. 1985. pap. 9.95 (ISBN 0-8245-0689-8). Crossroad NY.

Paris, Ginette. Pagan Meditations: The Worlds of Aphrodite, Artemis, & Hestia. Moore, Gwendolyn, tr. from Fr. LC 86-6675. 204p. (Orig.). 1986. pap. 13.50 (ISBN 0-88214-330-1). Spring Pubns.

Tiwari, J. N. Goddess Cults in Ancient India. (Illus.). 250p. 1986. 62.50x (ISBN 0-8364-1819-0, Pub. by Chanakya India). South Asia Bks.

GODDESSES, HINDU

Chaudhuri, Dulal. Goddess Durga: The Great Mother. 1985. 7.50x (ISBN 0-8364-1289-3, Pub. by Mrimol). South Asia Bks.

Gatwood, Lynn E. Devi & the Spouse Goddess: Women, Sexuality & Marriage in India. LC 85-61077. 206p. 1985. 18.00 (ISBN 0-913215-01-5). Riverdale Co.

Harshananda, Swami. Hindu Gods & Goddesses. (Illus., Orig.). 1985. pap. 4.25 (ISBN 0-87481-522-3, Pub. by Ramakrishna Math Madras India). Vedanta Pr.

Hawley, John S. & Wulff, Donna M., eds. The Divine Consort: Radha & the Goddesses of India. LC 86-47759. (Illus.). 432p. 1987. pap. 11.95 (ISBN 0-8070-1303-X, BP-734). Beacon Pr.

Preston, James J. Cult of the Goddess: Social & Religious Change in a Hindu Temple. (Illus.). 109p. 1985. pap. text ed. 6.95x (ISBN 0-88133-135-X). Waveland Pr.

GODDESSES, MOTHER

see Mother-Goddesses

GODS

see also Kings and Rulers (In Religion, Folk-Lore, etc.); Mother-Goddesses; Myth; Mythology; Religions

Barre, Michael. The God-List in the Treaty Between Hannibal & Philip V of Macedonia: A Study in Light of the Ancient Near Eastern Treaty Tradition. LC 82-13961. (Near Eastern Studies). 208p. 1983. text ed. 26.00x (ISBN 0-8018-2787-6). Johns Hopkins.

Blofeld, John. Bodhisattva of Compassion: The Mystical Tradition of Kuan Yin. LC 77-91352. (Illus.). 155p. 1978. pap. 9.95 (ISBN 0-87773-126-8, 73609-5). Shambhala Pubns.

Budge, Ernest A. Egyptian Ideas of the Future Life. LC 73-18839. Repr. of 1899 ed. 14.00 (ISBN 0-404-11330-3). AMS Pr.

Calverton, V. F. The Passing of the Gods. 326p. 1982. Repr. of 1934 ed. lib. bdg. 35.00 (ISBN 0-89987-123-2). Darby Bks.

Gallagher, Eugene V. Divine Man or Magician? Celsus & Origin on Jesus. (SBL Dissertation Ser.). 1982. pap. 13.50 (ISBN 0-89130-542-4, 06 01 64). Scholars Pr GA.

Gimbutas, Marija. Goddesses & Gods of Old Europe, 7000 to 3500 B.C. Myths, Legends, & Cult Images. 1982. pap. 14.95 (ISBN 0-520-04655-2, CAL 565). U of Cal Pr.

The Gods. (Enchanted World Ser.). 1987. 16.95 (ISBN 0-8094-5273-1). Time-Life.

Green, Miranda J. The Gods of Roman Britain. (Shire Archeaology Ser.: No. 34). (Illus.). 64p. (Orig.). 1983. pap. 5.95 (ISBN 0-85263-634-2, Pub. by Shire Pubns England). Seven Hills Bks.

Harshananda, Swami. Hindu Gods & Goddesses. (Illus., Orig.). 1985. pap. 4.25 (ISBN 0-87481-522-3, Pub. by Ramakrishna Math Madras India). Vedanta Pr.

Heschel, Abraham J. Man's Quest for God: Studies in Prayer & Symbolism. LC 54-10371. (Hudson River Edition Ser.). 1981. 22.50x (ISBN 0-684-16829-4, ScribT). Scribner.

Jayne, Walter A. The Healing Gods of Ancient Civilizations. LC 75-23728. Repr. of 1925 ed. 49.00 (ISBN 0-404-13286-3). AMS Pr.

Schwab, Gustav. Gods & Heroes. LC 47-873. 1977. pap. 9.95 (ISBN 0-394-73402-5). Pantheon.

Shell, Harvey. The Gods of China. Chamberlin, Roxanna, ed. (Illus.). 1985. pap. 4.95 (ISBN 0-914347-02-0). Ahio Pub Co.

--The Gods of Japan. (Illus.). 1984. pap. 4.95 (ISBN 0-914347-01-2). Ahio Pub Co.
Simon, Erika. Festivals of Attica: An Archaeological Commentary. LC 81-70160. 160p. 1983. text ed. 26.50x (ISBN 0-299-09180-5). U of Wis Pr.
Von Daniken, Erich. The Gods & Their Grand Design. Hemon, Michael, tr. from Ger. 1984. 18.95 (ISBN 0-399-12961-8, Putnam). Putnam Pub Group.
--Pathways to the Gods: The Stones of Kiribati. Heron, Michael, tr. from Ger. (Illus.). 288p. 1983. 16.95 (ISBN 0-399-12751-8, Putnam). Putnam Pub Group.
Whitehead, Henry. Village Gods of South India. (Illus.). 175p. 1986. Repr. 15.00X (ISBN 0-8364-1709-7, Pub. by Usha). South Asia Bks.

GODS IN ART
see also Idols and Images
Cartari, Vincenzo. Le Imagini...Degli Dei. LC 75-27855. (Renaissance & the Gods Ser.: Vol. 12). (Illus.). 602p. 1976. Repr. of 1571 ed. lib. bdg. 88.00 (ISBN 0-8240-2061-8). Garland Pub.
Henle, Jane. Greek Myths: A Vase Painter's Notebook. LC 72-75639. (Illus.). 256p. 1973. 35.00x (ISBN 0-253-32635-4); pap. 7.95x (ISBN 0-253-32636-2). Ind U Pr.
Krishna Sastri, H. South Indian Images of Gods & Goddesses. 308p. 1986. Repr. 37.50X (ISBN 0-8364-1710-0, Pub. by Chanakya India). South Asia Bks.
Matthews, Caitlin. Goddess. (Art & Imagination Ser.). (Illus.). 1983. pap. cancelled (ISBN 0-500-81031-1). Thames-Hudson.
Pal, Pratapaditya. Bronzes of Kashmir. LC 75-902. (Illus.). 205p. 1975. lib. bdg. 40.00 (ISBN 0-87817-158-4). Hacker.
Seznec, Jean. The Survival of the Pagan Gods: The Mythological Tradition & Its Place in Renaissance Humanism & Art. Sessions, Barbara, tr. (Bollingen Ser.: Vol. 38). (Illus.). 108p. 1972. pap. 9.50x (ISBN 0-691-01783-2). Princeton U Pr.
Spence, Joseph. Polymetis. LC 75-27886. (Renaissance & the Gods Ser.: Vol. 41). (Illus.). 1976. Repr. of 1747 ed. lib. bdg. 88.00 (ISBN 0-8240-2090-1). Garland Pub.
Tempesta, Antonio. Metamorphoseon...Ovidianarum. LC 75-27861. (Renaissance & the Gods Ser.: Vol. 19). (Illus.). 1976. Repr. of 1606 ed. lib. bdg. 88.00 (ISBN 0-8240-2067-7). Garland Pub.

GOG AND MAGOG
Anderson, Andrew R. Alexander's Gate, Gog & Magog & the Inclosed Nations. 1932. 7.50x (ISBN 0-910956-07-3). Medieval Acad.

GOOD AND EVIL
see also Evil in Literature; Guilt; Providence and Government of God; Sin; Theodicy
Bacon, Francis. Essays & Colours of Good & Evil. LC 72-56. (Select Bibliographies Reprint Ser.). 1972. Repr. of 1862 ed. 20.25 (ISBN 0-8369-9951-7). Ayer Co Pubs.
Bayley, Robert G. Deliver Us from the Evil One. 36p. 1987. pap. 2.95 (ISBN 0-934421-09-9). Presby Renewal Pubns.
Becker, Ernest. Escape from Evil. LC 75-12059. 1976. pap. 8.95 (ISBN 0-02-902450-1). Free Pr.
Breton, Denise. This Lie Called Evil. LC 82-80906. 130p. (Orig.). 1983. pap. 8.50 (ISBN 0-942958-02-0). Kappeler Inst Pub.
Brim, Frank M. Satan's Secret Revealed: From the Files of a Christian Exorcist. 176p. 1983. pap. 5.00 (ISBN 0-9612676-0-7). World Wide Mini.
Brown, Stuart, ed. Reason & Religion. LC 77-3115. 336p. 1977. pap. 12.95x (ISBN 0-8014-9166-5). Cornell U Pr.
Buber, Martin. Good & Evil. 185p. pap. text ed. 7.95 (ISBN 0-684-16990-8). Scribner.
--Good & Evil: Two Interpretations. 1953. pap. 3.95 (ISBN 0-684-71723-9, SL45, ScribT). Scribner.
Bunyan, John. Holy War. 324p. 1986. pap. 6.95 (ISBN 0-8010-0924-3). Baker Bk.
Camus, Albert. Homme Revolte: Essai. (Coll. Soleil). 1951. 16.50 (ISBN 0-685-11234-9); pap. 4.95 (ISBN 0-686-66425-6). French & Eur.
Conn, Charles W. Anatomy of Evil. 1984. pap. text ed. 6.95 (ISBN 0-87148-018-2). Pathway Pr.
Cuss, Gladys. Hidden Manna Revealed by the Comforter. 200p. 1981. 9.00 (ISBN 0-682-49768-1). Exposition Pr FL.
Darrow, Clarence & Lewis, Arthur. Darrow-Lewis Debate on the Theory of Non-Resistance to Evil. 26p. 1987. pap. write for info. (ISBN 0-911826-48-3). Am Atheist.
Davis, Stephen T., ed. Encountering Evil: Live Options in Theodicy. LC 80-84647. 1981. pap. 9.95 (ISBN 0-8042-0517-5). John Knox.
Deffner, Donald. I Hear Two Voices, God! LC 12-2817. 1983. pap. 4.95 (ISBN 0-570-03882-0). Concordia.
Evans, G. R. Augustine on Evil. LC 81-21793. 220p. 1983. 34.50 (ISBN 0-521-24526-5). Cambridge U Pr.
Ewing, Alfred C. The Definition of Good. LC 78-59021. 1979. Repr. of 1947 ed. 20.25 (ISBN 0-88355-695-2). Hyperion Conn.
Ferre, Nels F. Evil & the Christian Faith. facsimile ed. LC 71-134075. (Essay Index Reprints - Reason & the Christian Faith Ser.: Vol. 2). Repr. of 1947 ed. 18.00 (ISBN 0-8369-2393-6). Ayer Co Pubs.
Fontenrose, Joseph. Python. 1959. 25.00 (ISBN 0-8196-0285-X). Biblo.
Fromm, Erich. The Heart of Man: Its Genius for Good & Evil. LC 64-18053. 1980. pap. 6.95 (ISBN 0-06-090795-9, CN 795, PL). Har-Row.
Galligan, Michael. God & Evil. LC 75-36172. 96p. 1976. pap. 2.95 (ISBN 0-8091-1925-0). Paulist Pr.
Geisler, Norman L. The Roots of Evil. (Christian Free University Curriculum Ser.). 1978. pap. 4.95 (ISBN 0-310-35751-9, 12655P). Zondervan.
Giran, Etienne. A Modern Job: An Essay on the Problem of Evil. 92p. 1916. 1.95 (ISBN 0-317-40399-0). Open Court.
Gottemoller, Bartholomew. Why Good People Suffer: A Practical Treatise on the Problem of Evil. 1987. 9.95 (ISBN 0-533-07107-0). Vantage.
Green, Michael. I Believe in Satan's Downfall. (I Believe Ser.). 256p. (Orig.). 1981. pap. 6.95 (ISBN 0-8028-1892-7). Eerdmans.
Hagerty, Cornelius. The Problem of Evil. LC 77-3022. 1978. 9.95 (ISBN 0-8158-0352-4). Chris Mass.
Harris, Errol E. & Litt, D. The Problem of Evil. LC 77-72325. (Aquinas Lecture Ser.). 1977. 7.95 (ISBN 0-87462-142-9). Marquette.
Heagle, John. Suffering & Evil. (Guidelines for Contemporary Catholics Ser.). (Orig.). 1987. pap. 7.95 (ISBN 0-88347-212-0). Thomas More.
Herman, A. L. The Problem of Evil & Indian Thought. 1976. 13.95 (ISBN 0-8426-0991-1). Orient Bk Dist.
Hick, John H. Evil & the God of Love. rev. ed. LC 76-62953. 1977. pap. 6.95 (ISBN 0-06-063902-4, RD219, HarpR). Har-Row.
James, Henry, Sr. The Nature of Evil: Considered in a Letter to the Rev. Edward Beecher, D.D. LC 72-920. (The Selected Works of Henry James, Sr.: Vol. 6). 352p. 1983. Repr. of 1855 ed. 37.50 (ISBN 0-404-10086-4). AMS Pr.
Jenyns, Soame. A Free Enquiry into the Nature & Origin of Evil. 2nd ed. Wellek, Rene, ed. LC 75-11226. (British Philosophers & Theologians of the 17th & 18th Centuries: Vol. 28). 1976. Repr. of 1757 ed. lib. bdg. 51.00 (ISBN 0-8240-1780-3). Garland Pub.
Jooharigian, Robert B. God & Natural Evil. 85p. (Orig.). 1985. pap. 6.95x (ISBN 0-932269-30-3). Wyndham Hall.
Kelsey, Morton. Discernment: A Study in Ecstasy & Evil. LC 78-58958. 168p. 1978. pap. 7.95 (ISBN 0-8091-2157-3). Paulist Pr.
King, William. An Essay on the Origin of Evil. Bd. with Dissertations Concerning the Fundamental Principle & Immediate Criterion of Virtue. LC 75-11228. (British Philosophers & Theologians of the 17th & 18th Centuries Ser.). 391p. 1978. lib. bdg. 51.00 (ISBN 0-8240-1782-X). Garland Pub.
Kite, Roger. Evil & Suffering. 1985. 19.00x (ISBN 0-7062-3911-3, Pub. by Ward Lock Educ Co Ltd). State Mutual Bk.
Knoch, A. E. The Problem of Evil & the Judgments of God. 351p. 1976. pap. text ed. 4.00 (ISBN 0-910424-59-4). Concordant.
Lewis, C. S. The Problem of Pain. 1978. pap. 3.95 (ISBN 0-02-086850-2, Collier). Macmillan.
Lowe, Walter. Evil & the Unconscious. LC 82-19147. (AAR Studies in Religion Ser.). 142p. 1983. 16.50 (ISBN 0-89130-600-5, 01 00 30). Scholars Pr GA.
M. Lord God of Truth Within. 1976. Repr. of 1940 ed. 12.00 (ISBN 0-911662-56-1). Yoga.
McKeever, Jim. Knowledge of Good & Evil. 1981. 1.00 (ISBN 0-86694-084-7). Omega Pubns OR.
Maritain, Jacques. Saint Thomas & the Problem of Evil. (Aquinas Lecture). 1942. 7.95 (ISBN 0-87462-106-2). Marquette.
Martell, Dwane K. The Enigma of God & Man's Proclivity to Evil. (Institute for Religious Research Library). (Illus.). 77p. 1983. 47.75 (ISBN 0-89920-049-4). Am Inst Psych.
Midgley, Mary. Wickedness. 232p. 1986. pap. 8.95 (ISBN 0-7448-0053-6, 0053W). Methuen Inc.
Murdoch, Iris. The Sovereignty of Good. 116p. 1985. pap. 5.95 (ISBN 0-7448-0028-5, Ark Paperbks). Methuen Inc.
Murphy, Elspeth. Sometimes I'm Good, Sometimes I'm Bad. (David & I Talk to God Ser.). (Illus.). 24p. 1981. pap. 2.95 (ISBN 0-89191-368-8, 53686). Cook.
O'Flaherty, Wendy D. The Origins of Evil in Hindu Mythology Hermeneutics. (Studies in the History of Religions). 1977. pap. 6.95 (ISBN 0-520-04098-8, CAL 456). U of Cal Pr.
Peck, M. Scott. People of the Lie: The Hope for Healing Human Evil. LC 83-13631. 269p. 1983. 15.95 (ISBN 0-671-45492-7). S&S.
--People of the Lie: The Hope for Healing Human Evil. 1985. pap. 7.95 (ISBN 0-671-52816-5, Touchstone Bks). S&S.
Plantinga, Alvin. God, Freedom, & Evil. 1978. pap. 7.95 (ISBN 0-8028-1731-9). Eerdmans.
Portillo, Carlos E. Evil Side of Good. LC 85-52117. 200p. (Orig.). Date not set. pap. price not set (ISBN 0-937365-04-1). WCP Pubns.
Reichenbach, Bruce. Evil & a Good God. LC 82-71120. xviii, 198p. 1982. 22.50 (ISBN 0-8232-1080-4); pap. 9.00 (ISBN 0-8232-1081-2). Fordham.
Rice, Philip B. On the Knowledge of Good & Evil. LC 75-8968. 299p. 1975. Repr. of 1955 ed. lib. bdg. 22.50x (ISBN 0-8371-8124-0, RIGE). Greenwood.
Ricoeur, Paul. Symbolism of Evil. Buchanan, Emerson, tr. LC 67-11506. 1969. pap. 11.95x (ISBN 0-8070-1567-9, BPA18). Beacon Pr.
Rosenthal, Abigail L. A Good Look at Evil. 264p. 1987. 24.95 (ISBN 0-87722-456-0). Temple U Pr.
Saint Augustine. On Free Choice of the Will. Benjamin, A. S. & Hackstaff, L. H., trs. LC 63-16932. (Orig.). 1964. pap. 7.20 scp (ISBN 0-672-60368-3, LLAS150). Bobbs.
Sanford, John A. Evil: The Shadow Side of Reality. 176p. 1981. 10.95 (ISBN 0-8245-0037-7); pap. 9.95 (ISBN 0-8245-0526-3). Crossroad NY.
Schilling, S. Paul. God & Human Anguish. LC 77-5857. Repr. of 1977 ed. 76.00 (ISBN 0-8357-9009-6, 2016362). Bks Demand UMI.
Schulweis, Harold M. Evil & the Morality of Ged. (Hebrew Union College Jewish Perspectives Ser.: No. 3). 1984. 15.00 (ISBN 0-87820-502-0). Hebrew Union Coll Pr.
Schwartz, Richard B. Samuel Johnson & the Problem of Evil. LC 74-27314. 128p. 1975. 27.50x (ISBN 0-299-06790-4). U of Wis Pr.
Smith, Donald. How to Cure Yourself of Positive Thinking. LC 77-70191. 1977. 7.95 (ISBN 0-912458-80-1). E A Seemann.
Steiner, Rudolf. The Deed of Christ & the Opposing Spiritual Powers Lucifer, Ahriman, Mephistopheles, Asuras. 2.75 (ISBN 0-919924-02-6, Pub by Steiner Book Centre Canada). Anthroposophic.
--The Influences of Lucifer & Ahriman: Man's Responsibility for the Earth. Osmond, D. S., tr. from Ger. 84p. 1976. pap. 6.95 (ISBN 0-919924-00-X). Anthroposophic.
--The Origin of Suffering, The Origin of Evil, Illness & Death. Cotterell, Mabel & Watkin, V. E., trs. (Ger.). 31p. 1980. pap. 2.95 (ISBN 0-919924-12-3, Pub. by Steiner Book Centre Canada). Anthroposophic.
Surin, Kenneth. Theology & the Problem of Evil. (Signposts in Theology Ser.). 192p. 1986. text ed. 39.95 (ISBN 0-631-14664-4); pap. text ed. 14.95 (ISBN 0-631-14663-6). Basil Blackwell.
Thompson, William I. Evil & World Order. (World Perspectives Ser.). 1977. pap. 4.95x (ISBN 0-06-131951-1, TB1951, Torch). Har-Row.
Villafranca, Anthony L. The Theory of Sin & the Equilibrium Between the Emotional & the Rational in Man. (Illus.). 104p. 1986. 88.50 (ISBN 0-89266-568-8). Am Classical Coll Pr.
Wenham, John W. The Enigma of Evil: Can We Believe in the Goodness of God? 224p. (Orig.). 1985. pap. 7.95 (ISBN 0-310-29871-7, 12449P). Zondervan.
Zappulli, Cesare. The Power of Goodness. 1980. 3.00 (ISBN 0-8198-5800-5); pap. 2.00 (ISBN 0-8198-5801-3). Dghtrs St Paul.
Zimmer, Heinrich. King & the Corpse: Tales of the Soul's Conquest of Evil. Campbell, Joseph, ed. (Bollingen Ser.: Vol. 11). 1971. pap. 9.50 (ISBN 0-691-01776-X). Princeton U Pr.
Zodhiates, Spiros. Jesus & the Demon World. LC 82-71842. 1982. pap. 5.95 (ISBN 0-89957-556-0). AMG Pubs.

GOOD FRIDAY
Becker, Ralph. Lent, Good Friday & Easter. pap. 0.50 (ISBN 0-685-41825-1). Reiner.
Grimbol, William. The Darkest Day. 1986. 1.75 (ISBN 0-89536-789-0, 6807). CSS of Ohio.
Hoefler, Richard C. At Noon on Friday. 1983. 3.50 (ISBN 0-89536-557-X, 0111). CSS of Ohio.
Leary, Norma. Good Friday Unchanged. (Orig.). 1982. pap. 3.75 (ISBN 0-937172-34-0). JLJ Pubs.
Orbaker, Douglas & Blake, Robert A. Day of Redemption. Sherer, Michael L., ed. (Orig.). 1987. pap. 2.25 (ISBN 0-89536-848-X, 7807). CSS of Ohio.

GOOD WORKS (THEOLOGY)
see also Antinomianism; Corporal Works of Mercy; Justification; Reward (Theology)
Rogers, Dale E. Angel Unaware. (Orig.). 1984. pap. 2.50 (ISBN 0-515-08952-4). Jove Pubns.

GOSPEL, SOCIAL
see Social Gospel

GOSPEL AND LAW
see Law and Gospel

GOSPEL MUSIC
see also Spirituals (Songs)
Ferlita, Ernest. Gospel Journey. 120p. (Orig.). 1983. pap. 5.95 (ISBN 0-86683-685-3, HarpR). Har-Row.
Gospel. (The Ultimate Ser.). 288p. 1983. plastic comb 17.95 (ISBN 0-9607350-6-2, 00241008); pap. 14.95 (ISBN 0-9607350-7-0, 00241009). H Leonard Pub Corp.
Heilbut, Anthony. The Gospel Sound: Good News & Bad Times. rev. updated ed. LC 84-26122. (Illus.). 416p. 1985. pap. 9.95 (ISBN 0-87910-034-6). Limelight Edns.
Jackson, Irene V., compiled by. Afro-American Religious Music: A Bibliography & a Catalogue of Gospel Music. LC 78-60527. (Illus.). 1979. lib. bdg. 35.00 (ISBN 0-313-20560-4, JGM/). Greenwood.
Lovell, John, Jr. Black Song: The Forge & the Flame. (Illus.). 704p. 1986. pap. 12.95 (ISBN 0-913729-53-1). Paragon Hse.
McRae, Shirley W. Glow Ree Bee (11 Traditional Black Spiritual Arrangements) Bennett, Michael D., ed. 28p. (Orig.). 1982. pap. text ed. 5.95 (ISBN 0-934017-02-6). Memphis Musicraft.
Martin-Marrero, Vernetta. The Gospel Church Choir Organizer. 150p. 1984. 3 ring hard storage binder 29.95 (ISBN 0-9613430-0-1). Martin-Marrero.
Ricks, George R. Some Aspects of the Religious Music of the United States Negro. Dorson, Richard M., ed. LC 77-70621. (International Folklore Ser.). 1977. Repr. of 1977 ed. lib. bdg. 36.50x (ISBN 0-405-10123-6). Ayer Co Pubs.
Sankey, Ira D., et al. Gospel Hyms, 6 vols, No. 1-6. facsimile ed. LC 70-171076. (Earlier American Music Ser.: No. 5). 512p. 1972. Repr. of 1895 ed. lib. bdg. 37.50 (ISBN 0-306-77305-8). Da Capo.
Shinn, Duane & Hoffman, Diane. Evangelistic Embellishments: How to Make Hymns & Gospel Songs Come Alive. 1980. spiral bdg. 49.95 (ISBN 0-912732-49-0). Duane Shinn.
Sizer, Sandra S. Gospel Hymns & Social Religion: The Rhetoric of Nineteenth-Century Revivalism. LC 78-10165. (American Civilization Ser.). 222p. 1979. lib. bdg. 27.95 (ISBN 0-87722-142-1). Temple U Pr.
Wells, Edmund E. Wells of Salvation. (Orig.). pap. 2.00 (ISBN 0-686-30400-4). WOS.

GOTHIC ARCHITECTURE
see Architecture, Gothic

GOTHIC ART
see Art, Gothic

GOTHIC SCULPTURE
see Sculpture, Gothic

GOVERNORS–UNITED STATES
Almaraz, Felix D., Jr. Tragic Cavalier: Governor Manuel Salcedo of Texas, 1808-1813. 218p. 1971. pap. text ed. 6.95 (ISBN 0-292-78039-7). U of Tex Pr.
Hinckley, Ted C. Alaskan John G. Brady: Missionary, Businessman, Judge, & Governor, 1878-1918. LC 81-19030. (Illus.). 415p. 1982. 40.00x (ISBN 0-8142-0336-1). Ohio St U Pr.

GOVINDA SIMBA, 10TH GURU OF THE SIKHS, 1666-1708
Singh, Khushwant & Singh, Suneet V. Homage to Guru Gobind Singh. 1970. pap. 2.75 (ISBN 0-88253-088-7). Ind-US Inc.

GRACE (THEOLOGY)
see also Covenants (Theology); Law and Gospel
Boff, Leonardo. Liberating Grace. Drury, John, tr. from Port. LC 79-4206. Tr. of A graca libertadoro no mundo. 256p. (Orig.). 1979. pap. 9.95 (ISBN 0-88344-282-5). Orbis Bks.
Booth, Abrh. The Reign of Grace. 5.95 (ISBN 0-685-88390-6). Reiner.
Bro. Stanley. Pure Grace. 96p. 1984. 6.95 (ISBN 0-89962-414-6). Todd & Honeywell.
Bunyan, John. Doctrine of Law & Grace Unfolded. 1974. pap. 2.95 (ISBN 0-685-52817-0). Reiner.
--Saved by Grace. pap. 2.25 (ISBN 0-685-88393-0). Reiner.
Chafer, Lewis S. Grace. pap. 11.95 (ISBN 0-310-22331-8, 6305P). Zondervan.
Cheesman, John, et al. The Grace of God in the Gospel. 1976. pap. 3.45 (ISBN 0-85151-153-8). Banner of Truth.
Cowen, Deborah, ed. The Year of Grace of the Lord. 254p. (Orig.). 1980. pap. 8.95 (ISBN 0-913836-68-0). St Vladimirs.
Custance, Arthur C. Sovereignty of Grace. 1979. 12.95 (ISBN 0-87552-160-6). Presby & Reformed.
Davey, James E. Riches of Grace. pap. 0.95 (ISBN 0-87509-127-X). Chr Pubns.
Davis, Ron L. The Healing Choice. 160p. 1986. 9.95 (ISBN 0-8499-0466-8, 0466-8). Word Bks.
De Lubac, Henri. A Brief Catechesis on Nature & Grace. Arnandez, Richard, tr. from Fr. LC 83-82108. Tr. of Petite Catechese sur Nature et Grace. 308p. (Orig.). 1984. pap. 10.95 (ISBN 0-89870-035-3). Ignatius Pr.

Drewery, Benjamin. Origen & the Doctrine of Grace. LC 61-19395. 1960. text ed. 17.50x (ISBN 0-8401-0579-7). A R Allenson.
The Grace Divine. 236p. (Orig.). 1984. pap. 3.50 (ISBN 0-87481-524-X, Pub. by Ramakrishna Math Madras India). Vedanta Pr.
Grossman, Siegfried. Stewards of God's Grace. 192p. (Orig.). 1981. pap. text ed. 8.95 (ISBN 0-85364-287-7). Attic Pr.
Hagin, Kenneth E. Five Hindrances to Growth in Grace. 1981. pap. 0.50 mini bk (ISBN 0-89276-253-5). Hagin Ministries.
Haight, Roger. The Experience & Language of Grace. LC 79-84403. 192p. 1979. pap. 7.95 (ISBN 0-8091-2200-6). Paulist Pr.
Hendriksen, William. The Covenant of Grace. 1978. pap. 2.95 (ISBN 0-8010-4196-1). Baker Bk.
Hess, Nancy B. By the Grace of God. 1979. 12.50 (ISBN 0-87813-207-4). Park View.
Jeeves, Malcolm A., et al. Free to Be Different. American ed. LC 84-10525. Repr. of 1985 ed. 40.80 (2027547). Bks Demand UMI.
John-Roger. Baraka: Movement of Spiritual Inner Awareness. 1978. pap. 5.00 (ISBN 0-914829-01-7). Baraka Bk.
Keating, Thomas, et al. Finding Grace at the Center. rev. ed. LC 78-10514. 1979. 2.50 (ISBN 0-932506-20-8); pap. 2.50 (ISBN 0-932506-00-3). St Bedes Pubns.
Kevan, Ernest F. The Grace of Law. 9.95 (ISBN 0-8010-5373-0). Baker Bk.
Liderbach, Daniel. The Theology of Grace & the American Mind: A Representation of Catholic Doctrine. LC 83-22154. (Toronto Studies in Theology: Vol. 15). 170p. 1983. lib. bdg. 39.95x (ISBN 0-88946-761-7). E Mellen.
MacDonald, William. Grace of God. pap. 1.95 (ISBN 0-937396-18-4). Walterick Pubs.
Matthews, Edward M. A Means of Grace. 58p. 1946. pap. 1.50 (ISBN 0-935461-08-6). St Alban Pr CA.
Moffatt, James. Grace in the New Testament. 419p. 1981. Repr. of 1931 ed. lib. bdg. 45.00 (ISBN 0-89984-339-5). Century Bookbindery.
Murray, Andrew. Secret of the Throne of Grace. (Secret Ser.). (Orig.). 1980. pap. 1.95 (ISBN 0-87508-393-5). Chr Lit.
Nee, Watchman. Full of Grace & Truth, Vol. II. Kaung, Stephen, tr. 1981. pap. 3.25 (ISBN 0-935008-51-9). Christian Fellow Pubs.
Neilands, David L. Studies in the Covenant of Grace. 1981. pap. 5.75 (ISBN 0-87552-365-X). Presby & Reformed.
O'Donovan, L. J. A World of Grace. 1980. pap. 14.95x (ISBN 0-8245-0406-2). Crossroad NY.
Pinnock, Clark H. Grace Unlimited. LC 75-22161. 272p. 1975. pap. 8.95 (ISBN 0-87123-185-9, 210185). Bethany Hse.
Read, David H. This Grace Given. 144p. (Orig.). 1984. pap. 7.95 (ISBN 0-8028-0025-4). Eerdmans.
Riggle, H. M. The Two Works of Grace. 56p. pap. 0.40 (ISBN 0-686-29168-9); pap. 1.00 3 copies (ISBN 0-686-29169-7). Faith Pub Hse.
Roberts, Donald. Grace: God's Special Gift. 1982. pap. 3.95 (ISBN 0-570-04060-4, 56-1363). Concordia.
Ryrie, Charles C. The Grace of God. rev., new ed. 128p. 1975. pap. 4.95 (ISBN 0-8024-3250-6). Moody.
--La Gracia de Dios. Orig. Title: The Grace of God. (Span.). 160p. 1979. pap. 3.50 (ISBN 0-8254-1630-2). Kregel.
Schulz, Thomas. Charis: The Meaning of Grace in the New Testament. 78p. 1971. pap. 3.95 (ISBN 0-911620-06-0). Westcott.
Segundo, Jean L. Grace & the Human Condition. Drury, John, tr. from Span. LC 72-85794. (A Theology for Artisans of a New Humanity Ser.: Vol. 2). Orig. Title: Gracia y Condicion Humana. 221p. 1973. pap. 7.95 (ISBN 0-88344-488-7). Orbis Bks.
Spurgeon, C. H. Exposition of the Doctrines of Grace. 1975. 1.50 (ISBN 0-686-09096-9). Pilgrim Pubns.
--Grace. 1976. pap. 1.50 (ISBN 0-686-16843-7). Pilgrim Pubns.
Spurgeon, Charles H. All of Grace. (Moody Classics Ser.). 1984. pap. 3.50 (ISBN 0-8024-0001-9). Moody.
--Solamente Por Gracia. (Span.). 128p. 1982. pap. 3.25 (ISBN 0-8254-1678-7). Kregel.
Steiner, Rudolf. The Concepts of Original Sin & Grace. Osmond, D. S., tr. from Ger. 32p. 1973. pap. 1.95 (ISBN 0-85440-275-6, Pub. by Steinerbooks). Anthroposophic.
Sumner, Robert L. Saved by Grace...for Service. 1979. 8.95 (ISBN 0-87398-797-7, Pub. by Bibl Evang Pr). Sword of Lord.
Teasley, D. O. The Double Cure, or Redemption Twofold. 160p. pap. 1.50 large print (ISBN 0-686-29147-6). Faith Pub Hse.
Thomas, J. D. The Biblical Doctrine of Grace. LC 76-56472. (Way of Life Ser: No. 111). (Orig.). 1977. pap. 3.95 (ISBN 0-89112-111-0, Bibl Res Pr). Abilene Christ U.
Twombly, Gerald & Kennedy, Timothy. A Taste of Grace, Vol. 1. (Illus.). 182p. 1982. pap. 7.50 (ISBN 0-910219-04-4). Little People.
Van Til, Cornelius. Common Grace & the Gospel. 1972. pap. 8.95 (ISBN 0-87552-482-6). Presby & Reformed.
Wallace, Dewey D., Jr. Puritans & Predestination: Grace in English Protestant Theology, 1525 to 1695. LC 81-11563. (Studies in Religion). xiii, 289p. 1982. 29.95x (ISBN 0-8078-1499-7). U of NC Pr.
Wilson, William P. Croitre dans la Grace. Orig. Title: The Grace to Grow. (Fr.). 1986. write for info. (ISBN 0-8297-0745-X). Life Pubs Intl.
Wilson, William P. & Slattery, Kathryn. El Poder Sanador de la Gracia. Llerena, Mario, ed. Bernal, Luis, tr. from Span. Orig. Title: The Grace to Grow. 176p. 1985. pap. text ed. 2.95 (ISBN 0-8297-0744-1). Life Pubs Intl.

GRACE, GIFTS OF
see Gifts, Spiritual

GRACE AT MEALS
Beilenson, Nick, ed. Table Graces. LC 86-61119. (Illus.). 63p. 1986. 5.95 (ISBN 0-88088-509-2). Peter Pauper.
Kwatera, Michael & Reinhart, Dietrich. Prayers at Meals. 48p. 1983. pap. 0.50 (ISBN 0-8146-1318-7). Liturgical Pr.
Simons, Thomas G. Blessings: A Reappraisal of Their Nature, Purpose, & Celebration. LC 80-54275. 1981. pap. 9.95 (ISBN 0-89390-026-5). Resource Pubns.
Table Graces for the Family. rev. ed. 128p. 1984. 4.95 (ISBN 0-8407-5369-1). Nelson.
Tengbom, Mildred. Mealtime Prayers. LC 85-9041. 128p. 1985. pap. 4.95 (ISBN 0-8066-2127-3, 10-4306). Augsburg.
Tengbom, Mildred, compiled by. Table Prayers: New Prayers, Old Favorites, Songs, & Responses. LC 77-72451. 1977. pap. 4.95 (ISBN 0-8066-1594-X, 10-6185). Augsburg.
Tudor, Tasha. First Graces. LC 59-12017. (Illus.). 1955. 4.95 (ISBN 0-8098-1953-8). McKay.

GRAHAM, WILLIAM FRANKLIN, 1918-
Ashman, Chuck. The Gospel According to Billy. 1977. 8.95 (ISBN 0-8184-0251-2). Lyle Stuart.
Brown, Joan W., compiled by. Dia-Tras-Dia Con Billy Graham. Orig. Title: Day by Day with Billy Graham. 192p. 1982. Repr. of 1978 ed. 3.95 (ISBN 0-311-40039-6, Edit Mundo). Casa Bautista.
--Day-by-Day with Billy Graham. 1976. pap. 5.95 (ISBN 0-89066-000-X). World Wide Pubs.
Cornwell, Patricia D. A Time for Remembering. 496p. 1985. pap. 16.95 (ISBN 0-8027-2501-5). Walker & Co.
Frist, Betty. My Neighbors, the Billy Grahams. LC 83-70368. 1983. 8.95 (ISBN 0-8054-7229-0). Broadman.
Westman, Paul. Billy Graham: Reaching Out to the World. LC 81-9912. (Taking Part Ser.). (Illus.). 48p. 1981. PLB 8.95 (ISBN 0-87518-220-8). Dillon.
Wilson, Jean. Crusader for Christ (Billy Graham) 1973. pap. 2.50 (ISBN 0-87508-602-0). Chr Lit.

GRAIL
Cavendish, Richard. King Arthur & the Grail: The Arthurian Legends & Their Meaning. LC 79-14034. 238p. 1985. pap. 6.95 (ISBN 0-8008-4466-1). Taplinger.
Cooney, Ellen. The Quest for the Holy Grail. LC 80-67333. 85p. (Orig.). 1981. pap. 5.95 (ISBN 0-9602912-3-7). Duir Press.
Evans, Sabastian, tr. High History of the Holy Graal. (Illus.). 395p. 1969. 16.95 (ISBN 0-227-67727-7). Attic Pr.
Fisher, Lizette A. Mystic Vision in the Grail Legend & in the Divine Comedy. LC 79-168029. Repr. of 1917 ed. 16.50 (ISBN 0-404-02389-4). AMS Pr.
Hall, Manly P. Orders of the Quest - the Holy Grail. 5.95 (ISBN 0-89314-533-5). Philos Res.
Heline, Corinne. Mysteries of the Holy Grail. pap. 3.95 (ISBN 0-87613-015-5). New Age.
Kahane, Henry & Kahane, Renee. The Krater & the Grail: Hermetic Sources of the Parzival. LC 84-16179. 216p. 1965. 31.00 (ISBN 0-252-01196-1). U of Ill Pr.
Locke, Frederick W. Quest for the Holy Grail. LC 70-181948. (Stanford University. Stanford Studies in Language & Literature: No. 21). Repr. of 1960 ed. 22.50 (ISBN 0-404-51831-1). AMS Pr.
Lovelich, Henry. The History of the Holy Grail, Pts. 1-5. Furnivall, F. J., ed. (EETS, ES Ser.: Nos. 20, 24, 28, 30, 95). Repr. of 1875 ed. Pts. I & II. 45.00 (ISBN 0-527-00234-8); Pts. 3-5, 1877 - 1905. 29.00 (ISBN 0-527-00235-6). Kraus Repr.
Matarasso, P. M., tr. Quest of the Holy Grail. (Classics Ser.). 304p. 1969. pap. 4.95 (ISBN 0-14-044220-0). Penguin.
Matthews, John. At the Table of the Grail: Magic & the Use of Imagination. 224p. (Orig.). 1984. pap. 10.95 (ISBN 0-7100-9938-X). Methuen Inc.
Newstead, Helaine. Bran the Blessed in Arthurian Romance. LC 40-4360. Repr. of 1939 ed. 14.50 (ISBN 0-404-04687-8). AMS Pr.
Nutt, Alfred. Studies on the Legend of the Holy Grail with Special Reference to the Hypothesis of Its Celtic Origin. (Folk-Lore Society, London, Monographs: Vol. 23). pap. 29.00 (ISBN 0-8115-0510-3). Kraus Repr.
Nutt, Alfred T. Legends of the Holy Grail. LC 78-139176. (Popular Studies in Mythology, Romance & Folklore: No. 14). Repr. of 1902 ed. 5.50 (ISBN 0-404-53514-3). AMS Pr.
Prophet, Elizabeth C., ed. Mysteries of the Holy Grail: Archangel Gabriel. LC 83-51154. (Illus.). 430p. 1984. pap. 12.95 (ISBN 0-916766-64-0). Summit Univ.
Ravenscroft, Trevor. The Cup of Destiny: The Quest for the Grail. LC 82-60160. 194p. 1982. pap. 6.95 (ISBN 0-87728-546-2). Weiser.
Waite, Arthur E. Hidden Church of the Holy Graal. 710p. 1975. Repr. of 1909 ed. 12.00 (ISBN 0-911662-54-5). Yoga.
Webb, James, ed. A Quest Anthology. LC 75-36916. (Occult Ser.). 1976. Repr. of 1976 ed. 46.50x (ISBN 0-405-07971-0). Ayer Co Pubs.
Weston, Jessie L. From Ritual to Romance. McLaughlin, Mary M., tr. 13.75 (ISBN 0-8446-3162-0). Peter Smith.
--The Quest of the Holy Grail. LC 72-10823. (Arthurian Legend & Literature Ser., No. 1). 1973. Repr. of 1913 ed. lib. bdg. 75.00x (ISBN 0-8383-0642-X). Haskell.

GRANDPARENTS
Christian, Mary B. Grandfathers: God's Gift to Children. 1982. pap. 2.75 (ISBN 0-570-04069-8, 56-1372). Concordia.
--Grandmothers: God's Gift to Children. 1982. pap. 2.75 (ISBN 0-570-04068-X, 56-1371). Concordia.
Isler, Betty. Thank You for My Grandchild. 1983. pap. 4.95 (ISBN 0-570-03915-0, 12-2850). Concordia.
Madden, Myron C. & Madden, Mary B. For Grandparents: Wonders & Worries. LC 80-12778. (Christian Care Bks.: Vol, 9). 118p. 1980. pap. 7.95 (ISBN 0-664-24325-8). Westminster.

GRAVES
see Burial; Epitaphs; Funeral Rites and Ceremonies; Sepulchral Monuments; Tombs

GRAVESEND, RICHARD, BP. OF LONDON, d. 1303
Hale, William H. & Ellacombe, H. T., eds. Account of the Executors of Richard Bishop of London 1303, & of the Executors of Thomas Bishop of Exeter 1310. 1874. 27.00 (ISBN 0-384-20950-5). Johnson Repr.

GRAVESTONES
see Sepulchral Monuments

GRAY FRIARS
see Franciscans

GREAT AWAKENING
Here are entered works dealing with the revival of religion that occurred in the American colonies in the 18th century.
see also Evangelical Revival
Gaustad, Edwin S. The Great Awakening in New England. 13.75 (ISBN 0-8446-1491-2). Peter Smith.
Heimert, Alan E. & Miller, Perry, eds. Great Awakening: Documents Illustrating the Crisis & Its Consequences. LC 66-23537. (Orig.). 1967. pap. 14.47 scp (ISBN 0-672-60044-7, AHS34). Bobbs.
Maxson, Charles H. The Great Awakening in the Middle Colonies. 12.00 (ISBN 0-8446-1306-1). Peter Smith.
Rutman, Darrett B., ed. The Great Awakening: Event & Exegesis. LC 77-10540. 208p. 1977. pap. text ed. 8.00 (ISBN 0-88275-605-2). Krieger.
Whitefield, George. Journals of George Whitefield, 1737-1741. LC 73-81363. (Illus.). 1969. Repr. of 1905 ed. 75.00x (ISBN 0-8201-1069-8). Schol Facsimiles.

GREAT BRITAIN–ANTIQUITIES
Burl. The Stone Circles of the British Isles. 1976. 46.00x (ISBN 0-300-01972-6); pap. 22.50x (ISBN 0-300-02398-7, Y-341). Yale U Pr.
Burl, Aubrey. Rites of the Gods. (Illus.). 272p. 1981. text ed. 26.50x (ISBN 0-460-04313-7, BKA 04660, Pub. by J M Dent England). Biblio Dist.
Chambers, Robert, ed. Book of Days: A Miscellany of Popular Antiquities in Connection with the Calendar, Including Anecdote, Biography & History, Curiosities of Literature, & Oddities of Human Life & Character, 2 Vols. LC 67-13009. (Illus.). 1967. Repr. of 1862 ed. 125.00x (ISBN 0-8103-3002-4). Gale.
Dawes, Jean D. & Magilton, J. R. Cemetery of St. Helen-on-the-Walls, Aldwark, York. (Archaeology of York Ser: Vol. 12). 132p. 1980. pap. text ed. 25.00x (ISBN 0-900312-88-2, Pub. by Coun Brit Archaeology). Humanities.
Dobson, R. & Donaghey, S. The History of Clementhorpe Nunnery. (The Archaeology of York-Historical Sources for York Archaeology after AD 1100,). 40p. 1984. pap. text ed. 10.50x (ISBN 0-906780-40-3, Pub. by Council British Archaeology England). Humanities.
Green, Miranda J. The Gods of Roman Britain. (Shire Archeaology Ser.: No. 34). (Illus.). 64p. (Orig.). 1983. pap. 5.95 (ISBN 0-85263-634-2, Pub. by Shire Pubns England). Seven Hills Bks.
Jones, Michael J. The Defences of the Upper Roman Enclosure. (Archaeology of Lincoln Ser.: Vol. 7). 62p. 1980. pap. text ed. 25.00x (ISBN 0-906780-00-4, Pub. by Coun Brit Archaeology). Humanities.
Magilton, J. R. The Church of St. Helen on the Walls, Aldwark, York. (Archaeology of York Ser.: Vol. 10). 64p. 1980. pap. text ed. 15.00x (ISBN 0-900312-98-X, Pub. by Coun Brit Archaeology). Humanities.
Stukeley, William. Stonehenge, a Temple Restored to the British Druids; Abury, a Temple of the British Druids. Feldman, Burton & Richardson, Robert D., eds. LC 78-60898. (Myth & Romanticism Ser.). 1984. lib. bdg. 80.00 (ISBN 0-8240-3572-0). Garland Pub.

GREAT BRITAIN–CHURCH HISTORY
see also Celtic Church
Bourdillon, A. F. C. The Order of Minoresses in England. 115p. Repr. of 1926 ed. text ed. 33.12x (ISBN 0-576-99212-7, Pub. by Gregg Intl Pubs England). Gregg Intl.
Bready, John W. England, Before & after Wesley: The Evangelical Revival & Social Reform. LC 72-139906. (Illus.). 463p. 1971. Repr. of 1938 ed. 17.00x (ISBN 0-8462-1533-0). Russell.
Bright, William. Chapters in Early English Church History. 3rd ed. 1897. 25.00 (ISBN 0-8337-4005-9). B Franklin.
Burke, Arthur M. Key to the Ancient Parish Registers of England & Wales. LC 62-6577. (Illus.). 163p. 1981. Repr. of 1908 ed. 15.00 (ISBN 0-8063-0445-6). Genealog Pub.
Cheney, C. R. Medieval Texts & Studies. 1973. 55.00x (ISBN 0-19-822399-4). Oxford U Pr.
Dodd, Charles. Dodd's Church History of England, 1500-1688, 5 Vols. Tierney, M. A., ed. LC 75-119152. Repr. of 1843 ed. Set. 262.00 (ISBN 0-404-02150-6); 52.50 ea. Vol. 1 (ISBN 0-404-02151-4). Vol. 2 (ISBN 0-404-02152-2). Vol. 3 (ISBN 0-404-02153-0). Vol. 4 (ISBN 0-404-02154-9). Vol. 5 (ISBN 0-404-02155-7). AMS Pr.
Faulkner, Harold U. Chartism & the Churches. LC 79-76712. (Columbia University. Studies in the Social Sciences: No. 173). Repr. of 1916 ed. 12.50 (ISBN 0-404-51173-2). AMS Pr.
--Chartism & the Churches: A Study in Democracy. 152p. 1970. Repr. of 1916 ed. 32.50x (ISBN 0-7146-1308-8, F Cass Co). Biblio Dist.
Gater, George H. & Hiorns, F. R. The Parish of St. Martin-in-the Fields: Trafalgar Square & Neighborhood, Pt. 3. LC 70-37852. (London County Council. Survey of London: No. 20). Repr. of 1940 ed. 74.50 (ISBN 0-404-51670-X). AMS Pr.
Martin, Edward J. A History of the Iconoclastic Controversy. (Church Historical Society London N. S. Ser.: No. 2). Repr. of 1930 ed. 55.00 (ISBN 0-8115-3126-0). Kraus Repr.
Moorman, John R. A History of the Church in England. 3rd rev ed. 485p. 1973. 19.95 (ISBN 0-8192-1282-2). Morehouse.
Neilson, N., ed. The Cartulary & Terrier of the Priory of Bilsongton, Kent. (British Academy, London, Records of the Social & Economic History of England & Wales Ser.: Vol. 7). pap. 36.00 (ISBN 0-8115-1247-9). Kraus Repr.
Norman, Edward. Roman Catholicism in England from the Elizabethan Settlement to the Second Vatican Council. (OPUS). 160p. 1985. 18.95x (ISBN 0-19-219181-0); pap. 9.95 (ISBN 0-19-281935-6). Oxford U Pr.
Nuttall, Geoffrey F. & Chadwick, O., eds. From Uniformity to Unity, 1662-1962. LC 63-2539. 1962. 20.00x (ISBN 0-8401-1746-9). A R Allenson.
Randall, Gerald. The English Parish Church. 192p. 1982. 35.00 (ISBN 0-8419-6402-5). Holmes & Meier.
Rodes, Robert. Lay Authority & Reformation in the English Church. LC 82-7038. 319p. 1982. 25.00 (ISBN 0-268-01265-2). U of Notre Dame Pr.
Rodwell, Warwick. The Archaeology of the English Church. (Illus.). 192p. 1981. 34.95 (ISBN 0-7134-2590-3, Pub. by Batsford England). David & Charles.
Schwartz, Hillel. Knaves, Fools, Madmen & That Subtile Effluvium: A Study of the Opposition to the French Prophets in England, 1706-1710. LC 78-1692. (University of Florida Social Sciences Monographs: No. 62). 1978. pap. 5.50 (ISBN 0-8130-0505-1). U Presses Fla.
Stephens, William R., et al. History of the English Church, 8 vols. in 9. Repr. of 1910 ed. Set. 265.50 (ISBN 0-404-50750-6); 29.50 ea. AMS Pr.

Suffling, Ernest R. English Church Brasses from the 13th to the 17th Century, a Manual for Antiquaries, Archaeologists & Collectors. LC 73-126133. (Illus.). 456p. 1970. Repr. of 1910 ed. 22.50 (ISBN 0-8063-0437-5). Genealog Pub.

Thompson, E. Margaret. The Carthusian Order in England. (Church Historical Society London N. S. Ser.: No. 3). Repr. of 1930 ed. 80.00 (ISBN 0-8115-3127-9). Kraus Repr.

Tierney, M. A. Dodd's Church History of England, eith Notes Additions & A Continuation, 5 Vols. 2512p. 1839. text ed. 331.20x (ISBN 0-576-78535-0, Pub. by Gregg Intl Pubs England). Gregg Intl.

Wallis, John E. A History of the Church of Blackburnshire. (Church Historical Society London, New Ser.: No. 7). Repr. of 1932 ed. 40.00 (ISBN 0-8115-3131-7). Kraus Repr.

Yates, Nigel. The Anglican Revival in Victorian Portsmouth. 1981. 42.00x (ISBN 0-317-43792-5, Pub. by City of Portsmouth). State Mutual Bk.

GREAT BRITAIN–CHURCH HISTORY–SOURCES

Foliot, G. The Letters & Charters of Gilbert Foliot. Morey, A. & Brooke, C. N., eds. 1967. Cambridge U Pr.

Gee, Henry & Hardy, William J., eds. Documents Illustrative of English Church History. LC 83-45580. Date not set. Repr. of 1896 ed. 62.50 (ISBN 0-404-19898-8). AMS Pr.

Hunter, Joseph, ed. Ecclesiastical Documents. 1840. 19.00 (ISBN 0-384-24935-3). Johnson Repr.

GREAT BRITAIN–CHURCH HISTORY–TO 843

Fuller, Thoams. The Church History of Britain, from the Birth of Jesus Christ Until the Year 1648, 6 Vols. 3202p. 1845. text ed. 621.00x (ISBN 0-576-78882-1, Pub. by Gregg Intl Pubs England). Gregg Intl.

Hunt, William. English Church from Its Foundation to the Norman Conquest, 597-1066. LC 2-21442. (History of the English Church: No. 1). Repr. of 1899 ed. 29.50 (ISBN 0-404-50751-4). AMS Pr.

Lumby, F. R., ed. Be Domes Daege (Bede's de Die Judicii) (EETS OS Ser.: Vol. 65). Repr. of 1876 ed. 15.00 (ISBN 0-8115-3419-7). Kraus Repr.

Saklatvala, Beram. The Christian Island. LC 75-92561. (Illus.). 150p. 1970. 15.00 (ISBN 0-8386-7571-9). Fairleigh Dickinson.

GREAT BRITAIN–CHURCH HISTORY–ANGLO-SAXON PERIOD, 449-1066

Allison, Thomas. English Religious Life in the Eighth Century. LC 75-106708. Repr. of 1929 ed. lib. bdg. 22.50x (ISBN 0-8371-3438-2, ALRL). Greenwood.

--English Religious Life in the Eighth Century As Illustrated by Contemporary Letters. LC 70-136409. Repr. of 1929 ed. 9.00 (ISBN 0-404-00348-6). AMS Pr.

Beda. The History of the Church of Englande. (English Experience Ser.: No. 234). 382p. Repr. of 1565 ed. 55.00 (ISBN 90-221-0234-3). Walter J Johnson.

Bede. Historical Works, 2 Vols. (Loeb Classical Library: No. 246, 248). 13.95x ea. Vol. 1 (ISBN 0-674-99271-7). Vol. 2 (ISBN 0-674-99273-3). Harvard U Pr.

Bede the Venerable. Ecclesiastical History of England. Giles, John A., ed. LC 78-136367. (Bohn's Antiquarian Lib.). (Illus.). Repr. of 1849 ed. 42.50 (ISBN 0-404-50001-3). AMS Pr.

--Ecclesiastical History of the English People. Colgrave, Bertram & Minors, R. A., eds. (Oxford Medieval Texts Ser). 1969. 87.00x (ISBN 0-19-822202-5). Oxford U Pr.

--Ecclesiastical History of the English Nation & Other Writings. Stevens, John, tr. 1978. Repr. of 1910 ed. 12.95x (ISBN 0-460-00479-4, Evman). Biblio Dist.

--History of the English Church & People. Sherley-Price, tr. (Classics Ser.). (Orig.). 1955. pap. 4.95 (ISBN 0-14-044042-9). Penguin.

Fuller, Thoams. The Church History of Britain, from the Birth of Jesus Christ Until the Year 1648, 6 Vols. 3202p. 1845. text ed. 621.00x (ISBN 0-576-78882-1, Pub. by Gregg Intl Pubs England). Gregg Intl.

Soames, Henry. The Anglo-Saxon Church: Its History, Revenues & General Character. 4th ed. LC 80-2212. Repr. of 1856 ed. 39.50 (ISBN 0-404-18786-2). AMS Pr.

Sottovagina, Hugh. The History of the Church of York, 1066-1127. Johnson, Charles, tr. from Lat. & intro. by. LC 80-2227. Repr. of 1961 ed. 38.00 (ISBN 0-404-18764-1). AMS Pr.

GREAT BRITAIN–CHURCH HISTORY–MEDIEVAL PERIOD, 1066-1485

Cantor, Norman F. Church, Kingship & Lay Investiture in England, 1089-1135. 1969. lib. bdg. 26.00x (ISBN 0-374-91273-4, Octagon). Hippocrene Bks.

Capes, William W. English Church in the Fourteenth & Fifteenth Centuries, 1272-1486. LC 2-21441. (History of the English Church: No. 3). Repr. of 1900 ed. 29.50 (ISBN 0-404-50753-0). AMS Pr.

Cutts, Edward L. Parish Priests & Their People in the Middle Ages in England. LC 74-107457. Repr. of 1898 ed. 32.50 (ISBN 0-404-01898-X). Ams Pr.

Fuller, Thoams. The Church History of Britain, from the Birth of Jesus Christ Until the Year 1648, 6 Vols. 3202p. 1845. text ed. 621.00x (ISBN 0-576-78882-1, Pub. by Gregg Intl Pubs England). Gregg Intl.

Gasquet, Francis A. Eve of the Reformation. LC 75-118522. 1971. Repr. of 1900 ed. 35.00x (ISBN 0-8046-1144-0, Pub. by Kennikat). Assoc Faculty Pr.

Hunt, R. W. & Gibson, Margaret. The Schools & the Cloister: The Life & the Writings of Alexander Nequam, 1157-1217. 1984. 49.00x (ISBN 0-19-822398-6). Oxford U Pr.

Matthew, Donald. The Norman Monasteries & Their English Possessions. LC 78-26293. (Oxford Historical Ser.). 1979. Repr. of 1962 ed. lib. bdg. 24.75x (ISBN 0-313-20847-6, MANM). Greenwood.

Netter, Thomas. Fasciculi Zizaniorium Magistri Johannis Wyclif Cum Tritico. Shirley, Walter W., ed. (Rolls Ser.: No. 5). Repr. of 1858 ed. 60.00 (ISBN 0-8115-1006-9). Kraus Repr.

Ordericus, Vitalis. Historiae Ecclesiasticae Libri Tredecim, 5 Vols. Le Prevost, A., ed. Set. 240.00 (ISBN 0-384-43511-4); Set. pap. 210.00 (ISBN 0-384-43512-2). Johnson Repr.

Stephens, William R. English Church from the Norman Conquest to the Accession of Edward First, 1066-1272. LC 2-21443. (History of the English Church Ser.: No. 2). Repr. of 1901 ed. 29.50 (ISBN 0-404-50752-2). AMS Pr.

Trevelyan, George M. England in the Age of Wycliffe. 3rd ed. LC 78-178560. Repr. of 1900 ed. 34.50 (ISBN 0-404-56677-4). AMS Pr.

Warren, Ann K. Anchorites & Their Patrons in Medieval England. LC 84-24091. 1985. 42.00x (ISBN 0-520-05278-1). U of Cal Pr.

GREAT BRITAIN–CHURCH HISTORY–16TH CENTURY

see also Reformation–England

Burnet, Gilbert. The History of the Reformation of the Church of England, 7 vols. rev. ed. LC 83-45575. Date not set. Repr. of 1865 ed. Set. 425.00 (ISBN 0-404-19893-7). Ams Pr.

Child, Gilbert W. Church & State Under the Tudors. LC 72-183695. 452p. 1974. Repr. of 1890 ed. lib. bdg. 29.50 (ISBN 0-8337-4041-5). B Franklin.

Church of England Staff. A Parte of a Register, Contayninge Sundrie Memorable Matters, Written by Diuers Godly & Learned in Our Time, Which Stande for the Reformation of Our Church. LC 72-5981. (English Experience Ser.: No. 509). 1973. Repr. of 1593 ed. 67.00 (ISBN 90-221-0509-1). Walter J Johnson.

Faulkner, Robert K. Richard Hooker & the Politics of a Christian England. LC 79-65776. 195p. 1981. 31.00x (ISBN 0-520-03993-9). U of Cal Pr.

Frere, Walter H. English Church in the Reigns of Elizabeth & James First, 1558-1625. (History of the English Church: No. 5). Repr. of 1904 ed. 29.50 (ISBN 0-404-50755-7). AMS Pr.

--The English Church in the Reigns of Elizabeth & James I: 1558-1625. 1977. lib. bdg. 59.95 (ISBN 0-8490-1773-4). Gordon Pr.

Fuller, Thoams. The Church History of Britain, from the Birth of Jesus Christ Until the Year 1648, 6 Vols. 3202p. 1845. text ed. 621.00x (ISBN 0-576-78882-1, Pub. by Gregg Intl Pubs England). Gregg Intl.

Gairdner, James. English Church in the Sixteenth Century, from the Accession of Henry Eighth to the Death of Mary, 1509-1558. LC 72-168089. (History of the English Church Ser.: No. 4). Repr. of 1902 ed. 29.50 (ISBN 0-404-50754-9). AMS Pr.

Gee, Henry. The Elizabethan Clergy & the Settlement of Religion, 1558-64. LC 83-45581. Date not set. Repr. of 1898 ed. 39.50 (ISBN 0-404-19899-6). AMS Pr.

Heal, Felicity & O'Day, Rosemary. Church & Society in England: Henry VIII to James I. LC 76-51728. vi, 206p. 1977. 23.50 (ISBN 0-208-01649-X, Archon). Shoe String.

Jordan, W. K. The Development of Religious Toleration in England, 4 vols. Incl. Vol. 1. From the Beginning of the English Reformation to the Death of Queen Elizabeth (ISBN 0-8446-1251-0); Vol. 2. From the Accession of James One to the Convention of the Long Parliament; Vol. 3. From the Convention of the Long Parliament to the Restoration (ISBN 0-8446-1253-7); Vol. 4. Attainment of the Theory & Accommodations in Thought & Institutions (ISBN 0-8446-1254-5). 1932. 16.50 ea. Peter Smith.

Kreider, Alan. English Chantries: The Road to Dissolution. LC 78-12453. (Harvard Historical Studies: No. 97). 1979. 22.50x (ISBN 0-674-25560-7). Harvard U Pr.

Mutschmann, Heinrich & Wentersdorf, Karl. Shakespeare & Catholicism. LC 71-105107. 1970. Repr. of 1952 ed. 31.50 (ISBN 0-404-04547-2). AMS Pr.

Overton, John H. & Relton, Frederic. English Church from the Accession of George First to the End of the Eighteenth Century, 1714-1800. (History of the English Church Ser.: No. 7). Repr. of 1906 ed. 29.50 (ISBN 0-404-50757-3). AMS Pr.

Pierce, William. Historical Introduction to the Marprelate Tracts: A Chapter in the Evolution of Religious & Civil Liberty in England. 1908. 23.50 (ISBN 0-8337-2762-1). B Franklin.

Plummer, Alfred. English Church History: From the Death of Archbishop Parker to the Death of King Charles I. 1977. lib. bdg. 59.95 (ISBN 0-8490-1772-6). Gordon Pr.

Pollen, John H. English Catholics in the Reign of Queen Elizabeth: A Study of Their Politics, Civil Life & Government. 1971. Repr. of 1920 ed. lib. bdg. 24.50 (ISBN 0-8337-2798-2). B Franklin.

Porter, H. C., ed. Puritanism in Tudor England. LC 75-145532. (History in Depth Ser). xvi, 312p. 1971. 17.95x (ISBN 0-87249-222-2); pap. 7.95x (ISBN 0-87249-223-0). U. of SC Pr.

Saint German, Christopher. A Treatise Concernynge the Division Betwene the Spiritualitie & Temporalitie. LC 72-6027. (English Experience Ser.: No. 453). 94p. 1972. Repr. of 1532 ed. 14.00 (ISBN 90-221-0453-2). Walter J Johnson.

Thompson, Craig R. The English Church in the Sixteenth Century. LC 79-65981. (Folger Guides to the Age of Shakespeare Ser.). 1979. pap. 3.95 (ISBN 0-918016-08-8). Folger Bks.

White, Helen C. Social Criticism in Popular Religious Literature of the Sixteenth-Century. 1965. lib. bdg. 20.50x (ISBN 0-374-98455-7, Octagon). Hippocrene Bks.

GREAT BRITAIN–CHURCH HISTORY–17TH CENTURY

Cragg, Gerald R. Puritanism in the Period of the Great Persecution, 1660-1688. LC 76-143557. 1971. Repr. of 1957 ed. 16.00x (ISBN 0-8462-1578-0). Russell.

Frere, Walter H. English Church in the Reigns of Elizabeth & James First, 1558-1625. (History of the English Church: No. 5). Repr. of 1904 ed. 29.50 (ISBN 0-404-50755-7). AMS Pr.

--The English Church in the Reigns of Elizabeth & James I: 1558-1625. 1977. lib. bdg. 59.95 (ISBN 0-8490-1773-4). Gordon Pr.

Green, I. M. The Re-Establishment of the Church of England, 1660-1663. (Oxford Historical Monographs). 1978. 42.00x (ISBN 0-19-821867-2). Oxford U Pr.

Haller, William. Liberty & Reformation in the Puritan Revolution. LC 54-6482. 410p. 1955. pap. 14.00x (ISBN 0-231-08547-8). Columbia U Pr.

Havran, Martin J. The Catholics in Caroline England. 1962. 17.50x (ISBN 0-8047-0112-1). Stanford U Pr.

Jordan, W. K. The Development of Religious Toleration in England, 4 vols. Incl. Vol. 1. From the Beginning of the English Reformation to the Death of Queen Elizabeth (ISBN 0-8446-1251-0); Vol. 2. From the Accession of James One to the Convention of the Long Parliament; Vol. 3. From the Convention of the Long Parliament to the Restoration (ISBN 0-8446-1253-7); Vol. 4. Attainment of the Theory & Accommodations in Thought & Institutions (ISBN 0-8446-1254-5). 1932. 16.50 ea. Peter Smith.

McGregor, J. F. Radical Religion in the English Revolution. Reay, B., ed. 219p. 1984. 34.95x (ISBN 0-19-873044-6); pap. 14.95x (ISBN 0-19-873045-4). Oxford U Pr.

Miller, J. Popery & Politics in England, 1660-1688. LC 73-79306. (Illus.). 278p. 1973. 44.50 (ISBN 0-521-20236-1). Cambridge U Pr.

Overton, John H. & Relton, Frederic. English Church from the Accession of George First to the End of the Eighteenth Century, 1714-1800. (History of the English Church Ser.: No. 7). Repr. of 1906 ed. 29.50 (ISBN 0-404-50757-3). AMS Pr.

Plummer, Alfred. English Church History: From the Death of Archbishop Parker to the Death of King Charles I. 1977. lib. bdg. 59.95 (ISBN 0-8490-1772-6). Gordon Pr.

Rupp, Gordon. Religion in England: 1688-1781. (History of the Christian Church Ser.). 520p. 1987. 79.00x (ISBN 0-19-826918-8). Oxford U Pr.

Schlatter, Richard B. Social Ideas of Religious Leaders, Sixteen Sixty to Sixteen Sixty-Eight. LC 77-120663. 1970. Repr. lib. bdg. 18.50x (ISBN 0-374-97102-1, Octagon). Hippocrene Bks.

Shaw, William A. A History of the English Church During the Civil Wars & under the Commonwealth, 1640-1660. LC 78-184708. 1974. Repr. of 1900 ed. lib. bdg. 57.50 (ISBN 0-8337-4389-9). B Franklin.

Sommerville, C. John. Popular Religion in Restoration England. LC 77-7618. (University of Florida Social Sciences Monographs: No. 59). 1977. pap. 4.50 (ISBN 0-8130-0564-7). U Presses Fla.

Sprunger, Keith L. The Learned Doctor William Ames: Dutch Backgrounds of English & American Puritanism. LC 77-175172. pap. 76.30 (ISBN 0-317-08400-3, 2020215). Bks Demand UMI.

Sykes, Norman. From Sheldon to Secker: Aspects of English Church History, 1660-1768. LC 59-2371. (The Ford Lectures: 1958). pap. 62.50 (ISBN 0-317-20808-X, 2024534). Bks Demand UMI.

Ward, Nathaniel. Simple Cobler of Aggawam in America. Zall, Paul M., ed. LC 69-19107. xviii, 81p. 1969. 7.50x (ISBN 0-8032-0188-5). U of Nebr Pr.

Whiting, Charles E. Studies in English Puritanism from the Restoration to the Revolution, 1660-1688. LC 68-56060. 1968. Repr. of 1931 ed. 37.50x (ISBN 0-678-05203-4). Kelley.

GREAT BRITAIN–CHURCH HISTORY–MODERN PERIOD, 1485-

Clark, Ruth. Strangers & Sojourners at Port Royal. 1972. lib. bdg. 26.00x (ISBN 0-374-91664-0, Octagon). Hippocrene Bks.

Flynn, John S. Influence of Puritanism. LC 72-102569. 1970. Repr. of 1920 ed. 23.00x (ISBN 0-8046-0729-X, Pub. by Kennikat). Assoc Faculty Pr.

Hunt, John. Religious Thought in England from the Reformation to the End of the Last Century, 3 Vols. LC 72-153593. Repr. of 1873 ed. Set. 125.00 (ISBN 0-404-09480-5). AMS Pr.

Hutton, Ronald. The Restoration: A Political & Religious History of England & Wales 1658-1667. (Illus.). 379p. 1985. 29.95x (ISBN 0-19-822698-5). Oxford U Pr.

Lee, Umphrey. Historical Backgrounds of Early Methodist Enthusiasm. LC 31-18047. (Columbia University. Studies in the Social Sciences: No. 339). Repr. of 1931 ed. 17.50 (ISBN 0-404-51339-5). AMS Pr.

Seaton, Alexander A. The Theory of Toleration under the Later Stuarts. 1972. lib. bdg. 23.00x (ISBN 0-374-97233-8, Octagon). Hippocrene Bks.

GREAT BRITAIN–CHURCH HISTORY–18TH CENTURY

Clarke, Basil. The Building of the Eighteenth Century Church. LC 66-37309. (Illus.). 1963. text ed. 20.00x (ISBN 0-8401-0404-9). A R Allenson.

Rupp, Gordon. Religion in England: 1688-1781. (History of the Christian Church Ser.). 520p. 1987. 79.00x (ISBN 0-19-826918-8). Oxford U Pr.

Schwartz, Hillel. The French Prophets: The History of a Millenarian Group in Eighteenth-Century England. LC 78-65459. (Illus.). 1980. 42.00x (ISBN 0-520-03815-0). U of Cal Pr.

Sykes, Norman. From Sheldon to Secker: Aspects of English Church History, 1660-1768. LC 59-2371. (The Ford Lectures: 1958). pap. 62.50 (ISBN 0-317-20808-X, 2024534). Bks Demand UMI.

GREAT BRITAIN–CHURCH HISTORY–19TH CENTURY

Bentley, James. Ritualism & Politics in Victorian Britain. (Oxford Theological Monographs). (Illus.). 1978. 37.00x (ISBN 0-19-826714-2). Oxford U Pr.

Elliott-Binns, L. The Development of English Theology in the Later Nineteenth Century. LC 72-122411. ix, 137p. 1971. Repr. of 1952 ed. 17.50 (ISBN 0-208-01045-9, Archon). Shoe String.

Helmstadter, Richard J. & Phillips, Paul T., eds. Religion in Victorian Society: A Sourcebook of Documents. 484p. (Orig.). 1986. lib. bdg. 36.00 (ISBN 0-8191-4994-2); pap. text ed. 17.75 (ISBN 0-8191-4995-0). U Pr of Amer.

Machin, G. I. Politics & the Churches in Great Britain, 1832-1868. 1977. 57.00x (ISBN 0-19-826436-4). Oxford U Pr.

Martin, Roger H. Evangelicals United: Ecumenical Stirrings in Pre-Victorian Britain, 1795-1830. LC 82-10784. (Studies in Evangelicalism: No. 4). 244p. 1983. 19.00 (ISBN 0-8108-1586-9). Scarecrow.

Newman, John H. The Letters & Diaries of John Henry Newman. Dessain, Charles S. & Gornall, Thomas, eds. Incl. Vol. 23. Defeat at Oxford-Defence at Rome, January to December 1867. 38.50x (ISBN 0-19-920040-8); Vol. 24. A Grammar of Ascent, January 1868 to December 1869. 38.50x (ISBN 0-19-920043-2); Vol. 25. The Vatican Council, January 1870 to December 1871. 42.00x (ISBN 0-19-920055-6); Vol. 26. Aftermaths, January 1872 to December 1873. 42.00x (ISBN 0-19-920056-4). 1973. Oxford U Pr.

Newsome, David H. Wilberforces & Henry Manning: The Parting of Friends. LC 67-2. (Illus.). 1966. 30.00x (ISBN 0-674-95280-4, Belknap Pr). Harvard U Pr.
Overton, John H. The English Church in the Nineteenth Century (1800-1833) (Victorian Age Ser.). 1894. Repr. 35.00 (ISBN 0-8482-5454-6). Norwood Edns.

GREAT BRITAIN–FOREIGN RELATIONS–CATHOLIC CHURCH

Gasquet, Francis A. Monastic Life in the Middle Ages, 1792-1806. facs. ed. LC 76-137377. (Select Bibliographies Reprint Ser). 1922. 16.00 (ISBN 0-8369-5578-1). Ayer Co Pubs.
Hachey, Thomas, ed. Anglo-Vatican Relations, 1914-1939: Confidential Annual Reports of the British Ministers to the Holy See. 1972. lib. bdg. 23.00 (ISBN 0-8161-0991-5, Hall Reference). G K Hall.
Sayers, Jane E. Papal Government & England During the Pontificate of Honorius III (1216-1227) LC 84-1853. (Cambridge Studies in Medieval Life & Thought: 3rd Ser., Vol. 21). 1985. 49.50 (ISBN 0-521-25911-8). Cambridge U Pr.
Wilkie, W. E. The Cardinal Protectors of England: Rome & the Tudors Before the Reformation. LC 73-82462. 224p. 1974. 44.50 (ISBN 0-521-20332-5). Cambridge U Pr.

GREAT BRITAIN–HISTORY–MEDIEVAL PERIOD, 1066-1485

Here are entered works on the Medieval period as a whole as well as those on parts of the period.

Adams, G. B. History of England from the Norman Conquest to the Death of John, 1066-1216. (Political History of England Monograph). Repr. of 1905 ed. 35.00 (ISBN 0-527-00847-8). Kraus Repr.
Chew, Helena M. The English Ecclesiastical Tenants-in-Chief & Knight Service, Especially in the Thirteenth & Fourteenth Centuries. LC 80-2310. Repr. of 1932 ed. 37.50 (ISBN 0-404-18558-4). AMS Pr.
Chronicon Petroburgense. 1849. 24.00 (ISBN 0-384-08985-2). Johnson Repr.
Corfe, Tom. The Murder of Archbishop Thomas. LC 76-22419. (Cambridge Topic Bks). (Illus.). 1977. PLB 8.95 (ISBN 0-8225-1202-5). Lerner Pubns.
Davis, H. W., ed. Medieval England. new ed. Orig. Title: Bernard's Companion to English History. 1977. Repr. of 1924 ed. lib. bdg. 45.00 (ISBN 0-8495-1006-6). Arden Lib.
DeAngeli, Marguerite. The Door in the Wall: Story of Medieval London. LC 64-7025. (Illus.). 111p. 10.95a (ISBN 0-385-07283-X). Doubleday.
Giles, John A., ed. Chronicon Angliae Petriburgense. 1966. Repr. of 1845 ed. 24.00 (ISBN 0-8337-1342-6). B Franklin.
Jessopp, Augustus. The Coming of the Friars & Other Historic Essays. facsimile ed. (Select Bibliographies Reprint Ser). Repr. of 1892 ed. 21.00 (ISBN 0-8369-6696-1). Ayer Co Pubs.
--Studies by a Recluse in Cloister, Town & Country. 3rd ed. 1969. Repr. of 1883 ed. lib. bdg. 20.50 (ISBN 0-8337-1841-X). B Franklin.
Kelly, Henry A. Divine Providence in the England of Shakespeare's Histories. LC 75-111485. 1970. 22.50x (ISBN 0-674-21292-4). Harvard U Pr.
Knowles, David. Thomas Becket. LC 77-143785. 1971. 15.00x (ISBN 0-8047-0766-9). Stanford U Pr.
Platt, Colin. Medieval England: A Social History & Archaeology from the Conquest to 1600 A. D. (Illus.). 1978. encore ed. 9.95 (ISBN 0-684-17247-X, ScribT). Scribner.
Robertson, James C. & Sheppard, J. B., eds. Materials for the History of Thomas Becket, 7 vols. (Rolls Ser.: No. 67). Repr. of 1885 ed. Set. 308.00 (ISBN 0-8115-1135-9). Kraus Repr.
Stubbs, William. Historical Introduction to the Rolls Series. LC 77-158211. Repr. of 1902 ed. 11.50 (ISBN 0-404-06302-0). AMS Pr.
Vitalis, Orderic. The Ecclesiastical History of Orderic Vitalis, Vol. 5, Bks. 9 & 10. Chibnall, Majorie, ed. & tr. from Fr. (Oxford Medieval Texts Ser). 1975. 65.00x (ISBN 0-19-822232-7). Oxford U Pr.

GREAT BRITAIN–HISTORY–PURITAN REVOLUTION, 1642-1660

Ashley, Maurice. Financial & Commercial Policy under Cromwellian Protectorate. 2nd ed. 190p. 1962. Repr. of 1934 ed. 28.50x (ISBN 0-7146-1265-0, BHA 01265, F Cass Co). Biblio Dist.
Barker, Arthur E. Milton & the Puritan Dilemma, 1641-1660. LC 58-3195. 1942. 30.00x (ISBN 0-8020-5025-5); pap. 8.50 o. p. (ISBN 0-8020-6306-3). U of Toronto Pr.
Clarke, William. Clarke Papers, 4 Vols. Firth, C. H., ed. 105.00 (ISBN 0-384-09232-2); 27.00 ea. Johnson Repr.
Fletcher, Anthony. The Outbreak of the English Civil War. 480p. 1985. pap. text ed. 19.95 (ISBN 0-7131-6454-9). E Arnold.
Gardiner, Samuel R. Cromwell's Place in History. LC 76-94270. (Select Bibliographies Reprint Ser). 1897. 15.00 (ISBN 0-8369-5044-5). Ayer Co Pubs.
--The First Two Stuarts & the Puritan Revolution: 1603-1660. 1977. Repr. of 1891 ed. lib. bdg. 25.00 (ISBN 0-8495-1911-X). Arden Lib.
Harrison, Frederic. Oliver Cromwell. LC 78-39196. (Select Bibliographies Reprint Ser.). Repr. of 1888 ed. 18.00 (ISBN 0-8369-6798-4). Ayer Co Pubs.
Hunt, William. The Puritan Moment: The Coming of Revolution in an English County. (Harvard Historical Studies: No. 102). (Illus.). 384p. 1983. text ed. 36.00x (ISBN 0-674-73903-5). Harvard U Pr.
--The Puritan Moment: The Coming of Revolution in an English County. (Harvard Historical Studies: No. 102). 384p. 1985. pap. text ed. 8.95x (ISBN 0-674-73904-3). Harvard U Pr.
Morton, A. L. The World of the Ranters: Religious Radicalism in the English Revolution. 232p. 1970. 14.95x (ISBN 0-8464-0980-1). Beekman Pubs.
Newman, P. R. Atlas of the English Civil War. (Illus.). 144p. 1985. text ed. 35.00x (ISBN 0-02-906540-2). Macmillan.
Reay, Barry. The Quakers & the English Revolution. LC 84-22355. 200p. 1985. 22.50 (ISBN 0-312-65808-7). St Martin.
Solt, Leo F. Saints in Arms. LC 74-153355. (Stanford University. Stanford Studies in History, Economics & Political Science: No. 18). Repr. of 1959 ed. 19.00 (ISBN 0-404-50976-2). AMS Pr.
Taylor, Philip A., ed. Origins of the English Civil War: Conspiracy, Crusade, or Class Conflict. (Problems in European Civilization Ser.). 1960. pap. text ed. 5.50 (ISBN 0-669-24174-1). Heath.
Underdown, David. Pride's Purge: Politics in the Puritan Revolution. 440p. 1985. pap. text ed. 13.50x (ISBN 0-04-822045-0). Allen Unwin.
Wolfe, Don M. Milton in the Puritan Revolution. 1963. text ed. 22.50x (ISBN 0-391-00477-8). Humanities.

GREAT BRITAIN–HISTORY–RESTORATION, 1660-1688

Draper, Maurice L. Restoration Studies, Vol. II. 1983. pap. 13.00 (ISBN 0-8309-0362-3). Herald Hse.
Hutton, Ronald. The Restoration: A Political & Religious History of England & Wales 1658-1667. (Illus.). 379p. 1985. 29.95x (ISBN 0-19-822698-5). Oxford U Pr.
Mensing, Raymond C. Toleration & Parliament, Sixteen Sixty to Seventeen Nineteen. LC 79-63260. 1979. pap. text ed. 10.75 (ISBN 0-8191-0723-9). U Pr of Amer.

GREAT BRITAIN–RELIGION

Allison, Thomas. English Religious Life in the Eighth Century. LC 75-106708. Repr. of 1929 ed. lib. bdg. 22.50x (ISBN 0-8371-3438-2, ALRL). Greenwood.
--English Religious Life in the Eighth Century As Illustrated by Contemporary Letters. LC 70-136409. Repr. of 1929 ed. 9.00 (ISBN 0-404-00348-6). AMS Pr.
Atkinson, Clarissa W. Mystic & Pilgrim: The "Book" & the World of Margery Kempe. LC 82-22219. 248p. (Orig.). 1983. 27.50x (ISBN 0-8014-1521-7); pap. text ed. 8.95x (ISBN 0-8014-9895-3). Cornell U Pr.
Bebbington, D. W. The Nonconformist Conscience: Chapel & Politics 1870-1914. 192p. 1982. text ed. 24.95x (ISBN 0-04-942173-5). Allen Unwin.
Bede the Venerable. The Ecclesiastical History of the English People. Hereford, Philip, ed. Stapleton, Thomas, tr. from Latin. 1983. Repr. of 1935 ed. lib. bdg. 45.00 (ISBN 0-89760-062-2). Telegraph Bks.
Bell, G. K. The English Church. 10.00 (ISBN 0-8414-1634-6). Folcroft.
Bertocci, P. A. Empirical Argument for God in Late British Thought. Repr. of 1938 ed. 36.00 (ISBN 0-527-07300-8). Kraus Repr.
Buschkuhl, Matthias. Great Britain & the Holy See 1746-1870. (Illus.). 260p. 1982. text ed. 40.00x (ISBN 0-7165-0290-9, Pub. by Irish Academic Pr Ireland). Biblio Dist.
Calderwood, David. A Solution of Doctor Resolutus, His Resolutions for Kneeling. LC 79-84093. (English Experience Ser.: No. 913). 60p. 1979. Repr. of 1619 ed. lib. bdg. 8.00 (ISBN 90-221-0913-5). Walter J Johnson.
Cashmore, Ernest. Rastaman: The Rastafarian Movement in England. (Illus.). 272p. 1980. pap. text ed. 9.95x (ISBN 0-04-301116-0). Allen Unwin.
Clark, David. Between Pulpit & Pew: Folk Religion in a North Yorkshire Fishing Village. LC 81-18166. (Illus.). 216p. 1982. 32.50 (ISBN 0-521-24071-9). Cambridge U Pr.
Cockshut, A. O., ed. Religious Controversies of the Nineteenth Century: Selected Documents. LC 66-18225. vi, 265p. 1966. 19.95x (ISBN 0-8032-0019-6). U of Nebr Pr.
Cowling, Maurice. Religion & Public Doctrine in Modern England: Assaults, Vol. 2. (Cambridge Studies in the History & Theory of Politics). 403p. 1985. 49.50 (ISBN 0-521-25959-2). Cambridge U Pr.
--Religion & Public Doctrine in Modern England. (Cambridge Studies in the History & Theory of Politics). 498p. 1981. 59.50 (ISBN 0-521-23289-9). Cambridge U Pr.
Crosby, Thomas. History of the English Baptists: 1740 Ed, 4 vols. in 2 vols. Set. 45.00 (ISBN 0-686-12405-7). Church History.
D'Aubigne, Merle. The Reformation in England, 2 vols. 1977. Vol. 1. pap. 13.95 (ISBN 0-85151-486-3); Vol. 2. pap. 13.95 (ISBN 0-85151-487-1); Set. o. p. 25.95 (ISBN 0-85151-488-X). Banner of Truth.
Davies, Horton. The Ecumenical Century: 1900-1965. (Worship & Theology in England Ser.: Vol. 5). 1965. 39.50x (ISBN 0-691-07145-4). Princeton U Pr.
Finlayson, Michael G. Historians, Puritanism & the English Revolution: The Religious Factor in English Politics before & after the Interregnum. LC 83-215172. pap. 54.50 (2026454). Bks Demand UMI.
Firth, Katherine R. The Apocalyptic Tradition in Reformation Britain 1530-1645. (Historical Monographs). (Illus.). 1979. 45.00x (ISBN 0-19-821868-0). Oxford U Pr.
Fraser, Hilary. Beauty & Belief: Aesthetics & Religion in Victorian Literature. 306p. 1986. 34.50 (ISBN 0-521-30767-8). Cambridge U Pr.
Fulbrook, Mary. Piety & Politics: Religion & the Rise of Absolutism in England, Wurttemberg & Prussia. LC 83-5316. 224p. 1984. 37.50 (ISBN 0-521-25612-7); pap. 13.95 (ISBN 0-521-27633-0). Cambridge U Pr.
Greaves, Richard L. Society & Religion in Elizabethan England. LC 81-2530. pap. 160.00 (2056201). Bks Demand UMI.
Haigh, C. Last Days of the Lancashire Monasteries & the Pilgrimage of Grace. 182p. 1969. 30.00 (ISBN 0-7190-1150-7, Pub. by Manchester Univ Pr). Longwood Pub Group.
Hanley, Thomas O. Their Rights & Liberties. 160p. 1984. 9.95 (ISBN 0-8294-0471-6). Loyola.
Hardie, Frank & Herrman, Irwin. Britain & Zion: The Fateful Entanglement. 192p. 1980. 11.95 (ISBN 0-85640-229-X, Pub. by Blackstaff Pr). Longwood Pub Group.
Hayes, A. J. & Gowland, D. A., eds. Scottish Methodism in the Early Victorian Period: The Scottish Correspondence of the Rev. Jabez Bunting 1800-57. 1981. 40.00x (ISBN 0-85224-412-6, Pub. by Edinburgh Univ England). State Mutual Bk.
Hill, Christopher. The Collected Essays of Christopher Hill: Religion & Politics in Seventeenth-Century England, Vol. 2. LC 84-16446. 368p. 1986. lib. bdg. 27.50x (ISBN 0-87023-503-6). U of Mass Pr.
Hunt, John. Religious Thought in England in the Nineteenth Century. 424p. Repr. of 1896 ed. text ed. 62.10x (ISBN 0-576-29211-7, Pub. by Gregg Intl Pubs England). Gregg Intl.
Jay, Elisabeth. Faith & Doubt in Victorian Britain. (Context & Commentary Ser.). (Illus.). 152p. 1986. text ed. 29.95 (ISBN 0-333-37658-7, Pub. by Macmillan Pubs UK); pap. text ed. 9.95 (ISBN 0-333-37659-5). Humanities.
Jeffrey, David L., ed. A Burning & a Shining Light: English Spirituality in the Age of Wesley. 512p. (Orig.). 1987. pap. 16.95 (ISBN 0-8028-0234-6). Eerdmans.
Kelly, Faye L. Prayer in Sixteenth Century England. LC 66-64090. (U of Fla. Humanities Monographs: No. 22). 1966. pap. 3.50 (ISBN 0-8130-0127-7). U Presses Fla.
Kirk, John. Biographies of English Catholics in the Eighteenth Century. xvi, 293p. 1985. Repr. of 1901 ed. lib. bdg. 39.00 (ISBN 0-932051-45-6, Pub. by Am Repr Serv). Am Biog Serv.
MacCulloch, Diarmaid. Suffolk & the Tudors: Politics & Religion in an English County 1500-1600. (Illus.). 360p. 1987. text ed. 66.00 (ISBN 0-19-822914-3). Oxford U Pr.
McIntire, C. T. England Against the Papacy: 1858-1861. LC 82-9405. (Illus.). 280p. 1983. 44.50 (ISBN 0-521-24237-1). Cambridge U Pr.
McLeod, H. Religion & the Working Class in Nineteenth Century Britain. (Studies in Economic & Social History). 72p. 1984. pap. text ed. 7.95x (ISBN 0-333-28115-2, Pub. by Macmillan UK). Humanities.
Martin, Roger H. Evangelicals United: Ecumenical Stirrings in Pre-Victorian Britain, 1795-1830. LC 82-10784. (Studies in Evangelicalism: No. 4). 244p. 1983. 19.00 (ISBN 0-8108-1586-9). Scarecrow.
Mensing, Raymond C. Toleration & Parliament, Sixteen Sixty to Seventeen Nineteen. LC 79-63260. 1979. pap. text ed. 10.75 (ISBN 0-8191-0723-9). U Pr of Amer.
Needham, G. I., ed. Lives of Three English Saints. rev. ed. 119p. 1979. pap. text ed. 7.95x (ISBN 0-85989-076-7, Pub. by U Exeter UK). Humanities.
Parry, J. P. Democracy & Religion: Gladstone & the Liberal Party, 1867-1876. (Cambridge Studies in the History & Theory of Politics). 520p. 1986. 59.50 (ISBN 0-521-30948-4). Cambridge U Pr.
Pattison, Mark. Essays & Reviews: Tendencies of Religious Thought in England. Jowett, Benjamin, ed. 434p. 1982. Repr. of 1861 ed. lib. bdg. 75.00 (ISBN 0-89987-040-6). Darby Bks.
Pritchard, Arnold. Catholic Loyalism in Elizabethan England. LC 78-10208. xiii, 243p. 1979. 22.50x (ISBN 0-8078-1345-1). U of NC Pr.
Pruett, John H. The Parish Clergy under the Later Stuarts: The Leicestershire Experience. LC 78-8174. 203p. 1978. 19.95 (ISBN 0-252-00662-3). U of Ill Pr.
Reid, William, ed. Authentic Records of Revival, Now in Progress in the United Kingdom. (Revival Library). viii, 478p. 1980. Repr. of 1860 ed. lib. bdg. 15.95 (ISBN 0-940033-17-8). R O Roberts.
Religion, 3 vols. (British Parliamentary Papers Ser.). 1971. Set. 284.00x (ISBN 0-7165-1498-2, Pub. by Irish Academic Pr Ireland). Biblio Dist.
Stoughton, John. History of Religion in England, 8 vols. 1977. lib. bdg. 800.00 (ISBN 0-8490-1984-2). Gordon Pr.
Sykes, Norman. The English Religious Tradition: Sketches of Its Influence on Church, State & Society. LC 78-59045. 1986. Repr. of 1953 ed. 15.00 (ISBN 0-88355-717-7). Hyperion Conn.
Sykes, S. W., ed. England & Germany: Studies in Theological Diplomacy. (IC-Studies in the Intercultural History of Christianity: Vol. 25). 170p. 1981. pap. 22.15 (ISBN 3-8204-5854-9). P Lang Pubs.
Thornton, Martin. English Spirituality. 330p. 1986. 24.95 (ISBN 0-936384-38-7); pap. 11.95 (ISBN 0-936384-31-X). Cowley Pubns.
Valenze, Deborah M. Prophetic Sons & Daughters: Female Preaching & Popular Religion in Industrial England. LC 85-42755. (Illus.). 344p. 1985. 38.50x (ISBN 0-691-05455-X). Princeton U Pr.
Voltaire. Letters Concerning the English Nation. LC 74-728. 224p. 1974. Repr. of 1926 ed. lib. bdg. 19.00 (ISBN 0-8337-4467-4). B Franklin.
--Lettres Philosophiques. Pomeau, Rene, ed. 192p. 1964. 18.95 (ISBN 0-686-55754-9). French & Eur.
Von Arx, Jeffrey P. Progress & Pessimism: Religion, Politics & History in Late Nineteenth Century Britain. (Harvard Historical Studies: No. 104). 256p. 1985. text ed. 25.00x (ISBN 0-674-71375-3). Harvard U Pr.
Wark, K. R. Elizabethan Recusancy in Cheshire. 1971. 30.00 (ISBN 0-7190-1154-X, Pub. by Manchester Univ Pr). Longwood Pub Group.
Wright, T. R. The Religion of Humanity: The Impact of Comtean Positivism on Victorian Britain. (Illus.). 325p. 1986. 44.50 (ISBN 0-521-30671-X). Cambridge U Pr.

GREAT SCHISM

see Schism; Schism–Eastern and Western Church; Schism, the Great Western, 1378-1417

GREAT WESTERN SCHISM

see Schism, the Great Western, 1378-1417

GREATER VEHICLE

see Mahayana Buddhism

GRECO-ROMAN SCHISM

see Schism–Eastern and Western Church

GREECE–ANTIQUITIES

Burford, A. The Greek Temple Builders at Epidauros. (Liverpool Monographs in Archaeology & Oriental Studies). 274p. 1969. text ed. 25.00x (ISBN 0-85323-080-3, Pub. by Liverpool U Pr). Humanities.
Grinnell, Isabel H. Greek Temples. LC 79-168420. (Metropolitan Museum of Art Publications in Reprint Ser.). (Illus.). 138p. 1972. Repr. of 1943 ed. 35.50 (ISBN 0-405-02258-1). Ayer Co Pubs.
Rouse, William H. Greek Votive Offerings: An Essay in the History of Greek Religion. facsimile ed. LC 75-10654. (Ancient Religion & Mythology Ser.). (Illus.). 1976. Repr. of 1902 ed. 36.50x (ISBN 0-405-07262-7). Ayer Co Pubs.
Tataki, A. B. Sounion: The Temple of Poseidon. (Illustrated Travel Guides Ser.). (Illus.). 1979. pap. 9.95 (ISBN 0-89241-104-X). Caratzas.
Woodford, Susan. The Parthenon. (Cambridge Introduction to the History of Mankind Ser.). 1981. pap. 4.95 (ISBN 0-521-22629-5). Cambridge U Pr.

GREECE–RELIGION

Adam, James. The Religious Teachers of Greece. LC 65-22806. (Library of Religious & Philosophical Thought). 1966. Repr. of 1908 ed. lib. bdg. 35.00x (ISBN 0-678-09950-2, Reference Bk Pubs). Kelley.
Adeney, Walter F. The Greek & Eastern Churches. LC 65-22087. (Library of Religious & Philosophical Thought). 1966. Repr. of 1908 ed. lib. bdg. 45.00x (ISBN 0-678-09951-0, Reference Bk Pubs). Kelley.

Angus, S. The Religious Quests of the Graeco-Roman World. 1929. 30.00 (ISBN 0-686-20108-6). Quality Lib.
Armstrong, A. H., ed. Classical Mediterranean Spirituality. (World Spirituality Ser.). 499p. 1986. 49.50x (ISBN 0-8245-0764-9). Crossroad NY.
Bevan, Edwyn R., ed. Later Greek Religion. LC 76-179282. (Library of Greek Thought: No. 9). Repr. of 1927 ed. 12.50 (ISBN 0-404-07807-9). AMS Pr.
Bookidis, Nancy & Stroud, Ronald. Demeter & Persephone in Ancient Corinth. (Corinth Notes Ser.: No. 2). (Illus.). 32p. (Orig.). 1987. pap. 3.00. Am Sch Athens.
Bremmer, Jan. The Early Greek Concept of the Soul. LC 82-47583. 190p. 1983. 23.00x (ISBN 0-691-03131-2). Princeton U Pr.
Burkert, Walter. Greek Religion. 504p. 1987. pap. text ed. 9.95x (ISBN 0-674-36281-0). Harvard U Pr.
Burkert, William. Greek Religion. Raffan, John, tr. from Ger. LC 84-25209. 493p. 1985. text ed. 30.00x (ISBN 0-674-36280-2). Harvard U Pr.
Cambridge School Classics Project Foundation Course Staff. Foundation Course Folder III: Greek Religion. 1974. 13.95x (ISBN 0-521-08724-4). Cambridge U Pr.
Campbell, Lewis. Religion in Greek Literature: A Sketch in Outline. facsimile ed. LC 79-148874. (Select Bibliographies Reprint Ser). Repr. of 1898 ed. 22.00 (ISBN 0-8369-5645-1). Ayer Co Pubs.
Cornford, Francis M., ed. Greek Religious Thought from Homer to the Age of Alexander. LC 79-98637. (Library of Greek Thought: No. 2). Repr. of 1923 ed. 21.50 (ISBN 0-404-01734-7). AMS Pr.
Cumont, Franz. Astrology & Religion among the Greeks & Romans. 1912. pap. 3.50 (ISBN 0-486-20581-9). Dover.
Dietrich, B. C. The Origins of Greek Religion. 314p. 1973. 84.00x (ISBN 3-11-003982-6). De Gruyter.
Dietrich, Bernard C. Tradition in Greek Religion. xvi, 213p. 1986. 66.00x (ISBN 3-11-010695-7). De Gruyter.
Earp, Frank R. Way of the Greeks. LC 75-136393. Repr. of 1929 ed. 21.50 (ISBN 0-404-02234-0). AMS Pr.
Easterling, P. E. & Muir, J. V., eds. Greek Religion & Society. (Illus.). 264p. 1985. 39.50 (ISBN 0-521-24552-4); pap. 12.95 (ISBN 0-521-28785-5). Cambridge U Pr.
Farnell, L. R. The Higher Aspects of Greek Religion. vii, 155p. 1977. 10.00 (ISBN 0-89005-206-9). Ares.
Farnell, Lewis R. Greece & Babylon: A Comparative Sketch of Mesopotamian, Anatolian, & Hellenic Religions. 1977. lib. bdg. 59.95 (ISBN 0-8490-1906-0). Gordon Pr.
--The Higher Aspects of Greek Religion. LC 77-27158. (Hibbert Lectures Ser.: 1911). Repr. of 1912 ed. 20.00 (ISBN 0-404-60413-7). AMS Pr.
--Outline History of Greek Religion. 160p. (Orig.). 1986. 10.00 (ISBN 0-89005-025-2); pap. 10.00 (ISBN 0-89005-442-8). Ares.
Festugiere, Andre-Jean. Personal Religion among the Greeks. (Sather Classical Lecture Ser.: No. 26). 186p. 1984. Repr. of 1954 ed. lib. bdg. 25.00 (ISBN 0-313-23209-1, FERG). Greenwood.
Foucart, Paul F. Des Associations Religieuses chez les Grecs: Thiases, Eranes, Orgeons. facsimile ed. LC 75-10637. (Ancient Religion & Mythology Ser.). (Fr.). 1976. Repr. of 1873 ed. 20.00x (ISBN 0-405-07014-4). Ayer Co Pubs.
Furley, William D. Studies in the Use of Fire in the Ancient Greek Religion. rev. ed. Connor, W. R., ed. LC 80-2650. (Monographs in Clasical Studies). (Illus.). 1981. lib. bdg. 29.00 (ISBN 0-405-14037-1). Ayer Co Pubs.
Garland, Robert. The Greek Way of Death. LC 85-470. (Illus.). 208p. 1985. text ed. 22.50x (ISBN 0-8014-1823-2). Cornell U Pr.
Graf, Fritz. Eleusis und die Orphische Dichtung Athens in Vorhellenistischer Zeit. (Religionsgeschichtliche Versuche und Vorarbeiten, Vol. 33). xii, 224p. 1974. 33.60x (ISBN 3-11-004498-6). De Gruyter.
Grant, F. C. Hellenistic Religions: Grant. 1953. pap. text ed. write for info. (ISBN 0-02-345640-X). Macmillan.
Grant, Frederick C., ed. Hellenistic Religions: The Age of Syncretism. 1953. pap. 13.24 scp (ISBN 0-672-60342-X, LLA134). Bobbs.
Gruppe, Otto. Griechische Mythologie und Religionsgeschichte, 2 vols. facsimile ed. LC 75-10638. (Ancient Religion & Mythology Ser.). (Ger.). 1976. Repr. of 1906 ed. 144.00x set (ISBN 0-405-07015-2). Ayer Co Pubs.
Guthrie, William K. Greeks & Their Gods. (Orig.). 1955. pap. 8.95x (ISBN 0-8070-5793-2, BPA16). Beacon Pr.
Habert, Isaac. Liber Pontificalis Graecae. 790p. Repr. of 1643 ed. text ed. 124.20x (ISBN 0-576-99140-6, Pub. by Gregg Intl Pubs England). Gregg Intl.
Harrison, Jane. Prolegomena to the Study of Greek Religion. 682p. 1981. text ed. 27.50x (ISBN 0-85036-262-8, Pub. by Merlin Pr UK); pap. 17.50x. Humanities.
Harrison, Jane E. Prolegomena to the Study of Greek Religion. facsimile ed. LC 75-10639. (Ancient Religion & Mythology Ser.). (Illus.). 1976. Repr. of 1922 ed. 57.50x (ISBN 0-405-07018-7). Ayer Co Pubs.
--The Religion of Ancient Greece. 1979. Repr. of 1905 ed. lib. bdg. 27.00 (ISBN 0-8495-2325-7). Arden Lib.
--The Religion of Ancient Greece. 66p. 1921. 0.95 (ISBN 0-317-40433-4). Open Court.
Hyde, Walter W. Greek Religion & Its Survivals. LC 63-10268. (Our Debt to Greece & Rome Ser). 1963. Repr. of 1930 ed. 18.50x (ISBN 0-8154-0117-5). Cooper Sq.
Jaeger, Werner. Early Christianity & Greek Paideia. 160p. 1985. pap. text ed. 5.95x (ISBN 0-674-22052-8, Belknap Pr). Harvard U Pr.
Kephala, Euphrosyne. The Church of the Greek People. LC 77-87528. Repr. of 1930 ed. 14.50 (ISBN 0-404-16594-X). AMS Pr.
Kerenyi, Carl. Archetypal Images in Greek Religion, 5 vols. Manheim, R., tr. Incl. Vol. 1. Prometheus: Archetypal Image of Human Existence. 1963; Vol. 2. Dionysos: Archetypal Image of Industructible Life. 1975; Vol. 3. Asklepios: Archetypal Image of the Physician's Existence. 1959. 37.00x (ISBN 0-691-09703-8); Vol. 4. Eleusis: Archetypal Image of Mother & Daughter. 1967; Vol. 5. Zeus & Hera-Archetypal Image of Father, Husband & Wife. Holme, tr. 1975. (Bollingen Ser.: Vol. 65). Princeton U Pr.
Kerenyi, Karoly. The Religion of the Greeks & Romans. LC 72-9823. (Illus.). 303p. 1973. Repr. of 1962 ed. lib. bdg. 24.75x (ISBN 0-8371-6605-5, KERG). Greenwood.
Kimpel, Ben. A Philosophy of the Religions of Ancient Greeks & Israelites. LC 83-6512. 362p. (Orig.). 1983. lib. bdg. 30.00 (ISBN 0-8191-3225-X); pap. text ed. 15.50 (ISBN 0-8191-3226-8). U Pr of Amer.
Leuven, J. V. Prehistoric Religion in Greece. (Illus.). 280p. 1987. lib. bdg. 72.00 (Pub. by A. M. Hakkert). Coronet Bks.
Mikalson, Jon D. Athenian Popular Religion. LC 82-25616. xi, 142p. 1987. pap. text ed. 8.95x (ISBN 0-8078-4194-3). U of NC Pr.
Mommsen, A. Athenae Christianae. (Illus.). 177p. 1977. 12.50 (ISBN 0-89005-216-6). Ares.
Murray, Gilbert. Five Stages of Greek Religion. LC 76-27675. 1976. Repr. of 1925 ed. lib. bdg. 22.50x (ISBN 0-8371-9080-0, MUFS). Greenwood.
--Five Stages of Greek Religion: Studies Based on a Course of Lectures Delivered in April 1912 at Columbia University. LC 75-41202. Repr. of 1925 ed. 12.50 (ISBN 0-404-14577-9). AMS Pr.
Nilsson, Martin P. Greek Folk Religion. 1972. pap. 10.95x (ISBN 0-8122-1034-4, Pa. Paperbacks). U of Pa Pr.
Otto, Walter F. The Homeric Gods: The Spiritual Significance of Greek Religion. Bolle, Kees W., ed. LC 77-79149. (Mythology Ser.). 1978. Repr. of 1954 ed. lib. bdg. 22.00x (ISBN 0-405-10558-4). Ayer Co Pubs.
--The Homeric Gods: The Spiritual Significance of Greek Religion. 1978. Repr. of 1954 ed. lib. bdg. 24.00x (ISBN 0-88254-845-X, Octagon). Hippocrene Bks.
Parke, H. W. Festivals of the Athenians. LC 76-12819. (Aspects of Greek & Roman Life Ser.). (Illus.). 288p. 1986. pap. text ed. 8.95x (ISBN 0-8014-9440-0). Cornell U Pr.
Reitzenstein, Richard. The Hellenistic Mystery-Religions. Steely, John E., tr. from Ger. LC 77-12980. (Pittsburgh Theological Monographs: No. 15). Orig. Title: Die Hellenistischen Mysterienreligionen Nach Ihren Arundgedanken und Wirkungen. 1978. pap. text ed. 17.75 (ISBN 0-915138-20-4). Pickwick.
Rexine, John E. Religion in Plato & Cicero. LC 68-28581. 72p. Repr. of 1959 ed. lib. bdg. 22.50x (ISBN 0-8371-0198-0, RERP). Greenwood.
Rice, David G. & Stambaugh, John E. Sources for the Study of Greek Religion. LC 79-18389. (Society of Biblical Literature. Sources for Biblical Study Ser.: No. 14). 1979. pap. 9.95 (ISBN 0-89130-347-2, 060314). Scholars Pr GA.
Rohde, Erwin. Psyche: The Cult of Souls & Belief in Immortality Among the Greeks. facsimile ed. LC 75-37911. (Select Bibliographies Reprint Ser). Repr. of 1920 ed. 32.00 (ISBN 0-8369-6749-6). Ayer Co Pubs.
Rouse, William H. Greek Votive Offerings: An Essay in the History of Greek Religion. facsimile ed. LC 75-10654. (Ancient Religion & Mythology Ser.). (Illus.). 1976. Repr. of 1902 ed. 36.50x (ISBN 0-405-07262-7). Ayer Co Pubs.
Simon, Erika. Festivals of Attica: An Archaeological Commentary. LC 81-70160. 160p. 1983. text ed. 26.50x (ISBN 0-299-09180-5). U of Wis Pr.
Stengel, Paul. Die Griechischen Kultusaltertumer. facsimile ed. LC 75-10656. (Ancient Religion & Mythology Ser.). (Ger.). 1976. Repr. of 1920 ed. 22.00x (ISBN 0-405-07264-3). Ayer Co Pubs.
Zielinski, T. The Religion of Ancient Greece. x, 235p. pap. 10.00 (ISBN 0-89005-090-2). Ares.
Zielinski, Thaddeus. Religion of Ancient Greece. facsimile ed. Noyes, George R., tr. LC 76-107838. (Select Bibliographies Reprint Ser). 1926. 17.00 (ISBN 0-8369-5222-7). Ayer Co Pubs.

GREEK ARCHITECTURE
see Architecture, Greek

GREEK CHURCH
see Orthodox Eastern Church, Greek

GREEK CIVILIZATION
see Hellenism

GREEK CULTUS
see Cultus, Greek

GREEK HYMNS
see Hymns, Greek

GREEK LANGUAGE, BIBLICAL
Comprises the language of the Septuagint and the New Testament.

Berry, Harold J. Treasures from the Original. 1985. pap. 4.95 (ISBN 0-8024-2956-4). Moody.
Boyer, James L. A Manual of Greek Forms. pap. 4.95 (ISBN 0-88469-007-5). BMH Bks.
Chapman, Benjamin. Card-Guide to New Testament Greek. 1.95 (ISBN 0-8010-2388-2). Baker Bk.
--New Testament Greek Notebook. 1976. looseleaf 19.95 (ISBN 0-8010-2389-0). Baker Bk.
Dicharry, Warren F. Greek Without Grief: An Outline Guide to New Testament Greek. 5th ed. (Illus.). 1985. pap. 8.95 (ISBN 0-9608630-3-6). Vincentian.
Gingrich, F. Wilbur. Shorter Lexicon of the Greek New Testament. 2nd ed. 256p. 1983. 22.00 (ISBN 0-310-25030-7, 18075). Zondervan.
Goodrick, Edward W. Do It Yourself Hebrew & Greek. 2nd ed. LC 79-25463. 1980. pap. text ed. 9.95 (ISBN 0-930014-35-9); with cassette 14.95 (ISBN 0-930014-42-1). Multnomah.
Guillemette, Pierre. The Greek New Testament Analyzed. LC 86-81317. 480p. 1986. 29.95 (ISBN 0-8361-3418-4). Herald Pr.
Institut fuer Neutestamentliche Textforschung, Muenster-Westf. & Aland, Kurt, eds. Vollstaendige Konkordanz zum griechischen Neuen Testament, 2 vols. viii, 96p. Vol. 1, 2 pts., 1983. 908.00 (ISBN 3-11-009698-6); Vol. 2, 1978. 105.00 (ISBN 3-11-007349-8). De Gruyter.
Louw, J. P. Semantics of New Testament Greek. LC 81-67308. (Semeia Studies). 176p. 1982. pap. 12.95 (ISBN 0-8006-1511-5). Fortress.
--Semantics of New Testament Greek. (Semeia Studies). pap. 12.95 (ISBN 0-89130-693-5, 06 06 11). Scholars Pr GA.
Mare, W. Harold. Mastering New Testament Greek. 1979. 14.95 (ISBN 0-8010-6064-8). Baker Bk.
Martin, Raymond. An Introduction to New Testament Greek. 1980. text ed. 7.50x (ISBN 0-915948-07-9). Bks Distinction.
Metzger, Bruce M. Manuscripts of the Greek Bible: An Introduction to Paleography. (Illus.). 1981. 19.95x (ISBN 0-19-502924-0). Oxford U Pr.
Powers, B. Ward. Learn to Read the Greek New Testament. 300p. 1982. 21.00 (ISBN 0-85364-291-5); pap. text ed. 13.95 cancelled (ISBN 0-85364-292-3). Attic Pr.
Powers, Ward. Learn to Read the Greek New Testament. 336p. 1982. 19.95 (ISBN 0-8028-3578-3). Eerdmans.
Story, Cullen I K. Greek to Me: An Easy Way to Learn New Testament Greek Through Memory Visualization. LC 79-1769. (Illus.). 1979. pap. text ed. 12.45 (ISBN 0-06-067705-8, RD 307, HarpR). Har-Row.
Zerwick, Max. A Grammatical Analysis of Greek New Testament. (Scripta Pontificii Instituti Biblici Ser.: Vol. 1). 1974. pap. 16.00 (ISBN 88-7653-553-5). Loyola.
Zodhiates, Spiros, ed. Learn or Review New Testament Greek: The Answer Book. 1977. pap. 2.95 (ISBN 0-89957-519-6); wkbk. 9.95 (ISBN 0-89957-566-8); answer bk. avail. (ISBN 0-89957-567-6). AMG Pubs.

GREEK LANGUAGE, BIBLICAL–DICTIONARIES

Abbott-Smith, G. A Manual Greek Lexicon of the New Testament. 3rd ed. 528p. 1937. 21.95 (ISBN 0-567-01001-5, Pub. by T & T Clark Ltd UK). Fortress.
Alsop, John R. An Index to the Revised Bauer Arndt, Gingrich Greek Lexicon. 2nd ed. (Gr.). 1981. 14.95 (ISBN 0-310-44031-9, 6773P). Zondervan.
Bauer, Walter, et al, eds. A Greek-English Lexicon of the New Testament & Other Early Christian Literature. Arndt, William F., tr. from Ger. LC 78-14293. (2nd rev. & augmented edition). 1979. lib. bdg. 47.50x (ISBN 0-226-03932-3). U of Chicago Pr.
Brown, Colin. The New International Dictionary of New Testament Theology, 3 vols. Set. 109.95 (ISBN 0-310-21928-0, 11137P). Zondervan.
Cremer, Hermann. Biblico-Theological Lexicon of New Testament Greek. Urwick, William, tr. (Gr.). 960p. 1895. 35.95 (ISBN 0-567-01004-X, Pub. by T & T Clark Ltd UK). Fortress.
Gingrich, Wilbur F., et al. Greek-English Lexicon of the New Testament & Other Early Christian Literature. rev 2nd. ed. 1979. 45.00 (ISBN 0-310-20570-0, 6768). Zondervan.
Holly, David. A Complete Categorized Greek-English New Testament Vocabulary. (Gr. & Eng.). 1980. pap. 6.95 (ISBN 0-8010-4224-0). Baker Bk.
Kittel, Gerhard & Friedrich, Gerhard, eds. Theological Dictionary of the New Testament, 10 vols. Incl. Vol. 1. 1964. 29.95 (ISBN 0-8028-2243-6); Vol. 2. 1965. 29.95 (ISBN 0-8028-2244-4); Vol. 3. 1966. 29.95 (ISBN 0-8028-2245-2); Vol. 4. 1967. 29.95 (ISBN 0-8028-2246-0); Vol. 5. 1968. 29.95 (ISBN 0-8028-2247-9); Vol. 6. 1969. 29.95 (ISBN 0-8028-2248-7); Vol. 7. 1970. 29.95 (ISBN 0-8028-2249-5); Vol. 8. 1972. 29.95 (ISBN 0-8028-2250-9); Vol. 9. 1973. 29.95 (ISBN 0-8028-2322-X); Vol; Vol. 10. 1976. 29.95 (ISBN 0-8028-2323-8); Vol. 10. 1976. 29.95 (ISBN 0-8028-2323-8). Set. 299.50 (ISBN 0-8028-2324-6). Eerdmans.
Morrison, Clinton D. & Barnes, David H. New Testament Word Lists. 1964. pap. 3.95 (ISBN 0-8028-1141-8). Eerdmans.
Richards, Lawrence O. Expository Dictionary of Bible Words. 596p. 1985. 24.95 (ISBN 0-310-39000-1, 18300). Zondervan.
Smith, J. B. Greek-English Concordance. LC 55-12260. 430p. 1955. 29.95 (ISBN 0-8361-1368-3). Herald Pr.
Souter, Alexander, ed. Pocket Lexicon to the Greek New Testament. 1916. 17.95x (ISBN 0-19-864203-2). Oxford U Pr.
Thayer, John. The New Thayer's Greek Lexicon. 784p. 1981. 19.95 (ISBN 0-913573-22-1). Hendrickson MA.
Thayer, Joseph H. Greek-English Lexicon of the New Testament. 1956. 19.95 (ISBN 0-310-36850-2, 10906); pap. 10.95 (ISBN 0-310-36851-0, 10906P). Zondervan.
--Thayer's Greek-English Lexicon of the New Testament. LC 78-67264. (Gr. & Eng.). 1978. pap. 16.95 (ISBN 0-8054-1376-6). Broadman.
Wigram, George V. New Englishmans Greek Concordance & Lexicon. 960p. 1982. 34.95 (ISBN 0-913573-23-X). Hendrickson MA.
Zerwick, Maximilian. Biblical Greek. (Scripta Pontificci Instituti Biblica Ser.: Vol. 114). 1963. 12.00 (ISBN 88-7653-554-3). Loyola.

GREEK LANGUAGE, BIBLICAL–GLOSSARIES, VOCABULARIES, ETC.

Holly, David. A Complete Categorized Greek-English New Testament Vocabulary. (Eng. & Gr.). 141p. 1978. 9.50 (ISBN 0-85150-119-2). Attic Pr.
Kubo, Sakae. A Reader's Greek-English Lexicon of the New Testament & a Beginner's Guide for the Translation of New Testament Greek. (Andrews University Monographs, Studies in Religion: Vol. IV). x, 327p. 1975. text ed. 14.95 (ISBN 0-943872-04-9). Andrews Univ Pr.
Metzger, Bruce M. Lexical Aids for Students of New Testament Greek. 3rd ed. LC 70-73197. 1969. pap. 4.95x (ISBN 0-8401-1618-7). A R Allenson.
Moulton, J. H. & Milligan, G. The Vocabulary of the Greek Testament: Illustrated from the Papyri & Other Non-Literary Sources, 2 vols. 1977. lib. bdg. 250.00 (ISBN 0-8490-2800-0). Gordon Pr.
Moulton, James H. & Milligan, George. Vocabulary of the Greek New Testament. (Gr.). 1949. 35.95 (ISBN 0-8028-2178-2). Eerdmans.
Vine, W. E. Expository Dictionary of New Testament Words. 1396p. 14.95 (ISBN 0-8007-0089-9); thumb index ed. 16.95 (ISBN 0-8007-0090-2). Revell.

GREEK LANGUAGE, BIBLICAL–GRAMMAR

Blass, F. & Debrunner, A. Greek Grammar of the New Testament & Other Early Christian Literature. Funk, Robert W., tr. 28.00 (ISBN 0-310-24780-2, 18076). Zondervan.

Chamberlain, William D. Exegetical Grammar of the Greek New Testament. 1979. pap. 7.95 (ISBN 0-8010-2438-2). Baker Bk.
Colwell, Ernest C. & Tune, E. W. A Beginner's Reader-Grammar for New Testament Greek. 1965. 11.00 (ISBN 0-06-061530-3, HarpR). Har-Row.
Dana, H. E. & Mantey, R. Manual Grammar of the Greek New Testament: With Index. 1957. text ed. write for info. (ISBN 0-02-327070-5, 32707). Macmillan.
Davis, Guillermo H. Gramatica Elemental del Griego del Nuevo Testamento. McKibben, Jorge F., tr. 240p. 1984. Repr. of 1980 ed. 4.75 (ISBN 0-311-42008-7). Casa Bautista.
Davis, William H. Beginner's Grammar of the Greek New Testament. 1923. 12.45 (ISBN 0-06-061710-1, HarpR). Har-Row.
Drumwright, Huber L. An Introduction to New Testament Greek. 2nd ed. LC 78-59982. 1980. 11.95 (ISBN 0-8054-1368-5). Broadman.
Funk, Robert W., ed. Greek Grammar of the New Testament & Other Early Christian Literature. LC 61-8077. 1961. 32.00x (ISBN 0-226-27110-2). U of Chicago Pr.
Gignac, Francis T. An Introductory New Testament Greek Course. 4.20 (ISBN 0-8294-0223-3). Loyola.
Greenlee, J. Harold. Concise Exegetical Grammar of New Testament Greek. (Orig.). 1963. pap. 3.95 (ISBN 0-8028-1092-6). Eerdmans.
--A Concise Exegetical Grammar of New Testament Greek. 5th, rev. ed. 88p. (Orig.). 1987. pap. text ed. 5.95 (ISBN 0-8028-0173-0). Eerdmans.
Hale, Clarence B. Let's Study Greek. rev. ed. LC 82-3619. 1982. 14.95 (ISBN 0-8024-4666-3). Moody.
Hanna, Robert. A Grammatical Aid to the Greek New Testament. 1983. 16.95 (ISBN 0-8010-4272-0). Baker Bk.
Kubo, Sakae. A Beginner's New Testament Greek Grammar. LC 79-64247. 1979. pap. text ed. 11.00 (ISBN 0-8191-0761-1). U Pr of Amer.
LaSor, William S. Handbook of New Testament Greek: An Inductive Approach Based on the Greek Text of Acts, 2 vols. 1973. pap. text ed. 24.95 (ISBN 0-8028-2341-6). Eerdmans.
Machen, J. Gresham. New Testament Greek for Beginners. 1923. text ed. write for info. (ISBN 0-02-373480-9). Macmillan.
Marshall, Alfred. New Testament Greek Primer. 176p. (Orig.). 1981. leather edition 49.95 (ISBN 0-310-20540-9, 6246). Zondervan.
Moulton, James H. A Prolegomena to a Grammar of New Testament, Vol. I. (Moulton's Grammar of New Testament Greek Ser.). 320p. 1906. 19.95 (ISBN 0-567-01011-2, Pub. by T & T Clark Ltd UK). Fortress.
Moulton, James H. & Howard, Wilbert F. Accidence & Word Formation, Vol. 2. (Moulton's Grammar of New Testament Greek Ser.). 572p. 1929. 21.95 (ISBN 0-567-01012-0, Pub. by T & T Clark Ltd UK). Fortress.
Mueller, Walter. Grammatical Aids for Students of New Testament Greek. 1972. pap. 3.95 (ISBN 0-8028-1447-6). Eerdmans.
Nunn, Henry P. Short Syntax of New Testament Greek. 5th ed. 1931. text ed. 10.95 (ISBN 0-521-09941-2). Cambridge U Pr.
Rienecker, Fritz & Rogers, Cleon. Linquistic Key to the Greek New Testament. 912p. 1982. 29.95 (ISBN 0-310-32050-X, 6277). Zondervan.
Robertson, Archibald T. Grammar of the Greek New Testament in the Light of Historical Research. 1947. 45.00 (ISBN 0-8054-1308-1). Broadman.
Summers, Ray. Essentials of New Testament Greek. 1950. text ed. 11.95 (ISBN 0-8054-1309-X). Broadman.
Turner, Nigel. Syntax, Vol. 3. (Moulton's Grammar of New Testament Greek Ser.). 438p. 1963. 21.95 (ISBN 0-567-01013-9, Pub. by T & T Clark Ltd UK). Fortress.
Vaughan, Curtis & Gideon, Virtus E. A Greek Grammar of the New Testament. LC 78-74504. 1979. 11.95 (ISBN 0-8054-1378-2). Broadman.
Voelz, James W. Fundamental Greek Grammar. 320p. 1986. 14.95 (ISBN 0-570-04226-7, 15-2185). Concordia.
Wenham, John W. Elements of New Testament Greek. 1966. text ed. 11.95 (ISBN 0-521-09842-4); key 4.95 (ISBN 0-521-06769-3). Cambridge U Pr.

GREEK LANGUAGE, BIBLICAL–READERS

Colwell, Ernest C. & Tune, E. W. A Beginner's Reader-Grammar for New Testament Greek. 1965. 11.00 (ISBN 0-06-061530-3, HarpR). Har-Row.

GREEK LANGUAGE, BIBLICAL–SEMANTICS

Butler, Roy F. The Meaning of Agapao & Phileo in the Greek New Testament. 1977. 6.50x (ISBN 0-87291-089-X). Coronado Pr.
Morris, Leon. Apostolic Preaching of the Cross. 1956. pap. 5.95 (ISBN 0-8028-1512-X). Eerdmans.

GREEK LANGUAGE, BIBLICAL–SYNTAX

Brooks, James A. & Winbery, Carlton L. Syntax of New Testament Greek. LC 78-51150. 1978. pap. text ed. 8.00 (ISBN 0-8191-0473-6). U Pr of Amer.
Burton, Ernest D. Syntax of Moods & Tenses of New Testament Greek. 240p. 1898. 11.95 (ISBN 0-567-01002-3, Pub. by T & T Clark Ltd UK). Fortress.
Moule, Charles F. Idiom Book of New Testament Greek. 2nd ed. 1959. 39.50 (ISBN 0-521-05774-4); pap. text ed. 13.95 (ISBN 0-521-09237-X). Cambridge U Pr.
Thompson, Steven. The Apocalypse & Semitic Syntax. LC 84-12081. (Society for New Testament Studies Monograph: No. 52). 160p. 1985. 32.50 (ISBN 0-521-26031-0). Cambridge U Pr.

GREEK LITERATURE (COLLECTIONS)

Here are entered collections in the Greek language.

Warmington, E. H., ed. Greek Anthology, 5vols. Incl. Vol. 1. Book 1, Christian Epigrams. Book 2 Christoclorus of Thebes in Egypt. Book 3, Cyzicene Epigrams. Book 4, Proems of the Different Anthologies. Book 5, Amatory Epigrams. Book 6, Dedicatory Epigrams (ISBN 0-674-99074-9); Vol. 2. Book 7, Sepulchral Epigrams. Book 8, Epigrams of St. Gregory the Theologian (ISBN 0-674-99075-7); Vol. 3. Book 9, Declamatory Epigrams (ISBN 0-674-99093-5); Vol. 4. Book 10, Hortatory & Admonitory Epigrams. Book 11, Convivial & Satirical Epigrams. Book 12, Strato's Musa Puerilis (ISBN 0-674-99094-3); Vol. 5. Book 13, Epigrams in Various Metres. Book 14, Arithmetical Problems, Riddles, Oracles. Book 15, Miscellanea. Book 16, Epigrams of Planudean Anthology Not in the Palatine Manuscript (ISBN 0-674-99095-1). (Loeb Classical Library: No. 67-68, 84-86). (Gr. & Eng.). 13.95x ea. Harvard U Pr.

GREEK LITERATURE–HISTORY AND CRITICISM

Campbell, Lewis. Religion in Greek Literature: A Sketch in Outline. facsimile ed. LC 79-148874. (Select Bibliographies Reprint Ser). Repr. of 1898 ed. 22.00 (ISBN 0-8369-5645-1). Ayer Co Pubs.
Clinton, Henry F. Fasti Romani: The Civil & Literary Chronology of Rome & Constantinople from the Death of Augustus to the Death of Justin the 2nd, 2 Vols. 1965. Repr. of 1850 ed. Set. 105.50 (ISBN 0-8337-0602-0). B Franklin.
Jaeger, Werner. Paideia: The Ideals of Greek Culture, 3 vols. Highet, Gilbert, tr. from Ger. Incl. Vol. 1. Archaic Greece; The Mind of Athens. 2nd ed. 1945 (ISBN 0-19-500399-3); Vol. 2. In Search of the Divine Center. 1943 (ISBN 0-19-500592-9); Vol. 3. The Conflict of Cultural Ideals in the Age of Plato. 1944 (ISBN 0-19-500593-7). 35.00x ea. Oxford U Pr.
Philo. Philonis Alexandrini in Flaccum. Connor, W. R., ed. LC 78-18570. (Greek Texts & Commentaries Ser.). 1979. Repr. of 1939 ed. lib. bdg. 17.00x (ISBN 0-405-11414-1). Ayer Co Pubs.
Wacholder, Ben Z. Eupolemus: A Study of Graeco-Judean Literature. 1974. 20.00x (ISBN 0-87820-401-6). Ktav.

GREEK PHILOSOPHY

see Philosophy, Ancient

GREGOIRE, HENRI, ABBE, 1750-1831

Necheles, Ruth F. Abbe Gregoire, 1787-1831: The Odyssey of an Egalitarian. LC 75-105987. 1971. lib. bdg. 29.95 (ISBN 0-8371-3312-2, NAG/&). Greenwood.

GREGORIAN CHANT

see Chants (Plain, Gregorian, etc.)

GREGORIUS 1ST, THE GREAT, SAINT, POPE, 540-604

Baasten, Matthew. Pride According to Gregory the Great: A Study of the Moralia. LC 86-18057. (Studies in the Bible & Early Christianity: Vol. 7). 216p. 1986. lib. bdg. 49.95 (ISBN 0-88946-606-8). E Mellen.
Colgrave, Bertram, ed. The Earliest Life of Gregory the Great. 192p. 1985. 37.50 (ISBN 0-521-30924-7); pap. 12.95 (ISBN 0-521-31384-8). Cambridge U Pr.
King Alfred's West-Saxon Version of Gregory's Pastoral Care, 2 pts. Sweet, Henry, ed. (EETS, OS Ser.: No. 50). Repr. of 1872 ed. Pt. I. 18.00 (ISBN 0-527-00041-8); Pt. II. 13.00 (ISBN 0-527-00042-6). Kraus Repr.
Richards, Jeffrey. Consul of God. 1980. 27.95x (ISBN 0-7100-0346-3). Methuen Inc.

GREGORIUS 7TH, SAINT, POPE, 1015-1085

Gregory Seventh, Pope The Correspondence of Pope Gregory VII. Emerton, E., tr. (Columbia University Records of Civilization Ser.). 1969. pap. 5.95x (ISBN 0-393-09859-1). Norton.
Macdonald, Allan J. Hildebrand: A Life of Gregory the Seventh. (Great Medieval Churchmen Ser.). 254p. 1977. Repr. of 1932 ed. lib. bdg. 17.50x (ISBN 0-915172-26-7). Richwood Pub.
Vogel, Juergen. Gregor VII & Heinrich IV. 1982. 59.20 (ISBN 3-11-008959-9). De Gruyter.

GREGORY, SAINT, BP. OF NYSSA, 322-398

Burghardt, W. J., et al, eds. St. Gregory the Great: Pastoral Care. (ACW Ser.: No. 11). 282p. 1950. 13.95 (ISBN 0-8091-0251-X). Paulist Pr.
Cavarnos, John P. St. Gregory of Nyssa on the Origin & Destiny of the Soul. 12p. 1982. pap. 0.90 (ISBN 0-914744-60-7). Inst Byzantine.
Cherniss, Harold F. Platonism of Gregory of Nyssa. 1971. Repr. of 1930 ed. lib. bdg. 18.50 (ISBN 0-8337-0556-3). B Franklin.
Malherbe, Abraham, tr. Gregory of Nyssa: The Life of Moses. LC 78-56352. (Classics of Western Spirituality Ser.). (Illus.). 224p. 1978. 12.95 (ISBN 0-8091-0239-0); pap. 7.95 (ISBN 0-8091-2112-3). Paulist Pr.
Zahirsky, Valerie G. The Conversion of Armenia. (Armenian Church Classics Ser.). (Illus.). 48p. (Orig.). 1985. pap. 5.00 (ISBN 0-934728-16-X). D O A C.

GRELLET, STEPHEN, 1773-1855

Dalglish, Doris N. People Called Quakers. facsimile ed. LC 78-90628. (Essay Index Reprint Ser). 1938. 15.00 (ISBN 0-8369-1254-3). Ayer Co Pubs.

GRIEF

see also Church Work with the Bereaved; Consolation

Archives of the Foundation of Thanatology, Vol. 8: Acute Grief III: Continuum of Anticipatory Grief; Dying & Death; Acute Grief; Bereavement; Recovery from Bereavement, or Pathological Bereavement; & Lifelong Bereavement, No. 4. pap. 14.00 (ISBN 0-405-13074-0). Ayer Co Pubs.
Berkus, Rusty. To Heal Again: Toward Serenity & the Resolution of Grief. (Illus.). 32p. (Orig.). 1986. pap. 13.95 (ISBN 0-9609888-2-3). Red Rose Pr.
Bernstein, Joanne. Loss & How to Cope with It. LC 76-50027. 8.95 (ISBN 0-395-28891-6, Clarion). HM.
Bissell, Charles B., III. Letters I Never Wrote, Conversations I Never Had: Dealing with Unresolved Grief & Anger. 58p. (Orig.). 1983. pap. 4.95 (ISBN 0-9612604-0-8). C Bissell.
Bright, Ruth. Grieving: A Handbook for Those Who Care. vi, 229p. 1986. pap. 19.50 (ISBN 0-918812-46-1). MMB Music.
Carlson, Roberta. Moments of Grace: Lessons from Grief. 128p. (Orig.). 1987. pap. 4.95 (ISBN 0-8423-4602-3). Tyndale.
Carpenter, Jan. Turning Sorrow into Song. 154p. 1986. 9.95 (ISBN 0-89066-081-6). World Wide Pubs.
Carr, Arthur C., et al, eds. Grief: Selected Readings. 155p. 1974. pap. 7.50 (ISBN 0-930194-76-4). Ctr Thanatology.
Cato, Sid. Healing Life's Great Hurts. 64p. 5.95 (ISBN 0-914091-51-4). Chicago Review.
Clark, Martha B. Are You Weeping with Me, God? LC 86-17194. (Orig.). 1987. pap. 5.95 (ISBN 0-8054-5436-5). Broadman.
Coniaris, A. M. Christ's Comfort for Those Who Sorrow. 1978. pap. 3.95 (ISBN 0-937032-00-X). Light&Life Pub Co MN.
D'Arcy, Paula. Song for Sarah: A Young Mother's Journey Through Grief, & Beyond. LC 79-14684. 124p. 1979. 6.95 (ISBN 0-87788-778-0); pap. 2.50 (ISBN 0-87788-780-2). Shaw Pubs.
Day, Gwynn M. The Joy Beyond. 1979. 3.95 (ISBN 0-8010-2893-0). Baker Bk.
DeBellis, Robert, et al, eds. Suffering: Psychological & Social Aspects in Loss, Grief, & Care. LC 85-31744. (Loss, Grief & Care Ser.: Vol. 1(1-2)). 196p. 1986. text ed. 32.95 (ISBN 0-86656-558-2). Haworth Pr.
Fulton, Robert. Death, Grief & Bereavement: A Bibliography, 1845-1975. Kastenbaum, Robert, ed. LC 76-19572. (Death and Dying Ser.). 1976. PLB 27.50 (ISBN 0-405-09570-8). Ayer Co Pubs.
Great Expectations. (Pocket Power Ser.). 16p. (Orig.). 1986. pap. 0.50 (ISBN 0-89486-366-5). Hazelden.
Grollman, Earl A. Time Remembered: A Journal for Survivors. LC 86-47753. 98p. 1987. 10.00 (ISBN 0-8070-2704-9). Beacon Pr.
Grollman, Earl A., ed. What Helped Me When My Loved One Died. LC 80-68166. 168p. 1982. pap. 7.95 (ISBN 0-8070-3229-8, BP 626). Beacon Pr.
Guthmann, Robert F., Jr. & Womack, Sharon K. Death, Dying & Grief: A Bibliography. LC 77-82084. 1978. pap. text ed. 5.50 (ISBN 0-918626-01-3, Pied Publications). Word Serv.
Hershey, Terry. Beginning Again: Involvement Guide. 64p. 1986. cancelled (ISBN 0-8407-3084-5). Nelson.
--Beginning Again: Life after a Relationship Ends. 152p. 1986. pap. 7.95 (ISBN 0-8407-3075-6). Nelson.
Howard, Donald. Christians Grieve Too. 1980. pap. 1.45 (ISBN 0-85151-315-8). Banner of Truth.
Jackson, Jewell N. The Agony of Grief. LC 85-52320. (Illus.). 96p. (Orig.). 1986. pap. 8.95 (ISBN 0-934955-02-6). Watercress Pr.
Jones, Jean G. Time Out for Grief: A Practical Guide to Passing Through Grief to Happiness. LC 81-85051. 228p. 1982. pap. 4.50 (ISBN 0-87973-654-2, 654). Our Sunday Visitor.
Koers, Shirley. The Eyes Are Sunlight: A Journey Through Grief. LC 86-82036. 200p. (Orig.). 1986. pap. 4.95 (ISBN 0-87793-345-6). Ave Maria.
Kreis, Bernadine & Pattie, Alice. Up from Grief: Patterns of Recovery. 160p. 1982. pap. 5.95 (ISBN 0-8164-2364-4, AY7442, HarpR). Har-Row.
Kreis, Bernardine & Pattie, Alice. Up from Grief. 292p. 1984. pap. 9.95 large print ed. (ISBN 0-8027-2486-8). Walker & Co.
Krumroy, Jeri. Grief Is Not Forever. 128p. (Orig.). 1985. pap. 6.95 (ISBN 0-87178-326-6). Brethren.
Kutscher, Austin H. & Kutscher, M. L., eds. Bibliography of Books on Death, Bereavement, Loss & Grief, Supplement, 1935-1971. 170p. 1970. pap. 9.95 (ISBN 0-930194-79-9). Ctr Thanatology.
Linn, Dennis, et al. Healing the Greatest Hurt: Healing Grief & the Family Tree. LC 85-60407. 258p. (Orig.). 1985. pap. 5.95 (ISBN 0-8091-2714-8). Paulist Pr.
Lombardo, Victor S. & Lombardo, Edith F. Kids Grieve Too! (Illus.). 88p. 1986. 17.75x (ISBN 0-398-05275-1). C C Thomas.
McDonald, Peter C. Grieving: A Healing Process. 24p. (Orig.). 1985. pap. 0.95 (ISBN 0-89486-318-5). Hazelden.
Manning, Doug. Comforting Those Who Grieve: A Guide for Helping Others. LC 84-48226. 112p. 1985. 10.45 (ISBN 0-06-065418-X, HarpR). Har-Row.
Margolis, Otto S. Grief & the Meaning of the Funeral. 15.50 (ISBN 0-405-12501-1). Ayer Co Pubs.
Marshall, George. Facing Death & Grief. LC 80-84402. (Library of Liberal Religion Ser.). 200p. 1981. 18.95 (ISBN 0-87975-140-1); pap. 11.95 (ISBN 0-87975-169-X). Prometheus Bks.
Miller, Jack S. The Healing Power of Grief. 125p. 1985. pap. 7.95 (ISBN 0-914373-02-1). Wieser & Wieser.
Miller, Jolonda. You Can Become Whole Again: A Guide to Healing for Christians in Grief. LC 80-84652. 1981. pap. 6.50 (ISBN 0-8042-1156-6). John Knox.
Miller, Roger F. What Can I Say? Lambert, Herbert, ed. 96p. (Orig.). 1987. pap. 4.95 (ISBN 0-8272-4220-4). CBP.
Monsma, Hester. Devotions for Those Who Sorrow. 30p. 1984. pap. 1.25 (ISBN 0-8010-2944-9). Baker Bk.
Montgomery, Herb & Montgomery, Mary. Beyond Sorrow: Reflections on Death & Grief. rev. ed. 32p. 1985. pap. 6.95 (ISBN 0-86683-461-3, HarpR). Har-Row.
Murphey, Cecil. Comforting Those Who Grieve. LC 78-71052. 64p. 1979. pap. 1.00 (ISBN 0-8042-1099-3). John Knox.
Myers, Edward. When Parents Die: A Guide for Adults. 208p. 1986. 13.95 (ISBN 0-670-80771-0). Viking.
Nimeth, Albert J. In Your Time of Sorrow. 1976. pap. 0.50 (ISBN 0-685-77503-8). Franciscan Herald.
Novak, Michael, ed. Democracy & Mediating Structures: A Theological Inquiry. 1980. 13.25 (ISBN 0-8447-2175-1); pap. 7.25 (ISBN 0-8447-2176-X). Am Enterprise.
Oates, Wayne E. Your Particular Grief. LC 81-3328. 114p. 1981. pap. 6.95 (ISBN 0-664-24376-2). Westminster.
O'Connor, Nancy. Letting Go with Love: The Grieving Process. LC 84-61538. 186p. 1985. 18.95x (ISBN 0-9613714-1-2); pap. 9.95x (ISBN 0-9613714-0-4). La Mariposa.
Osgood, Judy, ed. Meditations for Bereaved Parents. LC 86-15003. (Gilgal Meditations Ser.). 70p. (Orig.). 1984. pap. 5.95 (ISBN 0-916895-00-9). Gilgal Pubns.
Peretz, David, et al, eds. Death & Grief: Selected Readings for the Medical Student. 270p. 1977. pap. 6.95 (ISBN 0-930194-82-9). Ctr Thanatology.
Rando, Therese A., ed. Loss & Anticipatory Grief. LC 85-45082. 256p. 1986. 27.00 (ISBN 0-669-11144-9). Lexington Bks.
Rank, Maureen. Free to Grieve: Coping with the Trauma of Miscarriage. 176p. 1985. pap. 5.95 (ISBN 0-87123-806-3, 210806). Bethany Hse.
Robinson, Haddon W. Grief. 24p. 1976. pap. 3.50 (ISBN 0-310-32261-8, 9772P). Zondervan.
Silverman, Phyllis R. Helping Women Cope with Grief. (Sage Human Services Guides Ser.: Vol. 25). 111p. 1981. pap. 9.95 (ISBN 0-8039-1735-X). Sage.
Simpson, M. A. Dying, Death, & Grief: A Critically Annotated Bibliography & Source Book of Thanatology & Terminal Care. LC 78-27273. 300p. 1979. 35.00x (ISBN 0-306-40147-9, Plenum Pr). Plenum Pub.

Smith, Elwyn A. A Spiritual Exercise for the Grieving. LC 84-47935. 64p. 1984. pap. 3.50 (ISBN 0-8006-1807-6, 1-1807). Fortress.
Stern, Marvin. Death, Grief & Friendship in the Eighteenth Century: Edward Gibbon & Lord Sheffield. 1985. pap. 11.95 (ISBN 0-930194-35-7). Ctr Thanatology.
Sullender, R. Scott. Grief & Growth: Pastoral Resources for Emotional & Spiritual Growth. LC 84-61024. 240p. (Orig.). 1985. pap. 9.95 (ISBN 0-8091-2652-4). Paulist Pr.
Tallmer, Margot, et al, eds. The Implications of Death & Loss for Women. (Current Thanatology Ser.). 100p. 1986. pap. 13.95 (ISBN 0-930194-40-3). Ctr Thanatology.
Tanner, Ira J. Healing the Pain of Everyday Loss. 188p. 1980. pap. 4.95 (ISBN 0-03-057849-3, HarpR). Har-Row.
Towns, James E. Growing Through Grief. 1984. pap. 2.95 (ISBN 0-87162-395-1, D4000). Warner Pr.
Updike, L. Wayne. Ministry to the Bereaved. 1986. pap. 6.00 (ISBN 0-8309-0450-6). Herald Hse.
Veninga, Robert L. A Gift of Hope: How We Survive Our Tragedies. (Large Print Bks.). 404p. 1986. lib. bdg. 16.95 (ISBN 0-8161-4101-0, Large Print Bks). G K Hall.
Williams, Mary L. Sorrow Speaks. 1968. pap. 2.95 (ISBN 0-8272-3405-8). CBP.
Williams, Steve. The Death of a Child. 1977. 3.95 (ISBN 0-88027-005-5). Firm Foun Pub.

GROSSETESTE, ROBERT, BP. OF LINCOLN, 1175-1253

McEvoy, James. The Philosophy of Robert Grosseteste. 450p. 1986. pap. 19.95x (ISBN 0-19-824939-X). Oxford U Pr.
Southern, Richard. Robert Grosseteste: The Growth of an English Mind in Medieval Europe. 300p. 1986. 55.00x (ISBN 0-19-826450-X). Oxford U Pr.
Stevenson, F. S. Robert Grosseteste, Bishop of Lincoln: A Contribution to the Religious, Political & Intellectual History of the Thirteenth Century. (Medieval Studies Ser.). Repr. of 1899 ed. lib. bdg. 39.50 (ISBN 0-697-00018-4). Irvington.

GROTESQUE

Wildridge, Thomas T. Grotesque in Church Art. LC 68-30633. 1969. Repr. of 1899 ed. 35.00x (ISBN 0-8103-3077-6). Gale.

GROUP PRAYER

see Prayer Groups

GROUP WORK, CHURCH

see Church Group Work

GRUBER, FRANZ XAVIER, 1787-1863

Rosel, Paul. Silent Night, Holy Night. (Illus.). 1969. 3.25 (ISBN 0-8066-0928-1, 11-9388). Augsburg.

GRUBER, FRANZ XAVIER, 1787-1863–JUVENILE LITERATURE

Moore, John Travers. Story of Silent Night. LC 65-19252. 1965. 5.95 (ISBN 0-570-03430-2, 56-1056). Concordia.

GUADALUPE, NUESTRA SENORA DE

Carroll, Warren H. Our Lady of Guadalupe & the Conquest of Darkness. 123p. (Orig.). pap. 4.95 (ISBN 0-931888-12-3). Christendom Pubns.
Dooley, L. M. That Motherly Mother of Guadalupe. 2.25 (ISBN 0-8198-0634-X); pap. 1.25 (ISBN 0-8198-0635-8). Dghtrs St Paul.
Johnston, Francis. The Wonder of Guadalupe. LC 81-53041. 143p. 1981. pap. 4.50 (ISBN 0-89555-168-3). TAN Bks Pubs.
Lafaye, Jacques. Quetzalcoatl & Guadalupe: The Formation of Mexican National Consciousness, 1531-1813. Keen, Benjamin, tr. from Fr. LC 75-20889. 1976. lib. bdg. 26.00x (ISBN 0-226-46794-5). U of Chicago Pr.
Smith, Jody B. Image of Guadalupe: Myth or Miracle? LC 80-2066. (Illus.). 216p. 1984. pap. 6.95 (ISBN 0-385-19705-5, Im). Doubleday.

GUILDFORD, RICHARD, SIR, 1455-1506

Ellis, Henry, ed. Pylgrymage of Sir Richard Guylforde to the Holy Land, A. D. 1506. LC 75-166023. (Camden Society, London. Publications, First Ser.: No. 51). Repr. of 1851 ed. 19.00 (ISBN 0-404-50151-6). AMS Pr.

GUILLAUME D'AUVERGNE, BP. OF PARIS, d. 1249

Valois, Noel. Guillaume d'Auvergne: Eveque de Paris (1228-1249), Sa vie & Ses ouvrages (Medieval Studies Ser.) (Medieval Studies Ser.). (Fr.). Repr. of 1880 ed. lib. bdg. 44.00x (ISBN 0-697-00019-2). Irvington.

GUILLAUME DE CHAMPEAUX, BP., 1070?-1121

Michaud, E. Guillaume de Champeaux et les Ecoles de Paris. 2nd ed. (Medieval Studies Reprint Ser.). (Fr.). Repr. of 1867 ed. lib. bdg. 45.00x (ISBN 0-697-00011-7). Irvington.

GUILLAUME DE DEGUILLEVILLE, 14TH CENTURY

Wharey, James B. Study of the Sources of Bunyan's Allegories(with Special Reference to Deguileville's Pilgrimage of Man. LC 68-59038. 136p. 1968. Repr. of 1904 ed. 15.00x (ISBN 0-87752-120-4). Gordian.

GUILT

see also Atonement; Sin

Agudo, Philomena, et al. Guilt: Issues of Emotional Living in an Age of Stress for Clergy & Religious. Kelley, Kathleen E., ed. LC 80-10747. 144p. 1980. pap. 5.00 (ISBN 0-89571-008-0). Affirmation.
Amato, Joseph A., II. Guilt & Gratitude: A Study of the Origins of Contemporary Conscience. LC 81-6991. (Contributions in Philosophy Ser.: No. 20). xxv, 218p. 1982. lib. bdg. 29.95 (ISBN 0-313-22946-5, AGG/). Greenwood.
Caldwell, Louis O. You Can Stop Feeling Guilty. (Christian Counseling Aids Ser.). 1978. pap. 1.25 (ISBN 0-8010-2414-5). Baker Bk.
Freeman, Lucy C. & Strean, Herbert S. Guilt: Letting Go. LC 86-15873. 288p. 1987. 14.95 (ISBN 0-471-83636-2). Wiley.
Hamroque, John & Krastel, Joseph. Guilt: How to Deal with It. 48p. 1986. pap. 1.50 (ISBN 0-89243-256-X). Liguori Pubns.
Hughes, Don. Free from Guilt & Condemnation. (Orig.). 1977. pap. 0.75 minibook (ISBN 0-89274-048-5, HH-048). Harrison Hse.
Kirkpatrick, Jean. The Nature of Guilt. 16p. 1983. pap. 1.50 (ISBN 0-318-19524-0). WFS.
Kurtz, Ernest. Shame & Guilt: Characteristics of the Dependency Cycle. 68p. 4.95 (ISBN 0-89486-132-8, 1940A). Hazelden.
Moore, Marvin. How to Handle Guilt. (Better Living Ser.). 1977. pap. 0.99 (ISBN 0-8127-0158-5). Review & Herald.
Morris, Herbert. On Guilt & Innocence: Essays in Legal Philosophy & Moral Psychology. 1976. pap. 3.95 (ISBN 0-520-03944-0, 434). U of Cal Pr.
Narramore, S. Bruce. No Condemnation: Rethinking Guilt Motivation in Counseling, Preaching & Parenting. 208p. 1984. pap. 8.95 (ISBN 0-310-30401-6, 11244P). Zondervan.
Ross, Alf. On Guilt, Responsibility & Punishment. LC 73-94446. 1974. 33.00x (ISBN 0-520-02717-5). U of Cal Pr.
Westphal, Merold. God, Guilt & Death: An Existential Phenomenology of Religion. LC 83-48525. (Studies in Phenomenology & Existential Philosophy). 320p. 1987. 27.50x (ISBN 0-253-32586-2); pap. 9.95 (ISBN 0-253-32586-2). Ind U Pr.

GURDJIEFF, GEORGE IVANOVITCH, 1872-1949

Anderson, Margaret. The Unknowable Gurdjieff. 1st 1973 ed. (Illus.). 212p. (Orig.). 1969. pap. 7.50 (ISBN 0-87728-219-6). Weiser.
Bennett, J. G. Gurdjieff: A Very Great Enigma 1973. LC 72-91951. 100p. (Orig.). 1984. pap. 4.50 (ISBN 0-87728-581-0). Weiser.
Bennett, John G. Deeper Man. LC 84-73170. 254p. 1985. 8.95 (ISBN 0-934254-07-9). Claymont Comm.
--What Are We Living for. 4.95 (ISBN 0-900306-07-6, Pub. by Coombe Springs Pr.). Claymont Comm.
Butkovsky-Hewitt, Anna. With Gurdjieff in St. Petersburg. 1978. 9.95 (ISBN 0-7100-8527-3). Weiser.
Cox, Jan. Death of Gurdjieff in the Foothills of Georgia: Secret Papers of an American Work Group. 316p. 1980. 9.00 (ISBN 0-936380-03-9). Chan Shal Imi.
Da Silva, Andrew J. Do from the Octave of Man Number Four: The Awakening & Crisis, Vol. 1. Sajkovic, Olivera, ed. LC 85-71128. 128p. 1985. 12.00 (ISBN 0-9614941-0-7). Borderline NY.
De Hartmann, Thomas. Our Life with Mister Gurdjieff. LC 64-22661. (Illus.). 1964. 17.50x (ISBN 0-8154-0058-6). Cooper Sq.
De Hartmann, Thomas & De Hartmann, Olga. Our Life with Mr. Gurdjieff. rev. ed. LC 83-47722. 160p. 1983. pap. 7.95 (ISBN 0-06-061865-5, RD 469, HarpR). Har-Row.
Gurdjieff Foundation of California & Driscoll, J. Walter. Gurdjieff: An Annotated Bibliography. LC 83-49296. (Reference Library of Social Science). 390p. 1985. lib. bdg. 50.00 (ISBN 0-8240-8972-3). Garland Pub.
Hulme, Kathryn. Undiscovered Country: In Search of Gurdjieff. 1972. pap. 4.95 (ISBN 0-316-38138-1, Pub. by Atlantic Monthly Pr). Little.
Lefort, Rafael. The Teachers of Gurdjieff. LC 66-68145. 157p. (Orig.). 1975. pap. 6.95 (ISBN 0-87728-283-8). Weiser.
Nicoll, Maurice. Psychological Commentaries on the Teaching of Gurdjieff & Ouspensky, Vol. 1. LC 83-25194. 371p. (Orig.). 1984. pap. 15.95 (ISBN 0-87773-269-8). Shambhala Pubns.
--Psychological Commentaries on the Teachings of Gurdjieff & Ouspensky, Vol. 2. LC 83-25194. 404p. (Orig.). 1984. pap. 18.95 (ISBN 0-87773-270-1). Shambhala Pubns.
--Psychological Commentaries on the Teachings of Gurdjieff & Ouspensky, Vol. 3. LC 83-25194. 447p. (Orig.). 1984. pap. 11.95 (ISBN 0-87773-271-X). Shambhala Pubns.
--Psychological Commentaries on the Teaching of Gurdjieff & Ouspensky, Vol. 4. LC 83-25194. 268p. 1984. pap. 11.95 (ISBN 0-87773-287-6, 72695-2). Shambhala Pubns.
--Psychological Commentaries on the Teaching of Gurdjieff & Ouspensky, Vol. 5. LC 83-25194. 253p. 1984. pap. 11.95 (ISBN 0-87773-288-4, 72694-4). Shambhala Pubns.
Nott, C. S. Teachings of Gurdjieff: The Journal of a Pupil. (Illus., Orig.). 1974. pap. 7.95 (ISBN 0-87728-395-8). Weiser.
Ouspensky, P. D. Fourth Way. 1971. pap. 7.95 (ISBN 0-394-71672-8, Vin). Random.
--In Search of the Miraculous: Fragments of an Unknown Teaching. 399p. 1965. pap. 6.95 (ISBN 0-15-644508-5, Harv). HarBraceJ.
Ridley, Gustave. From Boredom to Bliss. Campbell, Jean, ed. (Illus.). 160p. (Orig.). 1983. pap. 8.95 (ISBN 0-9610544-0-9). Harmonious Pr.
Speeth, Kathleen R. & Friedlander, Ira. Gurdjieff: The Early Years. LC 78-24696. (Illus.). 1979. pap. 5.95 (ISBN 0-06-090693-6, CN-693, PL). Har-Row.
Staveley, A. L. Memories of Gurdjieff. LC 78-56109. 1978. 8.95 (ISBN 0-89756-000-0). Two Rivers.
Vaysse, Jean. Toward Awakening: An Approach to the Teaching of Gurdjieff. LC 79-1779. 1979. pap. 5.95i (ISBN 0-06-068860-2, RD 304, HarpR). Har-Row.
Walker, Kenneth. Gurdjieff: A Study of His Teaching. (Unwin Paperbacks Ser.). 221p. (Orig.). 1980. pap. 5.95 (ISBN 0-04-294106-7). Allen Unwin.
--The Making of Man. 1963. 14.95 (ISBN 0-7100-2248-4). Methuen Inc.
Wilson, Colin. The War Against Sleep: The Philosophy of Gurdjieff. 96p. 1980. pap. 6.95 (ISBN 0-85030-198-X). Weiser.
Zuber, Rene. Who Are You Monsieur Gurdjieff? Koralek, Jenny, tr. 80p. 1980. pap. 4.95 (ISBN 0-7100-0674-8). Methuen Inc.

GUYON JEANNE MARIE (BOUVIER DE LA MOTTE) 1648-1717

Coslet, Dorothy. Madame Jeanne Guyon: Child of Another World. 219p. (Orig.). 1984. pap. 3.95 (ISBN 0-87508-144-4). Chr Lit.

GYPSIES

Block, Martin. Gypsies: Their Life & Their Customs. Kuczynski, Barbara & Taylor, Duncan, trs. LC 75-3451. (Illus.). Repr. of 1939 ed. 31.50 (ISBN 0-404-16886-8). AMS Pr.
Burton, Richard F. The Jew, the Gypsy & el Islam. 1974. Repr. of 1898 ed. 6.00 (ISBN 0-913022-11-X). Angriff Pr.
Leland, Charles G. The Gypsies. LC 75-3460. Repr. of 1882 ed. 27.00 (ISBN 0-404-16891-4). AMS Pr.

H

HABANS

see Anabaptists

HABE (AFRICAN PEOPLE)

see Dogons (African People)

HADES

see Future Life; Hell

HADITH

Here are entered works on the oral traditions concerning the deeds and sayings of Muhammad, the prophet, solely.

Azami, M. M. Early Hadith Literature. LC 77-90341. 1978. 10.50 (ISBN 0-89259-012-2). Am Trust Pubns.
Azami, Mustafa. Studies in Hadith Methodology & Literature. Beg, Anwer, ed. LC 77-90335. 1978. pap. 5.50 (ISBN 0-89259-011-4); pap. text ed. 5.50. Am Trust Pubns.
Azizullah. Glimpses of Hadith, 3. pap. 6.50 (ISBN 0-686-18380-0). Kazi Pubns.
Doi, A. R. Hadith: An Introduction. 1980. pap. 6.50 (ISBN 0-686-64661-4). Kazi Pubns.
Guillaume, Alfred. The Traditions of Islam. LC 79-52552. (Islam Ser.). 1980. Repr. of 1924 ed. lib. bdg. 16.00x (ISBN 0-8369-9260-1). Ayer Co Pubs.
Juynboll, G. H. Muslim Tradition: Studies in Chronology, Provenance & Authorship of Early Hadith. LC 82-19778. (Cambridge Studies in Islamic Civilization). 264p. 1983. 62.50 (ISBN 0-521-25382-9). Cambridge U Pr.
Qazi, M. A. Bilal in Hadith. pap. 1.25 (ISBN 0-686-18324-X). Kazi Pubns.
Rauf, A. Hadith for Children. pap. 5.95 (ISBN 0-686-63901-4). Kazi Pubns.

HAECKEL, ERNST HEINRICH PHILIPP AUGUST, 1834-1919

Slosson, Edwin E. Major Prophets of To-Day. facs. ed. LC 68-8493. (Essay Index Reprint Ser.). 1914. 20.00 (ISBN 0-8369-0882-1). Ayer Co Pubs.

HAENDEL, GEORG FRIEDRICH, 1685-1759

Deutsch, Otto. Handel: A Documentary Biography. LC 74-3118. (Music Ser.). 942p. 1974. Repr. of 1954 ed. lib. bdg. 85.00 (ISBN 0-306-70624-5). Da Capo.
Hadden, James C. Life of Handel: The Kelkel Edition. LC 74-24096. Repr. of 1904 ed. 15.00 (ISBN 0-404-12941-2). AMS Pr.
Handel, George F. Complete Concerti Grossi in Full Score. 20.25 (ISBN 0-8446-5890-1). Peter Smith.
Harris, Ellen T. Handel & The Pastoral Tradition. (Illus.). 1980. 47.00x (ISBN 0-19-315236-3). Oxford U Pr.
Jacobi, Peter. The Messiah Book: The Life & Times of G. F. Handel's Greatest Hit. (Illus.). 169p. 1982. 10.95 (ISBN 0-312-53072-2). St Martin.
Myers, Robert M. Handel, Dryden & Milton. 1956. lib. bdg. 32.50 (ISBN 0-8414-6129-5). Folcroft.
--Handel's Messiah: A Touchstone of Taste. LC 72-159747. 338p. 1971. Repr. of 1948 ed. lib. bdg. 27.50x (ISBN 0-374-96035-6, Octagon). Hippocrene Bks.
Quillin, Roger T. Meeting Christ in Handel's Messiah: Lent & Easter Messages Based on Handel's Texts & Music. 96p. 1984. pap. 4.95 (ISBN 0-8066-2118-4, 10-4318). Augsburg.
Smith, William C. Concerning Handel: His Life & Works. LC 78-59044. (Encore Music Editions). (Illus.). 1979. Repr. of 1948 ed. 27.50 (ISBN 0-88355-716-9). Hyperion Conn.
Tobin, John. Handel's Messiah. LC 69-13491. (Illus.). 1969. 35.00 (ISBN 0-312-35840-7). St Martin.
Young, Percy M. Messiah, a Study in Interpretation. (Student's Music Library Ser.). 1961. 13.95 (ISBN 0-234-77215-8). Dufour.

HAGIOGRAPHY

Here are entered works on the lives of the saints, and how to write them. The lives themselves are entered under the heading Saints.

Clogan, Paul M., ed. Medieval Hagiography & Romance. LC 75-16872. (Medievalia et Humanistica Ser.: No. 6). pap. 59.30 (2029216). Bks Demand UMI.
Holtzclaw, Robert F. The Saints Go Marching In. rev. ed. LC 84-52751. (Illus.). 194p. (Orig.). 1984. write for info.; pap. 10.00 (ISBN 0-933144-00-8). Keeble Pr.
Kieckhefer, Richard. Unquiet Souls: Fourteenth-Century Saints & Their Religious Milieu. LC 84-210. 248p. 1984. lib. bdg. 24.95x (ISBN 0-226-43509-1). U of Chicago Pr.
Petin, L. M. Dictionnaire Hagiographique, 2 vols. Migne, J. P., ed. (Encyclopedie Theologique Ser.: Vols. 40-41). (Fr.). 1580p. Repr. of 1850 ed. lib. bdg. 240.00x (ISBN 0-89241-246-1). Caratzas.
White, Helen C. Tudor Books of Saints & Martyrs. LC 63-13741. pap. 73.00 (ISBN 0-317-07866-6, 2004164). Bks Demand UMI.

HAILE SELASSIE 1ST EMPEROR OF ETHIOPIA, 1891-1975

Nicholas, Tracy. Rastafari: A Way of Life. LC 77-76285. (Illus.). 1979. pap. 9.95 (ISBN 0-385-11575-X, Anch). Doubleday.

HAITI

Courlander, Harold & Bastien, Remy. Religion & Politics in Haiti. LC 66-26633. (Illus.). 1970. 3.95 (ISBN 0-911976-00-0). ICR.
Franklin, James. Present State of Hayti: Saint Domingo-with Remarks on Its Agriculture, Commerce, Laws, Religion, Finance & Population. LC 79-109325. Repr. of 1828 ed. 25.00x (ISBN 0-8371-3591-5, FRH&). Greenwood.

HAITI–SOCIAL LIFE AND CUSTOMS

Courlander, Harold. The Drum & the Hoe: Life & Lore of the Haitian People. (California Library Reprint: No. 31). (Illus.). 436p. 1981. 40.00x (ISBN 0-520-02364-1); pap. 10.95 (ISBN 0-520-05449-0, CAL 731). U of Cal Pr.
Taft, Edna. Puritan in Voodoo-Land. LC 73-174115. (Tower Bks). (Illus.). 1971. Repr. of 1938 ed. 43.00x (ISBN 0-8103-3919-6). Gale.

HALACHA

see Jewish Law; Talmud; Tradition (Judaism)

HALLUCINOGENIC DRUGS AND RELIGIOUS EXPERIENCE

Castaneda, Carlos. Journey to Ixtlan. 1983. pap. 4.95 (ISBN 0-671-60658-1). WSP.
--Tales of Power. 1982. pap. 4.95 (ISBN 0-671-55329-1). WSP.
--The Teachings of Don Juan: A Yaqui Way of Knowledge. LC 68-17303. 1968. pap. 5.95 (ISBN 0-520-02258-0, CAL253). U of Cal Pr.
Harner, Michael J., ed. Hallucinogens & Shamanism. (Illus.). 1973. pap. 9.95x (ISBN 0-19-501649-1). Oxford U Pr.
Huxley, Aldous. Moksha: Writings on Psychedelics & the Visionary Experience (1931-1963) Horowitz, Michael & Palmer, Cynthia, eds. LC 81-21239. 300p. 1982. pap. 7.95 (ISBN 0-87477-208-7). J P Tarcher.
Kleps, Arthur J. Boo Hoo Bible: The Neo-American Church Catechism & Handbook. rev. ed. LC 73-29356. Orig. Title: Neo-American Church Catechism. (Illus.). 218p. 1971. pap. 5.00 (ISBN 0-9600388-1-7). Neo-Am Church.
Leary, Timothy & Metzner, Ralph. The Psychedelic Experience: A Manual Based on the Tibetan Book of the Dead. 1976. pap. 4.95 (ISBN 0-8065-0552-4). Citadel Pr.

HAMMARSKJOLD, DAG HJALMAR AGNE CARL, 1905-1961

Aulen, Gustaf. Dag Hammarskjold's Fortress White Book: An Analysis of Markings. LC 75-84608. pap. 40.50 (2026974). Bks Demand UMI.

Hammarskjold, Dag. Markings. (Epiphany Bks.). 1985. pap. 3.50 (ISBN 0-345-32741-1). Ballantine.

HANDICAPPED

see also Church Work with the Handicapped

Cox-Gedmark, Jan. Coping with Physical Disability. LC 79-28275. (Christian Care Bks.). 118p. 1980. pap. 7.95 (ISBN 0-664-24297-9). Westminster.

Eareckson, Joni & Estes, Steve. A Step Further. 2nd ed. (Illus.). 192p. 1980. pap. 5.95 (ISBN 0-310-23971-0, 12007P). Zondervan.

HANDICRAFT

see also Creative Activities and Seatwork; Glass Painting and Staining; Illumination of Books and Manuscripts; Mosaics; Mural Painting and Decoration

American School of Needlework Staff. The Great Christmas Craft Book. (Illus.). 144p. 1983. 19.95 (ISBN 0-8069-5498-1). Sterling.

Aulson, Nan & Aulson, Pam. Fun 'n Festive Holiday Trimmers. (Illus.). 1983. pap. 3.00 (ISBN 0-9601896-6-1). Patch as Patch.

Better Homes & Gardens Editors. Better Homes & Gardens Christmas Joys to Craft & Stitch. (Illus.). 80p. 1985. pap. 6.95 (ISBN 0-696-01432-7). BH&G.

Braga, Meg. Cosas Que Hacer para Navidad. (Editorial Mundo Hispano). (YA) 1981. Repr. of 1980 ed. 3.25 (ISBN 0-311-26607-X). Casa Bautista.

Brokering, L. Thirty Six Creative Ideas for Children in the Church School. LC 12-2958. 1982. pap. 4.95 (ISBN 0-570-03865-0). Concordia.

Everist, Burton. The Christian Family Craftbook. LC 78-62064. (Illus.). 1978. pap. 5.95 (ISBN 0-8192-1239-3). Morehouse.

Fitzpatrick, Nancy J., ed. Creative Ideas for Christmas, 1986. (Illus.). 160p. 1986. 17.95 (ISBN 0-8487-0683-8). Oxmoor Hse.

Foose, Sandra L. Scrap Saver's Christmas Stitchery. (Illus.). 160p. 1986. 19.95 (ISBN 0-8487-0646-3). Oxmoor Hse.

Frost, Marie H. Fifty-Two Primary Crafts. 48p. (Orig.). 1984. pap. 2.95 (ISBN 0-87239-726-2, 2106). Standard Pub.

Hagans, Marilyn T. All Good Gifts: Crafts for Christian Gift-Giving. LC 82-62924. 128p. (Orig.). 1983. pap. 5.95 (ISBN 0-8091-2543-9). Paulist Pr.

Hart, Joanna. Fifty-Two Preschool Crafts. 48p. (Orig.). 1984. pap. 2.95 (ISBN 0-87239-725-4, 2105). Standard Pub.

Nelson, Jane S. Christ-Centered Crafts for Children's Classes. LC 81-8711. 1981. pap. 2.50 (ISBN 0-87227-078-5). Reg Baptist.

Reese, Loretta. Fifty-Four Crafts with Easy Patterns. LC 78-62788. (Illus.). 1979. pap. 4.95 (ISBN 0-87239-175-2, 2134). Standard Pub.

Rowland, Jacqueline. Fifty-Two Middler-Junior Crafts. 48p. (Orig.). 1984. pap. 2.95 (ISBN 0-87239-727-0, 2107). Standard Pub.

Russell, Susan. Fifty-Two Teen Crafts. 48p. (Orig.). 1984. pap. 2.95 (ISBN 0-87239-728-9, 2108). Standard Pub.

Schomas, Rhonda. My Book of Gospel Treasures. (Illus.). 63p. (Orig.). 1980. pap. 3.95 (ISBN 0-87747-839-2). Deseret Bk.

Sharon, Ruth. Arts & Crafts the Year Round, 2 Vols. (Illus.). 1965. Set. 29.00x (ISBN 0-8381-0213-1). United Syn Bk.

Sibbett, Ed, Jr. Easy-to-Make Christmas & Holiday Lightcatchers: With Full-Size Template for 66 Stained Glass Projects. 64p. 1984. pap. 4.50 (ISBN 0-486-24706-6). Dover.

Sock Bunnies: Christmas & Spring Edition. Date not set. pap. 4.98 (ISBN 0-317-03192-9). Gick.

Stewart, Linda, ed. Christmas Is Coming! 1986: Holiday Projects for Children & Parents. (Illus.). 128p. 1986. 17.95 (ISBN 0-8487-0688-9). Oxmoor Hse.

Stringer, Leslea & Bowman, Lea. Crafts Handbook for Children's Church: Graded Activities for Ages 3-7. (Teaching Help Ser.). (Orig.). 1981. pap. 8.95 (ISBN 0-8010-8197-1). Baker Bk.

Stuart, Sally. All-Occasion Craft & Gift Book. (Illus.). 96p. (Orig.). 1984. pap. 5.95 (ISBN 0-87239-709-2, 2138). Standard Pub.

Thirty Five Handicraft Projects for Children. LC 12-2957. 1982. pap. 4.95 (ISBN 0-570-03864-2). Concordia.

Wright, Sandra L. Country Handcrafts Christmas Collection. 34p. 1985. pap. 5.95 (ISBN 0-89821-069-0). Reiman Assocs.

HANDICRAFT–JUVENILE LITERATURE

Beegle, Shirley, ed. Creative Craft Ideas for All Ages. (Illus., Orig.). 1966. pap. 6.95 (ISBN 0-87239-321-6, 2795). Standard Pub.

Bennett, Marian. Preschool Pattern Book. (Illus.). 48p. (Orig.). 1973. pap. 4.95 (ISBN 0-87239-339-9, 2145). Standard Pub.

Cutler, Katherine N. & Bogle, Kate C. Crafts for Christmas. (Illus.). 96p. 1975. pap. 1.95 (ISBN 0-688-46663-X). Lothrop.

Frost, Marie H. Fifty-Two Nursery Patterns. (Illus.). 48p. (Orig.). 1979. pap. 4.95 (ISBN 0-87239-341-0, 42046). Standard Pub.

Things to Make & Do for Thanksgiving. (Things to Make & Do Ser.). 1977. lib. bdg. 8.90 (ISBN 0-531-01324-3). Watts.

Vonk, Idalee W. Elementary Activity Patterns: For Year 'Round Use. (Illus.). 48p. (Orig.). 1973. pap. 4.95 (ISBN 0-87239-323-2, 2142). Standard Pub.

--Fifty-Two Elementary Patterns. (Illus.). 48p. (Orig.). 1979. pap. 4.95 (ISBN 0-87239-340-2, 3366). Standard Pub.

HANUKKAH (FEAST OF LIGHTS)

Adler, David A. A Picture Book of Hanukkah. LC 82-2942. (Illus.). 1985. pap. 5.95 (ISBN 0-8234-0574-5). Holiday.

Bloch, Charles E. The First Chanukah. LC 56-12405. (Illus.). 1957. pap. 2.25 (ISBN 0-8197-0450-4). Bloch.

Chaikin, Miriam. Light Another Candle: The Story & Meaning of Hanukkah. LC 80-28137. (Illus.). 80p. 1981. 10.50 (ISBN 0-395-31026-1, Clarion); pap. 3.95 (ISBN 0-89919-057-X). HM.

D'Addio, Janie & Bach, Othello. Monicas Hannukah House. (Illus.). 64p. 1983. 14.95 (ISBN 0-914759-01-9). Preferred Pr.

Geller, Norman. It's Not the Jewish Christmas. (Illus.). 20p. 1985. pap. 4.95 (ISBN 0-915753-09-X). N Geller Pub.

Goodman, Philip, ed. The Hanukkah Anthology. LC 75-44637. (Illus.). xxxiv, 466p. 1976. 15.95 (ISBN 0-8276-0080-1, 392). Jewish Pubns.

Greenberg, David & Bernards, Solomon S. The Living Heritage of Hanukkah. 47p. 1.50 (ISBN 0-686-74963-4). ADL.

Greene, Jacqueline D. A Classroom Hanukah. (Illus.). 32p. (Orig.). 1980. pap. 3.00 (ISBN 0-938836-01-3). Pascal Pubs.

Hirsh, Marilyn. The Hanukkah Story. LC 77-22183. (Illus.). 1977. pap. 4.95 (ISBN 0-88482-761-5, Bonim Bks). Hebrew Pub.

Kaplan, Aryeh. The Laws of Chanukah. 124p. pap. 5.45 (ISBN 0-940118-28-9). Maznaim.

Lieberman, Donald. Heroes of Hanukkah. 1980. 8.95x (ISBN 0-87068-866-9). Ktav.

Nulman, Louis. What is Chanukah? A Programmed Text. text ed. 2.25 (ISBN 0-914131-73-7, A30). Torah Umesorah.

Rockland, Mae S. The Hanukkah Book. (Illus.). 190p. 1985. pap. 9.95 (ISBN 0-8052-0792-9). Schocken.

Sanders, James. Fun-in-Learning About Chanukah. LC 76-189390. (Illus.). 1972. 3.95 (ISBN 0-8246-0135-1). Jonathan David.

Saypol, Judyth R. & Wikler, Madeline. My Very Own Chanukah Book. LC 77-23682. (Illus.). 32p. 1977. pap. 2.95 (ISBN 0-930494-03-2). Kar-Ben.

Wengrov, Charles. Hanukkah Song & Story. (Illus.). 1960. pap. 4.00 (ISBN 0-914080-29-6). Shulsinger Sales.

Wurtzel, Yehuda & Wurtzel, Sara. Lights: A Fable of Hanukahkah. LC 84-18297. (Illus.). 64p. 1985. pap. 7.95 (ISBN 0-940646-56-0). Rossel Bks.

HANUKKAH (FEAST OF LIGHTS)–JUVENILE LITERATURE

Adler, David A. Hanukkah Fun Book: Puzzles, Riddles, Magic & More. LC 76-47459. (Illus.). 1976. pap. 3.95 (ISBN 0-88482-754-2, Bonim Bks). Hebrew Pub.

--Hanukkah Game Book: Games, Riddles, Puzzles & More. (Fun-to-Do Bk). (Illus.). 1978. pap. 3.95 (ISBN 0-88482-764-X, Bonim Bks). Hebrew Pub.

--A Picture Book of Hanukkah. LC 82-2942. (Illus.). 32p. 1982. reinforced bdg. 12.95 (ISBN 0-8234-0458-7). Holiday.

Bearman, Jane. The Eight Nights: A Chanukah Counting Book. Syme, Daniel B., ed. LC 78-60781. (Illus.). 1979. pap. 4.50 (ISBN 0-8074-0025-4, 102562). UAHC.

Behrens, June. Hanukkah. LC 82-17890. (Ethnic & Traditional Holidays Ser.). (Illus.). 32p. 1983. PLB 10.60 (ISBN 0-516-02386-1); pap. 2.95 (ISBN 0-516-42386-X). Childrens.

Burns, Marilyn. The Hanukkah Book. (Illus.). 128p. 1981. 9.95 (ISBN 0-02-716140-4, Four Winds). Macmillan.

Chaikin, Miriam. Light Another Candle: The Story & Meaning of Hanukkah. LC 80-28137. (Illus.). 80p. 1981. 10.50 (ISBN 0-395-31026-1, Clarion); pap. 3.95 (ISBN 0-89919-057-X). HM.

Chiel, Kinneret. Complete Book of Hanukah. (Illus.). pap. 6.95x (ISBN 0-87068-367-5). Ktav.

Drucker, Malka. Hanukkah: Eight Nights, Eight Lights. LC 80-15852. (A Jewish Holidays Book). (Illus.). 96p. 1980. reinforced bdg. 12.95 (ISBN 0-8234-0377-7). Holiday.

Gellman, Ellie. It's Chanukah. LC 85-80782. (Illus.). 12p. 1985. bds. 4.95 (ISBN 0-930494-51-2). Kar Ben.

Greenfeld, Howard. Chanukah. LC 76-6527. 1976. 6.95 (ISBN 0-03-015566-5). H Holt & Co.

Hirsh, Marilyn. The Hanukkah Story. LC 77-22183. (Illus.). 1977. pap. 4.95 (ISBN 0-88482-761-5, Bonim Bks). Hebrew Pub.

Parish, Peggy. December Decorations: A Holiday How-to Book. LC 75-14285. (Illus.). 64p. 1975. 9.95 (ISBN 0-02-769920-X). Macmillan.

Scharfstein, Eythe & Scharfstein, Sol. Book of Chanukah. (Illus.). 1959. 5.95x (ISBN 0-87068-357-8). Ktav.

Simon, Norma. Hanukah in My House. (Festival Series of Picture Story Books). (Illus.). 1960. plastic cover 4.50 (ISBN 0-8381-0705-2). United Syn Bk.

--Hanukkah. LC 66-10065. (Holiday Ser.). (Illus.). 1966. PLB 12.89 (ISBN 0-690-36953-0, Crowell Jr Bks). HarpJ.

The Story of Chanukah for Children. 2.95 (ISBN 0-8249-8020-4). Ideals.

Stuhlman, Daniel D. My Own Hanukah Story. (Illus., Orig.). 1980. pap. 3.95 personalized version (ISBN 0-934402-07-8); decorations 1.00 (ISBN 0-934402-08-6); trade version 2.50 (ISBN 0-934402-12-4). BYLS Pr.

Vered, Ben. Why Is Hanukkah. (Illus.). 1961. pap. 2.50 (ISBN 0-914080-59-8). Shulsinger Sales.

Wengrov, Charles. The Story of Hanukkah. (Holiday Ser.). (Illus.). 1965. pap. 1.50 (ISBN 0-914080-52-0). Shulsinger Sales.

HAPPINESS

see also Joy and Sorrow

Anderson, Leith. Making Happiness Happen. 132p. 1987. pap. 5.95 (ISBN 0-89693-776-3). Victor Bks.

Ashford, Ray. The Surrender & the Singing: Happiness Through Letting Go. 168p. (Orig.). 1985. pap. 7.95 (ISBN 0-86683-964-X, AY8546, HarpR). Har-Row.

Beecher, Catherine E. Letters to the People on Health & Happiness. (The Works of Catherine E. Beecher Ser.). vi, 222p. Repr. of 1855 ed. lib. bdg. 29.00 (ISBN 0-932051-03-0, Pub by Am Repr Serv). Am Biog Serv.

Boethius. The Consolation of Philosophy. Green, Richard H., tr. LC 62-11788. 1962. pap. 5.44 scp (ISBN 0-672-60273-3, LLA86). Bobbs.

--Consolation of Philosophy. Buchanan, James J., ed. LC 57-8649. (Milestones of Thought Ser.). 7.00 (ISBN 0-8044-5149-4); pap. 3.95 (ISBN 0-8044-6057-4). Ungar.

Cooper, Irving S. Secret of Happiness. LC 75-26815. 75p. 1976. pap. 1.75 (ISBN 0-8356-0469-1, Quest). Theos Pub Hse.

DeHaan, Richard W. Como Ser Feliz. Orig. Title: How to Be Happy. (Span.). 64p. 1978. pap. 2.25. Kregel.

Dreier, Patricia, compiled by. Happiness Is a Journey. (Illus.). 1983. boxed 8.00 (ISBN 0-8378-1804-4). Gibson.

Elbin, Paul N. Making Happiness a Habit. (Festival Ser.). 192p. 1981. pap. 2.75 (ISBN 0-687-23030-6). Abingdon.

Fing, Wing F. Fuck, YES! A Guide to the Happy Acceptance of Everything. (Illus.). 270p. (Orig.). 1987. pap. 8.50 (ISBN 0-940183-21-8). Shepherd Bks.

Gompertz, Rolf. Sparks of Spirit: A Handbook for Personal Happiness. LC 83-50870. 168p. 1983. velo binding 10.00 (ISBN 0-918248-04-3). Word Doctor.

Graham, Billy. The Secret of Happiness. rev. & enl. ed. 160p. 1985. 11.95 (ISBN 0-8499-0508-7, 0508-7); pap. 9.95 (ISBN 0-8499-3034-0, 3034-0). Word Bks.

Harries, Richard. Prayer & the Pursuit of Happiness. 160p. (Orig.). 1985. pap. 6.95 (ISBN 0-8028-0089-0). Eerdmans.

Heywood, Ellis. Il Moro: Ellis Heywood's Dialogue in Memory of Thomas More. Deakins, Roger L., tr. LC 75-184107. 176p. 1972. 12.50x (ISBN 0-674-58735-9). Harvard U Pr.

How to Be Happy. 192p. (Orig.). 1985. pap. 5.95 (ISBN 1-85063-025-9, Ark Paperbks). Methuen Inc.

Kelley, Kathleen, et al. Happiness: Issues of Emotional Living in an Age of Stress for Clergy & Religious. Kane, T. A., ed. LC 82-1733. 128p. (Orig.). 1982. pap. 5.00 (ISBN 0-89571-014-5). Affirmation.

Marra, William A. Happiness & Christian Hope: A Phenomenological Analysis. 1979. 8.95 (ISBN 0-8199-0770-7). Franciscan Herald.

Morse, Lois. Two Blocks from Happiness. 176p. 1985. pap. 6.95 (ISBN 0-87239-860-9, 3005). Standard Pub.

Muller, Robert. Most of All They Taught Me Happiness. LC 78-52110. 1985. pap. 7.95 (ISBN 0-385-19914-7, Im). Doubleday.

Parrott, Leslie. The Habit of Happiness. 192p. 1987. 10.95 (ISBN 0-8499-0607-5). Word Bks.

Peale, Norman V. & Blanton, Smiley. The Art of Real Happiness. 1976. pap. 2.50 (ISBN 0-449-24062-2, Crest). Fawcett.

St. Thomas Aquinas. Treatise on Happiness. Oesterle, John A., tr. LC 83-17091. 224p. 1983. text ed. 15.95x (ISBN 0-268-01848-0, 85-18482); pap. text ed. 5.95x (ISBN 0-268-01849-9, 85-18490). U of Notre Dame Pr.

Samra, Cal. Jesus Put on a Happy Face: The Healing Power of Joy & Humor. LC 85-60257. (Illus.). 234p. (Orig.). 1985. pap. 7.95 (ISBN 0-933453-00-0). Rosejoy Pubns.

Schuller, Robert. The Be-Happy Attitudes. 1985. 12.95 (ISBN 0-8499-0363-7). Word Bks.

--The Be-Happy Attitudes. lg. print ed. 1986. 12.95 (ISBN 0-8499-3055-3). Word Bks.

Warner, Richard. Freedom, Enjoyment, & Happiness: An Essay on Moral Psychology. LC 86-19696. (Illus.). 208p. 1987. text ed. 19.95x (ISBN 0-8014-1977-8). Cornell U Pr.

Zodhiates, Spiros. The Pursuit of Happiness. 2nd ed. 665p. 1982. pap. 9.95 (ISBN 0-89957-508-0). AMG Pubs.

HARDENBERG, FRIEDRICH LEOPOLD, FREIHERR VON, 1772-1801

Hiebel, Friedrich. Novalis: German Poet, European Thinker, Christian Mystic. LC 54-62201. (North Carolina University Studies in the Germanic Languages & Literatures: No. 10). Repr. of 1953 ed. 27.00 (ISBN 0-404-50910-X). AMS Pr.

Scholz, Joachim J. Blake & Novalis. (European University Studies: Series 18, Comparative Literature, Vol. 19). 404p. 1978. 40.40 (ISBN 3-261-02576-X). P Lang Pubs.

HARE KRISHNA SECT

Birla, Shri B. Alive in Krishna: Living Memories of the Vedic Quest. (Patterns of World Spirituality Ser.). 160p. 1986. pap. 8.95 (ISBN 0-913757-65-9, Pub. by New Era Bks). Paragon Hse.

Burr, Angela. I Am Not My Body: A Study of the International Hare Krishna Sect. 352p. 1984. text ed. 35.00x (ISBN 0-7069-2296-4, Pub by Vikas India). Advent NY.

Dasa Goswami, Satsvarupa. Handbook for Krishna Consciousness. 380p. 1983. 5.95 (ISBN 0-318-03098-5). Gita Nagari.

--He Lives Forever. Dasa, Mandalesvara, ed. 80p. 1980. 2.00 (ISBN 0-318-03099-3). Gita Nagari.

Gelberg. The Hare Krishna Movement. 1985. lib. bdg. 23.00 (ISBN 0-8240-8751-8). Garland Pub.

Gelberg, Steven, ed. Hare Krishna Hare Krishna: Five Distinguished Scholars in Religion Discuss the Krishna Movement in the West. LC 82-21055. (Press Eastern Philosophy & Literature Ser.). 224p. (Orig.). 1983. pap. 7.95 (ISBN 0-394-62454-8, E845, Ever). Grove.

Judah, J. Stillson. Hare Krishna & the Counterculture. LC 74-8209. (Contemporary Religious Movements Ser.). pap. 80.00 (ISBN 0-317-07867-4, 2007717). Bks Demand UMI.

Kenny, J. Frank & Poling, Tommy H. The Hare Krishna Character Type: A Study of the Sensate Personality. (Studies in Religion & Society: No. 15). 202p. 1986. 49.95 (ISBN 0-88946-859-1). E Mellen.

Kirtanananda Bhaktipada. Christ & Krishna: The Path of Pure Devotion. LC 85-73024. 182p. 1986. 10.95 (ISBN 0-317-43353-9); pap. 6.95 (ISBN 0-317-43354-7). Bhaktipada Bks.

Knott, Kim. My Sweet Lord: The Hare Krishna Movement. 112p. 1986. pap. 11.95. Newcastle Pub.

--My Sweet Lord: The Hare Krishna Movement. LC 86-18810. 176p. 1986. lib. bdg. 19.95x (ISBN 0-8095-7023-8). Borgo Pr.

Shinn, Larry D. The Dark Lord: Cult Images & the Hare Krishnas in America. 204p. (Orig.). 1987. pap. 16.95 (ISBN 0-664-24170-0). Westminster.

Venkatesananda, Swami. Christ Krishna & You. 168p. (Orig.). 1983. write for info. Chiltern Yoga.

Yanoff, Morris. Where Is Joey? Lost among the Hare Krishnas. LC 81-11280. x, 260p. 1982. 15.95 (ISBN 0-8040-0414-5, Pub by Swallow). Ohio U Pr.

HARMONY (COSMOLOGY)

see Harmony of the Spheres

HARMONY OF THE SPHERES

Murchie, Guy. Music of the Spheres: The Material Universe from Atom to Quasar, Simply Explained, 2 vols. (Illus.). 28.00 set (ISBN 0-8446-0815-7). Peter Smith.

HARTSHORNE, CHARLES, 1897-

Davaney, Sheila G. Divine Power: A Study of Karl Barth & Charles Hartshorne. LC 85-45502. (Harvard Dissertions in Religion Ser.). 224p. 1986. pap. 16.95 (ISBN 0-8006-7072-8, 1-7072). Fortress.

Goodwin, George L. The Ontological Argument of Charles Hartshorne. LC 78-2821. 1978. pap. 9.95 (ISBN 0-89130-228-X, 01-01-20). Scholars Pr GA.

Gunton, Colin E. Becoming & Being: The Doctrine of God in Charles Hartshorne & Karl Barth. (Theological Monographs). 1978. text ed. 39.95x (ISBN 0-19-826713-4). Oxford U Pr.

Moskop, John C. Divine Omniscience & Human Freedom: Thomas Aquinas & Charles Hartshorne. LC 84-1172. xviii, 105p. 1984. 14.95 (ISBN 0-86554-123-X, MUP/H102). Mercer Univ Pr.

Viney, Donald W. Charles Hartshorne & the Existence of God. (Philosophy Ser.). 192p. 1984. 44.50 (ISBN 0-87395-907-8); pap. 14.95 (ISBN 0-87395-908-6). State U NY Pr.

Whitney, Barry L. Evil & the Process God: The Problem of Evil in Charles Hartshorne's Thought. LC 84-25505. (Toronto Studies in Theology: Vol. 19). 247p. 1985. 49.95x (ISBN 0-88946-760-9). E Mellen.

HASIDISM

Aron, Milton. Ideas & Ideals of the Hassidim. 1969. 7.95 (ISBN 0-8065-0319-X). Citadel Pr.

--Ideas & Ideals of the Hassidim. 1980. pap. 5.95 (ISBN 0-8065-0722-5). Citadel Pr.

Buber, Martin. For the Sake of Heaven. Lewisohn, Ludwig, tr. LC 77-97311. Repr. of 1953 ed. lib. bdg. 60.50x (ISBN 0-8371-2592-8, BUSH). Greenwood.

--For the Sake of Heaven: A Chronicle. Lewisohn, Ludwig, tr. LC 58-8531. (Temple Bks.). 1969. pap. 9.95 (ISBN 0-689-70026-1, T2). Atheneum.

--Hasidism & Modern Man. LC 58-10225. 256p. 1972. pap. 5.95 (ISBN 0-8180-1326-5). Horizon.

--The Legend of the Baal-Shem. LC 76-86849. 1969. pap. 7.95 (ISBN 0-8052-0233-1). Schocken.

--Mamre, Essays in Religion. Hort, Greta, tr. LC 72-97271. Repr. of 1946 ed. lib. bdg. 15.00x (ISBN 0-8371-2591-X, BUMA). Greenwood.

--The Origin & Meaning of Hasidism. LC 60-8161. 256p. 1972. pap. 5.95 (ISBN 0-8180-1315-X). Horizon.

--The Prophetic Faith. 15.75 (ISBN 0-8446-6206-2). Peter Smith.

--Tales of the Hasidim, 2 vols. Incl. The Early Masters. pap. 6.95 (ISBN 0-8052-0001-0); The Later Masters. pap. 5.95 (ISBN 0-8052-0002-9). LC 47-2952. 1961. pap. Schocken.

--Ten Rungs: Hasidic Sayings. LC 62-13135. 1962. pap. 3.95 (ISBN 0-8052-0018-5). Schocken.

--Way of Man. 1966. pap. 2.95 (ISBN 0-87574-106-1, 106). Citadel Pr.

Buchler, Adolf. Types of Jewish-Palestinian Piety from 70 BCE to 70 CE. 264p. Repr. of 1922 ed. text ed. 62.10x (ISBN 0-576-80135-6, Pub by Gregg Intl Pubs England). Gregg Intl.

Carlebach, Shlomo. Holy Beggar Teachings: Jewish Hasidic Stories, 1975-1977. Maimes, Steven L. & Rappaport, Elana, eds. 1979. pap. 4.95 (ISBN 0-917246-06-3). Maimes.

Cooper, Eli L. Am Seguliah: A Treasured People. LC 82-91010. 148p. 1984. 10.00 (ISBN 0-533-05673-X). Vantage.

Dan, Joseph, ed. The Teachings of Hasidism. (Orig.). 1983. pap. text ed. 9.95x (ISBN 0-87441-346-X). Behrman.

Dresner, Samuel H. Portraits of a Hasidic Master: Levi Yitzhak of Berditchev. 1986. pap. 8.95 (ISBN 0-933503-59-8). Shapolsky Pubs.

Green, Arthur. Tormented Master: A Life of Rabbi Nahman of Bratslav. LC 78-16674. (Judaic Studies: No. 9). (Illus.). 400p. 1979. 30.00 (ISBN 0-8173-6907-4). U of Ala Pr.

Heifetz, Harold, ed. Zen & Hasidism. LC 78-9073. 1978. 10.95 (ISBN 0-8356-0514-0). Theos Pub Hse.

Heschel, Abraham J. The Circle of Baal Shem Tov: Studies in Hasidism. Dresner, Samuel H., ed. 280p. 1985. 24.95 (ISBN 0-226-32960-7). U of Chicago Pr.

Horodezky, Samuel A. Religiose Stromungen Judentum: Mit besondered Berucksichtigung des Chassidismus. Katz, Steven, ed. LC 79-7137. (Jewish Philosophy, Mysticism & History of Ideas Ser.). 1980. Repr. of 1920 ed. lib. bdg. 23.00x (ISBN 0-405-12263-2). Ayer Co Pubs.

Jacobs, Louis. Hasidic Prayer. (Littman Library of Jewish Civilization). 1972. 17.95x (ISBN 0-19-710024-4). Oxford U Pr.

Kantor, Mattis. Chassidic Insights: A Guide for the Entangled. pap. 6.95x (ISBN 0-87068-679-8). Ktav.

Kaplan, Aryeh. The Light Beyond: Adventure in Hassidic Thought. 384p. 1981. 15.95 (ISBN 0-940118-33-5). Maznaim.

Katz, Steven, ed. Studies by Samuel Horodezky: An Original Anthology. LC 79-51391. (Jewish Philosophy, Mysticism & History of Ideas Ser.). 1980. lib. bdg. 17.00x (ISBN 0-405-12233-0). Ayer Co Pubs.

Langer, Jiri. Nine Gates to the Chassidic Mysteries. new ed. Rossel, Seymour, ed. Jolly, Stephen, tr. from Czech, Fr. LC 76-5859. (Jewish Legacy Ser.). 266p. 1976. pap. text ed. 4.95x (ISBN 0-87441-241-2). Behrman.

Mahler, Raphael. Hasidism & the Jewish Enlightenment: Their Confrontation in Galicia & Poland in the First Half of the Nineteenth Century. Orenstein, Eugene, et al, trs. from Yiddish & Hebrew. 432p. 1985. 29.95 (ISBN 0-8276-0233-2). Jewish Pubns.

Mintz, Jerome R. Legends of the Hasidim: An Introduction to Hasidic Culture & Oral Tradition in the New World. LC 68-16707. 504p. 1974. pap. 14.95 (ISBN 0-226-53103-1, P612, Phoen). U of Chicago Pr.

Newman, Louis I., ed. & tr. from Hebrew, Yiddish & Ger. The Hasidic Anthology: Tales & Teachings of the Hasidim. LC 63-11041. 576p. 1987. pap. 12.95 (ISBN 0-8052-0836-4). Schocken.

Rabinowicz, Harry. Hasidism & the State of Israel. (Littman Library of Jewish Civilization). (Illus.). 1982. 24.95x (ISBN 0-19-710049-X). Oxford U Pr.

Rajneesh, Bhagwan Shree. The True Sage. Chaitanya, Swami Christ, ed. LC 83-183323. (Hasids Ser.). (Illus.). 410p. (Orig.). 1976. 16.50 (ISBN 0-88050-159-6). Chidvilas Found.

Rotenberg, Mordechai. Dialogue with Deviance: The Hasidic Ethic & the Theory of Social Contraction. LC 81-13309. 224p. 1983. text ed. 27.50 (ISBN 0-89727-031-2). ISHI PA.

Rubinstein, Aryeh, ed. Hasidism. 128p. pap. 4.50 (ISBN 0-686-95129-8). ADL.

Safran, Bezalel, ed. Hasidism: Continuity or Innovation? (Harvard Judaic Texts & Studies: No. V). 60p. 1985. text ed. 5.00x (ISBN 0-674-38120-3). Harvard U Ctr Jewish.

Schachter, Zalman M. & Hoffman, Edward. Sparks of Light: Counseling in the Hasidic Tradition. LC 83-42804. 208p. (Orig.). 1983. pap. 9.95 (ISBN 0-87773-240-X). Shambhala Pubns.

Sharot, Stephen. Messianism, Mysticism, & Magic: A Sociological Analysis of Jewish Religious Movements. LC 81-11688. (Studies in Religion). ix, 306p. 1987. pap. 12.95x (ISBN 0-8078-4170-6). U of NC Pr.

Spector, Sheila A. Jewish Mysticism: An Annotated Bibliography on the Kabbalah in English. LC 83-48224. (Reference Library of Social Science Ser.). 1984. lib. bdg. 45.00 (ISBN 0-8240-9042-X). Garland Pub.

Twersky, Abraham J. Generation to Generation: Recollections of a Chassidic Legacy. 256p. 1985. 14.95 (ISBN 0-933711-17-4). Traditional Pr.

Wiesel, Elie. Four Hasidic Masters & Their Struggle Against Melancholy. LC 78-1419. (Ward-Phillips Lectures in English Language & Literature Ser: No. 9). (Illus.). 1978. 9.95 (ISBN 0-268-00944-9). U of Notre Dame Pr.

--Four Hasidic Masters & Their Struggle Against Melancholy. LC 78-1419. (Ward-Phillips Lectures in English Language & Literature: No. 9). (Illus.). 1979. pap. text ed. 4.95x (ISBN 0-268-00947-3). U of Notre Dame Pr.

HASMONAEANS

see Maccabees

HATHA YOGA

see Yoga, Hatha

HAUGE, HANS NIELSEN, 1771-1824

Shaw, Joseph M. Pulpit under the Sky: A Life of Hans Nielson Hauge. LC 78-12391. 1979. Repr. of 1955 ed. lib. bdg. 24.75x (ISBN 0-313-21123-X, SHPU). Greenwood.

HAWAII–RELIGION

Beckley, Timothy G. & Carta, Maria. Kahuna: Authentic Chants, Prayers & Rituals of the Legendary Hawaiians. (Illus.). 200p. Date not set. 17.95x (ISBN 0-938294-52-0); pap. 9.95x (ISBN 0-938294-53-9). Global Comm.

Buck, Peter & Hiroa, Te Rangi. Arts & Crafts of Hawaii: Religion. (Special Publication Ser.: No. 45 (11)). (Illus.). 77p. 1957. pap. 3.00 (ISBN 0-910240-44-2). Bishop Mus.

Gutmanis, June. Na Pule Kahiko: Ancient Hawaiian Prayers. LC 83-80256. (Illus.). 136p. 1983. 17.50 (ISBN 0-9607938-6-0); deluxe ed. 100.00 (ISBN 0-9607938-7-9). Editions Ltd.

Kepelino. Kepelino's Traditions of Hawaii. Beckwith, Martha W., ed. (BMB). Repr. of 1932 ed. 25.00 (ISBN 0-527-02201-2). Kraus Repr.

Melville, Leinani. Children of the Rainbow: The Religions, Legends & Gods of Pre-Christian Hawaii. LC 69-17715. (Illus.). 1969. pap. 5.95 (ISBN 0-8356-0002-5, Quest). Theos Pub Hse.

Nau, Erika S. Self-Awareness Through Huna-Hawaii's Ancient Wisdom. Grunwald, Stefan, ed. LC 80-27842. (Orig.). 1981. pap. 5.95 (ISBN 0-89865-099-2, Unilaw). Donning Co.

Phaigh, Bethal. Gestalt & the Wisdom of the Kahunas. LC 82-50928. 112p. 1983. pap. 5.95 (ISBN 0-87516-498-6). De Vorss.

Rodman, Julius S. The Kahuna Sorcerers of Hawaii, Past & Present: With a Glossary of Ancient Religious Terms & the Books of the Hawaiian Royal Dead. (Illus.). 1979. 20.00 (ISBN 0-682-49196-9, Banner). Exposition Pr FL.

Spurrier, Joseph H. Great Are the Promises unto the Isle of the Sea: The Church of Jesus Christ of Latter-Day Saints in the Hawaiian Islands. (Orig.). 1978. pap. 2.95 (ISBN 0-89036-114-2). Hawkes Pub Inc.

HEALERS

Caleron, Eduardo, et al. Eduardo el Curandero: The Words of a Peruvian Healer. (Illus.). 200p. 1982. 20.00 (ISBN 0-913028-94-0); pap. 7.95 (ISBN 0-913028-95-9). North Atlantic.

De Rosny, Eric. Healers in the Night. Barr, Robert R., tr. from Fr. LC 85-5659. Tr. of Les Yeaux de Ma Chevre sur les Pas des Maitres de la Nuit en Pays Douala. 304p. (Orig.). 1985. pap. 13.95 (ISBN 0-88344-199-3). Orbis Bks.

Firas, Shihab. Healer, Ash-Shafuja, an Ismaili Treatise. Makarem, Sami N., ed. 1966. pap. 15.95x (ISBN 0-8156-6026-X, Am U Beirut). Syracuse U Pr.

Phillips, Vera & Robertson, Edwin. J. B. Phillips: The Wounded Healer. 120p. (Orig.). 1985. pap. 5.95 (ISBN 0-8028-0073-4). Eerdmans.

Ramsey, Russell. A Lady, A Healer. Graves, Helen, ed. LC 85-40891. 213p. (Orig.). 1986. pap. 3.95 (ISBN 1-55523-006-7). Winston-Derek.

Ross, A. C. Arnica: The Amazing Healer. 96p. (Orig.). 1986. pap. 2.50 (ISBN 0-7225-0374-1, Dist. by Inner Traditions International). Thorsons Pubs.

HEALING (IN RELIGION, FOLK-LORE, ETC.)

Adams, Walter E. You Can Be Absolutely Irrefutably Supernaturally Healed by God Today. 100p. (Orig.). 1987. pap. 4.95 (ISBN 0-937408-39-5). GMI Pubns Inc.

Answers to the Difficult Questions Concerning Healing. (Divine Healing & Health Ser.). 1.25 (ISBN 0-89985-025-1). Christ Nations.

Backmen, Richard J. & Nerheim, Steven J. Toward a Healing Ministry: Exploring & Implementing a Congregational Ministry. 72p. (Orig.). 1985. pap. 5.95 (ISBN 0-8066-2176-1, 12-2022). Augsburg.

Bayley, Robert G. The Healing Ministry of the Local Church. 32p. 1983. 1.95 (ISBN 0-934421-03-X). Presby Renewal Pubns.

Bek, Lilla & Pullar, Philippa. The Seven Levels of Healing. 160p. 1987. pap. 11.95 (ISBN 0-7126-9473-0, Pub. by Century Hutchinson). David & Charles.

Brooks, Nona. In the Light of Healing: Sermons by Nona L. Brooks. Zarlengo, Patricia, compiled by. (Illus.). 75p. (Orig.). 1986. pap. write for info. First Divine Sci Ch Denver.

Burns, Echo B. Hands that Heal. (Orig.). 1986. pap. 7.95 (ISBN 0-917086-76-7). A C S Pubns Inc.

Cassell, Eric J. The Healer's Art. 240p. 1985. pap. 7.95 (ISBN 0-262-53062-7). MIT Pr.

Catholic Health Association Staff. The Ministry of Healing: Readings in the Catholic Health Care Ministry. LC 81-12201. 120p. 1981. pap. 7.50 (ISBN 0-686-85771-2). Cath Health.

Chaitow, Boris R. My Healing Secrets. 128p. 1980. 14.95 (ISBN 0-8464-1066-4). Beekman Pubs.

Cranor, Phoebe. Five Loaves & Two Fishes: New Life Through Inner Healing. 1987. pap. 4.95. Paulist Pr.

Disciples of Donato the Christ. Healing: A Thought Away, Vol. 2. 438p. 1981. pap. 10.00 (ISBN 0-935146-61-X). Morningland.

Disciples of the Master Donato the Christ. Healing: As It Is, Vol. 4. 418p. (Orig.). pap. 10.00 (ISBN 0-935146-65-2). Morningland.

Durodola, James I. Scientific Insights into Yoruba Traditional Medicine. (Traditional Healing Ser.). 1985. 27.50 (ISBN 0-686-85813-1). Conch Mag.

East, Reginald. Heal the Sick. LC 77-80678. 160p. (Orig.). 1977. pap. 2.95 (ISBN 0-87123-232-4, 200232). Bethany Hse.

Eddy, Mary B. Science & Health with Key to the Scriptures. (Pol.). 25.00 (ISBN 0-87952-200-3). First Church.

--Science & Health with Key to the Scriptures. pap. 10.50 Spanish ed. (ISBN 0-87952-225-9); pap. 10.50 German ed. (ISBN 0-87952-150-3); pap. 10.50 French ed. (ISBN 0-87952-116-3). First Church.

Ellens, J. Harold. God's Grace & Human Health. 1982. pap. 8.75 (ISBN 0-687-15326-3). Abingdon.

Farnsworth, Kenneth C. Journey to Healing. Lambert, Herbert, ed. LC 85-3838. (Orig.). 1985. pap. 8.95 (ISBN 0-8272-1706-4). CBP.

Finkelstein, Adrian. Your Past Lives & the Healing Process. 233p. (Orig.). 1985. pap. 9.95x. A Finkelstein.

Fischer, Bernhard, ed. Healing Education Based on Anthroposophy's Image of Man: Living, Learning, Working with Children & Adults in Need of Special Soul Care. Mier, C. A. & Mier, G. F., trs. from Ger. (Illus.). 227p. 1974. pap. 11.00 (ISBN 3-772506-39-9). Anthroposophic.

Fishbein, Morris. Fads & Quackery in Healing. LC 75-23708. Repr. of 1932 ed. 45.00 (ISBN 0-404-13260-X). AMS Pr.

Geiger, Lura J. Healing: Drawing on God's Strength. (Orig.). 1987. pap. 34.50; cassette incl. LuraMedia.

Gordon, S. D. The Healing Christ. rev. ed. 160p. (Orig.). 1985. pap. 3.95 (ISBN 0-89283-271-1, Pub. by Vine Books). Servant.

Grassi, Joseph A. Healing the Heart: The Power of Biblical Heart Imagery. (Orig.). 1987. 7.95 (ISBN 0-8091-2862-4). Paulist Pr.

Hagin, Kenneth E. Healing Belongs to Us. 1969. pap. 1.00 (ISBN 0-89276-016-8). Hagin Ministries.

--How to Keep Your Healing. 1980. pap. 0.50 mini bk (ISBN 0-89276-059-1). Hagin Ministries.

--The Key to Scriptural Healing. 2nd ed. 1983. pap. 1.00 (ISBN 0-89276-008-7). Hagin Ministries.

Hagin, Kenneth, Jr. Healing: A Forever-Settled Subject. 1981. pap. 0.50 mini bk. (ISBN 0-89276-707-3). Hagin Ministries.

Hall, Manly P. Healing: Divine Art. 10.00 (ISBN 0-89314-510-6); pap. 6.95 (ISBN 0-89314-390-1). Philos Res.

Hall, Marion P. The Healing Coin. 86p. 1984. pap. 5.50 (ISBN 0-87516-542-7). De Vorss.

Hati, Aten. Astro-Change. 53p. 1981. pap. 5.00 (ISBN 0-935146-64-4). Morningland.

Hay, Louise L. Heal Your Body. rev. ed. 48p. 1984. pap. 3.00 (ISBN 0-937611-00-X). Hay House.

--I Love My Body. 80p. 1985. pap. 5.00 (ISBN 0-937611-02-6). Hay House.

--You Can Heal Your Life. 224p. (Orig.). 1984. lib. bdg. 10.00 (ISBN 0-317-52419-4); pap. 10.00 (ISBN 0-937611-01-8). Hay House.

Hunt, Roland. The Seven Keys to Color Healing: Successful Treatment Through Color. LC 81-47849. (Library of Spiritual Wisdom). 128p. 1982. pap. 7.95 (ISBN 0-06-064080-4, CN 4028, HarpR). Har-Row.

Israel, Martin. Healing As Sacrament: The Santification of the World. LC 84-72482. 116p. 1985. pap. 6.00 (ISBN 0-936384-23-9). Cowley Pubns.

Lawrence, Roy. Christian Healing Rediscovered. LC 80-7470. 128p. (Orig.). 1980. pap. 3.95 (ISBN 0-87784-621-9). Inter-Varsity.

Levine, Stephen. Just This Much: Healing Into Life & Death. 288p. 1987. 16.95 (ISBN 0-385-23371-X, Anch); pap. 8.95 (ISBN 0-385-23372-8, Anch). Doubleday.

Lindsay, Gordon. How You Can Be Healed. (Divine Healing & Health Ser.). 1.25 (ISBN 0-89985-026-X). Christ Nations.

Lovett, C. S. Jesus Wants You Well. 1973. pap. 6.45 (ISBN 0-938148-29-X). Personal Christianity.

McCrossan, T. J. Bodily Healing & the Atonement. 1982. pap. 3.50 (ISBN 0-89276-505-4). Hagin Ministries.

Matzat, Don. Inner Healing: Deliverance or Deception? 224p. (Orig.). 1987. pap. 6.95 (ISBN 0-89081-584-4). Harvest Hse.

Mayes, Charles W. A Look at the Modern Healing Movement. 1979. pap. write for info. (ISBN 0-88469-113-6). BMH Bks.

Mengle, Kathy. Tools for Healing: Working Toward Harmony & Balance. LC 84-72359. (Illus.). 172p. (Orig.). 1985. pap. 9.95 (ISBN 0-87516-548-6). De Vorss.

Morningland Publications, Inc., ed. Healing: As It Is, 2 vols. (Illus.). 320p. (Orig.). 1981. Set. pap. 10.00 (ISBN 0-935146-59-8). Morningland.

Muramoto, Naboru. Healing Ourselves. Abehsera, Michael, compiled by. (Illus.). 150p. 1974. pap. 9.95 (ISBN 0-380-00900-5, 60168-0). Avon.

Neal, Emily G. Healing Ministry. 176p. 1985. pap. 7.95 (ISBN 0-8245-0688-X). Crossroad NY.

Owens, Bill. Health & Healing: God's Way. (Illus.). 124p. (Orig.). Date not set. pap. 5.00 (ISBN 0-936801-01-8). Christ Serv Ctrs.

Phillips, Vera & Robertson, Edwin. J. B. Phillips: The Wounded Healer. 120p. (Orig.). 1985. pap. 5.95 (ISBN 0-8028-0073-4). Eerdmans.

Popoff, Peter. Seven Delivery Systems for God's Healing Power. Tanner, Don, ed. LC 81-69730. (Illus.). 70p. 1981. pap. 1.50 (ISBN 0-938544-07-1). Faith Messenger.

Range, Cornelius. Heal Me or Kill Me! LC 85-71350. 1985. pap. 5.95 (ISBN 0-88270-592-X). Bridge Pub.

Ross, A. C. Arnica: The Amazing Healer. 96p. (Orig.). 1986. pap. 2.50 (ISBN 0-7225-0374-1, Dist. by Inner Traditions International). Thorsons Pubs.

Sanford, Agness. The Healing Gifts of the Spirit. LC 83-48998. 240p. 1984. pap. 6.95 (ISBN 0-06-067052-5, RD 519, HarpR). Har-Row.

Simpson, A. B. The Gospel of Healing. rev. ed. LC 86-70736. 180p. 1986. pap. 5.45 (ISBN 0-87509-376-0). Chr Pubns.

Sterner, Eugene. Healing & Wholeness. (Doctrinal Material of the Church of God Ser.: No. 2). 1978. pap. text ed. 3.95 (ISBN 0-87162-201-7, D4285). Warner Pr.

Urquhart, Colin. Receive Your Healing. 312p. 1987. pap. 10.95 (ISBN 0-8245-0807-6). Crossroad NY.

Wilson, Jim. Healing Through the Power of Christ. 64p. 1969. pap. 2.50 (ISBN 0-227-67478-2). Attic Pr.

Wise, Robert L. Healing of the Past. 40p. 1984. 2.00 (ISBN 0-318-04134-0). Presby Renewal Pubns.

Wood, Betty. The Healing Power of Color: How to Use Color to Improve Your Mental, Physical & Spiritual Well-Being. 112p. 1985. pap. 9.95 (ISBN 0-89281-110-2). Inner Tradit.

Yogi Ramacharaka. Practical Water Cure. leatherette 3.00 (ISBN 0-911662-12-X). Yoga.

Zysk, Kenneth G. Religious Healing in the Veda. LC 84-45899. (Transaction Ser.: Vol. 75 Pt. 7). 300p. 1986. 30.00 (ISBN 0-87169-757-2). Am Philos.

HEALING, MENTAL

see Mental Healing

HEALING IN THE BIBLE

The Biblical Pattern for Divine Healing. 1979. pap. 1.00 (ISBN 0-88469-108-X). BMH Bks.

Freemesser, George F. Learning to Live from Within: A Glimpse of Jesus As Healer. 1985. 8.95 (ISBN 0-87193-242-3). Dimension Bks.

Gordon, S. D. The Healing Christ. rev. ed. 160p. (Orig.). 1985. pap. 3.95 (ISBN 0-89283-271-1, Pub. by Vine Books). Servant.

Mayhue, Richard. Divine Healing Today. 1983. pap. 6.96 (ISBN 0-88469-154-3). BMH Bks.

Simpson, A. B. The Gospel of Healing. rev. ed. LC 86-70736. 180p. 1986. pap. 5.45 (ISBN 0-87509-376-0). Chr Pubns.

HEALTH THOUGHTS

see Mental Healing

HEALY, JAMES AUGUSTINE, BISHOP, 1830-1900

Foley, Albert S. Bishop Healy: Beloved Outcaste. LC 79-94130. (American Negro: His History & Literature, Ser. No. 3). 1970. Repr. of 1954 ed. 17.00 (ISBN 0-405-01925-4). Ayer Co Pubs.

HEARD, GERALD, 1889-

Savage, D. S. Mysticism & Aldous Huxley. LC 77-23247. 1947. lib. bdg. 12.50 (ISBN 0-8414-7805-8). Folcroft.

HEATHENISM

see Paganism

HEAVEN

see also Angels; Beatific Vision; Future Life; Paradise

Arendzen, J. P. Purgatory & Heaven. (Canterbury Ser.). 1972. pap. 2.00 (ISBN 0-89555-045-8). TAN Bks Pubs.

Baker, Don. Heaven: A Glimpse of Your Future Home. expanded ed. (Orig.). 1986. pap. 3.95 (ISBN 0-88070-168-4). Multnomah.

Bayly, Joseph. Heaven. LC 77-71035. (Illus.). 1977. pap. 2.95 (ISBN 0-89191-070-0). Cook.

Beiderwieden, George. Heaven. 1957. 1.50 (ISBN 0-570-03680-1, 74-1008). Concordia.

Boehme, Jacob. Of Heaven & Hell: A Dialogue Between Junius, a Scholar & Theophorus, His Master. 1986. pap. 3.95 (ISBN 0-916411-53-2). Sure Fire.

Boudreau, J. The Happiness of Heaven. LC 83-51548. 258p. 1984. pap. 6.00 (ISBN 0-89555-232-9). TAN Bks Pubs.

Bounds, E. M. Catching a Glimpse of Heaven. 150p. 1985. pap. text ed. 3.50 (ISBN 0-88368-167-6). Whitaker Hse.

--Heaven: A Place, a City, a Home. (Direction Bks). 152p. 1975. pap. 3.50 (ISBN 0-8010-0648-1). Baker Bk.

Brown, Walton J. Home at Last. (Discovery Ser.). 96p. pap. 5.95 (ISBN 0-317-01321-1). Review & Herald.

Bullinger, Ethelbert W. Witness of the Stars. LC 68-16762. 212p. 1984. pap. 10.95 (ISBN 0-8254-2245-0). Kregel.

Bunyan, John. The Strait Gate. pap. 2.25 (ISBN 0-685-88394-9). Reiner.

Carretto, Carlo. Made in Heaven. 4.95 (ISBN 0-87193-135-4). Dimension Bks.

Church, F. Forester. Entertaining Angels: A Guide to Heaven or Atheists & True Believers. 1987. 13.95. Har-Row.

Daughters of St. Paul. Heaven. 1977. 3.50 (ISBN 0-8198-0419-3); pap. 2.50 (ISBN 0-8198-0420-7). Dghtrs St Paul.

Eaton, Dave. How Do We Get to Heaven? (Questions, Questions Ser.). 32p. 1986. 2.95 (ISBN 0-89081-549-6). Harvest Hse.

A Guide for the Still Perplexed: Heaven, Bk. I. 65p. (Orig.). 1986. pap. 4.95 (ISBN 0-940733-00-5). Dimona Pr.

Hutson, Joan. Heaven & Earth. (Little Learner Ser.). 24p. 1985. 5.95 (ISBN 0-570-08952-2, 56-1544). Concordia.

Keith, M. R. How I Found Out About Heaven. 1970. 4.95 (ISBN 0-910122-23-7). Amherst Pr.

--So You're Going to Heaven. 1965. 4.95 (ISBN 0-910122-22-9). Amherst Pr.

Kohler, Kaufmann. Heaven & Hell in Comparative Religion. 1923. 25.00 (ISBN 0-8414-5601-1). Folcroft.

Kreeft, Peter J. Everything You Ever Wanted to Know About Heaven-But Never Dreamed of Asking. LC 82-47747. 160p. (Orig.). 1982. pap. 7.95 (ISBN 0-06-064777-9, RD/413, HarpR). Har-Row.

--Heaven: The Heart's Deepest Longing. LC 80-7747. 160p. 1980. 10.00 (ISBN 0-06-064776-0, HarpR). Har-Row.

Lairdon, Roberts, ed. I Saw Heaven. 31p. 1983. pap. 2.00 (ISBN 0-915693-00-3). Christian Pub.

Lauterbach, William A. Heaven Bound. LC 74-34277. 128p. 1974. pap. 5.50 (ISBN 0-570-03028-5, 6-1156). Concordia.

Lightner, Robert P. Heaven for Those Who Can't Believe. LC 76-50303. 1977. pap. 1.95 (ISBN 0-87227-035-1). Reg Baptist.

Lindsay, Gordon. Within the Gates. (Sorcery & Spirit World Ser.). 1.75 (ISBN 0-89985-095-2). Christ Nations.

McKnight, Mid. Vestibules of Heaven. 1982. pap. 3.95 (ISBN 0-89225-219-7). Gospel Advocate.

Mayer, Fred S. Why Two Worlds: Relation of Physical to Spiritual Realities. LC 78-134425. Repr. of 1934 ed. 21.00 (ISBN 0-404-08465-6). AMS Pr.

Mullen, E. Theodore, Jr. The Assembly of the Gods: The Divine Council in Canaanite & Early Hebrew Literature. LC 80-10128. (Harvard Semitic Museum Monographs: No. 24). 1980. 10.50x (ISBN 0-89130-380-4, 04 00 24). Scholars Pr GA.

Nee, Watchman. The King & the Kingdom of Heaven. Kaung, Stephen, tr. from Chinese. 1978. pap. 5.00 (ISBN 0-935008-24-1). Christian Fellow Pubs.

Nelson, James E. What We Know about Heaven. 80p. 1987. 2.95, paper (ISBN 0-8423-7921-5). Tyndale.

Patch, Howard R. Other World, According to Descriptions in Medieval Literature. LC 77-96164. 1970. Repr. of 1950 ed. lib. bdg. 27.50x (ISBN 0-374-96289-8, Octagon). Hippocrene Bks.

Quadrupani, R. P. Light & Peace. LC 79-67860. 193p. 1980. pap. 3.50 (ISBN 0-89555-133-0). TAN Bks Pubs.

Sayers, Stanley E. The Nature of Things to Come. 1972. 7.95 (ISBN 0-88027-013-6). Firm Foun Pub.

Springer, Rebecca. Within Heaven's Gates. 128p. 1984. pap. 3.50 (ISBN 0-88368-125-0). Whitaker Hse.

Swedenborg, Emanuel. Heaven & Hell. LC 77-93044. cancelled (ISBN 0-87785-167-0); student ed. 12.00 (ISBN 0-87785-066-6); pap. 5.95 (ISBN 0-87785-153-0). Swedenborg.

Tilotta, Becky. Do You Want to Go to Heaven? 1967. 0.60 (ISBN 0-88027-106-X). Firm Foun Pub.

Toon, Peter. Heaven & Hell: A Biblical & Theological Overview. 160p. 1986. pap. 8.95 (ISBN 0-8407-5967-3). Nelson.

Wheeler, Penny E. More Than Harps of Gold. (Outreach Ser.). 1981. pap. 1.25 (ISBN 0-8163-0424-6). Pacific Pr Pub Assn.

Worcester. Heaven. 1967. pap. 1.25 (ISBN 0-317-03716-1). College Pr Pub.

Wormhoudt, Arthur. Diwan Hassan ibn Thabit. (Arab Translation Ser.: No. 69). 180p. (Orig.). pap. 6.50x (ISBN 0-916358-21-6). Wormhoudt.

HEBER, REGINALD, 1783-1826

Laird, M. A., ed. Bishop Heber in Northern India: Selections from Heber's Journal. LC 70-123673. (European Understanding of India Ser). (Illus.). 1971. 39.50 (ISBN 0-521-07873-3). Cambridge U Pr.

HEBREW ART

see Art, Jewish

HEBREW CALENDAR

see Calendar, Jewish

HEBREW CHRONOLOGY

see Chronology, Jewish

HEBREW IMPRINTS

Harvard University Library. Catalogue of Hebrew Books, 6 Vols. LC 68-22146. (Yiddish & Heb). 1968. Set. 225.00x (ISBN 0-674-10150-2). Harvard U Pr.

HEBREW LANGUAGE

Beall, Todd & Banks, William. Old Testament Parsing Guide: Genesis - Esther. (Orig.). 1986. 25.95 (ISBN 0-8024-6315-0). Moody.

Bergman, Bella. Hebrew Level Two. Band, Ora, ed. (Illus.). 243p. 1983. pap. text ed. 7.95x (ISBN 0-87441-360-5). Behrman.

Blumberg, Harry & Lewittes, Mordecai. Modern Hebrew: Ivrit Hayah, Vol. 1. 3rd ed. 449p. pap. 8.95x (ISBN 0-88482-718-6). Hebrew Pub.

Chomsky, Noam. Morphophonemics of Modern Hebrew. Hankamer, Jorge, ed. LC 78-66579. (Outstanding Dissertations in Linguistics Ser.). 1979. 15.00 (ISBN 0-8240-9688-6). Garland Pub.

Davidson, Benjamin. Analytical Hebrew & Chaldee Lexicon. 784p. Date not set. 24.95 (ISBN 0-913573-03-5). Hendrickson MA.

Efros, Israel I. Philosophical Terms in the Moreh Nebukim. LC 73-164764. (Columbia University. Oriental Studies: No. 22). Repr. of 1924 ed. 17.00 (ISBN 0-404-50512-0). AMS Pr.

Eitan, Israel. Contribution to Biblical Lexicography. (Columbia University. Contributions to Oriental History & Philology: No. 10). Repr. of 1924 ed. 12.50 (ISBN 0-404-50540-6). AMS Pr.

Finley, Harvey E. & Isbell, Charles D. Biblical Hebrew. 213p. 1975. pap. text ed. 13.95 (ISBN 0-8341-0350-8). Beacon Hill.

Foreign Service Institute. Hebrew Basic Course. (Hebrew.). 552p. 1980. plus 24 cassettes 215.00x (ISBN 0-88432-040-5, H345). J Norton Pubs.

Friedman, Jerome. The Most Ancient Testimony: Sixteenth-Century Christian-Hebraica in the Age of Renaissance Nostalgia. LC 82-18830. x, 279p. 1983. text ed. 26.95x (ISBN 0-8214-0700-7). Ohio U Pr.

Greenspahn, Frederick E. Hapax Legomena in Biblical Hebrew. LC 83-20021. (SBL Dissertation Ser.). 274p. 1984. 10.50 (ISBN 0-89130-660-9, 06 01 74); pap. 10.95 (ISBN 0-89130-785-0). Scholars Pr GA.

Greenspan, Jay Seth. Hebrew Calligraphy: A Step-by-Step Guide. LC 79-12718. (Illus.). 1980. pap. 8.95 (ISBN 0-8052-0664-7). Schocken.

Heuman, Fred S. The Uses of Hebraisms in Recent Bible Translations. 154p. 1977. 9.95 (ISBN 0-8022-2190-4). Philos Lib.

James, J. Courtenay. Hebrew & English: Some Likenesses, Psychic & Linguistic. Repr. of 1920 ed. lib. bdg. 20.00 (ISBN 0-8495-2723-6). Arden Lib.

Kamhi, D. J. Modern Hebrew: An Introductory Course. (OUP for the School of Oriental & African Studies Ser.). 1982. 15.95x (ISBN 0-19-713594-3). Oxford U Pr.

Kugel, James L. The Idea of Biblical Poetry: Parallelism & Its History. LC 80-25227. August 1983, 351p. pap. 10.95 (ISBN 0-300-03101-7, Y-470). Yale U Pr.

Lapide, Pinchas. Hebrew in the Church. 208p. (Orig.). 1985. 24.95x (ISBN 0-8028-3615-1). Eerdmans.

LaSor, William S. Handbook of Biblical Hebrew, 3 vols. Set. 14.95x (ISBN 0-8028-2379-3). Eerdmans.

Lewittes, Mordecai. Easy Hebrew (Iurit Kallah) 5.95 (ISBN 0-88482-682-1). Hebrew Pub.

Mansoor, Menahem. Biblical Hebrew Step by Step II: Readings from the Book of Genesis. 230p. (Orig.). 1984. pap. 13.95 (ISBN 0-8010-6151-2); cassette 7.95 (ISBN 0-8010-6198-9). Baker Bk.

Marks, Cara G. A Handbook of Hebrew Calligraphy: The ABC's of the Alef-Bet. (Illus.). 128p. 1983. cancelled (ISBN 0-89961-010-2); pap. cancelled (ISBN 0-89961-011-0). SBS Pub.

Mozeson, Isaac E. The Word: The English from Hebrew Dictionary. 1986. 16.95 (ISBN 0-933503-44-X). Shapolsky Pubs.

Revell, E. J. Biblical Texts with Palestinian Pointing & Their Accents. LC 77-8893. (Society of Biblical Literature. Masoretic Studies). 1977. pap. 10.95 (ISBN 0-89130-141-0, 060504). Scholars Pr GA.

Saulex, William H. The Romance of the Hebrew Language. 243p. 1983. Repr. of 1913 ed. lib. bdg. 30.00 (ISBN 0-8482-6303-0). Norwood Edns.

Saulez, William H. The Romance of the Hebrew Language. 1979. Repr. of 1913 ed. lib. bdg. 27.50 (ISBN 0-8414-8013-3). Folcroft.

Saulson, Scott B. Institutionalized Language Planning: Documents & Analysis of the Revival of Hebrew. (Contributions to the Sociology of Language Ser.: No. 23). 1979. text ed. 24.80x (ISBN 90-279-7567-1). Mouton.

Sawyer, John F. A Modern Introduction to Biblical Hebrew. (Orig.). 1976. pap. 14.95x (ISBN 0-85362-159-4, Oriel). Methuen Inc.

Tarnor, Pearl & Tarnor, Norman. Hebrew & Heritage, Vol. II: Siddur Track. 1982. 3.95x (ISBN 0-87441-375-3); tchr's. guide 12.50 (ISBN 0-87441-377-X). Behrman.

--Siddur Program, II to Hebrew & Heritage. (Illus.). 128p. 1982. pap. text ed. 3.95x (ISBN 0-87441-330-3). Behrman.

--Siddur Program III to Hebrew & Heritage. (Illus.). 128p. 1983. pap. text ed. 3.95x (ISBN 0-87441-359-1). Behrman.

Tregelles, Samuel P., tr. Gesenius' Hebrew & Chaldee Lexicon. (Reference Set). 919p. 1982. Repr. of 1979 ed. 24.95 (ISBN 0-915134-70-5). Mott Media.

Uveeler & Bronznick. Hayesod: Fundamentals of Hebrew. LC 72-86858. 16.95x (ISBN 0-87306-071-7). Feldheim.

Vaughan, P. H. Meaning of Bama in the Old Testament. LC 73-89004. (Society for Old Testament Study Monographs: No. 3). (Illus.). 96p. 1974. 29.95 (ISBN 0-521-20425-9). Cambridge U Pr.

Wickes, William. Two Treatises on the Accentuation of the Old Testament. rev. ed. 1970. 35.00x (ISBN 0-87068-004-8). Ktav.

Yates, Kyle M. & Owens, J. J. Nociones Esenciales Del Hebreo Biblico. Daglio, S. Daniel, tr. 308p. 1984. Repr. of 1980 ed. 6.75 (ISBN 0-311-42056-7). Casa Bautista.

Yonay, Shahar & Yonay, Rina. Systematic Hebrew. 1986. 12.95 (ISBN 0-9616783-0-5). S Yonay.

HEBREW LANGUAGE–COMPOSITION AND EXERCISES

Harper, William R. Introductory Hebrew: Method & Manual. rev. ed. Smith, James M., ed. LC 59-7624. (Midway Reprint Ser.). 1974. pap. 15.00x (ISBN 0-226-31683-1). U of Chicago Pr.

Sellers, Ovid R. & Voigt, E. E. Biblical Hebrew for Beginners. 12th corr ed. 1963. pap. 3.95x (ISBN 0-8401-2163-6). A R Allenson.

Weingreen, Jacob. Classical Hebrew Composition. 1957. 16.95x (ISBN 0-19-815423-2). Oxford U Pr.

HEBREW LANGUAGE–DICTIONARIES

Ben-Yehuda, Eliezer, ed. Dictionary & Thesaurus of the Hebrew Language, 8 Vols. Set. 150.00 (ISBN 0-498-07038-7, Yoseloff); lea. bd. set o.p. 250.00 (ISBN 0-498-08915-0). A S Barnes.

Davidson, Benjamin. Analytical Hebrew & Chaldee Lexicon. (Hebrew.). 27.95 (ISBN 0-310-20290-6, 6263, Pub. by Bagster). Zondervan.

Debahy, Moses. Dictionary Hebrew Verbs. (Hebrew & Arabic.). 1974. 15.00x (ISBN 0-86685-123-2). Intl Bk Ctr.

Einspahr, Bruce, compiled by. Index to the Brown, Driver & Briggs Hebrew Lexicon. LC 76-25479. (Hebrew.). 1976. 25.95 (ISBN 0-8024-4082-7). Moody.

Jastrow, Marcus. Hebrew-Aramaic-English Dictionary, a Dictionary of Talmud Babli & Talmud Yerushalmi Targum & Midrash, 2 Vols. (Hebrew, Aramaic & Eng.). 75.00 (ISBN 0-87559-019-5). Shalom.

Levenston, Edward A. & Sivan, Reuven. The New Bantam-Megiddo Hebrew Dictionary. (Hebrew.). 736p. 1975. pap. 4.95 (ISBN 0-553-26387-0). Bantam.

Mitchel, Larry A. A Student's Vocabulary for Biblical Hebrew & Aramaic. 128p. 1984. pap. 5.95 (ISBN 0-310-45461-1, 11607P). Zondervan.

Richards, Lawrence O. Expository Dictionary of Bible Words. 596p. 1985. 24.95 (ISBN 0-310-39000-1, 18300). Zondervan.

Skoss, Solomon, ed. Hebrew-Arabic Dictionary of the Bible Known As Kitab Jami-Al-Alfaz, 2 vols. (Yale Oriental Researches Ser.: No. XX, XXI). (Hebrew & Arabic.). 1945. 50.00x ea.; 95.00x set (ISBN 0-686-57837-6). Elliots Bks.

HEBREW LANGUAGE–DICTIONARIES–ENGLISH

Alcalay, Reuben. Complete English-Hebrew, Hebrew-English Dictionary, 3 vols. (Eng. & Hebrew.). 7180p. 1980. Repr. of 1965 ed. 69.00 set (ISBN 0-89961-017-X). Vol. 1 (ISBN 0-89961-003-X). Vol. 2 (ISBN 0-89961-007-2). Vol. 3 (ISBN 0-89961-008-0). SBS Pub.

--The Massada English-Hebrew Student Dictionary. (Eng. & Hebrew.). 734p. 1980. Repr. 18.95 (ISBN 0-89961-006-4). SBS Pub.

Armstrong, Terry, et al, eds. A Reader's Hebrew-English Lexicon of the Old Testament: Genesis-II Kings. (Hebrew & Eng.). 1982. 16.95 (ISBN 0-310-37040-X, 6291). Zondervan.

Furst, Gesenius. Hebrew-English Dictionary: Hebrew & Chaldee Lexicon to the Old Testament. rev. ed. Mitchell, Edward C., ed. (Hebrew & Eng.). 47.50 (ISBN 0-87559-021-7); thumb indexed 52.50 (ISBN 0-87559-022-5). Shalom.

Gesenius, William. Hebrew & English Lexicon to the Old Testament. 2nd ed. Brown, Francis, et al, eds. Robinson, Edward, tr. (Hebrew & Eng.). 1959. Repr. of 1907 ed. 34.95x (ISBN 0-19-864301-2). Oxford U Pr.

Goldberg, Nathan. New Functional Hebrew-English, English-Hebrew Dictionary. (Hebrew & Eng.). 1958. 5.00x (ISBN 0-87068-379-9). Ktav.

--New Illustrated Hebrew-English Dictionary for Young Readers. (Hebrew & Eng., Illus.). 1958. pap. 6.95x (ISBN 0-87068-370-5). Ktav.

Harkavy, Alexander, ed. Yiddish-English-Hebrew Dictionary. LC 86-31414. 624p. 1987. Repr. 29.95 (ISBN 0-8052-4027-6). Schocken.

Hebrew-English Lexicon. (Hebrew & Eng.). 6.95 (ISBN 0-310-20360-0, Pub. by Bagster). Zondervan.

Hebrew-English Lexicon of the Bible. LC 74-26705. (Hebrew & Eng.). 296p. (Orig.). 1975. pap. 7.50 (ISBN 0-8052-0481-4). Schocken.

Sheheen, Dennis, ed. A Child's Picture English-Hebrew Dictionary. (Children's Picture Dictionaries Ser.). (Illus.). 1987. 9.95 (ISBN 0-915361-75-2, Dist. by Watts). Adama Pubs Inc.

Sivan, Reuven & Levenston, Edward A. The New Bantam-Megiddo Hebrew & English Dictionary. LC 77-75289. (Hebrew & Eng.). 1977. 24.95 (ISBN 0-8052-3666-X). Schocken.

Weinberg, W. How Do You Spell Chanukah? A General-Purpose Romanization of Hebrew for Speakers of English. (Bibliographica Judaica Ser: No. 5). 10.00x (ISBN 0-87820-903-4, HUC Pr). Ktav.

HEBREW LANGUAGE–GRAMMAR

Bailey, D. Waylon & Strange, John O. Biblical Hebrew Grammar. LC 85-60960. 246p. 1985. 17.00 (ISBN 0-914520-23-7). Insight Pr.

Chomsky, William. Hebrew: The Eternal Language. LC 57-8140. 322p. 1975. 5.95 (ISBN 0-8276-0077-1, 384). Jewish Pubns.

Gesunius, William. Gesenius' Hebrew Grammar. 2nd ed. Kautzsch, E. & Cowley, A. E., eds. 1910. 29.95x (ISBN 0-19-815406-2). Oxford U Pr.

Greenberg, Moshe. Introduction to Hebrew. 1964. text ed. write for info. (ISBN 0-13-484469-6). P-H.

Harper, William R. Elements of Hebrew by an Inductive Method. LC 59-7625. (Midway Reprint Ser). 204p. 1974. pap. 9.00x (ISBN 0-226-31681-5). U of Chicago Pr.

--Introductory Hebrew: Method & Manual. rev. ed. Smith, James M., ed. LC 59-7624. (Midway Reprint Ser.). 1974. pap. 15.00x (ISBN 0-226-31683-1). U of Chicago Pr.

Hebrew Verb Tables. 1982. pap. 5.95x (ISBN 0-686-76516-8). Feldheim.

Horowitz, Edward. How the Hebrew Language Grew. rev. ed. 1967. pap. 9.95x (ISBN 0-87068-066-8). Ktav.

Lambin, Thomas O. An Introduction to Biblical Hebrew. 345p. 1971. text ed. write for info. (ISBN 0-02-367250-1, Pub. by Scribner). Macmillan.

Landes, George M. A Student's Vocabulary of Biblical Hebrew. 56p. (Orig.). 1961. pap. text ed. write for info. (ISBN 0-02-367410-5, Pub. by Scribner). Macmillan.

Muraoka, T. Modern Hebrew for Biblical Scholars: An Annotated Chrestomathy with an Outline Grammar & Glossary. (Journal for the Study of the Old Testament Ser.: Manuals 2). 220p. 1982. text ed. 25.00 (ISBN 0-905774-36-1, Pub. by JSOT Pr England); pap. text ed. 14.50 (ISBN 0-905774-37-X, Pub. by JSOT Pr England). Eisenbrauns.

Qimron, Elisha. The Hebrew of the Dead Sea Scrolls. (Harvard Semitic Ser.: No. 29). 1986. text ed. 13.95 (ISBN 0-89130-989-6, 04-04-29). Scholars Pr GA.

Segal, M. H. A Grammar of Mishnaic Hebrew. 1978. pap. text ed. 15.95x (ISBN 0-19-815454-2). Oxford U Pr.

Sellers, Ovid R. & Voigt, E. E. Biblical Hebrew for Beginners. 12th corr ed. 1963. pap. 3.95x (ISBN 0-8401-2163-6). A R Allenson.

Waltke, Bruce K. An Intermediate Hebrew Grammar. 1987. text ed. write for info. (ISBN 0-931464-31-5). Eisenbrauns.

Weingreen, Jacob. Practical Grammar for Classical Hebrew. 2nd ed. 1959. 15.95x (ISBN 0-19-815422-4). Oxford U Pr.

Yates, Kyle M. Essentials of Biblical Hebrew. rev. ed. Owens, J. J., ed. 1955. 13.95 (ISBN 0-06-069710-5, HarpR). Har-Row.

HEBREW LANGUAGE–PROGRAMMED INSTRUCTION

Bridger, David. Programmed Hebrew Series, 2 vols. Incl. Vol. 1. 1971. pap. text ed. 3.50x (ISBN 0-87441-079-7); Vol. 2. 1971. pap. text ed. 3.50x (ISBN 0-87441-080-0). (Reshit Tefillah V'lashon). 62p. (Prog. Bk.). (YA) pap. Behrman.

Chavez, Moises. Hebreo Biblico Juego de Dos Tomos, 2 vols. (Span., Vol. I - 568 pgs., Vol. II - 240 pgs.). 1984. Set. pap. 28.95 (ISBN 0-311-42070-2, Edit Mundo). Casa Bautista.

HEBREW LANGUAGE–READERS

Adler, L. W. & Castberg, C. Reading Hebrew. 1972. pap. 3.95x (ISBN 0-87441-042-8). Behrman.

Armstrong, Terry A., et al. Reader's Hebrew-English Lexicon of the Old Testament: Isaiah-Malachi, Vol. 3. 208p. 1985. 14.95 (ISBN 0-310-37010-8, 6293). Zondervan.

Harper, William R. Introductory Hebrew: Method & Manual. rev. ed. Smith, James M., ed. LC 59-7624. (Midway Reprint Ser.). 1974. pap. 15.00x (ISBN 0-226-31683-1). U of Chicago Pr.

Harvard University Library. Catalogue of Hebrew Books: Supplement I, 3 vols. LC 68-22416. 1972. Set. 185.00x (ISBN 0-674-10173-1). Harvard U Pr.

Rabin, Chaim. Hebrew. 1977. Repr. of 1949 ed. lib. bdg. 17.00 (ISBN 0-8492-2311-3). R West.

HEBREW LANGUAGE–SELF-INSTRUCTION

Goodrick, Edward W. Do It Yourself Hebrew & Greek. 2nd ed. LC 79-25463. 1980. pap. text ed. 9.95 (ISBN 0-930014-35-9); with cassette 14.95 (ISBN 0-930014-42-1). Multnomah.

--Do It Yourself Hebrew & Greek: Everybody's Guide to the Language Tools. 256p. (Orig.). 1980. pap. 11.95 (ISBN 0-310-41741-4, 6245P). Zondervan.

Harrison, Roland K. Teach Yourself Biblical Hebrew. (Teach Yourself Ser.). pap. 6.95 (ISBN 0-679-10180-2). McKay.

Levy, Harold. Hebrew for All. 260p. 1976. Repr. of 1970 ed. 15.00x (ISBN 0-85303-191-6, Pub. by Vallentine Mitchell England). Biblio Dist.

Mansoor, Menahem. Biblical Hebrew Step by Step: A Significant Breakthrough for Learning Biblical Hebrew. 1978. pap. 12.95 (ISBN 0-8010-6041-9); cassette 7.95 (ISBN 0-8010-6074-5). Baker Bk.

Mansoor, Menham. Key to the Biblical Hebrew, No. 2. 7.95 (ISBN 0-8010-6182-2). Baker Bk.

Reif, Joseph A. & Levinson, Hanna. FSI Hebrew Basic Course. 1976. pap. text ed. 15.00X (ISBN 0-686-10730-6); 35 cassettes 210.00x (ISBN 0-686-10731-4). Intl Learn Syst.

--Spoken Modern Hebrew. (Spoken Language Ser.). 590p. 1980. pap. 15.00x (ISBN 0-87950-683-0); cassettes, 31 dual track 180.00x (ISBN 0-87950-684-9); text & cassettes 190.00x (ISBN 0-87950-685-7). Spoken Lang Serv.

Steinberg, Samuel. Living Hebrew. (YA) 1958. 17.95 (ISBN 0-517-00133-0); records, manual & dictionary incl. Crown.

HEBREW LANGUAGE–SYNTAX

Andersen, Francis I. The Sentence in Biblical Hebrew. (Janua Linguarum, Ser. Practica: No. 231). 209p. 1974. pap. text ed. 23.20x (ISBN 90-2792-673-5). Mouton.

HEBREW LANGUAGE–TEXTBOOKS FOR CHILDREN

Amery & Haron. First Thousand Words in Hebrew. (First Thousand Words Ser.). (Illus.). 62p. 1985. PLB 10.95 (ISBN 0-86020-863-X, Pub. by Usborne). EDC.

Shumsky, Abraham & Shumsky, Adaia. Ahavat Chesed - Love Mercy: Reader. (Mah Tov Hebrew Teaching Ser.: Bk. 2). (Illus.). 1970. text ed. 5.50 (ISBN 0-8074-0175-7, 405304); tchrs'. guide 3.50 (ISBN 0-8074-0176-5, 205305); wkbk. 5.00 (ISBN 0-8074-0177-3, 405303). UAHC.

--Alef-Bet: A Hebrew Primer. (Illus.). 1979. pap. text ed. 6.00 (ISBN 0-8074-0026-2, 405309). UAHC.

--Asot Mishpat. (Mah Tov Hebrew Teaching Ser.: Bk. 1). (Illus.). 1969. text ed. 5.50 (ISBN 0-8074-0178-1, 405301); tchrs'. guide 3.50 (ISBN 0-8074-0179-X, 205302); wkbk. 5.00 (ISBN 0-8074-0180-3, 405300). UAHC.

HEBREW LAW

see Jewish Law

HEBREW LITERATURE

see also Apocalyptic Literature; Cabala; Rabbinical Literature; Talmud

Agnon, S. Y. A Simple Story. Halkin, Hillel, tr. from Hebrew. & afterword by. LC 85-2481. 256p. 1985. 14.95 (ISBN 0-8052-3999-5). Schocken.

Amram, David. Makers of Hebrew Books in Italy. 350p. 1983. 55.00 (ISBN 0-87556-013-X). Saifer.

Berg, Philip S. Wheels of a Soul. (Hebrew.). 160p. 1986. 12.95 (ISBN 0-943688-41-8); pap. 9.95 (ISBN 0-943688-42-6). Res Ctr Kabbalah.

--Wheels of a Soul. (Span.). 256p. 1986. 12.95 (ISBN 0-943688-45-0); pap. 9.95 (ISBN 0-943688-46-9). Res Ctr Kabbalah.

Bleiweiss, Robert M., ed. Torah at Brandeis Institute: The Layman Expounds. LC 76-7776. (Illus.). 1976. 8.95 (ISBN 0-916952-00-2). Brandeis-Bardin Inst.

Clay, Albert T. Hebrew Deluge Story in Cuneiform. (Yale Oriental Researches Ser.: No. V, Pt. III). 1922. 19.50x (ISBN 0-685-69802-5). Elliots Bks.

Daud, Abraham I. The Book of Tradition: Sefer ha-Qabbalah. Cohen, Gerson D., ed. & tr. from Hebrew. (LLJC Ser.). 486p. 1967. Repr. of 1967 ed. 39.95x (ISBN 0-19-710019-8). Oxford U Pr.

Fishelis, Avrahams. Kol Rom, Vol. I. 3rd ed. (Hebrew.). 208p. 5.50 (ISBN 0-9605560-0-1). A Fishelis.

--Kol Rom, Vol. II. (Hebrew.). 292p. 6.50 (ISBN 0-9605560-2-8). A Fishelis.

--Kol Rom, Vol. III. (Hebrew.). 431p. 12.00 (ISBN 0-9605560-3-6). A Fishelis.

Gaster, Moses. Studies & Texts in Folklore, Magic, Medieval Romance, Hebrew Apocrypha & Samaritan Archaeology, 3 Vols. rev. ed. 1970. Set. 45.00x (ISBN 0-87068-056-0). Ktav.

Goldstein, David. Hebrew Incunables in the British Isles: A Preliminary Census. (Illus.). 50p. (Orig.). 1985. pap. 14.25 (ISBN 0-7123-0047-3, Pub. by British Lib). Longwood Pub Group.

--Hebrew Manuscript Painting. LC 85-18995. (Illus.). 80p. (Orig.). 1985. pap. 8.95 (ISBN 0-7123-0054-6, Pub. by British Lib). Longwood Pub Group.

Guber, Rivka. Village of the Brothers. LC 78-54568. (Illus.). 1979. 10.00 (ISBN 0-88400-059-1). Shengold.

Hayward, Robert. Divine Name & Presence: The Memra. LC 81-10928. (Publications of the Oxford Centre for Postgraduate Hebrew Study). 208p. 1981. 25.50x (ISBN 0-86598-067-5). Allanheld.

Kee, Howard C. The Origins of Christianity: Sources & Documents. LC 73-4830. 320p. 1973. P-H.

Mansoor, Menahem. Modern Hebrew Literature Reader for Advanced Students, 2 vols. 1971. Vol. 1. 14.95x; Vol. 2. 16.95x (ISBN 0-685-27921-9). Ktav.

Mekhilta, Munich. Early Hebrew Manuscripts in Facsimile, Vol. 7. Edelmann, Martin & Schmelzer, Menahem, eds. 220p. 1980. 450.00x (ISBN 0-8018-2464-8); pap. 410.00x (ISBN 0-8018-2465-6). Johns Hopkins.

Pearl, Chaim & Brookes, Reuben. The Guide to Jewish Knowledge. rev. ed. LC 75-25366. 142p. 1976. 8.95 (ISBN 0-87677-138-X). Hartmore.

HEBREW LITERATURE–BIBLIOGRAPHY

Fletcher, Harris F. Milton's Rabbinical Readings. LC 67-30701. 344p. 1967. Repr. of 1930 ed. 29.50x (ISBN 0-87752-034-8). Gordian.

--Milton's Rabbinical Readings. LC 67-22303. 344p. 1967. Repr. of 1930 ed. 29.50 (ISBN 0-208-00335-5, Archon). Shoe String.

Harvard University Library. Catalogue of Hebrew Books: Supplement I, 3 vols. LC 68-22416. 1972. Set. 185.00x (ISBN 0-674-10173-1). Harvard U Pr.

Steinschneider, Moritz. Die Geschichtsliteratur der Juden. Katz, Steven, ed. LC 79-7153. (Jewish Philosophy, Mysticism & History of Ideas Ser.). 1980. Repr. of 1905 ed. lib. bdg. 16.00x (ISBN 0-405-12290-X). Ayer Co Pubs.

Zeithlin, William & Katz, Steven, eds. Bibliotheca Hebraica Post-Mendelssohniana. LC 79-7154. (Jewish Philosophy, Mysticism & History of Ideas Ser.). 1980. Repr. of 1895 ed. lib. bdg. 45.00x (ISBN 0-405-12291-8). Ayer Co Pubs.

HEBREW LITERATURE–HISTORY AND CRITICISM

Abrahams, Israel. By-Paths in Hebraic Bookland. LC 77-174368. Repr. of 1920 ed. 17.00 (ISBN 0-405-08177-4, Pub. by Blom Publications). Ayer Co Pubs.

Abramson, Glenda & Parfitt, Tudor, eds. The Great Transition: The Recovery of the Lost Centres of Modern Hebrew Literature. (Oxford Centre for Postgraduate Hebrew Studies). 184p. 1985. 35.00x (ISBN 0-8476-7437-1, Rowman & Allanheld). Rowman.

Aschkenasy, Nehama. Eve's Journey: Feminine Images In Hebraic Literary Tradition. LC 85-29427. 176p. 1986. text ed. 29.95 (ISBN 0-8122-8033-4); pap. 15.95. U of Pa Pr.

Bridger, David. Hebrew & Heritage, 4 vols. LC 75-1812. (Illus.). 1976. Vol. I. pap. 3.95x (ISBN 0-87441-254-4); Vol. II. pap. 3.95x (ISBN 0-87441-252-8); Vol. III. pap. 3.95x (ISBN 0-87441-259-5); Vol. IV. pap. 3.95x (ISBN 0-87441-274-9). Behrman.

Brooke, George J. Exegesis at Qumran: Four Q Florilegium in Its Jewish Context. (JSOT Supplement Ser.: No. 29). 370p. 1984. text ed. 28.50x (ISBN 0-905774-76-0, Pub. by JSOT Pr England); pap. text ed. 13.50x (ISBN 0-905774-77-9, Pub. by JSOT Pr England). Eisenbrauns.

Burke, David G., ed. The Poetry of Baruch: A Reconstruction & Analysis of the Original Hebrew Text of Baruch 3: 9-5: 9. LC 80-10271. (Society of Biblical Literature, Septuagint & Cognate Studies: No. 10). pap. 15.95 (ISBN 0-89130-382-0, 06-04-10). Scholars Pr GA.

Chiesa, Bruno. The Emergence of Hebrew Biblical Pointing, Vol. 1. (Judentum v. Umwelt Ser.: Vol. 1). 92p. 1979. pap. 17.70 (ISBN 3-8204-6419-0). P Lang Pubs.

Chilton, Bruce D. The Glory of Israel: The Theology & Provenience of the Isaiah Targum. (JSOT Supplement Ser.: No. 23). ix, 178p. 1984. text ed. 28.00x (ISBN 0-905774-46-9, Pub. by JSOT Pr England); pap. text ed. 18.50 (ISBN 0-905774-47-7, Pub. by JSOT Pr England). Eisenbrauns.

Clines, David J. The Esther Scroll: Its Genesis, Growth, & Meaning. (JSOT Supplement Ser.: No. 30). 260p. 1984. text ed. 29.50x (ISBN 0-905774-66-3, Pub. by JSOT Pr England); pap. text ed. 13.50x (ISBN 0-905774-67-1, Pub. by JSOT Pr England). Eisenbrauns.

Driver, S. R. Introduction to the Literature of the Old Testament. 16.50 (ISBN 0-8446-1998-1). Peter Smith.

Fletcher, Harris F. Milton's Rabbinical Readings. LC 67-30701. 344p. 1967. Repr. of 1930 ed. 29.50x (ISBN 0-87752-034-8). Gordian.

--Milton's Rabbinical Readings. LC 67-22303. 344p. 1967. Repr. of 1930 ed. 29.50 (ISBN 0-208-00335-5, Archon). Shoe String.

Freedman, D. N. & Mathews, K. A. The Paleo-Hebrew Leviticus Scroll. (Illus.). xii, 135p. 1985. text ed. 19.95x (ISBN 0-89757-007-3). Am Sch Orient Res.

Golb, Norman & Pritsak, Omeljan. Khazarian Hebrew Documents of the Tenth Century. 152p. 1982. 45.00x (ISBN 0-8014-1221-8). Cornell U Pr.

Greenstein, Edward L. & Preminger, Alex, eds. Hebrew Bible in Literary Criticism. (Library of Literary Criticism). 635p. 1986. 65.00x (ISBN 0-8044-3266-X). Ungar.

Kersten, John C. Understanding Hebrew Literature: A Guide to a Better Understanding of the Bible As a Source Book for the Humanities. 2.25 (ISBN 0-89942-145-8, 145/04). Catholic Bk Pub.

Mintz, Alan. Hurban: Responses to Catastrophe in Hebrew Literature. LC 83-23979. 288p. 1984. 27.50x (ISBN 0-231-05634-6). Columbia U Pr.

Mullen, E. Theodore, Jr. The Assembly of the Gods: The Divine Council in Canaanite & Early Hebrew Literature. LC 80-10128. (Harvard Semitic Museum Monographs: No. 24). 1980. 10.50x (ISBN 0-89130-380-4, 04 00 24). Scholars Pr GA.

Neubauer, A. Catalogue of the Hebrew Mss in the Jew's College, London. (Descriptive Catalogue of the Hewbrew Mss of the Montefiore Library). 274p. Repr. of 1904 ed. text ed. 74.52x (ISBN 0-576-80128-3, Pub. by Gregg Intl Pubs England). Gregg Intl.

Shepard, Sanford. Shem Tov: His World & His Words. LC 76-62685. (Coleccion De Estudios Hispanicos). 1978. pap. 10.00 (ISBN 0-89729-189-1). Ediciones.

Silberschlag, Eisig. From Renaissance to Renaissance: Hebrew Literature 1492-1967, Vol. I. 1972. 25.00x (ISBN 0-87068-184-2). Ktav.

Wacholder, Ben Z. Eupolemus: A Study of Graeco-Judean Literature. 1974. 20.00x (ISBN 0-87820-401-6). Ktav.

HEBREW LITERATURE–TRANSLATIONS INTO ENGLISH

Chavel, C. B., tr. The Disputation at Barcelona. 48p. 1983. pap. 2.95 (ISBN 0-88328-025-6). Shilo Pub Hse.

Leviant, Curt. Masterpieces of Hebrew Literature: A Treasury of Two Thousand Years of Jewish Creativity. 1969. pap. 14.95x (ISBN 0-87068-079-X). Ktav.

Neusner, Jacob. The Tosefta, Translated from the Hebrew: Pt. III Nashim. The Order of Women. 45.00x (ISBN 0-87068-684-4). Ktav.

Wilson, Epiphanius, intro. by. Hebrew Literature (Comprising of Talmudic Treatises, Hebrew Melodies & the Kabbalah Unveiled) 400p. 1986. Repr. of 1901 ed. PLB 60.00 (ISBN 0-89760-658-2). Telegraph Bks.

HEBREW LITERATURE, MODERN–BIBLIOGRAPHY

Goell, Yohai. Bibliography of Modern Hebrew Literature in English Translation. 132p. 1968. casebound 14.95x (ISBN 0-87855-187-5). Transaction Bks.

HEBREW PHILOLOGY

Andersen, Francis I. The Hebrew Verbless Clause in the Pentateuch. (SBL Monograph). 8.95 (ISBN 0-89130-321-9, 06-00-14). Scholars Pr GA.

HEBREW POETRY

Alter, Robert. The Art of Biblical Poetry. LC 85-47550. 272p. 1985. 17.95 (ISBN 0-465-00430-X). Basic.

--The Art of Biblical Poetry. LC 85-47550. 228p. 1987. pap. 8.95 (ISBN 0-465-00431-8, PL 5180). Basic.

HEBREW POETRY (COLLECTIONS)

Carmi, T., ed. The Penguin Book of Hebrew Verse. (Hebrew & Eng.). 448p. (Orig.). 1981. pap. 13.95 (ISBN 0-14-042197-1). Penguin.

Davidson, Israel. Thesaurus of Medieval Hebrew Poetry, 4 Vols. rev. ed. (Library of Jewish Classics). 1970. Set. 150.00x (ISBN 0-87068-003-X). Ktav.

Kohut, George A., ed. A Hebrew Anthology: A Collection of Poems & Dramas Inspired by the Old Testament & Post Biblical Tradition Gathered from Writings of English Poets, from the Elizabethan Period & Earlier to the Present Day, 2 vols. 1399p. Repr. of 1913 ed. Set. lib. bdg. 250.00 (ISBN 0-918377-86-2). Russell Pr.

Weinberger, Leon J. Anthology of Hebrew Poetry in Greece, Anatolia & the Balkans. LC 75-34119. 270p. 1975. pap. 16.50 (ISBN 0-8173-8525-8). U of Ala Pr.

HEBREW POETRY–HISTORY AND CRITICISM

Freedman, D. N. Pottery, Poetry & Prophecy: Studies in Early Hebrew Poetry. 1980. text ed. 20.00 (ISBN 0-931464-04-8). Eisenbrauns.

Geller, Stephen A. Parallelism in Early Biblical Poetry. LC 78-27255. (Harvard Semitic Monographs: No. 20). 1979. 12.00 (ISBN 0-89130-275-1, 040020). Scholars Pr GA.

Greenberg, Moshe. Biblical Prose Prayer: As a Window to the Popular Religion of Ancient Israel. LC 83-47662. (Taubman Lectures in Jewish Studies: No. 6). 78p. 1983. 16.50x (ISBN 0-520-05011-8); pap. 3.95 (ISBN 0-520-05012-6, CAL 680). U of Cal Pr.

Guthrie, Harvey H., Jr. Israel's Sacred Songs: A Study of Dominant Themes. 256p. 1984. pap. text ed. 11.50 (ISBN 0-8191-4027-9, Co-Pub. by Episcopal Div Sch). U Pr of Amer.
Hoeckmann, Olaf. Dance in Hebrew Poetry. Adams, Doug, ed. 1987. pap. 3.00 (ISBN 0-941500-44-6). Sharing Co.
Kugel, James L. The Idea of Biblical Poetry: Parallelism & Its History. LC 80-25227. August 1983, 351p. pap. 10.95 (ISBN 0-300-03101-7, Y-470). Yale U Pr.
O'Connor, Michael. Hebrew Verse Structure. 1980. 18.75x (ISBN 0-931464-02-1). Eisenbrauns.
Robinson, Theodore H. The Poetry of the Old Testament. LC 75-41233. Repr. of 1947 ed. 15.00 (ISBN 0-404-14593-0). AMS Pr.
White, John B. A Study of the Language of Love in the Song of Songs & Ancient Egyptian Poetry. LC 77-13399. (Society of Biblical Literature. Dissertation Ser.: Vol. 38). 1978. pap. 10.25 (ISBN 0-89130-192-5, 060138). Scholars Pr GA.
Yoder, Sanford C. Poetry of the Old Testament. 426p. 1948. pap. 9.95 (ISBN 0-8361-1709-3). Herald Pr.

HEBREW POETRY–TRANSLATIONS INTO ENGLISH

Jacobs, Steven L. Shirot Bialik: A New & Annotated Translation of Chaim Nachman Bialik's Epic Poems. (The Hebraica-Judaica Bookshelf Ser.). Date not set. price not set (ISBN 0-933771-03-7). Alpha Pub Co.

HEBREWS

see Jews

HECKER, ISAAC THOMAS, 1819-1888

Elliott, Walter. The Life of Father Hecker. LC 75-38446. (Religion in America, Ser. 2). 456p. 1972. Repr. of 1891 ed. 28.00 (ISBN 0-405-04065-2). Ayer Co Pubs.
Farina, John. An American Experience of God: The Spirituality of Isaac Hecker. LC 81-80875. 240p. 1981. 11.95 (ISBN 0-8091-0321-4). Paulist Pr.
--Hecker Studies: Essays on the Thought of Isaac Hecker. LC 83-60654. 196p. (Orig.). 1983. pap. 7.95 (ISBN 0-8091-2555-2). Paulist Pr.
Holden, Vincent F. The Early Years of Isaac Thomas Hecker (1819-1844) LC 73-3583. (Catholic University of America. Studies in American Church History: No. 29). Repr. of 1939 ed. 29.00 (ISBN 0-404-57779-2). AMS Pr.
McSorley, Joseph. Isaac Hecker & His Friends. 314p. 1972. pap. 1.45 (ISBN 0-8091-1605-7). Paulist Pr.
Portier, William L. Isaac Hecker & the First Vatican Council, Including Hecker's Notes in Italy: 1869-1870. LC 85-3034. (Studies in American Religion: Vol. 15). 360p. 1984. 59.95x (ISBN 0-88946-653-X). E Mellen.

HEDONISM

see also Altruism; Happiness

Mitchell, Thomas A. Hedonism & Eudonism in Aquinas. 1983. 2.00 (ISBN 0-686-45793-5). Franciscan Herald.
Powys, Llewelyn. Rats in the Sacristy. facs. ed. LC 67-30226. (Essay Index Reprint Ser). 1937. 17.00 (ISBN 0-8369-0798-1). Ayer Co Pubs.

HEGEL, GEORG WILHELM FRIEDRICH, 1770-1831

Beach, Edward. Dance of the Dialectic: A Dramatic Dialogue Presenting Hegel's Philosophy of Religion. LC 78-63255. pap. text ed. 6.75 (ISBN 0-8191-0615-1). U Pr of Amer.
Christensen, Darrel E. The Search for Concreteness-Reflections on Hegel & Whitehead: A Treatise on Self-Evidence & Critical Method in Philosophy. LC 85-63421. 516p. 1986. 45.00x (ISBN 0-941664-22-8, Pub. by Susquehanna U Pr). Assoc Univ Prs.
Croce, Benedetto. What Is Living & What Is Dead of the Philosophy of Hegel. Ainslie, Douglas, tr. from Ital. 268p. 1985. pap. text ed. 10.50 (ISBN 0-8191-4279-4). U Pr of Amer.
Derrida, Jacques. Glas. Leavey, John P., Jr. & Rand, Richard, trs. from Fr. LC 85-28877. vi, 262p. 1986. 50.00x (ISBN 0-8032-1667-X). U of Nebr Pr.
Dunning, Stephen N. The Tongues of Men: Hegel & Hamann on Religious Language & History. LC 79-10729. (American Academy of Religion, Dissertation Ser.: No. 27). 1979. 14.00 (ISBN 0-89130-283-2, 010127); pap. 9.95 (ISBN 0-89130-302-2). Scholars Pr GA.
Hegel, G. W. Hegel: Phenomenology of Spirit. Miller, A. V. & Findlay, J. N., trs. 1977. 34.95x (ISBN 0-19-824530-0); pap. 13.95 (ISBN 0-19-824597-1). Oxford U Pr.
--Hegel's System of Ethical Life & First Philosophy of Spirit. Harris, H. S. & Knox, T. M., eds. Harris, H. S. & Knox, T. M., trs. LC 79-11477. 1979. 39.50 (ISBN 0-87395-386-X). State U NY Pr.
Houlgate, Stephen. Hegel, Nietzsche & the Criticism of Metaphysics. 304p. 1987. 39.50 (ISBN 0-521-32255-3). Cambridge U Pr.
Kainz, Howard P. Hegel's Phenomenology, Part II: The Evolution of Ethical & Religious Consciousness to the Absolute Standpoint. LC 82-22444. xii, 211p. 1983. text ed. 23.95x (ISBN 0-8214-0677-9); pap. 12.95x (ISBN 0-8214-0738-4). Ohio U Pr.
Kolb, David. The Critique of Pure Modernity: Hegel, Heidegger, & After. LC 85-24510. 334p. 1987. lib. bdg. 25.00 (ISBN 0-226-45031-7). U of Chicago Pr.
Lauer, Quentin. Hegel's Concept of God. 432p. 1982. 44.50 (ISBN 0-87395-597-8); pap. 16.95 (ISBN 0-87395-598-6). State U NY Pr.
Lucas, George R. Two Views of Freedom in Process & Thought. LC 79-12287. (American Academy of Religion, Dissertation Ser.: No. 28). 1979. 14.00 (ISBN 0-89130-285-9, 010128); pap. 9.95 (ISBN 0-89130-304-9). Scholars Pr GA.
McTaggart, John M. Studies in Hegelian Cosmology. 2nd ed. 1986. lib. bdg. 25.00x (ISBN 0-935005-59-5); pap. text ed. 13.00x (ISBN 0-935005-60-9). Ibis Pub VA.
Pochmann, Henry A. New England Transcendentalism & St. Louis Hegelianism. LC 68-55163. (Studies in Comparative Literature, No. 35). 1969. Repr. of 1948 ed. lib. bdg. 39.95x (ISBN 0-8383-0610-1). Haskell.
Rosen, Michael. Hegel's Dialectic & Its Criticism. LC 81-24211. 210p. 1982. 29.95 (ISBN 0-521-24484-6). Cambridge U Pr.
Schmidt, Erik. Hegels System der Theologie. LC 73-81703. (Theologische Bibliothek Toepelmann 26). 210p. 1974. 26.80x (ISBN 3-11-004463-3). De Gruyter.
Seth, Andrew. The Development from Kant to Hegel. 1975. lib. bdg. 49.95 (ISBN 0-8490-0020-3). Gordon Pr.
--The Development from Kant to Hegel, with Chapters on the Philosophy of Religion. Beck, Lewis W., ed. LC 75-32044. (The Philosophy of Immanuel Kant Ser.: Vol. 7). 1976. Repr. of 1882 ed. lib. bdg. 24.00 (ISBN 0-8240-2331-5). Garland Pub.
Solomon, Robert C. In the Spirit of Hegel: A Study of G. W. F. Hegel's "Phenomenology of Spirit". (Illus.). 1983. 32.50x (ISBN 0-19-503169-5); pap. 14.95x (ISBN 0-19-503650-6). Oxford U Pr.
Stillman, Peter G., ed. Hegel's Philosophy of Spirit. (SUNY Series in Hegelian Studies). 223p. 1986. 39.50x (ISBN 0-88706-476-0); pap. 12.95x (ISBN 0-88706-477-9). State U NY Pr.
Sussman, Henry. The Hegelian Aftermath: Readings in Hegel, Kierkegaard, Freud, Proust & James. LC 82-47971. 172p. 1982. text ed. 22.50x (ISBN 0-8018-2852-X). Johns Hopkins.
Warminski, Andrzej. Readings in Interpretation: Holderlin, Hegel, Heidegger. (Theory & History of Literature Ser.: Vol. 26). 272p. (Orig.). 1987. 29.50 (ISBN 0-8166-1239-0); pap. 12.95 (ISBN 0-8166-1240-4). U of Minn Pr.
Williamson, Raymond K. An Introduction to Hegel's Philosophy of Religion. (Hegelian Studies). 376p. 1984. 49.50 (ISBN 0-87395-827-6); pap. 17.95 (ISBN 0-87395-826-8). State U NY Pr.
Yerkes, James. The Christology of Hegel. (SUNY Hegelian Studies). 240p. 1982. 49.50 (ISBN 0-87395-648-6); pap. 18.95 (ISBN 0-87395-649-4). State U NY Pr.

HEIDEGGER, MARTIN, 1889-1976

Caputo, John D. The Mystical Element in Heidegger's Thought. LC 77-92251. xvi, 292p. 1978. 28.95x (ISBN 0-8214-0372-9). Ohio U Pr.
--The Mystical Element in Heidegger's Thought. rev. ed. xxviii, 292p. 1986. pap. 12.50 (ISBN 0-8232-1153-3). Fordham.
Knowles, Richard T. Human Development & Human Possibility: Erikson in the Light of Heidegger. LC 85-20498. (Illus.). 224p. (Orig.). 1986. lib. bdg. 26.00 (ISBN 0-8191-4992-6); pap. text ed. 12.25 (ISBN 0-8191-4993-4). U Pr of Amer.
Kolb, David. The Critique of Pure Modernity: Hegel, Heidegger, & After. LC 85-24510. 334p. 1987. lib. bdg. 25.00 (ISBN 0-226-45031-7). U of Chicago Pr.
Macquarrie, John. Martin Heidegger. LC 68-11970. (Makers of Contemporary Theology Ser). 1968. pap. 3.95 (ISBN 0-8042-0659-7). John Knox.
Robinson, James M. & Cobb, John B., Jr., eds. The Later Heidegger & Theology. LC 78-23619. 1979. Repr. of 1963 ed. lib. bdg. 22.50x (ISBN 0-313-20783-6, ROLH). Greenwood.
Schalow, Frank. Imagination & Existence: Heidegger's Retrieval of the Kantian Ethic. 192p. (Orig.). 1986. lib. bdg. 24.75 (ISBN 0-8191-5114-9); pap. text ed. 11.75 (ISBN 0-8191-5115-7). U Pr of Amer.
Warminski, Andrzej. Readings in Interpretation: Holderlin, Hegel, Heidegger. (Theory & History of Literature Ser.: Vol. 26). 272p. (Orig.). 1987. 29.50 (ISBN 0-8166-1239-0); pap. 12.95 (ISBN 0-8166-1240-4). U of Minn Pr.
Williams, John R. Martin Heidegger's Philosophy of Religion. 190p. 1977. pap. text ed. 9.95x (ISBN 0-919812-03-1, Pub. by Wilfrid Laurier Canada). Humanities.

HEIDELBERG CATECHISM

Barth, Karl. Learning Jesus Christ Through the Heidelberg Catechism. 144p. (Orig.). 1982. pap. 4.95 (ISBN 0-8028-1893-5). Eerdmans.
Heidelberg Catechism with Scripture Texts. (Orig.). 1981. pap. 4.95 (ISBN 0-933140-21-5). CRC Pubns.
Theleman. Aid to Heidelberg Catechism. 5.95 (ISBN 0-686-23483-9). Rose Pub MI.
Thompson, Bard, et al. Essays on the Heidelberg Catechism. LC 63-21522. 1963. pap. 5.95 (ISBN 0-8298-0325-4). Pilgrim NY.
Verhey, Allen. Living the Heidelberg, the Heidelberg Catechism & the Moral Life. LC 85-31386. 120p. (Orig.). 1986. pap. text ed. 7.95 (ISBN 0-930265-21-1). CRC Pubns.

HEINRICH VON DEM TURLIN, fl. 1220

Boll, Lawrence L. Relation of Diu Krone to La Mule Sanz Frain. LC 77-140018. (Catholic University Studies in German Ser.: No. 2). Repr. of 1929 ed. 18.00 (ISBN 0-404-50222-9). AMS Pr.

HELL

see also Future Punishment

Adams, Judith. Against the Gates of Hell. 152p. pap. 2.50 (ISBN 0-87509-232-2). Chr Pubns.
Blodgett, Ralph. Hell: Will the Wicked Burn Forever? (Outreach Ser.). 1981. pap. 0.99 (ISBN 0-8163-0375-4). Pacific Pr Pub Assn.
Boehme, Jacob. Of Heaven & Hell: A Dialogue Between Junius, a Scholar & Theophorus, His Master. 1986. pap. 3.95 (ISBN 0-916411-53-2). Sure Fire.
Bryson, Harold T. The Reality of Hell & the Goodness of God. LC 83-51674. 192p. 1984. pap. 4.95 (ISBN 0-8423-5279-1). Tyndale.
Cribb, C. C. The Devil's Empire. LC 77-70211. pap. 2.95 (ISBN 0-932046-02-9). Manhattan Ltd NC.
Ferguson, John. The Place of Suffering. 137p. 1972. 7.95 (ISBN 0-227-67803-6). Attic Pr.
Fudge, Edward W. The Fire That Consumes: A Biblical & Historical Study of Final Punishment. 1983. 19.95 (ISBN 0-89890-018-2). Providential Pr.
Hagin, Kenneth E. I Went to Hell. 1982. pap. 0.50 mini bk. (ISBN 0-89276-257-8). Hagin Ministries.
Kater, John. The Letter of John to James. (Illus.). 64p. (Orig.). 1981. pap. 3.95 (ISBN 0-8164-2344-X, HarpR). Har-Row.
Kelley, P. J. So High the Price. LC 68-28104. (St. Paul Editions). 1968. 3.00 (ISBN 0-8198-0148-8). Dghtrs St Paul.
Kohler, Kaufmann. Heaven & Hell in Comparative Religion. 1923. 25.00 (ISBN 0-8414-5601-1). Folcroft.
Lehner, Ernst & Lehner, Johanna. Picture Book of Devils, Demons, & Witchcraft. LC 72-137002. 1972. pap. 6.50 (ISBN 0-486-22751-0). Dover.
Lindsay, Gordon. Hades-Abode of the Unrighteous Dead. (Sorcery & Spirit World Ser.). 1.25 (ISBN 0-89985-082-0). Christ Nations.
Macculluch, John A. The Harrowing of Hell: A Comparative Study of an Early Christian Doctrine. LC 79-8113. 1983. Repr. of 1930 ed. 33.50 (ISBN 0-404-18426-X). AMS Pr.
Mew, James. Traditional Aspects of Hell. LC 73-140321. 1971. Repr. of 1903 ed. 48.00x (ISBN 0-8103-3693-6). Gale.
Patch, Howard R. Other World, According to Descriptions in Medieval Literature. LC 77-96164. 1970. Repr. of 1950 ed. lib. bdg. 27.50x (ISBN 0-374-96289-8, Octagon). Hippocrene Bks.
Sayers, Stanley E. The Nature of Things to Come. 1972. 7.95 (ISBN 0-88027-013-6). Firm Foun Pub.
Shedd, W. G. The Doctrine of Endless Punishment. 1980. 8.25 (ISBN 0-86524-019-1, 9803). Klock & Klock.
Swedenborg, Emanuel. Heaven & Hell. LC 77-93044. cancelled (ISBN 0-87785-167-0); student ed. 12.00 (ISBN 0-87785-066-6); pap. 5.95 (ISBN 0-87785-153-0). Swedenborg.
Teller, Woolsey & Gauvin, Marshall. Hell, A Christian Doctrine. (Illus.). 47p. pap. cancelled (ISBN 0-910309-01-9). Am Atheist.
Toon, Peter. Heaven & Hell: A Biblical & Theological Overview. 160p. 1986. pap. 8.95 (ISBN 0-8407-5967-3). Nelson.
Worley, Win. Annihilating the Hosts of Hell: The Battle Royal, Vol. I. 1981. 5.00 (ISBN 0-686-75479-4). HBC.

HELLENISM

see also Neoplatonism

Bevan, Edwyn R. Hellenism & Christianity. facs. ed. LC 67-26714. (Essay Index Reprint Ser). 1921. 18.00 (ISBN 0-8369-0207-6). Ayer Co Pubs.
Jews in the Hellenistic World: Josephus, Aristeas, the Sibylline Oracles, Eupolemus. (Cambridge Commentaries on the Writings of the Jewish & Christian World 200 B. C. to 200 A. D.). (Illus.). 224p. 1985. 42.50 (ISBN 0-521-24246-0); pap. 12.95 (ISBN 0-521-28551-8). Cambridge U Pr.
Koebner, Richard, ed. Studies in Classics & Jewish Hellenism. (Scripts Hierosolymitana Ser.: Vol. 1). pap. 39.00 (ISBN 0-317-28711-7, 2051594). Bks Demand UMI.
Kraeling, Carl H. Anthropos & Son of Man. LC 27-23162. (Columbia University. Oriental Studies: No. 25). Repr. of 1927 ed. 18.50 (ISBN 0-404-50515-5). AMS Pr.
Makrakis, Apostolos. Hellenism & the Unfinished Revolution. Orthodox Christian Educational Society, ed. Stephanou, Archimandrite E., tr. from Hellenic. 191p. (Orig.). 1968. pap. 5.00x (ISBN 0-938366-26-2). Orthodox Chr.
Tcherikover, Victor. Hellenistic Civilization & the Jews. Applebaum, S., tr. LC 59-8518. (Temple Bk.). 1970. pap. 9.95x (ISBN 0-689-70248-5, T22). Atheneum.

HENRI 4TH, KING OF FRANCE, 1553-1610–FICTION

Weyman, Stanley J. From the Memoirs of a Minister of France. LC 77-113694. (Short Story Index Reprint Ser.). 1895. 24.50 (ISBN 0-8369-3423-7). Ayer Co Pubs.

HENRY 2ND, KING OF ENGLAND, 1133-1189

Warren, W. L. Henry II. (English Monarchs Ser.). 1973. pap. 14.95 (ISBN 0-520-03494-5, CAL367). U of Cal Pr.

HENRY 8TH, KING OF ENGLAND, 1491-1547

Du Boys, Albert. Catherine of Aragon & the Sources of the English Reformation, 2 vols in 1. Yonge, Charlotte M., ed. 1969. Repr. of 1881 ed. 35.50 (ISBN 0-8337-0931-3). B Franklin.
Froude, James A. Divorce of Catherine of Aragon. 2nd ed. LC 68-58379. Repr. of 1891 ed. 31.50 (ISBN 0-404-02626-5). AMS Pr.
Gasquet, Francis A. Henry the Eighth & the English Monasteries, 2 vols. LC 74-39467. (Select Bibliography Reprint Ser.). 1972. Repr. of 1888 ed. 56.75 (ISBN 0-8369-9905-3). Ayer Co Pubs.
--Henry VIII & the English Monasteries, 2 vols. (Select Bibliographies Reprint Ser.). Repr. of 1888 ed. lib. bdg. 55.00 set (ISBN 0-8290-0849-7). Irvington.
Harpsfield, Nicholas. Treatise on the Pretended Divorce Between Henry Eighth & Catharine of Aragon. Pocock, N., ed. 1878. 27.00 (ISBN 0-384-21420-7). Johnson Repr.
Henry VIII. A Copy of the Letters Wherein Kyng Henry the Eyght Made Answere into a Certayn Letter of Martyn Luther. LC 72-204. (English Experience Ser.: No. 322). 100p. 1971. Repr. of 1528 ed. 14.00 (ISBN 90-221-0322-6). Walter J Johnson.
Kelly, Henry A. The Matrimonial Trials of Henry VIII. LC 75-7483. xiv, 334p. 1976. 27.50x (ISBN 0-8047-0895-9). Stanford U Pr.
Palmer, M. D. Henry VIII. 2nd ed. (Seminar Studies in History Ser.). (Illus.). 1983. pap. text ed. 6.95x (ISBN 0-582-35437-4). Longman.
Scarisbrick, J. J. Henry VIII. LC 68-10995. (English Monarchs Series). (Illus.). 1968. pap. 8.95 (ISBN 0-520-01130-9, CAL195). U of Cal Pr.
Waldman, Milton. Some English Dictators. LC 77-112820. 1970. Repr. of 1940 ed. 24.50x (ISBN 0-8046-1087-8, Pub.by Kennikat). Assoc Faculty Pr.

HENSON, JOSIAH, 1789-1883

Cavanah, Frances. The Truth about the Man Behind the Book That Sparked the War Between the States. LC 75-11566. (Illus.). 188p. 1975. 7.95 (ISBN 0-664-32572-6). Westminster.
Henson, Josiah. Father Henson's Story of His Own Life. LC 70-99381. (Illus.). vii, 212p. 1972. Repr. of 1858 ed. lib. bdg. 12.50 (ISBN 0-8411-0052-7). Metro Bks.

HEORTOLOGY

see Church Calendar; Church Year; Fasts and Feasts; Saints–Calendar

HERBERT, GEORGE, 1593-1633

Bennett, Joan. Five Metaphysical Poets: Donne, Herbert, Vaughan, Crashaw, Marvell. 1964. 32.50 (ISBN 0-521-04156-2); pap. 9.95 (ISBN 0-521-09238-8). Cambridge U Pr.
Freer, Coburn. Music for a King: George Herbert's Style & the Metrical Psalms. LC 76-179136. pap. 67.50 (ISBN 0-317-42332-0, 2025815). Bks Demand UMI.
Grant, Patrick. The Transformation of Sin: Studies in Donne, Herbert, Vaughan & Traherne. LC 73-93174. 308p. 1974. 20.00x (ISBN 0-87023-158-8). U of Mass Pr.

--The Transformation of Sin: Studies in Donne, Herbert, Vaughan & Traherne. LC 73-93174. pap. 63.50 (ISBN 0-317-26444-3, 2023850). Bks Demand UMI.

Miller, Edmund. Drudgerie Divine: The Rhetoric of God & Man in George Herbert. Hogg, James, ed. (Elizabethan & Renaissance Studies). 250p. (Orig.). 1979. pap. 15.00 (ISBN 0-317-40130-0, Pub by Salzburg Studies). Longwood Pub Group.

Todd, Richard. The Opacity of Signs: Acts of Interpretation in George Herbert's The Temple. LC 83-36133. (Illus.). 240p. 1986. text ed. 27.00 (ISBN 0-8262-0609-3). U of Mo Pr.

Wall, John N., ed. George Herbert: The Country Parson & the Temple. LC 81-80287. (Classics of Western Spirituality Ser.). 384p. 13.95 (ISBN 0-8091-0317-6); pap. 10.95 (ISBN 0-8091-2298-7). Paulist Pr.

White, Helen C. The Metaphysical Poets: A Study in Religious Experience. LC 83-45866. 1936. 39.50 (ISBN 0-404-20285-3, PR549). AMS Pr.

HERESIES AND HERETICS

For general descriptive and historical works. Works on heresy in the abstract are entered under the heading Heresy.

Aldridge, John W. In Search of Heresy: American Literature in an Age of Conformity. LC 74-3618. 208p. 1974. Repr. of 1956 ed. lib. bdg. 82.50x (ISBN 0-8371-7452-X, ALSH). Greenwood.

Barthlet, John. The Pedegrewe of Heretiques. LC 79-76432. (English Experience Ser.: No. 76). 180p. 1969. Repr. of 1566 ed. 21.00 (ISBN 90-221-0076-6). Walter J Johnson.

Batman, Stephen. The Golden Booke of the Leaden Gods, Repr. Of 1577 Ed. Bd. with The Third Part of the Countess of Pembroke's Yvychurch. Fraunce, Abraham. Repr. of 1592 ed; The Fountaine of Ancient Fiction. Lynche, Richard. Repr. of 1599 ed. LC 75-27856. (Renaissance & the Gods Ser.: Vol. 13). (Illus.). 1976. lib. bdg. 88.00 (ISBN 0-8240-2062-6). Garland Pub.

Belloc, Hilaire. Great Heresies. facs. ed. LC 68-16908. (Essay Index Reprint Ser). 1938. 18.00 (ISBN 0-8369-0189-4). Ayer Co Pubs.

Chesterton, Gilbert K. Heretics. facs. ed. LC 75-128220. (Essay Index Reprint Ser). 1905. 19.00 (ISBN 0-8369-1869-X). Ayer Co Pubs.

Emery, Richard W. Heresy & Inquisition in Narbonne. LC 75-166031. (Columbia University Studies in the Social Sciences: No. 480). 17.50 (ISBN 0-404-51480-4). AMS Pr.

The Encyclopedia of Unbelief, 2 vols. LC 85-43327. 819p. 1985. Set. 99.95 (ISBN 0-87975-307-2). Prometheus Bks.

Fritchman, Stephen. Heretic. pap. 6.95 (ISBN 0-933840-19-5). Unitarian Univ.

Heath, Carl. Social & Religious Heretics in Five Centuries. LC 78-147622. (Library of War & Peace; Non-Resis. & Non-Vio.). 1972. lib. bdg. 46.00 (ISBN 0-8240-0397-7). Garland Pub.

Herrick, Samuel E. Some Heretics of Yesterday. LC 83-45614. Date not set. Repr. of 1885 ed. 37.50 (ISBN 0-404-19832-5). AMS Pr.

Hutchinson, Roger. Works. 1842. 31.00 (ISBN 0-384-25120-X). Johnson Repr.

Ingram, T. Robert. New Liturgy, Old Heresy. LC 81-52116. (Orig.). 1981. pap. 4.50 (ISBN 0-686-75087-X). St Thomas.

Le Goff, Jacques. Heresies et Societes Dans L'europe Pre-Industrielle 11e-18e Siecles: Communications et Debats Du Colloque De Royaumont. (Civilisations et Societes: No. 10). 1968. pap. 28.40x (ISBN 90-2796-079-8). Mouton.

Metcalfe, J. C. There Must Be Heresies. 1963. pap. 2.25 (ISBN 0-87508-922-4). Chr Lit.

Meyer, Samuel. The Deacon & the Jewess: Adventures in Heresy. LC 80-84734. 208p. 1982. 10.00 (ISBN 0-8022-2379-6). Philos Lib.

Nelli, Rene. Dictionnaire Des Heresies Meridionales. (Fr.). 384p. 18.50 (ISBN 0-686-56886-9, F-21110). French & Eur.

Pluquet, F. A. Dictionnaire des Heresies des Erreurs et des Schismes, 2 vols. Migne, J. P., ed. (Encyclopedie Theologique Ser.: Vols. 11-12). (Fr.). 1374p. Repr. of 1847 ed. lib. bdg. 175.00x (ISBN 0-89241-235-6). Caratzas.

HERESIES AND HERETICS–EARLY CHURCH, ca. 30-600

see also Gnosticism; Manichaeism

Burton, Edward. An Inquiry into the Heresies of the Apostolic Age. LC 78-63166. (Heresies of the Early Christian & Medieval Era: Second Ser.). Repr. of 1829 ed. 62.50 (ISBN 0-404-16179-0). AMS Pr.

Douais, Celestin. Les Albigeois. 2nd ed. LC 78-63182. (Heresies of the Early Christian & Medieval Era: Second Ser.). Repr. of 1879 ed. 64.50 (ISBN 0-404-16221-5). AMS Pr.

Grant, Robert M., ed. Gnosticism: A Source Book of Heretical Writings from the Early Christian Period. LC 77-85274. Repr. of 1961 ed. 32.50 (ISBN 0-404-16108-1). AMS Pr.

Grobel, Kendrick, tr. The Gospel of Truth. LC 78-63167. (Heresies of the Early Christian & Medieval Era: Second Ser.). Repr. of 1960 ed. 26.00. AMS Pr.

Mansel, Henry L. The Gnostic Heresies of the First & Second Centuries. Lightfoot, J. B., ed. LC 78-63170. (Heresies of the Early Christian & Medieval Era: Second Ser.). Repr. of 1875 ed. 42.00 (ISBN 0-404-16185-5). AMS Pr.

Marcion Of Sinope. The Gospel of the Lord. Hill, James H., tr. LC 78-63171. (Heresies of the Early Christian & Medieval Era: Second Ser.). Repr. of 1891 ed. 19.50 (ISBN 0-404-16186-3). AMS Pr.

O'Callaghan, Joseph F., ed. Heresies of the Early Christian & Medieval Era, 67 titles in 92 vols. (An AMS Reprint Ser.). 1965. Repr. of 1816 ed. write in info. (ISBN 0-404-16090-5). AMS Pr.

Turner, Henry E. The Pattern of Christian Truth: A Study in the Relations Between Orthodoxy & Heresy in the Early Church. LC 77-84707. (Bampton Lectures: 1954). 1977. Repr. of 1954 ed. 47.50 (ISBN 0-404-16114-6). AMS Pr.

Wand, John W. The Four Great Heresies. LC 78-63174. (Heresies of the Early Christian & Medieval Era: Second Ser.). Repr. of 1955 ed. 29.00 (ISBN 0-404-16189-8). AMS Pr.

Wolfson, Harry A. Philosophy of the Church Fathers: Faith, Trinity, Incarnation. 3rd rev. ed. LC 70-119077. 1970. 32.50x (ISBN 0-674-66551-1). Harvard U Pr.

HERESIES AND HERETICS–MIDDLE AGES, 600-1500

see also Sects, Medieval

Alphandery, Paul. Les Idees Morales Chez les Heterodoxes Latins Au Debut Du Xiiie Siecle. LC 78-63184. (Heresies of the Early Christian & Medieval Era: Second Ser.). Repr. of 1903 ed. 27.50 (ISBN 0-404-16198-7). AMS Pr.

Douais, Celestin. Les Albigeois. 2nd ed. LC 78-63182. (Heresies of the Early Christian & Medieval Era: Second Ser.). Repr. of 1879 ed. 64.50 (ISBN 0-404-16221-5). AMS Pr.

Gebhart, E. Mystics & Heretics in Italy at the End of the Middle Ages. 1977. lib. bdg. 59.95 (ISBN 0-8490-2321-1). Gordon Pr.

Grobel, Kendrick, tr. The Gospel of Truth. LC 78-63167. (Heresies of the Early Christian & Medieval Era: Second Ser.). Repr. of 1960 ed. 26.00. AMS Pr.

Guiraud, Jean. The Medieval Inquisition. Messenger, E. C., tr. LC 78-63181. (Heresies of the Early Christian & Medieval Era: Second Ser.). Repr. of 1929 ed. 31.00 (ISBN 0-404-16222-3). AMS Pr.

Hus, Jan. Mag. Johannis Hus Tractatus Responsiyus. LC 78-63201. (Heresies of the Early Christian & Medieval Era: Second Ser.). Repr. of 1927 ed. 34.50 (ISBN 0-404-16229-0). AMS Pr.

Lambert, Malcolm. Medieval Heresy: Popular Movements from Bogomil to Hus. LC 76-49949. 446p. 1977. 54.50x (ISBN 0-8419-0298-4). Holmes & Meier.

Marcion Of Sinope. The Gospel of the Lord. Hill, James H., tr. LC 78-63171. (Heresies of the Early Christian & Medieval Era: Second Ser.). Repr. of 1891 ed. 19.50 (ISBN 0-404-16186-3). AMS Pr.

Moore, R. I. The Origins of European Dissent. 338p. 1985. pap. 12.95x (ISBN 0-631-14404-8). Basil Blackwell.

Moore, R. I., ed. The Birth of Popular Heresy. LC 75-32934. (Documents of Medieval History Ser.). 176p. 1976. 25.00 (ISBN 0-312-08190-1). St Martin.

More, St. Thomas, et al, eds. A Dialogue Concerning Heresies: Complete Works of St. Thomas More, Vol. 6, Pts. 1 & 2. LC 63-7949. (Illus.). 910p. 1981. Set. text ed. 87.00x (ISBN 0-300-02211-5). Yale U Pr.

Nelli, Rene. Spiritualite de l'Heresie: le Catharisme. LC 78-63189. (Heresies of the Early Christian & Medieval Era: Second Ser.). Repr. of 1953 ed. 31.00 (ISBN 0-404-16226-6). AMS Pr.

O'Callaghan, Joseph F., ed. Heresies of the Early Christian & Medieval Era, 67 titles in 92 vols. (An AMS Reprint Ser.). 1965. Repr. of 1816 ed. write in info. (ISBN 0-404-16090-5). AMS Pr.

Schmidt, Charles G. Histoire et Doctrine de la Secte des Cathares ou Albigeois, 2 vols. LC 78-63191. (Heresies of the Early Christian & Medieval Era: Second Ser.). 1979. Repr. of 1849 ed. 57.50 set (ISBN 0-404-16180-4). AMS Pr.

Shannon, Albert C. The Popes & Heresy in the Thirteenth Century. LC 78-63192. (Heresies of the Early Christian & Medieval Era: Second Ser.). Repr. of 1949 ed. 31.00 (ISBN 0-404-16228-2). AMS Pr.

Wand, John W. The Four Great Heresies. LC 78-63174. (Heresies of the Early Christian & Medieval Era: Second Ser.). Repr. of 1955 ed. 29.00 (ISBN 0-404-16189-8). AMS Pr.

Wilson, Robert S. Marcion. LC 78-63176. (Heresies of the Early Christian & Medieval Era: Second Ser.). Repr. of 1933 ed. 32.00 (ISBN 0-404-16194-4). AMS Pr.

HERESIES AND HERETICS–MODERN PERIOD, 1500-

see also Sects

Genzburg, Carlo. The Cheese & the Worms: The Cosmos of a Sixteenth-Century Miller. LC 79-3654. pap. 51.80 (2026706). Bks Demand UMI.

Rifkin, Jeremy. Declaration of a Heretic. 150p. 1985. 19.95 (ISBN 0-7102-0709-3); pap. 7.95 (ISBN 0-7102-0710-7). Methuen Inc.

HERESY

see also Apostasy; Liberty of Speech in the Church; Schism

Brown, Harold O. Heresies: The Image of Christ in the Mirror of Heresy & Orthodoxy from the Apostles to the Present. LC 80-2558. (Illus.). 504p. 1984. 17.95 (ISBN 0-385-15338-4). Doubleday.

Peters, Edward, ed. Heresy & Authority in Medieval Europe. LC 79-5262. (Middle Ages Ser.). 384p. 1980. 39.00x (ISBN 0-8122-7779-1); pap. 15.95x (ISBN 0-8122-1103-0). U of Pa Pr.

St. Philastrius Bishop of Brescia. Sancti Filastrii Episcopi Brixiensis Diversarum Hereseon Liber. Repr. of 1898 ed. 50.00 (ISBN 0-384-46225-1). Johnson Repr.

Weber, Martin. Some Call It Heresy. Woolsey, Raymond, ed. 128p. (Orig.). 1985. pap. 6.95 (ISBN 0-8280-0248-7). Review & Herald.

Whiteford-Boyle, John E. Graffiti on the Wall of Time: Thirty Poems Celebrating the Triumph of Western Heresy. 1983. 5.00. Wheat Forders.

--The Indra Web: The Renewal of Ancient Oriental Concepts in Modern Western Thought. 1983. 10.00. Wheat Forders.

HERMENEUTICS

Barwick, D., et al. Metaphors of Interpretation: Essays in Honour of W. E. H. Stanner. LC 84-71361. (Illus.). 318p. 1987. pap. 28.00 (ISBN 0-08-029875-3). Pergamon.

Bernstein, Richard. Beyond Objectivism & Relativism: Science, Hermeneutics, & Praxis. 320p. (Orig.). 1983. 28.95x (ISBN 0-8122-7906-9); pap. 10.95 (ISBN 0-8122-1165-0). U of Pa Pr.

Birdsong, Robert E. The Challenge of the Aquarian Age. (Aquarian Academy Monograph, Ser. A: Lecture No. 7). 1978. pap. 1.25 (ISBN 0-917108-25-6). Sirius Bks.

Bright, John. The Authority of the Old Testament. (Twin Brooks Ser.). 272p. 1975. pap. 6.95 (ISBN 0-8010-0637-6). Baker Bk.

Bryant, Darrol & Foster, Durwood, eds. Hermeneutics & Unification Theology. LC 80-66201. (Conference Ser.: No. 5). (Illus.). 154p. (Orig.). 1980. pap. 7.95 (ISBN 0-932894-05-4, Pub. by New Era Bks). Paragon Hse.

--Hermeneutics & Unification Theology. LC 80-66201. 154p. (Orig.). 1980. pap. 7.95. Rose Sharon Pr.

Carson, D. A. & Woodbridge, John D., eds. Hermeneutics, Authority & Canon. 480p. 1986. pap. 14.95 (ISBN 0-310-43991-4, 12644P). Zondervan.

Ferster, J. Chaucer on Interpretation. LC 84-23188. 194p. 1985. 29.95 (ISBN 0-521-26661-0). Cambridge U Pr.

Flinn, Frank K., ed. Hermeneutics & Horizons: The Shape of the Future. LC 82-50053. (Conference Ser.: No. 11). xvii, 445p. (Orig.). 1982. pap. text ed. 11.95 (ISBN 0-932894-11-9, Pub. by New Era Bks). Paragon Hse.

Frei, Hans W. The Eclipse of Biblical Narrative: A Study in Eighteenth & Nineteenth-Century Hermeneutics. LC 73-86893. 384p. 1974. pap. 10.95x (ISBN 0-300-02602-1). Yale U Pr.

Gadamer, Hans-Georg. Truth & Method. 516p. 1982. pap. 16.95x (ISBN 0-8264-0431-6). Continuum.

Hansburg, Mary E. Myth, Faith & Hermeneutics. 85p. (Orig.). 1985. pap. 6.95x (ISBN 0-932269-23-0). Wyndham Hall.

Hekman, Susan J. Hermeneutics & the Sociology of Knowledge. LC 85-52311. 224p. 1986. text ed. 29.95x (ISBN 0-268-01083-8). U of Notre Dame Pr.

Hirsch, E. D., Jr. The Aims of Interpretation. LC 75-21269. 1978. pap. 7.00x (ISBN 0-226-34241-7, P767, Phoen). U of Chicago Pr.

Hollinger, Robert, ed. Hermeneutics & Praxis. LC 85-40599. (Revisions Ser.: Vol. 6). 320p. 1985. text ed. 29.95x (ISBN 0-268-01080-3, 85-10802, Dist. by Har-Row); pap. text ed. 12.95x (ISBN 0-268-01081-1, 85-10810). U of Notre Dame Pr.

Ihde, Don. Hermeneutic Phenomenology: The Philosophy of Paul Ricoeur. (Studies in Phenomenology & Existential Philosophy). 1971. 20.95 (ISBN 0-8101-0347-8); pap. 11.95 (ISBN 0-8101-0611-6). Northwestern U Pr.

Klemm, David E., ed. Hermeneutical Inquiry, Vol. I: The Interpretations of Texts. (American Academy of Religion, Studies in Religion). 299p. 1986. 22.95 (ISBN 1-55540-032-9, 01-00-43); pap. 16.95 (ISBN 1-55540-033-7). Scholars Pr GA.

--Hermeneutical Inquiry, Vol. II: The Interpretation of Existence. (American Academy of Religion, Studies in Religion). 409p. 1986. 26.95 (ISBN 1-55540-034-5, 01-00-44); pap. 19.95 (ISBN 1-55540-035-3). Scholars Pr GA.

Kloppenborg, John S. The Formation of Q: Trajectories in Ancient Wisdom Collections. LC 86-45225. 416p. 1987. 39.95 (ISBN 0-8006-3101-3). Fortress.

Lukacher, Ned. Primal Scenes: Literature, Philosophy, Psychoanalysis. LC 85-25513. 368p. 1986. text ed. 24.95x (ISBN 0-8014-1886-0). Cornell U Pr.

Machlis, Gary E., ed. Interpretive Views: Opinions on Evaluating Interpretation. LC 86-61991. (Illus., Orig.). 1986. pap. 9.95 (ISBN 0-940091-15-1). Natl Parks & Cons.

Miller, Donald G., ed. The Hermeneutical Quest: Essays in Honor of James Luther Mays on His Sixty-Fifth Birthday. (Princeton Theological Monograph Ser.: No. 4). 1986. pap. 27.95 (ISBN 0-915138-86-7). Pickwick.

Oliver, Harold H. Relatedness: Essays in Metaphysics & Theology. LC 84-1152. xvi, 178p. 1984. 14.50 (ISBN 0-86554-141-8, MUP/H132). Mercer Univ Pr.

Olson, Alan M. Transcendence & Hermeneutics. (Studies in Philosophy & Religion: No. 2). 1979. lib. bdg. 35.00 (ISBN 90-247-2092-3, Pub. by Martinus Nijhoff Netherlands). Kluwer Academic.

Ommen, Thomas B. The Hermeneutic of Dogma. LC 75-29493. (American Academy of Religion. Dissertation Ser.). 1975. pap. 9.95 (ISBN 0-89130-039-2, 010111). Scholars Pr GA.

Palmer, Richard E. Hermeneutics: Interpretation Theory in Schleiermacher, Dilthey, Heidegger, & Gadamer. LC 68-54885. (Studies in Phenomenology & Existential Philosophy). 1969. 22.95 (ISBN 0-8101-0027-4); pap. 9.95 (ISBN 0-8101-0459-8). Northwestern U Pr.

Pannenberg, Wolfhart. Basic Questions in Theology: Collected Essays, Vol. I. LC 82-15984. 256p. 1983. pap. 12.95 (ISBN 0-664-24466-1). Westminster.

Polka, Brayton. The Dialectic of Biblical Critique: Interpretation & Existence. LC 84-26216. 192p. 1986. 25.00 (ISBN 0-312-19874-4). St Martin.

Raschke, Carl A. The Alchemy of the Word: Language & the End of Theology. LC 79-15490. (American Academy of Religion, Studies in Religion: No. 20). 1979. 14.00 (ISBN 0-89130-319-7, 01-00-20); pap. 9.95 (ISBN 0-89130-320-0). Scholars Pr GA.

Schleiermacher, Friedrich. Hermeneutics: The Handwritten Manuscripts. Kimmerle, Heinz, ed. Duke, James & Forstman, Jack, trs. from Ger. LC 77-13969. (American Academy of Religion. Text & Translations Ser.: No. 1). 1978. pap. text ed. 10.25 (ISBN 0-89130-186-0, 010201). Scholars Pr GA.

Schrag, Calvin O. Communicative Praxis & the Space of Subjectivity. LC 84-48647. (Studies in Phenomenology & Existential Philosophy). 232p. 1986. 27.50x (ISBN 0-253-31383-X). Ind U Pr.

Seung, T. K. Semiotics & Thematics in Hermeneutics. LC 82-4345. 256p. 1982. 27.50 (ISBN 0-231-05410-6). Columbia U Pr.

Tracy, David. Plurality & Ambiguity: Religion As Test Case for Hermeneutics. 175p. 1985. 14.95 (ISBN 0-86683-983-6, 8567, HarpR). Har-Row.

Wachterhauser, Brice R., ed. Hermeneutics & Modern Philosophy. 536p. (Orig.). 1986. 49.50x (ISBN 0-88706-295-4); pap. 16.95x (ISBN 0-88706-296-2). State U NY Pr.

Walhout, Clarence, et al. The Responsibility of Hermeneutics. 160p. (Orig.). 1985. pap. 8.95x (ISBN 0-8028-0029-7). Eerdmans.

Warminski, Andrzej. Readings in Interpretation: Holderlin, Hegel, Heidegger. (Theory & History of Literature Ser.: Vol. 26). 272p. (Orig.). 1987. 29.50 (ISBN 0-8166-1239-0); pap. 12.95 (ISBN 0-8166-1240-4). U of Minn Pr.

Weinsheimer, Joel C. Gadamer's Hermeneutics: A Reading of Truth & Method. LC 84-27028. 288p. 1985. 20.00x (ISBN 0-300-03320-6). Yale U Pr.

Winquist, Charles E. The Communion of Possibility. LC 75-859. (The Religions Quest Ser: Vol. 2). 160p. 1975. pap. text ed. 6.95x (ISBN 0-914914-04-9). New Horizons.

HERMITS

see also Carthusians

Clay, Rotha M. Hermits & Anchorites of England. LC 68-21759. (Illus.). 1968. Repr. of 1914 ed. 40.00x (ISBN 0-8103-3424-0). Gale.

Fitzell, John. Hermit in German Literature: From Lessing to Eichendorff. LC 74-168033. (North Carolina. University. Studies in the Germanic Languages & Literatures: No. 30). Repr. of 1961 ed. 27.00 (ISBN 0-404-50930-4). AMS Pr.

Jerome. Life of Saint Hilarion. 1976. 1.95 (ISBN 0-686-15462-2). Eastern Orthodox.

Sheils, W. J., ed. Monks, Hermits & the Ascetic Tradition. (Studies in Church History: Vol. 22). 500p. 1985. 45.00x (ISBN 0-631-14351-3). Basil Blackwell.

Warren, Ann K. Anchorites & Their Patrons in Medieval England. LC 84-24091. 1985. 42.00x (ISBN 0-520-05278-1). U of Cal Pr.

Weaver, Charles P. The Hermit in English Literature from the Beginnings to 1660. LC 73-515. 1973. lib. bdg. 25.00 (ISBN 0-8414-1456-4). Folcroft.

HEROD 1ST, THE GREAT, KING OF JUDEA, d. 4 B.C.

Schalit, Abraham. Koenig Herodes: Der Mann und sein Werk. Amir, Jehoshua, tr. (Studia Judaica, No. 4). (Ger). 1969. 80.00x (ISBN 3-11-001346-0). De Gruyter.

HEROD 1ST, THE GREAT, KING OF JUDEA, d. 4 B.C.–DRAMA

Greenberg, Noah & Smoldon, W. L., eds. Play of Herod: A Twelfth-Century Musical Drama. (Illus.). 1965. pap. 4.25 (ISBN 0-19-385196-2). Oxford U Pr.

Hebbel, Friedrich. Herod & Mariamne. Curts, Paul H., tr. LC 51-895. (North Carolina. University. Studies in the Germanic Languages & Literatures: No. 3). Repr. of 1950 ed. 27.00 (ISBN 0-404-50903-7). AMS Pr.

Valency, Maurice J. Tragedies of Herod & Mariamne. LC 70-8450. Repr. of 1940 ed. 19.50 (ISBN 0-404-06750-6). AMS Pr.

HEROES

see also Martyrs; Mythology; Saints

Bentley, Eric. The Cult of the Superman. Orig. Title: A Century of Hero Worship. 11.50 (ISBN 0-8446-0486-0). Peter Smith.

Brinton, Daniel G. American Hero-Myths: A Study in the Native Religions of the Western Continent. LC 15-7574. (American Studies Ser). Repr. of 1882 ed. 18.00 (ISBN 0-384-05860-4). Johnson Repr.

Daughters of St. Paul. Heroes from Every Walk of Life. 1981. 5.00 (ISBN 0-8198-3303-7); pap. 4.00 (ISBN 0-8198-3304-5). Dghtrs St Paul.

Dumezil, Georges. The Destiny of the Warrior. Hiltebeitel, Alf, tr. LC 75-113254. 184p. 1971. pap. write for info. (ISBN 0-226-16971-5). U of Chicago Pr.

Fox, Robert J. Saints & Heroes Speak. 512p. 1983. 7.95 (ISBN 0-911988-43-2). Ami Pr.

Hadas, Moses & Smith, Morton. Heroes & Gods: Spiritual Biographies in Antiquity. facsimile ed. LC 77-117800. (Essay Index Reprints - Religious Perspectives Ser.: Vol. 13). Repr. of 1965 ed. 19.00 (ISBN 0-8369-1880-0). Ayer Co Pubs.

Linenthal, Edward T. Changing Images of the Warrior Hero in America: A History of Popular Symbolism. LC 82-22885. (Studies in American Religion: Vol. 6). 296p. 1983. 49.95 (ISBN 0-88946-921-0). E Mellen.

Raglan, FitzRoy. The Hero: A Study in Tradition, Myth, & Drama. LC 75-23424. 296p. 1975. Repr. of 1956 ed. lib. bdg. 45.00x (ISBN 0-8371-8138-0, RATH). Greenwood.

HEROINES

see Women; Women in the Bible

HERRNHUT, GERMANY–HISTORY

Gollin, Gillian L. Moravians in Two Worlds: A Study of Changing Communities. LC 67-19653. 302p. 1967. 31.00x (ISBN 0-231-03033-9). Columbia U Pr.

HERRNHUTER

see Bohemian Brethren; Moravians

HESED (THE WORD)

Finkel, Nosson. Chessed as an Expression of Emunah: A Schmuess. Kaminetsky, Joseph, ed. 0.50 (ISBN 0-914131-10-9, I30). Torah Umesorah.

Glueck, Nelson. Hesed in the Bible. 1968. 12.50x (ISBN 0-87820-104-1, Pub. by Hebrew Union). Ktav.

HEWLETT, MAURICE HENRI, 1861-1923

Haworth, Peter. English Hymns & Ballads. 1927. lib. bdg. 16.50 (ISBN 0-8414-4975-9). Folcroft.

Muir, P. H. A Bibliography of the First Editions of Books by Maurice Henry Hewlett. LC 73-14788. 1927. Repr. lib. bdg. 17.50 (ISBN 0-8414-5981-9). Folcroft.

HICKS, EDWARD, 1780-1849

Ford, Alice E. Edward Hicks, Painter of the Peaceable Kingdom. LC 52-13392. (Illus.). 1973. Repr. of 1952 ed. 63.00 (ISBN 0-527-30400-X). Kraus Repr.

Mather, Eleanore P. Edward Hicks, Primitive Quaker. LC 75-110287. (Illus., Orig.). 1970. pap. 2.50x (ISBN 0-87574-170-3, 170). Pendle Hill.

Mather, Eleanore P. & Miller, Dorothy C. Edward Hicks: His Peaceable Kingdoms & Other Paintings. LC 81-71405. (Illus.). 224p. 1983. 40.00 (ISBN 0-87413-208-8). U Delaware Pr.

HICKS, ELIAS, 1748-1830

Forbush, Bliss. Elias Hicks: Quaker Liberal. LC 56-6250. pap. 95.80 (ISBN 0-317-08431-3, 2050181). Bks Demand UMI.

HIERATIC INSCRIPTIONS

see Egyptian Language–Inscriptions

HIGH HOLY DAYS

see also Rosh Ha-Shanah; Yom Kippur

Bernards, Solomon S., ed. The Living Heritage of the High Holy Days. 31p. 0.50 (ISBN 0-686-74964-2). ADL.

Freehof, Solomon B. Preaching the Bible. 1974. 12.50x (ISBN 0-87068-244-X). Ktav.

HIGHER LAW

see Divine Right of Kings

HILDEGARD, SAINT, 1098?-1178

Hildegard of Bingen. Hildegard of Bingen's Book of Divine Works with Music & Letters. Fox, Matthew, ed. 408p. (Orig.). 1987. pap. 14.95 (ISBN 0-939680-32-7). Bear & Co.

Newman, Barbara. Sister of Wisdom: St. Hildegard's Theology of the Feminine. 1987. 30.00. U of Cal Pr.

--Sister of Wisdom: St. Hildegard's Theology of the Feminine. 288p. 1987. 18.95 (ISBN 0-520-05810-0). U of Cal Pr.

HILTON, WALTER, d. 1396

Kennedy, David G. Incarnational Element in Hiltons Spirituality. Hogg, James, ed. (Elizabethan & Renaissance Studies). 312p. (Orig.). 1982. pap. 15.00 (ISBN 0-317-40146-7, Pub by Salzburg Studies). Longwood Pub Group.

Thomson, Ogilvie. Walter Hilton's Mixed Life. Hogg, James, ed. (Elizabethan & Renaissance Studies). (Orig.). 1985. pap. 15.00 (ISBN 3-7052-0756-3, Pub. by Salzburg Studies). Longwood Pub Group.

HINDI POETRY

Bryant, Kenneth E. Poems to the Child-God: Structures & Strategies in the Poetry of Surdas. LC 77-80467. (Center for South & Southeast Asia Studies, UC Berkeley). 1978. 33.00x (ISBN 0-520-03540-2). U of Cal Pr.

White, Charles S., ed. The Caurasi Pad of Sri Hit Harivams: Introduction, Translation, Notes, & Edited Hindi Text. LC 76-54207. (Asian Studies at Hawaii Ser: No. 16). 212p. 1977. pap. text ed. 10.50x (ISBN 0-8248-0359-0). UH Pr.

HINDU ARCHITECTURE

see Architecture, Hindu

HINDU CIVILIZATION

see Civilization, Hindu

HINDU ETHICS

Bandyopadhyaya, Narayan C. Development of Hindu Polity & Political Theories. 1980. text ed. 28.50x. Coronet Bks.

Dubois, J. A. & Beauchamp, Henry K. Hindu Manners, Customs & Ceremonies. 800p. 1986. Repr. 17.50X (ISBN 0-8364-1760-7, Pub. by Manohar India). South Asia Bks.

Hindery, Roderick. Comparative Ethics in Hindu & Buddhist Traditions. 1978. 18.95 (ISBN 0-89684-017-4, Pub. by Motilal Banarsidass India). Orient Bk Dist.

Krishnamurti, Jiddu. Commentaries on Living, 3 Bks. 3 ser ed. Rajagopal, D., ed. (Ser. 1, LC 67-8405; Ser. 2, LC 67-8407; Ser. 3, LC 67-8416). 1967. Ser. 1. pap. 4.75 (ISBN 0-8356-0390-3, Quest); Ser. 2. pap. 5.50 (ISBN 0-8356-0415-2); Ser. 3. pap. 5.50 (ISBN 0-8356-0402-0). Theos Pub Hse.

Singh, B. Hindu Ethics. 200p. 1984. text ed. 22.50 (ISBN 0-391-02933-9). Humanities.

HINDU HYMNS

Aurobindo, Sri. Hymns to the Mystic Fire. 506p. 1985. pap. 14.00 (ISBN 0-89071-298-0, Pub. by Sri Aurobindo Ashram India). Matagiri.

--Love Treasures: "The Mother", Book One. (Illus.). 98p. 1985. 36.00x (ISBN 0-89071-333-2, Pub. by Sri Aurobindo Ashram India). Matagiri.

Frawley, David. Hymns from the Golden Age: Selected Hymns from the Rig Veda with Yogic Interpretation. 256p. 1986. 22.00 (ISBN 81-208-0072-9, Pub. by Motilal Banarsidass). South Asia Bks.

Griffith, Ralph T., tr. from Sanskrit. Sam-Veda Sanhita. 338p. 1978. Repr. of 1907 ed. 22.00 (ISBN 0-89684-160-X). Orient Bk Dist.

Hindu Samskaras: Sacraments. Date not set. pap. price not set (ISBN 0-938924-17-6). Sri Shirdi Sai.

Maurer, Walter. Pinnacles of India's Past: Selections from the Rgveda. LC 85-30784. (University of Pennsylvania Studies on South Asia: No. 2). 350p. 1986. 44.00x (ISBN 0-915027-62-3); pap. 20.00x (ISBN 0-915027-83-6). Benjamins North Am.

Mukerjee, Radhakamal, tr. The Song of the Self Supreme: Astavakra Gita. LC 74-24308. 293p. 1981. 9.95 (ISBN 0-913922-14-5). Dawn Horse Pr.

Muller, F. & Oldenberg, H. Vedic Hymns. (Sacred Bks. of the East: Vols. 32, 46). both vols. 30.00 (ISBN 0-89581-529-X); 15.00 ea. Asian Human Pr.

Muller, Max, ed. Sacred Book of the East: Vedic Hymns, 2 vols. 250.00 (ISBN 0-87968-438-0). Krishna Pr.

HINDU LAW

Chadha, P. N. Hindu Law. 354p. 1982. 60.00x (Pub. by Eastern Bk India). State Mutual Bk.

--Hindu Law: Edition. abr. ed. 354p. 1982. 60.00x (Pub. by Eastern Bk India). State Mutual Bk.

Doongaji, Damayanti. Law of Crime & Punishment in Ancient Hindu Society. 310p. 1986. 48.50X (ISBN 81-202-0168-X, Pub. by Ajanta). South Asia Bks.

Kern, H., tr. The Saddharma-Pundarika: Lotus of True Law. lib. bdg. 79.95 (ISBN 0-87968-530-1). Krishna Pr.

Lariviere, Richard W. The Divyatattva of Raghunandana Bhattacarya: Ordeals in Classical Hindu Law. 1982. 22.00x (ISBN 0-8364-0854-3, Pub. by Manohar India). South Asia Bks.

Markby, William. An Introduction to Hindu & Mohammedan Law. LC 78-58189. 1978. Repr. of 1906 ed. lib. bdg. 25.00 (ISBN 0-89341-509-X). Longwood Pub Group.

Nagpal, R. C. Modern Hindu Law. (Hindi.). 815p. 1984. 225.00x (Pub. by Eastern Bk India). State Mutual Bk.

--Modern Hindu Law. 992p. 1983. 360.00x (Pub. by Eastern Bk India). State Mutual Bk.

Sharma, K. P. Hindu Vidhi (Hindu Law in Hindi) 390p. 1980. 90.00x (Pub. by Eastern Bk India). State Mutual Bk.

HINDU LITERATURE

see also Hinduism–Sacred Books (Selections: Extracts, etc.)

Arnold, Edwin. Song Celestial. 1971. pap. 1.50 (ISBN 0-8356-0418-7, Quest). Theos Pub Hse.

Atma: Contemporary Vedic Library Series Based on the Teachings of A. C. Bhaktivedanta Swami Prabhupada. 1.50 (ISBN 0-89213-122-5). Bhaktivedanta.

Bhagavad-Gita. The Song of God. Prabhavananda, Swami & Isherwood, C., trs. pap. 2.95 (ISBN 0-451-62576-5, Ment). NAL.

Bhattacharya, Bhabani, ed. Contemporary Indian Short Stories, 2 vols. 1967. Vol. 1. 3.50 (ISBN 0-88253-409-2); Vol. 2. 3.50 (ISBN 0-88253-327-4). Ind-US Inc.

Burton, Richard, tr. The Kama Sutra of Vatsyayana. (Hindustani.). 340p. 1986. 16.95 (ISBN 0-88029-089-7, Pub. by Dorset). Hippocrene Bks.

Dasa Goswaini, Satsvarupa. Living with the Scriptures, Vol. 1. Dattatreya dasa, ed. 120p. 1984. text ed. 5.00 (ISBN 0-911233-26-1). Gita Nagari.

Dasa Goswami, Satsvarupa. Prabhupada Nectar, Vol. 3. Bimala dasi, ed. 160p. 1985. pap. text ed. 2.00 (ISBN 0-911233-24-5). Gita Nagari.

Das Goswami, Satsvarupa. Prabhupada Nectar, Bk. 2. Dasi, Bimala, ed. 145p. pap. 4.99 (ISBN 0-911233-23-7). Gita Nagari.

Hindu Literature. 474p. 1986. Repr. 25.00X (ISBN 0-8364-1763-1, Pub. by Manohar India). South Asia Bks.

Lutze, Lothar. Hindu Writings in Post-Colonial India. 1985. 27.00x (ISBN 0-8364-1422-5, Pub. by Manohar India). South Asia Bks.

Mishra, V. B. From the Vedas to the Manu-Samhita: A Cultural Study. 160p. 1982. text ed. 19.95x (ISBN 0-391-02705-0). Humanities.

Murthy, B. Srinivasa, tr. from Sanskrit. The Bhagavad Gita: Translated with Introduction & Notes. LC 84-82433. 150p. 1985. pap. 9.95 (ISBN 0-941910-01-6). Long Beach Pubns.

Naravane, V. S. Premchand: His Life & Work. 280p. 1980. text ed. 25.00x (ISBN 0-7069-1091-5, Pub. by Vikas India). Advent NY.

Nivedita, Sr. Complete Works of Sister Nivedita, 4 vols. Incl. Vol. 1. Our Master & His Message, the Master As I Saw Him, Kali the Mother, Lectures & Articles (ISBN 0-87481-112-0); Vol. 2. The Web of Indian Life, an Indian Study on Love & Death, Studies from an Eastern Home, Lectures & Articles (ISBN 0-87481-113-9); Vol. 3. Indian Art, Cradle Tales of Hinduism, Religion & Dharma (ISBN 0-87481-114-7); Vol. 4. Footfalls of Indian History, Bodh-Gaya, Civic Ideal & Indian Nationality, Hints on National Education in India (ISBN 0-87481-115-5); Vol. V. Lectures & Writings (ISBN 0-87481-226-7). 60.00x set (ISBN 0-87481-216-X). Vedanta Pr.

--Cradle Tales of Hinduism. (Illus.). 329p. 1972. pap. 5.95 (ISBN 0-87481-131-7). Vedanta Pr.

Panikkar, Raimundo. Mantramanjari: An Anthology of the Veclas for Modern Man & Contemporary Celebration. 1977. 55.00x (ISBN 0-520-02854-6). U of Cal Pr.

Prabhavananda, Swami & Manchester, Frederick, trs. Upanishads: Breath of the Eternal. LC 48-5935. pap. 6.95 (ISBN 0-87481-040-X). Vedanta Pr.

Sri Aurobindo. Essays on the Gita. 1976. pap. 8.75 (ISBN 0-89071-222-0). Matagiri.

Swami Vivekananda. Religion of Love. 114p. pap. 2.50 (ISBN 0-87481-129-5). Vedanta Pr.

--What Religion Is in the Words of Vivekananda. Yale, John, ed. pap. 5.95 (ISBN 0-87481-213-5). Vedanta Pr.

Talib, Gubachana S. Bani of Sri Guru Amardas. 1979. text ed. 29.50 (ISBN 0-89684-078-6, Pub. by Sterling New Delhi). Orient Bk Dist.

Thomas, P. Kama Kalpa or the Hindu Ritual of Love. 14th ed. (Illus.). ix, 151p. 1981. text ed. 35.00x (ISBN 0-86590-031-0, Pub. by Taraporevala India). Apt Bks.

Valmiki. Sundara Kandam of Srimad Valmiki Ramayana. Swami Tapasyananda, tr. from Sanskrit. 286p. 1984. 15.00 (ISBN 0-87481-527-4, Pub. by Ramakrishna Math Madras India). Vedanta Pr.

Wade, A. The Ten Principal Upanishads. 75.00 (ISBN 0-8490-1183-3). Gordon Pr.

Zaehner, R. C., ed. & tr. Hindu Scriptures. 1978. 11.95x (ISBN 0-460-10944-8, Evman); pap. 5.95x (ISBN 0-460-11944-3, Evman). Biblio Dist.

HINDU MUSIC

see Music, Indic

HINDU MYSTICISM

see Mysticism–Hinduism

HINDU SCULPTURE

see Sculpture, Hindu

HINDU SECTS

see also Shaktism; Vaishnavism

Bergaigne, Abel. Vedic Religion. Paranjpe, V. G., tr. 1978. 25.00 (ISBN 0-89684-006-9, Pub. by Motilal Banarsidass India). Orient Bk Dist.

Bhagowalia, Urmila. Vaisnavism & Society in Northern India. 1980. 22.00x (ISBN 0-8364-0664-8, Pub. by Intellectual India). South Asia Bks.

Bhaktivedanta, Swami A. C. Srimad Bhagavatam: First Canto, 3 vols. LC 73-169353. (Illus.). 1972. 12.95 ea. Vol. 1 (ISBN 0-912776-27-7). Vol. 2 (ISBN 0-912776-29-3). Vol. 3 (ISBN 0-912776-34-X). Bhaktivedanta.

--Srimad Bhagavatam: Fourth Canto, 4 vols. LC 73-169353. (Illus.). 1974. 12.95 ea. Vol. 1 (ISBN 0-912776-38-2). Vol. 2 (ISBN 0-912776-47-1). Vol. 3 (ISBN 0-912776-48-X). Vol. 4 (ISBN 0-912776-49-8). Bhaktivedanta.

--Srimad Bhagavatam: Second Canto, 2 vols. LC 73-169353. (Illus.). 1972. 12.95 ea. Vol. 1 (ISBN 0-912776-28-5). Vol. 2 (ISBN 0-912776-35-8). Bhaktivedanta.

--Srimad Bhagavatam: Third Canto, 4 vols. LC 73-169353. (Illus.). 1974. 12.95 ea. Vol. 1 (ISBN 0-912776-37-4). Vol. 2 (ISBN 0-912776-44-7). Vol. 3 (ISBN 0-912776-46-3). Vol. 4 (ISBN 0-912776-75-7). Bhaktivedanta.

Bhandarkar, R. G. Vaisnavism Saivism & Minor Religious Systems. 238p. 1986. Repr. 14.00X (ISBN 0-8364-1704-6, Pub. by Minerva India). South Asia Bks.

Chatterji, J. C. Kashmir Shaivaism. (Cultural Perspectives Ser.). 176p. (Orig.). 1986. 29.50x (ISBN 0-88706-179-6); pap. 9.95x (ISBN 0-88706-180-X). State U NY Pr.

Chattopadhyaya, S. Evolution of Hindu Sects. 1970. text ed. 18.00x. Coronet Bks.

Kinsley, David R. The Divine Player: A Study of Krishna Lila. 1978. 17.95 (ISBN 0-89684-019-0, Pub. by Motilal Barnarsidass India). Orient Bk Dist.

Mudugula, I. S. The Acarya: Sandara of Kaladi - A Story. (Illus.). 142p. 1985. 16.00 (ISBN 0-317-46523-6, Pub. by Motilal Banarsidass India). Orient Bk Dist.

Mukherjee, Prabhat. History of the Chaitanya Faith in Orissa. 1979. 14.00x (ISBN 0-8364-0547-1). South Asia Bks.

Muktananda, Swami. A Book for the Mind. 40p. (Orig.). 1976. pap. 1.75 (ISBN 0-685-99448-1). SYDA Found.

--God Is with You. (Illus.). 40p. (Orig.). 1978. pap. 1.75 (ISBN 0-914602-57-8). SYDA Found.

Nair, P. T., ed. Bruton's Visit of Lord Jagannath 350 Years Ago: British Beginnings in Orissa. 1986. 14.00x (ISBN 0-8364-1610-4, Pub. by Minerva India). South Asia Bks.

Nandimath, S. C. A Handbook of Virasaivism. 1979. 15.00 (ISBN 0-89684-053-0, Pub. by Motilal Banarsidass India). Orient Bk Dist.

Oman, J. C. The Mystics, Ascetics & Saints of India: A Study of Sadhmaism with an Account of the Yogis, Sanyasis, Bairagis, & other Strange Hindu Sectarians. 308p. 1984. text ed. 38.50x (ISBN 0-89563-650-6). Coronet Bks.

Seth, S. J. The Divinity of Krishna. 1984. text ed. 14.00x. Coronet Bks.

Sherring. Hindu Tribes & Castes, 3 vols. 1219p. 1974. Repr. of 1881 ed. Set. text ed. 120.00. Vol. 1, Benares. Vol. 2, Mohamedan Tribes of the North West Frontier & Aboriginal Tribes of the Central Provinces. Vol. 3 Natural History of the Hindu Caste, Unity of the Hindu Race. Coronet Bks.

Swami Muktananda. In the Company of a Siddha: Interviews & Conversations with Swami Muktananda. rev. ed. LC 78-65085. 192p. 1978. 5.95. SYDA Found.

--Swami Muktananda American Tour 1970. LC 76-670007. 103p. 1974. 2.95 (ISBN 0-914602-25-X). SYDA Found.

HINDU SOCIOLOGY

see Sociology, Hindu

HINDUISM

see also Advaita; Bhakti; Brahmanism; Civilization, Hindu; Dharma; God (Hinduism); Hindu Hymns; Hindu Sects; Jains; Karma; Maya (Hinduism); Mysticism–Hinduism; Tantrism; Vedanta; Vedas; Women in Hinduism; Yoga

Aggarwal, Manju. I Am a Hindu. LC 85-50166. (My Heritage Ser.). (Illus.). 32p. 1985. PLB 9.90 (ISBN 0-531-10018-9). Watts.

Anand, Balwant S. Guru Tegh Bahadur. 1979. text ed. 11.95 (ISBN 0-89684-076-X, Pub. by Sterling New Delhi). Orient Bk Dist.

Andersen, Walter K. & Damle, Shridhar D. The Brotherhood in Saffron: The Rashtriya Swayamsevak Sangh & Hindu Revivalism. (Special Studies on South & Southeast Asia). 246p. 1987. pap. 27.50 (ISBN 0-8133-7358-1). Westview.

Bahree, Pat. Hinduism. (World Religions Ser.). (Illus.). 72p. 1984. 16.95 (ISBN 0-7134-3654-9, Pub. by Batsford England). David & Charles.

Bhaktivedanta, Swami A. C. Prahlad, Picture & Story Book. LC 72-2032. (Illus.). 1973. pap. 2.95 (ISBN 0-685-47513-1). Bhaktivedanta.

--Raja-Vidya: The King of Knowledge. LC 72-84845. (Illus.). 1973. pap. 1.95 (ISBN 0-912776-40-4). Bhaktivedanta.

Boger, Ann C. & DeOreo, Joellen K. Sacred India: Hinduism, Buddhism, Jainism. LC 85-19559. (Illus.). 60p. 1986. pap. 7.95 (ISBN 0-910386-84-6, Pub. by Cleveland Mus Art). Ind U Pr.

Brabazon, Francis. In Dust I Sing. 150p. 1974. 8.95 (ISBN 0-940700-08-5); pap. 4.95 (ISBN 0-940700-07-7). Meher Baba Info.

--The Word at World's End. 88p. 1971. 5.95 (ISBN 0-940700-04-2); pap. 3.45 (ISBN 0-940700-03-4). Meher Baba Info.

Channa, V. C. Hinduism. 1985. 17.50x (ISBN 0-8364-1451-9, Pub. by National Sahitya Akademi). South Asia Bks.

Chapple, Christopher. Karma & Creativity. (Religion Ser.). 128p. (Orig.). 1986. 29.50x (ISBN 0-88706-250-4); pap. 9.95x (ISBN 0-88706-251-2). State U NY Pr.

Chaudhuri, Nirad C. Hinduism: A Religion to Live by. 1979. pap. 9.95. Oxford U Pr.

Chennakesvan, Sarasvati. A Critical Study of Hinduism. 1980. 12.50x (ISBN 0-8364-0614-1). South Asia Bks.

Crompton, Yorke. Hinduism. 1985. 13.00 (ISBN 0-7062-3598-3, Pub. by Ward Lock Educ Co Ltd). State Mutual Bk.

Da Free John. The Eating Gorilla Comes in Peace. LC 75-24582. 1979. 12.95 (ISBN 0-913922-19-6). Dawn Horse Pr.

Dange, Sindhu S. Hindu Domestic Rituals. 1986. 12.00x (ISBN 81-202-0138-8, Pub. by Ajanta). South Asia Bks.

Danielou, Alain. The Gods of India. (Illus.). 441p. (Orig.). 1985. pap. 18.95 (ISBN 0-89281-101-3). Inner Tradit.

Das, Veena. Structure & Cognition: Aspects of Hindu Caste & Ritual. 2nd ed. 1982. 24.95x (ISBN 0-19-561395-3). Oxford U Pr.

Das Goswami, Satsvar upa. Reading Reform. Dattatreya dasa, ed. 120p. 1985. pap. text ed. 4.00 (ISBN 0-911233-28-8). Gita Nagari.

Das Goswami, Satsvarupa. Living with the Scriptures, Vol. 2. Dattatreya dasa, ed. 120p. 1985. text ed. 5.00 (ISBN 0-911233-27-X). Gita Nagari.

--Prabhupada: He Built a House in Which the Whole World Could Live. 7.95 (ISBN 0-89213-133-0). Bhaktivedanta.

--Prabhupada Nectar, Vol. 4. Bimala dasi, ed. 160p. 1985. pap. text ed. 2.00 (ISBN 0-911233-29-6). Gita Nagari.

Das Goswami, Satvarupa. Prabhupada Nectar, Vol. 5. Bimala dasi, ed. 160p. 1986. pap. text ed. 4.00 (ISBN 0-911233-31-8). Gita Nagari.

Dash, Bhagwan & Kashyap, Lalitesh. Basic Principles of Ayurveda. (Illus.). 628p. 1980. 44.95x (ISBN 0-940500-34-5). Asia Bk Corp.

Death Rites. Date not set. pap. price not set (ISBN 0-938924-18-4). Sri Shirdi Sai.

Dell, David J., et al. Guide to Hindu Religion. 1981. lib. bdg. 47.00 (ISBN 0-8161-7903-4, Hall Reference). G K Hall.

De Maillard, Benjamin. Hindu Theology, Egyptian Civilization & the Growth of European Culture. (Illus.). 156p. 1986. 137.50 (ISBN 0-89266-548-3). Am Classical Coll Pr.

Desai, Santosh N. Hinduism in Thai Life. 163p. 1980. 23.95x (ISBN 0-940500-66-3, Pub by Popular Prakashan India). Asia Bk Corp.

Donato, Sri. The Day of Brahma. Morningland Publications, Inc., ed. (Illus.). 377p. 1981. pap. 10.00 (ISBN 0-935146-20-2). Morningland.

Dwivedi, A. N. Essentials of Hinduism, Jainism & Buddhism. 148p. 1979. 12.00 (ISBN 0-88065-083-4, Pub. by Messers Today & Tomorrows Printers & Publishers India). Scholarly Pubns.

Ellwood, Rober S., ed. Eastern Spirituality in America: Selected Writings. (Sources of American Spirituality Ser.). 256p. 1987. pap. 16.95 (ISBN 0-8091-0388-5). Paulist Pr.

Embree, Ainslie T., ed. The Hindu Tradition. 448p. 1972. pap. 5.95 (ISBN 0-394-71702-3, V696, Vin). Random.

Feldhaus, Anne, ed. The Deeds of God in Rddhipur. LC 83-21949. 1984. 27.00x (ISBN 0-19-503438-4). Oxford U Pr.

Frazier, Allie M., ed. Readings in Eastern Religious Thought, 3 vols. Incl. Vol. 1. Hinduism; Vol. 2. Buddhism; Vol. 3. Chinese & Japanese Religions. (ISBN 0-664-24848-9). LC 69-14197. 1969. Westminster.

Ghurye, G. S. Gods & Men. 1962. 39.50x (ISBN 0-317-27474-0). Elliots Bks.

Guenon, Rene. Studies in Hinduism. 1986. 18.50x (ISBN 0-8364-1548-5, Pub. by Navrang). South Asia Bks.

Hansadutta. The Book: What the Black Sheep Said. LC 85-5636. (Illus.). 1160p. (Orig.). 1985. pap. text ed. 9.95 (ISBN 0-933593-03-1). Hansa Pub.

Hawkridge, Emma. Indian Gods & Kings: The Story of a Living Past. facs. ed. LC 68-24853. (Essay Index Reprint Ser). 1935. 21.50 (ISBN 0-8369-0521-0). Ayer Co Pubs.

Hazra, R. C. Studies in the Puranic Records on Hindu Rites & Customs. 2nd ed. 1975. 28.00 (ISBN 0-8426-0965-2). Orient Bk Dist.

Hefner, Robert W. Hindu Javanese: Tengger Tradition & Islam. LC 85-3426. (Illus.). 300p. 1985. text ed. 36.00x (ISBN 0-691-09413-6). Princeton U Pr.

Hindu Samskaras: Sacraments. Date not set. pap. price not set (ISBN 0-938924-17-6). Sri Shirdi Sai.

Hobson, John. Hinduism & Its Relation to Christianity. 1977. lib. bdg. 59.95 (ISBN 0-8490-1951-6). Gordon Pr.

Holland, Barron, compiled by. Popular Hinduism & Hindu Mythology: An Annotated Bibliography. LC 79-7188. 1979. lib. bdg. 45.00 (ISBN 0-313-21358-5, HPH/). Greenwood.

Ironbiter, Suzanne. Devl. 125p. (Orig.). 1987. pap. 6.95 (ISBN 0-938999-02-8). Yuganta Pr.

Kalchuri, Bhau. Meher Roshani. 144p. (Orig.). Date not set. pap. 10.00 (ISBN 0-932947-06-9). Manifestation.

Kanitkar, V. P. Hinduism. (Religions of the World Ser.). (Illus.). 48p. 1986. PLB 10.90 (ISBN 0-531-18068-9, Pub. by Bookwright). Watts.

Kaye, G. R. Hindu Astronomy: Ancient Science of the Hindus. 134p. 1981. text ed. 42.00x. Coronet Bks.

Kinsley, David. Hinduism: A Cultural Perspective. (Illus.). 200p. 1982. 17.00 (ISBN 0-13-388975-0). P-H.

Kumarappa, Bharatan. Realism & Illusionism in Hinduism. xvi, 356p. 1986. Repr. text ed. 40.00x (ISBN 81-7047-012-9, Pub. by Mayur Pubns India). Apt Bks.

McDermott, Robert A., ed. Focus on Hinduism: Audio Visual Resources for Teaching Religion. 2nd, enl. ed. Morgan, Kenneth W. & Smith, Daniel. LC 81-8085. (Focus on Hinduism & Buddhism Ser.). 160p. 1981. text ed. 14.50 (ISBN 0-89012-018-8); pap. text ed. 7.95 (ISBN 0-89012-019-6). Anima Pubns.

Mahaprajna, Yuvacharya. Mysteries of Mind. 225p. 1982. 11.00 (ISBN 0-88065-223-3, Pub. by Messers Today & Tomorrow Printers & Publishers). Scholarly Pubns.

Maharaj, Rabindranath R. & Hunt, Dave. Death of a Guru. Rev. ed. LC 84-81212. 208p. 1986. pap. 5.95 (ISBN 0-89081-434-1). Harvest Hse.

Maitra, H. Hinduism: The World Ideal. 34.95 (ISBN 0-8490-0302-4). Gordon Pr.

Matrisciana, Caryl. Gods of the New Age. (Orig.). 1985. pap. 6.95 (ISBN 0-89081-445-7). Harvest Hse.

Mishr, R. P. Hinduism: The Faith of the Future. 131p. 1981. 15.95x (ISBN 0-940500-17-5, Pub. by S S Pubs India). Asia Bk Corp.

--Hinduism: The Faith of the Future. 131p. 1981. text ed. 15.00x (ISBN 0-391-02515-5). Humanities.

Monier-Williams, Monier. Indian Wisdom. 575p. 1978. Repr. of 1893 ed. 21.00x (ISBN 0-89684-105-7, Pub. by Cosmo Pubns India). Orient Bk Dist.

Moor, Edward. Hindu Pantheon. 45.00 (ISBN 0-89314-409-6). Philos Res.

Morgan, Kenneth W., ed. The Religion of the Hindus: Interpreted by Hindus. LC 53-10466. Repr. of 1953 ed. 112.00 (ISBN 0-8357-9975-1, 2015620). Bks Demand UMI.

Morinis, E. Alan, ed. Pilgrimage in the Hindu Tradition: A Case Study of West Bengal. (Illus.). 1984. 34.95x (ISBN 0-19-561412-7). Oxford U Pr.

Mukherjee, Prabhat. History of the Chaitanya Faith in Orissa. 1979. 14.00x (ISBN 0-8364-0547-1). South Asia Bks.

Nurbakhsh, Javad. Traditions of the Prophet (Ahadith) Rothschild, Jeffrey, et al, eds. Lewisehn, Leonard & Nurbakhsh, Ali-Reza, trs. 104p. 1981. pap. 6.00x (ISBN 0-933546-06-8). KhaniQahi-Nimatullahi-Sufi.

O'Malley, Lewis S. Popular Hinduism: The Religion of the Masses. LC 70-142072. 1971. Repr. of 1935 ed. 24.00 (ISBN 0-384-43305-7). Johnson Repr.

Organ, Troy W. Hindu Quest for the Perfection of Man. x, 439p. 1970. pap. 14.00x (ISBN 0-8214-0575-6). Ohio U Pr.

Origins: Contemporary Vedic Library Series Based on the Teachings of A. C. Bhaktivedanta Swami Prabhupada. 1.50 (ISBN 0-89213-137-3). Bhaktivedanta.

Osborne, Arthur. The Incredible Sai Baba: The Life & Miracles of a Modern-Day Saint. 102p. 1985. pap. text ed. 5.00x (ISBN 0-86125-105-9, Pub. by Orient Longman Ltd India). Apt Bks.

Pal, Pratapaditya. Hindu Religion & Iconology According to the Tantrasara. LC 81-52893. (Tantric Tradition Ser.). Orig. Title: Tantrasara. (Illus.). 172p. 1982. pap. 10.95 (ISBN 0-941582-00-0). Vichitra Pr.

Patel, Satyavrata. Hinduism: Religion & Way of Life. 165p. 1980. 15.95x (ISBN 0-940500-25-6). Asia Bk Corp.

Podgorski, Frank R. Hinduism: A Beautiful Mosaic. LC 85-51907. i, 61p. 1984. pap. text ed. 6.95x (ISBN 0-932269-12-5). Wyndham Hall.

Prabhavananda, Swami. Religion in Practice. 6.95 (ISBN 0-87481-016-7). Vedanta Pr.

Radhakrishnan, S. Hindu View of Life. (Unwin Paperbacks Ser.). 92p. 1980. pap. 4.95 (ISBN 0-04-294115-6). Allen Unwin.

Richards, Glyn, ed. A Source Book of Modern Hinduism. 220p. 1985. 20.00 (ISBN 0-7007-0173-7). Salem Hse Pubs.

Ross, Nancy W. Three Ways of Asian Wisdom: Hinduism, Buddhism, Zen. (Illus.). 1978. pap. 12.95 (ISBN 0-671-24230-X, Touchstone Bks). S&S.

Sahukar, Mani. Sai Baba, the Saint of Shirdi. LC 75-29273. 1977. 3.95 (ISBN 0-913922-11-0). Dawn Horse Pr.

Sarma, D. S. A Primer of Hinduism. 170p. 1987. pap. 3.25 (ISBN 0-87481-532-0, Pub. by Ramakrishna Math Madras India). Vedanta Pr.

Satyaprakash, ed. Hinduism: A Select Bibliography. 1984. 46.50x (ISBN 0-8364-1121-8, Pub. by Indian Doc Serv India). South Asia Bks.

Sen, Kshitimohan M. Hinduism. (Orig.). 1962. pap. 5.95 (ISBN 0-14-020515-2, Pelican). Penguin.

Shah, Priyabala. Tilaka: Hindu Marks. (Illus.). 108p. 1985. 29.95x (ISBN 0-318-20319-7, Pub. by New Order Bk Co India). Humanities.

Sharma, Arvind. Textual Studies in Hinduism. 1985. 12.50x (ISBN 0-8364-1291-5, Pub. by Manohar India). South Asia Bks.

Shivkumar, Muni. The Doctrine of Liberation in Indian Religion. 1984. text ed. 14.00x (ISBN 0-89563-286-1). Coronet Bks.

Shourie, Arun. Hinduism: Essence & Consequence. 1980. text ed. 40.00x (ISBN 0-7069-0834-1, Pub. by Vikas India). Advent NY.

Singh, Balbir. Hindu Metaphysics. 256p. 1986. text ed. 25.00x (ISBN 0-391-03408-1). Humanities.

Singh, Fauja. Guru Amar Das. 196p. 1979. text ed. 9.95 (ISBN 0-89684-080-8, Pub. by Sterling New Delhi). Orient Bk Dist.

Singh, Harbans. Guru Gobind Singh. 1979. text ed. 6.95 (ISBN 0-89684-073-5, Pub. by Sterling New Delhi). Orient Bk Dist.

Sinha, B. C. Hinduism & Symbol Worship. 1985. 17.50x (ISBN 0-8364-1297-4, Pub. by Agam Kala Prakashan). South Asia Bks.

Smart, Ninian & Purnananda, Swami. Prophet of the New Hindu Age: The Life & Times of Archarya Pranavananda. (Illus.). 256p. 1985. 15.00 (ISBN 0-04-922032-2); pap. 9.50 (ISBN 0-04-922033-0). Allen Unwin.

Smith, Robert S. In the Image of God. 150p. (Orig.). 1987. pap. 5.95 (ISBN 0-938999-01-X). Yuganta Pr.

Srinivasan, A. V. A Hindu Primer: Yaksha Prashna. (Illus.). 78p. 1984. pap. 7.70 (ISBN 0-86578-249-0, 6203). Ind-US Inc.

Svarupa dasa, Ravindra. Encounters with the Lord of the Universe. Swami, Jayadvaita & Dravida dasa, eds. 130p. 1985. pap. text ed. 3.50 (ISBN 0-911233-20-2). Gita Nagari.

Swami Bhaktivedanta. Sri Isopanisad: Discovering the Original Person. 1985. 7.95; pap. 2.95 (ISBN 0-89213-138-1). Bhaktivedanta.

Thomas, P. Hindu Religion, Customs & Manners. 6th ed. (Illus.). 144p. 1981. text ed. 35.00x (ISBN 0-86590-036-1, Pub. by Taraporevala India). Apt Bks.

Vable, D. The Arya Samaj: Hindu without Hinduism. 1983. text ed. 25.00x (ISBN 0-7069-2131-3, Pub. by Vikas India). Advent NY.

Vetalapancavimsati. Vikram & the Vampire, or Tales of the Hindu Diety. Burton, Isadel, ed. Burton, Richard F., tr. (Illus.). 264p. Repr. of 1893 ed. text ed. 20.00x. Coronet Bks.

Walker, Benjamin. Hindu World: An Encyclopedic Survey of Hinduism, 2 vols. 1983. Set. text ed. 72.00x. Coronet Bks.

Wedding: (Hindu) (Illus.). Date not set. pap. price not set (ISBN 0-938924-16-8). Sri Shirdi Sai.

Who Are They? (Contemporary Vedic Library Series Based on the Teachings of A. C. Bhaktivedanta Swami Prabhupada). 1.50 (ISBN 0-89213-111-X). Bhaktivedanta.

Wilson, H. H. Religion of the Hindus. 416p. 1978. Repr. of 1862 ed. 13.95x (ISBN 0-89684-135-9). Orient Bk Dist.

Yogeshananda, Swami. Way of the Hindu. (The Way Ser.). pap. 5.95 (ISBN 0-7175-0626-6). Dufour.

Zaehner, Robert C. Hinduism. 1962. pap. 8.95 (ISBN 0-19-888012-X). Oxford U Pr.

HINDUISM–ADDRESSES, ESSAYS, AND LECTURES

Ashby, Philip H. Modern Trends in Hinduism. LC 73-20262. (Lectures in the History of Religions Ser.: No. 10). 143p. 1974. 22.50x (ISBN 0-231-03768-6). Columbia U Pr.

Aurobindo, Sri. Essays on the Gita. 588p. 1983. 12.50 (ISBN 0-89071-297-2, Pub. by Sri Aurobindo Ashram India); pap. 8.75 (ISBN 0-89071-296-4, Pub. by Sri Aurobindo Ashram India). Matagiri.

Babb, Lawrence A. The Divine Hierarchy: Popular Hinduism in Central India. LC 75-61693. (Illus.). 266p. 1975. 27.50x (ISBN 0-231-03882-8). Columbia U Pr.

Brockington, J. L. The Sacred Thread: Hinduism in Continuity & Diversity. 222p. 1981. pap. 10.50x (ISBN 0-85224-393-6, Pub. by Edinburgh U Pr Scotland). Columbia U Pr.

Coomaraswamy, Ananda K. Hinduism & Buddhism. LC 78-138215. 1971. Repr. of 1943 ed. lib. bdg. 22.50x (ISBN 0-8371-5570-3, COHB). Greenwood.

Dubash, P. N. Hindoo Art in Its Social Setting. (Illus.). 278p. 1986. Repr. 30.00X (ISBN 0-8364-1752-6, Pub. by Usha). South Asia Bks.

Eck, Diana L. Banaras: City of Light. LC 81-48134. (Illus.). 1982. 25.00 (ISBN 0-394-51971-X). Knopf.

Guenon, Rene. Studies in Hinduism. 1986. 18.50x (ISBN 0-8364-1548-5, Pub. by Navrang). South Asia Bks.

Isherwood, Christopher. My Guru & His Disciple. 352p. 1981. pap. 4.95 (ISBN 0-14-005837-0). Penguin.

Kinsley, David. Hindu Goddesses: Visions of the Divine Feminine in the Hindu Religious Tradition. LC 84-28000. (Hermeneutics: Studies in the History of Religions). 1985. 35.00x (ISBN 0-520-05393-1). U of Cal Pr.

Marglin, Frederique A. Wives of the God-King: The Rituals of the Devadasis of Puri. (Illus.). 1985. 29.95x (ISBN 0-19-561731-2). Oxford U Pr.

Monier-Williams, M. Hinduism: Non-Christian Religious Systems. lib. bdg. 79.95 (ISBN 0-87968-546-8). Krishna Pr.

Nikhilananda, Swami. Hinduism: Its Meaning for the Liberation of the Spirit: a Survey of Hinduism. LC 58-6155. 189p. 5.50 (ISBN 0-911206-13-2). Ramakrishna.

Ramanayyan, Venkata. An Essay on the Origin of the South Indian Temples. (Illus.). 92p. 1986. Repr. 15.00X (ISBN 0-8364-1725-9, Pub. by Manohar India). South Asia Bks.

Rammohun Roy, R. The English Works of Raja Ramohun Roy. Ghose, Jogendra C., ed. LC 75-41220. Repr. of 1906 ed. 49.50 (ISBN 0-404-14738-0). AMS Pr.

Schweitzer, Albert. Indian Thought & Its Development. 1962. 11.00 (ISBN 0-8446-2893-X). Peter Smith.

Sharma, Arvind. Textual Studies in Hinduism. 1985. 12.50x (ISBN 0-8364-1291-5, Pub. by Manohar India). South Asia Bks.

Smith, F. H. Outline of Hinduism. 59.95 (ISBN 0-8490-0788-7). Gordon Pr.

Swami Swahananda. Hindu Symbology & Other Essays. 266p. (Orig.). 1983. pap. 4.95 (ISBN 0-87481-526-6, Pub. by Ramakrishna Math Madras India). Vedanta Pr.

Swami Vivekananda. Complete Works of Swami Vivekananda, 8 vols. pap. 55.00x (ISBN 0-87481-176-7). Vedanta Pr.

HINDUISM–DICTIONARIES

Coward, Harold G. Sphota Theory of Language. 1981. 12.00x (ISBN 0-8364-0692-3). South Asia Bks.

Dowson, John. A Classical Dictionary of Hindu Mythology & Religion, Geography, History & Literature. 11th ed. 26.95 (ISBN 0-7100-1302-7). Methuen Inc.

Gauba, Om P. Sandarbh-MulAK Shabd-Kosh: Hindi-English-Hindi Dictionary of Phrase & Fable Including Symbolic & Idiomatic Expressions. viii, 258p. 1986. text ed. 35.00x (ISBN 81-7018-363-4, Pub. by B. R. Pub Corp Delhi). Apt Bks.

Stutley, Margaret & Stutley, James. Harper's Dictionary of Hinduism: Its Mythology, Folklore, Philosophy, Literature & History. LC 76-9999. 400p. 1984. pap. 16.95 (ISBN 0-06-067767-8, RD 479, HarpR). Har-Row.

Whitmarsh, Katherine. A Concordance to the Gospel of Sri Ramakrishna. LC 85-50340. 640p. (Orig.). 1985. pap. text ed. 59.95x (ISBN 0-87481-042-6). Vedanta Pr.

HINDUISM–RELATIONS–CHRISTIANITY

Akhilananda, Swami. Hindu View of Christ. pap. 12.00 (ISBN 0-8283-1355-5). Branden Pub Co.

Cave, Sydney. Redemption, Hindu & Christian: The Religious Quest of India. facsimile ed. LC 73-102230. (Select Bibliographies Reprint Ser). 1919. 24.50 (ISBN 0-8369-5115-8). Ayer Co Pubs.

Griffiths, Bede. Vedanta & Christian Faith. LC 73-88179. 85p. 1973. pap. 3.95 (ISBN 0-913922-04-8). Dawn Horse Pr.

Marshall, Peter J. The British Discovery of Hinduism in the 18th Century. 318p. 1970. text ed. 32.00x. Coronet Bks.

Pathak, Sushil M. American Missionaries & Hinduism: A Study of Their Contacts from 1813-1918. 294p. 1967. text ed. 20.00x. Coronet Bks.

Satprakashananda, Swami. Hinduism & Christianity: Jesus Christ & His Teachings in the Light of Vedanta. LC 75-32598. 196p. 1975. 8.95 (ISBN 0-916356-53-1). Vedanta Soc St Louis.

HINDUISM–RELATIONS–ISLAM

Bharati, Agehananda. Hindu Views & Ways & the Hindu-Muslim Interface: An Anthropological Assessment. 107p. 1982. Repr. of 1981 ed. 8.95 (ISBN 0-915520-54-0). Ross Erikson.

Hefner, Robert W. Hindu Javanese: Tengger Tradition & Islam. LC 85-3426. (Illus.). 300p. 1985. text ed. 36.00x (ISBN 0-691-09413-6). Princeton U Pr.

Sarkar, J. N. Hindu-Muslim Relations in Medieval Bengal. 130p. 1986. 15.00x (ISBN 0-8364-1806-9, Pub. by Chanakya India). South Asia Bks.

HINDUISM–SACRED BOOKS (SELECTIONS: EXTRACTS, ETC.)

Atma: Contemporary Vedic Library Series Based on the Teachings of A. C. Bhaktivedanta Swami Prabhupada. 1.50 (ISBN 0-89213-122-5). Bhaktivedanta.

Aurobindo, Sri. The Secret of the Veda. 581p. 1982. 15.00 (ISBN 0-89071-303-0, Pub. by Sri Aurobindo Ashram India); pap. 10.00 (ISBN 0-89071-302-2, Pub. by Sri Aurobindo Ashram India). Matagiri.

Badarayana. Brahma-Sutras (Vedanta-Sutras) Vireswarananda, Swami, tr. (Sanskrit & Eng.). 11.95 (ISBN 0-87481-076-0). Vedanta Pr.

Baman Das Basu, ed. The Sacred Books of the Hindus, 47 vols. Repr. of 1937 ed. 1251.50 (ISBN 0-404-19548-2). AMS Pr.

Banabhatta. Harshacarita: Text of Uchchhvasas I-VIII. Kane, P. V., ed. 645p. 1986. Repr. 22.00 (ISBN 81-208-0032-X, Pub. by Motilal Banarsidass). South Asia Bks.

Bhaktivedanta, Swami A. C. Srimad Bhagavatam: First Canto, 3 vols. LC 73-169353. (Illus.). 1972. 12.95 ea. Vol. 1 (ISBN 0-912776-27-7). Vol. 2 (ISBN 0-912776-29-3). Vol. 3 (ISBN 0-912776-34-X). Bhaktivedanta.

--Srimad Bhagavatam: Fourth Canto, 4 vols. LC 73-169353. (Illus.). 1974. 12.95 ea. Vol. 1 (ISBN 0-912776-38-2). Vol. 2 (ISBN 0-912776-47-1). Vol. 3 (ISBN 0-912776-48-X). Vol. 4 (ISBN 0-912776-49-8). Bhaktivedanta.

--Srimad Bhagavatam: Second Canto, 2 vols. LC 73-169353. (Illus.). 1972. 12.95 ea. Vol. 1 (ISBN 0-912776-28-5). Vol. 2 (ISBN 0-912776-35-8). Bhaktivedanta.

--Srimad Bhagavatam: Third Canto, 4 vols. LC 73-169353. (Illus.). 1974. 12.95 ea. Vol. 1 (ISBN 0-912776-37-4). Vol. 2 (ISBN 0-912776-44-7). Vol. 3 (ISBN 0-912776-46-3). Vol. 4 (ISBN 0-912776-75-7). Bhaktivedanta.

Bloomfield, Maurice. Religion of the Veda. LC 70-94310. (BCL Ser. II). Repr. of 1908 ed. 18.00 (ISBN 0-404-00912-3). AMS Pr.

Buhler, Georg, ed. The Sacred Laws of the Aryas. (Sacred Bks. of the East: Vols. 2 & 14). both vols. 30.00 (ISBN 0-686-97474-3); 15.00 ea. Asian Human Pr.

Davids, T. W. Jaina, Sutras. (Sacred Bks. of the East Ser.: Vol. 22, 45). both vols. 36.00 (ISBN 0-89581-525-7); 15.00 ea. Asian Human Pr.

Davids, T. W. & Oldenberg, H. Vinaya Texts. (Sacred Bks. of the East: Vols. 13, 17, 20). 3 vols. 45.00 (ISBN 0-89581-522-2); 15.00 ea. Asian Human Pr.

The Dharam Shastra: Hindu Religious Codes, 6 vols. Incl. Vol. I. 267p. 1978 (ISBN 0-89684-137-5); Vol. II. 230p. 1979 (ISBN 0-89684-138-3); Vol. III. 309p. 1979 (ISBN 0-89684-139-1); Vol. IV. 187p. 1979 (ISBN 0-89684-140-5); Vol. V. 438p. 1979 (ISBN 0-89684-141-3); Vol. VI. 222p. 1979 (ISBN 0-89684-142-1). Repr. of 1908 ed. 100.00 set (ISBN 0-686-77519-8, Pub. by Cosmo Pubns India). Orient Bk Dist.

Eggeling, Julius. The Satapatha Brahmana. (Sacred Bks. of the East: Vols. 12, 26, 41, 43, 44). 5 vols. 75.00 (ISBN 0-686-97483-2); 15.00 ea. Asian Human Pr.

Eggeling, Julius, ed. The Satapatha Brahmana, 5 vols. 1974. lib. bdg. 500.00 (ISBN 0-8490-0994-4). Gordon Pr.

Gambhirananda, Swami, tr. from Sanskrit. Aitereya Upanishad. (Upanishads with Shankara's Commentary Ser.). 75p. 1980. pap. 1.25 (ISBN 0-87481-200-3). Vedanta Pr.

--Katha Upanishad. (Upanishads with Shankara's Commentary Ser.). 136p. pap. 2.95 (ISBN 0-87481-201-1). Vedanta Pr.

--Mandukya Upanishad. (Upanishads with Shankara's Commentary Ser.). 240p. 1980. pap. 3.50 (ISBN 0-87481-202-X). Vedanta Pr.

--Mundaka Upanishad with Commentary of Shankara. 100p. pap. 1.25 (ISBN 0-87481-203-8). Vedanta Pr.

--Prasna Upanishad. (Upanishads with Shankara's Commentary Ser.). 104p. 1980. pap. 2.25 (ISBN 0-87481-204-6). Vedanta Pr.

Hatengdi, M. U. & Chetanananda, Swami. Nitya Sutras: The Revelations of Nityananda from the Chidakash Gita. (Illus.). 224p. (Orig.). 1985. pap. 11.95 (ISBN 0-915801-02-7). Rudra Pr.

Jolly, Julius, ed. The Institutes of Vishnu. (Sacred Bks. of the East: Vol. 7). 15.00 (ISBN 0-89581-517-6). Asian Human Pr.

Kalidasa. Kumarasambhava. Kale, M. R., ed. 1986. Repr. 17.50 (ISBN 81-208-0160-1, Pub. by Motilal Banarsidass). South Asia Bks.

Kern, H. The Saddharma-Pundarika or the Lotus of the Good Law. (Sacred Bks. of the East: Vol. 21). 15.00 (ISBN 0-89581-524-9). Asian Human Pr.

Klaiman, M. H., tr. Singing the Glory of Lord Krishna Baru Candidasa's Srikrsnakirtana: Baru Candidasa's Srikrsnakirtana. LC 84-3905. (SP AAR Classics in Religious Studies). 1984. 28.75 (ISBN 0-89130-736-2, 01 05 05); pap. 20.75 (ISBN 0-89130-737-0). Scholars Pr GA.

Mahanarayanopanisad. Vimalananda, Swami, tr. from Sanskrit. 1979. pap. 6.50 (ISBN 0-87481-492-8). Vedanta Pr.

Muller, F. Max, ed. The Upanishads. (Sacred Bks. of the East: Vol 1 & 15). both vols. 30.00 (ISBN 0-686-97473-5); 15.00 ea. Asian Human Pr.

Muller, Max, ed. Sacred Book of the East: Vedic Hymns, 2 vols. 250.00 (ISBN 0-87968-438-0). Krishna Pr.

Murthy, B. Srinivasa, tr. from Sanskrit. The Bhagavad Gita: Translated with Introduction & Notes. LC 84-82433. 150p. 1985. pap. 9.95 (ISBN 0-941910-01-6). Long Beach Pubns.

Pinkham, Mildred W. Woman in the Sacred Scriptures of Hinduism. LC 41-7015. Repr. of 1941 ed. 16.50 (ISBN 0-404-05055-7). AMS Pr.

Puranas, Bhagavatapurana. The Bhakti-Ratnavali: With the Commentary of Visnu Puri. LC 73-3794. (Sacred Books of the Hindus: No. 7 Pt.3). Repr. of 1912 ed. 25.00 (ISBN 0-404-57835-7). AMS Pr.

Rajneesh, Bhagwan S. The Rajneesh Bible, Vol. III. Rajneesh Academy Staff, ed. LC 85-42539. 1072p. (Orig.). 1985. pap. 6.95 (ISBN 0-88050-202-9). Chidvilas Found.

Rajneesh, Bhagwan Shree. Don't Let Yourself Be Upset by the Sutra: Rather Upset the Sutra Yourself. Prabhu, Swami Krishna, ed. LC 85-43054. (Initiation Talks Ser.). 560p. (Orig.). 1985. pap. 5.95 (ISBN 0-88050-584-2). Chidvilas Found.

Sharma, Arvind. Textual Studies in Hinduism. 1980. lib. bdg. 14.95x (ISBN 0-914914-15-4). New Horizons.

Shastri, J. L., ed. Brahma Purana, Pt. I. (Ancient Tradition & Mythology Ser.: Vol. 33). 240p. 1985. 18.50 (ISBN 81-208-0003-6, Pub. by Motilal Banarsidass India). Orient Bk Dist.

Swami Vivekananda. Complete Works of Swami Vivekananda, 8 vols. pap. 55.00x (ISBN 0-87481-176-7). Vedanta Pr.

Thibaut, G. The Vedanta Sutras. (Sacred Bks. of the East: Vols. 34, 38). both vols. 30.00 (ISBN 0-89581-530-3); 15.00 ea. Asian Human Pr.

Vasu, Srisa Chandra. A Catechism of Hindu Dharma. 2nd, rev. & enl. ed. Vidyarnava, Srisa Chandra, tr. LC 73-3829. (Sacred Books of the Hindus: No. 3). Repr. of 1919 ed. 14.50 (ISBN 0-404-57847-0). AMS Pr.

--The Daily Practice of the Hindus Containing the Morning & Midday Duties. 3rd, rev. & enl. ed. Vidyarnava, Srisa Chandra, tr. LC 73-3812. (Sacred Books of the Hindus: No. 20). Repr. of 1918 ed. 14.50 (ISBN 0-404-57820-9). AMS Pr.

Vijnanananda. The Sri Mad Devi Bhagavatam. LC 73-3819. (Sacred Books of the Hindus: No. 26, Bks. 1-12). Repr. of 1921 ed. 79.50 (ISBN 0-404-57826-8). AMS Pr.

Winternitz, M. Index. (Sacred Bks. of the East: Vol. 50). 15.00 (ISBN 0-89581-535-4). Asian Human Pr.

Woodroffe, John. The World As Power. new ed. Bd. with Mahamaya: Power As Consciousness. Woodroffe, John & Mukhyopadhyaya, Pramatha N.. 1981. 24.00 (ISBN 0-89744-119-2, Pub. by Ganesh & Co. India). Auromere.

HINDUISM–SECTS

see Hindu Sects

HINDUS

Brown, Brian. The Wisdom of the Hindus. 320p. 1981. pap. 18.00 (ISBN 0-89540-093-6, SB-093). Sun Pub.

Dass, Ram. Miracle of Love: Stories About Neem Karoli Baba. (Illus.). 1979. pap. 12.95 (ISBN 0-525-47611-3, 01257-380). Dutton.

Dubois, J. A. & Beauchamp, Henry K. Hindu Manners, Customs & Ceremonies. 800p. 1986. Repr. 17.50X (ISBN 0-8364-1760-7, Pub. by Manohar India). South Asia Bks.

Isherwood, Christopher. Ramakrishna & His Disciples. LC 65-17100. 384p. 1980. pap. 8.95 (ISBN 0-87481-037-X). Vedanta Pr.

Jones, Kenneth W. Arya Dharm: Hindu Consciousness in Nineteenth-Century Punjab. LC 74-27290. 350p. 1976. 41.95x (ISBN 0-520-02919-4). U of Cal Pr.

Larus, Joel. Culture & Political-Military Behavior: The Hindus in Pre-Modern India. 1980. 16.50x (ISBN 0-8364-0038-0). South Asia Bks.

Nikhilananda, Swami. Holy Mother: Being the Life of Sri Sarada Devi, Wife of Sri Ramakrishna & Helpmate in His Mission. LC 62-13423. (Illus.). 384p. pap. 7.95 (ISBN 0-911206-20-5). Ramakrishna.

Ward, W. History, Literature & Mythology of the Hindoos, 4 vols. 1986. Repr. of 1817 ed. text ed. 200.00x (ISBN 81-7018-240-9, Pub. by B R Pub Corp Delhi). Vol. 1: 354. Vol. 2: 505. Vol. 3: 288. Vol. 4: 344. Apt Bks.

HIPPOLYTUS

Euripides. Hippolytus in Drama & Myth. Sutherland, Donald, tr. LC 60-13112. vi, 124p. 1960. pap. 4.50x (ISBN 0-8032-5195-5, BB 103, Bison). U of Nebr Pr.

HIRSCH, EMIL GUSTAV, 1851-1923

Hirsch, David E. Rabbi Emil G. Hirsch: The Reform Advocate. LC 68-24717. 1968. pap. 3.00x (ISBN 0-87655-502-4). Collage Inc.

Hirsch, David E., ed. Theology of Emil G. Hirsch. 1977. pap. text ed. 12.50x (ISBN 0-87655-539-3). Collage Inc.

HISPANOS

see Mexican Americans

HISTORY–PHILOSOPHY

see also Church History–Philosophy; Demythologization; History (Theology)

American Catholic Historic Association Staff. Catholic Philosophy of History, Vol. 3. facs. ed. LC 67-23190. (Essay Index Reprint Ser). 1936. 16.00 (ISBN 0-8369-0285-8). Ayer Co Pubs.

Becker, Carl L. Heavenly City of the Eighteenth-Century Philosophers. (Storrs Lectures Ser.). 1932. pap. 6.95x (ISBN 0-300-00017-0, Y5). Yale U Pr.

Dawson, Christopher H. Progress & Religion, an Historical Enquiry. LC 79-104266. Repr. of 1929 ed. lib. bdg. 27.50x (ISBN 0-8371-3917-1, DAPR). Greenwood.

Keyes, G. L. Christian Faith & the Interpretation of History: A Study of St. Augustine's Philosophy of History. LC 66-10314. xiv, 206p. 1966. 17.50x (ISBN 0-8032-0091-9). U of Nebr Pr.

Lowith, Karl. Meaning in History: The Theological Implications of the Philosophy of History. LC 57-7900. 1957. pap. 7.50x (ISBN 0-226-49555-8, P16, Phoen). U of Chicago Pr.

Lukacher, Ned. Primal Scenes: Literature, Philosophy, Psychoanalysis. LC 85-25513. 368p. 1986. text ed. 24.95x (ISBN 0-8014-1886-0). Cornell U Pr.

Masaryk, Thomas G. Masaryk on Thought & Life. LC 78-135840. (Eastern Europe Collection Ser.). 1970. Repr. of 1938 ed. 16.00 (ISBN 0-405-02782-6). Ayer Co Pubs.

Mathews, Shailer. The Spiritual Interpretation of History. 1977. lib. bdg. 59.95 (ISBN 0-8490-2661-X). Gordon Pr.

Montgomery, John W. The Shape of the Past. LC 75-26651. 400p. 1975. pap. 9.95 (ISBN 0-87123-535-8, 210535). Bethany Hse.

Niebuhr, Reinhold. Beyond Tragedy: Essays on the Christian Interpretation of History. facsimile ed. LC 76-167397. (Essay Index Reprint Ser). Repr. of 1937 ed. 23.95 (ISBN 0-8369-2437-1). Ayer Co Pubs.

--Beyond Tragedy: Essays on the Christian Interpretation of History. 1937. pap. text ed. 7.95 (ISBN 0-684-16410-8, SL38, ScribT). Scribner.

--Faith & History: A Comparison of Christian & Modern Views of History. (Lib. Rep. Ed.). 1949. 25.00 (ISBN 0-684-15318-1, ScribT). Scribner.

Rockwood, Raymond O., ed. Carl Becker's Heavenly City Revisited. LC 68-11256. xxxii, 227p. 1968. Repr. of 1958 ed. 23.00 (ISBN 0-208-00421-1, Archon). Shoe String.

Schluchter, Wolfgang. The Rise of Western Rationalism: Max Weber's Developmental History. Roth, Guenther, tr. from Ger. LC 81-2763. 300p. 1981. 24.50x (ISBN 0-520-04060-0); pap. 9.95 (ISBN 0-520-05464-4, CAL 747). U of Cal Pr.

Shine, Hill. Carlyle & the Saint Simonians. LC 71-120666. 1970. Repr. lib. bdg. 17.00x (ISBN 0-374-97360-1, Octagon). Hippocrene Bks.

Volney, C. F. A New Translation of Volney's Ruins, 2 vols. Feldman, Burton & Richardson, Robert D., eds. LC 78-60900. (Myth & Romanticism Ser.: Vol. 25). (Illus.). 1979. Set. lib. bdg. 160.00 (ISBN 0-8240-3574-7). Garland Pub.

HISTORY–THEOLOGY

see History (Theology)

HISTORY (THEOLOGY)

see also Time (Theology)

Altizer, Thomas J. Total Presence: The Language of Jesus & the Language of Today. 128p. 1980. 9.95 (ISBN 0-8164-0461-5, HarpR). Har-Row.

Gilkey, Langdon. Reaping the Whirlwind: A Christian Interpretation of History. 1977. (HarpR); pap. 12.95 (ISBN 0-8164-2317-2). Har-Row.

Joachim Pillai, C. A. The Apostolic Interpretation of History: A Commentary on Acts 13: 16-41. 1980. 9.00 (ISBN 0-682-49404-6, University). Exposition Pr FL.

Markus, R. A. Saeculum: History & Society in the Theology of St Augustine. LC 71-87136. 1970. 54.50 (ISBN 0-521-07621-8). Cambridge U Pr.

Montgomery, John W. Where Is History Going? LC 69-11659. 256p. 1969. 7.95 (ISBN 0-87123-640-0, 210640). Bethany Hse.

Ratzinger, J. Theology of History According to St. Bonaventure. 12.50 (ISBN 0-8199-0415-5). Franciscan Herald.

Severinghaus, Leslie R. Religions & History: A Textbook for the Enlightenment of 12th Graders in our Tax-Supported Public High Schools. 1985. 13.95 (ISBN 0-533-06577-1). Vantage.

Showers, Renald E. What on Earth Is God Doing? Satan's Conflict with God. LC 73-81551. 1973. pap. 3.95 (ISBN 0-87213-784-8). Loizeaux.

Trimingham, J. Spencer. History in Two Dimensions: A Christian Interpretation of History as Being an Equation Between Time & Eternity. 1983. 11.95 (ISBN 0-533-05395-1). Vantage.

Vandeman, George E. Cry of a Lonely Planet. 352p. 1983. pap. 7.95 (ISBN 0-8163-0519-6). Pacific Pr Pub Assn.

HISTORY, ANCIENT

see also Bible–Chronology; Civilization, Ancient also names of ancient races and peoples, e.g. hittites and names of countries of antiquity

Bouquet, A. C. Everyday Life in New Testament Times. (Hudson River Editions). (Illus.). 1953. lib. rep. ed. 20.00 (ISBN 0-684-14833-1, ScribT). Scribner.

Burton, O. E. Study in Creative History. LC 71-105821. (Classics Ser). 1971. Repr. of 1932 ed. 26.00x (ISBN 0-8046-1197-1, Pub. by Kennikat). Assoc Faculty Pr.

Connor, W. R., ed. The Acts of the Pagan Martyrs. LC 78-18588. (Greek Texts & Commentaries Ser.). 1979. Repr. of 1954 ed. lib. bdg. 25.50x (ISBN 0-405-11430-3). Ayer Co Pubs.

Finegan, Jack. Light from the Ancient Past, 2 vols. 2nd ed. (Illus.). 1959. Vol. 1 2nd Ed. 52.50 (ISBN 0-691-03550-4); Vol. 1 2nd Edition. pap. 16.50 (ISBN 0-691-00207-X); Vol. 2. 50.00 (ISBN 0-691-03551-2); Vol. 2. pap. 15.50x (ISBN 0-691-00208-8); Set. 90.00 (ISBN 0-686-76901-5). Princeton U Pr.

Weeks, Kent R. Classic Christian Townsite at Arminna West, Vol. 3. LC 67-26194. 1967. 25.00 (ISBN 0-686-00130-3). Penn-Yale Expedit.

HISTORY, CHURCH

see Church History

HISTORY, ECCLESIASTICAL

see Church History

HISTORY, MEDIEVAL

see Middle Ages–History

HISTORY, MODERN–PHILOSOPHY

see History–Philosophy

HISTORY, MODERN–20TH CENTURY

MacEoin, Gary. Memoirs & Memories. 308p. (Orig.). 1986. pap. 9.95 (ISBN 0-89622-317-5). Twenty-Third.

HISTORY, PHILOSOPHY OF

see History–Philosophy

HISTORY, UNIVERSAL

see World History

HISTORY AND SCIENCE

see Science and Civilization

HITTITES

Cowley, A. E. The Hittites. (British Academy, London; Schweich Lectures on Biblical Archaeology Series, 1918). pap. 19.00 (ISBN 0-8115-1260-6). Kraus Repr.

Gurney, O. R. Some Aspects of Hittite Religion. (Schweich Lectures on Biblical Archaeology). (Illus.). 80p. 1976. 10.25 (ISBN 0-85672-740-7, Pub. by British Acad). Longwood Pub Group.

Hogarth, D. G. Kings of the Hittites. (British Academy, London, Schweich Lectures on Biblical Archaeology Ser.). pap. 19.00 (ISBN 0-8115-1266-5). Kraus Repr.

HOAXES

see Impostors and Imposture

HOCKING, WILLIAM ERNEST, 1873-1966

Rouner, Leroy S. Within Human Experience: The Philosophy of William Ernest Hocking. LC 71-75433. (Illus.). 1969. text ed. 20.00x (ISBN 0-674-95380-0). Harvard U Pr.

HODGE, CHARLES, 1797-1878

Hodge, Archibald A. Life of Charles Hodge, Professor in the Theological Seminary, Princeton, New Jersey. LC 71-83425. (Religion in America, Ser. 1). 1969. Repr. of 1881 ed. 32.00 (ISBN 0-405-00250-5). Ayer Co Pubs.

Noll, Mark A., ed. Charles Hodge: The Way of Life & Selected Writings. 1987. 12.95. Paulist Pr.

HODGSON, FRANCIS, 1781-1852

Hodgson, James T. Memoir of the Rev. Francis Hodgson, B.D., Scholar, Poet, & Divine, 2 vols. LC 75-26864. 1975. Repr. of 1878 ed. lib. bdg. 75.00 (ISBN 0-8414-4804-3). Folcroft.

--Memoirs of the Rev. Francis Hodgson, 2 Vols. LC 76-169470. Repr. of 1878 ed. Set. 65.00 (ISBN 0-404-07374-3). Vol. 1 (ISBN 0-404-07375-1). Vol. 2 (ISBN 0-404-07376-X). AMS Pr.

HOLIDAY DECORATIONS

see also Christmas Decorations

Deems, Betty. Easy-to-Make Felt Ornaments for Christmas & Other Occasions. LC 76-18405. (Dover Needlework Ser). (Illus.). 32p. (Orig.). 1976. pap. 3.50 (ISBN 0-486-23389-8). Dover.

Katz, Ruth. Pumpkin Personalities. (Illus.). 1979. 5.95 (ISBN 0-8027-6364-2); PLB 5.85 (ISBN 0-8027-6365-0). Walker & Co.

Sullivan, Eugene T. & Sullivan, Marilynn C., eds. Celebrate! No. V. LC 75-24148. 1978. pap. 11.99 (ISBN 0-912696-22-2). Wilton.

HOLIDAYS

see also Christmas; Fasts and Feasts; Schools–Exercises and Recreations; Sunday Legislation; Thanksgiving Day

Bauer, Caroline F. Celebrations: Read-Aloud Holiday & Theme Book Programs. LC 85-714. (Illus.). 301p. 1985. 35.00 (ISBN 0-8242-0708-4). Wilson.

Brand, John. Observations on the Popular Antiquities of Great Britain: Chiefly Illustrating the Origin of Our Vulgar & Provincial Customs, Ceremonies & Superstitions, 3 vols. LC 67-23896. 1969. Repr. of 1849 ed. Set. 68.00x (ISBN 0-8103-3256-6). Gale.

Bruno, Giordano. The Ash Wednesday Supper. Jaki, Stanley L., tr. Tr. of La Cena de Le Ceneri. (Illus.). 174p. 1975. text ed. 19.60x (ISBN 90-2797-581-7). Mouton.

Chambers, Robert, ed. Book of Days: A Miscellany of Popular Antiquities in Connection with the Calendar, Including Anecdote, Biography & History, Curiosities of Literature, & Oddities of Human Life & Character, 2 Vols. LC 67-13009. (Illus.). 1967. Repr. of 1862 ed. 125.00x (ISBN 0-8103-3002-4). Gale.

Chase, William D. Chases' Calendar of Annual Events: Special Days, Weeks & Months in 1980. rev. ed. LC 57-14540. (Illus., Orig.). 1979. lib. bdg. 14.95 (ISBN 0-913082-27-9); pap. 9.95 (ISBN 0-913082-26-0). Apple Tree.

Deems, Edward M., ed. Holy-Days & Holidays: A Treasury of Historical Material, Sermons in Full & in Brief, Suggestive Thoughts & Poetry, Relating to Holy Days & Holidays. LC 68-17940. 1968. Repr. of 1902 ed. 65.00x (ISBN 0-8103-3352-X). Gale.

DuCharme, Jerome J. The Reader's Guide to Proclamation: For Sundays & Major Feasts in Cycle A. 160p. 1974. pap. 2.95 (ISBN 0-8199-0577-1). Franciscan Herald.

Dyer, Wayne W. Happy Holidays: How to Enjoy the Christmas & Chanukkah Season to the Fullest. Nast, Thomas, tr. LC 86-2448. (Illus.). 96p. 1986. 9.95 (ISBN 0-688-06466-3). Morrow.

Emmens, Carol A. & Maglione, Harry, eds. An Audio-Visual Guide to American Holidays. LC 78-6230. 284p. 1978. lib. bdg. 20.00 (ISBN 0-8108-1140-5). Scarecrow.

Gregory, Ruth W. Special Days: The Book of Anniversaries & Holidays. 1978. pap. 5.95 (ISBN 0-8065-0659-8). Citadel Pr.

Hatch, Jane M., ed. American Book of Days. LC 78-16239. 1212p. 1978. 73.00 (ISBN 0-8242-0593-6). Wilson.

Ladendecker, Dianne. Holidays & Holy Days. 36p. 1986. pap. text ed. 6.95 (ISBN 0-8497-4854-2, C8630). Kjos.

Lamm, Norman. Supplement for the Days of Remembrance & Thanksgiving. 1973. 0.85x (ISBN 0-87306-079-2). Feldheim.

Lenz, Friedel. Celebrating the Festivals with Children. Tr. of Mit Kindren Feste feiern. 20p. (Orig.). 1986. pap. 3.95 (ISBN 0-88010-151-2). Anthroposophic.

Munoz, A. Lopez. Programas Para Dias Especiales Tomo II. 64p. 1984. pap. 1.95 (ISBN 0-311-07006-X). Casa Bautista.

Powers, Mala. Follow the Year: A Family Celebration of Christian Holidays. LC 85-42791. (Illus.). 128p. 1985. 14.45 (ISBN 0-06-066693-5, HarpR). Har-Row.

Sullivan, Eugene T. & Sullivan, Marilynn C., eds. Celebrate! No. V. LC 75-24148. 1978. pap. 11.99 (ISBN 0-912696-22-2). Wilton.

Tietjen, Mary L. Holidays & Celebrations: Activities, Crafts & Stories for Children. LC 82-62416. 1983. pap. 4.95 (ISBN 0-8091-2531-5). Paulist Pr.

Webster, Hutton. Rest Days, the Christian Sunday, the Jewish Sabbath & Their Historical & Anthropological Prototypes. LC 68-58165. 1968. Repr. of 1916 ed. 48.00x (ISBN 0-8103-3342-2). Gale.

HOLIDAYS–DRAMA

De Deiros, Norma H. C. Dramatizaciones Infantiles Para Dias Especiales. 96p. 1985. pap. 2.50 (ISBN 0-311-07606-8). Casa Bautista.

Munoz, A. Lopez. Programas Para Dias Especiales Tomo I. 107p. 1984. pap. 1.95 (ISBN 0-311-07005-1). Casa Bautista.

HOLIDAYS–JUVENILE LITERATURE

Banh Chung Banh Day: The New Year's Rice Cakes. 1972. 2.50 (ISBN 0-686-10279-7). Asia Resource.

Ritchie, Judith & Niggemeyer, Vickie. Holy Days: Holidays. LC 78-23841. (Illus.). 1978. 7.95 (ISBN 0-915134-48-9). Mott Media.

Scharfstein, Sol. What to Do on a Jewish Holiday? 1985. 6.95 (ISBN 0-88125-170-4). Ktav.

Van Straalen, Alice. The Book of Holidays Around the World. (Illus.). 192p. 1986. 12.95 (ISBN 0-525-44270-7). Dutton.

HOLINESS

see also Pentecostal Churches; Perfection; Sanctification

Armstrong, John. The Idea of Holiness & the Humane Response: A Study of the Concept of Holiness & Its Social Consequences. 177p. 1982. 16.95 (ISBN 0-04-200042-4). Allen Unwin.

Arnoudt, Peter J. The Imitation of the Sacred Heart of Jesus. LC 79-112463. 1974. pap. 10.00 (ISBN 0-89555-012-1). TAN Bks Pubs.

Baker, S. Hidden Manna. pap. 5.00 (ISBN 0-686-12875-3). Schmul Pub Co.

Baldwin, H. A. Holiness & the Human Element. pap. 3.95 (ISBN 0-686-12876-1). Schmul Pub Co.

Bernard, David K. Practical Holiness: A Second Look. 336p. (Orig.). 1985. pap. 6.95 (ISBN 0-912315-91-1). Word Aflame.

Bernard, Loretta A. & Bernard, David K. In Search of Holiness. 288p. (Orig.). 1981. pap. 6.95 (ISBN 0-912315-40-7). Word Aflame.

Bray, Gerald L. Holiness & the Will of God: Perspectives on the Theology of Tertullian. LC 79-5211. (New Foundations Theological Library). (Peter Toon & Ralph Martin series editors). 1980. 3.25 (ISBN 0-8042-3705-0). John Knox.

Bridges, Jerry. The Pursuit of Holiness. LC 78-18109. 158p. 1978. pap. 3.95 (ISBN 0-89109-430-X). NavPress.

--The Pursuit of Holiness. 192p. 1985. pap. 9.95 (ISBN 0-8027-2507-4). Walker & Co.

Brooks, Noel. Scriptural Holiness. 3.95 (ISBN 0-911866-53-1); pap. 2.95 (ISBN 0-911866-54-X). Advocate.

Bunyan, John. Holy Life: The Beauty of Christianity. pap. 1.95 (ISBN 0-685-19832-4). Reiner.

Cavarnos, Constantine. Paths & Means to Holiness. 85p. (Orig.). 1986. pap. 5.00 (ISBN 0-911165-08-8). Ctr Trad Orthodox.

Cook. New Testament Holiness. 4.95 (ISBN 0-686-12895-8). Schmul Pub Co.

Dieter, Melvin E. The Holiness Revival of the Nineteenth Century. LC 80-17259. (Studies in Evangelicalism: No. 1). 366p. 1980. 26.00 (ISBN 0-8108-1328-9). Scarecrow.

Fenelon, Francois. Christian Perfection. Whiston, Charles F., ed. Stillman, Mildred W., tr. from Fr. LC 75-22545. 208p. 1976. pap. 4.95 (ISBN 0-87123-083-6, 200083). Bethany Hse.

Fenhagen, James C. Invitation to Holiness. LC 85-42774. 128p. 1985. 12.45 (ISBN 0-06-062351-9, HarpR). Har-Row.

Finney, Charles G. Principles of Holiness. LC 83-25769. 274p. 1984. pap. 5.95 (ISBN 0-87123-403-3, 210403). Bethany Hse.

Girvin, E. A. Phineas F. Bresse: A Prince in Israel. Dayton, Donald W., ed. (The Higher Christian Life Ser.). 464p. 55.00 (ISBN 0-8240-6407-0). Garland Pub.

Hills, A. M. Holiness & Power for the Church & the Ministry. Dayton, Donald W., ed. (The Higher Christian Life Ser.). 386p. 1984. 50.00 (ISBN 0-8240-6422-4). Garland Pub.

Holmes, Theda. Holiness & Honor of Praise. LC 85-62801. 1986. pap. 3.50 (ISBN 0-88270-599-7). Bridge Pub.

Jones, Charles E. Guide to the Study of the Holiness Movement. LC 74-659. (ATLA Bibliography Ser.: No. 1). 946p. 1974. 57.50 (ISBN 0-8108-0703-3). Scarecrow.

--Perfectionist Persuasion: The Holiness Movement & American Methodism, 1867-1936. LC 74-13766. (ATLA Monograph: No. 5). (Illus.). 262p. 1974. 22.50 (ISBN 0-8108-0747-5). Scarecrow.

Jones, Kenneth E. Commitment to Holiness. 1985. pap. 5.95 (ISBN 0-87162-413-3, D1350). Warner Pr.

Kreider, Alan. Journey Towards Holiness. LC 86-22838. 304p. (Orig.). 1987. pap. 9.95 (ISBN 0-8361-3423-0). Herald Pr.

McLean, A. & Easton, J. W. Penuel; or Face to Face with God. Dayton, Donald W., ed. (The Higher Christian Life Ser.). 483p. 1985. 60.00 (ISBN 0-8240-6427-5). Garland Pub.

Murray, Andrew. The Believer's Secret of Holiness. LC 84-2973. 208p. 1984. pap. 3.95 (ISBN 0-87123-432-7). Bethany Hse.

Nicholl, Donald. Holiness. 176p. (Orig.). 1981. pap. 8.95 (ISBN 0-8164-2336-9, HarpR). Har-Row.

Palmer, Phoebe & Dayton, Donald W., eds. Pioneer Experiences. (The Higher Christian Life Ser.). 368p. 1985. 45.00 (ISBN 0-8240-6433-X). Garland Pub.

Paul, Cecil & Lanham, Jan. Choices: In Pursuit of Wholeness. 88p. 1982. pap. 3.95 (ISBN 0-8341-0807-0). Beacon Hill.

Purkiser, W. T. Exploring Christian Holiness, Vol. I: The Biblical Foundations, 3 Vols. (Exploring Christian Holiness Ser.). 280p. 1983. 10.95 (ISBN 0-8341-0843-7). Beacon Hill.

--These Earthen Vessels. 118p. 1985. pap. 4.95 (ISBN 0-8341-0977-8). Beacon Hill.

Redpath, Alan. Victorious Christian Living: Studies in the Book of Joshua. 256p. 1955. 10.95 (ISBN 0-8007-0336-7). Revell.

Rees, Seth C. Miracles in the Slums. (The Higher Christian Life Ser.). 301p. 1985. lib. bdg. 40.00 (ISBN 0-8240-6440-2). Garland Pub.

Roberts, Roger. Holiness: Every Christian's Calling. LC 85-11330. 1985. pap. 5.95 (ISBN 0-8054-1956-X). Broadman.

Ryle, J. C. Holiness. 352p. 1977. Repr. of 1959 ed. 12.50 (ISBN 0-227-67482-0). Attic Pr.

Ryle, John C. Holiness. 352p. 1979. 12.95 (ISBN 0-8007-1066-5). Revell.

Salter, Darius L. Spirit & Intellect: Thomas Upham's Holiness Theology. LC 86-10048. (Studies in Evangelicalism: No. 7). 283p. 1986. 27.50 (ISBN 0-8108-1899-X). Scarecrow.

Shaw, S. B., ed. Echoes of the General Holiness Assembly. (The Higher Christian Life Ser.). 345p. 1985. lib. bdg. 45.00 (ISBN 0-8240-6442-9). Garland Pub.

Shelhamer. Holiness: How Obtained & Retained. 2.50 (ISBN 0-686-12878-8). Schmul Pub Co.

Sproul, R. C. The Holiness of God. 256p. 1985. 10.95 (ISBN 0-8423-1493-8). Tyndale.

Spurgeon, C. H. Exposition of the Doctrines of Grace. 1975. 1.50 (ISBN 0-686-09096-9). Pilgrim Pubns.

Taylor, Jeremy. Holy Living & Holy Dying. Hinten, Marvin D., ed. 80p. 1986. pap. 3.95 (ISBN 0-8423-1350-8). Tyndale.

Taylor, Richard S. Exploring Christian Holiness, Vol. 3: The Theological Formulations. (Exploring Christian Holiness Ser.). 300p. 1985. 12.95 (ISBN 0-8341-1077-6). Beacon Hill.

Taylor, Richard S., ed. Great Holiness Classics, Vol. 3: Leading Wesleyan Thinkers. 436p. 1985. 21.95 (ISBN 0-8341-1069-5). Beacon Hill.

HOLISM

Bauman, David M. Spiritual Life for the Overbusy. 96p. (Orig.). 1987. pap. price not set (ISBN 0-88028-065-4). Forward Movement.

Biermann, June & Toohey, Barbara. The Woman's Holistic Headache Relief Book. 212p. Repr. of 1979 ed. 8.95 (ISBN 0-686-35967-4). Sugarfree.

Birch, L. C. & Cobb, J. B. The Liberation of Life: From the Cell to the Community. LC 80-42156. 300p. 1982. 42.50 (ISBN 0-521-23787-4). Cambridge U Pr.

Blate, Michael. The Tao of Health: The Way of Total Well-Being. (Illus., Orig.). 1978. pap. 6.95 (ISBN 0-916878-05-8). Falkynor Bks.

Chernin, Dennis K. & Manteuffel, Gregory. Health: A Holistic Approach. LC 84-40270. (Illus.). 285p. (Orig.). 1984. pap. 7.50 (ISBN 0-8356-0590-6, Quest). Theos Pub Hse.

Cornelius, Martin P., III. Til Death Do Us Part: A Basic Education in Total Health: How to Keep Body & Soul Happily Together. 256p. (Orig.). 1981. pap. 15.00 (ISBN 0-9607142-0-0). Health Ed & Life Exp Res.

Day, Albert E. & Wagner, James K. Letters on the Healing Ministry. 144p. 1986. pap. 6.95 incl. study guide (ISBN 0-317-30215-9, ICN 606462, Dist. by Abingdon Pr). Upper Room.

Drahos, Mary. To Touch the Hem of His Garment. 224p. (Orig.). 1983. pap. 7.95 (ISBN 0-8091-2548-X). Paulist Pr.

Hafen, Brent & Frandsen, Katherine. From Acupuncture to Yoga: Alternative Methods of Healing. (Illus.). 136p. 1983. 12.95 (ISBN 0-13-330845-6). P-H.

Hodgson, Joan. A White Eagle Lodge Book of Health & Healing. 240p. 1983. text ed. 10.50 (ISBN 0-85487-063-6). De Vorss.

Jafolla, Mary-Alice, et al. Nourishing the Life Force. LC 82-51301. 200p. 1983. 6.95 (ISBN 0-87159-114-6). Unity School.

Legere, Thomas E. Thoughts on the Run: Glimpses of Wholistic Spirituality. 144p. 1983. pap. 7.95 (ISBN 0-86683-698-5, HarpR). Har-Row.

Ouellette, Raymond. Holistic Healing & the Edgar Cayce Readings. LC 80-80446. 384p. 1980. 11.95 (ISBN 0-936450-07-X); pap. 7.75. Aero Pr.

Peacocke, Christopher A. Holistic Explanation: Action, Space, Interpretation. 1979. 28.50x (ISBN 0-19-824605-6). Oxford U Pr.

Powellson, Jack. Holistic Economics & Social Protest. 1983. pap. 2.50x (ISBN 0-87574-250-5, 250). Pendle Hill.

Sonnier, Isadore L., ed. Methods & Techniques of Holistic Education. (Illus.). 184p. 1985. 21.50 (ISBN 0-398-05054-6). C C Thomas.

Van Nuys, Kelvin. A Holist Pilgrimage. LC 80-84738. 400p. 1981. 15.00 (ISBN 0-8022-2383-4). Philos Lib.

The Way to Peace. 11.95 (ISBN 0-87418-037-6). Coleman Pub.

HOLOCAUST, JEWISH (1939-1945)

Abells, Chana B. The Children We Remember. LC 85-24876. (Illus.). 48p. 1986. 9.95 (ISBN 0-688-06371-3); PLB 10.88 (ISBN 0-688-06372-1). Greenwillow.

Abrahamsen, Samuel. The Holocaust in Norway: An Historical Perspective. 1987. 20.95 (ISBN 0-89604-116-6); pap. 13.95 (ISBN 0-89604-117-4). Holocaust Pubns.

Abrams, Alan. Special Treatment: The Untold Story of the Survival of Thousands of Jews in Hitler's Third Reich. (Illus.). 261p. 1985. 14.95 (ISBN 0-8184-0364-0). Lyle-Stuart.

Ainstein, Reuben. The Warsaw Ghetto Revolt. (Illus.). 238p. 1979. pap. 10.95 (ISBN 0-89604-007-0). Holocaust Pubns.

Alexander, Edward. The Resonance of Dust: Essays on Holocaust Literature & Jewish Fate. LC 79-15515. 276p. 1979. 20.00 (ISBN 0-8142-0303-5). Ohio St U Pr.

Altshuler, David A. Hitler's War Against the Jews - the Holocaust: A Young Reader's Version of the War Against the Jews: 1933-1945 by Lucy Dawidowicz. LC 78-5418. (Illus.). 1978. 8.95x (ISBN 0-87441-293-5); pap. 6.50x (ISBN 0-87441-222-6). Behrman.

America & the Holocaust. (American Jewish History Ser.: Vol. 70, Pt. 3). 1981. 6.00 (ISBN 0-911934-20-0). Am Jewish Hist Soc.

American Jewish Committee. The Jewish Communities of Nazi-Occupied Europe. 400p. 1982. Repr. of 1944 ed. 42.50x (ISBN 0-86527-337-5). Fertig.

--The Jews in Nazi Germany. x, 177p. 1982. Repr. of 1935 ed. 22.50x (ISBN 0-86527-110-0). Fertig.

Amery, Jean. Radical Humanism: Selected Essays. Rosenfeld, Sidney & Rosenfeld, Stella P., eds. Rosenfeld, Stella & Rosenfeld, Sidney, trs. from Fr. LC 83-49525. 160p. 1984. 22.50x (ISBN 0-253-34770-X). Ind U Pr.

Anti-Defamation League of B'nai Brith Staff. The Holocaust & Genocide: A Search for Conscience, An Anthology for Students. 217p. 9.95 (ISBN 0-317-03375-1). ADL.

--The Holocaust & Genocide: A Search for Conscience, A Curriculum Guide. 184p. 12.00 (ISBN 0-317-03374-3). ADL.

Apenszlak, Jacob, ed. The Black Book of Polish Jewry: An Account of the Martyrdom of Polish Jewry Under Nazi Occupation. xvi, 343p. 1982. Repr. of 1943 ed. 27.50x (ISBN 0-86527-340-5). Fertig.

App, Austin J. Hitler-Himmler Order on the Jews. 1984. lib. bdg. 79.95 (ISBN 0-87700-516-8). Revisionist Pr.

--Holocaust: Sneak Attack on Christianity. 1984. lib. bdg. 79.95 (ISBN 0-87700-517-6). Revisionist Pr.

Aptecker, George. Beyond Despair. (Illus.). 72p. 1980. 25.00 (ISBN 0-9604286-0-7). Kahn & Kahan.

Arad, Yitzhak. Belzec, Sobibor, Treblinka: The Operation Reinhard Death Camps. 1987. 29.95 (ISBN 0-253-34293-7). Ind U Pr.

--Ghetto in Flames. LC 80-50198. (Illus.). 500p. 1982. pap. 14.95 (ISBN 0-89604-043-7). Holocaust Pubns.

--The Partisan. LC 78-71299. (Illus.). 288p. 1979. 16.95 (ISBN 0-317-06371-5); pap. 10.95 (ISBN 0-89604-011-9). Holocaust Pubns.

Arad, Yitzhak, compiled by. The Einsatzgruppen Reports: Selections from the Official Dispatches of the Nazi Death Squads' Campaign Against the Jews. 1986. 15.95 (ISBN 0-89604-057-7); pap. 10.95 (ISBN 0-89604-058-5). Holocaust Pubns.

Aronsfeld, C. C. The Text of the Holocaust: A Documentation of the Nazis' Extermination Propaganda from 1919-45. 1985. 16.00 (ISBN 0-916288-17-X); pap. 10.00 (ISBN 0-916288-18-8). Micah Pubns.

Aronsfeld, Caesar C. The Ghosts of Fourteen Ninety-Two. (Conference on Jewish Social Studies). 1979. 10.00x (ISBN 0-910430-00-4, Pub by Conf Jewish Soc Studies). Columbia U Pr.

Atkinson, Linda. In Kindling Flame: The Story of Hannah Senesh 1921-1944. LC 83-24392. 256p. 1985. 13.50 (ISBN 0-688-02714-8). Lothrop.

Atrocities & Other Conditions in Concentration Camps in Germany. (Witness to the Holocaust Ser.: No. 3). 21p. 1980. 1.00. Witness Holocaust.

Ayalon, O., et al. The Holocaust & Its Perseverance. (SANAI Ser.: No. 2). 64p. 1983. pap. text ed. 9.95x (Pub. by Van Gorcum Holland). Humanities.

Ayalon, Ofra, et al. The Holocaust & Its Perserverance: Stress, Coping, & Disorder. (Sinai-Papers, Studies in Integral Psychology). 80p. 1983. pap. text ed. 8.00 (Pub. by Van Gorcum Holland). Longwood Pub Group.

Balshone, Benjamin. Determined! 1984. 15.95 (ISBN 0-8197-0494-6). Bloch.

Bauer, Yehuda. American Jewry & the Holocaust: The American Jewish Joint Distribution Committee, 1939-1945. LC 80-26035. 522p. 1981. 35.00x (ISBN 0-8143-1672-7). Wayne St U Pr.

--They Chose Life: Jewish Resistance in the Holocaust. LC 73-89085. (Illus.). 64p. (Orig.). 1973. pap. 2.00 (ISBN 0-87495-000-7). Am Jewish Comm.

Bauer, Yehuda & Keren, Nili. A History of the Holocaust. 453p. 1982. 17.95 (ISBN 0-531-09862-1); 12.95 (ISBN 0-531-05641-4). Watts.

Berkovits, Eliezer. Faith After the Holocaust. 1973. pap. 7.95x (ISBN 0-87068-193-1). Ktav.

Berkowitz, Sarah B. In Search of Ashes. LC 83-50495. 128p. 1984. 7.95 (ISBN 0-88400-099-0). Shengold.

Bilik, Dorothy S. Immigrant-Survivors: Post-Holocaust Consciousness in Recent Jewish-American Literature. LC 80-15326. 217p. 1981. 17.50x. Wesleyan U Pr.

Blumenthal, David R., ed. Emory Studies on the Holocaust. LC 84-52494. 178p. (Orig.). 1985. pap. 5.00 (ISBN 0-912313-01-3). Witness Holocaust.

Boas, Jacob. Boulevard des Miseres: The Story of Transit Camp Westerbork. LC 85-1435. (Illus.). 174p. 1985. lib. bdg. 22.50 (ISBN 0-208-01977-4, Archon Bks). Shoe String.

Braham, Randolph L. The Hungarian Jewish Catastrophe: Selected & Annotated Bibliography. 501p. 1984. 45.00x (ISBN 0-88033-054-6). East Eur Quarterly.

--Perspectives on the Holocaust. (Holocaust Studies). 1983. lib. bdg. 20.00 (ISBN 0-89838-124-X). Kluwer Nijhoff.

Braham, Randolph L., ed. Contemporary Views on the Holocaust. 1983. lib. bdg. 31.50 (ISBN 0-89838-141-X). Kluwer Nijhoff.

Brenner, Reeve R. The Faith & Doubt of Holocaust Survivors. LC 79-6764. 1980. 12.95 (ISBN 0-02-904420-0). Free Pr.

Browning, Christopher R. Fateful Months: Essays on the Emergence of the Final Solution, 1941-1942. LC 84-9089. (Illus.). 100p. 1985. text ed. 24.95x (ISBN 0-8419-0967-9). Holmes & Meier.

--The Final Solution & the German Foreign Office. LC 78-8996. 276p. 1978. text ed. 35.00x (ISBN 0-8419-0403-0). Holmes & Meier.

Cargas, Harry J. & Corrigan, John T. The Holocaust: An Annotated Bibliography. 1977. pap. text ed. 4.00 (ISBN 0-87507-005-1). Cath Lib Assn.

Cargas, Henry J., ed. When God & Man Failed: Non-Jewish Views of the Holocaust. 320p. 1981. 16.95 (ISBN 0-02-521300-8). Macmillan.

Carr, Joseph J. Christian Heroes of the Holocaust. LC 85-70538. 1985. pap. 3.50 (ISBN 0-88270-582-2). Bridge Pub.

Carroll, Thomas M. The Abomination of Desolation: The Great Persecution. 96p. 1983. pap. 5.95 (ISBN 0-87881-103-6). Mojave Bks.

Central Commission for the Investigation of German Crimes in Poland Staff. German Crimes in Poland, 2 vols. in one. 1982. Repr. of 1947 ed. 45.00x (ISBN 0-86527-336-7). Fertig.

Charny, Israel W. & Rapaport, Chanan. Genocide: The Human Cancer. 1983. pap. 10.95 (ISBN 0-87851-313-2). Hearst Bks.

Chartock, Roselle & Spencer, Jack. The Holocaust Years: Society on Trial. 244p. Repr. 2.95 (ISBN 0-686-95069-0). ADL.

Cohen, Richard I. Burden of Conscience: French Jewry's Response to the Holocaust. (The Modern Jewish Experience Ser.). 351p. 1987. 27.50 (ISBN 0-253-31263-9). Ind U Pr.

Costanza, Mary S. The Living Witness: Art in the Concentration Camps & Ghettos. 1982. 19.95 (ISBN 0-02-906660-3). Free Pr.

Curtis, Denis, et al. Dead Martyrs & Living Heroes. LC 83-61651. 260p. 13.95 (ISBN 0-88400-097-4). Shengold.

Dachau. LC 79-51047. (Witness to the Holocaust Ser.: No. 2). 67p. 1982. 2.75. Witness Holocaust.

Dawidowicz, Lucy. Holocaust Reader. LC 75-33740. pap. 9.95x (ISBN 0-87441-236-6). Behrman.

--The Jewish Presence: Essays on Identity & History. LC 78-6236. 308p. 1978. pap. 3.95 (ISBN 0-15-646221-4, Harv). HarBraceJ.

Dawidowicz, Lucy S. Holocaust & the Historians. LC 80-29175. (Illus.). 200p. 1983. pap. 16.50x (ISBN 0-674-40566-8); pap. text ed. 6.95 (ISBN 0-674-40567-6). Harvard U Pr.

--The War Against the Jews: 1933-1945. 640p. 1976. pap. 10.95 (ISBN 0-553-34302-5). Bantam.

Dicker, Herman. Creativity, Holocaust, Reconstruction: Jewish Life in Wuertemberg, Past & Present. (Illus.). 1984. 18.50 (ISBN 0-87203-118-7). Hermon.

Dimensions of the Holocaust: A Series of Lectures Presented at Northwestern University & Coordinated by the Department of History. 64p. 3.50 (ISBN 0-88464-091-4). ADL.

Dimsdale, Joel E., ed. Survivors, Victims & Perpetrators: Essays on the Nazi Holocaust. LC 79-24834. (Illus.). 474p. 1980. text ed. 42.50 (ISBN 0-89116-145-7); pap. text ed. 32.95 (ISBN 0-89116-351-4). Hemisphere Pub.

Donat, Alexander. The Holocaust Kingdom. LC 77-89067. 361p. (Orig.). 1963. pap. 12.95 (ISBN 0-89604-001-1). Holocaust Pubns.

--The Holocaust Kingdom: A Memoir. 368p. pap. 5.95 (ISBN 0-686-95070-4). ADL.

Donat, Alexander, ed. The Death Camp Treblinka. LC 79-53471. (Illus.). 320p. (Orig.). 1979. 16.95 (ISBN 0-89604-008-9); pap. 12.95 (ISBN 0-89604-009-7). Holocaust Pubns.

Dorian, Emil. The Quality of Witness: A Romanian Diary, 1937-1944. Dorian, Marguerite, ed. Vamos, Mara S., tr. from Romanian. 352p. 1983. 19.95 (ISBN 0-8276-0211-1). Jewish Pubns.

Druks, Herbert. Jewish Resistance During the Holocaust. LC 83-14. 132p. 1983. text ed. 14.95x (ISBN 0-8290-1295-8). Irvington.

--Not in Vain: A Holocaust Documentary. 125p. 1984. text ed. 14.95x (ISBN 0-8290-1499-3). Irvington.

Eckardt, A. Roy. Jews & Christians: The Contemporary Meeting. LC 85-45327. 192p. 1986. 19.95x (ISBN 0-253-33162-5). Ind U Pr.

Eckardt, A. Roy & Eckardt, Alice L. Long Night's Journey into Day - Life & Faith After the Holocaust. LC 81-14788. 206p. 1982. 19.50x (ISBN 0-8143-1692-1). Wayne St U Pr.

Ehrenburg, Iiya & Grossman, Vasily. The Black Book. LC 81-81519. 595p. 1980. 24.95 (ISBN 0-89604-031-3); pap. 14.95 (ISBN 0-89604-032-1). Holocaust Pubns.

Eisenberg, Azriel, ed. The Lost Generation: Children in the Holocaust. 384p. 1982. 17.95 (ISBN 0-8298-0498-6). Pilgrim NY.

Eliach, Yaffa. Hasidic Tales of the Holocaust. 1982. 17.95 (ISBN 0-19-503199-7). Oxford U Pr.

Fackenheim, Emil L. The Jewish Return into History: Reflections in the Age of Auschwitz & a New Jerusalem. LC 77-87861. 1978. 14.95 (ISBN 0-8052-3677-5). Schocken.

Fein, Helen. Accounting for Genocide: National Response & Jewish Victimization During the Holocaust. LC 78-53085. (Illus.). 1979. 17.95 (ISBN 0-02-910220-0). Free Pr.

--Accounting for Genocide: National Responses & Jewish Victimization During the Holocaust. LC 83-24219. (Illus.). xxii, 469p. 1984. pap. 13.95 (ISBN 0-226-24034-7). U of Chicago Pr.

Feingold, Henry L. The Politics of Rescue. LC 80-81713. (Illus.). 432p. (Orig.). 1970. pap. 12.95 (ISBN 0-89604-019-4). Holocaust Pubns.

--The Politics of Rescue: The Roosevelt Administration & the Holocaust, 1938-1945. LC 75-127049. 1970. 40.00 (ISBN 0-8135-0664-6). Rutgers U Pr.

Ferencz, Benjamin B. Less Than Slaves: Jewish Forced Labor & the Quest for Compensation. LC 79-10690. 1979. 17.50x (ISBN 0-674-52525-6). Harvard U Pr.

Finger, Seymour M. American Jewry During the Holocaust. 1984. pap. 14.95x (ISBN 0-9613537-3-2). Am Jewish Holo.

Fischel, Jack R. & Pinsker, Sanford, eds. The Churches' Response to the Holocaust. (Holocaust Studies Annual: Vol. II). 200p. 1986. 20.00 (ISBN 0-913283-12-6). Penkevill.

Fleischner, E., ed. Auschwitz - Beginning of a New Era? Reflections on the Holocaust. 35.00x (ISBN 0-87068-499-X); pap. 16.95. Ktav.

Fleming, Gerald. Hitler & the Final Solution. LC 83-24535. (Illus.). 219p. 1984. 25.00 (ISBN 0-520-05103-3). U of Cal Pr.

Flender, Harold. Rescue in Denmark. LC 80-81716. (Illus.). 281p. (Orig.). 1963. pap. 10.95 (ISBN 0-89604-018-6). Holocaust Pubns.

Frank, Anne. The Works of Anne Frank. LC 73-16643. (Illus.). 332p. 1974. Repr. of 1959 ed. lib. bdg. 32.50x (ISBN 0-8371-7206-3, FRWO). Greenwood.

Frey, Robert S. & Thompson-Frey, Nancy. The Imperative of Response: The Holocaust in Human Context. 186p. 1985. lib. bdg. 24.25 (ISBN 0-8191-4633-1); pap. text ed. 10.75 (ISBN 0-8191-4634-X). U Pr of Amer.

Friedlander, Saul. When Memory Comes. Lane, Helen, tr. from Fr. 192p. 1979. 9.95 (ISBN 0-374-28898-4). FS&G.

Friedling, Sheila, ed. The Pit & the Trap: Leyb Rochman. Kohn, Moshe, tr. (Yiddish., Illus.). 288p. (Orig.). 1983. 16.95 (ISBN 0-8052-5044-1); pap. 10.95 (ISBN 0-8052-5045-X). Holocaust Pubns.

Friedman, Philip. Roads to Extinction: Essays on the Holocaust. Friedman, Ada J., ed. LC 79-89818. 616p. 1980. 27.50 (ISBN 0-8276-0170-0, 446). Jewish Pubns.

--Their Brothers' Keepers. LC 57-8773. 232p. 1978. pap. 12.95 (ISBN 0-89604-002-X). Holocaust Pubns.

Friedman, Saul S. No Haven for the Oppressed: United States Policy Toward Jewish Refugees, 1938-1945. LC 72-2271. 315p. 1973. 25.00x (ISBN 0-8143-1474-0). Wayne St U Pr.

Gar, Josef. Biblyografye Fun Artiklen Vegn Khurbn un Gvure. Incl. Vol. 1. LC 67-2416. (Yad Vashem-Yivo Joint Documentary Projects Bibliographical Ser.: No.). 306p. 1966. 10.00 (ISBN 0-914512-22-6); Vol. 2. (Yad Vashem-Yivo Joint Documentary Projects Bibliographical Ser.: No. 10). 338p. 1969. 15.00 (ISBN 0-914512-10-2). Yivo Inst.

Gilbert, Martin. The Final Journey: The Fate of the Jews in Nazi Europe. (Illus.). 1980. 12.50 (ISBN 0-8317-3325-X, Mayflower Bks). Smith Pubs.

--The Holocaust. 64p. 1979. pap. 6.95 (ISBN 0-8090-1389-4). Hill & Wang.

--The Holocaust: A History of the Jews of Europe during the Second World War. LC 85-5523. (Illus.). 900p. 1986. 19.45 (ISBN 0-317-44733-5). H Holt & Co.

--The Holocaust: The History of the Jews of Europe During the Second World War. LC 85-5523. (Illus.). 488p. 1985. 24.95 (ISBN 0-03-062416-9). H Holt & Co.

--Macmillan Atlas of the Holocaust. (Quality Paperbacks Ser.). (Illus.). 256p. 1984. pap. 13.95 (ISBN 0-306-80218-X). Da Capo.

Gordon, Sarah. Hitler, Germans, & the "Jewish Question". LC 83-43073. 416p. 1984. 42.00 (ISBN 0-691-05412-6); pap. 15.00 (ISBN 0-691-10162-0). Princeton U Pr.

Grobman, Alex, ed. Simon Wiesenthal Center Annual, Vol. 1. (Illus.). 256p. 1984. text ed. 17.95x (ISBN 0-940646-30-7). Rossel Bks.

Grobman, Alex, et al, eds. Genocide: Critical Issues of the Holocaust. LC 83-3052. (Illus.). 502p. 1983. 19.95 (ISBN 0-940646-04-8, Co-pub. by Simon Wiesenthal Center); pap. 12.95 (ISBN 0-940646-38-2). Rossel Bks.

--Genocide: Critical Issues of the Holocaust. 1986. pap. 12.95 (ISBN 0-317-42656-7). Shapolsky Pubs.

Gurdus, Luba K. The Death Train. LC 78-54657. (Illus.). 1979. 12.95 (ISBN 0-8052-5005-0, Pub. by Holocaust Library). Schocken.

--The Death Train. LC 78-54657. (Illus.). 165p. (Orig.). 1978. 12.95 (ISBN 0-89604-005-4). Holocaust Pubns.

--Painful Echoes: From the Diary of Luba Krugman Gurdus. pap. 12.95 (ISBN 0-89604-059-3). Holocaust Pubns.

Gursan-Salzmann, Ayse & Salzmann, Laurence. Last Jews of Radauti. LC 82-22176. (Illus.). 192p. 1983. 29.95 (ISBN 0-385-27808-X, Dial). Doubleday.

Gutman, Y. & Zuroff, E., eds. Rescue Attempts During the Holocaust. 25.00x (ISBN 0-87068-345-4). Ktav.

Gutman, Yisrael. The Jews of Warsaw, 1939-1943: Ghetto, Underground, Revolt. Friedman, Ina, tr. LC 81-47570. (Illus.). 512p. 1982. 24.95x (ISBN 0-253-33174-9). Ind U Pr.

Gutman, Yisrael, ed. The Holocaust in Documents. 1982. 22.50 (ISBN 0-686-85569-8). ADL.

Gutman, Yisrael & Krakowski, Shmuel, eds. The Angel of Death: The Untold Story of Josef Mengele. 1986. 16.95 (ISBN 0-933503-62-8). Shapolsky Pubs.

Haft, Cynthia J. The Bargain & the Bridle: The General Union of the Israelites of France, 1941-1944. 150p. (Orig.). 1983. pap. 14.95 (ISBN 0-914153-00-5). Dialog.

Heinemann, Marlene E. Gender & Destiny: Women Writers & the Holocaust. LC 86-367. (Contributions in Women's Studies: No. 72). 158p. 1986. 27.95 (ISBN 0-313-24665-3, HGD/). Greenwood.

Hellman, Peter, text by. The Auschwitz Album. 1987. 25.00 (ISBN 0-89604-085-2). Holocaust Pubns.

Hemmendinger, Judith. Survivors: Children of the Holocaust. Tr. of Les Enfants De Buchenwald. 200p. (Orig.). 1986. Repr. of 1984 ed. 15.95 (ISBN 0-915765-24-1). Natl Pr Inc.

Hillesum, Etty. An Interrupted Life: The Diaries of Etty Hillesum 1941-1943. Pomerans, Arno, tr. LC 83-47750. 226p. 1984. 13.45 (ISBN 0-394-53217-1). Pantheon.

Hirschfeld, Gerhard, ed. The Policies of Genocide: Jews & Soviet Prisoners of War in Nazi Germany. (Illus.). 176p. 1986. text ed. 24.95x (ISBN 0-04-943045-9); pap. text ed. 9.95x (ISBN 0-04-943046-7). Allen Unwin.

Hirshaut, Julien. Jewish Martyrs of Pawiak. LC 81-85301. 256p. 1982. 16.95 (ISBN 0-8052-5039-5); pap. 10.95 (ISBN 0-8052-5040-9). Holocaust Pubns.

Huneke, Douglas K. The Moses of Rovno: The Stirring Story of Fritz Graeve, a German Christian Who Risked His Life to Lead Hundreds of Jews to Safety During the Holocaust. (Holocaust Studies). (Illus.). 236p. 1985. 17.95 (ISBN 0-396-08714-0). Dodd.

Imposed Jewish Governing Bodies Under Nazi Rule: Yivo Colloquium Dec. 2-5, 1967. LC 73-150304. 1972. pap. 5.00 (ISBN 0-914512-03-X). Yivo Inst.

Isaacman, Clara & Grossman, Joan A. Clara's Story. LC 84-14339. 180p. 1984. 11.95 (ISBN 0-8276-0243-X). Jewish Pubns.

Kaganovoch, Moshe. Jewish Partisans of Eastern Europe. 1984. 17.95 (ISBN 0-89604-048-8); pap. 13.95 (ISBN 0-89604-049-6). Holocaust Pubns.

Kantor, Alfred. The Book of Alfred Kantor: An Artist's Journal of the Holocaust. (Illus.). 224p. 1987. 25.00x (ISBN 0-8052-4029-2); pap. 16.95x (ISBN 0-8052-0825-9). Schocken.

Karas, Joza. Music in Terezin Nineteen Forty-One to Nineteen Forty Five. LC 84-24411. (Illus.). 212p. 1985. 16.95x (ISBN 0-918728-34-7). Pendragon NY.

Katz, Esther & Ringelheim, Joan M. Women Surviving: The Holocaust-Proceedings of the Conference. (Occasional Papers: No. 1). 100p. (Orig.). 1983. pap. write for info. (ISBN 0-913865-00-1). Inst Res Hist.

Katz, Steven T. Post-Holocaust Dialogues: Critcal Studies in Modern Jewish Thought. 416p. 1983. 45.00x (ISBN 0-8147-4583-0). NYU Pr.

--Post-Holocaust Dialogues: Critical Studies in Modern Jewish Thought. 1985. pap. 15.00 (ISBN 0-8147-4587-3). NYU Pr.

Kirschner, Robert S., ed. Rabbinic Responsa of the Holocaust Era. LC 84-23509. 204p. 1985. 17.95 (ISBN 0-8052-3978-2). Schocken.

Klarsfeld, Serge. The Children of Izieu: A Human Tragedy. (Illus.). 128p. 1985. pap. 9.95 (ISBN 0-8109-2307-6). Abrams.

Klein, Gerda W. Promise of a New Spring: The Holocaust & Renewal. (Illus.). 64p. 1981. 10.95 (ISBN 0-940646-50-1); pap. 5.95 (ISBN 0-940646-51-X). Rossel Bks.

Koblik, Steven. The Stones Cry Out: Sweden's Response to Persecution of the Jews 1933-1945. 1987. 20.95 (ISBN 0-89604-118-2); pap. 13.95 (ISBN 0-89604-119-0). Holocaust Pubns.

Kogon, Eugen, et al, eds. Zyklon B: Nazi Mass Murder by Poison Gas. 1987. 19.95 (ISBN 0-89604-110-7); pap. 13.95 (ISBN 0-89604-111-5). Holocaust Pubns.

Kohn, Nahum & Roiter, Howard. A Voice from the Forest. LC 80-81685. (Illus.). 256p. (Orig.). 1985. 16.95 (ISBN 0-89604-020-8); pap. 10.95 (ISBN 0-89604-021-6). Holocaust Pubns.

Kohner, Hanna, et al. Hanna & Walter. 224p. 1985. pap. 3.50 (ISBN 0-445-20109-6, Popular Lib). Warner Bks.

Kopeck. In the Shadow of the Flames: Six Lectures on the Holocaust. LC 82-72377. (Witness to the Holocaust Ser.: No. 4). 86p. 1982. 6.75. Witness Holocaust.

Korczak, Janusz. Ghetto Diary. LC 77-91911. (Illus.). 192p. 1978. 16.95 (ISBN 0-89604-004-6); pap. 10.95 (ISBN 0-317-06362-6). Holocaust Pubns.

Kowalski, Isaac. Anthology on Armed Jewish Resistance 1939-1945, Vol. 1. (Illus.). 648p. 1984. Repr. 30.00x. Jewish Com Pub.

Kren, George M. & Rappoport, Leon H. Holocaust & the Crisis of Human Behavior. LC 79-23781. 200p. 1980. text ed. 29.50x (ISBN 0-8419-0544-4). Holmes & Meier.

Kulka, Erich. Escape from Auschwitz. (Illus.). 192p. (Orig.). 1986. 27.95 (ISBN 0-89789-088-4); pap. 12.95 (ISBN 0-89789-089-2). Bergin & Garvey.

KZ: A Pictoral Report from Five Concentration Camps. (Witness to the Holocaust Ser.: No. 5). (Illus.). 54p. 1983. 3.00 (ISBN 0-317-46949-5). Witness Holocaust.

Lapon, Lenny. Mass Murderers in White Coats: Psychiatric Genocide in Nazi Germany & the United States. (Orig.). 1986. pap. 9.00 (ISBN 0-9614961-9-3). Psych Genocide Res.

Laska, Vera, ed. Women in the Resistance & in the Holocaust: The Voices of Eyewitnesses. LC 82-12018. (Contributions in Women Studies: No. 37). xv, 330p. 1983. lib. bdg. 29.95 (ISBN 0-313-23457-4, LWH/). Greenwood.

Latour, Anny. The Jewish Resistance In France. LC 80-84246. (Illus.). 287p. 1981. 16.95 (ISBN 0-89604-025-9); pap. 10.95 (ISBN 0-89604-026-7). Holocaust Pubns.

Leo Baeck Institute Yearbook, Vol. 29: Enlightenment & Acculturation Persecution under the Nazi Regime. (Illus.). 560p. 1984. 28.00 (ISBN 0-436-25543-X, Pub. by Secker & Warburg UK). David & Charles.

Letgers, Lyman H., ed. Western Society after the Holocaust. (Replica Editon Ser.). 200p. 1984. 20.00x (ISBN 0-86531-985-5). Westview.

Leuchter, Sara, ed. Guide to Wisconsin Survivors of the Holocaust: A Documentary Project of the Wisconsin Jewish Archives. 192p. 1983. pap. 12.50 (ISBN 0-87020-216-2). State Hist Soc Wis.

Levin, Meyer. Eva: A Novel of the Holocaust. LC 79-14440. 1979. pap. text ed. 5.95x (ISBN 0-87441-283-8). Behrman.

Levin, Nora. The Holocaust: The Destruction of European Jewry, 1933-1945. LC 67-23676. (Illus.). 784p. 1973. pap. 12.95 (ISBN 0-8052-0376-1). Schocken.

Lifton, Robert J. The Nazi Doctors: Medical Killing & the Psychology of Genocide. LC 85-73874. 576p. 1986. 19.95 (ISBN 0-465-04904-4). Basic.

Lipstadt, Deborah. Beyond Belief: The American Press & the Coming of the Holocaust. 336p. 19.95 (ISBN 0-02-919160-2). Free Pr.

Littell, Marcia S., ed. Liturgies on the Holocaust: An Interfaith Anthology. LC 86-23507. 208p. 1986. lib. bdg. 39.95x (ISBN 0-88946-030-2). E Mellen.

Luel, Steven & Marcus, Paul. Psychoanalytic Reflections on the Holocaust: Selected Essays. 1985. 25.00 (ISBN 0-88125-041-4). Ktav.

Medoff, Rafael. The Deafening Silence: American Jewish Leaders & the Holocaust, 1933-1945. 1986. 14.95 (ISBN 0-933503-63-6). Shapolsky Pubs.

Meed, Vladka. On Both Sides of the Wall. Meed, Steven, tr. LC 78-71300. (Illus.). 304p. 1979. 16.95 (ISBN 0-89604-012-7); pap. 10.95 (ISBN 0-89604-013-5). Holocaust Pubns.

Meltzer, Milton. Never to Forget: The Jews of the Holocaust. 192p. 1977. pap. 3.25 (ISBN 0-440-96070-3, LFL); tchr's. guide by Max Nadel 0.50. Dell.

--Never to Forget: The Jews of the Holocaust. LC 75-25409. (YA) 1976. PLB 13.89 (ISBN 0-06-024175-6). HarpJ.

Mendelsohn, J. The Final Solution in the Extermination Camps & the Aftermath. LC 81-80320. (The Holocaust Ser.). 250p. 1982. lib. bdg. 61.00 (ISBN 0-8240-4886-5). Garland Pub.

--The Judicial System & the Jews in Nazi Germany. LC 81-80321. (The Holocaust Ser.). 245p. 1982. lib. bdg. 61.00 (ISBN 0-8240-4887-3). Garland Pub.

--Relief & Rescue of Jews from Nazi Oppression, 1943-1945. LC 81-80322. (The Holocaust Ser.). 264p. 1982. lib. bdg. 61.00 (ISBN 0-8240-4888-1). Garland Pub.

--Relief in Hungary & the Failure of the Joel Brand Mission. LC 81-80323. (The Holocaust Ser.). 256p. 1982. lib. bdg. 61.00 (ISBN 0-8240-4889-X). Garland Pub.

--Rescue to Switzerland: The Mussy & Saly Mayer Affair. LC 81-80324. (The Holocaust Ser.). 280p. 1982. lib. bdg. 61.00 (ISBN 0-8240-4890-3). Garland Pub.

--The Wannsee Protocol & a 1944 Report on Auschwitz by the Office of Strategic Services. LC 81-80319. (The Holocaust Ser.). 264p. 1982. lib. bdg. 61.00 (ISBN 0-8240-4885-7). Garland Pub.

Mendelsohn, John. Deportation of the Jews to the East: Settin, 1940 to Hungary 1944. LC 81-80316. (The Holocaust Ser.). 256p. 1982. lib. bdg. 61.00 (ISBN 0-8240-4882-2). Garland Pub.

--The Einsatzgruppen or Murder Commandos. LC 81-80318. (The Holocaust Ser.). 256p. 1982. lib. bdg. 61.00 (ISBN 0-8240-4884-9). Garland Pub.

--Jewish Emigration: The SS St. Louis Affair & Other Cases. LC 81-80315. (The Holocaust Ser.: Vol. 7). 274p. 1982. lib. bdg. 61.00 (ISBN 0-8240-4881-4). Garland Pub.

--Jewish Emigration 1938-1940: Rublee & Intergovernmental Committee. LC 81-80314. (The Holocaust Ser.). 250p. 1982. lib. bdg. 61.00 (ISBN 0-8240-4880-6). Garland Pub.

--Medical Experiments on Jewish Inmates of Concentration Camps. LC 81-80317. (The Holocaust Ser.). 282p. 1982. lib. bdg. 61.00 (ISBN 0-8240-4883-0). Garland Pub.

--Propaganda & Aryanization, 1938-1944. LC 81-80312. (The Holocaust Ser.). 255p. 1982. lib. bdg. 61.00 (ISBN 0-8240-4878-4). Garland Pub.

--Punishing the Perpetrators of the Holocaust: The Ohlendorf & Von Weizsaecker Cases. LC 81-80326. (The Holocaust Ser.). 310p. 1982. lib. bdg. 61.00 (ISBN 0-8240-4892-X). Garland Pub.

Mendelsohn, John & Detwiler, Donald S. Jewish Emigration from 1933 to the Evian Conference of 1938. LC 81-80313. (The Holocaust Ser.). 260p. 1982. lib. bdg. 61.00 (ISBN 0-8240-4879-2). Garland Pub.

Michelson, Frida. Rumbuli. Goodman, Wolf, tr. from Rus. 224p. 1981. 16.95 (ISBN 0-89604-029-1); pap. 10.95 (ISBN 0-89604-030-5). Holocaust Pubns.

Milner, Sonia. Sonia: Survival in War & Peace. LC 83-50758. 1983. pap. 4.95 (ISBN 0-88400-102-4). Shengold.

Milton, Sybil & Friedlander, Henry, eds. The Simon Wiesenthal Center Annual, Vol. 3. 1986. lib. bdg. 35.00 (ISBN 0-527-96490-5). Kraus Intl.

Morley, John F. Vatican Diplomacy & the Jews During the Holocaust, 1939-1943. 1980. 25.00x (ISBN 0-87068-701-8). Ktav.

--Vatican Diplomacy & the Jews During the Holocaust 1939-1943. 320p. 25.00. ADL.

Neimark, Anne E. One Man's Valor: Leo Baeck & the Holocaust. (Jewish Biography Ser.). (Illus.). 128p. 1986. 14.95 (ISBN 0-525-67175-7, 01451-440). Lodestar Bks.

Neusner, Jacob. Stranger at Home: "The Holocaust," Zionism, & American Judaism. LC 80-19455. x, 214p. 1985. pap. 8.95 (ISBN 0-226-57629-9). U of Chicago Pr.

Nurenberger, M. J. The Scared & the Doomed: The Jewish Establishment vs. the Six Million. (Illus.). 320p. (Orig.). 1986. pap. 12.95 (ISBN 0-88962-289-2). Riverrun NY.

Pankiewicz, Tadeusz. The Cracow Ghetto Pharmacy. 1987. 16.95 (ISBN 0-89604-114-X); pap. 10.95 (ISBN 0-89604-115-8). Holocaust Pubns.

Penkower, Monty N. The Jews Were Expendable: Free World Diplomacy & the Holocaust. LC 82-17490. 446p. 1983. 27.50 (ISBN 0-252-00747-6). U of Ill Pr.

Pinsker, Sanford & Fischel, Jack, eds. America & the Holocaust, Vol. I. (Holocaust Studies Annual). 200p. 1984. lib. bdg. 15.00 (ISBN 0-913283-02-9). Penkevill.

Poliakov, Leon. Harvest of Hate. LC 78-71294. 350p. 1979. pap. 12.95 (ISBN 0-89604-006-2). Holocaust Pubns.

--Harvest of Hate: The Nazi Program for the Destruction of the Jews in Europe. LC 74-110836. 1971. Repr. of 1954 ed. lib. bdg. 22.50x (ISBN 0-8371-2635-5, POHH). Greenwood.

--Harvest of Hate: The Nazi Program for the Destruction of the Jews of Europe. rev ed. LC 78-71294. 1979. pap. 5.95 (ISBN 0-8052-5006-9, Pub. by Holocaust Library). Schocken.

Porter, Jack N. Confronting History & Holocaust: Collected Essays: 1972-1982. LC 83-3572. (Illus.). 168p. (Orig.). 1983. lib. bdg. 26.00 (ISBN 0-8191-3107-5); pap. text ed. 11.25 (ISBN 0-8191-3108-3). U Pr of Amer.

Quaytman, Wilfred, ed. Holocaust Survivors: Psychological & Social Sequelae. LC 80-80071. (A Special Issue of Journal of Contemporary Psychotherapy: Vol. 11, No. 1). 88p. 1981. pap. 9.95 (ISBN 0-89885-016-9). Human Sci Pr.

Rabinowitz, Dorothy. About the Holocaust: What We Know & How We Know It. LC 79-51801. (Illus.). 48p. 1979. pap. 1.50 (ISBN 0-87495-014-7). Am Jewish Comm.

Rabinsky, Leatrice & Mann, Gertrude. Journey of Conscience: Young People Respond to the Holocaust. 112p. Repr. 1.50 (ISBN 0-686-95073-9). ADL.

Ramras-Rauch, Gila & Michman-Melkman, Joseph, eds. Facing the Holocaust. 1986. 16.95 (ISBN 0-8276-0253-7). Jewish Pubns.

Rausch, David A. A Legacy of Hatred: Why Christians Must Not Forget the Holocaust. 1984. 9.95 (ISBN 0-8024-0341-7). Moody.

Rautkallio, Hannu. Finland & the Holocaust: The Finnish Experience. 1987. 20.95 (ISBN 0-89604-120-4); pap. 13.95 (ISBN 0-89604-121-2). Holocaust Pubns.

Reitlinger, Gerald. The Final Solution: The Attempt to Exterminate the Jews of Europe 1939-45. 622p. 1987. Repr. of 1953 ed. 40.00 (ISBN 0-87668-951-9). Aronson.

Renn, Walter, et al. The Treatment of the Holocaust in Textbooks: The Federal Republic of Germany, Israel, the United States. (Holocaust Studies). 288p. 1987. text ed. 30.00 (ISBN 0-88033-955-1). East Eur Quarterly.

Ringelheim, Joan & Katz, Esther, eds. Catalogue of Audio & Video Testimonies of the Holocaust. (Occasional Papers from the Institute for Research in History Ser.: No. 5). 150p. (Orig.). Date not set. pap. 7.50 (ISBN 0-913865-04-4). Inst Res Hist.

Rittner, Carol & Myers, Sondra. Courage to Care: Rescuers of Jews During the Holocaust. 176p. 1986. 24.95 (ISBN 0-8147-7397-4). NYU Pr.

Robinson, Jacob & Sachs, Henry. The Holocaust: The Nuremberg Evidence, Part I: Documents, Digest, Index & Chronological Tables. (Yad Vashem-Yivo. Joint Documentary Projects). 1976. 30.00 (ISBN 0-914512-37-4). Yivo Inst.

Roden, Rudolph G. & Roden, Eva. Lives on Borrowed Time. 1984. 6.95 (ISBN 0-8062-2316-2). Carlton.

Romano, Elio. A Generation of Wrath. 228p. 1986. 14.95 (ISBN 0-7278-2039-7). Salem Hse Pubs.

Rosenbaum, I. Holocaust & Halakhah. (Library of Jewish Law & Ethics: No. 2). 15.00x (ISBN 0-87068-296-2); pap. 9.95. Ktav.

Rosenfeld, Alvin H. A Double Dying: Reflections on Holocaust Literature. LC 79-3006. 224p. 1980. 17.50x (ISBN 0-253-13337-8). Ind U Pr.

Rosenfeld, Alvin H. & Greenberg, Irving, eds. Confronting the Holocaust: The Impact of Elie Wiesel. LC 78-15821. pap. 61.80 (ISBN 0-317-27853-3, 2056054). Bks Demand UMI.

Rosenthal, Ludwig. The Final Solution to the Jewish Question: Mass-Murder or Hoax? (Illus.). 145p. (Orig.). 1984. pap. 9.95 (ISBN 0-318-04673-3). Magnes Mus.

Roskies, David G. Against the Apocalypse: Responses to Catastrophe in Modern Jewish Culture. LC 83-18663. (Illus.). 392p. 1986. pap. 9.95 (ISBN 0-674-00916-9). Harvard U Pr.

Roskies, Diane. Teaching the Holocaust to Children: A Review & Bibliography. pap. 7.50x (ISBN 0-87068-469-8). Ktav.

Ross, Robert W. So It Was True: The American Protestant Press & the Nazi Persecution of the Jews. LC 80-196. 1980. 20.00 (ISBN 0-8166-0948-9); pap. 9.95 (ISBN 0-8166-0951-9). U of Minn Pr.

Rothchild, Sylvia, ed. Voices from the Holocaust. 464p. 1982. pap. 10.95 (ISBN 0-452-00860-3, Mer). NAL.

Rousset, David. The Other Kingdom. Guthrie, Ramon, tr. from Fr. LC 81-12572. 173p. 1982. Repr. of 1947 ed. lib. bdg. 21.50 (ISBN 0-86527-339-1). Fertig.

Rubenstein, Richard. The Cunning of History: The Holocaust & the American Future. price not set (ISBN 0-8446-5860-X). Peter Smith.

Rubenstein, Richard L. After Auschwitz: Radical Theology & Contemporary Judism. 1966. pap. text ed. write for info. (ISBN 0-02-404210-2). Macmillan.

Ryan, Michael D., ed. Human Responses to the Holocaust: Perpetrators, Victims, Bystanders & Resisters-Papers of the 1979 Bernhard E. Olson Scholar's Conference on the Church Struggle & the Holocaust Sponsored by the National Conference of Christians & Jews. LC 81-38331. (Texts & Studies in Religion: Vol. 9). 300p. 1981. 49.95x (ISBN 0-88946-902-4). E Mellen.

Sachar, Abram. The Redemption of the Unwanted: The Post-Holocaust Years. 334p. 1985. pap. 9.95 (ISBN 0-312-66730-2, Pub. by Marek). St Martin.

Schoenfeld, Joachim. Holocaust Memoirs: Jews in the Lwow Ghetto, the Janowski Concentration Camp, & as Deportees in Siberia. 1985. text ed. 17.50x (ISBN 0-88125-074-0). Ktav.

Schulman, Elias. The Holocaust in Yiddish Literature. 96p. 1983. pap. 4.00 (ISBN 0-318-20364-2). Workmen's Circle.

Schupack, Joseph. The Dead Years: Surviving the Holocaust. LC 86-81286. 1987. 16.95 (ISBN 0-89604-066-6); pap. 10.95 (ISBN 0-89604-067-4). Holocaust Pubns.

Seventy First Infantry Division, U.S. Army. The Seventy-First Came to Gunskirchen Lager. Crawford, Fred R., intro. by. LC 79-51047. (Witness to the Holocaust Ser.: No. 1). (Illus.). 28p. 1983. pap. 1.50 (ISBN 0-89937-036-5). Witness Holocaust.

Sevillias, Errikos. Athens-Auschwitz. 109p. 1984. 11.95 (ISBN 0-930685-00-8). Cadmus Press.

Shepherd, Naomi. A Refuge from Darkness: Wilfrid Israel & the Rescue of the Jews. LC 83-22000. 18.45 (ISBN 0-394-52503-5). Pantheon.

Sherwin, Byron & Ament, Susan. Encountering the Holocaust: An Interdisciplinary Survey. LC 79-9126. 500p. 1979. 22.50 (ISBN 0-88482-936-7). Impact Pr IL.

Shulman, Abraham. The Case of Hotel Polski. LC 81-81519. 240p. 1982. 16.95 (ISBN 0-89604-033-X); pap. 10.95 (ISBN 0-89604-034-8). Holocaust Pubns.

Shur, Irene G. & Littell, Franklin H. Reflection on the Holocaust. Lambert, Richard D., ed. LC 80-66618. (The Annals of the American Academy of Political & Social Science: No. 450). 272p. 1980. pap. text ed. 7.95 (ISBN 0-87761-253-6). Am Acad Pol Soc Sci.

Smolar, Hersh. The Minsk Ghetto. Rosenfeld, Max, tr. from Yiddish. 1987. 18.95 (ISBN 0-89604-068-2); pap. 13.95 (ISBN 0-89604-069-0). Holocaust Pubns.

Spanjaard, Barry. Don't Fence Me In: An American Teenager in the Holocaust. 8th ed. Spanjaard, Bunnie J., ed. LC 81-68713. (Illus.). 224p. (Orig.). 1981. pap. 8.95 (ISBN 0-9607008-0-3). B & B Pub CA.

Stadtler, Bea. The Holocaust: A History of Courage & Resistance. Bial, Morrison D., ed. LC 74-11469. Orig. Title: The Test. (Illus.). 210p. 1975. pap. text ed. 5.50x (ISBN 0-87441-231-5). Behrman.

--The Holocaust: A History of Courage & Resistance. 210p. Repr. 5.50 (ISBN 0-686-95067-4). ADL.

Stein, R. Conrad. The Holocaust. LC 85-31415. (World at War Ser.). (Illus.). 48p. 1986. PLB 10.60 (ISBN 0-516-04767-1); pap. 2.95 (ISBN 0-516-44767-X). Childrens.

Steiner, Erich G. The Story of "Patria". LC 81-85302. 224p. 1982. 16.95 (ISBN 0-8052-5036-0); pap. 10.95 (ISBN 0-8052-5037-9). Holocaust Pubns.

Steinhorn, Harriet. Shadows of the Holocaust. LC 83-14887. 80p. 1983. pap. text ed. 8.95 (ISBN 0-930494-25-3). Kar Ben.

Strauss, Herbert A. & Kampe, Norbert, eds. Jewish Immigrants of the Nazi Period in the U. S. A. The Expulsion & Migration of German Jews 1933-45 - Annotated Sources. (Jewish Immigrants of the Nazi Period in the U. S. A. Ser.: Vol. 4). 225p. 1988. lib. bdg. 50.00 (ISBN 3-598-08009-3). K G Saur.

Szajkowski, Soza. An Illustrated Sourcebook on the Holocaust, Vols. 1 & 2. Incl. Vol. 1. Prelude to Holocaust: The Jew Must Disappear. o. p 50.00 (ISBN 0-87068-294-6); Vol. 2. The Ghetto & Death Camp Walls Speak (ISBN 0-87068-295-4). 45.00x ea. Ktav.

Szajkowski, Zosa. An Illustrated Sourcebook on the Holocaust, Vol. III. 1979. 40.00x (ISBN 0-87068-690-9). Ktav.

Truth in History Committee. The Six Million Reconsidered. Grimstad, William N., ed. (Illus.). 1979. pap. 8.00 (ISBN 0-911038-50-7). Noontide.

The Warsaw Ghetto in Pictures: Illustrated Catalog. LC 79-26657. (Yivo Institute for Jewish Research Guide & Catalogs Ser.: No. 1). (Illus.). 1970. pap. 5.00 (ISBN 0-914512-08-0). Yivo Inst.

Weber, Charles E. The Holocaust: One Hundred Twenty Questions & Answers. (Illus.). 60p. (Orig.). 1983. pap. 4.00 (ISBN 0-939484-07-2). Inst Hist Rev.

Wells, L. The Death Brigade. LC 77-89068. 305p. 1978. pap. 10.95 (ISBN 0-89604-000-3). Holocaust Pubns.

Wiesel, Elie. Legends of Our Time. 1980. pap. 2.50 (ISBN 0-380-00931-5, 49429, Bard). Avon.

Wiesel, Elie, pref. by. Selected & Annotated Resource List of Materials on the Holocaust. 65p. 5.00 (ISBN 0-686-74934-0). ADL.

Wiesel, Elie, et al. Dimensions of the Holocaust. 1978. 10.95 (ISBN 0-8101-0469-5); pap. 6.95x (ISBN 0-8101-0470-9). Northwestern U Pr.

Wilson, Doric. A Perfect Relationship. LC 83-61708. 98p. (Orig.). 1983. pap. 5.95 (ISBN 0-933322-12-7). Sea Horse.

With Fury Poured Out: A Torah Perspective on the Holocaust. 300p. 1987. 16.95 (ISBN 0-88125-107-0). KTAV.

Wyman, David S. The Abandonment of the Jews. LC 84-42711. 480p. 1986. pap. 8.95 (ISBN 0-394-74077-7). Pantheon.

--The Abandonment of the Jews: America & the Holocaust, 1941-1945. LC 84-42711. 450p. 1984. 6.00 (ISBN 0-394-42813-7). Pantheon.

Yuter, Alan J. The Holocaust in Hebrew Literature: From Genocide to Rebirth. LC 83-9973. (Judaic Studies). 152p. 1983. 18.00x (ISBN 0-8046-5322-4, Natl U). Assoc Faculty Pr.

Zimmels, H. J. The Echo of the Nazi Holocaust in Rabbinic Literature. 25.00x (ISBN 0-87068-427-2). Ktav.

Zvi. LC 78-56149. 1978. pap. 3.95 (ISBN 0-915540-23-1). Friends Israel-Spearhead Pr.

HOLOCAUST, JEWISH (1939-1945)–ERRORS, INVENTIONS, ETC.

Faurisson, Robert. The Holocaust Debate: Revisionist Historians Versus Six Million Jews. 1980. lib. bdg. 59.95 (ISBN 0-686-62797-0). Revisionist Pr.

Hoffman, Michael A., II. Blaspheming Against the Holy Peoples Holy Hoax. 1986. pap. 2.00 (ISBN 0-317-53014-3). Noontide.

--The Great Holocaust Trial. (Illus.). 95p. (Orig.). 1985. pap. 5.95 (ISBN 0-939484-22-6). Inst Hist Rev.

--The Great Holocaust Trial. (Illus.). 95p. 1986. pap. 5.95 (ISBN 0-317-53011-9). Noontide.

Staeglich, Wilhelm. The Auschwitz Myth. O'Keefe, Theodore J., ed. Francis, Thomas, tr. from Ger. Tr. of Der Auschwitz Mythos. (Illus.). 408p. 1986. 19.95 (ISBN 0-939484-23-4). Inst Hist Rev.

HOLOCAUST, JEWISH (1939-1945)–PERSONAL NARRATIVES

Amery, Jean. At the Mind's Limits: Contemplations by a Survivor on Auschwitz & Its Realities. Rosenfeld, Sidney & Rosenfeld, Stella P., trs. 128p. 1986. pap. 5.95 (ISBN 0-8052-0761-9). Schocken.

Axelrad, Albert S. Refusenik: Voices of Struggle & Hope. 75p. (Orig.). 1986. pap. text ed. 9.95x (ISBN 0-932269-56-7). Wyndham Hall.

Biber, Jacob. Survivors: A Personal Story of the Holocaust. LC 85-22415. (Studies in Judaica & the Holocaust: No. 2). 208p. 1986. lib. bdg. 18.95x (ISBN 0-89370-370-2); pap. text ed. 8.95x (ISBN 0-89370-470-9). Borgo Pr.

Dolinsky, Benjamin. Our Miracle. LC 86-43253. 116p. 1987. pap. 5.95 (ISBN 0-88400-126-1). Shengold.

Hillesum, Etty. Letters from Westerbork. Pomerans, Arnold, tr. LC 86-42625. (Dutch.). 160p. 1986. 14.95 (ISBN 0-394-55350-0). Pantheon.

Oliner, Samuel P. Restless Memories: Recollections of the Holocaust Years. rev., 2nd ed. LC 85-82084. 215p. (Orig.). 1986. pap. 9.95 (ISBN 0-943376-28-9). Magnes Mus.

Schlamm, J. Vera & Friedman, Bob. Pursued. rev. ed. LC 86-600. 189p. 1986. pap. 3.95 (ISBN 0-8307-1146-5, 5018631). Regal.

Sender, Ruth M. The Cage. LC 86-8562. 252p. 1986. 13.95 (ISBN 0-02-781830-6). Macmillan.

Shelley, Lore, ed. Secretaries of Death: Accounts by Former Prisoners Who Worked in the Administrative Offices of Auschwitz. LC 85-43608. 450p. 1986. 20.00 (ISBN 0-88400-123-7). Shengold.

Strygler, Rosa. Rosa: A Story of Two Survivals. 190p. 15.95 (ISBN 0-88400-125-3). Shengold.

Tec, Nechama. When Light Pierced the Darkness: Christian Rescue of Jews in Nazi-Occupied Poland. (Illus.). 320p. 1986. 19.95 (ISBN 0-19-503643-3). Oxford U Pr.

HOLOCAUST SURVIVORS

Here are entered works on Jews who survived the Jewish Holocaust of 1939-1945, with emphasis on their lives since 1945. Works consisting of personal accounts of the Jewish Holocaust are entered under Holocaust, Jewish 1939-1945)–Personal Narratives.

Amery, Jean. At the Mind's Limits: Contemplations by a Survivor on Auschwitz & Its Realities. Rosenfeld, Sidney & Rosenfeld, Stella P., trs. 128p. 1986. pap. 5.95 (ISBN 0-8052-0761-9). Schocken.

Levi, Primo. The Reawakening. 224p. 1987. 4.95 (ISBN 0-02-022370-6, Collier). Macmillan.

Milton, Sybil, et al, eds. Simon Wiesenthal Center Annual, Vol. 2. 1985. lib. bdg. 30.00 (ISBN 0-527-96489-1). Kraus Intl.

Ringelheim, Joan & Katz, Esther, eds. Catalogue of Audio & Video Testimonies of the Holocaust. (Occasional Papers from the Institute for Research in History Ser.: No. 5). 150p. (Orig.). Date not set. pap. 7.50 (ISBN 0-913865-04-4). Inst Res Hist.

Rubinstein, Erna F. The Survivor in Us All: Four Young Sisters in the Holocaust. 185p. 1986. 19.50 (ISBN 0-208-02025-X, Archon); pap. 12.50x (ISBN 0-208-02128-0). Shoe String.

Schlamm, J. Vera & Friedman, Bob. Pursued. rev. ed. LC 86-600. 189p. 1986. pap. 3.95 (ISBN 0-8307-1146-5, 5018631). Regal.

Strygler, Rosa. Rosa: A Story of Two Survivals. 190p. 15.95 (ISBN 0-88400-125-3). Shengold.

Zuccotti, Susan. The Italians & the Holocaust: Persecution, Rescue & Survival. LC 86-47738. (Illus.). 344p. 1987. 19.95 (ISBN 0-465-03622-8). Basic.

HOLY, THE

see also Theism

Beasley-Murray, Stephen. Toward a Metaphysics of the Sacred: Development of the Concept of the Holy. LC 82-8288. viii, 110p. 1982. 7.95x (ISBN 0-86554-038-1, MUP-M08). Mercer Univ Pr.

Olson, Alan M.. & Rouner, Leroy S., eds. Transcendence & the Sacred. LC 81-50456. 256p. 1981. 19.95 (ISBN 0-268-01841-3). U of Notre Dame Pr.

Turner, Harold W. From Temple to Meeting House: The Phenomenology & Theology of Sacred Space. 1979. text ed. 39.20x (ISBN 90-279-7977-4). Mouton.

HOLY ALLIANCE

Knapton, Ernest J. Lady of the Holy Alliance: The Life of Julie De Krudener. LC 39-14081. Repr. of 1939 ed. 22.45 (ISBN 0-404-03732-1). AMS Pr.

HOLY CROSS

Ajijola, A. D. Myth of the Cross. pap. 9.50 (ISBN 0-686-63907-3). Kazi Pubns.

Berna, Kurt. Christ Did Not Perish on the Cross: Christ's Body Buried Alive. (Illus.). 1975. 14.50 (ISBN 0-682-48139-4). Exposition Pr FL.

Carley, Ed. Way of the Cross. 1985. 9.95 (ISBN 0-89837-101-5, Pub. by Pflaum Press). Peter Li.

De Brand, Roy E. The Cross & Beyond. LC 83-70374. 1984. pap. 4.95 (ISBN 0-8054-2250-1). Broadman.

Forsyth, Peter T. The Cruciality of the Cross. 104p. 1983. pap. 5.95 (ISBN 0-913029-00-9). Stevens Bk Pr.

Guenon, Rene. The Symbolism of the Cross. 134p. 1975. 35.00x (ISBN 0-317-39165-8, Pub. by Luzac & Co Ltd); pap. 19.00x (ISBN 0-317-39166-6). State Mutual Bk.

Lloyd-Jones, Martyn. The Cross. 192p. 1986. pap. 6.95 (ISBN 0-89107-382-5, Crossway Bks). Good News.

Miller, Calvin. Once upon a Tree. 1978. pap. 3.95 (ISBN 0-8010-6050-8). Baker Bk.

Prenter, Regin. Luther's Theology of the Cross. Anderson, Charles S., ed. LC 71-152368. (Facet Bks.). 32p. 1971. pap. 2.50 (ISBN 0-8006-3062-9, 1-3062). Fortress.

Stevens, William O. The Cross in the Life & Literature of the Anglo-Saxons. 69.95 (ISBN 0-87968-970-6). Gordon Pr.

HOLY GHOST

see Holy Spirit

HOLY GRAIL

see Grail

HOLY LANCE

Ravenscroft, Trevor. The Spear of Destiny: The Occult Power Behind the Spear Which Pierced the Side of Christ... & How Hitler Inverted the Force in a Bid to Conquer the World. LC 82-60165. 384p. 1982. pap. 9.95 (ISBN 0-87728-547-0). Weiser.

HOLY LEAGUE, 1576-1593

Jensen, DeLamar. Diplomacy & Dogmatism: Bernardino de Mendoza & the French Catholic League. LC 63-20769. (Illus.). 1964. 22.50x (ISBN 0-674-20800-5). Harvard U Pr.

HOLY OFFICE

see Inquisition

HOLY ORDERS

see Clergy–Office

HOLY ORTHODOX EASTERN CATHOLIC AND APOSTOLIC CHURCH

see Orthodox Eastern Church

HOLY PLACES

see Shrines

HOLY ROMAN EMPIRE

Bahree, Patricia. The Hindu World. LC 83-50691. (Religions of the World Ser.). 48p. 1983. lib. bdg. 14.96 (ISBN 0-382-06718-5); 9.25 (ISBN 0-382-06931-5). Silver.

Bryce, James. The Holy Roman Empire. 1978. Repr. of 1911 ed. lib. bdg. 65.00 (ISBN 0-8495-0333-7). Arden Lib.

--The Holy Roman Empire. 1911. 47.50 (ISBN 0-8482-7383-4). Norwood Edns.

Bryce, James B. The Holy Roman Empire. new enl. rev. ed. LC 75-41045. (BCL Ser. II). Repr. of 1913 ed. 28.50 (ISBN 0-404-14516-7). AMS Pr.

Falco, Giorgio. The Holy Roman Republic: A Historic Profile of the Middle Ages. Kent, K. V., tr. from Italian. LC 80-19696. Orig. Title: La Santa Romana Republica. 336p. 1980. Repr. of 1965 ed. lib. bdg. 42.50x (ISBN 0-313-22395-5, FAHR). Greenwood.

HOLY ROMAN EMPIRE–HISTORY–843-1273

Besozzi, Cerbonio. Chronik Des Cerbonio Besozzi: 1548-1563. 185p. pap. 23.00 (ISBN 0-384-15678-9). Johnson Repr.

Gagliardo, John G. Reich & Nation: The Holy Roman Empire As Idea & Reality, 1763-1806. LC 79-2170. 384p. 1980. 25.00x (ISBN 0-253-16773-6). Ind U Pr.

Innocent Third, Pope Register Innocenz' 3rd Uber Die Reichsfrage, 1198-1209. Tangl, Georgine, ed. 1923. 23.00 (ISBN 0-384-07885-0). Johnson Repr.

Mathews, Shailer. Select Medieval Documents & Other Material Illustrative in the History of Church & Empire, 754 A.D.-1254 A.D. LC 70-178566. (Lat.). Repr. of 1900 ed. 21.00 (ISBN 0-404-56628-6). AMS Pr.

Zophy, Jonathan W., ed. The Holy Roman Empire: A Dictionary Handbook. LC 79-8282. (Illus.). xxvii, 551p. 1980. lib. bdg. 49.95 (ISBN 0-313-21457-3, ZHR/). Greenwood.

HOLY SEE

see Papacy; Popes

HOLY SHROUD

Adams, Frank O. Sindon: A Layman's Guide to the Shroud of Turin. DeSalvo, John A., ed. LC 82-90138. (Illus.). 1982. 12.50 (ISBN 0-86700-008-2, Synergy Bks). P Walsh Pr.

Drews, Robert. In Search of the Shroud of Turin: New Light on Its History & Origins. LC 83-24586. (Illus.). 148p. 1984. 19.95x (ISBN 0-8476-7349-9, Rowman & Allanheld). Rowman.

Heller, John. The Report on the Shroud of Turin. 1984. pap. 8.95 (ISBN 0-395-36568-6). HM.

Heller, John H. Report on the Shroud of Turin. LC 83-127. 1983. 15.95 (ISBN 0-395-33967-7). HM.

Maher, Robert W. Science, History & the Shroud of Turin. 1986. 8.95 (ISBN 0-533-06641-7). Vantage.

Nickell, Joe. Inquest on the Shroud of Turin. LC 82-62457. (Illus.). 178p. 1982. 18.95 (ISBN 0-87975-194-0). Prometheus Bks.

O'Connell, Patrick & Carty, Charles. The Holy Shroud & Four Visions: The Holy Shroud New Evidence Compared with the Visions of St. Bridget of Sweden, Maria d'Agreda, Anne Catherine Emmerich, & Teresa Neumann. (Illus.). 1974. pap. 1.50 (ISBN 0-89555-102-0). TAN Bks Pubs.

Rinaldi, Peter M. I Saw the Holy Shroud. LC 83-71121. (Illus.). 112p. 1983. 4.95 (ISBN 0-89944-072-X); pap. 2.85 (ISBN 0-89944-069-X). Don Bosco Multimedia.

--When Millions Saw the Shroud. LC 79-53065. (Illus.). 1979. 6.95 (ISBN 0-89944-023-1); pap. 2.95 (ISBN 0-89944-024-X). Don Bosco Multimedia.

Smith, Donald M. The Letter. Parker, Diane, et al, eds. LC 83-91201. (Illus.). 217p. 20.00 (ISBN 0-914731-00-9). DMS Publishing Co.

Stevenson, Kenneth, ed. Proceedings of the Nineteen Seventy-Seven United States Conference of Research on the Shroud of Turin. (Illus.). 244p. (Orig.). 1980. pap. 10.00 (ISBN 0-9605516-0-3). Shroud of Turin.

Tribbe, Frank C. Portrait of Jesus? The Illustrated Story of the Shroud of Turin. 176p. 1983. 19.95 (ISBN 0-8128-2904-2). Stein & Day.

Wilson, Ian. The Shroud of Turin: The Burial Cloth of Jesus Christ. LC 77-81551. (Illus.). 1979. pap. 5.50 (ISBN 0-385-15042-3, Im). Doubleday.

HOLY SPIRIT

see also Church–Foundation; Gifts, Spiritual; Pentecost; Spirit; Trinity

Abbott, Stan. Holy Spirit: The Anointing of God. (Illus.). 86p. (Orig.). 1984. pap. 2.95 (ISBN 0-915545-00-4). S R Abbott Mini.

Alberione, James. The Spirit in My Life. 1977. pap. 0.95 (ISBN 0-8198-0460-6). Dghtrs St Paul.

Arnold, Eberhard. The Inner Land, Vol. 4: Light & Fire & the Holy Spirit. LC 75-16303. 1975. 3.50 (ISBN 0-87486-156-X). Plough.

Augsburger, Myron S. Practicing the Presence of the Spirit. LC 81-20170. 200p. (Orig.). 1982. pap. 7.95 (ISBN 0-8361-1990-8). Herald Pr.

Barney, Kenneth D. The Fellowship of the Holy Spirit. LC 77-70475. 96p. 1977. pap. 1.25 (ISBN 0-88243-515-9, 02-0515). Gospel Pub.

Bearer of the Holy Spirit. 2.00 (ISBN 0-8198-1112-2). Dghtrs St Paul.

Bennett, Dennis & Bennett, Rita. Holy Spirit & You Supplement. LC 73-75963. (To be used with The Holy Spirit & You). 1973. pap. 3.95 (ISBN 0-88270-031-6). Bridge Pub.

--Trinity of Man. LC 79-67378. (Illus.). 1979. pap. text ed. 6.95 (ISBN 0-88270-287-4). Bridge Pub.

Berkhof, Hendrikus. Doctrine of the Holy Spirit. LC 64-16279. 1976. pap. 6.95 (ISBN 0-8042-0551-5). John Knox.

Bickersteth, Edward H. Holy Spirit. LC 59-13640. 192p. 1976. pap. 5.95 (ISBN 0-8254-2227-2). Kregel.

Biederwolf, William E. Study of the Holy Spirit. LC 84-25099. 128p. 1985. pap. 5.95 (ISBN 0-8254-2244-2). Kregel.

Black, Garth. The Holy Spirit. rev. ed. (Way of Life Ser: No. 102). 1967. pap. 3.95 (ISBN 0-89112-102-1, Bibl Res Pr). Abilene Christ U.

Black, R. L. Holy Ghost & Speaking in Tongues. 180p. (Orig.). 1983. pap. 4.95 (ISBN 0-934942-35-8, 1869). White Wing Pub.

Bogorodskii, N. The Doctrine of St. John Damascene on the Procession of the Holy Spirit. LC 80-2351. Tr. of Uchenie Sv. Ioann Damaskina Ob' Iskhozhdenii Sv. Dukha. Repr. of 1879 ed. 28.50 (ISBN 0-404-18903-2). AMS Pr.

Boles, H. Leo. The Holy Spirit. 10.95 (ISBN 0-89225-102-6). Gospel Advocate.

Bradford, Brick. Releasing the Power of the Holy Spirit. 32p. 1983. 1.95x (ISBN 0-934421-00-5). Presby Renewal Pubns.

Brengle, Samuel L. When the Holy Ghost Is Come. 1980. pap. 3.95 (ISBN 0-86544-009-3). Salv Army Suppl South.

Briscoe, D. Stuart. Spirit Life. 160p. 1983. pap. 5.95 (ISBN 0-8007-5185-X). Revell.

Bruner, Frederick D. Theology of the Holy Spirit. LC 76-103445. 1970. pap. 9.95 (ISBN 0-8028-1547-2). Eerdmans.

Bruner, Frederick D. & Hordern, William E. The Holy Spirit-Shy Member of the Trinity. LC 83-72124. 112p. (Orig.). 1984. pap. 5.95 (ISBN 0-8066-2068-4, 10-3070). Augsburg.

Brunk, George R., ed. Encounter with the Holy Spirit. LC 72-2053. 240p. 1972. pap. 5.95 (ISBN 0-8361-1693-3). Herald Pr.

Buchanan, James. Office & Work of the Holy Spirit. 488p. 1984. Repr. of 1843 ed. 11.95 (ISBN 0-85151-089-2). Banner of Truth.

Buess, Bob. You Can Receive the Holy Ghost Today. 1967. pap. 2.50 (ISBN 0-934244-14-6). Sweeter Than Honey.

Buntain, D. N. The Holy Ghost & Fire. 100p. 1956. 1.25 (ISBN 0-88243-525-6, 02-0525). Gospel Pub.

Bunyan, John. Holy War. 1975. 12.95 (ISBN 0-685-52819-7). Reiner.

Burns, J. Patout & Fagin, Gerald M. The Holy Spirit. (Message of the Fathers of the Church Ser.: Vol. 3). 16.95 (ISBN 0-89453-343-6); pap. 10.95 (ISBN 0-89453-315-0). M Glazier.

Carter, Pat H. Vivamos En el Espiritu Cada Dia. 160p. 1982. pap. 3.25 (ISBN 0-311-09089-3). Casa Bautista.

Chadwick, Samuel. Way to Pentecost. 1960. pap. 2.95 (ISBN 0-87508-096-0). Chr Lit.

Chambers, Oswald. He Shall Glorify Me. 1965. 3.95 (ISBN 0-87508-111-8). Chr Lit.

Chantry, Walter. Signs of the Apostles. 1979. pap. 3.95 (ISBN 0-85151-175-9). Banner of Truth.

The Charismatica. (Illus.). 1979. 6.95 (ISBN 0-911346-03-1). Christianica.

Chinnici, Joseph P., ed. Devotion to the Holy Spirit in American Catholicism. LC 85-60956. (Sources of American Spirituality Ser.: Vol. 3). 256p. 1985. 12.95 (ISBN 0-8091-0366-4). Paulist Pr.

Clark, Glenn. Holy Spirit. pap. 0.50 (ISBN 0-910924-07-4). Macalester.

Congar, Yves. I Believe in the Holy Spirit, 3 Vols. Smith, David, tr. from Fr. Incl. Vol. I. The Experience of the Spirit. 173p. 24.95 (ISBN 0-8164-0518-2); Vol. 2. Lord & Giver of Life. 230p. 24.95 (ISBN 0-8164-0535-2); Vol. 3. The River of Life Flows in the East & in the West. 274p. 24.95 (ISBN 0-8164-0537-9). 300p. 1983. Set. 70.00 (ISBN 0-8164-0540-9, Winston-Seabury). Har-Row.

--The Word & the Spirit. 192p. 1986. 15.95 (ISBN 0-86683-538-5, HarpR). Har-Row.

Coppin, Ezra M. Slain in the Spirit. LC 75-36001. 96p. 1976. pap. 2.50 (ISBN 0-89221-010-9). New Leaf.

Cummings, James E. A Handbook on the Holy Spirit. LC 77-79551. 208p. 1977. pap. 3.95 (ISBN 0-87123-541-2, 200541). Bethany Hse.

DeCelles, Charles. The Unbound Spirit: God's Universal, Sanctifying Work. LC 85-20047. 367p. (Orig.). 1985. pap. 9.95 (ISBN 0-8189-0486-0). Alba.

De Valle, Francisca J. About the Holy Spirit. 120p. 5.00 (ISBN 0-912414-31-6). Lumen Christi.

DeWelt, Don. Nine Lessons on the Holy Spirit. 187p. 1978. cancelled (ISBN 0-89900-116-5). College Pr Pub.

--The Power of the Holy Spirit, Vol. III. 3rd ed. 1972. pap. 3.95 (ISBN 0-89900-125-4). College Pr Pub.

--Power of the Holy Spirit, Vol. IV. 2nd ed. (Orig.). 1976. pap. 6.95 (ISBN 0-89900-126-2). College Pr Pub.

--Power of the Holy Spirit, Vol. II. 5th ed. (Orig.). 1971. pap. 3.95 (ISBN 0-89900-124-6). College Pr Pub.

--Power of the Holy Spirit, Vol. I. 8th ed. (Orig.). 1963. pap. 3.95 (ISBN 0-89900-123-8). College Pr Pub.

Dunn, James D. Baptism in the Holy Spirit: A Re-Examination of the New Testament Teaching on the Gift of the Spirit in Relation to Pentacostalism Today. LC 77-3995. 256p. 1977. pap. 8.95 (ISBN 0-664-24140-9). Westminster.

Eifert, Frank & Stenbock, Evelyn. They Sang with the Spirit. 104p. 1983. pap. 3.95 (ISBN 0-8341-0824-0). Beacon Hill.

Ervin, Howard M. Conversion-Initiation & the Baptism in the Holy Spirit. 108p. 1985. pap. 9.95 (ISBN 0-913573-12-4). Hendrickson MA.

Fortman, Edmund. Activities of the Holy Spirit. LC 84-13786. 199p. 1984. 12.00 (ISBN 0-8199-0881-9). Franciscan Herald.

Frost, Robert. Set My Spirit Free. LC 73-84475. 234p. 1973. pap. 4.95 (ISBN 0-88270-058-8). Bridge Pub.

Geissler, Eugene S., compiled by. The Spirit Bible. LC 73-88004. 272p. 1973. pap. 2.25 (ISBN 0-87793-062-7). Ave Maria.

Gelpi, Donald L. The Divine Mother: A Trinitarian Theology of the Holy Spirit. LC 84-11921. 260p. (Orig.). 1984. lib. bdg. 27.25 (ISBN 0-8191-4034-1); pap. text ed. 12.50 (ISBN 0-8191-4035-X). U Pr of Amer.

Gesswein, Armin R. With One Accord in One Place. 93p. (Orig.). 1978. pap. 1.75 (ISBN 0-87509-161-X). Chr Pubns.

God's Gift-the Holy Spirit. 1978. 2.95 (ISBN 0-8198-0377-4); pap. 1.95 (ISBN 0-8198-0378-2). Dghtrs St Paul.

Goodwin, Thomas. Holy Spirit in Salvation. 1979. 15.95 (ISBN 0-85151-279-8). Banner of Truth.

Gordon, A. J. The Ministry of the Spirit. 160p. 1986. pap. 3.95 (ISBN 0-87123-843-8, 210843). Bethany Hse.

Gordon, Adoniram J. Holy Spirit in Missions. pap. 2.25 (ISBN 0-87509-094-X). Chr Pubns.

Graham, Billy. El Espiritu Santo. Sipowicz, A. Edwin, tr. from Eng. Orig. Title: The Holy Spirit. (Span.). 252p. 1981. pap. 6.25 (ISBN 0-311-09096-6). Casa Bautista.
--The Holy Spirit. 1978. 3.95 (ISBN 0-8499-4153-9). Word Bks.
--How to Be Born Again. LC 77-76057. 1977. 3.95 (ISBN 0-8499-4119-9). Word Bks.
Green, Michael. Creo en el Espiritu Santo. Vilela, Ernesto S., tr. from Eng. LC 77-164. (Serie Creo). Tr. of I Believe in the Holy Spririt. (Span.). 267p. 1977. pap. 5.95 (ISBN 0-89922-090-8). Edit Caribe.
--I Believe in the Holy Spirit. (I Believe Ser). 224p. 1975. pap. 8.95 (ISBN 0-8028-1609-6). Eerdmans.
Gresk, Grace E. Come Holy Spirit-I Need Thee. 48p. 1985. 5.95 (ISBN 0-533-06177-6). Vantage.
Gunkel, Hermann. The Influence of the Holy Spirit: The Popular View of the Apostolic Age & the Teaching of the Apostle Paul. Harrisville, Roy A. & Quanbeck, Philip A., II, trs. LC 78-20022. 144p. 1979. 3.00 (ISBN 0-8006-0544-6, 1-544). Fortress.
Hagin, Kenneth E. The Holy Spirit & His Gifts. 1974. pap. 5.00 (ISBN 0-89276-082-6). Hagin Ministries.
Hall, Manly P. Mystery of Holy Spirit. pap. 2.50 (ISBN 0-89314-333-2). Philos Res.
Hall, Robert B. Receiving the Holy Spirit. 1964. pap. 1.00 (ISBN 0-686-14948-3). Episcopal Ctr.
Haughey, John C. Conspiracy of God: The Holy Spirit in Men. LC 73-80730. 120p. 1976. pap. 2.95 (ISBN 0-385-11558-X, Im). Doubleday.
Heijkoop, H. J. Holy Spirit Is a Divine Person. 5.95 (ISBN 0-88172-084-4); pap. 4.95 (ISBN 0-88172-085-2). Believers Bkshelf.
Heron, Alasdair I. The Holy Spirit. LC 82-24705. 224p. (Orig.). 1983. pap. 11.95 (ISBN 0-664-24439-4). Westminster.
Hession, Roy. Be Filled Now. 1968. pap. 1.50 (ISBN 0-87508-235-1). Chr Lit.
Hicks, Robert & Bewes, Richard. The Holy Spirit. (Understanding Bible Truth Ser.). (Orig.). 1981. pap. 0.95 (ISBN 0-89840-021-X). Heres Life.
Holdcroft, Thomas L. The Holy Spirit: A Pentecostal Interpretation. LC 79-54991. (Illus.). 272p. 1979. Repr. 5.95 (ISBN 0-88243-554-X, 02-0554). Gospel Pub.
Ironside, H. A. Holy Spirit: Mission of, & Praying in. pap. 2.95 (ISBN 0-87213-366-4). Loizeaux.
Israel, Martin. Smouldering Fire: The Work of the Holy Spirit. LC 81-9794. 192p. 1981. 10.95 (ISBN 0-8245-0072-5). Crossroad NY.
Iverson, Dick. The Holy Spirit Today. (Illus.). 1977. pap. 5.50 (ISBN 0-914936-24-7). Bible Temple.
Jensen, Richard A. Touched by the Spirit: One Man's Struggle to Understand His Experience of the Holy Spirit. LC 75-2838. 160p. 1975. pap. 7.95 (ISBN 0-8066-1484-6, 10-6675). Augsburg.
Jepson, J. W. What You Should Know about the Holy Spirit. LC 85-81719. 160p. 1986. pap. 3.95 (ISBN 0-88243-639-2, 02-0639). Gospel Pub.
Kelly, W. Lectures on the Doctrine of the Holy Spirit. 7.95 (ISBN 0-88172-095-X). Believers Bkshelf.
Kidd, Sunnie D. & Kidd, James W. Brother Jerry's Stories: Following the Inspirations of the Holy Spirit. 34p. (Orig.). 1982. pap. text ed. 3.50 (ISBN 0-910727-00-7). Golden Phoenix.
King, George D. Lessons on the Holy Spirit. (Orig.). 1987. pap. 6.95 (ISBN 0-8054-1153-4). Broadman.
Koren, Henry J. To the Ends of the Earth: A General History of the Congregation of the Holy Ghost. 656p. 1982. text ed. 18.50x (ISBN 0-8207-0157-2). Duquesne.
The Life in the Spirit Seminars Team Manual: Catholic Edition. 1979. pap. 4.95 (ISBN 0-89283-065-4). Servant.
Lindsay, Gordon. Gifts of the Spirit, 4 vols. 2.50 ea. Vol. 1 (ISBN 0-89985-195-9). Vol. 2 (ISBN 0-89985-196-7). Vol. 3 (ISBN 0-89985-197-5). Vol. 4 (ISBN 0-89985-199-1). Christ Nations.
Linzey, Stanford E. Why I Believe in the Baptism with the Holy Spirit. 1962. pap. 0.75 (ISBN 0-88243-764-X, 02-0764). Gospel Pub.
Lloyd-Jones, Martyn, ed. Joy Unspeakable: Power & Renewal in the Holy Spirit. 284p. 1985. pap. 7.95 (ISBN 0-87788-441-2). Shaw Pubs.
Lockyer, Herbert. The Holy Spirit of God. 240p. (Orig.). 1983. pap. 5.50 (ISBN 0-687-17323-X). Abingdon.
Lovett, C. S. Dealing with the Devil. 1967. pap. 5.45 (ISBN 0-938148-05-2). Personal Christianity.
Lowery, T. L., ed. El Don del Espiritu Santo. (Span.). 80p. 1978. pap. 2.25 (ISBN 0-87148-307-6). Pathway Pr.
McBride, Alfred. The Gospel of the Holy Spirit. 1975. pap. 1.50 (ISBN 0-88479-951-4). Arena Lettres.
McConkey, James H. El Triple Secreto Del Espiritu Santo. Agostini, Beatrice, tr. from Eng. Orig. Title: The Three Fold Secret of the Holy Spirit. (Span.). 112p. 1980. pap. 1.95 (ISBN 0-311-09090-7). Casa Bautista.
Mains, David. Getting to Know the Holy Spirit. (Chapel Talks Ser.). 64p. 0.95 (ISBN 0-89191-262-2, 52621). Cook.
Manning, Brennan. Prophets & Lovers: In Search of the Holy Spirit. 1985. 4.95 (ISBN 0-87193-013-7). Dimension Bks.
Manteau-Bonamy, H. M. Immaculate Conception & the Holy Spirit: The Marian Teachings of Father Kolbe. Geiger, Bernard M., ed. Arnandez, Richard, tr. from Fr. LC 77-93104. Tr. of Doctrine mariale du Pere Kolbe, Esprit-Saint et Conception Immaculee. (Illus.). 1977. pap. 4.00 (ISBN 0-913382-00-0, 101-20). Prow Bks-Franciscan.
Marsh, F. E. Emblems of the Holy Spirit. LC 63-11465. 268p. 1974. pap. 9.95 (ISBN 0-8254-3222-7). Kregel.
Martinez, Luis M. The Sanctifier. 1981. 7.50 (ISBN 0-8198-6803-5); pap. 6.00 (ISBN 0-8198-6804-3). Dghtrs St Paul.
Matheson, George. Voices of the Spirit. (Direction Bks). 1979. pap. 3.45 (ISBN 0-8010-6078-8). Baker Bk.
Montague, George T. The Holy Spirit: Growth of Biblical Tradition. LC 76-4691. 384p. 1976. pap. 10.95 (ISBN 0-8091-1950-1). Paulist Pr.
Moody, Dwight L. & Martin, Walter. Secret Power. rev. ed. 1987. pap. 7.95 (ISBN 0-8307-1219-4). Regal.
Mooth, Verla A. The Spirit-Filled Life. 1978. 6.00 (ISBN 0-682-49113-6). Exposition Pr FL.
Morgan, G. Campbell. The Spirit of God. (Morgan Library). 240p. 1981. pap. 4.95 (ISBN 0-8010-6119-9). Baker Bk.
Morgan, James. The Biblical Doctrine of the Holy Spirit. 510p. 1985. Repr. lib. bdg. 19.00 (ISBN 0-86524-185-6, 8805). Klock & Klock.
Mozumdar, A. K. The Triumphant Spirit. 1978. pap. 6.50 (ISBN 0-87516-261-4). De Vorss.
Murphy, Roland, et al. Presence of God. LC 78-107214. (Concilium Ser.: Vol. 50). 215p. 7.95 (ISBN 0-8091-0116-5). Paulist Pr.
Newell, Arlo F. Receive the Holy Spirit. 1984. pap. 2.95 (ISBN 0-87162-409-5, D6431). Warner Pr.
Nystrom, Carolyn. The Holy Spirit in Me. (Children's Bible Ser.). 32p. 1980. pap. 4.95 (ISBN 0-8024-5994-3). Moody.
On the Holy Spirit & on Prayer. LC 81-9305. (Word & Spirit Ser.: Vol. 3). (Orig.). 1981. pap. 6.00 (ISBN 0-932506-15-1). St Bedes Pubns.
Owen, John. The Holy Spirit, His Gifts & Power. LC 60-16514. 1977. pap. 11.95 (ISBN 0-8254-3413-0). Kregel.
Owens, Valerie. The Holy Spirit of God. 168p. (Orig.). 1985. pap. text ed. 6.50 (ISBN 0-914307-39-8). Word Faith.
Pache, Rene. Person & Work of the Holy Spirit. 1960. pap. 7.50 (ISBN 0-8024-6471-8). Moody.
Pack, Frank. Tongues & the Holy Spirit. (Way of Life Ser: No. 127). (Orig.). 1972. pap. text ed. 3.95 (ISBN 0-89112-127-7, Bibl Res Pr). Abilene Christ U.
Packer, J. T. Keep in the Step with the Spirit. Date not set. pap. 7.95 (ISBN 0-8007-5235-X, Power Bks). Revell.
Pallenberg, Esward H. The Amazing Discovery of the Holy Ghost. (Illus.). 98p. 1984. pap. 23.75 (ISBN 0-89266-487-8). Am Classical Coll Pr.
Palmer, Edwin H. The Holy Spirit: His Person & Ministry. 200p. (Orig.). 1985. pap. 5.95 (ISBN 0-87552-367-6). Presby & Reformed.
Peck, John. What the Bible Teaches about the Holy Spirit. 1979. pap. 3.95 (ISBN 0-8423-7882-0). Tyndale.
Pegram, Don R. Sinning Against the Holy Spirit. 1982. pap. 1.25 (ISBN 0-89265-085-0). Randall Hse.
Petts, David. The Dynamic Difference: How the Holy Spirit Can Add an Exciting New Dimension to Your Life. LC 77-91483. 64p. 1978. pap. 0.95 (ISBN 0-88243-484-5, 02-0484, Radiant Bks). Gospel Pub.
Philippe, Thomas. The Fire of Contemplation: A Guide for Interior Souls. Doran, Verda C., tr. from Fr. LC 81-8099. 128p. (Orig.). 1981. pap. 4.95 (ISBN 0-8189-0414-3). Alba.
Pierson, A. T. Acts of the Holy Spirit. 127p. 1980. pap. 3.25 (ISBN 0-87509-274-8). Chr Pubns.
Pink, Arthur W. Holy Spirit. 1970. pap. 6.95 (ISBN 0-8010-7041-4). Baker Bk.
Pittenger, Norman. The Holy Spirit. LC 74-10839. 128p. 1974. 5.50 (ISBN 0-8298-0284-3). Pilgrim NY.
Potgieter, Pieter. Victory: The Work of the Spirit. 42p. 1984. pap. 1.45 (ISBN 0-85151-430-8). Banner of Truth.
The Power Filled Christian: The Work of the Holy Spirit in Man. LC 83-6658. 144p. 1984. pap. 4.95 (ISBN 0-310-33471-3, 6658P, Clarion Class). Zondervan.
Price, Frederick K. The Holy Spirit the Missing Ingredient. 1978. pap. text ed. 1.95 (ISBN 0-89274-081-7). Harrison Hse.
Prince, Derek. Baptism in the Holy Spirit. 1966. pap. 1.95 (ISBN 0-934920-07-9, B-19). Derek Prince.
Pugh, J. T. How to Receive the Holy Ghost. 63p. (Orig.). 1969. pap. 1.95 (ISBN 0-912315-45-8). Word Aflame.
Pursey, Barbara. The Gifts of the Holy Spirit. 40p. 1984. 1.95 (ISBN 0-934421-02-1). Presby Renewal Pubns.
Pursey, Barbara A. The Charismatic Renewal & You. Orig. Title: The Holy Spirit, the Church & You. 43p. (Orig.). 1987. pap. 2.95 (ISBN 0-934421-08-0). Presby Renewal Pubns.
Religous Education Staff. The Spirit Alive in Liturgy: Spirit Masters. 1981. 9.95 (ISBN 0-686-84105-0). Wm C Brown.
--The Spirit Alive in You: Spirit Masters. 1982. 9.95 (ISBN 0-697-01805-9). Wm C Brown.
Richardson, Jim. Praying in the Holy Ghost. 1983. pap. 1.75 (ISBN 0-911739-02-5). Abbott Loop.
Roberts, Sharon L. Somebody Lives Inside: The Holy Spirit. (Concept Ser.). (Illus.). 24p. (Orig.). 1986. pap. 3.95 saddlestitched (ISBN 0-570-08530-6, 56-1557). Concordia.
Rogers, Richard. Holy Spirit of God. 85p. (Orig.). 1980. pap. text ed. 3.50 (ISBN 0-931097-04-5). Sentinel Pub.
Rouner, Arthur A., Jr. Receiving the Spirit at Old First Church. LC 81-19959. 96p. (Orig.). 1982. pap. 5.95 (ISBN 0-8298-0492-7). Pilgrim NY.
Rowlands, Gerald. Coming Alive in the Spirit: The Spirit-led Life. (Basic Bible Study). Orig. Title: The Holy Spirit & His Fruit. 64p. 1985. pap. 2.95 (ISBN 0-930756-90-8, 521019). Aglow Pubns.
--The Holy Spirit & His Gifts. Sekowsky, Jo Anne, ed. (Aglow Basic Bible Study Ser.). 64p. 1984. pap. 2.95 (ISBN 0-930756-83-5, 521017). Aglow Pubns.
--How to Know the Fullness of the Spirit. (Cornerstone Ser.). (Illus.). 32p. 1982. pap. 2.00 (ISBN 0-930756-68-1, 533005). Aglow Pubns.
Roy, Elmer L. Work of Holy Spirit. pap. 2.50 (ISBN 0-89315-108-4). Lambert Bk.
Ryrie, Charles C. El Espiritu Santo. Orig. Title: The Holy Spirit. (Span.). 192p. 1978. pap. 3.95 (ISBN 0-8254-1629-9). Kregel.
--Holy Spirit. LC 65-14610. (Orig.). 1965. pap. 5.95 (ISBN 0-8024-3565-3). Moody.
St. Basil The Great. On the Holy Spirit. Anderson, David, tr. from Gr. LC 80-25502. 118p. (Orig.). 1980. pap. 4.95 (ISBN 0-913836-74-5). St Vladimirs.
Sanders, J. Oswald. Holy Spirit & His Gifts. (Contemporary Evangelical Perspectives Ser). kivar 5.95 (ISBN 0-310-32481-5, 6520P). Zondervan.
Scragg, W. R. The In-Between God. Wheeler, Gerald, ed. 128p. pap. price not set (ISBN 0-8280-0374-2). Review & Herald.
Seamands, John T. On Tiptoe with Love. (Direction Bk). pap. 1.95 (ISBN 0-8010-7991-8). Baker Bk.
Sekowsky, JoAnne. How to Walk in the Spirit. 32p. 1976. pap. 0.95 (ISBN 0-930756-17-7, 541004). Aglow Pubns.
Selby, Thomas G. The Holy Spirit & the Christian Privilege. 1978. Repr. lib. bdg. 20.00 (ISBN 0-8495-4858-6). Arden Lib.
Seven Gifts of the Holy Spirit. 1980. plastic 1.75 (ISBN 0-8198-6807-8); pap. 1.00 (ISBN 0-8198-6808-6). Dghtrs St Paul.
Seyda, Robert. Transforming Love. LC 82-91022. 162p. 1984. 12.50 (ISBN 0-533-05687-X). Vantage.
Sheed, F. J. The Holy Spirit in Action. 148p. 1981. pap. 3.95 (ISBN 0-89283-109-X). Servant.
Sherry, Patrick. Spirit, Saints & Immortality. 200p. 1984. 39.50x (ISBN 0-87395-755-5); pap. 14.95x (ISBN 0-87395-756-3). State U NY Pr.
Shevkenek, Alice. Things the Baptism in the Holy Spirit Will Do for You. 1976. pap. 1.00 (ISBN 0-89350-005-4). Fountain Pr.
Simpson, A. B. The Gentle Love of the Holy Spirit. 157p. 1983. pap. 5.95 (ISBN 0-87509-334-5). Chr Pubns.
--Holy Spirit, 2 Vols. 7.95; Vol. 1. 7.95 ea. (ISBN 0-87509-015-X). Vol. 2 (ISBN 0-87509-016-8). pap. 5.95 ea. Vol. 1 (ISBN 0-87509-018-4). Vol. 2 (ISBN 0-87509-019-2). Chr Pubns.
Simpson, Albert B. When the Comforter Came. pap. 2.95 (ISBN 0-87509-042-7). Chr Pubns.
Sims, John. Power with Purpose. 1985. text ed. 8.95 (ISBN 0-87148-717-9); pap. text ed. 7.95 (ISBN 0-87148-716-0). Pathway Pr.
Smeaton, George. Doctrine of the Holy Spirit. 1980. 15.95 (ISBN 0-85151-187-2). Banner of Truth.
Smith, Bertha. How the Spirit Filled My Life. LC 73-87068. 7.50 (ISBN 0-8054-5540-X). Broadman.
Spurgeon, C. H. Holy Spirit. 1978. pap. 1.95 (ISBN 0-686-23025-6). Pilgrim Pubns.
--Personality of the Holy Ghost. 1977. pap. 0.95 (ISBN 0-686-23222-4). Pilgrim Pubns.
Stagg, Frank. The Holy Spirit Today. LC 73-85701. 1974. pap. 3.75 (ISBN 0-8054-1919-5). Broadman.
Steinberg, Hardy W. The Church of the Spirit. (Charismatic Bk.). 64p. 1972. pap. 0.69 (ISBN 0-88243-922-7, 02-0922). Gospel Pub.
Stephens, John F. Spirit Filled Family, No. 11. 48p. (Orig.). 1980. pap. 1.95 (ISBN 0-89841-008-8). Zoe Pubns.
Stott, John R. Baptism & Fullness: The Work of the Holy Spirit Today. LC 76-21457. 1976. pap. 2.95 (ISBN 0-87784-648-0). Inter-Varsity.
--Sed Llenos del Espiritu Santo. rev. ed. Cook, David A., tr. from Eng. LC 77-162. Tr. of Be Filled with the Holy Spirit. (Span.). 112p. 1977. pap. 3.50 (ISBN 0-89922-084-3). Edit Caribe.
Strauss, Lehman. Third Person. 1954. 7.95 (ISBN 0-87213-827-5). Loizeaux.
Surath, Sri. Holy Spirit - the Living Love. 1978. pap. 3.00 (ISBN 0-685-58453-4). Ranney Pubns.
Swails, John W. The Holy Spirit & the Messianic Age. 4.95 (ISBN 0-911866-73-6). Advocate.
Synan, Vinson. In the Latter Days: The Outpouring of the Holy Spirit in the Twentieth Century. 168p. (Orig.). 1984. pap. 4.95 (ISBN 0-89283-191-X). Servant.
Tapscott, Betty. Fruit of the Spirit. 1978. pap. 4.95 (ISBN 0-917726-26-X). Hunter Bks.
Taylor, John V. The Go-Between God: The Holy Spirit & the Christian Mission. 1979. pap. 7.95 (ISBN 0-19-520125-6). Oxford U Pr.
Teasley, D. O. The Holy Spirit & Other Spirits. 192p. pap. 1.75 (ISBN 0-686-29150-6). Faith Pub Hse.
Tillsley, Bramwell H. Life in the Spirit. 109p. (Orig.). 1986. pap. 4.95 (ISBN 0-86544-037-9). Salv Army Suppl South.
Torrey, A. Holy Spirit: Who He Is & What He Does. 208p. 1927. 11.95 (ISBN 0-8007-0139-9). Revell.
Torrey, R. A. Como Obtener la Plenitud del Poder. Rivas, Jose G., tr. from Eng. Orig. Title: How to Obtain Fullness of Power. (Span.). 112p. 1983. pap. 2.20 (ISBN 0-311-46083-6). Casa Bautista.
--The Person & the Work of the Holy Spirit. 2nd ed. 1985. pap. text ed. 7.95 (ISBN 0-310-33301-6, 10902P). Zondervan.
Torrey, Reuben A. Person & Work of the Holy Spirit. 1968. 7.95 (ISBN 0-310-33300-8, 10902P). Zondervan.
Tozer, A. W. How to Be Filled with the Holy Spirit. 58p. pap. 1.75 (ISBN 0-87509-187-3). Chr Pubns.
Tozer, A. W. & Smith, G. B. When He Is Come. Orig. Title: Tozer Pulpit, Vol. 2: Ten Sermons on the Ministry of the Holy Spirit. 146p. (Orig.). 1980. pap. 3.45 (ISBN 0-87509-221-7). Chr Pubns.
Tucker, Ronald D. The Holy Spirit. (Illus.). 34p. (Orig.). 1983. pap. 1.75 (ISBN 0-933643-15-2). Grace World Outreach.
Underwood, B. E. Gifts of the Spirit. 3.95 (ISBN 0-911866-64-7); pap. 2.95 (ISBN 0-911866-65-5). Advocate.
Unger, Merrill F. The Baptism & Gifts of the Holy Spirit. LC 74-2931. 192p. 1974. pap. text ed. 6.95 (ISBN 0-8024-0467-7). Moody.
Van Impe, Jack. Baptism of the Holy Spirit. 45p. 1985. pap. 1.95 (ISBN 0-934803-02-1). J Van Impe.
Vaughan, C. R. The Gifts of the Holy Spirit. 1975. 15.95 (ISBN 0-85151-222-4). Banner of Truth.
Venden, Morris. Your Friend the Holy Spirit. (Anchor Ser.). 80p. (Orig.). 1987. pap. 6.95 (ISBN 0-8163-0682-6). Pacific Pr Pub Assn.
Wagner, C. Peter. Your Spiritual Gifts Can Help Your Church Grow. LC 78-53353. 272p. 1979. pap. 7.95 (ISBN 0-8307-0644-5, 5410606). Regal.
Walvoord, John F. Holy Spirit. 1958. 15.95 (ISBN 0-310-34060-8, 6388). Zondervan.
Wesley, John. The Holy Spirit & Power. Weakley, Clare, ed. LC 77-91883. 1977. pap. 4.95 (ISBN 0-88270-262-9). Bridge Pub.
Wierwille, Victor P. Receiving the Holy Spirit Today. LC 82-71185. 298p. 1983. 5.95 (ISBN 0-910068-49-6). Am Christian.
Williams, John. The Holy Spirit, Lord & Life-Giver: A Biblical Introduction to the Doctrine of the Holy Spirit. LC 79-27891. 1980. 8.50 (ISBN 0-87213-950-6); pap. 5.95 (ISBN 0-87213-951-4); study guide 3.25 (ISBN 0-87213-952-2). Loizeaux.
Wilson, Patricia F. Who Put All These Cucumbers in My Garden? LC 83-51398. 144p. (Orig.). 1984. pap. 5.50 (ISBN 0-8358-0475-5). Upper Room.
Winslow, Octavius. Work of the Holy Spirit. 223p. 1984. pap. 5.45 (ISBN 0-85151-152-X). Banner of Truth.

HOLY SPIRIT ASSOCIATON FOR THE UNIFICATION OF WORLD CHRISTIANITY
Ahlberg, Sture. Messianic Movements: A Comparative Analysis of the Sabbatians, the People's Temple & the Unification Church. 128p. (Orig.). pap. text ed. 19.00x (ISBN 91-22-00787-3, Pub. by Almqvist & Wiksell). Coronet Bks.
Barker, Eileen. The Making of a Moonie: Choice or Brainwashing? (Illus.). 299p. 1984. 19.95 (ISBN 0-631-13246-5). Basil Blackwell.
Bettis, Joseph & Johannesen, S. K., eds. The Return of the Millennium. LC 83-82671. 247p. 1984. pap. 11.95 (ISBN 0-913757-02-0). Rose Sharon Pr.
Biermans, John T. The Odyssey of New Religious Movements: Persecution, Struggle, Legitimation - a Case Study of the Unification Church. (Symposium Ser.). 232p. text ed. 49.95 (ISBN 0-88946-710-2). E Mellen.
Bjornstad, James. Sun Myung Moon & the Unification Church. 160p. 1984. pap. 2.95 (ISBN 0-87123-301-0, 210301). Bethany Hse.
Bromley, David G. & Shupe, Anson D., Jr. Moonies in America: Cult, Church, & Crusade. LC 79-16456. (Sage Library of Social Research: Vol. 92). 269p. 1979. 29.00 (ISBN 0-8039-1060-6). Sage.
Bryant, Darrol, ed. Proceedings of the Virgin Islands' Seminar on Unification Theology. LC 80-52594. (Conference Ser.: No. 6). (Illus.). xv, 323p. (Orig.). 1980. pap. text ed. 9.95 (ISBN 0-932894-06-2). Unif Theol Sem.
--Unification Theology Seminar, Virgin Islands: Proceedings. LC 80-52594. 323p. 1980. pap. 9.95. Rose Sharon Pr.
Bryant, Darrol & Foster, Durwood, eds. Hermeneutics & Unification Theology. LC 80-66201. 154p. (Orig.). 1980. pap. 7.95. Rose Sharon Pr.
Bryant, Darrol & Hodges, Susan, eds. Exploring Unification Theology. LC 78-63274. 168p. (Orig.). 1978. pap. 7.95. Rose Sharon Pr.
Bryant, M. Darrol & Richardson, Herbert W. A Time for Consideration: A Scholarly Appraisal of the Unification Church. 2nd ed. LC 78-61364. (Symposium Ser.: Vol. 3). xi, 332p. 1978. 19.95x (ISBN 0-88946-954-7). E Mellen.
Bryant, M. Darrol & Hodges, Susan, eds. Exploring Unification Theology. 2nd ed. LC 78-63274. (Conference Ser.: No. 1). 168p. 1978. pap. text ed. 7.95x (ISBN 0-932894-00-3, Pub. by New Era Bks). Paragon Hse.
Communism: A Critique & Counter Proposal. 1975. pap. 2.00 (ISBN 0-686-13413-3). Unification Church.
Divine Principle. 1977. write for info.; pap. write for info. Rose Sharon Pr.
Durst, Mose. To Bigotry, No Sanction: The Reverend Sun Myung Moon & the Unification Church. LC 84-60571. (Illus.). 196p. 1984. pap. 6.95 (ISBN 0-89526-829-9). Regnery Bks.
Elkins, Chris. Heavenly Deception. 1980. pap. 3.95 (ISBN 0-8423-1402-4). Tyndale.
Ferme, Deane W., ed. Restoring the Kingdom. LC 83-82671. 226p. 1984. pap. 11.95 (ISBN 0-913757-06-3). Rose Sharon Pr.
Fichter, Joseph H. The Holy Family of Father Moon. LC 84-82549. 155p. (Orig.). 1985. pap. 7.95 (ISBN 0-934134-13-8, Leaven Pr). Sheed & Ward MO.
Flinn, Frank, ed. Hermeneutics & Horizons: The Shape of the Future. LC 82-50053. 445p. (Orig.). 1982. pap. 12.95. Rose Sharon Pr.
Grace, James H. Sex & Marriage in the Unification Movement: A Sociological Study. LC 85-2961. (Studies in Religion & Society: Vol. 13). 304p. 1985. 49.95x (ISBN 0-88946-861-3). E Mellen.
Hodges, Susan & Bryant, M. Darrol, eds. Exploring Unification Theology. LC 78-51957. 226p. 1978. write for info. E Mellen.
James, Gene G., ed. The Family & the Unification Church. LC 83-80638. (Conference Ser.: No. 17). 1983. 14.95 (ISBN 0-932894-19-4, Pub. by New Era Bks); pap. text ed. 10.95 (ISBN 0-932894-17-8). Paragon Hse.
--The Family & the Unification Church. LC 83-80638. 269p. (Orig.). 1983. 15.95; pap. 11.95. Rose Sharon Pr.
Johnson, Rose & Ratzlaff, Don. As Angels of Light. LC 80-82926. (Illus.). 160p. (Orig.). 1980. pap. 4.95 (ISBN 0-937364-00-2). Kindred Pr.
Kim, Young O. An Introduction to Theology. LC 82-84722. 190p. 1983. pap. 8.95 (ISBN 0-318-11687-1). Rose Sharon Pr.
--Unification Theology. LC 80-52872. 294p. 1980. pap. 8.95 (ISBN 0-318-11689-8). Rose Sharon Pr.
--Unification Theology & Christian Thought. LC 74-32590. 302p. 1976. pap. 6.95 (ISBN 0-318-11688-X). Rose Sharon Pr.
Kim, Dr. Young Oon. Unification Theology & Christian Thought. pap. 4.00 (ISBN 0-686-13407-9). Unification Church.
Kwak, Chung Hwan, ed. Home Study Course, 6 vols. (Orig.). Date not set. Set. 24.95 (ISBN 0-910621-09-8). HSA Pubns.
Lee, Sang H. Explaining Unificatiion Thought. LC 80-54858. 356p. pap. 10.95 (ISBN 0-9606480-0-3). Rose Sharon Pr.
--Explaining Unification Thought. LC 80-54858. 356p. (Orig.). 1981. pap. 9.95 (ISBN 0-9606480-0-3). HSA Pubns.
Lewis, Warren, ed. Towards a Global Congress of the World's Religions. LC 79-56121. 63p. 1979. pap. 2.95 (ISBN 0-932894-03-8). Rose Sharon Pr.
--Towards a Global Congress of the Worlds's Religions. LC 78-73771. 1978. write for info. (ISBN 0-932894-01-1). Rose Sharon Pr.
--Towards a Global Congress of World's Religions. LC 80-53764. 79p. 1980. pap. 3.25 (ISBN 0-932894-07-0). Rose Sharon Pr.
Matczak, Sebastian A., ed. God in Contemporary Thought. LC 75-31391. 1119p. 1977. 55.00 (ISBN 0-910621-25-X). Rose Sharon Pr.
Mickler, Michael J. The Unification Church in America: Sects & Cults in America. LC 83-48225. (Bibliographical Guides Ser.). 130p. 1986. lib. bdg. 19.00 (ISBN 0-8240-9040-3). Garland Pub.
Moon, Sun M. The Divine Principle. 2nd rev. ed. 536p. 1973. 10.95 (ISBN 0-910621-05-5). HSA Pubns.
--The Divine Principle. 2nd rev. ed. 536p. 1973. pap. 7.95 (ISBN 0-910621-04-7). HSA Pubns.
--The Divine Principle. 5th rev. ed. 536p. 1977. pap. 5.95 (ISBN 0-910621-03-9). HSA Pubns.
--Home Church. LC 82-88432. (Illus.). 474p. 1983. 14.95 (ISBN 0-318-03061-6); pap. 11.95 (ISBN 0-910621-21-7). HSA Pubns.
--The Way of Tradition I. 326p. (Orig.). Date not set. pap. 6.95 (ISBN 0-910621-22-5). HSA Pubns.
--Way of Tradition II. 295p. Date not set. pap. 6.95 (ISBN 0-910621-23-3). HSA Pubns.
--The Way of Tradition III. 541p. Date not set. pap. 6.95 (ISBN 0-910621-24-1). HSA Pubns.
--The Way of Tradition IV. 462p. 1980. pap. 8.00 (ISBN 0-910621-35-7). HSA Pubns.
Moon, Sun Myung. Christianity in Crisis. pap. 3.00 (ISBN 0-686-13410-9). HSA Pubns.
Owen, R. J. The Moonies: A Critical Look at a Controversial Group. 1985. 20.00x (ISBN 0-7062-4149-5, Pub. by Ward Lock Educ Co Ltd). State Mutual Bk.
Quebedeaux, Richard, ed. Lifestyle: Conversations with Members of the Unification Church. LC 82-50799. (Conference Ser.: No. 13). (Orig.). 1982. 12.95 (ISBN 0-932894-18-6, Pub. by New Era Bks); pap. 9.95 (ISBN 0-932894-13-5, Pub. by New Era Bks). Paragon Hse.
--Lifestyles. LC 82-50799. 214p. (Orig.). 1982. 14.95; pap. 10.95. Rose Sharon Pr.
Quebedeaux, Richard & Sawatsky, Rodney, eds. Evangelical-Unification Dialogue. LC 79-89421. (Conference Ser.: No. 3). 374p. (Orig.). 1979. pap. text ed. 7.95 (ISBN 0-932894-02-X, Pub. by New Era Bks). Paragon Hse.
--Evangelical-Unification Dialog. LC 79-89421. 374p. (Orig.). pap. 7.95. Rose Sharon Pr.
Richardson, Herbert. New Religions & Mental Health. 177p. 1980. pap. 11.95. Rose Sharon Pr.
--Ten Theologians Respond to the Unification Church. LC 81-70679. 199p. 1981. pap. 10.95. Rose Sharon Pr.
Richardson, Herbert, ed. Ten Theologians Respond to the Unification Church. LC 81-70679. (Conference Ser.: No. 10). xv, 199p. (Orig.). 1981. pap. text ed. 9.95 (ISBN 0-932894-10-0, Pub. by New Era Bks). Paragon Hse.
Thompson, Henry O., ed. Unity in Diversity. LC 83-51715. 436p. (Orig.). 1984. pap. 12.95 (ISBN 0-932894-20-8). Rose Sharon Pr.
Tsirpanlis, Constantine N., ed. Orthodox-Unification Dialog. 139p. (Orig.). pap. 7.95. Rose Sharon Pr.
--Orthodox-Unification Dialogue. LC 80-54586. (Conference Ser.: No. 8). (Illus.). x, 139p. (Orig.). 1981. pap. text ed. 7.95 (ISBN 0-932894-08-9, Pub. by New Era Bks). Paragon Hse.
Unification Thought. 1975. pap. 5.00 (ISBN 0-686-13405-2); Study Guide. pap. text ed. 1.50 (ISBN 0-686-13406-0). Unification Church.

HOLY WEEK
see also Easter; Good Friday
Flood, Edmund. Making More of Holy Week. 1984. pap. 3.95 pamphlet (ISBN 0-8091-5184-7). Paulist Pr.
Freeman, Eileen E. The Holy Week Book. new ed. LC 78-73510. (Illus.). 1979. pap. 19.95 (ISBN 0-89390-007-9). Resource Pubns.
Fuller, Reginald H. Holy Week. Achtemeier, Elizabeth, ed. LC 84-6011. (Proclamation 3: Aids for Interpreting the Lessons of the Church Year Ser. B). 64p. 1984. pap. 3.75 (ISBN 0-8006-4104-3). Fortress.
Grimbol, William. Perspectives on the Passion. 1984. 5.95 (ISBN 0-89536-665-7, 1645). CSS of Ohio.
Hansen, Paul G. Portraits of the Passion. 1983. 6.25 (ISBN 0-89536-582-0, 1624). CSS of Ohio.
Harrisville, Roy. Holy Week. LC 84-18756. (Proclamation 3 C Ser.). 64p. 1985. pap. 3.75 (ISBN 0-8006-4128-0). Fortress.
Jeske, Richard L. & Barr, Browne. Holy Week. Achtemeier, Elizabeth, et al, eds. LC 79-7377. (Proclamation 2: Aids for Interpreting the Lessons of the Church Year, Ser. A). 64p. (Orig.). 1980. pap. 3.75 (ISBN 0-8006-4094-2, 1-4094). Fortress.
Kirby, Wallace H. Sounds of the Passion. 1984. 4.25 (ISBN 0-89536-647-9, 1944). CSS of Ohio.
Newhouse, Flower A. Drama of Incarnation. 4th ed. 1948. 7.50 (ISBN 0-910378-04-5). Christward.
Numrich, Charles. Passion Play. 1983. 4.95 (ISBN 0-89536-601-0, 1627). CSS of Ohio.
Rouse, Richard & Rouse, Susan. The Last Week. 1985. 1.00 (ISBN 0-89536-726-2, 5810). CSS of Ohio.
Stendahl, Krister. Holy Week Preaching. LC 84-48714. (Resources for Preaching Ser.). 64p. 1985. pap. 3.95 (ISBN 0-8006-1851-3, 1-1851). Fortress.
Terrien, Samuel. Holy Week. LC 84-18756. (Proclamation 3A Ser.). 64p. 1986. pap. 3.75 (ISBN 0-8006-4120-5). Fortress.

HOLY-WEEK SERMONS
Erickson, Craig D. Under the Shadow of Your Wings. Sherer, Michael L., ed. (Orig.). 1987. pap. 6.75 (ISBN 0-89536-844-7, 7803). CSS of Ohio.
Grimbol, William. Passion Paths. Sherer, Michael L., ed. (Orig.). 1987. pap. 3.95 (ISBN 0-89536-842-0, 7801). CSS of Ohio.
Harrisville, Roy A. & Hackett, Charles D. Holy Week. Achtemeier, Elizabeth, et al, eds. LC 79-7377. (Proclamation 2: Aids for Interpreting the Lessons of the Church Year, Ser. B). 64p. 1981. pap. 3.75 (ISBN 0-8006-4086-1, 1-4086). Fortress.
Hazelton, Roger. Graceful Courage: A Venture in Christian Humanism. LC 84-48706. 128p. 1985. pap. 4.95 (ISBN 0-8006-1850-5, 1-1850). Fortress.
Kalas, J. Ellsworth. A Pilgrimage. Sherer, Michael L., ed. (Orig.). 1987. pap. 3.95 (ISBN 0-89536-845-5, 7804). CSS of Ohio.
Murray, Andrew. Spirit of Christ. 1970. pap. 4.50 (ISBN 0-87508-395-1). Chr Lit.

HOLY WELLS
Hope, Robert C. Legendary Lore of the Holy Wells of England. LC 68-21775. (Illus.). 1968. Repr. of 1893 ed. 35.00x (ISBN 0-8103-3445-3). Gale.
Masani, Rustom P. Folklore of Wells. LC 77-11936. 1977. Repr. lib. bdg. 32.00 (ISBN 0-8414-6216-X). Folcroft.

HOME ECONOMICS
see also Cookery; Food
Bouma, Mary L. The Creative Homemaker. LC 73-17234. 192p. 1973. pap. 3.95 (ISBN 0-87123-078-X, 200084). Bethany Hse.
Curtis, June. The Gracious Woman: Developing A Servant's Heart Through Hospitality. 176p. (Orig.). 1985. pap. 4.95 (ISBN 0-89081-489-9). Harvest Hse.
Lockerbie, Jeanette W. Salt in My Kitchen. (Quiet Time Books). 1967. pap. 3.50 (ISBN 0-8024-7500-0). Moody.
Otto, Donna. All in Good Time. 240p. 1985. 12.95 (ISBN 0-8407-5963-0). Nelson.
Random Sampler: Helpful Hints for Latter-day Living from the Ensign. LC 86-1465. 220p. 1986. 7.95 (ISBN 0-87747-977-1). Deseret Bk.

HOME MISSIONS
see Missions, Home

HOMER
Clay, Jenny S. The Wrath of Athena. LC 83-2996. 240p. 1983. 29.00x (ISBN 0-691-06574-8). Princeton U Pr.
Gordon, Cyrus H. Homer & Bible: The Origin & Character of East Mediterranean Literature. 1967. pap. 4.95 (ISBN 0-911566-03-1). Ventnor.
Lamberton, Robert. Homer the Theologian: Neoplatonist Allegorical Rading & the Growth of the Epic Tradition. LC 85-1184. (Transformation of the Classical Heritage Ser.: No. 9). 375p. 1986. text ed. 40.00x (ISBN 0-520-05437-7). U of Cal Pr.
--Homer the Theologian: Neoplatonist Allegorical Reading & the Growth of the Epic Tradition, Vol. 10. Date not set. price not set. Oxford U Pr.
Smith, Peter. Nursling of Mortality: A Study of the Homeric Hymn to Aphrodite. (Studien zur klassischen Philologie: Vol. 3). 155p. 1980. pap. 20.65 (ISBN 3-8204-6111-6). P Lang Pubs.
Weil, Simone. Iliad or the Poem of Force. LC 57-6026. 1956. pap. 2.50x (ISBN 0-87574-091-X). Pendle Hill.

HOMILETICAL ILLUSTRATIONS
see also Bible–Homiletical Use; Exempla; Fables; Legends; Parables
Buttrick, David G. Homiletic. LC 86-45208. 544p. 1987. 24.95 (ISBN 0-8006-0777-5, 1-777). Fortress.
Cockayne, O., ed. Hali Meidenhad, Alliterative Homily of 13th Century. (EETS OS Ser.: No. 18). Repr. of 1922 ed. 11.00 (ISBN 0-527-00020-5). Kraus Repr.
Deems, Edward M., ed. Holy-Days & Holidays: A Treasury of Historical Material, Sermons in Full & in Brief, Suggestive Thoughts & Poetry, Relating to Holy Days & Holidays. LC 68-17940. 1968. Repr. of 1902 ed. 65.00x (ISBN 0-8103-3352-X). Gale.
Fichtner, Joseph. Proclaim His Word: Homiletic Themes for Sundays & Holy Days-Cycle A, Vol. 2. new ed. LC 73-5726. 239p. (Orig.). 1974. pap. 4.95 (ISBN 0-8189-0292-2). Alba.
Fowler, J. B., Jr. Living Illustrations. LC 85-4175. 1985. pap. 5.95 (ISBN 0-8054-2260-9). Broadman.
Knight, Walter B. Knight's Master Book of New Illustrations. 1956. pap. 13.95 (ISBN 0-8028-1699-1). Eerdmans.
Koenig, John. Stories to Learn by. (Illus.). 5.00 (ISBN 0-8198-0333-2); pap. 4.00 (ISBN 0-8198-0334-0). Dghtrs St Paul.
Lehman, Louis P. How to Find & Develop Effective Illustrations. LC 75-12109. 102p. 1985. pap. 4.95 (ISBN 0-8254-3133-6). Kregel.
Liptak, David Q. Biblical-Catechetical Homilies for Sundays & Holy Days (A, B & C) Based on the Lectionary & Reflecting the Syllabus of the Pastoral Homiletic Plan. LC 79-27895. 370p. (Orig.). 1980. pap. 10.95 (ISBN 0-8189-0400-3). Alba.
Lufburrow, Bill. Illustrations Without Sermons. 128p. (Orig.). 1985. pap. 7.95 (ISBN 0-687-18677-3). Abingdon.
Newman, Louis I., ed. Maggidim & Hasidim: Their Wisdom. 1962. 14.95x (ISBN 0-8197-0161-0). Bloch.
Price, Leo. The Tree That Always Said No. LC 73-90617. (Illus.). 1973. plastic bdg. 2.75 (ISBN 0-8198-0330-8); pap. 1.75 (ISBN 0-8198-0331-6). Dghtrs St Paul.
Smith, James. Handfuls on Purpose, 5 vols. 1943. 69.95 set (ISBN 0-8028-8139-4). Eerdmans.
Westphal, Arnold C. Junior Surprise Sermons with Handmade Objects, 2 bks. Set. pap. 9.90 (ISBN 0-686-70924-1); No. 1. pap. 4.50 (ISBN 0-915398-18-4); No. 2. pap. 4.95 (ISBN 0-915398-19-2). Visual Evangels.

HOMILETICS
see Preaching

HOMILIES
see Sermons

HOMOSEXUALITY
see also Gay Liberation Movement
Baars, Conrad. The Homosexual's Search for Happiness. (Synthesis Ser.). 1977. pap. 1.25 (ISBN 0-8199-0709-X). Franciscan Herald.
Babuscio, Jack. We Speak for Ourselves: Experiences in Homosexual Counseling. LC 77-78623. pap. 40.00 (2026837). Bks Demand UMI.
Bailey, D. Sherwin. Homosexuality & the Western Christian Tradition. LC 75-34384. xii, 181p. 1975. Repr. of 1955 ed. 22.50 (ISBN 0-208-01492-6, Archon). Shoe String.
Barnett, Walter. Homosexuality & the Bible: An Interpretation. LC 79-84920. 1979. pap. 2.50x (ISBN 0-87574-226-2). Pendle Hill.
Batchelor, Edward, Jr., ed. Homosexuality & Ethics. rev. ed. LC 80-10533. 1982. 15.95 (ISBN 0-8298-0392-0); pap. 8.95 (ISBN 0-8298-0615-6). Pilgrim NY.
Borhek, Mary V. Coming Out to Parents: A Two-Way Survival Guide for Lesbians & Gay Men & Their Parents. LC 83-3971. 224p. 1983. pap. 9.95 (ISBN 0-8298-0665-2). Pilgrim NY.
Bradford, Brick, ed. Healing for the Homosexual. 64p. 1983. 1.95 (ISBN 0-934421-06-4). Presby Renewal Pubns.
Chesebro, James W., ed. Gayspeak: Gay Male & Lesbian Communication. LC 82-355. 384p. 1981. 17.95 (ISBN 0-8298-0472-2); pap. 9.95 (ISBN 0-8298-0456-0). Pilgrim NY.
Coleman, Gerald. Homosexuality - an Appraisal. 1978. 0.75 (ISBN 0-685-89391-X). Franciscan Herald.
Drakeford, John W. A Christian View of Homosexuality. LC 76-41474. 1977. pap. 3.95 (ISBN 0-8054-5620-1). Broadman.
Flood, Gregory. I'm Looking for Mr. Right, But I'll Settle for Mr. Right Away: AIDS, True Love, the Perils of Safe Sex, & Other Spiritual Concerns of the Gay Male. 136p. (Orig.). 1987. pap. 6.95 (ISBN 0-938407-00-7). Brob Hse Bks.
Horner, Tom. Jonathan Loved David: Homosexuality in Biblical Times. LC 77-15628. 164p. 1978. pap. 8.95 (ISBN 0-664-24185-9). Westminster.
Ide, Arthur F. Gomorrah & the Rise of Homophobia. (Illus.). 114p. (Orig.). 1985. pap. 5.95 (ISBN 0-934659-01-X). Liberal Pr.
Moses, A. Elfin & Hawkins, Robert O., Jr. Counseling Lesbian Women & Gay Men: A Life-Issues Approach. 263p. 1982. pap. text ed. 19.95 (ISBN 0-675-20599-9). Merrill.
Pearson, Carol L. Good-Bye, I Love You. LC 85-23235. 240p. 1986. 15.95 (ISBN 0-394-55032-3). Random.

Pesek-Marous, Georgia. The Bull: A Religious & Secular History of Phallus Worship & Male Homosexuality. (Illus.). 185p. (Orig.). 1984. pap. 9.95 (ISBN 0-916453-01-4). Tau Pr.

Sergent, Bernard. Homosexuality in Greek Myth. Goldhammer, Arthur, tr. from Fr. LC 85-73369. 360p. 1986. 21.95 (ISBN 0-8070-5700-2). Beacon Pr.

Switzer, David K. & Switzer, Shirley A. Parents of the Homosexual, Vol. 11. LC 80-13748. (Christian Care Bks.). 118p. 1980. pap. 7.95 (ISBN 0-664-24327-4). Westminster.

Symonds, John A. Problem in Greek Ethics. LC 71-163126. (Studies in Philosophy, No. 40). 1971. lib. bdg. 31.95x (ISBN 0-8383-1253-5). Haskell.

Vanggaard, Thorkil. Phallos: A Symbol & Its History in the Male World. LC 72-80553. (Illus.). 266p. 1972. text ed. 22.50 (ISBN 0-8236-4135-X); pap. text ed. 17.95 (ISBN 0-8236-8192-0, 24135). Intl Univs Pr.

Weltge, Ralph, ed. Same Sex: An Appraisal of Homosexuality. LC 71-88184. 1969. pap. 3.95 (ISBN 0-8298-0118-9). Pilgrim NY.

Yungblut, John. Sex & the Human Psyche. LC 75-19951. 32p. (Orig.). 1975. pap. 2.50x (ISBN 0-87574-203-3, 203). Pendle Hill.

HOMOSEXUALITY AND CHRISTIANITY

Baker, Don. Beyond Rejection: The Church, Homosexuality, & Hope. LC 85-8789. 1985. 8.95 (ISBN 0-88070-108-0). Multnomah.

Boswell, John. Christianity, Social Tolerance, & Homosexuality: Gay People in Western Europe from the Beginning of the Christian Era to the Fourteenth Century. LC 79-11171. (Illus.). xviii, 424p. 1980. 35.00x (ISBN 0-226-06710-6); pap. 12.95 (ISBN 0-226-06711-4). U of Chicago Pr.

Boyd, Malcolm. Gay Priests: An Inner Journey. 208p. 1986. 14.95 (ISBN 0-312-31797-2). St Martin.

Damian, Peter. Book of Gomorrah: An Eleventh-Century Treatise Against Clerical Homosexual Practices. Payer, Pierre J., tr. 120p. 1982. pap. text ed. 10.50x (ISBN 0-88920-123-4, Pub. by Wilfrid Laurier Canada). Humanities.

Dicker, Gordon S., ed. Homosexuality & the Church. 71p. (Orig.). 1985. pap. 6.95 (ISBN 0-85819-505-4, Pub. by Uniting Church). ANZ Religious Pubns.

DiMaria-Kuiper, Johannes W. Hot under the Collar: Self-Portrait of a Gay Pastor. LC 83-60016. 177p. (Orig.). 1983. pap. 7.95 (ISBN 0-912393-00-9). Mercury Pr.

Flatt, Bill, et al. Counseling the Homosexual. 11.00 (ISBN 0-934916-49-7). Natl Christian Pr.

Flood, Gregory. I'm Looking for Mr. Right, But I'll Settle for Mr. Right Away: AIDS, True Love, the Perils of Safe Sex, & Other Spiritual Concerns of the Gay Male. 136p. (Orig.). 1987. pap. 6.95 (ISBN 0-938407-00-7). Brob Hse Bks.

Fowler, Richard A. & House, H. Wayne. The Christian Confronts His Culture. 228p. (Orig.). 1983. pap. 7.95 (ISBN 0-8024-0232-1). Moody.

Gallagher, John, ed. Homosexuality & the Magisterium: Documents from the Vatican & U. S. Bishops, 1975-1985. 109p. 1986. 9.95 (ISBN 0-935877-00-2). New Ways Min.

Goodich, Michael. The Unmentionable Vice: Homosexuality in the Later Medieval Period. LC 78-13276. 179p. 1980. pap. 7.95 (ISBN 0-87436-300-4). Ross-Erikson.

Gramick, Jeannine, ed. Homosexuality & the Catholic Church. 176p. 1985. 8.95 (ISBN 0-88347-149-3). New Ways Min.

Homosexuality: A Christian Evaluation & Response. 1980. 0.75 (ISBN 0-911802-47-9). Free Church Pubns.

Horner, Tom. Homosexuality & the Judeo-Christian Tradition: An Annotated Bibliography. LC 81-889. (ATLA Bibliography Ser.: No. 5). 141p. 1981. 16.50 (ISBN 0-8108-1412-9). Scarecrow.

Ide, Arthur F. Idol Worshippers in Twentieth Century America. (Illus.). 150p. (Orig.). 1984. pap. 10.95 (ISBN 0-930383-02-8). Monument Pr.

Johnson, Paul R. Gays & Fundamentalism. (Illus.). 56p. (Orig.). 1983. pap. 2.95 (ISBN 0-910097-02-X). Paul R Johnson.

--Gays & the Bible. (Illus.). 52p. (Orig.). 1983. pap. 2.95 (ISBN 0-910097-00-3). Paul R Johnson.

--Gays & the Church. (Illus.). 48p. (Orig.). 1983. pap. 2.95 (ISBN 0-910097-04-6). Paul R Johnson.

Johnston, Maury. Gays Under Grace: A Gay Christian's Response to the Moral Majority. LC 82-51217. 250p. 1983. 15.95 (ISBN 0-938232-20-7). Winston-Derek.

McNaught, Brian R. A Disturbed Peace: Selected Writings of an Irish Catholic Homosexual. LC 81-67627. 125p. (Orig.). 1981. pap. 5.95 (ISBN 0-940680-00-9). Dignity Inc.

Malloy, Edward A. Homosexuality & the Christian Way of Life. LC 81-40385. 382p. (Orig.). 1981. lib. bdg. 32.50 (ISBN 0-8191-1794-3); pap. text ed. 14.75 (ISBN 0-8191-1795-1). U Pr of Amer.

Moberly, Elizabeth. Homosexuality: A New Christian Ethic. 64p. 1983. pap. 6.95 (ISBN 0-227-67850-8, Pub. by J Clarke UK). Attic Pr.

Nugent, Robert, ed. A Challenge to Love: Gay & Lesbian Catholics in the Church. LC 82-19850. 256p. 1983. pap. 10.95 (ISBN 0-8245-0518-2). Crossroad NY.

Rigsbee, Ron & Bakker, Dorothy. The Agony of Deception. LC 83-81285. 288p. (Orig.). 1983. pap. 6.95 (ISBN 0-910311-07-2). Huntington Hse Inc.

Scanzoni, Letha & Mollenkott, Virginia R. Is the Homosexual My Neighbor? Another Christian View. LC 77-20445. 176p. 1980. pap. 8.95 (ISBN 0-06-067076-2, RD 337, HarpR). Har-Row.

Scroggs, Robin. The New Testament & Homosexuality. LC 82-48588. 160p. 1984. pap. 8.95 (ISBN 0-8006-1854-8, 1-1854). Fortress.

Sherwood, Zalmon. Kairos: Confessions of a Gay Priest. 150p. (Orig.). 1987. pap. 7.95 (ISBN 1-55583-102-8). Alyson Pubns.

Smith, Herbert F. Sexual Inversion: The Questions-with Catholic Answers. 1979. 2.95 (ISBN 0-8198-0612-9); pap. 1.95 (ISBN 0-8198-0613-7). Dghtrs St Paul.

Uhrig, Larry. Sex Positive. 160p. (Orig.). 1985. pap. 6.95 (ISBN 0-932870-82-1). Alyson Pubns.

Wright, Ezekiel & Inesse, Daniel. God Is Gay: An Evolutionary Spiritual Work. 2nd, rev. ed. 1982. pap. 4.95 (ISBN 0-934350-01-9). Tayu Pr.

HONESTY

see also Business Ethics; Wealth, Ethics Of

Furse, Margaret L. Nothing but the Truth: What It Takes to Be Honest. LC 81-3501. 128p. 1981. 8.75 (ISBN 0-687-28130-X). Abingdon.

Moncure, Jane B. Honesty. LC 80-39571. (Values to Live by Ser.). (Illus.). 32p. 1981. PLB 10.35 (ISBN 0-516-06523-8). Childrens.

Narot, Joseph R. The Lost Honesty. pap. 1.25 (ISBN 0-686-15804-0). Rostrum Bks.

HONI HA-MEAGGEL, 1ST CENTURY B.C.

Gershator, Phillis. Honi & His Magic Circle. LC 79-84931. (Illus.). 1979. 6.95 (ISBN 0-8276-0167-0, 443). Jewish Pubns.

HOOKER, THOMAS, 1586-1647

Bush, Sargent, Jr. The Writings of Thomas Hooker: Spiritual Adventure in Two Worlds. LC 79-5404. 400p. 1980. 29.50x (ISBN 0-299-08070-6). U of Wis Pr.

Paget, Francis. An Introduction to the Fifth Book of Hooker's Treatise of the Laws of Ecclesiastical Polity. 265p. 1981. Repr. of 1899 ed. lib. bdg. 85.00 (ISBN 0-8495-4402-5). Arden Lib.

Power, M. Susan. Before the Convention: Religion & the Founders. LC 84-12004. 268p. (Orig.). 1984. lib. bdg. 26.25 (ISBN 0-8191-4133-X); pap. text ed. 13.25 (ISBN 0-8191-4134-8). U Pr of Amer.

Shuffelton, Frank. Thomas Hooker, 1586-1647. LC 76-45912. 1977. 38.00x (ISBN 0-691-05249-2). Princeton U Pr.

Walker, George L. Thomas Hooker: Preacher, Founder, Democrat. 1972. Repr. of 1891 ed. lib. bdg. 19.00 (ISBN 0-8422-8120-7). Irvington.

HOPE

see also Despair

Allen. Faith, Hope & Love. 5.95 (ISBN 0-318-18178-9). WCTU.

Augsburger, David. When Enough Is Enough. LC 84-11644. 1984. pap. 5.95 (ISBN 0-8307-0979-7, 5418273). Regal.

Banas, Jackie. Hope & the Purple Onion. (Illus.). 39p. (Orig.). 1984. wkbk. 5.00 (ISBN 0-9614014-1-9). Know Him Pr.

Carroll, W. H., et al. Reasons for Hope. rev. ed. 254p. 1982. pap. 6.95 (ISBN 0-931888-07-7, Chris. Coll. Pr.). Christendom Pubns.

Eyer, Richard C. Devotions of Hope. 1984. 1.95 (ISBN 0-89536-653-3, 0418). CSS of Ohio.

Flynn, Leslie B. The Sustaining Power of Hope. 132p. 1985. pap. 4.95 (ISBN 0-89693-600-7). Victor Bks.

Galot, Jean. The Mystery of Christian Hope. LC 77-1222. 1977. 4.95 (ISBN 0-8189-0346-5). Alba.

Getz, Gene A. Measure of a Church. LC 75-17160. (Orig.). 1975. pap. 3.50 (ISBN 0-8307-0398-5, 5014700). Regal.

Goff, James & Goff, Margaret. In Every Person Who Hopes... (Orig.). 1980. pap. 3.75 (ISBN 0-377-00096-5). Friend Pr.

Hawkins, Peter S. Getting Nowhere: Christian Hope & Utopian Dream. LC 85-12758. 133p. (Orig.). 1985. pap. 8.95 (ISBN 0-936384-28-X). Cowley Pubns.

Hebblethwaite, Brian. The Christian Hope. 248p. (Orig.). 1985. pap. 9.95 (ISBN 0-8028-0054-8). Eerdmans.

Hicks, Roy H. Whatever Happened to Hope. 1978. mini book 0.75 (ISBN 0-89274-074-4). Harrison Hse.

Hoffman, Oswald C. There Is Hope. 104p. 1985. 9.95 (ISBN 0-570-03979-7, 15-2184). Concordia.

John Paul II, Pope Healing & Hope. 266p. 1982. 5.00 (ISBN 0-8198-3317-7, EP0545); pap. 3.50 (ISBN 0-8198-3318-5). Dghtrs St Paul.

Kuasten, J. & Plumpe, J., eds. St. Augustine, Faith, Hope & Charity. Arand, Louis A., tr. LC 78-62450. (Ancient Christian Writers Ser.: No. 3). 165p. 1947. 10.95 (ISBN 0-8091-0045-2). Paulist Pr.

Leonard of Taize, Brother. Listening to People of Hope. 180p. 1985. pap. 6.95 (ISBN 0-8298-0544-3). Pilgrim NY.

Muller, Robert. A Plants of Hope. (Chrysalis Bk). (Illus.). 128p. 1986. pap. 7.95 (ISBN 0-916349-04-7). Amity Hous Inc.

Pieper, Josef. On Hope. McCarthy, Mary F., tr. from Ger. LC 85-82177. Orig. Title: Uber die Hoffnung. 99p. (Orig.). 1986. pap. 6.95 (ISBN 0-89870-067-1). Ignatius Pr.

Underwood, Walter L. Being Human Being Hopeful. 112p. 1987. 9.95 (ISBN 0-687-02815-9). Abingdon.

Van Impe, Rexella. Hope & Fear Not. 32p. 1985. pap. 1.95 (ISBN 0-934803-14-5). J Van Impe.

Wiersbe, Warren W. Be Hopeful. 1982. pap. 5.95 (ISBN 0-88207-382-6). Victor Bks.

Words of Hope. (Words of... Ser.). (Illus.). 48p. 1983. 3.95 (ISBN 0-8407-5335-7). Nelson.

Young, Mildred B. Insured by Hope. LC 56-8831. (Orig.). pap. 2.50x (ISBN 0-87574-090-1). Pendle Hill.

HOPE–BIBLICAL TEACHING

Brueggemann, Walter. Hope Within History. LC 86-45353. 144p. (Orig.). 1986. pap. 8.95 (ISBN 0-8042-0918-9). John Knox.

Bunyan, John. Israel's Hope Encouraged. pap. 1.95 (ISBN 0-685-19836-7). Reiner.

Capps, Charles. Hope: A Partner to Faith. 38p. (Orig.). 1986. pap. 1.25 mini-book (ISBN 0-89274-396-4). Harrison Hse.

Gordon, Arthur. A Song Called Hope. 48p. 1985. 6.95 (ISBN 0-8378-5081-9). Gibson.

Rest, Friedrich. Fourteen Messages of Hope. (Pulpit Library). 96p. 1985. pap. 3.95 (ISBN 0-8010-7733-8). Baker Bk.

Zodhiates, Spiros. The Patience of Hope. (Trilogy Ser.: Vol. 1). pap. 4.95 (ISBN 0-89957-543-9). AMG Pubs.

HOPKINS, GERARD MANLEY, 1844-1889

Downes, David A. Hopkins' Sanctifying Imagination. LC 85-11071. 134p. (Orig.). 1985. lib. bdg. 22.00 (ISBN 0-8191-4755-9); pap. text ed. 8.75 (ISBN 0-8191-4756-7). U Pr of Amer.

Harris, Daniel A. Inspirations Unbidden: The "Terrible Sonnets" of Gerard Manley Hopkins. LC 81-11497. 200p. 1982. 26.50x (ISBN 0-520-04539-4). U of Cal Pr.

Peters, W. A. Gerard Manley Hopkins: A Tribute. 80p. 1984. pap. 5.95 (ISBN 0-8294-0456-2). Loyola.

HOPKINS, SAMUEL, 1721-1803

Conforti, Joseph A. Samuel Hopkins & the New Divinity Movement: Calvinism, the Congregational Ministry, & Reform in New England Between the Great Awakenings. LC 80-28268. pap. 62.30 (ISBN 0-317-08398-8, 2020840). Bks Demand UMI.

Kuklick, Bruce. Samuel Hopkins Works, 3 vols. (American Religious Thought of the 18th & 19th Centuries Ser.). 1838p. 1987. Set. lib. bdg. 240.00 (ISBN 0-8240-6951-X). Garland Pub.

HOPKINSON, FRANCIS, 1737-1791

Sonneck, Oscar G. Francis Hopkinson, the First American Poet-Composer, & James Lyon, Patriot, Preacher, Psalmodist. 2nd ed. LC 65-23393. (Music Reprint Ser.). 213p. 1966. Repr. of 1905 ed. lib. bdg. 32.50 (ISBN 0-306-70918-X). Da Capo.

HORAE (BOOKS OF HOURS)

see Hours, Books Of

HORNS (IN RELIGION, FOLK-LORE, ETC.)

see also Religion, Primitive

Mellinkoff, Ruth. The Horned Moses in Medieval Art & Thought. LC 77-85450. (California Studies in the History of Art: No. XIV). (Illus.). 1970. 40.00x (ISBN 0-520-01705-6). U of Cal Pr.

HOSEA, THE PROPHET

Beacon Bible Commentary Staff. Hosea-Malachi, Vol. V. 13.95 (ISBN 0-8010-0692-9). Baker Bk.

Cohen, Gary & Vandermey, H. Ronald, eds. Hosea & Amos. (Everyman's Bible Commentary). 128p. 1981. pap. 5.95 (ISBN 0-8024-2028-1). Moody.

Emmerson, Grace I. Hosea: An Israelite Prophet in Judean Perspective. (JSOT Supplement Ser.: No. 28). 224p. 1984. text ed. 28.50x (ISBN 0-905774-68-X, Pub. by JSOT Pr England); pap. text ed. 11.95x (ISBN 0-905774-69-8, Pub. by JSOT Pr England). Eisenbrauns.

Rand, Howard B. Study in Hosea. 1955. 8.00 (ISBN 0-685-08815-4). Destiny.

HOSPITALERS

Bedford, William K. The Order or the Hospital of St. John of Jerusalem. LC 76-29831. Repr. of 1902 ed. 31.25 (ISBN 0-404-15412-3). AMS Pr.

Gervers, Michael, ed. The Cartulary of the Knights of St. John of Jerusalem in England. (Records of Social & Economic History Ser.). 1982. 195.00x (ISBN 0-19-725996-0). Oxford U Pr.

King, Edwin J. The Grand Priory of the Order of the Hospital of St. John of Jerusalem in England: A Short History. LC 76-29826. Repr. of 1924 ed. 28.00 (ISBN 0-404-15420-4). AMS Pr.

Philippus De Thame. Knights Hospitallers in England: Being the Report of Prior Phillip De Thame to the Grand Master Elyan De Villanova for A. D. 1338. Larking, Lambert B., ed. (Camden Society, London. Publications, First Ser.: No. 65). Repr. of 1857 ed. 37.00 (ISBN 0-404-50165-6). AMS Pr.

HOURS (TIME)

see Days; Time

HOURS, BOOKS OF

Fouquet, Jean. The Hours of Etienne Chevalier. LC 78-160131. (Illus.). 128p. 1971. slipcased 40.00 (ISBN 0-8076-0618-9). Braziller.

Knapp, Elsie M. Horary Art & It's Synthesis. 1974. 5.00x (ISBN 0-686-17210-8). Sandollar Pr.

The Liturgy of the Hours, 4 vols. Incl. Vol. 1. Advent & Christmas. 24.50 (ISBN 0-89942-401-5, 401/10); Vol. 2. Lent & Easter. 26.00 (ISBN 0-89942-402-3, 402/10); Vol. 3. Ordinary Time-Weeks 1 to 17. 24.50 (ISBN 0-89942-403-1, 403/10); Vol. 4. Ordinary Time-Weeks 18 to 34. 24.50 (ISBN 0-89942-404-X, 404/10). Boxed. gift set 96.00 (ISBN 0-89942-409-0, 409-05); St. Joseph guide for 1986 o.s.i. 1.25 (ISBN 0-89942-400-7, 400-G); Boxed. deluxe gift set 136.00, leather, gold edges (ISBN 0-89942-411-2, 409/13). Blue (401C). Red (402C). Brown (403C). Green (404C). Catholic Bk Pub.

Miller, Charles E. Making Holy the Day: A Commentary in the Liturgy of the Hours. red flexible bdg. 0.95 (ISBN 0-89942-410-4, 410/04). Catholic Bk Pub.

Plummer, John, intro. by. The Hours of Catherine of Cleves. LC 66-23096. (Illus.). 360p. 1975. 50.00 (ISBN 0-8076-0379-1). Braziller.

Smith, Webster. The Farnese Hours. LC 76-4041. (Library of Illuminated Manuscripts). (Illus.). 168p. 1976. slipcase 45.00 (ISBN 0-8076-0856-4). Braziller.

Thomas, Marcel, ed. The Grandes Heures of Jean, Duke of Berry. LC 75-167761. (Illus.). 192p. 1971. 80.00 (ISBN 0-8076-0613-8). Braziller.

Vinck, Catherine D. Readings: "John at Patmos" & "A Book of Hours". LC 78-55341. 68p. 1978. 5.75 (ISBN 0-911726-32-2); pap. 3.75 (ISBN 0-911726-33-0). Alleluia Pr.

HSUAN-TSANG, 596?-664

Watters, Thomas. On Yuan Chwang's Travels in India 629-645 A. D. LC 74-158213. Repr. of 1905 ed. Set. 45.00 (ISBN 0-404-06878-2). AMS Pr.

HSUN-TZE

Dubs, Homer H. Hsuntze, the Moulder of Ancient Confucianism. 339p. Repr. of 1927 ed. text ed. 22.50x (ISBN 0-89644-006-0, Pub. by Chinese Matl Ctr). Coronet Bks.

HUBMAIER, BALTHASAR, d. 1528

Vedder, Henry C. Baltahsar Hubmaier: The Leader of the Anabaptists. LC 79-149670. Repr. of 1905 ed. 24.50 (ISBN 0-404-06755-7). AMS Pr.

HUGUENOTS

Baird, Henry M. History of the Rise of the Huguenots of France, 2 Vols. LC 79-130236. Repr. of 1879 ed. Set. 90.00 (ISBN 0-404-00520-9); 45.00 ea. Vol. 1 (ISBN 0-404-00521-7). Vol. 2 (ISBN 0-404-00522-5). AMS Pr.

Grant, Arthur J. The Huguenots. LC 69-11552. 255p. 1969. Repr. of 1934 ed. 27.50 (ISBN 0-208-00745-8, Archon). Shoe String.

Minet, William & Waller, William C., eds. Registers of the Church Known As La Patente in Spittlefields from 1689-1785. Bd. with Register of Baptisms in the Dutch Church at Colchester from 1645-1728. Moens, William J., ed. Repr. of 1905 ed; Pt. 2. Registers of the French Church. Moens, W. J., ed. Repr. of 1899 ed. (Hugenot Society of London Publications Ser.: Vols. 11-13). Repr. of 1898 ed. 135.00 (ISBN 0-8115-1648-2). Kraus Repr.

Rothrock, George A. The Huguenots: A Biography of a Minority. LC 78-23476. (Illus.). 228p. 1979. 21.95x (ISBN 0-88229-277-3). Nelson-Hall.

Schwartz, Hillel. Knaves, Fools, Madmen & That Subtile Effluvium: A Study of the Opposition to the French Prophets in England, 1706-1710. LC 78-1692. (University of Florida Social Sciences Monographs: No. 62). 1978. pap. 5.50 (ISBN 0-8130-0505-1). U Presses Fla.

HUGUENOTS IN FOREIGN COUNTRIES
Gwynn, Robin D. Huguenot Heritage: The History & Contribution of the Huguenots in England. (Illus.). 256p. 1985. 34.95x (ISBN 0-7102-0420-5). Methuen Inc.
Hovenden, Robert, ed. The Registers of the Walloon or Strangers' Church in Canterbury, 3 pts. (Huguenot Society of London Publications Ser.: Vol. 5). Repr. of 1891 ed. Set. 107.00 (ISBN 0-8115-1644-X). Kraus Repr.
Schwartz, Hillel. The French Prophets: The History of a Millenarian Group in Eighteenth-Century England. LC 78-65459. (Illus.). 1980. 42.00x (ISBN 0-520-03815-0). U of Cal Pr.
HUGUENOTS IN FRANCE
see also Edict of Nantes; Holy League, 1576-1593
Baird, Henry M. History of the Rise of the Huguenots of France, 2 Vols. LC 79-130236. Repr. of 1879 ed. Set. 90.00 (ISBN 0-404-00520-9); 45.00 ea. Vol. 1 (ISBN 0-404-00521-7). Vol. 2 (ISBN 0-404-00522-5). AMS Pr.
--Huguenots & Henry of Navarre, 2 Vols. LC 76-130987. Repr. of 1903 ed. Set. 74.50 (ISBN 0-404-00540-3). AMS Pr.
--The Huguenots & the Revocation of the Edict of Nantes, 2 vols. LC 76-161752. Repr. of 1895 ed. Set. 74.50 (ISBN 0-404-08003-0). AMS Pr.
--The Huguenots & the Revocation of the Edict of Nantes, 2 vols. 1977. lib. bdg. 250.00 (ISBN 0-8490-2025-5). Gordon Pr.
Bien, David D. The Calas Affair: Persecution, Toleration, & Heresy in Eighteenth-Century Toulouse. LC 78-12393. 1979. Repr. of 1960 ed. lib. bdg. cancelled (ISBN 0-313-21206-6, BICA). Greenwood.
Browning, William S. The History of the Huguenots During the Sixteenth Century, 2 vols. LC 83-45604. Date not set. Repr. of 1829 ed. Set. 59.50 (ISBN 0-404-19871-6). AMS Pr.
Grant, Arthur J. The Huguenots. LC 69-11552. 255p. 1969. Repr. of 1934 ed. 27.50 (ISBN 0-208-00745-8, Archon). Shoe String.
Gray, Janet G. The French Huguenots. LC 81-67172. 200p. (Orig.). 1981. pap. 8.95 (ISBN 0-8010-3758-1). Baker Bk.
Kelly, Caleb G. French Protestantism, Fifteen Fifty-Nine to Fifteen Sixty-Two. LC 83-45621. Date not set. Repr. of 1918 ed. 24.50 (ISBN 0-404-19839-2). AMS Pr.
Le Fanu, Thomas P., ed. Registers of the French Non-Conformist Churches of Lucy Lane & Peter Street, Dublin. Bd. with History of the Walloon & Huguenot Church at Canterbury. Cross, F. W. Repr. of 1898 ed; Pt. 3. Registers of the French Church. Colyer-Fergusson, T. C., ed. Repr. of 1906 ed. (Hugenot Society of London Publication Ser.: Vols. 14-16). Repr. of 1901 ed. 135.00 (ISBN 0-8115-1649-0). Kraus Repr.
Peet, Henry, ed. Register of Baptisms of the French Protestant Refugees Settled at Thorney, Cambridgeshire, 1654-1727. Bd. with Letters of Denization. Shaw, William A., ed. Repr. of 1911 ed; Registers of the French Church of Portarlington, Ireland. Le Fanu, Thomas P., ed. Repr. of 1908 ed; Registers of the French Churches of Bristol. Lart, Charles E., ed. Repr. of 1912 ed; Register of the French Church at Thorpe-le-Spoken. Waller, William C., ed. Repr. of 1912 ed. (Huguenot Society of London Publications Ser.: Vols. 17 & 20). Repr. of 1903 ed. 144.00 (ISBN 0-317-17885-7). Kraus Repr.
Schwartz, Hillel. The French Prophets: The History of a Millenarian Group in Eighteenth-Century England. LC 78-65459. (Illus.). 1980. 42.00x (ISBN 0-520-03815-0). U of Cal Pr.
Sutherland, N. M. The Huguenot Struggle for Recognition. LC 79-64070. 1980. text ed. 40.00x (ISBN 0-300-02328-6). Yale U Pr.
HULMECAS
see Olmecs
HUMAN ACTS
see also Free Will and Determinism; Sin; Virtue and Virtues
More, Paul E. On Being Human. 1978. Repr. of 1936 ed. lib. bdg. 25.00 (ISBN 0-8414-2308-3). Folcroft.
HUMAN ECOLOGY-MORAL AND RELIGIOUS ASPECTS
Abrecht, Paul. Faith, Science, & the Future. LC 79-7035. pap. 60.00 (2026942). Bks Demand UMI.
McElwain, Hugh T. Theology of Limits & the Limits of Theology: Reflections on Language, Environment & Death. LC 83-1331. 190p. (Orig.). 1983. lib. bdg. 26.00 (ISBN 0-8191-3093-1); pap. text ed. 11.50 (ISBN 0-8191-3094-X). U Pr of Amer.
Zink, Jorg. Turn Toward Life: The Bible & Peacemaking. Rhodin, Victoria, tr. from Ger. LC 84-48709. 128p. 1985. pap. 7.95 (ISBN 0-8006-1829-7, 1-1829). Fortress.
HUMAN GENETICS-MORAL AND RELIGIOUS ASPECTS
Anderson, J. K. Genetic Engineering: The Ethical Issues. 128p. (Orig.). 1982. pap. 6.95 (ISBN 0-310-45051-9, 12707). Zondervan.
Hilton, Bruce, et al, eds. Ethical Issues in Human Genetics: Genetic Counseling & the Use of Genetic Knowledge. LC 72-93443. 468p. 1973. 35.00x (ISBN 0-306-30715-4, Plenum Pr). Plenum Pub.
Kowles, Richard V. Genetics, Society, & Decisions. 1985. Repr. text ed. write for info. (ISBN 0-673-18678-4). Scott F.
HUMAN RELATIONS
see Interpersonal Relations
HUMANISM
see also Classical Philology; Hellenism; Humanistic Ethics; Philosophical Anthropology; Renaissance
Abel, Reuben E., ed. Humanistic Pragmatism: The Philosophy of F. C. S. Schiller. (Orig.). 1966. pap. text ed. 6.95 (ISBN 0-02-900120-X). Free Pr.
Abelard, Peter. Historia Calamitatum: Story of My Misfortunes. 59.95 (ISBN 0-8490-0305-9). Gordon Pr.
Allen, Ronald B. The Majesty of Man: The Dignity of Being Human. LC 84-984. (Critical Concern Ser.). 1984. 11.95 (ISBN 0-88070-065-3). Multnomah.
Baker, Herschel. The Wars of Truth: Studies in the Decay of Christian Humanism in the Earlier 17th Century. 11.75 (ISBN 0-8446-0472-0). Peter Smith.
Baxter, Ern, et al. Secular Humanism. 1986. pap. 2.95 (ISBN 0-8010-0936-7). Baker Bk.
Bentley, Jerry H. Humanists & Holy Writ. LC 83-42547. 264p. 1983. 25.50x (ISBN 0-691-05392-8). Princeton U Pr.
Blackham, H. J., et al. Objections to Humanism. LC 73-16796. 128p. 1974. Repr. of 1963 ed. lib. bdg. 22.50x (ISBN 0-8371-7235-7, BLOH). Greenwood.
Braunthal, Alfred. Salvation & the Perfect Society: The Eternal Quest. LC 79-4705. 448p. 1979. lib. bdg. 25.00x (ISBN 0-87023-273-8). U of Mass Pr.
Conn, Harry. Four Trojan Horses of Humanism. 141p. 1982. pap. 5.95 (ISBN 0-88062-009-9). Mott Media.
D'Amico, John F. Renaissance Humanism in Papal Rome: Humanists & Churchmen on the Eve of the Reformation. LC 82-49059. (Studies in Historical & Political Science). 352p. 1983. text ed. 32.50x (ISBN 0-8018-2860-0). Johns Hopkins.
Einstein, Albert. Essays in Humanism. 130p. 1983. pap. 4.95 (ISBN 0-8022-2417-2). Philos Lib.
Fussell, Paul. The Rhetorical World of Augustan Humanism: Ethics & Imagery from Swift to Burke. LC 66-1724. pap. 80.80 (ISBN 0-317-29155-6, 2055599). Bks Demand UMI.
Gilmore, David B. The Essence & the Vocation of Man. (Illus.). 123p. 1980. deluxe ed. 57.50 (ISBN 0-89920-009-5). Am Inst Psych.
Glover, Willis B. Biblical Origins of Modern Secular Culture. LC 84-14868. xx, 300p. 1984. 23.95 (ISBN 0-86554-138-8, MUP-H129). Mercer Univ Pr.
Goodsell, Willystine. Conflict of Naturalism & Humanism. LC 74-176814. (Columbia University. Teachers College. Contributions to Education: No. 33). Repr. of 1910 ed. 22.50 (ISBN 0-404-55033-9). AMS Pr.
Gragg, Florence A., ed. The Latin Writings of the Italian Humanists. (College Classical Ser.). xxxvi, 434p. 1981. lib. bdg. 30.00 (ISBN 0-89241-356-5); pap. text ed. 17.50 (ISBN 0-89241-110-4). Caratzas.
Greville, Brooke R. The Nature of Truth, It's Union & Unity with the Soule. 210p. Repr. of 1640 ed. text ed. 33.12x (ISBN 0-576-02144-X, Pub. by Gregg Intl Pubs England). Gregg Intl.
Hitchcock, James. What Is Secular Humanism? Why Humanism Became Secular & How It Is Changing Our World. (Illus.). 158p. 1982. pap. 6.95 (ISBN 0-89283-163-4). Servant.
Hodges, Donald C. Socialist Humanism: The Outcome of Classical European Morality. LC 73-96983. 384p. 1974. 19.75 (ISBN 0-87527-042-5). Green.
Hume, David. Dialogues Concerning Natural Religion. Popkin, Richard H., ed. LC 79-25349. 132p. 1980. lib. bdg. 15.00 (ISBN 0-915144-46-8); pap. text ed. 2.95 (ISBN 0-915144-45-X). Hackett Pub.
Jaeger, Werner. Humanism & Theology. (Aquinas Lecture). 1943. 7.95 (ISBN 0-87462-107-0). Marquette.
Klemke, E. D., intro. by. Humanism vs Theism. 154p. 1982. pap. 8.50x (ISBN 0-8138-0916-9). Iowa St U Pr.
Kristeller, Paul O. Renaissance Thought: The Classic, Scholastic & Humanistic Strains. 15.50 (ISBN 0-8446-2405-5). Peter Smith.
Kurtz, Paul, ed. Humanist Manifestos One & Two. 32p. 1973. pap. 2.95 (ISBN 0-87975-031-6). Prometheus Bks.
Labadie, Laurance. Humanism & Morality. (Men & Movements in the History & Philosophy of Anarchism Ser.). 1979. lib. bdg. 59.95 (ISBN 0-685-96397-7). Revisionist Pr.
Lamont, Corliss. The Philosophy of Humanism. 6th ed. LC 81-70127. 340p. 1982. 15.95 (ISBN 0-8044-5997-5); pap. 9.95 (ISBN 0-8044-6379-4). Ungar.
--Philosophy of Humanism. 5th ed. LC 65-16612. 10.50 (ISBN 0-8044-5595-3); pap. 10.95 (ISBN 0-8044-6378-6). Ungar.
Mackail, John W. Studies in Humanism. facs. ed. LC 73-84322. (Essay Index Reprint Ser). 1938. 17.75 (ISBN 0-8369-1092-3). Ayer Co Pubs.
Mahoney, Edward P., ed. Philosophy & Humanism: Renaissance Essays in Honor of Paul Oskar Kristeller. LC 75-42285. 624p. 1976. 65.00 (ISBN 0-231-03904-2). Columbia U Pr.
Maritain, Jacques. Freedom & the Modern World. O'Sullivan, Richard, tr. LC 77-150414. 231p. 1971. Repr. of 1936 ed. 15.00x (ISBN 0-87752-147-6). Gordian.
--True Humanism. Adamson, M. R., tr. LC 71-114888. (Select Bibliographies Reprint Ser). 1938. 22.00 (ISBN 0-8369-5292-8). Ayer Co Pubs.
--True Humanism. 3rd ed. Adamson, Margot, tr. Repr. of 1941 ed. lib. bdg. 35.00x (ISBN 0-8371-2902-8, MAHU). Greenwood.
Mitchell, Basil. Morality-Religious & Secular: The Dilemma of the Traditional Conscience. 1980. 29.95x (ISBN 0-19-824537-8). Oxford U Pr.
Morison, Richard. Humanist Scholarship & Public Order: Two Tracts Against the Pilgrimage of Grace, & a Collection of Related Contemporary Documents. Berkowitz, David S., ed. LC 79-89983. 280p. 1983. text ed. 28.50 (ISBN 0-918016-01-0). Folger Bks.
Pollard, T. E. Fullness of Humanity: Christ's Humanness & Ours. 128p. 1982. text ed. 19.95x (ISBN 0-907459-10-2, Pub. by Almond Pr England); pap. text ed. 9.95x (ISBN 0-907459-11-0, Pub. by Almond Pr England). Eisenbrauns.
Reiser, Oliver. Cosmic Humanism & World Unity. new ed. LC 73-86468. (World Institute Creative Findings Ser.). (Illus.). 286p. 1975. 49.50 (ISBN 0-677-03870-4); pap. 21.00 (ISBN 0-677-03875-5). Gordon & Breach.
Rowe, H. Edward. New Age Globalism: Humanist Agenda for Building a New World Without God. 95p. (Orig.). 1985. pap. 4.95 (ISBN 0-931225-11-6). Growth Pub.
Saumur, Lucien. The Humanist Evangel. LC 81-85573. 128p. 1982. 16.95 (ISBN 0-87975-172-X); pap. 13.95 (ISBN 0-87975-114-2). Prometheus Bks.
Schultz, H. Milton & Forbidden Knowledge. (MLA RFS). 1955. 22.00 (ISBN 0-527-80600-5). Kraus Repr.
Sloane, Thomas O. Donne, Milton, & the End of Humanist Rhetoric. LC 83-24315. 1985. 38.50x (ISBN 0-520-05212-9). U of Cal Pr.
Soper, Kate. Humanism & Anti-Humanism. 154p. 1986. 9.95 (ISBN 0-8126-9017-6). Open Court.
Southern, R. W. Medieval Humanism: And Other Stories. (Illus.). 288p. 1984. pap. 12.95x (ISBN 0-631-13649-5). Basil Blackwell.
Streeting, Cecilian. Devout Humanism as a Style. LC 70-128930. (Catholic University. Romance Literature: No. 50). Repr. of 1954 ed. 23.80 (ISBN 0-404-50350-0). AMS Pr.
Valdes, Juan de & Benedetto, Don. The Benefit of Christ. LC 84-9282. (Classics of Faith & Devotion Ser.). 1984. 10.95 (ISBN 0-88070-063-7). Multnomah.
Webber, Robert E. Secular Humanism. 144p. 1985. pap. 5.95 (ISBN 0-310-36671-2, 12208P). Zondervan.
HUMANISM, RELIGIOUS
Adams, James L. On Being Human Religiously. 2nd ed. Stackhouse, Max L., ed. 1986. pap. 10.95 (ISBN 0-933840-29-2, Skinner Hse Bks). Unitarian Univ.
Chambers, Claire. The Siecus Circle. LC 75-41650. 1977. pap. 6.95 (ISBN 0-88279-119-2). Western Islands.
Clark, John R. The Great Living System. 1984. pap. 7.95 (ISBN 0-933840-24-1). Unitarian Univ.
Erasmus. Christian Humanism & the Reformation: Selected Writings with the Life of Erasmus by Beatus Rhenanus. Olin, John C., ed. 11.25 (ISBN 0-8446-2035-1). Peter Smith.
Friedman, Maurice. The Human Way. LC 81-8011. (Religion & Human Experience Ser.). 168p. 1982. 13.95 (ISBN 0-89012-025-0). Anima Pubns.
Goodman, Don. Cory Hears with His Heart. LC 82-12272. (A Cory Story Ser.). 32p. 1982. pap. 2.95 (ISBN 0-8307-0858-8, 5608318). Regal.
Irish Bishop's Pastoral. Human Life Is Sacred. 1977. pap. 1.50 (ISBN 0-8198-0416-9). Dghtrs St Paul.
Jorgenson, Dale A. Christianity & Humanism. LC 83-70878. 115p. (Orig.). 1983. pap. 2.95 (ISBN 0-89900-149-1). College Pr Pub.
Ledwith, Miceal, tr. from Lat. Propositions on the Dignity & Rights of the Human Person. (International Theological Commission Ser.). 28p. (Orig.). 1986. pap. 1.95 (ISBN 1-55586-997-1). US Catholic.
McShane, Philip. The Shaping of the Foundations: Being at Home in the Transcendental Method. 12.25 (ISBN 0-8191-0209-1). U Pr of Amer.
Molnar, Thomas. Christian Humanism, a Critique of the Secular City & Its Ideology. 1978. 7.95 (ISBN 0-8199-0694-8). Franciscan Herald.
Phelps, William L. Human Nature & the Gospel. 1977. Repr. of 1925 ed. lib. bdg. 30.00 (ISBN 0-8414-6807-9). Folcroft.
Reines, Alvin J. Polydoxy: Explorations in a Philosophy of Liberal Religion. 200p. 1987. 29.95 (ISBN 0-87975-399-4). Prometheus Bks.
Robbins, Keith, ed. Religion & Humanism: Papers Read at the Eighteenth Summer Meeting & the Nineteenth Winter Meeting of the Ecclesiastical History Society. (Studies in Church History: Vol. 17). (Illus.). 378p. 1981. 45.00x (ISBN 0-631-18050-8). Basil Blackwell.
Shaw, Joseph M., et al, eds. Readings in Christian Humanism. LC 82-70963. (Orig.). 1982. pap. 24.95 (ISBN 0-8066-1938-4, 10-5400). Augsburg.
Stinson, Linda L. Process & Conscience: Toward a Theology of Human Emergence. 202p. (Orig.). 1986. lib. bdg. 22.50 (ISBN 0-8191-5206-4); pap. text ed. 11.50 (ISBN 0-8191-5207-2). U Pr of Amer.
Williams, George H. The Law of Nations & the Book of Nature. Franklin, R. W., ed. LC 84-72274. (New Essays in Christian Humanism: Vol. 1). (Illus.). 60p. (Orig.). 1985. pap. 4.95x (ISBN 0-9613867-0-3). St Johns Univ Christ Hum.
Yonker, Nicolas. God, Man & the Planetary Age: Preface for a Theistic Humanism. LC 78-4233. 168p. 1978. 11.00x (ISBN 0-87071-322-1). Oreg St U Pr.
HUMANIST ETHICS
see Humanistic Ethics
HUMANISTIC ETHICS
Hume, David. An Enquiry Concerning the Principles of Morals. Schneewind, J. B., ed. LC 82-11679. (HPC Philosophical Classics Ser.). 132p. 1983. lib. bdg. 15.00 (ISBN 0-915145-46-4); pap. text ed. 3.45 (ISBN 0-915145-45-6). Hackett Pub.
Kurtz, Paul, ed. Moral Problems in Contemporary Society: Essays in Humanistic Ethics. 2nd ed. 301p. 1973. pap. 10.95 (ISBN 0-87975-022-7). Prometheus Bks.
Saumur, Lucien. The Humanist Evangel. LC 81-85573. 128p. 1982. 16.95 (ISBN 0-87975-172-X); pap. 13.95 (ISBN 0-87975-114-2). Prometheus Bks.
Storer, Morris B., ed. Humanist Ethics. LC 80-7456. 313p. 1980. 19.95 (ISBN 0-87975-117-7); pap. 13.95 (ISBN 0-87975-118-5). Prometheus Bks.
HUMANITARIANISM (RELIGION)
see Jesus Christ-Divinity; Positivism; Trinity; Unitarianism
HUMBUG
see Impostors and Imposture
HUMILITY
Chrysostomos, Archimandrite & Williams, Theodore. Humility, Vol. 1. LC 82-74509. (Themes in Orthodox Patristic Psychology Ser.). 90p. (Orig.). 1983. pap. text ed. 4.50 (ISBN 0-911165-01-0); pap. write for info. (ISBN 0-911165-02-9). Ctr Trad Orthodox.
Furey, Robert J. So I'm Not Perfect: A Psychology of Humility. 131p. (Orig.). 1986. pap. 6.95 (ISBN 0-8189-0499-2). Alba.
Leo, Pope The Practice of Humility. O'Connor, John F., tr. 1976. lib. bdg. 59.95 (ISBN 0-8490-2462-5). Gordon Pr.
--The Practice of Humility. O'Conor, John F., tr. 1980. lib. bdg. 59.95 (ISBN 0-8490-3177-X). Gordon Pr.
Mary da Bergamo, Cajetan. Humility of Heart. Vaughan, Herbert C., tr. 240p. 1978. pap. 4.50 (ISBN 0-89555-067-9). Tan Bks Pubs.
Practice of Humilty. 1978. 2.50 (ISBN 0-8198-0546-7); pap. 1.50 (ISBN 0-8198-0547-5). Dghtrs St Paul.
HUNGARIAN MYTHOLOGY
see Mythology, Finno-Ugrian
HUNGER
Grassi, Joseph A. Broken Bread & Broken Bodies: The Eucharist & World Hunger. LC 84-18888. 128p. (Orig.). 1985. pap. 6.95 (ISBN 0-88344-193-4). Orbis Bks.
Hessel, Dietert T. & Conner, John T., eds. Agricultural Mission of Churches & Land-Grant Universities: A Report of an Informal Consultation. 1979. pap. text ed. 8.50x (ISBN 0-8138-0920-7). Iowa St U Pr.
Sider, Ronald J. Rich Christians in an Age of Hunger: A Biblical Study. 2nd, rev. ed. LC 84-4549. (Illus.). 257p. 1984. pap. 7.95 (ISBN 0-87784-977-3). Inter-Varsity.

HUS, JOHN, 1369-1415

Denis, Ernest. Huss et les guerres hussites. LC 77-8424. Repr. of 1930 ed. 46.50 (ISBN 0-404-16126-X). AMS Pr.

Gillett, Ezra H. The Life & Times of John Huss: The Bohemian Reformation of the Fifteenth Century, 2 vols. LC 77-85271. Repr. of 1863 ed. Set. 94.50 (ISBN 0-404-16150-2). AMS Pr.

Jones, Bob. Prologue: A Drama of John Hus. (Illus.). 85p. 1968. pap. 3.95 (ISBN 0-89084-195-0). Bob Jones Univ Pr.

Kitts, Eustace J. Pope John the Twenty-Third & Master John Hus of Bohemia. LC 77-84726. Repr. of 1910 ed. 47.00 (ISBN 0-404-16127-8). AMS Pr.

Loserth, Johann. Wiclif & Hus. Evans, M. J., tr. LC 78-63198. (Heresies of the Early Christian & Medieval Era: Second Ser.). 1979. Repr. of 1884 ed. 48.00 (ISBN 0-404-16236-3). AMS Pr.

Lutzow, Franz. The Life & Times of Master John Hus. LC 77-84728. (Illus.). Repr. of 1909 ed. 40.00 (ISBN 0-404-16128-6). AMS Pr.

Schaff, D. S. John Huss. 59.95 (ISBN 0-8490-0451-9). Gordon Pr.

Spinka, Matthew. John Hus: A Biography. LC 78-14366. (Illus.). 1978. Repr. of 1968 ed. lib. bdg. 37.50 (ISBN 0-313-21050-0, SPJH). Greenwood.

HUSAIN, MAQBOOL FIDA

Ali, S. V. Husain the Savior of Islam. LC 81-51900. 252p. 1981. 5.95 (ISBN 0-940368-05-6); pap. 3.95 (ISBN 0-940368-03-X). Tahrike Tarsile Quran.

HUSBAND AND WIFE

see also Divorce

Campion, Michael & Zehr, Wilmer. Especially for Husbands. (When Was the Last Time Ser.). (Illus.). 112p. 1978. pap. 5.95 (ISBN 0-87123-136-0, 210136). Bethany Hse.

Dillow, Linda. Creative Counterpart. rev. & updated ed. 228p. 1986. pap. 7.95 (ISBN 0-8407-3067-5). Nelson.

Dobson, James. What Wives Wish Their Husbands Knew about Women. 1977. pap. 5.95 (ISBN 0-8423-7889-8); pap. 3.50 (ISBN 0-8423-7896-0, Living Books). Tyndale.

Durkin, Henry P. Forty-Four Hours to Change Your Life: Marriage Encounter. (Orig.). pap. write for info (ISBN 0-515-09442-0). Jove Pubns.

Leman, Kevin. Sex Begins in the Kitchen. LC 80-54004. 1983. pap. 5.95 (ISBN 0-8307-1190-2, 5419017). Regal.

Rowatt, G. Wade, Jr. & Rowatt, Mary Jo. The Two-Career Marriage. LC 79-28408. (Christian Care Bks.: Vol. 5). 120p. 1980. pap. 7.95 (ISBN 0-664-24298-7). Westminster.

Shivanandan, Mary. When Your Wife Wants to Work. LC 79-51278. (When Bks). (Illus.). 1980. pap. 2.45 (ISBN 0-87029-151-3, 20237-4). Abbey.

Stanley, Charles F. A Man's Touch. LC 77-80948. 120p. 1977. pap. 3.95 (ISBN 0-88207-753-8). Victor Bks.

Williams, Patti. Husbands. LC 75-7477. 1976. 4.95 (ISBN 0-88270-148-7). Bridge Pub.

HUSSITES

see also Moravians

Bartos, F. M. The Hussite Revolution: Fourteen Twenty-Four to Fourteen Thirty-Seven. 256p. 1986. 25.00 (ISBN 0-88033-097-X). East Eur Quarterly.

Kautsky, Karl. Communism in Central Europe in the Time of the Reformation. Mulliken, J. L. & Mulliken, E. G., trs. LC 66-22631. 1966. Repr. of 1897 ed. 29.50x (ISBN 0-678-00193-6). Kelley.

Macek, Josef. The Hussite Movement in Bohemia. Fried, Vilem & Milner, Ian, trs. LC 78-63207. (Heresies of the Early Christian & Medieval Era: Second Ser.). Repr. of 1958 ed. 39.50 (ISBN 0-404-16237-1). AMS Pr.

Zeman, Jarold K. The Hussite Movement & the Reformation in Bohemia, Moravia & Slovakia, 1350-1650: A Bibliographic Study Guide. 1977. 15.00 (ISBN 0-930042-00-X). Mich Slavic Pubns.

HUTTERITE BRETHREN

Arnold, Eberhard. Foundation & Orders of Sannerz & the Rhon Bruderhof: Introductory History: The Basis for Our Orders, Vol. 1. LC 76-5856. 1976. pap. 2.50 (ISBN 0-87486-162-4). Plough.

--Why We Live in Community. 1976. pap. 1.50 (ISBN 0-87486-168-3). Plough.

Arnold, Emmy. Gegen Den Strom. (Ger.). 200p. 1983. pap. 5.50 (ISBN 3-87067-206-4, Pub. by Brendow-Verlag, West Germany). Plough.

--Ein Inneres Wort Fur Jeden Tag Des Jahres. LC 76-10987. 192p. 1976. 4.50 (ISBN 0-87486-166-7). Plough.

Blumhardt, Johann C. & Blumhardt, Christoph. Now Is Eternity. LC 76-10251. 1976. 4.00 (ISBN 0-87486-209-4); pap. 3.00 (ISBN 0-87486-219-1). Plough.

Braitmichel, Kasper, et al. The Chronicle of the Hutterian Brethren, Vol. 1. Hutterian Brethren, ed. (Ger. & Eng., Illus.). 900p. 1987. 36.00 (ISBN 0-87486-021-0). Plough.

Ehrenpreis, Andreas & Felbinger, Claus. Brotherly Community, the Highest Command of Love: Two Anabaptist Documents of 1650 & 1560. LC 78-21065. 1979. pap. 5.00 (ISBN 0-87486-190-X). Plough.

Gross, Leonard. The Golden Years of the Hutterites. LC 80-10711. (Studies in Anabaptist & Mennonite History: Vol. 23). 1980. 17.95x (ISBN 0-8361-1227-X). Herald Pr.

--Golden Years of the Hutterites, 1565-1578. LC 80-10711. 280p. 1980. 15.00 (ISBN 0-317-47160-0). Plough.

Horsch, John. Hutterian Brethren. 189p. 1931. 9.95x (ISBN 0-8361-1188-5). Herald Pr.

--Hutterian Brethren, 1528-1931. 190p. 1931. 7.00 (ISBN 0-317-47168-6). Plough.

Horst, Irvin B. The Radical Brethren. 216p. 1972. 30.00x (ISBN 0-8361-1193-1). Herald Pr.

Hostetler, John A. Hutterite Life. 2nd ed. LC 82-83962. (Illus., Orig.). 1983. pap. 4.95 (ISBN 0-8361-3329-3). Herald Pr.

--Hutterite Society. LC 74-6827. (Illus.). 420p. 1974. 30.00x (ISBN 0-8018-1584-3). Johns Hopkins.

Hostetler, John A. & Huntington, Gertrude E. The Hutterites in North America. LC 79-19718. 141p. 1980. pap. text ed. 9.95 (ISBN 0-03-045391-7, HoltC). HR&W.

Howells, W. W. Hutterite Age Differences in Body Measurements. LC 78-115048. (Peabody Museum Papers: Vol. 57, No. 2). 1970. pap. 10.00x (ISBN 0-87365-168-5). Peabody Harvard.

Peter, Karl A. The Dynamics of Hutterite Society: An Analytical Approach. 250p. 1986. 27.50x (ISBN 0-88864-108-7, Univ of Atla Pr Canada); pap. 16.95x (ISBN 0-88864-109-5). U of Nebr Pr.

Pickering, W. S. The Hutterists: Christians Who Practice a Communal Way of Life. 1985. 20.00 (ISBN 0-7062-4163-0, Pub. by Ward Lock Educ Co Ltd). State Mutual Bk.

HYMN TUNES

Breed, David R. The History & Use of Hymns & Hymn Tunes. LC 76-39525. Repr. of 1903 ed. 20.00 (ISBN 0-404-09906-8). AMS Pr.

Butterworth, Hezekiah. Story of Hymns & Tunes. 1981. Repr. lib. bdg. 79.00x (ISBN 0-403-00107-2). Scholarly.

Hays, Henry B. Swayed Pines Song Book. x, 88p. 1981. wirebound 7.95 (ISBN 0-8146-1238-5). Liturgical Pr.

Lyon, James. Urania: A Choice Collection of Psalm-Tunes, Anthems & Hymns. LC 69-11667. (Music Reprint Ser.). 198p. 1974. Repr. of 1761 ed. lib. bdg. 37.50 (ISBN 0-306-71198-2). Da Capo.

Mason, H. Lowell. Hymn-Tunes of Lowell Mason. LC 74-24144. Repr. of 1944 ed. 15.00 (ISBN 0-404-13035-6). AMS Pr.

HYMN WRITERS

Aaberg, J. C. Hymns & Hymnwriter of Denmark. 170p. Repr. of 1945 ed. 29.00 (ISBN 0-932051-28-6, Pub. by Am Repr Serv). Am Biog Serv.

Goodenough, Caroline L. High Lights on Hymnists & Their Hymns. LC 72-1626. Repr. of 1931 ed. 32.50 (ISBN 0-404-08310-2). AMS Pr.

Hatfield, Edwin F. Poets of the Church: A Series of Biographical Sketches of Hymn-Writers, with Notes on Their Hymns. 1979. Repr. of 1884 ed. 110.00x (ISBN 0-8103-4291-X). Gale.

Reynolds, William J. Hymns of Our Faith. LC 64-14049. 1964. 18.95 (ISBN 0-8054-6805-6). Broadman.

Stebbins, George C. Reminiscences & Gospel Hymn Stories. LC 74-144689. Repr. of 1924 ed. 24.50 (ISBN 0-404-07203-8). AMS Pr.

HYMNOLOGY

see Hymns

HYMNS

see also Carols; Children's Hymns; Church Music; Gospel Music; Hymn Tunes; Psalmody; Religious Poetry; Sunday-Schools–Hymns

Aaberg, J. C. Hymns & Hymnwriter of Denmark. 170p. Repr. of 1945 ed. 29.00 (ISBN 0-932051-28-6, Pub. by Am Repr Serv). Am Biog Serv.

Aitken, John. Compilations of Litanies & Vesper Hymns. 25.00x (ISBN 0-87556-004-0). Saifer.

Anderson, Fred R. Singing Psalms of Joy & Praise. LC 86-1550. 78p. (Orig.). 1986. pap. 5.95 ea. (ISBN 0-664-24696-6). Westminster.

Andrews, Edward D. Gift to Be Simple. (Illus.). 1940. pap. 3.95 (ISBN 0-486-20022-1). Dover.

--Gift to Be Simple: Songs, Dances & Rituals of the American Shakers. (Illus.). 12.75 (ISBN 0-8446-1536-6). Peter Smith.

Banks, Louis A. Immortal Hymns & Their Story. LC 77-75198. 1977. Repr. of 1899 ed. lib. bdg. 30.00 (ISBN 0-89341-088-8). Longwood Pub Group.

Barrett, James E., ed. The Hymnary: A Table for Service Planning. 95p. 1979. incl. binder 16.00 (ISBN 0-942466-01-2); 13.50 (ISBN 0-942466-00-4). Hymnary Pr.

Bausch, Michael & Duck, Ruth. Everflowing Streams. LC 81-701. 96p. (Orig.). 1981. pap. 4.95 (ISBN 0-8298-0428-5). Pilgrim NY.

Bay, Bill. Mel Bay's Deluxe Guitar Praise Book. 64p. (Orig.). 1973. pap. 2.95 (ISBN 0-89228-007-7). Impact Bks MO.

--Mel Bay's Guitar Hymnal. 80p. (Orig.). 1972. pap. 2.95 (ISBN 0-89228-009-3). Impact Bks MO.

Beckwith, Paul, et al, eds. Hymns II. LC 76-47503. 1976. text ed. 12.95 (ISBN 0-87784-898-X); pap. text ed. 7.95 (ISBN 0-87784-783-5); pap. text ed. 10.95 spiral text (ISBN 0-87784-750-9). Inter-Varsity.

Beierle, Herbert L. Song of the Spirit. 1978. 20.00 (ISBN 0-940480-01-8). U of Healing.

Bennett, Marian, ed. Songs for Preschool Children. LC 80-25091. 96p. (Orig.). 1981. pap. 7.95 (ISBN 0-87239-429-8, 5754). Standard Pub.

Benson, Louis. The English Hymn. (Music Reprint Ser.). 624p. 1985. Repr. of 1915 ed. 65.00 (ISBN 0-306-76261-7). Da Capo.

Blue. Pilgrim Hymnal. 1958. 9.95x (ISBN 0-8298-0460-9). Pilgrim NY.

Bock, Fred & Leech, Bryan J., eds. The Hymnal Companion. 1979. 12.95 (ISBN 0-89477-004-7). Paragon Benson.

--Hymns for the Family of God. 1976. 7.95 (ISBN 0-89477-000-4, Dist. by Alexandria House); looseleaf 6.95 (ISBN 0-89477-002-0); pap. 7.95 (ISBN 0-89477-001-2). Paragon Benson.

Boring, Holland, ed. Songs of Hope. 1979. pap. 2.75 (ISBN 0-88027-059-4). Firm Foun Pub.

Brunk, J. D., ed. Church & Sunday School Hymnal with Supplement. LC 72-2053. 384p. (532 hymns & songs, & 50 german songs, words only, 1902; supplement 1911). 1902. 7.95x (ISBN 0-8361-1110-9). Herald Pr.

Cantate Domino: An Ecumenical Hymn Book. full music ed. 1980. 24.50x (ISBN 0-19-143371-3). Oxford U Pr.

Christ-Janer, Albert, et al, eds. American Hymns Old & New: Notes on the Hymns & Biographies of the Authors & Composers, 2 vols. LC 79-4630. (Illus.). 1454p. 1980. 72.00 (ISBN 0-231-05148-4). Columbia U Pr.

Cirou, Joseph, et al. The Johannine Hymnal. LC 75-14542. (Melody ed). 1970. 3.95 (ISBN 0-915866-00-5). Am Cath Pr.

Coffman, S. F., ed. Life Songs Number Two. 288p. (With Responsive Readings). 1938. 6.95x (ISBN 0-8361-1116-8). Herald Pr.

Cokesbury Worship Hymnal. 288p. 1976. 4.95 (ISBN 0-687-08863-1); pap. 4.95 (ISBN 0-687-08865-8); accompanist ed. 3.95 (ISBN 0-687-08866-6). Abingdon.

Coleman, Robert E. Songs of Heaven. 160p. 1982. pap. 5.95 (ISBN 0-8007-5097-7, Power Bks). Revell.

Colquhoun, Frank. A Hymn Companion. 288p. 1985. pap. 8.95 (ISBN 0-8192-1368-3). Morehouse.

Crockett, Richard H. & Horsch, James E. Jesus Life Songbook. 134p. 1975. pap. 3.95 (ISBN 0-317-37867-8). Herald Pr.

Davies, Walford, ed. Let's Sing Together. 25.00x (ISBN 0-946095-14-0, Pub. by Gresham England); pap. 20.00x (ISBN 0-946095-13-2, Pub. by Gresham England). State Mutual Bk.

Davisson, A., ed. Kentucky Harmony: A Collection of Psalms, Tunes, Hymns & Anthems. 1976. 16.00 (ISBN 0-8066-1546-X, 11-9249). Augsburg.

Dearmer, Percy. Songs of Praise. Vaughan Williams, Ralph & Shaw, Martin, eds. Incl. Music Ed. rev. & enl. ed. 1932. 19.95x (ISBN 0-19-231207-3). Oxford U Pr.

Diehl, Katharine S. Hymns & Tunes: An Index. LC 66-13743. 1242p. 1979. lib. bdg. 65.00 (ISBN 0-8108-0062-4). Scarecrow.

Drillock, David, et al. Holy Week. (Music Ser.: Vol. I). 186p. (Orig.). 1980. 18.00 (ISBN 0-913836-67-2); pap. 14.00 (ISBN 0-913836-66-4). St Vladimirs.

Emurian, Ernest K. Living Stories of Famous Hymns. (Interlude Bks). 1971. pap. 4.95 (ISBN 0-8010-3260-1). Baker Bk.

English Hymnal. 1933. 20.00x (ISBN 0-19-231111-5); words only o.p. 9.95x (ISBN 0-19-231108-5). Oxford U Pr.

English Praise: A Supplement to the English Hymnal, Full Music Edition. 1975. pap. 5.95x (ISBN 0-19-231126-3). Oxford U Pr.

Evening Light Songs. 512p. 6.00 (ISBN 0-686-29108-5). Faith Pub Hse.

Faber, Fredrick W. Hymns. 1977. Repr. of 1881 ed. 20.00 (ISBN 0-8274-4295-5). R West.

Favorite Hymns for Senior Adults. LC 77-80939. 1977. pap. 4.95 (ISBN 0-8054-3303-1). Broadman.

Ferntheil, Carol, ed. Songs of Cheer. (Illus.). 16p. (Orig.). 1979. pap. 0.85 (ISBN 0-87239-345-3, 7948). Standard Pub.

Hall, Roger L. The Stoughton Musical Society's Centennial Collection of Sacred Music. (Earlier American Music Ser.: No. 23). 304p. 1980. Repr. of 1878 ed. lib. bdg. 37.50 (ISBN 0-306-79618-X). Da Capo.

Hanson, Handt. Spirit Touching Spirit, A Contemporary Hymnal. 240p. 1986. 10.95 (ISBN 0-933173-01-6). Prince Peace Pub.

Harlow, Louis K. The World's Best Hymns. Churchill, J. W., ed. 1978. Repr. of 1893 ed. lib. bdg. 25.00 (ISBN 0-8495-2323-0). Arden Lib.

Heaton, Charles H., ed. Hymnbook for Christian Worship. LC 69-14339. 1970. Red. 7.95x (ISBN 0-8272-8020-3). Blue. 7.95x (ISBN 0-8272-8021-1); Beige. 7.95x (ISBN 0-8272-8024-6); 19.50x (ISBN 0-8272-8023-8); 8.95x (ISBN 0-8272-8022-X); brown gift 8.50x (ISBN 0-8272-8027-0). CBP.

Henry, Victor. La Magie dans L'Inde Antique: Paris, 1904. LC 78-74261. (Oriental Religions Ser.: Vol. 5). 325p. 1980. lib. bdg. 40.00 (ISBN 0-8240-3903-3). Garland Pub.

Hogrogian, Nonny, illus. The Pearl: Hymn of the Robe of Glory. LC 79-66092. (Illus.). 1979. 7.95 (ISBN 0-89756-002-7). Two Rivers.

Hostetler, Lester & Yoder, Walter E., eds. Mennonite Hymnal. LC 69-18131. 1969. 7.50x (ISBN 0-87303-515-1). Faith & Life.

Hume, Alexander. Hymns & Sacred Songs. Repr. of 1599 ed. 20.00 (ISBN 0-384-24880-2). Johnson Repr.

Huntington, F. D. Hymns of the Ages, 3 vols. 1977. 300.00 (ISBN 0-8490-2031-X). Gordon Pr.

The Hymnal. 7.95 (ISBN 0-664-10033-3). Westminster.

Hymnal for Juniors in Worship & Study. 2.25 (ISBN 0-664-10082-1). Westminster.

Hymnbook for Christian Worship. red 6.95 (ISBN 0-8170-9018-5). Judson.

The Hymnbook: The Johannine Hymnal: Organ Edition. rev. ed. (Illus.). 1978. 24.95x (ISBN 0-915866-08-0). Am Cath Pr.

Hymns & Songs of the Spirit. LC 66-12542. 1966. 4.95 (ISBN 0-8272-8017-3). CBP.

Hymns for Church & School. (Orig.). 1983. 35.00x (ISBN 0-905418-05-0, Pub. by Gresham England); pap. 30.00x (ISBN 0-9502121-5-6, Pub. by Gresham England). State Mutual Bk.

Hymns for Creative Living. 3.95 (ISBN 0-8170-9009-6). Judson.

Hymns for Praise & Worship. 1984. 7.95 (ISBN 0-916035-09-3); text ed. 15.00 organist copy (ISBN 0-916035-10-7). Evangel Indiana.

Hymns for Worship. 1963. 6.50 (ISBN 0-916035-02-6, BE-30); organist copy o.p. 15.00 (ISBN 0-916035-03-4). Evangel Indiana.

Hymns from the Four Winds: A Collection of Asian American Hymns. 240p. (Orig.). 1983. pap. 7.50 (ISBN 0-687-18126-7). Abingdon.

Hymns of the Christian Life. 698p. 1978. 7.95 (ISBN 0-87509-278-0); deluxe ed. 9.50 (ISBN 0-87509-249-7); organist-pianist version 12.95. Chr Pubns.

Hyneman, Charles S., ed. Hymns Ancient & Modern for Use in the Services of the Church, with Accompanying Tunes. LC 74-24123. (Illus.). Repr. of 1909 ed. 150.00 (ISBN 0-404-12981-1). AMS Pr.

Jones, Joseph. Poems & Hymn Tunes As Songs: Metrical Partners. 84p. 1983. with 2 audio cassettes 24.50, (ISBN 0-88432-119-3, S1560). J Norton Pubs.

Kalas, Ellsworth. Our First Song: Evangelism in the Hymns of Charles Wesley. LC 84-70133. 64p. (Orig.). 1984. pap. 2.95 (ISBN 0-88177-010-8, DRO10B). Discipleship Res.

Kings School Canterbury Hymn Book. 578p. (Orig.). 1983. 38.00x (ISBN 0-905418-93-X, Pub. by Gresham England). State Mutual Bk.

Klepper, Robert F. Methodist Hymnal Concordance. LC 86-29811. 800p. 1987. 62.50 (ISBN 0-8108-1968-6). Scarecrow.

Lemmons, Reuel, ed. The Majestic Hymnal, No. 2. 1959. 2.75x (ISBN 0-88027-056-X). Firm Foun Pub.

Leupold, Ulrich S. & Lehmann, Helmut T., eds. Luther's Works: Liturgy & Hymns, Vol. 53. LC 55-9893. 1965. 19.95 (ISBN 0-8006-0353-2, 1-353). Fortress.

Lodge, Ann, ed. Creation Sings. 1980. pap. 1.25 (ISBN 0-664-10091-0). Westminster.

Lund, Lynn S. Songs of Eternal Faith: Artistic Piano Arrangements of Best-Loved Hymns. LC 81-80954. 56p. (Orig.). 1982. pap. 5.95 (ISBN 0-88290-184-2, 2901). Horizon Utah.

Lyon, Lawrence A. Choral Settings for Six LDS Hymns. 56p. (Orig.). 1975. pap. 4.95 (ISBN 0-87747-605-5). Deseret Bk.

McNeil, Margaret C. Come Sing with Me. 1971. pap. 2.95 (ISBN 0-8170-0535-8); bk. & record o.p. 5.95 (ISBN 0-685-01111-9). Judson.

Marshall, Madeleine F. & Todd, Janet M. English Congregational Hymns in the Eighteenth Century. LC 82-40176. 192p. 1982. 16.00x (ISBN 0-8131-1470-5). U Pr of Ky.

Mearns, James. Early Latin Hymnaries. 127p. Repr. of 1913 ed. lib. bdg. 38.50X (Pub. by G Olms BRD). Coronet Bks.

The Mennonite Hymnal. 640p. 1960. round notes 7.95 (ISBN 0-317-37871-6); shape notes 7.95 (ISBN 0-317-37872-4); large print 11.95 (ISBN 0-317-37873-2). Herald Pr.

The Mennonite Hymnal Loose-Leaf Edition. 640p. 1969. round notes 14.95 (ISBN 0-317-37874-0); shape notes 14.95 (ISBN 0-317-37875-9). Herald Pr.

Miller, Max B. & Drew, Louise C., eds. Sing of Life & Faith. LC 68-22233. (Illus.). 1969. 5.95 (ISBN 0-8298-0123-5). Pilgrim NY.

Milosz, Czeslaw. Hymn O Perle: Hymn to the Pearl. (Michigan Slavic Materials Ser.: No. 21). 1982. 10.00 (ISBN 0-930042-45-X). Mich Slavic Pubns.

Mudditt, B. Howard, ed. Christian Worship (Hymns) 716p. 1976. text ed. 15.00x (ISBN 0-85364-194-3). Attic Pr.

The New Saint Joseph Sunday Missal & Hymnal. complete ed. (Illus., References, Calendar, Bold Sense-Lines, Two Color Ordinary, Perpetual). red flexible vinyl 9.25 (ISBN 0-89942-820-7, 820/09); green cloth, colored edges 10.95 (ISBN 0-89942-819-3, 820/22-GN); black cloth hard bdg. 10.95 (ISBN 0-89942-818-5, 820/22-B); brown flexible bdg., colored edges 11.95 (ISBN 0-89942-817-7, 820/10-BN); white durocoat, marriage cert, gold edges 12.95 (ISBN 0-89942-816-9, 820/51W); dlx. white sim. pearl, gold edges 15.00 (ISBN 0-89942-815-0, 820/82W). Catholic Bk Pub.

Newman, Henry. Hymns. 1983. 9.95 (ISBN 0-87193-199-0). Dimension Bks.

Olson, Ruth L., ed. Hymns & Songs for Church Schools. LC 62-13898. (Illus.). 1962. 7.95 ea. (12-1500). 25 or more 7.65 ea. Augsburg.

Osbeck, Kenneth W. One Hundred One Hymn Stories. LC 81-17165. 288p. 1982. pap. 8.95 (ISBN 0-8254-3416-5). Kregel.

--One Hundred One More Hymn Stories. LC 84-27847. 328p. (Orig.). 1985. pap. 9.95 (ISBN 0-8254-3420-3). Kregel.

--Singing with Understanding: Including 101 Beloved Hymn Backgrounds. LC 78-19960. 324p. 1979. 14.95 (ISBN 0-8254-3414-9). Kregel.

Polack, W. G. The Handbook to the Lutheran Hymnal. 3rd rev. ed. 1975. Repr. of 1942 ed. lib. bdg. 16.95 (ISBN 0-8100-0003-2, 03-0700). Northwest Pub.

Poteat, Hubert M. Practical Hymnology. LC 72-1693. Repr. of 1921 ed. 14.50 (ISBN 0-404-09912-2). AMS Pr.

Ramsey, Dale E. Sing Praises! Management of Church Hymns. 30p. (Orig.). 1983. pap. 3.50 (ISBN 0-8272-3300-0). CBP.

Red. Pilgrim Hymnal. 1958. 9.95x (ISBN 0-8298-0107-3). Pilgrim NY.

Reeves, J. B. The Hymn As Literature. 59.95 (ISBN 0-8490-0378-4). Gordon Pr.

Reformed Church in America. Rejoice in the Lord: A Hymn Companion to the Scriptures. Routley, Erik, ed. 608p. 1985. 12.95x (ISBN 0-8028-9009-1). Eerdmans.

Reynolds, William J. & Price, Milburn. A Joyful Sound: Christian Hymnody. 2nd ed. LC 77-12048. 1978. 26.95 (ISBN 0-03-040831-8, HoltC). HR&W.

Rice, Cathy. Singing in Signs. LC 81-18830. 160p. 1982. 7.95 (ISBN 0-8407-9006-6). Nelson.

Robertson, Leroy J., ed. Hymns from the Crossroads. (Illus.). 51p. 1965. pap. 6.00 (ISBN 0-8258-0137-0, 0-4516). Fischer Inc NY.

Rodeheaver, Homer A. Hymnal Handbook for Standard Hymns & Gospel Songs. LC 72-1686. Repr. of 1931 ed. 17.50 (ISBN 0-404-09913-0). AMS Pr.

Ross, Joe. NESFA Hymnal. 2nd ed. 220p. pap. 10.00 (ISBN 0-915368-69-2). New Eng SF Assoc.

Sandford, Frank W., intro. by. Warrior Songs for the White Cavalry. 4th ed. 1972. 7.50 (ISBN 0-910840-14-8). Kingdom.

Savas, Savas J. The Treasury of Orthodox Hymnology: The Triodion. 1983. pap. 4.95 (ISBN 0-937032-32-8). Light&Life Pub Co MN.

Sborniki Dukhovno-Muzikal'nikh Proizvjedenij Borisa Mikhajlovicha Ledkovskago, 3 Vols. Tr. of Collections of Sacred Hymns Composed by Boris M. Ledkovsky. 1972. Vol. 1, 47p. 5.00 (ISBN 0-317-30399-6); Vol. 2, 88p. 8.00 (ISBN 0-317-30400-3); Vol. 3, 185p. 15.00 (ISBN 0-317-30401-1). Holy Trinity.

Schmidt, Orlando. Sing & Rejoice! LC 79-84367. 192p. 1979. 6.95x (ISBN 0-8361-1210-5); pap. 5.95x (ISBN 0-8361-1211-3). Herald Pr.

Schuller, Eileen M. Non-Canonical Psalms from Qumran: A Pseudepigraphic Collection. (Harvard Semitic Studies). 1987. 23.95 (ISBN 0-89130-943-8, 04-04-28). Scholars Pr GA.

Shakers. A Collection of Millennial Hymns Adapted to the Present Order of the Church. LC 72-2991. (Communal Societies in America Ser). Repr. of 1847 ed. 21.50 (ISBN 0-404-10753-2). AMS Pr.

Sheppard, W. Great Hymns & Their Stories. lib. bdg. 69.95 (ISBN 0-87968-350-3). Gordon Pr.

Shiplett, Gary R. Worship & Hymnody. (Illus.). 122p. (Orig.). 1980. pap. text ed. 8.95 (ISBN 0-916260-08-9). Meriwether Pub.

Shull, Eva & Shull, Russell. CFO Songs. 1972. pap. 2.50 (ISBN 0-910924-53-8); pap. 3.95 spiral bdg. (ISBN 0-910924-54-6). Macalester.

Sievers, Eduard. Murbacher Hymnen, nach den Handschriften Herausgegeben. Repr. of 1874 ed. 27.00 (ISBN 0-384-55359-1). Johnson Repr.

Sing & Rejoice! Introductory Kit. with cassette 8.25 (ISBN 0-8361-1219-9). Herald Pr.

Sing to God: Songs & Hymns for Christian Education. (Orig.). 1984. pap. 9.95 leader's ed. (ISBN 0-8298-0688-1); student's ed. 4.95 (ISBN 0-8298-0689-X); spiral bd. leaders guide 12.95 (ISBN 0-8298-0716-0). Pilgrim NY.

Sizer, Sandra S. Gospel Hymns & Social Religion: The Rhetoric of Nineteenth-Century Revivalism. LC 78-10165. (American Civilization Ser.). 222p. 1979. lib. bdg. 27.95 (ISBN 0-87722-142-1). Temple U Pr.

Smith, H. Augustine. Lyric Religion: The Romance of Immortal Hymns. 517p. Repr. of 1931 ed. lib. bdg. 75.00 (ISBN 0-918377-84-6). Russell Pr.

Spiritual Life Songs. 19.41 (ISBN 0-687-39228-4); 2.00 ea. Abingdon.

Stauffer, J. Mark, ed. Our Hymns of Praise. (Illus.). 168p. 1958. 4.95x (ISBN 0-8361-1126-5). Herald Pr.

Stevenson, Arthur L. Story of Southern Hymnology. LC 72-1676. Repr. of 1931 ed. 17.50 (ISBN 0-404-08334-X). AMS Pr.

Sutton, Brett. Primitive Baptist Hymns of the Blue Ridge. (American Folklore Recordings Ser.). 28p. 1982. pap. 15.00x incl. records (ISBN 0-8078-4083-1). U of NC Pr.

Sydnor, James R. Hymns & Their Uses. LC 81-71795. 155p. (Orig.). 1982. pap. 6.95 (ISBN 0-916642-18-6). Hope Pub.

Syndor, James R. Hymns: A Congregational Study. 100p. (Orig.). 1983. pap. text ed. 4.95 (ISBN 0-916642-19-4, 778); tchrs' ed 2.95 (ISBN 0-916642-20-8, 779). Agape Il.

Teddlie, Tillit S. Great Christian Hymnal. 1965. 4.25 (ISBN 0-89137-600-3). Quality Pubns.

Troeger, Thomas H. New Hymns for the Lectionary: To Glorify the Maker's Name. 144p. (Music by Carol Doran). 1986. 7.95 (ISBN 0-19-385729-4). Oxford U Pr.

Tserkovno-Pjevcheskiji Sbornik, 5 Vols. Incl. Vol. 1. Vsjenoshchnoje Bdjenije. Tr. of All Night Vigil. 394p. 27.00 (ISBN 0-317-30454-2); Vol. 2. Bozhestvjennaja Liturgija (Nachjalo) Tr. of Divine Liturgy (Beginning) 381p. Pt. 1. 26.00 (ISBN 0-317-30455-0); Vol. 2. Bozhestvjennaja Liturgija (Konjets) Tr. of Divine Liturgy (End) 621p. Pt. 2. 33.00 (ISBN 0-317-30456-9); Vol. 3. Triod' Postnaja. Tr. of Lenten Triodion. 532p. Pt. 1. 31.00 (ISBN 0-317-30457-7); Vol. 3. Strastnaja Sedmitsa. Tr. of Passion Week. 1059p. Pt. 2. 40.00 (ISBN 0-317-30458-5); Vol. 4. Triod' Tsvjetnaja. Tr. of Pentacostarion. 882p. 33.00 (ISBN 0-317-30459-3); Vol. 5. Oktojikh. Tr. of Octoechos. 421p. 26.00 (ISBN 0-317-30460-7). Tr. of Collection of Sacred Hymns. 216.00 set (ISBN 0-317-30453-4). Holy Trinity.

Voznesensky, J. Obshchjedostupnija Chtenija o Tserkovnom Peniji. Tr. of Popular Readings in Church Singing. 48p. 1969. pap. 2.00 (ISBN 0-317-30383-X). Holy Trinity.

Wake, Arthur N. Companion to Hymnbook for Christian Worship. LC 72-129621. 1970. 8.95 (ISBN 0-8272-8025-4). CBP.

Walpole, Arthur S. Early Latin Hymns. 473p. Repr. of 1922 ed. lib. bdg. 68.50X (Pub. by G Olms BRD). Coronet Bks.

Watters, Cyril. It's Easy to Play Hymns. 1981. pap. 5.95. Music Sales.

Willcocks, David, ed. Hymns for Choirs. 1976. pap. 6.00 (ISBN 0-19-353556-4). Oxford U Pr.

Winkworth, Catherine. The Choral Hymn Book for England. 59.95 (ISBN 0-87968-859-9). Gordon Pr.

Wither, George. Hymnes & Songs of the Church. (1623, 1881 Reprint 1967). 54.00 (ISBN 0-8337-3937-9). B Franklin.

Wofford, Nat, ed. Showers of Blessings: Hymns for the Shower. 16p. 1986. pap. 4.95 (ISBN 0-942820-18-5). Steam Pr MA.

World Church Congregational Music Committee. Hymns of the Saints. text ed. 10.50 (ISBN 0-8309-0326-7). Herald Hse.

Worship Hymnal. 671p. 1971. 6.95 (ISBN 0-318-18907-0); piano ed. 16.00 (ISBN 0-919797-30-X). Kindred Pr.

Wright, David & Wright, Jill. Thirty Hymns of the Wesleys. 65p. 1986. pap. 4.95 (ISBN 0-85364-414-4, Pub. by Paternoster UK). Attic Pr.

Young, Carlton R., ed. Supplement to the Book of Hymns. 160p. (Orig.). 1981. pap. 4.75 (ISBN 0-687-03757-3); pap. 6.75 accompanist ed. (ISBN 0-687-03758-1). Abingdon.

Young, Carlton R., et al, eds. Ecumenical Praise. 1977. 14.95x (ISBN 0-916642-07-0). Hope Pub.

HYMNS–ACCOMPANIMENT

Schilling, S. Paul. The Faith We Sing. LC 82-21749. 262p. 1983. pap. 14.95 (ISBN 0-664-24434-3). Westminster.

Schoenhals, Lawrence R. Companion to Hymns of Faith & Life. (Orig.). 1980. pap. 6.95 (ISBN 0-89367-040-5). Light & Life.

UCC. Pilgrim Hymnal: Organist's Edition. 1981. 15.00 (ISBN 0-8298-0454-4). Pilgrim NY.

HYMNS–BIBLIOGRAPHY

Dearmer, Percy. A Subject Index of Hymns in the English Hymnal & Songs of Praise. 59.95 (ISBN 0-8490-1159-0). Gordon Pr.

Glen, Irma, ed. Religious Science Hymnal. 3rd ed. 225p. 1982. Repr. of 1956 ed. 8.00 (ISBN 0-87516-489-7). De Vorss.

Hatfield, Edwin F. Poets of the Church: A Series of Biographical Sketches of Hymn-Writers, with Notes on Their Hymns. 1979. Repr. of 1884 ed. 110.00x (ISBN 0-8103-4291-X). Gale.

Metcalf, Frank J. American Psalmody. 2nd ed. LC 68-13274. (Music Reprint Ser.). (Illus.). 1968. Repr. of 1917 ed. lib. bdg. 19.50 (ISBN 0-306-71132-X). Da Capo.

Warrington, James. Short Titles of Books Relating to or Illustrating the History & Practice of Psalmody in the U. S., 1620-1820. LC 77-178095. (American Classics in History & Social Science Ser.: No. 218). 102p. 1972. Repr. of 1898 ed. lib. bdg. 19.00 (ISBN 0-8337-5357-6). B Franklin.

HYMNS–CONCORDANCES

Sheppard, W. L. Great Hymns & Their Stories. 1979. pap. 4.95 (ISBN 0-87508-492-3). Chr Lit.

HYMNS–DICTIONARIES, INDEXES, ETC.

Claghorn, Gene. Women Composers & Hymnists: A Concise Biographical Dictionary. LC 83-20429. 288p. 1984. 22.50 (ISBN 0-8108-1680-6). Scarecrow.

Hustad, Donald P. & Shorney, George H, Jr. Dictionary-Handbook to Hymns for the Living Church. LC 77-75916. 1978. 14.95 (ISBN 0-916642-09-7). Hope Pub.

Julian, J., ed. A Dictionary of Hymnology: Origin & History of Christian Hymns, 4 vols. 1977. Set. lib. bdg. 600.00 (ISBN 0-8490-1719-X). Gordon Pr.

Julian, John. Dictionary of Hymnology, 2 vols. LC 83-8373. 1786p. 1985. Repr. of 1907 ed. 120.00 (ISBN 0-8254-2960-9). Kregel.

Richardson, Alice M. Index to Stories of Hymns. LC 72-1690. Repr. of 1929 ed. 11.50 (ISBN 0-404-09911-4). AMS Pr.

Ross, Joe. NESFA Hymnal. 2nd ed. 220p. pap. 10.00 (ISBN 0-915368-69-2). New Eng SF Assoc.

Shaw, John M. The Poetry of Sacred Song. 1972. 3.00 (ISBN 0-9607778-6-5). Friends Fla St.

HYMNS–HISTORY AND CRITICISM

see also Church Music; Hymn Writers

Bonner, Clint. Hymn Is Born. LC 59-9694. 1959. 10.95 (ISBN 0-8054-6801-3). Broadman.

Breed, David R. The History & Use of Hymns & Hymn Tunes. LC 76-39525. Repr. of 1903 ed. 20.00 (ISBN 0-404-09906-8). AMS Pr.

--The History & Use of Hymns & Hymn Tunes. 59.95 (ISBN 0-8490-0313-X). Gordon Pr.

Brock, Earl E. Devotional Interpretation of Familiar Hymns. facsimile ed. LC 72-93319. (Essay Index Reprint Ser.). 1947. 14.00 (ISBN 0-8369-1395-7). Ayer Co Pubs.

Butterworth, H. The Story of the Hymns. 59.95 (ISBN 0-8490-1139-6). Gordon Pr.

Butterworth, Hezekiah. Story of Hymns & Tunes. 1981. Repr. lib. bdg. 79.00x (ISBN 0-403-00107-2). Scholarly.

Cobb, Buell E., Jr. The Sacred Harp: A Tradition & Its Music. LC 76-12680. 256p. 1978. 15.00x (ISBN 0-8203-0426-3). U of Ga Pr.

Colquhoun, Frank. Hymns That Live. LC 81-1458. 320p. 1981. pap. 6.95 (ISBN 0-87784-473-9). Inter Varsity.

Curran, Michael. The Antiphonary of Bangor. 272p. 1984. 60.00x (ISBN 0-7165-0338-7, BBA 05250, Pub. by Irish Academic Pr Ireland). Biblio Dist.

Dahle, John, ed. Library of Christian Hymns, 3 vols. in 2. LC 72-1649. Repr. of 1928 ed. 74.50 set (ISBN 0-404-13202-2). AMS Pr.

Dircks, Henry. Naturalistic Poetry, Selected from Psalms & Hymns of the Last Three Centuries: In Four Essays, Developing the Progress of Nature-Study, in Connection with Sacred Song. 1979. Repr. of 1872 ed. lib. bdg. 20.00 (ISBN 0-8482-0622-3). Norwood Edns.

Duffield, Samuel W. English Hymns: Their Authors & History. 1980. Repr. of 1886 ed. lib. bdg. 60.00 (ISBN 0-89341-441-7). Longwood Pub Group.

Emurian, Ernest K. Living Stories of Famous Hymns. (Interlude Bks). 1971. pap. 4.95 (ISBN 0-8010-3260-1). Baker Bk.

--Stories of Christmas Carols. (Paperback Program Ser). 1969. pap. 4.95 (ISBN 0-8010-3265-2). Baker Bk.

George, Emery. Holderlin's "Ars Poetica". A Part-Rigorous Analysis of Information Structure in the Late Hymns. (De Proprietatibu Litterarum Ser. Practica: No. 32). text ed. 60.80x (ISBN 90-2792-381-7). Mouton.

Goodenough, Caroline L. High Lights on Hymnists & Their Hymns. LC 72-1626. Repr. of 1931 ed. 32.50 (ISBN 0-404-08310-2). AMS Pr.

Haworth, Peter. English Hymns & Ballads. 1927. lib. bdg. 16.50 (ISBN 0-8414-4975-9). Folcroft.

The History of Hymn Singing As Told Through One Hundred One Famous Hymns. LC 82-83452. (Illus.). 232p. 1982. 19.95 (ISBN 0-87319-016-5). C Hallberg.

Horn, Dorothy D. Sing to Me of Heaven: A Study of Folk & Early American Materials in Three Old Harp Books. LC 74-99212. (Illus.). 1970. 10.00 (ISBN 0-8130-0293-1). U Presses Fla.

Idle, Christopher. Stories of Our Favorite Hymns. (Illus.). 80p. 1980. 12.95 (ISBN 0-8028-3535-X). Eerdmans.

Jackson, George P. White & Negro Spirituals, Their Life Span & Kinship. (Music Reprint Ser.). (Illus.). xii, 349p. 1975. Repr. of 1944 ed. lib. bdg. 42.50 (ISBN 0-306-70667-9). Da Capo.

Jackson, George P., ed. Spiritual Folk-Songs of Early America. 11.25 (ISBN 0-8446-2297-4). Peter Smith.

Johnson, Guye. Treasury of Great Hymns: And Their Stories. 382p. (Orig.). 1985. pap. 9.95 (ISBN 0-89084-249-3). Bob Jones Univ Pr.

Jones, F. A. Famous Hymns & Their Authors. 59.95 (ISBN 0-8490-0154-4). Gordon Pr.

Mc Cutchan, Robert G. Hymn Tune Names: Their Sources & Significance. Repr. of 1957 ed. 39.00x (ISBN 0-403-03608-9). Scholarly.

Ninde, Edward S. The Story of the American Hymn. LC 72-1708. (Illus.). Repr. of 1921 ed. 29.75 (ISBN 0-404-09914-9). AMS Pr.

Osbeck, Kenneth W. One Hundred One Hymn Stories. LC 81-17165. 288p. 1982. pap. 8.95 (ISBN 0-8254-3416-5). Kregel.

Patterson, Daniel W. The Shaker Spiritual. LC 77-85557. (Illus.). 1979. text ed. 90.00x (ISBN 0-691-09124-2). Princeton U Pr.

Phelps, Austin, et al. Hymns & Choirs. LC 78-144671. Repr. of 1860 ed. 29.50 (ISBN 0-404-07207-0). AMS Pr.

Pratt, Waldo S. Musical Ministries in the Church. LC 74-24193. Repr. of 1923 ed. 18.75 (ISBN 0-404-13095-X). AMS Pr.

Reynolds, William J. Hymns of Our Faith. LC 64-14049. 1964. 18.95 (ISBN 0-8054-6805-6). Broadman.

Reynolds, William J. & Price, Milburn. A Joyful Sound: Christian Hymnody. 2nd ed. LC 77-12048. 1978. 26.95 (ISBN 0-03-040831-8, HoltC). HR&W.

Routley, Erik. Christian Hymns Observed: When in Our Music God Is Glorified. LC 82-61841. 121p. (Orig.). 1982. pap. text ed. 12.95 (ISBN 0-911009-00-0). Prestige Pubns.

--The English Carol. LC 73-9129. (Illus.). 272p. 1973. Repr. of 1959 ed. lib. bdg. 22.50x (ISBN 0-8371-6989-5, ROEC). Greenwood.

Sankey, Ira D. My Life & the Story of the Gospel Hymns & of Sacred Songs & Solos. LC 72-1682. Repr. of 1907 ed. 32.50 (ISBN 0-404-08332-3). AMS Pr.

Schroeder, M. J. Mary-Verse in "Meistergesang". (Catholic University Studies in German: No. 16). 1970. Repr. of 1942 ed. 30.00 (ISBN 0-404-50236-9). AMS Pr.

Seton, Bernard E. Our Heritage of Hymns: A Swift Survey. LC 84-71734. 160p. (Orig.). 1984. pap. 10.95 (ISBN 0-943872-89-8). Andrews Univ Pr.

Spencer, Donald A. Hymn & Scripture Selection Guide. LC 76-48529. 1977. text ed. 9.85 (ISBN 0-8170-0705-9). Judson.

Tamke, Susan S. Make a Joyful Noise Unto the Lord: Hymns As a Reflection of Victorian Social Attitudes. LC 76-51693. 209p. 1978. 12.00x (ISBN 0-8214-0371-0); pap. text ed. 5.00x (ISBN 0-8214-0382-6). Ohio U Pr.

Wells, Amos R. Treasure of Hymns. facs. ed. LC 70-128330. (Essay Index Reprint Ser). 1945. 19.50 (ISBN 0-8369-2096-1). Ayer Co Pubs.

HYMNS–JUVENILE LITERATURE

Ford, Bud & Ford, Donna. The Dulcimer Hymn Book. 72p. 1979. wkbk 4.95 (ISBN 0-89228-054-9). Impact Bks MO.

Griffin, Steve. Children's Guitar Hymnal. 32p. 1978. wkbk 1.95 (ISBN 0-89228-052-2). Impact Bks MO.

Konkel, Wilbur. Living Hymn Stories. 128p. 1982. pap. 3.95 (ISBN 0-87123-317-7, 210317). Bethany Hse.

Peterson, Meg. Hymns for Auto Harp. 56p. 1978. wkbk 4.95 (ISBN 0-89228-053-0). Impact Bks MO.

HYMNS, ASSYRO-BABYLONIAN

Clay, Albert T. Epics, Hymns, Omens & Other Texts. LC 78-63519. (Babylonian Records in the Library of J. Pierpont Morgan: 4). Repr. of 1923 ed. 30.00 (ISBN 0-404-60124-3). AMS Pr.

Schollmeyer, Anastasius, ed. Sumerisch-Babylonische Hymnen und Gebete an Samas. Repr. of 1912 ed. 12.00 (ISBN 0-384-54240-9). Johnson Repr.

HYMNS, ASSYRO-BABYLONIAN–HISTORY AND CRITICISM

Cumming, Charles G. Assyrian & Hebrew Hymns of Praise. LC 34-3318. (Columbia University. Oriental Studies: No. 12). Repr. of 1934 ed. 16.50 (ISBN 0-404-50502-3). AMS Pr.

HYMNS, GERMAN

Andrews, J. S. A Study of German Hymns in Current English Hymnals. (German Language & Literature-European University Studies: No. 1, Vol. 614). 398p. 1982. pap. 36.30 (ISBN 3-261-05068-3). P Lang Pubs.

Lambert, James F. Luther's Hymns. LC 83-45646. Date not set. Repr. of 1917 ed. 34.50 (ISBN 0-404-19855-4). AMS Pr.

Liedersammlung, 2 vols. Incl. Vol. B. Collection of 148 German Hymns Without Notes. 1917. 5.95x (ISBN 0-8361-1144-3); Vol. G. Collection of 317 German Hymns Without Notes. 6.95x (ISBN 0-8361-1163-X). Repr. of 1928 ed. Herald Pr.

Seipt, A. A. Schwenkfelder Hymnology. LC 77-134414. Repr. of 1909 ed. 14.50 (ISBN 0-404-09908-4). AMS Pr.

HYMNS, GREEK

Holy Transfiguration Monastery Staff. Selected Byzantine Hymns. 2nd ed. 120p. (Orig.). 1987. pap. 10.00x (ISBN 0-913026-59-X, Holy Transfiguration). St Nectarios.

Kambylis, Athanasios, ed. Symeon Neos Theologos, Hymnen Einleitung und kritischer Text. (Supplementa Byzantina, Vol. 3). 1976. 234.00x (ISBN 3-11-004888-4). De Gruyter.

Tillyard, Henry J. Byzantine Music & Hymnography. LC 74-24242. Repr. of 1923 ed. 11.50 (ISBN 0-404-13116-6). AMS Pr.

Wellesz, Egon. History of Byzantine Music & Hymnography. 2nd ed. 1961. 49.95x (ISBN 0-19-816111-5). Oxford U Pr.

Ziehn, Bernhard. The Doric Hymns of Mesomedes. 1979. pap. 1.75 (ISBN 0-911028-11-0). Newberry.

HYMNS, HEBREW

Newsom, Carol. The Songs of the Sabbath Sacrifice: Edition, Translation, & Commentary. (Harvard Semitic Museum Ser.). 1985. 34.95 (ISBN 0-89130-837-7, 04-04-27). Scholars Pr GA.

HYMNS, HINDU

see Hindu Hymns

HYMNS, LATIN

Blume, Clemens, ed. Hymnodia Gotica. Repr. of 1909 ed. 60.00 ea. Vol. 1. (ISBN 0-384-04766-1); Vol. 2. (ISBN 0-384-04767-X). Johnson Repr.

--Thesauri Hymnologica Hymnarium, 2 Vols. Repr. of 1909 ed. 60.00 ea. Johnson Repr.

--Thesauri Hymnologica Prosarium, 2 Vols in 3. (Illus.). Repr. of 1922 ed. 60.00 ea. Johnson Repr.

Boncore Di Santa Vittoria Staff. Boncore Di Santa Victoria Novus Liber Hymnorum Ac Orationum. Repr. of 1903 ed. 60.00 (ISBN 0-384-12867-X). Johnson Repr.

Dreves, Guido M., ed. Cantiones Bohemicae. 1886. 60.00 (ISBN 0-384-12860-2). Johnson Repr.

--Cantiones et Muteti, 3 vols. (Illus.). 1895-1904. 60.00 ea. (ISBN 0-384-12865-3). Johnson Repr.

--Historiae Rhythmicae, 8 Vols. 1889-1904. 60.00 ea. (ISBN 0-384-12880-7). Johnson Repr.

--Hymni Inediti, 7 Vols. 1888-1903. 60.00 ea. Johnson Repr.

--Hymnodia Hiberica: Liturgische Reimofficien, Aus Spanischen Brevieren. (Illus.). 1894. 60.00 (ISBN 0-384-12915-3). Johnson Repr.

--Hymnodia Hiberica: Spanische Hymnen Des Mittelalters. 1894. 60.00 (ISBN 0-384-12920-X). Johnson Repr.

--Pia Dictamina, 7 Vols. 1893-1905. 60.00 ea. (ISBN 0-384-12950-1). Johnson Repr.

--Psalteria Rhythmica, 2 Vols. 1900-01. 60.00 ea. (ISBN 0-384-12960-9) (ISBN 0-384-12961-7). Johnson Repr.

Moissac France Benedictine Abbey. Hymnarius Moissiacensis. 1888. 60.00 (ISBN 0-384-39520-1). Johnson Repr.

Stocklin, Ulrich V. Psalteria Wessofontana. Dreves, Guido M., ed. Repr. of 1902 ed. 60.00 (ISBN 0-384-58320-2). Johnson Repr.

--Udalricus Wessofontanus. Dreves, Guido M., ed. Repr. 60.00 (ISBN 0-384-58330-X). Johnson Repr.

HYMNS, LATIN–HISTORY AND CRITICISM

Duffield, Samuel W. The Latin Hymn-Writers & Their Hymns. 1980. Repr. of 1889 ed. lib. bdg. 50.00 (ISBN 0-89341-440-9). Longwood Pub Group.

Messenger, Ruth E. Ethical Teachings in the Latin Hymns of Medieval England. LC 30-20975. (Columbia University. Studies in the Social Sciences: No. 321). Repr. of 1930 ed. 18.50 (ISBN 0-404-51321-2). AMS Pr.

Shoham, S. Giora. Rebellion, Creativity & Revelation. Cherns, Albert, intro. by. 320p. 1986. 29.95 (ISBN 0-905927-61-3). Transaction Bks.

Van Assendelft, Marion M. Sol Ecce Surgit Igneus: A Commentary on the Morning & Evening Hymns of Prudentius. vii, 275p. 1976. 30.00x (ISBN 90-6088-060-9, Pub. by Boumas Boekhuis Netherlands). Benjamins North AM.

HYMNS, SANSKRIT

Advaita Ashrama Staff, ed. Altar Flowers: A Bouquet of Choicest Sanskrit Hymns. (Eng. & Sanskrit). 1974. pap. 5.95 (ISBN 0-87481-146-5). Vedanta Pr.

Sanskrit Mantras. 1977. 10.00x (ISBN 0-930736-03-6); cassett tape recording incl. (ISBN 0-685-32618-7). E W Cultural Ctr.

HYMNS, SPANISH

Eck, Ellen, tr. from Eng. Himnos de la Vida Cristiana. 1980. 3.95 (ISBN 0-87509-277-2); pap. 2.25 (ISBN 0-87509-275-6); With music. pap. 4.50. Chr Pubns.

Himnario Cristiano. (Span.). 6.95x (ISBN 0-8361-1198-2). Herald Pr.

Himnos de Gloria. 150p. pap. 0.75 (ISBN 0-686-29116-6). Faith Pub Hse.

McConnell, Cecil. Conozcamos Nuestro Himnario. 144p. 1980. pap. 3.75 (ISBN 0-311-32432-0). Casa Bautista.

HYMNS, SUMERIAN

Cohen, Mark E. Sumerian Hymnology: The Ersemma. 1981. 18.75x (ISBN 0-87820-601-9). Ktav.

Klein, Jacob. Royal Hymns of Shulgi, King of Ur: Man's Quest for Immortal Fame. LC 81-65929. (Transactions Ser.: Vol. 71, Pt. 7.). 1981. 6.00 (ISBN 0-87169-717-3). Am Philos.

Schollmeyer, Anastasius, ed. Sumerisch-Babylonische Hymnen und Gebete an Samas. Repr. of 1912 ed. 12.00 (ISBN 0-384-54240-9). Johnson Repr.

Vanderburgh, Frederick A., ed. Sumerian Hymns from Cuneiform Texts in the British Museum. LC 68-23118. (Columbia University. Contributions to Oriential History & Philology: No. 1). Repr. of 1908 ed. 14.00 (ISBN 0-404-50531-7). AMS Pr.

HYMNS, SUMERIAN–HISTORY AND CRITICISM

Stummer, Friedrich. Summerisch-Akkadische Parallelen Zum Aufbau Alttestamentlicher Psalmen. Repr. of 1922 ed. 15.00 (ISBN 0-384-58710-0). Johnson Repr.

HYPERDULIA

see Mary, Virgin–Cultus

HYPNOTISM–MORAL AND RELIGIOUS ASPECTS

Bobgan, Martin & Bobgan, Deidre. Hypnosis & the Christian. LC 83-21401. 64p. (Orig.). 1984. pap. 2.95 (ISBN 0-87123-402-5, 210402). Bethany Hse.

HYPOSTATIC UNION

Chemnitz, Martin. Two Natures in Christ. Preus, J. A., tr. LC 74-115465. Orig. Title: De Duabus Naturis in Christo. 1970. 24.95 (ISBN 0-570-03210-5, 15-2109). Concordia.

I

I CHING

Anthony, Carol K. Guide to I Ching. 3rd ed. 400p. Date not set. pap. write for info. Anthony Pub Co.

Chih-hsu, Ou-i. The Buddhist I Ching. Cleary, Thomas, tr. from Chinese. LC 86-31460. (Dragon Ser.). 290p. 1987. pap. 10.95 (ISBN 0-87773-408-9). Shambhala Pubns.

Colmer, Michael. Executive I Ching: The Business Oracle. 176p. 1987. 17.95 (ISBN 0-7137-1934-6, Pub. by Blandford Pr England). Sterling.

Damian-Knight, Guy. Karma & Destiny in the I Ching. 256p. 1987. pap. 12.95 (ISBN 1-85063-038-0, 30380, Ark Paperbks). Methuen Inc.

Hook, Diane F. The I Ching & You. 160p. 1985. pap. 8.95 (ISBN 0-7100-8042-5). Methuen Inc.

Liu Da. T'ai Chi Ch'uan & I Ching: A Choreography of Body & Mind. LC 79-183640. 1987. pap. 5.95 (ISBN 0-06-091309-6, PL-1309, PL). Har-Row.

Stahl, John. Arcane Commentaries. 9p. 1973. pap. 2.00 (ISBN 0-318-21744-9). Evanescent Pr.

--An Original Commentary on the I Ching. 32p. 1976. 10.00 (ISBN 0-318-21738-4). Evanescent Pr.

--Patterns of Illusion & Change. (Illus.). 24p. 1984. pap. 3.50 (ISBN 0-318-21732-5). Evanescent Pr.

--The World Union Company. 60p. 1980. pap. 5.00 (ISBN 0-318-21734-1). Evanescent Pr.

Walker, Barbara. The I Ching of the Goddess. LC 86-45029. (Illus.). 176p. (Orig.). 1986. pap. 12.95 (ISBN 0-06-250924-1, HarpR). Har-row.

IBADAN, NIGERIA

Parrinder, Geoffrey. Religion in an African City. LC 74-142921. (Illus.). Repr. of 1953 ed. 22.50x (ISBN 0-8371-5947-4, PAC&, Pub. by Negro U Pr). Greenwood.

IBN AL-ARABI, 1165-1240

Affifi, Abul E. The Mystical Philosophy of Muhyid Din-Ibnul 'Arabi. LC 77-180312. (Mid-East Studies). Repr. of 1939 ed. 12.00 (ISBN 0-404-56205-1). AMS Pr.

Corbin, Henry. Creative Imagination in the Sufism of Ibn Arabi. Manheim, R., tr. (Bollingen Ser.: Vol. 91). 1969. 40.00 (ISBN 0-691-09852-2); pap. 12.95 (ISBN 0-691-01828-6). Princeton U Pr.

Husaini. Ibn-Al-Arabi. pap. 1.75 (ISBN 0-686-18320-7). Kazi Pubns.

Husaini, S. A. The Pantheistic Monism of Ibn Al-Arabi. 1970. 9.30x (ISBN 0-87902-164-0). Orientalia.

Nasr, Seyyed H. Three Muslim Sages. LC 75-14430. 192p. 1976. pap. text ed. 10.00x (ISBN 0-88206-500-9). Caravan Bks.

IBURG, GERMANY–BENEDICTINE ABBEY

Norbert. Das Leben des Bischofs Benno der Zweiter von Osnabruck. Bd. with Ausfuehrliches Namenregister und Sachregister Mit Genauem Inhalsverzeichnis der Seither Erschienene Baende 1-90. (Die Geschichtschreiber der Deutschen Vorzeit Ser: Vol. 91). (Ger.). 12.00 (ISBN 0-384-41895-3). Johnson Repr.

ICELANDIC AND OLD NORSE LITERATURE

see also Eddas

Anderson, R. B. Norse Mythology or the Religion of Our Forefathers. LC 77-6879. 1977. Repr. of 1891 ed. lib. bdg. 25.00 (ISBN 0-89341-147-7). Longwood Pub Group.

ICHTHYS

see Fish (In Religion, Folk-Lore, etc.)

ICONOGRAPHY

see Christian Art and Symbolism; Idols and Images

Von Barghahn, Barbara. Age of Gold, Age of Iron: Renaissance Spain & Symbols of Monarchy. (The Imperial Legacy of Charles V & Philip II Royal Castles, Palace-Monasteries, Princely Houses Ser.: 2 vols.). (Illus.). 1036p. 1985. Set. lib. bdg. 204.75 (ISBN 0-8191-4739-7). U Pr of Amer.

ICONS

Archbishop Metodies. O Znamjenii Obnovlenija Svatykh Ikon. Tr. of On the Signs of the Renewing of Holy Icons. 82p. 1963. pap. 3.00 (ISBN 0-317-29041-X). Holy Trinity.

Baines, J. Fecundity Figures: Egyptian Personification & the Iconology of a Genre. (Illus.). 200p. 1983. 60.00 (ISBN 0-85668-087-7, Pub. by Aris & Phillips UK). Humanities.

Balabanov, Kosta. Freske i Ikone u Makedoniji, iv-xv vek (Frescos & Icons in Macedonia, iv-xv Century) 158p. 1983. 20.00 (ISBN 0-918660-26-2). Ragusan Pr.

Browne. Icons of America. LC 77-84917. 1978. 14.95 (ISBN 0-87972-090-5); pap. 6.95 (ISBN 0-87972-091-3). Bowling Green Univ.

Collet's Holdings, Ltd. Staff, ed. Early Russian Painting 11th to Early 13th Centuries: Mosaics, Frescoes & Icons. 308p. 1982. 125.00x (ISBN 0-317-39496-7, Pub. by Collets UK). State Mutual Bk.

Dabovich, Sebastian. Holy Orthodox Church: Its Ritual, Services, & Sacraments. 1898. pap. 2.95 (ISBN 0-686-00253-9). Eastern Orthodox.

Damascene, John & Oecumenical Synod Seventh. The Icon. Cavarnos, Constantine, tr. from Gr. (Illus.). 11p. 1979. pap. 0.90 (ISBN 0-914744-19-4). Inst Byzantine.

Iconmakers' Handbook of the Stroganov School of Icon Painting. 1974. 12.50 (ISBN 0-686-10192-8). Eastern Orthodox.

Icons in the Eastern Orthodox Church, a Brief Theological Introduction: Jeremiah, Patriarch of Constantinople & St. John of Damascus. pap. 0.50 (ISBN 0-686-01294-1). Eastern Orthodox.

Irimie, Cornel & Focsa, Marcela. Romanian Icons Painted on Glass. (Illus.). 1971. 75.00 (ISBN 0-393-04309-6). Norton.

John of Damascus, St. Veneration of Icons. pap. 0.50 (ISBN 0-686-05666-3). Eastern Orthodox.

Kaplan, Paul H. The Rise of the Black Magus in Western Art. Seidel, Linda, ed. LC 85-8461. (Studies in the Fine Arts: Iconography: No. 10). 344p. 1985. 49.95 (ISBN 0-8357-1667-8). UMI Res Pr.

Lazarer, V. N. Novgorodian Icon-Painting. (Illus.). 40.00 (ISBN 0-912729-00-7). Newbury Bks.

Lossky, Vladimir & Ouspensky, Leonid. The Meaning of Icons. 1981. pap. 52.50x (ISBN 0-913836-77-X, Pub. by Mowbrays Pub Div). State Mutual Bk.

McKenzie, A. Dean. Russian Icons in the Santa Barbara Museum of Art. LC 82-62426. (Illus.). 54p. (Orig.). 1982. pap. 8.25 (ISBN 0-89951-049-3). Santa Barb Mus Art.

Moon, Warren G., ed. Ancient Greek Art & Iconography. LC 83-47765. (Illus.). 368p. 1983. 50.00 (ISBN 0-299-09250-X). U of Wis Pr.

Mukhopadhyay, Somnath. Candi in Art & Iconography. 1984. 34.00x (ISBN 0-8364-1146-3, Pub. by Agam India). South Asia Bks.

Ouspensky, Leonid. Theology of the Icon. Meyendorff, Elizabeth, tr. from Fr. LC 77-11882. (Illus.). 232p. 1978. pap. 12.95 (ISBN 0-913836-42-7). St Vladimirs.

Roth, Catherine, tr. St. Theodore the Studite on the Holy Icons. LC 81-18319. 115p. (Orig.). pap. 4.95 (ISBN 0-913836-76-1). St Vladimirs.

Salko, N. The Illustrious Relic of the Kulikovo Battle. 1985. 39.00x (ISBN 0-569-08567-5, Pub. by Collets (UK)). State Mutual Bk.

Sinding-Larsen, Staale. Iconography & Ritual: A Study of Analytical Perspectives. 260p. 1985. 30.00x (ISBN 82-00-07184-7). Oxford U Pr.

Stutley, Margaret. The Illustrated Dictionary of Hindu Iconography. (Illus.). 200p. 1985. 36.95 (ISBN 0-317-17180-1). Methuen Inc.

Taylor, John. Icon Painting. LC 78-25925. (The Mayflower Gallery Ser.). (Illus.). 1979. 12.50 (ISBN 0-8317-4813-3, Mayflower Bks); pap. 6.95 (ISBN 0-8317-4814-1). Smith Pubs.

Vorobyev, Nicolai. The History & Art of the Russian Icon from the X to the XX Century. Maxym, Lucy, ed. & tr. from Rus. (Illus.). 144p. 1986. 50.00 (ISBN 0-940202-06-9). Siamese Imports.

Weitzman, Kurt. The Icon: Holy Images 6th to 14th Century. LC 78-6495. (Magnificant Paperback Art Ser.). 136p. 1978. 24.95 (ISBN 0-8076-0892-0); pap. 14.95 (ISBN 0-8076-0893-9). Braziller.

Weitzmann, Kurt. The Monastery of Saint Catherine at Mount Sinai, The Icons I: From the Sixth to the Tenth Century. LC 75-3482. 276p. 1976. 205.00x (ISBN 0-691-03543-1). Princeton U Pr.

Weitzmann, Kurt, et al. The Icon. LC 82-47840. (Illus.). 419p. 1982. 60.00 (ISBN 0-394-52551-5). Knopf.

IDEALISM

see also Dualism; Transcendentalism

Dilthey, Wilthelm. Philosophy of Existence: Introduction to Weltanschauugslehre. LC 78-5673. 1978. Repr. of 1957 ed. lib. bdg. 22.50x (ISBN 0-313-20460-8, DIPH). Greenwood.

Fausset, High I. Studies in Idealism. 278p. 1982. Repr. of 1923 ed. lib. bdg. 30.00 (ISBN 0-89760-230-7). Telegraph Bks.

Gram, Moltke S. The Transcendental Turn: The/Foundation of Kant's Idealism. LC 84-22047. xii, 260p. 1985. 30.00 (ISBN 0-8130-0787-9). U Presses Fla.

Hammond, Phillip E. The Role of Ideology in Church Participation. Zuckerman, Harriet & Merton, Robert K., eds. LC 79-9003. (Dissertations on Sociology Ser.). 1980. lib. bdg. 27.50x (ISBN 0-405-12972-6). Ayer Co Pubs.

Hoernle, R. F. Idealism, as a Philosophical Doctrine. 1979. Repr. of 1924 ed. lib. bdg. 25.00 (ISBN 0-8495-2281-1). Arden Lib.

Howard, Claud. Coleridge's Idealism. LC 72-191125. 1924. lib. bdg. 17.50 (ISBN 0-8414-5131-1). Folcroft.

Hunt, John. Pantheism & Christianity. LC 78-102573. 1970. Repr. of 1884 ed. 25.50 (ISBN 0-8046-0733-8, Pub. by Kennikat). Assoc Faculty Pr.

Jackson, Holbrook. Dreamers of Dreams: The Rise & Fall of 19th Century Idealism. LC 78-15808. 1978. Repr. of 1948 ed. lib. bdg. 35.00 (ISBN 0-8414-5410-8). Folcroft.

Knappen, Marshall M. Tudor Puritanism: A Chapter in the History of Idealism. LC 39-10082. 1965. pap. 3.45x (ISBN 0-226-44627-1, P194, Phoen). U of Chicago Pr.

Lloyd, Alfred H. Dynamic Idealism. LC 75-3243. Repr. of 1898 ed. 17.00 (ISBN 0-404-59233-3). AMS Pr.

Wollheim, R. The Good Self & the Bad Self: The Moral Psychology of British Idealism & the English School of Psychoanalysis Compared. (Dawes Hicks Lectures on Philosophy). 1975. pap. 2.50 (ISBN 0-85672-278-2, Pub. by British Acad). Longwood Pub Group.

IDENTIFICATION (RELIGION)

Bhaktivedanta, Swami. The Science of Self Realization. (Illus.). 1977. 3.95 (ISBN 0-89213-101-2). Bhaktivedanta.

Cooper, Norman W. Finding Your Self. new ed. 96p. 1974. pap. 4.50 (ISBN 0-87516-183-9). De Vorss.

Freeman, David. Know Your Self. 1976. pap. 3.95 (ISBN 0-934532-11-7). Presby & Reformed.

Goldberg, Michael. Jews & Christians, Getting Our Stories Straight: The Exodus & the Passion...Resurrection. 240p. (Orig.). 1985. pap. 12.95 (ISBN 0-687-20330-9). Abingdon.

Goldsmith, Joel S. Man Was Not Born to Cry. 1984. pap. 5.95 (ISBN 0-8065-0915-5). Citadel Pr.

Haught, John F. Religion & Self-Acceptance: A Study of the Relationship Between Belief in God & the Desire to Know. LC 80-5872. 195p. 1980. lib. bdg. 24.75 (ISBN 0-8191-1296-8); pap. text ed. 10.50 (ISBN 0-8191-1297-6). U Pr of Amer.

Hulme, William & Hulme, Dale. Who Am I Lord... & Why Am I Here? LC 83-25175. 1984. pap. 4.95 (ISBN 0-570-03926-6, 12-2860). Concordia.

Keyes, Dick. Beyond Identity: Finding Your Self in the Image & Character of God. 264p. (Orig.). 1984. pap. 7.95 (ISBN 0-89283-137-5). Servant.

Mata, Sri Daya. Only Love. LC 75-44633. (Illus.). 295p. 1976. 6.50 (ISBN 0-87612-215-2). Self Realization.

Murray, Donal. Life & Sacrament: Reflections on the Catholic Vision. (Theology & Life Ser.: Vol. 4). 1983. pap. 6.95 (ISBN 0-89453-299-5). M Glazier.

O'Flaherty, Vincent M. Who...Me? A Study in Identification by Seeking the Will of God. 200p. 1974. 4.95 (ISBN 0-8199-0540-2). Franciscan Herald.

Taimni. Secret of Self-Realization. 4.50 (ISBN 0-8356-7640-4). Theos Pub Hse.

--Self-Realization Through Love. 4.75 (ISBN 0-8356-7522-X). Theos Pub Hse.

Van Kaam, Adrian, et al. The Emergent Self, 4 bks. in 1. 1968. cancelled (ISBN 0-87193-165-6). Dimension Bks.

--The Participant Self, 2 vols. in 1. 1985. write for info. (ISBN 0-87193-160-5). Dimension Bks.

IDENTITY

Agus, Jacob B. Jewish Identity in an Age of Ideologies. LC 76-14230. 1978. 25.00 (ISBN 0-8044-5018-8). Ungar.

Butchvarov, Panayot. Being Qua Being: A Theory of Identity, Existence & Predication. LC 78-13812. 288p. 1979. 22.50x (ISBN 0-253-13700-4). Ind U Pr.

IDENTITY (PSYCHOLOGY)

Barnhouse, Ruth T. Identity. LC 84-3664. (Choices: Guides for Today's Woman Ser.,: Vol. 7). 120p. (Orig.). 1984. pap. 6.95 (ISBN 0-664-24545-5). Westminster.

Damrell, Joseph. Search for Identity: Youth, Religion, & Culture. LC 78-5887. (Sage Library of Social Research: No. 64). 232p. 24.50 (ISBN 0-8039-0987-X); pap. 14.50 (ISBN 0-8039-0988-8). Sage.

Micks, Marianne H. Our Search for Identity: Humanity in the Image of God. LC 81-70592. 176p. 1982. pap. 1.00 (ISBN 0-8006-1627-8). Fortress.

IDEOLOGY

Dilthey, Wilthelm. Philosophy of Existence: Introduction to Weltanschauugslehre. LC 78-5673. 1978. Repr. of 1957 ed. lib. bdg. 22.50x (ISBN 0-313-20460-8, DIPH). Greenwood.

IDOLS AND IMAGES

see also Gods in Art

Barfield, Owen. Saving the Appearances: A Study in Idolatry. LC 65-23538. 190p. 1965. pap. 4.95 (ISBN 0-15-679490-X, Harv). HarBraceJ.

Bevan, Edwyn R. Holy Images: An Inquiry into Idolatry & Image-Worship in Ancient Paganism & in Christianity. LC 77-27191. (Gifford Lectures: 1933). Repr. of 1940 ed. 22.50 (ISBN 0-404-60489-7). AMS Pr.

Brehier, Louis. La Querelle des Images Huitieme-Neuvieme Siecle. 1969. 14.00 (ISBN 0-8337-0362-5). B Franklin.

De Montault, X. Barbier. Traite d'Iconographie Chretienne. (Fr., Illus.). 972p. Repr. of 1890 ed. lib. bdg. 200.00x (ISBN 0-89241-137-6). Caratzas.

Huggins, William H. & Entwisle, Doris R. Iconic Communication: An Annotated Bibliography. LC 73-8130. (Illus.). 184p. 1974. 18.50x (ISBN 0-8018-1528-2). Johns Hopkins.

Knipping, John B. Iconography of the Counter Reformation in the Netherlands: Heaven on Earth, 2 vols. LC 73-85234. (Illus.). 539p. 1974. Set. text ed. 195.00x (Pub. by B De Graaf Netherlands). Coronet Bks.

L'Orange, H. P. Studies on the Iconography of Cosmic Kingship in the Ancient World. (Illus.). 206p. 1982. Repr. of 1953 ed. lib. bdg. 50.00X (ISBN 0-89241-150-3). Caratzas.

Malyala, Panduranga R. Temples & Idol Worship. Date not set. 4.99 (ISBN 0-938924-02-8). Sri Shirdi Sai.

Pandurangarao, Malyala. Consecration of Idols. (Illus.). 32p. (Orig.). 1984. pap. 2.00x (ISBN 0-938924-21-4). Sri Shirdi Sai.

Pasztory, Esther. The Iconography of the Teotihuacan Tlaloc. LC 74-16543. (Studies in Pre-Columbian Art & Archaeology: No. 15). (Illus.). 22p. 1974. pap. 3.00x (ISBN 0-88402-059-2). Dumbarton Oaks.

Schellhas, P. Representation of Deities of the Maya Manuscripts. (Hupmaen Ser.: Vol. 4, No. 1). (Illus.). 1904. pap. 15.00 (ISBN 0-527-01198-3). Kraus Repr.

Schulz, Reuel J. Idols: Dead or Alive? 7.95 (ISBN 0-686-91886-X, 12N1724). Northwest Pub.

Simmons, D. R. Iconography of New Zealand Maori Religion. (Iconography of Religions Ser.: Pt. II/1). (Illus.). ix, 33p. 1986. pap. 27.25 (ISBN 90-04-07588-7, Pub. by E J Brill). Heinman.

Stern, Jean, ed. The Cross & the Sword. LC 76-9415. Tr. of La Cruz y la Espada. (Eng. & Span., Illus.). 144p. 1982. pap. 10.00 (ISBN 0-295-95916-9, Pub. by San Diego Museum Art). U of Wash Pr.

Van Oort, H. A. The Iconography of Chinese Buddhism in Traditional China, 2 pts. (Iconography of Religions Ser.: XII-5). (Illus.). 1986. Pt. 1, xii, 30p. pap. 25.50 (ISBN 90-04-07822-3, Pub. by E J Brill); Pt. 2, viii, 27p. pap. 24.75 (ISBN 90-04-07823-1). Heinman.

IFUGAOS

Barton, R. F. Religion of the Ifugaos. LC 48-3664. (American Anthropological Association Memoirs Ser). Repr. of 1946 ed. 21.00 (ISBN 0-527-00564-9). Kraus Repr.

Barton, Roy F. Philippine Pagans: The Autobiographies of Three Ifugaos. LC 76-44686. Repr. of 1938 ed. 30.00 (ISBN 0-404-15903-6). AMS Pr.

Dumia, Mariano A. The Ifugao World. Edades, Jean, ed. (Illus.). 1979. pap. 6.00x (ISBN 0-686-24953-4, Pub. by New Day Pub). Cellar.

IGNATIUS, SAINT, BP. OF ANTIOCH, 1ST CENTURY

Brown, Milton P., Jr. Authentic Writings of Ignatius: A Study of Linguistic Criteria. LC 63-19458. pap. 33.30 (ISBN 0-8357-9096-7, 2017888). Bks Demand UMI.

Ignatius, Saint Epistles of St. Ignatius. Lightfoot, J. D., tr. pap. 1.25 (ISBN 0-686-25549-6). Eastern Orthodox.

Richardson, Cyril C. Christianity of Ignatius of Antioch. LC 35-7948. Repr. of 1935 ed. 14.50 (ISBN 0-404-05297-5). AMS Pr.

Schoedel, William. Ignatius of Antioch: A Commentary on the Seven Letters of Ignatius. LC 84-48731. (Hermeneia Ser.). 320p. 1985. 34.95 (ISBN 0-8006-6016-1, 20-6016). Fortress.

IKONS

see Icons

ILLINOIS

Mikkelsen, M. A. The Bishop Hill Colony, a Religious Communistic Settlement in Henry County, Illinois. pap. 9.00 (ISBN 0-384-38850-7). Johnson Repr.

--The Bishop Hill Colony: A Religious, Communistic Settlement in Henry County, Illinois. LC 72-187466. (The American Utopian Adventure Ser.). 1973. Repr. of 1892 ed. lib. bdg. 19.50x (ISBN 0-87991-014-3). Porcupine Pr.

ILLUMINATION OF BOOKS AND MANUSCRIPTS

see also Hours, Books Of

Alexander, J. J., ed. Italian Renaissance Illuminations. LC 77-2841. (Magnificent Paperback Ser.). (Illus.). 1977. 19.95 (ISBN 0-8076-0863-7); pap. 11.95 (ISBN 0-8076-0864-5). Braziller.

Arnold, Thomas W. Painting in Islam. (Illus.). 16.25 (ISBN 0-8446-1553-6). Peter Smith.

Berenson, Bernard. Studies in Medieval Painting. LC 73-153884. (Graphic Art Ser.). (Illus.). 148p. 1971. Repr. of 1930 ed. lib. bdg. 39.50 (ISBN 0-306-70292-4). Da Capo.

Buchtal, Hugo. The Miniatures of the Paris Psalter: A Study in Middle Byzantine Painting. (Warburg Institute Studies: Vol. 2). Repr. of 1938 ed. 88.00 (ISBN 0-8115-1379-3). Kraus Repr.

Buchtal, Hugo & Kurz, Otto. Hand List of Illuminated Oriental Christian Manuscripts. (Warburg Institute Studies: Vol. 12). Repr. of 1942 ed. 20.00 (ISBN 0-8115-1389-0). Kraus Repr.

Dynes, Wayne. The Illuminations of the Stavelot Bible. LC 77-94693. (Outstanding Dissertations in the Fine Arts Ser.). (Illus.). 1978. lib. bdg. 44.00 (ISBN 0-8240-3225-X). Garland Pub.

Folda, Jaroslav. Crusader Manuscript Illumination at Saint-Jean D'Acre, 1275-1291. LC 75-2991. (Illus.). 646p. 1975. 70.50x (ISBN 0-691-03907-0). Princeton U Pr.

Hatch, William H. Greek & Syrian Miniatures in Jerusalem. (Illus.). 1931. 15.00x (ISBN 0-910956-04-9). Medieval Acad.

Hindman, Sandra. Text & Image in Fifteenth-Century Illustrated Dutch Bibles (1977) (Corpus Sacrae Scripturae Neerlandicae Medii Aevi Ser.: Miscellanea: Vol. 1). (Illus.). 35.00 (ISBN 90-04-04901-0). Heinman.

Lichten, Frances. Fraktur: The Illuminated Manuscripts of the Pennsylvania Dutch. 1958. wrappers 1.00 (ISBN 0-911132-10-4). Phila Free Lib.

Lowden, John. Illuminated Prophet Books: A Study of Byzantine Manuscripts of the Major & Minor Prophets. LC 86-43164. 250p. 1987. 49.75x (ISBN 0-271-00604-8). Pa St U Pr.

Mercier, Jacques. Ethiopian Magic Scrolls. Molinaro, Ursule, tr. from Fr. LC 78-9330. (Illus.). 1979. 24.95 (ISBN 0-8076-0896-3); pap. 12.95 (ISBN 0-8076-0897-1). Braziller.

Nelson, Robert S. The Iconography of Preface & Miniature in the Byzantine Gospel Book. LC 80-15335. (College Art Association Monograph Ser.: Vol. 36). (Illus.). 180p. 1985. Repr. of 1980 ed. 30.00x (ISBN 0-271-00404-5). Pa St U Pr.

Nordenfalk, Carl, ed. Medieval & Renaissance Miniatures from the National Gallery of Art. LC 74-28397. (Illus.). pap. 8.95 (ISBN 0-89468-017-X). Natl Gallery Art.

Ohlgren, Thomas H., compiled by. Insular & Anglo-Saxon Illuminated Manuscripts: An Iconographic Catalogue c. A.D. 625 to 1100. LC 85-20446. (Illus.). 480p. 75.00 (ISBN 0-8240-8651-1). Garland Pub.

Plummer, John, intro. by. The Hours of Catherine of Cleves. LC 66-23096. (Illus.). 360p. 1975. 50.00 (ISBN 0-8076-0379-1). Braziller.

Seguy, Marie-Rose. The Miraculous Journey of Mahomet. LC 77-5140. (Library of Illuminated Manuscripts). (Illus.). 1977. 40.00 (ISBN 0-8076-0868-8). Braziller.

Thomas, Marcel, ed. The Grandes Heures of Jean, Duke of Berry. LC 75-167761. (Illus.). 192p. 1971. 80.00 (ISBN 0-8076-0613-8). Braziller.

Wormald, Francis. The Miniatures in the Gospels of St. Augustine: Corpus Christi College Ms. 286. LC 54-4312. (Sandars Lectures in Bibliography Ser.: 1948). (Illus.). pap. 20.00 (ISBN 0-317-09509-9, 2051474). Bks Demand UMI.

ILLUMINATION OF BOOKS AND MANUSCRIPTS–CATALOGS

Kup, Karl. Christmas Story in Medieval & Renaissance Manuscripts from the Spencer Collection, the New York Public Library. LC 70-98680. (Illus.). 128p. 1969. pap. 10.00 (ISBN 0-87104-053-0). NY Pub Lib.

ILLUMINATION OF BOOKS AND MANUSCRIPTS–HISTORY

Carr, Annemarie W. Byzantine Illumination Eleven Fifty to Twelve Fifty: The Study of a Provincial Tradition. (Studies in Medieval Manuscript Illumination Chicago Visual Library: No. 47). (Illus.). 448p. 1987. lib. bdg. 85.00 text-fiche (ISBN 0-226-68863-1). U of Chicago Pr.

Hatch, William H. Greek & Syrian Miniatures in Jerusalem. (Illus.). 1931. 15.00x (ISBN 0-910956-04-9). Medieval Acad.

ILLUMINATION OF BOOKS AND MANUSCRIPTS–SPECIMENS, REPRODUCTIONS, ETC.

Hatch, William H. Greek & Syrian Miniatures in Jerusalem. (Illus.). 1931. 15.00x (ISBN 0-910956-04-9). Medieval Acad.

Pelekanidis, S. M., et al. The Treasures of Mount Athos: Illuminated Manuscripts, Vol. 1. (Patriarchal Institute for Patristic Studies). (Illus.). 500p. 1975. cancelled (ISBN 0-89241-003-5). Caratzas.

ILLUSTRATIONS, HOMILETICAL

see Homiletical Illustrations

IMAGE OF GOD

Brizee, Robert. Where in the World Is God? God's Presence in Every Moment of Our Lives. 160p. 1987. pap. 6.95 (ISBN 0-8358-0556-5). Upper Room.

Masson, Robert, ed. The Pedagogy of God's Image: Essays on Symbol & the Religious Imagination. 214p. 1986. lib. bdg. 23.00 (ISBN 0-8191-5721-X, Pub. by College Theology Society); pap. text ed. 13.00 (ISBN 0-8191-5619-1, Pub. by College Theology Society). U Pr of Amer.

IMAGES AND IDOLS

see Idols and Images

IMMACULATE CONCEPTION

see also Mary, Virgin; Virgin Birth

Brown, Raymond E. The Virginal Conception & Bodily Resurrection of Jesus. LC 72-97399. 1973. pap. 5.95 (ISBN 0-8091-1768-1). Paulist Pr.

Clasen, Souphronius, ed. Henrici De Werla, O. F. M. Opera Omnia: Tractatus De Immaculata Conceptione Beatae Mariae Virginis. (Text Ser). 1955. 6.00 (ISBN 0-686-11555-4). Franciscan Inst.

Manteau-Bonamy, H. M. Immaculate Conception & the Holy Spirit: The Marian Teachings of Father Kolbe. Geiger, Bernard M., ed. Arnandez, Richard, tr. from Fr. LC 77-93104. Tr. of Doctrine mariale du Pere Kolbe, Esprit-Saint et Conception Immaculee. (Illus.). 1977. pap. 4.00 (ISBN 0-913382-00-0, 101-20). Prow Bks-Franciscan.

IMMANENCE OF GOD

see also Jesus Christ–Mystical Body; Mystical Union; Mysticism; Transcendence of God

Bontrager, Ida B. Under God's Arrest. 1974. 11.50 (ISBN 0-87813-508-1). Christian Light.

Bowne, Borden P. The Immanence of God. LC 75-3071. Repr. of 1905 ed. 24.50 (ISBN 0-404-59070-5). AMS Pr.

Daly, Gabriel. Transcendence & Immanence: A Study in Catholic Modernism & Integralism. 1980. 37.50x (ISBN 0-19-826652-9). Oxford U Pr.

Divine Principle. 1977. write for info.; pap. write for info. Rose Sharon Pr.

Farrelly, John. God's Work in a Changing World. 346p. (Orig.). 1985. lib. bdg. 28.50 (ISBN 0-8191-4523-8); pap. text ed. 14.50 (ISBN 0-8191-4524-6). U Pr of Amer.

Hunter, Charles & Hunter, Frances. Don't Limit God. 1976. pap. 4.95 (ISBN 0-917726-04-9). Hunter Bks.

Paulk, Earl. Held in the Heavens until... 256p. (Orig.). 1985. pap. 7.95 (ISBN 0-917595-07-6). K-Dimension.

--To Whom Is God Betrothed? 200p. (Orig.). 1985. pap. 4.95 (ISBN 0-917595-10-6). K-Dimension.

IMMERSION, BAPTISMAL

see Baptism

IMMORTALISM

Here are entered works on the concept of living indefinitely in the flesh. For works on the concept of the survival of the soul after death, see Immortality.

see also Immortality

Stuart, Friend. How to Conquer Physical Death. 1980. vinyl 29.95 (ISBN 0-912132-02-7). Dominion Pr.

IMMORTALITY

Here are entered works on the concept of the survival of the soul after death. For works on the concept of living indefinitely in the flesh, see Immortalism.

see also Eschatology; Future Life; Soul

Alden, Henry M. A Study of Death: Works of Henry Mills Alden. (Works of Henry Mills Alden Ser.). vii, 335p. 1985. Repr. of 1895 ed. 39.00 (Pub. by Am Repr Serv). Am Biog Serv.

Altasen, J., et al. Immortality. 733p. 1978. 7.45 (ISBN 0-8285-0939-5, Pub. by Progress Pubs USSR). Imported Pubns.

Badham, Paul & Badham, Linda. Death & Immortality in the Religions of the World. 256p. 1987. 22.95 (ISBN 0-913757-54-3, Pub. by New Era Bks); pap. 12.95 (ISBN 0-913757-67-5, Pub. by New Era Bks). Paragon Hse.

Balaramiah, V. The Art of Deathlessness. (Illus.). 128p. 1980. pap. 4.95 (ISBN 0-937698-01-6). Golden Mean.

Banerji, Barenya K. Towards Quiescence & Immortality. LC 80-81693. 149p. 1981. 10.95 (ISBN 0-8022-2366-4). Philos Lib.

Birdsong, Robert E. Way of the Immortal Threefold Self: The Straight Path. (Aquarian Academy Monograph: Ser. E, No. 4). 1980. pap. 1.45 (ISBN 0-917108-29-9). Sirius Bks.

--Way of the Soul: The "Heart Path" to Human Perfection. (Aquarian Academy Monograph: Ser. D, No. 2). 1980. pap. 1.45 (ISBN 0-917108-28-0). Sirius Bks.

--Way of the Spirit: The "Head Path" to Human Perfection, Ser. C, No. 2. (Aquarian Academy Monograph). 1980. pap. 1.45 (ISBN 0-917108-27-2). Sirius Bks.

Bixler, Julius S. Immortality & the Present Mood. LC 75-3047. Repr. of 1931 ed. 16.00 (ISBN 0-404-59044-6). AMS Pr.

Brown, Stuart, ed. Reason & Religion. LC 77-3115. 336p. 1977. pap. 12.95x (ISBN 0-8014-9166-5). Cornell U Pr.

Burns, Norman T. Christian Mortalism from Tyndale to Milton. LC 72-75406. 224p. 1972. 16.50x (ISBN 0-674-12875-3). Harvard U Pr.

Carrington, Hereward. Death: The Causes & Phenomena with Special Reference to Immortality. Kastenbaum, Robert, ed. LC 76-19563. (Death & Dying Ser.). 1977. lib. bdg. 27.50 (ISBN 0-405-09559-7). Ayer Co Pubs.

Case, Charles J. Beyond Time: Ideas of the Great Philosophers on Eternal Existence & Immortality. LC 85-17864. 144p. (Orig.). 1985. lib. bdg. 20.75 (ISBN 0-8191-4933-0); pap. text ed. 8.25 (ISBN 0-8191-4934-9). U Pr of Amer.

Charleton, Walter. The Immorality of the Human Soul, Demonstrated by the Light of Nature: In Two Dialogues. LC 83-46043. (Scientific AWakeningin the Restoration Ser.: No. 2). (Illus.). 224p. 1985. Repr. of 1657 ed. 87.50 (ISBN 0-404-63302-1). AMS Pr.

Clarke, William N. Immortality. 1920. 29.50x (ISBN 0-686-83578-6). Elliots Bks.

Clymer, R. Swinburne. Philosophy of Immortality. 208p. 1960. 6.95 (ISBN 0-932785-39-5). Philos Pub.

--The Way to Life & Immortality. 244p. 1948. 7.95 (ISBN 0-932785-48-4). Philos Pub.

Compton, Arthur H. Man's Destiny in Eternity. LC 75-117821. (Essay Index Reprint Ser). 1949. 19.00 (ISBN 0-8369-1762-6). Ayer Co Pubs.

Davis, Roy E. Conscious Immortality. 150p. 1978. pap. 2.95 (ISBN 0-87707-216-7). CSA Pr.

De Unamuno, Miguel. Tragic Sense of Life. 14.00 (ISBN 0-8446-3100-0). Peter Smith.
Dr. Clem Davies Ministry Inc., et al. Immortality: The Next Giant Step for Mankind. LC 83-90890. 138p. 1985. 10.00 (ISBN 0-533-05910-0). Vantage.
Ducasse, C. J. Critical Examination of the Belief in a Life after Death. 336p. 1974. pap. 39.50x spiral (ISBN 0-398-03037-5). C C Thomas.
Fechner, Gustav T. The Little Book of Life After Death. Kastenbaum, Robert, ed. LC 76-19570. (Death & Dying Ser.). 1977. Repr. of 1904 ed. lib. bdg. 15.00x (ISBN 0-405-09565-1). Ayer Co Pubs.
Flew, Antony. God, Freedom & Immortality: A Critical Analysis. LC 84-42543. 183p. 1984. pap. text ed. 10.95 (ISBN 0-87975-251-3). Prometheus Bks.
Fontinell, Eugene. Self, God & Immortality: A Jamesian Investigation. 320p. 1986. 34.95 (ISBN 0-87722-428-5). Temple U Pr.
Garfield, Samuel. The Immortality of the Soul & the Perfectibility of Man. (Illus.). 1977. 45.00 (ISBN 0-89266-026-0). Am Classical Coll Pr.
Hall, Manly P. Science & Immortality. pap. 2.50 (ISBN 0-89314-351-0). Philos Res.
Harris, Murray J. Raised Immortal: Resurrection & Immortality in the New Testament. 320p. (Orig.). 1985. pap. 10.95 (ISBN 0-8028-0053-X). Eerdmans.
Hickok, Laurens P. Humanity Immortal: Or, Man Tried, Fallen & Redeemed. LC 75-3180. Repr. of 1872 ed. 25.00 (ISBN 0-404-59183-3). AMS Pr.
Hirsch, W. Rabbinic Psychology. LC 73-2208. (The Jewish People; History, Religion, Literature Ser.). Repr. of 1947 ed. 24.50 (ISBN 0-405-05272-3). Ayer Co Pubs.
James, William. The Will to Believe & Human Immortality. pap. 5.95 (ISBN 0-486-20291-7). Dover.
--Will to Believe & Other Essays in Popular Philosophy & Human Immortality. 15.75 (ISBN 0-8446-2313-X). Peter Smith.
Koepke, Fred T. How to Be Sure of Immortality. 1985. 6.95 (ISBN 0-533-06491-0). Vantage.
Lamont, Corliss. Illusion of Immortality. 4th ed. LC 65-25140. 1965. pap. 6.95 (ISBN 0-8044-6377-8). Ungar.
Lifton, Robert J. The Future of Immortality: And Other Essays for a Nuclear Age. LC 86-47763. 368p. 1987. 21.95 (ISBN 0-465-02597-8). Basic.
McConnell, S. D. The Evolution of Immortality. 1978. Repr. of 1901 ed. lib. bdg. 25.00 (ISBN 0-8495-3508-5). Arden Lib.
McTaggart, John. Human Immortality & Pre-Existence. Repr. of 1916 ed. 23.00 (ISBN 0-527-59950-6). Kraus Repr.
--Some Dogmas of Religion. LC 7-7484. 1968. Repr. of 1906 ed. 23.00 (ISBN 0-527-60000-8). Kraus Repr.
Mohammed, O. Averroes' Doctrine of Immorality: A Matter of Controversy. (Editions Ser.: No. 6). 232p. 1984. pap. text ed. 11.95x (ISBN 0-88920-178-1, Wilfrid Laurier Canada). Humanities.
Montagu, Henry. Contemplatio Mortis et Immortalitatis. LC 72-218. (English Experience Ser.: No. 337). 148p. 1971. Repr. of 1631 ed. 11.50 (ISBN 90-221-0337-4). Walter J Johnson.
Moore, Clifford H. Ancient Beliefs in the Immortality of the Soul. LC 63-10283. (Our Debt to Greece & Rome Ser.). 183p. 1963. Repr. of 1930 ed. 20.00x (ISBN 0-8154-0154-X). Cooper Sq.
Paramananda, Swami. Reincarnation & Immortality. 2nd ed. 1961. 4.50 (ISBN 0-911564-05-5). Vedanta Ctr.
Pelikan, Jaroslav J. The Shape of Death: Life, Death, & Immortality in the Early Fathers. LC 78-6030. 1978. Repr. of 1961 ed. lib. bdg. 22.50x (ISBN 0-313-20458-6, PESD). Greenwood.
Perry, John R. A Dialogue on Personal Identity & Immortality. LC 78-52943. 60p. 1978. lib. bdg. 15.00 (ISBN 0-915144-91-3); pap. text ed. 2.95 (ISBN 0-915144-53-0). Hackett Pub.
Plato. Phaedo. Church, F. J., tr. LC 51-10496. 1951. pap. 4.24 scp (ISBN 0-672-60192-3, LLA30). Bobbs.
--Phaedo. Grube, G. M., tr. LC 76-49565. 72p. 1977. pap. 2.50 (ISBN 0-915144-18-2). Hackett Pub.
--Plato's Phaedo. Bluck, R. S., tr. 1955. pap. 7.87 scp (ISBN 0-672-60308-X, LLA110). Bobbs.
Reesman, Richard T. Contributions of the Major Philosophers into the Problem of Body Resurrection & Personal Immortality. (Illus.). 117p. 1981. 61.85 (ISBN 0-89920-021-4). Am Inst Psych.
Rosin, Jacob. In God's Image. LC 75-86507. 1969. 6.00 (ISBN 0-8022-2299-4). Philos Lib.
Royce, Josiah. Conception of Immortality. 1968. Repr. of 1900 ed. lib. bdg. 22.50x (ISBN 0-8371-0207-3, ROCI). Greenwood.
St. Augustine. Immortality of the Soul & Other Works. (Fathers of the Church Ser.: Vol. 4). 489p. 1947. 29.95x (ISBN 0-8132-0004-0). Cath U Pr.
Schmahl, Phillip. Logic of Faith. LC 65-20327. 250p. 1965. 5.95 (ISBN 0-8022-1503-3). Philos Lib.
Seth, Pattison A. Idea of Immortality. Repr. of 1922 ed. 18.00 (ISBN 0-527-81506-3). Kraus Repr.
Strauss, Lehman. We Live Forever. 1947. pap. 5.95 (ISBN 0-87213-830-5). Loizeaux.
Streeter, Burnett H., et al. Immortality: An Essay in Discovery, Co-Ordinating Scientific, Physical, & Biblical Research. 1977. Repr. of 1917 ed. lib. bdg. 27.50 (ISBN 0-8492-2418-7). R West.
Stringfellow, William. Instead of Death: New & Expanded Edition. rev. ed. 1976. pap. 3.95 (ISBN 0-8164-2120-X, HarpR). Har-Row.
Transformation-Night, Immortality-Dawn. 1975. 2.00 (ISBN 0-88497-111-2). Aum Pubns.
Unamuno, Miguel. Tragic Sense of Life. Flitch, J. Crawford, tr. 1921. pap. 6.00 (ISBN 0-486-20257-7). Dover.
Wilson, Everett L. Jesus & the End-Time. 1977. pap. 3.95 (ISBN 0-910452-32-6). Covenant.

IMPOSTORS AND IMPOSTURE

Matthews, Ronald. English Messiahs: Studies of Six English Religious Pretenders, 1656-1927. LC 76-172553. Repr. of 1936 ed. 12.75 (ISBN 0-405-18187-6, Pub. by Blom). Ayer Co Pubs.
Thomas, Fred W. Masters of Deception. pap. 4.95 (ISBN 0-8010-8779-1). Baker Bk.

IMPRECATION

see Blessing and Cursing

IMPROPRIATION

see Secularization

INCANTATIONS

see also Blessing and Cursing

Isbell, Charles D. Corpus of the Aramaic Incantation Bowls. LC 75-15949. (Society of Biblical Literature. Dissertation Ser.: No. 17). pap. 40.70 (ISBN 0-317-10143-9, 2017519). Bks Demand UMI.
Kilpatrick, Jack F. & Kilpatrick, Anna G. Run Toward the Nightland: Magic of the Oklahoma Cherokees. LC 67-19814. (Illus.). 1967. pap. 9.95 (ISBN 0-87074-084-9). SMU Press.
Thompson, Reginald C. The Devils & Evil Spirits of Babylonia, 2 vols. LC 73-18855. (Luzac's Semitic Text & Translation Ser.: Nos. 14-15). (Illus.). Repr. of 1904 ed. 47.50 set (ISBN 0-404-11353-2). AMS Pr.

INCARNATION

see also Theophanies

Anderson, Norman. The Mystery of the Incarnation. LC 79-13879. 1979. pap. 3.95 (ISBN 0-87784-530-1). Inter-Varsity.
Andrews, Samuel J. & Gifford, E. H. Man & the Incarnation: The Study of Philippians 2 & Psalm 110. 1981. lib. bdg. 15.00 (ISBN 0-86524-078-7, 9510). Klock & Klock.
Anselm of Canterbury. Trinity, Incarnation, & Redemption: Theological Treatises. (Anselm Ser.: No. 6). 1974. 9.95 (ISBN 0-88946-008-6). E Mellen.
Athanasius, Saint On the Incarnation of the Word. pap. 2.95 (ISBN 0-686-25556-9). Eastern Orthodox.
Blackwood, Andrew W., Jr. When God Came Down. (Pocket Paperback Library Ser.). 1978. pap. 1.45 (ISBN 0-8010-0753-4). Baker Bk.
Conway, Charles A., Jr. The Vita Christi of Ludolph of Saxony & Late Medieval Devotion Centered on the Incarnation: A Descriptive Analysis. Hogg, James, ed. (Analecta Cartusiana Ser.: No. 34). 153p. (Orig.). 1976. pap. 25.00 (ISBN 3-7052-0036-4, Pub. by Salzburg Studies). Longwood Pub Group.
Crawford, Robert G. The Saga of God Incarnate. 120p. 1985. 13.95 (ISBN 0-86981-309-9, Pub. by T&T Clark Ltd UK). Fortress.
Galot. Who Is Christ? A Theology of the Incarnation. Bouchard, M. Angeline, tr. 423p. 1981. 10.00 (ISBN 0-8199-0813-4). Franciscan Herald.
Gorodetzky, Nadejda. The Humiliated Christ in Modern Russian Thought. LC 79-168159. Repr. of 1938 ed. 18.75 (ISBN 0-404-02883-7). AMS Pr.
Hick, John, ed. The Myth of God Incarnate. LC 77-9965. 224p. 1978. pap. 7.95 (ISBN 0-664-24178-6). Westminster.
Kung, Hans. The Incarnation of God. 660p. 1987. 34.50 (ISBN 0-8245-0793-2). Crossroad NY.
Morris, Thomas V. The Logic of God Incarnate. LC 85-21252. (Illus.). 224p. 1986. text ed. 19.95x (ISBN 0-8014-1846-1). Cornell U Pr.
Parrinder, Geoffrey. Avatar & Incarnation. 1982. Repr. of 1970 ed. 15.95 (ISBN 0-19-520361-5). Oxford U Pr.
St. Anthanasius. St. Athanasius on the Incarnation. 120p. 1977. pap. 4.95 (ISBN 0-913836-40-0). St Vladimirs.
Schlitzer, Albert L. Our Life in Christ. (University Theology Ser.: Vols. 1 & 2). 1962. Set. 12.95 (ISBN 0-268-00201-0). U of Notre Dame Pr.
Spurgeon, C. H. Christ's Incarnation-"Good Tidings of Great Joy". 1978. pap. 2.50 (ISBN 0-686-00498-1). Pilgrim Pubns.
Surath, Sri. God Is Now Here. 1976. 5.00 (ISBN 0-685-58439-9). Ranney Pubns.
Torrance, Thomas F. Space, Time & Incarnation. 1969. pap. 4.95 (ISBN 0-19-520082-9). Oxford U Pr.
Weinandy, Thomas. Does God Change? The Word's Becoming in the Incarnation. LC 84-26241. (Studies in Historical Theology). 1985. pap. 17.95 (ISBN 0-932506-35-6). St Bedes Pubns.
Whitton, Joel. Life Between Life: Scientific Explorations into the Void Separating One Incarnation from the Next. LC 86-4573. 192p. 1986. 14.95 (ISBN 0-385-23274-8, Dolp). Doubleday.
Williams, Charles. He Came Down from Heaven. 160p. 1984. pap. 3.95 (ISBN 0-8028-0033-5). Eerdmans.
Wolfson, Harry A. Philosophy of the Church Fathers: Faith, Trinity, Incarnation. 3rd rev. ed. LC 70-119077. 1970. 32.50x (ISBN 0-674-66551-1). Harvard U Pr.
Zodhiates, Spiros. The Perfect Gift. (Illus.). 1973. pap. 1.75 (ISBN 0-89957-511-0). AMG Pubs.

INCEST

Peters, David B. A Betrayal of Innocence. 160p. 1986. 11.95 (ISBN 0-8499-0502-8, 0502-8). Word Bks.
Rawlings, Meridel. Honor Thy Father. Keith, Bill, ed. (Orig.). 1986. pap. 6.95 (ISBN 0-910311-39-0). Huntington Hse Inc.
Ricks, Chip. Carol's Story. 192p. 1981. pap. 6.95 (ISBN 0-8423-0208-5). Tyndale.

INDEPENDENCY (CHURCH POLITY)

see Congregationalism

INDETERMINISM

see Free Will and Determinism

INDIA–ANTIQUITIES

Charish, Chandra B. Sacred City of Anuradhapura. (Illus.). 132p. 1986. Repr. 26.00X (ISBN 0-8364-1746-1, Pub. by Abhinav India). South Asia Bks.
Cousens, H. The Architectural Antiquities of Western India. (Illus.). 1983. text ed. 34.00x. Coronet Bks.
Ramanayyan, Venkata. An Essay on the Origin of the South Indian Temples. (Illus.). 92p. 1986. Repr. 15.00X (ISBN 0-8364-1725-9, Pub. by Manohar India). South Asia Bks.

INDIA–BIOGRAPHY

Abbott, Justin E. Life of Eknath. cancelled (ISBN 0-8364-0746-6, Pub. by Motilal Banarsidass). South Asia Bks.
Aiyar, M. S. Thiagaraja: A Great Musician Saint. 238p. 1986. Repr. 20.00X (ISBN 0-8364-1766-6, Pub. by Usha). South Asia Bks.
Anand, Balwant S. Guru Nanak: His Life Was His Message - A Biography. 1985. 9.00x (ISBN 0-8364-1456-X, Pub. by Nanak Dev Univ India). South Asia Bks.
Borthwick, Meredith. Keshub Chunder Sen: A Search for Cultural Synthesis in India. 1978. 13.50x (ISBN 0-88386-904-7). South Asia Bks.
Burke, Marie L. Swami Vivekananda in the West: New Discoveries: His Prophetic Mission, 2 Vols, Vol. 1. new ed. (Illus.). 515p. text ed. 12.95x (ISBN 0-317-03702-1, Pub. by Advaita Ashrama India). Vedanta Pr.
Devi, Indira & Roy, Dilip K. Pilgrims of the Stars. 2nd ed. (Illus.). 406p. 1985. pap. 14.95 (ISBN 0-931454-10-7). Timeless Bks.
Dhar, Niranjan. Aurobindo, Gandhi & Roy: A Yogi, a Mahatma & a Rationalist. 1986. 13.50x (ISBN 0-8364-1578-7, Pub. by Minerva India). South Asia Bks.
Engle, Jon. Servants of God: The Lives of the 10 Gurus of the Sikhs. LC 79-63457. (Illus.). 192p. 1980. pap. 6.00 (ISBN 0-89142-035-5). Sant Bani Ash.
Husain, A. M. Tughluq Dynasty. (Illus.). 1976. Repr. of 1935 ed. 30.00x (ISBN 0-89684-461-7). Orient Bk Dist.
Jain, Naresh K., ed. Muslims in India: A Biographical Dictionary, Vol. II. 1984. 40.00x (ISBN 0-8364-1150-1, Pub. by Manohar India). South Asia Bks.
Langley, G. H. Sri Aurobindo. 59.95 (ISBN 0-8490-1119-1). Gordon Pr.
Max Mueller, F. Keshub Chunder Sen. rev. ed. Mookerjee, Nanda, ed. 1976. 6.00x (ISBN 0-88386-862-8). South Asia Bks.
Natu, Bal. Glimpses of the God-Man, Meher Baba: Vol. III, February 1952 - February 1953. LC 79-913293. (Illus.). 344p. (Orig.). 1982. pap. 7.95 (ISBN 0-913078-44-1). Sheriar Pr.
Nayyar, Sushila. Kasturba, Wife of Gandhi. 1983. pap. 2.50x (ISBN 0-87574-000-6, 000). Pendle Hill.
Osborne, Arthur. The Incredible Sai Baba: The Life & Miracles of a Modern-Day Saint. 102p. 1985. pap. text ed. 5.00x (ISBN 0-86125-105-9, Pub. by Orient Longman Ltd India). Apt Bks.
Pillai, Ananda R., et al. The Private Diary of Ananda Ranga Pillai in 12 Volumes. Price, J. F. & Rangachari, eds. Dupleix, Joseph F., tr. 1986. Repr. per Set 420.00X (PUb. by Abhinav by India). South Asia Bks.
Rajneesh, Bhagwan Shree. The Sound of Running Water. Asha, Ma Prem, ed. LC 83-180798. (Photobiography Ser.). (Illus.). 564p. 1980. 100.00 (ISBN 0-88050-134-0). Chidvilas Found.
Ramakrisnananda, Swami. Life of Sri Ranauja. 1979. pap. 8.95 (ISBN 0-87481-446-4). Vedanta Pr.
Ravindra. The White Lotus: At the Feet of the Mother. (Illus.). 1978. 8.50x (ISBN 0-89684-466-8). Orient Bk Dist.
Roy-Chaudhury, P. C. Gandhi & His Contemporaries. 336p. 1972. 25.00x (ISBN 0-89684-394-7). Orient Bk Dist.
Satsvarupa dasa Goswami. A Lifetime in Preparation: Srila Prabhupada-lilamrta, Vol. 1. (Illus.). 357p. 1980. 12.95 (ISBN 0-686-71685-X). Bhaktivedanta.
Sethi, V. K. Kabir: The Weaver of God's Name. 762p. 1986. 23.00X (ISBN 0-8364-1673-2, Pub. by Manohar India). South Asia Bks.
Smart, Ninian & Purnananda, Swami. Prophet of the New Hindu Age: The Life & Times of Archarya Pranavananda. (Illus.). 256p. 1985. 15.00 (ISBN 0-04-922032-2); pap. 9.50 (ISBN 0-04-922033-0). Allen Unwin.
Waghore, Joanne P. Images of Dharma: The Epic World of C. Rajagopalachari. 1985. 25.00x (ISBN 0-8364-1426-8, Pub. by Chanakya India). South Asia Bks.
Yuvacharya Shri Mahaprajna. Shraman Mahavir: His Life & Teachings. 334p. 1980. 12.00 (ISBN 0-88065-213-6, Pub. by Messers Today & Tomorrows Printers & Publishers India). Scholarly Pubns.

INDIA–CHURCH HISTORY

Neill, Stephen. A History of Christianity in India 1707-1858. (Illus.). 592p. 1985. 79.50 (ISBN 0-521-30376-1). Cambridge U Pr.

INDIA–CIVILIZATION

Ali, Abdullah Yusuf. A Cultural History of India During the British Period. LC 75-41006. Repr. of 1940 ed. 25.50 (ISBN 0-404-14723-2). AMS Pr.
Basham, A. L., ed. A Cultural History of India. (Illus.). 1975. 29.95x (ISBN 0-19-561520-4). Oxford U Pr.
Bhattacharyya, et al, eds. The Cultural Heritage of India, 5 vols. Incl. Vol. 1. Early Phases. Radhakrishnan, S., intro. by. (ISBN 0-87481-560-6); Vol. 2. Itihasas, Puranas, Dharma & Other Shastras (ISBN 0-87481-561-4); Vol. 3. The Philosophies (ISBN 0-87481-562-2); Vol. 4. The Religions (ISBN 0-87481-563-0); Vol. 5: Languages & Literatures (ISBN 0-87481-564-9). (Illus.). 40.00x ea.; Set. 175.00x (ISBN 0-87481-558-4). Vedanta Pr.
Davids, Thomas W. Buddhist India. LC 78-38349. (Select Bibliographies Reprint Ser). Repr. of 1903 ed. 28.00 (ISBN 0-8369-6766-6). Ayer Co Pubs.
Drekmeier, Charles. Kingship & Community in Early India. LC 62-9565. 1962. 27.50x (ISBN 0-8047-0114-8). Stanford U Pr.
Jain, J. Life in Ancient India as Depicted in Jaina Canon & Commentaries. 2nd ed. 1984. text ed. 34.00x. Coronet Bks.
Joshi, N. P. Iconography of Balarama. 1979. 16.50x (ISBN 0-8364-0538-2). South Asia Bks.
Macdonell, Arthur A. India's Past: A Survey of Her Literatures, Religions, Languages & Antiquities. LC 78-20481. 1979. Repr. of 1927 ed. text ed. 29.00 (ISBN 0-88355-858-0). Hyperion Conn.
Roy, Girish C. Indian Culture. 1977. write for info. (ISBN 0-686-22664-X). Intl Bk Dist.
Saletore, R. N. Encyclopaedia of Indian Culture, V-Z, Vol. 5. 324p. 1985. text ed. 50.00x (ISBN 0-391-02978-9, Pub. by Sterling India). Humanities.
Singer, Milton, ed. Traditional India: Structure & Change. (American Folklore Society Bibliographical & Special Ser.: No. 10). 356p. 1959. pap. 9.95x (ISBN 0-292-73504-9). U of Tex Pr.
Slater, G. The Dravidian Element in Indian Culture. (Illus.). 192p. 1986. Repr. 14.00X (ISBN 0-8364-1706-2, Pub. by Manohar India). South Asia Bks.

INDIA–HISTORY–EARLY TO 1000 A.D

Al-Biruni. Alberni's India: An Account of the Religion, Philosophy, Literature, Geography, Chronology, Astronomy, Customs, Laws & Astrology of India about AD 1030, 2 vols. Sachau, Edward C., tr. Repr. of 1888 ed. Set. text ed. 54.00x. Coronet Bks.
Davids, Thomas W. Buddhist India. LC 78-38349. (Select Bibliographies Reprint Ser). Repr. of 1903 ed. 28.00 (ISBN 0-8369-6766-6). Ayer Co Pubs.
Havell, Ernest B. The History of Aryan Rule in India. LC 72-900073. (Illus.). 613p. 1972. Repr. of 1918 ed. 22.50x (ISBN 0-89684-400-5). Orient Bk Dist.

Hawkridge, Emma. Indian Gods & Kings: The Story of a Living Past. facs. ed. LC 68-24853. (Essay Index Reprint Ser). 1935. 21.50 (ISBN 0-8369-0521-0). Ayer Co Pubs.

Lane-Poole, S. Medieval India under Mohammedan Rule: A. D. 712-1764, 2 Vols. in 1. LC 52-33515. Repr. of 1951 ed. 29.00 (ISBN 0-527-54300-4). Kraus Repr.

Mcauliffe, Max A. The Sikh Religion, 6 vols. in 3. 1963. text ed. 100.00. Coronet Bks.

Maurice, Thomas. The History of Hindostan. Feldman, Burton & Richardson, Robert D., eds. LC 78-60888. (Myth & Romanticism Ser.). 1984. lib. bdg. 240.00 (ISBN 0-8240-3566-6). Garland Pub.

Sharma, R. N. Brahmins Through the Ages. 1977. 18.00x (ISBN 0-686-22659-3). Intl Bk Dist.

Smith, Vincent A. History of India from the Sixth Century B.C. to the Mohammedan Conquest, Including the Invasion of Alexander the Great. LC 72-14391. (History of India Ser.: No. 2). Repr. of 1906 ed. 32.00 (ISBN 0-404-09002-8). AMS Pr.

Vijnanananda, Swami, tr. from Sanskrit. The Srimad Devi Bhagawatam, Pts. I & II. LC 75-985029. 1977. 55.00x (ISBN 0-89684-455-2). Orient Bk Dist.

INDIA–INTELLECTUAL LIFE

Oman, John C. The Mystics, Ascetics & Saints of India. lib. bdg. 75.00 (ISBN 0-8490-0698-8). Gordon Pr.

INDIA–RELIGION

Abbott, J. Indian Ritual & Belief. Orig. Title: Keys of Power: A Study of Indian Religion & Ritual. 1985. Repr. of 1932 ed. 40.00x (ISBN 0-8364-1294-X, Pub. by Usha). South Asia Bks.

Agrawala, P. K. Goddesses in Ancient India. 180p. 1983. text ed. 50.00x (ISBN 0-391-02960-6). Humanities.

Ahir, D. C. Buddhist Shrines in India. (Illus.). xii, 132p. 1986. text ed. 25.00x (ISBN 81-7018-326-X, Pub. by D K Pub Corp Delhi). Apt Bks.

Ahluwalia, B. K., ed. Muslims & India's Freedom Movement. 1985. 26.50x (ISBN 0-8364-1349-0, Pub. by Heritage India). South Asia Bks.

Alexander, Horace. Quakerism in India. 1983. pap. 2.50x (ISBN 0-87574-031-6, 031). Pendle Hill.

Allens, Alexi. Images of Sai Baba. (Illus.). 104p. (Orig.). 1985. pap. 12.95 (ISBN 0-318-18477-X). Masterpiece Pub.

Anirvan. Buddhiyoga of the Gita & Other Essays. LC 84-900102. 1984. 16.00x (ISBN 0-8364-1120-X, Pub. by Biblia Impex). South Asia Bks.

Apurvananda, Swami. Acharya Shankara. 362p. 1985. pap. 7.95 (ISBN 0-87481-529-0, Pub. by Ramakrishna Math Madras India). Vedanta Pr.

Aurobindo, Sri. Letters on Yoga, 2 vols. (Life Companion Library Bible Paper Ser.). 1984p. 40.00 (ISBN 0-89744-014-5). Auromere.

--Santan Dharma Ka Mahatva: (Uttarpara Speech) 14p. 3.00 (ISBN 0-317-17480-0). Auromere.

--Sri Aurobindo Birth Centenary Library: Complete Writings of Sri Aurobindo, 30 vols. 1979. Set. 300.00x (ISBN 0-89744-964-9); lib. bdg. 400.00x (ISBN 0-89744-965-7). Auromere.

--Synthesis of Yoga. 6th ed. 1979p. 36.00 (ISBN 0-89744-931-2). Auromere.

--Synthesis of Yoga. 1979p. 30.00 (ISBN 0-89744-932-0). Auromere.

--Synthesis of Yoga. (Life Companion Bible Bks.). 1984p. 24.95 (ISBN 0-89744-017-X). Auromere.

Avadhuta. Avadhuta Gita: The Song of the Ever-Free. Chetanananda, tr. from Sanskrit. 138p. 1985. text ed. 3.50 (ISBN 0-87481-224-0, Pub. by Advaita Ashram India). Vedanta Pr.

Babb, Lawrence A. The Divine Hierarchy: Popular Hinduism in Central India. LC 75-61693. (Illus.). 266p. 1975. 27.50x (ISBN 0-231-03882-8). Columbia U Pr.

Baird, Robert D. & Bloom, Alfred. Religion & Man: Indian & Far Eastern Religious Traditions. (Religion & Man: An Introduction, Pts. 2 & 3). 1972. pap. text ed. 14.95 scp (ISBN 0-06-040448-5, HarpC). Har-Row.

Bannerjee, Brojendra N. Religious Conversions in India. 384p. 1982. 29.95x (ISBN 0-940500-28-0, Pub. by Harnam Pub India). Asia Bk Corp.

Barth, A. Religions of India. 6th ed. Wood, J., tr. from Fr. 309p. 1980. Repr. of 1880 ed. 23.95x (ISBN 0-940500-64-7). Asia Bk Corp.

--The Religions of India. 1980. text ed. 22.00x (ISBN 0-89563-630-1). Coronet Bks.

--The Religions of India. 332p. 25.00X (ISBN 0-317-52150-0, Pub. by S Chand India). State Mutual Bk.

Barth, M. A. Bulletin of Religion, ISPP Vol. 1, No. 4. 60p. 1974. Repr. 2.00 (ISBN 0-88065-050-8, Pub. by Messers Today & Tomorrow Printers & Publishers India). Scholarly Pubns.

Bhagat, M. G. Ancient Indian Asceticism. LC 76-904001. 1976. 18.50x (ISBN 0-88386-865-2). South Asia Bks.

Bhaktivedanta, Swami. The Science of Self Realization. (Illus.). 1977. 3.95 (ISBN 0-89213-101-2). Bhaktivedanta.

Bhaktivedanta, Swami A. C. Beyond Birth & Death. LC 72-84844. (Illus.). 1972. pap. 1.95 (ISBN 0-912776-41-2). Bhaktivedanta.

--Nectar of Devotion. LC 78-118082. (Illus.). 1970. 12.95 (ISBN 0-912776-05-6). Bhaktivedanta.

--Sri Caitanya Caritamrta: Antya-Lila, 5 vols. (Illus.). 1975. 12.95 ea. Vol. 1 (ISBN 0-912776-72-2). Vol. 2 (ISBN 0-912776-73-0). Vol. 3 (ISBN 0-912776-74-9). Vol. 4 (ISBN 0-912776-76-5). Vol. 5 (ISBN 0-912776-77-3). Bhaktivedanta.

--Sri Caitanya-Caritamrta: Madhya-Lila, 9 vols. (Illus.). 1975. 12.95 ea. Vol. 1 (ISBN 0-912776-63-3). Vol. 2 (ISBN 0-912776-64-1). Vol. 3 (ISBN 0-912776-65-X). Vol. 4 (ISBN 0-912776-66-8). Vol. 5 (ISBN 0-912776-67-6). Vol. 6 (ISBN 0-912776-68-4). Vol. 7 (ISBN 0-912776-69-2). Vol. 8, (ISBN 0-912776-70-6), Vol. 9 (ISBN 0-912776-71-4). Bhaktivedanta.

Bhaktivendanta, Swami A. C. Srimad Bhagavatam: Ninth Canto, 3 vols. LC 73-169353. (Sanskrit & Eng., Illus.). 1977. 12.95 ea. Vol. 1 (ISBN 0-912776-94-3). Vol. 2 (ISBN 0-912776-95-1). Vol. 3 (ISBN 0-912776-96-X). Bhaktivedanta.

Bhandarkar, R. G. Vaisnavism Saivism & Minor Religious Systems. 238p. 1986. Repr. 14.00X (ISBN 0-8364-1704-6, Pub. by Minerva India). South Asia Bks.

Bhattacharya, Aparna. Religious Movements of Bengal, 1800-1850. 1984. pap. 9.00x (ISBN 0-8364-1118-8, Pub. by New Times). South Asia Bks.

Bhattacharya, Vivek. The Spirit of Indian Culture: Saints of India. 622p. 1980. 29.95 (ISBN 0-940500-40-X). Asia Bk Corp.

Blavatsky, Helena P. The Caves & Jungles of Hindustan. De Zirkoff, Boris, ed. LC 74-26605. (Illus.). 750p. 1975. 18.50 (ISBN 0-8356-0219-2). Theos Pub Hse.

Bose, D. N. The Yoga Vasistha Ramayana. rev. ed. 1984. Repr. of 1954 ed. 12.50x (ISBN 0-8364-1181-1, Pub. by Mukhopadhyaya India). South Asia Bks.

Brooke, Tal. Avatar of Night: The Hidden Side of Sai Baba. 392p. 1982. pap. text ed. 6.95x (ISBN 0-686-91763-4, Pub. by Vikas India). Advent NY.

Burghart, Richard & Cantlie, Audrey, eds. Indian Religion. LC 84-15115. 320p. 1985. 27.50 (ISBN 0-312-41400-5). St Martin.

Carpenter, J. Estlin. Theism in Medieval India. 1977. Repr. of 1921 ed. 22.50x (ISBN 0-89684-457-9). Orient Bk Dist.

--Theism in Medieval India. 564p. Repr. of 1921 ed. text ed. 37.50x. Coronet Bks.

Carpenter, Joseph E. Theism in Medieval India. LC 77-27152. (Hibbert Lectures: 1919). Repr. of 1921 ed. 48.00 (ISBN 0-404-60419-6). AMS Pr.

Carpenter, K. Theism in Medieval India. 1977. 22.50x (ISBN 0-8364-0100-X). South Asia Bks.

Cenker, William. A Tradition of Teachers: Sankara & the Jagadgurus Today. 1983. 18.50 (ISBN 0-8364-0944-2); text ed. 13.00 (ISBN 0-8364-1058-0). South Asia Bks.

Chakravarti, S. C. Bauls: The Spiritual Vikings. 1981. 10.00x (ISBN 0-8364-0671-0, Pub. by Mukhopadhyay India). South Asia Bks.

Chatterjee, Margaret. The Religious Spectrum. (Studies in an Indian Context). 196p. 1984. 23.95x (ISBN 0-317-39860-1, Pub. by Allied Pubs India). Asia Bk Corp.

Chinmoy, Sri. Mother India's Lighthouse: India's Spiritual Leaders. LC 74-189998. 288p. 1973. pap. cancelled (ISBN 0-89345-219-X, Steinerbks). Garber Comm.

Chopra, P. N., ed. Religions & Communities of India. 1982. 59.00x (ISBN 0-85692-081-9, Pub. by E-W Pubns England). State Mutual Bk.

Christanand, M. The Philosophy of Indian Monotheism. 1979. 12.00x (ISBN 0-8364-0558-7, Pub. by Macmillan India). South Asia Bks.

Colebrooke, H. T. Essays on History, Literature & Religion of Ancient India, 2 vols. 1024p. Repr. of 1873 ed. text ed. 57.50x. Coronet Bks.

Convention of Religions in India. 215p. 1983. text ed. 27.50x (ISBN 0-86590-205-4). Apt Bks.

Crawford, S. Cromwell. Ram Mohan Roy: Social, Political & Religious Reform in 19th Century India. 288p. 1986. 22.95 (ISBN 0-913729-15-9). Paragon Hse.

Creel, Austin. Dharma in Hindu Ethics. 1978. 11.00x (ISBN 0-88386-999-3). South Asia Bks.

Dabois, Abee J. State of Christianity in India - During the Early Nineteenth Century. 1977. 11.00x (ISBN 0-686-12059-0). Intl Bk Dist.

Dahlquist, Allan. Megasthenes & Indian Religion. 1977. 11.50 (ISBN 0-89684-277-0, Pub. by Motilal Banarsidass India). Orient Bk Dist.

Dash, Vaidya B. Handbook of Ayurveda. 221p. (Orig.). 1983. 28.00 (ISBN 0-317-17437-1, Pub. by Cultural Integration). Auromere.

Dass, Baba Hari. Sweeper to Saint: Stories of Holy India. Renu, Ma, ed. LC 80-52021. (Illus.). 208p. (Orig.). 1980. pap. 6.95 (ISBN 0-918100-03-8). Sri Rama.

Dave, H. T. Life & Philosophy of Shree Swaminarayan. new ed. Shepard, Leslie, ed. (Illus.). 274p. 1974. 8.95 (ISBN 0-04-294082-6). Weiser.

Deloria, Vine, Jr. God Is Red. 1983. pap. 3.95 (ISBN 0-440-33044-0, LE). Dell.

Drekmeier, Charles. Kingship & Community in Early India. LC 62-9565. 1962. 27.50x (ISBN 0-8047-0114-8). Stanford U Pr.

Dutt, Nalinaksha. Buddhist Sects in India. 1978. (Pub. by Motilal Banarsidass India); pap. 7.50 (ISBN 0-89684-044-1). Orient Bk Dist.

Eck, Diana L. Darsan: Seeing the Divine Image in India. 2nd, enl. ed. 97p. 1985. pap. 5.95 (ISBN 0-89012-042-0). Anima Pubns.

Engineer, Asghar A. Indian Muslims: A Study of Minority Problems in India. 1986. 28.00x (ISBN 81-202-0139-6, Pub. by Ajanta). South Asia Bks.

Firishtah, Muhammed Kasim. History of the Rise of the Mahomedan Power in India till the Year A.D. 1612, 4 Vols. Briggs, John, tr. LC 79-154112. Repr. of 1910 ed. Set. 225.00 (ISBN 0-404-56300-7). AMS Pr.

French, Hal W. & Sharma, Arvind. Religious Ferment in Modern India. 1982. 19.95x (ISBN 0-312-67134-2). St Martin.

Gambhirananda, Swami. History of the Ramakrishna Math & Mission. rev. ed. 344p. 1983. 10.00 (ISBN 0-87481-215-1, Pub. by Advaita Ashram India). Vedanta Pr.

Gokak, Vinayak K. Narahari: Prophet of New India. 298p. 1972. pap. 7.95 (ISBN 0-317-20882-9). CSA Pr.

Gonda, J. Change & Continuity in Indian Religion. 1984. text ed. 30.00x. Coronet Bks.

--Visnuism & Sivaism: A Comparison. LC 71-545904. 1976. 12.50x (ISBN 0-89684-465-X). Orient Bk Dist.

Hardy, Friedhelm E. Viraha-Bhakti: The Early History of Krsna Devotion in South India. (Illus.). 1983. 55.00x (ISBN 0-19-561251-5). Oxford U Pr.

Hawley, John S. & Wulff, Donna M., eds. The Divine Consort: Radha & the Goddesses of India. LC 86-47759. (Illus.). 432p. 1987. pap. 11.95 (ISBN 0-8070-1303-X, BP-734). Beacon Pr.

Hopkins, Edward W. The Religions of India. LC 77-94585. 1979. Repr. of 1895 ed. lib. bdg. 65.00 (ISBN 0-89341-312-7). Longwood Pub Group.

Jagadiswarananda, Swami, tr. Devi-Mahatmyam (the Chandi) (Sanskrit & Eng). pap. 3.25 (ISBN 0-87481-426-X). Vedanta Pr.

Jha, Akhileshwar. The Imprisoned Mind: Guru Shisya Tradition in Indian Culture. 1980. 18.50x (ISBN 0-8364-0665-6, Pub. by Ambika India). South Asia Bks.

Jindel, Rajendra. Culture of a Sacred Town: Sociological Study of Nathdwara. 233p. 1986. 12.00X (ISBN 0-8364-1672-4, Pub. by Popular Prakashan). South Asia Bks.

Kar, Bijayananda. Indian Philosophy: An Analytical Study. 1986. 17.00x (ISBN 0-317-44233-3, Pub. by Ajanta). South Asia Bks.

Kawamura, Leslie S. Bodhisattva Doctrine. 306p. 1981. pap. text ed. 11.95x (ISBN 0-919812-12-0, Pub. by Wilfrid Laurier Canada). Humanities.

Keith, Arthur B. The Religion & Philosophy of the Veda & Upanishads, 2 vols. LC 71-109969. Repr. of 1925 ed. lib. bdg. 34.00x (ISBN 0-8371-4475-2, KEVU). Greenwood.

Keyt, George, tr. Song of Love. Orig. Title: Gita Govinda. 123p. 1969. pap. 2.00 (ISBN 0-88253-048-8). Ind-US Inc.

Kim, Young O. World Religions II: India's Religious Quest & the Faiths of the Far East. 2nd rev. ed. 415p. 1982. pap. 7.75 (ISBN 0-910621-37-3). HSA Pubns.

Klostermaier, K. Mythologies & Philosophies of Salvation in the Theistic Traditions of India. (Editions SR Ser.: No. 5). 549p. 1984. pap. text ed. 23.95x (ISBN 0-88920-158-7, Pub. by Wilfrid Laurier Canada). Humanities.

Krishna Prasad. Religious Freedom under Indian Constitution. 1976. 9.00x (ISBN 0-88386-839-3). South Asia Bks.

Kuppuswamy, B. Elements of Ancient Indian Psychology. 305p. 1986. text ed. 30.00x (ISBN 0-7069-2620-X, Pub. by Vikas India); pap. text ed. 10.95x (ISBN 0-7069-2620-X, Pub. by Vikas India). Advent NY.

Lalwani, K. C. Sramana Bhagavan Mahavira: Life & Doctrine. LC 75-904150. 1975. 10.00x (ISBN 0-88386-533-5). South Asia Bks.

Law, Bimala C. History of Buddha's Religion. (Bibliotheca Indo-Buddhica Ser.: No. 29). 174p. 1986. Repr. of 1952 ed. 24.00 (ISBN 81-7030-011-8, Pub. by SRI SATGURU Pubns India). Orient Bk Dist.

Liebert, Gosta. Iconographic Dictionary of the Indian Religions: Hinduism, Buddhism, Jainism. (Illus.). 377p. 1986. Repr. lib. bdg. 75.00 (ISBN 81-7030-098-3, Pub. by Sri Satguru Pubns India). Orient Bk Dist.

Ling, Trevor. Karl Marx & Religion: In Europe & India. LC 79-55947. 168p. 1980. text ed. 28.50x (ISBN 0-06-494294-5). B&N Imports.

MacDougall, John. Land or Religion? The Sardar & Kherwar Movements in Bihar, 1858-1895. 1986. 27.00x (ISBN 0-8364-1591-4, Pub. by Manohar India). South Asia Bks.

McGavran, Donald A. Ethnic Realities & the Church: Lessons from India. LC 78-11517. (Illus.). 1979. pap. 8.95 (ISBN 0-87808-168-2). William Carey Lib.

MacMunn, George. The Religions & Hidden Cults of India. (Illus.). xii, 244p. 1983. text ed. 30.00x (ISBN 0-86590-107-4). Apt Bks.

Madhava, K. G. Religions in Coastal Karnataka: 1500-1763. (Illus.). 206p. 1985. text ed. 37.50x (ISBN 0-86590-585-1, Inter India Pubns Delhi). Apt Bks.

Malyala, Panduranga R. Bhagavadgeeta-Bible-Khuran (Krishna-Jesus Mohammad) Date not set. 3.99 (ISBN 0-938924-04-4). Sri Shirdi Sai.

--Sri Ganesh Puja (Worship of God of Obstacles) (Illus.). 56p. 1982. 2.00 (ISBN 0-938924-03-6). Sri Shirdi Sai.

Martin, E. Osborn. The Gods of India: A Brief Description of Their History, Character, & Worship. LC 77-87621. 1977. Repr. of 1914 ed. lib. bdg. 40.00 (ISBN 0-89341-302-X). Longwood Pub Group.

Mathur, A. P. Radhasoami Faith: A Historical Study. 1974. 9.00 (ISBN 0-686-20296-1). Intl Bk Dist.

Miri, Sujata. Religion & Society of North-East India. 128p. 1980. text ed. 13.95x (ISBN 0-7069-1136-9, Pub. by Vikas India). Advent NY.

Mishra, K. C. The Cult of Jagannatha. 2nd, Rev. ed. 1985. 28.50x (ISBN 0-317-17545-9, Pub. by Mukhopadhyaya India). South Asia Bks.

Mookenthottam, Antony. Indian Theological Tendencies. (IC-Studies in the Intercultural History of Christianity: Vol. 21). 320p. 1979. pap. 34.80 (ISBN 3-261-04613-9). P Lang Pubs.

Mother India's Lighthouse: India's Spiritual Leaders & Flame-Heights of the West. LC 74-189998. 1973. 1.95 (ISBN 0-685-61448-4). Aum Pubns.

Mueller, Friedrich M. Lectures on the Origin & Growth of Religion, as Illustrated by the Religions of India. LC 73-18816. Repr. of 1882 ed. 34.50 (ISBN 0-404-11440-7). AMS Pr.

Murphet, Howard. Sai Baba Avatar: A New Journey into Power & Glory. LC 77-83643. 1977. 10.25 (ISBN 0-9600958-2-9); pap. 5.40 (ISBN 0-9600958-3-7). Birth Day.

Mushir-Ul-Haq. Islam in Secular India. (Indian Institute of Advanced Study Monographs Ser). 110p. 1972. 8.00x (ISBN 0-89684-426-9). Orient Bk Dist.

Nandi, R. N. Religious Institutions & Cults in the Deccan. 1973. 8.50 (ISBN 0-8426-0564-9). Orient Bk Dist.

Narayan, R. K. The Ramayana of R. K. Narayan: A Shortened Modern Prose Version of the Indian Epic, Suggested by the Tamil Version of Kamban. LC 79-189514. (Illus.). 192p. 1972. 13.95 (ISBN 0-670-58950-0). Viking.

Narla, V. R. Gods, Goblins & Men. 1979. 12.00x (ISBN 0-8364-0559-5, Pub. by Minerva Associates). South Asia Bks.

Newbigin, James E. The Reunion of the Church: A Defence of the South India Scheme. LC 79-4205. 1979. Repr. of 1960 ed. lib. bdg. cancelled (ISBN 0-313-20797-6, NERU). Greenwood.

Nikopol, Georg R. The Artistic & Mystical Significance of Indian & Egyptian Temples. (Illus.). 187p. 1984. 137.45 (ISBN 0-86650-131-2). Gloucester Art.

Nisargadatta Maharaj. Prior to Consciousness: Talks with Sri Nisargadatta Maharaj. Dunn, Jean, ed. LC 85-71544. ix, 159p. (Orig.). pap. 9.95 (ISBN 0-317-19710-X). Acorn NC.

Oddie, G. A. Social Protest in India: British Protestant Missionaries & Social Reforms, Eighteen Fifty to Nineteen Hundred. 1979. 17.50x (ISBN 0-8364-0195-6). South Asia Bks.

O'Flaherty, Wendy D. Karma & Rebirth in Classical Indian Traditions. LC 79-64475. 400p. 1980. 41.00x (ISBN 0-520-03923-8). U of Cal Pr.

O'Malley, Lewis S. Popular Hinduism: The Religion of the Masses. LC 70-142072. 1971. Repr. of 1935 ed. 24.00 (ISBN 0-384-43305-7). Johnson Repr.

Oman, J. C. Brahmans, Theists & Muslims of India. 1973. 24.00 (ISBN 0-89684-371-8). Orient Bk Dist.

Oman, John C. Cults, Customs, & Superstitions of India: Being a Revised & Enlarged Edition of Indian Life, Religious & Social. LC 70-179232. (Illus.). Repr. of 1908 ed. 36.00 (ISBN 0-404-54859-8). AMS Pr.

--The Mystics, Ascetics & Saints of India. lib. bdg. 75.00 (ISBN 0-8490-0698-8). Gordon Pr.
Osborne, Arthur. The Incredible Sai Baba: The Life & Miracles of a Modern-Day Saint. 102p. 1985. pap. text ed. 5.00x (ISBN 0-86125-105-9, Pub. by Orient Longman Ltd India). Apt Bks.
Panda, Sadhu C. Naga Cult in Orissa. xx, 142p. 1986. text ed. 30.00x (ISBN 81-7018-356-1, Pub. by B. R. Pub Corp Delhi). Apt Bks.
Paramananda, Swami. Srimad-Bhagavad-Gita. 7th ed. Orig. Title: Bhagavad-Gita, Srimad. 1981. 5.75 (ISBN 0-911564-03-9); lexitone bdg. 3.50. Vedanta Ctr.
Parratt, Saroj Nalini. The Religion of Manipur. 1980. 13.00x (ISBN 0-8364-0594-3, Pub. by Mukhopadhyaya India). South Asia Bks.
Pavitrananda, Swami. A Short Life of the Holy Mother. pap. 1.75 (ISBN 0-87481-122-8). Vedanta Pr.
Pillai, V. R. Temple Culture of South India. (Illus.). xii, 201p. 1986. text ed. 45.00x (ISBN 81-210-0168-4, Pub. by Inter India Pubns N Delhi). Apt Bks.
Radhakrishnan, S. Indian Religions. 1979. 7.00x (ISBN 0-8364-0367-3). South Asia Bks.
Raj Gupta, Giri, ed. Religions in Modern India. (Main Currents in Indian Sociology Ser.: Vol. 5). 368p. 1983. text ed. 37.50x (ISBN 0-7069-0793-0, Pub. by Vikas India). Advent NY.
Ramacharaka, Yogi. Philosophies & Religions of India. 8.00 (ISBN 0-911662-05-7). Yoga.
Ramakrishna, Sri. Sayings of Sri Ramakrishna. 5.50 (ISBN 0-87481-431-6). Vedanta Pr.
--Words of the Master. Brahmananda, Swami, ed. pap. 1.50 (ISBN 0-87481-135-X). Vedanta Pr.
Ramakrisnananda, Swami. Life of Sri Ranauja. 1979. pap. 8.95 (ISBN 0-87481-446-4). Vedanta Pr.
Ramanayyan, Venkata. An Essay on the Origin of the South Indian Temples. (Illus.). 92p. 1986. Repr. 15.00X (ISBN 0-8364-1725-9, Pub. by Manohar India). South Asia Bks.
Ramprasad. Ramprasad: The Melodius Mystic. Buddhananda, tr. 72p. 1985. pap. 2.00 (ISBN 0-87481-568-1, Pub. by Ramakrishna Math Madras India). Vedanta Pr.
Rao, K. L. Mahatma Gandhi & Comparative Religion. 1979. 15.00x (ISBN 0-89684-034-4). South Asia Bks.
Renou, Louis. Religions of Ancient India. 147p. Repr. of 1953 ed. text ed. 19.95x. Coronet Bks.
Rolland, Romain. Life of Ramakrishna. 5.95 (ISBN 0-87481-080-9). Vedanta Pr.
--La Vie de Ramakrishna. 1978. 16.95 (ISBN 0-686-55279-2). French & Eur.
--La Vie de Vivekananda. 352p. 1978. 16.95 (ISBN 0-686-55280-6). French & Eur.
Saletore, R. N. Encyclopaedia of Indian Culture, V-Z, Vol. 5. 324p. 1985. text ed. 50.00x (ISBN 0-391-02978-9, Pub. by Sterling India). Humanities.
Saradeshananda. The Mother as I Saw Her. Dey, J. N., tr. from Bengali. 247p. 1985. pap. 4.95 (ISBN 0-87481-530-4, Pub. by Ramakrishna Math Madras India). Vedanta Pr.
Sarkar, R. M. Regional Cults & Rural Traditions: An Interacting Pattern of Divinity & Humanity in Rural Bengal. (Illus.). xx, 351p. 1986. text ed. 50.00x (ISBN 81-210-0095-5, Pub. by Inter India Pubns N Delhi). Apt Bks.
Schweitzer, Albert. Indian Thought & Its Development. 1962. 11.00 (ISBN 0-8446-2893-X). Peter Smith.
Sethi, V. K. Kabir: The Weaver of God's Name. 762p. 1986. 23.00X (ISBN 0-8364-1673-2, Pub. by Manohar India). South Asia Bks.
Sharma, Kamalesh. Role of Muslims in Indian Politics, 1857-1947. 295p. 1986. text ed. 45.00x (ISBN 81-210-0028-9, Pub. by Inter India Pubns N Delhi). Apt Bks.
Sharma, T. N. Religious Thought in India. 1980. 11.00x (ISBN 0-8364-0619-2, Pub. by Ramneek). South Asia Bks.
Singh, Khushwant. Gurus, Godman & Good People. (Illus.). 134p. 1975. text ed. 13.95x (ISBN 0-86125-087-7, Pub. by Orient Longman India). Apt Bks.
Sinha, V. K. Secularism in India. 1968. 6.25 (ISBN 0-89684-521-4). Orient Bk Dist.
Sircar, D. C. Studies in the Religious Life of Ancient & Medieval India. 1971. 9.95 (ISBN 0-89684-326-2). Orient Bk Dist.
Smith, W. C. Modern Islam in India. 1985. Repr. of 1946 ed. 18.50x (ISBN 0-8364-1338-5, Pub. by Usha). South Asia Bks.
Spiritual Practices of India. pap. 1.25 (ISBN 0-8065-0057-3). Citadel Pr.
Sri Aurobindo Album. 55p. Date not set. 15.00 (ISBN 0-317-17482-7). Auromere.
Srivastava, Rama. Comparative Religion. LC 74-904268. 1974. 14.00x (ISBN 0-88386-565-3). South Asia Bks.
Subramanian, Anna A. Saints of India. (Illus.). 1978. pap. 3.25 (ISBN 0-87481-479-0). Vedanta Pr.
Swami Muktananda. Lalleshwari. LC 81-50160. 92p. 1981. pap. 3.95. SYDA Found.
Tapasyananda, Swami. Aratrika Hymns & Ram Nam. 1979. pap. 1.50 (ISBN 0-87481-476-6). Vedanta Pr.
Taranath. Taranatha's History of Buddhism in India. Chattopadhyaya, Debiprsdad & Chattopadhyaya, A., eds. 1980. Repr. of 1970 ed. 27.00x (ISBN 0-8364-1597-3, Pub. by KP Bagchi & Co.). South Asia Bks.
Tiwari, J. N. Goddess Cults in Ancient India. (Illus.). 250p. 1986. 62.50x (ISBN 0-8364-1819-0, Pub. by Chanakya India). South Asia Bks.
Troisi, J. Tribal Religion: Religious Beliefs & Practices Among the Santals. 1979. 18.00x (ISBN 0-8364-0197-2). South Asia Bks.
Tyagaraja. Spiritual Heritage of Tyagaraja. Ramanujachari, C., tr. (Sanskrit, Telegu & Eng.). 15.00 (ISBN 0-87481-440-5). Vedanta Pr.
Upanishads: The Crown of India's Soul. 1972. pap. 2.00 (ISBN 0-87847-012-3). Aum Pubns.
Uprety, Prem R. Religion & Politics in the Punjab in the 1920's. 1981. 20.00x (ISBN 0-8364-0757-1, Pub. by Sterling). South Asia Bks.
Vakil, AK. Three Dimensions of Hindu-Muslim Confrontation. 1982. 6.00 (ISBN 0-8364-0844-6, Pub. By Minerva India). South Asia Bks.
Varadpande, M. L. Religion & Theatre. 100p. 1982. text ed. 15.00x (ISBN 0-391-02794-8). Humanities.
Vijnananda. At the Feet of Ski Ramakrishna. 66p. 1985. pap. 1.50 (ISBN 0-87481-225-9, Pub. by Ramakrishna Math Madras India). Vedanta Pr.
Waghorne, Joanne Punzo, et al, eds. Gods of Flesh-Gods of Stone: The Embodiment of Divinity in India. LC 84-18543. (Orig.). 1985. pap. 12.95 (ISBN 0-89012-037-4). Anima Pubns.
Warder, A. K. Indian Buddhism. rev. 2nd ed. 580p. 1980. text ed. 22.00 (ISBN 0-89684-094-8, Pub. by Motilal Banarsidass India). Orient Bk Dist.
Warrier, A. G. God in Advaita. 1977. text ed. 15.00x (ISBN 0-8426-1047-2). Verry.
Watters, Thomas. On Yuan Chwang's Travels in India 629-645 A. D. LC 74-158213. Repr. of 1905 ed. Set. 45.00 (ISBN 0-404-06878-2). AMS Pr.
Werner, Karel. Perspectives on Indian Religion. Connolly, Peter, ed. 253p. 1986. lib. bdg. 56.00 (ISBN 0-85424-021-7, Pub. by Sri Satguru Pubns India). Orient Bk Dist.
Whitehead, Henry. Village Gods of South India. (Illus.). 175p. 1986. Repr. 15.00X (ISBN 0-8364-1709-7, Pub. by Usha). South Asia Bks.

INDIAN FOLK-LORE

see Folk-Lore, Indian

INDIAN POETRY

Bierhorst, John, ed. The Sacred Path: Spells, Prayers & Power Songs of the American Indians. LC 82-14118. (Illus.). 191p. 1983. PLB 10.25 (ISBN 0-688-01699-5). Morrow.
Sharpe, J. Edward, ed. American Indian Prayers & Poetry. (Illus.). 32p. 1985. pap. 3.00 (ISBN 0-935741-09-7). Cherokee Pubns.

INDIANS–ANTIQUITIES

Aveni, Anthony F., ed. Native American Astronomy. LC 76-53569. (Illus.). 304p. 1977. text ed. 18.95x (ISBN 0-292-75511-2). U of Tex Pr.

INDIANS–FOLK-LORE

see Folk-Lore, Indian

INDIANS–PICTURE WRITING

see Picture-Writing, Indian

INDIANS–RELIGION AND MYTHOLOGY

Bierhorst, John, ed. The Sacred Path: Spells, Prayers & Power Songs of the American Indians. LC 82-14118. (Illus.). 191p. 1983. PLB 10.25 (ISBN 0-688-01699-5). Morrow.
Brinton, D. G. Myths of the New World: A Treatise on the Symbolism & Mythology of the Red Race of America. LC 68-24972. (American History & Americana Ser., No. 47). 1969. Repr. of 1876 ed. lib. bdg. 75.00x (ISBN 0-8383-0918-6). Haskell.
Brinton, Daniel G. The Myths of the New World. LC 71-144901. 331p. 1972. Repr. of 1876 ed. 10.00 (ISBN 0-403-00839-5). Scholarly.
--Myths of the New World: A Treatise on the Symbolism & Mythology of the Red Race of America. 2nd ed. LC 69-13839. 1969. Repr. of 1876 ed. lib. bdg. 22.50x (ISBN 0-8371-2040-3, BRMN). Greenwood.
--Myths of the New World: A Treatise on the Symbolism & Mythology of the Red Race of America. LC 78-31682. 1979. Repr. of 1868 ed. lib. bdg. 30.00 (ISBN 0-89341-326-7). Longwood Pub Group.
Brinton, Daniel G., ed. Rig Veda Americanus. LC 73-83463. (Library of Aboriginal American Literature Ser.: No. 8). Repr. of 1890 ed. 30.00 (ISBN 0-404-52188-6). AMS Pr.
Brown, Vinson. Voices of Earth & Sky. LC 76-41761. (Illus.). 177p. 1976. pap. 6.95 (ISBN 0-87961-060-3). Naturegraph.
Bullchild, Percy. The Sun Came Down: The History of the World as My Blackfeet Elders Told It. LC 85-42771. (Illus.). 384p. 1985. 22.45 (ISBN 0-06-250107-0, HarpR). Har-Row.
Castaneda, Carlos. Journey to Ixtlan. 1983. pap. 4.95 (ISBN 0-671-60658-1). WSP.
--Tales of Power. 1982. pap. 4.95 (ISBN 0-671-55329-1). WSP.
Coward, Harold G., ed. Language in Indian Philosophy & Religion. 98p. 1978. pap. text ed. 9.95x (ISBN 0-919812-07-4, Pub. by Wilfrid Laurier Canada). Humanities.
Ely, Evelyn & Hughes, Phyllis. Ojos de Dios. (Illus.). 1972. pap. 2.50 (ISBN 0-89013-056-6). Museum NM Pr.
Herrick, Eduard F. Old Indian Temples, Idols & Worship. (Illus.). 154p. 1985. Repr. of 1882 ed. 91.45 (ISBN 0-89901-209-4). Found Class Reprints.
Highwater, Jamake. Native Land: Sagas of the Indian Americas. 1986. 24.95 (ISBN 0-316-36087-2). Little.
Luomala, K. Oceanic, American Indian, & African Myths of Snaring the Sun. (BMB Ser.). Repr. of 1940 ed. 11.00 (ISBN 0-527-02276-4). Kraus Repr.
Mackenzie, Donald. Indian Myth & Legend. LC 77-85615. 1978. Repr. of 1913 ed. lib. bdg. 50.00 (ISBN 0-89341-316-X). Longwood Pub Group.
MacKenzie, Donald A. Myths of Pre-Columbian America. LC 77-94602. 1978. Repr. of 1923 ed. lib. bdg. 40.00 (ISBN 0-89341-314-3). Longwood Pub Group.
Mooney, James. Myths of the Cherokee. LC 16-5534. (Landmarks in Anthropology Ser). Repr. of 1900 ed. 37.00 (ISBN 0-384-39920-7). Johnson Repr.
Peet, Stephen O. Myths & Symbols, or Aboriginal Religions in America. LC 76-27515. (Illus.). 1976. Repr. of 1905 ed. lib. bdg. 45.00 (ISBN 0-89341-039-X). Longwood Pub Group.
Poor, Laura E. Sanskrit & Its Kindred Literatures. LC 76-27525. 1976. Repr. of 1880 ed. lib. bdg. 35.00 (ISBN 0-89341-038-1). Longwood Pub Group.
Srivastava. Mother Goddess in Indian Art, Archaeology & Literature. 1980. 32.00x (ISBN 0-686-65576-1, Pub. by Agam India). South Asia Bks.
Williams, Raymond B. A New Face of Hinduism: The Swaminarayan Religion. LC 83-7197. 256p. 1984. 37.50 (ISBN 0-521-25454-X); pap. 13.95 (ISBN 0-521-27473-7). Cambridge U Pr.

INDIANS OF CENTRAL AMERICA–RELIGION AND MYTHOLOGY

Alexander, Hartley B. Latin American Mythology. LC 63-19096. (Mythology of All Races Ser.: Vol. 11). (Illus.). 1964. Repr. of 1932 ed. 30.00x (ISBN 0-8154-0006-3). Cooper Sq.
Gifford, Douglas. Warriors, Gods & Spirits from Central & South American Mythology. (World Mythologies Ser.). (Illus.). 132p. 1983. 15.95 (ISBN 0-8052-3857-3). Schocken.
Le Plongeon, Augustus. Sacred Mysteries among the Mayas & the Quiches. LC 73-76094. (Secret Doctrine Reference Ser). (Illus.). 200p. 1985. Repr. of 1886 ed. 12.00 (ISBN 0-913510-02-5). Wizards.
Recinos, Adrian & Goetz, Delia, trs. Popol Vuh: The Sacred Book of the Ancient Quiche Maya: Spanish Version of the Original Maya. (Civilization of the American Indian Ser.: No. 29). (Eng). 1983. Repr. of 1950 ed. 16.95 (ISBN 0-8061-0205-5). U of Okla Pr.
Spence, Lewis. The Myths of Mexico & Peru. LC 76-27516. (Illus.). 1976. Repr. of 1914 ed. lib. bdg. 45.00 (ISBN 0-89341-031-4). Longwood Pub Group.
--Popol Vuh: Mythic & Heroic Sagas of the Kiches of Central America. LC 75-139178. (Popular Studies in Mythology, Romance & Folklore: No. 16). Repr. of 1908 ed. 5.50 (ISBN 0-404-53516-X). AMS Pr.

INDIANS OF MEXICO–ANTIQUITIES

Sahagun, Bernardino de. Florentine Codex, General History of the Things of New Spain, 13 bks. Anderson, Arthur J. & Dibble, Charles E., trs. Incl. Introductory Volume: Introductions, Sahagun's Prologues & Interpolations, General Bibliography, General Indices. 1982. 35.00x (ISBN 0-87480-165-6); Bk. 1. Gods. rev., 2nd ed. 1970. 17.50 (ISBN 0-87480-000-5); Bk. 2. Ceremonies. rev., 2nd ed. 1981. 40.00x (ISBN 0-87480-194-X); Bk. 3. Origins of the Gods. rev., 2nd ed. 1979. 17.50x (ISBN 0-87480-002-1); Bks. 4 & 5. The Soothsayers, the Omens. Repr. of 1979 ed. 40.00x (ISBN 0-87480-003-X); Bk. 6. Rhetoric & Moral Philosophy. 1976. 40.00x (ISBN 0-87480-010-2); Bk. 7. Sun, Moon & Stars, & the Binding of the Years. Repr. of 1977 ed. 17.50 (ISBN 0-87480-004-8); Bk. 8. Kings & Lords. Repr. of 1979 ed. 20.00x (ISBN 0-87480-005-6); Bk. 9. Merchants. Repr. of 1976 ed. 20.00x (ISBN 0-87480-006-4); Bk. 10. People. Repr. of 1974 ed. 30.00x (ISBN 0-87480-007-2); Bk. 11. Earthly Things. Repr. of 1975 ed. 45.00x (ISBN 0-87480-008-0); Bk. 12. Conquest of Mexico. rev., 2nd ed. 1975. 27.50x (ISBN 0-87480-096-X). 1982. Set. 350.00x (ISBN 0-87480-082-X). U of Utah Pr.

INDIANS OF MEXICO–MISSIONS

Braden, Charles S. Religious Aspects of the Conquest of Mexico. LC 74-181914. Repr. of 1930 ed. 37.50 (ISBN 0-404-00925-5). AMS Pr.
Dunner, Peter M. Pioneer Jesuits in Northern Mexico. LC 78-10566. (Illus.). 1979. Repr. of 1944 ed. lib. bdg. 24.75x (ISBN 0-313-20653-8, DUPJ). Greenwood.
Shiels, William E. Gonzalo De Tapia, 1561-1594: Founder of the First Permanent Jesuit Mission in North America. LC 74-12835. (U. S. Catholic Historical Society Monograph: No. XIV). 1978. Repr. of 1934 ed. lib. bdg. 22.50x (ISBN 0-8371-7758-8, SHGT). Greenwood.

INDIANS OF MEXICO–RELIGION AND MYTHOLOGY

see also Mayas–Religion and Mythology

Alexander, Hartley B. Latin American Mythology. LC 63-19096. (Mythology of All Races Ser.: Vol. 11). (Illus.). 1964. Repr. of 1932 ed. 30.00x (ISBN 0-8154-0006-3). Cooper Sq.
Aveni, Anthony F. Skywatchers of Ancient Mexico. (Texas Pan American Ser.). (Illus.). 369p. 1980. text ed. 30.00x (ISBN 0-292-77557-1). U of Tex Pr.
Braden, Charles S. Religious Aspects of the Conquest of Mexico. LC 74-181914. Repr. of 1930 ed. 37.50 (ISBN 0-404-00925-5). AMS Pr.
Brenner, Anita. Idols Behind Altars. LC 67-19527. (Illus.). 1929. 18.00 (ISBN 0-8196-0190-X). Biblo.
Brundage, Burr C. The Fifth Sun: Aztec Gods, Aztec World. (Texas Pan American Ser.). (Illus.). 283p. 1979. pap. 8.95 (ISBN 0-292-72438-1). U of Tex Pr.
Caso, Alfonso. Aztecs: People of the Sun, Vol. 50. Dunham, Lowell, tr. (Civilization of the American Indian Ser.: No. 50). (Illus.). 142p. 1978. Repr. of 1958 ed. 24.95 (ISBN 0-8061-0414-7). U of Okla Pr.
Castaneda, Carlos. The Teachings of Don Juan: A Yaqui Way of Knowledge. LC 68-17303. 1968. pap. 5.95 (ISBN 0-520-02258-0, CAL253). U of Cal Pr.
Nuttall, Zelia. Penitential Rite of the Ancient Mexicans. (HU PMP Ser.). 1904. pap. 10.00 (ISBN 0-527-01189-4). Kraus Repr.
Ruiz de Alarcon, Hernando. Treatise on the Heathen Superstitions that Today Live among the Indians Native to this New Spain, 1629. Andrews, J. Richard & Hassig, Ross, eds. LC 83-47842. (The Civilization of the American Indian Ser.: Vol. 164). (Illus.). 540p. 1984. text ed. 48.50x (ISBN 0-8061-1832-6). U of Okla Pr.
Sandstrom, Alan R. Traditional Curing & Crop Fertility Rituals Among Otomi Indians of the Sierra de Puebla, Mexico: The Lopez Manuscripts. (Occasional Papers & Monographs: No. 3). (Illus.). vi, 104p. 1981. 4.00 (ISBN 0-9605982-0-0). W H Mathers Mus.
Sandstrom, Alan R. & Sandstrom, Pamela E. Traditional Papermaking & Paper Cult Figures of Mexico. LC 85-40947. (Illus.). 336p. 1986. 24.95 (ISBN 0-8061-1972-1). U of Okla Pr.
Spence, Lewis. The Mythologies of Ancient Mexico & Peru. 80p. 1921. 0.95 (ISBN 0-317-40437-7). Open Court.
--Myths of Mexico & Peru. 1976. lib. bdg. 60.00 (ISBN 0-8490-0700-3). Gordon Pr.
--The Myths of Mexico & Peru. LC 76-27516. (Illus.). 1976. Repr. of 1914 ed. lib. bdg. 45.00 (ISBN 0-89341-031-4). Longwood Pub Group.
Tedlock, Barbara. Time & the Highland Maya. LC 80-54569. (Illus.). 245p. 1981. pap. 10.95x (ISBN 0-8263-0835-X). U of NM Pr.
Vogt, Evon Z. Tortillas for the Gods: A Symbolic Analysis of Zinacanteco Rituals. 256p. 1976. 18.00x (ISBN 0-674-89554-1). Harvard U Pr.

INDIANS OF NORTH AMERICA–CIVILIZATION

see Indians of North America–Culture

INDIANS OF NORTH AMERICA–CULTURE

Here is entered literature dealing with the cultural condition (i.e. arts, industries, religion and mythology, etc.) of the Indian at a given time or period.

Begay, Shirley M. & Clinton-Tullie, Verna. Kinaalada: A Navajo Puberty Ceremony. rev. ed. LC 83-61661. (Illus.). 171p. 1983. 15.00x (ISBN 0-936008-11-3); pap. 11.00x. Navajo Curr.
Bierhorst, John, ed. The Sacred Path: Spells, Prayers, & Power Songs of the American Indians. LC 83-19460. (Illus.). 192p. 1984. pap. 8.20 (ISBN 0-688-02647-8, Quill). Morrow.
Bingham, Sam & Bingham, Janet, eds. Between Sacred Mountains: Navajo Stories & Lessons from the Land. LC 82-82827. (Illus.). 296p. 1982. 30.00 (ISBN 0-910675-00-7); pap. 19.95 (ISBN 0-910675-01-5). Rock Point.
Boyd, Doug. Rolling Thunder. 273p. 1986. pap. 9.95 (ISBN 0-385-28859-X, Delta). Dell.

Haeberlin, Herman K. The Idea of Fertilization in the Culture of the Pueblo Indians. LC 16-25723. (American Anthro. Association Memoirs). pap. 15.00 (ISBN 0-527-00512-6). Kraus Repr.

Marriott, Alice. The Ten Grandmothers. LC 45-1584. (The Civilization of the American Indians Ser.: Vol. 26). 306p. 1985. pap. 9.95 (ISBN 0-8061-1825-3). U of Okla Pr.

Mills, George. The People of the Saints. (Illus.). 1967. 5.00 (ISBN 0-916537-30-7, Taylor Museum). CO Springs Fine Arts.

Smith, Marian W. Puyallup-Nisqually. LC 73-82360. (Columbia Univ. Contributions to Anthropology Ser.: Vol. 32). 1969. Repr. of 1940 ed. 34.50 (ISBN 0-404-50582-1). AMS Pr.

Statement on American Indians. pap. cancelled (ISBN 0-686-15373-1, B-124). US Catholic.

Teit, James A. The Lillooet Indians. LC 73-3520. (Jesup North Pacific Expedition. Publications: No. 2, Pt. 5). Repr. of 1906 ed. 20.00 (ISBN 0-404-58121-8). AMS Pr.

Wilson, Gilbert L. The Horse & the Dog in Hidatsa Culture. LC 76-43895. (AMNH Anthropological Papers: Vol. 15, Pt. 2). Repr. of 1924 ed. 23.00 (ISBN 0-404-15751-3). AMS Pr.

INDIANS OF NORTH AMERICA–DANCES

see also Ghost Dance

Fletcher, Alice C. Indian Games & Dances with Native Songs. LC 75-136369. Repr. of 1915 ed. 14.50 (ISBN 0-404-07229-1). AMS Pr.

Kurath, Gertrude P. Iroquois Music & Dance: Ceremonial Arts of Two Seneca Longhouses. Repr. of 1964 ed. 39.00x (ISBN 0-403-03618-6). Scholarly.

Laubin, Reginald & Laubin, Gladys. Indian Dances of North America: Their Importance to Indian Life. LC 75-40962. (The Civilization of the American Indian Ser: No.141). 1979. 32.50 (ISBN 0-8061-1319-7). U of Okla Pr.

Lesser, Alexander. Pawnee Ghost Dance Hand Game. LC 79-82340. (Columbia Univ. Contributions to Anthropology Ser.: Vol. 16). 1969. Repr. of 1933 ed. 37.00 (ISBN 0-404-50566-X). AMS Pr.

Michelson, Truman. Notes on the Buffalo-Head Dance of the Bear Gens of the Fox Indians. Repr. of 1928 ed. 29.00x (ISBN 0-403-03668-2). Scholarly.

Speck, Frank G. Oklahoma Delaware Ceremonies, Feasts & Dances. LC 76-43845. (Memoirs of the American Philosophical Sociey: Vol. 7). Repr. of 1937 ed. 21.50 (ISBN 0-404-15696-7). AMS Pr.

Spier, Leslie. The Prophet Dance of the Northwest & Its Derivatives: The Source of the Ghost Dance. LC 76-43853. Repr. of 1935 ed. 18.00 (ISBN 0-404-15708-4). AMS Pr.

Walker, J. R. The Sun Dance & Other Ceremonies of the Oglala Division of the Teton Dakota. LC 76-43886. (AMNH Anthropological Papers: Vol. 16, Pt. 2). Repr. of 1917 ed. 21.50 (ISBN 0-404-15745-9). AMS Pr.

INDIANS OF NORTH AMERICA–LEGENDS

see also Folk-Lore, Indian

Barnouw, Victor. Wisconsin Chippewa Myths & Tales & Their Relation to Chippewa Life. LC 76-53647. 304p. 1977. 25.00x (ISBN 0-299-07310-6). U of Wis Pr.

Beckwith, Martha W. Mandan-Hidatsa Myths & Ceremonies. LC 38-19412. (American Folklore Society Memoirs). Repr. of 1938 ed. 29.00 (ISBN 0-527-01084-7). Kraus Repr.

Benedict, Ruth. Zuni Mythology, 2 Vols. LC 75-82366. (Columbia Univ. Contributions to Anthropology Ser.: No. 21). 1969. Repr. of 1935 ed. Set. 70.00 (ISBN 0-404-50571-6); 35.00 ea. AMS Pr.

Bierhorst, John, ed. The Red Swan: Myths and Tales of the American Indians. LC 76-196. 368p. 1976. pap. 7.95 (ISBN 0-374-51393-7). FS&G.

--The Sacred Path: Spells, Prayers, & Power Songs of the American Indians. LC 83-19460. (Illus.). 192p. 1984. pap. 8.20 (ISBN 0-688-02647-8, Quill). Morrow.

Bloomfield, Leonard. Plains Cree Texts. LC 73-3552. (American Ethnological Society. Publications Ser.: No. 16). Repr. of 1934 ed. 36.00 (ISBN 0-404-58166-8). AMS Pr.

--Sacred Stories of the Sweet Grass Cree. LC 74-7933. Repr. of 1930 ed. 34.50 (ISBN 0-404-11821-6). AMS Pr.

Boas, Franz. The Mythology of the Bella Coola Indians. LC 73-3510. (Jesup North Pacific Expedition. Publications: Vol. 1, Pt. 2). Repr. of 1898 ed. 20.00 (ISBN 0-404-58113-7). AMS Pr.

Boatright, Mody C., ed. The Sky Is My Tipi. LC 49-1690. (Texas Folklore Society Publications: No. 22). (Illus.). 1966. Repr. of 1949 ed. 13.95 (ISBN 0-87074-010-5). SMU Press.

Brown, Virginia P. & Owens, Laurella, eds. Southern Indian Myths & Legends. (Illus.). 160p. 1985. 15.95 (ISBN 0-912221-02-X). Beechwood.

Curtin, Jeremiah. Myths of the Modocs: Indian Legends from the Northwest. LC 74-170711. Repr. of 1912 ed. 20.00 (ISBN 0-405-08415-3, Blom Pubns). Ayer Co Pubs.

Dutton, Bertha P. & Olin, Caroline. Myths & Legends of the Indian Southwest. (Bk 2). (Illus.). 1978. pap. 2.95 (ISBN 0-88388-062-8). Bellerophon Bks.

Erodes, Richard & Ortiz, Alfonso. American Indian Myth & Legends. LC 84-42669. (Illus.). 504p. 1984. 19.45 (ISBN 0-394-50796-7). Pantheon.

Espinosa, Carmen G. The Freeing of the Deer & Other New Mexico Indian Myths. LC 85-16406. (Illus.). 83p. 1985. 9.95 (ISBN 0-8263-0840-6). U of NM Pr.

Faraud, Henri J. Dix-Huit Ans Chez Les Sauvages: Voyages Et Missions De Monseigneur Henry Faraud. Repr. of 1866 ed. 28.00 (ISBN 0-384-15135-3). Johnson Repr.

Goddard, Pliny E. Myths & Tales from the San Carlos Apache. LC 76-43715. (AMNH. Anthropological Pap.: Vol. 29, Pt. 1). Repr. of 1918 ed. 16.50 (ISBN 0-404-15548-0). AMS Pr.

Goodwin, Grenville, ed. Myths & Tales of the White Mountain Apache. LC 39-33959. (AFS M). Repr. of 1939 ed. 29.00 (ISBN 0-527-01085-5). Kraus Repr.

Henry Tall Bull & Weist, Tom. Cheyenne Legends of Creation. (Indian Culture Ser.). 1972. 1.95 (ISBN 0-89992-025-X). Coun India Ed.

Hilbert, Vi, ed. & tr. Haboo: Native American Stories from Puget Sound. LC 85-40397. (Illus.). 228p. 1985. pap. 9.95 (ISBN 0-295-96270-4). U of Wash Pr.

Jacobs, Melville. Content & Style of an Oral Literature: Clackamas Chinook Myths & Tales. LC 58-5617. 1959. 17.50x (ISBN 0-226-38973-1). U of Chicago Pr.

Johnson, F. Roy. North Carolina Indian Legends & Myths. (Illus.). 112p. 1981. 8.50 (ISBN 0-930230-43-4). Johnson NC.

Link, Margaret S., retold by. The Pollen Path: A Collection of Navajo Myths. LC 56-7272. (Illus.). 1956. 17.50x (ISBN 0-8047-0473-2). Stanford U Pr.

Mooney, James. Myths of the Cherokee. LC 70-108513. (American Indian History Sers). 1970. Repr. of 1900 ed. 89.00 (ISBN 0-403-00221-4). Scholarly.

Olin, Caroline & Olin, D. Caroline. Myths & Legends of the Indian Southwest, Bk 1. 1st ed. (Illus.). 1978. pap. 2.95 (ISBN 0-88388-049-0). Bellerophon Bks.

Opler, Morris E. Myths & Legends of the Lipan Apache Indians. LC 40-13687. (Amer. Folklore SocietyMemoirs Ser.). Repr. of 1940 ed. 21.00 (ISBN 0-527-01088-X). Kraus Repr.

--Myths & Tales of the Chiricahua Apache Indians. LC 43-2944. (Amer. Folklore Society Memoirs Ser.). Repr. of 1942 ed. 15.00 (ISBN 0-527-01089-8). Kraus Repr.

--Myths & Tales of the Jicarilla Apache Indians. LC 38-22477. (American Folklore Society Memoirs). Repr. of 1938 ed. 37.00 (ISBN 0-527-01083-9). Kraus Repr.

Parker, Arthur C. Seneca Myths & Folk Tales. LC 76-43803. (Buffalo Historical Society. Publication: Vol. 27). Repr. of 1923 ed. 35.00 (ISBN 0-404-15659-2). AMS Pr.

Rachlin & Marriott. Plains Indian Mythology. 224p. 1977. pap. 3.95 (ISBN 0-452-00766-6, Mer). NAL.

Radin, Paul. Literary Aspects of North American Mythology. (Folklore Ser). 20.00 (ISBN 0-8482-5887-8). Norwood Edns.

Rossman, Douglas A. Where Legends Live. (Illus.). 48p. (Orig.). 1986. pap. 5.00x (ISBN 0-935741-10-0). Cherokee Pubns.

Schoolcraft, H. R. Myth of Hiawatha, & Other Oral Legends, Mythologic & Allegoric, of the North American Indians. Repr. of 1856 ed. 28.00 (ISBN 0-527-80350-2). Kraus Repr.

Spence, L. Myths & Legends of the North American Indian. LC 72-81598. (Illus.). 396p. 1975. pap. cancelled (ISBN 0-8334-1745-2, Steinerbks). Garber Comm.

Swanton, John R. Haida Texts & Myths: Skidegate Dialect. LC 5-41613. (Landmarks in Anthropology Ser). Repr. of 1905 ed. 34.00 (ISBN 0-384-59020-9). Johnson Repr.

Troughton, Joanna, retold by. & illus. How Rabbit Stole the Fire: A North American Indian Folk Tale. LC 85-15629. (Folk-Tales of the World Ser.). (Illus.). 28p. 1986. 10.95 (ISBN 0-87226-040-2, Bedrick Blackie). P Bedrick Bks.

VanEtten, Teresa. Ways of Indian Wisdom. LC 86-5924. 96p. (Orig.). 1987. pap. 8.95 (ISBN 0-86534-090-0). Sunstone Pr.

Wild, Peter & Coss, Hal. The Saguaro Forest. LC 86-60514. (Western Horizons Ser.). (Illus.). 96p. (Orig.). 1986. pap. 11.95 (ISBN 0-87358-405-8). Northland.

Williams, Terry T. Pieces of White Shell. (Illus.). 176p. 1987. pap. 8.95 (ISBN 0-8263-0969-0). U of NM Pr.

INDIANS OF NORTH AMERICA–LEGENDS–JUVENILE LITERATURE

Beckwith, Martha W. Myths & Hunting Stories of the Mandan & Hidatsa Sioux. LC 76-43665. (Vassar College Folklore Foundation: Publication No. 10). 1977. Repr. of 1930 ed. 16.00 (ISBN 0-404-15498-0). AMS Pr.

Levin, Beatrice. Indian Myths from the Southeast. (Indian Culture Ser.). 1974. 1.95 (ISBN 0-89992-071-3). Coun India Ed.

INDIANS OF NORTH AMERICA–MAGIC

Andrews, Lynn V. Star Woman: We Are Made from Stars & to the Stars We Must Return. LC 86-40038. 256p. 1986. 16.95 (ISBN 0-446-51316-4). Warner Bks.

Freesoul, John Redtail. Breath of the Invisible. LC 86-40124. (Illus.). 226p. (Orig.). 1986. pap. 6.95 (ISBN 0-8356-0611-2). Theos Pub Hse.

Harrington, Mark R. Sacred Bundles of the Sac & Fox Indians. LC 76-43732. (Univivesity of Pennsylvania Museum Anthropological Publications: Vol. 4, No. 1). (Illus.). 192p. Repr. of 1914 ed. 30.00 (ISBN 0-404-15573-1). AMS Pr.

Kilpatrick, Jack F. & Kilpatrick, Anna G. Run Toward the Nightland: Magic of the Oklahoma Cherokees. LC 67-19814. (Illus.). 1967. pap. 9.95 (ISBN 0-87074-084-9). SMU Press.

Kluckhohn, Clyde. Navaho Witchcraft. 1962. pap. 8.95x (ISBN 0-8070-4697-3, BP243). Beacon Pr.

Steiger, Brad. American Indian Magic: Sacred Pow Wows & Hopi Prophecies. (Illus.). 210p. 1986. 17.95 (ISBN 0-938294-19-9); pap. 9.95 (ISBN 0-938294-20-2). Global Comm.

Whiting, Beatrice B. Paiute Sorcery. Repr. of 1950 ed. 19.00 (ISBN 0-384-68180-8). Johnson Repr.

INDIANS OF NORTH AMERICA–MEDICINE

see also Medicine-Man

Bahr, Donald M., et al. Piman Shamanism & Staying Sickness: Ka: cim Mumkidag. LC 72-92103. 332p. 1974. pap. 9.95 (ISBN 0-8165-0303-6). U of Ariz Pr.

Boyd, Doug. Rolling Thunder. 273p. 1986. pap. 9.95 (ISBN 0-385-28859-X, Delta). Dell.

Corlett, William T. The Medicine-Man of the American Indian & His Cultural Background. LC 75-23699. Repr. of 1935 ed. 47.50 (ISBN 0-404-13249-9). AMS Pr.

Densmore, Frances. Menominee Music. LC 72-1882. (Music Ser.). (Illus.). 286p. 1972. Repr. of 1932 ed. lib. bdg. 29.50 (ISBN 0-306-70510-9). Da Capo.

Dow, James. The Shaman's Touch: Otomi Indian Symbolic Healing. (Illus.). 180p. (Orig.). 1986. 13.95 (ISBN 0-87480-257-1). U of Utah Pr.

Freesoul, John Redtail. Breath of the Invisible. LC 86-40124. (Illus.). 226p. (Orig.). 1986. pap. 6.95 (ISBN 0-8356-0611-2). Theos Pub Hse.

Kluckhohn, Clyde & Wyman, L. C. Introduction to Navaho Chant Practice. LC 42-2722. (HU PMP Ser.). 1940. 21.00 (ISBN 0-527-00552-5). Kraus Repr.

Linderman, Frank B. Pretty-shield: Medicine Woman of the Crows. LC 72-3273. (Illus.). 256p. 1974. pap. 6.95 (ISBN 0-8032-5791-0, BB 580, Bison). U of Nebr Pr.

Luckert, Karl W. Coyoteway: A Navajo Holyway Healing Ceremonial. LC 78-10358. 243p. 1979. pap. 13.95 (ISBN 0-8165-0655-8). U of Ariz Pr.

Reichard, Gladys. Navajo Medicine Man Sand Paintings. (Illus.). 1977. pap. 8.95 (ISBN 0-486-23329-4). Dover.

Stone, Eric P. Medicine Among the American Indians. LC 75-23657. (Clio Medica: 7). (Illus.). Repr. of 1932 ed. 20.00 (ISBN 0-404-58907-3). AMS Pr.

Tantaquidgeon, Gladys. Folk Medicine of the Delaware & Related Algonkian Indians. LC 73-620801. (Pennsylvania Historical & Museum Commission Anthropological Ser.: No. 3). (Illus.). 145p. 1972. 7.50 (ISBN 0-911124-70-5); pap. 4.50 (ISBN 0-911124-69-1). Pa Hist & Mus.

--A Study of Delaware Indian Medicine Practice & Folk Beliefs. LC 76-43864. (Pennsylvania Historical Commission). Repr. of 1942 ed. 18.00 (ISBN 0-404-15724-6). AMS Pr.

Vogel, Virgil J. American Indian Medicine. LC 69-10626. (Civilization of the American Indian Ser.: Vol. 95). (Illus.). 1970. 29.95 (ISBN 0-8061-0863-0). U of Okla Pr.

Walker, James R. Lakota Belief & Ritual. DeMallie, Raymond J. & Jahner, Elaine A., eds. LC 79-19816. (Illus.). xxx, 369p. 1980. 21.50 (ISBN 0-8032-2551-2). U of Nebr Pr.

Wildschut, William. Crow Indian Medicine Bundles. 2nd ed. Ewers, John C., ed. LC 74-33115. (Illus.). 1975. soft cover 10.00 (ISBN 0-934490-34-1). Mus Am Ind.

Wyman, L. C. & Kluckhohn, Clyde. Navaho Classification of Their Song Ceremonials. LC 38-23008. (American Anthro. Association Memoirs). 1938. pap. 15.00 (ISBN 0-527-00549-5). Kraus Repr.

INDIANS OF NORTH AMERICA–MISSIONS

see also Jesuits–Missions

Barton, Winifred W. John P. Williamson: A Brother to the Sioux. LC 80-53176. (Illus.). 308p. 1980. Repr. of 1919 ed. 16.00 (ISBN 0-9610012-0-8). Sunnycrest Pub.

Beatty, Charles. Journal of a Two-Months Tour, with a View to Promoting Religion. LC 72-108459. 1768. 25.00x (ISBN 0-403-00456-X). Scholarly.

Berkhofer, Robert F. Salvation & the Savage: An Analysis of Protestant Missions & American Indian Response, 1787-1862. LC 77-22857. 1977. Repr. of 1965 ed. lib. bdg. 22.50x (ISBN 0-8371-9745-7, BESSA). Greenwood.

Berkhofer, Robert F., Jr. Salvation & the Savage: An Analysis of Protestant Missions & American Indian Response, 1787-1862. LC 65-11826. 1972. pap. text ed. 4.95x (ISBN 0-689-70290-6, 184). Atheneum.

Bowden, Henry W. American Indians & Christian Missions: Studies in Cultural Conflict. LC 80-27840. (Chicago History of American Religion Ser.). 1981. 18.00x (ISBN 0-226-06811-0). U of Chicago Pr.

--American Indians & Christian Missions: Studies in Cultural Conflict. LC 84-27840. (Chicago History of American Religion Ser). xx, 256p. 1985. pap. 7.95 (ISBN 0-226-06812-9). U of Chicago Pr.

Brainerd, David, ed. Memoirs of the Reverend David Brainerd: Missionary to the Indians on the Border of New York, New Jersey & Pennsylvania. LC 70-108477. (American Indian History Sers). 1970. Repr. of 1822 ed. 49.00x (ISBN 0-403-00233-8). Scholarly.

Burns, Louis F., ed. Osage Mission Baptisms, Marriages, & Interments, 1820-1886. (Osage Indian & Eng.). 869p. 1986. 35.00 (ISBN 0-942574-08-7). Ciga Pr.

Caldwell, Martha B. Annals of Shawnee Methodist Mission & Indian Manual Labor School. 2nd ed. LC 39-28738. (Illus.). 120p. 1977. pap. 2.95 (ISBN 0-87726-005-2). Kansas St Hist.

Coolidge, Grace. Teepee Neighbors. LC 83-40487. 200p. 1984. pap. 7.95 (ISBN 0-8061-1889-X). U of Okla Pr.

DeSmet, Pierre-Jean. Indian Missions. 67p. 1985. 10.95. Ye Galleon.

Faraud, Henri J. Dix-Huit Ans Chez Les Sauvages: Voyages Et Missions De Monseigneur Henry Faraud. Repr. of 1866 ed. 28.00 (ISBN 0-384-15135-3). Johnson Repr.

--Dix-Huit Ans Chez les Sauvages: Voyages et Missions De Mgr. Henry Faraud Paris-Bruxelles 1866. (Canadiana Avant 1867: No.12). 1966. 26.00x (ISBN 90-2796-329-0). Mouton.

Garrand, Victor. Augustine Laure, S. J., Missionary to the Yakimas. 36p. 1977. 8.00_o.s.i (ISBN 0-87770-176-8); pap. 5.95 (ISBN 0-87770-187-3). Ye Galleon.

Gray, Elma E. & Gray, Leslie R. Wilderness Christians: The Moravian Mission to the Delaware Indians. LC 72-84988. (Illus.). xiv, 354p. 1973. Repr. of 1956 ed. 22.00x (ISBN 0-8462-1701-5). Russell.

Haile, Berard. Cathechism & Guide: Navaho-English. (Orig.). 1937. pap. 3.00 (ISBN 0-686-32657-1). St Michaels.

Hare, Lloyd C. Thomas Mayhew, Patriarch to the Indians, 1593-1682. LC 76-104347. (Illus.). Repr. of 1932 ed. 20.00 (ISBN 0-404-03108-0). AMS Pr.

Kocher, Paul. Alabado, a Story of Old California. 1978. 6.95 (ISBN 0-8199-0689-1). Franciscan Herald.

Kutsche, Paul. A Guide to Cherokee Documents in the Northeastern United States. LC 85-11798. (Native American Bibliography Ser.: No. 7). 541p. 1986. 75.00 (ISBN 0-8108-1827-2). Scarecrow.

McCoy, Isaac. History of Baptist Indian Missions. LC 19-11605. 1970. Repr. of 1840 ed. 36.00 (ISBN 0-384-36590-6). Johnson Repr.

Mengarini, Gregory. Recollections of the Flathead Mission. Lothrop, Gloria, ed. LC 74-27573. (Illus.). 1977. 16.95 (ISBN 0-87062-111-4). A H Clark.

Milner, Clyde A., II & O'Neil, Floyd A., eds. Churchmen & the Western Indians, 1820-1920. LC 85-40477. (Illus.). 272p. 1985. 19.95 (ISBN 0-8061-1950-0). U of Okla Pr.

Morfi, Fray J. History of Texas, Sixteen Seventy-Three to Seventeen Seventy-Nine, 2 pts. Castaneda, Carlos E., ed. LC 67-24718. (Quivira Society Publications Ser.: Vol. 6). 1967. Repr. of 1935 ed. 34.00 (ISBN 0-405-19053-0). Ayer Co Pubs.

Mudge, Zachariah A. Sketches of Mission Life among the Indians of Oregon. 1983. 12.50 (ISBN 0-87770-308-6). Ye Galleon.

Olson. Bruchko. LC 73-81494. 1977. pap. 5.95 (ISBN 0-88419-133-8). Creation Hse.

Pitrone, Jean. Great Black Robe. (Illus.). 1965. 4.00 (ISBN 0-8198-0050-3); pap. 3.00 (ISBN 0-8198-0051-1). Dghtrs St Paul.

Shea, John D. History of the Catholic Missions Among the Indian Tribes of the United States, 1529-1854. LC 73-175853. Repr. of 1855 ed. 28.50 (ISBN 0-404-07176-7). AMS Pr.

Shea, John G. History of the Catholic Missions Among the Indian Tribes of the United States, 1529-1854. LC 70-83436. (Religion in America, Ser. 1). 1969. Repr. of 1857 ed. 26.50 (ISBN 0-405-00263-7). Ayer Co Pubs.

Smith, Defost. Martyrs of the Oblong & Little Nine. 1948. 6.00 (ISBN 0-910294-11-9). Brown Bk.

Tache, Alexandre A. Vingt Annees De Missions Dans le Nord-Ouest De L'amerique. (Canadiana Before 1867 Ser). (Fr). Repr. of 1866 ed. 18.00 (ISBN 0-384-59425-5). Johnson Repr.

--Vingt Annees De Missions Dans le Nord-Ouest De L'amerique Par Mgr. Alex. Tache Eveque De Saint-Boniface (Montreal, 1866) (Canadiana Avant 1867: NO. 21). 1970. 16.80x (ISBN 90-2796-343-6). Mouton.

Teiwes, Helga. Mission San Xavier del Bac: A Photographic Essay on the Desert People & Their Church. (Illus.). 32p. 1973. pap. 3.50 (ISBN 0-8165-0423-7). U of Ariz Pr.

Webb, Edith B. Indian Life at the Old Missions. LC 82-23871. (Illus.). xxx, 378p. 1983. Repr. of 1952 ed. 35.00 (ISBN 0-8032-4724-9). U of Nebr Pr.

Wilken, Robert L. Anselm Weber, O.F.M. Missionary to the Navaho. 1955. 12.50 (ISBN 0-686-32658-X, 55-1235). St Michaels.

INDIANS OF NORTH AMERICA–MUSIC

Bierhorst, John, ed. The Sacred Path: Spells, Prayers, & Power Songs of the American Indians. LC 83-19460. (Illus.). 192p. 1984. pap. 8.20 (ISBN 0-688-02647-8, Quill). Morrow.

Boas, Franz. The Social Organization & Secret Societies of the Kwakiutl Indians. Based on Personal Observations Notes Made by Mr. George Hunt. (Landmarks in Anthropology Ser). Repr. of 1897 ed. 60.00 (ISBN 0-384-04872-2). Johnson Repr.

Densmore, Frances. Menominee Music. LC 72-1882. (Music Ser.). (Illus.). 286p. 1972. Repr. of 1932 ed. lib. bdg. 29.50 (ISBN 0-306-70510-9). Da Capo.

Fewkes, Jessie W. & Gilman, Benjamin I. A Few Summer Ceremonials at Zuni Pueblo: Zuni Melodies, Reconnaissance of Ruins in or Near the Zuni Reservation. LC 76-21216. (A Journal of American Ethnology & Archaeology: Vol. 1). Repr. of 1891 ed. 25.00 (ISBN 0-404-58041-6). AMS Pr.

Graber, David, ed. Tsese-Ma'Heone-Nemeototse: Cheyenne Spiritual Songs. LC 82-83401. (Eng. & Cheyenne.). 227p. 1982. 29.95 (ISBN 0-87303-078-8). Faith & Life.

Kluckhohn, Clyde & Wyman, L. C. Introduction to Navaho Chant Practice. LC 42-2722. (HU PMP Ser.). 1940. 21.00 (ISBN 0-527-00552-5). Kraus Repr.

Kurath, Gertrude P. Dance & Song Rituals of Six Nations Reserve, Ontario. (Illus.). 205p. 1968. pap. text ed. 5.50x (ISBN 0-660-02066-1, 56320-0, Pub. by Natl Mus Canada). U of Chicago Pr.

--Iroquois Music & Dance: Ceremonial Arts of Two Seneca Longhouses. Repr. of 1964 ed. 39.00x (ISBN 0-403-03618-6). Scholarly.

McAllester, David P. Peyote Music. pap. 19.00 (ISBN 0-384-36490-X). Johnson Repr.

Wyman, L. C. & Kluckhohn, Clyde. Navaho Classification of Their Song Ceremonials. LC 38-23008. (American Anthro. Association Memoirs). 1938. pap. 15.00 (ISBN 0-527-00549-5). Kraus Repr.

INDIANS OF NORTH AMERICA–MYTHOLOGY

see Folk-Lore, Indian; Indians of North America–Legends; Indians of North America–Religion and Mythology

Brown, Virginia P. & Owens, Laurella, eds. Southern Indian Myths & Legends. (Illus.). 160p. 1985. 15.95 (ISBN 0-912221-02-X). Beechwood.

INDIANS OF NORTH AMERICA–RELIGION AND MYTHOLOGY

see also Indians of North America–Dances; Indians of North America–Magic; Peyotism; Totems

Alexander, Hartley B. North American Mythology. LC 63-19095. (Mythology of All Races Ser.: Vol. 10). (Illus.). 1964. Repr. of 1932 ed. 30.00x (ISBN 0-8154-0007-1). Cooper Sq.

Andrews, Lynn V. Flight of the Seventh Moon: The Teaching of the Shields. LC 83-48414. (Illus.). 208p. 1984. 13.45 (ISBN 0-06-250027-9, HarpR). Har-Row.

Bagley, Clarence B. Indian Myths of the Northwest. (Shorey Indian Ser.). (Illus.). 145p. pap. 8.95 (ISBN 0-8466-4041-4, I41). Shorey.

Bailey, Paul. Ghost Dance Messiah: The Jack Wilson Story. LC 75-135152. 12.95 (ISBN 0-87026-025-1). Westernlore.

Barney, Garold D. Mormons, Indians & the Ghost Dance Religion of 1890. LC 85-29509. (Illus.). 258p. (Orig.). 1986. lib. bdg. 28.00 (ISBN 0-8191-5227-7); pap. text ed. 13.50 (ISBN 0-8191-5228-5). U Pr of Amer.

Beck, Peggy V. & Walters, Anna L. The Sacred: Ways of Knowledge, Sources of Life. (Illus.). 384p. 1977. 16.00x (ISBN 0-912586-24-9). Navajo Coll Pr.

Benedict, Ruth F. Concept of the Guardian Spirit in North America. LC 24-872. (American Anthropology Association Memoirs). 1923. 12.00 (ISBN 0-527-00528-2). Kraus Repr.

Bierhorst, John. The Mythology of North America: Intro to Classic American Gods, Heroes & Tricksters. LC 86-12207. (Illus.). 256p. 1986. pap. 6.95 (ISBN 0-688-06666-6, Quill). Morrow.

Bierhorst, John, ed. The Sacred Path: Spells, Prayers, & Power Songs of the American Indians. LC 83-19460. (Illus.). 192p. 1984. pap. 8.20 (ISBN 0-688-02647-8, Quill). Morrow.

Blanchard, Kendall. The Economics of Sainthood: Religious Change among the Rimrock Navajos. LC 75-10141. (Illus.). 244p. 1976. 22.50 (ISBN 0-8386-1770-0). Fairleigh Dickinson.

Bloomfield, Leonard. Sacred Stories of the Sweet Grass Cree. LC 74-7933. Repr. of 1930 ed. 34.50 (ISBN 0-404-11821-6). AMS Pr.

Boas, Franz. Kwakiutl Culture As Reflected in Mythology. LC 36-6760. (American Folklore Society Memoirs). Repr. of 1935 ed. 19.00 (ISBN 0-527-01080-4). Kraus Repr.

--Religion of the Kwakiutl Indians, 2 Vols. LC 72-82368. (Columbia Univ. Contributions to Anthropology Ser.: No. 10). Repr. of 1930 ed. Set. 60.00 (ISBN 0-404-50560-0); 30.00 ea. AMS Pr.

Boissiere, Robert. Meditations With the Hopi. LC 86-70257. (Meditations With Ser.). (Illus.). 144p. (Orig.). 1986. pap. 6.95 (ISBN 0-939680-27-0). Bear & Co.

Brinton, Daniel G. The Myths of the New World: A Treatise on the Symbolism & Mythology of the Red Race in America. LC 74-1038. 360p. 1974. Repr. of 1896 ed. 30.00x (ISBN 0-8103-3959-5). Gale.

--Myths of the New World: The Symbolism & Mythology of the Indians of the Americas. LC 72-81594. (Illus.). 348p. pap. cancelled (ISBN 0-89345-207-6, Steinerbks). Garber Comm.

Brown, Joseph E. Spiritual Legacy of American Indian. 160p. 1984. pap. 8.95 (ISBN 0-8245-0618-9). Crossroad NY.

--Spiritual Legacy of the American Indian. LC 64-17425. (Illus., Orig.). 1964. pap. 2.50x (ISBN 0-87574-135-5). Pendle Hill.

Brown, Vinson. Voices of Earth & Sky. LC 76-41761. (Illus.). 177p. 1976. pap. 6.95 (ISBN 0-87961-060-3). Naturegraph.

Brundage, Burr C. The Phoenix of the Western World: Quetzalcoatl & the Sky Religion. LC 81-40278. (The Civilization of the American Indian Ser.: Vol. 160). (Illus.). 320p. 1982. 22.50x (ISBN 0-8061-1773-7). U of Okla Pr.

Capps, Walter H., ed. Seeing with a Native Eye: Contributions to the Study of Native American Religion. LC 76-9980. 1976. pap. 6.95xi (ISBN 0-06-061312-2, RD-177, HarpR). Har-Row.

Chupco, Lee & Coachman, Ward. Creek (Muscogee) New Testament Concordance. 167p. 1982. spiral bdg. 12.50x (ISBN 0-940392-10-0). Indian U Pr OK.

Clark, Ella. Guardian Spirit Quest. (Indian Culture Ser.). 1974. pap. 1.95 (ISBN 0-89992-045-4). Coun India Ed.

Colton, Harold S. Hopi Kachina Dolls with a Key to Their Identification. rev ed. LC 59-5480. (Illus.). 150p. 1971. pap. 8.95 (ISBN 0-8263-0180-0). U of NM Pr.

Cooke, Grace. Sun Men of the Americas. pap. 5.95 (ISBN 0-85487-057-1). De Vorss.

Cooper, Guy H. Development & Stress in Navajo Religion. 126p. (Orig.). 1984. pap. text ed. 20.00x (ISBN 91-7146-337-2). Coronet Bks.

Cooper, John M. The Northern Algonquian Supreme Being. LC 76-43682. (Catholic University of America Anthropological Ser.: No. 2). Repr. of 1934 ed. 14.00 (ISBN 0-404-15515-4). AMS Pr.

Curtin, Jeremiah. Creation Myths of Primitive America. 1980. 31.00 (ISBN 0-405-13697-8, 1710). Ayer Co Pubs.

--Myths of the Modocs: Indian Legends from the Northwest. LC 74-170711. Repr. of 1912 ed. 20.00 (ISBN 0-405-08415-3, Blom Pubns). Ayer Co Pubs.

Cushing, Frank H. Zuni Fetishes. LC 66-23329. (Illus.). 43p. 1966. pap. 3.00 (ISBN 0-916122-03-4). KC Pubns.

Dewdney, Selwyn. Sacred Scrolls of the Southern Ojibway. LC 73-90150. 1974. 27.50x (ISBN 0-8020-3321-0). U of Toronto Pr.

Dorsey, G. A. & Voth, H. R. Oraibi Soyal Ceremony, & Oraibi Powamu Ceremony, & Mishongnovi Ceremonies of the Snake & Antelope Fraternities, & Oraibi Summer Snake Ceremony, 4 wks. in 1 vol. 1901-03. (Chicago Field Museum of Natural History). 70.00 (ISBN 0-527-01863-5). Kraus Repr.

Dunigan, Jack. The Pastor's Handbook. (Orig.). 1985. pap. 6.95 (ISBN 0-932943-00-4). Life Lines.

Duran, Fr. Diego. Book of the Gods & Rites & the Ancient Calendar. Horcasitas, Fernando & Heyden, Doris, trs. LC 73-88147. (Civilization of the American Indian Ser.: No. 102). (Illus.). 1977. pap. 12.95 (ISBN 0-8061-1201-8). U of Okla Pr.

Earle, Edwin & Kennard, Edward A. Hopi Kachinas. 2nd ed. LC 71-139867. (Illus.). 1971. 12.50 (ISBN 0-934490-11-2). Mus Am Ind.

Eastman, Charles A. The Soul of the Indian: An Interpretation. LC 79-26355. xvi, 170p. 1980. pap. 5.95 (ISBN 0-8032-6701-0, BB 735, Bison). U of Nebr Pr.

Emerson, Ellen. Indian Myths. 59.95 (ISBN 0-8490-0400-4). Gordon Pr.

Fenton, William N. The False Faces of the Iroquois. (Illus.). 1987. 75.00. U of Okla Pr.

Fewkes, Jesse W. & Owens, John G. A Few Summer Ceremonials at the Tusayon Pueblos: Natal Ceremonies of the Hopi Indians,& a Report on the Present Condition of a Ruin in Arizona Called Casa Grande. LC 76-21217. (A Journal of American Ethnology & Archaeology: Vol. 2). 1977. Repr. of 1892 ed. 30.00 (ISBN 0-404-58042-4). AMS Pr.

Fewkes, Jesse W., et al. The Snake Ceremonials at Walpi. LC 76-17497. (A Journal of American Ethnology & Archaeology: Vol. 4). Repr. of 1894 ed. 25.00 (ISBN 0-404-58044-0). AMS Pr.

Fishler, Stanley A. In the Beginning: A Navaho Creation Myth. (Utah Anthropological Papers: No. 13). Repr. of 1953 ed. 26.50 (ISBN 0-404-60613-X). AMS Pr.

Geertz, Armin W. & Lomatuway'ma, Michael. Children of Cottonwood: Piety & Ceremonialism in Hopi Indian Puppetry. (American Tribal Religions Ser.: Vol. 12). (Illus.). viii, 412p. 1987. 24.95x (ISBN 0-8032-2127-4); pap. 14.95x (ISBN 0-8032-7021-6). U of Nebr Pr.

Gill, Sam. Native American Religions. 208p. 1981. pap. text ed. write for info. (ISBN 0-534-00973-5). Wadsworth Pub.

Gill, Sam D. Sacred Words: A Study of Navajo Religion & Prayer. LC 80-659. (Contributions in Intercultural & Comparative Studies: No. 4). (Illus.). xxvi, 257p. 1981. lib. bdg. 29.95 (ISBN 0-313-22165-0, GSW/). Greenwood.

Goddard, Pliny E. Myths & Tales from the San Carlos Apache. LC 76-43715. (AMNH. Anthropological Pap.: Vol. 29, Pt. 1). Repr. of 1918 ed. 16.50 (ISBN 0-404-15548-0). AMS Pr.

Haeberlin, Herman K. The Idea of Fertilization in the Culture of the Pueblo Indians. LC 16-25723. (American Anthro. Association Memoirs). pap. 15.00 (ISBN 0-527-00512-6). Kraus Repr.

Haile, Berard. Love-Magic & Butterfly People: The Slim Curly Version of the Ajilee & Mothway Myths. LC 78-59705. (American Tribal Religions Ser.: Vol. 2). (Illus.). xii, 172p. 1978. pap. 13.95x (ISBN 0-89734-026-4, Pub by Mus Nothern Ariz). U of Nebr Pr.

--Waterway. LC 79-66605. (American Tribal Religions Ser.: Vol. 5). (Illus.). vi, 153p. 1979. pap. 12.95x (ISBN 0-89734-030-2, Pub. by Mus Northern Ariz). U of Nebr Pr.

Harrington, M. R. Sacred Bundles of the Sac & Fox Indians. (Anthropological Publications Ser.: Vol. 4-2). (Illus.). 142p. 1914. 10.50x (ISBN 0-686-24093-6). Univ Mus of U.

Harrington, Mark R. Religion & Ceremonies of the Lenape. LC 76-43731. (MAI Indian Notes & Monographs. Miscellaneous). Repr. of 1921 ed. 31.50 (ISBN 0-404-15572-3). AMS Pr.

Harrod, Howard L. Renewing the World: Northern Plains Indian Religion. LC 87-5010. 210p. 1987. 22.50x (ISBN 0-8165-0958-1). U of Ariz Pr.

Harwell, Henry O. & Harwell, Delores T. The Creek Verb. 57p. 1981. 6.00x (ISBN 0-940392-03-8). Indian U Pr OK.

Hausman, Gerald. Meditations With Animals: A Native American Bestiary. LC 86-70259. (Meditations With Ser.). (Illus.). 141p. (Orig.). 1986. pap. 6.95 (ISBN 0-939680-26-2). Bear & Co.

Heath, Virginia S. Dramatic Elements in American Indian Ceremonials. (American History & Americana Ser., No. 47). 1970. pap. 22.95x (ISBN 0-8383-0093-6). Haskell.

Heckewelder, John. Narrative of the Mission of the United Brethren Among the Delaware & Mohegan Indians. LC 79-146399. (First American Frontier Ser). 1971. Repr. of 1820 ed. 29.00 (ISBN 0-405-02852-0). Ayer Co Pubs.

Hendren, Samuel R. Government & Religion of the Virginia Indians. LC 78-63845. (Johns Hopkins University. Studies in the Social Sciences. Thirteenth Ser. 1895: 11-12). Repr. of 1895 ed. 11.50 (ISBN 0-404-61102-8). AMS Pr.

Hewitt, John N. Iroquoian Cosmology, 2 pts. in 1. LC 73-8095. Repr. of 1928 ed. 60.00 (ISBN 0-404-11202-1). AMS Pr.

Hildreth, Dolly, et al. The Money God. (Indian Culture Ser.). 1972. 1.95 (ISBN 0-89992-031-4). Coun India Ed.

Hultkrantz, Ake. Belief & Worship in Native North America. Vecsey, Christopher, ed. LC 81-18356. (Illus.). 358p. 1981. 30.00x (ISBN 0-8156-2248-1). Syracuse U Pr.

--The Religions of the American Indians. LC 73-90661. (Hermeneutics: Studies in the History of Religions). 1979. 20.95x (ISBN 0-520-02653-5); pap. 7.95 (ISBN 0-520-04239-5, CAL 463). U of Cal Pr.

--The Study of American Indian Religions. Vecsey, Christopher, ed. LC 82-10533. (The American Academy of Religion - Studies in Religion). 142p. 1983. 12.95 (ISBN 0-89130-587-4, 01 00 29). Scholars Pr GA.

Johnson, F. Roy. North Carolina Indian Legends & Myths. (Illus.). 112p. 1981. 8.50 (ISBN 0-930230-43-4). Johnson NC.

Jorgensen, Joseph G. The Sun Dance Religion: Power for the Powerless. LC 70-182089. 1972. pap. 12.50x (ISBN 0-226-41085-4). U of Chicago Pr.

--The Sun Dance Religion: Power for the Powerless. LC 70-182089. (Illus.). xii, 360p. 1986. pap. 14.95 (ISBN 0-226-41086-2). U of Chicago Pr.

Kessell, John L. Mission of Sorrows: Jesuit Guevari & the Pimas, 1691-1767. LC 79-101098. pap. 60.00 (ISBN 0-317-28586-6, 2055248). Bks Demand UMI.

Kilpatrick, Jack F. & Kilpatrick, Anna G. Run Toward the Nightland: Magic of the Oklahoma Cherokees. LC 67-19814. (Illus.). 1967. pap. 9.95 (ISBN 0-87074-084-9). SMU Press.

Klah, Hasteen. Navajo Creation Myth: The Story of Emergence. LC 76-43762. (Museum of Navajo Ceremonial Art. Religion Ser.: Vol. 1). Repr. of 1942 ed. 24.50 (ISBN 0-404-15615-0). AMS Pr.

Kluckhohn, Clyde & Wyman, L. C. Introduction to Navaho Chant Practice. LC 42-2722. (HU PMP Ser.). 1940. 21.00 (ISBN 0-527-00552-5). Kraus Repr.

Kroeber, Alfred L. Yurok Myths. LC 75-3772. 460p. 1976. 31.00x (ISBN 0-520-02977-1); pap. 6.95 (ISBN 0-520-03639-5, CAL 386). U of Cal Pr.

LaBarre, Weston. The Peyote Cult. 4th ed. LC 75-19425. (Illus.). xix, 296p. 1975. 27.50 (ISBN 0-208-01456-X, Archon). Shoe String.

Link, Margaret S., retold by. The Pollen Path: A Collection of Navajo Myths. LC 56-7272. (Illus.). 1956. 17.50x (ISBN 0-8047-0473-2). Stanford U Pr.

Locke, Raymond F. The Book of the Navajo. 3rd ed. pap. 4.95 (ISBN 0-87687-400-6, Pub. by Mankind Pub). Borden.

Lowie, Robert H. The Religion of the Crow Indians. LC 74-7986. Repr. of 1922 ed. 15.00 (ISBN 0-404-11876-3). AMS Pr.

Luckert, Karl W. A Navajo Bringing-Home Ceremony: The Claus Chee Sonny Version of Deerway Ajilee. LC 78-59701. (Illus.). 14p. 1978. pap. 14.95x (ISBN 0-89734-027-2). Mus Northern Ariz.

McClintock, Walter. The Old North Trail; or, Life, Legends & Religion of the Blackfeet Indians. LC 68-13651. (Illus.). xxvii, 539p. 1968. pap. 11.50 (ISBN 0-8032-5130-0, BB 379, Bison). U of Nebr Pr.

McDonald, W. H. Creation Tales from the Salish. (Indian Culture Ser.). 1973. 1.95 (ISBN 0-89992-061-6). Coun India Ed.

Malotki, Ekkehart & Lomatuway'ma, Michael. Maasaw: Profile of a Hopi God. LC 87-163. (American Tribal Religions Ser.: Vol. 11). (Illus.). vi, 432p. 1987. 24.95x (ISBN 0-8032-3118-0); pap. 14.95x (ISBN 0-8032-8148-X, Bison). U of Nebr Pr.

--Stories of Maasaw, a Hopi God. LC 87-164. (American Tribal Religions Ser.: Vol. 10). (Illus.). vi, 388p. 1987. 23.95x (ISBN 0-8032-3117-2); pap. 13.95x (ISBN 0-8032-8147-1). U of Nebr Pr.

Marriott, Alice. The Ten Grandmothers. LC 45-1584. (The Civilization of the American Indians Ser.: Vol. 26). 306p. 1985. pap. 9.95 (ISBN 0-8061-1825-3). U of Okla Pr.

Marriott, Alice & Rachlin, Carol K. American Indian Mythology. 258p. (YA) 1972. pap. 3.50 (ISBN 0-451-62327-4, ME2327, Ment). NAL.

Meredith, Howard & Milan, Virginia E. A Cherokee Vision of Eloh' Proctor, Wesley, tr. (Eng. & Cherokee.). 37p. 1981. pap. 8.00x (ISBN 0-940392-04-6); write for info. Indian U Pr OK.

Meredith, Howard & Smith, Adeline. A Cherokee Prayerbook. (Eng. & Cherokee.). 44p. 1981. pap. 1.50x (ISBN 0-940392-02-X). Indian U Pr OK.

Miller, David H. Ghost Dance. LC 85-5876. (Illus.). xviii, 318p. 1985. 23.95x (ISBN 0-8032-3099-0); pap. 8.95 (ISBN 0-8032-8130-7, BB 943, Bison). U of Nebr Pr.

Modesto, Ruby & Mount, Guy. Not for Innocent Ears: Spiritual Traditions of a Desert Cahuilla Medicine Woman. rev. ed. (Illus.). 128p. 1986. pap. 7.95 (ISBN 0-9604462-0-6). Sweetlight.

Mooney, James. Ghost-Dance Religion & the Sioux Outbreak of 1890. Wallace, Anthony F., ed. LC 64-24971. (Orig.). 1965. pap. 14.00 (ISBN 0-226-53517-7, P176, Phoen). U of Chicago Pr.

--Myths of the Cherokee & Sacred Formulas of the Cherokees. LC 72-188151. (Illus.). 1982. 20.00 (ISBN 0-918450-05-5); pap. 14.00x (ISBN 0-918450-22-5). C Elder.

Myerhoff, Barbara G. Peyote Hunt: The Sacred Journey of the Huichol Indians. LC 73-16923. (Symbol, Myth & Ritual Ser.). (Illus.). 288p. 1976. pap. 9.95x (ISBN 0-8014-9137-1). Cornell U Pr.

Opler, Morris E. Myths & Tales of the Jicarilla Apache Indians. LC 38-22477. (American Folklore Society Memoirs). Repr. of 1938 ed. 37.00 (ISBN 0-527-01083-9). Kraus Repr.

Painter, Muriel T. With Good Heart: Yaqui Beliefs & Ceremonies in Pascua, Village. Spicer, Edward H. & Kaemlein, Wilma, eds. LC 86-893. (Illus.). 533p. 1986. 35.00x (ISBN 0-8165-0875-5). U of Ariz Pr.

Parker, Arthur C. Seneca Myths & Folk Tales. LC 76-43803. (Buffalo Historical Society. Publication: Vol. 27). Repr. of 1923 ed. 35.00 (ISBN 0-404-15659-2). AMS Pr.

Parsons, Elsie C. Hopi & Zuni Ceremonialism. LC 34-5260. (American Anthro. Associatiom Memoirs). 1933. 11.00 (ISBN 0-527-00538-X). Kraus Repr.

--Scalp Ceremonial of Zuni. LC 25-1663. (American Anthro. Association Memoirs). 1924. pap. 15.00 (ISBN 0-527-00530-4). Kraus Repr.

Powers, William. Sacred Language: The Nature of Supernatural Discourse in Lakota. LC 86-40079. (Civilization of the American Indians Ser.: Vol. 179). (Illus.). 320p. 1986. 24.95x (ISBN 0-8061-2009-6). U of Okla Pr.

Powers, William K. Oglala Religion. LC 76-30614. (Illus.). xxii, 237p. 1977. pap. 6.95 (ISBN 0-8032-8706-2, BB 802, Bison). U of Nebr Pr.

Rachlin & Marriott. Plains Indian Mythology. 224p. 1977. pap. 3.95 (ISBN 0-452-00766-6, Mer). NAL.

Radin, Paul. Literary Aspects of North American Mythology. (Folklore Ser). 20.00 (ISBN 0-8482-5887-8). Norwood Edns.

--Trickster: A Study in American Indian Mythology. Repr. of 1956 ed. lib. bdg. 28.75x (ISBN 0-8371-2112-4, RATT). Greenwood.

--The Trickster: A Study in American Indian Mythology. LC 74-88986. 223p. 1972. pap. 6.95 (ISBN 0-8052-0351-6). Schocken.

Reichard, Gladys A. Analysis of Coeur D'Alene Indian Myths. LC 48-2411. (AFS M). Repr. of 1947 ed. 21.00 (ISBN 0-527-01093-6). Kraus Repr.

--Navaho Religion: A Study of Symbolism. LC 83-5082. 804p. 1983. pap. 19.95x (ISBN 0-8165-0834-8). U of Ariz Pr.

Riggs, Stephen R. Tah-Koo Wah-Kan; Or, the Gospel Among the Dakotas. LC 78-38460. (Religion in America, Ser. 2). 534p. 1972. Repr. of 1869 ed. 33.00 (ISBN 0-405-04081-4). Ayer Co Pubs.

Sharpe, J. Edward, ed. American Indian Prayers & Poetry. (Illus.). 32p. 1985. pap. 3.00 (ISBN 0-935741-09-7). Cherokee Pubns.

Siskin, Edgar E. Washo Shamans & Peyotists: Religious Conflict in an American Indian Tribe. (Illus.). 300p. 1983. 25.00x (ISBN 0-87480-223-7). U of Utah Pr.

Smithson, Carma L. & Euler, Robert C. Havasupai Religion & Mythology. (Utah Anthropological Papers: No. 68). Repr. of 1964 ed. 14.00 (ISBN 0-404-60668-7). AMS Pr.

--Havasupai Religion & Mythology. viii, 112p. Repr. of 1964 ed. 19.00 (ISBN 0-384-56210-8). Johnson Repr.

Snyder, Gary. He Who Hunted Birds in His Father's Village: The Dimensions of a Haida Myth. LC 78-16935. 154p. 1979. pap. 5.95 (ISBN 0-912516-38-0). Grey Fox.

Spencer, Katherine. Mythology & Values: An Analysis of Navaho Chantway Myths. (American Folklore Society Memoir Ser: No. 48). 248p. 1957. pap. 6.95x (ISBN 0-292-73528-6). U of Tex Pr.

--Reflections of Social Life in the Navaho Origin Myth. LC 76-43850. (Univ. of New Mexico. Publications in Anthropology: No. 3). 1983. Repr. of 1947 ed. 20.00 (ISBN 0-404-15705-X). AMS Pr.

Steinmetz, Paul. Meditations with Native Americans: Lakota Spirituality. LC 83-71961. (Meditations with Ser.). (Illus.). 144p. (Orig.). 1984. pap. 6.95 (ISBN 0-939680-13-0). Bear & Co.

Swanton, John R. Myths & Tales of the Southeastern Indians. LC 74-9011. (Smithsonian Institution. Bureau of American Enthnology. Bulletin: 88). Repr. of 1929 ed. 20.00 (ISBN 0-404-11908-5). AMS Pr.

--Tlingit Myths & Texts. Repr. of 1909 ed. 34.00 (ISBN 0-384-59050-0). Johnson Repr.

--Tlingit Myths & Texts. Repr. of 1909 ed. 49.00 (ISBN 0-403-03710-7). Scholarly.

Tedlock, Dennis & Tedlock, Barbara, eds. Teachings from the American Earth: Indian Religion & Philosophy. (Illus.). 304p. 1976. pap. 7.95 (ISBN 0-87140-097-9). Liveright.

Thomas, George. Christian Indians & Indian Nationalism, 1885-1950: An Interpretation in Historical & Theological Perspectives. (IC-Studies in the Intercultural History of Christianity: Vol. 22). 271p. 1979. 28.10 (ISBN 3-8204-6399-2). P Lang Pubs.

Tyler, Hamilton A. Pueblo God & Myths. LC 64-11317. (The Civilization of the American Indians Ser.: Vol. 71). (Illus.). 336p. 1984. pap. 8.95 (ISBN 0-8061-1112-7). U of Okla Pr.

Underhill, Ruth M. Papago Indian Religion. LC 74-82363. (Columbia Univ. Contributions to Anthropology Ser.: Vol. 33). Repr. of 1946 ed. 37.50 (ISBN 0-404-50583-X). AMS Pr.

--Red Man's Religion: Beliefs & Practices of the Indians North of Mexico. LC 65-24985. 1972. pap. 10.00 (ISBN 0-226-84167-7, P481, Phoen). U of Chicago Pr.

Underhill, Ruth M., et al. Rainhouse & Ocean: Speeches for the Papago Year. LC 79-66733. (American Tribal Religions Ser.: Vol. 4). (Illus.). vi, 154p. 1979. pap. 12.95x (ISBN 0-89734-029-9, Pub by Mus Northern Ariz). U of Nebr Pr.

Vecsey, Christopher. Traditional Ojibwa Religion & Its Historical Changes. LC 83-72209. (Mem. Ser.: Vol. 152). 1983. 12.00 (ISBN 0-87169-152-3). Am Philos.

Walker, James R. Lakota Belief & Ritual. DeMallie, Raymond J. & Jahner, Elaine A., eds. LC 79-19816. (Illus.). xxx, 369p. 1980. 21.50 (ISBN 0-8032-2551-2). U of Nebr Pr.

--Lakota Myth. Jahner, Elaine A., ed. LC 83-3454. xiv, 428p. 1983. 29.95x (ISBN 0-8032-4726-5); pap. 14.95 (ISBN 0-8032-9706-8, BB 848, Bison). U of Nebr Pr.

Wheelwright, Mary C. The Myth & Prayers of the Great Star Chant & the Myth of the Coyote Chant. (Illus.). 191p. 1987. 14.00 (ISBN 0-912586-58-3); pap. 10.00 (ISBN 0-912586-61-3). Navajo Coll Pr.

Wissler, Clark. Social Organization & Ritualistic Ceremonies of the Blackfoot Indians, 2 parts in 1 vol. LC 74-9020. (Anthropological Papers of the American Museum of Natural History: Vol. 7). (Illus.). Repr. of 1912 ed. 24.00 (ISBN 0-404-11917-4). AMS Pr.

Wissler, Clark & Duvall, D. C. Mythology of the Blackfoot Indians. LC 74-9019. (Anthropological Papers of the American Museum of Natural History: Vol. 2, Pt. 1). (Illus.). Repr. of 1909 ed. 17.00 (ISBN 0-404-11916-6). AMS Pr.

Wood, Charles E. A Book of Tales, Being Myths of the North American Indians. 59.95 (ISBN 0-87968-770-3). Gordon Pr.

Wright, B. Pueblo Cultures. (Iconography of Religions X Ser.: No. 4). (Illus.). xii, 29p. 1986. pap. 26.25 (ISBN 90-04-07106-7, Pub. by E J Brill). Heinman.

Wyman, L. C. & Kluckhohn, Clyde. Navaho Classification of Their Song Ceremonials. LC 38-23008. (American Anthro. Association Memoirs). 1938. pap. 15.00 (ISBN 0-527-00549-5). Kraus Repr.

Wyman, Leland C. Blessingway. LC 66-28786. (Illus.). 660p. 1970. U of Ariz Pr.

INDIANS OF NORTH AMERICA–RITES AND CEREMONIES

see also Peyotism

Alexander, Hartley B. The World's Rim: Great Mysteries of the North American Indians. LC 53-7703. (Illus.). xx, 259p. 1967. pap. 7.95 (ISBN 0-8032-5003-7, BB 160, Bison). U of Nebr Pr.

Beckwith, Martha W. Mandan-Hidatsa Myths & Ceremonies. LC 38-19412. (American Folklore Society Memoirs). Repr. of 1938 ed. 29.00 (ISBN 0-527-01084-7). Kraus Repr.

Boyd, Doug. Rolling Thunder. 273p. 1986. pap. 9.95 (ISBN 0-385-28859-X, Delta). Dell.

Brown, Joseph E., ed. The Sacred Pipe: Black Elk's Account of the Seven Rites of Oglala Sioux. LC 53-8810. (Civilization of the American Indian Ser.: No. 36). (Illus.). 1981. 17.95 (ISBN 0-8061-0272-1). U of Okla Pr.

Clark, Ella. Guardian Spirit Quest. (Indian Culture Ser.). 1974. pap. 1.95 (ISBN 0-89992-045-4). Coun India Ed.

Collier, John. On the Gleaming Way: Navajos, Eastern Pueblos, Zunis, Hopis, Apaches & Their Land, & Their Meanings to the World. LC 62-12407. 163p. (Photos, Orig). 1962. pap. 5.95 (ISBN 0-8040-0232-0, SB). Ohio U Pr.

Eaton, Evelyn. I Send a Voice. LC 78-7273. (Illus., Orig.). 1978. 10.95 (ISBN 0-8356-0513-2). Theos Pub Hse.

Fenton, William N. The False Faces of the Iroquois. (Illus.). 1987. 75.00. U of Okla Pr.

Fewkes, Jesse W. Hopi Snake Ceremonies: An Eyewitness Account. LC 86-1127. (Bureau of American Ethnology Ser.). (Illus.). 160p. 1986. Repr. of 1897 ed. 16.95 (ISBN 0-936755-00-8). Avanyu Pub.

Frisbie, Charlotte J., ed. Southwestern Indian Ritual Drama. LC 79-2308. (School of American Research Advanced Seminar Ser.). (Illus.). 384p. 1980. 30.00x (ISBN 0-8263-0521-0). U of NM Pr.

Gilliland, Hap. Coyote's Pow-Wow. (Indian Culture Ser.). 1972. 1.95 (ISBN 0-89992-022-5). Coun India Ed.

Haile, Berard. Head & Face Masks in Navaho Ceremonialism. LC 76-43722. Repr. of 1947 ed. 17.50 (ISBN 0-404-15565-0). AMS Pr.

Harrington, Mark R. Religion & Ceremonies of the Lenape. LC 76-43731. (MAI Indian Notes & Monographs. Miscellaneous). Repr. of 1921 ed. 31.50 (ISBN 0-404-15572-3). AMS Pr.

LaBarre, Weston. The Peyote Cult. 4th ed. LC 75-19425. (Illus.). xix, 296p. 1975. 27.50 (ISBN 0-208-01456-X, Archon). Shoe String.

Luckert, Karl W. Coyoteway: A Navajo Holyway Healing Ceremonial. LC 78-10358. 243p. 1979. pap. 13.95 (ISBN 0-8165-0655-8). U of Ariz Pr.

--A Navajo Bringing-Home Ceremony: The Claus Chee Sonny Version of Deerway Ajilee. LC 78-59701. (Illus.). 14p. 1978. pap. 14.95x (ISBN 0-89734-027-2). Mus Northern Ariz.

Matthews, Washington. The Night Chant: A Navaho Ceremony. LC 74-7991. Repr. of 1902 ed. 70.00 (ISBN 0-404-11880-1). AMS Pr.

Painter, Muriel T. With Good Heart: Yaqui Beliefs & Ceremonies in Pascua, Village. Spicer, Edward H. & Kaemlein, Wilma, eds. LC 86-893. (Illus.). 533p. 1986. 35.00x (ISBN 0-8165-0875-5). U of Ariz Pr.

Radin, Paul. Road of Life & Death. (Bollingen Ser.: Vol. 5). 1945. 33.00 (ISBN 0-691-09819-0). Princeton U Pr.

Simmons, Marc. Witchcraft in the Southwest: Spanish & Indian Supernaturalism on the Rio Grande. LC 79-18928. (Illus.). xiv, 184p. 1980. pap. 5.50 (ISBN 0-8032-9116-7, BB 729, Bison). U of Nebr Pr.

Simmons, William S. Cautantowwit's House: An Indian Burial Ground on the Island of Conanicut in Narragansett Bay. LC 77-111456. (Illus.). pap. 49.50 (ISBN 0-317-41779-7, 2025642). Bks Demand UMI.

Speck, Frank G. Oklahoma Delaware Ceremonies, Feasts & Dances. LC 76-43845. (Memoirs of the American Philosophical Sociey: Vol. 7). Repr. of 1937 ed. 21.50 (ISBN 0-404-15696-7). AMS Pr.

--A Study of the Delaware Indian Big House Ceremony: In Native Text Dictated by Witapanoxwe. LC 76-43846. (Publications of the Pennsylvania Historical Commission: Vol. 2). Repr. of 1931 ed. 24.00 (ISBN 0-404-15698-3). AMS Pr.

Tooker, Elisabeth, ed. Native North American Spirituality of the Eastern Woodlands: Sacred Myths, Dreams, Vision Speeches, Healing Formulas, Rituals & Ceremonials. LC 79-66573. (Classics of Western Spirituality Ser.). 320p. 1979. pap. 9.95 (ISBN 0-8091-2256-1). Paulist Pr.

Voth, H. R. Oraibu Marau Ceremony-Brief Miscellaneous Hopi Papers. (Chicago Field Museum of Natural History Fieldiana Anthropology Ser.). 1912. 44.00 (ISBN 0-527-01871-6). Kraus Repr.

Walker, J. R. The Sun Dance & Other Ceremonies of the Oglala Division of the Teton Dakota. LC 76-43886. (AMNH Anthropological Papers: Vol. 16, Pt. 2). Repr. of 1917 ed. 21.50 (ISBN 0-404-15745-9). AMS Pr.

Wyman, Leland C. The Mountainway of the Navajo. LC 74-83333. 271p. 1975. 14.50x (ISBN 0-8165-0412-1). U of Ariz Pr.

INDIANS OF SOUTH AMERICA–LEGENDS

see also Folk-Lore, Indian

Levi-Strauss, Claude. From Honey to Ashes. (Science of Mythology Ser.). 1980. Repr. of 1973 ed. lib. bdg. 34.50x (ISBN 0-374-94952-2, Octagon). Hippocrene Bks.

Roe, Peter G. The Cosmic Zygote: Cosmology in the Amazon Basin. (Illus.). 451p. 1982. 42.00x (ISBN 0-8135-0896-7). Rutgers U Pr.

Whittaker, Arabelle & Warkentin, Viola. Chol Texts on the Supernatural. (Publications in Linguistics & Related Fields Ser.: No. 13). 171p. 1965. microfiche (2) 4.00. Summer Inst Ling.

Wilbert, Johannes & Simoneau, Karin, eds. Folk Literature of the Chorote Indians. LC 85-9961. (Latin American Studies Ser.: Vol. 60). 288p. 1985. lib. bdg. 27.50x (ISBN 0-87903-060-7). UCLA Lat Am Ctr.

INDIANS OF SOUTH AMERICA–MISSIONS

Loewen, Jacob A. Culture & Human Values: Christian Intervention in Anthropological Perspective. Smalley, William A., ed. LC 75-12653. (Applied Cultural Anthropology Ser.). 443p. (Orig.). 1975. pap. 10.95x (ISBN 0-87808-722-2). William Carey Lib.

Rippy, J. Fred & Nelson, Jean T. Crusaders of the Jungle. LC 76-123495. 1971. Repr. of 1936 ed. 31.50x (ISBN 0-8046-1382-6, Pub. by Kennikat). Assoc Faculty Pr.

INDIANS OF SOUTH AMERICA–RELIGION AND MYTHOLOGY

Alexander, Hartley B. Latin American Mythology. LC 63-19096. (Mythology of All Races Ser.: Vol. 11). (Illus.). 1964. Repr. of 1932 ed. 30.00x (ISBN 0-8154-0006-3). Cooper Sq.

Brown, Michael F. Tsewa'a Gift: Magic & Meaning in an Amazonian Society. LC 85-40401. (Ethnographic Inquiry Ser.). (Illus.). 220p. 1986. 19.95x (ISBN 0-87474-294-3, BRTG). Smithsonian.

Gifford, Douglas. Warriors, Gods & Spirits from Central & South American Mythology. (World Mythologies Ser.). (Illus.). 132p. 1983. 15.95 (ISBN 0-8052-3857-3). Schocken.

Hadingham, Evan. Lines to the Mountain Gods: Nazca & the Mysteries of Peru. LC 86-10137. (Illus.). 256p. 1986. 22.50 (ISBN 0-394-54235-5). Random.

Haile, Berard. The Upward Moving & Emergence Way: The Gishin Biye Version. Luckert, Karl W., ed. LC 81-7441. (American Tribal Religions Ser.: Vol. 7). xvi, 239p. 1981. 19.95x (ISBN 0-8032-2320-X); pap. 11.95x (ISBN 0-8032-7212-X, BB 786, Bison). U of Nebr Pr.

--Women versus Men: A Conflict of Navajo Emergence. Luckert, Karl W., ed. LC 81-7433. (American Tribal Religions Ser.: Vol. 6). viii, 119p. 1981. 14.95x (ISBN 0-8032-2319-6); pap. 9.95x (ISBN 0-8032-7211-1, BB 785, Bison). U of Nebr Pr.

Hugh-Jones, S. The Palm & the Pleiades. LC 78-5533. (Studies in Social Anthropology: No. 24). (Illus.). 1979. 37.50 (ISBN 0-521-21952-3). Cambridge U Pr.

Hultkrantz, Ake. The Religions of the American Indians. LC 73-90661. (Hermeneutics: Studies in the History of Religions). 1979. 20.95x (ISBN 0-520-02653-5); pap. 7.95 (ISBN 0-520-04239-5, CAL 463). U of Cal Pr.

Lowie, Robert H. Myths & Traditions of the Crow Indians. LC 74-7981. Repr. of 1918 ed. 24.00 (ISBN 0-404-11872-0). AMS Pr.

Markham, Clements R., ed. & tr. Narratives of the Rites & Laws of the Yncas. (Hakluyt Society First Ser.: No. 48). (Illus.). 1964. Repr. of 1873 ed. 26.50 (ISBN 0-8337-2232-8). B Franklin.

Metraux, Alfred. Myths of the Toba & Pilaga Indians of the Gran Chaco. LC 46-4565. (Amer. Folklore Society Memoirs Ser.). Repr. of 1946 ed. 15.00 (ISBN 0-527-01092-8). Kraus Repr.

Osborne, Harold. South American Mythology. LC 85-28567. (The Library of the World's Myths & Legends). (Illus.). 144p. 1986. 18.95 (ISBN 0-87226-043-7). P Bedrick Bks.

Powlison, Paul S. Yagua Mythology: Epic Tendencies in a New World Mythology. Merrifield, William R., ed. LC 84-63152. (International Museum of Cultures Publications: No. 16). (Illus.). 132p. (Orig.). 1985. pap. 14.00 (ISBN 0-88312-172-7); microfiche (2) 4.00 (ISBN 0-88312-254-5). Summer Inst Ling.

Reichel-Dolmatoff, Gerardo. Amazonian Cosmos: The Sexual & Religious Symbolism of the Tukano Indians. Reichel-Dolmatoff, Gerardo, tr. from Span. LC 73-133491. xxiv, 290p. 1974. pap. 7.95X (ISBN 0-226-70732-6, P574, Phoen). U of Chicago Pr.

Spence, Lewis. The Mythologies of Ancient Mexico & Peru. 80p. 1921. 0.95 (ISBN 0-317-40437-7). Open Court.

--The Myths of Mexico & Peru. LC 76-27516. (Illus.). 1976. Repr. of 1914 ed. lib. bdg. 45.00 (ISBN 0-89341-031-4). Longwood Pub Group.

Teit, James A. Mythology of the Thompson Indians. LC 73-3529. (Jesup North Pacific Expeditions. Publications: No. 8, Pt. 2). Repr. of 1912 ed. 27.50 (ISBN 0-404-58125-0). AMS Pr.

Vaughan, Alden T. & Clark, Edward W., eds. Puritans among the Indians: Accounts of Captivity & Redemption, 1676-1724. (John Harvard Library). 288p. 1986. pap. text ed. 7.95x (ISBN 0-674-73899-3, Belknap Pr). Harvard U Pr.

Wilbert, Johannes & Simoneau, Karin, eds. Folk Literature of the Chorote Indians. LC 85-9961. (Latin American Studies Ser.: Vol. 60). 288p. 1985. lib. bdg. 27.50x (ISBN 0-87903-060-7). UCLA Lat Am Ctr.

INDIC PHILOSOPHY
see Philosophy, Indic

INDIFFERENTISM (RELIGION)
see also Liberalism (Religion)

Cizik, Richard. The High Cost of Indifference. LC 84-15957. 1984. pap. 6.95 (ISBN 0-8307-1000-0, 5418377). Regal.

Grotius, Hugo. True Religion Explained & Defended. Coventry, F., tr. LC 72-201. (English Experience Ser.: No. 318). 350p. 1971. Repr. of 1632 ed. 28.00 (ISBN 90-221-0318-8). Walter J Johnson.

INDONESIA–RELIGION

Evans, Ivor H. The Religion of the Tempusak Dusuns of North Borneo. LC 77-86972. Repr. of 1953 ed. 40.00 (ISBN 0-404-16707-1). AMS Pr.

Haire, James. The Character & Theological Struggle of the Church in Halmahera, Indonesia, 1941-1979. (IC-Studies in the Intercultural History of Christianity: Vol. 26). xii, 382p. 1981. pap. 42.05 (ISBN 3-8204-5888-3). P Lang Pubs.

Kipp, Rita S. & Rodgers, Susan, eds. Indonesian Religions in Transition. LC 86-30742. 304p. 1987. 29.95x (ISBN 0-8165-1020-2). U of Ariz Pr.

Willis, Avery T., Jr. Indonesian Revival: Why Two Million Came to Christ. LC 77-12811. (Illus.). 1977. pap. 6.95 (ISBN 0-87808-428-2). William Carey Lib.

INDULGENCES
see also Absolution; Catholic Church–Discipline; Purgatory

Enchiridion of Indulgences. rev. ed. maroon cloth 5.00 (ISBN 0-89942-555-0, 555/22). Catholic Bk Pub.

Herbst, Winfrid. New Regulations on Indulgences. 47p. 1970. pap. 1.50 (ISBN 0-89555-103-9). TAN Bks Pubs.

Lea, Henry C. History of Auricular Confession & Indulgences in the Latin Church, 3 Vols. LC 68-19287. 1968. Repr. of 1896 ed. lib. bdg. 67.25x (ISBN 0-8371-0140-9, LEHC). Greenwood.

Thurston, Herbert. The Holy Year of the Jubilee: An Account of the History & Ceremonial of the Roman Jubilee. LC 78-63481. Repr. of 1900 ed. 38.45 (ISBN 0-404-16547-8). AMS Pr.

INDUSTRY (PSYCHOLOGY)
see Work

INEBRIETY
see Alcoholism

INEQUALITY
see Equality

INFALLIBILITY OF THE CHURCH
see Catholic Church–Infallibility

INFALLIBILITY OF THE POPE
see Popes–Infallibility

INFANT BAPTISM
see also Baptism; Predestination

Bromiley, Geoffrey W. Children of Promise: The Case for Baptizing Infants. LC 79-10346. 1979. pap. 3.95 (ISBN 0-8028-1797-1). Eerdmans.

Johnson, Maxwell E. Beginnings: Preparing for Your Child's Baptism. (Pass Along Ser.). 32p. (Orig.). 1986. pap. 2.95 (ISBN 0-933350-47-3). Morse Pr.

Newman, Albert H. History of Anti-Pedobaptism: From the Rise of Pedobaptism to A.D. 1609. LC 71-144664. Repr. of 1897 ed. 26.45 (ISBN 0-404-04686-X). AMS Pr.

Sartelle, John P. Infant Baptism: What Christian Parents Should Know. 32p. 1985. pap. 1.95 (ISBN 0-87552-429-X); shrinkwrapped package of 12 19.50 (ISBN 0-87552-438-9). Presby & Reformed.

Wittenback, Janet. God Makes Me His Child in Baptism. LC 85-7689. 24p. 1985. pap. 2.95 (ISBN 0-570-04126-0, 56-1537). Concordia.

INGLIS, CHARLES, BP. OF NOVA SCOTIA, 1734-1816

Lydekker, John W. The Life & Letters of Charles Inglis: His Ministry in America & Consecration As First Colonial Bishop from 1759 to 1787. (Church Historical Society London N. S. Ser.: No. 20). Repr. of 1936 ed. 50.00 (ISBN 0-8115-3144-9). Kraus Repr.

INITIATIONS (IN RELIGION, FOLK-LORE, ETC.)
see also Baptism

Archdiocese of Dubuque Staff. R. C. I. A. Foundations of Christian Initiation. 96p. 1982. wire coil 7.95 (ISBN 0-697-01781-8). Wm C Brown.

Barbernitz, Patricia. RCIA: The Rite of Christian Initiation of Adults. 48p. 1983. pap. 2.95 (ISBN 0-89243-190-3). Liguori Pubns.

Droogers, Andre. The Dangerous Journey: Symbolic Aspects of Boys' Initiation Among the Wagenia of Kisangani, Zaire. (Change & Continuity in Africa Ser.). 1979. pap. text ed. 23.60x (ISBN 90-279-3357-X). Mouton.

Eliade, Mircea. Rites & Symbols of Initiation: The Mysteries of Birth & Rebirth. Orig. Title: Birth & Rebirth. pap. 5.95x (ISBN 0-06-131236-3, TB1236, Torch). Har-Row.

--Rites & Symbols of Initiation: The Mysteries of Birth & Rebirth. 16.75 (ISBN 0-8446-2027-0). Peter Smith.

Harley, George W. Notes on the Poro in Liberia. (HU PMP). 1941. 12.00 (ISBN 0-527-01248-3). Kraus Repr.

Henderson, Joseph L. Thresholds of Initiation. LC 67-24110. 1967. pap. 10.95 (ISBN 0-8195-6061-8). Wesleyan U Pr.

Herdt, Gilbert H., ed. Rituals of Manhood: Male Initiation in Papua New Guinea. 392p. 1982. 38.50x (ISBN 0-520-04448-7); pap. 10.95 (ISBN 0-520-04454-1, CAL 564). U of Cal Pr.

Jensen, Adolf E. Beschneidung und Reifezeremonien Bei Naturvoelkern. 1933. 19.00 (ISBN 0-384-27160-X). Johnson Repr.

Murphy Center for Liturgical Research. Made, Not Born: New Perspectives on Christian Initiation & the Catechumenate. 192p. 1976. pap. 6.95 (ISBN 0-268-01337-3). U of Notre Dame Pr.

Steiner, Rudolf. Initiation & Its Results. 134p. 1984. pap. 8.00 (ISBN 0-89540-148-7, SB-148). Sun Pub.

--Man in the Past, the Present, & the Future: The Sun-Initiation of the Druid Priest & His Moon-Science. Goddard, E., tr. from Ger. 82p. 1982. pap. 5.00 (ISBN 0-85440-403-1, Pub by Steinerbooks). Anthroposophic.

INNER LIGHT

Thurman, Howard. Inward Journey. LC 77-70182. 1973. pap. 7.95 (ISBN 0-913408-03-4). Friends United.

--Mysticism & the Experience of Love. LC 61-13708. (Orig.). 1961. pap. 2.50x (ISBN 0-87574-115-0). Pendle Hill.

Viereck, Peter. Inner Liberty. 1983. pap. 2.50x (ISBN 0-87574-095-2, 095). Pendle Hill.

INNOCENTIUS 3RD, POPE, 1160 or 61-1216

Elliott-Binns, L. Innocent III. LC 68-15343. xi, 212p. 1968. Repr. of 1931 ed. 19.50 (ISBN 0-208-00393-2, Archon). Shoe String.

Smith, Charles E. Innocent Three, Church Defender. LC 79-88939. 1971. Repr. of 1951 ed. lib. bdg. 55.00x (ISBN 0-8371-3145-6, SMIN). Greenwood.

Tillmann, H. Pope Innocent III. (Europe in the Middle Ages Selected Studies: Vol. 12). 374p. 1980. 64.00 (ISBN 0-444-85137-2, North-Holland). Elsevier.

INQUISITION
see also Persecution

Alcala, Angel, ed. The Spanish Inquisition & the Inquisitional Mind. (Atlantic Studies: No. 49). write for info (ISBN 0-88033-952-7). Brooklyn Coll Pr.

Andrzejewski, Jerzy. The Inquisitors. Syrop, Konrad, tr. from Polish. LC 76-6896. 1976. Repr. of 1960 ed. lib. bdg. 22.50x (ISBN 0-8371-8868-7, ANIN). Greenwood.

Bernardus Guidonis. Manuel de l'Inquisiteur, 2 vols. in 1. Mollat, G., ed. LC 78-63183. (Heresies of the Early Christian & Medieval Era: Second Ser.). Repr. of 1927 ed. 57.50 set (ISBN 0-404-16199-5). AMS Pr.

Braunstein, Baruch. The Chuetas of Majorca. rev. ed. 1971. 25.00x (ISBN 0-87068-147-8). Ktav.

Cadoux, Cecil J. Philip of Spain & the Netherlands: An Essay on Moral Judgments in History. LC 69-15788. xv, 251p. 1969. Repr. of 1947 ed. 27.50 (ISBN 0-208-00735-0, Archon). Shoe String.

Coulton, George G. Inquisition. LC 74-18020. 1974. Repr. of 1929 ed. lib. bdg. 16.50 (ISBN 0-8414-3647-9). Folcroft.

Grendler, Paul F. The Roman Inquisition & the Venetian Press, 1540-1605. LC 76-45900. 1978. text ed. 42.00x (ISBN 0-691-05245-X). Princeton U Pr.

Grigulevich, I. Historia de la Inquisicion. (Span.). 414p. 1980. 8.95 (ISBN 0-8285-1813-0, Pub. by Progress Pubs USSR). Imported Pubns.

Guiraud, Jean. The Medieval Inquisition. Messenger, E. C., tr. LC 78-63181. (Heresies of the Early Christian & Medieval Era: Second Ser.). Repr. of 1929 ed. 31.00 (ISBN 0-404-16222-3). AMS Pr.

Haliczer, Stephen, ed. Inquisition & Society in Early Modern Europe. LC 86-26493. 208p. 1987. 28.50x (ISBN 0-389-20700-4). B&N Imports.

Hamilton, Bernard. The Medieval Inquisition. 112p. 1981. 25.00x (ISBN 0-7131-6251-1, Pub. by E Arnold England). State Mutual Bk.

--Medieval Inquisition: Foundations of Medieval History. LC 80-27997. 110p. (Orig.). 1981. 24.50x (ISBN 0-8419-0718-8); pap. text ed. 14.95x (ISBN 0-8419-0695-5). Holmes & Meier.

Haureau, Barthelemy. Bernard Delicieux et l'Inquisition Albigeoise, 1300-1320. LC 78-63180. (Heresies of the Early Christian & Medieval Era: Second Ser.). Repr. of 1877 ed. 31.00 (ISBN 0-404-16223-1). AMS Pr.

Henningsen, Gustav. The Witches' Advocate: Basque Witchcraft & the Spanish Inquisition, 1609-1614. LC 79-20340. (Basque Book Ser.). (Illus.). xxxii, 607p. 1980. 24.00 (ISBN 0-87417-056-7). U of Nev Pr.

Henningsen, Gustav & Tedeschi, John, eds. The Inquisition in Early Modern Europe: Studies on Sources & Methods. 254p. 1986. 27.50 (ISBN 0-87580-102-1). N Ill U Pr.

Herculano, Alexandre. History of the Origin & Establishment of the Inquisition in Portugal. Branner, John C., tr. LC 68-54274. (Stanford University. Stanford Studies in History, Economics, & Political Science: No. 1, Pt. 2). Repr. of 1926 ed. 20.00 (ISBN 0-404-50962-2). AMS Pr.

--History of the Origin & Establishment of the Inquisition in Portugal. rev. ed. 1971. 35.00x (ISBN 0-87068-153-2). Ktav.

Kamen, Henry. Inquisition & Society in Spain in the Sixteenth & Seventeenth Centuries. LC 85-10804. (Illus.). 320p. 1985. 27.50x (ISBN 0-253-33015-7); pap. 10.95x (ISBN 0-253-22775-5). Ind U Pr.

Lea, Henry. Moriscos of Spain, Their Conversion & Expulsion. LC 68-26358. (Studies in Spanish Literature, No. 36). 1969. Repr. of 1901 ed. lib. bdg. 51.95x (ISBN 0-8383-0266-1). Haskell.

Lea, Henry C. Chapters from the Religious History of Spain Connected with the Inquisition. LC 68-56760. (Research & Source Work Ser.: No. 245). 1967. Repr. of 1890 ed. 26.00 (ISBN 0-8337-2035-X). B Franklin.

--History of the Inquisition of Spain, 4 Vols. LC 72-181943. Repr. of 1907 ed. Set. 145.00 (ISBN 0-404-03920-0). Vol. 1 (ISBN 0-404-03921-9). Vol. 2 (ISBN 0-404-03922-7). Vol. 3 (ISBN 0-404-03923-5). Vol. 4 (ISBN 0-404-03924-3). AMS Pr.

--Moriscos of Spain. LC 68-56783. 1968. Repr. of 1901 ed. 20.50 (ISBN 0-8337-4218-3). B Franklin.

--Moriscos of Spain: Their Conversion & Expulsion. 1968. Repr. of 1901 ed. lib. bdg. 23.50x (ISBN 0-8371-0141-7, LEMS). Greenwood.

Liebman, Seymour B. The Inquisitors & the Jews in the New World: Summaries of Procesos 1500-1810, & Bibliographical Guide. LC 72-85110. 160p. 1973. 12.95x (ISBN 0-87024-245-8). U of Miami Pr.

--Jews in New Spain: Faith, Flame & the Inquisition. LC 70-91213. (Illus.). 1970. 19.95x (ISBN 0-87024-129-X). U of Miami Pr.

Maistre, Joseph M. De, tr. Letters on the Spanish Inquisition. LC 77-24949. 1977. Repr. of 1843 ed. 35.00x (ISBN 0-8201-1293-3). Schol Facsimiles.

Molinier, Charles. Inquisition Dans le Midi De la France Au Treizieme et Au Quatorzieme Seicle: Etude Sur les Sources De Son Histoire. 1965. Repr. of 1880 ed. 32.00 (ISBN 0-8337-2421-5). B Franklin.

Roth, Cecil. A History of the Marranos. LC 74-10149. 448p. 1974. pap. 10.95 (ISBN 0-8052-0463-6). Schocken.

--Spanish Inquisition. (Illus., Orig.). 1964. pap. 7.95 (ISBN 0-393-00255-1, Norton Lib). Norton.

Shannon, Albert C. The Medieval Inquisition. 168p. 1983. 15.00 (ISBN 0-9612336-0-5, 83-72869); pap. 10.00 (ISBN 0-9612336-1-3). Augustinian Coll Pr.

Vacandard, Elphege. The Inquisition: A Critical & Historical Study of the Coercive Power of the Church. Conway, Bertrand L., tr. from Fr. LC 76-1127. 195p. 1977. Repr. of 1926 ed. lib. bdg. 20.00 (ISBN 0-915172-09-7). Richwood Pub.

INSCRIPTIONS, ARAMAIC

Hackett, Jo Ann. The Balaam Text from Deir Alla. LC 83-27125. (Harvard Semitic Museum - Monograph). 160p. 1984. 11.95 (ISBN 0-89130-723-0, 04 00 31). Scholars Pr GA.

Parihar, Subhash. Muslim Inscriptions in the Punjab, Haryana & Himachal Pradesh. (Illus.). 79p. 1986. text ed. 40.00x (ISBN 81-210-0017-3, Pub. by Inter India Pubns N Delhi). Apt Bks.

INSCRIPTIONS, DEMOTIC
see Egyptian Language–Inscriptions

INSCRIPTIONS, EGYPTIAN
see Egyptian Language–Inscriptions

INSCRIPTIONS, HIERATIC
see Egyptian Language–Inscriptions

INSCRIPTIONS, INDIC

Vijayaraghavacharya, V., ed. Epigraphical Glossary. (Tirupathi Devasthanam Inscription Ser.: Vol. VI, Pt. 2). 420p. 1984. Repr. of 1938 ed. lib. bdg. 65.00x (ISBN 81-7030-074-6, Pub. by Sri Satguru Pubns India). Orient Bk Dist.

INSCRIPTIONS, ISLAMIC

Parihar, Subhash. Muslim Inscriptions in the Punjab, Haryana & Himachal Pradesh. (Illus.). 79p. 1986. text ed. 40.00x (ISBN 81-210-0017-3, Pub. by Inter India Pubns N Delhi). Apt Bks.

INSCRIPTIONS, LATIN

Gaeng, Paul A. An Inquiry into the Local Variations in Vulgar Latin As Reflected in the Vocalism of Christian Inscriptions. (Studies in the Romance Languages & Literatures: No. 77). 300p. 1968. pap. 16.50x (ISBN 0-8078-9077-4). U of NC Pr.

Marucchi, Orazio. Christian Epigraphy. Willis, J. Armine, tr. from It. LC 74-82057. 472p. 1975. 20.00 (ISBN 0-89005-070-8). Ares.

INSCRIPTIONS, SAFAITIC

Grimme, Hubert. Texte und Untersuchungen Zur Safatenisch - Arabischen Religion. 1929. pap. 15.00 (ISBN 0-384-20070-2). Johnson Repr.

Oxtoby, Willard B. Some Inscriptions of the Safaitic Bedouin. (American Oriental Ser.: Vol. 50). (Illus.). 1968. pap. 8.00x (ISBN 0-940490-50-1). Am Orient Soc.

INSPIRATION
see also Bible–Inspiration; Enthusiasm; Revelation

Addington, Cornelia & Addington, Jack. All about Prosperity & How You Can Prosper. LC 83-73342. (Orig.). 1984. pap. 4.95 (ISBN 0-87516-533-8). De Vorss.

Addington, Jack E. Psychogenesis: Everything Begins in the Mind. 1987. pap. 8.95 (ISBN 0-396-09021-4). Dodd.

Aldrich, Joseph C. Love for All Your Worth! A Quest for Personal Value & Lovability. LC 85-11420. 1985. pap. 6.95 (ISBN 0-88070-119-6). Multnomah.

Amen, Carol. Hyacinths to Feed the Soul. LC 74-33850. (Better Living Ser.). 64p. 1975. pap. text ed. 0.99 (ISBN 0-8127-0094-5). Review & Herald.

And You, Who Do You Say I Am? 3.50 (ISBN 0-318-02212-5). Chrstphrs NY.

Arkin, Alan. Halfway Through the Door: First Steps on a Path of Enlightenment. LC 83-48415. 112p. 1984. pap. 5.95 (ISBN 0-06-060307-0, CN 4094, HarpR). Har-Row.

Bales, James. You Believe. pap. 2.95 (ISBN 0-89315-425-3). Lambert Bk.

Barnard, Jerry. Something Worse Than Hell & Better Than Heaven. 1979. pap. 3.25 (ISBN 0-917726-31-6). Hunter Bks.

Baumann, Dan. Which Way to Happiness? LC 81-50302. 144p. 1981. pap. 3.50 (ISBN 0-8307-0773-5, S351100). Regal.

Bechtel, Faythelma. The Creative Touch, No. 1. 1973. 5.50x (ISBN 0-87813-909-5). Christian Light.

Bevan, Edwyn R. Sibyls & Seers. 1979. Repr. of 1928 ed. lib. bdg. 39.50 (ISBN 0-8495-0510-0). Arden Lib.

Bigart, Lois S. You Can Have Joy. 1984. 5.00 (ISBN 0-8062-2414-2). Carlton.

Bingham, Opha & Bingham, Robert E. One Step More, Lord! LC 84-4942. 1984. pap. 7.95 (ISBN 0-8054-5432-2). Broadman.

Birky, Lela & Conley, Lucy. The Building Christian English Series. 1973. write for info. (ISBN 0-686-05606-X); tchr's. ed. avail. (ISBN 0-686-05607-8). Rod & Staff.

Boyd, Charles E. At Liberty on Bear Creek, 1835-1985. 1984. 14.95; pap. 9.95. Banner Pr AL.

Una Buena Familia Hace un Mundo Mejor. (Span.). 3.50 (ISBN 0-318-02210-9). Chrstphrs NY.

Catoir, John. Gozad del Senor. (Span.). 3.50 (ISBN 0-318-02209-5). Chrstphrs NY.

Cioran, E. M. The Trouble with Being Born. Howard, Richard, tr. from Fr. LC 81-51526. Orig. Title: L' Inconvenient d'etre Ne. Tr. of L' Inconvenient d'Etre Ne. 208p. 1981. pap. 5.95 (ISBN 0-394-17847-5). Seaver Bks.

Cirino, Andre. In the Womb of the Cave. 36p. 1981. 14.00 (ISBN 0-933402-26-0); pap. 9.00 (ISBN 0-933402-25-2). Charisma Pr.

Coniaris, A. M. God Speaks from the Cross. 1984. pap. 4.95 (ISBN 0-937032-33-6). Light&Life Pub Co MN.

Crum, Jesse K. The Art of Inner Listening. LC 74-21643. (Orig.). 1975. pap. 2.25 (ISBN 0-8356-0303-2, Quest). Theos Pub Hse.

Custer, Stewart. Does Inspiration Demand Inerrancy? 1968. pap. 3.50 (ISBN 0-934532-07-9). Presby & Reformed.

Davis, William F. Every Cloud Has One. 1985. 7.95 (ISBN 0-8062-2477-0). Carlton.

Deal, William S. Unequally Yoked. 2nd ed. LC 80-67387. 112p. 1987. pap. 4.95 (Crossway Bks). Good News.

Del Mazza, Valentino. Our Lady among Us. 1978. 4.00 (ISBN 0-8198-0363-4); pap. 3.00 (ISBN 0-8198-0364-2). Dghtrs St Paul.

DeMello, Anthony. Song of the Bird. LC 84-10105. (Illus.). 192p. 1984. pap. 6.95 (ISBN 0-385-19615-6, Im). Doubleday.

Dorsett, Lyle W. And God Came In: The Extraordinary Story of Joy Davidman; Her Life & Marriage to C. S. Lewis. (Illus.). 192p. 1984. pap. 2.95 (ISBN 0-345-31787-4). Ballantine.

Durfield, Richard. How Shall We Escape. 1983. pap. 3.95 (ISBN 0-938612-07-7). Revival Press.

Fallowell, Duncan & Ashley, April. April Ashley's Odyssey. (Illus.). 287p. 1983. 15.95 (ISBN 0-224-01849-3, Pub. by Jonathan Cape). Salem Hse Pubs.
Ferguson, Howard E. The Edge. (Illus.). 340p. 1983. text ed. 29.95x (ISBN 0-9611180-0-8). H E Ferguson.
Fisher, Mary P. Heart of Gold: The Light Within Life. LC 85-81211. (Illus.). 72p. (Orig.). 1985. pap. 6.00 (ISBN 0-9615149-5-7). Fenton Valley Pr.
Galde, Dorothy. You Write the Ticket, Lord. 144p. 1983. pap. 5.95 (ISBN 0-89840-047-3). Heres Life.
Gauchat, Dorothy & Lyons, Arthur. All God's Children. 224p. 1985. pap. 2.50 (ISBN 0-345-31988-5). Ballantine.
Gerrick, David J. God Stories to Scare the Hell Out of You. 1979. pap. text ed. 4.95 (ISBN 0-916750-24-8). Dayton Labs.
Giniger, Ken S., compiled by. Compact Treasury of Inspiration. 320p. (Orig.). 1983. pap. 3.50 (ISBN 0-515-07442-X). Jove Pubns.
Grubb, Norman P. Deep Things of God. 1970. pap. 4.95 (ISBN 0-87508-209-2). Chr Lit.
Hager, Wesley H. Consider the Grass: God Cares for You. (Contempo Ser.). pap. 0.95 (ISBN 0-8010-4102-3). Baker Bk.
Hagin, Kenneth E. Casting Your Cares Upon the Lord. 1981. pap. 1.00 (ISBN 0-89276-023-0). Hagin Ministries.
--How God Taught Me About Prosperity. 1985. mini bk. 0.50 (ISBN 0-89276-265-9). Hagin Ministries.
--Learning to Forget. 1985. mini bk. 0.50 (ISBN 0-89276-266-7). Hagin Ministries.
Hagin, Kenneth, Jr. How to Make the Dream God Gave You Come True. 1981. pap. 1.00 (ISBN 0-89276-708-1). Hagin Ministries.
Hayes, Bernard. Who Is This God You Pray To. 96p. (Orig.). 1981. pap. 2.95 (ISBN 0-914544-41-1). Living Flame Pr.
Hemenway, Joan E. Holding on... While Letting Go. (Looking Up Ser.). (Orig.). 1985. pap. 1.25 (ISBN 0-8298-0548-6). Pilgrim NY.
Hill, Elsie Isensce & Dudley, Cliff. Abused But Chosen. LC 83-61439. 144p. 1983. 4.95 (ISBN 0-89221-106-7). New Leaf.
Hill, Harold & Harrell, Irene. How to Be a Winner. LC 76-31676. 1976. (Pub. by Logos); pap. 2.95 (ISBN 0-88270-456-7). Bridge Pub.
Howell, Clinton T., ed. Lines to Live By. 200p. 1984. Repr. 12.95 (ISBN 0-8407-5389-6). Nelson.
--Seasons of Inspiration. 160p. 1984. Repr. 10.95 (ISBN 0-8407-5345-4). Nelson.
Hunter, Charles. Follow Me! 1975. pap. 4.95 (ISBN 0-917726-35-9). Hunter Bks.
Hunter, Charles & Hunter, Frances. Angels on Assignment. 1979. pap. 4.95 (ISBN 0-917726-33-2). Hunter Bks.
--The Two Sides of a Coin. 1973. pap. 3.95 (ISBN 0-917726-36-7). Hunter Bks.
Hunter, Frances. Come Alive. 1975. pap. 4.95 (ISBN 0-917726-34-0). Hunter Bks.
--A Confession a Day Keeps the Devil Away. 1980. pap. 4.95 (ISBN 0-917726-37-5). Hunter Bks.
Hunter, Frances & Hunter, Charles. Since Jesus Passed By. 1973. pap. 3.95 (ISBN 0-917726-38-3). Hunter Bks.
Inrig, Gary. Quality Friendship. LC 81-38379. 192p. (Orig.). 1981. pap. 5.95 (ISBN 0-8024-2891-6). Moody.
Inspiration & Motivation. LC 81-23459. 1982. 9.95 (ISBN 0-9603174-6-5). Bks of Value.
Institute for Religious & Social Studies. Hour of Insight. facsimile ed. MacIver, R. M., ed. LC 70-167366. (Essay Index Reprint Ser). Repr. of 1954 ed. 15.00 (ISBN 0-8369-2655-2). Ayer Co Pubs.
Johnson, L. C. Chapel Messages. 1982. pap. 5.95 (ISBN 0-89265-081-8). Randall Hse.
Kaplan, David & Phillips, Marcia. Cheers. (Inspirational Ser.). (Illus.). 96p. 1981. pap. 4.95 (ISBN 0-939944-04-9). M & L Sales.
Kelly, Kelly B. Bread for the Eating. 121p. (Orig.). 1982. pap. 3.50 (ISBN 0-914544-39-X). Living Flame Pr.
Keyes, Ken, Jr. & Burkan, Bruce. How to Make Your Life Work. 1976. pap. 3.95 (ISBN 0-346-12226-0). Cornerstone.
Kidd, Sunnie D. & Kidd, James W. The Dynamic Aspects of Inspiration. 38p. (Orig.). 1982. pap. text ed. 3.50 (ISBN 0-910727-02-3). Golden Phoenix.
Large Type Treasury of Inspiration. 1986. 8.98 (625334). Outlet Bk Co.
Larson, Muriel. Praise Every Day. 135p. 1984. 10.95 (ISBN 0-910311-11-0). Huntington Hse Inc.
Lefebvre, Dom G. God Present. 1979. pap. 3.95 (ISBN 0-03-053436-4, HarpR). Har-Row.
Lewis, John M. Revelation, Inspiration, Scripture. LC 83-71822. (Layman's Library of Christian Doctrine Ser.). 1985. 5.95 (ISBN 0-8054-1633-1). Broadman.
The Little Book of Inspiration: Seven Famous Classics, 1 vol. 290p. Date not set. pap. 9.95 (ISBN 0-87983-424-2). Keats.
Little, Mark. Handbook for Advanced Souls: Eternal Reminders for the Present Moment. (Illus.). 136p. 1984. 6.95 (ISBN 0-9613783-0-1). M A Little.
McCann, Edna. The Heritage Book, 1985. (Illus.). 192p. 1984. 5.95 (ISBN 0-02-582880-0). Macmillan.
McCarthy, David S. Our Constant Companion. 96p. 1984. pap. 2.95 (ISBN 0-8170-1019-X). Judson.
McClain, Alva J. The "Problems" of Verbal Inspiration. 1968. pap. write for info. (ISBN 0-88469-116-0). BMH Bks.
McPhee, Arthur G. Have a Great Day Every Day. LC 84-565. 160p. 1984. pap. 6.50 (ISBN 0-8361-3352-8). Herald Pr.
McWhirter, David. Millenial Harbinger - Index. LC 81-65031. (Millenial Harbinger Ser.). 776p. 1981. 19.95 (ISBN 0-89900-228-5). College Pr Pub.
Maloney, George A. The Returning Sun: Hope for a Broken World. 63p. (Orig.). 1982. pap. 2.50 (ISBN 0-914544-42-X). Living Flame Pr.
Mara. The Middle Sphere. LC 81-67349. (Earth Song Ser.). (Illus.). 57p. (Orig.). 1981. pap. 4.95 (ISBN 0-9605170-1-4). Earth-Song.
Mason, Mike. The Mystery of Marriage: As Iron Sharpens Iron. LC 85-3048. 190p. 1985. 10.95 (ISBN 0-88070-097-1). Multnomah.
Maxwell, Neal A. Plain & Precious Things. LC 83-72478. 103p. 1983. 6.95 (ISBN 0-87747-979-8). Deseret Bk.
Meadows, Della A. Good Morning in the Dawn, Dear Son. 200p. 1985. 11.95 (ISBN 0-8059-2952-5). Dorrance.
Mehl, Duane. At Peace with Failure. LC 83-721141. 128p. (Orig.). 1984. pap. 5.95 (ISBN 0-8066-2058-7, 10-0472). Augsburg.
Michael, Arnold. Brothers of the Grape. LC 76-142525. 1972. pap. 6.95 (ISBN 0-87516-149-9). De Vorss.
Montgomery, Ruth. A Search for the Truth. 256p. (Orig.). 1986. pap. 3.50 (ISBN 0-449-21085-5, Crest). Fawcett.
Moore, Charles. Life-There's More to It Than Meets the Eye. 1983. 5.95 (ISBN 0-8062-2110-0). Carlton.
Morneau, Robert F. There Is a Season: An Inspirational Journal. LC 84-11622. (Illus.). 175p. 1984. 18.95 (ISBN 0-13-914755-1, Busn); pap. 9.95 (ISBN 0-13-914706-3). P-H.
Muller, Robert. Most of All They Taught Me Happiness. LC 78-52110. 1985. pap. 7.95 (ISBN 0-385-19914-7, Im). Doubleday.
Muto, Susan A. & Kaam, Adrian Van. Celebrating the Single Life. LC 81-43770. 1985. pap. 6.95 (ISBN 0-385-19915-5, Im). Doubleday.
Nightingale, Earl. Earl Nightingale's Greatest Discovery: The Strangest Secret...Revisited. (PMA Ser.). 1987. 17.95 (ISBN 0-396-08928-3). Dodd.
Oda, Stephanie C., ed. Seasons of the Heart. (A Reader's Digest-C. R. Gibson Bk.). (Illus.). 96p. 1984. 8.00 (ISBN 0-8378-1806-0). Gibson.
Parker, D. Coffey. Feed My Sheep. (Illus.). 1983. 3.00. Harlo Pr.
Pate, Ernest. Dreams for a Quiet Night. LC 83-73639. 80p. (Orig.). 1984. pap. 4.95 (ISBN 0-87516-535-4). De Vorss.
Paulk, Earl. Divine Runner. LC 78-71967. 142p. (Orig.). 1978. pap. 3.25 (ISBN 0-917595-00-9). K-Dimension.
Paulsell, William & Kelty, Matthew. Letters from a Hermit. 1978. 7.95 (ISBN 0-87243-086-3). Templegate.
Peale, Norman V. Treasury of Joy & Enthusiasm. 224p. 1982. pap. 2.50 (ISBN 0-449-24550-0, Crest). Fawcett.
Peale, Ruth S. Secrets of Staying in Love. 272p. 1984. pap. 5.95 (ISBN 0-8407-5910-X). Nelson.
Phillips, Dorothy B., et al, eds. The Choice Is Always Ours. rev. ed. 480p. (Orig.). 1975. pap. 3.95 (ISBN 0-8356-0302-4, Quest). Theos Pub Hse.
Pitcher, Arthur. Memoirs of Peter. 1981. 3.95 (ISBN 0-86544-015-8). Salv Army Suppl South.
Pollnow, Jim. My God, Why? A Mastectomy from a Husbands Point of View. LC 79-55888. 127p. 1980. pap. 2.95x (ISBN 0-9603708-0-3). J L Pollnow.
Ponder, Catherine. Open Your Mind to Prosperity. rev. ed. LC 70-155720. 184p. 1984. pap. 5.50 (ISBN 0-87516-531-1). De Vorss.
Power Words for Prosperous Living! 120p. 1984. pap. 4.95 (ISBN 0-9602166-1-8). Golden Key.
Powers, John. Coping with a Gentle God. 1984. pap. 6.95 (ISBN 0-89453-443-2). M Glazier.
Quenon, Paul. Carved in Stone. (Illus.). 40p. 1979. pap. 2.50 (ISBN 0-87793-195-X). Ave Maria.
Quezada, Adolfo. A Desert Place. (Illus.). 96p. (Orig.). 1982. pap. 2.95 (ISBN 0-914544-40-3). Living Flame Pr.
Ranaghan, Dorothy. A Day in Thy Courts. LC 84-70866. 144p. (Orig.). 1984. pap. 4.95 (ISBN 0-943780-05-5, 8055). Charismatic Ren Servs.
Robbins, James R. At The River I Stand. 5.95 (ISBN 0-8062-2426-6). Carlton.
Robertson, Dede. The New You. 1984. 12.95 (ISBN 0-8407-5408-6). Nelson.
Rosage, David E. Linger with Me: Moments Aside with Jesus. 212p. (Orig.). 1979. pap. 3.95 (ISBN 0-914544-29-2). Living Flame Pr.
--Living Here & Hereafter. (Christian Dying, Death & Resurection Ser.). 128p. (Orig.). 1982. pap. 2.95 (ISBN 0-914544-44-6). Living Flame Pr.
Sanders, Bill. Tough Turf. 168p. (Orig.). 1985. pap. 5.95 (ISBN 0-8007-5212-0). Revell.
Satir, Virginia. Meditations & Inspirations. LC 85-13302. 96p. (Orig.). 1985. pap. 5.95 (ISBN 0-89087-421-2). Celestial Arts.
Sato, Chiaki. Inspirational Lines. 1986. 5.95 (ISBN 0-533-06789-8). Vantage.
Schaffer, Ulrich. Growing into the Blue. LC 83-48463. (Illus.). 96p. (Orig.). 1984. pap. 14.95 (ISBN 0-06-067089-4, RD 509, HarpR). Har-Row.
Schuller, Robert. Daily Power Thoughts. 384p. 1984. pap. 3.95 (ISBN 0-515-08164-7). Jove Pubns.
Scott, Albert C. Mini Miracles & Words with a Little Wisdom. 1984. 6.95 (ISBN 0-8062-2320-0). Carlton.
Sit, Amy. Sing It! 1979. pap. 3.50 (ISBN 0-917726-39-1). Hunter Bks.
Smith. Christian Secret of a Happy Life. 2.50 (ISBN 0-318-18169-X). WCTU.
Snyder, Bernadet M. Dear God, I Have This Terrible Problem: A Housewife's Secret Letters. 96p. 1983. pap. 2.95 (ISBN 0-89243-188-1). Liguori Pubns.
Standhardt, Robert T. Journey to the Magical City: A Quadriplegic Person's Reflections on Suffering & Love. LC 83-80413. 96p. (Orig.). 1983. pap. 4.50 (ISBN 0-8358-0458-5). Upper Room.
Stanley, Gary. The Garimus File. LC 82-72301. (Illus., Orig.). 1983. pap. 6.95 (ISBN 0-86605-107-4). Heres Life.
Swami Rama. Inspired Thoughts of Swami Rama. 260p. (Orig.). pap. 8.95 (ISBN 0-89389-086-3). Himalayan Pubs.
Swift, Helen. In Search of Peace. 1983. pap. 3.75 (ISBN 0-89243-192-X). Liguori Pubns.
Talmadge, Virginia. Dear God Little Prayers to a Big God. 1981. cloth 3.25 (ISBN 0-86544-016-6). Salv Army Suppl South.
Teilhard de Chardin, Pierre. On Love & Happiness. LC 83-48979. 96p. 1984. 9.45 (ISBN 0-06-068151-9, HarpR). Har-Row.
Temple of the People Publications Staff, ed. The Teachings of the Temple, 3 vols. 1985. Set. 25.00 (ISBN 0-933797-08-7); Vol. 1, 661p. 11.25 ea. (ISBN 0-933797-03-6). Vol. 2, 400p (ISBN 0-933797-04-4). Vol. 3, 400p (ISBN 0-933797-05-2) (ISBN 0-933797-05-2). Halcyon Bk.
That Your Joy May Be Full. 3.50 (ISBN 0-318-02211-7). Chrstphrs NY.
Theophan the Recluse. Misli na Kazhdij Den' Goda. Tr. of Thoughts on Every Day of the Year. 186p. 1982. pap. 7.00 (ISBN 0-317-28912-8). Holy Trinity.
Thornton, Edward E., ed. A Love That Heals. LC 83-21083. 1984. pap. 3.75 (ISBN 0-8054-5105-6). Broadman.
The Unforgotten Things. (Illus.). 6.95 (ISBN 0-686-46782-5). Inspiration Conn.
Van Dyke, Henry. The Story of the Other Wise Man. 96p. 1986. pap. 2.95 (ISBN 0-345-31882-X, Pub. by Ballantine Epiphany). Ballantine.
Varner, K. H. Prevail: A Handbook for the Overcomer. 172p. 1982. pap. 3.95 (ISBN 0-938612-06-9). Revival Press.
Vigeveno, Henk S. Thirteen Men Who Changed the World. LC 86-3209. (Illus.). 154p. 1986. pap. 5.95 (ISBN 0-8307-1150-3, 5418817) (ISBN 0-8307-1174-0, 6102292). Regal.
Vining, Elizabeth G. Harnessing Pegasus: Inspiration & Meditation. 1983. pap. 2.50x (ISBN 0-87574-221-1, 221). Pendle Hill.
Waggoner, Dorene. I Will Not Leave You Comfortless. (Illus.). 32p. 1984. 4.95 (ISBN 0-8378-2040-5). Gibson.
White, Ruthe. Touch Me Again, Lord. LC 82-84453. 136p. (Orig.). 1983. pap. 5.95 (ISBN 0-89840-038-4). Heres Life.
Wilder, Garnett M. Using Your Emotions Creatively. 80p. 1984. pap. 2.95 (ISBN 0-8170-1020-3). Judson.
Wilkerson. Have You Felt Like Giving Up Lately? 2.50 (ISBN 0-318-18174-6). WCTU.
Williams, Steve. The Death of a Child. 1977. 3.95 (ISBN 0-88027-005-5). Firm Foun Pub.
Worthington, Everett L., Jr. How to Help the Hurting. LC 85-23070. (Illus.). 192p. 1986. pap. 5.95 (ISBN 0-87784-388-0). Inter-Varsity.
Wright, Ralph. Ripples of Stillness. 1978. 5.95 (ISBN 0-8198-0365-0). Dghtrs St Paul.
You Are Loved. (Four Very Special Gift Bks.). 48p. 1985. 2.25 (ISBN 0-8407-6680-7). Nelson.
You Are Not Alone. (Four Very Special Gift Bks.). 48p. 1985. 2.25 (ISBN 0-8407-6679-3). Nelson.
You Can Be Full of Joy. (Four Very Special Gift Bks.). 48p. 1985. 2.25 (ISBN 0-8407-6681-5). Nelson.
You Can Still Change the World. 3.50 (ISBN 0-318-02218-4). Chrstphrs NY.
Young, H. Edwin. The Purpose of Suffering: Knowing the God Who Comforts. LC 85-80488. 144p. (Orig.). 1985. pap. 4.95 (ISBN 0-89081-496-1). Harvest Hse.
Young Ideas. 3.50 (ISBN 0-318-02217-6). Chrstphrs NY.

INSTALLATION SERVICE (CHURCH OFFICERS)

Ammerman, Leila T. Installation Services That Inspire. LC 81-67371. 1982. pap. 5.50 (ISBN 0-8054-3616-2). Broadman.
Mall, E. Jane. Abingdon Manual of Installation Services. 80p. (Orig.). 1983. pap. 4.95 (ISBN 0-687-00367-9). Abingdon.
White, Gladyce E. Installations with Corresponding Devotionals. Crankshaw, Andrea, ed. 70p. (Orig.). Date not set. pap. 6.50 (ISBN 0-9615371-0-8). Adlen Bks.

INSTITUTIONAL CHURCH

see Church Work

INSTITUTIONS, ASSOCIATIONS, ETC.

see Associations, Institutions, etc.

INSTITUTIONS, CHARITABLE AND PHILANTHROPIC

see Charities

INSTITUTIONS, ECCLESIASTICAL

see Religious and Ecclesiastical Institutions

INTEGRATION, RACIAL

see Race Relations

INTEMPERANCE

see Alcoholism; Temperance

INTERCOMMUNION

see also Church Membership

Raphael, Bishop. Anglican-Orthodox Intercommunion. pap. 0.25 (ISBN 0-686-05405-9). Eastern Orthodox.
Ware, K. Communion & Intercommunion. 1980. pap. 1.95 (ISBN 0-937032-20-4). Light&Life Pub Co MN.

INTERMENT

see Burial

INTERNATIONAL AFFAIRS AND CHRISTIANITY

see Christianity and International Affairs

INTERNATIONAL LAW (ISLAMIC LAW)

Khadduri, Majid, intro. by. & tr. The Islamic Law of Nations: Shaybani's Siyar. 366p. 1966. 34.50x (ISBN 0-8018-0334-9). Johns Hopkins.

INTERNATIONAL RELATIONS-MORAL AND RELIGIOUS ASPECTS

Beitz, Charles R., et al, eds. International Ethics: A Philosophy & Public Affairs Reader. LC 84-42938. 352p. 1985. text ed. 24.50 (ISBN 0-691-07683-9); pap. 8.95 (ISBN 0-691-02234-8). Princeton U Pr.
Hero, Alfred O. American Religious Groups View Foreign Policy: Trends in Rank & File Opinion, 1937-1969. LC 72-81335. pap. 141.00 (ISBN 0-317-26767-1, 2023400). Bks Demand UMI.
Thompson, Kenneth W. Christian Ethics & the Dilemmas of Foreign Policy. LC 59-15344. pap. 30.40 (ISBN 0-8357-9098-3, 2017937). Bks Demand UMI.

INTERPERSONAL RELATIONS

Allen, Ronald & Allen, Beverly. Liberated Traditionalism: Men & Women in Balance. LC 85-8969. (Critical Concern Bks.). 1985. 11.95 (ISBN 0-88070-112-9). Multnomah.
Arnold, William V., et al. Divorce: Prevention or Survival. LC 77-22066. 128p. 1977. pap. 5.95 (ISBN 0-664-24142-5). Westminster.
Bonino, Jose M. Room to Be People: An Interpretation of the Message of the Bible for Today's World. Leach, Vickie, tr. from Span. LC 78-14662. 80p. 1979. pap. 4.50 (ISBN 0-8006-1349-X, 1-1349). Fortress.
Booher, Dianna D. Getting along with People Who Don't Get Along. LC 83-14406. (Orig.). 1984. pap. 3.75 (ISBN 0-8054-5209-5). Broadman.
Carlson, Dwight L. Overcoming Hurts & Anger. LC 80-83852. 1981. pap. 4.95 (ISBN 0-89081-277-2). Harvest Hse.
Costello, Andrew. How to Deal with Difficult People. LC 80-81751. 112p. (Orig.). 1980. pap. 3.95 (ISBN 0-89243-128-8). Liguori Pubns.
Crabb, Lawrence J., Jr. & Allender, Dan B. Encouragement: The Key to Caring. 144p. 1984. 9.95 (ISBN 0-310-22590-6, 10182). Zondervan.
DeVille, Jard. Pastor's Handbook on Interpersonal Relationships. 145p. 1986. pap. 8.95 (ISBN 0-8010-2961-9). Baker Bk.
Diehm, William J. Criticizing. LC 86-17372. (Christian Growth Bks). 128p. (Orig.). 1986. pap. 6.95 (ISBN 0-8066-2211-3, 10-1722). Augsburg.

--Finding Your Life Partner. 128p. 1984. pap. 4.95 (ISBN 0-8170-1028-9). Judson.

Dobson, James. What Wives Wish Their Husbands Knew about Women. 1975. 9.95 (ISBN 0-8423-7890-1). Tyndale.

Dyer, William G. Creating Closer Families: Principles of Positive Family Interaction. LC 75-20169. (Illus.). 144p. 1975. pap. 6.95 (ISBN 0-8425-0726-4). Brigham.

Genne, Elizabeth S. & Genne, William H. First of All Persons: A New Look at Men-Women Relationships. (Orig.). 1973. pap. 1.95 (ISBN 0-377-03041-4). Friend Pr.

Getz, Gene A. Building up One Another. LC 76-19918. 120p. 1976. pap. 4.95 (ISBN 0-88207-744-9). Victor Bks.

Gossett, Don. If Nobody Reaches, Nobody Gets Touched. 128p. (Orig.). 1983. pap. 2.95 (ISBN 0-88368-127-7). Whitaker Hse.

Gratton, Carolyn. Trusting: Theory & Practice. LC 82-9760. 240p. 1982. 17.50 (ISBN 0-8245-0496-8). Crossroad NY.

Headington, Bonnie J. Communication in the Counseling Relationship. LC 78-9026. 1979. cloth 16.50x (ISBN 0-910328-23-4); pap. 11.00x (ISBN 0-910328-24-2). Carroll Pr.

Held, Ronald G. Learning Together. LC 76-9515. 128p. 1976. pap. 1.25 (ISBN 0-88243-571-X, 02-0571). Gospel Pub.

Hembree, Ron. The Speck in Your Brother's Eye: How to Be a More Loving Christian. 192p. 1985. 9.95 (ISBN 0-8007-1426-1). Revell.

Hershey, Terry & McAfee, Lisa. Beginning Again. 64p. 1984. involvement guide 4.95 (ISBN 0-915929-11-2). Merit Bks.

--How to Start a Beginning Again Ministry. 64p. 1984. 4.95 (ISBN 0-915929-15-5). Merit Bks.

Hunter, Robert L. Helping When It Hurts: A Practical Guide to Helping Relationships. LC 85-47738. 80p. 1985. pap. 3.95 (ISBN 0-8006-1879-3, 1-1879). Fortress.

Joy, Donald. Bonding: Relationships in the Image of God. LC 84-27121. 192p. 1985. 9.95 (ISBN 0-8499-0440-4, 0440-4). Word Bks.

Keating, Charles J. Dealing with Difficult People. LC 83-82018. 224p. 1984. pap. 7.95 (ISBN 0-8091-2596-X). Paulist Pr.

Kennedy, D. James. Learning to Live with the People You Love. 200p. (Orig.). 1987. pap. text ed. 3.95 (ISBN 0-88368-190-0). Whitaker Hse.

Landorf, Joyce. Tough & Tender. rev. ed. 160p. 1981. 9.95 (ISBN 0-8007-1283-8). Revell.

Littauer, Florence. How to Get along with Difficult People. LC 83-83371. 1984. pap. 4.95 (ISBN 0-89081-429-5). Harvest Hse.

--Pursuit of Happiness. LC 80-85333. 1981. pap. 4.95 (ISBN 0-89081-284-5). Harvest Hse.

Lockerbie, Jeannie. By Ones & By Twos: Single & Double Missionaries. LC 83-7272. (Mission Candidate Aids Ser.). 96p. 1983. pap. 4.95 (ISBN 0-87808-194-1). William Carey Lib.

McDowell, Josh. The Secret of Loving. (Living Bks.). 240p. Repr. 3.95 (ISBN 0-8423-5845-5). Tyndale.

Mack, Wayne. Homework Manual for Biblical Counseling: Personal & Interpersonal Problems, Vol. 1. 1979. pap. 5.50 (ISBN 0-87552-356-0). Presby & Reformed.

McMinn, Gordon & Libby, Larry. Choosing to Be Close: Fill Your Life with the Rewards of Relationships. LC 84-3297. 1984. pap. 5.95 (ISBN 0-88070-053-X). Multnomah.

Molton, Warren L. Friends, Partners, & Lovers. 1979. pap. 6.95 (ISBN 0-8170-0815-2). Judson.

Nystrom, Carolyn & Floding, Matthew. Relationships: Face to Face. (Young Fisherman Bible Studyguide Ser.). 64p. (Orig.). (YA) 1986. pap. 2.95 student ed. (ISBN 0-87788-722-5); tchr's ed. 4.95 (ISBN 0-87788-723-3). Shaw Pubs.

Ogilvie, Lloyd J. The Beauty of Caring. LC 80-80464. 1981. pap. 5.95 (ISBN 0-89081-244-6). Harvest Hse.

--The Beauty of Sharing. LC 80-8880. (Orig.). 1981. pap. 5.95 (ISBN 0-89081-246-2). Harvest Hse.

Rauch, Gerry. Handling Conflicts: Taking the Tension Out of Difficult Relationships. (Living as a Christian Ser.). 160p. (Orig.). 1985. pap. 3.95 (ISBN 0-89283-187-1). Servant.

Russell, Letty M. The Future of Partnership. LC 78-20805. 198p. 1979. pap. 8.95 (ISBN 0-664-24240-5). Westminster.

Sammon, Sean D., et al. Fidelity: Issues of Emotional Living in an Age of Stress for Clergy & Religious. Hart, Joseph L., ed. LC 81-533. 148p. (Orig.). 1981. pap. 5.00 (ISBN 0-89571-011-0). Affirmation.

Scalf, Cherie & Waters, Kenneth. Dating & Relating. 160p. 1982. pap. 7.95 (ISBN 0-8499-2890-7). Word Bks.

Schmidt, Paul F. Coping with Difficult People. LC 79-27486. (Christian Care Bks.: Vol. 6). 120p. 1980. pap. 7.95 (ISBN 0-664-24299-5). Westminster.

Senter, Ruth. The Seasons of Friendship: A Search for Intimacy. 160p. 1982. 9.95 (ISBN 0-310-38830-9, 11226). Zondervan.

Shelton, Robert R. Loving Relationships. 272p. (Orig.). 1987. pap. 11.95 (ISBN 0-87178-542-0). Brethren.

Smalley, Gary & Scott, Steve. The Joy of Committed Love: A Valuable Guide to Knowing, Understanding & Loving Each Other. LC 83-18248. 336p. 1984. 12.95 (ISBN 0-310-44900-6, 18248). Zondervan.

Smith, Harold I. Tear Catchers. 160p. (Orig.). 1984. pap. 9.50 (ISBN 0-687-41184-X). Abingdon.

Solomon, Charles R. The Rejection Syndrome. 144p. 1982. pap. 5.95 (ISBN 0-8423-5417-4). Tyndale.

Sternberg, Patricia. Be My Friend: The Art of Good Relationships. LC 83-10254. 192p. 1983. pap. 8.95 (ISBN 0-664-26007-1, A Bridgebooks Publication). Westminster.

Swindoll, Charles A. Dropping Your Guard. 1986. deluxe ed. 9.95 (ISBN 0-8499-3850-3). Word Bks.

Tamiazzo, John. Love & Be Loved: A How-To Book. 176p. 1986. pap. 7.95 (ISBN 0-87877-087-9, Greenbriar Books). Newcastle Pub.

Vissell, Barry & Vissell, Joyce. The Shared Heart: Relationship Initiations & Celebrations. LC 85-10981. 192p. 1985. Repr. lib. bdg. 19.95x (ISBN 0-89370-883-6). Borgo Pr.

Welwood, John. Challenge of the Heart: Love, Sex & Intimacy in Changing Times. LC 85-2461. 283p. (Orig.). 1985. pap. 9.95 (ISBN 0-87773-331-7, 74200-1). Shambhala Pubns.

White, Ellen G. How to Get Along with Others. (Uplook Ser.). 1964. pap. 0.99 (ISBN 0-8163-0072-0, 08835-1). Pacific Pr Pub Assn.

White, Ernest. The Art of Human Relations. LC 85-5953. 1985. pap. 6.95 (ISBN 0-8054-5008-4). Broadman.

Zerof, Herbert G. Finding Intimacy: The Art of Happiness in Living Together. 224p. (Orig.). 1981. pap. 6.95 (ISBN 0-86683-618-7, HarpR). Har-Row.

INTERPRETATION

see Hermeneutics

INTOLERANCE

see Fanaticism; Liberty of Conscience; Religious Liberty; Toleration

INTOXICATION

see Alcoholism; Temperance

INVESTITURE

see also Bishops; Church and State

Cantor, Norman F. Church, Kingship & Lay Investiture in England, 1089-1135. 1969. lib. bdg. 26.00x (ISBN 0-374-91273-4, Octagon). Hippocrene Bks.

Morrison, Karl E., ed. The Investiture Controversy: Issues, Ideals & Results. LC 77-15654. (European Problem Studies). 144p. 1976. pap. text ed. 5.95 (ISBN 0-88275-634-6). Krieger.

Robinson, Ian S. Authority & Resistance in the Investiture Contest. LC 78-9110. 189p. 1978. text ed. 44.50x (ISBN 0-8419-0407-3). Holmes & Meier.

INVISIBLE WORLD

see Spirits

INVOCATION OF SAINTS

see Saints–Cultus

IRAN–RELIGION

Akhavi, Shahrough. Religion & Politics in Contemporary Iran. LC 79-22084. 1980. 44.50 (ISBN 0-87395-408-4); pap. 16.95 (ISBN 0-87395-456-4). State U NY Pr.

Arjomand, Said A. The Shadow of God & the Hidden Iman: Religion, Political Order & Societal Change in Shi'ite Iran from the Beginning to 1890. LC 83-27196. (Publications of the Center for the Middle Eastern Studies: No. 17). (Illus.). xii, 356p. 1984. lib. bdg. 28.00x (ISBN 0-226-02782-1). U of Chicago Pr.

Bayat, Mangol. Mysticism & Dissent: Socioreligious Thought in Qajar Iran. LC 82-5498. 320p. 1982. 25.00x (ISBN 0-8156-2260-0). Syracuse U Pr.

Bowman, Raymond A. Aramaic Ritual Texts from Persepolis. LC 65-55148. (Oriental Institute Pubns. Ser: No. 91). 1970. 35.00x (ISBN 0-226-62194-4). U of Chicago Pr.

Irfani, Suroosh. Iran's Islamic Revolution: Popular Liberation or Religious Dictatorship? (Illus.). 278p. 1983. 29.50x (ISBN 0-86232-157-3, Pub. by Zed Pr England); pap. 10.75 (ISBN 0-86232-158-1). Humanities.

Keddie, Nikki R. Religion & Politics in Iran: Shi'ism from Quiestism to Revolution. LC 82-17351. 288p. 1983. text ed. 28.50x (ISBN 0-300-02874-1). Yale U Pr.

--Religion & Rebellion in Iran: The Iranian Tobacco Protest of 1891-1892. 163p. 1966. 27.50x (ISBN 0-7146-1971-X, F Cass Co). Biblio Dist.

Keddie, Nikki R., ed. Religion & Politics in Iran: Shi'ism from Quietism to Revolution. LC 82-17351. 288p. 1984. pap. 9.95x (ISBN 0-300-03245-5, Y-504). Yale U Pr.

Kedourie, Elie & Haim, Sylvia G., eds. Towards a Modern Iran: Studies in Thought, Politics & Society. 262p. 1980. 29.50x (ISBN 0-7146-3145-0, F Cass Co). Biblio Dist.

Malandra, William W. An Introduction to Ancient Iranian Religion: Readings from the "Avesta" & "Achaemenid" Inscriptions. (Minnesota Publications in the Humanities Ser.: No. 2). 201p. 1983. 29.50 (ISBN 0-8166-1114-9); pap. 14.95x (ISBN 0-8166-1115-7). U of Minn Pr.

Mills, Lawrence H. Our Own Religion in Ancient Persia. LC 74-21262. Repr. of 1913 ed. 45.00 (ISBN 0-404-12811-4). AMS Pr.

Mottahedeh, Roy. The Mantle of the Prophet: Religion & Politics in Iran. LC 86-42737. 416p. 1986. pap. 9.95 (ISBN 0-394-74865-4). Pantheon.

Mulla Firuz Bin Kaus, tr. from Mahabhadian. The Desatir. LC 73-84045. (Secret Doctrine Reference Ser.). 208p. 1980. pap. 9.00 (ISBN 0-913510-33-5). Wizards.

Wilson, Samuel G. Persian Life & Customs. 3rd ed. LC 76-178305. Repr. of 1900 ed. 24.50 (ISBN 0-404-06996-7). AMS Pr.

IRELAND–CHURCH HISTORY

see also Celtic Church

Bell, Philip. Disestablishment in Ireland & Wales. LC 73-488607. (Church Historical Society Ser.: No. 90). 1969. pap. 21.50x (ISBN 0-8401-5090-3). A R Allenson.

Burke, Thomas. Hibernia Dominicana, Sive Historia Provinciae: Hiberniae Ordinis Praedicatorum. 966p. Repr. of 1762 ed. text ed. 124.20x (ISBN 0-576-78541-5, Pub. by Gregg Intl Pubs England). Gregg Intl.

D'Arcy, Mary R. The Saints of Ireland. 241p. 1985. pap. 9.95 (ISBN 0-9614900-0-4). Irish Am Cult.

Eipper, Chris. The Ruling Trinity: A Community Study of Chruch, State & Business in Ireland. 1986. text ed. 42.00 (ISBN 0-566-05173-7, Pub. by Gower Pub England). Gower Pub Co.

Gallagher, Eric. Christians in Ulster, Nineteen Sixty-Eight to Nineteen Eighty. 1982. 19.95x (ISBN 0-19-213237-7). Oxford U Pr.

Harney, Martin P. Medieval Ties Between Italy & Ireland. 1963. 1.50 (ISBN 0-8198-0101-1). Dghtrs St Paul.

Hickey, John. Religion & the Northern Ireland Problem. LC 83-26612. 162p. 1984. 23.50x (ISBN 0-389-20448-X, 08012). B&N Imports.

Watt, John. The Church in Medieval Ireland, Vol. 5. (Gill History of Ireland Ser.). 1973. 18.50 (ISBN 0-7171-0562-8, Pub. by Gill & Macmillan Ireland). Irish Bk Ctr.

Whyte, J. H. Church & State in Modern Ireland: 1923 to 1979. 2nd ed. LC 79-55700. 491p. 1980. 32.50x (ISBN 0-389-20010-7). B&N Imports.

World Book, Inc. Christmas in Ireland. LC 84-51015. (Round the World Christmas Program Ser.). (Illus.). 80p. 1985. write for info. (ISBN 0-7166-0885-5). World Bk.

IRENICS

see Christian Union

ISAAC, THE PATRIARCH

Heap, Norman L. Abraham, Isaac, & Jacob, Servants & Prophets of God. 1987. 12.50 (ISBN 0-533-07272-7). Vantage.

Kelly, W. Isaac. 135p. pap. 4.95 (ISBN 0-88172-144-1). Believers Bkshelf.

Lindsay, Gordon. Isaac & Rebekah. (Old Testament Ser.). 1.25 (ISBN 0-89985-127-4). Christ Nations.

Nee, Watchman. Changed into His Likeness. 1969. 4.95 (ISBN 0-87508-411-7); pap. 3.95 (ISBN 0-87508-410-9). Chr Lit.

Spiegel, Shalom. The Last Trial: On the Legend & Lore of the Command to Abraham to Offer Isaac As a Sacrifice - the Akedah. LC 79-12664. (The Jewish Legacy Ser.). 1979. pap. 7.95x (ISBN 0-87441-290-0). Behrman.

Stern, Chaim. Isaac: The Link in the Chain. 1977. text ed. 9.95 (ISBN 0-8315-0077-8). Speller.

Watchman, Nee. Changed into His Likeness. 1978. pap. 3.95 (ISBN 0-8423-0228-X). Tyndale.

ISAIAH, THE PROPHET

Allis, Oswald T. The Unity of Isaiah: A Study in Prophecy. 1974. pap. 4.50 (ISBN 0-8010-0111-0). Baker Bk.

Cothen, Joe H. & Strange, John O. The Preacher's Notebook on Isaiah. LC 82-24596. 96p. 1983. pap. 6.95 (ISBN 0-88289-365-3). Pelican.

Gileadi, Avraham. The Apocalyptic Book of Isaiah: A New Translation with Interpretative Key. Gileadi, Avraham, tr. (Hebrew.). 207p. 1982. 10.95 (ISBN 0-910511-00-4). Hebraeus Pr.

Heifner, Fred. Isaiah: Messenger for God. (BibLearn Ser.). (Illus.). 1978. 5.95 (ISBN 0-8054-4243-X, 4242-43). Broadman.

Isaiah: A New Translation. LC 78-188581. (Illus.). 192p. 1973. 12.50 (ISBN 0-686-73768-7, 150); pap. 4.00 (ISBN 0-8276-0005-4, 151). Jewish Pubns.

Lindsay, Gordon. Isaiah & Jeremiah. (Old Testament Ser.). 1.25 (ISBN 0-89985-155-X). Christ Nations.

Lindsey, F. Duane. The Servant Songs: A Study in Isaiah. 1985. pap. 7.95 (ISBN 0-8024-4093-2). Moody.

Ludlow, Victor L. Isaiah: Prophet, Poet, & Seer. LC 82-1444. (Illus.). 578p. 1982. 13.95 (ISBN 0-87747-884-8). Deseret Bk.

Martin, Loren D. Isaiah: An Ensign to the Nations. LC 81-92840. (Isaiah Ser.: Vol. 1). (Illus.). 180p. 1982. 9.95 (ISBN 0-9608244-0-5); Set of Multivolumes. write for info. (ISBN 0-9608244-2-1). Valiant Pubns.

Siegel, Jonathan P. The Severus Scroll & 1Q1SA. LC 75-28372. (Society of Biblical Literature, Masoretic Studies). 1975. pap. 8.95 (ISBN 0-89130-028-7, 060502). Scholars Pr GA.

Skousen, Cleon W. Isaiah Speaks to Modern Times. 800p. 1984. 15.95 (ISBN 0-910558-25-6). Ensign Pub.

ISIDORIUS, SAINT, BP. OF SEVILLE, d. 636

Brehaut, Ernest. Encyclopedist of the Dark Ages, Isidore of Seville. (Columbia University. Studies in History, Economics, & Public Law: Vol. 48, No. 1). 1967. Repr. of 1912 ed. 21.50 (ISBN 0-8337-0361-7). B Franklin.

ISIS

Brady, Thomas A. Sarapis & Isis: Collected Essays. Mitchel, Fordyce, ed. 129p. 1978. 25.00 (ISBN 0-89005-253-0). Ares.

ISLAM

see also Caliphate; Civilization, Islamic; Koran; Muslims

also special headings with Islam added in parentheses; subdivision Islam under special topics, e.g. Marriage–Islam; headings beginning with the words Islamic and Muslim

Abdalati, Hammudah. The Family Structure in Islam. LC 77-79635. 1976. 10.95 (ISBN 0-89259-004-1); pap. 8.50. Am Trust Pubns.

--Islam in Focus. 2nd ed. LC 75-4382. (Illus.). 211p. 1975. pap. 5.00 (ISBN 0-89259-000-9). Am Trust Pubns.

Abdul, M. A. The Quran, Sh. Tabarsi's Commentary. 15.95 (ISBN 0-317-01596-6). Kazi Pubns.

Abu-Saud, Mahmoud. Concept of Islam. Quinlan, Hamid, ed. LC 83-70184. 147p. 1983. pap. 6.50 (ISBN 0-89259-043-2). Am Trust Pubns.

Affifi, A. E. Mystical Philosophy of Muhyid Din Ibn-Ul-Arabi. 1964. 12.00x (ISBN 0-87902-035-0). Orientalia.

Ahemd, Akbar S. & Hart, David M., eds. Islam in Tribal Societies: From the Atlas to the Indus. 320p. (Orig.). 1984. pap. 21.95x (ISBN 0-7100-9320-9). Methuen Inc.

Ahmad, Akbar S. Towards Islamic Anthropology. 80p. (Orig.). 1986. pap. 7.50 (ISBN 0-317-52455-0). New Era Pubns MI.

Ahmad, K. Islam & the West. pap. 2.00 (ISBN 0-686-18572-2). Kazi Pubns.

Ahmad, Khurshid. Family Life in Islam. 38p. (Orig.). 1974. pap. 2.25x (ISBN 0-86037-016-X, Pub by Islamic Found UK). New Era Pubns MI.

Ahmad, Khurshid, ed. Islam: Its Meaning & Message. 279p. (Orig.). 1976. pap. 8.95 (ISBN 0-86037-000-3, Pub. by Islamic Found UK). New Era Pubns MI.

Ahmed, K. Fanaticism, Intolerance & Islam. pap. 1.00 (ISBN 0-686-18491-2). Kazi Pubns.

Ahsan, Manazir. Islam: Faith & Practice. (Illus.). 48p. (Orig.). 1980. pap. 3.00 (ISBN 0-86037-001-1, Pub. by Islamic Found UK). New Era Pubns MI.

Ajijola, A. D. Essence of Faith in Islam. pap. 12.50 (ISBN 0-686-63898-0). Kazi Pubns.

Al Farugi, I. R. Towards Islamic Arabic. 64p. (Orig.). 1986. pap. 5.00 (ISBN 0-317-52453-4). New Era Pubns MI.

--Trialogue of Abrahamic Faiths. 88p. (Orig.). 1986. pap. 7.50 (ISBN 0-317-52454-2). New Era Pubns MI.

Al-Ghazali. Inner Dimensions of Islamic Worship. Holland, Muhtar, tr. from Arabic. 142p. (Orig.). 1983. pap. 6.95 (ISBN 0-86037-125-5, Pub. by Islamic Found UK). New Era Pubns MI.

Al-Ghazzali. The Book of Knowledge. 1970. 15.00x (ISBN 0-87902-106-3). Orientalia.

--Just Balance. 6.50 (ISBN 0-317-01603-2). Kazi Pubns.

--Worship in Islam. Calverley, Edwin E., ed. LC 79-2860. 242p. 1981. Repr. of 1925 ed. 23.00 (ISBN 0-8305-0032-4). Hyperion Conn.

Al-Gita, Kashif, ed. The Shia Origin & Faith. Haq, M. Fazal, tr. from Arabic. 284p. 1984. pap. 7.50 (ISBN 0-941724-23-9). Islamic Seminary.

Al-Husaini, Ishak M. The Moslem Brethren: The Greatest of the Modern Islamic Movements. LC 79-2866. 186p. 1987. Repr. of 1956 ed. 21.00 (ISBN 0-8305-0039-1). Hyperion Conn.

Ali, A. Yusuf, tr. Qur'an: The Holy. (Eng. & Arabic.). 1862p. 1983. text ed. 20.00 (ISBN 0-940368-32-3); pap. 10.00 (ISBN 0-940368-31-5). Tahrike Tarsile Quran.

Ali, Abdullah. The Spirit & the Future of Islam, 2 vols. 155p. 1983. Set. 187.50x (ISBN 0-86722-051-1). Inst Econ Pol.

Ali, Muhammad K., ed. Islamic Unity & Happiness. Pazargali, Alaedin, tr. from Persian. 1985. pap. 3.95 (ISBN 0-940368-47-1). Tahrike Tarsile Quran.

Ali, Zaki. Islam in the World. LC 74-180314. (Mid-East Studies). Repr. of 1947 ed. 31.00 (ISBN 0-404-56209-4). AMS Pr.

Al-Islam, Da'i. The Companions of the Cave. 23p. 1985. pap. 3.95 (ISBN 0-940368-55-2). Tahrike Tarsile Quran.

--Prophet Sulaiman. 32p. 1985. pap. 3.95 (ISBN 0-940368-53-6). Tahrike Tarsile Quran.

Al-Khui, Ayatullah A. Articles of Islamic Acts. Haq, M. Fazal, tr. from Arabic. 236p. 1983. pap. 6.00 (ISBN 0-941724-21-2). Islamic Seminary.

Al-Mufid, Shaykh. Kitab Al-Irshad: The Book of Guidance into the Lives of the Twelve Imams. Howard, I. K., tr. 616p. 1986. lib. bdg. 55.00 (ISBN 0-7103-0151-0). Methuen Inc.

Al-Muzaffar, Muhammad. The Faith of Shi'a Islam. LC 83-50153. 80p. pap. 4.00 (ISBN 0-940368-26-9). Tahrike Tarsile Quran.

Al-Muzaffar, Muhammad Rida. The Faith of Shi'ia Islam. 89p. 1982. 20.00x (ISBN 0-317-39062-7, Pub. by Luzac & Co Ltd). State Mutual Bk.

Al Sadr, Muhammad B. Awaited Saviour. 110p. 1983. pap. text ed. 4.00 (ISBN 0-686-90398-6). Islamic Seminary.

Al-Sayed, Abdul M. Social Ethics of Islam: Classical Islamic Political Theory & Practice. 1982. 14.95 (ISBN 0-533-04671-8). Vantage.

Ansari, F. R. Islam & the Western Civilization. pap. 1.50 (ISBN 0-686-18533-1). Kazi Pubns.

--Philosophy of Worship in Islam. pap. 1.00 (ISBN 0-686-18603-6). Kazi Pubns.

--Through Science & Philosophy to Religion. pap. 1.25 (ISBN 0-686-18536-6). Kazi Pubns.

Arberry, Arthur J. Revelation & Reason in Islam. LC 80-1936. (BCL: Series I & II). Repr. of 1957 ed. 20.00 (ISBN 0-404-18952-0). AMS Pr.

Arnold, E. Pearls of the Faith: Islam's Rosary. pap. 3.50x (ISBN 0-87902-044-X). Orientalia.

Arnold, T. Preaching of Islam. 1968. 27.50x (ISBN 0-87902-045-8). Orientalia.

Arnold, T. W. Preaching of Islam. 32.50 (ISBN 0-686-18455-6). Kazi Pubns.

Arnold, T. W. & Guillaume, A. The Legacy of Islam. 1976. lib. bdg. 75.00 (ISBN 0-8490-2141-3). Gordon Pr.

Asad, Muhammad. Islam at the Crossroads. 104p. (Orig.). 1982. 8.95 (ISBN 0-317-52459-3, Pub. by Dar Al Andalus). New Era Pubns MI.

--Message of the Quran. 998p. (Orig.). 1980. 49.95 (ISBN 0-317-52456-9, Pub. by Dar Al Andalus). New Era Pubns MI.

--Road to Mecca. 380p. (Orig.). 1981. 14.95 (ISBN 0-317-52460-7, Pub. by Dar Al Andalus). New Era Pubns MI.

--Sahih Al-Bukhari: The Early Years. 306p. (Orig.). 1981. 24.95 (ISBN 0-317-52458-5, Pub. by Dar Al Andalus). New Era Pubns MI.

Ashraf. Lessons in Islam, 5. 8.50 (ISBN 0-686-18391-6). Kazi Pubns.

Asifi, Allama M. Al-Salat. 1983. pap. 4.00 (ISBN 0-941724-10-7). Islamic Seminary.

--Children's Guide to Islam. 112p. 1983. pap. 5.00 (ISBN 0-941724-11-5). Islamic Seminary.

Atemed, M. G. The Teachings of Islam: A Solution of Five Fundamental Religious Problems from the Muslim Point of View. 208p. 1984. text ed. 23.00. Coronet Bks.

Ati, H. A. Islam in Focus. pap. 9.50 (ISBN 0-686-18504-8). Kazi Pubns.

Audah, A. Q. Islam Between Ignorant Followers & Incapable Scholars. pap. 4.50 (ISBN 0-686-18505-6). Kazi Pubns.

Avicenna. Avicenna on Theology. Arberry, Arthur J., tr. LC 78-59000. 1983. Repr. of 1951 ed. 15.00 (ISBN 0-88355-676-6). Hyperion Conn.

Ayoub, M. Great Tiding: Thirtieth Part of Holy Quran. pap. 4.50 (ISBN 0-317-01597-4). Kazi Pubns.

Ayoub, Mahmoud. Redemptive Suffering in Islam. (Religion & Society Ser.: No. 10). 1978. 35.25 (ISBN 90-279-7948-0). Mouton.

Azzam, Abd-Al-Rahman. Eternal Message of Muhammad. 1964. 9.50 (ISBN 0-8159-5401-8). Devin.

Baali, F. Ibn Khaldun's Science of Human Culture. 16.50 (ISBN 0-317-01604-0). Kazi Pubns.

Badri, M. C. Islam & Alcoholism. LC 76-42173. 1976. pap. 2.75 (ISBN 0-89259-005-X). Am Trust Pubns.

Baillie, N. B. Digest of Moohammudan Law, 2 Vols. 1965. 65.50x (ISBN 0-87902-048-2). Orientalia.

Barnes, Bruce. Introduction to Islam. (Illus.). 192p. (Orig.). 1984. pap. text ed. 7.00 (ISBN 0-913811-01-7). Northeast A S.

Bawa Muhaiyaddeen, M. R. The Asma'ul-Husna: The 99 Beautiful Names of Allah. LC 79-19619. (Illus.). 211p. 1979. pap. 4.95 (ISBN 0-914390-13-9). Fellowship Pr PA.

Bell, Joseph N. Love Theory in Later Hanbalite Islam. LC 78-5904. 1979. PLB 49.50x (ISBN 0-87395-244-8). State U NY Pr.

Boisard, Marcel. Humanism in Islam. Al-Jarrahi, Abdussamad, tr. from Fr. LC 82-70456. 200p. (Orig.). Date not set. pap. 8.00 (ISBN 0-89259-035-1). Am Trust Pubns.

Bouhdiba, Abdelwahab. Sexuality in Islam. 288p. 1985. 42.50x (ISBN 0-7100-9608-9). Methuen Inc.

Bourghei, S. R., et al. Piety. Tavakoli, Amir, tr. from Persian. 1980. pap. 1.00 (ISBN 0-318-03827-7). Book-Dist-Ctr.

Brill, E. J. Encyclopedia of Islam. 1983. text ed. write for info. (ISBN 0-02-903770-0). Macmillan.

Brinner, William M. & Ricks, Stephen D., eds. Studies in Islamic & Judaic Traditions. (Brown Judaic Studies). 287p. 1986. 29.95 (ISBN 1-55540-047-7, 14-01-10); pap. 24.95 (ISBN 1-55540-048-5). Scholars Pr GA.

Broomhall, Marshall. Islam in China: A Neglected Problem. 1980. lib. bdg. 75.00 (ISBN 0-8490-3137-0). Gordon Pr.

Brown, Marguerite. Magnificent Muslims. LC 81-80056. 98p. 1981. 8.00 (ISBN 0-911026-10-X). New World Press NY.

Bukhari, Sohail, tr. Abuzar. 200p. 1985. pap. 9.00 (ISBN 0-941724-35-2). Islamic Seminary.

Bukhsh, S. K. Islamic Studies. 16.50 (ISBN 0-686-18357-6). Kazi Pubns.

Burton, Richard F. The Jew, the Gypsy & el Islam. 1974. Repr. of 1898 ed. 6.00 (ISBN 0-913022-11-X). Angriff Pr.

Carra de Vaux, Bernard. Les Penseurs de l'Islam, 5 vols. LC 80-2197. Repr. of 1926 ed. Set. 200.00 (ISBN 0-404-18990-3). AMS Pr.

Chattopadhya, A. Why Have I Accepted Islam? pap. 1.75 (ISBN 0-686-18476-9). Kazi Pubns.

Chirri, Imam Mohamad Jawad. The Faith of Islam. 24p. Date not set. pap. 3.00 (ISBN 0-317-52358-9). Islamic Ctr.

Christopher, John B. The Islamic Tradition. (Major Traditions in World Civilization Ser.). 1972. pap. text ed. 11.95 scp (ISBN 0-06-041283-6, HarpC). Har-Row.

Dale, Stephen F. Islamic Society on the South Asian Frontier: The Mappilas of Malabar, 1498 - 1922. (Illus.). 1980. 55.00x (ISBN 0-19-821571-1). Oxford U Pr.

Dekmejian, R. Hrair. Islam in Revolution: Fundamentalism in the Arab World. (Contemporary Issues in the Middle East Ser.). 224p. 1985. text ed. 28.00x (ISBN 0-8156-2329-1); pap. text ed. 13.95x (ISBN 0-8156-2330-5). Syracuse U Pr.

Denny, Frederick M. An Introduction to Islam. 368p. 1985. text ed. write for info. (ISBN 0-02-328520-6). Macmillan.

Dermenghem, Emile. Muhammad & the Islamic Tradition. Watt, Jean M., tr. LC 81-47412. 192p. pap. 9.95 (ISBN 0-87951-170-2). Overlook Pr.

Diamond, Michael J. & Gowing, Peter G. Islam & Muslims: Some Basic Information. 100p. 1981. pap. 3.75x (ISBN 0-686-30367-9, Pub. by New Day Publishers Philippines). Cellar.

Dobbins, Frank A. The Contributions of Mohammedanism to the Historical Growth of Mankind & Its Future Prospects. (Illus.). 103p. Repr. of 1883 ed. 97.75 (ISBN 0-89901-111-X). Found Class Reprints.

Donaldson, Dwight M. The Shi'ite Religion: A History of Islam in Persia & Irak. LC 80-1933. 49.50 (ISBN 0-404-18959-8). AMS Pr.

Donohue, John J. & Esposito, John L., eds. Islam in Transition: Muslim Perspectives. 1982. 28.00x (ISBN 0-19-503022-2); pap. 12.95x (ISBN 0-19-503023-0). Oxford U Pr.

Doray, S. J. Gateway to Islam, 4. pap. 9.50 (ISBN 0-686-18395-9). Kazi Pubns.

Dorman, Harry G. Toward Understanding Islam: Contemporary Apologetic of Islam & Missionary Policy. LC 79-176727. (Columbia University. Teachers College. Contributions to Education: No. 940). Repr. of 1948 ed. 22.50 (ISBN 0-404-55940-9). AMS Pr.

Eickelman, Dale F. Moroccan Islam: Tradition & Society in a Pilgrimage Center. (Modern Middle East Ser.: No. 1). 323p. 1976. pap. text ed. 12.95x (ISBN 0-292-75062-5). U of Tex Pr.

El Droubie, Riadh. Islam. 1985. 13.00 (ISBN 0-7062-3595-9, Pub. by Ward Lock Educ Co Ltd). State Mutual Bk.

El Farra, Muhammad. Years of No Decision. 350p. 1987. 37.50 (ISBN 0-7103-0215-0, Kegan Paul). Methuen Inc.

Esposito, John L., ed. Voices of Resurgent Islam. 1983. 27.00x (ISBN 0-19-503339-6); pap. 12.95x (ISBN 0-19-503340-X). Oxford U Pr.

Ewert, Christian. Islamische Funde in Balaguer und die Aljaferia in Zaragoza. (Madrider Forschungen, Vol. 7). (Illus.). 281p. 1971. 96.00 (ISBN 3-11-003613-4). De Gruyter.

Farah, Caesar E. Islam: Beliefs & Observances. rev. ed. LC 72-135505. (Orig.). (YA) 1970. pap. 6.50 (ISBN 0-8120-0277-6). Barron.

Farid, A. H. Prayers of Muhammad. 1969. 10.75x (ISBN 0-87902-050-4). Orientalia.

Ferber, Stanley, ed. Islam & the Medieval West. (Illus.). 1979. pap. 29.50x (ISBN 0-87395-802-0). State U NY Pr.

Ghazzali, Al. Mysteries of Worship in Islam: The Book of the Ihya' on Worship Translated with Commentary & Introduction. Calverley, E. E., tr. pap. 11.00 (ISBN 0-87902-200-0). Orientalia.

Ghosh, A. The Koran & the Kafir: Islam & the Infidel. (Illus.). 190p. 1983. pap. 5.95 (ISBN 0-9611614-0-X). Ghosh A.

Gibb, H. A. & Kramers, J. H., eds. Shorter Encyclopaedia of Islam. (Illus.). 678p. 1957. 85.00x (ISBN 0-8014-0150-X). Cornell U Pr.

Gibb, Hamilton A., ed. Whither Islam? A Survey of Modern Movements in the Moslem World. LC 73-180338. Repr. of 1932 ed. 27.00 (ISBN 0-404-56263-9). AMS Pr.

Gilliland, Dean S. African Religion Meets Islam: Religious Change in Northern Nigeria. 250p. (Orig.). 1986. lib. bdg. 24.50 (ISBN 0-8191-5634-5); pap. text ed. 12.75 (ISBN 0-8191-5635-3). U Pr of Amer.

Guillaume, Alfred. Islam. 1954. pap. 6.95 (ISBN 0-14-020311-7, Pelican). Penguin.

Haddad, Yvonne Y. Contemporary Islam & the Challenge of History. LC 81-8732. 272p. 1982. 49.50 (ISBN 0-87395-543-9); pap. 19.95 o. s. i. (ISBN 0-87395-544-7). State U NY Pr.

Haddad, Yvonne Y., et al, eds. The Islamic Impact. (Contemporary Issues in the Middle East Ser.). (Illus.). 264p. 1983. text ed. 30.00x o. p. (ISBN 0-8156-2304-6); pap. text ed. 13.95x (ISBN 0-8156-2299-6). Syracuse U Pr.

Hakim, K. A. Islam & Communism. pap. 15.95 (ISBN 0-686-18576-5). Kazi Pubns.

--Islamic Ideology. 16.50 (ISBN 0-686-18571-4). Kazi Pubns.

Hameed, Hakeem A., ed. Islam at a Glance. 125p. 1981. (Pub. by Vikas India); pap. 4.95x (ISBN 0-7069-1413-9). Advent NY.

Hameedullah, M. Introduction to Islam. pap. 14.95 (ISBN 0-686-18488-2). Kazi Pubns.

--Islam, a General Picture. pap. 4.50 (ISBN 0-686-63903-0). Kazi Pubns.

Hameedullah, Muhammad. Introduction to Islam. 276p. (Orig.). 1977. pap. 6.50 (ISBN 0-939830-13-2, Pub. by IIFSO Kuwait). New Era Pubns MI.

Hashim, A. S. Eleven Surahs Explained. (Islamics Books for Children: Bk. 3). pap. 4.95 (ISBN 0-686-18412-2); pap. 45.00 entire ser. (ISBN 0-686-18413-0). Kazi Pubns.

--Ibadat. (Islamic Books for Children: Bk. 2). pap. 4.95 (ISBN 0-686-18414-9); pap. 40.00 entire ser. (ISBN 0-686-18415-7). Kazi Pubns.

--Iman, Basic Beliefs. (Islamic Books for Children: Bk. 1). pap. 4.95 (ISBN 0-686-18416-5); pap. 45.00 entire ser. (ISBN 0-686-18417-3). Kazi Pubns.

Hitti, Philip K. Islam: A Way of Life. 1971. pap. 7.50 (ISBN 0-89526-992-9). Regnery Bks.

Hourani, George F., ed. Essays on Islamic Philosophy & Science. LC 74-13493. 1974. 49.50 (ISBN 0-87395-224-3). State U Ny Pr.

Hovannisian, Richard G. & Vryonis, Speros, Jr., eds. Islam's Understanding of Itself. LC 82-50987. (Giorgio Levi Della Vida Biennial Conference Ser.: Vol. 8). viii, 151p. 1983. pap. 18.50x (ISBN 0-89003-135-5). Undena Pubns.

Hughes. Dictionary of Islam. 45.00 (ISBN 0-686-18366-5). Kazi Pubns.

Hughes, Thomas P. A Dictionary of Islam, 2 vols. 1980. Set. lib. bdg. 199.95 (ISBN 0-8490-3121-4). Gordon Pr.

--Dictionary of Islam. (Illus.). 750p. 1977. Repr. of 1885 ed. 48.00x (ISBN 0-89684-103-0, Pub. by Cosmo Pubns India). Orient Bk Dist.

--A Dictionary of Islam. 1976. Repr. 37.50x (ISBN 0-8364-0395-9). South Asia Bks.

--A Dictionary of Islam: A Cyclopedia of the Muhammadan Religion. (Reprints in History). (Illus.). 750p. lib. bdg. 34.00 (ISBN 0-697-00053-2). Irvington.

--Notes on Muhammadanism: Being Outlines of the Religious System of Islam. LC 74-83164. (Islam & MidEast Ser). 1976. Repr. of 1877 ed. 33.00 (ISBN 0-8420-1756-9). Scholarly Res Inc.

Humayun, Kabir. Science, Democracy, & Islam: And Other Essays. LC 80-2195. Repr. of 1955 ed. 20.00 (ISBN 0-404-18967-9). AMS Pr.

Hurgronje, Christian S. Mohammedanism: Lectures in Its Origin, Its Religious & Political Growth, & Its Present State. LC 79-2865. 184p. 1980. Repr. of 1916 ed. 18.00 (ISBN 0-8305-0038-3). Hyperion Conn.

Hussain, J. M. The Occultation of the Twelfth Imam: A Historical Background. 221p. 1982. 35.00x (ISBN 0-317-39132-1, Pub. by Luzac & Co Ltd). State Mutual Bk.

Hussain, Jassim M. The Occulation of Imam: A Historical Background. 221p. 1986. lib. bdg. 30.00 (ISBN 0-7103-0158-8). Methuen Inc.

Hussain, M. Shamail Tirmidhi. 22.50 (ISBN 0-317-01594-X). Kazi Pubns.

Imam. Introduction to Islam: The First & Final Religion. abr. ed. 18p. (Orig.). 1983. pap. 1.50 (ISBN 0-916157-01-6). African Islam Miss Pubns.

Iqbal, A. Diplomacy in Islam. 14.95 (ISBN 0-686-18588-9). Kazi Pubns.

Iqbal, M. The Reconstruction of Religious Thoughts in Islam. 15.50 (ISBN 0-686-18482-3). Kazi Pubns.

Iqbal, Muhammad. Way of the Muslim. (The Way Ser.). pap. 5.95 (ISBN 0-7175-0632-0). Dufour.

Irving, Thomas B. The World of Islam. Orig. Title: The Tide of Islam. (Illus.). 200p. 1985. 17.50 (ISBN 0-915597-20-9); pap. 9.95 (ISBN 0-915597-18-7). Amana Bks.

Irving, Washington. Mahomet & His Successors, 2 Vols. 1983. Repr. of 1868 ed. lib. bdg. 200.00 set (ISBN 0-89987-405-3). Darby Bks.

Islam: A Code of Social Life. 4.00. Islamic Seminary.

Izetbegovic, Alija A. Islam Between East & West. LC 84-45552. 248p. (Orig.). 1984. pap. 12.00 (ISBN 0-89259-057-2). Am Trust Pubns.

Izutsu, Toshihiko. The Concept of Belief in Islamic Theology. LC 79-52553. (Islam Ser.). 1980. Repr. of 1965 ed. lib. bdg. 20.00x (ISBN 0-8369-9261-X). Ayer Co Pubs.

Jameelah, M. Islam & Modernism. pap. 10.50 (ISBN 0-686-18574-9). Kazi Pubns.

--Islam & Orientalism. pap. 6.50 (ISBN 0-686-18573-0). Kazi Pubns.

--Islam in Theory & Practice. pap. 14.50 (ISBN 0-686-18501-3). Kazi Pubns.

--Islam vs, Ahl-al-Kitab, Past & Present. pap. 15.95 (ISBN 0-686-18570-6). Kazi Pubns.

--Islam vs the West. pap. 1.75 (ISBN 0-686-18568-4). Kazi Pubns.

Jang, A. Notes on Islam. pap. 1.50 (ISBN 0-686-18487-4). Kazi Pubns.

Kamal, A. A. Everyday Fight, 2 vols. Set. pap. 18.00 (ISBN 0-686-63899-9). Kazi Pubns.

Kasravi, Ahmad. On Religion: Shi'ism & on Islam, Bk. 1. Jazayery, Mohammad A., ed. Ghanoonparvar, M. R., tr. from Persian. 180p. Date not set. lib. bdg. write for info. (ISBN 0-939214-39-3); pap. text ed. write for info. (ISBN 0-939214-42-3). Mazda Pubs.

Kattani, Sulayman. Imam Ali: Source of Light, Wisdom & Might. Howard, I. K., tr. 148p. Date not set. text ed. 25.00 (ISBN 0-7103-0153-7). Methuen Inc.

Kazi, M. Adhan over Anatolia. pap. 7.95. Am Trust Pubns.

Keddie, Nikki R., ed. Scholars, Saints & Sufis: Muslim Religious Institutions Since 1500. LC 77-153546. (Near Eastern Center, UCLA). 350p. 1972. pap. 9.95x (ISBN 0-520-03644-1, CAMPUS 210). U of Cal Pr.

Kedourie, Elie. Afghani & Abduh: Essay on Religious Unbelief & Political Activism in Modern Islam. 97p. 1966. 28.50x (ISBN 0-7146-1989-2, F Cass Co). Biblio Dist.

Kelly, Marjorie, ed. Islam: The Religious & Political Life of a World Community. LC 84-13307. 336p. 1984. 42.95 (ISBN 0-275-91204-3); pap. 16.95 (ISBN 0-03-001087-X); study guide 9.95 (ISBN 0-03-001084-5). Praeger.

--Islam: The Religious & Political Life of a World Community. LC 84-13307. 325p. 1984. 39.95; pap. 16.95. Foreign Policy.

Khalidi, Tarif. Classical Arab Islam: The Culture & Heritage of the Golden Age. LC 84-70416. 158p. 1985. 16.95 (ISBN 0-87850-047-2). Darwin Pr.

Khan, M. Y. God, Soul & Universe in Science & Islam. 1969. 3.50 (ISBN 0-87902-170-5). Orientalia.

Khomeini, Imam. Practical Laws of Islam. LC 83-50077. 1983. pap. 9.00 (ISBN 0-940368-25-0). Tahrike Tarsile Quran.

Klein, F. A. The Religion of Islam. 8.95x (ISBN 0-317-20253-7). Intl Bk Ctr.

--The Religion of Islam. 248p. 1985. pap. text ed. 12.50x (ISBN 0-7007-0190-7, Pub by Curzon Pr UK). Humanities.

Kramer, Martin. Islam Assembled: The Advent of the Muslim Congresses. LC 84-21407. 280p. 1985. 30.00x (ISBN 0-231-05994-9). Columbia U Pr.

Kurdi, Abdulrahman A. The Islamic State: A Study Based on the Qur'an & Sunnah. 147p. 1984. 33.00x (ISBN 0-7201-1725-9). Mansell.

Kyani, A. S. Islam & Muslims in Red Regimes. pap. 4.50 (ISBN 0-686-18575-7). Kazi Pubns.

Lalljee, Yousuf N. Know Your Islam. LC 81-51707. 256p. 1981. pap. 7.00 (ISBN 0-940368-02-1). Tahrike Tarsile Quran.

Lammens, Henri. Islam: Beliefs & Institutions. 1976. lib. bdg. 59.95 (ISBN 0-8490-2080-8). Gordon Pr.

--Islam: Beliefs & Institutions. Ross, E. Denison, tr. from Fr. 265p. Repr. of 1929 ed. text ed. 23.50x. Coronet Bks.

Le Gai Eaton, Charles. Islam & the Destiny of Man. (Islam Ser.). 256p. 1985. 44.50x (ISBN 0-88706-161-3); pap. 14.95 (ISBN 0-88706-163-X). State U NY Pr.

Le Tourneau, Roger. L'Islam Contemporain. LC 80-1922. Repr. of 1950 ed. 24.50 (ISBN 0-404-18975-X). AMS Pr.

Lewis, B., et al, eds. Encyclopedia of Islam, 4 vols. Incl. Vol. 1. A-B: Fasc. 1-22. Gibb, H. A., et al, eds. 1960. text ed. 185.75x (ISBN 90-040-0530-7); Vol. 2. C-G: Fasc. 23-40. Lewis, B., et al, eds. 1965; Vol. 3. H-Iram: Fasc. 41-60. 1969. text ed. 226.25x (ISBN 90-040-3275-4); Vols. 4 & 5. I-Ram &K-Ha: Fasc. 61-78. 1978. text ed. 275.50. Humanities.
Lewis, Bernard. The Muslim Discovery of Europe. (Illus.). 352p. 1982. 19.95 (ISBN 0-393-01529-7). Norton.
Lichtenstadter, Ilse. Islam & the Modern Age. 228p. 1958. text ed. 29.00x (ISBN 0-8290-0179-4). Irvington.
Lippman, Thomas W. Islam: Politics & Religion in the Muslim World. (Headline Series 258). (Illus.). 64p. 1982. pap. 4.00 (ISBN 0-87124-075-0). Foreign Policy.
--Understanding Islam: An Introduction to the Moslem World. LC 81-85142. 208p. 1982. pap. 3.50 (ISBN 0-451-62501-3, ME2079, Ment). NAL.
Macdonald, Duncan B. Aspects of Islam. facsimile ed. LC 77-179530. (Select Bibliographies Reprint Ser). Repr. of 1911 ed. 25.50 (ISBN 0-8369-6659-7). Ayer Co Pubs.
--Development of Muslim Theology, Jurisprudence & Constitutional Theory. LC 65-18818. 1965. Repr. of 1903 ed. 14.00 (ISBN 0-89684-381-5). Orient Bk Dist.
--Religious Attitude & Life in Islam. LC 70-121277. Repr. of 1909 ed. 20.50 (ISBN 0-404-04125-6). AMS Pr.
MacDonald Presentation Volume: A Tribute to Duncan Black Macdonald, Consisting of Articles by Former Students, Presented to Him on His Seventieth Birthday, April 9, 1933. facs. ed. LC 68-22109. (Essay Index Reprint Ser.). 1933. 24.25 (ISBN 0-8369-0645-4). Ayer Co Pubs.
McDowell, Josh & Gilchrist, John. The Islam Debate. (Orig.). 1983. pap. 6.95 (ISBN 0-86605-104-X). Campus Crusade.
MacEoin, Denis & Al-Shahi, Ahmed, eds. Islam in the Modern World. LC 83-8992. 148p. 1983. 22.50 (ISBN 0-317-13515-5). St Martin.
McWilliam, H. O. Muhammad & the World of Islam. Reeves, Marjorie, ed. (Then & There Ser.). (Illus.). 96p. (Orig.). 1977. pap. text ed. 4.75 (ISBN 0-582-20537-9). Longman.
Margoliouth, David S. Mohammed & the Rise of Islam. LC 73-14455. Repr. of 1905 ed. 30.00 (ISBN 0-404-58273-7). AMS Pr.
Martin, Richard C. Islam: A Cultural Perspective. (Illus.). 192p. 1982. pap. text ed. 17.00 (ISBN 0-13-506345-0). P-H.
Martin, Richard C., ed. Approaches to Islam in Reglious Studies. LC 85-1099. 1985. 18.95x (ISBN 0-8165-0868-2). U of Ariz Pr.
Maududi, A. A. Fundamentals of Islam. 12.50 (ISBN 0-686-18489-0). Kazi Pubns.
--Political Theory of Islam. pap. 1.00 (ISBN 0-686-18547-1). Kazi Pubns.
--The Religion of Truth. pap. 1.00 (ISBN 0-686-18537-4). Kazi Pubns.
--Towards Understanding Islam. pap. 5.50 (ISBN 0-686-18479-3). Kazi Pubns.
Maududi, Abul A. Towards Understanding Islam. Ahmad, Khurshid, tr. from Urdu. 116p. (Orig.). pap. 5.95x (ISBN 0-86037-053-4, Pub. by Islamic Found UK). New Era Pubns MI.
Maududi, S. A. Towards Understanding Islam. 5.50x (ISBN 0-87902-065-2). Orientalia.
Maulana-Muhammad-Ali. Religion of Islam. 1978. 42.50x (ISBN 0-89684-447-1). Orient Bk Dist.
Mawdudi, Sayyid A. Towards Understanding Islam. Ahmad, Khurshid, tr. from Urdu. Tr. of Risala-e-Diniyat. 179p. (Orig.). 1980. pap. 5.95 (ISBN 0-939830-22-1, Pub. by IIFSO Kuwait). New Era Pubns MI.
Mez, Adam. The Renaissance of Islam. Bukhsl, Salahuddin K & Margoliovth, D. S., trs. LC 70-180361. Repr. of 1937 ed. 27.00 (ISBN 0-404-56293-0). AMS Pr.
Mohamed. The Philosophical Essence of Islam. (The Essential Library of the Great Philosophies). (Illus.). 143p. 1985. 117.50 (ISBN 0-317-19583-2). Am Inst Psych.
Morgan, Kenneth W., ed. Islam the Straight Path: Islam Interpreted by Muslims. LC 58-9807. pap. 115.80 (ISBN 0-317-08489-5, 2012383). Bks Demand UMI.
Mortimer, Edward. Faith & Power: The Politics of Islam. (Illus.). 425p. 1982. 6.36 (ISBN 0-394-71173-4). Random.
Mott, John R. Moslem World of Today. xv, 420p. 1986. text ed. 50.00x (ISBN 81-210-0016-5, Pub. by Inter India Pubns N Delhi). Apt Bks.
Mozaffari, Mehdi. Authority in Islam. Vale, Michel, tr. from Fr. Tr. of Pouvoic Islamique. 156p. 1987. 39.95 (ISBN 0-87332-388-2). M E Sharpe.
Muhajir, A. M. Islam in Practical Life. 1968. 7.25x (ISBN 0-87902-067-9). Orientalia.
--Tenets of Islam. 1969. 7.25x (ISBN 0-87902-107-1). Orientalia.
Muhajir, M. R. Islam in Practical Life. 12.50 (ISBN 0-686-18502-1). Kazi Pubns.
Mutahhari, Murtaza. The Nature of Imam Hussein'n Movement. Ali, Muhammed K., ed. Pazargadi, Alaedin, tr. 20p. 1984. pap. 2.95 (ISBN 0-940368-33-1). Tahrike Tarsile Quran.
Mutahhery, Murtaza. The Martyr. Ansari, M. A., tr. 62p. 1983. pap. 4.00 (ISBN 0-941724-13-1). Islamic Seminary.
--Master & Mastership. Ansari, M. A., tr. 124p. 1983. pap. 5.00 (ISBN 0-941724-15-8). Islamic Seminary.
--Rationality of Islam. Ansari, M. A., tr. 170p. 1983. pap. 6.00 (ISBN 0-941724-17-4). Islamic Seminary.
Nabi, Malik B. The Quranic Phenomenon. Kirkari, Abu B., tr. from Fr. LC 82-70460. (Illus.). 187p. (Orig.). 1982. pap. 6.00 (ISBN 0-89259-023-8). Am Trust Pubns.
Nadui, A. H. Islam: The Perfect Religion & a Way of Life. pap. 1.00 (ISBN 0-686-18498-X). Kazi Pubns.
Nadvi. An Easy History of the Prophet of Islam. pap. 3.95 (ISBN 0-686-18309-6). Kazi Pubns.
--Saviors of Islamic Spirit, 3 Vols. 60.00 set (ISBN 0-686-18312-6); 20.00 ea. Kazi Pubns.
Nadvi, A. Islam: The Only Way. pap. 1.00 (ISBN 0-686-18499-8). Kazi Pubns.
Nadvi, A. H. Four Pillars of Islam. 14.95 (ISBN 0-686-18597-8). Kazi Pubns.
--Islam & the World. 14.50 (ISBN 0-686-18625-7). Kazi Pubns.
--Religion & Civilization. 4.00 (ISBN 0-686-18566-8). Kazi Pubns.
Nasr, Seyyed H. Islam & the Plight of Modern Man. LC 75-29014. (World of Islam Ser.). 1976. text ed. 26.00x (ISBN 0-582-78053-5). Longman.
--Traditional Islam in the Modern World. 320p. 1987. text ed. 39.95 (ISBN 0-7103-0177-4). Methuen Inc.
Naumani, M. What Islam Is? 10.50 (ISBN 0-686-18477-7). Kazi Pubns.
Nazir-Ali, Michael. Islam: A Christian Perspective. LC 84-3615. 186p. 1984. pap. 11.95 (ISBN 0-664-24527-7). Westminster.
Nigosian, Solomon. Islam. (Crucible Ser.). 208p. 1987. pap. 9.95 (ISBN 0-85030-490-3). Thorsons Pubs.
Nizami, Ashraf F. Namaz the Yoga of Islam. (Illus.). xxiii, 46p. 1981. text ed. 5.95x (ISBN 0-86590-052-3, Pub. by Taraporevala India). Apt Bks.
Nu'man, Muhammad A. What Every American Should Know about Islam & the Muslims. 74p. (Orig.). 1985. pap. 5.00 (ISBN 0-933821-04-2). New Mind Prod.
Obermann, Julian, ed. Nissim Ibn Shahin: The Arabic Original of Ibn Shahin's Book of Comfort. LC 78-63561. (Yale Oriental Ser. Researches: No. 17). Repr. of 1933 ed. 72.50 (ISBN 0-404-60287-8). AMS Pr.
O'Leary, De Lacy E. Islam at the Cross Roads: A Brief Survey of the Present Position & Problems of the World of Islam. LC 80-1916. 1981. Repr. of 1923 ed. 26.50 (ISBN 0-404-18983-0). AMS Pr.
Palacios, Miguel A. Islam & the Divine Comedy. 295p. 1968. Repr. of 1926 ed. 30.00x (ISBN 0-7146-1995-7, F Cass Co). Biblio Dist.
Parshall, Phil. New Paths in Muslim Evangelism: Evangelical Approaches to Contextualization. 200p. (Orig.). 1980. pap. 8.95 (ISBN 0-8010-7056-2). Baker Bk.
Peacock, James L. Muslim Puritans: Reformist Psychology in Southeast Asian Islam. LC 76-55571. 1978. 36.00x (ISBN 0-520-03403-1). U of Cal Pr.
Peters, Rudilph. Islam & Colonialism. (Religion & Society Ser.). 1984. text ed. 37.75x (ISBN 90-279-3347-2); pap. 14.95 (ISBN 3-11-010022-3). Mouton.
Pickthall, Muhammad, tr. Qur'an: The Glorious. 767p. 1983. pap. 8.00 (ISBN 0-940368-30-7). Tahrike Tarsile Quran.
Pipes, Daniel. In the Path of God: Islam & Political Power. LC 83-70764. 384p. 1985. pap. 9.95 (ISBN 0-465-03452-7, PL-5138). Basic.
Planhol, Xavier de. The World of Islam. 153p. 1959. pap. 8.95x (ISBN 0-8014-9830-9). Cornell U Pr.
Qaderi, M. Taleem-Ul-Islam, 4. pap. 7.50 (ISBN 0-686-18387-8). Kazi Pubns.
Qazi, M. A. Bilal: The First Muadhdhin of the Prophet of Islam. pap. 4.50 (ISBN 0-686-18325-8). Kazi Pubns.
Quasem, M. A. Salvation of the Soul & Islamic Devotion. 200p. (Orig.). 1984. pap. 12.95 (ISBN 0-7103-0033-6, Kegan Paul). Methuen Inc.
Quraishi, M. Tariq, ed. Islam, A Way of Life & a Movement. LC 83-71408. 221p. (Orig.). 1986. pap. 9.50 (ISBN 0-89259-055-6). Am Trust Pubns.
Qutb, M. Islam: The Misunderstood Religion. pap. 8.50 (ISBN 0-686-18500-5). Kazi Pubns.
Qutb, Sayved. Islam & Universal Peace. LC 77-89635. 1977. pap. 2.85 (ISBN 0-89259-007-6). Am Trust Pubns.
Qutb, Sayyid. Al-Mustaqbal li-hadha ad-Din. (Arabic.). 118p. (Orig.). 1978. pap. 2.35x (ISBN 0-939830-16-7, Pub. by IIFSO Kuwait). New Era Pubns MI.
--Hadha ad-Din. (Arabic.). 96p. (Orig.). 1978. pap. 1.75x (ISBN 0-939830-18-3, Pub. by IIFSO Kuwait). New Era Pubns MI.
--Ma alim fi at-Tariq. (Arabic.). 186p. (Orig.). 1978. pap. 3.75x (ISBN 0-939830-17-5, Pub. by IIFSO Kuwait). New Era Pubns MI.
--Milestones. Tr. of Ma alim fi at-Tariq. 303p. (Orig.). 1978. pap. 5.95 (ISBN 0-939830-07-8, Pub. by IIFSO Kuwait). New Era Pubns MI.
--This Religion of Islam. Tr. of Hadha ad-Din. 104p. (Orig.). 1977. pap. 2.95x (ISBN 0-939830-08-6, Pub. by IIFSO Kuwait). New Era Pubns MI.
Rahman, A. Encyclopaedia of Seerah I-IV. 55.00 ea. (ISBN 0-317-46105-2). Kazi Pubns.
--Essentials of Islam. pap. 4.95 (ISBN 0-686-67786-2). Kazi Pubns.
Ramadhan, S. Islam & Nationalism. pap. 1.00 (ISBN 0-686-18586-2). Kazi Pubns.
Rauf, Abdul. Bilal Ibn Rabah. LC 76-49691. 1977. pap. 3.95 (ISBN 0-89259-008-4). Am Trust Pubns.
Rauf, M. A. Islamic Religious Knowledge, 3 vols. 9.50 (ISBN 0-686-18392-4). Kazi Pubns.
Rippin, A. & Knappert, J., eds. Islam (Textual Sources for the Study of Islam) LC 86-22190. (Textual Sources for the Study of Religion). 256p. 1986. 23.50x (ISBN 0-389-20677-6); pap. 11.75 (ISBN 0-389-20678-4). B&N Imports.
Rizvi, Allama S. Element of Islamic Studies. Anwarali, Maulana, ed. Rizvi, Saeed A., tr. LC 84-52745. 60p. 1984. pap. 3.95 (ISBN 0-940368-44-7). Tahrike Tarsile Quran.
Roboz, Steven & Steiner, Rudolf. Islam: Study Notes. Roboz, Steven, ed. 33p. 1980. pap. 2.95 (ISBN 0-88010-050-8, Pub. by Steiner Book Centre Canada). Anthroposophic.
Robson, J., tr. Mishkat Al-Masabih, 2 vols. Set. 65.00x (ISBN 0-87902-068-7); Vol. 1. 35.00 (ISBN 0-87902-297-3); Vol. 2. 35.00 (ISBN 0-87902-298-1). Orientalia.
Rosenthal, Erwin I. Studia Semitica, 2 vols. Incl. Vol. 1. Jewish Themes. 59.50 (ISBN 0-521-07958-6); Vol. 2. Islamic Themes. 49.50 (ISBN 0-521-07959-4). (Oriental Publications Ser.: Nos. 16 & 17). Cambridge U Pr.
Sabini, J. Islam: A Primer. 127p. 1984. 30.00x (ISBN 0-317-39197-6, Pub. by Luzac & Co Ltd). State Mutual Bk.
Sabini, John. Islam: A Primer. LC 83-61987. (Illus.). 127p. 1983. pap. 7.50x (ISBN 0-918992-05-2). Middle East Edit.
Sabiq, Sayyed. Figh Al Sunnah. Quilan, Hamid, ed. Izzidien, Movel Y., tr. from Arabic. LC 82-70450. 1700p. (Orig.). 1983. text ed. 30.00 (ISBN 0-89259-033-5); pap. 20.00 (ISBN 0-686-81828-8). Am Trust Pubns.
Sachedina, Abdulaziz A. Islamic Messianism: The Idea of Mahdi in Twelver Shi'ism. LC 80-16767. 1980. 49.50x (ISBN 0-87395-442-4); pap. 19.95x (ISBN 0-87395-458-0). State U NY Pr.
Sakr, A. Names of Quran in Holy Quran. pap. 2.50 (ISBN 0-317-01599-0). Kazi Pubns.
Sanderson, Richard N. The Islamic Movement & the Threat to Western Civilization. (Illus.). 141p. 1980. deluxe ed. 67.45x (ISBN 0-930008-59-6). Inst Econ Pol.
Saud, M. A. Concepts of Islam. pap. 6.95 (ISBN 0-317-01600-8). Kazi Pubns.
Sayili, Aydin. The Observatory in Islam. Cohen, I. Bernard, ed. LC 80-2144. (Development of Science Ser.). (Illus.). 1981. lib. bdg. 45.00x (ISBN 0-405-13951-9). Ayer Co Pubs.
Schacht, Joseph & Bosworth, C. E., eds. The Legacy of Islam. 2nd ed. (Legacy Ser). (Illus.). 1974. text ed. 29.95x (ISBN 0-19-821913-X). Oxford U Pr.
Schaefer, Udo. The Light Shineth in Darkness: Five Studies in Revelation after Christ. Neri, Helene M. & Coburn, Oliver, trs. 208p. 1977. 15.95 (ISBN 0-85398-091-8); pap. 9.95 (ISBN 0-85398-072-1). G Ronald Pub.
Schimmel, Annemarie. Islamic Calligraphy. (Illus.). 1970. 103.25x (ISBN 0-685-00757-X). Adlers Foreign Bks.
Schuon, Frithjof. Understanding Islam. Matheson, D. M., tr. (Unwin Paperback Ser.). 1976. pap. 5.95 (ISBN 0-04-297035-0). Allen Unwin.
Servier, Andre. Islam & the Psychology of the Musulman. 1977. lib. bdg. 59.95 (ISBN 0-8490-2079-4). Gordon Pr.
Shad, A. R. Do's & Do Nots in Islam. Tr. of Al-Halal wal-Haram. 15.95 (ISBN 0-317-01588-5). Kazi Pubns.
--From Adam to Muhammad. 16.95 (ISBN 0-317-01593-1). Kazi Pubns.
--Riadh-us-Salihin. (Eng. & Arabic.). 29.00 (ISBN 0-317-01590-7). Kazi Pubns.
Shah, Sirdar I. A. The Golden Caravan. 1983. 15.95 (ISBN 0-86304-026-8, Pub. by Octagon Pr England). Ins Study Human.
Sharafuddin, Sadruddin. Ammar Yasir. Haq, M. Fazal, tr. Orig. Title: Halif al-Makhzum. 264p. 1985. pap. 9.00 (ISBN 0-941724-40-9). Islamic Seminary.
Shariati, Ali. An Approach to Understanding of Islam. Kiavantash, Venus, tr. from Persian. 26p. 1980. pap. 1.00x (ISBN 0-941722-14-7). Book-Dist-Ctr.
--Man & Islam. Marjani, Fathollah, tr. from Persian. 150p. (Orig.). 1981. 9.95 (ISBN 0-941722-02-3); pap. 4.95 (ISBN 0-941722-00-7). Book Dist Ctr.
Shari'ati, Ali. On the Sociology of Islam. 3rd ed. Algar, Hamid, tr. from Persian. LC 79-83552. 1980. 15.95 (ISBN 0-933782-01-2); pap. 5.95 (ISBN 0-933782-00-4). Mizan Pr.
Sheik, Ali B. Islam: A Cultural Orientation. 10.00x (ISBN 0-8364-0802-0, Pub. by Macmillan India). South Asia Bks.
Siddique, Kaukab. Islam-the Wave of the Future. LC 82-83624. 75p. (Orig.). 1983. pap. 2.00 (ISBN 0-942978-04-8). Am Soc Ed & Rel.
--Towards Understanding the Basics of Islam: Texts from Qur'an & Hadith. 52p. (Orig.). 1986. pap. 2.50 (ISBN 0-942978-01-3). Am Soc Ed & Rel.
Siddiqui, A. A. Elementary Teachings of Islam. pap. 4.50 (ISBN 0-686-18397-5). Kazi Pubns.
Siddiqui, A. H. Islam & the Remaking of Humanity. pap. 9.95 (ISBN 0-686-63904-9). Kazi Pubns.
--What Islam Gave to Humanity? pap. 2.50 (ISBN 0-686-63918-9). Kazi Pubns.
Siddiqui, M. M. Women in Islam. 1969. 10.50 (ISBN 0-87902-069-5). Orientalia.
Siddiqui, M. S. Call to Islam. pap. 2.00 (ISBN 0-686-63897-2). Kazi Pubns.
Siddiqui, Muhammad A. Elementary Teachings of Islam. Date not set. 1.75 (ISBN 0-89259-022-X). Am Trust Pubns.
Sivan, Emmanuel. Interpretations of Islam: Past & Present. LC 84-70415. 256p. 1985. 19.95 (ISBN 0-87850-049-9). Darwin Pr.
Smith, Wilfred C. Islam in Modern History. 1957. 37.00 (ISBN 0-691-03030-8); pap. 10.50x (ISBN 0-691-01991-6). Princeton U Pr.
Subhan, S. A. Islam: Its Belief & Practices. 1938. 5.25x (ISBN 0-87902-190-X). Orientalia.
Swartz, Merlin L., et al. Studies on Islam. 1981. 22.50x (ISBN 0-19-502716-7); pap. 10.95x (ISBN 0-19-502717-5). Oxford U Pr.
Swarup, Ram. Understanding Islam Through Hadis: Religious Faith or Fanaticism? 1983. 13.95 (ISBN 0-682-49948-X). Exposition Pr FL.
Tabataba'I, Allamah. A Shi'ite Anthology. Chittick, William C., ed. 152p. 1986. text ed. 25.00 (ISBN 0-7103-0159-6); pap. text ed. 12.95 (ISBN 0-317-40555-1). Methuen Inc.
Tabbarah, Afif. The Spirit of Islam. 20.00x (ISBN 0-86685-029-5). Intl Bk Ctr.
Tabibi, Abdul H. Daa, Wah & Jihad. 40p. (Orig.). 1984. pap. 3.00 (ISBN 0-911119-05-1). Igram Pr.
Taleghani, Sayyid M. Society & Economics in Islam. Campbell, R., tr. from Persian. LC 82-2115. (Contemporary Islamic Thought Ser.). 225p. 1983. 17.95 (ISBN 0-933782-08-X). Mizan Pr.
Tames, Richard. The Muslim World. LC 83-50694. (Religions of the World Ser.). 48p. 1983. 14.96 (ISBN 0-382-06719-3); pap. 9.25 (ISBN 0-382-06932-3). Silver.
Taylor, John B. The World of Islam. (Orig.). 1979. pap. 3.95 (ISBN 0-377-00086-8). Friend Pr.
Tenets of Islam. 12.50 (ISBN 0-686-18485-8). Kazi Pubns.
Tibawi, A. L. Islamic Education: Its Traditions & Modernization into the Arab National Systems. 256p. 1979. Repr. 60.00x (ISBN 0-317-39091-0, Pub. by Luzac & Co Ltd). State Mutual Bk.
Tritton, Arthur S. Islam: Belief & Practices. LC 79-2883. 200p. 1986. Repr. of 1950 ed. 20.00 (ISBN 0-8305-0051-0). Hyperion Conn.
Ullah, Mohammad Z. The Islamic Concept of God. 116p. 1985. pap. 9.95 (ISBN 0-7103-0127-8, Kegan Paul). Methuen Inc.
Uthman, Ali Bin. Kashef-Al-Mahjub. 19.95 (ISBN 0-317-01606-7). Kazi Pubns.
Voll, John O. Islam: Continuity & Change in the Modern World. LC 82-2829. 398p. 1982. 32.00x (ISBN 0-89158-931-7); pap. text ed. 14.50x (ISBN 0-89158-983-X). Westview.
Von Grunebaum, G. E. Muhammaden Festivals: Typical Elements of Islamic Ritual, Prayer & Pilgrimage. new ed. (Illus.). 1976. text ed. 9.95x (ISBN 0-7007-0087-0). Humanities.
Von Grunebaum, Gustave E. Modern Islam: The Search for Cultural Identity. LC 83-11508. viii, 303p. 1983. Repr. of 1962 ed. lib. bdg. 39.75x (ISBN 0-313-24087-6, VGMI). Greenwood.
Waddy, Charis. The Muslim Mind. 2nd ed. LC 82-7778. (Illus.). 232p. 1983. 25.00x (ISBN 0-582-78346-1); pap. 8.95x (ISBN 0-582-78345-3). Longman.

Walther, Wiebke. Woman in Islam. (Image of Women Ser.). (Illus.). 192p. 1982. 35.00 (ISBN 0-8390-0256-4, Allanheld & Schram). Abner Schram Ltd.

Watt, Montgomery. What Is Islam? 1968. 25.00x (ISBN 0-685-77133-4). Intl Bk Ctr.

Watt, W. Montgomery. What Is Islam? 2nd ed. (Arab Background Ser.). 1979. text ed. 29.95x (ISBN 0-582-78302-X). Longman.

Wensinck, Arent J. The Muslim Creed: Its Genesis & Historical Development. 311p. 1932. Repr. text ed. 22.00x. Coronet Bks.

Wright, Robin. Sacred Rage: The Wrath of Militant Islam. 336p. 1986. pap. 7.95 (ISBN 0-671-62811-9, Touchstone Bks). S&S.

Yakan, Fathi. Islamic Movement: Problems & Perspective. Al-Johani, Maneh, tr. from Arabic. pap. 5.00 (ISBN 0-89259-051-3). Am Trust Pubns.

Zakariya, M. The Virtues of Salat. 1970. 3.95x (ISBN 0-87902-193-4). Orientalia.

Zakeriyya, M. Teachings of Islam (Tablighi Nisab) Date not set. 25.00 (ISBN 0-933511-09-4). Kazi Pubns.

Zubairi, M. Yameen. The Purpose of Islam. LC 84-90999. 100p. (Orig.). 1984. pap. text ed. write for info. (ISBN 0-930895-02-9). Byron Daven Pub.

Zuhur-U'D, A. M. M. An Examination of the Mystical Tendencies in Islam. 224p. 1973. 8.50x (ISBN 0-87902-252-3). Orientalia.

ISLAM–BIBLIOGRAPHY

Ede, David, et al. Guide to Islam. 265p. 1983. lib. bdg. 59.50 (ISBN 0-8161-7905-0, Hall Reference). G K Hall.

Pearson, J. D. & Behn, Wolfgang, eds. Index Islamicus, Fifth Supplement 1976-1980. 944p. 1983. Set. 159.00x (ISBN 0-7201-1650-3); Pt. 1: Articles. 96.00 (ISBN 0-7201-1669-4); Pt. 2: Monographs. 64.00 (ISBN 0-7201-1668-6). Mansell.

--Index Islamicus: First Supplement 1956-1960. 344p. 1978. Repr. of 1962 ed. 53.00x (ISBN 0-7201-0381-9). Mansell.

--Index Islamicus: Primary Sequence 1906-1955. 933p. 1958. 75.00x (ISBN 0-7201-0380-0). Mansell.

--Index Islamicus: Second Supplement, 1961-1965. 372p. 1967. 53.00 (ISBN 0-7201-0382-7). Mansell.

--Index Islamicus: Third Supplement 1966-1970. 420p. 1972. 53.00x (ISBN 0-7201-0282-0). Mansell.

Pearson, J. D. & Walsh, Ann, eds. Index Islamicus, Fourth Supplement: Part 2, 1972-73. 108p. 1974. 64.00 (ISBN 0-7201-0286-3). Mansell.

--Index Islamicus: Fourth Supplement, Part 4, 1974-1975. 128p. 1975. pap. 10.00x (ISBN 0-7201-0288-X). Mansell.

Roberts, Dennis. Islam: A Concise Introduction. LC 81-47845. 224p. 1982. pap. 7.95 (ISBN 0-06-066880-6, CN 4026, HarpR). Har-Row.

Sardar, Ziauddin. Islam: Outline of a Classification Scheme. 81p. 1979. 17.50 (ISBN 0-85157-285-5, Pub. by Bingley England). Shoe String.

Siddiq, Akhtar H. The Muslim World: A Selected Bibliography on Its Socio-Economic Development. (Public Administration Ser.: P 1372). 74p. 1984. pap. 11.25 (ISBN 0-88066-832-6). Vance Biblios.

Sumarti, Muljanto. Islamic Education in Indonesia: A Bibliography. 133p. (Orig.). 1984. pap. text ed. 21.00x (ISBN 9971-902-57-5, Pub. by Inst Southeast Asian Stud). Gower Pub Co.

Tabatabai, Hossein M. Introduction to Shii Law: A Bibliographical Study. 258p. 1985. text ed. 22.00 (ISBN 0-86372-015-3, Pub. by Ithaca England). Evergreen Dist.

ISLAM–HISTORIOGRAPHY

Easwaran, Eknath. A Man to Match His Mountains: Badshah Khan, Nonviolent Soldier of Islam. (Illus.). 1985. 15.95 (ISBN 0-915132-33-8); pap. 7.95 (ISBN 0-915132-34-6). Nilgiri Pr.

Rasul, M. G. Origin & Development of Muslim Historiography. 1970. 5.00x (ISBN 0-87902-183-7). Orientalia.

Thanvi, A. A. Bahishti Zewar (Heavenly Ornaments) 14.95 (ISBN 0-686-63896-4). Kazi Pubns.

Waardenburg, Jean-Jacques. L'islam Dans le Miroir De L'Occident: Comment Quelques Orientalistes Occidentaux Se Sont Penches Sur L'islam et Se Sont Forme une Image De Cette Religion. 3 ed. (Recherches Mediterraneennes: Etudes 3). 1970. 26.80x (ISBN 90-2796-304-5). Mouton.

ISLAM–HISTORY

Al-Askari, Allama M. Hadith: A Probe into the History of. Haq, M. Fazal, tr. 120p. 1983. pap. 4.00 (ISBN 0-941724-16-6). Islamic Seminary.

Ali ibn Isma'il, A. H., et al. Al ibanah 'an usul addiyanah. Klein, W. C., tr. (American Oriental Ser.: Vol. 19). 1940. 18.00 (ISBN 0-527-02693-X). Kraus Repr.

Al-Sayyid-Marsot, A. L., ed. Society & the Sexes in Medieval Islam. LC 79-63268. (Giorgio Levi Della Vida Biennial Conference Ser.: Vol. 6). 149p. 1979. pap. 18.50x (ISBN 0-89003-033-2). Undena Pubns.

Al-Tabari. The History of al-Tabari, Vol. 4: The Ancient Kingdoms. Yarshater, Ehsan, et al, eds. Perlmann, Moshe, tr. (The History of al-Tabari Ser.). 160p. 1986. 39.50x (ISBN 0-88706-181-8); pap. 14.95x (ISBN 0-88706-182-6). State U NY Pr.

Ansari, M. A., tr. from Persian. Man & His Destiny. Tr. of Insan wa Sarnawisht. 124p. 1985. pap. 5.00 (ISBN 0-941724-39-5). Islamic Seminary.

Arnold, Thomas W. The Preaching of Islam: A History of Propagation of the Muslim Faith. LC 72-180319. (Mid-East Studies). Repr. of 1913 ed. 27.50 (ISBN 0-404-56214-0). AMS Pr.

Ayati, Ibrahim. A Probe into the History of Ashura. Tr. of Barasi Tarkh-i-Ashura. 234p. 1985. pap. 9.00 (ISBN 0-941724-41-7). Islamic Seminary.

Azzam, Salem. Islam & Contemporary Society. LC 82-253. 256p. 1982. 16.95x (ISBN 0-582-78323-2); pap. 7.95x (ISBN 0-582-78322-4). Longman.

Becker, Carl H. Beitrage zur Geschicte Agyptens unter Dem Islam, 2 vols. in 1. LC 77-10579. (Studies in Islamic History: No. 5). 1978. Repr. of 1903 ed. lib. bdg. 25.00x (ISBN 0-87991-454-8). Porcupine Pr.

Bosworth, C. E. The Islamic Dynasties. 243p. 1980. pap. 10.00 (ISBN 0-85224-402-9, Pub. by Edinburgh U Pr Scotland). Columbia U Pr.

Bosworth, C. E., ed. Iran & Islam. 574p. 1972. 35.00x (ISBN 0-85224-200-X, Pub. by Edinburgh U Pr Scotland). Columbia U Pr.

Bukhsh, S. K. The Renaissance of Islam. 1981. 29.00 (ISBN 0-686-97863-3). Kazi Pubns.

Bulliet, Richard W. Conversion to Islam in the Medieval Period: An Essay in Quantitative History. (Illus.). 158p. 1979. text ed. 16.50x (ISBN 0-674-17035-0). Harvard U Pr.

Chejne, Anwar G. Islam & the West: The Moriscos. LC 82-703. 368p. 1983. 49.50 (ISBN 0-87395-603-6); pap. 19.95 (ISBN 0-87395-606-0). State U NY Pr.

Crone, Patricia. Meccan Trade & the Rise of Islam. 320p. 1986. text ed. 30.00 (ISBN 0-691-05480-0). Princeton U Pr.

Crone, Patricia & Cook, M. Hagarism: The Making of the Islamic World. LC 75-41714. 268p. 1977. 37.50 (ISBN 0-521-21133-6). Cambridge U Pr.

Crone, Patricia & Hinds, Martin. God's Caliph: Religious Authority in the First Centuries of Islam. (Oriental Publications Ser.: No. 37). 200p. 1986. 39.50 (ISBN 0-521-32185-9). Cambridge U Pr.

Dessouki, Ali E. Hillal. Islamic Resurgence in the Arab World. LC 81-12135. 286p. 1982. 40.95 (ISBN 0-03-059673-4). Praeger.

Donaldson, Dwight M. The Shi, Its Religion: A History of Islam in Persia & Iraq. 1976. lib. bdg. 59.95 (ISBN 0-8490-2598-2). Gordon Pr.

Donner, Fred M. The Early Islamic Conquests. LC 80-8544. (Princeton Studies on the Near East). (Illus.). 328p. 1981. 19.95x (ISBN 0-691-10182-5). Princeton U Pr.

Duckworth, John, et al. Muhammad & the Arab Empire. Yapp, Malcolm & Killingray, Margaret, eds. (World History Ser.). (Illus.). 1980. lib. bdg. 6.95 (ISBN 0-89908-036-7); pap. text ed. 2.45 (ISBN 0-89908-011-1). Greenhaven.

Endress, Gerhard. An Introduction to Islamic History. 220p. 1986. cancelled (ISBN 0-85224-496-7, Pub. by Edinburgh U Pr Scotland). Columbia U Pr.

--Islam: A Historical Introduction. Hillenbrand, Carole, tr. from Ger. 205p. 1987. text ed. 25.00 (ISBN 0-231-06580-9); pap. text ed. 12.00 (ISBN 0-231-06579-5). Columbia U Pr.

Engineer, Asghar A. The Origin & Development of Islam. 248p. 1980. 18.95x (ISBN 0-940500-33-7). Asia Bk Corp.

--The Origin & Development of Islam: An Essay on Its Socio-Economic Growth. 248p. 1980. text ed. 18.95x (ISBN 0-86131-174-4, Pub. by Orient Longman Ltd India). Apt Bks.

Esposito, John L., ed. Islam & Development: Religion & Sociopolitical Change. LC 80-25119. (Contemporary Issues in the Middle East Ser.). 292p. 1980. pap. text ed. 9.95x (ISBN 0-8156-2230-9). Syracuse U Pr.

Faizi, A. Q. The Prince of Martyrs: A Brief Account of Imam Husayn. 74p. 1977. pap. 3.50 (ISBN 0-85398-073-X). G Ronald Pub.

Faqih, I. Glimpses of Islamic History. 16.50 (ISBN 0-686-63900-6). Kazi Pubns.

Gibb, Hamilton A. Mohammedanism: An Historical Survey. 2nd ed. 1953. pap. 5.95x (ISBN 0-19-500245-8, 90). Oxford U Pr.

Graham, William A. Divine Word & Prophetic Word in Early Islam: A Reconsideration of the Sources, with Special Reference to the Divine Saying or Hadith Qudsi. (Religion & Society Ser.). 1977. text ed. 37.50x (ISBN 90-279-7612-0). Mouton.

Green, Arnold H., ed. In Quest of an Islamic Humanism: Arabic & Islamic Studies in Memory of Mohamed al-Nowaihi. 288p. 1986. pap. 27.50 (ISBN 977-424-027-8, Pub. by Am Univ Cairo Pr). Columbia U Pr.

Gulati, S. P. Quintessence of Islamic History & Culture. 225p. 1986. 23.00X (ISBN 81-85061-44-0, Pub. by Manohar India). South Asia Bks.

Haneef, S. What Everyone Should Know about Islam & Muslims. pap. 9.95 (ISBN 0-686-63919-7). Kazi Pubns.

Hawting, G. R. The First Dynasty of Islam: The Umayyad Caliphate A.D. 661-750. 160p. 1986. text ed. 24.95x (ISBN 0-8093-1324-3). S Ill U Pr.

Heyd, Uriel, ed. Studies in Islamic History & Civilization. (Scripta Hierosolymitana Ser.: Vol. 9). pap. 60.00 (ISBN 0-317-08597-2, 2051596). Bks Demand UMI.

Hodgson, Marshall G. Venture of Islam: Conscience & History in World Civilization, 3 vols. LC 73-87243. 1975. 30.00x ea.; Vol. 2. (ISBN 0-226-34680-3); Vol. 3. (ISBN 0-226-34681-1). U of Chicago Pr.

Holt, P. M., et al, eds. Cambridge History of Islam. Incl. Vol. 1A. Central Islamic Lands from Pre-Islamic Times to the First World War. 67.50 (ISBN 0-521-21946-9); pap. 29.95 (ISBN 0-521-29135-6); Vol. 1B. Central Islamic Lands Since 1918. 62.50 (ISBN 0-521-21947-7); pap. 24.95 (ISBN 0-521-29136-4); Vol. 2A. The Indian Subcontinent, Southeast Asia, Africa & the Muslim West. 64.50 (ISBN 0-521-21948-5); pap. 24.95 (ISBN 0-521-29137-2); Vol. 2B. Islamic Society & Civilization. 77.50 (ISBN 0-521-21949-3); pap. 32.95 (ISBN 0-521-29138-0). 1977-78. Set. 250.00 (ISBN 0-521-22310-5); Set. pap. 90.00 (ISBN 0-521-08755-4). Cambridge U Pr.

Hooker, M. B., ed. Islam in South East Asia. 272p. 1983. text ed. 39.95x (ISBN 0-686-46644-6, Pub. by EJ Brill Holland). Humanities.

Husayn, Sayyid S. The Early History of Islam. 360p. 1984. pap. 7.50 (ISBN 0-941724-25-5). Islamic Seminary.

Iqbal, Afzal. The Life & Work of Muhammed Jalal-ud-Din Rumi. 1983. 29.95 (ISBN 0-86304-033-0, Pub. by Octagon England). Ins Study Human.

Islam & the Medieval West: Aspects of Intercultural Relations. LC 79-18678. 1979. 44.50x (ISBN 0-87395-409-2); pap. 16.95x (ISBN 0-87395-455-6). State U NY Pr.

Israeli, Raphael, ed. The Crescent in the East: Islam in Asia Major. 240p. 1981. 30.00x (ISBN 0-7007-0143-5, Pub. by Curzon England). State Mutual Bk.

Karim, F. Heroes of Islam. Incl. Bk. 1. Muhammad; Bk. 2. Abu Bakr; Bk. 3. Umar; Bk. 4. Othman; Bk. 5. Ali; Bk. 6. Khalid Bin Walid; Bk. 7. Mohammad Bin Qasim; Bk. 8. Mahmood of Ghazni; Bk. 9. Mohyuddin; Bk. 10. Sultan Tipu; Bk. 11. Aisha the Truthful; Bk. 12. Hussain the Martyr; Bk. 13. Some Companions of the Prophet-I; Bk. 14. Some Companions of the Prophet-II; Bk. 15. Some Companions of the Prophet-III. pap. 37.50 complete set (ISBN 0-686-18393-2); pap. 2.50 ea bk. Kazi Pubns.

Kramer, Joel J. Humanism in the Renaissance of Islam: The Cultural Revival During the Buyid Age. ix, 329p. 1986. 54.50 (ISBN 90-04-07259-4, Pub. by E J Brill). Heinman.

Lapidus, Ira M. Contemporary Islamic Movements in Historical Perspective. LC 83-82308. (Policy Papers in International Affairs: No. 18). viii, 76p. 1983. pap. 4.95x (ISBN 0-87725-518-0). U of Cal Intl St.

Leiden, Carl. The Conflict of Traditionalism & Modernism in the Muslim Middle East: A Symposium. LC 68-59178. pap. 40.50 (ISBN 0-317-08447-X, 2000823). Bks Demand UMI.

Levtzion, Nehemia, ed. Conversion to Islam. LC 77-26771. 265p. 1979. text ed. 39.50x (ISBN 0-8419-0343-3). Holmes & Meier.

Levy, Reuben. A Baghdad Chronicle. LC 77-10580. (Studies in Islamic History: No. 17). (Illus.). 1978. Repr. of 1929 ed. lib. bdg. 27.50x (ISBN 0-87991-466-1). Porcupine Pr.

Margoliouth, David S. The Early Development of Mohammedanism. LC 77-27156. (Hibbert Lectures: 1913). Repr. of 1914 ed. 22.50 (ISBN 0-404-60415-3). AMS Pr.

Martin, B. G. Muslim Brotherhoods in 19th Century Africa. LC 75-35451. (African Studies Ser.: No. 18). 1977. 44.50 (ISBN 0-521-21062-3). Cambridge U Pr.

Memon, Muhammed U. Ibn Taimaya's Struggle Against Popular Religion with an Annotated Translation of His Kitab Iqtida Assirat Al Mustaquin Mukhalafat Ashab Al-Jahim. (Religion & Society: No. 1). 1976. text ed. 59.00x (ISBN 90-2797-591-4). Mouton.

Miskawayh, et al. The Eclipse of the Abbasid Caliphate, 7 vols. Amedroz, H. F. & Margoliouth, D. S., trs. from Arabic. Repr. of 1920 ed. lib. bdg. 500.00. Caratzas.

Nadawi, Abul H. Islam & the World. Kidwai, Mohammad A., tr. from Arabic. Tr. of Madha Khasira al-Alam bi-Inhtat al-Muslimin. 218p. (Orig.). 1977. pap. 5.95x (ISBN 0-939830-04-3, Pub. by IIFSO Kuwait). New Era Pubns MI.

Nadvi. Saviors of Islamic Spirit, 3 Vols. 60.00 set (ISBN 0-686-18312-6); 20.00 ea. Kazi Pubns.

Naff, Thomas & Owen, Roger, eds. Studies in Eighteenth-Century Islamic History. LC 77-22012. 462p. 1977. 24.95x (ISBN 0-8093-0819-3). S Ill U Pr.

Price, David. Mahommedan History, 3 vols. Orig. Title: Chronological Retrospect or the Principal Events of Mahommedan History. (Illus.). 2291p. 1984. Repr. of 1811 ed. Set. text ed. 400.00x (ISBN 0-86590-393-X, Inter India Pubns Delhi). Apt Bks.

Razwy, Sayed A. Salman el-Farsi. 1985. pap. 3.95 (ISBN 0-933543-02-6). Aza Khana.

Rosenthal, Erwin I. Political Thought in Medieval Islam: An Introductory Outline. LC 85-21909. ix, 345p. 1985. Repr. of 1958 ed. lib. bdg. 47.50x (ISBN 0-313-25094-4, JA82). Greenwood.

Saunders, J. J. A History of Medieval Islam. (Illus.). 1978. pap. 9.95x (ISBN 0-7100-0050-2). Methuen Inc.

Schacht, Joseph & Bosworth, C. E., eds. The Legacy of Islam. 2nd ed. (Illus.). 1974. pap. 8.95 (ISBN 0-19-285081-4). Oxford U Pr.

Scott, S. P. History of the Moorish Empire in Europe, 3 vols. 1977. Set. lib. bdg. 300.00 (ISBN 0-8490-2004-2). Gordon Pr.

Shaban, M. A. Islamic History: A.D. 750 to 1055, (A.H. 132 to 448) New Interpretation II. LC 75-39390. (Illus.). 190p. 1976. 49.50 (ISBN 0-521-21198-0); pap. 16.95 (ISBN 0-521-29453-3). Cambridge U Pr.

Shah, Idries, ed. The Exploits of the Incomparable Mulla Nasrudin. 1983. Repr. of 1968 ed. 14.95 (ISBN 0-86304-022-5, Pub. by Octagon Pr England). Ins Study Human.

Shariati, Ali. Red Shi'ism. Shirazi, Habib, tr. from Persian. 1980. pap. 1.00 (ISBN 0-941722-17-1). Book-Dist-Ctr.

--Reflection of Humanity. 2nd ed. Marjani, Fathollah, tr. from Persian. 37p. 1984. pap. 2.00 (ISBN 0-941722-11-2). Book-Dist-Ctr.

Siddiqui, A. H. Philosophical Interpretation of History. 14.95 (ISBN 0-686-83884-X). Kazi Pubns.

Siddiqui, M. M. Development of Islamic State & Society. 1986. 22.50 (ISBN 0-317-46088-9). Kazi Pubns.

Sluglett, Peter, compiled by. Theses on Islam, Middle East, & Northwest Africa, 1880-1978. 160p. 1983. 27.00x (ISBN 0-7201-1651-1). Mansell.

Smith-Savage, E. & Smith, M. B. Islamic Geomancy & a Thirteenth-Century Divinatory Device. LC 79-65001. (Studies in Near Eastern Culture & Society: Vol. 2). 91p. 1981. pap. 15.25x (ISBN 0-89003-038-3). Undena Pubns.

Spuler, Bertold, ed. The Muslim World: A Historical Survey of Modern Times, Pt. IV, Fascicule 1. x, 370p. 1981. text ed. 49.95x (ISBN 90-04-06196-7, Pub. by E J Brill Holland). Humanities.

Tabatabai, Muhammad. Muhammad in the Mirror of Islam. Chittick, William, tr. from Persian. 21p. 1979. pap. 1.00 (ISBN 0-941722-18-X). Book-Dist-Ctr.

--Shi'ite Islam. Nasr, Sayyed H., tr. from Persian. 253p. 1979. pap. 4.95 (ISBN 0-941722-19-8). Book-Dist-Ctr.

Tibawl, A. L. The Islamic Pious Foundations in Jerusalem. 163p. 1978. 20.00x (ISBN 0-317-39095-3, Pub. by Luzac & Co Ltd). State Mutual Bk.

Watt, W. M. The Influence of Islam Upon Medieval Europe. 125p. 1973. pap. 10.00x (ISBN 0-85224-439-8, Pub. by Edinburgh U Pr Scotland). Columbia U Pr.

Wellhausen, Julius. Medina vor dem Islam, Muhammeds Gemeindeordnung Von Medina: Seine Schriften und Die Gesandtschaften an Ihn. (Skizzen und Vorarbeiten: 4 Heft). (Ger. & Arabic.). 272p. 1985. 63.00x (ISBN 3-11-009764-8). De Gruyter.

--Prolegomena zur Altesten Geschichte des Islam: Verschiedenes (Unveraenderter Photomechanischer Nachdruck der 1. Auflage 1899) (Skizzen und Vorarbeiten: 6 Heft). (Ger.). viii, 260p. 1985. 61.00x (ISBN 3-11-002215-X). De Gruyter.

Williams, John A., ed. & tr. The History of al-Tabari, Vol. 27: The Abbasid Revolution A. D. 743-750 - A. H.126-132) (Near Eastern Studies). 192p. 1985. 39.50 (ISBN 0-87395-884-5). State U NY Pr.

Wismar, Adolph L. Study in Tolerance As Practiced by Muhammed & His Immediate Successors. LC 27-24455. (Columbia University. Contributions to Oriental History & Philology: No. 13). Repr. of 1927 ed. 14.00 (ISBN 0-404-50543-0). AMS Pr.

Zaydan, Jirji. Umayyads & Abbasids. Margoliuth, D. S., tr. from Arabic. LC 79-2889. 325p. 1982. Repr. of 1907 ed. 29.00 (ISBN 0-8305-0056-1). Hyperion Conn.

ISLAM–JUVENILE LITERATURE

Aggarwal, Manju. I Am a Muslim. (My Heritage Ser.). 32p. 1985. PLB 9.90 (ISBN 0-531-10020-0). Watts.

Barlow, Christopher. Islam. (Today's World Ser.). (Illus.). 72p. 1983. 16.95 (ISBN 0-7134-3659-X, Pub. by Batsford England). David & Charles.

Chaudhry, Saida. Call to Prophethood. (Illus.). pap. 4.00. Am Trust Pubns.

--We Are Muslim Children. pap. 4.00 (ISBN 0-89259-050-5). Am Trust Pubns.

Hood, Abdul Latif Al. Islam: Religions of the World Ser. (Illus.). 48p. 1987. lib. bdg. 11.40 (ISBN 0-531-18063-8, Pub. by Bookwright Pr). Watts.

Keene, Michael. Looking into Being a Muslim. (Looking into World Religions Ser.). (Illus.). 64p. 1987. 16.95 (ISBN 0-7134-4667-6, Pub. by Batsford England). David & Charles.

Kishta, Leila. ABC Rhymes for Young Muslims. Quinlan, Hamid, ed. LC 83-70183. (Illus.). 32p. 1983. pap. 3.00 (ISBN 0-89259-044-0). Am Trust Pubns.

ISLAM–RELATIONS

Al-Qaradawl, Yusuf. Non Muslims in the Islamic Society. Hamad, Khalil M. & Shah, Sayed M., trs. LC 83-72763. 68p. (Orig.). 1985. pap. 3.75 (ISBN 0-89259-049-1). Am Trust Pubns.

Arnold, Thomas W. The Preaching of Islam: A History of Propagation of the Muslim Faith. LC 72-180319. (Mid-East Studies). Repr. of 1913 ed. 27.50 (ISBN 0-404-56214-0). AMS Pr.

Bury, George W. Pan-Islam. LC 80-1938. Repr. of 1919 ed. 30.00 (ISBN 0-404-18956-3). AMS Pr.

Hassan, Farooq. The Concept of State & Law in Islam. LC 80-69038. 321p. (Orig.). 1981. lib. bdg. 29.25 (ISBN 0-8191-1426-X); pap. text ed. 13.75 (ISBN 0-8191-1427-8). U Pr of Amer.

Johnson, Nels. Islam & the Politics of Meaning in Palestinian Nationalism. 111p. 1983. 21.95x (ISBN 0-7103-0021-2). Methuen Inc.

Kamil, A. Abd-Al-Qadir. Islam & the Race Question. 65p. (Orig.). 1970. pap. 5.00 (ISBN 92-3-100833-1, U342, UNESCO). Bernan-Unipub.

Lichtenstadter, Ilse. Islam & the Modern Age. 228p. 1958. text ed. 29.00x (ISBN 0-8290-0179-4). Irvington.

Musavi, Sayyed M. Western Civilization Through Muslim Eyes. Goulding, F. J., tr. from Persian. 146p. 1977. 4.95 (ISBN 0-941722-20-1); pap. 3.95 (ISBN 0-941722-06-6). Book-Dist-Ctr.

Proctor, Jesse H., ed. Islam & International Relations. LC 80-1914. 1981. Repr. of 1965 ed. 27.50 (ISBN 0-404-18969-5). AMS Pr.

Roy, Asim. The Islamic Syncretistic Tradition in Bengal. LC 83-42574. 312p. 1984. 31.50x (ISBN 0-691-05387-1). Princeton U Pr.

Siddique, Kaukab. Islam and Revolution: Basic Issues Facing the Muslim World. LC 82-154032. 112p. 1981. pap. 10.00 (ISBN 0-942978-00-5). Am Soc Ed & Rel.

Siddiqui, A. H. The Democracy & the Islamic State. 2.50 (ISBN 0-686-83892-0). Kazi Pubns.

ISLAM–RELATIONS–CHRISTIANITY

see also Jesus Christ–Islamic Interpretations; Missions to Muslims

Al-Qaradawl, Yusuf. Non Muslims in the Islamic Society. Hamad, Khalil M. & Shah, Sayed M., trs. LC 83-72763. 68p. (Orig.). 1985. pap. 3.75 (ISBN 0-89259-049-1). Am Trust Pubns.

Ansari, F. R. Islam & Christianity in the Modern World. pap. 14.95 (ISBN 0-686-18577-3). Kazi Pubns.

Basetti-Sami, Giulio. Koran in the Light of Christ. 1977. 8.50 (ISBN 0-8199-0713-8). Franciscan Herald.

Becker, C. H. Christianity & Islam. Chaytor, H. J., tr. LC 74-608. 120p. 1974. Repr. of 1909 ed. lib. bdg. 18.50 (ISBN 0-8337-4816-5). B Franklin.

Browne, Lawrence E. The Eclipse of Christianity in Asia. 1967. Repr. 27.50x (ISBN 0-86527-049-X). Fertig.

Deedat, A. Is Bible God's Word? 1981. 2.75 (ISBN 0-686-97857-9). Kazi Pubns.

Lochhaas, Philip H. How to Respond to Islam. 1981. pap. 1.95 (ISBN 0-570-07687-0, 12-2788). Concordia.

Maybaum, Ignay. Trialogue Between Jew, Christian & Muslim. (Littman Library of Jewish Civilization). 192p. 1973. 18.50x (ISBN 0-19-710032-5). Oxford U Pr.

Parshall, Phil. Bridges to Islam: A Christian Perspective on Folk Islam. 120p. 1983. pap. 6.95 (ISBN 0-8010-7081-3). Baker Bk.

Southern, R. W. Western Views of Islam in the Middle Ages. LC 62-13270. 1978. 12.50x (ISBN 0-674-95055-0); pap. 4.95x (ISBN 0-674-95065-8). Harvard U Pr.

Wismer, Don. The Islamic Jesus: An Annotated Bibliography of Sources in English & French. LC 76-24737. (Reference Library of the Humanities Ser.: Vol. 58). 1977. lib. bdg. 40.00 (ISBN 0-8240-9940-0). Garland Pub.

ISLAM–RELATIONS–JUDAISM

Al-Qaradawl, Yusuf. Non Muslims in the Islamic Society. Hamad, Khalil M. & Shah, Sayed M., trs. LC 83-72763. 68p. (Orig.). 1985. pap. 3.75 (ISBN 0-89259-049-1). Am Trust Pubns.

Maybaum, Ignay. Trialogue Between Jew, Christian & Muslim. (Littman Library of Jewish Civilization). 192p. 1973. 18.50x (ISBN 0-19-710032-5). Oxford U Pr.

Patai, Raphael. The Seed of Abraham: Jews & Arabs in Contact & Conflict. 384p. 1986. 29.95 (ISBN 0-87480-251-2). U of Utah Pr.

Torrey, Charles C. Jewish Foundation of Islam. rev. ed. LC 67-18817. 1968. 20.00x (ISBN 0-87068-117-6). Ktav.

ISLAM–AFRICA

Abun-Nasr, Jamil M. A History of the Maghrib in the Islamic Period. (Illus.). 512p. Date not set. price not set (ISBN 0-521-33184-6); pap. price not set (ISBN 0-521-33767-4). Cambridge U Pr.

Alhaji Obaba Abdullahi Muhammad. Three Little Africans. (Illus.). 36p. (Orig.). 1978. pap. 2.50 (ISBN 0-916157-00-8). African Islam Miss Pubns.

Atterbury, Anson P. Islam in Africa. LC 73-91254. Repr. of 1899 ed. 22.50x (ISBN 0-8371-2064-0, ATI&, Pub. by Negro U Pr). Greenwood.

Berger, Morroe. Islam in Egypt Today: Social & Political Aspects of Popular Religion. LC 70-113597. 1970. 34.50 (ISBN 0-521-07834-2). Cambridge U Pr.

Bravmann, Rene A. African Islam. LC 83-21174. (Illus.). 120p. 1984. pap. 16.95 (ISBN 0-87474-281-1, BRAIP). Smithsonian.

Brett, Michael, ed. Northern Africa: Islam & Modernization. 156p. 1973. 28.50x (ISBN 0-7146-2972-3, F Cass Co). Biblio Dist.

Bunger, Robert L. Islamization among the Upper Pokomo. 2nd ed. LC 80-242. (Foreign & Comparative Studies-African Ser.: No. 33). 128p. (Orig.). 1979. pap. 7.00x (ISBN 0-915984-55-5). Syracuse U Foreign Comp.

Clarke, Peter. West Africa & Islam. 280p. 1982. pap. text ed. 19.95 (ISBN 0-7131-8029-3). E Arnold.

Cohen, R. Dominance & Defiance: A Study of Marital Instability in an Islamic African Society. (Anthropological Studies: No. 6). 1971. pap. 6.00 (ISBN 0-686-36563-1). Am Anthro Assn.

Fluehr-Lobban, Carolyn. Islamic Law & Society in the Sudan. 275p. 1986. 32.50x (ISBN 0-7146-3280-5, F Cass Co). Biblio Dist.

Friedmann, Yohanan. Prophecy Continuous: Aspects of Ahmadi Religious Thoughts & Its Medieval Background. 370p. 1987. text ed. 35.00x. U of Cal Pr.

Imam Alhaji Obaba Muhammadu. The African Islamic Mission. 38p. (Orig.). 1982. pap. 1.00 (ISBN 0-916157-04-0). African Islam Miss Pubns.

Lewis, I. M., ed. Islam in Tropical Africa. 2nd ed. LC 79-3292. 324p. 1980. 25.00x (ISBN 0-253-14956-8); pap. 10.95x (ISBN 0-253-28514-3). Ind U Pr.

Lubeck, Paul M. Islam & Urban Labor in Northern Nigeria: The Making of a Muslim Working Class. (African Studies Ser.: No. 52). (Illus.). 368p. Date not set. 49.50 (ISBN 0-521-30942-5). Cambridge U Pr.

Mason, John P. Island of the Blest: Islam in a Libyan Oasis Community. LC 77-620016. (Papers in International Studies: Africa Ser.: No. 31). (Illus.). 1977. pap. 10.00x (ISBN 0-89680-063-6, Ohio U Ctr Intl). Ohio U Pr.

Monteil, Vincent. Black Islam: Africa's Rising Religion. 464p. cancelled (ISBN 0-86356-114-4, Pub. by Zed Pr England); pap. cancelled (ISBN 0-86356-024-5, Pub. by Zed Pr England). Humanities.

Oded, Arye. Islam in Uganda. 382p. 1974. casebound 19.95x (ISBN 0-87855-171-9). Transaction Bks.

Ofori, Patrick E. Islam in Africa South of the Sahara: A Select Bibliographic Guide. 223p. 1977. lib. bdg. 42.00 (ISBN 3-262-00003-5). Kraus Intl.

Pouwels, Randall L. Horn & Crescent: Cultural Change & Traditional Islam on the East African Coast, 800-1900. (African Studies Ser.: No. 53). (Illus.). 288p. Date not set. price not set (ISBN 0-521-32308-8). Cambridge U Pr.

Roy, Olivier. Islam & Resistance in Afghanistan. (Cambridge Middle East Library). (Illus.). 256p. 1986. 24.95 (ISBN 0-521-32833-0). Cambridge U Pr.

Trimingham, J. Spencer. History of Islam in West Africa. (Oxford Paperback Ser.). 1962. pap. 8.95x (ISBN 0-19-285038-5). Oxford U Pr.

--The Influence of Islam Upon Africa. 2nd ed. (Arab Background Ser.). (Illus.). 1980. text ed. 27.00x (ISBN 0-582-78499-9). Longman.

--Islam in Ethiopia. (Illus.). 299p. 1965. Repr. of 1952 ed. 29.50x (ISBN 0-7146-1731-8, F Cass Co). Biblio Dist.

Trimingham, John S. Islam in East Africa. LC 79-52567. (Islam Ser.). 1980. Repr. of 1964 ed. lib. bdg. 18.00x (ISBN 0-8369-9270-9). Ayer Co Pubs.

--Islam in West Africa. 1959. 29.95x (ISBN 0-19-826511-5). Oxford U Pr.

Trimingham, Spencer. Influence of Islam Upon Africa. 25.00x (ISBN 0-685-85423-X). Intl Bk Ctr.

Tully, Dennis. Culture & Context in Sudan: The Process of Market Incorporation in Dar Masalit. (SUNY Series in Middle Eastern Studies). (Illus.). 272p. 1987. text ed. 49.50x (ISBN 0-88706-502-3); pap. 18.95x (ISBN 0-88706-504-X). State U NY Pr.

Willis, John R., ed. Studies in West African Islamic History: The Cultivators of Islam, Vol. 1. (Illus.). 325p. 1979. 39.50x (ISBN 0-7146-1737-7, F Cass Co). Biblio Dist.

Works, John A., Jr. Pilgrims in a Strange Land: Hausa Communities in Chad. LC 76-23138. 1976. 32.00x (ISBN 0-231-03976-X). Columbia U Pr.

ISLAM–EGYPT

Berger, Morroe. Islam in Egypt Today: Social & Political Aspects of Popular Religion. LC 70-113597. 1970. 34.50 (ISBN 0-521-07834-2). Cambridge U Pr.

Harris, Christina. Nationalism & Revolution in Egypt: The Role of the Muslim Brotherhood. LC 79-2861. 276p. 1987. Repr. of 1964 ed. 25.00 (ISBN 0-8305-0034-0). Hyperion Conn.

Hussain, Asaf. Islamic Movements in Egypt, Pakistan & Iran: An Annotated Bibliography. 182p. 1983. 36.00x (ISBN 0-7201-1648-1). Mansell.

Smith, Charles D. Islam & the Search for Social Order in Modern Egypt: A Biography of Muhammad Husayn Haykal. (Middle East Studies). 256p. 1983. 49.50 (ISBN 0-87395-710-5); pap. 18.95 (ISBN 0-87395-711-3). State U NY Pr.

ISLAM–INDIA

Ahmad, Aziz. An Intellectual History of Islamic India. 1970. 13.00x (ISBN 0-85224-057-0, Pub. by Edinburgh U Pr Scotland). Columbia U Pr.

Ashraf, Mujeeb. Muslim Attitudes Toward British Rule & Western Culture in India. 1983. 19.00x (ISBN 0-8364-1076-9, Pub. by Idarah). South Asia Bks.

Firishtah, Muhammad. History of the Rise of the Mahomedan Power in India until AD 1612, 4 vols. Biggs, John, tr. Repr. of 1910 ed. Set. text ed. 125.00x. Coronet Bks.

Israel, Milton & Wagle, N. K., eds. Islamic Society & Culture: Essays in Honour of Professor Aziz Ahmad. 1983. 32.50x (ISBN 0-8364-1047-5, Pub. by Manohar India). South Asia Bks.

Izzidien, Mouel Y. Nisab Al Ihtisab. Quinlan, Hamid, ed. LC 82-70458. (Illus.). 230p. (Orig.). Date not set. pap. 5.00 (ISBN 0-89259-031-9). Am Trust Pubns.

Jain, C. R. Gems of Islam: Lifting of the Veil, Pt. I. 196p. 1975. 6.00 (ISBN 0-88065-136-9, Pub. by Messers Today & Tomorrows Printers & Publishers India). Scholarly Pubns.

Khan, Syed A. Sir Sayyid Ahmad Khan's History of Bijnor Rebellion. Malik, Hafeez, tr. 1983. 13.50x (ISBN 0-8364-1080-7, Pub. by Idarah). South Asia Bks.

Madhok, Balraj. Punjab Problem: The Muslim Connection. 1985. 14.00x (ISBN 0-8364-1519-1, Pub. by Vision). South Asia Bks.

Metcalf, Barbara D. Islamic Revival in British India: Deoband, 1860-1900. LC 81-47934. (Illus.). 400p. 1982. 31.50 (ISBN 0-691-05343-X). Princeton U Pr.

Metcalf, Barbara D., ed. Moral Conduct & Authority: The Place of Adab in Sout h Asian Islam. LC 83-1361. 350p. 1984. text ed. 40.00x (ISBN 0-520-04660-9). U of Cal Pr.

Nanji, Azim. The Nizari Ismaili Tradition in the Indo-Pakistan Subcontinent. LC 78-12990. (Monographs in Islamic Religion & Theology). 1979. 30.00x (ISBN 0-88206-020-1). Caravan Bks.

Nath, R. Islamic Architecture & Culture in India. (Illus.). 228p. 1983. text ed. 40.00x (ISBN 0-86590-135-X). Apt Bks.

Prasad, Yuvaraj D. The Indian Muslims & World War I. 1985. 20.00x (ISBN 0-8364-1489-6, Pub. by Nanaki Prakashan). South Asia Bks.

Rahbar, Daud, ed. & tr. from Urdu. Urdu Letters of Mirza Asadu'llah Khan Ghalib. 628p. 1987. 48.50 (ISBN 0-88706-412-4). State U NY Pr.

Rahman, M. From Consultation to Confrontation: A Study of the Muslim League in British Indian Politics, 1906-1912. 313p. 1985. 52.00x (ISBN 0-317-39069-4, Pub. by Luzac & Co Ltd). State Mutual Bk.

Shakir, Moin. Islam in Indian Politics. 1983. 11.00x (ISBN 0-8364-1032-7, Pub. by Ajanta). South Asia Bks.

Smith, W. C. Modern Islam in India. 1985. Repr. of 1946 ed. 18.50x (ISBN 0-8364-1338-5, Pub. by Usha). South Asia Bks.

Smith, Wilfred C. Modern Islam in India: A Social Analysis. LC 70-179243. Repr. of 1946 ed. 17.00 (ISBN 0-404-54869-5). AMS Pr.

Troll, Christian W., ed. Islam in India-Studies & Commentaries: Vol. 1, The Akbar Mission & Miscellaneous Studies. 240p. 1982. text ed. 32.50x (ISBN 0-7069-1889-4, Pub. by Vikas India). Advent NY.

ISLAM–INDONESIA

Archer, Raymond L. Muhammadan Mysticism in Sumatra. LC 77-87487. (Royal Asiatic Society, Malayan Branch. Journal: Vol. 15). Repr. of 1937 ed. 16.50 (ISBN 0-404-16695-4). AMS Pr.

Federspiel, Howard. Persatuan Islam: Islamic Reform in Twentieth Century Indonesia. (Monograph Ser.). (Orig.). 1970. pap. 7.50 (ISBN 0-87763-013-5). Cornell Mod Indo.

Noer, Deliar. Administration of Islam in Indonesia. (Monograph Ser.). 1978. pap. 4.50 (ISBN 0-87763-002-X). Cornell Mod Indo.

Siegel, James T. The Rope of God. LC 69-15942. (Center for South & Southeast Asia Studies, California Library Reprint Ser.: No. 96). 1978. Repr. of 1969 ed. 35.00x (ISBN 0-520-03714-6). U of Cal Pr.

Van Nieuwenhuijze, C. A. Aspects of Islam in Post-Colonial Indonesia: Five Essays. 1958. 23.75x (ISBN 0-686-21860-4). Mouton.

ISLAM–IRAN

Abraham, Antoine J. Khoumani, Islamic Fundamentalists & the Contributions of Islamic Sciences to Modern Civilization. 60p. (Orig.). 1985. pap. 5.95x (ISBN 0-932269-51-6). Wyndham Hall.

Arjomand, Said A. The Shadow of God & the Hidden Inam: Religion, Political Order, & Societal Change in Shi'ite Iran from the Beginning to 1890. LC 83-27196. (Publications of the Center for Middle Eastern Studies: No. 117). (Illus.). 344p. 1987. lib. bdg. price not set; pap. text ed. price not set (ISBN 0-226-02784-8). U of Chicago Pr.

Benard, Cheryl & Khalilzad, Zalmay. The Government of God: Iran's Islamic Republic. LC 83-20880. 232p. 1984. 28.00x (ISBN 0-231-05376-2); pap. 12.50 (ISBN 0-231-05377-0). Columbia U Pr.

Hussain, Asaf. Islamic Iran: Revolution & Counter-Revolution. LC 85-40078. 250p. 1985. 27.50 (ISBN 0-312-43745-5). St Martin.

--Islamic Movements in Egypt, Pakistan & Iran: An Annotated Bibliography. 182p. 1983. 36.00x (ISBN 0-7201-1648-1). Mansell.

Irfani, Suroosh. Iran's Islamic Revolution: Popular Liberation or Religious Dictatorship? (Illus.). 278p. 1983. 29.50x (ISBN 0-86232-157-3, Pub. by Zed Pr England); pap. 10.75 (ISBN 0-86232-158-1). Humanities.

Khomeini, Imam. Islam & Revolution: Writings & Declarations. Algar, Hamid, tr. 460p. 1986. pap. 19.95 (ISBN 0-7103-0098-0, Kegan Paul). Methuen Inc.

Petrushevsky, I. P. Islam in Iran. Evans, Hubert, tr. (Series in Near Eastern Studies). 400p. 1985. 49.50x (ISBN 0-88706-070-6). State U NY Pr.

Subhani, Jafar. The Message. Haq, M. Fazal, tr. from Persian. 784p. 1985. pap. 25.00 (ISBN 0-941724-38-7). Islamic Seminary.

ISLAM–PAKISTAN

Ahmed, Abkar S. Religion & Politics in Muslim Society: Order & Conflict in Pakistan. LC 82-14774. (Illus.). 225p. 1983. 44.50 (ISBN 0-521-24635-0). Cambridge U Pr.

Asghar Khan, Mohammad, ed. Islam, Politics & the State - The Pakistan Experience. 320p. 1985. 32.95x (ISBN 0-86232-471-8, Pub. by Zed Pr England); pap. 12.95 (ISBN 0-86232-472-6, Pub. by Zed Pr England). Humanities.

Hashmi, A. H. Nationalism, Islam & Pakistan. pap. 14.95 (ISBN 0-317-46108-7). Kazi Pubns.

Hussain, Asaf. Islamic Movements in Egypt, Pakistan & Iran: An Annotated Bibliography. 182p. 1983. 36.00x (ISBN 0-7201-1648-1). Mansell.

Iqbal, Afzal. Islamization of Pakistan. 1985. 15.00x (ISBN 0-8364-1493-4, Pub. by Idarah). South Asia Bks.

Nanji, Azim. The Nizari Ismaili Tradition in the Indo-Pakistan Subcontinent. LC 78-12990. (Monographs in Islamic Religion & Theology). 1979. 30.00x (ISBN 0-88206-020-1). Caravan Bks.

Weiss, Anita M., ed. Islamic Reassertion in Pakistan: Islamic Laws in a Modern State. (Contemporary Issues in the Middle East Ser.). 176p. 1986. text ed. 19.95x (ISBN 0-8156-2375-5). Syracuse U Pr.

ISLAM–SAUDI ARABIA

Al-Tabari. History of al-Tabari, Vol. 7: Foundation of the Community - Muhammad at al-Madina, A. D. 622-626, Hijra-4 A.H. McDonald, V. M. & Watt, Montgomery, eds. McDonald, V. M., tr. from Ancient Parsi. (Series in Near Eastern Studies). 154p. (Orig.). 1987. 44.50x (ISBN 0-88706-344-6); pap. 16.95x (ISBN 0-88706-345-4). State U NY Pr.

ISLAM–SYRIA

Abdallah, Umar F. The Islamic Struggle in Syria. 24.95 (ISBN 0-933782-10-1). Mizan Pr.

ISLAM–TURKEY

Leder, Arnold. Catalysts of Change: Marxist versus Muslim in a Turkish Community. LC 76-29323. (Middle East Monograph: No. 1). 70p. 1976. pap. text ed. 3.95x (ISBN 0-292-71042-9, Pub. by Ctr Mid East Stud). U of Tex Pr.

ISLAM AND ECONOMICS

Ahmad, Khurshid, ed. Studies in Islamic Economics. 390p. (Orig.). 1980. 31.50x (ISBN 0-86037-066-6, Pub. by Islamic Found UK); pap. 15.95 (ISBN 0-86037-067-4). New Era Pubns MI.

Al Sadr, Muhammad B. Islam & Schools of Economics. Ansari, M. A., tr. 160p. 1983. pap. text ed. 6.00 (ISBN 0-686-90405-2). Islamic Seminary.

Archaisme et Modernisme dans l'Islam Contemporain. (Economies et Societes Series V: No. 3). 1961. pap. 26.00 (ISBN 0-8115-0805-6). Kraus Repr.

Bazargan, Mehdi. Work & Islam. Yousefi, Mohammack, tr. from Persian. 62p. 1979. 4.00 (ISBN 0-941722-04-X). Book-Dist-Ctr.

Choudhury, Masudul A. Contributions to Islamic Economic Theory: A Study in Social Economics. LC 85-22149. 224p. 1986. 29.95 (ISBN 0-312-16881-0). St Martin.

Mannan, M. A. The Frontiers of Islamic Economics. 1985. 15.00x (ISBN 0-8364-1505-1, Pub. by Idarah). South Asia Bks.

Naqvi, Syed N. H. Ethics & Economics: An Islamic Synthesis. 176p. (Orig.). 1981. 17.25x (ISBN 0-86037-079-8, Pub by Islamic Found UK); pap. 9.95x (ISBN 0-86037-080-1). New Era Pubns MI.

Qureshi, A. I. Fiscal System of Islam. 1981. 10.50 (ISBN 0-686-97866-8). Kazi Pubns.

Siddiqi, Muhammad N. Muslim Economic Thinking: A Survey of Contemporary Literature. 130p. (Orig.). 1981. 10.50x (ISBN 0-86037-082-8, Pub. by Islamic Found UK); pap. 5.25x (ISBN 0-86037-081-X). New Era Pubns MI.

Siddiqui, M. I. Economic Security in Islam. 1981. 19.95 (ISBN 0-686-97853-6). Kazi Pubns.

Taymiya, Ibn. Public Duties in Islam: The Institution of the Hisba. Holland, Muhtar, tr. from Arabic. 159p. (Orig.). 1982. pap. 6.95x (ISBN 0-86037-113-1, Pub by Islamic Found UK). New Era Pubns MI.

ISLAM AND SCIENCE

Al-Hassan, Ahmed & Hill, Donald. Islamic Technology: An Illustrated History. (Illus.). 300p. 1987. 39.50 (ISBN 0-521-26333-6). Cambridge U Pr.

ISLAM AND STATE

see also Jihad

Ahmed, Ishtiaq. The Concept of an Islamic State: An Analysis of the Ideological Controversy in Pakistan. 266p. (Orig.). 1985. pap. text ed. 37.50x (ISBN 91-7146-458-1, Pub. by Almqvist & Wiksell). Coronet Bks.

Asghar Khan, Mohammad, ed. Islam, Politics & the State - The Pakistan Experience. 320p. 1985. 32.95x (ISBN 0-86232-471-8, Pub. by Zed Pr England); pap. 12.95 (ISBN 0-86232-472-6, Pub. by Zed Pr England). Humanities.

Dawisha, Adeed, ed. Islam in Foreign Policy. LC 83-7458. 250p. 1984. 29.95 (ISBN 0-521-25815-4). Cambridge U Pr.

Dobbin, Christine. Islamic Revivalism in a Changing Peasant Economy: Central Sumatra, 1784-1847. 328p. 1981. 40.00x (ISBN 0-7007-0155-9, Pub. by Curzon England). State Mutual Bk.

Heper, Metin & Israeli, Raphael, eds. Islam & Politics in the Modern Middle East. LC 84-40042. 131p. 1984. 25.00 (ISBN 0-312-43742-0). St Martin.

Islam, Fida E. The Political Personality of Islam. 280p. 1985. pap. 6.95 (ISBN 0-940368-37-4). Tahrike Tarsile Quran.

Ismael, Tareq Y. & Ismael, Jacqueline S. Government & Politics in Islam. LC 85-2265. 177p. 1985. 27.50 (ISBN 0-312-34126-1). St Martin.

Kelly, Marjorie, ed. Islam: The Religious & Political Life of a World Community. LC 84-13307. 325p. 1984. 39.95; pap. 16.95. Foreign Policy.

Muhaiyaddeen, M. R. Islam & World Peace. LC 87-11921. 150p. 1987. 6.95 (ISBN 0-914390-25-2). Fellowship Pr PA.

Peel, J. D. & Stewart, Charles C., eds. Popular Islam South of the Sahara. (African Studies). 128p. 1986. pap. 15.00 (ISBN 0-7190-1975-3, Pub. by Manchester Univ Pr). Longwood Pub Group.

Piscatori, James P., ed. Islam in the Political Process. LC 82-9745. 272p. 1983. 42.50 (ISBN 0-521-24941-4); pap. 16.95 (ISBN 0-521-27434-6). Cambridge U Pr.

Rahman, M. From Consultation to Confrontation: A Study of the Muslim League in British Indian Politics, 1906-1912. 313p. 1985. 52.00x (ISBN 0-317-39069-4, Pub. by Luzac & Co Ltd). State Mutual Bk.

Royal Institute of International Affairs & Piscatori, James P. Islam in a World of Nation-States. LC 86-8275. 1986. 34.50 (ISBN 0-521-32985-X); pap. 12.95 (ISBN 0-521-33867-0). Cambridge U Pr.

Sivan, Emmanuel. Radical Islam: Medieval Theology & Modern Politics. LC 84-20999. 224p. 1985. 20.00x (ISBN 0-300-03263-3). Yale U Pr.

Tabatabai, Hossein M. Introduction to Shii Law: A Bibliographical Study. 258p. 1985. text ed. 22.00 (ISBN 0-86372-015-3, Pub. by Ithaca England). Evergreen Dist.

Zaidi, A. M. Evolution of Muslim Political Thought in India, 6 vols. 1973. Set. text ed. 295.00x. Vol. 1, From Sayed to the Emergence of Jinnah. Vol. 2, Sectarian Nationalism & Khilafat. Vol. 3, Parting of Ways. Vol. 4, The Communal Award. Vol. 5, Demand for Pakistan. Vol. 6, Freedom at Last. Coronet Bks.

ISLAMIC ARCHITECTURE

see Architecture, Islamic

ISLAMIC CIVILIZATION

see Civilization, Islamic

ISLAMIC COUNTRIES

Daniel, Norman A. Islam & the West. 26.00x (ISBN 0-85224-109-7, Pub. by Edinburgh U Pr Scotland). Columbia U Pr.

Geertz, Clifford. Islam Observed: Religious Development in Morocco & Indonesia. 1971. pap. 6.00x (ISBN 0-226-28511-1, P439, Phoen). U of Chicago Pr.

Israeli, Raphael. The Crescent in the East: Islam in Asia Major. 240p. 1981. 30.00x (ISBN 0-7007-0143-5, Pub. by Curzon England). State Mutual Bk.

Lewis, B., et al, eds. Encyclopedia of Islam, 4 vols. Incl. Vol. 1. A-B: Fasc. 1-22. Gibb, H. A., et al, eds. 1960. text ed. 185.75x (ISBN 90-040-0530-7); Vol. 2. C-G: Fasc. 23-40. Lewis, B., et al, eds. 1965; Vol. 3. H-Iram: Fasc. 41-60. 1969. text ed. 226.25x (ISBN 90-040-3275-4); Vols. 4 & 5. I-Ram &K-Ha: Fasc. 61-78. 1978. text ed. 275.50. Humanities.

Linant De Bellefonds, Y. Traite De Droit Musulman Compare: Filiation - Incapacites - Liberalites Entre Vifs, Tome 3. (Recherches Mediterraneennes: No. 9). 1973. pap. 34.40x (ISBN 90-2797-199-4). Mouton.

Siddiqui, M. I. Qualities of Holy Quran. 1981. 2.50 (ISBN 0-686-97854-4). Kazi Pubns.

Toynbee, Arnold J. The Islamic World since the Peace Settlement. Repr. of 1927 ed. 50.00 (ISBN 0-384-61120-6). Johnson Repr.

Udovitch, A. L., ed. Islamic Middle East 700-1900: Studies in Economic & Social History. LC 79-52703. (Illus.). 838p. 1981. 29.95x (ISBN 0-87850-030-8). Darwin Pr.

ISLAMIC COUNTRIES–POLITICS

Al Tunisi, Khayr. Surest Path: The Political Treatise of a Nineteenth-Century Muslim Statesman. Brown, Leon C., tr. LC 67-25399. (Middle Eastern Monographs Ser: No. 16). pap. 5.00x (ISBN 0-674-85695-3). Harvard U Pr.

Cleveland, William L. Islam Against the West: Shakib Arslan & the Campaign for Islamic Nationalism. (Modern Middle East Ser.: No. 10). (Illus.). 247p. 1985. 19.95 (ISBN 0-292-77594-6). U of Tex Pr.

Cudsi, Alex & Dessouki, Ali E. Hillal, eds. Islam & Power in the Contemporary Muslim World. LC 81-47608. 208p. 1981. text ed. 25.00x (ISBN 0-8018-2697-7). Johns Hopkins.

Dawisha, Adeed, ed. Islam in Foreign Policy. 202p. 1985. pap. 11.95 (ISBN 0-521-27740-X). Cambridge U Pr.

Dessouki, Ali E. Hillal. Islamic Resurgence in the Arab World. LC 81-12135. 286p. 1982. 40.95 (ISBN 0-03-059673-4). Praeger.

Doi, A. R. Non-Muslims Under Shari'ah. 1981. 6.50 (ISBN 0-686-97861-7). Kazi Pubns.

El-Awa, M. S. On the Political System of the Islamic State. pap. 4.50. Am Trust Pubns.

Keddie, Hikke R. An Islamic Response to Imperialism: Political & Religious Writings of Sayyid Jamal ad-Din "al-Afghani". LC 68-13224. (California Library Reprint Ser. Near Eastern Center, UCLA: No. 119). 224p. 1983. 35.00x (ISBN 0-520-04766-4); pap. 7.95 (ISBN 0-520-04774-5, CAL 586). U of Cal Pr.

Lippman, Thomas W. Islam: Politics & Religion in the Muslim World. (Headline Series 258). (Illus.). 64p. 1982. pap. 4.00 (ISBN 0-87124-075-0). Foreign Policy.

Lupinin, Nickolas B. Religious Revolt in the Seventeenth Century: The Schism of the Russian Church. 220p. 1984. 24.00 (ISBN 0-940670-12-7). Kingston Pr.

Moinuddin, Hasan. The Charter of the Islamic Conference: The Legal & Economic Framework. LC 86-802. 256p. 1986. 59.00x (ISBN 0-19-825524-1). Oxford U Pr.

Pipes, Daniel. In the Path of God: Islam & Political Power. LC 83-70764. 373p. 1983. text ed. 22.50 (ISBN 0-465-03451-9). Basic.

Qureshi, A. I. Fiscal System of Islam. 1981. 10.50 (ISBN 0-686-97866-8). Kazi Pubns.

Sanderson, Richard N. The Islamic Movement & the Threat to Western Civilization, 2 vols. (Illus.). 309p. 1985. Set. 227.50 (ISBN 0-86722-113-5). Inst Econ Finan.

Siddiqui, M. I. Economic Security in Islam. 1981. 19.95 (ISBN 0-686-97853-6). Kazi Pubns.

--Qualities of Holy Quran. 1981. 2.50 (ISBN 0-686-97854-4). Kazi Pubns.

ISLAMIC EMPIRE–HISTORY

Al-din, Minhaj. General History of Muhammadan Dynasties of Asia from 810 to 1260 AD, 2 vols. Raverty, H. C., tr. from Persian. Repr. of 1881 ed. Set. text ed. 77.50x. Coronet Bks.

Al-Tabari. History of al-Tabari, Vol. 7: Foundation of the Community - Muhammad at al-Madina, A. D. 622-626, Hijra-4 A.H. McDonald, V. M. & Watt, Montgomery, eds. McDonald, V. M., tr. from Ancient Parsi. (Series in Near Eastern Studies). 154p. (Orig.). 1987. 44.50x (ISBN 0-88706-344-6); pap. 16.95x (ISBN 0-88706-345-4). State U NY Pr.

Bulliet, Richard W. Conversion to Islam in the Medieval Period: An Essay in Quantitative History. (Illus.). 158p. 1979. text ed. 16.50x (ISBN 0-674-17035-0). Harvard U Pr.

Hawting, G. R. The First Dynasty of Islam: The Umayyad Caliphate A.D. 661-750. 160p. 1986. text ed. 24.95x (ISBN 0-8093-1324-3). S Ill U Pr.

ISLAMIC ETHICS

Abdul-Rauf, Muhammad. A Muslim's Reflections on Democratic Capitalism. 1984. pap. 4.95 (ISBN 0-8447-3537-X). Am Enterprise.

Adb al-Wahhab ibn Ali, Taj. Kitab Mu'id an-Ni'am Wa-Mubid an-Niqam: The Restorer of Favours & the Restrainer of Chastisements. LC 78-53829. (Luzac's Semitic Text & Translation Ser.: Vol. 18). 1978. Repr. of 1908 ed. 32.50 (ISBN 0-404-11291-9). AMS Pr.

Al-Ghazali. On the Duties of Brotherhood in Islam. Holland, Muhtar, tr. from Arabic. 95p. (Orig.). 1980. pap. 4.95 (ISBN 0-86037-068-2, Pub. by Islamic Found UK). New Era Pubns MI.

Al-Qaradawi, Yusuf. The Lawful & the Prohibited in Islam. Siddiqui, Mohammed M., et al, trs. from Arabic. LC 80-81562. Orig. Title: Al-Halal Wal-Haram Fil Islam. (Eng.). 355p. (Orig.). 1981. pap. 10.00 (ISBN 0-89259-016-5). Am Trust Pubns.

Dar, B. A. Quranic Ethics. pap. 3.50 (ISBN 0-686-18602-8). Kazi Pubns.

--Qur'anic Ethics. 1970. 5.00x (ISBN 0-87902-160-8). Orientalia.

Hashim, A. S. Islamic Ethics. (Islamic Books for Children: Bk. 7). pap. 4.95 (ISBN 0-686-18404-1); pap. 45.00 entire set (ISBN 0-686-18405-X). Kazi Pubns.

Hourani, G. F. Reason & Tradition in Islamic Ethics. 282p. 1985. 39.50 (ISBN 0-521-26712-9). Cambridge U Pr.

Hovannisian, R., ed. Ethics in Islam. (Giorgio Levi Della Vida Biennial Conference Ser.: Vol. 9). 150p. 1984. pap. 20.50x (ISBN 0-89003-182-7). Undena Pubns.

McDonough, S. Muslim Ethics & Modernity. (Comparative Ethics Ser.: No. 1). 126p. 1984. pap. 11.95x (ISBN 0-88920-162-5, Pub. by Wilfrid Laurier Canada). Humanities.

McDonough, Sheila. The Authority of the Past. LC 76-141690. (American Academy of Religion. Studies in Religion). 46p. pap. 8.95 (ISBN 0-89130-153-4, 010001). Scholars Pr GA.

Makari, Victor E. Ibn Taymiyyah's Ethics: The Social Factor. LC 81-1019. (American Academy of Religion Academy Ser.). pap. write for info. (ISBN 0-89130-477-0). Scholars Pr GA.

Maududi, A. A. Ethical Viewpoint of Islam. pap. 1.00 (ISBN 0-686-18492-0). Kazi Pubns.

Maududi, Abul A. Human Rights in Islam. 39p. (Orig.). 1981. pap. 1.95 (ISBN 0-9503954-9-8, Pub. by Islamic Found UK). New Era Pubns MI.

Morewedge, Parviz, ed. Islamic Philosophy & Mysticism. LC 80-14364. (Studies in Islamic Philosophy & Science). 1981. 45.00x (ISBN 0-88206-302-2). Caravan Bks.

Naqvi, Syed N. H. Ethics & Economics: An Islamic Synthesis. 176p. (Orig.). 1981. 17.25x (ISBN 0-86037-079-8, Pub by Islamic Found UK); pap. 9.95x (ISBN 0-86037-080-1). New Era Pubns MI.

Quasem, Mohammad A. The Ethics of Al-Ghazali. LC 78-15259. (Monographs in Islamic Religion & Theology). 1978. 35.00x (ISBN 0-88206-021-X). Caravan Bks.

Quasem, Muhammad A. The Ethics of al-Ghazali: A Composite Ethics in Islam. 1975. 17.85 (ISBN 0-686-18952-3); pap. 9.00 (ISBN 0-686-18953-1). Quasem.

Shad, A. R. Muslim Etiquettes. 1981. 16.50 (ISBN 0-686-77429-9). Kazi Pubns.

Taymiya, Ibn. Public Duties in Islam: The Institution of the Hisba. Holland, Muhtar, tr. from Arabic. 159p. (Orig.). 1982. pap. 6.95x (ISBN 0-86037-113-1, Pub by Islamic Found UK). New Era Pubns MI.

ISLAMIC INTERNATIONAL LAW

see International Law (Islamic Law)

ISLAMIC LAW

Al-Azmeh, Aziz, ed. Islamic Law: Social & Historical Contents. 1986. 39.00 (ISBN 0-7099-0588-2, Pub. by Croom Helm Ltd). Longwood Pub Group.

Algar, Hamid, tr. from Persian. Constitution of the Islamic Republic of Iran. 94p. 1980. 9.95 (ISBN 0-933782-07-1); pap. 4.95 (ISBN 0-933782-02-0). Mizan Pr.

Al-Qaradawi, Yusuf. The Lawful & the Prohibited in Islam. Siddiqui, Mohammed M., et al, trs. from Arabic. LC 80-81562. Orig. Title: Al-Halal Wal-Haram Fil Islam. (Eng.). 355p. (Orig.). 1981. pap. 10.00 (ISBN 0-89259-016-5). Am Trust Pubns.

Anderson, James N. Islamic Law in the Modern World. LC 75-31816. 106p. 1976. Repr. of 1959 ed. lib. bdg. 22.50x (ISBN 0-8371-8451-7, ANIL). Greenwood.

Audah, Abdul Q. Al-Islam bain Jahl 'Abna'ihi wa Ajz Ulama'ihi. (Arabic.). 79p. (Orig.). 1980. pap. 1.55x (ISBN 0-939830-12-4, Pub. by IIFSO Kuwait). New Era Pubns MI.

Audah, Adbul Q. Islam Between Ignorant Followers & Incapable Scholars. Tr. of Al-Islam bain Jahl 'Abna'ihi wa Ajz Ulama'ihi. 115p. (Orig.). pap. 3.50 (ISBN 0-939830-01-9, Pub. by IIFSO Kuwait). New Era Pubns MI.

Ayatullah Al-Khu'i. Islamic Practical Law, Pts. I & II. Shaikh Muhammad Sarwar, tr. from Arabic. 1981. 15.00 (ISBN 0-941724-08-5); pap. 10.00 (ISBN 0-941724-01-8). Islamic Seminary.

--Rules of HAJJ. Shaikh Muhammad Sarwar, tr. from Arabic. 50p. 1981. pap. 3.00 (ISBN 0-941724-02-6). Islamic Seminary.

Badawi, G. A. Polygamy in Islamic Law. pap. 1.00 (ISBN 0-686-18440-8). Kazi Pubns.

Burton, John. The Collection of the Qur'an. LC 76-27899. 1977. 49.50 (ISBN 0-521-21439-4); pap. 15.95 (ISBN 0-521-29652-8). Cambridge U Pr.

Chaudhri, A. R. Substance of Muhammahan Law. 1970. 4.25x (ISBN 0-87902-157-8). Orientalia.

Chejne, Anwar. Succession to the Rule in Muslim. 154p. (Orig.). 1981. pap. 4.75 (ISBN 0-88004-001-7). Sunwise Turn.

Coulson, Noel. A History of Islamic Law. 264p. 1964. pap. 10.00 (ISBN 0-85224-354-5, Pub. by Edinburgh U Pr Scotland). Columbia U Pr.

Crone, Patricia. Roman, Provincial & Islamic Law: The Origins of the Islamic Patronate. (Cambridge Studies in Islamic Civilization). 200p. Date not set. price not set (ISBN 0-521-32253-7). Cambridge U Pr.

El Awa, M. S. Punishment in Islamic Law. 162p. Date not set. pap. 6.00 (ISBN 0-89259-015-7). Am Trust Pubns.

Esposito, John L. Women in Muslim Family Law. LC 81-18273. (Contemporary Issues in the Middle East Ser.). 172p. 1982. pap. text ed. 10.95X (ISBN 0-8156-2278-3). Syracuse U Pr.

Fyzee, Asaf A. Outlines of Muhammadan Law. 5th ed. Pearl, David, ed. 520p. 1986. pap. 13.95x (ISBN 0-19-561393-7). Oxford U Pr.

Goldziher, Ignaz. Introduction to Islamic Theology & Law. Lewis, Bernard, ed. Hamori, Andras & Hamori, Ruth, trs. from Ger. LC 80-7523. (Modern Classics in Near Eastern Studies). 325p. 1981. 32.00 (ISBN 0-691-07257-4); pap. 14.50 LPE (ISBN 0-691-10099-3). Princeton U Pr.

Guraya, M. Y. Origins of Islamic Jurisprudence. 18.00 (ISBN 0-317-46093-5). Kazi Pubns.

Hamilton, C. The Hedaya: A Commentary on the Muslim Laws. 1963. 130.00 (ISBN 0-87902-163-2). Orientalia.

Khadduri, Majid. Law of War & Peace in Islam: A Study of Moslem International Law. LC 76-147599. (Library of War & Peace; International Law). lib. bdg. 42.00 (ISBN 0-8240-0360-8). Garland Pub.

Khomeini, Imam. Practical Laws of Islam. LC 83-50077. 1983. pap. 9.00 (ISBN 0-940368-25-0). Tahrike Tarsile Quran.

MacDonald, D. B. Development of Muslim Jurisprudence & Constitutional Theory. 1964. 29.00 (ISBN 0-87902-173-X). Orientalia.

Macnauhten, William H. Principles of Muhammadan Law. 140p. (Orig.). 1981. pap. 6.50 (ISBN 0-88004-010-6). Sunwise Turn.

Markby, William. An Introduction to Hindu & Mohammedan Law. LC 78-58189. 1978. Repr. of 1906 ed. lib. bdg. 25.00 (ISBN 0-89341-509-X). Longwood Pub Group.
Maududi, A. Islamic Law & Constitution. 1969. pap. 14.95 (ISBN 0-87902-176-4). Orientalia.
Maududi, A. A. Questions of Dress. pap. 1.50 (ISBN 0-686-63910-3). Kazi Pubns.
Maududi, Abul A. Human Rights in Islam. 39p. (Orig.). 1981. pap. 1.95 (ISBN 0-9503954-9-8, Pub. by Islamic Found UK). New Era Pubns MI.
Merchant, M. V. Qur'anic Laws. 1971. 8.50x (ISBN 0-87902-177-2). Orientalia.
Nasir, Jamal J. The Islamic Law of Personal Status. Date not set. 79.00 (ISBN 0-317-53173-5); deluxe ed. 132.00 (ISBN 0-86010-503-2). Graham & Trotman.
Powers, David S. Studies in Qur'an & Hadith: The Formation of the Islamic Law of Inheritance. 1986. text ed. 30.00x (ISBN 0-520-05558-6). U of Cal Pr.
Qadri, A. A. Islamic Jurisprudence in the Modern World. 45.00 (ISBN 0-317-46102-8). Kazi Pubns.
Quadri, A. A. Islamic Jurisprudence in the Modern World. 35.00 (ISBN 0-317-01602-4). Kazi Pubns.
Qureshi, Hafiz M. The Qur'an and Slavery. Siddique, Kaukab, tr. from Urdu. 39p. (Orig.). 1984. pap. 2.00 (ISBN 0-942978-07-2). Am Soc Ed & Rel.
Rahim, Abdur. The Principles of Muhammadan Jurisprudence According to the Hanali, Maliki, Shafi'i & Hanbali Schools. LC 79-2879. 443p. 1981. Repr. of 1911 ed. 34.50 (ISBN 0-8305-0047-2). Hyperion Conn.
Rashid, Khalid. Muslim Law. 376p. 1985. 60.00x (Pub. by Eastern Bk India). State Mutual Bk.
Roberts, Robert. The Social Laws of the Qoran. 136p. 1982. text ed. 11.95x (ISBN 0-7007-0009-9, Pub. by Curzon Pr England). Apt Bks.
Sadr, Muhammad B. Introduction to Islamic Political System. Ansari, M. A., tr. 112p. 1985. pap. 6.00 (ISBN 0-941724-34-4). Islamic Seminary.
Sadr, Muhhammad B. A Short History of Iluml Usul. Ansari, M. A., tr. from Arabic. 130p. 1985. pap. 5.00 (ISBN 0-941724-37-9). Islamic Seminary.
Saxena, K. P. Muslim Law. 4th ed. 1306p. 1963. 105.00x (Pub. by Eastern Bk India). State Mutual Bk.
Schacht, Joseph. Introduction to Islamic Law. 1964. pap. 18.95x (ISBN 0-19-825473-3). Oxford U Pr.
Siddiqui, A. H. Jehad in Islam. pap. 2.75 (ISBN 0-686-63906-5). Kazi Pubns.
Siddiqui, M. I. The Family Laws of Islam. Date not set. 22.00. Kazi Pubns.
--Penal Law of Islam. 1980. 16.50 (ISBN 0-686-64662-2). Kazi Pubns.
Siddiqui, M. S. Islamic Sharia & the Muslims. pap. 2.50 (ISBN 0-686-63905-7). Kazi Pubns.
Valiuddin, Mir. The Quranic Sufism. 221p. 1981. pap. 13.25 (ISBN 0-88004-007-6). Sunwise Turn.

ISLAMIC LAW–AFRICA

Fluehr-Lobban, Carolyn. Islamic Law & Society in the Sudan. 275p. 1986. 32.50x (ISBN 0-7146-3280-5, F Cass Co). Biblio Dist.

ISLAMIC LEARNING AND SCHOLARSHIP

Ahmad, Nafis. Muslim Contributions to Geography. (Illus.). 178p. (Orig.). 1981. pap. 10.25 (ISBN 0-88004-014-9). Sunwise Turn.
Eickelman, Dale F. Knowledge & Power in Morocco: The Education of a Twentieth-Century Notable. LC 85-3444. (Princeton Studies on the Near East). (Illus.). 325p. 1985. text ed. 32.50x (ISBN 0-691-09415-2). Princeton U Pr.

ISLAMIC LITERATURE–HISTORY AND CRITICISM

Arberry, Arthur J. Aspects of Islamic Civilization as Depicted in the Original Text. 1967. pap. 9.95 (ISBN 0-472-06130-5, 130, AA). U of Mich Pr.
Faris, Nabih A., ed. The Arab Heritage. LC 84-27929. (Illus.). xii, 279p. 1985. Repr. of 1944 ed. lib. bdg. 55.00x (ISBN 0-313-23371-3, FAAH). Greenwood.
Pfannmueller, Gustav. Handbuch der Islam-Literatur. (Ger.). viii, 436p. 1974. Repr. of 1923 ed. 68.00x (ISBN 3-11-002488-8). De Gruyter.
Schimmel, Annemarie. And Muhammad Is His Messenger: The Veneration of the Prophet in Islamic Piety. LC 84-17374. (Studies in Religion). (Illus.). xii, 377p. 1985. 32.00x (ISBN 0-8078-1639-6); pap. 9.95x (ISBN 0-8078-4128-5). U of NC Pr.
--As Through a Veil: Mystical Poetry in Islam. 359p. 1987. pap. text ed. 14.50 (ISBN 0-231-05247-2). Columbia U Pr.
Stories of Great Muslims. Date not set. 4.00 (ISBN 0-89259-020-3). Am Trust Pubns.
Wansbrough, J. Quranic Studies: Sources & Methods of Scriptural Interpretations, Vol. 31. (London Oriental Ser). 1977. 55.00x (ISBN 0-19-713588-9). Oxford U Pr.

ISLAMIC MYSTICISM

see Mysticism–Islam

ISLAMIC PAINTING

see Painting, Islamic

ISLAMIC PHILOSOPHY

see Philosophy, Islamic

ISLAMIC SECTS

see also Assassins (Ismailites); Bektashi; Motazilites; Shiites

Abd-Al-Kahir Ibn-Tahir Ibn Muhammad, Abu M. Moslem Schisms & Sects: Being the History of the Various Philosophic Systems Developed in Islam. Seelye, Kate C., tr. LC 75-158216. (Columbia University Oriental Studies: No. 15). 1920. 20.00 (ISBN 0-404-50505-8). AMS Pr.
Al-Din, Shaykh M. The Rising of al-Husayn: Its Impact on the Consciousness of Muslim Society. Howard, I. K., tr. Date not set. pap. 15.95 (ISBN 0-7103-0191-X, Kegan Paul). Methuen Inc.
Al-Muzaffar, Muhammed R. The Faith of Shi'a Islam. 89p. (Orig.). 1986. pap. text ed. 8.95 (ISBN 0-7103-0157-X). Methuen Inc.
Norton, Augustus R. Amal & the Shi'a: Struggle for the Soul of Lebanon. (Modern Middle East Ser.: No. 13). (Illus.). 264p. 1987. text ed. 25.00x (ISBN 0-292-73039-X); pap. 10.95 (ISBN 0-292-73040-3). U of Tex Pr.
Shahrastani, Muhammad B. Moslem Sects & Divisions: The Section on Muslim Sects in Kitab Al-Milal Wa L-Nihal. Kazi, A. K. & Flynn, J. G., trs. 180p. 1984. 29.95x (ISBN 0-7103-0063-8, Kegan Paul). Methuen Inc.
Sivan, Emmanuel. Radical Islam. LC 84-20999. 224p. 1987. pap. 9.95x (ISBN 0-300-03888-7). Yale U Pr.

ISLAMIC SECTS–MISSIONS

Parshall, Phil. Beyond the Mosque. 312p. 1985. pap. 9.95 (ISBN 0-8010-7089-9). Baker Bk.

ISLAMIC SOCIOLOGY

see Sociology, Islamic

ISLAMIC THEOLOGY

see also God (Islam); Mysticism–Islam

Akbar, Na'im. Chains & Images of Psychological Slavery. 76p. (Orig.). pap. 3.50 (ISBN 0-933821-00-X). New Mind Prod.
Ali, B. Hajjat-ul-Wada: Last Sermon. 1981. 1.25 (ISBN 0-686-97858-7). Kazi Pubns.
Al-Kulayni Ar-Razi. Al-Kafi: The Book of Divine Proof, II. Hasan-Rizvi, S. Muhammad, tr. from Arabic. LC 85-52242. 80p. (Orig.). 1985. pap. 6.00 (ISBN 0-940368-65-X). Tahrike Tarsile Quran.
--Al-Kafi: The Book of Divine Proof, IV. Hasan-Rizvi, S. Muhammad, tr. from Arabic. LC 85-52242. 90p. (Orig.). 1986. pap. 12.00 (ISBN 0-940368-66-8). Tahrike Tarsile Quran.
Al-Qibrisi, Shaykh N. Mercy Oceans: Teachings of Maulana Abdullah al-Faiza ad-Daghestani. 190p. (Orig.). 1980. pap. 4.75x (ISBN 0-939830-11-6, Pub. by Leon). New Era Pubns MI.
Al-Sadr, Ayatullah B. He His Messenger & His Message. x ed. Ansari, M. A., tr. from Arabic. 116p. pap. 6.00 (ISBN 0-941724-12-3). Islamic Seminary.
Al-Wahhab, Muhammad I. Kitab Al Tawhid. (Arabic.). 120p. (Orig.). 1978. pap. 4.95 (ISBN 0-939830-20-5, Pub. by IIFSO Kuwait). New Era Pubns MI.
Ansari, M. A., tr. from Persian. Man & His Destiny. Tr. of Insan wa Sarnawisht. 124p. 1985. pap. 5.00 (ISBN 0-941724-39-5). Islamic Seminary.
Arberry, A. J., ed. & tr. Al-Niffari, Muhammad ibn'Abdi 'L-Jabbar. 276p. 1985. Repr. of 1978 ed. 50.00x (ISBN 0-317-39030-9, Pub. by Luzac & Co Ltd). State Mutual Bk.
Boewering, Gerhard. The Mystical Vision of Existence in Classical Islam. (Studien zur Sprache, Geschichte und Kultur des islamischen Orients, Beihefte zur "der Islam"). 296p. 1979. text ed. 70.50x (ISBN 3-11-007546-6). De Gruyter.
Bukhsh, S. K. The Renaissance of Islam. 1981. 29.00 (ISBN 0-686-97863-3). Kazi Pubns.
Busool, A. N. Forty Ahadith: Asqalani. 1981. 4.50 (ISBN 0-686-97860-9). Kazi Pubns.
Calverley, E. E. The Mysteries of Worship in Islam. 1981. 6.50 (ISBN 0-686-97865-X). Kazi Pubns.
Cook, M. Early Muslim Dogma. 256p. 1981. 54.50 (ISBN 0-521-23379-8). Cambridge U Pr.
Craig, William L. The Kalam Cosmological Argument. LC 77-17232. (Library of Philosophy & Religion Ser.). 216p. 1979. text ed. 28.50x (ISBN 0-06-491308-2). B&N Imports.
Dabas, M. S. & Zarabozo, J. M., trs. from Arabic. Fiqh us-Sunnah Purification & Prayer, Vol. 1. LC 85-73207. 205p. 1986. Repr. of 1985 ed. text ed. 15.00 (ISBN 0-89259-060-2). Am Trust Pubns.
Deedat, A. Is Bible God's Word? 1981. 2.75 (ISBN 0-686-97857-9). Kazi Pubns.
--Quran, the Ultimate Miracle. pap. 2.95 (ISBN 0-686-63913-8). Kazi Pubns.
Doi, A. R. Non-Muslims Under Shari'ah. 1981. 6.50 (ISBN 0-686-97861-7). Kazi Pubns.
--Quran, an Introduction. pap. 5.50 (ISBN 0-686-63911-1). Kazi Pubns.
Farook, Omar & Rauf, A. Quran for Children. pap. 5.95 (ISBN 0-686-63912-X). Kazi Pubns.
Fox, Robert J. Rediscovering Fatima. LC 82-60667. (Illus.). 144p. (Orig.). 1982. pap. 4.50 (ISBN 0-87973-657-7, 657). Our Sunday Visitor.
Frank, Richard M. Beings & Their Attributes: The Teaching of the Bastian School of the Matzzila in the Classical Period. LC 78-6957. 1978. 49.50x (ISBN 0-87395-378-9). State U NY Pr.
Ghazi, A. Mercy for the Mankind, Vol. II. 1981. 4.00 (ISBN 0-686-97848-X). Kazi Pubns.
--Messenger of Allah, Vol. II. 1981. 4.50 (ISBN 0-686-97851-X). Kazi Pubns.
--Our Prophet, Vol. II. 1981. 3.50 (ISBN 0-686-97846-3). Kazi Pubns.
Gilani, A. Maududi, Thought & Movements. 25.00 (ISBN 0-317-46091-9). Kazi Pubns.
Goldziher, Ignaz. Introduction to Islamic Theology & Law. Lewis, Bernard, ed. Hamori, Andras & Hamori, Ruth, trs. from Ger. LC 80-7523. (Modern Classics in Near Eastern Studies). 325p. 1981. 32.00 (ISBN 0-691-07257-4); pap. 14.50 LPE (ISBN 0-691-10099-3). Princeton U Pr.
Hakim, Khalifa A. The Metaphysics of Rumi. 157p. 1981. pap. 3.95 (ISBN 0-88004-004-1). Sunwise Turn.
Haq, M. Fazal, tr. Islamic Teaching, V. 102p. 1985. pap. 6.00 (ISBN 0-317-19682-0). Islamic Seminary.
--Islamic Teachings, VI. 140p. 1985. pap. 6.00 (ISBN 0-317-19685-5). Islamic Seminary.
--Islamic Teachings, VII. 192p. 1985. pap. 9.00 (ISBN 0-941724-33-6). Islamic Seminary.
Husayn at-Tabatabai, S. Muhammad & S. Saeed, Akhtar-Rizvi. Al-Mizan: An Exegesis of the Qur'an, Vol. 1. LC 85-52243. 366p. (Orig.). 1985. pap. 30.00 (ISBN 0-940368-57-9). Tahrike Tarsile Quran.
Hussain, Ahmed. The Philosophy of Faqirs. 126p. (Orig.). 1981. pap. 5.25 (ISBN 0-88004-006-8). Sunwise Turn.
Iqbal, Mohammed. Shikwa & Jawab-I-Shikwa (Answer) Iqbal's Dialogue with Allah. Singh, Krushwant, tr. from Urdu. 96p. (Orig.). 1981. pap. 7.95x (ISBN 0-19-561324-4). Oxford U Pr.
Islamic Perspective to the Divine Principle. LC 80-84970. 198p. (Orig.). 1980. pap. 7.00 (ISBN 0-910621-18-7). HSA Pubns.
Keddie, Nikki R., ed. Scholars, Saints & Sufis: Muslim Religious Institutions since 1500. 1983. 14.50 (ISBN 0-8446-5970-3). Peter Smith.
Khan, K. The Secrets of Anal-Haqq. 1981. 12.50 (ISBN 0-686-97864-1). Kazi Pubns.
Klein, F. A. The Religion of Islam. 248p. 1985. text ed. 17.95x (ISBN 0-7007-0010-2, Pub. by Curzon Pr England); pap. text ed. 8.95 (ISBN 0-7007-0190-7). Apt Bks.
--Religion of Islam. 241p. 1978. Repr. of 1906 ed. 16.50 (ISBN 0-89684-153-7). Orient Bk Dist.
Malik, Charles, ed. God & Man in Contemporary Islamic Thought. 1972. 16.95x (ISBN 0-8156-6035-9, Am U Beirut). Syracuse U Pr.
Marmura, Michael E., ed. Islamic Theology & Philosophy: Studies in Honor of George F. Hourani. 344p. 1983. 49.50 (ISBN 0-87395-746-6); pap. 18.95 (ISBN 0-87395-747-4). State U NY Pr.
Mas'Ud Ibn Umar Al-Taftazani. A Commentary on the Creed of Islam. LC 79-52565. (Islam Ser.). 1980. Repr. of 1950 ed. lib. bdg. 18.00x (ISBN 0-8369-9268-7). Ayer Co Pubs.
Morewedge, Parviz, ed. Islamic Philosophical Theology. LC 79-14405. 1979. 55.50x (ISBN 0-87395-242-1). State U NY Pr.
Murd, M. A. Intellectual Modernism of Shibli Nu'mani: An Exposition of His Religious & Political Ideas. pap. 19.95 (ISBN 0-317-46099-4). Kazi Pubns.
Qayyum, A. On Striving to Be a Muslim. pap. 12.50 (ISBN 0-686-63908-1). Kazi Pubns.
Rahman, A. Prayer, Its Significance & Benefits. pap. 12.50 (ISBN 0-317-46106-0). Kazi Pubns.
Rahman, Fazlur. Health & Medicine in the Islamic Tradition. 176p. 1987. 16.95x (ISBN 0-8245-0797-5). Crossroad NY.
Revealed Book. Qur'an Made Easy. 132p. 1983. pap. 6.00 (ISBN 0-941724-09-3). Islamic Seminary.
Saporetti, C. Assur 14446: La famiglia "A". (Cybernetica Mesopotamica, Data Sets: Cuneiform Texts Ser.: Vol. 1). 140p. 1979. pap. 12.00x soft only (ISBN 0-89003-036-7). Undena Pubns.
Sarwar, Shaikh M. Religious Teachings for Children, Bk. 1. 44p. pap. 5.00 (ISBN 0-941724-03-4). Islamic Seminary.
--Religious Teachings for Children, Bk. 2. 66p. pap. 5.00 (ISBN 0-941724-04-2). Islamic Seminary.
--Religious Teachings for Children, Bk. 3. 80p. pap. 5.00 (ISBN 0-941724-05-0). Islamic Seminary.
--Religious Teachings for Children, Bk. 4. 72p. 1981. pap. 5.00 (ISBN 0-941724-06-9). Islamic Seminary.
Shariati, Ali. Culture & Ideology. Marjani, Fathollah, tr. from Persian. 23p. 1980. pap. 1.00x (ISBN 0-941722-12-0). Book-Dist-Ctr.
--Selection & Election. Ghasemy, Ali A., tr. from Persian. 12p. 1980. pap. 0.75 (ISBN 0-941722-13-9). Book-Dist-Ctr.
Shariff, A. A. Muslim Thought, Its Origin & Achievements. pap. 10.50 (ISBN 0-317-46100-1). Kazi Pubns.
Siddigui, A. H. The Islamic Concept of Religion & Its Revival. 1981. 19.00 (ISBN 0-686-77428-0). Kazi Pubns.
Siddiqui, A. H. Selections from Quran & Hadith. pap. 22.50 ea. (ISBN 0-686-63914-6). Kazi Pubns.
Siddiqui, M. I. What Agitates the Mind of the East. 1981. 1.25 (ISBN 0-686-97862-5). Kazi Pubns.
--Why Islam Forbids Intoxicants & Gambling. 1981. 15.75 (ISBN 0-686-97852-8). Kazi Pubns.
Sivan, Emmanuel. Radical Islam: Medieval Theology & Modern Politics. LC 84-20999. 224p. 1985. 20.00x (ISBN 0-300-03263-3). Yale U Pr.
Sweetman, James W. Islam & Christian Theology: A Study of the Interpretations of Theological Ideas in the Two Religions, 3 vols. 1980. Set. lib. bdg. 229.95 (ISBN 0-8490-3136-2). Gordon Pr.
Talib, Ali B. Abi. Peak of Eloquence-Nahjul Balagha. x ed. Jafery, Askari, tr. 558p. 1983. Repr. 10.00 (ISBN 0-941724-18-2). Islamic Seminary.
Talib, Ali-Ibne-Abu. Nahjul Balagha. Jafery, Syded A., tr. from Arabic. LC 84-51778. 691p. 1984. text ed. 19.95 (ISBN 0-940368-43-9); pap. 9.00 (ISBN 0-940368-42-0). Tahrike Tarsile Quran.
Taymiyah, Ibn. A Muslim Theologian's Response to Christianity: A Translation of Ibn Taymiyya's Jawab al-Sahih li-man Baddala din al-Masih. Michel, Thomas F., tr. LC 83-15430. (Studies in Islamic Philosophy & Science). 60.00x (ISBN 0-88206-058-9). Caravan Bks.
Tritton, Arthur S. Muslim Theology. LC 79-2885. 218p. 1980. Repr. of 1947 ed. 22.00 (ISBN 0-8305-0052-9). Hyperion Conn.
Von Grunebaum, G. E. Muhammadam Festivals: Typical Elements of Islamic Rituals, Prayers & Pilgrimage. 144p. 1981. 20.00x (ISBN 0-7007-0087-0, Pub. by Curzon England). State Mutual Bk.
Wansbrough, J. Quranic Studies: Sources & Methods of Scriptural Interpretations, Vol. 31. (London Oriential Ser). 1977. 55.00x (ISBN 0-19-713588-9). Oxford U Pr.
Wilson, Stephen, ed. Saints & Their Cults: Studies in Religious Sociology, Folklore & History. LC 82-25296. 416p. 1984. 62.50 (ISBN 0-521-24978-3). Cambridge U Pr.
Wolfson, Harry A. The Philosophy of the Kalam. LC 74-78718. 864p. 1976. 40.00x (ISBN 0-674-66580-5). Harvard U Pr.

ISLAMIC WOMEN

see Women, Muslim

ISMAILITES

see also Assassins (Ismailites); Fatimites

Corbin, Henry. Cyclical Time & Ismaili Gnosis. (Islamic Texts & Contexts Ser.). 193p. 1983. 24.95x (ISBN 0-7103-0047-6, Kegan Paul); pap. 13.95 (ISBN 0-7103-0048-4). Methuen Inc.
Lewis, Bernard. The Origins of Isma'ilism: A Study of the Historical Background of the Fatimid Caliphate. LC 74-180357. Repr. of 1940 ed. 22.50 (ISBN 0-404-56289-2). AMS Pr.
Tajdin, Nagib. Bibliography of Ismailism. LC 85-26960. 1986. 25.00x (ISBN 0-88206-063-5). Caravan Bks.

ISRAEL

see also Palestine

Baal-Teshuva, Jacob. Mission of Israel. 1963. 10.95 (ISBN 0-8315-0046-8). Speller.
Baron, David. Israel in the Plan of God. LC 82-18678. 320p. 1983. 14.95 (ISBN 0-8254-2241-8). Kregel.
Bruce, F. F. Israel y las Naciones. Orig. Title: Israel & the Nations. (Span.). 298p. 1979. 8.95 (ISBN 0-8254-1076-2). Kregel.
Buber, Martin & Magnes, J. L., eds. Towards Union in Palestine: Essays on Zionism & Jewish-Arab Cooperation. LC 76-97272. (Judaica Ser.). 124p. 1972. Repr. of 1947 ed. lib. bdg. 22.50x (ISBN 0-8371-2564-2, BUUP). Greenwood.
Ceperley, Gordon. A Promised Land for a Chosen People. LC 79-65616. (Illus., Orig.). 1979. pap. 2.50 (ISBN 0-915540-25-8). Friends Israel-Spearhead Pr.
Cohen, Gary & Kirban, Salem. Israel, Land of Promise, Land of Peace. LC 74-77252. (Illus.). 1974. pap. 5.95 (ISBN 0-912582-16-2). Kirban.

Cohen, Israel, ed. The Rebirth of Israel. LC 75-6427. (The Rise of Jewish Nationalism & the Middle East Ser.). 338p. 1975. Repr. of 1952 ed. 25.85 (ISBN 0-88355-314-7). Hyperion Conn.

--Zionist Work in Palestine. LC 75-6428. (The Rise of Jewish Nationalism & the Middle East Ser.). (Illus.). 208p. 1975. Repr. of 1911 ed. 24.75 (ISBN 0-88355-315-5). Hyperion Conn.

Davis, Moshe, ed. World Jewry & the State of Israel. LC 77-72730. (Indivual Publications Ser.). 1977. lib. bdg. 14.00x (ISBN 0-405-10305-0). Ayer Co Pubs.

Douglas, C. H. The Land for the Chosen People Racket. 1982. lib. bdg. 55.00 (ISBN 0-87700-415-3). Revisionist Pr.

Ellis, Harry B. The Dilemma of Israel. 1970. pap. 5.25 (ISBN 0-8447-1041-5). Am Enterprise.

Essrig, Harry & Segal, Abraham. Israel Today. rev. ed. LC 77-7536. (Illus.). (YA) 1977. text ed. 8.50 (ISBN 0-8074-0007-6, 142601); tchr's guide o.p. 5.00 (ISBN 0-686-83000-8, 202601). UAHC.

Fabian, Larry L. & Schiff, Ze'ev, eds. Israelis Speak: About Themselves & the Palestinians. LC 75-51150. 1977. text ed. 10.00 (ISBN 0-87003-007-8); pap. text ed. 5.00 (ISBN 0-87003-008-6). Carnegie Endow.

Fine, Leon. Will the Real Israel Please Stand Up? 2nd ed. (Illus.). 278p. (Orig.). 1984. pap. 10.95 (ISBN 965-10-0003-1, Pub. by Massada Israel). Hermon.

Friedlander, Dov & Goldscheider, Calvin. The Population of Israel: Growth, Policy & Implications. LC 78-13139. 264p. 1979. 31.00x (ISBN 0-231-04572-7). Columbia U Pr.

Hertz, Joseph H., ed. A Book of Jewish Thoughts. 1976. Repr. 8.95 (ISBN 0-8197-0252-8). Bloch.

Jansen, G. H. Zionism, Israel & Asian Nationalism. 347p. 1971. 6.00 (ISBN 0-88728-112-5); pap. 3.00 (ISBN 0-88728-113-3). Inst Palestine.

Kirban, Salem. The Day Israel Dies! (Illus.). 1975. pap. 2.95 (ISBN 0-912582-21-9). Kirban.

Kittel, Rudolf. Great Men & Movements in Israel. rev. ed. LC 66-29121. (Library of Biblical Studies). 1968. 20.00x (ISBN 0-87068-071-4). Ktav.

Leroy-Beaulieu, Anatole. Israel among the Nations: A Study of the Jews & Antisemitism. facsimile ed. Hellman, Frances, tr. from Fr. LC 74-27996. (Modern Jewish Experience Ser.). (Eng.). 1975. Repr. of 1904 ed. 32.00x (ISBN 0-405-06723-2). Ayer Co Pubs.

Lewittes, M. Religious Foundations of the Jewish State: The Concept & Practice of Jewish Statehood from Biblical Times to the Modern State of Israel. 25.00x (ISBN 0-87068-433-7). Ktav.

Lindsay, Gordon. The Miracle of Israel. 1.95 (ISBN 0-89985-188-6). Christ Nations.

McEleney, Neil J. Melody of Israel. (Bible Ser.). pap. 1.00 (ISBN 0-8091-5089-1). Paulist Pr.

Mark, Emanuel, ed. A Composite Portrait of Israel. LC 80-40889. 1981. 55.50 (ISBN 0-12-476450-9). Acad Pr.

Mehdi, M. T., ed. Palestine & the Bible. LC 71-114557. 1971. pap. 4.00 (ISBN 0-911026-06-1). New World Press NY.

Meyer, F. B. Israel. 1972. pap. 4.50 (ISBN 0-87508-347-1). Chr Lit.

Meyer, Lawrence. Israel Now: Portrait of a Troubled Land. 1982. 16.95 (ISBN 0-385-28475-6). Delacorte.

Meyer, Nathan M. The Land of Miracles. (Illus.). pap. 2.00 (ISBN 0-88469-021-0). BMH Bks.

Miller, Irving. Israel: The Eternal Idea. 1955. 19.50x (ISBN 0-686-50046-6). Elliots Bks.

Naamani, Israel T. The State of Israel. LC 79-12757. (Illus.). 1980. pap. 6.95x (ISBN 0-87441-278-1). Behrman.

Orlinsky, H. M. Israel Exploration Journal Reader, 2 vols. (The Library of Biblical Studies). 1982. Set. 99.50x (ISBN 0-87068-267-9). Ktav.

Rapaport, et al. Early Child Care in Israel. (International Monograph on Early Child Care). 212p. 1976. 38.50 (ISBN 0-677-05270-7). Gordon & Breach.

Reich, Bernard. Israel: Land of Tradition & Conflict. (Profiles-Nations of the Contemporary Middle East Ser.). 240p. 1985. 28.00x (ISBN 0-8133-0211-0); pap. text ed. 13.95x (ISBN 0-8133-0215-3). Westview.

Rossel, Seymour. Israel: Covenant People, Covenant Land. (Illus.). 256p. 1985. pap. 8.95 (ISBN 0-941232-06-9, 147500). UAHC.

Rubin, Gail. Psalmist with a Camera. LC 79-5086. (Illus.). 116p. 1979. 19.95 (ISBN 0-89659-076-3); pap. 14.95 (ISBN 0-89659-071-2). Abbeville Pr.

Satan & Israel. Date not set. pap. 0.95 (ISBN 0-937408-13-1). GMI Pubns Inc.

Simon, Merill. Jerry Falwell & the Jews. LC 83-22266. 172p. 1983. 12.50 (ISBN 0-8246-0300-1). Jonathan David.

Sinai, Anne & Sinai, Robert I., eds. Israel & the Arabs: Prelude to the Jewish State. LC 78-161364. (A Facts on File Publication). pap. 64.00 (2025158). Bks Demand UMI.

Wagner, George. Practical Truths from Israel's Wanderings. LC 82-18706. 384p. 1983. 14.95 (ISBN 0-8254-4017-3). Kregel.

Walvoord, John F. Israel in Prophecy. 1978. pap. 4.95 (ISBN 0-310-34081-0, 10970P). Zondervan.

Zweig, Ferdynand. Israel: The Sword & the Harp. LC 74-86291. 326p. 1970. 24.50 (ISBN 0-8386-7534-4). Fairleigh Dickinson.

ISRAEL–DESCRIPTION AND TRAVEL

Agnon, S. Y. In the Heart of the Seas: A Story of a Journey to the Land of Israel. Lask, I. M., tr. from Hebrew. LC 66-30349. (Illus.). 128p. 1980. pap. 6.95 (ISBN 0-8052-0647-7). Schocken.

Alexander, Morris. Israel & Me. (Illus.). 278p. 1977. 14.50x (ISBN 0-87073-204-8). Schenkman Bks Inc.

Bellow, Saul. To Jerusalem & Back. 1977. pap. 1.95 (ISBN 0-380-01676-1, 33472-0). Avon.

Dowley, Tom. High above the Holy Land. Roe, Earl O., ed. LC 86-6422. (Illus.). 64p. 1986. 15.95 (ISBN 0-8307-1153-8, 5111590). Regal.

Jacoby, Hilla & Jacoby, Max, photos by. The Land of Israel. (Illus.). 1978. 25.00f. Thames Hudson.

Kesich, Veselin & Kesich, Lydia W. Treasures of the Holy Land: A Visit to the Places of Christian Origins. LC 85-18403. (Illus., Orig.). 1985. pap. 6.95 (ISBN 0-88141-045-4). St Vladimirs.

Koch, Kurt E. The Coming One. LC 72-85597. 96p. 1974. pap. 2.95 (ISBN 0-8254-3011-9). Kregel.

Maidat, Rita. The Twins Visit Israel. (Shayna & Keppi Ser.). (Illus.). 1978. pap. 2.00 (ISBN 0-914080-72-5). Shulsinger Sales.

Serruya, Colette. Lake Kinneret: Lake of Tiberias, Sea of Galilee. (Monographiae Biologicae: No.32). 1978. lib. bdg. 68.50 (ISBN 90-619-3085-5, Pub. by Junk Pubs Netherlands). Kluwer Academic.

ISRAEL–HISTORY

Bain, Kenneth R. The March to Zion: United States Policy & the Founding of Israel. LC 79-7413. 256p. 1980. 18.50 (ISBN 0-89096-076-3). Tex A&M Univ Pr.

Balabkins, Nicholas. West German Reparations to Israel. LC 70-152724. 1971. 32.00 (ISBN 0-8135-0691-3). Rutgers U Pr.

Blenkinsopp, J. Gibeon & Israel: The Role of Gibeon & the Gibeonites in the Political and Religious History of Early Israel. LC 74-171672. (Society for Old Testament Studies Monographs). 1972. 34.50 (ISBN 0-521-08368-0). Cambridge U Pr.

Bright, John. A History of Israel. 3rd ed. LC 80-22774. (Illus.). 528p. 1981. 18.95 (ISBN 0-664-21381-2). Westminster.

Burney, C. F. Israel's Settlement in Canaan: The Biblical Tradition & Its Historical Background. 3rd ed. (British Academy, London, Schweich Lectures on Biblical Archaeology Series, 1917). pap. 19.00 (ISBN 0-8115-1259-2). Kraus Repr.

Cameron, James. The Making of Israel. LC 77-76041. (Illus.). 1977. 7.95 (ISBN 0-8008-5084-X). Taplinger.

Castel, Francois. History of Israel & Judah: From the Beginnings to the Second Century A. D. 288p. (Orig.). 1985. pap. 8.95 (ISBN 0-8091-2701-6). Paulist Pr.

Cohen, Mitchell. Zion & State: Nation, Class & the Shaping of Modern Israel. 288p. 1987. 24.95 (ISBN 0-631-15243-1). Basil Blackwell.

Cornhill, Carl H. History of the People of Israel. 325p. 1943. 4.95 (ISBN 0-317-40441-5); pap. 2.95 (ISBN 0-317-40442-3). Open Court.

Davis, John J. & Whitcomb, John C. A History of Israel. (Old Testament Studies). 1980. 17.95 (ISBN 0-8010-2888-4). Baker Bk.

--History of Israel. 17.95 (ISBN 0-88469-061-X). BMH Bks.

De Vaux, Roland. The Early History of Israel. LC 78-1883. 914p. 1978. Westminster.

Edelman, Lily. Israel. 1958. 20.00 (ISBN 0-686-17232-9). Scholars Ref Lib.

Ellison, H. L. The Mystery of Israel: An Exposition of Romans 9-11. 3rd ed. 117p. 1976. pap. 4.95 (ISBN 0-85364-169-2). Attic Pr.

Elon, Amos. Understanding Israel: A Social Studies Approach. Sugarman, Morris J., ed. LC 76-18282. (Illus.). 256p. 1976. pap. text ed. 6.95x (ISBN 0-87441-234-X). Behrman.

Fohrer, Georg. Geschichte der Israelitischen Religion. (Ger.). xvi, 367p. 1969. 20.80x (ISBN 3-11-002652-X). De Gruyter.

Forster, Arnold. Report from Israel. 72p. pap. 1.25 (ISBN 0-686-74976-6). ADL.

Grand, Tamar & Grand, Samuel. Children of Israel. (Illus.). 1972. text ed. 5.50 (ISBN 0-8074-0131-5, 121320); tchr's guide 2.25 (ISBN 0-8074-0132-3, 201320); fun & act bk. 4.50 (ISBN 0-8074-0133-1, 121322). UAHC.

Grant, Michael. The History of Ancient Israel. (Illus.). 360p. 1984. pap. 14.95 (ISBN 0-684-18084-7, ScribT); 19.95 (ISBN 0-684-18081-2). Scribner.

--The History of Ancient Israel. 360p. 1984. pap. text ed. write for info. (ISBN 0-02-345620-5, Pub. by Scribner). Macmillan.

Hartman, David. Joy & Responsibility: Israel, Modernity & the Renewal of Judaism. 286p. 12.50 (ISBN 0-686-95138-7). ADL.

Heaton, E. W. Everyday Life in Old Testament Times. LC 76-29288. (Illus.). 1977. lib. rep. ed. 17.50H (ISBN 0-684-14836-6). Scribner.

Hoffman, Lawrence A. The Land of Israel: Jewish Perspectives. LC 86-40241. (Studies in Judiasm & Christianity in Antiquity: Vol. 6). 352p. 1986. text ed. 29.95x (ISBN 0-268-02180-5). U of Notre Dame Pr.

Horowitz, Aharon. The Quarternary of Israel. LC 78-8855. 1979. 45.00 (ISBN 0-12-356170-1). Acad Pr.

Horowitz, Dan & Lissak, Moshe. Origins of the Israeli Polity: Palestine Under the Mandate. Hoffman, Charles, tr. LC 78-3175. (Illus.). 320p. 1979. lib. bdg. 24.00x (ISBN 0-226-35366-4). U of Chicago Pr.

Horowitz, David. State in the Making. Meltzer, Julian, tr. from Hebrew. LC 81-6649. viii, 349p. 1981. Repr. of 1953 ed. lib. bdg. 28.75x (ISBN 0-313-23011-0, HOSI). Greenwood.

Ishida, Tomoo. The Royal Dynasties in Ancient Israel. 1977. 45.25 (ISBN 3-1100-6519-3). De Gruyter.

Jaffe, Eliezer D. Pleaders & Protesters: The Future of Citizens' Organizations in Israel. LC 80-68431. 40p. 1980. pap. 2.50 (ISBN 0-87495-028-7). Am Jewish Comm.

Jagersma, Henk. A History of Israel from Alexander the Great to Bar Kochba. Kok, J. H., tr. LC 85-45497. 256p. 1986. pap. 12.95 (ISBN 0-8006-1890-4, 1-1890). Fortress.

--A History of Israel in the Old Testament Period. Bowden, John, tr. LC 82-48548. 320p. 1983. pap. 13.95 (ISBN 0-8006-1692-8). Fortress.

The Jewish Agency for Palestine: The Jewish Plan for Palestine. Repr. of 1947 ed. 77.00 (ISBN 3-601-00327-9). Kraus Repr.

Kampelman, Max M. Jewish Power: Myth or Reality. 21p. 1.50 (ISBN 0-686-74974-X). ADL.

Kedourie, Elie & Haim, Sylvia G., eds. Palestine & Israel in the Nineteenth & Twentieth Centuries. (Illus.). 286p. 1982. 39.50x (ISBN 0-7146-3121-3, F Cass Co). Biblio Dist.

Klein, Herbert A. The Peoples of Israel: Fifty-Seven Centuries of Presence. rev. & enl. ed. Simon, Joseph, ed. Orig. Title: Israel - Land of the Jews. (Illus.). 240p. 1986. Repr. of 1972 ed. 23.50 (ISBN 0-934710-13-9). J Simon.

Koppejan, Helene. Strange Parallel: Zebulun a Tribe of Israel. Rev. ed. LC 83-73689. (Illus.). 96p. 1984. pap. 4.00 (ISBN 0-934666-13-X). Artisan Sales.

Kuntz, J. Kenneth. The People of Ancient Israel: An Introduction to the Old Testament Literature, History & Thought. (Illus.). 1974. pap. text ed. 21.95 scp (ISBN 0-06-043822-3, HarpC). Har-Row.

Lemche, Niels P. Ancient Israel: A New History of Israelite Society. (The Biblical Seminar Ser.: No. 5). 250p. 1987. pap. text ed. 9.50x (ISBN 1-85075-017-3, Pub. by JSOT Pr England). Eisenbrauns.

Levine, Lee I., ed. The Jerusalem Cathedra: Studies in the History, Archaeology, Geography, & Ethnography of the Land of Israel, Vol. 1. (Illus.). 362p. 1982. 35.00x (ISBN 0-8143-1691-3). Wayne St U Pr.

Lewisohn, Ludwig. Israel. LC 76-138122. 1971. Repr. of 1925 ed. lib. bdg. 22.50x (ISBN 0-8371-5698-X, LEIS). Greenwood.

Lindblom, Johannes. Prophecy in Ancient Israel. LC 63-907. pap. 120.00 (2029298). Bks Demand UMI.

Lods, Adolphe. Israel, from Its Beginning to the Middle of the Eighth Century. Hooke, S. H., tr. LC 75-41180. 1948. 34.75 (ISBN 0-404-14569-8). AMS PR.

Meyer, Nathan M. The Land of Miracles. (Illus.). pap. 2.00 (ISBN 0-88469-021-0). BMH Bks.

Miller, J. Maxwell & Hayes, John H. A History of Ancient Israel & Judah. LC 85-11468. (Illus.). 524p. 1986. 27.95 (ISBN 0-664-21262-X). Westminster.

Moo, Douglas J. The Old Testament in the Gospel Passion Narratives. xii, 468p. 1983. text ed. 29.95x (ISBN 0-907459-28-5, Pub. by Almond Pr England); pap. text ed. 17.95x (ISBN 0-907459-29-3). Eisenbrauns.

Neilson, Francis. From UR to Nazareth: An Economic Inquiry into the Religious & Political History of Israel. 75.00 (ISBN 0-87700-010-7). Revisionist Pr.

Neusner, Jacob. Messiah in Context: Israel's History & Destiny in Formative Judaism. LC 83-20542. (Foundations of Judaism Ser.). 304p. 1984. 26.95 (ISBN 0-8006-0716-3, 1-716). Fortress.

Neusner, Jacob, et al, eds. Judaic Perspectives on Ancient Israel. LC 86-45908. 356p. 1987. 34.95 (ISBN 0-8006-0832-1, 1-832). Fortress.

O'Brien, Conor C. The Siege: The Saga of Israel & Zionism. 800p. 1986. 24.95 (ISBN 0-671-60044-3). S&S.

Parmelee, Alice. A History of the People of Israel, Bk. 4. LC 80-81097. (All About the Bible). 148p. (Orig.). 1980. pap. 5.95 (ISBN 0-8192-1273-3). Morehouse.

Ramsey, George W. Quest for the Historical Israel. LC 80-82188. 208p. (Orig.). 1981. pap. 13.95 (ISBN 0-8042-0187-0). John Knox.

Raymond, E. The Gem Stones in the Breastplate. (Illus.). 48p. (Orig.). 1987. pap. price not set (ISBN 0-934666-18-0). Artisan Sales.

Regan, Geoffrey B. Israel & the Arabs: Cambridge Introduction to the History of Mankind. (Illus.). 48p. 1984. pap. 4.95 (ISBN 0-521-27580-6). Cambridge U Pr.

Ritchie, John. From Egypt to Canaan. LC 82-220. 102p. 1982. pap. 4.50 (ISBN 0-8254-3614-1). Kregel.

Robinson, H. Wheeler. History of Israel. rev. ed. Brockington, L. H., ed. (Studies in Theology: No. 42). 1964. pap. 8.95x (ISBN 0-8401-6042-9). A R Allenson.

--The History of Israel. (Studies in Theology). 206p. 1967. pap. 13.50 (ISBN 0-7156-0163-6, Pub. by Duckworth London). Longwood Pub Group.

Rowley, Gwyn, ed. Israel into Palestine. LC 83-22167. 198p. 1983. 31.00x (ISBN 0-7201-1674-0). Mansell.

Sachar, Howard M. A History of Israel: From the Rise of Zionism to Our Time. LC 76-13710. (Illus.). 1979. 14.95 (ISBN 0-394-73679-6). Knopf.

Samuel, Rinna. Israel: Promised Land to Modern State. (Illus.). 175p. 1971. Repr. of 1969 ed. 18.50x (ISBN 0-85303-135-5, Pub. by Vallentine Mitchell England). Biblio Dist.

Smith, George A. The Early Poetry of Israel in Its Physical & Social Origins. (British Academy, London, Schweich Lectures on Biblical Archaeology Series, 1910). pap. 19.00 (ISBN 0-8115-1252-5). Kraus Repr.

Smith, James E. Divided We Fall. LC 79-67439. 96p. (Orig.). 1980. pap. 2.25 (ISBN 0-87239-381-X, 40086). Standard Pub.

Soggin, J. Albert. A History of Ancient Israel. Bowden, John, tr. from Italian. LC 84-27010. (Illus.). 452p. 1985. 29.95 (ISBN 0-664-21258-1). Westminster.

Telpaz, Gideon. Israeli Childhood Stories of the Sixties. LC 83-14202. (Brown Judaic Studies). 222p. 1983. pap. 18.00 (ISBN 0-89130-610-2, 14 00 40). Scholars Pr GA.

Teringo, J. Robert. The Land & People Jesus Knew. 250p. 1985. 24.95 (ISBN 0-87123-797-0, 230797). Bethany Hse.

Torrey, Charles C. Chronicler's History of Israel: Chronicles-Ezra-Nehemiah Restored to Its Original Form. 1954. 17.50x (ISBN 0-686-37866-0). Elliots Bks.

Whitelam, Keith W. The Just King: Monarchical Judicial Authority in Ancient Israel. (Journal for the Study of the Old Testament Supplement Ser.: No. 12). 1979. text ed. 19.95x (ISBN 0-905774-18-3, Pub. by JSOT Pr England). Eisenbrauns.

Wood, Leon & O'Brien, David. A Survey of Israel's History. rev. ed. 416p. 1986. 19.95 (ISBN 0-310-34770-X, 6505). Zondervan.

ISRAEL–JUVENILE LITERATURE

Amos, C. M. Israel Becomes a Nation. (Discovering the Bible Ser.). pap. 8.95 (ISBN 0-7175-1160-X). Dufour.

Bamberger, David. A Young Person's History of Israel. Mandelkern, Nicholas, ed. (Illus.). 150p. (Orig.). 1985. pap. 6.95 (ISBN 0-87441-393-1). Behrman.

Hoffman, Gail. The Land & People of Israel. rev. ed. LC 77-37286. (Portraits of the Nations Ser.). (Illus.). 1972. PLB 11.89i (ISBN 0-397-31258-X, Lipp Jr Bks). HarpJ.

Israel. (Library of Nations). (YA) 1986. lib. bdg. 18.60 (ISBN 0-8094-5313-4, Pub. by Time-LIfe). Silver.

Kubie, Nora B. Jews of Israel: History & Sources. Silberman, Mark, ed. LC 75-18510. (Illus.). 128p. (Orig.). 1975. pap. text ed. 3.95x (ISBN 0-87441-246-3). Behrman.

Lehman, Emil. Israel: Idea & Reality. (Illus.). 3.95x (ISBN 0-8381-0205-0, 10-205). United Syn Bk.

Rutland, Jonathan. Take a Trip to Israel. (Take a Trip to Ser.). (Illus.). 32p. 1981. lib. bdg. 9.90 (ISBN 0-531-04318-5). Watts.

Shaw, Lee H., Jr. How to Live Forever in the New Jerusalem. 56p. (Orig.). (YA) 1985. pap. 3.00x (ISBN 0-9614311-0-5). Elijah-John.

Zohar, Danah. Israel. LC 77-88352. (Countries Ser.). (Illus.). 1978. PLB 14.96 (ISBN 0-382-06146-2). Silver.

ISRAEL–RELIGION

Abramov, S. Zalman. Perpetual Dilemma: Jewish Religion in the Jewish State. 1979. pap. 7.50 (ISBN 0-8074-0088-2, 382500, WUPJ). UAHC.

Aviad, Janet. Return to Judaism: Religious Renewal in Israel. LC 82-17663. xiv, 194p. 1985. pap. 8.95 (ISBN 0-226-03235-3). U of Chicago Pr.

Blenkinsopp, J. Gibeon & Israel: The Role of Gibeon & the Gibeonites in the Political and Religious History of Early Israel. LC 74-171672. (Society for Old Testament Studies Monographs). 1972. 34.50 (ISBN 0-521-08368-0). Cambridge U Pr.

Campbell, Roderick. Israel & the New Covenant. 1982. 12.95 (ISBN 0-87552-161-4). Presby & Reformed.

Coggins, R. J. & Phillips, Anthony C., eds. Israel's Prophetic Tradition. LC 81-17065. (Illus.). 290p. 1982. 44.50 (ISBN 0-521-24223-1). Cambridge U Pr.

Cross, Frank M. Canaanite Myth & Hebrew Epic: Essays in the History of the Religion of Israel. LC 72-76564. 1973. 25.00x (ISBN 0-674-09175-2). Harvard U Pr.

Dowley, Tom. High above the Holy Land. Roe, Earl O., ed. LC 86-6422. (Illus.). 64p. 1986. 15.95 (ISBN 0-8307-1153-8, 5111590). Regal.

Elazar, Daniel J. & Aviad, Janet. Religion & Politics in Israel: The Interplay of Judaism & Zionism. 32p. 1981. pap. 2.50 (ISBN 0-87495-033-3). Am Jewish Comm.

Fohrer, Georg. Geschichte der Israelitischen Religion. (Ger.). xvi, 367p. 1969. 20.80x (ISBN 3-11-002652-X). De Gruyter.

Goldberg, Louis. Turbulence over the Middle East: Israel & the Nations in Confrontation & the Coming Kingdom of Peace on Earth. (Illus.). 320p. 1982. pap. 7.95 (ISBN 0-87213-240-4). Loizeaux.

Harrelson, Walter J. From Fertility Cult to Worship: A Reassessment for the Modern Church. LC 66-14929. (Scholars Press Reprint Ser.: No. 4). pap. 10.25x (ISBN 0-89130-379-0, 00 07 04). Scholars Pr GA.

Holmes, Reed M. The Church in Israel. (Illus.). 1983. pap. 10.00 (ISBN 0-8309-0383-6). Herald Hse.

Kaufmann, Yehezkel. The Religion of Israel: From Its Beginnings to the Babylonian Exile. Greenberg, Moshe, tr. LC 60-5466. 304p. 1972. pap. 10.95 (ISBN 0-8052-0364-8). Schocken.

Kloos, Carola. Yhwh's Combat with the Sea: A Canaanite Tradition in the Religion of Ancient Israel. 243p. 1986. pap. 35.75 (ISBN 90-04-08096-1, Pub. by E J Brill). Heinman.

Liebman, Charles S. & Don-Yehiya, Eliezer. Religion & Politics in Israel. LC 83-48172. (Jewish Political & Social Studies Ser.). 160p. 1984. 17.50x (ISBN 0-253-34497-2). Ind U pr.

Mayes, Andrew D. Israel in the Period of the Judges. (Studies in Biblical Theology, Second Ser.: No. 29). 1974. pap. text ed. 10.00x (ISBN 0-8401-3079-1). A R Allenson.

Neusner, Jacob, ed. The Talmud of the Land of Israel: A Preliminary Translation & Explanation, Vol. 22: Ketubot. (Chicago Studies in the History of Judaism). 384p. 1985. lib. bdg. 49.00x (ISBN 0-226-57681-7). U of Chicago Pr.

Ottensoser, Max & Roberg, Alex, eds. Israelitische Lehrerbildungsanstalt Wurzburg. LC 81-81930. (Illus.). 256p. 1982. 12.95 (ISBN 0-8187-0046-7). Harlo Pr.

Petersen, David L., ed. Prophecy in Israel: Search for an Identity. LC 85-45584. (Issues in Religion & Theology Ser.). 176p. 1986. pap. 7.95 (ISBN 0-317-47042-6, 1-773). Fortress.

Sanchez, Benjamin M. Israel & the Prophecies. pap. 3.10 (ISBN 0-913558-06-0). Educator Pubns.

Shavit, Yaacov. The New Hebrew Nation: A Study in Israeli Heresy & Fantasy. 1987. 29.50 (ISBN 0-7146-3302-X, F Cass Co). Biblio Dist.

Strong, James. Tabernacle of Israel. LC 85-8100. (Illus.). 208p. 1987. pap. 10.95 (ISBN 0-8254-3745-8). Kregel.

Ten Words of Freedom: An Introduction to the Faith of Iarael. LC 75-139344. pap. 60.00 (2026879). Bks Demand UMI.

Thomson, J. The Samaritans: Their Testimony to the Religion of Israel. 1976. lib. bdg. 59.95 (ISBN 0-8490-2564-8). Gordon Pr.

Tigay, Jeffrey H. You Shall Have No Other Gods: Israelite Religion in the Light of Hebrew Inscriptions. (Harvard Semitic Studies). 130p. 1987. 16.95 (ISBN 1-55540-063-9, 04-04-31). Scholars Pr GA.

Van Impe, Jack. Israel's Final Holocaust. 172p. 1979. pap. 4.95 (ISBN 0-934803-08-0). J Van Impe.

Zucker, Norman L. The Coming Crisis in Israel: Private Faith & Public Policy. 1973. pap. 7.95x (ISBN 0-262-74012-5). MIT Pr.

ISRAEL, ELECTION OF

see Jews–Election, Doctrine Of

ISRAEL AND THE DIASPORA

Hammer, Gottlieb. Good Faith & Credit. LC 85-13962. (Illus.). 280p. 1986. 17.95 (ISBN 0-8453-4798-5, Cornwall Bks). Assoc Univ Prs.

ISTANBUL–ANTIQUITIES

Belting, Hans, et al. The Mosaics & Frescoes of St. Mary Pammakaristos (Fethiye Camii) at Istanbul. LC 77-99268. (Dumbarton Oaks Studies: Vol. 15). (Illus.). 118p. 1978. 30.00x (ISBN 0-88402-075-4). Dumbarton Oaks.

ISTANBUL–CHURCH OF THE HOLY APOSTLES

Dvornik, Francis. The Idea of Apostolicity in Byzantium & the Legend of the Apostle Andrew. (Dumbarton Oaks Studies: Vol. 4). 342p. (LC A58-8640). 1958. 25.00x (ISBN 0-88402-004-5). Dumbarton Oaks.

Runciman, Steven. The Great Church in Captivity: A Study of the Patriarchate of Constantinople from the Eve of the Turkish Conquest to the Greek War of Independence. 465p. Date not set. pap. price not set. Cambridge U Pr.

ISTANBUL–HISTORY

see also Crusades–Fourth, 1202-1204

De Villehardouin, Geoffroi. De la Conqueste de Constantinoble. Paris, Paulin, ed. 1965. 39.00 (ISBN 0-685-92799-7); pap. 33.00 (ISBN 0-384-64581-X). Johnson Repr.

De Villehardouin, Geoffroy. Conqueste de Constantinople. White, Julian E., Jr., ed. LC 68-16196. (Medieval French Literature Ser). (Fr., Orig.). 1968. pap. text ed. 5.95x (ISBN 0-89197-102-5). Irvington.

Gadolin, A. A. A Theory of History & Society, with Special Reference to the Chronographia of Michael Psellus: Eleventh Century Byzantium. 2nd ed. (Illus.). 244p. 1986. lib. bdg. 45.00x (ISBN 90-256-0906-6, Pub. by A M Hakkert). Coronet Bks.

Gerostergios, Asterios. St. Photios the Great. LC 80-82285. (Illus.). 125p. 1980. 8.50 (ISBN 0-914744-50-X); pap. 5.50 (ISBN 0-914744-51-8). Inst Byzantine.

Godfrey, John. Twelve Hundred & Four-the Unholy Crusade. (Illus.). 1980. 39.95x (ISBN 0-19-215834-1). Oxford U Pr.

Nelson, Lynn H. & Shirk, Melanie. Liutprand of Cremona, Mission to Constantinople 968 A.D. 62p. 1972. pap. 1.00x (ISBN 0-87291-039-3). Coronado Pr.

ISTANBUL (PATRIARCHATE)–HISTORY

Runciman, Steven. The Great Church in Captivity: A Study of the Patriarchate of Constantinople from the Eve of the Turkish Conquest to the Greek War of Independence. LC 68-29330. pap. 116.30 (ISBN 0-317-26393-5, 2024531). Bks Demand UMI.

Vaporis, Nomikos M. Codex Beta of the Ecumenical Patriarchate of Constantinople: Aspects of the History of the Church of Constantinople. (The Archbishop Iakovos Library of Ecclesiastical & Historical Sources). 166p. 1975. pap. 4.95 (ISBN 0-916586-03-0). Holy Cross Orthodox.

--Codex Gamma of the Ecumenical Patriarchate of Constantinople. (The Archbishop Iakovos Library of Ecclesiastical & Historical Sources Ser.). 154p. 1974. pap. 4.95 (ISBN 0-916586-01-4). Holy Cross Orthodox.

ITALIANS IN THE UNITED STATES

Caliaro, Marco & Francesconi, Mario. John Baptist Scalabrini: Apostle to Emigrants. Zizzamia, Alba I., tr. from It. LC 76-44922. (Illus.). 580p. 1977. lib. bdg. 15.00x (ISBN 0-913256-24-2). Ctr Migration.

Orsi, Robert A. The Madonna of One Hundred Fifteenth Street: Faith & Community in Italian Harlem, 1880 to 1950. LC 85-10799. (Illus.). 366p. 1985. 29.95x (ISBN 0-300-03262-5). Yale U Pr.

Sartorio, Enrico C. Social & Religious Life of Italians in the United States. LC 73-13520. 1974. Repr. of 1918 ed. 19.50x (ISBN 0-678-01364-0). Kelley.

Scarpaci, Jean, ed. The Interaction of Italians & Jews in America. 1974. 9.95 (ISBN 0-934675-07-4). Am Italian.

Smith, Judith E. Family Connections: A History of Italian & Jewish Immigrant Lives in Providence, Rhode Island, 1900-1940. (SUNY Series in American Social History). 256p. 1985. 44.50 (ISBN 0-87395-964-7); pap. 16.95 (ISBN 0-87395-965-5). State U NY Pr.

ITALY–CHURCH HISTORY

Collett, Barry. Italian Benedictine Scholars & the Reformation: The Congregation of Santa Giustina of Padua. (Historical Monographs). 300p. 1985. 48.00x (ISBN 0-19-822934-8). Oxford U Pr.

Genzburg, Carlo. The Cheese & the Worms: The Cosmos of a Sixteenth-Century Miller. LC 79-3654. pap. 51.80 (2026706). Bks Demand UMI.

J

JACKSON, MAHALIA, 1911-1972

Cornell, Jean G. Mahalia Jackson: Queen of Gospel Song. LC 73-14713. (Americans All Ser.). (Illus.). 96p. 1974. PLB 7.12 (ISBN 0-8116-4581-9). Garrard.

Jackson, Jesse. Make a Joyful Noise unto the Lord: The Life of Mahalia Jackson, Queen of Gospel Singers. LC 72-7549. (Women of America Ser.). 1974. 12.70 (ISBN 0-690-43344-1, Crowell Jr Bks). HarpJ.

JACOB, THE PATRIARCH

Heap, Norman L. Abraham, Isaac, & Jacob, Servants & Prophets of God. 1987. 12.50 (ISBN 0-533-07272-7). Vantage.

Jacob. 1979. 0.75 (ISBN 0-8198-0581-5). Dghtrs St Paul.

L'Engle, Madeleine. A Stone for a Pillow: Journeys with Jacob. (Wheaton Literary Ser.). 240p. (Orig.). 1986. 11.95 (ISBN 0-87788-789-6); pap. cancelled. Shaw Pubs.

Lindsay, Gordon. Jacob & His Son, Joseph. (Old Testament Ser.). 1.25 (ISBN 0-89985-129-0). Christ Nations.

--Jacob, The Supplanter Who Became a Prince with God. (Old Testament Ser.). 1.25 (ISBN 0-89985-128-2). Christ Nations.

Nee, Watchman. Changed into His Likeness. 1969. 4.95 (ISBN 0-87508-411-7); pap. 3.95 (ISBN 0-87508-410-9). Chr Lit.

Paamoni, Zev. The Adventures of Jacob. (Biblical Ser.). (Illus.). 1970. 4.00 (ISBN 0-914080-26-1). Shulsinger Sales.

Shearburn, Wally M. Jacob's Ladder: A Choral Reading. 1980. 4.00 (ISBN 0-89536-441-7, 1014). CSS of Ohio.

Small, Dwight H. No Rival Love. 201p. (Orig.). 1985. pap. 4.95 (ISBN 0-87508-495-8). Chr Lit.

Watchman, Nee. Changed into His Likeness. 1978. pap. 3.95 (ISBN 0-8423-0228-X). Tyndale.

JACOBINS (DOMINICANS)

see Dominicans

JACOBITE CHURCH

Baumstark, Anton. Festbrevier und Kirchenjahr der Syrischen Jakobiten. Repr. of 1910 ed. 22.00 (ISBN 0-384-03575-2). Johnson Repr.

Brooks-Davies, Douglas. Pope's Dunciad & the Queen of Night: A Study in Emotional Jacobitism. LC 84-17135. 190p. 1985. 35.00 (ISBN 0-7190-1735-1, Pub. by Manchester Univ Pr); pap. write for info. Longwood Pub Group.

JADE

Laufer, Berthold. Jade: A Study in Chinese Archaeology & Religion. (Field Museum of Natural History). (Illus.). 1912. 41.00 (ISBN 0-527-01870-8). Kraus Repr.

--Jade: A Study in Chinese Archaeology & Religion. (Illus.). 15.25 (ISBN 0-8446-5214-8). Peter Smith.

JAFFRAY, ROBERT ALEXANDER, 1873-1945

Tozer, Aiden W. Let My People Go. pap. 4.45 (ISBN 0-87509-189-X). Chr Pubns.

JAINAS

see Jains

JAINISM

Bist, Umrao S. Jaina Theories of Reality & Knowledge. 1985. 6.50x (ISBN 0-8364-1362-8, Pub. by Eastern). South Asia Bks.

Boger, Ann C. & DeOreo, Joellen K. Sacred India: Hinduism, Buddhism, Jainism. LC 85-19559. (Illus.). 60p. 1986. pap. 7.95 (ISBN 0-910386-84-6, Pub. by Cleveland Mus Art). Ind U Pr.

Bothra, Pushpa. Jaina Theory of Perception. 1976. 11.95 (ISBN 0-89684-229-0). Orient Bk Dist.

Chatterjee, Asim K. A Comprehensive History of Jainism. 1978. 20.00x (ISBN 0-8364-0225-1). South Asia Bks.

Dwivedi, A. N. Essentials of Hinduism, Jainism & Buddhism. 148p. 1979. 12.00 (ISBN 0-88065-083-4, Pub. by Messers Today & Tomorrows Printers & Publishers India). Scholarly Pubns.

Dwivedi, R. C. Contributions of Jainism to Indian Culture. 1975. 12.95 (ISBN 0-8426-0953-9). Orient Bk Dist.

Fischer, Eberhard & Jain, Jyotindra. Art & Rituals: Twenty Five Hundred Years of Jainism in India. LC 78-670055. (Illus.). 1977. 20.00 (ISBN 0-89684-369-6). Orient Bk Dist.

Ghosh, A. Jaina Art & Architecture, 3 vols. (Illus.). 1974. Set. text ed. 110.00x. Coronet Bks.

Homage to Shravana Belgola. 1981. 35.00x (ISBN 0-8364-0761-X, Pub. by Marg India). South Asia Bks.

Jain, J. Life in Ancient India as Depicted in Jaina Canon & Commentaries. 2nd ed. 1984. text ed. 34.00x. Coronet Bks.

Jaini, Jagmandar L. Outlines of Jainism. Thomas, F. W., ed. LC 78-14128. (Illus.). 1981. Repr. of 1940 ed. 21.00 (ISBN 0-88355-801-7). Hyperion Conn.

Jaini, Manak C. Life of Mahavira. 1986. 8.00X (ISBN 0-8364-1559-0, Pub. by Academic India). South Asia Bks.

Jaini, Padmanabh S. The Jaina Path of Purification. LC 77-73496. 1979. 35.95x (ISBN 0-520-03459-7). U of Cal Pr.

Lalwani, K. C., tr. Jaina Stories. 1985. 15.00x (ISBN 0-317-31633-8, Pub. by Arthat Prakashon). South Asia Bks.

Marathe, M. P., et al, eds. Studies in Jainism. 267p. 1986. pap. 9.50X (ISBN 0-8364-1665-1, Pub. by Abhinav India). South Asia Bks.

Mookerjee, Satkari. The Jaina Philosophy of Non-Absolutism. 1978. 15.00 (ISBN 0-89684-021-2, Pub. by Motilal Banarsidass India). Orient Bk Dist.

--The Jaina Philosophy of Non-Absolutism. 2nd ed. 24.00x (ISBN 0-89684-021-2). South Asia Bks.

Nevaskar, Balwant S. Capitalists Without Capitalism: The Jains of India & the Quakers of the West. LC 72-98709. (Contributions in Sociology: No. 6). 1971. lib. bdg. 29.95 (ISBN 0-8371-3297-5, NCA/). Greenwood.

Pereira, Jose. Monolithic Jinas. 1977. 11.50 (ISBN 0-8426-1027-8, Pub. by Motilal Banarsidass India). Orient Bk Dist.

Sandal, Mohan L. Introduction to the Mimamsa Sutras of Jaimini. LC 73-3821. (Sacred Books of the Hindus: No. 28). Repr. of 1925 ed. 24.50 (ISBN 0-404-57828-4). AMS Pr.

Satyaprakash. Jainism: A Select Bibliography. 1984. 12.50x (ISBN 0-8364-1224-9, Pub. by Indian Doc Serv India). South Asia Bks.

Schubring, Walther. The Doctrine of the Jainas. Buerlen, Wolfgang, tr. 1978. Repr. 15.00 (ISBN 0-89684-005-0, Pub. by Motilal Banarsidass India). Orient Bk Dist.

Schweitzer, Albert. Indian Thought & Its Development. 1962. 11.00 (ISBN 0-8446-2893-X). Peter Smith.

Singh, R. B. Jainism in Early Medieval Karnataka. 1976. 9.95 (ISBN 0-8426-0981-4). Orient Bk Dist.

Umasvati. Tattvarthadhigama Sutra (A Treatise on the Essential Principles of Jainism) Jaini, J. L., ed. & intro. by. LC 73-3836. (Sacred Books of the Jainas: No. 2). Repr. of 1920 ed. 21.50 (ISBN 0-404-57702-4). AMS Pr.

JAINS

Caillat, Collette. Jain Cosmology. (Illus.). 192p. 1982. 55.00 (ISBN 0-517-54662-0, Harmony). Crown.

Ghoshal, Sarat C., ed. The Sacred Books of the Jainas (Bibliotheca Jainica, 11 vols. Repr. of 1940 ed. 324.00 (ISBN 0-404-19549-0). AMS Pr.

Roy, A. K. A History of the Jainas. 1984. 22.50x (ISBN 0-8364-1136-6, Pub. by Gitanjali Prakashan). South Asia Bks.

Sanghavi, Vilas. Jaina Community. 2nd ed. 455p. 1980. 29.95 (ISBN 0-317-12346-7, Pub. by Popular Pubns India). Asia Bk Corp.

JALAL AL-DIN RUMI, MAWLANA, 1207-1273

Aflaki. The Whirling Ecstasy. Huart, C., tr. (Illus.). 30p. (Orig.). 1973. pap. 1.95 (ISBN 0-915424-02-9, Prophecy Pressworks). Sufi Islamia-Prophecy.

Hakim, Khalifa A. The Metaphysics of Rumi. 157p. 1981. pap. 3.95 (ISBN 0-88004-004-1). Sunwise Turn.

JAMES 1ST, KING OF GREAT BRITAIN, 1566-1625

Donne, John. Pseudo-Martyr. LC 74-16215. 450p. 1974. 60.00x (ISBN 0-8201-1140-6). Schol Facsimiles.

Gordon, John. Englands & Scotlands Happiness in Being Reduced to Unitie of Religion. LC 75-38190. (English Experience Ser.: No. 461). 50p. 1972. Repr. of 1604 ed. 7.00 (ISBN 90-221-0461-3). Walter J Johnson.

Parsons, Robert. The Judgment of a Catholicke English-Man Living in Banishment for His Religion. LC 57-9033. 1978. Repr. of 1608 ed. 30.00x (ISBN 0-8201-1240-2). Schol Facsimiles.

Rose, Elliot. Cases of Conscience: Alternatives Open to Recusants & Puritans under Elizabeth I & James I. LC 74-76947. pap. 68.50 (2027243). Bks Demand UMI.

JAMES, SAINT, APOSTLE

Christensen, Chuck & Christensen, Winnie. James: Faith in Action. LC 75-33442. (Fisherman Bible Studyguide Ser.). 55p. 1975. saddle-stitched 2.95 (ISBN 0-87788-421-8). Shaw Pubs.

King, Georgianna G. The Way of St. James, 3 vols. LC 78-63469. Repr. of 1920 ed. Set. 140.00 (ISBN 0-404-17160-5). AMS Pr.

Lightner, Robert P. James: Apostle of Practical Christianity. LC 81-70775. (The Chosen Messengers Ser.). 128p. (Orig.). 1982. pap. text ed. 3.50 (ISBN 0-89636-079-2). Accent Bks.

JAMES, WILLIAM, 1842-1910

Fontinell, Eugene. Self, God & Immortality: A Jamesian Investigation. 320p. 1986. 34.95 (ISBN 0-87722-428-5). Temple U Pr.

Levinson, Henry S. Science, Metaphysics, & the Chance of Salvation: An Interpretation of the Thought of William James. LC 78-7383. 1978. pap. 9.95 (ISBN 0-89130-234-4, 01-01-24). Scholars Pr GA.

Levinson, Henry S. & Levering, Ralph. The Religious Investigations of William James. LC 80-26109. (Studies in Religion). xii, 316p. 1981. 27.50x (ISBN 0-8078-1468-7). U of NC Pr.

Sahay, R. R. Religious Philosophy of William James. 1980. text ed. 18.95x. Coronet Bks.

Vanden Burgt, Robert J. The Religious Philosophy of William James. LC 80-22936. 176p. 1981. text ed. 19.95x (ISBN 0-88229-594-2); pap. text ed. 9.95x (ISBN 0-88229-767-8). Nelson-Hall.

JANSENISTS

see also Old Catholic Church

Clark, Ruth. Strangers & Sojourners at Port Royal. 1972. lib. bdg. 26.00x (ISBN 0-374-91664-0, Octagon). Hippocrene Bks.

De Sainte-Beuve, Charles-Augustin. Port-Royal, 3 tomes. 1953-1955. Set. 79.95 (ISBN 0-685-11502-X). French & Eur.

Mikkelsen, M. A. The Bishop Hill Colony, a Religious Communistic Settlement in Henry County, Illinois. pap. 9.00 (ISBN 0-384-38850-7). Johnson Repr.

--The Bishop Hill Colony: A Religious, Communistic Settlement in Henry County, Illinois. LC 72-187466. (The American Utopian Adventure Ser.). 1973. Repr. of 1892 ed. lib. bdg. 19.50x (ISBN 0-87991-014-3). Porcupine Pr.

Neale, John M. A History of the So-Called Jansenist Church of Holland. LC 71-133820. Repr. of 1858 ed. 26.50 (ISBN 0-404-04656-8). AMS Pr.

Pascal, Blaise. Les Provinciales. 1966. 4.95 (ISBN 0-686-54852-3). French & Eur.

Pascal, Blaise & Adam, Antoine. Lettres Escrites a un Provincial. 320p. 1967. 4.50 (ISBN 0-686-54847-7). French & Eur.

Saint-Beuve. Port Royal, 3 vols. Vol. 1. 37.50 (ISBN 0-686-56564-9); Vol. 2. 37.50 (ISBN 0-686-56565-7); Vol. 3. 35.95 (ISBN 0-686-56566-5). French & Eur.

Sedgwick, Alexander. Jansenism in Seventeenth-Century France: Voices from the Wilderness. LC 77-2812. 243p. 1977. 20.00x (ISBN 0-8139-0702-0). U Pr of Va.

Van Kley, Dale. The Jansenists & the Expulsion of the Jesuits from France, 1757-1765. LC 74-26390. (Yale Historical Publication. Miscellany Ser.: No. 107). pap. 70.50 (ISBN 0-317-09445-9, 2022046). Bks Demand UMI.

JAPAN–CHURCH HISTORY

Boxer, C. R. The Christian Century in Japan: Fifteen Forty-Nine to Sixteen Fifty. (California Library Reprint Ser: No. 51). (Illus.). 552p. 1974. Repr. of 1967 ed. 49.50x (ISBN 0-520-02702-7). U of Cal Pr.

Hammer, Raymond. Japan's Religious Ferment: Christian Presence Amid Faiths Old & New. LC 85-14867. (Christian Presence Ser.). 207p. 1985. Repr. of 1962 ed. lib. bdg. 39.75x (ISBN 0-313-24921-0, HAJR). Greenwood.

JAPAN–CIVILIZATION

Hearn, Lafcadio. Kokoro: Hints & Echoes of Japanese Inner Life. LC 79-184814. 1972. pap. 6.50 (ISBN 0-8048-1035-4). C E Tuttle.

--Kokoro: Hints & Echoes of Japanese Inner Life. Repr. of 1896 ed. lib. bdg. 22.50x (ISBN 0-8371-1633-3, HEKO). Greenwood.

Mackenzie, Donald A. The Myths of China & Japan. LC 77-6878. 1977. Repr. of 1923 ed. lib. bdg. 45.00 (ISBN 0-89341-149-3). Longwood Pub Group.

Suzuki, D. T. Zen & Japanese Culture. (Bollingen Ser.: Vol. 64). (Illus.). 1959. 52.00x (ISBN 0-691-09849-2); pap. 10.95x (ISBN 0-691-01770-0). Princeton U Pr.

JAPAN–RELIGION

Anesaki, Masaharu. History of Japanese Religion. LC 63-19395. 1963. Repr. of 1930 ed. 23.50 (ISBN 0-8048-0248-3). C E Tuttle.

Ashton, W. G. Shinto: The Ancient Religion of Japan. 83p. 1921. 0.95 (ISBN 0-317-40426-1). Open Court.

Basabe, Fernando M. Religious Attitudes of Japanese Men. LC 68-57415. 1969. bds. 15.00 (ISBN 0-8048-0651-9). C E Tuttle.

Batchelor, John. The Ainu of Japan: The Religion, Superstitions, & General History of the Hairy Aborigines of Japan. 26.00 (ISBN 0-8369-7153-1, 7985). Ayer Co Pubs.

Bellah, Robert N. Tokugawa Religion. 272p. pap. 9.95 (ISBN 0-02-902460-9). Free Pr.

Blacker, Carmen. The Catalpa Bow: A Study of Shamanistic Practices in Japan. 2nd ed. (Illus.). 382p. 1986. pap. 14.95 (ISBN 0-04-398008-2). Allen Unwin.

Bunce, William K., ed. Religions in Japan. LC 59-9234. 216p. 1981. pap. 5.25 (ISBN 0-8048-0500-8). C E Tuttle.

Cary, Otis. History of Christianity in Japan, Roman Catholic & Greek Orthodox Missions, 2 Vols. 1971. Repr. of 1909 ed. Set. 18.00 (ISBN 0-403-00252-4). Scholarly.

Davis, Roy E. Miracle Man of Japan: The Life & Work of Masaharu Taniguchi, One of the Most Influential Spiritual Leaders of Our Time. (Illus.). 160p. (Orig.). pap. 3.00 (ISBN 0-87707-048-2). CSA Pr.

Earhart, H. Byron. Japanese Religion: Unity & Diversity. 3rd ed. 288p. 1982. pap. text ed. write for info. (ISBN 0-534-01028-8). Wadsworth Pub.

Ellwood, Robert S. & Pilgrim, Richard. Japanese Religion: A Cultural Perspective. (Illus.). 192p. 1985. pap. text ed. 16.00 (ISBN 0-13-509282-5). P-H.

Folk Religion & Spiritual Belief in Modernizing Japan. 23p. 1979. pap. 5.00 (ISBN 92-808-0108-2, TUNU078, UNU). Bernan-Unipub.

Griffis, William E. Religions of Japan: From the Dawn of History to the Era of Meiji. facsimile ed. LC 70-37469. (Essay Index Reprint Ser). Repr. of 1895 ed. 21.00 (ISBN 0-8369-2550-5). Ayer Co Pubs.

Guthrie, Stewart E. A Japanese New Religion: Rissho Kosei-Kai in a Mountain Hamlet. LC 86-33446. (Michigan Papers in Japanese Studies: No. 16). 1987. text ed. 20.00 (ISBN 0-939512-33-5); pap. 10.00 (ISBN 0-939512-34-3). U Mi Japan.

Hammer, Raymond. Japan's Religious Ferment: Christian Presence Amid Faiths Old & New. LC 85-14867. (Christian Presence Ser.). 207p. 1985. Repr. of 1962 ed. lib. bdg. 39.75x (ISBN 0-313-24921-0, HAJR). Greenwood.

Hardacre, Helen. Kurozumikyo & the New Religions of Japan. LC 85-43287. (Illus.). 232p. 1986. text ed. 28.00 (ISBN 0-691-06675-2). Princeton U Pr.

--The Religion of Japan's Korean Minority: The Preservation of Ethnic Identity. (Korea Research Monographs: No. 9). (Illus.). 155p. (Orig.). 1984. pap. text ed. 12.00x (ISBN 0-912966-67-X). IEAS.

Hashim Amir-Ali. Message of the Qur'an: Presented in Perspective. LC 73-84906. 1974. 25.00 (ISBN 0-8048-0976-3). C E Tuttle.

Hearn, Lafcadio. Glimpses of Unfamiliar Japan, 2 Vols. LC 70-101093. Repr. of 1894 ed. 32.50 (ISBN 0-404-03205-2). AMS Pr.

Hori, Ichiro. Folk Religion in Japan: Continuity & Change. Kitagawa, Joseph M. & Miller, Alan L., eds. LC 67-30128. (Midway Reprint Ser.). xvi, 278p. 1983. pap. text ed. 15.00x (ISBN 0-226-35335-4). U of Chicago Pr.

Japanese Religion: A Survey by the Agency for Cultural Affairs. LC 80-85584. (Illus.). 272p. 1981. pap. 6.25 (ISBN 0-87011-467-0). Kodansha.

Kitagawa, Joseph M. Religion in Japanese History. LC 65-23669. 475p. 1966. 35.00x (ISBN 0-231-02834-2). Columbia U Pr.

Knox, George W. The Development of Religion in Japan. LC 78-72456. Repr. of 1907 ed. 27.00 (ISBN 0-404-17325-X). AMS Pr.

Lebra, William P. Okinawan Religion: Belief, Ritual, & Social Structure. 256p. 1985. pap. text ed. 8.95x (ISBN 0-87022-450-6). Uh Pr.

McFarland, H. Neill. Rush Hour of the Gods. 1967. 11.95x (ISBN 0-02-583200-X). Macmillan.

Morioka, Kiyomi. Religion in Changing Japanese Society. 231p. 1975. 29.50 (ISBN 0-86008-131-1, Pub. by U of Tokyo Japan). Columbia U Pr.

Murakami, Shigeyoshi. Japanese Religion in the Modern Century. Earhart, H. Byron, tr. 186p. 1979. 18.50x (ISBN 0-86008-260-1, Pub. by U of Tokyo Japan). Columbia U Pr.

Nanjio, Bunyiu, tr. from Japanese. Short History of the Twelve Buddhist Sects. (Studies in Japanese History & Civilization). 1979. Repr. of 1886 ed. 19.75 (ISBN 0-89093-252-2). U Pubns Amer.

Norbeck, Edward. Religion & Society in Modern Japan. (Rice University Studies: Vol. 56, No. 1). 232p. 1970. pap. 10.00x (ISBN 0-89263-203-8). Rice Univ.

Okakura, Y. The Japanese Spirit. lib. bdg. 79.95 (ISBN 0-87968-549-2). Krishna Pr.

Ono, Sokyo. Shinto: The Kami Way. LC 61-14033. 1962. 8.50 (ISBN 0-8048-0525-3). C E Tuttle.

Palmer, Aaron H. Documents & Facts Illustrating the Origin of the Mission to Japan. LC 72-82105. (Japan Library Ser.). 1973. Repr. of 1857 ed. lib. bdg. 11.00 (ISBN 0-8420-1399-7). Scholarly Res Inc.

Paske-Smith, Montague, ed. Japanese Traditions of Christianity: Being Some Old Translations from the Japanese, with British Consular Reports of the Persecutions of 1868-1872. (Studies in Japanese History & Civilization). 1979. Repr. of 1930 ed. 17.50 (ISBN 0-89093-257-3). U Pubns Amer.

Picken, Stuart D. Christianity & Japan: Meeting, Conflict, Hope. LC 82-48787. (Illus.). 80p. 1983. 18.95 (ISBN 0-87011-571-5). Kodansha.

Pye, Michael. Zen & Modern Japanese Religions. 1985. 13.00 (ISBN 0-7062-3148-1, Pub. by Ward Lock Educ Co Ltd). State Mutual Bk.

Supreme Commander for the Allied Powers. Civil Information & Education Section. Religions in Japan: Buddhism, Shinto, Christianity. LC 77-13855. 1978. Repr. of 1955 ed. lib. bdg. 22.50x (ISBN 0-8371-9874-7, SURJ). Greenwood.

Thelle, Notto R. Buddhism & Christianity in Japan: From Conflict to Dialogue, 1854-1899. (Illus.). 384p. 1987. text ed. 30.00x. UH Pr.

Thomsen, Harry. The New Religions of Japan. LC 77-13846. (Illus.). 1978. Repr. of 1963 ed. lib. bdg. 25.75x (ISBN 0-8371-9878-X, THNR). Greenwood.

Yamamori, Tetsunao. Church Growth in Japan. LC 74-4009. (Illus.). 184p. (Orig.). 1974. pap. 4.95 (ISBN 0-87808-412-6). William Carey Lib.

JAPANESE FOLK-LORE

see Folk-Lore, Japanese

JAPANESE LEGENDS

see Legends, Japanese

JASPER, JOHN, 1812-1901

Hatcher, W. John Jasper: Negro Philosopher & Preacher. 59.95 (ISBN 0-8490-0452-7). Gordon Pr.

Hatcher, William E. John Jasper, the Unmatched Negro Philosopher & Preacher. LC 71-88413. Repr. of 1908 ed. 22.50x (ISBN 0-8371-1842-5, HAJ&, Pub. by Negro U Pr). Greenwood.

JASPERS, KARL, 1883-1969

Ehrlich, Leonard H. Karl Jaspers: Philosophy As Faith. LC 73-79505. 292p. 1975. 20.00x (ISBN 0-87023-153-7). U of Mass Pr.

Samay, Sebastian. Reason Revisited: The Philosophy of Karl Jaspers. LC 72-160423. pap. 79.50 (ISBN 0-317-26140-1, 2024371). Bks Demand UMI.

Wallraff, Charles F. Karl Jaspers: An Introduction to His Philosophy. 1970. 27.50 (ISBN 0-691-07164-0); pap. 10.50 (ISBN 0-691-01971-1). Princeton U Pr.

JEANNE D'ARC, SAINT, 1412-1431

Barstow, Anne L. Joan of Arc: Heretic, Mystic, Shaman. LC 86-12756. (Studies in Women & Religion: No. 17). (Illus.). 156p. 1986. lib. bdg. 49.95 (ISBN 0-88946-532-0). E Mellen.

Beevers, John. St. Joan of Arc. 1974. pap. 5.00 (ISBN 0-89555-043-1). TAN Bks Pubs.

Clemens, Samuel L. Personal Recollections of Joan of Arc by the Sieur Louis De Conte. LC 80-23663. (Illus.). xiv, 461p. 1980. Repr. of 1906 ed. lib. bdg. 60.50x (ISBN 0-313-22373-4, CLPR). Greenwood.

Cristiani, Leon. St. Joan of Arc, Virgin-Soldier. 1977. 3.95 (ISBN 0-8198-0465-7); pap. 2.95 (ISBN 0-8198-0466-5). Dghtrs St Paul.

De Monstrelet, Enguerrend. Chronique D'Enguerrand De Monstrelet, 6 Vols. Douet D'Arcq, L., ed. 1857-62. Set. 255.00 (ISBN 0-384-39781-6); Set. pap. 220.00 (ISBN 0-384-39780-8). Johnson Repr.

Jeanne D'Arc, Saint. Proces De Condamnation et De Rehabilitation De Jeanne D'Arc, 5 Vols. Quicherat, Jules, ed. 1841-1849. Set. 230.00 (ISBN 0-384-27070-0); Set. pap. 200.00 (ISBN 0-384-27071-9). Johnson Repr.

Michelet, Jules. Joan of Arc. Guerard, Albert, tr. 1957. pap. 6.95 (ISBN 0-472-06122-4, 122, AA). U of Mich Pr.

Oliphant, Margaret O. Jeanne d'Arc. LC 73-14460. (Heroes of the Nations Series). Repr. of 1896 ed. 30.00 (ISBN 0-404-58278-8). AMS Pr.

Pernoud, Regine. Joan of Arc: By Herself & Her Witnesses. LC 66-24807. 1969. pap. 10.95 (ISBN 0-8128-1260-3). Stein & Day.

Sabatini, Rafael. Heroic Lives. facs. ed. LC 70-99648. (Essay Index Reprint Ser.). 1934. 19.50 (ISBN 0-8369-2071-6). Ayer Co Pubs.

Sackville-West, V. Saint Joan of Arc. LC 84-9125. 416p. 1984. pap. 7.95 (ISBN 0-8398-2856-X, Gregg). G K Hall.

Warner, Marina. Joan of Arc: The Image of Female Heroism. LC 80-2720. (Illus.). 1981. 19.95 (ISBN 0-394-41145-5). Knopf.

--Joan of Arc: The Image of Female Heroism. LC 81-69565. (Illus.). 400p. 1982. pap. 9.95 (ISBN 0-394-75333-X, Vin). Random.

JEANNE D'ARC, SAINT, 1412-1431–DRAMA

Anouilh, Jean. Alouette. 1963. pap. 3.95 (ISBN 0-685-10991-7, 1153). French & Eur.

--Lark. Fry, Christopher, tr. 1956. 10.95x (ISBN 0-19-500393-4). Oxford U Pr.

Nieto, J. C. Mystic, Rebel, Saint: A Study on St. Joan of the Cross. (Illus.). 148p. (Orig.). 1979. pap. text ed. 38.00x (Pub. by Droz Switzerland). Coronet Bks.

Searle, William. The Saint & the Skeptics: Joan of Arc in the World of Mark Twain, Anatole France, & Bernard Shaw. LC 75-26709. 178p. 1976. text ed. 22.50x (ISBN 0-8143-1541-0). Wayne St U Pr.

Shaw, Bernard. Saint Joan, a Screenplay. Dukore, Bernard F., ed. LC 68-11039. (Illus.). 224p. 1968. 15.00x (ISBN 0-295-97885-6); pap. 5.95x (ISBN 0-295-95072-2, WP56). U of Wash Pr.

--Saint Joan, Major Barbara, Androcles. Bd. with Major Barbara; Androcles & the Lion. LC 56-5413. 6.95 (ISBN 0-394-60480-6). Modern Lib.

Shaw, George Bernard. Saint Joan. (Penguin Plays Ser.). (YA) 1950. pap. 2.95 (ISBN 0-14-048005-6). Penguin.

Von Schiller, Friedrich. Maiden of Orleans. 2nd rev. ed. Krumpelmann, John T., tr. LC 63-62703. (North Carolina. University. Studies in the Germanic Languages & Literatures: No. 37). Repr. of 1962 ed. 18.50 (ISBN 0-404-50937-1). AMS Pr.

JEANNE D'ARC, SAINT, 1412-1431–JUVENILE LITERATURE

Daughters Of St. Paul. Wind & Shadows. (Encounter Ser.). 3.00 (ISBN 0-8198-0174-7); pap. 2.00 (ISBN 0-8198-0175-5). Dghtrs St Paul.

Ready, Dolores. Joan, the Brave Soldier: Joan of Arc. LC 77-86597. (Stories About Christian Heroes). (Illus.). 1977. pap. 1.95 (ISBN 0-86683-764-7, HarpR). Har-Row.

Storr, Catherine. Joan of Arc. LC 84-18346. (Raintree Stories Ser.). (Illus.). 32p. 1985. PLB 14.65 (ISBN 0-8172-2111-5); pap. 9.27 (ISBN 0-8172-2254-5). Raintree Pubs.

JEFFERSON, THOMAS, PRES. U. S., 1743-1826

Adams, Dickinson W., ed. Jefferson's Extracts from the Gospels: "The Philosophy of Jesus" & "The Life & Morals of Jesus". LC 82-61371. (The Papers of Thomas Jefferson, Second Ser.). 456p. 1986. text ed. 31.50 (ISBN 0-691-04699-9); pap. text ed. 14.50 (ISBN 0-691-10210-4). Princeton U Pr.

Jayne, Allen. The Religious & Moral Wisdom of Thomas Jefferson: An Anthology. 1984. 12.95 (ISBN 0-533-05800-7). Vantage.

Sanford, Charles B. The Religious Life of Thomas Jefferson. LC 83-21649. 246p. 1984. 13.95x (ISBN 0-8139-0996-1). U Pr of Va.

JEHOVAH, SERVANT OF

see Servant of Jehovah

JEHOVAH'S WITNESSES

Beier, Lucinda. Mormans, Jehovah's Witnesses & Christian Scientists. 1985. 13.00x (ISBN 0-7062-3880-X, Pub. by Ward Lock Educ Co Ltd). State Mutual Bk.

Bergman, Jerry. Jehovah's Witness & Kindred Groups: An Historical Compendium & Bibliography. LC 83-47603. (Social Science Ser.). 414p. 1985. lib. bdg. 58.00 (ISBN 0-8240-9109-4). Garland Pub.

Bjornstad, James. Counterfeits at Your Door. LC 78-72864. 160p. 1979. pap. text ed. 2.95 (ISBN 0-8307-0610-0, S124254). Regal.

Botting, Heather & Botting, Gary. The Orwellian World of Jehovah's Witnesses. (Illus.). 224p. 1984. pap. 10.95 (ISBN 0-8020-6545-7). U of Toronto Pr.

Bowser, Arthur M. What Every Jehovah's Witness Should Know. 1975. micro book 1.95 (ISBN 0-916406-35-0). Accent Bks.

Cetnar, William & Cetnar, Jean. Questions for Jehovah's Witnesses. 1983. pap. 3.95 (ISBN 0-87552-162-2). Presby & Reformed.

Chretien, Leonard & Chretien, Marjorie. Witnesses of Jehovah. 208p. (Orig.). 1987. pap. 6.95 (ISBN 0-89081-587-9). Harvest Hse.

Countess, Robert H. The Jehovah's Witnesses' New Testament: A Critical Analysis. 1982. pap. 5.95 (ISBN 0-87552-210-6). Presby & Reformed.

Dencher, Ted. Why I Left Jehovah's Witnesses. 1966. pap. 5.95 (ISBN 0-87508-183-5). Chr Lit.

Duggar, Gordon E. Jehovah's Witness: Not Just Another Denomination. (Illus.). 144p. 1982. 8.00 (ISBN 0-682-49874-2). Exposition Pr FL.

--Jehovah's Witnesses: Watchout for the Watchtower! 144p. 1985. pap. 5.95 (ISBN 0-8010-2955-4). Baker Bk.

Franz, Raymond. Crisis of Conscience: The Struggle between Loyalty to God & Loyalty to One's Religion. LC 83-62637. (Illus.). 384p. 1983. 10.95 (ISBN 0-914675-00-1); pap. 7.95 (ISBN 0-914675-03-6). Comment Pr.

Gerstner, John H. Teachings of Jehovah's Witnesses. pap. 1.95 (ISBN 0-8010-3718-2). Baker Bk.

Gruss, Edmond C. Jehovah's Witnesses & Prophetic Speculation. pap. 5.95 (ISBN 0-8010-3710-7). Baker Bk.

--Jehovah's Witnesses & Prophetic Speculation. 1972. pap. 5.95 (ISBN 0-87552-306-4). Presby & Reformed.

--We Left Jehovah's Witnesses. pap. 5.95 (ISBN 0-8010-3696-8). Baker Bk.

--We Left Jehovah's Witnesses: A Non-Prophet Organization. 1974. pap. 5.95 (ISBN 0-87552-307-2). Presby & Reformed.

Hartog, John. Enduring to the End: Jehovah's Witnesses & Bible Doctrine. 200p. 1987. pap. write for info. (ISBN 0-87227-118-8). Reg Baptist.

Hewitt, Joe B. I Was Raised a Jehovah's Witness. LC 78-73255. 1979. pap. 3.95 (ISBN 0-89636-018-0). Accent Bks.

Hickman, Richard, ed. A Jehovah's Witness Finds the Truth. 115p. (Orig.). 1983. pap. 4.95 (ISBN 0-914605-00-3). Love Agape Min.

Hoekema, Anthony A. The Four Major Cults. 1963. 24.95 (ISBN 0-8028-3117-6). Eerdmans.

--Jehovah's Witnesses. 1974. pap. 4.95 (ISBN 0-8028-1489-1). Eerdmans.

Kern, Herbert. How to Respond to Jehovah's Witnesses. (The Response Ser.). 1977. 1.95 (ISBN 0-570-07679-X, 12-2664). Concordia.

Kirban, Salem. Jehovah's Witnesses. (Illus.). 1972. pap. 4.95 (ISBN 0-912582-03-0). Kirban.

Lambert, O. C. Russellism Unveiled. 1940. pap. 3.50 (ISBN 0-88027-090-X). Firm Foun Pub.

Lewis, Gordon. Bible, Christians & Jehovah's Witnesses. pap. 1.25 (ISBN 0-8010-5568-7). Baker Bk.

Lindsay, Gordon. What About Jehovah's Witnesses? 1.25 (ISBN 0-89985-017-0). Christ Nations.

Magnani, Duane & Barrett, Arthur. The Watchtower Files. 340p. (Orig.). 1985. pap. 6.95 (ISBN 0-87123-816-0, 210816). Bethany Hse.

Martin, Walter. Jehovah's Witnesses. 64p. 1969. pap. 2.95 (ISBN 0-87123-270-7, 210270). Bethany Hse.

Martin, Walter & Klann, Norman H. Jehovah of the Watchtower. 192p. 1981. pap. 5.95 (ISBN 0-87123-267-7, 210267). Bethany Hse.

Morey, Robert A. How to Answer a Jehovah's Witness. LC 79-25502. 112p. (Orig.). 1980. pap. 3.95 (ISBN 0-87123-206-5, 210206). Bethany Hse.

Nelson, M. W. Los Testigos de Jehova. 130p. 1984. pap. 2.50 (ISBN 0-311-06352-7). Casa Bautista.

Passantino, Robert, et al. Answers to the Cultist at Your Door. LC 80-83850. 1981. pap. 5.95 (ISBN 0-89081-275-6). Harvest Hse.

Price, E. B. Is It the Watchtower? LC 67-30889. 1967. pap. 1.25 (ISBN 0-8163-0106-9, 09665-1). Pacific Pr Pub Assn.

Reed, David A. Jehovah's Witnesses Answered Verse By Verse. 1987. pap. 5.95 (ISBN 0-8010-7739-7). Baker Bk.

Rumble, Leslie. The Incredible Creed of the Jehovah Witnesses. 1977. pap. 0.60 (ISBN 0-89555-025-3). TAN Bks Pubs.

Schnell, William J. How to Witness to a Jehovah's Witness. Orig. Title: Christians, Awake! 160p. 1975. pap. 3.95 (ISBN 0-8010-8048-7). Baker Bk.

--Jehovah's Witnesses Errors Exposed. pap. 6.95 (ISBN 0-8010-8074-6). Baker Bk.

--Thirty Years a Watchtower Slave. (Direction Bks). pap. 3.95 (ISBN 0-8010-7933-0). Baker Bk.

Sustar, T. David. Witnessing to Jehovah's Witnessess. (Truthway Ser.). 31p. (Orig.). 1981. pap. text ed. 1.25 (ISBN 0-87148-915-5). Pathway Pr.

JEREMIAH THE PROPHET

Blank, Sheldon. Jeremiah, Man & Prophet. 1961. 12.50x (ISBN 0-87820-100-9, Pub. by Hebrew Union). Ktav.

Fettke, Steven M. Messages to a Nation in Crisis: An Introduction to the Prophecy of Jeremiah. LC 82-19997. (Illus.). 72p. (Orig.). 1983. pap. text ed. 7.75 (ISBN 0-8191-2839-2). U Pr of Amer.

Holladay, William L. Jeremiah: Spokesman Out of Time. LC 74-7052. 160p. 1974. pap. 5.95 (ISBN 0-8298-0283-5). Pilgrim NY.

Janzen, John G. Studies in the Text of Jeremiah. LC 73-81265. (Harvard Semitic Monographs: Vol. 6). pap. 64.00 (ISBN 0-317-09145-X, 2021591). Bks Demand UMI.

Lindsay, Gordon. Isaiah & Jeremiah. (Old Testament Ser.). 1.25 (ISBN 0-89985-155-X). Christ Nations.

Maurice, Frederick D. Theological Essays. 436p. (Orig.). Date not set. pap. write for info. (ISBN 0-87921-048-6). Attic Pr.

Meyer, F. B. Jeremiah. 1972. pap. 4.50 (ISBN 0-87508-355-2). Chr Lit.

Peterson, Eugene. Run with the Horses. LC 83-13005. 216p. (Orig.). 1983. pap. 6.95 (ISBN 0-87784-905-6). Inter-Varsity.

Rand, Howard B. Study in Jeremiah. 1947. 12.00 (ISBN 0-685-08816-2). Destiny.

JEROME, SAINT (HIERONYMUS, SAINT)

Berschin, Walter. Greek Letters & the Latin Middle Ages: From Jerome to Nicholas of Cusa. Frakes, Jerold C., tr. from Ger. Tr. of Griechisch-lateinisches mittelater von Hieronymus zu Nikolaus von Kues. 1987. price not set (ISBN 0-8132-0606-5). Cath U Pr.

Brewer, James W., Jr. Jerome. 15th ed. (Illus.). 1976. pap. 0.50 (ISBN 0-911408-16-9). SW Pks Mnmts.

Hornblower, Jane. Hieronymus of Cardia. (Classical & Philosophical Monographs). 1981. text ed. 52.00x (ISBN 0-19-814717-1). Oxford U Pr.

Jerome, Saint Letters of Saint Jerome, Vol. 1. Quasten & Burqhardt, eds. (Ancient Christian Writers Ser: Vol. 33). 1963. 11.95 (ISBN 0-8091-0087-8). Paulist Pr.

Rice, Eugene F., Jr. Saint Jerome in the Renaissance. LC 84-21321. (Symposia in Comparative History Ser.: No. 13). (Illus.). 272p. 1985. text ed. 24.00x (ISBN 0-8018-2381-1). Johns Hopkins.

JERUSALEM

Bovis, H. Eugene. Jerusalem Question: 1917-1968. LC 73-149796. (Studies Ser.: No. 29). (Illus.). 175p. 1971. 9.95x (ISBN 0-8179-3291-7). Hoover Inst Pr.

Collins, Larry & Lapierre, Dominique. O Jerusalem. 1980. pap. 3.95 (ISBN 0-671-83684-6). PB.

Coretto, Carlo, frwd. by. The Jerusalem Community: Rule of Life. 144p. (Orig.). 1985. pap. 5.95 (ISBN 0-8091-2712-1). Paulist Pr.

Elkins, Dov P., ed. Rejoice with Jerusalem. 1972. pap. 1.95 (ISBN 0-87677-065-0). Prayer BK.

Goldberg, Hillel. Wherever I Go, I Go to Jerusalem. 240p. 1986. 12.95 (ISBN 0-940646-09-9); pap. 8.95 (ISBN 0-940646-10-2). Rossel Bks.

Lindsey, Hal. A Prophetical Walk Through the Holy Land. LC 83-80121. 200p. 1983. text ed. 29.95 (ISBN 0-89081-381-7). Harvest Hse.

Loti, Pierre. Jerusalem. 15.00 (ISBN 0-8482-4859-7). Norwood Edns.

Malgo, Wim. Jerusalem: Focal Point of the World. 3.95 (ISBN 0-937422-08-8). Midnight Call.

Miller, J. Maxwell. Introducing the Holy Land. LC 82-14424. x, 189p. 1982. 13.95 (ISBN 0-86554-034-9, MUP-H38). Mercer Univ Pr.

Peters, F. E. Jerusalem & Mecca: The Typology of the Holy City in the Near East. 272p. 1987. 45.00 (ISBN 0-8147-6598-X). NYU Pr.

Prince, Lydia. Appointment in Jerusalem. 1975. 9.95 (ISBN 0-934920-24-9, B-26); pap. 5.95 (ISBN 0-934920-27-3, B 26A). Derek Prince.

Wilson, Evan M. Jerusalem, Key to Peace. LC 70-119026. (James Terry Duce Ser.: Vol. 2). 1970. 5.95 (ISBN 0-916808-08-4). Mid East Inst.

JERUSALEM–ANTIQUITIES

Couasnon, C. The Church of the Holy Sepulchre, Jerusalem. (Schweich Lectures on Biblical Archaeology). (Illus.). 62p. 1972. 10.25 (ISBN 0-85672-735-0, Pub. by British Acad). Longwood Pub Group.

Dever, William G. Gezer Two. 1974. 35.00x (ISBN 0-685-56198-4). Ktav.

Mare, W. Harold. Archaeology of the Jerusalem Area. 1986. 19.95 (ISBN 0-8010-6126-1). Baker Bk.

Merrill, Selah. Ancient Jerusalem. Davis, Moshe, ed. LC 77-70724. (America & the Holy Land Ser.). (Illus.). 1977. Repr. of 1908 ed. lib. bdg. 40.00x (ISBN 0-405-10267-4). Ayer Co Pubs.

O'Brien, Christian. The Genius of the Few: The Story of Those who Founded the Garden of Eden. 320p. 1985. pap. 12.95 (ISBN 0-85500-214-X). Newcastle Pub.

Pearlman, Moshe & Yannai, Yaacov. Historical Sites in the Holy Land. 286p. 1985. 16.95 (ISBN 0-8170-1086-6). Judson.

JERUSALEM–CHURCHES

Bludau, August. Die Pilgerreise der Aetheria. pap. 22.00 (ISBN 0-384-04760-2). Johnson Repr.

Duckworth, Henry T. The Church of the Holy Sepulchre. LC 78-63361. (BCL Ser.). (Illus.). Repr. of 1922 ed. 32.00 (ISBN 0-404-17014-5). AMS Pr.

Duncan, Alistair. The Noble Heritage: Jerusalem & Christianity - a Portrait of the Church of the Resurrection. 1974. 12.95x (ISBN 0-86685-011-2). Intl Bk Ctr.

JERUSALEM–DESCRIPTION

Davis, Moshe, ed. Holy Land Missions & Missionaries: An Original Anthology. LC 77-70703. (America & the Holy Land Ser.). (Illus.). 1977. lib. bdg. 20.00x (ISBN 0-405-10259-3). Ayer Co Pubs.

Gafni, Shlomo S. & Van der Heyden, A. The Glory of Jerusalem: An Explorer's Guide. LC 81-17053. 128p. 1982. o. p. 16.95 (ISBN 0-521-24613-X). Cambridge U Pr.

Ganz, Yaffa. Our Jerusalem. (Illus.). 1979. pap. 3.50x (ISBN 0-87441-308-7). Behrman.

Geyer, Paul, ed. Itinera Hierosolymitana, Saeculi 3-8. (Corpus Scriptorum Ecclesiasticorum Latinorum Ser: Vol. 39). Repr. of 1898 ed. 40.00 (ISBN 0-384-18270-4). Johnson Repr.

Hostetler, Marian. Journey to Jerusalem. LC 77-19347. (Illus.). 128p. 1978. pap. 3.95 (ISBN 0-8361-1848-0). Herald Pr.

Johnson, Sarah B. Hadji in Syria: Three Years in Jerusalem. Davis, Moshe, ed. LC 77-70708. (America & the Holy Land Ser.). (Illus.). 1977. Repr. of 1858 ed. lib. bdg. 26.50x (ISBN 0-405-10258-5). Ayer Co Pubs.

Le Strange, Guy, tr. Palestine under the Moslems. LC 70-180356. Repr. of 1890 ed. 47.50 (ISBN 0-404-56288-4). AMS Pr.

Leymarie, Jean, intro. by. The Jerusalem Windows of Marc Chagall. LC 62-18146. (Illus.). 120p. 1975. 15.00 (ISBN 0-8076-0423-2); pap. 9.95 (ISBN 0-8076-0807-6). Braziller.

Merrill, Selah. Ancient Jerusalem. Davis, Moshe, ed. LC 77-70724. (America & the Holy Land Ser.). (Illus.). 1977. Repr. of 1908 ed. lib. bdg. 40.00x (ISBN 0-405-10267-4). Ayer Co Pubs.

Odenheimer, William H. Jerusalem & Its Vicinity: Familiar Lectures on the Sacred Localities Connected with the Week Before the Resurrection. Davis, Moshe, ed. (America & the Holy Land Ser.). (Illus.). 1977. Repr. of 1855 ed. lib. bdg. 20.00x (ISBN 0-405-10272-0). Ayer Co Pubs.

Pearlman, Moshe & Yannai, Yaacov. Historical Sites in the Holy Land. 286p. 1985. 16.95 (ISBN 0-8170-1086-6). Judson.

Shaw, Lee H., Jr. How to Live Forever in the New Jerusalem. 56p. (Orig.). (YA) 1985. pap. 3.00x (ISBN 0-9614311-0-5). Elijah-John.

Timberlake, Henry. A True & Strange Discourse of the Travailes of Two English Pilgrimes. LC 74-80228. (English Experience Ser.: No. 699). 28p. 1974. Repr. of 1603 ed. 3.50 (ISBN 90-221-0699-3). Walter J Johnson.

Vester, Bertha H. Our Jerusalem: An American Family in the Holy City, 1881-1949. Davis, Moshe, ed. LC 77-70752. (America & the Holy Land Ser.). 1977. Repr. of 1950 ed. lib. bdg. 30.00x (ISBN 0-405-10296-8). Ayer Co Pubs.

Walker, Shoshana. Haggadah. 104p. 1982. 24.95 (ISBN 965-220-017-4, Carta Maps & Guides Pub Isreal). Hippocrene Bks.

Wallace, Edwin S. Jerusalem the Holy: History of Ancient Jerusalem with an Account of the Modern City & Its Conditions Political, Religious & Social. Davis, Moshe, ed. LC 77-70753. (America & the Holy Land Ser.). (Illus.). 1977. Repr. of 1898 ed. lib. bdg. 30.00x (ISBN 0-405-10298-4). Ayer Co Pubs.

Zangwill, Israel. The Voice of Jerusalem. 1976. lib. bdg. 59.95 (ISBN 0-8490-2801-9). Gordon Pr.

JERUSALEM–DESCRIPTION–GUIDEBOOKS

Clark, W. Joseph. The Holy Land. LC 86-61593. 204p. (Orig.). 1986. pap. 7.95 (ISBN 0-87973-546-5, 546). Our Sunday Visitor.

JERUSALEM–HISTORY

Baldwin, Marshall W. Raymond III of Tripolis & the the Fall of Jerusalem: 1140-1187. LC 76-29830. Repr. of 1936 ed. 28.50 (ISBN 0-404-15411-5). AMS Pr.

Bernadotte Af Wisborg, Folke G. To Jerusalem. LC 75-6424. (The Rise of Jewish Nationalism & the Middle East Ser.). 280p. 1975. Repr. of 1951 ed. 23.65 (ISBN 0-88355-311-2). Hyperion Conn.

Clifford, David. The Two Jerusalems in Prophecy. LC 78-14922. (Illus.). 1978. pap. 3.50 (ISBN 0-87213-081-9). Loizeaux.

Cohen, Amnon. Jewish Life under Islam: Jerusalem in the Sixteenth Century. (Illus.). 288p. 1984. text ed. 30.00x (ISBN 0-674-47436-8). Harvard U Pr.

Cohen, Saul B. Jerusalem: A Geopolitical Perspective. 1977. 10.00 (ISBN 0-930832-54-X). Herzl Pr.

Ganz, Yaffa. Our Jerusalem. (Illus.). 1979. pap. 3.50x (ISBN 0-87441-308-7). Behrman.

Gerlitz, Menaham. The Heavenly City. Weinbach, Sheindel, tr. from Hebrew. Tr. of Yerushalayim Shel Ma'ala. 1978. 6.95 (ISBN 0-87306-147-0). Feldheim.

Gulston, Charles. Jerusalem: The Tragedy & the Triumph. 1977. 12.95 (ISBN 0-310-35510-9). Zondervan.

Jeremias, Joachim. Jerusalem in the Time of Jesus: An Investigation into Economic & Social Conditions During the New Testament Period. Cave, F. H. & Cave, C. H., trs. from Ger. LC 77-81530. 434p. 1975. pap. 7.95 (ISBN 0-8006-1136-5, 1-1136). Fortress.

Kraemer, Joel L., ed. Jerusalem: Problems & Prospects. LC 80-19418. 256p. 1980. 38.95 (ISBN 0-03-057733-0); pap. 17.95 (ISBN 0-03-057734-9). Praeger.

Mackowski, Richard M. Jerusalem: City of Jesus: An Exploration of the Traditions, Writings, & Remains of the Holy City from the Time of Christ. LC 79-28093. pap. 57.80 (ISBN 0-317-30152-7, 2025334). Bks Demand UMI.

New Jerusalem. 24p. (Orig.). 1982. pap. 0.95 (ISBN 0-937408-18-2). GMI Pubns Inc.

O'Rourke, David K. The Holy Land As Jesus Knew It: Its People, Customs & Religion. 160p. 1983. pap. 4.95 (ISBN 0-89243-182-2). Liguori Pubns.

Peters, F. E. Jerusalem: The Holy City in the Eyes of Chroniclers, Visitors, Pilgrims, & Prophets from the Days of Abraham to the Beginnings of Modern Times. LC 85-42699. (Illus.). 712p. 1985. 37.00 (ISBN 0-691-07300-7). Princeton U Pr.

Vincent, Hughes. Jerusalem, 2 vols. in 4. LC 78-63368. (The Crusades & Military Orders: Second Ser.). Repr. of 1926 ed. Set. 495.00 (ISBN 0-404-17060-9). AMS Pr.

Williams, Colin. Jerusalem: A Universal Cultural & Historical Resource. 18p. (Orig.). 1975. pap. text ed. 5.00 (ISBN 0-8191-5907-7, Pub. by Aspen Inst for Humanistic Studies). U Pr of Amer.

JERUSALEM–HISTORY–LATIN KINGDOM, 1099-1244

Ben-Ami, Aharon. Social Change in a Hostile Environment: The Crusaders' Kingdom of Jerusalem. (Princeton Studies on the Near East Ser.). (Illus.). 1969. 25.50x (ISBN 0-691-09344-X). Princeton U Pr.

Chalandon, Ferdinand. Histoire de la premiere croisade jusqu'a l'election de Godefroi de Bouillon. 380p. 1972. Repr. of 1925 ed. lib. bdg. 25.50 (ISBN 0-8337-0515-6). B Franklin.

Dodu, Gaston J. Histoire des institutions monarchiques dans le Royaume latin de Jerusalem, 1099-1291. LC 76-29820. (Fr.). Repr. of 1894 ed. 32.50 (ISBN 0-404-15415-8). AMS Pr.

Enlart, Camille. Les Monuments des Croises dans le Royaume de Jerusalem, 4 vols. LC 78-63336. (The Crusades & Military Orders: Second Ser.). Repr. of 1927 ed. Set. 495.00 (ISBN 0-404-17050-1). AMS Pr.

Richard, J. The Latin Kingdom of Jerusalem, 2 Pts. (Europe in the Middle Ages Selected Studies: Vol. 11). 514p. 1978. Set. 91.50 (ISBN 0-444-85092-9, North-Holland). Elsevier.

Richard, Jean. Le Royaume Latin de Jerusalem. LC 78-63359. (The Crusades & Military Orders: Second Ser.). Repr. of 1953 ed. 28.50 (ISBN 0-404-17029-3). AMS Pr.

JERUSALEM–TEMPLE

see also Tabernacle

Edersheim, Alfred. Temple, Its Ministry & Services. 1950. 5.95 (ISBN 0-8028-8133-5). Eerdmans.

Parrot, Andre. The Temple of Jerusalem. Hooke, Beatrice E., tr. from Fr. LC 85-8037. (Studies in Biblical Archaeology: No. 5). Tr. of Le Temple de Jerusalem. (Illus.). 112p. 1985. Repr. of 1957 ed. lib. bdg. 35.00x (ISBN 0-313-24224-0, PATJ). Greenwood.

JESUITS

Arnauld, Antoine. The Arrainment of the Whole Societie of Jesuites in Fraunce: Holden-the Twelfth & Thirteenth of July, 1594. LC 79-84084. (English Experience Ser.: No. 904). 68p. 1979. Repr. of 1594 ed. lib. bdg. 8.00 (ISBN 0-686-71069-X). Walter J Johnson.

Arrupe, Pedro. One Jesuit's Spiritual Journey: Autobiographical Conversations with Jean-Claude Dietsch, S. J. Ganss, George E., frwd. by. Bradley, Ruth, tr. LC 84-81990. Orig. Title: Itineraire d'un Jesuite. Entretiens avec Jean-Claude Dietsch, S. J. 174p. 1986. 10.00 (ISBN 0-912422-69-6); smyth sewn 8.00 (ISBN 0-912422-68-8). Inst Jesuit.

--Other Apostolates Today: Selected Letters & Addresses - III. Aixala, Jerome, ed. LC 81-80741. 380p. 1981. 9.00 (ISBN 0-912422-81-5); pap. 8.00 smyth sewn (ISBN 0-912422-80-7). Inst Jesuit.

Aveling, J. C. The Jesuits. LC 81-40482. 396p. 1982. 19.95 (ISBN 0-8128-2838-0). Stein & Day.

Bangert, William. Claude Jay & Alfonso Salmeron: Two Early Jesuits. 1985. 15.95 (ISBN 0-8294-0459-7). Loyola.

Bangert, William V. A Bibliographical Essay on the History of the Society of Jesus. Ganss, George E., ed. LC 76-12667. (Study Aids on Jesuit Topics Ser.: No. 6). 72p. 1976. pap. 1.50 (ISBN 0-912422-16-5); Smyth Sewn. pap. 2.50 (ISBN 0-912422-21-1). Inst Jesuit.

--A History of the Society of Jesus. 2nd, rev. ed. Ganss, George E., ed. LC 85-80693. 587p. 1986. pap. 21.00 (ISBN 0-912422-73-4); smyth sewn 17.50 (ISBN 0-912422-74-2). Inst Jesuit.

Barthel, Manfred. The Jesuits: History & Legend of the Society of Jesus. Howson, Mark, tr. 324p. 1987. pap. 8.95 (ISBN 0-688-06970-3, Quill). Morrow.

--The Jesuits: Legend & Truth of the Society of Jesus - Yesterday, Today, Tomorrow. Howson, Mark, tr. LC 84-60446. (Illus.). 384p. 1984. 17.95 (ISBN 0-688-02861-6). Morrow.

Boehmer, H. The Jesuits. 69.95 (ISBN 0-87968-199-3). Gordon Pr.

Broderick, James. The Economic Morals of the Jesuits. LC 76-38248. (The Evolution of Capitalism Ser.). 168p. 1972. Repr. of 1934 ed. 12.00 (ISBN 0-405-04113-6). Ayer Co Pubs.

Brodrick, James. Origin of the Jesuits. LC 70-138604. 1971. Repr. of 1940 ed. lib. bdg. 22.50x (ISBN 0-8371-5523-1, BROJ). Greenwood.

--The Origin of the Jesuits. LC 83-45590. Date not set. Repr. of 1940 ed. 33.50 (ISBN 0-404-19883-X). AMS Pr.

Calvez, J. Y., et al. Conferences on the Chief Decrees of the Jesuit General Congregation XXXII: A Symposium by Some of Its Members. LC 76-2977. (Study Aids on Jesuit Topics Ser.: No. 4). 173p. 1976. smyth sewn 4.50 (ISBN 0-912422-17-3); pap. 3.50 (ISBN 0-912422-13-0). Inst Jesuit.

Campbell, Thomas J. The Jesuits, Fifteen Thirty-Four to Nineteen Twenty-One, 2 vols. 1977. lib. bdg. 250.00 (ISBN 0-8490-2093-X). Gordon Pr.

--Jesuits: Fifteen Thirty-Four to Nineteen Twenty-One. LC 77-82144. (Reprints Ser). 1970. Repr. of 1921 ed. lib. bdg. 45.00 (ISBN 0-87821-018-0). Milford Hse.

Campion, Donald R. & Louapre, Albert C., eds. Documents of the Thirty-Third General Congregation of the Society of Jesus: An English Translation of the Official Latin Texts. LC 84-80080. 116p. pap. 3.00 (ISBN 0-912422-64-5). Inst Jesuit.

Clancy, Thomas H. The Conversational Word of God: A Commentary on the Doctrine of St. Ignatius of Loyola Concerning Spiritual Conversation, with Four Early Jesuit Texts. Ganss, George E., frwd. by. LC 78-51343. (Study Aids on Jesuit Topics: No. 8 in Ser. IV). 83p. 1978. 5.00 (ISBN 0-912422-33-5); pap. 2.50 smyth sewn (ISBN 0-912422-34-3). Inst Jesuit.

--An Introduction to Jesuit Life: The Constitutions & History Through 435 Years. Ganss, George E., ed. LC 75-46080. (Study Aids on Jesuit Topics Ser.: No. 3). 422p. 1976. 12.00 (ISBN 0-912422-15-7). Inst Jesuit.

Culley, Thomas D. Jesuits & Music. 401p. 1970. 29.00 (ISBN 88-7041-582-1). Jesuit Hist.

D'Alembert, Jean. An Account of the Destruction of the Jesuits. 59.95 (ISBN 0-87968-575-1). Gordon Pr.

De Guibert, Joseph. The Jesuits: Their Spiritual Doctrine & Practice. Young, W. J., tr. LC 64-21430. 717p. 1964. pap. 15.00 (ISBN 0-912422-09-2). Inst Jesuit.

Derrick, Christopher. Words & the Word. 134p. 1987. pap. 6.95 (ISBN 0-89870-130-9). Ignatius Pr.

Diehl, Katharine S. Jesuits, Lutherans, & the Printing Press in South India. (Printers & Printing in the East Indies to 1850 Ser.: Vol. III). write for info. Caratzas.

Egan, Harvey D. The Spiritual Exercises & the Ignatian Mystical Horizon. LC 76-5742. (Study Aids on Jesuit Topics, Series 4: No. 5). xii, 216p. 1976. smyth sewn 7.00 (ISBN 0-912422-18-1); pap. 6.00 (ISBN 0-912422-14-9). Inst Jesuit.

Faase, Thomas P. Making the Jesuits More Modern. LC 81-40388. (Illus.). 478p. (Orig.). 1981. lib. bdg. 31.50 o. p. (ISBN 0-8191-1761-7); pap. text ed. 18.75 (ISBN 0-8191-1762-5). U Pr of Amer.

Fulop-Miller, Rene. The Power & Secret of the Jesuits. 1930. 29.50 (ISBN 0-8414-4288-6). Folcroft.

Futrell, John C. Making an Apostolic Community of Love: The Role of the Superior According to St. Ignatius of Loyola. LC 73-139365. (Original Studies Composed in English Ser.). 239p. 1970. smyth sewn 5.00 (ISBN 0-912422-19-X); pap. 4.00 (ISBN 0-912422-08-4). Inst Jesuit.

Ganss, George E., ed. Jesuit Religious Life Today: The Principal Features of its Spirit, in Excerpts... from Official Documents. LC 77-78816. (Jesuit Primary Sources in English Translation Ser.: No. 3). 190p. 1977. pap. 3.00 (ISBN 0-912422-27-0). Inst Jesuit.

Griesinger, Theodor. The Jesuits: A Complete History of Their Open & Secret Proceedings, 2 vols. 1977. Set. lib. bdg. 200.00 (ISBN 0-8490-2092-1). Gordon Pr.

Harris, Angela & Friedrich, Dick, eds. A Priest for All Reason: William B. Faherty 50 Years a Jesuit. LC 81-52127. (Illus., Orig.). 1981. pap. 6.95 (ISBN 0-933150-27-X). River City MO.

Hauser, Judith A. Jesuit Rings from Fort Michilimackinac & Other European Contact Sites. LC 83-100548. (Archaeological Completion Report Ser.: No. 5). (Illus.). 69p. (Orig.). 1983. pap. 5.00 (ISBN 0-911872-45-0). Mackinac Island.

Hughes, Thomas A. Loyola & the Educational System of the Jesuits. LC 83-45594. Date not set. Repr. of 1892 ed. 35.00 (ISBN 0-404-19887-2). AMS Pr.

--Loyola & the Educational Systems of the Jesuits. 1892. 39.00 (ISBN 0-403-00121-8). Scholarly.

Ignatius Of Loyola, St. The Constitutions of the Society of Jesus. Ganss, George E., tr. & commentary by. LC 72-108258. (Jesuit Primary Sources in English Translation Ser.: No. 1). 432p. 1970. pap. 12.00 smyth sewn (ISBN 0-912422-20-3). Inst Jesuit.

Iparraguirre, Ignacio. Contemporary Trends in Studies on the Constitutions of the Society of Jesus: Annotated Bibliographical Orientations. Ganss, George E., ed. Meenan, Daniel F., tr. from Span. LC 74-77120. (Study Aids on Jesuit Topics Ser.: No. 1). 96p. 1974. pap. 2.00 (ISBN 0-912422-10-6). Inst Jesuit.

Laverdiere & Casgrain, eds. Le Journal des Jesuites. (French-Canadian Civilization Ser.). (Fr.). Repr. of 1871 ed. lib. bdg. 46.00x (ISBN 0-697-00050-8). Irvington.

McCabe, Joseph. A Candid History of the Jesuits. 1977. lib. bdg. 59.95 (ISBN 0-8490-1567-7). Gordon Pr.

McCabe, William H. An Introduction to the Jesuit Theater: A Posthumous Work. Oldani, Louis J., intro. by. LC 83-81114. (Series III-Original Studies, Composed in English: No. 6). xxiv, 338p. 1983. pap. 19.00 smyth sewn (ISBN 0-912422-62-9). Inst Jesuit.

MacLagan, E. The Jesuits & the Great Mogul. LC 71-159212. 1971. Repr. of 1932 ed. lib. bdg. 26.00x (ISBN 0-374-95248-5, Octagon). Hippocrene Bks.

Martin, Malachi. The Jesuits: Revolt of Angels. 704p. 1987. 19.95 (ISBN 0-671-54505-1, Linden Pr). S&S.

Moore, James T. Indian & Jesuit: A Seventeenth Century Encounter. 1982. 12.95 (ISBN 0-8294-0395-7). Loyola.

Negri, Giulio. Istoria Degli Scrittori Fiorentini. 570p. Date not set. Repr. of 1722 ed. text ed. 144.90x (ISBN 0-576-72205-7, Pub. by Gregg Intl Pubs England). Gregg Intl.

Paris, Edmond. The Secret History of the Jesuits. rev. ed. 208p. 1982. pap. 5.95 (ISBN 0-937958-10-7). Chick Pubns.

Pascal, Blaise. Les Provinciales. 1966. 4.95 (ISBN 0-686-54852-3). French & Eur.

Pascal, Blaise & Adam, Antoine. Lettres Escrites a un Provincial. 320p. 1967. 4.50 (ISBN 0-686-54847-7). French & Eur.

Pieper, Josef. No One Could Have Known: An Autobiography-- The Early Years. Harrison, Graham, tr. from Ger. LC 86-72509. Tr. of Noch Wusste es Niemand. (Illus.). 227p. (Orig.). 1987. pap. 9.95 (ISBN 0-89870-131-7). Ignatius Pr.

Rahner, Karl. The Religious Life Today. 1976. 5.95 (ISBN 0-8245-0371-6). Crossroad NY.

Ravier, Andre. Ignatius of Loyola & the Founding of Society of Jesus. Daly, Maura, et al, trs. from Fr. Tr. of Ignace de Loyola Fonde la Compagnie de Jesus. 498p. (Orig.). 1987. 29.95 (ISBN 0-89870-036-1). Ignatius Pr.

Ribadeneira, Pedro. Bibliotheca Scriptorum Societatis Jesu. 1022p. Date not set. Repr. of 1676 ed. text ed. 207.00x (ISBN 0-576-78529-6, Pub. by Gregg Intl Pubs England). Gregg Intl.

Ridley, Francis A. The Jesuits: A Study in Counter-Reformation. LC 83-45595. Date not set. Repr. of 1938 ed. 35.00 (ISBN 0-404-19888-0). AMS Pr.

Roberts, Kenneth J. Playboy to Priest. LC 78-169145. 304p. 1974. pap. 4.95 (ISBN 0-87973-782-4). Our Sunday Visitor.

Ronan & Hanisch. Epistolario de Juan Ignacio Molina. (Span.). 1980. 11.60 (ISBN 0-8294-0360-4). Loyola.

Rose, Stewart. Ignatius Loyola & the Early Jesuits. LC 83-45596. Date not set. Repr. of 1870 ed. 52.00 (ISBN 0-404-19889-9). AMS Pr.

Schutte, Josef F. Valignano's Mission Principles for Japan: Vol. I (1573-1582), Pts. I & II: The Problem 1573-1580 & The Solution 1580 to 1582. Ganss, G. E. & Fischer, P. C., eds. LC 78-69683. (Modern Scholarly Studies about the Jesuits, in English Translations: No. 5). Orig. Title: Valignanos Missionsgrundsatze Fur Japan. Tr. of Ger. 398p. 1985. 16.00 (ISBN 0-912422-76-9); pap. 14.00 sewn (ISBN 0-912422-75-0). Inst Jesuit.

Smith, Gerard, ed. Jesuit Thinkers of the Renaissance. 1939. 8.95 (ISBN 0-87462-431-2). Marquette.

Sullivan, Kevin. Joyce among the Jesuits. LC 84-25241. x, 259p. 1985. Repr. of 1957 ed. lib. bdg. 39.75x (ISBN 0-313-24745-5, SUJJ). Greenwood.

Terrien, James S., tr. Prophecies & Revelations about the Jesuits. 143p. pap. 3.98 (ISBN 0-913452-27-0). Jesuit Bks.

Thompson, R. W. The Footprints of the Jesuits. 1981. lib. bdg. 75.00 (ISBN 0-686-71628-0). Revisionist Pr.

Tylenda, Joseph N. Jesuit Saints & Martyrs. 503p. 1984. 15.95 (ISBN 0-8294-0447-3). Loyola.

Tylenda, Joseph N., ed. Counsels for Jesuits: Selected Letters & Instructions of Saint Ignatius Loyola. 152p. 1985. pap. 4.95 (ISBN 0-8294-0496-1). Loyola.

Valles, Carlos G. Living Together in a Jesuit Community. LC 84-81259. (Study Aids on Jesuit Topics: Ser. IV, No. 10). 128p. 1985. pap. 4.00 Smyth Sewn (ISBN 0-912422-66-1). Inst Jesuit.

Van Kley, Dale. The Jansenists & the Expulsion of the Jesuits from France, 1757-1765. LC 74-26390. (Yale Historical Publication. Miscellany Ser.: No. 107). pap. 70.50 (ISBN 0-317-09445-9, 2022046). Bks Demand UMI.

JESUITS–EDUCATION

Ganss, George E. The Jesuit Educational Tradition & Saint Louis University: Some Bearings for the University's Sesquicentennial, 1818-1968. LC 75-87922. (Illus.). 70p. 1969. 3.25 (ISBN 0-912422-02-5). Inst Jesuit.

Owen, Lewis. The Running Register: Recording the State of the English Colledges in All Forraine Parts. LC 68-54654. (English Experience Ser.: No. 19). 118p. 1968. Repr. of 1626 ed. 13.00 (ISBN 90-221-0019-7). Walter J Johnson.

Scaglione, Aldo. The Liberal Arts & the Jesuit College System. LC 86-17507. (Paperback Ser.: No. 6). (Illus.). v, 229p. 1986. 44.00x (ISBN 0-915027-76-3); pap. 20.00x (ISBN 0-915027-77-1). Benjamins North Am.

Schwickerat, Robert. Jesuit Education. 59.95 (ISBN 0-8490-0442-X). Gordon Pr.

JESUITS–MISSIONS

see also Catholic Church–Missions

Correia-Afonso, John, ed. & tr. Letters from the Mughal Court: The First Jesuit Mission to Akbar (1580-1583) LC 81-81766. (Jesuit Primary Sources in English Translation Ser.: No. 4). (Illus.). 150p. 1982. 9.00 (ISBN 0-912422-57-2). Inst Jesuit.

Du Creux, Francois. History of Canada, or New France, 2 Vols. Conacher, James B., ed. Robinson, Percy J., tr. LC 69-14507. 1969. Repr. of 1951 ed. Vol. 1. lib. bdg. 26.75x (ISBN 0-8371-5070-1, DUHI); Vol. 2. lib. bdg. 25.75x (ISBN 0-8371-5071-X, DUHJ). Greenwood.

Dunne, George H. Generation of Giants. 1962. 19.95 (ISBN 0-268-00109-X). U of Notre Dame Pr.

Graham, Robert B. Vanished Arcadia: Being Some Account of the Jesuits in Paraguay. LC 68-25238. (Studies in Spanish Literature, No. 36). 1969. Repr. of 1901 ed. lib. bdg. 50.95x (ISBN 0-8383-0949-6). Haskell.

The Jesuit Mission of St. Mary's County. 2nd ed. LC 77-75320. 422p. 1976. 20.00 (ISBN 0-686-24147-9). E W Beitzell.

Kenny, Michael. Romance of the Floridas. LC 70-120573. (Illus.). Repr. of 1934 ed. 15.00 (ISBN 0-404-03656-2). AMS Pr.

Le Clercq, Chretien. First Establishment of the Faith in New France, 2 Vols. LC 77-172312. Repr. of 1881 ed. Set. 67.50 (ISBN 0-404-03914-6). Vol. 1 (ISBN 0-404-03915-4). Vol. 2 (ISBN 0-404-03916-2). AMS Pr.

McCoy, James C. Jesuit Relations of Canada, 1632-1673: A Bibliography. LC 76-153038. (Illus.). xv, 346p. 1972. Repr. of 1937 ed. lib. bdg. 23.50 (ISBN 0-8337-2314-6). B Franklin.

McNaspy, C. J. Lost Cities of Paraguay: The Art & Architecture of the Jesuit Reductions. 1982. 24.95 (ISBN 0-8294-0396-5). Loyola.

Mengarini, Gregory. Recollections of the Flathead Mission. Lothrop, Gloria, ed. LC 74-27573. (Illus.). 1977. 16.95 (ISBN 0-87062-111-4). A H Clark.

Roca, Paul M. Spanish Jesuit Churches in Mexico's Tarahumara. LC 78-14467. 369p. 1979. pap. 11.50x (ISBN 0-8165-0572-1). U of Ariz Pr.

Schutte, Josef F. Valignano's Mission Principles for Japan: Vol. I (1573-1582), Pt. I - The Problem (1573-1580) Coyne, John J., tr. from Ger. LC 78-69683. (Modern Scholarly Studies About the Jesuits, in English Translations, Ser. II: No. 3). (Illus.). xxiv, 428p. 1980. 14.00 (ISBN 0-912422-36-X); pap. 12.00 smyth sewn (ISBN 0-912422-35-1). Inst Jesuit.

Shiels, William E. Gonzalo De Tapia, 1561-1594: Founder of the First Permanent Jesuit Mission in North America. LC 74-12835. (U. S. Catholic Historical Society Monograph: No. XIV). 1978. Repr. of 1934 ed. lib. bdg. 22.50x (ISBN 0-8371-7758-8, SHGT). Greenwood.

Taraval, Sigismundo. Indian Uprising in Lower California, 1734-1737. LC 79-137296. Repr. of 1931 ed. 24.00 (ISBN 0-404-06337-3). AMS Pr.

JESUITS IN CANADA

Dalton, Roy C. The Jesuits' Estates Question, 1760-1888: A Study of the Background for the Agitation of 1889. LC 74-393033. (Canada Studies in History & Government: No. 11). pap. 53.30 (ISBN 0-317-26918-6, 2023608). Bks Demand UMI.

Donnelly, Joseph P. Thwaites' Jesuit Relations, Errata & Addenda. LC 66-27701. (The American West Ser). 1967. 6.95 (ISBN 0-8294-0025-7). Loyola.

McCoy, James C. Jesuit Relations of Canada, 1632-1673: A Bibliography. LC 76-153038. (Illus.). xv, 346p. 1972. Repr. of 1937 ed. lib. bdg. 23.50 (ISBN 0-8337-2314-6). B Franklin.

JESUITS IN CHINA

Borri, Christoforo. Cochin-China: Containing Many Admirable Rarities of That Countrey. LC 71-25710. (English Experience Ser.: No. 223). 1970. Repr. of 1633 ed. 9.50 (ISBN 90-221-0223-8). Walter J Johnson.

D'Orleans, Pierre J. History of the Two Tartar Conquerors of China. LC 75-162706. 1963. Repr. of 1668 ed. 26.00 (ISBN 0-8337-3630-2). B Franklin.

Jesuit Missionaries. China. (Illus.). 216p. 150.00 (ISBN 0-8478-5402-7). Rizzoli Intl.

Jesuits at the Court of Peking. (Studies in Chinese History & Civilization). Repr. of 1935 ed. 23.00 (ISBN 0-89093-077-5). U Pubns Amer.

JESUITS IN ENGLAND

Edwards, Francis. The Jesuits in England from 1850 to the Present Day. LC 85-12048. 333p. text ed. cancelled (ISBN 0-268-01204-0, Pub. by Burns & Oates London). U of Notre Dame Pr.

Foley, Henry. Records of the English Province of the Society of Jesus, 7 Vols. in 8. (Illus.). Repr. of 1883 ed. Set. 690.00 (ISBN 0-384-16310-6). Johnson Repr.

Law, Thomas G., ed. The Archpriest Controversy, 2 Vols. Repr. of 1898 ed. 54.00 (ISBN 0-384-31730-8). Johnson Repr.

Martin, A. L. Henry III & the Jesuit Politicians. 264p. (Orig.). 1973. pap. text ed. 48.50x (Pub. by Droz Switzerland). Coronet Bks.

JESUITS IN LATIN-AMERICA

Cushner, Nicholas P. Jesuit Ranches & the Agrarian Development of Colonial Argentina, 1650-1767. 350p. 1982. 49.50x (ISBN 0-87395-707-5); pap. 19.95 (ISBN 0-87395-706-7). State U NY Pr.

Morner, Magnus. The Political & Economic Activities of the Jesuits in the Plata Region. 1976. lib. bdg. 59.95 (ISBN 0-8490-2451-X). Gordon Pr.

JESUITS IN MEXICO

Dunner, Peter M. Pioneer Jesuits in Northern Mexico. LC 78-10566. (Illus.). 1979. Repr. of 1944 ed. lib. bdg. 24.75x (ISBN 0-313-20653-8, DUPJ). Greenwood.

Ronan, Charles E. Francisco Javier Clavigero, S. J., Figure of the Mexican Enlightment: His Life & Work. 1978. pap. 26.00x (ISBN 88-7041-340-3). Jesuit Hist.

JESUITS IN NORTH AMERICA

Bolton, Herbert E. Wider Horizons of American History. 1967. pap. 5.95x (ISBN 0-268-00301-7). U of Notre Dame Pr.

McCoy, James C. Jesuit Relations of Canada, 1632-1673: A Bibliography. LC 76-153038. (Illus.). xv, 346p. 1972. Repr. of 1937 ed. lib. bdg. 23.50 (ISBN 0-8337-2314-6). B Franklin.

Parkman, Francis. The Jesuits in North America. 586p. 1970. Repr. of 1895 ed. 22.50 (ISBN 0-87928-016-6). Corner Hse.

Polzer, Charles. Rules & Precepts of the Jesuit Missions of Northwestern New Spain. LC 75-8456. 141p. 1976. pap. 4.50 (ISBN 0-8165-0488-1). U of Ariz Pr.

Schoenberg, Wilfred. Paths to the Northwest: A Jesuit History of the Oregon Province. 477p. 1983. 27.50 (ISBN 0-8294-0405-8). Loyola.

JESUITS IN POLAND

Pollard, Alfred F. Jesuits in Poland. LC 76-116799. (Studies in Philosophy, No. 40). 1970. Repr. of 1902 ed. lib. bdg. 39.95x (ISBN 0-8383-1041-9). Haskell.

JESUITS IN THE UNITED STATES

Broderick, James. The Economic Morals of the Jesuits. LC 76-38248. (The Evolution of Capitalism Ser.). 168p. 1972. Repr. of 1934 ed. 12.00 (ISBN 0-405-04113-6). Ayer Co Pubs.

Burns, Robert. Jesuits & the Indian Wars of the Northwest. LC 65-22314. 550p. (Orig.). 1985. pap. 12.95 (ISBN 0-89301-110-X). U of Idaho Pr.

Burrus, Ernest. Ducrue's Account of Expulsion of the Jesuits from Lower California. 1967. pap. 20.00 (ISBN 88-7041-502-3). Jesuit Hist.

Burrus, Ernest J., ed. Jesuit Relations, Baja California, 1716-1762. (Baja California Travels Ser.: Vol. 47). (Illus.). 280p. 1984. 60.00 (ISBN 0-87093-243-8). Dawsons.

Curran, Francis X. The Return of the Jesuits. LC 66-29559. 1966. 3.00 (ISBN 0-8294-0018-4). Loyola.

Delanglez, Jean. The French Jesuits in Lower Louisiana (1700-1763) LC 73-3576. (Catholic University of America. Studies in American Church History: No. 21). Repr. of 1935 ed. 46.00 (ISBN 0-404-57771-7). AMS Pr.

FitzGerald, Paul A. Governance of Jesuit Colleges in the United States, 1920-1970. LC 83-25927. 328p. 1984. text ed. 20.00 (ISBN 0-268-01010-2, 85-10109). U of Notre Dame Pr.

Gache, Louis-Hippolyte. A Frenchman, a Chaplain, a Rebel: The War Letters of Pere Louis-Hippolyte Gache, S. J. Buckley, Cornelius M., tr. 282p. 1981. 8.95 (ISBN 0-8294-0376-0). Loyola.

Garraghan, Gilbert J. The Jesuits of the Middle United States, 3 vols. 1938. Repr. 162.00 (ISBN 0-405-10831-1, 11838). Ayer Co Pubs.

Gruenberg, Gladys W. Labor Peacemaker: The Life & Works of Father Leo. C. Brown, S. J. Ganss, George E., ed. LC 80-83552. (Original Studies Composed in English Ser.: No. 4). (Illus.). 176p. 1981. 8.50 (ISBN 0-912422-54-8); pap. 7.00 smythsewn paperbound (ISBN 0-912422-53-X); pap. 6.00 (ISBN 0-912422-52-1). Inst Jesuit.

The Jesuit Mission of St. Mary's County. 2nd ed. LC 77-75320. 422p. 1976. 20.00 (ISBN 0-686-24147-9). E W Beitzell.

Lapomarda, Vincent A. The Jesuit Heritage in New England. LC 76-42896. (Illus., Orig.). 1977. 8.00x (ISBN 0-9606294-0-8). Jesuits Holy Cross.

Walsh, J. J. American Jesuits. 59.95 (ISBN 0-87968-605-7). Gordon Pr.

Walsh, James J. American Jesuits. facs. ed. LC 68-29251. (Essay Index Reprint Ser). 1934. 18.25 (ISBN 0-8369-0970-4). Ayer Co Pubs.

JESUS, SOCIETY OF

see Jesuits

JESUS CHRIST

see also Antichrist; Atonement; Christianity; Crosses; Incarnation; Logos; Lord's Supper; Mercersburg Theology; Messiah; Millennium; Redemption; Salvation; Second Advent; Trinity

Adams, Jay E. Christ & Your Problems. 1976. pap. 1.25 (ISBN 0-8010-0035-1). Baker Bk.

Albritton, Clarice. The Untold Story: Jesus Son of God. LC 83-73188. 1983. pap. 5.95 (ISBN 0-318-00817-3). W P Brownell.

Aldwinckle, Russell. Jesus: A Savior or the Savior? Religious Pluralism in Christian Perspective. LC 81-19033. viii, 232p. 1982. 15.95 (ISBN 0-86554-023-3, MUP-H24). Mercer Univ Pr.

Allen, R. C. Immortal Words of Jesus Christ. 1981. pap. 4.95 (ISBN 0-910228-11-6). Best Bks.

Association for Research & Enlightenment, Readings Research Dept., compiled by. Christ Consciousness. (Library: Vol. 11). 277p. 1980. 10.95 (ISBN 0-87604-124-1). ARE Pr.

--Jesus the Pattern: Library. (Vol. 10). 336p. 1980. 10.95 (ISBN 0-87604-123-3). ARE Pr.

Augustinus, Aurelius. De Perfectione Ivstitiae Hominis, De Gestis Pelagii, De Gratia Christi et De Peccato Originali Liber Duo. (Corpus Scriptorum Ecclesiasticorum Latinorum Ser: Vol. 42). Repr. of 1902 ed. 50.00 (ISBN 0-384-02495-5). Johnson Repr.

Baird, J. Arthur. Audience Criticism & the Historical Jesus. 1969. 6.50 (ISBN 0-664-20846-0). Biblical Res Assocs.

Ball, Barbara. Coffee Talk: Sharing Christ Through Friendly Gatherings. LC 79-53980. 80p. 1980. pap. 4.95 (ISBN 0-934396-08-6). Churches Alive.

Barclay, William. Jesus of Nazareth. 1977. pap. 1.95 (ISBN 0-345-27253-6). Ballantine.

Barrois, Georges A. The Face of Christ in the Old Testament. 172p. 1974. pap. 6.95 (ISBN 0-913836-22-2). St Vladimirs.

Baumgartner, Aline & Fisher, Carl, eds. Jesus: Friend, Teacher, Leader. (Illus.). 1986. dupl. masterbook 9.95 (ISBN 0-89837-104-X, Pub. by Pflaum Pr). Peter Li.

Beechick, Allen. The Pre-Tribulation Rapture. LC 79-53291. 256p. (Orig.). 1980. pap. 4.95 (ISBN 0-89636-040-7). Accent Bks.

Betz, Hans D., ed. Christology & a Modern Pilgrimage: A Discussion with Norman Perrin. rev. ed. LC 79-31605. pap. 27.30 (ISBN 0-317-28877-6, 2020268). Bks Demand UMI.

Bjerregard, Carl H. Jesus: A Poet, Prophet, Mystic & Man of Freedom. 1976. lib. bdg. 59.95 (ISBN 0-8490-2094-8). Gordon Pr.

Boff, Leonardo. Jesus Christ Liberator: A Critical Christology for Our Time. Hughes, Patrick, tr. from Portuguese. LC 78-969. Tr. of Jesus Cristo Libertador Ensaio de Crista logia Critica para o nosso Tempo. 335p. (Orig.). 1978. pap. 9.95 (ISBN 0-88344-236-1). Orbis Bks.

Bonhoeffer, Dietrich. Christ the Center: A New Translation. new ed. LC 78-4747. (Harper's Ministers Paperback Library Ser.). 1978. pap. 5.95 (ISBN 0-06-060815-3, RD 285, HarpR). Har-Row.

Booty, John. The Christ We Know. LC 87-6779. (Illus.). 174p. 1987. pap. 9.95 (ISBN 0-936384-48-4). Cowley Pubns.

Boykin, James H. Political Intrigue in the Establishment of the Identity of Jesus & Mary. LC 86-90957. 286p. 1986. pap. 15.00x (ISBN 0-9603342-6-2). Boykin.

Bradlaugh, Charles. Jesus, Shelley, & Malthus. 1978. Repr. of 1877 ed. lib. bdg. 10.00 (ISBN 0-8495-0441-4). Arden Lib.

Broeckhover, Egide van. A Friend to All Men. 5.95 (ISBN 0-317-06463-0). Dimension Bks.

Brown, Harold O. Heresies: The Image of Christ in the Mirror of Heresy & Orthodoxy from the Apostles to the Present. LC 80-2558. (Illus.). 504p. 1984. 17.95 (ISBN 0-385-15338-4). Doubleday.

Bruce, F. F. Jesus & Paul: Places They Knew. 128p. 1983. Repr. of 1981 ed. 12.95 (ISBN 0-8407-5281-4). Nelson.

--What the Bible Teaches about What Jesus Did. 1979. pap. 3.95 (ISBN 0-8423-7885-5). Tyndale.

Brungardt, Helen. The Mystical Meaning of Jesus the Christ: Significant Episodes in the Life of the Master. 2nd ed. (Illus.). 64p. 1983. pap. 5.00 (ISBN 0-941992-03-9). Los Arboles Pub.

Bryditzki, Victor V. The Selling of Jesus. (Illus.). 128p. (Orig.). 1985. pap. 3.95 (ISBN 0-937958-22-0). Chick Pubns.

Buchanan, George Wesley. Jesus: The King & His Kingdom. LC 83-24939. xx, 348p. 1984. 21.95 (ISBN 0-86554-072-1, H66). Mercer Univ Pr.

Bultmann, Rudolf. Jesus Christ & Mythology. 1958. pap. text ed. 5.95 (ISBN 0-684-17228-3, ScribT). Scribner.

--Jesus Christ & Mythology. 94p. 1981. pap. text ed. write for info. (ISBN 0-02-305570-7, Pub. by Scribner). Macmillan.

Bunyan, John. Come & Welcome to Jesus Christ. 1974. pap. 2.50 (ISBN 0-685-52815-4). Reiner.

--Saints Knowledge of Christ's Love. pap. 1.50 (ISBN 0-685-19843-X). Reiner.

Burns, Jim. The Incredible Christ. (LifeSources for Youth Ser.: No. 3). 64p. (Orig.). 1987. wkbk. 3.95 (ISBN 0-89081-575-5). Harvest Hse.

Cabasilas, Nicholas. The Life in Christ. Decatanzaro, Carmino J., tr. 229p. 1974. pap. 8.95 (ISBN 0-913836-12-5). St Vladimirs.

Cadoux, C. John. The Historic Mission of Jesus: A Constructive Re-Examination of the Eschatological Teaching in the Synoptic Gospels with an Extensive Bibliography. 1977. lib. bdg. 59.95 (ISBN 0-8490-1955-9). Gordon Pr.

Campbell, Alexander. Stories of Jesus, Stories of Now. 80p. (Orig.). 1980. pap. 12.95 (ISBN 0-940754-04-5). Ed Ministries.

Carpenter, Humphrey. Jesus. (Past Masters Ser.). 1980. pap. 4.95 (ISBN 0-19-283016-3). Oxford U Pr.

Carroll, Gerry. Creation, Christ & Credibility: How & Why Mankind Has Failed to Discredit the Bible. LC 83-72663. (Illus.). 204p. (Orig.). 1983. pap. 5.95 (ISBN 0-914569-01-5). Creat Pubns B P C M.

Chamberlain, Eugene. Jesus: God's Son, Saviour, Lord. (BibLearn Ser.). (Illus.). pap. 5.95 (ISBN 0-8054-4226-X, 4242-26). Broadman.

Cheney, Johnston M. The Life of Christ in Stereo. Ellisen, Stanley A., ed. LC 84-8280. 275p. 1984. pap. 6.95 (ISBN 0-88070-068-8). Multnomah.

Christ. Date not set. pap. 0.95 (ISBN 0-937408-14-X). GMI Pubns Inc.

The Christ Papers, Vol. I. LC 82-90717. 150p. (Orig.). pap. 5.95 (ISBN 0-937408-22-0). GMI Pubns Inc.

Christenson, Larry. Christ & His Church. (Trinity Bible Ser.). 160p. 1973. pap. 4.95 spiral wkbk. (ISBN 0-87123-550-1, 240550). Bethany Hse.

Christopher, George, Jr. Jesus of Nazareth: The Man, the Myth, the Enigma. 50p. 1984. 4.95 (ISBN 0-89697-176-7). Intl Univ Pr.

Clancy, Bill. Jesus: The Ultimate E.T. Howard, Dick, ed. 40p. (Orig.). 1983. pap. 1.75 (ISBN 0-912573-00-7). Believers Faith.

Clark, Glenn. Three Mysteries of Jesus. 1978. 0.95 (ISBN 0-910924-85-6). Macalester.

Colton, Ann R. The King. 72p. 1968. 5.00 (ISBN 0-917187-08-3). A R C Pub.

Cornier, Henri. The Humor of Jesus. Heiman, David, tr. from Fr. LC 77-9887. Orig. Title: L Humour De Jesus. 1977. pap. 5.95 (ISBN 0-8189-0356-2). Alba.

Corsini, Eugenio. The Apocalypse: The Perennial Revelation of Jesus Christ. Moloney, ed. (Good News Studies: Vol. 5). 1983. pap. 5.95 (ISBN 0-89453-310-X). M Glazier.

Cotter, James F. Inscape: The Christology & Poetry of Gerald Manley Hopkins. LC 73-189857. pap. 92.30 (ISBN 0-317-26639-X, 2025436). Bks Demand UMI.

Coventry, John. Faith in Jesus Christ. 54p. 1982. pap. 3.95 (ISBN 0-86683-620-9, HarpR). Har-Row.

Crawley-Boevey, Mateo. Jesus King of Love. 1978. 5.50 (ISBN 0-8198-0521-1); pap. 3.95 (ISBN 0-8198-0522-X). Dghtrs St Paul.

Cristo y Su Ley de Amor. (Span. & Eng.). pap. text ed. 2.00 (ISBN 0-8198-1437-7); 1.80 (ISBN 0-8198-1438-5). Dghtrs St Paul.

Crock, Clement H. No Cross No Crown. 1974. Repr. 3.00 (ISBN 0-8198-0510-6). Dghtrs St Paul.

Cross, Dorothy. Around the World with Jesus. 0.60 (ISBN 0-88027-102-7). Firm Foun Pub.

Crossan, John D. In Fragments: The Aphorisms of Jesus. LC 83-47719. 384p. 1983. 29.45 (ISBN 0-06-061608-3, HarpR). Har-Row.

Crossley, Alan. Jesus Psychi Super Star. 64p. 1984. 29.00x (ISBN 0-7212-0683-2, Pub. by Regency Pr). State Mutual Bk.

Cuando Jesus Nacio. (Span.). 1.25 (ISBN 0-8198-1425-3). Dghtrs St Paul.

Cullmann, Oscar. The Christology of the New Testament. rev. ed. Guthrie, Shirley C. & Hall, Charles A. M., trs. LC 59-10178. 364p. 1980. pap. 12.95 (ISBN 0-664-24351-7). Westminster.

Davie, Ian. Jesus Purusha. LC 85-23113. 176p. (Orig.). 1985. pap. 8.95 (ISBN 0-89281-069-6, Lindisfarne Pr). Inner Tradit.

Davies, Chris, et al, eds. Jesus: One of Us. 148p. 1981. pap. 3.95 (ISBN 0-87784-618-9). Inter Varsity.

Dawson, W. J. The Man Jesus Christ. 1977. lib. bdg. 59.95 (ISBN 0-8490-2199-5). Gordon Pr.

Dean, Jay & Dean, Claire. How Damage is Done in The Name of Christ! LC 82-90134. 102p. (Orig.). 1982. pap. 3.95 (ISBN 0-943416-00-0). Plus Seven Bks.

DeHaan, Martin R. Religion o Cristo? Orig. Title: Religion or Christ. (Span.). 64p. 1970. pap. 2.25 (ISBN 0-8254-1153-X). Kregel.

DeJonge, M. Christology in Context. price not set. Westminster.

De Lacey, D. R. Jesus & the Gospels. (Discovering the Bible Ser.). pap. 8.95 (ISBN 0-7175-1162-6). Dufour.

De La Fuente, Tomas. La Hermosa Historia de Jesus: Ordenada, Simplificada y Brevemente Explicada. 1983. pap. 4.95 (ISBN 0-311-04658-4). Casa Bautista.

Delanghe, Jules A. The Philosophy of Jesus: Real Love. LC 72-96805. 1973. 4.95 (ISBN 0-8059-1821-3). Dorrance.

De Margerie, Bertrand. Human Knowledge of Christ. 1980. 2.95 (ISBN 0-8198-3301-0); pap. 1.50 (ISBN 0-8198-3302-9). Dghtrs St Paul.

Denny, James. Jesus & the Gospel. 1977. lib. bdg. 59.95 (ISBN 0-8490-2095-6). Gordon Pr.

De Pressense, E. Jesus Christ: His Times, Life & Work. 1978. Repr. of 1898 ed. lib. bdg. 50.00 (ISBN 0-8495-1032-5). Arden Lib.

Dooley, Kate C. The Jesus Book. LC 82-61422. 48p. (Orig.). 1983. pap. 2.95 (ISBN 0-8091-2514-5). Paulist Pr.

Drane, John. Jesus & the Gospels. LC 77-20448. 1979. pap. 9.95 (ISBN 0-06-062066-8, RD264, HarpR). Har-Row.

Drew, George. The Original Ideas of Jesus That Are Changing the World. 45p. (Orig.). 1980. pap. 5.45 (ISBN 0-940754-05-3). Ed Ministries.

Drohan, Francis B. Jesus Who? The Greatest Mystery Never Told. LC 84-16654. 270p. 1985. 15.00 (ISBN 0-8022-2475-X). Philos Lib.

Duling, Dennis C. Jesus Christ Through History. 324p. 1979. pap. text ed. 13.95 (ISBN 0-15-547370-0, HC). HarBraceJ.

Duncan, Anthony. Jesus: Essential Readings. (Crucible Ser.). 176p. 1987. pap. 9.95 (ISBN 0-85030-395-8). Thorsons Pubs.

Dunn, James D. Christology in the Making: A New Testament Inquiry into the Origins of the Doctrine of the Incarnation. LC 80-16968. 462p. 1980. pap. 24.50 (ISBN 0-664-24356-8). Westminster.

--Jesus & the Spirit: A Study of the Religious & Charismatic Experience of Jesus & the First Christians as Reflected in the New Testament. LC 75-9802. 528p. 1979. pap. 15.95 (ISBN 0-664-24290-1). Westminster.

An Eastern View of Jesus Christ. write for info. Birth Day.

Edwards, O. C., Jr. Luke's Story of Jesus. LC 81-43076. 96p. 1981. pap. 4.50 (ISBN 0-8006-1611-1, 1-1611). Fortress.

Egelkraut, Helmuth L. Jesus' Mission to Jerusalem: Theology, Vol. 80. (European University Studies: Ser. 23). x, 258p. 1977. pap. 28.70 (ISBN 3-261-02133-0). P Lang Pubs.

Elizondo, Virgilio P. Creemos en Jesucristo. (Span.). 128p. 1982. pap. 2.95 (ISBN 0-89243-153-9). Liguori Pubns.

Emmerich, Anne C. The Dolorous Passion of Our Lord Jesus Christ. LC 83-70406. 382p. 1983. pap. 10.00 (ISBN 0-89555-210-8). TAN Bks Pubs.

Endo, Shusaku. A Life of Jesus. Schuchert, Richard, tr. from Japanese. LC 78-61721. 192p. 1979. pap. 3.95 (ISBN 0-8091-2319-3). Paulist Pr.

Epstein, Leslie. King of the Jews. 352p. 1986. pap. 7.95 (ISBN 0-452-25823-5, Plume). NAL.

Estevez, Kent. The Untold Story of Jesus Christ. LC 86-81086. 100p. (Orig.). 1986. pap. 10.00 (ISBN 0-9616660-0-5). Holland Pub Hse.

Ewing, Upton C. The Essene Christ. 438p. pap. 12.95 (ISBN 0-317-07627-2). Edenite.

Failing, George E. Did Christ Die for All? 1980. 1.25 (ISBN 0-937296-02-3, 222-B). Presence Inc.

Fairweather, William. Jesus & the Greeks. 1977. lib. bdg. 59.95 (ISBN 0-8490-2096-4). Gordon Pr.

Falk, Harvey. Jesus the Pharisee: New Look at the Jewishness of Jesus. (Orig.). 1985. pap. 8.95 (ISBN 0-8091-2677-X). Paulist Pr.

Farmer, William R. Jesus & the Gospel. LC 81-43078. 320p. 1982. 22.95 (ISBN 0-8006-0666-3). Fortress.

Finley, Merrill. Christ & the Colonel. 120p. 1987. pap. write for info. (ISBN 0-911826-51-3). Am Atheist.

Finnegan, Robert E. Christ & Satan: A Critical Edition. 169p. 1977. pap. text ed. 15.95x (ISBN 0-88920-041-6, Pub. by Wilfrid Laurier Canada); pap. text ed. 10.50 (ISBN 0-88920-040-8). Humanities.

Fitzmyer, Joseph A. A Christological Catechism: New Testament Answers. 160p. (Orig.). 1982. pap. 4.95 (ISBN 0-8091-2453-X). Paulist Pr.

Flinn, Frank, ed. Christology: The Center & the Periphery. 256p. 1987. 21.95 (ISBN 0-913757-75-6). Paragon Hse.

Floyd, Tony. United to Christ. (Illus.). 80p. (Orig.). 1983. pap. 5.95 (ISBN 0-85819-420-1, Pub. by JBCE). ANZ Religious Pubns.

Ford, J. Massyngbaerd. My Enemy Is My Guest. LC 84-5812. 192p. 1984. pap. 9.95 (ISBN 0-88344-348-1). Orbis Bks.

Gandhi, Mohandas K. The Message of Jesus Christ. Hingorani, A. T., ed. 64p. (Orig.). 1980. pap. 1.25 (ISBN 0-934676-20-8). Greenlf Bks.

Gautrey, Robert M. The Burning Cataracts of Christ. 1980. Repr. of 1933 ed. lib. bdg. 30.00 (ISBN 0-8482-4193-2). Norwood Edns.

Gendrot, Marcel, ed. Make Way for Jesus Christ. pap. 4.95 (ISBN 0-910984-52-2). Montfort Pubns.

Goodier, Alban. The Prince of Peace. 152p. 1982. 3.25 (ISBN 0-8198-5807-2, SP0585); pap. 2.25 (ISBN 0-8198-5808-0). Dghtrs St Paul.

Graves, Robert. King Jesus. 356p. 1983. Repr. of 1946 ed. lib. bdg. 25.00 (ISBN 0-8495-2139-4). Arden Lib.

Grillmeier, Aloys. Christ in the Christian Tradition, Vol. 2, Pt. 1. Allen, Pauline & Cawte, John, trs. 1987. 34.95 (ISBN 0-8042-0493-4). John Knox.

Grogan, Geoffrey W. What the Bible Teaches about Jesus. 1979. pap. 3.95 (ISBN 0-8423-7884-7). Tyndale.

Gunn, George S. Indispensable Christ: Sermons. 266p. 1962. 6.50 (ISBN 0-227-67661-0). Attic Pr.

Gunn, James. Christ: The Fullness of the Godhead, a Study in New Testament Christology. 256p. 1983. pap. 5.50 (ISBN 0-87213-283-8). Loizeaux.

Habig, Marion. Christ the Prisoner. 1976. pap. 0.50 (ISBN 0-685-77502-X). Franciscan Herald.

Hackwood, F. W. Christ Lore. 59.95 (ISBN 0-87968-861-0). Gordon Pr.

Hagin, Kenneth, Jr. Because of Jesus. 2nd ed. 1979. 1.00 (ISBN 0-89276-701-4). Hagin Ministries.

Hall, Charles C. Christ & the Eastern Soul: Oriental Consciousness & Jesus. 1977. lib. bdg. 59.95 (ISBN 0-8490-1613-4). Gordon Pr.

Hall, Miriam J. Jesus, the Children's Friend. 64p. (Orig.). 1983. pap. 1.95 (ISBN 0-8341-0815-1). Beacon Hill.

Hall, Thor. The Evolution of Christology. LC 81-14838. 128p. (Orig.). 1982. pap. 6.50 (ISBN 0-687-12190-6). Abingdon.

Hamson, Robert L. Signature of God: A Positive Identification of Christ & His Prophets by Computer Wordprints. LC 81-51809. (Illus.). 111p. 1982. 8.95 (ISBN 0-940356-01-5). Sandpiper CA.

Harnish, James A. What Will You Do with King Jesus. 128p. (Orig.). 1986. pap. 5.95 (ISBN 0-8358-0530-1, ICN 613108, Dist. by Abingdon Pr). Upper Room.

Harper, George. Jesus: A Whole in One Down. (H. B. & His-Her Adventures Ser.). 224p. (Orig.). 1986. pap. 5.95 (ISBN 0-937959-12-X). Falcon Pr Mt.

Hayford, Jack W. Newborn: Alive in Christ, the Savior. (Orig.). 1984. pap. 2.95 (ISBN 0-916847-00-4). Living Way.

Heijkoop, H. L. Beginning with Christ. 6.95 (ISBN 0-88172-081-X); pap. 4.95 (ISBN 0-88172-082-8). Believers Bkshelf.

Heiner, Wolfgang. Jesus Is Different. 112p. 1983. pap. 4.50 (ISBN 0-85364-344-X, Pub. by Paternoster UK). Attic Pr.

Hendricks, William. Quien es Jesuscristo? Martinez, Jose L., tr. from Eng. (Biblioteca de Doctrina Cristiana Ser.). Tr. of Who is Jesus Christ? (Span.). 164p. 1986. pap. 5.95 (ISBN 0-311-09112-1). Casa Bautista.

Hengel, Martin. Between Jesus & Paul. LC 83-48003. 256p. 1983. pap. 14.95 (ISBN 0-8006-1720-7). Fortress.

Henry, Philip. Christ All in All. 7.95 (ISBN 0-685-88369-8). Reiner.

Hicks, Robert & Bewes, Richard. Jesus Christ. (Understanding Bible Truth Ser.). (Orig.). 1981. pap. 0.95 (ISBN 0-89840-026-0). Heres Life.

Hirst, Edward W. Jesus & the Moralists. 1977. lib. bdg. 59.95 (ISBN 0-8490-2097-2). Gordon Pr.

Hocking, W. J. The Son of His Love. 6.25 (ISBN 0-88172-088-7). Believers Bkshelf.

Hoffmann, R. Joseph. Jesus Outside the Gospels. LC 84-42862. (The Skeptic's Bookshelf Ser.). 132p. 1984. 17.95 (ISBN 0-87975-263-7). Prometheus Bks.

Hoffmann, R. Joseph & Larue, Gerald. Jesus in History & Myth. 300p. 1986. 21.95 (ISBN 0-87975-332-3). Prometheus Bks.

Holl, Adolf. Jesus in Bad Company. 1978. pap. 1.65 (ISBN 0-380-00022-9, 19281, Discus). Avon.

Holland, Thomas W. God & Jesus: Nothing More Than Four-Letter Words. 1987. 6.95 (ISBN 0-533-07206-9). Vantage.

Holmes, George. He Is Lord. LC 76-20891. (Radiant Life Ser.). 128p. 1977. pap. 2.50 (ISBN 0-88243-902-2, 02-0902); teacher's ed 3.95 (ISBN 0-88243-172-2, 32-0172). Gospel Pub.

Hoonacker, A. Van. Une Communaute Judeo-Arameenne a Elephantine en Egypte aux VI et V Siecles avant Jesus-Christ. (British Academy, London, Schweich Lectures on Biblical Archaeology Series, 1914). pap. 19.00 (ISBN 0-8115-1256-8). Kraus Repr.

Horton, Stanley M. Welcome Back Jesus. 1975. pap. 1.25 (ISBN 0-88243-629-5, 02-0629). Gospel Pub.

Hubbard, Elbert. Jesus Was an Anarchist. 1974. lib. bdg. 59.95 (ISBN 0-87700-304-1). Revisionist Pr.

Inter-Varsity Staff. Christ in You. pap. 0.75 (ISBN 0-87784-175-6). Inter Varsity.

Javad, Nurbakhsh. Jesus in the Eyes of the Sufis. Graham, Terry, et al, trs. 1983. pap. 6.00 (ISBN 0-317-07015-0). KhaniQahi-Nimatullahi-Sufi.

Jervell, Jacob. Jesus in the Gospel of John. Cleven, Harry T., tr. LC 84-14547. 96p. (Orig.). 1984. pap. 5.95 (ISBN 0-8066-2089-7, 10-3516). Augsburg.

Jesus. 1979. 0.75 (ISBN 0-8198-0582-3). Dghtrs St Paul.

Jesus. 23p. 1982. pap. 7.55 (ISBN 0-88479-034-7). Arena Lettres.

Jesus. rev. ed. (Time of Life Learning Ser.). (Illus.). 32p. pap. 2.95 (ISBN 0-89622-244-6). Twenty-Third.

Jesus Christ & the Faith: A Collection of Studies by Philippe H. Menoud. LC 78-15551. (Pittsburgh Theological Monographs: No. 18). Orig. Title: Jesus-Christ et la Foi. 1978. 16.75 (ISBN 0-915138-22-0). Pickwick.

Jewett, Robert. Semeia Thirty, Christology & Exegesis: New Approaches. (SBL-Semeia Ser.). 1985. pap. 9.95 (ISBN 0-317-38906-8, 06-20-30). Scholars Pr Ga.

John of Smolensk. Iisus Khristos Pred Sudom Sovemjennogo Razuma. Tr. of Jesus Christ Before the Judgement of Contemporaty Intellect. 16p. pap. 1.00 (ISBN 0-317-28988-8). Holy Trinity.

Jones, E. Stanley. Christ at the Round Table. 328p. 1981. Repr. of 1928 ed. lib. bdg. 30.00 (ISBN 0-89984-267-4). Century Bookbindery.

Jordan, Lawrence W. Christian Psychiatry. 112p. 1984. pap. 8.95 (ISBN 0-8059-2910-X). Dorrance.

Joyce, Jon L. Jesus on Our Hands. (Orig.). 1983. pap. 4.95 (ISBN 0-937172-57-X). JLJ Pubs.

Jukes, Andrew. Four Views of Christ. LC 82-7800. 128p. 1982. pap. 5.95 (ISBN 0-8254-2953-6). Kregel.

Kaiser, Bill. Who Is Christ. 152p. (Orig.). 1983. pap. text ed. 4.95 (ISBN 0-914307-01-0, Dist. by Harrison Hse). Word Faith.

Karris, Robert. Following Jesus: A Guide to the Gospels. (Biblical Ser.). 1973. pap. 1.25 (ISBN 0-8199-0514-3). Franciscan Herald.

Kaspar, Walter. God of Jesus Christ. rev. ed. 450p. 1986. text ed. 14.95 (ISBN 0-8245-0777-0). Crossroad NY.

Katter, Reuben L. Jesus Christ: The Divine Executive; Architect of the Universe (Why the Universe Was Created) 400p. 1986. 18.95. Theotes.

Kee, Howard C. Jesus in History: An Approach to the Study of the Gospels. 2nd ed. LC 77-75349. 312p. 1977. pap. text ed. 13.95 (ISBN 0-15-547382-4, HC). HarBraceJ.

Keller, W. Phillip. A Layman Looks at the Lamb of God. LC 82-4568. 122p. (Orig.). 1982. 7.95 (ISBN 0-87123-313-4, 230314); pap. 3.95 (ISBN 0-87123-314-2, 210314). Bethany Hse.

Knight, G. Wilson. Christ & Nietzsche: An Essay in Poetic Wisdom. 1982. 17.00 (ISBN 0-8495-3135-7). Arden Lib.

Kraeling, Carl H. Anthropos & Son of Man. LC 27-23162. (Columbia University. Oriental Studies: No. 25). Repr. of 1927 ed. 18.50 (ISBN 0-404-50515-5). AMS Pr.

Labadie, Laurance. Jesus As an Anarchist. (Men & Movements in the History & Philosophy of Anarchism Ser.). 1979. lib. bdg. 59.95 (ISBN 0-685-96404-3). Revisionist Pr.

Lewis, H. Spencer. The Mystical Life of Jesus. 25th ed. LC 54-20988. 1982. 11.95 (ISBN 0-912057-06-8, G-503). AMORC.

Lindars, B. & Smalley, S. S. Christ & Spirit in the New Testament. LC 72-91367. 300p. 1974. 72.50 (ISBN 0-521-20148-9). Cambridge U Pr.

Lindemann, Emil R. Jesus' Revelation of What Is True. Wegener, Wilfried W., ed. 154p. (Orig.). 1983. pap. text ed. 4.00 (ISBN 0-9612192-0-3). E R Lindemann.

Lindsay, Gordon. Did Politics Influence Jesus? 86p. (Orig.). 1982. pap. 2.50 (ISBN 0-89985-113-4, 1002). Christ Nations.

Lockyer, Herbert. Retratos del Salvador. Tr. of Portraits of the Savior. (Span.). 192p. 1986. pap. 3.50 (ISBN 0-8297-0741-7). Life Pubs Intl.

Lovasik, Lawrence G. The Lord Jesus. (Illus.). hard bd 3.95 (ISBN 0-89942-419-8, 419/22). Catholic Bk Pub.

MacDonald, George. Getting to Know Jesus. 160p. 1987. pap. 2.95 (ISBN 0-345-34307-7, Pub. by Ballantine Epiphany). Ballantine.

McDowell, Josh. More Than a Carpenter. 1980. pap. 2.95 (ISBN 0-8423-4552-3). Tyndale.

McGloin, Joseph T. The Way I See Him: A Writer's Look at Jesus. LC 86-8030. 212p. (Orig.). 1986. pap. 6.95 (ISBN 0-8189-0498-4). Alba.

McGrath, Allister E. Understanding Jesus: Who Jesus Christ Is & Why He Matters. Van der Maas, E., ed. (Orig.). 1987. Repr. write for info. (ISBN 0-310-29810-5). Zondervan.

McKenna, Megan & Ducote, Darryl. New Testament Understanding of Jesus. LC 78-71529. (Followers of the Way Ser.: Vol. 2). 1979. 22.50 (ISBN 0-8091-9543-7); cassette 7.50 (ISBN 0-8091-7667-X). Paulist Pr.

Mackey, James P. Jesus, the Man & the Myth. LC 78-61627. 320p. 1979. pap. 10.95 (ISBN 0-8091-2169-7). Paulist Pr.

Maloney, George. Centering on the Lord Jesus: The Whole Person at Prayer. (Ways of Prayer Ser.: Vol. 3). 1982. 8.95 (ISBN 0-89453-427-0). M Glazier.

Marney, Carlyle. The Carpenter's Son. 96p. 1984. pap. 6.95 (ISBN 0-913029-02-5). Stevens Bk Pr.

Massabki, Charles. Christ: Liberation of the World Today. Mescall, Sr. Eloise T., tr. from Fr. LC 78-12998. 1979. pap. 6.95 (ISBN 0-8189-0374-0). Alba.

Metcalfe, J. C. Jesus Christ Our Lord. 1970. pap. 2.25 (ISBN 0-87508-919-4). Chr Lit.

Mooth, Verla A. Completeness in Christ. 144p. 1984. pap. 5.95 (ISBN 0-8059-2954-1). Dorrance.

Morton, H. V. In the Steps of the Master. (Illus.). 408p. 1984. pap. 12.95 (ISBN 0-396-08415-X). Dodd.

Most, William G. The Consciousness of Christ. LC 80-68761. 232p. (Orig.). 1980. pap. text ed. 6.95 (ISBN 0-931888-03-4, Chr Coll Pr). Christendom Pubns.

Muccie, Frank J., Jr. The Essene Humane Gospel of Jesus. 174p. pap. 4.95 (ISBN 0-938520-02-4). Edenite.

Murray, Andrew. Abide in Christ. (Large Print Christian Classic). 192p. 1983. Repr. 14.95 (ISBN 0-87983-334-3). Keats.

--Jesus Himself. 27p. 1966. pap. 0.95 (ISBN 0-87509-096-6). Chr Pubns.

Murry, John M. The Betrayal of Christ by the Churches. 59.95 (ISBN 0-87968-724-X). Gordon Pr.

Nee, Watchman. Not I, But Christ. Kaung, Stephen, tr. (Basic Lesson Ser.: Vol. 4). 1974. 4.50 (ISBN 0-935008-11-X); pap. 3.25 (ISBN 0-935008-12-8). Christian Fellow Pubs.

Newman, John H. Taking on the Heart of Christ. 1985. Repr. 4.95 (ISBN 0-87193-114-1). Dimension Bks.

Norris, Richard A., Jr. & Rusch, William G., eds. The Christological Controversy. Norris, Richard A., tr. LC 79-8890. (Sources of Early Christian Thought). 176p. 1980. pap. 7.95 (ISBN 0-8006-1411-9, 1-1411). Fortress.

O'Connor, James. The Father's Son. 324p. 1984. 7.00 (ISBN 0-8198-2621-9); pap. 6.00 (ISBN 0-8198-2622-7). Dghtrs St Paul.

Ogden, Schubert M. The Point of Christology. LC 81-47842. 224p. 1982. 14.00i (ISBN 0-06-066352-9, HarpR). Har-Row.

O'Grady, Ron. The Song of Jesus. (Illus.). 80p. (Orig.). 1984. pap. 9.95 (ISBN 0-85819-470-8, Pub. by JBCE). ANZ Religious Pubns.

Pannenberg, Wolfhart. Jesus: God & Man. 2nd ed. Wilkins, Lewis L. & Priebe, Duane A., trs. LC 76-26478. 428p. 1982. pap. 13.95 (ISBN 0-664-24468-8). Westminster.

Paramananda, Swami. Christ & Oriental Ideals. 4th ed. 1968. 4.50 (ISBN 0-911564-14-4). Vedanta Ctr.

Pascal, Blaise. The Mystery of Jesus & of the Jewish People, 2 vols. (Illus.). 245p. 1985. 207.50 (ISBN 0-89901-228-0). Found Class Reprints.

Patricia. Jesus I: The Man. Morningland Publications, Inc., ed. (Ser. of Three Books Called Jesus). (Illus.). 439p. 1980. pap. 10.00 (ISBN 0-935146-15-6). Morningland.

--Jesus II: The Mission. Morningland Publications, Inc., ed. (Ser. of Three Books Called Jesus). (Illus.). 461p. 1980. pap. 10.00 (ISBN 0-935146-17-2). Morningland.

--Jesus III: The Return. Morningland Publications, Inc., ed. (Ser. of Three Books Called Jesus). (Illus.). 470p. (Orig.). 1980. pap. 10.00 (ISBN 0-935146-18-0). Morningland.

Pelikan, Jaroslav. Jesus Through the Centuries: His Place in the History of Culture. LC 86-45679. (Illus.). 288p. 1987. pap. 8.95 (ISBN 0-06-097080-4, PL 7080, PL). Har-Row.

Perrin, Norman. Jesus & the Language of the Kingdom: Symbol & Metaphor in New Testament Interpretation. LC 80-20822. 240p. 1980. pap. 11.95 (ISBN 0-8006-1432-1, 1-1432). Fortress.

Phipps, William E. Was Jesus Married? The Distortion of Sexuality in the Christian Tradition. LC 85-32319. 250p. 1986. pap. text ed. 11.75 (ISBN 0-8191-5191-2). U Pr of Amer.

Prajnanananda. Christ the Savior & Christ Myth. rev. ed. 7.95 (ISBN 0-87481-652-1, Pub. by Ramakrishna Math Madras India). Vedanta Pr.

Ralph, Margaret. Historias Que Jesus Conto. (Serie Jirafa). Orig. Title: Stories Jesus Told. 28p. 1979. 3.95 (ISBN 0-311-38537-0, Edit Mundo). Casa Bautista.

Ramm, Bernard. An Evangelical Christology: Ecumenic & Historic. 224p. 1985. 14.95 (ISBN 0-8407-7518-0). Nelson.

Richard, Lucien J. A Kenotic Christology: In the Humanity of Jesus the Christ, the Compassion of Our God. LC 80-40915. 342p. (Orig.). 1982. lib. bdg. 32.00 (ISBN 0-8191-2199-1); pap. text ed. 14.50 (ISBN 0-8191-2200-9). U Pr of Amer.

Rodgers, Peter. Knowing Jesus. LC 82-14832. 64p. (Orig.). pap. 1.95 (ISBN 0-87784-383-X). Inter-Varsity.

Rorick, William G. Your Brain & the Mind of Christ. LC 84-50081. 140p. 1984. 4.95 (ISBN 0-938232-43-6). Winston-Derek.

Runia, Klaus. The Present-Day Christological Debate. Marshall, I. Howard, ed. LC 84-6554. (Issues in Contemporary Theology Ser.). 120p. 1984. pap. 7.95 (ISBN 0-87784-937-4). Inter-Varsity.

Sanders, J. Oswald. Le Christ Incomparable. Tr. of The Incomparable Christ. (Fr.). 1986. pap. 3.90 (ISBN 0-8297-1344-1). Life Pubs Intl.

--The Incomparable Christ. rev. ed. 256p. 1982. pap. 8.95 (ISBN 0-8024-4081-9). Moody.

Schaberg, Jane. The Illegitimacy of Jesus: A Feminist Theological Interpretation. 240p. 1985. 16.95 (ISBN 0-86683-972-0, HarpR). Har-Row.

Scheffczyk, Leo, ed. Faith in Christ & the Worship of Christ. Harrison, Graham, tr. from Ger. LC 85-82174. Orig. Title: Christusglaube und Christusverehrung. 216p. (Orig.). 1986. pap. 9.95 (ISBN 0-89870-057-4). Ignatius Pr.

Schillebeeckx, Edward. Jesus: An Experiment in Christology. 1979. pap. 12.95 (ISBN 0-8245-0405-4). Crossroad NY.

Schillebeeckx, Edward & Metz, Johannes-Baptist, eds. Jesus, Son of God? (Concilium Ser.: Vol. 153). 128p. 1982. pap. 6.95 (ISBN 0-8164-2384-9, HarpR). Har-Row.

Schuetze, Armin W. & Habezk, Irwin J. The Shepherd Under Christ. LC 74-81794. 1974. text ed. 14.95 (ISBN 0-8100-0046-6, 15N0351). Northwest Pub.

Schweitzer, Albert. The Mystery of the Kingdom of God: The Secret of Jesus' Messiahship & Passion. LC 85-60625. 174p. 1985. pap. 11.95 (ISBN 0-87975-294-7). Prometheus Bks.

--Psychiatric Study of Jesus. 14.75 (ISBN 0-8446-2894-8). Peter Smith.

Schweizer, Eduard. Jesus Christ: The Man from Nazareth & the Exalted Lord. Gloer, Hulitt, ed. 128p. (Orig.). 1986. 14.95 (ISBN 0-86554-225-2, MUP-H201); pap. 9.95 (ISBN 0-86554-226-0, MUP-P30). Mercer Univ Pr.

Scott, Bernard B. Jesus, Symbol-Maker for the Kingdom. LC 80-2388. pap. 47.50 (2029610). Bks Demand UMI.

Simmons, Billy E. The Incomparable Christ. 128p. 1983. pap. 4.00 (ISBN 0-914520-21-0). Insight Pr.

Simons, Frans. Man Kann Wieder Christ Sein: Eine Abrechnung mit der Theologie und der "kritischen" Bibelwissenschaft. 231p. 1978. 27.80 (ISBN 3-261-03011-9). P Lang Pubs.

Sloyan, Gerard S. Is Christ the End of the Law? LC 77-27454. (Biblical Perspectives on Current Issues). 210p. 1978. softcover 4.95 (ISBN 0-664-24190-5). Westminster.

--The Jesus Tradition: Images of Jesus in the West. 128p. (Orig.). 1986. pap. 5.95 (ISBN 0-89622-285-3). Twenty-Third.

Snook, Lee N. The Anonymous Christ: Jesus As Savior in Modern Theology. LC 86-14117. 192p. (Orig.). 1986. pap. 10.95 (ISBN 0-8066-2220-2, 10-0370). Augsburg.

Sobrino, Jon. Christology at the Crossroads: A Latin American Approach. Drury, John, tr. from Span. LC 77-25025. Orig. Title: Cristologia desde America Latina. 458p. (Orig.). 1978. pap. 13.95 (ISBN 0-88344-076-8). Orbis Bks.

Solomon, Bernard A. The Zaddick Christ: A Suite of Wood Engravings. (Illus.). 84p. 1974. 16.95 (ISBN 0-87921-022-2). Attic Pr.

Sproul, R. C. Who Is Jesus? 96p. 1983. pap. 2.95 (ISBN 0-8423-8216-X). Tyndale.

Spurgeon, C. H. Christ Crucified. 1978. pap. 0.95 (ISBN 0-686-26193-3). Pilgrim Pubns.

Stead, Julian. There Shines Forth Christ. 1983. pap. 8.95 (ISBN 0-932506-29-1). St Bedes Pubns.

Steiner, Rudolf. Jesus & Christ. 1976. pap. 2.00 (ISBN 0-910142-74-2). Anthroposophic.

--Pre-Earthly Deeds of Christ. 16p. 1976. pap. 2.75 (ISBN 0-919924-01-8, Pub. by Steiner Book Centre Canada). Anthroposophic.

--The Waking of the Human Soul & the Forming of Destiny - The Need for Understanding Christ. Wannamaker, Olin D., tr. (Ger.). 25p. 1983. pap. 3.00 (ISBN 0-919924-19-0, Pub by Steiner Book Centre Canada). Anthroposophic.

Stewart, Ed. Here Comes Jesus. LC 77-90584. 160p. 1977. pap. 3.50 (ISBN 0-8307-0553-8, S101157). Regal.

Strait, C. Neil. The Conquering Christ. 56p. 1975. pap. 1.25 (ISBN 0-8341-0273-0). Beacon Hill.

Strange, Roderick. Newman & the Gospel of Christ. (Oxford Theological Monographs). 1981. 39.00x (ISBN 0-19-826718-5). Oxford U Pr.

Stranges, Frank E. The Authority of Jesus Christ. 12p. 1985. pap. text ed. 2.00 (ISBN 0-933470-08-8). Intl Evang.

Stroup, George W. Jesus Christ for Today. LC 82-13494. (Library of Living Faith: Vol. 7). 116p. 1982. pap. 5.95 (ISBN 0-664-24450-5). Westminster.

Sutherland, Stewart R. God, Jesus & Belief: The Legacy of Theism. 160p. 1984. 29.95x (ISBN 0-631-13548-0); pap. 12.95 (ISBN 0-631-13591-X). Basil Blackwell.

Talmage, James E. Jesus the Christ. (Classics in Mormon Literature Ser.). 804p. 1982. 10.95 (ISBN 0-87747-903-8). Deseret Bk.

Tavard, George H. Images of the Christ: An Enquiry into Christology. LC 81-40582. 134p. (Orig.). 1982. lib. bdg. 24.25 (ISBN 0-8191-2129-0); pap. text ed. 9.50 (ISBN 0-8191-2130-4). U Pr of Amer.

Tester, Sylvia R. The World into Which Jesus Came. LC 82-9430. (Illus.). 96p. 1982. PLB 12.95 (ISBN 0-89565-232-3, 4951, Pub. by Childs World). Standard Pub.

Thomas, W. Griffith. Christianity Is Christ. LC 80-85341. (Shepherd Illustrated Classics Ser.). (Illus.). 200p. 1981. pap. 5.95 (ISBN 0-87983-238-X). Keats.

Thomas a Kempis. Imitation of Christ. 1978. plastic bdg. 3.50 (ISBN 0-8198-0533-5). Dghtrs St Paul.

--Imitation of Christ. 1967. 5.95 (ISBN 0-88088-320-0). Peter Pauper.

--The Imitation of Christ. Rooney, John, tr. 214p. 1980. pap. 5.95 (ISBN 0-87243-097-9). Templegate.

Thompson, William M. The Jesus Debate: A Survey & Synthesis. 512p. (Orig.). 1985. pap. 12.95 (ISBN 0-8091-2666-4). Paulist Pr.

Thurman, Howard. Jesus & the Disinherited. LC 81-70333. 112p. 1981. pap. 5.95 (ISBN 0-913408-77-8). Friends United.

Tolliver, Gene, ed. Did Jesus Die Twice? LC 85-63545. 100p. (Orig.). 1986. pap. 3.75 (ISBN 0-937357-00-6). Substance Faith.

Torrance, Thomas F. The Mediation of Christ. LC 83-25330. Repr. of 1984 ed. 27.00 (2027551). Bks Demand UMI.

Tozer, A. W. Christ, the Eternal Son. Smith, G. B., ed. 136p. 1982. pap. 3.45 (ISBN 0-87509-230-6). Chr Pubns.

Tylenda, Joseph. The Imitation of Christ: New Translation from the Original Latin Text. 1984. pap. 7.95 (ISBN 0-89453-432-7). M Glazier.

Tyrrell, Bernard J. Christotherapy II: A New Horizon for Counselors, Spiritual Directors & Seekers of Healing & Growth in Christ. LC 82-60597. (Orig.). 1982. 12.95 (ISBN 0-8091-0332-X); pap. 8.95 (ISBN 0-8091-2482-3). Paulist Pr.

Urs von Balthasar, Hans. Does Jesus Know Us? Do We Know Him? Harrison, Graham, tr. from Ger. LC 82-84581. Orig. Title: Kennt Uns Jesus-Kennen Wir Ihn? 99p. (Orig.). 1983. pap. 6.95 (ISBN 0-89870-023-X). Ignatius Pr.

Valdes, Juan de & Benedetto, Don. The Benefit of Christ. LC 84-9282. (Classics of Faith & Devotion Ser.). 1984. 10.95 (ISBN 0-88070-063-7). Multnomah.

Van Impe, Jack. Heart Disease in Christ's Body. 328p. 1984. pap. 6.95 (ISBN 0-934803-04-8). J Van Impe.

Vano, Manolo O. God's Beloved Son. 82p. (Orig.). 1984. pap. 4.00x (ISBN 971-10-0099-7, Pub. by New Day Philippines). Cellar.

Venkatesananda, Swami. Christ Krishna & You. 168p. (Orig.). 1983. write for info. Chiltern Yoga.

Vine, W. E. The Divine Sonship of Christ. 246p. 1984. smythe sewn 9.50 (ISBN 0-86524-179-1, 9520). Klock & Klock.

Von Kietzel, F. Behold the Lamb of God. 5.95 (ISBN 0-88172-136-0). Believers Bkshelf.

Von Wellnitz, Marcus. Christ & the Patriarchs: New Light from Apocryphal Literature & Tradition. LC 80-83035. 400p. 1980. 9.95 (ISBN 0-88290-164-8, 2045). Horizon Utah.

Wainwright, Arthur. Beyond Biblical Criticism: Encountering Jesus Christ in the Scripture. LC 81-85327. 153p. 1982. pap. 4.99 (ISBN 0-8042-0007-6). John Knox.

Waldrop, Charles T. Karl Barth's Christology: Its Basic Alexandrian Character. LC 84-20701. (Religion & Reason: Vol. 21). xvi, 265p. 1984. 52.50 (ISBN 90-279-3109-7). Mouton.

Wallis, Arthur. Jesus of Nazareth, Who Is He. 1959. pap. 1.50 (ISBN 0-87508-558-X). Chr Lit.

Walvoord, John F. Jesus Christ Our Lord. LC 70-80941. 318p. 1974. pap. 8.95 (ISBN 0-8024-4326-5). Moody.

Wells, David F. The Person of Christ: A Biblical & Historical Analysis of the Incarnation. LC 84-70979. (Foundations for Faith Ser.). 224p. 1984. pap. 8.95 (ISBN 0-89107-315-9, Crossway Bks). Good News.

Wenley, R. M. Socrates & Christ. 1977. 59.95 (ISBN 0-8490-2621-0). Gordon Pr.

White, Leland J. Christ & the Christian Movement: Jesus in the New Testament, the Creeds & Modern Theology. LC 85-11190. 296p. (Orig.). 1985. pap. 10.95 (ISBN 0-8189-0484-4). Alba.

White, Reginald E. Stranger of Galilee. LC 60-10096. (Pivot Family Reader Ser). 240p. 1975. pap. 2.25 (ISBN 0-87983-108-1). Keats.

Wiersbe, Warren. Be Loyal: Formerly Title Meet Your King. LC 79-92552. 216p. 1980. pap. 5.95 (ISBN 0-88207-799-6). Victor Bks.

Wierwille, Victor P. Jesus Christ Is Not God. LC 81-66710. 180p. 1981. 6.95 (ISBN 0-910068-33-X). Am Christian.

--Jesus Christ Our Passover. LC 80-68401. 527p. 1980. 10.95 (ISBN 0-910068-30-5). Am Christian.

Wilkins, Ronald J. The Jesus Book: Short Ed. (To Live Is Christ Ser.). 112p. 1979. pap. 4.20 (ISBN 0-697-01695-1); tchr's manual 4.00 (ISBN 0-697-01714-1). Wm C Brown.

Wilson, Ian. Jesus: The Evidence. LC 84-48234. (Illus.). 208p. 1985. 17.45 (ISBN 0-06-069433-5, HarpR). Har-Row.

Wilson-Kastner, Patricia. Faith, Feminism & the Christ. LC 83-5688. 160p. 1983. pap. 8.95 (ISBN 0-8006-1746-0). Fortress.

Winter, David. Closer Than a Brother. LC 71-181991. (Illus.). 160p. 1976. pap. 3.50 (ISBN 0-87788-129-4). Shaw Pubs.

Wise, Charles C., Jr. Picture Windows on the Christ. LC 78-69928. (Illus.). 354p. 1979. 11.95 (ISBN 0-917023-03-X); pap. 5.95 (ISBN 0-917023-04-8). Magian Pr.

Wurmbrand, Richard. Where Christ is Still Tortured. 160p. 1982. pap. 3.95 (ISBN 0-88264-162-X). Diane Bks.

Zahl, Paul F. Who Will Deliver Us? 96p. (Orig.). 1983. pap. 5.95 (ISBN 0-8164-2468-3, HarpR). Har-Row.

Zodhiates, Spiros. Jesus & the Demon World. LC 82-71842. 1982. pap. 5.95 (ISBN 0-89957-556-0). AMG Pubs.

JESUS CHRIST–APPEARANCES

see also Theophanies

Menendez, Josefa. The Way of Divine Love. LC 79-112493. 504p. 1972. pap. 12.00 (ISBN 0-89555-030-X). TAN Bks Pubs.

Simpson, A. B. Christ in the Tabernacle. LC 85-70720. 150p. 1985. 4.95 (ISBN 0-87509-361-2). Chr Pubns.

JESUS CHRIST–ART

see also Bible–Pictures, Illustrations, etc.; Christian Art and Symbolism; Fish (In Religion, Folk-Lore, etc.); Icons

Beauchamp, Virgil. The Life of Christ in the Paintings by Tissot. 1979. deluxe ed. 49.75 (ISBN 0-930582-29-2). Gloucester Art.

Brooks, Neil C. The Sepulchre of Christ in Art & Liturgy. pap. 9.00 (ISBN 0-384-05925-2). Johnson Repr.

Chesnut, Glenn F. Images of Christ: An Introduction to Christology. 160p. (Orig.). 1984. pap. 8.95 (ISBN 0-86683-875-9, 7918, HarpR). Har-Row.

Emerson, James C., ed. The Life of Christ in the Conception & Expression of Chinese & Oriental Artists. (The Great Art Masters of the World Ser.). (Illus.). 117p. 1983. 97.50 (ISBN 0-86650-054-5). Gloucester Art.

Henkes, Robert. The Crucifixion in American Painting. 1978. lib. bdg. 79.95 (ISBN 0-8490-1370-4). Gordon Pr.

Hurll, E. M. The Life of Our Lord in Art. 59.95 (ISBN 0-8490-0534-5). Gordon Pr.

Hurll, Estelle M. Life of Our Lord in Art: With Some Account of the Artistic Treatment of the Life of St. John the Baptist. LC 76-89272. 1969. Repr. of 1898 ed. 31.00 (ISBN 0-8103-3137-3). Gale.

Kitzinger, Ernst & Senior, Elizabeth. Portraits of Christ. (Illus.). 62p. 1983. Repr. of 1940 ed. lib. bdg. 25.00 (ISBN 0-89987-459-2). Darby Bks.

Parker, Elizabeth C. The Descent from the Cross: Its Relation to the Extra-Liturgical Depositio Drama. LC 77-94713. (Outstanding Dissertations in the Fine Arts Ser.). 1978. lib. bdg. 41.00 (ISBN 0-8240-3245-4). Garland Pub.

Phillips, J. B. The Living Gospels. 288p. 1981. 24.95 (ISBN 0-8317-3948-7, Rutledge Pr). Smith Pubs.

Poortvliet, Rien. He Was One of Us: The Life of Jesus of Nazareth. LC 85-29270. 128p. 1986. 14.95 (ISBN 0-385-13576-9). Doubleday.

Sledge, Linda C. Shivering Babe, Victorious Lord: The Nativity in Poetry & Art. LC 81-9728. pap. 49.80 (ISBN 0-317-30162-4, 2025344). Bks Demand UMI.

Wegner, Susan E. Images of the Madonna & Child by Three Tuscan Artists of the Early Seicento: Vanni, Roncalli & Manetti. LC 86-70511. (Occasional Papers: No. III). (Illus.). 42p. (Orig.). 1986. pap. 9.00 (ISBN 0-916606-10-4). Bowdoin Coll.

JESUS CHRIST–ASCENSION

Bey, Serapis. Dossier on the Ascension. 212p. 1979. pap. 5.95 (ISBN 0-916766-21-7). Summit Univ.

Milligan, William. The Ascension & Heavenly Priesthood of Our Lord. 416p. 1977. Repr. of 1894 ed. 12.50 (ISBN 0-87921-034-6). Attic Pr.

--The Ascension of Christ. 1980. 15.00 (ISBN 0-86524-061-2, 9505). Klock & Klock.

Saffen, Wayne. The Second Season: Lent, Easter, Ascension. LC 72-87064. pap. 24.00 (2026827). Bks Demand UMI.

JESUS CHRIST–ATONEMENT

see Atonement

JESUS CHRIST–BEATITUDES

see Beatitudes

JESUS CHRIST–BIOGRAPHY

Arndt, Herman. Why Did Jesus Fast? 87p. 1962. pap. 7.95 (ISBN 0-88697-039-3). Life Science.

Ault, Norman. Poets's Life of Christ. LC 72-2513. (Select Bibliographies Reprint Ser). 1972. Repr. of 1922 ed. 22.00 (ISBN 0-8369-6847-6). Ayer Co Pubs.

Bailey, Keith M. Learning to Live. 64p. (Orig.). 1978. pap. 0.95 (ISBN 0-87509-158-X). Chr Pubns.

Bales, James. Jesus the Master Respondent. 2.50 (ISBN 0-89315-130-0). Lambert Bk.

Barclay, William. Jesus As They Saw Him. LC 78-18224. 1978. pap. 7.95 (ISBN 0-8028-1775-0). Eerdmans.

--Jesus of Nazareth. 288p. 1985. pap. 12.95 (ISBN 0-8407-5759-X). Nelson.

--The Life of Jesus for Everyman. LC 75-12282. 96p. 1975. pap. 5.72 (ISBN 0-06-060404-2, RD 319, HarpR). Har-Row.

Barnett, Walter. Jesus: the Story of His Life: A Modern Retelling Based on the Gospels. LC 75-28260. 1976. 19.95x (ISBN 0-88229-308-7). Nelson Hall.

Barrois, Georges A. Jesus Christ & the Temple. LC 80-19700. 163p. 1980. pap. 6.95 (ISBN 0-913836-73-7). St Vladimirs.

Bauman, Edward W. Life & Teaching of Jesus. LC 60-7038. 240p. 1978. pap. 6.95 (ISBN 0-664-24221-9). Westminster.

Bock, Janet L. The Jesus Mystery: Of Lost Years & Unknown Travels. LC 80-67420. (Illus.). 231p. (Orig.). 1980. pap. 6.95 (ISBN 0-937736-00-7). Aura Bks.

Boultwood, Alban. Christ in Us: Reflections on Redemption. LC 81-8371. 144p. (Orig.). 1981. pap. 5.50 (ISBN 0-8146-1234-2). Liturgical Pr.

Bramley, William. Jesus & Mary. 450p. 1987. 21.95 (ISBN 0-940291-02-9). Dahlin Family Pr.

Bultmann, Rudolf. Jesus & the Word. (Hudson River Edition). 20.00 (ISBN 0-684-17596-7, ScribT). Scribner.

Caine, Hall. Life of Christ. 1310p. 1985. Repr. of 1938 ed. lib. bdg. 45.00 (ISBN 0-89987-194-1). Darby Bks.

Carol, J. B. The Absolute Primacy & Predestination of Jesus & His Virgin Mother. 1981. 7.50 (ISBN 0-8199-0848-7). Franciscan Herald.

Cary, Diane M. Master. 1981. 9.95 (ISBN 0-8062-1763-4). Carlton.

Case, Shirley J. Jesus, a New Biography. LC 70-95149. (BCL Ser. II). Repr. of 1927 ed. 17.50 (ISBN 0-404-01406-2). AMS Pr.

--Jesus: A New Biography. LC 68-57594. 1968. Repr. of 1927 ed. lib. bdg. 22.50x (ISBN 0-8371-0342-8, CAJE). Greenwood.

--Jesus, a New Biography. 1928. 30.00 (ISBN 0-932062-36-9). Sharon Hill.

Cassandre. Life When Jesus Was a Boy. 48p. 1981. pap. 6.95 (ISBN 0-8170-0913-2). Judson.

Chesterton, G. K. The Everlasting Man. LC 72-11233. 344p. 1974. Repr. of 1925 ed. lib. bdg. 22.50x (ISBN 0-8371-6636-5, CEVM). Greenwood.

Clark, Dennis E. Jesus Christ, His Life & Teaching. 324p. pap. 4.95 (ISBN 0-89191-117-0, 23341). Cook.

Colquhoun, Frank. Four Portraits of Jesus. LC 85-4248. Orig. Title: Fourfold Portrait of Jesus. 84p. 1985. pap. 2.95 (ISBN 0-87784-450-X). Inter-Varsity.

Colton, Ann R. The Jesus Story. 396p. 1969. 10.00 (ISBN 0-917187-04-0). A R C Pub.

Conn, Charles P. The Man from Galilee. LC 74-83547. 1974. pap. 1.99 (ISBN 0-87148-565-6). Pathway Pr.

Culver, Robert D. Life of Christ. LC 76-17967. 272p. 1976. pap. 9.95 (ISBN 0-8010-2498-6). Baker Bk.

Dale, Alan T. Portrait of Jesus. (Illus.). 1979. 6.95 (ISBN 0-8317-7091-0, Mayflower Bks). Smith Pubs.

Daniel-Rops, Henri. Daily Life in the Time of Jesus. O'Brian, Patrick, tr. from Fr. (Illus.). 518p. 1981. pap. 8.95 (ISBN 0-89283-085-9). Servant.

Dawe, Donald G. Jesus: The Death & Resurrection of God. LC 85-5192. 252p. 1985. pap. 15.95 (ISBN 0-8042-0527-2). John Knox.

Deck, Gladys E. A Mother's Soliloquy. 115p. 1986. 7.50 (ISBN 0-913382-38-8, 101-38). Prow Bks-Franciscan.

DeGroat, Florence. Tales from Galilee. 96p. (Orig.). 1982. pap. 4.50 (ISBN 0-87516-485-4). De Vorss.

Demarest, Bruce A. Who Is Jesus? 132p. 1983. pap. 4.50 (ISBN 0-88207-103-3). SP Pubns.

--Who Is Jesus. Chen, Ruth T., tr. (Basic Doctrine Ser.: Bk. 1). 1985. pap. write for info. (ISBN 0-941598-26-8). Living Spring Pubns.

Denney, James. The Death of Christ. LC 81-81100. (The Shephard Illustrated Classics Ser.). (Illus.). 372p. 1981. pap. 6.95 (ISBN 0-87983-258-4). Keats.

DeVries, Henri. Incarnate Son of God. pap. 2.75 (ISBN 0-87509-095-8). Chr Pubns.

Dickens, Charles. The Life of Our Lord. LC 80-22131. (Illus.). 128p. 1981. Repr. of 1934 ed. 10.95 (ISBN 0-664-21382-0). Westminster.

Edersheim, Alfred. Jesus the Messiah. 1959. pap. 10.95 (ISBN 0-8028-8131-9). Eerdmans.

--Life & Times of Jesus the Messiah. 1972. 25.95 (ISBN 0-8028-8027-4). Eerdmans.

Edwards, F. H. Life & Ministry of Jesus. 1982. pap. 14.00 (ISBN 0-686-95353-3). Herald Hse.

Emmerich, Anne C. Life of Jesus Christ & Biblical Revelations, 4 vols. Schmoeger, C. E., ed. LC 79-90066. 1979. Set. pap. 30.00 (ISBN 0-89555-127-6); Vol. 1. (ISBN 0-89555-123-3); Vol. 2. pap. (ISBN 0-89555-124-1); Vol. 3. (ISBN 0-89555-125-X); Vol. 4. (ISBN 0-89555-126-8). TAN Bks Pubs.

--The Life of Jesus Christ & Biblical Revelations. Schmoger, Carl E., ed. LC 86-50154. 1986. Repr. of 1914 ed. Set. 67.00 (ISBN 0-89555-293-0); Vol. 1, 486 p. 16.75 ea (ISBN 0-89555-289-2). Vol. 2, 481 p (ISBN 0-89555-290-6). Vol. 3, 594 p (ISBN 0-89555-291-4). Vol. 4, 476 p (ISBN 0-89555-292-2). TAN Bks Pubs.

Enns, Peter & Forsberg, Glen. Six Stories of Jesus. (Stories that Live Ser.: Bk. 5). (Illus.). 24p. 1985. 4.95 (ISBN 0-936215-05-4); cassette incl. STL Intl.

Farrar, Frederic W. Life of Christ. 1980. 15.00 (ISBN 0-911376-01-1). Fountain Publications Oregon.

--Life of Christ. 1982. lib. bdg. 24.95 (ISBN 0-86524-089-2, 9508). Klock & Klock.

Fosdick, Harry E. The Man from Nazareth: As His Contemporaries Saw Him. LC 78-16469. 1978. Repr. of 1949 ed. lib. bdg. 24.25x (ISBN 0-313-20603-1, FOMN). Greenwood.

Foster, R. C. Studies in the Life of Christ. 1979. Repr. 29.95 (ISBN 0-8010-3452-3). Baker Bk.

Fowler, Harlan D. Behold the Flaming Sword: A Biography of John & Jesus. (Illus.). 1983. 35.00 (ISBN 0-533-05059-6). Vantage.

France, R. T. The Evidence for Jesus. Green, Michael, ed. LC 86-20927. (The Jesus Library). 144p. 1986. pap. 6.95 (ISBN 0-87784-986-2). Inter-Varsity.

Fruchtenbaum, Arnold G. Jesus Was a Jew. Rev. ed. LC 74-75670. 156p. 1981. pap. 2.95 (ISBN 0-8054-6209-0). Ariel Pr CA.

Furst, Jeffrey, ed. Edgar Cayce's Story of Jesus. 1984. pap. 3.95 (ISBN 0-425-09534-7, Medallion). Berkley Pub.

Fusselle, Warner E. Scenes with the Savior. LC 84-11389. 1984. pap. 3.75 (ISBN 0-8054-1532-7). Broadman.

Galeone, Victor. The Great Drama of Jesus: A Life of Christ for Teens Who Want to be Challenged. (Illus.). 207p. (Orig.). 1979. pap. 5.95 (ISBN 0-913382-31-0, 101-28). Prow Bks-Franciscan.

George, Bill. His Story: The Life of Christ. LC 76-53630. 1977. pap. text ed. 3.95 (ISBN 0-87148-406-4). Pathway Pr.

Ghezzi, Bert. Becoming More Like Jesus. LC 86-63424. 160p. 1987. pap. 5.95 (ISBN 0-87973-518-X, 518). Our Sunday Visitor.

Glover, T. R. The Jesus of History. LC 78-25986. 30.00 (ISBN 0-8414-4488-9). Folcroft.

Goguel, Maurice. The Life of Jesus. Wyon, Olive, tr. LC 75-41114. Repr. of 1933 ed. 32.50 (ISBN 0-404-14546-9). AMS Pr.

Goodier, A. Public Life of Our Lord Jesus Christ, 2 vols. 1978. Set. 15.95 (ISBN 0-8198-0551-3); Set. pap. 13.95 (ISBN 0-8198-0552-1). Dghtrs St Paul.

Goodspeed, Edgar J. A Life of Jesus. LC 78-21540. 1979. Repr. of 1950 ed. lib. bdg. 24.75x (ISBN 0-313-20728-3, GOLJ). Greenwood.

Gorman, Ralph. Last Hours of Jesus. 1960. 4.50 (ISBN 0-8362-0221-X, Pub. by Sheed). Guild Bks.

Graesser, Erich, et al. Jesus in Nazareth. (Beiheft 40 zur Zeitschrift fuer die alttes tamentliche Wissenschaft). 153p. 1972. 41.50x (ISBN 3-11-004004-2). De Gruyter.

Gray, Donald P. Jesus: The Way to Freedom. LC 79-66823. (Illus.). 1979. pap. text ed. 4.95 (ISBN 0-88489-112-7). St Mary's.

Guardini, Romano. Lord. 1978. pap. 9.95 (ISBN 0-89526-909-0). Regnery Bks.

Guthrie, Donald. Shorter Life of Christ. LC 71-120039. (Contemporary Evangelical Perspectives Ser). 1970. kivar 8.95 (ISBN 0-310-25441-8, 6500P). Zondervan.

Hackwood, Frederick W. Christ Lore: Being the Legends, Traditions, Myths, Symbols, Customs, & Superstitions of the Christian Church. LC 69-16064. (Illus.). 1971. Repr. of 1902 ed. 34.00x (ISBN 0-8103-3528-X). Gale.

Harrison, Everett. A Short Life of Christ. (Highlights in the Life of Christ). 1968. pap. 8.95 (ISBN 0-8028-1824-2). Eerdmans.

Hirschmann, Maria A. & Pershing, Betty. Follow Me: A Study of the Life of Christ. LC 79-84331. (Bible Study & Sharing Ser.: No. 2). 224p. (Orig.). 1979. pap. 4.95 (ISBN 0-932878-01-6, HB/01). Hansi.

Hodson, Geoffrey. The Christ Life from Nativity to Ascension. LC 75-4169. 540p. 1975. pap. 5.50 (ISBN 0-8356-0467-5, Quest). Theos Pub Hse.

Hughes, R. Kent. Behold the Man. LC 84-50144. 180p. 1984. pap. 5.95 (ISBN 0-89693-379-2). Victor Bks.

Hull, Bill. Jesus Christ, Disciplemaker. LC 84-70471. 216p. 1984. 5.95 (ISBN 0-89109-516-0). NavPress.

Hunt, Marigold. A Life of Our Lord. 191p. 1959. 5.00 (ISBN 0-912414-25-1). Lumen Christi.

Hurll, Estelle M. Life of Our Lord in Art: With Some Account of the Artistic Treatment of the Life of St. John the Baptist. LC 76-89272. 1969. Repr. of 1898 ed. 31.00 (ISBN 0-8103-3137-3). Gale.

Ingraham, F. & Anderson, Eric. Prince of the House of David. Orig. Title: Three Years in the Holy City. 363p. 1980. Repr. text ed. 15.95 (ISBN 0-89841-003-7). Zoe Pubns.

Janda, J. The Legend of the Holy Child of Atocha. (Illus.). 48p. (Orig.). 1986. pap. 2.95 (ISBN 0-8091-6559-7). Paulist Pr.

Jefferson, Thomas. The Life & Morals of Jesus of Nazareth. LC 76-17582. 1976. Repr. of 1904 ed. lib. bdg. 30.00 (ISBN 0-8414-5323-3). Folcroft.

--The Life & Morals of Jesus of Nazareth. 82p. 1983. Repr. of 1904 ed. lib. bdg. 25.00 (ISBN 0-8492-5611-9). R West.

--Thomas Jefferson's Life of Jesus. 1976. 2.95 (ISBN 0-87243-056-1). Templegate.

Jesus in the Gospel. (Illus.). 1980. 12.00 (ISBN 0-8198-0618-8). Dghtrs St Paul.

Johnson, Eric W. An Introduction to Jesus of Nazareth. (Illus.). 512p. (Orig.). 1981. pap. 11.95x (ISBN 0-88334-146-8). Ind Sch Pr.

Kelber, Werner H. Mark's Story of Jesus. LC 78-14668. 96p. 1979. pap. 4.50 (ISBN 0-8006-1355-4, 1-1355). Fortress.

Keller, W. Phillip. Rabboni. 256p. 1980. pap. 6.95 (ISBN 0-8007-5053-5, Power Bks). Revell.

Kissinger, Warren S. The Lives of Jesus: A History & Bibliography. LC 83-48284. 200p. 1985. lib. bdg. 39.00 (ISBN 0-8240-9035-7). Garland Pub.

Klausner, Joseph. Jesus of Nazareth: His Life, Times & Teaching. Danby, Herbert, tr. from Hebrew. 1978. 15.95x (ISBN 0-932232-01-9); pap. 12.95 (ISBN 0-932232-02-7). Menorah Pub.

Levi. The Aquarian Gospel of Jesus Christ. 1972. 7.95 (ISBN 0-87516-041-7); pap. 6.95 (ISBN 0-87516-168-5). De Vorss.

Levin, S. Jesus Alias Christ. LC 71-81814. 1969. 6.95 (ISBN 0-8022-2293-5). Philos Lib.

Lewis, E. R. Life & Teaching of Jesus Christ: According to the Synoptic Gospels. (London Divinity Ser.). 170p. 1977. pap. 3.95 (ISBN 0-227-67519-3). Attic Pr.

Life of Christ, Vols. 1 & 2. 6.49 ea. (0140594). CEF Press.

Lindars, Barnabas. Jesus, Son of Man. 256p. (Orig.). 1984. pap. 9.95 (ISBN 0-8028-0022-X). Eerdmans.

Lindsay, Gordon. Life & Teachings of Christ, Vol. 1. (Life of Christ & Parable Ser.). 238p. (Orig.). 1980. pap. 5.00 (ISBN 0-89985-967-4, 4101). Christ Nations.

--Life & Teachings of Christ, Vol. 2. (Life of Christ & Parable Ser.). 244p. (Orig.). 1980. pap. 5.00 (ISBN 0-89985-968-2). Christ Nations.
--Life & Teachings of Christ, Vol. 3. (Life of Christ & Parable Ser.). 288p. 1980. pap. 5.75 (ISBN 0-89985-969-0). Christ Nations.
Maccoby, Hyam. Revolution in Judaea: Jesus & the Jewish Resistance. LC 80-16752. 256p. 1980. 9.95 (ISBN 0-8008-6784-X). Taplinger.
McConkie, Bruce R. The Mortal Messiah: From Bethlehem to Calvary, 4 vols, Bk. 1. LC 79-19606. 536p. 1979. 16.95 (ISBN 0-87747-784-1). Deseret Bk.
--The Mortal Messiah: From Bethlehem to Calvary, Bk. 2. LC 79-19606. 424p. 1980. 16.95 (ISBN 0-87747-803-1). Deseret Bk.
--The Mortal Messiah, from Bethlehem to Calvary, Bk. 3. LC 79-19606. 486p. 1980. 14.95 (ISBN 0-87747-825-2). Deseret Bk.
--The Mortal Messiah: From Bethlehem to Calvary, Bk. 4. LC 79-19606. (The Mortal Messiah Ser.). 447p. 1981. 14.95 (ISBN 0-87747-856-2). Deseret Bk.
Makrakis, Apostolos. The Human Nature of Christ: Growth & Perfection. Orthodox Christian Educational Society, ed. Cummings, D., tr. from Hellenic. 52p. (Orig.). 1965. pap. 1.00x (ISBN 0-938366-28-9). Orthodox Chr.
Marsh, F. E. Why Did Christ Die? LC 85-18093. Orig. Title: The Greatest Theme in the World. 204p. 1985. pap. 6.95 (ISBN 0-8254-3249-9). Kregel.
Mathews, Basil. A Life of Jesus. (Illus.). 1979. Repr. of 1931 ed. lib. bdg. 25.00 (ISBN 0-8495-3817-3). Arden Lib.
Matthews, Mary. Jacob & the Star. 1986. pap. 7.95 (ISBN 0-8192-1384-5). Morehouse.
Menendez, Josefa. Christ's Appeal for Love. Keppel, L., tr. from Span. 1975. pap. 4.00 (ISBN 0-89555-013-X). TAN Bks Pubs.
Millar, John F. A Complete Life of Christ. LC 85-51584. (Illus.). 180p. (Orig.). 1986. 15.95 (ISBN 0-934943-04-4); pap. 8.95 (ISBN 0-934943-01-X). Thirteen Colonies Pr.
Modras, Ronald. Jesus of Nazareth: A Life Worth Living. (Nazareth Bks). 128p. 1983. pap. 4.95 (ISBN 0-86683-713-2, HarpR). Har-Row.
Montgomery, Mary & Montgomery, Herb. The Jesus Story. 1974. pupil pack 5.55 (ISBN 0-03-012951-6, 125, HarpR); tchr's. manual 8.95 (ISBN 0-03-012956-7, 126). Har-Row.
Morgan, Howard M. The God-Man of Galilee. 1983. pap. 14.95 (ISBN 0-8359-2561-7). Reston.
Murry, J. Middleton. The Life of Jesus. 1982. Repr. of 1927 ed. lib. bdg. 35.00 (ISBN 0-8495-3939-0). Arden Lib.
Nelson, Carl G. The Prince of Peace. LC 79-63954. (Illus., Ltd. ed-600copies). 1979. 10.00 (ISBN 0-930954-11-4). Tidal Pr.
Nevins, Albert J. The Life of Jesus Christ. 248p. (Orig.). 1987. pap. 12.95 (ISBN 0-87973-500-7, 500). Our Sunday Visitor.
Nieman, Charles. Life of Jesus. 55p. (Orig.). 1984. wkbk. 2.75 (ISBN 0-914307-25-8). Word Faith.
Nolan, Albert. Jesus Before Christianity. LC 78-6708. 156p. (Orig.). 1978. pap. 8.95 (ISBN 0-88344-230-2). Orbis Bks.
Notovich, N. The Unknown Life of Jesus Christ. 69.95 (ISBN 0-87968-073-3). Gordon Pr.
O'Driscoll, Herbert. A Certain Life: Contemporary Meditations on the Way of Christ. 96p. (Orig.). 1980. pap. 5.95 (ISBN 0-8164-2040-8, HarpR). Har-Row.
Oursler, Fulton. Greatest Story Ever Told. 1949. pap. 4.95 (ISBN 0-385-08028-X, D121, Im). Doubleday.
Pals, Daniel L. The Victorian "Lives" of Jesus. LC 82-81018. (Trinity University Monograph Series in Religion). 225p. 1982. 20.00 (ISBN 0-911536-95-7). Trinity U Pr.
Panciatichi, Ermenegildo. The Stations of the Cross of Our Lord & Master Jesus Christ. (Illus.). 156p. 1987. 88.85 (ISBN 0-86650-211-4). Gloucester Art.
Phillips, J. B. The Living Gospels. 288p. 1981. 24.95 (ISBN 0-8317-3948-7, Rutledge Pr). Smith Pubs.
Pignatelli, Gaspare. The Christ Nobody Knows: A Sentimental Vision of His Life. (Illus.). 121p. 1987. 88.85 (ISBN 0-89266-576-9). Am Classical Coll Pr.
Pollack, John. The Master: A Life of Jesus. 240p. 1985. 12.95 (ISBN 0-89693-315-6). Victor Bks.
Potter, C. F. The Lost Years of Jesus Revealed. 1982. pap. 2.25 (ISBN 0-449-12468-1, GM). Fawcett.
Priestly, Joseph L. The Way Jesus Walked: Spontaneous Reflections on the Way of the Cross. 224p. (Orig.). 1982. pap. 6.95 (ISBN 0-89962-252-6). Todd & Honeywell.
Prophet, Elizabeth C. The Lost Years of Jesus. (Illus.). 401p. 1984. pap. 14.95 (ISBN 0-916766-61-6). Summit Univ.
Ramsay, William M. The Education of Christ. LC 80-84438. (Shepherd Illustrated Classics Ser.). (Illus.). 168p. 1981. pap. 5.95 (ISBN 0-87983-236-3). Keats.
Rasi, Humberto. Life of Jesus. 9.95 ea. (ISBN 0-8163-0573-0). No.1, 1984. No.2, 1985 (ISBN 0-8163-0602-8). No. 3, 1985 (ISBN 0-8163-0607-9). Pacific Pr Pub Assn.
Rosenberg, Roy A. Who Was Jesus? LC 85-29523. 132p. (Orig.). 1986. lib. bdg. 23.75 (ISBN 0-8191-5177-7); pap. 9.25 (ISBN 0-8191-5178-5). U Pr of Amer.
Ross, Pearl, ed. Jesus the Pagan. 84p. 1972. 7.00 (ISBN 0-8022-2097-5). Philos Lib.
Rumble, L. A Brief Life of Christ. 54p. 1974. pap. 1.50 (ISBN 0-89555-096-2). TAN Bks Pubs.
Russell, Marjorie H. A Handbook of Christian Meditation. (Illus.). pap. 5.95 (ISBN 0-8159-6110-3). Devin.
Samuels, David G. Birth & Youth of Jesus, by Mary, Mother of Jesus. 5.00 (ISBN 0-686-12714-5). New Age Min Spiritualist.
Savoy, Gene. Jamil: The Child Christ. LC 73-92360. (Sacred Teachings of Light Ser.: Codex I). 118p. 1976. text ed. 25.00 (ISBN 0-936202-00-9). Intl Comm Christ.
Seeley, John R. Ecce Homo. 1970. Repr. of 1908 ed. 12.95x (ISBN 0-460-00305-4, Evman). Biblio Dist.
Sheed, F. J. To Know Christ Jesus. 1980. pap. 4.95 (ISBN 0-89283-080-8). Servant.
Sheen, Fulton J. Life of Christ. LC 77-81295. 1977. pap. 8.95 (ISBN 0-385-13220-4, Im). Doubleday.
Shepard, John W. Christ of the Gospels. rev. ed. 1946. 15.95 (ISBN 0-8028-1779-3). Eerdmans.
Shoemaker, Mary E. Anno Domini Number One. (Orig.). 1981. pap. 2.95 (ISBN 0-937172-25-1). JLJ Pubs.
Sloyan, Gerard S. Jesus in Focus: A Life in Its Setting. 207p. (Orig.). 1983. pap. 7.95 (ISBN 0-89622-191-1). Twenty-Third.
Smith, Ester M. & Sutton, Maurice L. The Last Eight Days. LC 85-40202. 125p. (Orig.). 1985. pap. 6.95 (ISBN 0-938232-82-7). Winston-Derek.
Smith, Robert O. A Biography of Jesus Christ. 1987. 14.95 (ISBN 0-533-07232-8). Vantage.
Smyth, Alexander. The True Life of Jesus of Nazareth - the Confessions of St. Paul. (Illus.). 1968. 7.95 (ISBN 0-932642-15-2); pap. write for info. (ISBN 0-932642-56-X). Unarius Pubns.
Stalker, James. The Life of Jesus Christ. Whyte, A. & Moffatt, J., eds. (Handbooks for Bible Classes & Private Students Ser.). 160p. 1922. pap. 7.95 (ISBN 0-567-28130-2, Pub. by T & T Clark Ltd UK). Fortress.
--Vida de Jesucristo. (Span.). 177p. pap. 3.50. Edit Caribe.
Stalker, James A. The Life of Jesus Christ. (Stalker Trilogy Ser.). 160p. 1984. pap. 5.95 (ISBN 0-310-44191-9, 12618P). Zondervan.
Stephens, William H. Where Jesus Walked. LC 80-67422. 1981. soft cover 14.95 (ISBN 0-8054-1138-0). Broadman.
Stevens, Clifford. A Life of Christ. LC 83-60102. 196p. (Orig.). 1983. pap. 5.95 (ISBN 0-87973-617-8, 617). Our Sunday Visitor.
Stewart, James S. The Life & Teaching of Jesus Christ. 1982. pap. 3.95 (ISBN 0-687-21744-X, Festival). Abingdon.
Strauss, David F. Life of Jesus Critically Examined, 2 Vols. Evans, Marian, tr. LC 74-107193. 1970. Repr. of 1860 ed. Set. 59.00x (ISBN 0-403-00238-9). Scholarly.
Sutton, Hilton. He's Coming! 149p. (Orig.). 1983. pap. 2.95 (ISBN 0-89274-256-9). Harrison Hse.
Tambasco, Anthony J. In the Days of Jesus: The Jewish Background & Unique Teaching of Jesus. LC 82-62919. 128p. (Orig.). 1983. pap. 3.95 (ISBN 0-8091-2536-6). Paulist Pr.
Thomas a Kempis. Of the Imitation of Christ. Whytford, Richard & Flint, W. Russell, trs. 264p. 1983. Repr. of 1909 ed. lib. bdg. 95.00 (ISBN 0-89984-921-0). Century Bookbindery.
Thurman, Thomas D. The Jesus Years: A Chronological Study of the Life of Christ. LC 77-80314. (Illus.). 1977. pap. 5.95 (ISBN 0-87239-136-1, 40061). Standard Pub.
Vallotton, Annie. Priority: Jesus' Life in Sixty Drawings. (Illus.). 64p. 1969. pap. 0.95 (ISBN 0-8361-1901-0). Herald Pr.
Warschauer, J. The Historical Life of Christ. 1977. lib. bdg. 69.95 (ISBN 0-8490-1960-5). Gordon Pr.
Weatherhead, Leslie D. The Autobiography of Jesus: What He Said about Himself. (Festival Bks.). 1980. pap. 1.95 (ISBN 0-687-02318-1). Abingdon.
Wells, G. A. Did Jesus Exist? 24.95 (ISBN 0-87975-394-3); pap. 14.95 (ISBN 0-87975-395-1). Prometheus Bks.
When Jesus Was a Little Boy. 32p. 1981. pap. 2.95 (ISBN 0-8249-8009-3). Ideals.
Wightman, W. M. Saint Luke's Life of Christ. pap. 1.00x (ISBN 0-685-02586-1). Outlook.
Zanzig, Thomas. Jesus of History, Christ of Faith. LC 81-86361. (Illus.). 192p. (Orig.). 1981. pap. text ed. 7.20x (ISBN 0-88489-145-3); tchr's. manual 9.00 (ISBN 0-88489-146-1); spiritmasters 9.95. St Mary's.

JESUS CHRIST–BIOGRAPHY–APOCRYPHAL AND LEGENDARY LITERATURE

Belben, Howard. The Mission of Jesus. 96p. 1985. pap. 4.95 (ISBN 0-89109-529-2). NavPress.
Beskow, Per. Strange Tales About Jesus: A Survey of Unfamiliar Gospels. LC 82-16001. 144p. 1983. pap. 9.95 (ISBN 0-8006-1686-3, 1-1686). Fortress.
Goodspeed, Edgar J. Strange New Gospels. 1979. Repr. of 1931 ed. lib. bdg. 22.50 (ISBN 0-8495-2000-2). Arden Lib.
--Strange New Gospels. facsimile ed. LC 70-156652. (Essay Index Reprint Ser). Repr. of 1931 ed. 12.00 (ISBN 0-8369-2364-2). Ayer Co Pubs.
Goodspeed, Edgar J., ed. Apocrypha. 1959. pap. 5.95 (ISBN 0-394-70163-1, V163, Vin). Random.
Holmes, Fenwicke & McEathron, Margaret. Philip's Cousin Jesus: The Untold Story. LC 81-65247. 425p. 1982. pap. 9.95. Reading Hse.
Hudson, Thomson J. Physical Manifestations & Philosophy of Christ. 1978. pap. 4.50 deluxe (ISBN 0-87852-003-1). Inst Human Growth.
Jesus, Way, Truth, Life. 7.00 (ISBN 0-8198-3913-2); 6.00 (ISBN 0-8198-3914-0). Dghtrs St Paul.
Levi. The Aquarian Gospel of Jesus Christ. 1972. 7.95 (ISBN 0-87516-041-7); pap. 6.95 (ISBN 0-87516-168-5). De Vorss.
Life of Christ: A Stanzaic Life of Christ Compiled from Higden's Polychronicon & the Legenda Aurea. (EETS, OS Ser.: No. 166). Repr. of 1926 ed. 70.00 (ISBN 0-527-00163-5). Kraus Repr.

JESUS CHRIST–BIOGRAPHY–HISTORY AND CRITICISM

Blomberg, Don W. Good News of the Kingdom. 1985. 8.75 (ISBN 0-317-13203-2). Carlton.
Coscia, Louis W., pseud. The Promised One. 192p. 1983. 10.95. Todd & Honeywell.
Foote, G. W. & Wheeler, J. M., eds. The Jewish Life of Christ: Being Sepher Toldoth Jeshu. (Illus.). 49p. 1982. pap. 3.00 (ISBN 0-910309-02-7). Am Atheist.
Haley, Jay. The Power Tactics of Jesus Christ, & Other Essays. 2nd ed. 160p. 1986. 14.95 (ISBN 0-931513-04-9, Dist. by W. W. Norton, Inc). Triang Pr.
Hoffmann, R. Joseph. Jesus Outside the Gospels. LC 84-42862. (The Skeptic's Bookshelf Ser.). 132p. 1984. 17.95 (ISBN 0-87975-263-7). Prometheus Bks.
Maier, Paul A. Caspar Schwenckfeld on the Person & Work of Christ. 115p. 1959. write for info. Concordia Schl Grad Studies.
Massey, Marilyn C., ed. In Defense of My "Life of Jesus" Against the Hegelians by David Friedrich Strauss. LC 83-10644. 112p. 1983. 17.50 (ISBN 0-208-02017-9, Archon Bks). Shoe String.
Moore, T. V. The Last Days of Jesus. 212p. (Orig.). 1981. pap. 4.95 (ISBN 0-85151-321-2). Banner of Truth.
Painter, John. Theology As Hermeneutics: Rudolf Bultmann's Theology of the History of Jesus. (Historic Texts & Interpreters Ser.: No. 4). 220p. 1986. text ed. 23.95x (ISBN 1-85075-050-5, Pub. by Almond Pr England); pap. text ed. 14.95x (ISBN 1-85075-051-3). Eisenbrauns.
Salter, Elizabeth. Nicolas Love's Myrrour of the Blessed Lyf of Jesu Christ. Hogg, James, ed. (Analecta Carusiana Ser.: No. 10). (Orig.). 1974. pap. 25.00 (ISBN 3-7052-0011-9, Pub by Salzburg Studies). Longwood Pub Group.
Schillebeeckx, Edward. Interim Report on the Books Jesus & Christ. 160p. 1980. 9.95 (ISBN 0-8245-0029-6). Crossroad NY.
Senior, Donald. God the Son. LC 81-69109. (Illus.). 95p. 1982. pap. 5.95 (ISBN 0-89505-065-X). Argus Comm.
Smith, Morton. Jesus the Magician. LC 76-9986. 224p. 1982. pap. 12.95 (ISBN 0-06-067413-X, RD 372, HarpR). Har-Row.
Vermes, Geza. Jesus the Jew: A Historian's Reading of the Gospels. LC 80-2381. 288p. 1981. pap. 9.95 (ISBN 0-8006-1443-7, 1-1443). Fortress.
Wise, Melvin J. Survey of the Life of Christ, 2 vols. 2.50 ea.; Vol. 1. (ISBN 0-89315-288-9); Vol. 2. (ISBN 0-89315-289-7). Lambert Bk.

JESUS CHRIST–BIOGRAPHY–JUVENILE LITERATURE

see also Jesus Christ–Nativity–Juvenile Literature; Jesus Christ–Parables–Juvenile Literature; Jesus Christ–Resurrection–Juvenile Literature

Alexander, Patricia, ed. The Life & Words of Jesus. LC 83-47715. (Illus.). 96p. 1983. 10.95 (ISBN 0-06-065255-1, HarpR). Har-Row.
Brittain, Grady B. Platy: The Child in Us. LC 81-6503. (Illus.). 53p. (Orig.). 1981. pap. 0.50 (ISBN 0-86663-761-3). Ide Hse.
Broughton, Pamela, retold by. Jesus at the Temple. LC 85-81162. (Golden Bible Stories). (Illus.). 32p. 1986. 3.95 (ISBN 0-307-11624-7, Pub. by Golden Bks). Western Pub.
--The Life of Jesus. LC 85-51852. (Golden Bible Stories). (Illus.). 32p. 1986. 3.95 (ISBN 0-307-11626-3, Pub. by Golden Bks). Western Pub.
Carr, Dan. Our Savior Is Born. 1984. 6.50 (ISBN 0-570-04092-2, 56-1460). Concordia.
Dotts, Maryann J. When Jesus Was Born. LC 79-3958. (Illus.). 1979. 9.95 (ISBN 0-687-45020-9). Abingdon.
Dyer, Heather. Stories Jesus Told. Incl. The Good Samaritan (ISBN 0-89191-286-X); The Good Shepherd (ISBN 0-89191-283-5); The Great Feast (ISBN 0-89191-284-3); The House Built on Sand (ISBN 0-89191-288-6); The Prodigal Son (ISBN 0-89191-285-1); The Rich Man (ISBN 0-89191-287-8). (Illus.). 1980. Repr. 2.50 ea. Cook.
Egermeier, Elsie E. Egermeier's Picture-Story Life of Jesus. (Illus.). 1969. 7.95 (ISBN 0-87162-008-1, D2015). Warner Pr.
Enns, Peter & Forsberg, Glen. Jesus Is Alive! & Five Other Stories. (Stories that Live Ser.: Bk. 6). 24p. 1985. book & cassette 4.95 (ISBN 0-936215-06-2). STL Intl.
Hayes, Wanda. Jesus Makes Me Happy. (A Happy Day Book). (Illus.). 24p. 1979. 1.59 (3620). Standard Pub.
Henry, Kay V. Jesus Was a Helper. LC 86-17540. (Bible-&-Me Ser.). 1987. pap. 5.95 (ISBN 0-8054-4176-X). Broadman.
Hill, Dave. Most Wonderful King. (Arch Bks.: Set 5). (Illus.). 1968. laminated bdg. 0.99 (ISBN 0-570-06032-X, 59-1145). Concordia.
Hilliard, Dick & Valenti-Hilliard, Beverly. Happenings. (Center Celebration Ser.). (Illus.). 60p. 1981. pap. text ed. 3.95 (ISBN 0-89390-033-8). Resource Pubns.
Jones, Mary A. Favorite Stories of Jesus. LC 81-50278. (Rand McNally "Favorite" Ser.). (Illus.). 112p. 1981. 9.95 (ISBN 0-02-689035-6). Macmillan.
Kageyama, Akiko. Journey to Bethlehem. 26p. 1983. 7.95 (ISBN 0-8170-1012-2). Judson.
Kanaar, Barbara. A Child's Story of Jesus. (Happy Day Bks.). (Illus.). 24p. 1986. 1.59 (ISBN 0-87403-023-4, 3483). Standard Pub.
Lorenz, Ed B. Jesus: A Biography. (Illus.). 1977. 4.95 (ISBN 0-89328-011-9). Lorenz Pr.
Mann, C. Stephen. Man for All Time. LC 75-161567. 1971. pap. 2.50 (ISBN 0-8192-1127-3). Morehouse.
Odor, Ruth. The Life of Jesus. (Flip-a-Bible-Story Bks.). (Illus.). 16p. (Orig.). 1982. pap. 3.95 (ISBN 0-87239-559-6, 2733). Standard Pub.
Otting, Rae. When Jesus Was a Lad. (Illus.). 1978. pap. 1.25 (ISBN 0-89508-055-9). Rainbow Bks.
Peterson, Esther A. A Child's Life of Christ. (Illus.). 44p. 1987. 6.95 (ISBN 1-55523-045-8). Winston-Derek.
Ralph, Margaret. Jesus: Historias de su Vida. LaValle, Teresa, tr. (Serie Jirafa). Orig. Title: The Life of Jesus. (Illus.). 28p. 1979. 3.95 (ISBN 0-311-38536-2, Edit Mundo). Casa Bautista.
Richards, Jean H. A Boy Named Jesus. LC 77-71036. (Illus.). 1978. 3.95 (ISBN 0-8054-4415-7, 4244-15); film & cassette 19.00 (4436-38). Broadman.
Royer, Katherine. Nursery Stories of Jesus. (Illus.). 48p. 1957. pap. 2.95 (ISBN 0-8361-1276-8). Herald Pr.
Schrage, Alice. The King Who Lives Forever. LC 81-50590. (Bible Biography Ser.). 128p. 1981. pap. text ed. 1.95 (ISBN 0-8307-0766-2, 5810604). Regal.
Sheen, Fulton J. Jesus, Son of Mary: A Book for Children. (Illus.). 32p. 1980. 8.95 (ISBN 0-8164-0470-4, HarpR). Har-Row.
Sherlock, Connie. Life of Jesus. (Think 'N Check Quizzes Ser.). (Illus.). 16p. (Orig.). 1983. pap. 1.95 (ISBN 0-87239-689-4, 2793). Standard Pub.
Stevens, Clifford. Man of Galilee. LC 79-88086. 1979. pap. 2.50 (ISBN 0-87973-302-0). Our Sunday Visitor.
Stevenson, J. Sinclair. The Friend of Little Children: Story of Our Lord's Life Told for Children. 1978. Repr. lib. bdg. 25.00 (ISBN 0-8495-4876-4). Arden Lib.
Stirrup Associates, Inc. My Jesus Pocketbook of Scripture Pictures. LC 82-80351. (Illus.). 32p. (Orig.). 1982. pap. 0.49 (ISBN 0-937420-02-6). Stirrup Assoc.
Stowell, Gordon. Jesus & the Fisherman. (Little Fish Bks.: Bk. II). (Illus.). 14p. 1982. pap. 0.59 (ISBN 0-8307-0831-6, 5608150). Regal.
--Jesus Feeds the People. (Little Fish Bks.: Bk. II). (Illus.). 14p. 1982. pap. 0.59 (ISBN 0-8307-0832-4, 5608167). Regal.
--Jesus Heals. (Little Fish Bks.: Bk. II). (Illus.). 14p. 1982. pap. 0.59 (ISBN 0-8307-0828-6, 5608122). Regal.
--Jesus Lives. (Little Fish Bks.: Bk. II). (Illus.). 14p. 1982. pap. 0.59 (ISBN 0-8307-0834-0, 5608181). Regal.

--Jesus Loves. (Little Fish Bks.: Bk. II). 14p. 1982. pap. 0.59 (ISBN 0-8307-0830-8, 5608145). Regal.

--Jesus Teaches. (Little Fish Bks.: Bk. II). (Illus.). 14p. 1982. pap. 0.59 (ISBN 0-8307-0829-4, 5608138). Regal.

--Jesus Tells Some Stories. (Little Fish Bks.: Bk. II). (Illus.). 14p. 1982. pap. 0.59 (ISBN 0-8307-0833-2, 5608176). Regal.

Tallach, Isobel. Life of Jesus. (Orig.). 1984. pap. 1.75 (ISBN 0-85151-345-X). Banner of Truth.

Van Vechten, Schuyler. The Bethlehem Star: Children's Newspaper Reports of the Life of Jesus. 1972. 4.95 (ISBN 0-8027-6097-X). Walker & Co.

Wangerin, Walter, Jr. My First Book about Jesus. 1984. 8.95 (ISBN 0-528-82403-1). Macmillan.

Wolf, Bob. Just Like Jesus. (Illus.). 24p. (Orig.). 1982. pap. 0.75 (ISBN 0-89323-034-0). Bible Memory.

Youngman, Bernard R. Palestine of Jesus. (Background to the Bible Ser.: Vol. 3). pap. 8.95 (ISBN 0-7175-0418-2). Dufour.

JESUS CHRIST–BIOGRAPHY–SOURCES

see also Jesus Christ–Historicity

Bruce, F. F. Jesus & Christian Origins Outside the New Testament. 1974. pap. 5.95 (ISBN 0-8028-1575-8). Eerdmans.

Burkitt, F. Crawford. The Earliest Sources for the Life of Jesus. 1977. lib. bdg. 59.95 (ISBN 0-8490-1736-X). Gordon Pr.

Downing, Francis G. Church & Jesus. LC 78-3050. (Studies in Biblical Theology, 2nd Ser.: No. 10). 1968. pap. 10.00x (ISBN 0-8401-3060-0). A R Allenson.

JESUS CHRIST–BIOGRAPHY–SOURCES, BIBLICAL

Here are entered works purporting to give a life of Jesus Christ in the words of the four Gospels, harmonized into a continuous narrative.

Beck, William F., tr. Christ of the Gospels. rev. ed. LC 59-11068. 1959. pap. 6.95 (ISBN 0-570-03724-7, 12-2626). Concordia.

Carter, John F. Layman's Harmony of the Gospel. 1961. 12.95 (ISBN 0-8054-1326-X). Broadman.

O'Driscoll, Herbert. A Certain Life: Contemporary Meditations on the Way of Christ. 96p. (Orig.). 1980. pap. 5.95 (ISBN 0-8164-2040-8, HarpR). Har-Row.

Reumann, John. Jesus in the Church's Gospels: Modern Scholarship & the Earliest Sources. LC 68-10983. 564p. 1973. pap. 9.95 (ISBN 0-8006-1091-1, 1-1091). Fortress.

Schaller, John. Biblical Christology. 1981. 10.95 (ISBN 0-8100-0126-8, 15N0372). Northwest Pub.

Shank, Robert, tr. Jesus, His Story: The Four Gospels As One Narrative in Language for Today. LC 62-17864. (Illus.). 256p. 1962. 7.95 (ISBN 0-911620-00-1). Westcott.

What the Gospels Say about Jesus. LC 78-53636. (Journeys Ser). 1978. pap. text ed. 6.00x (ISBN 0-88489-103-8); tchrs' guide 6.00x (ISBN 0-88489-105-4). St Marys.

JESUS CHRIST–BIOGRAPHY–STUDY

Burgess, Edward E., ed. Christ, the Crown of the Torah. 220p. 1986. pap. 7.95 (ISBN 0-310-41621-3, 9942P). Zondervan.

Cole, Clifford A. The Mighty Act of God. 192p. 1984. pap. text ed. 12.00 (ISBN 0-8309-0393-3). Herald Hse.

Colina, Tessa & Westers, Jacqueline, eds. Jesus & Me Teacher: Primary Study in the Life of Christ. 1978. pap. 7.95 (ISBN 0-87239-165-5, 3243). Standard Pub.

Crowther, Duane S. Atlas & Outline of the Life of Christ. LC 83-82414. 120p. (Orig.). 1983. pap. 6.95 (ISBN 0-88290-207-5). Horizon Utah.

Elwood, Douglas J. & Magdamo, Patricia L. Christ in the Philippine Context. 1971. newsprint 6.75 (ISBN 0-686-18694-X). Cellar.

Hayes, Bernard. To Live As Jesus Did. new ed. 128p. (Orig.). 1981. pap. 2.95 (ISBN 0-914544-35-7). Living Flame Pr.

Miller, T. Franklin. Life & Teachings of Jesus. rev. ed. 1971. pap. 1.95 (ISBN 0-87162-114-2, D5200). Warner Pr.

Stalker, James M. Life of Jesus Christ. 160p. 10.95 (ISBN 0-8007-0177-1). Revell.

Wilson, Seth. Learning from Jesus. Gardner, Lynn, ed. LC 77-155407. (The Bible Study Textbook Ser.). (Illus.). 1977. 15.90 (ISBN 0-89900-056-8). College Pr Pub.

JESUS CHRIST–BIRTH

see Jesus Christ–Nativity; Virgin Birth

JESUS CHRIST–CHARACTER

Adler, Denise R. Jesus, the Man Who Changes Lives. 1982. pap. 2.50 (ISBN 0-8423-1872-0). Tyndale.

Bangley, Bernard. Growing in His Image. LC 82-19579. (Illus.). 155p. 1983. pap. 3.50 (ISBN 0-87788-328-9). Shaw Pubs.

Barton, Bruce. Man Nobody Knows. 1925. pap. 6.95 (ISBN 0-672-50743-9). Bobbs.

Bell, D. Rayford. The Philosophy of Christ. LC 80-67408. 104p. 1980. 6.95 (ISBN 0-9604820-0-8); pap. 4.95 (ISBN 0-9604820-1-6). D R Bell.

Canale, Andrew. Understanding the Human Jesus: A Journey in Scripture & Imagination. LC 84-61027. 208p. 1985. pap. 7.95 (ISBN 0-8091-2654-0). Paulist Pr.

Glover, T. R. The Jesus of History. LC 78-25986. 30.00 (ISBN 0-8414-4488-9). Folcroft.

Hardy, Edward R., ed. Christology of the Later Fathers. LC 54-9949. (Library of Christian Classics). 396p. 1977. pap. 10.95 (ISBN 0-664-24152-2). Westminster.

Jones, Kenneth R. The Winner's Circle: Triumph of Jesus Christ. 1987. 16.95 (ISBN 0-533-07092-9). Vantage.

Kappen, Sebastian. Jesus & Freedom. LC 76-25927. 186p. (Orig.). 1977. 4.48 (ISBN 0-88344-232-9). Orbis Bks.

McCaughney, J. D. Diversity & Unity in the New Testament Picture of Christ. (Lectures in Biblical Studies: No. III). 1969. pap. 2.00x (ISBN 0-85564-016-2, Pub. by U of W Austral Pr). Intl Spec Bk.

McKeever, James. Become Like Jesus. 408p. 1984. write for info. (ISBN 0-86694-101-0); pap. 9.95 (ISBN 0-86694-100-2). Omega Pubns OR.

Manson, William. Jesus & the Christian. 236p. 1967. 14.00 (ISBN 0-227-67723-4). Attic Pr.

Matthew the Poor. Communion of Love. LC 84-10561. 234p. (Orig.). 1984. pap. text ed. 8.95 (ISBN 0-88141-036-5). St Vladimirs.

Miguez-Bonino, Jose, ed. Faces of Jesus: Latin American Christologies. Barr, Robert R., tr. from Span. LC 83-19375. Tr. of Jesus ni Vencido ni Monarca Celestial. 192p. 1984. pap. 10.95 (ISBN 0-88344-129-2). Orbis Bks.

Segundo, Juan L. The Historical Jesus of the Synoptics. Drury, John, tr. from Span. LC 85-7146. (Jesus of Nazareth Yesterday & Today Ser.: Vol. II). Tr. of Historia y Actualidad: Sinopticos y Pablo El Hombre de Hoy Ante Jesus de Nazareth. 240p. (Orig.). 1985. pap. 9.95 (ISBN 0-88344-220-5). Orbis Bks.

Trueblood, Elton. The Humor of Christ. LC 75-12280. 128p. 1975. pap. 4.95 (ISBN 0-06-068631-6, RD 298, HarpR). Har-Row.

Wahlberg, Rachel C. Jesus According to a Woman. LC 74-27461. 112p. 1975. pap. 4.95 (ISBN 0-8091-1861-0). Paulist Pr.

Youssef, Michael. The Leadership Style of Jesus. 168p. 1986. pap. 5.95 (ISBN 0-89693-168-4). Victor Bks.

JESUS CHRIST–CHILDHOOD

Bangham, Mary D. When Jesus Was Four-or Maybe Five. (Illus., Orig.). 1968. pap. 3.95 (ISBN 0-8066-0824-2, 10-7058). Augsburg.

Buchanan, Duncan. The Counselling of Jesus. Green, Michael, ed. LC 85-19736. (The Jesus Library). 160p. 1985. pap. 6.95 (ISBN 0-87784-931-5). Inter-Varsity.

Cammaerts, Emile. The Childhood of Christ: As Seen by the Primitive Masters. 1978. Repr. of 1922 ed. lib. bdg. 20.00 (ISBN 0-8495-0766-9). Arden Lib.

Lorber, Jakob. The Three Days Scene at the Temple in Jerusalem. 2nd ed. Nordewin, Dr. & Von Koerber, Hildegard, trs. from Ger. LC 82-83492. 128p. 1982. pap. 6.00 (ISBN 0-934616-10-8). Valkyrie Pub Hse.

Otting, Rae. When Jesus Was a Lad. (Illus.). 1978. pap. 1.25 (ISBN 0-89508-055-9). Rainbow Bks.

Petersham, Maud & Petersham, Miska. Christ Child. 63p. 1931. 12.95 (ISBN 0-385-07260-0); PLB (ISBN 0-385-07319-4); pap. 5.95 (ISBN 0-385-15841-6, Zephyr). Doubleday.

JESUS CHRIST–CHRONOLOGY

Hoehner, Harold W. Chronological Aspects of the Life of Christ. 1976. pap. text ed. 9.95 (ISBN 0-310-26211-9, 10841P). Zondervan.

Ogg, George. Chronology of the Public Ministry of Jesus. 1980. lib. bdg. 75.00 (ISBN 0-8490-3142-7). Gordon Pr.

JESUS CHRIST–CRUCIFIXION

see also Holy Cross

Adams, Thomas. A Crucifix: A Message on Christ's Sufferings. pap. 0.75 (ISBN 0-685-88372-8). Reiner.

Baldwin, Stanley C. When Death Means Life: Choosing the Way of the Cross. (Living Theology Ser.). 1986. pap. 6.95 (ISBN 0-88070-161-7). Multnomah.

Beattie, Frank. Jesus on the Cross. (Orig.). 1981. pap. 2.95 (ISBN 0-937172-17-0). JLJ Pubs.

Berna, Kurt. Christ Did Not Perish on the Cross: Christ's Body Buried Alive. (Illus.). 1975. 14.50 (ISBN 0-682-48139-4). Exposition Pr FL.

Bishop, Jim. The Day Christ Died. LC 57-6125. 1978. pap. 4.95 (ISBN 0-06-060786-6, HJ 38, HarpR). Har-Row.

Carinat, Alois. The Fully Illustrated Book in Colours of the Crucifixion. (Illus.). 101p. 1983. 275.50x (ISBN 0-86650-078-2). Gloucester Art.

Cohn, H. The Trial & Death of Jesus. 14.95x (ISBN 0-87068-432-9). Ktav.

Deedat, A. Was Jesus Crucified? pap. 1.50 (ISBN 0-686-63916-2). Kazi Pubns.

Denny, James. Death of Christ. 1982. lib. bdg. 12.50 (ISBN 0-86524-090-6, 9507). Klock & Klock.

Dinsmore, M. H. What Really Happened When Christ Died. LC 79-52539. 1979. pap. 4.95 (ISBN 0-89636-025-3). Accent Bks.

Escriva, Josemaria. The Way of the Cross. (Illus.). 123p. 1983. 10.95 (ISBN 0-906138-05-1); pap. 6.95 (ISBN 0-906138-06-X); pocket size 3.95 (ISBN 0-906138-07-8). Scepter Pubs.

Grace, V. V., ed. The Most Memorable Utterances of Our Lord & Master Jesus Christ. (Illus.). 98p. 1987. 97.85 (ISBN 0-89266-580-7). Am Classical Coll Pr.

Green, Michael. The Empty Cross of Jesus. LC 84-19312. (The Jesus Library). 224p. 1984. pap. 7.95 (ISBN 0-87784-930-7). Inter-Varsity.

Harvey, James M., ed. A Letter: The Crucifixion by an Eye Witness. 7th ed. LC 70-161624. (Supplemental Harmonic Ser.: Vol. 4). 107p. 1972. pap. 3.95 (ISBN 0-686-01242-9). Harvey J M.

Hengel, Martin. Crucifixion: In the Ancient World & the Folly of the Message of the Cross. Bowden, John, tr. from Ger. LC 77-78629. 118p. 1977. pap. 5.50 (ISBN 0-8006-1268-X, 1-1268). Fortress.

Henkes, Robert. The Crucifixion in American Painting. 1978. lib. bdg. 79.95 (ISBN 0-8490-1370-4). Gordon Pr.

Hirsch, David E. Rabbi Emil G. Hirsch: The Reform Advocate. LC 68-24717. 1968. pap. 3.00x (ISBN 0-87655-502-4). Collage Inc.

Holloway, Richard. The Killing. 77p. 1985. pap. 5.95 (ISBN 0-8192-1367-5). Morehouse.

Jacobs, James P. Rome, Judea & Christianity: The Crucifixion. 300p. 1987. pap. 7.95 (ISBN 0-9617280-0-0). James Pr Inc.

Jesus' Vigil of the Hour "Watch with Me". 1965. 1.95 (ISBN 0-685-79133-5). Summit Univ.

Joyce, Jon L. For My Sins, He Died. (Orig.). 1981. pap. 3.25 (ISBN 0-937172-20-0). JLJ Pubs.

--Perspectives on the Cross. (Orig.). 1982. pap. 3.25 (ISBN 0-937172-33-2). JLJ Pubs.

Kilpack, Gilbert. Ninth Hour. 1983. pap. 2.50x (ISBN 0-87574-063-4, 063). Pendle Hill.

Lightner, Robert P. The Death Christ Died. LC 67-30992. 1975. pap. 3.25 (ISBN 0-87227-012-2). Reg Baptist.

Lindsay, Gordon. Death & Resurrection of Christ. (Life of Christ Ser.: Vol. 3). (Span.). 1.50 (ISBN 0-89985-983-6). Christ Nations.

Logsdon, S. Franklin. Lingering at Calvary. 157p. (Orig.). 1981. pap. 3.95 (ISBN 0-89323-025-1). Bible Memory.

McIntosk & Twyman, trs. The Archko Volume. LC 74-33199. 248p. 1975. 9.95 (ISBN 0-87983-067-0). Keats.

Martin, Hugh. Shadow of Calvary. 1983. pap. 5.95 (ISBN 0-85151-373-5). Banner of Truth.

Moltmann, Jurgen. The Crucified God. LC 73-18694. 352p. 1974. 18.45 (ISBN 0-06-065901-7, HarpR). Har-Row.

Moore, Sebastian. The Crucified Jesus Is No Stranger. 1977. (HarpR); pap. 5.95 (ISBN 0-86683-891-0). Har-Row.

--The Fire & the Rose Are One. 176p. 1980. 9.95 (ISBN 0-8164-0468-2, HarpR). Har-Row.

Murray, Andrew. The Blood of the Cross. 144p. 1981. pap. 3.50 (ISBN 0-88368-103-X). Whitaker Hse.

Nicholson, William R. Six Miracles of Calvary. (Moody Classics Ser.). 1928. pap. 3.50 (ISBN 0-8024-7834-4). Moody.

Nutting, George L. & Nutting, Ruth S. A Parable of the Ninth Hour. 165p. (Orig.). 1983. pap. 2.95 (ISBN 0-9612266-0-9). Numard Bks.

Paulk, Earl. Wounded Body of Christ. 2nd ed. 160p. 1985. pap. 4.95 (ISBN 0-917595-06-8). K-Dimension.

Peusch, Leonard. The Three Crosses. 1978. 0.75 (ISBN 0-8199-0723-5). Franciscan Herald.

Pio, Padre. The Agony of Jesus. 40p. 1974. pap. 1.00 (ISBN 0-89555-097-0). TAN Bks Pubs.

Rivkin, Ellis. What Crucified Jesus? The Political Execution of a Charismatic. 128p. 1984. pap. 7.50 (ISBN 0-687-44637-6). Abingdon.

Sauer, Erich. El Triunfo del Crucificado. Orig. Title: The Triumph of the Crucified. (Span.). 288p. 1980. pap. 6.50 (ISBN 0-8254-1655-8). Kregel.

Stott, John R. The Cross of Christ. LC 86-21293. 480p. (Orig.). 1986. Repr. 14.95 (ISBN 0-87784-998-6). Inter-Varsity.

Tozer, A. W. Who Put Jesus on the Cross. 1976. pap. 3.45 (ISBN 0-87509-212-8). Chr Pubns.

Tyson, Joseph B. The Death of Jesus in Luke-Acts. 212p. 1986. text ed. 17.95 (ISBN 0-87249-461-6). U of SC Pr.

Williams, Robert. The Veil. 20p. 1976. pap. 3.95 (ISBN 0-89536-247-3, 2200). CSS of Ohio.

Zeitlin, Solomon. Who Crucified Jesus? 1976. pap. 6.95x (ISBN 0-8197-0013-4). Bloch.

Zugibe, Frederick T. The Cross & the Shroud: A Medical Examination of the Crucifixion. (Illus.). 240p. 1987. 21.95 (ISBN 0-913729-75-2); pap. 9.95 (ISBN 0-913729-46-9). Paragon Hse.

JESUS CHRIST–DESCENT INTO HELL

Reicke, Bo I. The Disobedient Spirits & Christian Baptism: Study of First Peter, III-19 & Its Context. LC 79-8117. 288p. 1984. Repr. of 1946 ed. 41.50 (ISBN 0-404-18430-8). AMS Pr.

JESUS CHRIST–DEVOTIONAL LITERATURE

see also Jesus Christ–Passion–Devotional Literature

Ackland, Donald P. Day by Day with the Master. LC 83-70209. 1985. pap. 5.95 (ISBN 0-8054-5196-X). Broadman.

Adams, Robert E. Encuentro con Jesus. (Illus.). 80p. 1977. pap. 1.50 (ISBN 0-311-04657-6). Casa Bautista.

Armstrong, Garner T. The Real Jesus. 1983. pap. 2.25 (ISBN 0-380-40055-3, 40055-3). Avon.

Ashton, Marvin J. Ye Are My Friends. 151p. 1982. 7.95 (ISBN 0-87747-934-8). Deseret Bk.

Bailey, Keith M. Aprender a Vivir: Learning to Live. Bucher, Dorothy, tr. (Span.). 125p. 1980. 1.50 (ISBN 0-87509-299-3). Chr Pubns.

Barclay, William. Turning to God. 1978. pap. 3.25x (ISBN 0-7152-0388-6). Outlook.

Bartel, Bonnie. Night the Animals Talked. 1982. pap. 3.25 (ISBN 0-89536-551-0, 1410). CSS of Ohio.

Bass, George M. The Man, the Message, & the Mission. 1982. 6.95 (ISBN 0-89536-565-0, 1336). CSS of Ohio.

Beattie, Frank A., Jr. I Went to School with Jesus. (Orig.). 1982. pap. 1.95 (ISBN 0-937172-37-5). JLJ Pubs.

Benjamin, Dick. Finding Your Place in the Body of Christ. 1980. pap. text ed. 3.95 (ISBN 0-911739-07-6). Abbott Loop.

--Pleading the Case of the Fatherless. 1982. pap. 0.95 (ISBN 0-911739-09-2). Abbott Loop.

Bernardin, Joseph L. Christ Lives in Me: A Pastoral Reflection on Jesus & His Meaning for Christian Life. (Illus.). 69p. (Orig.). 1985. pap. 3.95 (ISBN 0-86716-044-6). St Anthony Mess Pr.

Berry, Nancee. At Home with Jesus. (Come Unto Me Library). 1979. pap. 1.65 (ISBN 0-8127-0236-0). Review & Herald.

--When Jesus Comes. (Come Unto Me Library). 1979. pap. 1.65 (ISBN 0-8127-0210-7). Review & Herald.

Bickimer, David Arthur. Christ the Placenta. LC 82-24097. 239p. (Orig.). 1983. pap. 12.95 (ISBN 0-89135-034-9). Religious Educ.

Billheimer, Paul E. Destined for the Throne. LC 83-15151. 140p. (Orig.). 1983. pap. 4.95 (ISBN 0-87123-309-6, 210309). Bethany Hse.

Bixler, Russell. Learning to Know God As Provider. 96p. 1982. pap. 3.50 (ISBN 0-88368-120-X). Whitaker Hse.

Bloch, Carl, illus. Jesus, the Son of Man. (Illus.). 80p. 1983. pap. 12.95 (ISBN 0-87973-652-6, 652). Our Sunday Visitor.

Boring, Holland, Sr. & Cox, Bill. Gems for His Crown. 1977. pap. 2.25 (ISBN 0-88027-054-3). Firm Foun Pub.

Bradford, Charles E. The God Between. Coffen, Richard W., ed. 96p. 1984. pap. 4.95 (ISBN 0-8280-0243-6). Review & Herald.

Breech, James. The Silence of Jesus: The Authentic Voice of the Historical Man. LC 82-71825. 192p. 1983. 14.95 (ISBN 0-8006-0691-4, 1-691). Fortress.

Brokering, Herbert. The Night Before Jesus. (Continued Applied Christianity Ser.). 1983. 6.50 (ISBN 0-570-04084-1, 56-1439). Concordia.

Bruce, F. F. Jesus: Lord & Savior. Green, Michael, ed. LC 86-7157. (Jesus Library). 228p. 1986. pap. 7.95 (ISBN 0-87784-932-3). Inter-Varsity.

Burrows, Ruth. To Believe in Jesus. 6.95 (ISBN 0-87193-154-0). Dimension Bks.

Cannon, William R. A Disciple's Profile of Jesus. LC 75-2956. 1975. 2.95x (ISBN 0-8358-0322-8). Upper Room.

Carver, Estelle C. Newness of Life. rev. ed. Helms, Hal M., ed. (Living Library Ser.). 150p. pap. 4.95 (ISBN 0-941478-19-X). Paraclete Pr.

Cavert, Walter D. With Jesus on the Scout Trail. (Orig.). 1970. pap. 3.75 (ISBN 0-687-45849-8). Abingdon.

Chantry, Walter J. Shadow of the Cross: Studies in Self-denial. 79p. (Orig.). 1981. pap. 3.45 (ISBN 0-85151-331-X). Banner of Truth.

Chappell, Clovis G. The Best of C. G. Chappell. (Best Ser.). 240p. 1984. pap. 5.95 (ISBN 0-8010-2500-1). Baker Bk.

Christ in You. 224p. 1983. pap. 5.95 (ISBN 0-87516-506-0). De Vorss.

Clark, Robert. Who Is Jesus? Leader's Guide. Chao, Lorna Y., tr. (Basic Doctrine Ser.). 1986. pap. write for info. (ISBN 0-941598-33-0). Living Spring Pubns.

Craft, Hazel S. Jesus God's Gift of Peace to You. 100p. (Orig.). 1983. pap. 5.95 (ISBN 0-88144-013-2, CPS-013). Christian Pub.

Criswell, W. A. What a Savior! LC 77-82399. 1978. 7.50 (ISBN 0-8054-5155-2). Broadman.

Cushing, Richard J. Eternal Thoughts from Christ the Teacher, 2 Vols. 1962. 3.50 ea. Vol. 1 (ISBN 0-8198-0606-4). Vol. 2 (ISBN 0-8198-0607-2). Dghtrs St Paul.

Daughters of St. Paul. Alive in the Spirit. rev. ed. (Way, Truth & Life Ser.). (Illus.). 1974. text ed. 2.75 (ISBN 0-8198-0282-4); tchr's manual 6.25 (ISBN 0-8198-0283-2); activity bk. 1.50 (ISBN 0-8198-0284-0); parents' guide 01.25 (ISBN 0-8198-0285-9). Dghtrs St Paul.

--Christ Lives in Me. rev. ed. (Way, Truth & Life Ser.). (Illus.). 1973. text ed. 2.00 (ISBN 0-8198-0308-1); tchr's manual 6.25 (ISBN 0-8198-0309-X); activity bk. 1.00 (ISBN 0-8198-0310-3); parent guide 1.25 (ISBN 0-8198-0311-1). Dghtrs St Paul.

--Christ: Our Way to the Father. rev. ed. (Way, Truth & Life Ser.). (Illus.). 1973. text ed. 2.00 (ISBN 0-8198-0300-6); tchrs. manual 6.25 (ISBN 0-8198-0301-4); activity bk. 1.00 (ISBN 0-8198-0302-2); parent guide 0.95 (ISBN 0-8198-0303-0). Dghtrs St Paul.

--Christ's Law of Love. rev. ed. (Way, Truth & Life Ser.). (Illus.). 1973. text ed. 2.50 (ISBN 0-8198-0296-4); tchrs manual 6.25 (ISBN 0-8198-0297-2); activity bk. 1.50 (ISBN 0-8198-0298-0); parent guide 1.25 (ISBN 0-8198-0299-9). Dghtrs St Paul.

--Drawing Near Him with Confidence. 1976. 3.95 (ISBN 0-8198-0403-7); pap. 2.95 (ISBN 0-8198-0404-5). Dghtrs St Paul.

--God the Father Sent His Son. rev. ed. (Way, Truth & Life Ser.). (Illus.). 1973. text ed. 2.00 (ISBN 0-8198-0286-7); tchrs. manual 6.25 (ISBN 0-8198-0287-5); activity bk. 1.00 (ISBN 0-8198-0288-3); parent guide 1.25 (ISBN 0-8198-0289-1). Dghtrs St Paul.

--His Saving Love. rev. ed. (Way, Truth & Life Ser.). (Illus.). 1976. text ed. 2.75 (ISBN 0-8198-0340-5); tchrs. manual 6.95 (ISBN 0-8198-0341-3); activity bk. 1.60 (ISBN 0-8198-0342-1); parent guide 1.50 (ISBN 0-8198-0343-X). Dghtrs St Paul.

--Live the Mass. rev. ed. (Way, Truth & Life Ser.). (Illus.). text ed. 1.75 (ISBN 0-8198-0272-7); tchr's. manual 6.25 (ISBN 0-8198-0273-5); activity bk. 0.85 (ISBN 0-8198-0274-3); parent guide 0.69 (ISBN 0-8198-0275-1). Dghtrs St Paul.

--Live the Truth-Give the Truth. rev. ed. (Way, Truth & Life Ser.). (Illus.). 1976. text ed. 2.75 (ISBN 0-8198-0304-9); tchr's. manual 8.00 (ISBN 0-8198-0305-7); activity bk. 1.60 (ISBN 0-8198-0306-5); parent guide 1.50 (ISBN 0-8198-0307-3). Dghtrs St Paul.

--Preparing to Receive Jesus Christ. (Way, Truth & Life Ser.). 1978. 1.75 (ISBN 0-8198-0548-3); tchr's manual 3.50 (ISBN 0-8198-0549-1); activity book 1.00 (ISBN 0-8198-0550-5). Dghtrs St Paul.

Davis, John F. An Audience with Jesus. 134p. 1982. 4.00 (ISBN 0-8198-0721-4, SP0008); pap. 3.00 (ISBN 0-8198-0722-2). Dghtrs St Paul.

De la Cruz Aymes, Maria, et al. Growing with Jesus. 144p. (Orig.). 1983. pap. text ed. 3.69 (ISBN 0-8215-1122-X); 10.86 (ISBN 0-8215-1132-7); wkbk. 1.65 (ISBN 0-8215-1152-1); compact ed. 3.18 (ISBN 0-8215-1102-5). Sadlier.

Devotion to the Infant Jesus of Prague. 32p. 1975. pap. 0.40 (ISBN 0-89555-106-3). TAN Bks Pubs.

De Waters, Lillian. The Christ Within. 5.95 (ISBN 0-686-05717-1). L De Waters.

Dodd, Robert V. Praying the Name of Jesus. 96p. (Orig.). 1985. pap. 4.95 (ISBN 0-8358-0514-X). Upper Room.

Douglass, James W. Lightning East to West: Jesus, Gandhi & the Nuclear Age. 112p. 1983. pap. 6.95 (ISBN 0-8245-0587-5). Crossroad NY.

Duncan, George. Every Day with Jesus. 288p. 1984. pap. 6.95 (ISBN 0-89066-059-X). World Wide Pubs.

Edwards, Ruth. Answer Me. LC 83-61453. (Illus., Orig.). 1983. pap. 7.95 (ISBN 0-89390-041-9); pap. text ed. 6.95. Resource Pubns.

Faricy, Robert & Wicks, Robert J. Contemplating Jesus. 48p. (Orig.). 1986. pap. 2.95 (ISBN 0-8091-2757-1). Paulist Pr.

Fawcett, John. Christ Precious to Those That Believe. 1979. 10.00 (ISBN 0-86524-026-4, 8901). Klock & Klock.

Fearon, Mary & Hirstein, Sandra J. Celebrating the Gift of Jesus. 64p. 1982. pap. 3.50 (ISBN 0-697-01794-X); program manual 6.95 (ISBN 0-697-01795-8). Wm C Brown.

Fichtl, Frank. The Great Day of the Lord. 256p. 1986. 12.95 (ISBN 0-89962-510-X). Todd & Honeywell.

Fraser, Donald. The Metaphors of Christ. 384p. 1985. smythe sewn 15.25 (ISBN 0-86524-188-0, 9523); lib. bdg. 15.25 smythe sewn (ISBN 0-317-40599-3). Klock & Klock.

Freeman, Bill. Gaining Christ in Daily Life. 12p. 1983. pap. 0.25 (ISBN 0-914271-02-4). NW Christian Pubns.

Gardner, Dudley. Angel with a Bushy Beard. 1980. pap. 8.95x (ISBN 0-7152-0425-4). Outlook.

Goodier, A. Public Life of Our Lord Jesus Christ, 2 vols. 1978. Set. 15.95 (ISBN 0-8198-0551-3); Set. pap. 13.95 (ISBN 0-8198-0552-1). Dghtrs St Paul.

Goodier, Alban. The Crown of Sorrow. 156p. 1982. 3.25 (ISBN 0-8198-1422-9, SP0093); pap. 2.25 (ISBN 0-8198-1423-7). Dghtrs St Paul.

Gratian Of Paris. I Know Christ. (Spirit & Life Ser). 1957. 2.00 (ISBN 0-686-11569-4). Franciscan Inst.

Guyon, Jeanne M. Experiencing the Depths of Jesus Christ. 3rd ed. Edwards, Gene, ed. 1975. pap. 5.95 (ISBN 0-940232-00-6). Christian Bks.

Hall, Barbara. Joining the Conversation: Jesus, Matthew, Luke & Us. LC 84-72480. (Parish Life Sourcebooks: Vol. 1). 103p. (Orig.). 1985. pap. 6.95 (ISBN 0-936384-25-5). Cowley Pubns.

Hannah, Kenneth. Soon Coming World Emperor. 48p. (Orig.). pap. 2.95 (CPS-012). Christian Pub.

Harper, Michael. The Healings of Jesus. Green, Michael, ed. LC 86-20971. (The Jesus Library). 228p. 1986. pap. 6.95 (ISBN 0-87784-987-0). Inter-Varsity.

Harralson, David M. Jesus of Nazareth. (Literacy Volunteers of America Readers Ser.). 48p. (Orig.). 1983. pap. 1.95 (ISBN 0-8428-9608-2). Cambridge Bk.

Hart, Thomas N. To Know & Follow Jesus: Contemporary Christology. 160p. (Orig.). 1984. pap. 6.95 (ISBN 0-8091-2636-2). Paulist Pr.

Hayes, Zachary. To Whom Shall We Go: Christ & the Mystery of Man. (Synthesis Ser). 96p. 1975. 1.25 (ISBN 0-8199-0702-2). Franciscan Herald.

Hays, Richard B. The Faith of Jesus Christ. LC 82-10660. (SBL Dissertation Ser.). 316p. 1983. pap. 15.00 (ISBN 0-89130-589-0, 06 01 56). Scholars Pr GA.

Hazelip, Harold. Lord, Help Me When I'm Hurting. pap. 3.95 (ISBN 0-8010-4285-2). Baker Bk.

Heijkoop, H. L. Unto Christ. 47p. pap. 0.60 (ISBN 0-88172-087-9). Believers Bkshelf.

Holly, Donna. Jesus, Our Savior. (Illus.). 16p. (Orig.). 1984. pap. 0.60 (ISBN 0-87239-701-7, 2307). Standard Pub.

Hornsby, Sarah. Who I Am in Jesus. (Illus.). 160p. 1986. 8.95 (ISBN 0-8007-9087-1). Revell.

Hunton, Johnny. In Time of Need: Jesus. 35p. (Orig.). 1983. pap. 2.25 (ISBN 0-89323-041-3). Bible Memory.

Hutchinson, Gloria. Jesus' Saving Questions. 118p. (Orig.). 1984. pap. text ed. 4.95 (ISBN 0-86716-028-4). St Anthony Mess Pr.

Huxhold, Harry N. Followers of the Cross. LC 85-22823. 80p. (Orig.). 1985. pap. 4.95 (ISBN 0-8066-2184-2, 10-2346). Augsburg.

Hybels, Bill. Christians in the Marketplace. 144p. 1982. pap. 5.95 (ISBN 0-88207-314-1). Victor Bks.

In Jesus Name We Pray. 1975. 1.25 (ISBN 0-915952-01-7). Lord's Line.

Ingram, Kristen J. With the Huckleberry Christ: A Spiritual Journey. 96p. (Orig.). 1985. pap. 5.95 (ISBN 0-86683-798-1, HarpR). Har-Row.

Jacobson, Pearl. I Can't Help Singing for Jesus Gives the Song. 192p. (Orig.). 1983. pap. 3.95 (ISBN 0-88144-010-8, CPS-010). Christian Pub.

Jahsmann, Allan H. It's All about Jesus. LC 74-21233. (Illus.). 160p. 1975. pap. 5.95 (ISBN 0-570-03031-5, 6-1157). Concordia.

John Of Landsburg. A Letter of Jesus Christ. Griffiths, John, ed. LC 81-126. (The Spiritual Classics Ser.). 176p. 1981. 9.95 (ISBN 0-8245-0080-6). Crossroad NY.

Joyce, Jon L. Glory of the Only Son. (Orig.). 1982. pap. 4.95 (ISBN 0-937172-43-X). JLJ Pubs.

Kasemann, Ernst. The Testament of Jesus: A Study of the Gospel of John in the Light of Chapter 17. LC 78-104781. 96p. (Orig.). 1978. pap. 3.95 (ISBN 0-8006-1399-6, 1-1399). Fortress.

Keller, W. Phillip. As a Tree Grows: Reflections on Growing in the Image of Christ. 96p. 1985. pap. 2.95 (ISBN 0-89283-248-7, Pub. by Vine Bks). Servant.

Kempis, Thomas a. The Imitation of Christ. 217p. 1986. 16.95 (ISBN 0-88029-078-1, Pub. by Dorset). Hippocrene Bks.

Lamb, Bob. Speaking Blood: Speaking Faith. 1983. pap. 2.95 (ISBN 0-910709-09-2). PTL Repro.

Lenta, Clementine. What Can I Do for Christ? 5.50 (ISBN 0-910984-17-4). Montfort Pubns.

L'Estrange, Francis L. Random Talks with the Living Christ. 107p. 1986. 30.00X (ISBN 0-7223-2038-8, Pub. by A H Stockwell England). State Mutual Bk.

Liguori, St. Alphonsus. Love Is Prayer - Prayer Is Love. LC 72-97592. 1973. pap. 2.95 (ISBN 0-89243-047-8, 41500). Liguori Pubns.

The Lord Loves His People. 1980. plastic bdg. 5.00 (ISBN 0-8198-4400-4). Dghtrs St Paul.

Lovasik, Lawrence. Jesus, Joy of the Suffering. 3.00 (ISBN 0-8198-0641-2); pap. 2.00 (ISBN 0-8198-0642-0). Dghtrs St Paul.

MacArthur, John, Jr. The Superiority of Christ. (John MacArthur's Bible Studies). (Orig.). 1986. pap. 3.95 (ISBN 0-8024-5344-9). Moody.

McCord, David. The King Is Coming. 112p. (Orig.). 1984. pap. 2.95 (ISBN 0-87239-670-3, 41026). Standard Pub.

MacDonald, William. Christ Loved the Church. pap. 2.95 (ISBN 0-937396-09-5). Walterick Pubs.

McWilliams, Warren. Free in Christ. LC 84-2812. 1984. pap. 3.75 (ISBN 0-8054-1609-9). Broadman.

Madauss, Martyria. Jesus: A Portrait of Love. 1972. 6.50 (ISBN 3-87209-603-6). Evang Sisterhood Mary.

Main, John. Moment of Christ: The Path of Meditation. 144p. 1984. 10.95 (ISBN 0-8245-0679-0); pap. 7.95 (ISBN 0-8245-0660-X). Crossroad NY.

Maloney, George A. Who Do You Say You Are? Christ's Love for Us. (Orig.). 1986. pap. 4.95 (ISBN 0-914544-64-0). Living Flame Pr.

Marshall, John F. In the Shadow of His Cross. (Spirit & Life Ser). 1969. 2.00 (ISBN 0-686-11577-5). Franciscan Inst.

Martin, Hugh. The Abiding Presence. LC 83-11337. 256p. 1984. 5.95 (ISBN 0-310-28921-1, 11337P, Clarion Class). Zondervan.

Martin, Paul. Good Morning, Lord: Devotions for Teens. (Good Morning Lord Ser.). 1962. 4.95 (ISBN 0-8010-5879-1). Baker Bk.

Maxwell, Neal A. Even As I Am. 128p. 1982. 8.95 (ISBN 0-87747-943-7). Deseret Bk.

Mead, George R. The Hymn of Jesus. 78p. 1973. pap. 1.00 (ISBN 0-8356-0432-2, Quest). Theos Pub Hse.

Meditations on the Life & Passion of Christ. (EETS, OS Ser.: No. 158). Repr. of 1921 ed. 34.00 (ISBN 0-527-00155-4). Kraus Repr.

Meilach, Michael, ed. There Shall Be One Christ. (Spirit and Life Ser). 1968. 2.50 (ISBN 0-686-11576-7). Franciscan Inst.

Miethe, Terry. The New Christian's Guide to Following Jesus. 144p. 1984. pap. 4.95 (ISBN 0-87123-439-4, 210439). Bethany Hse.

Miles, Delos. How Jesus Won Persons. LC 82-70049. 1982. pap. 5.95 (ISBN 0-8054-6236-8). Broadman.

Morton, H. V. In the Steps of the Master. 1935. lib. bdg. 32.59 (ISBN 0-8414-6678-5). Folcroft.

Mother Teresa. Jesus, the Word to Be Spoken. 176p. (Orig.). 1986. pocket-size 3.95 (ISBN 0-89283-304-1). Servant.

Muggeridge, Malcolm. Jesus Rediscovered. 1979. pap. 7.95 (ISBN 0-385-14654-X, Galilee). Doubleday.

Muller, Richard A. Christ & the Decree: Christology & Predestination in Reformed Theology from Calvin to Perkins. (Studies in Historical Theology: Vol. 2). 250p. 1986. lib. bdg. 30.00x (ISBN 0-939464-39-X). Labyrinth Pr.

Murray, Andrew. The True Vine. 112p. 1983. pap. text ed. 3.50 (ISBN 0-88368-118-8). Whitaker Hse.

Nouwen, Henri J. The Wounded Healer: Ministry in Contemporary Society. LC 72-186312. 1979. pap. 3.50 (ISBN 0-385-14803-8, Im). Doubleday.

O'Driscoll, Herbert. A Certain Life: Contemporary Meditations on the Way of Christ. 192p. 1985. pap. 8.95 large print ed. (ISBN 0-8027-2491-4); pap. cancelled (ISBN 0-8027-7274-9). Walker & Co.

Ogilvie, Lloyd J. Why Not? Accept Christ's Healing & Wholeness. 192p. 1984. 9.95 (ISBN 0-8007-1223-4). Revell.

--You've Got Charisma. 177p. 1983. pap. 4.35 (ISBN 0-687-47268-7). Abingdon.

Padgett, James E. True Gospel of Salvation Revealed Anew by Jesus, 3 Vols. Vol. I, III. pap. 7.50 ea. (ISBN 0-686-37147-X); Vols. II, III. pap. 9.00 ea. New Age Min Spiritualist.

Paone, Anthony J. My Life with Christ. LC 62-17359. 1962. pap. 4.95 (ISBN 0-385-03361-3, D185, Im). Doubleday.

Papadopoulos, Gerasimos. Orthodoxy, Faith & Life: Christ in the Gospels, Vol. 1. 164p. 1980. 9.50 (ISBN 0-916586-38-3); pap. 4.95 (ISBN 0-916586-37-5). Holy Cross Orthodox.

Pearson, Arthur. In Christ Jesus. pap. 6.95 (ISBN 0-89957-573-0). AMG Pubs.

Peffley, Bill. Prayerful Pauses with Jesus & Mary. (Illus.). 96p. (Orig.). 1985. pap. 5.95 (ISBN 0-89622-251-9). Twenty-Third.

Pennington, M. Basil. Daily We Touch Him: Practical Religious Experiences. LC 76-20836. 1977. pap. 3.50 (ISBN 0-385-14802-X, Im). Doubleday.

Pope Paul The Sixth. Who Is Jesus? LC 72-80446. pap. 2.25 (ISBN 0-8198-0325-1). Dghtrs St Paul.

Portilla, Lorraine. He Brought Me Out of a Horrible Pit. DeLellis, Leatrice, ed. (Orig.). Date not set. pap. 5.00 (ISBN 0-9616892-0-X). Your New Beginning.

Powers, Isaias. Letters from an Understanding Friend: Jesus on the Way to Jerusalem. 112p. (Orig.). 1985. pap. 4.95 (ISBN 0-89622-215-2). Twenty-Third.

--Quiet Places with Jesus. LC 78-64452. 128p. 1978. pap. 4.95 (ISBN 0-89622-086-9). Twenty-Third.

Quezada, Adolfo. Wholeness: The Legacy of Jesus. 89p. (Orig.). 1983. pap. 2.95 (ISBN 0-914544-48-9). Living Flame Pr.

Ragusa, Isa & Green, Rosalie B., eds. Meditations on the Life of Christ: An Illustrated Manuscript of the Fourteenth Century. (Monographs in Art & Archeology: No. 35). (Illus.). 501p. 1975. 52.50x (ISBN 0-691-03829-5). Princeton U Pr.

Reynolds, R. Gene. Assurance. 128p. 1982. pap. 3.95 (ISBN 0-8423-0088-0). Tyndale.

Roberts, Augustine. Centered on Christ. LC 79-4036. 1979. pap. 7.95 (ISBN 0-932506-03-8). St Bedes Pubns.

Roberts, William P. Encounters with Christ: An Introduction to the Sacraments. 256p. (Orig.). 1985. pap. 8.95 (ISBN 0-8091-2707-5). Paulist Pr.

Rogers, Richard. The Love of Christ. 26p. 1981. pap. text ed. 1.50 (ISBN 0-931097-12-6). Sentinel Pub.

Rohrbach, Peter T. Conversation with Christ. LC 82-50586. 171p. 1982. pap. 5.00 (ISBN 0-89555-180-2). TAN Bks Pubs.

Rolls, Charles J. The Indescribable Christ. Rev. ed. 1984. pap. 5.95 (ISBN 0-87213-731-7). Loizeaux.

Ross, Alan. The Jesus Messages. Boster, Gregory, ed. (Illus.). 24p. (Orig.). pap. 3.49 (ISBN 0-9617038-0-6). Divine Love Pub.

Runk, Wesley T. Let's Share Jesus-Together. 1982. 4.50 (ISBN 0-89536-554-5, 1243). CSS of Ohio.

--On the Move with Jesus. 1984. 4.50 (ISBN 0-89536-670-3, 1511). CSS of Ohio.

Salerno, Tony. Life in Christ. 288p. (Orig.). 1985. pap. 9.95 (ISBN 0-87123-887-X, 210887). Bethany Hse.

Sanders, J. Oswald. Consider Him. 2nd ed. 1979. pap. 1.50 (ISBN 9971-83-778-1). OMF Bks.

Savelle, Jerry. Sharing Jesus Effectively. 125p. (Orig.). 1982. pap. 3.95 (ISBN 0-89274-251-8). Harrison Hse.

Schillebeeckx, Edward. Christ: The Experience of Jesus As Lord. 928p. 1983. pap. 17.95 (ISBN 0-8245-0605-7). Crossroad NY.

Schlink, Basilea. Behold His Love. 144p. 1973. pap. 3.50 (ISBN 0-87123-039-9). Bethany Hse.

--The Grace of Love. 1974. gift edition 0.95 (ISBN 3-87209-662-1). Evang Sisterhood Mary.

--Those Who Love Him. LC 69-11639. 96p. 1981. pap. 2.95 (ISBN 0-87123-609-5, 200609). Bethany Hse.

Scott, Raymond L. The Hiding God: Jesus in the Old Testament. 192p. 1982. pap. 4.95 (ISBN 0-8010-8221-8). Baker Bk.

Seashore, Gladys. Let's Talk About Jesus. (Illus.). 1978. pap. 1.75 (ISBN 0-911802-40-1). Free Church Pubns.

Sheed, Frank. What Difference Does Jesus Make? LC 76-162382. 264p. 1982. pap. 6.95 (ISBN 0-87973-810-3, 810). Our Sunday Visitor.

Spong, John S. This Hebrew Lord. 1976. pap. 4.95 (ISBN 0-8164-2133-1, HarpR). Har-Row.

Spurgeon, C. H. Looking Unto Jesus. 1976. pap. 0.10 (ISBN 0-686-16841-0). Pilgrim Pubns.

Stalker, James. The Example of Jesus Christ: Imago Christi. LC 80-82322. (Shepherd Illustrated Classics Ser.). (Orig.). 1980. pap. 5.95 (ISBN 0-87983-231-2). Keats.

Steele. Jesus Exultant. pap. 2.95 (ISBN 0-686-12885-0). Schmul Pub Co.

Steiner, Rudolf. How Can Mankind Find the Christ Again? 2nd ed. Hahn, Galdys, ed. Dawson, Frances E. & Hahn, Gladys, trs. from Ger. 1984. 15.00 (ISBN 0-88010-078-8); pap. 8.95 (ISBN 0-88010-079-6). Anthroposophic.

--Knowledge & Initiation: Cognition of the Christ through Anthroposophy. Adams, George, tr. from Ger. 31p. 1983. pap. 3.25 (ISBN 0-919924-21-2). Anthroposophic.

Stevens, Weston A. Jesus As We Knew Him. LC 85-73771. (Illus.). 137p. 1986. pap. 5.95 (ISBN 0-9605818-2-0). John Alden Bks.

Stewart, James S. Man in Christ. (James S. Stewart Library). 1975. pap. 7.95 (ISBN 0-8010-8045-2). Baker Bk.

Strauss, Lehman. Second Person. 1951. 7.95 (ISBN 0-87213-826-7). Loizeaux.

Stuart, Friend. The Revenant Christ. 1983. pap. 4.95 (ISBN 0-912132-15-9). Dominion Pr.

Tatum, W. Barnes. In Quest of Jesus: A Guidebook. 1983. pap. 9.95 (ISBN 0-8042-0275-3). John Knox.

Taylor, John V. Weep Not for Me: Meditations on the Cross & the Resurrection. (Risk Book Ser.). 56p. 1986. pap. 3.50 (ISBN 2-8254-0850-6). Wrld Coun Churches.

Thomas a Kempis. Imitation of Christ. LC 55-8729. 1955. pap. 4.50 (ISBN 0-385-02861-X, D17, Im). Doubleday.

--The Imitation of Christ. 20.00 (ISBN 0-8274-2557-0). R West.

--The Imitation of Christ. LC 82-80472. (Treasures from the Spiritual Classics Ser.). 64p. 1982. pap. 2.95 (ISBN 0-8192-1307-1). Morehouse.

--The Imitation of Christ. Zomberg, P. G., tr. LC 84-71574. Tr. of De imitatione Christi. (Lat., Illus.). 272p. 1985. 12.00 (ISBN 0-930995-00-7, 00-7). Dunstan Pr.

Tollett, T. O., compiled by. We Preach Jesus. 40p. 1971. pap. 1.00 (ISBN 0-89114-063-8). Baptist Pub Hse.

Vogl, Carl. Begone Satan. 48p. 1973. pap. 1.50 (ISBN 0-89555-098-9). TAN Bks Pubs.

Von Balthasar, Hans U. Life out of Death: Meditations on the Easter Mystery. LC 84-48704. 64p. 1985. pap. 3.50 (ISBN 0-8006-1821-1, 1-1821). Fortress.

Von Balthasar, Hans Urs. The Heart of the World. Leiva, Erasmo, tr. from Ger. LC 79-84879. Orig. Title: Das Herz der Welt. 219p. (Orig.). 1980. pap. 9.95 (ISBN 0-89870-001-9). Ignatius Pr.

Von Trapp, Maria. When King Was Carpenter. LC 75-46021. 142p. 1976. pap. 2.95 (ISBN 0-89221-018-4). New Leaf.

Watchman Nee. The Messenger of the Cross. Kaung, Stephen, tr. (Orig.). 1980. pap. text ed. 3.25 (ISBN 0-935008-50-0). Christian Fellow Pubs.

Weiser, Alfons. The Miracle of Jesus: Then & Now. Karris, Robert, ed. Tiede, David L., tr. (Herald Biblical Bklts.). 1972. pap. 1.25 (ISBN 0-8199-0519-4). Franciscan Herald.

White, Ellen G. Christ in His Sanctuary. LC 70-94869. (Dimension Ser.). 1969. pap. 6.95 (ISBN 0-8163-0128-X, 03254-0). Pacific Pr Pub Assn.

--Steps to Christ. LC 56-7169. 134p. 1956. 6.95 (ISBN 0-8163-0045-3, 19543-8); pap. 1.25 (ISBN 0-8163-0046-1, 19547-9). Pacific Pr Pub Assn.

Wickens, Paul A. Christ Denied. LC 82-50585. 49p. 1982. pap. 1.25 (ISBN 0-89555-183-7). TAN Bks Pubs.

Wierwille, Victor P. Jesus Christ Our Promised Seed. LC 82-72672. 306p. 1982. 10.95 (ISBN 0-910068-42-9). Am Christian.

Wijngaards, John N. Experiencing Jesus. LC 81-52295. 176p. (Orig.). 1981. pap. 4.95 (ISBN 0-87793-235-2). Ave Maria.

Wild, Robert. His Face Shone Like the Sun: Encountering the Transfigured Christ in Scripture. LC 86-8054. 126p. (Orig.). 1986. pap. 5.95 (ISBN 0-8189-0501-8). Alba.

Wilson, Everett L. Christ Died for Me. 164p. 1980. pap. 4.50 (ISBN 0-910452-45-8). Covenant.

Winter, David. The Search for the Real Jesus. 160p. (Orig.). 1982. pap. 6.95 (ISBN 0-8192-1318-7). Morehouse.

Wiseman, Lawrence. Discipling for Jesus. LC 83-70959. 1983. pap. 4.95 (ISBN 0-89900-199-8). College Pr Pub.

Womack, David. Alive in Christ. LC 75-22609. (Radiant Life Ser.). 128p. 1975. pap. 2.50 (ISBN 0-88243-888-3, 02-0888, Radiant Books); teacher's ed 3.95 (ISBN 0-88243-162-5, 32-0162). Gospel Pub.

Zanzig, Thomas. Jesus Is Lord! LC 82-62337. (Illus.). 208p. pap. 7.95 (ISBN 0-88489-149-6). St Marys.

JESUS CHRIST–DIVINITY

see also Trinity; Unitarianism

Anderson, Robert. The Lord from Heaven. LC 78-9533. (Sir Robert Anderson Library). 120p. 1978. pap. 3.50 (ISBN 0-8254-2127-6). Kregel.

Brown, Raymond E. Jesus, God & Man. LC 67-29587. (Impact Books). 1967. pap. 4.95 (ISBN 0-02-084000-4, Collier). Macmillan.

Carballosa, Evis L. La Deidad de Cristo. Orig. Title: The Deity of Christ. (Span.). 168p. 1982. pap. 3.50 (ISBN 0-8254-1102-5). Kregel.

Chemnitz, Martin. Two Natures in Christ. Preus, J. A., tr. LC 74-115465. Orig. Title: De Duabus Naturis in Christo. 1970. 24.95 (ISBN 0-570-03210-5, 15-2109). Concordia.

Guthrie, Donald. Jesus the Messiah. 400p. 1981. pap. 12.95 (ISBN 0-310-25431-0, 12223P). Zondervan.

Herrmann, Robert A. Oneness, the Trinity & Logic. Wallace, Mary, ed. 112p. 1984. pap. 4.95 (ISBN 0-912315-80-6). Word Aflame.

Jesus Christ Is God! 329p. 1985. pap. 9.95 (ISBN 0-914012-23-1, Pub. by Bibl Evang Pr). Sword of Lord.

King, Joseph H. Christ: God's Love Gift. 3.50 (ISBN 0-911866-84-1). Advocate.

Knox, John. Humanity & Divinity of Christ. (Orig.). pap. 9.95 (ISBN 0-521-09414-3). Cambridge U Pr.

Liddon, Henry P. The Divinity of Our Lord. 1978. 20.50 (ISBN 0-86524-130-9, 9801). Klock & Klock.

McDowell, Josh & Larson, Bart. Jesus: A Biblical Defense of His Deity. 144p. (Orig.). 1983. pap. 5.95. Campus Crusade.

McIntosh, Hugh. Is Christ Infallible & the Bible True? 1981. lib. bdg. 27.00 (ISBN 0-86524-076-0, 8603). Klock & Klock.

Menendez, Josefa. The Way of Divine Love. 506p. 1981. pap. 5.00 (ISBN 0-89555-276-0). TAN Bks Pubs.

Migne, J. P., ed. Dictionnaires des Preuves de la Divinite de Jesus Christ. (Troisieme et Derniere Encyclopedie Theologique Ser.: Vol. 37). (Fr.). 516p. Repr. of 1858 ed. lib. bdg. 66.50x (ISBN 0-89241-316-6). Caratzas.

Nee, Watchman. God's Plan & the Overcomers. Kaung, Stephen, tr. from Chinese. 1977. pap. 2.50 (ISBN 0-935008-19-5). Christian Fellow Pubs.

Santayana, George. The Idea of Christ in the Gospels: Or, God in Man, a Critical Essay. LC 75-3338. Repr. of 1946 ed. 30.00 (ISBN 0-404-59341-0). AMS Pr.

Sullivan, Peter. Christ: The Answer. (Orig.). pap. 1.95 (ISBN 0-8198-0026-0). Dghtrs St Paul.

Williams, J. Floyd. Christ Jesus: The God-Man. 3.95 (ISBN 0-911866-72-8). Advocate.

JESUS CHRIST–DRAMA

see also Christmas Plays; Easter–Drama

Dobie, J. Frank, ed. Spur-Of-The-Cock. LC 34-1434. (Texas Folklore Society Publications: No. 11). 1965. Repr. of 1933 ed. 11.95 (ISBN 0-87074-043-1). SMU Press.

Elliott, John R., Jr. & Runnalls, Graham A., eds. The Baptism & Temptation of Christ: The First Day of a Medieval French Passion Play. LC 78-6564. 1978. 24.50x (ISBN 0-300-02199-2). Yale U Pr.

Sayers, Dorothy L. The Man Born to Be King. 343p. 1983. 13.95 (ISBN 0-575-00366-9, Pub. by Gollancz England). David & Charles.

JESUS CHRIST–ETHICS

Kappeler, Max. The Christ Idea. LC 79-868476. 30p. 1975. pap. 3.50 (ISBN 0-85241-079-4). Kappeler Inst Pub.

JESUS CHRIST–EVANGELISTIC METHODS

Bright, Bill. How to Introduce Others to Christ. (Transferable Concepts Ser.). 64p. 1981. pap. 1.25 (ISBN 0-918956-93-5). Campus Crusade.

--How to Witness in the Spirit. (Transferable Concepts Ser.). 64p. 1981. pap. 1.25 (ISBN 0-918956-92-7). Campus Crusade.

Goodman, Clarke E. Preaching the Gospel of Jesus Christ. LC 84-90077. 101p. 1985. 8.95 (ISBN 0-533-06156-3). Vantage.

JESUS CHRIST–EXAMPLE

Adams, Jay E. Christ & Your Problems. 33p. 1973. pap. 1.25 (ISBN 0-87552-011-1). Presby & Reformed.

Babaja, Thomas. Take Jesus for Example. (Illus.). 66p. (Orig.). 1985. pap. text ed. 3.50 (ISBN 0-318-18797-3). Dovehaven Pr Ltd.

Brusselmans, C., ed. Jesus Loves Children. 5.95 (ISBN 0-8215-9889-9). Sadlier.

Fry, Caroline. Christ Our Example. 155p. 1976. pap. 3.95 (ISBN 0-685-53618-1). Reiner.

Hayes, Bernard. To Live As Jesus Did. new ed. 128p. (Orig.). 1981. pap. 2.95 (ISBN 0-914544-35-7). Living Flame Pr.

Hengel, Martin. The Charismatic Leader & His Followers. LC 81-9708. 124p. 1981. 10.95 (ISBN 0-8245-0137-3). Crossroad NY.

Kaung, Stephen. The Splendor of His Ways. Fader, Herbert L., ed. 1974. 5.00 (ISBN 0-935008-42-X); pap. 3.25 (ISBN 0-935008-43-8). Christian Fellow Pubs.

Kliewer, Marilyn P. Have the Mind of Christ. LC 85-81041. (Faith & Life Bible Studies). 90p. 1985. pap. 4.95 (ISBN 0-87303-104-0). Faith & Life.

Ryan, Arthur H. Mirroring Christ's Splendour. Rev. ed. 216p. 1984. pap. 7.00 (ISBN 0-912414-40-5). Lumen Christi.

St. Clair. Following Jesus. 1983. 4.95 (ISBN 0-88207-301-X). Victor Bks.

Tennis, Diane. Is God the Only Reliable Father. LC 84-20899. 118p. (Orig.). 1985. pap. 7.95 (ISBN 0-664-24594-3). Westminster.

Thomas a Kempis. Of the Imitation of Christ. (Large Print Christian Classic Ser.). 1982. 14.95 (ISBN 0-87983-288-6). Keats.

We Follow Jesus. 2.82 (ISBN 0-02-649490-6, 64949); tchr's manual 2.52 (ISBN 0-02-649500-7, 64950). Benziger Pub Co.

JESUS CHRIST–FICTION

Bishop, Jim. The Day Christ Died. LC 57-6125. 1978. pap. 4.95 (ISBN 0-06-060786-6, HJ 38, HarpR). Har-Row.

Dostoyevsky, Fyodor. The Grand Inquisitor. LC 56-7503. (Milestones of Thought Ser.). pap. 2.95x (ISBN 0-8044-6125-2). Ungar.

--Grand Inquisitor on the Nature of Man. Garnett, Constance, tr. 1948. pap. 4.79 scp (ISBN 0-672-60237-7, LLA63). Bobbs.

Douglas, Lloyd C. Robe. 1942. 12.95 (ISBN 0-395-07635-8). HM.

Gibran, Kahlil. Jesus the Son of Man. (Illus.). 1928. 14.95 (ISBN 0-394-43124-3). Knopf.

Gompertz, Rolf. My Jewish Brother Jesus. LC 76-55591. 200p. 1977. 15.00 (ISBN 0-918248-03-5); pap. 10.00 (ISBN 0-918248-02-7). Word Doctor.

Jacobs, Joseph. Jesus as Others Saw Him: A Retrospect A.D. 54. LC 73-2211. (The Jewish People; History, Religion, Literature Ser.). Repr. of 1925 ed. 21.00 (ISBN 0-405-05275-8). Ayer Co Pubs.

Lawrence, David H. Saint Mawr. Bd. with The Man Who Died. 1959. pap. 3.95 (ISBN 0-394-70071-6, Vin). Random.

Newcomb, Robert T. Janissa. 1943. 8.00 (ISBN 0-685-08807-3). Destiny.

O'Byrne, Cathal. From Green Hills of Galilee. facsimile ed. LC 71-167464. (Short Story Index Reprint Ser.). Repr. of 1935 ed. 14.00 (ISBN 0-8369-3990-5). Ayer Co Pubs.

Wallace, Lew. Ben Hur. (Classics Ser). (YA) pap. 2.95 (ISBN 0-8049-0074-4, CL-74). Airmont.

Ziolkowski, Theodore. Fictional Transfiguration of Jesus. LC 70-39794. 536p. 1972. 34.00 (ISBN 0-691-06235-8); pap. 13.50 (ISBN 0-691-01346-2). Princeton U Pr.

JESUS CHRIST–FORTY DAYS IN THE WILDERNESS

see Jesus Christ–Temptation

JESUS CHRIST–FOUNDATION OF THE CHURCH

see Church–Foundation

JESUS CHRIST–FRIENDS AND ASSOCIATES

Goodwin, Bennie E. How to Be a Growing Christian. LC 86-33737. 40p. (Orig.). 1986. pap. 1.95 (ISBN 0-87784-573-5). Inter-Varsity.

MacGregor, G. H. & Purdy, A. C. Jew & Greek: Tutors Unto Christ. 59.95 (ISBN 0-8490-0444-6). Gordon Pr.

Marquart, M. Jesus' Second Family. (Arch Book Series Fourteen). 1977. pap. 0.99 (ISBN 0-570-06111-3, 59-1229). Concordia.

Moltmann-Wendel, Elisabeth. The Women Around Jesus. LC 82-72478. 160p. 1982. pap. 7.95 (ISBN 0-8245-0535-2). Crossroad NY.

Narramore, Kathy & Hill, Alice. Kindred Spirits. 144p. (Orig.). 1985. pap. 5.95 (ISBN 0-310-30531-4, 11245P). Zondervan.

Richardson, P. & Hurd, J. From Jesus to Paul: Studies in Honour of Francis Wright Beare. 256p. 1984. pap. text ed. 16.50x (ISBN 0-88920-138-2, Pub. by Wilfrid Laurier Canada). Humanities.

JESUS CHRIST–HISTORICITY

see also Jesus Christ–Biography–Sources

Bammel, E. & Moule, C. F., eds. Jesus & the Politics of His Day. 320p. 1985. pap. 17.95 (ISBN 0-521-31344-9). Cambridge U Pr.

Cadbury, Henry J. Eclipse of the Historical Jesus. LC 64-12998. (Orig.). 1964. 2.50x (ISBN 0-87574-133-9, 133). Pendle Hill.

Carmichael, Joel. The Death of Jesus. 296p. (Orig.). 1982. pap. 8.95 (ISBN 0-8180-0826-1). Horizon.

Cook, Michael L. The Historical Jesus. (Guidelines for Contemporary Catholics). (Orig.). 1986. pap. 7.95 (ISBN 0-88347-188-4). Thomas More.

Crossan, John D. In Parables: The Challenge of the Historical Jesus. LC 73-7067. 141p. 1985. pap. 8.95 (ISBN 0-06-061609-1, HarpR). Har-Row.

Cullman, Oscar. Christ & Time: The Primitive Christian Conception of Time & History. 1977. lib. bdg. 59.95 (ISBN 0-8490-1614-2). Gordon Pr.

Edersheim, Alfred. The Life & Times of Jesus the Messiah. 1568p. Date not set. 24.95 (ISBN 0-917006-12-7). Hendrickson MA.

Fries, Paul R. & Nersoyan, Tiran, eds. Christ in East & West. 240p. 1987. 31.95 (ISBN 0-86554-267-8, MUP H-228); pap. 14.95 (ISBN 0-86554-277-5). Mercer Univ Pr.

Goodier, A. Public Life of Our Lord Jesus Christ, 2 vols. 1978. Set. 15.95 (ISBN 0-8198-0551-3); Set. pap. 13.95 (ISBN 0-8198-0552-1). Dghtrs St Paul.

Habermas, Gary R. Ancient Evidence for the Life of Jesus: Historical Records of His Death & Resurrection. 1985. pap. 6.95 (ISBN 0-8407-5919-3). Nelson.

Hiers, Richard H. The Historical Jesus & the Kingdom of God: Present & Future in the Message & Ministry of Jesus. LC 73-2623. (University of Florida Humanities Monographs: No. 38). 1973. pap. 3.50 (ISBN 0-8130-0386-5). U Presses Fla.

Keck, Leander E. A Future for the Historical Jesus: The Place of Jesus in Preaching & Theology. LC 81-43081. pap. 70.80 (2029605). Bks Demand UMI.

Kevane, Eugene. The Lord of History. 1980. 4.00 (ISBN 0-8198-0636-6); pap. 3.00 (ISBN 0-8198-0637-4). Dghtrs St Paul.

Marshall, I. Howard. I Believe in the Historical Jesus. (I Believe Ser). 1977. pap. 4.95 (ISBN 0-8028-1691-6). Eerdmans.

Murray, Andrew. Secret of Christ Our Life. (Secret Ser.). (Orig.). 1980. pap. 1.95 (ISBN 0-87508-385-4). Chr Lit.

Robinson, James M. A New Quest of the Historical Jesus & Other Essays. LC 82-48586. 224p. 1983. pap. 12.95 (ISBN 0-8006-1698-7). Fortress.

Wagner, Al. Historical Records Concerning Jesus the Christ. 64p. 1984. 10.50 (ISBN 0-89962-347-6). Todd & Honeywell.

Wells, G. A. The Historical Evidence for Jesus. LC 82-60381. 350p. 1982. 20.95 (ISBN 0-87975-180-0). Prometheus Bks.

Zanzig, Thomas. Jesus of History, Christ of Faith. LC 81-86361. (Illus.). 192p. (Orig.). 1981. pap. text ed. 7.20x (ISBN 0-88489-145-3); tchr's. manual 9.00 (ISBN 0-88489-146-1); spiritmasters 9.95. St Mary's.

JESUS CHRIST–HISTORY OF DOCTRINES

Aulen, Gustaf E. Reformation & Catholicity. Wahlstrom, Eric H., tr. from Swedish. LC 78-25981. 1979. Repr. of 1961 ed. lib. bdg. 22.50x (ISBN 0-313-20809-3, AURC). Greenwood.

Barth, Karl. The Doctrine of Reconciliation: Jesus Christ the True Witness. Bromiley, G. W. & Torrance, T. F., eds. Bromiley, G. W., tr. from Ger. (Church Dogmatics Ser.: Vol. 4, Pt. 3, 2nd Half). 492p. 1962. 29.95 (ISBN 0-567-09044-2, Pub. by T & T Clark Ltd UK). Fortress.

Carmody, John. The Heart of the Christian Matter: An Ecumenical Approach. 304p. (Orig.). 1983. pap. 12.95 (ISBN 0-687-16765-5). Abingdon.

Conn, Charles W. Christ & the Gospels. 109p. 1964. pap. 4.25 (ISBN 0-87148-150-2). Pathway Pr.

De Jonge, Marinus. Jesus: Stranger from Heaven & Son of God. Steely, John E., ed. LC 77-9984. (Society of Biblical Literature. Sources for Biblical Studies: No. 11). Repr. of 1977 ed. 61.50 (ISBN 0-8357-9575-6, 2017532). Bks Demand UMI.

Deschner, John. Wesley's Christology: An Interpretation. LC 85-2274. 244p. pap. 12.95x (ISBN 0-87074-200-0). SMU Press.

Fuller, Reginald & Perkins, Pheme. Who Is This Christ? Gospel Christology & Contemporary Faith. LC 82-48590. 176p. 1983. pap. 8.95 (ISBN 0-8006-1706-1, 1-1706). Fortress.

Grillmeier, Aloys. Christ in Christian Tradition: From the Apostolic Age to Chalcedon, Vol. 1. rev. ed. Bowden, John S., tr. from Ger. LC 75-13456. 451p. 1975. 29.95 (ISBN 0-8042-0492-6). John Knox.

Hale, Robert. Christ & the Universe. Meilach, Michael, ed. (Theilhard de Chardin & the Universe Ser). 5.50 (ISBN 0-8199-0449-X). Franciscan Herald.

Marxsen, Willi. The Beginnings of Christology: Together with the Lord's Supper As a Christological Problem. LC 79-7384. pap. 31.80 (2029295). Bks Demand UMI.

Moule, Charles F. The Origin of Christology. LC 76-11087. 1977. 29.95 (ISBN 0-521-21290-1); pap. 11.95 (ISBN 0-521-29363-4). Cambridge U Pr.

O'Collins, Gerald. What Are They Saying about Jesus? Rev. ed. LC 77-70640. 1982. pap. 3.95 (ISBN 0-8091-2521-8). Paulist Pr.

Rogers, Jack, et al. Case Studies in Christ & Salvation. LC 76-53765. 176p. 1977. pap. 7.95 (ISBN 0-664-24133-6). Westminster.

Sabourin, Leopold. Christology: Basic Texts in Focus. LC 84-12304. 259p. (Orig.). 1984. pap. 9.95 (ISBN 0-8189-0471-2). ALBA.

Stanton, G. N. Jesus of Nazareth in New Testament Preaching. LC 73-92782. (Society of New Testament Studies: No. 27). 228p. 1975. 44.50 (ISBN 0-521-20465-8). Cambridge U Pr.

JESUS CHRIST–HOLY SHROUD

see Holy Shroud

JESUS CHRIST–HUMANITY

Brown, Raymond E. Jesus, God & Man. LC 67-29587. (Impact Books). 1967. pap. 4.95 (ISBN 0-02-084000-4, Collier). Macmillan.

Chemnitz, Martin. Two Natures in Christ. Preus, J. A., tr. LC 74-115465. Orig. Title: De Duabus Naturis in Christo. 1970. 24.95 (ISBN 0-570-03210-5, 15-2109). Concordia.

Comblin, Jose. Jesus of Nazareth: Meditations on His Humanity. Kabat, Carl, tr. from Port. LC 75-29580. Orig. Title: Jesus De Nazare. 176p. (Orig.). 1976. pap. 3.48 (ISBN 0-88344-239-6). Orbis Bks.

Fast, H. A. Jesus & Human Conflict. LC 58-10315. 215p. 1959. 7.95 (ISBN 0-8361-1382-9). Herald Pr.

Glover, T. R. Jesus in the Experience of Men. LC 78-23617. 1921. 30.00 (ISBN 0-8414-4616-4). Folcroft.

Ivar, Asheim. Christ & Humanity. LC 73-10426. pap. 50.80 (2026913). Bks Demand UMI.

Johnson, Harry. Humanity of the Saviour. 1962. 8.50x (ISBN 0-8401-1248-3). A R Allenson.

Knox, John. Humanity & Divinity of Christ. (Orig.). pap. 9.95 (ISBN 0-521-09414-3). Cambridge U Pr.

Murray, Andrew. Secret of Christ Our Life. (Secret Ser.). (Orig.). 1980. pap. 1.95 (ISBN 0-87508-385-4). Chr Lit.

Stewart, Marjorie. Looking at Jesus with Luke. 24p. 1978. pap. 0.75 (ISBN 0-88243-756-9, 02-0756). Gospel Pub.

JESUS CHRIST–INCARNATION
see Incarnation

JESUS CHRIST–INFLUENCE

Carl, Joseph B. Jesus in Our Affluent Society. 208p. 1981. 9.95 (ISBN 0-938234-01-3); pap. 5.95 (ISBN 0-938234-00-5). Ministry Pubns.

Cramer, Raymond L. Psicologia de Jesus y la Salud Mental. Vargas, Carlos A., tr. from Eng. LC 76-16438. Tr. of Paychology of Jesus & Mental Health. (Span.). 191p. 1976. pap. 5.95 (ISBN 0-89922-074-6). Edit Caribe.

Dreyfus, Francois. Did Jesus Know He Was God? Date not set. price not set (ISBN 0-8199-0899-1). Franciscan Herald.

Griffiths, Michael. The Example of Jesus. LC 84-6739. (The Jesus Library). 180p. 1985. pap. 6.95 (ISBN 0-87784-929-3). Inter-Varsity.

Hunt, Arnold D. Christ & the World's Religious. 124p. (Orig.). 1970. pap. 8.45 (ISBN 0-85819-003-6, Pub. by JBCE). ANZ Religious Pubns.

Murray, Andrew. Secret of Christ Our Life. (Secret Ser.). (Orig.). 1980. pap. 1.95 (ISBN 0-87508-385-4). Chr Lit.

Pelikan, Jaroslav. Jesus Through the Centuries: His Place in the History of Culture. LC 85-2428. (Illus.). 272p. 1985. 22.50 (ISBN 0-300-03496-2). Yale U Pr.

JESUS CHRIST–ISLAMIC INTERPRETATIONS

Basetti-Sami, Giulio. Koran in the Light of Christ. 1977. 8.50 (ISBN 0-8199-0713-8). Franciscan Herald.

Wismer, Don. The Islamic Jesus: An Annotated Bibliography of Sources in English & French. LC 76-24737. (Reference Library of the Humanities Ser.: Vol. 58). 1977. lib. bdg. 40.00 (ISBN 0-8240-9940-0). Garland Pub.

JESUS CHRIST–JEWISH INTERPRETATIONS

Borowitz, Eugene B. Contemporary Christologies: A Jewish Response. LC 80-81051. 208p. (Orig.). 1980. pap. 8.95 (ISBN 0-8091-2305-3). Paulist Pr.

Brown, Raymond. The Message of Hebrews. Motyer, J. A. & Stott, John R., eds. LC 82-15321. (The Bible Speaks Today Ser.). 272p. (Orig.). 1982. pap. 7.95 (ISBN 0-87784-289-2). Inter-Varsity.

Dalman, Gustaf. Jesus Christ in the Talmud, Midrash, Zohar, & the Liturgy of the Synagogue. LC 73-2190. (The Jewish People; History, Religion, Literature Ser.). Repr. of 1893 ed. 11.00 (ISBN 0-405-05256-1). Ayer Co Pubs.

Hirsch, Emil G. My Religion. Levi, Gerson B., ed. Incl. The Crucifixion Viewed from a Jewish Standpoint (1908. LC 73-2207. (The Jewish People; History, Religion, Literature Ser.). Repr. of 1925 ed. 33.00 (ISBN 0-405-05271-5). Ayer Co Pubs.

Lapide, Pinchas. The Resurrection of Jesus: A Jewish Perspective. Linss, Wilhelm C., tr. LC 83-70514. 160p. (Orig.). 1983. pap. 8.95 (ISBN 0-8066-2020-X, 10-5485). Augsburg.

Pawlikowski, John T. Christ in the Light of the Christian-Jewish Dialogue. LC 81-83186. (Stimulus Bks.). 208p. (Orig.). 1982. pap. 7.95 (ISBN 0-8091-2416-5). Paulist Pr.

Sandmel, Samuel. We Jews & Jesus. LC 65-11529. 1965. pap. 7.95 (ISBN 0-19-501676-9). Oxford U Pr.

Schoenle, Volker. Johannes, Jesus und die Juden. (Beitroge zur Biblischen Exegese und Theologie: Vol. 17). (Ger.). 288p. 1982. 40.00 (ISBN 3-8204-5877-8). P Lang Pubs.

Slomowitz, Samuel W. Jesus Christ-Sam. 1987. 7.95 (ISBN 0-533-07158-5). Vantage.

Umen, Samuel. Pharisaism & Jesus. LC 62-20875. 1962. 5.00 (ISBN 0-8022-1752-4). Philos Lib.

Vermes, Geza. Jesus & the World of Judaism. LC 83-16535. 224p. 1984. pap. 10.95 (ISBN 0-8006-1784-3, 1-1784). Fortress.

Walker, Thomas T. Jewish Views of Jesus: An Introduction & an Appreciation. LC 73-2229. (The Jewish People; History, Religion, Literature Ser.). Repr. of 1931 ed. 16.00 (ISBN 0-405-05290-1). Ayer Co Pubs.

Weiss-Rosmarin, T., ed. Jewish Expressions on Jesus. 14.95x (ISBN 0-87068-470-1). Ktav.

Zurer, Rachel. A Jew Examines Christianity. LC 83-82999. 181p. (Orig.). 1985. 12.50 (ISBN 0-941752-03-8); pap. 8.50 (ISBN 0-941752-01-1). Jenna Pr.

JESUS CHRIST–JUVENILE LITERATURE
see also Jesus Christ–Biography–Juvenile Literature; Jesus Christ–Nativity–Juvenile Literature; Jesus Christ–Parables–Juvenile Literature; Jesus Christ–Resurrection–Juvenile Literature

Angers, Joann. Meeting the Forgiving Jesus: A Child's First Penance Book. 32p. 1984. pap. 1.75 (ISBN 0-89243-201-2). Liguori Pubns.

Balika, Susan S. Jesus Is My Special Friend. LC 81-86702. (Happy Day Bks.). (Illus.). 24p. (Orig.). 1982. pap. 1.59 (ISBN 0-87239-541-3, 3587). Standard Pub.

Beckmann, Beverly. From. (Illus.). 1980. pap. 3.95 (ISBN 0-570-03489-2, 56-1343). Concordia.

Beegle, Shirley. Jesus Quizzes. 1985. pap. 0.69 (ISBN 0-87239-824-2, 2814). Standard Pub.

Bennett, Marian. Baby Jesus ABC's. (Little Happy Day Bks.). (Illus.). 24p. (Orig.). 1983. pap. 0.49 (ISBN 0-87239-651-7, 2121). Standard Pub.

--Jesus, God's Son. (Surprise Bks.). (Illus.). 14p. (Orig.). 1982. pap. 4.95 (ISBN 0-87239-564-2, 2705). Standard Pub.

Bracken, Carolyn, illus. The Baby Jesus. (Tuck-A-Toy Bks.). (Illus.). 7p. 1985. 3.95 (ISBN 0-8407-6666-1). Nelson.

Brennan-Nichols, Patricia. Getting to Know Jesus. (Illus.). 68p. (Orig.). 1984. pap. 3.95 (ISBN 0-89505-130-3). Argus Comm.

Brown, Alice & Kirk, Pat. Jesus: His Story for Children. (Illus.). 1986. 10.95 (ISBN 0-915720-21-3). Brownlow Pub Co.

Buerger, Jane. Growing as Jesus Grew. (Child's World Books of Understanding). (Illus.). 1985. PLB 5.95 (ISBN 0-89565-173-4, R4924). Standard Pub.

Burrow, Dan. When Jesus Was a Baby. LC 84-70244. (Augsburg Open Window Bks.). (Illus.). 12p. (Orig.). 1984. pap. 4.95 (ISBN 0-8066-2078-1, 10-7082). Augsburg.

Caffrey, Stephanie & Kenslea, Timothy. The Shepherds Find a King. (Rainbow Books (Bible Story Books for Children)). 16p. 1978. pap. 1.00 (ISBN 0-8192-1232-6). Morehouse.

Campbell, Alexander & Haff, Gerry. Live with Jesus. 90p. (Orig.). 1984. pap. 12.95 (ISBN 0-940754-20-7). Ed Ministries.

Carwell, L'Ann. Baby's First Book About Jesus. (Illus.). 1979. 1.25 (ISBN 0-570-08001-0, 56-1326). Concordia.

Churchwell, Kay. Baby Jesus. LC 85-24335. (Bible-&-Me Ser.). (Illus.). 1986. 5.95 (ISBN 0-8054-4170-0). Broadman.

Coleman, William. Jesus, My Forever Friend. (Wonderful World of the Bible Ser.). (Illus.). 1981. 9.95 (ISBN 0-89191-370-X, 53702). Cook.

Colina, Tessa, ed. Jesus, My Teacher: (Pupil Activities Book Two) (Jesus & Me Ser.). (Illus.). 16p. 1978. pap. 1.50 (ISBN 0-87239-269-4, 2441). Standard Pub.

D. C. Cook Editors. Jesus, the Friend of Children. LC 77-72722. (Illus.). 1977. 9.95 (ISBN 0-89191-077-8). Cook.

Daniels, Rebecca. Book X-His Last Days. (Life of Jesus Ser.). 32p. (YA) 1984. wkbk. 3.95 (ISBN 0-86653-231-5). Good Apple.

Daughters of St. Paul. Always with Jesus. 1973. 3.95 (ISBN 0-8198-0265-4); pap. 2.95 (ISBN 0-8198-0714-1). Dghtrs St Paul.

Davis, Robert. Great Day in the Morning. (Jesus & His Disciples Ser.: Vol 2). (Illus.). 40p. 1986. 5.40 (ISBN 0-9615877-1-7). Davis Pub.

DePaola, Tomie. The Miracles of Christ. LC 86-18297. (Illus.). 1987. price not set reinforced bdg. (ISBN 0-8234-0635-0). Holiday.

Diamond, Lucy. Jesus by the Sea of Galilee. (Ladybird Ser). (Illus.). 1958. bds. 2.50 (ISBN 0-87508-840-6). Chr Lit.

--Jesus Calls His Disciples. (Ladybird Ser). (Illus.). 1959. bds. 2.50 (ISBN 0-87508-842-2). Chr Lit.

Erickson, Mary. Don't Cry for Anna. LC 85-10975. (Jesus, the Wonder Worker Ser.). 48p. 1985. pap. 3.95 (ISBN 0-89191-683-0, 56838, Chariot Bks). Cook.

Fletcher, Cynthia H. My Jesus Pocketbook of ABC's. LC 81-80218. (Illus.). 32p. (Orig.). 1981. pap. 0.49 (ISBN 0-937420-01-8). Stirrup Assoc.

Fogle, Jeanne S. Symbols of God's Love: Codes & Passwords. Ducket, Mary Jean & Lane, W. Benson, eds. LC 86-12014. (Illus.). 32p. (Orig.). 1986. pap. 4.95 (ISBN 0-664-24050-X, A Geneva Press Publication). Westminster.

Galambos, Edith P. Loving Hands for Jesus. (Little Learner Ser.). 24p. 1985. 5.95 (ISBN 0-570-08951-4, 56-1543). Concordia.

Galusha, David. The First Christmas. LC 81-82147. (Illus.). 32p. 1981. wkbk. 3.95 (ISBN 0-87973-662-3, 662). Our Sunday Visitor.

Garlow, Willa R. Jesus Is a Special Person. LC 85-24361. (Bible & Me Ser.). (Illus.). 1986. 5.95 (ISBN 0-8054-4166-2). Broadman.

Griffin, Henry W. Jesus for Children. (Illus.). 132p. 1985. 12.95 (HarpR); pap. 4.95 (ISBN 0-86683-866-X). Har-Row.

Groth, Lynn. Jesus Loves Children. (A Cradle Roll Program Ser.). 16p. (Orig.). 1985. pap. 1.25 (ISBN 0-938272-78-0). Wels Board.

--A Very Special Baby-Jesus. (A Cradle Roll Program Ser.). 8p. (Orig.). 1985. pap. 1.25 (ISBN 0-938272-76-4). Wels Board.

Haas, Lois J. Tell Me about Jesus: 16 Lessons, Vol. 2. (Tiny Steps of Faith Ser.). 1967. complete kit 12.95 (ISBN 0-86508-014-3); text only 2.95 (ISBN 0-86508-015-1); color & action book 0.90 (ISBN 0-86508-016-X). BCM Intl Inc.

Hayes, Wanda. My Jesus Book. (Illus.). 32p. 1963. pap. 5.95 (ISBN 0-87239-239-2, 3046). Standard Pub.

Hodges, Graham R. Did Jesus Go to Church? And Fifty-One Other Children's Sermons. LC 81-20585. 128p. (Orig.). 1982. pap. 5.95 (ISBN 0-687-10762-8). Abingdon.

Humphrey, Rilda. Jesus Story & Color Book. (Illus.). 64p. (Orig.). 1982. pap. 2.95 (ISBN 0-87239-583-9, 2398). Standard Pub.

Ife, Elaine & Sutton, Rosalind, eds. The Birth of Jesus. (Now You Can Read Stories from the Bible Ser.). (Illus.). 24p. 1984. 2.50 (ISBN 0-8407-5393-4). Nelson.

--The Childhood of Jesus. (Now You Can Read Stories from the Bible Ser.). (Illus.). 24p. 1985. 2.50 (ISBN 0-8407-5394-2). Nelson.

Jones, Vera R. Stories of Jesus. 1983. 6.95 (ISBN 0-8062-2242-5). Carlton.

Kendrick, Rosalyn. In the Steps of Jesus. 128p. 1985. pap. 8.95 (ISBN 0-7175-1309-2). Dufour.

Kepes, Joanne L. Jesus & His Parables. 1982. 9.95 (ISBN 0-89837-087-6, Pub. by Pflaum Pr). Peter Li.

Klug, Ron & Klug, Lyn. Jesus Lives. LC 82-72848. 32p. (Orig.). 1983. pap. 3.95 (ISBN 0-8066-1952-X, 10-3527). Augsburg.

Klug, Ron, et al. Jesus Loves: Stories about Jesus for Children. LC 86-81807. (Illus.). 32p. (Orig.). 1986. pap. 4.95 saddlestitch (ISBN 0-8066-2235-0, 10-3526). Augsburg.

LeFevre, Greg L. Life of Jesus. (Bible Quiz 'N Tattletotals Ser.). 16p. (Orig.). 1982. pap. 0.98 (ISBN 0-87239-579-0, 2806). Standard Pub.

Lindvall, Ella K. Jesus Begins His Work. (People of the Bible Ser.). (Illus.). 1983. 4.95 (ISBN 0-8024-0394-8). Moody.

Lloyd, Rawson. Stories Jesus Told. (Children's Picture Bible Ser.). 1982. 7.95 (ISBN 0-86020-516-9, Usborne-Hayes); PLB 12.96 (ISBN 0-88110-097-8); pap. 4.95 (ISBN 0-86020-521-5). EDC.

Lynn, Claire. No Crib for a Bed. (Doctrinal Ser.: Bk. 2). (Illus., Orig.). 1983. pap. 1.95 (ISBN 0-89323-029-4). Bible Memory.

McMillan, Mary. Baby Jesus. (Color, Cut & Paste Ser.). 48p. 1986. wkbk. 4.95 (ISBN 0-86653-369-9). Good Apple.

Marchand, Roger. Meeting Jesus in Holy Communion. 32p. 1984. pap. 1.75 (ISBN 0-89243-202-0). Liguori Pubns.

Marshall, Martha. What Child Is This? LC 82-7239. (Illus.). 1982. lib. bdg. 6.95 (ISBN 0-89693-204-4). Dandelion Hse.

Maschke, Ruby. Life of Christ Story-N-Puzzle Book. 48p. (Orig.). 1981. pap. 2.50 (ISBN 0-87239-449-2, 2839). Standard Pub.

Melang, Karen. Jesus: The Servant. (Concept Ser.). (Illus.). 24p. (Orig.). 1986. pap. 3.95 saddlestitched (ISBN 0-570-08532-2, 56-1559). Concordia.

My Book about Jesus. (Little Books to Treasure). (Illus.). 32p. 1985. 1.95 (ISBN 0-225-66388-0, HarpR). Har-Row.

Nystrom, Carolyn. Jesus Is No Secret. (Children's Bible Basics Ser.). (Illus.). 1983. 4.95 (ISBN 0-8024-0193-7). Moody.

--Who Is Jesus? (Children's Bible Basics Ser.). 32p. 1980. pap. 4.95 (ISBN 0-8024-5993-5). Moody.

Podhaizer, Mary E. Following Christ: Activity Book. Puccetti, Patricia I., ed. (Faith & Life Ser.). 41p. (Orig.). 1985. pap. 2.50 (ISBN 0-89870-066-3). Ignatius Pr.

Pugh, Nathanael. Living in the Tower. LC 86-18888. 96p. (Orig.). 1986. pap. 4.95 (ISBN 0-932581-01-3). Word Aflame.

Rawson & Lloyd. The Miracles of Jesus. (Children's Picture Bible Ser.). 1982. 7.95 (ISBN 0-86020-518-5, Usborne-Hayes); PLB 12.96 (ISBN 0-88110-099-4); pap. 4.95 (ISBN 0-86020-523-1). EDC.

The Real Jesus. 128p. pap. 2.95 (ISBN 0-89191-066-2, 08243). Cook.

Richards, Jean H. Jesus Went about Doing Good. LC 80-70475. 1983. 5.95 (ISBN 0-8054-4289-8, 4242-89). Broadman.

Rostron, Hilda L. Stories About Jesus the Friend. (Ladybird Ser). (Illus.). 1961. bds. 2.50 (ISBN 0-87508-862-7). Chr Lit.

--Stories About Jesus the Helper. (Ladybird Ser). (Illus.). 1961. bds. 2.50 (ISBN 0-87508-864-3). Chr Lit.

Schraff, Francis, et al. Learning about Jesus. rev. ed. 80p. 1980. pap. 1.95 (ISBN 0-89243-129-6). Liguori Pubns.

Smith, Mary P. The Story of Jesus. (Illus.). 32p. (Orig.). 1980. pap. 1.95 (ISBN 0-87516-420-X). De Vorss.

Sparks, Judy, ed. Yes!, Jesus Loves Me. (Happy Day Bks.). (Illus.). 24p. 1985. 1.59 (ISBN 0-87239-882-X, 3682). Standard Pub.

Stifle, J. M. ABC Book About Jesus. 1981. pap. 3.95 (ISBN 0-570-04054-X, 56-1715). Concordia.

Stoner, Laura M. Jesus: A Story Color Book. (Illus.). 80p. (Orig.). 1985. pap. 3.95 wkbk. (ISBN 0-934426-07-4). Napsac Reprods.

Storr, Catherine, as told by. Jesus & John the Baptist. (People of the Bible Ser.). (Illus.). 32p. 1985. PLB 10.65 (ISBN 0-8172-2037-2). Raintree Pubs.

--Jesus the Healer. (People of the Bible Ser.). (Illus.). 32p. 1985. PLB 10.65 (ISBN 0-8172-2041-0). Raintree Pubs.

Story of Jesus Pop-Up Book. (Pop-Up Bks.). (Illus.). 1.98 (ISBN 0-517-43888-7). Outlet Bk Co.

Svensson, Borje. Great Miracles of Jesus. (Change-the-Picture Storybooks). (Illus.). 10p. 1985. 6.95 (ISBN 0-89191-940-6, 59402, Chariot Bks). Cook.

Tiner, John H. They Followed Jesus: Word Search Puzzles. 48p. pap. 2.50 (ISBN 0-87239-586-3, 2784). Standard Pub.

Vanier, Jean. I Meet Jesus: He Tells Me "I Love You". LC 81-82109. 208p. 1982. pap. 3.95 (ISBN 0-8091-2725-3). Paulist Pr.

Ward, Alton. Ten Pennies for Jesus. (Illus.). 24p. (Orig.). 1986. pap. 3.50 (ISBN 0-570-04132-5, 56-1560). Concordia.

Watson, Elizabeth E. Tell Me about Jesus. 1980. pap. 3.95 (ISBN 0-570-03484-1, 56-1705). Concordia.

Williams-Ellis, Virginia. The Baby Jesus. (Board Bks.). (Illus.). 10p. 1984. 2.95 (ISBN 0-8249-8082-4). Ideals.

Wyatt, Margaret. My Friend Jesus. LC 86-90051. (Illus.). 20p. (Orig.). 1986. pap. 2.25 (ISBN 0-9616117-0-7). M Wyatt.

JESUS CHRIST–KINGDOM
see also Jesus Christ–Mystical Body

Cribb, C. C. The Coming Kingdom. LC 77-70213. pap. 2.95 (ISBN 0-932046-04-5). Manhattan Ltd NC.

Sauer, Erich. The King of the Earth. 256p. 1979. pap. 10.95 (ISBN 0-85364-009-2). Attic Pr.

JESUS CHRIST–LAST WORDS
see Jesus Christ–Seven Last Words

JESUS CHRIST–LIFE
see Jesus Christ–Biography

JESUS CHRIST–LOGOS DOCTRINE
see Logos

JESUS CHRIST–LORD'S SUPPER
see Lord's Supper

JESUS CHRIST–MESSIAHSHIP
see also Messiah

Anderson, Julian G. The Story of Jesus the Messiah, Four Gospels. LC 76-52054. (A Life of Christ Wkbk). (Illus.). 1977. pap. 3.95 (ISBN 0-9602128-1-7). Anderson Publ.

--The Story of Jesus the Messiah, Old Testament. (An Old Testament Wkbk). (Illus.). 1977. pap. 3.95 (ISBN 0-9602128-2-5). Anderson Publ.

Brown, Raymond E. The Birth of the Messiah: A Commentary on the Infancy Narratives in Matthew & Luke. LC 76-56271. 1977. pap. 9.95 (ISBN 0-385-05405-X, Im). Doubleday.

Gloag, P. J. & Delitzsch, F. The Messiahship of Christ. 628p. 1983. lib. bdg. 23.50 Smythe Sewn (ISBN 0-86524-146-5, 9514). Klock & Klock.

Grant, F. W. The Crowned Christ. pap. 4.25 (ISBN 0-88172-073-9). Believers Bkshelf.

Hall, Willard S. The Lamb of God; the Theme Eternal. 35p. 1974. 4.95 (ISBN 0-87881-033-1). Mojave Bks.

Hugel, Friedrich Von. Essays & Addresses on the Philosophy of Religion. LC 72-9828. 308p. 1974. Repr. of 1921 ed. lib. bdg. 29.50x (ISBN 0-8371-6219-X, HUPR). Greenwood.

Juster, Daniel. Jewishness & Jesus. 1977. pap. 0.75 (ISBN 0-87784-163-2). Inter-Varsity.

MacArthur, John, Jr. The Supernatural Power of Jesus. (John MacArthur's Bible Studies). 1985. pap. 3.50 (ISBN 0-8024-5113-6). Moody.

McConkie, Bruce R. The Promised Messiah. LC 78-3478. 1978. 17.95 (ISBN 0-87747-702-7). Deseret Bk.

Miranda, Jose P. Being & the Messiah: The Message of St. John. Eagleson, John, tr. from Span. LC 77-5388. Orig. Title: El Ser y el Mesias. 253p. (Orig.). 1977. 8.95x (ISBN 0-88344-027-X). Orbis Bks.

Shofner, David. Soul Winning. (Illus.). 96p. (Orig.). 1980. pap. 2.95 (ISBN 0-89957-051-8). AMG Pubs.

JESUS CHRIST–MIRACLES

Allen, Charles L. Touch of the Master's Hand: Christ's Miracles for Today. 160p. 1956. pap. 2.75 (ISBN 0-8007-8093-0, Spire Bks). Revell.

Allen, Ronald J. Our Eyes Can Be Opened: Preaching the Miracle Stories of the Synoptic Gospels Today. LC 81-43679. 146p. 1983. pap. text ed. 9.50 (ISBN 0-8191-2671-3). U Pr of Amer.

Barclay, William. And He Had Compassion. LC 75-28099. 272p. 1976. pap. 5.95 (ISBN 0-8170-0686-9). Judson.

Brown, Colin. That You May Believe: Miracles & Faith-Then & Now. 224p. (Orig.). 1985. pap. 8.95 (ISBN 0-8028-0086-6). Eerdmans.

Bruce, A. B. The Miracles of Christ. 1980. 20.00 (ISBN 0-86524-060-4, 9504). Klock & Klock.

Daughters of St. Paul. The Teachings & Miracles of Jesus. 1981. 5.00 (ISBN 0-686-73821-7); pap. 4.00 (ISBN 0-8198-7302-0). Dghtrs St Paul.

Freemesser, George F. Learning to Live from Within: A Glimpse of Jesus As Healer. 1985. 8.95 (ISBN 0-87193-242-3). Dimension Bks.

Habershon, Ada R. Study of the Miracles. LC 62-19174. 336p. 1967. 12.95 (ISBN 0-8254-2801-7); pap. 9.95 (ISBN 0-8254-2851-3). Kregel.

Kremers, Edward. Christ the Healer. 24p. 1911. pap. 0.95 (ISBN 0-317-40411-3). Open Court.

Laidlaw, John. Studies in the Miracles of Our Lord. 390p. 1984. lib. bdg. 14.75 (ISBN 0-86524-168-6, 9518). Klock & Klock.

Lindsay, Gordon. Christ the Great Physician. (Divine Healing & Health Ser.). 1.25 (ISBN 0-89985-024-3). Christ Nations.

--The Forgotten Miracles of the Bible. (Miracles in the Bible Ser.: Vol. 6). 0.95 (ISBN 0-89985-183-5). Christ Nations.

--Four Hundred & Fifty-Year Judgment Cycles. (Miracles in the Bible Ser.: Vol. 5). 0.95 (ISBN 0-89985-182-7). Christ Nations.

--Miracles of Christ, 2 parts, Vols. 2 & 3. (Miracles in the Bible Ser.). 0.95 ea. Vol. 2 (ISBN 0-89985-960-7). Vol. 3 (ISBN 0-89985-960-7). Christ Nations.

--Old Testament Healings. (Miracles in the Bible Ser.: Vol. 1). 0.95 (ISBN 0-89985-179-7). Christ Nations.

Lovasik, Lawrence G. The Miracles of Jesus. (Saint Joseph Picture Bks.). flexible dg. 0.95 (ISBN 0-89942-279-9, 279). Catholic Bk Pub.

Maier, Paul A. Caspar Schwenckfeld on the Person & Work of Christ. 115p. 1959. write for info. Concordia Schl Grad Studies.

Murray, Andrew. Power of the Blood of Jesus. LC 85-62802. 1985. pap. 3.50 (ISBN 0-88270-597-0). Bridge Pub.

Osborn, T. L. Miracles: Proof of God's Power. 96p. (Orig.). 1981. pap. 1.50 (ISBN 0-89274-185-6, HH-185). Harrison Hse.

Pentecost, Dwight. A Harmony of the Words & Works of Jesus Christ. 272p. 1981. 12.95 (ISBN 0-310-30950-6, 17016); pap. 8.95 (ISBN 0-310-30951-4, 17016P). Zondervan.

Pentecost, J. Dwight. The Words & Works of Jesus Christ. 576p. 1981. 19.95 (ISBN 0-310-30940-9, 17015). Zondervan.

Richards, Hubert J. The Miracles of Jesus: What Really Happened? (What Really Happened? Ser.). 128p. 1986. pap. 5.95 (ISBN 0-89622-287-X). Twenty-Third.

Storr, Catherine, as told by. Jesus the Healer. (People of the Bible Ser.). (Illus.). 32p. 1985. PLB 10.65 (ISBN 0-8172-2041-0). Raintree Pubs.

Storr, Catherine, retold by. Miracles by the Sea. LC 82-23022. (People of the Bible). (Illus.). 32p. 1983. PLB 10.65 (ISBN 0-8172-1983-8). Raintree Pubs.

Tregay, William, ed. The Miracles of Jesus for the Intellectual. LC 85-63853. 128p. (Orig.). 1986. pap. text ed. write for info. (ISBN 0-936435-03-8). Church Man pub.

Trench, R. C. Notes on the Miracles. (Twin Brooks Ser.). pap. 7.95 (ISBN 0-8010-8776-7). Baker Bk.

Weiser, Alfons. The Miracle of Jesus: Then & Now. Karris, Robert, ed. Tiede, David L., tr. (Herald Biblical Bklts.). 1972. pap. 1.25 (ISBN 0-8199-0519-4). Franciscan Herald.

Woolston, Thomas. Discourses on the Miracles of Our Savior. Wellek, Rene, ed. LC 75-11268. (British Philosophers & Theologians of the 17th & 18th Centuries Ser.: Vol. 67). 565p. 1979. lib. bdg. 51.00 (ISBN 0-8240-1778-1); lib. bdg. 2700.00 set of 101 vols. (ISBN 0-686-60102-5). Garland Pub.

JESUS CHRIST–MIRACLES–JUVENILE LITERATURE

Bergey, Alyce. Beggar's Greatest Wish. (Arch Bks: No. 6). 1969. pap. 0.99 (ISBN 0-570-06040-0, 59-1155). Concordia.

--Fishermen's Surprise. (Arch Bks: Set 4). 1967. laminated cover 0.99 (ISBN 0-570-06028-1, 59-1139). Concordia.

Hill, Dave. Boy Who Gave His Lunch Away. (Arch Bks: Set 4). 1967. laminated bdg. 0.99 (59-1138). Concordia.

Prior, Brenda. Little Sleeping Beauty. (Arch Bks: Set 6). 1969. laminated bdg. 0.99 (ISBN 0-570-06041-9, 59-1156). Concordia.

Warren, Mary P. & Rada. Little Boat That Almost Sank. LC 64-23371. (Arch Bks: Set 2). 1965. pap. 0.99 (ISBN 0-570-06010-9, 59-1111). Concordia.

Warren, Mary P. & Wind, Betty. Lame Man Who Walked Again. (Arch Bks: Set 3). 1966. laminated bdg. 0.99 (ISBN 0-570-06020-6, 59-1129). Concordia.

JESUS CHRIST–MISCELLANEA

Elliott, Maurice. The Psychic Life of Jesus. 69.95 (ISBN 0-87968-185-3). Gordon Pr.

Gaffney, J. Patrick. Inexhaustible Presence: The Mystery of Jesus. 210p. 1986. 11.95 (ISBN 0-87193-249-0). Dimension Bks.

Hellwig, Monika K. Jesus, the Compassion of God: New Perspectives on the Tradition of Christianity. 1983. 12.95 (ISBN 0-89453-365-7); pap. 7.95 (ISBN 0-89453-375-4). M Glazier.

McKenna, Megan & Ducote, Darryl. Jesus Living the Father's Values. LC 78-71530. (Followers of the Way Ser.: Vol. 3). 1979. 22.50 (ISBN 0-8091-9544-5); cassette 7.50 (ISBN 0-8091-7668-8). Paulist Pr.

Pike, Diane K. Cosmic Unfoldment: The Individualizing Process as Mirrored in the Life of Jesus. LC 76-45344. 99p. 1976. pap. 2.00 (ISBN 0-916192-08-3). L P Pubns.

Rappoport, Angelo S. Mediaeval Legends of Christ. LC 76-15555. 1976. Repr. of 1934 ed. lib. bdg. 32.50 (ISBN 0-8414-7346-3). Folcroft.

Spurgeon, C. H. Remembrance of Christ. 1977. pap. 0.95 (ISBN 0-686-23223-2). Pilgrim Pubns.

Stewart, Don. One Hundred & One Questions People Ask Most about Jesus. 224p. (Orig.). 1987. pap. 5.95 (ISBN 0-8423-4748-8). Tyndale.

JESUS CHRIST–MYSTICAL BODY

see also Church–Foundation; Communion of Saints; Mystical Union; Priesthood, Universal

Baillie, Donald M. God Was in Christ. 232p. 1977. pap. 6.50 (ISBN 0-571-05685-7). Faber & Faber.

Collins, John H. Mystical Body of Christ. 1977. 2.00 (ISBN 0-8198-0435-5); pap. 0.95 (ISBN 0-8198-0436-3). Dghtrs St Paul.

Lewis, H. Spencer. Mystical Life of Jesus. LC 54-20988. (Illus.). 320p. 1986. pap. 9.95 (ISBN 0-912057-46-7, G-658). AMORC.

Mersch, E. The Whole Christ. 638p. 1981. 39.00x (ISBN 0-234-77051-1, Pub. by Dobson Bks England). State Mutual Bk.

Messori, Vittorio. Faith's Answer: The Mystery of Jesus. Brown, Eugene, ed. Whitehead, Kenneth, tr. from Ital. LC 86-13509. Tr. of Ipotesi su Jesu. 312p. (Orig.). 1986. lib. bdg. 16.95 (ISBN 0-89944-083-5); pap. 12.95 (ISBN 0-89944-084-3). Don Bosco Multimedia.

Nee, Watchman. The Body of Christ: A Reality. Kaung, Stephen, tr. 1978. pap. 2.50 (ISBN 0-935008-13-6). Christian Fellow Pubs.

Reader, J. The Divine Mystery. 79p. pap. 4.95 (ISBN 0-88172-117-4). Believers Bkshelf.

JESUS CHRIST–NAME

see also Servant of Jehovah; Son of Man

Churchwell, Kay. Baby Jesus. LC 85-24335. (Bible-&-Me Ser.). (Illus.). 1986. 5.95 (ISBN 0-8054-4170-0). Broadman.

Derk, Francis H. Names of Christ: A Pocket Guide. LC 75-44928. 176p. 1976. pap. 3.95 (ISBN 0-87123-390-8, 210390). Bethany Hse.

Duran, Manuel & Kluback, William, trs. Luis de Leon: Names of Christ. (Classics of Western Spirituality Ser.). 1984. 14.95 (ISBN 0-8091-0346-X); pap. 11.95 (ISBN 0-8091-2561-7). Paulist Pr.

Gillet, Lev. On the Invocation of the Name of Jesus. 1985. pap. 4.95 (ISBN 0-87243-133-9). Templegate.

Hausherr, Irenee. The Name of Jesus. Cummings, Charles, tr. LC 77-10559. (Cistercian Studies: No. 44). 358p. 1978. 15.95 (ISBN 0-87907-844-8); pap. 8.00 (ISBN 0-87907-944-4). Cistercian Pubns.

Raya, Joseph. Acathist Hymn to the Name of Jesus. Vinck, Jose D., ed. 40p. 1983. 6.00x (ISBN 0-911726-45-4). Alleluia Pr.

Rolls, Charles J. His Glorious Name. (Names & Titles of Jesus Christ Ser.: No. 5). 267p. 1986. pap. 5.95 (ISBN 0-87213-735-X). Loizeaux.

--Name above Every Name: The Names & Titles of Jesus Christ Beginning with P-S. rev. ed. LC 65-26585. 1985. pap. 5.95 (ISBN 0-87213-734-1). Loizeaux.

--Time's Noblest Name: The Names & Titles of Jesus Christ, L-O. New rev. ed. pap. 5.95 (ISBN 0-87213-733-3). Loizeaux.

Spurgeon, Charles H. Spurgeon's Sermons on Christ's Names & Titles. Cook, Charles T., ed. 1965. Repr. of 1961 ed. 7.95 (ISBN 0-87921-033-8). Attic Pr.

JESUS CHRIST–NATIVITY

see also Christmas; Star of Bethlehem; Virgin Birth

Aust-Schminke, Janith. From Mary's Side: Summons for Change. 160p. (Orig.). Date not set. price not set (ISBN 0-916865-00-2); pap. price not set (ISBN 0-916865-01-0). Sansper.

Bainton, Roland H., tr. Martin Luther Christmas Book with Celebrated Woodcuts by His Contemporaries. LC 59-2930. 80p. 1948. pap. 3.95 (ISBN 0-8006-1843-2, 1-1843). Fortress.

Bishop, Jim. The Day Christ Was Born. LC 60-13444. 1978. pap. 2.95i (ISBN 0-06-060785-8, HJ 37, HarpR). Har-Row.

Carus, Paul, ed. Virgil's Prophecy on the Saviour's Birth. 97p. 1918. 2.95 (ISBN 0-317-40414-8). Open Court.

Daughters of St. Paul. When Jesus Was Born. (Illus.). 1973. plastic bdg. 2.00 (ISBN 0-8198-0326-X); pap. 1.25 (ISBN 0-8198-0327-8). Dghtrs St Paul.

Gromacki, Robert G. The Virgin Birth of Christ. 200p. 1981. pap. 5.95 (ISBN 0-8010-3765-4). Baker Bk.

Hecht, Johanna, notes by. The Nativity. LC 81-65400. (Illus.). 1981. pop-up bk. 9.95 (ISBN 0-385-28713-5). Delacorte.

Laurentin, Rene. The Truth of Christmas Beyond the Myths: The Gospel of the Infancy of Christ. (Studies in Scripture: Vol. III). 1986. pap. 29.95 (ISBN 0-932506-34-8). St Bedes Pubns.

Lidden, H. P. & Orr, J. The Birth of Christ. 1980. 15.25 (ISBN 0-86524-058-2, 9502). Klock & Klock.

Long, Edward S. Two Nativity Dramas. 1984. 4.75 (ISBN 0-89536-697-5, 4874). CSS of Ohio.

McDowell, Josh. Bien Plus Qu'un Charpentier. Cosson, Annie, ed. Flammanc, Solveng, tr. Orig. Title: More Than a Carpenter. 128p. 1982. pap. 1.75 (ISBN 0-8297-1248-8). Life Pubs Intl.

Maier, Paul L. First Christmas: The True & Unfamiliar Story in Words & Pictures. LC 76-163162. (Illus.). 1971. 10.45i (ISBN 0-06-065396-5, HarpR). Har-Row.

Midwood, Bart. The Nativity. 56p. 1982. 9.95 (ISBN 0-9607118-0-5). Bel Esprit.

Northrup, Marguerite. Christmas Story: From the Gospels of Matthew & Luke. LC 65-23504. (Illus.). 1966. 8.95 (ISBN 0-87099-047-0, 139459, Pub. by Metro Mus Art). NYGS.

Samuels, David G. Birth & Youth of Jesus, by Mary, Mother of Jesus. 5.00 (ISBN 0-686-12714-5). New Age Min Spiritualist.

Schrage, Alice. Birth of the King. LC 80-53874. (Bible Biography Ser.). 128p. 1981. pap. 2.50 (ISBN 0-8307-0765-4, 5810507). Regal.

Skaballanovitch, M. Rozhdestvo Khristovo. Tr. of The Nativity of Christ. 195p. pap. 7.00 (ISBN 0-317-29162-9). Holy Trinity.

--Rozhdestvo Presvjatia Bogoroditsi. Tr. of The Nativity of the Holy Mother of God. 134p. pap. 5.00 (ISBN 0-317-29149-1). Holy Trinity.

Stewart, Frances T. & Stewart, Charles P. The Birth of Jesus. (Stick & Learn Book Ser.). (Orig.). 1985. pap. 6.95 (ISBN 0-8054-4171-9). Broadman.

Two Hermits. The Revelation of Bethlehem. 1985. pap. 3.50 (ISBN 0-932506-41-0). St Bedes Pubns.

Weber, Hans-Reudi. Immanuel: The Coming of Jesus in Art & the Bible. (Illus.). 128p. 1984. 12.95 (ISBN 0-8028-3603-8). Eerdmans.

Younger, Dory. The Nativity. 1983. pap. 3.75 (ISBN 0-89536-614-2, 1416). CSS of Ohio.

JESUS CHRIST–NATIVITY–ART

see Jesus Christ–Art

JESUS CHRIST–NATIVITY–JUVENILE LITERATURE

Bennett, Marian. The Story of Baby Jesus. (Illus.). 24p. (Orig.). 1983. pap. 0.49 (ISBN 0-87239-654-1, 2124). Standard Pub.

Bennett, Marian, ed. Baby Jesus. (My Shape Book Ser.). (Illus.). 10p. 1985. 2.95 (ISBN 0-87239-907-9, 2747). Standard Pub.

Brandt, Catharine. The Story of Christmas for Children. LC 74-79366. (Illus.). 20p. (Orig.). 1974. pap. 5.95 (ISBN 0-8066-2030-7, 10-6041). Augsburg.

Butterworth, Nick & Inkpen, Mick. The Nativity Play. (Illus.). 32p. 1985. 10.95 (ISBN 0-316-11903-2). Little.

Forell, Betty & Wind, Betty. Little Benjamin & the First Christmas. (Arch Bks: Set 1). (Illus.). 1964. laminated bdg. 0.99 (ISBN 0-570-06005-2, 59-1113). Concordia.

Frost, Marie H. Jesus Is Born. (First Happy Day Bks.). (Illus.). 20p. 1986. casebound 1.29 (ISBN 0-87403-131-1, 2001). Standard Pub.

Irland, Nancy. Baby Jesus' Birthday. (Cut & Color Bks.). (Illus.). 16p. (Orig.). 1982. pap. 0.95 (ISBN 0-87239-585-5, 2389). Standard Pub.

Klug, Ron & Klug, Lyn. Jesus Comes: the Story of Jesus' Birth for Children. LC 86-81808. (Illus.). 32p. (Orig.). 1986. pap. 4.95 saddlestitch (ISBN 0-8066-2234-2, 10-3497). Augsburg.

Kramer-Lampher, A. H. Baby Born in a Stable. LC 65-15145. (Arch Bks.: Set. 2). 1965. pap. 0.99 (ISBN 0-570-06013-3, 59-1118). Concordia.

Laurence, Margaret. The Christmas Birthday Story. LC 79-27159. (Illus.). 32p. 1980. PLB 6.99 (ISBN 0-394-94361-9). Knopf.

Mahany, Patricia, ed. Jesus is Born. (Classroom Activity Bks.). (Illus.). 48p. (Orig.). 1984. pap. 2.95 (ISBN 0-87239-719-X, 2449). Standard Pub.

Make Your Own Nativity Scene. pap. 2.95 (ISBN 0-89191-810-8, 28100). Cook.

Marshall, Martha. What Child Is This? 1982. text ed. 4.95 (Sonflower Bks). SP Pubns.

Mullen, Sharon. When Jesus Was Born. LC 86-17558. (Bible-&-Me Ser.). 1987. 5.95 (ISBN 0-8054-4177-8). Broadman.

Odor, Ruth. The Very Special Night. (A Happy Day Book). (Illus.). 24p. (Orig.). 1980. 1.59 (ISBN 0-87239-405-0, 3637). Standard Pub.

Rostron, Hilda L. Baby Jesus. (Ladybird Ser.). (Illus.). 1961. bds. 2.50 (ISBN 0-87508-832-5). Chr Lit.

Stowell, Gordon. Jesus Is Born. (Little Fish Bks.: Bk. II). (Illus.). 14p. 1982. pap. 0.59 (ISBN 0-8307-0827-8, 5608119). Regal.

JESUS CHRIST–NATIVITY–SERMONS

see Christmas Sermons

JESUS CHRIST–NATURES

see also Jesus Christ–Divinity; Jesus Christ–Humanity

Simpson, A. B. El Evangelio Cuadruple: Fourfold Gospel, Spanish. Bucher, Dorothy, tr. from Eng. 96p. 1981. pap. 2.00 (ISBN 0-87509-268-3). Chr Pubns.

JESUS CHRIST–NEW THOUGHT INTERPRETATIONS

Bostick, W. F. Jesus & Socrates. 59.95 (ISBN 0-8490-0443-8). Gordon Pr.

Dunne, Carrin. Buddha & Jesus: Conversations. 1975. pap. 4.95 (ISBN 0-87243-057-X). Templegate.

Fillmore, Charles. Mysteries of John. 1946. 5.95 (ISBN 0-87159-105-7). Unity School.

Hagin, Kenneth E. The Precious Blood of Jesus. 1984. pap. 0.50 mini bk. (ISBN 0-89276-263-2). Hagin Ministries.

Kissinger, Warren S. The Parables of Jesus: A History of Interpretation & Bibliography. LC 78-23271. (American Theological Library Association (ATLA) Bibliography Ser.: No. 4). 463p. 1979. lib. bdg. 30.00 (ISBN 0-8108-1186-3). Scarecrow.

Moum, Margaret R. Guidebook to the Aquarian Gospel of Jesus the Christ. 93p. 1974. pap. 3.95 (ISBN 0-917200-05-5). ESPress.

Vogel, Arthur A. The Jesus Prayer for Today. LC 81-84349. 128p. (Orig.). 1982. pap. 5.95 (ISBN 0-8091-2413-0). Paulist Pr.

Wilson, Clifford. The Passover Plot Exposed. LC 77-73814. 1977. pap. 2.95 (ISBN 0-89051-032-6). Master Bks.

JESUS CHRIST–PARABLES

Barclay, William. And Jesus Said: A Handbook on the Parables of Jesus. LC 77-120410. 224p. 1970. pap. 7.95 (ISBN 0-664-24898-5). Westminster.

Booth, Julianne. Parables of Jesus. (Arch Bks.). 1982. pap. 0.99 (ISBN 0-570-06163-6, 59-1309). Concordia.

Bruce, A. B. The Parables of Christ. 1980. 15.50 (ISBN 0-86524-059-0, 9503). Klock & Klock.

Bunyan, John. Barren Fig Tree. pap. 1.25 (ISBN 0-685-19824-3). Reiner.

--Groans of a Lost Soul. LC 68-6571. 1967. pap. 3.25 (ISBN 0-685-19830-8). Reiner.

Buttrick, George A. The Parables of Jesus. (Minister's Paperback Library Ser). 274p. 1973. pap. 6.95 (ISBN 0-8010-0597-3). Baker Bk.

Capon, Robert F. The Parables of the Kingdom. 192p. 1985. 10.95 (ISBN 0-310-42670-7, 17040). Zondervan.

Carlozzi, Carl G. & Parkes, Ellen. Pocket Parables. 80p. (Orig.). 1985. pap. 2.95 (ISBN 0-8423-4919-7). Tyndale.

Carothers, J. Edward. Living with the Parables: Jesus & the Reign of God. 141p. (Orig.). 1984. pap. 9.95 (ISBN 0-377-00146-5). Friend Pr.

Crossan, John D. In Parables: The Challenge of the Historical Jesus. LC 73-7067. 141p. 1985. pap. 8.95 (ISBN 0-06-061609-1, HarpR). Har-Row.

Dale, Alan T. God Cares for Everybody, Everywhere. (Rainbow Books (Bible Story Books for Children)). (Orig.). 1978. pap. 1.00 (ISBN 0-8192-1237-7). Morehouse.

Filby, P. Gwyn. Stories of Jesus, Tell Them to Me. 200p. 1986. 45.00x (ISBN 0-947939-01-6, Pub. by Elmcrest UK). State Mutual Bk.

--Tell Them to Me. 200p. 1986. 40.00x (ISBN 0-947939-01-6, Pub. by Elmcrest Uk). State Mutual Bk.

Griffith, Harry C. The Ways of God: Paths into the New Testament. 149p. 1986. pap. 7.95 (ISBN 0-8192-1377-2). Morehouse.

Grimes, Bobbie M. The Parable of Jesus & Santa. LC 84-90331. (Illus.). 40p. 1984. 14.95 (ISBN 0-9613328-0-8). B & D Pub.

Gross, Arthur W. Stories Jesus Told. 1981. 6.95 (ISBN 0-570-04059-0, 56YY1352). Concordia.

Harrington, Wilfrid J. Parables Told by Jesus: Contemporary Approach. LC 74-12395. 135p. (Orig.). 1974. pap. 3.95 (ISBN 0-8189-0296-5). Alba.

Hunt, Gladys. Stories Jesus Told. (Fisherman Bible Studyguide Ser.). 96p. (Orig.). pap. 2.95 (ISBN 0-87788-791-8). Shaw Pubs.

Hunter, Archibald M. The Parables Then & Now. LC 72-170113. 128p. 1972. pap. 5.95 (ISBN 0-664-24940-X). Westminster.

Jeremias, Joachim. The Parables of Jesus. 2nd ed. LC 63-22114. (Illus.). 248p. 1972. pap. text ed. 8.95 (ISBN 0-02-360510-3, Pub. by Scribner). Macmillan.

Jewett, Robert. Jesus Against the Rapture: Seven Unexpected Prophecies. LC 78-31759. 148p. 1979. pap. 5.95 (ISBN 0-664-24253-7). Westminster.
Keller, Phillip. Master's Hands: Understanding the Parable of the Potter & the Clay. (Christian Essentials Ser.). 48p. (Orig.). Date not set. pap. 1.95 (ISBN 0-89283-330-0, Pub. by Vine Books). Servant.
Kissinger, Warren S. The Parables of Jesus: A History of Interpretation & Bibliography. LC 78-23271. (American Theological Library Association (ATLA) Bibliography Ser.: No. 4). 463p. 1979. lib. bdg. 30.00 (ISBN 0-8108-1186-3). Scarecrow.
Kistemaker, Simon. The Parables of Jesus. 264p. 1980. 11.95 (ISBN 0-8010-5462-1). Baker Bk.
Lambrecht, Jan. Once More Astonished: The Parables of Jesus Christ. 262p. 1981. pap. 9.95 (ISBN 0-8245-0093-8). Crossroad NY.
Lawson, LeRoy. Cracking the Code. LC 76-57045. 1977. pap. 2.25 (ISBN 0-87239-125-6, 40042). Standard Pub.
--The Lord of Parables: Instructor Edition. LC 83-12640. 128p. (Orig.). 1984. pap. 2.95 (ISBN 0-87239-706-8, 39980); pap. 2.50 student edition (ISBN 0-87239-707-6, 39981). Standard Pub.
Lightfoot, Neil R. Parables of Jesus, 2 vols. (Way of Life Ser.). 1986. pap. 3.95 ea. Vol. 1, 95p; Vol. 2, 95p. Abilene Christ U.
Lindsay, Gordon. Parables of Christ, Vol. 1. (Span.). 1.50 (ISBN 0-89985-980-1). Christ Nations.
Lowery, Daniel L. The Parables of Jesus: Twenty Stories with a Message. 64p. 1987. pap. 1.95 (ISBN 0-89243-266-7). Liguori Pubns.
McFague, Sallie. Speaking in Parables: A Study in Metaphor & Theology. LC 74-26338. 192p. 1975. pap. 5.95 (ISBN 0-8006-1097-0, 1-1097). Fortress.
Marcus, Joel. The Mystery of the Kingdom of God. (Dissertation Ser.). 270p. 1986. 17.95 (ISBN 0-89130-983-7, 06-01-90); pap. 12.95 (ISBN 0-89130-984-5). Scholars Pr GA.
Michaels, J. Ramsey. Servant & Son: Jesus in Parable & Gospel. LC 80-84651. 322p. 1982. pap. 9.95 (ISBN 0-8042-0409-8). John Knox.
Millais, John E. The Parables of Our Lord & Savior Jesus Christ. 7.75 (ISBN 0-8446-5225-3). Peter Smith.
Morgan, G. Campbell. Parables & Metaphors of Our Lord. 352p. 1956. 15.95 (ISBN 0-8007-0245-X). Revell.
Mueller, Michael. The Sinner's Return to God: Or, the Prodigal Son. LC 82-74244. 224p. 1983. pap. 6.00 (ISBN 0-89555-205-1). TAN Bks Pubs.
Nicoll, Maurice. The New Man: An Interpretation of Some Parables & Miracles of Christ. LC 83-20279. 153p. (Orig.). 1984. pap. 9.95 (ISBN 0-87773-268-X). Shambhala Pubns.
Pentecost, J. Dwight. The Parables of Jesus. 160p. 1982. 9.95 (ISBN 0-310-30960-3, 17017). Zondervan.
Pentz, Croft M. Outlines on the Parables of Jesus. (Sermon Outline Ser.). (Orig.). 1980. pap. 2.50 (ISBN 0-8010-7055-4). Baker Bk.
Perkins, Pheme. Hearing the Parables of Jesus. LC 80-84508. 228p. (Orig.). 1981. pap. 7.95 (ISBN 0-8091-2352-5). Paulist Pr.
Poovey, W. A. Prodigals & Publicans: Dramas & Meditations on Six Parables. LC 79-54111. 100p. 1979. pap. 5.95 (ISBN 0-8066-1763-2, 10-5247). Augsburg.
Purdy, John C. Parables at Work. LC 84-17323. 132p. 1986. 10.95 (ISBN 0-664-21268-9); pap. 7.95 (ISBN 0-664-24640-0). Westminster.
Richardson, William. The Restoring Father. 64p. 1987. pap. price not set (ISBN 0-87403-257-1, 39966). Standard Pub.
Seale, Ervin. Learn to Live. 256p. 1966. pap. 6.95 (ISBN 0-911336-08-7). Sci of Mind.
Sherman, Cecil E. A Kingdom of Surprises. LC 85-4699. (Orig.). 1985. pap. 3.75 (ISBN 0-8054-1533-5). Broadman.
Smith, Charles W. The Jesus of the Parables. LC 74-26816. 255p. 1975. 8.95 (ISBN 0-8298-0267-3). Pilgrim NY.
Stein, Robert H. An Introduction to the Parables of Jesus. LC 81-11564. 180p. 1981. pap. 8.95 (ISBN 0-664-24390-8). Westminster.
Storr, Catherine, retold by. The Prodigal Son. LC 82-23011. (People of the Bible). (Illus.). 32p. 1983. PLB 10.65 (ISBN 0-8172-1982-X). Raintree Pubs.
Tambiah, Stanley J. Culture, Thought, & Social Action: An Anthropological Perspective. (Illus.). 432p. 1985. text ed. 30.00x (ISBN 0-674-17969-2). Harvard U Pr.
Tapia, Geraldine. The Parables of Jesus. 144p. 1987. 10.95 (ISBN 0-317-53382-7). Todd & Honeywell.
Taylor, William M. Parables of Our Saviour. LC 74-79943. 1975. 14.95 (ISBN 0-8254-3805-5). Kregel.
Thielicke, Helmut. The Waiting Father. Doberstein, J. W., tr. from Ger. 192p. 1978. Repr. 13.95 (ISBN 0-227-67634-3). Attic Pr.
--The Waiting Father. LC 75-12284. 192p. 1981. 5.95 (ISBN 0-06-067991-3, RD-364, HarpR). Har-Row.
Trench, R. C. Notes on the Parables of Our Lord. (Twin Brooks Ser). pap. 5.95 (ISBN 0-8010-8774-0). Baker Bk.
Van Horn, Bill. The Good Samaritan. 1983. 3.60 (ISBN 0-89536-588-X, 0730). CSS of Ohio.
Wiersbe, Warren W. Windows on the Parables. rev. ed. 160p. 1984. pap. 2.95 (ISBN 0-89693-710-0). Victor Bks.
Wilder, Amos N. Jesus' Parables & the War of Myths: Essays on Imagination in the Scriptures. LC 81-43083. 176p. 1982. 3.50 (ISBN 0-8006-0668-X, 1-668). Fortress.
Young, Norman. Rebuke & Challenge: The Point of Jesus' Parables. Coffen, Richard W., ed. 96p. (Orig.). 1985. pap. 6.95 (ISBN 0-8280-0286-X). Review & Herald.

JESUS CHRIST–PARABLES–JUVENILE LITERATURE

Bull, Norman. Parables of Jesus. (Bible Story & Its Background Ser.: Vol. 6). 9.95 (ISBN 0-7175-0452-2). Dufour.
Dale, Alan T. Who's My Friend? (Rainbow Books (Bible Story Books for Children)). 16p. 1978. pap. 1.00 (ISBN 0-8192-1236-9). Morehouse.
--God Cares for Everybody, Everywhere. (Rainbow Books (Bible Story Books for Children)). (Orig.). 1978. pap. 1.00 (ISBN 0-8192-1237-7). Morehouse.
Diamond, Lucy. Two Stories Jesus Told. (Ladybird Ser). (Illus.). 1959. bds. 2.50 (ISBN 0-87508-870-8). Chr Lit.
Elmer, Irene & Mathews. Boy Who Ran Away. LC 63-23143. (Arch Bks: Set 1). (Illus.). 1964. laminated bdg. 0.99 (ISBN 0-570-06001-X, 59-1104). Concordia.
Hilliard, Dick & Valenti-Hilliard, Beverly. Wonders. (Center Celebration Ser.). (Illus.). 60p. (Orig.). 1981. pap. text ed. 3.95 (ISBN 0-89390-032-X). Resource Pubns.
Kramer, Janice & Mathews. Good Samaritan. LC 63-23369. (Arch Bks: Set 1). (Illus.). 1964. laminated bdg 0.99 (ISBN 0-570-06000-1, 59-1102). Concordia.
Lane, Virginia. Little Lamb & the Good Shepherd. (Illus.). 48p. 1983. 6.95 (ISBN 0-89274-254-2). Harrison Hse.
Latourette, Jane & Wind, Betty. Jon & the Little Lost Lamb. LC 65-15145. (Arch Bks: Set 2). 1965. pap. 0.99 (ISBN 0-570-06008-7, 59-1106). Concordia.
LeFevre, G. L. Parables & Miracles of Jesus. (Bible Quiz 'N Tattletotals Ser.). 16p. (Orig.). 1982. pap. 0.98 (ISBN 0-87239-580-4, 2807). Standard Pub.
Mahany, Patricia. Stories Jesus Told. (Coloring Bks.). (Illus.). 16p. (Orig.). 1982. pap. 0.89 (ISBN 0-87239-601-0, 2390). Standard Pub.
Reid, John C. Parables from Nature. 1954. 3.95 (ISBN 0-8028-4025-6). Eerdmans.
Titus, Susan. Parables for Young Teens: Twenty-Six Junior High Programs. 1986. 4.95 (ISBN 0-87403-150-8, 3412). Standard Pub.

JESUS CHRIST–PARABLES–SERMONS

Boice, James M. The Parables of Jesus. 1983. pap. 6.95 (ISBN 0-8024-0163-5). Moody.
St. Bonaventure. What Manner of Man. (Sermons on Christ Ser). 1974. 5.95 (ISBN 0-8199-0497-X). Franciscan Herald.
Tolbert, Mary Ann. Perspectives on the Parables: An Approach to Multiple Interpretations. LC 78-54563. 144p. 1978. 9.95 (ISBN 0-8006-0527-6, 1-527). Fortress.
Ward, C. M. The Playboy Comes Home. LC 75-32603. 112p. (Orig.). 1976. pap. 1.25 (ISBN 0-88243-572-8, 02-0572). Gospel Pub.

JESUS CHRIST–PASSION

see also Holy Week; Jesus Christ–Relics of the Passion; Lent; Stations of the Cross

Allison, Dale C., Jr. The End of the Ages Has Come: An Early Interpretation of the Passion & Resurrection of Jesus. LC 85-47732. 208p. 1985. 19.95 (ISBN 0-8006-0753-8, 1-753). Fortress.
Anderson, Norman. Jesus Christ: The Witness of History. LC 84-15703. 210p. 1985. pap. 6.95 (ISBN 0-87784-336-8). Inter-Varsity.
Baier, Walter. Untersuchungen zu den Passionbetrachtungen in der "Vita Christi" des Ludolfvon Sachsen: Ein Quellen-Kritischer Beitrag zu Leben und Werk Ludolfs und Zur Geschichte des Passionsthelogie, 3 Vols. Hogg, James, ed. (Analecta Cartsiana Ser.: No. 44-1, 2, 3). (Ger.). 614p. (Orig.). 1977. pap. 32.00 (ISBN 3-7052-0060-7, Pub. by Salzburg Studies). Longwood Pub Group.
Blackwell, John. The Passion As Story: The Plot of Mark. LC 85-16209. (Fortress Resources for Preaching Ser.). 96p. 1986. pap. 5.95 (ISBN 0-8006-1144-6, 1-1144). Fortress.
Boff, Leonardo. Passion of Christ, Passion of the World: The Facts, Their Interpretation & Their Meaning Yesterday & Today. Barr, Robert R., tr. from Port. 160p. (Orig.). 1987. 19.95 (ISBN 0-88344-564-6); pap. 9.95 (ISBN 0-88344-563-8). Orbis Bks.
Bruland, Esther B. & Mott, Stephen C. A Passion for Jesus: A Passion for Justice. 176p. 1983. pap. 9.95 (ISBN 0-8170-0994-9). Judson.
Emmerich, Anne C. Dolorous Passion of Our Lord Jesus Christ. 1980. lib. bdg. 64.95 (ISBN 0-8490-3100-1). Gordon Pr.
--The Dolorous Passion of Our Lord Jesus Christ. LC 83-70406. 382p. 1983. pap. 10.00 (ISBN 0-89555-210-8). TAN Bks Pubs.
Freedberg, David. Rubens: The Life of Christ after the Passion, Pt. VII. (Corpus Rubenianum Ludwig Burchand). (Illus.). 1983. 74.00 (ISBN 0-19-921032-2). Oxford U Pr.
Gritter, George. When God Was at Calvary: Messages on the Seven Words. (Pocket Pulpit Library). 144p. 1982. pap. 3.50 (ISBN 0-8010-3785-9). Baker Bk.
Kesich, Veselin. The Passion of Christ. 84p. pap. 1.95 (ISBN 0-913836-80-X). St Vladimirs.
Kripalvanandji, Shri. The Passion of Christ. LC 83-80214. 51p. 1983. pap. 4.50 (ISBN 0-940258-09-9). Kripalu Pubns.
Lacomara, Aelred, ed. The Language of the Cross. 1977. 5.95 (ISBN 0-8199-0617-4). Franciscan Herald.
Lucado, Max. No Wonder They Call Him the Savior: Chronicles of the Cross. LC 85-31026. 1986. 6.95 (ISBN 0-88070-133-1). Multnomah.
McQuaid, Elwood. The Outpouring: Jesus in the Feasts of Israel. (Orig.). 1986. pap. 5.95 (ISBN 0-8024-6101-8). Moody.
Marin, Louis. The Semiotics of the Passion Narratives. Johnson, Alfred M., Jr., tr. (Pittsburgh Theological Monographs: No. 25). 1980. 12.95 (ISBN 0-915138-23-9). Pickwick.
Marison, Fiscar, tr. The Passion of Our Lord. 302p. 1980. pap. 4.50 (ISBN 0-911988-38-6). AMI Pr.
Neyrey, Jerome. The Passion According to Luke. 232p. (Orig.). 1985. pap. 8.95 (ISBN 0-8091-2688-5). Paulist Pr.
Odenheimer, William H. Jerusalem & Its Vicinity: Familiar Lectures on the Sacred Localities Connected with the Week Before the Resurrection. Davis, Moshe, ed. (America & the Holy Land Ser.). (Illus.). 1977. Repr. of 1855 ed. lib. bdg. 20.00x (ISBN 0-405-10272-0). Ayer Co Pubs.
Reid, William. Blood of Jesus. pap. 1.50x (ISBN 0-914053-02-7). Liberty Bell Pr.
Schilder, Klass. The Trilogy, 3 vols. 1978. Set. 48.00 (ISBN 0-86524-126-0, 9501). Klock & Klock.
Senior, Donald. The Passion of Jesus in the Gospel of Mark. (Passion Ser.: Vol. 2). 1984. pap. 8.95 (ISBN 0-89453-436-X). M Glazier.
Southwell, Robert. Marie Magdalens Funeral Teares. LC 74-22099. 180p. 1975. 30.00x (ISBN 0-8201-1144-9). Schol Facsimiles.
Wilson, Ernest C. Week That Changed the World. 1968. 5.95 (ISBN 0-87159-170-7). Unity School.
Wright, E. A. Ystoire de la Passion. Repr. of 1944 ed. 14.00 (ISBN 0-384-70484-0). Johnson Repr.

JESUS CHRIST–PASSION–ART

see Jesus Christ–Art

JESUS CHRIST–PASSION–DEVOTIONAL LITERATURE

see also Paschal Mystery

Aho, Gerhard, et al. Glory in the Cross-Fruit of the Spirit from the Passion of Christ. 1984. pap. 7.95 (ISBN 0-570-03940-1, 12-2876). Concordia.
Arrastia, Cecilio. Itinerario De la Pasion: Meditaciones De la Semana Santa. 1985. pap. 2.95 (ISBN 0-311-43036-8). Casa Bautista.
Bennett, J. A. Poetry of the Passion: Studies in Twelve Centuries of English Verse. 1982. 37.50x (ISBN 0-19-812804-5); pap. 16.95x (ISBN 0-19-812832-0). Oxford U Pr.
Boevey, Mateo C. Twenty Holy Hours. 1978. pap. 5.00 (ISBN 0-8198-0563-7). Dghtrs St Paul.
Lohfink, Gerhard. The Last Day of Jesus. Attanasio, Salvator, tr. from Ger. LC 83-73026. Tr. of De Letzte Tag Jesu. 80p. 1984. pap. 2.95 (ISBN 0-87793-312-X). Ave Maria.
Taylor, John V. Weep Not for Me. 64p. 1987. pap. 3.95 (ISBN 0-89622-313-2). Twenty-Third.
--Weep Not for Me: Meditations on the Cross & the Resurrection. (Risk Book Ser.). 56p. 1986. pap. 3.50 (ISBN 2-8254-0850-6). Wrld Coun Churches.

JESUS CHRIST–PASSION–DRAMA

see Jesus Christ–Drama; Passion-Plays

JESUS CHRIST–PERSON AND OFFICES

see also Hypostatic Union

Baillie, Donald M. God Was in Christ. 1948. pap. 8.95x (ISBN 0-684-17474-X, PG56, ScribT); lib. bdg. 20.00 lib. rep. ed. (ISBN 0-684-16470-1, PG104HRE). Scribner.
Barclay, William. The Mind of Jesus. LC 61-7332. 352p. 1976. pap. 8.95 (ISBN 0-06-060451-4, RD143, HarpR). Har-Row.
Bornkamm, Gunther. Jesus of Nazareth. LC 61-5256. 240p. 1975. pap. 6.00 (ISBN 0-06-060932-X, RD113, HarpR). Har-Row.
Chemnitz, Martin. Two Natures in Christ. Preus, J. A., tr. LC 74-115465. Orig. Title: De Duabus Naturis in Christo. 1970. 24.95 (ISBN 0-570-03210-5, 15-2109). Concordia.
Cleverly, D. W. Preaching Through the Life of Christ. Lambert, Herbert, ed. LC 85-19002. 112p. 1986. pap. 7.95 (ISBN 0-8272-2930-5). CBP.
Conzelmann, Hans. Jesus. Reumann, John, ed. Lord, J. Raymond, tr. from Gr. LC 73-79011. 128p. 1973. pap. 4.25 (ISBN 0-8006-1000-8, 1-1000). Fortress.
Davis, R. M. The Woods: The Human Self & the Realism of Jesus. 79p. 1971. pap. 4.00 (ISBN 0-9600434-0-3, 03). Camda.
Driver, Tom F. Christ in a Changing World: Toward an Ethical Christology. LC 81-5552. 224p. 1981. 12.95 (ISBN 0-8245-0105-5). Crossroad NY.
Echegaray, Hugo. The Practice of Jesus. O'Connell, Matthew J., tr. from Span. LC 83-19341. Orig. Title: La Practica de Jesus. 176p. (Orig.). 1984. pap. 7.95 (ISBN 0-88344-397-X). Orbis Bks.
Galot, Jean. The Person of Christ: Covenant Between God & Man. Bouchard, Angeline, tr. LC 84-5982. 102p. 1983. 7.50 (ISBN 0-8199-0832-0). Franciscan Herald.
Guzie, Tad W. Jesus & the Eucharist. LC 73-90069. 168p. 1974. pap. 5.95 (ISBN 0-8091-1858-0). Paulist Pr.
Helminiak, Daniel A., ed. The Same Jesus: A Contemporary Christology. 368p. 1986. 15.95 (ISBN 0-8294-0521-6). Loyola.
Hendricks, William L. Who Is Jesus Christ? LC 83-71265. (Layman's Library of Christian Doctrine Ser.). 1985. 5.95 (ISBN 0-8054-1632-3). Broadman.
Hooper, John. The Early Writings of John Hooper. 1843. 51.00 (ISBN 0-384-24210-3). Johnson Repr.
Jay, E. G. Son of Man, Son of God. 1965. 4.95c (ISBN 0-7735-0029-4). McGill-Queens U Pr.
Johnson, Robert C. The Meaning of Christ. LC 58-6120. (Layman's Theological Library). 96p. 1958. pap. 3.45 (ISBN 0-664-24009-7). Westminster.
Kappen, Sebastian. Jesus & Freedom. LC 76-25927. 186p. (Orig.). 1977. 4.48 (ISBN 0-88344-232-9). Orbis Bks.
Kasper, Walter. Jesus the Christ. LC 76-20021. 294p. 1977. pap. 9.95 (ISBN 0-8091-2081-X). Paulist Pr.
Ketcham, Charles B. A Theology of Encounter: The Ontological Ground for a New Christology. LC 77-21905. 1978. 22.50x (ISBN 0-271-00520-3). Pa St U Pr.
Koyama, Kosuke. No Handle on the Cross: An Asian Meditation on the Crucified Mind. LC 76-23160. pap. 32.00 (ISBN 0-317-26647-0, 2025120). Bks Demand UMI.
Lane, Dermont A. The Reality of Jesus. LC 77-70635. (Exploration Book Ser.). 180p. 1977. pap. 6.95 (ISBN 0-8091-2020-8). Paulist Pr.
Maritain, Jacques. De la Grace et de l'Humanite de Jesus. 2nd ed. 156p. 1967. 8.95 (ISBN 0-686-56347-6). French & Eur.
Meilach, M. D. From Order to Omega. pap. 0.95 (ISBN 0-8199-0038-9, L38249). Franciscan Herald.
Meilach, Michael D. Primacy of Christ. 1964. 4.95 (ISBN 0-8199-0087-7, L38655). Franciscan Herald.
Moltmann, Jurgen. The Crucified God. LC 73-18694. 352p. 1974. 18.45 (ISBN 0-06-065901-7, HarpR). Har-Row.
O'Grady, John-F. Models of Jesus. LC 82-45076. (Illus.). 224p. 1982. pap. 4.95 (ISBN 0-385-17321-0, Im). Doubleday.
Rahner, Karl. The Love of Jesus & the Love of Neighbor. LC 82-23523. 96p. 1983. pap. 5.95 (ISBN 0-8245-0570-0). Crossroad NY.
Rice, George E. Christ in Colision. (Harvest Ser.). 112p. 1982. pap. 4.95 (ISBN 0-8163-0473-4). Pacific Pr Pub Assn.
Schweizer, Eduard. Jesus. LC 76-107322. 1979. pap. 7.95 (ISBN 0-8042-0331-8). John Knox.
Senior, Donald. Jesus: A Gospel Portrait. 192p. (Orig.). 1975. pap. 2.95 (ISBN 0-8278-9003-6, Pub. by Pflaum Pr). Peter Li.
Skinner, John E. The Christian Disciple. LC 83-21772. 92p. (Orig.). 1984. lib. bdg. 20.50 (ISBN 0-8191-3657-3); pap. text ed. 7.75 (ISBN 0-8191-3658-1). U Pr of Amer.
Suggs, M. Jack. Wisdom, Christology, & Law in Matthew's Gospel. LC 75-95930. Repr. of 1970 ed. 36.00 (ISBN 0-8357-9185-8, 2017749). Bks Demand UMI.
Sykes, S. W. & Clayton, J. P. Christ, Faith & History. LC 70-176257. (Cambridge Studies in Christology). (Illus.). 280p. 1972. pap. text ed. 14.95 (ISBN 0-521-29325-1). Cambridge U Pr.
Talec, Pierre. Christ & the Sacrament Church. 144p. 1983. pap. 9.95 (ISBN 0-8164-2455-1, HarpR). Har-Row.
Tripole, Martin R. The Jesus Event & Our Response. LC 79-27896. 248p. (Orig.). 1980. pap. 7.95 (ISBN 0-8189-0399-6). Alba.

Trocme, Andre. Jesus & the Nonviolent Revolution. Shenk, Michel, tr. from Fr. LC 73-9934. (Christian Peace Shelf Ser.). 216p. 1974. pap. 12.95 (ISBN 0-8361-3320-X). Herald Pr.

Vick, Edward W. H. Jesus: The Man. LC 78-10253. (Anvil Ser.). 1979. pap. 6.95 (ISBN 0-8127-0220-4). Review & Herald.

Warfield, B. B. The Person & Work of Christ. 12.95 (ISBN 0-8010-9588-3). Baker Bk.

Warfield, Benjamin B. Person & Work of Christ. 1950. 12.95 (ISBN 0-87552-529-6). Presby & Reformed.

Williams, Trevor. Form & Vitality in the World & God: A Christian Perspective. 1985. 29.95x (ISBN 0-19-826671-5). Oxford U Pr.

Yoder, John H. The Politics of Jesus. 176p. 1972. pap. 7.95 (ISBN 0-8028-1485-9). Eerdmans.

JESUS CHRIST–PERSONALITY

see Jesus Christ–Character

JESUS CHRIST–PICTURES, ILLUSTRATIONS, ETC.

see Jesus Christ–Art

JESUS CHRIST–POETRY

Babin, Lawrence J. Agony in the Garden. LC 75-158476. 1971. deluxe ed. 3.00x (ISBN 0-912492-25-2); pap. 1.00 (ISBN 0-912492-00-7). Pyquag.

Bennett, J. A. Poetry of the Passion: Studies in Twelve Centuries of English Verse. 1982. 37.50x (ISBN 0-19-812804-5); pap. 16.95x (ISBN 0-19-812832-0). Oxford U Pr.

Brown, Beatrice. The Southern Passion. LC 74-10772. 1927. 20.00 (ISBN 0-8414-3122-1). Folcroft.

Clark, Thomas C., ed. Master of Men. fascimile ed. LC 72-116396. (Granger Index Reprint Ser.). 1930. 15.00 (ISBN 0-8369-6137-4). Ayer Co Pubs.

Crow, Martha F. Christ in the Poetry of Today: An Anthology from American Poets. 1978. Repr. of 1917 ed. lib. bdg. 25.00 (ISBN 0-8495-0912-2). Arden Lib.

Cynewulf. The Christ of Cynewulf; a Poem in Three Parts: The Advent, the Ascension, & the Last Judgement. Cook, Albert S., ed. LC 73-178524. Repr. of 1900 ed. 32.50 (ISBN 0-404-56538-7). AMS Pr.

Hojeda, Diego de. Christiada: Introduction & Text. Corcoran, Sr. Mary H., ed. LC 35-9384. (Catholic University of America. Studies in Romance Languages & Literatures: No. 11). Repr. of 1935 ed. 49.50 (ISBN 0-404-50311-X). AMS Pr.

Marchant, James. Anthology of Jesus. Wiersbe, Warren W., ed. LC 80-25038. 382p. 1981. Repr. of 1926 ed. 11.95 (ISBN 0-8254-4015-7). Kregel.

Miller, Basil, compiled by. Beautiful Poems on Jesus. facs. ed. LC 68-58826. (Granger Index Reprint Ser). 1948. 17.00 (ISBN 0-8369-6029-7). Ayer Co Pubs.

Oetting, R. When Jesus Was a Lad. LC 68-56816. (Illus.). 1968. PLB 9.26x (ISBN 0-87783-047-9). Oddo.

Sledge, Linda C. Shivering Babe, Victorious Lord: The Nativity in Poetry & Art. LC 81-9728. pap. 49.80 (ISBN 0-317-30162-4, 2025344). Bks Demand UMI.

Stubbs, Charles W. The Christ of English Poetry. LC 73-1787. 1973. lib. bdg. 25.00 (ISBN 0-8414-2621-X). Folcroft.

Thomas, Joan G. If Jesus Came to My House. (Illus.). 1951. 10.25 (ISBN 0-688-40981-4). Lothrop.

Vida, Marco G. The Christiad: Latin-English Edition. Drake, Gertrude C. & Forbes, Clarence A., eds. LC 78-1430. 288p. 1978. 9.85x (ISBN 0-8093-0814-2). S Ill U Pr.

JESUS CHRIST–PRAYERS

see also Lord's Prayer

Daughters of St. Paul. I Pray with Jesus. 1978. deluxe ed. 7.00 (ISBN 0-8198-0535-1); plastic bdg. 3.00 (ISBN 0-8198-0537-8). Dghtrs St Paul.

Donehoo, Paris. Prayer in the Life of Jesus. (Orig.). 1984. pap. 3.95 (ISBN 0-8054-5101-3). Broadman.

Dueland, Joy. The Blessings of Jesus. (Illus.). 1979. 8.95 (ISBN 0-931942-02-0). Phunn Pubs.

Jeremias, Joachim. The Prayers of Jesus. Bowden, John, et al, trs. from Ger. LC 77-10427. 132p. 1978. pap. 4.95 (ISBN 0-8006-1322-8, 1-1322). Fortress.

MacArthur, John, Jr. Jesus' Pattern of Prayer. LC 81-3947. 200p. 1981. 5.95 (ISBN 0-8024-4962-X). Moody.

Mitchell, Curtis C. Praying Jesus' Way. 160p. 1977. 10.95 (ISBN 0-8007-0843-1). Revell.

Reyes, Benito F. The Eternal Christ: Sonnet Prayer for the Second Coming. 18p. 1977. pap. 5.50 (ISBN 0-939375-00-1). World Univ Amer.

Sjogren, Per-Olof. The Jesus Prayer. Linton, Sydney, tr. from Swedish. LC 75-18789. 96p. 1975. pap. 3.95 (ISBN 0-8006-1216-7, 1-1216). Fortress.

Trueblood, Elton. The Prayers of Christ. LC 65-10706. Orig. Title: The Lord's Prayers. 1982. pap. 3.95 (ISBN 0-932970-24-9). Prinit Pr.

Wallis, Arthur. Jesus Prayed. 1966. pap. 1.50 (ISBN 0-87508-559-8). Chr Lit.

Ward, J. Neville. The Personal Faith of Jesus as Revealed in the Lord's Prayer. 128p. 1982. pap. 6.95 (ISBN 0-86683-678-0, HarpR). Har-Row.

JESUS CHRIST–PRIESTHOOD

Bunyan, John. Work of Jesus Christ As an Advocate. pap. 3.95 (ISBN 0-685-19844-8). Reiner.

Milligan, William. The Ascension & Heavenly Priesthood of Our Lord. 416p. 1977. Repr. of 1894 ed. 12.50 (ISBN 0-87921-034-6). Attic Pr.

Vanhoye, Albert. Old Testament Priests & the New Priest. Orchard, Bernard, tr. from Fr. LC 85-2171. (Studies in Scripture: Vol. II). Tr. of Pretres anciens, pretre nouveau selon le nouveau testament. 1986. pap. 24.95 (ISBN 0-932506-38-0). St Bedes Pubns.

JESUS CHRIST–PRIMACY

see also Jesus Christ–Mystical Body; Logos

Meilach, M. D. From Order to Omega. pap. 0.95 (ISBN 0-8199-0038-9, L38249). Franciscan Herald.

Pancheri, Francesco S. The Universal Primacy of Christ. Carol, Juniper B., tr. from Italian. Orig. Title: Il Primato universale de Christo. 144p. (Orig.). 1984. pap. 6.95 (ISBN 0-931888-16-6). Christendom Pubns.

JESUS CHRIST–PROPHECIES

Bayer, Hans F. Jesus' Predictions of Vindication & Resurrection: The Provenance, Meaning, & Correlation of the Synoptic Predictions. 290p. 1986. pap. 50.00x (ISBN 3-16-145014-0, Pub. by J C B Mohr BRD). Coronet Bks.

Carus, Paul, ed. Virgil's Prophecy on the Saviour's Birth. 97p. 1918. 2.95 (ISBN 0-317-40414-8). Open Court.

Lucas, DeWitt B. God Tells the World. 1964. pap. 2.50 (ISBN 0-910140-08-1). C & R Anthony.

Robertson, O. Palmer. The Christ of the Covenants. 1981. pap. 9.95 (ISBN 0-87552-418-4). Presby & Reformed.

Wallace, Arthur, compiled by. America's Witness for Jesus Christ. 70p. 1978. pap. 1.95x (ISBN 0-937892-04-1). LL Co.

Wilkerson, David. The Pocket Promise Book. gift ed. LC 72-86208. 96p. 1981. imitation leather 3.95 (ISBN 0-8307-0789-1, 5007953). Regal.

JESUS CHRIST–PROPHETIC OFFICE

Howes, Fred. This Is the Prophet Jesus. LC 82-72741. 276p. 1983. pap. 8.95 (ISBN 0-87516-497-8). De Vorss.

Murray, Andrew. Jesus Christ: Prophet-Priest. 64p. 1967. pap. 2.95 (ISBN 0-87123-271-5, 200271). Bethany Hse.

JESUS CHRIST–RELICS OF THE PASSION

see also Holy Cross; Holy Lance; Holy Shroud

Stevenson, Kenneth, ed. Proceedings of the Nineteen Seventy-Seven United States Conference of Research on the Shroud of Turin. (Illus.). 244p. (Orig.). 1980. pap. 10.00 (ISBN 0-9605516-0-3). Shroud of Turin.

Wilson, Ian. The Shroud of Turin: The Burial Cloth of Jesus Christ. LC 77-81551. (Illus.). 1979. pap. 5.50 (ISBN 0-385-15042-3, Im). Doubleday.

JESUS CHRIST–RESURRECTION

see also Easter; Jesus Christ–Appearances; Paschal Mystery

Allison, Dale C., Jr. The End of the Ages Has Come: An Early Interpretation of the Passion & Resurrection of Jesus. LC 85-47732. 208p. 1985. 19.95 (ISBN 0-8006-0753-8, 1-753). Fortress.

Austin, E. L. Earth's Greatest Day. 96p. (Orig.). 1980. pap. 3.95 (ISBN 0-8010-0163-3). Baker Bk.

Barth, Karl. The Resurrection of the Dead. Kastenbaum, Robert, ed. LC 76-19559. (Death and Dying Ser.). 1977. Repr. of 1933 ed. lib. bdg. 23.50x (ISBN 0-405-09555-4). Ayer Co Pubs.

Brown, Raymond E. The Virginal Conception & Bodily Resurrection of Jesus. LC 72-97399. 1973. pap. 5.95 (ISBN 0-8091-1768-1). Paulist Pr.

Chevrot, Georges. On the Third Day. 208p. 1961. 5.95 (ISBN 0-933932-10-3); pap. 2.95 (ISBN 0-933932-11-1). Scepter Pubs.

Craig, William L. The Historical Argument for the Resurrection of Jesus. LC 85-21570. (Texts & Studies in Religion: Vol. 23). 688p. 1985. lib. bdg. 69.95x (ISBN 0-88946-811-7). E Mellen.

Drillock, David, et al. Pascha: The Resurrection of Christ. (Music Ser.). 274p. 1980. pap. 15.00 (ISBN 0-913836-50-8); 20.00 (ISBN 0-913836-65-6). St Vladimirs.

Fishel, Kent & Rayds, John. Resurrection Evidences. (Cornerstone Ser.). 1985. pap. 2.95 (ISBN 0-310-46102-2, 12675P). Zondervan.

Fitch, Alger M., Jr. Afterglow of Christ's Resurrection. LC 75-14692. (New Life Bks). (Illus.). 136p. 1975. pap. 3.95 (ISBN 0-87239-055-1, 40030). Standard Pub.

Habermas, Gary & Flew, Anthony. Did Jesus Rise from the Dead? 1987. 14.95 (HarpR). Har-Row.

Habermas, Gary R. The Resurrection of Jesus: An Apologetic. 188p. 1984. pap. text ed. 11.50 (ISBN 0-8191-3750-2). U Pr of Amer.

Jansen, John F. The Resurrection of Jesus Christ in New Testament Theology. LC 80-231. 188p. 1980. pap. 9.95 (ISBN 0-664-24309-6). Westminster.

Kelsey, Morton T. Resurrection: Release from Oppression. LC 84-62150. 201p. 1985. pap. 8.95 (ISBN 0-8091-2673-7). Paulist Pr.

Kesich, Veselin. The First Day of the New Creation: The Resurrection & the Christian Faith. LC 81-21516. 206p. 1982. pap. 7.95 (ISBN 0-913836-78-8). St Vladimirs.

Ladd, George E. Creo en la Resurreccion de Jesus. Blanch, Miguel, tr. from Eng. LC 77-79934. (Serie Creo). Tr. of I Believe in the Resurrection of Jesus. (Span.). 204p. 1977. pap. 5.95 (ISBN 0-89922-091-6). Edit Caribe.

Lapide, Pinchas. The Resurrection of Jesus: A Jewish Perspective. Linss, Wilhelm C., tr. LC 83-70514. 160p. (Orig.). 1983. pap. 8.95 (ISBN 0-8066-2020-X, 10-5485). Augsburg.

Lindsay, Gordon. Death & Resurrection of Christ. (Life of Christ Ser.: Vol. 3). (Span.). 1.50 (ISBN 0-89985-983-6). Christ Nations.

Luebering, Carol & Schmitz, Robert E. Nothing to Fear: Unleashing the Power of the Resurrection. (Illus.). 104p. 1985. pap. text ed. 4.50 (ISBN 0-86716-047-0). St Anthony Mess Pr.

McDowell, Josh. The Resurrection Factor. 180p. (Orig.). 1981. (ISBN 0-918956-71-4, Dist. by Here's Life Publishers Inc.); pap. 6.95 (ISBN 0-918956-72-2). Campus Crusade.

Marxsen, Willi. Resurrection of Jesus of Nazareth. Kohl, Margaret, tr. from Ger. LC 76-120083. 192p. (Orig.). 1970. pap. 4.95 (ISBN 0-8006-0001-0, 1-1). Fortress.

Morison, Frank. Who Moved the Stone. pap. 3.95 (ISBN 0-310-29562-9, 10371P). Zondervan.

Moule, H. C. & Orr, J. The Resurrection of Christ. 1980. 20.00 (ISBN 0-86524-062-0, 9506). Klock & Klock.

Mouton, Boyce. By This Shall All Men Know. LC 79-56541. 1980. pap. 2.95 (ISBN 0-89900-139-4). College Pr Pub.

Nutting, George. Resurrection Is Not a Fairy Tale. 1981. 5.75 (ISBN 0-8062-1649-2). Carlton.

O'Collins, Gerald. Jesus Risen: An Historical, Fundamental & Systematic Examination of Christ's Resurrection. 240p. 1987. 13.95 (ISBN 0-8091-2849-7); pap. 16.95 (ISBN 0-8091-0393-1). Paulist Pr.

--The Resurrection of Jesus Christ. LC 73-2613. 160p. 1973. pap. 3.50 (ISBN 0-8170-0614-1). Judson.

Osborne, Grant R. The Resurrection Narratives: A Redactional Study. 288p. 1984. pap. 11.95 (ISBN 0-8010-6708-1). Baker Bk.

Owen, Valerie. Christ, Resurrection Life. 268p. (Orig.). 1985. pap. text ed. 7.95 (ISBN 0-914307-32-0). Word Faith.

Perrin, Norman. Resurrection According to Matthew, Mark, & Luke. LC 76-47913. 96p. (Orig.). 1977. pap. 3.95 (ISBN 0-8006-1248-5, 1-1248). Fortress.

Perry, Charles A. The Resurrection Promise: An Interpretation of the Easter Narratives. 152p. (Orig.). 1987. pap. 8.95 (ISBN 0-8028-0249-4). Eerdmans.

Price, Nelson L. The Destruction of Death. LC 82-72464. 1983. 4.50 (ISBN 0-8054-1528-9). Broadman.

Richards, Hubert J. The First Easter: What Really Happened? (What Really Happened? Ser.). 144p. 1986. pap. 5.95 (ISBN 0-89622-282-9). Twenty-Third.

Risen Jesus. 4.00 (ISBN 0-8198-6411-0); 3.00 (ISBN 0-8198-6412-9). Dghtrs St Paul.

Shaw, John M. The Resurrection of Christ. 218p. 1920. 10.95 (ISBN 0-567-02252-8, Pub. by T & T Clark Ltd UK). Fortress.

Smith, Robert H. Easter Gospels: The Resurrection of Jesus According to the Four Evangelists. LC 83-70518. 272p. (Orig.). 1983. pap. 15.95 (ISBN 0-8066-2024-2, 10-1988). Augsburg.

Spong, John S. The Easter Moment. 176p. 1980. 9.95 (ISBN 0-8164-0133-0, HarpR). Har-Row.

Stevenson, Kenneth & Habermas, Gary B. Verdict on the Shroud: Evidence for the Death & Resurrection of Jesus Christ. (Illus.). 220p. 1981. pap. 6.95 (ISBN 0-89283-174-X). Servant.

Stott, John R. The Authentic Jesus. LC 85-23831. 96p. 1986. pap. 2.95 (ISBN 0-87784-619-7). Inter-Varsity.

Taylor, John V. Weep Not for Me: Meditations on the Cross & the Resurrection. (Risk Book Ser.). 56p. 1986. pap. 3.50 (ISBN 2-8254-0850-6). Wrld Coun Churches.

Tregay, William. The Original Meaning of the Resurrection. 60p. (Orig.). Date not set. pap. price not set. Church Man Pub.

Wenham, John. Easter Enigma: Are the Resurrection Accounts in Conflict? 176p. 1984. pap. 6.95 (ISBN 0-310-29861-X, 12448P). Zondervan.

Williams, Rowan. Resurrection: Interpreting the Easter Gospel. 144p. (Orig.). 1985. pap. 5.95 (ISBN 0-8298-0727-6). Pilgrim NY.

Zodhiates, Spiros. Resurrection: True or False? (Illus.). 1978. pap. 3.95 (ISBN 0-89957-524-2). AMG Pubs.

JESUS CHRIST–RESURRECTION–JUVENILE LITERATURE

Enns, Peter & Forsberg, Glen. Jesus Is Alive! & Five Other Stories. (Stories that Live Ser.: Bk. 6). 24p. 1985. book & cassette 4.95 (ISBN 0-936215-06-2). STL Intl.

JESUS CHRIST–SAYINGS

see Jesus Christ–Words

JESUS CHRIST–SECOND ADVENT

see Second Advent

JESUS CHRIST–SERMON ON THE MOUNT

see Sermon on the Mount

JESUS CHRIST–SEVEN LAST WORDS

Chappell, Clovis G. The Seven Words: The Words of Jesus on the Cross Reveal the Heart of the Christian Faith. (Pocket Pulpit Library). 80p. 1976. pap. 2.95 (ISBN 0-8010-2387-4). Baker Bk.

Cocoris, G. Michael. The Last Sayings of the Savior from the Cross. 25p. (Orig.). 1985. pap. 1.00 (ISBN 0-935729-01-1). Church Open Door.

Pink, Arthur W. Seven Sayings of Our Saviour on the Cross. (Summit Bks). 1977. pap. 4.95 (ISBN 0-8010-7084-8). Baker Bk.

Sheen, Fulton J. The Seven Last Words. 1982. pap. 2.95 (ISBN 0-8189-0438-0). Alba.

Smith, H. The Last Words. pap. 4.75 (ISBN 0-88172-124-7). Believers Bkshelf.

Spurgeon, C. H. Words of Jesus Christ from the Cross. 1978. pap. 2.75 (ISBN 0-686-23028-0). Pilgrim Pubns.

Spurgeon, Charles H. Christ's Words from the Cross. (Spurgeon Library Ser.). 120p. 1981. pap. 4.95 (ISBN 0-8010-8207-2). Baker Bk.

Stier, Rudolf E. Words of the Risen Christ. 1982. lib. bdg. 8.25 (ISBN 0-86524-088-4, 9512). Klock & Klock.

Strauss, Lehman. Listen! Our Dying Savior Speaks. Orig. Title: The Day God Died. 113p. 1987. pap. 5.95 (ISBN 0-87213-828-3). Loizeaux.

Ward, Neville. Friday Afternoon: Reflections on the Seven Last Words. 144p. 1984. pap. 5.95 (ISBN 0-86683-744-2, AY8397, HarpR). Har-Row.

Wolfe, Charles E. The Seven Words from the Cross: A Commentary. 1980. pap. 4.65 (ISBN 0-89536-420-4, 1962). CSS of Ohio.

JESUS CHRIST–SIGNIFICANCE

Alexander, John W. Hope for a Troubled World. 32p. 1978. pap. 0.75 (ISBN 0-87784-165-9). Inter-Varsity.

Berkey, Robert F. & Edwards, Sarah A., eds. Christological Perspectives. 320p. 18.95 (ISBN 0-8298-0491-9); pap. 10.95 (ISBN 0-8298-0606-7). Pilgrim NY.

Blanchard, John. Right with God. LC 78-6809. 1978. pap. 3.50 (ISBN 0-8024-7357-1). Moody.

Cassidy, Richard J. Jesus, Politics, & Society: A Study of Luke's Gospel. LC 78-735. 238p. (Orig.). 1978. 15.95 (ISBN 0-88344-238-8); pap. 7.95 (ISBN 0-88344-237-X). Orbis Bks.

McGuckin, John A. The Transfiguration of Christ in Scripture & Tradition. LC 86-23892. (Studies in Bible & Early Christianity: Vol. 9). 333p. 1987. 59.95 (ISBN 0-88946-609-2). E Mellen.

Mohr, Victor. The Advent of Christ. 116p. 1985. pap. cancelled (ISBN 0-934616-16-7). Valkyrie Pub Hse.

Muggeridge, Malcolm. Jesus. LC 74-28794. 176p. 1976. pap. 9.95 (ISBN 0-06-066042-2, RD149, HarpR). Har-Row.

Neill, Stephen. The Supremacy of Jesus. LC 84-47740. (The Jesus Library Ser.). 216p. 1984. pap. 6.95 (ISBN 0-87784-928-5). Inter-Varsity.

Ouweneel, W. J. What Is the Sonship of Christ? pap. 2.25 (ISBN 0-88172-170-0). Believers Bkshelf.

Sheldon, Charles M. In His Steps. (Pivot Family Reader Ser). 256p. 1972. pap. 1.95 (ISBN 0-87983-012-3). Keats.

Smith, Joyce Marie. The Significance of Jesus. 1976. pap. 2.95 (ISBN 0-8423-5887-0). Tyndale.

Wurmbrand, Richard. Where Christ Still Suffers. Tr. of Where Christ Is Still Tortured. 1984. pap. 3.50 (ISBN 0-88270-578-4). Bridge Pub.

JESUS CHRIST–SPIRITUALISTIC INTERPRETATION

see also Bible and Spiritualism

Blaikie, W. G. & Law, R. The Inner Life of Christ. 459p. 1982. lib. bdg. 17.25 Smythe Sewn (ISBN 0-86524-156-2, 9515). Klock & Klock.

Lightfoot, Neil R. Jesus Christ Today. LC 76-42590. 360p. 1976. pap. 8.95 (ISBN 0-8010-5604-7). Baker Bk.

Murray, Andrew. The Spirit of Christ. 2nd ed. 240p. 1984. pap. 3.50 (ISBN 0-88368-126-9). Whitaker Hse.

Nee, Watchman. Christ the Sum of All Spiritual Things. Kaung, Stephen, tr. 1973. pap. 2.50 (ISBN 0-935008-14-4). Christian Fellow Pubs.

Prajnanananda, Swami. Christ the Savior & Christ Myth. rev. ed. 7.59. Vedanta Pr.

Richard, Lucien. What Are They Saying about Christ & World Religions? LC 81-80878. 96p. (Orig.). 1981. pap. 4.95 (ISBN 0-8091-2391-6). Paulist Pr.

JESUS CHRIST–TEACHING METHODS

Alfonso, Regina M. How Jesus Taught: The Methods & Techniques of the Master. (Illus.). 129p. (Orig.). 1986. pap. 6.95 (ISBN 0-8189-0506-9). Alba.

Conaway, John. Teaching the Bible. (Complete Teacher Training Meeting ser.). 48p. 1986. tchr's ed 9.95 (ISBN 0-89191-319-X). Cook.

Delnay, Robert G. Teach As He Taught: How to Apply Jesus' Teaching Methods. (Orig.). 1987. pap. 5.95 (ISBN 0-8024-4340-0). Moody.

Disciples of Jesus Junior-Junior High Teacher. 1984. pap. 2.25 (ISBN 0-915374-48-X). Rapids Christian.

Goodwin, Wayne & Cook, Gregory D. The Serving Sunday School. (Complete Teacher Training Meeting Ser.). 48p. 1986. tchr's ed 9.95 (ISBN 0-89191-315-7). Cook.

Grassi, Joseph A. Teaching the Way: Jesus, the Early Church & Today. LC 82-7054. 176p. 1982. lib. bdg. 26.75 (ISBN 0-8191-2501-6); pap. text ed. 11.50 (ISBN 0-8191-2502-4). U Pr of Amer.

Hall, Sandra. Christ & His Church: Teacher Guide. 96p. (Orig.). 1985. pap. 6.95 (ISBN 0-87123-801-2). Bethany Hse.

--The Kingdom: Teacher's Guide. 96p. (Orig.). 1985. pap. 6.95. Bethany Hse.

Horne, Herman H. Teaching Techniques of Jesus. LC 64-16634. 224p. 1971. pap. 5.95 (ISBN 0-8254-2804-1). Kregel.

Klausmeier, Robert. Preschool Teacher Survival Kit. 80p. 1986. tchr's ed 9.95 (ISBN 0-89191-362-9). Cook.

--Teen Teacher Survival Kit. 80p. 1986. tchr's ed 9.95 (ISBN 0-89191-364-5). Cook.

Leary, Michael. Christ & the Catechist: The Spiritual Life of the Christian Teacher. LC 86-83017. 128p. 1987. pap. 6.95 (ISBN 0-89870-139-2). Ignatius Pr.

McBride, Neal F. Teacher! A Christlike Model in Students. (Complete Teacher Training Meeting Ser.). 48p. 1986. 9.95 (ISBN 0-89191-313-0). Cook.

Meet Jesus in the Sunday Gospels, Vol. 1. 1986. pap. 8.95 (ISBN 0-937032-41-7). Light&Life Pub Co MN.

Merril, Dean. Teaching for Life-Response. (Complete Teacher Training Meeting Ser.). 48p. 1986. 9.95 (ISBN 0-89191-316-5). Cook.

Miller, Carol E. Disciples of Jesus, Beginner-Primary Teacher. 1984. pap. 1.75 (ISBN 0-915374-47-1). Rapids Christian.

Stein, Robert H. The Method & Message of Jesus' Teachings. LC 78-16427. 202p. 1978. pap. 8.95 (ISBN 0-664-24216-2). Westminster.

Thomas a Kempis. Imitation of Christ. Bechtel, Paul M., ed. (Moody Classics Ser.). 1984. pap. 4.50 (ISBN 0-8024-4005-3). Moody.

Townsend, Jim. The Personal Bible Study. (Complete Teacher Training Meeting Ser.). 48p. 1986. tchr's ed 9.95 (ISBN 0-89191-320-3). Cook.

JESUS CHRIST–TEACHINGS

Abernathy, David & Perrin, Norman. Understanding the Teaching of Jesus. 288p. (Orig.). 1983. pap. 13.95 (ISBN 0-8164-2438-1, HarpR). Har-Row.

Allen, James. As a Man Thinketh. 1985. 4.95 (ISBN 0-915720-20-5). Brownlow Pub Co.

Anderson, Norman. The Teachings of Jesus. LC 83-4312. (The Jesus Library). 216p. 1983. pap. 6.95 (ISBN 0-87784-926-9). Inter-Varsity.

Baldwin, Stanley C. What Did Jesus Say about That? 224p. 1984. pap. 2.95 missal size (ISBN 0-89693-312-1). Victor Bks.

Bauman, Edward W. Life & Teaching of Jesus. LC 60-7038. 240p. 1978. pap. 6.95 (ISBN 0-664-24221-9). Westminster.

Beasley-Murray, George R. Jesus & the Kingdom of God. 512p. 1986. 29.95 (ISBN 0-8028-3609-7). Eerdmans.

Blaikie, William G. The Public Ministry of Christ. 356p. 1984. lib. bdg. 13.25 (ISBN 0-86524-167-8, 9517). Klock & Klock.

Borg, Marcus J. Conflict, Holiness & Politics in the Teachings of Jesus. LC 84-9029. (Studies in the Bible & Early Christianity: Vol. 5). 410p. 1984. 59.95x (ISBN 0-88946-603-3). E Mellen.

Brestin, Dee. Examining the Claims of Jesus. (A Core Study in the Fisherman Bible Studyguides). 48p. 1985. pap. 2.95 (ISBN 0-87788-246-0). Shaw Pubs.

Bruce, F. F. The Hard Sayings of Jesus. LC 83-10793. (The Jesus Library). 216p. 1983. pap. 7.95 (ISBN 0-87784-927-7). Inter-Varsity.

Bruce, F. F., ed. Promise & Fulfilment. 216p. 1963. 15.95 (ISBN 0-567-02055-X, Pub. by T & T Clark Ltd UK). Fortress.

Burtis, Warren D. Jesus: The First Human Behaviorist. 128p. 1981. pap. text ed. 5.95 (ISBN 0-939530-00-7). Burtis Ent.

Butterworth, Eric. Discover the Power Within You. LC 68-17583. 1968. 13.45 (ISBN 0-06-061266-5, HarpR). Har-Row.

Cesar, Joseph V. The Teaching of the Master. 120p. (Orig.). pap. text ed. 5.95 (ISBN 0-937816-01-9). Tech Data.

Chilton, Bruce, ed. The Kingdom of God in the Teaching of Jesus. LC 83-20569. (Issues in Religion & Theology Ser.). 192p. 1984. pap. 7.95 (ISBN 0-8006-1769-X, 1-769). Fortress.

Chilton, Bruce D. A Galilean Rabbi & His Bible: Jesus' Use of the Interpreted Scripture of His Time. (Good News Studies Ser.: Vol. 8). 7.95 (ISBN 0-89453-374-6). M Glazier.

Coniaris, A. M. Christ's Comfort for Those Who Sorrow. 1978. pap. 3.95 (ISBN 0-937032-00-X). Light&Life Pub Co MN.

--The Great I Came's of Jesus. 1980. pap. 7.95 (ISBN 0-686-27069-X). Light&Life Pub Co MN.

--No Man Ever Spoke As This Man. 1969. pap. 4.95 (ISBN 0-937032-18-2). Light&Life Pub Co MN.

Connick, C. Milo. Jesus: The Man, the Mission, & the Message. 2nd ed. (Illus.). 512p. 1974. 29.95 (ISBN 0-13-509521-2). P-H.

Cumming, William K. Follow ME. 6.95 (ISBN 0-917920-01-5); pap. 1.95 (ISBN 0-917920-00-7). Mustardseed.

Curtis, Donald. The Christ-Based Teachings. LC 75-40657. 1976. 5.95 (ISBN 0-87159-016-6). Unity School.

Daughters of St. Paul. The Teachings & Miracles of Jesus. 1981. 5.00 (ISBN 0-686-73821-7); pap. 4.00 (ISBN 0-8198-7302-0). Dghtrs St Paul.

Davis, R. M. The Woods: The Human Self & the Realism of Jesus. 79p. 1971. pap. 4.00 (ISBN 0-9600434-0-3, 03). Camda.

Dean, Bessie. Lessons Jesus Taught. (Children's Inspirational Coloring Books). (Illus.). 72p. (Orig.). 1980. pap. 2.50 (ISBN 0-88290-146-X). Horizon Utah.

Finlan, Stephen. The Forgotten Teachings of Jesus. (Illus.). 49p. (Orig.). 1984. pap. 3.00 perfect bound (ISBN 0-9614275-0-7). Spiritual.

--The Forgotten Teachings of Jesus. rev. ed. (Illus.). 46p. 1985. pap. 4.50 (ISBN 0-9615301-1-1). Dilman Pr.

Getz, Gene. Loving One Another. LC 79-63450. 143p. 1979. pap. 5.95 (ISBN 0-88207-786-4). Victor Bks.

Giordani, Igino. Social Message of Jesus. 1977. 4.50 (ISBN 0-8198-0467-3); pap. 3.50 (ISBN 0-8198-0468-1). Dghtrs St Paul.

Goppelt, Leonard. Theology of the New Testament: Jesus & the Gospels, Vol I. Alsup, John E., tr. LC 80-28947. 316p. 1981. 15.95 (ISBN 0-8028-2384-X). Eerdmans.

Hamerton-Kelly, Robert. God the Father: Theology & Patriarchy in the Teaching of Jesus, No. 4. Brueggemann, Walter & Donahue, John R., eds. LC 78-54551. (Overtures to Biblical Theology Ser.). 144p. 1979. pap. 8.95 (ISBN 0-8006-1528-X, 1-1528). Fortress.

Haring, Bernard. Free & Faithful in Christ: The Truth Will Set You Free. (Free & Faithful in Christ Ser.: Vol. 2). 592p. pap. 14.95 (ISBN 0-8245-0501-8). Crossroad NY.

Harrington, Wilfrid. Christ & Life. 160p. 1976. 7.95 (ISBN 0-8199-0571-2). Franciscan Herald.

Harris, Dale L. Jesus Christ's World Utopia. rev. ed. (Illus.). 1984. pap. text ed. 4.95 (ISBN 0-318-00118-7). Christian Freedom.

Harris, John. The Teaching Methods of Christ: Characteristics of Our Lord's Ministry. 444p. 1984. lib. bdg. 16.75 (ISBN 0-86524-161-9, 9516). Klock & Klock.

Hayes, Norvel. Jesus Taught Me to Cast Out Devils. 90p. (Orig.). 1982. pap. 2.75 (ISBN 0-89274-272-0). Harrison Hse.

Hiers, Richard H. The Historical Jesus & the Kingdom of God: Present & Future in the Message & Ministry of Jesus. LC 73-2623. (University of Florida Humanities Monographs: No. 38). 1973. pap. 3.50 (ISBN 0-8130-0386-5). U Presses Fla.

Holmes, Ernest. Philosophy of Jesus. Kinnear, Willis, ed. 94p. 1973. pap. 4.50 (ISBN 0-911336-51-6). Sci of Mind.

Josephson, Emanuel. The Unheeded Teachings of Jesus Christ or Christ Rejected: The Strangest Story Never Told. LC 59-15870. (Blacked-Out History Ser.). (Illus.). 96p. 1959. 3.50 (ISBN 0-686-32441-2); pap. 3.00 (ISBN 0-686-32442-0). A-albionic Res.

Josephson, Emanuel M. Unheeded Teachings of Christ or Christ Rejected. 1979. write for info. (ISBN 0-685-96472-8). Revisionist Pr.

--Unheeded Teachings of Jesus: Christ Rejected. (Illus.). 50.00 (ISBN 0-685-07976-7). Chedney.

Lapide, Pinchas & Luz, Ulrich. Jesus in Two Perspectives. LC 85-15760. Tr. of Der Jude Jesus. 176p. 1985. pap. 8.95 (ISBN 0-8066-2171-0, 10-3517). Augsburg.

Lawler, Ronald, et al. Teaching of Christ. 2nd ed. LC 75-34852. 640p. 1983. pap. 9.95 (ISBN 0-87973-850-2, 850). Our Sunday Visitor.

Lawson, LeRoy. Lord of Promises. LC 82-17034. 112p. 1983. pap. 2.50 (ISBN 0-87239-611-8, 39988). Standard Pub.

Leslie, Robert C. Jesus As Counselor. (Festival Ser.). 144p. 1982. pap. 4.50 (ISBN 0-687-19930-1). Abingdon.

Lewis, E. R. Life & Teaching of Jesus Christ: According to the Synoptic Gospels. (London Divinity Ser.). 170p. 1977. pap. 3.95 (ISBN 0-227-67519-3). Attic Pr.

Lindsay, Gordon. Life & Teachings of Christ, Vol. 1. (Life of Christ & Parable Ser.). 238p. (Orig.). 1980. pap. 5.00 (ISBN 0-89985-967-4, 4101). Christ Nations.

--Life & Teachings of Christ, Vol. 2. (Life of Christ & Parable Ser.). 244p. (Orig.). 1980. pap. 5.00 (ISBN 0-89985-968-2). Christ Nations.

--Life & Teachings of Christ, Vol. 3. (Life of Christ & Parable Ser.). 288p. 1980. pap. 5.75 (ISBN 0-89985-969-0). Christ Nations.

Lockyer, Herbert. Everything Jesus Taught. LC 83-48431. 576p. 1984. pap. 6.95 (ISBN 0-06-065259-4, RD 503, HarpR). Har-Row.

Lohfink, Gerhard. Jesus & Community: The Social Dimension of Christian Faith. 224p. 1985. pap. 9.95 (ISBN 0-8091-2661-3). Paulist Pr.

Long, Max F. What Jesus Taught in Secret. (Illus.). 144p. 1983. pap. 5.95 (ISBN 0-87516-510-9). De Vorss.

The Lost Gospel of Jesus of Nazareth. LC 85-72544. write for info. (ISBN 0-936435-00-3). Church Man Pub.

Marsh, John. Confronting Jesus. LC 84-60895. 112p. (Orig.). 1984. pap. 3.50 (ISBN 0-89109-518-7). NavPress.

Maschke, Ruby. Promises of Jesus from the Bibles: Puzzle Book. (Illus.). 48p. 1983. pap. 2.50 (ISBN 0-87239-591-X, 2789). Standard Pub.

Meyer, Marvin W., tr. The Secret Teachings of Jesus: Four Gnostic Gospels. LC 84-42528. 224p. 1984. 15.45 (ISBN 0-394-52959-6). Random.

Montefiore, Claude G. Some Elements of the Religious Teaching of Jesus According to the Synoptic Gospels. LC 73-2223. (The Jewish People; History, Religion, Literature Ser.). Repr. of 1910 ed. 17.00 (ISBN 0-405-05285-5). Ayer Co Pubs.

Murray, Andrew. Money: Christ's Perspective on the Use & Abuse of Money. 80p. 1978. pap. 2.95 (ISBN 0-87123-382-7, 200382). Bethany Hse.

--True Vine. (Andrew Murray Ser.). pap. 3.50 (ISBN 0-8024-8798-X). Moody.

Niwano, Nichiko. My Father My Teacher: A Spiritual Journey. Gage, Richard L., tr. from Jap. 143p. (Orig.). 1982. pap. 3.50 (ISBN 4-333-01095-0, Pub. by Kosei Pub Co Japan). C E Tuttle.

Norden, Rudolph F. Day by Day with Jesus. 400p. (Orig.). 1985. pap. 10.95 (ISBN 0-570-03971-1, 12-3006). Concordia.

Norquist, Marilyn. Thy Kingdom Come: The Basic Teachings of Jesus. 64p. 1986. pap. 1.50 (ISBN 0-89243-244-6). Liguori Pubns.

O'Collins, Gerald. Interpreting Jesus. 1983. pap. 9.95 (ISBN 0-8091-2572-2). Paulist Pr.

Overton, Basil. When Christ Was Preached to Christ. pap. 5.50 (ISBN 0-89137-545-7). Quality Pubns.

Pennock, Michael. Jesus & You: Student Text. rev. ed. LC 84-70384. (High School Religion Text Ser.). (Illus.). 224p. 1984. pap. 5.95 (ISBN 0-87793-315-4). Ave Maria.

--Jesus & You: Teacher Manual. Rev. ed. (High School Religion Text Ser.). 144p. 1984. pap. 7.95 (ISBN 0-87793-316-2). Ave Maria.

Perrin, Norman. Rediscovering the Teachings of Jesus. LC 67-11510. 1976. pap. 6.95xi (ISBN 0-06-066493-2, RD 151, HarpR). Har-Row.

Peterson, Ralph H. Did Jesus Know What He Was Talking About? 112p. 1982. 6.95 (ISBN 0-8187-0045-9). Am Developing.

Piper, John. Love Your Enemies. LC 77-95449. (Society for New Testament Studies: No. 38). 1980. 34.50 (ISBN 0-521-22056-4). Cambridge U Pr.

Price, J. M. & Estudio, Guias de. Guia de Estudios Sobre Jesus el Maestro. 50p. 1982. pap. 3.25 (ISBN 0-311-43501-7). Casa Bautista.

Prophet, Mark L. & Prophet, Elizabeth C. The Lost Teachings of Jesus, Vol. I. LC 81-52784. (Illus.). 425p. (Orig.). 1986. 19.95 (ISBN 0-916766-45-4). Summit Univ.

--The Lost Teachings of Jesus, Vol. 1. LC 81-52784. (Illus.). 425p. (Orig.). pap. 14.95 (ISBN 0-916766-71-3). Summit Univ.

--The Lost Teachings of Jesus, Vol. 2. LC 81-52784. (Illus.). 598p. (Orig.). 1986. pap. 21.95 (ISBN 0-916766-72-1). Summit Univ.

Prophet, Mark L. & Prophet, Elizabeth C., eds. Corona Class Lessons. LC 83-51445. 455p. (Orig.). 1986. pap. 12.95 (ISBN 0-916766-65-9). Summit Univ.

Putnam, Roy C. Those He Came to Save. LC 77-13764. Repr. of 1978 ed. 35.50 (ISBN 0-8357-9029-0, 2016414). Bks Demand UMI.

Rauschenbusch, Walter. The Social Principles of Jesus. LC 76-50566. 1976. Repr. of 1916 ed. lib. bdg. 22.00 (ISBN 0-8414-7308-0). Folcroft.

Riches, John. Jesus & the Transformation of Judaism. 264p. (Orig.). 1982. pap. 10.95 (ISBN 0-8164-2361-X, HarpR). Har-Row.

Saraydarian, Torkom. Dialogue with Christ. LC 77-86722. 1979. pap. 4.00 (ISBN 0-911794-42-5). Aqua Educ.

Savoy, Gene. The Lost Gospel of Jesus: The Hidden Teachings of Christ. authorized millennium ed. LC 78-71277. (The Sacred Teachings of Light, Codex VIII Ser.). (Illus.). xv, 91p. 1984. text ed. 39.50 (ISBN 0-936202-08-4). Intl Comm Christ.

--The Millennium Edition of the Decoded New Testament: Origins & History of the Paradosis or Secret Tradition of the Oral Law Called the Gospel, with Commentary on the Canonical New Testament, Apocrypha, Pseudepigrapha, Old Testament, Dead Sea Scrolls, Ancient Fragments, & Other Religious Texts. Revised ed. LC 83-80523. (The Sacred Teachings of Light, Codex II Ser.). Orig. Title: The Decoded New Testament. (Illus.). 207p. 1983. text ed. 39.50 (ISBN 0-936202-06-8). Intl Comm Christ.

Sayings of Jesus. 5.95 (ISBN 0-88088-351-0). Peter Pauper.

Segundo, Juan L. The Historical Jesus of the Synoptics. Drury, John, tr. from Span. LC 85-7146. (Jesus of Nazareth Yesterday & Today Ser.: Vol. II). Tr. of Historia y Actualidad: Sinopticos y Pablo El Hombre de Hoy Ante Jesus de Nazareth. 240p. (Orig.). 1985. pap. 9.95 (ISBN 0-88344-220-5). Orbis Bks.

Sigal, Phillip. The Halakah of Jesus of Nazareth According to the Gospel of Matthew. 282p. (Orig.). 1986. lib. bdg. 23.75 (ISBN 0-8191-5210-2); pap. text ed. 13.25 (ISBN 0-8191-5211-0). U Pr of Amer.

Stewart, James S. The Life & Teaching of Jesus Christ. 1982. pap. 3.95 (ISBN 0-687-21744-X, Festival). Abingdon.

Szekely, Edmond B. The Essene Gospel of Peace, Bk. 1. (Illus.). 72p. 1981. pap. 1.00 (ISBN 0-89564-000-7). IBS Intl.

--The Essene Gospel of Peace, Bk. 2. (Illus.). 132p. 1981. pap. 5.80 (ISBN 0-89564-001-5). IBS Intl.

--The Essene Gospel of Peace, Bk. 3: Lost Scrolls of the Essene Brotherhood. (Illus.). 144p. 1981. pap. 5.60 (ISBN 0-89564-002-3). IBS Intl.

--The Essene Gospel of Peace, Bk. 4: Teachings of the Elect. (Illus.). 40p. 1981. pap. 4.50 (ISBN 0-89564-003-1). IBS Intl.

--The Essene Jesus. (Illus.). 72p. 1977. pap. 4.50 (ISBN 0-89564-007-4). IBS Intl.

--The Essene Origins of Christianity. (Illus.). 184p. 1981. pap. 8.50 (ISBN 0-89564-015-5). IBS Intl.

Teachings of Christ Ungame Cards. 1.50 (ISBN 0-317-15786-8). Chr Marriage.

Tiner, John H. Jesus the Teacher Word Search. 48p. 1986. pap. 2.50 (ISBN 0-87403-049-8, 2693). Standard Pub.

Van Beeck, Frans J. Christ Proclaimed: Christology As Rhetoric. LC 79-66459. 632p. 1979. pap. 9.95 (ISBN 0-8091-2208-1). Paulist Pr.

Vinck, Jose D. The Words of Jesus, with Key Readings from New & Old Testaments. 320p. 1977. deluxe ed. 30.00 boxed, slipcover, hand-made full morocco (ISBN 0-911726-26-8). Alleluia Pr.

Walsh, Vincent M. Spirit of Jesus. 1984. pap. 5.00 (ISBN 0-943374-10-3). Key of David.

Waterman, Leroy. The Religion of Jesus: Christianity's Unclaimed Heritage of Prophetic Religion. LC 78-16405. 1978. Repr. of 1952 ed. lib. bdg. 22.50x (ISBN 0-313-20586-8, WARJ). Greenwood.

Weber, Hans-Ruedi. Jesus & the Children: Biblical Resources for Study & Preaching. LC 79-87754. 1980. pap. 5.95 (ISBN 0-8042-1316-X). John Knox.

Weiss, Johannes. Jesus' Proclamation of the Kingdom of God. Hiers, Richard H. & Holland, Larrimore D., eds. (Reprints & Translations). 1985. pap. 9.75 (ISBN 0-89130-859-8, 00-07-08). Scholars Pr GA.

Wilder, Amos N. Eschatology & Ethics in the Teaching of Jesus. LC 78-16425. 1978. Repr. of 1950 ed. lib. bdg. 27.50 (ISBN 0-313-20585-X, WIEE). Greenwood.

Wilson, Dora. The Totalitarian Claim of the Gospels. 1983. pap. 2.50x (ISBN 0-87574-004-9, 004A). Pendle Hill.

JESUS CHRIST–TEMPTATION

Bale, John. Temptation of Christ. LC 74-133636. (Tudor Facsimile Texts. Old English Plays: No. 22). Repr. of 1909 ed. 49.50 (ISBN 0-404-53322-1). AMS Pr.

Bien, Peter. Tempted by Happiness: Razantzakis Post-Christian Christ. 1984. pap. 2.50x (ISBN 0-317-12307-6, 253). Pendle Hill.

Bussell, Harold. Lord, I Can Resist Anything but Temptation. (Orig.). 1985. pap. 5.95 (ISBN 0-310-37271-2, 12389P). Zondervan.

Coombe, Jack. The Temptation. 1984. pap. 6.95 (ISBN 0-89896-127-0). Larksdale.

Davis, Robert W. Jesus Meets Nick. (Jesus & His Disciples Ser.: Vol. I). (Illus.). 24p. 1985. 4.95 (ISBN 0-9615877-0-9). Davis Pub.

Kelly, W. Christ Tempted & Sympathizing. 3.95 (ISBN 0-88172-091-7). Believers Bkshelf.

Simpson, Albert B. Christ of the Forty Days. pap. 1.25 (ISBN 0-87509-004-4). Chr Pubns.

Thurman, Howard. Temptations of Jesus. LC 78-74718. 1979. pap. 3.95 (ISBN 0-913408-47-6). Friends United.

Welch, Reuben. His Victory & Ours: The Temptations of Jesus. 78p. (Orig.). 1983. pap. 3.50 (ISBN 0-8341-0871-2). Beacon Hill.

JESUS CHRIST–THEOSOPHICAL INTERPRETATIONS

Bailey, Alice A. From Bethlehem to Calvary. 1975. 19.00 (ISBN 0-85330-007-0); pap. 7.00 (ISBN 0-85330-107-7). Lucis.

--The Reappearance of the Christ. 1978. 18.00 (ISBN 0-85330-014-3); pap. 7.00 (ISBN 0-85330-114-X). Lucis.

Besant, Annie. Esoteric Christianity. 8th ed. 1966. 7.00 (ISBN 0-8356-7052-X). Theos Pub Hse.

Jakubowsky, Frank. The Psychological Patterns of Jesus Christ. 342p. (Orig.). 1982. pap. 14.95 (ISBN 0-932588-02-6). Jakubowsky.

Kralik, A. F. Jesus: Fact, Fable or Myth. 1985. 6.50 (ISBN 0-8062-2480-0). Carlton.

Ruether, Rosemary R. To Change the World: Christology & Cultural Criticism. LC 81-9703. 96p. 1983. pap. 5.95 (ISBN 0-8245-0573-5). Crossroad NY.

St. Thomas Aquinas. The Grace of Christ. (Summa Theologial Ser.: Vol. 49). 1974. 18.95 (ISBN 0-07-002024-8). McGraw.

Saraydarian, Haroutiun. Christ, Avatar of Sacrificial Love. LC 74-11760. 1974. 9.00 (ISBN 0-911794-38-7); pap. 8.00 (ISBN 0-911794-39-5). Aqua Educ.

Segundo, Juan L. The Humanist Christology of Paul: Jesus of Nazareth Yesterday & Today, Vol. 3. Drury, John, tr. from Span. LC 86-8480. 256p. (Orig.). 1986. pap. 14.95 (ISBN 0-88344-221-3). Orbis Bks.

Sellers, Robert V. Two Ancient Christologies: A Study in the Christological Thought of the Schools of Alexandria & Antioch in the Early History of Christian Doctrine. (Church Historical Society London N. S. Ser.: No. 39). Repr. of 1940 ed. 50.00 (ISBN 0-8115-3162-7). Kraus Repr.

Steiner, Rudolf. Christ in Relation to Lucifer & Ahriman. Mollenhauer, Peter, tr. 1978. pap. 2.00 (ISBN 0-910142-77-7). Anthroposophic.

--The Four Sacrifices of Christ. 2nd ed. Church, Gilbert, ed. Laird-Brown, May, tr. from Ger. 20p. (Orig.). 1981. pap. 1.00 (ISBN 0-88010-026-5). Anthroposophic.

--From Jesus to Christ. 185p. 1973. 16.95 (ISBN 0-85440-277-2). Anthroposophic.

Watson, David & Jenkins, Simon. Jesus Then & Now. Keely, R., ed. 192p. 1987. pap. 9.95 (ISBN 0-7459-1318-0). Lion USA.

JESUS CHRIST–TRANSFIGURATION

De Petri, Catharose. Transfiguracion. (Span.). 1987. pap. 6.00. Rosycross Pr.

Moscow Synod. Staff, ed. Preobrazhenije Gospodnje. Tr. of The Rransfiguration of the Lord. 128p. pap. 6.00 (ISBN 0-317-29169-6). Holy Trinity.

St. Gregory & Balfour, David. Discourse on the Tranfiguration. LC 85-13299. 170p. 1985. Repr. lib. bdg. 19.95x (ISBN 0-89370-862-3). Borgo Pr.

Van Rijckenborgh, Jan. What Is Transfiguration? 40p. 1987. pap. 1.50. Rosycross Pr.

Wild, Robert. His Face Shone Like the Sun: Encountering the Transfigured Christ in Scripture. LC 86-8054. 126p. (Orig.). 1986. pap. 5.95 (ISBN 0-8189-0501-8). Alba.

JESUS CHRIST–TRIAL

Brandon, S. G. The Trial of Jesus of Nazareth. LC 68-9206. (Illus.). 1979. pap. 4.95 (ISBN 0-8128-6018-7). Stein & Day.

Breed, David K. The Trial of Christ: From a Legal & Scriptural Viewpoint. (Pocket Pulpit Library). 96p. 1982. pap. 2.95 (ISBN 0-8010-0829-8). Baker Bk.

Chandler. The Trial of Jesus. (Illus.). 24.95 (ISBN 0-686-90784-1); deluxe ed. 44.95 (ISBN 0-686-90785-X); pap. 9.95 (ISBN 0-686-90786-8). Harrison Co GA.

Chandler, Walter M. The Trial of Jesus from a Lawyer's Standpoint, 2 vols. LC 83-82312. 1983. Repr. of 1925 ed. 115.00 set (ISBN 0-89941-294-7). W S Hein.

Cohn, H. The Trial & Death of Jesus. 14.95x (ISBN 0-87068-432-9). Ktav.

Innes, A. T. & Powell, F. J. The Trial of Christ. 287p. 1982. lib. bdg. 10.75 (ISBN 0-86524-138-4, 9513). Klock & Klock.

Juel, Donald. Messiah & Temple: The Trial of Jesus in the Gospel of Mark. LC 76-46397. (Society of Biblical Literature. Dissertation Ser.: No. 31). Repr. of 1977 ed. 43.60 (ISBN 0-8357-9578-0, 2017527). Bks Demand UMI.

Rosadi, Giovanni. The Trial of Jesus. 1977. lib. bdg. 59.95 (ISBN 0-8490-2767-5). Gordon Pr.

Sloyan, Gerard S. Jesus on Trial: The Development of the Passion Narratives & Their Historical & Ecumenical Implications. (Illus.). 156p. pap. 3.75 (ISBN 0-686-95173-5). ADL.

Tyson, Joseph B. The Death of Jesus in Luke-Acts. 212p. 1986. text ed. 17.95 (ISBN 0-87249-461-6). U of SC Pr.

Vassilakos, Aristarchus. The Trial of Jesus Christ. Orthodox Christian Educational Society, ed. 64p. (Orig.). 1950. pap. 2.75x (ISBN 0-938366-47-5). Orthodox Chr.

Winter, Paul. On the Trial of Jesus. 2nd ed. Burkill, T. A. & Vermes, G., eds. (Studia Judaica, Vol. 1). 1973. 31.00x (ISBN 3-11-002283-4). De Gruyter.

JESUS CHRIST–TYPOLOGY

see Typology (Theology)

JESUS CHRIST–WORDS

see also Jesus Christ–Seven Last Words

Berrigan, Daniel. The Words Our Saviour Gave Us. 1978. pap. 4.95 (ISBN 0-87243-081-2). Templegate.

Bivin, David. Understanding the Difficult Words of Jesus. LC 83-61850. (Illus.). 172p. (Orig.). 1983. pap. 8.95 (ISBN 0-918873-00-2). Ctr Judaic-Christ Studies.

Boring, M. Eugene. Sayings of the Risen Jesus: Christian Prophecy in the Synoptic Tradition. LC 81-18022. (Society for New Testament Studies Monograph: No. 46). (Illus.). 310p. 1981. 44.50 (ISBN 0-521-24117-0). Cambridge U Pr.

Bouyer, L. & Cawley, M. Christology. LC 83-4420. (Word & Spirit Ser.: Vol. V). 1983. pap. 7.00 (ISBN 0-932506-28-3). St Bedes Pubns.

Campbell, Benjamin P. No Alien Power. (Orig.). 1985. pap. 1.75 (ISBN 0-88028-050-6). Forward Movement.

Campbell, Robert C. Jesus Still Has Something to Say. 192p. 1987. pap. 9.95 (ISBN 0-8170-1114-5). Judson.

Crossan, John D. Sayings Parallels: A Workbook for the Jesus Tradition. LC 85-16220. (Foundations & Facets Ser.). 256p. 1986. 24.95 (ISBN 0-8006-2109-3, 1-2109); pap. 14.95 (ISBN 0-8006-1909-9, 1-1909). Fortress.

Dalman, Gustaf H. Words of Christ. 1981. lib. bdg. 13.50 (ISBN 0-86524-080-9, 9509). Klock & Klock.

Dunnam, Maxie. Jesus' Claims-Our Promise: A Study of the "I Am" Sayings of Jesus. LC 84-51831. 128p. (Orig.). 1984. pap. 5.95 (ISBN 0-8358-0502-6). Upper Room.

Failing, George E. Did Christ Die for All? 1980. 1.25 (ISBN 0-937296-02-3, 222-B). Presence Inc.

Hills, Christopher. The Christ Book: What Did He Really Say? Hills, Norah, ed. LC 80-5865. (Illus.). 224p. 1980. gift ed. 15.95; text ed. 10.95 (ISBN 0-916438-37-6). Univ of Trees.

Hunter, Archibald M. The Work & Words of Jesus. rev. ed. LC 73-7559. 230p. 1973. pap. 8.95 (ISBN 0-664-24976-0). Westminster.

Jakubowsky, Frank. The Psychological Patterns of Jesus Christ. 342p. (Orig.). 1982. pap. 14.95 (ISBN 0-932588-02-6). Jakubowsky.

Kistler, Don. The Father & Sons Shall Be One, Vol. 1. 141p. (Orig.). 1978. pap. 3.50x (ISBN 0-940532-01-8). AOG.

Kline, Leslie L. The Sayings of Jesus in the Pseudo-Clementine Homilies. LC 75-1645. (Society of Biblical Literature. Dissertation Ser.: No. 14). Repr. of 1975 ed. 52.00 (ISBN 0-8357-9579-9, 2017517). Bks Demand UMI.

Langdon, Larry, ed. The Words of Jesus on Peace. LC 84-28866. (Illus.). 72p. 1985. pap. 3.95 (ISBN 0-943726-02-6). Langdon Pubns.

Lindsay, Gordon. Amazing Discoveries in the Words of Jesus. 4.50 (ISBN 0-89985-112-6). Christ Nations.

Matura, Thaddee. Gospel Radicalism: A Study of the Hard Sayings of Jesus. Despot, Maggi & Lachance, Paul, trs. from Fr. LC 83-6249. Orig. Title: Le Radicalisme Evangelique Aux Sources de la vie Chretienne. 208p. (Orig.). 1984. pap. 8.95 (ISBN 0-88344-182-9). Orbis Bks.

Menedez, Josefa, et al. Words of Love. LC 84-51596. 95p. (Orig.). 1985. pap. 3.00 (ISBN 0-89555-244-2). Tan Bks Pubs.

Menendez, Josefa. I Wait for You: Jesus' Lament Over Man's Indifference (Excerpts from the Way of Divine Love) 32p. (Orig.). 1985. pap. 0.50 (ISBN 0-89555-285-X). Tan Bks Pubs.

Michaels, Louis. The Words of Jesus: Arranged for Meditation. 1977. 6.95 (ISBN 0-87243-071-5). Templegate.

Neil, William. The Difficult Sayings of Jesus. 1977. pap. 2.95 (ISBN 0-8028-1668-1). Eerdmans.

Neil, William & Travis, Stephen. More Difficult Sayings of Jesus. 128p. (Orig.). 1982. pap. 5.95 (ISBN 0-8028-1937-0). Eerdmans.

Pelikan, Judy, illus. The Words of Christ. Golbitz, Pat, ed. LC 86-60824. (Illus.). 64p. 1986. 14.95 (ISBN 0-688-06240-7). Morrow.

Pentecost, Dwight. A Harmony of the Words & Works of Jesus Christ. 272p. 1981. 12.95 (ISBN 0-310-30950-6, 17016); pap. 8.95 (ISBN 0-310-30951-4, 17016P). Zondervan.

Pentecost, J. Dwight. The Words & Works of Jesus Christ. 576p. 1981. 19.95 (ISBN 0-310-30940-9, 17015). Zondervan.

Rajneesh, Bhagwan Shree. Come Follow Me, Vol. III. Swami Deva Paritosh, ed. LC 80-8343. (Jesus Ser.). (Illus.). 272p. (Orig.). 1976. 12.95 (ISBN 0-88050-036-0). Chidvilas Found.

--Come Follow Me, Vol. IV. Ma Yoga Sudha, ed. LC 80-8343. (Jesus Ser.). (Illus.). 286p. (Orig.). 1977. 12.95 (ISBN 0-88050-037-9). Chidvilas Found.

--Come Follow Me, Vol. II. Ma Satya Bharti, ed. LC 80-8343. (Jesus Ser.). (Illus.). 316p. (Orig.). 1977. 12.95 (ISBN 0-88050-035-2). Chidvilas Found.

--Come Follow Me, Vol. I. Ma Satya Bharti, ed. LC 80-8343. (Jesus Ser.). (Illus.). 292p. (Orig.). 1976. 12.95 (ISBN 0-88050-034-4). Chidvilas Found.

--I Say unto You, 2 vols. Asha, Ma Prem, ed. LC 82-245650. (Jesus Ser.). (Illus., Orig.). 1980. Vol. I, 384. 19.50 (ISBN 0-88050-085-9); Vol. II. pap. 15.95 (ISBN 0-88050-586-9); pap. 4.95 wkbk. (ISBN 0-88050-585-0). Chidvilas Found.

Sanford, John A. Kingdom Within: A Study of the Inner Meaning of Jesus' Sayings. LC 77-105548. 1970. Har-Row.

Stier, Rudolf E. Words of the Risen Christ. 1982. lib. bdg. 8.25 (ISBN 0-86524-088-4, 9512). Klock & Klock.

Stuart, Friend. Master Thoughts, 3 vols. 600p. 1985. Set. vinyl 50.00 (ISBN 0-912132-05-1). Dominion Pr.

Youngblood, Ronald & Inch, Morris, eds. The Living & Active Word of God: Studies in Honor of Samuel J. Schultz. 1983. 20.00 (ISBN 0-931464-11-0). Eisenbrauns.

JESUS CHRIST IN ART

see Jesus Christ–Art

JESUS CHRIST IN FICTION, DRAMA, POETRY, ETC.

Adams, Dickinson W., ed. Jefferson's Extracts from the Gospels: "The Philosophy of Jesus" & "The Life & Morals of Jesus". LC 82-61371. (The Papers of Thomas Jefferson, Second Ser.). 456p. 1986. text ed. 31.50 (ISBN 0-691-04699-9); pap. text ed. 14.50 (ISBN 0-691-10210-4). Princeton U Pr.

Clark, Ira. Christ Revealed: The History of the Neotypological Lyric in the English Renaissance. LC 82-2696. (University of Florida Humanities Monographs: No. 51). xiv, 218p. 1982. pap. 15.00x (ISBN 0-8130-0712-7). U Presses Fla.

Ditsky, John. The Onstage Christ: Studies in the Persistence of a Theme. (Critical Studies Ser.). 188p. 1980. 28.50x (ISBN 0-389-20059-X). B&N Imports.

Eastman, Fred. Christ in the Drama: A Study of the Influence of Christ on the Drama of England & America. facsimile ed. LC 79-167336. (Essay Index Reprints - Shaffer Lectures of Northwestern University, 1946). Repr. of 1947 ed. 15.00 (ISBN 0-8369-2647-1). Ayer Co Pubs.

Kremen, Kathryn R. The Imagination of the Resurrection: The Poetic Continuity of a Religious Motif in Donne, Blake, & Yeats. LC 71-168812. (Illus.). 344p. 1972. 26.50 (ISBN 0-8387-7940-9). Bucknell U Pr.

Morrison, George H. Christ in Shakespeare. 142p. 1981. Repr. of 1928 ed. lib. bdg. 30.00 (ISBN 0-89984-342-5). Century Bookbindery.

Roberts, Richard. The Jesus of Poets & Prophets. 1977. Repr. of 1920 ed. lib. bdg. 25.00 (ISBN 0-8492-2312-1). R West.

JESUS CHRIST IN LITERATURE

see Jesus Christ in Fiction, Drama, Poetry, etc.

JESUS MOVEMENT

see Jesus People

JESUS PEOPLE

Enroth, Ronald M., et al. The Story of the Jesus People: A Factual Survey. (Illus.). 256p. 1972. pap. 3.95 (ISBN 0-85364-131-5). Attic Pr.

Kelly, W. Lectures on the Church of God. 7.50 (ISBN 0-88172-092-5). Believers Bkshelf.

Larsen, Earnest. Whatever Happened to Good Old Plastic Jesus? 144p. 1978. pap. 3.95 (ISBN 0-697-01696-X). Wm C Brown.

Mills, Watson E. Charismatic Religion in Modern Research: A Bibliography. Scholer, David M., ed. LC 85-127327. (National Association of Baptist Professors of Religion Bibliographic Ser.: No. 1). viii, 178p. 1985. text ed. 14.50 (ISBN 0-86554-143-4, MUP/M010). Mercer Univ Pr.

Richardson, James T., et al. Organized Miracles: A Study of a Contemporary, Youth, Communal, Fundamentalist Organization. LC 78-55937. 368p. 1979. 19.95 (ISBN 0-87855-284-7). Transaction Bks.

Ryan, John J. Jesus People. 1970. text ed. 2.95 (ISBN 0-914070-03-7). ACTA Found.

Wilkerson, David. Jesus Person Pocket Promise Book. LC 72-86208. 96p. 1979. pap. 2.50 (ISBN 0-8307-0191-5, 5007801). Regal.

JETTATURA

see Evil Eye

JEWEL, JOHN BP. OF SALISBURY, 1522-1571

Cooper, Thomas. An Answer in Defence of the Truth Against the Apology of Private Mass. 1850. 21.00 (ISBN 0-384-09790-1). Johnson Repr.

Southgate, Wyndham M. John Jewel & the Problem of Doctrinal Authority. LC 62-9430. (Historical Monographs: No. 49). (Illus.). 1962. 16.50x (ISBN 0-674-47750-2). Harvard U Pr.

Weiser, David K. The Prose Style of John Jewel. Hogg, James, ed. (Elizabethan & Renaissance Studies). 194p. (Orig.). 1973. pap. 15.00 (ISBN 3-7052-0658-3, Pub. by Salzburg Studies). Longwood Pub Group.

JEWISH-ARAB RELATIONS

Alexander, Yonah & Kittrie, Nicholas N. F., eds. Crescent & Star: Arab & Israeli Perspectives on the Middle East Conflict. LC 72-5797. (AMS Studies in Modern Society: Political & Social Issues). 37.50 (ISBN 0-404-10522-X); pap. 14.00 (ISBN 0-404-10523-8). AMS Pr.

Allen, Richard. Imperialism & Nationalism in the Fertile Crescent: Sources & Prospects of the Arab-Israeli Conflict. (Illus.). 1974. 29.95x (ISBN 0-19-501782-X). Oxford U Pr.

Black, Ian. Zionism & the Arabs, Nineteen Thirty-Six to Nineteen Thirty-Nine. (Outstanding Theses from the London School of Economics & Political Science Ser.). 500p. 1987. lib. bdg. 75.00 (ISBN 0-8240-1911-3). Garland Pub.

Carmichael, Joel. Open Letter to Moses & Mohammed. LC 68-9705. (Open Letter Ser). (Orig.). 1968. pap. 4.95 (ISBN 0-685-11973-4, 18). Heineman.

Cohen, Amnon & Baer, Gabriel, eds. Egypt & Palestine: A Millennium of Association (868-1948) LC 84-16109. 400p. 1985. 32.50 (ISBN 0-312-23927-0). St Martin.

Eaford & Ajaz. Judaism or Zionism? What Difference for the Middle East? 320p. 1986. 32.50 (ISBN 0-86232-475-0, Pub. by Zed Pr England); pap. 12.50 (ISBN 0-86232-476-9, Pub. by Zed Pr England). Humanities.

Elmessiri, Abdelwahab M. The Land of Promise: A Critique of Political Zionism. LC 77-83664. 1977. text ed. 11.95x (ISBN 0-930244-02-8); pap. text ed. 7.95x (ISBN 0-930244-01-X). North American Inc.

Esco Foundation For Palestine Inc. Palestine: A Study of Jewish, Arab, & British Policies, 2 Vols. LC 47-2569. Repr. of 1947 ed. Set. 192.00 (ISBN 0-527-27750-9). Kraus Repr.

Givet, Jacques. The Anti-Zionist Complex. Abel, Evelyn, tr. from Fr. LC 81-16693. Tr. of Israel et le Genocide Inacheve. 192p. 1982. 11.95 (ISBN 0-89961-019-6). SBS Pub.

Goitein, S. D. Jews & Arabs: Their Contacts Through the Ages. 3rd ed. LC 74-9141. 271p. 1974. pap. 6.95 (ISBN 0-8052-0464-4). Schocken.

Haddad, Heskel M. The Jews of Arab & Islamic Countries: History, Problems & Solutions. LC 83-5065. 168p. 1984. 12.95 (ISBN 0-88400-100-8). Shengold.

Haim, Yehoyada. Abandonment of Illusions: Zionist Political Attitudes Toward Palestinian Arab Nationalism, 1936-1939. (Relica Edition Ser.). 170p. 1983. softcover 22.50x (ISBN 0-86531-971-5). Westview.

Israeli, Raphuel. Peace Is in the Eye of the Beholder. xxiv, 389p. 1985. text ed. 62.00 (ISBN 0-89925-077-7). Mouton.

Lorch, Netanel. One Long War. 1976. 8.00 (ISBN 0-685-82597-3). Herzl Pr.

Magnes, Judah L. & Buber, Martin. Arab-Jewish Unity: Testimony Before the Anglo-American Inquiry for the Ihud (Union) LC 75-7678. (The Rise of Jewish Nationalism & the Middle East Ser). 96p. 1975. Repr. of 1947 ed. 15.00 (ISBN 0-88355-348-1). Hyperion Conn.

Mandel, Neville. The Arabs & Zionism Before World War One. LC 73-78545. 1977. pap. 4.95 (ISBN 0-520-03940-8, CAL 430). U of Cal Pr.

Margoliouth, D. S. The Relations Between Arabs & Israelis Prior to the Rise of Islam. (British Academy, London, Schweich Lectures on Biblical Archaeology Series, 1921). pap. 19.00 (ISBN 0-8115-1263-0). Kraus Repr.

Memmi, Albert. Jews & Arabs. Levieux, Eleanor, tr. from Fr. LC 75-10697. (Eng.). 224p. 1975. 9.95 (ISBN 0-87955-327-8); pap. 7.95 (ISBN 0-87955-328-6). O'Hara.
Patai, Raphael. The Seed of Abraham: Jews & Arabs in Contact & Conflict. 384p. 1986. 29.95 (ISBN 0-87480-251-2). U of Utah Pr.
Regan, Geoffrey B. Israel & the Arabs: Cambridge Introduction to the History of Mankind. (Illus.). 48p. 1984. pap. 4.95 (ISBN 0-521-27580-6). Cambridge U Pr.
Rowley, Gwyn, ed. Israel into Palestine. LC 83-22167. 198p. 1983. 31.00x (ISBN 0-7201-1674-0). Mansell.
Rubinstein, Leon. The First Swallows. LC 83-45138. (Illus.). 216p. 1986. 14.50 (ISBN 0-8453-4758-6, Cornwall Bks). Assoc Univ Prs.
Sereni, Ezo H. & Ashery, R. E., eds. Jews & Arabs in Palestine: Studies in a National & Colonial Problem. LC 75-6455. (The Rise of Jewish Nationalism & the Middle East Ser). 416p. 1975. Repr. of 1936 ed. 31.35 (ISBN 0-88355-341-4). Hyperion Conn.
Sherman, John. Arab-Israeli Conflict, Nineteen Forty-Five to Nineteen Seventy-One: A Bibliography. LC 77-83360. (Reference Library of Social Science Ser.). 1978. lib. bdg. 63.00 (ISBN 0-8240-9829-3). Garland Pub.
Ziff, William B. The Rape of Palestine. LC 73-97310. (Illus.). 612p. 1975. Repr. of 1938 ed. lib. bdg. 29.25x (ISBN 0-8371-2639-8, ZIRP). Greenwood.

JEWISH ART AND SYMBOLISM
see also Symbolism in the Bible
Altmann, Alexander. Essays in Jewish Intellectual History. LC 80-54471. 336p. 1981. 30.00x (ISBN 0-87451-192-5). U Pr of New Eng.
Davidovitch, David. The Ketuba: Jewish Marriage Contracts Through the Ages. LC 82-1247. (Illus.). 120p. 1985. 29.95 (ISBN 0-915361-21-3, 09745-5, Dist. by Watts). Adama Pubs Inc.
Eis, Ruth. Ornamented Bags for Tallit & Tefllin. Cassuto, Nelda, ed. LC 83-83059. (The Magnes Museum Collection Ser.). 99p. (Orig.). 1984. pap. text ed. 22.50 (ISBN 0-318-01125-5). Magnes Mus.
Goldman, Bernard. The Sacred Portal: A Primary Symbol in Ancient Judaic Art. LC 86-10983. (Brown Classics in Judaica Ser.). (Illus.). 260p. 1986. pap. text ed. 15.75 (ISBN 0-8191-5269-2). U Pr of Amer.
Gutmann, Joseph. Beauty in Holiness: Studies in Jewish Ceremonial Art & Customs. 1970. 50.00x (ISBN 0-87068-012-9). Ktav.
--No Graven Images: Studies in Art & the Hebrew Bible. (Library of Biblical Studies). 1970. 50.00x (ISBN 0-87068-063-3). Ktav.
Heschel, Abraham J. Man's Quest for God: Studies in Prayer & Symbolism. LC 54-10371. 1954. 5.95 (ISBN 0-684-13582-5, ScribT). Scribner.
Joseph Breuer Foundation, ed. Collected Writings of Samson Raphael Hirsch, Vol. III: Jewish Symbolism. (The Hirsch Heritage Ser.). Tr. of Gessamelte Schriften. 260p. 1984. 15.75 (ISBN 0-87306-924-2). Feldheim.
Kampf, Avram. Contemporary Synagogue Art: Developments in the United States, 1945-1965. LC 65-25292. (Illus.). 1976. 15.00 (ISBN 0-8074-0085-8, 382630). UAHC.
Kanof, Abram, intro. by. Ceremonial Art in the Judaic Tradition. LC 75-126321. (Illus.). 92p. 1975. pap. 3.00 (ISBN 0-88259-078-2). NCMA.
Reider, Rimma. Jewish Ceremonial Designs. (International Design Library). (Illus.). 48p. 1987. pap. 3.95 (ISBN 0-88045-087-8). Stemmer Hse.
Samuel, Edith. Your Jewish Lexicon. (Hebrew.). 192p. (Orig.). 1982. 10.00 (ISBN 0-8074-0054-8); pap. 5.95 (ISBN 0-8074-0061-0). UAHC.
Steinberger, Heidi. Let's Learn About Jewish Symbols. LC 68-9347. (Illus.). 1969. pap. text ed. 6.00 (ISBN 0-8074-0144-7, 101035). UAHC.
The Symbols of Judaism: The Challenge to Learn & Create. pap. 4.00 (ISBN 0-686-96080-7). United Syn Bk.

JEWISH CALENDAR
see Calendar, Jewish

JEWISH CHANT
see Chants (Jewish)

JEWISH CHILDREN
Bernard, Jacqueline. The Children You Gave Us. LC 72-87122. (Illus.). 1972. 8.95x (ISBN 0-8197-0356-7). Bloch.
Bernstein, Fred. The Jewish Mothers' Hall of Fame. LC 85-24541. (Illus.). 192p. 1986. pap. 6.95 (ISBN 0-385-23377-9, Dolp). Doubleday.
Bial, Morrison D. Your Jewish Child. Syme, Daniel B., ed. 1978. pap. 5.00 (ISBN 0-8074-0012-2, 101200). UAHC.
Birnhack, Sarah. Happy Is the Heart: A Year in the Life of a Jewish Girl. (Illus.). 1976. 7.95 (ISBN 0-87306-131-4); pap. 5.95. Feldheim.
Donin, Hayim H. To Raise a Jewish Child: A Guide for Parents. LC 76-7679. 1977. 15.95 (ISBN 0-465-08626-8). Basic.
Horowitz, Tamar R., ed. Between Two Worlds: Children from the Soviet Union in Israel. LC 86-11071. 240p. (Orig.). 1986. lib. bdg. 26.00 (ISBN 0-8191-5454-7); pap. text ed. 12.75 (ISBN 0-8191-5455-5). U Pr of Amer.
Matzner-Bekerman, Shoshana. The Jewish Child: Halakhic Perspectives. LC 83-19950. 314p. 1984. 20.00x (ISBN 0-88125-017-1); pap. 11.95 (ISBN 0-88125-024-4). Ktav.
Mayer, Egon. Children of Intermarriage: A Study in Pattern of Identification & Family Life. LC 83-82077. 56p. 1983. pap. 2.50 (ISBN 0-87495-055-4). Am Jewish Comm.
Shulman, Avi. Criticizing Children: A Parents Guide to Helping Children. (Dynamics of Personal Achievement Ser.). 48p. (Orig.). 1984. pap. 2.95 (ISBN 0-87306-365-1). Feldheim.
Wolf, Hannie. Child of Two Worlds. (Illus.). 156p. 1979. 13.00 (ISBN 0-931068-02-9). Purcells.

JEWISH CHRISTIANS
Here are entered works dealing with Christians of Jewish antecedence.
see also Converts from Judaism
Berger, David & Wyschogrod, Michael. Jews & Jewish Christianity. 3.95x (ISBN 0-87068-675-5). Ktav.
Jocz, Jakob. The Jewish People & Jesus Christ. 1979. pap. 7.95 (ISBN 0-8010-5085-5). Baker Bk.
Longenecker, Richard N. The Christology of Early Jewish Christianity. (Twin Brooks Ser.). 178p. 1981. pap. 8.95 (ISBN 0-8010-5610-1). Baker Bk.
Pruter, Karl. Jewish Christians in the U. S. A Bibliography. LC 84-48881. 250p. 1985. lib. bdg. 30.00 (ISBN 0-8240-8741-0). Garland Pub.
--Jewish Christians in the United States: A Bibliography Sects & Cults in America. LC 86-48881. (Garland Reference Library of Social Sciences Ser.). 1987. lib. bdg. 38.00. Garland Pub.
Rausch, David A., ed. Eminent Hebrew Christians of the Nineteenth Century: Brief Biographical Sketches. LC 83-22013. (Texts & Studies in Religion: Vol. 17). 184p. lib. bdg. 39.95x (ISBN 0-88946-806-0). E Mellen.

JEWISH CHRONOLOGY
see Chronology, Jewish

JEWISH CIVILIZATION
see Jews–Civilization

JEWISH CONVERTS TO CHRISTIANITY
see Converts from Judaism

JEWISH CULTUS
see Cultus, Jewish

JEWISH DAY OF ATONEMENT
see Yom Kippur

JEWISH DEVOTIONAL LITERATURE
see also Jews–Prayer-Books and Devotions
As a Tree by the Waters. 1981. 9.95 (ISBN 0-87306-237-X). Feldheim.
Baal Shem of Michelstadt. 1981. pap. 4.95 (ISBN 0-686-76481-1). Feldheim.
Birkas Hashulchan. 1980. 5.95 (ISBN 0-686-76484-6). Feldheim.
Bitzer, Heinrich, ed. Light on the Path: Daily Scripture Readings in Hebrew & Greek. 400p. (Orig.). 1982. pap. 9.95 (ISBN 0-8010-0822-0). Baker Bk.
Challenge of Sinai. (Illus.). 1981. 12.95 (ISBN 0-686-76489-7). Feldheim.
Chumash Koren. 1982. 6.95 (ISBN 0-686-76491-9). Feldheim.
Faith & Courage. 1986. 6.95 (ISBN 0-87306-258-2). Feldheim.
Gates of Repentance. 1982. 10.95 (ISBN 0-87306-252-3). Feldheim.
Goldberg, Hillel. Wherever I Go, I Go to Jerusalem. 240p. 1986. 12.95 (ISBN 0-940646-09-9); pap. 8.95 (ISBN 0-940646-10-2). Rossel Bks.
Grace after Meals. 1982. pap. 0.35 small (ISBN 0-686-76511-7). Feldheim.
Hertz, Joseph H. Pirke Aboth: Sayings of the Fathers. 1945. pap. 3.95x (ISBN 0-87441-155-6). Behrman.
Hirsch Siddur. 1982. deluxe leatherbound 45.00 (ISBN 0-686-76517-6). Feldheim.
Kafra Haggadah. 1982. 27.50 (ISBN 0-686-76527-3). Feldheim.
Koren Tanach. 1982. small 7.95 (ISBN 0-686-76529-X); medium 14.95 (ISBN 0-686-76530-3); large 75.00 (ISBN 0-686-76531-1). Feldheim.
Lehavin Ulehaskil. 1982. 8.95 (ISBN 0-686-76535-4); pap. 6.95. Feldheim.
Lehmann, Marcus. Just in Time: A Novel about Medieval Jewish Community. 1982. pap. 6.95 (ISBN 0-87306-257-4). Feldheim.
--Royal Resident. 1981. 6.95 (ISBN 0-686-76251-7). Feldheim.
Leo Jung Jubilee Volume. cancelled (ISBN 0-686-76536-2). Feldheim.
Maaser Kesafim. 1982. 9.95 (ISBN 0-87306-238-8). Feldheim.
Matter of Return. 1982. pap. 4.95 (ISBN 0-686-76543-5). Feldheim.
Meditations on the Siddur. 1982. 9.95 (ISBN 0-686-76545-1). Feldheim.
Mishna Berurah, Vol. 3A. 1980. regular ed. 12.95 (ISBN 0-87306-233-7); large ed. 15.95 (ISBN 0-87306-198-5). Feldheim.
Mitzvoth. cancelled (ISBN 0-686-76550-8). Feldheim.
Practical Guide to Kashruth. 1982. 7.50 (ISBN 0-686-76247-9); pap. 6.00. Feldheim.
Prisoner & Other Tales of Faith. 1980. pap. 5.95 (ISBN 0-87306-243-4). Feldheim.
Rabbi's Blessing. 1982. 7.50 (ISBN 0-686-76249-5). Feldheim.
Road Back. 1981. pap. 6.95 (ISBN 0-87306-264-7). Feldheim.
Rothschild, Zeev. Knowing Your Tefilen & Mezuzos: A Layman's Guide to Understanding & Appreciating Tefilin & Mezuzos. 80p. (Orig.). 1982. pap. 2.50 (ISBN 0-686-76528-1). Feldheim.
Seder Mincha U'Maariv. 1982. pap. 0.99 (ISBN 0-686-76256-8). Feldheim.
Shemuel Hanagid. 1982. 7.95 (ISBN 0-87306-220-5); pap. 5.95. Feldheim.
Sign & Glory. cancelled (ISBN 0-686-76258-4). Feldheim.
Silverstein, Shragu. Antidote. 1980. pap. 3.95 (ISBN 0-87306-173-X). Feldheim.
The Sins of Omission: The Neglected Child. 1982. pap. 5.95 (ISBN 0-686-76259-2). Feldheim.
Sparks of the Holy Tongue. 1982. pap. 4.95 (ISBN 0-87306-240-X). Feldheim.
Taamim Lakorim. 1982. pap. 7.50 (ISBN 0-686-76267-3); cassette 7.50 (ISBN 0-686-76268-1); book & cassette 12.00 (ISBN 0-686-76269-X). Feldheim.
A Time to Build Joseph Breuer. 1982. Vol. 2. 8.95 (ISBN 0-686-76270-3). Feldheim.
Vilna Goan Views Life. 1982. 4.00 (ISBN 0-686-76275-4). Feldheim.
Weltwende. 1982. pap. 6.00 (ISBN 0-686-76278-9). Feldheim.
Yossef Mokir Shabbos: Hebrew-English. 1982. pap. 4.95 (ISBN 0-87306-189-6). Feldheim.
Yossef Mokir Shabbos: Hebrew-French. 1982. pap. 4.95 (ISBN 0-686-76282-7). Feldheim.
Yossef Mokir Shabbos: Hebrew-Yiddish. 1982. pap. 4.95 (ISBN 0-686-76283-5). Feldheim.
Zechariah, Fendel. Anvil of Sinai. 1980. 12.95 (ISBN 0-686-76479-X). Feldheim.
Zemiros Shabbos. 1982. pap. 1.50 large (ISBN 0-686-76284-3); pap. 1.25 medium; pap. 0.50 small. Feldheim.

JEWISH ETHICS
see Ethics, Jewish

JEWISH HOLOCAUST (1939-1945)
see Holocaust, Jewish (1939-1945)
Littell, Franklin H. The Crucifixion of the Jews. (Reprints of Scholarly Excellence: No. 12). 160p. 1986. Repr. of 1975 ed. 10.95 (ISBN 0-86554-227-9). Mercer Univ Pr.

JEWISH LANGUAGE
see Hebrew Language

JEWISH LAW
see also Commandments (Judaism); Commandments, Ten; Jews–Dietary Laws; Responsa
Appel, G. The Concise Code of Jewish Law: Daily Prayers & Religious Observances in the Life-Cycle of the Jew, Vol. 1. 11.95 (ISBN 0-87068-298-9). Ktav.
Associations of Orthodox Jewish Scientists Staff. Proceedings, Vol. 3 & 4. Rosner, Fred, ed. 248p. 1976. pap. 9.95 (ISBN 0-87306-074-1). Feldheim.
Atkin, Abraham. Darkeinu Aleph & Bais: In One Volume. pap. text ed. 3.50 (ISBN 0-686-33046-3, A13). Torah Umesorah.
--Darkeinu Daled. text ed. 3.75 (ISBN 0-914131-13-3, A15). Torah Umesorah.
Atkins, Abraham. Darkeinu Gimel. text ed. 3.50 (ISBN 0-686-33046-3, A14). Torah Umesorah.
Bahnsen, Greg L. By This Standard. 432p. 1985. pap. 4.95 (ISBN 0-930464-06-0). Dominion Pr.
Bazak, Jacob. Jewish Law & Jewish Life, 8 bks. in 4 vols. Passamaneck, Stephen M., ed. Incl. Bk. 1. Selected Rabbinical Response (ISBN 0-8074-0034-3, 180210); Bks. 2-4. Contracts, Real Estate, Sales & Usury (180211); Bks. 5-6. Credit, Law Enforcement & Taxation (180212); Bks. 7-8. Criminal & Domestic Relations (ISBN 0-8074-0037-8, 180213). 1978. pap. 12.50 complete vol. (ISBN 0-8074-0038-6, 180218); pap. 5.00 ea. UAHC.
Bergren, Victor. The Prophets & the Law. 15.00x (ISBN 0-87820-403-2, Pub. by Hebrew Union College Press). Ktav.
Berkovits, Eliezer. Crisis & Faith. 224p. 1975. 8.95 (ISBN 0-88482-903-0, Sanhedrin Pr). Hebrew Pub.
--Not in Heaven: The Nature & Function of Halakha. LC 82-23255. 131p. 1983. 12.00x (ISBN 0-88125-003-1). Ktav.
Biale, Rachel. Women & Jewish Law: An Exploration of Women's Issues in Halakhic Sources. LC 83-40457. 256p. 1984. 18.95 (ISBN 0-8052-3887-5). Schocken.
--Women & Jewish Law: An Exploration of Women's Issues in Halakhic Sources. 304p. 1986. pap. 8.95 (ISBN 0-8052-0810-0). Schocken.
Blackman, Philip, tr. The Mishnah, 7 vols. with index vol. (Eng. & Hebrew.). 4050p. 1962. 75.00 (ISBN 0-910818-00-2). Judaica Pr.
Bleich, D. J. Contemporary Halakhic Problems, Vol. I. (The Library of Jewish Law & Ethics: No. 4). 20.00x (ISBN 0-87068-450-7); pap. 14.95. Ktav.
Bleich, David J. Contemporary Halakhic Problems, Vol.II. 20.00x (ISBN 0-87068-275-X); pap. 14.95. Ktav.
Brooks, Roger. Support for the Poor in the Mishnaic Law of Agriculture: Tractate Peah. LC 83-8719. (Brown Judaic Studies: No. 43). 220p. 1983. pap. 21.00 (ISBN 0-89130-632-3, 14 00 43). Scholars Pr GA.
Carmichael, Calum M. Law & Narrative in the Bible: The Evidence of the Deuteronomic Laws & the Decalogue. LC 85-4214. 352p. 1985. text ed. 35.00x (ISBN 0-8014-1792-9). Cornell U Pr.
Cohen, Abraham. Everyman's Talmud. LC 75-10750. 446p. 1975. pap. 11.25 (ISBN 0-8052-0497-0). Schocken.
Cohen, Alfred S. Halacha & Contemporary Society. LC 84-741. 1985. pap. 9.95 (ISBN 0-88125-043-0). Ktav.
Cohen, Boaz. Jewish & Roman Law, 2 Vols. 1966. Set. 15.00x (ISBN 0-8381-4100-5). United Syn Bk.
--Law & Tradition in Judaism. 1959. 12.50x (ISBN 0-87068-023-4). Ktav.
Cohn, Haim H. Human Rights in Jewish Law. LC 83-14846. 266p. 1984. 25.00x (ISBN 0-88125-036-8). Ktav.
Dorff, Elliot. Jewish Law & Modern Ideology. 1970. pap. 6.50x (ISBN 0-8381-0209-3). United Syn Bk.
Dorff, Elliot N. & Rosett, Arthur. A Living Tree: Materials on the Jewish Legal Tradition with Comparative Notes. 680p. 1987. 49.50x (ISBN 0-88706-459-0); pap. 19.95x (ISBN 0-88706-460-4). State U NY Pr.
Dresner, Samuel & Siegel, Seymour. Jewish Dietary Laws. rev. ed. LC 83-235401. 110p. pap. 2.95x (ISBN 0-8381-2105-5). United Syn Bk.
Elon, Menachem, ed. The Principles of Jewish Law. 866p. 1975. 50.00 (ISBN 0-87855-188-3). Transaction Bks.
Feldman, David M. Marital Relations, Birth Control, & Abortion in Jewish Law. LC 68-15338. 336p. 1974. pap. 8.95 (ISBN 0-8052-0438-5). Schocken.
Fuss, Abraham, ed. Studies in Jewish Jurisprudence. (Studies in Jewish Jurisprudence Ser.: Vol. 4). 320p. 1975. 14.50 (ISBN 0-87203-058-X). Hermon.
Ganzfried, Solomon. Code of Jewish Law: Kitzur Shulhan Arukh, 4 vols. Goldin, Hyman E., tr. (Eng. & Hebrew.). 1961. Set. 49.50 (ISBN 0-88482-412-8). Hebrew Pub.
Gilmer, Harry. The If-You Form an Israelite Law. LC 75-23136. (Society of Biblical Literature. Dissertation Ser.: No. 15). Repr. of 1975 ed. 36.80 (ISBN 0-8357-9572-1, 2017518). Bks Demand UMI.
Ginzberg, Louis. Of Jewish Law & Lore. LC 55-6707. (Temple Bks). 1970. pap. 5.95 (ISBN 0-689-70231-0, T12). Atheneum.
Graff, Gil. Separation of Church & State: Dina de-Malkhuta Dina in Jewish Law, 1750-1848. LC 84-24061. (Judaic Studies Ser.). ix, 224p. 1985. 29.50 (ISBN 0-8173-0264-6). U of Ala Pr.
Halivni, David W. Midrash, Mishnah & Gemara: The Jewish Predilection for Justified Law. 176p. 1986. text ed. 22.50x (ISBN 0-674-57370-6). Harvard U Pr.
Hamelsdorf, Ora, et al, eds. Jewish Women & Jewish Law: Bibliography. 60p. 1981. pap. 3.00 (ISBN 0-9602036-2-1). Biblio NY.
Hayyim, Hafetz, pseud. Ahavath Chesed: The Love of Kindness As Required by G-D. 2nd & rev. ed. Oschry, Leonard, tr. from Hebrew. Orig. Title: Ahavath Hesed. 1976. 9.95 (ISBN 0-87306-110-1). Feldheim.
Herzog, Isaac. Judaism-Law & Ethics. 227p. 1974. 9.95 (ISBN 0-900689-73-0). Soncino Pr.
--Main Institutions of Jewish Law, 2 Vols. Set. pap. 15.95x (ISBN 0-900689-14-5). Bloch.
--The Main Institutions of Jewish Law, 2 vols. 1939. Set. pap. 15.95 (ISBN 0-900689-14-5). Soncino Pr.
Jackson, Bernard S. & Jewish Law Association, International Congress Staff. Studies in Jewish Law I: The Touro Conference Volume. LC 84-1329. (SP Occasional Papers & Proceedings: No. 3). 1985. 26.75 (ISBN 0-89130-732-X, 15-00-01); pap. 17.75 (ISBN 0-89130-868-7). Scholars Pr GA.
Jackson, Bernard S., ed. Jewish Law Association Studies II: The Jerusalem Conference Volume. (Occasional Papers & Proceedings). 208p. 26.95 (ISBN 0-89130-950-0, 15-00-02); pap. 19.95 (ISBN 0-89130-951-9). Scholars Pr GA.

Jacob, Walter, ed. American Reform Responsa. 561p. 1983. pap. text ed. 20.00 (ISBN 0-916694-83-6). Central Conf.
Jacobs, Louis. Jewish Law. LC 68-27329. (Chain of Tradition Ser). 1968. pap. text ed. 5.95x (ISBN 0-87441-010-X). Behrman.
--The Talmudic Argument: A Study in Talmudic Reasoning & Methodology. LC 84-4351. 240p. 1984. 44.50 (ISBN 0-521-26370-0). Cambridge U Pr.
--A Tree of Life: Diversity, Creativity, & Flexibility in Jewish Law. (Littman Library of Jewish Civilization). 32.50x (ISBN 0-19-710039-2). Oxford U Pr.
Johns, C. H. The Relations Between the Laws of Babylonia & the Laws of the Hebrew Peoples. (British Academy, London, Schweich Lectures on Biblical Archaeology Series, 1912). pap. 19.00 (ISBN 0-8115-1254-1). Kraus Repr.
Kahana, K. Case for Jewish Civil Law in the Jewish State. 6.25x (ISBN 0-685-01037-6). Bloch.
--The Case for Jewish Civil Law in the Jewish State. 120p. 1960. 6.50. Soncino Pr.
Kaplan, Aryeh. The Story of Tisha B'Av. 160p. (Orig.). 1981. pap. 2.95 (ISBN 0-940118-32-7). Maznaim.
Karo, Joseph Ben Ephraim. The Traditional Jewish Law of Sale: Shulhan Arukh Hoshen Mishpat, Chapters 189-240. Passamaneck, Stephen M., tr. LC 83-4287. (Hebrew Union College Monographs No. 9). 1983. 20.00x (ISBN 0-87820-408-3). Hebrew Union Coll Pr.
Katz, Mordecai. Protection of the Weak in the Talmud. LC 26-5707. (Columbia University. Oriental Studies: No. 24). Repr. of 1925 ed. 12.50 (ISBN 0-404-50514-7). AMS Pr.
Katz, Mordechai. Lishmor Velaasos: Guide to Basic Principles of Jewish Law & Their Applications in Theory & Practice. (Rothman Foundation Ser.). 159p. 1981. 8.95 (ISBN 0-87306-974-9); pap. 6.95 (ISBN 0-317-42416-5). Feldheim.
Katz, Yoseph. She'erit Yoseph. Siev, Asher, ed. LC 83-50567. 350p. 1984. 15.00 (ISBN 0-87203-116-0). Hermon.
Kirschenbaum, Aaron. Self-Incrimination in Jewish Law. 1970. 8.00x (ISBN 0-8381-3111-5). United Syn Bk.
Klein, Isaac. Responsa & Halakhic Studies. 15.00x. Ktav.
Kramer, Ralph M. & Schild, Philip, eds. The Bay Area Jewish Forum Hagadah. rev. ed. (Illus.). 69p. 1985. 13.95 (ISBN 0-917883-00-4). Benmir Bks.
Levine, Aaron. Free Enterprise & Jewish Law: Aspects of Jewish Business Ethics. 1979. 20.00 (ISBN 0-87068-702-6). Ktav.
Levita, Elijah. Massoreth Ha Massoreth. rev. ed. LC 67-11894. (Library of Biblical Studies). 1969. 39.50x (ISBN 0-87068-081-1). Ktav.
Lew, Dayan. Humanity of Jewish Law. 198p. 1986. 11.95 (ISBN 0-900689-87-0). Soncino Pr.
Lewittes, Mendell. Principles & Development of Jewish Law. 200p. Date not set. 19.95x (ISBN 0-8197-0512-8); pap. 10.95x (ISBN 0-8197-0506-3). Bloch.
Link-Salinger, Ruth. Jewish Law in Our Time. 183p. 22.50x (ISBN 0-8197-0486-5); pap. 12.95x (ISBN 0-8197-0487-3). Bloch.
McEleney, Neil J. Law Given Through Moses. (Bible Ser.). pap. 0.50 (ISBN 0-8091-5079-4). Paulist Pr.
Maimonides Codex: The Laws of Moses Ben Maimon (1135-1204) (Jewish Legal System in Hebrew Ser.). 1982. 390.00x (ISBN 0-686-44755-7, Pub. by Collets (UK)). State Mutual Bk.
Maimonides, Moses. The Code of Maimonides, Bks. 5-6 & 8-14. Incl. Bk. 5. The Book of Holiness. Rabinowitz, Louis I. & Grossman, Philip, trs. xxxiv, 429p. 1965. 50.00x (ISBN 0-300-00846-5); Bk. 6. The Book of Asseverations. Klien, B. D., tr. 273p. 1962. 30.00x (ISBN 0-300-00633-0); Bk. 8. The Book of Temple Service. Lewittes, Mendell, tr. (Illus.). xxvii, 525p. 1957. 55.00x (ISBN 0-300-00717-5); Bk. 9. The Book of Offerings. Danby, Herbert, tr. xxi, 236p. 1950. 27.50x (ISBN 0-300-00398-6); Bk. 10. The Book of Cleanness. Danby, Herbert, tr. (Illus.). xiv, 645p. 1954. 60.00x (ISBN 0-300-00397-8); Bk. 11. The Book of Torts. Klein, Hyman, tr. xvii, 299p. 1954. 35.00x (ISBN 0-300-00632-2); Bk. 12. The Book of Acquisition. Klein, Isaac, tr. xv, 335p. 1951. 40.00x (ISBN 0-300-00631-4); Bk. 13. The Book of Civil Laws. Rabinowitz, Jacob J., tr. xxiv, 345p. 1949. 45.00 (ISBN 0-300-00845-7); Bk. 14. The Book of Judges. Hershman, Abraham M., tr. xxv, 335p. 1949. 40.00x (ISBN 0-300-00548-2). (Judaica Ser.). Yale U Pr.
Marcus, Ralph. Law in the Apocrypha. LC 29-9822. (Columbia University. Oriental Studies: No. 26). Repr. of 1927 ed. 15.00 (ISBN 0-404-50516-3). AMS Pr.
Mayer, Mordecai. Israel's Wisdom in Modern Life: Essays & Interpretations of Religious & Cultural Problems Based on the Talmudic & Midrashic Literature. 32.50 (ISBN 0-87559-147-7). Shalom.
Medical Hulacha for Everyone. 1982. 10.95 (ISBN 0-87306-218-3). Feldheim.
Meiselman, M. Jewish Woman in Jewish Law. (Library of Jewish Law & Ethics: Vol. 6). 9.95x (ISBN 0-87068-329-2). Ktav.
Meislin, Bernard. Jewish Law in American Trials & Tribunals. 25.00x (ISBN 0-87068-288-1). Ktav.
Mendelsohn, Samuel. The Criminal Jurisprudence of the Jews. (Studies in Jewish Jurisprudence: Vol. 6). 280p. 1986. 19.50 (ISBN 0-87203-122-5). Hermon.
Narot, Joseph R. A Primer for Temple Life. pap. 1.00 (ISBN 0-686-15808-3). Rostrum Bks.
Neusner, Jacob. Tosefta: Structure & Sources. (Brown University Ser.). 1986. 39.95 (ISBN 1-55540-049-3, 14-01-12). Scholars Pr GA.
--The Tosefta, Translated from the Hebrew: Pt. II. Moed. The Order of Appointed Times. 45.00x (ISBN 0-87068-691-7). Ktav.
Novak, David. Halakhah in a Theological Dimension: Essays on the Interpenetration of Law & Theology in Judaism. Neusner, Jacob, ed. LC 84-10661. (Brown Judaic Studies: No. 68). 1985. 19.75 (ISBN 0-89130-757-5, 14-00-68); pap. 16.25 (ISBN 0-89130-829-6). Scholars Pr GA.
Patrick, Dale. Old Testament Law. LC 84-4418. 228p. (Orig.). 1984. 15.95 (ISBN 0-8042-0133-1). John Knox.
Practical Medical Halacha. 1982. 5.00 (ISBN 0-87306-221-3). Feldheim.
Quint, Emanuel & Hecht, Neil S. Jewish Jurisprudence: Its Sources & Modern Applications Ser, Vol. 1. (Jurisprudence-Its Sources & Modern Applications Ser.). 268p. 1980. 46.25 (ISBN 3-7186-0054-4); pap. 13.95 (ISBN 3-7186-0055-2). Harwood Academic.
Quint, Emanuel B. & Hecht, Neil S. Jewish Jurisprudence: Its Sources & Modern Applications. (Jewish Jurisprudence Ser.: Vol. 2). 193p. 1986. text ed. 65.00 (ISBN 3-7186-0064-1); pap. text ed. 18.00 (ISBN 3-7186-0293-8). Harwood Academic.
Rosenbaum, I. Holocaust & Halakhah. (Library of Jewish Law & Ethics: No. 2). 15.00x (ISBN 0-87068-296-2); pap. 9.95. Ktav.
Roth, Joel. The Halakhic Process: A Systemic Analysis. (Moreshet Ser.: Vol. 13). 1987. 35.00 (ISBN 0-87334-035-3). Jewish Sem.
Schatz, Elihu A. Proof of the Accuracy of the Bible. LC 73-10726. (Illus.). xxvi, 740p. 1973. 15.00x (ISBN 0-8246-0161-0). Jonathan David.
Schiffman, Lawrence. Sectarian Laws in the Dead Sea Scrolls: Courts, Testimony & the Penal Code. LC 82-837. (Brown Judaic Studies). 294p. 1983. pap. 27.50 (ISBN 0-89130-569-6). Scholars Pr GA.
Schodde, tr. Book of Jubilees. LC 80-53467. 96p. 1980. pap. 4.00 (ISBN 0-934666-07-5). Artisan Sales.
Schreiber, Aaron. Jewish Law & Decision-Making: A Study Through Time. 456p. 1980. lib. bdg. 39.95 (ISBN 0-87722-120-0). Temple U Pr.
Schultz, Samuel J. Old Testament Survey: Law & History. rev. ed. LC 64-10037. 96p. 1968. pap. text ed. 4.95 (ISBN 0-910566-01-1); Perfect bdg. instr's. guide 5.95 (ISBN 0-910566-20-8). Evang Tchr.
Sheinkopf, David I. Gelatin & Jewish Law. 132p. 1983. pap. 7.95x (ISBN 0-8197-0488-1). Bloch.
Siegel, S., ed. Conservative Judaism & Jewish Law. 20.00x (ISBN 0-87068-428-0); pap. 9.95. Ktav.
Sigal, Phillip. The Halakah of Jesus of Nazareth According to the Gospel of Matthew. 282p. (Orig.). 1986. lib. bdg. 23.75 (ISBN 0-8191-5210-2); pap. text ed. 13.25 (ISBN 0-8191-5211-0). U Pr of Amer.
Smith, John M. The Origin & History of Hebrew Law. LC 79-1620. 1980. Repr. of 1960 ed. 23.65 (ISBN 0-88355-924-2). Hyperion Conn.
Sobel, Ronald & Wallach, Sidney. Justice, Justice, Shalt Thou Pursue. 10.00x (ISBN 0-87068-458-2). Ktav.
Sonsino, Rifat. Motive Clauses in Hebrew Law: Biblical Forms & Near Eastern Parallels. LC 79-15024. (Society of Biblical Literature Dissertation Ser.: No. 45). 15.95 (ISBN 0-89130-317-0, 060145); pap. 10.95 (ISBN 0-89130-318-9). Scholars Pr GA.
Twersky, I. Studies in Jewish Law & Philosophy. 39.50x (ISBN 0-87068-335-7). Ktav.
The Yamin Nora'im-Laws of the Synagogue. write for info. United Syn Bk.
Zevin, Shlomo Y. The Festivals in Halachah, Vol. II. Kaploon, Uri, ed. Fox-Ashrei, Meir, tr. from Hebrew. (Artscroll Judica Classics Ser.). 336p. 1981. 14.95 (ISBN 0-89906-908-8); pap. 11.95 (ISBN 0-89906-909-6). Mesorah Pubns.

JEWISH LEARNING AND SCHOLARSHIP
see also Jews–Intellectual Life

Berlin, Charles. Index to Festschriften in Jewish Studies. 1971. 50.00x (ISBN 0-87068-133-8). Ktav.
Crenshaw, James L. Studies in Ancient Israelite Wisdom. 1974. 59.50x (ISBN 0-87068-255-5). Ktav.
Epstein, David & Stutman, Suzanne. Torah with Love: A Guide for Strengthening Jewish Values Within the Family. (Illus.). 208p. 1986. 16.95 (ISBN 0-13-925371-8). P-H.
Friedlander, Gerald, tr. from Heb. Pirke De Rabbi Eliezer (The Chapters of Rabbi Eliezer the Great) LC 80-545920. (The Judaic Studies Library: No. SPH6). 552p. 1981. pap. 14.95 (ISBN 0-87203-095-4). Hermon.
Gamoran, Emanuel. Changing Conceptions in Jewish Education. facsimile ed. LC 74-27986. (Modern Jewish Experience Ser.). 1975. Repr. of 1924 ed. 36.50x (ISBN 0-405-06713-5). Ayer Co Pubs.
Gateway to Learning. pap. 3.95 (ISBN 0-87306-253-1). Feldheim.
Gratz, Rebecca. Letters of Rebecca Gratz. facsimile ed. LC 74-27987. (Modern Jewish Experience Ser.). 1975. Repr. of 1929 ed. 38.50x (ISBN 0-405-06714-3). Ayer Co Pubs.
Heilman, Samuel. Inside the Jewish Schools: A Study of the Cultural Setting for Jewish Education. 50p. 1984. pap. 2.50 (ISBN 0-87495-057-0). Am Jewish Comm.
Kolatch, A. J. The Jewish Book of Why's. 1985. gift set 28.95 (ISBN 0-8246-0314-1). Jonathan David.
Lamm, Norman. Torah Lishmah: The Study of Torah for Its Own Sake in the Work of Rabbi Hayyim of Volozhin & His Contemporaries. 1987. 25.00 (ISBN 0-88125-117-8); pap. 16.95 (ISBN 0-88125-133-X). Ktav.
Lieberman, Saul. Alexander Marx Jubilee Volume, 2 vols. 1950. 35.00x (ISBN 0-685-31434-0, Pub. by Jewish Theol Seminary). KTAV.
Mason, Philip P. Directory of Jewish Archival Institutions. LC 75-15504. 72p. 1975. pap. text ed. 7.95x (ISBN 0-8143-1547-X). Wayne St U Pr.
Monson, Rela G. Jewish Campus Life: A Survey of Student Attitudes Toward Marriage & Family. LC 84-70026. 52p. 1984. pap. 3.00 (ISBN 0-87495-060-0). Am Jewish Comm.
Naiman, Charles S., ed. Proceedings of the Associations of the Associations of Orthodox Jewish Scientists, Vols. 8-9. (Illus.). 304p. (Orig.). 1987. pap. 14.95 (ISBN 0-87203-125-X). Hermon.
Neusner, Jacob. History & Torah: Essays on Jewish Learning. 128p. 1965. text ed. 8.50x (ISBN 0-686-37017-1, Pub. by Vallentine Michell England). Biblio Dist.
Peterson, James L. & Zill, Nicholas. American Jewish High School Students: A National Profile. LC 84-72249. vi, 32p. (Orig.). 1984. pap. 2.50 (ISBN 0-87495-065-1). Am Jewish Comm.
Rosner, Fred. Medicine in the Mishneh Torah of Maimonides. 1983. 20.00x (ISBN 0-88125-020-1); pap. 11.95 (ISBN 0-88125-021-X). Ktav.
Rossel, Seymour. When a Jew Seeks Wisdom: The Sayings of the Fathers. LC 75-14119. (Jewish Values Ser.). pap. 6.95x (ISBN 0-87441-089-4). Behrman.
Scholarship of Dr. Samuel Belkin. pap. cancelled (ISBN 0-686-76254-1). Feldheim.
Tarcov, Edith & Tarcov, Oscar. Illustrated Book of Jewish Knowledge. (Illus.). 1959. 6.00x (ISBN 0-87068-358-6, Pub. by Friendly Hse). Ktav.
Twersky, Isadore, ed. Rabbi Moses Nahmanides: Explorations in His Religious & Literary Virtuosity. (Center for Jewish Studies Ser.). 110p. (Orig.). 1983. pap. text ed. 9.50x (ISBN 0-674-74560-4). Harvard U Pr.

JEWISH LEARNING AND SCHOLARSHIP–JUVENILE LITERATURE

Karp, Deborah. Heroes of Jewish Thought. (Illus.). 1965. pap. 6.95x (ISBN 0-87068-538-4). Ktav.
--Heroes of Modern Jewish Thought. (Illus.). 1966. pap. 6.95x (ISBN 0-87068-539-2). Ktav.

JEWISH LITERATURE (COLLECTIONS)
see also Apocalyptic Literature; Cabala; Hebrew Literature; Midrash; Rabbinical Literature; Talmud; Yiddish Literature

Alcalay. Basic Encyclopedia of Jewish Proverbs, Quotations, Folk Wisdom. 19.95 (ISBN 0-87677-153-3). Hartmore.
Antin, Mary. From Plotzk to Boston. Sarna, Jonathan D., ed. (Masterworks of Modern Jewish Writing Ser.). 140p. 1986. pap. 6.95 (ISBN 0-910129-45-2, Dist. by Schocken). Wiener Pub Inc.
Benjamin, Chaya, ed. The Copenhagen Haggadah. LC 86-63514. (Hebrew., Illus.). 68p. 1987. 40.00 (ISBN 0-8478-0820-3). Rizzoli Intl.
Blinkin, Meir. Stories. Rosenfeld, Max, tr. from Yiddish. (Modern Jewish Literature & Culture Ser.). 166p. 1984. 10.95x (ISBN 0-87395-818-7). State U NY Pr.
Caplan, Samuel & Ribalow, Harold. The Great Jewish Books. 1983. pap. 10.95 (ISBN 0-8180-1135-1). Horizon.
Eisenberg, Azriel. Modern Jewish Life in Literature, 2 Vols. 1952-1968. Vol. 1. 4.50x (ISBN 0-8381-0201-8); Vol. 2. 4.50x (ISBN 0-8381-0207-7). United Syn Bk.
Fleg, Edmond. The Jewish Anthology. Samuel, Maurice, tr. LC 72-142934. 399p. 1975. Repr. of 1925 ed. lib. bdg. 22.50x (ISBN 0-8371-5824-9, FLJA). Greenwood.
Gersonides, pseud. The Wars of the Lord, Vol. 2, bks. 2, 3, & 4. Feldman, Seymour, tr. from Hebrew. 288p. 1987. 23.95 (ISBN 0-8276-0275-8). Jewish Pubns.
Goldreich, Gloria, ed. A Treasury of Jewish Literature: From Biblical Times to Today. LC 81-6967. 256p. 1982. 13.45 (ISBN 0-03-053831-9). H Holt & Co.
Goodman, Philip, ed. Yom Kippur Anthology. LC 72-151312. (Illus.). 399p. 1971. 9.95 (ISBN 0-8276-0026-7, 245). Jewish Pubns.
Grossman, Cheryl S. & Engman, Suzy. Jewish Literature for Children: A Teaching Guide. 230p. (Orig.). 1985. text ed. 19.00 (ISBN 0-86705-018-7); pap. text ed. 15.00. AIRE.
Handler, Andrew, ed. & tr. Ararat: A Collection of Hungarian-Jewish Short Stories. LC 75-5244. 153p. 1978. 18.00 (ISBN 0-8386-1733-6). Fairleigh Dickinson.
Howe, Irving, ed. Jewish-American Stories. 1977. pap. 4.95 (ISBN 0-451-62515-3, ME2302, Ment). NAL.
Kabakoff, Jacob. Jewish Book Annual, Vol. 37. 1979. 12.00 (ISBN 0-914820-07-9). JWB.
Kabakoff, Jacob, ed. Jewish Book Annual, Vol. 38. 1980. 15.00 (ISBN 0-914820-33-8). JWB.
Kalechofsky, Roberta, ed. South African Jewish Voices. LC 81-83903. (Echad 2: a Global Anthology Ser.). 280p. 1982. pap. text ed. 10.00 (ISBN 0-916288-10-2). Micah Pubns.
Lieberman, Leo, ed. Classics of Jewish Literature. Beringause, Arthur. LC 86-8124. 432p. 1986. 24.95 (ISBN 0-8022-2092-4). Philos Lib.
Lubetski, Edith & Lubetski, Meir. Building a Judaica Library Collection: A/Resource Guide. 185p. 1983. lib. bdg. 30.00 (ISBN 0-87287-375-7). Libs Unl.
Mazow, Julia W., ed. The Woman Who Lost Her Names: Selected Writings by American Jewish Women. LC 79-2986. 240p. 1981. pap. text ed. 10.00 (ISBN 0-06-250567-X, CN 4017, HarpR). Har-Row.
Mihaly, E. A Song to Creation: A Dialogue with a Text. (Jewish Perspectives Ser.: Vol. 1). 7.50x (ISBN 0-87820-500-4, HUC Pr). Ktav.
Nemoy, Leon, tr. Karaite Anthology: Excerpts from the Early Literature. (Judaica Ser.: No. 7). 1952. 45.00x (ISBN 0-300-00792-2). Yale U Pr.
Neusner, J. The Tosefta Translated from the Hebrew: The Order of Purities, Pt. 6. 45.00x (ISBN 0-87068-430-2). Ktav.
Neusner, Jacob. The Tosefta Translated from the Hebrew IV. Neziqin: The Order of Damages. 1981. 45.00x (ISBN 0-87068-692-5). Ktav.
--The Tosefta Translated from the Hebrew I. Zeraim: The Order of Seeds. 1986. 45.00x. Ktav.
--The Tosefta Translated from the Hebrew V. Qodoshim: The Order of Holy Things. 1980. 45.00x (ISBN 0-87068-340-3). Ktav.
Newman, Louis I. The Hasidic Anthology. 740p. 1987. 40.00 (ISBN 0-87668-968-3). Aronson.
Patai, Raphael. Gates to the Old City. 928p. 1980. pap. 12.95 (ISBN 0-380-76091-6, 76091-6). Avon.
--Messiah Texts: Jewish Legends of Three Thousound Years. LC 79-5387. 426p. 1979. 25.95x (ISBN 0-8143-1652-2). Wayne St U Pr.
Roth, C., intro. by. The Sarajevo Haggadah. 50.00 (ISBN 0-87068-761-1). Ktav.
Sabar, Yona, ed. The Folk Literature of the Kurdistani Jews: An Anthology. LC 81-43605. (Judaica Ser.: No. 23). 320p. 1982. 35.00x (ISBN 0-300-02698-6). Yale U Pr.
Shakow, Zara, compiled by. Curtain Time: Plays, Readings, Sketches, Cantatas, & Poems for Jewish Programs. 1985. pap. 9.95 (ISBN 0-8246-0310-9). Jonathan David.
USY Parshat HaShavuan Series. 10.00 (ISBN 0-686-96100-5). United Syn Bk.
Wallenrod, Reuben. The Literature of Modern Israel. LC 80-12709. 256p. 1980. Repr. of 1956 ed. lib. bdg. 20.00x (ISBN 0-374-98198-1, Octagon). Hippocrene Bks.

JEWISH LITERATURE–BIBLIOGRAPHY

Atid Bibliography. pap. 5.00 (ISBN 0-686-96097-1). United Syn Bk.
Berliant, Howard M. & Arbit, Bruce, eds. Jewish Literary Marketplace: A Directory of the Press, Periodicals, Publishers, & Booksellers. LC 79-18114. 1979. pap. 9.95 (ISBN 0-930038-16-9). Arbit.
Eichstadt, V. Bibliographie zur Geschichte der Judenfrage, BD 1, 1750-1848. 278p. Date not set. Repr. of 1939 ed. text ed. 66.24x (ISBN 0-576-80137-2, Pub. by Gregg Intl Pubs England). Gregg Intl.

Gittleman, Sol. Sholom Aleichem: A Non-Critical Introduction. (De Proprietatibus Litterarum Ser. Didactica: No. 3). 1974. pap. text ed. 13.60x (ISBN 90-2792-606-9). Mouton.

Grossfeld, B. Bibliography of Targum Literature: Supplement, Vol. 2. (Bibliographica Judaica Ser: No. 8). 39.50x (ISBN 0-87820-905-0, HUC Pr). Ktav.

Kabakoff, Jacob. Jewish Book Annual, Vol. 35. 1977. 10.00 (ISBN 0-914820-05-2). JWB.

--Jewish Book Annual, Vol. 41. 1983. 17.50 (ISBN 0-914820-12-5). JWB.

--Jewish Book Annual, Vol. 42. 18.00 (ISBN 0-914820-13-3). JWB.

--Jewish Book Annual, Vol. 43. 1985. 18.00 (ISBN 0-914820-14-1). JWB.

Kabakoff, Jacob, ed. Jewish Book Annual, Vol. 36. 1978. 10.00 (ISBN 0-914820-06-0). JWB.

Leikind, Miriam, et al. Index to Jewish Periodicals. Per Volume. 80.00 (ISBN 0-686-75688-6). IJP.

Levy, Jane & Helzel, Florence B. The Jewish Illustrated Book. LC 86-80427. (Illus.). 150p. (Orig.). 1986. pap. 16.00 (ISBN 0-943376-33-5). Magnes Mus.

New York Public Library, Research Libraries. Dictionary Catalog of Jewish Collection, 14 Vols. 1960. Set. 1240.00 (ISBN 0-8161-0409-3, Pub. by Hall Library). G K Hall.

Singerman, Robert. Jewish Serials of the World: A Research Bibliography of Secondary Sources. LC 86-344. 399p. 1986. lib. bdg. 55.00 (ISBN 0-313-24493-6, SJE/). Greenwood.

JEWISH LITERATURE–HISTORY AND CRITICISM

Abrahams, Israel. By-Paths in Hebraic Bookland. LC 77-174368. Repr. of 1920 ed. 17.00 (ISBN 0-405-08177-4, Pub. by Blom Publications). Ayer Co Pubs.

--A Short History of Jewish Literature. 1906. Repr. 20.00 (ISBN 0-8274-3400-6). R West.

Agus, Jacob B., et al, eds. The Jewish People: History, Religion, Literature, 41 bks. 1973. Set. 1106.50 (ISBN 0-405-05250-2). Ayer Co Pubs.

Bargad, Warren. Ideas in Fiction: The Works of Hayim Hazaz. LC 81-13621. (Brown Judiac Studies). 1982. pap. 13.50 (ISBN 0-89130-518-1, 14-00-31). Scholars Pr GA.

Basser, Herbert W. Midrashic Interpretations of the Song of Moses. LC 83-49003. (American University Studies VII: Vol. 2). 312p. 1983. pap. text ed. 28.85 (ISBN 0-8204-0065-3). P Lang Pubs.

Baumgarten, Murray. City Scriptures: Modern Jewish Writing. LC 81-6879. 240p. 1982. text ed. 17.50x (ISBN 0-674-13278-5). Harvard U Pr.

Beck, Norman A. Mature Christianity: The Recognition & Repudiation of the Anti-Jewish Polemic of the New Testament. LC 83-51047. (Illus.). 328p. 1985. 19.50 (ISBN 0-941664-03-1). Assoc Univ Prs.

Berenson, Bernard. Contemporary Jewish Fiction. 1976. lib. bdg. 59.95 (ISBN 0-87968-939-0). Gordon Pr.

Bloom, Harold, ed. & intro. by. Jewish Literature: The Bible Through 1789. (Critical Cosmos--Other European & Latin American Literature Ser.). 1987. 49.95 (ISBN 1-55546-101-8). Chelsea Hse.

--Modern Jewish Literature. (Critical Cosmos--Other European & Latin American Literature Ser.). 1987. 49.95 (ISBN 1-55546-102-6). Chelsea Hse.

Davidson, Israel. Parody in Jewish Literature. LC 77-163670. (Columbia University. Oriental Studies: No. 2). Repr. of 1907 ed. 24.50 (ISBN 0-404-50492-2). AMS Pr.

Diamond, James S. Barukh Kurzweil & Modern Hebrew Literature. LC 82-16770. (Brown Judaic Studies). 232p. 1983. pap. 18.00 (ISBN 0-89130-595-5, 14 00 39). Scholars Pr GA.

Fine, Ellen S. Legacy of Night: The Literary Universe of Elie Wiesel. LC 81-14601. (Modern Jewish Literature & Culture Ser.). 276p. 1982. 44.50 (ISBN 0-87395-589-7); pap. 14.95 (ISBN 0-87395-590-0). State U NY Pr.

Fletcher, Harris F. Milton's Rabbinical Readings. LC 67-22303. 344p. 1967. Repr. of 1930 ed. 29.50 (ISBN 0-208-00335-5, Archon). Shoe String.

Glatzer, Nahum. The Judaic Tradition. 352p. 1982. pap. text ed. 9.95x (ISBN 0-87441-344-3). Behrman.

Goldwurm, Hersh, et al. Mishnah-Moed, Vol. 3. (Art Scroll Mishnah Ser.). 1980. 16.95 (ISBN 0-89906-256-3); pap. 13.95 (ISBN 0-89906-257-1). Mesorah Pubns.

Greenspan, Ezra. The Schlemiel Comes to America. LC 83-14399. 258p. 1983. 20.00 (ISBN 0-8108-1646-6). Scarecrow.

Grossfield, B. A Bibliography of Targum Literature, Vol. 1. 1972. 39.50x. Ktav.

Guttman, Alexander. Struggle over Reform in Rabbinic Literature. LC 75-45046. 1977. 13.50 (ISBN 0-8074-0005-X, 382790). UAHC.

Handelman, Susan A. The Slayers of Moses: The Emergence of Rabbinic Interpretation in Modern Literary Theory. LC 81-16522. (Modern Jewish Literature & Culture Ser.). 284p. 1982. 49.50x (ISBN 0-87395-576-5); pap. 18.95 (ISBN 0-87395-577-3). State U NY Pr.

Jacobs, Joseph. Jewish Ideals & Other Essays. LC 72-311. (Essay Index Reprint Ser.). Repr. of 1896 ed. 18.00 (ISBN 0-8369-2795-8). Ayer Co Pubs.

Kaplan, Aryeh, tr. The Book of Esther. 268p. 8.95 (ISBN 0-686-27543-8); pap. 6.45 (ISBN 0-940118-21-1). Maznaim.

Karpeles, Gustav. Jewish Literature & Other Essays. facsimile ed. LC 78-37159. (Essay Index Reprint Ser). Repr. of 1895 ed. 22.00 (ISBN 0-8369-2512-2). Ayer Co Pubs.

Knopp, Josephine Z. The Trial of Judaism in Contemporary Jewish Writing. LC 74-18319. 164p. 1975. 15.95 (ISBN 0-252-00386-1). U of Ill Pr.

Lehrmann, Charles C. Jewish Influences on European Thought. Klin, George & Carpenter, Victor, trs. LC 72-3264. 323p. 1976. 27.50 (ISBN 0-8386-7908-0). Fairleigh Dickinson.

Lvov-Rogachevsky, V. A History of Russian Jewish Literature: Including Russian Literature & the Jews. Levin, Arthur, tr. from Rus. 1979. 15.00 (ISBN 0-88233-271-6); pap. 5.50 (ISBN 0-88233-272-4). Ardis Pubs.

Mann, Jacob. Texts & Studies in Jewish History & Literature, 2 Vols. rev. ed. 1970. Set. 99.50x (ISBN 0-87068-085-4). Ktav.

Neusner, Jacob. Canon & Connection: Intertextuality in Judaism. (Studies in Judaism). 316p. (Orig.). 1987. lib. bdg. 27.50 (ISBN 0-8191-5796-1, Pub. by Studies in Judaism); pap. text ed. 15.75 (ISBN 0-8191-5797-X). U Pr of Amer.

Oring, Elliott. Israeli Humor: The Content & Structure of the Chizbat of the Palmah. LC 80-25483. (Modern Jewish Literature & Culture Ser.). 210p. 1981. 44.50 (ISBN 0-87395-512-9); pap. 14.95x (ISBN 0-87395-513-7). State U NY Pr.

Pearl, Chaim & Brookes, Reuben. The Guide to Jewish Knowledge. rev. ed. LC 75-25366. 142p. 1976. 8.95 (ISBN 0-87677-138-X). Hartmore.

Philipson, David, et al. Studies in Jewish Literature Issued in Honor of Professor Kaufmann Kohler, Ph.D. Katz, Steven, ed. LC 79-7167. (Jewish Philosophy, Mysticism & History of Ideas Ser.). 1980. Repr. of 1913 ed. lib. bdg. 26.50x (ISBN 0-405-12283-7). Ayer Co Pubs.

Pinsker, Sanford. Schlemiel As Metaphor: Studies in the Yiddish & American Jewish Novel. LC 77-132487. (Crosscurrents-Modern Critiques Ser.). 185p. 1971. 6.95x (ISBN 0-8093-0480-5). S Ill U Pr.

Rabinovitch, Nachum L. Probability & Statistical Inference in Ancient & Medieval Jewish Literature. LC 79-187394. pap. 54.80 (ISBN 0-317-08544-1, 2014349). Bks Demand UMI.

Rowland, Christopher. The Open Heaven: The Study of Apocalyptic in Judaism & Early Christianity. LC 82-7409. 540p. 1982. 29.50x (ISBN 0-8245-0455-0). Crossroad NY.

Rylaarsdam, John C. Revelation in Jewish Wisdom Literature. (Midway Reprint Ser.). pap. 35.00 (ISBN 0-317-26582-2, 2024065). Bks Demand UMI.

Schwab, Moise. Repertoire des Articles Relatifs a l'Histoire et a la Litterature Juives Parus dans les Periodiques De 1665 a 1900. rev. ed. (Fr.). 1971. 79.50 (ISBN 0-87068-163-X). Ktav.

Sicher, Efraim. Beyond Marginality: Anglo-Jewish Literature after the Holocaust. (Modern Jewish Literature & Culture Ser.). 224p. 1985. 44.50x (ISBN 0-87395-976-0); pap. 14.95x (ISBN 0-87395-975-2). State U NY Pr.

Steinschneider, Moritz. Gesammelte Schriften. Katz, Steven, ed. LC 79-7152. (Jewish Philosophy, Mysticism & History of Ideas Ser.). 1980. Repr. of 1925 ed. lib. bdg. 55.50x (ISBN 0-405-12289-6). Ayer Co Pubs.

Trenchard, Warren C. Ben Sira's View of Women: A Literary Analysis. LC 82-16755. (Brown Judaic Studies: No. 38). 352p. 1982. pap. 15.75 (ISBN 0-89130-593-9, 14-00-38). Scholars Pr GA.

Twersky, Isadore, ed. Studies in Medieval Jewish History & Literature, Vol. 2. (Harvard Judaic Monographs: No. V). 460p. 1985. text ed. 25.00x (ISBN 0-674-85193-5). Harvard U Ctr Jewish.

Waxman, Meyer. A History of Jewish Literature, 6 vols. 50.00 set (ISBN 0-8453-8640-9, Cornwall Bks). Assoc Univ Prs.

Whittaker, Molly. Jews & Christians: Graeco-Roman Views. (Commentaries on Writings of the Jewish & Christian World 200 B.C. to A.D. 200: Vol. 6). 304p. 1985. 47.50 (ISBN 0-521-24251-7); pap. 18.95 (ISBN 0-521-28556-9). Cambridge U Pr.

Yudkin, Leon I. Escape into Siege: A Survey of Israeli Literature Today. (Littman Library of Jewish Civilization). 1974. 18.50x (ISBN 0-19-710016-3). Oxford U Pr.

--Jewish Writing & Identity in the Twentieth Century. LC 82-827. 180p. 1982. 22.50x (ISBN 0-312-44234-3). St Martin.

Zimmels, H. J. The Echo of the Nazi Holocaust in Rabbinic Literature. 25.00x (ISBN 0-87068-427-2). Ktav.

Zinberg, Israel. A History of Jewish Literature, 12 vols. 22.50x ea. (ISBN 0-685-56219-0). Ktav.

JEWISH LITURGICAL MUSIC

see Synagogue Music

JEWISH PENTECOST

see Shavu'Oth (Feast of Weeks)

JEWISH PHILOSOPHY

see Philosophy, Jewish

JEWISH POETRY

see also Hebrew Poetry

Benson, Clarence H. Old Testament Survey: Poetry & Prophecy. rev. ed. 96p. 1972. pap. text ed. 4.95 (ISBN 0-910566-02-X); Perfect bdg. instr's. guide 5.95 (ISBN 0-910566-21-6). Evang Tchr.

Gans, Manfred, ed. Yeshiva Children Write Poetry: From the Heart We Sing. 6.95 (ISBN 0-914131-76-1, D43). Torah Umesorah.

Jacobs, Steven L. Shirot Bialik: A New & Annotated Translation of Chaim Nachman Bialik's Epic Poems. (The Hebraica-Judaica Bookshelf Ser.). Date not set. price not set (ISBN 0-933771-03-7). Alpha Pub Co.

Oelman, Timothy, ed. & tr. Marrano Poets of the Seventeenth Century: An Anthology of the Poetry of Joao Pinto Delgado, Antonio Enriquez Gomez & Miguel de Barrios. (Littman Library of Jewish Civilization). (Illus.). 1985. 24.95x (ISBN 0-19-710047-3). Oxford U Pr.

Poems of the Holocaust: From the Diary of Luba Krugman Gurdus. bilingual ed. (Illus.). 1985. 12.95 (ISBN 0-8052-5059-X, Dist. by Schocken). Holocaust Pubns.

Sachs, Michael. Die Religiose Poesie der Juden in Spanien. Katz, Steven, ed. LC 79-7150. (Jewish Philosophy, Mysticism & History of Ideas Ser.). 1980. Repr. of 1901 ed. lib. bdg. 37.00x (ISBN 0-405-12285-3). Ayer Co Pubs.

Schmelzer, Menahem. Isaac ben Abraham ibn Ezra Poems (in Hebrew) 15.00x (ISBN 0-87334-011-6). Ktav.

Schwartz, Howard & Rudolf, Anthony, eds. Voices Within the Ark. 1983. pap. 15.95 (ISBN 0-380-76109-2, 80119). Avon.

Shakow, Zara, compiled by. Curtain Time: Plays, Readings, Sketches, Cantatas, & Poems for Jewish Programs. 1985. pap. 9.95 (ISBN 0-8246-0310-9). Jonathan David.

Smith, George A. The Early Poetry of Israel in Its Physical & Social Origins. (British Academy, London, Schweich Lectures on Biblical Archaeology Series, 1910). pap. 19.00 (ISBN 0-8115-1252-5). Kraus Repr.

Spiegel, Marcia C. & Kremsdorf, Deborah L., eds. Women Speak To God: The Prayers & Poems of Jewish Women. LC 86-51498. 100p. (Orig.). 1987. pap. 9.98 (ISBN 0-9608054-6-X). Womans Inst-Cont Jewish Ed.

JEWISH RABBIS

see Rabbis

JEWISH RELIGIOUS EDUCATION

Atkin, Abraham. Chelkeinu. 200p. text ed. 5.50 (ISBN 0-914131-09-5, A16). Torah Umesorah.

--Darkeinu Aleph & Bais: In One Volume. pap. text ed. 3.50 (ISBN 0-686-33046-3, A13). Torah Umesorah.

--Darkeinu Daled. text ed. 3.75 (ISBN 0-914131-13-3, A15). Torah Umesorah.

Atkins, Abraham. Darkeinu Gimel. text ed. 3.50 (ISBN 0-686-33046-3, A14). Torah Umesorah.

Best of Olomeinu Back Cover Stories: Series II - Events in the Lives of Torah Personalities. 2.75 (ISBN 0-914131-04-4, D31). Torah Umesorah.

Best of Olomeinu Back Cover Stories: Series I - Little Stories with Great Meanings. 2.75 (ISBN 0-914131-03-6, D30). Torah Umesorah.

B'ikvoseihem. Vol. I, Stories 1-31. 3.50 (ISBN 0-686-33098-6, I01); Vol. II, Stories 32-72. 3.75 (ISBN 0-914131-06-0, I01A). Torah Umesorah.

Birkat HaMazon Manual. pap. write for info. (ISBN 0-686-96116-1). United Syn Bk.

Bokser, Ben Z., tr. Minhah & Maariv Service. 45p. 1958. pap. 1.50 (ISBN 0-88482-125-0). Hebrew Pub.

Building Jewish Ethical Character. 319p. 6.00 (ISBN 0-914131-08-7, I20). Torah Umesorah.

Bulman, Nachman. Reason, Emotion & Habit in the Training of a Torah Personality. (Annual Fryer Memorial Lecture Ser.). 0.75 (ISBN 0-914131-53-2, I34). Torah Umesorah.

Chazan, Barry. Language of Jewish Education. LC 77-21638. 1978. 10.00 (ISBN 0-87677-146-0). Hartmore.

Citron, Samuel J. Dramatics for Creative Teaching. (Illus.). 1961. 9.50x (ISBN 0-8381-0212-3). United Syn Bk.

Cohen, Dovid. The Relevancy of Torah to the Social & Ethical Issues of Our Time. (Annual Fryer Memorial Lecture Ser.). 0.50 (ISBN 0-914131-57-5, I36). Torah Umesorah.

Day School Directory. 7.00 (ISBN 0-914131-15-X, E30). Torah Umesorah.

The Dean's Administrative Manual, 2 pts. 180p. Set. 12.00 (ISBN 0-914131-16-8, C20). Torah Umesorah.

Dessler, N. W. Suggested Curriculum for the Day School. 7.00 (ISBN 0-914131-63-X, C01). Torah Umesorah.

Divrei Rabboseinu. (Hebrew.). 1.00 (ISBN 0-914131-17-6, E01). Torah Umesorah.

Dresner, Samuel & Sherwin, Byron. Judaism: The Way of Sanctification. 1978. text ed. 6.50 (ISBN 0-8381-0222-0). United Syn Bk.

Epstein, Ita. Ba'sha'ar: Yahadus & Middos Text & Workbook. (Illus.). text ed. 4.00 (ISBN 0-914131-02-8, A10). Torah Umesorah.

The Expanding Role of the Yeshiva Educator. 1.50 (ISBN 0-914131-19-2, C26). Torah Umesorah.

Finkel, Nosson. Chessed as an Expression of Emunah: A Schmuess. Kaminetsky, Joseph, ed. 0.50 (ISBN 0-914131-10-9, I30). Torah Umesorah.

Fischer, John. The Olive Tree Connection: Sharing Israel's Messiah. LC 83-12645. 192p. (Orig.). 1983. pap. 8.95 (ISBN 0-87784-848-3). Inter-Varsity.

Friedman, Murray. Solving Ethical Problems. 0.50 (ISBN 0-914131-58-3, I38). Torah Umesorah.

Galupkin, Esther. Kindergarten Curriculum for the Day School. 1.50 (ISBN 0-914131-39-7, C05). Torah Umesorah.

Garber, Zev, ed. Methodology in the Academic Teaching of Judaism. (Studies in Judaism). 308p. (Orig.). 1987. lib. bdg. 28.00 (ISBN 0-8191-5723-6, Pub. by Studies in Judaism); pap. text ed. 15.75 (ISBN 0-8191-5724-4). U Pr of Amer.

Ginzberg, Louis. Students Scholars & Saints. LC 85-9089. (Brown Classics in Judaica Ser.). 312p. 1985. pap. text ed. 12.75 (ISBN 0-8191-4490-8). U Pr of Amer.

Goble, Phillip E., ed. Everything You Need to Grow a Messianic Yeshiva. LC 81-1032. 312p. (Orig.). 1981. pap. 10.95 (ISBN 0-87808-181-X). William Carey Lib.

Golinkin, Noah. Ayn Keloheynu. LC 81-51960. (Illus.). 128p. 1981. pap. 7.95x (ISBN 0-88400-076-1). Shengold.

Gorodetsky, Benjamin. Light in the Darkness. Schreiber, Mordecai, tr. LC 85-63010. (Illus.). 224p. 1986. 14.95 (ISBN 0-88400-120-2). Shengold.

Greene, Roberta M. & Heavenrich, Elaine. A Question in Search of an Answer: Understanding Learning Disability in Jewish Education. LC 8-18059. (Illus.). 262p. 1981. pap. 5.00 (ISBN 0-8074-0029-7). UAHC.

Gross, Sukey. How & What to Teach: A Pre-School & Kindergarten Curriculum Guide for the Day School. 8.00 (ISBN 0-914131-33-8, C04). Torah Umesorah.

Habershon, Ada R. Outline Study of the Tabernacle. LC 73-85298. 1974. pap. 2.95 (ISBN 0-8254-2820-3). Kregel.

Harlow, Jules. Lessons from Our Living Past. LC 72-2055. (Illus.). 128p. 1972. text ed. 6.95x (ISBN 0-87441-085-1). Behrman.

Hebrew Day School Education: An Overview. 310p. 10.00 (ISBN 0-914131-32-X, E08). Torah Umesorah.

Implementation of a Diagnostic & Remedial Program at a Hebrew Day School. 1.00 (ISBN 0-686-33114-1, N02). Torah Umesorah.

In God's Image. pap. 5.00 (ISBN 0-686-96040-8). United Syn Bk.

In Their Footsteps. 3.75 (ISBN 0-914131-36-2, I03); tchr's guide 20.00 (ISBN 0-914131-37-0, I10). Torah Umesorah.

The Jewish Face. (Illus.). 1.50 (ISBN 0-914131-38-9, D44). Torah Umesorah.

Jick, Leon A. The Teaching of Judaica in American Universities: Proceedings. 1970. 10.00x (ISBN 0-87068-127-3). Ktav.

Kadima Hagim Series, 8 vols. Incl. No. 1-Pesach, Pesach, Pesach Time Is Here; No. 2-Tikun Lel Chatzot Shavuot; No. 3-Rosh Chodesh Programming; No. 4-Purim Programming; No. 5-Shlosha Yamim: Three New Holidays; No. 6-A Kadima Chanukah Party; No. 7-Yom Yerushalayim; No. 8-Dreidel Factory. Set. pap. 6.50 (ISBN 0-686-95960-4); pap. 1.00 ea. vol. United Syn Bk.

Kadima Kesher Series, 16 vols. Incl. No. 1. Bar-Bat Mitzvah Simulation Game; No. 2. Build Your Own Sukkah; No. 3. Russian Jewry Situation Game; No. 4. Izzy Queer; No. 5. Kasher In; No. 6. Teaching Shira is More Than Clapping Hands; No. 7. T-O-R-A-H; No. 8. Values Auction; No. 9. Kadima Family Programming Seudah Shleesheet; No. 10. How to Create a Creative Service; No. 11. Kadima Sports Manual; No. 12. Grandparents Shabbat; No. 13. Shabbat Cantata; No. 14. Prejudice; No. 15. Yad B'Yad Bowl-A-Thon; No. 16. Different Choices-A Game of Jewish Survival. Set. 11.00 (ISBN 0-686-95953-1); vol. 1.00 ea. United Syn Bk.

Kaminetsky, Joseph & Gross, Alexander. The Founder of Torah Umesorah. pap. 1.00 (ISBN 0-914131-21-4, E-23). Torah Umesorah.

Kopin, Rita. The Lively Jewish Classroom: Games & Activities for Learning. (Illus.). 132p. 1980. pap. text ed. 8.75 (ISBN 0-86705-014-4). AIRE.

Langsam, Aviva. Nichtov M'aleph V'ad Tav: Spirit Duplicating Primer. text ed. 15.00 (ISBN 0-915152-03-7, A05). Torah Umesorah.

Langsam, Avivia. M'aleph V'ad Tav: Spirit Duplicating Primer. text ed. 15.00 (ISBN 0-915152-02-9, A04). Torah Umesorah.

Leibowitz, A. H. Chochmas Hamussar. (Annual Fryer Memorial Lectures Ser.). 1.00 (ISBN 0-914131-11-7, I37). Torah Umesorah.

Lister, Rebecca & Lister, Louis. The Smaller Religious School: A Manual. 1977. pap. text ed. 5.00 (ISBN 0-685-88426-0, 241850). UAHC.

Marcus, Audrey F. & Zwerin, Raymond A., eds. The Jewish Principals Handbook. LC 83-70198. 525p. 1983. text ed. 45.00 (ISBN 0-86705-035-7); pap. text ed. 39.95 (ISBN 0-86705-010-1). AIRE.

Minchah-Maariv: Pocket Size Siddur. 0.60 (ISBN 0-914131-45-1, B75). Torah Umesorah.

Newman, Shirley & Newman, Louis. A Child's Introduction to Torah. LC 72-2056. (Illus.). 128p. 1972. text ed. 6.95x (ISBN 0-87441-067-3). 2.25x ea., wkbk in 2 pts. Behrman.

Nulman, Louis. What is Chanukah? A Programmed Text. text ed. 2.25 (ISBN 0-914131-73-7, A30). Torah Umesorah.

--What is Kosher? A Programmed Text. text ed. 2.50 (ISBN 0-914131-74-5, A40). Torah Umesorah.

Oschry, Leonard. The Story of the Vilna Gaon. 1.50 (ISBN 0-914131-62-1, D52). Torah Umesorah.

Outline of Administrative Responsibilities in a Hebrew Day School. 0.25 (ISBN 0-914131-47-8, C25). Torah Umesorah.

Prager, Moshe. Rabbi Yisroel Baal Shem Tov. (Hebrew., Illus.). 1.75 (ISBN 0-914131-51-6, D50). Torah Umesorah.

PTA with a Purpose. 2.00 (ISBN 0-914131-49-4, L01). Torah Umesorah.

Rabinonwitz, C. D. A Teacher's Guide for Sefer Yehoshua. (Hebrew.). 4.00 (ISBN 0-914131-68-0, B41). Torah Umesorah.

Rabinowitz, C. D. A Teacher's Guide for Melachim I: A Teacher's Guide. 5.00 (ISBN 0-914131-66-4, B45). Torah Umesorah.

--The Teaching of Prayer: A Teacher's Guide. 2.25 (ISBN 0-914131-71-0, B50). Torah Umesorah.

Rabinowitz, Chaim D. Divrei Y'mei Yisroel: In Hebrew. text ed. 10.00 (ISBN 0-914131-18-4, A80). Torah Umesorah.

Rashi Vocalized for Beginners. text ed. 2.50 (ISBN 0-914131-52-4, B01). Torah Umesorah.

Rivkin, Nacha. Reishis Chochmah. (Illus.). 64p. text ed. 3.50 (ISBN 0-914131-54-0, A01); wkbk. 3.00 (ISBN 0-914131-55-9). Torah Umesorah.

--Reishis Chochmah, Vol. II. (Illus.). 100p. 4.75 (ISBN 0-914131-56-7, A03). Torah Umesorah.

Rosenberg, Amye. Tzedakah. (Jewish Awareness Ser.). (Illus.). 1979. pap. text ed. 2.95x (ISBN 0-87441-279-X). Behrman.

Rosenfeld, Israel. Gemorah L'mas'chillim. 4.75 (ISBN 0-914131-23-0, A40); tchr's. guide 3.00 (ISBN 0-914131-24-9, A41). Torah Umesorah.

--Targilon for Sefer Bamidbar, Vol. 1. text ed. 4.00 (ISBN 0-914131-64-8, A23). Torah Umesorah.

--Targilon for Sefer Bemidbar, Vol. II. text ed. 4.00 (ISBN 0-914131-65-6, A24). Torah Umesorah.

Schwartz, Earl. Moral Development: A Practical Guide for Jewish Teachers. LC 83-70196. 188p. 1983. pap. text ed. 10.00 (ISBN 0-86705-037-3). AIRE.

Seldin, Ruth. Teacher's Guide to Jews & Their Religion. 150p. 5.95 (ISBN 0-88464-041-8); pap. 2.95 (ISBN 0-686-99468-X). ADL.

Selichot Reader. pap. 0.75 (ISBN 0-686-96114-5). United Syn Bk.

Shapiro, Alexander M. & Cohen, Burton I. Studies in Jewish Education & Judaica in Honor of Louis Newman. 1984. 20.00 (ISBN 0-317-13172-9). Ktav.

Sharon, Ruth. Arts & Crafts the Year Round, 2 Vols. (Illus.). 1965. Set. 29.00x (ISBN 0-8381-0213-1). United Syn Bk.

Shulman, Avi. A Guide to the Bais Hamikosh. rev. ed. 2.75 (ISBN 0-914131-25-7, B20). Torah Umesorah.

--How to Teach, Enjoy & Survive Primary Grades. 2.50 (ISBN 0-914131-34-6, B65). Torah Umesorah.

Shulman, Shaindy. Torah Teddy Learns Colors. 1985. 3.95 (ISBN 0-87306-942-0). Feldheim.

--Torah Teddy Learns to Count. 1985. 3.95 (ISBN 0-87306-943-9). Feldheim.

Shurin, Israel. Morei Ha'umah, Bk. 2. (Illus.). 4.00 (ISBN 0-914131-46-X, D45). Torah Umesorah.

Siegel, Seymour & Gertel, Elliot. God in the Teachings of Conservative Judaism. 278p. 1985. 20.00 (ISBN 0-88125-066-X). Ktav.

Soloveitchik, Aaron. The Fire of Sinai. (Annual Fryer Memorial Lecture Ser.). 1.00 (ISBN 0-914131-20-6, I32). Torah Umesorah.

--Law & Morality in Modern Society. (Annual Fryer Memorial Lecture Ser.). 0.75 (ISBN 0-914131-40-0, I33). Torah Umesorah.

Special Education in the Jewish Community. 3.00 (N03). Torah Umesorah.

Spero, Shubert. The Story of the Chasam Sofer. (Illus.). 80p. 2.00 (ISBN 0-914131-61-3, D53). Torah Umesorah.

A Teacher's Guide for Sefer Shoftim. (Hebrew.). 4.00 (ISBN 0-914131-67-2, B42). Torah Umesorah.

Ury, Zalman F. The Story of Rabbi Yisroel Salanter. 3.75 (ISBN 0-914131-60-5, D54). Torah Umesorah.

Yachas Harav V'hatalmid. (Hebrew.). 0.50 (ISBN 0-914131-75-3, E05). Torah Umesorah.

JEWISH SECTS

see also Conservative Judaism; Essenes; Karaites; Orthodox Judaism; Pharisees; Qumran Community; Reconstructionist Judaism; Reform Judaism; Zealots (Jewish Party)

Ashkenazim & Sephardim: Their Relations, Differences & Problems As Reflected in the Rabbinical Responsa. 25.00x (ISBN 0-87068-349-7). Ktav.

Blau, Joseph L. Modern Varieties of Judaism. LC 66-10732. (Lectures on the History of Religion Ser.). 217p. 1966. 24.50x (ISBN 0-231-02867-9); pap. 11.00x (ISBN 0-231-08668-7). Columbia U Pr.

Grad, Eli & Roth, Bette. Congregation Shaarey Zedek: 5622-5742 1861-1981. LC 82-48650. (Illus.). 198p. 1982. 25.00x (ISBN 0-8143-1713-8). Wayne St U Pr.

Kahn, Paul, ed. Proceedings of the Association of Orthodox Jewish Scientists, Vol. 7. 240p. 1984. pap. 9.95. Hermon.

Levin, S. I. & Boyden, Edward A. Kosher Code of the Orthodox Jew. LC 76-76170. (Illus.). 264p. 1983. pap. 9.75 (ISBN 0-87203-011-3). Hermon.

Lightley, John W. Jewish Sects & Parties in the Time of Jesus. 1980. lib. bdg. 75.00 (ISBN 0-8490-3150-8). Gordon Pr.

Porter, Jack N., compiled by. Jews & the Cults: Bibliography-Guide. LC 81-67448. 50p. 1981. pap. 3.50 (ISBN 0-9602036-4-8). Biblio NY.

Ross, Dan. Acts of Faith: A Journey to the Fringes of Jewish Identity. LC 83-40468. (Illus.). 256p. 1984. pap. 8.95 (ISBN 0-8052-0759-7). Schocken.

JEWISH SOCIOLOGY

see Sociology, Jewish

JEWISH SYMBOLISM AND ART

see Jewish Art and Symbolism

JEWISH THEOLOGY

see also Judaism

Bamberger, Bernard J. The Search for Jewish Theology. new ed. LC 77-28457. 1978. pap. 4.95x (ISBN 0-87441-300-1). Behrman.

Blank, S. H. Prophetic Thought: Essays & Addresses. (Jewish Perspectives Ser: Vol. 2). 15.00x (ISBN 0-87820-501-2, HUC Pr). Ktav.

Cohn-Sherbok, Dan. On Earth As It Is in Heaven: Jews, Christians, & Liberation Theology. LC 86-23509. 128p. (Orig.). 1987. pap. 7.95 (ISBN 0-88344-410-0). Orbis Bks.

Daud, Abraham I. The Exalted Faith. Weiss, Gershon, ed. Samuelson, Norbert, tr. LC 83-49341. (Hebrew.). 408p. 1986. 75.00x (ISBN 0-8386-3185-1). Fairleigh Dickinson.

Ellis, Marc H. Toward a Jewish Theology of Liberation. LC 86-23553. 160p. (Orig.). 1987. pap. 9.95 (ISBN 0-88344-358-9). Orbis Bks.

Epstein, Isidore. Step by Step in the Jewish Religion. PLB 4.95x. Bloch.

Fackenheim, Emil. L. Quest for Past & Future: Essays in Jewish Theology. LC 83-12692. 336p. 1983. Repr. of 1968 ed. lib. bdg. 39.75x (ISBN 0-313-22738-1, FAQP). Greenwood.

Friedlander, M. Jewish Religion: Describing & Explaining the Philosophy & Rituals of the Jewish Faith. 35.00 (ISBN 0-87559-117-5). Shalom.

Hayes, John H. & Prussner, Frederick. Old Testament Theology: Its History & Development. LC 84-47798. 336p. 1984. pap. 15.95 (ISBN 0-8042-0146-3). John Knox.

Jacobs, Louis. Jewish Theology. LC 73-17442. 384p. 1973. pap. 9.95x (ISBN 0-87441-248-X). Behrman.

--Theology in the Responsa. (Littman Library of Jewish Civilization). 1975. 35.50x (ISBN 0-19-710022-8). Oxford U Pr.

Joseph, Howard, et al, eds. Truth & Compassion: Essays on Judaism & Religion in Memory of Rabbi Dr. Solomon Frank, Vol. 12. 217p. 1983. pap. text ed. 13.95x (ISBN 0-919812-17-1, Pub. by Wilfrid Laurier Canada). Humanities.

Kaplan, Aryeh. The Handbook of Jewish Thought. 307p. 13.95 (ISBN 0-940118-27-0). Maznaim.

Kellerman, Eli. Jewish Ceremonial: A Guide to Jewish Prayer & Ritual. 69p. 1983. pap. 9.95 (ISBN 965-220-038-7, Carta Pub Isreal). Hippocrene Bks.

Kosovsky, Binyamin. Otzar Leshon Ho-Tannaim-Mekilta d'rabi Ishmael, 4 vols. 1965. Set. 75.00x (ISBN 0-685-31425-1, Pub. by Jewish Theol Seminary). Ktav.

Lieberman, Saul. Siphre Zutta. 1968. 10.00x (ISBN 0-685-31431-6, Pub. by Jewish Theol Seminary). Ktav.

--The Tosefta, 5 Vols. 25.00x ea. (ISBN 0-685-31430-8, Pub. by Jewish Theol Seminary). KTAV.

Maimonides, Moses. Guide for the Perplexed. Friedlander, M., tr. 1904. pap. 6.95 (ISBN 0-486-20351-4). Dover.

--Guide for the Perplexed: Morah Nevochim. (Heb, & Eng). 37.50 (ISBN 0-87559-079-9). Shalom.

--Guide of the Perplexed, 2 vols. Pines, Shlomo, tr. LC 62-18113. 1963. 25.00x ea.; Vol. 1. (ISBN 0-226-50232-5). Vol. 2 (ISBN 0-226-50233-3). U of Chicago Pr.

--The Guide of the Perplexed. Pines, Shlomo, tr. LC 62-18113. 1974. Vol. 1. pap. 15.95 (ISBN 0-226-50230-9, P609, Phoen); Vol. 2. pap. 15.95 (ISBN 0-226-50231-7, P610). U of Chicago Pr.

Marmorstein, A. Studies in Jewish Theology. 376p. Repr. of 1950 ed. text ed. 49.68x (ISBN 0-576-80153-4, Pub. by Gregg Intl Pubs England). Gregg Intl.

Meynell, Hugo A. The Theology of Bernard Lonergan. (Studies in Religion). 1986. text ed. 15.95 (ISBN 1-55540-015-9, 01-00-42); pap. 11.95 (ISBN 1-55540-016-7). Scholars Pr GA.

Narot, Joseph R. An Introduction to a Faith. pap. 1.00 (ISBN 0-686-15807-5). Rostrum Bks.

--Why I Am a Jew. pap. 0.95 (ISBN 0-686-15802-4). Rostrum Bks.

Nathanael Ibn Al-Fayyumi. Bustan Al-Ukul. Levine, David, tr. LC 8-4311. (American Geographical Society. Oriental Explorations & Studies: No. 6). 20.75 (ISBN 0-404-50496-5). AMS Pr.

Neusner, Jacob. Understanding Jewish Theology. 1973. pap. 11.95x (ISBN 0-87068-215-6). Ktav.

--Understanding Jewish Theology: Classsical Issues & Modern Perspective. 280p. pap. 9.95 (ISBN 0-686-95185-9). ADL.

Neusner, Jacob, ed. Our Sages, God & Israel: An Anthology of the Jerusalem Talmud. LC 84-23793. 179p. 1985. 19.95 (ISBN 0-940646-18-8). Rossel Bks.

Pearl, Chaim. The Medieval Jewish Mind. LC 76-184221. 208p. 1973. 8.95 (ISBN 0-87677-043-X). Hartmore.

Philosophy: Basic Judaism. (Home Study Program Ser.: No. 601). 5.00 (ISBN 0-686-96129-3). United Syn Bk.

Rubenstein, Richard J. After Auschwitz: Essays in Contemporary Judaism. (Orig.). 1966. pap. 10.28 scp (ISBN 0-672-61150-3). Bobbs.

Schechter, Solomon. Aspects of Rabbinic Theology: Major Concepts of the Talmud. LC 61-14919. 1961. pap. 8.95 (ISBN 0-8052-0015-0). Schocken.

Talmage, F., ed. AJS Review, Vol. 1. 1976. 20.00x (Pub. by Assoc. for Jewish Studies). Ktav.

--AJS Review, Vol. 2. 1977. 20.00x (ISBN 0-685-55539-9, Pub. by Assoc. for Jewish Studies). Ktav.

JEWISH WAY OF LIFE

see also Women, Jewish

Angel, Marc D. The Rhythms of Jewish Living: The Sephardic Approach. LC 86-25993. 208p. 1987. 14.95 (ISBN 0-87203-125-X). Hermon.

Bazak, Jacob. Jewish Law & Jewish Life, 8 bks. in 4 vols. Passamaneck, Stephen M., ed. Incl. Bk. 1. Selected Rabbinical Response (ISBN 0-8074-0034-3, 180210); Bks. 2-4. Contracts, Real Estate, Sales & Usury (180211); Bks. 5-6. Credit, Law Enforcement & Taxation (180212); Bks. 7-8. Criminal & Domestic Relations (ISBN 0-8074-0037-8, 180213). 1978. pap. 12.50 complete vol. (ISBN 0-8074-0038-6, 180218); pap. 5.00 ea. UAHC.

Blue, Lionel. Bright Blue. 96p. 1985. 11.95 (ISBN 0-312-09626-7). St Martin.

Bogart, Shirley. The New Jewish Homemaker: A Treasury of Tips, Crafts, Foods & Stories. 256p. 16.95t (ISBN 0-940646-20-X). Rossel Bks.

Booker, Richard. Blow the Trumpet in Zion. LC 85-62152. 208p. (Orig.). 1985. pap. 5.95 (ISBN 0-932081-02-9). Victory Hse.

Brand, Sandra. I Dared to Live. LC 78-52142. 1978. pap. 8.95 (ISBN 0-88400-058-3). Shengold.

Buber, Martin. The Way of Man. 44p. 1985. pap. 3.50 (ISBN 0-8065-0024-7). Citadel Pr.

Bubis, G. B., ed. Serving the Jewish Family. 25.00x (ISBN 0-87068-439-6). Ktav.

Bubis, Gerald B. & Wasserman, Harry. Synagogue Havurot: A Comparative Study. LC 82-23912. 160p. (Orig.). 1983. lib. bdg. 25.50 (ISBN 0-8191-2969-0, Co-pub. by Ctr Jewish Comm Studies); pap. text ed. 10.50 (ISBN 0-8191-2970-4). U Pr of Amer.

Bulka, Reuven P. The Jewish Pleasure Principle. LC 86-20839. 168p. 1987. text ed. 24.95 (ISBN 0-89885-328-1). Human Sci Pr.

Cardozo, Arlene. Jewish Family Celebrations. (Illus.). 288p. 1985. pap. 6.95 (ISBN 0-312-44232-7). St Martin.

Cohen, Jack S. The Jewish Heart: Essays on Jewish Sensitivities. LC 84-27837. 217p. 1985. 15.00 (ISBN 0-88125-065-1). Ktav.

Cohen, Seymour. Affirming Life. 350p. 1987. 20.00x (ISBN 0-88125-112-7). Ktav.

Cohen, Steven M. & Hyman, Paula E., eds. The Jewish Family. 256p. 1986. text ed. 42.50x (ISBN 0-8419-0860-5). Holmes & Meier.

DaCosta, I. Noble Families among the Sephardic Jews. 1976. lib. bdg. 134.95 (ISBN 0-8490-2349-1). Gordon Pr.

Dashefsky, Arnold, ed. Contemporary Jewry, Vol. 8. 160p. 1987. 19.95 (ISBN 0-88738-097-2). Transaction Bks.

Davis, Nancy & Levitt, Joy. The Guide to Everything Jewish in New York. LC 86-10927. 334p. 1986. pap. 14.95 (ISBN 0-915361-47-7, Dist. by Watts). Adama Pubs Inc.

Dawidowicz, Lucy. The Jewish Presence: Essays on Identity & History. 13.75 (ISBN 0-8446-6217-8). Peter Smith.

Diller, Jerry V. Ancient Roots & Modern Meanings. LC 77-99196. 1978. 12.50 (ISBN 0-8197-0457-1); pap. 7.95 (ISBN 0-685-27177-3). Bloch.

Donin, Hayim. To Be a Jew. LC 72-89175. 1972. 17.95 (ISBN 0-465-08624-1). Basic.

Eisen, Arnold M. Galut: Modern Jewish Reflections on Homelessness & Homecoming. LC 85-45763. (Modern Jewish Experience Ser.). 224p. 1986. pap. 27.50x (ISBN 0-253-32550-1). Ind U Pr.

Elkins, Dov P., ed. Being Jewish, Being Human: A Gift Book of Poems & Readings. LC 79-88298. Date not set. pap. 16.50 (ISBN 0-918834-07-4). Growth Assoc.

Epstein, Jane G. The Jewish Working Parent: Determining Priorities. 4.95. United Synagogue.

Frankel, William, ed. Survey of Jewish Affairs, 1985. 280p. 1985. 25.00x (ISBN 0-8386-3269-6). Fairleigh Dickinson.

Gastwirt, Harold P. Fraud Corruption & Holiness: The Controversy over the Supervision of Jewish Dietary Practice in New York City. LC 74-77649. 1974. 23.95x (ISBN 0-8046-9056-1, Pub. by Kennikat). Assoc Faculty Pr.

Gilman, Sander L. Jewish Self-Hatred: Anti-Semitism & the Hidden Language of the Jews. LC 85-45050. 480p. 1986. text ed. 28.50x (ISBN 0-8018-3276-4). Johns Hopkins.

Gittelsohn, Roland B. The Extra Dimension. 228p. 1983. pap. 7.95 (ISBN 0-8074-0170-6, 168500). UAHC.

--Love, Sex & Marriage: A Jewish View. (Illus.). 1980. pap. 7.95x (ISBN 0-8074-0046-7, 142683). UAHC.

Goldberg, M. Hirsh. Just Because They're Jewish. 1978. 9.95 (ISBN 0-8128-2518-7). Stein & Day.

Greenberg, Simon. A Jewish Philosophy & Pattern of Life. LC 81-2153. (Moreshet Series, Studies in Jewish History, Literature & Thought: Vol. 9). 550p. 1982. 25.00x (ISBN 0-87334-012-4, Pub. by Jewish Theol Seminary). Ktav.

Hadassah Magazine Staff. Jewish Traveler. Tigay, Alan M., ed. LC 86-8917. (Illus.). 416p. 1987. 19.95 (ISBN 0-385-23811-8); pap. 12.95 (ISBN 0-385-23451-1). Doubleday.

Heilman, Samuel C. The People of the Book: Drama, Fellowship, & Religion. LC 82-13369. 264p. 1983. lib. bdg. 25.00x (ISBN 0-226-32492-3). U of Chicago Pr.

--Synagogue Life: A Study in Symbolic Interaction. LC 75-36403. 1976. 12.95x (ISBN 0-226-32488-5); pap. 9.95x (ISBN 0-226-32490-7, P824, Phoen). U of Chicago Pr.

Herzog, Yaacov D. The Mishnah. 15.00x (ISBN 0-686-84235-9). Bloch.

Horowitz, George. The Spirit of Jewish Law. LC 53-7535. 1979. Repr. of 1953 ed. text ed. 40.00x (ISBN 0-87632-167-8). Bloch.

Humphreys, W. Lee. Crisis & Story: Introduction to the Old Testament. LC 78-64594. (Illus.). 313p. 1979. text ed. 21.95 (ISBN 0-87484-437-1). Mayfield Pub.

Hurwitz, Shimon. Being Jewish. rev. ed. 1979. pap. 5.95 (ISBN 0-87306-196-9). Feldheim.

Janowitz, Morris. Judaism of the Next Generation. pap. 2.00 (ISBN 0-686-15805-9). Rostrum Bks.

Jewish Book of Days. (Illus.). 128p. 1987. 9.95 (ISBN 0-88363-388-4). H L Levin.

Juster, Daniel C. Growing to Maturity: A Messianic Jewish Guide. 2nd ed. (Illus.). 278p. (Orig.). 1985. pap. 7.00 (ISBN 0-9614555-0-0). Union Messianic Jew Pub.

Kadima Hagim Series, 8 vols. Incl. No. 1-Pesach, Pesach, Pesach Time Is Here; No. 2-Tikun Lel Chatzot Shavuot; No. 3-Rosh Chodesh Programming; No. 4-Purim Programming; No. 5-Shlosha Yamim: Three New Holidays; No. 6-A Kadima Chanukah Party; No. 7-Yom Yerushalayim; No. 8-Dreidel Factory. Set. pap. 6.50 (ISBN 0-686-95960-4); pap. 1.00 ea. vol. United Syn Bk.

Kahane, Meir. Why Be Jewish? Intermarriage, Assimilation, & Alienation. LC 77-8774. 264p. 1982. pap. 7.95 (ISBN 0-8128-6129-9). Stein & Day.

Karp, Abraham J. The Jewish Way of Life & Thought. 1981. pap. 9.95x (ISBN 0-87068-717-4). Ktav.

Kasher, Menachem M. Israel Passover Haggadah. LC 64-17316. (Illus.). 1983. Repr. of 1964 ed. 15.00 (ISBN 0-88400-018-4). Shengold.

Katz, Jacob. Jewish Emancipation & Self-Emancipation. 179p. 1986. 14.95 (ISBN 0-8276-0261-8). Jewish Pubns.

--The Traditional Jewish Family in Historical Perspective. 1983. pap. 1.00 (ISBN 0-87495-048-1). Am Jewish Comm.

Kipper, Lenore & Bogot, Howard. Alef-Bet of Jewish Values: Code Words of Jewish Life. (Illus.). 64p. 1985. pap. text ed. 6.00 (ISBN 0-8074-0267-2, 101087). UAHC.

Kitov, A. E. The Jew & His Home. 14th ed. Bulman, Nathan, tr. LC 63-17660. 233p. 1976. 12.50 (ISBN 0-88400-004-4). Shengold.

Klein, Judith W. Jewish Identity & Self-Esteem: Healing Wounds Through Ethnotherapy. 64p. 1980. 2.75. Am Jewish Comm.

Koeppel, Josephine, tr. from Ger. Edith Stein: Life in a Jewish Family. LC 84-25164. (Illus.). 576p. (Orig.). 1986. pap. 10.95x (ISBN 0-935216-04-9). ICS Pubns.

Kolatch, Alfred J. The Jewish Book of Why. 1981. 12.95 (ISBN 0-8246-0256-0). Jonathan David.

Lamm, Norman, ed. Treasury of Tradition. Wurzburger, Walter S. 462p. 1967. 9.95 (ISBN 0-88482-434-9). Hebrew Pub.

Latner, Helen. The Book of Modern Jewish Etiquette: A Guide To Contemporary Manners & Religious Customs. LC 86-45124. 400p. 1986. pap. 9.95 (ISBN 0-06-097054-5, PL-7054, PL). Har-Row.

--Your Jewish Wedding. LC 83-45567. (Illus.). 224p. 1985. pap. 4.95 (ISBN 0-385-18873-0). Doubleday.

Lehrman, S. M. The Jewish Design for Living. LC 76-24242. 1976. 11.95 (ISBN 0-88400-003-6). Shengold.

Lemelman, Martin. My Jewish Home: Sinchah Ba'ambatyah - Fun in the Bathtub. (Illus.). 10p. 1987. polyvinyl 3.95 (ISBN 0-8074-0327-X). UAHC.

Let Us Make Man: Self Esteem Through Jewishness. 208p. 1987. 14.95 (ISBN 0-933711-01-8). Traditional Pr.

Levi, Miriam. Effective Jewish Parenting. 1986. 10.95 (ISBN 0-87306-405-4). Feldheim.

Levita, Elijah. Massoreth Ha Massoreth. rev. ed. LC 67-11894. (Library of Biblical Studies). 1969. 39.50x (ISBN 0-87068-081-1). Ktav.

Lightman, Sidney, ed. The Jewish Travel Guide, 1986. (Illus.). 296p. (Orig.). 1986. pap. 9.25 (ISBN 0-317-39976-4, Pub. by Jewish Chronicle Pubns England). Hermon.

Linzer, Norman. The Jewish Family: Authority & Tradition in Modern Perspectives. 217p. 1984. 34.95 (ISBN 0-89885-149-1); pap. 14.95 (ISBN 0-89885-191-2). Human Sci Pr.

Lion The Printer. Seven Days a Week. (Illus.). 1977. spiral 2.00 (ISBN 0-914080-62-8). Shulsinger Sales.

Maimonodes, Moses. Guide of the Perplexed. abr. ed. Guttman, Julius W., ed. Rabin, Chaim, tr. 1978. pap. text ed. 5.95 (ISBN 0-85222-208-4, East & West Lib). Hebrew Pub.

Mayer, Egon & Sheingold, Carl. Intermarriage & the Jewish Future. LC 79-63378. 46p. 1980. pap. 2.00 (ISBN 0-87495-031-7). Am Jewish Comm.

Monson, Rela G. Jewish Campus Life: A Survey of Student Attitudes Toward Marriage & Family. LC 84-70026. 52p. 1984. pap. 3.00 (ISBN 0-87495-060-0). Am Jewish Comm.

Moskowitz, Nachama S. Original Bulletin Boards on Jewish Themes. 128p. (Orig.). 1986. pap. text ed. 12.50 (ISBN 0-86705-019-5). AIRE.

Narot, Joseph R. For Whom the Rabbi Speaks. pap. 1.65 (ISBN 0-686-15800-8). Rostrum Bks.

--Judaism Without Guilt. pap. 0.75 (ISBN 0-686-15811-3). Rostrum Bks.

--A Preface to Well Being. pap. 1.00 (ISBN 0-686-15806-7). Rostrum Bks.

--What I Believe About God. pap. 0.95 (ISBN 0-686-15803-2). Rostrum Bks.

National Council of Jewish Women. Our Heritage Speaks: Applying Jewish Values to Contemporary Issues. (Module I - Care of Aging Parents). (Illus.). 30p. (Orig.). 1985. pap. 3.50 (ISBN 0-941840-23-9). NCJW.

National Council of Jewish Women Staff. Our Heritage Speaks: Applying Jewish Values to Contempary Issues. (Jewish Values Ser.: Choices in Action & Advocacy: Module II). 19p. (Orig.). pap. 3.50 (ISBN 0-941840-28-X). NCJW.

Nelson, Zev K. The Light Within. LC 78-56774. 1979. 8.95 (ISBN 0-88400-060-5). Shengold.

Neusner, Jacob. Vanquished Nation, Broken Spirit: The Virtues of the Heart in Formative Judaism. 208p. Date not set. price not set (ISBN 0-521-32832-2); pap. price not set (ISBN 0-521-33801-8). Cambridge U Pr.

New Approach to Jewish Life. 4.95 (ISBN 0-87677-142-8). Hartmore.

Olan, Levi A. Maturity in an Immature World. 1984. 15.00 (ISBN 0-88125-049-X). Ktav.

Patai, Raphael. The Jewish Mind. 384p. 1985. pap. 14.95 (ISBN 0-684-16321-7, ScribT). Scribner.

Pechota, Vratislav. The Right to Know One's Human Rights: A Road Toward Marriage & Family. LC 83-72868. 52p. 1983. pap. 2.50 (ISBN 0-87495-056-2). Am Jewish Comm.

Peli, Pinchas. Shabbat Shalom: A Renewed Encounter with the Sabbath. 120p. 1986. pap. 7.95 (ISBN 0-940646-37-4). Rossel Bks.

Petuchowski, Jacob J. Freedom of Expression in the Jewish Tradition. 34p. 1984. pap. 2.50 (ISBN 0-87495-062-7). Am Jewish Comm.

Plesur, Milton. Jewish Life in Twentieth Century America: Challenge & Accommodation. LC 81-11196. (Illus.). 264p. 1982. text ed. 21.95x (ISBN 0-88229-639-6). Nelson-Hall.

Podwal, Mark. A Book of Hebrew Letters. LC 78-70076. (Illus.). 64p. 1979. pap. 5.95 (ISBN 0-8276-0118-2, 435). Jewish Pubns.

Raphael, Chaim. Encounters with the Jewish People. LC 79-14424. 1979. pap. text ed. 6.95x (ISBN 0-87441-282-X). Behrman.

Reisman, Bernard. The Chavurah: A Contemporary Jewish Experience. 1977. pap. 7.50 (ISBN 0-8074-0048-3, 140050). UAHC.

Reisman, Bernard & Rosen, Gladys. Single-Parent Families at Camp: The Essence of an Experience. LC 84-70480. 54p. 1984. pap. 2.50 (ISBN 0-87495-061-9). Am Jewish Comm.

Riemer, Jack & Stampfer, Nathaniel, eds. Ethical Wills: A Jewish Tradition. LC 82-19160. 192p. 1983. 16.95 (ISBN 0-8052-3839-5). Schocken.

Roskies, Diane K. & Roskies, David G. The Shtetl Book. rev ed. pap. 9.95x (ISBN 0-87068-455-8). Ktav.

Sachar, Howard M. Diaspora: An Inquiry into the Contemporary Jewish World. LC 84-48190. 480p. 1985. 27.00i (ISBN 0-06-015403-9, HarpT). Har-Row.

Santo, Lori, ed. Jews & Hispanics in America: The Meeting of Two Historic Cultures. 31p. 1982. pap. 2.50 (ISBN 0-87495-061-9). Am Jewish Comm.

Schostak, Zev. Taharath Hamishpacha: Jewish Family Laws. 1982. 3.95 (ISBN 0-87306-100-4). Feldheim.

Shaanan, Alexander. Dear God, Is Justice Still With You? (Illus.). 144p. 1983. 8.95 (ISBN 0-89962-306-9). Todd & Honeywell.

Shaham, Nathan. The Other Side of the Wall: Three Novellas. Gold, Leonard, tr. from Hebrew. 256p. 1983. 13.95 (ISBN 0-8276-0223-5, 607). Jewish Pubns.

Shapolsky, Ian. The Jewish Trivia & Information Book. 400p. 1985. pap. 5.95 (ISBN 0-317-39894-6). Shapolsky Pubs.

--The Second Jewish Trivia & Information Book. (Illus.). 400p. 1986. pap. 6.95 (ISBN 0-933503-45-8). Shapolsky Pubs.

Shmueli Family, 2 bks. Incl. Bk. 1. A Cartoon Adventure. 5.00x (ISBN 0-685-55046-X, 405310); Bk. 2. More Cartoon Adventures. 5.00x (ISBN 0-685-55047-8, 405311). 1975. 6.00. UAHC.

Singer, David. Focus on the Jewish Family: A Selected Annotated Bibliography, 1970-1982. 32p. 1984. pap. 2.00 (ISBN 0-87495-058-9). Am Jewish Comm.

Sklare, Marshall, et al. Not Quite at Home: How an American Jewish Community Lives with Itself & Its Neighbors. LC 77-81092. (Institute of Human Relations Press Paperback Ser). x, 85p. (Orig.). 1969. pap. 1.00 (ISBN 0-87495-017-1). Am Jewish Comm.

Soloveitchik, Joseph B. Halakhic Man. Kaplan, Lawrence, tr. from Hebrew. 182p. 1984. 12.95 (ISBN 0-8276-0222-7, 606). Jewish Pubns.

Strassfeld, Michael & Strassfeld, Sharon, eds. The Second Jewish Catalog: Sources & Resources. LC 73-11759. (Illus.). 464p. 1976. 8.95 (ISBN 0-8276-0084-4, 391). Jewish Pubns.

Strassfeld, Sharon & Kurzweil, Arthur. Behold a Great Image. LC 78-1168. (Illus.). 224p. 1978. 22.95 (ISBN 0-8276-0105-0, 417). Jewish Pubns.

Trepp, Leo. The Complete Book of Jewish Observance. LC 79-1352. (Illus.). 1979. 16.50 (ISBN 0-87441-281-1). Behrman.

Weinreich, Uriel. College Yiddish; An Introduction to the Yiddish Language & to Jewish Life & Culture. 5th ed. LC 76-88208. 399p. 1979. 15.00 (ISBN 0-914512-04-8). Yivo Inst.

Women's League for Conservative Judaism. Welcome to the World - A Jewish Baby's Record Book. (Illus.). 40p. 1985. 12.95 (ISBN 0-936293-00-4). WLCJ.

Wouk, Herman. This Is My God: The Jewish Way of Life. 1986. pap. 8.95 (ISBN 0-671-62258-7, Touchstone Bks). S&S.

JEWISH WIT AND HUMOR

Ausubel, Nathan, ed. Treasury of Jewish Humor. LC 51-10639. 1951. 17.95 (ISBN 0-385-04499-2). Doubleday.

Chetkin, Len. Guess Who's Jewish? (You'll Never Guess) Friedman, Robert S., ed. LC 85-13200. (Illus.). 164p. (Orig.). 1985. pap. 4.95 (ISBN 0-89865-403-3). Donning Co.

Cohen, Sarah B., ed. Jewish Wry: Essays on Jewish Humor. (Jewish Literature & Culture Ser.). 1987. 27.50 (ISBN 0-253-33185-4). Ind U Pr.

Fuchs, Esther. Encounters with Israeli Authors. LC 82-62086. (Illus.). 95p. 1983. pap. 7.50 (ISBN 0-916288-14-5). Micah Pubns.

Kleinman, Isador. Lach a Bisl: Laugh a Little. 1985. pap. 5.95 (ISBN 0-910818-61-4). Judaica Pr.

Kruger, Mollee. Daughters of Chutzpah: Humorous Verse on the Jewish Woman. LC 82-71394. (Illus.). 112p. (Orig.). 1983. pap. 5.00 (ISBN 0-9602036-7-2). Biblio NY.

--More Unholy Writ: Jewish Verses & Vices. 100p. 1973. pap. 2.25 (ISBN 0-913184-02-0). Maryben Bks.

Landau, Ron. The Book of Jewish Lists. LC 81-40500. 192p. 1982. 14.95 (ISBN 0-8128-2839-9). Stein & Day.

Nero, pseud. By My Laugh Its Jewish. 1982 ed. (Illus.). 110p. Date not set. 12.50x (ISBN 0-85303-197-5, Pub. by Vallentine Mitchell England); pap. 6.50x (ISBN 0-85303-198-3). Biblio Dist.

Novak, William & Waldoks, Moshe. Big Book of Jewish Humor. LC 81-47234. (Illus.). 320p. 1981. pap. 14.95 (ISBN 0-06-090917-X, CN 917, PL). Har-Row.

Olsvanger, Immanuel, ed. Royte Pomerantsen or How to Laugh in Yiddish. 1979. pap. 6.95 (ISBN 0-8052-0099-1). Schocken.

Rosten, Leo. Joys of Yiddish. 1968. 19.95 (ISBN 0-07-053975-8). McGraw.

--Joys of Yiddish. 534p. 1970. pap. 4.95 (ISBN 0-671-47349-2). WSP.

Schwartz, David. Hanukkah Latkes & Rothschild's Millions. 1961. 14.95x (ISBN 0-8084-0036-3). New Coll U Pr.

Simon, Solomon. Wise Men of Helm. 1942. pap. 4.95 (ISBN 0-87441-125-4). Behrman.

Spalding, H. D., ed. Joys of Jewish Humor. LC 84-23822. (Illus.). 360p. 1985. pap. 8.95 (ISBN 0-8246-0257-9). Jonathan David.

Spalding, Henry D. Jewish Laffs. LC 82-9990. (Illus.). 96p. 1982. pap. 3.95 (ISBN 0-8246-0290-0). Jonathan David.

--A Treasure-Trove of American Jewish Humor. LC 75-40192. 429p. 1976. 16.95 (ISBN 0-8246-0204-8). Jonathan David.

Spalding, Henry D., ed. Encyclopedia of Jewish Humor. LC 68-21429. 1978. 16.95 (ISBN 0-8246-0021-5). Jonathan David.

Wigoder, J. Contemporary Jewry: Studies in Honor of Moshe Davis. 431p. 1984. text ed. 35.00x (ISBN 965-223-499-0, Pub. by Magnes Pr Israel). Humanities.

JEWISH WOMEN

see Women, Jewish

JEWISH YOUTH

see Youth, Jewish

JEWS

see also Anglo-Israelism; Falashas; Patriarchs (Bible); Prophets; Sephardim; Youth, Jewish

Agus, Jacob B. Jewish Identity in an Age of Ideologies. LC 76-14230. 1978. 25.00 (ISBN 0-8044-5018-8). Ungar.

Anti-Gentilism: Jews As Anti-Gentiles. 1984. lib. bdg. 79.95 (ISBN 0-87700-596-6). Revisionist Pr.

Belloc, Hilaire. The Jews. 1981. lib. bdg. 75.00 (ISBN 0-8490-3220-2). Gordon Pr.

--The Jews. 1986. pap. 6.50 (ISBN 0-317-53001-1). Noontide.

Burton, Richard F. The Jew, the Gypsy & el Islam. 1974. Repr. of 1898 ed. 6.00 (ISBN 0-913022-11-X). Angriff Pr.

Cohen, Arthur A. The Natural & the Supernatural Jew: An Historical and Theological Introduction. LC 79-13038. 1979. pap. text ed. 6.95x (ISBN 0-87441-291-9). Behrman.

Cohen, Bernard L. Jews Among the Nations. LC 77-79171. 338p. 1978. 10.95 (ISBN 0-8022-2209-9). Philos Lib.

Cohen, Michael J. Churchill & the Jews. (Illus). 408p. 1985. 25.00x (ISBN 0-7146-3254-6, F Cass Co). Biblio Dist.

Cohen, P. S., ed. Jewish Radicals & Radical Jews. LC 80-41227. 1981. 53.00 (ISBN 0-12-178780-X). Acad Pr.

Cohen, Steven M., et al, eds. Perspectives in Jewish Population Research. LC 84-50660. (Replica Edition). 275p. 1984. 22.50x (ISBN 0-86531-853-0). Westview.

Dalven, Rachel. The Jews of Jannina. 1986. write for info. (ISBN 0-930685-02-4). Cadmus Press.

Dashefsky, Arnold, ed. Contemporary Jewry, Vol. 7. 160p. 1986. 19.95x (ISBN 0-87855-979-5). Transaction Bks.

Davis, Moshe, ed. World Jewry & the State of Israel. LC 77-72730. (Indivual Publications Ser.). 1977. lib. bdg. 14.00x (ISBN 0-405-10305-0). Ayer Co Pubs.

Feldman, Emanuel, ed. The Biblical Echo: Reflection on Bible, Jews & Judaism. 1986. text ed. 17.50x (ISBN 0-88125-104-6). Ktav.

Feuerlight, M. M. Where the Jews Fail. 1984. lib. bdg. 79.95 (ISBN 0-87700-569-9). Revisionist Pr.

Fishman, Isidore. Remember the Days of Old. LC 79-100058. 1969. 4.95 (ISBN 0-87677-000-6). Hartmore.

Ford, Henry. The International Jew. 59.95 (ISBN 0-8490-0418-7). Gordon Pr.

--The International Jew, 4 vols. 1984. lib. bdg. 500.95 (ISBN 0-87700-586-9). Revisionist Pr.

Frieman, Donald G. Milestones in the Life of a Jew. LC 65-15710. 1980. pap. 3.95 (ISBN 0-8197-0002-9). Bloch.

Jacobs, Sidney J. & Jacobs, Betty J. Clues about Jews for People Who Aren't. LC 85-90337. 128p. (Orig.). 1985. pap. 8.95 (ISBN 0-933647-00-X). Jacobs Ladder Pubns.

Jacoby, Hilla & Jacoby, Max. The Jews: God's People. (Illus.). 224p. 1984. 49.95 (ISBN 0-310-42430-5, 18369). Zondervan.

The Jewish Problem as Dealt with by the Popes. 1982. lib. bdg. 59.95 (ISBN 0-87700-344-0). Revisionist Pr.

Kabakoff, Jacob, ed. Jewish Book Annual, Vol. 39. 1981. 15.00 (ISBN 0-914820-34-6). JWB.

Kac, Arthur W. Spiritual Dilemma of the Jewish People. 5.95 (ISBN 0-8010-5456-7). Baker Bk.

Katz, Jacob. Exclusiveness & Tolerance: Studies in Jewish-Gentile Relations in Medieval & Modern Times. LC 80-12181. (Scripta Judaica: No. III). xv, 200p. 1980. Repr. of 1961 ed. lib. bdg. 24.75x (ISBN 0-313-22387-4, KAEX). Greenwood.

Keech, L. Is There a Difference Between a Khazar Jew & a Palestinian Jew? 1982. lib. bdg. 59.95 (ISBN 0-87700-335-1). Revisionist Pr.

Kertzer, Morris N. What Is a Jew. rev. ed. LC 73-77280. 217p. 1973. Repr. of 1953 ed. 8.95x (ISBN 0-8197-0299-4). Bloch.

--What Is a Jew? 4th ed. 1978. pap. 4.95 (ISBN 0-02-086350-0, Collier). Macmillan.

Kraines, Oscar. The Impossible Dilemma: Who Is a Jew in the State of Israel? 1976. 8.95x (ISBN 0-8197-0392-3). Bloch.

Kushner, Harold. Commanded to Live. LC 73-91738. 1973. 10.95x (ISBN 0-87677-154-1). Hartmore.

Leese, A. The Jewish War of Survival. 1982. lib. bdg. 59.95 (ISBN 0-87700-347-5). Revisionist Pr.

Levine, Naomi & Hochbaum, Martin, eds. Poor Jews: An American Awakening. LC 73-85097. 206p. 1974. 19.95 (ISBN 0-87855-073-9); pap. 8.95x (ISBN 0-87855-570-6). Transaction Bks.

Lieberman, Saul & Hyman, Arthur, eds. Salo Wittmayer Baron Jubilee Volume: On the Occasion of His Eightieth Birthday, 3 vols. new ed. LC 74-82633. 1533p. 1975. 112.00x set (ISBN 0-685-51945-7); Vol. 1. (ISBN 0-231-03911-5); Vol. 2. (ISBN 0-231-03912-3); Vol. 3. (ISBN 0-231-03913-1). Columbia U Pr.

Louw, Eric. The Jewish Problem in South Africa. 1982. lib. bdg. 59.95 (ISBN 0-87700-342-4). Revisionist Pr.

Lutzweiler, D. Who Are "The Jews" Today? 1984. lib. bdg. 79.95 (ISBN 0-87700-568-0). Revisionist Pr.

MacArthur, John F., Jr. Hebrews. 1983. 14.95 (ISBN 0-88469-155-1). BMH Bks.

Mandlebaum, Bernard. Live with Meaning. 1980. pap. 7.95 (ISBN 0-87677-182-7). Hartmore.

Nyburg, Sidney L. The Chosen People. Sarna, Jonathan D., ed. (Masterworks of Modern Jewish Writing Ser.). 382p. 1986. pap. 9.95 (ISBN 0-910129-47-9, Distr. by Schcken Books). Wiener Pub Inc.

Ornitz, Samuel. Alrightniks Row: The Making of a Professional Jew, Haunch, Paunch & Jowl. Gabriel, Milley, ed. LC 85-40730. (Masterworks of Modern Jewish Writing Ser.). 320p. 1986. 18.85 (ISBN 0-910129-49-5, Distribited by Schocken Books); pap. 9.95 (ISBN 0-910129-46-0). Wiener Pub Inc.

Pentz, Croft M. Expository Outlines on Hebrews. (Sermon Outline Ser.). pap. 1.95 (ISBN 0-8010-7045-7). Baker Bk.

Raphael, Chaim. Encounters with the Jewish People. LC 79-14424. 1979. pap. text ed. 6.95x (ISBN 0-87441-282-X). Behrman.

Raskas, Bernard S., ed. Living Thoughts. LC 76-22418. 1976. 12.50 (ISBN 0-87677-145-2). Hartmore.

Rohling, A. The Jew According to the Talmud. 1982. lib. bdg. 69.95 (ISBN 0-87700-361-0). Revisionist Pr.

Samuel, Maurice. Gentleman & the Jew. LC 77-6666. pap. 5.95x (ISBN 0-87441-264-1). Behrman.

Sanning, Walter N. The Dissolution of Eastern European Jewry. (Illus.). 239p. 1986. pap. 8.00 (ISBN 0-317-53010-0). Noontide.

Seltzer, Sandford. Jews & Non-Jews Falling in Love. 1976. 4.00 (ISBN 0-8074-0098-X, 164050). UAHC.

Shulman, Avi. Time Is Life. (Dynamics of Personal Achievement Ser.). 96p. (Orig.). 1985. pap. 4.95 (ISBN 0-87306-927-7). Feldheim.

Silberschlag, Eisig, compiled by. An Exhibition of Judaica & Hebraica. (Illus.). 26p. 1973. pap. 3.50 (ISBN 0-87959-034-3). U of Tex H Ransom Ctr.

Silverman, Hillel E. From Week to Week. LC 74-16211. 1975. 10.95x (ISBN 0-87677-156-8). Hartmore.

Strassfeld, Michael, et alcompiled by. The Jewish Catalog: A Do-It Yourself Kit. LC 73-11759. (Illus.). 1973. pap. 8.95 (ISBN 0-8276-0042-9, 338). Jewish Pubns.

Strassfeld, Sharon & Strassfeld, Michael, eds. Third Jewish Catalog: Creating Community. LC 80-19818. (Illus.). 416p. 1980. 9.95 (ISBN 0-8276-0183-2, 466). Jewish Pubns.

Szajkowski, Soza. Jews in the French Foreign Legion. 25.00x (ISBN 0-87068-285-7). Ktav.

Valensi, Lucette & Udovitch, Abraham L. The Last Arab Jews: The Communities of Jerba. (Social Orders: A Series of Monographs & Tracts). 180p. 1984. 36.00 (ISBN 3-7186-0135-4). Harwood Academic.

Vermes, Geza & Neusner, Jacob, eds. Essays in Honour of Yigael Yadin. (Publications of the Oxford Centre for Postgraduate Hebrew Studies: Vol. 6). (Illus.). 618p. 1983. text ed. 45.00x (ISBN 0-86598-102-7). Allanheld.

Von Verschuer, Otmar. Racial Biology of the Jews. (Illus.). 1984. lib. bdg. 79.95 (ISBN 0-87700-560-5). Revisionist Pr.

--Racial Biology of the Jews. 1987. lib. bdg. 75.00 (ISBN 0-8490-3945-2). Gordon Pr.

JEWS–ADDRESSES, ESSAYS, LECTURES

American Jewish Committee. The Jewish Communities of Nazi-Occupied Europe. 400p. 1982. Repr. of 1944 ed. 42.50x (ISBN 0-86527-337-5). Fertig.

Chiel, Arthur A., ed. Perspectives on Jews & Judaism: Essays in Honor of Wolfe Kelman. 25.00x (ISBN 0-87068-683-6). Ktav.

Dawidowicz, Lucy. The Jewish Presence: Essays on Identity & History. LC 78-6236. 308p. 1978. pap. 3.95 (ISBN 0-15-646221-4, Harv). HarBraceJ.

--The Jewish Presence: Essays on Identity & History. 13.75 (ISBN 0-8446-6217-8). Peter Smith.

Goldstein, Israel. Toward a Solution. facs. ed. LC 79-128248. (Essay Index Reprint Ser). 1940. 21.00 (ISBN 0-8369-1877-0). Ayer Co Pubs.

Gordon, A. D. Selected Essays. LC 73-2201. (The Jewish People; History, Religion, Literature Ser.). Repr. of 1938 ed. 25.50 (ISBN 0-405-05266-9). Ayer Co Pubs.

Herzog, Yaacov. A People That Dwells Alone. Louvish, Misha, ed. 282p. 1975. 10.95 (ISBN 0-88482-895-6, Sanhedrin Pr). Hebrew Pub.

Jewish Frontier (Periodical) Anthology, Nineteen Thirty-Four to Nineteen Forty-Four. facsimile ed. LC 76-167370. (Essay Index Reprint Ser). Repr. of 1945 ed. 31.00 (ISBN 0-8369-2459-2). Ayer Co Pubs.

Karpeles, Gustav. Jewish Literature & Other Essays. facsimile ed. LC 78-37159. (Essay Index Reprint Ser). Repr. of 1895 ed. 22.00 (ISBN 0-8369-2512-2). Ayer Co Pubs.

Malino, Frances & Albert, Phyllis C., eds. Essays in Modern Jewish History: A Tribute to Ben Halpern. LC 80-70585. 500p. 1981. 27.50 (ISBN 0-8386-3095-2). Fairleigh Dickinson.

Proctor, Samuel, et al, eds. Jews of the South: Selected Essays. LC 83-25060. viii, 131p. 1984. 12.95 (ISBN 0-86554-102-7, H94). Mercer Univ Pr.

Scholem, Gershom. Messianic Idea in Judaism & Other Essays on Jewish Spirituality. 376p. pap. 7.95 (ISBN 0-686-95141-7). ADL.

Wiesel, Elie. A Jew Today. Weisel, Marion, tr. from Fr. LC 79-11251. 1979. pap. 4.95 (ISBN 0-394-74057-2, Vin). Random.

JEWS–ANTIQUITIES

see also Ark of the Covenant; Bible–Antiquities; Dancing (In Religion, Folk-Lore, etc.); Priests, Jewish–Vestments; Tabernacle

Figueras, P. Decorated Jewish Ossuaries. (Documenta et Monumenta Orientis Antiqui Ser.: No. 20). (Illus.). 119p. 1983. text ed. 39.95x (ISBN 90-04-06579-2, Pub. by EJ Brill Holland). Humanities.

Goodenough, E. R. Jewish Symbols in the Greco-Roman Period, 13 vols. Incl. Vols. 1-3. Archeological Evidence from Palestine & the Diaspora. 1953; Vol. 4. The Problem of Method; Symbols from Jewish Cult. 1954; Vols. 5 & 6. Fish, Bread, & Wine, 2 vols. 1956; Vols. 7 & 8. Pagan Symbols in Judaism. 1958. o.p. (ISBN 0-691-09755-0); Vols. 9-11. Symbolism in the Dura Synagogue. 1964; Vol. 12. Summary & Conclusions. 1965. 34.00x (ISBN 0-691-09757-7); Vol. 13. General Index & Maps. 1969. (Bollingen Ser.). Princeton U Pr.

Hirsh, Ethel S. Jewish Buildings & Cemeteries Guide to Visual Resources: International Holdings in Israel, Vol. I. 75p. 1982. pap. 10.00 (ISBN 0-943376-17-3). Magnes Mus.

Josephus. Works of Josephus, 9 vols. Warmington, E. H., ed. Incl. Vol. 1. Life; Against Apion (ISBN 0-674-99205-9); Vols 2-3. Jewish War. Vol. 2, Bks 1-3. (ISBN 0-674-99223-7); Vol. 3, Bks. 4-7, Index To Vols. 2 & 3. (ISBN 0-674-99232-6); Vols 4-9. Antiquities. Vol. 4, Bks 1-4. (ISBN 0-674-99267-9); Vol. 5, Bks 5-8. (ISBN 0-674-99310-1); Vol. 6, Bks 9-11. (ISBN 0-674-99360-8); Vol. 7, Bks 12-14. (ISBN 0-674-99402-7); Vol. 8, Bks 15-17. (ISBN 0-674-99451-5); Vol. 9, Bks 18-20, General Index. (ISBN 0-674-99477-9). (Loeb Classical Library: No. 186, 203, 210, 242, 281, 326, 365, 410, 433). 13.95x ea. Harvard U Pr.

Josephus, Flavius. Complete Works of Josephus. Whiston, William, tr. LC 60-15405. 840p. (Orig.). 1974. 18.95 (ISBN 0-8254-2951-X); kivar 14.95 (ISBN 0-8254-2952-8). Kregel.

Krauss, Samuel. Talmudische Archaologie, 3 vols. Finley, Moses, ed. LC 79-4988. (Ancient Economic History). (Ger., Illus.). 1980. Repr. of 1912 ed. Set. lib. bdg. 172.00x (ISBN 0-405-12373-6); lib. bdg. 57.50x ea. Vol. 1 (ISBN 0-405-12374-4). Vol. 2 (ISBN 0-405-12375-2). Vol. 3 (ISBN 0-405-12376-0). Ayer Co Pubs.

Pritchard, James B. Archaeology & the Old Testament. LC 58-10053. pap. 69.80 (ISBN 0-317-08485-2, 2016011). Bks Demand UMI.

JEWS–APOLOGETICS

see Judaism–Apologetic Works

JEWS–BIBLIOGRAPHY

Atid Bibliography. pap. 5.00 (ISBN 0-686-96097-1). United Syn Bk.

Baron, Salo W. The Jewish Community, 3 vols. LC 74-97269. 1972. Repr. of 1942 ed. Set. lib. bdg. 53.50x (ISBN 0-8371-3274-6, BAJC). Greenwood.

Berlin, Charles. Studies in Jewish Bibliography, History & Literature: In Honor of I. Edward Kiev. 1971. 50.00x (ISBN 0-87068-143-5). Ktav.

Bloch, ed. Journal of Jewish Bibliography, 4 vols. Set. 35.00 (ISBN 0-685-48593-5). Feldheim.

Cutter, Charles & Oppenheim, Micha F. Jewish Reference Sources: A Select, Annotated Bibliographic Guide. LC 82-15434. (Reference Library of Social Science: Vol. 126). 180p. 1982. lib. bdg. 24.00 (ISBN 0-8240-9347-X). Garland Pub.

Eppler, Elizabeth E., ed. International Bibliography of Jewish Affairs 1966-1967: A Select List of Books & Articles Published in the Diaspora. LC 74-84654. 365p. 1976. 35.00x (ISBN 0-8419-0177-5). Holmes & Meier.

Gar, Josef. Biblyografye Fun Artiklen Vegn Khurbn un Gvure. Incl. Vol. 1. LC 67-2416. (Yad Vashem-Yivo Joint Documentary Projects Bibliographical Ser.: No.). 306p. 1966. 10.00 (ISBN 0-914512-22-6); Vol. 2. (Yad Vashem-Yivo Joint Documentary Projects Bibliographical Ser.: No. 10). 338p. 1969. 15.00 (ISBN 0-914512-10-2). Yivo Inst.

Lyman, Darryl. Great Jews in Music. 500p. 1986. 24.95 (ISBN 0-8246-0315-X). Jonathan David.

New York Public Library, Research Libraries. Dictionary Catalog of Jewish Collection, 14 Vols. 1960. Set. 1240.00 (ISBN 0-8161-0409-3, Pub. by Hall Library). G K Hall.

--Dictionary Catalog of the Jewish Collection, First Supplement, 8 vols. 5424p. 1975. Set. lib. bdg. 875.00 (ISBN 0-8161-0773-4, Hall Library). G K Hall.

Schweinfurth, Georg. Studies in Jewish Bibliography & Related Subjects in Memory of Abraham Solomon Freidus (1867-1923) 814p. 1929. Repr. text ed. 124.20x (ISBN 0-576-80130-5, Pub. by Gregg Intl Pubs England). Gregg Intl.

Stuhlman, Daniel D. Library of Congress Headings for Judaica. LC 82-73398. (Orig.). 1983. pap. 5.00 (ISBN 0-934402-13-2); pap. 1.50 (ISBN 0-934402-15-9). BYLS Pr.

Yivo Biblyografye 1942-1950: Bibliography of the Publications of the Yiddish Scientific Institute, Vol. 2. LC 47-36672. (Yivo Institute for Jewish Research, Organizatsye Fun der Yidisher Visnshaft: No. 38). (Yiddish.). 158p. 1955. 5.00 (ISBN 0-914512-30-7). Yivo Inst.

JEWS–BIOGRAPHY

see also Rabbis; Women, Jewish;
also Jews in Germany; Jews in the United States and similar headings

Alkow, Jacob. In Many Worlds. LC 84-52110. (Illus.). 260p. 1985. pap. 13.95 (ISBN 0-88400-111-3). Shengold.

Arad, Yitzhak. The Partisan: From the Valley of Death to Mount Zion. LC 78-71299. 1979. 16.95 (ISBN 0-8052-5011-5, Pub. by Holocaust Library); pap. 10.95 (ISBN 0-8052-5010-7, Pub. by Holocaust Library). Schocken.

Araten, Rachel S. Michalina, Daughter of Israel: True Story of A Jewish Girl Abducted by the Catholic Church. 1986. 12.95 (ISBN 0-87306-412-7). Feldheim.

Axelrad, Albert S. Meditations of a Maverick Rabbi. Whitfield, Stephen, ed. 256p. (Orig.). 1985. pap. 8.95 (ISBN 0-940646-12-9). Rossel Bks.

Bardin, Shlomo, ed. Self-Fulfillment Through Zionism: A Study in Jewish Adjustment. LC 70-142605. (Biography Index Reprint Ser). Repr. of 1943 ed. 17.00 (ISBN 0-8369-8076-X). Ayer Co Pubs.

Ben, I., ed. Who's Who in Israel & Jewish Personalities from All over the World, 1985-86. 20th ed. (Who's Who in Israel Ser.). 1985. 100.00x (ISBN 0-318-18965-8). Heinman.

Berger, Elmer. Memoirs of an Anti-Zionist Jew. 159p. 1978. 4.00 (ISBN 0-88728-127-3). Inst Palestine.

Best of Olomeinu Back Cover Stories: Series II - Events in the Lives of Torah Personalities. 2.75 (ISBN 0-914131-04-4, D31). Torah Umesorah.

Biale, David. Gershom Scholem: Kabbalah & Counter-History. 2nd ed. 240p. 1982. pap. text ed. 7.95x (ISBN 0-674-36332-9). Harvard U Pr.

Bokser, Ben Zion, tr. Abraham Isaac Kook: The Lights of Penitance, Lights of Holiness. the Moral Principles. Essays, Letters & Poems. LC 78-70465. (Classics of Western Spirituality Ser.). 448p. 1978. 13.95 (ISBN 0-8091-0278-1); pap. 10.95 (ISBN 0-8091-2159-X). Paulist Pr.

Boxer, Tim. The Jewish Celebrities Hall of Fame. 1986. pap. 7.95 (ISBN 0-318-21398-2). Shapolsky Pubs.

Brin, Herb. ICH Bin Ein Jude. LC 81-15256. 146p. 1983. 9.95 (ISBN 0-8246-0275-7). Jonathan David.

Burnshaw, Stanley. My Friend, My Father. (Galaxy Books). 160p. 1986. pap. 7.95 (ISBN 0-19-503723-5). Oxford U Pr.

Dresner, Samuel H. Portraits of a Hasidic Master: Levi Yitzhak of Berditchev. 1986. pap. 8.95 (ISBN 0-933503-59-8). Shapolsky Pubs.

Drucker, Malka. Eliezer Ben-Yehuda: The Father of Modern Hebrew. LC 86-15213. (Jewish Biography Ser.). (Illus.). 128p. 1987. 13.95 (ISBN 0-525-67184-6, 01354-410). Lodestar Bks.

Eccles, Robert S. Erwin Ramsdell Goodenough: A Personal Pilgrimage. (SBL-Biblical Scholarship in North America). 1985. 22.95 (ISBN 0-89130-907-1, 01-11-11); pap. 16.95 (ISBN 0-89130-908-X). Scholars Pr GA.

Fierman, Floyd S. Guts & Ruts: The Jewish Pioneer on the Trail in the American Southwest. (Illus.). 1985. 20.00 (ISBN 0-88125-061-9). Ktav.

Friedling, Sheila, ed. The Pit & the Trap: Leyb Rochman. Kohn, Moshe, tr. (Yiddish., Illus.). 288p. (Orig.). 1983. 16.95 (ISBN 0-8052-5044-1); pap. 10.95 (ISBN 0-8052-5045-X). Holocaust Pubns.

Geiger, Abraham. Salomo Gabirol und seine Dichtungen. Katz, Steven, ed. LC 79-7130. (Jewish Philosophy, Mysticism & History of Ideas Ser.). 1980. Repr. of 1867 ed. lib. bdg. 14.00x (ISBN 0-405-12254-3). Ayer Co Pubs.

Gilmovsky, Norman. My Life, My Destiny. LC 82-46083. (Illus.). 320p. 1984. 22.50 (ISBN 0-317-02674-7, Cornwall Bks). Assoc Univ Prs.

Golan, Matti. Shimon Peres: A Biography. Friedman, Ina, tr. LC 82-7354. (Hebrew., Illus.). 275p. 1982. 25.00 (ISBN 0-312-71736-9). St Martin.

Goldstein, Israel. My World as a Jew, Vol. 1. LC 82-42721. (Illus.). 352p. 1984. 27.50 (ISBN 0-8453-4765-9, Cornwall Bks). Assoc Univ Prs.

--My World as a Jew, Vol. 2. LC 82-42621. (Illus.). 416p. 1984. 27.50 (ISBN 0-8453-4780-2, Cornwall Bks). Assoc Univ Prs.

Greenberg, Marian. The Down Side of Up. LC 86-80657. (Illus.). 264p. 1986. pap. 8.95 (ISBN 0-941404-40-4). Falcon Pr AZ.

Handler, Andrew. Dori: The Life & Times of Theodor Herzl in Budapest, 1860-1878. LC 82-8509. (Judaic Studies). (Illus.). 176p. 1983. text ed. 16.95 (ISBN 0-8173-0125-9). U of Ala Pr.

Hilberg, Raul & Staron, Stanislaw, eds. The Warsaw Diary of Adam Czerniakow: Prelude to Doom. 480p. Repr. 14.00 (ISBN 0-686-95101-8). ADL.

Hillesum, Etty. An Interrupted Life: The Diaries of Etty Hillesum 1941-1943. Pomerans, Arno, tr. LC 83-47750. 226p. 1984. 13.45 (ISBN 0-394-53217-1). Pantheon.

Inger, Judith. Victory Dances: The Story of Fred Berk, a Modern Day Jewish Dancing Master. 225p. pap. 15.95 (ISBN 0-934682-11-9). Emmett.

Jung, Leo. Sages & Saints. (The Jewish Library: Vol. X). 1987. pap. 20.00. Ktav.

Kalderon, Albert E. Abraham Galante: A Biography. (Illus.). 124p. 1983. 10.00 (ISBN 0-87203-111-X). Hermon.

Kazin, Alfred. New York Jew. LC 77-20359. 1978. 12.95 (ISBN 0-394-49567-5). Knopf.

Klein, Nancy I. Heritage of Faith: Two Pioneers of Judaism in America. 16.95 (ISBN 0-88125-119-4). Ktav.

Kohn, Nahum & Roiter, Howard. A Voice from the Forest: Memoirs of a Jewish Partisan. (Illus.). 288p. pap. 5.95 (ISBN 0-686-95099-2). ADL.

Koren, Nathan, ed. Jewish Physicians: A Biographical Index. 275p. 1973. 25.00 (ISBN 0-87855-184-0). Transaction Bks.

Landman, Leo. Rabbi Joseph H. Lookstein Memorial Volume. 1979. 35.00x (ISBN 0-87068-705-0). Ktav.

Levinger, Elma E. Great Jews Since Bible Times. (Illus.). 2.50x (ISBN 0-87441-053-3). Behrman.

MacPherson, Malcolm C. The Blood of His Servants: The True Story of One Man's Search for His Family's Friend & Executioner. LC 83-40089. (Illus.). 310p. 1984. 16.95 (ISBN 0-8129-1098-2). Times Bks.

Marcus, Jacob R. Israel Jacobson: The Founder of the Reform Movement in Judaism. 12.50x (ISBN 0-87820-000-2, Pub. by Hebrew Union). Ktav.

Markell, Jan. Gone the Golden Dream. LC 79-16718. 176p. 1979. pap. 4.95 (ISBN 0-87123-049-6, 210049). Bethany Hse.

Marx, Alexander. Essays in Jewish Biography. (Brown Classics in Judaica Ser.). 322p. 1986. pap. text ed. 14.25 (ISBN 0-8191-5022-3). U Pr of Amer.

Mechoulan, Henry & Nahon, Gerard, eds. Menasseh ben Israel: The Hope of Israel. (Litman Library of Jewish Civilzation). (Illus.). 224p. 37.00 (ISBN 0-19-710054-6). Oxford U Pr.

Patai, Raphael. Nahum Goldmann: His Missions to the Gentiles. LC 85-24518. (Judaic Studies Ser.). (Illus.). 345p. 1987. 29.95 (ISBN 0-8173-0294-8). U of Ala Pr.

Raz, Simcha. A Tzaddik in Our Time. Wengrow, Charles, tr. from Hebrew. (Illus.). 1976. 13.95 (ISBN 0-87306-130-6). Feldheim.

Reschke, Meier M. Hugo Zuckermann: A Great Jewish Leader. LC 84-90055. 45p. 1985. 7.95 (ISBN 0-533-06136-9). Vantage.

Robinson, Ira, ed. Cyrus Adler: Selected Letters. 1000p. 1985. 2 vols. boxed 50.00 (ISBN 0-8276-0224-3). Jewish Pubns.

Rosenbaum, S. E. A Voyage to America in Eighteen Forty-Seven: The Diary of a Bohemian Jew on His Voyage from Hamburg to New York in 1847. (Studies in Judaica & the Holocaust: No. 3). 60p. 1987. lib. bdg. 19.95x (ISBN 0-89370-371-0); pap. text ed. 9.95x (ISBN 0-89370-471-7). Borgo Pr.

Rossini, Lillian M. Rabbi Letters, No. 1. (Illus.). 32p. 1986. 5.95 (ISBN 0-89962-506-1). Todd & Honeywell.

Roston, Scott. Nightmare in Israel. 1987. 14.95 (ISBN 0-533-07157-7). Vantage.

Roth, Cecil. Dona Gracia of the House of Nasi. LC 77-92984. 208p. 1978. pap. 4.95 (ISBN 0-8276-0099-2, 415). Jewish Pubns.

Rothman, Frances. My Father, Edward Bransten: His Life & Letters. (Illus.). 109p. 1983. pap. 5.00 (ISBN 0-943376-18-1). Magnes Mus.

Rubenstein, Richard L. Power Struggle. LC 86-16000. 214p. 1986. pap. text ed. 12.75 (ISBN 0-8191-5428-8). U Pr of Amer.

Rubinstein, Leon. The First Swallows. LC 83-45138. (Illus.). 216p. 1986. 14.50 (ISBN 0-8453-4758-6, Cornwall Bks). Assoc Univ Prs.

Sanford, John. The Waters of Darkness: Scenes from the Life of an American Jew, Vol. 2. 294p. (Orig.). 1986. 20.00 (ISBN 0-87685-672-5); signed cloth 30.00 (ISBN 0-87685-673-3); pap. 12.50 (ISBN 0-87685-671-7). Black Sparrow.

Schulzinger, Morris S. The Tale of a Litvak. LC 84-7693. (Illus.). 379p. 1985. 24.95 (ISBN 0-8022-2454-7). Philos Lib.

Segal, Yocheved. Our Sages Showed the Way, Vol. 2. Falk, Esther, tr. from Hebrew. (Jewish Youth Classics Ser.). (Illus.). 192p. 1982. text ed. 9.95 (ISBN 0-87306-200-0). Feldheim.

Segre, Dan V. Memoirs of a Fortunate Jew: An Italian Story. LC 86-17495. 274p. 1987. 16.95 (ISBN 0-917561-32-5). Adler & Adler.

Shaanan, Alexander. Dear God, Is Justice Still With You? (Illus.). 144p. 1983. 8.95 (ISBN 0-89962-306-9). Todd & Honeywell.

Shainberg, Maurice. Breaking from the K. G. B. 1986. 15.95 (ISBN 0-933503-54-7). Shapolsky Pubs.

Shamir, Ruth. All Our Vows. LC 82-61795. 1983. 11.95 (ISBN 0-88400-090-7). Shengold.

Sherman, Shlomoh. Escape from Jesus: One Man's Search for a Meaningful Judaism. 1983. 14.95 (ISBN 0-915474-03-4). Effective Learn.

Slater, Robert. Great Jews in Sports. LC 82-19953. (Illus.). 304p. 1983. 14.95 (ISBN 0-8246-0285-4). Jonathan David.

Spiegelman, J. Marvin & Jacobson, Abraham, eds. A Modern Jew in Search of a Soul. 320p. 1986. pap. 12.95 (ISBN 0-941404-33-1). Falcon Pr AZ.

Strauss, Herbert A. & Rogrbaugh, Dennis, eds. Jewish Immigrants of the Nazi Period in the U. S. A. An Oral History Record. (Jewish Immigrants of the Nazi Period in the U. S. A. Ser.: Vol. 5). 308p. 1986. lib. bdg. 60.00 (ISBN 3-598-08010-7). K G Saur.

Sutton, Joseph A. D. Magic Carpet: Aleppo in Flatbush: The Story of a Unique Ethnic Jewish Community. 3rd ed. LC 79-65516. (Illus.). 336p. 1986. text ed. 19.95x (ISBN 0-686-27080-0). Thayer-Jacoby.

Tauber, Rhea. Rhea's World. LC 86-16989. (Paperback Ser.). 217p. 1987. pap. 7.95 (ISBN 0-8022-2499-7). Philos Lib.

Temchin, Michael. The Witch Doctor: Memoirs of a Partisan. (Illus.). 192p. (Orig.). 1983. 16.95 (ISBN 0-8052-5046-8); pap. 10.95 (ISBN 0-8052-5047-6). Holocaust Pubns.

Ury, Zalman F. The Story of Rabbi Yisroel Salanter. 3.75 (ISBN 0-914131-60-5, D54). Torah Umesorah.

Weissmann Klein, Gerda. A Passion for Sharing: The Life of Edith Rosenwald Stern. (Illus.). 448p. 1984. 18.95 (ISBN 0-940646-15-3). Rossel Bks.

Whitney, George G. Born to Survive, Nineteen Thirty-Six to Nineteen Forty-Six. (Illus.). 200p. 1982. pap. 12.95 (ISBN 0-916224-72-4). Banyan Bks.

JEWS-CABALA

see Cabala

JEWS-CHARITIES

Raphael, Marc L. Understanding American Jewish Philanthropy. 20.00x (ISBN 0-87068-689-5). Ktav.

JEWS-CHILDREN

see Jewish Children

JEWS-CHOSEN PEOPLE

see Jews-Election, Doctrine of

JEWS-CIVILIZATION

Alon, Gedaliah. The Jews in Their Land in the Talmudic Age, Vol. 1. Gershon, Levi, tr. from Hebrew. 324p. 1980. text ed. 32.50x (ISBN 965-223-352-8, Pub. by Magnes Pr Israel). Humanities.

Alon, Gedalyahu. Jews, Judaism & the Classical World. Abrahams, Israel, tr. from Hebrew. 499p. 1977. text ed. 38.50x (Pub. by Magnes Pr Israel). Humanities.

Baron, Salo W. A Social & Religious History of the Jews, 18 vols. 2nd, rev. & enl. ed. Incl. Vol. 1. Ancient Times to the Beginning of the Christian Era. 1952 (ISBN 0-231-08838-8); Vol. 2. Ancient Times: Christian Era: the First Five Centuries. 1952 (ISBN 0-231-08839-6); Vol. 3. High Middle Ages: Heirs of Rome & Persia. 1957 (ISBN 0-231-08840-X); Vol. 4. High Middle Ages: Meeting of the East & West. 1957 (ISBN 0-231-08841-8); Vol. 5. High Middle Ages: Religious Controls & Dissensions. 1957 (ISBN 0-231-08842-6); Vol. 6. High Middle Ages: Laws, Homilies & the Bible. 1958 (ISBN 0-231-08843-4); Vol. 7. High Middle Ages: Hebrew Language & Letters. 1958 (ISBN 0-231-08844-2); Vol. 8. High Middle Ages: Philosophy & Science. 1958 (ISBN 0-231-08845-0); Vol. 9. Late Middle Ages & Era of European Expansion, 1200-1650: Under Church & Empire. 1965 (ISBN 0-231-08846-9); Vol. 10. Late Middle Ages & Era of European Expansion, 1200-1650: On the Empire's Periphery. 1965 (ISBN 0-231-08847-7); Vol. 11. Late Middle Ages & Era of European Expansion, 1200-1650: Citizen or Alien Conjurer. 1967 (ISBN 0-231-08848-5); Vol. 12. Late Middle Ages & Era of European Expansion, 1200-1650: Economic Catalyst. 1967 (ISBN 0-231-08849-3); Vol. 13. Late Middle Ages & Era of European Expansion, 1200-1650: Inquisition, Renaissance & Reformation. 1969 (ISBN 0-231-08850-7); Vol. 14. Late Middle Ages & Era of European Expansion, 1200-1650: Catholic Restoration & Wars of Religion. 1969 (ISBN 0-231-08851-5); Vol. 15. Late Middle Ages & Era of European Expansion, 1200-1650: Resettlement & Exploration. 1973 (ISBN 0-231-08852-3); Index. 32.00x (ISBN 0-231-08877-9). LC 52-404. 45.00x ea. Columbia U Pr.

Blau, Joseph L., ed. Essays on Jewish Life & Thought. LC 57-11757. 458p. 1959. 31.00x (ISBN 0-231-02171-2). Columbia U Pr.

Chouraqui, Andre. The People & the Faith of the Bible. Gugli, William V., tr. LC 74-21237. 224p. 1975. 15.00x (ISBN 0-87023-172-3). U of Mass Pr.

Contemporary Jewish Civilization. 14.50 (ISBN 0-8160-1473-6). Facts on File.

Davis, Nancy & Levitt, Joy. The Guide to Everything Jewish in New York. LC 86-10927. 334p. 1986. pap. 14.95 (ISBN 0-915361-47-7, Dist. by Watts). Adama Pubs Inc.

Dawidowicz, L. S., et al, eds. For Max Weinreich on His Seventieth Birthday: Studies in Jewish Language, Literature & Society. 1964. 66.00x (ISBN 0-686-22430-2). Mouton.

Eban, Abba. Heritage: Civilization & the Jews. (Illus.). 352p. 1984. 32.95 (ISBN 0-671-44103-5). Summit Bks.

Goldberg, M. Hirsch. The Jewish You Wouldn't Believe It Book. (Illus.). 252p. 1986. pap. 7.95 (ISBN 0-933503-51-2). Shapolsky Pubs.

Goldin, Judah, ed. & The Jewish Expression. LC 75-27866. 512p. 1976. pap. 10.95 (ISBN 0-300-01975-0). Yale U Pr.

Hallo, William & Ruderman, David. Heritage: Civilization & the Jews; a Study Guide. 302p. 1984. 34.95 (ISBN 0-03-000484-5); pap. 12.95 (ISBN 0-03-000483-7). Praeger.

Hallo, William & Ruderman, David, eds. Heritage: Civilization & the Jews; a Source Reader. 332p. 1984. 34.95 (ISBN 0-03-000479-9); pap. 13.95 (ISBN 0-03-000482-9). Praeger.

Halpern, Joel M., ed. Bibliography of Judaic Cultures, Nos. 749-750. 1975. 8.00 (ISBN 0-686-20342-9). CPL Biblios.

Hartman, David, ed. Crisis & Leadership: Epistles of Maimonides. Halkin, Abraham, tr. from Hebrew. 292p. 1985. 15.95 (ISBN 0-8276-0238-3). Jewish Pubns.

Horowitz, George. The Spirit of Jewish Law. LC 53-7535. 1979. Repr. of 1953 ed. text ed. 40.00x (ISBN 0-87632-167-8). Bloch.

Hyman, Frieda C. The Jewish Experience: Book I. 1975. 5.25x (ISBN 0-8381-0191-7). United Syn Bk.

International Center for University Teaching of Jewish Civilization Staff & Shimmoni, Gideon, eds. Contemporary Jewish Civilization. LC 85-40515. (Selected Course Outlines & Curriculum Resources Ser.). 250p. 1985. pap. text ed. 14.50x (ISBN 0-910129-28-2). Wiener Pub Inc.

International Center for University Teaching of Jewish Civilization Staff & Verbit, Mervin, eds. World Register of University Teaching of Jewish Civilization. LC 85-40514. (Selected Syllabi in University Teaching of Jewish Civilization Ser.). 250p. 1985. pap. text ed. 14.50x (ISBN 0-910129-30-4). Wiener Pub Inc.

Kent, Maxwell. A Comparative Analysis of the Italians & the Jews: The Two People Who Contributed the Most to the Civilization of Mankind with Strange & Unexpected Conclusions. (Illus.). 1977. 117.25 (ISBN 0-89266-056-2). Am Classical Coll Pr.

Koebner, Richard, ed. Studies in Classics & Jewish Hellenism. (Scripts Hierosolymitana Ser.: Vol. 1). pap. 39.00 (ISBN 0-317-28711-7, 2051594). Bks Demand UMI.

Lehrmann, Charles C. Jewish Influences on European Thought. Klin, George & Carpenter, Victor, trs. LC 72-3264. 323p. 1976. 27.50 (ISBN 0-8386-7908-0). Fairleigh Dickinson.

Litvin & Hoenig. Jewish Identity. 13.95 (ISBN 0-87306-096-2). Feldheim.

Montefiore, C. G. Ancient Jewish & Greek Consolation. LC 75-184052. 86p. 1973. text ed. 7.95 (ISBN 0-87677-045-6). Hartmore.

Patai, Raphael. The Jewish Mind. LC 76-58040. 1977. 14.95 (ISBN 0-684-14878-1, ScribT). Scribner.

Raphael, Chaim. Memoirs of a Special Case. rev. ed. LC 62-9548. 208p. 1985. 12.95 (ISBN 0-940646-16-1); pap. 7.95 (ISBN 0-940646-17-X). Rossel Bks.

--The Springs of Jewish Life. LC 82-70853. 1982. 16.50 (ISBN 0-465-08192-4). Basic.

Roth, Cecil. The Jewish Contribution to Civilizaton. 1978. pap. 5.95 (ISBN 0-85222-217-3, East & West Lib). Hebrew Pub.

Shiblak, Abbas. The Lure of Zion--the Case of the Iraqi Jews. 178p. 1986. 29.95 (ISBN 0-86356-121-7, Pub. by Al Saqi Bks UK); pap. 9.95 (ISBN 0-86356-033-4, Pub. by Al Saqi Bks UK). Humanities.

Steinberg, Milton. The Making of the Modern Jew. (Brown Classics in Judaica Ser.). 318p. 1987. pap. text ed. 14.50 (ISBN 0-8191-4492-4). U Pr of Amer.

Szarmach, Paul E., ed. Aspects of Jewish Culture in the Middle Ages: Papers from the Eighth Annual CEMERS Conference. 230p. 10.00 (ISBN 0-87395-165-4, Pub. by SUNY Pr). Medieval & Renaissance NY.

Twain, Mark. Concerning the Jews. LC 84-27665. 32p. (Orig.). 1985. lib. bdg. 12.90 (ISBN 0-89471-336-1); pap. 3.95 (ISBN 0-89471-335-3). Running Pr.

Van Den Haag, Ernest. The Jewish Mystique. LC 76-56974. 1977. pap. 6.95 (ISBN 0-8128-2189-0). Stein & Day.

Voegelin, Eric. Order & History, 4 vols. Incl. Vol. 1. Israel & Revelation. LC 56-11670. xxvi, 534p. 1956 (ISBN 0-8071-0818-9); Vol. 2. The World of the Polis. LC 57-11670. xvii, 390p. 1957 (ISBN 0-8071-0819-7); Vol. 3. Plato & Aristotle. LC 57-11670. xviii, 384p. 1957 (ISBN 0-8071-0820-0); Vol. 4. The Ecumenic Age. LC 56-11670. 1974 (ISBN 0-8071-0081-1). 19.95 ea. La State U Pr.

Weinreich, Uriel. Yidish Launiversitah: Hebrew Edition of "College Yiddish". Bahat, S. & Goldwasser, M., trs. (Illus.). 1977. pap. text ed. write for info. (ISBN 0-914512-35-8). Yivo Inst.

World Register of University Studies in Jewish Civilization. 14.50 (ISBN 0-8160-1475-2). Facts on File.

JEWS-CONVERTS TO CHRISTIANITY

see Converts from Judaism

JEWS-DIASPORA

see also Israel and the Diaspora; Jews-Migrations

Auraham, Samuel & Kushner, Arlene. Treacherous Journey: My Escape from Ethiopia. 1986. 14.95 (ISBN 0-933503-46-6). Shapolsky Pubs.

Bendix, Reinhard. From Berlin to Berkeley: German-Jewish Identities. LC 85-8578. 320p. 1985. 29.95 (ISBN 0-88738-067-0). Transaction Bks.

Collins, John J. Between Athens & Jerusalem: Jewish Indentity in the Hellenistic Diaspora. 272p. 1983. 27.50x (ISBN 0-8245-0491-7). Crossroad NY.

Kochan, Lionel. The Jew & His History. (Scholars Press Reprints & Translations: No. 1). 1985. pap. 8.25 (ISBN 0-89130-821-0, 00 07 06). Scholars Pr GA.

Kushner, Arlene. Falasha No More: An Ethiopian Jewish Child Comes Home. (Illus.). 58p. 1986. 9.95 (ISBN 0-933503-43-1). Shapolsky Pubs.

Schmelz, U. O. Studies in Jewish Demography. 1983. 25.00x (ISBN 0-88125-013-9). Ktav.

JEWS-DICTIONARIES AND ENCYCLOPEDIAS

see also Judaism-Dictionaries

Ausubel, Nathan. Book of Jewish Knowledge. (Illus.). 1962. 23.95 (ISBN 0-517-09746-X). Crown.

Ben-Asher, Naomi & Leaf, Hayim, eds. Junior Jewish Encyclopedia. 10th, rev. ed. LC 84-51583. (Illus.). 1984. 19.95 (ISBN 0-88400-110-5). Shengold.

Bridger & Wolk. The New Jewish Encyclopedia. rev. ed. LC 76-15251. (Illus.). 542p. 1976. 14.95 (ISBN 0-87441-120-3). Behrman.

Markowitz, Endel. The Encyclopedia Yiddishanica. LC 79-89973. (Illus.). 450p. 1980. 19.95 (ISBN 0-933910-02-9); pap. write for info. (ISBN 0-933910-04-5). Haymark.

Roth, Cecil & Widoger, Geoffrey, eds. The Concise Jewish Encyclopedia. 576p. (Orig.). 1980. pap. 8.95 (ISBN 0-452-00526-4, F526, Mer). NAL.

Singer, I., ed. The Jewish Encyclopedia, 12 vols. 1976. Set. lib. bdg. 998.95 (ISBN 0-8490-2101-4). Gordon Pr.

Werblowsky, Zvi & Wigoder, Geoffrey, eds. The Encyclopedia of the Jewish Religion. LC 86-10932. (Illus.). 478p. 1986. 39.95 (ISBN 0-915361-53-1, Dist. by Watts). Adama Pubs Inc.

JEWS-DIETARY LAWS

Berman, Louis A. Vegetarianism & the Jewish Tradition. LC 81-11729. 120p. 1982. 10.00x (ISBN 0-87068-756-5); pap. 7.95. Ktav.

David, Suzy, ed. The Sephardic Kosher Kitchen. LC 84-8150. (Illus.). 228p. 1985. 14.95 (ISBN 0-8246-0303-6). Jonathan David.

Grossman, Bob. The New Chinese-Kosher Cookbook. rev. ed. LC 77-79248. (Illus.). 1978. 5.95 (ISBN 0-8397-6308-5); pap. 4.95 (ISBN 0-8397-6309-3). Eriksson.

Grunfeld. The Jewish Dietary Laws, 2 vols. 1973. Set. 32.95x (ISBN 0-900689-09-9). Bloch.

Grunfeld, Dayan I. The Jewish Dietary Laws, 2 vols. 246p. 1972. Vol. 1, 246 pgs. pap. 29.95 (ISBN 0-900689-10-2); Vol. 2, 285 pgs. pap. 32.95 slipcased (ISBN 0-900689-11-0). Soncino Pr.

Kahn, Ada P. Diabetes Control & the Kosher Diet. LC 84-51535. 180p. 1985. pap. 9.95x (ISBN 0-930121-00-7). Wordscope Inc.

Kemelman, Y. A Guide to the Jewish Dietary Laws. 3rd ed. 1971. pap. 2.50x (ISBN 0-685-40445-5); pap. 13.00 (ISBN 0-231-05147-6). Bloch.

Munk, Michael L. & Munk, Eli, eds. Shechita: Religious & Historical Research on the Method of Slaughter. (Illus.). 1976. 9.95 (ISBN 0-87306-992-7). Feldheim.

Simon, Bennet. Kosher Konnection: The Los Angeles Dining Guide to the Best of Kosher, Delis & Natural Foods. LC 79-67671. (Orig.). 1980. pap. 4.95 (ISBN 0-935618-00-7). Rossi Pubns.

Spear, Tziporah. Kosher Calories. 1985. 12.95 (ISBN 0-317-38550-X); pap. 9.95 (ISBN 0-317-38551-8). Mesorah Pubns.

JEWS-DIVORCE

see Divorce (Jewish Law)

JEWS-EDUCATION

see also Jewish Religious Education

Ben-Horin, Meir. Common Faith-Uncommon People: Essays in Reconstructionist Judaism. LC 71-80691. 245p. 1970. 7.50 (ISBN 0-935457-03-8). Reconstructionist Pr.

Brumberg, Stephan F. Going to America Going to School: The Jewish Immigrant Public School Encounter in Turn-of-the-Century New York City. LC 85-16791. 300p. 1986. 29.95 (ISBN 0-03-062574-2, C2030). Praeger.

Drazin, Nathan. History of Jewish Education from 515 B. C. E. to 220 C. E. 1979. 16.00 (ISBN 0-405-10598-3). Ayer Co Pubs.

Dushkin, Alexander M. Jewish Education: Selected Writings. 180p. 1980. text ed. 10.00x (ISBN 965-223-353-6, Pub. by Magnes Pr Israel). Humanities.

Heilman, Samuel. Inside the Jewish Schools: A Study of the Cultural Setting for Jewish Education. 50p. 1984. pap. 2.50 (ISBN 0-87495-057-0). Am Jewish Comm.

Kohn, Eugene. Good to Be a Jew. LC 59-13350. 180p. 1959. pap. 8.95 (ISBN 0-935457-23-2). Reconstructionist Pr.

Leviticus. Sefer Ha'hinnuch: The Book of Education, Vols. 2 & 3. 1985. 29.95 (ISBN 0-87306-145-4). Feldheim.

Oren, Dan A. Joining the Club: A History of Jews & Yale. LC 85-14252. (The Yale Scene, University Ser.: No. 4). 448p. 1986. 29.95x (ISBN 0-300-03330-3). Yale U Pr.

Peterson, James L. & Zill, Nicholas. American Jewish High School Students: A National Profile. LC 84-72249. vi, 32p. (Orig.). 1984. pap. 2.50 (ISBN 0-87495-065-1). Am Jewish Comm.

Schein, Jeffrey L. & Staub, Jacob J., eds. Creative Jewish Education. 256p. (Orig.). 1985. pap. 7.95 (ISBN 0-940646-33-1). Rossel Bks.

Sefer Hahinnuch, Vol. IV: Numbers & Part I. of Deuteronomy. (Hebrew & Eng.). 500p. 1987. 17.95 (ISBN 0-317-42725-3). Feldheim.

Shapiro, Alexander M., ed. Lilmod u-Lelamed: Studies in Jewish Education & Judaica in Honor of Louis Newman. 1984. 20.00x (ISBN 0-88125-038-4). Ktav.

Shuart, Adele K. Signs in Judaism: A Resource Book for the Jewish Deaf Community. 196p. 1986. pap. 16.95x (ISBN 0-8197-0505-5). Bloch.

Walsh, Vincent M. Teach My People. 104p. 1983. pap. 4.00 (ISBN 0-943374-04-9). Key of David.

JEWS-ELECTION, DOCTRINE OF

Douglas, C. H. The Land for the Chosen People Racket. 1982. lib. bdg. 55.00 (ISBN 0-87700-415-3). Revisionist Pr.

Malgo, Wim. Israel's God Does Not Lie. 4.95 (ISBN 0-937422-06-1). Midnight Call.

Roth, Samuel. Jews Must Live. 1980. lib. bdg. 69.95 (ISBN 0-8490-3204-0). Gordon Pr.

Sandmel, Samuel. The Several Israels. 1971. 12.50x. Ktav.

JEWS–ETHICS

see Ethics, Jewish

JEWS–EXODUS

see Exodus, the

JEWS–HISTORY

see also Chronology, Jewish

Abrahams, Israel & Buchler, Adolf. The Foundations of Jewish Life: Three Studies. LC 73-2197. (The Jewish People; History, Religion, Literature Ser.). 38.50 (ISBN 0-405-05263-4). Ayer Co Pubs.

Agus, Jacob B. The Evolution of Jewish Thought. LC 73-2185. (The Jewish People; History, Religion, Literature Ser.). Repr. of 1959 ed. 30.00 (ISBN 0-405-05251-0). Ayer Co Pubs.

Agus, Jacob B., et al, eds. The Jewish People: History, Religion, Literature, 41 bks. 1973. Set. 1106.50 (ISBN 0-405-05250-2). Ayer Co Pubs.

Ahimaaz Ben Paltiel. Chronicle of Ahimaaz. Salzman, Marcus, tr. LC 79-158233. (Columbia University Oriental Studies: No. 18). Repr. of 1924 ed. 15.75 (ISBN 0-404-50508-2). AMS Pr.

Alpher, Joseph, ed. Encyclopedia of Jewish History. (Illus.). 288p. 1986. 35.00x (ISBN 0-8160-1220-2). Facts on File.

--Encyclopedia of Jewish History: Events & Eras of the Jewish People. Amir, Haya, tr. LC 85-23941. (Illus.). 285p. 1985. 35.00. Facts on File.

Anderson, George K. The Legend of the Wandering Jew. LC 65-14290. (Brown University Bicentennial Publication Ser.). pap. 125.80 (ISBN 0-317-52056-3, 2027498). Bks Demand UMI.

Angel, Marc D., ed. Studies in Sephardic Culture: The David N. Barocas Memorial Volume. LC 79-92737. (Illus.). 190p. 1980. 15.00 (ISBN 0-87203-090-3). Hermon.

Ashtor, Eliyahu. The Jews of Moslem Spain, Vol. III. Klein, Aaron & Klein, Jenny M., trs. from Hebrew. 380p. 1985. 19.95 (ISBN 0-8276-0237-5). Jewish Pubns.

Ausubel, Nathan. Pictorial History of the Jewish People: From Biblical Times to Our Own Day Throughout the World. rev ed. (Illus.). 1984. 19.95 (ISBN 0-517-55283-3). Crown.

--Pictorial History of the Jewish People. (Illus.). 1953. 19.95 (ISBN 0-517-09757-5). Crown.

Bamberger, David. My People: Abba Eban's History of the Jews, Vol. II. (Illus.). 1979. pap. 6.95x (ISBN 0-87441-280-3); tchr's guide by Geoffrey Horn 12.50 (ISBN 0-87441-341-9). Behrman.

--My People: Abba Eban's History of the Jews, Vol. I. LC 77-10667. (Illus.). 1978. pap. text ed. 6.95x (ISBN 0-87441-263-3). Behrman.

Bammel, Ernst. Judaica. 330p. 1986. lib. bdg. 82.50x (ISBN 3-16-144971-1, Pub. by J C B Mohr BRD). Coronet Bks.

Baron, Salo W. A Social & Religious History of the Jews, 18 vols. 2nd, rev. & enl. ed. Incl. Vol. 1. Ancient Times to the Beginning of the Christian Era. 1952 (ISBN 0-231-08838-8); Vol. 2. Ancient Times: Christian Era: the First Five Centuries. 1952 (ISBN 0-231-08839-6); Vol. 3. High Middle Ages: Heirs of Rome & Persia. 1957 (ISBN 0-231-08840-X); Vol. 4. High Middle Ages: Meeting of the East & West. 1957 (ISBN 0-231-08841-8); Vol. 5. High Middle Ages: Religious Controls & Dissensions. 1957 (ISBN 0-231-08842-6); Vol. 6. High Middle Ages: Laws, Homilies & the Bible. 1958 (ISBN 0-231-08843-4); Vol. 7. High Middle Ages: Hebrew Language & Letters. 1958 (ISBN 0-231-08844-2); Vol. 8. High Middle Ages: Philosophy & Science. 1958 (ISBN 0-231-08845-0); Vol. 9. Late Middle Ages & Era of European Expansion, 1200-1650: Under Church & Empire. 1965 (ISBN 0-231-08846-9); Vol. 10. Late Middle Ages & Era of European Expansion, 1200-1650: On the Empire's Periphery. 1965 (ISBN 0-231-08847-7); Vol. 11. Late Middle Ages & Era of European Expansion, 1200-1650: Citizen or Alien Conjurer. 1967 (ISBN 0-231-08848-5); Vol. 12. Late Middle Ages & Era of European Expansion, 1200-1650: Economic Catalyst. 1967 (ISBN 0-231-08849-3); Vol. 13. Late Middle Ages & Era of European Expansion, 1200-1650: Inquisition, Renaissance & Reformation. 1969 (ISBN 0-231-08850-7); Vol. 14. Late Middle Ages & Era of European Expansion, 1200-1650: Catholic Restoration & Wars of Religion. 1969 (ISBN 0-231-08851-5); Vol. 15. Late Middle Ages & Era of European Expansion, 1200-1650: Resettlement & Exploration. 1973 (ISBN 0-231-08852-3); Index. 32.00x (ISBN 0-231-08877-9). LC 52-404. 45.00x ea. Columbia U Pr.

Bauer, Yehuda. The Jewish Emergence from Powerlessness. LC 78-25830. pap. 25.80 (ISBN 0-317-26941-0, 2023592). Bks Demand UMI.

Beck, Norman A. Mature Christianity: The Recognition & Repudiation of the Anti-Jewish Polemic of the New Testament. LC 83-51047. (Illus.). 328p. 1985. 19.50 (ISBN 0-941664-03-1). Assoc Univ Prs.

Ben-Sasson, Haim H., ed. A History of the Jewish People. (Illus.). 1108p. 1985. pap. 18.95 (ISBN 0-674-39731-2). Harvard U Pr.

Ben-Sasson, Haim H., et al. History of the Jewish People. (Illus.). 1040p. 1976. 60.00 (ISBN 0-674-39730-4). Harvard U Pr.

Biale, David. Power & Powerlessness in Jewish History. 1986. 18.95 (ISBN 0-8052-4015-2). Schocken.

Bialik, Hayyim N. And It Came to Pass. 281p. 1938. 6.95 (ISBN 0-88482-887-5). Hebrew Pub.

Biberfeld, Philip. Universal Jewish History, 4 vols. Vol. 1. 8.95 (ISBN 0-87306-052-0, Spero Foundation); Vol. 2. 8.95 (ISBN 0-87306-053-9); Vol. 3. 10.95 (ISBN 0-87306-054-7); Set. cancelled (ISBN 0-87306-051-2). Feldheim.

Birmingham, Stephen. The Rest of Us: The Rise of America's Eastern European Jews. 432p. 1985. pap. 4.50 (ISBN 0-425-08074-9). Berkley Pub.

Bloch, Abraham P. The Biblical & Historical Backround of Jewish Customs & Ceremonies. 1979. 20.00x (ISBN 0-87068-658-5); pap. 11.95. Ktav.

Booker, Richard. Blow the Trumpet in Zion. LC 85-62152. 208p. (Orig.). 1985. pap. 5.95 (ISBN 0-932081-02-9). Victory Hse.

Brooten, Bernadette J. Women Leaders in the Ancient Synagogue: Inscriptional Evidence & Background Issues. LC 82-10658. (Brown Judaic Studies). 292p. 1982. pap. 20.00 (ISBN 0-89130-587-4, 14 00 36). Scholars Pr GA.

Cohn, Emil B. This Immortal People: A Short History of the Jewish People. LC 84-62563. 180p. (Orig.). 1985. pap. 5.95 (ISBN 0-8091-2693-1). Paulist Pr.

Dan, Joseph. Gershom Scholem & the Mystical Dimension of Jewish History. 350p. 1987. 50.00x (ISBN 0-8147-1779-9). NYU Pr.

Davis, Myer D. Shetaroth, Hebrew Deeds of English Jews Before 1290. 410p. 1888. text ed. 74.52x (ISBN 0-576-80111-9, Pub. by Gregg Intl Pubs England). Gregg Intl.

Dawidowicz, Lucy. The Jewish Presence: Essays on Identity & History. 13.75 (ISBN 0-8446-6217-8). Peter Smith.

Dimont, Max I. The Indestructible Jews. 480p. 1973. pap. 4.95 (ISBN 0-451-13878-3, Sig). NAL.

Dresner, Samuel H. Between the Generations. pap. 1.75 (ISBN 0-87677-042-1). Hartmore.

Dubnov, Simon. History of the Jews, Vol. 1. 18.00 (ISBN 0-8453-6410-3, Cornwall Bks). Assoc Univ Prs.

--History of the Jews, Vol. 2. 18.00 (ISBN 0-8453-6659-9, Cornwall Bks). Assoc Univ Prs.

--History of the Jews, Vol.3. 18.00 (ISBN 0-8453-6822-2, Cornwall Bks). Assoc Univ Prs.

--History of the Jews, Vol. 4. 18.00 (ISBN 0-8453-7537-7, Cornwall Bks). Assoc Univ Prs.

--History of the Jews, Vol. 5. 18.00 (ISBN 0-8453-7691-8, Cornwall Bks). Assoc Univ Prs.

Dubnow, Semen M. Jewish History: An Essay in the Philosophy of History. LC 72-5481. (Select Bibliographies Reprint Ser.). 1972. Repr. of 1903 ed. 16.00 (ISBN 0-8369-6903-0). Ayer Co Pubs.

Eban, Abba. Heritage: Civilization & the Jews. 356p. 1986. pap. 16.95 (ISBN 0-671-62881-X). Summit Bks.

--My People: The Story of the Jews. LC 68-27328. (Illus.). 1968. 25.00 (ISBN 0-87441-294-3). Behrman.

Eisenberg, Azriel. Jewish Historical Treasures. LC 68-57432. (Illus.). 300p. 1969. 12.50 (ISBN 0-8197-0076-2). Bloch.

Eisenberg, Azriel, et al, eds. Eyewitnesses to American Jewish History: 1492-1793, Pt. 1. 1976. pap. 5.00 (ISBN 0-686-77106-0, 144060); tchrs'. guide 5.00 (ISBN 0-8074-0019-X, 204061). UAHC.

Ellison, H. L. From Babylon to Bethlehem: The People of God from the Exile to the Messiah. LC 78-24504. 144p. 1984. pap. 5.95 (ISBN 0-8010-3412-4). Baker Bk.

Epstein, Morris. A Picture Parade of Jewish History. 1977. pap. 4.95 (ISBN 0-8197-0024-X). Bloch.

Fast, Howard. The Jews: Story of a People. 384p. 1978. pap. 3.95 (ISBN 0-440-34444-1). Dell.

Fast, Howard & Fast, Bette. The Picture Book History of the Jews. 60p. 1942. 5.95 (ISBN 0-88482-771-2). Hebrew Pub.

Flannery, Edward. The Anguish of the Jews: Twenty-Three Centuries of Antisemitism. rev. ed. LC 85-60298. 384p. 1985. pap. 12.95 (ISBN 0-8091-2702-4). Paulist Pr.

Fleg, Edmond. Why I Am a Jew. Wise, Louise W., tr. from Fr. LC 75-4124. 1985. pap. 4.95 (ISBN 0-8197-0009-6). Bloch.

Ford, Henry. The International Jew. 1978. pap. 5.00x (ISBN 0-911038-45-0). Noontide.

Foster, Charles K. The Unknown History of the Jewish People, 2 vols. (Illus.). 247p. 1986. Set. 187.45. Found Class Reprints.

Franzos, Karl E. The Jews of Barnow. facsimile ed. Macdowall, M. W., tr. from Ger. LC 74-27985. (Modern Jewish Experience Ser.). (Eng.). 1975. Repr. of 1883 ed. 30.00x (ISBN 0-405-06712-7). Ayer Co Pubs.

Gelberman, Joseph H. Haggadah: The Story of Thanksgiving. 35p. (Orig.). 1983. pap. 4.00 (ISBN 0-942494-55-5). Coleman Pub.

Gill, John, ed. Notices of the Jews & Their Country by the Classic Writers of Antiquity. LC 70-97281. (Judaica Ser). 180p. 1972. Repr. of 1872 ed. lib. bdg. 22.50x (ISBN 0-8371-2603-7, GINJ). Greenwood.

Glanz, Rudolf. Aspects of the Social, Political, & Economic History of the Jews in America. 1984. 29.50x (ISBN 0-87068-463-9). Ktav.

Goldberg, Israel. Israel: A History of the Jewish People. LC 72-162629. 715p. 1949. Repr. lib. bdg. 29.50x (ISBN 0-8371-6196-7, GOIS). Greenwood.

Goldberg, M. Hirsch. The Jewish You Wouldn't Believe It Book. (Illus.). 252p. 1986. pap. 7.95 (ISBN 0-933503-51-2). Shapolsky Pubs.

Gordon, A. D. Selected Essays. LC 73-2201. (The Jewish People; History, Religion, Literature Ser.). Repr. of 1938 ed. 25.50 (ISBN 0-405-05266-9). Ayer Co Pubs.

Grad, Eli & Roth, Bette. Congregation Shaarey Zedek: 5622-5742 1861-1981. LC 82-48650. (Illus.). 198p. 1982. 25.00x (ISBN 0-8143-1713-8). Wayne St U Pr.

Graetz, Heinrich. The Structure of Jewish History & Other Essays. 20.00x (ISBN 0-87068-466-3); pap. 14.95x (ISBN 0-685-56206-9). Ktav.

Grayzel, Solomon. History of the Jews. rev. ed. (Illus.). 908p. 1968. Repr. of 1947 ed. 12.95 (ISBN 0-8276-0142-5, 190). Jewish Pubns.

--A History of the Jews. 768p. 1968. pap. 4.95 (ISBN 0-452-00694-5, Mer). NAL.

Greer, Rowan. The Captain of Our Salvation: A Study in the Patristic Exegesis of Hebrews. 325p. 1973. lib. bdg. 52.00x (Pub. by J C B Mohr BRD). Coronet Bks.

Gutman, Y. & Rothkirchen, L., eds. The Catastrophe of European Jewry: Antecedents, History, Reflections. 25.00x (ISBN 0-87068-336-5). Ktav.

Hartman, David, ed. Crisis & Leadership: Epistles of Maimonides. Halkin, Abraham, tr. from Hebrew. 292p. 1985. 15.95 (ISBN 0-8276-0238-3). Jewish Pubns.

Heathcote, A. W. From the Death of Solomon to the Captivity of Judah. (London Divinity Ser.). 140p. 1977. pap. 3.95 (ISBN 0-227-67462-6). Attic Pr.

--From the Exile to Herod the Great. (London Divinity Ser). 140p. 1964. 3.95 (ISBN 0-227-67658-0). Attic Pr.

Hebrew Union College Annual, 10 Vols. 1969. 650.00x (ISBN 0-87068-065-X). Ktav.

Heller, Celia S. On the Edge of Destruction: Jews of Poland Between the Two World Wars. LC 79-24645. 384p. 1980. pap. 8.95 (ISBN 0-8052-0651-5). Schocken.

Hoffman, Lawrence A. The Canonization of the Synagogue Service. LC 78-62972. (Studies in Judaism & Christianity in Antiquity: No. 4). 1979. text ed. 18.95 (ISBN 0-268-00727-6). U of Notre Dame Pr.

Huber, Friedrich. Jahwe, Juda und die anderen Voelker beim Proheton Jesaja. (Beiheft 137 Zur Zeitschrift Fuer die Alttestamentliche Wissenschaft). (Ger.). 1976. 46.40 (ISBN 3-11-005729-8). De Gruyter.

Hughley, Ella J. The Truth about Black Biblical Hebrew Israelites (Jews) (Orig.). 1982. pap. 5.00 (ISBN 0-9605150-1-1). Hughley Pubns.

Jakobovits, Immanuel. The Timely & the Timeless: Jews, Judaism & Society in a Storm-Tossed Decade. 432p. 1977. 25.00x (ISBN 0-85303-189-4, Pub. by Vallentine Mitchell England). Biblio Dist.

Johnson, Paul. A History of the Jews. LC 85-42575. 448p. 1987. 24.50i (ISBN 0-06-015698-8, HarpT). Har-Row.

Josephus. Works of Josephus, 9 vols. Warmington, E. H., ed. Incl. Vol. 1. Life; Against Apion (ISBN 0-674-99205-9); Vols 2-3. Jewish War. Vol. 2, Bks 1-3. (ISBN 0-674-99223-7); Vol. 3, Bks. 4-7, Index To Vols. 2 & 3. (ISBN 0-674-99232-6); Vols 4-9. Antiquities. Vol. 4, Bks 1-4. (ISBN 0-674-99267-9); Vol. 5, Bks 5-8. (ISBN 0-674-99310-1); Vol. 6, Bks 9-11. (ISBN 0-674-99360-8); Vol. 7, Bks 12-14. (ISBN 0-674-99402-7); Vol. 8, Bks 15-17. (ISBN 0-674-99451-5); Vol. 9, Bks 18-20, General Index. (ISBN 0-674-99477-9). (Loeb Classical Library: No. 186, 203, 210, 242, 281, 326, 365, 410, 433). 13.95x ea. Harvard U Pr.

Josephus, Flavius. Great Roman-Jewish War: A.D. 66-70. Whiston, tr. 11.25 (ISBN 0-8446-0729-0). Peter Smith.

Jospe, Raphael & Wagner, Stanley M. Great Schisms in Jewish History. 1980. 25.00x (ISBN 0-87068-784-0). Ktav.

Kahan, Arcadius. Essays in Jewish Social & Economic History. Weiss, Roger, ed. LC 86-1427. xx, 208p. 1986. lib. bdg. 27.50x (ISBN 0-226-42240-2). U of Chicago Pr.

Karp, Deborah. Heroes of American Jewish History. Effron, Benjamin, ed. 155p. pap. 6.95 (ISBN 0-686-95130-1). ADL.

Katchen, Aaron L. Christian Hebraists & Dutch Rabbis: Seventeenth Century Apologetics & the Study of Maimonides' Mishneh Torah. (Harvard Judaic Texts & Studies: No. 3). 430p. 1985. text ed. 28.00x (ISBN 0-674-12865-6). Harvard U Ctr Jewish.

Katz, Jacob. The Traditional Jewish Family in Historical Perspective. 1983. pap. 1.00 (ISBN 0-87495-048-1). Am Jewish Comm.

Katzburg, Nathaniel. Hungary & the Jews: Policy & Legislation 1920-1943. 299p. cancelled (ISBN 965-226-020-7). Hermon.

Kent, Charles. The Egyptian Background of Hebrew History. (Illus.). 133p. 1982. Repr. of 1908 ed. 73.45 (ISBN 0-89901-068-7). Found Class Reprints.

Kitov, Eliyahu. The Book of Our Heritage, 3 vols. Bulman, Nathan, tr. from Hebrew. Orig. Title: Sefer HaToda'ah. 1978. 32.50 (ISBN 0-87306-151-9); slipcased ed. 33.95 (ISBN 0-87306-157-8). Feldheim.

Klaperman, Gilbert & Klaperman, Libby. The Story of the Jewish People, 4 vols. Incl. Vol. 1. From Creation to the Second Temple. pap. text ed. 4.50x (ISBN 0-87441-207-2); Vol. 2. From the Building of the Second Temple Through the Age of the Rabbis. pap. text ed. 4.50x (ISBN 0-87441-208-0); Vol. 3. From the Golden Age in Spain Through the European Emancipation. pap. text ed. 5.50x (ISBN 0-87441-209-9); Vol. 4. From the Settlement of America Through Israel Today. pap. text ed. 5.50x (ISBN 0-87441-210-2). LC 56-12175. (Illus.). 1974. pap. Behrman.

Kobler, Franz. Letters of Jews Through the Ages, Vol. 2. 1978. pap. 7.95 (ISBN 0-85222-213-0, East & West Lib). Hebrew Pub.

Kobler, Franz, ed. Letters of Jews Through the Ages, Vol. 1. 1978. pap. 7.95 (ISBN 0-85222-212-2, East & West Lib). Hebrew Pub.

Kochan, Lionel. The Jew & His History. (Scholars Press Reprints & Translations: No. 1). 1985. pap. 8.25 (ISBN 0-89130-821-0, 00 07 06). Scholars Pr GA.

Kohn, Gary J. The Jewish Experience: A Guide to Manuscript Sources in the Library of Congress. (Monographs of the American Jewish Archives). 250p. 1986. text ed. write for info. (ISBN 0-87820-014-2, Pub. by Am Jewish Archives). Ktav.

Kornberg, Jacques, ed. At the Crossroads: Essays on Ahad Ha'am. (Modern Jewish History Ser.). 242p. 1983. 44.50 (ISBN 0-87395-738-5); pap. 14.95 (ISBN 0-87395-739-3). State U NY Pr.

Kosovsky, Binyamin. Otzar Leshon Ha-Tannaim-Sifra-Tarat Kohanim, 4 vols. 1967. Set. 75.00x (ISBN 0-685-31426-X, Pub. by Jewish Theol Seminary). Ktav.

Lange, Nicholas de. Atlas of the Jewish World. (Cultiral Atlas Ser.). (Illus.). 240p. 1984. 35.00 (ISBN 0-87196-043-5). Facts on File.

Lash, Neil A. & Lash, Jamie S. A Jewish Wedding. (Jewish Jewels Ser.: Vol. 2). (Illus.). 24p. 1985. pap. 1.50 (ISBN 0-915775-03-4). Love Song Mess Assn.

Leo Baeck Institute Yearbook, Vol. 17. 1972. 28.00 (ISBN 0-436-24425-X, Pub. by Secker & Warburg UK). David & Charles.

Leo Baeck Institute Yearbook, Vol. 18. 400p. 1973. 28.00 (ISBN 0-436-24426-8, Pub. by Secker & Warburg UK). David & Charles.

Leo Baeck Institute Yearbook, Vol. 19. 380p. 1974. 28.00 (ISBN 0-436-24427-6, Pub. by Secker & Warburg UK). David & Charles.

Leo Baeck Institute Yearbook, Vol 20. 420p. 1975. 28.00 (ISBN 0-436-24428-4, Pub. by Secker & Warburg UK). David & Charles.

Leo Baeck Institute Yearbook, Vol. 22. (Illus.). 388p. 1977. 28.00 (ISBN 0-436-24430-6, Pub. by Secker & Warbug UK). David & Charles.

Leo Baeck Institute Yearbook, Vol. 23. 486p. 1978. 28.00 (ISBN 0-436-24431-4, Pub. by Secker & Warburg UK). David & Charles.

Leo Baeck Institute Yearbook, Vol. 25. 504p. 1980. 28.00 (ISBN 0-436-24433-0, Pub. by Secker & Warburg UK). David & Charles.

Leo Baeck Institute Yearbook, Vol. 26. 504p. 1981. 28.00 (ISBN 0-436-24434-9, Pub. by Secker & Warburg UK). David & Charles.

Leo Baeck Institute Yearbooks Index: Volumes I-XX, 1956-1975. 224p. 1982. 32.00 (ISBN 0-436-25541-3, Pub. by Secker & Warburg UK). David & Charles.

Levenson, Dode B., et al. Jewish Trivia. LC 84-63112. (Illus.). 195p. (Orig.). 1985. pap. 7.95 (ISBN 0-9611268-7-6). Quinlan Pr.

Lewittes, M. Religious Foundations of the Jewish State: The Concept & Practice of Jewish Statehood from Biblical Times to the Modern State of Israel. 25.00x (ISBN 0-87068-433-7). Ktav.

Lewittes, Mordecai. Heroes of Jewish History: From Abraham to Moses, Vol. 1. 255p. 1952. pap. 6.95x (ISBN 0-88482-626-0). Hebrew Pub.

--Highlights of Jewish History: From Dan to Ramban, Vol. 3. 303p. 1955. pap. 6.95x (ISBN 0-88482-628-7). Hebrew Pub.

--Highlights of Jewish History: From Joshua to Jeremiah, Vol. 2. 288p. 1953. pap. 6.95x (ISBN 0-88482-627-9). Hebrew Pub.

--Highlights of Jewish History: From Middle Ages to Modern Times, Vol. 4. 319p. 1957. 6.95x (ISBN 0-88482-629-5). Hebrew Pub.

Lods, Adolphe. Prophets & the Rise of Judaism. Hooke, S. H., tr. LC 77-109772. (Illus.). 1971. Repr. of 1937 ed. lib. bdg. 25.75x (ISBN 0-8371-4262-8, LOPR). Greenwood.

Loeb, Sorel G. & Kadden, Barbara B. Jewish History - Moments & Methods: An Activity Source Book for Teachers. LC 82-71283. (Illus.). 150p. (Orig.). 1982. pap. text ed. 10.00 (ISBN 0-86705-008-X). AIRE.

McCalden, David. Exiles from History. (Illus.). 40p. (Orig.). 1982. pap. 5.00 (ISBN 0-910607-00-1). Truth Missions.

Maier, Johann. Geschichte der Juedischen Religion: Von der Zeit Alexanders des Grossen bis zur Aufklaerung. Mit einem Ausblick auf das 19.-20. Jahrhundert. LC 72-77437. (Ger.). xx, 641p. 1972. 29.60x (ISBN 3-11-002448-9). De Gruyter.

Malino, Frances & Albert, Phyllis C., eds. Essays in Modern Jewish History: A Tribute to Ben Halpern. LC 80-70585. 500p. 1981. 27.50 (ISBN 0-8386-3095-2). Fairleigh Dickinson.

Mann, Jacob. Texts & Studies in Jewish History & Literature, 2 Vols. rev. ed. 1970. Set. 99.50x (ISBN 0-87068-085-4). Ktav.

Marcus, Jacob R. Jew in the Medieval World: A Source Book: 315-1791. LC 60-8666. (Temple Books). 1969. pap. text ed. 10.95x (ISBN 0-689-70133-0, T7). Atheneum.

--Studies in American Jewish History. 1969. 15.00x (ISBN 0-87820-003-7, Pub. by Hebrew Union). Ktav.

Margolis, Max L. & Marx, Alexander. History of the Jewish People. LC 70-90074. (Temple Books). 1969. pap. text ed. 10.95x (ISBN 0-689-70134-9, T8). Atheneum.

Marx, A. Studies in Jewish History & Booklore. 472p. 1944. text ed. 49.68x (ISBN 0-576-80136-4, Pub. by Gregg Intl Pubs England). Gregg Intl.

Mauro, Phillip. God's Pilgrims. 192p. 1969. pap. 3.00 (ISBN 0-87509-090-7). Chr Pubns.

Mendelssohn, Sidney. The Jews of Asia: Especially in the Sixteenth & Seventeenth Centuries. LC 77-87612. (Illus.). 256p. Repr. of 1920 ed. 29.50 (ISBN 0-404-16436-6). AMS Pr.

Meyer, Michael A., ed. Ideas of Jewish History. LC 73-19960. (Library of Jewish Studies). 384p. 1974. 15.95x (ISBN 0-87441-202-1). Behrman.

Moore, Deborah D. B'nai B'rith & the Challenge of Ethnic Leadership. LC 81-906. (Modern Jewish History Ser.). 292p. 1981. 18.95x (ISBN 0-87395-480-7). State U NY Pr.

Neher, Andre. The Exile of the Word: From the Silence of the Bible to the Silence of Auschwitz. LC 80-12612. 224p. 1980. 17.95 (ISBN 0-8276-0176-X, 465). Jewish Pubns.

Neusner, Jacob. The Jewish War Against the Jews: Reflections on Golah, Shoah, & Torah. LC 84-9657. 157p. 1984. 12.95 (ISBN 0-88125-050-3). Ktav.

Neusner, Jacob, tr. The Fathers According to Rabbi Nathan. (Brown Judaic Studies). 274p. 1986. 41.95 (ISBN 1-55540-051-5, 14-01-14). Scholars Pr GA.

Noth, Martin. History of Israel: Biblical History. 2nd ed. LC 58-5195. 1960. 16.95xi (ISBN 0-06-066310-3, HarpR). Har-Row.

One a Day: An Anthology of Jewish Historical Sketches for Every Day of the Year. 20.00 (ISBN 0-88125-108-9). Ktav.

Potok, Chaim. Wanderings: Chaim Potok's History of the Jews. LC 78-54915. 1978. 29.95 (ISBN 0-394-50110-1). Knopf.

Rabinbach, Anson & Zipes, Jack D., eds. Germans & Jews since the Holocaust: The Changing Situation in West Germany. 300p. 1986. text ed. 37.50 (ISBN 0-8419-0924-5); pap. text ed. 17.95 (ISBN 0-8419-0925-3). Holmes & Meier.

Raphael, Chaim. The Road from Babylon: The Story of the Sephardic & Oriental Jews. LC 85-42587. (Illus.). 320p. 1986. 22.45i (ISBN 0-06-039048-4, C&M Bessie Bks). Har-Row.

Reddish, Robert O., Jr. The Burning Burning Bush. LC 73-85938. (Illus.). 1974. 11.95 (ISBN 0-686-05480-6). Rorge Pub Co.

Rischin, Moses, ed. Modern Jewish Experience, 59 vols. 1975. Set. 1630.50x (ISBN 0-405-06690-2). Ayer Co Pubs.

Rodinson, Maxime. Cult, Ghetto, & State: The Persistence of the Jewish Question. Rothschild, Jon, tr. from Fr. 239p. (Orig.). 1984. pap. 10.95 (ISBN 0-86356-020-2, Pub. by Al Saqi UK). Evergreen Dist.

Rosenzweig, Rachel. Solidaritaet mit den Leidenden im Judentum. (Studia Judaica: Vol. 10). 1978. 46.40x (ISBN 3-11-005939-8). De Gruyter.

Rossel, Seymour. Journey Through Jewish History, Vol. II. (Illus.). 128p. 1983. pap. text ed. 5.95x (ISBN 0-87441-366-4). Behrman.

Roth, Cecil. A History of the Jews: From Earliest Times Through the Six Day War. rev. ed. LC 74-121042. 1970. pap. 8.95 (ISBN 0-8052-0009-6). Schocken.

--Short History of the Jewish People. rev. ed. 1969. 14.95; pap. 6.95 (ISBN 0-87677-183-5). Hartmore.

Rothstein, Raphael. The Story of Masada. (Illus.). 296p. 1983. cancelled (ISBN 0-89961-012-9). SBS Pub.

Sachar, A. L. History of the Jews. rev. ed. 1967. 20.00 (ISBN 0-394-42871-4). Knopf.

Sachar, Howard M. Diaspora: An Inquiry into the Contemporary Jewish World. LC 84-48190. (Illus.). 539p. 1986. pap. 10.95 (ISBN 0-06-091347-9, PL-1347, PL). Har-Row.

Schauss, Hayyim. Lifetime of a Jew: Throughout the Ages of Jewish History. rev. ed. (Illus.). (YA) 1976. pap. 7.95 (ISBN 0-8074-0096-3, 383473). UAHC.

Schwab, Moise. Repertoire des Articles Relatifs a l'Histoire et a la Litterature Juives Parus dans les Periodiques De 1665 a 1900. rev. ed. (Fr.). 1971. 79.50 (ISBN 0-87068-163-X). Ktav.

Segal, Yocheved. Our Sages Showed the Way, Vol. 2. Falk, Esther, tr. from Hebrew. (Jewish Youth Classics Ser.). (Illus.). 192p. 1982. text ed. 9.95 (ISBN 0-87306-200-0). Feldheim.

Shapiro, Harry L. The Jewish People: A Biological History. 1978. lib. bdg. 59.95 (ISBN 0-685-62297-5). Revisionist Pr.

Shapolsky, Ian. The Jewish Trivia & Information Book. 400p. 1985. pap. 5.95 (ISBN 0-317-39894-6). Shapolsky Pubs.

--The Second Jewish Trivia & Information Book. (Illus.). 400p. 1986. pap. 6.95 (ISBN 0-933503-45-8). Shapolsky Pubs.

Shiblak, Abbas. The Lure of Zion--the Case of the Iraqi Jews. 178p. 1986. 29.95 (ISBN 0-86356-121-7, Pub. by Al Saqi Bks UK); pap. 9.95 (ISBN 0-86356-033-4, Pub. by Al Saqi Bks UK). Humanities.

Shneiderman, S. L. The River Remembers. LC 77-93935. (Illus.). 1978. 8.95 (ISBN 0-8180-0821-0). Horizon.

Shulvass, Moses A. The History of the Jewish People, Vol. 1: The Antiquity. LC 81-85564. 250p. 1982. 14.95 (ISBN 0-89526-660-1). Regnery Bks.

Simonsohn, S. History of the Jews in the Duchy of Mantua. 35.00x (ISBN 0-87068-341-1). Ktav.

Singer, Betty J. Friends of the Jews. (Illus.). 1976. pap. text ed. 2.75 (ISBN 0-917400-01-1). Options.

Slater, Robert. Great Jews in Sports. LC 82-19953. (Illus.). 304p. 1983. 14.95 (ISBN 0-8246-0285-4). Jonathan David.

Steinberg, Aaron. History As Experience. 1983. 35.00x (ISBN 0-88125-001-5). Ktav.

Stern, Shirley. Exploring Jewish History. 1978. pap. 8.95x (ISBN 0-87068-651-8). Ktav.

Stone, Michael E. Scriptures, Sects & Visions: A Profile of Judaism from Ezra to the Jewish Revolts. LC 78-54151. 160p. 1980. 11.95 (ISBN 0-8006-0641-8, 1-641). Fortress.

Sutton, Joseph A. D. Magic Carpet: Aleppo in Flatbush: The Story of a Unique Ethnic Jewish Community. 3rd ed. LC 79-65516. (Illus.). 336p. 1986. text ed. 19.95x (ISBN 0-686-27080-0). Thayer-Jacoby.

Szjakowski, Soza. Jews, War & Communism. Incl. Vol. 1. The Attitude of American Jews to World War I, the Russian Revolution of 1917, and Communism, 1917 to 1945. 1972. 35.00x (ISBN 0-87068-182-6); Vol. 2. 1974. 35.00x (ISBN 0-87068-239-3). Ktav.

Tarnor, Pearl & Tarnor, Norman. Hebrew & Heritage, Vol. II: Siddur Track. 1982. 3.95x (ISBN 0-87441-375-3); tchr's. guide 12.50 (ISBN 0-87441-377-X). Behrman.

Time Line Display of Jewish History: Mural Edition. 1981. 18.00 (ISBN 0-686-46788-4). T Black.

Time Line Display of Jewish History: Poster Edition. 1982. 10.00 (ISBN 0-686-46792-2). T Black.

Twersky, Abraham J. Generation to Generation: Recollections of a Chassidic Legacy. 256p. 1985. 14.95 (ISBN 0-933711-17-4). Traditional Pr.

Twersky, Isadore, ed. Danzig: Between East & West. (Harvard Judaica Texts & Studies: Vol. IV). 185p. 1984. text ed. 21.00x (ISBN 0-674-19255-9); pap. text ed. 14.00x (ISBN 0-674-19256-7). Harvard U Pr.

Uchill, Ida L. Pioneers, Peddlers, & Tsadikim: The Story of the Jews in Colorado. 2nd ed. LC 57-57817. 327p. 1979. pap. 9.95 (ISBN 0-9604468-0-X). Uchill.

Universal Jewish History: The Exodous, Vol. 4. 1982. 9.95 (ISBN 0-686-76273-8). Feldheim.

Ussher, Arland. The Magic People. 12.95 (ISBN 0-8159-6200-2). Devin.

Vishniac, Roman. A Vanished World. LC 83-16420. (Illus.). 192p. 1983. 65.00 (ISBN 0-374-28247-1). FS&G.

Waagenaar, Sam. The Pope's Jews. (Illus.). 500p. 1974. 9.95 (ISBN 0-912050-49-7, Library Pr). Open Court.

Wacholder, Ben Z. The Dawn of Quran: The Sectarian Torah & the Teacher of Righteousness. 310p. 1983. 25.00 (ISBN 0-686-88437-X). Ktav.

Wellhausen, Julius. Abriss der Geschichte Israels und Judas: Lieder der Hudhailiten. (Skizzen und Vorarbeiten, l.Heft). (Ger. & Arabic.). iv, 175p. 1985. 70.50x (ISBN 3-11-009765-6). De Gruyter.

Wiesenthal, Simon. Every Day Remembrance Day: A Chronicle of Jewish Martyrdom. (Illus.). 480p. 1987. 19.95 (ISBN 0-8050-0098-4). H Holt & Co.

Wolfe, Robert. Dark Star. 266p. (Orig.). 1984. 12.00 (ISBN 0-318-19328-0); pap. 6.00 (ISBN 0-318-19329-9). Memory Bks.

Wollman-Tsamir, Pinchas. The Graphic History of the Jewish Heritage. (Illus.). 224p. 1982. 22.50. Shengold.

Wurmbrand, Max & Roth, Cecil. The Jewish People: Four Thousand Years of Survival. rev. ed. (Illus.). 480p. 1987. 39.95 (ISBN 0-915361-64-7, Dist. by Watts). Adama Pubs Inc.

Yerushalmi, Yosef H. Zakhor: Jewish History & Jewish Memory. LC 82-15989. (Samuel & Althea Stroum Lectures in Jewish Studies). 162p. 1982. 17.50x (ISBN 0-295-95939-8). U of Wash Pr.

JEWS–HISTORY–CHRONOLOGY

Conservative Judaism: Our Ancestors to Our Descendants. 7.95 (ISBN 0-686-96053-X); pap. 5.00 (ISBN 0-686-99689-5); tchr's. guide 3.00 (ISBN 0-686-99690-9). United Syn Bk.

Howard, Dale A. Golden Ark of Covenant. (Illus.). 40p. 1987. pap. 5.00 (ISBN 0-940517-04-3). JCMC Louisiana.

JEWS–HISTORY–JUVENILE LITERATURE

Bull, Norman. Church of the Jews. (Bible Story & Its Background Ser.: Vol. 4). 9.95 (ISBN 0-7175-0450-6). Dufour.

--Founders of the Jews. (Bible Story & Its Background Ser.: Vol. 1). pap. 9.95 (ISBN 0-7175-0977-X). Dufour.

Chaikin, Miriam. Shake a Palm Branch: The Story & Meaning of Sukkot. LC 84-5022. (Illus.). 80p. 1984. PLB 12.95 (ISBN 0-89919-254-8, Clarion). HM.

Charry, Elias & Segal, Abraham. The Eternal People. (Illus.). 448p. 7.50x (ISBN 0-8381-0206-9, 10-206). United Syn Bk.

Connolly, Peter. A History of the Jewish People in the Time of Jesus: From Herod the Great to Masada. LC 86-28890. (Illus.). 96p. 1987. 15.95 (ISBN 0-87226-007-0). P Bedrick Bks.

Dimont, Max I. The Amazing Adventures of the Jewish People. LC 84-16806. 175p. (YA) 1984. pap. 3.95 (ISBN 0-87441-391-5). Behrman.

Gersh, Harry, et al. Story of the Jew. rev. ed. LC 64-22514. (Illus.). 1965. 5.95x (ISBN 0-87441-019-3). Behrman.

Harlow, Jules. Lessons from Our Living Past. LC 72-2055. (Illus.). 128p. 1972. text ed. 6.95x (ISBN 0-87441-085-1). Behrman.

Jacobs, Louis. Way of the Jews. (The Way Ser.). pap. 5.95 (ISBN 0-7175-0875-7). Dufour.

Lipson, Ruth. Modeh Ani Means Thank You. (Illus.). 1986. 5.95 (ISBN 0-317-42732-6). Feldheim.

Meltzer, Milton. The Jews in America: A Picture Album. LC 84-14344. (Illus.). 1985. 12.95 (ISBN 0-8276-0246-4). Jewish Pubns.

Pessin, Deborah. Jewish People, 3 Vols. (Illus.). 1951-53. pap. 4.25x ea. Vol. I (ISBN 0-8381-0182-8). Vol. II (ISBN 0-8381-0185-2). Vol. III (ISBN 0-8381-0187-9). pap. 2.50x ea. pupils' activity bks. Vol. I Activity Bk (ISBN 0-8381-0183-6). Vol. II Activity Bk (ISBN 0-8381-0186-0). Vol. III Activity Bk (ISBN 0-8381-0188-7). United Syn Bk.

Rossel, Seymour. Introduction to Jewish History. Kozodoy, Neil, ed. (Illus.). 128p. 1981. pap. text ed. 5.95x (ISBN 0-87441-335-4). Behrman.

Rothstein, Chaya L. The Mentchkins Make Shabbos. (Sifrei Rimon Ser.). 1986. pap. 2.50 (ISBN 0-317-42728-8). Feldheim.

Samuels, Ruth. Pathways Through Jewish History. rev ed. (Illus.). 1977. pap. 9.00x (ISBN 0-87068-520-1). Ktav.

Soloff, Mordecai I. The Covenant People, Vol. 1: The First 2,000 Years of Jewish Life. LC 72-97080. (Illus.). 1973. 3.95x (ISBN 0-8246-0154-8); tchr's guide 8.95x (ISBN 0-685-30240-7); wkbk 2.95x (ISBN 0-8246-0155-6). Jonathan David.

--The Covenant People, Vol. 2: The Battle for Survival from Talmudic Times to the End of World War I. LC 72-97080. (Illus.). 1974. 3.95x; tchr's guide 8.95x (ISBN 0-685-47972-2); wkbk 2.95x (ISBN 0-8246-0155-6). Jonathan David.

Wengrov, Charles. The Twelve Tribes of Israel. (Illus.). 1960. pap. 0.99 (ISBN 0-914080-64-4). Shulsinger Sales.

JEWS–HISTORY–PHILOSOPHY

Maritain, Jacques. Le Mystere d'Israel. 260p. 1965. 9.95 (ISBN 0-686-56358-1). French & Eur.

Neusner, Jacob. Self-Fulfilling Prophecy: Exile & Return As the History of Judaism. LC 86-47756. 320p. 1987. 25.00 (ISBN 0-8070-3606-4). Beacon Pr.

JEWS–HISTORY–TO 586 B.C.

see also Exodus, The

Albright, William F. Biblical Period from Abraham to Ezra: A Historical Survey. pap. 4.95x (ISBN 0-06-130102-7, TB102, Torch). Har-Row.

Bright, John. Covenant & Promise: The Prophetic Understanding of the Future in Pre-Exilic Israel. LC 76-13546. 208p. 1976. 10.00 (ISBN 0-664-20752-9). Westminster.

Connolly, Peter. A History of the Jewish People in the Times of Jesus: From Herod the Great to Masada. LC 86-28890. 1987. 15.95. P Bedrick Bks.

Gottwald, Norman K. The Tribes of Yahweh: A Sociology of the Religion of Liberated Israel, 1250-1050 B.C. LC 78-24333. 944p. (Orig.). 1979. pap. 19.95 (ISBN 0-88344-499-2). Orbis Bks.

Hardinge, Leslie. The Conquerors. (Anchor Ser.). 112p. 1983. pap. 5.95 (ISBN 0-8163-0509-9). Pacific Pr Pub Assn.

Heaton, Eric W. Hebrew Kingdoms. (New Clarendon Bible Ser.). 1968. 10.95x (ISBN 0-19-836922-0). Oxford U Pr.

Kraeling, Emil G. Aram & Israel Or, Aramaeans in Syria & Mesopotamia. LC 18-9797. (Columbia University. Oriental Studies: No. 13). Repr. of 1918 ed. 17.00 (ISBN 0-404-50503-1). AMS Pr.

Lindsay, Gordon. The Decline & Fall of Israel & Judah. (Old Testament Ser.). 1.25 (ISBN 0-89985-153-3). Christ Nations.

--Gideon & the Early Judges. (Old Testament Ser.). 1.25 (ISBN 0-89985-135-5). Christ Nations.

Meek, Theophile J. Hebrew Origins. 1960. 11.25 (ISBN 0-8446-2572-8). Peter Smith.

Pascal, Blaise. The Mystery of Jesus & of the Jewish People, 2 vols. (Illus.). 245p. 1985. 207.50 (ISBN 0-89901-228-0). Found Class Reprints.

Payne, David F. Kingdoms of the Lord: A History of the Hebrew Kingdoms from Saul to the Fall of Jerusalem. LC 81-3197. (Illus.). pap. 85.00 (ISBN 0-317-11122-1, 2020852). Bks Demand UMI.

Rattey, B. K. A Short History of the Hebrews: From the Patriarchs to Herod the Great. 3rd ed. (Illus.). 1976. pap. 11.50x (ISBN 0-19-832121-X). Oxford U Pr.

Robinson, T. H. Decline & Fall of the Hebrew Kingdoms. LC 74-137284. Repr. of 1926 ed. 21.50 (ISBN 0-404-05376-9). AMS Pr.

Weippert, Manfred. Settlement of the Israelite Tribes in Palestine. Martin, James, tr. from Ger. LC 74-131587. (Studies in Biblical Theology, 2nd Ser.: No. 21). (Orig.). 1970. pap. 12.00x (ISBN 0-8401-3071-6). A R Allenson.

Wellhausen, Julius. Prolegomena to the History of Ancient Israel. 14.25 (ISBN 0-8446-3147-7). Peter Smith.

JEWS–HISTORY–TO 70 A.D.

Bruce, Frederick F., ed. Israel & the Nations. LC 63-22838. 1963. pap. 7.95 (ISBN 0-8028-1450-6). Eerdmans.

Eller, Meredith F. The Beginnings of the Christian Religion: A Guide to the History & Literature of Judaism & Christianity. 1958. 16.95x (ISBN 0-8084-0392-3); pap. 12.95x (ISBN 0-8084-0393-1). New Coll U Pr.

Feldman, Louis H. Josephus & Modern Scholarship: 1937-1980. LC 84-1879. xvi, 1055p. 1984. 248.00x (ISBN 3-11-008138-5). De Gruyter.

Grant, Michael. Jews in the Roman World. LC 72-11118. 1973. lib. rep. ed. 20.00x (ISBN 0-684-15494-3, ScribT). Scribner.

Greenspahn, Frederick E., et al, eds. Nourished with Peace: Studies in Hellenistic Judaism in Memory of Samuel Sandmel. (Scholars Press Homage Ser.: No. 9). 23.95 (ISBN 0-89130-740-0, 00 16 09). Scholars Pr GA.

Herrmann, Siegfried. A History of Israel in Old Testament Times. 2nd, rev. & enl. ed. Bowden, John, tr. from Ger. LC 81-43092. Tr. of Geschichte Israels in alttestamentlicher Zeit. 456p. 1981. pap. 16.95 (ISBN 0-8006-1499-2, 1-1499). Fortress.

Hoenig, Sidney B. The Era of the Second Temple. LC 74-79271. Orig. Title: Korot Am Olam. 480p. 1974. 11.95 (ISBN 0-88400-009-5). Shengold.

Kennett, R. H. Ancient Hebrew Social Life & Custom As Indicated in Law, Narrative & Metaphor. (British Academy, London, Schweich Lectures on Biblical Archaeology Series, 1931). pap. 19.00 (ISBN 0-8115-1273-8). Kraus Repr.

Neusner, Jacob. The Religious Study of Judaism: Description, Analysis & Interpretation. LC 85-30411. (Studies in Judaism Ser.: Vol. 1). 188p. (Orig.). 1986. lib. bdg. 22.50 (ISBN 0-8191-5393-1, Pub. by Studies in Judaism); pap. text ed. 9.75 (ISBN 0-8191-5394-X). U Pr of Amer.

--The Religious Study of Judaism: Description, Analysis, Interpretation-The Centrality of Context. LC 85-30411. (Studies in Judaism: Vol. 2). 230p. (Orig.). 1986. lib. bdg. 24.50 (ISBN 0-8191-5450-4, Pub. by Studies in Judaism); pap. text ed. 12.75 (ISBN 0-8191-5451-2). U Pr of Amer.

Neusner, Jacob, ed. Ancient Judaism: Debates & Disputes. LC 84-5532. (Brown Judaic Studies). 292p. 31.50 (ISBN 0-89130-755-9); pap. 20.95 (ISBN 0-89130-746-X, 14 00 64). Scholars Pr GA.

Orlinsky, Harry M. Ancient Israel. 2nd ed. (Development of Western Civilization Ser.). (Illus.). 164p. (Orig.). 1960. pap. text ed. 5.95x (ISBN 0-8014-9849-X). Cornell U Pr.

--Ancient Israel. LC 82-2937. (The Development of Western Civilization Ser.). xii, 164p. 1982. Repr. of 1954 ed. lib. bdg. 24.75x (ISBN 0-313-23559-7, ORAN). Greenwood.

Ringgren, Helmer. Israelite Religion. Green, David E., tr. from Ger. LC 66-10757. 408p. 1975. pap. 7.95 (ISBN 0-8006-1121-7, 1-1121). Fortress.

Schurer, Emil. History of the Jewish People in the Age of Jesus Christ, Vol. 3, Pt. 2. Vermes, Geza, et al, eds. 250p. 1986. 29.95 (ISBN 0-567-09373-5, Pub. by T & T Clark Ltd UK). Fortress.

--History of the Jewish People in the Age of Jesus Christ, Vol. 3, Pt. 1. Vermes, Geza, et al, eds. 704p. 1986. 48.50 (ISBN 0-567-02244-7, Pub. by T & T Clark Ltd UK). Fortress.

Schweltzer, Frederick. A History of the Jews Since the First Century A. D. 319p. pap. 1.95 (ISBN 0-686-95171-9). ADL.

Steinberg, Milton. The Making of the Modern Jew. (Brown Classics in Judaica Ser.). 318p. 1987. pap. text ed. 14.50 (ISBN 0-8191-4492-4). U Pr of Amer.

Sukenik, E. L. Ancient Synagogues in Palestine & Greece. (British Academy, London, Schweich Lectures on Biblical Archaeology Series, 1930). pap. 19.00 (ISBN 0-8115-1272-X). Kraus Repr.

Williams, Trevor. Form & Vitality in the World & God: A Christian Perspective. 1985. 29.95x (ISBN 0-19-826671-5). Oxford U Pr.

Wilson, Robert R. Sociological Approaches to the Old Testament. LC 83-16607. (Guides to Biblical Scholarship). 96p. 1984. pap. 4.50 (ISBN 0-8006-0469-5, 1-469). Fortress.

Zeitlin, Solomon. Studies in the Early History of Judaism. Vol. 3. 49.50x (ISBN 0-87068-278-4); Vol. 4. 49.50x (ISBN 0-87068-454-X). Ktav.

--Studies in the Early History of Judaism, Vol. 1. 1973. 59.50x (ISBN 0-87068-208-3). Ktav.

JEWS–HISTORY–586 B.C.-70 A.D.

see also Maccabees

Bickerman, Elias. From Ezra to the Last of the Maccabees: Foundations of Post-Biblical Judaism. 1962. pap. 5.95 (ISBN 0-8052-0036-3). Schocken.

Ironside, H. A. Four Hundred Silent Years. pap. 3.50 (ISBN 0-87213-361-3). Loizeaux.

Jews in the Hellenistic World: Josephus, Aristeas, the Sibylline Oracles, Eupolemus. (Cambridge Commentaries on the Writings of the Jewish & Christian World 200 B. C. to 200 A. D.). (Illus.). 224p. 1985. 42.50 (ISBN 0-521-24246-0); pap. 12.95 (ISBN 0-521-28551-8). Cambridge U Pr.

Josephus, Flavius. Hegesippi Qui Dicitur Historiae, Libri 5. Ussani, V., ed. (Corpus Scriptorum Ecclesiasticorum Latinorum Ser: Vol. 66). 1932. 31.00 (ISBN 0-384-27880-9). Johnson Repr.

--The Jewish War. Smallwood, E. Mary, ed. Williamson, G. A., tr. (Classics Ser.). 512p. (Orig.). 1984. pap. 6.95 (ISBN 0-14-044420-3). Penguin.

Kasher, Aryek. The Jews in Hellenistic & Roman Egypt: The Struggle for Equal Rights. 442p. 1985. lib. bdg. 90.00x (ISBN 3-16-144829-4, Pub. by J C B Mohr BRD). Coronet Bks.

Lightstone, Jack N. The Commerce of the Sacred. LC 83-20180. (Brown Judaic Ser.). 234p. 1984. pap. 18.75 (ISBN 0-89130-664-1, 14 00 59). Scholars Pr GA.

Nadich, Judah. Jewish Legends of the Second Commonwealth. 508p. 1983. 25.00 (ISBN 0-8276-0212-X, 490). Jewish Pubns.

Pearl, Chaim & Brookes, Reuben. The Guide to Jewish Knowledge. rev. ed. LC 75-25366. 142p. 1976. 8.95 (ISBN 0-87677-138-X). Hartmore.

Pfeiffer, Charles F. Between the Testaments. pap. 4.95 (ISBN 0-8010-6873-8). Baker Bk.

Pfeiffer, Robert H. History of New Testament Times. LC 77-138125. 561p. 1972. Repr. of 1949 ed. lib. bdg. 23.00x (ISBN 0-8371-3559-1, PFNT). Greenwood.

Radin, Max. The Jews Among the Greeks & Romans. LC 73-2224. (The Jewish People; History, Religion, Literature Ser.). Repr. of 1915 ed. 33.00 (ISBN 0-405-05286-3). Ayer Co Pubs.

Rattey, B. K. A Short History of the Hebrews: From the Patriarchs to Herod the Great. 3rd ed. (Illus.). 1976. pap. 11.50x (ISBN 0-19-832121-X). Oxford U Pr.

Russell, D. S. Between the Testaments. LC 77-74742. 176p. 1960. pap. 5.95 (ISBN 0-8006-1856-4, 1-1856). Fortress.

--The Jews from Alexander to Herod. 1967. pap. 13.95x (ISBN 0-19-836913-1). Oxford U Pr.

Schurer, Emil. A History of the Jewish People in the Time of Jesus. Glatzer, Nahum N., ed. LC 61-8195. 1961. pap. 7.95 (ISBN 0-8052-0008-8). Schocken.

--Schurer's History of the Jewish People in the Age of Jesus Christ, 2 vols. Vermes, Geza, et al, eds. 42.95 ea. (Pub. by T & T Clark Ltd UK). Vol. 1, 1973, 608 pgs (ISBN 0-567-02242-0). Vol. 2, 1979, 608 pgs (ISBN 0-567-02243-9). Fortress.

Shmuelevitz, A. The Jews of the Ottoman Empire in the Late Fifteenth & the Sixteenth Centuries. 201p. 1984. pap. text ed. 35.00x (ISBN 90-04-07071-0, Pub. by EJ Brill Holland). Humanities.

Tcherikover, Victor. Hellenistic Civilization & the Jews. Applebaum, S., tr. LC 59-8518. (Temple Bk.). 1970. pap. 9.95x (ISBN 0-689-70248-5, T22). Atheneum.

Wardle, William L. The History & Religion of Israel. LC 78-11741. (The Clarendon Bible, Old Testament Ser.: Vol. I). (Illus.). 1979. Repr. of 1942 ed. lib. bdg. 24.75x (ISBN 0-313-21016-0, WAHR). Greenwood.

JEWS–HISTORY–70-1789

Adler, Elkan N., ed. Jewish Travellers in the Middle Ages: Nineteen Firsthand Accounts. 416p. 1987. pap. 8.95 (ISBN 0-486-25397-X). Dover.

Albright, William F. Archaeology of Palestine. rev. ed. 11.25 (ISBN 0-8446-0003-2). Peter Smith.

American Academy for Jewish Research Staff. Facets of Medieval Judaism: Proceedings. (Jewish People; History, Religion, Literature Ser.). 19.00 (ISBN 0-405-05262-6). Ayer Co Pubs.

Bachrach, Bernard S. Jews in Barbarian Europe. 1977. 7.50x (ISBN 0-87291-088-1). Coronado Pr.

Berliner, Abraham. Aus dem Leben der Deuschen Juden im Mittelalter. Katz, Steven, ed. LC 79-7127. (Jewish Philosophy, Mysticism & History of Ideas Ser.). 1980. Repr. of 1900 ed. lib. bdg. 14.00x (ISBN 0-405-12241-1). Ayer Co Pubs.

Blumenthal, David R. Approaches to Judaism in Medieval Times. LC 83-18886. (Brown Judaic Ser.). 188p. pap. 14.95 (ISBN 0-89130-659-5, 14 00 54). Scholars Pr GA.

Calmann, Marianne. The Carriere of Carpentras. LC 82-48692. (Littman Library of Jewish Civilization). (Illus.). 286p. 1984. 32.50x (ISBN 0-19-710037-6). Oxford U Pr.

Chazan, Robert. Church, State & Jew in the Middle Ages. new ed. Kozodoy, Neal, ed. LC 78-27221. (Library of Jewish Studies). 1979. pap. text ed. 9.95x (ISBN 0-87441-302-8). Behrman.

--Medieval Jewry in Northern France: A Poltical & Social History. LC 73-8129. (Johns Hopkins University Studies in Historical & Political Science: 91st; 2). pap. 63.00 (ISBN 0-317-20643-5, 2024132). Bks Demand UMI.

Cohen, Amnon. Jewish Life under Islam: Jerusalem in the Sixteenth Century. (Illus.). 288p. 1984. text ed. 30.00x (ISBN 0-674-47436-8). Harvard U Pr.

Cohen, Jeremy. The Friars & the Jews: The Evolution of Medieval Anti-Judaism. LC 81-15210. 304p. 1984. pap. 10.95x (ISBN 0-8014-9266-1). Cornell U Pr.

Cutler, Allan H. & Cutler, Helen E. The Jew As Ally of the Muslim: Medieval Roots of Anti-Semitism. LC 84-40295. 594p. 1986. text ed. 50.00 (ISBN 0-268-01190-7, 85-11909). U of Notre Dame Pr.

Jews in the Hellenistic World: Josephus, Aristeas, the Sibylline Oracles, Eupolemus. (Cambridge Commentaries on the Writings of the Jewish & Christian World 200 B. C. to 200 A. D.). (Illus.). 224p. 1985. 42.50 (ISBN 0-521-24246-0); pap. 12.95 (ISBN 0-521-28551-8). Cambridge U Pr.

Katz, S. Jews in the Visigothic & Frankish Kingdoms of Spain & Gaul. (Mediaeval Academy of America Publications). 1937. 21.00 (ISBN 0-527-01697-7). Kraus Repr.

Maccoby, Hyman. Judaism on Trial: Jewish-Christian Disputations in the Middle Ages. (Littman Library of Jewish Civilization). 246p. 1982. 34.00x (ISBN 0-19-710046-5). Oxford U Pr.

Marcus, Jacob R. The Jew in the Medieval World: A Source Book, 315-1791. LC 71-97295. 504p. 1975. Repr. of 1938 ed. lib. bdg. 22.50x (ISBN 0-8371-2619-3, MAJM). Greenwood.

Meisl, Josef. Haskalah: Geschichte der Aufklarungsbewegung unter den Juden in Russland. Katz, Stephen, ed. LC 79-7147. (Jewish Philosophy, Mysticism & History of Ideas Ser.). 1980. Repr. of 1919 ed. lib. bdg. 21.00x (ISBN 0-405-12277-2). Ayer Co Pubs.

Moreen, Vera B. Iranian Jewry's Hour of Peril & Heroism. (A Study of the American Academy for Jewish Research). 247p. 1987. text ed. 25.00 (ISBN 0-231-06578-7). Columbia U Pr.

Parkes, James W. The Jew in the Medieval Community. 456p. 1976. pap. 12.95 (ISBN 0-87203-060-1). Hermon.

Poliakov, Leon. Jewish Barbers & the Holy See: From the Thirteenth to the Seventeenth-Century. Kochan, Miriam, tr. from Fr. (Littman Library of Jewish Civilization). 288p. 1977. 29.00x (ISBN 0-19-710028-7). Oxford U Pr.

Richardson, Henry G. The English Jewry under Angevin Kings. LC 83-18539. ix, 313p. 1983. Repr. of 1960 ed. lib. bdg. 35.00x (ISBN 0-313-24247-X, RIEJ). Greenwood.

Roth, Cecil. Gleanings: Essays in Jewish History, Letters & Art. 1967. 10.00x (ISBN 0-8197-0178-5). Bloch.

--The Jews in the Renaissance. LC 59-8516. (Illus.). 378p. 1978. pap. 8.95 (ISBN 0-8276-0103-4, 321). Jewish Pubns.

Schurer, Emil. Schurer's History of the Jewish People in the Age of Jesus Christ, 2 vols. Vermes, Geza, et al, eds. 42.95 ea. (Pub. by T & T Clark Ltd UK). Vol. 1, 1973, 608 pgs (ISBN 0-567-02242-0). Vol. 2, 1979, 608 pgs (ISBN 0-567-02243-9). Fortress.

Shulman, Nisson E. Authority & Community: Polish Jewry in the Sixteenth Century. 288p. 1986. text ed. 20.00x (ISBN 0-88125-101-1). Ktav.

Sirat, Colette. A History of Jewish Philosophy in the Middle Ages. 476p. 1985. 59.50 (ISBN 0-521-26087-6). Cambridge U Pr.

Stillman, Norman A. The Jews of Arab Lands: A History & Source Book. LC 78-70078. (Illus.). 416p. 1979. 10.95 (ISBN 0-8276-0116-6, 426). Jewish Pubns.

Szarmach, Paul E., ed. Aspects of Jewish Culture in the Middle Ages. LC 77-29046. (Illus.). 208p. 1979. 44.50 (ISBN 0-87395-165-4). State U NY Pr.

Twersky, Isadore, ed. Studies in Medieval Jewish History & Literature, Vol. 2. (Harvard Judaic Monographs: No. V). 460p. 1985. text ed. 25.00x (ISBN 0-674-85193-5). Harvard U Ctr Jewish.

Twersky, Isadore & Septimus, Bernard, eds. Jewish Thought in the Seventeenth Century. (Harvard Judaic Texts & Studies: VI). 425p. 1986. text ed. 25.00x (ISBN 0-674-47465-1); pap. text ed. 12.50x (ISBN 0-674-47466-X). Harvard U Pr.

Vetulani, A. The Jews of Medieval Poland. 1978. lib. bdg. 59.95 (ISBN 0-685-62298-3). Revisionist Pr.

Yerushalmi, Y. H. The Lisbon Massacre of 1506 & the Royal Image in the Shebet Yehuda. (Hebrew Union College Annual Supplements: Vol. 1). 12.50x (ISBN 0-87820-600-0, HUC Pr). Ktav.

JEWS–HISTORY–1789-

Adler, Cyrus & Margalith, Aaron M. With Firmness in the Right: American Diplomatic Action Affecting Jews, 1840-1945. Davis, Moshe, ed. LC 77-70651. (America & the Holy Land Ser.). 1977. Repr. of 1946 ed. lib. bdg. 40.00x (ISBN 0-405-10222-4). Ayer Co Pubs.

Almog, Shmuel. Zionism & History: Zionist Attitudes to the Jewish Historical Past, 1896-1906. Friedman, Ina, tr. from Hebrew. 350p. 1986. 29.95 (ISBN 0-312-89885-1). St Martin.

Ben-Ami, Yitshaq. Years of Wrath, Days of Glory. 2nd ed. LC 83-60834. (Illus.). 620p. 1983. Repr. of 1982 ed. 17.50 (ISBN 0-88400-096-6). Shengold.

Carmilly-Weinberger, Moshe, ed. The Rabbinical Seminary of Budapest, 1877-1977: A Centennial Volume. (Illus.). 420p. 1986. 35.00 (ISBN 0-87203-148-9). Hermon.

Dobroszycki, Lucjan & Kirshenblatt-Gimblett, Barbara. Image Before My Eyes: A Photographic History of Jewish Life in Poland, 1864-1939. LC 75-35448. (Illus.). 1979. pap. 19.95 (ISBN 0-8052-0634-5). Schocken.

Eisenberg, Azriel, et al, eds. Eyewitnesses to American Jewish History: East European Immigration 1881-1920, Pt. 3. (Illus.). 1978. pap. 5.00 (ISBN 0-8074-0017-3, 144061); tchrs'. guide 5.00 (ISBN 0-8074-0021-1, 204063). UAHC.

--Eyewitnesses to American Jewish History: The German Immigration 1800-1875, Pt. 2. (Illus.). 1977. pap. 5.00 (ISBN 0-8074-0016-5, 144059); tchrs'. guide 5.00 (ISBN 0-8074-0020-3, 204062). UAHC.

Grupper, David & Klein, David G. The Paper Shtetl: A Complete Model of an East European Jewish Town. LC 83-42714. (Illus., Orig.). 1984. pap. 11.95 (ISBN 0-8052-0749-X). Schocken.

Kurzweil, Arthur & Strauss, Ruby. My Generations: A Course in Jewish Family History. (Illus.). 128p. 1984. pap. 6.50x (ISBN 0-87441-383-4). Behrman.

Meisl, Josef. Haskalah: Geschichte der Aufklarungsbewegung unter den Juden in Russland. Katz, Stephen, ed. LC 79-7147. (Jewish Philosophy, Mysticism & History of Ideas Ser.). 1980. Repr. of 1919 ed. lib. bdg. 21.00x (ISBN 0-405-12277-2). Ayer Co Pubs.

Parkes, James W. Emergence of the Jewish Problem, 1878-1939. Repr. of 1946 ed. lib. bdg. 22.50x (ISBN 0-8371-2794-7, PJPR). Greenwood.

Polonsky, Antony, et al. The Jews in Poland. 288p. 1986. 24.95 (ISBN 0-631-14857-4). Basil Blackwell.

Sachar, Abram L. The Redemption of the Unwanted: From the Liberation of the Death Camps to the Founding of Israel. LC 83-3025. (Illus.). 320p. 1983. 19.95 (ISBN 0-312-66729-9, Pub. by Marek). St Martin.

Stillman, Norman A. The Jews of Arab Lands: A History & Source Book. LC 78-70078. (Illus.). 416p. 1979. 10.95 (ISBN 0-8276-0116-6, 426). Jewish Pubns.

Tamir, Nachman, ed. The Polish Jews, 1914-1939. LC 85-47709. (Illus.). 216p. 1986. 19.95 (ISBN 0-8453-4791-8, Cornwall Bks). Assoc Univ Prs.

Vago, Bela & Mosse, George L., eds. Jews & Non-Jews in Eastern Europe, 1918-1945. pap. 88.00 (ISBN 0-317-27256-X, 2024158). Bks Demand UMI.

JEWS–INTELLECTUAL LIFE

see also Jewish Learning and Scholarship

Bloom, Alexander. Prodigal Sons: The New York Intellectuals & Their World. 461p. 1986. 24.95 (ISBN 0-19-503662-X). Oxford U Pr.

Crenshaw, James L. Studies in Ancient Israelite Wisdom. 1974. 59.50x (ISBN 0-87068-255-5). Ktav.

Goldsmith, Emanuel S. Architects of Yiddishism at the Beginning of the Twentieth Century: A Study in Jewish Cultural History. LC 73-2894. 309p. 1976. 27.50 (ISBN 0-8386-1384-5). Fairleigh Dickinson.

Kampf, Avram. Jewish Experience in the Art of the Twentieth-Century. (Illus.). 240p. 1984. 49.50 (ISBN 0-89789-039-6). Bergin & Garvey.

Schwarz, Leo W., ed. Great Ages & Ideas of the Jewish People. LC 83-5464. 7.95 (ISBN 0-394-60413-X). Modern Lib.

JEWS–LAW

see Jewish Law

JEWS–LEARNING AND SCHOLARSHIP

see Jewish Learning and Scholarship

JEWS–LITERATURE

see Hebrew Literature

JEWS–LITURGY AND RITUAL

see also Chants (Jewish); Cultus, Jewish

Artz, Max. Joy & Remembrance. 1979. 12.50 (ISBN 0-87677-147-9). Hartmore.

Book of Life-Sefer Hachaim. (Heb, & Eng). 18.50 (ISBN 0-87559-102-7). Shalom.

Chanover, Hyman. Haggadah for the School. (Illus.). 1964. pap. 2.25x (ISBN 0-8381-0175-5). United Syn Bk.

Cohen, Eugene J. Guide to Ritual Circumcision & Redemption of the First-Born Son. 210p. 1984. 15.00x (ISBN 0-88125-017-1); pap. 9.95 (ISBN 0-88125-023-6). Ktav.

Conner, Kevin J. Feasts of Israel. (Illus.). 122p. 1980. pap. 7.95 (ISBN 0-914936-42-5). Bible Temple.

Day of Joy. (Hebrew & Eng.). 7.50 (ISBN 0-87559-103-5). Shalom.

Donin, Hayim H. To Pray As a Jew. LC 80-50554. 384p. 1980. 17.95 (ISBN 0-465-08628-4). Basic.

Fredman, Ruth G. The Passover Seder. 1982. pap. 5.95 (ISBN 0-452-00606-6, Mer). NAL.

Gilbert, Arthur. The Passover Seder. (Illus.). 1965. pap. 2.95x (ISBN 0-87068-504-X). Ktav.

Glatzer, Nahum N., ed. Passover Haggadah: Including Readings on the Holocaust, with English Translation, Introduction & Commentary. 3rd ed. LC 69-10846. (Illus., Bilingual ed). 1979. pap. 3.95 (ISBN 0-8052-0624-8). Schocken.

A Guide to Sabbath Observance & Enjoyment. pap. 8.95 (ISBN 0-686-96036-X). United Syn Bk.

Heinemann, Joseph. Prayer in the Talmud: Forms & Patterns. (Studia Judaica: Vol. 9). 1977. 61.00 (ISBN 3-11-004289-4). De Gruyter.
Hertz, Joseph H. Authorized Daily Prayer Book. (Eng. & Hebrew.). 1948. 25.00x (ISBN 0-8197-0094-0). Bloch.
Hirsch, Samson R. The Hirsch Siddur. Samson Raphael Hirsch Publication Society Staff, tr. from Ger. Tr. of Tefilot Yisrael. 1978. 16.95 (ISBN 0-87306-141-1); compact ed 9.95 (ISBN 0-87306-142-X). Feldheim.
Hoffman, Lawrence A. The Canonization of the Synagogue Service. LC 78-62972. 245p. 1986. pap. 12.95 (ISBN 0-268-00756-X). U of Notre Dame Pr.
Hynes, Arleen. Passover Meal. LC 76-187207. 64p. 1972. pap. 2.50 (ISBN 0-8091-1653-7). Paulist Pr.
Idelsohn, Abraham Z. Jewish Music in Its Historical Development. LC 80-24235. (Illus.). xi, 535p. 1981. Repr. of 1948 ed. lib. bdg. 35.00 (ISBN 0-313-22749-7, IDJM). Greenwood.
Kohler, Kaufmann. The Origins of the Synagogue & the Church. Enelow, H. G., ed. LC 73-2213. (The Jewish People; History, Religion, Literature Ser.). Repr. of 1929 ed. 24.50 (ISBN 0-405-05277-4). Ayer Co Pubs.
Lamm, Maurice. Jewish Way in Death & Mourning. rev. ed. LC 69-11684. 1972. pap. 7.95 (ISBN 0-8246-0126-2). Jonathan David.
Levin, Meyer. Israel Haggadah. rev. ed. LC 70-99933. (Illus.). 1977. pap. 5.95 (ISBN 0-8109-2040-9). Abrams.
Mann, Jacob. The Bible As Read & Preached in the Old Synagogue, Vol. 1. rev. ed. (Library of Biblical Studies). 1970. 59.50x (ISBN 0-87068-083-8). Ktav.
Millgram, Abraham E. Jewish Worship. LC 77-151316. (Illus.). 1971. 15.95 (ISBN 0-8276-0003-8, 179). Jewish Pubns.
Neusner, Jacob. The Enchantments of Judaism: Rites of Transformation from Birth Through Death. LC 87-47507. 192p. 1987. 15.95 (ISBN 0-465-01964-1). Basic.
Noth, Martin & Anderson, Berhard W. History of Pentateuchal Traditions. LC 80-24937. (Scholars Press Reproductions Ser.). 1981. 22.00_o.s. (ISBN 0-89130-446-0, 00-07-05); text ed. 17.50 (ISBN 0-89130-954-3). Scholars Pr GA.
Oesterley, William O. The Jewish Background of the Christian Liturgy. 1925. 11.75 (ISBN 0-8446-1329-0). Peter Smith.
--A Short Survey of the Literature of Rabbinical & Medieval Judaism. LC 72-82352. 328p. 1973. Repr. of 1920 ed. lib. bdg. 24.50 (ISBN 0-8337-3944-1). B Franklin.
Olivestone, Ceil & Olivestone, David. Let's Go to Synagogue. LC 81-516. (Illus.). 24p. 1981. 4.95 (ISBN 0-89961-018-8). SBS Pub.
Otzar Hazmiros. (Heb). 7.50 (ISBN 0-87559-089-6); pap. 5.00 (ISBN 0-87559-088-8). Shalom.
Peli, Pinchas. Shabbat Shalom: A Renewed Encounter with the Sabbath. 120p. 1986. pap. 7.95 (ISBN 0-940646-37-4). Rossel Bks.
Petuchowski, Jakob J. Prayerbook Reform in Europe: The Liturgy of European Liberal & Reform Judaism. LC 68-8262. (Illus.). 1969. 13.50 (ISBN 0-8074-0091-2, 387580, Pub. by World Union). UAHC.
Pollak, Gabriel, ed. Transliterated Haggadah: Passover Haggadah. (Heb, & Eng). deluxe ed. 18.50 leatherette bdg. (ISBN 0-87559-082-9). Shalom.
Pollak, P. S. Halel Vzimrah: Commentary in Hebrew on the Passover Haggadah. (Heb). 12.50 (ISBN 0-87559-100-0); pap. 9.50 (ISBN 0-87559-099-3). Shalom.
--Nefesh Hayah: Commentary & Interpretation on the Passover Haggadah with the Haggadah Text. (Hebrew.). 9.50 (ISBN 0-87559-091-8). Shalom.
Rossel, Seymour. When a Jew Prays. Borowitz, Eugene B. & Chanover, Hyman, eds. LC 73-1233. (Illus.). 192p. 1973. pap. text ed. 6.95x (ISBN 0-87441-093-2). Behrman.
Roth, Cecil. The Haggadah. 109p. 1975. pap. 4.95 (ISBN 0-900689-72-2). Soncino Pr.
Silverman, Morris & Hillel. Tishah B'av Service. pap. 2.95x (ISBN 0-87677-068-5). Prayer Bk.
Silverman, Morris, ed. Passover Haggadah. rev. ed. (Illus.). 1986. 10.00 (ISBN 0-87677-025-1); pap. 4.95 (ISBN 0-87677-029-4). Prayer Bk.
Stavsky, David. For Thou Art with Me: A Manual of Mourning. 1965. pap. 1.50 (ISBN 0-87306-093-8). Feldheim.
Trepp, Leo. The Complete Book of Jewish Observance. LC 79-1352. (Illus.). 1979. 16.50 (ISBN 0-87441-281-1). Behrman.
Werner, Eric. The Sacred Bridge. (Music Reprint Ser.). 1979. Repr. of 1959 ed. lib. bdg. 65.00 (ISBN 0-306-79581-7). Da Capo.
Wildman, Joshua A. And Let Us Say Amen. Wengrov, Charles, tr. from Hebrew. Tr. of V'imru Amen. 1978. pap. 6.95 (ISBN 0-87306-148-9). Feldheim.

JEWS–MIGRATIONS

see also Jews–Diaspora; Refugees, Jewish

Abella, Irving & Troper, Harold. None is Too Many: Canada & the Jews of Europe, 1933-1948. LC 83-42864. 368p. 1983. 17.95 (ISBN 0-394-53328-3). Random.
Berger, David. The Legacy of Jewish Migration: Eighteen Eighty-One & Its Impact. (Social Science Monographs, Brooklyn College Studies on Society in Change). 189p. 1983. 26.00x (ISBN 0-88033-026-0). East Eur Quarterly.
Bierman, John. Odyssey. 288p. 1984. 16.95 (ISBN 0-671-50156-9). S&S.
Gilbert, Martin. Exile & Return: The Struggle for a Jewish Homeland. (Illus.). 364p. 1978. 12.95 (ISBN 0-397-01249-7). Brown Bk.
Kushner, Arlene. The Ethiopian Jews: Photographs & Letters. 1986. pap. 9.95 (ISBN 0-933503-47-4). Shapolsky Pubs.
--Falasha No More: An Ethiopian Jewish Child Comes Home. (Illus.). 58p. 1986. 9.95 (ISBN 0-933503-43-1). Shapolsky Pubs.
Leftwich, Joseph & Chertoff, Mordecai S., eds. Why Do the Jews Need a Land of Their Own? LC 83-45297. 242p. 1984. 19.95 (ISBN 0-8453-4774-8, Cornwall Bks). Assoc Univ Prs.
Marinbach, Bernard. Galveston: Ellis Island of the West. (Modern Jewish History Ser.). 384p. 1983. 49.50x (ISBN 0-87395-700-8); pap. 17.95 (ISBN 0-87395-701-6). State U NY Pr.
Mendelsohn, John. Jewish Emigration: The SS St. Louis Affair & Other Cases. LC 81-80315. (The Holocaust Ser.: Vol. 7). 274p. 1982. lib. bdg. 61.00 (ISBN 0-8240-4881-4). Garland Pub.
--Jewish Emigration 1938-1940: Rublee & Intergovernmental Committee. LC 81-80314. (The Holocaust Ser.). 250p. 1982. lib. bdg. 61.00 (ISBN 0-8240-4880-6). Garland Pub.
Rosenbaum, S. E. A Voyage to America in Eighteen Forty-Seven: The Diary of a Bohemian Jew on His Voyage from Hamburg to New York in 1847. (Studies in Judaica & the Holocaust: No. 3). 60p. 1987. lib. bdg. 19.95x (ISBN 0-89370-371-0); pap. text ed. 9.95x (ISBN 0-89370-471-7). Borgo Pr.
Shoshuk, Levi & Eisenberg, Azriel, eds. Momentous Century: Personal & Eyewitness Accounts of the Rise of the Jewish Homeland & State, 1875-1978. LC 81-86164. (Illus.). 472p. 1984. 25.00 (ISBN 0-8453-4748-9, Cornwall Bks). Assoc Univ Prs.
Simon, Rita J., ed. New Lives: The Adjustment of Soviet Jewish Immigrants in the United States & Israel. 208p. 1985. 19.95 (ISBN 0-669-09767-5). Lexington Bks.
Strauss, Herbert A., ed. Jewish Immigrants of the Nazi Period in the U. S. A. Essays on the History, Persecution, & Emigration of the German Jews. (Jewish Immigrants of the Nazi Period in the U. S. A. Ser.: Vol. 6). 430p. 1987. lib. bdg. 74.00 (ISBN 3-598-08011-5). K G Saur.
Strauss, Herbert A. & Kampe, Norbert, eds. Jewish Immigrants of the Nazi Period in the U. S. A. The Expulsion & Migration of German Jews 1933-45 - Annotated Sources. (Jewish Immigrants of the Nazi Period in the U. S. A. Ser.: Vol. 4). 225p. 1988. lib. bdg. 50.00 (ISBN 3-598-08009-3). K G Saur.

JEWS–MISCELLANEA

Blum, Jakub & Rich, Vera. The Image of the Jew in Soviet Literature. LC 84-12196. 276p. 1985. 25.00 (ISBN 0-88125-062-7). Ktav.
Isaacs, Ron & Isaacs, Leora. A Jewish Grandparents' Book of Memories. 100p. 1987. 20.00 (ISBN 0-87668-976-4). Aronson.

JEWS–MISSION

see Jews–Election, Doctrine of

JEWS–NATIONALISM

see Nationalism–Jews

JEWS–PERSECUTIONS

see also Holocaust, Jewish (1939-1945); Refugees, Jewish

Adler, Cyrus & Margalith, Aaron M. With Firmness in the Right: American Diplomatic Action Affecting Jews, 1840-1945. Davis, Moshe, ed. LC 77-70651. (America & the Holy Land Ser.). 1977. Repr. of 1946 ed. lib. bdg. 40.00x (ISBN 0-405-10222-4). Ayer Co Pubs.
Anti-Semitism in the Soviet Union: Its Roots & Consequences. 664p. 1984. 35.00 (ISBN 0-88464-051-5); pap. 16.95 (ISBN 0-88464-052-3). ADL.
Arendt, Hannah. Eichmann in Jerusalem: A Report of the Banality of Evil. rev ed. 1977. pap. 6.95 (ISBN 0-14-004450-7). Penguin.
Chazan, Robert. European Jewry & the First Crusade. 1987. 37.50. U of Cal Pr.
Dawidowicz, Lucy S. The War Against the Jews, 1933-1945. 496p. 1986. 22.95 (ISBN 0-02-908030-4). Free Pr.
Gordon, Sarah. Hitler, Germans, & the "Jewish Question". LC 83-43073. 416p. 1984. 42.00 (ISBN 0-691-05412-6); pap. 15.00 (ISBN 0-691-10162-0). Princeton U Pr.
Graeber, Isacque & Britt, Steuart H. Jews in a Gentile World: The Problem of Anti-Semitism. LC 78-26329. (Illus.). 1979. Repr. of 1942 ed. lib. bdg. 32.50x (ISBN 0-313-20878-6, GRJE). Greenwood.
Grobman, Alex, et al, eds. Genocide: Critical Issues of the Holocaust. LC 83-3052. (Illus.). 502p. 1983. 19.95 (ISBN 0-940646-04-8, Co-pub. by Simon Wiesenthal Center); pap. 12.95 (ISBN 0-940646-38-2). Rossel Bks.
Gutman, Yisrael. The Jews of Warsaw, 1939-1943: Ghetto, Underground, Revolt. Friedman, Ina, tr. LC 81-47570. (Illus.). 512p. 1982. 24.95x (ISBN 0-253-33174-9). Ind U Pr.
Hirschfeld, Gerhard, ed. The Policies of Genocide: Jews & Soviet Prisoners of War in Nazi Germany. (Illus.). 176p. 1986. text ed. 24.95x (ISBN 0-04-943045-9); pap. text ed. 9.95x (ISBN 0-04-943046-7). Allen Unwin.
Historical Views of Judaism: Four Selections. LC 73-2209. (The Jewish People; History, Religion, Literature Ser.). 35.00 (ISBN 0-405-05273-1). Ayer Co Pubs.
Laub, Morris. Last Barrier to Freedom: Internment of Jewish Holocaust Survivors on Cyprus 1946-1949. LC 84-82475. (Illus., Orig.). 1985. pap. 8.95 (ISBN 0-943376-25-4). Magnes Mus.
Lee, Albert. Henry Ford & the Jews. LC 79-3694. 252p. 1980. 12.95 (ISBN 0-8128-2701-5). Stein & Day.
Moreen, Vera B. Iranian Jewry's Hour of Peril & Heroism. (A Study of the American Academy for Jewish Research). 247p. 1987. text ed. 25.00 (ISBN 0-231-06578-7). Columbia U Pr.
Poliakov, Leon. The History of Anti-Semitism, Vol. 2: From Mohammed to the Marranos. Gerardi, Natalie, tr. from Fr. LC 65-10228. Tr. of Histoire De l'antisemitisme: De Mahomet Aux Marranes. 399p. 1974. 19.50 (ISBN 0-8149-0701-6). Vanguard.
Poliakov, Leon & Sabille, Jacques. Jews under the Italian Occupation. LC 81-22202. 208p. 1983. Repr. of 1955 ed. 23.50x (ISBN 0-86527-344-8). Fertig.
Prager, Dennis & Telushkin, Joseph. Why the Jews? The Reason for Anti-Semitism. 224p. 1983. 14.95 (ISBN 0-671-45270-3). S&S.
Ross, Robert W. So It Was True: The American Protestant Press & the Nazi Persecution of the Jews. 374p. pap. 9.95 (ISBN 0-686-95052-6). ADL.
Roth, Cecil. Spanish Inquisition. (Illus., Orig.). 1964. pap. 7.95 (ISBN 0-393-00255-1, Norton Lib). Norton.
Strauss, Herbert A., ed. Jewish Immigrants of the Nazi Period in the U. S. A. Essays on the History, Persecution, & Emigration of the German Jews. (Jewish Immigrants of the Nazi Period in the U. S. A. Ser.: Vol. 6). 430p. 1987. lib. bdg. 74.00 (ISBN 3-598-08011-5). K G Saur.
Trachtenberg, Joshua. The Devil & the Jews: The Medieval Conception of the Jew & Its Relation to Modern Anti - Semitism. 288p. 1983. pap. 6.95 (ISBN 0-8276-0227-8, 610). Jewish Pubns.
Trunk, Isaiah. Jewish Responses to Nazi Persecution. (Illus.). 371p. Repr. 13.00 (ISBN 0-686-95071-2). ADL.
Wiesenthal, Simon. Every Day Remembrance Day: A Chronicle of Jewish Martyrdom. (Illus.). 480p. 1987. 19.95 (ISBN 0-8050-0098-4). H Holt & Co.
World Committee For The Relief Of The Victims Of German Fascism. The Reichstag Fire Trial: The Second Brown Book of the Hitler Terror. LC 68-9605. 1969. Repr. of 1934 ed. 32.50 (ISBN 0-86527-165-8). Fertig.
Zweigenhaft, Richard L. Who Gets to the Top? Executive Suite Discrimination in the Eighties. LC 84-70044. 48p. 1984. pap. 3.00 (ISBN 0-87495-059-7). Am Jewish Comm.

JEWS–PHILOSOPHY

see Philosophy, Jewish

JEWS–POLITICAL AND SOCIAL CONDITIONS

see also Jews–Diaspora; Zealots (Jewish Party); Zionism

Adler, Cyrus & Margalith, Aaron M. With Firmness in the Right: American Diplomatic Action Affecting Jews, 1840-1945. Davis, Moshe, ed. LC 77-70651. (America & the Holy Land Ser.). 1977. Repr. of 1946 ed. lib. bdg. 40.00x (ISBN 0-405-10222-4). Ayer Co Pubs.
Baron, Salo W. The Jewish Community, 3 vols. LC 74-97269. 1972. Repr. of 1942 ed. Set. lib. bdg. 53.50x (ISBN 0-8371-3274-6, BAJC). Greenwood.
--A Social & Religious History of the Jews, 18 vols. 2nd, rev. & enl. ed. Incl. Vol. 1. Ancient Times to the Beginning of the Christian Era. 1952 (ISBN 0-231-08838-8); Vol. 2. Ancient Times: Christian Era: the First Five Centuries. 1952 (ISBN 0-231-08839-6); Vol. 3. High Middle Ages: Heirs of Rome & Persia. 1957 (ISBN 0-231-08840-X); Vol. 4. High Middle Ages: Meeting of the East & West. 1957 (ISBN 0-231-08841-8); Vol. 5. High Middle Ages: Religious Controls & Dissensions. 1957 (ISBN 0-231-08842-6); Vol. 6. High Middle Ages: Laws, Homilies & the Bible. 1958 (ISBN 0-231-08843-4); Vol. 7. High Middle Ages: Hebrew Language & Letters. 1958 (ISBN 0-231-08844-2); Vol. 8. High Middle Ages: Philosophy & Science. 1958 (ISBN 0-231-08845-0); Vol. 9. Late Middle Ages & Era of European Expansion, 1200-1650: Under Church & Empire. 1965 (ISBN 0-231-08846-9); Vol. 10. Late Middle Ages & Era of European Expansion, 1200-1650: On the Empire's Periphery. 1965 (ISBN 0-231-08847-7); Vol. 11. Late Middle Ages & Era of European Expansion, 1200-1650: Citizen or Alien Conjurer. 1967 (ISBN 0-231-08848-5); Vol. 12. Late Middle Ages & Era of European Expansion, 1200-1650: Economic Catalyst. 1967 (ISBN 0-231-08849-3); Vol. 13. Late Middle Ages & Era of European Expansion, 1200-1650: Inquisition, Renaissance & Reformation. 1969 (ISBN 0-231-08850-7); Vol. 14. Late Middle Ages & Era of European Expansion, 1200-1650: Catholic Restoration & Wars of Religion. 1969 (ISBN 0-231-08851-5); Vol. 15. Late Middle Ages & Era of European Expansion, 1200-1650: Resettlement & Exploration. 1973 (ISBN 0-231-08852-3); Index. 32.00x (ISBN 0-231-08877-9). LC 52-404. 45.00x ea. Columbia U Pr.
Cohen, Steven M. The National Survey of American Jews, 1984: Political & Social Outlooks. iv, 60p. (Orig.). 1985. pap. 4.00 (ISBN 0-87495-069-4). Am Jewish Comm.
Cuddihy, John M. The Ordeal of Civility: Freud, Marx, Levi-Strauss, & the Jewish Struggle with Modernity. LC 86-47757. 272p. 1987. pap. 9.95 (ISBN 0-8070-3609-9, BP-738). Beacon Pr.
Dawidowicz, Lucy S. The Golden Tradition: Jewish Life & Thought in Eastern Europe. LC 84-5560. 512p. 1984. pap. 11.95 (ISBN 0-8052-0768-6). Schocken.
Elazar, Daniel J. Kinship & Consent: The Jewish Political Tradition & Its Contemporary Uses. LC 82-21851. 412p. 1983. lib. bdg. 29.50 (ISBN 0-8191-2800-7, Co-pub. by Ctr Jewish Comm Studies); pap. text ed. 14.50 (ISBN 0-8191-2801-5). U Pr of Amer.
Elazar, Daniel J. & Cohen, Stuart A. The Jewish Polity: Jewish Political Organization from Biblical Times to the Present. LC 83-48648. (Jewish Political & Social Studies). (Illus.). 384p. 1984. 27.50x (ISBN 0-253-33156-0). Ind U Pr.
Frick, Frank S. The Formation of the State in Ancient Israel: A Survey of Models & Theories. (The Social World of Biblical Antiquity Ser.). 219p. 1985. text ed. 24.95x (ISBN 0-907459-51-X, Pub. by Almond Pr England); pap. text ed. 10.95 (ISBN 0-907459-52-8). Eisenbrauns.
Gilbert, Martin. The Jews of Hope. (Nonfiction Ser.). 272p. 1985. pap. 7.95 (ISBN 0-14-008510-6). Penguin.
Glanz, Rudolf. Aspects of the Social, Political, & Economic History of the Jews in America. 1984. 29.50x (ISBN 0-87068-463-9). Ktav.
Goldman, Edward A., ed. Jews in a Free Society: Challenges & Opportunities. 12.50x (ISBN 0-87820-112-2). Ktav.
Goldscheider, Calvin. Jewish Continuity & Change: Emerging Patterns in America. LC 84-48746. (Jewish Political & Social Studies). (Illus.). 214p. 1986. 24.95x (ISBN 0-253-33157-9). Ind U Pr.
Grupper, David & Klein, David G. The Paper Shtetl: A Complete Model of an East European Jewish Town. LC 83-42714. (Illus., Orig.). 1984. pap. 11.95 (ISBN 0-8052-0749-X). Schocken.
Hentoff, Nat, ed. Black Anti-Semitism & Jewish Racism. LC 70-89955. 1970. pap. 3.75 (ISBN 0-8052-0280-3). Schocken.
International Center for University Teaching of Jewish Civilization Staff, et al, eds. Jewish Political Traditions. LC 85-40516. (Selected Course Outlines & Curriculum Resources from Leading Universities Ser.). 250p. 1985. pap. text ed. 14.50 (ISBN 0-910129-29-0). Wiener Pub Inc.
Jewish Peace Fellowship, ed. The Jewish Tradition of Peace. 1984. lib. bdg. 79.95 (ISBN 0-87700-626-1). Revisionist Pr.
--Judaism & Peacemaking. 1984. lib. bdg. 79.95 (ISBN 0-87700-627-X). Revisionist Pr.
--Roots of Jewish Nonviolence. 1984. lib. bdg. 79.95 (ISBN 0-87700-628-8). Revisionist Pr.

Kahan, Arcadius. Essays in Jewish Social & Economic History. Weiss, Roger, ed. LC 86-1427. xx, 208p. 1986. lib. bdg. 27.50x (ISBN 0-226-42240-2). U of Chicago Pr.
Kahane, Meir. Uncomfortable Questions for Comfortable Jews. 288p. 1987. 18.00 (ISBN 0-8184-0438-8). Lyle Stuart.
Kautsky, Karl. Foundations of Christianity. Hartmann, Jacob W., tr. from Ger. LC 72-81774. 512p. 1972. pap. 15.00 (ISBN 0-85345-262-8, PB-2628). Monthly Rev.
--Foundations of Christianity. Hartmann, Jacob W., tr. from Ger. LC 72-81774. Repr. of 1972 ed. 120.00 (ISBN 0-8357-9441-5, 2016442). Bks Demand UMI.
Kolitz, Zvi. Survival for What. LC 70-75761. 234p. 1969. 10.00 (ISBN 0-8022-2272-2). Philos Lib.
Korn, Yitshak. Jews at the Crossroads. LC 81-86479. 208p. 1983. 12.95 (ISBN 0-8453-4754-3, Cornwall Bks). Assoc Univ Prs.
Lesser, Allen. Israel's Impact, Nineteen Hundred Fifty to Fifty-One: A Personal Record. LC 84-12013. (Orig.). 1984. lib. bdg. 28.00 (ISBN 0-8191-4125-9); pap. text ed. 15.50 (ISBN 0-8191-4126-7). U Pr of Amer.
Levin, Nora. Jewish Socialist Movements, Eighteen Seventy-One to Nineteen Seventeen: While Messiah Tarried. (Littman Library of Jewish Civilization). (Illus.). 566p. 1978. 32.00x (ISBN 0-19-710029-5). Oxford U Pr.
Levine, Etan, ed. Diaspora: Exile & the Contemporary Jewish Condition. 363p. 1986. 18.95 (ISBN 0-933503-50-4). Shapolsky Pubs.
Levkov, Ilya. Bitburg & Beyond. 1986. 14.95 (ISBN 0-933503-52-0). Shapolsky Pubs.
Lewittes, M. Religious Foundations of the Jewish State: The Concept & Practice of Jewish Statehood from Biblical Times to the Modern State of Israel. 25.00x (ISBN 0-87068-433-7). Ktav.
Maccoby, Hyman. Judaism on Trial: Jewish-Christian Disputations in the Middle Ages. (Littman Library of Jewish Civilization). 246p. 1982. 34.00x (ISBN 0-19-710046-5). Oxford U Pr.
Marcus, Jacob R. Jew in the Medieval World: A Source Book: 315-1791. LC 60-8666. (Temple Books). 1969. pap. text ed. 10.95x (ISBN 0-689-70133-0, T7). Atheneum.
Mayer, Egon. Love & Tradition: Marriage Between Jews & Christians. 312p. 1985. (full discount avail.) 17.95 (ISBN 0-306-42043-0, Plenum Pr). Plenum Pub.
Morton, Leah, pseud. I Am a Woman & a Jew. (Masterworks of Modern Jewish Writing Ser.). (Illus.). 380p. 1986. pap. 9.95 (ISBN 0-910129-56-8, Distr. by Schocken Books). Wiener Pub Inc.
Mosse, George L. Germans & Jews. LC 68-9631. 260p. 1985. 25.00x. Fertig.
National Council of Jewish Women. Self Help for Seniors. 30p. (Orig.). 1983. pap. text ed. 4.00 (ISBN 0-941840-14-X). NCJW.
The Protocols of the Learned Elders of Zion. 299p. 1986. pap. 7.00 (ISBN 0-317-53280-4). Noontide.
Schneid, Hayyim, ed. The Family. LC 73-11760. (Popular Judaica Library). (Illus.). 120p. 1974. pap. 3.95 (ISBN 0-8276-0029-1, 341). Jewish Pubns.
Selzer, Michael. Politics & Jewish Purpose. 45p. 1972. pap. 2.50 (ISBN 0-934676-12-7). Greenlf Bks.
Shorris, Earl. Jews without Mercy: A Lament. 1982. 14.95 (ISBN 0-385-17853-0). Brown Bk.
Starr, Joshua. Romania: The Jewries of the Levant After the Fourth Crusade. 1943. 10.00x (ISBN 0-87068-108-7). Ktav.
Steinberg, Milton. The Making of the Modern Jew. (Brown Classics in Judaica Ser.). 318p. 1987. pap. text ed. 14.50 (ISBN 0-8191-4492-4). U Pr of Amer.
Wistrich, Robert S. Socialism & the Jews: The Dilemmas of Assimilation in Germany & Austria-Hungary. (Littman Library of Jewish Civilization). 1982. 37.50x (ISBN 0-19-710053-8). Oxford U Pr.

JEWS–PRAYER-BOOKS AND DEVOTIONS

Birnbaoum, Philip. Hasiddur Hashalem Daily Prayer Book: Sephardic. 860p. 1969. 17.00 (ISBN 0-88482-053-X). Hebrew Pub.
Birnbaum, Philim. Hasiddur Hashalem: Daily Prayer Book. 790p. 1977. pap. 9.95 pocket flexible ed. (ISBN 0-88482-054-8). Hebrew Pub.
Birnbaum, Philip. Hasiddur Hashalem (Daily Prayer Book) 790p. 1964. 17.00 (ISBN 0-88482-045-9). Hebrew Pub.
--Mahzor Hashalem: High Holiday Prayer Book, Vol. 1, Rosh Hashahah. 646p. 1960. 14.00 (ISBN 0-88482-246-X). Hebrew Pub.
--Mahzor Hashalem: High Holyday Prayer Book, 5 Vols. 1971. Set. 58.00 (ISBN 0-88482-169-2). Hebrew Pub.
--Mahzor Hashalem: High Holyday Prayer Book, 2 Vols. 1960. Set. 26.50 (ISBN 0-88482-170-6). Hebrew Pub.
--Mahzor Hashalem: High Holyday Prayer Book, 1 Vol. 1042p. 1951. 17.00 (ISBN 0-88482-240-0). Hebrew Pub.
--Mahzor Hashalem: Prayer Book for Pesah, Vol. 4. 459p. 1971. 11.50 (ISBN 0-88482-172-2). Hebrew Pub.
--Mahzor Hashalem: Prayer Book for Shavuot, Vol. 5. 358p. 1971. 11.50 (ISBN 0-88482-173-0). Hebrew Pub.
--Mahzor Hashalem: Prayer Book for Sukkot, Vol. 3. 478p. 1971. 11.50 (ISBN 0-88482-174-9). Hebrew Pub.
--Mahzor Leshalosh Regalim: Prayer Book for Three Festivals. 641p. 1971. 15.00 (ISBN 0-88482-149-8). Hebrew Pub.
--Mazhor Hashalem High Holiday Prayer Book, Vol. 2: Yom Kippur. 770p. 1960. 14.00 (ISBN 0-88482-247-8). Hebrew Pub.
--Siddur Leshabbat Veyom Tov: Prayer Book for Sabbath & Festivals with Torah Readings. 724p. 1950. 14.50 (ISBN 0-88482-062-9). Hebrew Pub.
Bokser, Ben. Hasiddur: The Prayer Book. 842p. 1957. pap. 9.00 pocket flexible ed. (ISBN 0-88482-069-6). Hebrew Pub.
Dresner, Samuel. Prayer, Humility & Compassion. 4.95 (ISBN 0-87677-006-5). Hartmore.
Eisenberg, Azriel & Arian, Philip. The Story of the Prayer Book. pap. 5.95x (ISBN 0-87677-017-0). Hartmore.
Feuer, Avrohom C. Tashlich. (Art Scroll Mesorah Ser.). 64p. 1979. 6.95 (ISBN 0-89906-158-3); pap. 4.95 (ISBN 0-89906-159-1). Mesorah Pubns.
Freedman, Jacob. Polychrome Historical Prayerbook: Siddur 'Bet Yosef' (Illus.). 400p. 1984. 125.00x (ISBN 0-686-12113-9). J Freedman Liturgy.
Gates of Mitzvah: A Guide to the Jewish Life Cycle. (Shaarei Mitzvah Ser.). (Illus.). 7.95 (ISBN 0-916694-53-4). Central Conf.
Gates of the House (Shaarei Habayit) The New Union Home Prayerbook. 9.00 (ISBN 0-916694-35-6). Central Conf.
Gates of Understanding: for the Days of Awe, Vol. II. (Shaarei Bina Ser..). pap. 7.95 flexbook binding (ISBN 0-916694-84-4). Central Conf.
Greenberg, Sidney & Sugarman, Allan S. Junior Contemporary Prayer Book for the High Holidays. pap. 4.95 (ISBN 0-87677-054-5). Prayer Bk.
Greenberg, Sidney, ed. Contemporary Prayers & Readings. 1972. pap. 3.95 (ISBN 0-87677-050-2). Prayer BK.
Heilman, Samuel C. The People of the Book: Drama, Felloship, & Religion. LC 82-13369. x, 338p. 1987. pap. text ed. price not set (ISBN 0-226-32493-1). U of Chicago Pr.
Hirsch. Psalms, 2 vols. 1975. 26.95 (ISBN 0-87306-025-3). Feldheim.
Hoffman, Edward. The Heavenly Ladder: A Jewish Guide to Inner Growth. LC 85-42779. 160p. (Orig.). 1986. pap. 8.95 (ISBN 0-06-064001-4, HarpR). Har-Row.
Hoffman, Lawrence, ed. Gates of Understanding, Vol. 1. 1977. 5.95 (ISBN 0-916694-43-7). Central Conf.
Jewish Reconstructionist Foundation. The New Haggadah. 3rd rev. ed. Kaplan, Mordecai M., et al, eds. LC 77-16803. (Illus.). 1978. pap. text ed. 3.95x (ISBN 0-87441-304-4). Behrman.
Karff, Samuel E. Agada: The Language of Jewish Faith. 15.00x (ISBN 0-87820-114-9). Ktav.
Klein, Earl. Jewish Prayer: Concepts & Customs. LC 85-23944. (The Hebraica-Judaica Bookshelf Ser.). (Orig.). 1986. 17.95 (ISBN 0-933771-01-0). Alpha Pub Co.
Labovitz, Annette & Labovitz, Eugene. Time for My Soul: A Treasury of Jewish Stories for Our Holy Days. LC 86-32243. 400p. 1987. 30.00 (ISBN 0-87668-954-3). Aronson.
Lipman, Zev, illus. Baruch Ata Befi Hataf: Illustrated Prayers & Blessings for Young Children. (Illus.). 4.95 (ISBN 0-685-84974-0). Feldheim.
Nachman of Breslov & Nathan of Breslov. Outpouring of the Soul. Kaplan, Aryeh, tr. from Hebrew. Tr. of Hishtap'kuth HaNefesh. 96p. (Orig.). 1980. pap. 2.50 (ISBN 0-930213-14-9). Breslov Res Inst.
Prayerbook: Service of the Heart. (Home Study Program Ser.: No. 302). 6.00 (ISBN 0-686-96123-4). United Syn Bk.
Rosenfield, Abraham. Kinot for the Ninth of Av. 482p. 1956. 12.95 (ISBN 0-910818-16-9). Judaica Pr.
--Selichot for the Whole Year. 832p. 1956. 13.95 (ISBN 0-910818-10-X). Judaica Pr.
Rothenberg, Benno, ed. Archaeological Haggadah. LC 86-1052. (Illus.). 1986. 12.95 (ISBN 0-915361-36-1, 09713-7, Dist. by Watts). Adama Pubs Inc.
Sabbath & Festival Praybook. 9.85 (ISBN 0-686-96035-1). United Syn Bk.
Schuller, Eileen M. Non-Canonical Psalms from Qumran: A Pseudepigraphic Collection. (Harvard Semitic Studies). 1987. 23.95 (ISBN 0-89130-943-8, 04-04-28). Scholars Pr GA.
Silbermann, A. M., ed. The Children's Haggadah. Wartski, Isidore & Super, Arthur S., trs. (Illus.). 100p. 1972. 14.95 (ISBN 0-87306-984-6). Feldheim.
Silverman, Morris. High Holiday Prayer Book. 12.00 (ISBN 0-87677-051-0); simulated leather 13.50 (ISBN 0-87677-012-X). Prayer Bk.
--Prayers of Consolation. 1972. 8.95x (ISBN 0-87677-062-6); pap. 6.95x (ISBN 0-87677-063-4). Prayer BK.
Silverman, Morris & Arzt, Max. Selihot Service. rev. ed. pap. 2.95x (ISBN 0-87677-066-9). Prayer Bk.
Silverman, Morris & United Synagogue. Weekday Prayer Book. 8.95 (ISBN 0-87677-071-5). Prayer Bk.
Spiro, Jack. A Time to Mourn. LC 67-30744. 160p. 1985. pap. text ed. 8.95 (ISBN 0-8197-0497-0). Bloch.
The Standard Siddur-Prayerbook. 1974. 8.95 (ISBN 0-87306-990-0). Feldheim.
Steinsaltz, Adin. Teshuvah: A Guide for the Newly Observant Jew. 192p. 1987. 19.95 (ISBN 0-02-931150-0). Free Pr.
Stern, Chaim. Gates of the House. 1977. cancelled (ISBN 0-916694-42-9); lib. bdg. cancelled. Central Conf.
Stern, Chaim, ed. Gates of Prayer. pulpit ed. 1975. English ed. 20.00 (ISBN 0-916694-46-1); Hebrew 20.00 (ISBN 0-916694-03-8). Central Conf.
--Gates of Prayer for Weekdays & at a House of Mourning. 1975. pap. 2.75 (ISBN 0-916694-04-6). Central Conf.
--Gates of Prayer: The New Union Prayerbook. 1975. English ed. 15.00 (ISBN 0-916694-01-1); Hebrew ed. 16.00 (ISBN 0-916694-00-3). Central Conf.
Strassfeld, Michael. A Shabbat Haggadah for Celebration & Study. LC 80-83430. 124p. 1980. pap. 5.50 (ISBN 0-87495-025-2). Am Jewish Comm.
Tolley, Jackie, ed. On Our Spiritual Journey: A Creative Shabbat Service. (Illus.). 74p. (Orig.). 1984. pap. 5.95 (ISBN 0-9608054-3-5). Womans Inst-Cont Jewish Ed.
Union Home Prayerbook. 1951. 7.95 ea. (ISBN 0-916694-19-4); leatherbound 7.00 ea. (ISBN 0-916694-60-7). Central Conf.
Weekday Prayerbook. 6.25 (ISBN 0-686-96031-9). United Syn Bk.
Wengrow, C., tr. The Hafetz Hayyim on the Siddur. 10.95 (ISBN 0-87306-996-X). Feldheim.

JEWS–PRIESTS
see Priests, Jewish

JEWS–RELIGION
see Judaism

JEWS–RESTORATION
see also Jews–Diaspora; Zionism

Cohen, Richard I., ed. Vision & Conflict in the Holy Land. LC 85-1972. 350p. 1985. 29.95 (ISBN 0-312-84967-2). St Martin.
Davis, Moshe, ed. Call to America to Build Zion: An Original Anthology. LC 77-70723. (America & the Holy Land Ser.). 1977. lib. bdg. 20.00x (ISBN 0-405-10306-9). Ayer Co Pubs.
--Christian Protagonists for Jewish Restoration: An Original Anthology. LC 77-70678. (America & the Holy Land Ser.). 1977. lib. bdg. 20.00x (ISBN 0-405-10221-6). Ayer Co Pubs.
--Holy Land Missions & Missionaries: An Original Anthology. LC 77-70703. (America & the Holy Land Ser.). (Illus.). 1977. lib. bdg. 20.00x (ISBN 0-405-10259-3). Ayer Co Pubs.
Mehdi, M. T., ed. Palestine & the Bible. LC 71-114557. 1971. pap. 4.00 (ISBN 0-911026-06-1). New World Press NY.

JEWS–RITES AND CEREMONIES
see also Bar Mitzvah; Jewish Way of Life

Agnon, Y. Days of Awe: A Treasury of Tradition, Legends & Learned Commentaries Concerning Rosh Hashanah, Yom Kippur & the Days Between. LC 48-8316. 1965. pap. 8.95 (ISBN 0-8052-0100-9). Schocken.
Bloch, Abraham P. The Biblical & Historical Backround of Jewish Customs & Ceremonies. 1979. 20.00x (ISBN 0-87068-658-5); pap. 11.95. Ktav.
Cashman, Greer F. & Frankel, Alona. Jewish Days & Holidays. LC 86-70789. (Illus.). 61p. 1986. 9.95 (ISBN 0-915361-58-2, Dist. by Watts). Adama Pubs Inc.
Caspi, M. M., ed. Jewish Tradition in the Diaspora: Studies in Memory of Professor Walter J. Fischel. 314p. 1981. 19.95 (ISBN 0-943376-16-5). Magnes Mus.
Chanover, Hyman, adapted by. Service for the High Holy Days Adapted for Youth. new ed. LC 72-2058. 192p. 1972. pap. 3.95x (ISBN 0-87441-123-8). Behrman.
Chill, Abraham. The Minhagim: The Customs & Ceremonies of Judaism, Their Origins & Rationale. 2nd corrected ed. LC 78-62153. (Illus.). 339p. 1980. 14.95 (ISBN 0-87203-076-8); pap. 10.95 (ISBN 0-87203-077-6). Hermon.
Dembitz, Lewis N. Jewish Services in Synagogue & Home. facs. ed. LC 74-27977. (Modern Jewish Experience Ser.). 1975. Repr. of 1898 ed. 40.00x (ISBN 0-405-06706-2). Ayer Co Pubs.
Diamant, Anita. New Jewish Wedding. 272p. 1986. 8.95 (ISBN 0-671-62882-8). Summit Bks.
Donin, Hayim. To Be a Jew. LC 72-89175. 1972. 17.95 (ISBN 0-465-08624-1). Basic.
Drucker, Malka. Celebrating Life: Jewish Rites of Passage. LC 84-4684. (Illus.). 112p. 1984. reinforced bdg. 11.95 (ISBN 0-8234-0539-7). Holiday.
Epstein, Morris. All about Jewish Holidays & Customs. rev. ed. 1969. pap. 7.95x (ISBN 0-87068-500-7). Ktav.
Goldin, Hyman E. Jew & His Duties. 246p. 1953. pap. 6.95 (ISBN 0-88482-429-2). Hebrew Pub.
Gutmann, Joseph. Beauty in Holiness: Studies in Jewish Ceremonial Art & Customs. 1970. 50.00x (ISBN 0-87068-012-9). Ktav.
--The Jewish Sanctuary. (Inconography of Religions, Section Ser.: Vol. 23). (Illus.). 33p. 1983. pap. text ed. 32.50x (ISBN 90-04-06893-7, Pub. by EJ Brill Holland). Humanities.
Israel Ministry. What Is a Jew? 1975. 30.00 (ISBN 0-379-13904-9). Oceana.
Klein, I. A Guide to Jewish Religious Practice. (Moreshet Ser: No. 6). 20.00x (ISBN 0-87334-004-3, Pub. by Jewish Theol Seminary). Ktav.
Kolatch, A. J. The Second Jewish Book of Why. LC 84-21477. 432p. 1985. 13.95 (ISBN 0-8246-0305-2). Jonathan David.
Kolatch, Alfred J. Family Seder. rev. ed. LC 67-17778. (Illus.). 1972. pap. 3.95 (ISBN 0-8246-0132-7). Jonathan David.
Lash, Neil A. & Lash, Jamie S. A Jewish Wedding. (Jewish Jewels Ser.: Vol. 2). (Illus.). 24p. 1985. pap. 1.50 (ISBN 0-915775-03-4). Love Song Mess Assn.
Levi, Shonie B. & Kaplan, Sylvia R. Guide for the Jewish Homemaker. 2nd ed. LC 59-12039. (Illus.). 1965. pap. 6.95 (ISBN 0-8052-0087-8). Schocken.
Levy, B. H. Savannah's Old Jewish Community Cemeteries. LC 83-1045. vii, 118p. 1983. 10.95 (ISBN 0-86554-076-4, H68). Mercer Univ Pr.
Marcus, Ralph. Law in the Apocrypha. LC 29-9822. (Columbia University. Oriental Studies: No. 26). Repr. of 1927 ed. 15.00 (ISBN 0-404-50516-3). AMS Pr.
Maslin, Simeon J., ed. Shaarei Mitzvah: Gates of Mitzvah. (Illus.). 1979. 9.95 (ISBN 0-916694-37-2); pap. 7.95 (ISBN 0-916694-53-4). Central Conf.
Peli, Pinchas. Shabbat Shalom: A Renewed Encounter with the Sabbath. 120p. 1986. pap. 7.95 (ISBN 0-940646-37-4). Rossel Bks.
Philosophy: Ritual-Shabbat & Kashrut. (Home Study Program Ser.: No. 602). 6.00 (ISBN 0-686-96133-1). United Syn Bk.
Reik, Theodore. Ritual. pap. text ed. 19.95 (ISBN 0-8236-8269-2, 025840). Intl Univs Pr.
Rosenau, William. Jewish Ceremonial Institutions & Customs. rev. ed. 3rd. ed. LC 70-78222. (Illus.). 1971. Repr. of 1925 ed. 35.00x (ISBN 0-8103-3402-X). Gale.
Rosoff, David. The Tefillin Handbook. (Orig.). 1984. pap. 4.95 (ISBN 0-87306-373-2). Feldheim.
Silverman, Morris. Memorial Service at the Cemetery. pap. 0.95 (ISBN 0-685-64878-8). Prayer Bk.
Sperling, Abraham I. Reasons for Jewish Customs & Traditions. Matts, Abraham, tr. LC 68-31711. cancelled. (ISBN 0-8197-0184-X); pap. cancelled (ISBN 0-8197-0008-8). Bloch.
Stone, Michael E., ed. Jewish Writings of the Second Temple Period: Apocrypha, Pseudipigrapha, Qumran, Sectarian Writings, Philo, Josephus. LC 83-48926. (Compendia Rerum Iudaicarum ad Novum Testamentum Ser.). 656p. 1984. 35.95 (ISBN 0-8006-0603-5, 1-603). Fortress.
Strassfeld, Michael & Strassfeld, Sharon, eds. The Second Jewish Catalog: Sources & Resources. LC 73-11759. (Illus.). 464p. 1976. 8.95 (ISBN 0-8276-0084-4, 391). Jewish Pubns.
Trepp, Leo. The Complete Book of Jewish Observance. LC 79-1352. (Illus.). 1979. 16.50 (ISBN 0-87441-281-1). Behrman.
--The Complete Book of Jewish Observance. LC 79-1352. (Behrman House Book). (Illus.). 370p. 1980. 14.95 (ISBN 0-671-41797-5). Summit Bks.
--History of the Jewish Experience: Eternal Faith, Eternal People. rev. ed. LC 73-3142. Orig. Title: Eternal Faith, Eternal People: a Journey into Judaism. 296p. 1973. pap. text ed. 9.95x (ISBN 0-87441-072-X). Behrman.
Unterman, Alan. The Jews. (Library of Religious Beliefs & Practices). 212p. 1986. pap. text ed. 14.95 (ISBN 0-7100-0842-2). Methuen Inc.
Weisenberg, David H. Jewish Way. (Illus.). 1969. 8.95 (ISBN 0-8158-0026-6). Chris Mass.

JEWS–SECTS
see Jewish Sects

JEWS–SOCIAL LIFE AND CUSTOMS
see also Jewish Way of Life

Abrahams, Israel. Jewish Life in the Middle Ages. LC 58-11933. (Temple Books). 1969. pap. text ed. 7.95x (ISBN 0-689-70001-6, T1). Atheneum.

Berliner, Abraham. Aus dem Leben der Deuschen Juden im Mittelalter. Katz, Steven, ed. LC 79-7127. (Jewish Philosophy, Mysticism & History of Ideas Ser.). 1980. Repr. of 1900 ed. lib. bdg. 14.00x (ISBN 0-405-12241-1). Ayer Co Pubs.

Biale, David. Childhood, Marriage & the Family in the Eastern European Jewish Enlightement. 24p. 1983. pap. 1.50 (ISBN 0-87495-049-X). Am Jewish Comm.

Bloch, Abraham P. The Biblical & Historical Backround of Jewish Customs & Ceremonies. 1979. 20.00x (ISBN 0-87068-658-5); pap. 11.95. Ktav.

Bowen, Barbara M. Strange Scriptures That Perplex the Western Mind. 1940. pap. 3.95 (ISBN 0-8028-1511-1). Eerdmans.

Bulka, Reuven P. Torah Therapy: Reflections on the Weekly Sedra & Special Occasions. LC 83-6155. 1983. 15.00x (ISBN 0-88125-033-3). Ktav.

Cashman, Greer F. & Frankel, Alona. Jewish Days & Holidays. LC 86-70789. (Illus.). 61p. 1986. 9.95 (ISBN 0-915361-58-2, Dist. by Watts). Adama Pubs Inc.

Cohen, Steven M. American Modernity & Jewish Identity. 250p. 1983. 24.00x (ISBN 0-422-77740-4, NO.3467); pap. 9.95 (ISBN 0-422-77750-1, NO.3495). Methuen Inc.

Cohen, Steven M. & Hyman, Paula E., eds. The Jewish Family. 256p. 1986. text ed. 42.50x (ISBN 0-8419-0860-5). Holmes & Meier.

Dawidowicz, Lucy S. The Golden Tradition: Jewish Life & Thought in Eastern Europe. LC 84-5560. 512p. 1984. pap. 11.95 (ISBN 0-8052-0768-6). Schocken.

Diamant, Anita. The New Jewish Wedding. LC 84-24102. (Illus.). 1985. 16.95 (ISBN 0-671-49527-5). Summit Bks.

Drachman, Bernard. From the Heart of Israel. LC 72-110183. (Short Story Index Reprint Ser.). 1905. 23.50 (ISBN 0-8369-3334-6). Ayer Co Pubs.

Feldman, David M. Health & Medicine in the Jewish Tradition: The Pursuit of Wholeness. 176p. 1986. 15.95x (ISBN 0-8245-0707-X). Crossroad NY.

Friedman, Natalie & Rogers, Theresa F. The Jewish Community & Children of Divorce: A Pilot Study of Perceptions & Responses. 32p. 1983. pap. 2.00 (ISBN 0-87495-051-1). Am Jewish Comm.

Galas, Yechiel. Halacha. 192p. 1973. pap. 4.95 (ISBN 0-910818-13-4). Judaica Pr.

Gilman, Sander L. Jewish Self-Hatred: Anti-Semitism & the Hidden Language of the Jews. LC 85-45050. 480p. 1986. text ed. 28.50x (ISBN 0-8018-3276-4). Johns Hopkins.

Goodman, Philip, ed. Jewish Marriage Anthology. Goodman, Hanna. LC 65-17045. (Illus.). 1965. 13.95 (ISBN 0-8276-0145-X, 236). Jewish Pubns.

Groner, Judyth S. & Wikler, Madeline. My Very Own Jewish Community. LC 83-22215. (Illus.). 40p. 1984. pap. 4.95 (ISBN 0-930494-32-6). Kar Ben.

Heilman, Samuel C. The People of the Book: Drama, Fellowship, & Religion. LC 82-13369. 264p. 1983. lib. bdg. 25.00x (ISBN 0-226-32492-3). U of Chicago Pr.

Horowitz, George. The Spirit of Jewish Law. LC 53-7535. 1979. Repr. of 1953 ed. text ed. 40.00x (ISBN 0-87632-167-8). Bloch.

Jung, Leo. Love & Life. LC 79-87873. 84p. 1979. 7.50 (ISBN 0-8022-2355-9). Philos Lib.

Kaplan, Benjamin. Jew & His Family. LC 67-21376. 1967. 25.00x (ISBN 0-8071-0545-7). La State U Pr.

Katz, Jacob. The Traditional Jewish Family in Historical Perspective. 1983. pap. 1.00 (ISBN 0-87495-048-1). Am Jewish Comm.

Kennett, R. H. Ancient Hebrew Social Life & Custom As Indicated in Law, Narrative & Metaphor. (British Academy, London, Schweich Lectures on Biblical Archaeology Series, 1931). pap. 19.00 (ISBN 0-8115-1273-8). Kraus Repr.

Kushner, Arlene. Falasha No More: An Ethiopian Jewish Child Comes Home. (Illus.). 58p. 1986. 9.95 (ISBN 0-933503-43-1). Shapolsky Pubs.

Lash, Neil A. & Lash, Jamie S. A Jewish Wedding. (Jewish Jewels Ser.: Vol. 2). (Illus.). 24p. 1985. pap. 1.50 (ISBN 0-915775-03-4). Love Song Mess Assn.

Latner, Helen. The Book of Modern Jewish Etiquette: A Guide To Contemporary Manners & Religious Customs. LC 86-45124. 400p. 1986. pap. 9.95 (ISBN 0-06-097054-5, PL-7054, PL). Har-Row.

L'ayla L'ayla. pap. 6.95 (ISBN 0-686-96043-2); tchr's guide 4.00 (ISBN 0-686-99686-0). United Syn Bk.

Levi, Shonie B. & Kaplan, Sylvia R. Guide for the Jewish Homemaker. 2nd ed. LC 59-12039. (Illus.). 1965. pap. 6.95 (ISBN 0-8052-0087-8). Schocken.

Levita, Elijah. Massoreth Ha Massoreth. rev. ed. LC 67-11894. (Library of Biblical Studies). 1969. 39.50x (ISBN 0-87068-081-1). Ktav.

Life Cycle Chapter Study Kit. pap. 3.00 (ISBN 0-686-96087-4). United Syn Bk.

Loeb, L., ed. Outcaste: Jewish Life in Southern Iran. (Library of Anthroplogy). 354p. 1977. 42.95 (ISBN 0-677-04530-1). Gordon & Breach.

Lutske, Harvey. The Book of Jewish Customs. LC 86-2362. 300p. 1986. 25.00 (ISBN 0-87668-916-0). Aronson.

Marcus, Jacob R. The Jew in the Medieval World: A Source Book, 315-1791. LC 71-97295. 504p. 1975. Repr. of 1938 ed. lib. bdg. 22.50x (ISBN 0-8371-2619-3, MAJM). Greenwood.

Neusner, Jacob. Vanquished Nation, Broken Spirit: The Virtues of the Heart in Formative Judaism. 208p. Date not set. price not set (ISBN 0-521-32832-2); pap. price not set (ISBN 0-521-33801-8). Cambridge U Pr.

Pechota, Vratislav. The Right to Know One's Human Rights: A Road Toward Marriage & Family. LC 83-72868. 52p. 1983. pap. 2.50 (ISBN 0-87495-056-2). Am Jewish Comm.

Petuchowski, Jacob J. Freedom of Expression in the Jewish Tradition. 34p. 1984. pap. 2.50 (ISBN 0-87495-062-7). Am Jewish Comm.

Rockland, Mae S. The Jewish Party Book: A Contemporary Guide to Customs, Crafts & Foods. LC 78-54387. (Illus.). 284p. 1987. pap. 10.95 (ISBN 0-8052-0829-1). Schocken.

Schlesinger, Benjamin. The Jewish Family: A Survey & Annotated Bibliography. Strakhovsky, Florence, ed. LC 79-151389. pap. 46.80 (ISBN 0-317-09749-0, 2014401). Bks Demand UMI.

Seltzer, Robert M. Jewish People, Jewish Thought. (Illus.). 1980. text ed. write for info. (ISBN 0-02-408950-8). Macmillan.

Shin'ar, Uri. The Animated Hagaddah. Date not set. 14.95. Jonathan David.

Sidon, Ephraim. The Animated Megillah. (Animated Holydays Ser.). 54p. 1987. 14.95 (ISBN 0-8246-0324-9). Jonathan David.

Singer, David. Focus on the Jewish Family: A Selected Annotated Bibliography, 1970-1982. 32p. 1984. pap. 2.00 (ISBN 0-87495-058-9). Am Jewish Comm.

Snyder, Charles R. Alcohol & the Jews: A Cultural Study of Drinking & Sobriety. LC 77-24885. (Arcturus Books Paperbacks). 240p. 1978. pap. 6.95x (ISBN 0-8093-0846-0). S Ill U Pr.

Stopler, Pinchas. Jewish Alternatives in Love, Dating & Marriage. 100p. (Orig.). 1985. lib. bdg. 10.50 (ISBN 0-8191-4475-4); pap. text ed. 5.95 (ISBN 0-8191-4476-2). U Pr of Amer.

Szarmach, Paul E., ed. Aspects of Jewish Culture in the Middle Ages. LC 77-29046. (Illus.). 208p. 1979. 44.50 (ISBN 0-87395-165-4). State U NY Pr.

Tarrant, Christ. Life in Bible Times. 48p. (Orig.). 1986. pap. 5.95 (ISBN 0-687-21850-0). Abingdon.

Tzorchei Tzibbur: Community & Responsibility in the Jewish Tradition. 6.00 (ISBN 0-686-96047-5); tchr's ed. 8.50 (ISBN 0-686-99687-9). United Syn Bk.

Women's League for Conservative Judaism. Welcome to the World - A Jewish Baby's Record Book. (Illus.). 40p. 1985. 12.95 (ISBN 0-936293-00-4). WLCJ.

JEWS–WOMEN
see Women, Jewish

JEWS–ZIONISM
see Zionism

JEWS, YEMENITE

Ahroni, Reuben. Yemenite Jewry: Origins, Culture, & Literature. LC 84-48649. (Jewish Literature and Culture Ser.). (Illus.). 288p. 1986. 27.50x (ISBN 0-253-36807-3). Ind U Pr.

Ozeri, Zion M. Yemenite Jews: A Photographic Essay. (Illus.). 96p. 1985. 19.95 (ISBN 0-8052-3980-4). Schocken.

JEWS IN AFRICA

Auraham, Samuel & Kushner, Arlene. Treacherous Journey: My Escape from Ethiopia. 1986. 14.95 (ISBN 0-933503-46-6). Shapolsky Pubs.

Boykin, James H. Black Jews. LC 81-90626. iv, 98p. (Orig.). 1982. pap. 3.25x (ISBN 0-9603342-1-1). Boykin.

De Felice, Renzo. Jews in an Arab Land: Libya, 1835-1970. Roumani, Judith, tr. 436p. 1985. 27.50x (ISBN 0-292-74016-6). U of Tex Pr.

Friedman, Elizabeth. Colonialism & After: An Algerian Jewish Community. (Critical Studies in Work & Community). 288p. 1987. text ed. 34.95 (ISBN 0-89789-095-7). Bergin & Garvey.

Kushner, Arlene. The Ethiopian Jews: Photographs & Letters. 1986. pap. 9.95 (ISBN 0-933503-47-4). Shapolsky Pubs.

--Falasha No More: An Ethiopian Jewish Child Comes Home. (Illus.). 58p. 1986. 9.95 (ISBN 0-933503-43-1). Shapolsky Pubs.

Mendelssohn, Sidney. The Jews of Africa, Especially in the 16th & 17th Centuries. 59.95 (ISBN 0-8490-0446-2). Gordon Pr.

Parfitt, Tudor. Operation Moses: The Untold Story of the Secret Exodus of the Falasha Jews from Ethiopia. LC 85-40240. (Illus.). 192p. 1986. 16.95 (ISBN 0-8128-3059-8). Stein & Day.

Williams, Joseph J. Hebrewisms of West Africa: From Nile to Niger with the Jews. LC 67-19534. (Illus.). 1930. 20.00 (ISBN 0-8196-0194-2). Biblo.

JEWS IN ARABIA

Haddad, Heskel M. The Jews of Arab & Islamic Countries: History, Problems & Solutions. LC 83-5065. 168p. 1984. 12.95 (ISBN 0-88400-100-8). Shengold.

Patai, Raphael. The Seed of Abraham: Jews & Arabs in Contact & Conflict. 384p. 1986. 29.95 (ISBN 0-87480-251-2). U of Utah Pr.

Sassoon, David S. A History of the Jews in Baghdad. LC 77-87645. (Illus.). 264p. Repr. of 1949 ed. 34.00 (ISBN 0-404-16427-7). AMS Pr.

Torrey, Charles C. Jewish Foundation of Islam. rev. ed. LC 67-18817. 1968. 20.00x (ISBN 0-87068-117-6). Ktav.

JEWS IN AUSTRIA

Pennell, Joseph. The Jew at Home: Impressions of Jewish Life in Russia & Austria. 1976. lib. bdg. 134.95 (ISBN 0-8490-2098-0). Gordon Pr.

Rozenblit, Marsha L. The Jews of Vienna, 1867-1914: Assimilation & Identity. (Modern Jewish History Ser.). 368p. 1984. 44.50 (ISBN 0-87395-844-6); pap. 16.95 (ISBN 0-87395-845-4). State U NY Pr.

Schoenfeld, Joachim. Shtetl Memoirs: Jewish Life in Galicia under the Austro-Hungarian Empire & in the Polish Republic, 1898-1939. 400p. 1985. text ed. 17.50x (ISBN 0-88125-075-9). Ktav.

Sichrovsky, Peter. Strangers in Their Own Land: Young Jews in Germany & Austria Today. Steinberg, Jean, tr. LC 85-43108. 208p. 1986. 14.95 (ISBN 0-465-08211-4). Basic.

JEWS IN BABYLONIA

Mann, Jacob. The Responsa of the Babylonian Geonim As a Source of Jewish History. LC 73-2215. (The Jewish People; History, Religion, Literature Ser.). Repr. of 1921 ed. 23.50 (ISBN 0-405-05279-0). Ayer Co Pubs.

Neusner, Jacob. A History of the Jews in Babylonia: The Parthian Period. LC 84-5363. (Brown Judaic Studies). 292p. pap. 21.00 (ISBN 0-89130-738-9, 14 00 62). Scholars Pr GA.

--Israel & Iran in Talmudic Times: A Political History. (Illus.). 266p. (Orig.). 1987. lib. bdg. 27.50 (ISBN 0-8191-5729-5, Pub. by Studies in Judaism); pap. text ed. 14.75 (ISBN 0-8191-5730-9). U Pr of Amer.

--Israel's Politics in Sasanian Iran: Jewish Self-Government in Talmudic Times. (Studies in Judaism). (Illus.). 202p. (Orig.). 1987. lib. bdg. 24.75 (ISBN 0-8191-5725-2, Pub. by Studies in Judaism); pap. text ed. 12.25 (ISBN 0-8191-5726-0). U Pr of Amer.

--Judaism, Christianity & Zoroastrianism in Talmudic Babylonia. (Studies in Judaism). 240p. (Orig.). 1987. lib. bdg. 26.50 (ISBN 0-8191-5727-9, Pub. by Studies in Judaism); pap. text ed. 13.50 (ISBN 0-8191-5728-7). U Pr of Amer.

JEWS IN CANADA

Brown, Michael. Jew of Juif? Jews in Canada, 1759-1914. (Illus.). 336p. 1987. 16.95 (ISBN 0-8276-0271-5). Jewish Pubns.

Klein, A. M. Beyond Sambation: Selected Essays & Editorials, 1928-1955. Steinberg, M. W. & Kaplan, Usher, eds. (The Collected Works of A. M. Klein). 1982. 35.00 (ISBN 0-8020-5566-4). U of Toronto Pr.

Rosen, Oded, ed. The Encyclopedia of Jewish Institutions: United States & Canada. 512p. 1983. 55.00 (ISBN 0-913185-00-0). Mosadot Pubns.

Sack, Benjamin G. History of the Jews in Canada. LC 65-1899. pap. 79.00 (ISBN 0-317-28422-3, 2022315). Bks Demand UMI.

JEWS IN CHINA

Leslie, Donald D. The Survival of the Chinese Jews: The Jewish Community of Kaifeng. (Illus.). 270p. 1973. text ed. 59.95 (ISBN 90-040-3413-7). Humanities.

Lord, James H. The Jews in India & the Far East. LC 70-97292. 1976. Repr. of 1907 ed. lib. bdg. 22.50x (ISBN 0-8371-2615-0, LOJI). Greenwood.

Pollak, Michael. Mandarins, Jews & Missionaries: The Jewish Experience in the Chinese Empire. LC 79-84732. (Illus.). 439p. 1983. pap. 10.95 (ISBN 0-8276-0229-4). Jewish Pubns.

Shapiro, Sidney, ed. Jews in Old China: Studies by Chinese Historians. (Illus.). 224p. 1984. 15.95 (ISBN 0-88254-996-0). Hippocrene Bks.

JEWS IN COMMUNIST COUNTRIES

Meyer, Peter. Jews in the Soviet Satellites. LC 79-97297. 1971. Repr. of 1953 ed. lib. bdg. 45.00x (ISBN 0-8371-2621-5, MEJS). Greenwood.

Strom, Yale & Blue, Brian. The Last Jews of Eastern Europe. LC 86-25354. (Illus.). 250p. 1986. 29.95 (ISBN 0-8022-2520-9). Philos Lib.

Tamir, Vicki. Bulgaria & Her Jews: The History of a Dubious Symbiosis. LC 78-62154. (Illus.). 1979. 14.95 (ISBN 0-87203-075-X). Hermon.

JEWS IN EGYPT

Gordon, Benjamin L. New Judea: Jewish Life in Modern Palestine & Egypt. Davis, Moshe, ed. LC 77-70697. (America & the Holy Land Ser.). (Illus.). 1977. Repr. of 1919 ed. lib. bdg. 30.00x (ISBN 0-405-10251-8). Ayer Co Pubs.

Porten, Bezalel. Archives from Elephantine: The Life of an Ancient Jewish Military Colony. (Illus.). 1968. 47.50x (ISBN 0-520-01028-0). U of Cal Pr.

JEWS IN EUROPE

Best, Gary D. To Free a People: American Jewish Leaders & the Jewish Problem in Eastern Europe, 1890 to 1914. LC 81-4265. (Contributions in American History Ser.: No. 98). xi, 240p. 1982. lib. bdg. 32.95 (ISBN 0-313-22532-X, BTO/). Greenwood.

Biale, David. Childhood, Marriage & the Family in the Eastern European Jewish Enlightement. 24p. 1983. pap. 1.50 (ISBN 0-87495-049-X). Am Jewish Comm.

Braham, Randolph L., ed. The Tragedy of the Jews in Hungary: Essays & Documents. (East European Monographs: No. 208). 288p. 1986. 30.00 (ISBN 0-88033-105-4). East Eur Quarterly.

Brin, Herb. ICH Bin Ein Jude. LC 81-15256. 146p. 1983. 9.95 (ISBN 0-8246-0275-7). Jonathan David.

Bristow, Edward J. Prostitution & Prejudice: The Jewish Fight Against White Slavery 1870-1939. 368p. 1983. 21.95 (ISBN 0-8052-3866-2). Schocken.

Carmilly-Weinberger, Moshe, ed. The Rabbinical Seminary of Budapest, 1877-1977: A Centennial Volume. (Illus.). 420p. 1986. 35.00 (ISBN 0-87203-148-9). Hermon.

Dawidowicz, Lucy S. The Golden Tradition: Jewish Life & Thought in Eastern Europe. LC 84-5560. 512p. 1984. pap. 11.95 (ISBN 0-8052-0768-6). Schocken.

Edelstein, Alan. An Unacknowledged Harmony: Philo-Semitism & the Survival of European Jewry. LC 81-1563. (Contributions in Ethnic Studies: No. 4). xii, 235p. 1982. lib. bdg. 29.95 (ISBN 0-313-22754-3, EDP/). Greenwood.

Elazar, Daniel J. & Friedenreich, Harriet P. The Balkan Jewish Communities: Yugoslavia, Bulgaria, Greece, & Turkey. (Illus.). 208p. (Orig.). 1984. lib. bdg. 22.00 (ISBN 0-8191-3473-2, Co-Pub. by Ctr Jewish Comm Studies); pap. text ed. 10.25 (ISBN 0-8191-3474-0). U Pr of Amer.

Engelman, Uriah Z. The Rise of the Jew in the Western World. LC 73-2194. (The Jewish People; History, Religion, Literature Ser.). Repr. of 1944 ed. 22.00 (ISBN 0-405-05260-X). Ayer Co Pubs.

Fishberg, Maurice. Materials for the Physical Anthropology of the Eastern European Jews. LC 6-2111. (American Anthro. Association Memoirs). 1905. 14.00 (ISBN 0-527-00500-2). Kraus Repr.

Glanz, Rudolf. The German Jewish Women, Vol. 2. 25.00x (ISBN 0-87068-462-0). Ktav.

Grupper, David & Klein, David G. The Paper Shtetl: A Complete Model of an East European Jewish Town. LC 83-42714. (Illus., Orig.). 1984. pap. 11.95 (ISBN 0-8052-0749-X). Schocken.

Gursan-Salzmann, Ayse & Salzmann, Laurence. Last Jews of Radauti. LC 82-22176. (Illus.). 192p. 1983. 29.95 (ISBN 0-385-27808-X, Dial). Doubleday.

Heschel, Abraham J. The Earth Is the Lord's: The Inner World of the Jew in Eastern Europe. 109p. 1978. 8.95 (ISBN 0-374-14613-6); pap. 5.95. FS&G.

Hilberg, Raul. The Destruction of the European Jews, 3 vols. rev. ed. LC 84-18369. 1312p. 1985. Boxed Set. text ed. 159.50x (ISBN 0-8419-0832-X); pap. 14.95 student ed. (ISBN 0-8419-0910-5). Holmes & Meier.

Imposed Jewish Governing Bodies Under Nazi Rule: Yivo Colloquium Dec. 2-5, 1967. LC 73-150304. 1972. pap. 5.00 (ISBN 0-914512-03-X). Yivo Inst.

Israel, Jonathan L. European Jewry in the Age of Mercantilism, 1550-1750. 1985. 34.50x (ISBN 0-19-821928-8). Oxford U Pr.

Joseph, Samuel. Jewish Immigration to the United States from 1881 to 1910. LC 14-15042. (Columbia University. Studies in the Social Sciences: No. 145). Repr. of 1914 ed. 7.50 (ISBN 0-404-51145-7). AMS Pr.

--Jewish Immigration to the United States from 1881 to 1910. LC 69-18781. (American Immigration Collection Ser., No. 1). (Illus.). 1969. Repr. of 1914 ed. 10.00 (ISBN 0-405-00529-6). Ayer Co Pubs.

Kaganovich, Moshe. Jewish Partisans of Eastern Europe. 340p. 1985. 15.95 (ISBN 0-8052-5053-0); pap. 11.95 (ISBN 0-8052-5054-9). Schocken.

Katz, Jacob. Jews & Freemasons in Europe, 1723-1939. Oschry, Leonard, tr. from Heb. LC 71-115475. 1970. 22.50x (ISBN 0-674-47480-5). Harvard U Pr.

--Out of the Ghetto: The Social Background of Jewish Emancipation, 1770-1870. LC 72-86386. 1973. 18.50x (ISBN 0-674-64775-0). Harvard U Pr.

Katz, Jacob, ed. Toward Modernity: The European Jewish Model. 246p. (Orig.). 1986. 24.95 (ISBN 0-88738-092-1). Transaction Bks.

Meltzer, Milton. World of Our Fathers: The Jews of Eastern Europe. LC 74-14755. (Illus.). 256p. 1974. 11.95 (ISBN 0-374-38530-0). FS&G.

Mendelsohn, Ezra. The Jews of East Central Europe between the World Wars. LC 81-48676. (Illus.). 320p. 1983. 27.50x (ISBN 0-253-33160-9). Ind U Pr.

Meyer, Peter. Jews in the Soviet Satellites. LC 79-97297. 1971. Repr. of 1953 ed. lib. bdg. 45.00x (ISBN 0-8371-2621-5, MEJS). Greenwood.

Parkes, James W. The Jew in the Medieval Community. 456p. 1976. pap. 12.95 (ISBN 0-87203-060-1). Hermon.

Philipson, David. Old European Jewries. LC 74-178586. Repr. of 1895 ed. 27.50 (ISBN 0-404-56663-4). AMS Pr.

Pullan, Brian. The Jews of Europe & The Inquisition of Venice, 1550-1670. LC 83-7147. 364p. 1983. 32.50x (ISBN 0-389-20414-5). B&N Imports.

Sachs, Abraham S. Worlds That Passed. facsimile ed. Berman, Harold & Joffe, Judah, trs. from Yiddish. LC 74-29521. (Modern Jewish Experience Ser.). (Eng.). 1975. Repr. of 1928 ed. 24.50x (ISBN 0-405-06746-1). Ayer Co Pubs.

Sanning, Walter N. The Dissolution of Eastern European Jewry: An Analysis of the Six Million Myth. 1983. lib. bdg. 79.95 (ISBN 0-87700-463-3). Revisionist Pr.

Shainberg, Maurice. Breaking from the K. G. B. 1986. 15.95 (ISBN 0-933503-54-7). Shapolsky Pubs.

Stern, Selma. The Court Jew: A Contribution to the History of Absolutism in Europe. 316p. 1985. 29.95 (ISBN 0-88738-019-0). Transaction Bks.

Strom, Yale & Blue, Brian. The Last Jews of Eastern Europe. LC 86-25354. (Illus.). 250p. 1986. 29.95 (ISBN 0-8022-2520-9). Philos Lib.

Suhl, Yuri. They Fought Back: The Story of Jewish Resistance in Nazi Europe. 316p. Repr. 7.95 (ISBN 0-686-95093-3). ADL.

Tama, M. Diogene, tr. Transactions of the Parisian Sanhedrim. (Brown Classics in Judaica Ser.). 364p. 1985. pap. text ed. 15.25 (ISBN 0-8191-4488-6). U Pr of Amer.

Trunk, Isaiah. Judenrat. LC 70-173692. 1977. pap. 8.95 (ISBN 0-8128-2170-X). Stein & Day.

Vago, Bela & Mosse, George L., eds. Jews & Non-Jews in Eastern Europe, 1918-1945. pap. 88.00 (ISBN 0-317-27256-X, 2024158). Bks Demand UMI.

Vishniac, Roman. A Vanished World. (Illus.). 192p. 1986. pap. 19.95 (ISBN 0-374-52023-2). FS&G.

Waagenaar, Sam. The Pope's Jews. (Illus.). 500p. 1974. 9.95 (ISBN 0-912050-49-7, Library Pr). Open Court.

Wolf, Hannie. Child of Two Worlds. (Illus.). 156p. 1979. 13.00 (ISBN 0-931068-02-9). Purcells.

Zimmer, Eric. Harmony & Discord: An Analysis of the Decline of Jewish Self-Government in Fifteenth Century Central Europe. 276p. 1970. 10.00x (ISBN 0-685-26214-6, Pub. by Yeshiva U. Pr.). Bloch.

JEWS IN FRANCE

Agus, Irving A. Heroic Age of Franco-German Jewry. LC 75-94444. 1969. 20.00x (ISBN 0-8197-0053-3). Bloch.

Albert, Phyllis C. The Modernization of French Jewry: Consistory & Community in the Nineteenth Century. LC 76-50680. (Illus.). 472p. 1977. 40.00x (ISBN 0-87451-139-9). U Pr of New Eng.

Bensimon-Donath, Doris. L'Integration des Juifs Nord-Africains en France. (Publications de l'Institut d'Etudes et de Recherches Interethniques et Interculturelles: No. 1). 1971. pap. 14.00x (ISBN 90-2796-930-2). Mouton.

Calmann, Marianne. The Carriere of Carpentras. LC 82-48692. (Littman Library of Jewish Civilization). (Illus.). 286p. 1984. 32.50x (ISBN 0-19-710037-6). Oxford U Pr.

Chazan, Robert. Medieval Jewry in Northern France: A Poltical & Social History. LC 73-8129. (Johns Hopkins University Studies in Historical & Political Science: 91st; 2). pap. 63.00 (ISBN 0-317-20643-5, 2024132). Bks Demand UMI.

Cohen, Richard I. Burden of Conscience: French Jewry's Response to the Holocaust. (The Modern Jewish Experience Ser.). 351p. 1987. 27.50 (ISBN 0-253-31263-9). Ind U Pr.

Epstein, Simon. Cry of Cassandra: The Resurgence of European Anti-Semitism. Posel, Norman S., tr. from Fr. Tr. of Antisemitism Francais. 256p. 1986. 15.95 (ISBN 0-915765-13-6, Pub. by Zenith Edit); pap. 7.95 (ISBN 0-915765-14-4, Pub. by Zenith Edit). Natl Pr Inc.

Green, Nancy L. Pletzl of Paris: Jewish Immigrant Workers in the Belle Epoque. 278p. 1985. 39.55 (ISBN 0-8419-0995-4). Holmes & Meier.

Hertzberg, Arthur. The French Enlightenment & the Jews. LC 68-18996. pap. 108.00 (ISBN 0-317-26825-2, 2023485). Bks Demand UMI.

Inbar, Michael & Adler, Chaim. Ethnic Integration in Israel: A Comparative Study of Moroccan Brothers Who Settled in France & in Israel. LC 76-27933. (Illus.). 120p. 1977. lib. bdg. 16.95 (ISBN 0-87855-204-9). Transaction Bks.

Kahn, Leon. Les Juifs de Paris Pendant la Revolution. (Research & Source Works Ser.: No. 198). 1968. Repr. of 1899 ed. 30.50 (ISBN 0-8337-1892-4). B Franklin.

Klarsfeld, Serge. The Children of Izieu: A Human Tragedy. (Illus.). 128p. 1985. pap. 9.95 (ISBN 0-8109-2307-6). Abrams.

Latour, Anny. The Jewish Resistance in France, Nineteen Forty to Nineteen Forty-Four. (Illus.). 1981. 14.95 (ISBN 0-8052-5025-5, Pub. by Holocaust Library); pap. 8.95 (ISBN 0-8052-5024-7). Schocken.

Malino, Frances. The Sephardic Jews of Bordeaux: Assimilation & Emancipation in Revolutionary & Napoleonic France. LC 77-22659. (Judaic Studies: Vol. 7). 200p. 1978. 15.75 (ISBN 0-8173-6903-1). U of Ala Pr.

Marrus, Michael R. & Paxton, Robert O. Vichy France & the Jews. LC 82-16869. 432p. (Orig.). 1983. pap. 12.95 (ISBN 0-8052-0741-4). Schocken.

Muhlstein, Anka. Baron James: The Rise of the French Rothschilds. LC 84-40015. 224p. 1984. pap. 7.95 (ISBN 0-394-72608-1, Vin). Random.

Poliakov, Leon & Sabille, Jacques. Jews under the Italian Occupation. LC 81-22202. 208p. 1983. Repr. of 1955 ed. 23.50x (ISBN 0-86527-344-8). Fertig.

Schnapper, Dominique. Jewish Identities in France: An Analysis of Contemporary French Jewry. Goldhammer, Arthur, tr. LC 82-17495. (Illus.). 224p. 1983. lib. bdg. 25.00x (ISBN 0-226-73910-4). U of Chicago Pr.

Schwartzfuchs, Simon. Napoleon, the Jews & the Sanhedria. (Littman Library of Jewish Civilization). 1979. 24.00x (ISBN 0-19-710023-6). Oxford U Pr.

Shatzmiller, Joseph. Recherches sur la Communaute Juive De Manosque Au Moyen Age (1241-1329) (Etudes Juives: No. 15). 1973. pap. 14.00x (ISBN 90-2797-188-9). Mouton.

Szajkowski, Soza. Analytical Franco-Jewish Gazetteer, 1939-1945. 1966. 50.00 (ISBN 0-87068-112-5). Ktav.

--Jews & the French Revolution of 1789, 1830 & 1848. 1969. 59.50x (ISBN 0-87068-112-5). Ktav.

Tama, M. Diogene, tr. Transactions of the Parisian Sanhedrim. (Brown Classics in Judaica Ser.). 364p. 1985. pap. text ed. 15.25 (ISBN 0-8191-4488-6). U Pr of Amer.

Timayenis, Telemachus T. The Original Mr. Jacobs: Startling Expose. Grob, Gerald, ed. LC 76-46107. (Anti-Movements in America). 1977. Repr. of 1888 ed. lib. bdg. 24.50x (ISBN 0-405-09978-9). Ayer Co Pubs.

Weinberg, David H. A Community on Trial: The Jews of Paris in the 1930's. LC 77-2999. 1977. 22.00x (ISBN 0-226-88507-0). U of Chicago Pr.

Weinstein, Frida S. A Hidden Childhood: A Jewish Girl's Sanctuary in a French Convent, 1942-1945. Kennedy, Barbara L., tr. 160p. 1986. pap. 6.95 (ISBN 0-8090-1529-3). Hill & Wang.

Wilson, Nelly. Bernard-Lazare. LC 77-82524. 1979. 47.50 (ISBN 0-521-21802-0). Cambridge U Pr.

Wilson, Stephen. Ideology & Experience: Antisemitism in France at the Time of the Dreyfus Affair. LC 81-65467. (Illus.). 832p. 1982. 60.00 (ISBN 0-8386-3037-5). Fairleigh Dickinson.

JEWS IN GERMANY

Agus, Irving A. Heroic Age of Franco-German Jewry. LC 75-94444. 1969. 20.00x (ISBN 0-8197-0053-3). Bloch.

Arendt, Hannah. Rahel Varnhagen: The Life of a Jewish Woman. Winston, Richard & Winston, Clara, trs. from Ger. LC 74-6478. (Illus.). 236p. 1974. pap. 7.95 (ISBN 0-15-676100-9, Harv). HarBraceJ.

Bach, H. I. The German Jew: A Synthesis of Judaism & Western Civilization, 1730-1930. (Litman Library of Jewish Civilization). 1985. 29.95x (ISBN 0-19-710033-3). Oxford U Pr.

Bendix, Reinhard. From Berlin to Berkeley: German-Jewish Identities. LC 85-8578. 320p. 1985. 29.95 (ISBN 0-88738-067-0). Transaction Bks.

Chazan, Robert. European Jewry & the First Crusade. 1987. 37.50. U of Cal Pr.

Dicker, Herman. Creativity, Holocaust, Reconstruction: Jewish Life in Wuertemberg, Past & Present. (Illus.). 1984. 18.50 (ISBN 0-87203-118-7). Hermon.

Eidelberg, Shlomo, ed. Jews & the Crusaders: The Hebrew Chronicles of the First & Second Crusades. (Illus.). 200p. 1977. 24.95x (ISBN 0-299-07060-3). U of Wis Pr.

Gluckel. The Memoirs of Gluckel of Hameln. Lowenthal, Marvin, tr. from Ger. LC 77-75290. 1977. pap. 7.95 (ISBN 0-8052-0572-1). Schocken.

Graupe, Heinz M. The Rise of Modern Judaism: An Intellectual History of German Jewry 1650-1942. LC 77-9059. 344p. 1979. lib. bdg. 24.00 (ISBN 0-88275-395-9); pap. text ed. 10.50 (ISBN 0-89874-562-4). Krieger.

Henry, Frances. Victims & Neighbors: A Small Town in Nazi Germany Remembered. (Illus.). 216p. 1984. 27.95 (ISBN 0-89789-047-7); pap. 12.95 (ISBN 0-89789-048-5). Bergin & Garvey.

Herz, E. Emil. Before the Fury. LC 66-18484. 1967. 7.95 (ISBN 0-8022-0710-3). Philos Lib.

Historical Views of Judaism: Four Selections. LC 73-2209. (The Jewish People; History, Religion, Literature Ser.). 35.00 (ISBN 0-405-05273-1). Ayer Co Pubs.

Kaplan, Marion. The Jewish Feminist Movement in Germany: The Campaigns of the Judischer Frauenbund, 1904-1938. LC 78-67567. (Contributions in Women's Studies: No. 8). (Illus.). lib. bdg. 29.95 (ISBN 0-313-20736-4, KGJ/). Greenwood.

Katz, Jacob, ed. Toward Modernity: The European Jewish Model. 246p. (Orig.). 1986. 24.95 (ISBN 0-88738-092-1). Transaction Bks.

Koehn, Ilse. Mischling, Second Degree: My Childhood in Nazi Germany. LC 77-6189. 240p. 1977. 13.00 (ISBN 0-688-80110-2); PLB 12.88 (ISBN 0-688-84110-4). Greenwillow.

Lamberti, Marjorie. Jewish Activism in Imperial Germany: The Struggle for Civil Equality. LC 77-17325. (Yale Historical Publications: No. 119). 1978. 27.50x (ISBN 0-300-02163-1). Yale U Pr.

Leo Baeck Institute Yearbook, Vol. 18. 400p. 1973. 28.00 (ISBN 0-436-24426-8, Pub. by Secker & Warburg UK). David & Charles.

Leo Baeck Institute Yearbook, Vol. 19. 380p. 1974. 28.00 (ISBN 0-436-24427-6, Pub. by Secker & Warburg UK). David & Charles.

Leo Baeck Institute Yearbook, Vol 20. 420p. 1975. 28.00 (ISBN 0-436-24428-4, Pub. by Secker & Warburg UK). David & Charles.

Leo Baeck Institute Yearbook, Vol. 22. (Illus.). 388p. 1977. 28.00 (ISBN 0-436-24430-6, Pub. by Secker & Warbug UK). David & Charles.

Leo Baeck Institute Yearbook, Vol. 23. 486p. 1978. 28.00 (ISBN 0-436-24431-4, Pub. by Secker & Warburg UK). David & Charles.

Leo Baeck Institute Yearbook, Vol. 25. 504p. 1980. 28.00 (ISBN 0-436-24433-0, Pub. by Secker & Warburg UK). David & Charles.

Leo Baeck Institute Yearbook, Vol. 26. 504p. 1981. 28.00 (ISBN 0-436-24434-9, Pub. by Secker & Warburg UK). David & Charles.

Leo Baek Institute Yearbook: Jewry in the German Reich II, No. 28. 464p. 1983. 28.00 (ISBN 0-436-25542-1, Pub. by Secker & Warburg UK). David & Charles.

Liberles, Robert. Religious Conflict in Social Context: The Resurgence of Orthodox Judaism in Frankfurt Am Main, 1838-1877. LC 84-27981. (Contributions to the Study of Religion Ser.: No. 13). xvi, 297p. 1985. lib. bdg. 29.95 (ISBN 0-313-24806-0, LRX/). Greenwood.

Low, Alfred D. Jews in the Eyes of the Germans: From the Enlightenment to Imperial Germany. LC 79-334. (Illus.). 528p. 1979. 19.95 (ISBN 0-915980-86-X). ISHI PA.

Mandelbaum, Hugo. Jewish Life in Village Communities of Southern Germany. (Illus.). 96p. 1986. 6.95 (ISBN 0-87306-382-1). Feldheim.

Marcus, Jacob R. The Rise & Destiny of the German Jew. rev. ed. 1971. 15.00x (ISBN 0-87068-148-6). Ktav.

Mosse, George L. Germans & Jews: The Right, the Left, & the Search for a 'Third Force' in Pre-Nazi Germany. LC 68-9631. 1970. 23.50 (ISBN 0-86527-081-3). Fertig.

Nicosia, Francis R. The Third Reich & the Palestine Question. 335p. 1986. text ed. 35.00x (ISBN 0-292-72731-3). U of Tex Pr.

Niewyk, Donald L. The Jews in Weimar Germany. LC 79-26234. 262p. 1980. 27.50x (ISBN 0-8071-0661-5). La State U Pr.

Poppel, Stephen M. Zionism in Germany 1897-1933: The Shaping of a Jewish Identity. LC 76-14284. 229p. 1977. 7.95 (ISBN 0-8276-0085-2, 395). Jewish Pubns.

Reinharz, Jehuda & Schatzberg, Walter, eds. The Jewish Response to German Culture: From the Enlightenment to the Second World War. LC 85-14185. 368p. 1985. 32.50x (ISBN 0-87451-345-6). U Pr of New Eng.

Robinson, Jacob. Guide to Jewish History Under Nazi Impact. 1974. 45.00x (ISBN 0-87068-231-8). Ktav.

Schleunes, Karl A. The Twisted Road to Auschwitz: Nazi Policy Toward German Jews, 1933-1939. LC 74-102024. pap. 72.00 (ISBN 0-317-11169-8, 2011134). Bks Demand UMI.

Sichrovsky, Peter. Strangers in Their Own Land: Young Jews in Germany & Austria Today. Steinberg, Jean, tr. LC 85-43108. 208p. 1986. 14.95 (ISBN 0-465-08211-4). Basic.

Stanford, Julian C. Reflection: Diary of a German Jew in Hiding. 1965. 4.50 (ISBN 0-943376-00-9). Magnes Mus.

Strauss, Herbert A. & Kampe, Norbert, eds. Jewish Immigrants of the Nazi Period in the U. S. A. The Expulsion & Migration of German Jews 1933-45 - Annotated Sources. (Jewish Immigrants of the Nazi Period in the U. S. A. Ser.: Vol. 4). 225p. 1988. lib. bdg. 50.00 (ISBN 3-598-08009-3). K G Saur.

Strauss, Herbert A. & Rogrbaugh, Dennis, eds. Jewish Immigrants of the Nazi Period in the U. S. A. An Oral History Record. (Jewish Immigrants of the Nazi Period in the U. S. A. Ser.: Vol. 5). 308p. 1986. lib. bdg. 60.00 (ISBN 3-598-08010-7). K G Saur.

Strauss, Walter, ed. Signs of Life: Jews from Wuerttemberg-Reports for the Period after 1933 in Letters & Descriptions. 25.00x. Ktav.

Tal, Uriel. Christians & Jews in Germany: Religion, Politics, & Ideology in the Second Reich, 1870-1914. Jacobs, Noah J., tr. from Hebrew. LC 74-21612. (Illus.). 359p. 1975. 35.00x (ISBN 0-8014-0879-2). Cornell U Pr.

Weinreich, Max. Hitlers Professors. LC 47-42580. (Yiddish., Illus.). 325p. 1947. pap. 10.00x (ISBN 0-914512-26-9). Yivo Inst.

JEWS IN GREAT BRITAIN

Davis, Myer D. Shetaroth, Hebrew Deeds of English Jews Before 1290. 410p. 1888. text ed. 74.52x (ISBN 0-576-80111-9, Pub. by Gregg Intl Pubs England). Gregg Intl.

Glassman, Bernard. Anti-Semitic Stereotypes Without Jews: Images of the Jews in England, 1290-1700. LC 75-16391. 218p. 1975. 22.50x (ISBN 0-8143-1545-3). Wayne St U Pr.

Hein, Virginia H. The British Followers of Theodor Herzl: English Zionist Leaders, 1896-1904. McNeill, William H. & Stansky, Peter, eds. (Modern European History Ser.). 325p. 1987. lib. bdg. 50.00 (ISBN 0-8240-7815-2). Garland Pub.

Holmes, Colin. Anti-Semitism in British Society Eighteen Seventy-Six to Nineteen Thirty-Nine. LC 78-21023. 328p. 1979. text ed. 49.50x (ISBN 0-8419-0459-6). Holmes & Meier.

Kokosalakis, N. Ethnic Identity & Religion: Tradition & Change in Liverpool Jewry. LC 82-13609. (Illus.). 276p. 1983. lib. bdg. 29.75 (ISBN 0-8191-2732-9); pap. text ed. 13.25 (ISBN 0-8191-2733-7). U Pr of Amer.

Pollins, Harold. Economic History of the Jews in England. (Littman Library of Jewish Civilization). 1983. 37.50x (ISBN 0-19-710048-1). Oxford U Pr.

Richardson, Henry G. The English Jewry under Angevin Kings. LC 83-18539. ix, 313p. 1983. Repr. of 1960 ed. lib. bdg. 35.00x (ISBN 0-313-24247-X, RIEJ). Greenwood.

Salbstein, Michail. The Emancipation of the Jews in Britain: The Question of Admission of the Jews to Parliament, 1828-1860. (Littman Library of Jewish Civilization). 1982. 24.95x (ISBN 0-19-710050-3). Oxford U Pr.

Schoffler, Herbert. Abendland und Altes Testament. pap. 10.00 (ISBN 0-384-54210-7). Johnson Repr.

JEWS IN HUNGARY

Braham, Randolph L., ed. The Tragedy of the Jews in Hungary: Essays & Documents. (East European Monographs: No. 208). 288p. 1986. 30.00 (ISBN 0-88033-105-4). East Eur Quarterly.

Handler, Andrew. Dori: The Life & Times of Theodor Herzl in Budapest, 1860-1878. LC 82-8509. (Judaic Studies). (Illus.). 176p. 1983. text ed. 16.95 (ISBN 0-8173-0125-9). U of Ala Pr.

Schoenfeld, Joachim. Shtetl Memoirs: Jewish Life in Galicia under the Austro-Hungarian Empire & in the Polish Republic, 1898-1939. 400p. 1985. text ed. 17.50x (ISBN 0-88125-075-9). Ktav.

JEWS IN IRAQ

Rejwan, Nissim. The Jews of Iraq. 288p. 1986. 30.00 (ISBN 0-8133-0348-6). Westview.

JEWS IN ITALY

Calimani, Riccardo. The Ghetto of Venice. Wolfthal, Katherine, tr. (Illus.). 400p. 1987. 19.95 (ISBN 0-87131-484-3). M Evans.

Hughes, H. Stuart. Prisoners of Hope: The Silver Age of the Italian Jews, 1924-1974. 184p. 1983. text ed. 15.00x (ISBN 0-674-70727-3). Harvard U Pr.

Segre, Dan V. Memoirs of a Fortunate Jew: An Italian Story. LC 86-17495. 274p. 1987. 16.95 (ISBN 0-917561-32-5). Adler & Adler.

Yerushalmi, Yosef H. From Spanish Court to Italian Ghetto: Isaac Cardoso, A Study in Seventeenth-Century Marranism & Jewish Apologetics. LC 76-109544. (Illus.). 548p. 1981. pap. 12.50x (ISBN 0-295-95824-3). U of Wash Pr.

Zuccotti, Susan. The Italians & the Holocaust: Persecution, Rescue & Survival. LC 86-47738. (Illus.). 344p. 1987. 19.95 (ISBN 0-465-03622-8). Basic.

JEWS IN LATIN AMERICA

Cohen, Martin. Jewish Experience in Latin America, 2 Vols. 1971. Set. 50.00x (ISBN 0-87068-136-2, Pub by Am Jewish Hist Soc). Ktav.

Elkin, Judith L. & Merkx, Gilbert, eds. The Jewish Presence in Latin America. (Thematic Studies in Latin America). 256p. 1987. text ed. 34.95x (ISBN 0-04-497012-9); pap. text ed. 13.95x (ISBN 0-04-497013-7). Allen Unwin.

Niehaus, Thomas, et al. Resources for Latin American Jewish Studies: Essays on Using Jewish Reference Sources for the Study of Latin American Jewry; U. S. Library Collections on L. A. Jews; & U. S. Archival Resources for the Study of Jews in L. A. Elkin, Judith L., ed. LC 84-80219. (LAJSA Publication Ser.: No. 1). 59p. (Orig.). 1984. pap. text ed. 10.00 (ISBN 0-916921-00-X). Lat Am Jewish Assn.

Sable, Martin H. Latin American Jewry: A Research Guide. LC 77-18527. (Bibliographica Judaica: No. 6). Repr. of 1978 ed. 160.00 (ISBN 0-317-42036-4, 2025695). Bks Demand UMI.

JEWS IN LITERATURE

Baumgarten, Murray. City Scriptures: Modern Jewish Writing. LC 81-6879. 240p. 1982. text ed. 17.50x (ISBN 0-674-13278-5). Harvard U Pr.

Bilik, Dorothy S. Immigrant-Survivors: Post-Holocaust Consciousness in Recent Jewish-American Literature. LC 80-15326. 217p. 1981. 17.50x. Wesleyan U Pr.

Blackman, Murray. A Guide to Jewish Themes in American Fiction, 1940-1980. LC 80-24953. 271p. 1981. lib. bdg. 19.00 (ISBN 0-8108-1380-7). Scarecrow.

Blum, Jakub & Rich, Vera. The Image of the Jew in Soviet Literature. LC 84-12196. 276p. 1985. 25.00 (ISBN 0-88125-062-7). Ktav.

Brayer, Menachem M. Jewish Woman in Rabbinic Literature: A Psychosocial Perspective. 300p. 1986. text ed. 20.00x (ISBN 0-88125-071-6); pap. text ed. 11.95x (ISBN 0-88125-070-8). Ktav.

Cardozo, Jacob L. The Contemporary Jew in the Elizabethan Drama. (Research & Source Works Ser: No. 175). Repr. of 1925 ed. 15.00 (ISBN 0-8337-0466-4). B Franklin.

Chametzky, Jules. Our Decentralized Literature: Cultural Mediations in Selected Jewish & Southern Writers. LC 86-1259. 168p. 1986. lib. bdg. 25.00x (ISBN 0-87023-527-3); pap. text ed. 9.95 (ISBN 0-87023-540-0). U of Mass Pr.

Charlton, H. B. Shakespeare's Jew. 1934. lib. bdg. 12.50 (ISBN 0-8414-3560-X). Folcroft.

Coleman, Edward D. Bible in English Drama: An Annotated Bibliography. rev. ed. 1969. 25.00x (ISBN 0-87068-034-X). Ktav.

--Bible in English Drama: An Annotated List of Plays. 1969. 6.95 (ISBN 0-87104-021-2, Co-Pub by Ktav). NY Pub Lib.

--Jew in English Drama: An Annotated Bibliography. rev. ed. LC 67-11901. 1969. 25.00x (ISBN 0-87068-011-0). Ktav.

--Jew in English Drama: An Annotated Bibliography. LC 67-11901. 1968. Repr. of 1943 ed. with The Jew in Western Drama by Edgar Rosenberg 8.95 (ISBN 0-87104-101-4, Co-Pub by Ktav). NY Pub Lib.

Ezrahi, Sidra D. By Words Alone: The Holocaust in Literature. LC 79-56908. 1980. 19.00x (ISBN 0-226-23335-9). U of Chicago Pr.

Friedlander, Gerald. Shakespeare & the Jew. LC 74-168084. Repr. of 1921 ed. 18.00 (ISBN 0-404-02579-X). AMS Pr.

Gill, John, ed. Notices of the Jews & Their Country by the Classic Writers of Antiquity. LC 70-97281. (Judaica Ser). 180p. 1972. Repr. of 1872 ed. lib. bdg. 22.50x (ISBN 0-8371-2603-7, GINJ). Greenwood.

Goldstein, David I. Dostoyevsky & the Jews. (University of Texas Press Slavic Ser.: No. 3). 256p. 1981. 20.00x (ISBN 0-292-71528-5). U of Tex Pr.

Gross, Theodore L. Literature of American Jews. LC 72-93311. 1973. 14.95 (ISBN 0-02-913190-1). Free Pr.

Harap, Louis. Creative Awakening: The Jewish Presence in Twentieth-Century American Literature, 1900-1940s-Published in Cooperation with the American Jewish Archives. LC 86-14986. (Contributions in Ethnic Studies: No. 17). 216p. 1987. lib. bdg. 29.95 (ISBN 0-313-25386-2, HFI). Greenwood.

--The Image of the Jew in American Literature. LC 74-12887. 608p. 1975. 10.00 (ISBN 0-8276-0054-2, 357). Jewish Pubns.

Kaufmann, David. George Eliot & Judaism. LC 75-130251. (English Literature Ser., No. 33). 1970. Repr. of 1888 ed. lib. bdg. 27.95x (ISBN 0-8383-1141-5). Haskell.

Kayser, Rudolf. The Saints of Qumran: Stories & Essays on Jewish Themes. Zohn, Harry, ed. LC 76-20273. 188p. 1977. 18.00 (ISBN 0-8386-2024-8). Fairleigh Dickinson.

Landa, Myer J. Jew in Drama. LC 68-26290. 1968. Repr. of 1926 ed. 23.00x (ISBN 0-8046-0257-3, Pub. by Kennikat). Assoc Faculty Pr.

Lea, Charlene A. Emancipation, Assimilation & Stereotype: The Image of the Jew in German & Austrian Drama (1800-1850) (Modern German Studies: Vol. 2). viii, 171p. (Orig.). 1978. pap. 18.00x (ISBN 3-416-01420-0, Pub. by Bouvier Verlag W Germany). Benjamins North Am.

Lehrmann, Charles C. Jewish Influences on European Thought. Klin, George & Carpenter, Victor, trs. LC 72-3264. 323p. 1976. 27.50 (ISBN 0-8386-7908-0). Fairleigh Dickinson.

Naman, Anne A. The Jew in the Victorian Novel: Some Relationships Between Prejudice & Art. LC 79-8634. (AMS Studies in the 19th Century: No. 1). 1980. 29.50 (ISBN 0-404-18023-X). AMS Pr.

Panitz, Esther L. The Alien in Their Midst: Image of Jews in English Literature. LC 78-75183. 192p. 1981. 20.00 (ISBN 0-8386-2318-2). Fairleigh Dickinson.

Philipson, David. Jew in English Fiction. LC 76-42290. 1889. lib. bdg. 25.00 (ISBN 0-8414-6796-X). Folcroft.

--The Jew in English Fiction. LC 76-30568. (English Literature Ser, No. 33). 1977. lib. bdg. 47.95x (ISBN 0-8383-2150-X). Haskell.

Prawer, S. S. Heine's Jewish Comedy: A Study of His Portraits of Jews & Judaism. 846p. 1986. pap. 19.95x (ISBN 0-19-815834-3). Oxford U Pr.

Rosenberg, Edgar. From Shylock to Svengali: Jewish Stereotypes in English Fiction. (Illus.). 1960. 27.50x (ISBN 0-8047-0586-0). Stanford U Pr.

Rubin, Abba. Images in Transition: The English Jew in English Literature, 1660-1830. LC 83-22730. (Contributions of the Study of World Literature Ser.: No. 4). iv, 157p. 1984. lib. bdg. 29.95 (ISBN 0-313-23779-4, RUJ/). Greenwood.

Sinsheimer, Hermann. Shylock: The History of a Character. LC 63-23188. (Illus.). Repr. of 1947 ed. 15.00 (ISBN 0-405-08977-5, Pub. by Blom). Ayer Co Pubs.

Van Der Veen, H. R. Jewish Characters in Eighteenth Century Fiction & Drama. 1970. 25.00x (ISBN 0-87068-076-5). Ktav.

Wilk, Melvin. The Jewish Presence in Eliot & Kafka. (Brown Judaic Studies). 228p. 1986. 31.95 (ISBN 0-89130-915-2, 14-00-82). Scholars Pr GA.

JEWS IN LITHUANIA

Levin, Dov. Fighting Back: Lithuanian Jewry's Armed Resistance to the Nazis. 325p. 1985. text ed. 49.50x (ISBN 0-8419-0831-1). Holmes & Meier.

Schulzinger, Morris S. The Tale of a Litvak. LC 84-7693. (Illus.). 379p. 1985. 24.95 (ISBN 0-8022-2454-7). Philos Lib.

JEWS IN PALESTINE

Avi-Yonah, Michael. The Jews under Roman & Byzantine Rule: A Political History of Palestine from the Bar-Kokhba War to the Arab Conquest. LC 84-5612. Orig. Title: The Jews of Palestine. (Illus.). 304p. 1984. Repr. 23.00x (ISBN 0-8052-3580-9). Schocken.

Chissin, Chaim. A Palestine Diary. 1976. 10.00 (ISBN 0-685-82598-1). Herzl Pr.

Davis, Moshe, ed. Israel: Its Role in Civilization. LC 77-70673. (America & the Holy Land Ser.). 1977. Repr. of 1956 ed. lib. bdg. 31.00 (ISBN 0-405-10241-0). Ayer Co Pubs.

--Pioneer Settlement in the Twenties: An Original Anthology. LC 77-70699. (America & the Holy Land Ser.). 1977. lib. bdg. 20.00x (ISBN 0-405-10250-X). Ayer Co Pubs.

Frankl, Ludwig A. The Jews in the East, 2 vols. Beaton, P., tr. LC 78-97278. 1975. Repr. of 1859 ed. Set. lib. bdg. 28.50x (ISBN 0-8371-2596-0, FRJE). Greenwood.

Friedman, Isaiah. Germany, Turkey, & Zionism, 1897-1918. 1977. 59.00x (ISBN 0-19-822528-8). Oxford U Pr.

Gordon, Benjamin L. New Judea: Jewish Life in Modern Palestine & Egypt. Davis, Moshe, ed. LC 77-70697. (America & the Holy Land Ser.). (Illus.). 1977. Repr. of 1919 ed. lib. bdg. 30.00x (ISBN 0-405-10251-8). Ayer Co Pubs.

Hoofien, Sigfried. Report of Mr. S. Hoofien to the Joint Distribution Committee of the American Funds for Jewish War Sufferers,New York. Davis, Moshe, ed. LC 77-70702. (America & the Holy Land Ser.). (Illus.). 1977. Repr. of 1918 ed. lib. bdg. 17.00x (ISBN 0-405-10254-2). Ayer Co Pubs.

Lieberman, Saul. Texts & Studies. 1973. 35.00x (ISBN 0-87068-210-5). Ktav.

Nachmani, Amikam. Great Power Discord in Palestine: The Anglo-American Committee of Inquiry into the Problems of European Jewry & Palestine 1945-1946. (Illus.). 296p. 1986. 30.00 (ISBN 0-7146-3298-8, F Cass Co). Biblio Dist.

Ruppin, Arthur. Three Decades of Palestine: Speeches & Papers on the Upbuilding of the Jewish National Home. LC 70-97301. (Illus.). 342p. 1975. Repr. of 1936 ed. lib. bdg. 22.50x (ISBN 0-8371-2629-0, RUPA). Greenwood.

Samuel, Maurice. Harvest in the Desert. LC 82-985. 316p. 1982. Repr. lib. bdg. 27.50x (ISBN 0-313-23354-3, SAHA). Greenwood.

Simon, Rita J., ed. New Lives: The Adjustment of Soviet Jewish Immigrants in the United States & Israel. 208p. 1985. 19.95 (ISBN 0-669-09767-5). Lexington Bks.

Sneersohn, Haym Z. Palestine & Roumania: A Description of the Holy Land & the Past & Present State of Roumania & the Roumanian Jews. Davis, Moshe, ed. LC 77-70745. (America & the Holy Land Ser.). 1977. Repr. of 1872 ed. lib. bdg. 17.00x (ISBN 0-405-10291-7). Ayer Co Pubs.

Sukenik, E. L. Ancient Synagogues in Palestine & Greece. (British Academy, London, Schweich Lectures on Biblical Archaeology Series, 1930). pap. 19.00 (ISBN 0-8115-1272-X). Kraus Repr.

JEWS IN POLAND

Banas, Josef. The Scapegoats: The Exodus of the Remnants of Polish Jewry. Szafar, Tadeusz, tr. 221p. 1979. text ed. 34.50 (ISBN 0-8419-6303-7). Holmes & Meier.

Baskerville, B. C. The Polish Jew. 75.00 (ISBN 0-8490-0870-0). Gordon Pr.

De Pomiane, Edouard. The Jews of Poland: Recollections & Recipes. Bacon, Josephine, tr. from Fr. (Jewish Cookery Classics Ser.). Tr. of Cuisine Juive: Ghettos Modernes. (Illus.). 256p. 1985. 9.95 (ISBN 0-910231-02-8); pap. 9.95. Pholiota.

Dobroczcki, L. & Kirshenblatt-Gimblett, B. Image Before My Eyes: A Photographic History of Jewish Life in Poland, 1864-1939. (Illus.). 1977. 25.00; pap. text ed. 15.00 (ISBN 0-914512-38-2). Yivo Inst.

Dobroszycki, Lucjan & Kirshenblatt-Gimblett, Barbara. Image Before My Eyes: A Photographic History of Jewish Life in Poland, 1864-1939. LC 75-35448. (Illus.). 1977. 29.95 (ISBN 0-8052-3607-4). Schocken.

--Image Before My Eyes: A Photographic History of Jewish Life in Poland, 1864-1939. LC 75-35448. (Illus.). 1979. pap. 19.95 (ISBN 0-8052-0634-5). Schocken.

Dobroszycki, Lucjan, ed. The Chronicle of the Lodz Ghetto, 1941-1944. LC 84-3614. (Illus.). 603p. 1984. 37.50x (ISBN 0-300-03208-0). Yale U Pr.

Gilmovsky, Norman. My Life, My Destiny. LC 82-46083. (Illus.). 320p. 1984. 22.50 (ISBN 0-317-02674-7, Cornwall Bks). Assoc Univ Prs.

Gurdus, Luba K. The Death Train. LC 78-54657. (Illus.). 1979. 12.95 (ISBN 0-8052-5005-0, Pub. by Holocaust Library). Schocken.

Heller, Celia. On the Edge of Destruction: Jews in Poland Between the Two World Wars. LC 76-22646. (Illus.). 1977. 36.00x (ISBN 0-231-03819-4). Columbia U Pr.

Heller, Celia S. On the Edge of Destruction: Jews of Poland Between the Two World Wars. LC 79-24645. 384p. 1980. pap. 8.95 (ISBN 0-8052-0651-5). Schocken.

Hirshaut, Julien. Jewish Martyrs of Pawiak. LC 81-85301. 256p. 1982. 16.95 (ISBN 0-8052-5039-5); pap. 10.95 (ISBN 0-8052-5040-9). Holocaust Pubns.

Kallen, Horace M. Frontiers of Hope. Davis, Moshe, ed. LC 77-70711. (America & the Holy Land Ser.). 1977. Repr. of 1929 ed. lib. bdg. 37.50x (ISBN 0-405-10260-7). Ayer Co Pubs.

Klepfisz, Heszel. Culture of Compassion: The Spirit of Polish Jewry from Hasidism to the Holocaust. LC 83-13626. 265p. 1983. 25.00x (ISBN 0-88125-037-6). Ktav.

Krakowski, Shmuel. The War of the Doomed: Jewish Armed Resistance in Poland, 1942-1944. LC 83-18537. 340p. 1984. text ed. 44.50x (ISBN 0-8419-0851-6). Holmes & Meier.

Kruk, Herman. Togbukh Fun Vilner Geto. Bernstein, Mordecai W., ed. LC 62-56072. (Yivo Institute for Jewish Research, Memoirs Ser.: No. 1). (Yiddish., Illus.). 620p. 1961. 10.00 (ISBN 0-914512-29-3). Yivo Inst.

Kugelmass, Jack & Boyarin, Jonathan. From a Ruined Garden: The Memorial Books of Polish Jewry. (Illus.). 309p. 1985. pap. 8.95 (ISBN 0-8052-0789-9). Schocken.

Litman, Jacob. The Economic Role of Jews in Medieval Poland: The Contribution of Yitzhak Schipper. (Illus.). 320p. (Orig.). 1985. lib. bdg. 29.50 (ISBN 0-8191-4244-1); pap. text ed. 15.25 (ISBN 0-8191-4245-X). U Pr of Amer.

Marcus, Joseph. Social & Political History of the Jews in Poland, 1919-1939. LC 82-22420. (New Babylon, Studies in the Social Sciences: No. 37). xviii, 569p. 1983. 88.50x (ISBN 90-279-3239-5). Mouton.

Niezabitowska, Malgorzata. Remnants: The Last Jews of Poland. Brand, William & Dobosiewicz, Hanna, trs. from Polish. LC 86-1468. (Illus.). 272p. 1986. 35.00 (ISBN 0-914919-05-9). Friendly Pr NY.

Oliner, Samuel P. Restless Memories: Recollections of the Holocaust Years. rev., 2nd ed. LC 85-82084. 215p. (Orig.). 1986. pap. 9.95 (ISBN 0-943376-28-9). Magnes Mus.

Polonsky, Antony, et al. The Jews in Poland. 288p. 1986. 24.95 (ISBN 0-631-14857-4). Basil Blackwell.

Ringelblum, Emmanuel. Polish-Jewish Relations During the Second World War. Allon, Dafna, et al, trs. LC 76-1394. 330p. 1976. 35.00x (ISBN 0-86527-155-0). Fertig.

Schoenfeld, Joachim. Shtetl Memoirs: Jewish Life in Galicia under the Austro-Hungarian Empire & in the Polish Republic, 1898-1939. 400p. 1985. text ed. 17.50x (ISBN 0-88125-075-9). Ktav.

Shatzky, Jacob. Geshikhte Fun Yidn in Varshe, 3 vols. LC 48-15791. (Yiddish.). 1953. Set. 10.00 (ISBN 0-914512-27-7); 10.00 ea. Vol. 1 (ISBN 0-914512-32-3). Vol. 2 (ISBN 0-914512-33-1). Vol. 3 (ISBN 0-914512-34-X). Yivo Inst.

Shneiderman, S. L. The River Remembers. LC 77-93935. (Illus.). 1978. 8.95 (ISBN 0-8180-0821-0). Horizon.

Shulman, Nisson E. Authority & Community: Polish Jewry in the Sixteenth Century. 288p. 1986. text ed. 20.00x (ISBN 0-88125-101-1). Ktav.

Tamir, Nachman, ed. The Polish Jews, 1914-1939. LC 85-47709. (Illus.). 216p. 1986. 19.95 (ISBN 0-8453-4791-8, Cornwall Bks). Assoc Univ Prs.

Vetulani, A. The Jews of Medieval Poland. 1978. lib. bdg. 59.95 (ISBN 0-685-62298-3). Revisionist Pr.

Vinecour, Earl. Polish Jews: The Final Chapter. LC 77-83266. (Illus.). 1977. 17.50x (ISBN 0-8147-8756-8). NYU Pr.

Vinecour, Earl & Fishman, Charles. Polish Jews: The Final Chapter. (Paperbacks Ser). (Orig.). 1977. pap. 5.95 (ISBN 0-07-067490-6). McGraw.

Vishniac, Roman. Polish Jews: A Pictorial Record. LC 65-25413. (Illus.). 1968. pap. 7.95 (ISBN 0-8052-0360-5). Schocken.

The Warsaw Ghetto in Pictures: Illustrated Catalog. LC 79-26657. (Yivo Institute for Jewish Research Guide & Catalogs Ser.: No. 1). (Illus.). 1970. pap. 5.00 (ISBN 0-914512-08-0). Yivo Inst.

Zvi. LC 78-56149. 1978. pap. 3.95 (ISBN 0-915540-23-1). Friends Israel-Spearhead Pr.

JEWS IN RUMANIA

Dorian, Emil. The Quality of Witness: A Romanian Diary, 1937-1944. Dorian, Marguerite, ed. Vamos, Mara S., tr. from Romanian. 352p. 1983. 19.95 (ISBN 0-8276-0211-1). Jewish Pubns.

Sneersohn, Haym Z. Palestine & Roumania: A Description of the Holy Land & the Past & Present State of Roumania & the Roumanian Jews. Davis, Moshe, ed. LC 77-70745. (America & the Holy Land Ser.). 1977. Repr. of 1872 ed. lib. bdg. 17.00x (ISBN 0-405-10291-7). Ayer Co Pubs.

Sternberg, G. Stefanesti: Portrait of a Romanian Shtetl. (Illus.). 320p. 1984. 30.00 (ISBN 0-08-030840-6). Pergamon.

JEWS IN SPAIN

Ashtor, Eliyahu. The Jews of Moslem Spain, Vol. III. Klein, Aaron & Klein, Jenny M., trs. from Hebrew. 380p. 1985. 19.95 (ISBN 0-8276-0237-5). Jewish Pubns.

--The Jews of Moslem Spain, Vol. 1. Machlowitz Klein, Aaron, tr. from Heb. LC 73-14081. (Illus.). 469p. 1974. 12.00 (ISBN 0-8276-0017-8, 352). Jewish Pubns.

--The Jews of Moslem Spain, Vol. 2. 381p. 1978. 12.00 (ISBN 0-8276-0100-X, 411). Jewish Pubns.

Avni, Haim. Spain, the Jews & Franco. Shimoni, Emanuel, tr. from Hebrew. LC 80-39777. 320p. 1981. 19.95 (ISBN 0-8276-0188-3, 469). Jewish Pubns.

Baer, Yitzhak. History of the Jews in Christian Spain, 2 Vols. LC 61-16852. 1966. pap. 6.95 ea. (ISBN 0-8276-0115-8, 425). Jewish Pubns.

Beinart, Haim. Trujillo: A Jewish Community in Extremadura on the Eve of Expulsion from Spain. (Hispania Judaica Ser.: No. 2). 372p. 1980. text ed. 22.50x (ISBN 965-223-349-8, Pub. by Magnes Pr Israel). Humanities.

Isaacs, A. Lionel. The Jews of Majorca. 1976. lib. bdg. 59.95 (ISBN 0-8490-2105-7). Gordon Pr.

Katz, S. Jews in the Visigothic & Frankish Kingdoms of Spain & Gaul. (Mediaeval Academy of America Publications). 1937. 21.00 (ISBN 0-527-01697-7). Kraus Repr.

Kayserling, Meyer. Biblioteca Espanola-Portugeza-Judaica. rev. ed. 1971. 35.00x (ISBN 0-87068-146-X). Ktav.

Lindo, Elias H. History of the Jews of Spain & Portugal. LC 71-112055. (Research & Source Works Ser: No. 4). (Illus.). 1970. Repr. of 1848 ed. 32.50 (ISBN 0-8337-2109-7). B Franklin.

M, Nectario. Juan Colon, Alias Cristobal Colon, Alias Christopher Columbus, Was a Spanish Jew. Josephson, E., ed. 1985. lib. bdg. 79.95 (ISBN 0-87700-867-1). Revisionist Pr.

Moore, Kenneth. Those of the Street: The Catholic-Jews of Mallorca. LC 76-636. 1979. pap. text ed. 7.95x (ISBN 0-268-01836-7). U of Notre Dame Pr.

Neuman, Abraham A. Jews in Spain: Their Social, Political & Cultural Life During the Middle Ages, 2 vols. LC 70-105964. 1970. Repr. of 1942 ed. lib. bdg. 54.50x (ISBN 0-374-96061-5, Octagon). Hippocrene Bks.

Oelman, Timothy, ed. & tr. Marrano Poets of the Seventeenth Century: An Anthology of the Poetry of Joao Pinto Delgado, Antonio Enriquez Gomez & Miguel de Barrios. (Littman Library of Jewish Civilization). (Illus.). 1985. 24.95x (ISBN 0-19-710047-3). Oxford U Pr.

Roth, Cecil. Spanish Inquisition. (Illus., Orig.). 1964. pap. 7.95 (ISBN 0-393-00255-1, Norton Lib). Norton.

Singerman, Robert. The Jews in Spain & Portugal: A Bibliography. LC 75-1166. (Reference Library of Social Science: No. 11). 376p. 1975. lib. bdg. 52.00 (ISBN 0-8240-1089-2). Garland Pub.

JEWS IN THE ISLAMIC EMPIRE

Fischel, Walter. Jews in the Economic & Political Life of Medieval Islam. rev. ed. LC 68-25719. 1969. Repr. of 1937 ed. 15.00x (ISBN 0-87068-047-1). Ktav.

Goitein, S. D. Jews & Arabs: Their Contacts Through the Ages. 3rd ed. LC 74-9141. 271p. 1974. pap. 6.95 (ISBN 0-8052-0464-4). Schocken.

--A Mediterranean Society: The Jewish Communities of the Arab World As Portrayed in the Documents of the Cairo Geniza. Bd. with Vol. I. Economic Foundations. 1968; Vol. 2. The Community. 1971; Vol. 3. The Family. 1978. 48.50x (ISBN 0-520-03265-9); Vol. 4. Daily Life. 1983. 42.00x (ISBN 0-520-04869-5). LC 67-22430. (Near Eastern Center, UCLA). U of Cal Pr.

Ye'or, Bat. The Dhimmi: Jews & Christians under Islam. Maisel, David, et al, trs. from French. LC 84-47749. (Illus.). 444p. 1985. 25.00 (ISBN 0-8386-3233-5); pap. 9.95 (ISBN 0-8386-3262-9). Fairleigh Dickinson.

JEWS IN THE LEVANT

Frankl, Ludwig A. The Jews in the East, 2 vols. Beaton, P., tr. LC 78-97278. 1975. Repr. of 1859 ed. Set. lib. bdg. 28.50x (ISBN 0-8371-2596-0, FRJE). Greenwood.

Starr, Joshua. Romania: The Jewries of the Levant After the Fourth Crusade. 1943. 10.00x (ISBN 0-87068-108-7). Ktav.

JEWS IN THE NETHERLANDS

Gans, Mozes Heiman. Memorbook: Pictorial History of Dutch Jewry from the Renaissance to 1940. (Illus.). 852p. 1983. 125.00x (ISBN 0-8143-1749-9). Wayne St U Pr.

Hes, Hindle S. Jewish Physicians in the Netherlands 1600-1940. 248p. 1980. pap. text ed. 14.50 (ISBN 0-317-51979-4, Pub. by Van Gorcum Holland). Longwood Pub Group.

Hillesum, Etty. An Interrupted Life: The Diaries of Etty Hillesum 1941-1943. Pomerans, Arno, tr. LC 83-47750. 226p. 1984. 13.45 (ISBN 0-394-53217-1). Pantheon.

Katchen, Aaron L. Christian Hebraists & Dutch Rabbis: Seventeenth Century Apologetics & the Study of Maimonides' Mishneh Torah. (Harvard Judaic Texts & Studies: No. 3). 430p. 1985. text ed. 28.00x (ISBN 0-674-12865-6). Harvard U Ctr Jewish.

Mechoulan, Henry & Nahon, Gerard, eds. Menasseh ben Israel: The Hope of Israel. (Litman Library of Jewish Civilization). (Illus.). 224p. 37.00 (ISBN 0-19-710054-6). Oxford U Pr.

JEWS IN THE SOVIET UNION

Altshuler, Mordechai. Soviet Jewry since the Second World War: Population & Social Structure. LC 86-12139. (Studies in Population & Urban Demography: No. 5). (Illus.). 296p. 1987. lib. bdg. 37.95 (ISBN 0-313-24494-4, ASO). Greenwood.

Anti-Defamation League Staff. Perspectives on Soviet Jewry. 150p. pap. 2.50 (ISBN 0-686-95144-1). ADL.

Anti-Semitism in the Soviet Union: Its Roots & Consequences. 664p. 1984. 35.00 (ISBN 0-88464-051-5); pap. 16.95 (ISBN 0-88464-052-3). ADL.

Berk, Stephen M. Year of Crisis, Year of Hope: Russian Jewry & the Pogroms of 1881-1882. LC 84-25216. (Contributions in Ethnic Studies Ser.: No. 11). xvi, 231p. 1985. lib. bdg. 39.95 (ISBN 0-313-24609-2, BPG/). Greenwood.

Ber Of Bolechow. The Memoirs of Ber of Bolechow (1723-1805) LC 73-2186. (The Jewish People; History, Religion, Literature Ser.). Repr. of 1922 ed. 19.00 (ISBN 0-405-05252-9). Ayer Co Pubs.

Biber, Jacob. Survivors: A Personal Story of the Holocaust. LC 85-22415. (Studies in Judaica & the Holocaust: No. 2). 208p. 1986. lib. bdg. 18.95x (ISBN 0-89370-370-2); pap. text ed. 8.95x (ISBN 0-89370-470-9). Borgo Pr.

Chalidze, Valery. The Soviet Human Rights Movement: A Memoir. LC 84-72146. xii, 50p. 1984. pap. 2.50 (ISBN 0-87495-064-3). AM Jewish Comm.

Chesler, Evan R. The Russian Jewry Reader. 147p. pap. 2.45 (ISBN 0-686-95145-X). ADL.

Davitt, Michael. Within the Pale: The True Story of Anti-Semitic Persecutions in Russia. facsimile ed. LC 74-27976. (Modern Jewish Experience Ser.). 1975. Repr. of 1903 ed. 25.50x (ISBN 0-405-06705-4). Ayer Co Pubs.

Frankel, Jonathan. Prophecy & Politics: Socialism, Nationalism, & the Russian Jews, 1862-1917. LC 80-14414. 686p. 1984. pap. 19.95 (ISBN 0-521-26919-9). Cambridge U Pr.

Frederic, Harold. New Exodus: A Study of Israel in Russia. LC 71-115538. (Russia Observed, Series I). 1970. Repr. of 1892 ed. 19.00 (ISBN 0-405-03027-4). Ayer Co Pubs.

Gilbert, Martin. The Jews of Hope. (Nonfiction Ser.). 272p. 1985. pap. 7.95 (ISBN 0-14-008510-6). Penguin.

--The Jews of Hope: The Plight of Soviet Jewry Today. LC 84-40461. (Illus.). 237p. 1985. 15.95 (ISBN 0-670-80377-4, E. Sifton Bks). Viking.

--Scharansky: Hero of our Time. 512p. 1986. 24.95 (ISBN 0-317-46605-4). Viking.

--Shcharansky: Hero of Our Time. (Illus.). 512p. 1986. 24.95 (ISBN 0-670-81418-0). Viking.

Gilboa, Yehoshuna A. A Language Silenced: Hebrew Culture in the Soviet Union. LC 80-70920. 320p. 1982. 25.00 (ISBN 0-8386-3072-3). Fairleigh Dickerson.

Goldberg, Ben Z. The Jewish Problem in the Soviet Union: Analysis & Solution. LC 82-15842. (Illus.). x, 374p. 1982. Repr. of 1961 ed. lib. bdg. 45.00x (ISBN 0-313-23692-5, GOJE). Greenwood.

Greenberg, Louis. Jews in Russia: The Struggle for Emancipation, 2 Vols. in 1. LC 79-161769. Repr. of 1965 ed. 27.50 (ISBN 0-404-09023-0). AMS Pr.

--The Jews in Russia: The Struggle for Emancipation, 1772-1917, 2 vols. in 1. Wishnitzer, Mark, ed. LC 75-36489. 234p. 1976. pap. 11.95 (ISBN 0-8052-0525-X). Schocken.

Hundert, Gershon D. & Bacon, Gershon C. The Jews in Poland & Russia: Bibliographical Essays. LC 83-49285. (The Modern Jewish Experience Ser.). 288p. 1985. 25.00x (ISBN 0-253-33158-7). Ind U Pr.

Kallen, Horace M. Frontiers of Hope. Davis, Moshe, ed. LC 77-70711. (America & the Holy Land Ser.). 1977. Repr. of 1929 ed. lib. bdg. 37.50x (ISBN 0-405-10260-7). Ayer Co Pubs.

Kochan, Lionel, ed. The Jews in Soviet Russia Since 1917. 3rd ed. (Illus.). 1978. pap. 9.95 (ISBN 0-19-281199-1). Oxford U Pr.

La Zebnik, Edith. Such a Life. 1979. pap. 2.50 (ISBN 0-671-82282-9). PB.

Lenin, V. I. Lenin on the Jewish Question. Lumer, Hyman, ed. LC 74-6278. (Eng.). 156p. 1974. 7.50 (ISBN 0-7178-0398-8); pap. 2.75 (ISBN 0-7178-0399-6). Intl Pubs Co.

Leskov, Nikolai. The Jews in Russia. Schefski, Harold K., ed. & tr. from Rus. 143p. 1986. 21.00 (ISBN 0-940670-29-1). Kingston Pr.

Levin, Nora. The Jews in the Soviet Union: A History from 1917 to the Present, 2 vols. (Illus.). 864p. 1987. Set. text ed. 75.00 (ISBN 0-8147-5018-4); Vol. 1 (432p.) text ed. 45.00 (ISBN 0-8147-5034-6); Vol. 2 (432p.) text ed. 45.00 (ISBN 0-8147-5035-4). NYU Pr.

Levin, Shmarya. Youth in Revolt. facsimile ed. Samuel, Maurice, tr. LC 74-27998. (Modern Jewish Experience Ser.). (Eng.). 1975. Repr. of 1930 ed. 24.50x (ISBN 0-405-06725-9). Ayer Co Pubs.

Marsden, Norman, ed. A Jewish Life under the Tsars: The Autobiography of Chaim Aronson, 1825-1888, Vol. 3. LC 81-10963. (Publications of the Oxford Centre for Postgraduate Hebrew Study). 368p. 1983. 23.95 (ISBN 0-86598-066-7). Allanheld.

Meisl, Josef. Haskalah: Geschichte der Aufklarungsbewegung unter den Juden in Russland. Katz, Stephen, ed. LC 79-7147. (Jewish Philosophy, Mysticism & History of Ideas Ser.). 1980. Repr. of 1919 ed. lib. bdg. 21.00x (ISBN 0-405-12277-2). Ayer Co Pubs.

Miller, Jack, ed. Jews in Soviet Culture. 325p. 1983. 24.95 (ISBN 0-87855-495-5). Transaction Bks.

Pennell, Joseph. The Jew at Home: Impressions of Jewish Life in Russia & Austria. 1976. lib. bdg. 134.95 (ISBN 0-8490-2098-0). Gordon Pr.

Pinkus, Benjamin. The Soviet Government & the Jews, Nineteen Forty-Eight to Nineteen Sixty-Seven: A Documented Study. 675p. 1984. 62.50 (ISBN 0-521-24713-6). Cambridge U Pr.

Porath, Jonathan D. Jews in Russia: The Last Four Centuries. 1973. pap. 3.75x (ISBN 0-8381-0220-4). United Syn Bk.

Rogger, Hans. Jewish Policies & Right-Wing Politics in Imperial Russia. LC 85-1006. 1985. 30.00x (ISBN 0-520-04596-3). U of Cal Pr.

Rosensaft, Menachem Z. The Legal Status of Soviet Jewry: De Jure Equality & De Facto Discrimination. 30p. 1.00 (ISBN 0-686-74962-6). ADL.

Rothenberg, Joshua. The Jewish Religion in the Soviet Union. 1971. 20.00x (ISBN 0-87068-156-7). Ktav.

Roziner, Felix. Shcharansky: The Man. 1986. 16.95 (ISBN 0-318-21401-6); pap. 10.95. Shapolsky Pubs.

Roziner, Felix, ed. The Shcharansky Chronicles: A Complete Documentary. 1986. 18.95 (ISBN 0-318-21399-0); pap. 11.95. Shapolsky Pubs.

Rubinow, Isaac M. Economic Conditions of the Jews in Russia. facsimile ed. LC 74-29519. (Modern Jewish Experience Ser.). 1975. Repr. of 1907 ed. 15.00x (ISBN 0-405-06744-5). Ayer Co Pubs.

Rudin, A. James & Gillen, Ann, eds. The Struggle for Religious Survival in the Soviet Union. LC 86-72630. 76p. 1986. pap. 5.00 (ISBN 0-87495-085-6). Am Jewish Comm.

Rukhadze, Avtandil. Jews in the U. S. S. R. Figures, Facts, Comment. 112p. 1984. pap. 5.00x (ISBN 0-317-53875-6, Pub. by Collets (UK)). State Mutual Bk.

Schulman, Elias. A History of Jewish Education in the Soviet Union, 1918-1948. 1971. 25.00x (ISBN 0-87068-145-1). Ktav.

Schwarz, Solomon M. The Jews in the Soviet Union. LC 72-4298. (World Affairs Ser.: National & International Viewpoints). 398p. 1972. Repr. of 1951 ed. 22.00 (ISBN 0-405-04589-1). Ayer Co Pubs.

Semenov, E. P. The Russian Government & the Massacres. LC 70-97304. (Judaica Ser.). 265p. 1972. Repr. of 1907 ed. lib. bdg. 29.75 (ISBN 0-8371-2632-0, SERG). Greenwood.

Shield, 5 vols. in 1. Incl. Vol. 1. Russia & the Jews. Gorky, Maxim; Vol. 2. First Step. Andreyev, Leonid; Vol. 3. Jewish Question in Russia. Milyukov, Paul; Vol. 4. Jewish Question As a Russian Question. Merezhovsky, Dmitry; Vol. 5. Jew, A Story. Artzibashef, Michael. (Eng.). Repr. of 1917 ed. lib. bdg. 15.00 (ISBN 0-8371-2633-9, GOSH). Greenwood.

Simon, Rita J., ed. New Lives: The Adjustment of Soviet Jewish Immigrants in the United States & Israel. 208p. 1985. 19.95 (ISBN 0-669-09767-5). Lexington Bks.

Stanislawski, Michael. Tsar Nicholas I & the Jews: The Transformation of Jewish Society in Russia, 1825-1855. (Illus.). 272p. 1983. 18.95 (ISBN 0-8276-0216-2, 497). Jewish Pubns.

Tobias, Henry J. Jewish Bund in Russia from Its Origins to 1905. LC 75-153820. 1972. 30.00x (ISBN 0-8047-0764-2). Stanford U Pr.

Wiesel, Elie. The Jews of Silence: A Personal Report on Soviet Jewry. LC 63-11041. 160p. 1987. pap. 8.95 (ISBN 0-8052-0826-7). Schocken.

--Zalem, or the Madness of God. 171p. 1985. pap. 7.95 (ISBN 0-8052-0777-5). Schocken.

Zaslavsky, Victor & Brym, Robert J. Soviet-Jewish Emigration & Soviet Nationality Policy. LC 83-3160. 172p. 1983. 22.50 (ISBN 0-312-74844-2). St Martin.

Zipperstein, Steven J. The Jews of Odessa: A Cultural History, 1794-1881. LC 84-50152. 232p. 1986. 32.50x (ISBN 0-8047-1251-4). Stanford U Pr.

JEWS IN THE UNITED STATES

Altfeld, E. Milton. The Jews' Struggle for Religious & Civil Liberty in Maryland. LC 78-99859. (Civil Liberties in American History Ser). 1970. Repr. of 1924 ed. lib. bdg. 29.50 (ISBN 0-306-71859-6). Da Capo.

American Jewish Business Enterprise. (American Jewish Historical Quarterly: Vol. 66, Pt.1). 1976. 8.00 (ISBN 0-911934-03-0). Am Jewish Hist Soc.

American Jewish Year Book, 1986, Vol. 80. Date not set. price not set. Am Jewish Comm.

Anti-Semitism in America, 1878-1939. An Original Anthology. LC 76-46110. (Anti-Movements in America). (Illus.). 1977. lib. bdg. 35.00 (ISBN 0-405-09981-9). Ayer Co Pubs.

Barnard, Harry. Forging of an American Jew: The Life & Times of Judge Julian W. Mack. 1974. 7.95 (ISBN 0-685-52984-3). Herzl Pr.

Bauer, Yehuda. American Jewry & the Holocaust: The American Jewish Joint Distribution Committee, 1939-1945. LC 80-26035. 522p. 1981. 35.00x (ISBN 0-8143-1672-7). Wayne St U Pr.

Bendix, Reinhard. From Berlin to Berkeley: German-Jewish Identities. LC 85-8578. 320p. 1985. 29.95 (ISBN 0-88738-067-0). Transaction Bks.

Berkson, Isaac B. Theories of Americanization: A Critical Study. LC 77-87743. (American Education: Its Men, Institutions & Ideas, Ser. 1). 1969. Repr. of 1920 ed. 15.00 (ISBN 0-405-01387-6). Ayer Co Pubs.

--Theories of Americanization: A Critical Study, with Special Reference to the Jewish Group. LC 78-176558. (Columbia University. Teachers College. Contributions to Education: No. 109). Repr. of 1920 ed. 22.50 (ISBN 0-404-55109-2). AMS Pr.

Berlin, William S. On the Edge of Politics: The Roots of Jewish Political Thought in America. (Contributions in Political Science Ser.: No. 14). 1978. lib. bdg. 29.95x (ISBN 0-313-20422-5, BEP/). Greenwood.

Berman, Myron. Richmond's Jewry, Seventeen Sixty-Nine to Nineteen Seventy-Six. LC 78-6377. 438p. 1979. 20.00x (ISBN 0-8139-0743-8). U Pr of Va.

Birmingham, Stephen. The Grandees. 384p. 1985. pap. 4.50 (ISBN 0-425-08390-X). Berkley Pub.

Bloomfield, Brynna C., et al. Traveling Jewish in America: For Business & Pleasure. rev. ed. 420p. (Orig.). 1987. pap. 9.95 (ISBN 0-9617104-1-1). Wandering You Pr.

Bomzer, Herbert W. The Kolel in America. LC 85-63012. 184p. 1986. 15.95 (ISBN 0-88400-118-0). Shengold.

Bookstaber, Philip D. Judaism & the American Mind: In Theory & Practice. LC 78-26404. 1979. Repr. of 1939 ed. lib. bdg. cancelled (ISBN 0-313-20875-1, BOJU). Greenwood.

Bothwell, Etta K. Alienation in the Jewish American Novel of the Sixties. LC 78-3559. 1979. pap. 10.00 (ISBN 0-8477-3191-X). U of PR Pr.

Boykin, James H. Black Jews. LC 81-90626. iv, 98p. (Orig.). 1982. pap. 3.25x (ISBN 0-9603342-1-1). Boykin.

Brooks, Juanita. The History of the Jews in Utah & Idaho, 1853-1950. 252p. 1973. 9.95 (ISBN 0-914740-12-1). Western Epics.

Bunim, Irving M. Ever since Sinai. Wengrov, Charles, ed. 1978. 13.95 (ISBN 0-87306-138-1). Feldheim.

Cogan, Sara, compiled by. The Jews of San Francisco & the Greater Bay Area: 1849 to 1919. (Western Jewish Americana Ser.: No. 2). 1972. 22.00 (ISBN 0-943376-03-3). Magnes Mus.

--The Jews of Los Angeles, No. 3. (Western Jewish Americana Ser. Publications). 237p. 1980. 24.95 (ISBN 0-943376-12-2); pap. 14.95 (ISBN 0-943376-11-4). Magnes Mus.

Cohen, Naomi. American Jews & the Zionist Idea. pap. 9.95x (ISBN 0-87068-272-5). Ktav.

--Encounter with Emancipation: The German Jews in the United States, 1830 to 1914. (Illus.). 407p. 1984. 25.95 (ISBN 0-8276-0236-7). Jewish Pubns.

Cohen, Steven M. The National Survey of American Jews, 1984: Political & Social Outlooks. iv, 60p. (Orig.). 1985. pap. 4.00 (ISBN 0-87495-069-4). Am Jewish Comm.

Crawford, Albert G. & Monson, Rela G. Academy & Community: A Study of the Jewish Identity & Involvement of Professors. LC 80-68432. 40p. 1980. pap. 2.00. Am Jewish Comm.

Daly, C. P. Settlement of the Jews in North America. 59.95 (ISBN 0-8490-1027-6). Gordon Pr.

Davis, Moshe. From Dependence to Mutuality: The American Jewish Community & World Jewry. (Texts & Studies). (Hebrew.). 1970. 10.00 (ISBN 0-911934-07-3). Am Jewish Hist Soc.

Dawidowicz, Lucy. The Jewish Presence: Essays on Identity & History. LC 78-6236. 308p. 1978. pap. 3.95 (ISBN 0-15-646221-4, Harv). HarBraceJ.

Dawidowicz, Lucy S. On Equal Terms: Jews in America 1881-1981. 1984. pap. 6.95 (ISBN 0-03-071058-8). H Holt & Co.

Dinnerstein, Leonard & Palsson, Mary D., eds. Jews in the South. LC 72-89114. viii, 392p. 1973. 32.50x (ISBN 0-8071-0226-1). La State U Pr.

Eichhorn. Evangelizing the American Jew. LC 77-28975. 1978. 12.50 (ISBN 0-8246-0225-0). Jonathan David.

Eis, Ruth. Torah Binders of the Judah L. Magnes Museum. LC 79-83877. 80p. 1979. pap. 18.00 (ISBN 0-943376-15-7). Magnes Mus.

Eisen, Arnold M. The Chosen People in America: A Study in Jewish Religious Ideology. LC 82-49296. (Modern Jewish Experience Ser.). 254p. 1983. 20.00x (ISBN 0-253-31365-1). Ind U Pr.

Elazar, Daniel J. Community & Polity: The Organizational Dynamics of American Jewry. LC 75-8167. (Illus.). 448p. 1976. pap. 9.95 (ISBN 0-8276-0068-2, 377). Jewish Pubns.

Endelman, Judith E. The Jewish Community of Indianapolis, 1849 to the Present. LC 83-49513. (The Modern Jewish Experience Ser.). (Illus.). 316p. 1985. 17.50x (ISBN 0-253-33150-1). Ind U Pr.

Epstein, Melech. Jewish Labor in the U. S. A., 1882-1952. rev. ed. 1969. 45.00x (ISBN 0-87068-042-0). Ktav.

Feldman, Steven, et al, eds. Guide to Jewish Boston & New England. LC 85-90430. 235p. (Orig.). pap. text ed. 10.95 (ISBN 0-9615649-0-3). Genesis Two.

Finger, Seymour M. Their Brother's Keepers: American Jewry & the Holocaust. 300p. 1988. text ed. 34.50x (ISBN 0-8419-1036-7). Holmes & Meier.

Fishman, Joshua A. Yiddish in America: Socio-Linguistic Description & Analysis. LC 65-63395. (General Publications Ser: Vol. 36). (Orig.). 1965. pap. text ed. 9.95x (ISBN 0-87750-110-6). Res Ctr Lang Semiotic.

Ginzberg, Eli. Agenda for American Jews. 90p. 1964. pap. 4.50 (ISBN 0-935457-12-7). Reconstructionist Pr.

Glanz, Rudolf. The Jewish Female in America: Two Female Generations, 1820-1929, Vol. 1. The Eastern European Jewish Woman 25.00x (ISBN 0-87068-461-2). Ktav.

Glazer, Nathan. American Judaism. rev. ed. LC 57-8574. (Chicago History of American Civilization Ser). 1972. 12.50x (ISBN 0-226-29839-6); pap. 7.50 (ISBN 0-226-29841-8, CHAC7). U of Chicago Pr.

Goldberg, Nathan, et al. The Classification of Jewish Immigrants & Its Implications: A Survey of Opinion. LC 45-6587. (Yivo English Translation Ser.). 154p. 1945. pap. 2.00 (ISBN 0-914512-13-7). Yivo Inst.

Goldscheider, Calvin. The American Jewish Community: Social Science Research & Policy Implications. (Brown Judaic Studies). 183p. 1986. 27.95 (ISBN 1-55540-081-7, 14-50-03). Scholars Pr GA.

--American Jewish Fertility. (Brown Studies on Jews & Their Societies). 1986. text ed. 23.95 (ISBN 0-89130-919-5, 14-50-01); pap. 18.95 (ISBN 0-89130-920-9). Scholars Pr GA.

Goldstein, Sidney & Goldscheider, Calvin. Jewish Americans: Three Generations in a Jewish Community. (Brown Classics in Judaica Ser.). (Illus.). 294p. 1985. pap. text ed. 13.50 (ISBN 0-8191-4721-4). U Pr of Amer.

Gordon, Albert I. Jews in Suburbia. LC 73-11749. 264p. 1973. Repr. of 1959 ed. lib. bdg. 15.00x (ISBN 0-8371-7088-5, COJS). Greenwood.

Grossman, Brigite S. Experiencing Jewish Boston. LC 80-85316. (Illus.). 54p. (Orig.). 1981. pap. 3.50 (ISBN 0-9605624-0-0). Jewish Comm Ctr.

Halpern, Ben. The American Jew: A Zionistic Analysis. LC 82-16875. 192p. 1983. pap. 6.95 (ISBN 0-8052-0742-2). Schocken.

Handlin, Mimi & Layton, Marilyn S. Let Me Hear Your Voice: Portraits of Aging Immigrant Jews. LC 83-47974. (Illus.). 112p. 1984. 19.95 (ISBN 0-295-96039-6). U of Wash Pr.

Hapgood, Hutchins. Spirit of the Ghetto. facsimile ed. Rischin, Moses, ed. LC 67-12099. (The John Harvard Library). (Illus.). 1967. 22.50x (ISBN 0-674-83265-5). Harvard U Pr.

Hardon, John A. American Judaism. LC 72-148264. 1971. 5.95 (ISBN 0-8294-0199-7). Loyola.

Hartstein, Jacob I. & Miller, Benjamin. Jews in America: Heritage & History. (Illus.). 1978. 6.50 (ISBN 0-686-26239-5). Board Jewish Educ.

Hendel-Sebestyen, Giselle. The Sephardic Home: Ethnic Homogeneity & Cultural Traditions in a Total Institution. LC 83-45356. (Immigrant Communities & Ethnic Minorities in the United States & Canada Ser.). 1986. 67.50 (ISBN 0-404-19409-5). AMS Pr.

Hendrick, Burton J. The Jews in America. Grob, Gerald, ed. LC 76-46081. (Anti-Movements in America). 1977. Repr. of 1923 ed. lib. bdg. 17.00x (ISBN 0-405-09954-1). Ayer Co Pubs.

Hertzberg, Arthur. Being Jewish in America: The Modern Experience. LC 78-54390. 320p. 1980. pap. 7.95 (ISBN 0-8052-0654-X). Schocken.

Himmelfarb, Milton & Singer, David, eds. American Jewish Year Book, Vol 86. LC 99-4040. 516p. 1986. 25.95 (ISBN 0-8276-0269-3). Am Jewish Comm.

Howe, Irving. World of Our Fathers. LC 75-16342. (Illus.). 714p. 1976. 14.95 (ISBN 0-15-146353-0). HarBraceJ.

Israel, Fred L., ed. Jews. (Let's Meet the Peoples of North America Ser.). (Illus.). 112p. 1987. lib. bdg. 15.95 (ISBN 0-87754-887-0). Chelsea Hse.

Janowsky, Oscar I., ed. American Jew. facs. ed. LC 76-142647. (Essay Index Reprint Ser). 1942. 18.00 (ISBN 0-8369-2166-6). Ayer Co Pubs.

Joseph, Samuel. History of the Baron DeHirsch Fund: The Americanization of the Jewish Immigrant. LC 76-52987. (Illus.). Repr. of 1935 ed. lib. bdg. 32.50x (ISBN 0-678-01151-6). Kelley.

--Jewish Immigration to the United States from 1881 to 1910. LC 14-15042. (Columbia University. Studies in the Social Sciences: No. 145). Repr. of 1914 ed. 7.50 (ISBN 0-404-51145-7). AMS Pr.

--Jewish Immigration to the United States from 1881 to 1910. LC 69-18781. (American Immigration Collection Ser., No. 1). (Illus.). 1969. Repr. of 1914 ed. 10.00 (ISBN 0-405-00529-6). Ayer Co Pubs.

Kaganoff, Nathan M., ed. Solidarity & Kinship: Essays on American Zionism. (Illus.). 1980. 5.00 (ISBN 0-911934-14-6). Am Jewish Hist Soc.

Kamen, Robert M. Growing up Hasidic: Education & Socialization in the Bobover Hasidic Community. LC 83-45358. (Immigrant Communities & Ethnic Minorities in the United States & Canada Ser.). 1985. 30.00 (ISBN 0-404-19411-7). AMS Pr.

Kaplan, Mordecai M. Future of the American Jew. LC 67-31309. 571p. 1981. pap. 13.95 (ISBN 0-935457-13-5). Reconstructionist Pr.

Karp, Abraham J. To Give Life: The UJA in the Shaping of the American Jewish Community. LC 80-16487. 224p. 1980. 12.95 (ISBN 0-8052-3751-8). Schocken.

Kazin, Alfred. New York Jew. LC 77-20359. 1978. 12.95 (ISBN 0-394-49567-5). Knopf.

Kessner, Thomas. The Golden Door: Italian & Jewish Immigrant Mobility in New York City, 1880-1915. 1977. text ed. 22.50x (ISBN 0-19-502116-9); pap. 8.95x (ISBN 0-19-502161-4). Oxford U Pr.

Kurtz, Seymour. Jewish America. LC 84-10065. (Illus.). 250p. 1985. 29.95 (ISBN 0-07-035655-6). McGraw.

Lavender, Abraham D., ed. A Coat of Many Colors: Jewish Subcommunities in the United States. LC 77-71865. (Contributions in Family Studies: No. 1). 1977. lib. bdg. 29.95 (ISBN 0-8371-9539-X, LCM/). Greenwood.

Learsi, Rufus. The Jew in America: A History. rev. ed. 1972. 11.95x (ISBN 0-87068-177-X). Ktav.

Leiser, Joseph. American Judaism: The Religion & Religious Institutions of the Jewish People in the United States. LC 78-26230. 1979. Repr. of 1925 ed. lib. bdg. 22.50x (ISBN 0-313-20879-4, LEAJ). Greenwood.

Lipsky, Louis. Thirty Years of American Zionism, Vol.1. Davis, Moshe, ed. LC 77-70718. (America & the Holy Land Ser.). 1977. Repr. of 1927 ed. lib. bdg. 26.50x (ISBN 0-405-10263-1). Ayer Co Pubs.

London, Hannah. Miniatures & Silhouttes of Early American Jews. (Illus.). 199p. 25.00 (ISBN 0-686-47008-7). Apollo.

London, Hannah R. Miniatures & Silhouettes of Early American Jews. LC 78-87797. (Illus.). 1969. Repr. 16.50 (ISBN 0-8048-0657-8). C E Tuttle.

--Portraits of Jews by Gilbert Stuart & Other Early American Artists. LC 69-19613. (Illus.). 1969. Repr. 13.75 (ISBN 0-8048-0459-1). C E Tuttle.

Marcus, Jacob R. Jewish Americana. 1954. 7.50x (ISBN 0-87068-799-9, Pub. by Hebrew Union). Ktav.

Marcus, Jacob R. & Peck, Abraham J., eds. Studies in the American Jewish Experience II: Contributions from the Fellowship Programs of the American Jewish Archives. 228p. (Orig.). 1984. lib. bdg. 25.25 (ISBN 0-8191-3714-6); pap. text ed. 12.25 (ISBN 0-8191-3715-4). U Pr of Amer.

Markens, Isaac. The Hebrews in America: A Series of Historical & Biographical Sketches. facsimile ed. LC 74-29504. (Modern Jewish Experiences). 1975. Repr. of 1888 ed. 30.00x (ISBN 0-405-06731-3). Ayer Co Pubs.

Miller, Alan W. God of Daniel S: In Search of the American Jew. (Brown Classics in Judaica Ser.). 260p. 1986. pap. text ed. 13.25 (ISBN 0-8191-5047-9). U Pr of Amer.

Milton, Sybil, et al, eds. Simon Wiesenthal Center Annual, Vol. 2. 1985. lib. bdg. 30.00 (ISBN 0-527-96489-1). Kraus Intl.

Myerhoff, Barbara. Number Our Days. 1980. 8.95 (ISBN 0-671-25430-8, Touchstone). S&S.

Neusner, Jacob. American Judaism: Adventure in Modernity. pap. 9.95x (ISBN 0-87068-681-X). Ktav.

--Stranger at Home: "The Holocaust," Zionism, & American Judaism. LC 80-19455. x, 214p. 1985. pap. 8.95 (ISBN 0-226-57629-9). U of Chicago Pr.

O'Brien, Lee. American Jewish Organizations & Israel. LC 85-29117. 330p. 1985. pap. 24.95 (ISBN 0-88728-153-2). Inst Palestine.

Orthodox Judaism in America. (American Jewish History Ser.: Vol. 69, Pt. 2). 1980. 6.00 (ISBN 0-911934-13-8). Am Jewish Hist Soc.

Plesur, Milton. Jewish Life in Twentieth Century America: Challenge & Accommodation. LC 81-11196. (Illus.). 264p. 1982. text ed. 21.95x (ISBN 0-88229-639-6). Nelson-Hall.

Postal, Bernard & Koppman, Lionel. American Jewish Landmarks: A Travel Guide & History, Vol. 1. LC 76-27401. (Orig.). 1977. 25.00 (ISBN 0-8303-0151-8); pap. 15.00 (ISBN 0-8303-0152-6). Fleet.

--American Jewish Landmarks: A Travel Guide & History, the South & Southwest, Vol. II. LC 76-27401. 1979. 21.95 (ISBN 0-8303-0155-0); pap. 11.95 (ISBN 0-8303-0157-7). Fleet.

Raphael, Marc L. Jews & Judaism in a Midwestern Community: Columbus, Ohio, 1840-1975. (Illus.). 296p. 1979. 10.00 (ISBN 0-318-00876-9). Ohio Hist Soc.

--Profiles in American Judaism: The Reform, Conservative, Orthodox & Reconstructionist Traditions in Historical Perspective. LC 84-47734. 288p. 1985. 20.45 (ISBN 0-06-066801-6, HarpR). Har-Row.

Rischin, Moses, ed. The Jews of the West: The Metropolitan Years. (Illus.). 1979. 5.95 (ISBN 0-911934-11-1). Am Jewish Hist Soc.

Rose, Peter I. Strangers in Their Midst: Small-Town Jews & Their Neighbors. 1977. lib. bdg. 12.95 (ISBN 0-915172-32-1). Richwood Pub.

Rosen, Oded, ed. The Encyclopedia of Jewish Institutions: United States & Canada. 512p. 1983. 55.00 (ISBN 0-913185-00-0). Mosadot Pubns.

Rosenbaum, Fred. Architects of Reform: Congregation & Community Leadership, Emanuel of San Francisco. 1849-1980. LC 80-54032. 241p. 1980. 19.95 (ISBN 0-943376-14-9); pap. 9.95 (ISBN 0-943376-13-0). Magnes Mus.

Rosenberg, Stuart E. New Jewish Identity in America. LC 84-10938. 384p. 1985. 19.95 (ISBN 0-88254-997-9). Hippocrene Bks.

Rosenthal, Gilbert S. Contemporary Judaism: Patterns of Survival. 2nd ed. 401p. 1986. 39.95 (ISBN 0-89885-260-9, Dist. by Independent Publishers Group); pap. 16.95 (ISBN 0-89885-277-3). Human Sci Pr.

Sarna, Jonathan D. Jacksonian Jew: The Two Worlds of Mordecai Noah. LC 79-24379. 245p. 1981. text ed. 35.00x (ISBN 0-8419-0567-3). Holmes & Meier.

Scarpaci, Jean, ed. The Interaction of Italians & Jews in America. 1974. 9.95 (ISBN 0-934675-07-4). Am Italian.

Shulman, Abraham. The Adventures of a Yiddish Lecturer. LC 79-28734. 1980. 7.95 (ISBN 0-8298-0391-2). Pilgrim NY.

Silberman, Charles E. A Certain People: American Jews & Their Lives Today. 464p. 1986. pap. 9.95 (ISBN 0-671-62877-1). Summit Bks.

Singer, David & Seldin, Ruth. American Jewish Year Book, 1987. 1986. write for info. Am Jewish Comm.

Sklare, Marshall. America's Jews. 1971. pap. 9.00 (ISBN 0-394-31645-2, RanC). Random.

--Conservative Judaism: An American Religious Movement. cancelled. Transaction Bks.

Sklare, Marshall, ed. Understanding American Jewry. LC 81-14795. 300p. 1982. text ed. 21.95x (ISBN 0-87855-454-8). Transaction Bks.

Slavin, Stephen L. & Pradt, Mary A. The Einstein Syndrome: Corporate Anti-Semitism in America Today. LC 81-43767. (Illus., Orig.). 1982. lib. bdg. 26.25 (ISBN 0-8191-2370-6); pap. text ed. 11.25 (ISBN 0-8191-2371-4). U Pr of Amer.

Sloan, Irving J. The Jews in America 1621-1977: A Chronology & Fact Book. 2nd ed. LC 77-26768. (No. 3). 1978. lib. bdg. 8.50 (ISBN 0-379-00530-1). Oceana.

Strassfeld, Michael & Strassfeld, Sharon, eds. The Second Jewish Catalog: Sources & Resources. LC 73-11759. (Illus.). 464p. 1976. 8.95 (ISBN 0-8276-0084-4, 391). Jewish Pubns.

Tebeau, Charlton W. Synagogue in the Central City: Temple Israel of Greater Miami, 1922-1972. LC 71-85107. (Illus.). 144p. 1972. 9.95 (ISBN 0-87024-239-3). U of Miami Pr.

Tobias, Henry J. The Jews in Oklahoma. LC 79-6723. (Newcomers to a New Land Ser.: Vol. 10). (Illus.). 96p. (Orig.). 1980. pap. 3.95 (ISBN 0-8061-1676-5). U of Okla Pr.

Uchill, Ida L. Pioneers, Peddlers, & Tsadikim: The Story of the Jews in Colorado. 2nd ed. LC 57-57817. 327p. 1979. pap. 9.95 (ISBN 0-9604468-0-X). Uchill.

Van Den Haag, Ernest. The Jewish Mystique. LC 76-56974. 1977. pap. 6.95 (ISBN 0-8128-2189-0). Stein & Day.

Whitfield, Stephen J. Voices of Jacob, Hands of Esau: Jews in American Life & Thought. LC 83-25720. x, 322p. 1984. lib. bdg. 25.00 (ISBN 0-208-02024-1, Archon Bks). Shoe String.

Wieder, Alan. Immigration, the Public School, & the 20th Century American Ethos: The Jewish Immigrant As a Case Study. 124p. (Orig.). 1985. lib. bdg. 24.00 (ISBN 0-8191-4793-1); pap. text ed. 8.75 (ISBN 0-8191-4794-X). U Pr of Amer.

Wise, Isaac. Reminiscences. Philipson, David, ed. LC 73-2233. (The Jewish People; History, Religion, Literature Ser.). Repr. of 1901 ed. 30.00 (ISBN 0-405-05294-4). Ayer Co Pubs.

Wise, James W. Jews Are Like That. facs. ed. LC 70-84348. (Essay Index Reprint Ser). 1928. 16.75 (ISBN 0-8369-1114-8). Ayer Co Pubs.

Woocher, Jonathan S. Sacred Survival: The Civil Religion of American Jews. LC 85-45790. (Jewish Political & Social Studies). (Illus.). 224p. 1986. 25.00x (ISBN 0-253-35041-7). Ind U Pr.

JEWS IN THE UNITED STATES–BIOGRAPHY

Abramson, Ruth. Benjamin: Journey of a Jew. (The Life-Cycle Bookshelf Ser.). (Orig.). 1987. pap. 10.00 (ISBN 0-933771-02-9). Alpha Pub Co.

Birmingham, Stephen. Our Crowd: The Great Jewish Families of New York. 528p. 1985. pap. 4.50 (ISBN 0-425-07557-5). Berkley Pub.

Coser, Lewis A. Refugee Scholars in America: Their Impact & Their Experiences. LC 84-40193. 384p. 1984. 27.50x (ISBN 0-300-03193-9). Yale U Pr.

Cowett, Mark. Birmingham's Rabbi: Morris Newfield & Alabama, 1895-1940. LC 85-20897. 379p. 1986. 22.50 (ISBN 0-8173-0284-0). U of Ala Pr.

Freedland, Michael. So Let's Hear the Applause: The Story of the Jewish Entertainer. (Illus.). 250p. 1986. 16.50x (ISBN 0-85303-215-7, Pu. by Valentine Mitchell England). Biblio Dist.

Hartmann, Heinz. Once a Doctor, Always a Doctor: The Memoirs of a German-Jewish Immigrant Physician. 130p. Date not set. 18.95 (ISBN 0-87975-342-0). Prometheus Bks.

Lipstadt, Deborah E. The Zionist Career of Louis Lipsky, 1900-1921. 35.00 (ISBN 0-405-14086-X). Ayer Co Pubs.

Polner, Murray. American Jewish Biographies. (Illus.). 500p. 1982. 39.95x (ISBN 0-87196-462-7). Facts on File.

Ribalow, Harld V. & Ribalow, Meir. The Jewish Baseball Stars. (Illus.). 1984. 12.95 (ISBN 0-88254-898-0). Hippocrene Bks.

Sanford, John. The Color of the Air: Scenes from the Life of an American Jew, Vol. 1. 305p. (Orig.). 1985. 20.00 (ISBN 0-87685-644-X); pap. 12.50 (ISBN 0-87685-643-1). Black Sparrow.

--The Waters of Darkness: Scenes from the Life of an American Jew, Vol. 2. 294p. (Orig.). 1986. 20.00 (ISBN 0-87685-672-5); signed cloth 30.00 (ISBN 0-87685-673-3); pap. 12.50 (ISBN 0-87685-671-7). Black Sparrow.

Silverman, Morris. Hartford Jews: Sixteen Fifty-Nine to Nineteen Seventy. (Illus.). 449p. 1970. 10.00 (ISBN 0-940748-21-5). Conn Hist Soc.

Wolf, Hannie. Child of Two Worlds. (Illus.). 156p. 1979. 13.00 (ISBN 0-931068-02-9). Purcells.

JEWS IN THE UNITED STATES - BIBLIOGRAPHY

Alexander, Morris. Israel & Me. (Illus.). 278p. 1977. 14.50x (ISBN 0-87073-204-8). Schenkman Bks Inc.

American Jewish Archives, Cincinnati Staff, ed. Manuscript Catalog of the American Jewish Archives, 4 vols. 1971. Set. lib. bdg. 400.00 (ISBN 0-8161-0899-4, Hall Library). G K Hall.

Brickman, William E., ed. & compiled by. The Jewish Community in America: An Annotated & Classified Bibliographical Guide. (Ethnic Bibliographical Ser: No. 2). 1977. PLB 19.95 (ISBN 0-89102-057-8). B Franklin.

Glanz, Rudolph. German Jew in America: An Annotated Bibliography Including Books, Pamphlets & Articles of Special Interest. 1969. 39.50x (ISBN 0-87068-061-7). Ktav.

The Jewish Experience in America: A Historical Bibliography. LC 82-22823. (ABC-Clio Research Guides Ser.: No. 1). 190p. 1982. lib. bdg. 25.00 (ISBN 0-87436-034-X). ABC-Clio.

Marcus, Jacob R. An Index to Articles on American Jewish History. 1971. 20.00x (ISBN 0-87068-139-7). Ktav.

Rosenbach, Abraham S. An American Jewish Bibliography: Being a List of Books & Pamphlets by Jews, or Relating to Them, Printed in the United States from the Establishment of the Press in the Colonies until 1850. (American Jewish Historical Society Publications: No. 30). (Illus.). pap. 127.30 (ISBN 0-317-09938-8, 2017816). Bks Demand UMI.

JEWS IN THE UNITED STATES–FICTION

Rosewaike, Ira. The Edge of Greatness: A Portrait of American Jewry in the Early National Period. (Illus.). 1985. 25.00 (ISBN 0-87820-013-4, Pub. by Am Jewish Archives). Ktav.

JEWS IN THE UNITED STATES–HISTORY

America & the Holocaust. (American Jewish History Ser.: Vol. 70, Pt. 3). 1981. 6.00 (ISBN 0-911934-20-0). Am Jewish Hist Soc.

American Jews & the Labor Movement. (American Jewish Historical Quarterly: Vol. 65, Pt.3). 1976. 4.00 (ISBN 0-911934-05-7). Am Jewish Hist Soc.

Baron, Salo W. Steeled in Adversity. (Texts & Studies). (Hebrew.). 1977. 15.00 (ISBN 0-911934-15-4). Am Jewish Hist Soc.

Benjamin, Israel B. Three Years in America: 1859-1862, 2 vols. in 1. facsimile ed. Reznikoff, Charles, tr. from Ger. LC 74-27962. (Modern Jewish Experience Ser.). (Eng.). 1975. Repr. of 1956 ed. 52.00x (ISBN 0-405-06693-7). Ayer Co Pubs.

Bernstein, Philip. To Dwell in Unity: The Jewish Federation Movement in America, 1960-1980. LC 83-9867. 394p. 1983. 19.95 (ISBN 0-8276-0228-6, 608). Jewish Pubns.

Birmingham, Stephen. The Rest of Us: The Rise of America's Eastern European Jews. 384p. 1984. 19.95 (ISBN 0-316-09647-4). Little.

--The Rest of Us: The Rise of America's Eastern European Jews. 432p. 1985. pap. 4.50 (ISBN 0-425-08074-9). Berkley Pub.

Blau, Joseph L. Judaism in America: From Curiosity to Third Faith. LC 75-5069. (Chicago History of American Religion Ser.). 176p. 1976. 6.00x (ISBN 0-226-05727-5). U of Chicago Pr.

Blau, Joseph L., et al, eds. The Jews of the United States, 1790-1840: A Documentary History, 3 Vols. LC 64-10108. 1034p. 1964. Set. 140.00x (ISBN 0-231-02651-X). Columbia U Pr.

Blumanthal, David. Understanding Jewish Mysticism: The Philosophic-Mystical Tradition & the Hasidic Tradition, Vol.II. 20.00x (ISBN 0-87068-205-9); pap. 9.95 (ISBN 0-87068-225-3). Ktav.

Brandes, Joseph & Douglas, Martin. Immigrants to Freedom: Jewish Communities in Rural New Jersey Since 1882. LC 76-122384. 1971. 27.50x (ISBN 0-8122-7620-5). U of Pa Pr.

Brumberg, Stephan F. Going to America Going to School: The Jewish Immigrant Public School Encounter in Turn-of-the-Century New York City. LC 85-16791. 300p. 1986. 29.95 (ISBN 0-03-062574-2, C2030). Praeger.

Chotzinoff, Samuel. A Lost Paradise: Early Reminiscences. facsimile ed. LC 74-27970. (Modern Jewish Experience Ser.). 1975. Repr. of 1955 ed. 31.00x (ISBN 0-405-06700-3). Ayer Co Pubs.

Covey, Cyclone. Calalus: A Roman Jewish Colony in America from the Time of Charlemagne Through Alfred the Great. 190p. 1975. 10.00 (ISBN 0-533-01209-0). Vantage.

Dimont, Max. The Jews in America. 1980. 6.95 (ISBN 0-671-25412-X, Touchstone). S&S.

Drazin, Nathan. History of Jewish Education from 515 B. C. E. to 220 C. E. 1979. 16.00 (ISBN 0-405-10598-3). Ayer Co Pubs.

Ehrmann, E. L. Readings in Jewish History: From the American Revolution to the Present. 9.95x (ISBN 0-87068-447-7). Ktav.

Eisenberg, Azriel. Eyewitnesses to American Jewish History, Pt. 4: The American Jew 1915 to 1969. 1979. 6.00 (ISBN 0-8074-0018-1, 044062). UAHC.

Eisenberg, Azriel, et al, eds. Eyewitnesses to American Jewish History: 1492-1793, Pt. 1. 1976. pap. 5.00 (ISBN 0-686-77106-0, 144060); tchrs'. guide 5.00 (ISBN 0-8074-0019-X, 204061). UAHC.

Elzas, Barnett A. The Jews of South Carolina, from the Earliest Times to the Present Day. LC 77-187364. (Illus.). 352p. 1972. Repr. of 1905 ed. 23.50 (ISBN 0-87152-092-3). Reprint.

Essays in American Jewish History, in Honor of Jacob Rader Marcus. 35.00x (ISBN 0-87068-459-0). Ktav.

Feingold, Henry L. Zion in America. rev. ed. (American Immigrant Ser.). 1981. pap. 10.95 (ISBN 0-88254-592-2). Hippocrene Bks.

Feldman, Abraham J. The American Jew: A Study of Backgrounds. LC 78-26254. 1979. Repr. of 1937 ed. lib. bdg. cancelled (ISBN 0-313-20876-X, FEAJ). Greenwood.

Feldman, Jacob. The Jewish Experience in Western Pensylvania, 1755-1945. (Illus.). 1986. 9.95 (ISBN 0-936340-03-7). Hist Soc West Pa.

Fierman, Floyd S. Roots & Boots: From Crypto-Jew in New Spain to Community Leader in the American Southwest. 1987. 20.00 (ISBN 0-88125-114-3). KTAV.

Fine, Jo Renee & Wolfe, Gerard R. The Synagogues of New York's Lower East Side. LC 75-15126. (Illus.). 1978. 27.50 (ISBN 0-8147-2559-7). NYU Pr.

Finger, Seymour M. American Jewry During the Holocaust. 1984. pap. 14.95x (ISBN 0-9613537-3-2). Am Jewish Holo.

--American Jewry During the Holocaust. 412p. (Orig.). 1984. pap. text ed. 17.95 (ISBN 0-8419-7506-X). Holmes & Meier.

Foster, Geraldine S. The Jews in Rhode Island: A Brief History. Conley, Patrick T., ed. (Rhode Island Ethnic Heritage Pamphlet Ser.). (Illus.). 48p. (Orig.). 1985. pap. 2.75 (ISBN 0-917012-80-1). RI Pubns Soc.

Friedman, Lee M. Pilgrims in a New Land. LC 78-26208. (Illus.). 1979. Repr. of 1948 ed. lib. bdg. 32.50x (ISBN 0-313-20877-8, FRPI). Greenwood.

Friedman, Murray, ed. Jewish Life in Philadelphia, 1830-1940. LC 83-10763. (Illus.). 360p. 1983. 19.95 (ISBN 0-89727-050-9). ISHI PA.

Gerber, David A., ed. Anti-Semitism in American History. 440p. 1986. 29.95 (ISBN 0-252-01214-3). U of Ill Pr.

Goldberg, Robert A. Back to the Soil: The Jewish Farmers of Clarion, Utah, & Their World. (Utah Centennial Ser.: Vol. 2). (Illus.). 208p. 1986. 19.95 (ISBN 0-87480-263-6). U of Utah Pr.

Goldmark, Josephine. Pilgrims of Forty-Eight. facsimile ed. LC 74-27989. (Modern Jewish Experience Ser.). (Illus.). 1975. Repr. of 1930 ed. 29.00x (ISBN 0-405-06716-X). Ayer Co Pubs.

Goren, Arthur A. New York Jews & the Quest for Community. LC 76-129961. 1979. 34.00x (ISBN 0-231-03422-9); pap. 17.00x (ISBN 0-231-08368-8). Columbia U Pr.

Grinstein, Hyman. A Short History of the Jews in the United States. 208p. 1980. 20.00 (ISBN 0-900689-50-1). Soncino Pr.

Gurock, Jeffrey S. American Jewish History: A Bibliograhical Guide. 1983. 6.95 (ISBN 0-88464-037-X). ADL.

Handlin, Oscar. American Jews: Their Story. 48p. 2.50 (ISBN 0-88464-011-6). ADL.

Herscher, Uri D., ed. The East European Jewish Experience in America: A Century of Memories, 1882-1982. LC 83-6416. (Monographs of the American Jewish Archives: No. 9). 192p. 1983. 15.75x (ISBN 0-87820-011-8). Ktav.

Howe, Irving. World of Our Fathers. 560p. 1983. pap. 12.95 (ISBN 0-671-49252-7, Touchstone). S&S.

The Jewish Experience in America: A Historical Bibliography. LC 82-22823. (ABC-Clio Research Guides Ser.: No. 1). 190p. 1982. lib. bdg. 25.00 (ISBN 0-87436-034-X). ABC-Clio.

Jick, Leon A. The Americanization of the Synagogue, 1820-1870. LC 75-18213. (Illus.). 260p. 1976. 25.00x (ISBN 0-87451-119-4). U Pr of New Eng.

Kaganoff, Nathan M. & Urofsky, Melvin I., eds. Turn to the South: Essays on Southern Jewry. LC 78-9306. 205p. 1979. 10.95x (ISBN 0-8139-0742-X). U Pr of Va.

Karp, Abraham J. Haven & Home: A History of the Jews in America. LC 84-5530. 416p. 1985. 24.95 (ISBN 0-8052-3920-0). Schocken.

Karp, Abraham. J. Haven & Home: A History of the Jews in America. 416p. 1986. pap. 9.95 (ISBN 0-8052-0817-8). Schocken.

Koppman, Lionel & Postol, Bernard. Guess Who's Jewish in American History. 336p. 1986. pap. 7.95 (ISBN 0-933503-55-5). Shapolsky Pubs.

Korn, Bertram W. American Jewry: The Formative Years. (Texts & Studies). (Hebrew.). 1971. 10.00 (ISBN 0-911934-04-9). Am Jewish Hist Soc.

Libo, Kenneth & Howe, Irving. We Lived There Too: A Documentary History of Pioneer Jews & the Westward Movement of America, 1630-1930. LC 84-11787. (Illus.). 352p. 1984. 24.95 (ISBN 0-312-85866-3, Pub. by Marek). St Martin.

--We Lived There Too: In Their Own Words & Pictures-Pioneer Jews & the Westward Movement of America 1630-1930. (Illus.). 352p. 1985. pap. 13.95 (ISBN 0-312-85867-1, Pub. by Marek). St Martin.

Marcus, J. R., ed. Jews & the American Revolution: A Bicentennial Documentary. 7.50x (ISBN 0-87068-875-8). Ktav.

Marcus, Jacob R. The American Jewish Woman: A Documentary History. 1981. 35.00x (ISBN 0-87068-752-2). Ktav.

--An Introduction to Early American Jewish History. (Texts & Studies). (Hebrew.). 1971. 10.00 (ISBN 0-911934-09-X). Am Jewish Hist Soc.

Marcus, Jacob R., ed. The American Jewish Woman: 1654-1980. 1981. 15.00x (ISBN 0-87068-579-1). Ktav.

Mayer, Egon. From Suburb to Shtetl: The Jews of Boro Park. (Illus.). 196p. 1979. 29.95 (ISBN 0-87722-161-8). Temple U Pr.

Medoff, Rafael. The Deafening Silence: American Jewish Leaders & the Holocaust, 1933-1945. 1986. 14.95 (ISBN 0-933503-63-6). Shapolsky Pubs.

Meyer, Isidore S., ed. American Jew in the Civil War. Repr. of 1962 ed. 11.00 (ISBN 0-527-03218-2). Kraus Repr.

Mitchell, William E. Mishpokhe: A Study of New York City Jewish Family Clubs. (New Babylon Studies in the Social Sciences Ser.: No. 30). (Illus.). 1978. 20.50x (ISBN 90-279-7695-3). Mouton.

Narrell, Irena. Our City: The Jews of San Francisco. LC 80-21216. 1980. 25.00 (ISBN 0-8310-7122-2). Howell-North.

Nurenberger, M. J. The Scared & the Doomed: The Jewish Establishment vs. the Six Million. (Illus.). 320p. (Orig.). 1986. pap. 12.95 (ISBN 0-88962-289-2). Riverrun NY.

On Common Ground: The Boston Jewish Community 1649-1980. (Illus.). 1981. 6.00 (ISBN 0-911934-19-7). Am Jewish Hist Soc.

Pessin, Deborah. History of the Jews in America. (Illus.). 1957. pap. 4.95x (ISBN 0-8381-0189-5). United Syn Bk.

Postal, Bernard & Koppman, Lionel. American Jewish Landmarks: A Travel Guide & History, the South & Southwest, Vol. II. LC 76-27401. 1979. 21.95 (ISBN 0-8303-0155-0); pap. 11.95 (ISBN 0-8303-0157-7). Fleet.

--Jewish Landmarks of New York: A Travel Guide & History. LC 76-27400. (Orig.). 1978. 15.95 (ISBN 0-8303-0153-4). Fleet.

Rischin, Moses. The Promised City: New York's Jews, 1870-1914. (Illus.). 342p. 1977. pap. 8.95x (ISBN 0-674-71501-2); text ed. 22.50x (ISBN 0-674-71502-0). Harvard U Pr.

Rischin, Moses, ed. The Jews of the West: The Metropolitan Years. (Illus.). 156p. 1975. pap. 5.95 (ISBN 0-943376-10-6). Magnes Mus.

Rochlin, Harriett. Pioneer Jews: A New Life in the Far West. LC 83-12647. (Illus.). 1984. 17.95 (ISBN 0-395-31832-7). HM.

Rockaway, Robert. The Jews of Detroit: From the Beginning, 1762-1914. LC 86-15866. (Illus.). 175p. 1986. 15.95X (ISBN 0-8143-1808-8). Wayne St U Pr.

Rosen, Gladys. Jewish Life in America: Historical Perspectives. 12.50x (ISBN 0-87068-346-2); pap. 9.95 (ISBN 0-686-52683-X). Ktav.

Rosen, Gladys L., ed. Jewish Life in America: Historical Perspectives. LC 78-16560. 198p. 1978. pap. 6.95 (ISBN 0-686-74514-0). Am Jewish Comm.

Rosenbaum, S. E. A Voyage to America in Eighteen Forty-Seven: The Diary of a Bohemian Jew on His Voyage from Hamburg to New York in 1847. (Studies in Judaica & the Holocaust: No. 3). 60p. 1987. lib. bdg. 19.95x (ISBN 0-89370-371-0); pap. text ed. 9.95x (ISBN 0-89370-471-7). Borgo Pr.

Rosewaike, Ira. The Edge of Greatness: A Portrait of American Jewry in the Early National Period. (Illus.). 1985. 25.00 (ISBN 0-87820-013-4, Pub. by Am Jewish Archives). Ktav.

Rothchild, Sylvia. A Special Legacy: An Oral History of Soviet Jewish Emigres in the United States. 336p. 1986. pap. 8.95 (ISBN 0-671-62817-8, Touchstone). S&S.

Sanders, Ronald & Gillon, Edmund V. The Lower East Side: A Guide to Its Jewish Past with Ninety-Nine New Photographs. (Illus.). 1980. pap. 5.95 (ISBN 0-486-23871-7). Dover.

Sarna, Jonathan D. The American Jewish Experience. 336p. 1986. text ed. 35.00x (ISBN 0-8419-0934-2); pap. text ed. 19.50x (ISBN 0-8419-0935-0). Holmes & Meier.

Sarna, Jonathan D., ed. People Walk on Their Heads: Moses Weinberger's Jews & Judaism in New York. 137p. 1982. text ed. 24.50x (ISBN 0-8419-0707-2); pap. text ed. 12.95x (ISBN 0-8419-0731-5). Holmes & Meier.

Sarna, Jonathan D., et al. Jews & the Founding of the Republic. LC 85-40513. (American History in Documents Ser.). (Illus.). 240p. (Orig.). 1985. pap. text ed. 14.50x (ISBN 0-910129-44-4). Wiener Pub Inc.

Schmier, Louis, ed. Reflections of Southern Jewry: The Letters of Charles Wessolowsky. LC 81-16995. viii, 184p. 1982. 12.95 (ISBN 0-86554-020-9, MUP-H15). Mercer Univ Pr.

Silverman, Morris. Hartford Jews: Sixteen Fifty-Nine to Nineteen Seventy. (Illus.). 449p. 1970. 10.00 (ISBN 0-940748-21-5). Conn Hist Soc.

Simon, Rita J., ed. New Lives: The Adjustment of Soviet Jewish Immigrants in the United States & Israel. 208p. 1985. 19.95 (ISBN 0-669-09767-5). Lexington Bks.

Sklare, Marshall. Conservative Judaism: An American Religious Movement. (Illus.). 336p. 1985. pap. text ed. 12.75 (ISBN 0-8191-4480-0, Co-Pub. by Ctr Jewish Comm Studies). U Pr of Amer.

Smith, Judith E. Family Connections: A History of Italian & Jewish Immigrant Lives in Providence, Rhode Island, 1900-1940. (SUNY Series in American Social History). 256p. 1985. 44.50 (ISBN 0-87395-964-7); pap. 16.95 (ISBN 0-87395-965-5). State U NY Pr.

Strauss, Herbert, ed. Jewish Immigrants of the Nazi Period in the U. S. A, 6 Vols. Set. lib. bdg. 130.00 (ISBN 0-317-11838-2); Vol. 1. 35.00 (ISBN 3-598-08006-9). Vol. 2 (ISBN 3-598-08007-7). Vol. 3, Pt. 1 (ISBN 3-598-08008-5). Vol. 3, Pt. 2 (ISBN 3-598-08013-1). K G Saur.

Strauss, Herbert A., ed. Jewish Immigrants of the Nazi Period in the U. S. A. Essays on the History, Persecution, & Emigration of the German Jews. (Jewish Immigrants of the Nazi Period in the U. S. A. Ser.: Vol. 6). 430p. 1987. lib. bdg. 74.00 (ISBN 3-598-08011-5). K G Saur.

Tcherikower, Elias, ed. Geshikhte Fun der Yidisher Arbeterbavegung, Vol. 2. LC 45-13072. (Yiddish., Illus.). 1945. 20.00 (ISBN 0-914512-18-8). Yivo Inst.

Turitz, Leo & Turitz, Evelyn. Jews in Early Mississippi. LC 82-25093. (Illus.). 144p. (Orig.). 1983. pap. 20.00 (ISBN 0-87805-178-3). U Pr of Miss.

Waxman, Chaim I. America's Jews in Transition. 290p. 1983. 29.95 (ISBN 0-87722-321-1); pap. 12.95 (ISBN 0-87722-329-7). Temple U Pr.

Wolf, Edwin, 2nd & Whiteman, Maxwell. History of the Jews of Philadelphia: From Colonial Times to the Age of Jackson. LC 56-7780. (Illus.). 552p. 1975. 8.50 (ISBN 0-8276-0075-5, 372). Jewish Pubns.

Wolf, Hannie. Child of Two Worlds. (Illus.). 156p. 1979. 13.00 (ISBN 0-931068-02-9). Purcells.

Wolf, Simon. The American Jew As Patriot, Soldier, & Citizen. LC 72-8739. (American Revolutionary Ser.). 1979. Repr. of 1895 ed. lib. bdg. 47.00x (ISBN 0-8398-2179-4). Irvington.

JEWS IN THE UNITED STATES–HISTORY–SOURCES

Butwin, Frances. Jews of America: History & Sources. Blecher, Arthur C., ed. LC 73-2253. (Illus.). 160p. 1973. pap. text ed. 3.95x (ISBN 0-87441-062-2). Behrman.

Cowen, Philip. Memories of an American Jew. facsimile ed. LC 74-27974. (Modern Jewish Experience Ser.). (Illus.). 1975. Repr. of 1932 ed. 37.50x (ISBN 0-405-06703-8). Ayer Co Pubs.

Karp, Abraham J., intro. by. Beginnings: Early American Judaica a Collection of Ten Publications in Facsimile, Illustrative of the Religious, Communal, Cultural & Political Life of American Jewry, 1761-1845. LC 75-23405. (Illus.). 1975. 20.00 (ISBN 0-8276-0076-3, 376). Jewish Pubns.

Levy, Harriet L. Nine-Twenty O'Farrell Street. facsimile ed. LC 74-29501. (Modern Jewish Experience Ser.). (Illus.). 1975. Repr. of 1947 ed. 23.50x (ISBN 0-405-06728-3). Ayer Co Pubs.

JEWS IN THE UNITED STATES–JUVENILE LITERATURE

Karp, Deborah. Heroes of American Jewish History. 1972. pap. 6.95x (ISBN 0-87068-394-2). Ktav.

JEWS IN THE UNITED STATES–SOCIAL LIFE AND CUSTOMS

Bloomfield, Brynna C. & Moskowitz, Jane M. Traveling Jewish in America: The Complete Guide for 1986 for Business & Pleasure. 407p. (Orig.). 1986. pap. 9.95 (ISBN 0-9617104-0-3). Wandering You Pr.

Cohen, Bernard. Sociocultural Changes in American Jewish Life As Reflected in Selected Jewish Literature. LC 75-146162. 282p. 1972. 24.50 (ISBN 0-8386-7848-3). Fairleigh Dickinson.

Davis, Nancy & Levitt, Joy. The Guide to Everything Jewish in New York. LC 86-10927. 334p. 1986. pap. 14.95 (ISBN 0-915361-47-7, Dist. by Watts). Adama Pubs Inc.

Heilman, Samuel C. Synagogue Life: A Study in Symbolic Interaction. LC 75-36403. 1976. 12.95x (ISBN 0-226-32488-5); pap. 9.95x (ISBN 0-226-32490-7, P824, Phoen). U of Chicago Pr.

Kaplan, Mordecai M. Judaism As a Civilization: Toward a Reconstruction of American-Jewish Life. LC 81-6057. 601p. 1981. 25.00 (ISBN 0-8276-0193-X, 474); pap. 12.95 (ISBN 0-8276-0194-8, 480). Jewish Pubns.

Mayer, Egon. From Suburb to Shtetl: The Jews of Boro Park. (Illus.). 196p. 1979. 29.95 (ISBN 0-87722-161-8). Temple U Pr.

Neusner, Jacob. Judaism in the American Humanities. LC 81-1798. (Brown Judaic Studies). 1981. pap. text ed. 20.00 (ISBN 0-89130-480-0, 14-00-28). Scholars Pr GA.

Raphael, Marc L., ed. Jews & Judaism in the United States: A Documentary History. 352p. 1983. pap. text ed. 9.95x (ISBN 0-87441-347-8). Behrman.

Sandberg, Neil C. Jewish Life in Los Angeles: A Window to Tomorrow. LC 86-11025. (Illus.). 224p. 1986. lib. bdg. 17.50 (ISBN 0-8191-5439-3). U Pr of Amer.

Shepard, Richard F., et al. Live & Be Well: A Celebration of Yiddish Culture in America from the First Immigrants to the Second World War. (Illus.). 192p. 1982. 19.50 (ISBN 0-345-30752-6); pap. 9.95 (ISBN 0-345-29435-1). Ballantine.

Silberman, Charles. A Certain People: American Jews & Their Lives Today. 1985. 19.95 (ISBN 0-671-44761-0). Summit Bks.

Sklare, Marshall, ed. American Jews. 352p. 1983. pap. text ed. 9.95x (ISBN 0-87441-348-6). Behrman.

Wilde, Larry. The Ultimate Official Jewish Joke Book. 192p. (Orig.). 1986. pap. 2.95 (ISBN 0-553-26227-0). Bantam.

JEZEBEL, WIFE OF AHAB, KING OF ISRAEL–FICTION

Hesky, Olga. Painted Queen. 1962. 12.95 (ISBN 0-8392-1083-3). Astor-Honor.

JEZIDES

see Yezidis

JIB, AL, JORDAN

Pritchard, James B. Gibeon, Where the Sun Stood Still: The Discovery of a Biblical City. 1962. 31.50 (ISBN 0-691-03517-2); pap. 9.50x (ISBN 0-691-00210-X). Princeton U Pr.

JIHAD

Nima, Ramy. The Wrath of Allah: Islamic Revolution & Reaction in Iran. 170p. (Orig.). 1983. pap. 9.50 (ISBN 0-86104-733-8, Pub by Pluto Pr). Longwood Pub Group.

Sobini, John. Armies in the Sand: The Struggle for Mecca & Medina. (Illus.). 223p. 11.95 (ISBN 0-500-01246-6). Brown Bk.

JOACHIM, ABBOT OF FIORE, 1132-1202

Gregorich, Barbara. Colors. Hoffman, Joan, ed. (A Get Ready! Bk.). (Illus.). 32p. 1983. pap. text ed. 1.95 (ISBN 0-938256-64-5). Sch Zone Pub Co.

JOB, A SLAVE

Brodsky, Beverley, adapted by. & illus. The Story of Job. LC 85-24303. (Illus.). 40p. 14.95 (ISBN 0-8076-1142-5). Braziller.

JOB, THE PATRIARCH

Besserman, Lawrence L. The Legend of Job in the Middle Ages. LC 78-14936. (Illus.). 1979. 15.00x (ISBN 0-674-52385-7, Belknap Pr). Harvard U Pr.

Bloem, Diane B. Into the Midst of Suffering: A Woman's Workshop on Job. (Woman's Workshop Ser.). (Orig.). 1985. Leader's ed., 64pp. pap. 3.95 (ISBN 0-310-42771-1, 11213P); Student's ed., 112pp. pap. 2.95 (ISBN 0-310-42781-9, 11213P). Zondervan.

Brodsky, Beverley, adapted by. & illus. The Story of Job. LC 85-24303. (Illus.). 40p. 14.95 (ISBN 0-8076-1142-5). Braziller.

Gordis, Robert. The Book of God & Man. LC 65-25126. 1978. pap. 12.95x (ISBN 0-226-30410-8, P771, Phoen). U of Chicago Pr.

Roth, Joseph. Job: The Story of a Simple Man. Thompson, Dorothy, tr. from Ger. LC 81-18901. (A Tusk Bk.). 252p. 1985. 22.50 (ISBN 0-87951-149-4); pap. 8.95 (ISBN 0-87951-202-4). Overlook Pr.

Shestov, Lev. In Job's Balances: On the Sources of the Eternal Truths. Coventry, Camilla & Macartney, C. A., trs. from Ger. LC 73-92902. (Eng.). l, 379p. 1975. 20.00x (ISBN 0-8214-0143-2, 82-81461). Ohio U Pr.

Vawter, Bruce. Job & Jonah: Questioning the Hidden God. LC 82-62413. 1983. pap. 4.95 (ISBN 0-8091-2524-2). Paulist Pr.

JOB SATISFACTION

Hubbard, L. Ron. The Problems of Work. 20.00 (ISBN 0-686-30789-5). Church Scient NY.

JOGGING

Gilmore, Haydn. Jog for Your Life. new ed. (Illus.). 1979. pap. 1.95 (ISBN 0-310-25022-6). Zondervan.

Lovett, C. S. Jogging with Jesus. (Illus.). 1978. pap. 3.95 (ISBN 0-938148-34-6). Personal Christianity.

JOHN 23RD, POPE, 1881-1963

Bonnot, Bernard R. Pope John Twenty-Third: A Clever, Pastoral Leader. LC 79-1770. 1980. 9.95 (ISBN 0-8189-0388-0). Alba.

Calvez, Jean Y. The Social Thought of John Twenty-Third: Mater et Magistra. McKenzie, George J., tr. LC 75-40992. 1977. Repr. of 1965 ed. lib. bdg. 22.50x (ISBN 0-8371-8711-7, CASCJ). Greenwood.

Cousins, Norman. The Improbable Triumvirate: John F. Kennedy, Pope John, Nikita Khrushchev. (Illus.). 176p. 1984. pap. 4.95 (ISBN 0-393-30162-1). Norton.

Hansen, William P. & Haney, John, eds. Pope John XXIII. (World Leaders--Past & Present Ser.). (Illus.). 112p. 1987. lib. bdg. 16.95 (ISBN 0-87754-535-9). Chelsea Hse.

Hebblethwaite, Peter. Pope John XXIII: Shepherd of the Modern World. LC 82-45484. (Illus.). 576p. 1985. 19.95 (ISBN 0-385-17298-2). Doubleday.

Kitts, Eustace J. Pope John the Twenty-Third & Master John Hus of Bohemia. LC 77-84726. Repr. of 1910 ed. 47.00 (ISBN 0-404-16127-8). AMS Pr.

Lecaro, Giacomo. John Twenty Third: Simpleton or Saint. 1968. 3.50 (ISBN 0-8199-0055-9, L38351). Franciscan Herald.

Lorit, Sergius C. Everybody's Pope: The Life of John 23rd. LC 67-15775. 1966. pap. 2.95 (ISBN 0-911782-06-0). New City.

Zizola, Giancarlo. The Utopia of Pope John XXIII. Barolini, Helen, tr. from Ital. LC 79-4347. Orig. Title: L' Utopia de Papa Giovanni. 391p. (Orig.). 1979. pap. 2.49 (ISBN 0-88344-520-4). Orbis Bks.

JOHN 23RD, POPE, 1881-1963–JUVENILE LITERATURE

McGravie, Anne. The Boyhood of Pope John XXIII. (Stories about Christian Heroes Ser.). (Illus.). 1979. pap. 1.95 (ISBN 0-03-049446-X, HarpR). Har-Row.

JOHN, SAINT, APOSTLE

Barnes, Arthur S. Christianity at Rome in the Apostolic Age. LC 72-114462. (Illus.). 1971. Repr. of 1938 ed. lib. bdg. 55.00x (ISBN 0-8371-4760-3, BACR). Greenwood.

Booth, A. E. Ministry of Peter, John & Paul. 1982. pap. 1.25 (ISBN 0-88172-004-6). Believers Bkshelf.

Bo Yin Ra. The Wisdom of St. John. Reichenbach, Bodo A., tr. from Ger. LC 74-15272. 112p. 1975. 8.00 (ISBN 0-915034-01-8). Kober Pr.

Culpepper, R. Alan. The Johannine School: An Evaluation of the Johannine-School Hypothesis Based on an Investigation of the Nature of Ancient Schools. LC 75-34235. (Society of Biblical Literature. Dissertation Ser.: No. 26). Repr. of 1975 ed. 62.40 (ISBN 0-8357-9576-4, 2017525). Bks Demand UMI.

Eldridge, Charlotte. The Watcher. (Orig.). 1981. pap. write for info. Shamar Bk.

Ellis, E. Earle. The World of St. John: The Gospels & the Epistles. 96p. (Orig.). 1984. pap. 4.95 (ISBN 0-8028-0013-0). Eerdmans.

Fowler, Harlan D. Behold the Flaming Sword: A Biography of John & Jesus. (Illus.). 1983. 35.00 (ISBN 0-533-05059-6). Vantage.

Hardy, Richard P. Search for Nothing: Life of John of the Cross. 160p. 1987. pap. 8.95 (ISBN 0-8245-0815-7). Crossroad NY.

Helick, R. Martin. The Complex Vision of Philo St. John. LC 75-27035. 1975. 10.00 (ISBN 0-912710-07-1). Regent Graphic Serv.

Johan the Evangelist. LC 71-133689. (Tudor Facsimile Texts. Old English Plays: No. 24). Repr. of 1907 ed. 49.50 (ISBN 0-404-53324-8). AMS Pr.

Laux, Dorothy. John: Beloved Apostle. (BibLearn Ser.). (Illus.). 1977. bds. 5.95 (ISBN 0-8054-4234-0, 4242-34). Broadman.

McQuay, Earl. John-Apostle of Love. LC 81-70774. (Chosen Messenger Ser.). 128p. (Orig.). 1982. pap. text ed. 3.50 (ISBN 0-89636-080-6). Accent Bks.

Meinardus, Otto F. St. John of Patmos & the Seven Churches of the Apocalypse. LC 78-51245. (In the Footsteps of the Saints Ser.). (Illus.). 160p. 1979. 17.50 (ISBN 0-89241-070-1); pap. 6.95 (ISBN 0-89241-043-4). Caratzas.

Riggs, Robert F. The Apocalypse Unsealed. LC 80-81698. 328p. 1981. pap. 9.95 (ISBN 0-8022-2367-2). Philos Lib.

Schoenle, Volker. Johannes, Jesus und die Juden. (Beitroge zur Biblischen Exegese und Theologie: Vol. 17). (Ger.). 288p. 1982. 40.00 (ISBN 3-8204-5877-8). P Lang Pubs.

Thomas, W. H. The Apostle John: His Life & Writings. LC 84-785. 376p. 1984. pap. 10.95 (ISBN 0-8254-3822-5). Kregel.

Traylor, Ellen G. John, Son of Thunder. 1980. pap. 4.95 (ISBN 0-8423-1903-4). Tyndale.

Vinck, Catherine D. Readings: "John at Patmos" & "A Book of Hours". LC 78-55341. 68p. 1978. 5.75 (ISBN 0-911726-32-2); pap. 3.75 (ISBN 0-911726-33-0). Alleluia Pr.

JOHN CHRYSOSTOM, SAINT, d. 407

Krupp, R. A. Saint John Chrysostom: A Scripture Index. LC 84-21028. 270p. 1985. lib. bdg. 27.50 (ISBN 0-8191-4380-4). U Pr of Amer.

JOHN OF SALISBURY, BP. OF CHARTRES, d. 1180

John of Salisbury. The Metalogicon of John of Salisbury: A Twelfth-Century Defense of Verbal & Logical Arts of the Trivium. McGarry, Daniel D., tr. from Latin. LC 82-2989. xxvii, 305p. 1982. Repr. of 1955 ed. lib. bdg. 39.75x (ISBN 0-313-23539-2, JOME). Greenwood.

Lloyd, Roger B. Golden Middle Age. LC 75-90654. (Essay Index Reprint Ser). 1939. 18.00 (ISBN 0-8369-1208-X). Ayer Co Pubs.

Wilks, Michael J., ed. The World of John of Salisbury. (Studies in Church History: Subsidia 3). 400p. 1985. text ed. 45.00x (ISBN 0-631-13122-1). Basil Blackwell.

JOHN OF THE CROSS, SAINT, 1542-1591

Arraj, James. St. John of the Cross & Dr. C. G. Jung: Christian Mysticism in the Light of Jungian Psychology. LC 86-11315. 200p. (Orig.). 1986. pap. 11.95 (ISBN 0-914073-02-8). Tools for Inner.

Brenan, Gerald. St. John of the Cross: His Life & Poetry. LC 72-83577. pap. 61.30 (ISBN 0-317-26068-5, 2024428). Bks Demand UMI.

Frost, Bede. Saint John of the Cross: Doctor of Divine Love, an Introduction to His Philosophy, Theology & Spirituality. 1977. lib. bdg. 59.95 (ISBN 0-8490-2559-1). Gordon Pr.

Hardy, Richard P. The Search for Nothing: The Life of John of the Cross. LC 82-13081. 160p. 1982. 10.95 (ISBN 0-8245-0499-2). Crossroad NY.

Icaza, Sr. Rosa M. Stylistic Relationship Between Poetry & Prose in the Cantico Espiritual of San Juan De la Cruz. LC 76-94191. (Catholic University of America Studies in Romance Languages & Literatures Ser: No. 54). 1969. Repr. of 1957 ed. 21.00 (ISBN 0-404-50354-3). AMS Pr.

Kavanaugh, Kieran & Rodriguez, Otilio, trs. from Span. The Collected Works of St. John of the Cross. 2nd ed. LC 78-65789. 1979. 14.95x (ISBN 0-9600876-5-6); pap. 8.95x (ISBN 0-9600876-7-2). ICS Pubns.

MacDonald, James M. The Life & Writings of St. John of the Cross. 1977. lib. bdg. 59.95 (ISBN 0-8490-2164-2). Gordon Pr.

Meyer, Robert T., ed. Palladius: Dialogue on the Life of St. John Chrysostom. (ACW Ser.: No. 45). 1985. text ed. 16.95 (ISBN 0-8091-0358-3). Paulist Pr.

Nemeck, Francis K. Receptivity. 135p. 1985. 10.00 (ISBN 0-533-06057-5). Vantage.

Peers, E. Allison. St. John of the Cross & Other Lectures & Addresses. 1977. lib. bdg. 59.95 (ISBN 0-8490-2558-3). Gordon Pr.

Peers, Edgar A. St. John of the Cross, & Other Lectures & Addresses, 1920-1945. facs. ed. LC 70-136650. (Biography Index Reprint Ser.). 1946. 16.00 (ISBN 0-8369-8045-X). Ayer Co Pubs.

JOHN PAUL II, POPE, 1920-

Annese, Lucius. Pope John Paul II in America. LC 79-56497. 1980. 50.00 (ISBN 0-933402-10-4). Charisma Pr.

Bland, Joan, ed. The Pastoral Vision of John Paul II. 1982. 7.95 (ISBN 0-8199-0839-8). Franciscan Herald.

Bonic. The Picture Life of Pope John Paul II. Date not set. lib. bdg. 9.90 (ISBN 0-531-04806-3). Watts.

Brzezinski, Zbigniew & Kupperman, Robert H. The International Implications of the Papal Assassination Attempt: A Case of State-Sponsored Terrorism. (Significant Issues Ser.: Vol. VI, No. 20). 23p. 1984. 12.95 (ISBN 0-89206-073-5). CSI Studies.

Craig, Mary. Pope John Paul II. (Profiles Ser.). (Illus.). 64p. 1982. 8.95 (ISBN 0-241-10711-3, Pub. by Hamish Hamilton England). David & Charles.

--Pope Paul II. (Illus.). 80p. 1982. pap. 2.50 (ISBN 0-686-40828-4, Pub by Penguin England). Irish Bk Ctr.

Douglas, Robert W. John Paul II: The Pilgrim Pope. LC 79-24930. (Picture-Story Biographies Ser.). (Illus.). 32p. 1980. PLB 10.60 (ISBN 0-516-03563-0). Childrens.

Frossard, Andre & Pope John Paul II. Be Not Afraid! John Paul II Speaks Out on His Life, His Beliefs & His Inspiring Vision for Humanity. Foster, J. R., tr. from Fr. 252p. 1984. 13.95 (ISBN 0-312-07021-7). St Martin.

Henze, Paul. The Plot to Kill the Pope. 224p. 1985. pap. 4.50 rack size (ISBN 0-684-18357-9). Scribner.

Hogan, Richard M. & Levoir, John M. Covenant of Love: Pope John Paul II on Sexuality, Marriage, & Family in the Modern World. LC 86-4395. 264p. 1986. pap. 7.95 (ISBN 0-385-23240-3, Im). Doubleday.

John Paul II. Pope John Paul II: Pilgrim of Peace. 1987. 25.00 (ISBN 0-517-56423-8, Harmony). Crown.

John Paul II, Pope Prayers of Pope John Paul II. McDonald, John F., ed. LC 82-72495. 108p. 1982. pap. 6.95 (ISBN 0-8245-0537-9). Crossroad NY.

Johnson, Paul. Pope John Paul II & the Catholic Restoration. 224p. 1982. 11.95 (ISBN 0-312-63032-8). St Martin.

Longford, Lord. Pope John Paul II: An Authorized Biography. LC 82-8001. (Illus.). 208p. 1982. 20.50 (ISBN 0-688-01393-7). Morrow.

Pilgrim to Poland: Pope John Paul II. 1979. 5.00 (ISBN 0-686-63640-6); pap. 3.50 (ISBN 0-8198-0627-7). Dghtrs St Paul.

Pope John Paul II At the United Nations. pap. 4.95 (E. 80.1.8); pap. 4.95 (ISBN 92-1-100166-8). UN.

Pope John Paul II: He Came to Us As a Father. (Illus.). 1979. gift edition 14.95 (ISBN 0-8198-0628-5). Dghtrs St Paul.

Pope John Paul. Puebla: A Pilgrimage of Faith. 1979. pap. 2.00 (ISBN 0-8198-0629-3). Dghtrs St Paul.

Pope John Paul II. Africa: Apostolic Pilgrimage. 1980. 8.00 (ISBN 0-8198-0708-7); pap. 7.00 (ISBN 0-8198-0709-5). Dghtrs St Paul.

--Canada: Celebrating Our Faith. 370p. 1985. 7.00 (ISBN 0-317-18636-1); pap. 6.00 (ISBN 0-8198-1441-5). Dghtrs St Paul.

--Ireland: In the Footsteps of St. Patrick. 1979. 3.95 (ISBN 0-8198-0624-2); pap. 2.95 (ISBN 0-8198-0625-0). Dghtrs St Paul.

--Reflections on Humanae Vitae. 96p. 1984. 3.76 (ISBN 0-8198-6409-9); pap. 2.75 (ISBN 0-8198-6410-2). Dghtrs St Paul.

--Toward a Philosophy of Praxis. Bloch, A. & Czuckza, G. T., eds. LC 80-21239. 152p. 1981. 10.95 (ISBN 0-8245-0033-4). Crossroad NY.

--Turkey: Ecumenical Pilgrimage. 3.50 (ISBN 0-8198-0650-1); pap. 2.50 (ISBN 0-8198-0651-X). Dghtrs St Paul.

--U. S. A. The Message of Justice, Peace & Love. 1979. 5.95 (ISBN 0-8198-0630-7); pap. 4.95 (ISBN 0-8198-0631-5). Dghtrs St Paul.

--Words of Certitude: Excerpts from His Talks & Writings As Bishop & Pope. Buono, Anthon, tr. from It. LC 80-81440. 136p. 1980. pap. 3.95 (ISBN 0-8091-2302-9). Paulist Pr.

--You Are My Favorites. 1980. 6.95 (ISBN 0-8198-8701-3). Dghtrs St Paul.

Pope John Paul II & Frossard, Andre. Be Not Afraid: Pope John Paul II Speaks Out on His Life, His Beliefs, & His Inspiring Vision for Humanity. LC 85-2322. 216p. 1985. pap. 7.95 (ISBN 0-385-23151-2, Im). Doubleday.

Pope Paul II. Pope John Paul II & the Family & Text. LC 82-13308. 416p. 1983. 15.00 (ISBN 0-8199-0851-7). Franciscan Herald.

Schall, J. V. The Church, the State & Society in the Thought of John Paul II. 1982. 7.50 (ISBN 0-8199-0838-X). Franciscan Herald.

Williams, George H. The Law of Nations & the Book of Nature. Franklin, R. W., ed. LC 84-72274. (New Essays in Christian Humanism: Vol. 1). (Illus.). 60p. (Orig.). 1985. pap. 4.95x (ISBN 0-9613867-0-3). St Johns Univ Christ Hum.

--The Mind of John Paul II: Origins of His Thought & Action. LC 80-19947. 415p. 1981. 26.95 (ISBN 0-8164-0473-9, HarpR). Har-Row.

Wolfe, Rinna. The Singing Pope: The Story of Pope John Paul II. (Illus.). 128p. 1980. 8.95 (ISBN 0-8164-0472-0, HarpR). Har-Row.

JOHN PAUL II, POPE, 1920-–ASSASSINATION ATTEMPT, 1981

Herman, Edward S. & Brodhead, Frank. The Rise & Fall of the Bulgarian Connection. 270p. (Orig.). 1986. 19.95 (ISBN 0-940380-07-2); pap. text ed. 9.95 (ISBN 0-940380-06-4). Sheridan Square Pubns.

Raine, Linnea P. The International Implications of the Papal Assassination Attempt: A Case of State-Sponsored Terrorism. (Significant Issues Ser.: Vol. VI, No. 20). 32p. (Orig.). 1985. pap. text ed. 6.95 (ISBN 0-8191-5935-2, Pub. by CSIS). U Pr of Amer.

JOHN THE BAPTIST, SAINT, ca. 5 B.C.-ca. 30 A.D.

Battersby, W. J. De la Salle: A Pioneer of Modern Education. 236p. 1981. Repr. of 1949 ed. lib. bdg. 40.00 (ISBN 0-89987-065-1). Darby Bks.

Dallison, Dennis. The Apology of John the Baptist. Norman, Ruth, ed. 66p. (Orig.). 1982. pap. 2.50 (ISBN 0-932642-75-6). Unarius Pubns.

--Reflections of My Life: The Apology of John the Baptist. Norman, Ruth, ed. 77p. (Orig.). 1982. pap. text ed. 2.50 (ISBN 0-932642-75-6). Unarius Pubns.

Human, Johnnie. John the Baptist: Forerunner of Jesus. (BibLearn Ser.). (Illus.). 1978. 5.95 (ISBN 0-8054-4240-5, 4242-40). Broadman.

Meyer, F. B. John the Baptist. 1975. pap. 4.50 (ISBN 0-87508-345-5). Chr Lit.

St. John Chrysostom. Sermon on the Decollation of St. John the Baptist, & on Herodias, & on Good & Evil Women. (Early Slavic Literatures, Studies, Texts, & Seminar Materials: Vol. 3). Orig. Title: V 29 den' mesiatsa avgusta slovo Ioanna Zlatoustogo na useknovenie glavy. (Slavic & Gr.). 45p. 1982. pap. 4.00 (ISBN 0-933884-23-0). Berkeley Slavic.

Storr, Catherine, as told by. Jesus & John the Baptist. (People of the Bible Ser.). (Illus.). 32p. 1985. PLB 10.65 (ISBN 0-8172-2037-2). Raintree Pubs.

JOHN THE BAPTIST,–ART

Hurll, Estelle M. Life of Our Lord in Art: With Some Account of the Artistic Treatment of the Life of St. John the Baptist. LC 76-89272. 1969. Repr. of 1898 ed. 31.00 (ISBN 0-8103-3137-3). Gale.

JOHNSON, SAMUEL, 1696-1772

Burke, John J., Jr. & Kay, Donald, eds. The Unknown Samuel Johnson. LC 81-70159. (Illus.). 224p. 1983. 32.50x (ISBN 0-299-09150-3). U of Wis Pr.

Johnson, Samuel. Johnson: Selected Writings. Cruttwell, Patrick, ed. 1982. pap. 6.95 (ISBN 0-14-043033-4). Penguin.

Pierce, Charles R., Jr. The Religious Life of Samuel Johnson. LC 82-13938. 184p. 1982. lib. bdg. 21.50 (ISBN 0-208-01992-8, Archon). Shoe String.

JOHNSON, SAMUEL, 1709-1784

Cairns, William T. Religion of Dr. Johnson. facsimile ed. LC 71-93324. (Essay Index Reprint Ser). 1946. 17.00 (ISBN 0-8369-1279-9). Ayer Co Pubs.

Schwartz, Richard B. Samuel Johnson & the Problem of Evil. LC 74-27314. 128p. 1975. 27.50x (ISBN 0-299-06790-4). U of Wis Pr.

Wieder, Robert. Le Docteur Johnson, Critique Litteraire (1709-1784) Essai De Biographie Psychologique. 201p. 1982. lib. bdg. 25.00 (ISBN 0-89984-528-2). Century Bookbindery.

JONAH, THE PROPHET

Bob & Couchman, Win. Ruth & Jonah: People in Process. (Carpenter Studyguide). 80p. 1983. saddle-stiched member's handbk. 1.95 (ISBN 0-87788-736-5); leader's handbook 2.95 (ISBN 0-87788-737-3). Shaw Pubs.

Briscoe, Jill. Jonah & the Worm. LC 83-6323. (Illus.). 120p. 1983. 5.95 (ISBN 0-8407-5289-X). Nelson.

Exell, Joseph S. Practical Truths from Jonah. LC 82-18671. 240p. 1983. 11.95 (ISBN 0-8254-2525-5). Kregel.

Ferguson, Sinclair. Man Overboard. 1982. pap. 3.95 (ISBN 0-8423-4015-7); leader's guide 2.95 (ISBN 0-8423-4016-5). Tyndale.

Hutton, Warwick. Jonah & the Great Fish. LC 83-15477. (Illus.). 32p. 1984. 12.95 (ISBN 0-689-50283-4, McElderly Bk). Macmillan.

Lacocque, Andre & Lacocque, Pierre. Jonah Complex. LC 80-84649. 1981. pap. 8.95 (ISBN 0-8042-0092-0). John Knox.

Price, Brynmor F. & Nida, Eugene A. A Translator's Handbook on the Book of Jonah. (Helps for Translators Ser.). 95p. 1978. 3.30x (ISBN 0-8267-0199-X, 08552, Pub. by United Bible). Am Bible.

Vawter, Bruce. Job & Jonah: Questioning the Hidden God. LC 82-62413. 1983. pap. 4.95 (ISBN 0-8091-2524-2). Paulist Pr.

JONAH, THE PROPHET–JUVENILE LITERATURE

Jonah. LC 76-11275. (Sunshine Bks). (Illus.). 20p. 1976. pap. 1.50 (ISBN 0-8006-1577-8, 1-1577). Fortress.

Spier, Peter. Book of Jonah. LC 85-1676. (Illus.). 40p. 1985. 11.95 (ISBN 0-385-19334-3); PLB 11.95 (ISBN 0-385-19335-1). Doubleday.

Storr, Catherine, retold by. Jonah & the Whale. LC 82-23023. (People of the Bible). (Illus.). 32p. 1983. PLB 10.65 (ISBN 0-8172-1984-6). Raintree Pubs.

JONES, RUFUS MATTHEW, 1863-1948

Hinshaw, David. Rufus Jones, Master Quaker. facsimile ed. LC 74-133522. (Select Bibliographies Reprint Ser.). Repr. of 1951 ed. 19.00 (ISBN 0-8369-5554-4). Ayer Co Pubs.

Vining, Elizabeth G. Friend of Life: A Biography of Rufus M. Jones. 2nd ed. (Illus.). 347p. 1981. pap. 8.95 (ISBN 0-941308-00-6). Religious Soc Friends.

JORDAN–ANTIQUITIES

De Hass, Frank S. Buried Cities Recovered: Explorations in Bible Lands. Davis, Moshe, ed. LC 77-70774. (America & the Holy Land). (Illus.). 1977. lib. bdg. 40.00x (ISBN 0-405-10242-9). Ayer Co Pubs.

Pritchard, James B. Hebrew Inscriptions & Stamps from Gibeon. (University Museum Monographs: No. 17). (Illus.). 32p. 1959. 5.00 (ISBN 0-934718-10-5). Univ Mus of U PA.

JORDAN–HISTORY

Kirkbride, Alec. From the Wings: Amman Memoirs, 1947-1951. 194p. 1976. 28.50x (ISBN 0-7146-3061-6, F Cass Co). Biblio Dist.

JOSEPH, SAINT

Fox, Robert J. St. Joseph: His Life As He Might Tell It. 1983. pap. 1.00 (ISBN 0-911988-55-6). AMI Pr.

Larsen, Sandy. Joseph: Non Stop Faith. (Young Fisherman Bible Studyguides). 64p. (Orig.). 1987. pap. 4.95 tchr's. ed. (ISBN 0-87788-438-2); pap. 2.95 student ed. (ISBN 0-87788-437-4). Shaw Pubs.

Levy, Rosalie M. Joseph, the Just Man. 4.00 (ISBN 0-8198-3901-9); pap. 3.00 (ISBN 0-8198-3902-7). Dghtrs St Paul.

Lovasik, Lawrence G. Good St. Joseph. (Saint Joseph Picture Bks.). (Illus.). flexible bdg. 0.95 (ISBN 0-89942-283-7, 283). Catholic Bk Pub.

Meyer, F. B. Joseph. 1975. pap. 4.50 (ISBN 0-87508-356-0). Chr Lit.

Nicklesburg, George W., ed. Studies on the Testament of Joseph. LC 75-26923. (Society of Biblical Literature. Septurgint & Cognate Studies). 153p. 1975. pap. 13.50 (ISBN 0-89130-027-9, 060405). Scholars Pr GA.

The Story of Joseph. 79p. pap. 0.50 (ISBN 0-686-29167-0). Faith Pub Hse.

Suarez, Federico. Joseph of Nazareth. Mascarenhas, Ives & Kearns, Patrick, trs. from Span. Tr. of Jose, Esposo de Maria. 222p. (Orig.). 1984. pap. 7.95 (ISBN 0-906138-08-6). Scepter Pubs.

Thompson, Edward H. Life & Glories of St. Joseph. LC 80-53744. 1980. pap. 7.50 (ISBN 0-89555-161-6). Tan Bks Pubs.

JOSEPH, THE PATRIARCH

Boruch, Behn. Coat of Many Colors. 1959. 3.95 (ISBN 0-88482-728-3). Hebrew Pub.

Getz, Gene A. Joseph: From Prison to Palace. LC 82-18571. 1983. pap. 5.95 (ISBN 0-8307-0870-7, 5417907). Regal.

Joseph. 1979. 0.75 (ISBN 0-8198-0583-1). Dghtrs St Paul.

Landorf, Joyce. Joseph. 1985. pap. 7.95 (ISBN 0-8007-5197-3, Power Bks.). Revell.

Lindsay, Gordon. Jacob & His Son, Joseph. (Old Testament Ser.). 1.25 (ISBN 0-89985-129-0). Christ Nations.

--Joseph & His Brethren. (Old Testament Ser.). 1.25 (ISBN 0-89985-130-4). Christ Nations.

Yadon, Loren A. More Than a Dream. Wallace, Mary, ed. 128p. (Orig.). 1984. pap. 4.95 (ISBN 0-912315-66-0). Word Aflame.

JOSEPH, THE PATRIARCH–FICTION

Mann, Thomas. Joseph & His Brothers. (YA) 1948. 35.00 (ISBN 0-394-43132-4). Knopf.

JOSEPH, THE PATRIARCH–JUVENILE LITERATURE

Barrett, Ethel. Joseph. LC 79-65232. (Bible Biography Bible Ser.). 128p. 1979. pap. 1.95 (ISBN 0-8307-0715-8, 5607701). Regal.

Bergey, Alyce & Wind, Betty. Boy Who Saved His Family. (Arch Bks: Set 3). 1966. laminated cover 0.99 (ISBN 0-570-06017-6, 59-1126). Concordia.

Broughton, Pamela, retold by. Joseph & the Coat of Many Colors. LC 85-81156. (Golden Bible Stories). (Illus.). 32p. 1986. 3.95 (ISBN 0-307-11627-1, Pub. by Golden Bks). Western Pub.

Citrin, Paul J. Joseph's Wardrobe. (Illus.). 1987. pap. 6.95 (ISBN 0-8074-0319-9). UAHC.

Diamond, Lucy. Story of Joseph. (Ladybird Ser). (Illus.). 1954. bds. 2.50 (ISBN 0-87508-868-6). Chr Lit.

Lindvall, Ella K. Joseph & His Brothers. (People of the Bible Ser.). (Illus.). 1983. 4.95 (ISBN 0-8024-0395-6). Moody.

Maniscalco, Joe. Joseph. LC 74-28725. (Bible Hero Stories). (Illus.). 48p. (Orig.). 1975. pap. 2.00 (ISBN 0-87239-332-1, 2737). Standard Pub.

Shimoni, S. Legends of Joseph & His Brothers. (Biblical Ser.). (Illus.). 1975. 3.00 (ISBN 0-914080-11-3). Shulsinger Sales.

Storr, Catherine, as told by. Joseph & the Famine. (People of the Bible Ser.). (Illus.). 32p. 1985. PLB 10.65 (ISBN 0-8172-2038-0). Raintree Pubs.

Summers, Jester. Joseph: the Forgiver. (BibLearn Ser.). (Illus.). 1976. bds. 5.95 (ISBN 0-8054-4224-3, 4242-24). Broadman.

JOSEPH OF ARIMATHEA

Lewis, Lionel S. St. Joseph of Arimathea at Glastonbury. (Illus.). 212p. 1983. pap. 8.95 (ISBN 0-227-67868-0). Attic Pr.

JOSEPHUS FLAVIUS

Feldman, Louis, ed. Josephus, Judaism & Christianity. Hata, Gohei, tr. from Japanese. 336p. 1987. 39.95X (ISBN 0-8143-1831-2); pap. 13.95X (ISBN 0-8143-1832-0). Wayne St U Pr.

Feldman, Louis H. Josephus & Modern Scholarship: 1937-1980. LC 84-1879. xvi, 1055p. 1984. 248.00x (ISBN 3-11-008138-5). De Gruyter.

Feuchtwanger, Lion. Josephus: A Historical Romance. LC 32-28823. (Temple Bks). 1972. pap. 12.95 (ISBN 0-689-70345-7, T25). Atheneum.

Josephus, Flavius. Complete Works of Josephus, 4 vols. 39.95 set (ISBN 0-8010-5056-1). Baker Bk.

Rajak, Tessa. Josephus: The Historian & His Society. LC 83-16538. 256p. 1984. 24.95 (ISBN 0-8006-0717-1, 1-717). Fortress.

Ulrich, Eugene C., Jr. The Qumran Text of Samuel & Josephus. LC 78-15254. (Harvard Semitic Museum. Harvard Semitic Monographs: No. 19). 1978. 15.00 (ISBN 0-89130-256-5, 040019). Scholars Pr GA.

JOSHUA, SON OF NUN

Auld, A. Graeme. Joshua, Moses & the Land. 158p. 1981. 19.95 (ISBN 0-567-09306-9, Pub. by T & T Clark Ltd UK). Fortress.

Bush, George. Joshua & Judges. 1981. 17.95 (ISBN 0-86524-100-7, 0602). Klock & Klock.

Campbell, Donald K. Joshua: Leader under Fire. 144p. pap. 5.95 (ISBN 0-89693-502-7). Victor Bks.

Enns, Paul P. Joshua: Bible Study Commentary. (Bible Study Commentary). 160p. (Orig.). 1981. pap. 4.95 (ISBN 0-310-44041-6, 11830P). Zondervan.

Girzone, Joseph F. Joshua. 320p. 1983. 12.00 (ISBN 0-911519-03-3). Richelieu Court.

Jordan, Bernice C. Fighting Giants: Joshua-Solomon 14 Lessons, Vol. 3. (Footsteps of Faith Ser.). 1957. pap. text ed. 2.50 (ISBN 0-86508-031-3); figures text 11.45 (ISBN 0-86508-032-1). BCM Intl Inc.

Kappeler, Max. Joshua, Judges. Larson, Rory, tr. from Ger. LC 82-80904. (The Bible in the Light of Christian Science Ser.: Vol. 3). Orig. Title: Die Wissenschaft der Bibel, Das Buch Josua und Das Buch der Richter. 210p. (Orig.). 1983. pap. 12.00 (ISBN 0-942958-07-1). Kappeler Inst Pub.

Katz, Mordechai. Lilmod Ulelamade on Joshua. (Rothman Foundation Ser.). 1984. 8.95 (ISBN 0-87306-925-0); pap. 6.95 (ISBN 0-87306-926-9). Feldheim.

Lindsay, Gordon. Joshua, Conqueror of Canaan. (Old Testament Ser.). 1.25 (ISBN 0-89985-134-7). Christ Nations.

Meyer, F. B. Joshua. 1977. pap. 4.50 (ISBN 0-87508-357-9). Chr Lit.

Schaeffer, Francis A. Joshua & the Flow of Biblical History. LC 74-31847. 216p. 1975. pap. text ed. 7.95 (ISBN 0-87784-773-8). Inter-Varsity.

Totten, C. A. Joshua's Long Day. 1968. 5.00 (ISBN 0-685-08808-1). Destiny.

JOSHUA, SON OF NUN–JUVENILE LITERATURE

Barrett, Ethel. Joshua. LC 79-65233. (Bible Biography Ser.). 128p. 1979. pap. 2.50 (ISBN 0-8307-0707-7, 5607000). Regal.

Hill, Dave. Walls Came Tumbling Down. (Arch Bks.: Set 4). 1967. laminated bdg 0.99 (ISBN 0-570-06024-9, 59-1135). Concordia.

Shimoni, S. Legends of Joshua. (Biblical Ser.). (Illus.). 1975. 3.00 (ISBN 0-914080-12-1). Shulsinger Sales.

Thompson, Don. General Joshua. (Rainy Day Survival Bk.: No. 2). 32p. pap. 0.99 (ISBN 0-87123-697-4, 220697). Bethany Hse.

JOURNALISM, RELIGIOUS

Burrell, David B. & Kane, Franzita, eds. Evangelization in the American Context. LC 76-22403. 1976. pap. 2.95x (ISBN 0-268-00902-3). U of Notre Dame Pr.

Hensley, Dennis E. & Adkins, Rose A. Writing for Religious & Other Specialty Markets. (Orig.). 1987. pap. 8.95 (ISBN 0-8054-7911-2). Broadman.

Knight, Walter W. How to Publish a Church Newsletter. LC 83-70372. (Orig.). 1983. pap. 6.95 (ISBN 0-8054-3108-X). Broadman.

Marty, Martin E., et al. The Religious Press in America. LC 72-6844. 184p. 1973. Repr. of 1963 ed. lib. bdg. 22.50x (ISBN 0-8371-6500-8, MARP). Greenwood.

Polen, O. W. Editorially Speaking. 1975. pap. 2.25 (ISBN 0-87148-300-9). Pathway Pr.

Thaman, Mary P. Manners & Morals of the Nineteen Twenties: A Survey of the Religious Press. LC 77-8129. 1977. Repr. of 1954 ed. lib. bdg. 22.50x (ISBN 0-8371-9679-5, THMM). Greenwood.

Verploegh, Harry, compiled by. The Next Chapter after the Last. (Orig.). Date not set. pap. price not set (ISBN 0-87509-391-4). Chr Pubns.

JOY AND SORROW

see also Church Work with the Bereaved; Happiness

Billheimer, Paul E. Destined for the Throne. 1983. pap. 4.95 (ISBN 0-87508-040-5). Chr Lit.

--Don't Waste Your Sorrows. LC 83-15821. 144p. (Orig.). 1983. pap. 4.95 (ISBN 0-87123-310-X, 210310). Bethany Hse.

Draper, James T., Jr. Discover Joy: Studies in Philippians. 1983. pap. 4.95 (ISBN 0-8423-0606-4); leader's guide 2.95 (ISBN 0-8423-0607-2). Tyndale.

Ellwood, Robert. Finding Deep Joy. LC 84-40167. 156p. (Orig.). 1984. pap. 4.50 (ISBN 0-8356-0586-8). Theos Pub Hse.

Evans, Colleen T. A New Joy. (Orig.). 1975. pap. 1.50 (ISBN 0-89129-015-X). Jove Pubns.

Eyre, Linda & Eyre, Richard. Teaching Children Joy. LC 84-201498. 240p. 1986. pap. 3.50 (ISBN 0-345-32704-7). Ballantine.

Flint, Carol. Flat in Bliss. 1980. 2.00 (ISBN 0-936814-06-3). New Collage.

Hicks, Roy H. He Who Laughs...Lasts...& Lasts...& Lasts. (Orig.). 1976. pap. 2.95 (ISBN 0-89274-003-5). Harrison Hse.

Jamison-Peterson, Vicki. How You Can Have Joy. 130p. 1976. pap. 2.95 (ISBN 0-88144-054-X). Christian Pub.

Leih, Virginia K. Enjoy! 124p. 1983. pap. 3.95 (ISBN 0-8341-0814-3). Beacon Hill.

McDowell, Josh & Bellis, Dale. Evidence for Joy. 192p. 1986. pap. 3.50 (ISBN 0-553-26153-3). Bantam.

Mathis, Mary E. A Scriptural Treasury of Joy. 1981. pap. 0.40 (ISBN 0-570-08353-2, 12-2933). Concordia.

Moncure, Jane B. Joy. LC 82-1145. (What Does the Bible Say? Ser.). (Illus.). 32p. 1982. PLB 5.95 (ISBN 0-89565-222-6, 4940, Pub. by Childs World). Standard Pub.

--Joy. (Values to Live by Ser.). 1982. 10.35 (ISBN 0-516-06527-0). Childrens.

Pope Paul VI. On Christian Joy. 1975. pap. 0.30 (ISBN 0-8198-0448-7). Dghtrs St Paul.

Powell, Paul W. Why Me, Lord? 120p. 1981. pap. 4.95 (ISBN 0-89693-007-6). Victor Bks.

Samra, Cal. Jesus Put on a Happy Face: The Healing Power of Joy & Humor. LC 85-60257. (Illus.). 234p. (Orig.). 1985. pap. 7.95 (ISBN 0-933453-00-0). Rosejoy Pubns.

Townsend, Janice M. Joy Before Us. LC 81-7198. 1982. pap. 8.00 (ISBN 0-8309-0327-5). Herald Hse.

Word of Joy. (Words of... Ser.). (Illus.). 48p. 1983. 3.95 (ISBN 0-8407-5336-5). Nelson.

JUBILEE INDULGENCES

see Indulgences

JUBILEE SINGERS

Marsh, J. B. Story of the Jubilee Singers with Their Songs. rev. ed. LC 72-165509. (Illus.). Repr. of 1880 ed. 14.00 (ISBN 0-404-04189-2). AMS Pr.

--Story of the Jubilee Singers, with Their Songs. rev. ed. LC 79-78583. (Illus.). Repr. of 1881 ed. 22.50x (ISBN 0-8371-1424-1, MAJ&, Pub. by Negro U Pr). Greenwood.

Pike, Gustavus D. Jubilee Singers, & Their Campaign for Twenty Thousand Dollars. LC 72-1692. Repr. of 1873 ed. 18.50 (ISBN 0-404-08329-3). AMS Pr.

--The Singing Campaign for Ten Thousand Pounds. rev. ed. LC 75-164392. (Black Heritage Library Collection). Repr. of 1875 ed. 18.25 (ISBN 0-8369-8851-5). Ayer Co Pubs.

JUDAH, HA-LEVI, 12TH CENTURY

Miller, J. Maxwell & Hayes, John H. A History of Ancient Israel & Judah. LC 85-11468. (Illus.). 524p. 1986. 27.95 (ISBN 0-664-21262-X). Westminster.

Strauss, Leo. Persecution & the Art of Writing. LC 73-1407. 204p. 1973. Repr. of 1952 ed. lib. bdg. 19.75 (ISBN 0-8371-6801-5, STPA). Greenwood.

JUDAICA

see Jews

JUDAISM

Here are entered works on Jewish faith and practice in which the main stream of orthodox Judaism is treated and no cleavage is stressed. see also Cabala; Commandments, Ten; Cultus, Jewish; Fasts and Feasts–Judaism; Jesus Christ–Jewish Interpretations; Jewish Theology; Jews; Messiah; Mythology, Jewish; Rabbis; Reform Judaism; Sabbath; Synagogues

Abraham Ben Moses Ben Maimon. High Ways to Perfection of Abraham Maimonides. Rosenblatt, Samuel, tr. LC 74-158221. (Columbia University Oriental Studies: No. 27). 1927. 19.00 (ISBN 0-404-50517-1); Suppl., 1982. 35.00; Supp., 1983. 43.50. AMS Pr.

Agus, Jacob B. The Jewish Quest: Essays on Basic Concepts of Jewish Theology. LC 83-258. 264p. 1983. 25.00x (ISBN 0-88125-012-0). Ktav.

Agus, Jacob B., et al, eds. The Jewish People: History, Religion, Literature, 41 bks. 1973. Set. 1106.50 (ISBN 0-405-05250-2). Ayer Co Pubs.

Alexander, Philip, ed. & tr. Judaism. (Textual Sources for the Study of Religion). 240p. 1987. pap. 11.75 (ISBN 0-389-20719-5). B&N Imports.

Alexander, Philip S., ed. Judaism. LC 84-6199. (Textual Sources for the Study of Religion Ser.). 208p. 1984. 23.50x (ISBN 0-389-20477-3, BNB 08039); pap. 11.75x (ISBN 0-389-20719-5). B&N Imports.

Alpert, Rebecca T. & Staub, Jacob J. Exploring Judaism: A Reconstructionist Approach. 108p. 1985. 11.95 (ISBN 0-935457-01-1); pap. 5.95 (ISBN 0-935457-00-3). Reconstructionist Pr.

Alter, Robert, ed. Modern Hebrew Literature. LC 75-9928. (Library of Jewish Studies). 384p. 1975. pap. text ed. 9.95x (ISBN 0-87441-235-8); cloth 15.95x. Behrman.

Amsel. Judaism & Psychology. pap. 5.95 (ISBN 0-87306-064-4). Feldheim.

Amsel, Avrohom. Rational Irrational Man: Torah Psychology. 1976. pap. 7.95 (ISBN 0-87306-129-2). Feldheim.

Asheri, Michael. Living Jewish: The Lore & the Law of the Practicing Jew. 446p. 1983. pap. 9.95 (ISBN 0-396-08263-7). Dodd.

Aviad, Janet. Return to Judaism: Religious Renewal in Israel. LC 82-17663. xiv, 194p. 1985. pap. 8.95 (ISBN 0-226-03235-3). U of Chicago Pr.

Axelrad, Albert S. Call to Conscience: Jews, Judaism, & Conscientious Objection. LC 85-24010. 207p. 1986. text ed. 25.00x (ISBN 0-88125-092-9); pap. 14.95x (ISBN 0-88125-081-3). Ktav.

Baeck, Leo. Essence of Judaism. rev. ed. LC 61-8992. 1961. pap. 8.50 (ISBN 0-8052-0006-1). Schocken.

Bamberger, Bernard J. Story of Judaism. rev. ed. 1970. 9.95 (ISBN 0-8074-0193-5, 959291). UAHC.

Barish, Louis & Barish, Rebecca. Varieties of Jewish Belief. 1979. Repr. 9.95 (ISBN 0-8246-0242-0). Jonathan David.

Belin, David. Why Choose Judaism: New Dimensions of Jewish Outreach. 32p. 1985. pap. text ed. 4.00 (ISBN 0-8074-0302-4, 381900). UAHC.
Belkin, Samuel. In His Image: The Jewish Philosophy of Man As Expressed in Rabbinic Tradition. LC 78-10192. 1979. Repr. of 1960 ed. lib. bdg. 27.50x (ISBN 0-313-21234-1, BEIH). Greenwood.
Ben-Horin, Meir. Common Faith-Uncommon People: Essays in Reconstructionist Judaism. LC 71-80691. 245p. 1970. 7.50 (ISBN 0-935457-03-8). Reconstructionist Pr.
Berger, Rabbi E., et al. Judaism, Zionism, & Anti-Semitism. 72p. (Orig.). 1985. pap. 2.50 (ISBN 0-935177-01-9). Palestine Focus.
Berkovits, Eliezer. With God in Hell: Judaism in the Ghettos & Deathcamps. 1979. 9.95 (ISBN 0-88482-937-5, Sanhedrin Pr). Hebrew Pub.
Berman, Lawrence V., et al, eds. The Study of Judaism: Vol. 2. 25.00x (ISBN 0-87068-486-8). Ktav.
Bernstein, Philip S. What the Jews Believe. LC 77-28446. (Illus.). 1978. Repr. of 1951 ed. lib. bdg. 22.50x (ISBN 0-313-20228-1, BEWJ). Greenwood.
Blackman, Philip. Ethics of the Fathers. 166p. 1980. pap. 4.95 (ISBN 0-910818-15-0). Judaica Pr.
Bleich, David. With Perfect Faith. 1982. 25.00x (ISBN 0-87068-891-X); pap. 14.95. Ktav.
Blumanthal, David. Understanding Jewish Mysticism: The Philosophic-Mystical Tradition & the Hasidic Tradition, Vol.II. 20.00x (ISBN 0-87068-205-9); pap. 9.95 (ISBN 0-87068-225-3). Ktav.
Blumenthal, David R. The Place of Faith & Grace in Judaism. 29p. (Orig.). 1985. pap. 3.50 (ISBN 0-918873-03-7). Ctr Judaic-Christ Studies.
Bokser, Ben Zion. Judaism & Modern Man. 153p. 1958. 5.95 (ISBN 0-8022-0148-2). Philos Lib.
Bookstaber, Philip D. Judaism & the American Mind: In Theory & Practice. LC 78-26404. 1979. Repr. of 1939 ed. lib. bdg. cancelled (ISBN 0-313-20875-1, BOJU). Greenwood.
Borowitz, Eugene. Understanding Judaism. 1979. 7.50 (ISBN 0-8074-0027-0, 341800). UAHC.
Brafman, Morris & Schimel, David. Trade for Freedom. LC 75-26371. 96p. 1975. 6.95 (ISBN 0-88400-043-5). Shengold.
Breslauer, S. Daniel. The Ecumenical Perspective & the Modernization of Jewish Religion: A Study in the Relationship Between Theology & Myth. 1978. pap. 9.00 (ISBN 0-89130-236-0, 140005). Scholars Pr GA.
Breuer, Isaac. Concepts of Judaism. Levinger, Jacob S., tr. 1974. 10.00 (ISBN 0-87306-058-X). Feldheim.
Breuer, Jacob. Fundamentals of Judaism. 1969. pap. 6.95 (ISBN 0-87306-208-6). Feldheim.
Brinner, William M. & Ricks, Stephen D., eds. Studies in Islamic & Judaic Traditions. (Brown Judaic Studies). 287p. 1986. 29.95 (ISBN 1-55540-047-7, 14-01-10); pap. 24.95 (ISBN 1-55540-048-5). Scholars Pr GA.
Britton, F. L. Behind Communism: The Jewish Background of Communism. 1982. lib. bdg. 59.95 (ISBN 0-87700-425-0). Revisionist Pr.
Buber, Martin. On Judaism. Glatzer, Nahum, ed. LC 67-28091. 256p. 1972. pap. 7.50 (ISBN 0-8052-0343-5). Schocken.
--The Tales of Rabbi Nachman. LC 56-12330. 214p. 1972. 5.95 (ISBN 0-8180-1325-7). Horizon.
Bulka, Reuven P. & Spero, Moshe H. A Psychology-Judaism Reader. (Illus.). 338p. 1982. pap. 27.00x (ISBN 0-398-04582-8). C C Thomas.
Carlson, Paul R. O Christian! O Jew! LC 74-78937. 256p. (Orig.). 1974. pap. 1.95 (ISBN 0-912692-39-1). Cook.
Chaim, B., ed. Neturei Karta; Voice of Anti-Zionist Judaism: A Study. 1980. 75.00 (ISBN 0-87700-273-8). Revisionist Pr.
Chait, Baruch, ed. Perek Shira & Zemirot. 100p. (Orig.). 1986. text ed. 4.95 (ISBN 0-88125-095-3). Ktav.
Charing, Douglas. The Jewish World. LC 83-50693. (Religions of the World Ser.). 48p. 1983. PLB 14.96 (ISBN 0-382-06720-7); 9.25 (ISBN 0-382-06930-7). Silver.
Claudel, Paul. Une Voix sur Israel. 46p. 1950. 2.95 (ISBN 0-686-54445-5). French & Eur.
Cohen, A. The Twelve Prophets. 368p. 1948. 10.95 (ISBN 0-900689-31-5). Soncino Pr.
Cohen, Henry. Why Judaism? A Search for Meaning in Jewish Identity. 192p. 1973. pap. 5.00 (ISBN 0-8074-0077-7, 161901). UAHC.
Davies, W. D. The Territorial Dimension of Judaism. LC 81-53. (A Quantum Bk.). 160p. 1982. 15.95x (ISBN 0-520-04331-6). U of Cal Pr.
De Lange, Nicholas. Judaism. 224p. 1986. 14.95 (ISBN 0-19-219198-5). Oxford U Pr.
De Poncins, Leon. Judaism & the Vatican. 1982. lib. bdg. 65.00 (ISBN 0-87700-381-5). Revisionist Pr.
Deutscher, Isaac. The Non-Jewish Jew. 170p. 1982. pap. 5.95 (ISBN 0-932870-18-X). Alyson Pubns.
Domnitz, Myer. Judaism. 1985. 13.00 (ISBN 0-7062-3596-7, Pub. by Ward Lock Educ Co Ltd). State Mutual Bk.
Donin, Hayim H. To Raise a Jewish Child: A Guide for Parents. LC 76-7679. 1977. 15.95 (ISBN 0-465-08626-8). Basic.
Dresner, Samuel H. Zaddik: The Doctrine of the Zaddik According to the Writings of Rabbi Yaakov Yosef of Polnoy. LC 60-7228. 312p. 1974. pap. 4.95 (ISBN 0-8052-0437-7). Schocken.
Duties of the Heart, Chovoth Halevovoth, 2 vols. 1978. Set. pap. 11.95 (ISBN 0-87306-161-6). Feldheim.
Edersheim, Alfred. Temple, Its Ministry & Services. 1950. 5.95 (ISBN 0-8028-8133-5). Eerdmans.
Eichenbaum, Sharon & Goldin, Alice. Jewish Awareness Worksheets, 2 vols. pap. 2.95x ea. Vol. 1 (ISBN 0-87441-266-8). Vol. 2 (ISBN 0-87441-270-6). Behrman.
Eisen, Arnold M. The Chosen People in America: A Study in Jewish Religious Ideology. LC 82-49296. (Modern Jewish Experience Ser.). 254p. 1983. 20.00x (ISBN 0-253-31365-1). Ind U Pr.
Eisenstein, Ira. Judaism under Freedom. LC 56-12814. 262p. 1956. pap. 6.95 (ISBN 0-935457-05-4). Reconstructionist Pr.
--Reconstructing Judaism: An Autobiography. 1986. 17.95 (ISBN 0-935457-37-2). Reconstructionist Pr.
The Emergence of Contemporary Judaism: A Survey of Judaism from the 7th to the 17th Centuries, Vol. 2. LC 77-831. (Pittsburgh Theological Monographs: No. 12). 1977. Set. pap. text ed. 15.25 (ISBN 0-915138-14-X). Pickwick.
Epstein, Isadore. The Faith of Judaism. 418p. 1954. pap. 8.75 (ISBN 0-900689-13-7). Soncino Pr.
--Step by Step in the Jewish Religion. 143p. 1958. pap. 4.95 (ISBN 0-900689-12-9). Soncino Pr.
Epstein, Isidore. Faith of Judaism. pap. 8.75x (ISBN 0-900689-13-7). Bloch.
Essrig, Harry. Judaism. 1984. Barron.
Fackenheim, Emil L. Encounters Between Judaism & Modern Philosophy: A Preface to Future Jewish Thought. LC 80-16437. 288p. 1980. pap. 7.95 (ISBN 0-8052-0656-6). Schocken.
Fackenhein, Emil L. To Mend the World: Foundations of Future Jewish Thought. LC 81-16614. 352p. (Orig.). 1982. pap. 12.95 (ISBN 0-8052-0699-X). Schocken.
Feinsilver, A. Aspects of Jewish Belief. 1973. pap. 5.95x (ISBN 0-87068-225-3). Ktav.
Feldman, Emanuel, ed. The Biblical Echo: Reflection on Bible, Jews & Judaism. 1986. text ed. 17.50x (ISBN 0-88125-104-6). Ktav.
Finegan, Jack. Light from the Ancient Past, 2 vols. 2nd ed. (Illus.). 1959. Vol. 1 2nd Ed. 52.50 (ISBN 0-691-03550-4); Vol. 1 2nd Edition. pap. 16.50 (ISBN 0-691-00207-X); Vol. 2. 50.00 (ISBN 0-691-03551-2); Vol. 2. pap. 15.50x (ISBN 0-691-00208-8); Set. 90.00 (ISBN 0-686-76901-5). Princeton U Pr.
Finkelstein, et al. Religions of Democracy. 1941. 9.50 (ISBN 0-8159-6708-X). Devin.
Fisch, Dov A. Jews for Nothing: On Cults, Assimilation & Intermarriage. 368p. 1984. 13.95 (ISBN 0-87306-347-3). Feldheim.
Fishbane, Michael. Judaism. LC 85-42775. (Religious Traditions of the World Ser.). 128p. (Orig.). 1985. 6.95 (ISBN 0-06-062655-0, HarpR). Har-Row.
Fleg, Edmond. Why I Am a Jew. 2nd facsimile ed. Wise, Louise W., tr. from Fr. LC 74-27984. (Modern Jewish Experience Ser.). (Eng.). 1975. Repr. of 1945 ed. 13.00 (ISBN 0-405-06711-9). Ayer Co Pubs.
Frankel, William, ed. Survey of Jewish Affairs 1983. 320p. 1985. 25.00 (ISBN 0-8386-3244-0). Fairleigh Dickinson.
Frensdorff, Salomon. Ochlah W'Ochlah. 35.00x (ISBN 0-87068-194-X). Ktav.
Frey, Jean B. Corpus Inscriptionum Judaicarum. rev. ed. (Library of Biblical Studies). 1970. 100.00x (ISBN 0-87068-103-6). Ktav.
Friedlander, Albert. Out of the Whirlwind. 1968. 10.95 (ISBN 0-8074-0043-2, 959065). UAHC.
Friedlander, Gerald. Jewish Sources of the Sermon on the Mount. 1976. lib. bdg. 59.95 (ISBN 0-8490-2102-2). Gordon Pr.
Friedman, Alexander Z. Wellsprings of Torah. Hirschler, Gertrude, tr. from Yiddish. 584p. 1980. slipcased 18.95 (ISBN 0-910818-20-7); pap. 16.95 (ISBN 0-910818-04-5). Judaica Pr.
Frymer, Berl. Jewish Horizons. LC 81-65057. 256p. 1982. 12.95 (ISBN 0-8453-4705-5, Cornwall Bks). Assoc Univ Prs.
Gereboff, Joel. Rabbi Tarfon: The Tradition, the Man & Early Rabbinic Judaism. LC 78-15220. (Brown Judaic Studies: No. 7). 1979. 16.50 (ISBN 0-89130-257-3, 140007); pap. 12.00 (ISBN 0-89130-299-9). Scholars Pr GA.
Glazer, Nathan. American Judaism. rev. ed. LC 57-8574. (Chicago History of American Civilization Ser). 1972. 12.50x (ISBN 0-226-29839-6); pap. 7.50 (ISBN 0-226-29841-8, CHAC7). U of Chicago Pr.
Goebbels, Joseph. Communism with the Mask Off: The Jewish Origin of Communism. 1982. lib. bdg. 59.95 (ISBN 0-87700-406-4). Revisionist Pr.
Goldberg, Harvey E., ed. Judaism Viewed from Within & from Without: Anthropological Studies. (Anthropolgy & Judaic Studies). 348p. 1986. 44.50X (ISBN 0-88706-354-3); pap. 16.95X (ISBN 0-88706-356-X). STate U NY Pr.
Goldstein-Alpern, Neva G. Beginning of the World. (Board Bks.). (Illus.). 12p. 1987. 5.95. Judaica Pr.
Goodman, S. L. The Faith of Secular Jews. (Library of Judaic Learning). 25.00x (ISBN 0-87068-489-2); pap. 11.95. Ktav.
Gordis, Robert. Root & the Branch: Judaism & the Free Society. LC 62-17133. 1962. 20.00x (ISBN 0-226-30411-6). U of Chicago Pr.
Green, Arthur. Jewish Spirituality: Vol 1. Cousins, Ewert, ed. (World Spirituality Ser.). 496p. 1985. 49.50x (ISBN 0-8245-0762-2). Crossroad NY.
Green, William S. Approaches to Ancient Judaism II. LC 76-57656. (Brown Judaic Studies). 1980. 15.00 (ISBN 0-89130-447-9, 14-00-09); pap. 10.50 (ISBN 0-89130-448-7). Scholars Pr GA.
Green, William S., ed. Approaches to Ancient Judaism III. LC 76-57656. (Brown Judaic Studies). 220p. 1981. pap. 15.00 (ISBN 0-89130-553-X, 14 00 11). Scholars Pr GA.
Greenberg, Sidney & Levine, Jonathan D. Mahzor Hadash. rev. ed. 12.50 (ISBN 0-87677-075-8); simulated leather 14.95. Prayer Bk.
Greenberg, Sidney, ed. Light from Jewish Lamps: A Modern Treasury of Jewish Thoughts. LC 86-71270. 465p. 1986. 30.00 (ISBN 0-87668-918-7). Aronson.
Greenberg, Simon. A Jewish Philosophy & Pattern of Life. LC 81-2153. (Moreshet Series, Studies in Jewish History, Literature & Thought: Vol. 9). 550p. 1982. 25.00x (ISBN 0-87334-012-4, Pub. by Jewish Theol Seminary). Ktav.
Greenspahn, Frederick E. The Human Condition in the Jewish & Christian Conditions. 1985. text ed. 25.00x (ISBN 0-88125-084-8). Ktav.
Greenstein, Howard R. Judaism: An Eternal Covenant. LC 82-17601. 176p. 1983. pap. 10.95 (ISBN 0-8006-1690-1, 1-1690). Fortress.
Grimstad, William. Antizion: The Jewish & Zionist Question Through the Ages. 1982. lib. bdg. 69.95 (ISBN 0-686-97529-4). Revisionist Pr.
Guttman, Julius. Philosophies of Judaism: The History of Jewish Philosophy from Biblical Times to Franz Rosenzweig. LC 63-11875. 560p. 1973. pap. 13.50 (ISBN 0-8052-0402-4). Schocken.
Gwynne, H. The Cause of World Unrest: The Jews. 1982. lib. bdg. 69.95 (ISBN 0-87700-340-8). Revisionist Pr.
Ha-Cohen, Yisroel Meir. Mishnah Bervrah, Vol. 3C. Orenstein, Aviel, tr. from Herbrew. 1984. 13.95 (ISBN 0-87306-351-1); large type ed. 17.95 (ISBN 0-87306-350-3). Feldheim.
--Mishnah Bervrah, Vol. 3B. Feldman, Aharon & Orenstein, Aviel, trs. 402p. 1981. 12.95 (ISBN 0-87306-276-0); large type ed. 15.95 (ISBN 0-87306-275-2). Feldheim.
Halevi, Judah. The Kuzari: An Argument for the Faith of Israel. LC 64-15222. 1966. pap. 6.95 (ISBN 0-8052-0075-4). Schocken.
Halevi, Yehudah. Book of Kuzari. (Hebrew & Eng.). 37.50 (ISBN 0-87559-077-2). Shalom.
Hansen, James. The Ministry of the Cantor. (Ministry Ser.). 40p. 1985. pap. 1.25 (ISBN 0-8146-1387-X). Liturgical Pr.
Harland, Henry. Yoke of the Thorah, by Sidney Luska. Repr. of 1887 ed. 23.00 (ISBN 0-384-21370-7). Johnson Repr.
Harris, Lis. Holy Days: The World of a Hasidic Family. 272p. 1986. pap. 8.95 (ISBN 0-02-020970-3, Collier). Macmillan.
Hartman, David. A Living Covenant: The Innovative Spirit in Traditional Judaism. 384p. 1985. 21.60x (ISBN 0-02-914140-0). Free Pr.
Haskelevich, B., tr. from Hebrew. Disputation at Barcelona, Nachmanides(Ramban) With Introduction & Commentaries. Tr. of Vikkuakh Hazamban. (Rus.). (1982) 6.00 (ISBN 0-938666-03-7); pap. 3.75 (1981) (ISBN 0-938666-00-2). CHAMAH Pubs.
Hecht, Shea & Clorfene, Chaim. Confessions of a Jewish Cultbuster. Crossen, Chaya, ed. 256p. 1985. 8.37 (ISBN 0-318-18531-8); pap. 5.97 (ISBN 0-318-18532-6). Tosefos.
Herberg, Will. Judaism & Modern Man. LC 59-12913. (Temple Bks). 1970. pap. text ed. 8.95x (ISBN 0-689-70232-9, T13). Atheneum.
Hertz, J. H. Affirmations of Judaism. 338p. 1975. 9.95 (ISBN 0-900689-54-4). Soncino Pr.
Herzog, Isaac. Judaism-Law & Ethics. 227p. 1974. 9.95 (ISBN 0-900689-73-0). Soncino Pr.
Heschel, Abraham J. Between God & Man, an Interpretation of Judaism. 1965. pap. 8.95 (ISBN 0-02-914510-4). Free Pr.
--God in Search of Man: A Philosophy of Judaism. 464p. 1976. pap. 10.95 (ISBN 0-374-51331-7). FS&G.
--God in Search of Man: Philosophy of Judaism. 437p. 1987. Repr. of 1955 ed. 30.00 (ISBN 0-87668-955-1). Aronson.
Hexter, Jack H. The Judaeo Christian Tradition. (Orig.). 1966. pap. text ed. 10.95 scp (ISBN 0-06-042815-5, HarpC). Har-Row.
Hirsch, Emil G. My Religion. Levi, Gerson B., ed. Incl. The Crucifixion Viewed from a Jewish Standpoint (1908. LC 73-2207. (The Jewish People; History, Religion, Literature Ser.). Repr. of 1925 ed. 33.00 (ISBN 0-405-05271-5). Ayer Co Pubs.
Hirsch, S. R. Horeb, 1 vol. Set. 19.95x (ISBN 0-900689-40-4). Bloch.
--Judaism Eternal, 2 Vols. 1956. Set. 29.95 (ISBN 0-900689-70-6). Soncino Pr.
Hirsch, Samson R. The Nineteen Letters of Ben Uziel on Judaism. Drachman, Bermard, tr. LC 69-131727. 1969. 4.95 (ISBN 0-87306-045-8). Feldheim.
Hirsch, Somson R. Nineteen Letters of Ben Uziel: A Spiritual Presentation of the Principles of Judaism. Drachman, Bernard, tr. (Eng. & Ger., Heb). 27.50 (ISBN 0-87559-076-4). Shalom.
Holmgren, Frederick. The God Who Cares: A Christian Looks at Judaism. LC 78-52445. (Orig.). 1979. pap. 1.95 (ISBN 0-8042-0588-4). John Knox.
Humphreys, W. Lee. Crisis & Story: Introduction to the Old Testament. LC 78-64594. (Illus.). 313p. 1979. text ed. 21.95 (ISBN 0-87484-437-1). Mayfield Pub.
Institute of Contemporary Jewry of The Hebrew University of Jerusalem. Studies in Contemporary Jewry, Vol.I. (Illus.). 608p. 1984. 22.50X (ISBN 0-253-39511-9). Ind U Pr.
Jacobs, Louis. The Book of Jewish Belief. 250p. (Orig.). 1984. pap. text ed. 7.95x (ISBN 0-87441-379-6). Behrman.
--The Book of Jewish Values. (The Limited Editions Reprints). 160p. 1984. pap. text ed. 6.95 (ISBN 0-940646-06-4, 83-21278). Rossel Bks.
Jamison, A. Leland, ed. Tradition & Change in Jewish Experience: B.G. Rudolph Lectures in Judaic Studies. 1978. pap. 5.95x (ISBN 0-8156-8097-X). Syracuse U Pr.
Joy, Donald M., ed. Moral Development Foundations: Judeo-Christian Alternatives to Piaget-Kohlberg. 240p. (Orig.). 1983. pap. 13.95 (ISBN 0-687-27177-0). Abingdon.
Jung, Leo. The Jewish Library. Incl. Vol. 1. Faith. 9.50x (ISBN 0-685-23058-9); Vol. 2. Folk. 9.50x (ISBN 0-685-23059-7); Vol. 3. Women. 9.50x (ISBN 0-685-23060-0); Vol. 4. Judaism in a Changing World. 9.50x (ISBN 0-685-23061-9); Vol. 5. Panorama of Judaism: Part 1. 9.50x (ISBN 0-685-23062-7); Vol. 6. Panorama of Judaism: Part 2. 9.50x (ISBN 0-685-23063-5). Bloch.
--Judaism in a Changing World. 273p. 1971. 9.50 (ISBN 0-900689-08-0). Soncino Pr.
Jung, Leo, ed. Panorama of Judaism, 2 pts. 1974. Pt. 1, 275 pp. 9.50 (ISBN 0-900689-48-X); Pt. 2, 243 pp. 9.50 (ISBN 0-900689-49-8). Soncino Pr.
Kabakoff, Jacob, ed. Jewish Book Annual, Vol. 40. 1982. 17.50 (ISBN 0-914820-10-9). JWB.
Kac, Arthur W. Spiritual Dilemma of the Jewish People. 5.95 (ISBN 0-8010-5456-7). Baker Bk.
Kadushin, Max. A Conceptual Approach to the Mekilta. 11.95x (ISBN 0-87334-014-0). Ktav.
Kagan, Berl. Hebrew Subscription Lists. 50.00x (ISBN 0-87068-282-2, Pub. by Jewish Theol. Seminary). Ktav.
Kalir, Joseph. Introduction to Judaism. LC 79-6758. 170p. 1980. text ed. 25.00 (ISBN 0-8191-0948-7); pap. text ed. 10.75 (ISBN 0-8191-0949-5). U Pr of Amer.
Kaniel, Michael. Timeless Judaism for Our Time. 1985. pap. 2.95 (ISBN 0-87306-944-7). Feldheim.
Kaplan, Aryeh. The Handbook of Jewish Thought. 307p. 13.95 (ISBN 0-940118-27-0). Maznaim.
Kaplan, Mordecai M. Dynamic Judaism: The Essential Writings of Mordecai M. Kaplan. Goldsmith, Emanuel S. & Scult, Mel, eds. LC 85-2391. 256p. (Orig.). 1985. text ed. 22.00x (ISBN 0-8052-3997-9); pap. 12.95 (ISBN 0-8052-0786-4). Schocken.
--Greater Judaism in the Making. LC 59-15683. 565p. 1967. pap. 12.95 (ISBN 0-935457-14-3). Reconstructionist Pr.
--Judaism Without Supernaturalism. LC 58-10056. 254p. 1958. pap. 6.50 (ISBN 0-935457-18-6). Reconstructionist Pr.
--The Meaning of God in Modern Jewish Religion. 1975. pap. 10.95 (ISBN 0-935457-19-4). Reconstructionist Pr.
--Questions Jews Ask. Rev ed. LC 56-8577. 532p. 1956. pap. 10.50 (ISBN 0-935457-21-6). Reconstructionist Pr.

Kaplan, Mordecai M. & Cohen, Arthur A. If Not Now, When? LC 72-95901. 134p. 1973. 7.95 (ISBN 0-935457-15-1). Reconstructionist Pr.

Karp, Abraham J. The Jewish Way of Life & Thought. 1981. pap. 9.95x (ISBN 0-87068-717-4). Ktav.

Karta, Neturei. Judaism & Zionism: Principles & Definitions. 1980. lib. bdg. 59.95 (ISBN 0-87700-305-X). Revisionist Pr.

Katz, Mordechai. Menucha Vesimcha. (Rothman Foundation Ser.). 1982. 7.95 (ISBN 0-87306-977-3); pap. 5.95 (ISBN 0-317-42411-4). Feldheim.

Katz, Steven T., ed. Jewish Philosophy, Mysticism & History of Ideas Series, 50 bks. (Illus.). 1980. Set. lib. bdg. 2389.00x (ISBN 0-405-12229-2). Ayer Co Pubs.

Kellner, Menachem. Dogma in Medieval Jewish Thought: From Maimonides to Abravanel. (Littman Library of Jewish Civilization). 350p. 1987. 45.00 (ISBN 0-19-710044-9). Oxford U Pr.

Kimpel, Ben. A Philosophy of the Religions of Ancient Greeks & Israelites. LC 83-6512. 362p. (Orig.). 1983. lib. bdg. 30.00 (ISBN 0-8191-3225-X); pap. text ed. 15.50 (ISBN 0-8191-3226-8). U Pr of Amer.

Knopp, Josephine Z. The Trial of Judaism in Contemporary Jewish Writing. LC 74-18319. 164p. 1975. 15.95 (ISBN 0-252-00386-1). U of Ill Pr.

Kohn, Eugene. Good to Be a Jew. LC 59-13350. 180p. 1959. pap. 8.95 (ISBN 0-935457-23-2). Reconstructionist Pr.

Kosovsky, Binyamin. Concordance of the Sifrei. 75.00x (ISBN 0-685-56222-0, Pub. by Jewish Theol Seminary). Ktav.

Kukoff, Lydia. Choosing Judaism. (Orig.). 1981. 10.00 (ISBN 0-8074-0151-X); pap. 5.95 (ISBN 0-8074-0150-1). UAHC.

--Choosing Judaism. 152p. (Orig.). 1983. pap. 5.95 (ISBN 0-686-88518-X, Pub. by UAHC Israel). Hippocrene Bks.

Kurzweil, Zvi. The Modern Impulse of Traditional Judaism. LC 84-28892. 156p. 1985. 12.95 (ISBN 0-88125-068-6). Ktav.

Kushner, Lawrence. The River of Light: Spirituality, Judaism, & the Evolution of Consciousness. LC 80-7738. 192p. (Orig.). 1981. pap. 7.95 (ISBN 0-06-064902-X, RD 370, HarpR). Har-Row.

--The River of Light: Spirituality, Judaism, & the Evolution of Consciousness. LC 80-7738. 192p. 1981. 12.95 (ISBN 0-940646-00-5). Rossel Bks.

Lady Queenborough. Judaism. 1982. lib. bdg. 55.95 (ISBN 0-87700-410-2). Revisionist Pr.

Laifer, Miryam. Edmond Jabes: Un Judaisme Apres Dieu. (American University Studies II: Romance Languages & Literature: Vol. 39). 165p. 1986. pap. 33.70 (ISBN 0-8204-0283-4). P Lang Pubs.

Lash, Neil A. & Lash, Jamie S. Looking for Leaven. (Jewish Jewels: Vol. 1). (Illus.). 21p. (Orig.). 1985. pap. 1.50 (ISBN 0-915775-02-6). Love Song Mess Assn.

Leese, A. Bolshevism Is Jewish. 1982. lib. bdg. 59.95 (ISBN 0-87700-409-9). Revisionist Pr.

Leibowitz. Studies in the Shemoth, 2 vols. 1976. 17.50 (ISBN 0-685-71930-8). Feldheim.

Leiser, Joseph. American Judaism: The Religion & Religious Institutions of the Jewish People in the United States. LC 78-26230. 1979. Repr. of 1925 ed. lib. bdg. 22.50x (ISBN 0-313-20879-4, LEAJ). Greenwood.

Levin, Michael G. Journey to Tradition: The Odyssey of a Born-Again Jew. 129p. 1986. 14.95 (ISBN 0-88125-093-7). Ktav.

Levine, Etan, ed. Diaspora. LC 82-6723. 350p. 1983. 20.00 (ISBN 0-87668-601-3). Aronson.

Lieberman, Chaim. The Grave Concern. LC 68-58650. 202p. 1968. 10.00 (ISBN 0-88400-016-8). Shengold.

Luzatto, Moshe C. Derech HaShem: The Way of G-D. Kaplan, Aryeh, tr. from Hebrew. 1978. 12.95 (ISBN 0-87306-136-5); pap. 9.95. Feldheim.

Maimonides, Moses. Code of Maimonides, Bk. 3, Treatise 8, Sanctification Of The New Moon. Gandz, Solomon, tr. (Judaica Ser: No. 11). 1956. 23.50x (ISBN 0-300-00476-1). Yale U Pr.

--Code of Maimonides - Book Three: The Book of Seasons. Gandz, Solomon & Klein, Hyman, trs. (Judaica Ser: No. 14). 1961. 60.00x (ISBN 0-300-00475-3). Yale U Pr.

--Guide for the Perplexed. 2nd ed. 16.00 (ISBN 0-8446-2512-4). Peter Smith.

Mann, Denese B. The Woman in Judaism. 1979. pap. 5.50 (ISBN 0-9603348-0-7). Jonathan Pubns.

Martin, Bernard, ed. Movements & Issues in American Judaism: An Analysis & Sourcebook of Developments Since 1945. LC 77-87971. 1978. lib. bdg. 35.00 (ISBN 0-313-20044-0, MCJ/). Greenwood.

Meiseles, Meir. Judaism, Thought & Legend. Schonfeld-Brand, Rebecca & Newman, Aryeh, trs. from Hebrew. 1978. pap. 9.95 (ISBN 0-87306-140-3). Feldheim.

Mendelssohn, Moses. Jerusalem: Or on Religious Power & Judaism. Altmann, Alexander, intro. by. Arkush, Allan, tr. LC 83-40015. 262p. 1983. 20.00x (ISBN 0-87451-263-8); pap. 10.00x (ISBN 0-87451-264-6). U Pr of New Eng.

Menuhin, Moshe. The Decadence of Judaism in Our Time. 1981. lib. bdg. 59.95 (ISBN 0-686-73181-6). Revisionist Pr.

Merkle, John C. Abraham Joshua Heschel: Exploring His Life & Thought. 184p. 1985. 17.95x (ISBN 0-02-920970-6). Macmillan.

Migas, Abraham I. Kevod Elohim. 27.50 (ISBN 0-405-12616-6). Ayer Co Pubs.

Mills, Lawrence H. Zarathushtra, Philo, the Achaemenids & Israel. LC 74-21261. Repr. of 1906 ed. 34.50 (ISBN 0-404-12815-7). AMS Pr.

Mirsky, Norman B. Unorthodox Judaism. LC 78-8683. 227p. 1978. 17.50 (ISBN 0-8142-0283-7). Ohio St U Pr.

Mishnayoth Tohoroth, 2 vols. 36.00 (ISBN 0-910218-88-9). Bennet Pub.

Moshe, Beth. Judaism's Truth versus the Missionaries. 354p. 1987. 14.95 (ISBN 0-8197-0515-2). Bloch.

Musaph-Andriesse, R. G. From Torah to Kabbalah: A Basic Introduction to the Writings of Judaism. 1982. pap. 4.95x (ISBN 0-19-520364-X). Oxford U Pr.

Narot, Joseph R. Letters to the Now Generation. pap. 1.95 (ISBN 0-686-15801-6). Rostrum Bks.

--Old Wine in Old Bottles. pap. 0.75 (ISBN 0-686-15809-1). Rostrum Bks.

Neuser, Jacob. Reading & Believing. (Brown Judaic Studies). 138p. 1986. 25.50 (ISBN 0-89130-976-4, 14-01-13); pap. 20.50 (ISBN 0-89130-977-2). Scholars Pr GA.

Neusner, Jacob. The Academic Study of Judaism: Essays & Reflections I. (Third Ser.). 20.00x (ISBN 0-87068-712-3). Ktav.

--Ancient Judaism & Modern Category Formation: "Judaism," "Midrash," "Messianism," & Canon in the Past Quarter-Century. LC 85-30416. (Studies in Judaism Ser.). 138p. (Orig.). 1986. lib. bdg. 22.50 (ISBN 0-8191-5395-8, Pub. by Studies in Judaism); pap. text ed. 9.75 (ISBN 0-8191-5396-6). U Pr of Amer.

--Formative Judaism II. LC 82-25072. (Brown Judiac Studies). 198p. 1983. pap. 13.50 (ISBN 0-89130-614-5, 14 00 41). Scholars Pr GA.

--Formative Judaism: Religious, Historical & Literary Studies-Third Series. LC 83-8662. (Brown Judaic Studies). 212p. 1983. pap. 15.00 (ISBN 0-89130-633-1, 14 00 46). Scholars Pr GA.

--Judaism & Scripture: The Evidence of Leviticus Rabbah. LC 85-20497. (CSHJ Ser.). 664p. 1986. 50.00x (ISBN 0-226-57614-0). U of Chicago Pr.

--Judaism in the Beginning of Christianity. LC 83-48000. 112p. 1984. pap. 5.95 (ISBN 0-8006-1750-9, 1-1750). Fortress.

--Judaism: The Evidence of the Mishnah. LC 80-26080. xx, 420p. 1981. 25.00x (ISBN 0-226-57617-5); pap. 15.95 (ISBN 0-226-57619-1). U of Chicago Pr.

--Major Trends in Formative Judaism: First Series. LC 83-20176. (Brown Judaic Studies). 126p. 1983. pap. 14.25 (ISBN 0-89130-668-4, 14 00 60). Scholars Pr GA.

--Major Trends in Formative Judaism: Second Series: Texts, Contents, & Contexts. LC 83-20176. (Brown Judaic Studies). 160p. 1984. pap. text ed. 15.00 (ISBN 0-89130-727-3, 14 00 61). Scholars Pr GA.

--Major Trends in Formative Judaism: Third Series: The Three Stages in the Formation of Judaism. (Brown Judaic St00553869x). 1985. 22.95 (ISBN 0-89130-898-9, 14-00-99); pap. 18.25 (ISBN 0-89130-899-7). Scholars Pr GA.

--Method & Meaning in Ancient Judaism. LC 79-9881. (Brown Judaic Ser.: No. 10). 1979. 18.00 (ISBN 0-89130-281-6, 140010); pap. 13.50 (ISBN 0-89130-300-6). Scholars Pr GA.

--Religious Study of Judaism: Context, Text, Circumstance, Vol. 3. (Studies in Judaism). 234p. (Orig.). 1987. lib. bdg. 25.50 (ISBN 0-8191-6047-4, Pub. by Studies in Judaism); pap. 13.75 (ISBN 0-8191-6048-2, Pub. by Studies in Judaism). U Pr of Amer.

--Understanding American Judaism: Toward the Description of a Modern Religion, 2 vols. Incl. Vol. 1. The Synagogue & the Rabbi (ISBN 0-87068-279-2); Vol. 2. Reform, Orthodoxy, Conservatism, & Reconstructionism (ISBN 0-87068-280-6). pap. 11.95 ea. Ktav.

--Vanquished Nation, Broken Spirit: The Virtues of the Heart in Formative Judaism. 208p. Date not set. price not set (ISBN 0-521-32832-2); pap. price not set (ISBN 0-521-33801-8). Cambridge U Pr.

--The Way of Torah: An Introduction to Judaism. 3rd ed. 164p. 1979. pap. text ed. write for info. (ISBN 0-87872-217-3). Wadsworth Pub.

--The Way of Torah: An Introduction to Judaism. 4th ed. Fullerton, Sheryl, ed. 192p. (Orig.). 1987. price not set. Wadsworth Pub.

Neusner, Jacob, ed. Contemporary Judaic Fellowship in Theory & Practice. 1972. 20.00x (ISBN 0-87068-187-7). Ktav.

--Take Judaism, for Example: Studies Toward the Comparison of Religion. LC 82-16039. 1983. 22.50x (ISBN 0-226-57618-3). U of Chicago Pr.

Neusner, Jacob & Frerichs, Ernest S., eds. Goodenough on the History of Religion & on Judaism. (Brown Judaic Studies). 168p. 1987. pap. 29.95 (ISBN 1-55540-062-0, 14-01-21). Scholars Pr GA.

New Pockets of Jewish Energy: A Study of Adults Who Found Their Way Back to Judaism. 32p. 1982. 2.50 (ISBN 0-87495-046-5). Am Jewish Comm.

Newman, Louis I. Jewish Influence on Christian Reform Movements. LC 26-883. (Columbia University. Oriental Studies: No. 23). Repr. of 1925 ed. 45.00 (ISBN 0-404-50513-9). AMS Pr.

Nigosian, Solomon. Judaism. (Crucible Ser.). 208p. 1987. pap. 9.95 (ISBN 0-85030-429-6). Thorsons Pubs.

Novak, David. The Image of the Non-Jew in Judaism: An Historical & Constructive Study of the Noahide Laws. LC 83-21989. (Toronto Studies in Theology: Vol. 14). 500p. 1984. 69.95x (ISBN 0-88946-759-5). E Mellen.

Novak, David & Samuelson, Norbert, eds. Creation & the End of Days - Judaism & Scientific Cosmology: Proceedings of the 1984 Meeting of the Academy for Jewish Philosophy. LC 86-19062. 336p. (Orig.). 1986. 26.75 (ISBN 0-8191-5524-1, Pub. by Studies in Judaism); pap. text ed. 14.50 (ISBN 0-8191-5525-X, Pub. by Studies in Judaism). U Pr of Amer.

Obermann, Julian, ed. Nissim Ibn Shahin: The Arabic Original of Ibn Shahin's Book of Comfort. LC 78-63561. (Yale Oriental Ser. Researches: No. 17). Repr. of 1933 ed. 72.50 (ISBN 0-404-60287-8). AMS Pr.

Pearl, Chaim & Brookes, Reuben. The Guide to Jewish Knowledge. rev. ed. LC 75-25366. 142p. 1976. 8.95 (ISBN 0-87677-138-X). Hartmore.

Pesahim, 2 vols. 30.00 (ISBN 0-910218-55-2). Bennet Pub.

Petuchowski, Jakob J. The Theology of Haham David Nieto. 1970. 10.00x (ISBN 0-87068-015-3). Ktav.

Phillips, McCandlish. The Bible, the Supernatural & the Jews. LC 77-92532. 1970. pap. 8.95 (ISBN 0-87123-036-4, 210036). Bethany Hse.

Philosophy: Basic Judaism. (Home Study Program Ser.: No. 601). 5.00 (ISBN 0-686-96129-3). United Syn Bk.

Posner, Zalman I. Think Jewish: A Contemporary View of Judaism, a Jewish View of Today's World. LC 78-71323. 1979. 8.95 (ISBN 0-9602394-0-5); pap. 4.95 (ISBN 0-9602394-1-3). Kesher.

Prager, Dennis & Telushkin, Joseph. Nine Questions People Ask About Judaism. 1981. 14.95 (ISBN 0-671-42593-5). S&S.

--The Nine Questions People Ask about Judaism. 1986. pap. 7.95 (ISBN 0-671-62261-7, Touchstone Bks). S&S.

Rabin. Jewish Lights: Substitute Teachers Kit. 1984. 3.00x (ISBN 0-940646-28-5). Rossel Bks.

Raphael, Marc L. Profiles in American Judaism: The Reform, Conservative, Orthodox & Reconstructionist Traditions in Historical Perspective. LC 84-47734. 288p. 1985. 20.45 (ISBN 0-06-066801-6, HarpR). Har-Row.

Raphael, Marc L., ed. Approaches to Modern Judaism, Vol. II. (Brown Judaic Studies: No. 56). 128p. 1985. 19.95 (ISBN 0-89130-793-1, 14 00 56); pap. 16.95 (ISBN 0-89130-794-X). Scholars Pr GA.

Raskas, Bernard S. Heart of Wisdom, Bk. III. 10.50. United Synagogue.

Rosenberg, A. J. Book of Twelve Prophets, Vol. II. (Book of the Prophets Ser.). 270p. 1987. 14.95. Judaica Pr.

Rosenthal, Erwin I. Studia Semitica, 2 vols. Incl. Vol. 1. Jewish Themes. 59.50 (ISBN 0-521-07958-6); Vol. 2. Islamic Themes. 49.50 (ISBN 0-521-07959-4). (Oriental Publications Ser.: Nos. 16 & 17). Cambridge U Pr.

Rosenthal, Gilbert S. The Many Faces of Judaism. Rossel, Seymour, ed. LC 78-25898. 1979. pap. 4.95x (ISBN 0-87441-311-7). Behrman.

Rosenzweig, Franz. The Star of Redemption. Hallo, William W., tr. from Ger. LC 84-40833. 464p. 1985. text ed. 30.00 (ISBN 0-268-01717-4, 85-17179); pap. text ed. 12.95 (ISBN 0-268-01718-2, 85-17187). U of Notre Dame Pr.

Roth, Leon. Judaism, a Portrait. LC 61-5918. 240p. 1972. pap. 4.95 (ISBN 0-8052-0344-3). Schocken.

Rothenberg, Joshua. The Jewish Religion in the Soviet Union. 1971. 20.00x (ISBN 0-87068-156-7). Ktav.

Rubenstein, Richard J. After Auschwitz: Essays in Contemporary Judaism. (Orig.). 1966. pap. 10.28 scp (ISBN 0-672-61150-3). Bobbs.

Rubenstein, Richard L. After Auschwitz: Radical Theology & Contemporary Judism. 1966. pap. text ed. write for info. (ISBN 0-02-404210-2). Macmillan.

Salluste, A. Marxism & Judaism. 1982. lib. bdg. 69.95 (ISBN 0-87700-329-7). Revisionist Pr.

Sanders, James A. Torah & Canon. LC 72-171504. 144p. (Orig.). 1972. pap. 5.95 (ISBN 0-8006-0105-X, 1-105). Fortress.

Sandmel, Samuel. Judaism & Christian Beginnings. pap. 11.95x (ISBN 0-19-502282-3). Oxford U Pr.

Schaefer, Peter. Rivalitaet zwischen Engeln und Menschen: Untersuchungen zur rabbinischen Engelvorstellung. (Studia Judaica, Vol. 8). xiv, 280p. 1975. 38.80x (ISBN 3-11-004632-6). De Gruyter.

Schiller, Mayer. The Road Back: A Discovery of Judaism Without Embellishments. new ed. 1978. 9.95 (ISBN 0-87306-164-0). Feldheim.

Schochet, Elijah J. Taz Rabbi David Halevi. 10.00x (ISBN 0-87068-687-9). Ktav.

Segal, Abraham. One People: A Study in Comparative Judaism. Zlotowitz, Bernard M., ed. 160p. (Orig.). 1983. pap. text ed. 6.95 (ISBN 0-8074-0169-2, 140025). UAHC.

Seltzer, Robert M. Jewish People, Jewish Thought. (Illus.). 1980. text ed. write for info. (ISBN 0-02-408950-8). Macmillan.

Shabbath, 3 vols. 45.00 (ISBN 0-317-39580-7). Bennet Pub.

Shain, Ruchoma. All for the Boss. 439p. 1984. 13.95 (ISBN 0-87306-346-5). Feldheim.

Sharot, Stephen. Judaism: A Sociology. LC 75-37727. 240p. 1976. text ed. 29.50x (ISBN 0-8419-0250-X). Holmes & Meier.

Shenker, Israel. Coat of Many Colors: Pages from Jewish Life. LC 82-45338. 408p. 1985. 19.95 (ISBN 0-385-15811-4). Doubleday.

Sherman, Shlomoh. Escape from Jesus: One Man's Search for a Meaningful Judaism. 1983. 14.95 (ISBN 0-915474-03-4). Effective Learn.

Shulman, Albert M. Gateway to Judaism, 2 vols. 30.00 set (ISBN 0-8453-6896-6, Cornwall Bks). Assoc Univ Prs.

Shumsky, Abraham. Sabbath Service: Shaharit L'Shabbat. Date not set. pap. 3.95x (ISBN 0-940646-35-8). Rossel Bks.

Shunami, S. Bibliography of Jewish Bibliographies. enl. 2nd ed. 1969. 50.00x (ISBN 0-87068-882-0). Ktav.

Silver, Abba H. Where Judaism Differed. 1972. pap. 5.95 (ISBN 0-02-089360-4, Collier). Macmillan.

Soloveitchik, Joseph B. The Halakhic Mind: Rabbinic Judaism & Modern Thought. 128p. 1986. 16.95 (ISBN 0-02-930040-1). Free Pr.

Spero, Moshe H. Judaism & Psychology: Halakhic Perspectives. 25.00x (ISBN 0-87068-693-3). Ktav.

Stadelmann, Luis I. Hebrew Conception of the World. (Analecta Biblica: Vol. 39). 1970. pap. 15.00 (ISBN 88-7653-039-8). Loyola.

Steinberg, Milton. Basic Judaism. LC 47-30768. 1965. pap. 3.95 (ISBN 0-15-610698-1, Harv). HarBraceJ.

--Basic Judaism. 180p. 1987. 22.00 (ISBN 0-87668-975-6). Aronson.

Studies in Bamidbor (Numbers) 1982. 12.95 (ISBN 0-686-76263-0). Feldheim.

Studies in Bereshis (Genesis) 1982. 12.95 (ISBN 0-686-76261-4). Feldheim.

Studies in Devorim (Deuteronomy) 1982. 12.95 (ISBN 0-686-76264-9). Feldheim.

Studies in Vayikra. 1982. 8.95 (ISBN 0-686-76262-2). Feldheim.

Szlakmann, Charles. Judaism for Beginners. (Documentary Comic Bks.). (Illus.). 189p. Date not set. pap. 6.95 (ISBN 0-86316-101-4). Writers & Readers.

Ta'anith, 1 vol. 15.00 (ISBN 0-910218-62-5). Bennet Pub.

Tabak, Israel. Judaic Lore in Heine. LC 78-19266. 25.50 (ISBN 0-405-10632-7). Ayer Co Pubs.

Taylor, Charles W. Sayings of the Jewish Fathers. 59.95 (ISBN 0-8490-0995-2). Gordon Pr.

Thackeray, H. St. J. The Septuagint of Jewish Worship. (British Academy of London Ser.). pap. 19.00 (ISBN 0-8115-1262-2). Kraus Repr.

Trepp, Leo. Judaism: Development & Life. 3rd ed. 384p. 1981. pap. text ed. write for info. (ISBN 0-534-00999-9). Wadsworth Pub.

Tsa'ar Ba'ale Hayim. 1976. 6.95 (ISBN 0-87306-127-6). Feldheim.

Umansky, Ellen M. Lily Montagu & the Advancement of Liberal Judaism: From Vision to Vocation. LC 83-22005. (Studies in Women & Religion: Vol. 12). 305p. 1984. 49.95x (ISBN 0-88946-537-1). E Mellen.

Umen, Samuel. Jewish Concepts & Reflections. LC 62-9774. 190p. 1962. 10.00 (ISBN 0-8022-1748-6). Philos Lib.

Unterman, Alan. The Art & Practices of Judaism. 96p. 1985. 20.00x (ISBN 0-7062-4126-6, Pub. by Ward Lock Educ Co Ltd). State Mutual Bk.

Van Buren, Paul M. A Christian Theology of the People Israel. (A Theology of the Jewish-Christian Reality Ser.: Pt. II). 320p. (Orig.). 1983. pap. 26.95 (ISBN 0-8164-0548-4, HarpR). Har-Row.

Wagner, Richard. Judaism in Music. 1982. lib. bdg. 79.95 (ISBN 0-87700-354-8). Revisionist Pr.

Weiss-Rosmarin, T. Jewish Survival. 6.95x (ISBN 0-87068-426-4). Ktav.

Wengrov, Charles, tr. from Hebrew. Sefer Ha'hinnuch, the Book of Education: Genesis-Exodus. (Anonymous Attributed to R. Aharon Halevi). 1978. Vol. 1. 14.95 (ISBN 0-87306-179-9). Feldheim.

Wewers, Gerd S. Geheimnis und Geheimhaltung im Rabbinischen Judentum. (Religionsgeschichtliche Versuche und Vorarbeiten, Vol. 35). (Ger.). 1975. 33.60x (ISBN 3-11-005858-8). De Gruyter.

Wicks, Henry J. The Doctrine of God in the Jewish Apocryphal & Apocalyptic Literature. Repr. of 1915 ed. 29.00x (ISBN 0-87068-149-4). Ktav.

Wiener, Aharon. The Prophet Elijah in the Development of Judaism. (Littman Library of Jewish Civilization). 250p. 1978. 24.00x (ISBN 0-19-710010-4). Oxford U Pr.

Wiesel, Elie. Witness for Life. 12.95 (ISBN 0-87068-766-2); pap. 7.95x (ISBN 0-87068-767-0). Ktav.

Williams, Jay G. Judaism. LC 80-51551. 204p. 1981. pap. 5.50 (ISBN 0-8356-0540-X, Quest). Theos Pub Hse.

Wine, Sherwin T. Judaism Beyond God. LC 85-61942. 286p. (Orig.). 1985. pap. 13.95 (ISBN 0-912645-08-3). Soc Humanistic.

--Judaism Beyond God: A Radical New to Be Jewish. 286p. 1986. pap. 13.95 (ISBN 0-87975-363-3). Prometheus Bks.

Wouk, Herman. This Is My God. LC 79-78741. 1959. 14.95 (ISBN 0-385-02158-5). Doubleday.

Wyschogrod, Michael. The Body of Faith: Judaism As Corporeal Election. 320p. (Orig.). 1983. pap. 24.95 (ISBN 0-8164-0549-2, HarpR). Har-Row.

Yaakov, Bat. The Tenth Famine: Judaism Without God. 96p. (Orig.). 1986. pap. 7.95 (ISBN 0-9617361-0-0). Bat Yaakov Pubns.

Yonah, Rabbeinu. Gates of Repentance, Shaarei Teshuvah. 1976. pap. 7.95 (ISBN 0-87306-112-8). Feldheim.

Zahalon, Yom-Tov B. Sefer lekarth tov: Perush le-megilat Ester, Tsfat, 1577. 31.00 (ISBN 0-405-11952-6). Ayer Co Pubs.

Zeitlin, Joseph. Disciples of the Wise. LC 71-121517. (Essay Index Reprint Ser). 1945. 19.00 (ISBN 0-8369-1859-2). Ayer Co Pubs.

Zeitlin, Solomon. Rise & Fall of the Judaean State, 3 vols. LC 61-11708. 1978. Vol. 3, 66-120 C. E. 534 Pgs. 12.50 (ISBN 0-686-91516-X). Jewish Pubns.

Zucker, Norman L. The Coming Crisis in Israel: Private Faith & Public Policy. 1973. pap. 7.95x (ISBN 0-262-74012-5). MIT Pr.

JUDAISM–ADDRESSES, ESSAYS, LECTURES

Alexander Kohut Memorial Foundation Staff. Jewish Studies in Memory of Israel Abrahams. Katz, Steven, ed. LC 79-7164. (Jewish Philosophy, Mysticism & History of Ideas Ser.). (Illus.). 1980. Repr. of 1927 ed. lib. bdg. 45.00x (ISBN 0-405-12274-8). Ayer Co Pubs.

Appel, Gersion. Samuel K. Mirsky Memorial Volume. 1970. 25.00x (ISBN 0-87068-084-6). Ktav.

Bemporad, J., ed. A Rational Faith: Essays in Honor of Levi A. Olan. 15.00x (ISBN 0-87068-448-5). Ktav.

Birnbaum, Philip, ed. The New Treasury of Judaism. 1977. 15.00 (ISBN 0-88482-410-1, Sanhedrin Pr); pap. 9.95 (ISBN 0-88482-411-X, Sanhedrin Pr). Hebrew Pub.

Bland, Kalman P. Epistle on the Possibility of Conjunction with the Active Intellect by Ibn Rushd with the Commentary of Moses Narboni. LC 81-20788. 314p. 1982. 35.00x (ISBN 0-87334-005-1). Ktav.

Brann, M. & Rosenthal, F. Gedenkbuch zur Erinnerung an David Kaufmann. Katz, Steven, ed. LC 79-7142. (Jewish Philosophy, Mysticism & History of Ideas Ser.). 1980. Repr. of 1900 ed. lib. bdg. 68.50x (ISBN 0-405-12292-6). Ayer Co Pubs.

Brauner, R. A., ed. Shiv'im: Essays & Studies in Honor of Ira Eisenstein. 20.00x (ISBN 0-87068-442-6). Ktav.

Buber, Martin. Israel & the World: Essays in a Time of Crisis. LC 48-9322. 1963. pap. 6.50 (ISBN 0-8052-0066-5). Schocken.

--Mamre, Essays in Religion. Hort, Greta, tr. LC 72-97271. Repr. of 1946 ed. lib. bdg. 15.00x (ISBN 0-8371-2591-X, BUMA). Greenwood.

--The Prophetic Faith. 15.75 (ISBN 0-8446-6206-2). Peter Smith.

Chiel, Arthur A., ed. Perspectives on Jews & Judaism: Essays in Honor of Wolfe Kelman. 25.00x (ISBN 0-87068-683-6). Ktav.

Dawidowicz, Lucy. The Jewish Presence: Essays on Identity & History. LC 78-6236. 308p. 1978. pap. 3.95 (ISBN 0-15-646221-4, Harv). HarBraceJ.

Eppenstein, Simon, et al. Festschriftum, 3 vols. Katz, Steven, ed. LC 79-7161. (Jewish Philosophy, Mysticism & History of Ideas Ser.). 1980. Repr. of 1914 ed. Set. lib. bdg. 69.00x (ISBN 0-405-12247-0); lib. bdg. 23.00x ea. Vol. 1 (ISBN 0-405-12248-9). Vol. 2 (ISBN 0-405-12249-7). Vol. 3 (ISBN 0-405-12304-3). Ayer Co Pubs.

Fraenckelscher, Stiftung. Festschrift Seventy-Five Jahrigen Bestehen Des Judich-Theologischen Seminars, 2 vols. Katz, Steven, ed. LC 79-7159. (Jewish Philosophy, Mysticism & History of Ideas Ser.). 1980. Repr. of 1929 ed. Set. lib. bdg. 80.00x (ISBN 0-405-12243-8). Ayer Co Pubs.

Frank, Luanne T. & George, Emery E., eds. Husbanding the Golden Grain: Studies in Honor of Henry W. Nordmeyer. 337p. 1973. 12.50x (ISBN 0-913950-01-7). M S Rosenberg.

Freiman, A., et al, eds. Festschrift zum Siebzigsten Geburtstage A. Berliner's. LC 79-7165. (Jewish Philosophy, Mysticism & History of Ideas Ser.). 1980. Repr. of 1903 ed. lib. bdg. 45.00x (ISBN 0-405-12252-7). Ayer Co Pubs.

Gammie, John G., ed. Israelite Wisdom: Theological & Literary Essays in Honor of Samuel Terrien. LC 77-17862. 1978. pap. 18.00 (ISBN 0-89130-208-5, 00-16-03). Scholars Pr GA.

Geiger, Abraham. Nachgelassene Schriften, 5 vols. in 3. Katz, Steven, ed. LC 79-7132. (Jewish Philosophy, Mysticism & History of Ideas Ser.). 1980. Repr. of 1875 ed. Set. lib. bdg. 172.50x (ISBN 0-405-12255-1); lib. bdg. 57.50x ea. Vol. 1 (ISBN 0-405-12256-X). Vol. 2 (ISBN 0-405-12257-8). Vol. 3 (ISBN 0-405-12228-4). Ayer Co Pubs.

Gesellschaft zur Forderung der Wissenschaft des Judentums. Festschrift Siebzigsten Geburtstage Jakob Guttmanns. Katz, Steven, ed. LC 79-7155. (Jewish Philosophy, Mysticism & History of Ideas Ser.). 1980. Repr. of 1915 ed. lib. bdg. 25.50x (ISBN 0-405-12253-5). Ayer Co Pubs.

Greenberg, Blu. On Women & Judaism: A View from Tradition. LC 81-11779. 192p. 1983. pap. 5.95 (ISBN 0-8276-0195-6, 482). Jewish Pubns.

Gunzburg, D., et al, eds. Festschrift zu Ehren des Dr. A. Harkavy. LC 79-7160. (Jewish Philosophy, Mysticism & History of Ideas Ser.). 1980. Repr. of 1908 ed. lib. bdg. 60.00x (ISBN 0-405-12259-4). Ayer Co Pubs.

Ha-am, Achad, pseud. Ten Essays on Zionism & Judaism. LC 73-2202. (The Jewish People; History, Religion, Literature Ser.). Repr. of 1922 ed. 26.50 (ISBN 0-405-05267-7). Ayer Co Pubs.

Hirsch, S. R. Collected Writings of Samson Raphael Hirsch, Vol. 2: The Jewish Year, Elul-Adar. (The Hirsch Heritage Ser.). 1985. 15.75 (ISBN 0-87306-951-X). Feldheim.

Hoffman, Lawrence, ed. Gates of Understanding. LC 77-23488. 1977. pap. text ed. 4.95 (ISBN 0-8074-0009-2, 142689). UAHC.

Huxley, Thomas H. Science & Hebrew Tradition: Essays. 1979. Repr. of 1894 ed. lib. bdg. 30.00 (ISBN 0-8495-2263-3). Arden Lib.

Jacobs, Louis. Jewish Thought Today. LC 73-116679. (Chain of Tradition Ser). (Illus.). 1970. pap. 5.95x (ISBN 0-87441-014-2). Behrman.

Joseph Brever Foundation, ed. Collected Writings of Samson Raphael Hirsch, Vol. I: The Jewish Year, Nissan-Av. (The Hirsch Heritage). Tr. of Gessamelte Schriften. 391p. 1984. 15.75 (ISBN 0-87306-364-3). Feldheim.

Jung, Leo. Heirloom: Sermons, Lectures & Studies. 1961. 7.50 (ISBN 0-87306-107-1). Feldheim.

Junior Judaica, 6 vols. (Encyclopedia Judaica for Youth Ser.). 69.00 (ISBN 0-942500-00-8, Keter Pub). Maccabee Pub.

Kallen, Horace M. Judaism at Bay: Essays Toward the Adjustment of Judaism to Modernity. LC 74-38451. (Religion in America, Ser. 2). 268p. 1972. Repr. of 1932 ed. 20.00 (ISBN 0-405-04071-7). Ayer Co Pubs.

Katz, Steven, et al, eds. Judaica Festschrift zu Hermann Cohens Siebzigstem Geburtstage. LC 79-7156. (Jewish Philosophy, Mysticism & History of Ideas Ser.). 1980. Repr. of 1912 ed. lib. bdg. 60.00x (ISBN 0-405-12246-2). Ayer Co Pubs.

Konvitz, Milton R. Judaism & the American Idea. LC 78-58028. 265p. 1978. 19.50x (ISBN 0-8014-1181-5). Cornell U Pr.

Korn, Bertram. A Bicentennial Festschrift for Jacob Rader Marcus. 35.00x (ISBN 0-87068-457-4). Ktav.

Krauss, Samuel & Katz, Steven, eds. Festschrift Adolf Schwarz zum Siebzigsten Geburtstage. LC 79-7162. (Jewish Philosophy, Mysticism & History of Ideas Ser.). (Illus.). 1980. Repr. of 1917 ed. lib. bdg. 57.50x (ISBN 0-405-12275-6). Ayer Co Pubs.

Lauterbach, Jacob Z. Rabbinic Essays. LC 52-18170. pap. 146.50 (ISBN 0-317-42031-3, 2025693). Bks Demand UMI.

Lazarus, Josephine. Spirit of Judaism. facsimile ed. LC 77-38031. (Essay Index Reprint Ser). Repr. of 1895 ed. 16.00 (ISBN 0-8369-2602-1). Ayer Co Pubs.

Mandelbaum, Bernard. Wisdom of Solomon Schechter. 1963. pap. 2.50 (ISBN 0-8381-3103-4). United Syn Bk.

Modern Jewish Thought: Selected Issues, 1889-1966. LC 73-2221. (The Jewish People; History, Religion, Literature Ser.). 22.00 (ISBN 0-405-05283-9). Ayer Co Pubs.

Neusner, Jacob. The Academic Study of Judaism: Essays & Reflections. LC 75-5782. (Brown Judaic Studies). pap. 16.50 (14-00-35). Scholars Pr GA.

--Understanding Jewish Theology. 1973. pap. 11.95x (ISBN 0-87068-215-6). Ktav.

--Understanding Seeking Faith: Essays on the Case of Judaism Vol. 1: Dabates on Method Reports of Results. (Brown University Ser.). 158p. 1986. 25.95 (ISBN 1-55540-053-1, 14-01-16). Scholars Pr GA.

Quispel, Gilles & Scholem, Gershom. Jewish & Gnostic Man. LC 85-26137. (Eranos Lectures Ser.: No. 3). 46p. (Orig.). 1986. pap. 7.50 (ISBN 0-88214-403-0). Spring Pubns.

Schechter, Solomon. Seminary Addresses. 1959. pap. 2.45 (ISBN 0-8381-2109-8). United Syn Bk.

--Seminary Addresses & Other Papers. LC 79-83435. (Religion in America, Ser. 1). 1969. Repr. of 1915 ed. 19.00 (ISBN 0-405-00260-2). Ayer Co Pubs.

Scholem, Gershom. Messianic Idea in Judaism & Other Essays on Jewish Spirituality. 376p. pap. 7.95 (ISBN 0-686-95141-7). ADL.

--On Jews & Judaism in Crisis: Selected Essays. Dannhauser, Werner J., ed. LC 75-37010. 1978. 16.50 (ISBN 0-8052-3613-9). Schocken.

Slonimsky, Henry. Essays. 10.00x (ISBN 0-87068-884-7). Ktav.

Steinberg, Milton. Believing Jew: The Selected Writings. facsimile ed. LC 76-152215. (Essay Index Reprint Ser). Repr. of 1951 ed. 18.00 (ISBN 0-8369-2256-5). Ayer Co Pubs.

JUDAISM–APOLOGETIC WORKS

Gudemann, Moritz. Judische Apologetik. Katz, Steven, ed. LC 79-7133. (Jewish Philosophy, Mysticism & History of Ideas Ser.). 1980. Repr. of 1906 ed. lib. bdg. 23.00x (ISBN 0-405-12258-6). Ayer Co Pubs.

Hilsenrad, Zalman A. My Soul Thirsts Still. 1985. 13.95 (ISBN 0-87306-923-4). Feldheim.

Kolitz, Zvi. Survival for What. LC 70-75761. 234p. 1969. 10.00 (ISBN 0-8022-2272-2). Philos Lib.

Peck, Alan. The Priestly Gift in Mishnah: A Study of Tractate Terumot. LC 81-2764. (Brown BJS Ser.). 1981. pap. 16.50 (ISBN 0-89130-488-6, 140020). Scholars Pr GA.

Rankin, Oliver S. Jewish Religious Polemic. rev. ed. 1969. 20.00x (ISBN 0-87068-007-2). Ktav.

Runes, Dagobert D. Of God, the Devil & the Jews. 1952. 5.00 (ISBN 0-8022-1444-4). Philos Lib.

Yerushalmi, Yosef H. From Spanish Court to Italian Ghetto: Isaac Cardoso, A Study in Seventeenth-Century Marranism & Jewish Apologetics. LC 76-109544. (Illus.). 548p. 1981. pap. 12.50x (ISBN 0-295-95824-3). U of Wash Pr.

JUDAISM–BIBLIOGRAPHY

Brisman, S. A History & Guide to Judaic Bibliography. (Bibliographica Judaica Ser.: No. 7). 35.00x (ISBN 0-87820-900-X, HUC Pr). Ktav.

Frank, Ruth S. & Wolheim, William. The Book of Jewish Books: A Readers' Guide to Judaism. LC 86-45014. (Illus.). 272p. (Orig.). 1986. 15.95 (ISBN 0-06-063008-6, HarpR); pap. 8.95 (ISBN 0-06-063009-4, HarpR). Har-Row.

Kaplan, Jonathan, ed. International Bibliography of Jewish History & Thought. 483p. 1984. lib. bdg. 41.00 (ISBN 3-598-07503-0). K G Saur.

Starkey, Edward D. Judaism & Christianity: A Guide to the Reference Literature. (Reference Sources in the Humanities Ser.). 250p. 1987. lib. bdg. 27.50 (ISBN 0-87287-533-4). Libs Unl.

The Study of Judaism: Bibliographical Essays, Vol. 1. 229p. 12.50 (ISBN 0-686-95147-6). ADL.

JUDAISM–CEREMONIES AND PRACTICES

see Jews–Rites and Ceremonies

JUDAISM–COLLECTIONS

Davis, Moshe. Mordecai M. Kaplan Jubilee Volume, 2 Vols. 1953. Set. 50.00x (ISBN 0-685-13740-6, Pub. by Jewish Theol Seminary). Ktav.

Hirsch, Samson R. The Nineteen Letters of Ben Uziel. Paritzky, Karen, tr. from Ger. 6.95 (ISBN 0-87306-180-2). Feldheim.

Leslau, Wolf, tr. Falasha Anthology. (Judaica Ser.: No. 6). (Illus.). 1951. 26.00x (ISBN 0-300-00681-0). Yale U Pr.

Shear-Yashuv, Aharon. The Theology of Salomon Ludwig Steinheim. (Studies in Judaism in Modern Times: Vol. 7). (Illus.). x, 115p. 1986. 27.23 (ISBN 90-04-07670-0, Pub. by E J Brill). Heinman.

Underground Literature, 2 vols. in 1. 80p. 1.95 (ISBN 0-686-74969-3). ADL.

World Union of Jewish Studies, ed. Eighth World Congress of Jewish Studies. 242p. 1983. pap. text ed. 25.00x (Pub. by Magnes Pr Israel). Humanities.

JUDAISM–DEVOTIONAL EXERCISES

see Jews–Prayer-Books and Devotions

JUDAISM–DICTIONARIES

see also Jews–Dictionaries and Encyclopedias

Ausubel, Nathan. Book of Jewish Knowledge. (Illus.). 1962. 23.95 (ISBN 0-517-09746-X). Crown.

Cohen, Arthur A. & Mendes-Flohr, Paul, eds. Contemporary Jewish Religious Thought. LC 86-11856. 1986. 75.00 (ISBN 0-684-18628-4). Scribner.

Encyclopedia Talmudica, 3 vols. 25.00 ea. Vol. I (ISBN 0-87306-209-4). Vol. II (ISBN 0-87306-210-8). Vol. III (ISBN 0-87306-211-6). Feldheim.

Glustrom, Simon. Language of Judaism. rev. ed. 1973. pap. 9.95x (ISBN 0-87068-224-5). Ktav.

Koehler, Ludwig & Baumgartner, Walter. Lexicon in Veteris Testamenti Libros: Hebrew-Aramaic Lexicon, Incl. Supplement. (Hebrew & Aramaic.). 1951-53. 49.50x (ISBN 0-8028-2176-6). Eerdmans.

Marwick, Lawrence. Biblical & Judaic Acronyms. 39.00x (ISBN 0-87068-438-8). Ktav.

Runes, Dagobert D. Dictionary of Judaism. 236p. 1981. 5.95 (ISBN 0-8065-0787-X). Citadel Pr.

Schonfield, Hugh J. Popular Dictionary of Judaism. 1966. pap. 1.75 (ISBN 0-8065-0075-1, 232). Citadel Pr.

Werblowsky, Zvi & Wigoder, Geoffrey, eds. The Encyclopedia of the Jewish Religion. LC 86-10932. (Illus.). 478p. 1986. 39.95 (ISBN 0-915361-53-1, Dist. by Watts). Adama Pubs Inc.

JUDAISM–HISTORY

see also Jews–History–To 70 A.D.

Abrahams, Israel. Jewish Life in the Middle Ages. LC 58-11933. (Temple Books). 1969. pap. text ed. 7.95x (ISBN 0-689-70001-6, T1). Atheneum.

Abramov, S. Zalman. Perpetual Dilemma: Jewish Religion in the Jewish State. 1979. pap. 7.50 (ISBN 0-8074-0088-2, 382500, WUPJ). UAHC.

Ackroyd, Peter R. Israel under Babylon & Persia. (New Clarendon Bible Ser.). 1970. 15.95x (ISBN 0-19-836917-4). Oxford U Pr.

Albright, William F. Yahweh & the Gods of Canaan: An Historical Analysis of Two Contrasting Faiths. 1978. Repr. of 1968 ed. 12.00x (ISBN 0-931464-01-3). Eisenbrauns.

Anderson, G. W. The History & Religion of Israel. (New Clarendon Bible-OT Ser.). (Illus.). 1966. pap. 11.95x (ISBN 0-19-836915-8). Oxford U Pr.

Ayers, Robert H. Judaism & Christianity: Origins, Developments & Recent Trends. LC 83-3548. (Illus.). 478p. (Orig.). 1983. lib. bdg. 35.75 (ISBN 0-8191-3156-3); pap. text ed. 16.50 (ISBN 0-8191-3157-1). U Pr of Amer.

Bamberger, Bernard J. Story of Judaism. rev. 3rd ed. LC 64-16463. 1964. pap. 12.95 (ISBN 0-8052-0077-0). Schocken.

Baskin, Judith R. Pharaoh's Counsellors: Job, Jethro, & Balaam in Rabbinic & Patristic Tradition. LC 83-11535. (Brown Judaic Studies). 200p. 1983. pap. 18.00 (ISBN 0-89130-637-4, 14 00 47). Scholars Pr GA.

Beck, Norman A. Mature Christianity: The Recognition & Repudiation of the Anti-Jewish Polemic of the New Testament. LC 83-51047. (Illus.). 328p. 1985. 19.50 (ISBN 0-941664-03-1). Assoc Univ Prs.

Berlin, Charles. Studies in Jewish Bibliography, History & Literature: In Honor of I. Edward Kiev. 1971. 50.00x (ISBN 0-87068-143-5). Ktav.

Bickerman, Elias. From Ezra to the Last of the Maccabees: Foundations of Post-Biblical Judaism. 1962. pap. 5.95 (ISBN 0-8052-0036-3). Schocken.

--Studies in Jewish & Christian History, Pt. 3. (Arbeiten zur Geschichte des antiken Judentums und des Urchritentums Ser.: Band 9). xvi, 392p. 1986. 93.50 (ISBN 90-04-07480-5, Pub. by E J Brill). Heinman.

Blizzard, Roy B., Jr. Let Judah Go up First: A Study in Praise, Prayer, & Worship. 46p. (Orig.). 1984. pap. 3.50 (ISBN 0-918873-01-0). Ctr Judaic-Christ Studies.

Blumenthal, David R. Approaches to Judaism in Medieval Times, Vol. II. (Brown Judaic Studies). 1985. 23.95 (ISBN 0-89130-848-2, 14-00-57); pap. 18.95 (ISBN 0-89130-849-0). Scholars Pr GA.
Bokser, Baruch M. History of Judaism: The Next Ten Years. Neusner, Jacob, ed. LC 80-25501. (Brown Judaic Studies). 1980. 15.00 (ISBN 0-89130-450-9, 14-00-21); pap. 10.50 (ISBN 0-89130-451-7). Scholars Pr GA.
--Post Mishnaic Judaism in Transition: Samuel in Berakhot & the Beginnings of Gemara. LC 80-19702. (Brown Judaic Studies). 543p. 1980. 19.50 (ISBN 0-89130-432-0, 14 00 17); pap. 15.00 (ISBN 0-89130-433-9). Scholars Pr GA.
Bokser, Ben Z. Pharisaic Judaism in Transition. LC 73-2189. (The Jewish People; History, Religion, Literature Ser.). Repr. of 1935 ed. 18.00 (ISBN 0-405-05255-3). Ayer Co Pubs.
Butwin, Frances. Jews of America: History & Sources. Blecher, Arthur C., ed. LC 73-2253. (Illus.). 160p. 1973. pap. text ed. 3.95x (ISBN 0-87441-062-2). Behrman.
Cohen, Mark R. Jewish Self-Government in Medieval Egypt: The Origins of the Office of the Head of the Jews. LC 80-7514. (Princeton Studies on the Near East). 425p. 1981. 41.00 (ISBN 0-691-05307-3). Princeton U Pr.
Collins, John J. & Nickelsburg, George W., eds. Ideal Figures in Ancient Judaism: Profiles & Paradigms. LC 80-19878. 1980. 17.95 (ISBN 0-89130-434-7, 060412); pap. 11.95 (ISBN 0-89130-435-5). Scholars Pr GA.
Culi, Yaakov. The Torah Anthology: Mem Lo'ez, 9 vols. Kaplan, Aryeh, tr. Incl. Vol. 1. Beginnings: From Creation Until Abraham. 540p. 14.95 (ISBN 0-940118-01-7); Vol. 2. The Patriarchs: From Abraham Until Jacob. 600p. 15.95 (ISBN 0-940118-02-5); Vol. 3. The Twelve Tribes: From Jacob Until Joseph. 708p; Vol. 4. Israel in Egypt: Subjugation & Prelude to the Exodus. 280p. 12.95 (ISBN 0-940118-04-1); Vol. 5. Redemption: The Exodus from Egypt. 436p. 15.95 (ISBN 0-940118-05-X); Vol. 6. The Ten Commandments: Revelation at Sinai. 534p. 16.95 (ISBN 0-940118-06-8); Vol. 7. The Law: The First Codification. 363p. 13.95 (ISBN 0-940118-07-6); Vol. 8. Acceptance: Establishing the Covenant. 250p. 12.95 (ISBN 0-940118-08-4); Vol. 9. The Tabernacle: Plans for the Sanctuary. 413p. 15.95 (ISBN 0-940118-09-2). (MeAm Lo'ez Ser.). (Illus.). 1977-1980. Maznaim.
Davies, W. D. The Gospel & the Land: Early Christianity & Jewish Territorial Doctrine. LC 72-82228. 1974. 32.50x (ISBN 0-520-02278-5). U of Cal Pr.
--Jewish & Pauline Studies. LC 82-48620. 432p. 1983. text ed. 29.95 (ISBN 0-8006-0694-9). Fortress.
Davies, W. D., ed. Cambridge History of Judaism: Introduction, the Persian Period, Vol. 1. Finkelstein, Louis. LC 77-85704. 461p. 1984. 62.50 (ISBN 0-521-21880-2). Cambridge U Pr.
Dilling, Elizabeth. The Jewish Religion: Its Influence Today. (Illus.). 300p. 1983. pap. 8.00 (ISBN 0-939482-07-X). Noontide.
Eckardt, A. Roy. Jews & Christians: The Contemporary Meeting. LC 85-45327. 192p. 1986. 19.95x (ISBN 0-253-33162-5). Ind U Pr.
Epstein, Isidore. Judaism. (Orig.). 1959. pap. 6.95 (ISBN 0-14-020440-7, Pelican). Penguin.
Fairweather, William. The Background of the Gospels. 464p. 1916. 15.95 (ISBN 0-567-02101-7, Pub. by T & T Clark Ltd UK). Fortress.
Fine, Jo Renee & Wolfe, Gerard R. The Synagogues of New York's Lower East Side. LC 75-15126. (Illus.). 1978. 27.50 (ISBN 0-8147-2559-7). NYU Pr.
Fiorenza, Elizabeth S., ed. Aspects of Religious Propaganda in Judaism & Early Christianity. LC 74-27890. (University of Notre Dame. Center for the Study of Judaism & Christianity in Antiquity Ser: No. 2). pap. 51.30 (2029308). Bks Demand UMI.
Foerster, Werner. From the Exile to Christ: Historical Introduction to Palestinian Judaism. Harris, Gordon E., ed. LC 64-18151. 264p. 1964. pap. 10.95 (ISBN 0-8006-0978-6, 1-978). Fortress.
Friedman, Richard E. The Poet & the Historian: Essays in Literary & Historical Biblical Criticism. LC 83-9035. (Harvard Semitic Studies). 172p. 1983. 13.50 (ISBN 0-89130-629-3, 04 04 26). Scholars Pr GA.
Geiger, Abraham. Judaism & It's History: In Two Parts. Newburgh, Charles, tr. from Ger. LC 85-9043. (Brown Classics in Judaica Ser.). 414p. 1985. pap. text ed. 17.50 (ISBN 0-8191-4491-6). U Pr of Amer.
Ginsberg, Louis H. The Israelian Heritage of Judaism. 15.00x (ISBN 0-87334-013-2). Ktav.
Ginzberg, Louis. Students Scholars & Saints. LC 85-9089. (Brown Classics in Judaica Ser.). 312p. 1985. pap. text ed. 12.75 (ISBN 0-8191-4490-8). U Pr of Amer.
Gowan, Donald E., ed. Bridge Between the Testaments: Reappraisal of Judaism from the Exile to the Birth of Christianity. 3rd, rev. ed. LC 86-9327. (Pittsburgh Theological Monographs: No. 14). 1986. text ed. 32.95 (ISBN 0-915138-88-3). Pickwick.
Grant, Frederick C. Ancient Judaism & the New Testament. LC 77-18848. 1978. Repr. of 1959 ed. lib. bdg. cancelled (ISBN 0-313-20204-4, GRAJ). Greenwood.
Graupe, Heinz M. The Rise of Modern Judaism: An Intellectual History of German Jewry 1650-1942. LC 77-9059. 344p. 1979. lib. bdg. 24.00 (ISBN 0-88275-395-9); pap. text ed. 10.50 (ISBN 0-89874-562-4). Krieger.
Green, Arthur. Jewish Spirituality: Vol 1. Cousins, Ewert, ed. (World Spirituality Ser.). 496p. 1985. 49.50x (ISBN 0-8245-0762-2). Crossroad NY.
Green, William S. Approaches to Ancient Judaism, Vol. IV. (Brown Judaic Studies). 208p. 1983. pap. 17.00 (ISBN 0-89130-673-0, 14 00 27). Scholars Pr GA.
--Approaches to Ancient Judaism: Theory & Practice. LC 76-57656. 1978. pap. 16.50 (ISBN 0-89130-130-5, 14-00-01). Scholars Pr GA.
Green, William S., ed. Approaches to Ancient Judaism, Vol. V. (Brown Judaic Studies: No. 32). 1985. 20.95 (ISBN 0-89130-797-4, 14 00 32); pap. 17.25 (ISBN 0-89130-798-2). Scholars Pr GA.
Hartman, David. Joy & Responsibility: Israel, Modernity & the Renewal of Judaism. 286p. 12.50 (ISBN 0-686-95138-7). ADL.
Hebrew Union College Annual, 10 Vols. 1969. 650.00x (ISBN 0-87068-065-X). Ktav.
Hengel, Martin. Judaism & Hellenism: Studies in Their Encounter in Palestine During the Early Hellenistic Period, 2 Vols. pap. 160.00 (2027202). Bks Demand UMI.
Heschel, Abraham J. Theology of Ancient Judaism, 2 vols. (Hebrew.). 1973. Set. 14.95x (ISBN 0-685-32988-7). Bloch.
Higgens, Elford. Hebrew Idolatry & Superstition. 1971. Repr. of 1893 ed. 19.50x (ISBN 0-8046-1150-5, Pub. by Kennikat). Assoc Faculty Pr.
History of the Religion of Israel: From the Babylonian Captivity to the End of the Prophecy, Vol. 4. 45.00x (ISBN 0-685-56209-3). Ktav.
Humphreys, W. Lee. The Tragic Vision & the Hebrew Tradition. LC 85-47724. (Overtures to Biblical Theology Ser.). 176p. 1985. pap. 9.95 (ISBN 0-8006-1542-5). Fortress.
Hyman, Frieda C. The Jewish Experience, Bk. 2. (Illus.). 1978. text ed. 6.95x (ISBN 0-8381-0192-5). United Syn Bk.
Joseph, Howard, et al, eds. Truth & Compassion: Essays on Judaism & Religion in Memory of Rabbi Dr. Solomon Frank, Vol. 12. 217p. 1983. pap. text ed. 13.95x (ISBN 0-919812-17-1, Pub. by Wilfrid Laurier Canada). Humanities.
Kaufmann, Yehezkel. Religion of Israel. Greenberg, Moshe, tr. LC 60-5466. 1960. 36.00x (ISBN 0-226-42728-5). U of Chicago Pr.
Kent, Charles F. The Messages of Israel's Lawgivers. Sanders, Frank K., ed. 386p. 1981. Repr. of 1916 ed. lib. bdg. 25.00 (ISBN 0-89760-430-X). Telegraph Bks.
Klein, Herbert A. The Peoples of Israel: Fifty-Seven Centuries of Presence. rev. & enl. ed. Simon, Joseph, ed. Orig. Title: Israel - Land of the Jews. (Illus.). 240p. 1986. Repr. of 1972 ed. 23.50 (ISBN 0-934710-13-9). J Simon.
Kraft, Robert A., et al, eds. Early Judaism & Its Modern Interpreters. (SBL Bible & Its Modern Interpreters Ser.). 1986. 24.95 (ISBN 0-89130-669-2, 06-14-02); pap. 19.95 (ISBN 0-89130-884-9). Scholars Pr GA.
Lange, Nicholas de. Atlas of the Jewish World. (Cultiral Atlas Ser.). (Illus.). 240p. 1984. 35.00 (ISBN 0-87196-043-5). Facts on File.
Lilker, Shalom. Kibbutz Judaism: A New Tradition in the Making. (Kibbutz, Cooperative Society, & Alternative Social Policy Ser.: Vol. 7). 264p. 1982. lib. bdg. 19.50 (ISBN 0-8482-4876-7). Norwood Edns.
Lods, Adolphe. Prophets & the Rise of Judaism. Hooke, S. H., tr. LC 77-109772. (Illus.). 1971. Repr. of 1937 ed. lib. bdg. 25.75x (ISBN 0-8371-4262-8, LOPR). Greenwood.
Magriso, Yitzchak. Avoth. Barocas, David N., tr. Kaplan, Aryeh, intro. by. & 400p. 15.95 (ISBN 0-940118-22-X). Maznaim.
Markowitz, Sidney L. What You Should Know about Jewish Religion, History, Ethics, & Culture. 226p. 1973. pap. 5.95 (ISBN 0-8065-0028-X). Citadel Pr.
Meek, Theophile J. Hebrew Origins. 1960. 11.25 (ISBN 0-8446-2572-8). Peter Smith.
Meyer, Michael A. The Origins of the Modern Jew: Jewish Identity & European Culture in Germany, 1749-1824. LC 67-12384. (Waynebooks Ser: No. 32). 250p. 1972. o. p. 9.95x (ISBN 0-8143-1315-9); pap. 7.95x (ISBN 0-8143-1470-8). Wayne St U Pr.
Montefiore, Claude J. Lectures on the Origin & Growth of Religion as Illustrated by the Religion of the Ancient Hebrews. 3rd ed. LC 77-27162. (Hibbert Lectures: 1892). Repr. of 1892 ed. 46.50 (ISBN 0-404-60410-2). AMS Pr.
Neher, Andre. Jewish Thought & the Scientific Revolution of the Sixteenth Century: David Gans (1541-1613) & His Times. Maisel, David, tr. (Littman Library of Jewish Civilization). (Illus.). 240p. 1986. 29.95x (ISBN 0-19-710057-0). Oxford U Pr.
Neuberger, Julia. The Story of the Jews. (Cambridge Books for Children). (Illus.). 32p. 1987. 7.95 (ISBN 0-521-30601-9); pap. 3.95 (ISBN 0-521-31580-8). Cambridge U Pr.
Neusner, Jacob. The Death & Birth of Judaism: The Impact of Christianity, Secularism & the Holocaust on Jewish Faith. LC 86-47733. 352p. 1987. 21.95 (ISBN 0-465-01577-8). Basic.
--First-Century Judaism in Crisis: Yohanan ben Zakkai & the Renaissance of Torah. X ed. 1982. 14.95x (ISBN 0-87068-728-X). Ktav.
--Formative Judaism. LC 82-16746. (Brown Judaic Studies). 182p. 1982. pap. 13.50 (ISBN 0-89130-594-7, 14 00 37). Scholars Pr GA.
--Formative Judaism - Religious Historical & Literary Studies: Fourth Series - Problems of Classification & Composition. (Brown Judaic Studies: No. 76). 222p. 1984. 24.95 (ISBN 0-89130-782-6, 14 00 76); pap. 16.95 (ISBN 0-89130-783-4). Scholars Pr GA.
--Formative Judaism: Religious, Historical, & Literary Studies. (Brown Judaic Studies). (Fifth Series Revisioning the Written Records of a Nascent Religion). 1985. 29.95 (ISBN 0-89130-850-4, 14-00-91); pap. 21.95 (ISBN 0-89130-851-2). Scholars Pr Ga.
--Judaism in Society: The Evidence of the Yerushalmi, Toward the Natural History of a Religion. LC 83-4916. (Chicago Studies in the History of Judaism). 272p. 1984. lib. bdg. 25.00x (ISBN 0-226-57616-7). U of Chicago Pr.
--Messiah in Context: Israel's History & Destiny in Formative Judaism. LC 83-20542. (Foundations of Judaism Ser.). 304p. 1984. 26.95 (ISBN 0-8006-0716-3, 1-716). Fortress.
--Method & Meaning in Ancient Judaism II. LC 80-21781. (Brown Judaic Studies). 1981. pap. 27.50 (ISBN 0-89130-416-9, 140015). Scholars Pr GA.
--Method & Meaning in Ancient Judaism III. LC 80-19449. (Brown Judaic Studies). 1981. pap. 27.50 (ISBN 0-89130-418-5, 14-00-16). Scholars Pr GA.
--Self-Fulfilling Prophecy: Exile & Return As the History of Judaism. LC 86-47756. 320p. 1987. 25.00 (ISBN 0-8070-3606-4). Beacon Pr.
--Understanding Rabbinic Judaism: From Talmudic to Modern Times. 1974. pap. 11.95x (ISBN 0-685-56200-X). Ktav.
Neusner, Jacob & Frerichs, Ernest S., eds. To See Ourselves As Others See Us: Christians Jews, "Others" in Late Antiquity. (Scholars Press Studies in the Humanities). (Orig.). 1985. 38.95 (ISBN 0-89130-819-9, 00-01-09); pap. 25.95 (ISBN 0-89130-820-2). Scholars Pr GA.
Nickelsburg, George W. & Stone, Michael E. Faith & Piety in Early Judaism: Texts & Documents. LC 82-71830. 272p. 1983. 19.95 (ISBN 0-8006-0679-5). Fortress.
Nickelsburg, George W. & Kraft, Robert A., eds. Early Judaism & Its Modern Interpreters. LC 85-45491. (The Bible & its Modern Interpreters Ser.). 544p. 1986. 24.95 (ISBN 0-8006-0722-8). Fortress.
Noth, Martin & Anderson, Berhard W. History of Pentateuchal Traditions. LC 80-24937. (Scholars Press Reproductions Ser.). 1981. 22.00_o.s. (ISBN 0-89130-446-0, 00-07-05); text ed. 17.50 (ISBN 0-89130-954-3). Scholars Pr GA.
Oesterley, William O. Jews & Judaism During the Greek Period: The Background of Christianity. LC 74-102580. 1970. Repr. of 1941 ed. 23.00x (ISBN 0-8046-0740-0, Pub. by Kennikat). Assoc Faculty Pr.
Patai, Raphael. The Hebrew Goddess. 1984. pap. 2.95 (ISBN 0-380-39289-5, 39289, Discus). Avon.
Raisin, Jacob S. The Haskalah Movement in Russia. 1976. Repr. of 1913 ed. 40.00 (ISBN 0-8274-2471-X). R West.
Rausch, David A. Messianic Judaism: Its History, Theology & Polity. LC 82-20382. (Texts & Studies in Religion: Vol. 14). 304p. 1983. 49.95x (ISBN 0-88946-802-8). E Mellen.
Reinharz, Jehuda, et al, eds. Mystics, Philosophers, & Politicians: Essays in Jewish Intellectual History in Honor of Alexander Altman. LC 81-5540. (Duke Monographs in Medieval & Renaissance Studies: No. 5). xv, 372p. 1982. 36.75 (ISBN 0-8223-0446-5). Duke.
Rosenberg, Stuart E. Judaism. 159p. pap. 2.45 (ISBN 0-686-95139-5). ADL.
Rosenthal, Gilbert S. Contemporary Judaism: Patterns of Survival. 2nd ed. 401p. 1986. 39.95 (ISBN 0-89885-260-9, Dist. by Independent Publishers Group); pap. 16.95 (ISBN 0-89885-277-3). Human Sci Pr.
Rudavsky, David. Modern Jewish Religious Movements. 3rd rev. ed. LC 79-11266. 1979. pap. text ed. 9.95x (ISBN 0-87441-286-2). Behrman.
Russell, D. S. Between the Testaments. LC 77-74742. 176p. 1960. pap. 5.95 (ISBN 0-8006-1856-4, 1-1856). Fortress.
--From Early Judaism to Early Church. LC 85-31776. 1986. pap. 5.95 (ISBN 0-8006-1921-8). Fortress.
--The Jews from Alexander to Herod. 1967. pap. 13.95x (ISBN 0-19-836913-1). Oxford U Pr.
Sanders, E. P. Paul & Palestinian Judaism: A Comparison of Patterns of Religion. LC 76-62612. 648p. 1977. pap. 19.95 (ISBN 0-8006-1899-8, 1-1899). Fortress.
--Paul, the Law & the Jewish People. LC 82-17487. 240p. 1983. pap. 9.95 (ISBN 0-8006-1878-5, 1-1878). Fortress.
Schechter, Solomon. Studies in Judaism. facsimile ed. LC 78-38775. (Essay Index Reprint Ser). Repr. of 1896 ed. 19.50 (ISBN 0-8369-2670-6). Ayer Co Pubs.
Scholem, Gershom. The Messianic Idea in Judaism: And Other Essays on Jewish Spirituality. LC 70-130212. 384p. 1972. pap. 8.95 (ISBN 0-8052-0362-1). Schocken.
Sigal, Phillip. The Emergence of Contemporary Judaism: From Medievalism to Proto-Modernity in the 16th & 17th Century, Vol. 3. (Pittsburgh Theological Monographs New Ser.: No. 17). 1986. pap. text ed. 31.90 (ISBN 0-915138-57-3). Pickwick.
--Emergence of Contemporary Judaism: The Foundation of Judaism from Biblical Origins to the Sixth Century A. D, Vol. 1, Pts. 1 & 2. Incl. Pt. 1. From the Origins to the Separation of Christianity. (Pittsburgh Theological Monographs: No. 29). pap. text ed. 22.25 (ISBN 0-915138-30-1); Pt. 2. Rabbinic Judaism. (Pittsburgh Theological Monographs: No. 29a). pap. text ed. 20.25 (ISBN 0-915138-46-8). 1980. pap. text ed. 39.75 set (ISBN 0-915138-46-8). Pickwick.
Silver, Abba H. Where Judaism Differed. 318p. 1987. Repr. of 1956 ed. 25.00 (ISBN 0-87668-957-8). Aronson.
Silver, Daniel J. & Martin, Bernard. History of Judaism, 2 vols. Incl. Vol. 1. From Abraham to Maimonides; Vol. 2. Europe & the New World. pap. 10.95 o.s.i (ISBN 0-465-03005-X). LC 73-90131. 1974. Basic.
Simon, Marcal. Verus Israel. McKeating, H., tr. 592p. 1985. 57.00x (ISBN 0-19-710035-X). Oxford U Pr.
Simpson, Cuthbert A. Revelation & Response in the Old Testament. LC 73-76022. Repr. of 1947 ed. 15.00 (ISBN 0-404-06056-0). AMS Pr.
Smith, Jonathan Z. Imagining Religion: From Babylon to Jonestown. LC 82-2734. (Studies in the History of Judaism). 1982. 17.50x (ISBN 0-226-76358-7). U of Chicago Pr.
Steinschneider, Moritz. Gesammelte Schriften. Katz, Steven, ed. LC 79-7152. (Jewish Philosophy, Mysticism & History of Ideas Ser.). 1980. Repr. of 1925 ed. lib. bdg. 55.50x (ISBN 0-405-12289-6). Ayer Co Pubs.
--Die Geschichtsliteratur der Juden. Katz, Steven, ed. LC 79-7153. (Jewish Philosophy, Mysticism & History of Ideas Ser.). 1980. Repr. of 1905 ed. lib. bdg. 16.00x (ISBN 0-405-12290-X). Ayer Co Pubs.
Trepp, Leo. The Complete Book of Jewish Observance. LC 79-1352. (Behrman House Book). (Illus.). 370p. 1980. 14.95 (ISBN 0-671-41797-5). Summit Bks.
--History of the Jewish Experience: Eternal Faith, Eternal People. rev. ed. LC 73-3142. Orig. Title: Eternal Faith, Eternal People: a Journey into Judaism. 296p. 1973. pap. text ed. 9.95x (ISBN 0-87441-072-X). Behrman.
Twersky, Isadore, ed. Studies in Medieval Jewish History & Literature. LC 79-11588. (Judaic Monographs: No. 2). 1979. text ed. 25.00x (ISBN 0-674-85192-7). Harvard U Pr.
Understanding the Jewish Experience. 54p. 2.00 (ISBN 0-686-74981-2). ADL.
Wardle, William L. The History & Religion of Israel. LC 78-11741. (The Clarendon Bible, Old Testament Ser.: Vol. I). (Illus.). 1979. Repr. of 1942 ed. lib. bdg. 24.75x (ISBN 0-313-21016-0, WAHR). Greenwood.
Weber, Max. Ancient Judaism. Martindale, Don, ed. Gerth, Hans H., tr. LC 52-8156. 484p. 1967. pap. text ed. 12.95x (ISBN 0-02-934130-2). Free Pr.
Wellhausen, Julius. Prolegomena to the History of Ancient Israel. 14.25 (ISBN 0-8446-3147-7). Peter Smith.
Young, Brad. The Jewish Background to the Lord's Prayer. 54p. (Orig.). 1984. pap. 3.95 (ISBN 0-918873-02-9). Ctr Judaic-Christ Studies.

Zeitlin, Irving M. Ancient Judaism: Biblical Criticism from Max Weber to the Present. 328p. 1985. 29.95x (ISBN 0-7456-0059-X). Basil Blackwell.

--Ancient Judaism: Biblical Criticism from Max Weber to the Present. 328p. 1986. pap. 12.95 (ISBN 0-7456-0297-5). Basil Blackwell.

Zeitlin, Solomon. Studies in the Early History of Judaism, Vol. 2. 1973. 59.50x (ISBN 0-87068-209-1). Ktav.

JUDAISM–HISTORY–SOURCES

Ackerman, Walter. Out of Our People's Past: Sources for the Study of Jewish History. 1978. 7.50x (ISBN 0-8381-0221-2). United Syn Bk.

American Academy for Jewish Research Staff. Facets of Medieval Judaism: Proceedings. (Jewish People; History, Religion, Literature Ser.). 19.00 (ISBN 0-405-05262-6). Ayer Co Pubs.

Holladay, Carl R. Fragments from Hellenistic Jewish Authors: Historians, Vol. I. LC 79-18090. (SBL Texts & Translations). 404p. 1983. pap. 16.50 (ISBN 0-89130-349-9, 06 02 20). Scholars Pr GA.

Holtz, Barry, ed. Back to the Sources: Reading the Classic Jewish Texts. (Illus.). 416p. 1984. 19.95 (ISBN 0-671-45467-6). Summit Bks.

Marcus, Jacob R. An Index to the Picture Collection of the American Jewish Archives. 7.50 (ISBN 0-87820-005-3). Ktav.

Neusner, Jacob. Judaism in the American Humanities: Second Series. (Brown Judaic Ser.). 136p. 1983. pap. 13.50 (ISBN 0-89130-618-8, 14 00 42). Scholars Pr GA.

White, Paul F. Index to the American Jewish Archives, Vols. I-X. 25.00x (ISBN 0-87820-004-5). Ktav.

Zeitlin, Solomon. Studies in the Early History of Judaism, Vol. 1. 1973. 59.50x (ISBN 0-87068-208-3). Ktav.

JUDAISM–HISTORY–TANNAITIC PERIOD, 10-220

see Tannaim

JUDAISM–JUVENILE LITERATURE

Bogot, Howard. Yoni. 1982. pap. 4.00 (ISBN 0-686-82564-0). UAHC.

Borovetz, Fran. Ha Motzi Bracha Kit. (Illus.). 32p. (Orig.). 1985. pap. text ed. 13.95 (ISBN 0-933873-03-4). Torah Aura.

Burstein, Chaya M. The Jewish Kids Catalog. (Illus.). 224p. 1983. pap. 10.95 (ISBN 0-8276-0215-4, 603). Jewish Pubns.

Chanover, Hyman, adapted by. Service for the High Holy Days Adapted for Youth. new ed. LC 72-2058. 192p. 1972. pap. 3.95x (ISBN 0-87441-123-8). Behrman.

Domnitz, Myer. Judaism. (Religions of the World Ser.). (Illus.). 48p. 1986. PLB 10.90 (ISBN 0-531-18066-2, Pub. by Bookwright). Watts.

Ganz, Yaffa. Follow the Moon: A Journey Through the Jewish Year. 1984. 8.95 (ISBN 0-87306-369-4). Feldheim.

--Who Knows One? A Book of Jewish Numbers. 1981. 8.95 (ISBN 0-87306-285-X). Feldheim.

Gellman, Ellie. It's Rosh-Hashanah. LC 85-80783. (Illus.). 12p. 1985. bds. 4.95 (ISBN 0-930494-50-4). Kar Ben.

--Shai's Shabbat Walk. LC 85-80780. (Illus.). 12p. 1985. bds. 4.95 (ISBN 0-930494-49-0). Kar Ben.

Gevirtz, Eliezer. Shmittah: What It's All About. (Orig.). 1987. write for info. Torah Umesorah.

Goldman, Alex J. Child's Dictionary of Jewish Symbols. (Illus.). 5.00 (ISBN 0-685-09470-7). Feldheim.

Golomb, Morris. Know Jewish Living & Enjoy It. LC 78-54569. (Illus.). 1981. 11.95 (ISBN 0-88400-054-0). Shengold.

Greenfeld, Howard. Bar Mitzvah. LC 81-5104. (Illus.). 32p. 1981. 7.95 (ISBN 0-03-053861-0). H Holt & Co.

Grishaver, Joel L. Being Torah Student Commentary, 2 Vols. (Illus.). 72p. (Orig.). 1986. pap. text ed. 3.25 ea. Vol. 1 (ISBN 0-933873-09-3). Vol. 2 (ISBN 0-933873-10-7). Torah Aura.

--Torah Toons I. (Illus.). 115p. (Orig.). 1985. pap. text ed. 5.50 (ISBN 0-933873-01-8). Torah Aura.

--Torah Toons II. (Illus.). 114p. (Orig.). 1985. pap. text ed. 5.50 (ISBN 0-933873-02-6). Torah Aura.

Jacobs, Louis. Chain of Tradition Series, 4 vols. Incl. Vol. 1. Jewish Law. LC 68-27329. pap. text ed. 5.95x (ISBN 0-87441-211-0); Vol. 2. Jewish Ethics, Philosophy & Mysticism. LC 71-80005. pap. text ed. 5.95x (ISBN 0-87441-212-9); Vol. 3. Jewish Thought Today. LC 73-116679. (Illus.). 1974. pap. text ed. 5.95x (ISBN 0-87441-213-7); Vol. 4. Hasidic Thought; Vol. 5. Jewish Biblical Exegesis. LC 78-1487. (Illus.). 1974. pap. Behrman.

Karlinsky, Isaiah & Karlinsky, Ruth. My First Book of Mitzvos. (Illus.). 1986. 7.95 (ISBN 0-87306-388-0). Feldheim.

Keene, Michael & Wood, Angela. Looking into Being Jewish. (Looking into World Religions Ser.). (Illus.). 64p. 1987. 16.95 (ISBN 0-7134-4668-4, Pub. by Batsford England). David & Charles.

Kripke, Dorothy K. & Levin, Meyer. God & the Story of Judaism. LC 62-17078. (Jewish Heritage Ser: Vol. 1). 1962. 5.95x (ISBN 0-87441-000-2). Behrman.

Kushner, Lawrence. The Book of Miracles: A Young Person's Guide to Jewish Spirituality. 96p. (Orig.). (YA) 1987. pap. text ed. 8.95 (ISBN 0-8074-0323-7). UAHC.

Lawton, Clive. I Am a Jew. Sloan, Frank, ed. LC 85-50167. (My Heritage Ser.). 32p. 1985. PLB 9.40 (ISBN 0-531-10019-7). Watts.

Levin, Meyer. Beginnings in Jewish Philosophy. LC 76-116677. (Jewish Heritage Ser). (Illus.). 192p. 1971. text ed. 5.95x (ISBN 0-87441-063-0). Behrman.

Levin, Meyer & Kurzband, Toby. Story of the Jewish Way of Life. LC 59-13487. (Jewish Heritage Ser: Vol. 3). 1959. 5.95x (ISBN 0-87441-003-7). Behrman.

Orovitz, Norma A. Puzzled! The Jewish Word Search. LC 77-83177. 1977. pap. 3.95 (ISBN 0-8197-0022-3). Bloch.

Rabinowitz, Jan. The Tzedakah Workbook. (Illus.). 32p. (Orig.). 1986. pap. text ed. 3.95 (ISBN 0-933873-07-7). Torah Aura.

Rosenberg, Amye. Mitzvot. (Illus.). 30p. pap. text ed. 2.95x (ISBN 0-87441-387-7). Behrman.

Saypol, Judyth & Wikler, Madeline. My Very Own Haggadah. Rev. ed. LC 83-6. (Illus.). 32p. pap. text ed. 2.95 (ISBN 0-930494-23-7). Kar Ben.

Schachnowitz, Selig. Light from the West. Leftwich, Joseph, tr. 7.95 (ISBN 0-87306-124-1). Feldheim.

Shapolsky, Ian. The Beginners' Jewish Book of Why & What. (YA) 1987. 11.95. Shapolsky Pubs.

Silberman, Shoshana. A Family Haggadah. 1987. pap. 3.95; Songs for a Family Seder. cassette 6.95. Kar Ben.

Silverman, William B. Judaism & Christianity. LC 68-27330. pap. 5.95x (ISBN 0-87441-016-9). Behrman.

Simms, Laura & Kozodoy, Ruth. Exploring Our Living Past. Harlow, Jules, ed. (Our Living Past Ser). (Illus.). 1978. pap. 6.95x (ISBN 0-87441-309-5). Behrman.

Singer, Isaac B. The Power of Light: Eight Stories for Hanukkah. LC 80-20263. (Illus.). 87p. 1980. 10.95 (ISBN 0-374-36099-5). FS&G.

Union of American Hebrew Congregations. All in My Jewish Family. (Illus.). 32p. 1984. pap. 5.00 wkbk. (ISBN 0-8074-0266-4, 103800). UAHC.

Weinbach, Sheindel. Avi Names His Price. (Illus.). 1976. 6.95 (ISBN 0-87306-119-5). Feldheim.

Wood, Angela. Judaism. (World Religions Ser.). (Illus.). 72p. 1984. 16.95 (ISBN 0-7134-3656-5, Pub. by Batsford England). David & Charles.

Zar, Rose. In the Mouth of the Wolf. 224p. 1983. 10.95 (ISBN 0-8276-0225-1, 611). Jewish Pubns.

JUDAISM–QUOTATIONS, MAXIMS, ETC.

Hertz, Joseph H., ed. A Book of Jewish Thoughts. 1976. Repr. 8.95 (ISBN 0-8197-0252-8). Bloch.

Hirsch, Sampson R. From the Wisdom of Mishle. Paritzky-Joshua, Karin, tr. 260p. 1976. pap. 7.95 (ISBN 0-87306-040-7). Feldheim.

Kent, Charles F. The Messages of Israel's Lawgivers. Sanders, Frank K., ed. 386p. 1981. Repr. of 1916 ed. lib. bdg. 25.00 (ISBN 0-89760-430-X). Telegraph Bks.

Why Don't You Believe What We Tell You. 39p. 1983. pap. 1.00 (ISBN 0-939482-06-1). Noontide.

Zaretsky, David & Wengrov, Charles. The Stories & Parables of the Hafetz Hayyim. Orig. Title: Mishle Hafetz Hayyim. 1976. 8.95 (ISBN 0-87306-132-2). Feldheim.

JUDAISM–RECONSTRUCTIONIST MOVEMENT

see Reconstructionist Judaism

JUDAISM–REFORM MOVEMENT

see Reform Judaism

JUDAISM–RELATIONS

see also Jews–Election, Doctrine Of

Carter, George W. Zoroastrianism & Judaism. LC 70-112489. 1970. Repr. of 1918 ed. 14.00 (ISBN 0-404-01396-1). AMS Pr.

Eisenberg, Gary. Smashing the Idols: A Jewish Inquiry into the Cults. 325p. 1987. 25.00 (ISBN 0-87668-974-8). Aronson.

Freud, Sigmund. Moses & Monotheism. Jones, Katherine, ed. 1955. pap. 4.95 (ISBN 0-394-70014-7, V14, Vin). Random.

McKay, John. Religion in Judah under the Assyrians. LC 72-97460. (Studies in Biblical Theology, 2nd Ser.: No. 26). 1973. pap. text ed. 10.00x (ISBN 0-8401-3076-7). A R Allenson.

Patai, Raphael. The Jewish Mind. LC 76-58040. 1977. 14.95 (ISBN 0-684-14878-1, ScribT). Scribner.

Rowley, Harold H. Prophecy & Religion in Ancient China & Israel. LC 56-12074. 1956. 12.00x (ISBN 0-8401-2059-1). A R Allenson.

JUDAISM–RELATIONS–CHRISTIANITY

Althouse, LaVonne. When Jew & Christian Meet. (Illus.). 1966. pap. 1.50 (ISBN 0-377-36221-2). Friend Pr.

Arno Press Staff. Judaism & Christianity: Selected Accounts, 1892-1962. LC 73-2212. (The Jewish People; History, Religion, Literature Ser.). 22.00 (ISBN 0-405-05276-6). Ayer Co Pubs.

Croner, Helga. More Stepping Stones to Jewish Christian Relations. (Stimulus Bk.). 240p. (Orig.). 1985. pap. 7.95 (ISBN 0-8091-2708-3). Paulist Pr.

De Lange, N. R. Origen & the Jews. LC 75-36293. (Oriental Publications Ser.: No. 25). 160p. 1977. 39.50 (ISBN 0-521-20542-5). Cambridge U Pr.

DePoncins, Leon V. Judaism & the Vatican. 59.95 (ISBN 0-8490-0466-7). Gordon Pr.

Fleischner, Eva. Judaism in German Christian Theology since 1945: Christianity & Israel Considered in Terms of Mission. LC 75-22374. (ATLA Monograph: No. 8). 205p. 1975. 17.50 (ISBN 0-8108-0835-8). Scarecrow.

Friedman, Jerome. The Most Ancient Testimony: Sixteenth-Century Christian-Hebraica in the Age of Renaissance Nostalgia. LC 82-18830. x, 279p. 1983. text ed. 26.95x (ISBN 0-8214-0700-7). Ohio U Pr.

Grant, Frederick C. Ancient Judaism & the New Testament. LC 77-18848. 1978. Repr. of 1959 ed. lib. bdg. cancelled (ISBN 0-313-20204-4, GRAJ). Greenwood.

Luttikhuizen, Gerard P. The Revelation of Elchasai: Investigations into the Evidence for a Mesopotamian Jewish Apocalypse of the Second Century & Its Reception by Judeo-Christian Propagandists. 263p. 1985. lib. bdg. 60.00x (ISBN 3-16-144935-5, Pub. by J C B Mohr BRD). Coronet Bks.

Marks, Stanley J. & Marks, Ethel M. Judaism Looks at Christianity: 7 BC-1985 C. E. 1985. pap. 19.95; 24.95. Bur Intl Aff.

Maybaum, Ignay. Trialogue Between Jew, Christian & Muslim. (Littman Library of Jewish Civilization). 192p. 1973. 18.50x (ISBN 0-19-710032-5). Oxford U Pr.

Neusner, Jacob & Frerichs, Ernest S., eds. To See Ourselves As Others See Us: Christians Jews, "Others" in Late Antiquity. (Scholars Press Studies in the Humanities). (Orig.). 1985. 38.95 (ISBN 0-89130-819-9, 00-01-09); pap. 25.95 (ISBN 0-89130-820-2). Scholars Pr GA.

Oesterley, William O. The Jewish Background of the Christian Liturgy. 1925. 11.75 (ISBN 0-8446-1329-0). Peter Smith.

--Jews & Judaism During the Greek Period: The Background of Christianity. LC 74-102580. 1970. Repr. of 1941 ed. 23.00x (ISBN 0-8046-0740-0, Pub. by Kennikat). Assoc Faculty Pr.

Oesterreicher, John M. The New Encounter Between Christians & Jews. LC 85-26033. 472p. 1986. 25.00 (ISBN 0-8022-2496-2). Philos Lib.

Parkes, James. Conflict of the Church & the Synagogue: A Study in the Origins of Antisemitism. LC 61-11472. (Temple Books). 1969. pap. text ed. 6.95x (ISBN 0-689-70151-9, T9). Atheneum.

Rhyne, C. Thomas. Faith Establishes the Law. Kee, Howard, ed. LC 81-1794. (Society of Biblical Literature Dissertation Ser.). 1981. pap. 13.50 (ISBN 0-89130-483-5, 06-01-55). Scholars Pr GA.

Sanders, E. P. Jesus & Judaism. LC 84-48806. 448p. 1985. 19.95 (ISBN 0-8006-0743-0, 1-743). Fortress.

Sandmel, Samuel. A Jewish Understanding of the New Testament. 1974. 11.95x (ISBN 0-87068-102-8); pap. 9.95x (ISBN 0-87068-262-8). Ktav.

Schaeffer, Edith. Christianity Is Jewish. 1977. pap. 6.95 (ISBN 0-8423-0242-5). Tyndale.

Schiffman, Lawrence H. Who Was Jew: Rabbinic & Halakhic Perspectives on the Jewish-Christian Schism. (Illus.). 140p. 1985. 14.95 (ISBN 0-88125-053-8); pap. 8.95 (ISBN 0-88125-054-6). Ktav.

Schoffler, Herbert. Abendland und Altes Testament. pap. 10.00 (ISBN 0-384-54210-7). Johnson Repr.

Silcox, Claris E. Catholics, Jews, & Protestants: A Study of Relationships in the United States & Canada. LC 78-21101. 1979. Repr. of 1934 ed. lib. bdg. 24.75x (ISBN 0-313-20882-4, SICJ). Greenwood.

Silverman, William B. Judaism & Christianity. LC 68-27330. pap. 5.95x (ISBN 0-87441-016-9). Behrman.

Simon, Marcal. Verus Israel. McKeating, H., tr. 592p. 1985. 57.00x (ISBN 0-19-710035-X). Oxford U Pr.

Simon, Merill. Jerry Falwell & the Jews. LC 83-22266. 172p. 1983. 12.50 (ISBN 0-8246-0300-1). Jonathan David.

Tal, Uriel. Christians & Jews in Germany: Religion, Politics, & Ideology in the Second Reich, 1870-1914. Jacobs, Noah J., tr. from Hebrew. LC 74-21612. (Illus.). 359p. 1975. 35.00x (ISBN 0-8014-0879-2). Cornell U Pr.

Voss, Carl H. Rabbi & Minister: The Friendship of Stephen S. Wise & John Haynes Holmes. LC 80-7453. (The Library of Liberal Religion). 384p. 1980. pap. 11.95 (ISBN 0-87975-130-4). Prometheus Bks.

Weiss-Rosmarin, Trude. Judaism & Christianity: The Differences. 1965. pap. 4.95 (ISBN 0-8246-0044-4). Jonathan David.

JUDAISM–RELATIONS–ISLAM

Lewis, Bernard. The Jews of Islam. LC 84-42575. (Illus.). 259p. 1984. 42.50x (ISBN 0-691-05419-3). Princeton U Pr.

--The Jews of Islam. 280p. 1987. pap. 8.95 (ISBN 0-691-00807-8). Princeton U Pr.

Maybaum, Ignay. Trialogue Between Jew, Christian & Muslim. (Littman Library of Jewish Civilization). 192p. 1973. 18.50x (ISBN 0-19-710032-5). Oxford U Pr.

Patai, Raphael. The Seed of Abraham: Jews & Arabs in Contact & Conflict. 384p. 1986. 29.95 (ISBN 0-87480-251-2). U of Utah Pr.

Torrey, Charles C. Jewish Foundation of Islam. rev. ed. LC 67-18817. 1968. 20.00x (ISBN 0-87068-117-6). Ktav.

JUDAISM–RITUALS

see Jews–Rites and Ceremonies

JUDAISM–WORKS TO 1900

Abrahams, Israel. The Book of Delight & Other Papers. Katz, Steven, ed. LC 79-7124. (Jewish Philosophy, Mysticism & History of Ideas Ser.). 1980. Repr. of 1912 ed. lib. bdg. 26.50x (ISBN 0-405-12238-1). Ayer Co Pubs.

Grob, Gerald, ed. A Course of Lectures on the Jews: By Ministers of the Established Church in Glasgow. LC 76-46095. (Anti-Movements in America). 1977. lib. bdg. 37.50x (ISBN 0-405-09968-1). Ayer Co Pubs.

Harrington, Daniel J., ed. & tr. from Heb. The Hebrew Fragments of Pseudo-Philo. LC 73-89170. (Socity of Biblical Literature. Texts & Translation-Psuedepigrapha Ser.). 1974. pap. 7.50_o.s. (ISBN 0-88414-036-9, 060203). Scholars Pr GA.

Kraft, Robert A. & Purintun, Ann-Elizabeth. Paraleipomena Jeremiou. LC 72-88436. (Society of Biblical Literature. Texts & Translation-Psuedepigrapha Ser.). 49p. 1972. pap. 8.95 (ISBN 0-89130-169-0, 06 02 01). Scholars Pr GA.

Rosenblatt, Samuel, tr. Saadia Gaon Book of Beliefs & Opinions. (Judaica Ser.: No. 1). 1948. 55.00x (ISBN 0-300-00865-1). Yale U Pr.

Shear-Yashuv, Aharon. The Theology of Salomon Ludwig Steinheim. (Studies in Judaism in Modern Times: Vol. 7). (Illus.). x, 115p. 1986. 27.23 (ISBN 90-04-07670-0, Pub. by E J Brill). Heinman.

JUDAISM, ORTHODOX

see Orthodox Judaism

JUDAISM, RECONSTRUCTIONIST

see Reconstructionist Judaism

JUDAISM, REFORM

see Reform Judaism

JUDAISM AND SOCIAL PROBLEMS

Rotenberg, Mordechai. Dialogue with Deviance: The Hasidic Ethic & the Theory of Social Contraction. LC 81-13309. 224p. 1983. text ed. 27.50 (ISBN 0-89727-031-2). ISHI PA.

Silver, Daniel J. Judaism & Ethics. 1970. 20.00x (ISBN 0-87068-010-2). Ktav.

JUDAISM AND STATE

Assault on the Bill of Rights: The Jewish Stake. LC 83-182603. 1983. 12.00. UAHC.

Friedman, Murray. The Utopian Dilemma: American Judaism & Public Policy. LC 85-7068. 125p. (Orig.). 1985. 12.00 (ISBN 0-89633-092-3); pap. 7.95 (ISBN 0-89633-093-1). Ethics & Public Policy.

Neusner, Jacob. The Public Side of Learning: The Political Consequences of Scholorship in the Context of Judaism. (Studies in Religion). 1985. 17.95 (ISBN 0-89130-860-1); pap. 11.95 (ISBN 0-89130-861-X, 01-00-40). Scholars Pr GA.

JUDAS ISCARIOT

Schaumberg, Ethel L. Judas: The Unforgiven Man. 1981. 4.75 (1002). CSS of Ohio.

JUDAS MACCABAEUS, d. 160 B.C.

Hansen, William P. & Haney, John, eds. Judas Maccabeus. (World Leaders--Past & Present Ser.). (Illus.). 112p. 1987. lib. bdg. 16.95 (ISBN 0-87754-539-1). Chelsea Hse.

JUDGMENT (ETHICS)

Arkes, Hadley. First Things: An Inquiry into the First Principles of Morals & Justice. LC 85-43267. 480p. 1986. text ed. 45.00 (ISBN 0-691-07702-9); pap. 9.95 (ISBN 0-691-02247-X). Princeton U Pr.

Colby, Anne & Kohlberg, Lawrence. The Measurement of Moral Judgement, 2 vols, Vols. 1-2. Date not set. Vol. 1: Theoretical Foundations & Research, 425 pgs. price not set (ISBN 0-521-24447-1); Vol. 2: Standard Issue Scoring Manual, 1200 pgs. price not set (ISBN 0-521-32501-3); price not set (ISBN 0-521-32565-X). Cambridge U Pr.

Muelder, Walter G. Moral Law in Christian Social Ethics. LC 66-15972. 198p. lib. bdg. 19.95x (ISBN 0-88946-011-6). E Mellen.

Raphael, David D. Moral Judgment. LC 77-28440. 1978. Repr. of 1955 ed. lib. bdg. 22.25x (ISBN 0-313-20246-X, RAMJ). Greenwood.
Ravenhill, Leonard. The Judgement Seat of Christ: Your Day in Court. 200p. (Orig.). 1986. pap. 6.95 (ISBN 0-910311-34-X). Huntington Hse Inc.
Yerman, Ron. Religion: Innocent or Guilty. LC 85-90019. 180p. 1985. 11.95 (ISBN 0-533-06540-2). Vantage.

JUDGMENT DAY
see also Second Advent
Batman, Stephen. Doom & Warning All Men to the Judgement. LC 84-1441. 1984. Repr. of 1581 ed. 60.00x (ISBN 0-8201-1393-X). Schol Facsimiles.
Brown, Vinson, et al. Prevent Doomsday! Anti-Nuclear Anthology. new ed. (Illus.). 96p. 1983. pap. 4.95 (ISBN 0-8283-1875-1). Branden Pub Co.
Collins, Adela Y. Apocalypse. (New Testament Message Ser.: Vol. 22). 172p. 1979. 9.95 (ISBN 0-89453-210-3); pap. 6.95 (ISBN 0-89453-145-X). M Glazier.
Culligan, Emmett J. The Last World War & the End of Time. (Illus.). 210p. 1981. pap. 6.00 (ISBN 0-89555-034-2). TAN Bks Pubs.
Jonsson, Carl O. & Herbst, Wolfgang. The "Sign" of the Last Days--When? LC 86-72140. (Illus.). 288p. 1987. pap. 7.95 (ISBN 0-914675-09-5). Comment Pr.
Kenna. Man's Judgement Call-the Irrevocable Master Contract. Date not set. price not set. Port Love Intl.
Kettler, Wilfried. Das Juengste Gericht Philologische Studien zu den Eschatologie Vorstellungen in den Alt-und Fruehmittel-Hochdeutschen Denkmaelern. (Quellen und Forschungen Zur Sprach-und Kulturgeschichte der Germanischen Voelker: Vol.70). 1977. 38.80x (ISBN 3-11-007345-5). De Gruyter.
LaSor, William S. The Truth about Armageddon. 240p. 1987. pap. 6.95 (ISBN 0-8010-5637-3). Baker Bk.
Lindsay, Gordon. The Great Day of the Lord. (Revelation Ser.). 1.25 (ISBN 0-89985-037-5). Christ Nations.
--The Great Judgment Throne & the Seven Seals. (Revelation Ser.). 1.25 (ISBN 0-89985-036-7). Christ Nations.
--The Great Trumpets & the Vial Judgments. (End of the Age Ser.: Vol. 6). 1.25 (ISBN 0-89985-072-3). Christ Nations.
--The Judgment Seat of Christ, Vol. 7. (End of the Age Ser.). 1.25 (ISBN 0-89985-073-1). Christ Nations.
--The Vial Judgments, or, The Seven Last Plagues. (Revelation Ser.). 1.25 (ISBN 0-89985-045-6). Christ Nations.
Morse, Charlotte C. The Pattern of Judgement in the "Queste" & "Cleanness". LC 77-25158. (Illus.). 248p. 1978. 19.00x (ISBN 0-8262-0242-X). U of Mo Pr.
Prince, Derek. Eternal Judgment. (Foundation Ser.: Bk. VII). 1965-66. pap. 2.95 (ISBN 0-934920-06-0, B-16). Derek Prince.
Ravenhill, Leonard. The Judgement Seat of Christ: Your Day in Court. 200p. (Orig.). 1986. pap. 6.95 (ISBN 0-910311-34-X). Huntington Hse Inc.
Sayers, Stanley E. The Nature of Things to Come. 1972. 7.95 (ISBN 0-88027-013-6). Firm Foun Pub.
Swedenborg, Emanuel. Apocalypse Explained, 6 vols. Student ed. LC 76-46145. 12.00 ea. Vol. 1 (ISBN 0-87785-000-3). Vol. 2 (ISBN 0-87785-001-1). Vol. 3 (ISBN 0-87785-002-X). Vol. 4 (ISBN 0-87785-003-8). Vol. 5 (ISBN 0-87785-004-6). Vol. 6 (ISBN 0-87785-005-4). 72.00 set (ISBN 0-87785-006-2). Swedenborg.

JUDSON, ADONIRAM, 1788-1850
Bailey, Faith C. Adoniram Judson. (Golden Oldies Ser.). 128p. 1980. pap. 3.50 (ISBN 0-8024-0287-9). Moody.
Conant, D. C. The Earnest Man; or the Character & Labors of Adoniram Judson. 1978. Repr. of 1856 ed. lib. bdg. 20.00 (ISBN 0-8492-3943-5). R West.

JUDSON, ANN (HASSELTINE) MRS., 1789-1826
Hubbard, Ethel D. Ann of Ava. LC 76-160921. (Biography Index Reprint Ser.). (Illus.). Repr. of 1941 ed. 17.25 (ISBN 0-8369-8084-0). Ayer Co Pubs.
Pitman, E. R. Ann H. Judson of Burma. 1974. pap. 2.95 (ISBN 0-87508-601-2). Chr Lit.

JULIUS 2ND, POPE, 1443-1513
Colledge, Edmund, et al, eds. Julian of Norwich, "Showings". LC 77-90953. (Classics of Western Spirituality). 384p. 1978. 13.95 (ISBN 0-8091-0234-X); pap. 9.95 (ISBN 0-8091-2091-7). Paulist Pr.
Count Gobineau, Arthur. The Renaissance Savonarola. Levy, Oscar, ed. Cohen, Paul V., tr. (Fr., Illus.). 349p. 1986. Repr. of 1913 ed. lib. bdg. 75.00 (ISBN 0-89760-264-1). Telegraph Bks.
Gobineau, Joseph A. Golden Flower. facsimile ed. Redman, B. R., tr. LC 68-54347. (Essay Index Reprint Ser). 1924. 15.00 (ISBN 0-8369-0477-X). Ayer Co Pubs.

JUNG, CARL GUSTAV, 1875-1961
Avens, Roberts. Imaginal Body: Para-Jungian Reflections on Soul, Imagination & Death. LC 81-43814. 264p. (Orig.). 1982. lib. bdg. 29.00 (ISBN 0-8191-2411-7); pap. text ed. 13.25 (ISBN 0-8191-2412-5). U Pr of Amer.
Bryant, Christopher. Jung & the Christian Way. 144p. (Orig.). 1984. pap. 7.95 (ISBN 0-86683-872-4, 7917, HarpR). Har-Row.
Clift, Wallace B. Jung & Christianity: The Challenge of Reconciliation. 169p. 1982. 12.95 (ISBN 0-8245-0409-7). Crossroad NY.
--Jung & Christianity: The Challenge of Reconciliation. LC 81-17395. 192p. 1983. pap. 8.95 (ISBN 0-8245-0552-2). Crossroad NY.
Cowan, Lyn. Masochism: A Jungian View. LC 82-16957. 137p. (Orig.). 1982. pap. 12.00 (ISBN 0-88214-320-4). Spring Pubns.
Evans, Richard I. Dialogue with C. G. Jung. LC 81-15371. 256p. 1981. 36.95 (ISBN 0-03-059927-X). Praeger.
Gay, Volney P. Reading Jung: Science, Psychology, & Religion. LC 84-1322. (AAR-Studies in Religion). 166p. 1984. pap. 8.25 (ISBN 0-89130-731-1, 01 00 34). Scholars Pr GA.
Heisig, James W. Imago Dei: A Study of C. G. Jung's Psychology of Religion. LC 77-74405. 256p. 1978. 26.50 (ISBN 0-8387-2076-5). Bucknell U Pr.
Hillman, James, ed. Spring 1982: An Annual of Archetypal Psychology & Jungian Thought. 316p. (Orig.). 1982. pap. 15.00 (ISBN 0-88214-017-5). Spring Pubns.
Hoeller, Stephen. The Gnostic Jung & the Seven Sermons to the Dead. LC 82-50220. 282p. (Orig.). 1982. 13.95 (ISBN 0-8356-0573-6). Theos Pub Hse.
Jung, Emma & Von Franz, Marie-Louise. The Grail Legend. 452p. (Orig.). 1986. 27.50 (ISBN 0-938434-07-1); pap. 14.95 (ISBN 0-938434-08-X). Sigo Pr.
Kelsey, Morton T. Prophetic Ministry: The Psychology & Spirituality of Pastoral Care. 258p. 1982. 12.95 (ISBN 0-8245-0441-0). Crossroad NY.
Martin, Luther H. & Goss, James, eds. Essays on Jung & the Study of Religion. LC 85-17865. 214p. (Orig.). 1986. lib. bdg. 29.50 (ISBN 0-8191-4923-3); pap. text ed. 12.75 (ISBN 0-8191-4924-1). U Pr of Amer.
Meier, C. A. The Psychology of C. G. Jung. Rolfe, Eugene, tr. (The Unconscious in Its Empirical Manifestations Ser.: Vol. I). (Illus.). 256p. 1985. 25.50 (ISBN 0-938434-10-1). Sigo Pr.
Mooney, Lucindi F. Storming Eastern Temples. LC 76-4903. 1976. 9.75x (ISBN 0-8356-0482-9). Theos Pub Hse.
Moreno, Antonio. Jung, Gods, & Modern Man. LC 73-122047. pap. 72.00 (ISBN 0-317-29683-3, 2022073). Bks Demand UMI.
Rollins, Wayne G. Jung & the Bible. LC 82-48091. 156p. 1983. pap. 10.95 (ISBN 0-8042-1117-5). John Knox.
Stein, Murray. Jung's Treatment of Christianity: The Psychotherapy of a Religious Tradition. 2nd ed. LC 85-4739. 194p. 1985. 24.95 (ISBN 0-933029-14-4). Chiron Pubns.
Stein, Murray & Moore, Robert, eds. Jung's Challenge to Contemporary Religion. 175p. 1987. pap. 14.95 (ISBN 0-933029-09-8). Chiron Pubns.
Stern, E. Mark, ed. Carl Jung & Soul Psychology. Tr. of Voices: The Art & Science of Psychotherapy. 196p. (Orig.). Repr. of 1986 ed. text ed. write for info. (ISBN 0-86656-632-5). Haworth Pr.
Welch, John. Spiritual Pilgrims: Carl Jung & Teresa of Avila. LC 82-80164. 208p. 1982. 8.95 (ISBN 0-8091-2454-8). Paulist Pr.
Wilmer, Harry A. Practical Jung: Nuts & Bolts of Jungian Psychotherapy. 250p. 1987. 17.95 (ISBN 0-933029-16-0). Chiron Pubns.

JUNIPERUS, OF ASISSI, BROTHER, 13TH CENTURY
Bodo, Murray. Juniper: Friend of Francis, Fool of God. 90p. pap. text ed. cancelled (ISBN 0-86716-021-7). St Anthony Mess Pr.

JUSTICE
Dengevin, K. The Idea of Justice in Christian Perspective. 1978. pap. 2.95 (ISBN 0-88906-102-5). Radix Bks.
Kaplan, Morton A. Justice, Human Nature, & Political Obligation. LC 76-8145. 1976. 18.95 (ISBN 0-02-916890-2). Free Pr.
Kelly, Margaret, ed. Justice & Health Care: Christian Perspectives. LC 84-9459. 1985. pap. 16.50 (ISBN 0-87125-097-7). Cath Health.
Kiefer, Howard E. & Munitz, Milton K., eds. Ethics & Social Justice. (Contemporary Philosophic Thought: Vol. 4). 1970. 49.50 (ISBN 0-87395-054-2). State U NY Pr.
Krolikowski, Walter, ed. Faith & Justice. 174p. 1982. pap. text ed. 6.95 (ISBN 0-8294-0397-3). Loyola.
Lebacqz, Karen. Six Theories of Justice: Perspectives from Philosophical & Theological Ethics. LC 86-26457. 144p. (Orig.). 1986. pap. 9.95 (ISBN 0-8066-2245-8, 10-5820). Augsburg.
McGeachy, Pat. Beyond the Facts, Acts. (Orig.). 1973. pap. 1.95 (ISBN 0-377-03051-1). Friend Pr.
Marongiu, Pietro & Newman, Graeme. Vengeance: The Fight Against Injustice. 176p. 1987. 27.50. Rowman.
Niebuhr, Reinhold. Love & Justice: Selections from the Shorter Writings of Reinhold Niebuhr. Robertson, D. B., ed. 12.50 (ISBN 0-8446-2659-7). Peter Smith.
O'Brien, David J. & Shannon, Thomas A., eds. Renewing the Earth: Catholic Documents on Peace, Justice & Liberation. LC 76-52008. 1977. pap. 6.95 (ISBN 0-385-12954-8, Im). Doubleday.
Peace Education Council & Sister Loretta Carey. Directions for Justice-Peace Education in the Catholic Elementary School. 44p. 1985. 4.80 (ISBN 0-318-20608-0). Natl Cath Educ.
St. Thomas Aquinas. Political Ideas of St. Thomas Aquinas. Bigongiari, Dino, ed. (Library of Classics Ser.: No. 15). 1973. pap. text ed. 7.95x (ISBN 0-02-840380-0). Hafner.
Tillich, Paul. Love, Power & Justice. 1954. pap. 7.95 (ISBN 0-19-500222-9). Oxford U Pr.
True, Michael. Homemade Social Justice: Teaching Peace & Justice in the Home. 2nd ed. 168p. 1983. pap. 5.95 (ISBN 0-89622-202-0). Twenty-Third.
Wilczak, Paul F., ed. Healing in the Family. LC 79-53515. (Marriage & Family Living in Depth Bk.). 1979. pap. 2.45 (ISBN 0-87029-158-0, 20244-0). Abbey.
Wright, Elliott. Go Free. 128p. (Orig.). 1973. pap. 1.75 (ISBN 0-377-03011-2). Friend Pr.

JUSTIFICATION
see also Assurance (Theology); Faith; Law and Gospel
Buchanan, James. The Doctrine of Justification. 514p. 1985. Repr. of 1867 ed. 15.95 (ISBN 0-85151-440-5). Banner of Truth.
Bull, George. Harmony on Justification, Defense of the Nicene Creed, Judgement of the Catholic Church, 5 vols. LC 71-39556. (Library of Anglo-Catholic Theology: No. 4). Repr. of 1855 ed. Set. 150.00 (ISBN 0-404-52070-7). AMS Pr.
De Soto, Domingo. De Natura et Gratia. 612p. Repr. of 1549 ed. text ed. 99.36 (ISBN 0-576-99423-5, Pub. by Gregg Intl Pubs England). Gregg Intl.
Gerstner, John H. A Primer on Justification. 32p. 1983. pap. 1.50 (ISBN 0-87552-276-9). Presby & Reformed.
Hordern, William. Living by Grace. LC 75-6548. 208p. 1975. pap. 7.95 (ISBN 0-664-24763-6). Westminster.
Justification. pap. 1.25 (ISBN 0-686-12888-5). Schmul Pub Co.
McGrath, Alister E. Iustitia Dei: A History of the Doctrine of Justification. 250p. 1986. 39.50 (ISBN 0-521-30887-9). Cambridge U Pr.
Pappas, George S. & Swain, Marshall, eds. Essays on Knowledge & Justification. LC 77-10299. (Illus.). 384p. 1978. 42.50x (ISBN 0-8014-1086-X); pap. 10.95x (ISBN 0-8014-9865-1). Cornell U Pr.
Servetus, Michael. Two Treatises of Servetus on the Trinity. Wilbur, Earl M., tr. (Harvard Theological Studies). 1932. 24.00 (ISBN 0-527-01016-2). Kraus Repr.
Tavard, George H. Justification: An Ecumenical Study. 144p. (Orig.). 1983. pap. 7.95 (ISBN 0-8091-2549-8). Paulist Pr.
Wiersbe, Warren W. Be Right. LC 77-154327. 175p. 1977. pap. 5.95 (ISBN 0-88207-729-5). Victor Bks.

JUSTIFICATION–HISTORY OF DOCTRINES
Buchanan, James. The Doctrine of Justification. 514p. 1985. Repr. of 1867 ed. 15.95 (ISBN 0-85151-440-5). Banner of Truth.
Leaver, Robin A. Luther on Justification. LC 74-11781. 1975. pap. 4.75 (ISBN 0-570-03188-5, 12-2590). Concordia.
McGrath, Alister E. Iustitia Dei: A History of the Doctrine of Justification, Vol. II--From the Reformation to the Present Day. 272p. 1986. 39.50 (ISBN 0-521-32274-X). Cambridge U Pr.

JUVENILE DRINKING
see Alcohol and Youth

JUVENILE LITERATURE
see Children's Literature (Collections)

K

KABBALA
see Cabala

KAFIRS (AFRICAN PEOPLE)
see also Zulus
Hewat, Matthew L. Bantu Folk Lore. LC 77-129948. Repr. of 1906 ed. 22.50x (ISBN 0-8371-4992-4, HBF&, Pub. by Negro U Pr). Greenwood.

KAGAWA, TOYOHIKO, 1888-1960
Davey, Cyril. Saint in the Slums (Kagawa of Japan) 1968. pap. 2.95 (ISBN 0-87508-620-9). Chr Lit.

KAHANE, MEIR, 1932-
Breslauer, S. Daniel. Meir Kahane, Ideologue, Hero, & Thinker. LC 86-21703. (Jewish Studies: Vol. 1). 168p. 1986. text ed. 39.95x (ISBN 0-88946-252-6). E Mellen.
Kotler, Yair. Heil Kahane: The Life of a Fanatic Whose Influence is Growing. Levin, Ed, tr. from Hebrew. LC 86-1035. 212p. 1986. 17.95 (ISBN 0-915361-35-3, 09712-9, Dist. by Watts). Adama Pubs Inc.

KAILA
see Falashas

KAIRWAN MOSQUE OF SIDI OKBA
Boddy, A. A. To Kairwan the Holy. 320p. 1985. 49.00x (ISBN 0-317-39199-2, Pub. by Luzac & Co Ltd). State Mutual Bk.

KALAM
see Islamic Theology

KALI
Kinsley, David R. The Sword & the Flute-Kali & Krsna: Dark Visions of the Terrible & the Sublime in Hindu Mythology. LC 73-91669. (Hermeneutics: Studies in the History of Religions). 175p. 1975. pap. 10.95x (ISBN 0-520-03510-0). U of Cal Pr.
Noble, Margaret. Kali the Mother. 110p. 1985. pap. 2.00 (ISBN 0-87481-104-X, Pub. by Advaita Ashrama India). Vedanta Pr.
Woodroffe, John. Hymns to the Goddess - Hymn to Kali. LC 81-84749. 350p. 1982. 11.00 (ISBN 0-941524-00-0). Lotus Light.

KANNA'IM
see Zealots (Jewish Party)

KANT, IMMANUEL, 1724-1804
Allison, Henry E. Kant's Transcendental Idealism. LC 85-5756. 400p. 1986. 12.95x (ISBN 0-300-03629-9, Y-567). Yale U Pr.
Andersen, Svend. Ideal und Singularitat: Uber die Funktion des Gottesbegriffes in Kants theoretischer Philosophie. 278p. 1983. 28.80 (ISBN 3-11-009649-8). De Gruyter.
Arendt, Hannah. Lectures on Kant's Political Philosophy. Beiner, Ronald, ed. LC 82-4817. 192p. 1982. 17.50 (ISBN 0-226-02594-2). U of Chicago Pr.
Aune, Bruce. Kant's Theory of Morals. LC 79-17938. 1980. 26.50 (ISBN 0-691-07238-8). Princeton U Pr.
Auxter, Thomas. Kant's Moral Teleology. LC 82-7838. xvi, 194p. 1982. 16.95 (ISBN 0-86554-022-5, MUP-H23). Mercer Univ Pr.
Ewing, A. C. A Short Commentary on Kant's "Critique of Pure Reason". viii, 278p. Date not set. pap. text ed. 16.00 (ISBN 0-226-22779-0, Midway Reprint). U of Chicago Pr.
Gauchhwal, B. S. Concept of Perfection in the Teachings of Kant & the Gita. 1967. 4.95 (ISBN 0-89684-186-3). Orient Bk Dist.
Gram, Moltke S. The Transcendental Turn: The/Foundation of Kant's Idealism. LC 84-22047. xii, 260p. 1985. 30.00 (ISBN 0-8130-0787-9). U Presses Fla.
Gram, Moltke S., ed. Interpreting Kant. LC 82-13627. 1982. text ed. 18.00 (ISBN 0-87745-118-4). U of Iowa Pr.
Hegel, G. W. Faith & Knowledge: The Reflective Philosophy of Subjectivity. Harris, H. S. & Cerf, Walter, eds. Harris, H. S. & Cerf, Walter., trs. from Ger. LC 76-10250. 1977. 39.50 (ISBN 0-87395-338-X). State U NY Pr.
Heidegger, Martin. What Is a Thing? Barton, W. B. & Deutsch, Vera, trs. from Ger. 320p. 1985. pap. text ed. 8.75 (ISBN 0-8191-4545-9). U Pr of Amer.
Howard, Claud. Coleridge's Idealism. LC 72-191125. 1924. lib. bdg. 17.50 (ISBN 0-8414-5131-1). Folcroft.
Kant, Immanuel. The Reconstruction in Schematic Representations of Kant's Psychological Theory of God. (Illus.). 110p. 1983. 87.45x (ISBN 0-89266-430-4). Am Classical Coll Pr.
Michalson, G. E. The Historical Dimensions of Rational Faith: The Role of History in Kant's Religious Thought. 1977. 12.25 (ISBN 0-8191-0308-X). U Pr of Amer.
Monarch Notes in Kant's Philosophy. pap. 2.95 (ISBN 0-671-00530-8). Monarch Pr.
Novak, David. Suicide & Morality: The Theories of Plato, Aquinas & Kant & Their Relevance for Suicidology. LC 75-37543. x, 136p. 1976. lib. bdg. 7.50 (ISBN 0-685-69079-2). Scholars Studies.

Palmer, Humphrey. Presupposition & Transcendental Inference. LC 84-18384. 108p. 1985. 27.50 (ISBN 0-312-64173-7). St Martin.

Peccorini, Francisco L. On to the World of "Freedom": A Kantian Meditation on Finite Selfhood. LC 82-40233. 370p. (Orig.). 1982. lib. bdg. 30.25 o. p. (ISBN 0-8191-2643-8); pap. text ed. 15.75 (ISBN 0-8191-2644-6). U Pr of Amer.

Richardson, J. & Co. Staff. Book of Kant, Vol. 5. 1983. 57.50x (ISBN 0-317-54273-7, Pub. by J Richardson UK); pap. 40.00x (ISBN 0-317-54274-5). State Mutual Bk.

Riley, Patrick. Kant's Political Philosophy. LC 82-573. (Philosophy & Society Ser.). 224p. 1983. text ed. 31.50x (ISBN 0-8476-6763-4). Rowman.

Ross, Sir William D. Kant's Ethical Theory: A Commentary on the Grundlegung zur Metaphysik der Sitten. LC 78-6730. 1978. Repr. of 1954 ed. lib. bdg. 22.50x (ISBN 0-8371-9059-2, ROKE). Greenwood.

Schalow, Frank. Imagination & Existence: Heidegger's Retrieval of the Kantian Ethic. 192p. (Orig.). 1986. lib. bdg. 24.75 (ISBN 0-8191-5114-9); pap. text ed. 11.75 (ISBN 0-8191-5115-7). U Pr of Amer.

Scheler, Max. Formalism in Ethics & Non-Formal Ethics of Values: A New Attempt Toward the Foundation of an Ethical Personalism. Frings, Manfred S. & Funk, Roger L., trs. from Ger. LC 72-97416. (Studies in Phenomenology & Existential Philosophy). Orig. Title: Der Formalismus der Ethik und die Materiale Wertethik. 750p. 1973. text ed. 29.95 (ISBN 0-8101-0415-6); 14.95 (ISBN 0-8101-0620-5). Northwestern U Pr.

Seth, Andrew. The Development from Kant to Hegel. 1975. lib. bdg. 49.95 (ISBN 0-8490-0020-3). Gordon Pr.

--The Development from Kant to Hegel, with Chapters on the Philosophy of Religion. Beck, Lewis W., ed. LC 75-32044. (The Philosophy of Immanuel Kant Ser.: Vol. 7). 1976. Repr. of 1882 ed. lib. bdg. 24.00 (ISBN 0-8240-2331-5). Garland Pub.

Shell, Susan M. The Rights of Reason: A Study of Kant's Philosophy & Politics. LC 79-19801. 1979. 23.50x (ISBN 0-8020-5462-5). U of Toronto Pr.

Somerset, Douglas P. The Destructive Conception of God in Kant's "Philosophy of Man". (Illus.). 129p. 1982. 73.45 (ISBN 0-89266-355-3). Am Classical Coll Pr.

Walker, Ralph C. Kant. 1982. pap. 10.95 (ISBN 0-7100-0009-X). Methuen Inc.

Walker, Ralph C., ed. Kant on Pure Reason. (Illus.). 1982. pap. text ed. 7.95x (ISBN 0-19-875056-0). Oxford U Pr.

Walsh, W. H. Kant's Moral Theology. (Dawes Hicks Lectures on Philosophy). 1963. pap. 2.25 (ISBN 0-85672-270-7, Pub. by British Acad). Longwood Pub Group.

Webb, C. J. Kant's Philosophy of Religion. Repr. of 1926 ed. 18.00 (ISBN 0-527-94912-4). Kraus Repr.

Wenley, R. M. Kant & His Philosophical Revolution. 302p. 1982. Repr. of 1910 ed. lib. bdg. 40.00 (ISBN 0-89987-894-6). Darby Bks.

Wood, Allen W. Kant's Rational Theology. LC 78-58059. 144p. 1978. 22.50x (ISBN 0-8014-1200-5). Cornell U Pr.

KARAITES

Al-Qirqisani, Ya'Qub. Kitab Al-Anwar Wal-Maraoib: Code of Karaite Law, 3 vols. Incl. Vol. 1. First Discourse - Historical Introduction; Second Discourse - Philosophical & Theological Principles of JurisPrudence; Vol. 2. Third Discourse - Criticism of Sectarian Doctrines; Fourth Discourse - Methods of Construction & Interpretation of Law; Vol. 3. Fifth Discourse - Circumcion - Sabbath; Sixth Discourse - Civil & Criminal Law Liturgy. pap. 49.50 ea. in arabic; Set. pap. 125.00x (ISBN 0-686-52167-6). Elliots Bks.

Ankori, Zvi. Karaites in Byzantium: The Formative Years, 970-1100. LC 71-158258. (Columbia University Studies in the Social Sciences: No. 597). Repr. of 1959 ed. 28.50 (ISBN 0-404-51597-5). AMS Pr.

Mann, Jacob. Texts & Studies in Jewish History & Literature, 2 Vols. rev. ed. 1970. Set. 99.50x (ISBN 0-87068-085-4). Ktav.

Nemoy, Leon, tr. Karaite Anthology: Excerpts from the Early Literature. (Judaica Ser.: No. 7). 1952. 45.00x (ISBN 0-300-00792-2). Yale U Pr.

Schecter, Solomon. Documents of Jewish Sectaries, 2 Vols. in 1. rev. ed. (Library of Biblical Studies Ser). (Illus.). 1970. 35.00 (ISBN 0-87068-016-1). Ktav.

KARMA

see also Anthroposophy

Abhedananda, Swami. Doctrine of Karma. 5.95 (ISBN 0-87481-608-4). Vedanta Pr.

Anand, Kewal K. Indian Philosophy: The Concept of Karma. 396p. 1982. 34.95 (ISBN 0-940500-91-4, Pub by Bharatiya Vidya Prakashan India). Asia Bk Corp.

Bajaj, Harbhajan S. Meaning of Things in Life. 1986. 6.95 (ISBN 0-533-06697-2). Vantage.

--What Is Karma & All about God. 1987. 6.95 (ISBN 0-533-06697-2). Vantage.

Besant. Study in Karma. 2.25 (ISBN 0-8356-7292-1). Theos Pub Hse.

Besant, Annie. Karma. 10th ed. 1975. 3.50 (ISBN 0-8356-7035-X). Theos Pub Hse.

Bhikshu, Yogi. Karma Yoga. 1928. 6.00 (ISBN 0-911662-20-0). Yoga.

Birdsong, Robert E. Physical Experience & Karmic Liability. (Aquarian Academy Monograph: Ser. A, Lecture No. 6). 38p. 1977. pap. 1.50 (ISBN 0-917108-20-5). Sirius Bks.

Blavatsky, Helena P., et al. Karma Lore: One. 71p. (Orig.). 1983. pap. 3.95 (ISBN 0-912181-02-8). East School Pr.

Carus, Paul. Karma Nirvana: Two Buddhist Tales. LC 73-82781. (Illus.). 160p. 1973. 15.95 (ISBN 0-87548-249-X); pap. 6.95 (ISBN 0-87548-359-3). Open Court.

Chapple, Christopher. Karma & Creativity. (Religion Ser.). 128p. (Orig.). 1986. 29.50x (ISBN 0-88706-250-4); pap. 9.95x (ISBN 0-88706-251-2). State U NY Pr.

Damian-Knight, Guy. Karma & Destiny in the I Ching. 256p. 1987. pap. 12.95 (ISBN 1-85063-038-0, 30380, Ark Paperbks). Methuen Inc.

Hanson, Virginia, ed. Karma. 2nd rev. ed. Stewart, Rosemarie. LC 80-53951. 200p. 1980. pap. 4.95 (ISBN 0-8356-0543-4, Quest). Theos Pub Hse.

Humphreys, Christmas. Karma & Rebirth. 110p. 1983. pap. 5.75 (ISBN 0-8356-0306-7, Quest). Theos Pub Hse.

Keyes, Charles F. & Daniel, E. Valentine. Karma: An Anthropological Inquiry. LC 81-19719. 328p. 1983. text ed. 33.00x (ISBN 0-520-04429-0). U of Cal Pr.

LaFleur, William R. The Karma of Words: Buddhism & the Literary Arts in Medieval Japan. LC 82-45909. 232p. 1983. text ed. 30.00x (ISBN 0-520-04600-5); pap. 9.95 (ISBN 0-520-05622-1, CAL764). U of Cal Pr.

MacGregor, Geddes. The Christening of Karma. LC 83-40234. 200p. (Orig.). 1984. pap. 6.95 (ISBN 0-8356-0581-7, Quest). Theos Pub Hse.

Perinbanayagam, R. S. The Karmic Theater: Self, Society & Astrology in Jaffna. LC 82-6997. 224p. 1982. lib. bdg. 22.50x (ISBN 0-87023-374-2). U of Mass Pr.

Rama, Swami. Freedom from the Bondage of Karma. 2nd ed. 92p. pap. 5.95 (ISBN 0-89389-031-6). Himalayan Pubs.

Saraydarian, Torkom. Questioning Traveller & Karma. 1979. pap. 2.50 (ISBN 0-911794-45-X). Aqua Educ.

Schulman, Martin. Karmic Relationships. LC 84-51376. 1984. pap. 7.95 (ISBN 0-87728-508-X). Weiser.

Sharma, I. C. Cayce, Karma & Reincarnation. LC 81-23214. 186p. 1982. pap. 5.50 (ISBN 0-8356-0563-9, Quest). Theos Pub Hse.

Steiner, Rudolf. The Karma of Materialism. Tr. of Menschliche und menschheitliche Entwicklungswanrheiten. 173p. (Orig.). 1986. 20.00 (ISBN 0-88010-130-X); pap. 9.95 (ISBN 0-88010-129-6). Anthroposophic.

--The Karma of Vocation. 2nd ed. Mollenhauer, Peter & Church, Gilbert, eds. Wannamaker, Olin, et al, trs. from Ger. 270p. 1984. 17.00 (ISBN 0-88010-085-0); pap. 10.95 (ISBN 0-88010-086-9). Anthroposophic.

--Karmic Relationships, 8 vols. Incl. Vol. 1. 205p. 14.50 (ISBN 0-85440-260-8); Vol. 2. 1974. 14.50 (ISBN 0-85440-281-0); Vol. 3. 12.95 (ISBN 0-85440-313-2); Vol. 4. 157p. 1983. 14.00 (ISBN 0-85440-412-0); Vol. 5. 10.95 (ISBN 0-685-36131-4); Vol. 6. 14.50 (ISBN 0-85440-242-X); Vol. 7. 140p. 1973. 9.95 (ISBN 0-85440-276-4); Vol. 8. 102p. 1975. 9.95 (ISBN 0-85440-018-4). Anthroposophic.

--Karmic Relationships: Esoteric Studies, Vol. I. Adams, George, tr. from Ger. 205p. 1981. 14.50 (ISBN 0-85440-260-8, Pub by Steinerbooks). Anthroposophic.

--Karmic Relationships: Esoteric Studies, Vol. 2. Adams, George & Cotterell, M., trs. from Ger. Davy, C. & Osmond, D. S. 1974. 14.50 (ISBN 0-85440-281-0, Pub. by Steinerbooks). Anthroposophic.

--Karmic Relationships: Esoteric Studies, Vol. 4. 2nd ed. Adams, George, et al, trs. 157p. 1983. 14.00 (ISBN 0-85440-412-0, Pub by Steinerbooks). Anthroposophic.

--Karmic Relationships: Esoteric Studies, Vol. 7. Osmond, D. S., tr. from Ger. 140p. 1973. 9.95 (ISBN 0-85440-276-4, Pub. by Steinerbooks). Anthroposophic.

--Karmic Relationships: Esoteric Studies, Vol. 8. Osmond, D. S., tr. from Ger. Orig. Title: Cosmic Christianity & the Impulse of Michael. 102p. 1975. 9.95 (ISBN 0-85440-018-4, Pub. by Steinerbooks). Anthroposophic.

--Karmic Relationships: Esoteric Studies (The Karmic Relationships of the Anthroposophics Movement, Vol. 3. 3rd ed. Adams, George, tr. 179p. 1977. 12.95 (ISBN 0-85440-313-2, Pub. by Steinerbooks). Anthroposophic.

--Manifestations of Karma. 3rd ed. 262p. 1984. pap. 10.95 (ISBN 0-317-18543-8, Pub. by Steinerbooks). Anthroposophic.

Szekely, Edmond B. Creative Work: Karma Yoga. (Illus.). 32p. 1973. pap. 2.95 (ISBN 0-89564-066-X). IBS Intl.

Van Pelt, Gertrude W. The Doctrine of Karma. Small, W. Emmett & Todd, Helen, eds. (Theosophical Manual: No. 3). 64p. 1975. pap. 2.00 (ISBN 0-913004-16-2). Point Loma Pub.

Woodward, Mary A. Edgar Cayce's Story of Karma. 1984. pap. 3.50 (ISBN 0-425-07697-0, Medallion). Berkley Pub.

KARNAK, EGYPT

Epigraphic Survey - Reliefs & Inscriptions at Karnak, 3 vols. Incl. Vol. 1. Ramses the Third's Temple Within the Great Inclosure of Amon, Part One. Nelson, Harold H. (Oriental Institute Pubns. Ser: No. 25). 1936. 60.00x (ISBN 0-226-62121-9); Vol. 2. Ramses the Third's Temple Within the Inclosure of Amon, Part Two, & Ramses the Third's Temple in the Precinct of Mut. (Oriental Institute Pubns. Ser: No. 35). 1936. 60.00x (ISBN 0-226-62132-4); Vol. 3. The Bubastic Portal. Hughes, George R. (Oriental Institute Pubns. Ser: No. 74). 1954. 50.00x (ISBN 0-226-62175-8). LC 36-11240. U of Chicago Pr.

Epigraphic Survey. The Temple of Khonsu: Vol. 2, Scenes & Inscriptions in the Court & the First Hypostyle Hall. LC 80-82999. (Oriental Institute Publications Ser.: Vol. 103). 1981. pap. 95.00x incl. 96 plates in portfolio (ISBN 0-918986-29-X). Oriental Inst.

KEBLE, JOHN, 1792-1866

Coleridge, John T. A Memoir of the Rev. John Keble, 2 vols. in 1. 2nd rev. ed. LC 75-30019. Repr. of 1869 ed. 38.50 (ISBN 0-404-14024-6). AMS Pr.

Donaldson, Augustas B. Five Great Oxford Leaders: Keble, Newman, Pusey, Liddon & Church. 1978. Repr. of 1900 ed. lib. bdg. 35.00 (ISBN 0-8495-1036-8). Arden Lib.

Griffin, John R. John Keble, Saint of Anglicanism. 128p. 1987. 24.95 (ISBN 0-86554-249-X). Mercer Univ Pr.

Lock, Walter. John Keble. 1977. Repr. of 1895 ed. lib. bdg. 20.00 (ISBN 0-8495-3221-3). Arden Lib.

--John Keble. 1895. Repr. 20.00 (ISBN 0-8274-2626-7). R West.

Martin, Brian W. John Keble: Priest, Professor & Poet. 191p. 1976. 25.00 (ISBN 0-85664-381-5, Pub. by Croom Helm Ltd). Methuen Inc.

Wood, Edward L. John Keble: Leaders of the Church 1800-1900. Russell, George W., ed. 1909. Repr. 25.00 (ISBN 0-8274-2627-5). R West.

KEMPE, MARGERY (BURNHAM), b. 1373

Cholmeley, Katharine. Margery Kempe, Genius & Mystic. LC 78-7811. 1978. Repr. of 1947 ed. lib. bdg. 17.50 (ISBN 0-8414-0296-5). Folcroft.

KEN, THOMAS, BP. OF BATH AND WELLS, 1637-1711

Marston, E. Thomas Ken & Izaak Walton: A Sketch of Their Lives & Family Connection. 1908. Repr. 35.00 (ISBN 0-8274-3613-0). R West.

Rice, Hugh A. L. Thomas Ken: Bishop & Non-Juror. LC 58-4172. 1958. 10.00x (ISBN 0-8401-2008-7). A R Allenson.

KENNEDY, JOHN FITZGERALD, PRES. U. S., 1917-1963–POETRY

Nachant, Frances G. Song of Peace. 1969. cancelled (ISBN 0-8233-0126-5). Golden Quill.

KENOSIS (THEOLOGY)

see Incarnation

KENYON COLLEGE, GAMBIER, OHIO

Caswall, Henry. America, & the American Church. LC 77-83413. (Religion in America Ser). 1969. Repr. of 1839 ed. 21.00 (ISBN 0-405-00234-3). Ayer Co Pubs.

KERALA, INDIA (STATE)

Alexander, P. C. Buddhism in Kerala. LC 78-72369. Repr. of 1949 ed. 37.50 (ISBN 0-404-17216-4). AMS Pr.

Gladstone, J. W. Protestant Christianity & People's Movements in Kerala, 1850-1936. 470p. 1986. 12.50x (ISBN 0-8364-1821-2, Pub. by Somaiya). South Asia Bks.

Miller, Roland. Mapilla Muslims of Kerala: A Study of Islamic Trends. LC 76-901758. 1976. 14.00x (ISBN 0-88386-080-5). South Asia Bks.

KERYGMA

Althaus, Paul. Fact & Faith in the Kerygma of Today. Cairas, David, tr. 89p. 1978. Repr. of 1959 ed. lib. bdg. cancelled (ISBN 0-313-20446-2, ALFA). Greenwood.

McDonald, J. H. Kerygma & Didache: The Articulation & Structure of the Earliest Christian Message. LC 77-95446. (Society for New Testament Studies Monograph: No. 37). 1980. 29.95 (ISBN 0-521-22055-6). Cambridge U Pr.

KESWICK MOVEMENT

Bundy, David D. Keswick: A Bibliographic Introduction to the Higher Life Movements. LC 76-369083. (Occasional Bibliographic Papers of the B. L. Fisher Library: No. 3). 89p. 1975. 3.00 (ISBN 0-914368-03-6). Asbury Theological.

Figgis, John B. Keswick from Within. Dayton, Donald W., ed. (The Higher Christian Ser.). 192p. 1985. 25.00 (ISBN 0-8240-6417-8). Garland Pub.

KHALIFAT

see Caliphate

KHILAFAT

see Caliphate

KHOTANESE LANGUAGE

Bailey, Harold W. Khotanese Buddhist Texts. rev. ed. LC 80-41425. (University of Cambridge Oriental Publications Ser.: No. 31). 168p. 1981. 57.50 (ISBN 0-521-23717-3). Cambridge U Pr.

KIERKEGAARD, SOREN AABYE, 1813-1855

Attwater, Donald, ed. Modern Christian Revolutionaries. facsimile ed. LC 76-156608. (Essay Index Reprint Ser). Repr. of 1947 ed. 23.00 (ISBN 0-8369-2304-9). Ayer Co Pubs.

Becker, Ernest. The Denial of Death. LC 73-1860. 1973. 19.95 (ISBN 0-02-902150-2); pap. 8.95 (ISBN 0-02-902380-7). Free Pr.

Burgess, Andrew J. Passion, Knowing How, & Understanding: An Essay on the Concept of Faith. LC 75-31550. (American Academy of Religion. Dissertation Ser.). 1975. pap. 9.95 (ISBN 0-89130-044-9, 010109). Scholars Pr GA.

Colette. Histoire et Absolu: Essai Sur Kierkegaard. 19.95 (ISBN 0-686-54575-3). French & Eur.

Diem, Hermann. Kierkegaard's Dialectic of Existence. Knight, Harold, tr. from German. LC 77-18886. 1978. Repr. of 1959 ed. lib. bdg. 22.50x (ISBN 0-313-20220-6, DIKD). Greenwood.

Duncan, Elmer H. Soren Kierkegaard. Patterson, Bob E., ed. LC 76-2862. (Markers of the Modern Theological Mind Ser.). 1976. 8.95 (ISBN 0-87680-463-6, 80463). Word Bks.

Klemke. Studies in the Philosophy of Kierkegaard. 1976. pap. 16.00 (ISBN 90-247-1852-X, Pub. by Martinus Nijhoff Netherlands). Kluwer Academic.

Lowrie, Walter. Kierkegaard, 2 vols. Set. 28.50 (ISBN 0-8446-0778-9). Peter Smith.

--Short Life of Kierkegaard. 1942. pap. 9.50x (ISBN 0-691-01957-6). Princeton U Pr.

Malantschuk, Gregor. Kierkegaard's Thought. Hong, Howard V. & Hong, Edna H., trs. from Dan. LC 77-155000. (Eng.). 400p. 1972. 38.50 (ISBN 0-691-07166-7, 317); pap. 10.00 (ISBN 0-691-01982-7). Princeton U Pr.

Nielsen, H. A. Where the Passion Is: A Reading of Kierkegaard's Philosophical Fragments. LC 83-6923. 209p. 1983. 20.00 (ISBN 0-8130-0742-9). U Presses Fla.

Pojman, Louis P. The Logic of Subjectivity: Kierkegaard's Philosophy of Religion. LC 83-1053. 174p. 1984. 17.50x (ISBN 0-8173-0166-6). U of Ala Pr.

Sontag, Frederick. A Kierkegaard Handbook. LC 79-87741. 1980. pap. 7.25 (ISBN 0-8042-0654-6). John Knox.

Stack, George J. Kierkegaard's Existential Ethics. LC 75-16344. (Studies in Humanities: No. 16). 240p. 1977. 15.00 (ISBN 0-8173-6624-5); pap. 5.50 (ISBN 0-8173-6626-1). U of Ala Pr.

Sullivan, F. Russell. Faith & Reason in Kierkegaard. LC 78-60695. 1978. pap. text ed. 9.50 (ISBN 0-8191-0559-7). U Pr of Amer.

Sussman, Henry. The Hegelian Aftermath: Readings in Hegel, Kierkegaard, Freud, Proust & James. LC 82-47971. 172p. 1982. text ed. 22.50x (ISBN 0-8018-2852-X). Johns Hopkins.

Thomte, Reidar. Kierkegaard's Philosophy of Religion. Repr. of 1948 ed. lib. bdg. 27.50x (ISBN 0-8371-0979-5, THKI). Greenwood.

KINDNESS

Brister, C. W. Caring for the Caregivers. LC 85-3793. 1985. pap. 8.95 (ISBN 0-8054-5537-X). Broadman.

Chaim, Chafetz, pseud. Ahavath Chesed: The Love of Kindness As Required by G-D. Oschry, Leonard, tr. from Hebrew. 1978. pap. 6.95 (ISBN 0-87306-167-5). Feldheim.

MacKenthun, Carole & Dwyer, Paulinus. Kindness. (Fruit of the Spirit Ser.). (Illus.). 48p. 1987. pap. 5.95 (ISBN 0-86653-379-6, SS880). Good Apple.

Martin, Grant. Please Don't Hurt Me. 180p. 1987. pap. 6.95 (ISBN 0-89693-743-7). Victor Bks.

Moncure, Jane B. Kindness. LC 80-15286. (What Does the Bible Say? Ser.). (Illus.). 32p. 1980. PLB 5.95 (ISBN 0-89565-167-X). Childs World.

KING, CORETTA SCOTT, 1927-

Patterson, Lillie. Coretta Scott King. LC 76-19077. (American All Ser.). (Illus.). 96p. 1977. PLB 7.12 (ISBN 0-8116-4585-1). Garrard.

KING, MARTIN LUTHER, 1929-1968

Collins, David R. Not Only Dreamers. Eller, David, ed. 160p. (Orig.). 1986. pap. 7.95 (ISBN 0-87178-612-5). Brethren.

Crawford, Fred R., et al. Certain Reactions by the Atlanta Public to the Death of the Rev. Dr. Martin Luther King Jr. LC 73-85669. 1969. pap. 3.00 (ISBN 0-89937-023-3). Ctr Res Soc Chg.

An Explanation of Dr. Martin Luther's Small Catechism. 265p. 1982. write for info. (ISBN 0-89279-043-1). Board Pub Evang.

Fairclough, Adam. To Redeem the Soul of America: The Southern Christian Leadership Conference & Martin Luther King, Jr. (Illus.). 456p. 1987. 35.00 (ISBN 0-8203-0898-6); pap. 17.95 (ISBN 0-8203-0938-9). U of Ga Pr.

Pitre, David W. To Martin Luther King, with Love: A Southern Quaker's Tribute. 1984. pap. 2.50x (ISBN 0-87574-254-8, 254). Pendle Hill.

Rahming, Philip A. Martin Luther King, Jr. His Religion, His Philosophy. LC 86-911950. 96p. (Orig.). 1986. pap. text ed. 10.00 (ISBN 0-682-40301-6). Exposition Pr FL.

Ramsay, William M. Four Modern Prophets: Walter Rauschenbusch, Martin Luther King, Jr., Gustavo Gutierrez, Rosemary Radford Ruether. LC 86-45351. 108p. (Orig.). 1986. pap. 6.95 (ISBN 0-8042-0811-5). John Knox.

Shuker, Nancy F. Martin Luther King. (World Leaders: Past & Present Ser.). (Illus.). 112p. 1985. lib. bdg. 16.95x (ISBN 0-87754-567-7). Chelsea Hse.

Smith, Ervin. The Ethics of Martin Luther King Jr. LC 81-18976. (Studies in American Religion: Vol. 2). 226p. 1982. 49.95x (ISBN 0-88946-974-1). E Mellen.

KINGDOM OF GOD

see also Covenants (Theology)

Allchin, A. M. The Kingdom of Love & Knowledge: The Encounter Between Orthodoxy & the West. 224p. (Orig.). 1982. 14.95 (ISBN 0-8164-0532-8, HarpR). Har-Row.

Anderson, Gerald H., ed. Witnessing to the Kingdom: Melbourne & Beyond. LC 82-3530. 176p. (Orig.). 1982. pap. 7.95 (ISBN 0-88344-708-8). Orbis Bks.

Anglican Consultative Council Staff. For the Sake of the Kingdom. 72p. (Orig.). 1986. pap. 2.25 (ISBN 0-88028-054-9). Forward Movement.

Augustine, Saint City of God, 2 Vols. Tasker, R. V., ed. Healey, John, tr. 1973. Repr. of 1945 ed. 12.95x ea. (ISBN 0-686-66408-6, Evman). Vol. 1 (ISBN 0-460-00982-6). Vol. 2 (ISBN 0-460-00983-4). Biblio Dist.

--City of God Against the Pagans, 7 vols. (Loeb Classical Library: No. 411-417). 13.95x ea. Harvard U Pr.

Augustinus, Saint Aurelius. De Civitate Dei Liber 22: Sec. 5, 2 pts, Pts. 1 & 2. (Corpus Scriptorum Ecclesiasticorum Latinorum Ser: Vol. 40). Repr. of 1899 ed. 50.00 ea. (ISBN 0-384-02370-3). Johnson Repr.

Christenson, Larry. The Kingdom. (Trinity Bible Ser.). 160p. 1972. pap. 5.95x (ISBN 0-87123-548-X, 240548). Bethany Hse.

Davis, John J. Christ's Victorious Kingdom. 144p. 1987. pap. 6.95 (ISBN 0-8010-2970-8). Baker Bk.

Driver, John. Kingdom Citizens. LC 80-16171. 160p. (Orig.). 1980. pap. 6.95 (ISBN 0-8361-1935-5). Herald Pr.

Eldridge, Paul. Kingdom Without God. 15p. 1951. pap. cancelled (ISBN 0-911826-50-5). Am Atheist.

Fern, Deane W., ed. Restoring the Kingdom. 240p. (Orig.). 1984. pap. text ed. 10.95 (ISBN 0-913757-06-3, Pub. by New Era Bks). Paragon Hse.

Godsey, John D. Preface to Bonhoeffer: The Man & Two of His Shorter Writings. LC 79-7378. 80p. 1979. pap. 3.50 (ISBN 0-8006-1367-8, 1-1367). Fortress.

Jabay, Earl. Kingdom of Self. LC 73-89494. 1974. pap. 3.95 (ISBN 0-88270-062-6). Bridge Pub.

Kraybill, Donald B. The Upside-Down Kingdom. LC 78-9435. (Christian Peace Shelf Ser.). 328p. 1978. pap. 6.95 (ISBN 0-8361-1860-X). Herald Pr.

Ladd, George E. L' Evangile du Royaume. Cosson, Annie L., ed. Martin, Marie-Therese, tr. Tr. of The Gospel of the Kingdom. (Fr.). 192p. 1985. pap. text ed. 2.25 (ISBN 0-8297-1012-4). Life Pubs Intl.

--Gospel of the Kingdom. 1959. pap. 4.95 (ISBN 0-8028-1280-5). Eerdmans.

--The Presence of the Future: The Eschatology of Biblical Realism. 1973. pap. 7.95 (ISBN 0-8028-1531-6). Eerdmans.

McClain, Alva J. The Greatness of the Kingdom. 11.95 (ISBN 0-88469-011-3). BMH Bks.

Millet, Robert. Perfected Millenial Kingdom. 1974. pap. 2.00 (ISBN 0-89036-034-0). Hawkes Pub Inc.

Pannenberg, Wolfhart. Theology & the Kingdom of God. LC 69-12668. 144p. 1969. pap. 5.95 (ISBN 0-664-24842-X). Westminster.

Paulk, Earl. Ultimate Kingdom. 2nd ed. 264p. (Orig.). 1987. pap. 7.95 (ISBN 0-917595-13-0). K-Dimension.

Rand, Howard B. Digest of the Divine Law. 1943. 8.00 (ISBN 0-685-08802-2). Destiny.

Robertson, Pat. Le Royaume Secret. Cosson, Annie L., ed. Gimenez, Anne, tr. Tr. of The Secret Kingdom. (Fr.). 261p. 1985. pap. 2.75 (ISBN 0-8297-1277-1). Life Pubs Intl.

St. Augustine. City of God, Bks. 1-7. LC 63-19613. (Fathers of the Church Ser.: Vol. 8). 401p. 1950. 29.95x (ISBN 0-8132-0008-3). Cath U Pr.

Snyder, Howard A. A Kingdom Manifesto. LC 85-10725. 108p. (Orig.). 1985. pap. 5.95 (ISBN 0-87784-408-9). Inter-Varsity.

Talese, Gay. The Kingdom & the Power. 672p. 1981. pap. 5.95 (ISBN 0-440-14397-7). Dell.

Walton, F. A. Keys to the Kingdom. (Illus.). 80p. 1985. 8.00 (ISBN 0-682-40247-8). Exposition Pr FL.

Weiss, Johannes. Jesus' Proclamation of the Kingdom of God. Hiers, Richard H. & Holland, Larrimore D., eds. (Reprints & Translations). 1985. pap. 9.75 (ISBN 0-89130-859-8, 00-07-08). Scholars Pr GA.

Williams, Charles. He Came Down from Heaven. 160p. 1984. pap. 3.95 (ISBN 0-8028-0033-5). Eerdmans.

KINGDOM OF GOD–BIBLICAL TEACHING

Beasley-Murray, George R. Jesus & the Kingdom of God. 512p. 1986. 29.95 (ISBN 0-8028-3609-7). Eerdmans.

Bright, John. Kingdom of God. rev. ed. (Series A). 1957. pap. 7.50 (ISBN 0-687-20908-0, Apex). Abingdon.

Chilton, Bruce, ed. The Kingdom of God in the Teaching of Jesus. LC 83-20569. (Issues in Religion & Theology Ser.). 192p. 1984. pap. 7.95 (ISBN 0-8006-1769-X, 1-769). Fortress.

McClain, Alva J. The Greatness of the Kingdom. 11.95 (ISBN 0-88469-011-3). BMH Bks.

Marcus, Joel. The Mystery of the Kingdom of God. (Dissertation Ser.). 270p. 1986. 17.95 (ISBN 0-89130-983-7, 06-01-90); pap. 12.95 (ISBN 0-89130-984-5). Scholars Pr GA.

Ribberbos, Herman N. Coming of the Kingdom. 1962. pap. 11.95 (ISBN 0-87552-408-7). Presby & Reformed.

Stephens, Julius H. The Churches & the Kingdom. LC 78-5676. 1978. Repr. of 1959 ed. lib. bdg. cancelled (ISBN 0-313-20488-8, STCK). Greenwood.

Van Horn, Bill. The Key to the Kingdom. 1982. 4.25 (ISBN 0-89536-555-3, 1101). CSS of Ohio.

Wilder, Amos N. Eschatology & Ethics in the Teaching of Jesus. LC 78-16425. 1978. Repr. of 1950 ed. lib. bdg. 27.50 (ISBN 0-313-20585-X, WIEE). Greenwood.

KINGS AND RULERS (IN RELIGION, FOLK-LORE, ETC.)

see also Emperor Worship

Capt, E. Raymond. Jacob's Pillar. LC 79-116385. (Illus.). 96p. 1977. pap. 3.00 (ISBN 0-934666-03-2). Artisan Sales.

Frankfort, Henri. Kingship & the Gods: A Study of Ancient Near Eastern Religion As the Integration of Society & Nature. LC 48-5158. 1978. pap. 12.95 (ISBN 0-226-26011-9, P766, Phoen). U of Chicago Pr.

Gerbrandt, Gerald E. Kingship According to Deuteronomistic History. (Society of Biblical Literature Dissertation Ser.). 1986. 17.95 (ISBN 0-89130-968-3, 06 01 87); pap. 12.95 (ISBN 0-89130-969-1). Scholars Pr GA.

Hadfield, P. Traits of Divine Kingship in Africa. LC 78-32120. 1979. Repr. of 1949 ed. lib. bdg. 22.50x (ISBN 0-8371-5189-9, HDK&, Pub. by Negro U Pr). Greenwood.

Ludwig, Charles. Ludwig's Handbook of New Testament Cities & Rulers. LC 83-71619. 244p. (Orig.). 1983. pap. 6.95 (ISBN 0-89636-111-X). Accent Bks.

KINGSLEY, CHARLES, 1819-1875

Brown, W. Henry. Charles Kingsley. LC 73-12770. 1924. lib. bdg. 17.50 (ISBN 0-8414-3231-7). Folcroft.

Clare, Maurice. A Day with Charles Kingsley. Repr. 10.00 (ISBN 0-8274-2148-6). R West.

Ellis, James J. Charles Kingsley. 1890. Repr. 25.00 (ISBN 0-8274-3799-4). R West.

Kaufmann, M. Charles Kingsley: Christian Social Reformer. LC 77-20677. 1892. Repr. 30.00 (ISBN 0-8492-1416-5). R West.

--Charles Kingsley: Christian Socialist & Social Reformer. 1978. Repr. of 1892 ed. lib. bdg. 25.00 (ISBN 0-8495-3010-5). Arden Lib.

Kendall, Guy. Charles Kingsley & His Ideas. LC 72-6679. (English Biography Ser., No. 31). 195p. 1972. Repr. of 1937 ed. lib. bdg. 39.95x (ISBN 0-8383-1639-5). Haskell.

Kingsley, Charles. Charles Kingsley: His Letters & Memories of His Life, 2 Vols. LC 74-148803. (Illus.). Repr. of 1877 ed. Set. 37.50 (ISBN 0-404-08869-4); deluxe ed. 19.00 ea. Vol. 1 (ISBN 0-404-08870-8). Vol. 2 (ISBN 0-404-08871-6). AMS Pr.

Seaver, George. Charles Kingsley: Poet. LC 73-1252. 1973. lib. bdg. 10.00 (ISBN 0-8414-1540-4). Folcroft.

Stubbs, Charles W. Charles Kingsley & the Christian Social Movement. LC 70-148310. Repr. of 1899 ed. 17.50 (ISBN 0-404-08914-3). AMS Pr.

Thorp, Margaret F. Charles Kingsley, Eighteen Nineteen to Eighteen Seventy-Five. LC 70-96170. 1969. Repr. of 1937 ed. lib. bdg. 18.50x (ISBN 0-374-97942-1, Octagon). Hippocrene Bks.

Webb, Catherine. Lives of Great Men & Women: Charles Kingsley, John Ruskin, William Morris. 1911. Repr. 25.00 (ISBN 0-8274-2976-2). R West.

KINLOSS ABBEY

Ferrerio, Giovanni. Ferrerii Historia Abbatum De Kynlos. LC 78-168018. (Bannatyne Club, Edinburgh. Publications: No. 63). Repr. of 1839 ed. 15.00 (ISBN 0-404-52774-4). AMS Pr.

KINO, EUSBIUS FRANCISCO, 1644-1711

Bolton, Herbert E. Padre on Horseback. LC 63-13248. (Illus.). 1963. Repr. of 1962 ed. 3.00 (ISBN 0-8294-0003-6). Loyola.

--Rim of Christendom: A Biography of Eusebio Francisco Kino, Pacific Coast Pioneer. LC 84-8814. 644p. 1984. Repr. of 1960 ed. 40.00x (ISBN 0-8165-0863-1). U of Ariz Pr.

Cabat, Erni & Polzer, Charles W. Father Eusebio Francisco Kino & His Missions of the Pimeria Alta: Facing the Missions, Bk. II. Prezelski, Carmen V., tr. LC 82-50219. (Illus.). 36p. 1983. pap. 5.00 (ISBN 0-915076-09-8). SW Mission.

Polzer, Charles. Kino Guide II. LC 82-50218. (Illus.). 76p. 1982. pap. 5.00 (ISBN 0-915076-07-1). SW Mission.

KNIGHTS OF MALTA

Cavaliero, Roderick. The Last of the Crusaders. LC 78-63337. (The Crusades & Military Orders: Second Ser.). Repr. of 1960 ed. 34.25 (ISBN 0-404-17006-4). AMS Pr.

Knights of Malta. The Rule Statutes & Customs of the Hospitallers, 1099-1310. LC 78-63347. (The Crusades & Military Orders: Second Ser.). 272p. Repr. of 1934 ed. 29.00 (ISBN 0-404-16246-0). AMS Pr.

Mifsud, Alfred. Knights Hospitallers of the Venerable Tongue of England in Malta. LC 78-63348. (The Crusades & Military Orders: Second Ser.). (Illus.). Repr. of 1914 ed. 34.50 (ISBN 0-404-17009-9). AMS Pr.

Philippus De Thame. Knights Hospitallers in England. Repr. of 1857 ed. 37.00 (ISBN 0-384-46330-4). Johnson Repr.

Schermerhorn, Elizabeth W. Malta of the Knights. LC 76-29838. Repr. of 1929 ed. 40.00 (ISBN 0-404-15429-8). AMS Pr.

KNIGHTS OF SAINT CRISPIN

Lescohier, Don D. Knights of St. Crispin, Eighteen Sixty-Seven to Eighteen Seventy-Four. LC 77-89748. (American Labor from Conspiracy to Collective Bargaining, Ser. 2). 101p. 1969. Repr. of 1910 ed. 14.00 (ISBN 0-405-02136-4). Ayer Co Pubs.

KNIGHTS TEMPLARS (MASONIC)

see Freemasons–Knights Templars

KNIGHTS TEMPLARS (MONASTIC AND MILITARY ORDER)

see Templars

KNOWABLENESS OF GOD

see God–Knowableness

KNOWLEDGE, THEORY OF (RELIGION)

see also Faith and Reason; God–Knowableness

Apczynski, John V. Doers of the Word. LC 76-51640. (American Academy of Religion. Dissertation Ser.). 1977. pap. 10.50 (ISBN 0-89130-128-3, 010118). Scholars Pr GA.

Bateson, Gregory & Bateson, May C. Angels Fear: Towards an Epistemology of the Sacred. 224p. 1987. 18.95 (ISBN 0-02-507670-1). Macmillan.

Biardeau, Madeleine. Theorie De la Connaissance et Philosophie De la Parole Dans le Brahmanisme Classique. (Le Monde D'outre-Mer Passe et Present, Etudes: No. 23). 1963. pap. 34.80x (ISBN 90-2796-178-6). Mouton.

Brandt, Richard B. Philosophy of Schleiermacher: The Development of His Theory of Scientific & Religious Knowledge. LC 68-19265. 1968. Repr. of 1941 ed. lib. bdg. 27.00x (ISBN 0-8371-0027-5, BRPS). Greenwood.

Bubacz, Bruce. St. Augustine's Theory of Knowledge: A Contemporary Analysis. LC 81-18754. (Texts & Studies in Religion: Vol. 11). 248p. 1982. 39.95x (ISBN 0-88946-959-8). E Mellen.

Furse, Margaret L., et al. The Problem of Religious Knowledge. (Rice University Studies: Vol. 60, No. 1). 129p. 1974. pap. 10.00x (ISBN 0-89263-219-4). Rice Univ.

Jain, C. R. Key of Knowledge: The Key to Unlock the Mysteries of Important Religions of the World. 1012p. 1975. 35.00 (ISBN 0-88065-137-7, Pub. by Messers Today & Tomorrows Printers & Publishers India). Scholarly Pubns.

Lynch, John E. The Theory of Knowledge of Vital Du Four. (Philosophy Ser). 1972. 17.00 (ISBN 0-686-11546-5). Franciscan Inst.

McCarthy, Gerald. The Ethics of Belief Debate. (AAR Studies in Religion). 1986. 20.95 (ISBN 0-89130-892-X, 01-00-41); pap. 15.95 (ISBN 0-89130-893-8). Scholars Pr GA.

Matthew of Aquasparta. Knowledge & Deceit in the Intellectual Life of Man. (Illus.). 87p. 1984. pap. 23.75 (ISBN 0-89266-491-6). Am Classical Coll Pr.

Mavrodes, George I. Belief in God: A Study in the Epistemology of Religion. LC 81-40788. 128p. 1981. pap. text ed. 7.50 (ISBN 0-8191-1816-8). U Pr of Amer.

Nature of Religious Experience: Essays in Honor of Douglas Clyde Macintosh. facsimile ed. LC 78-152202. (Essay Index Reprint Ser). Repr. of 1937 ed. 16.00 (ISBN 0-8369-2286-7). Ayer Co Pubs.

Nee, Watchman. Spiritual Knowledge. Kaung, Stephen, tr. 1973. 4.00 (ISBN 0-935008-36-5); pap. 2.75 (ISBN 0-935008-37-3). Christian Fellow Pubs.

Pearlman, Myer. Knowing the Doctrines of the Bible. 400p. 1937. 7.95 (ISBN 0-88243-534-5, 02-0534). Gospel Pub.

Preus, Mary. Eloquence & Ignorance in Augustine's "On the Nature & Origin of the Soul". (AAR Academy Ser.). 1986. 19.95 (ISBN 0-89130-927-6, 01-01-51); pap. 15.25 (ISBN 0-89130-928-4). Scholars Pr Ga.

Reymond, Robert. The Justification of Knowledge. 1976. pap. 6.95 (ISBN 0-87552-406-0). Presby & Reformed.

St. Thomas Aquinas. Providence & Predestination: Questions 5 & 6 of "Truth". Mulligan, Robert W., tr. 154p. 1961. pap. 5.95 (ISBN 0-89526-937-6). Regnery Bks.

Santoni, Ronald E., ed. Religious Language & the Problem of Religious Knowledge. LC 68-27352. Repr. of 1968 ed. 95.50 (ISBN 0-8357-9238-2, 2017640). Bks Demand UMI.

Van Til, Cornelius. A Survey of Christian Epistemology. 1967. pap. 6.95 (ISBN 0-87552-495-8). Presby & Reformed.

Warfield, Benjamin B. Studies in Tertullian & Augustine. Repr. of 1930 ed. lib. bdg. 29.00x (ISBN 0-8371-4490-6, WATT). Greenwood.

Williams, William J. The Miracle of Abduction. LC 84-82540. 160p. (Orig.). 1985. 12.95 (ISBN 0-930371-02-X); pap. 8.95 (ISBN 0-930371-03-8). Epistemics.

KNOWLEDGE OF GOD

see God–Knowableness

KNOX, JOHN, 1505-1572

Cowan, Henry. John Knox: The Hero of the Scottish Reformation. LC 70-133817. (Illus.). Repr. of 1905 ed. 27.50 (ISBN 0-404-01788-6). AMS Pr.

Harland, Marion. John Knox. 1900. 25.00 (ISBN 0-686-19912-X). Quaker City.

Innes, A. Taylor. John Knox. 1978. Repr. of 1896 ed. lib. bdg. 17.50 (ISBN 0-8414-5057-9). Folcroft.

McCrie, Thomas. Life of John Knox. LC 83-45584. (Illus.). Date not set. Repr. of 1898 ed. 57.50 (ISBN 0-404-19902-X). AMS Pr.

Muir, Edwin. John Knox: Portrait of a Calvinist. facsimile ed. LC 76-148892. (Select Bibliographies Reprint Ser). Repr. of 1929 ed. 21.00 (ISBN 0-8369-5656-7). Ayer Co Pubs.

--John Knox: Portrait of a Calvinist. 1978. Repr. of 1930 ed. lib. bdg. 30.00 (ISBN 0-8414-6246-1). Folcroft.

--John Knox: Portrait of a Calvinist. LC 78-159096. 1971. Repr. of 1929 ed. 28.00x (ISBN 0-8046-1639-6, Pub. by Kennikat). Assoc Faculty Pr.

Pearce, G. R. John Knox. 1936. Repr. 25.00 (ISBN 0-8274-3855-9). R West.

Preedy, George R. The Life of John Knox. 1940. Repr. 35.00 (ISBN 0-8274-2933-9). R West.

Reid, W. Stanford. Trumpeter of God: A Biography of John Knox. 372p. 1982. pap. 8.95 (ISBN 0-8010-7708-7). Baker Bk.

Smith, G. Barnett & Martin, Dorothy. John Knox: Apostle of the Scottish Reformation. LC 82-12608. (Golden Oldies Ser.). 128p. 1982. pap. 3.95 (ISBN 0-8024-4354-0). Moody.

Walker, Ralph S. John Knox: Historia of the Reformation in Scotland. 72p. 1985. 22.00x (ISBN 0-85411-021-6, Pub. by Saltire Soc.). State Mutual Bk.

KOAN

Franck, Frederick. The Supreme Koan: An Artist's Spiritual Journey. LC 81-22037. (Illus.). 1982. pap. 12.95 (ISBN 0-8245-0430-5). Crossroad NY.

Grimstone, A. V., ed. Two Zen Classics: Mumonkan & Hekiganroku. Sekida, Katsuki, tr. from Chinese. LC 77-2398. 1977. 13.50 (ISBN 0-8348-0131-0); pap. 8.95 (ISBN 0-8348-0130-2). Weatherhill.

Leggett, Trevor. The Warrior Koans: Early Zen in Japan. 256p. 1985. pap. 8.95 (Ark Paperbks). Methuen Inc.

Low, Albert. The Iron Cow of Zen. LC 85-40413. 226p. (Orig.). 1985. pap. 6.50 (ISBN 0-8356-0598-1, Quest). Theos Pub Hse.

Miura, Isshu & Sasaki, Ruth F. The Zen Koan. LC 65-19104. (Illus.). 156p. 1966. pap. 7.95 (ISBN 0-15-699981-1, Harv). HarBraceJ.

KOLBE, MAXIMILLAN

Dewar, Diana. The Saint of Auschwitz: The Story of Maximilian Kolbe. LC 82-48926. (Illus.). 160p. (Orig.). 1983. pap. 5.95 (ISBN 0-06-061901-5, RD/460, HarpR). Har-Row.

Franciscan Friars of Marytown, ed. The Hero of Auschwitz. (Illus.). 47p. 1979. pap. 0.75 (ISBN 0-913382-11-6, 105-29). Prow Bks-Franciscan.

Manteau-Bonamy, H. M. Immaculate Conception & the Holy Spirit: The Marian Teachings of Father Kolbe. Geiger, Bernard M., ed. Arnandez, Richard, tr. from Fr. LC 77-93104. Tr. of Doctrine mariale du Pere Kolbe, Esprit-Saint et Conception Immaculee. (Illus.). 1977. pap. 4.00 (ISBN 0-913382-00-0, 101-20). Prow Bks-Franciscan.

Ricciardi, Antonio. St. Maximilian Kolbe. Daughters of St. Paul, tr. from Ital. (Illus.). 314p. 1982. 7.95 (ISBN 0-8198-6838-8, ST0283); pap. 6.50 (ISBN 0-8198-6837-X). Dghtrs St Paul.

Romb, Anselm. Kolbe Reader. (Orig.). Date not set. pap. price not set (ISBN 0-913382-35-3, 101-35). Prow Bks-Franciscan.

Treece, Patricia. A Man for Others: Maximilian Kolbe, Saint of Auschwitz. 208p. 1986. pap. 5.95 (ISBN 0-87973-519-8, 519). Our Sunday Visitor.

--Soldier of God. 32p. 1982. pap. 1.00 (ISBN 0-913382-22-1, 111-1). Prow Bks-Franciscan.

KONARAK, INDIA–TEMPLE

Ebersole, Robert. Black Pagoda. LC 57-12929. (Illus.). 1957. 8.50 (ISBN 0-8130-0070-X). U Presses Fla.

KORAN

Ahmad, Mufassir M. The Koran. LC 81-52147. (Illus.). 600p. 1981. pap. 30.00 (ISBN 0-940368-04-8). Tahrike Tarsile Quran.

Al-Esman, Mashef, ed. Quran. (Arabic.). 25.00x (ISBN 0-86685-135-6). Intl Bk Ctr.

Ali, A. A. Holy Qur'an, 2 Vols. 29.50x (ISBN 0-87902-038-5). Orientalia.

Ali, A. Yusuf, tr. from Arabic. Holy Qur'an. lib. bdg. 14.00. Am Trust Pubns.

Ali, Abdullah Y. & Ali, Abdullah Y. The Meaning of the Glorious Qur'an, 2 Vols. Set. 24.00 (ISBN 0-686-37146-1). New World Press NY.

Ali, M. M. Introduction to the Study of the Holy Qur'an. 5.25x (ISBN 0-87902-040-7). Orientalia.

Ali, S. V., tr. from Arabic. The Holy Qur'an. 550p. 1981. text ed. 9.00 (ISBN 0-940368-08-0); pap. 4.95 (ISBN 0-940368-07-2). Tahrike Tarsile Quran.

Ali, Yousuf. The Holy Quran with Arabic Text Commentary & Translation. 25.75 (ISBN 0-686-18528-5). Kazi Pubns.

Ali, Yusef. The Holy Quran. (Arabic & Eng.). 20.00x (ISBN 0-86685-167-4). Intl Bk Ctr.

Ali, Yusuf. The Holy Quran. LC 77-78098. 1915p. 14.00 (ISBN 0-89259-006-8). Am Trust Pubns.

Al-Muminin, Amir. Supplications (Du'a) Chittick, William C., tr. from Arabic & Eng. 63p. 1986. text ed. 24.95 (ISBN 0-7103-0156-1). Methuen Inc.

Ar-Razi, Al-Kulayni. Al-Kafi: The Book of Divine Unity. Rizvi, S. Muhammad, tr. from Arabic. LC 85-52265. 70p. (Orig.). 1985. pap. 12.00 (ISBN 0-940368-62-5). Tahrike Tarsile Quran.

--Al-Kafi: The Book of Excellence of Knowledge. Rizvi, S. Muhammad, tr. from Arabic. LC 85-52264. 72p. (Orig.). 1985. pap. 12.00 (ISBN 0-940368-61-7). Tahrike Tarsile Quran.

As-Said, Labib. Recited Koran: A History of the First Recorded Version. Weiss, Bernard, ed. LC 73-20717. (Illus.). 156p. 1975. 10.00 (ISBN 0-87850-024-3). Darwin Pr.

At-Tabatabai, S. Muhammad. Al-Mizan: En Exegesis of the Quran, Vol. 3. Rizvi, S. Saeed, tr. from Arabic. LC 85-52243. 334p. (Orig.). 1985. pap. 30.00 (ISBN 0-940368-58-7). Tahrike Tarsile Quran.

Ayoub, Mahmoud M. The Qur'an & Its Interpreters, Vol. 1. LC 82-21713. 290p. 1984. 29.50x (ISBN 0-87395-727-X). State U NY Pr.

Azizullah. Glimpses of the Holy Quran. pap. 6.50 (ISBN 0-686-18517-X). Kazi Pubns.

Basetti-Sami, Giulio. Koran in the Light of Christ. 1977. 8.50 (ISBN 0-8199-0713-8). Franciscan Herald.

Baydun, M., ed. Quran. (Arabic.). medium sized. 25.00x (ISBN 0-86685-134-8). Intl Bk Ctr.

Behlim, S. A. Quran Made Easy (Yassar nal Quran) Date not set. pap. 7.50 (ISBN 0-317-43010-6). Kazi Pubns.

Binark, Ismet & Eren, Halit. World Bibliography of Translations of the Meanings of the Holy Qur'an: Printed Translations 1515-1980. 600p. 1987. text ed. 125.00 (ISBN 0-7103-0229-0, Kegan Paul). Methuen Inc.

Bucaille, Maurice. The Bible, the Quran & Science. Beg, Anwer, ed. Bucaille, Maurice & Pannell, Alastair D., trs. from Fr. LC 77-90336. 253p. 1978. 11.95 (ISBN 0-89259-010-6); pap. 8.50. Am Trust Pubns.

Burton, John. The Collection of the Qur'an. LC 76-27899. 1977. 49.50 (ISBN 0-521-21439-4); pap. 15.95 (ISBN 0-521-29652-8). Cambridge U Pr.

Chipa, A. K. Beauty & Wisdom of the Holy Qur'an. 1971. 3.25x (ISBN 0-87902-159-4). Orientalia.

Cragg, Kenneth. The Pen & the Faith: Eight Modern Muslim Writers & the Qur'an. 188p. 1985. text ed. 16.00x (ISBN 0-04-297044-X). Allen Unwin.

Cross, Frank M. & Talmon, Shemaryahu, eds. Qumran & the History of the Biblical Text. LC 75-12529. 415p. 1975. text ed. 25.00x (ISBN 0-674-74360-1); pap. text ed. 9.95x (ISBN 0-674-74362-8). Harvard U Pr.

Faruqi, I. Azad. The Tarjuman Al-Qura'n: A Critical Analysis of Maulana Abul Kalam Azad's Approach to the Understanding of the Qura'n. 128p. 1983. text ed. 15.95x (ISBN 0-7069-1342-6, Pub. by Vikas India). Advent NY.

Gauhar, Altaf. Translation from the Quran. 16.95 (ISBN 0-686-18511-0). Kazi Pubns.

Ghosh, A. The Koran & the Kafir: Islam & the Infidel. rev., 2nd ed. (Illus.). 200p. (Orig.). 1983. pap. 7.35 (ISBN 0-9611614-1-8). Ghosh A.

Haeri, Shaykh F. Heart of Qu'ran & Perfect Mizan. 140p. 1987. pap. 18.95 (ISBN 0-7103-0222-3, Kegan Paul). Methuen Inc.

--Journey of the Universe As Expounded in the Qur'an. 120p. 1985. 29.95x (ISBN 0-7103-0149-9, Kegan Paul). Methuen Inc.

--Man in Qur'an & the Meaning of Furqan. 210p. 1987. pap. 18.95 (ISBN 0-7103-0223-1, Pub. by Routledge UK). Methuen Inc.

Haeri, Shykh F. The Mercy of Qur'an & the Advent of Zaman. 164p. 1987. pap. 18.95 (ISBN 0-7103-0224-X, 02231, Kegan Paul). Methuen Inc.

Hafiz, M. Virtues of the Holy Quran. pap. 7.50 (ISBN 0-686-18508-0). Kazi Pubns.

Hamidullah, D. M. Holy Quran, 2 vols. (Arabic, Fr.). 1981. Set. french & arabic 69.00 (ISBN 0-686-77430-2). Kazi Pubns.

Haque, Muhammad S. Al-Qur'anal-Karim, The Holy Qur'an: Surah Al-Fatiha, Section 1 of Surah Baqarah, Ayatul Kursi, Surah Nas thru Surah Naba with Modern English Translations, & Reading Guide, Prayer modes & Qaidah, Pt. 30. LC 84-63148. (Arabic & Eng., Illus.). viii, 80p. (Orig.). 1985. pap. text ed. 3.00 (ISBN 0-933057-02-4). Namuk Intl Inc.

--The Holy Qur'an (With Modern English Translations & Annotations) 800p. 1987. text ed. 20.00 (ISBN 0-933057-05-9). Namuk Intl Inc.

Hingora. The Prophecies of the Holy Quran. pap. 4.50 (ISBN 0-686-18509-9). Kazi Pubns.

The Holy Quran. (Arabic.). 19.95 (ISBN 0-686-18522-6); deluxe ed. 29.50. Kazi Pubns.

The Holy Quran. 2nd ed. write for info. (ISBN 0-89259-018-1). Am Trust Pubns.

Husayn at-Tabatabai, S. Muhammad. Al-Mizan: An Exegesis of the Qur'an, Vol. 4. Rizvi, S. Saeed, tr. from Arabic. LC 85-52243. 336p. (Orig.). 1985. pap. 30.00 (ISBN 0-940368-59-5). Tahrike Tarsile Quran.

--Al-Mizan: An Exegesis of the Qur'an, Vol. 5. Rizvi, S. Saeed, tr. from Arabic. LC 85-52243. 288p. (Orig.). 1985. pap. 30.00 (ISBN 0-940368-60-9). Tahrike Tarsile Quran.

Husayn at-Tabatabai, S. Muhammad & S. Saeed, Akhtar-Rizvi. Al-Mizan: An Exegesis of the Qur'an, Vol. 1. LC 85-52243. 366p. (Orig.). 1985. pap. 30.00 (ISBN 0-940368-57-9). Tahrike Tarsile Quran.

Irving, T. B., tr. The Qur'an: The First American Version. LC 84-72242. 500p. (Orig.). 1985. 17.50 (ISBN 0-915597-08-X). Amana Bks.

Irving, T. B., et al. The Quran: Basic Teachings. 278p. (Orig.). 1979. pap. 10.00 (ISBN 0-86037-021-6, Pub by Islamic Found UK). New Era Pubns MI.

Izutsu, Toshihiko. God & Man in the Koran. LC 79-52554. (Islam Ser.). 1980. Repr. of 1964 ed. lib. bdg. 20.00x (ISBN 0-8369-9262-8). Ayer Co Pubs.

Jeffery, Arthur. The Qur'an As Scripture. LC 80-1924. Repr. of 1952 ed. 18.00 (ISBN 0-404-18970-9). AMS Pr.

Jeffery, Arthur, ed. Materials for the History of the Text of the Qur'an. LC 79-180350. Repr. of 1937 ed. 57.50 (ISBN 0-404-56282-5). AMS Pr.

Jones, John D. The Apostles of Christ. 268p. 1982. lib. bdg. 10.00 Smythe Sewn (ISBN 0-86524-139-2, 8403). Klock & Klock.

Jung, N. An Approach to the Study of the Quran. pap. 4.75 (ISBN 0-686-18520-X). Kazi Pubns.

--An Approach to the Study of the Qur'an. 1970. 4.75x (ISBN 0-87902-168-3). Orientalia.

Jung, Nizamat. An Approach to the Study of the Qur'an. 84p. (Orig.). 1981. pap. 4.50 (ISBN 0-88004-002-5). Sunwise Turn.

Karim, A. Beauty & Wisdom of the Holy Quran. 4.95 (ISBN 0-686-18519-6). Kazi Pubns.

Kassis, Hanna E. A Concordance of the Qur'an. LC 82-40100. 1400p. 1984. 95.00x (ISBN 0-520-04327-8). U of Cal Pr.

Katsh, Abraham I. Judaism in Islam: Biblical & Talmudic Background of the Koran & Its Commentaries. 3rd ed. LC 80-50001. 1980. pap. 9.75 (ISBN 0-87203-086-5). Hermon.

Khalifa, R. A. Koran, Hadith, & Islam. 90p. (Orig.). 1983. 6.00 (ISBN 0-934894-35-3). Islamic Prods.

Khalifa, Rashad. Koran: The Final Scripture. 600p. (Orig.). 1981. 13.30 (ISBN 0-934894-19-1). Islamic Prods.

Khan, M. M. The Noble Qur'an, Arabic-English: A Summarized Version of At-Tabari, Al-Qurtubi & Ibn Kathir with comments from Sahih Al-Bukhari, Vol I. 49.00 (ISBN 0-317-46109-5). Kazi Pubns.

Khan, M. M. & Hilali, T. Noble Quran, Vol. 1. 1986. 49.95 (ISBN 0-317-43012-2). Kazi Pubns.

Khan, Muhammed Z., tr. The Quran: Arabic Text with English Translation. 736p. 1981. 40.00x (ISBN 0-7007-0148-6, Pub. by Curzon England). State Mutual Bk.

Kur'An. Here Begynneth a Lytell Treatyse of the Turkes Lawe Called Alcaron. LC 77-7411. (English Experience Ser.: No. 876). 1977. Repr. of 1519 ed. lib. bdg. 3.50 (ISBN 90-221-0876-7). Walter J Johnson.

Latif, S. A. The Mind Al-Quran Builds. 200p. 1983. 9.95 (ISBN 0-935782-16-8). Kazi Pubns.

Maudadi, A. A. Tafhimul - Quran: Urdu Translation & Commentary. 95.00 (ISBN 0-686-18523-4). Kazi Pubns.

Maududi, A. A. The Meaning of the Quran, 12 vols. 10.50 ea. Kazi Pubns.

Mir Ahmad Ali, tr. Koran. LC 83-80220. 440p. Date not set. pap. 4.95 (ISBN 0-940368-36-6). Tahrike Tarsile Quran.

Muhajir. Lessons from the Stories of the Quran. pap. 14.95 (ISBN 0-686-18515-3). Kazi Pubns.

Muhajir, A. M. Lessons from the Stories of the Quran. 1969. 14.95x (ISBN 0-87902-066-0). Orientalia.

Muhammad. The Qur'an: A New Translation with a Critical Rearrangement of the Surahs, 2 vols. Bell, Richard, tr. 14.95 ea. (Pub. by T & T Clark Ltd UK). Vol. 1, 348 pgs (ISBN 0-567-02027-4). Vol. 2, 352 pgs (ISBN 0-567-02028-2). Fortress.

Mutahhari, Morteza. Understanding the Quran. Tawheedi, Mohammad S., tr. from Persian. LC 84-50586. 64p. 1985. pap. 3.95 (ISBN 0-940368-35-8). Tahrike Tarsile Quran.

Nadui, S. M. A Geographical History of the Qur'an. 1970. 10.50 (ISBN 0-87902-300-7). Orientalia.

Nadvi, A. H. A Geographical History of the Qur'an. 12.50 (ISBN 0-686-18521-8). Kazi Pubns.

Nadvi, T. The Object of Life According to the Holy Qur'an. 1972. 3.50x (ISBN 0-87902-181-0). Orientalia.

Nelson, Kristina. The Art of Reciting the Qur'an. (Modern Middle East Ser.: No. 11). 271p. 1986. text ed. 25.00x (ISBN 0-292-70367-8). U of Tex Pr.

Peckthall, Mardaduke, tr. Holy Quaran. 1986. Repr. of 1983 ed. 20.00x (ISBN 0-8364-1623-6, Pub. by Rajesh). South Asia Bks.

Penrice, J. A Dictionary & Glossary of the Koran, with Copious Grammatical References & Explanations of the Text. 176p. 1978. text ed. 26.00. Coronet Bks.

Penrice, John. Dictionary & Glossary of the Koran. (Arabic & Eng.). 20.00x (ISBN 0-86685-088-0). Intl Bk Ctr.

--A Dictionary & Glossary of the Koran. 180p. 1985. 15.00x (ISBN 0-7007-0001-3, Pub. by Curzon Pr England). Humanities.

--Dictionary & Glossary of the Koran, with Copious Grammatical References & Explanations. LC 70-90039. (Arabic.). 1969. Repr. of 1873 ed. 20.00 (ISBN 0-8196-0252-3). Biblo.

--A Dictionary & Glossary of the Koran with Grammatical References & Explanations. 1980. lib. bdg. 55.00 (ISBN 0-8490-3123-0). Gordon Pr.

Pickthall. The Holy Quran: Text & Explanatory Translation. 1983. 25.50 (ISBN 0-686-18527-7). Kazi Pubns.

--The Meaning of the Glorious Quran. pap. 4.95 (ISBN 0-686-18531-5). Kazi Pubns.

Pickthall, M., ed. Holy Quran. 1983. Repr. of 1977 ed. 18.50x (ISBN 0-8364-0989-2, Pub. by R Taj Co). South Asia Bks.

Pickthall, M. M., ed. Holy Quran with English Translation. 1976. Repr. 17.50x (ISBN 0-8364-0415-7). South Asia Bks.

Pickthall, M. M., tr. The Meaning of the Illustrious Qur'an: Arabic & English. 1970. 45.00x (ISBN 0-87902-182-9). Orientalia.

Pickthall, Marmaduke, ed. The Glorious Koran. bilingual ed. 1696p. 1976. text ed. 50.00x (ISBN 0-04-297036-9). Allen Unwin.

Pickthall, Mohammed M., tr. Meaning of the Glorious Koran. pap. 4.50 (ISBN 0-451-62305-3, ME2305, Ment). NAL.

Quasem, Muhammad A. The Jewels of the Qur'an: Al-Ghazali's Theory. 1977. 12.00 (ISBN 0-686-23467-7). Quasem.

--The Jewels of the Qur'an: Al-Ghazali's Theory. 240p. (Orig.). 1984. pap. 12.95 (ISBN 0-7103-0034-4, Kegan Paul). Methuen Inc.

The Quran: A New English Translation, with the Arabic Text. 736p. 1985. 17.00 (ISBN 0-7007-0148-6). Salem Hse Pubs.

Qutb, S. In the Shade of the Qur'an, 30th Part. pap. 14.95 (ISBN 0-317-46111-7). Kazi Pubns.

Rahaman, A. Quranic Sciences. pap. 14.95 (ISBN 0-317-46103-6). Kazi Pubns.

Rahman, A. Subject Index of Holy Quran. 29.00 (ISBN 0-317-14644-0). Kazi Pubns.

Rahman, Fazlur. Major Themes of the Qur'an. LC 79-54189. 1980. 30.00x (ISBN 0-88297-026-7); pap. 16.00x (ISBN 0-88297-027-5). Bibliotheca.

Raza, A. Musa. Muhammad in the Holy Quran. 15.95 (ISBN 0-317-14646-7). Kazi Pubns.

Razwy, Sayed A., ed. The Holy Koran. rev. ed. Ali, A. Yusuf, tr. 424p. 1986. pap. 4.50 (ISBN 0-940368-77-3). Tahrike Tarsile Quran.

Rodwell, J. M., ed. & tr. Koran. 1978. pap. 3.50x (ISBN 0-460-01380-7, Evman). Biblio Dist.

Sales, George & Wherry, E. M., eds. Comprehensive Commentary on the Qur'an, 4 Vols. LC 79-153620. Repr. of 1896 ed. Set. 145.00 (ISBN 0-404-09520-8); 27.50 ea. Vol. 1 (ISBN 0-404-09521-6). Vol. 2 (ISBN 0-404-09522-4). Vol. 3 (ISBN 0-404-09523-2). Vol. 4 (ISBN 0-404-09524-0). AMS Pr.

Sarwar, H. G. Philosophy of the Quran. 4.50 (ISBN 0-686-18604-4). Kazi Pubns.

--Philosophy of the Qur'an. 1969. 7.25x (ISBN 0-87902-187-X). Orientalia.

Seale, M. S. Qur'an & Bible: Studies in Interpretation & Dialogue. 124p. 1978. 23.50 (ISBN 0-85664-818-3, Pub. by Croom Helm Ltd). Methuen Inc.

Shah, A. Miftah-ul-Quran: Glossary of Quran, 2 vols. 22.50 (ISBN 0-686-18525-0). Kazi Pubns.

Shaikh Muhammad Sarwar, tr. from Arabic. The Holy Qur'an. 418p. pap. 10.00 (ISBN 0-941724-00-X). Islamic Seminary.

Shakin, M. H. Holy Quran. (Arabic & Eng.). 634p. 1982. 49.00x (ISBN 0-317-39404-5, Pub. by Luzac & Co Ltd). State Mutual Bk.

Shakir, H. M., tr. Koran. LC 85-51993. (Arabic & Eng.). 672p. 1985. pap. text ed. 6.00 (ISBN 0-940368-56-0). Tahrike Tarsile Quran.

Shakir, M. H., tr. Holy Quran. (Eng. & Arabic.). 660p. 1982. 15.00 (ISBN 0-940368-17-X); pap. 9.00 (ISBN 0-940368-16-1). Tahrike Tarsile Quran.

Shakir, M. H., tr. from Arabic. Koran. 440p. 1985. 15.00 (ISBN 0-933543-05-0); pap. 9.00 (ISBN 0-933543-04-2). Aza Khana.

Shakir, Mahomodali H. The Holy Qur'an. 320p. 1986. text ed. 29.95 (ISBN 0-7103-0162-6); pap. text ed. 20.00 (ISBN 0-7103-0161-8). Methuen Inc.

Sherif, Faruq, ed. A Guide to the Contents of the Qur'an. (Middle East Cultures Ser.: No. 9). 172p. 1985. 25.00 (ISBN 0-86372-030-7, Pub. by Ithaca Pr UK). Humanities.

Siddigi, K. N. The Qur'An & the World Today. 295p. 1971. 7.25x (ISBN 0-87902-249-3). Orientalia.

Siddiqui, A. H. The Holy Quran: Text, Translation & Explanatory Notes, I-VIII. (Avail. in sep. parts). pap. 4.00 ea. Kazi Pubns.

Sirdar Ikbal Ali Shah. Selections from the Koran. 1980. 10.85 (ISBN 0-900860-85-5, Pub. by Octagon Pr England). Ins Study Human.

Stanton, H. U. Teaching of the Qur'An, with an Account of Its Growth & Subject Index. LC 74-90040. 1969. Repr. 18.00 (ISBN 0-8196-0253-1). Biblo.

Tariq, M. A. Holy Quran Made Easy. 1968. 5.35x (ISBN 0-87902-070-9). Orientalia.

Torrey, Charles C. Jewish Foundation of Islam. rev. ed. LC 67-18817. 1968. 20.00x (ISBN 0-87068-117-6). Ktav.

KOREA–RELIGION

Clark, Donald N. Christianity in Modern Korea. LC 86-9092. (Asian Agenda Report: No. 5). 70p. (Orig.). 1986. lib. bdg. 12.75 (ISBN 0-8191-5384-2, Pub. by the Asia Soc); pap. text ed. 4.75 (ISBN 0-8191-5385-0). U Pr of Amer.

Covell, Alan C. Ecstasy: Shamanism in Korea. LC 83-81487. (Illus.). 107p. 1983. 19.50x (ISBN 0-930878-33-7). Hollym Intl.

De Bary, William T. & Haboush, Jahyun K., eds. The Rise of Neo-Confucianism in Korea. 512p. 1985. 40.00x (ISBN 0-231-06052-1). Columbia U pr.

Kendall, Laurel & Dix, Griffin, eds. Religion & Ritual in Korean Society. LC 86-82390. (Korea Research Monograph Ser.: No. 12). xii, 240p. 1987. pap. 15.00x. IEAS.

Lee, Kwan-Jo. Search for Nirvana. (Illus.). 124p. 1984. 24.00 (ISBN 0-8048-1417-1, Pub. by Seoul Intl Publishing House). C E Tuttle.

Palmer, Spencer J. Confucian Rituals in Korea. (Religions of Asia Ser.). (Illus.). 270p. 1984. 30.00 (ISBN 0-89581-457-9). Asian Human Pr.

KOSHER FOOD

see Jews–Dietary Laws

KRISHNA

Bhaktivedanta, Swami A. C. Krsna Consciousness: The Matchless Gift. LC 73-76634. (Illus.). 1974. pap. 1.95 (ISBN 0-912776-61-7). Bhaktivedanta.

--Krsna: The Supreme Personality of Godhead, 3 vols. LC 74-118081. (Illus.). 1970. Vol. 1. pap. 12.95 (ISBN 0-89213-136-5). Bhaktivedanta.

--Srimad Bhagavatam: First Canto, 3 vols. LC 73-169353. (Illus.). 1972. 12.95 ea. Vol. 1 (ISBN 0-912776-27-7). Vol. 2 (ISBN 0-912776-29-3). Vol. 3 (ISBN 0-912776-34-X). Bhaktivedanta.

--Srimad Bhagavatam: Fourth Canto, 4 vols. LC 73-169353. (Illus.). 1974. 12.95 ea. Vol. 1 (ISBN 0-912776-38-2). Vol. 2 (ISBN 0-912776-47-1). Vol. 3 (ISBN 0-912776-48-X). Vol. 4 (ISBN 0-912776-49-8). Bhaktivedanta.

--Srimad Bhagavatam: Second Canto, 2 vols. LC 73-169353. (Illus.). 1972. 12.95 ea. Vol. 1 (ISBN 0-912776-28-5). Vol. 2 (ISBN 0-912776-35-8). Bhaktivedanta.

--Srimad Bhagavatam: Third Canto, 4 vols. LC 73-169353. (Illus.). 1974. 12.95 ea. Vol. 1 (ISBN 0-912776-37-4). Vol. 2 (ISBN 0-912776-44-7). Vol. 3 (ISBN 0-912776-46-3). Vol. 4 (ISBN 0-912776-75-7). Bhaktivedanta.

Bhaktivendanta, Swami A. C. Srimad Bhagavatam: Ninth Canto, 3 vols. LC 73-169353. (Sanskrit & Eng., Illus.). 1977. 12.95 ea. Vol. 1 (ISBN 0-912776-94-3). Vol. 2 (ISBN 0-912776-95-1). Vol. 3 (ISBN 0-912776-96-X). Bhaktivedanta.

Choudhary, Bani R. The Story of Krishna. (Illus.). 1979. 7.25 (ISBN 0-89744-134-6). Auromere.

Daner, Francine J. The American Children of Krsna: Case Studies in Cultural Anthrology. LC 75-15616. 1976. pap. text ed. 9.95 (ISBN 0-03-013546-X, HoltC). HR&W.

Elkin, Judith L. Krishna Smiled: Assignment in Southeast Asia. LC 72-737. pap. 63.30 (2027638). Bks Demand UMI.

Greene, Joshua, retold by. Krishna, Master of All Mystics. (Illus.). 16p. 1981. pap. 4.00 (ISBN 0-89647-010-5). Bala Bks.

Guelinboin, Marie T., illus. Krishna & the Demons. (Illus.). 16p. 1978. pap. 2.50 (ISBN 0-89647-005-9). Bala Bks.

Gupta, Ram C. Sri Krishna: A Socio-Political & Philosophical Study. xiv, 188p. 1984. text ed. 30.00x (ISBN 0-86590-376-X, Pub. by B R Pub Corp Delhi). Apt Bks.

Hawley, John S. At Play with Krishna: Pilgrimage Dramas from Brindavan. LC 80-8552. (Illus.). 360p. 1985. 37.00x (ISBN 0-691-06470-9); pap. 10.95x (ISBN 0-691-01419-1). Princeton U Pr.

Hutchins, Francis G. Young Krishna. LC 80-66834. (Illus.). 132p. 1980. 29.50 (ISBN 0-935100-01-6); pap. 14.00 (ISBN 0-935100-05-9). Amarta Pr.

Johnson, Una, et al. Krishna Reddy: A Retrospective. (Illus.). 78p. (Orig.). 1981. pap. 10.00 (ISBN 0-89062-138-1, Pub by Bronx Museum Arts). Pub Ctr Cult Res.

Kinsley, David R. The Divine Player: A Study of Krishna Lila. 1978. 17.95 (ISBN 0-89684-019-0, Pub. by Motilal Barnarsidass India). Orient Bk Dist.

--The Divine Player: A Study of Krishna Lila. 1979. 22.00x (ISBN 0-89684-019-0). South Asia Bks.

--The Sword & the Flute-Kali & Krsna: Dark Visions of the Terrible & the Sublime in Hindu Mythology. LC 73-91669. (Hermeneutics: Studies in the History of Religions). 175p. 1975. pap. 10.95x (ISBN 0-520-03510-0). U of Cal Pr.

Klaiman, M. H., tr. Singing the Glory of Lord Krishna Baru Candidasa's Srikrsnakirtana: Baru Candidasa's Srikrsnakirtana. LC 84-3905. (SP AAR Classics in Religious Studies). 1984. 28.75 (ISBN 0-89130-736-2, 01 05 05); pap. 20.75 (ISBN 0-89130-737-0). Scholars Pr GA.

Losty, Jeremiah P. Krishna: A Hindu Vision of God. (Illus.). 52p. (Orig.). 1980. pap. 3.75 (ISBN 0-904654-51-6, Pub. by British Lib). Longwood Pub Group.

Mirabai & Nandy, Pritish. Krishna: Devotional Songs of Mirabai. 68p. (Orig.). 1982. pap. text ed. O.P. (ISBN 0-7069-1495-3, Pub. by Vikas India); text ed. 5.25x (ISBN 0-7069-1494-5). Advent NY.

Pal, P. Krishna: The Cowherd King. LC 70-185825. 1972. pap. 4.95x (ISBN 0-87587-048-1). LA Co Art Mus.

Poddar, Hanumanprasad. Gopis' Love for Sri Krishna. (Illus.). 51p. 1981. pap. 9.95 (ISBN 0-913922-51-X). Dawn Horse Pr.

Prabhavananda, Swami. Bhagavatam, Srimad: The Wisdom of God. 1978. Repr. of 1943 ed. 5.95 (ISBN 0-87481-483-9). Vedanta Pr.

Rajneesh, Bhagwan Shree. Krishna: The Man & His Philosophy. Sambuddha, Swami Anand, ed. LC 85-43055. (Early Writings & Discourses Ser.). 880p. 1985. pap. 5.95 (ISBN 0-88050-713-6). Chidvilas Found.

Saradananda, Swami. Ramakrishna, Sri: The Great Master, Pts. 1 & 2. rev. ed. Swami Jagadananda, tr. (Illus.). 1980. Pt. 1, 563p. pap. 8.50x ea. (ISBN 0-87481-495-2). Pt. 2 (ISBN 0-87481-496-0). Vedanta Pr.

Satsvarupa dasa Goswami. A Lifetime in Preparation: Srila Prabhupada-lilamrta, Vol. 1. (Illus.). 357p. 1980. 12.95 (ISBN 0-686-71685-X). Bhaktivedanta.

Singer, Milton, ed. Krishna: Myths, Rites, & Attitudes. LC 65-20585. 1969. pap. 12.00x (ISBN 0-226-76101-0, P329, Phoen). U of Chicago Pr.

Singer, Milton B., ed. Krishna: Myths, Rites, & Attitudes. LC 80-29194. xvii, 277p. 1981. Repr. of 1966 ed. lib. bdg. 27.50x (ISBN 0-313-22822-1, SIKR). Greenwood.

Singh, Bhagat. The Story of Krishna. (Illus.). 20p. (Orig.). 1976. pap. 1.75 (ISBN 0-89744-135-4, Pub. by Hemkunt India). Auromere.

Swami, Shri P., tr. The Geeta. 96p. (Orig.). 1965. pap. 5.95 (ISBN 0-571-06157-5). Faber & Faber.

Wilson, Frances, ed. & tr. The Love of Krishna: The Krsnakarnamrta of Lilasuka Bilvamangala. LC 74-153426. (Haney Foundation Ser.). 448p. 1975. 24.00x (ISBN 0-8122-7655-8). U of Pa Pr.

KRISHNA IN ART, LITERATURE, ETC.

Dimock, Edward C., Jr. & Levertov, Denise, trs. In Praise of Krishna: Songs from the Bengali. (Illus.). xii, 96p. 1981. 6.95 (ISBN 0-226-15231-6, Phoen). U of Chicago Pr.

Isacco, Enrico & Dallapiccola, Anna L., eds. Krishna: The Divine Lover. LC 82-83044. (Illus.). 224p. 1983. 75.00 (ISBN 0-87923-457-1). Godine.

Lewis, Samuel L. The Rejected Avatar. (Illus.). 24p. (Orig.). 1968. pap. 1.25 saddlestitched (ISBN 0-915424-00-2, Prophecy Pressworks). Sufi Islamia-Prophecy.

Seth, S. J. The Divinity of Krishna. 1984. text ed. 14.00x. Coronet Bks.

White, Charles S., ed. The Caurasi Pad of Sri Hit Harivams: Introduction, Translation, Notes, & Edited Hindi Text. LC 76-54207. (Asian Studies at Hawaii Ser: No. 16). 212p. 1977. pap. text ed. 10.50x (ISBN 0-8248-0359-0). UH Pr.

KRISHNAMURTI, JIDDU, 1895-

Chandmal, Asit. One Thousand Moons: Krishnamurti at Eighty-Five. (Illus.). 128p. 1985. 25.00 (ISBN 0-8109-1209-0). Abrams.

Fouere, Rene. Krishnamurti: The Man & His Teaching. 1974. lib. bdg. 69.95 (ISBN 0-8490-0477-2). Gordon Pr.

Jayakar, Pupul. Krishnamurti: A Biography. LC 85-45739. (Illus.). 525p. 1986. 22.95 (ISBN 0-06-250401-0, HarpR). Har-Row.

Krishnamurti. Krishnamurti's Journal. Lutyens, Mary, ed. LC 81-48210. 1982. pap. 5.95 (ISBN 0-06-064841-4, RD-396, HarpR). Har-Row.

Krishnamurti, J. Early Writings of Krishnamurti, 2 Vols. 1974. lib. bdg. 250.00 (ISBN 0-87968-533-6). Krishna Pr.

Lutyens, Mary. Krishnamurti: The Years of Fulfillment. 248p. 1983. 15.50 (ISBN 0-374-18224-8). FS&G.

Methorst-Kuiper, A. J. Krishnamurti: A Biography. 1974. lib. bdg. 79.95 (ISBN 0-87968-545-X). Krishna Pr.

Powell, Robert. The Great Awakening. Nicholson, Shirley, ed. LC 83-70688. Orig. Title: Zen & Reality. 179p. 1983. pap. 6.50 (ISBN 0-8356-0577-9, Quest). Theos Pub Hse.

Shringy, R. K. Philosophy of J. Krishnamurti: A Systematic Study. LC 78-670076. 1977. 24.00x (ISBN 0-89684-442-0). Orient Bk Dist.

Suares, Carlo. Krishnamurti & the Unity of Man. 1974. lib. bdg. 69.95 (ISBN 0-8490-0476-4). Gordon Pr.

KUHN, ISOBEL

Kuhn, Isobel. By Searching. 1959. pap. 3.95 (ISBN 0-8024-0053-1). Moody.

Reason, Joyce. Searcher for God (Isabel Kuhn) 1963. pap. 2.95 (ISBN 0-87508-621-7). Chr Lit.

Tallach, John. God Made Them Great. 144p. 1982. pap. 5.45 (ISBN 0-85151-190-2). Banner of Truth.

KUKAI, 774-835

Hakeda, Yoshita S., tr. from Japanese. Kukai: Major Works, Translated with an Account of His Life & a Study of His Thought. LC 72-3124. (Records of Civilization, Sources, Studies & Translations of the Oriental Classics Ser.). 303p. 1972. 30.00x (ISBN 0-231-03627-2); pap. 14.00x (ISBN 0-231-05933-7). Columbia U Pr.

Shaner, David E. The Bodymind Experience in Japanese Buddhism: A Phenomenological Study of Kukai & Dogen. (Series in Buddhist Studies). 202p. 1986. 44.50x (ISBN 0-88706-061-7); pap. 14.95x (ISBN 0-88706-062-5). State U NY Pr.

Statler, Oliver. Japanese Pilgrimage. (Illus.). 352p. 1985. pap. 9.95 (ISBN 0-688-04834-X, Quill). Morrow.

KUMRAN COMMUNITY

see Qumran Community

KUNDALI YOGA

see Yoga, Hatha

KUNG, HANS, 1928-

LaCugna, Catherine M. The Theological Methodology of Hans Kung. LC 81-16654. (American Academy of Religion Academy Ser.). 1982. 12.95 (ISBN 0-89130-546-7, 01 01 39). Scholars Pr GA.

L

LABOR AND THE CHURCH

see Church and Labor

LAITY

see also Lay Readers; Priesthood, Universal

Anderson, James D. & Jones, Ezra E. Ministry of the Laity. LC 84-48211. 224p. 1985. 14.45 (ISBN 0-06-060194-9, HarpR). Har-Row.

Congar, Yves. Lay People in the Church. 518p. 1985. pap. 14.95 (ISBN 0-87061-114-3). Chr Classics.

Directory of Lay Ministry Training Programs. 1986. pap. 9.95 (ISBN 1-55586-109-1). US Catholic.

Doohan, Leonard. The Laity: A Bibliography. LC 87-45006. (Theological & Biblical Resources). 160p. (Orig.). 1987. pap. 8.95 (ISBN 0-89453-617-6). M Glazier.

--Laity's Mission in the Local Church. 204p. (Orig.). 1986. pap. 8.95 (ISBN 0-86683-490-7, HarpR). Har-Row.

Droel, William & Pierce, Gregory. Confident & Competent: A Challenge for the Lay Church. LC 86-72789. 112p. (Orig.). 1987. pap. 3.95 (ISBN 0-87793-351-0). Ave Maria.

Duquoc, Christian, ed. Spirituality in Church & World. LC 65-28868. (Concilium Ser.: Vol. 9). 174p. 7.95 (ISBN 0-8091-0139-4). Paulist Pr.

Flood, Edmund. The Laity Today & Tomorrow. 120p. (Orig.). 1987. pap. 4.95 (ISBN 0-8091-2848-9). Paulist Pr.

Gifts: A Laity Reader, Selected Articles from the Gifts Journal 1979-1983. 124p. 1983. pap. 3.95 (ISBN 1-55586-879-7). US Catholic.

Guia Para Damas Auxiliares. (Span.). 102p. pap. 2.95 (ISBN 0-87148-361-0). Pathway Pr.

Gustafson, Gus. I Was...Called To Be a Layman. 176p. (Orig.). 1982. pap. 7.95 (ISBN 0-687-18604-8). Abingdon.

Hall, Cameron P. Lay Action: The Church's Third Force. (Orig.). 1974. pap. 3.50 (ISBN 0-377-00018-3). Friend Pr.

Howington, Nolan P. A Royal Priesthood. LC 85-22376. 1986. pap. 4.95 (ISBN 0-8054-1622-6). Broadman.

Lindgren, Alvin J. & Shawchuck, Norman. Let My People Go: Empowering Laity for Ministry. LC 80-16035. 144p. (Orig.). 1982. pap. 7.95 (ISBN 0-687-21377-0). Abingdon.

Liptak, David Q. & Sheridan, Philip A. The New Code: Laity & Deacons. 128p. (Orig.). 1986. pap. 7.95 (ISBN 0-941850-20-X). Sunday Pubns.

Peck, George & Hoffman, John S., eds. The Laity in Ministry. 176p. 1984. pap. 7.95 (ISBN 0-8170-1041-6). Judson.

Rowthorn, Anne W. The Liberation of the Laity. 232p. (Orig.). 1986. pap. 9.95 (ISBN 0-8192-1395-0). Morehouse.

Shockey, Richard W. Training for Hospital Visitation: A Three-Week Course for Laypersons. LC 86-42930. 40p. (Orig.). 1986. pap. 4.00 (ISBN 0-937021-01-6). Sagamore Bks MI.

Southard, Samuel. Training Church Members for Pastoral Care. 96p. 1982. pap. 4.95 (ISBN 0-8170-0944-2). Judson.

Stevens, R. Paul. Liberating the Laity. LC 85-10856. 192p. (Orig.). 1985. pap. 5.95 (ISBN 0-87784-613-8). Inter-Varsity.

Stott, John. One People. Rev. ed. 128p. 1982. pap. 4.95 (ISBN 0-8007-5099-3, Power Bks). Revell.

To Build & Be Church, Lay Ministry Resource Packet. 73p. 1979. pap. 6.50 (ISBN 1-55586-621-2). US Catholic.

Vaillancourt, Jean-Guy. Papal Power: A Study of Vatican Control Over Lay Catholic Elites. 375p. 1980. 24.95x (ISBN 0-520-03733-2). U of Cal Pr.

Whitehead, James D. & Whitehead, Evelyn E. Emerging Laity: Returning Leadership to the Community of Faith. LC 85-31201. 240p. 1986. 15.95 (ISBN 0-385-23612-3). Doubleday.

LAMAISM

see also Bon (Tibetan Religion)

Avedon, John F. An Interview with the Dalai Lama. LC 80-83015. (Illus.). 83p. (Orig.). 1980. pap. 6.95 (ISBN 0-937896-00-4). Littlebird.

Chapman, F. Spencer. Lhasa the Holy City. facsimile ed. LC 75-37875. (Select Bibliographies Reprint Ser). Repr. of 1940 ed. 32.00 (ISBN 0-8369-6712-7). Ayer Co Pubs.

David-Neel, Alexandra. Secret Oral Teachings in Tibetan Buddhist Sects. 1967. pap. 4.95 (ISBN 0-87286-012-4). City Lights.

Ekvall, Robert B. The Lama Knows: A Tibetan Legend Is Born. LC 81-4160. (Illus.). 144p. 1981. pap. 5.95 (ISBN 0-88316-541-4). Chandler & Sharp.

Ellam, J. E. The Religion of Tibet: Study of Lamaism. 59.95 (ISBN 0-8490-0940-5). Gordon Pr.

Fourteenth Dalai Lama His Holiness Tenzin Gyatso. Kindness, Clarity & Insight. Hopkins, Jeffrey & Napper, Elizabeth, eds. LC 84-51198. (Illus.). 250p. (Orig.). 1984. pap. 10.95 (ISBN 0-937938-18-1). Snow Lion.

Goodman, Michael H. The Last Dalai Lama. LC 85-27906. 400p. 1987. pap. 14.95 (ISBN 0-87773-400-3). Shambhala Pubns.

Hoffmann, Helmut. The Religions of Tibet. LC 78-11420. (Illus.). 1979. Repr. of 1961 ed. lib. bdg. 24.75x (ISBN 0-313-21120-5, HORT). Greenwood.

Mullin, Glenn, et al. Selected Works of the Dalai Lama I: Bridging the Sutras & Tantras. Rev. ed. LC 85-8333. (Teachings of the Dalai Lamas Ser.). Orig. Title: Bridging the Sutras & Tantras. (Tibetan., Illus.). 288p. (Orig.). 1985. pap. 12.95 (ISBN 0-937938-27-0). Snow Lion.

Mullin, Glenn H. Selected Works of the Dalai Lama VII: Songs of Spiritual Change. Rev. ed. LC 85-8332. (Teachings of the Dalai Lamas Ser.). Orig. Title: Songs of Spiritual Change. (Tibetan., Illus.). 225p. 1985. pap. 10.95 (ISBN 0-937938-30-0). Snow Lion.

Mullin, Glenn H., et al. Selected Works of the Dalai Lama II: The Tantric Yogas of the Sister Niguma. LC 85-40081. (Teachings of the Dalai Lamas Ser.). (Tibetan., Illus.). 240p. (Orig.). 1985. pap. 10.95 (ISBN 0-937938-28-9). Snow Lion.

--Selected Works of the Dalai Lama III: Essence of Refined Gold. Rev. ed. LC 85-8359. (Teachings of the Dalai Lamas Ser.). Orig. Title: Essence of Refined Gold. (Tibetan.). 264p. 1985. pap. 10.95 (ISBN 0-937938-29-7). Snow Lion.

Pozdneyev, Aleksei M. Religion & Ritual in Society: Lamaist Buddhism in Late 19th-Century Mongolia. Krueger, John R., ed. Raun, Alo & Raun, Linda, trs. from Rus. (Occasional Papers Ser.: No. 10). Orig. Title: Ocherki Byta Buddiiskikh Monastyrei. pap. 15.00x (ISBN 0-910980-50-0). Mongolia.

Rampa, T. Lobsang. Third Eye. 1974. pap. 2.50 (ISBN 0-345-29023-2). Ballantine.

Waddell, Austine. Buddhism & Lamaism of Tibet. 1985. text ed. 40.00x (ISBN 0-86590-615-7, Pub. by Sterling Pubs India). Apt Bks.

--Tibetan Buddhism with Its Mystic Cults Symbolism & Mythology, & in Its Relation to Indian Buddhism. (Illus.). 598p. 1972. pap. 8.95 (ISBN 0-486-20130-9). Dover.

LAMBETH CONFERENCE

Curtis, William R. Lambeth Conferences: The Solution for Pan-Anglican Organization. LC 68-58565. (Columbia University Studies in the Social Sciences: No. 488). Repr. of 1942 ed. 24.50 (ISBN 0-404-51488-X). AMS Pr.

Smyth, Norman. Story of Church Unity: The Lambeth Conference of Anglican Bishops & the Congregational-Episcopal Approaches. 1923. 29.50x (ISBN 0-686-83788-6). Elliots Bks.

Stephenson, Alan M. First Lambeth Conference. LC 67-95915. (Church Historical Society Ser.: No. 88). 1967. 22.50x (ISBN 0-8401-5088-1). A R Allenson.

LANGLAND, WILLIAM, 1330-1400

Chambers, R. W. Poets & Their Critics: Langland & Milton. 1942. lib. bdg. 10.00 (ISBN 0-685-10478-8). Folcroft.

--Text of Piers Plowman. LC 72-195253. lib. bdg. 10.00 (ISBN 0-8414-3015-2). Folcroft.

Holloway, Julia B. THe Pilgrim & the Book: A Study of Dante, Langland & Chaucer. (American University Studies IV- English Language & Literature: Vol. 42). 343p. 1987. text ed. 30.75 (ISBN 0-8204-0345-8). P Lang Pubs.

Hort, Greta. Piers Plowman & Contemporary Religious Thought. LC 72-193685. lib. bdg. 15.00 (ISBN 0-8414-5129-X). Folcroft.

Taitt, Peter S. Incubus & Ideal: Ecclesiastical Figures In Chaucer & Langland. Hogg, James, ed. (Elizabethan & Renaissance Studies). 228p. (Orig.). 1975. pap. 15.00 (ISBN 3-7052-0690-7, Pub. by Salzburg Studies). Longwood Pub Group.

LANGO (AFRICAN TRIBE)

Curley, Richard T. Elders, Shades, & Women: Ceremonial Change in Lango, Uganda. LC 70-634788. 1973. 32.50x (ISBN 0-520-02149-5). U of Cal Pr.

Hayley, Thomas T. Anatomy of Lango Religion & Groups. LC 74-100263. Repr. of 1947 ed. cancelled (ISBN 0-8371-2871-4, HLR&, Pub. by Negro U Pr). Greenwood.

LANGUAGE AND LANGUAGES–RELIGIOUS ASPECTS

see Language Question in the Church; Religion and Language

LANGUAGE AND RELIGION

see Religion and Language

LANGUAGE QUESTION IN THE CHURCH

see also Bible–Publication and Distribution; Bible–Versions; Latin Language–Church Latin

Weinstein, Brian. The Civic Tongue: Political Consequences of Language Choices. LC 82-15268. (Professional Studies in Political Communication & Policy). 213p. 1982. 22.50x (ISBN 0-582-29010-4). Longman.

LANGUAGES–RELIGIOUS ASPECTS

see also Bible–Language, Style; Bible–Versions; Greek Language, Biblical; Hebrew Language; Language Question in the Church; Latin Language–Church Latin; Religion and Language

Wild, Laura H. The Romance of the English Bible. 1929. 15.00 (ISBN 0-8274-3303-4). R West.

LAO-TZU

Harris, Iverson L. The Wisdom of Laotse. 36p. 1972. pap. 0.75 (ISBN 0-913004-05-7). Point Loma Pub.

Men-Ching, Cheng. Lao-Tzu: My Words Are Very Easy to Understand. 2nd ed. Gibbs, Tam & Huang, Juh-Hua, trs. (Eng. & Chinese.). 256p. 1981. pap. 8.95 (ISBN 0-913028-91-6). North Atlantic.

Rump, Ariane & Chan, Wing-Tsit, trs. Commentary on the Lao Tzu by Wang Pi. LC 79-11212. (Society for Asian & Comparative Philosophy Monograph: No. 6). 266p. 1979. pap. text ed. 8.00x (ISBN 0-8248-0677-8). UH Pr.

Welch, Holmes. Taoism: The Parting of the Way. Orig. Title: Parting of the Way. 1966. pap. 6.95 (ISBN 0-8070-5973-0, BP224). Beacon Pr.

LAPPISH MYTHOLOGY

see Mythology, Finno-Ugrian

LARGE TYPE BOOKS

Brians, Bert. Leoni Meadows Experiences. large print ed. 62p. 1984. pap. 9.00 (ISBN 0-914009-07-9). VHI Library.

Brians, Charlene. How I Use Herbs. large print ed. 37p. 1985. pap. 5.50 (ISBN 0-914009-43-5). VHI Library.

Brians, Charline. Light after Ellen White. large print ed. 32p. 1985. pap. 5.00 (ISBN 0-914009-06-0). VHI Library.

--Sunday Sister. large print ed. 24p. 1985. pap. 4.00 (ISBN 0-914009-53-2). VHI Library.

--Testing Myself As a Prophet. large print ed. 1985. pap. 5.00 (ISBN 0-914009-10-9). VHI Library.

Brians, Pearl. Adventist Evangelist's Diary. large print ed. 1985. pap. 4.00 (ISBN 0-914009-25-7). VHI Library.

--Appetite Control for Christians. large print ed. 28p. 1985. pap. 4.50 (ISBN 0-914009-30-3). VHI Library.

--Carelessness & Indifference. large print ed. 25p. 1985. pap. 5.00 (ISBN 0-914009-39-7). VHI Library.

--Defending the Blind Man. large print ed. 1985. pap. 4.00 (ISBN 0-914009-28-1). VHI Library.

--During My Conversion. large print ed. 44p. 1984. pap. 8.00 (ISBN 0-914009-11-7). VHI Library.

--Indecision about Baptism. large print ed. 34p. 1985. pap. 5.00 (ISBN 0-914009-41-9). VHI Library.

--Ingathering Experience, Vol. 1. large print ed. 33p. 1985. pap. 5.00 (ISBN 0-914009-32-X). VHI Library.

--Mama's Life on a Missouri Farm. large print ed. 86p. pap. 8.00 (ISBN 0-914009-26-5). VHI Library.

--My Appetite Control. large print ed. 1985. pap. 6.00 (ISBN 0-914009-40-0). VHI Library.

--My First SDA Camp Meeting. large print ed. 44p. 1985. pap. 6.00 (ISBN 0-914009-27-3). VHI Library.

--Out of Confusion-into the Light. large print ed. 58p. 1984. pap. 9.50 (ISBN 0-914009-12-5). VHI Library.

--Overeaters Feelings & Faith. large print ed. 40p. 1985. pap. 5.50 (ISBN 0-914009-31-1). VHI Library.

--Pleading with the Father. large print ed. 27p. 1985. pap. 4.50 (ISBN 0-914009-36-2). VHI Library.

--Prayer Changes My Life. large print ed. 23p. 1985. pap. 4.00 (ISBN 0-914009-35-4). VHI Library.

--Prayer Meeting at Our House. large print ed. 25p. 1985. pap. 4.00 (ISBN 0-914009-33-8). VHI Library.

--Recovery from Compulsive Overeating. large print ed. 31p. 1985. pap. 5.00 (ISBN 0-914009-29-X). VHI Library.

Buechner, Frederick. The Sacred Journey. 224p. 1984. pap. 8.95 large print ed. (ISBN 0-8027-2479-5). Walker & Co.

Calkins & White. Talk to God about The Sabbath. large type ed. 70p. 1984. pap. 8.50x (ISBN 0-914009-22-2). VHI Library.

Coburn, John B. Prayer & Personal Religion. LC 85-10477. 160p. 1985. pap. 8.95 (ISBN 0-8027-2509-0). Walker & Co.

Dailey, Janet. For the Love of God. (Nightingale Paperbacks Ser.). 1984. pap. 9.95 (ISBN 0-8161-3697-1, Large Print Bks). G K Hall.

Drury, Michael. The Adventure of Spiritual Healing. 304p. 1985. pap. 9.95 large print ed. (ISBN 0-8027-2493-0). Walker & Co.

Edwards, Tilden. Living Simply Through the Day. 444p. 1985. pap. 9.95 large print ed. (ISBN 0-8027-2492-2). Walker & Co.

Graham, Billy & Ten Boom, Corrie. To God Be the Glory. 62p. 1985. pap. text ed. 4.95 large print ed. (ISBN 0-8027-2473-6). Walker & Co.

Hayes, Helen. A Gathering of Hope. 222p. 1985. pap. 7.95 large print ed. (ISBN 0-8027-2467-1). Walker & Co.

Helleberg, Marilyn M. A Guide to Christian Meditation. 258p. 1985. pap. 9.95 large print ed. (ISBN 0-8027-2489-2). Walker & Co.

Hersey, Jean. The Touch of the Earth. 396p. 1985. pap. 10.95 large print ed. (ISBN 0-8027-2481-7). Walker & Co.

Kreis, Bernardine & Pattie, Alice. Up from Grief. 292p. 1984. pap. 9.95 large print ed. (ISBN 0-8027-2486-8). Walker & Co.

Kushner, Harold S. When Bad Things Happen to Good People. (General Ser.). 1982. lib. bdg. 13.95 (ISBN 0-8161-3465-0, Large Print Bks). G K Hall.

Large Type Treasury of Inspiration. 1986. 8.98 (625334). Outlet Bk Co.

Lauterbach, William. Es Will Abend Werden. Kujath, Mentor, ed. 1978. pap. 2.25 (ISBN 0-8100-0101-2, 26-0511). Northwest Pub.

L'Engle, Madeleine. The Irrational Season. 430p. 1985. pap. 13.95 large print ed. (ISBN 0-8027-2476-0). Walker & Co.

Lewis, C. S. A Grief Observed. 120p. 1985. pap. 5.95 large print ed. (ISBN 0-8027-2470-1). Walker & Co.

--The Screwtape Letters. Bd. with Screwtape Proposes a Toast. 1964-67. 9.95 (ISBN 0-02-571240-3). Macmillan.

Meyer, Frederick B. The Shepherd Psalm. (Large Print Christian Classics Ser.). (Illus.). 1984. large print 9.95 (ISBN 0-87983-361-0). Keats.

Moss, Michele & Brians, Charlene. Latter Rain. large print ed. 24p. 1984. pap. 5.00 (ISBN 0-914009-03-6). VHI Library.

Mother Teresa. Words to Love By. 160p. 1985. pap. 6.95 large print ed. (ISBN 0-8027-2478-7). Walker & Co.

Nouwen, Henri. With Open Hands. 96p. 1985. pap. 4.95 large print ed. (ISBN 0-8027-2475-2). Walker & Co.

Nouwen, Henri J. The Genesee Diary: Report from a Trappist Monastery. LC 85-7150. 352p. 1985. pap. 12.95 (ISBN 0-8027-2500-7). Walker & Co.

O'Driscoll, Herbert. A Certain Life: Contemporary Meditations on the Way of Christ. 192p. 1985. pap. 8.95 large print ed. (ISBN 0-8027-2491-4); pap. cancelled (ISBN 0-8027-7274-9). Walker & Co.

Oke, Janette. Love's Abiding Joy. 217p. 1985. Large Print. pap. 6.95 (ISBN 0-317-20707-5). Bethany Hse.

--Love's Long Journey. 207p. 1985. Large Print. pap. 6.95 (ISBN 0-317-20714-8). Bethany Hse.

--Love's Unending Legacy. 224p. 1985. Large Print. pap. 6.95 (ISBN 0-87123-855-1). Bethany Hse.

Paton, Alan. Instrument of Thy Peace. 124p. 1985. pap. text ed. 8.95 large print ed. (ISBN 0-8027-2494-9). Walker & Co.

Peale, Norman V. The Power of Positive Thinking. 552p. 1985. pap. 15.95 large print ed. (ISBN 0-8027-2465-5). Walker & Co.

Pocketpac Bks. Promises for the Golden Years. 96p. 1983. pap. 2.50 (ISBN 0-87788-320-3). Shaw Pubs.

Pope John Paul II. Words of Certitude. 266p. 1985. pap. 7.95 large print ed. (ISBN 0-8027-2477-9). Walker & Co.

Read, David H. The Christian Faith. LC 85-10473. 256p. 1985. pap. 9.95 (ISBN 0-8027-2515-5). Walker & Co.

Ripple, Paula. Walking with Loneliness. 318p. 1985. pap. 9.95 large print ed. (ISBN 0-8027-2490-6). Walker & Co.

Russell, Arthur J., ed. God Calling: A Devotional Diary. 10.95 (ISBN 0-396-02621-4). Dodd.

Schuller, Robert. The Be-Happy Attitudes. lg. print ed. 1986. 12.95 (ISBN 0-8499-3055-3). Word Bks.

--Tough Times Never Last but Tough People Do! 256p. 1984. pap. 3.95 (ISBN 0-553-24245-8). Bantam.

Schuller, Robert H. Robert H. Schuller Tells You How to Be an Extraordinary Person in an Ordinary World. Schuller, Robert A., ed. 1987. 16.95 (Large Print Bks). G K Hall.

--Tough Minded Faith for Tender Hearted People. Date not set. 16.95 (ISBN 0-8161-3806-0, Large Print Bks); pap. 9.95 (ISBN 0-8161-3815-X). G K Hall.

--Tough Times Never Last, but Tough People Do! (General Ser.). 1984. lib. bdg. 13.95 (ISBN 0-8161-3677-7, Large Print Bks). G K Hall.

Trine, Ralph W. In Tune with the Infinite. (Large Type Christian Classics Ser.). 1984. large print 10.95 (ISBN 0-87983-360-2). Keats.

Veninga, Robert L. A Gift of Hope: How We Survive Our Tragedies. (Large Print Bks.). 404p. 1986. lib. bdg. 16.95 (ISBN 0-8161-4101-0, Large Print Bks). G K Hall.

White, Ellen. The Broad Road. large print ed. 32p. 1985. pap. 5.00 (ISBN 0-914009-47-8). VHI Library.

--Forbidden Marriages & Divorce. large print ed. 27p. 1985. pap. 5.00 (ISBN 0-914009-38-9). VHI Library.

--Overeating: A Common Sin. large print ed. 52p. 1985. pap. 6.50 (ISBN 0-914009-45-1). VHI Library.

--Passions. 1985. pap. 6.00 (ISBN 0-914009-55-9). VHI Library.

--Passions among God's People. large print ed. 35p. 1985. pap. 6.00 (ISBN 0-914009-46-X). VHI Library.

--Subdue Sins. large print ed. 41p. 1985. pap. 5.50 (ISBN 0-914009-44-3). VHI Library.

Yates, Elizabeth. A Book of Hours. 128p. 1985. pap. 4.95 large print ed. (ISBN 0-8027-2484-1). Walker & Co.

Zahl, Paul. Who Will Deliver Us? 170p. 1985. pap. 7.95 large print ed. (ISBN 0-8027-2487-6). Walker & Co.

LAS CASAS, BARTOLOME DE, 1474-1566

Helps, Arthur. The Life of las Casas: The Apostle of the Indies. 1976. lib. bdg. 75.00 (ISBN 0-8490-2165-0). Gordon Pr.

MacNutt, Francis A. Bartholomew De Las Casas: His Life, His Apostolate, & His Writings. LC 70-172712. Repr. of 1909 ed. 32.45 (ISBN 0-404-07146-5). AMS Pr.

LAST JUDGMENT

see Judgment Day

LAST SUPPER

Here are entered works on the final meal of Christ with his apostles when the sacrament of the Lord's Supper was instituted.

see also Lord's Supper

Daughters of St. Paul. Living & Growing Through the Eucharist. 1976. 7.00 (ISBN 0-8198-0432-0); pap. 6.00 (ISBN 0-8198-0433-9). Dghtrs St Paul.

Lamb, Bob. The Lord's Supper: More Than a Ritual. 1983. pap. 2.95 (ISBN 0-910709-08-4). PTL Repro.

Lussier, Ernest. Christ's Farewell Discourse. LC 79-19798. 90p. (Orig.). 1980. pap. 3.95 (ISBN 0-8189-0394-5). Alba.

Marshall, I. Howard. Last Supper & Lord's Supper. (Orig.). 1981. pap. 6.95 (ISBN 0-8028-1854-4). Eerdmans.

LATIMER, HUGH, BP, OF WORCESTER, 1485-1555

Chester, Allan G. Hugh Latimer, Apostle to the English. 1978. Repr. of 1954 ed. lib. bdg. 20.00x (ISBN 0-374-91492-3, Octagon). Hippocrene Bks.

Latimer, Hugh. Selected Sermons of Hugh Latimer. Chester, Allan G., ed. (Documents Ser). 1978. 16.00x (ISBN 0-918016-43-6). Folger Bks.

Stuart, Clara. Latimer: Apostle to the English. 320p. 1986. 15.95 (ISBN 0-310-41370-2). Zondervan.

LATIN AMERICA–RELIGION

Belli, Humberto. Breaking Faith: The Sandinista Revolution & Its Impact on Freedom & the Christian Faith in Nicaragua. LC 85-70475. 288p. 1985. pap. 8.95 (ISBN 0-89107-359-0, Crossway Bks). Good News.

Bermudez, Fernando. Death & Resurrection in Guatemala. Barr, Robert R., tr. from Span. LC 85-48305. Tr. of Cristo Muere y Resucita en Guatemala. 96p. (Orig.). 1986. pap. 7.95 (ISBN 0-88344-268-X). Orbis Bks.

Cleary, Edward L. Crisis & Change: The Church in Latin America Today. LC 84-16478. 208p. (Orig.). 1985. pap. 11.95 (ISBN 0-88344-149-7). Orbis Bks.

Cole, Jeffrey A., ed. The Church & the Society in Latin American. 379p. 1984. pap. 12.00 (ISBN 0-317-43435-7). Tulane U Ctr Lat.

Costas, O., et al, eds. Hacia Una Teologia Evangelica Latinoamericana. 154p. 1984. pap. 3.95 (ISBN 0-89922-238-2). Edit Caribe.

Das Goswami, Satsvarupa. Srila Prbhupada in Latin America. Dasa, Mandalesvara & Dasi, Bimala, eds. (Prabhupada-lila). (Orig.). Vol. 7. pap. text ed. 2.00 (ISBN 0-911233-05-9). Gita-Nagari.

Dussel, Enrique. The History of the Church in Latin America: Colonialism to Liberation. Neely, Alan, tr. 368p. 1981. 21.95 (ISBN 0-8028-3548-1). Eerdmans.

Galdamez, Pablo. Faith of a People: The Life of a Basic Christian Community in El Salvador. Barr, Robert R., tr. from Span. LC 85-30981. Tr. of La Fe de un Pueblo: Historia de una Comunidad Cristiana en El Salvador. 112p. (Orig.). 1986. pap. 7.95 (ISBN 0-88344-270-1). Orbis Bks.

Gutierrez, Gustavo. We Drink from Our Own Wells: The Spiritual Journey of a People. O'Connell, Matthew J., tr. from Span. LC 83-22008. Orig. Title: Beber en Supropio Pozo: En el Itinerario Espiritual de un Pueblo. 208p. (Orig.). 1984. pap. 7.95 (ISBN 0-88344-707-X). Orbis Bks.

Latorre Cabal, Hugo. The Revolution of the Latin American Church. Hendricks, Frances K. & Berler, Beatrice, trs. from Span. LC 77-9117. 1978. 14.95x (ISBN 0-8061-1449-5). U of Okla Pr.

Lee, Elizabeth M. He Wears Orchids & Other Latin American Stories. LC 76-117327. (Biography Index Reprint Ser). 1951. 19.00 (ISBN 0-8369-8019-0). Ayer Co Pubs.

Levine, Daniel H., ed. Religion & Political Conflict in Latin America. LC 85-24525. xiii, 266p. 1986. 24.95x (ISBN 0-8078-1689-2); pap. 9.95x (ISBN 0-8078-4150-1). U of NC Pr.

Perez-Esquivel, Adolfo. Christ in a Poncho: Witnesses to the Nonviolent Struggles in Latin America. Barr, Robert R., tr. from Fr. LC 82-18760. Tr. of Le Christ au poncho, suivi de Temoignages de luttes nonviolentes en Amerique Latine. 139p. (Orig.). 1983. pap. 7.95 (ISBN 0-88344-104-7). Orbis Bks.

Peruvian Bishops' Commission for Social Action. Between Honesty & Hope: Documents from & about the Church in Latin America. LC 78-143185. (Maryknoll Documentation Ser.). pap. 67.80 (ISBN 0-317-26635-7, 2025116). Bks Demand UMI.

Sobrino, Jon. Jesus in Latin America. LC 86-23485. Tr. of Jesus en America Latina: Su significada para la fe y la cristologia. 192p. (Orig.). 1987. pap. 11.95 (ISBN 0-88344-412-7). Orbis Bks.

Stafford Poole, C. M. Pedro Moya de Contreras: Catholic Reform & Royal Power in New Spain, 1571-1591. LC 86-1410. 350p. 1987. text ed. 30.00 (ISBN 0-520-05551-9). U of Cal Pr.

Zwerneman, Andrew J. In Bloody Terms: The Betrayal of the Church in Marxist Grenada. LC 85-82316. 113p. (Orig.). 1986. pap. text ed. 6.95 (ISBN 0-937779-00-8). Greenlawn Pr.

LATIN HYMNS

see Hymns, Latin

LATIN INSCRIPTIONS

see Inscriptions, Latin

LATIN LANGUAGE–CHURCH LATIN

Galfridus Anglicus. Promptorium Parvulorum Sive Clericorum, Dictionarius Anglolatinus Princeps, 3 Pts. Repr. of 1865 ed. 37.00 ea. Johnson Repr.

Gavaert, Francois A. Les Origines du Chant Litturgique de l'Eglise Latin. 93p. Repr. of 1890 ed. lib. bdg. 30.00x (Pub. by G. Olms BRD). Coronet Bks.

Mearns, James. Early Latin Hymnaries. 127p. Repr. of 1913 ed. lib. bdg. 38.50X (Pub. by G Olms BRD). Coronet Bks.

Mitropolsky, S. Kratkaja Grammatika Tserkovno-Slavjanskago Jazika. Tr. of A Concise Grammer of the Church-Slavonic Language. 92p. 1980. pap. 5.00 (ISBN 0-317-30307-4). Holy Trinity.

Rosenstock-Huessy, Eugen & Battles, Ford L. Magna Carta Latina: The Privilege of Singing, Articulating & Reading a Language & Keeping It Alive. 2nd ed. LC 75-23378. (Pittsburgh Reprint Ser.: No. 1). 1975. pap. text ed. 9.95 (ISBN 0-915138-07-7). Pickwick.

Walpole, Arthur S. Early Latin Hymns. 473p. Repr. of 1922 ed. lib. bdg. 68.50X (Pub. by G Olms BRD). Coronet Bks.

LATTER-DAY SAINTS

see Mormons and Mormonism

LAUD, WILLIAM ABP. OF CANTERBURY, 1573-1645

Collins, William E., ed. Archbishop Laud Commemoration, 1895. (Bibliography & Reference Ser: No. 257). 1969. Repr. of 1895 ed. 23.50 (ISBN 0-8337-0628-4). B Franklin.

Laud, William. Articles Exhibited in Parliament Against William, Archbishop of Canterbury. LC 72-212. (English Experience Ser.: No. 333). 16p. 1971. Repr. of 1640 ed. 7.00 (ISBN 90-221-0333-1). Walter J Johnson.

LAW, WILLIAM, 1686-1761
Baker, Frank, ed. Heart of True Spirituality: Selections from William Law, Vol. 1. 2nd ed. 128p. 1985. pap. 5.95 (ISBN 0-310-39621-2, 17064P). Zondervan.
Law, William. William Law & Eighteenth-Century Quakerism. Hobhouse, Stephen, ed. LC 77-175870. (Illus.). Repr. of 1927 ed. 24.50 (ISBN 0-405-08736-5). Ayer Co Pubs.
Stanwood, Paul & Warren, Austin, eds. William Law: A Serious Call to a Devout & Holy Life & the Spirit of Love. LC 78-61418. (Classics of Western Spirituality). 542p. 1978. 14.95 (ISBN 0-8091-0265-X); pap. 9.95 (ISBN 0-8091-2144-1). Paulist Pr.
LAW–JEWS
see Jewish Law
LAW–RELIGIOUS ASPECTS
see Religion and Law
LAW (THEOLOGY)
see also Antinomianism; Law and Gospel
Coppenger, Mark T. A Christian View of Justice. LC 82-70867. 1983. pap. 6.95 (ISBN 0-8054-6126-4). Broadman.
Raisanen, Heikki. Paul & the Law. 330p. 1983. lib. bdg. 67.50x (ISBN 3-16-144629-1, Pub. by J C B Mohr BRD). Coronet Bks.
Rhyne, C. Thomas. Faith Establishes the Law. Kee, Howard, ed. LC 81-1794. (Society of Biblical Literature Dissertation Ser.). 1981. pap. 13.50 (ISBN 0-89130-483-5, 06-01-55). Scholars Pr GA.
Sanders, E. P. Paul, the Law & the Jewish People. LC 82-17487. 240p. 1983. pap. 9.95 (ISBN 0-8006-1878-5, 1-1878). Fortress.
Suggs, M. Jack. Wisdom, Christology, & Law in Matthew's Gospel. LC 75-95930. Repr. of 1970 ed. 36.00 (ISBN 0-8357-9185-8, 2017749). Bks Demand UMI.
LAW, ECCLESIASTICAL
see Ecclesiastical Law
LAW, HEBREW
see Jewish Law
LAW, HINDU
see Hindu Law
LAW, JEWISH
see Jewish Law
LAW, MOSAIC
see Jewish Law
LAW, NATURAL
see Natural Law
LAW, SUNDAY
see Sunday Legislation
LAW AND CHRISTIANITY
see Religion and Law
LAW AND ETHICS
Bayne, David C. Conscience, Obligation & the Law: The Moral Binding Power of the Civil Law. LC 66-12757. (Jesuit Studies). 1966. 3.45 (ISBN 0-8294-0001-X). Loyola.
Bentham, Jeremy & Hart, H. L. Introduction to the Principles of Morals & Legislation. 385p. 1982. 14.95x (ISBN 0-416-31910-6, NO. 3710). Methuen Inc.
Horwitz, Robert H. Moral Foundations of the American Republic. 2nd ed. LC 79-20387. 275p. 1982. 15.00x (ISBN 0-8139-0853-1). U Pr of Va.
St. John-Stevas, Norman. Life, Death & the Law: A Study of the Relationship Between Law & Christian Morals in the English & American Legal Systems. 375p. 1981. Repr. of 1961 ed. lib. bdg. 32.50x (ISBN 0-8377-1119-3). Rothman.
St. Thomas Acquinas. On Law, Morality, & Politics. Regan, Richard J. & Baumgarth, William P., eds. (HPC Classics Ser.). 300p. 1987. 27.50 (ISBN 0-87220-032-9); pap. text ed. 7.95 (ISBN 0-87220-031-0). Hackett Pub.
Shaffer, Thomas L. On Being a Christian & a Lawyer. LC 80-25215. 288p. 1981. 12.95 (ISBN 0-8425-1833-9). Brigham.
Shienbaum, Kim E., ed. Legislating Morality: Private Choices on the Public Agenda. 256p. 1987. 28.95 (ISBN 0-87073-689-2); pap. 18.95 (ISBN 0-87073-690-6). Schenkman Bks Inc.
LAW AND GOSPEL
see also Freedom (Theology); Law (Theology)
Huck, Albert. Synopsis of the First Three Gospels With the Addition of the Johannine Parallels. 1982. 22.50x (ISBN 0-8028-3568-6). Eerdmans.
Walther, Carl F. Proper Distinction Between Law & Gospel. Dau, W. H., tr. 1929. 15.50 (ISBN 0-570-03248-2, 15-1601). Concordia.
LAW AND MORALS
see Law and Ethics
LAW AND RELIGION
see Religion and Law
LAW IN THE BIBLE
see Jewish Law
LAW OF NATURE
see Natural Law
LAY APOSTOLATE
see Catholic Action
LAY LEADERSHIP
see Christian Leadership
LAY READERS
Gifts: A Laity Reader, Selected Articles from the Gifts Journal 1979-1983. 124p. 1983. pap. 3.95 (ISBN 1-55586-879-7). US Catholic.
Partridge, Edmund. Church in Perspective: Standard Course for Layreaders. rev. ed. 1976. 5.95 (ISBN 0-8192-1210-5). Morehouse.
Sleeth, Ronald E. Look Who's Talking: A Guide for Lay Speakers in the Church. LC 77-1171. 1982. pap. 5.50 (ISBN 0-687-22630-9). Abingdon.
Tate, Judith. Manual for Lectors. (Orig.). 1975. 2.95 (ISBN 0-8278-0030-4, Pub. by Pflaum Pr). Peter Li.
LAYMEN
see Laity
LAZARUS, SAINT
Cornish, John. The Raising of Lazarus. 1979. pap. 2.95 (ISBN 0-916786-36-6). St George Bk Serv.
Kastenbaum, Robert, ed. Return to Life: Two Imaginings of the Lazarus Theme. an original anthology ed. LC 76-19587. (Death & Dying Ser.). 1977. Repr. of 1976 ed. lib. bdg. 19.00x (ISBN 0-405-09582-1). Ayer Co Pubs.
North, Brownlow. The Rich Man & Lazarus. 1979. pap. 2.95 (ISBN 0-85151-121-X). Banner of Truth.
LEARNING AND SCHOLARSHIP–JEWS
see Jewish Learning and Scholarship
LEARNING DISABILITIES
Cherne, J. The Learning Disabled Child in Your Church School. LC 12-2818. (09). 1983. pap. 3.25 (ISBN 0-570-03883-9). Concordia.
Greene, Roberta M. & Heavenrich, Elaine. A Question in Search of an Answer: Understanding Learning Disability in Jewish Education. LC 8-18059. (Illus.). 262p. 1981. pap. 5.00 (ISBN 0-8074-0029-7). UAHC.
Rolando, Mary J. Recognizing & Helping the Learning Disabled Child in Your Classroom. 24p. 1978. 2.40 (ISBN 0-686-39949-8). Natl Cath Educ.
LECTIONARIES
Barrett, James E., ed. The Daily Lectionary. 70p. 1982. 2.45 (ISBN 0-942466-02-0). Hymnary Pr.
Beck, Norman A. Scripture Notes: Series B (Common Consensus Lectionary) 1984. 7.25 (ISBN 0-89536-687-8, 4863). CSS of Ohio.
Bower, Peter C. Handbook for the Common Lectionary. 300p. (Orig.). 1987. pap. 10.95 (ISBN 0-664-24048-8, A Geneva Press Publication). Westminster.
Catholic Church, Sacred Congregation for Divine Worship. Lectionary for Mass: Cycle A, Sundays & Solemnities. Hartdegen, Steven J., ed. International Committee on English in the Liturgy Confraternity of Christian Doctrine for the New American Bible, tr. from Lat. (Lectionary for Mass Ser.). 1974. 14.50 (ISBN 0-916134-01-6). Pueblo Pub Co.
Catholic Church, Sacred Congregation of Divine Worship Staff. Lectionary for Mass: Cycle C, Sundays & Solemnities. Hartdegen, Steven J., ed. International Committee on English in the Liturgy Confraternity of Christian Doctrine for the New American Bible, tr. from Lat. (Lectionary for Mass). 1973. 27.50 (ISBN 0-916134-03-2). Pueblo Pub Co.
--The Study Edition (Lectors' Guide) of the Lectionary for Mass, Cycle A Sundays & Solemnities. International Committee on English in the Liturgy, Confraternity of Christian Doctrine for the New American Bible, tr. (The Study Edition (Lector's Guide) of the Lectionary for Mass Ser.: Texts from the New American Bible). 1977. pap. 6.95 (ISBN 0-916134-04-0). Pueblo Pub Co.
--The Study Edition (Lectors' Guide) of the Lectionary for Mass, Cycle B Sundays & Solemnities. 1978. pap. 6.95 (ISBN 0-916134-05-9). Pueblo Pub Co.
Chapman, Geoffrey. Lectionary, 3 vols. 3500p. 1985. Vol. 1: The Proper of the Seasons, Sundays in Ordinary Time. 60.00 (ISBN 0-225-66350-3, HarpR). Vol. 2: Weekdays in Ordinary Time, Proper of Saints, Commons. Vol. 3: Rituals Celebrations, Masses for Various Needs & Occasions, Votive Masses, Masses for the Dead. Har-Row.
Corl, Heth. Lectionary Worship Aids C (Common) 1985. 9.95 (ISBN 0-89536-760-2, 5867). CSS of Ohio.
Corl, Heth H. Lectionary Worship Aids A: Common Lectionary. rev. ed. Sherer, Michael L., ed. 1986. pap. 9.95 (ISBN 0-89536-814-5, 6843). CSS of Ohio.
Craddock, Fred B., et al. Preaching the New Common Lectionary. 176p. (Orig.). 1984. pap. 8.50 (ISBN 0-687-33845-X). Abingdon.
--Preaching the New Common Lectionary: Year B: Lent, Holy Week, Easter, 2 vols. 256p. (Orig.). 1984. Vol. 2, 256 pgs. pap. 9.95 (ISBN 0-687-33846-8); Vol. 3, 304 pgs. pap. 11.95 (ISBN 0-687-33847-6). Abingdon.
--Preaching the New Common Lectionary: Year C-Advent, Christmas, Epiphany. 176p. (Orig.). 1985. pap. 9.50 (ISBN 0-687-33848-4). Abingdon.
Crotty, Robert & Manley, Gregory. Commentaries on the Readings of the Lectionary: Cycles A, B, C. 1975. pap. 12.95 (ISBN 0-916134-20-2). Pueblo Pub Co.
Harrison, G. B. & McCabe, John. Proclaiming the Word. 2nd ed. 1976. pap. 4.95 (ISBN 0-916134-00-8). Pueblo Pub Co.
Inclusive-Language Lectionary Committee, Division of Education & Ministry, National Council of Churches of Christ in the U. S. A. An Inclusive-Language Lectionary: Readings for Year A. rev. & enl. ed. 292p. 1986. pap. 10.95 (ISBN 0-664-24051-8). Westminster.
Johnson, Sherman E. The Year of the Lord's Favor: Preaching the Three-Year Lectionary. 300p. 1983. pap. 13.95 (ISBN 0-8164-2359-8, HarpR). Har-Row.
Laughlin, Paul A. Lectionary Worship Aids B: Series II. (Orig.). 1987. pap. price not set (ISBN 0-89536-886-2, 7872). CSS of Ohio.
Lectionary: New American Bible Version. small size ed. 23.00 (ISBN 0-89942-025-7, 25/22). Catholic Bk Pub.
Lectionary: New American Bible Version. large size ed. (Large Red & Black type, Ribbon Markers). red simulated leather 42.00 (ISBN 0-89942-035-4, 35/02); protective jacket o.s.i. 1.50; genuine leather, gold edges 75.00 (ISBN 0-89942-036-2, 35/13). Catholic Bk Pub.
Lectionary Reader C (Common, RSV) 1985. 14.25 (ISBN 0-89536-772-6, 5877). CSS of Ohio.
Lectionary Reader C (Common, TEV) 1985. 14.25 (ISBN 0-89536-776-9, 5879). CSS of Ohio.
Lectionary Series from the Common (Consensus) Lectionary: Series B (TEV) 1984. 14.25 (ISBN 0-89536-693-2, 4870). CSS of Ohio.
The Lectionary Texts, Year C: From the Common Lectionary RSV. 312p. 1985. UM 49.95 (ISBN 0-687-21337-1). Plain (ISBN 0-687-21334-7). Abingdon.
Morentz, Jim & Morentz, Doris. Children's Object Lesson Sermons Based on the Common Lectionary Year. 112p. (Orig.). 1984. pap. 6.95 (ISBN 0-687-06499-6). Abingdon.
National Council of Churches of Christ. An Inclusive Language Lectionary: Readings for Year B. 192p. (Orig.). 1984. pap. 8.95 (ISBN 0-8298-0719-5). Pilgrim NY.
Rossow, Francis & Aho, Gerhard. Lectionary Preaching Resources. (Illus.). 224p. 1987. pap. 14.95 (ISBN 0-570-04468-5). Concordia.
Russell, Joseph. The Daily Lectionary-Year 1: Advent-Easter. (Orig.). 1986. pap. 2.50 (ISBN 0-88028-057-3). Forward Movement.
Russell, Joseph P. The Daily Lectionary: A Weekly Guide for Daily Bible Readings, the Sundays After Pentecost Year One. (Daily Lectionary Ser.). 136p. (Orig.). 1987. pap. 3.25 (ISBN 0-88028-060-3). Forward Movement.
Sherer, Michael L., ed. The Lectionary Series from the Common Lectionary: Series A (RSV) rev. ed. 1986. 14.25 (ISBN 0-89536-810-2, 6839). CSS of Ohio.
--The Lectionary Series from the Common Lectionary: Series A (TEV) rev. ed. 1986. 14.25 (ISBN 0-89536-811-0, 6840). CSS of Ohio.
--The Lectionary Series from the Common Lectionary: Series B (RSV) (Orig.). 1987. pap. price not set (ISBN 0-89536-884-6, 7870). CSS of Ohio.
Sloyan, Gerard S. Commentary on the New Lectionary. LC 75-22781. 444p. 1975. pap. 11.95 (ISBN 0-8091-1895-5). Paulist Pr.
Staack, Hagen. Lectionary Preaching Workbook on the Psalms. (Ser. C). 1982. 14.25 (ISBN 0-89536-573-1, 1263). CSS of Ohio.
The Study Edition (Lectors' Guide) of the Lectionary for Mass, Cycle C, Sunday & Solemnities. International Committee on English in the Liturgy, tr. from Latin. (The Study Edition (Lectors' Guide) of the Lectionary for Mass Ser.: Texts from the New American Bible). 1976. pap. 6.95 (ISBN 0-916134-06-7). Pueblo Pub Co.
LEE, JAMES PRINCE, BP. OF MANCHESTER, 1804-1869
Newsome, David. Godliness & Good Learning: Four Studies on a Victorian Ideal. (Illus.). 1961. 21.00 (ISBN 0-7195-1015-5). Transatl Arts.
LEE, JESSE, 1758-1816
Lee, Jesse & Thrift, Minton. Memoir of the Reverend Jesse Lee, with Extracts from His Journals. LC 72-83428. (Religion in America, Ser. 1). 1969. Repr. of 1823 ed. 19.00 (ISBN 0-405-00253-X). Ayer Co Pubs.
LEGENDS
see also Fables; Folk-Lore; Mythology; Saints also subdivisions Legends under special subjects, e.g. Mary, Virgin–Legends
Davis, Hubert J. Myths & Legends of the Great Dismal Swamp. (Illus.). 112p. 1981. 7.50 (ISBN 0-930230-42-6). Johnson NC.
Pettazzoni, Raffaele & Bolle, Kees W., eds. Miti E. Leggende: Myths & Legends, 4 vols. in 1. LC 77-79151. (Mythology Ser.). (Ital.). 1978. Repr. of 1959 ed. lib. bdg. 186.00x (ISBN 0-405-10560-6). Ayer Co Pubs.
LEGENDS–HISTORY AND CRITICISM
Gripkey, Sr. M. Vincentine. Blessed Virgin Mary As Mediatrix in the Latin & Old French Legend Prior to the Fourteenth Century. LC 72-94166. (Catholic University of America Studies in Romance Languages & Literatures Ser: No. 17). 1969. Repr. of 1938 ed. 26.00 (ISBN 0-404-50317-9). Ams Pr.
Harper, G. M. The Legend of the Holy Grail. 59.95 (ISBN 0-8490-0502-7). Gordon Pr.
Leach, ed. Funk & Wagnalls Standard Dictionary of Folklore, Mythology & Legend. LC 72-78268. (Funk & W Bk.). 23.00i (ISBN 0-308-40090-9). T Y Crowell.
LEGENDS, BUDDHIST
Budge, Ernest A., ed. Baralam & Yewasef - Baralaam & Joasaph, 3 pts. in 2 vols. LC 73-18832. (Illus.). Repr. of 1923 ed. Set. 67.50 (ISBN 0-404-11300-1). AMS Pr.
Burlingame, E. W. Buddhist Parables. lib. bdg. 79.95 (ISBN 0-87968-494-1). Krishna Pr.
Somadeva, Bhatta. The Buddhist Legend of Jimutavahana. LC 78-70116. Repr. of 1911 ed. 20.50 (ISBN 0-404-17373-X). AMS Pr.
LEGENDS, CHINESE
Mui, Shan. The Seven Magic Orders. Tabrah, Ruth, ed. LC 72-86743. (Illus.). 1973. 5.95 (ISBN 0-89610-011-1). Island Heritage.
Werner, E. T. Myths & Legends of China. LC 71-172541. (Illus.). Repr. of 1922 ed. 33.00 (ISBN 0-405-09059-5, Pub. by Blom). Ayer Co Pubs.
--Myths & Legends of China. 2nd ed. (Illus.). 453p. 1984. pap. 15.00 (ISBN 9971-947-55-2, Pub. by Graham Brash Singapore). Three Continents.
LEGENDS, CHRISTIAN
Bousset, Wilhelm. The Antichrist Legend: A Chapter in Christian & Jewish Folklore. 1977. lib. bdg. 59.95 (ISBN 0-8490-1439-5). Gordon Pr.
Douhet, J. Dictionnaire des Legendes du Christianisme. Migne, J. P., ed. (Troisieme et Derniere Encyclopedie Theologique Ser.: Vol. 14). (Fr.). 764p. Repr. of 1855 ed. lib. bdg. 97.50x (ISBN 0-89241-276-6). Caratzas.
Every, George. Christian Legends. LC 86-22242. (Library of the World's Myths & Legends). (Illus.). 144p. 1987. 18.95 (ISBN 0-87226-046-1). P Bedrick Bks.
Metford, J. C. A Dictionary of Christian Lore & Legend. LC 82-50815. (Illus.). 272p. 1983. 24.95f (ISBN 0-500-11020-4). Thames Hudson.
LEGENDS, EGYPTIAN
King, L. W. Legends of Babylon & Egypt in Relation to Hebrew Tradition. 59.95 (ISBN 0-8490-0504-3). Gordon Pr.
King, Leonard W. Legends of Babylonia & Egypt in Relation to the Hebrew Tradition. LC 77-94593. 1979. Repr. of 1918 ed. lib. bdg. 20.00 (ISBN 0-89341-310-0). Longwood Pub Group.
LEGENDS, JAPANESE
Chiba, Reiko. Seven Lucky Gods of Japan. LC 65-25467. (Illus.). 1966. 12.95 (ISBN 0-8048-0521-0). C E Tuttle.
Davis, F. Hadland. Myths & Legends of Japan. (Illus.). 1978. Repr. of 1912 ed. lib. bdg. 45.00 (ISBN 0-8495-1008-2). Arden Lib.
LEGENDS, JEWISH
Agnon, Y. Days of Awe: A Treasury of Tradition, Legends & Learned Commentaries Concerning Rosh Hashanah, Yom Kippur & the Days Between. LC 48-8316. 1965. pap. 8.95 (ISBN 0-8052-0100-9). Schocken.
Bousset, Wilhelm. The Antichrist Legend: A Chapter in Christian & Jewish Folklore. 1977. lib. bdg. 59.95 (ISBN 0-8490-1439-5). Gordon Pr.
Field, Claud H. Jewish Legends of the Middle Ages. LC 76-48141. 1976. Repr. of 1930 ed. lib. bdg. 25.00 (ISBN 0-8414-6771-4). Folcroft.
Gaster, Moses. The Chronicles of Jerahmeel. rev. ed. 1971. 35.00x (ISBN 0-87068-162-1). Ktav.
Gaster, Moses, tr. from Judeo-German. Ma'aseh Book: Book of Jewish Tales & Legends. LC 81-80356. 694p. 1981. pap. 10.95 (ISBN 0-8276-0189-1, 471). Jewish Pubns.
Ginzberg, Louis. Legends of the Jews, 7 Vols. LC 76-58650. 1956. Set. 80.00 (ISBN 0-8276-0148-4); 11.95 ea. Vol. 1 (172). Vol. 2 (173). Vol. 3 (174). Vol. 4 (175). Vol. 5 (176). Vol. 6 (177). Vol. 7 (178). Jewish Pubns.
Glenn, Menachem. Jewish Tales & Legends. 441p. 1929. 6.95 (ISBN 0-88482-857-3). Hebrew Pub.
King, Leonard W. Legends of Babylonia & Egypt in Relation to the Hebrew Tradition. LC 77-94593. 1979. Repr. of 1918 ed. lib. bdg. 20.00 (ISBN 0-89341-310-0). Longwood Pub Group.
Mendelssohn, S. Judaic or Semitic Legends & Customs Amongst South African Natives. 1976. lib. bdg. 59.95 (ISBN 0-8490-2111-1). Gordon Pr.

Nadich, Judah. Jewish Legends of the Second Commonwealth. 508p. 1983. 25.00 (ISBN 0-8276-0212-X, 490). Jewish Pubns.

Rappoport, Angelo S. Myth & Legend of Ancient Israel, 3 Vols. rev. ed. 1966. Set. 39.50x (ISBN 0-87068-099-4). Ktav.

Rubin, Gershon. The Hebrew Saga. LC 84-1745. 204p. 1984. 15.00 (ISBN 0-8022-2451-2). Philos Lib.

Snowman, Joel. The Legends of Israel. Levner, J. B., tr. from Hebrew. (Illus.). 233p. 1983. Repr. of 1946 ed. lib. bdg. 85.00 (ISBN 0-8495-5060-2). Arden Lib.

Vilnay, Zev. Legends of Galilee, Jordan & Sinai. LC 73-168156. (Sacred Land Ser.: Vol. 3). (Illus.). 378p. 1978. 10.95 (ISBN 0-8276-0106-9, 419). Jewish Pubns.

--Legends of Jerusalem. LC 72-12180. (The Sacred Land Ser.: Vol. 1). (Illus.). 338p. 1973. 8.95 (ISBN 0-8276-0004-6, 323). Jewish Pubns.

LEGION OF MARY

Duff, Frank. Miracles on Tap. 5.00 (ISBN 0-910984-14-X); pap. 3.50 (ISBN 0-910984-15-8). Montfort Pubns.

LEISURE

Hansel, Tim. When I Relax I Feel Guilty. LC 78-73460. 1979. pap. 6.95 (ISBN 0-89191-137-5). Cook.

Koenig, Norma E. Ventures in Leisure-Time Christian Education. (Orig.). 1979. pap. 4.15 (ISBN 0-687-43670-2). Abingdon.

Lehman, Harold D. In Praise of Leisure. LC 74-16399. 200p. 1974. 6.95 (ISBN 0-8361-1752-2); leader's guide o.p. 1.75 (ISBN 0-8361-1750-6). Herald Pr.

Oswalt, John. The Leisure Crisis. 168p. 1987. pap. 5.95 (ISBN 0-89693-241-9). Victor Bks.

LE MANS–CHURCH HISTORY–SOURCES–HISTORY AND CRITICISM

Goffart, Walter A. Le Mans Forgeries: A Chapter from the History of Church Property in the Ninth Century. LC 66-18246. (Historical Studies: No. 76). 1966. 25.00x (ISBN 0-674-51875-6). Harvard U Pr.

LENT

see also Easter; Good Friday; Holy Week

Alessi, Vincie. Programs for Lent & Easter, Vol. 2. 64p. 1983. pap. 5.95 (ISBN 0-8170-1016-5). Judson.

Alessi, Vincie, ed. Programs for Lent & Easter. 1979. pap. 3.95 (ISBN 0-8170-0861-6). Judson.

Becker, Ralph. Lent, Good Friday & Easter. pap. 0.50 (ISBN 0-685-41825-1). Reiner.

Bosch, Paul. The Paschal Cycle. 1979. pap. 6.75 (ISBN 0-570-03796-4, 12-2778). Concordia.

Brokhoff, John R. Lent: A Time of Tears. 1984. 4.25 (ISBN 0-89536-649-5, 1267). CSS of Ohio.

Change My Heart: Family Lenten Handbook. 1.25 (ISBN 0-8091-9173-3). Paulist Pr.

Cole, Joan. A Lenten Journey with Jesus. 48p. 1982. pap. 1.50 (ISBN 0-89243-172-5). Liguori Pubns.

Council, Raymond. The One Who Made His Cross. 1986. 2.95 (ISBN 0-89536-793-9, 6811). CSS of Ohio.

Davidson, Robert G., ed. Creative Ideas for Lent. 120p. (Orig.). 1985. pap. 9.95 (ISBN 0-940754-25-8). Ed Ministries.

De Gidio, Sandra. Re-Treat Your Family to Lent. 50p. (Orig.). 1983. pap. text ed. 1.95 (ISBN 0-86716-022-5). St Anthony Mess Pr.

Dunnam, Maxie. The Sanctuary for Lent, 1985. 48p. (Orig.). 1985. pap. 30.00 per 100 (ISBN 0-687-36847-2). Abingdon.

Ehlen-Miller, Margaret, et al. A Time of Hope: Family Celebrations & Activities for Lent & Easter. (Illus., Orig.). 1979. pap. 4.95 (ISBN 0-8192-1247-4). Morehouse.

Ellebracht, Mary P. Easter Passage: The RCIA Experience. 204p. 1983. pap. 11.95 (ISBN 0-86683-693-4, HarpR). Har-Row.

Fadness, Arley. Blueprint for Lent. 1983. 10.00 (ISBN 0-89536-603-7, 0219). CSS of Ohio.

Fillmore, Charles. Keep a True Lent. 1982. 5.95 (ISBN 0-87159-076-X). Unity School.

Furnish, Victor. Lent. LC 84-18756. (Proclamation 3A Ser.). 64p. 1986. pap. 3.75 (ISBN 0-8006-4119-1, 1-4119). Fortress.

Gomes, Peter. Lent. LC 84-18756. (Proclamation 3 C Ser.). 64p. 1985. pap. 3.75 (ISBN 0-8006-4127-2). Fortress.

Griggs, Patricia & Griggs, Donald. Teaching & Celebrating Lent-Easter. (Griggs Educational Resources Ser.). 1980. pap. 6.95 (ISBN 0-687-41081-9). Abingdon.

Gunning, Peter. Paschal or Lent Fast. LC 70-168214. (Library of Anglo-Catholic Theology: No. 7). Repr. of 1845 ed. 27.50 (ISBN 0-404-52088-X). AMS Pr.

Irwin, Kevin. Lent, a Guide to the Eucharist & Hours. (Liturgical Seasons Ser.). 300p. (Orig.). 1985. pap. 12.95 (ISBN 0-916134-68-7). Pueblo Pub Co.

Kennedy, James W. Holy Island. 2nd ed. 144p. 1984. pap. 1.70 (ISBN 0-88028-028-X). Forward Movement.

Kingsbury, Jack D. & Pennington, Chester. Lent. Achtemeier, Elizabeth, et al, eds. LC 79-7377. (Proclamation 2: Aids for Interpreting the Lessons of the Church Year, Ser. A). 64p. (Orig.). 1980. pap. 3.75 (ISBN 0-8006-4093-4, 1-4093). Fortress.

Lowery, Daniel L. Day by Day Through Lent: Reflections, Prayers, Practices. 160p. 1983. pap. 3.95 (ISBN 0-89243-194-6). Liguori Pubns.

Micks, Marianne H. & Ridenhour, Thomas E. Lent. Achtemeier, Elizabeth, et al, eds. LC 79-7377. (Proclamation 2: Aids for Interpreting the Lessons of the Church Year Ser. C). 64p. 1979. pap. 3.75 (ISBN 0-8006-4082-9, 1-4082). Fortress.

Mother Mary & Archimandrite Kallistos Ware, trs. The Lenten Triodion. LC 83-20750. 699p. (Orig.). 1984. pap. 17.95 (ISBN 0-571-13243-X). Faber & Faber.

Nerney, Catherine. Called to Be Faithful: Reflections on Cycle B Readings for the Sundays of Lent. 1.95 (ISBN 0-8091-9339-6). Paulist Pr.

--The Experience of Lent with the Risen Christ. 1.95 (ISBN 0-8091-9308-6). Paulist Pr.

O'Dea, Barbara. Of Fast & Festival: Celebrating Lent & Easter. 1982. pap. 3.95 (ISBN 0-8091-2426-2). Paulist Pr.

Perkins, Pheme. Lent: Series B. Achtemeier, Elizabeth, ed. LC 84-6010. (Proclamation 3: Aids for Interpreting the Lessons of the Church Year Ser.). 64p. 1984. pap. 3.75 (ISBN 0-8006-4103-5). Fortress.

Quillin, Roger T. Meeting Christ in Handel's Messiah: Lent & Easter Messages Based on Handel's Texts & Music. 96p. 1984. pap. 4.95 (ISBN 0-8066-2118-4, 10-4318). Augsburg.

Rathert, Donna R. Lent Is for Remembering. LC 56-1613. 24p. (Orig.). 1987. pap. 2.95 (ISBN 0-570-04147-3). Concordia.

Recker, Colane. All the Days of Lent. LC 78-73825. (Illus.). 64p. 1978. pap. 2.45 (ISBN 0-87793-168-2). Ave Maria.

Ryan, Pat & Ryan, Rosemary. Lent Begins at Home. 1979. pap. 1.50 (ISBN 0-89243-101-6). Liguori Pubns.

Saffen, Wayne. The Second Season: Lent, Easter, Ascension. LC 72-87064. pap. 24.00 (2026827). Bks Demand UMI.

Steinke, Peter L. Preaching the Theology of the Cross: Sermons & Worship Ideas for Lent & Easter. LC 82-72638. 128p. (Orig.). 1983. pap. 6.95 (ISBN 0-8066-1944-9, 10-5144). Augsburg.

Sullivan, Barbara. Page a Day for Lent 1987. 56p. (Orig.). 1987. pap. 2.95 (ISBN 0-8091-2852-7). Paulist Pr.

Tickle, Phyllis A. Final Sanity: Essays on Lent & Easter. 128p. (Orig.). 1987. pap 6.95 (ISBN 0-8358-0545-X). Upper Room.

Wean, Ronald. One Must Die: Six-Week Lenten Drama Series. 1986. 6.50 (ISBN 0-89536-794-7, 6812). CSS of Ohio.

LENT–PRAYER BOOKS AND DEVOTIONS

Breckenridge, Marilyn S. Jesse Tree Devotions: A Family Activity for Lent. 40p. (Orig.). 1985. pap. 4.95 (ISBN 0-8066-2154-0, 10-3475). Augsburg.

Buchanan, Ray, ed. GLEANINGS: Hunger Meditations for Lent. rev. ed. 112p. pap. 5.50 (ISBN 0-939485-02-8). St Andrew Pr.

Fillmore, Charles. Guarda una Cuaresma Verdadera. (Span.). 214p. 1983. 5.95 (ISBN 0-87159-048-4). Unity School.

Griffin, James A. Sackcloth & Ashes: Liturgical Reflections for Lenten Weekdays. LC 74-44463. 1976. pap. 4.00 (ISBN 0-8189-0336-8). Alba.

Hayes, Paul J. Meditations for Lent. 1985. pap. 1.95 (ISBN 0-8198-4719-4). Dghtrs St Paul.

Hohenstein, Herbert E. Upper Room to Garden Tomb: Messages for Lent & Easter on the Passion Narrative in Mark. LC 84-21735. 80p. (Orig.). 1984. pap. 4.95 (ISBN 0-8066-2117-6, 10-6840). Augsburg.

Hopko, Thomas. The Lenten Spring. LC 83-4278. 229p. 1983. pap. text ed. 5.95 (ISBN 0-88141-014-4). St Vladimirs.

McCoy, Charles S. & McCoy, Marjorie C. The Transforming Cross. LC 77-10884. Repr. of 1977 ed. 27.80 (ISBN 0-8357-9030-4, 2016417). Bks Demand UMI.

Manning, Michael. Pardon My Lenten Smile: Daily Homily-Meditation Themes for the Weekdays of Lent. 90p. 1976. pap. 5.95 (ISBN 0-8189-0325-2). Alba.

Montgomery, Mary & Montgomery, Herb. Easter Is Coming: Lenten Celebrations for the Family. (Illus.). 120p. (Orig.). 1982. pap. 7.95 (ISBN 0-86683-609-8, HarpR). Har-Row.

Myers, Rawley. Lent: A Journey to Resurrection Prayers & Reflections for the Penitential Season. LC 83-63084. 192p. 1984. pap. 5.95 (ISBN 0-87973-605-4). Our Sunday Visitor.

Newhouse, Flower A. Through Lent to Resurrection. Bengtson, Melodie N., ed. LC 77-77088. (Illus.). 1977. pap. 5.00 (ISBN 0-910378-13-4). Christward.

O'Neal, Debbie T. An Easter People: Family Devotional Activities for Lent & Easter. 32p. (Orig.). 1986. pap. 3.95 (ISBN 0-8066-2255-5, 10-1990). Augsburg.

Rosage, David E. A Lenten Pilgrimage: Scriptural Meditations in the Holy Land. (Orig.). 1980. pap. 3.50 (ISBN 0-89283-081-6). Servant.

Schmemann, Alexander. Great Lent: Journey to Pascha. 1974. pap. 5.95 (ISBN 0-913836-04-4). St Vladimirs.

Sheen, Fulton J. Cross-Ways: A Book of Inspiration. LC 83-45272. (Illus.). 80p. 1984. pap. 7.95 (ISBN 0-385-19205-3, Im). Doubleday.

Shelton, Joan A. Stone Turning into Star: Prayer & Meditations for Lent. 168p. (Orig.). 1986. pap. 5.95 (ISBN 0-8091-2736-9). Paulist Pr.

Sims, Edward R. A Season with the Savior: Meditations on Mark. 1979. 6.95 (ISBN 0-8164-0413-5, HarpR); pap. 3.95 (ISBN 0-8164-2195-1). Har-Row.

Skatrud-Mickelson, Ellen. Draw Near the Cross: Lenten Devotions for Children & Those Who Love Them. 48p. (Orig.). 1985. pap. 2.95 (ISBN 0-8066-2200-8, 23-1604). Augsburg.

Smith, Delia. A Feast for Lent. 96p. pap. 3.95 (ISBN 0-89622-220-9). Twenty-Third.

Stuhlmueller, Carroll. Biblical Meditations for Lent. rev. ed. LC 77-91366. 190p. 1978. pap. 4.95 (ISBN 0-8091-2089-5). Paulist Pr.

LENTEN MUSIC

see Passion–Music

LENTEN SERMONS

Here are entered sermons preached during the season of Lent. If they are limited in their scope to the passion of Jesus Christ, entry is made under Jesus Christ–Passion–Sermons.

Albert, Harold & Morentz, James. The Compleat Sermon Program for Lent. 1982. 4.35 (ISBN 0-89536-533-2, 0347). CSS of Ohio.

Allen, Robert. Hot & Cold & in Between. 1985. 4.25 (ISBN 0-89536-717-3, 5801). CSS of Ohio.

Andersen, R. & Barlag, R. They Were There. 1977. pap. 4.50 (ISBN 0-570-03769-7, 12-2704). Concordia.

Bond, Alan. The Sevenfold Path to Peace. 1986. 4.50 (ISBN 0-89536-774-2, 6801). CSS of Ohio.

Currin, Beverly M. The Hope That Never Disappoints. 128p. (Orig.). 1983. pap. 8.75 (ISBN 0-687-17415-5). Abingdon.

Erickson, Craig D. Under the Shadow of Your Wings. Sherer, Michael L., ed. (Orig.). 1987. pap. 6.75 (ISBN 0-89536-844-7, 7803). CSS of Ohio.

Fiorenza, Elisabeth S. & Holmes, Urban T. Lent. Achtemeier, Elizabeth & Krodel, Gerhard, eds. LC 79-7377. (Proclamation 2: Aids for Interpreting the Lessons of the Church Year, Ser. B). 64p. 1981. pap. 3.75 (ISBN 0-8006-4070-5, 1-4070). Fortress.

Hegele, Paul. When Messiah Comes. Sherer, Michael L., ed. (Orig.). 1986. pap. 6.25 (ISBN 0-89536-823-4, 6832). CSS of Ohio.

Jarrett, Bede. No Abiding City. 1.95 (ISBN 0-87243-012-X). Templegate.

Jensen, Richard. The Crucified Ruler. (Orig.). 1987. pap. price not set (ISBN 0-89536-870-6, 7856). CSS of Ohio.

Kalas, J. Ellsworth. A Pilgrimage. Sherer, Michael L., ed. (Orig.). 1987. pap. 3.95 (ISBN 0-89536-845-5, 7804). CSS of Ohio.

Kolsti, Arthur H. The Lion Roars. 1985. 4.95 (ISBN 0-89536-720-3, 5804). CSS of Ohio.

Liptak, David Q. Biblical Lenten Homilies for Preaching & Meditation. rev. & exp. ed. pap. 11.95 (ISBN 0-941850-05-6). Sunday Pubns.

McCabe, Kendall K. The Path of the Phoenix. Sherer, Michael L., ed. (Orig.). 1986. pap. 7.25 (ISBN 0-89536-818-8, 6827). CSS of Ohio.

Powell, Larry. On His Way. 1984. 5.00 (ISBN 0-89536-681-9, 4857). CSS of Ohio.

Puffenberger, Allen. Words for the Weary. (Orig.). 1987. pap. price not set (ISBN 0-89536-875-7, 7861). CSS of Ohio.

Richter, Robert L. The Last Enemy. 1983. 3.75 (ISBN 0-89536-960-5, 7511). CSS of Ohio.

Shaw, Amy. Our Family Lenten Experience. 1983. 4.95 (ISBN 0-89536-590-1, 1506). CSS of Ohio.

Shelby, Donald J. Bold Expectations of the Gospel. LC 82-50943. 96p. (Orig.). 1983. pap. 3.95 (ISBN 0-8358-0454-2). Upper Room.

Swanson, Steven. Biblical Pictures of Bread. 1985. 3.95 (ISBN 0-89536-718-1, 5802). CSS of Ohio.

LEO 10TH, POPE, 1475-1521

Count Gobineau, Arthur. The Renaissance Savonarola. Levy, Oscar, ed. Cohen, Paul V., tr. (Fr., Illus.). 349p. 1986. Repr. of 1913 ed. lib. bdg. 75.00 (ISBN 0-89760-264-1). Telegraph Bks.

Gobineau, Joseph A. Golden Flower. facsimile ed. Redman, B. R., tr. LC 68-54347. (Essay Index Reprint Ser). 1924. 15.00 (ISBN 0-8369-0477-X). Ayer Co Pubs.

Roscoe, William. Life & Pontificate of Pope Leo the Tenth, 2 vols. rev. ed. 6th ed. Roscoe, Thomas, ed. LC 75-174965. Repr. of 1853 ed. 92.50 (ISBN 0-404-05430-7). AMS Pr.

LESBIAN NUNS

Brown, Judith C. Immodest Acts: The Life of a Lesbian Nun in Renaissance Italy. (Studies in the History of Sexuality). 221p. 1985. 14.95 (ISBN 0-19-503675-1). Oxford U Pr.

Curb, Rosemary & Manahan, Nancy. Lesbian Nuns: Breaking Silence. 400p. 1986. pap. 3.95 (ISBN 0-446-32659-3). Warner Bks.

Curb, Rosemary & Manahan, Nancy, eds. Lesbian Nuns: Breaking Silence. LC 84-29594. 432p. 1985. 16.95 (ISBN 0-930044-63-0); pap. 9.95 (ISBN 0-930044-62-2). Naiad Pr.

LESSING, GOTTHOLD EPHRAIM, 1729-1781

Fittbogen, Gottfried. Die Religion Lessings. 1967. 36.00; pap. 31.00 (ISBN 0-685-13575-6). Johnson Repr.

Lamport, F. J. Lessing & the Drama. 1981. text ed. 39.00x (ISBN 0-19-815767-3). Oxford U Pr.

Michalson, Gordon E., Jr. Lessing's "Ugly Ditch". A Study of Theology & History. LC 84-42991. 224p. 1985. 22.50x (ISBN 0-271-00385-5). Pa St U Pr.

Wessell, Leonard P. G.E Lessing's Theology: A Reinterpretation, a Study in the Problematic Nature of the Enlightenment. 1977. 20.00x (ISBN 90-279-7801-8). Mouton.

LETTERS

Ambrose, St. Complete Letters. LC 67-28583. (Fathers of the Church Ser.: Vol. 26). 515p. 1954. 26.95x (ISBN 0-8132-0026-1). Cath U Pr.

Augustine, St. Letters, Nos. 1-82. LC 64-19948. (Fathers of the Church Ser.: Vol. 12). 420p. 1951. 22.95x (ISBN 0-8132-0012-1). Cath U Pr.

--Letters, Nos. 131-164. (Fathers of the Church Ser.: Vol. 20). 398p. 1953. 34.95x (ISBN 0-8132-0020-2). Cath U Pr.

--Letters, Nos. 83-130. LC 64-19948. (Fathers of the Church Ser.: Vol. 18). 401p. 1953. 34.95x (ISBN 0-8132-0018-0). Cath U Pr.

Barker, A. Trevor, compiled by. The Letters of H. P. Blavatsky to A. P. Sinnett. facsimile of 1925 ed. LC 73-84138. 1973. 12.00 (ISBN 0-911500-23-5). Theos U Pr.

--The Mahatma Letters to A. P. Sinnett. facsimile of 1926, 2nd ed. LC 75-10574. 1975. 12.00 (ISBN 0-911500-20-0); pap. 7.00 (ISBN 0-911500-21-9). Theos U Pr.

Basil, St. Letters, Nos. 1-185. (Fathers of the Church Ser.: Vol. 13). 345p. 1951. 18.95x (ISBN 0-8132-0013-X). Cath U Pr.

--Letters, Nos. 186-368. LC 65-18318. (Fathers of the Church Ser.: Vol. 28). 369p. 1955. 19.95x (ISBN 0-8132-0028-8). Cath U Pr.

Cyprian, St. Complete Letters. LC 65-12906. (Fathers of the Church Ser.: Vol. 51). 352p. 1964. 19.95x (ISBN 0-8132-0051-2). Cath U Pr.

Doty, William G. Letters in Primitive Christianity. Via, Dan O., Jr., ed. LC 72-87058. (Guides to Biblical Scholarship: New Testament Ser.). 96p. 1973. pap. 4.50 (ISBN 0-8006-0170-X, 1-170). Fortress.

Goodall, Blake. The Homilies of St. John Chrysostom on the Letters of St. Paul to Titus & Philemon. (Univ. of California Publications in Classical Studies: Vol. 20). 1979. 19.95x (ISBN 0-520-09596-0). U of Cal Pr.

Leo The Great, St. Selected Letters. LC 63-18826. (Fathers of the Church Ser: Vol. 34). 312p. 1957. 15.95x (ISBN 0-8132-0034-2). Cath U Pr.

Teresa, Saint The Letters of St. Teresa, 4 vols. Gasquet, Cardinal, ed. 1977. Set. lib. bdg. 400.00 (ISBN 0-8490-2154-5). Gordon Pr.

LETTERS, PAPAL

Pope John Paul II. Faithfulness to the Gospel. Daughters of St. Paul, compiled by. 335p. 1982. 4.50 (ISBN 0-8198-2614-6, EP0482); pap. 3.50 (ISBN 0-8198-2615-4). Dghtrs St Paul.

LEWIS, CLIVE STAPLES, 1898-1963

Beversluis, John. C. S. Lewis & the Search for Rational Religion. 179p. (Orig.). 1985. pap. 9.95 (ISBN 0-8028-0046-7). Eerdmans.

Christopher, J. R. & Ostling, Joan K. C. S. Lewis: An Annotated Checklist. LC 73-76556. (Serif Ser.: No. 30). 402p. 1974. 20.00x (ISBN 0-87338-138-6). Kent St U Pr.

Christopher, Joe R. C. S. Lewis. (Twayne's English Authors Ser.). 160p. 1987. lib. bdg. 16.95 (ISBN 0-8057-6944-7, TEAS 442, Twayne). G K Hall.

Green, Roger L. & Hooper, Walter. C. S. Lewis: A Biography. LC 75-29425. 320p. 1976. pap. 7.95 (ISBN 0-15-623205-7, Harv). HarBraceJ.

Hooper, Walter. Through Joy & Beyond: A Pictorial Biography of C. S. Lewis. LC 82-9884. 192p. 1982. 15.75 (ISBN 0-02-553670-2). Macmillan.

Lewis, W. H., ed. The Letters of C. S. Lewis. LC 74-13416. (Illus.). 308p. 1975. pap. 5.95 (ISBN 0-15-650870-2, Harv). HarBraceJ.

Lindskoog, Kathryn. Mere Christian. 264p. Date not set. pap. 9.95 (ISBN 0-87788-543-5). Shaw Pubs.

Payne, Leanne. Real Presence: The Holy Spirit in the Works of C. S. Lewis. LC 78-71945. 183p. 1979. pap. 6.95 (ISBN 0-89107-164-4, Crossway Bks). Good News.

Putrill, Richard L. C. S. Lewis's Case for the Christian Faith. LC 81-47435. 160p. 1985. pap. 6.68 (ISBN 0-06-066713-3, HarpR). Har-Row.

Sayer, George. Jack: C. S. Lewis & His Times. LC 84-48778. (Illus.). 416p. 1985. 25.95 (ISBN 0-06-067072-X, HarpR). Har-Row.

Sibley, Brian. C. S. Lewis Through the Shadowlands. LC 86-13096. (Illus.). 160p. 1986. pap. text ed. 10.95 (ISBN 0-8007-1509-8). Revell.

Tripp, R. P., Jr., ed. Man's Natural Powers: Essays for & About C. S. Lewis. (Orig.). 1975. pap. 5.00 (ISBN 0-905019-01-6). Soc New Lang Study.

Urang, Gunnar. Shadows of Heaven: Religion & Fantasy in the Writing of C. S. Lewis, Charles Williams & J. R. R. Tolkien. LC 73-153998. 208p. 1971. 7.95 (ISBN 0-8298-0197-9). Pilgrim NY.

Walsh, Chad. C. S. Lewis: Apostle to the Skeptics. LC 78-689. 1974. Repr. of 1949 ed. lib. bdg. 32.50 (ISBN 0-8414-9647-1). Folcroft.

Walsh, Chad, ed. The Visionary Christian: One Hundred & Thirty-One Readings from C. S. Lewis. 288p. 1984. 5.95 (ISBN 0-02-086730-1, Collier). Macmillan.

Willis, John R. Pleasures Forevermore: The Theology of C. S. Lewis. 157p. 1983. 12.95 (ISBN 0-8294-0446-5). Loyola.

LIBERAL CATHOLIC CHURCH

Cooper, Irving S. Ceremonies of the Liberal Catholic Rite. 2nd ed. (Illus.). 225p. 1981. Repr. of 1934 ed. 16.50 (ISBN 0-935461-07-8). St Alban Pr CA.

General Episcopal Synod. The Liturgy According to the Use of the Liberal Catholic Church, Prepared for the Use of English-Speaking Congregations. 3rd ed. 421p. 1987. Repr. of 1942 ed. price not set (ISBN 0-935461-11-6). St Alban Pr CA.

LIBERAL JUDAISM

see Reform Judaism

LIBERAL THEOLOGY

see Liberalism (Religion)

LIBERALISM (RELIGION)

Ayala, Francisco. El Problema de Liberalismo. 2nd ed. pap. 4.35 (ISBN 0-8477-2402-6). U of PR Pr.

Bernstein, George L. Liberalism & Liberal Politics in Edwardian England. 256p. 1986. text ed. 34.95x (ISBN 0-04-942198-0); pap. text ed. 14.95x (ISBN 0-04-942199-9). Allen Unwin.

Bonino, Jose M. Doing Theology in a Revolutionary Situation. Lazareth, William H., ed. LC 74-80424. 208p. 1975. pap. 5.95 (ISBN 0-8006-1451-8, 1-1451). Fortress.

Boys, Don. Liberalism: A Rope of Sand. 1979. 4.95 (ISBN 0-686-25591-7). Freedom Univ-FSP.

Coleman, Richard J. Issues of Theological Conflict: Evangelicals & Liberals. Rev. ed. LC 79-19494. pap. 74.00 (ISBN 0-317-19816-5, 2023209). Bks Demand UMI.

Collini, Stefan. Liberalism & Sociology: L. T. Hobhouse & Political Argument in English, 1880-1914. LC 78-23779. 1979. 37.50 (ISBN 0-521-22304-0). Cambridge U Pr.

Haight, Roger S. An Alternative Vision: An Interpretation of Liberation Theology. (Orig.). 1985. 10.95 (ISBN 0-8091-2679-6). Paulist Pr.

Horton, Walter M. Realistic Theology. 207p. 1982. Repr. of 1934 ed. lib. bdg. 30.00 (ISBN 0-89760-362-1). Telegraph Bks.

Jedin, Hubert & Dolan, John P., eds. The Church in the Age of Liberalism. (History of the Church: Vol. 8). 1981. 59.50x (ISBN 0-8245-0011-3). Crossroad NY.

Luker, Ralph. A Southern Tradition in Theology & Social Criticism, 1830-1930: The Religious Liberalism & Social Conservatism of James Warley Miles, William Porcher Dubose & Edgar Gardner Murphy. LC 84-8954. (Studies in American Religion: Vol. 11). 476p. 1984. 69.95x (ISBN 0-88946-655-6). E Mellen.

McCann, Dennis P. Christian Realism & Liberation Theology: Practical Theologies in Creative Conflict. LC 80-23163. 256p. (Orig.). 1981. pap. 9.95 (ISBN 0-88344-086-5). Orbis Bks.

Machen, J. Gresham. Christianity & Liberalism. 1923. pap. 6.95 (ISBN 0-8028-1121-3). Eerdmans.

Opton, Frank. Liberal Religion: Principles & Practices. LC 81-81129. (Library of Liberal Religion). 295p. 1981. 20.95 (ISBN 0-87975-155-X). Prometheus Bks.

Orton, William A. Liberal Tradition. 1945. 12.50x (ISBN 0-686-83606-5). Elliots Bks.

Perrens, Francois T. Libertins en France au Dix-Septieme Siecle. LC 72-168701. (Fr.). 428p. 1973. Repr. of 1896 ed. lib. bdg. 29.00 (ISBN 0-8337-2728-1). B Franklin.

Quade, Quentin L., ed. The Pope & Revolution: John Paul II Confronts Liberation Theology. LC 82-4971. 205p. 1982. 12.00 (ISBN 0-89633-059-1); pap. 7.00 (ISBN 0-89633-054-0). Ethics & Public Policy.

Reardon, B. Liberalism & Tradition. LC 75-7214. 320p. 1975. Cambridge U Pr.

Richesin, L. Dale, ed. The Challenge of Liberation Theology: A First World Response. Mahan, Brian. LC 81-9527. 152p. (Orig.). 1981. pap. 7.95 (ISBN 0-88344-092-X). Orbis Bks.

Rochester, Stuart I. American Liberal Disillusionment in the Wake of World War I. LC 76-47613. 1977. 22.50x (ISBN 0-271-01233-1). Pa St U Pr.

Rupp, George. Culture-Protestantism: German Liberal Theology at the Turn of the Twentieth Century. LC 77-13763. (American Academy of Religion. Studies in Religion: No. 15). 1977. pap. 8.95 (ISBN 0-89130-197-6, 010015). Scholars Pr GA.

Sandmel, Samuel. The Several Israels. 1971. 12.50x. Ktav.

Tambasco, Anthony J. The Bible for Ethics: Juan Luis Segundo & First-World Ethics. LC 80-6253. 286p. (Orig.). 1981. lib. bdg. 27.50 (ISBN 0-8191-1556-8); pap. text ed. 12.75 (ISBN 0-8191-1557-6). U Pr of Amer.

Wieman, Henry N. Creative Freedom: Vocation of Liberal Religion. Creighton, W. & Axel, Larry E., eds. LC 82-10182. 128p. (Orig.). 1982. pap. 7.95 (ISBN 0-8298-0623-7). Pilgrim NY.

LIBERATION THEOLOGY

Araya, Victorio. God of the Poor. Barr, Robert R., tr. from Span. 224p. (Orig.). 1987. 19.95 (ISBN 0-88344-566-2); pap. 9.95 (ISBN 0-88344-565-4). Orbis Bks.

Bayer, Charles H. A Guide to Liberation Theology for Middle-Class Congregations. Lambert, Herbert, ed. LC 86-6111. 176p. (Orig.). 1986. pap. 10.95 (ISBN 0-8272-1233-X). CBP.

Berghoef, Gerard & DeKoster, Lester. Liberation Theology: The Church's Future Shock. 197p. 1984. 14.95 (ISBN 0-934874-07-7). Chr Lib Pr.

Berryman, Phillip. Liberation Theology: Essential Facts about the Revolutionary Movement in Latin America & Beyond. LC 86-42638. 224p. 1986. 16.95 (ISBN 0-394-55241-5); pap. 6.95 (ISBN 0-394-74652-X). Pantheon.

Boff, Leonardo. Ecclesiogenesis: The Base Communities Reinvent the Church. Barr, Robert R., tr. from Port. LC 85-15600. 128p. (Orig.). 1986. pap. 9.95 (ISBN 0-88344-214-0). Orbis Bks.

Boff, Leonardo & Boff, Clodovis. Introducing Liberation Theology. Burns, Paul, tr. from Port. LC 87-5672. Tr. of Como Fazer Teologia da Libertacao. 112p. (Orig.). 1987. 16.95 (ISBN 0-88344-575-1); pap. 7.95 (ISBN 0-88344-550-6). Orbis Bks.

Bonpane, Blase. Guerrillas of Peace: Liberation Theology & the Central American Revolution. 120p. (Orig.). 1986. 25.00 (ISBN 0-89608-311-X); pap. 8.00 (ISBN 0-89608-310-1). South End Pr.

Castillo-Cardenas, Gonzalo. Liberation Theology from Below: The Life & Thought of Manuel Quintin Lame. LC 86-21812. 224p. (Orig.). 1987. pap. 16.95 (ISBN 0-88344-408-9). Orbis Bks.

Cohn-Sherbok, Dan. On Earth As It Is in Heaven: Jews, Christians, & Liberation Theology. LC 86-23509. 128p. (Orig.). 1987. pap. 7.95 (ISBN 0-88344-410-0). Orbis Bks.

Cone, James H. A Black Theology of Liberation. 2nd ed. LC 85-18749. 176p. 1986. pap. 9.95 (ISBN 0-88344-245-0). Orbis Bks.

--Speaking the Truth: Ecumenism, Liberation, & Black Theology. 176p. (Orig.). 1986. pap. 8.95 (ISBN 0-8028-0226-5). Eerdmans.

Ferm, Deane W., ed. Third World Liberation Theologies: A Reader. LC 85-15302. 400p. (Orig.). 1986. pap. 16.95 (ISBN 0-88344-516-6). Orbis Bks.

Gonzalez, Juan G. The New Libertarian Gospel: Pitfalls of the Theology of Liberation. 1977. 7.95 (ISBN 0-8199-0682-4). Franciscan Herald.

Gutierrez, Gustavo. On Job: God-Talk & the Suffering of the Innocent. O'Connell, Matthew, tr. from Span. LC 87-5661. Tr. of Hablar de Dios desde el Sufrimento del Inocente. 144p. (Orig.). 1987. 10.95 (ISBN 0-88344-577-8); pap. 8.95 (ISBN 0-88344-552-2). Orbis Bks.

Instruction on Christian Freedom & Liberation. 60p. (Orig.). 1986. pap. 1.95 (ISBN 1-55586-995-5). US Catholic.

Jesudasan, Ignatius. A Gandhian Theology of Liberation. LC 83-19486. 192p. (Orig.). 1984. pap. 10.95 (ISBN 0-88344-154-3). Orbis Bks.

Kloppenberg, Bonaventure. Temptations for the Theology of Liberation. (Synthesis Ser.). 1974. 0.75 (ISBN 0-8199-0362-0). Franciscan Herald.

Mieth, Dietmar & Pohier, Jacques, eds. The Ethics of Liberation: The Liberation of Liberation, Vol. 172. (Concilium Ser.). 128p. 1984. pap. 6.95 (ISBN 0-567-30052-8, Pub. by T & T Clark Ltd UK). Fortress.

Nash, Ronald H., ed. Liberation Theology. 1986. text ed. 15.95 (ISBN 0-8010-6745-6). Baker Bk.

Nottingham, William J. Practice & Preaching of Liberation. Lambert, Herbert, ed. LC 85-18997. 96p. (Orig.). 1986. pap. 9.95 (ISBN 0-8272-2931-3). CBP.

Nunez, Emilio. Liberation Theology. 1985. text ed. 15.95 (ISBN 0-8024-4893-3). Moody.

Rodes, Robert E. Law & Liberation. LC 85-41011. 240p. 1986. text ed. 24.95 (ISBN 0-268-01279-2). U of Notre Dame Pr.

Schaffner, Franklin J. Worthington Miner: A Directors Guild of America Oral History. LC 84-22184. 323p. 1985. 22.50 (ISBN 0-8108-1757-8). Scarecrow.

Shivkumar, Muni. The Doctrine of Liberation in Indian Religion. 1984. text ed. 14.00x (ISBN 0-89563-286-1). Coronet Bks.

Tabb, William K., ed. Churches in Struggle: Liberation Theologies & Social Change in North America. 331p. 1986. 27.00 (ISBN 0-85345-692-5); pap. 11.00 (ISBN 0-85345-693-3). Monthly Rev.

Welch, Sharon D. Communities of Resistance & Solidarity: A Feminist Theology of Liberation. LC 85-4809. 112p. (Orig.). 1985. pap. 7.95 (ISBN 0-88344-204-3). Orbis Bks.

Williams, George H. The Law of Nations & the Book of Nature. Franklin, R. W., ed. LC 84-72274. (New Essays in Christian Humanism: Vol. 1). (Illus.). 60p. (Orig.). 1985. pap. 4.95x (ISBN 0-9613867-0-3). St Johns Univ Christ Hum.

Witvliet, Theo. A Place in the Sun: Liberation Theology in the Third World. Bowden, John, tr. from Dutch. LC 84-27229. Tr. of Fen Plaats onder de zon Bevrijdingstheologie in de Derde Wereld. 208p. (Orig.). 1985. pap. 8.95 (ISBN 0-88344-404-6). Orbis Bks.

LIBERTY (THEOLOGY)

see Freedom (Theology)

LIBERTY OF CONSCIENCE

see also Free Thought; Persecution; Religious Liberty

Pestana, Carla G. Liberty of Conscience & the Growth of Religious Diversity in Early America, 1636-1786. (Illus.). 104p. 1986. pap. 30.00 (ISBN 0-916617-02-5); bibliographical suppl. 10.00 (ISBN 0-916617-03-3). J C Brown.

Putnam, George H. Censorship of the Church of Rome & Its Influence upon the Production & Distribution of Literature, 2 Vols. LC 67-12455. 1967. Repr. of 1906 ed. 55.00 (ISBN 0-405-08869-8); 27.50 ea. Vol. 1 (ISBN 0-405-08870-1). Vol. 2 (ISBN 0-405-08871-X). Ayer Co Pubs.

Swancara, Frank. Obstruction of Justice by Religion: A Treatise on Religious Barbarities of the Common Law, & a Review of Judicial Oppressions of the Non-Religious in the U. S. LC 70-139581. (Civil Liberties in American History Ser). (Illus.). 1971. Repr. of 1936 ed. lib. bdg. 32.50 (ISBN 0-306-71964-9). Da Capo.

LIBERTY OF RELIGION

see Religious Liberty

LIBERTY OF SPEECH IN THE CHURCH

Rahner, Karl. Free Speech in the Church. LC 79-8717. Orig. Title: Das Freie Wort in der Kirche. 112p. 1981. Repr. of 1959 ed. lib. bdg. 22.50x (ISBN 0-313-20849-2, RAFS). Greenwood.

Seaton, Alexander A. The Theory of Toleration under the Later Stuarts. 1972. lib. bdg. 23.00x (ISBN 0-374-97233-8, Octagon). Hippocrene Bks.

LIBERTY OF THE WILL

see Free Will and Determinism

LIBRARIES, CATHOLIC

Brown, James, et al. The Relationship of the Library to Instructional Systems. Corrigan, John T., ed. (Catholic Library Association Studies in Librarianship: No. 2). 1978. pap. 3.00 (ISBN 0-87507-006-X). Cath Lib Assn.

Cashel Diocesan Library, County Tipperary, Republic of Ireland Staff. Catalogue of the Cashel Diocesan Library. 1973. 100.00 (ISBN 0-8161-1065-4, Hall Library). G K Hall.

Harvey, John F., ed. Church & Synagogue Libraries. LC 80-11736. 299p. 1980. 20.00 (ISBN 0-8108-1304-1). Scarecrow.

Hyland, Anne M. Manual: School Library-Media Skills Test. 50p. 1986. pap. text ed. 5.00 (ISBN 0-87287-524-5). Libs Unl.

Pilley, Catherine M. & Wilt, Matthew R., eds. Catholic Subject Headings. rev. ed. 257p. 1981. pap. 25.00x (ISBN 0-87507-009-4). Cath Lib Assn.

LIBRARIES, CHURCH

Anderson, Jacqulyn, compiled by. How to Administer & Promote a Church Media Library. LC 84-21452. 1985. pap. 5.95 (ISBN 0-8054-3711-8). Broadman.

Deitrick, Bernard E. A Basic Book List for Church Libraries. 2nd rev ed. LC 77-4093. 1983. pap. 3.95x (ISBN 0-915324-10-5); pap. 3.00 members. CSLA.

Hammack, Mary L. How to Organize Your Church Library & Resource Center. 128p. 1985. pap. 5.95 (ISBN 0-8170-1066-1). Judson.

Hannaford, Claudia. The ABC's of Financing Church & Synagogue Libraries, No. 13. LC 85-13286. (CSLA Guide Ser.). (Illus.). 36p. (Orig.). 1985. pap. 5.95X (ISBN 0-915324-23-7). CSLA.

Harvey, John F., ed. Church & Synagogue Libraries. LC 80-11736. 299p. 1980. 20.00 (ISBN 0-8108-1304-1). Scarecrow.

John, Erwin E. Key to a Successful Church Library. rev. ed. LC 58-13940. (Orig.). 1967. pap. 5.95 (ISBN 0-8066-0711-4, 10-3684). Augsburg.

Kohl, Rachel & Rodda, Dorothy. Church & Synagogue Library Resources. 4th ed. LC 75-1178. 1984. pap. 3.95x (ISBN 0-915324-08-3); pap. 3.00 members. CSLA.

Korty, Margaret B. Audio-Visual Materials in the Church Library: How to Select, Catalog, Process, Store, Circulate & Promote. LC 77-74780. (Illus.). 102p. 1977. spiral bdg. 4.95 (ISBN 0-9603060-0-5). Church Lib.

Laugher, Charles T. Thomas Bray's Grand Design: Libraries of the Church of England in America, 1695-1785. LC 73-16332. (ACRL Publications in Librarianship Ser.: No. 35). pap. 31.30 (ISBN 0-317-29444-X, 2024224). Bks Demand UMI.

Merryweather, F. Somner. Bibliomania in the Middle Ages. rev. ed. Copinger, H. B., ed. LC 72-83748. Repr. of 1933 ed. 22.00 (ISBN 0-405-08787-X, Pub. by Blom). Ayer Co Pubs.

Newton, LaVose. The Church Library Handbook. Rev. ed. 1987. Repr. of 1972 ed. 12.95 (ISBN 0-89081-563-1). Harvest Hse.

Oliver, Andrew & Peabody, James B., eds. The Records of Trinity Church, Boston, 1728-1830. LC 80-68230. 519p. 1980. 30.00x (ISBN 0-8139-0950-3, Colonial Soc Ma). U Pr of Va.

Paris, Janelle A. Planning Bulletin Boards for Church & Synagogue Libraries. LC 83-7331. (CSLA Guide Two Ser. No. 11). (Orig.). 1983. pap. 6.95 (ISBN 0-915324-20-2); pap. 5.50 members. CSLA.

Scheer, Gladys E. The Church Library: Tips & Tools. LC 73-10093. (Orig.). 1973. pap. 3.95 (ISBN 0-8272-0435-3). CBP.

Smith, Ruth S. Getting the Books Off the Shelves: Making the Most of Your Congregation's Library, No. 12. rev. ed. LC 85-11650. (CSLA Guide Ser.). (Illus.). 40p. 1985. pap. 6.95X (ISBN 0-915324-22-9). CSLA.

--Running a Library: Managing the Congregation's Library with Care, Confidence, & Common Sense. 144p. (Orig.). 1982. pap. 7.95 (ISBN 0-8164-2413-6, HarpR). Har-Row.

Standards for Church & Synagogue Libraries. LC 77-6634. (Guide Ser.: No. 6). 1977. pap. 4.95x (ISBN 0-915324-12-1); pap. 3.95 members. CSLA.

Walls, Francine E. The Church Library Workbook. 144p. 1980. pap. 8.95 (ISBN 0-89367-048-0). Light & Life.

LIBRARIES, PARISH

see Libraries, Church

LIBRARIES, THEOLOGICAL

see Theological Libraries

LIBRARY CATALOGS

Cashel Diocesan Library, County Tipperary, Republic of Ireland Staff. Catalogue of the Cashel Diocesan Library. 1973. 100.00 (ISBN 0-8161-1065-4, Hall Library). G K Hall.

Ecole Biblique et Archeologique Francaise. Jerusalem. Catalogue de la Bibliotheque de l'ecole Biblique et Archeologique Francaise (Catalog of the Library of the French Biblical & Archaeological School, 13 vols. 1975. lib. bdg. 1405.00 (ISBN 0-8161-1154-5, Hall Library). G K Hall.

Pontifical Institute of Medieval Studies, Ontario. Dictionary Catalogue of the Library of the Pontifical Institute of Medieval Studies, 5 vols. 1972. Set. lib. bdg. 505.00 (ISBN 0-8161-0970-2, Hall Library). G K Hall.

World Council of Churches, Geneva, Switzerland. Classified Catalog of the Ecumenical Movement, 2 vols. 1972. lib. bdg. 198.00 (ISBN 0-8161-0925-7, Hall Library). G K Hall.

LIFE

see also Conduct of Life; Death; Ethics; Old Age; Ontology; Philosophical Anthropology

Bendit, Laurence J. Mirror of Life & Death. 1965. pap. 1.35 (ISBN 0-8356-0411-X, Quest). Theos Pub Hse.

Bergson, Henri. Creative Evolution. Mitxhell, Arthur, tr. LC 83-19859. 460p. 1984. pap. text ed. 13.50 (ISBN 0-8191-3553-4). U Pr of Amer.
Chaudhuri, Haridas. Mastering the Problems of Living. new ed. LC 75-4172. 222p. 1975. pap. 2.75 (ISBN 0-8356-0463-2, Quest). Theos Pub Hse.
Crockett, William J. Life: Voices from the Heart. 15p. 1985. pap. 3.00 (ISBN 0-934383-05-7). Pride Prods.
Dunne, John S. Time & Myth. LC 74-32289. 128p. 1975. pap. 4.95 (ISBN 0-268-01828-6). U of Notre Dame Pr.
Greg, William R. Enigmas of Life. LC 72-323. (Essay Index Reprint Ser.). Repr. of 1879 ed. 21.00 (ISBN 0-8369-2794-X). Ayer Co Pubs.
Hocking, William E. The Meaning of Immortality in Human Experience, Including Thoughts on Death & Life. rev. ed. 263p. 1973. Repr. of 1957 ed. lib. bdg. 27.50x (ISBN 0-8371-6621-7, HOMI). Greenwood.
Hutson, Joan. Heaven & Earth. (Little Learner Ser.). 24p. 1985. 5.95 (ISBN 0-570-08952-2, 56-1544). Concordia.
Jasson, Wilbur A. Beyond Evolution. LC 84-52700. (Illus.). 141p. 1986. 14.95 (ISBN 0-9614464-0-4); pap. 8.95 (ISBN 0-9614464-1-2). Sarasota Sci.
Kniazev, V. V. Zhizn' dlja vsjekh i smert' za vsjekh. Tr. of Life is for All & Death is for All. 1971. pap. 1.00 (ISBN 0-317-30338-4). Holy Trinity.
Krishnamurti, J. The Wholeness of Life. LC 78-19495. 256p. 1981. pap. 8.95 (ISBN 0-06-064868-6, RD362, HarpR). Har-Row.
Lawson, Brian C. Life, Death, Eternity & the Secret of the Universe. (Illus.). 1979. 47.45 (ISBN 0-89266-207-7). Am Classical Coll Pr.
Mandelbaum, Bernard. Choose Life. 1972. pap. 5.95 (ISBN 0-8197-0006-1). Bloch.
Nagel, T. Mortal Questions. LC 78-58797. 1979. 32.50 (ISBN 0-521-22360-1); pap. 10.95 (ISBN 0-521-29460-6). Cambridge U Pr.
Nelson, J. Robert. Human Life: A Biblical Perspective for Bioethics. LC 83-48140. 208p. 1984. pap. 10.95 (ISBN 0-8006-1754-1, 1-1754). Fortress.
O'Connor, John J. In Defense of Life. 1980. 4.00 (ISBN 0-686-74344-X); pap. 3.00 (ISBN 0-8198-3601-X). Dghtrs St Paul.
The Philosophy of Life & the Philosophy of Death: Considerations & Anticipations of the Future Universe & of Man's Existence in It. 2nd ed. (Illus.). 1977. 47.25 (ISBN 0-89266-058-9). Am Classical Coll Pr.
Rogers, Carl R. Therapist's View of Personal Goals. LC 60-11607. (Orig.). 1960. pap. 2.50x (ISBN 0-87574-108-8). Pendle Hill.
Steiner, Rudolf. Philosophy of Freedom. Wilson, Michael, tr. from Ger. 226p. 1973. pap. 7.95 (ISBN 0-910142-52-1). Anthroposophic.
Thomasma, David C. An Apology for the Value of Human Life. LC 83-7335. 169p. 1983. pap. 18.00 (ISBN 0-87125-085-3). Cath Health.
Tully, Mary J. A Family Book of Praise. (Illus.). 128p. (Orig.). 1980. pap. 5.95 (ISBN 0-8215-6542-7). Sadlier.
Vinck, Jose D. The Yes Book. 1976. pap. 3.75 (ISBN 0-685-77499-6). Franciscan Herald.
--The Yes Book: An Answer to Life (a Manual of Christian Existentialism) LC 77-190621. 200p. 1972. 12.75 (ISBN 0-911726-12-8); pap. 8.75 (ISBN 0-911726-11-X). Alleluia Pr.
Words of Life. (Words of... Ser.). (Illus.). 48p. 1983. 3.95 (ISBN 0-8407-5337-3). Nelson.

LIFE-ORIGIN
see also Man–Origin
Bliss, Richard B. & Parker, Gary E. Origin of Life. LC 78-58477. (Illus.). 1978. pap. 4.95 (ISBN 0-89051-053-9). Master Bks.
Eccles, Sir John. The Human Mystery. LC 78-12095. (Illus.). 1978. 25.00 (ISBN 0-387-09016-9). Springer-Verlag.
Gish, Duane T. Speculations & Experiments Related to the Origin of Life: A Critique. (ICR Technical Monograph: No. 1). (Illus.). 41p. 1972. pap. 5.95 (ISBN 0-89051-010-5). Master Bks.
Strickling, James E., Jr. Origins: Today's Science, Tomorrow's Myth. 1986. 11.95 (ISBN 0-317-40170-X). Vantage.
Szekely, Edmond B. The Cosmotherapy of the Essenes. (Illus.). 64p. 1975. pap. 3.50 (ISBN 0-89564-012-0). IBS Intl.
--The Discovery of the Essene Gospel of Peace: The Essenes & the Vatican. (Illus.). 96p. 1977. pap. 4.80 (ISBN 0-89564-004-X). IBS Intl.
--The Essene Communions with the Infinite. (Illus.). 64p. 1979. pap. 3.95 (ISBN 0-89564-009-0). IBS Intl.
--The Essene Science of Life. (Illus.). 64p. 1976. pap. 3.50 (ISBN 0-89564-010-4). IBS Intl.
--The Essene Way: Biogenic Living. (Illus.). 200p. 1981. pap. 8.80 (ISBN 0-89564-019-8). IBS Intl.
--The Essene Way: World Pictures & Cosmic Symbols. (Illus.). 40p. 1978. pap. 1.80 (ISBN 0-89564-050-3). IBS Intl.
--The First Essene. (Illus.). 240p. 1981. pap. 9.50 (ISBN 0-89564-018-X). IBS Intl.
--The Teachings of the Essenes from Enoch to the Dead Sea Scrolls. (Illus.). 112p. 1981. pap. 4.80 (ISBN 0-89564-006-6). IBS Intl.
--The Tender Touch: Biogenic Fulfillment. (Illus.). 120p. 1977. text ed. 5.50 (ISBN 0-89564-020-1). IBS Intl.

LIFE, FUTURE
see Future Life

LIFE, JEWISH WAY OF
see Jewish Way of Life

LIFE AFTER DEATH
see Future Life; Immortality

LIGHT, INNER
see Inner Light

LIGHT AND DARKNESS (IN RELIGION, FOLK-LORE, ETC.)
Feagins, Mary E. Tending the Light. 1984. pap. 2.50x (ISBN 0-87574-255-6, 255). Pendle Hill.

LIGHTS, FEAST OF
see Hanukkah (Feast of Lights)

LIGUORI, ALFONSO MARIA DE, SAINT, 1696-1787
Oppitz, Joseph. Autumn Memoirs of St. Alphonsus Liguori. 96p. 1986. pap. 3.95 (ISBN 0-89243-253-5). Liguori Pubns.

LILBURNE, JOHN, 1614?-1657
Haller, William & Davies, Godfrey, eds. The Leveller Tracts: 1647-1653. 1964. 11.75 (ISBN 0-8446-1218-9). Peter Smith.
Pease, T. C. The Leveller Movement. 11.75 (ISBN 0-8446-1345-2). Peter Smith.

LINCOLN, ABRAHAM, PRES. U. S., 1809-1865
Bassuk, Daniel. Abraham Lincoln & the Quakers. (Orig.). 1987. pap. 2.50x (ISBN 0-87574-273-4). Pendle Hill.
Johnson, William J. Abraham Lincoln the Christian. (Great American Christian Ser.). (Illus.). 1976. pap. 3.95 (ISBN 0-915134-13-6). Mott Media.
Jones, Edgar D. Lincoln & the Preachers. (Biography Index Reprint Ser). 1948. 21.00 (ISBN 0-8369-8018-2). Ayer Co Pubs.
Owen, G. Frederick. Abraham Lincoln: The Man & His Faith. 232p. 1981. pap. 6.95 (ISBN 0-8423-0000-7). Tyndale.
Wolf, William J. Lincoln's Religion. LC 70-123035. Orig. Title: Almost Chosen People. 1970. pap. 2.25 (ISBN 0-8298-0181-2). Pilgrim NY.

LINDISFARNE ABBEY
Backhouse, Janet. The Lindisfarne Gospels. LC 81-65990. (Cornell Phaidon Bks.). (Illus.). 96p. 1981. 29.95 (ISBN 0-8014-1354-0). Cornell U Pr.

LIPPI, FRA FILIPPO, 1412-1469
Strutt, Edward C. Fra Filippo Lippi. LC 78-176460. Repr. of 1901 ed. 11.50 (ISBN 0-404-06299-7). AMS Pr.

LITANIES
Hebert, Albert, compiled by. A Prayerbook of Favorite Litanies: 116 Favorite Catholic Litanies & Responsory Prayers. LC 84-51818. 192p. 1985. pap. 7.50 (ISBN 0-89555-252-3). Tan Bks Pubs.

LITERATURE–INFLUENCE
see Literature and Morals

LITERATURE–MORAL AND RELIGIOUS ASPECTS
see Literature and Morals; Religion and Literature

LITERATURE, APOCALYPTIC
see Apocalyptic Literature

LITERATURE, PRIMITIVE
see Folk Literature

LITERATURE AND MORALS
see also Censorship
Clark, Glenn. God's Voice in the Folklore. 4.95 (ISBN 0-910924-06-6). Macalester.
Humphries, Jefferson. The Puritan & the Cynic: Moralists & Theorists in French Letters. 144p. 1986. 15.95 (ISBN 0-19-504180-1). Oxford U Pr.
Kort, Wesley A. Moral Fiber: Character & Belief in Recent American Fiction. LC 81-71389. 160p. 1982. pap. 1.00 (ISBN 0-8006-1624-3, 1-1624). Fortress.
MacIver, R. M., ed. Great Moral Dilemmas. (Religion & Civilization Ser). 189p. 1964. Repr. of 1956 ed. 21.50x (ISBN 0-8154-0145-0). Cooper Sq.

LITERATURE AND RELIGION
see Religion and Literature

LITURGICAL APOSTOLATE
see Liturgical Movement–Catholic Church

LITURGICAL DRAMA
see also Mysteries and Miracle-Plays
Bennett, Gordon C. Reader's Theatre Comes to Church. 2nd ed. LC 85-61999. 128p. 1985. pap. 7.95 (ISBN 0-916260-33-X, B-191). Meriwether Pub.
Collins, Fletcher, Jr. Production of Medieval Church Music-Drama. LC 78-168610. (Illus.). xiii, 356p. 1972. 25.00x (ISBN 0-8139-0373-4). U Pr of Va.
Parker, Elizabeth C. The Descent from the Cross: Its Relation to the Extra-Liturgical Depositio Drama. LC 77-94713. (Outstanding Dissertations in the Fine Arts Ser.). 1978. lib. bdg. 41.00 (ISBN 0-8240-3245-4). Garland Pub.

LITURGICAL DRAMAS
Greenberg, Noah & Smoldon, W. L., eds. Play of Herod: A Twelfth-Century Musical Drama. (Illus.). 1965. pap. 4.25 (ISBN 0-19-385196-2). Oxford U Pr.

LITURGICAL MOVEMENT
Here are entered works dealing with the revived interest in liturgical matters, which began about 1890 in Catholic circles and spread over to Protestantism.
McNally, Dennis. Sacred Space: An Aesthetic for the Liturgical Environment. 215p. (Orig.). 1985. pap. 8.95x (ISBN 0-932269-45-1). Wyndham Hall.
Simon, Thomas G. & Fitzpatrick, James M. The Ministry of Liturgical Environment. 48p. (Orig.). 1984. pap. 1.25 (ISBN 0-8146-1354-3). Liturgical Pr.

LITURGICAL MOVEMENT–CATHOLIC CHURCH
Del Mazza, Valentino. Good News for the Liturgical Community: Cycle C. rev. ed. 1981. 5.95 (ISBN 0-8198-0573-4); pap. 4.95 (ISBN 0-8198-3003-8). Dghtrs St Paul.
Hovda, Robert W. Strong, Loving & Wise: Presiding in Liturgy. 5th ed. (Illus.). 96p. 1983. pap. 5.95 (ISBN 0-8146-1253-9). Liturgical Pr.

LITURGICAL YEAR
see Church Year

LITURGICS
see also Bible–Liturgical Use; Chants (Plain, Gregorian, etc.); Christian Art and Symbolism; Church Music; Church Vestments; Church Year; Fasts and Feasts; Liturgical Movement; Lord's Supper (Liturgy); Sacraments (Liturgy)
Baker, Thomas & Ferrone, Frank. Liturgy Committee Basics: A No-nonsense Guide. (Orig.). 1985. pap. 6.95 (ISBN 0-912405-11-2). Pastoral Pr.
Barrois, Georges A. Scripture Readings in Orthodox Worship. 197p. 1977. pap. 6.95 (ISBN 0-913836-41-9). St Vladimirs.
Beachy, Alvin J. Worship As Celebration of Covenant & Incarnation. LC 68-57497. 1968. pap. 2.00 (ISBN 0-87303-940-8). Faith & Life.
Booty, John E., ed. The Divine Drama in History & Liturgy: Essays Presented to Horton Davies on His Retirement from Princeton University. (Pittsburgh Theological Monographs: New Ser. 10). 1984. pap. 16.50 (ISBN 0-915138-67-0). Pickwick.
Bouyer, Louis. Rite & Man: Natural Sacredness & Christian Liturgy. Costelloe, Joseph, tr. 224p. 1985. pap. text ed. 12.25 (ISBN 0-8191-4340-5). U Pr of Amer.
Chupungco, Anscar J. Cultural Adaptation of the Liturgy. 117p. (Orig.). 1982. pap. 4.95 (ISBN 0-8091-2452-1). Paulist Pr.
Collins, Mary & Power, David, eds. A Creative Tradition. (Concilium 1983: Vol. 162). 128p. (Orig.). 1983. pap. 6.95 (ISBN 0-8164-2442-X, HarpR). Har-Row.
Darcy-Berube, Francoise & Berube, John-Paul. Come, Let Us Celebrate. 64p. 1984. 3.95 (ISBN 0-7773-8007-2, 8514, HarpR). Har-Row.
Davies, J. G., ed. The New Westminster Dictionary of Liturgy & Worship. LC 86-9219. (Illus.). 560p. 1986. 29.95 (ISBN 0-664-21270-0). Westminster.
Deiss, Lucien. Springtime of the Liturgy: Liturgical Texts of the First Four Centuries. rev. ed. O'Connell, Matthew J., tr. from Fr. LC 79-15603. 307p. 1979. pap. 10.00 (ISBN 0-8146-1023-4). Liturgical Pr.
Deitering, Carolyn. The Liturgy As Dance & the Liturgical Dancer. (Illus.). 144p. 1984. pap. 8.95 (ISBN 0-8245-0654-5). Crossroad NY.
Del Mazza, Valentino. Good News for the Liturgical Community: Cycle B. 1980. 5.95 (ISBN 0-8198-3004-6); pap. 4.95 (ISBN 0-8198-3005-4). Dghtrs St Paul.
Dix, Dom G. The Shape of the Liturgy. 816p. 1982. 24.50 (ISBN 0-8164-2418-7, HarpR). Har-Row.
Feuer, Avrohom C. Tashlich. (Art Scroll Mesorah Ser.). 64p. 1979. 6.95 (ISBN 0-89906-158-3); pap. 4.95 (ISBN 0-89906-159-1). Mesorah Pubns.
Fischer, Edward. Everybody Steals from God: Communication as Worship. LC 77-3711. 1977. text ed. 10.95x (ISBN 0-268-00904-X). U of Notre Dame Pr.
Fleming, Austin H. Preparing for Liturgy: A Theology & Sprituality. (Orig.). 1985. pap. 6.95 (ISBN 0-912405-16-3). Pastoral Pr.
Freburger, William J. Liturgy: Work of the People. 112p. (Orig.). 1984. pap. 4.95 (ISBN 0-89622-214-4). Twenty-Third.
Gallen, John, ed. Christians at Prayer. LC 76-22407. (Liturgical Studies). 1977. pap. text ed. 5.95 (ISBN 0-268-00719-5). U of Notre Dame Pr.
Gardner, Johann V. Alliluija (Liturgijnaja), 8-mi Glasov. Tr. of Alleluia (for Divine Liturgy) Eight Tones. 1966. pap. 3.00 (ISBN 0-317-30391-0). Holy Trinity.
Gogol, Nikolai. Razmishljenije o Bozhestvennoj Liturgii. Tr. of Meditations on the Divine Liturgy. 48p. pap. 2.00 (ISBN 0-317-29135-1). Holy Trinity.
Hamilton, James E. The Liturgical Coordinator. 64p. (Orig.). 1984. pap. text ed. 10.00 (ISBN 0-942466-06-3); Looseleaf 9.50 (ISBN 0-942466-05-5). Hymnary Pr.
Hatchett, Marion J. Sanctifying Life, Time & Space: An Introduction to Liturgical Study. 1976. (HarpR); pap. 8.95 (ISBN 0-8164-2396-2). Har-Row.
Hoffman, Lawrence. Beyond the Text: A Holistic Approach to Liturgy. (Jewish Literature & Culture Ser.). 1987. 35.00 (ISBN 0-253-31199-3). Ind U Pr.
Hughes, Dom A., compiled by. Liturgical Terms for Music Students: A Dictionary. LC 70-166236. 1972. Repr. of 1940 ed. 29.00x (ISBN 0-403-01363-1). Scholarly.
International Committee on English in the Liturgy. Documents on the Liturgy, 1963-1979: Conciliar, Papal & Curial Texts. O'Brien, Thomas C., ed. LC 82-83580. 1496p. 1983. text ed. 49.95 (ISBN 0-8146-1281-4). Liturgical Pr.
Jones, Cheslyn, et al, eds. The Study of Liturgy. 1978. 27.00x (ISBN 0-19-520075-6); pap. 13.95x (ISBN 0-19-520076-4). Oxford U Pr.
Keifer, Ralph A. Liturgy Against Itself. 128p. (Orig.). 1986. pap. 7.95 (ISBN 0-06-254480-2, HarpR). Har-Row.
Kern, Walter. New Liturgy & Old Devotions. LC 78-73623. (Illus., Orig.). 1979. pap. 3.50 (ISBN 0-8189-1151-4, 151, Pub. by Alba Bks). Alba.
Kucharek, Casimir. The Byzantine Slav Liturgy of St. John Chrysostom, Its Origin & Evolution. LC 74-147735. (Illus.). 840p. 1971. 18.75 (ISBN 0-911726-06-3, BSL). Alleluia Pr.
Leclercq, Dom H. & Marron, Henri. Dictionnaire d'Archeologie Chretienne et de Liturgie, 28 vols. (Fr.). 1903. Set. 1995.00 (ISBN 0-686-57001-4, M-6342). French & Eur.
Lehmann, Arnold O. Lehmann's Little Dictionary of Liturgical Terms. 1980. 3.75 (ISBN 0-8100-0127-6, 15N0371). Northwest Pub.
Liturgy of St. John Chrysostom. (Eng. & Arabic.). 104p. 1978. pap. 3.00 (ISBN 0-911726-39-X). Alleluia Pr.
Machado, Mary K. How to Plan Children's Liturgies. LC 86-60892. (Orig.). 1985. pap. 9.95 (ISBN 0-89390-074-5). Resource Pubns.
McKenna, Megan & Ducote, Darryl. Sacraments, Liturgy & Prayer. LC 78-71531. (Followers of the Way Ser.: Vol. 5). 221p. 1979. 22.50 (ISBN 0-8091-9546-1); cassette 7.50 (ISBN 0-8091-7670-X). Paulist Pr.
Martimort, A. G. The Church at Prayer: The Liturgy & Time, Vol. 4. 304p. 1986. pap. 14.95 (ISBN 0-8146-1366-7). Liturgical Pr.
Maxwell, Jack M. Worship & Reformed Theology: The Liturgical Lessons of Mercersburg. LC 75-45492. (Pittsburgh Theological Monographs: No. 10). 1976. pap. 12.00 (ISBN 0-915138-12-3). Pickwick.
Monks of New Skete. Transfiguration of Christ. Reverend Laurence Mancuso, tr. (Liturgical Music Series I: Great Feasts: Vol. 1). 40p. (Orig.). 1986. pap. text ed. 12.00 (ISBN 0-935129-02-2). Monks of New Skete.
Monks of New Skete Staff. Birth of the Theotokos. (Liturgical Music Series I: Great Feasts: Vol. 3). 25p. 1986. pap. text ed. 10.00 (ISBN 0-935129-04-9). Monks of New Skete.
--Dormition of the Theotokos. Reverend Laurence Mancuso, tr. (Liturgical Music Series I: Great Feasts: Vol. 2). 40p. (Orig.). 1986. pap. text ed. 12.00 (ISBN 0-935129-03-0). Monks of New Skete.
--Entry of the Theotokos. Reverend Laurence Mancuso, tr. from Gr. & Church Slavonic. (Liturgical Music Series I: Great Feasts: Vol. 5). 40p. 1986. pap. text ed. 12.00 (ISBN 0-935129-06-5). Monks of New Skete.
--Great & Holy Pascha. Reverend Laurence Mancuso, tr. from Gr. & Church Slavonic. (Liturgical Music Series I: Great Feasts: Vol. 6). 60p. (Orig.). 1986. pap. text ed. 15.00 (ISBN 0-935129-07-3). Monks of New Skete.
Neale, John M. Essays on Liturgiology & Church History. LC 70-173070. Repr. of 1863 ed. 32.50 (ISBN 0-404-04667-3). AMS Pr.
Neville, Gwen K. & Westerhoff, John H., III. Learning Through Liturgy. 189p. 1983. pap. 6.95 (ISBN 0-8164-2423-3, HarpR). Har-Row.
O'Connell, Matthew J. Temple of the Holy Spirit. 345p. 1983. pap. 17.50 (ISBN 0-916134-64-4). Pueblo Pub Co.
Ramshaw-Schmidt, Gail. Christ in Sacred Speech: The Meaning of Liturgical Language. LC 85-45486. 144p. 1986. pap. 9.95 (ISBN 0-8006-1907-2, 1-1907). Fortress.

Reeder, Rachel. Liturgy: Advent, Christmas, Epiphany, Vol. 4, No. 3. (The Quarterly Journal of the Lit. Conference Ser.). (Illus.). 88p. (Orig.). 1984. pap. 7.95 (ISBN 0-918208-36-X). Liturgical Conf.

Reeder, Rachel, ed. Liturgy: Dressing the Church. (The Quarterly Journal of the Liturgical Conference Ser.: Vol.5, No. 4). (Illus.). 103p. (Orig.). Date not set. pap. 7.95 (ISBN 0-918208-40-8). Liturgical Conf.

--Liturgy: In Spirit & Truth. (The Quarterly Journal of the Liturgical Conference: Vol. 5, No. 3). (Illus.). 96p. (Orig.). pap. text ed. 7.95 (ISBN 0-918208-39-4). Liturgical Conf.

--Liturgy: Language & Metaphor, Vol. 4, No.4. (The Quarterly Journal of the Lit. Conference Ser.). (Illus.). 95p. (Orig.). 1985. pap. 7.95 (ISBN 0-918208-35-1). Liturgical Conf.

--Liturgy: Ministries to the Sick. (Quarterly Journal of the Liturgical Conference Ser.: Vol. 2, No. 2 of Liturgy). (Illus.). 80p. 1982. 7.95 (ISBN 0-918208-26-2). Liturgical Conf.

--Liturgy: One Church, Many Churches. (Quarterly Journal of The Liturgical Conference: Vol. 3, No. 2). (Illus.). 96p. (Orig.). 1983. pap. text ed. 7.95 (ISBN 0-918208-30-0). Liturgical Conf.

--Liturgy: Scripture & the Assembly. (Quarterly Journal of the Liturgical Conference Ser.: Vol. 2, No. 3 of Liturgy). (Illus.). 80p. 1982. 7.95 (ISBN 0-918208-27-0). Liturgical Conf.

--Liturgy: Teaching Prayer. (The Quarterly Journal of the Liturgical Conference Ser.: Vol. 5, No. 1). (Illus.). 96p. (Orig.). pap. text ed. 7.95 (ISBN 0-918208-37-8). Liturgical Conf.

--Liturgy: The Church & Culture. (The Quarterly Journal of the Liturgical Conference Ser.: Vol. 6, No. 1). (Illus.). 96p. (Orig.). Date not set. pap. 7.95 (ISBN 0-918208-41-6). Liturgical Conf.

--Liturgy: With All the Saints. (The Quarterly Journal of the Liturgy Conference Ser.: Vol. 5, No. 2). (Illus.). 112p. (Orig.). pap. text ed. 7.95 (ISBN 0-918208-38-6). Liturgical Conf.

Reilly, Bernard F. Santiago, St. Denis, & St. Peter: The Reception of the Roman Liturgy in Leon-Castile in 1080. (Illus.). xvi, 216p. 1985. 37.50 (ISBN 0-8232-1125-8). Fordham.

Schulz, Hans-Joachim. The Byzantine Liturgy. O'Connell, Matthew J., tr. from Ger. (Orig.). 1986. pap. 17.50 (ISBN 0-916134-72-5). Pueblo Pub Co.

Searle, Mark, ed. Liturgy & Social Justice. LC 80-27011. 102p. 1980. pap. 5.50 (ISBN 0-8146-1209-1). Liturgical Pr.

Seasoltz, R. Kevin. New Liturgy, New Laws. LC 79-27916. 256p. 1980. pap. 7.95 (ISBN 0-8146-1077-3). Liturgical Pr.

Taft, Robert. The Liturgy of the Hours in East & West. 440p. 1986. pap. 14.95 (ISBN 0-8146-1405-1). Liturgical Pr.

Vasileios of Stavronikita. Hymn of Entry. Briere, Elizabeth, tr. from Gr. LC 84-5512. 138p. 1984. pap. text ed. 6.95 (ISBN 0-88141-026-8). St Vladimirs.

Von Hildebrand, Dietrich. Liturgy & Personality. LC 85-18388. 182p. 1986. 11.95 (ISBN 0-918477-03-4); pap. 7.95 (ISBN 0-918477-04-2). Sophia Inst Pr.

Weil, Louis. Sacraments & Liturgy. 116p. 1984. 24.95x (ISBN 0-631-13192-2); pap. 6.95 (ISBN 0-631-13229-5). Basil Blackwell.

Zappula, Robert, et al. The Modern Liturgy Planning Guide. 350p. 1987. 19.95 (ISBN 0-89390-088-5). Resource Pubns.

LITURGICS–CATHOLIC CHURCH

Aitken, John. Compilations of Litanies & Vesper Hymns. 25.00x (ISBN 0-87556-004-0). Saifer.

Collins, Patrick W. More Than Meets the Eye: Ritual & Parish Liturgy. LC 82-62920. 160p. (Orig.). 1983. pap. 6.95 (ISBN 0-8091-2539-0). Paulist Pr.

General Episcopal Synod. The Liturgy According to the Use of the Liberal Catholic Church, Prepared for the Use of English-Speaking Congregations. 3rd ed. 421p. 1987. Repr. of 1942 ed. price not set (ISBN 0-935461-11-6). St Alban Pr CA.

Irwin, Kevin W. Liturgy, Prayer & Spirituality. 1984. pap. 9.95 (ISBN 0-8091-2560-9). Paulist Pr.

Miller, Charles E. Making Holy the Day: A Commentary in the Liturgy of the Hours. red flexible bdg. 0.95 (ISBN 0-89942-410-4, 410/04). Catholic Bk Pub.

St. Maximus the Confessor. The Church, the Liturgy & the Soul of Man. Stead, Dom J., tr. from Gr. LC 82-10545. 1982. pap. 6.95 (ISBN 0-932506-23-2). St Bedes Pubns.

Tomasello, Andrew. Music & Ritual at Papal Avignon, 1309-1403. Buelow, George, ed. LC 83-18296. (Studies in Musicology: No. 75). 314p. 1983. 49.95 (ISBN 0-8357-1493-4). UMI Res Pr.

Webber, Robert E. Evangelicals on the Canterbury Trail: Why Evangelicals Are Attracted to the Liturgical Church. 160p. 1985. 13.95 (ISBN 0-8499-0402-1, 04021). Word Bks.

Westerhoff, John H., III & Willimon, William H. Liturgy & Learning Through the Life Cycle. 192p. (Orig.). 1985. pap. 9.95 (ISBN 0-86683-980-1, HarpR). Har-Row.

LITURGIES

see also Dedication Services; Funeral Service; Hours, Books of; Hymns; Installation Service (Church Officers); Liturgies; Marriage Service; Mass; Occasional Services; Pastoral Prayers; Ritual; Worship Programs

also subdivision Liturgy and Ritual, or name of ritual, under names of churches, e.g. Catholic Church–Liturgy and Ritual; Church of England–Book of Common Prayer

Bruck, Maria, ed. More Children's Liturgies. LC 81-80877. 256p. (Orig.). 1981. pap. 9.95 (ISBN 0-8091-2362-2). Paulist Pr.

Champlin, Joseph M. The Proper Balance. LC 81-68000. 144p. (Orig.). 1981. pap. 3.95 (ISBN 0-87793-233-6). Ave Maria.

DeAngelis, William. School Year Liturgies. (Illus.). 64p. (Orig.). 1985. pap. 9.95 (ISBN 0-89622-218-7). Twenty-Third.

Folkening, John. Handbells in the Liturgical Service. (Illus.). 52p. (Orig.). 1984. pap. 3.00 (ISBN 0-570-01328-3, 99-1254). Concordia.

Gilsdorf, Helen M., ed. Modern Liturgy Index. 2nd ed. 1984. pap. 6.95 (ISBN 0-89390-040-0). Resource Pubns.

Gogol, Nikolai. Meditations on the Divine Liturgy. 58p. (Orig.). 1985. pap. 3.00 (ISBN 0-317-30300-7). Holy Trinity.

Guerric of Igny Liturgical Sermons, 2 vols. Berkeley, Theodore, tr. from Latin. (Cistercian Father Ser.: No. 8 & No. 32). 378p. 1970-71. 15.00 set (ISBN 0-87907-400-0); Vol. 1. 7.95 (ISBN 0-87907-408-6); Vol. 2. o. p. 7.95 (ISBN 0-87907-432-9). Cistercian Pubns.

Herring, William. The Role of Music in the New Roman Liturgy. LC 75-14548. 1971. pap. 0.50 (ISBN 0-915866-01-3). Am Cath Pr.

Hilliard, Dick & Valenti-Hilliard, Beverly. Happenings. (Center Celebration Ser.). (Illus.). 60p. 1981. pap. text ed. 3.95 (ISBN 0-89390-033-8). Resource Pubns.

--Surprises. (Center Celebration Ser.). (Illus.). 60p. (Orig.). 1981. pap. text ed. 3.95 (ISBN 0-89390-031-1). Resource Pubns.

--Wonders. (Center Celebration Ser.). (Illus.). 60p. (Orig.). 1981. pap. text ed. 3.95 (ISBN 0-89390-032-X). Resource Pubns.

Hiscox, Edward T. Star Book for Ministers. rev. ed. 1967. 7.95 (ISBN 0-8170-0167-0). Judson.

Hobbs, James R. Pastor's Manual. 1940. 8.95 (ISBN 0-8054-2301-X). Broadman.

Ihli, Sr. Jan. Liturgy of the Word for Children. LC 79-90003. 176p. 1979. pap. 9.95 (ISBN 0-8091-2176-X). Paulist Pr.

Jeep, Elizabeth M. & Huck, Gabe. Celebrate Summer! Guidebook for Families & Congregations, 2 vols. 1973. 5.95 (ISBN 0-918208-98-X). Liturgical Conf.

Johnson, Dennis C. A Liturgical Narrative on the Service for the Day. 1984. 3.50 (ISBN 0-89536-657-6, 1268). CSS of Ohio.

Johnson, John R. Liturgy for the Free Church. LC 86-18782. 176p. 1986. lib. bdg. 19.95x (ISBN 0-89370-527-6). Borgo Pr.

Jung, Wolfgang. Liturgisches Woerterbuch. (Ger.). 1964. leatherette 13.50 (ISBN 3-87537-023-6, M-7544, Pub. by Merseburger Berlin). French & Eur.

Kenny, Bernadette. Children's Liturgies: Seventy-Four Eucharistic Liturgies, Prayer Services & Penance Services Designed for Primary, Middle & Junior High Children. LC 77-74582. 176p. 1977. pap. 9.95 (ISBN 0-8091-2030-5). Paulist Pr.

Klauser, Theodor. A Short History of the Western Liturgy. 2nd ed. Halliburton, John, tr. from Ger. 1979. pap. text ed. 10.95x (ISBN 0-19-213223-7). Oxford U Pr.

Lee, Frederick G. A Glossary of Liturgical & Ecclesiastical Terms. LC 76-174069. (Tower Bks.). (Illus.). xl, 452p. 1972. Repr. of 1877 ed. 44.00x (ISBN 0-8103-3949-8). Gale.

Liturgies & Occasional Forms of Prayer Set Forth in the Reign of Queen Elizabeth. 1847. 55.00 (ISBN 0-384-32940-3). Johnson Repr.

McBride, Alfred. Year of the Lord: Reflections on the Sunday Readings. 240p. cycle A 6.95 (ISBN 0-697-01847-4); cycle B 6.95 (ISBN 0-697-01848-2); cycle C 6.95 (ISBN 0-697-01849-0). Wm C Brown.

McNally, Dennis. Sacred Space: An Aesthetic for the Liturgical Environment. 215p. (Orig.). 1985. pap. 8.95x (ISBN 0-932269-45-1). Wyndham Hall.

Mazziotta, Richard. We Pray to the Lord: General Intercessions Based on the Scriptural Readings for Sundays & Holy Days. LC 84-71135. 208p. (Orig.). 1984. pap. 9.95 (ISBN 0-87793-323-5). Ave Maria.

Miguens, Manuel. Gospels for Sundays & Feasts: Cycle C. 1980. 7.50 (ISBN 0-8198-3000-3); pap. 6.00 (ISBN 0-8198-3001-1). Dghtrs St Paul.

Morse, Kenneth I. Move in Our Midst: Looking at Worship in the Life of the Church. 1977. pap. 2.95 (ISBN 0-87178-583-8). Brethren.

The Orthodox Liturgy. 1984. priest's ed. 29.95 (ISBN 0-19-143495-7); congregational ed. 21.95 (ISBN 0-19-143492-2). Oxford U Pr.

Reeder, Rachel, ed. Liturgy: Celebrating Marriage, Vol. 4, No. 2. (Illus.). 80p. 1984. pap. text ed. 7.95 (ISBN 0-918208-34-3). Liturgical Conf.

--Liturgy: Diakonia. (Journal of The Liturgical Conference: Vol. 2, No. 4). (Illus.). 84p. (Orig.). 1982. pap. 7.95 (ISBN 0-918208-28-9). Liturgical Conf.

--Liturgy: Putting on Christ, Vol. 4, No. 1. (Illus.). 80p. 1983. pap. text ed. 7.95 (ISBN 0-918208-33-5). Liturgical Conf.

--Liturgy: With Lyre & Harp. (Quarterly Journal of The Liturgical Conference: Vol. 3, No. 3). (Illus.). 88p. (Orig.). 1983. pap. text ed. 7.95 (ISBN 0-918208-31-9). Liturgical Conf.

Religious Education Staff. The Spirit Alive in Liturgy: Spirit Masters. 1981. 9.95 (ISBN 0-686-84105-0). Wm C Brown.

Rezy, Carol. Liturgies for Little Ones: Thirty-Eight Complete Celebrations for Grades One Through Three. LC 78-59926. (Illus.). 160p. 1978. pap. 4.95 (ISBN 0-87793-160-7). Ave Maria.

Richstatter, Thomas. Liturgical Law Today: New Style, New Spirit. LC 77-3008. pap. 67.80 (ISBN 0-317-28483-5, 2019104). Bks Demand UMI.

Sloyan, Virginia, ed. Signs, Songs & Stories. (Illus.). 160p. 1982. pap. 8.50 (ISBN 0-8146-1285-7). Liturgical Pr.

Stern, Chaim. Gates of Freedom: A Passover Haggadah. LC 81-84191. (Illus.). 130p. 1986. pap. 6.95 (ISBN 0-940646-21-8). Rossel Bks.

Stiller, Gunther. J. S. Bach & Liturgical Life in Liepzig. Leaver, Robin A., ed. Boutman, Herbert J., et al, trs. from Ger. Tr. of Johann Sebastian Bach und das Leipziger Gottesdienstliche Leben Seiner Zeit. (Illus.). 312p. (Orig.). 1984. pap. 24.95 (ISBN 0-570-01320-8, 99-1247). Concordia.

Thompson, Bard, ed. Liturgies of the Western Church. LC 80-8044. 448p. 1980. pap. 9.95 (ISBN 0-8006-1428-3, 1-1428). Fortress.

Tuthill, Marge. Art for Children's Liturgy: What You Need & How To Do It. LC 82-60855. 1982. pap. 4.95 (ISBN 0-8091-2478-5). Paulist Pr.

Two Liturgies, A. D. Fifteen Forty-Nine, & A. D. Fifteen Fifty-Seven. 1844. 51.00 (ISBN 0-384-62140-6). Johnson Repr.

Weil, Louis. Gathered to Pray: Understanding Liturgical Prayer. LC 86-17413. (Parish Life Sourcebooks Ser.: No. 3). 148p. (Orig.). 1986. pap. 6.95 (ISBN 0-936384-35-2). Cowley Pubns.

Zappula, Robert, et al. The Modern Liturgy Planning Guide. 350p. 1987. 19.95 (ISBN 0-89390-088-5). Resource Pubns.

LITURGIES–BIBLIOGRAPHY

Buono, Anthony. Liturgy: Our School of Faith. 177p. (Orig.). 1982. pap. 6.95 (ISBN 0-8189-0435-6). Alba.

Charles Louis De Bourbon. Bibliotheque liturgique, 2 vols. in 1. Ales, Anatole, ed. LC 72-130592. (Fr). 1970. Repr. of 1898 ed. lib. bdg. 40.50 (ISBN 0-8337-0036-7). B Franklin.

Zaccaria, Francesco A. Bibliotheca Ritualis, 2 vols. in 3. 1964. Repr. of 1781 ed. Set. 106.00 (ISBN 0-8337-3913-1). B Franklin.

LITURGIES, EARLY CHRISTIAN

see also Church Orders, Ancient

Bludau, August. Die Pilgerreise der Aetheria. pap. 22.00 (ISBN 0-384-04760-2). Johnson Repr.

Hamman, Adelbert. Mass: Ancient Liturgies & Patristic Texts. Halton, Thomas, ed. LC 67-15202. 1967. 5.95 (ISBN 0-8189-0086-5). Alba.

Jungmann, Josef A. Early Liturgy, to the Time of Gregory the Great. Brunner, Francis A., tr. (Liturgical Studies: No. 7). 1959. 10.95 (ISBN 0-268-00083-2). U of Notre Dame Pr.

Oesterley, William O. The Jewish Background of the Christian Liturgy. 1925. 11.75 (ISBN 0-8446-1329-0). Peter Smith.

Orthodox Eastern Church. Liturgies of Saints Mark, James, Clement, Chrysostom, & the Church of Malabar. LC 76-83374. Repr. of 1859 ed. 18.50 (ISBN 0-404-04658-4). AMS Pr.

--Liturgies of Saints Mark, James, Clement, Chrysostom, Basil. LC 79-80721. (Gr). 1969. Repr. of 1859 ed. 18.50 (ISBN 0-404-04657-6). AMS Pr.

Pink, Arthur W. Christians in Romans Seven. pap. 0.50 (ISBN 0-685-00738-3). Reiner.

Schermann, Theodor. Die Allgemeine Kirchenordnung Fruehchristliche Liturgien und Kirchliche Uberlieferung, 3 pts. Repr. of 1914 ed. Set. 55.00 (ISBN 0-384-53740-5). Johnson Repr.

Warren, Frederick E. Liturgy & Ritual of the Ante-Nicene Church. 2nd rev. ed. LC 78-177851. Repr. of 1912 ed. 25.00 (ISBN 0-404-06847-2). AMS Pr.

LITURGY

see Liturgics

LITURGY AND DRAMA

see also Religious Drama

Cargill, Oscar. Drama & Liturgy. LC 73-86272. 1969. Repr. of 1930 ed. lib. bdg. 17.00x (ISBN 0-374-91292-0, Octagon). Hippocrene Bks.

De Coussemaker, Edmond, ed. Drames liturgiques du moyen age, texte et musique. (Fr., Lat., Illus.). 370p. 1964. Repr. of 1860 ed. 57.50x (ISBN 0-8450-1004-2). Broude.

Kelley, Gail & Hershberger, Carol. Come Mime with Me: Ten Liturgical Dramas for Children. LC 86-62621. 100p. 1987. 11.95 (ISBN 0-89390-089-3). Resource Pubns.

LITURGY AND LITERATURE

Martimort, A. G., ed. The Church at Prayer: Part One-The Liturgy. 264p. 1969. text ed. 17.50x (ISBN 0-7165-0511-8, Pub. by Irish Academic Pr Ireland). Biblio Dist.

Ramshaw-Schmidt, Gail. Christ in Sacred Speech: The Meaning of Liturgical Language. LC 85-45486. 144p. 1986. pap. 9.95 (ISBN 0-8006-1907-2, 1-1907). Fortress.

LIVINGSTONE, DAVID, 1813-1873

Blackie, W. W. David Livingstone. (Heroes of the Faith Ser.). 1986. 6.95 (ISBN 0-916441-48-2). Barbour & Co.

Blaikie, William G. Personal Life of David Livingstone. LC 69-19353. (Illus.). 1880. 22.50x (ISBN 0-8371-0518-8, BLL&). Greenwood.

Buel, J. W. Heroes of the Dark Continent. facs. ed. LC 73-138333. (Black Heritage Library Collection). 1889. 32.75 (ISBN 0-8369-8725-X). Ayer Co Pubs.

Campbell, Reginald J. Livingstone. LC 77-138212. (Illus.). 295p. 1972. Repr. of 1930 ed. lib. bdg. 22.50x (ISBN 0-8371-5567-3, CALI). Greenwood.

Latham, Robert O. Trail Maker (David Livingstone) 1973. pap. 2.95 (ISBN 0-87508-626-8). Chr Lit.

Stocker, Fern N. David Livingstone: Glorifying God, Not Himself. (Guessing Bks.). (Orig.). 1986. pap. 3.95 (ISBN 0-8024-4758-9). Moody.

Worchester, J. H., Jr. David Livingstone. (Golden Oldies Ser.). 128p. 1980. pap. 3.50 (ISBN 0-8024-4782-1). Moody.

LOCKE, JOHN, 1632-1704

Acton, Henry. Religious Opinions & Example of Milton, Locke, & Newton. LC 71-158223. Repr. of 1833 ed. 11.50 (ISBN 0-404-00283-8). AMS Pr.

Colman, John. John Locke's Moral Philosophy. 280p. 1982. 27.50x (ISBN 0-85224-445-2, Pub. by Edinburgh U Pr Scotland). Columbia U Pr.

Cox, Richard H. Locke on War & Peace. LC 82-42514. 240p. 1983. pap. text ed. 12.50 (ISBN 0-8191-2662-4). U Pr of Amer.

Edwards, John. Some Thoughts Concerning the Several Causes & Occasions of Atheism, Especially in the Present Age. LC 80-48568. (The Philosophy of John Locke Ser.). 268p. 1984. lib. bdg. 35.00 (ISBN 0-8240-5603-5). Garland Pub.

Jenkins, J. J. Understanding Locke. 192p. 1983. 15.00x (ISBN 0-85224-449-5, Pub. by Edinburgh U Pr Scotland). Columbia U Pr.

Lowde, James. Disclosure Concerning the Nature of Man, 1694. LC 75-11233. (British Philosophers & Theologians in the 17th & 18th Century Ser.). 271p. 1979. lib. bdg. 51.00 (ISBN 0-8240-1786-2). Garland Pub.

McLachlan, Herbert. The Religious Opinions of Milton, Locke & Newton. LC 74-20740. 1974. Repr. of 1941 ed. lib. bdg. 35.00 (ISBN 0-8414-5930-4). Folcroft.

Norris, John. Christian Blessedness (with) Reflections upon a Late Essay Concerning Human Understanding. Wellek, Rene, ed. LC 75-11241. (British Philosophers & Theologians of the 17th & 18th Centuries Ser.). 1978. Repr. of 1690 ed. lib. bdg. 51.00 (ISBN 0-8240-1793-5). Garland Pub.

Tuveson, Ernest L. Imagination As a Means of Grace. LC 73-21543. 218p. 1973. Repr. of 1960 ed. 20.00x (ISBN 0-87752-173-5). Gordian.

Watts, Issac. Logic: Or, the Right Use of Reason in the Enquiry after Truth, with a Variety of Rules to Guard Against Error, in the Affairs of Religion & Human Life as Well as the Sciences. LC 83-48579. (The Philosophy of John Locke Ser.). 365p. 1984. lib. bdg. 44.00 (ISBN 0-8240-5615-9). Garland Pub.

White, Morton. Science & Sentiment in America: Philosophical Thought from Jonathan Edwards to John Dewey. 1972. 25.00x (ISBN 0-19-501519-3). Oxford U Pr.

LOGIC–EARLY WORKS TO 1800

Gyekye, Kwame, ed. & tr. Arabic Logic: Ibn al-Tayyib on Porphyry's "Eisagoge". LC 76-4071. 1979. 49.50x (ISBN 0-87395-308-8). State U NY Pr.

Wade, Francis C. John of Saint Thomas: Outlines of Formal Logic. 2nd ed. (Medieval Philosophical Texts in Translation: No. 8). 1962. pap. 7.95 (ISBN 0-87462-208-5). Marquette.

LOGIC AND FAITH
see Faith and Reason

LOGOS

Brinton, Howard H. Evolution & the Inward Light. LC 77-137101. (Orig.). 1970. pap. 2.50x (ISBN 0-87574-173-8). Pendle Hill.

Carey, John J. Kairos & Logos: Studies in the Roots & Implications of Tillich Society. LC 84-6738. xxii, 284p. 1984. Repr. of 1978 ed. 15.95 (ISBN 0-86554-106-X, MUP/H100). Mercer Univ Pr.

Christou, Evangelos. The Logos of the Soul. Hillman, James, ed. (Dunquin Ser.: No. 2). 1963. pap. 6.50 (ISBN 0-88214-202-X). Spring Pubns.

Kuhlewind, Georg. Becoming Aware of the Logos. LC 85-23126. 195p. (Orig.). 1985. pap. 9.95 (ISBN 0-89281-071-8, Lindisfarne Pr). Inner Tradit.

Mills, Lawrence H. Zarathushtra, Philo, the Achaemenids & Israel. LC 74-21261. Repr. of 1906 ed. 34.50 (ISBN 0-404-12815-7). AMS Pr.

Pascher, Josef. Der Konigsweg Zu Wiedergeburt und Vergottung Bei Philon Von Alexandreia. Repr. of 1931 ed. 22.00 (ISBN 0-384-45050-4). Johnson Repr.

Schain, Richard. A Contemporary Logos. 20p. (Orig.). 1984. pap. 2.00 (ISBN 0-9609922-2-7). Garric Pr.

LOLLARDS

Aston, Margaret. Lollards & Reformers: Images & Literacy in Late Medieval Religion. 405p. 1984. 35.00 (ISBN 0-907628-03-6). Hambledon Press.

Carrick, J. C. Wycliffe & the Lollards. 1977. lib. bdg. 59.95 (ISBN 0-8490-2824-8). Gordon Pr.

Dickens, A. G. Lollards & Protestants in the Diocese of York. (No. 10). 280p. 1983. 27.00 (ISBN 0-907628-05-2); pap. 12.00 (ISBN 0-907628-06-0). Hambledon Press.

Gairdner, James. Lollardy & the Reformation in England: An Historical Survey, 4 Vols. 1965. Repr. of 1913 ed. 141.00 (ISBN 0-8337-1268-3). B Franklin.

Kendall, Ritchie D. The Drama of Dissent: The Radical Poetics of Nonconformity, 1380-1590. LC 86-1289. (Studies in Religion). 286p. 1986. 27.50x (ISBN 0-8078-1700-7). U of NC Pr.

Powell, Edgar & Trevelyan, G. M., eds. The Peasants' Rising & the Lollards. LC 78-63202. (Heresies of the Early Christian & Medieval Era: Second Ser.). Repr. of 1899 ed. 24.00 (ISBN 0-404-16238-X). AMS Pr.

Summers, William H. The Lollards of the Chiltern Hills. LC 80-12770. (Heresies of the Early Christian & Medieval Era: Second Ser.). Repr. of 1906 ed. 31.51 (ISBN 0-404-16245-2). AMS Pr.

Wycliffe, John. Apology for Lollard Doctrines, Attributed to Wycliffe. LC 80-312858. Repr. of 1842 ed. 28.00 (ISBN 0-404-50120-6). AMS Pr.

--Apology for Lollard Doctrines, Attributed to Wycliffe. 28.00 (ISBN 0-384-69838-7). Johnson Repr.

--Wycliffite Sermons, Vol. 1. Hudson, Anne, ed. (Oxford English Texts). (Illus.). 1983. 105.00x (ISBN 0-19-812704-9). Oxford U Pr.

LONDON-CHURCHES

Brooke-Hunt, Violet. Story of Westminster Abbey. 1977. lib. bdg. 59.95 (ISBN 0-8490-2692-X). Gordon Pr.

Gray, Ronald. Christopher Wren & St. Paul's Cathedral. LC 81-13696. (Cambridge Topic Bks.). (Illus.). 52p. 1982. PLB 8.95 (ISBN 0-8225-1222-X). Lerner Pubns.

Harvey, Barbara. Westminster Abbey & Its Estates in the Middle Ages. (Illus.). 1977. text ed. 55.00x (ISBN 0-19-822455-9). Oxford U Pr.

His Majesties Commission & Further Declaration Concerning the Reparation of Saint Pauls Church. LC 75-171754. (English Experience Ser.: No. 379). 1971. Repr. of 1633 ed. 7.00 (ISBN 90-221-0379-X). Walter J Johnson.

His Majesties Commission to Enquire of the Decayes of the Cathedral Church of St. Paul. LC 72-185. (English Experience Ser.: No. 355). 1971. Repr. of 1631 ed. 8.00 (ISBN 90-221-0355-2). Walter J Johnson.

Holton, Susan & Jones, David L. Spirit Aflame: Luis Palau's Mission to London. 258p. 1985. 7.95 (ISBN 0-8010-4293-3). Baker Bk.

Lethaby, William R. Westminster Abbey Re-Examined. LC 69-13244. (Illus.). Repr. of 1925 ed. 27.50 (ISBN 0-405-08744-6, Pub. by Blom). Ayer Co Pubs.

London - St. Paul'S Cathedral. Documents Illustrating the History of St. Paul's Cathedral. Simpson, W. S., ed. 1880. 27.00 (ISBN 0-384-55530-6). Johnson Repr.

Paul, Robert S. The Assembly of the Lord. (Illus.). 624p. 1985. 39.95 (ISBN 0-567-09341-7, Pub. by T&T Clark Ltd UK). Fortress.

Pilkington, James. Works of James Pilkington, Lord Bishop of Durham. 1842. Repr. of 1842 ed. 55.00 (ISBN 0-384-46530-7). Johnson Repr.

LONDON-RELIGION

Liu, Tai. Puritan London: A Study of Religion & Society in the City Parishes. LC 85-40534. 256p. 1986. 38.50x (ISBN 0-87413-283-5, Pub. by U Delaware Pr). Assoc Univ Prs.

LONELINESS
see also Consolation

Doherty, Catherine D. Doubts, Loneliness & Rejection. LC 81-19115. (Illus.). 93p. 1982. pap. 4.50 (ISBN 0-8189-0419-4). Alba.

Durham, Charles. When You Are Feeling Lonely. LC 84-10499. 180p. (Orig.). 1984. pap. 5.95 (ISBN 0-87784-915-3). Inter-Varsity.

Hulme, William E. Creative Loneliness. LC 76-27083. 112p. 1977. pap. 5.95 (ISBN 0-8066-1556-7, 10-1715). Augsburg.

Jeremiah, David. Overcoming Loneliness. LC 83-48411. 143p. 1983. pap. 5.95 (ISBN 0-89840-049-X). Heres Life.

Kennedy, Eugene. Loneliness & Everyday Problems. LC 82-45971. 160p. 1983. pap. 3.95 (ISBN 0-385-18797-1, Im). Doubleday.

Lauder, Robert E. Loneliness Is for Loving. LC 77-94033. (Illus.). 144p. 1978. pap. 2.95 (ISBN 0-87793-147-X). Ave Maria.

Lidmus, Susan B. Church Family Ministry: Changing Loneliness to Fellowship in the Church. 1985. pap. 6.95 (ISBN 0-570-03945-2, 12-2878). Concordia.

Moore, Sebastian. The Inner Loneliness. LC 82-14862. 125p. 1982. 9.95 (ISBN 0-8245-0515-8). Crossroad NY.

--Inner Loneliness. 1984. pap. 6.95 (ISBN 0-8245-0619-7). Crossroad NY.

Neale, Robert E. Loneliness, Solitude, & Companionship. LC 83-26065. 132p. (Orig.). 1984. pap. 9.95 (ISBN 0-664-24621-4). Westminster.

Ripple, Paula. Walking with Loneliness. LC 82-73048. 176p. (Orig.). 1982. pap. 4.95 (ISBN 0-87793-259-X). Ave Maria.

--Walking with Loneliness. 318p. 1985. pap. 9.95 large print ed. (ISBN 0-8027-2490-6). Walker & Co.

Rolheiser, Ronald. The Loneliness Factor: Its Religious & Spiritual Meaning. 8.95 (ISBN 0-87193-168-0). Dimension Bks.

Wakin, Edward & Cooney, Sean. Beyond Loneliness. 112p. (Orig.). 1985. pap. 5.95 (ISBN 0-89622-248-9). Twenty-Third.

Wellington, Paul A., ed. Loneliness. 1980. pap. 4.50 (ISBN 0-8309-0287-2). Herald Hse.

Wright, Norman. An Answer to Loneliness. (Orig.). pap. 1.95 (ISBN 0-89081-077-X). Harvest Hse.

LORD'S DAY
see Sabbath; Sunday

LORD'S PRAYER

Barclay, William. The Beatitudes & the Lord's Prayer for Everyman. LC 75-9309. 256p. 1975. pap. 7.95 (ISBN 0-06-060393-3, RD112, HarpR). Har-Row.

Bast, Henry. The Lord's Prayer. 2.50 (ISBN 0-686-23480-4). Rose Pub MI.

Boff, Leonardo. The Lord's Prayer: The Prayer of Integral Liberation. Morrow, Theodore, tr. from Portuguese. LC 82-18811. Tr. of O Pai-nosso: A Oracao da Libertacao. 144p. (Orig.). 1983. pap. 6.95 (ISBN 0-88344-299-X). Orbis Bks.

Buhring, Gernot, ed. Vaterunser Polyglott: The Lord's Prayer in 42 Languages (Sprachen Mit 75 Text Fassungen) (Ger.). 278p. 1984. 10.00x (ISBN 3-87118-666-X, Pub. by Helmut Buske Verlag Hamburg). Benjamins North AM.

Clark, Glenn. Lord's Prayer. pap. 0.50 (ISBN 0-910924-08-2). Macalester.

Coburn, John B. Deliver Us from Evil: The Prayer of Our Lord. 96p. 1976. pap. 4.95 (ISBN 0-8164-2124-2, HarpR). Har-Row.

Cottle, Ronald E. The Lord's Prayer. 48p. 1980. 0.95 (ISBN 0-88243-566-3, 02-0566). Gospel Pub.

Crosby, Michael H. Thy Will Be Done: Praying the Our Father As Subversive Activity. LC 77-5118. 262p. (Orig.). 1977. pap. 6.95 (ISBN 0-88344-497-6). Orbis Bks.

Dods, Marcus. The Prayer That Teaches to Pray. LC 80-82323. (Shepherd Illustrated Classics Ser.). (Illus.). 1980. pap. 5.95 (ISBN 0-87983-232-0). Keats.

Elliott, Norman. How to Be the Lord's Prayer. pap. 2.95 (ISBN 0-910924-26-0). Macalester.

Errico, Rocco A. The Ancient Aramaic Prayer of Jesus. (Illus.). 82p. 1978. pap. 4.95 (ISBN 0-911336-69-9). Sci of Mind.

Jeremias, Joachim. The Lord's Prayer. Reumann, John, ed. & tr. from Ger. LC 64-11859. (Facet Bks.). 56p. 1964. pap. 2.50 (ISBN 0-8006-3008-4, 1-3008). Fortress.

Kappeler, Max. Compendium for the Study of Christian Science: No. 3, The Commandments, the Beatitudes, the Lord's Prayer. 29p. 1951. pap. 3.50 (ISBN 0-85241-057-3). Kappeler Inst Pub.

Keller, Phillip, tr. Meditacoes De Um Leigo. (Portugese Bks.). Tr. of A Layman Looks at the Lord's Prayer. (Port.). 1979. 1.60 (ISBN 0-8297-0788-3). Life Pubs Intl.

Keller, W. Phillip. A Layman Looks at the Lord's Prayer. 160p. 1976. pap. 5.95 (ISBN 0-8024-4644-2). Moody.

--A Layman Looks at the Lord's Prayer. (Moody Press Electives Ser.). 1985. pap. text ed. 3.95 (ISBN 0-8024-0699-8); leader's guide 2.50 (ISBN 0-8024-0701-3). Moody.

LaVerdiere, Eugene. When We Pray: Meditation on the Lord's Prayer. LC 82-73512. 176p. 1983. pap. 4.95 (ISBN 0-87793-263-8). Ave Maria.

Mangan, Celine. Can We Still Call God "Father"? A Woman Looks at the Lord's Prayer Today. (Ways of Prayer Ser.: Vol. 12). 110p. 1984. pap. 4.95 (ISBN 0-89453-384-3). M Glazier.

Maurice, Frederick D. The Prayer Book & the Lord's Prayer. 416p. 1977. Repr. of 1880 ed. 12.50 (ISBN 0-87921-038-9). Attic Pr.

Overduin, Daniel. Reflections on the Lord's Prayer. 1980. pap. 1.95 (ISBN 0-570-03815-4, 12-2783). Concordia.

Rommel, Kurt. Our Father Who Art in Heaven. Cooperrider, Edward A., tr. from Ger. LC 80-2373. Tr. of Einladung zum Gesprach mit Gott: Gedanken uber das Vaterunser. 96p. 1981. pap. 4.95 (ISBN 0-8006-1448-8, 1-1448). Fortress.

Seilhamer, Frank H. No Empty Phrases. 1985. 4.25 (ISBN 0-89536-732-7, 5816). CSS of Ohio.

Shelton, Ingrid. The Lord's Prayer. (Arch Bks.). 1982. pap. 0.99 (ISBN 0-570-06161-X, 59-1308). Concordia.

Shriver, Donald W., Jr. The Lord's Prayer: A Way of Life. LC 83-9843. 108p. (Orig.). 1983. pap. 4.95 (ISBN 0-8042-2409-9). John Knox.

Sikorsky, Igor I. Message of the Lord's Prayer. 1963. 10.95 (ISBN 0-8392-1068-X). Astor-Honor.

Steiner, Rudolf. The Lord's Prayer: An Esoteric Study. McKnight, Floyd, tr. from Ger. 26p. 1977. pap. 2.95 (ISBN 0-88010-029-X). Anthroposophic.

Thielicke, Helmut. The Prayer That Spans the World. Doberstein, J. W., tr. from Ger. 160p. 1978. Repr. 13.95 (ISBN 0-227-67671-8). Attic Pr.

Very, Alice. The Lord's Prayer. 1975. 10.00 (ISBN 0-8283-1629-5). Branden Pub Co.

Wainwright, Geoffrey. Eucharist & Eschatology. 1981. 21.95x (ISBN 0-19-520248-1); pap. text ed. 8.95 (ISBN 0-19-520249-X). Oxford U Pr.

Ward, J. Neville. The Personal Faith of Jesus as Revealed in the Lord's Prayer. 128p. 1982. pap. 6.95 (ISBN 0-86683-678-0, HarpR). Har-Row.

Watson, Thomas. Lord's Prayer. 1978. 9.95 (ISBN 0-85151-145-7). Banner of Truth.

Young, Brad. The Jewish Background to the Lord's Prayer. 54p. (Orig.). 1984. pap. 3.95 (ISBN 0-918873-02-9). Ctr Judaic-Christ Studies.

Zodhiates, Spiros. The Lord's Prayer. 352p. pap. 8.95 (ISBN 0-89957-049-6). AMG Pubs.

LORD'S PRAYER-EARLY WORKS TO 1800

Hill, Robert. The Pathway to Prayer & Pietie. LC 74-28864. (English Experience Ser.: No. 744). 1975. Repr. of 1613 ed. 26.50 (ISBN 90-221-0744-2). Walter J Johnson.

LORD'S PRAYER-JUVENILE LITERATURE

Hernandez, Anna M. The Lords Prayer. (Illus.). 32p. 1987. 6.95 (ISBN 0-89962-601-7). Todd & Honeywell.

Hutson, Joan. The Lord's Prayer. LC 82-62736. (Happy Day Bks.). (Illus.). 24p. 1983. 1.59 (ISBN 0-87239-640-1, 3560). Standard Pub.

Lucy, Reda, pseud. The Lord's Prayer for Children. (Illus.). 24p. (Orig.). 1981. pap. 2.25 (ISBN 0-87516-437-4). De Vorss.

Webb, Barbara O. The Lord's Prayer: The Prayer Jesus Taught. (Concept Ser.). (Illus.). 24p. (Orig.). 1986. pap. 3.95 saddlestitched (ISBN 0-570-08529-2, 56-1556). Concordia.

LORD'S PRAYER-MEDITATIONS

Archilla, Rogelio. Meditaciones Sobre el Padrenuestro. (Span.). 96p. 1984. pap. 3.95 (ISBN 0-311-40046-9, Edit Mundo). Casa Bautista.

Burghardt, W. J. & Lawler, T. C., eds. St. Gregory of Nyssa, the Lord's Prayer, the Beatitudes. LC 78-62466. (ACW Ser.: No. 18). 216p. 1954. 14.95 (ISBN 0-8091-0255-2). Paulist Pr.

Davies, Merlin. Priorities in Praying: Learning from the Lord's Prayer. 104p. (Orig.). 1984. pap. 10.95 (ISBN 0-86474-002-6, Pub. by Interface Press). ANZ Religious Pubns.

Ebeling, Gerhard. On Prayer: The Lord's Prayer in Today's World. Leitch, James W., tr. LC 78-5079. pap. 27.80 (2026853). Bks Demand UMI.

Pfatteicher, Philip H. Foretaste of the Feast to Come: Devotions on Holy Communion. (Illus.). 64p. (Orig.). 1987. kivar paper 3.95 (ISBN 0-8066-2283-0, 10-2357). Augsburg.

LORD'S SUPPER
see also Agape; First Communion; Last Supper; Mass; Sacraments; Sacred Meals; Transubstantiation

Aelfric, Abbot. A Testimonie of Antique. LC 73-36208. (English Experience Ser.: No. 214). Repr. of 1567 ed. 13.00 (ISBN 90-221-0214-9). Walter J Johnson.

Asten, Dietrich V. Sacramental & Spiritual Communion. Glas, Werner, ed. (Orig.). 1984. pap. 2.50 (ISBN 0-88010-121-0). Anthroposophic.

Barclay, William. The Lord's Supper. LC 82-2774. 128p. 1982. pap. 7.95 (ISBN 0-664-24432-7). Westminster.

Bermejo, Luis M. Body Broken & Blood Shed. 368p. 1987. 8.95 (ISBN 0-8294-0554-2). Loyola.

Bernier, Paul. Bread Broken & Shared. LC 81-67539. 144p. 1981. pap. 3.95 (ISBN 0-87793-232-8). Ave Maria.

Biffi, Inos. The Story of the Eucharist. Drury, John, tr. from Ital. LC 85-82173. (Illustrated History of Christian Culture Ser.). Orig. Title: Storia dell' eucaristia. (Illus.). 125p. 1986. 11.95 (ISBN 0-89870-089-2). Ignatius Pr.

Bothwell, H. Roger. My First Book About Communion. (My Church Teaches Ser.). (Illus.). 1978. pap. 1.95 (ISBN 0-8127-0180-1). Review & Herald.

Bradford, John. Writings of John Bradford...Martyr, 1555, 2 Vols. Repr. of 1853 ed. Set. 92.00 (ISBN 0-384-05440-4). Johnson Repr.

Bridge, Donald & Phypers, David. Communion: The Meal That Unites? LC 82-62820. 192p. 1983. pap. 5.95 (ISBN 0-87788-160-X). Shaw Pubs.

Brokamp, Sr. Marlene & Brokamp, Sr. Marilyn. Eucharist: God's Gift of Love. (Illus.). 28p. (Orig.). 1976. pap. 1.95 (ISBN 0-912228-25-3). St Anthony Mess Pr.

Burr, David. Eucharistic Presence & Conversion in Late Thirteenth Century Franciscan Thought. LC 83-73283. (Transactions Ser.: Vol. 74 Pt. 3). 113p. 1984. 12.00 (ISBN 0-87169-743-2). Am Philos.

Champlin, Joseph M. An Important Office of Immense Love: A Handbook for Eucharistic Ministers. LC 80-80085. 152p. (Orig.). 1980. pap. 4.95 (ISBN 0-8091-2287-1). Paulist Pr.

Cullmann, Oscar & Leenhardt, Franz J. Essays on the Lord's Supper. LC 58-8979. 1958. pap. 4.95 (ISBN 0-8042-3748-4). John Knox.

Drower, Ethel S. Water into Wine: A Study of Ritual Idiom in the Middle East. LC 77-87663. Repr. of 1956 ed. 23.50 (ISBN 0-404-16401-3). AMS Pr.

Feeley-Harnik, Gillian. The Lord's Table: Eucharist & Passover in Early Christianity. 1981. text ed. 23.50x (ISBN 0-8122-7786-4). U of Pa Pr.

Fogle, Jeanne S. Signs of God's Love: Baptism & Communion. Duckert, Mary J. & Lane, W. Ben, eds. (Illus.). 32p. (Orig.). 1984. pap. 4.50 (ISBN 0-664-24636-2). Geneva Pr.

Ford, Bruce E. Notes on the Celebration of the Eucharist: A Supplement to the Ceremonial Directions of the Book of Common Prayer, 1979. LC 86-21523. 48p. (Orig.). 1986. pap. 7.50 (ISBN 0-942466-10-1). Hymnary Pr.

Garrison, Eileen & Albanese, Gayle. Eucharistic Manual for Children. LC 84-60217. (Illus.). 28p. (Orig.). 1984. pap. 3.95 (ISBN 0-8192-1343-8). Morehouse.

Grassi, Joseph A. Broken Bread & Broken Bodies: The Eucharist & World Hunger. LC 84-18888. 128p. (Orig.). 1985. pap. 6.95 (ISBN 0-88344-193-4). Orbis Bks.

Guzie, Tad W. Jesus & the Eucharist. LC 73-90069. 168p. 1974. pap. 5.95 (ISBN 0-8091-1858-0). Paulist Pr.

Habel, Norman C. Create in Me: A Form of the Eucharist in a Modern Idiom. 1978. 0.95 (ISBN 0-915644-14-2). Clayton Pub Hse.

Hagerty, Cornelius. The Holy Eucharist. 77p. 1967. pap. 1.50 (ISBN 0-912414-12-X). Lumen Christi.

Harrison, Russell F. More Brief Prayers for Bread & Cup. Lambert, Herbert, ed. LC 86-6076. 80p. (Orig.). 1986. pap. 4.95 (ISBN 0-8272-2319-6). CBP.

Hellwig, Monika. The Eucharist & the Hunger of the World. LC 76-18050. 100p. 1976. pap. 3.95 (ISBN 0-8091-1958-7). Paulist Pr.

Hooper, John. The Later Writings of Bishop Hooper. 1852. 55.00 (ISBN 0-384-24211-1). Johnson Repr.

Huels, John. One Table, Many Laws: Essays on Catholic Eucharistic Discipline. 112p. 1986. pap. 5.95 (ISBN 0-8146-1465-5). Liturgical Pr.

Johnson, Lawrence. The Word & Eucharist Handbook. LC 86-60896. 150p. (Orig.). 1985. pap. text ed. 9.95 (ISBN 0-89390-067-2). Resource Pubns.

Kater, John. Another Letter of John to James. (Illus.). 64p. (Orig.). 1982. pap. 3.95 (ISBN 0-8164-2376-8, HarpR). Har-Row.

Keating, J. F. Agape & the Eucharist in the Early Church: Studies in the History of Christian Love Feasts. LC 71-79511. Repr. of 1901 ed. 27.50 (ISBN 0-404-03640-6). AMS Pr.

Kelly, George A. Sacrament of the Eucharist in Our Time. 1978. 3.75 (ISBN 0-8198-0553-X); pap. 2.25 (ISBN 0-8198-0554-8). Dghtrs St Paul.

Kilpatrick, G. D. The Eucharist in Bible & Lithurgy: The Moorhouse Lectures 1975. LC 83-14315. 130p. 1984. 32.50 (ISBN 0-521-24675-X). Cambridge U Pr.

Kwatera, Michael. The Ministry of Communion. (Illus.). 48p. 1983. pap. text ed. 1.25 (ISBN 0-8146-1292-X). Liturgical Pr.

Langford, Alec J. Invitations to Communion. Lambert, Herbert, ed. LC 86-6116. 112p. (Orig.). 1986. pap. 7.95 (ISBN 0-8272-1607-6). CBP.

Lemons, Frank W. In Remembrance of Me. 1975. 4.95 (ISBN 0-87148-430-7); pap. 3.95 (ISBN 0-87148-431-5). Pathway Pr.

Livermore, Penny. Called to His Supper: The Biblical Eucharist. 2.95 (ISBN 0-89453-089-5). M Glazier.

The Lord's Supper. 1979. 15.95 (ISBN 0-570-03275-X, 15-2720). Concordia.

Lubich, Chiara. The Eucharist. LC 77-82230. 93p. 1977. pap. 2.50 (ISBN 0-911782-30-3). New City.

McEachern, Alton H. Here at Thy Table Lord. LC 77-1024. 1978. pap. 4.50 (ISBN 0-8054-2310-9). Broadman.

Macy, Gary. The Theologies of the Eucharist in the Early Scholastic Period. (Illus.). 1984. 32.00x (ISBN 0-19-826669-3). Oxford U Pr.

Martimort, A. G., ed. The Church at Prayer Part Two: The Eucharist. (Illus.). 250p. 1972. 17.50x (ISBN 0-7165-1107-X, BBA 01006, Pub. by Irish Academic Pr Ireland). Biblio Dist.

Marty, Martin E. The Lord's Supper. LC 79-6550. 80p. (Orig.). 1980. pap. 3.50 (ISBN 0-8006-1386-4, 1-1386). Fortress.

Merton, Thomas. The Living Bread. 157p. 1956. 12.95 (ISBN 0-374-14613-6); pap. 7.95 (ISBN 0-374-51520-4). FS&G.

Miller, Ronald H. The Holy Eucharist: Study Guide. 1977. pap. 2.95x (ISBN 0-8192-4075-3). Morehouse.

Mitchell, Nathan. Cult & Controversy: The Worship of the Eucharist Outside Mass. Kavanagh, Aidan, ed. (Studies in the Reformed Rites of the Catholic Church: Vol. IV). 460p. (Orig.). 1982. pap. 14.95 (ISBN 0-916134-50-4). Pueblo Pub Co.

Moloney, Raymond. Our Eucharistic Prayers in Worship, Preaching & Study. (Theology & Life Ser.: Vol. 14). 1985. pap. 8.95 (ISBN 0-89453-531-5). M Glazier.

More, Thomas. Answer to a Poisoned Book. Foley, Stepehn & Miller, Clarence H., eds. LC 63-7949. (Complete Works of St. Thomas More Ser.: Vol. II). 544p. 1985. text ed. 60.00 (ISBN 0-300-03129-7). Yale U Pr.

Murray, Andrew & Choy, Leona. Lord's Table. (Orig.). 1980. pap. 2.95 (ISBN 0-87508-380-3). Chr Lit.

Norbie, Donald L. The Lord's Supper: The Church's Love Feast. 1986. pap. 2.25 (ISBN 0-937396-67-2). Walterick Pubs.

Nuns of the Monastery of St. Clare, Balsbach, Germany, et al. The Celebration of the Eucharist: The Church's Festival of Love. Smith, David, tr. 1983. 6.00 (ISBN 0-8199-0866-5). Franciscan Herald.

Pennington, Basil. The Eucharist Yesterday & Today. 224p. 1984. 10.95 (ISBN 0-8245-0602-2). Crossroad NY.

--Eucharist: Yesterday & Today. 148p. pap. 6.95 (ISBN 0-8245-0690-1). Crossroad NY.

Pink, Arthur W. The Beatitudes & the Lord's Prayer. 140p. 1982. pap. 4.95 (ISBN 0-8010-7073-2). Baker Bk.

Pope John Paul II. Brazil, Journey in the Light of the Eucharist. 1980. 8.00 (ISBN 0-8198-1102-5); pap. 7.00 (ISBN 0-8198-1103-3). Dghtrs St Paul.

Rahner, Karl. Eucharist. 1970. 1.50 (ISBN 0-87193-106-0). Dimension Bks.

Reumann, John. The Supper of the Lord: The New Testament, Ecumenical Dialogues & Faith & Order on "Eucharist". LC 84-47932. 224p. 1984. pap. 13.95 (ISBN 0-8006-1816-5). Fortress.

Riggle, H. M. Christian Baptism, Feet Washing & the Lord's Supper. 264p. 3.50 (ISBN 0-686-29105-0). Faith Pub Hse.

Saunders, Landon B. The Power of Receiving. (Twentieth Century Sermons Ser.). 1979. 11.95 (ISBN 0-89112-312-1, Bibl Res Pr). Abilene Christ U.

Schweitzer, Albert & A. J. The Problem of the Lord's Supper. LC 81-22590. xiv, 144p. 1982. 10.95 (ISBN 0-86554-025-X, MUP-H25). Mercer Univ Pr.

Seasoltz, R., ed. Living Bread, Saving Cup: Readings on the Eucharist. LC 81-20813. 350p. 1982. pap. 12.95 (ISBN 0-8146-1257-1). Liturgical Pr.

Stevenson, Kenneth W. Eucharist & Offering. 300p. (Orig.). 1986. pap. 17.50 (ISBN 0-916134-77-6). Pueblo Pub Co.

Thurian, Max. The Mystery of the Eucharist. 88p. (Orig.). 1984. pap. 4.95 (ISBN 0-8028-0028-9). Eerdmans.

Thurian, Max & Wainwright, Geoffrey, eds. Baptism & Eucharist: Ecumenical Convergence in Celebration. LC 84-169338. 268p. (Orig.). 1984. pap. 11.95 (ISBN 0-8028-0005-X). Eerdmans.

Toler, Thomas. Elder at the Lord's Table. 1953. pap. 3.95 (ISBN 0-8272-0800-6). CBP.

Tyndale, William. An Answer to Sir Thomas More's Dialogue, the Supper of the Lord After the True Meaning of John 6 & or. 11. Repr. of 1850 ed. 31.00 (ISBN 0-384-62240-2). Johnson Repr.

Voillaume, Rene. Source of Life: The Eucharist & Christian Living. Livingstone, Dinah, tr. from Fr. 1977. pap. 2.95 (ISBN 0-914544-17-9). Living Flame Pr.

Watkins, Keith. The Feast of Joy: Ministering the Lord's Supper in the Free Tradition. LC 77-525. 1977. pap. 1.50 (ISBN 0-8272-1006-X). CBP.

Willimon, William H. Sunday Dinner. LC 81-52215. 1981. pap. 4.50x (ISBN 0-8358-0429-1). Upper Room.

LORD'S SUPPER–ANGLICAN COMMUNION

Britton, Colleen. Celebrate Communion. 79p. 1984. pap. 9.95 (ISBN 0-940754-26-6). Ed Ministries.

General Episcopal Synod. The Holy Eucharist, Longer Form & Other Services. rev. ed. 44p. 1986. pap. 1.50 (ISBN 0-935461-12-4). St Alban Pr CA.

Hill, Robert. The Pathway to Prayer & Pietie. LC 74-28864. (English Experience Ser.: No. 744). 1975. Repr. of 1613 ed. 26.50 (ISBN 90-221-0744-2). Walter J Johnson.

Hooper, John. The Early Writings of John Hooper. 1843. 51.00 (ISBN 0-384-24210-3). Johnson Repr.

Jewel, John. Works, 4 Vols. 1845-1850. Set. 204.00 (ISBN 0-384-27217-7). Johnson Repr.

The Liturgy of the Eucharist. 79p. (Orig.). 1984. pap. 3.95 (ISBN 0-908682-01-8, Pub. by Genesis). ANZ Religious Pubns.

LORD'S SUPPER–BIBLICAL TEACHING

Meagher, James L. How Christ Said the First Mass or the Lord's Last Supper. LC 82-74246. 438p. 1985. pap. 12.00 (ISBN 0-89555-207-8). Tan Bks Pubs.

Paris, Andrew. What the Bible Says about the Lord's Supper. LC 86-71103. (What the Bible Says Ser.). text ed. 13.95 (ISBN 0-89900-253-6). College Pr Pub.

LORD'S SUPPER–CATHOLIC CHURCH

Balasuriya, Tissa. The Eucharist & Human Liberation. LC 78-9160. 184p. (Orig.). 1979. pap. 6.95 (ISBN 0-88344-118-7). Orbis Bks.

Davies, Michael. Communion Under Both Kinds-an Ecumenical Surrender. 1980. pap. 1.00 (ISBN 0-89555-141-1). TAN Bks Pubs.

De Margerie, Bertrand. Remarried Divorcees & Eucharistic Communion. 1980. pap. 1.95 (ISBN 0-8198-6401-3). Dghtrs St Paul.

Duckworth, Robin, ed. This Is the Word of the Lord: Year A: The Year of Matthew. 1980. pap. 9.95 (ISBN 0-19-213248-2). Oxford U Pr.

Fahey, Michael A., ed. Catholic Perspectives on Baptism, Eucharist & Ministry: A Study Commissioned by the Catholic Theological Society of America. 240p. (Orig.). 1986. lib. bdg. 24.50 (ISBN 0-8191-5431-8, Pub. by Catholic Theological Soc of Amer); pap. text ed. 11.75 (ISBN 0-8191-5432-6). U Pr of Amer.

Meagher, James L. How Christ Said the First Mass or the Lord's Last Supper. LC 82-74246. 438p. 1985. pap. 12.00 (ISBN 0-89555-207-8). Tan Bks Pubs.

LORD'S SUPPER–FIRST COMMUNION

see First Communion

LORD'S SUPPER–HISTORY

Bouyer, Louis. Eucharist: Theology & Spirituality of the Eucharist Prayer. Quinn, Charles U., tr. LC 68-17064. 1968. pap. 13.95 (ISBN 0-268-00498-6). U of Notre Dame Pr.

Heron, Alasdair I. Table & Tradition. LC 83-14762. 206p. (Orig.). 1984. pap. 11.95 (ISBN 0-664-24516-1). Westminster.

Jasper, R. C. & Cuming, G. J., eds. Prayers of the Eucharist: Early & Reformed. 2nd ed. 1980. 17.95x (ISBN 0-19-520140-X); pap. 5.95 (ISBN 0-19-520141-8). Oxford U Pr.

Knox, David B. The Lord's Supper from Wycliffe to Crammer. 75p. 1986. pap. 6.25 (ISBN 0-85364-379-2, Pub. by Paternoster UK). Attic Pr.

Macdonald, Allan J. Berengar & the Reform of the Sacramental System. 444p. 1977. Repr. of 1930 ed. lib. bdg. 30.00 (ISBN 0-915172-25-9). Richwood Pub.

Marshall, I. Howard. Last Supper & Lord's Supper. (Orig.). 1981. pap. 6.95 (ISBN 0-8028-1854-4). Eerdmans.

Rordorf, Willy, et al. The Eucharist of the Early Christians. O'Connell, Matthew J., tr. from Fr. 1978. pap. 9.95 (ISBN 0-916134-33-4). Pueblo Pub Co.

LORD'S SUPPER–MEDITATIONS

Cowper, J. M. & Manning, Robert, eds. Mediations on the Supper of Our Lord. (EETS, OS Ser.: No. 60). Repr. of 1875 ed. 15.00 (ISBN 0-527-00054-X). Kraus Repr.

Fearon, Mary & Hirstein, Sandra J. The Eucharist Makes Us One. 1983. box set 84.95 (ISBN 0-697-01843-1); program dir. guide 4.95 (ISBN 0-697-01844-X); tchr's. manual, pre-school to junior levels 3.25 (ISBN 0-697-01845-8); write for info. student leaflets; attendance certificates 6.95 (ISBN 0-697-01973-X). Wm C Brown.

Gritter, George. Communion Mediations. 80p. 1984. pap. 5.95 (ISBN 0-8010-3805-7). Baker Bk.

Holy Transfiguration Monastery Staff. Prayers for Holy Communion. 120p. (Orig.). 1986. pap. 3.00x (ISBN 0-913026-60-3, Holy Transfiguration). St Nectarios.

Keifer, Ralph. Blessed & Broken: An Exploration of the Contemporary Experience of God in Eucharistic Celebration. (Message of the Sacraments Ser.: Vol. 3). 1982. 12.95 (ISBN 0-89453-393-2); pap. 8.95 (ISBN 0-89453-267-7). M Glazier.

Korth, Robert, ed. Communion Meditations & Prayers. LC 81-16668. 128p. (Orig.). 1982. pap. 4.95 (ISBN 0-87239-483-2, 3032). Standard Pub.

Landrum, Eli, Jr. More Than Symbol. LC 81-86669. (Orig.). 1983. pap. 3.95 (ISBN 0-8054-2304-4). Broadman.

Lussier, Ernest. The Eucharist: The Bread of Life. LC 77-3035. 248p. 1979. pap. 3.95 (ISBN 0-8189-0349-X). Alba.

McCord, David. Let Us Remember. 64p. 1986. pap. 2.95 (ISBN 0-87403-071-4, 3023). Standard Pub.

Ogilvie, Lloyde J. The Cup of Wonder: Communion Meditations. 142p. 1985. pap. 5.95 (ISBN 0-8010-6710-3). Baker Bk.

Weber, Gerard P., et al. Unite at the Lord's Table. (The Word Is Life Ser.). 4p. 1977. 3.92 (ISBN 0-02-658400-X); tchrs. ed. 8.00 (ISBN 0-02-658410-7); family handbook 1.00 (ISBN 0-02-658450-6). Benziger Pub Co.

LORD'S SUPPER–ORTHODOX EASTERN CHURCH

Ambrosius, Saint Concerning the Mysteries. 1977. pap. 1.25 (ISBN 0-686-19348-2). Eastern Orthodox.

Conomos, Dimitri E. The Late Byzantine & Slavonic Communion Cycle: Liturgy & Music. LC 84-12176. (Dumbarton Oaks Studies: Vol. 21). (Illus.). 222p. 1985. 25.00x (ISBN 0-88402-134-3). Dumbarton Oaks.

LORD'S SUPPER–PRAYER BOOKS AND DEVOTIONS

Buck, Carlton C. Communion Thoughts & Prayers. new ed. LC 76-46943. 1977. 5.95 (ISBN 0-8272-0440-X). CBP.

Korth, Robert, ed. Communion Meditations & Prayers. LC 81-16668. 128p. (Orig.). 1982. pap. 4.95 (ISBN 0-87239-483-2, 3032). Standard Pub.

LORD'S SUPPER–SACRIFICE

Smith, Preserved. A Short History of Christian Theophagy. 223p. 1922. 16.95 (ISBN 0-87548-241-4). Open Court.

LORD'S SUPPER–SERMONS

Here are entered sermons on the Lord's Supper itself. Sermons preached at, or in preparation for a communion service are entered under the heading Communion Sermons.

Belford, William J. Special Ministers of the Eucharist. 1979. pap. 1.95 (ISBN 0-916134-39-3). Pueblo Pub Co.

Hutchinson, Roger. Works. 1842. 31.00 (ISBN 0-384-25120-X). Johnson Repr.

LORD'S SUPPER (LITURGY)

Cook, Paul E. Communion Handbook. 96p. 1980. 5.95 (ISBN 0-8170-0877-2). Judson.

Frere, Walter H. The Anaphora or Great Eucharistic Prayer: An Eirenical Study in Liturgical History. (Church Historical Society, London, New Ser.: No. 26). Repr. of 1938 ed. 50.00 (ISBN 0-8115-3150-3). Kraus Repr.

Jasper, R. C. & Cuming, G. J., eds. Prayers of the Eucharist: Early & Reformed. 2nd ed. 1980. 17.95x (ISBN 0-19-520140-X); pap. 5.95 (ISBN 0-19-520141-8). Oxford U Pr.

The Liturgy of the Eucharist. 79p. (Orig.). 1984. pap. 3.95 (ISBN 0-908682-01-8, Pub. by Genesis). ANZ Religious Pubns.

Searle, Mark. Liturgy Made Simple. LC 81-4807. 96p. (Orig.). 1981. pap. 2.95 (ISBN 0-8146-1221-0). Liturgical Pr.

LORD'S SUPPER IN LITERATURE

Ross, Malcolm M. Poetry & Dogma. LC 78-86284. 1969. Repr. of 1954 ed. lib. bdg. 18.50x (ISBN 0-374-96973-6, Octagon). Hippocrene Bks.

LOST TRIBES OF ISRAEL

see also Anglo-Israelism; Mormons and Mormonism

Boudinot, Elias. Star in the West: A Humble Attempt to Discover the Long Lost Ten Tribes of Israel. facs. ed. LC 79-121499. (Select Bibliographies Reprint Ser). 1816. 17.00 (ISBN 0-8369-5457-2). Ayer Co Pubs.

Brough, R. Clayton. The Lost Tribes: History Doctrine, Prophecies & Theories About Israel's Lost Ten Tribes. LC 79-89351. 1979. 7.95 (ISBN 0-88290-123-0). Horizon Utah.

Dickey, C. R. One Man's Destiny. 1942. 8.00 (ISBN 0-685-08811-1). Destiny.

Even, Charles. The Lost Tribes of Israel: Or, the First of the Red Men. 26.50 (ISBN 0-405-10243-7, 14436). Ayer Co Pubs.

Gottwald, Norman K. The Tribes of Yahweh: A Sociology of the Religion of Liberated Israel, 1250-1050 B.C. LC 78-24333. 944p. (Orig.). 1979. pap. 19.95 (ISBN 0-88344-499-2). Orbis Bks.

Raymond, E. The Gem Stones in the Breastplate. (Illus.). 48p. (Orig.). 1987. pap. price not set (ISBN 0-934666-18-0). Artisan Sales.

LOUIS 9TH, SAINT, KING OF FRANCE, 1214-1270

De Joinville, Jean. Histoire de Saint Louis. De Wailly, N., ed. 1868. 38.00 (ISBN 0-384-27721-7); pap. 32.00 (ISBN 0-384-27720-9). Johnson Repr.

Guillaume De Berneville. La Vie De Saint Gilles. Paris, Gaston & Bos, Alphonse, eds. 34.00 (ISBN 0-384-20300-0); pap. 28.00 (ISBN 0-384-20285-3). Johnson Repr.

Jordan, William C. Louis the IX: The Challenge of the Crusade. LC 79-83996. (Illus.). 1979. 37.00 (ISBN 0-691-05285-9). Princeton U Pr.

Le Nain De Tillemont, Louis S. Vie De Saint Louis, Roi De France, 6 Vols. 255.00 (ISBN 0-384-32195-X); pap. 220.00 (ISBN 0-384-32196-8). Johnson Repr.

Perry, Frederick. Saint Louis: Louis IX of France, the Most Christian King. LC 73-14462. Repr. of 1901 ed. 30.00 (ISBN 0-404-58280-X). AMS Pr.

LOURDES

see also Bernadette, Saint (Bernadette Soubirous), 1844-1879

Bertrin, G. Lourdes: A History of Its Apparitions & Cures. 59.95 (ISBN 0-8490-0560-4). Gordon Pr.

Marnham, Patrick. Lourdes: A Modern Pilgrimage. LC 82-45299. 272p. 1982. pap. 4.95 (ISBN 0-385-18252-X, Im). Doubleday.

Odell, Catherine. On Pilgrimage with Father Ralph Diorio: Following the Footpaths of Faith through the Holyland, Rome & Lourdes. LC 85-7083. (Illus.). 192p. 1986. 16.95 (ISBN 0-385-19908-2). Doubleday.

LOVE

see also Friendship; Marriage

Allen. Faith, Hope & Love. 5.95 (ISBN 0-318-18178-9). WCTU.

Amen, Carol V. Love Goes 'Round the Circle. (Better Living Ser.). pap. 0.99 (ISBN 0-8280-1268-7). Review & Herald.

Bell, Joseph N. Love Theory in Later Hanbalite Islam. LC 78-5904. 1979. PLB 49.50x (ISBN 0-87395-244-8). State U NY Pr.

Boom, Corrie ten. Amazing Love. (Orig.). 1982. pap. 2.50 (ISBN 0-515-06735-0). Jove Pubns.

Cabot, Richard C. What Men Live By. 341p. 1985. Repr. of 1941 ed. lib. bdg. 35.00 (ISBN 0-89760-187-4). Telegraph Bks.

Campbell, D. Ross. How to Really Love Your Child. LC 77-89470. 132p. 1977. pap. 4.95 (ISBN 0-88207-751-1). Victor Bks.

Canfield, Muriel. I Wish I Could Say, "I Love You". 204p. (Orig.). 1983. pap. 5.95 (ISBN 0-87123-265-0, 210265). Bethany Hse.

Cohen, Alan. If We Only Have Love. (Illus.). 15p. (Orig.). 1984. pap. 1.00 (ISBN 0-910367-34-5). A Cohen.

Constable, Benjamin. The Mystical Symbolism of Universal Love. (Illus.). 1978. 47.50 (ISBN 0-89266-113-5). Am Classical Coll Pr.

Couer de Jesus d' Elbee, Jean du. I Believe In Love. Teichert, Marilyn & Stebbins, Madeline, trs. LC 82-24134. Tr. of Croire a l'amour. (Fr.). 1983. pap. 4.95 (ISBN 0-932506-21-6). St Bedes Pubns.

Desai, Yogi A. Love Is an Awakening. Sarasohn, Lisa, ed. (Illus.). 40p. (Orig.). 1985. pap. 2.00 (ISBN 0-940258-14-5). Kripalu Pubns.

Dominian, Jack. The Capacity to Love. 174p. (Orig.). 1985. text ed. 6.95 (ISBN 0-8091-2726-1). Paulist Pr.

Grau, Joseph A. Morality & the Human Future in the Thought of Teilhard De Chardin: A Critical Study. LC 74-4976. 389p. 1976. 28.50 (ISBN 0-8386-1579-1). Fairleigh Dickinson.

The Greatest Is Love. (Illus.). 48p. 1982. Repr. 7.95 (ISBN 0-86683-688-8, AY8289, HarpR). Har-Row.

Harper, Ralph. Human Love: Existential & Mystical. LC 66-24410. pap. 48.00 (2026322). Bks Demand UMI.

Hauck, Paul A. The Three Faces of Love. LC 83-10468. 174p. 1984. pap. 8.95 (ISBN 0-664-24486-6). Westminster.

Hershey, Terry. Intimacy: Where Do I Go To Find Love? 144p. 1984. text ed. 9.95 (ISBN 0-915929-06-6). Merit Bks.

Hobe, Phyllis. The Meaning of Love. LC 76-23415. 1982. Repr. of 1976 ed. 7.95 (ISBN 0-8054-5119-6). Broadman.

Hobe, Phyllis L. When Love Isn't Easy. 192p. 1986. pap. 3.50 (ISBN 0-553-26055-3). Bantam.

Iqbal, Sufi M. The Achievement of Love. Ahmad, Aftab, tr. from Arabic. 190p. 1987. pap. 9.95 (ISBN 0-915597-44-6). Amana Bks.

Kristeva, Julia. Tales of Love. Roudiez, Leon S., tr. from Fr. LC 86-28311. 448p. 1987. text ed. 30.00 (ISBN 0-231-06024-6). Columbia U Pr.

Lidiard, Victoria. Christianity: Faith, Love & Healing. LC 84-90145. 80p. 1985. 5.95 (ISBN 0-533-06204-7). Vantage.

Love. (The Inspirational Library Ser.). 24p. 3.95 (ISBN 0-8326-2006-8, 3253). World Bible.

Mac Carthy, Denis Florence. Love the Greatest Enchantment: The Sorceries of Sin, the Devotion of the Cross. 1861. 50.00 (ISBN 0-8274-3002-7). R West.

McDowell, Josh. The Secret of Loving. (Living Bks.). 240p. Repr. 3.95 (ISBN 0-8423-5845-5). Tyndale.

Murray, Andrew. Secret of Brotherly Love. (Secret Ser.). (Orig.). 1980. pap. 1.95 (ISBN 0-87508-390-0). Chr Lit.

Niebuhr, Reinhold. Love & Justice: Selections from the Shorter Writings of Reinhold Niebuhr. Robertson, D. B., ed. 12.50 (ISBN 0-8446-2659-7). Peter Smith.

Ogilvie, Lloyd J. The Beauty of Love. LC 80-80465. (Orig.). 1980. pap. 5.95 (ISBN 0-89081-245-4). Harvest Hse.

Peale, Ruth S. Secrets of Staying in Love. 272p. 1984. pap. 5.95 (ISBN 0-8407-5910-X). Nelson.

Powell, John. The Secret of Staying in Love. LC 74-84712. (Illus.). 1974. pap. 3.95 (ISBN 0-913592-29-3). Argus Comm.

Price, Eugenia. Make Love Your Aim. 192p. 1983. pap. 5.95 (ISBN 0-310-31311-2, 16243P). Zondervan.

Rajneesh, Bhagwan Shree. From Sex to Superconsciousness. Prem, Swami Krishna, ed. LC 77-20821. (Early Discourses & Writings Ser.). (Illus.). 256p. (Orig.). 1979. 15.50 (ISBN 0-88050-064-6). Chidvilas Found.

--The Path of Love. Sudha, Ma Yoga, ed. LC 83-181255. (Kabir Ser.). (Illus.). 350p. (Orig.). 1978. 16.50 (ISBN 0-88050-112-X); pap. 12.95 358p (ISBN 0-88050-612-1). Chidvilas Found.

Shelton, Robert R. Loving Relationships. 272p. (Orig.). 1987. pap. 11.95 (ISBN 0-87178-542-0). Brethren.

Smalley, Gary & Scott, Steve. The Joy of Committed Love: A Valuable Guide to Knowing, Understanding & Loving Each Other. LC 83-18248. 336p. 1984. 12.95 (ISBN 0-310-44900-6, 18248). Zondervan.

Smyly, Glenn A. & Smyly, Barbara J. All in the Name of Love. 116p. 1986. 17.95 (ISBN 0-9616707-0-3); pap. 9.95 (ISBN 0-9616707-1-1). Alivening Pubns.

Sweeting, George. Catch the Spirit of Love. 120p. 1983. pap. 4.95 (ISBN 0-88207-108-4). Victor Bks.

Tamiazzo, John. Love & Be Loved: A How-To Book. 176p. 1986. pap. 7.95 (ISBN 0-87877-087-9, Greenbriar Books). Newcastle Pub.

Thoughts on Love & Peace: To Commemorate the Visit of Pope John Paul II, India, 1986. 104p. (YA) 1986. text ed. 12.95x (ISBN 0-7069-3059-2, Pub. by Vikas India). Advent NY.

Tillich, Paul. Love, Power & Justice. 1954. pap. 7.95 (ISBN 0-19-500222-9). Oxford U Pr.

Walton, O. F. Nadie Me Quiere. Tr. of Nobody Loves Me. (Span.). 128p. 1984. 3.25 (ISBN 0-8254-1850-X). Kregel.

Welwood, John. Challenge of the Heart: Love, Sex & Intimacy in Changing Times. LC 85-2461. 283p. (Orig.). 1985. pap. 9.95 (ISBN 0-87773-331-7, 74200-1). Shambhala Pubns.

Word of Love. (Words of... Ser.). (Illus.). 48p. 1983. 3.95 (ISBN 0-8407-5338-1). Nelson.

Wright, Rusty & Wright, Linda R. How to Unlock the Secrets of Love & Sex in Marriage. 144p. 1985. pap. 3.95 (ISBN 0-916441-08-3). Barbour & Co.

LOVE (THEOLOGY)

see also Agape; God-Love; God-Worship and Love; Identification (Religion); Self-Love (Theology)

Abata, Russell M. Is Love in & Sin Out? LC 85-81325. 80p. 1985. pap. 2.95 (ISBN 0-89243-246-2). Liguori Pubns.

Abhedananda. Human Affection & Divine Love. 64p. 3.95 (ISBN 0-87481-610-6, Pub. by Ramakrishna Math Madras India). Vedanta Pr.

Allen, Joseph L. Love & Conflict: A Covenantal Model of Christian Ethics. 336p. 1984. pap. 12.95 (ISBN 0-687-22806-9). Abingdon.

Arnold, Eberhard. Love & Marriage in the Spirit. LC 64-24321. 1965. 7.00 (ISBN 0-87486-103-9). Plough.

Babris, Janina. The Covenant of Love. (Illus.). 228p. (Orig.). pap. 6.95 (ISBN 0-913382-19-1, 101-25). Prow Bks-Franciscan.

Baden. The Greatest Gift Is Love. LC 59-1314. (Arch Bks.). 24p. 1985. pap. 0.99 (ISBN 0-570-06196-2). Concordia.

Benn, Douglas R. Love-God's Greatest Gift. (Illus.). 1981. pap. 4.00 (ISBN 0-682-49736-3). Exposition Pr FL.

Bergan, Jacqueline & Schwan, S. Marie. Love: A Guide for Prayer. (Take & Receive Ser.). 96p. (Orig.). 1984. pap. 5.95 (ISBN 0-88489-168-2). St Mary's.

Billheimer, Paul. Love Covers. 1981. pap. 4.95 (ISBN 0-87508-006-5). Chr Lit.

Blair, Joe. When Bad Things Happen, God Still Loves. LC 85-13240. 1986. pap. 4.95 (ISBN 0-8054-5010-6). Broadman.

Bucer, Martin. Instruction in Christian Love. John Knox.

Butler, Roy F. The Meaning of Agapao & Phileo in the Greek New Testament. 1977. 6.50x (ISBN 0-87291-089-X). Coronado Pr.

Butterworth, Eric. Life Is for Loving. LC 73-6326. 128p. 1974. 10.53 (ISBN 0-06-061268-1, HarpR). Har-Row.

Cardenal, Ernesto. Love. 160p. 1981. pap. 4.95 (ISBN 0-8245-0043-1). Crossroad NY.

Chapian, Marie. Love & Be Loved. 192p. 1983. pap. 6.95 (ISBN 0-8007-5092-6, Power Bks). Revell.

Churches Alive, Inc. Staff. Esteeming. LC 79-52130. (Love One Another Bible Study Ser.). (Illus.). 1979. wkbk. 3.00 (ISBN 0-934396-03-5). Churches Alive.

Coleman, Bill & Coleman, Patty. Only Love Can Make It Easy, 2 vols. rev. ed. LC 80-52360. 1981. Couples' Wkbk. pap. 2.95x (ISBN 0-89622-131-8); Leader's Guide. pap. 8.50 (ISBN 0-89622-132-6). Twenty-Third.

De Coppens, Peter R. Spiritual Perspective II: The Spiritual Dimension & Implications of Love, Sex, & Marriage. LC 80-6302. 175p. (Orig.). 1981. pap. text ed. 10.75 (ISBN 0-8191-1512-6). U Pr of Amer.

Del Mastro, M. L., tr. Revelations of Divine Love: Juliana of Norwich. LC 76-52004. 1977. pap. 4.95 (ISBN 0-385-12297-7, Im). Doubleday.

Denninger, Richard. Anatomy of the Pure & of the Impure Love. (Intimate Life of Man Library Bk.). (Illus.). 1979. 97.95 (ISBN 0-89266-177-1); spiral bdg. 37.95 (ISBN 0-685-67718-4). Am Classical Coll Pr.

Desai, Yogi A. Loving Each Other. Sarasohn, Lisa, ed. (Illus.). 40p. 1985. pap. 2.00 (ISBN 0-940258-19-6). Kripalu Pubns.

Dominian, Jack. The Capacity to Love. 174p. (Orig.). 1985. text ed. 6.95 (ISBN 0-8091-2726-1). Paulist Pr.

Donnelly, Dorothy H. Radical Love: Toward a Sexual Spirituality. 144p. 1984. pap. 6.95 (ISBN 0-86683-817-1, AY8407, HarpR). Har-Row.

Doughty, Stephen. Answering Love's Call: Christian Love & a Life of Prayer. LC 86-81809. 128p. (Orig.). 1986. pap. 4.95 (ISBN 0-87793-348-0). Ave Maria.

Drummond, Henry. Greatest Thing in the World. 1959. 3.95 (ISBN 0-399-12828-X, G&D). Putnam Pub Group.

--Greatest Thing in the World. 64p. 1968. pap. 2.50 (ISBN 0-8007-8018-3, Spire Bks). Revell.

--The Greatest Thing in the World. 64p. 1981. pap. 2.95 (ISBN 0-88368-100-5). Whitaker Hse.

Elder, E. Rozanne, ed. The Way of Love. (Cistercian Fathers Ser.: No. 16). (Illus.). 1977. 7.95 (ISBN 0-87907-616-X); pap. 4.50 (ISBN 0-87907-966-5). Cistercian Pubns.

Finney, Charles G. Love Is Not a Special Way of Feeling. Orig. Title: Attributes of Love. 144p. 1963. pap. 3.50 (ISBN 0-87123-005-4, 200005). Bethany Hse.

Gesch, Roy. To Love & to Cherish. 1985. 4.95 (ISBN 0-570-04214-3, 15-2174). Concordia.

Getz, Gene A. Measure of a Church. LC 75-17160. (Orig.). 1975. pap. 3.50 (ISBN 0-8307-0398-5, 5014700). Regal.

The Gift of Love. LC 85-19655. 181p. 1985. pap. 6.95 (ISBN 0-88141-041-1). St Vladimirs.

Gillquist, Peter E. Love Is Now. new ed. 1970. 4.95 (ISBN 0-310-36941-X, 18054P). Zondervan.

Gocek, Matilda A. Love Is a Challenge. LC 78-12327. (Keepers of the Light Ser.). (Illus.). 72p. 1978. pap. 3.95 (ISBN 0-912526-22-X). Lib Res.

Goetz, Joan. El Amor y la Juventud. Montero, Lidia D., tr. from Eng. Tr. of Let's Look at Love. (Illus.). 96p. 1984. pap. 2.25 (ISBN 0-311-46058-5). Casa Bautista.

Griffin, Robert. I Never Said I Didn't Love You. LC 76-24442. (Emmaus Book Ser.). 128p. 1977. pap. 2.95 (ISBN 0-8091-1989-7). Paulist Pr.

Grigor, Jean C. Grow to Love. 1977. pap. 5.75x (ISBN 0-7152-0437-8). Outlook.

Guitton, Jean. Human Love. LC 66-17110. 253p. 1966. 4.50 (ISBN 0-8199-0046-X). Franciscan Herald.

Hanley, Boniface. No Greater Love: Maximilian Kolbe. LC 82-72656. (Illus.). 80p. (Orig.). 1982. pap. 3.95 (ISBN 0-87793-257-3). Ave Maria.

Herbert, Janet. Love Is Kind. (Sparkler Bks.). (Illus.). 32p. 1986. plastic comb bndg. 2.95 (ISBN 0-89191-928-7, 59287, Chariot Bks). Cook.

Hess, Margaret L. The Triumph of Love. 96p. 1987. pap. 4.95 (ISBN 0-89693-247-8). Victor Bks.

Hildebrand, Dietrich von. Man & Woman. LC 65-25840. pap. 25.80 (ISBN 0-317-28166-6, 2022575). Bks Demand UMI.

Howe, Reuel L. Herein Is Love. pap. 3.95 (ISBN 0-8170-0263-4). Judson.

Israel, Martin. Discipline of Love. 128p. (Orig.). 1986. pap. 8.95 (ISBN 0-8245-0739-8). Crossroad NY.

Kappeler, Max. Compendium for the Study of Christian Science: No. 10, Love. 23p. 1953. pap. 3.50 (ISBN 0-85241-064-6). Kappeler Inst Pub.

Kelsey, Morton T. Caring: How Can We Love One Another? LC 80-84659. 198p. (Orig.). 1981. pap. 8.95 (ISBN 0-8091-2366-5). Paulist Pr.

Keyes, Frances P. Three Ways of Love. 1975. 6.00 (ISBN 0-8198-0477-0); pap. 5.00 (ISBN 0-8198-0478-9). Dghtrs St Paul.

Koller, Carmeline. Walk in Love. 10.50 (ISBN 0-8199-0843-6). Franciscan Herald.

Lauder, Robert E. The Love Explosion: Human Experience & the Christian Mystery. 128p. (Orig.). 1979. pap. 2.95 (ISBN 0-914544-22-5). Living Flame Pr.

Lockyer, Herbert. Love Is Better Than Wine. LC 80-84903. 1981. pap. 3.95 (ISBN 0-89221-083-4). New Leaf.

Love. 1986. 8.95 (ISBN 0-87579-059-3). Deseret Bk.

Mignani, Rigo & Di Cesare, Mario A. A Concordance to Juan Ruiz's Libro De Buen Amor. 328p. 16.00 (ISBN 0-87395-322-3, Pub. by SUNY Pr). Medieval & Renaissance NY.

Miller, Judy. Cups Running Over. 1985. pap. 5.95 (ISBN 0-89225-278-2). Gospel Advocate.

Moncure, Jane B. Love. rev. ed. LC 80-27479. (What Is It? Ser.). (Illus.). 32p. 1981. PLB 7.45 (ISBN 0-89565-205-6). Childs World.

Morris, Leon. Testaments of Love: A Study of Love in the Bible. (Orig.). 1981. 12.95 (ISBN 0-8028-3502-3). Eerdmans.

Moss, Jean D. Godded with God: Hendrik Niclaes & His Family of Love. LC 81-68192. (Transactions Ser.: Vol. 71, Pt. 8). 1981. 10.00 (ISBN 0-87169-718-1). Am Philos.

Mother Teresa of Calcutta. The Love of Christ: Spiritual Counsels. LC 81-48216. 128p. 1982. 8.45 (ISBN 0-06-068229-9, HarpR). Har-Row.

Mouton, Boyce. These Two Commandments. 2nd ed. (Orig.). 1978. pap. 2.95 (ISBN 0-89900-138-6). College Pr Pub.

Murray, Andrew. Secret of Brotherly Love. (Secret Ser.). (Orig.). 1980. pap. 1.95 (ISBN 0-87508-390-0). Chr Lit.

Narada. Narada Bhakti Sutras: The Gospel of Divine Love. Tyagisananda, Swami, tr. (Sanskrit & Eng). pap. 4.95 (ISBN 0-87481-427-8). Vedanta Pr.

--Narada's Way of Divine Love: The Bhakti Sutras. 1st ed. Prabhavananda, Swami, tr. from Sansk. LC 75-161488. 1971. pap. 4.95 (ISBN 0-87481-508-8). Vedanta Pr.

Nighswander, Ada. The Little Martins Learn to Love. 6.50 (ISBN 0-686-30775-5). Rod & Staff.

Nyberg, Dorothea. We Still Love You, Bob. 144p. 1984. pap. 6.95 (ISBN 0-87178-925-6). Brethren.

Ogilvie, Lloyd J. Loved & Forgiven. LC 76-29889. 160p. 1977. pap. 3.50 (ISBN 0-8307-0442-6, S313103). Regal.

Ozment, Robert V. Love Is the Answer. 160p. 1986. pap. 5.95 (ISBN 0-8007-5227-9). Revell.

Parker, Margaret. Love, Acceptance & Forgiveness: Leader's Guide. LC 79-63763. 128p. 1984. pap. 3.95 (ISBN 0-8307-0989-4, 6101895). Regal.

Paulson, J. Sig. How to Love Your Neighbor. 184p. 1974. pap. 4.95 (ISBN 0-317-20873-X). CSA Pr.

Peil, William. Affirmation: The Touch of Life. LC 82-20655. (Illus.). 48p. 1983. pap. 1.95 (ISBN 0-89571-026-9). Affirmation.

Ponder, Catherine. The Prospering Power of Love. rev. ed. LC 66-25849. 126p. 1984. pap. 3.50 (ISBN 0-87516-525-7). De Vorss.

Post, Stephen G. Christian Love & Self-Denial: A Historical & Normative Study of Jonathan Edwards, Samuel Hopkins & American Theological Ethics. 138p. (Orig.). 1987. lib. bdg. 22.50 (ISBN 0-8191-5261-7); pap. text ed. 8.75 (ISBN 0-8191-5262-5). U Pr of Amer.

Puri, Ishwar C. On Love. Scott, Edward D., ed. 28p. (Orig.). 1984. pap. 2.00 (ISBN 0-937067-03-2). Inst Study Hum Aware.

Quoist, Michel. The Breath of Love. 167p. (Orig.). 1987. pap. 8.95 (ISBN 0-8245-0801-7). Crossroad NY.

Rahner, Karl. The Love of Jesus & the Love of Neighbor. LC 82-23523. 96p. 1983. pap. 5.95 (ISBN 0-8245-0570-0). Crossroad NY.

Rouner, Arthur A., Jr. How to Love. (Contemporary Discussion Ser.). 1974. pap. 1.25 (ISBN 0-8010-7622-6). Baker Bk.

St. Thomas Aquinas. Saint Thomas Aquinas: On Charity. Kendzierski, Lotti H., tr. (Medieval Philosophical Texts in Translation: No. 10). 1960. pap. 7.95 (ISBN 0-87462-210-7). Marquette.

Scott, Latayne C. To Love Each Other: A Woman's Workshop on First Corinthians. (Woman's Workshop Ser.). 112p. (Orig.). 1985. pap. 3.95 (ISBN 0-310-38921-6, 10454P). Zondervan.

Scroggie, W. Graham. Love Life: I Cor. 13. LC 79-2551. (W. Graham Scroggie Library). 96p. 1980. pap. 4.50 (ISBN 0-8254-3733-4). Kregel.

Sheen, Fulton J. Power of Love. 1968. pap. 2.95 (ISBN 0-385-01090-7, D235, Im). Doubleday.

Short, Ray E. Sex, Dating, & Love: Seventy-Seven Questions Most Often Asked. LC 83-72122. 144p. (Orig.). 1984. pap. 3.95 (ISBN 0-8066-2066-8, 10-5648). Augsburg.

Simpson, A. B. Walking in Love. 1975. Repr. 2.95 (ISBN 0-87509-040-0). Chr Pubns.

Slesinski, Robert. Pavel Florensky: A Metaphysics of Love. LC 83-27130. 256p. 1984. pap. text ed. 12.95 (ISBN 0-88141-032-2). St Vladimirs.

Smalley, Gary, et al. Decide to Love. 64p. (Orig.). 1985. tchr's. manual 19.95 (ISBN 0-310-44861-1, 18249P); student's manual 2.95 (ISBN 0-310-44331-8, 18253P). Zondervan.

Smith, Nelson M. What Is This Thing Called Love. 1970. 8.75 (ISBN 0-89137-505-8); pap. 4.95 (ISBN 0-89137-504-X). Quality Pubns.

Solovyov, Vladimir. The Meaning of Love. rev. ed. 144p. 1985. pap. 7.95 (ISBN 0-89281-068-8, Lindisfarne Pr). Inner Tradit.

Souter, John. Love. (Campus Magazine Ser.). 96p. (Orig.). 1985. pap. 4.95 (ISBN 0-8423-3851-9). Tyndale.

Steele. Love Enthroned. kivar 4.95 (ISBN 0-686-12891-5). Schmul Pub Co.

Steele, Sharon A. A New Commandment: Loving As Jesus Loved. (Basic Bible Study). 64p. 1986. pap. 2.95 (ISBN 0-932305-21-0, 521021). Aglow Pubns.

Swami Chetanananda. The Logic of Love. 288p. 1987. pap. 10.95 (ISBN 0-915801-05-1). Rudra Pr.

Swedenborg, Emanuel. Marital Love. LC 38-13542. 760p. 1974. student ed. 12.00 (ISBN 0-87785-150-6). Swedenborg.

Taylor, Mark L. God Is Love: A Study in the Theology of Karl Rahner. (AAR-Academy Ser.). 1986. 24.95 (ISBN 0-89130-925-X, 01-01-50); pap. 18.25 (ISBN 0-89130-926-8). Scholars Pr GA.

Thurman, Howard. Mysticism & the Experience of Love. LC 61-13708. (Orig.). 1961. pap. 2.50x (ISBN 0-87574-115-0). Pendle Hill.

Toyotome, M. Three Kinds of Love. pap. 0.75 (ISBN 0-87784-132-2). Inter-Varsity.

Tully, Mary Jo & Fearon, Mary. Focus on Loving. (Light of Faith Ser.). (Orig.). 1981. pap. text ed. 3.55 (ISBN 0-697-01763-X); tchrs.' ed. 12.95 (ISBN 0-697-01764-8); tests 12.95 (ISBN 0-697-01827-X). Wm C Brown.

Vanderhaar, Gerard A. Enemies & How to Love Them. 128p. (Orig.). 1985. pap. 4.95 (ISBN 0-89622-241-1). Twenty Third.

Vanstone, W. H. The Risk of Love. 1978. 11.95x (ISBN 0-19-520053-5). Oxford U Pr.

Vinck, Jose D. The Yes Book. 1976. pap. 3.75 (ISBN 0-685-77499-6). Franciscan Herald.

--The Yes Book: An Answer to Life (a Manual of Christian Existentialism) LC 77-190621. 200p. 1972. 12.75 (ISBN 0-911726-12-8); pap. 8.75 (ISBN 0-911726-11-X). Alleluia Pr.

Von Hildebrand, Alice. Love & Selfishness. 54p. 1970. pap. 0.75 (ISBN 0-8199-0376-0). Franciscan Herald.

Wilder, Kay W., ed. Season with Love. 288p. 1985. pap. 10.95 (ISBN 0-8341-1061-X). Beacon Hill.

William of St. Thierry. The Nature & Dignity of Love. Elder, E. R., ed. Davis, Thomas X., tr. from Lat. (Cistercian Fathers Ser.: No. 30). Orig. Title: De natura et dignitate amoris. 1981. 13.95 (ISBN 0-87907-330-6). Cistercian Pubns.

Williams, Charles. He Came Down from Heaven. 160p. 1984. pap. 3.95 (ISBN 0-8028-0033-5). Eerdmans.

Williams, Daniel D. The Spirit & the Forms of Love. LC 81-40368. 316p. 1981. lib. bdg. 27.75 (ISBN 0-8191-1691-2); pap. text ed. 12.25 (ISBN 0-8191-1692-0). U Pr of Amer.

Wilson, Earl D. Does God Really Love Me? LC 86-10616. 96p. (Orig.). 1986. pap. 2.95 (ISBN 0-87784-514-X). Inter-Varsity.

Wynanda, C. What Is Love. LC 83-12729. 96p. 1984. 7.95 (ISBN 0-310-37571-1). Zondervan.

Wynkoop, Mildred B. The Theology of Love. 327p. 1972. 8.95 (ISBN 0-8341-0102-5). Beacon Hill.

LOVE (THEOLOGY)–MEDITATIONS

Craig, Sidney D. Raising Your Child, Not by Force But by Love. LC 72-10436. 192p. 1982. pap. 6.95 (ISBN 0-664-24413-0). Westminster.

Finney, Charles G. Principles of Love. Parkhurst, Louis G., ed. 200p. 1986. pap. 5.95 (ISBN 0-87123-866-7, 210866). Bethany Hse.

Hobe, Phyllis, ed. The Wonder of Love. LC 82-8376. (Small Wonders Ser.). (Illus.). 112p. 1982. pap. 4.95 (ISBN 0-664-26001-2, A Bridgebooks Publication). Westminster.

McCausland, Clare. An Element of Love. Mobium Corporation & Ineman, K., eds. (Illus.). 140p. (Orig.). 1981. pap. 10.00 (ISBN 0-9607400-0-7). Children's Memorial.

Van Kaam, Adrian. Mystery of Transforming Love. 6.95 (ISBN 0-87193-182-6). Dimension Bks.

Welch, Reuben. We Really Do Need Each Other. 112p. 1982. pap. 4.95 (ISBN 0-310-70221-6, 14012P). Zondervan.

Wrightman, Paul. Paul's Early Letters: From Hope, Through Faith, to Love. LC 83-7126. 148p. (Orig.). 1983. pap. 6.95 (ISBN 0-8189-0440-2). Alba.

Zodhiates, Spiros. The Labor of Love. (Trilogy Ser.: Vol. 3). (Illus.). pap. 8.95 (ISBN 0-89957-541-2). AMG Pubs.

LOVE (THEOLOGY)–SERMONS

Finney, Charles G. Principles of Love. Parkhurst, Louis G., ed. 200p. 1986. pap. 5.95 (ISBN 0-87123-866-7, 210866). Bethany Hse.

LOVE OF SELF (THEOLOGY)

see Self-Love (Theology)

LOVEJOY, ELIJAH PARISH, 1802-1837

Lovejoy, Joseph C. & Lovejoy, Owen. Memoir of the Rev. Elijah P. Lovejoy. facsimile ed. LC 72-117882. (Select Bibliographies Reprint Ser). Repr. of 1838 ed. 21.00 (ISBN 0-8369-5335-5). Ayer Co Pubs.

Tanner, Henry. Martyrdom of Lovejoy: An Account of the Life, Trials, & Perils of Rev. Elijah P. Lovejoy. LC 68-18603. (Illus.). 1971. Repr. of 1881 ed. lib. bdg. 25.00x (ISBN 0-678-00744-6). Kelley.

LOYOLA, IGNACIO DE, SAINT, 1491-1556

Amey, Peter, et al. Luther, Erasmus & Loyola. Yapp, Malcolm, et al, eds. (World History Ser.). (Illus.). 1980. lib. bdg. 6.95 (ISBN 0-89908-043-X); pap. text ed. 2.45 (ISBN 0-89908-018-9). Greenhaven.

Brodrick, James. Origin of the Jesuits. LC 70-138604. 1971. Repr. of 1940 ed. lib. bdg. 22.50x (ISBN 0-8371-5523-1, BROJ). Greenwood.

Clancy, Thomas H. The Conversational Word of God: A Commentary on the Doctrine of St. Ignatius of Loyola Concerning Spiritual Conversation, with Four Early Jesuit Texts. Ganss, George E., frwd. by. LC 78-51343. (Study Aids on Jesuit Topics: No. 8 in Ser. IV). 83p. 1978. 5.00 (ISBN 0-912422-33-5); pap. 2.50 smyth sewn (ISBN 0-912422-34-3). Inst Jesuit.

Dalmases, Candido de. Ignatius of Loyola, Founder of the Jesuits: His Life & Work. Ganss, George E., frwd. by. Aixala, Jerome, tr. from Span. Index. LC 83-80349. (Series II-Scholarly Studies about the Jesuits in English Translations: No. 6). xxii, 362p. 1985. 16.00 (ISBN 0-912422-59-9); pap. 14.00 smyth sewn (ISBN 0-912422-58-0). Inst Jesuit.

De Nicolas, Antonio. Powers of Imagining: Ignatius de Loyola: A Philosophical Hermeneutic of Imagining through the Collected Works of Ignatius de Loyola with a Translation of These Works. 416p. 1986. 44.50x (ISBN 0-88706-109-5); pap. 19.95x (ISBN 0-88706-110-9). State U NY Pr.

Dudon, Paul. St. Ignatius of Loyola. Young, William J., tr. LC 83-45591. Date not set. Repr. of 1949 ed. 49.50 (ISBN 0-404-19884-8). AMS Pr.

Fleming, David L. A Contemporary Reading of the Spiritual Exercises: A Companion to St. Ignatius' Text. 2nd ed. Ganss, George E., ed. LC 80-81812. (Study Aids on Jesuit Topics Ser.:. No.2). 112p. 1980. pap. 3.00 (ISBN 0-912422-47-5); smyth sewn 4.00 (ISBN 0-912422-48-3). Inst Jesuit.

--The Spiritual Exercises of St. Ignatius: A Literal Translation & a Contemporary Reading. Ganss, George E., ed. LC 77-93429. (Study Aids on Jesuit Topics Ser.: No. 7). 290p. 1978. smyth sewn 9.00 (ISBN 0-912422-31-9). Inst Jesuit.

Ganss, George E. Saint Ignatius' Idea of a Jesuit University. 2nd ed. (Illus.). 1956. pap. 16.95 (ISBN 0-87462-437-1). Marquette.

Hughes, Thomas A. Loyola & the Educational System of the Jesuits. 34.95 (ISBN 0-8490-0565-5). Gordon Pr.

--Loyola & the Educational System of the Jesuits. LC 83-45594. Date not set. Repr. of 1892 ed. 35.00 (ISBN 0-404-19887-2). AMS Pr.

Ignatius, Saint Spiritual Exercises of St. Ignatius of Loyola. Delmage, Lewis, tr. 1978. 4.00 (ISBN 0-8198-0557-2); pap. 2.25 (ISBN 0-8198-0558-0). Dghtrs St Paul.

Ignatius of Loyola, Saint Letters of Saint Ignatius of Loyola. Young, William J., ed. LC 59-13459. 1959. 8.95 (ISBN 0-8294-0085-0). Loyola.

Joly, Henri. Saint Ignatius of Loyola. LC 70-170821. Repr. of 1899 ed. 21.00 (ISBN 0-404-03597-3). AMS Pr.

Marcuse, Ludwig. Soldier of the Church: The Life of Ignatius Loyola. LC 70-172842. Repr. of 1939 ed. 23.00 (ISBN 0-404-04187-6). AMS Pr.

Olin, John C., ed. Autobiography of St. Ignatius Loyola. 1974. pap. 6.95x (ISBN 0-06-131783-7, TB1783, Torch). Har-Row.

Pousset, Edouard. Life in Faith & Freedom: An Essay Presenting Gaston Fessard's Analysis of the Dialectic of the Spiritual Exercises of St. Ignatius. Ganss, G. E., frwd. by. LC 79-84200. (Modern Scholarly Studies About Jesuits, in English Translation Ser.: No. 4). 286p. 1980. 9.00 (ISBN 0-912422-41-6); pap. 8.00 smythsewn (ISBN 0-912422-40-8); pap. 7.00 (ISBN 0-912422-39-4). Inst Jesuit.

Proterra, Michael. Homo Spiritualis Nititur Fide: Martin Luther & Ignatius of Loyola, an Analytical & Comparative Study of a Hermeneutic Based on the Heuristic Structure of Discretio. LC 82-21837. 92p. (Orig.). 1983. lib. bdg. 22.00 (ISBN 0-8191-2938-0); pap. text ed. 8.50 (ISBN 0-8191-2939-9). U Pr of Amer.

Purcell, Mary. The First Jesuit. rev. ed. 225p. 1981. 10.00 (ISBN 0-8294-0371-X). Loyola.

Rahner, Hugo. The Spirituality of St. Ignatius Loyola: An Account of Its Historical Development. Smith, Francis J., tr. LC 53-5586. (Request Reprint). 1968. 3.50 (ISBN 0-8294-0066-4). Loyola.

Ravier, Andre. Ignatius of Loyola & the Founding of Society of Jesus. Daly, Maura, et al, trs. from Fr. Tr. of Ignace de Loyola Fonde la Compagnie de Jesus. 498p. (Orig.). 1987. 29.95 (ISBN 0-89870-036-1). Ignatius Pr.

Rose, Stewart. Ignatius Loyola & the Early Jesuits. LC 83-45596. Date not set. Repr. of 1870 ed. 52.00 (ISBN 0-404-19889-9). AMS Pr.

St. Ignatius Loyola. The Autobiography of St. Ignatius Loyola, with Related Documents. O'Callaghan, Joseph F., tr. 16.00 (ISBN 0-8446-5240-7). Peter Smith.

Sedgwick, Henry D. Ignatius Loyola. LC 83-45597. Date not set. Repr. of 1923 ed. 42.50 (ISBN 0-404-19890-2). AMS Pr.

Toner, Jules J. A Commentary on Saint Ignatius' Rules for the Discernment of Spirits: A Guide to the Principles & Practice. Ganss, George E., ed. LC 79-89606. (Original Studies Composed in English Ser.: No. 5). 352p. 1982. 14.00 (ISBN 0-912422-43-2); smyth sewn paper 11.00 (ISBN 0-912422-42-4). Inst Jesuit.

Wulf, F., et al. Ignatius of Loyola: His Personality & Spiritual Heritage, 1556-1956, Studies on the 400th Anniversary of His Death. LC 77-16677. (Modern Scholarly Studies About the Jesuits,in English Translations Ser.: No. 2). 318p. 1977. pap. 7.00 (ISBN 0-912422-22-X). Inst Jesuit.

LUIS DE GRANADA, 1504-1588

Brentano, Sr. Mary B. Nature in the Works of Fray Luis De Granada. LC 75-94164. (Catholic University. Studies in Romance Languages & Literatures: No. 15). Repr. of 1936 ed. 21.00 (ISBN 0-404-50315-2). AMS Pr.

Hagedorn, Maria. Reformation und Spanische Andachtsliteratur. 1934. 12.00 (ISBN 0-384-20770-7). Johnson Repr.

LUKE, SAINT

Bovon, Francois. Luke the Theologian: Thirty-Five Years of Research (1950-1985) McKinney, Ken, tr. from Fr. (Princeton Theological Monograph Ser.: No. 12). Tr. of Luc la theologien: Vingt-cinq ans de recherches (1950-1975) (Orig.). 1987. pap. price not set (ISBN 0-915138-93-X). Pickwick.

Brown, Robert. Luke: Doctor-Writer. (BibLearn Ser.). (Illus.). 1977. bds. 5.95 (ISBN 0-8054-4233-2, 4242-33). Broadman.

Hendriksen, William. Luke. (New Testament Commentary Ser.). 1978. 24.95 (ISBN 0-8010-4191-0). Baker Bk.

Jervell, Jacob. Luke & the People of God: A New Look at Luke-Acts. LC 72-78565. 208p. 1979. pap. 10.95 (ISBN 0-8066-1730-6, 10-4136). Augsburg.

Karris, Robert J. Luke, Artist & Theologian. LC 84-61030. 144p. (Orig.). 1985. pap. 7.95 (ISBN 0-8091-2651-6). Paulist Pr.

Keyes, Sharrel. Luke: Following Jesus. (Fisherman Bible Studyguide Ser.). 96p. 1983. pap. 2.95 saddlestitched (ISBN 0-87788-511-7). Shaw Pubs.

Marshall, I. Howard. Luke: Historian & Theologian. (Contemporary Evangelical Perspective Ser). 1971. kivar 7.95 (ISBN 0-310-28761-8, 10105P). Zondervan.

Thomas, W. Griffith. Outline Studies in Luke. LC 84-784. 408p. 1984. pap. text ed. 11.95 (ISBN 0-8254-3821-7). Kregel.

LUTHER, MARTIN, 1483-1546

Althaus, Paul. The Ethics of Martin Luther. Schultz, Robert C., tr. from Ger. LC 72-164552. 192p. 1972. pap. 8.95 (ISBN 0-8006-1709-6, 1-1709). Fortress.

--Theology of Martin Luther. Schultz, Robert C., tr. from Ger. LC 66-17345. 480p. 1966. pap. 12.95 (ISBN 0-8006-1855-6, 1-855). Fortress.

Amey, Peter, et al. Luther, Erasmus & Loyola. Yapp, Malcolm, et al, eds. (World History Ser.). (Illus.). 1980. lib. bdg. 6.95 (ISBN 0-89908-043-X); pap. text ed. 2.45 (ISBN 0-89908-018-9). Greenhaven.

Atkinson, James. Martin Luther & the Birth of Protestantism. LC 81-82356. 348p. 1981. pap. 5.25 (ISBN 0-8042-0941-3). John Knox.

--Martin Luther: Prophet to the Church Catholic. LC 83-16462. Repr. of 1983 ed. 58.00 (2027535). Bks Demand UMI.

Bainton, Roland H. Here I Stand: A Life of Martin Luther. pap. 3.95 (ISBN 0-451-62404-1, ME2103, Ment). NAL.

--Here I Stand: A Life of Martin Luther. 13.25 (ISBN 0-8446-6225-9). Peter Smith.

Barlow, William. A Dyaloge Descrybyng the Orygynall Ground of These Lutheran Saccyons, That Is, Faccyons. LC 74-80161. (English Experience Ser.: No. 641). 200p. 1974. Repr. of 1531 ed. 13.00 (ISBN 90-221-0641-1). Walter J Johnson.

Beard, Charles. Martin Luther & the Reformation in Germany until the Close of the Diet of Worms. LC 83-45638. Date not set. Repr. of 1889 ed. 49.50 (ISBN 0-404-19822-8). AMS Pr.

Benson, Kathleen. A Man Called Martin Luther. 1980. 7.50 (ISBN 0-570-03625-9, 39-1067). Concordia.

Boehmer, Heinrich. Luther & the Reformation in the Light of Modern Research. LC 83-45639. Date not set. Repr. of 1930 ed. 44.50 (ISBN 0-404-19823-6). AMS Pr.

--Luther in the Light of Recent Research. 1977. lib. bdg. 59.95 (ISBN 0-8490-2189-8). Gordon Pr.

Bornkamm, Heinrich. Luther in Mid-Career, 1521-1530. Bachmann, E. Theodore, tr. from German. LC 82-48591. 736p. 1983. 36.95 (ISBN 0-8006-0692-2, 1-692). Fortress.

Brecht, Martin. Martin Luther: His Road to Reformation, 1483-1521. Schaaf, James L., tr. LC 84-47911. 592p. 1985. 36.95 (ISBN 0-8006-0738-4, 1-738). Fortress.

Brokering, Herb. The Luther Journey. (Illus.). 96p. (Orig.). 1983. pap. 6.95 (ISBN 0-942562-02-X). Brokering Pr.

Brokering, Herb & Bainton, Roland. A Pilgrimage to Luther's Germany. 80p. 1983. 14.95 (ISBN 0-86683-629-2, HarpR). Har-Row.

Bruce, Gustav M. Luther As an Educator. LC 77-114482. (Illus.). 318p. Repr. of 1928 ed. lib. bdg. 35.00x (ISBN 0-8371-4771-9, BRLD). Greenwood.

Cargill-Thompson, W. D. The Political Thought of Martin Luther. Broadhead, Philip, ed. LC 83-27521. 204p. 1984. 27.50x (ISBN 0-389-20468-4, 08029). B&N Imports.

Charles, Elizabeth R. Luther: By Those Who Knew Him. 1983. pap. 5.95 (ISBN 0-8024-0314-X). Moody.

Crawford, James L. Catalogue of a Collection of 1500 Tracts by Martin Luther & His Contemporaries, 1511-1598. 1965. Repr. of 1903 ed. 32.00 (ISBN 0-8337-1001-X). B Franklin.

Cubitt, Heather. Luther & the Reformation. Reeves, Marjorie, ed. (Then & There Ser.). (Illus.). 96p. 1976. pap. text ed. 4.75 (ISBN 0-582-20542-5). Longman.

Curts, Paul. Luther's Variations in Sentence Arrangement From the Modern Literary Usage With Primary Reference to the Position of the Verb. 1910. 39.50x (ISBN 0-686-83611-1). Elliots Bks.

Davey, Cyril. Monk Who Shook the World (Martin Luther) 1960. pap. 2.95 (ISBN 0-87508-614-4). Chr Lit.

Davies, Rupert E. The Problems of Authority in the Continental Reformers: A Study of Luther, Zwingli, & Calvin. LC 78-5871. 1978. Repr. of 1946 ed. lib. bdg. cancelled (ISBN 0-313-20487-X, DAPA). Greenwood.

Dobneck, Johann. Commentaria. 372p. 1549. text ed. 124.40x (ISBN 0-576-72201-4, Pub. by Gregg Intl Pubs England). Gregg Intl.

Dunnhaupt, Gerhard, ed. The Martin Luther Quincentennial. LC 84-15239. 329p. 1984. 29.95x (ISBN 0-8143-1774-X). Wayne St U Pr.

Ebeling, Gerhard. Luther: An Introduction to His Thought. Wilson, R. A., tr. from Ger. LC 77-99612. 288p. 1970. pap. 6.95 (ISBN 0-8006-1162-4, 1-1162). Fortress.

Edwards, Mark & Tavard, George. Luther: A Reformer for the Churches. 1983. pap. 4.95 (ISBN 0-8091-2575-7). Paulist Pr.

Edwards, Mark & Tavard, George H. Luther: A Reformer for the Churches; An Ecumenical Study Guide. LC 83-48005. 96p. 1983. pap. 5.50 (ISBN 0-8006-1718-5, 1-1718). Fortress.

Edwards, Mark U., Jr. Luther & the False Brethren. LC 75-181. 1975. 20.00x (ISBN 0-8047-0883-5). Stanford U Pr.

--Luther's Last Battles: Politics & Polemics, 1531-1546. LC 82-72363. (Illus.). 272p. 1986. pap. text ed. 9.95x (ISBN 0-8014-9393-5). Cornell U Pr.

--Luther's Last Battles: Politics & Polemics, 1531-46. 272p. 1983. 24.95x (ISBN 0-8014-1564-0). Cornell U Pr.

Erikson, Erik H. Young Man Luther. 1962. pap. 5.95 (ISBN 0-393-00170-9). Norton.

Fabiny, T. Martin Luther's Last Will & Testament: A Facsimile of the Original Document, with an Account of Its Origins, Composition & Subsequent History. 51p. 1984. text ed. 25.00x (ISBN 0-904720-15-2, Pub. by Ussher Pr Ireland). Humanities.

Fagerberg, Holsten. A New Look at the Lutheran Confession. Lund, Gene J., tr. 336p. 1981. 15.50 (ISBN 0-570-03223-7, 15-2121). Concordia.

Febvre, Lucien P. Martin Luther: A Destiny. Tapley, Roberts, tr. LC 83-45640. Date not set. Repr. of 1929 ed. 37.50 (ISBN 0-404-19850-3). AMS Pr.

Fife, Robert H. Young Luther. LC 79-131040. 1970. Repr. of 1928 ed. 19.50 (ISBN 0-404-02385-1). AMS Pr.

Forell, George W. Faith Active in Love. LC 15-5702. 1954. kivar 7.95 (ISBN 0-8066-0186-8, 10-2165). Augsburg.

Freytag, Gustav. Doctor Luther. Reimer, G. C., tr. LC 83-45642. Date not set. Repr. of 1916 ed. 27.50 (ISBN 0-404-19851-1). AMS Pr.

--Martin Luther. LC 78-144612. Repr. of 1897 ed. 27.50 (ISBN 0-404-02577-3). AMS Pr.

Froude, James A. A Comparative Analysis of the Philosophies of Erasmus & Luther. (Illus.). 133p. 1981. Repr. of 1868 ed. 69.85 (ISBN 0-89901-038-5). Found Class Reprints.

Gerberich, Albert H. Luther & the English Bible. LC 83-45643. Date not set. Repr. of 1933 ed. 17.50 (ISBN 0-404-19852-X). AMS Pr.

Green, Lowell C. How Melanchthon Helped Luther Discover the Gospel: The Doctrine of Justification in the Reformation. 274p. 1980. 7.95 (ISBN 0-89890-010-7). Attic Pr.

Grisar, Hartmann. Martin Luther: His Life & Work. Preuss, Arthur, ed. LC 71-137235. Repr. of 1930 ed. 29.50 (ISBN 0-404-02935-3). AMS Pr.

Gritsch, Eric W. Martin - God's Court Jester: Luther in Retrospect. LC 83-48004. 304p. 1983. pap. 15.95 (ISBN 0-8006-1753-3, 1-1753). Fortress.

Hacker, Paul. Ego in Faith: Martin Luther & the Origins of Anthropocentric Religion. Wicks, Jared, ed. LC 70-85506. (Das Ich Im Glauben Bei Martin Luther). 1971. 6.50 (ISBN 0-8199-0406-6). Franciscan Herald.

Haendler, Gert. Luther on Ministerial Office & Congregational Function. Gritsch, Eric W., ed. Gritsch, Ruth C., tr. from Ger. LC 81-43075. Tr. of Amt und Gemeinde bei Luther im Kontext der Kirchengeschichte. 112p. 1981. 9.95 (ISBN 0-8006-0665-5, 1-665). Fortress.

Haile, H. G. Luther: An Experiment in Biography. LC 82-48569. 460p. 1983. 31.50x (ISBN 0-691-05374-X); pap. 10.50x (ISBN 0-691-00798-5). Princeton U Pr.

Hansen, William P. & Haney, John, eds. Luther. (World Leaders--Past & Present Ser.). (Illus.). 112p. 1986. lib. bdg. 16.95 (ISBN 0-87754-538-3). Chelsea Hse.

Harran, Marilyn J. Luther & Learning: The Wittenberg University Luther Symposium. LC 84-40810. (Illus.). 144p. 1985. 19.50 (ISBN 0-941664-13-9, Pub. by Susquehanna U Pr). Assoc Univ Prs.

--Luther on Conversion: The Early Years. LC 83-7194. 224p. 1983. 29.95x (ISBN 0-8014-1566-7). Cornell U Pr.

Hatznung, Ruth. Martin Luther: Man for Whom God Had Great Plans. 1974. pap. 1.95 (ISBN 0-8100-0060-1, 16-0757). Northwest Pub.

Headley, John M. Luther's View of Church History. 1963. 49.50x (ISBN 0-686-51413-0). Elliots Bks.

Hendrix, Scott H. Luther & the Papacy: Stages in a Reformation Conflict. LC 80-2393. pap. 56.30 (2027874). Bks Demand UMI.

Henry VIII. A Copy of the Letters Wherein Kyng Henry the Eyght Made Answere into a Certayn Letter of Martyn Luther. LC 72-204. (English Experience Ser.: No. 322). 100p. 1971. Repr. of 1528 ed. 14.00 (ISBN 90-221-0322-6). Walter J Johnson.

Hoffman, Bengt, ed. The Theologia Germanica of Martin Luther. LC 80-50155. (Classics of Western Spirituality). 224p. 1980. 12.95 (ISBN 0-8091-0308-7); pap. 8.95 (ISBN 0-8091-2291-X). Paulist Pr.

Hoffman, Manfred. Martin Luther & the Modern Mind: Freedom, Conscience, Toleration, Rights. LC 85-3054. (Toronto Studies in Theology: Vol. 22). 281p. 1985. 49.95x (ISBN 0-88946-766-8). E Mellen.

Hyma, Albert. Luther's Theological Development from Erfurt to Augsburg. LC 76-137247. Repr. of 1928 ed. 12.50 (ISBN 0-404-03479-9). AMS Pr.

Jacobs, Henry E. Martin Luther, the Hero of the Reformation. LC 72-170838. Repr. of 1898 ed. 27.50 (ISBN 0-404-03544-2). AMS Pr.

Janz, Denis. Luther & Late Medieval Thomism: A Study in Theological Anthropology. 191p. 1984. text ed. 25.00x (ISBN 0-88920-132-3). Humanities.

Johnson, Roger A., et al. Psychohistory & Religion: The Case of Young Man Luther. LC 76-7870. pap. 51.50 (2026895). Bks Demand UMI.

Johnson, Wayne G. Theological Method in Luther & Tillich: Law-Gospel & Correlation. LC 80-5691. 204p. 1982. lib. bdg. 27.50 (ISBN 0-8191-1895-8); pap. text ed. 12.50 (ISBN 0-8191-1896-6). U Pr of Amer.

Joyce, Jon L. Luther Had a Wife. (Orig.). 1985. pap. 2.95 (ISBN 0-937172-60-X). JLJ Pubs.

Kainz, Howard P. Wittenberg, Revisited: A Polymorphous Critique of Religion & Theology. LC 81-40729. 236p. (Orig.). 1982. lib. bdg. 27.50 (ISBN 0-8191-1949-0); pap. text ed. 12.50 (ISBN 0-8191-1950-4). U Pr of Amer.

Karant-Nunn, Susan C. Luther's Pastors: The Reformation in the Ernestine Countryside. LC 79-51539. (Transactions Ser.: Vol. 69, Pt. 8). 1979. 8.00 (ISBN 0-87169-698-3). Am Philos.

Kerr, Hugh T., Jr., ed. Compend of Luther's Theology. LC 43-16154. 276p. 1966. Westminster.

Kiessling, Elmer C. Early Sermons of Luther & Their Relation to the Pre-Reformation Sermon. LC 75-171064. Repr. of 1935 ed. 21.50 (ISBN 0-404-03669-4). AMS Pr.

Kirchner, Hubert. Luther & the Peasants' War. LC 73-171507. (Facet Books-Historical Ser.: No. 22). pap. 20.00 (2027181). Bks Demand UMI.

Kittelson, James M. Luther the Reformer: The Story of the Man & His Career. LC 86-17266. (Illus.). 320p. 1986. text ed. 24.95 (ISBN 0-8066-2240-7, 10-4148). Augsburg.

Klingner, Erich. Luther und der Deutsche Volksaberglaube. 18.00 (ISBN 0-384-29830-3); pap. 13.00 (ISBN 0-685-02277-3). Johnson Repr.

Kohler, Walther. Zwingli und Luther, Ihr Streit uber das Abendmahl nach Seinen Politischen und Religiosen Beziehung En. (Ger). 61.00 (ISBN 0-384-30019-7); pap. 55.00 (ISBN 0-384-30018-9). Johnson Repr.

Kolb, R. & Lumpp, D. Martin Luther: Companion of the Contemporary Christian. LC 12-2959. 1982. pap. 9.95 (ISBN 0-570-03866-9). Concordia.

Kostlin, Julius. Life of Luther. 1883. Repr. 50.00 (ISBN 0-8274-2894-4). R West.

Kraus, George. A Guide to a Year's Reading in Luther's Works. (Continued Applied Christianity Ser.). 1983. pap. 2.50 (ISBN 0-570-03902-9, 12-2984). Concordia.

Lambert, James F. Luther's Hymns. LC 83-45646. Date not set. Repr. of 1917 ed. 34.50 (ISBN 0-404-19855-4). AMS Pr.

Leaver, Robin A. Luther on Justification. LC 74-11781. 1975. pap. 4.75 (ISBN 0-570-03188-5, 12-2590). Concordia.

Letis, Theodore P. Martin Luther & Charismatic Ecumenism. (Orig.). 1979. pap. 1.95 (ISBN 0-936592-00-1). Reformation Res.

Lienhard, Marc. Luther: Witness to Jesus Christ: Stages & Themes of the Reformer's Christology. Robertson, Edwin H., tr. LC 81-52285. 432p. 1982. text ed. 24.95 (ISBN 0-8066-1917-1, 10-4149). Augsburg.

Lindhardt, Jan. Martin Luther: Knowledge and Mediation in the Renaissance. (Texts and Studies in Religion: Vol. 29). 270p. lib. bdg. 49.95 (ISBN 0-88946-817-6). E Mellen.

Lindsay, Thomas M. Luther & the Germany Reformation. facsimile ed. LC 71-133524. (Select Bibliographies Reprint Ser.). Repr. of 1900 ed. 18.00 (ISBN 0-8369-5556-0). Ayer Co Pubs.

Loewenich, Walther von. Martin Luther: The Man & His Work. Denef, Lawrence W., tr. from Ger. LC 83-70513. Tr. of Martin Luther: Der Mann und das Werk. 448p. 1986. text ed. 19.95 (ISBN 0-8066-2019-6, 10-4296). Augsburg.

Lohse, Bernhard. Martin Luther: An Introduction to His Life & Work. Schultz, Robert C., tr. from Ger. LC 85-45496. 304p. 1986. 26.95 (ISBN 0-8006-0764-3, 1-764); pap. 16.95 (ISBN 0-8006-1964-1, 1-1964). Fortress.

Ludwig, Martin. Religion und Sittlichkeit Bei Luther Bis Zum Sermon Von Den Guten Werken 1520. (Ger). 34.00 (ISBN 0-384-34151-9); pap. 28.00 (ISBN 0-384-34150-0). Johnson Repr.

Lundeen, Joel W., ed. Luther's Works-Index. LC 86-45197. 512p. 1986. 24.95 (ISBN 0-8006-0355-9). Fortress.

Luther, Martin. Basic Luther. 1984. pap. 14.95 (ISBN 0-87243-131-2). Templegate.

--Luther's Ninety-Five Theses. Jacobs, C. M., tr. 1957. pap. 0.95 (ISBN 0-8006-1265-5, 1-1265). Fortress.

--Luthers Werke in Auswahl, 8 vols. Clemen, Otto, ed. Incl. Vol. 1. Schriften von 1517 bis 1520. 6th rev. ed. (Illus.). xxxii, 512p. 1966. 20.00x (ISBN 3-11-003152-3); Vol. 2. Schriften von 1520 bis 1524. 6th rev. ed. vi, 464p. 1967. 20.00x (ISBN 3-11-003153-1); Vol. 3. Schriften von 1524 bis 1528. 6th rev. ed. vi, 516p. 1966. 20.00x (ISBN 3-11-003154-X); Vol. 4. Schriften von 1529 bis 1545. 6th rev. ed. vi, 428p. 1967. 20.00x (ISBN 3-11-003151-5); Vol. 5. Der Junge Luther. 3rd rev. ed. Vogelsang, Erich, ed. xi, 434p. 1963. 22.10 (ISBN 3-11-005609-7); Vol. 6. Luthers Briefe. 3rd rev. ed. Rueckert, Hanns, ed. xv, 451p. 1966. 22.10x (ISBN 3-11-005610-0); Vol. 7. Predigten. 3rd ed. Hirsch, Emanuel, ed. xii, 420p. 1962. 22.10x (ISBN 3-11-005611-9); Vol. 8. Tischreden. 3rd ed. Clemen, Otto, ed. x, 387p. 1962. 22.10 (ISBN 3-11-005612-7). De Gruyter.

McGiffert, Arthur C. Martin Luther, the Man & His Work. LC 83-45647. Date not set. Repr. of 1911 ed. 42.50 (ISBN 0-404-19856-2). AMS Pr.

McGoldrick, J. E. Luther's English Connection. 1979. pap. 7.50 (ISBN 0-8100-0070-9, 15-0368). Northwest Pub.

McGrath, Alister E. Luther's Theology of the Cross: Martin Luther on Justification 1509-1519. 224p. 1985. 34.95x (ISBN 0-631-13855-2). Basil Blackwell.

Mackinnon, James. Luther & the Reformation, 4 vols. LC 83-45648. Date not set. Repr. of 1925 ed. Set. 157.50 (ISBN 0-404-19857-0). AMS Pr.

Makolin, Jewell. Katie & Luther Speak. 1985. 4.95 (ISBN 0-89536-943-5, 7558). CSS of Ohio.

Malsch, Sara A. The Image of Martin Luther in the Writings of Novalis & Friedrich Schlegel: The Speculative Vision of History & Religion. (European University Studies: Series 1, German Language & Literature: Vol. 103). 165p. 1974. pap. 18.25 (ISBN 3-261-01453-9). P Lang Pubs.

Manns, Peter. Martin Luther: An Illustrated Biography. LC 83-1083. (Illus.). 128p. 1983. 14.95 (ISBN 0-8245-0563-8). Crossroad NY.

Manns, Peter & Meyer, Harding, eds. Luther's Ecumenical Significance: An Interconfessional Consultation. LC 83-48001. 336p. 1983. pap. 24.95 (ISBN 0-8006-1747-9, 1-1747). Fortress.

Marcello, Cristoforo. De Authoritate Summi Pontificis. 304p. Repr. of 1521 ed. text ed. 66.24x (ISBN 0-576-99483-9, Pub. by Gregg Intl Pubs England). Gregg Intl.

Maritain, Jacques. Three Reformers: Luther-Descartes-Rousseau. Repr. of 1950 ed. lib. bdg. 22.50x (ISBN 0-8371-2825-0, MATR). Greenwood.

Martin Luther: Portfolio Of Letters & Translations from Aesop. 126p. 150.00 (ISBN 0-8115-0906-0). Kraus Repr.

Masson, David. Three Devils: Luther's, Milton's & Goethe's. LC 72-193946. 1874. lib. bdg. 20.00 (ISBN 0-8414-6495-2). Folcroft.

Montgomery, John W. In Defense of Martin Luther. (Illus.). 1970. 2.50 (ISBN 0-8100-0026-1, 12N0339). Northwest Pub.

More, St. Thomas. Responsio Ad Lutherum, 2 Vols. Headley, John M., ed. LC 63-7949. (Complete Works of St. Thomas More Ser.: No. 5). 1969. Set. 85.00x (ISBN 0-300-01123-7). Yale U Pr.

Murray, Robert H. Erasmus & Luther: Their Attitude to Toleration. LC 83-45659. (The Zodiac Club Ser.). Date not set. Repr. of 1920 ed. 57.50 (ISBN 0-404-19809-0). AMS Pr.

Nestingen, James A. Martin Luther: His Life & Teachings. LC 82-71829. 80p. 1982. pap. 4.50 (ISBN 0-8006-1642-1, 1-1642). Fortress.

Olin, John C. & Smart, James D., eds. Luther, Erasmus & the Reformation: A Catholic-Protestant Reappraisal. LC 82-15500. x, 150p. 1982. Repr. of 1969 ed. lib. bdg. 22.50x (ISBN 0-313-23652-6, OLLE). Greenwood.

Olivier, D. Luther's Faith: The Cause of the Gospel in the Church. LC 12-2961. 1982. pap. 13.95 (ISBN 0-570-03868-5). Concordia.

Olivier, Daniel. The Trial of Luther. 1979. pap. 8.95 (ISBN 0-570-03785-9, 12-2743). Concordia.

O'Neill, Judith. Martin Luther. LC 74-12959. (Cambridge Introduction to the History of Mankind). (Illus.). 48p. 1975. pap. text ed. 4.95 (ISBN 0-521-20403-8). Cambridge U Pr.

Oswald, Hilton, ed. Luther's Works, Vol. 11. Bowman, Herbert J., tr. from Lat. LC 55-9893. 560p. 1976. 17.95 (ISBN 0-570-06411-2, 15-1753). Concordia.

Pascal, Roy. Social Basis of the German Reformation: Martin Luther & His Times. LC 68-30539. 1971. Repr. of 1933 ed. 25.00x (ISBN 0-678-00549-4). Kelley.

Pelikan, Jaroslav, ed. Luther the Expositor. 1959. 13.95 (ISBN 0-570-06431-7, 15-1741). Concordia.

Pelikan, Jaroslav, et al, trs. from Lat. Luther's Works, Vol. 15, Letters On Ecclesiastes, Song Of Solomon, & The Last Words Of David. LC 55-9893. 1971. 15.95 (ISBN 0-570-06415-5, 15-1757). Concordia.

Phillips, Leona R. Martin Luther & the Reformation: An Annotated Bibliography. 1985. lib. bdg. 79.95 (ISBN 0-8490-3242-3). Gordon Pr.

Plass, Ewald. This Is Luther. 1984. pap. 8.95 (ISBN 0-570-03942-8, 12-2875). Concordia.

Preus, Herman A. A Theology to Live By. 1977. pap. 7.95 (ISBN 0-570-03739-5, 12-2643). Concordia.

Preus, James S. From Shadow to Promise: Old Testament Interpretation from Augustine to the Young Luther. LC 69-12732. (Illus.). xii, 301p. 1969. 20.00x (ISBN 0-674-32610-5, Belkap Pr). Harvard U Pr.

Proterra, Michael. Homo Spiritualis Nititur Fide: Martin Luther & Ignatius of Loyola, an Analytical & Comparative Study of a Hermeneutic Based on the Heuristic Structure of Discretio. LC 82-21837. 92p. (Orig.). 1983. lib. bdg. 22.00 (ISBN 0-8191-2938-0); pap. text ed. 8.50 (ISBN 0-8191-2939-9). U Pr of Amer.

Reu, Johann M. Luther's German Bible. LC 83-45651. Date not set. Repr. of 1934 ed. 75.00 (ISBN 0-404-19860-0). AMS Pr.

--Thirty-Five Years of Luther Research. LC 79-13505. (Illus.). Repr. of 1917 ed. 16.50 (ISBN 0-404-05284-3). AMS Pr.

Ritter, Gerhard. Luther: His Life & Work. Riches, John, tr. from Ger. LC 78-2717. 1978. Repr. of 1963 ed. lib. bdg. 24.25x (ISBN 0-313-20347-4, RILU). Greenwood.

Rix, Herbert D. Martin Luther: The Man & the Image. 335p. 1983. text ed. 37.50x (ISBN 0-8290-0554-4). Irvington.

Robbert, G. S. Luther As Interpreter of Scripture. LC 12-2960. 1982. pap. 9.95 (ISBN 0-570-03867-7). Concordia.

Ross, Estelle. Martin Luther. LC 83-45673. (Illus.). Date not set. Repr. of 1927 ed. 28.00 (ISBN 0-404-19862-7). AMS Pr.

Rupp, E. G. & Drewery, Benjamin, eds. Martin Luther. (Documents of Modern History Ser.). 1970. pap. text ed. 11.95 (ISBN 0-312-51660-6). St Martin.

Schenker, Walter. Die Sprache Huldrych Zwinglis im Kontrast zur Sprache Luthers. (Studia Linguistica Germanica: Vol. 14). (Illus.). 1977. 66.00x (ISBN 3-11-006605-X). De Gruyter.

Schreiber, Clara S. Katherine: Life of Luther. 1981. 6.95 (ISBN 0-8100-0144-6, 15N0385). Northwest Pub.

Schwiebert, E. G. Luther's Ninety-Five Theses. pap. 0.75 (ISBN 0-570-03519-8, 14-1253). Concordia.

Schwiebert, Ernest G. Luther & His Times: The Reformation from a New Perspective. (Illus.). 1950. 24.95 (ISBN 0-570-03246-6, 15-1164). Concordia.

Sherman, Franklin & Lehman, Helmut T., eds. Luther's Works: The Christian in Society IV, Vol. 47. LC 55-9893. 1971. 19.95 (ISBN 0-8006-0347-8, 1-347). Fortress.

Siirala, Aarne. Divine Humanness. Kantonen, T. A., tr. LC 70-99460. pap. 48.00 (2026964). Bks Demand UMI.

Smith, Preserved. Luther's Table Talk. LC 78-127457. (Columbia University Studies in the Social Sciences: No. 69). 1970. Repr. of 1907 ed. 14.50 (ISBN 0-404-51069-8). AMS Pr.

Steinmetz, David. Luther in Context. LC 85-45313. (Midland Bks: No. 405). 160p. 1986. 25.00x (ISBN 0-253-33647-3); pap. 7.95x (ISBN 0-253-20405-4). Ind U Pr.

Steinmetz, David C. Luther & Staupitz: An Essay in the Intellectual Origins of the Protestant Reformation. LC 80-23007. (Duke Monographs in Medieval & Renaissance Studies: No. 4). xi, 149p. 1980. 18.50 (ISBN 0-8223-0447-3). Duke.

Steinwede, Dietrich. Reformation: A Picture Story of Martin Luther. Cooperrider, Edward A., tr. from German. LC 82-49055. (Illus.). 56p. 1983. pap. 6.95 (ISBN 0-8006-1710-X, 1-1710). Fortress.

Tierney, Brian, et al, eds. Martin Luther - Reformer or Revolutionary? 3rd ed. (Historical Pamphlets Ser.). 1977. pap. text ed. 1.95x (ISBN 0-394-32055-7). Random.

Todd, John. Luther: A Life. 416p. 1982. 17.50x (ISBN 0-8245-0479-8). Crossroad NY.

Tracy, James D. Luther & the Modern State in Germany. (Sixteenth Century Essays & Studies: Vol. VII). 110p. 1986. smyth sewn 25.00 (ISBN 0-940474-07-7). Sixteenth Cent.

Volz, Hans. Die Lutherpredigten Des Johannes Mathesius. (Ger). 34.00 (ISBN 0-384-64913-0); pap. 28.00 (ISBN 0-384-64912-2). Johnson Repr.

Von Loewenich, Walter. Luther's Theology of the Cross. Bouman, Herbert J., tr. LC 75-2845. 224p. (Orig.). 1982. pap. 10.95 (ISBN 0-8066-1490-0, 10-4233). Augsburg.

Waring, Luther H. Political Theories of Martin Luther. LC 68-15837. 1968. Repr. of 1910 ed. 21.50x (ISBN 0-8046-0488-6, Pub. by Kennikat). Assoc Faculty Pr.

Watson, Philip S. Let God Be God: An Interpretation of the Theology of Martin Luther. LC 83-45675. Date not set. Repr. of 1947 ed. 30.00 (ISBN 0-404-19864-3). AMS Pr.

Weidenschilling, J. M. Living with Luther. 1945. pap. text ed. 1.10 (ISBN 0-570-03523-6, 14-1155). Concordia.

Wicks, Jared. Luther & His Spiritual Legacy. (Theology & Life Ser.: Vol. 7). pap. 7.95 (ISBN 0-89453-338-X). M Glazier.

Wicks, Jared, ed. Catholic Scholars Dialogue with Luther. LC 78-105429. (Orig.). 1970. pap. 3.00 (ISBN 0-8294-0181-4). Loyola.

Wiener, Peter F. Martin Luther: Hitler's Spiritual Ancestor. (Illus.). 92p. 1985. saddle stiched 4.00 (ISBN 0-910309-21-3). Am Atheist.

Wolf, Ernst. Staupitz Und Luther. (Ger). 34.00 (ISBN 0-384-69019-X); pap. 28.00 (ISBN 0-384-69018-1). Johnson Repr.

Yule, George, ed. Luther: Theologian for the Catholics & Protestants. 208p. 1985. pap. 12.95 (ISBN 0-567-29119-7, Pub. by T&T Clark Ltd UK). Fortress.

Zeeden, Ernest W. The Legacy of Luther: Martin Luther & the Reformation in the Estimation of the German Lutherans from Luther's Death to the Beginning of the Age of Goethe. Bethell, Ruth M., tr. from Ger. LC 83-45685. Date not set. Repr. of 1954 ed. 30.00 (ISBN 0-404-19865-1). AMS Pr.

LUTHER, MARTIN, 1483-1546–DICTIONARIES, INDEXES, ETC.

Lundeen, Joel W., ed. Luther's Works: Index. through 12/31/86 19.95 (ISBN 0-317-52515-8, 1-355). Fortress.

LUTHER, MARTIN, 1483-1546–DRAMA

Brokering, Herb. The Luther Journey. (Illus.). 96p. (Orig.). 1983. pap. 6.95 (ISBN 0-942562-02-X). Brokering Pr.

Osborne, John. Luther. pap. 3.95 (ISBN 0-451-14474-0, Sig). NAL.

LUTHER, MARTIN, 1483-1546–JUVENILE LITERATURE

Fehlauer, Adolph. Life & Faith of Martin Luther. 1981. pap. 5.95 (ISBN 0-8100-0125-X, 15N0376). Northwest Pub.

Nohl, Frederick. Martin Luther: Hero of Faith. LC 62-14146. (Illus.). 1962. pap. 5.25 (ISBN 0-570-03727-1, 12-2629). Concordia.

O'Neill, Judith. Martin Luther. LC 78-56804. (Cambridge Topic Bks). (Illus.). 1978. PLB 8.95 (ISBN 0-8225-1215-7). Lerner Pubns.

LUTHERAN CHURCH

see also Evangelical Lutheran Church

Bergendoff, Conrad. One Hundred Years of Oratorio at Augustana: A History of the Handel Oratorio Society, 1881-1980. LC 81-52434. (Augustana Historical Society Publication Ser.: No. 29). 54p. 1981. 7.50 (ISBN 0-910184-00-3); pap. 5.00 (ISBN 0-910184-29-1). Augustana.

Braaten, Carl E., ed. The New Church Debate: Issues Facing American Lutheranism. LC 83-48008. 176p. 1984. pap. 7.95 (ISBN 0-8006-1715-0, 1-1715). Fortress.

Haendler, Gert. Luther on Ministerial Office & Congregational Function. Gritsch, Eric W., ed. Gritsch, Ruth C., tr. from Ger. LC 81-43075. Tr. of Amt und Gemeinde bei Luther im Kontext der Kirchengeschichte. 112p. 1981. 9.95 (ISBN 0-8006-0665-5, 1-665). Fortress.

Inter-Lutheran Commission on Worship. Lutheran Book of Worship. 10.50 (ISBN 0-8006-3330-X). Bd of Pubn LCA.

Kreider, Harry J. Lutheranism in Colonial New York. LC 78-38452. (Religion in America, Ser. 2). 184p. 1972. Repr. of 1942 ed. 13.00 (ISBN 0-405-04072-5). Ayer Co Pubs.

Luther, Martin. Martin Luther: Selections from His Writings. Dillenberger, John, ed. LC 61-9503. pap. 7.95 (ISBN 0-385-09876-6, Anch). Doubleday.

Lutz, Charles P. Abounding in Hope: A Family of Faith at Work through the Lutheran World Federation. LC 85-1216. 144p. (Orig.). 1985. pap. 5.95 (ISBN 0-8066-2158-3, 10-0123). Augsburg.

Marty, Martin. Health & Medicine in the Lutheran Tradition. 192p. 1983. 16.95x (ISBN 0-8245-0613-8). Crossroad NY.

Mastrantonis, George. Augsburg & Constantinople: The Correspondence Between Patriarch Jeremiah II & the Tubingen Theologians. 424p. 1981. 22.95 (ISBN 0-916586-81-2); pap. 14.95 (ISBN 0-916586-82-0). Hellenic Coll Pr.

Meitler, Neal D. & La Porte, Linda M. Standard Accounting System for Lutheran Congregations. 1981. 4.95 (ISBN 0-8100-0129-2, 21N2001). Northwest Pub.

Melanchthon, Philipp. Opera Quae Supersunt Omnia, 28 Vols. (Corpus Reformatorum). Repr. of 1860 ed. Set. 1650.00 (ISBN 0-384-38050-6); 60.00 ea. Johnson Repr.

--Selected Writings. Flack, Elmer E. & Satre, Lowell J., eds. Hill, Charles L., tr. LC 78-5175. 1978. Repr. of 1962 ed. lib. bdg. cancelled (ISBN 0-313-20384-9, MESW). Greenwood.

Polack, W. G. The Handbook to the Lutheran Hymnal. 3rd rev. ed. 1975. Repr. of 1942 ed. lib. bdg. 16.95 (ISBN 0-8100-0003-2, 03-0700). Northwest Pub.

Smith, Clifford N. Nineteenth-Century Emigration of "Old Lutherans" from Eastern Germany (Mainly Pomerania & Lower Silesia) to Australia, Canada, & the United States. (German-American Genealogical Research Monograph: No. 7). 1979. pap. 14.00 (ISBN 0-915162-06-7). Westland Pubns.

Stauderman, Albert P. Facts about Lutherans. 32p. 1959. pap. 0.95, 10 for 5.50 (ISBN 0-8006-1832-7, 1-1832). Fortress.

Tappert, Theodore G. & Lehmann, Helmut T., eds. Luther's Works: Table Talk, Vol. 54. Tappert, Theodore G., tr. LC 55-9893. 1967. 19.95 (ISBN 0-8006-0354-0, 1-354). Fortress.

Von Loewenich, Walter. Luther's Theology of the Cross. Bouman, Herbert J., tr. LC 75-2845. 224p. (Orig.). 1982. pap. 10.95 (ISBN 0-8066-1490-0, 10-4233). Augsburg.

Watson, Philip S. Let God Be God: An Interpretation of the Theology of Martin Luther. LC 83-45675. Date not set. Repr. of 1947 ed. 30.00 (ISBN 0-404-19864-3). AMS Pr.

LUTHERAN CHURCH–ADDRESSES, ESSAYS, LECTURES

Florinsky, N. I. Soslasno li c Evangelijem Dejstvoval i uchil Ljuter? Tr. of Were the Actions & Teachings of Luther in Accord with the Gospel? 166p. 1975. pap. text ed. 6.00 (ISBN 0-317-30257-4). Holy Trinity.

Norgren, William, et al, eds. What Can We Share? A Lutheran-Episcopal Resource & Study Guide. (Lutheran-Episcopal Dialogue Ser.). 88p. (Orig.). 1985. pap. 2.00 (ISBN 0-88028-047-6). Forward Movement.

Sittler, Joseph A. Grace Notes & Other Fragments. Herhold, Robert M. & Delloff, Linda M., eds. LC 80-8055. 128p. (Orig.). 1981. pap. 5.95 (ISBN 0-8006-1404-6, 1-1404). Fortress.

LUTHERAN CHURCH–CATECHISMS AND CREEDS

Bachmann, Theodore & Lehmann, Helmut T., eds. Luther's Works: Word & Sacrament I, Vol. 35. LC 55-9893. 426p. 1960. 19.95 (ISBN 0-8006-0335-4, 1-335). Fortress.

Bente, F. Historical Introduction to the Book of Concord. 1965. 12.95 (ISBN 0-570-03262-8, 15-1926). Concordia.

Fagerberg, Holsten. A New Look at the Lutheran Confession. Lund, Gene J., tr. 336p. 1981. 15.50 (ISBN 0-570-03223-7, 15-2121). Concordia.

Fischer, Robert H. & Lehmann, Helmut T., eds. Luther's Works: Word & Sacrament III, Vol. 37. LC 55-9893. 1961. 19.95 (ISBN 0-8006-0337-0, 1-337). Fortress.

Huggenvik, Theodore. We Believe. 1950. pap. 3.95 (ISBN 0-8066-0151-5, 15-7102). Augsburg.

Janzow, F. Samuel. Getting into Luther's Large Catechism. 1979. pap. 4.25 (ISBN 0-570-03783-2, 12-2737). Concordia.

Keller, Paul F. Studies in Lutheran Doctrine. LC 60-15574. (YA) 1959. pap. 5.50 (ISBN 0-570-03517-1, 14-1265); correction & profile chart 0.40 (ISBN 0-570-03526-0, 14-1267); tests 0.45 (ISBN 0-570-03525-2, 14-1266). Concordia.

Kurth, Edwin W. Catechetical Helps. 1981. pap. text ed. 4.95 (ISBN 0-570-03507-4, 14-1261). Concordia.

Kurth, Erwin, et al. Growing in Christ: Catechism. (Illus.). 1953. text ed. 4.85 (ISBN 0-570-01517-0, 22-1097); wkbk. 1.95 (ISBN 0-570-01518-9, 22-1100). Concordia.

Luther, Martin. The Chiefe & Prycypall Articles of the Christian Faythe. LC 72-6080. (English Experience Ser.: No. 84). 248p. 1969. Repr. of 1548 ed. 21.00 (ISBN 90-221-0084-7). Walter J Johnson.

--The Large Catechism of Martin Luther. Fischer, Robert H., tr. from Ger. LC 61-3802. 112p. 1959. 4.95 (ISBN 0-8006-0885-2, 1-885). Fortress.

--Luther's Large Catechism. Lenker, J. M., tr. 1967. flexible bdg. 6.95 (ISBN 0-8066-0720-3, 10-4211). Augsburg.

--Luther's Works, Vol. 17. Bouman, Herbert J., tr. LC 55-9893. 1972. 16.95 (ISBN 0-570-06417-1, 15-1759). Concordia.

--Small Catechism in Contemporary English. LC 15-6732. 1963. pap. 8.25 (ISBN 0-8066-0324-0, 15-6732). Augsburg.

Preus, Robert. Getting into the Theology of Concord. 1978. pap. 3.75 (ISBN 0-570-03767-0, 12-2702). Concordia.

Reumann, John. Righteousness in the New Testament: Justification in Lutheran-Catholic Dialogue. LC 81-43086. 320p. 1982. pap. 13.95 (ISBN 0-8006-1616-2, 1-1616). Fortress.

Tappert, Theodore G., ed. & tr. Book of Concord: The Confessions of the Evangelical Lutheran Church. LC 59-11369. 1959. 14.95 (ISBN 0-8006-0825-9, 1-825). Fortress.

Theiss, Herman C. Life with God. pap. 5.95 (ISBN 0-933350-05-8); tchrs. manual 3.00 (ISBN 0-933350-44-9). Morse Pr.

This We Believe. (Eng. & Ger.). pap. 0.60 (ISBN 0-8100-0004-0, 04-0622). Northwest Pub.

Wentz, Abdel R. & Lehmann, eds. Luther's Works: Word & Sacrament II, Vol. 36. LC 55-9893. 400p. 1959. 19.95 (ISBN 0-8006-0336-2, 1-336). Fortress.

LUTHERAN CHURCH–CLERGY

Lindberg, Duane R. Men of the Cloth & the Social-Cultural Fabric of the Norwegian Ethnic Community in North Dakota. Cordasco, Francesco, ed. LC 80-877. (American Ethnic Groups Ser.). 1981. lib. bdg. 38.00x (ISBN 0-405-13438-X). Ayer Co Pubs.

Winkler, Marion R. Church Polity: How the Clergy Run the Church. LC 82-91145. 271p. 1983. lib. bdg. 19.95 (ISBN 0-9610344-1-6); pap. 12.95 (ISBN 0-9610344-2-4). M R Winkler.

LUTHERAN CHURCH–DOCTRINAL AND CONTROVERSIAL WORKS

Bouman, H. J., tr. Luther's Works, Vol. 10. 1981. 16.95 (ISBN 0-570-06410-4, 15-1752). Concordia.

Braaten, Carl E. Principles of Lutheran Theology. LC 82-16542. 160p. 1983. pap. 8.95 (ISBN 0-8006-1689-8). Fortress.

Chemnitz, Martin. Examination of the Council of Trent. Kramer, Fred, tr. from Lat. LC 79-143693. 1971. 29.95 (ISBN 0-570-03213-X, 15-2113). Concordia.

Dinda, R. J., tr. Luther's Works, Vol. 18. 1980. 16.95 (ISBN 0-570-06418-X, 15-1760). Concordia.

Forde, Gerhard O. Where God Meets Man: Luther's Down-to-Earth Approach to the Gospel. LC 72-78569. 128p. 1972. pap. 6.95 (ISBN 0-8066-1235-5, 10-7060). Augsburg.

Forell, George W. & McCue, James F. Confessing One Faith: A Joint Commentary on the Augsburg Confession by Lutheran & Catholic Theologians. LC 80-65557. 368p. 1981. pap. 16.95 (ISBN 0-8066-1802-7, 10-1637). Augsburg.

Huggenvik, Theodore. We Believe. 1950. pap. 3.95 (ISBN 0-8066-0151-5, 15-7102). Augsburg.

Kolb, Robert A. Speaking the Gospel Today: A Theology for Evangelism. 1984. 16.95 (ISBN 0-570-04205-4, 15-2173). Concordia.

Krodel, Gottfried G. & Lehman, Helmut T., eds. Luther's Works: Letters I, Vol. 48. LC 55-9893. 1963. 19.95 (ISBN 0-8006-0348-6). Fortress.

Krodel, Gottfried G. & Lehmann, Helmut T., eds. Luther's Works: Letters III, Vol. 50. LC 74-76934. 416p. 1975. 19.95 (ISBN 0-8006-0350-8, 1-350). Fortress.

Mattison, Judith. Divorce-The Pain & the Healing: Personal Mediations When Marriage Ends. LC 85-11140. 96p. (Orig.). 1985. pap. 5.95 (ISBN 0-8066-2128-1, 10-1905). Augsburg.

Pelley, Ronn T. In Word & Deed: A Student's Beginning Guide to Understanding the Luthern Worship Service. (Pass Along Ser.). (Illus.). 32p. 1986. pap. 2.95 (ISBN 0-933350-49-X). Morse Pr.

Pieper, Francis. Christian Dogmatics, 4 Vols. Engelder, Theodore, et al, trs. 1950-1957. Vol. 1. 18.95 (ISBN 0-570-06712-X, 15-1001); Vol. 2. 18.95 (ISBN 0-570-06713-8, 15-1002); Vol. 3. 18.95 (ISBN 0-570-06714-6, 15-1003); Vol. 4. 25.95 (ISBN 0-570-06711-1, 15-1000); Set. 69.95 (ISBN 0-570-06715-4, 15-1852). Concordia.

Prenter, Regin. Luther's Theology of the Cross. Anderson, Charles S., ed. LC 71-152368. (Facet Bks.). 32p. 1971. pap. 2.50 (ISBN 0-8006-3062-9, 1-3062). Fortress.

Preus, Robert D. Theology of Post-Reformation Lutheranism: A Study of Theological Prolegomena. LC 70-121877. 1970. 16.95 (ISBN 0-570-03211-3, 15-2110). Concordia.

Rudnick, Milton L. Christianity Is for You. 1961. pap. 3.25 (ISBN 0-570-03503-1, 14-1271). Concordia.

Schmid, Heinrich. Doctrinal Theology of the Evangelical Lutheran Church. LC 66-13052. 1961. 25.95 (ISBN 0-8066-0107-8, 10-1930). Augsburg.

Three Tudor Dialogues. LC 78-14887. 1979. 35.00x (ISBN 0-8201-1319-0). Schol Facsimiles.

Truemper, David G. & Niedner, Frederick A., Jr. Keeping the Faith: A Guide to the Christian Message. LC 81-43072. 144p. 1981. pap. 6.95 (ISBN 0-8006-1608-1, 1-1608). Fortress.

LUTHERAN CHURCH–EDUCATION

Montgomery, Mary & Montgomery, Herb. Together at the Lord's Supper: Preparation for Holy Communion. (Illus.). 1977. pap. text ed. 3.25 (ISBN 0-03-021291-X, 141, HarpR); parent bk. 2.25 (ISBN 0-03-021286-3, 192); leader's guide 4.95 (ISBN 0-03-021296-0, 193). Har-Row.

Solberg, Richard W. Lutheran Higher Education in North America. LC 85-28757. 400p. (Orig.). 1985. pap. 9.95 (ISBN 0-8066-2187-7, 10-4168). Augsburg.

Solberg, Richard W. & Strommen, Merton P. How Church-Related Are Church-Related Colleges? Answers Based on a Comprehensive Survey of Supporting Constituencies of 18 LCA Colleges. LC 80-13833. 96p. (Orig.). 1980. pap. 3.95 (ISBN 0-8006-1388-0, 1-1388). Fortress.

Strauss, Gerald. Luther's House of Learning: Indoctrination of the Young in the German Reformation. LC 77-18705. pap. 101.30 (ISBN 0-317-20464-5, 2023003). Bks Demand UMI.

Whalen, William J. Reaching Out to the Lutherans with Heart & Mind. (Reaching Out to...Ser.). 32p. 1984. pap. 1.50 (ISBN 0-89243-206-3). Liguori Pubns.

LUTHERAN CHURCH–HISTORY

Abray, Lorna J. The People's Reformation: Magistrates, Clergy & Commons in Strasbourg, 1500-1598. LC 84-45805. 288p. 1985. text ed. 27.50x (ISBN 0-8014-1776-7). Cornell U Pr.

Bernheim, Gotthardt D. History of the German Settlements & of the Lutheran Church in North & South Carolina. LC 76-187361. 573p. 1972. Repr. of 1872 ed. 25.00 (ISBN 0-87152-089-3). Reprint.

Concordia Historical Institute Staff & Lutheran Historical Conference Staff. Lutheran Historical Conference: Essays & Reports. Suelflow, August R., ed. 7.50 (ISBN 0-318-04799-3). Concordia Hist.

Diehl, Katharine S. Jesuits, Lutherans, & the Printing Press in South India. (Printers & Printing in the East Indies to 1850 Ser.: Vol. III). write for info. Caratzas.

Elert, Werner. Structure of Lutheranism: The Theology & Philosophy of Life of Lutheranism, 16th & 17th Centuries, Vol. 1. Hansen, Walter A., tr. LC 62-19955. 1974. pap. 15.95 (ISBN 0-570-03192-3, 12-2588). Concordia.

Erb, Peter. Johann Arndt: True Christianity. LC 78-72046. (Classics of Western Spirituality). 320p. 1979. 12.95 (ISBN 0-8091-0281-1); pap. 9.95 (ISBN 0-8091-2192-1). Paulist Pr.

Haigler, Anne M. The Church Records of Saint Matthews Lutheran Church, Orangeburg, Co., S. C. Beginning in 1799, Giving Births, Christenings, Confirmations, Marriages, & Burials & "the Red Church", 1767-1838. (Illus.). 126p. 1985. 15.00 (ISBN 0-89308-563-4). Southern Hist Pr.

Jungkuntz, Theodore R. Formulators of the Formula of Concord. 1977. pap. 8.50 (ISBN 0-570-03740-9, 12-2644). Concordia.

Klug, Eugene F. Getting into the Formula of Concord. 1977. pap. 3.75 (ISBN 0-570-03742-5, 12-2646). Concordia.

Knudsen, Johannes. The Formation of the Lutheran Church in America. LC 77-15235. pap. 31.50 (2026956). Bks Demand UMI.

Ludolphy, Ingetraut. From Luther to Fifteen Eighty: A Pictorial Account. (Illus.). 1977. 15.95 (ISBN 0-570-03264-4, 15-2710). Concordia.

Lutz, Charles P., ed. Church Roots: Stories of Nine Immigrant Groups That Became the American Lutheran Church. LC 85-1217. 208p. (Orig.). 1985. pap. 9.95 (ISBN 0-8066-2156-7, 10-1366). Augsburg.

Nichol, Todd. All These Lutherans: Three Paths Toward a New Lutheran Church. LC 86-3638. (Illus.). 128p. (Orig.). 1986. pap. 6.95 (ISBN 0-8066-2208-3, 10-0228). Augsburg.

Pelikan, Jaroslav. Bach among the Theologians. LC 86-45219. 176p. 1986. 14.95 (ISBN 0-8006-0792-9, 1-792). Fortress.

Piepkorn, Arthur Carl. The Survival of the Historic Vestments in the Lutheran Church after Fifteen Fifty-Five. 120p. 1956. write for info. Concordia Schl Grad Studies.

Richard, James W. The Confessional History of the Lutheran Church. LC 83-45672. Date not set. Repr. of 1909 ed. 62.50 (ISBN 0-404-19861-9). AMS Pr.

Riforgiato, Leonard R. Missionary of Moderation: Henry Melchior Muhlenberg & the Lutheran Church in English America. LC 78-75203. 256p. 23.50 (ISBN 0-8387-2379-9). Bucknell U Pr.

Scaer, David. Getting into the Story of Concord. 1978. pap. 3.95 (ISBN 0-570-03768-9, 12-2703). Concordia.

Schmucker, Samuel S. American Lutheran Church, Historically, Doctrinally, & Practically Delineated in Several Discourses. LC 72-83436. (Religion in American Ser). 1969. Repr. of 1851 ed. 20.00 (ISBN 0-405-00261-0). Ayer Co Pubs.

Wittwer, Norman C., Jr. The Faithful & the Bold: The Story of the First Service of the Zion Evangelical Lutheran Church, Oldwick, New Jersey. (Illus.). 46p. 1984. 10.00x (ISBN 0-913186-10-4). Monocacy.

Zeeden, Ernest W. The Legacy of Luther: Martin Luther & the Reformation in the Estimation of the German Lutherans from Luther's Death to the Beginning of the Age of Goethe. Bethell, Ruth M., tr. from Ger. LC 83-45685. Date not set. Repr. of 1954 ed. 30.00 (ISBN 0-404-19865-1). AMS Pr.

LUTHERAN CHURCH–HYMNS

Lambert, James F. Luther's Hymns. LC 83-45646. Date not set. Repr. of 1917 ed. 34.50 (ISBN 0-404-19855-4). AMS Pr.

Leupold, Ulrich S. & Lehmann, Helmut T., eds. Luther's Works: Liturgy & Hymns, Vol. 53. LC 55-9893. 1965. 19.95 (ISBN 0-8006-0353-2, 1-353). Fortress.

Olson, Ruth L., ed. Hymns & Songs for Church Schools. LC 62-13898. (Illus.). 1962. 7.95 ea. (12-1500). 25 or more 7.65 ea. Augsburg.

Schalk, Carl. The Hymn of the Day & Its Use in Lutheran Worship. 48p. (Orig.). 1983. pap. 2.50 (ISBN 0-570-01322-4, 99-1252). Concordia.

Stulken, Marilyn K. Hymnal Companion to the Lutheran Book of Worship. LC 81-707. 672p. 1981. 34.95 (ISBN 0-8006-0300-1, 1-300). Fortress.

LUTHERAN CHURCH–LITURGY AND RITUAL

Lutheran Book of Worship, 7 vols. Incl. Pew Edition. 11.50 (ISBN 0-685-92595-1, 12-2000); Ministers Edition. 65.00 (ISBN 0-685-92596-X, 12-2001); Accompaniment Edition, Liturgy. 22.00 (ISBN 0-685-92597-8, 12-2002); Organist Edition, Hymns. 17.00 (ISBN 0-685-92598-6, 12-2003); Ministers Desk Edition. 18.00 (ISBN 0-685-92599-4, 12-2004); Gift Edition. 15.00 (ISBN 0-686-52336-9, 12-2005); Pocket Edition. 21.00 (ISBN 0-686-52337-7, 12-2006). LC 77-92169. 1978. Augsburg.

McClean, Charles, ed. The Conduct of the Services. (Illus.). 138p. 1975. pap. 6.50 (ISBN 0-915644-04-5). Clayton Pub Hse.

Mildenberger, Friedrich. Theology of the Lutheran Confessions. Lueker, Erwin, tr. LC 85-47727. 272p. 1986. 19.95 (ISBN 0-8006-0749-X). Fortress.

Pfatteicher, Philip H. & Messerli, Carlos R. Manual on the Liturgy: Lutheran Book of Worship. LC 78-68179. 1979. 18.00 (ISBN 0-8066-1676-8, 12-2015). Augsburg.

Schalk, Carl. Music in Lutheran Worship. 16p. (Orig.). 1983. pap. 1.25 (ISBN 0-570-01323-2, 99-1253). Concordia.

LUTHERAN CHURCH–MEMBERSHIP

Rudnick, Milton L. Christianity Is for You. 1961. pap. 3.25 (ISBN 0-570-03503-1, 14-1271). Concordia.

LUTHERAN CHURCH–MISSIONS

Mattison, Judith. Divorce-The Pain & the Healing: Personal Mediations When Marriage Ends. LC 85-11140. 96p. (Orig.). 1985. pap. 5.95 (ISBN 0-8066-2128-1, 10-1905). Augsburg.

LUTHERAN CHURCH–PRAYER-BOOKS AND DEVOTIONS

Brokering, Herbert F., ed. Luther Prayers. Kistler, Charles E., tr. LC 67-25366. 1967. lea. bdg. 7.95 (ISBN 0-8066-0721-1, 10-4231). Augsburg.

Gockel, Herman W. & Saleska, Edward J., eds. Child's Garden of Prayer. (Illus.). 1981. pap. 1.50 (ISBN 0-570-03412-4, 56-1016). Concordia.

Huxhold, Harry N. Family Altar. rev. ed. 1964. 12.95 (ISBN 0-570-03071-4, 6-1085). Concordia.

Little Folded Hands. rev. ed. LC 59-12074. 1959. 3.50 (ISBN 0-570-03417-5, 56-1038); pap. 1.85 laminated (ISBN 0-570-03416-7, 56-1037). Concordia.

Lutheran Book of Prayer. rev. ed. LC 76-119916. 1970. 4.50 (ISBN 0-570-03005-6, 6-1141). Concordia.

Lutheran Book of Worship, 13 Vols. Incl. Pew Edition. 10.50 (ISBN 0-317-12649-0); Ministers Altar Book. 50.00 (ISBN 0-317-12650-4); Minister Desk Edition. 16.50 (ISBN 0-317-12651-2); Accompaniment Edition. 20.00 (ISBN 0-317-12652-0); Organist Edition. 15.00 (ISBN 0-317-12653-9); Gift Edition. 21.50 (ISBN 0-317-12654-7); Pocket Edition. 19.00 (ISBN 0-317-12655-5); Braille Edition. 55.00 (ISBN 0-317-12656-3); Hymns Large. 5.25 (ISBN 0-317-12657-1); Holy Communion. 2.25 (ISBN 0-317-12658-X); Hymnal Companion. 32.50 (ISBN 0-317-12659-8); LBW Occasional Service. 23.50 (ISBN 0-317-12660-1); LBW Large Print. 40.00 (ISBN 0-317-12661-X). LC 77-92160. 1978-84. Fortress.

Nelson, Ruth Y. God's Song in My Heart: Daily Devotions. LC 56-11912. 432p. 1957. 8.95 (ISBN 0-8006-0254-4, 1-254). Fortress.

Pfatteicher, Philip H. Festivals & Commemorations: Handbook to the Calendar in Lutheran Book of Worship. LC 79-54129. 336p. 24.95 (ISBN 0-8066-1757-8, 10-2295). Augsburg.

Syverud, Genevieve W. This Is My Song of Songs. (Orig.). 1966. pap. 2.95 (ISBN 0-8066-0613-4, 11-9495). Augsburg.

Webb, Barbara O. In Christ, My Lord. 1982. pap. 4.95 (ISBN 0-570-03852-9, 12YY2807). Concordia.

Wiencke, Gustav K. & Lehman, Helmut T., eds. Luther's Works: Devotional Writings II, Vol. 43. LC 55-9893. 1968. 19.95 (ISBN 0-8006-0343-5, 1-343). Fortress.

LUTHERAN CHURCH–RELATIONS–CATHOLIC CHURCH

Arnold, Duane W. & Fry, C. George. The Way, the Truth, & the Life: An Introduction to Lutheran Christianity. (Illus.). 204p. (Orig.). 1982. pap. 9.95 (ISBN 0-8010-0189-7). Baker Bk.

Empie, Paul C., et al, eds. Lutherans & Catholics in Dialogue I-III. LC 74-83330. 1974. pap. 8.95 (ISBN 0-8066-1451-X, 10-4190). Augsburg.

Marty, Myron A. Lutherans & Roman Catholicism: The Changing Conflict, 1917-1963. 1968. 14.95 (ISBN 0-268-00162-6). U of Notre Dame Pr.

Reumann, John. Righteousness in the New Testament: Justification in Lutheran-Catholic Dialogue. LC 81-85385. 320p. (Orig.). 1982. pap. 13.95 (ISBN 0-8091-2436-X). Paulist Pr.

LUTHERAN CHURCH–SERMONS

Hillerbrand, Hans J. & Lehmann, Helmut T., eds. Luther's Works: Sermons II, Vol. 52. LC 55-9893. 416p. 1974. 19.95 (ISBN 0-8006-0352-4, 1-352). Fortress.

Kierkegaard, Soren. For Self-Examination & Judge for Yourself. (American-Scandinavian Foundation Ser.). 1944. pap. 8.50x (ISBN 0-691-01952-5). Princeton U Pr.

Kiessling, Elmer C. Early Sermons of Luther & Their Relation to the Pre-Reformation Sermon. LC 75-171064. Repr. of 1935 ed. 21.50 (ISBN 0-404-03669-4). AMS Pr.

Kolb, Robert. Andreae & the Formula of Concord. 1977. pap. 8.50 (ISBN 0-570-03741-7, 12-2645). Concordia.

Lehmann, Helmut T. & Doberstein, John W., eds. Luther's Works: Sermons I, Vol. 51. Doberstein, John W., tr. LC 55-9893. 1959. 19.95 (ISBN 0-8006-0351-6, 1-353). Fortress.

Lejeune, R. Christoph Blumhardt & His Message. LC 63-15816. 1963. 7.00 (ISBN 0-87486-200-0). Plough.

Steimle, Edmund A. God the Stranger: Reflections About Resurrection. LC 78-14674. 80p. 1979. pap. 4.95 (ISBN 0-8006-1354-6, 1-1354). Fortress.

Thielicke, Helmut. How the World Began: Man in the First Chapters of the Bible. Doberstein, John W., tr. from Ger. LC 61-6756. 324p. 1961. pap. 6.95 (ISBN 0-8006-1894-7, 1-1894). Fortress.

LUTHERAN CHURCH–YEARBOOKS

Pfatteicher, Philip H. Festivals & Commemorations: Handbook to the Calendar in Lutheran Book of Worship. LC 79-54129. 336p. 24.95 (ISBN 0-8066-1757-8, 10-2295). Augsburg.

LUTHERAN CHURCH IN SCANDINAVIA

Wordsworth, John. National Church of Sweden. LC 11-35349. 1911. 20.00x (ISBN 0-8401-2821-5). A R Allenson.

LUTHERAN CHURCH IN THE UNITED STATES

Bernheim, Gotthardt D. History of the German Settlements & of the Lutheran Church in North & South Carolina. LC 75-969. xvi, 557p. 1975. Repr. of 1872 ed. 20.00 (ISBN 0-8063-8001-2). Regional.

Graebner, Alan. Uncertain Saints. LC 75-1573. (Contributions in American History: No. 42). 320p. 1975. lib. bdg. 29.95 (ISBN 0-8371-7963-7, GUS/). Greenwood.

Groh, John E. & Smith, Robert H., eds. The Lutheran Church in North American Life: 1776-1976, 1580-1980. LC 78-71233. 1979. 5.95 (ISBN 0-915644-17-7, Clayton). Luth Acad.

Heintzen, Erich H. & Starr, Frank. Love Leaves Home. LC 72-94586. 1973. 3.50 (ISBN 0-570-03513-9, 14-2017). Concordia.

Kersten, Lawrence K. The Lutheran Ethic: The Impact of Religion on Laymen & Clergy. LC 71-102200. 310p. 1970. 25.00x (ISBN 0-8143-1416-3). Wayne St U Pr.

Knudsen, Johannes. The Formation of the Lutheran Church in America. LC 77-15235. pap. 31.50 (2026956). Bks Demand UMI.

Lindberg, Duane R. Men of the Cloth & the Social-Cultural Fabric of the Norwegian Ethnic Community in North Dakota. Cordasco, Francesco, ed. LC 80-877. (American Ethnic Groups Ser.). 1981. lib. bdg. 38.00x (ISBN 0-405-13438-X). Ayer Co Pubs.

Myers, Margaret E. Meyersville, Md., Lutheran Baptisms. Russell, Donna V., ed. (Illus.). 70p. 1986. pap. 10.00 (ISBN 0-914385-04-6). Catoctin Pr.

Norelius, Eric. The Pioneer Swedish Settlements & Swedish Lutheran Churches in America 1845-1860. Bergendoff, Conrad, tr. from Swedish. LC 84-71391. (Publication Ser.: No. 31). Orig. Title: De Svenska Luterska Forsamlingarnas och Svenska Historia i Amerika. 419p. 1984. 15.00 (ISBN 0-910184-31-3). Augustana.

Schmucker, Samuel S. American Lutheran Church, Historically, Doctrinally, & Practically Delineated in Several Discourses. LC 72-83436. (Religion in American Ser). 1969. Repr. of 1851 ed. 20.00 (ISBN 0-405-00261-0). Ayer Co Pubs.

Tietjen, John H. Which Way to Lutheran Unity? A History of Efforts to Unite the Lutherans of America. LC 66-25270. 176p. 1975. pap. text ed. 7.50 (ISBN 0-915644-01-0). Clayton Pub Hse.

Weiser, Frederick S., ed. Maryland German Church Records, Vol. 7: St. Mary's Lutheran Church 1783-1863, St. Mary's Reformed Church 1812-1866, & Jerusalem Lutheran Church 1799-1859. (Maryland German Church Records Ser.). (Orig.). 1987. pap. 15.00x (ISBN 0-913281-09-3). Noodle Doosey.

Weisheit, Eldon. The Zeal of His House. LC 73-76988. 1973. 3.50 (ISBN 0-570-03516-3, 14-2020). Concordia.

LUTHERANS IN NORTH AMERICA

Groh, John E. & Smith, Robert H., eds. The Lutheran Church in North American Life: 1776-1976, 1580-1980. LC 78-71233. 1979. 5.95 (ISBN 0-915644-17-7, Clayton). Luth Acad.

Nelson, E. Clifford, ed. Lutherans in North America. rev. ed. LC 74-26337. (Illus.). 576p. 1980. 22.50x (ISBN 0-8006-0409-1); pap. 16.95 (ISBN 0-8006-1409-7, 1-1409). Fortress.

LYMAN BEECHER LECTURES

Jones, Edgar D. Royalty of the Pulpit. LC 79-134105. (Essay Index Reprint Ser). 1951. 27.50 (ISBN 0-8369-1979-3). Ayer Co Pubs.

LYNDWOOD, WILLIAM, BP. OF ST. DAVID'S, 1375-1446

Ogle, Arthur. Canon Law in Mediaeval England: An Examination of William Lyndwood's Provinciale. LC 78-156390. (Research & Source Works Ser.: No. 731). 1971. Repr. of 1912 ed. lib. bdg. 20.50 (ISBN 0-8337-2603-X). B Franklin.

LYNN, JAMES JESSE, 1892-1955

Rajarsi Janakananda: A Great Western Yogi. (Illus.). 95p. 1984. pap. 1.95 (ISBN 0-87612-181-4). Self Realization.

LYON, JAMES

Sonneck, Oscar G. Francis Hopkinson, the First American Poet-Composer, & James Lyon, Patriot, Preacher, Psalmodist. 2nd ed. LC 65-23393. (Music Reprint Ser.). 213p. 1966. Repr. of 1905 ed. lib. bdg. 32.50 (ISBN 0-306-70918-X). Da Capo.

M

MACARIUS 3RD, PATRIARCH OF ANTIOCH, fl. 1636-1666

Ridding, Laura, ed. Travels of Macarius: Extracts from the Diary of the Travels of Macarius, Patriarch of Antioch. LC 77-115577. (Russia Observed Ser). 1971. Repr. of 1936 ed. 12.00 (ISBN 0-405-03089-4). Ayer Co Pubs.

Spiritual Direction: Letters of Starets Macarius of Optina Monastery. pap. 1.95 (ISBN 0-686-00254-7). Eastern Orthodox.

MCAULEY, JEREMIAH, 1839-1884

Offord, R. M., ed. Jerry McAuley, an Apostle to the Lost. facsimile ed. LC 75-124248. (Select Bibliographies Reprint Ser). (Illus.). Repr. of 1907 ed. 19.00 (ISBN 0-8369-5436-X). Ayer Co Pubs.

MACCABEES

Cohen, Shaye J. From the Maccabees to the Mishnah. Meeks, Wayne A., ed. LC 86-28077. (Library of Early Christianity: Vol. 7). 252p. 1987. 20.95 (ISBN 0-664-21911-X). Westminster.

Fischel, H. A., intro. by. The First Book of Maccabees. 124p. 1985. pap. 4.95 (ISBN 0-8052-0793-7). Schocken.

Hirsh, Marilyn. The Hanukkah Story. LC 77-22183. (Illus.). 1977. pap. 4.95 (ISBN 0-88482-761-5, Bonim Bks). Hebrew Pub.

MACCABEES–COMMENTARIES

Goldstein, Jonathan A., tr. & intro. by. Maccabees One. LC 75-32719. (Anchor Bible Ser.: Vol. 41). (Illus.). 18.00 (ISBN 0-385-08533-8, Anchor Pr). Doubleday.

MACCABEES, FEAST OF THE

see Hanukkah (Feast of Lights)

MCCULLOUGH, JOHN, 1832-1885

McCullough, William W., Jr. John McCullough: Pioneer Presbyterian Missionary in Texas. (Illus.). 9.50 (ISBN 0-8363-0055-6). Jenkins.

MACDONALD, GEORGE, 1824-1905

Hein, Rolland. The Harmony Within: The Spiritual Vision of George MacDonald. LC 82-1488. pap. 45.80 (ISBN 0-317-30142-X, 2025325). Bks Demand UMI.

Macdonald, Greville. George MacDonald & His Wife. Repr. of 1924 ed. 50.00 (ISBN 0-384-34777-0, E240). Johnson Repr.

Phillips, Michael. George MacDonald. 336p. 1987. 12.95 (ISBN 0-87123-944-2). Bethany Hse.

Reis, Richard H. George MacDonald. LC 71-125820. (Twayne's English Authors Ser.). 1972. lib. bdg. 17.95 (ISBN 0-8057-1356-5). Irvington.

MCGLYNN, EDWARD, 1837-1900

Bell, Stephen. Rebel, Priest & Prophet: A Biography of Dr. Edward McGlynn. LC 75-301. (The Radical Tradition in America Ser). 303p. 1975. Repr. of 1937 ed. 24.75 (ISBN 0-88355-206-X). Hyperion Conn.

Malone, Sylvester L. Dr. Edward McGlynn. 17.00 (ISBN 0-405-10841-9, 11847). Ayer Co Pubs.

MACK FAMILY

Smith, Lucy M. Biographical Sketches of Joseph Smith, the Prophet & His Progenitors for Many Generations. LC 73-83439. (Religion in America, Ser. 1). 1969. Repr. of 1853 ed. 15.00 (ISBN 0-405-00264-5). Ayer Co Pubs.

MADONNA

see Mary, Virgin

MAGI

Boa, Kenneth & Proctor, William. The Return of the Star of Bethlehem. 224p. (Orig.). 1985. pap. 7.95 (ISBN 0-310-33631-7, 12770P). Zondervan.

The Most Excellent Treatise of the Thre Kynges of Coleyne. LC 74-80169. (English Experience Ser: No. 648). (Illus.). 91p. 1974. Repr. of 1499 ed. 9.50 (ISBN 9-0221-0648-9). Walter J Johnson.

O'Rourke, John J. & Greenburg, S. Thomas, eds. Symposium on the Magisterium: A Positive Statement. 1978. 5.95 (ISBN 0-8198-0559-9); pap. 4.50 (ISBN 0-8198-0560-2). Dghtrs St Paul.

Wise, Charles C., Jr. The Magian Gospel of Brother Yeshua. LC 79-84277. (Illus.). 306p. 1979. 11.95 (ISBN 0-917023-05-6); pap. 5.95 (ISBN 0-917023-06-4). Magian Pr.

Zarathustra, Frater. Magickal Qaballah. LC 86-50965. (Illus.). 75p. (Orig.). 1986. pap. 15.00 (ISBN 0-939856-63-8). Tech Group.

MAGI–FICTION

Atiyeh, Wadeeha. Fourth Wise Man. 1959. pap. 3.00 (ISBN 0-8315-0038-7). Speller.

Blanco, Tomas. The Child's Gifts: A Twelfth Night Tale. LC 75-46530. (Eng. & Span., Illus.). 32p. 1976. 8.95 (ISBN 0-664-32595-5). Westminster.

MAGNIFICAT (MUSIC)

De La Rue, Pierre. Magnificat Quinti Toni. Davison, Nigel, ed. LC 65-26095. (Penn State Music Series, No. 8). 19p. 1965. pap. 3.00x (ISBN 0-271-73081-1). Pa St U Pr.

MAGYAR MYTHOLOGY

see Mythology, Finno-Ugrian

MAHABHARATA

Buck, William. Mahabarata. 272p. 1979. pap. 3.95 (ISBN 0-451-62347-9, ME1783, Ment). NAL.

--Mahabharata. (Illus.). 1973. pap. 8.95 (ISBN 0-520-04393-6, CAL 491). U of Cal Pr.

Goldman, Robert P. God's Priests & Warriors: The Bhrgus of the Mahabharata. LC 76-41255. (Studies in Oriental Culture). 195p. 1977. 23.00x (ISBN 0-231-03941-7). Columbia U Pr.

Hopkins, E. Washburn. Epic Mythology. rev. ed. LC 76-75358. 1968. Repr. of 1915 ed. 18.00 (ISBN 0-8196-0228-0). Biblo.

Lal, P. An Annotated Mahabharata Bibliography. 31p. 1973. 10.00 (ISBN 0-88253-306-1). Ind-US Inc.

--The Mahabharata. 352p. 1980. (Pub. by Vikas India); pap. 14.50 (ISBN 0-686-77530-9). Advent NY.

Murdoch, John. The Mahabharata. 160p. 1986. Repr. 14.00X (ISBN 0-8364-1762-3, Pub. by Manohar Inida). South Asia Bks.

Narasimhan, Chakravarthi V., tr. The Mahabharata. LC 64-10347. 254p. (English Version Based on Selected Verses). 1973. pap. 12.00x (ISBN 0-231-08321-1). Columbia U Pr.

Rameshwar Rao, S., tr. The Mahabharata. 2nd ed. Orig. Title: The Children's Mahabharata. 219p. 1976. pap. text ed. cancelled (ISBN 0-89253-041-3). Ind-US Inc.

Sorensen, S. An Index to the Names in the Mahabharata. 1978. Repr. 30.00 (ISBN 0-89684-011-5, Pub. by Motilal Banarsidass India). Orient Bk Dist.

Van Buitenen, J. A. The Mahabharata: The Book of the Beginning, Vol. 1. LC 72-97802. (Illus.). lii, 492p. 1980. pap. 18.00x (ISBN 0-226-84663-6, P879). U of Chicago Pr.

Van Buitenen, J. A., ed. & tr. from Sanskrit. The Mahabharata. Incl. Vol. 1. Book 1: The Book of the Beginning. 1974. 32.00x (ISBN 0-226-84648-2); Vol. II. Book 2: The Book of the Assembly Hall. 1976; Book 3: The Book of the Forest. 1976. LC 72-97802. lib. bdg. 42.00x set (ISBN 0-226-84649-0). U of Chicago Pr.

Van Buitenen, J. A., ed. & tr. The Mahabharata, Vol. 2, Bks. 2 & 3. LC 75-5067. 880p. 1981. Book 2 The Book Of The Assembly Hall. 15.00x (ISBN 0-226-84664-4, Phoen). Book 3 The Book Of The Forest. U of Chicago Pr.

Vyasa. Mahabharata. 6th ed. Rajagopalachari, Chakravarti, ed. Rajagapalachari, Chakravarti & Rao, N. R., trs. from Tamil. 332p. 1980. pap. 5.50 (ISBN 0-934676-16-X). Greenlf Bks.

MAHABHARATA, BHAGAVADGITA

Arnold, Edwin, tr. The Song Celestial or Bhaggvad-Gita: From the Mahabharata, Being a Discourse Between Arjuna, Prince of India, & the Supreme Being under the Form of Krishna. 1967. pap. 5.00 (ISBN 0-7100-6268-0). Methuen Inc.

Judge, William Q., ed. Bhagavad-Gita: Recension with Essays. LC 70-92964. 1977. 6.00 (ISBN 0-911500-27-8); pap. 3.50 (ISBN 0-911500-28-6). Theos U Pr.

Mahesh Yogi Maharishi, tr. Maharishi Mahesh Yogi on the Bhaqavad-Gita. (Orig.). 1969. pap. 8.95 (ISBN 0-14-002913-3). Penguin.

Srinivasachari, P. N. Ethical Philosophy of the Gita. 2.00 (ISBN 0-87481-454-5). Vedanta Pr.

MAHARSHI, SRI RAMANA

Osborne, Arthur, ed. The Collected Works of Ramana Maharshi. 192p. 1970. pap. 9.95 (ISBN 0-87728-070-3). Weiser.

MAHASHAY, NAG

Chakravarty, Sarat C. Nag Mahasaya: A Saintly Householder Disciple of Sri Ramakrishna. 1978. pap. 2.25 (ISBN 0-87481-481-2). Vedanta Pr.

MAHAYANA BUDDHISM

Asvaghosha. Acvaghosa's Discourse on the Awakening of Faith in the Mahayana. Suzuki, D. T., tr. from Chinese. 178p. 1900. Repr. text ed. 17.50x (ISBN 0-89644-475-9, Pub. by Chinese Matl Ctr). Coronet Bks.

Asvaghosha, B. Asvaghosha's Discourse on the Awakening of Faith in the Mahayana. lib. bdg. 79.95 (ISBN 0-87968-472-0). Krishna Pr.

Chang, Garma C. C., ed. A Treasury of Mahayana Sutras: Selections from the Maharatnakuta Sutra. Buddhist Association of the United States, tr. from Chinese. LC 82-42776. (Institute for Advanced Study of World Religions (IASWR) Ser.). 512p. 1983. 26.75x (ISBN 0-271-00341-3). Pa St U Pr.

Conze, Edward. Buddhist Thought in India. 1967. pap. 8.95 (ISBN 0-472-06129-1, 129, AA). U of Mich Pr.

Crowell, E. B. Buddhist Mahayana Texts. lib. bdg. 79.95 (ISBN 0-87968-499-2). Krishna Pr.

Dohanian, Diran D. The Mahayana Buddhist Sculpture of Ceylon. LC 76-23613. (Outstanding Dissertations in the Fine Arts). (Illus.). 1977. Repr. of 1964 ed. lib. bdg. 58.00 (ISBN 0-8240-2685-3). Garland Pub.

Dutt, Nalinaksha. Mahayana Buddhism. rev. ed. 1978. 12.95 (ISBN 0-89684-032-8, Pub. by Motilal Banarsidass India). Orient Bk Dist.

--Mahayana Buddhism. 1976. Repr. of 1973 ed. 11.00x (ISBN 0-8364-0430-0). South Asia Bks.

Getty, Alice. The Gods of Northern Buddhism. LC 62-15617. (Illus.). 1962. 39.50 (ISBN 0-8048-1129-6). C E Tuttle.

Hurvitz, Leon, tr. from Chin & Sanskrit. Scripture of the Lotus Blossom of the Fine Dharma: The Lotus Sutra. LC 75-45381. 1976. pap. 16.00x (ISBN 0-231-03920-4). Columbia U Pr.

Kato, Bunno, et al, trs. The Threefold Lotus Sutra. LC 74-23158. Orig. Title: Hokke Sambu-Kyo. 404p. 1975. 19.75 (ISBN 0-8348-0105-1); pap. 10.95 (ISBN 0-8348-0106-X). Weatherhill.

Kiyota, Minoru. Mahayana Buddhist Meditation: Theory & Practice. 327p. 1978. text ed. 17.50x (ISBN 0-8248-0556-9). UH Pr.

Lama Mi-phan. Golden Zephyr. Kawamura, Leslie S., tr. from Tibetan. LC 75-5259. (Tibetan Translation Ser.: Vol.4). (Illus.). 192p. (Orig.). 1975. 12.95 (ISBN 0-913546-22-4); pap. 6.95 (ISBN 0-913546-21-6). Dharma Pub.

McGovern, William M. Introduction to Mahayana Buddhism. LC 70-149665. Repr. of 1922 ed. 17.00 (ISBN 0-404-04129-9). AMS Pr.

O'Neil, Kevin. Awakening of Faith in Mahayana. (Orig.). 1984. pap. 14.95 (ISBN 0-86627-012-4). Crises Res Pr.

Pye, Michael. Skilful Means: A Concept in Mahayana Buddhism. 211p. 1978. 75.00 (ISBN 0-7156-1266-2, Pub. by Duckworth London). Longwood Pub Group.

Suzuki, Daisetz T. Studies in the Lankavatara Sutra: An Elucidation & Analysis of One of the Most Important Texts of Mahayana Buddhism, in Which Almost All Its Principal Tenets Are Presented Including the Teaching of Zen. 1968. Repr. of 1930 ed. 31.00 (ISBN 0-7100-6330-X). Methuen Inc.

Suzuki, Daisetz T., tr. The Lankavatara Sutra: A Mahayana Text. (Illus.). 1972. Repr. of 1932 ed. 27.00 (ISBN 0-7100-2165-8). Methuen Inc.

Thomas, E. J., tr. from Sanskrit. The Perfection of Wisdom: The Career of the Predestined Buddhas. LC 78-12005. 1979. Repr. of 1952 ed. lib. bdg. 22.50x (ISBN 0-313-20646-5, MAPWI). Greenwood.

Thurman, Robert A., tr. from Tibetan. The Holy Teaching of Vimalakirti: Mahayana Scripture. LC 75-27197. (Institute for Advanced Study of World Religions Ser.). 176p. 1976. 20.00x (ISBN 0-271-01209-9); pap. 10.00 (ISBN 0-271-00601-3). Pa St U Pr.

Tripitaka Master Hua, commentary by. Dharma Flower Sutra, Vol. II. Buddhist Text Translation Society, tr. from Chinese. (Chinese., Illus.). 324p. (Orig.). 1978. pap. 9.00 (ISBN 0-917512-22-7). Buddhist Text.

MAHDI

Bazargan, Mehdi. The Inevitable Victory. Yousefi, Mohammad, tr. from Persian. 35p. 1979. pap. 1.25x (ISBN 0-941722-03-1). Book-Dist-Ctr.

Wingate, F. R. Mahdiism & Egyptian Sudan. 2nd ed. (Illus.). 618p. 1968. 45.00x (ISBN 0-7146-1738-5, F Cass Co). Biblio Dist.

MAI-CHI SHAN CAVES

Sullivan, Michael. The Cave Temples of Maichishan. LC 69-15829. (Illus.). 1969. 70.00x (ISBN 0-520-01448-0). U of Cal Pr.

MAIER, WALTER ARTHUR, 1893-1950

Maier, Paul L. The Best of Walter A. Maier. 1980. pap. 7.95 (ISBN 0-570-03823-5, 12-2786). Concordia.

--A Man Spoke, a World Listened. 1980. pap. 8.95 (ISBN 0-570-03822-7, 12-2762). Concordia.

MAIMON, SOLOMON, 1754-1800

Maimon, Solomon. An Autobiography. Hadas, Moses, ed. 124p. 1985. pap. 4.95 (ISBN 0-8052-0150-5). Schocken.

MAITLAND, FREDERIC WILLIAM, 1850-1906

Elton, G. R. F. W. Maitland. LC 85-40439. 128p. 1985. 15.00x (ISBN 0-300-03528-4). Yale U Pr.

Milson, S. F. F. W. Maitland. (Master-Mind Lectures (Henriette Hertz Trust)). 1980. pap. 3.75 (ISBN 0-85672-241-3, Pub. by British Acad). Longwood Pub Group.

Ogle, Arthur. Canon Law in Mediaeval England: An Examination of William Lyndwood's Provinciale. LC 78-156390. (Research & Source Works Ser.: No. 731). 1971. Repr. of 1912 ed. lib. bdg. 20.50 (ISBN 0-8337-2603-X). B Franklin.

MAJOR ORDERS

see Bishops; Clergy

MALAWI

McCracken, J. Politics & Christianity in Malawi 1875-1940. LC 76-27905. (Cambridge Commonwealth Ser.). (Illus.). 1977. 49.50 (ISBN 0-521-21444-0). Cambridge U Pr.

MALEBRANCHE, NICOLAS, 1638-1715

Hobart, Michael E. Science & Religion in the Thought of Nicolas Malebranche. LC 81-7419. x, 196p. 1982. 19.95x (ISBN 0-8078-1487-3). U of NC Pr.

MALEDICTION

see Blessing and Cursing

MALTA

Vassallo, Mario. From Lordship to Stewardship: Religion & Social Change in Malta. 1979. text ed. 22.00x (ISBN 90-279-7967-7). Mouton.

MALTHUS, THOMAS ROBERT, 1766-1834

Bradlaugh, Charles. Jesus, Shelley, & Malthus. 1978. Repr. of 1877 ed. lib. bdg. 10.00 (ISBN 0-8495-0441-4). Arden Lib.

Greg, William R. Enigmas of Life. LC 72-323. (Essay Index Reprint Ser.). Repr. of 1879 ed. 21.00 (ISBN 0-8369-2794-X). Ayer Co Pubs.

MAN–ORIGIN

see also Evolution; Life–Origin

Cosgrove, Mark P. The Amazing Body Human. 160p. 1987. pap. 7.95 (ISBN 0-8010-2517-6). Baker Bk.

Geisler, Norman L. & Anderson, J. Kerby. Origin Science. 1987. pap. 8.95 (ISBN 0-8010-3808-1). Baker Bk.

Grayson, Donald K., ed. The Establishment of Human Antiquity (Monograph) LC 82-11571. 280p. 1983. 29.50 (ISBN 0-12-297250-3). Acad Pr.

Gribbin, John. Genesis: The Origins of Man & the Universe. (Illus., Orig.). 1982. pap. 8.95 (ISBN 0-385-28321-0, Delta). Dell.

Huxley, Thomas H. Evolution & Ethics, & Other Essays. LC 70-8391. 334p. 1897. Repr. 49.00x (ISBN 0-403-00041-6). Scholarly.

Moore, John N. How to Teach Origins. 1987. pap. 14.95 (ISBN 0-8010-6219-5). Baker Bk.

Morrison, Nathaniel. Human Roots, Fact or Fiction? 1983. 4.95 (ISBN 0-8062-2218-2). Carlton.

Tobin, Thomas H. The Creation of Man: Philo & the History of Interpretation. Vawter, Bruce, ed. LC 82-19891. (Catholic Biblical Quarterly Monographs: No. 14). viii, 199p. (Orig.). 1983. pap. 6.00x (ISBN 0-915170-13-2). Catholic Biblical.

Van Pelt, G. Man's Divine Parentage & Destiny: The Great Rounds & Races. Small, W. Emmett & Todd, Helen, eds. (Theosophical Manual: No. 7). 64p. 1975. pap. 2.00 (ISBN 0-913004-24-3, 913004-24). Point Loma Pub.

Von Daniken, Erich. Chariots of the Gods. 189p. 1985. 42.50 (ISBN 0-317-19961-7). Bern Porter.

Wilder-Smith, A. W. Man's Origin, Man's Destiny. LC 74-28508. 320p. 1975. pap. 7.95 (ISBN 0-87123-356-8, 210356). Bethany Hse.

Yereance, Robert A. Strangers, All Strangers. LC 79-27016. 1981. 14.95 (ISBN 0-87949-151-5). Ashley Bks.

MAN (PHILOSOPHY)

see Philosophical Anthropology

MAN (THEOLOGY)

see also Fall of Man; Humanism, Religious; Identification (Religion); Pelagianism; Sex (Theology); Sin; Soul; Work (Theology)

Amy, William O. & Recob, James B. Human Nature in the Christian Tradition. LC 82-45049. 118p. (Orig.). 1982. lib. bdg. 24.75 (ISBN 0-8191-2512-1); pap. text ed. 8.75 (ISBN 0-8191-2513-X). U Pr of Amer.

Anderson, Ray S. On Being Human: Essays in Theological Anthropology. 234p. (Orig.). 1982. pap. 9.95 (ISBN 0-8028-1926-5). Eerdmans.

Astley, H. J. Biblical Anthropology. 1977. Repr. of 1929 ed. 32.50 (ISBN 0-685-82796-8). Sharon Hill.

Bawa Muhaiyaddeen, M. R. Wisdom of Man: Selected Discourses. LC 80-20541. (Illus.). 168p. 1980. 7.95 (ISBN 0-914390-16-3). Fellowship Pr PA.

Brakhage, Pamela. The Theology of "La Lozana Andaluza". 27.50 (ISBN 0-916379-34-5). Scripta.

Buck, Peter H. Anthropology & Religion. 1939. 11.50x (ISBN 0-686-83471-2). Elliots Bks.

Burns, J. Patout, ed. Theological Anthropology. LC 81-43080. (Sources of Early Christian Thought Ser.). 1981. pap. 7.95 (ISBN 0-8006-1412-7). Fortress.

Carus, Paul. The Soul of Man. 59.95 (ISBN 0-8490-1090-X). Gordon Pr.

Clark, Gordon H. The Biblical Doctrine of Man. (Trinity Papers: No. 7). 95p. (Orig.). 1984. pap. 5.95 (ISBN 0-940931-07-9). Trinity Found.

Colbert-Thornton, Mollie. God's Purpose for Man: The Spirit & the Flesh. 141p. 1984. 8.95 (ISBN 0-533-05913-5). Vantage.

Delliquadri, Lyn, ed. Drawings: Eighty-First Exhibition by Artists of Chicago & Vicinity. 32p. (Orig.). 1985. pap. 6.95 (ISBN 0-86559-071-0). Art Inst Chi.

Doniger, Simon, ed. The Nature of Man in Theological & Psychological Perspective. LC 72-10819. (Essay Index Reprint Ser.). 1973. Repr. of 1962 ed. 18.00 (ISBN 0-8369-7213-9). Ayer Co Pubs.

Felins, Yehuda. Nature & Man in the Bible: Chapters in Biblical Ecology. 1982. 25.00x (ISBN 0-900689-19-6). Bloch.

Fisk, Samuel. Divine Sovereignty & Human Freedom. LC 73-81550. 1973. pap. 5.95 (ISBN 0-87213-166-1). Loizeaux.

Hamilton, William. The Christian Man. LC 56-8666. (Layman's Theological Library). 94p. 1956. pap. 1.00 (ISBN 0-664-24003-8). Westminster.

Howes, Elizabeth B. & Moon, Sheila. The Choicemaker. LC 76-54534. 1977. pap. 3.95 (ISBN 0-8356-0492-6, Quest). Theos Pub Hse.

Jabay, Earl. The God-Players. LC 69-11637. 155p. 1970. pap. 5.95 (ISBN 0-310-26541-X, 9939P). Zondervan.

--Kingdom of Self. LC 73-89494. 1974. pap. 3.95 (ISBN 0-88270-062-6). Bridge Pub.

Janz, Denis. Luther & Late Medieval Thomism: A Study in Theological Anthropology. 191p. 1984. text ed. 25.00x (ISBN 0-88920-132-3). Humanities.

Jeeves, Malcolm A., et al. Free to Be Different. American ed. LC 84-10525. Repr. of 1985 ed. 40.80 (2027547). Bks Demand UMI.

Kinigsberg, David. Modern Man & An Old-Fashioned God. 1985. 7.95 (ISBN 0-533-06659-X). Vantage.

Ledwith, Miceal, tr. from Lat. Propositions on the Dignity & Rights of the Human Person. (International Theological Commission Ser.). 28p. (Orig.). 1986. pap. 1.95 (ISBN 1-55586-997-1). US Catholic.

Liderbach, Daniel. The Theology of Grace & the American Mind: A Representation of Catholic Doctrine. LC 83-22154. (Toronto Studies in Theology: Vol. 15). 170p. 1983. lib. bdg. 39.95x (ISBN 0-88946-761-7). E Mellen.

McClanahan, John H. Man As Sinner. LC 84-20036. (Layman's Library of Christian Doctrine Ser.). 1987. 5.95 (ISBN 0-8054-1637-4). Broadman.

McGinn, Bernard. The Golden Chain: A Study in the Theological Anthropology of Isaac of Stella. LC 70-152487. (Cistercian Studies: No. 15). 280p. 1972. 7.50 (ISBN 0-87907-815-4). Cistercian Pubns.

McGinn, Bernard, ed. Three Treatises on Man: A Cistercian Anthropology. LC 77-184906. (Cistercian Fathers Ser.: No. 24). 1977. 13.95 (ISBN 0-87907-024-2). Cistercian Pubns.

Machiavelli, Niccolo. Machiavelli's Thoughts on the Management of Men. (Illus.). 119p. 1982. 107.50 (ISBN 0-89266-364-2). Am Classical Coll Pr.

McLean, Stuart. Humanity in the Thought of Karl Barth. 240p. 1981. 20.95 (ISBN 0-567-09304-2, Pub. by T&T Clark Ltd UK). Fortress.

Macquarrie, John. In Search of Humanity: A Theological & Philosophical Approach. LC 82-22077. 288p. 1983. 16.95 (ISBN 0-8245-0564-6). Crossroad NY.

Malina, Bruce J. Christian Origins & Cultural Anthropology: Practical Models for Biblical Interpretation. 288p. 1985. pap. 24.95 (ISBN 0-8042-0241-9). John Knox.

Man & God. (Miniature Ser.). 0.50 (ISBN 0-685-61383-6). Aum Pubns.

Mantzaridis, Georgios I. The Deification of Man. Sherrard, Liadain, tr. from Gr. 136p. (Orig.). 1984. pap. text ed. 7.95 (ISBN 0-88141-027-6). St Vladimirs.

Mascall, Eric L. Importance of Being Human. LC 74-12849. 118p. 1974. Repr. of 1958 ed. lib. bdg. 22.50 (ISBN 0-8371-7761-8, MABH). Greenwood.

Massey, Craig. Adjust or Self-Destruct. LC 77-4088. pap. 3.50 (ISBN 0-8024-0136-8). Moody.

Miles, Margaret R. Fullness of Life: Historical Foundations for a New Asceticism. LC 81-11535. 186p. 1981. pap. 11.95 (ISBN 0-664-24389-4). Westminster.

Moltmann, Jurgen. Man Christian Anthroplogy in the Conflicts of the Present. LC 73-88350. pap. 34.00 (2026872). Bks Demand UMI.

Morris, Brian. Anthropological Studies of Religion: An Introductory Text. (Illus.). 384p. 1987. 42.50 (ISBN 0-521-32794-6); pap. 12.95 (ISBN 0-521-33991-X). Cambridge U Pr.

O'Connell, Robert J. Saint Augustine's Early Theory of Man, A. D. 386-391. LC 68-21981. 1968. text ed. 20.00x (ISBN 0-674-78520-7, Belknap Pr). Harvard U Pr.

O'Reilly, Sean. In the Image of God. 92p. 1982. 2.95 (ISBN 0-8198-3607-9, MS0308); pap. 1.95 (ISBN 0-8198-3608-7). Dghtrs St Paul.

Pannenberg, Wolfhart. Anthropology in Theological Perspective. O'Connell, Matthew J., tr. from German. LC 84-22048. 552p. 1985. 38.95 (ISBN 0-664-21399-5). Westminster.

Pope John Paul II. The Whole Truth About Man. 1981. 7.95 (ISBN 0-686-73822-5); pap. 6.95 (ISBN 0-8198-8202-X). Dghtrs St Paul.

Purchas, Samuel. Purchas His Pilgrim Microcosmus: Or The Historie of Man. LC 76-25513. (English Experience Ser.: No. 146). 820p. 1969. Repr. of 1619 ed. 69.00 (ISBN 90-221-0146-0). Walter J Johnson.

Rough, Worth S. Synopsis: Past-Present-Future. LC 84-90177. 84p. 1984. 17.95 (ISBN 0-533-06227-6). Vantage.

Schwaller De Lubicz, R. A. The Temple in Man: Sacred Architecture & the Perfect Man. Lawlor, Robert & Lawlor, Deborah, trs. from Fr. LC 81-13374. (Illus.). 132p. 1981. pap. 6.95 (ISBN 0-89281-021-1). Inner Tradit.

Segundo, Jean L. Grace & the Human Condition. Drury, John, tr. from Span. LC 72-85794. (A Theology for Artisans of a New Humanity Ser.: Vol. 2). Orig. Title: Gracia y Condicion Humana. 221p. 1973. pap. 7.95 (ISBN 0-88344-488-7). Orbis Bks.

Siirala, Aarne. Divine Humanness. Kantonen, T. A., tr. LC 70-99460. pap. 48.00 (2026964). Bks Demand UMI.

Steiner, Rudolf. Man as a Being of Sense & Perception. Lenn, Dorothy, tr. from Ger. 53p. 1981. pap. 6.00 (ISBN 0-919924-11-5, Pub. by Steiner Book Centre Canada). Anthroposophic.

--Man as a Picture of the Living Spirit. Adams, George, tr. from Ger. 31p. (Orig.). 1972. pap. 1.95 (ISBN 0-85440-253-5, Pub. by Steinerbooks). Anthroposophic.

Stinson, Linda L. Process & Conscience: Toward a Theology of Human Emergence. 202p. (Orig.). 1986. lib. bdg. 22.50 (ISBN 0-8191-5206-4); pap. text ed. 11.50 (ISBN 0-8191-5207-2). U Pr of Amer.

Torrance, Thomas F. Calvin's Doctrine of Man. LC 77-5615. 1977. Repr. lib. bdg. 22.50x (ISBN 0-8371-9639-6, TOCD). Greenwood.

Tozer, Aiden W. Man, the Dwelling Place of God. 5.95 (ISBN 0-87509-188-1); pap. 4.45 (ISBN 0-87509-165-2); mass market 2.95 (ISBN 0-87509-166-0). Chr Pubns.

Viladesau, Richard. The Reason for Our Hope: A Introduction to Anthropology. LC 83-82019. 1984. pap. 10.95 (ISBN 0-8091-2574-9). Paulist Pr.

Vinoi, Lawrence. God & Man: The Essential Knowledge Which Everyone, but Absolutely Everyone Ought to Possess About Human Nature & the Nature of God & How the Two Are Related. (Essential Knowledge Ser. Books). (Illus.). 1978. plastic spiral bdg. 44.75 (ISBN 0-89266-118-6). Am Classical Coll Pr.

What, Then, Is Man? A Symposium. 356p. 1971. 10.50 (12-2361). Concordia.

MAN (THEOLOGY)–BIBLICAL TEACHING

Anderson, Ray S. On Being Human: Essays in Theological Anthropology. 234p. (Orig.). 1982. pap. 9.95 (ISBN 0-8028-1926-5). Eerdmans.

Flynn, Leslie B. What Is Man. Chao, Lorna Y., tr. (Chinese.). 1985. pap. write for info. (ISBN 0-941598-27-6). Living Spring Pubns.

Hicks, Robert & Bewes, Richard. Man. (Understanding Bible Truth Ser.). (Orig.). 1981. pap. 0.95 (ISBN 0-89840-025-2). Heres Life.

Portillo, Carlos E. Eternal Security Is Conditional. LC 85-52117. 150p. (Orig.). 1987. pap. write for info. (ISBN 0-937365-03-3). WCP Pubns.

Wolff, Hans W. Anthropology of the Old Testament. Kohl, Margaret, tr. from Ger. LC 74-21591. 304p. 1981. pap. 10.95 (ISBN 0-8006-1500-X, 1-1500). Fortress.

MAN, DOCTRINE OF

see Man (Theology)

MAN, FALL OF

see Fall of Man

MANDAEAN LANGUAGE

Macuch, Rudolf. Handbook of Classical & Modern Mandaic. 1965. 129.00x (ISBN 3-11-000261-2). De Gruyter.

MANDAEANS

Kraeling, Carl H. Anthropos & Son of Man. LC 27-23162. (Columbia University. Oriental Studies: No. 25). Repr. of 1927 ed. 18.50 (ISBN 0-404-50515-5). AMS Pr.

Macuch, Rudolf. Zur Sprache und Literatur der Mandaer: Mit Beitraegen von Kurt Rudolph & Eric Segelberg. 1976. 76.00x (ISBN 3-11-004838-8). De Gruyter.

MANDALA

Arguelles, Jose & Arguelles, Miriam. Mandala. LC 70-189856. (Illus.). 144p. 1972. pap. 14.95 (ISBN 0-87773-033-4, 73000-3). Shambhala Pubns.

Ngor Tharttse mKhanpo bSodnams rgyamtsho. Tibetan Mandalas: The Ngor Collection. Tachikawa, Musashi, ed. (Tibetan, Sanskrit, Japanese & Eng., Illus.). 1985. Set. boxed ltd. ed. 1500.00x (ISBN 0-87773-800-9). Vol. 1, 300p. Vol. 2, 340p. Shambhala Pubns.

MANGER IN CHRISTIAN ART AND TRADITION

see Crib in Christian Art and Tradition

MANICHAEISM

Alexander of Lycopolis. Alexander of Lycopolis Against Manichaeism. Koenen, Ludwig, ed. (Reprints & Translations). 1988. pap. write for info. (ISBN 0-89130-895-4, 00-07-12). Scholars Pr GA.

Alfaric, Prosper. Les Ecritures Manicheennes. (Reprints & Translations). Date not set. Vol. 1, Vue Generale. pap. price not set (ISBN 0-89130-896-2, 00-07-13). Vol. 2, Etude Analythique. Scholars Pr GA.

Asmussen, Jes P., compiled by. Manichaean Literature: Representative Texts, Chiefly from Middle Persian & Parthian Writings. LC 74-22063. (Unesco Collection of Representative Works, Oriental Ser.). 160p. 1975. lib. bdg. 30.00x (ISBN 0-8201-1141-4). Schol Facsimiles.

Augustinus, Aurelius. Contra Felicem De Natura Boni Epistula Secundini, Contra Secundinum, Pt. 2. Bd. with De Natura Boni Epistula Secundini; Contra Secundinum. (Corpus Scriptorum Ecclesiasticorum Latinorum Ser: Vol. 25). (Lat.). Repr. of 1892 ed. unbound 50.00 (ISBN 0-384-02365-7). Johnson Repr.

--De Utilitate Credendi, Pt. 1. Bd. with De Duabus Animabus; Contra Fortunatem; Contra Adimantum. (Corpus Scriptorum Ecclesiasticorum Latinorum Ser: Vol. 25). Repr. of 1891 ed. 50.00 (ISBN 0-384-02364-9). Johnson Repr.

Burkitt, Francis C. The Religion of the Manichees: Donnellan Lectures for 1924. LC 77-84698. Repr. of 1925 ed. 29.00 (ISBN 0-404-16105-7). AMS Pr.
Cameron, Ron & Dewey, Arthur J., trs. The Cologne Mani Codex. LC 79-14743. (Society of Biblical Literature Texts & Translations, 15. Early Christian Literature Ser.: No. 3). 1979. pap. 8.95 (ISBN 0-89130-312-X, 060215). Scholars Pr GA.
Jackson, Abraham V. Researches in Manichaeism with Special Reference to the Turfan Fragments. LC 32-9567. (Columbia University. Indo-Iranian Ser.: No. 13). Repr. of 1932 ed. 31.00 (ISBN 0-404-50483-3). AMS Pr.
Kraeling, Carl H. Anthropos & Son of Man. LC 27-23162. (Columbia University. Oriental Studies: No. 25). Repr. of 1927 ed. 18.50 (ISBN 0-404-50515-5). AMS Pr.
Liber de Duobus Principiis. Un Traite Neo-Manicheen du XIIIe siecle. LC 78-63185. (Heresies of the Early Christian & Medieval Era: Second Ser.). 1979. Repr. of 1939 ed. 32.00 (ISBN 0-404-16224-X). AMS Pr.
Lieu, Samuel N. Manichaeism in the Later Roman Empire & Medieval China. LC 84-26093. 240p. 1985. 54.00 (ISBN 0-7190-1088-8, Pub. by Manchester Univ Pr). Longwood Pub Group.
Serapion, Saint Against the Manichees. Casey, Robert P., ed. (Harvard Theological Studies). 1931. pap. 15.00 (ISBN 0-527-01015-4). Kraus Repr.

MANIFEST DESTINY (U. S.)
see Messianism, American

MANN, HORACE, 1796-1859
Culver, Raymond B. Horace Mann & Religion in the Massachusetts Public Schools. LC 72-89168. (American Education: Its Men, Institutions & Ideas, Ser. 1). 1969. Repr. of 1929 ed. 17.00 (ISBN 0-405-01406-6). Ayer Co Pubs.

MANNING, HENRY EDWARD, CARDINAL, 1808-1892
Donald, Gertrude. Men Who Left the Movement. facs. ed. LC 67-23207. (Essay Index Reprint Ser). 1933. 20.00 (ISBN 0-8369-0385-4). Ayer Co Pubs.
Fitzsimmons, John, ed. Manning: Anglican & Catholic. LC 78-11571. 1979. Repr. of 1951 ed. lib. bdg. cancelled (ISBN 0-313-21005-5, FIMA). Greenwood.
Newsome, David H. Wilberforces & Henry Manning: The Parting of Friends. LC 67-2. (Illus.). 1966. 30.00x (ISBN 0-674-95280-4, Belknap Pr). Harvard U Pr.
Purcell, Edmund S. Life of Cardinal Manning, Archbishop of Westminster, 2 vols. LC 70-126605. (Europe 1815-1945 Ser.). 1534p. 1973. Repr. of 1896 ed. Set. lib. bdg. 115.00 (ISBN 0-306-70050-6). Da Capo.
--Life of Cardinal Manning, Archbishop of Westminster, 2 vols. 1973. Repr. of 1896 ed. 50.00 set (ISBN 0-8274-1075-1). R West.
Strachey, Lytton. Eminent Victorians. 354p. 1969. pap. 6.95 (ISBN 0-15-628697-1, Harv). HarBraceJ.

MANORS
Addy, Sidney O. Church & Manor: A Study in English Economic History. LC 70-107902. (Illus.). 1970. Repr. of 1913 ed. 37.50x (ISBN 0-678-00632-6). Kelley.
London-St. Paul'S Cathedral. Domesday of Saint Paul of the Year Twelve Twenty-Two. Repr. of 1858 ed. 37.00 (ISBN 0-384-33475-X). Johnson Repr.

MANUS TRIBE
Buhler, G. The Laws of Manu. lib. bdg. 79.95 (ISBN 0-87968-492-5). Krishna Pr.

MANUSCRIPTS
see also Genizah; Illumination of Books and Manuscripts
Alexander, J. J., ed. The Decorated Letter. LC 78-6487. (Magnificent Paperback Ser.). 1978. 22.95 (ISBN 0-8076-0894-7); pap. 12.95 (ISBN 0-8076-0895-5). Braziller.
Charlesworth, James H. The New Discoveries in St. Catherine's Monastery: A Preliminary Report on the Manuscripts. Freedman, David N., intro. by. LC 81-10992. (American Schools of Oriental Research Monographs: No. 3). (Illus.). 45p. (Orig.). 1982. pap. text ed. 6.00x (ISBN 0-89757-403-6, Am Sch Orient Res). Eisenbrauns.
Forstemann, E. Commentary on the Maya Manuscript in the Royal Public Library of Dresden. (HU PMP). 1906. 25.00 (ISBN 0-527-01202-5). Kraus Repr.
Goldstein, David. Hebrew Manuscript Painting. LC 85-18995. (Illus.). 80p. (Orig.). 1985. pap. 8.95 (ISBN 0-7123-0054-6, Pub. by British Lib). Longwood Pub Group.
Gutmann, Joseph. Hebrew Manuscript Painting. (Magnificent Paperback Art Ser.). 1978. 22.95 (ISBN 0-8076-0890-4); pap. 12.95 (ISBN 0-8076-0891-2). Braziller.
Hatch, William H. Greek & Syrian Miniatures in Jerusalem. (Illus.). 1931. 15.00x (ISBN 0-910956-04-9). Medieval Acad.
Hughes, Andrew. Medieval Manuscripts for Mass & Office: A Guide to Their Organization & Terminology. 496p. 1981. 65.00x (ISBN 0-8020-5467-6). U of Toronto Pr.
Knorozov, Yuri V. & Proskouriakoff, Tatiana, eds. Selected Chapters from the Writings of the Maya Indians. Coe, Sophie, tr. LC 70-38502. (Harvard University. Peabody Museum of Archaeology & Ethnology. Russian Translation Ser.: No. 4). Repr. of 1967 ed. 28.00 (ISBN 0-404-52647-0). AMS Pr.
Latham, Robert, ed. Catalogue of the Pepys Library at Magdalene College Cambridge: Volume 5, Part 2: Modern Manuscripts, Vol. V - Pt. 2. 302p. 1981. 135.00x (ISBN 0-8476-7050-3). Rowman.
Morag, Shelomo. Vocalised Talmudic Manuscripts in the Cambridge Genizah Collections: Taylor-Schnechter Old Series, Vol. 1. (Cambridge University Library Genizan Ser.: No. 4). 60p. Date not set. Vol. I: Taylor-Schechter Old Series. price not set (ISBN 0-521-26863-X). Cambridge U Pr.
Post, Levi A. The Vatican Plato & Its Relations. (APA Philological Monographs). 22.50 (ISBN 0-89130-704-4, 40-00-04). Scholars Pr GA.
Sanders, Henry A. New Testament Manuscripts in the Freer Collection. Repr. of 1918 ed. 37.00 (ISBN 0-384-38809-4). Johnson Repr.
--Old Testament Manuscripts in the Freer Collection. Repr. of 1917 ed. 37.00 (ISBN 0-384-38808-6). Johnson Repr.
Schellhas, P. Representation of Deities of the Maya Manuscripts. (Hupmaen Ser.: Vol. 4, No. 1). (Illus.). 1904. pap. 15.00 (ISBN 0-527-01198-3). Kraus Repr.
Worrell, William H. The Coptic Manuscripts in the Freer Collection. Repr. of 1923 ed. 37.00 (ISBN 0-384-38810-8). Johnson Repr.

MANUSCRIPTS–BIBLIOGRAPHY
Kutsche, Paul. A Guide to Cherokee Documents in the Northeastern United States. LC 85-11798. (Native American Bibliography Ser.: No. 7). 541p. 1986. 75.00 (ISBN 0-8108-1827-2). Scarecrow.
Revell, Peter. Fifteenth-Century English Prayers & Meditations: A Bibliography of Manuscripts Preserved at the British Museum Library. LC 75-6579. (Reference Library of Humanities: Vol. 19). 150p. 1975. lib. bdg. 28.00 (ISBN 0-8240-1098-1). Garland Pub.

MANUSCRIPTS–CATALOGS
American Jewish Archives, Cincinnati Staff, ed. Manuscript Catalog of the American Jewish Archives, 4 vols. 1971. Set. lib. bdg. 400.00 (ISBN 0-8161-0899-4, Hall Library). G K Hall.
--Manuscript Catalog of the American Jewish Archives, Cincinnati: First Supplement. 1978. lib. bdg. 105.00 (ISBN 0-8161-0934-6, Hall Library). G K Hall.
Athos Monasteries Staff. Catalogue of the Greek Manuscripts in the Library of the Monastery of Vatopedi on Mt. Athos. (Harvard Theological Studies Ser.). 1924. 24.00 (ISBN 0-527-01011-1). Kraus Repr.
Leveen, J. Catalogue of the Hebrew & Samaritan Manuscripts in the British Museum: Introduction, Indexes, etc, Pt. 4. 224p. 1977. Repr. of 1935 ed. 22.50 (ISBN 0-7141-0619-4, Pub. by British Lib). Longwood Pub Group.
Mach, Rudolph. Catalogue of Arabic Manuscripts (Yahuda Section) in the Garrett Collection, Princeton University Library. LC 75-2999. (Illus.). 1976. 160.00x (ISBN 0-691-03908-9). Princeton U Pr.
McKinlay, A. P., ed. Arator: The Codices. 1942. 8.00x (ISBN 0-910956-18-9). Medieval Acad.
Margoliouth, G. Catalogue of the Hebrew & Samaritan Manuscripts in the British Museum, Pt. 3. 620p. 1965. Repr. of 1909 ed. 15.00 (ISBN 0-7141-0645-3, Pub. by British Lib). Longwood Pub Group.
Sinclair, Keith V., compiled by. French Devotional Texts of the Middle Ages: A Bibliographic Manuscript Guide. LC 79-7587. 1979. lib. bdg. 49.95x (ISBN 0-313-20649-X, SFT/). Greenwood.

MANUSCRIPTS–FACSIMILES
Hatch, William H. Greek & Syrian Miniatures in Jerusalem. (Illus.). 1931. 15.00x (ISBN 0-910956-04-9). Medieval Acad.
Thomas a Becket. Fragments D'une Vie de Saint Thomas de Cantorbery en Vers Accouples. 25.00 (ISBN 0-384-60189-8); pap. 19.00 (ISBN 0-384-60179-0). Johnson Repr.

MANUSCRIPTS (PAPYRI)
see also Egyptian Language–Papyri
Aland, Kurt, ed. Repertorium der Griechischen Christlichen Papyri, Pt.1: Biblische Papyri, Altes Testament, Neues Testament, Varia, Apokryphen. (Patristische Texte und Studien, Vol. 18). 473p. 1976. 63.20x (ISBN 3-11-004674-1). De Gruyter.
Bell, H. Idris & Skeat, T. C., eds. Fragments of an Unknown Gospel & Other Early Christian Papyri. (Illus.). 76p. 1935. Repr. of 1935 ed. 7.50 (ISBN 0-7141-0438-8, Pub. by British Lib). Longwood Pub Group.
Schuman, Verne B. Washington University Papyri I: Non-Literary Texts, Nos. 1-16. LC 79-14199. (American Society of Papyrologists Ser.: No. 310017). 15.00 (ISBN 0-89130-286-7, 310017). Scholars Pr GA.
Winlock, Herbert E., et al. The Monastery of Epiphanius at Thebes: Metropolitan Museum of Art Egyptain Expedition Publications, Vols. 3 & 4, 2 vols. LC 72-168413. (The Metropolitan Museum of Art Publication in Reprint Ser.). 1926. 88.00 set (ISBN 0-405-02249-2). Ayer Co Pubs.

MANUSCRIPTS, ILLUMINATED
see Illumination of Books and Manuscripts

MAORIS
Best, Elsdon. Maori Religion & Mythology. LC 75-35236. Repr. of 1924 ed. 45.00 (ISBN 0-404-14412-8). AMS Pr.
Simmons, David. Whakairo: Maori Tribal Art. (Illus.). 1985. 34.95x (ISBN 0-19-558119-9). Oxford U Pr.
Smith, Jean. Tapu Removal in Maori Religion. 96p. 1974. text ed. 12.00x (ISBN 0-8248-0591-7). UH Pr.

MARCEL, GABRIEL, 1887-
Keen, Sam. Gabriel Marcel. LC 67-11288. (Makers of Contemporary Theology Ser). pap. 15.00 (ISBN 0-8357-9258-7, 2015434). Bks Demand UMI.
McCown, Joe. Availability: Gabriel Marcel & the Phenomenology of Human Openness. LC 77-22358. (American Academy of Religion. Studies in Religion: No. 14). 1978. pap. 9.95 (ISBN 0-89130-144-5, 010014). Scholars Pr GA.

MARCION, OF SINOPE, 2ND CENTURY
Knox, John. Marcion & the New Testament. LC 78-63168. (Heresies of the Early Christian & Medieval Era: Second Ser.). Repr. of 1942 ed. 31.00 (ISBN 0-404-16183-9). AMS Pr.
Von Harnack, Adolf. Marcion: The Gospel of the Alien God. Steely, John E. & Bierma, Lyle D., trs. from Ger. Orig. Title: Marcion, das Evangelium vom Fremden Gott. 265p. 1987. lib. bdg. 24.95 (ISBN 0-939464-16-0). Labyrinth Pr.
Wilson, Robert S. Marcion. LC 78-63176. (Heresies of the Early Christian & Medieval Era: Second Ser.). Repr. of 1933 ed. 32.00 (ISBN 0-404-16194-4). AMS Pr.

MARIE DE L'INCARNATION, MOTHER, 1599-1672
L'Heureux, Mother Aloysius G. Mystical Vocabulary of Venerable Mere Marie De L'Incarnation & Its Problems. LC 72-94190. (Catholic University of America Studies in Romance Languages & Literatures Ser: No. 53). (Fr.). Repr. of 1956 ed. 24.00 (ISBN 0-404-50353-5). AMS Pr.

MARIIA, MOTHER, 1891-1945
Hackel, Sergei. Pearl of Great Price: The Life of Mother Maria Skobtsova 1891-1945. rev. ed. LC 81-21356. 192p. 1982. pap. 6.95 (ISBN 0-913836-85-0). St Vladimirs.

MARIOLATRY
see Mary, Virgin–Cultus

MARIONETTES
see Puppets and Puppet-Plays

MARITAIN, JACQUES, 1882-1973
Allard, Jean-Louis. Education for Freedom: The Philosophy of Education of Jacques Maritain. Nelson, Ralph C., tr. 130p. 1982. pap. text ed. 8.95 (ISBN 0-268-00909-0). U of Notre Dame Pr.
Doering, Bernard. Jacques Maritain & the French Catholic Intellectuals. LC 82-40377. 288p. 1983. text ed. 22.95. U of Notre Dame Pr.
Griffin, John H. & Simon, Yves R. Jacques Maritain: Homage in Words & Pictures. LC 73-85056. (Illus.). 1974. 12.95x (ISBN 0-87343-046-8). Magi Bks.
Smith, B. W. Jacques Maritain, Antimodern or Ultramodern? 1976. 27.95 (ISBN 0-444-99013-5, SIM/, Pub. by Elsevier). Greenwood.

MARITAL COUNSELING
see Marriage Counseling

MARK, SAINT
Vos, Howard F. Mark: A Bible Study Commentary. pap. 4.95 (ISBN 0-310-33873-5, 11044P). Zondervan.

MARRIAGE
see also Celibacy; Divorce; Family; Family Life Education; Marriage Counseling; Remarriage; Sex; Sex in Marriage; Sexual Ethics; Weddings; Wives
Allen, Charles L. Inspiring Thoughts for Your Marriage. 1985. 7.95 (ISBN 0-8007-1401-6). Revell.
Birdsong, Robert E. Soul Mates: The Facts & the Fallacies. (Aquarian Academy Supplementary Lecture Ser.: No. 9). 22p. (Orig.). 1980. pap. 1.25 (ISBN 0-917108-32-9). Sirius Bks.
Birner, Herbert A. Marriage Should Be Honored by All. 5.95 (ISBN 0-686-76769-1, 12N1719). Northwest Pub.
Bouma, Mary L. The Creative Homemaker. 3.95 (ISBN 0-87123-084-4, 200084). Bethany Hse.
Burkhart, Wanda. Submitting To A Sinning Husband. 64p. 1984. pap. 2.95 (ISBN 0-88144-042-6). Christian Pub.
Carter, Les. The Push-Pull Marriage. 1984. 7.95 (ISBN 0-8010-2497-8); pap. 5.95 (ISBN 0-8010-2490-0). Baker Bk.
Cook, Shirley. The Marriage Puzzle. 128p. (Orig.). 1985. pap. 5.95 (ISBN 0-310-33611-2, 11742P). Zondervan.
Daniel, R. P. Dating, Marriage, Sex & Divorce. 75p. pap. 3.95 (ISBN 0-88172-147-6). Believers Bkshelf.
DeMaria, Richard. Communal Love at Oneida: A Perfectionist Vision of Authority, Property & Sexual Order. 2nd. ed. LC 78-60958. (Texts & Studies in Religion: Vol. 2). 248p. 1983. 49.95x (ISBN 0-88946-988-1). E Mellen.
Dobson, James. What Wives Wish Their Husbands Knew about Women. 1975. 9.95 (ISBN 0-8423-7890-1). Tyndale.
Duty, Guy. Divorcio y Nuevo Matrimonio. 176p. 1975. 2.95 (ISBN 0-88113-060-5). Edit Betania.
Feeney, James H. Divorce & Marriage. 1980. pap. 1.75 (ISBN 0-911739-06-8). Abbott Loop.
Gibson, Dennis L. Live, Grow & Be Free: A Guide to Self-Parenting. LC 82-82412. 136p. 1982. pap. 5.95 (ISBN 0-89840-030-9). Here's Life.
Guernsey, Dennis. Thoroughly Married. 145p. 1984. pap. text ed. 5.95 (ISBN 0-8499-3000-6, 3000-6). Word Bks.
Jensen, Mary & Jensen, Andrew. Making Your Marriage Work. LC 85-7528. 144p. 1985. pap. 6.95 (ISBN 0-8066-2124-9, 10-4265). Augsburg.
Klausner, Abraham J. Weddings: A Guide to All Religious & Interfaith Marriage Services. LC 86-7892. (Life-Cycle Bookshelf Ser.). (Orig.). 1986. pap. 11.90 (ISBN 0-933771-00-2). Alpha Pub Co.
Krutza, William J. One Hundred One Ways to Enrich Your Marriage. 144p. 1982. pap. 4.95 (ISBN 0-8010-5452-4). Baker Bk.
LaHaye, Tim. How to Be Happy Though Married. (Living Book Ser.). 1979. 3.50 (ISBN 0-8423-1499-7). Tyndale.
Lavender, John A. Marriage at Its Best. LC 82-71375. 160p. (Orig.). 1982. pap. 4.95 (ISBN 0-89636-091-1). Accent Bks.
Linthorst, Ann T. A Gift of Love: Marriage As A Spiritual Journey. 166p. 1985. pap. 9.95 (ISBN 0-913105-17-1). PAGL Pr.
MacDonald, Gordon. Magnificent Marriage. 1976. pap. 3.50 1980 (ISBN 0-8423-3891-8). Tyndale.
McDowell, Josh. The Secret of Loving. (Living Bks.). 240p. Repr. 3.95 (ISBN 0-8423-5845-5). Tyndale.
Mace, David R. Whom God Hath Joined. rev. ed. LC 73-8871. 96p. 1984. pap. 6.95 (ISBN 0-664-24510-2). Westminster.
Mason, Mike. The Mystery of Ma-riage: As Iron Sharpens Iron. LC 85-3048. 190p. 1985. 10.95 (ISBN 0-88070-097-1). Multnomah.
Metz, Kenneth & Trokan, John. Pre-Marital Assessment Skills Training Program Leader Guide. 144p. 1986. pap. 12.95 (ISBN 0-8091-2809-8). Paulist Pr.
--Pre-Marital Assessment Skills Training Program: Team Couple Workbook. 96p. 1986. pap. 9.95 (ISBN 0-8091-2810-1). Paulist Pr.
Mickey, Paul & Proctor, William. Tough Marriage. Golbitz, Pat, ed. 256p. 1986. 14.95 (ISBN 0-688-05038-7). Morrow.
Miles, Herbert J. Sexual Happiness in Marriage. 2nd rev. ed. 208p. 1982. pap. 3.95 (ISBN 0-310-29222-0). Zondervan.
Morgan, Marabel. The Total Woman. 192p. 1973. spire bks. 3.50 (ISBN 0-8007-8218-6). Revell.
Petersen, J. Allan, compiled by. The Marriage Affair. 1971. pap. 9.95 (ISBN 0-8423-4171-4). Tyndale.
Purnell, Dick. The Thirty-One Day Experiment. LC 83-49023. 63p. (Orig.). 1984. pap. 2.95 (ISBN 0-89840-058-9). Heres Life.
Shedd, Charlie W. Letters to Philip. 128p. 1969. pap. 2.95 (ISBN 0-8007-8025-6, Spire Bks). Revell.
Steinmetz, Urban G. I Will. LC 71-84816. (Illus.). 136p. 1969. pap. 1.75 (ISBN 0-87793-010-4). Ave Maria.
Strauss, Richard L. Marriage Is for Love. 1982. pap. 4.95 (ISBN 0-8423-4178-1); leader's guide 2.95 (ISBN 0-8423-4179-X). Tyndale.
Sweatte, Appolles T. Marriage, Divorce, & the Believer. LC 85-91361. 53p. 1986. 6.95. Vantage.
Telford, Dr. Andrew. Miscarriage of Marriage. pap. 1.45 (ISBN 0-686-12750-1). Grace Pub Co.
Thompson, John & Thompson, Patti. Dance of the Broken Heart: A Family Love Story. 1986. 11.95 (ISBN 0-687-10080-1). Abingdon.
Van Pelt, Nancy. Your Future Mate. (Outreach Ser.). 32p. 1983. pap. 0.95 (ISBN 0-8163-0531-5). Pacific Pr Pub Assn.
Vissell, Barry & Vissell, Joyce. The Shared Heart: Relationship Initiations & Celebrations. LC 85-10981. 192p. 1985. Repr. lib. bdg. 19.95x (ISBN 0-89370-883-6). Borgo Pr.

Wells, Marian. With This Ring. LC 84-9301. 200p. (Orig.). 1984. pap. 4.95 (ISBN 0-87123-615-X, 210615). Bethany Hse.
Williams, Pat & Williams, Jill. Keep the Fire Glowing: How a Loving Marriage Builds a Loving Family. 160p. 1986. 9.95 (ISBN 0-317-46133-8). Revell.
Wood, Bobbye & Wood, Britton. Marriage Readiness. 1984. pap. 4.95 (ISBN 0-8054-5657-0). Broadman.
Wright, H. Norman. Seasons of a Marriage. LC 82-80010. 1983. pap. 4.95 (ISBN 0-8307-0912-6, 5418058). Regal.
Wright, Norman. Fulfilled Marriage. LC 76-21981. (Answer Ser.). 1976. pap. 1.95 (ISBN 0-89081-060-5, 0605). Harvest Hse.
Wright, Rusty & Wright, Linda R. How to Unlock the Secrets of Love & Sex in Marriage. 144p. 1985. pap. 3.95 (ISBN 0-916441-08-3). Barbour & Co.

MARRIAGE–ANNULMENT

see also Divorce

Noonan, John T., Jr. Power to Dissolve: Lawyers & Marriages in the Courts of the Roman Curia. LC 75-176044. (Illus.). 464p. 1972. 30.00x (ISBN 0-674-69575-5, Belknap Pr). Harvard U Pr.
Zwack, Joseph P. Annulment-Your Chance to Remarry Within the Catholic Church: A Step-by-Step Guide Using the New Code of Canon Law. LC 83-47739. (Using the New Code of Canon Law Ser.). 144p. (Orig.). 1983. pap. 5.95 (ISBN 0-06-250990-X, BN-3004, HarpR). Har-Row.

MARRIAGE–ANNULMENT (CANON LAW)

Tierney, Terence E. Annulment: Do You Have a Case? LC 78-6790. 1978. pap. 4.95 (ISBN 0-8189-0372-4). Alba.
Wrenn, Lawrence G. Annulments. 4th rev. ed. vi, 145p. (Orig.). 1983. pap. 4.00 (ISBN 0-943616-16-6). Canon Law Soc.

MARRIAGE–BIBLICAL TEACHING

Achtemeier, Elizabeth. The Committed Marriage. LC 76-7611. (Biblical Perspectives on Current Issues Ser.). 224p. 1976. pap. 8.95 (ISBN 0-664-24754-7). Westminster.
Adams, Jay E. Marriage, Divorce, & Remarriage in the Bible. (A Jay Adams Library). 128p. 1986. pap. 6.95 (ISBN 0-310-51111-9, 12123P). Zondervan.
Anderson, Ann K. I Gave God Time. 1982. 7.95 (ISBN 0-8423-1560-8); pap. 5.95 1984 (ISBN 0-8423-1559-4). Tyndale.
Augustine, St. Treatises on Marriage & Other Subjects. LC 73-75002. (Fathers of the Church Ser.: Vol. 27). 456p. 1955. 34.95x (ISBN 0-8132-0027-X). Cath U Pr.
Barber, Cyril J. & Barber, Aldyth A. Your Marriage Has Real Possibilities. LC 83-25537. 168p. (Orig.). 1984. pap. text ed. 6.95 (ISBN 0-8254-2249-3). Kregel.
Billheimer, Paul E. Love Covers. LC 83-15823. 174p. (Orig.). 1983. pap. 4.95 (ISBN 0-87123-400-9, 210400). Bethany Hse.
Bloem, Diane B. & Bloem, Robert C. A Women's Workshop on Bible Marriages. (Woman's Workshop Series of Study Books). 128p. (Orig.). 1980. pap. 2.95 student's manual (ISBN 0-310-21391-6, 10687); pap. 3.95 leader's manual (ISBN 0-310-21401-7, 10688). Zondervan.
Bryant, Al. Love Songs: Daily Meditations for Married Couples. 8.95 (ISBN 0-8499-3036-7). Word Bks.
Efird, James M. Marriage & Divorce: What the Bible Says. (Contemporary Christian Concerns Ser.). 96p. (Orig.). 1985. pap. 4.95 (ISBN 0-687-23619-3). Abingdon.
Geiseman, O. A. Make Yours a Happy Marriage. 1981. pap. 3.95 (ISBN 0-570-03133-8, 12-2383). Concordia.
Hard, Larry & Watts, Mark P. Preparing for Marriage. 1984. 2.95 (ISBN 0-89536-673-8, 1638). CSS of Ohio.
Kennedy, D. James. Learning to Live with the People You Love. 200p. (Orig.). 1987. pap. text ed. 3.95 (ISBN 0-88368-190-0). Whitaker Hse.
Killinger, John. Christ & the Seasons of Marriage. LC 86-17411. 1987. 7.95 (ISBN 0-8054-5666-X). Broadman.
Kriyananda, Swami. How to Spiritualize your Marriage. 2nd, enl. ed. 136p. 1982. pap. 6.95 (ISBN 0-916124-21-5). Dawn Pubns CA.
Mace, David & Mace, Vera. In the Presence of God: Readings for Christian Marriage. LC 84-26928. 116p. 1985. 8.95 (ISBN 0-664-21261-1). Westminster.
Mack, Wayne. Homework Manual for Biblical Counseling: Family & Marital Problems, Vol. 2. 1980. pap. 3.95 (ISBN 0-87552-357-9). Presby & Reformed.
Martens, Larry. Life with Promise: Marriage as a Covenant Venture. LC 82-81266. 76p. (Orig.). 1982. pap. 4.95 (ISBN 0-937364-03-7). Kindred Pr.
Mills, Dick. How to Have a Happy Marriage. 91p. (Orig.). 1985. pap. 2.95 (ISBN 0-89274-381-6). Harrison Hse.
Neill, Merrily & Tangedahl, Joanne. A New Blueprint for Marriage. 256p. 1981. pap. 6.50 (ISBN 0-942494-65-2). Coleman Pub.
Rahner, Karl. Marriage. 1.50 (ISBN 0-87193-118-4). Dimension Bks.
Robertson, John M. Together: Prayers & Promises for Newlyweds. 64p. 1982. pap. 2.50 (ISBN 0-8423-7282-2). Tyndale.
Shedd, Charlie & Shedd, Martha. Bible Study in Duet. 144p. 1984. 8.95 (ISBN 0-310-42380-5, 18360). Zondervan.
Small, Dwight H. Marriage As Equal Partnership. 1980. pap. 3.95 (ISBN 0-8010-8177-7). Baker Bk.
Sproul, R. C. The Intimate Marriage. 160p. (Orig.). 1986. pap. 5.95 (ISBN 0-8423-1595-0). Tyndale.
Stevens, R. Paul. Married for Good. LC 86-2881. 220p. (Orig.). 1986. pap. 5.95 (ISBN 0-87784-603-0). Inter-Varsity.
Stevenson, Kenneth, ed. Nuptial Blessing: A Study of Christian Marriage Rites. 1983. 22.50x (ISBN 0-19-520418-2); pap. 9.95x (ISBN 0-19-520419-0). Oxford U Pr.
Swindoll, Charles R. Strike the Original Match. LC 80-15639. 1980. pap. 6.95 (ISBN 0-930014-37-5); study guide 2.95 (ISBN 0-930014-49-9). Multnomah.
Tetlow, Elisabeth M. & Tetlow, Louis M. Partners in Service: Toward a Biblical Theology of Christian Marriage. LC 83-7016. 192p. (Orig.). 1983. lib. bdg. 26.00 (ISBN 0-8191-3206-3); pap. text ed. 11.25 (ISBN 0-8191-3207-1). U Pr of Amer.
Warren, Thomas B. Marriage is for Those Who Love God & One Another. 1976. 8.00 (ISBN 0-934916-37-3). Natl Christian Pr.
Warren, Thomas B., ed. Your Marriage Can Be Great. 1978. pap. 14.00 (ISBN 0-934916-44-6). Natl Christian Pr.
White, Ellen. Forbidden Marriages & Divorce. large print ed. 27p. 1985. pap. 5.00 (ISBN 0-914009-38-9). VHI Library.
Yarbrough, Larry O. Not Like the Gentiles: Marriage Rules in the Letters of Paul. (SBL Dissertation Ser.). 1985. 17.95 (ISBN 0-89130-874-1, 06-01-80); pap. 11.95 (ISBN 0-89130-875-X). Scholars Pr GA.

MARRIAGE–RELIGIOUS ASPECTS

Besson, Clyde T. Growing Together. 1987. pap. 5.95 (ISBN 0-317-54043-2). Baker Bk.
Crabb, Lawrence J., Jr. How to Become One with Your Mate. 1986. write for info. BMH Bks.
Dawson, Patsy R. Appreciating Marriage, Vol I. rev. ed. LC 86-22746. (Marriage: A Taste of Heaven Ser.). (Illus.). 544p. 1987. pap. 12.95 (ISBN 0-938855-40-9); Set. pap. 25.90 (ISBN 0-938855-44-1). Gospel Themes Pr.
--Learning to Love, Vol. II: God's People Make the Best Lovers. LC 86-22746. (Marriage: A Taste of Heaven Ser.). (Illus.). 544p. (Orig.). 1987. pap. 12.95 (ISBN 0-938855-41-7); Set. 25.90 (ISBN 0-938855-44-1). Gospel Themes Pr.
Dillow, Linda. Creative Counterpart. rev. & updated ed. 228p. 1986. pap. 7.95 (ISBN 0-8407-3067-5). Nelson.
Harley, Gary K. A Scriptural Guide to a Fulfilling Marriage: Two Shall Become One. 168p. (Orig.). 1987. cancelled (ISBN 0-932990-01-0). Ideals.
Heyer, Robert, ed. Enriching Your Marriage. 2.45 (ISBN 0-8091-2261-8). Paulist Pr.
Hine, James R. The Springtime of Love & Marriage. (Family Life Ser.). 160p. 1985. pap. 6.95 (ISBN 0-317-38064-8). Judson.
Kistler, Robert C. Marriage, Divorce, And... Woolsey, Raymond H., ed. 160p. (Orig.). 1987. 10.95 (ISBN 0-8280-0367-X). Review & Herald.
Linthorst, Ann T. Gift of Love: Marriage As a Spiritual Journey. 9.95 (ISBN 0-8091-0299-4). Paulist Pr.
MacArthur, John, Jr. Guidelines for Singleness & Marriage. (John MacArthur's Bible Studies). (Orig.). 1986. pap. 3.95 (ISBN 0-8024-5343-0). Moody.
Mickey, Paul & Proctor, William. Tough Marriage. Golbitz, Pat, ed. 256p. 1986. 14.95 (ISBN 0-688-05038-7). Morrow.
Pentar, Michael P. Building a Happy Marriage. pap. 2.95 (ISBN 0-8198-1114-9). Dghtrs St Paul.
Preister, Steven & Young, James J. Catholic Remarriage: Pastoral Issues & Preparation Models. 224p. (Orig.). 1986. pap. 12.95 (ISBN 0-8091-2808-X). Paulist Pr.
Reapsome, James & Reapsome, Martha. Marriage: God's Design for Intimacy. (LifeBuilder Bible Studies). 64p. (Orig.). 1986. pap. 2.95 (ISBN 0-8308-1056-0). Inter-Varsity.
Small, Dwight H. Remarriage & God's Renewing Grace. 184p. 1986. pap. 7.95 (ISBN 0-8010-8264-1). Baker Bk.
Theology of Marriage & Celibacy. 9.00 (ISBN 0-8198-7333-0); 8.00 (ISBN 0-8198-7334-9). Dghtrs St Paul.
Waggoner, Doreen. To Love & to Cherish. 48p. 1986. 6.95 (ISBN 0-8378-5094-0). Gibson.

MARRIAGE–RELIGIOUS ASPECTS–BAHAI FAITH

A Fortress for Well-Being: Baha'i Teachings on Marriage. (Comprehensive Deepening Program Ser.: Gift Ed.). 1974. 12.95 (ISBN 0-87743-093-4, 364-010). Baha'i.
Ruhe, Margaret. Some Thoughts on Marriage. 36p. 1982. pap. 1.95 (ISBN 0-933770-23-5). Kalimat.

MARRIAGE–RELIGIOUS ASPECTS–BRUDERHOF COMMUNITIES

Arnold, Eberhard. Love & Marriage in the Spirit. LC 64-24321. 1965. 7.00 (ISBN 0-87486-103-9). Plough.

MARRIAGE–RELIGIOUS ASPECTS–CATHOLIC CHURCH

Anderson, William. Journeying Toward Marriage. (Journeying with Christ Ser.). 176p. 1985. pap. 6.75 (ISBN 0-697-02059-2). Wm C Brown.
Balzano, Bill. Church of God & Roman Catholic Interfaith Marriage. (Truthway Ser.). 35p. (Orig.). 1981. pap. text ed. 1.25 (ISBN 0-87148-175-8). Pathway Pr.
Benjamin, Carol. So You're Getting Married! 1982. pap. 3.95 (ISBN 0-911739-15-7). Abbott Loop.
Carmody, Denise L. Caring for Marriage. LC 85-60412. 192p. (Orig.). 1985. pap. 7.95 (ISBN 0-8091-2721-0). Paulist Pr.
Catoir, John. Catholics & Broken Marriage. LC 78-74434. 72p. 1979. pap. 1.95 (ISBN 0-87793-176-3). Ave Maria.
Champlin, Joseph M. Together for Life: Regular Edition. rev. ed. (Illus.). 96p. 1970. pap. 1.50 (ISBN 0-87793-018-X). Ave Maria.
--Together for Life: Special Edition for Marriage Outside Mass. rev. ed. (Illus.). 96p. 1972. pap. 1.50 (ISBN 0-87793-118-6). Ave Maria.
Chartier, Myron & Chartier, Jan. Trusting Together in God. LC 83-73132. (Illus.). 172p. (Orig.). 1984. pap. 6.95 (ISBN 0-87029-193-9, 20285-3). Abbey.
Daughters of St. Paul Editorial Staff. Looking Ahead to Marriage. (Divine Master Ser.). (Illus.). 1969. 5.25 (ISBN 0-8198-0259-X); pap. 4.25 (ISBN 0-8198-0260-3); discussion & projects manual 2.75 (ISBN 0-8198-0261-1). Dghtrs St Paul.
Dominian, J. Marital Breakdown. 1969. 5.95 (ISBN 0-8199-0151-2, L38436). Franciscan Herald.
Die Ehe. (Ger.). pap. 2.55 (ISBN 0-686-32321-1). Rod & Staff.
Grunlan, Stephen A. Marriage & the Family: A Christian Perspective. 384p. 1984. pap. 10.95 (ISBN 0-310-36341-1, 11282P). Zondervan.
Hiesberger, Jean M., ed. Preparing for Marriage Handbook. LC 80-80386. (Paths of Life Ser.). 112p. 1980. 2.95 (ISBN 0-8091-2260-X). Paulist Pr.
Lawler, Michael. Secular Marriage, Christian Sacrament. 192p. (Orig.). 1985. pap. text ed. 8.95 (ISBN 0-89622-273-X). Twenty-Third.
LeClercq, Jean. Monks on Marriage: A Twelfth-Century View. 144p. 1982. 10.95 (ISBN 0-8164-0507-7, HarpR). Har-Row.
McGraw, Woody. Marriage According to God's Word: How to Succeed at Marriage. LC 83-9121. 86p. (Orig.). 1983. pap. 2.95 (ISBN 0-913309-00-1). Trinity House.
Mackin, Theodore. What is Marriage: Marriage in the Catholic Church. LC 81-84386. (Marriage in the Catholic Church Ser.: Vol. 1). 384p. (Orig.). 1982. pap. 11.95 (ISBN 0-8091-2442-4). Paulist Pr.
May, William E. Sex, Marriage & Chastity: Reflections of a Catholic Layman, Spouse & Parent. 1981. 6.95 (ISBN 0-8199-0821-5). Franciscan Herald.
Monks Of Solesmes, ed. Matrimony: One Hundred & Thirty-Eight Pronouncements from Benedict Fourteenth to John Twenty-Third. 5.50 (ISBN 0-8198-0098-8); pap. 4.50 (ISBN 0-8198-0099-6). Dghtrs St Paul.
Pico, Pancho. Matrimonio Sorprendente. 96p. 1981. pap. 1.90 (ISBN 0-311-37022-5). Casa Bautista.
Pope John Paul II. Love & Responsibility. Willetts, H. T., tr. 320p. 1981. 15.00 (ISBN 0-374-19247-2); pap. 7.95 (ISBN 0-374-51685-5). FS&G.
Rite of Marriage. (Large Type, Two Colors, Homiletic Notes). red cloth 8.50 (ISBN 0-89942-238-1, 238/22). Catholic Bk Pub.
Robbins, Jhan. Marriage Made in Heaven: The Story of Billy & Ruth Graham. 192p. 1983. 13.95 (ISBN 0-399-12849-2, Putnam). Putnam Pub Group.
Roberts, William P. Marriage: Sacrament of Hope & Challenge. 136p. 1983. pap. text ed. 4.75 (ISBN 0-86716-019-5). St Anthony Mess Pr.
Roberts, William P., ed. Commitment to Partnership: Exploring the Theology of Marriage. 1987. pap. 10.95. Paulist Pr.
Silbermann, Eileen Z. The Savage Sacrament: A Theology of Marriage after American Feminism. 128p. (Orig.). 1983. pap. 5.95 (ISBN 0-89622-165-2). Twenty-Third.
Smith & Smith. Growing Love in Christian Marriage: Pastors's Manual. 1981. pap. 4.75 (ISBN 0-687-15930-X). Abingdon.
Smith, Charles E. Papal Enforcement of Some Medieval Marriage Laws. LC 40-12564. pap. 59.30 (ISBN 0-317-28663-3, 2055314). Bks Demand UMI.
Talafous, Don. Planning a Christian Wedding. 36p. 1985. pap. 1.00 (ISBN 0-8146-1407-8). Liturgical Pr.
Twomey, Gerald S. When Catholics Marry Again: A Guide for the Divorced, Their Families & Those Who Minister to Them. 194p. (Orig.). 1982. pap. 7.95 (ISBN 0-86683-633-0, HarpR). Har-Row.
Vandenberg, Thomas L. Study Guide for Archbishop Hunthausen's Pastoral on Matrimony. rev. ed. LC 82-62716. 59p. 1984. pap. text ed. 2.95 (ISBN 0-911905-02-2). Past & Mat Rene Ctr.
Weiss, Gerald. On Becoming Married: The Art of a Loving Marriage. LC 81-85262. 108p. (Orig.). 1982. pap. 2.95 (ISBN 0-87973-664-X, 664). Our Sunday Visitor.
Whitehead, Evelyn & Whitehead, James. Marrying Well: Stages on the Journey of Christian Marriage. LC 81-43046. 504p. 1983. pap. 9.95 (ISBN 0-385-18829-3, Im). Doubleday.
Wojtyla, Karol. Fruitful & Responsible Love. (Orig.). 1979. pap. 2.95 (ISBN 0-8245-0310-4). Crossroad NY.
Young, James J. When You're Divorced & Catholic. LC 80-69090. (When Bk). 96p. 1980. pap. 2.45 (ISBN 0-87029-172-6, 20265-5). Abbey.

MARRIAGE–RELIGIOUS ASPECTS–CHRISTIANITY

Achtemeier, Elizabeth. The Committed Marriage. LC 76-7611. (Biblical Perspectives on Current Issues Ser.). 224p. 1976. pap. 8.95 (ISBN 0-664-24754-7). Westminster.
Adams, Jay E. Solving Marriage Problems. 1983. pap. 4.50 (ISBN 0-8010-0197-8). Baker Bk.
Allbritton, Cliff. How to Get Married: And Stay That Way. LC 82-71219. (Orig.). 1983. pap. 5.95 (ISBN 0-8054-5653-8). Broadman.
Amstutz, H. Clair. Marriage in Today's World. LC 78-955. 160p. 1978. pap. 6.95 (ISBN 0-8361-1849-9). Herald Pr.
Arnold, Heini. In the Image of God: Marriage & Chastity in Christian Life. LC 76-53542. 1977. pap. 3.50 (ISBN 0-87486-169-1). Plough.
Beardsley, Lou & Spry, Toni. The Fulfilled Woman. LC 74-29206. 1977. 3.25 (ISBN 0-89081-072-9). Harvest Hse.
Biddle, Perry H., Jr. The Goodness of Marriage: A Devotional Book for Newlyweds. LC 84-50840. 144p. 1984. 6.95 (ISBN 0-8358-0490-9). Upper Room.
Bloem, Diane B. & Bloem, Robert C. A Women's Workshop on Bible Marriages. (Woman's Workshop Series of Study Books). 128p. (Orig.). 1980. pap. 2.95 student's manual (ISBN 0-310-21391-6, 10687); pap. 3.95 leader's manual (ISBN 0-310-21401-7, 10688). Zondervan.
Buijs, Joseph A., ed. Christian Marriage Today: Growth or Breakdown? LC 85-10466. (Symposium Ser.: Vol. 16). 168p. 1985. 29.95x (ISBN 0-88946-707-2). E Mellen.
Bullinger, Heinrich. The Christian State of Matrimonye. Coverdale, Myles, tr. LC 74-80167. (English Experience Ser.: No. 646). 168p. 1974. Repr. of 1541 ed. 11.50 (ISBN 90-221-0646-2). Walter J Johnson.
Burghardt, W. J., et al, eds. Tertullian, Treatise on Marriage & Remarriage: To His Wife, an Exhortation to Chastity Monogamy. LC 78-62462. (Ancient Christian Writers Ser.: No. 13). 103p. 1951. 10.95 (ISBN 0-8091-0149-1). Paulist Pr.
Burtchaell, James T. For Better, for Worse. 160p. (Orig.). 1985. pap. 5.95 (ISBN 0-8091-2664-8). Paulist Pr.
Burtchaell, James T., et al. Marriage Among Christians: A Curious Tradition. LC 77-81396. (Illus.). 192p. 1977. pap. 3.50 (ISBN 0-87793-139-9). Ave Maria.
Calkin, Ruth H. Letters to a Young Bride. 112p. 1985. 10.95 (ISBN 0-8423-2134-9). Tyndale.
Canclini, Arnoldo. Cuando la Infidelidad Asoma. (Series on the Family). (Span.). 112p. (Orig.). 1986. pap. 3.50 (ISBN 0-311-46264-2). Casa Bautista.
Carmody, Denise L. Caring for Marriage. LC 85-60412. 192p. (Orig.). 1985. pap. 7.95 (ISBN 0-8091-2721-0). Paulist Pr.
Carmody, Denise L. & Carmody, John T. Becoming One Flesh. LC 84-50841. 160p. (Orig.). 1984. pap. 6.95 (ISBN 0-8358-0486-0). Upper Room.
Carroll, Anne Kristin. Together Forever. 256p. (Orig.). 1982. pap. 7.95 (ISBN 0-310-45021-7, 6885P). Zondervan.
Carter, Stephen J. & McKinney, Charles. Keeping a Good Thing Going. 1979. pap. 3.25 (ISBN 0-570-03787-5, 12-2745). Concordia.

Christenson, Larry & Christenson, Nordis. The Christian Couple. LC 77-24085. 1977. pap. 5.95 (ISBN 0-87123-051-8); study guide 1.50 (ISBN 0-87123-046-1, 210046). Bethany Hse.

A Christian Celebration of Marriage. 32p. 1987. pap. 3.25 (ISBN 0-8006-1973-0). Fortress.

Coleman, William L. Engaged. 1980. pap. 5.95 (ISBN 0-8423-0693-5). Tyndale.

Coniaris, A. Crown Them with Glory & Honor: Talks for Weddings. 1985. pap. 4.95 (ISBN 0-937032-40-9). Light&Life Pub Co MN.

Crabb, Lawrence J., Jr. The Marriage Builder: A Blueprint for Couples & Counselors. 176p. 1982. 9.95 (ISBN 0-310-22580-9, 10181). Zondervan.

Currie, Robert, et al. Churches & Churchgoers: Patterns of Church Growth in the British Isles since 1700. (Illus.). 1978. 42.00x (ISBN 0-19-827218-9). Oxford U Pr.

Daniels, Elam J. Como Ser Feliz en el Matrimonio. Orig. Title: How to Be Happily Married. 96p. 1984. pap. 2.10 (ISBN 0-311-46066-6). Casa Bautista.

Davis, Linda. How to be the Happy Wife of an Unsaved Husband. 165p. (Orig.). 1986. pap. text ed. 3.50 (ISBN 0-88368-189-7). Whitaker Hse.

Denton, Wallace & Denton, Juanita H. Creative Couples: The Growth Factor in Marriage. LC 82-17439. 154p. 1983. pap. 8.95 (ISBN 0-664-24453-X). Westminster.

Drescher, John M. When Opposites Attract. LC 79-53272. (When Bks.). (Illus., Orig.). 1979. pap. 2.45 (ISBN 0-87029-153-X, 20239-0). Abbey.

Elliot, Elisabeth. What God Has Joined. 32p. 1983. Repr. 1.50 (ISBN 0-89107-276-4). Good News.

The Encyclopedia of Christian Marriage. 414p. 1983. 16.95 (ISBN 0-8007-1376-1). Revell.

Esau, Truman & Burch, Beverly. Partners in Process. 156p. 1986. pap. 5.95 (ISBN 0-89693-372-5). Victor Bks.

Everett, William J. Blessed Be the Bond: Christian Perspectives on Marriage & Family. LC 84-48712. 144p. 1985. pap. 6.95 (ISBN 0-8006-1831-9, 1-1831). Fortress.

Faber, Stuart J. How to Get Rid of Your Wife: And No Court Will Ever Convict You. 200p. 1974. 7.95 (ISBN 0-685-50674-6). Good Life.

Foreman, Kenneth J. From This Day Forward: Thoughts about a Christian Marriage. pap. 2.95x (ISBN 0-685-02584-5). Outlook.

Getz, Gene A. The Measure of a Marriage. LC 78-53356. 144p. 1980. pap. 3.50 (ISBN 0-8307-0638-0, 5017203). Regal.

Grant, Brian W. Reclaiming the Dream: Marriage Counseling in the Parish Context. 176p. (Orig.). 1986. pap. 9.95 (ISBN 0-687-35729-2). Abingdon.

Groth, Jeanette. Thank You for My Spouse. LC 12-2826. 1983. pap. 2.50 (ISBN 0-570-03885-5). Concordia.

Guernsey, Dennis. Thoroughly Married. 145p. 1984. pap. text ed. 5.95 (ISBN 0-8499-3000-6, 3000-6). Word Bks.

Hardisty, Margaret. Your Husband & Your Emotional Needs. LC 80-81471. 176p. 1982. pap. text ed. 2.95 (ISBN 0-89081-312-4). Harvest Hse.

Hart, Thomas. Living Happily Ever after: Toward a Theology of Christian Marriage. LC 79-89475. 96p. 1979. pap. 3.95 (ISBN 0-8091-2213-8). Paulist Pr.

Hart, Thomas & Hart, Kathleen. The First Two Years of Marriage: Foundations for a Life Together. 144p. (Orig.). 1983. pap. 5.95 (ISBN 0-8091-2553-6). Paulist Pr.

Hauck, Paul A. Marriage Is a Loving Business. LC 77-2202. 116p. 1977. pap. 6.95 (ISBN 0-664-24137-9). Westminster.

Hayner, Jerry & Hayner, Karen. Marriage Can Be Meaningful. (Orig.). 1983. pap. 3.95 (ISBN 0-8054-2303-6). Broadman.

Hulme, William E. Building a Christian Marriage. LC 65-22192. 1968. pap. 5.95 (ISBN 0-8066-0813-7, 10-0940). Augsburg.

--When Two Become One: Reflections for the Newly Married. LC 76-176481. 1974. pap. 5.95 (ISBN 0-8066-1438-2, 10-7061). Augsburg.

Hunt, Joan & Hunt, Richard. Growing Love in Christian Marriage: Couple's Manual. 1981. pap. 2.50 (ISBN 0-687-15931-8). Abingdon.

Hunt, Joan A. & Hunt, Richard A. Preparing for Christian Marriage: Couples. LC 81-1770. 96p. 1982. 6.95 (ISBN 0-687-33919-7). Abingdon.

Kasper, Walter. Theology of Christian Marriage. LC 81-5444. 112p. 1983. pap. 7.95 (ISBN 0-8245-0559-X). Crossroad NY.

Kroll, Una. Flesh of My Flesh. 112p. 1975. pap. 6.50 (ISBN 0-232-51336-8). Attic Pr.

Krutza, William J. Twenty-Five Keys to a Happy Marriage. (Contempo Ser). pap. 1.75 (ISBN 0-8010-5447-8). Baker Bk.

LaHaye, Tim. How to Be Happy Though Married. 1968. pap. 5.95 (ISBN 0-8423-1501-2). Tyndale.

--Six Keys to a Happy Marriage. 1978. pap. 1.95 (ISBN 0-8423-5895-1). Tyndale.

LaHaye, Tim & LaHaye, Beverly. The Act of Marriage: The Beauty of Married Love. 1976. pap. 8.95 (ISBN 0-310-27061-8, 18077P); pap. 3.95 (ISBN 0-310-27062-6, 18083P). Zondervan.

Laney, J. Carl. The Divorce Myth. LC 81-7690. 152p. 1981. 8.95 (ISBN 0-87123-144-1, 230144). Bethany Hse.

Littauer, Florence. After Every Wedding Comes a Marriage. LC 81-80023. 208p. (Orig.). 1981. pap. 5.95 (ISBN 0-89081-289-6). Harvest Hse.

Ludwig, David. The Spirit of Your Marriage. LC 79-50088. 1979. pap. 6.95 (ISBN 0-8066-1721-7, 10-5890). Augsburg.

Lundstrom, Lowell. Heaven's Answer for the Home. rev. ed. 142p. 1985. pap. 3.50 (ISBN 0-938220-16-0). Whitaker Hse.

McDonald, Cleveland. Creating a Successful Christian Marriage. LC 74-20202. 1975. 14.95 (ISBN 0-8010-5957-7). Baker Bk.

--Creating a Successful Christian Marriage. LC 74-20202. 1975. 10.95 (ISBN 0-87227-038-6). Reg Baptist.

Mace, David & Mace, Vera. The Sacred Fire Christian Marriage Through the Ages. 1986. 16.95 (ISBN 0-687-36712-3). Abingdon.

Mace, David R. Success in Marriage. (Festival Ser.). 160p. 1980. pap. 3.95 (ISBN 0-687-40555-6). Abingdon.

McRae, William J. Preparing for Your Marriage. 160p. (Orig.). 1980. pap. 5.95 (ISBN 0-310-42761-4, 9366P). Zondervan.

McRoberts, Darlene. Second Marriage: The Promise & the Challenge. LC 77-84087. 1978. pap. 6.95 (ISBN 0-8066-1612-1, 10-5635). Augsburg.

Malone, Richard & Connery, John, eds. Contemporary Perspectives on Christian Marriage. 1984. 19.95 (ISBN 0-8294-0472-4). Loyola.

Martin, John R. Divorce & Remarriage: A Perspective for Counseling. LC 73-18038. 144p. 1974. pap. 6.95 (ISBN 0-8361-1328-4). Herald Pr.

Martin, LaJoyce. Happiness Is... Heaven Made Marriages. Wallace, Mary H., ed. LC 85-22522. (Illus.). 313p. (Orig.). 1985. pap. 6.95 (ISBN 0-912315-86-5). Word Aflame.

Mason, Mike. The Mystery of Marriage: As Iron Sharpens Iron. LC 85-3048. 190p. 1985. 10.95 (ISBN 0-88070-097-1). Multnomah.

Mazat, Alberta. That Friday in Eden. (Redwood Ser.). 1981. pap. 4.95 (ISBN 0-8163-0401-7). Pacific Pr Pub Assn.

Miller, Calvin. If This Be Love: The Journey of Two People Toward Each Other in Christian Love & Marriage. LC 83-48433. 112p. 1984. 11.45 (ISBN 0-06-065755-3, HarpR). Har-Row.

Moore, Donald. A Daily Guide to a Better Marriage. 32p. 1984. pap. 0.75 (ISBN 0-88144-021-3). Christian Pub.

More Than "I Do". Pastor's Resource Book for Premarital Counseling. (Orig.). 1983. pap. 4.95 (ISBN 0-8341-0865-8). Beacon Hill.

Morgan, Marabel. The Electric Woman. 1986. 3.95 (ISBN 0-8499-4175-X). Word Bks.

Ogden, Dunbar H. Wedding Bells. (Orig.). 1945. pap. 3.25 (ISBN 0-8042-1884-6). John Knox.

Osborne, Cecil. How to Have a Happier Wife. LC 85-14255. 64p. (Orig.). 1986. pap. 2.95 (ISBN 0-310-30622-1, 10478P). Zondervan.

Otto, Herbert A., ed. Marriage & Family Enrichment: New Perspectives & Programs. LC 75-30743. 1976. pap. 9.95 (ISBN 0-687-23620-7). Abingdon.

Palmer, Nehemiah M. Understanding Yourself, Society & Marriage. 288p. 1984. pap. 7.95 (ISBN 0-912315-82-2). Word Aflame.

Perersen, William J. C. S. Lewis Had a Wife. 160p. (Orig.). 1985. pap. 2.95 (ISBN 0-8423-0202-6). Tyndale.

Petersen, J. Allan. Before You Marry. 1974. pap. 3.95 (ISBN 0-8423-0104-6). Tyndale.

Petersen, William J. Catherine Marshall Had a Husband. (Living Books Ser.). 240p. (Orig.). 1986. mass 3.95 (ISBN 0-8423-0204-2). Tyndale.

--Martin Luther Had a Wife. 1983. pap. 3.95 (ISBN 0-8423-4104-8). Tyndale.

Prince, Derek & Prince, Ruth. God Is a Matchmaker. 1986. pap. 5.95 (ISBN 0-8007-9058-8, B35). Revell.

Rice, Max M. & Rice, Vivian B. When Can I Say, "I Love You"? LC 76-54926. 1977. pap. 4.95 (ISBN 0-8024-9436-6). Moody.

Richmond-Garland, Diana S. & Garland, David E. Beyond Companionship-Christians in Marriage. LC 86-7767. 192p. 1986. pap. 12.95 (ISBN 0-664-24018-6). Westminster.

Roberts, William P. Marriage: Sacrament of Hope & Challenge. 136p. 1983. pap. text ed. 4.75 (ISBN 0-86716-019-5). St Anthony Mess Pr.

Rodriguez, P. Pedro. Matrimono y Familia Cristiana. LC 84-7000069. 116p. 1984. pap. 2.95 (ISBN 0-915388-20-0). Buckley Pubns.

Sanford, Ruth. The First Years Together. 140p. (Orig.). 1983. pap. 5.95 (ISBN 0-89283-134-0). Servant.

Seagren, Daniel R. Togetherness. (Contempo Ser.). 32p. 1978. pap. 0.95 (ISBN 0-8010-8114-9). Baker Bk.

Self, Carolyn S. & Self, William L. A Survival Kit for Marriage. LC 81-66091. 1981. pap. 5.95 (ISBN 0-8054-5643-0). Broadman.

Small, Dwight H. Your Marriage Is God's Affair. 352p. 1979. pap. 7.95 (ISBN 0-8007-5024-1, Power Bks). Revell.

Smith, Antoinette & Smith, Leon. Preparing for Christian Marriage: Pastor's Edition. LC 80-28001. 112p. 1982. 7.75 (ISBN 0-687-33918-9). Abingdon.

Steele & Ryrie. Meant to Last. 1983. 5.95 (ISBN 0-686-46323-4). Victor Bks.

Steinmetz, Urban G. Strangers, Lovers, Friends. LC 80-69479. (Illus.). 176p. (Orig.). 1981. pap. 3.95 (ISBN 0-87793-217-4). Ave Maria.

Stuenkel, Omar. Marriage is for Two: How to Build a Marriage That Lasts & Works. LC 81-65640. 96p. (Orig.). 1981. pap. 4.95 (ISBN 0-8066-1876-0, 10-4290). Augsburg.

Swedenborg, Emanuel. Conjugal Love. Student ed. LC 79-93407. 12.00 (ISBN 0-87785-054-2). Swedenborg.

Taylor, Jack R. What Every Husband Should Know. LC 81-65389. 1981. 8.95 (ISBN 0-8054-5642-2). Broadman.

Thatcher, Floyd & Thatcher, Harriett. Long Term Marriage. 1981. 5.95 (ISBN 0-8499-2963-6). Word Bks.

Thomas, David M. Christian Marriage: A Journey Together. (Message of the Sacraments Ser.: Vol. 5). 13.95 (ISBN 0-89453-395-9); pap. 9.95 (ISBN 0-89453-231-6). M Glazier.

Timmons, Tim. Maximum Marriage. rev. & updated ed. 160p. pap. 5.95 (ISBN 0-8007-5106-X, Power Bks). Revell.

Timmons, Tim & McAfee, Lisa. Maximum Marriage. 64p. (Orig.). 1984. pap. 4.95 (ISBN 0-915929-08-2); leader's guide 1.95 (ISBN 0-915929-17-1). Merit Bks.

Tippit, Sammy & Jenkins, Jerry. You Me He. LC 77-95030. 119p. 1978. pap. 3.95 (ISBN 0-88207-766-X). Victor Bks.

Trent, John. Growing Together. 156p. 1985. pap. 5.95 (ISBN 0-89693-323-7). Victor Bks.

Van Bemmel, John & Van Bemmel, Dolores. We Celebrate Our Marriage. (Greeting Book Line Ser.). 32p. (Orig.). 1986. pap. 1.50 (ISBN 0-89622-304-3). Twenty-Third.

Voshell, Dorothy. Whom Shall I Marry? 1979. pap. 4.50 (ISBN 0-87552-509-1). Presby & Reformed.

Ward, C. M. Two Shall Be One. (Orig.). 1986. pap. text ed. 3.95 (ISBN 0-88368-184-6). Whitaker Hse.

Webb, Lance. Making Love Grow: Love That Can Make Incompatibility a Myth. LC 83-80410. 176p. (Orig.). 1983. pap. 6.50 (ISBN 0-8358-0462-3). Upper Room.

Wheat, Ed. How to Save Your Marriage Alone. 64p. 1983. pap. 2.50 (ISBN 0-310-42522-0, 10267P). Zondervan.

--Love Life for Every Married Couple. 288p. 1980. pap. 5.95 (ISBN 0-310-42511-5, 10266P). Zondervan.

Whiston, Lionel A. For Those in Love: Making Your Marriage Last a Lifetime. 128p. 1983. 10.95 (ISBN 0-687-13285-1). Abingdon.

Wilkins, Ronald & Gryczka, Mary. Christian Marriage: A Sacrament of Love. (To Live Is Christ Ser.). (YA) 1986. pap. text ed. 7.25 (ISBN 0-697-02071-1); tchr's. ed. 15.95 (ISBN 0-697-02072-X); test wkbk. 14.95 (ISBN 0-697-02112-2). Wm C Brown.

Wright, H. Norman. The Living Marriage. (Illus.). 128p. 1975. 12.95 (ISBN 0-8007-0722-2). Revell.

Wright, Norm. After You Say I Do. LC 79-66960. 80p. (Orig.). 1979. pap. 4.95 (ISBN 0-89081-205-5). Harvest Hse.

Wunsch, William F. Marriage: Ideals & Realizations. 155p. 1973. 1.75 (ISBN 0-87785-122-0). Swedenborg.

Yarbrough, Larry O. Not Like the Gentiles: Marriage Rules in the Letters of Paul. (SBL Dissertation Ser.). 1985. 17.95 (ISBN 0-89130-874-1, 06-01-80); pap. 11.95 (ISBN 0-89130-875-X). Scholars Pr GA.

MARRIAGE–RELIGIOUS ASPECTS–JUDAISM

Chigier, Moshe. Husband & Wife in Israeli Law. 281p. 1985. 17.50 (ISBN 0-87203-128-4, Pub. by Harry Fischel Institute for Research in Talmud Jerusalem Israel). Hermon.

Dorff, Elliot N. & Rosett, Arthur. A Living Tree: Materials on the Jewish Legal Tradition with Comparative Notes. 680p. 1987. 49.50x (ISBN 0-88706-459-0); pap. 19.95x (ISBN 0-88706-460-4). State U NY Pr.

Shoulson, Abraham B., ed. Marriage & Family Life: A Jewish View. 19.95x (ISBN 0-8084-0378-8). New Coll U Pr.

MARRIAGE–RELIGIOUS ASPECTS–ORTHODOX EASTERN CHURCH

Basaroff, F. The Sacrament of Matrimony According to the Doctrine & Ritual of the Eastern Orthodox Church. Bjerring, N., tr. from Russian. pap. 1.95 (ISBN 0-686-16370-2). Eastern Orthodox.

Constantelos, D. J. Marriage, Sexuality & Celibacy: A Greek Orthodox Perspective. 1975. pap. 4.95 (ISBN 0-937032-15-8). Light&Life Pub Co MN.

Evdokimov, Paul. The Sacrament of Love: The Nuptial Mystery in the Light of the Orthodox Tradition. Gythiel, Anthony P. & Steadman, Victoria, trs. from Fr. LC 85-2261. 192p. (Orig.). 1985. pap. 8.95 (ISBN 0-88141-042-X). St Vladimirs.

Harakas, S. Guidelines for Marriage in the Orthodox Church. 1980. pap. 1.45 (ISBN 0-937032-21-2). Light&Life Pub Co MN.

Meyendorff, John. Marriage: An Orthodox Perspective. LC 75-14241. 144p. 1975. pap. 5.95 (ISBN 0-913836-05-2). St Vladimirs.

MARRIAGE–GERMANY

Safley, Thomas M. Let No Man Put Asunder: The Control of Marriage in the German Southwest, 1550-1600. (Studies and Essays: Vol. II). 210p. 1984. 25.00x (ISBN 0-940474-02-6). Sixteenth Cent.

MARRIAGE–INDIA

Ahmad, Imtiaz, ed. Family, Kinship, & Marriage among the Muslims. LC 77-74484. 1977. 18.50x (ISBN 0-88386-757-5). South Asia Bks.

Archer, William G. Songs for the Bride: Wedding Rites of Rural India. Miller, Barbara S. & Archer, Mildred, eds. (Studies in Oriental Culture). 224p. 1985. 22.50x (ISBN 0-317-18769-4). Brooklyn Coll Pr.

Roy, Buddhaved. Marriage Rituals & Songs of Bengal. 1985. 6.50x (ISBN 0-8364-1290-7, Pub. by Mukhopadhyaya India). South Asia Bks.

MARRIAGE–UNITED STATES

Arnold, William V., et al. Divorce: Prevention or Survival. LC 77-22066. 128p. 1977. pap. 5.95 (ISBN 0-664-24142-5). Westminster.

George, Denise. The Student Marriage. LC 82-72230. (Orig.). 1983. pap. 4.95 (ISBN 0-8054-6939-7, 4269-39). Broadman.

MARRIAGE (CANON LAW)

see also Marriage–Annulment (Canon Law)

Alessio, Luis & Munoz, Hector. Marriage & the Family: The Domestic Church. Owen, Aloysius, tr. from Span. LC 82-6853. 121p. 1982. pap. 3.95 (ISBN 0-8189-0433-X). Alba.

Bontrager, G. Edwin. Divorce & the Faithful Church. LC 78-4671. 224p. 1978. 12.95 (ISBN 0-8361-1850-2); pap. 8.95 (ISBN 0-8361-1851-0). Herald Pr.

Doyle, Thomas P., ed. Marriage Studies: Reflections in Canon Law & Theology, Vol. 1. 155p. (Orig.). 1980. pap. 4.00 (ISBN 0-943616-03-4). Canon Law Soc.

--Marriage Studies: Reflections in Canon Law & Theology, Vol. 2. 202p. (Orig.). 1982. pap. 4.50 (ISBN 0-943616-04-2). Canon Law Soc.

--Marriage Studies, Vol. 3: Reflections in Canon Law & Theology. 207p. (Orig.). 1985. pap. 6.00 (ISBN 0-943616-25-5). Canon Law Soc.

Esmein, Adhemar. Mariage En Droit Canonique, 2 Vols. (Fr). 1969. Repr. of 1891 ed. Set. 47.00 (ISBN 0-8337-1072-9). B Franklin.

Mace, David R., ed. Modern Marriage & the Clergy. LC 74-19593. (Special Issues of Pastoral Psychology). 84p. 1978. 9.95 (ISBN 0-87705-368-5). Human Sci Pr.

Muggeridge, Malcolm, et al. Christian Married Love. Dennehy, Raymond, ed. Englund, Sergia & Leiva, Erasmo, trs. LC 81-85047. Tr. of Christlicher Stand. 132p. (Orig.). 1981. pap. 8.95 (ISBN 0-89870-008-6). Ignatius Pr.

Siegle, Bernad A. Marriage: According to the New Code of Canon Law. LC 86-10806. 297p. (Orig.). 1986. pap. 14.95 (ISBN 0-8189-0497-6). Alba.

Siegle, Bernard. Marriage: According to the New Code of Canon Law. new ed. LC 72-4055. 297p. (Orig.). Date not set. pap. 14.95 (ISBN 0-8189-0497-6). Alba.

Werth, Alvin, compiled by. Papal Pronouncements on Marriage & the Family: From Leo XIII to Pius XII (1878-1954) LC 82-6265. xxi, 189p. 1982. Repr. of 1955 ed. lib. bdg. 27.50x (ISBN 0-313-22521-4, WEPA). Greenwood.

MARRIAGE (ISLAMIC LAW)

Farah, Madelain. Marriage & Sexuality in Islam: A Translation of al-Ghazali's Book on the Etiquette of Marriage from the Ihya' 192p. 1984. 20.00 (ISBN 0-87480-231-8). U of Utah Pr.

Shukri, Ahmed. Muhammedan Law of Marriage & Divorce. (Columbia University. Contributions to Oriental History & Philology: No. 7). Repr. of 1917 ed. 15.25 (ISBN 0-404-50537-6). AMS Pr.

MARRIAGE, MIXED

Here are entered works on marriage between persons of different religions, or person of different denominations within christianity.

Baker, Andrew & Goodman, Lori. Working with the Intermarried: A Practical Guide for Workshop Leaders. LC 85-71160. 36p. (Orig.). 1985. pap. 4.00 (ISBN 0-87495-071-6). Am Jewish Comm.

Balzano, Bill. Church of God & Roman Catholic Interfaith Marriage. (Truthway Ser.). 35p. (Orig.). 1981. pap. text ed. 1.25 (ISBN 0-87148-175-8). Pathway Pr.

Beauchamp, Gary & Beauchamp, Deanna. Religiously Mixed Marriage. 4.95 (ISBN 0-89137-528-7). Quality Pubns.

Berry, Jo. Beloved Unbeliever: A Woman's Workshop. (Woman's Workshop Ser.). 176p. (Orig.). 1985. leader's manual 2.95 (ISBN 0-310-42661-8, 11219P); student's manual 5.95 (ISBN 0-310-42691-X, 11220P). Zondervan.

--Beloved Unbeliever: Loving Your Husband into the Faith. 176p. (Orig.). 1981. pap. 5.95 (ISBN 0-310-42621-9, 11215). Zondervan.

Besanceney, Paul H. Interfaith Marriages: Who & Why. 1970. 12.95x (ISBN 0-8084-0164-5); pap. 8.95x (ISBN 0-8084-0165-3). New Coll U Pr.

Billnitzer, Harold. Chances in a Mixed Marriage. 1978. pap. 1.95 (ISBN 0-933350-11-2). Morse Pr.

Bilnitzer. Check Your Chances of Success in a Mixed Marriage. pap. 1.75 (ISBN 0-686-12318-2). Christs Mission.

Cohen, Jack S. Intermarriage & Conversion: A Halakhic Solution. 1987. 14.95 (ISBN 0-88125-124-0); pap. 9.95 (ISBN 0-88125-125-9). Ktav.

Cowan, Paul & Cowan, Rachael. Mixed Blessings: Jews & Gentiles Confront Intermarriage. LC 87-480. 288p. 1987. 17.95 (ISBN 0-385-19502-8). Doubleday.

Crohn, Joel. Ethnic Identity & Marital Conflict: Jews, Italians & WASPs. LC 86-70084. 44p. (Orig.). 1986. pap. 2.50 (ISBN 0-87495-078-3). Am Jewish Comm.

Gordis, Robert. Love & Sex: A Modern Jewish Perspective. 290p. 1978. 8.95 (ISBN 0-374-19252-9). FS&G.

Klausner, Abraham J. Weddings: A Guide to All Religious & Interfaith Marriage Services. LC 86-7892. (Life-Cycle Bookshelf Ser.). (Orig.). 1986. pap. 11.90 (ISBN 0-933771-00-2). Alpha Pub Co.

Lawless, Richard M. When Love Unites the Church. LC 81-72000. (When Bks.). 88p. (Orig.). 1982. pap. 2.45 (ISBN 0-87029-181-5, 20273-9). Abbey.

Lunday, Berneice. Unblessed. LC 78-15244. (Orion Ser). 1979. pap. 3.50 (ISBN 0-8127-0200-X). Review & Herald.

Mayer, Egon. Becoming Jewish. 40p. (Orig.). Date not set. pap. price not set. Am Jewish Comm.

--Children of Intermarriage: A Study in Pattern of Identification & Family Life. LC 83-82077. 56p. 1983. pap. 2.50 (ISBN 0-87495-055-4). Am Jewish Comm.

--Love & Tradition: Marriage Between Jews & Christians. 312p. 1985. (full discount avail.) 17.95 (ISBN 0-306-42043-0, Plenum Pr). Plenum Pub.

--Love & Tradition: Marriage Between Jews & Christians. LC 86-24823. 312p. 1987. pap. 8.95 (ISBN 0-8052-0828-3). Schocken.

Mayer, John E. Jewish-Gentile Courtships: An Exploratory Study of a Social Process. LC 80-16130. x, 240p. 1980. Repr. of 1961 ed. lib. bdg. 24.75x (ISBN 0-313-22465-X, MAJG). Greenwood.

Schiappa, Barbara D. Mixing: Catholic-Protestant Marriages in the 1980's. LC 81-84387. 144p. (Orig.). 1982. pap. 5.95 (ISBN 0-8091-2443-2). Paulist Pr.

Thomas, John L. Beginning Your Marriage, 2 vols. 1980. 4.95 (ISBN 0-915388-25-1); pap. 2.50 (ISBN 0-915388-24-3). Buckley Pubns.

White, Ellen. Forbidden Marriages & Divorce. large print ed. 27p. 1985. pap. 5.00 (ISBN 0-914009-38-9). VHI Library.

MARRIAGE COUNSELING

Adams, Jay E. Solving Marriage Problems. 1983. pap. 4.50 (ISBN 0-8010-0197-8). Baker Bk.

--Solving Marriage Problems. 132p. 1983. pap. 5.95 (ISBN 0-87552-081-2). Presby & Reformed.

--Solving Marriage Problems: Biblical Solutions for Christian Counselors. (A Jay Adams Library). 144p. 1986. pap. 6.95 (ISBN 0-310-51081-3, 12120P). Zondervan.

Arnold, William V., et al. Divorce: Prevention or Survival. LC 77-22066. 128p. 1977. pap. 5.95 (ISBN 0-664-24142-5). Westminster.

Augsburger, Don A., ed. Marriages That Work. LC 84-15637. 112p. (Orig.). 1984. pap. 6.95 (ISBN 0-8361-3374-9). Herald Pr.

Bagot, Jean-Pierre. How to Understand Marriage. 144p. (Orig.). 1987. pap. 9.95 (ISBN 0-8245-0810-6). Crossroad NY.

Baker, Andrew & Goodman, Lori. Working with the Intermarried: A Practical Guide for Workshop Leaders. LC 85-71160. 36p. (Orig.). 1985. pap. 4.00 (ISBN 0-87495-071-6). Am Jewish Comm.

Barbeau, Clayton C. Joy of Marriage. Orig. Title: Creative Marriage: the Middle Years. 132p. 1980. pap. 5.95 (ISBN 0-86683-759-0, HarpR). Har-Row.

Besson, Clyde T. Growing Together. 1987. pap. 5.95 (ISBN 0-317-54043-2). Baker Bk.

Biddle, Perry. Abingdon Marriage Manual. 208p. pap. 12.95 (ISBN 0-687-00485-3). Abingdon.

Billnitzer, Harold. Before You Divorce. 1978. pap. 0.95 (ISBN 0-933350-12-0). Morse Pr.

Brown, Joan W. & Brown, Bill. Together Each Day. 288p. 1980. pap. 7.95 (ISBN 0-8007-5226-0). Revell.

Caldwell, Louis. The Adventure of Becoming One. (Ultra Bks.). 80p. 1981. 5.95 (ISBN 0-8010-2334-3). Baker Bk.

Canclini, Arnoldo. Cuando la Infidelidad Asoma. (Series on the Family). (Span.). 112p. (Orig.). 1986. pap. 3.50 (ISBN 0-311-46264-2). Casa Bautista.

Carter, Stephen & McKinney, Charles. More of a Good Thing. 1982. pap. 3.50 (ISBN 0-570-03840-5, 12-2943). Concordia.

Chapman, Gary. Toward a Growing Marriage. LC 79-21376. 1979. pap. 5.95 (ISBN 0-8024-8787-4). Moody.

Clinebell, Howard J. Growth Counseling for Marriage Enrichment: Pre-Marriage & the Early Years. Stone, Howard W., ed. LC 74-26335. (Creative Pastoral Care & Counseling Ser.). 96p. 1975. pap. 4.50 (ISBN 0-8006-0551-9, 1-551). Fortress.

--Growth Counseling for Mid-Years Couples. Stone, Howard W., ed. LC 76-7863. (Creative Pastoral Care & Counseling Ser.). 1977. pap. 0.50 (ISBN 0-8006-0558-6, 1-558). Fortress.

Dale, Robert D. & Dale, Carrie Kondy. Making Good Marriages Better. LC 78-60052. 1978. 6.95 (ISBN 0-8054-5631-7). Broadman.

Dana, Mark. Lifemating: New Hope for Those Who've Loved & Lost. 1985. 7.75 (ISBN 0-8062-2447-9). Carlton.

Deal, William S. Happiness & Harmony in Marriage. pap. 2.95 (ISBN 0-686-13723-X). Crusade Pubs.

--Picking a Partner. 2.95 (ISBN 0-686-13716-7). Crusade Pubs.

Del Vecchio, Anthony & Del Vecchio, Mary. Preparing for the Sacrament of Marriage. LC 80-67721. (Illus.). 144p. (Orig.). 1980. pap. 3.95 (ISBN 0-87793-208-5). Ave Maria.

Dobson, James C. Straight Talk to Men & Their Wives. 1980. 12.95 (ISBN 0-8499-0260-6). Word Bks.

Dominian, J. Marital Breakdown. 1969. 5.95 (ISBN 0-8199-0151-2, L38436). Franciscan Herald.

Dominian, Jack. Make or Break: A Guide to Marriage Counselling. (Pastoral Help Bks.: Vol. 1). 1985. pap. 8.95 (ISBN 0-89453-473-4). M Glazier.

Eyrich, Howard A. Three to Get Ready: A Christian Premarital Counselor's Manual. 1978. pap. 4.95 (ISBN 0-87552-259-9). Presby & Refomed.

Field, David. Marriage Personalities. 192p. (Orig.). 1986. pap. 5.95 (ISBN 0-89081-476-7). Harvest Hse.

Florio, Anthony. You Can Make Your Marriage Stronger. (Christian Counseling Aids Ser). 1978. pap. 1.25 (ISBN 0-8010-3484-1). Baker Bk.

Grant, Brian W. Reclaiming the Dream: Marriage Counseling in the Parish Context. 176p. (Orig.). 1986. pap. 9.95 (ISBN 0-687-35729-2). Abingdon.

Hauck, Paul A. Marriage Is a Loving Business. LC 77-2202. 116p. 1977. pap. 6.95 (ISBN 0-664-24137-9). Westminster.

Hawkins, Robert L. A Pastor's Primer for Premarital Guidance. 1978. pap. 3.95 (ISBN 0-9607764-0-0). R L Hawkins.

Jensen, Mary & Jensen, Andrew. Making Your Marriage Work. LC 85-7528. 144p. 1985. pap. 6.95 (ISBN 0-8066-2124-9, 10-4265). Augsburg.

Johnson, Douglas W. Ministry with Young Couples: A Pastor's Planbook. 128p. (Orig.). 1985. pap. 6.95 (ISBN 0-687-27043-X). Abingdon.

Joy, Donald. Lovers: Whatever Happened to Eden? 220p. 1987. 12.95 (ISBN 0-8499-0541-9). Word Bks.

Kenny, James & Kenny, Mary. When Your Marriage Goes Stale. LC 79-51277. (When Bks). (Illus.). 1979. pap. 2.45 (ISBN 0-87029-150-5, 20236-6). Abbey.

Kline, Donald L. One Flesh. 1985. 4.95 (ISBN 0-89536-730-0, 5814). CSS of Ohio.

Laz, Medard. Spiritual Guidance for the Separated & Divorced. 64p. 1982. pap. 1.95 (ISBN 0-89243-158-X). Liguori Pubns.

Lee, Mark W. How to Have a Good Marriage. LC 78-56794. 1981. pap. 5.95 (ISBN 0-915684-89-6). Chr Pubns.

Le Peau, Phyllis J. & Le Peau, Andrew T. One Plus One Equals One. 96p. (Orig.). 1981. pap. 3.95 (ISBN 0-87784-803-3). Inter-Varsity.

Mace, David & Mace, Vera. How to Have a Happy Marriage. 1983. pap. 3.95 (ISBN 0-687-17831-2, Festival). Abingdon.

--Marriage Enrichment in the Church. LC 76-49710. 1977. pap. 4.50 o. p. (ISBN 0-8054-5621-X). Broadman.

Mace, David R. Getting Ready for Marriage. 128p. 1985. pap. 5.95 (ISBN 0-687-14136-2). Abingdon.

Mason, Robert L. & Jacobs, Carrie. How to Choose the Wrong Marriage Partner & Live Unhappily Ever After. LC 78-52452. 1979. pap. 2.99 (ISBN 0-8042-2093-X). John Knox.

Mayhall, Jack & Mayhall, Carole. Marriage Takes More Than Love. LC 77-85736. 240p. 1978. pap. 5.95 (ISBN 0-89109-426-1). NavPress.

Meier, Paul D. You Can Avoid Divorce. (Christian Counseling Aids Ser). 1978. pap. 1.50 (ISBN 0-8010-6052-4). Baker Bk.

Mitman, John L. Premarital Counseling: A Manual for Clergy & Counselors. 128p. (Orig.). 1984. pap. 6.95 (ISBN 0-86683-879-1, 7874, HarpR). Har-Row.

Moore, Donald. A Daily Guide to a Better Marriage. 32p. 1984. pap. 0.75 (ISBN 0-88144-021-3). Christian Pub.

Phillips, Bob. How Can I Be Sure: A Pre-Marriage Inventory. LC 77-94448. 160p. (Orig.). 1978. pap. 3.95 (ISBN 0-89081-073-7). Harvest Hse.

Pitt, Theodore K. Premarital Counseling Handbook for Ministers. 192p. 1985. pap. 9.95 (ISBN 0-8170-1071-8). Judson.

Rickerson, Wayne. Newly Married. (Family Ministry Ser.). 96p. 1986. pap. 19.95 (ISBN 0-89191-967-8). Cook.

Ripple, Paula. The Pain & the Possibility. LC 78-67745. 144p. 1978. pap. 2.95 (ISBN 0-87793-162-3). Ave Maria.

Ruhnke, Robert. For Better & for Ever: Sponsor Couple Program for Christian Marriage Preparation. 1981. pap. 3.95 (ISBN 0-89243-143-1); dialogue packet wkbk. 3.75 (ISBN 0-89243-144-X). Liguori Pubns.

Smith, Harold I. More Than "I Do". An Engaged Couple's Premarital Handbook. (Orig.). 1983. pap. 2.95 (ISBN 0-8341-0864-X). Beacon Hill.

Smoke, Jim & Guest, Lisa. Growing Through Divorce: Working Guide. 96p. (Orig.). 1985. pap. 3.25 (ISBN 0-89081-477-5). Harvest Hse.

Swain, Clark. Enriching Your Marriage: A Tune-up for Partners in Love. LC 80-84568. 250p. 1982. 9.95 (ISBN 0-88290-171-0, 2015). Horizon Utah.

Tapley, William. Happily Ever after Is No Accident. Sherer, Michael L., ed. (Orig.). 1987. pap. 2.75 leaders guide (ISBN 0-89536-862-5, 7821); pap. 3.45 couples bk. (ISBN 0-89536-863-3, 7822). CSS of Ohio.

Thompson, David A. Five Steps Toward a Better Marriage. 96p. (Orig.). 1980. pap. 5.95 (ISBN 0-87123-164-6, 210164). Bethany Hse.

--A Premarital Guide for Couples & Their Counselors. 80p. 1979. pap. 4.95 (ISBN 0-87123-465-3, 210465). Bethany Hse.

Ulyat, Richard T. United in Marriage: A Guide to Premarital Counseling. 47p. 1984. pap. 3.50 (ISBN 0-86544-023-9). Salv Army Suppl South.

Van Pelt, Nancy. The Compleat Marriage. Rev. ed. LC 78-20770. (Orion Ser). 1979. pap. 6.95 (ISBN 0-8127-0218-2). Review & Herald.

Vath, Raymond E. & O'Neill, Daniel. Marrying for Life: A Handbook of Marriage Skills. (Illus.). 144p. (Orig.). 1982. pap. 6.95 (ISBN 0-86683-674-8, HarpR). Har-Row.

Vath, Raymond E. & O'Neill, Daniel W. Marrying for Life. (Illus., Orig.). 1981. pap. 8.00 (ISBN 0-939336-00-6). Messenger Comm.

Warren, Thomas B. Keeping the Lock in Wedlock. 1980. pap. 11.00 (ISBN 0-934916-26-8). Natl Christian Pr.

Watts, P. Mark. Living Through Your Separation or Divorce. Sherer, Michael L., ed. (Orig.). 1987. pap. 2.25 (ISBN 0-89536-864-1, 7823). CSS of Ohio.

Wright, H. Norman. Marital Counseling: A Biblical Behavioral Cognitive Approach. 370p. 1981. 16.95 (ISBN 0-938786-00-8). Chr Marriage.

Wright, Norman & Roberts, Wes. Before You Say I Do: Study Manual. LC 77-94133. 1978. 4.95 (ISBN 0-89081-119-9). Harvest Hse.

MARRIAGE CUSTOMS AND RITES

see also Wedding Etiquette

Ahmad, Imtiaz, ed. Family, Kinship, & Marriage among the Muslims. LC 77-74484. 1977. 18.50x (ISBN 0-88386-757-5). South Asia Bks.

Archer, William G. Songs for the Bride: Wedding Rites of Rural India. Miller, Barbara S. & Archer, Mildred, eds. (Studies in Oriental Culture). 224p. 1985. 22.50x (ISBN 0-317-18769-4). Brooklyn Coll Pr.

Aridas, Christopher. Your Catholic Wedding: A Complete Plan-Book. LC 81-43250. (Illus.). 192p. 1982. pap. 2.95 (ISBN 0-385-17731-3, Im). Doubleday.

Arnold, Caroline. How People Get Married. (Ceremonies & Celebrations Ser.). (Illus.). 32p. 1987. PLB 9.90 (ISBN 0-531-10096-0). Watts.

The Celebration & Blessing of a Marriage. 1977. pap. 0.95 (ISBN 0-8164-2152-8, HarpR). Har-Row.

Ch'en Kou-Chun. Studies in Marriage & Funerals of Taiwan Aborigines. (Asian Folklore & Social Life Monograph: No. 4). (Chinese.). 1970. 14.00 (ISBN 0-89986-007-9). Oriental Bk Store.

Daniels, Elam J. Como Ser Feliz en el Matrimonio. Orig. Title: How to Be Happily Married. 96p. 1984. pap. 2.10 (ISBN 0-311-46066-6). Casa Bautista.

Diamant, Anita. New Jewish Wedding. 272p. 1986. 8.95 (ISBN 0-671-62882-8). Summit Bks.

Evans-Pritchard, Edward E. Kinship & Marriage among the Nuer. (Illus.). 1951. 32.50x (ISBN 0-19-823104-0). Oxford U Pr.

MARRIAGE GUIDANCE

see Marriage Counseling

MARRIAGE LAW (ISLAMIC LAW)

see Marriage (Islamic Law)

MARRIAGE REGISTERS

see Registers of Births, Deaths, Marriages, Etc.

MARRIAGE SERVICE

Aridas, Christopher. Your Catholic Wedding: A Complete Plan-Book. LC 81-43250. (Illus.). 192p. 1982. pap. 2.95 (ISBN 0-385-17731-3, Im). Doubleday.

Christensen, James L. The Minister's Marriage Handbook. rev. ed. 160p. 1974. Repr. 10.95 (ISBN 0-8007-1424-5). Revell.

Follett, Barbara L. Checklist for a Perfect Wedding. rev. & expanded ed. LC 85-29206. (Illus.). 160p. 1986. pap. 3.95 (ISBN 0-385-23588-7). Doubleday.

Homburg, Arthur. A New Wedding Service For You. 1985. 5.95 (ISBN 0-89536-731-9, 5815). CSS of Ohio.

Hutton, Samuel W. Minister's Marriage Manual. 1968. 6.95 (ISBN 0-8010-4031-0). Baker Bk.

Knight, George W. Wedding Ceremony Idea Book. 96p. 1982. pap. 7.95 (ISBN 0-939298-01-5). J M Prods.

Marriage Service. boxed 4.50 (ISBN 0-664-21050-3); moire boxed 5.95 (ISBN 0-664-21075-9); pap. 15.50 pkg. of 10 (ISBN 0-664-29035-3). Westminster.

Office of Worship for the Presbyterian Church (U. S. A.) & the Cumberland Presbyterian Church Station. Christian Marriage. (Supplemental Liturgical Resource Ser.: 3). 120p. (Orig.). 1986. pap. 7.95 (ISBN 0-664-24033-X). Westminster.

Ruiz, Mario, ed. Manual de Ceremonias Matrimoniales. (Span.). 184p. 1982. 6.95 (ISBN 0-87148-581-8). Pathway Pr.

MARRIED PEOPLE–PRAYER-BOOKS AND DEVOTIONS

Bjorge, James R. Forty Ways to Say I Love You. LC 78-52179. 1978. pap. 5.95 (ISBN 0-8066-1654-7, 10-2360). Augsburg.

Deal, William S. Happiness & Harmony in Marriage. pap. 2.95 (ISBN 0-686-13723-X). Crusade Pubs.

Donnelly, Mark & Fenton, Nina. Search Heaven & Hell. Rappaport, Joh, ed. LC 86-81968. 500p. 1986. pap. 10.95 (ISBN 1-55666-001-4). Authors Unltd.

Drescher, John M. Meditations for the Newly Married. LC 69-10835. 142p. 1969. gift-boxed 9.95 (ISBN 0-8361-1571-6). Herald Pr.

Durkin, Henry P. Forty-Four Hours to Change Your Life: Marriage Encounter. (Orig.). pap. write for info (ISBN 0-515-09442-0). Jove Pubns.

Ruhnke, Robert. Nos Amaremos Toda la Vida: Paquete de Hojas para el Dialogo. Diaz, Olimpia, tr. (Span.). 96p. 1983. 3.75 (ISBN 0-89243-185-7). Liguori Pubns.

MARSHALL, PETER, 1902-1949

Marshall, Catherine. Man Called Peter. 1971. pap. 4.50 (ISBN 0-380-00894-7). Avon.

MARTIALL, JOHN, 1534-1597

Calfhill, James. An Answer to John Martiall's Treatise of the Cross. 1846. 31.00 (ISBN 0-384-07020-5). Johnson Repr.

Fulke, William. Stapleton's Fortress Overthrown: A Rejoinder to Martiall's Reply. Repr. of 1848 ed. 31.00 (ISBN 0-384-17240-7). Johnson Repr.

MARTIN, SAINT, BISHOP OF TOURS, 4TH CENT.

Donaldson, Christopher. Martin of Tours: Parish Priest, Mystic & Exorcist. (Illus.). 171p. 1985. pap. 8.95 (ISBN 0-7102-0682-8). Methuen Inc.

Severus, Sulpicius. The Life of Saint Martin of Tours. pap. 1.95 (ISBN 0-686-05653-1). Eastern Orthodox.

Stancliffe, Clare. St. Martin & His Hagiographer: History & Miracle in Sulpicius Severus. (Oxford Historical Monographs). (Illus.). 1983. 45.00x (ISBN 0-19-821895-8). Oxford U Pr.

MARTIN, GREGORY, d. 1582

Fulke, William. Defence of the Sincere & True Translations of the Holy Scriptures into the English Tongue. Repr. of 1843 ed. 51.00 (ISBN 0-384-17230-X). Johnson Repr.

MARTINEAU, HARRIET, 1802-1876

Martineau, Harriet. Autobiography. 962p. Repr. of 1877 ed. text ed. 62.10x (ISBN 0-576-02159-8). Gregg Intl.

Von Petzold, Gertrud. Harriet Martineau und Ihre Sittlich Religiose Weltschau. 1941. pap. 7.00 (ISBN 0-384-46100-X). Johnson Repr.

MARTYRDOM

see also Martyrs

Horbury, W. & McNeil, B., eds. Suffering & Martyrdom in the New Testament. LC 80-40706. 240p. 1981. 49.50 (ISBN 0-521-23482-4). Cambridge U Pr.

Ide, Arthur F. Martyrdom of Women in the Early Christian Church. LC 85-14741. (Illus.). 100p. 1985. pap. 6.95 (ISBN 0-934667-00-4). Tangelwuld.

Kolb, Robert. For All the Saints: Changing Perceptions of Martyrdom & Sainthood in the Lutheran Reformation. (Illus.). 192p. 1987. 29.95 (ISBN 0-86554-270-8, H233). Mercer Univ Pr.

Novitch, Miriam, ed. Sobibor: Martyrdom & Revolt. (Illus.). 168p. pap. 4.95 (ISBN 0-686-95087-9). ADL.

Wright, William. An Early Christian Syrian Martyrology: The Names of Our Lords the Confessors & Victors & the Days on Which They Gained Their Crowns. pap. 5.95 (ISBN 0-317-11387-9). Eastern Orthodox.

Wurmbrand, Richard. Tortured for Christ. 1973. pap. 2.95 (ISBN 0-88264-001-1). Diane Bks.

MARTYROLOGIES

Aengus, Saint Martyrology of St. Aengus. pap. 12.50 (ISBN 0-686-25554-2). Eastern Orthodox.

Budge, Ernest A., ed. Coptic Martyrdoms, Etc. in the Dialect of Upper Egypt. LC 77-3588. (Coptic Texts: Vol. 4). (Illus.). Repr. of 1914 ed. 60.00 (ISBN 0-404-11554-3). AMS Pr.

Catholic Church Staff. The Roman & British Martyrology. 1980. lib. bdg. 79.95 (ISBN 0-8490-3128-1). Gordon Pr.

White, Helen C. Tudor Books of Saints & Martyrs. LC 63-13741. pap. 73.00 (ISBN 0-317-07866-6, 2004164). Bks Demand UMI.

MARTYRS

see also Martyrdom

Acts of the Christian Martyrs. pap. 6.95 (ISBN 0-686-19380-6). Eastern Orthodox.

Delehaye, Hippolyte. Les Origines du Culte des martyrs. 2nd, rev. ed. LC 78-63459. (The Crusades & Military Orders: Second Ser.). Repr. of 1933 ed. 40.00 (ISBN 0-404-16518-4). AMS Pr.

Elliot, Elisabeth. Through Gates of Splendor. 1981. 3.95 (ISBN 0-8423-7151-6). Tyndale.

Fink, Benjamin. Life of John Kline. 7.95 (ISBN 0-87178-516-1). Brethren.

Forbush, W. B., ed. Fox's Book of Martyrs. 11.95 (ISBN 0-310-24390-4, 9636); pap. 6.95 (ISBN 0-310-24391-2, 9636P). Zondervan.

Fox, John. Foxe's Christian Martyrs of the World. 1985. 6.95 (ISBN 0-916441-12-1). Barbour & Co.

Foxe, John. Acts & Monuments, 8 Vols. Cattley, S. R. & Townsend, George, eds. LC 79-168132. Repr. of 1849 ed. Set. 400.00 (ISBN 0-404-02590-0). AMS Pr.

--Foxe's Book of Martyrs. Berry, W. Grinton, ed. (Giant Summit Bks). 1978. pap. 7.95 (ISBN 0-8010-3483-3). Baker Bk.

--Foxe's Book of Martyrs. 400p. pap. 3.95 (ISBN 0-8007-8013-2, Spire Bks). Revell.

--Foxe's Book of Martyrs. 400p. 1981. pap. 3.95 (ISBN 0-88368-095-5). Whitaker Hse.

Franciscan Friars of Marytown, ed. The Hero of Auschwitz. (Illus.). 47p. 1979. pap. 0.75 (ISBN 0-913382-11-6, 105-29). Prow Bks-Franciscan.

Graves, Kersey. The World's Sixteen Crucified Saviors. 436p. spiral bdg. 8.50. Truth Seeker.

Gregorius, Saint Les Livres des Miracles & Autres Opuscules, 4 Vols. 1863. Set. 149.00 (ISBN 0-384-19888-0); 38.00 ea.; pap. 32.00 ea.; Set. pap. 125.00 (ISBN 0-384-19889-9). Johnson Repr.

Hefley, James & Hefley, Marti. By Their Blood. 1986. pap. 8.95 (ISBN 0-8010-4312-3). Baker Bk.

--By Their Blood: Christian Martyrs of the Twentieth Century. LC 78-6187. 1979. pap. 7.95 (ISBN 0-915134-24-1). Mott Media.

Homan, Helen. Letters to the Martyrs. facs. ed. LC 79-148220. (Biography Index Reprint Ser.). 1951. 20.00 (ISBN 0-8369-8067-0). Ayer Co Pubs.

King, Marie G., ed. Foxe's Book of Martyrs. 50p. pap. 3.95 (ISBN 0-317-06922-5, 06742-3). Jove Pubns.

Lowry, James W. In the Whale's Belly & Other Martyr Stories. (Illus.). (YA) 1981. 4.70 (ISBN 0-87813-513-8). Christian Light.

McKee, John. A Martyr Bishop: The Life of St. Oliver Plunkett. 181p. 1975. 7.95 (ISBN 0-912414-21-9). Lumen Christi.

Marmorstein, Emil. The Murder of Jacob De Haan by the Zionists: A Martyr's Message. 1980. lib. bdg. 59.95 (ISBN 0-686-68747-7). Revisionist Pr.

Moiseyev, Ivan V. A Russian Martyr. 0.95 (ISBN 0-89985-107-X). Christ Nations.

Montague, H. Patrick. The Saints & Martyrs of Ireland: Feast Days Calendar. (Illus.). 138p. Date not set. 15.95 (ISBN 0-86140-106-9); pap. 5.95 (ISBN 0-86140-107-7). Dufour.

Musurillo, Herbert. The Acts of the Christian Martyrs: Text & Translations. (Oxford Early English Texts Ser). 1972. 52.00x (ISBN 0-19-826806-8). Oxford U Pr.

O'Malley, William J. The Voice of the Blood. LC 79-90055. (Five Christian Martyrs of Our Time Ser.: No. 633). 195p. (Orig.). 1980. pap. 1.99 (ISBN 0-88344-539-5). Orbis Bks.

Parbury, Kathleen. Women of Grace: A Biographical Dictionary of British Women Saints, Martyrs & Reformers. 224p. 1985. 25.00x (ISBN 0-85362-213-2, Oriel). Methuen Inc.

Protopresbyter Michael Polsky. Novije Mutcheniki Rossijskije, tom 2, Vol. 2. Tr. of The New Martyrs of Russia. 329p. 1957. pap. 11.00 (ISBN 0-317-29207-2). Holy Trinity.

Purcell, William. Martyrs of Our Time. Lambert, Herbert, ed. LC 85-4104. 1985. pap. 9.95 (ISBN 0-8272-2317-X). CBP.

Ruffin, C. Bernard. The Days of the Martyrs. LC 85-60517. 200p. (Orig.). 1985. pap. 7.95 (ISBN 0-87973-595-3, 595). Our Sunday Visitor.

Russo-Alesi, Anthony I. Martyrology Pronouncing Dictionary. LC 79-167151. 1973. Repr. of 1939 ed. 35.00x (ISBN 0-8103-3272-8). Gale.

St. John Ogilvie S.J., 1579-1615. 68p. 1979. 30.00x (Pub. by Third Eye Centre). State Mutual Bk.

Treece, Patricia. Soldier of God. 32p. 1982. pap. 1.00 (ISBN 0-913382-22-1, 111-1). Prow Bks-Franciscan.

Tylenda, Joseph N. Jesuit Saints & Martyrs. 503p. 1984. 15.95 (ISBN 0-8294-0447-3). Loyola.

Van Braght, Thieleman J. Martyrs' Mirror. (Illus.). 1157p. 1938. 29.95 (ISBN 0-8361-1390-X). Herald Pr.

MARVELL, ANDREW, 1621-1678

Bennett, Joan. Five Metaphysical Poets: Donne, Herbert, Vaughan, Crashaw, Marvell. 1964. 32.50 (ISBN 0-521-04156-2); pap. 9.95 (ISBN 0-521-09238-8). Cambridge U Pr.

Cullen, Patrick. Spenser, Marvell, & Renaissance Pastoral. LC 76-123566. pap. 42.60 (2014653). Bks Demand UMI.

Klause, John. The Unfortunate Fall: Theodicy & the Moral Imagination of Andrew Marvell. LC 83-13521. x, 208p. 1984. 22.50 (ISBN 0-208-02026-8, Archon Bks). Shoe String.

MARX, KARL, 1818-1883

Carlebach, Julius. Karl Marx & the Radical Critique of Judaism. (Littman Library of Jewish Civilization). 478p. 1978. 45.00x (ISBN 0-19-710031-7). Oxford U Pr.

Cartesius, Hugo. Individual & Society: Nature-Marx-Mao. 158p. 1977. 12.40 (ISBN 3-261-02063-6). P Lang Pubs.

Cuddihy, John M. The Ordeal of Civility: Freud, Marx, Levi-Strauss, & the Jewish Struggle with Modernity. LC 86-47757. 272p. 1987. pap. 9.95 (ISBN 0-8070-3609-9, BP-738). Beacon Pr.

Lash, Nicholas. A Matter of Hope: A Theologian's Reflections on the Thought of Karl Marx. LC 82-1980. 312p. 1982. text ed. 19.95 (ISBN 0-268-01352-7). U of Notre Dame Pr.

--A Matter of Hope: A Theologian's Reflections on the Thought of Karl Marx. LC 82-1980. 312p. 1984. pap. text ed. 9.95 (ISBN 0-268-01360-8, 85-13608). U of Notre Dame Pr.

Lenin, V. I. Marx-Engels-Marxism. 176p. 1977. pap. 1.40 (ISBN 0-8285-2194-8, Pub. by Progress Pubs USSR). Imported Pubns.

Lyon, David. Karl Marx: A Christian Assessment of His Life & Thought. LC 81-8268. 192p. (Orig.). 1981. pap. 5.95 (ISBN 0-87784-879-3). Inter-Varsity.

Miranda, Jose P. Marx Against the Marxists: The Christian Humanism of Karl Marx. Drury, John, tr. from Span. LC 80-14415. Orig. Title: El Christianism de Marx. 336p. (Orig.). 1980. pap. 12.95 (ISBN 0-88344-322-8). Orbis Bks.

Newell, William L. The Secular Magi: Marx, Nietzsche, & Freud on Religion. 264p. (Orig.). 1986. pap. 13.95 (ISBN 0-8298-0579-6). Pilgrim NY.

Smith, David. Marx's Kapital for Beginners. (Illus.). 1982. pap. 3.95 (ISBN 0-394-71265-X). Pantheon.

Worsley, Peter, ed. Marx & Marxism. LC 81-6848. (Key Sociologists Ser.). 126p. 1982. pap. 4.95x (ISBN 0-85312-375-6, NO. 3675 TAVISTOCK). Methuen Inc.

MARY, VIRGIN

Alberione, James. Mary, Queen of Apostles. rev. ed. 1976. 4.00 (ISBN 0-8198-0438-X); pap. 3.00 (ISBN 0-8198-0439-8). Dghtrs St Paul.

Berselli, Costante & Gharib, Georges, eds. Sing the Joys of Mary. Jenkins, Phil, tr. from Italian. Tr. of Lodi alla Madonna. (Eng.). 136p. (Orig.). 1983. pap. 7.95 (ISBN 0-8192-1329-2). Morehouse.

Blunt, J. H., ed. The Myroure of Oure Lady. (EETS, ES Ser.: No. 19). Repr. of 1873 ed. 40.00 (ISBN 0-527-00232-1). Kraus Repr.

Boykin, James H. Political Intrigue in the Establishment of the Identity of Jesus & Mary. LC 86-90957. 286p. 1986. pap. 15.00x (ISBN 0-9603342-6-2). Boykin.

Brown, Raymond E., et al, eds. Mary in the New Testament. LC 78-8797. 336p. 1978. pap. 6.95 (ISBN 0-8091-2168-9). Paulist Pr.

--Mary in the New Testament: A Collaborative Assessment by Protestant & Roman Catholic Scholars. LC 78-8797. 336p. 1978. pap. 6.95 (ISBN 0-8006-1345-7, 1-1345). Fortress.

Cadoux, T., pref. by. The Sorrowful & Immaculate Heart of Mary: Message of Berthe Petit, Franciscan Tertiary (1870-1943) 110p. 1966. pap. 3.00 (ISBN 0-913382-02-7, 101-2). Prow Bks-Franciscan.

Carberry, John. Mary Queen & Mother. 1979. 5.50 (ISBN 0-8198-0584-X); pap. 3.95 (ISBN 0-8198-0585-8). Dghtrs St Paul.

Carlisle, Thomas J. Beginning with Mary: Women of the Gospels in Portrait. 120p. (Orig.). 1986. pap. 5.95 (ISBN 0-8028-0194-3). Eerdmans.

Carol, J. B. The Absolute Primacy & Predestination of Jesus & His Virgin Mother. 1981. 7.50 (ISBN 0-8199-0848-7). Franciscan Herald.

Feuillet, Andre. Jesus & His Mother. Maluf, Leonard, tr. from Fr. LC 84-6790. (Studies in Scripture Ser.: Vol. I). Tr. of Jesus et sa Mere. 266p. (Orig.). 1984. pap. 19.95 (ISBN 0-932506-27-5). St Bedes Pubns.

Fox, Robert J. The Immaculate Heart of Mary: True Devotion. 200p. (Orig.). 1986. pap. 7.50 (ISBN 0-87973-550-3, 550). Our Sunday Visitor.

Giordani, Igino. Mary of Nazareth. (Orig.). 1965. 6.00 (ISBN 0-8198-0092-9); pap. 5.00 (ISBN 0-8198-0093-7). Dghtrs St Paul.

Gold, Penny S. The Lady & the Virgin: Image, Attitude & Experience in Twelfth-Century France. LC 84-23701. (Women in Culture & Society Ser.). (Illus.). 228p. 1985. lib. bdg. 20.00x (ISBN 0-226-30087-0). U of Chicago Pr.

Haring, Bernard. Mary & Your Everyday Life. LC 77-92897. 1978. pap. 4.95 (ISBN 0-89243-075-3). Liguori Pubns.

Healy, Kilian. The Assumption of Mary. (Mary Library Ser.). 1982. pap. 5.95 (ISBN 0-89453-288-X). M Glazier.

Hickey, Mary E., tr. from Fr. Novena of Confidence & Thanksgiving to the Sorrowful & Immaculate Heart of Mary. (Illus.). 20p. 1962. pap. 0.25 (ISBN 0-913382-21-3, 107-2). Prow Bks-Franciscan.

Hinnebusch, Paul. The Mother of Jesus: Present with Us. LC 79-93231. 1980. pap. 5.95 (ISBN 0-913382-32-9, 101-27). Prow Bks-Franciscan.

Jameson, Anna B. Legends of the Madonna, As Represented in the Fine Arts. LC 70-89273. (Tower Bks.). (Illus.). lxxvi, 344p. 1972. Repr. of 1890 ed. 42.00x (ISBN 0-8103-3114-4). Gale.

John Paul, II. A Year with Mary. Buono, Anthony M., tr. from Italian. 320p. (Orig.). 1986. pap. 6.00 (ISBN 0-89942-370-1, 370/22). Catholic Bk Pub.

Kosicki, George W. & Farrell, Gerald J. The Spirit & the Bride Say, "Come!". Mary's Role in the New Pentecost. 112p. pap. 3.95 (ISBN 0-911988-41-6). AMI Pr.

Lavasik, Lawrence. Mary My Hope. rev. ed. (Illus., LargeType). blue bdg., colored edges 4.95 (ISBN 0-89942-365-5, 365/00). Catholic Bk Pub.

Liguori, Alphonse. The Blessed Virgin Mary: Excerpt from the Glories of Mary. 96p. 1974. pap. 3.00 (ISBN 0-89555-177-2). TAN Bks Pubs.

Liguori, St. Alphonsus. Love Is Prayer - Prayer Is Love. LC 72-97592. 1973. pap. 2.95 (ISBN 0-89243-047-8, 41500). Liguori Pubns.

Long, Valentine. The Mother of God. 1977. 7.95 (ISBN 0-8199-0619-0). Franciscan Herald.

Lovasik, Lawrence G. Mary My Mother. rev. ed. (Saint Joseph Picture Bks). (Illus., LargeType). flexible bdg. 0.95 (ISBN 0-89942-280-2, 280). Catholic Bk Pub.

Madonna. (Illus.). 64p. (Orig.). 1984. 19.95 (ISBN 0-86683-827-9, 8467, HarpR); pap. 9.95 (ISBN 0-86683-812-0, 8291). Har-Row.

Malone, Mary T. Who Is My Mother? 144p. 1984. pap. 6.95 (ISBN 0-697-02019-3). Wm C Brown.

Maloney, George. Mary, the Womb of God. 6.95 (ISBN 0-87193-057-9). Dimension Bks.

Miguens, M. Mary, Servant of the Lord. 1978. 3.75 (ISBN 0-8198-0538-6); pap. 2.25 (ISBN 0-8198-0539-4). Dghtrs St Paul.

Myers, Rawley. The Book of Mary: Devotions for October & May. LC 84-61563. 208p. (Orig.). 1984. pap. 6.50 (ISBN 0-87973-804-9, 804). Our Sunday Visitor.

Newman, John H. Mary the Second Eve. 40p. 1982. pap. 1.50 (ISBN 0-89555-181-0). TAN Bks Pubs.

O'Carroll, Michael. Theotokos: A Theological Encyclopedia of the Blessed Virgin Mary. 1982. pap. 19.95 (ISBN 0-89453-268-5). M Glazier.

Pope Paul VI. Mary God's Mother & Ours. 1979. 4.75 (ISBN 0-8198-0571-8); pap. 3.50 (ISBN 0-8198-0572-6). Dghtrs St Paul.

Pozo, Candido. Mary & Scripture. Date not set. price not set (ISBN 0-8199-0906-8). Franciscan Herald.

Prophet, Mark & Prophet, Elizabeth. My Soul Doth Magnify the Lord! rev. ed. (Illus.). 350p. 1980. pap. 7.95 (ISBN 0-916766-35-7). Summit Univ.

Randall, John, et al. Mary: Pathway to Fruitfulness. (Orig.). 1978. pap. 2.95 (ISBN 0-914544-28-4). Living Flame Pr.

Rev. Frederick K. Jelly. Madonna: Mary in the Catholic Tradition. LC 86-61598. 210p. (Orig.). 1986. pap. 7.50 (ISBN 0-87973-536-8, 536). Our Sunday Visitor.

Ripley, Francis J. Mary, Mother of the Church: What Recent Popes Have Said about the Blessed Mother's Role in the Church. 1973. pap. 2.00 (ISBN 0-89555-094-6). TAN Bks Pubs.

Ruether, Rosemary R. Mary-the Feminine Face of the Church. LC 77-7652. 106p. 1977. pap. 6.95 (ISBN 0-664-24759-8). Westminster.

St. Alphonsus de Liguori. The Glories of Mary. LC 79-112485. 1977. pap. 13.50 (ISBN 0-89555-021-0). TAN Bks Pubs.

St. Dimitry of Rostov. The Assumption of Our Lady. 1976. pap. 1.50 (ISBN 0-317-30435-6). Holy Trinity.

Stacpoole, Alberic, ed. Mary's Place in Christian Dialogue. LC 83-61204. 282p. (Orig.). 1983. pap. 10.95 (ISBN 0-8192-1333-0). Morehouse.

Suarez, F. Mary of Nazareth. 259p. 1979. pap. 4.95x (ISBN 0-933932-42-1). Scepter Pubs.

Tambasco, Anthony J. What Are They Saying about Mary? (WATSA Ser.). (Orig.). 1984. pap. 4.95 (ISBN 0-8091-2626-5). Paulist Pr.

Worrell, William H. The Coptic Manuscripts in the Freer Collection. Repr. of 1923 ed. 37.00 (ISBN 0-384-38810-8). Johnson Repr.

Wright, John. Mary Our Hope. Almagno, Stephen, pref. by. LC 84-80015. 227p. (Orig.). 1984. pap. 8.95 (ISBN 0-89870-046-9). Ignatius Pr.

MARY, VIRGIN–APPARITIONS AND MIRACLES

see also Shrines

Claudel, Paul. Le Symbolisme de la Salette. 64p. 1952. 2.95 (ISBN 0-686-54437-4). French & Eur.

Delaney, John J., ed. Woman Clothed with the Sun. LC 60-5922. 1961. pap. 4.50 (ISBN 0-385-08019-0, Im). Doubleday.

Klien, James H. Thunder in the Valley: The Massabielle Saga. (Illus.). 92p. 4.00 (ISBN 0-8198-7316-0, MA0135); pap. 3.00 (ISBN 0-8198-7317-9). Dghtrs St Paul.

Kraljevic, Sveosar. Apparitions of Our Lady at Medugorje: An Historical Account with Interviews. Scanlan, Michael, ed. LC 84-5983. 217p. 1984. 9.50 (ISBN 0-8199-0878-9). Franciscan Herald.

Laurentin, Rene & Rupcic, Ljudevit. Is the Virgin Mary Appearing at Medjugorje? Martin, Francis, tr. from Fr. (Illus.). 170p. 1984. 12.95 (ISBN 0-932085-02-4); pap. 6.95 (ISBN 0-932085-00-8). Word Among Us.

Le Blanc, Sr. M. Francis. Cause of Our Joy. 1981. 4.00 (ISBN 0-8198-0391-X); pap. 3.00 (ISBN 0-8198-1414-8). Dghtrs St Paul.

Long, Valentine. The Mother of God. 1977. 7.95 (ISBN 0-8199-0619-0). Franciscan Herald.

McClure, Kevin. The Evidence for Visions of the Virgin Mary. (Illus.). 158p. (Orig.). 1984. pap. 5.95 (ISBN 0-85030-351-6, Pub. by Aquarian Pr England). Sterling.

Odell, Catherine M. Those Who Saw Her: The Apparitions of Mary. 200p. (Orig.). 1986. pap. 6.95 (ISBN 0-87973-720-4, 720). Our Sunday Visitor.

Osee, Johan. Call of the Virgin at San Damiano. (Illus.). 1977. pap. 6.95 (ISBN 0-8158-0354-0). Chris Mass.

Rooney, Lucy & Faricy, Robert. Mary, Queen of Peace: Is the Mother of God Appearing in Medjugorje? 98p. (Orig.). 1985. pap. 4.95 (ISBN 0-317-19369-4). Alba.

Sharkey, Don. The Woman Shall Conquer. rev. ed. 258p. 1976. pap. 4.95 (ISBN 0-913382-01-9, 101-1). Prow Bks-Franciscan.

Vega, Pablo A. The Apparitions of Our Blessed Mother in Cuapa, Nicaragua. 1984. pap. 1.00 (ISBN 0-911988-59-9). Ami Pr.

MARY, VIRGIN–ART

see also Icons; Jesus Christ–Art

Belvianes, Marcel. The Madonna in the Paintings of the Great Masters. (Illus.). 1980. Repr. 107.50 (ISBN 0-89901-010-5). Found Class Reprints.

Denny, Don. The Annunciation from the Right: From Early Christian Times to the Sixteenth Century. LC 76-23611. (Outstanding Dissertations in the Fine Arts - 2nd Ser. - Fifteenth Century). (Illus.). 1977. Repr. of 1965 ed. lib. bdg. 55.00 (ISBN 0-8240-2683-7). Garland Pub.

Forsyth, Ilene H. The Throne of Wisdom: Wood Sculptures of the Madonna in Romanesque France. LC 72-166372. pap. 77.30 (ISBN 0-317-41726-6, 2052061). Bks Demand UMI.

Goffen, Rona. Piety & Patronage in Renaissance Venice: Bellini, Titian, & Franciscans. LC 85-91280. 320p. 1986. 40.00 (ISBN 0-300-03455-5). Yale U Pr.

Hurlington, Vincent J. Great Art Madonnas Classed According to Their Significance As Types of Impressive Motherhood. (The Great Art Masters Library). (Illus.). 143p. 1981. 127.75 (ISBN 0-930582-97-7). Gloucester Art.

Salko, N. The Illustrious Relic of the Kulikovo Battle. 1985. 39.00x (ISBN 0-569-08567-5, Pub. by Collets (UK)). State Mutual Bk.

Wegner, Susan E. Images of the Madonna & Child by Three Tuscan Artists of the Early Seicento: Vanni, Roncalli & Manetti. LC 86-70511. (Occasional Papers: No. III). (Illus.). 42p. (Orig.). 1986. pap. 9.00 (ISBN 0-916606-10-4). Bowdoin Coll.

MARY, VIRGIN–ASSUMPTION

St. Dimitry of Rostov. The Assumption of Our Lady. 1976. pap. 1.50 (ISBN 0-317-30435-6). Holy Trinity.

MARY, VIRGIN–BIOGRAPHY

Agreda, Mary. The Mystical City of God: A Popular Abridgement. abr. ed. Marison, Fiscar & Blatter, George J., trs. from Sp. LC 78-62255. 1978. pap. 15.00 (ISBN 0-89555-070-9). TAN Bks Pubs.

Did the Virgin Mary Live & Die in England. 1986. 49.00x (Pub. by Megiddo Pr Cardiff). State Mutual Bk.

Emmerich, Anne C. The Life of the Blessed Virgin Mary. Palairet, Michael, tr. from Ger. 1970. pap. 10.00 (ISBN 0-89555-048-2). TAN Bks Pubs.

Emmerick, A. C. Life of the Blessed Virgin Mary. (Roman Catholic Ser.). 1979. lib. bdg. 69.95 (ISBN 0-8490-2959-7). Gordon Pr.

Heline, Corinne. The Blessed Virgin Mary: Her Life & Mission. (Illus.). 152p. 1986. pap. text ed. 8.95 (ISBN 0-933963-12-2). New Age Bible.

Johnson, Ann. Miryam of Nazareth: Woman of Strength & Wisdom. LC 84-71347. 128p. (Orig.). 1984. pap. 4.95 (ISBN 0-87793-321-9). Ave Maria.

Watson, Mary A. Mary, Woman of Faith. 32p. 1986. pap. 1.50 (ISBN 0-89243-260-8). Liguori Pubns.

MARY, VIRGIN–CULTUS

see also Mary, Virgin–Feasts; Sorrows of the Blessed Virgin Mary, Devotion To

Alberione, Rev. James. Glories & Virtues of Mary. 1970. 5.00 (ISBN 0-8198-3017-8); pap. 4.00 (ISBN 0-8198-3018-6). Dghtrs St Paul.

Begg, Ean. The Cult of the Black Virgin. (Illus.). 288p. (Orig.). 1985. pap. 11.95 (ISBN 1-85063-022-4, Ark Paperbks). Methuen Inc.

Carrol, Michael P. The Cult of the Virgin Mary: Psychological Origins. LC 85-43273. (Illus.). 325p. 1986. 25.00 (ISBN 0-691-09420-9). Princeton U Pr.

Warner, Marina. Alone of All Her Sex: The Myth & the Cult of the Virgin Mary. LC 82-40051. (Illus.). 488p. 1983. pap. 10.95 (ISBN 0-394-71155-6, Vin). Random.

MARY, VIRGIN–FEASTS

Von Krusenstierna, Sten, ed. Services of Our Lady. 70p. 1982. pap. text ed. 2.75 (ISBN 0-918980-11-9). St Alban Pr.

MARY, VIRGIN–ICONOGRAPHY

see Mary, Virgin–Art

MARY, VIRGIN–JUVENILE LITERATURE

Brem, M. M. Mary's Story. (Arch Bks.: Set 4). 1967. laminated bdg. 0.99 (ISBN 0-570-06029-X, 59-1140). Concordia.

Cutting, Edith. Mary, in Bethlehem. (Paper People Ser.). 48p. 1986. wkbk. 4.95 (ISBN 0-86653-370-2). Good Apple.

De Santis, Zerlina. Journeys with Mary. (Encounter Ser.). 155p. 1982. 3.00 (ISBN 0-8198-3900-0, EN0165); pap. 2.00 (ISBN 0-8198-3910-8). Dghtrs St Paul.

Hintze, Barbara. Mary: Mother of Jesus. (BibLearn Ser.). (Illus.). 1977. bds. 5.95 (ISBN 0-8054-4232-4, 4242-32). Broadman.

Mulqueen, Jack & Chatton, Ray. God's Mother Is My Mother. (Illus.). 28p. (Orig.). 1978. pap. 2.50 (ISBN 0-913382-49-3, 103-13). Prow Bks-Franciscan.

MARY, VIRGIN–LEGENDS

De Coinci, Gautier. Tumbler of Our Lady & Other Miracles. Kemp-Welch, A., tr. (Medieval Library). (Illus.). Repr. of 1926 ed. 17.50x (ISBN 0-8154-0076-4). Cooper Sq.

Gripkey, Sr. M. Vincentine. Blessed Virgin Mary As Mediatrix in the Latin & Old French Legend Prior to the Fourteenth Century. LC 72-94166. (Catholic University of America Studies in Romance Languages & Literatures Ser: No. 17). 1969. Repr. of 1938 ed. 26.00 (ISBN 0-404-50317-9). Ams Pr.

MARY, VIRGIN–MEDITATION

Gripkey, Sr. M. Vincentine. Blessed Virgin Mary As Mediatrix in the Latin & Old French Legend Prior to the Fourteenth Century. LC 72-94166. (Catholic University of America Studies in Romance Languages & Literatures Ser: No. 17). 1969. Repr. of 1938 ed. 26.00 (ISBN 0-404-50317-9). Ams Pr.

McGann, Dairmuid. The Journeying Self: The Gospel of Mark through a Jungian Perspective. 144p. (Orig.). 1985. pap. 7.95 (ISBN 0-8091-2662-1). Paulist Pr.

MARY, VIRGIN–MEDITATIONS

Allchin, A. M. The Joy of All Creation: An Anglican Meditation on the Place of Mary. LC 84-72479. 162p. 1985. pap. 7.50 (ISBN 0-936384-24-7). Cowley Pubns.

Budy, Bertrand. Mary, the Faithful Disciple. 160p. (Orig.). 1985. pap. 6.95 (ISBN 0-8091-2703-2). Paulist Pr.

Guste, Bob. Mary at My Side. 64p. (Orig.). 1985. pap. 3.95 (ISBN 0-89622-247-0). Twenty-Third.

Maestri, William, ed. Mary: Model of Justice: Reflections on the Magnificat. LC 86-22304. 87p. (Orig.). 1987. pap. 4.95 (ISBN 0-8189-0511-5). Alba.

O'Driscoll, Herbert. Portrait of a Woman. 96p. (Orig.). 1981. pap. 4.95 (ISBN 0-8164-2332-6, HarpR). Har-Row.

Peffley, Bill. Prayerful Pauses with Jesus & Mary. (Illus.). 96p. (Orig.). 1985. pap. 5.95 (ISBN 0-89622-251-9). Twenty-Third.

Pio, Padre. Meditation Prayer on Mary Immaculate. (Illus.). 28p. 1974. pap. 0.75 (ISBN 0-89555-099-7). Tan Bks Pubs.

Powers, Isaias. Quiet Places with Mary. 160p. (Orig.). 1986. pap. 4.95 (ISBN 0-89622-297-7). Twenty-THird.

Viano, Joseph A., ed. Two Months with Mary: Short Reflections for Every Day of May & October. (Illus.). 94p. (Orig.). 1984. pap. 4.95 (ISBN 0-8189-0466-6). Alba.

MARY, VIRGIN–POETRY

Goenner, M. E. Mary-Verse of the Teutonic Knights. LC 72-140022. (Catholic University of America Studies in German: No. 19). Repr. of 1943 ed. 20.00 (ISBN 0-404-50239-3). AMS Pr.

Heyden, A. B. The Blessed Virgin Mary in Early Christian Latin Poetry. 59.95 (ISBN 0-87968-755-X). Gordon Pr.

Laube, Clifford J. Their Music Is Mary. 3.50 (ISBN 0-910984-11-5). Montfort Pubns.

Lydgate, John. Here Endeth the Book of the Lyf of Our Lady. LC 73-38207. (English Experience Ser.: No. 473). 192p. 1972. Repr. of 1484 ed. 63.00 (ISBN 90-221-0473-7). Walter J Johnson.

Lynch, John W. A Woman Wrapped in Silence. 288p. 1976. pap. 4.95 (ISBN 0-8091-1905-6). Paulist Pr.

Ostrander, Frederick C. Li Romans Dou Lis. Repr. of 1915 ed. 16.50 (ISBN 0-404-50616-X). AMS Pr.

MARY, VIRGIN–PRAYER-BOOKS AND DEVOTIONS

Balskus, Pat. Mary's Pilgrim. LC 68-58160. (Encounter Ser.). 3.00 (ISBN 0-8198-0279-4). Dghtrs St Paul.

De Montfort, St. Louis Marie. True Devotion to the Blessed Virgin. 4.95 (ISBN 0-910984-49-2); pap. 3.95 (ISBN 0-910984-50-6). Montfort Pubns.

Denis, Gabriel. Reign of Jesus Thru Mary. 5.50 (ISBN 0-910984-03-4). Montfort Pubns.

Doherty, Eddie. True Devotion to Mary. pap. 2.00 (ISBN 0-910984-02-6). Montfort Pubns.

Gaffney, Patrick. Mary's Spiritual Maternity. 4.95 (ISBN 0-910984-18-2); pap. 2.95 (ISBN 0-910984-19-0). Montfort Pubns.

Hart, John. Regard the Lilies, Regard the Blood: Poems to the Blessed Virgin. 79p. 1983. pap. 6.00 (ISBN 0-682-49941-2). Exposition Pr FL.

Lelia, Mary. Leading the Little Ones to Mary. pap. 1.00 (ISBN 0-910984-13-1). Montfort Pubns.

Louis. True Devotion to Mary. Fathers of the Company of Mary, ed. LC 85-50571. 215p. 1985. pap. 5.00 (ISBN 0-89555-279-5). Tan Bks Pubs.

Miguens, M. Mary, Servant of the Lord. 1978. 3.75 (ISBN 0-8198-0538-6); pap. 2.25 (ISBN 0-8198-0539-4). Dghtrs St Paul.

Moran, Patrick R., ed. Day by Day with Mary. LC 83-60101. 204p. 1983. pap. 6.95 (ISBN 0-87973-613-5, 613). Our Sunday Visitor.

Pope Paul the Sixth. Devotion to the Blessed Virgin Mary. 1974. pap. 0.35 (ISBN 0-8198-0295-6). Dghtrs St Paul.

Roberto, D. The Love of Mary. LC 83-51545. 240p. 1985. pap. 5.00 (ISBN 0-89555-235-3). Tan Bks Pubs.

Roberts, Kenneth J. Mary, the Perfect Prayer Partner. Waters, Anna Marie, ed. LC 83-61151. (Illus.). 128p. (Orig.). 1983. pap. 3.95 (ISBN 0-9610984-1-4). Pax Tapes.

Romb, Anselm. Total Consecration to Mary, Spouse of the Holy Spirit. 64p. 1982. pap. 1.50 (ISBN 0-913382-13-2, 105-37). Prow Bks-Franciscan.

Von Krusenstierna, Sten, ed. Services of Our Lady. 70p. 1982. pap. text ed. 2.75 (ISBN 0-918980-11-9). St Alban Pr.

MARY, VIRGIN–SERMONS

Bernard Of Clairvaux & Amadeus Of Lausanne. Magnificat: Homilies in Praise of the Blessed Virgin Mary. LC 78-6249. (Cistercian Fathers Ser.: No. 18). 1979. 15.95 (ISBN 0-87907-118-4). Cistercian Pubns.

St. Francis of Sales. The Sermons of St. Francis de Sales on Our Lady. Fiorelli, Lewis S., ed. LC 85-51662. 197p. 1985. pap. 7.00 (ISBN 0-89555-259-0). Tan Bks Pubs.

MARY, VIRGIN–THEOLOGY

Bojorge, Horacio. The Image of Mary: According to the Evangelists. Owen, Aloysius, tr. from Span. LC 77-15516. (Illus.). 1978. pap. 4.00 (ISBN 0-8189-0362-7). Alba.

De Simoni, Felix. Mary Magdalene & the Theory of Sin, 2 vols. LC 72-84832. (Illus.). 35p. 1972. 179.50 (ISBN 0-913314-04-8). Am Classical Coll Pr.

Feuillet, Andre. Jesus & His Mother. Maluf, Leonard, tr. from Fr. LC 84-6790. (Studies in Scripture Ser.: Vol. I). Tr. of Jesus et sa Mere. 266p. (Orig.). 1984. pap. 19.95 (ISBN 0-932506-27-5). St Bedes Pubns.

Geagea, Nilo. Mary of the Koran: A Meeting Point Between Islam & Christianism. Fares, Lawrence T., tr. LC 82-3804. 324p. 1984. 17.50 (ISBN 0-8022-2395-8). Philos Lib.

Greeley, Andrew M. The Mary Myth: On the Femininity of God. 240p. 1977. 9.95 (ISBN 0-8164-0333-3, HarpR). Har-Row.

Jegen, Carol F. Mary According to Women. LC 84-82550. 163p. (Orig.). 1985. pap. 7.95 (ISBN 0-934134-31-6, Leaven Pr). Sheed & Ward MO.

Kung, Hans & Moltmann, Jurgen, eds. Mary in the Churches. (Concilium 1983: Vol. 168). 128p. (Orig.). 1983. pap. 6.95 (ISBN 0-8164-2448-9, HarpR). Har-Row.

Mariological Society of America. Tampa, Fla. Convention, 1986. Marian Studies: Proceedings, Vol. 37. 1987. 10.00. Mariological Soc.

Mariological Society of America. Washington, D.C. Convention, 1984. Marian Studies: Proceedings, Vol. 35. 190p. 10.00 (ISBN 0-318-17634-3). Mariological Soc.

Miravalle, Mark I. The Message of Medjugorje: The Marian Message to the Modern World. LC 86-1588. 168p. 1986. lib. bdg. 23.75 (ISBN 0-8191-5288-9); pap. 9.75 (ISBN 0-8191-5289-7). U Pr of Amer.

Pennington, M. Basil. Mary Today: The Challenging Woman. LC 86-29183. (Illus.). 168p. 1987. 13.95 (ISBN 0-385-23609-3). Doubleday.

Perrin, Joseph-Marie. Mary Mother of Christ & of Christians. Finley, Jean D., tr. from Fr. LC 77-26608. (Illus.). 1978. pap. 3.50 (ISBN 0-8189-0367-8). Alba.

Skaballanovitch, M. Vvedenije vo Khram Presvjatija Bogoroditsi. Tr. of The Entrance of the Mother of God into the Temple. 115p. pap. 4.00 (ISBN 0-317-29157-2). Holy Trinity.

MARY, VIRGIN, IN LITERATURE

Goenner, M. E. Mary-Verse of the Teutonic Knights. LC 72-140022. (Catholic University of America Studies in German: No. 19). Repr. of 1943 ed. 20.00 (ISBN 0-404-50239-3). AMS Pr.

Gripkey, Sr. M. Vincentine. Blessed Virgin Mary As Mediatrix in the Latin & Old French Legend Prior to the Fourteenth Century. LC 72-94166. (Catholic University of America Studies in Romance Languages & Literatures Ser: No. 17). 1969. Repr. of 1938 ed. 26.00 (ISBN 0-404-50317-9). Ams Pr.

Schroeder, M. J. Mary-Verse in "Meistergesang". (Catholic University Studies in German: No. 16). 1970. Repr. of 1942 ed. 30.00 (ISBN 0-404-50236-9). AMS Pr.

Vriend, Joannes. The Blessed Virgin Mary in Medieval Drama of England. 69.95 (ISBN 0-87968-756-8). Gordon Pr.

MARY MAGDALENE, SAINT

Garth, Helen M. Saint Mary Magdalene in Medieval Literature. LC 78-64210. (Johns Hopkins University. Studies in the Social Sciences. Sixty-Seventh Ser. 1949: 3). Repr. of 1950 ed. 15.50 (ISBN 0-404-61315-2). AMS Pr.

Robinson, T. The Life & Death of Mary Magdalene. Sommer, H. O., ed. (EETS ES Ser.: Vol. 78). pap. 15.00 (ISBN 0-8115-3401-4). Kraus Repr.

Southwell, Robert. Marie Magdalens Funeral Teares. LC 74-22099. 180p. 1975. 30.00x (ISBN 0-8201-1144-9). Schol Facsimiles.

Wager, Lewis. Repentance of Mary Magdalene. LC 70-133754. (Tudor Facsimile Texts. Old English Plays: No. 36). Repr. of 1908 ed. 49.50 (ISBN 0-404-53336-1). AMS Pr.

MARY MAGDALENE, SAINT–ART

De Jong, Ralph. The Life of Mary Magdalene in the Paintings of the Great Masters, 2 vols. (Illus.). 1979. deluxe ed. 117.45 (ISBN 0-930582-30-6). Gloucester Art.

MARY MAGDALENE, SAINT–FICTION

Saltus, Edgar. Mary Magdalen. LC 78-116002. Repr. of 1891 ed. 17.50 (ISBN 0-404-05517-6). AMS Pr.

MARYKNOLL SISTERS OF ST. DOMINIC

Cogan, Sr. Mary De Paul. Sisters of Maryknoll: Through Troubled Waters. LC 72-167329. (Essay Index Reprint Ser.). Repr. of 1947 ed. 18.00 (ISBN 0-8369-2764-8). Ayer Co Pubs.

MARYLAND–HISTORY

Carroll, Kenneth. Quakerism on the Eastern Shore. LC 70-112986. (Illus.). 328p. 1970. 15.00x (ISBN 0-938420-15-1). Md Hist.

Davis, Vernon P. & Rawlings, James S. The Colonial Churches of Virginia, Maryland, & North Carolina. 1985. pap. 25.00 (ISBN 0-87517-057-9). Dietz.

Hanley, Thomas O. Their Rights & Liberties. 160p. 1984. 9.95 (ISBN 0-8294-0471-6). Loyola.

Petrie, George. Church & State in Early Maryland. LC 78-63810. (Johns Hopkins University. Studies in the Social Sciences. Tenth Ser. 1892: 4). Repr. of 1892 ed. 11.50 (ISBN 0-404-61073-0). AMS Pr.

--Church & State in Early Maryland. 1973. pap. 9.00. Johnson Repr.

Randall, Daniel R. A Puritan Colony in Maryland. LC 78-63763. (Johns Hopkins University. Studies in the Social Sciences. Fourth Ser. 1886: 6). Repr. of 1886 ed. 11.50 (ISBN 0-404-61031-5). AMS Pr.

--A Puritan Colony in Maryland. 1973. pap. 9.00 (ISBN 0-384-49568-0). Johnson Repr.

MARYLAND–POLITICS AND GOVERNMENT

Ives, J. Moss. Ark & the Dove: The Beginnings of Civil & Religious Liberties in America. LC 76-79200. (Illus.). 1969. Repr. of 1936 ed. 32.50x (ISBN 0-8154-0293-7). Cooper Sq.

MASEFIELD, JOHN, 1878-1967

Gautrey, R. Moffat. The Burning Cataracts of Christ: An Evangelical Interpretation of John Mosefield's "The Ever-Lasting Mercy". LC 78-23716. 1933. lib. bdg. 20.00 (ISBN 0-8414-4483-8). Folcroft.

Gfollner, Adelheid. John Masefields Stellung Zum Religiosen. Hogg, James, ed. (Poetic Drama & Poetic Theory). 129p. (Orig.). 1979. pap. 15.00 (ISBN 3-7052-0880-2, Pub. by Salzburg). Longwood Pub Group.

Masefield, John. Letters to Margaret Bridges. Stanford, Donald, ed. 123p. 1984. 18.50 (ISBN 0-85635-477-5). Carcanet.

MASHONA

Berliner, Paul F. The Soul of Mbira: Music & Traditions of the Shona People of Zimbabwe. LC 76-24578. (Perspectives on Southern Africa Ser.: No. 26). 1978. 36.50x (ISBN 0-520-03315-9); pap. 6.95 (ISBN 0-520-04268-9, CAL 466). U of Cal Pr.

MASONIC ORDERS

see Freemasons

MASORAH

Frensdorff, Salomon. Massora Magna. rev. ed. LC 67-11896. (Library of Biblical Studies). (Heb). 1968. 35.00x (ISBN 0-87068-052-8). Ktav.

Jacob, Ben Chayyim. Introduction to the Rabbinic Bible of 1525. rev. ed. (Library of Biblical Studies Ser). 1969. 39.50x (ISBN 0-87068-067-6). Ktav.

Orlinsky, Harry M., ed. Masoretic Studies. 10.00x (ISBN 0-685-56221-2). Ktav.

Revell, E. J. Biblical Texts with Palestinian Pointing & Their Accents. LC 77-8893. (Society of Biblical Literature. Masoretic Studies). 1977. pap. 10.95 (ISBN 0-89130-141-0, 060504). Scholars Pr GA.

Yeivin, Israel. Introduction to the Tiberian Masorah. LC 79-24755. (Society of Biblical Literature Masoretic Studies: No. 5). pap. 14.50x (ISBN 0-89130-374-X, 06 05 05A). Scholars Pr Ga.

MASS

see also Altar Boys; Catholic Church–Liturgy and Ritual–Missal; Lord's Supper; Transubstantiation

Becon, Thomas. Prayers & Others Pieces of Thomas Becon, Chaplain to Archbishop Cranmer. Repr. of 1844 ed. 55.00 (ISBN 0-384-03730-5). Johnson Repr.

Buckley, Frank. Come Worship with Us: Explaining the Mass. 32p. 1987. pap. 1.95 (ISBN 0-89243-263-2). Liguori Pubns.

Catholic Church, Sacred Congregation for Divine Worship. Lectionary for Mass: Cycle B, Sundays & Solemnities. Hartdegen, Steven J., ed. (Lectionary for Mass Ser.). 1972. 27.50 (ISBN 0-916134-02-4). Pueblo Pub Co.

Cooper, Thomas. An Answer in Defence of the Truth Against the Apology of Private Mass. 1850. 21.00 (ISBN 0-384-09790-1). Johnson Repr.

Corless, Roger. I Am Food: The Mass in Planetary Perspective. LC 81-7836. 112p. 1981. 8.95 (ISBN 0-8245-0077-6). Crossroad NY.

Coyle, Thomas. This Is Our Mass. 144p. 1985. pap. 3.50 (ISBN 0-89622-233-0). Twenty-Third.

Cronin, Gaynell & Cronin, Jim. The Mass: Great Common Prayer. 1977. pap. 7.55 (ISBN 0-88479-006-1). Arena Lettres.

Georgi, D. De Liturgia Romani Pontificis in Solemni Celebratione Missarum, 3 vols. 1822p. Repr. of 1731 ed. text ed. 372.60 (ISBN 0-576-99174-0, Pub. by Gregg Intl Pubs England). Gregg Intl.

Goode, Teresa C. Gonzalo De Berceo. (Carl Ser.: No. 7). Repr. of 1933 ed. 21.00 (ISBN 0-404-50307-1). AMS Pr.

Hamman, Adelbert. Mass: Ancient Liturgies & Patristic Texts. Halton, Thomas, ed. LC 67-15202. 1967. 5.95 (ISBN 0-8189-0086-5). Alba.

Jungmann, Joseph A. The Mass of the Roman Rite: Its Origins and Development, 2 vols. Brunner, Francis A., tr. from German. 1050p. 1986. pap. 39.95 (ISBN 0-87061-129-1). Chr Classics.

Lanz, Kerry J. The Complete Server. (Illus.). 1978. 1.95 (ISBN 0-8192-1245-8). Morehouse.

Loret, Pierre. The Story of the Mass: From the Last Supper to the Present Day. LC 82-83984. 144p. 1983. pap. 3.50 (ISBN 0-89243-171-7). Liguori Pubns.

McGloin, Joseph T. How to Get More Out of the Mass. LC 74-80938. 1974. pap. 3.50 (ISBN 0-89243-011-7, 41230). Liguori Pubns.

McIntyre, Marie. Meditations on the Mass. (Greeting Book Line Ser.). 48p. 1983. pap. 1.50 (ISBN 0-89622-201-2). Twenty-Third.

Mick, Lawrence E. Understanding the Mass Today. 20p. 1985. pap. 0.30 (ISBN 0-8146-1390-X). Liturgical Pr.

Rietcheck, Robert & Korn, Daniel. Sunday Mass: What Part Do You Play? 32p. 1985. pap. 1.50 (ISBN 0-89243-235-7). Liguori Pubns.

St. Leonard. The Hidden Treasure: Holy Mass. 1971. pap. 2.50 (ISBN 0-89555-036-9). TAN Bks Pubs.

Schlitzer, Albert L. Prayerlife of the Church. 1962. 7.95x (ISBN 0-268-00214-2). U of Notre Dame Pr.

The Story of the Mass. 1.00. Paulist Pr.

Three Tudor Dialogues. LC 78-14887. 1979. 35.00x (ISBN 0-8201-1319-0). Schol Facsimiles.

Vasconcelos, B. Your Mass. 137p. 1961. 4.95 (ISBN 0-933932-13-8); pap. 2.50 (ISBN 0-933932-14-6). Scepter Pubs.

MASS–CELEBRATION

Gelineau, Joseph. Learning to Celebrate: The Mass & Its Music. 1985. pap. 6.95 (ISBN 0-317-38557-7). Pastoral Pr.

Guentert, Kenneth. Young Server's Book of the Mass. LC 86-60894. 1987. pap. 4.95 (ISBN 0-89390-078-8). Resource Pubns.

Hileman, Louis G. The Celebration of Holy Mass. 154p. 1976. pap. 2.95 (ISBN 0-912414-23-5). Lumen Christi.

Kershaw, Jack. Christ's Mass. LC 74-28633. 1975. 9.95 (ISBN 0-87695-178-7). Aurora Pubs.

Smolarski, Dennis C. How Not to Say Mass: Guidebook for All Concerned about Authentic Worship. 96p. 1986. pap. 5.95 (ISBN 0-8091-2811-X). Paulist Pr.

Weber, Gerard. The Mass: Finding Its Meaning for You & Getting More Out of It. (Illus., Orig.). 1985. pap. 4.95 (ISBN 0-86716-049-7). St Anthony Mess Pr.

MASS–JUVENILE LITERATURE

Curley, Ed. The Mass for Young Catholics. 1978. 9.95 (ISBN 0-686-89575-4, Pub. by Pflaum Pr). Peter Li.

Daughters of St. Paul. St. Paul Mass Book for Children. (Illus.). 1973. 1.75 (ISBN 0-8198-0336-7); pap. 1.00 (ISBN 0-8198-0337-5). Dghtrs St Paul.

Guentert, Kenneth. The Server's Book of the Mass. LC 86-60894. 64p. 1985. pap. 4.95 (ISBN 0-89390-078-8). Resource Pubns.

Leichner, J. Joy Joy, the Mass: Our Family Celebration. (Illus.). 1978. pap. 2.75 (ISBN 0-87973-350-0). Our Sunday Visitor.

MASS-BOOKS

see Catholic Church–Liturgy and Ritual–Missal

MASS MEDIA–MORAL AND RELIGIOUS ASPECTS

Alternative Museun Staff. Disinformation: The Manufacture of Consent. LC 85-70365. (Illus.). 64p. (Orig.). 1985. pap. text ed. 8.00 (ISBN 0-932075-01-0). Alternative Mus.

Corry, John. TV News & the Dominant Culture. Media Institute Staff, ed. LC 86-60785. (Media in Society Ser.). 54p. (Orig.). 1986. pap. 12.95 (ISBN 0-937790-34-6). Media Inst.

Daughters of St. Paul. Media Impact & You. 1981. 2.95 (ISBN 0-8198-4702-X); pap. 1.95 (ISBN 0-686-73820-9). Dghtrs St Paul.

Maddux, Bob. Fantasy Explosion. Beckwith, Mary, ed. LC 86-21938. 168p. (Orig.). pap. 5.95 (ISBN 0-8307-1163-5, 5418886). Regal.

Schwantes, Dave. Taming Your TV & Other Media. LC 79-16848. (Orion Ser.). 1979. pap. 3.95 (ISBN 0-8127-0246-8). Review & Herald.

Thayer, Lee, compiled by. Ethics, Morality & the Media: Reflections of American Culture. new ed. (Humanistic Studies in the Communication Arts). 320p. 1980. 22.00x (ISBN 0-8038-1957-9, Communication Arts); pap. text ed. 15.00x (ISBN 0-8038-1958-7). Hastings.

Wildmon, Donald. The Home Invaders. 180p. 1985. pap. 6.95 (ISBN 0-89693-521-3). Victor Bks.

MASS MEDIA IN RELIGION

see also Radio in Religion; Television in Religion

Robertson, Pat & Buckingham, Jamie. Shout It from the Housetops: The Story of the Founder of the Christian Broadcasting Network. LC 72-76591. 248p. 1972. pap. 3.95 (ISBN 0-88270-097-9). Bridge Pub.

Taylor, Rick. When You're the News. 112p. 1987. pap. 5.95 (ISBN 0-87403-225-3, 3185). Standard Pub.

MASSACHUSETTS–CHURCH HISTORY

Stoever, William K. A Faire & Easie Way to Heaven: Covenant Theology & Antinomianism in Early Massachusetts. LC 77-14851. 251p. 1978. 22.00x (ISBN 0-8195-5024-8). Wesleyan U Pr.

MASSACHUSETTS–HISTORY

Ballou, Adin. History of the Hopedale Community, from Its Inception to Its Virtual Submergence in the Hopedale Parish. Heywood, William S., ed. LC 72-2935. (Communal Societies in America Ser.). Repr. of 1897 ed. 14.00 (ISBN 0-404-10701-X). AMS Pr.

Emery, Helen F. The Puritan Village Evolves: A History of Wayland, Massachusetts. LC 81-5185. (Illus.). 384p. 1981. 15.00x (ISBN 0-914016-78-4). Phoenix Pub.

Hallowell, Richard P. The Quaker Invasion of Massachusetts. 13.50 (ISBN 0-8369-7139-6, 7972). Ayer Co Pubs.

Levy, Leonard. Blasphemy in Massachusetts: Freedom of Conscience & the Abner Kneeland Case. LC 70-16634. 592p. 1973. lib. bdg. 65.00 (ISBN 0-306-70221-5). Da Capo.

Pierce, Richard D., ed. Records of the First Church in Salem, Massachusetts, 1629-1736. LC 73-93302. 1974. 30.00 (ISBN 0-88389-050-X). Essex Inst.

MASSACHUSETTS–HISTORY–COLONIAL PERIOD, ca. 1600-1775

see also Pilgrims (New Plymouth Colony)

Adams, Charles F., ed. Antinomianism in the Colony of Massachusetts Bay, 1636-38, Including the Short Story & Documents. 1966. 26.00 (ISBN 0-8337-0010-3). B Franklin.

Bacon, Leonard. The Genesis of the New England Churches. LC 74-38435. (Religion in America, Ser. 2). 510p. 1972. Repr. of 1874 ed. 32.00 (ISBN 0-405-04056-3). Ayer Co Pubs.

Boyer, Paul & Nissenbaum, Stephen, eds. The Salem Witchcraft Papers: Verbatim Transcripts, 3 vols. (Civil Liberties in American History Ser.). 1977. Set. lib. bdg. 145.00 (ISBN 0-306-70655-5). Da Capo.

Bradford, William. Of Plymouth Plantation: The Pilgrims in America. 18.00 (ISBN 0-8446-1718-0). Peter Smith.

--Of Plymouth Plantation: 1620-1647. Morison, Samuel E., ed. (The American Past Ser). (Illus.). (YA) 1952. 19.95 (ISBN 0-394-43895-7). Knopf.

Ellis, George E. Puritan Age & Rule in the Colony of the Massachusetts Bay, 1629-1685. LC 75-122838. (Research & Source Ser.: No. 522). 1970. Repr. of 1888 ed. lib. bdg. 32.00 (ISBN 0-8337-1054-0). B Franklin.

Geller, Lawrence D. & Gomes, Peter J. The Books of the Pilgrims. LC 74-30056. (Reference Library of the Humanities: No. 13). (Illus.). 100p. 1975. lib. bdg. 25.00 (ISBN 0-8240-1065-5). Garland Pub.

Konig, David T. Law & Society in Puritan Massachusetts: Essex County, 1629-1692. xxi, 215p. 1981. pap. 9.95x (ISBN 0-8078-4081-5). U of NC Pr.

Rose-Troup, Frances. Massachusetts Bay Company & Its Predecessors. LC 68-56574. 1973. Repr. of 1930 ed. 22.50x (ISBN 0-678-00871-X). Kelley.

Steele, Ashbel. Chief of the Pilgrims: Or, the Life & Time of William Brewster. facs. ed. LC 72-133535. (Select Bibliographies Reprint Ser). (Illus.). 1857. 23.50 (ISBN 0-8369-5567-6). Ayer Co Pubs.

Weisman, Richard. Witchcraft, Magic & Religion in Seventeenth Century Massachusetts. LC 83-15542. 288p. 1985. pap. text ed. 9.95x (ISBN 0-87023-494-3). U of MAss Pr.

Young, Alexander. Chronicles of the Pilgrim Fathers of the Colony of Plymouth, 1602-1625. LC 78-87667. (Law, Politics & History Ser). 1971. Repr. of 1841 ed. lib. bdg. 42.50 (ISBN 0-306-71760-3). Da Capo.

MASSACHUSETTS–HISTORY–COLONIAL PERIOD, ca. 1600-1775–SOURCES

Wheelwright, John. John Wheelwright: His Writings, Including His Fast-Day Sermon, 1637. 1966. 24.00 (ISBN 0-8337-3763-5). B Franklin.

--John Wheelwright's Writings, Including His Fast-Day Sermon, 1637, & His Mercurius Americanus, 1645. facs. ed. LC 70-128897. (Select Bibliographies Reprint Ser). 1876. 18.00 (ISBN 0-8369-5517-X). Ayer Co Pubs.

MASSACHUSETTS–HISTORY, JUVENILE

Smith, E. Brooks & Meredith, Robert. Pilgrim Courage. (Illus.). 1962. 6.95 (ISBN 0-316-80045-7). Little.

MASSES

Isaac, Heirich. Five Polyphonic Masses. Cuyler, Louise, ed. LC 56-7145. pap. 38.50 (ISBN 0-317-09652-4, 2051077). Bks Demand UMI.

MATHER, COTTON 1663-1728

Beall, Otho T. & Shryock, Richard H. Cotton Mather. 1979. 21.00 (ISBN 0-405-10580-0). Ayer Co Pubs.

Cohen, I. Bernard. Cotton Mather & American Science & Medicine: With Studies & Documents Concerning the Introduction of Innoculation or Variolation, Vol. 1. 37.50 (ISBN 0-405-12520-8). Ayer Co Pubs.

--Cotton Mather & American Science & Medicine: With Studies & Documents Concerning the Introduction of Inoculation or Variolation, Vol. 2. 37.50 (ISBN 0-405-12521-6). Ayer Co Pubs.

Holmes, Thomas J. Cotton Mather: A Bibliography of His Works, 3 vols. 1395p. 1974. Repr. Set. 70.00x (ISBN 0-89020-000-9). Crofton Pub.

Holmes, Thomas S. Cotton Mather: A Bibliography of His Works. 1940. Set. 70.00 (ISBN 0-89020-000-9); Vol. 3. Brown Bk.

Levin, David. Cotton Mather: The Young Life of the Lord's Remembrancer, 1663-1703. LC 78-2355. (Illus.). 1978. 25.00x (ISBN 0-674-17507-7). Harvard U Pr.

--Did the Mathers Disagree about the Salem Witchcraft Trials? Proceedings of the American Antiquarian Society. 19p. 1985. pap. 3.95 (ISBN 0-912296-77-1, Dist. by U Pr of Va). Am Antiquarian.

Marvin, Abijah P. The Life & Times of Cotton Mather. LC 72-1979. (American Biography Ser., No. 32). 1972. Repr. of 1892 ed. lib. bdg. 59.95x (ISBN 0-8383-1454-6). Haskell.

Mather, Cotton. Magnalia Christi Americana, Bks. I & II In 1 vol. Murdock, Kenneth B., ed. (The John Harvard Library). 512p. 1976. text ed. 35.00x (ISBN 0-674-54155-3, Belknap Pr). Harvard U Pr.

--Paterna: The Autobiography of Cotton Mather. Bosco, Ronald A., ed. LC 76-10595. (Center for Editions of American Authors). 504p. 1976. lib. bdg. 75.00x (ISBN 0-8201-1273-9). Schol Facsimiles.

--Selected Letters of Cotton Mather. Silverman, Kenneth, ed. LC 78-142338. pap. 118.00 (ISBN 0-317-29860-7, 2019565). Bks Demand UMI.

Middlekauff, Robert. The Mathers: Three Generations of Puritan Intellectuals, 1596-1728. LC 79-140912. 1971. pap. 7.95 (ISBN 0-19-502115-0). Oxford U Pr.

Solberg, Winton U. Cotton Mather, the Christian Philosopher & the Classics. 44p. 1987. pap. write for info. (ISBN 0-912296-90-9). Am Antiquarian.

Wendell, Barrett. Cotton Mather. LC 80-23335. (American Men & Women of Letters Ser.). Orig. Title: Cotton Mather: the Puritan Priest. 328p. 1981. pap. 5.95 (ISBN 0-87754-166-3). Chelsea Hse.

--Cotton Mather: The Puritan Priest. 1978. Repr. of 1891 ed. lib. bdg. 35.00 (ISBN 0-8495-5626-0). Arden Lib.

MATHER, INCREASE, 1639-1723

Hall, Michael. The Last American Puritan: The Life of Increase Mather. 1987. 35.00 (ISBN 0-8195-5128-7). Wesleyan U Pr.

Levin, David. Did the Mathers Disagree about the Salem Witchcraft Trials? Proceedings of the American Antiquarian Society. 19p. 1985. pap. 3.95 (ISBN 0-912296-77-1, Dist. by U Pr of Va). Am Antiquarian.

Mather, Cotton. Ratio Disciplinae Fratrum Novanglorum: A Faithful Account of the Discipline Professed & Practised, in the Churches of New-England. LC 71-141114. (Research Library of Colonial Americana). 1971. Repr. of 1726 ed. 23.50 (ISBN 0-405-03327-3). Ayer Co Pubs.

Mather, Increase & Stoddard, Solomon. Increase Mather Vs. Solomon Stoddard: Two Puritan Tracts. LC 72-141117. (Research Library of Colonial Americana). 1971. Repr. of 1700 ed. 17.00 (ISBN 0-405-03328-1). Ayer Co Pubs.

Middlekauff, Robert. The Mathers: Three Generations of Puritan Intellectuals, 1596-1728. LC 79-140912. 1971. pap. 7.95 (ISBN 0-19-502115-0). Oxford U Pr.

MATRIMONIAL REGIME

see Husband and Wife

MATRIMONY

see Marriage

MATTHEW, SAINT, APOSTLE

Dickson, David. Matthew. (Geneva Ser. Commentaries). Orig. Title: A Brief Exposition of the Evangel of Jesus Christ According to Matthew. 416p. 1981. 15.95 (ISBN 0-85151-319-0). Banner of Truth.

Johnson, Luke T. Some Hard Blessings: Meditations on the Beatitudes in Matthew. LC 81-69108. 96p. 1981. pap. 3.95 (ISBN 0-89505-058-7, 21053). Argus Comm.

MAUNOIR, JULIEN, 1606-1683

Harney, Martin P. Good Father in Brittany. (Illus.). 1964. pap. 4.00 (ISBN 0-8198-0049-X). Dghtrs St Paul.

MAURIAC, FRANCOIS, 1885-1970

Heppenstall, Rayner. Double Image: Mutations of Christian Mythology in the Works of Four French Catholic Writers of Today & Yesterday. LC 72-93063. 1969. Repr. of 1947 ed. 23.00 (ISBN 0-8046-0676-5, Pub. by Kennikat). Assoc Faculty Pr.

Stratford, Philip. Faith & Fiction: Creative Process in Greene & Mauriac. 1964. pap. 9.95x (ISBN 0-268-00379-3). U of Notre Dame Pr.

MAURICE, FREDERICK DENISON, 1805-1872

Brose, Olive J. Frederick Denison Maurice: Rebellious Conformist, 1805-1872. LC 74-141380. xxiii, 308p. 1971. 16.00x (ISBN 0-8214-0092-4). Ohio U Pr.

Maurice, J. F. D. The Life of Frederick Denison Maurice, Chiefly Told in His Own Letters. 1294p. Repr. of 1884 ed. text ed. 99.36x (ISBN 0-576-02191-1). Gregg Intl.

MAUSOLEUMS

see Sepulchral Monuments; Tombs

MAXIMUS, SAINT, BP. OF TURIN, d. ca. 420

Berthold, George C., ed. Maximus the Confessor. (Classics of Western Spirituality Ser.: Vol. 45). 1985. 12.95 (ISBN 0-8091-0353-2); pap. 9.95 (ISBN 0-8091-2659-1). Paulist Pr.

Burghardt, W. J., et al, eds. St. Maximus the Confessor: The Ascetic Life, the Four Centuries on Charity. LC 55-8642. (ACW Ser.: No. 21). 293p. 1955. 13.95 (ISBN 0-8091-0258-7). Paulist Pr.

Holy Transfiguration Monastery, ed. The Life of St. Maximus the Confessor. Birchall, Christopher, tr. from Greek, & Russian. (Illus.). 73p. (Orig.). 1982. pap. 5.00 (ISBN 0-913026-52-2). St Nectarios.

Thunberg, Lars. Microcosm & Mediator: The Theological Anthropology of Maximus the Confessor. Allchin, A. L., rev. by. LC 80-2368. 1981. Repr. of 1965 ed. 58.00 (ISBN 0-404-18917-2). AMS Pr.

MAXIMUS CONFESSOR, SAINT, ca. 580-662

Obolensky, D. Italy, Mount Athos & Muscovy: The Three Worlds of Maximos the Greek. (Raleigh Lectures on History). 1981. pap. 3.00 (ISBN 0-85672-323-1, Pub. by British Acad). Longwood Pub Group.

MAYA (HINDUISM)

Tuck, Donald R. The Concept of Maya in Samkara & Radhakrishnan. 1986. 17.00x (ISBN 0-8364-1375-X). South Asia Bks.

MAYA ART

see Mayas–Art

MAYA MYTHOLOGY

see Mayas–Religion and Mythology

MAYAS

Cancian, F. What Are Norms? A Study of Beliefs & Action in a Maya Community. LC 74-77833. 256p. 1975. 34.50 (ISBN 0-521-20536-0). Cambridge U Pr.

Cancian, Francesca M. What Are Norms? A Study of Beliefs & Action in a Maya Community. LC 74-77833. pap. 55.50 (2027284). Bks Demand UMI.

Irving, Thomas B., ed. The Maya's Own Words: An Anthology Comprising Abridgements of the Popol-Vuh, Warrior of Rabinal, & Selections from the Memorial of Solola, the Book of Chilam Balam of Chumayel, & the Title of the Lords Of Totonicapan. LC 84-81822. (Illus.). 102p. (Orig.). 1985. pap. 12.00X (ISBN 0-911437-14-2). Labyrinthos.

Morley, Sylvanus G. & Brainerd, George W. The Ancient Maya. Rev., 4th ed. Sharer, Robert J., rev. by. LC 81-85451. (Illus.). xx, 708p. 1983. 38.50 (ISBN 0-8047-1137-2); pap. 14.95 (ISBN 0-8047-1288-3, SP 80). Stanford U Pr.

Nash, June. In the Eyes of the Ancestors: Belief & Behavior in a Mayan Community. (Illus.). 374p. 1985. pap. text ed. 11.95x (ISBN 0-88133-142-2). Waveland Pr.

Rodriguez, Alfonso. La Estructura Mitica del Popol Vuh. LC 84-81886. (Coleccion Polymita Ser.). (Span.). 108p. (Orig.). 1985. pap. 10.00 (ISBN 0-89729-360-6). Ediciones.

Thompson, J. Eric. Maya History & Religion. LC 72-88144. (Civilization of the American Indian Ser.: Vol. 99). 1976. Repr. of 1970 ed. 24.95 (ISBN 0-8061-0884-3). U of Okla Pr.

MAYAS–ART

Robicsek, Francis. The Smoking Gods: Tobacco in Maya Art, History, & Religion. LC 78-64904. (Illus.). 1978. 39.50 (ISBN 0-8061-1511-4). U of Okla Pr.

Scheke, Linda & Miller, Mary E. Blood of Kings: Dynasty & Ritual in Maya Art. 1986. 50.00 (ISBN 0-8076-1159-X). Braziller.

MAYAS–RELIGION AND MYTHOLOGY

Abreu Gomez, Emilio. Canek, History & Legend of a Maya Hero. Davila, Mario L. & Wilson, Carter, trs. from Span. LC 75-32674. 1979. 19.50x (ISBN 0-520-03148-2); pap. 2.95 (ISBN 0-520-03982-3, CAL 441). U of Cal Pr.

Arguelles, Jose. The Mayan Factor: Path Beyond Technology. (Illus.). 160p. (Orig.). 1987. pap. 10.95 (ISBN 0-939680-38-6). Bear & Co.

Bricker, Victoria R. The Indian Christ, the Indian King: The Historical Substrate of Maya Myth & Ritual. (Illus.). 382p. 1981. text ed. 45.00x (ISBN 0-292-73824-2). U of Tex Pr.

Brintnall, D. E. Revolt Against the Dead: The Modernization of a Mayan Community in the Highlands of Guatemala. (Library of Anthropology). 224p. 1979. 29.00x (ISBN 0-677-05170-0). Gordon & Breach.

Burns, Allan F., tr. An Epoch of Miracles: Oral Literature of the Yucatec Maya. (Texas Pan American Ser.). (Illus.). 282p. 1983. text ed. 24.50x (ISBN 0-292-72037-8). U of Tex Pr.

Colby, Benjamin N. & Colby, Lore M. The Daykeeper: The Life & Discource of As Ixtil Dviner. (Illus.). 352p. 1981. text ed. 27.50x (ISBN 0-674-19409-8). Harvard U Pr.

Craven, Roy C., Jr. Ceremonial Centers of the Maya. LC 74-2016. (Illus.). 152p. 1974. 20.00 (ISBN 0-8130-0447-0). U Presses Fla.

Crumrine, N. Ross. The Mayo Indians of Sonora: A People Who Refuse to Die. LC 76-8563. 167p. 1977. 12.50x (ISBN 0-8165-0605-1); pap. text ed. 5.95x (ISBN 0-8165-0473-3). U of Ariz Pr.

Edmonson, Munro S., tr. from Maya. Heaven Born Merida & Its Destiny: The Book of Chilam Balam of Chumayel. (Texas Pan American Ser.). (Illus.). 304p. 1986. 37.50x (ISBN 0-292-73027-6). U of Tex Pr.

Gossen, Gary. Chamulas in the World of the Sun: Time & Space in a Maya Oral Tradition. (Illus.). 382p. 1984. pap. text ed. 10.95x (ISBN 0-88133-091-4). Waveland Pr.

Goudriaan, Teun. Maya Divine & Human. 1978. 19.95 (ISBN 0-89684-040-9, Pub. by Motilal Banarsidass India). Orient Bk Dist.

Le Plongeon, Augustus. Sacred Mysteries among the Mayas & the Quiches. LC 73-76094. (Secret Doctrine Reference Ser). (Illus.). 200p. 1985. Repr. of 1886 ed. 12.00 (ISBN 0-913510-02-5). Wizards.

Roys, Ralph L., ed. Book of Chilam Balam of Chumayel. (Civilization of the American Indian Ser.: No. 87). (Illus.). 1973. pap. 19.95x (ISBN 0-8061-0735-9). U of Okla Pr.

Scheke, Linda & Miller, Mary E. Blood of Kings: Dynasty & Ritual in Maya Art. 1986. 50.00 (ISBN 0-8076-1159-X). Braziller.

Spence, Lewis. The Myths of Mexico & Peru. LC 76-27516. (Illus.). 1976. Repr. of 1914 ed. lib. bdg. 45.00 (ISBN 0-89341-031-4). Longwood Pub Group.

Teeple, John, ed. Maya Astronomy. (Classics of Anthropology Ser.). 20.00 (ISBN 0-8240-9624-X). Garland Pub.

MAZARIN, JULES, CARDINAL, 1602-1661

Hassall, Arthur. Mazarin. facs. ed. LC 73-137379. (Select Bibliographies Reprint Ser.). 1903. 17.00 (ISBN 0-8369-5580-3). Ayer Co Pubs.

Moreau, Celestin. Bibliographie Des Mazarinades, 3 Vols. Set. 113.00 (ISBN 0-384-40060-4); Set. pap. 95.00 (ISBN 0-384-40061-2). Johnson Repr.

Moreau, Celestin, ed. Choix de Mazarinades, 2 Vols. 1853. Set. 102.00 (ISBN 0-384-40103-1); Set. pap. 90.00 (ISBN 0-685-13377-X). Johnson Repr.

MAZDAISM

see Zoroastrianism

MECCA

De Gaury, Gerald. Rulers of Mecca. LC 78-63458. (Pilgrimages Ser.). (Illus.). 1982. Repr. of 1954 ed. 34.50 (ISBN 0-404-16517-6). AMS Pr.

Hureau, Jean. Mecca Today. (J. A. Editions: Today Ser.). (Illus.). 240p. 1980. 14.95 (ISBN 2-85258-214-7, Pub. by J. A. Editions France). Hippocrene Bks.

Makky, Ghazy A. Mecca, the Pilgrimage City: A Study of Pilgrim Accomodation. (Illus.). 95p. 1978. 28.00 (ISBN 0-85664-591-5, Pub. by Croom Helm Ltd). Methuen Inc.

MEDICAL ETHICS

see also Euthanasia; Medicine and Religion; Pastoral Medicine

Ashley, Benedict M. & O'Rourke, Kevin D. Health Care Ethics: A Theological Analysis. 2nd ed. LC 81-17973. 1982. 25.00 (ISBN 0-87125-075-6); pap. 16.00 (ISBN 0-87125-070-5). Cath Health.

Bondeson, William, et al, eds. New Knowledge in the Biomedical Sciences. 1982. lib. bdg. 29.50 (ISBN 90-277-1319-7, Pub. by Reidel Holland). Kluwer Academic.

Childress, James F. Priorities in Biomedical Ethics. LC 81-3. 144p. 1981. pap. 8.95 (ISBN 0-664-24368-1). Westminster.

Cowan, Dale H. Human Organ Transplantation: Societal, Medical-Legal, Regulatory, & Reimbursement Issues. LC 86-29478. 1987. price not set (ISBN 0-910701-20-2). Health Admin Pr.

Davis, et al, eds. Contemporary Issues in Biomedical Ethics. LC 78-71406. (Contemporary Issues in Biomedicine, Ethics, & Society Ser.). 300p. 1979. 29.50 (ISBN 0-89603-002-4). Humana.

Divett, Robert T. Medicine & the Mormons: An Introduction to the History of Latter-day Saint Health Care. LC 81-84588. 230p. 1981. pap. 9.95 (ISBN 0-88290-194-X, 2050). Horizon Utah.

Ethics, Humanisms & Medicine Conference, University of Michigan, Ann Arbor, MI. 1981 & Basson, Marc D. Troubling Problems in Medical Ethics: The Third Volume in a Series on Ethics, Humanism & Medicine, Proceedings. LC 81-20723. (Progress in Clinical & Biological Research: Vol. 76). 306p. 1981. 28.00 (ISBN 0-8451-0076-9). A R Liss.

Faulder, Carolyn. Whose Body Is It? The Troubling Issue of Informed Consent. 168p. (Orig.). 1986. pap. 6.95 (ISBN 0-86068-645-0, Pub. by Virago Pr). Salem Hse Pubs.

Glaser, John W. Caring for the Special Child. LC 84-82551. 97p. (Orig.). 1985. pap. 6.95 (ISBN 0-934134-14-6, Leaven Pr). Sheed & Ward MO.

Kelly, David F. The Emergence of Roman Catholic Medical Ethics in North America: An Historical-Methodological-Bibliographical Study. LC 79-66372. (Texts & Studies in Religion: Vol. 3). xi, 534p. 1982. Repr. 79.95x (ISBN 0-88946-877-X). E Mellen.

Lammers, Stephen E. & Verhey, Allen, eds. On Moral Medicine: Theological Perspectives in Medical Ethics. 680p. 1987. 35.00 (ISBN 0-8028-3629-1). Eerdmans.

Lapp, Rhonda S. Devotionals for Nurses. (Ultra Bks.). 4.95 (ISBN 0-8010-5539-3). Baker Bk.

Levine, Howard. Life Choices: Confronting the Life & Death Decisions Created by Modern Medicine. 304p. 1986. 16.95 (ISBN 0-671-55385-2). S&S.

Maestri, William. Bioethics: A Parish Resource. LC 81-40822. 64p. (Orig.). 1982. lib. bdg. 22.00 (ISBN 0-8191-2171-1); pap. text ed. 7.75 (ISBN 0-8191-2172-X). U Pr of Amer.

May, William E. Human Existence, Medicine, & Ethics. LC 77-8149. 43p. 1977. 5.25 (ISBN 0-8199-0677-8). Franciscan Herald.

May, William F. The Physician's Covenant: Images of the Healer in Medical Ethics. LC 83-16992. 204p. 1983. pap. 10.95 (ISBN 0-664-24497-1). Westminster.

Payne, Franklin E., Jr. Biblical-Medical Ethics. 1986. text ed. 19.95 (ISBN 0-8010-7099-6). Baker Bk.

Payne, Franklyn E., Jr. Biblical Medical Ethics. Goss, Leonard G., ed. 288p. 1985. write for info. (ISBN 0-88062-068-4). Mott Media.

Rosner, Fred. Modern Medicine & Jewish Ethics. LC 86-2910. 1986. text ed. 22.50 (ISBN 0-88125-091-0); pap. text ed. 14.95 (ISBN 0-88125-102-X). Ktav.

Schneider, Edward D., ed. Questions about the Beginning of Life. LC 85-15617. 192p. (Orig.). 1985. pap. 8.95 (ISBN 0-8066-2167-2, 10-5360). Augsburg.

Sharkey, Paul W., ed. Philosophy, Religion & Psychotherapy: Essays in the Philosophical Foundations of Psychotherapy. LC 81-40828. 242p. (Orig.). 1982. lib. bdg. 29.00 (ISBN 0-8191-2331-5); pap. text ed. 12.50 (ISBN 0-8191-2332-3). U Pr of Amer.

Sherlock, Richard. Preserving Life: Public Policy & the Life Not Worth Living. LC 86-21347. 1987. 15.95 (ISBN 0-8294-0526-7). Loyola.

Simmons, Paul D. Birth & Death: Bioethical Decision-Making. LC 82-20160. (Biblical Perspectives on Current Issues). 270p. 1983. pap. 13.95 (ISBN 0-664-24463-7). Westminster.

Smith, Harmon L. Ethics & the New Medicine. LC 76-124756. Repr. of 1970 ed. 43.50 (ISBN 0-8357-9005-3, 2016356). Bks Demand UMI.

Vaux, Kenneth, ed. Powers That Make Us Human: The Foundations of Medical Ethics. LC 84-28028. 152p. 1986. 16.95 (ISBN 0-252-01187-2). U of Ill Pr.

MEDICAL FOLK-LORE

see Folk Medicine

MEDICAL MISSIONS

see Missions, Medical

MEDICINE–RELIGIOUS ASPECTS

see also Spiritual Healing

Bleich, David J. Judaism & Healing: Halakhic Perspectives. 1981. pap. 9.95 (ISBN 0-87068-890-1). Ktav.

Bondeson, William, et al, eds. New Knowledge in the Biomedical Sciences. 1982. lib. bdg. 29.50 (ISBN 90-277-1319-7, Pub. by Reidel Holland). Kluwer Academic.

Brand, Paul & Yancey, Philip. Fearfully & Wonderfully Made. (Illus.). 224p. 1980. 11.95 (ISBN 0-310-35450-1, 10241). Zondervan.

Campbell, Alastair W. Professional Care: Its Meaning & Practice. LC 84-4081. 160p. 1984. pap. 7.95 (ISBN 0-8006-1812-2). Fortress.

Feldman, David M. Health & Medicine in the Jewish Tradition: The Pursuit of Wholeness. 176p. 1986. 15.95x (ISBN 0-8245-0707-X). Crossroad NY.

Fichter, Joseph H. Religion & Pain: The Spiritual Dimensions of Health Care. 128p. 1981. 9.95 (ISBN 0-8245-0102-0). Crossroad NY.

Finch, John G. Nishkamakarma. LC 82-83498. (Orig.). 1982. pap. 8.50 (ISBN 0-9609928-0-4). Integ Pr.

Fish, Sharon & Shelly, Judith A. Spiritual Care: The Nurse's Role. 2nd ed. LC 83-12604. (Illus.). 192p. 1983. pap. 7.95 (ISBN 0-87784-878-5). Inter-Varsity.

Fortunato, John E. AIDS, the Spiritual Dilemma. 1987. pap. 7.95. Har-Row.

Hamilton, Michael P. & Reid, Helen F. A Hospice Handbook. (Orig.). 1980. pap. 7.95 (ISBN 0-8028-1820-X). Eerdmans.

Hauerwas, Stanley. Suffering Presence: Theological Reflections on Medicine, the Mentally Handicapped & the Church. LC 85-40603. 224p. (Orig.). 1986. text ed. 19.95x (ISBN 0-268-01721-2, 85-17211, Dist. by Har-Row); pap. text ed. 9.95 (ISBN 0-268-01722-0, 85-17229). U of Notre Dame Pr.

Holifield, E. Brooks. Health & Medicine & the Methodist Tradition. 176p. 1986. 17.95x (ISBN 0-8245-0792-4). Crossroad NY.

Holst, Lawrence. Hospital Ministry. Marty, Martin E., intro. by. 256p. 1985. 19.95 (ISBN 0-8245-0697-9). Crossroad NY.

Hurley, Patricia S. Religion & Medicine: A Medical Subject Analysis & Research Index with Bibliography. LC 83-71656. 148p. 1985. 34.50 (ISBN 0-88164-032-8); pap. 26.50 (ISBN 0-88164-033-6). ABBE Pubs Assn.

Jackson, Edgar N. Your Health & You: How Awareness, Attitudes, & Faith Contribute to a Healthy Life. LC 86-22226. (Augsburg Religion & Medicine). 112p. (Orig.). 1986. pap. 5.95 (ISBN 0-8066-2221-0, 10-7426). Augsburg.

Jones, Kenneth, ed. Sickness & Sectarianism: Exploratory Studies in Medical & Religious Sectarianism. 517p. 1985. text ed. 28.95x (ISBN 0-566-00662-6). Gower Pub Co.

Koop, C. Everett. The Right to Live: the Right to Die. 1980. pap. 3.95 (ISBN 0-8423-5594-4). Tyndale.

Lammers, Stephen E. & Verhey, Allen, eds. On Moral Medicine: Theological Perspectives in Medical Ethics. 680p. 1987. 35.00 (ISBN 0-8028-3629-1). Eerdmans.

Larlham, Hattie. Dear Children. LC 82-25842. 152p. 1983. 9.95 (ISBN 0-8361-3325-0). Herald Pr.

McCormick, Richard A. Health & Medicine in the Roman Catholic Tradition: Tradition in Transition. 176p. 1984. 15.95x (ISBN 0-8245-0661-8). Crossroad NY.

MacFarlane, Gwyn. Howard Florey: The Making of a Great Scientist. (Illus.). 1979. 23.95x (ISBN 0-19-858161-0). Oxford U Pr.

McMillen, S. I. None of These Diseases. 160p. 1963. pap. 2.95 (ISBN 0-8007-8030-2, Spire Bks). Revell.

Martin, Marty E. Health Medicine & Faith Traditions: An Inquiry into Religion & Medicine. Vaux, Kenneth L., ed. LC 81-71383. pap. 90.50 (2026975). Bks Demand UMI.

O'Donnell, Thomas J. Medicine & Christian Morality. LC 75-41471. 1976. 9.95 (ISBN 0-8189-0323-6). Alba.

Paradis, Lenora F. Hospice Handbook: A Guide for Managers & Planners. 420p. 1985. 46.50 (ISBN 0-87189-104-2). Aspen Pub.

Parker, Paul E. & Enlow, David R. What's a Nice Person Like You Doing Sick? LC 74-82838. (Illus.). 80p. 1974. pap. 1.50 (ISBN 0-88419-082-X). Creation Hse.

Parkhill, Joe M. God Did Not Create Sickness or Disease. 160p. (Orig.). 1983. pap. text ed. 6.95 (ISBN 0-936744-05-7). Country Bazaar.

Pink, Arthur W. Divine Healing. pap. 0.75 (ISBN 0-685-00742-1). Reiner.

Pope John Center Staff. Technological Powers & the Person: Nuclear Energy & Reproductive Technology. Lossing, Larry D. & Bayer, Edward J., eds. (Illus.). 370p. (Orig.). 1983. pap. 15.95 (ISBN 0-935372-12-1). Pope John Ctr.

Rahman, Fazlur. Health & Medicine in the Islamic Tradition. 176p. 1987. 16.95x (ISBN 0-8245-0797-5). Crossroad NY.

Religious Congregations & Health Care Facilities: Accountability & Adaptation. LC 83-5228. 86p. (Orig.). 1983. pap. 7.00 (ISBN 0-87125-083-7). Cath Health.

Rosenbaum, Ernest H., et al. Rehabilitation Exercises for the Cancer Patient. (Illus., Orig.). 1980. pap. 4.95 (ISBN 0-915950-37-5). Bull Pub.

--Sexuality & Cancer. (Orig.). 1980. pap. 2.95 (ISBN 0-915950-39-1). Bull Pub.

Rosner, F. Medicine in the Bible & the Talmud: Selections from Classical Jewish Sources. (Library of Jewish Law & Ethics: Vol. 5). 9.95x (ISBN 0-87068-326-8). Ktav.

Sayers, William T. Body, Soul & Blood: Recovering the Human in Medicine. LC 79-56194. 112p. 1980. pap. 5.95 (ISBN 0-935718-00-1). Asclepiad.

Schneider, Edward D., ed. Questions about the Beginning of Life. LC 85-15617. 192p. (Orig.). 1985. pap. 8.95 (ISBN 0-8066-2167-2, 10-5360). Augsburg.

Shannon, Thomas A. & Faso, Charles N. Let Them Go Free: A Family Prayer Service & Guidelines for the Withdrawal of Life Support Systems. 1987. pap. 2.95. Paulist Pr.

Sharkey, Paul W., ed. Philosophy, Religion & Psychotherapy: Essays in the Philosophical Foundations of Psychotherapy. LC 81-40828. 242p. (Orig.). 1982. lib. bdg. 29.00 (ISBN 0-8191-2331-5); pap. text ed. 12.50 (ISBN 0-8191-2332-3). U Pr of Amer.

Sheils, W. J. & Baker, Derek, eds. The Church & Healing: Papers Read at the Twentieth Summer Meeting & the Twenty-First Winter Meeting. (Studies in Church History: Vol. 19). 400p. 1984. text ed. 45.00x (ISBN 0-631-13117-5). Basil Blackwell.

Shriver, Donald W., Jr., ed. Medicine & Religion: Strategies of Care. LC 79-23420. (Contemporary Community Health Ser.). 1980. 14.95x (ISBN 0-8229-3412-4). U of Pittsburgh Pr.

Thomsen, Russel J. The Bible Book of Medical Wisdom. 160p. 1985. pap. 3.95 (ISBN 0-916441-26-1). Barbour & Co.

Wilkinson, John. Health & Healing: Studies in New Testament Principles. 220p. 1980. 15.00x (ISBN 0-905312-08-2, Pub. by Scot Acad Pr). Longwood Pub Group.

Wilson, Dorothy C. I Will Be a Doctor! LC 83-3862. 160p. (Orig.). 1983. pap. 7.95 (ISBN 0-687-19727-9). Abingdon.

Winkelmann, John P., ed. The Catholic Pharmacist: 1985. (Vol. 18). 1985. 10.00. Natl Cath Pharm.

MEDICINE, AYURVEDIC

Dash, Bhagwan & Kashyap, Lalitesh. Basic Principles of Ayurveda. (Illus.). 628p. 1980. 44.95x (ISBN 0-940500-34-5). Asia Bk Corp.

Dash, Vaidya B. Handbook of Ayurveda. 221p. (Orig.). 1983. 28.00 (ISBN 0-317-17437-1, Pub. by Cultural Integration). Auromere.

Lad, Vasant. Ayurveda, the Science of Self-Healing: A Practical Guide. Elliot, Malinda & Slavitz, Harriet, eds. LC 83-80620. (Illus.). 176p. (Orig.). 1984. text ed. 37.95 (ISBN 0-914955-01-2); pap. text ed. 9.95 (ISBN 0-914955-00-4). Lotus Light.

MEDICINE, CLERICAL

see Pastoral Medicine

MEDICINE, HINDU

see Medicine, Ayurvedic

Dash, Vaidya B. Handbook of Ayurveda. 221p. (Orig.). 1983. 28.00 (ISBN 0-317-17437-1, Pub. by Cultural Integration). Auromere.

MEDICINE, PASTORAL

see Pastoral Medicine

MEDICINE, PRIMITIVE

see also Folk Medicine; Indians of North America–Medicine; Medicine-Man

Field, Margaret J. Religion & Medicine of the Ga People. LC 76-44718. 1977. Repr. of 1937 ed. 37.50 (ISBN 0-404-15923-0). AMS Pr.

Hewat, Matthew L. Bantu Folk Lore. LC 77-129948. Repr. of 1906 ed. 22.50x (ISBN 0-8371-4992-4, HBF&, Pub. by Negro U Pr). Greenwood.

Jayne, Walter A. The Healing Gods of Ancient Civilizations. LC 75-23728. Repr. of 1925 ed. 49.00 (ISBN 0-404-13286-3). AMS Pr.

Maddox, John L. The Medicine Man: A Sociological Study of the Character & Evolution of Shamanism. LC 75-23737. Repr. of 1923 ed. 45.00 (ISBN 0-404-13294-4). AMS Pr.

MEDICINE AND BUDDHISM

Tatz, Mark, tr. Buddhism & Healing: Demieville's Article "Byo" from Hobogirin. 108p. (Orig.). 1985. lib. bdg. 24.00 (ISBN 0-8191-4436-3); pap. text ed. 9.50 (ISBN 0-8191-4437-1). U Pr of Amer.

MEDICINE AND CHRISTIANITY

see Medicine and Religion

MEDICINE AND RELIGION

see Medicine–Religious Aspects

Numbers, Ronald L. & Amundsen, Darrel W., eds. Caring & Curing: Historical Essays on Health, Medicine, & the Faith Traditions. 576p. 1986. text ed. 35.00x (ISBN 0-02-919270-6). Macmillan.

MEDICINE-MAN

see also Shamanism

Bourke, John G. The Medicine Men of the Apache. LC 71-175003. (Illus.). 150p. 13.50 (ISBN 0-87026-049-9). Westernlore.

Corlett, William T. The Medicine-Man of the American Indian & His Cultural Background. LC 75-23699. Repr. of 1935 ed. 47.50 (ISBN 0-404-13249-9). AMS Pr.

John Lame Deer & Erdoes, Richard. Lame Deer Seeker of Visions: The Life of a Sioux Medicine Man. 288p. 1976. pap. 3.95 (ISBN 0-671-45586-9, 80391). WSP.

Krippner, Stanley & Villoldo, Alberto. The Realms of Healing. LC 75-7858. 320p. (Orig.). 1986. pap. 9.95 (ISBN 0-89087-474-3). Celestial Arts.

Mails, Thomas E. Fool's Crow. 1980. pap. 3.50 (ISBN 0-380-52175-X, 52175-X, Discus). Avon.

MEDIEVAL ARCHITECTURE

see Architecture, Medieval

MEDIEVAL ART

see Art, Medieval

MEDIEVAL HISTORY

see Middle Ages–History

MEDIEVAL SECTS

see Sects, Medieval

MEDINET-ABU

Hughes, George R. Medinet Habu - Epigraphic Survey: The Temple Proper, Part Three, the Third Hypostyle Hall, All Rooms Accessible from It, with Friezes of Scenes from the Roof Terraces & Exterior Walls of the Temple. LC 30-22847. (Oriental Institute Pubns. Ser). 1964. 65.00x (ISBN 0-226-62196-0, OIP93). U of Chicago Pr.

--Medinet Habu - Epigraphic Survey: The Temple Proper, Part Two, the Re Chapel, the Mortuary Complex, & Adjacent Rooms with Miscellaneous Material from Pylons, the Forecourts & the First Hypostyle Hall, Vol. 6. LC 30-22847. (Oriental Institute Pubns. Ser). 1963. 65.00x (ISBN 0-226-62185-5, OIP84). U of Chicago Pr.

Nelson, Harold H. & Holscher, Uvo. Medinet Habu, Nineteen Twenty Four-Twenty Eight. LC 29-13423. (Illus.). 1929. pap. 5.00x (ISBN 0-226-62320-3, OIC5). U of Chicago Pr.

MEDITATION

Here are entered works on meditation or mental prayer as a method of promoting the spiritual life. Works that contain collections of meditations are entered under the heading Meditations.

see also Contemplation; Retreats; Transcendental Meditation

Addington, Jack & Addington, Cornelia. The Joy of Meditation. LC 78-75078. 1979. pap. 4.95 (ISBN 0-87516-292-4). De Vorss.

Ajaya, Swami. Yoga Psychology: A Practical Guide to Meditation. rev. ed. LC 76-374539. 115p. 1976. pap. 5.95 (ISBN 0-89389-052-9). Himalayan Pubs.

Ajaya, Swami, ed. Meditational Therapy. 100p. (Orig.). pap. 3.95 (ISBN 0-89389-032-4). Himalayan Pubs.

Alcantara, S. Peter. A Golden Treatise of Mental Prayer. Hollings, G. S., ed. LC 77-18960. Repr. of 1978 ed. 35.20 (ISBN 0-8357-9135-1, 2019096). Bks Demand UMI.

Aldan, Daisy. Foundation Stone Meditation by Rudolf Steiner. 1981. pap. 2.00 (ISBN 0-916786-53-6). St George Bk Serv.

Alexander, Frank J. In the Hours of Meditation. pap. 1.75 (ISBN 0-87481-162-7). Vedanta Pr.

Amaldas, Swami. Christian Yogic Meditation. (Ways of Prayer Ser.: Vol. 8). pap. 5.95 (ISBN 0-89453-368-1). M Glazier.

Aron, Elaine & Aron, Arthur. The Maharishi Effect: A Revolution Through Meditation. 235p. (Orig.). 1986. pap. 9.95 (ISBN 0-913299-26-X, Dist. by NAL). Stillpoint.

The Art & Science of Meditation. Misra, L. K., ed. 112p. 1976. pap. 3.95 (ISBN 0-89389-018-9). Himalayan Pubs.

Arya, Pandit U. Superconcious Meditation. 150p. 1978. pap. 6.95 (ISBN 0-89389-035-9). Himalayan Pubs.

Ashcroft-Nowicki, Dolores. First Steps in Ritual: Safe, Effective Techniques for Experiencing the Inner Worlds. 96p. 1983. pap. 6.95 (ISBN 0-85030-314-1). Newcastle Pub.

Association for Research & Enlightenment, Readings Research Dept., compiled by. Meditation, 1: Healing, Prayer, & the Revelation. (Library: Vol. 2). 306p. 1974. 10.95 (ISBN 0-87604-072-5). ARE Pr.

Association for Research & Enlightenment, Readings Research Dept., ed. Meditation, 2: Meditation, Endocrine Glands, Prayer, & Affirmations. (Library: Vol. 3). 274p. 1975. 10.95 (ISBN 0-87604-082-2). ARE Pr.

Aveling, Harry, tr. Arjuna in Meditation. 1976. flexible cloth 8.00 (ISBN 0-89253-800-7). Ind-US Inc.

Bailey, Alice A. From Intellect to Intuition. 1973. 18.00 (ISBN 0-85330-008-9); pap. 7.00 (ISBN 0-85330-108-5). Lucis.

Baker, Douglas. In the Steps of the Master. 1982. 40.00x (ISBN 0-9505502-4-8, Pub. by Baker Pubns England). State Mutual Bk.

Brame, Grace A. Receptive Prayer: A Christian Approach to Meditation. Lambert, Herbert, ed. LC 84-29302. 144p. (Orig.). 1985. pap. 9.95 (ISBN 0-8272-3211-X). CBP.

Brooke, Avery. Doorway to Meditation. 1976. pap. 6.95 (ISBN 0-8164-0903-X, HarpR). Har-Row.

--Hidden in Plain Sight: The Practice of Christian Meditation. 144p. (Orig.). 1986. pap. 7.95 (ISBN 0-8358-0547-6). Upper Room.

Budhananda, Swami. The Mind & Its Control. 119p. (Orig.). 1972. pap. 1.75 (ISBN 0-87481-128-7). Vedanta Pr.

Carrington, Patricia. Freedom in Meditation. LC 76-6240. 384p. 1977. pap. 12.00. Pace Educ Systems.

Carrol, Frieda, compiled by. Meditation & Yoga Retreats: An International Directory. 200p. 1983. text ed. 4.75 (ISBN 0-913597-06-6, Pub. by Alpha Pyramis). Prosperity & Profits.

Cassianus, Joannes. Spiritual Life, a Guide for Those Seeking Perfection. 1977. pap. 4.95 (ISBN 0-686-19234-6). Eastern Orthodox.

Center for Self-Sufficiency, Research Division Staff. At Your Own Pace Reference on Meditation & Wholistic Healing. 30p. 1985. pap. text ed. 2.75 (ISBN 0-910811-71-7, Pub. by Center Self Suff). Prosperity & Profits.

Chaitow, Leon. Relaxation & Meditation Techniques: A Complete Stress-Proofing System. 128p. 1983. pap. cancelled (ISBN 0-7225-0737-2). Thorsons Pubs.

Chinmoy, Sri. Meditation: Man-Perfection in God-Satisfaction. (Illus.). 1979. pap. 6.95 (ISBN 0-88497-444-8). Aum Pubns.

Chu, Wen Kuan. Tao & Longevity: Mind Body Transformation. LC 82-60164. 192p. (Orig.). 1984. pap. 7.95 (ISBN 0-87728-542-X). Weiser.

Clowney, Edmund P. Christian Meditation. 1979. pap. 2.50 (ISBN 0-934532-06-0). Presby & Reformed.

Cooke, Grace. Meditation. 1955. pap. 4.95 (ISBN 0-85487-059-8). De Vorss.

Dass, Ram. Journey of Awakening: A Mediator's Guidebook. 1978. pap. 4.95 (ISBN 0-553-25845-1). Bantam.

Daughters of St Paul. Moments of Decision. 1976. 5.00 (ISBN 0-8198-0445-2); pap. 4.00 (ISBN 0-8198-0446-0). Dghtrs St Paul.

DeGroat, Florence. Universal Man. LC 80-69413. 117p. 1981. pap. 6.50 (ISBN 0-87516-428-5). De Vorss.

Devas, Dominic. Treatise on Prayer & Meditation. Repr. of 1926 ed. lib. bdg. 25.00 (ISBN 0-8495-1026-0). Arden Lib.

Dhiravamsa. The Dynamic Way of Meditation. 160p. 1983. pap. 8.95 (ISBN 0-85500-163-1). Newcastle Pub.

--The Way of Non-Attachment: The Practice of Insight Meditation. 160p. 1984. pap. 9.95 (ISBN 0-85500-210-7). Newcastle Pub.

Du Pont, Guigo. Della Contemplazione. Hogg, James, ed. Piovesan, Emilio, tr. & intro. by. (Analecta Cartusiana Ser.: No. 45). (Ital. & Lat.). 123p. (Orig.). 1979. pap. 25.00 (ISBN 3-7052-0061-5, Pub by Salzburg Studies). Longwood Pub Group.

Eastcott, Michal J. I: The Story of the Self. LC 80-51552. (Illus.). 201p. (Orig.). 1980. pap. 5.50 (ISBN 0-8356-0541-8, Quest). Theos Pub Hse.

Easwaran, Eknath. Instrucciones En la Meditacion. 1980. pap. 2.00 (ISBN 0-915132-23-0). Nilgiri Pr.

--Meditation: An Eight-Point Program. LC 78-10935. 240p. 1978. 15.00 (ISBN 0-915132-15-X); pap. 8.00. Nilgiri Pr.

Easwaran, Eknath, ed. God Makes the Rivers to Flow: Passages for Meditation. (Illus.). 96p. 1982. 12.00 (ISBN 0-915132-28-1); pap. 7.00 (ISBN 0-915132-29-X). Nilgiri Pr.

Edwards, F. Henry. Meditation & Prayer. LC 79-23708. 1980. pap. 12.00 (ISBN 0-8309-0271-6). Herald Hse.

Elliot, Elisabeth. A Slow & Certain Light: Thoughts on the Guidance of God. (Festival Ser.). 128p. 1982. pap. 1.95 (ISBN 0-687-38700-0). Abingdon.

Ellwood, Robert. Finding the Quiet Mind. LC 83-615. 155p. (Orig.). 1983. pap. 4.50 (ISBN 0-8356-0576-0, Quest). Theos Pub Hse.

Enzler, Clarence. In the Presence of God. pap. 4.95 (ISBN 0-87193-055-2). Dimension Bks.

Falconar, A. E. Gardens of Meditation. 128p. 9.95 (ISBN 0-86140-057-7). Dufour.

Fox, Douglas. Meditation & Reality: A Critical View. LC 85-45459. 192p. 1986. pap. 12.95 (ISBN 0-8042-0662-7). John Knox.

Freeman, Laurence. Light Within: The Inner Path of Meditation. 112p. 1987. pap. 7.95 (ISBN 0-8245-0785-1). Crossroad NY.

Fuller, Joy. The Gloricus Presence. LC 81-65753. 168p. (Orig.). 1981. pap. 2.95 (ISBN 0-87516-449-8). De Vorss.

G-Jo Institute. Meditative Relaxation. 1980. pap. 4.50 (ISBN 0-916878-13-9). Falkynor Bks.

Gawain, Shakti. Creative Visualization. LC 79-13760. (Illus.). 158p. 1978. pap. 7.95 (ISBN 0-931432-02-2). Whatever Pub.

Gidlow, Elsa. Makings for Meditation. (Illus.). 1973. 2.00 (ISBN 0-9606568-0-4). Druid Heights.

Ginsberg, Mitchell. The Far Shore. 100p. 1984. 21.00x (ISBN 0-7212-0577-1, Pub. by Regency Pr). State Mutual Bk.

Goldstein, Joseph. The Experience of Insight: A Simple & Direct Guide to Buddhist Meditation. LC 82-42682. 185p. (Orig.). 1983. pap. 7.95 (ISBN 0-87773-226-4). Shambhala Pubns.

Green, Richard J. Meditation, The Highway to Happiness. 3rd ed. 40p. 1980. pap. 3.00 (ISBN 0-87516-407-2). De Vorss.

Griffiths, Bede. Return to the Center. 1976. pap. 7.95 (ISBN 0-87243-112-6). Templegate.

Haddon, David & Hamilton, Vail. TM Wants You. (Direction Bks). 160p. 1976. pap. 1.95 (ISBN 0-8010-4151-1). Baker Bk.

Hall, Manly P. Meditation Disciplines. pap. 3.50 (ISBN 0-89314-800-8). Philos Res.

Hayes, Helen. A Gathering of Hope. 222p. 1985. pap. 7.95 large print ed. (ISBN 0-8027-2467-1). Walker & Co.

Helleberg, Marilyn M. Beyond T. M. A Practical Guide to the Lost Tradition of Christian Meditation. LC 80-82811. 144p. (Orig.). 1981. pap. 7.95 (ISBN 0-8091-2325-8). Paulist Pr.

--A Guide to Christian Meditation. 258p. 1985. pap. 9.95 large print ed. (ISBN 0-8027-2489-2). Walker & Co.

Hemenway, Joan E. Holding on... While Letting Go. (Looking Up Ser.). (Orig.). 1985. pap. 1.25 (ISBN 0-8298-0548-6). Pilgrim NY.

Herzog, Stephanie. Joy in the Classroom. Ray, Ann, ed. LC 82-4724. (Illus.). 224p. 1982. text ed. 7.95 (ISBN 0-916438-46-5). Univ of Trees.

Hesch, John B. Prayer & Meditation for Middle School Kids. 144p. (Orig.). 1985. pap. 7.95 (ISBN 0-8091-2723-7). Paulist Pr.

Hills, C., ed. The Secrets of Spirulina. LC 80-22087. 224p. 1980. 6.95 (ISBN 0-916438-38-4). Univ of Trees.

Hills, Christopher. Into Meditation Now: A Course on Direct Enlightenment. LC 79-5124. (Illus.). 128p. 1979. pap. 5.95 (ISBN 0-916438-30-9). Univ of Trees.

Himalayan Institute. Meditation in Christianity. rev. ed. 130p. pap. 5.95 (ISBN 0-89389-085-5). Himalayan Pubs.

--The Theory & Practice of Meditation. 2nd ed. 150p. (Orig.). 1986. pap. 5.95 (ISBN 0-89389-075-8). Himalayan Pubs.

Ho, Van H. Moving Meditation: Enlightenment of the Mind & Total Fitness. LC 79-88748. (Illus.). 214p. 1979. pap. 15.00 (ISBN 0-9602904-1-9). V H Ho.

Hora, Thomas. Can Meditation Be Done? (Discoures in Metapsychiatry Ser.). 33p. 1984. pap. 4.00 (ISBN 0-913105-09-0). PAGL Pr.

Hua, Ellen K., adapted by. Kung Fu Meditations & Chinese Proverbial Wisdom. LC 73-7731. (Illus.). 1973. o. p. 3.95 (ISBN 0-87407-511-4); pap. 3.00 (ISBN 0-87407-200-X, FPI). Thor.

Humphries, Christmas. Concentration & Meditation. 343p. 1981. pap. 18.00 (ISBN 0-89540-068-5, SD-068). Sun Pub.

Hyatt, Christopher S. Undoing Yourself with Energized Meditation & Other Devices. LC 82-83293. 114p. 1982. pap. 6.95 (ISBN 0-941404-06-4). Falcon Pr Az.

Ichazo, Oscar. Kinerhythm Meditation: A Multfaceted Concentration. (Illus.). 54p. 1978. pap. 12.95 (ISBN 0-916554-07-4). Arica Inst Pr.

Jivananda, Bhagavan. This Is It: It's How You Live It Now, the Endless Meditation. (Orig.). pap. cancelled (ISBN 0-941404-27-7). Falcon Pr AZ.

John-roger. Inner Worlds of Meditation. LC 76-56625. pap. 5.00 (ISBN 0-914829-11-4). Baraka Bk.

Johnson, Willard. Riding the Ox Home: A History of Meditation from Shamanism to Science. LC 86-47752. (Illus.). 262p. 1987. pap. 8.95 (ISBN 0-8070-1305-6, BP-735). Beacon Pr.

Johnston, William. Silent Music: The Science of Meditation. LC 73-18688. 1979. pap. 7.95 (ISBN 0-06-064196-7, RD 293, HarpR). Har-Row.

Jyotir Maya Nanda, Swami. Concentration & Meditation. (Illus.). 1971. 6.99 (ISBN 0-934664-03-X). Yoga Res Foun.

--Mantra, Kirtana, Yantra & Tantra. (Illus.). 1974. pap. 3.99 (ISBN 0-934664-06-4). Yoga Res Foun.

Kaplan, Aryeh. Jewish Meditation: A Practical Guide. LC 84-23589. 174p. 1985. 17.95 (ISBN 0-8052-4006-3); pap. 9.95 (ISBN 0-8052-0781-3). Schocken.

--Meditation & the Bible. reprinting ed. 1978. pap. 9.95 (ISBN 0-87728-617-5). Weiser.

Kaushik, R. P. Light of Exploration. LC 76-39622. 1977. pap. 5.95 (ISBN 0-918038-00-6). Journey Pubns.

Kelsey, Morton T. The Other Side of Silence: A Guide to Christian Meditation. LC 76-9365. 314p. 1976. pap. 9.95 (ISBN 0-8091-1956-0). Paulist Pr.

Kim, Ashida. Secrets of the Ninja. (Illus.). 168p. 1981. 16.95 (ISBN 0-87364-234-1). Paladin Pr.

King, S. Temple of Your Being. 1985. Book & Cassette Pack. 27.50x (ISBN 0-317-54328-8, Pub. by J Richardson UK). State Mutual Bk.

Kravette, Steve. Complete Meditation. (Illus.). 320p. (Orig.). 1982. pap. 10.95 (ISBN 0-914918-28-1). Para Res.

Kundalini Meditation: Manual for Intermediate Students. LC 85-11044. 70p. 1985. Repr. of 1984 ed. lib. bdg. 19.95x (ISBN 0-89370-885-2). Borgo Pr.

Kury, Zaher P. From a Gun to a Flower: Messages Through the Mediumship of Zaher P. Kury. (Illus.). 192p. 1984. 10.00 (ISBN 0-682-40160-9). Exposition Pr FL.

Langford, Anne. Meditation for Little People. LC 75-46191. (Illus.). 40p. 1976. pap. 3.00 (ISBN 0-87516-211-8). De Vorss.

Leen, Edward. Progress Through Mental Prayer. 1978. pap. 2.45 (ISBN 0-88479-012-6). Arena Lettres.

Lehodey, Dom V. The Ways of Mental Prayer. 408p. 1982. pap. 8.00 (ISBN 0-89555-178-0). TAN Bks Pubs.

Leichtman, Robert R. & Japikse, Carl. Active Meditation: The Western Tradition. LC 82-72785. 512p. 1983. 24.50 (ISBN 0-89804-040-X). Ariel OH.

LeShan, Lawrence. How to Meditate: A Guide to Self-Discovery. 176p. 1986. pap. 3.95 (ISBN 0-553-24453-1). Bantam.

Luk, Charles. Secrets of Chinese Meditation. (Illus.). 1969. pap. 6.95 (ISBN 0-87728-066-5). Weiser.

Lyman, Frederick C. Posture of Contemplation. LC 68-54973. 123p. 1969. 5.00 (ISBN 0-8022-2258-7). Philos Lib.

McCormick, Thomas & Fish, Sharon. Meditation: A Practical Guide to a Spiritual Discipline. 132p. (Orig.). 1983. pap. 3.95 (ISBN 0-87784-844-0). Inter-Varsity.

Mara. The Middle Sphere. LC 81-67349. (Earth Song Ser.). (Illus.). 57p. (Orig.). 1981. pap. 4.95 (ISBN 0-9605170-1-4). Earth-Song.

Masset, Evelyn. To Live Each Day Is to Meditate. (Illus.). 42p. 1982. pap. 5.00. Coleman Pub.

Massy, Robert. You Are What You Breathe: The Negative Ion Story. 32p. 1980. 1.50 (ISBN 0-916438-41-4, Dist. by New Era Pr). Univ of Trees.

Meditation as an Intervention in Stress Reactivity. (Stress in Modern Society Ser.: No. 10). 1986. write for info. (ISBN 0-404-63260-2). AMS Pr.

Mehta. Creative Silence. 4.75 (ISBN 0-8356-7224-7). Theos Pub Hse.

Mehta, Rohit. Science of Meditation. 1978. 11.95 (ISBN 0-89684-007-7, Pub. by Motilal Banarsidass India). Orient Bk Dist.

Meier, Paul. Meditating for Success. Mack, Jane, ed. 25p. (Orig.). 1985. pap. 2.95 (ISBN 0-8010-6207-1). Baker Bk.

Melcer, Donald. Self Development Through Meditative Practice. 1983. pap. 2.95 (ISBN 0-916786-70-6). St George Bk Serv.

Merton, Thomas. The Asian Journal of Thomas Merton. Stone, Naomi B., et al, eds. LC 71-103370. (Illus.). 448p. 1973. pap. 8.95 (ISBN 0-8112-0570-3, NDP394). New Directions.

--Mystics & Zen Masters. 303p. 1986. pap. 8.95 (ISBN 0-374-52001-1). FS&G.

--New Seeds of Contemplation. rev. ed. LC 61-17869. 1972. pap. 5.50 (ISBN 0-8112-0099-X, NDP337). New Directions.

Meserve, Harry C. The Practical Meditator. LC 80-15631. 137p. 1981. 19.95 (ISBN 0-87705-506-8); professional 16.95. Human Sci Pr.

Metaphysical Mediations. pap. 8.95 (ISBN 0-937134-17-1). Amrita Found.

Michaels, Louis. The Words of Jesus: Arranged for Meditation. 1977. 6.95 (ISBN 0-87243-071-5). Templegate.

Monks of the Ramakrishna Order. Meditation. Bhavyananda, Swami, ed. 1977. pap. 8.50 (ISBN 0-7025-0019-4). Vedanta Pr.

Moore, Christopher W. The Mediation Process: Practical Strategies for Resolving Conflicts. LC 85-23675. (Social & Behavioral Science Ser.). 1986. text ed. 24.95x (ISBN 0-87589-673-1). Jossey Bass.

Mouradian, Kay. Reflective Meditation. LC 82-50163. 175p. (Orig.). 1982. pap. 4.50 (ISBN 0-8356-0565-5, Quest). Theos Pub Hse.

Muktananda. Meditate. LC 80-20477. 84p. 1980. 9.95x (ISBN 0-87395-471-8); pap. 4.95x (ISBN 0-87395-472-6). State U NY Pr.

Murray, Andrew. Waiting on God. (Andrew Murray Ser.). pap. 3.50 (ISBN 0-8024-0026-4). Moody.
Newhouse, Flower A. Gateways into Light. 2nd ed. LC 74-75517. 160p. 1974. pap. 8.50 (ISBN 0-910378-09-6). Christward.
Norbu, Namkhai. The Crystal & the Way of Light: Meditation, Contemplation & Self Liberation. Shane, John, ed. (Illus.). 224p. 1986. pap. 14.95 (ISBN 0-7102-0833-2, 08332). Methuen Inc.
Odier, Daniel. Nirvana-Tao: The Secret Meditation Techniques of the Taoist & Buddhist Masters. (Illus.). 208p. (Orig.). 1986. pap. 9.95 (ISBN 0-89281-045-9). Inner Tradit.
Om! Meditation & Tranquility. 5.95 (ISBN 0-88088-456-8). Peter Pauper.
Ouseley, S. G. Colour Meditations. 96p. 1981. pap. 3.50 (ISBN 0-85243-062-0). Ariel OH.
Peck, Robert L. American Meditation & Beginning Yoga. 1976. 6.00 (ISBN 0-685-71846-8). Personal Dev Ctr.
Petersen, W. P. & Fehr, Terry. Meditation Made Easy. (Concise Guides Ser.). (Illus.). 1979. s&l 9.90 (ISBN 0-531-02894-1). Watts.
Progoff, Ira. The Practice of Process Meditation: The Intensive Journal Way to Spiritual Experience. LC 80-68847. 343p. 1980. 18.95 (ISBN 0-87941-008-6); pap. 9.95, 1980 (ISBN 0-87941-008-6). Dialogue Hse.
--Well & the Cathedral. 5th ed. LC 76-20823. (Entrance Meditation Ser.). 166p. 1983. 4.95; pap. 11.50 incl. cassette (ISBN 0-87941-005-1). Dialogue Hse.
Prophet, Elizabeth C., intro. by. Prayer & Meditation. LC 76-28086. (Illus.). 306p. (Orig.). 1978. pap. 9.95 (ISBN 0-916766-19-5). Summit Univ.
Puryear, Herbert B. & Thurston, Mark. Meditation & the Mind of Man. rev. ed. 1975. pap. 6.95 (ISBN 0-87604-105-5). ARE Pr.
Rajneesh, Bhagwan S. Meditation: The Art of Ecstasy. Bharti, Ma S., ed. 1978. pap. 3.50 (ISBN 0-06-080394-0, P394, PL). Har-Row.
Rajneesh, Bhagwan Shree. The Orange Book: The Meditation Techniques of Bhagwan Shree Rajneesh. 2nd ed. Rajneesh Foundation International, ed. LC 82-63117. (Meditation Ser.). 256p. 1983. pap. 3.95 (ISBN 0-88050-697-0). Chidvilas Found.
Reps, Paul. Ten Ways to Meditate. LC 70-83639. (Illus.). 64p. 1981. 9.95 (ISBN 0-8348-0163-9). Weatherhill.
Reyes, Benito F. Meditation: Cybernetics of Consciousness. Volz, Fred J., ed. 152p. 1978. pap. 7.50 (ISBN 0-939375-04-4). World Univ Amer.
Reynolds, David K. Naikan Psychotherapy: Meditation for Self-Development. LC 82-21862. 184p. 1983. 17.50x (ISBN 0-226-71029-7). U of Chicago Pr.
Rhoades, Gale R. Waybill to Lost Spanish Signs & Symbols. (Illus., Orig.). 1982. pap. 6.00 (ISBN 0-942688-02-3). Dream Garden.
Riccardo, Martin V. Mystical Consciousness: Exploring an Extraordinary State of Awareness. 1977. pap. 5.00 (ISBN 0-686-19170-6). MVR Bks.
Rozman, Deborah A. Meditating with Children: New Age Meditations for Children. LC 76-10480. (Illus.). 160p. (Orig.). 1975. pap. 7.95 (ISBN 0-916438-23-6). Univ of Trees.
Sadhu. Meditation. pap. 7.00 (ISBN 0-87980-096-8). Wilshire.
Saliers, Don E. The Soul in Paraphrase: Prayer & the Religious Affections. 160p. 1980. 8.95 (ISBN 0-8164-0121-7, HarpR). Har-Row.
Saraydarian, Haroutiun. Science of Meditation. LC 77-158995. 1971. 11.00 (ISBN 0-911794-29-8); pap. 9.00 (ISBN 0-911794-30-1). Aqua Educ.
Satprakashananda, Swami. Meditation: Its Process, Practice, & Culmination. LC 76-15722. 264p. 1976. 10.00 (ISBN 0-916356-55-8). Vedanta Soc St Louis.
Savary, Louis M. & Scheihing, Theresa O. Our Treasured Heritage: Teaching Christian Meditation to Children. LC 81-7818. 176p. 1981. 9.95 (ISBN 0-8245-0078-4). Crossroad NY.
Schwarz, Jack. The Path of Action. LC 77-2247. 1977. pap. 8.95 (ISBN 0-525-48231-8, 0869-260). Dutton.
Sechrist, Elsie. Meditation: Gateway to Light. rev. ed. 53p. 1972. pap. 3.95 (ISBN 0-87604-062-8). ARE Pr.
Shapiro, Deane H., Jr. Meditation: Self-Regulation Strategy & Altered States of Consciousness. LC 80-66454. 318p. 1980. 28.95x (ISBN 0-202-25132-2). De Gruyter Aldine.
Shapiro, Deane H., Jr. & Walsh, Roger N., eds. Meditation: Classic & Contemporary Perspectives. LC 84-300. 722p. 1984. lib. bdg. 64.95x (ISBN 0-202-25136-5). De Gruyter Aldine.
Shattock, E. H. The Rangoon, Burma, Thathana Yeiktha Meditation Course. 175p. 1985. 137.50 (ISBN 0-89920-094-X). Am Inst Psych.
Siddheswarananda, Swami. Meditation According to Yoga-Vedanta. pap. 4.95 (ISBN 0-87481-467-7). Vedanta Pr.
Simler, Joseph. Catechism of Mental Prayer. LC 84-51901. 69p. 1985. pap. 1.50 (ISBN 0-89555-256-6). Tan Bks Pubs.
Simmons, Patricia A. Between You & Me, God. LC 74-79486. 1974. pap. 5.95 (ISBN 0-8054-4412-2, 4244-12). Broadman.
Singh, Kirpal. The Light of Kirpal. LC 80-52537. xv, 446p. 1984. pap. 12.00 (ISBN 0-89142-033-9). Sant Bani Ash.
Stahl, Carolyn. Opening to God: Guided Imagery Meditation on Scripture. LC 77-87403. 1977. 3.50x (ISBN 0-8358-0357-0). Upper Room.
Stamm, Millie. Be Still & Know. 384p. 1981. pap. 7.95 (ISBN 0-310-32991-4, 10844P). Zondervan.
Steere, Douglas V. Contemplation & Leisure. rev. ed. LC 74-30803. 32p. 1975. pap. 2.50x (ISBN 0-87574-199-1, 199). Pendle Hill.
Steinbrecher, Edwin C. The Inner Guide Meditation. 4th ed. LC 78-60489. (Illus.). 1978. 12.95 (ISBN 0-685-65266-1); pap. 6.75 (ISBN 0-685-65267-X). Blue Feather.
Steiner, Rudolf. Knowledge of the Higher Worlds & Its Attainment. Metaxa, George & Monges, Henry B., trs. from Ger. LC 79-101595. 224p. 1983. 14.00 (ISBN 0-88010-045-1); pap. 6.95 (ISBN 0-88010-046-X). Anthroposophic.
Straughn, R. A. Meditation Techniques of the Kabalists, Vedantins & Taoists. (Illus.). 1976. pap. 6.95 (ISBN 0-917650-02-6). Maat Pub.
Subramuniya. The Fine Art of Meditation. pap. 1.00 (ISBN 0-87516-356-4). De Vorss.
--The Meditator. (On the Path Ser.). (Illus.). 72p. 1973. pap. 2.00 (ISBN 0-87516-351-3). De Vorss.
Swahananda, Swami. Meditation & Other Spiritual Disciplines. 171p. 6.50 (ISBN 0-87481-214-3, Pub. by Advaita Ashrama India). Vedanta Pr.
Swami Vivekananda. Meditation & Its Methods According to Swami Vivekananda. Swami Chetanananda, compiled by. LC 75-36392. (Orig.). 1976. pap. 4.95 (ISBN 0-87481-030-2). Vedanta Pr.
Szekely, Edmond B. Biogenic Meditation: Biogenic Self-Analysis, Creative Microcosmos. (Illus.). 40p. 1978. pap. 1.80 (ISBN 0-89564-051-1). IBS Intl.
Thakar, Vimala. Why Meditation. 82p. 1986. pap. 6.00 (ISBN 81-208-0047-8, Pub. by Motilal Banarsidass India). Orient Bk Dist.
Thomas, James. I Am That I Am: A Metaphysical Course on Consciousness. (Illus.). 168p. 1984. 14.95x (ISBN 0-931290-90-2); pap. 6.95x (ISBN 0-931290-91-0). Alchemy Bks.
Trungpa, Chogyam. Meditation in Action. 74p. (Orig.). 1969. pap. 4.95 (ISBN 0-87773-000-8). Shambhala Pubns.
Tulku, Tarthang. Gesture of Balance: A Guide to Awareness, Self-Healing & Meditation. LC 75-5255. (Illus.). 1976. 12.95 (ISBN 0-913546-17-8); pap. 7.95 (ISBN 0-913546-16-X). Dharma Pub.
Vining, Elizabeth G. Harnessing Pegasus: Inspiration & Meditation. 1983. pap. 2.50x (ISBN 0-87574-221-1, 221). Pendle Hill.
Watts, Alan. Om: Creative Meditations. LC 79-54101. 160p. 1984. pap. 6.95 (ISBN 0-89087-257-0). Celestial Arts.
Wedgewood. Meditation for Beginners. 2.50 (ISBN 0-8356-5050-2). Theos Pub Hse.
West, Serene. Very Practical Meditation. LC 79-20249. 116p. (Orig.). 1981. pap. 4.95 (ISBN 0-89865-006-2, Unilaw). Donning Co.
Wilson, Jim. First Steps in Meditation for Young People. pap. 2.50 (ISBN 0-227-67458-8, Pub. by J Clarke U K). Attic Pr.
Wise, Charles C., Jr. Mind Is It: Meditation, Prayer, Healing, & the Psychic. LC 77-82923. 191p. (Orig.). 1978. pap. 3.75 (ISBN 0-917023-02-1). Magian Pr.
Wood, Ernest. Concentration: An Approach Meditation. 6.75 (ISBN 0-8356-7337-5). Theos Pub Hse.
--Concentration: An Approach to Meditation. LC 67-2874. pap. 3.75 (ISBN 0-8356-0176-5, Quest). Theos Pub Hse.
Yatiswarananda, Swami. Meditation & Spiritual Life. 700p. 1980. 15.00x (ISBN 0-87481-403-0). Vedanta Pr.
Yuvacharya Shri Mahaprajna. Mind Beyond Mind: Perceptive Meditation, Form & Function. 186p. 1980. 9.00 (ISBN 0-88065-214-4, Pub. by Messers Today & Tomorrows Printers & Publishers India). Scholarly Pubns.

MEDITATION (BUDDHISM)

Arya, Usharbudh & Litt, D. Mantra & Meditation. LC 81-84076. 237p. (Orig.). 1981. pap. 8.95 (ISBN 0-89389-074-X). Himalayan Pubs.
Bucknell, R. S. & Stuart-Fox, Martin. The Twilight Language: Explanations in Buddhist Meditation & Symbolism. 227p. 1986. 27.50 (ISBN 0-312-82540-4). St Martin.
Goldstein, Joseph. The Experience of Insight: A Simple & Direct Guide to Buddhist Meditation. 1987. pap. 9.95. Shambhala Pubns.
Gregory, Peter N., ed. Traditions of Meditation in Chinese Buddhism. LC 86-19243. (Studies in East Asian Buddhism: No. 4). 272p. 1987. pap. text ed. 16.00x (ISBN 0-8248-1088-0). UH Pr.
Hanh, Thich N. The Miracle of Mindfulness! A Manual on Meditation. LC 76-7747. (Illus.). 1976. pap. 7.95 (ISBN 0-8070-1119-3, BP546). Beacon Pr.
Kongtrul, Jamgon. The Torch of Certainty. Hanson, Judith, tr. from Tibetan. LC 86-11835. 184p. 1986. pap. 12.95 (ISBN 0-87773-380-5). Shambhala Pubns.
Kriyananda, Goswami. Beginner's Guide to Meditation. 104p. (Orig.). pap. text ed. 3.95 (ISBN 0-317-43470-5). Temple Kriya Yoga.
Manjusrimitra. Primordial Experience: An Introduction to Dzog-chen Meditation. Lipman, Kennard & Norbu, Namkhai, trs. from Tibetan. LC 86-11842. Tr. of Rdo La Gser Zhun. 140p. 1986. pap. 11.95 (ISBN 0-87773-372-4). Shambhala Pubns.
Pradhan, Ayoda P. The Buddha's System of Meditation: Phase (I-VIII, 4 vols. 1986. text ed. 150.00x (ISBN 81-207-0140-2, Pub. by Sterling Pubs India). Apt Bks.
Roth, Martin & Stevens, John. Zen Guide: Where to Meditate in Japan. (Illus.). 152p. pap. 7.50 (ISBN 0-8348-0202-3). Weatherhill.
Sanadi, Lalita. Mantra Meditation. rev. ed. D'Auri, Laura, ed. (Illus.). 160p. pap. cancelled (ISBN 0-87407-204-2, FP-4). Thor.
Sekida, Katsuki. Zen Training: Methods & Philosophy. Grimstone, A. V., ed. LC 75-17573. (Illus.). 264p. 1975. 12.50 (ISBN 0-8348-0111-6); pap. 9.95 (ISBN 0-8348-0114-0). Weatherhill.
Sole-Leris, Amadeo. Tranquillity & Insight: An Introduction to the Oldest Form of Buddhist Meditation. LC 86-11834. 176p. 1986. pap. 7.95 (ISBN 0-87773-385-6). Shambhala Pubns.
Takpo Tashi Namgyal. Mahamudra: The Quintessance of Mind & Meditation. Lhalungpa, Lobsang P., tr. from Tibetan. LC 85-27963. (Orig.). 1986. pap. 25.00 (ISBN 0-87773-360-0). Shambhala Pubns.
Tulku, Tarthang. Kum Nye Relaxation, Vols. 1 & 2. (Nyingma Psychology Ser.). 1978. 14.95 ea. Vol. 1 (ISBN 0-913546-10-0). Vol. 2 (ISBN 0-913546-74-7). pap. 7.95 ea. Vol. 1 (ISBN 0-913546-25-9). Vol. 2 (ISBN 0-913546-75-5). Dharma Pub.
Watts, Alan. The Art of Contemplation. LC 72-10174. 1973. 4.95 (ISBN 0-394-70963-2). Pantheon.

MEDITATIONS

Here are entered works containing thoughts or reflections on spiritual truths. Works on the nature of meditation are entered under the heading Meditation.
see also Devotional Calendars; Devotional Literature; Jesus Christ–Devotional Literature; Spiritual Exercises;
also subdivisions Meditations under Bible, Jesus Christ, Lord's Supper, and similar headings

Adams, George. The Lemniscatory Ruled Surface in Space & Counterspace. Eberhart, Stephen, tr. from Ger. & Eng. (Illus.). 83p. 1979. pap. 9.95x (ISBN 0-686-43395-5, Pub. by Steinerbooks). Anthroposophic.
Addington, Jack & Addington, Cornelia. Your Needs Met. 156p. 1982. pap. 3.95 (ISBN 0-87516-490-0). De Vorss.
The Adept. 1983. pap. 4.95 (ISBN 0-913922-81-1). Dawn Horse Pr.
Alberione, James. Thoughts. 1973. 3.00 (ISBN 0-8198-0332-4). Dghtrs St Paul.
Allen, Charles L. La Siquiatria de Dios. 176p. 1975. 2.95 (ISBN 0-88113-280-2). Edit Betania.
Allen, Milton H. Why Do Good People Suffer? LC 82-82949. 1983. pap. 4.95 (ISBN 0-8054-5208-7). Broadman.
Allen, R. Earl. Let It Begin in Me. LC 84-19934. 1985. pap. 3.75 (ISBN 0-8054-5005-X). Broadman.
Ami Press Staff. The Message of Marienfried: According to Our Lady's Apparitions in 1946. 20p. 1983. 1.00 (ISBN 0-911988-50-5). AMI Pr.
Anandamurti, Shrii Shrii. Namami Krsnasundaram - Salutations to Lord Krsna. 252p. 1981. pap. 4.00 (ISBN 0-686-95432-7). Ananda Marga.
Anandanagar. Caryacarya, Vol. I & II. Vol. I - 37 p. pap. 2.00 (ISBN 0-686-95445-9); Vol. II - 49 p. pap. 1.00 (ISBN 0-686-99507-4). Ananda Marga.
Andersen, Richard. Inspirational Meditations for Sunday Church School Teachers. 1980. pap. 2.25 (ISBN 0-570-03810-3, 12-2919). Concordia.
Anderson, Margaret. Momentos Felices Con Dios. 192p. 1977. 3.95 (ISBN 0-88113-312-4). Edit Betania.
Armstrong, William H. Through Troubled Waters: A Young Father's Struggles with Grief. 96p. (Orig.). 1983. pap. 3.35 (ISBN 0-687-41895-X, Festival). Abingdon.
Arnold, Eberhard, et al. The Heavens Are Opened. LC 73-20715. (Illus.). 190p. 1974. 8.00 (ISBN 0-87486-113-6). Plough.
Arrington, Renee, et al. Voices of Inspiration. 34p. 1982. pap. 3.50 (ISBN 0-939296-04-7). Bond Pub Co.
Ashworth, Mae H. Candles in the Dark. LC 83-70253. 1983. 6.95 (ISBN 0-8054-5256-7). Broadman.
Atkinson, David. The Message of Ruth. LC 84-27785. (Bible Speaks Today Ser.). 128p. 1983. pap. 5.95 (ISBN 0-87784-294-9). Inter-Varsity.
Auden, W. H., et al. What I Believe. Booth, Mark, ed. 182p. 1984. 16.95 (ISBN 0-8245-0676-6); pap. 8.95 (ISBN 0-8245-0677-4). Crossroad NY.
Auer, Jim. Sorting It Out with God. 64p. 1982. pap. 1.95 (ISBN 0-89243-163-6). Liguori Pubns.
Augsburger, David. Caring Enough to Hear & Be Heard. LC 82-81000. (Caring Enough Bks.). 176p. (Orig.). 1982. pap. 4.95 (ISBN 0-8361-3307-2). Herald Pr.
Augustine, Aurelius. What Augustine Says. Geisler, Norman L., ed. 204p. (Orig.). 1982. pap. 8.95 (ISBN 0-8010-0185-4). Baker Bk.
Aurelius, Marcus. Meditations. Grube, G. M. A., ed. & tr. LC 83-22722. (HPC Philosophical Classics Ser.). 170p. 1984. lib. bdg. 16.50 (ISBN 0-915145-78-2); pap. text ed. 4.95 (ISBN 0-915145-79-0). Hackett Pub.
Aurobindo, tr. from Fr. Prayers & Meditations. rev. ed. 380p. (Orig.). 1979. pap. 16.00 (ISBN 0-89744-998-3, Sri Aurobindo Ashram Trust India); text ed. 21.00 (ISBN 0-89744-219-9). Auromere.
Azrael. Wisdom for the New Age. LC 81-85815. 208p. (Orig.). 1982. pap. 6.95 (ISBN 0-87516-477-3). De Vorss.
Bachelard, Gaston. Poetics of Reverie: Childhood, Language & the Cosmos. 1971. pap. 8.95x (ISBN 0-8070-6413-0, BP375). Beacon Pr.
Bachman, John W. Faith That Makes a Difference. LC 83-70508. 128p. (Orig.). 1983. pap. 6.95 (ISBN 0-8066-2014-5, 10-2193). Augsburg.
Backman, Robert L. Take Charge of Your Life. LC 83-70332. 168p. 1983. 7.95 (ISBN 0-87747-970-4). Deseret Bk.
Backus, William & Chaplan, Marie. Digase la Verdad. 1983. 3.75 (ISBN 0-88113-049-4). Edit Betania.
Bahaullah. Prayers & Meditations. Effendi, Shoghi, tr. 1978. 14.95 (ISBN 0-900125-39-X). Baha'i.
Bailey, Barry. Living with the Unexpected. 128p. 1984. 8.95 (ISBN 0-687-22366-0). Abingdon.
Baillie, John. Diario de Oracions Privada. pap. 2.75 (ISBN 0-8358-0412-7). Upper Room.
Baker, Don & Nester, Emery. Depression: Finding Hope & Meaning in Life's Darkest Shadow. LC 82-24609. (Critical Concern Ser.). 1983. 10.95 (ISBN 0-88070-011-4). Multnomah.
Baker, Pat A. In This Moment. LC 76-28802. Repr. of 1977 ed. 23.50 (ISBN 0-8357-9012-6, 2016370). Bks Demand UMI.
Baldwin, Lindley. Samuel Morris. 74p. 1980. 1.50 (ISBN 0-88113-319-1). Edit Betania.
Barclay, William. In the Hands of God. LC 80-25261. 154p. 1981. pap. 4.95 (ISBN 0-664-24362-2). Westminster.
Barker, Peggy. What Happened When Grandma Died. 4.95 (ISBN 0-570-04090-6, 56-1458). Concordia.
Barkman, Alma. Days Remembered. (Illus.). 96p. 1983. pap. 8.95 (ISBN 0-8024-0188-0). Moody.
Barr, Helen W. Thy Word Is True. 1986. 5.75 (ISBN 0-8062-2355-3). Carlton.
Bass, George M. Telling the Whole Story. 1983. 6.95 (ISBN 0-89536-642-8, 2007). CSS of Ohio.
Bauman, Elizabeth. Ascuas de Fuego. Patzan, Flora, tr. Tr. of Coals of Fire. (Span.). 128p. 1982. pap. 3.50 (ISBN 0-8361-3315-3). Herald Pr.
Bell, Martin. The Way of the Wolf. (Epiphany Ser.). 144p. 1983. pap. 2.95 (ISBN 0-345-30522-1). Ballantine.
Bellett, J. G. Short Meditations, 3 vols. pap. 13.95 set (ISBN 0-88172-003-8); pap. 4.95 ea. Believers Bkshelf.
Bellville, Cheryl W. All Things Bright & Beautiful. 64p. (Orig.). 1983. pap. 7.95 (ISBN 0-86683-722-1, AY8363, HarpR). Har-Row.
Benet, Juan. A Meditation. Rabassa, Gregory, tr. from Span. Tr. of Una Meditacion. 366p. 1983. 15.95; pap. 8.95 (ISBN 0-89255-065-1). Persea Bks.
Benjamin, Dick. Should I Tithe? 1977. pap. 1.75 (ISBN 0-911739-11-4). Abbott Loop.
Berry, Joan P. Reflections in a Shop Window. 1983. 4.25 (ISBN 0-89536-605-3, 1817). CSS of Ohio.
Bianco, Enzo. Salesian Cooperators: A Practical Way of Life. Swain, Peter, tr. (Salesian Family Ser.). 40p. 1983. pap. 3.25 (ISBN 0-89944-073-8). Don Bosco Multimedia.
Biggs, Mouzon, Jr. Moments to Hold Close. 144p. 1983. 9.95 (ISBN 0-687-27147-9). Abingdon.

Bimler, Richard W. Grand Opening. 1983. 3.75 (ISBN 0-89536-589-8, 0731). CSS of Ohio.
Bird, Bob. You Are a Special Person. 16p. (Orig.). 1974. pap. 1.50 (ISBN 0-934804-06-0). Inspiration MI.
Bisagno, John R. Love Is Something You Do. LC 75-9314. 1979. pap. 6.95 (ISBN 0-06-060793-9, RD-238, HarpR). Har-Row.
Bishop, Joseph P. The Eye of the Storm. 128p. (Orig.). 1983. pap. 3.95 (ISBN 0-87123-263-4, 210263). Bethany Hse.
Blackwood, Cheryl P. & Slattery, Kathryn. A Bright-Shining Place. (Epiphany Ser.). 240p. 1983. pap. 2.75 (ISBN 0-345-30698-8). Ballantine.
Blanchard, John. Right with God. rev. ed. 126p. 1985. pap. 2.95 (ISBN 0-85151-045-0). Banner of Truth.
Bloom, Anthony. Meditations. 3.95 (ISBN 0-87193-010-2). Dimension Bks.
Bloomfield, Arthur E. Antes de la Ultima Batalla-Armagedon. 192p. 1977. 3.75 (ISBN 0-88113-003-6). Edit Betania.
Bodhi Kalpa. 1978p. pap. 1.00 (ISBN 0-686-95470-X). Ananda Marga.
Bodo, Murray. Song of the Sparrow: Meditations & Poems to Pray by. (Illus.). 187p. (Orig.). 1976. pap. 3.95 (ISBN 0-912228-26-1). St Anthony Mess Pr.
Boff, Leonardo. The Way of the Cross: Way of Justice. Drury, John, tr. from Port. LC 79-23776. Tr. of Via-Sacra Da Justica. 144p. (Orig.). 1980. pap. 4.95 (ISBN 0-88344-701-0). Orbis Bks.
Bohlen, John R. How to Rule the World: Seek First the Kingdom of God. LC 81-90513. (Illus.). 271p. 1982. pap. 3.95 (ISBN 0-9607702-0-8). Kingdom God.
Bolding, Amy. Inspiring Devotions for Church Groups. 144p. 1985. pap. 4.95 (ISBN 0-8010-0889-1). Baker Bk.
--Words of Comfort. (Bolding Library). 132p. 1984. pap. 3.95 (ISBN 0-8010-0860-3). Baker Bk.
Bonar, Andrew. Heavenly Springs. 211p. (Orig.). 1986. pap. 4.95 (ISBN 0-85151-479-0). Banner of Truth.
Bonhoeffer, Dietrich. Meditating on the Word. Gracie, David, ed. & tr. from Ger. LC 86-16839. 152p. (Orig.). 1986. 11.95 (ISBN 0-936384-43-3); pap. 6.95 (ISBN 0-936384-41-7). Cowley Pubns.
Bosch, Henry G. The Gift of a Thorn. (Solace Ser.). 1984. pap. 1.50 (ISBN 0-8010-0866-2). Baker Bk.
--When Burdens Become Bridges. (Solace Ser.). 1984. pap. 1.50 (ISBN 0-8010-0867-0). Baker Bk.
Boulding, Maria. The Coming of God. 224p. 1983. pap. text ed. 9.00 (ISBN 0-8146-1278-4). Liturgical Pr.
Bowness, Charles. The Practice of Meditation 1971. rev. ed. (Paths to Inner Power Ser.). 1979. pap. 3.50 (ISBN 0-85030-182-3). Weiser.
Bradfield, Keith, tr. from Swedish. The Testament of Cain. Bradfield, Kieth. cancelled (ISBN 0-86538-019-8); pap. cancelled (ISBN 0-686-32482-X). Ontario Rev NJ.
Bradford, John. Writings of John Bradford...Martyr, 1555, 2 Vols. Repr. of 1853 ed. Set. 92.00 (ISBN 0-384-05440-4). Johnson Repr.
Bramer, Mary. This Is My Story, This Is My Song. 1984. pap. 6.95 (ISBN 0-570-03923-1, 12-2857). Concordia.
Brandt, L. Meditations on a Loving God. LC 12-2812. 1983. 10.95 (ISBN 0-570-03858-8). Concordia.
Brandt, Leslie F. Bible Reading for the Retired. LC 83-72117. 112p. (Orig.). 1984. pap. 3.95 (ISBN 0-8066-2061-7, 10-0683). Augsburg.
Brenneman, H. G. Meditaciones para la Nueva Madre. 80p. 1982. Repr. of 1978 ed. 2.85 (ISBN 0-311-40032-9). Casa Bautista.
Brenneman, Helen G. Meditaciones para la Nueva Madre. La Valle, Maria T., tr. Tr. of Meditations for the New Mother. (Span., Illus.). 80p. 1978. pap. 2.85 (ISBN 0-8361-1212-1). Herald Pr.
--Morning Joy. LC 80-26449. 80p. 1981. pap. 3.95 (ISBN 0-8361-1942-8). Herald Pr.
--Para la Futura Mama. Tr. of Meditations for the Expectant Mother. (Span.). 80p. 1979. pap. 2.85 (ISBN 0-8361-1216-4). Herald Pr.
Brokering, Herbert. Lord, If. 1977. pap. 2.95 (ISBN 0-570-03046-3, 6-1171). Concordia.
Brokering, Herbert F. Pilgrimage to Renewal. 96p. (Orig.). 1979. pap. 1.95 (ISBN 0-03-053791-6, HarpR). Har-Row.
Brokhoff, Barbara. Bitter-Sweet Recollections. 1983. 6.50 (ISBN 0-89536-638-X, 0238). CSS of Ohio.
Brokke, Harold J. Salvados por Su Vida. 224p. 1978. 2.50 (ISBN 0-88113-317-5). Edit Betania.
Brother Leonard of Taize. Along an Inner Shore: Echoes from the Gospel. 144p. (Orig.). 1986. pap. 8.95 (ISBN 0-8298-0733-0). Pilgrim NY.
Browneye, Ray. Through African Skies. 136p. 1983. pap. 5.95 (ISBN 0-8010-0853-0). Baker Bk.
Bruce, Robert G. & Bruce, Debra F. C.A.R.E.S. 1984. 5.50 (ISBN 0-89536-672-X, 0393). CSS of Ohio.
Bruce, Shelley. Tomorrow Is Today. LC 83-3797. (Illus.). 224p. 1983. 15.95 (ISBN 0-672-52756-1). Bobbs.
Bryant, Al, ed. New Every Morning: Three Hundred Sixty-Six Daily Meditations from Your Favorite Christian Writers. 224p. 1985. 9.95 (ISBN 0-8499-0507-9, 0507-9). Word Bks.
Buchanan, Ray, ed. GLEANINGS: Hunger Meditations for Lent. rev. ed. 112p. pap. 5.50 (ISBN 0-939485-02-8). St Andrew Pr.
Budd, Leonard H. Days Multiplied. 1984. 4.00 (ISBN 0-89536-666-5, 0424). CSS of Ohio.
Buddhist Text Translation Society, tr. from Chinese. Brahma Net Sutra, Vol. II Commentary by Hui Seng, Elder Master. (Illus.). 210p. (Orig.). 1982. pap. 10.00 (ISBN 0-917512-88-X). Buddhist Text.
--Brahma Net Sutra, text only. 70p. (Orig.). 1982. pap. 5.00 (ISBN 0-917512-56-1). Buddhist Text.
Buddhist Text Translation Society Staff, tr. Flower Adornment Sutra, Chapter 22: The Ten Inexhaustible Treasuries Commentary by Tripitka Master Hua. (Illus.). 184p. (Orig.). 1983. pap. 7.00 (ISBN 0-917512-38-3). Buddhist Text.
Buddhist Text Translation Society Staff, tr. from Chinese. Flower Adornment Sutra, Chapter 36: Universal Worthy's Conduct. (Illus.). 75p. (Orig.). 1983. pap. 5.00 (ISBN 0-88139-011-9). Buddhist Text.
--Flower Adornment Sutra, Chapter 39: Entering the Dharma Realm, Part VI. (Illus.). 320p. (Orig.). 1982. pap. 9.00 (ISBN 0-917512-48-0). Buddhist Text.
--Sutra of the Past Vows of Earth Store Bodhisattva. (Illus.). 120p. (Orig.). 1982. pap. 6.00 (ISBN 0-88139-502-1). Buddhist Text.
Buechner, Frederick. Now & Then. LC 82-48413. 128p. 1983. 12.45 (ISBN 0-06-061161-8, HarpR). Har-Row.
--The Sacred Journey. LC 81-47843. 128p. 1982. 12.45 (ISBN 0-06-061158-8, HarpR). Har-Row.
Buhler, Walther. Living with Your Body. Maloney, L., tr. from Ger. Tr. of Der Leib als Instrument der Seele. 117p. (Orig.). 1979. pap. 9.95 (ISBN 0-85440-345-0, Pub. by Steinerbooks). Anthroposophic.
Bull, Henry, ed. Christian Prayers & Holy Meditations. 1842. 21.00 (ISBN 0-384-06285-7). Johnson Repr.
Burke, Dennis. How to Meditate God's Word. 64p. 1982. pap. 2.25 (ISBN 0-89274-241-0, HH-241). Harrison Hse.
Burrows, Ruth. Our Father. (Illus.). 96p. 1986. 5.95 (ISBN 0-87193-255-5). Dimension Bks.
Caddy, Eileen. The Spirit of Findhorn. LC 75-36747. (Illus.). 1979. pap. 7.95 (ISBN 0-06-061291-6, RD 296, HarpR). Har-Row.
Caldwell, Happy. The Word System. 60p. 1981. pap. 1.50 (ISBN 0-89274-176-7). Harrison Hse.
Caldwell, Louis O. Congratulations: A Graduation Remembrance. (Ultra Books). 64p. 1983. 5.95 (ISBN 0-8010-2485-4). Baker Bk.
--Good Morning, Lord: Meditations for Modern Marrieds. (Good Morning Lord Ser.). 1974. 3.95 (ISBN 0-8010-2351-3). Baker Bk.
Camara, Helder. Hoping Against All Hope. O'Connell, Matthew J., tr. from Ger. LC 83-19348. Orig. Title: Hoffer Wider Alle Hoffnung. 96p. (Orig.). 1984. pap. 4.95 (ISBN 0-88344-192-6). Orbis Bks.
Campbell, Roger F. Prosperity in the End Time. 1983. pap. 2.95 (ISBN 0-87508-055-3). Chr Lit.
Capps, Charles. Changing the Seen & Shaping the Unseen. 1980. pap. 1.75 (ISBN 0-89274-165-1). Harrison Hse.
--Success Motivation Through the Word. 272p. 1982. pap. 3.95 (ISBN 0-89274-183-X, HH-183). Harrison Hse.
Cardwell, Julia C. The Moonshine Special. (Illus.). 1983. 5.75 (ISBN 0-8062-1908-4). Carlton.
Carothers, Merlin R. Answers to Praise. 169p. (Orig.). 1972. pap. 4.95 (ISBN 0-943026-07-5). Carothers.
--The Bible on Praise. 32p. (Orig.). 1981. pap. 2.25 (ISBN 0-943026-03-2). Carothers.
--Bringing Heaven into Hell. 120p. (Orig.). 1976. pap. 4.95 (ISBN 0-943026-10-5). Carothers.
--Power in Praise. 143p. 1972. pap. 4.95 (ISBN 0-943026-01-6). Carothers.
--Praise Works. 161p. (Orig.). 1973. pap. 4.95. Carothers.
--Prison to Praise. 106p. (Orig.). 1970. pap. 2.95 (ISBN 0-943026-02-4). Carothers.
--Prison to Praise: Giant Print. 106p. (Orig.). 1970. pap. 3.95 (ISBN 0-943026-08-3). Carothers.
--Victory on Praise Mountain. 175p. (Orig.). 1979. pap. 4.95 (ISBN 0-943026-04-0). Carothers.
--Walking & Leaping. 129p. (Orig.). 1974. pap. 4.95 (ISBN 0-943026-05-9). Carothers.
Carr, Kermit R. Moments to Live By - Years to Enjoy. 1986. 8.95 (ISBN 0-533-06945-9). Vantage.
Carretto, Carlo. Blessed Are You Who Believed. Wall, Barbara, tr. from Ital. LC 82-22504. Tr. of Beata te Che Hai Creduto. (Illus.). 96p. (Orig.). 1983. pap. 4.95 (ISBN 0-88344-038-5). Orbis Bks.
--Summoned by Love. Neame, Alan, tr. from Italian. LC 78-962. Orig. Title: Padre Mio me abbandono a Te. 1978. pap. 5.95 (ISBN 0-88344-472-0). Orbis Bks.
Carroll, Jane. Grace. (Illus.). 28p. 1987. 12.95 (ISBN 1-55523-041-5). Winston-Derek.
Carter, Les. Good 'n' Angry. 128p. 1983. 8.95 (ISBN 0-8010-2488-9); pap. 5.95 (ISBN 0-8010-2481-1). Baker Bk.
Casey, Karen. Love Book. (Hazelden Meditation Ser.). (Illus.). 110p. 1986. pap. 7.00 (ISBN 0-86683-505-9, HarpJ). Har-Row.
--The Love Book. (Hazelden Bks.). scp 7.50t (ISBN 0-317-46481-7). Har-Row.
--The Love Book. (Meditation Ser.). 110p. 1985. 7.95 (ISBN 0-89486-339-8). Hazelden.
--The Lovebook. 110p. 1985. pap. 5.95 (ISBN 0-89486-376-2). Hazelden.
Casey, Karen & Vanceburg, Martha. The Promise of a New Day. (Meditation Ser.). 400p. (Orig.). 1983. text ed. 7.95 (ISBN 0-89486-308-8). Hazelden.
Cecil, Martin. Meditations on the Lord's Prayer. 2nd ed. 1982. 10.95 (ISBN 0-686-27652-3). Cole-Outreach.
Chambers, Oswald. Daily Thoughts-Disciples. 1983. pap. 5.95 (ISBN 0-87508-143-6). Chr Lit.
Charles, Ronal. Street Walkin' (Illus.). 120p. (Orig.). 1986. pap. 9.95 (ISBN 1-55630-020-4). Brentwood Comm.
Chavis, Benjamin F., Jr. Psalms from Prison. 192p. 1983. 10.95 (ISBN 0-8298-0661-X); pap. 7.95 (ISBN 0-8298-0666-0). Pilgrim NY.
Cherubim. 2.25 (ISBN 0-8198-1436-9). Dghtrs St Paul.
Chiampi, Luke. Rebuild My Church. LC 72-87090. 105p. 1972. pap. 0.95 (ISBN 0-8199-0502-X). Franciscan Herald.
Chinmoy, Sri. Beauty-Drops. 51p. (Orig.). 1975. pap. 2.00 (ISBN 0-88497-224-0). Aum Pubns.
--Father's Day: Father with His European Children. 54p. (Orig.). 1976. pap. 2.00 (ISBN 0-88497-297-6). Aum Pubns.
--Inspiration-Garden & Aspiration-Leaves. 58p. (Orig.). 1977. pap. 2.00 (ISBN 0-88497-379-4). Aum Pubns.
--Justice-Light & Satisfaction-Delight. (Soulful Questions & Fruitful Answers on Law & Justice). 41p. (Orig.). 1977. pap. 2.00 (ISBN 0-88497-338-7). Aum Pubns.
--The Significance of a Smile. 52p. (Orig.). 1977. pap. 2.00 (ISBN 0-88497-367-0). Aum Pubns.
--The Silence of Death. (Illus.). 46p. (Orig.). 1973. pap. 2.00 (ISBN 0-88497-035-3). Aum Pubns.
--Something, Somehow, Somewhere, Someday. 70p. (Orig.). 1973. pap. 2.00 (ISBN 0-88497-025-6). Aum Pubns.
Chinn, Edward. The Wonder of Words, Bk. 2. (Orig.). 1987. pap. 7.50 (ISBN 0-88028-059-X, Co-Pub. by CSS of OH). Forward Movement.
Christensen, Ronald. The Death of Plato, the Aftermath. vii, 120p. 1983. lib. bdg. 8.95 (ISBN 0-938876-18-X). Entropy Ltd.
Christenson, Evelyn. Cambiame, Senor! 224p. 1980. 3.25 (ISBN 0-88113-035-4). Edit Betania.
--Perder Para Ganar. 1983. 3.75 (ISBN 0-88113-243-8). Edit Betania.
Christenson, Larry. Hacia Donde Va la Familia? 32p. 1978. 1.00 (ISBN 0-88113-110-5). Edit Betania.
--La Mente Renovada. 128p. 1975. 2.50 (ISBN 0-88113-199-7). Edit Betania.
--La Pareja Cristiana. 1982. 3.75 (ISBN 0-88113-314-0). Edit Betania.
Christopher. Our New Age: Words for the People. 1st ed. LC 77-72309. (Illus., Orig.). 1977. pap. 2.95 (ISBN 0-916940-01-2). World Light.
Clapp, Steve. Shalom: Hope for the World. 178p. (Orig.). 1982. pap. 8.00 (ISBN 0-914527-35-5). C-Four Res.
Clark, Miles. Glenn Clark: His Life & Writings. LC 75-6877. Repr. of 1975 ed. 30.40 (ISBN 0-8357-9008-8, 2016361). Bks Demand UMI.
Clark, Ovilene. Heirloom of Memories. 1983. 8.50 (ISBN 0-8062-2137-2). Carlton.
Cloyd, Betty S. Glory Beyond All Comparison. LC 81-52216. 1981. pap. 4.50x (ISBN 0-8358-0423-2). Upper Room.
Coburn, John B. Feeding Fire. LC 80-81103. 62p. 1980. 8.95 (ISBN 0-8192-1281-4). Morehouse.
Coffey, Thomas P. There Is a Singing Underneath: Meditations in Central Park. 128p. 1985. pap. 4.95 (ISBN 0-87193-217-2). Dimension Bks.
Cohen, Leonard. Book of Mercy. LC 84-40174. 88p. 1984. 9.95 (ISBN 0-394-53949-4, Pub. by Villard Bks). Random.
Coleman, William L. Escucha a los Animales. 144p. 1981. 3.25 (ISBN 0-88113-063-X). Edit Betania.
--Mi Maquina Maravillosa. 144p. 1982. 3.25 (ISBN 0-88113-309-4). Edit Betania.
Coleman, William V. Prayer-Talk: Casual Conversations with God. LC 82-74085. 112p. (Orig.). 1983. pap. 3.95 (ISBN 0-87793-265-4). Ave Maria.
Colman, Henry, ed. Divine Meditations (Sixteen Forty) 1979. 27.50x (ISBN 0-300-02305-7). Yale U Pr.
Colton, C. E. The Faithfulness of Faith. LC 85-9845. 1985. pap. 4.95 (ISBN 0-8054-1534-3). Broadman.
Connor, Paula. Walking in the Garden: Inner Peace from the Flowers of God. (Illus.). 170p. 1984. 14.95 (ISBN 0-13-944280-4); pap. 5.95 (ISBN 0-13-944264-2). P-H.
Cook, Charles, ed. Daily Meditations for Prayer. Gift Ed. 9.95 (ISBN 0-89107-160-1). Good News.
Cooke, Grace. The Illumined Ones. (Illus.). 1966. pap. 6.95 (ISBN 0-85487-058-X). De Vorss.
Corcoran, Paul A. With All Due Respect. 1983. 4.50 (ISBN 0-89536-609-6, 2354). CSS of Ohio.
Cornwall, Judson. La Alabanza Que Libera. 160p. 1976. 2.75 (ISBN 0-88113-002-8). Edit Betania.
--Give Me-Make Me. LC 79-64976. 1979. 1.25 (ISBN 0-88270-387-0). Bridge Pub.
Correu, Larry M., ed. The Best of These Days. LC 82-13415. 132p. 1983. 8.95 (ISBN 0-664-21391-X). Westminster.
Costello, Andrew. Thank God It's Friday: Meditations For Hard-Working Catholics. 1987. 12.95 (ISBN 0-88347-213-9). Thomas More.
Courtney, Ragan. Meditations for the Suddenly Single. pap. 5.95 (ISBN 0-310-70301-8). Zondervan.
Cowman, Mrs. Charles E. Cumbres De Inspiracion. Robleto, Adolfo, tr. 1982. pap. 4.25 (ISBN 0-311-40026-4). Casa Bautista.
Cox, Frank L. Bedside Meditations. 1967. pap. 2.00 (ISBN 0-88027-000-4). Firm Foun Pub.
Crabtree, Charles T. This I Believe. LC 81-84913. 160p. (Orig.). 1982. pap. 2.95 (ISBN 0-88243-758-5, 02-0758). Gospel Pub.
Crawley-Boevey, Mateo. Meditaciones. (Span.). 1978. plastic bdg. 2.00 (ISBN 0-8198-4706-2). Dghtrs St Paul.
Creme, Benjamin. Messages from Maitreya the Christ, Vol. 1. LC 80-52483. 209p. 1980. pap. 5.00 (ISBN 0-936604-01-8). Tara Ctr.
--The Reappearance of the Christ & the Masters of Wisdom. LC 80-50639. 253p. 1980. pap. 6.00 (ISBN 0-936604-00-X). Tara Ctr.
--Transmission: A Meditation for the New Age. rev. ed. 100p. 1985. pap. 3.50 (ISBN 0-936604-06-9). Tara Ctr.
Cristo Vive en Me. (Span. & Eng.). pap. text ed. 2.00 (ISBN 0-8198-1426-1); 1.00 (ISBN 0-8198-1427-X). Dghtrs St Paul.
Crossman, Eileen. Mountain Rain. 1982. pap. 3.95 (ISBN 9971-972-05-0). OMF Bks.
Cruden, Alexander. Cruden's Concordance. Eadie, ed. 1982. pap. 7.95 (ISBN 0-89081-362-0). Harvest Hse.
Cuffee, James W. Spiritual Automobile. Knickerbocker, Charles, ed. 44p. 1980. 4.75 (ISBN 0-682-48997-2). Exposition Pr FL.
Cushing, Richard J. Meditations for Religious. 1959. 3.00 (ISBN 0-8198-0102-X). Dghtrs St Paul.
Custodio, Sidney & Dudley, Cliff. Love-Hungry Priest. LC 82-61308. 192p. (Orig.). 1983. pap. 2.95 (ISBN 0-89221-099-0). New Leaf.
Dahl, Dolores. Where Heavens Hide. LC 84-51375. (Illus.). 48p. (Orig.). 1984. pap. 3.95 (ISBN 0-9608960-2-3). Single Vision.
Daily Meditations. 3.95 (ISBN 0-8198-1812-7); 2.95 (ISBN 0-8198-2315-5). Dghtrs St Paul.
D'Angelo, Louise. Too Busy for God? Think Again! LC 81-52423. 120p. 1981. pap. 2.50 (ISBN 0-89555-166-7). TAN Bks Pubs.
Dao, Wong Ming. Stone Made Smooth. 1982. pap. 5.95 (ISBN 0-907821-00-6). OMF Bks.
Davis, Burnie. How to Activate Miracles in Your Life & Ministry. 125p. 1982. pap. 3.95 (ISBN 0-89274-230-5, HH-230). Harrison Hse.
Davis, Melodie M. For the Next Nine Months: Meditations for Expectant Mothers. 256p. 1983. pap. 3.95 (ISBN 0-310-45542-1, 12477P). Zondervan.
Dawn, Marva J. I'm Lonely Lord-How Long? The Psalms for Today. LC 83-47721. 176p. 1984. 12.45 (ISBN 0-06-067201-3, HarpR). Har-Row.
Day by Day: Daily Meditations for Young Adults. (Hazelden Meditation Ser.). 1986. 5.95 (ISBN 0-317-46280-6). Har-Row.

Day by Day: Daily Meditations for Young Adults. (Hazelden Bks.). scp 5.95t (ISBN 0-317-46482-5). Har-Row.
Deal, William S. The Other Shepherd. 1982. 1.95 (ISBN 0-686-38053-3). Crusade Pubs.
Deffner, Donald. Please Talk to Me, God! (Continued Applied Christianity). 1983. pap. 4.95 (ISBN 0-570-03899-5, 12-2981). Concordia.
DeHaan, Richard W. & Bosch, Henry G. Our Daily Bread Favorites. rev. ed. 384p. 1986. pap. 9.95 large print ed. (ISBN 0-310-25877-4, 12587L). Zondervan.
Delaney, Sue. The Lord, the Lion & Mutn. pap. 0.95 (ISBN 0-89985-995-X). Christ Nations.
--Mutu Finds the Way to Heaven. pap. 0.95 (ISBN 0-89985-996-8). Christ Nations.
Dellinger, Annetta. You Are Special to Jesus. 1984. pap. 4.95 (ISBN 0-570-04089-2, 56-1457). Concordia.
DeMello, Anthony. Wellsprings: A Book of Spiritual Exercises. LC 84-13655. 216p. 1985. 13.95 (ISBN 0-385-19616-4). Doubleday.
Dennett, E. The Step I Have Taken. Daniel, R. P., ed. 53p. pap. 3.50 (ISBN 0-88172-140-9). Believers Bkshelf.
De Patterson, Paulina G. Te Damos Gracias, Dios. (Illus.). 28p. 1981. pap. 0.60 (ISBN 0-311-38508-7). Casa Bautista.
Dertinger, Charles J. Reflections. 1983. write for info. (ISBN 0-8062-2043-0). Carlton.
De Summers, Jessica. Gozo Al Grecer. 48p. 1981. pap. 1.10 (ISBN 0-311-38550-8, Edit Mundo). Casa Bautista.
Dickson, Albert A. Fascination of Faith. Keith, Gerald, ed. 268p. (Orig.). 1980. pap. 4.95x (ISBN 0-9604080-0-2). Gloria Pubs.
Dieleman, Dale, compiled by. The Praise Book. 1984. pap. 5.95 (ISBN 0-8010-2947-3). Baker Bk.
Dillow, Linda. La Esposa Virtuosa. 160p. 1981. 2.95 (ISBN 0-88113-064-8). Edit Betania.
Dios Padre Envia a Su Hijo. (Span. & Eng.). pap. text ed. 2.00 (ISBN 0-8198-1806-2); 1.00 (ISBN 0-8198-1807-0). Dghtrs St Paul.
Dobson, James. Preparemonos para la Adolescencia. 192p. 1981. 3.25 (ISBN 0-88113-253-5). Edit Betania.
Doerffler, Alfred. The Mind at Ease. rev. ed. LC 75-43869. (Large Print Ser.). 104p. 1976. pap. 5.50 (ISBN 0-570-03040-4, 6-1163). Concordia.
Doering, Jeanne. The Power of Encouragement. 176p. (Orig.). 1983. pap. 5.95 (ISBN 0-8024-0146-5). Moody.
Doherty, Catherine D. Doubts, Loneliness & Rejection. LC 81-19115. (Illus.). 93p. 1982. pap. 4.50 (ISBN 0-8189-0419-4). Alba.
Donne, John. Devotions upon Emergent Occasions. Bd. with Death's Duel. 1959. pap. 7.95 (ISBN 0-472-06030-9, 30, AA). U of Mich Pr.
--Devotions upon Emergent Occasions. Raspa, Anthony, ed. LC 76-361973. pap. 62.00 (ISBN 0-317-26281-5, 2024263). Bks Demand UMI.
Dowman, Kieth, tr. The Divine Madman: The Sublime Life & Songs of Drukpa Kunley. (Illus.). 180p. 1982. pap. 8.95 (ISBN 0-913922-75-7). Dawn Horse Pr.
Doyle, Brendan. Meditations with TM Julian of Norwich. LC 82-73955. (Meditations with TM). (Illus.). 135p. (Orig.). 1983. pap. 6.95 (ISBN 0-939680-11-4). Bear & Co.
The Dream of Ravan. (Institute of World Culture Ser.). 99p. pap. 8.75 (ISBN 0-88695-015-5). Concord Grove.
Drescher, John M. Spirit Fruit. rev. ed. LC 73-21660. 352p. 1978. pap. 8.95 (ISBN 0-8361-1867-7). Herald Pr.
Dresselhaus, Richard L. The Joy of Belonging. LC 78-66868. (Radiant Life Ser.). 128p. 1978. pap. 2.50 (ISBN 0-88243-526-4, 02-0526); tchr's ed. 3.95 (ISBN 0-88243-186-2, 32-0186). Gospel Pub.
Drummond, Lewis A. The Revived Life. LC 82-71217. 1982. pap. 6.50 (ISBN 0-8054-5205-2). Broadman.
Dubay, Thomas. Dawn of a Consecration. 1964. 4.00 (ISBN 0-8198-0034-1). Dghtrs St Paul.
Duda, William J. The Last Testament. 1987. 7.95 (ISBN 0-533-07114-3). Vantage.
Dunlap, Shirlee. Circle of Light. (Illus.). 183p. (Orig.). 1982. pap. 7.95 (ISBN 0-942494-19-9). Coleman Pub.
Dunne, John S. The Church of the Poor Devil: Reflections on a Riverboat Voyage & a Spiritual Journey. LC 83-14548. 1983. pap. text ed. 6.95 (ISBN 0-268-00746-2, 85-07469). U of Notre Dame Pr.
Eastman, Dick. Hour That Changes the World. (Direction Bks.). pap. 2.50 (ISBN 0-8010-3337-3). Baker Bk.
Edgar, Carlson M. The Classic Christian Faith: Chapel Meditations Based on Luther's Small Catechism. LC 59-9093. pap. 42.80 (2026912). Bks Demand UMI.
Edwards, Katherine. A House Divided. 144p. 1984. pap. 4.95 (ISBN 0-310-43501-3, 11169P). Zondervan.
Elliot, Elisabeth. As We Forgive Those. 16p. 1982. pap. 1.25 (ISBN 0-89107-255-1). Good News.
--No Graven Image. LC 81-71346. 256p. 1982. pap. 5.95 (ISBN 0-89107-235-7, Crossway Bks). Good News.
Ellis, Charles & Ellis, Norma. Wells of Salvation: Meditations of Isaiah. 224p. (Orig.). 1986. pap. 5.95 (ISBN 0-85151-457-X). Banner of Truth.
Elmo, Francis, tr. from Span. I, in Christ Arisen. LC 81-85745. Orig. Title: Yo, en Cristo Resucitado. 100p. 1982. pap. 4.00 (ISBN 0-9607590-0-X). Action Life Pubns.
El Morya. Morya. Prophet, Elizabeth C., ed. LC 81-85570. 412p. 1982. pap. 9.95 (ISBN 0-916766-52-7). Summit Univ.
Elvey, Linda B. Where Do I Go from Here. 1983. 6.00 (ISBN 0-8062-2194-1). Carlton.
Emswiler, Tom N. The Click in the Clock: Meditations for Junior Highs. LC 81-11875. 128p. (Orig.). 1981. pap. 5.95 (ISBN 0-8298-0470-6). Pilgrim NY.
Engstrom, Ted W. Un Lider No Nace, Se Hace. 256p. 1980. 4.25 (ISBN 0-88113-330-2). Edit Betania.
Envia Senor Tu Espiritu. (Span.). 3.00 (ISBN 0-8198-2302-3); 2.00 (ISBN 0-8198-2303-1). Dghtrs St Paul.
Erickson, Kenneth. The Power of Praise. 1984. pap. 4.95 (ISBN 0-570-03925-8, 12-2859). Concordia.
Escriva de Balaguer, Josemaria. The Way. Orig. Title: Camino. 1979. pap. 4.95 (ISBN 0-933932-01-4). Scepter Pubs.
Estrello, Francisco E. Senderos de Comunion. 1.75 (ISBN 0-8358-0416-X). Upper Room.
Etchison, Birdie L. Don't Drop the Sugar Bowl in the Sink! LC 84-80057. 144p. 1984. pap. 4.50 (ISBN 0-88243-485-3, 02-0485). Gospel Pub.
Evely, Louis. That Man Is You. Bonin, Edmond, tr. LC 63-23494. 297p. 1964. pap. 4.95 (ISBN 0-8091-1697-9). Paulist Pr.
Failing, George E. Secure & Rejoicing. 1980. 0.95 (ISBN 0-937296-03-1, 223-A). Presence Inc.
Fankhauser, Jerry. The Power of Affirmations. 56p. 1979. pap. 8.00 (ISBN 0-9617006-1-0). J Fankhauser.
Far West Editions. Speaking of My Life. 149p. 1979. pap. 4.95 (ISBN 0-686-47084-2). Far West Edns.
Farish, Starr. Voice of Silence. 5th ed. (Illus.). 119p. 1983. pap. 6.95 (ISBN 0-9605492-2-6). Touch Heart.
Farrell, Pat. Time for Me. (Everyday Ser.). (Illus.). 26p. (Orig.). 1983. pap. 3.00 (ISBN 0-915517-01-9). Everyday Ser.
Fator, Sue. The Adventures of Timoteo. pap. 1.25 (ISBN 0-89985-992-5). Christ Nations.
Featherstone, Vaughn J. Purity of Heart. LC 82-72728. 103p. 1982. 8.95 (ISBN 0-87747-914-3). Deseret Bk.
Ferguson, Sinclair B. Discovering God's Will. 125p. (Orig.). 1981. pap. 3.95 (ISBN 0-85151-334-4). Banner of Truth.
Fernandez, D. S. Los Falsos Testigos De Jehova. 46p. 1985. pap. 1.25 (ISBN 0-311-06351-9). Casa Bautista.
Fillmore, Charles. Jesucristo Sana (Jesus Christ Heals) (Span.). 200p. 1984. 5.95 (ISBN 0-87159-071-9). Unity School.
Finney, Charles G. Answers to Prayer. Parkhurst, Louis G., Jr., ed. LC 83-12253. 122p. (Orig.). 1983. pap. 3.95 (ISBN 0-87123-296-0). Bethany Hse.
--Principles of Prayer. Parkhurst, L. G., ed. LC 80-17856. 112p. (Orig.). 1980. pap. 3.95 (ISBN 0-87123-468-8, 210468). Bethany Hse.
Fischer, John. Dark Horse: The Story of a Winner. LC 83-11411. 100p. 1983. pap. 3.95 (ISBN 0-88070-016-5). Multnomah.
Fitzgerald, Ernest A. Diamonds Everywhere: Appreciating God's Gifts. 112p. (Orig.). 1983. pap. 7.75 (ISBN 0-687-10734-2). Abingdon.
Fleming, David L. Modern Spiritual Exercises: A Contemporary Reading of the Spiritual Exercises of St. Ignatius. LC 82-46055. 152p. 1983. pap. 3.95 (ISBN 0-385-18853-6, Im). Doubleday.
Floyd, Carol M. Anybody Listening? 1982. 2.50 (ISBN 0-89536-572-3, 0119). CSS of Ohio.
Folliet, Joseph. The Evening Sun. 183p. 1983. 12.50 (ISBN 0-8199-0817-7). Franciscan Herald.
Food for Thought: Daily Meditations for Overeaters. (Hazelden Bks.). scp 6.50t (ISBN 0-317-46482-5). Har-Row.
Ford, L. The Christian Persuader. LC 66-22043. 160p. 1976. pap. 6.00 (ISBN 0-06-062679-8, RD/157, HarpR). Har-Row.
Foreman, Max L. Rx for Living: Take as Needed. 1982. 20.00x (ISBN 0-8197-0490-3). Bloch.
Foust, Paul & Kortals, Richard. Reach Out. 1984. pap. 3.95 (ISBN 0-570-03933-9, 12-2868). Concordia.
Fox, Matt & Swimme, Brian. Manifesto for a Global Civilization. LC 82-71450. 54p. (Orig.). 1982. pap. 3.95 (ISBN 0-939680-05-X). Bear & Co.
Fox, Matthew. Meditations with TM Meister Eckhart. LC 82-71451. (Meditations with TM Ser.). (Illus.). 131p. (Orig.). 1982. pap. 6.95 (ISBN 0-939680-04-1). Bear & Co.
--Western Spirituality: Historical Roots, Ecumenical Routes. LC 81-67364. 440p. 1981. pap. 11.95 (ISBN 0-939680-01-7). Bear & Co.
--Whee! We, Wee All the Way Home: A Guide to a Sensual Prophetic Spirituality. LC 81-67365. 257p. 1981. pap. 8.95 (ISBN 0-939680-00-9). Bear & Co.
Francois De Sales. Oeuvres: Introduction a la Vie Devote & Traite de l'Amour de Dieu, etc. (Saint). 2024p. 46.95 (ISBN 0-686-56512-6). French & Eur.
Frank, Loraine C. My Book of Gold & Other Writings. 1987. 6.95 (ISBN 0-533-07072-4). Vantage.
Freeman, James D. Of Time & Eternity. LC 81-51069. 200p. 1981. 5.95 (ISBN 0-87159-122-7). Unity School.
Freeman, Lucy, ed. Listening to the Inner Self. LC 83-9988. 206p. 1984. 20.00 (ISBN 0-87668-640-4). Aronson.
Freeman, Nona. This Is the Day. Clanton, Charles, ed. 256p. (Orig.). 1978. pap. 4.95 (ISBN 0-912315-36-9). Word Aflame.
Freeman, Sean. Parables, Psalms, Prayers. 1985. 10.95 (ISBN 0-88347-185-X). Thomas More.
Frost, Gerhard. Homing in the Presence: Meditations for Daily Living. 125p. 1978. pap. 5.95 (ISBN 0-86683-756-6, HarpR). Har-Row.
Frost, Gerhard E. Kept Moments. 96p. (Orig.). 1982. pap. 5.95 (ISBN 0-86683-668-3, HarpR). Har-Row.
Fullman, Everett L. Living the Lord's Prayer. (Epiphany Ser.). 128p. 1983. pap. 2.50 (ISBN 0-345-30432-2). Ballantine.
Funk, Robert W. Parables & Presence. LC 82-71827. 224p. 1982. 3.00 (ISBN 0-8006-0688-4, 1-688). Fortress.
Furlong, Monica. Contemplating Now. LC 83-70991. 128p. 1983. pap. 6.00 (ISBN 0-936384-13-1). Cowley Pubns.
Gabriel. Divine Intimacy, Vol. II. 1983. 12.95 (ISBN 0-87193-201-6). Dimension Bks.
--Divine Intimacy, Vol. IV. 12.95 (ISBN 0-87193-204-0). Dimension Bks.
Galloway, Dale E. Una Nueva Ilusion. Ward, Rhode F., tr. Tr. of Dream a New Dream. (Span.). 169p. 1982. pap. 3.95 (ISBN 0-89922-158-0). Edit Caribe.
Garver. Stars in the Night. pap. 2.50 (ISBN 0-935120-01-7). Christs Mission.
Gayatri. (Illus.). 1983. pap. 3.00 (ISBN 0-938924-14-1). Sri Shirdi Sai.
Gaylor, Anne N. Lead Us Not into Penn Station. 1983. 5.00 (ISBN 0-318-00995-1). Freedom Rel Found.
Getz, Gene A. Looking up When You Feel Down Based on Ephesians 1-3. LC 85-2041. 158p. 1985. pap. 5.95 (ISBN 0-8307-1028-0, 5418463). Regal.
Gibb, C. C. More Than Enough. 83p. pap. 4.95 (ISBN 0-88172-071-2). Believers Bkshelf.
Gibble, Kenneth L. Yeast, Salt & Secret Agents. 1979. pap. 4.95 (ISBN 0-87178-968-X). Brethren.
Gibson, John. The Book of Hu & the Book of Tyana. LC 84-19096. (Illus.). 136p. 1984. 15.00 (ISBN 0-8022-2449-0). Philos Lib.
Giles, Mary E. The Poetics of Love: Meditations with John of the Cross. (American University Studies VII-Theology & Religion). 177p. 1987. text ed. 20.00 (ISBN 0-8204-0321-0). P Lang Pubs.
Gillet, Lev. In Thy Presence. LC 77-1040. 144p. 1977. pap. 3.95 (ISBN 0-913836-34-6). St Vladimirs.
Gilmore, G. Don. No Matter How Dark, the Valley: The Power of Faith in Times of Need. LC 81-48208. 141p. 1982. pap. 7.64 (ISBN 0-06-063121-X, RD-391, HarpR). Har-Row.
Gittner, Louis. There Is a Rainbow. (Illus.). 65p. (Orig.). 1981. pap. 5.95 (ISBN 0-9605492-1-8). Touch Heart.
Glick, Ferne P. & Pellman, Donald R. Breaking Silence: A Family Grows with Deafness. LC 82-6067. 208p. (Orig.). 1982. pap. 6.95 (ISBN 0-8361-3300-5). Herald Pr.
Gliner, Bob. Beyond Coping. 273p. (Orig.). 1982. pap. 5.95x (ISBN 0-910029-01-6). Dell.
Goldsmith, Joel S. Joel Goldsmith's Gift of Love. LC 82-11891. 96p. 1983. 8.95 (ISBN 0-686-92026-0, HarpR). Har-Row.
Grant, Myrna. La Jornada. 208p. 1980. 1.00 (ISBN 0-88113-200-4). Edit Betania.
--Vanya. 208p. 1976. 3.25 (ISBN 0-88113-310-8). Edit Betania.
Greene, Barbara & Gollancz, Victor, eds. God of a Hundred Names: Prayers & Meditations from Many Faiths & Cultures. 304p. 1985. pap. 7.95 (ISBN 0-575-03645-1, Pub. by Gollancz England). David & Charles.
Greene, Michael H. Program Your Own Life. 230p. 1982. 10.00 (ISBN 0-9610136-0-5). Behavorial Sys Inc.
Greenfield, Guy. We Need Each Other. 1984. 8.95 (ISBN 0-8010-3799-9); pap. 5.95 (ISBN 0-8010-3800-6). Baker Bk.
Griffiths, Michael. What on Earth Are You Doing? 1983. pap. 4.95 (ISBN 0-8010-3792-1). Baker Bk.
Groseclose, Kel. Coming up Short in a Tall World. (Illus.). 144p. 1984. pap. 3.95 (ISBN 0-87123-435-1). Bethany Hse.
Gvillo, Doris. Musing, Meditations, & Meanderings. 1984. 5.95 (ISBN 0-89536-982-6, 7531). CSS of Ohio.
Gyldenvand, Lily M. Joy in His Presence: Christian Reflections on Everyday Life. LC 81-67806. 112p. (Orig.). 1981. pap. 4.95 (ISBN 0-8066-1896-5, 10-3596). Augsburg.
Hagin, Kenneth, Jr. The Past Tense of God's Word. 1980. pap. 0.50 mini bk. (ISBN 0-89276-706-5). Hagin Ministries.
Hakes, Thomas L., ed. Mother Nature & Beauty, Vol. 1. 16p. 1984. pap. 3.25x (ISBN 0-915020-17-3). Bardic.
Hallesby, O. God's Word for Today: A Daily Devotional for the Whole Year. Carlsen, Clarence J., tr. LC 78-67940. 1979. pap. 5.95 (ISBN 0-8066-1682-2, 10-2741). Augsburg.
Hames. Deeper Things. pap. 2.95 (ISBN 0-686-12864-8). Schmul Pub Co.
Hammes, John A. In Praise of God: The Rosary in Scriptural Meditation. 154p. 1983. 1.98 (ISBN 0-911988-51-3). Ami Pr.
Hammond, Beth. Lord, Help Me! The Desperate Dieter. (Continued Applied Christianity Ser.). 1983. pap. 4.50 (ISBN 0-570-03896-0, 12-2978). Concordia.
Hansen, Paul H. All God's Children Got Dreams. (Orig.). 1980. pap. 2.95 (ISBN 0-937172-03-0). JLJ Pubs.
Hanson, Muriel. Honey & Salt. 2nd ed. LC 78-185512. 1971. pap. text ed. 1.50 (ISBN 0-911802-26-6). Free Church Pubns.
Hanson, Richard S. The Comings of God: Meditations for the Advent Season. LC 81-65645. 128p. (Orig.). 1981. pap. 5.95 (ISBN 0-8066-1881-7, 10-1590). Augsburg.
Harakas, Emily. Daily Lenten Meditations for Orthodox Christians. 1983. pap. 2.95 (ISBN 0-937032-27-1). Light&Life Pub Co MN.
Haring, Bernard. Heart of Jesus: Symbol of Redeeming Love. 160p. 1983. pap. 4.25 (ISBN 0-89243-191-1). Liguori Pubns.
Harless, Dan. Discoveries. 1982. pap. 4.95 (ISBN 0-89225-207-3). Gospel Advocate.
Harper, Michael. Poder para Vencer. 1982. 2.95 (ISBN 0-88113-245-4). Edit Betania.
Harrison, Norman B. His Comfort. 1973. pap. 0.75 (ISBN 0-911802-32-0). Free Church Pubns.
--His Joy. 1973. pap. 0.75 (ISBN 0-911802-35-5). Free Church Pubns.
--His Peace. 1972. pap. 0.75 (ISBN 0-911802-29-0). Free Church Pubns.
--Suffering. 1965. pap. 0.75 (ISBN 0-911802-34-7). Free Church Pubns.
Havner, Vance. Don't Miss Your Miracle. 74p. 1984. pap. 4.95 (ISBN 0-8010-4280-1). Baker Bk.
Hayden, Marshall. Two Hundred Stewardship Meditations. 112p. (Orig.). 1984. pap. 3.95 (ISBN 0-87239-780-7, 3034). Standard Pub.
Hayes, Helen. A Gathering of Hope. LC 83-1728. 112p. 1983. 9.95 (ISBN 0-8006-0705-8). Fortress.
Hayes, Norvel. The Seven Ways Jesus Heals. 142p. (Orig.). 1982. pap. 4.95 (ISBN 0-89274-235-6, HH-235). Harrison Hse.
Hayhurst, Emma L. I Will. 2nd ed. 1982. pap. 4.95 (ISBN 0-938736-09-4). Life Enrich.
Hayner, Jerry. God's Best to You. LC 81-71257. 1982. pap. 5.95 (ISBN 0-8054-5192-7). Broadman.
Haynes-Klassen, Joanne. Learning to Live, Learning to Love: A Book about You, A Book about Everyone. (Illus.). 150p. 1984. pap. 7.95 (ISBN 0-915190-38-9). Jalmar Pr.
Hays, Edward. Pray All Ways. LC 81-69329. (Illus.). 164p. (Orig.). 1981. pap. 7.95 (ISBN 0-939516-01-2). Forest Peace.
Hazelden Foundation Staff. Food for Thought. 400p. (Orig.). 1985. pap. 5.95 (ISBN 0-86683-503-2, HarpR). Har-Row.
He Carried Our Sorrows. (Illus.). 48p. 1983. 7.95 (ISBN 0-86683-746-9, AY8399, HarpR). Har-Row.
Hedeman, Robert. Arnold, Heaven's Loudest Angel. 1982. 3.75 (ISBN 0-89536-549-9, 0103). CSS of Ohio.
Hegre, T. A. Libre Para Vivir. 96p. 1964. 2.25 (ISBN 0-88113-020-6). Edit Betania.
--La Vida Que Nace de la Muerte. 272p. 1977. 2.95 (ISBN 0-88113-311-6). Edit Betania.
Hein, Marvin. The Ties That Bind: Moorings of a Life with God. LC 80-81705. 135p. (Orig.). 1980. pap. 5.95 (ISBN 0-937364-04-5). Kindred Pr.
Heline, Corinne. Healing & Regeneration Through Color & Music. 96p. 1983. pap. 3.95 (ISBN 0-87516-512-5). DE Vorss.
Hendricks, Howard. Las Familias Conviven Mejor con Amor. 48p. 1979. 1.65 (ISBN 0-88113-095-8). Edit Betania.

Hepburn, Daisy. Lead, Follow or Get Out of the Way! LC 81-84568. (Orig.). 1982. pap. 4.95 (ISBN 0-8307-0822-7, 5416209); Resource Manual o.p. 5.95 (ISBN 0-8307-0872-3, 5202802). Regal.
Hermanson, Renee. Here or Nowhere. LC 83-51401. 128p. (Orig.). 1984. pap. 5.50 (ISBN 0-8358-0478-X). Upper Room.
Hernandez, David & Page, Carole G. La Familia del Cirujano. 272p. 1982. 3.50 (ISBN 0-88113-090-7). Edit Betania.
Hersey, Jean. The Touch of the Earth. 396p. 1985. pap. 10.95 large print ed. (ISBN 0-8027-2481-7). Walker & Co.
Hicks, Robert F. The Gift of Faithfulness. Jenkins, Simon, ed. (The Gift of... Ser.). (Illus.). 24p. 1984. pap. 1.25 (ISBN 0-687-14700-X). Abingdon.
--The Gift of Gentleness. Jenkins, Simon, ed. (The Gift of... Ser.). (Illus.). 24p. 1984. pap. 1.25 (ISBN 0-687-14703-4). Abingdon.
--The Gift of Joy. Jenkins, Simon, ed. (The Gift of... Ser.). 24p. 1984. pap. 1.25 (ISBN 0-687-14704-2). Abingdon.
--The Gift of Love. Jenkins, Simon, ed. (The Gift of... Ser.). (Illus.). 24p. 1984. pap. 1.25 (ISBN 0-687-14705-0). Abingdon.
--The Gift of Patience. Jenkins, Simon, ed. (The Gift of... Ser.). (Illus.). 24p. 1984. pap. 1.25 (ISBN 0-687-14699-2). Abingdon.
--The Gift of Peace. Jenkins, Simon, ed. (The Gift of... Ser.). (Illus.). 24p. 1984. pap. 1.25 (ISBN 0-687-14701-8). Abingdon.
--The Gift of Self-Control. Jenkins, Simon, ed. (The Gift of... Ser.). (Illus.). 24p. 1984. pap. 1.25 (ISBN 0-687-14697-6). Abingdon.
Hifler, Joyce S. Put Your Mind at Ease. 128p. (Orig.). 1983. pap. 7.75 (ISBN 0-687-34929-X). Abingdon.
Hinton, Pat C. Images of Peace. 96p. 1983. pap. 4.95 (ISBN 0-86683-748-5, HarpR). Har-Row.
Hodgson, Joan. Our Father. (Illus.). 1977. pap. 2.95 (ISBN 0-85487-040-7). De Vorss.
Hoefler, Richard C. With Wings of Eagles. 1983. 5.35 (ISBN 0-89536-624-X, 2352). CSS of Ohio.
Hong, Edna. The Downward Ascent. LC 78-66942. 1979. pap. 5.95 (ISBN 0-8066-1679-2, 10-1955). Augsburg.
Hopkins, Jeffrey. Meditation on Emptiness. Napper, Elizabeth, ed. (Wisdom Advanced Book: Blue Ser.). (Illus.). 700p. 1983. 35.00 (ISBN 0-86171-014-2, Pub. by Wisdom Pubns). Great Traditions.
Hotchkiss, Burt. Have Miracles, Will Travel. 96p. 1982. pap. 4.95 (ISBN 0-8187-0047-5). Harlo Pr.
Howard, J. Grant. Balancing Life's Demands: A New Perpective on Priorities. LC 82-24581. 1983. pap. 6.95 (ISBN 0-88070-012-2); study guide 2.95 (ISBN 0-88070-033-5). Multnomah.
Howard, Vernon. There Is a Way Out. LC 75-11137. 173p. 1982. pap. 6.00 (ISBN 0-87516-472-2). De Vorss.
Hua, Tripitaka Master. The Shurangama Sutra, Vol. 7. Buddhist Text Translation Society, tr. from Chinese. (Illus.). 270p. (Orig.). 1982. pap. 8.50 (ISBN 0-917512-97-9). Buddhist Text.
Huggins, Larry. The Blood Speaks. 128p. 1982. pap. 3.95 (ISBN 0-89274-231-3, HH-231). Harrison Hse.
Hughes, John J. Proclaiming the Good News: Homilies for the A Cycle. LC 82-62554. 156p. 1983. pap. 14.95 (ISBN 0-87973-722-0, 722). Our Sunday Visitor.
Hughes, Phillip E. Hope for a Despairing World. LC 77-89680. (Canterbury Bks.). pap. 2.95 (ISBN 0-8010-4159-7). Baker Bk.
Hull, Walter E. God - Isn't There Any Other Way!? 1983. 5.95 (ISBN 0-8062-2173-9). Carlton.
Hunter, Charles. Born Again, What Do You Mean? 1982. pap. 0.75 (ISBN 0-917726-48-0). Hunter Bks.
--God's Conditions For Prosperity. rev. & enlarged ed. 1984. pap. 4.95 (ISBN 0-917726-41-3). Hunter Bks.
Hunter, Frances. Devil, You Can't Steal What's Mine. 1982. pap. 0.75 (ISBN 0-917726-42-1). Hunter Bks.
Huntley, Frank L. Bishop Joseph Hall & Protestant Meditation in Seventeenth-Century England: A Study, with Texts of the Art of Divine Meditation (1606) & Occasional Meditations (1633) (Medieval & Renaissance Texts & Studies: 1). (Illus.). 234p. (Orig.). 1981. 15.00 (ISBN 0-86698-000-8); pap. 9.00 (ISBN 0-86698-005-9). Medieval.
Hunttmiller, Patrique. The First Twelve Meditations: On Black American Philosophy & Theology - A Study into the Meaning of Genesis & the African Concept of the Great Past & African Time Concepts As Spiritual & Two Dimensional. 150p. Date not set. pap. 6.95 (ISBN 0-318-20332-4). Scojtia Renee.
Husserl. Cartesian Meditations. 1977. pap. 13.00 (ISBN 90-247-0068-X, Pub. by Martinus Nijhoff Netherlands). Kluwer Academic.
--Cartesianische Meditationen und Pariser Vortrage: Photomechanischer Nachdruck. (Husserliana Ser: No. 1). 1973. lib. bdg. 29.00 (ISBN 90-247-0214-3, Pub. by Martinus Nijhoff Netherlands). Kluwer Academic.
Hutson, Joan. Heal My Heart O Lord. LC 75-30493. 112p. 1976. pap. 2.95 (ISBN 0-87793-106-2). Ave Maria.
Huyck, Peter H. Scriptural Meditations for the Rosary. (Greeting Book Line Ser.). (Illus.). 48p. 1982. pap. 1.50 (ISBN 0-89622-157-1). Twenty-Third.
Inayat, Taj, et al. The Crystal Chalice. rev. ed. (Illus.). 170p. Date not set. pap. price not set (1011P). Omega Pr NM.
Ironside, H. A. The Continual Burnt Offering: Daily Meditations on the Word of God. 370p. 1981. pap. 4.95 (ISBN 0-87213-353-2). Loizeaux.
--The Daily Sacrifice: Daily Meditations on the Word of God. 370p. 1982. pap. 4.95 (ISBN 0-87213-356-7). Loizeaux.
Irsch, Ed. The Undisturbed Soldier. 1983. 4.25 (ISBN 0-89536-602-9, 2105). CSS of Ohio.
Irwin, James B. More Than Earthlings. LC 83-70369. 1983. 6.95 (ISBN 0-8054-5255-9). Broadman.
Isler, Betty. Here I Am Again, Lord. (Continued Applied Christianity Ser.). 1983. pap. 4.95 (ISBN 0-570-03895-2, 12-2977). Concordia.
Iyer, Pico. The Recovery of Innocence. (Illus.). 1984. 8.75 (ISBN 0-88695-019-8). Concord Grove.
Iyer, Raghavan. The Beacon Light. (Sangam Texts Ser.). 124p. 1984. pap. 8.75 (ISBN 0-88695-021-X). Concord Grove.
--The Society of the Future. 84. 8.75 (ISBN 0-88695-018-X). Concord Grove.
Jafolla, Richard. Soul Surgery: The Ultimate Self-Healing. LC 81-71018. 176p. (Orig.). 1982. pap. 5.95 (ISBN 0-87516-473-0). De Vorss.
Jaworski, Leon & Schneider, Dick. Encrucijadas. 1982. 3.95 (ISBN 0-88113-082-6). Edit Betania.
John, Da F. Do You Know What Anything Is? LC 84-70215. 1984. pap. 8.95 (ISBN 0-913922-87-0). Dawn Horse Pr.
--The Great Way of Wisdom: An Anthology of Written Teaching of Da Free John. Feuerstein, Georg, ed. 1984. pap. 3.95 (ISBN 0-913922-88-9). Dawn Horse Pr.
Johnson, Barry L. Visit of the Tomten. LC 81-70361. pap. 4.95x (ISBN 0-8358-0439-9). Upper Room.
Johnson, Buford. Seasonal Subjects. 1981. pap. 3.95 (ISBN 0-934942-25-0). White Wing Pub.
Johnson, C. Phillip. Will a Man Rob God? 1981. pap. 3.00 (ISBN 0-933184-29-8). Flame Intl.
Johnson, Connie. Living Our Visions of Peace. (Illus.). 35p. (Orig.). 1984. pap. 4.95 (ISBN 0-377-00141-4). Friend Pr.
Johnson, Lois W. Come as You Are. LC 82-70951. 112p. (Orig.). 1982. pap. 3.95 (ISBN 0-8066-1926-0, 10-1517). Augsburg.
--Gift in My Arms: Thoughts for New Mothers. LC 77-72448. 1977. pap. 5.95 (ISBN 0-8066-1586-9, 10-2549). Augsburg.
Jones, Alex. Seven Mansions of Color. LC 82-73248. (Illus.). 152p. 1983. pap. 7.95 (ISBN 0-87516-500-1). De Vorss.
Jones, Bob, Sr. Comments on Here & Hereafter. Haight, Grace W., ed. 189p. 1942. 3.95 (ISBN 0-89084-006-7). Bob Jones Univ Pr.
Jones, E. Stanley. Christian Maturity. (Festival Bks.). 1980. pap. 2.25 (ISBN 0-687-07453-3). Abingdon.
Jones, John E. Reconciliation. 164p. 1984. 8.95 (ISBN 0-87123-438-6); pap. 4.95 (ISBN 0-87123-862-4). Bethany Hse.
Jones, Russell B. Gold from Golgotha. (Orig.). 1978. pap. 1.50 (ISBN 0-89228-024-7). Impact Bks MO.
Jordan, Joseph A. We Can Make It...Together. (Illus.). 64p. 1984. 5.50 (ISBN 0-682-40157-9). Exposition Pr FL.
Joyce, Robert. Thoughts to Ponder. 1980. 6.00 (ISBN 0-8198-7305-5); pap. 5.00 (ISBN 0-8198-7306-3). Dghtrs St Paul.
Julian of Norwich. Enfolded in Love: Daily Readings with Julian of Norwich. Julian Shrine Members Staff, tr. 96p. (Orig.). 1981. pap. 4.95 (ISBN 0-8164-2318-0, HarpR). Har-Row.
Kagawa, Toyohiko. Meditations. LC 78-12761. 1979. Repr. of 1950 ed. lib. bdg. 22.50x (ISBN 0-313-21180-9, KAMD). Greenwood.
Kaiser, Walter. Malachi: God's Unchanging Love. 1984. pap. 6.95 (ISBN 0-8010-5464-8). Baker Bk.
Kameeta, Zephania. Why, O Lord? Psalms & Sermons from Namibia. LC 86-45211. 80p. 1987. pap. 3.95 (ISBN 0-8006-1923-4, 1-1923). Fortress.
Karay, Diane. All the Seasons of Mercy. LC 86-18948. 156p. (Orig.). 1987. pap. 7.95 (ISBN 0-664-24067-4). Westminster.
Karsten, Dennis. Are You Well, Why Not? 96p. (Orig.). 1983. pap. 2.95 (ISBN 0-88144-011-6). Christian Pub.
Keller, W. Phillip. Sea Edge. 120p. 1985. 9.95 (ISBN 0-8499-0457-9, 0457-9). Word Bks.
--Wonder O' the Wind. 1982. 9.95 (ISBN 0-8499-0337-8). Word Bks.
Kelly, Robert. How Do I Make Up My Mind, Lord? LC 82-70948. (Young Readers Ser.). (Orig.). 1982. pap. 3.95 (ISBN 0-8066-1923-6, 10-3168). Augsburg.
Kemper, Frederick & Bass, George M. You Are My Beloved Sermon Book. 1980. pap. 6.95 (ISBN 0-570-03821-9, 12-2761). Concordia.
Kendrick, Dolores. Now is the Thing to Praise. LC 83-82774. 116p. 1984. pap. 7.00 perf. bnd. (ISBN 0-916418-54-5). Lotus.
Kennedy, Eugene. Loneliness & Everyday Problems. LC 82-45971. 160p. 1983. pap. 3.95 (ISBN 0-385-18797-1, Im). Doubleday.
Kerl, Mary A. Where Are You, Lord? LC 82-70949. (Young Readers Ser.). 112p. (Orig.). 1982. pap. 3.95 (ISBN 0-8066-1924-4, 10-7069). Augsburg.
Khan, Hazrat I. Nature Meditations. LC 80-50829. (Collected Works of Hazrat Inayat Khan Ser.). (Illus.). 128p. (Orig.). 1980. pap. 6.95 (ISBN 0-930872-12-6). Omega Pr NM.
Kiemel, Ann. I'm Out to Change My World. 128p. 1983. pap. 4.95 (ISBN 0-310-70141-4, 14034P). Zondervan.
Killinger, John. Sea Breezes: Thoughts of God from a Summer Beach. 96p. (Orig.). 1985. pap. 6.95 (ISBN 0-687-37088-4). Abingdon.
Klenck, Robert H. Words Fitly Spoken: Reflections & Prayers. LC 79-13449. 1979. 10.95 (ISBN 0-934878-35-8, 07764-1, Dist. by W.W. Norton). Dembner Bks.
Knight, David M. Meditations for Priests. 1978. write for info. (ISBN 0-915488-05-1). Clarity Pub.
Knorr, Dandi. The Blessing Is in the Doing. LC 83-70643. (Orig.). 1983. pap. 4.95 (ISBN 0-8054-6001-2). Broadman.
Koyama, Kosuke. Fifty Meditations. LC 77-7026. (Illus.). 191p. (Orig.). 1979. pap. 6.95 (ISBN 0-88344-134-9). Orbis Bks.
Kramer, Joel. The Passionate Mind. 122p. 1983. pap. 7.95 (ISBN 0-938190-12-1). North Atlantic.
Krass, Alfred C. Evangelizing Neopagan North America. LC 81-23768. (Mennonite Missionary Study Ser.: No. 9). 256p. (Orig.). 1982. pap. 9.95 (ISBN 0-8361-1989-4). Herald Pr.
Kraus, George. The Pastor at Prayer. LC 6-1188. (Continued Applied Christianity Ser.). 1983. 15.95 (ISBN 0-570-03073-0, 6-1188). Concordia.
Kreeft, Peter J. Between Heaven & Hell. LC 82-8975. 144p. (Orig.). 1982. pap. 5.95 (ISBN 0-87784-389-9). Inter-Varsity.
Kuck, Glen. Help My Faith Grow, Lord! (Continued Applied Christianity Ser.). 1983. pap. 4.95 (ISBN 0-570-03894-4, 12-2976). Concordia.
Kuhn, Isobel. Second-Mile People. 1982. pap. 3.50 (ISBN 0-85363-145-X). OMF Bks.
Kuhne, Gary W. La Dinamica de Adiestrar Discipulos. 160p. 1980. 2.95 (ISBN 0-88113-040-0). Edit Betania.
LaHaye, Berverly & LaHaye, Tim. La Familia Sujeta al Espiritu. 208p. 1980. 3.75 (ISBN 0-88113-085-0). Edit Betania.
LaHaye, Beverly. La Mujer Sujeta al Espiritu. 208p. 1978. 3.25 (ISBN 0-88113-210-1). Edit Betania.
LaHaye, Tim. Como Estudiar la Biblia por Si Mismo. 192p. 1977. 3.75 (ISBN 0-88113-042-7); 3.75 (ISBN 0-88113-033-8). Edit Betania.
--El Varon y Su Temperamento. 217p. 1978. 3.95 (ISBN 0-88113-340-X). Edit Betania.
Lappin, Peter. Sunshine in the Shadows. LC 79-57184. 218p. 1980. pap. 6.95 (ISBN 0-89944-042-8). Don Bosco Multimedia.
Larson, Mobby. Prayers of a Christian Educator. (Greeting Book Line Ser.). 32p. (Orig.). 1985. pap. 1.50 (ISBN 0-89622-277-2). Twenty-Third.
Lavin, Ron. You Can't Start a Car with a Cross. 1984. 5.95 (ISBN 0-89536-648-7, 2507). CSS of Ohio.
Lawrence, Emeric. Believe the Good News: Daily Meditations on the Lenten Masses. LC 82-97. 144p. 1982. pap. 5.75 (ISBN 0-8146-1256-3). Liturgical Pr.
--Jesus Present & Coming: Daily Meditations on the Advent & Christmas Masses. LC 82-20380. 128p. 1982. pap. 7.95 (ISBN 0-8146-1284-9). Liturgical Pr.
--Risen & with You Always: Daily Meditations for the Easter Season Masses. 140p. 1986. pap. 5.95 (ISBN 0-8146-1448-5). Liturgical Pr.
Lawrence, John. Life's Choices: Discovering the Consequences of Sowing & Reaping. LC 82-3438. 120p. 1982. pap. 5.95 (ISBN 0-930014-85-5). Multnomah.
Leclercq, Jacques. This Day Is Ours. Livingstone, Dinah, tr. from Fr. LC 80-50314. Orig. Title: Le Jour de L'Homme. 128p. (Orig.). 1980. pap. 1.74 (ISBN 0-88344-504-2). Orbis Bks.
Lee, Linda, compiled by. Meditate Upon These Things. 2nd ed. (Illus.). 160p. 1981. pap. 5.00 (ISBN 0-87516-463-3). De Vorss.
Leech, Bryan J. Lift My Spirits, Lord: Prayers of a Struggling Christian. LC 84-9351. 128p. (Orig.). 1984. pap. 5.95 (ISBN 0-8066-2090-0, 10-3850). Augsburg.
Lehn, Cornelia. Peace Be with You. LC 80-70190. (Illus.). 126p. 1981. 12.95 (ISBN 0-87303-061-3). Faith & Life.
L'Engle, Madeleine. The Love Letters. (Epiphany Ser.). 384p. 1983. pap. 2.95 (ISBN 0-345-30617-1). Ballantine.
Lerner, Arthur. Words for All Seasons. (Illus.). 104p. (Orig.). 1983. pap. 6.95 (ISBN 0-938292-06-4). Being Bks.
Lessin, Roy. Como Disciplinar a Tus Hijos. 96p. 1982. 2.25 (ISBN 0-88113-032-X). Edit Betania.
Lewis, C. S. The Business of Heaven: Daily Readings from C. S. Lewis. 1984. pap. 7.95 (ISBN 0-15-614863-3, Harv). HarBraceJ.
--The Grand Miracle. (Epiphany Ser.). 176p. 1983. pap. 2.95 (ISBN 0-345-30539-6). Ballantine.
Lewis, Jim. The Great Commitment. LC 81-71542. 120p. (Orig.). 1982. pap. 7.50 (ISBN 0-942482-03-4). Unity Church Denver.
--Positive Thoughts for Successful Living. LC 80-50277. 138p. (Orig.). 1979. pap. 7.95 (ISBN 0-942482-00-X). Unity Church Denver.
--The Upward Path. LC 82-60277. 150p. (Orig.). 1982. pap. 7.95 (ISBN 0-942482-04-2). Unity Church Denver.
A Light to the Nations. 201p. 1983. pap. 3.95 (ISBN 0-88479-036-3). Arena Lettres.
Lindsay, Gordon. One Body, One Spirit, One Lord. pap. 3.95 (ISBN 0-89985-991-7). Christ Nations.
Long, Edward S. Go Forth into the World. 1983. 3.10 (ISBN 0-89536-604-5, 0732). CSS of Ohio.
Lorrance, Arleen. Musings for Meditation. LC 76-14783. (Illus.). 180p. (Orig.). 1976. pap. 4.50 (ISBN 0-916192-03-2). L P Pubns.
Lowery, Daniel. Following Christ: A Handbook of Catholic Moral Teaching. LC 82-84373. 160p. 1983. pap. 3.50 (ISBN 0-89243-173-3). Liguori Pubns.
Lowery, Fred. Whistling in the Dark: The Story of Fred Lowery, the Blind Whistler. McDowell, John, as told to. LC 83-4085. (Illus.). 416p. 1983. 15.95 (ISBN 0-88289-298-3). Pelican.
Lubich, Chiara. Meditations. LC 74-79452. 148p. 1974. pap. 4.95 (ISBN 0-911782-20-6). New City.
Luther, Martin. Day by Day We Magnify Thee. LC 82-2481. 448p. 1982. pap. 10.95 (ISBN 0-8006-1637-5, 1-1637). Fortress.
MacArthur, John, Jr. The Ultimate Priority. 1983. pap. 5.50 (ISBN 0-8024-0186-4). Moody.
McCarroll, Tolbert. Notes from the Song of Life: Spiritual Reflections. LC 77-7135. (Illus.). 1977. pap. 6.95 (ISBN 0-89087-200-7). Celestial Arts.
McClain, Ernest G. Meditations Through the Quran: Tonal Images in an Oral Culture. LC 81-82124. (Illus.). 166p. 1981. 12.95 (ISBN 0-89254-009-5). Nicolas-Hays.
McConnell, William T. The Gift of Time. LC 83-120. 132p. (Orig.). 1983. pap. 3.95 (ISBN 0-87784-838-6). Inter-Varsity.
McCord, David. Let Us Give. 64p. 1986. pap. 2.95 (ISBN 0-87403-098-6, 3024). Standard Pub.
McCumber, W. E. The Good News: Mark. 184p. 1982. pap. 4.95 (ISBN 0-8341-0699-X). Beacon Hill.
McDonnell, Thomas P., ed. Through the Year with Thomas Merton: Daily Meditations. LC 85-11827. (Illus.). 240p. 1985. pap. 7.95 (ISBN 0-385-23234-9, Im). Doubleday.
McFadden, Charles. Christianity Confronts Communism. 1983. 15.00 (ISBN 0-8199-0841-X). Franciscan Herald.
MacGregor, Geddes. He Who Lets Us Be. 194p. 1987. pap. 8.95 (ISBN 0-913729-61-2). Paragon Hse.
McIntyre, Marie. Little Things Mean a Lot: Minute Meditations. (Greeting Book Line Ser.). (Illus.). 48p. 1982. pap. 1.50 (ISBN 0-89622-155-5). Twenty-Third.
McKinney, Donald. Living with Joy. LC 76-8203. Repr. of 1976 ed. 24.00 (ISBN 0-8357-9014-2, 2016375). Bks Demand UMI.
Mackinnon, Donald. Enjoying the Harvest: Reflections for Your Mature Years. 48p. 1983. pap. 1.50 (ISBN 0-89243-196-2). Liguori Pubns.
McNamara, William. Earthy Mysticism: Contemplation & the Life of Passionate Presence. LC 82-33554. 128p. 1983. pap. 6.95 (ISBN 0-8245-0562-X). Crossroad NY.
Macquarrie, John. The Humility of God. LC 77-18707. 96p. 1978. pap. 4.65 (ISBN 0-664-24200-6). Westminster.
Madeline, Sr. Within the Castle. 1983. 9.50 (ISBN 0-8199-0820-7). Franciscan Herald.

Maestri, William F. A Time for Peace: Biblical Meditations for Advent. LC 83-22399. 94p. 1983. pap. 4.95 (ISBN 0-8189-0463-1). Alba.

--A Word in Season. LC 84-11026. 153p. (Orig.). 1983. pap. 6.95 (ISBN 0-8189-0459-3). Alba.

Makrakis, Apostolos. Orthodox Christian Meditations (Spiritual Discourses for the Orthodox Christians) Orthodox Christian Educational Society, ed. Cummings, Denver, tr. from Hellenic. 143p. (Orig.). 1965. pap. 3.50x (ISBN 0-938366-22-X). Orthodox Chr.

Malyala, Panduranga R. Aum: (Amen) Do, ed. (Illus.). 24p. (Orig.). 1983. pap. 2.00 (ISBN 0-938924-12-5). Sri Shirdi Sai.

Mapou, May. Love Is Forever. 1984. 4.95 (ISBN 0-8062-2196-8). Carlton.

Maria Reina de Los Apostolos. (Span.). 1.25 (ISBN 0-8198-4713-5). Dghtrs St Paul.

Mariechild, Diane. Crystal Visions: Nine Meditations for Personal & Planetary Peace. (Feminist Ser.). (Illus.). 128p. (Orig.). 1985. 15.95 (ISBN 0-89594-183-X); pap. 6.95 (ISBN 0-89594-182-1). Crossing Pr.

Maritain, Jacques. The Living Thoughts of Saint Paul. 135p. 1983. Repr. of 1942 ed. lib. bdg. 20.00 (ISBN 0-8495-3946-3). Arden Lib.

Marsh, Spencer. Beginnings: A Portrayal of the Creation. LC 81-18920. (Illus.). 72p. 1982. 16.95 (ISBN 0-930014-82-0); pap. 9.95 (ISBN 0-930014-81-2). Multnomah.

Marshall, Catherine. Algo Mas. 171p. 1981. 4.75 (ISBN 0-88113-001-X). Edit Betania.

--Aventuras en la Oracion. 192p. 1976. 2.95 (ISBN 0-88113-005-2). Edit Betania.

--El Ayudador. 208p. 1980. 3.25 (ISBN 0-88113-009-5). Edit Betania.

--A Closer Walk. LeSourd, Leonard, ed. 256p. 1986. 12.95 (ISBN 0-8007-9065-0). Revell.

Marshall, Catherine & LeSourd, Leonard. Mi Diario Personal de Oracion. 416p. 1981. 4.95 (ISBN 0-88113-306-X). Edit Betania.

Marshall, Catherine & Le Sourd, Leonard. My Personal Prayer Diary. (Epiphany Bks.). 1983. pap. 3.95 (ISBN 0-345-30612-0). Ballantine.

Marshall, Lillian. Stepping Stones: Meditations in a Garden. (Illus.). 64p. 1984. 4.95 (ISBN 0-88088-506-8). Peter Pauper.

Martin, Alfred & Martin, John A. Isaiah: The Glory of the Messiah. (Orig.). 1983. pap. 9.95 (ISBN 0-8024-0168-6). Moody.

Martin, Dorothy. The Story of Billy McCarrell. 160p. (Orig.). 1983. pap. 3.95 (ISBN 0-8024-0519-3). Moody.

Martin Luther: Portfolio Of Letters & Translations from Aesop. 126p. 150.00 (ISBN 0-8115-0906-0). Kraus Repr.

Martin, Paul. Good Morning, Lord: Devotions for Young People. (Good Morning, Lord Ser.). 1974. 4.95 (ISBN 0-8010-5958-5). Baker Bk.

Martin, Walter. Mormonismo. 48p. 1982. 1.95 (ISBN 0-88113-208-X). Edit Betania.

--Los Testigos de Jehova. 80p. 1982. 2.25 (ISBN 0-88113-285-3). Edit Betania.

Marty, Martin E. A Cry of Absence: Reflections for the Winter of the Heart. LC 82-48416. (Illus.). 176p. 1983. 12.45 (ISBN 0-06-065434-1, HarpR). Har-Row.

Maseroni, Robert S. Be Fruitful, No. 9. 1983. 0.80 (ISBN 0-89536-633-9, 0237). CSS of Ohio.

--The Gift of Aid, No. 6. 1983. 0.80 (ISBN 0-89536-630-4, 0738). CSS of Ohio.

--The Gift of Encouragement, No. 4. 1983. 0.80 (ISBN 0-89536-628-2, 0736). CSS of Ohio.

--The Gift of Mercy, No. 7. 1983. 0.80 (ISBN 0-89536-631-2, 0739). CSS of Ohio.

Master Hua, Tripitaka. The Shurangama Mantra: A Commentary, Vol. III. Buddhist Text Translation Society, tr. from Chinese. (Illus.). 156p. (Orig.). 1982. pap. 6.50 (ISBN 0-917512-36-7). Buddhist Text.

--Water Mirror Reflecting Heaven. Buddhist Text Translation Society, tr. from Chinese. (Illus.). 82p. (Orig.). 1982. pap. 4.00 (ISBN 0-88139-501-3). Buddhist Text.

May, Leland C. Good Morning, Lord: Meditations for College Students. (Good Morning Lord Ser.). 64p. (Orig.). 1981. 4.95 (ISBN 0-8010-6116-4). Baker Bk.

Melrose, Andrea LaSonde, ed. Nine Visions: A Book of Fantasies. 192p. 1983. pap. 8.95 (ISBN 0-8164-2490-X, HarpR). Har-Row.

Mendes, Reva. Words for the Quiet Moments. 35p. 1973. pap. 1.00 (ISBN 0-87516-185-5). De Vorss.

Merrill, Mary L., et al. A Light Unto My Path. (Illus.). 185p. 1981. Repr. of 1982 ed. 10.00 (ISBN 0-686-33180-X). Pathway Pubns.

Merton, Thomas. The New Man. 1983. 13.50 (ISBN 0-8446-5987-8). Peter Smith.

--Thoughts in Solitude. 124p. 1976. pap. 4.25 (ISBN 0-374-51325-2). FS&G.

Metz, Johannes B. & Moltmann, Jurgen. Meditations on the Passion. LC 78-70823. 48p. 1979. pap. 2.50 (ISBN 0-8091-2184-0). Paulist Pr.

Micks, Marianne H. The Joy of Worship. LC 81-19667. (Library of Living Faith: Vol, 1). 120p. 1982. pap. 5.95 (ISBN 0-664-24402-5). Westminster.

Miller, Alberta P. Dorcas Sews for Others. (Arch Book Ser.: No. 21). pap. 0.99 (59-1285). Concordia.

Miller, Barbara & Conn, Charles P. El Milagro de Kathy. 144p. 1982. 2.75 (ISBN 0-88113-170-9). Edit Betania.

Miller, Charles E. Opening the Treasures: A Book of Daily Homily Meditations. LC 81-19095. (Illus.). 557p. 1982. pap. 16.95 (ISBN 0-8189-0424-0). Alba.

Miller, Herbert. Fishing on the Asphalt. LC 83-10006. 208p. (Orig.). 1983. pap. 8.95 (ISBN 0-8272-1011-6). CBP.

Mitchell, Kurt. Poor Ralph. (Illus.). 32p. 1982. 8.95 (ISBN 0-89107-273-X, Crossway Bks). Good News.

Mohan, Robert P. Eternal Answers for an Anxious Age. LC 85-60518. 140p. (Orig.). 1985. pap. 6.95 (ISBN 0-87973-592-9, 592). Our Sunday Visitor.

Molnar, Paul J. Quotes & Notes to Share. Goebel, Patrice, ed. (Orig.). 1982. pap. 4.95 (ISBN 0-938736-06-X). Life Enrich.

Monsma, Hester. Devotions for Graduates. 25p. 1984. pap. 1.50 (ISBN 0-8010-2939-2). Baker Bk.

--Devotions for Mothers. 30p. 1984. pap. 1.25 (ISBN 0-8010-2942-2). Baker Bk.

--Devotions for Those God Loves. 30p. 1984. pap. 1.25 (ISBN 0-8010-2943-0). Baker Bk.

--Devotions for Those Who Sorrow. 30p. 1984. pap. 1.25 (ISBN 0-8010-2944-9). Baker Bk.

Moody, D. L. Thoughts for the Quiet Hour. pap. 3.50 (ISBN 0-8024-8729-7). Moody.

Morgan, Elise N. The Angel of the Presence. (Meditation Ser.). 1922. 3.50 (ISBN 0-87516-327-0). De Vorss.

--The Illimitable One. (Meditation Ser.). 1934. 3.50 (ISBN 0-87516-329-7). De Vorss.

--Now This Day. 1948. 3.50 (ISBN 0-87516-330-0). De Vorss.

--That We May Be Willing to Receive. (Meditation Ser.). 1938. 3.50 (ISBN 0-87516-331-9). De Vorss.

--The Way. (Meditation Ser.). 1972. 3.50 (ISBN 0-87516-332-7). De Vorss.

--Your Own Path. (Meditation Ser.). 1928. 4.50 (ISBN 0-87516-333-5). De Vorss.

Morgenroth, Anton. Splendor of the Faith: Meditations on the Credo of the People of God. 206p. (Orig.). 1983. pap. 7.95 (ISBN 0-931888-14-X). Christendom Pubns.

Morning, Evening Thoughts. 1967. 5.95 (ISBN 0-88088-444-4). Peter Pauper.

Morton, Craig & Burger, Robert. The Courage to Believe. (Epiphany Bks.). (Illus.). 1983. pap. 2.75 (ISBN 0-345-30564-7). Ballantine.

Mother Teresa. Words to Love By. 160p. 1985. pap. 6.95 large print ed. (ISBN 0-8027-2478-7). Walker & Co.

Mother Teresa of Calcutta & Roger of Taize. Meditations on the Way of the Cross. (Illus.). 64p. (Orig.). 1987. pap. 5.95 (ISBN 0-8298-0585-0). Pilgrim NY.

Mow, Anna B. Springs of Love. LC 79-11186. 1979. pap. 1.95 (ISBN 0-87178-810-1). Brethren.

Muggeridge, Kitty. Gazing on Truth: Meditations on Reality. 96p. (Orig.). 1985. pap. 4.95 (ISBN 0-8028-0072-6). Eerdmans.

Muhaiyaddeen, M. R. Bawa. Sheikh & Disciple. LC 83-1565. (Illus.). 120p. 1983. 7.95 (ISBN 0-914390-26-0). Fellowship Pr PA.

Muktananda, Swami. I Welcome You All with Love. 40p. (Orig.). 1978. pap. 1.75 (ISBN 0-914602-59-4). SYDA Found.

Murphree, Jon T. Made to Be Mastered: Managing Your Emotions Successfully--God's Way. 126p. (YA) 1984. pap. 5.95 (ISBN 0-8010-6169-5). Baker Bk.

Murphy, Elspeth C. Chalkdust: Prayer Meditations for a Teacher. 1978. 5.95 (ISBN 0-8010-6065-6). Baker Bk.

Murphy, Joseph. Special Meditations for Health, Wealth, Love. pap. 1.50 (ISBN 0-87516-336-X). De Vorss.

Murray, Andrew. The Believer's Prayer Life. rev. ed. LC 83-12254. (The Andrew Murray Prayer Library). 141p. 1983. pap. 3.95 (ISBN 0-87123-277-4). Bethany Hse.

--The Best of Andrew Murray. (Best Ser.). pap. 4.95 (ISBN 0-8010-6069-9). Baker Bk.

--Entrega Absoluta. 192p. 1981. 2.95 (ISBN 0-88113-079-6). Edit Betania.

--Every Day with Andrew Murray. rev. ed. Tr. of God's Best Secret. 208p. 1986. pap. 3.95 (ISBN 0-89283-302-5, Pub. by Vine Books). Servant.

--La Nueva Vida. 144p. 1979. 2.95 (ISBN 0-88113-220-9). Edit Betania.

Muto, Susan A. Meditation in Motion. LC 86-4690. 144p. 1986. 5.95 (ISBN 0-385-23533-X, Im). Doubleday.

My Book of Feelings. 1977. 6.95 (ISBN 0-8065-0585-0). Citadel Pr.

Nadzo, Stefan. There Is a Way. 129p. 1981. pap. 4.75 (ISBN 0-937226-00-9). Coleman Pub.

Nadzo, Stefan C. There Is a Way: Meditations for a Seeker. LC 80-66831. (Illus.). 129p. (Orig.). 1980. pap. 5.95 (ISBN 0-937226-00-9). Eden's Work.

National Master Ch'ing Liang. Flower Adornment Sutra Prologue: Vol. III: The Second Door, Part II. Tripitaka Master Hua, commentary by. Buddhist Text Translation Society Staff, tr. from Chinese. (Illus.). 220p. (Orig.). 1983. pap. 10.00 (ISBN 0-917512-98-7). Buddhist Text.

Nee, Watchman. La Liberacion del Espiritu. 112p. 1968. 2.95 (ISBN 0-88113-255-1). Edit Betania.

--Table in the Wilderness. 1969. pap. 4.95 (ISBN 0-87508-422-2). Chr Lit.

Neill, Mary, et al. How Shall We Find the Father? Meditations for Mixed Voices. 160p. (Orig.). 1983. pap. 8.95 (ISBN 0-8164-2623-6, HarpR). Har-Row.

Nestingen, James A. The Faith We Hold: The Living Witness of Luther & the Augsburg Confession. LC 83-70516. 96p. (Orig.). 1983. pap. 5.95 (ISBN 0-8066-2022-6, 10-2200). Augsburg.

Nethery, Susan. A Mother Shares: Meditations on Parenting. 128p. 1981. 5.95 (ISBN 0-8010-6736-7). Baker Bk.

Newman, John H. Blessed Art Thou among Women. 1985. 4.95 (ISBN 0-87193-076-5). Dimension Bks.

Nicholas, Ron, et al. Good Things Come in Small Groups. LC 85-778. 200p. 1985. pap. 6.95 (ISBN 0-87784-917-X). Inter-Varsity.

Night Light. 400p. (Orig.). pap. 5.95 (ISBN 0-89486-381-9). Hazelden.

Night Light: A Book of Nightime Meditations. (Hazelden Meditation Ser.). 1986. 5.95 (ISBN 0-06-255437-9). Har-Row.

Night Light: A Book of Nighttime Meditations. (Hazelden Bks.). scp 5.95t (ISBN 0-06-255437-9). Har-Row.

Nipham, Lama. Calm & Clear. 1985. 20.00x (ISBN 0-317-39045-7, Pub. by Luzac & Co Ltd). State Mutual Bk.

Nixon, David. The Year of the Locust. 138p. (Orig.). 1980. pap. 3.95 (ISBN 0-8341-0675-2). Beacon Hill.

Noblett, Robert A. A Main Street Gospel. 1983. 4.75 (ISBN 0-89536-608-8, 1341). CSS of Ohio.

Nomura, Yushi. Desert Wisdom: Sayings from the Desert Fathers. LC 82-45488. (Illus.). 128p. 1984. pap. 8.95 (ISBN 0-385-18079-9, Im). Doubleday.

Noonan, Hugh. Companion to the Clams. (Illus.). 1980. pap. 10.50 (ISBN 0-8199-0680-8). Franciscan Herald.

Nos Preparamos Para Recibir a Jesus. (Span. & Eng.). pap. text ed. 1.75 (ISBN 0-317-46869-3); activity bk. 1.00 (ISBN 0-8198-5102-7). Dghtrs St Paul.

Nouwen, Henri J. A Letter of Consolation. LC 81-48212. 96p. 1982. 10.45 (ISBN 0-686-81488-6, HarpR). Har-Row.

--Out of Solitude. (Illus.). 64p. 1974. pap. 1.95 (ISBN 0-87793-072-4). Ave Maria.

--The Way of the Heart. (Epiphany Bks.). 1983. pap. 2.50 (ISBN 0-345-30530-2). Ballantine.

O'Barr, Ann G. First Light. LC 83-70211. (Orig.). 1984. pap. 5.95 (ISBN 0-8054-7305-X). Broadman.

O'Collins, Gerald. A Month with Jesus. pap. 2.95 (ISBN 0-87193-097-8). Dimension Bks.

O'Connor, Elizabeth. Letters to Scattered Pilgrims. LC 78-3361. 176p. 1982. (HarpR); pap. 8.95 (ISBN 0-06-066334-0, RD-374). Har-Row.

O'Donnell, Edward. Priestly People. 64p. 1982. pap. 1.50 (ISBN 0-89243-168-7). Liguori Pubns.

O'Driscoll, Herbert. A Certain Life: Contemporary Meditations on the Way of Christ. 96p. (Orig.). 1980. pap. 5.95 (ISBN 0-8164-2040-8, HarpR). Har-Row.

--A Certain Life: Contemporary Meditations on the Way of Christ. 192p. 1985. pap. 8.95 large print ed. (ISBN 0-8027-2491-4); pap. cancelled (ISBN 0-8027-7274-9). Walker & Co.

--Crossroads: Times of Decision for People of God. 96p. 1983. pap. 5.95 (ISBN 0-8164-2432-2, HarpR). Har-Row.

Ogilvie, Lloyd. Let God Love You. 1978. pap. 7.95 (ISBN 0-8499-2831-1, 2831-1). Word Bks.

Ogilvie, Lloyd J. God's Best for My Life. LC 81-82390. 390p. (Orig.). 1981. text ed. 10.95 (ISBN 0-89081-293-4, 2934). Harvest Hse.

Oke, Janette. When Calls the Heart. LC 82-24451. 221p. (Orig.). 1983. pap. 5.95 (ISBN 0-87123-611-7, 210611). Bethany Hse.

--When Calls the Heart. Large type ed. (Canadian West Ser.). 221p. (Orig.). 1986. pap. 7.95 (ISBN 0-87123-885-3). Bethany Hse.

Oldenburg, Cornelius. Comfort Ye My People: Messages of Comfort for the Bereaved. (Solace Ser.). 1983. pap. 1.25 (ISBN 0-8010-6704-9). Baker Bk.

Olford, Stephen. The Grace of Giving. 1984. pap. 4.95 (ISBN 0-8010-6703-0). Baker Bk.

O'Malley, William J. Why Not? Daring to Live the Challenge of Christ. LC 86-14059. 169p. (Orig.). 1986. pap. 6.95 (ISBN 0-8189-0504-2). Alba.

Ortiz, Juan C. Discipulo. 192p. 1978. 3.75 (ISBN 0-88113-065-6). Edit Betania.

Osborne, Cecil G. The Joy of Understanding Your Faith. 192p. (Orig.). 1983. pap. 7.75 (ISBN 0-687-20594-8). Abingdon.

Osgood, Judy, ed. Meditations for Those Who Live with Alcoholism. 72p. 1987. pap. 5.95 (ISBN 0-916895-04-1). Gilgal Pubns.

--Meditations for the Divorced. (Gilgal Meditations Ser.). 167p. (Orig.). 1987. pap. text ed. 5.95 (ISBN 0-916895-02-5). Gilgal Pubns.

--Meditations for the Widowed. LC 86-15002. (Gilgal Meditations Ser.). 70p. (Orig.). 1985. pap. 5.95 (ISBN 0-916895-01-7). Gilgal Pubns.

Our Gift: Sunshine. 5.00 (ISBN 0-8198-6830-2); 4.00 (ISBN 0-8198-6831-0). Dghtrs St Paul.

Overberg, Kenneth R. To Comfort & Confront. 78p. (Orig.). 1983. pap. 2.95 (ISBN 0-914544-49-7). Living Flame Pr.

Owen, John. Sin & Temptation. Houston, James M., ed. LC 83-791. (Classics of Faith & Devotion). 1983. 10.95 (ISBN 0-88070-013-0). Multnomah.

Owen, Ray. Listening to Life. Penoi, Mary & Condit, Kay, eds. 124p. (Orig.). 1987. pap. 5.95 (ISBN 0-942316-14-2). Pueblo Pub Pr.

Padovano, Anthony. Dawn Without Darkness. LC 82-45117. (Illus.). 272p. 1982. pap. 4.95 (ISBN 0-385-18183-3, Im). Doubleday.

Page, Tom, ed. The Upper Room Disciplines, 1986. 382p. (Orig.). 1985. pap. 3.95 (ISBN 0-8358-0507-7). Upper Room.

Palau, Luis. Heart after God. LC 78-57676. 200p. 1982. pap. 3.50 (ISBN 0-930014-83-9). Multnomah.

--The Moment to Shout. LC 77-4593. 250p. 1982. pap. 3.50 (ISBN 0-930014-84-7). Multnomah.

Paramananda, Swami. Concentration & Meditation. 8th ed. 1974. pap. 3.50 (ISBN 0-911564-07-1). Vedanta Ctr.

Parks, Helen J. Holding the Ropes. LC 83-70004. 156p. 1983. 6.95 (ISBN 0-8054-5194-3). Broadman.

Parrott, JoAnn. The Sunshine Tree. 1979. pap. 2.50 (ISBN 0-911739-14-9). Abbott Loop.

Paterson, J. R. A Faith for the 1980s. 3.95x (ISBN 0-7152-0433-5). Outlook.

Paton, Alan. Instrument of Thy Peace. 124p. 1985. pap. text ed. 8.95 large print ed. (ISBN 0-8027-2494-9). Walker & Co.

Patterson, LeRoy. The Best Is Yet to Be. 192p. (Orig.). 1986. pap. 5.95 (ISBN 0-8423-0183-6). Tyndale.

Pearce, J. Winston. To Brighten Each Day. LC 83-70001. 1983. 9.95 (ISBN 0-8054-5220-6). Broadman.

Perry, Lloyd & Sell, Charles. Speaking to Life's Problems. 1983. pap. 12.95 (ISBN 0-8024-0170-8). Moody.

Peters, Dan, et al. Why Knock Rock? 272p. (Orig.). 1984. pap. 6.95 (ISBN 0-87123-440-8, 210440). Bethany Hse.

Peterson, Lorraine. If God Loves Me: Teacher's Guide. 128p. (Orig.). 1983. pap. 4.95 (ISBN 0-87123-586-2, 210586). Bethany Hse.

Pherson, Dave Mac. The Incredible Cover-Up. 1975. 8.95 (ISBN 0-88270-143-6); pap. 3.95 (ISBN 0-88270-144-4). Omega Pubns Or.

Phillips, Margaret. Songs of the Good Earth. LC 79-10731. 62p. 1980. pap. 4.95 (ISBN 0-88289-221-5). Pelican.

Phylos. A Dweller on Two Planets. LC 80-8896. (Harper's Library of Spiritual Wisdom). 424p. 1981. pap. 10.95 (ISBN 0-06-066565-3, CN 4010, HarpR). Har-Row.

Pierson, Paul E. Themes from Acts. LC 82-80153. (Bible Commentary for Laymen Ser.). (Orig.). 1982. pap. 3.50 (ISBN 0-8307-0819-7, S361107). Regal.

Piper, John. Desiring God: Meditations of a Christian Hedonist. (Critical Concern Ser.). 1987. 12.95 (ISBN 0-88070-169-2). Multnomah.

Plantinga, Cornelius, Jr. Beyond Doubt: A Devotional Response to Questions of Faith. LC 80-10647. (Illus.). 256p. (Orig.). 1980. pap. text ed. 8.95 (ISBN 0-933140-12-6); pap. text ed. 5.95 leader's guide (ISBN 0-933140-61-4). CRC Pubns.

Poganski, Donald J. Forty Object Lessons. LC 72-86233. 160p. 1973. pap. 4.50 (ISBN 0-570-03148-6, 12-2283). Concordia.

Pollard, Frank. Keeping Free. LC 82-73932. 1983. 4.95 (ISBN 0-8054-5216-8). Broadman.

Ponder, Catherine. Dare to Prosper. LC 82-74520. 80p. 1983. pap. 3.00 (ISBN 0-87516-511-7). De Vorss.

--Open Your Mind to Receive. LC 82-74283. 128p. 1983. pap. 4.50 (ISBN 0-87516-507-9). De Vorss.

Pope John Paul II. Words of Certitude. 266p. 1985. pap. 7.95 large print ed. (ISBN 0-8027-2477-9). Walker & Co.

Popoff, Peter. Set Free from Satan's Slavery. Tanner, Don, ed. LC 82-83455. 64p. 1982. pap. 2.00 (ISBN 0-938544-17-9). Faith Messenger.

Pratney, Winkey. El Joven y Su Dios. (El Joven y Sus Inquietudes Ser.). 1982. 2.95 (ISBN 0-88113-163-6). Edit Betania.

--El Joven y Su Mundo. (El Joven y Sus Inquietudes). 1982. 2.50 (ISBN 0-88113-164-4). Edit Betania.

--El Joven y Sus Amigos. (El Joven y Sus Inquietudes Ser). 1982. 2.25 (ISBN 0-88113-162-8). Edit Betania.

--El Joven y Sus Dilemas. (El Joven y Sus Inquietudes). 1982. 2.50 (ISBN 0-88113-165-2). Edit Betania.

The Prayer of Recollection: St. Teresa of Avila. 1983. 1.95 (ISBN 0-87193-208-3). Dimension Bks.

Price, Carl E. Writings in the Dust. 112p. (Orig.). 1984. pap. 4.75 (ISBN 0-8358-0474-7). Upper Room.

Price, Eugenia. What Really Matters. LC 82-25236. (Illus.). 120p. 1983. 7.95 (ISBN 0-385-27659-1, Dial). Doubleday.

Pronzato, Alessandro. Meditation on the Sand. LC 82-24513. (Ital.). 104p. (Orig.). 1983. pap. 5.95 (ISBN 0-8189-0457-7). Alba.

Prophet, Elizabeth C. Where the Eagles Gather: Vol. 24, Bks. I & II. LC 81-86682. 636p. 1982. 35.90; Bk. I. 17.95 (ISBN 0-916766-49-7); Bk. II. 17.95 (ISBN 0-916766-57-8). Summit Univ.

Prophet, Elizabeth C., ed. Pearls of Wisdom: A Prophecy of Karma, to the Earth & Her Evolutions, Vol. 23. LC 81-50418. 540p. 1980. 14.95 (ISBN 0-916766-41-1). Summit Univ.

--Pearls of Wisdom 1975: El Morya-On Discipleship East & West, Vol. 18. LC 79-64047. 349p. 1979. 18.95 (ISBN 0-916766-15-2). Summit Univ.

Prophet, Mark & Prophet, Elizabeth, eds. Pearls of Wisdom 1965: The Mechanization Concept. LC 79-89833. 297p. 1979. 16.95 (ISBN 0-916766-35-7). Summit Univ.

--Pearls of Wisdom 1969: Kuthumi-On Selfhood, Vol. 12. LC 79-53229. 314p. 1979. 17.95 (ISBN 0-916766-34-9). Summit Univ.

Pruitt, Robert J. And Then Shall the End Come. 1979. pap. 1.95 (ISBN 0-934942-20-X). White Wing Pub.

Purdy, Edna I. The Walk down the Road to Tomorrow. 1983. 6.95 (ISBN 0-8062-2172-0). Carlton.

Quoist, Michael. Prayers. 1975. pap. 5.95 (ISBN 0-380-00406-2, 60244-X). Avon.

Quoist, Michel. With Open Heart. 264p. (Orig.). 1983. pap. 8.95 (ISBN 0-8245-0569-7). Crossroad NY.

Rainbow Bridge II: Link with the Soul Purification. 1981. pap. 8.50 (ISBN 0-87613-078-3). New Age.

Raines, Robert A. A Faithing Oak: Meditations from the Mountain. LC 82-12720. 128p. 1982. 9.95 (ISBN 0-8245-0485-2). Crossroad NY.

Raphael, Audrey M. Growing Pains. (Illus.). 68p. 1985. 6.95 (ISBN 0-533-06210-1). Vantage.

Ravenhill, Leonard. Porque No Llega el Avivamiento. 144p. 1980. 2.75 (ISBN 0-88113-250-0). Edit Betania.

--Revival God's Way. LC 83-15589. 128p. 1983. text ed. 7.95 (ISBN 0-87123-580-3). Bethany Hse.

Redemptorist Pastoral Publication. Jesus Loves You. 80p. 1983. 4.95 (ISBN 0-89243-175-X). Liguori Pubns.

Reeve, Pamela. La Fe Es. Orig. Title: Faith Is. (Span.). 50p. 1983. spiral bd 4.95 (ISBN 0-930014-96-0). Multnomah.

Reid, David R. Thoughts for Growing Christians. LC 82-7913. 160p. 1982. pap. 3.95 (ISBN 0-8024-2200-4). Moody.

Rew, Lois J. God's Green Liniment. LC 81-84183. (Illus.). 208p. (Orig.). 1981. pap. 5.95 (ISBN 0-938462-02-4). Green Leaf CA.

Reyner, J. H. Gurdjieff in Action. 117p. 1982. 12.95 (ISBN 0-04-294117-2). Allen Unwin.

Richards, Franklin D. The Challenge & the Harvest. LC 82-74368. 208p. 1983. 7.95 (ISBN 0-87747-939-9). Deseret Bk.

Richter, Betts. Something Special Within. 2nd ed. (Illus.). 48p. 1982. pap. 4.50 (ISBN 0-87516-488-9). De Vorss.

Rifkin, Jeremy & Howard, Ted. The Emerging Order: God in the Age of Scarcity. (Epiphany Bks.). 1983. pap. 2.95 (ISBN 0-345-30464-0). Ballantine.

Roberts, Peg. Devotions for New Parents. 85p. 1984. 4.95 (ISBN 0-8010-7727-3). Baker Bk.

Robinson, James W. The Beauty of Being Prepared. 1982. 4.25 (ISBN 0-89536-548-0, 0213). CSS of Ohio.

Roeck, Alan L. Twenty-Four Hours a Day for Everyone. LC 78-52007. 383p. (Orig.). 1977. pap. 5.95 (ISBN 0-89486-040-2). Hazelden.

Roos, Richard. Christwalk. 208p. (Orig.). 1985. pap. 7.95 (ISBN 0-8091-2667-2). Paulist Pr.

Rosage, David E. Encountering the Lord in Daily Life. 160p. (Orig.). 1983. pap. 4.50 (ISBN 0-914544-45-4). Living Flame Pr.

Rosemergy, Jim. A Recent Revelation. LC 81-50146. 137p. 1981. 5.95 (ISBN 0-87159-002-6). Unity School.

Rowe, Lois. On Call. 1984. 8.95 (ISBN 0-8010-7724-9). Baker Bk.

Rowthorn, Jeffrey W. The Wideness of God's Mercy: Litanies to Enlarge Our Prayer, 2 vols. Set. pap. 29.95 (ISBN 0-86683-789-2, HarpR). Har-Row.

Rudowski, Peter. The Gospel in Madison Avenue. 1983. 3.85 (ISBN 0-89536-644-4, 0741). CSS of Ohio.

Russell, Letty M. Becoming Human. LC 81-23121. (Library of Living Faith: Vol. 2). 114p. 1982. pap. 5.95 (ISBN 0-664-24408-4). Westminster.

Russell, Marjorie H. Handbook of Christian Meditation. 1978. pap. 5.95 (ISBN 0-8159-5713-0). Devin.

Ruth & Naomi. (Arch Book Ser.: No. 21). 1984. pap. 0.99 (ISBN 0-570-06188-1, 59-1289). Concordia.

Rynberg, Elbert. Lithuania Calling Collect: An Exploration of the Roads to Love. 160p. 1983. 8.50 (ISBN 0-682-49970-6). Exposition Pr FL.

St. Catherine of Siena. The Dialogue of St. Catherine of Siena. Thorold, Algar, tr. from It. & intro. by. 1976. pap. 6.00 (ISBN 0-89555-037-7). TAN Bks Pubs.

Saloff-Astakhoff, N. I. Judith. 160p. 1980. 1.00 (ISBN 0-88113-290-X). Edit Betania.

Sanderson, Joyce. Why Are You Here Now? 83p. (Orig.). 1981. pap. 6.95 (ISBN 0-942494-10-5). Coleman Pub.

Sanford, Agnes. The Healing Touch of God. (Epiphany Ser.). 224p. 1983. pap. 2.50 (ISBN 0-345-30661-9). Ballantine.

Saraydarian, Torkom. I Was. LC 77-86723. 1981. pap. 5.00 (ISBN 0-911794-43-3). Aqua Educ.

--Psyche & Psychism, 2 vols. LC 80-67684. 1981. Set. 60.00 (ISBN 0-911794-06-9). Aqua Educ.

Satir, Virginia. Meditations & Inspirations. LC 85-13302. 96p. (Orig.). 1985. pap. 5.95 (ISBN 0-89087-421-2). Celestial Arts.

Savelle, Jerry. Man's Crown of Glory. 96p. (Orig.). 1983. pap. 2.75 (ISBN 0-89274-169-4, HH-169). Harrison Hse.

--Spirit of Might. 77p. (Orig.). 1982. pap. 2.50 (ISBN 0-89274-242-9, HH-242). Harrison Hse.

Schaeffer, Edith. Everybody Can Know. 1978. 8.95 (ISBN 0-8423-0786-9). Tyndale.

Schaeffer, Franky. A Time for Anger. LC 82-71981. 192p. 1982. pap. 6.95 (ISBN 0-89107-263-2, Crossway Bks). Good News.

Schaffer, Ulrich. For the Love of Children. LC 79-2984. 128p. (Orig.). 1980. pap. 3.95i (ISBN 0-06-067084-3, RD 310, HarpR). Har-Row.

Schall, James V. Unexpected Meditations Late in the Twentieth Century. 142p. 1986. 9.95 (ISBN 0-8199-0885-1). Franciscan Herald.

Scheing, Theresa & Savary, Lou. Our Treasured Heritage. 176p. 1986. pap. 8.95 (ISBN 0-8245-0731-2). Crossroad NY.

Schlink, Basilea. Asi Seremos Diferentes. 224p. 1976. 3.75 (ISBN 0-88113-004-4). Edit Betania.

--Secreto de la Oracion Diaria. 96p. 2.50 (ISBN 0-88113-201-2). Edit Betania.

Schreiber, B. C. Meditations for Mature Christians. LC 85-90050. 1985. 13.95 (ISBN 0-533-06578-X). Vantage.

Schroeder, David. Solid Ground: Facts of the Faith for Young Christians. Bubna, Paul, frwd. by. 255p. 1982. pap. 4.95 (ISBN 0-87509-323-X); Leader's guide 2.95 (ISBN 0-87509-326-4). Chr Pubns.

Schucman, Helen. Gifts of God. LC 81-70309. 1982. 20.00 (ISBN 0-9606388-1-4). Found Inner Peace.

Schuller, Robert H. Living Powerfully One Day at a Time. 400p. 1983. pap. 7.95 (ISBN 0-8007-5113-2, Power Bks). Revell.

Schumacher, Evelyn Ann, Sr. Presence Through the Word. 144p. (Orig.). 1983. pap. 2.95 (ISBN 0-914544-46-2). Living Flame Pr.

Scientific Healing Affirmations. pap. 7.95 (ISBN 0-937134-15-5). Amrita Found.

Scott, Robert L., Jr. God Is Still My Co-Pilot. 1967. 25.00 (ISBN 0-317-17716-8). Beachcomber Bks.

Seamands, John T. Power for the Day: 108 Meditations from Matthew. LC 75-45044. Repr. of 1976 ed. 28.00 (ISBN 0-8357-9020-7, 2016391). Bks Demand UMI.

Seymour, Peter, compiled by. Moments Bright & Shining: Three Hundred & Sixty-Five Thoughts to Enjoy Day by Day. (Illus.). 1979. 6.95 (ISBN 0-8378-1706-4). Gibson.

Shaffer, Floyd. If I Were a Clown. LC 84-11000. 112p. (Orig.). 1984. pap. 5.95 (ISBN 0-8066-2082-X, 10-3198). Augsburg.

Shannon, Foster H. God Is Light. LC 80-83606. (Illus.). 240p. (Orig.). 1981. pap. 6.95 (ISBN 0-938462-00-8). Green Leaf CA.

Shannon, Robert, et al. Sixty-Eight Communion Meditations & Prayers. 120p. (Orig.). 1984. pap. 3.95 (ISBN 0-87239-770-X, 3033). Standard Pub.

Sheng-Yen, Chang. Getting the Buddha Mind. LC 82-73979. 147p. (Orig.). 1982. pap. text ed. 5.95 (ISBN 0-9609854-0-9). Dharma Drum Pubs.

Shenk, Lois L. Out of Mighty Waters. LC 81-20116. 192p. (Orig.). 1982. 10.95 (ISBN 0-8361-1987-8); pap. 6.95 (ISBN 0-8361-1988-6). Herald Pr.

Shepherd, A. P. The Incarnation. 14p. (Orig.). 1976. pap. 1.50 (ISBN 0-88010-098-2). Anthroposophic.

Shepherd, J. Barrie. A Diary of Prayer: Daily Meditations on the Parables of Jesus. LC 80-27037. 132p. 1981. pap. 5.95 (ISBN 0-664-24352-5). Westminster.

Sherer, Michael L. Six Who Dared. 1984. 6.50 (ISBN 0-89536-663-0, 1971). CSS of Ohio.

Shilder, Joyce. God's Special Baby. (Little Learner Ser.). 24p. 1985. 5.95 (56-1553); pap. 2.95 (ISBN 0-570-04088-4). Concordia.

Shiva Das Floating Eagle Feather. Kiss of God. (Illus.). 100p. 1979. pap. 3.50 (ISBN 0-686-95426-2). Ananda Marga.

Shockley, Ann. Say Jesus & Come to Me. 288p. 1985. pap. 2.95 (ISBN 0-380-79657-0, 79657-0, Bard). Avon.

Short, Robert L. A Time to Be Born, A Time to Die. pap. 6.95i (ISBN 0-06-067677-9, RD 52, HarpR). Har-Row.

Shrii Prabhat Rainjain Sarkar. Problem of the Day. 64p. 1968. pap. 1.00 (ISBN 0-686-95454-8). Ananda Marga.

Shutt, V. Gladys. Food for Thought from God's Kettle. 1982. 8.95 (ISBN 0-533-05178-9). Vantage.

Siegel, Robert. The Kingdom of Wundle. 48p. 1982. 8.95 (ISBN 0-89107-261-6, Crossway Bks). Good News.

Simpson, A. B. Wholly Sanctified: Legacy Edition. Rev. ed. King, L. L., intro. by. 136p. 1982. pap. 4.95 (ISBN 0-87509-306-X). Chr Pubns.

Singer, Isaac B. Love & Exile: A Memoir. LC 79-7211. (Illus.). 384p. 1984. 17.95 (ISBN 0-385-14060-6). Doubleday.

Sittler, Joseph. Gravity & Grace: Reflections & Provocations. Delloff, Linda Marie, ed. LC 86-3547. 128p. (Orig.). 1986. pap. 6.95 (ISBN 0-8066-2205-9, 10-2888). Augsburg.

Smith, Chuck. Charisma vs. Charismania. LC 82-2241. 176p. (Orig.). 1983. pap. 3.95 (ISBN 0-89081-353-1). Harvest Hse.

Smith, Don I. By the River of No Return. LC 85-60311. (Illus.). 112p. 1985. pap. 5.95 (ISBN 0-932773-00-1). High Country Bks.

Smith, Edward J. There Is No Happiness Without a Feeling. 119p. 1984. 20.00 (ISBN 0-682-40130-7). Exposition Pr FL.

Smith, Gary. Songs for My Fathers. LC 83-82775. 78p. 1984. pap. 5.00 perf. bnd. (ISBN 0-916418-55-3). Lotus.

Smith, Hannah W. El Secreto de una Vida Feliz. 224p. 1980. 2.75 (ISBN 0-88113-270-5). Edit Betania.

Smith, Josie De. Senor: No Me Dejes Rodar. (Illus.). 96p. 1986. pap. 2.50 (ISBN 0-311-40042-6). Casa Bautista.

Smith, Katherine V. Chickens, Cookies, & Cuzzin George. 144p. (Orig.). 1983. pap. text ed. 7.75 (ISBN 0-687-06485-6). Abingdon.

Snyder, Bernadette. Graham Crackers, Galoshes & God. LC 82-82654. 96p. 1982. pap. 2.95 (ISBN 0-89243-164-4). Liguori Pubns.

Snyder, Bernadette M. Heavenly Hash: A Tasty Mix of a Mother's Meditations. LC 85-71564. 140p. (Orig.). 1985. pap. 6.95 (ISBN 0-87973-583-X, 583). Our Sunday Visitor.

--More Graham Crackers, Galoshes, & God. LC 85-80929. 96p. (Orig.). 1985. pap. 2.95 (ISBN 0-89243-243-8). Liguori Pubns.

Sophrony, Archimandrite. His Life Is Mine. Edmonds, Rosemary, tr. from Russian. LC 76-56815. 128p. 1977. pap. 5.95 (ISBN 0-913836-33-8). St Vladimirs.

Spell, Leonard, Sr. House of Prayer for All Nations. 174p. 1986. 12.95x (ISBN 0-9615439-1-4, 133997); pap. 9.95x (ISBN 0-9615439-2-2). Spell Assoc.

Spindle, Richard. They Never Stopped Teaching. 96p. 1982. pap. 2.50 (ISBN 0-8341-0735-X). Beacon Hill.

Spiritual Diary. 375p. (Orig.). pap. 7.95 (ISBN 0-89389-073-1). Himalayan Pubs.

Spohn, David, illus. Today's Gift. (Meditation Ser.). 400p. (Orig.). 1985. pap. 5.95 (ISBN 0-89486-302-9). Hazelden.

Sproul, R. C. In Search of Dignity. LC 82-18576. (In Search Of Ser.). 1983. 10.95 (ISBN 0-8307-0869-3, 5110407). Regal.

Sri Chinmoy. Lord, I Ask You for One Favour. 50p. (Orig.). 1975. pap. 2.00 (ISBN 0-685-61224-4). Aum Pubns.

--Lord, I Need You. 50p. 1975. pap. 2.00 (ISBN 0-88497-211-9). Aum Pubns.

--My Promise to God. 50p. (Orig.). 1975. pap. 2.00 (ISBN 0-88497-222-4). Aum Pubns.

--Supreme, Teach Me How to Cry. 100p. (Orig.). 1974. pap. 2.00 (ISBN 0-88497-120-1). Aum Pubns.

--Supreme, Teach Me How to Surrender. 100p. (Orig.). 1975. pap. 2.00 (ISBN 0-88497-237-2). Aum Pubns.

--When God-Love Descends. 50p. 1975. pap. 2.00 (ISBN 0-88497-210-0). Aum Pubns.

--When I Left God in Heaven. 50p. (Orig.). 1975. pap. 2.00 (ISBN 0-88497-223-2). Aum Pubns.

Steer, John L. & Dudley, Cliff. Vietnam, Curse or Blessing. LC 82-82016. (Illus.). 192p. (Orig.). 1982. pap. 5.95 (ISBN 0-89221-091-5). New Leaf.

Steiner, Rudolf. The Calendar of the Soul. Pusch, Ruth & Pusch, Hans, trs. from Ger. 62p. 1982. 7.95 (ISBN 0-88010-009-5). Anthroposophic.

--Verses & Meditations. Adams, George & Adams, Mary, trs. (Ger.). 253p. 1979. Repr. of 1961 ed. 9.95 (ISBN 0-85440-119-9, Pub. by Steinerbooks). Anthroposophic.

Stewart, James S. The Wind of the Spirit. 192p. 1984. pap. 6.95 (ISBN 0-8010-8250-1). Baker Bk.

Stone, James. How to Become a Great Man of God. 1981. pap. 1.95 (ISBN 0-934942-28-5). White Wing Pub.

--How to Understand the Church of God. 1981. pap. 1.95 (ISBN 0-934942-27-7). White Wing Pub.

Stum, Stephen B. Beyond Inspiration. 128p. 1984. 5.95 (ISBN 0-87159-011-5). Unity School.

Subhasita Samgraha, Vol. III & IV. Vol. III - 142 p. pap. 2.00 (ISBN 0-686-95449-1); Vol. IV - 128 p. pap. 2.00 (ISBN 0-686-99508-2). Ananda Marga.

Subramuniya. Gems of Wisdom. (Illus.). 234p. 1973. 7.00 (ISBN 0-87516-346-7); pap. 5.00 (ISBN 0-87516-345-9). De Vorss.

--Raja Yoga. (Illus.). 193p. 1973. 7.00 (ISBN 0-87516-348-3). De Vorss.

--Reflections. (On the Path Ser.). (Illus.). 72p. 1969. pap. 2.00 (ISBN 0-87516-354-8). De Vorss.

Sumrall, Lester. The Gifts & Ministries of the Holy Spirit. 1982. pap. 7.95 (ISBN 0-89274-189-9, HH-189). Harrison Hse.

--Victory & Dominion Over Fear. 104p. 1982. pap. 2.75 (ISBN 0-89274-233-X, HH-233). Harrison Hse.

Sutra, Jaina. Self-Purification. (Illus.). 8.75 (ISBN 0-88695-020-1). Concord Grove.

Swartz, Lois B. Soaring Beyond Problems: Meditations for Difficult Times. (Illus.). 72p. (Orig.). 1987. pap. 6.95 (ISBN 0-940045-00-1). Walnut Knoll Assocs.

Swift, Helen C. A Living-Room Retreat: Meditations for Home Use with a 12-Week Plan for Group Sharing. 100p. 1981. pap. text ed. 3.25 (ISBN 0-912228-95-4). St Anthony Mess Pr.

Swindoll, Charles R. Pasame Otro Ladrillo. 208p. 1980. 3.75 (ISBN 0-88113-315-9). Edit Betania.

--Standing Out: Being Real in an Unreal World. LC 82-24595. Orig. Title: Home: Where Life Makes Up Its Mind. 105p. 1983. pap. 9.95 (ISBN 0-88070-014-9). Multnomah.

Szekely, Edmond B. Father, Give Us Another Chance. (Illus.). 62p. 1969. pap. 6.80 (ISBN 0-89564-071-6). IBS Intl.

--Man in the Cosmic Ocean. (Illus.). 56p. 1970. pap. 3.50 (ISBN 0-89564-054-6). IBS Intl.

--Toward the Conquest of the Inner Cosmos. (Illus.). 64p. 1969. pap. 6.80 (ISBN 0-89564-053-8). IBS Intl.

Tales of Torture. 84p. 1977. pap. 2.00 (ISBN 0-686-95469-6). Ananda Marga.

Tari, Mel. Como un Viento Recio. 208p. 1972. 3.25 (ISBN 0-88113-041-9). Edit Betania.

Tash, Sharon. In the Potter's Hands Book. 32p. 1985. pap. 1.95 (ISBN 0-930756-96-7, 531020). Aglow Pubns.

Taylor, Blaine. Gee, You Look Good. 137p. (Orig.). 1984. pap. 6.00 (ISBN 0-914527-32-0). C-Four Res.

Taylor, Richard S. La Vida Disciplinada. 144p. 1979. 2.75 (ISBN 0-88113-341-8). Edit Betania.

Teilhard De Chardin, Pierre. Reflexions et Prieres dans L'espace-temps. 13.95 (ISBN 0-685-36601-4). French & Eur.

--Sur L'amour. pap. 6.25 (ISBN 0-685-36602-2). French & Eur.

--Sur le Bonheur. pap. 6.25 (ISBN 0-685-36603-0). French & Eur.

Ten Boom, Corrie. Each New Day. 1977. pap. 3.50 (ISBN 0-8007-8403-0, Spire Bks). Revell.

Thompson, Phyllis. Each to Her Post. 1982. pap. 3.95 (ISBN 0-340-26933-2). OMF Bks.

Thurman, Howard. The Centering Moment. LC 80-67469. 1980. pap. 6.95 (ISBN 0-913408-64-6). Friends United.

Timmons, Tim. Loneliness Is Not a Disease. (Epiphany Bks.). 1983. pap. 2.25 (ISBN 0-345-30509-4). Ballantine.

Today's Gift. (Hazelden Mediation Ser.). 400p. (Orig.). 1985. pap. 5.95 (ISBN 0-86683-504-0, HarpR). Har-Row.

Today's Gift: Daily Meditations for Families. (Hazelden Bks.). 1984. scp 6.50t (ISBN 0-86683-504-0). Har-Row.
Torres, Victor. El Hijo de la Calle Tenebrosa. 160p. 1975. 2.75 (ISBN 0-88113-100-8). Edit Betania.
Tournier, Paul. Guilt & Grace. LC 82-11882. 224p. 1983. pap. 7.95 (ISBN 0-06-068331-7, RD416, HarpR). Har-Row.
--The Meaning of Persons. LC 57-9885. 244p. 1982. pap. 7.95 (ISBN 0-686-97228-7, RD 411, HarpR). Har-Row.
Tozer, A. W. That Incredible Christian. 135p. 1964. pap. 4.45; 3.45 (ISBN 0-87509-304-3). Chr Pubns.
Tripitaka Master Hua, commentary by. Flower Adornment Sutra, Chapter 11: Pure Conduct. Buddhist Text Translation Society Staff, tr. from Chinese. (Illus.). 255p. (Orig.). 1983. pap. 9.00 (ISBN 0-917512-37-5). Buddhist Text.
--Flower Adornment Sutra, Chapter 24: Praises in the Tushita Heaven. Buddhist Text Translation Society, tr. from Chinese. (Illus.). 130p. (Orig.). 1982. pap. 5.00 (ISBN 0-917512-39-1). Buddhist Text.
--Flower Adornment Sutra, Chapter 5: Flower Adorned Sea of Worlds, Part 1. Buddhist Text Translation Society Staff, tr. from Chinese. (Illus.). 250p. (Orig.). 1983. pap. 8.50 (ISBN 0-917512-54-5). Buddhist Text.
--Flower Adornment Sutra, Chapter 9: Light Enlightenment. Buddhist Text Translation Society Staff, tr. from Chinese. (Illus.). 225p. (Orig.). 1983. pap. text ed. 8.50 (ISBN 0-88139-005-4). Buddhist Text.
Trobisch, Walter. My Journey Homeward. 140p. (Orig.). 1986. pap. 4.95 (ISBN 0-89283-299-1, Pub. by Vine Books). Servant.
Trotter, Mark. Grace All the Way Home. LC 81-52860. 1982. pap. 4.95 (ISBN 0-8358-0434-8). Upper Room.
Trueblood, D. Elton. Essays in Gratitude. LC 82-71215. 1982. 8.95 (ISBN 0-8054-6938-9). Broadman.
Tubesing, Donald A. & Tubesing, Nancy L. The Caring Question: You First or Me First - Choosing a Healthy Balance. LC 83-70501. 224p. (Orig.). 1983. pap. 3.95 (ISBN 0-8066-2007-2, 10-0968). Augsburg.
Tucker, Austin B. Morning Meditations. 99p. 1980. pap. 2.00 (ISBN 0-89323-011-1, 450). Bible Memory.
Tucker, Helen. Then the Sun Came Up. (Orig.). 1986. pap. 7.00 (ISBN 0-915541-10-6). Star Bks Inc.
Tulku, Tarthang. Crystal Mirror, Vol. III. (Illus.). 1974. pap. 6.95 (ISBN 0-913546-05-4). Dharma Pub.
Tulku, Tarthang, illus. Crystal Mirror, Vol. VII. (Illus.). 450p. (Orig.). 1984. 12.95 (ISBN 0-913546-92-5). Dharma Pub.
Twenty-Four Hours a Day. (Hazelden Bks.). scp 5.50t (ISBN 0-317-46478-7). Har-Row.
Tylenda, Joseph N., ed. Portraits in American Sanctity. 1983. 18.00 (ISBN 0-686-45830-3). Franciscan Herald.
Uhlein, Gabriele. Meditations with TM Hildegard of Bingen. LC 82-74151. (Meditations with TM). 129p. (Orig.). 1982. pap. 6.95 (ISBN 0-939680-12-2). Bear & Co.
Unruh, Fred. Questions I'd Like to Ask God. LC 80-67504. (Illus.). 64p. 1980. tchr's. guide 3.95 (ISBN 0-87303-041-9). Faith & Life.
Using Policy Simulation Analysis to Guide Correctional Reform - Utah. 7.00 (ISBN 0-318-20317-0). Natl Coun Crime.
Vander Shrier, Nettie. The Golden Thread. 169p. 1983. pap. 3.95 (ISBN 0-8024-0173-2). Moody.
Van Dusen, Wilson. The Natural Depth in Man. LC 72-78055. 197p. pap. 2.50 (ISBN 0-87785-165-4). Swedenborg.
Van Horn, Bill. Strangers. 1983. 4.00 (ISBN 0-89536-587-1, 1926). CSS of Ohio.
Vanier, Jean. I Meet Jesus: He Tells Me "I Love You". LC 81-82109. 208p. 1982. pap. 3.95 (ISBN 0-8091-2725-3). Paulist Pr.
Van Lutsenburg Maas, Adriaan. Guest among Guests. 1987. 8.95 (ISBN 0-533-06965-3). Vantage.
Vannorsdall, John W. Dimly Burning Wicks: Reflections on the Gospel after a Time Away. LC 81-70661. 112p. 1982. pap. 6.95 (ISBN 0-8006-1622-7, 1-1622). Fortress.
Van Nuys, Roscoe. Whole Man: Body Mind is Sprit. LC 77-145467. 134p. 1971. 6.95 (ISBN 0-8022-2050-9). Philos Lib.
Van Zeller, Hubert. Letters to a Soul. 1976. 7.95 (ISBN 0-87243-067-7). Templegate.
--To Be in Christ. LC 81-9793. (Illus.). 112p. 1981. 9.95x (ISBN 0-8245-0086-5). Crossroad NY.
Varberg, Mimi. Mischief, Messes & God's Grace. LC 53-1019. (Book Ser.). 56p. 1985. pap. 3.50 (ISBN 0-932305-34-2). Aglow Pubns.
Vasubhandu, Bodhisattva. The Hundred Dharmas. Master Hua, Tripitaka, commentary by. Buddhist Text Translation Society, tr. from Chinese. 130p. (Orig.). 1983. pap. 6.50 (ISBN 0-88139-003-8). Buddhist Text.
Vedanta Kesari Staff, ed. Paths of Meditation. 241p. 1980. pap. 3.25 (ISBN 0-87481-501-0). Vedanta Pr.
Veerman, David R., ed. Any Old Time, Bk. 7. 80p. 1987. pap. 5.95 (ISBN 0-89693-509-4). Victor Bks.
Verwer, George. Veintinueve Soldados de Plomo. 112p. 1981. 2.50 (ISBN 0-88113-331-0). Edit Betania.
Vishnewski, Stanley. Meditations-Dorothy Day. LC 73-133570. 104p. 1970. pap. 4.95 (ISBN 0-8091-1636-7). Paulist Pr.
Vivir la Misa. (Span.). pap. text ed. 2.75 (ISBN 0-8198-8007-8). Dghtrs St Paul.
Vivo en El Espiritu. (Span. & Eng.). pap. text ed. 2.75 (ISBN 0-8198-8006-X). Dghtrs St Paul.
Von Balthasar, Hans U. Life out of Death: Meditations on the Easter Mystery. LC 84-48704. 64p. 1985. pap. 3.50 (ISBN 0-8006-1821-1, 1-1821). Fortress.
--Origen: Spirit & Fire: A Thematic Anthology of His Writings by Hans Urs von Balthasar. Daly, Robert J., tr. LC 83-14368. 416p. 1984. 34.95x (ISBN 0-8132-0591-3). Cath U Pr.
Von Keitzell, F. By Many Infallible Proofs. 76p. pap. 4.95 (ISBN 0-88172-137-9). Believers Bkshelf.
Vuilleumier, Marion R. Meditations in the Mountains. 128p. (Orig.). 1983. pap. 7.75 (ISBN 0-687-24260-6). Abingdon.
Wagner, Clarence M. Seeds of Faith. (Vol. 11). 100p. 1981. pap. 4.00x (ISBN 0-937498-02-5). Tru-Faith.
Walchars, John. Voices on Fire: A Book of Meditations. LC 81-7767. 250p. 1981. pap. 7.95 (ISBN 0-8245-0094-6). Crossroad NY.
Walk According to the Spirit. 6.00 (ISBN 0-8198-8220-8); 5.00 (ISBN 0-8198-8221-6). Dghtrs St Paul.
Wallis, Arthur. El Ayuno Escogido por Dios. 176p. 1974. 2.95 (ISBN 0-88113-006-0). Edit Betania.
--Desafio a Triunfar. 128p. 1976. 2.50 (ISBN 0-88113-000-1). Edit Betania.
--Orad en el Espiritu. LC 82-23203. 144p. 1975. 2.75 (ISBN 0-88113-240-3). Edit Betania.
Wallis, Charles L., ed. Words of Life. 5th ed. LC 81-47850. (Illus.). 256p. 1982. 12.50 (ISBN 0-06-069239-1, HarpR). Har-Row.
Walsh, Vincent M. The Kingdom at Hand. 340p. 1982. pap. 6.00 (ISBN 0-943374-00-6). Key of David.
Ward, Benedicta, tr. Prayers & Meditations of St. Anselm. (Classics Ser.). 1979. pap. 5.95 (ISBN 0-14-044278-2). Penguin.
Watson, David. My God Is Real. LC 81-71343. 95p. 1982. pap. 4.95 (ISBN 0-89107-248-9). Good News.
Watson, Elizabeth E. Sometimes I'm Small, Sometime's I'm Tall. 1984. pap. 5.99 (ISBN 0-570-04091-4, 56-1459). Concordia.
Weatherhead, Leslie D. Antidoto Contra la Ansiedad. 1979. pap. 2.75 (ISBN 0-8358-0414-3). Upper Room.
Weir, William & Abata, Russell M. Dealing with Depression. LC 82-84045. 144p. 1983. pap. 3.50 (ISBN 0-89243-170-9). Liguori Pubns.
Weiser, Harold. The Victorious Decision. 1983. 6.75 (ISBN 0-8062-2002-3). Carlton.
Weising, Edward F. & Weising, Gwen. Singleness: An Opportunity for Growth & Fulfillment. LC 82-80197. (Radiant Life Ser.). 128p. (Orig.). 1982. pap. 2.50 (ISBN 0-88243-901-4, 02-0901); teacher's ed. 3.95 (ISBN 0-88243-196-X, 32-0196). Gospel Pub.
Wesner, Maralene & Wesner, Miles E. When God Can't Answer (Divine Limitations) LC 86-70753. 100p. 1986. pap. 4.95 (ISBN 0-936715-26-X). Diversity Okla.
Wesner, Marlene & Wesner, Miles E. The Living Word (God's Self-Disclosure) LC 86-70752. 164p. (Orig.). pap. cancelled (ISBN 0-936715-27-8). Diversity Okla.
Westphal, Arnold C. The Voyage of Life on a Paper Boat, No. 12. pap. 4.95 (ISBN 0-915398-22-2). Visual Evangels.
Wheat, Ed & De Wheat, Gaye. El Placer Sexual Ordenado por Dios. 224p. 1980. 4.25 (ISBN 0-88113-320-5). Edit Betania.
White Eagle. Prayer in the New Age. 1957. 3.95 (ISBN 0-85487-041-5). De Vorss.
Wiersbe, Warren. Thoughts for Men on the Move. 1970. pap. 3.50 (ISBN 0-8024-0132-5). Moody.
Wiersbe, Warren W. Bumps Are What You Climb On. 1980. pap. 4.95 (ISBN 0-8010-9629-4). Baker Bk.
Williams, J. L. The Fire Inside. 1984. 6.50 (ISBN 0-89536-654-1, 0634). CSS of Ohio.
Williamson, Nancy. Handy Helpful Household Hints. pap. cancelled (ISBN 0-89728-066-0). Omega Pubns Or.
Willimon, William H. On a Wild & Windy Mountain: And 25 other Mediations for the Christian Year. 144p. 1984. pap. 8.95 (ISBN 0-687-28846-0). Abingdon.
Willis, Elbert. Private Praise. 1977. 1.25 (ISBN 0-89858-009-9). Fill the Gap.
Wilson, Bob. The Good That Lives after Them. Kings, John, ed. (Illus.). 170p. 1982. 14.50 (ISBN 0-9608192-1-5); cassette 10.00. B Wilson.
Wilson, Jim. Meditation & the Fullness of Life. 76p. 1974. pap. text ed. 2.95 (ISBN 0-227-67810-9). Attic Pr.
Wing, Richard A. Three A. M. Meditations for the Middle of the Night. LC 21-786068. 144p. (Orig.). 1985. pap. 9.95 (ISBN 0-934849-00-5). Arthur Pub.
Wings of Song. 544p. 1984. 6.95 (ISBN 0-87159-176-6). Unity School.
Winters, Sandy & Brooks, Shirley. Flames of Power: A Study of Meditation, Candles & Special Insights. 64p. 1987. pap. 6.50 (ISBN 0-89540-164-9, SB-164). Sun Pub.
Wisler, G. Clifton. A Special Gift. (Voyager Ser.). 80p. 1983. pap. 3.50 (ISBN 0-8010-9661-8). Baker Bk.
Witt, Roselyn. W. Norman Cooper: A View of a Holy Man. LC 81-70657. 96p. 1982. 7.50 (ISBN 0-87516-492-7); pap. 4.50 (ISBN 0-87516-471-4). De Vorss.
Wood, June S. A Workable Faith. 1975. 6.95 (ISBN 0-8022-2152-1). Philos Lib.
Woodruff, Sue. Meditations with TM Mechtild of Magdeburg. LC 82-73366. (Meditations with TM Ser.). (Illus.). 132p. (Orig.). 1982. pap. 6.95 (ISBN 0-939680-06-8). Bear & Co.
Yeshe, Lama T. Introduction to Tantra. Landaw, Jonathan, ed. (Wisdom Basic Bk. Orange). 150p. (Orig.). 1984. pap. 8.95 (ISBN 0-86171-021-5, Wisdom Pubns). Great Traditions.
Yoder, Perry. From Word to Life. LC 81-20071. (Conrad Grebel Lecture Ser.). 288p. (Orig.). 1982. pap. 14.95x (ISBN 0-8361-1249-0). Herald Pr.
Yogananda, Paramahansa. Songs of the Soul. LC 83-60701. (Illus.). 200p. 1983. 6.50 (ISBN 0-87612-025-7). Self-Realization.
Zacharias, Paul. Celebrate Life. LC 79-93145. 78p. pap. 1.95 (ISBN 0-87785-162-X). Swedenborg.
Zahl, Paul. Who Will Deliver Us? 170p. 1985. pap. 7.95 large print ed. (ISBN 0-8027-2487-6). Walker & Co.
Zodhiates, Spiros. Why God Permits Accidents. LC 79-51340. 1982. pap. 2.25 (ISBN 0-89957-537-4). AMG Pubs.

MEETINGS, CHURCH
see Church Meetings

MEHER BABA, 1894-1969
Baba, Meher. The Narrow Lane. Le Page, William, ed. 148p. 1979. pap. 3.95 (ISBN 0-913078-39-5). Sheriar Pr.
Baba, Meher, et al. Treasures from the Meher Baba Journals. Haynes, Jane B., ed. LC 79-92169. (Illus.). 246p. 1980. pap. 6.95 (ISBN 0-913078-37-9). Sheriar Pr.
Craske, Margaret. The Dance of Love: My Life with Meher Baba. LC 80-53859. 180p. (Orig.). 1980. pap. 6.95 (ISBN 0-913078-40-9). Sheriar Pr.
Eaton, Bili. A Love So Amazing... Memories of Meher Baba. LC 84-23597. 144p. 1984. pap. 8.95 (ISBN 0-913078-55-7). Sheriar Pr.
Hopkinson, Tom & Hopkinson, Dorothy. Much Silence: The Life & Work of Meher Baba. 3rd ed. LC 74-26821. 232p. 1982. pap. 4.95 (ISBN 0-913078-53-0, Pub. by Meher Foun Australia). Sheriar Pr.
Irani, Adi K. Just to Love Him: Talks & Essays about Meher Baba. Berry, Steve & Booth, Peter, eds. LC 85-10709. 160p. (Orig.). 1985. pap. 8.95 (ISBN 0-913078-56-5). Sheriar Pr.
Kalchuri, Bhau. Let's Go to Meherabad. 120p. 1981. 10.95 (ISBN 0-940700-12-3); pap. 5.95 (ISBN 0-940700-11-5). Meher Baba Info.
Mistry, Jim, compiled by. Letters from the Mandali of Avatar Meher Baba, Vol 1. LC 83-142831. 152p. (Orig.). 1981. pap. 6.75 (ISBN 0-913078-42-5). Sheriar Pr.
Natu, Bal. Glimpses of the God-Man Meher, Baba, Vol. IV. LC 79-913293. (Illus.). 218p. (Orig.). 1984. pap. 7.95 (ISBN 0-913078-52-2). Sheriar Pr.
--Glimpses of the God-Man, Meher Baba, Vol. 2: Jan. 1949-Jan. 1952. (Illus.). 406p. 1979. pap. 7.95 (ISBN 0-913078-38-7). Sheriar Pr.
Schloss, Malcolm & Purdom, Charles. Three Incredible Weeks with Meher Baba. Frederick, Filis, ed. LC 80-109542. (Illus.). 165p. 1979. pap. 5.95 (ISBN 0-913078-36-0). Sheriar Pr.
Shifrin, Adah. Meher Baba Is Love. 2nd ed. (Illus.). 56p. pap. 6.95. Sheriar Pr.

MELANCHTHON, PHILIPP, 1497-1560
Fagerberg, Holsten. A New Look at the Lutheran Confession. Lund, Gene J., tr. 336p. 1981. 15.50 (ISBN 0-570-03223-7, 15-2121). Concordia.
Green, Lowell C. How Melanchthon Helped Luther Discover the Gospel: The Doctrine of Justification in the Reformation. 274p. 1980. 7.95 (ISBN 0-89890-010-7). Attic Pr.
Hildebrandt, Franz. Melanchthon: Alien or Ally. LC 46-3804. 1968. Repr. of 1946 ed. 16.00 (ISBN 0-527-40600-7). Kraus Repr.
Manschreck, Clyde L. Melanchthon: The Quiet Reformer. LC 73-21263. (Illus.). 350p. 1975. Repr. of 1958 ed. lib. bdg. 27.25x (ISBN 0-8371-6131-2, MAMQ). Greenwood.
Melanchthon, Philip. The Loci Communes of Philip Melanchthon. Hill, Charles L., tr. LC 83-45649. Date not set. Repr. of 1944 ed. 32.50 (ISBN 0-404-19858-9). AMS Pr.
Richard, James W. Philip Melanchthon, the Protestant Preceptor of Germany. LC 72-82414. 1974. Repr. of 1898 ed. lib. bdg. 25.50 (ISBN 0-8337-4341-4). B Franklin.

MELANESIA
Worsley, Peter. The Trumpet Shall Sound: A Study of Cargo Cults in Melanesia. LC 67-26995. (Illus.). 1968. pap. 8.95 (ISBN 0-8052-0156-4). Schocken.

MELVILLE, HERMAN, 1819-1891
Franklin, H. Bruce. The Wake of the Gods: Melville's Mythology. 1963. pap. 16.95x (ISBN 0-8047-0137-7). Stanford U Pr.
Friedrich, Gerhard. In Pursuit of Moby Dick. 1983. pap. 2.50x (ISBN 0-87574-098-7, 098). Pendle Hill.
Gross, Theodore L. & Wertheim, S. Hawthorne, Melville, Stephen Crane: A Critical Bibliography. LC 75-142364. 1971. 14.95 (ISBN 0-02-913220-7). Free Pr.
Hamilton, William. Melville & the Gods. (Scholars Press Studies in the Humanities: No. 7). 1985. pap. 13.25 (ISBN 0-89130-741-9, 00 01 07). Scholars Pr GA.
Herbert, T. Walter, Jr. Moby Dick & Calvinism: A World Dismantled. 1977. 27.00x (ISBN 0-8135-0829-0). Rutgers U Pr.
Kenny, Vincent. Herman Melville's "Clarel". A Spiritual Autobiography. LC 73-3074. xvi, 272p. 1973. 26.00 (ISBN 0-208-01226-5, Archon). Shoe String.
Sachs, Viola. La Contre-Bible de Melville: Moby-Dick Dechiffre. 122p. 1975. pap. text ed. 13.60x (ISBN 90-2797-586-8). Mouton.
Walker, Franklin. Irreverent Pilgrims: Melville, Browne & Mark Twain in the Holy Land. LC 74-10644. (Illus.). 246p. 1974. 16.50x (ISBN 0-295-95344-6). U of Wash Pr.

MEMOIRS
see Biography
also subdivision Correspondence, Reminiscences, etc. under classes of people, e.g. Actors–Correspondence, reminiscenses, etc.

MEMORIAL SERVICE
see also Funeral Service
Silverman, Morris. Memorial Service at the Cemetery. pap. 0.95 (ISBN 0-685-64878-8). Prayer Bk.

MEMORIAL TABLETS
see Sepulchral Monuments

MEN–PRAYER-BOOKS AND DEVOTIONS
Bingham, Mindy, et al. Challenges: A Young Man's Journal for Self-Awareness & Personal Planning. Greene, Barbara & Peters, Kathleen, eds. LC 84-70108. (Illus.). 240p. 1984. pap. 12.95 (ISBN 0-911655-24-7). Advocacy Pr.
Forbes, Harrison. Reflections from the Son: For Men. (Orig.). 1986. pap. 5.00 (ISBN 0-915541-07-6). Star Bks Inc.
Monsma, Hester. Devotions for Men. 30p. 1984. pap. 1.25 (ISBN 0-8010-2941-4). Baker Bk.
Overton, Basil. Mule Musings. 6.95 (ISBN 0-89137-105-2); pap. 4.25. Quality Pubns.
Swanson, Steve. Bible Readings for Men. LC 83-72116. 112p. (Orig.). 1984. pap. 3.95 (ISBN 0-8066-2060-9, 10-0682). Augsburg.
Vaughn, Joe & Klug, Ron. New Life for Men: A Book for Men & the Women Who Care about Them. LC 84-21685. 144p. 1984. pap. 4.95 (ISBN 0-8066-2114-1, 10-4642). Augsburg.

MENDAEANS
see Mandaeans

MENDICANT ORDERS
see Friars

MENNO SIMONS, 1496-1561
Horst, Irvin B. A Bibliography of Menno Simons. 157p. 1962. 45.00x (ISBN 0-8361-1104-4). Herald Pr.
Vernon, Louise A. Night Preacher. LC 73-94378. (Illus.). 134p. 1969. pap. 4.50 (ISBN 0-8361-1774-3). Herald Pr.

MENNONITES
see also Amish
Bechler, Leroy. The Black Mennonite Church in North America 1886-1986. LC 86-25691. 192p. 1986. 17.95x (ISBN 0-8361-1287-3). Herald Pr.
Bender, Harold S. & Smith, C. Henry, eds. Mennonite Encyclopedia, 4vols. 1956-1969. Set. 160.00x (ISBN 0-8361-1018-8); 45.00x ea. Vol. 1 (ISBN 0-8361-1118-4). Vol. 2 (ISBN 0-8361-1119-2). Vol. 3 (ISBN 0-8361-1120-6). Vol. 4 (ISBN 0-8361-1121-4). Herald Pr.

Boynton, Linda L. The Plain People: An Ethnography of the Holdeman Mennonites. (Illus.). 222p. (Orig.). 1986. pap. text ed. 9.95x (ISBN 0-88133-198-8). Sheffield Wisc.
Buffington, Albert F., et al. Something for Everyone, Something for You: Essays in Memoriam Albert Franklin Buffington, Vol. 14. (Illus.). 1980. 25.00 (ISBN 0-911122-41-9). Penn German Soc.
Cummings, Mary L., ed. Full Circle: Stories of Mennonite Women. LC 78-66879. 1978. pap. 5.25 (ISBN 0-87303-014-1). Faith & Life.
Drescher, John M. Now Is the Time to Love. LC 73-123411. 144p. 1970. pap. 1.50 (ISBN 0-8361-1641-0). Herald Pr.
Dyck, C. J., ed. Something Meaningful for God. LC 80-10975. (MCC Story Ser.: Vol. 4). 408p. (Orig.). 1981. pap. 7.95x (ISBN 0-8361-1244-X). Herald Pr.
Dyck, Cornelius J. Twelve Becoming, Biographies of Mennonite Disciples from the Sixteenth to the Twentieth Century. LC 73-75174. 1973. pap. 4.50 (ISBN 0-87303-865-7). Faith & Life.
Epp, Frank H. Mennonites in Canada, Nineteen Twenty to Nineteen Forty, Vol. II. LC 82-81339. 640p. 1982. text ed. 21.95x (ISBN 0-8361-1255-5). Herald Pr.
Erb, Paul. South Central Frontiers. LC 74-12108. (Studies in Anabaptist & Mennonite History, No. 17). (Illus.). 448p. 1974. 19.95x (ISBN 0-8361-1196-6). Herald Pr.
Eshleman, H. Frank. Historic Background & Annals of the Swiss & German Pioneer Settlers of Southeastern Pennsylvania & of Their Remote Ancestors. LC 77-86809. 386p. 1982. Repr. of 1917 ed. 20.00 (ISBN 0-8063-0105-8). Genealog Pub.
Froese, J. A. Witness Extraordinary: A Bibliography of Elder Heinrich Voth, 1851-1918. (Trailblazer Ser.). 60p. (Orig.). 1975. pap. 1.00 (ISBN 0-919797-20-2). Kindred Pr.
Gallardo, Jose. El Concepto Biblico de Justicia. LC 86-80343. (Title from Mennonite Faith Ser.). 80p. (Orig.). 1986. pap. 1.50X (ISBN 0-8361-1285-7). Herald Pr.
Glatfelter, Charles H. Pastors & People: German & Lutheran Reformed Churches in the Pennsylvania Field, 1717-1793, Vol. II, The History. LC 80-83400. (Penn. German Ser.: Vol. 15). (Illus.). 25.00 (ISBN 0-911122-44-3). Penn German Soc.
Goossen, Rachel W. Meetingplace: A History of the Mennonite Church of Normal 1912-1987. Stutzman, Terry, ed. LC 86-63769. (Illus.). 192p. 1987. text ed. 25.00 (ISBN 0-9617978-0-0); pap. text ed. 18.00 (ISBN 0-9617978-1-9). Mennonite Church.
Hartzler, Jonas S. Mennonites in the World War: Or, Nonresistance under Test. LC 76-137543. (Peace Movement in America Ser). 246p. 1972. Repr. of 1922 ed. lib. bdg. 18.95x (ISBN 0-89198-071-7). Ozer.
Hiebert, Clarence. The Holdeman People: The Church in Christ, Mennonite, 1869-1969. LC 72-94133. 1973. 17.95 (ISBN 0-87808-411-8). William Carey Lib.
Hiebert, Clarence, ed. Brothers in Deed to Brothers in Need. new ed. LC 74-76588. (Illus.). 486p. 1974. 29.95 (ISBN 0-87303-037-0). Faith & Life.
Horsch, John. Mennonites in Europe. (Illus.). 414p. 1950. 12.95 (ISBN 0-8361-1395-0). Herald Pr.
Hostetler, John A. Mennonite Life. 2nd ed. LC 82-83963. (Illus.). 48p. 1983. pap. 4.95 (ISBN 0-8361-1995-9). Herald Pr.
Hostetler, John A. & Huntington, Gertrude E. Children in Amish Society: Socialization & Community Education. LC 72-157454. (Case Studies in Education & Culture). 1971. pap. text ed. 9.95 (ISBN 0-03-077750-X, HoltC). HR&W.
Kennel, Leroy. Mennonites: Who & Why. LC 63-17081. 32p. 1966. pap. 1.00 (ISBN 0-8361-1396-9). Herald Pr.
Kisare. Kisare, A Mennonite of Kiseru: An Autobiography As Told to Joseph C. Shenk. Shenk, Joseph C., as told to. (Illus.). 194p. 1984. 5.00 (ISBN 0-9613368-1-1). E Mennonite Bd.
Kraus, C. Norman. The Authentic Witness. LC 78-24012. 200p. 1981. pap. 5.95 (ISBN 0-8361-1959-2). Herald Pr.
Kraybill, Donald B. Ethnic Education: The Impact of Mennonite Schooling. LC 77-81022. 1977. soft bdg. 11.95 (ISBN 0-88247-480-4). R & E Pubs.
Lapp, John A. The Mennonite Church in India: Eighteen Ninety-Seven to Nineteen Sixty-Two. LC 75-186445. 248p. 1972. 12.95 (ISBN 0-8361-1122-2). Herald Pr.
Mecenseffy, Grete. Osterreichische Tauferakten Two. (Tauferakten Kommission Ser.). 544p. 1973. 40.00x (ISBN 0-8361-1192-3). Herald Pr.
Mennonite Brethren Church Gesangbuch. 590p. 1955. 9.95x (ISBN 0-919797-17-2). Kindred Pr.
The Mennonite Encyclopedia, 4 vols. 3800p. Set. 160.00x (ISBN 0-8361-1018-8); 45.00ea (ISBN 0-317-37852-X). Herald Pr.
The Mennonite Hymnal. 640p. 1960. round notes 7.95 (ISBN 0-317-37871-6); shape notes 7.95 (ISBN 0-317-37872-4); large print 11.95 (ISBN 0-317-37873-2). Herald Pr.
The Mennonite Hymnal Loose-Leaf Edition. 640p. 1969. round notes 14.95 (ISBN 0-317-37874-0); shape notes 14.95 (ISBN 0-317-37875-9). Herald Pr.
The Mennonite Quarterly Review: Goshen, Ind., 1927-1976, Vols. 1-50. Set. lib. bdg. 2375.00 (ISBN 0-686-77268-7); lib. bdg. 47.50 ea. AMS Pr.
Miller, Levi. Our People: The Amish & Mennonites of Ohio. LC 82-84405. (Illus.). 56p. (Orig.). 1983. pap. 2.50 (ISBN 0-8361-3331-5). Herald Pr.
Miller, Paul M. Servant of God's Servants: The Work of a Christian Minister. LC 63-15499. (The Conrad Grebel Lectures: 1963). pap. 59.00 (ISBN 0-317-26613-6, 2025423). Bks Demand UMI.
Neff, Larry M. & Weiser, Frederick S., eds. The Account Book of Conrad Weiser: Berks County, Pennsylvania, 1746-1760. LC 81-84666. (Sources & Documents of the Pennsylvania Germans Ser.: No. 6). (Illus.). 1981. 15.00 (ISBN 0-911122-43-5). Penn German Soc.
Plett, C. F. The Story of the Kimmer Mennonite Brethren Church. pap. 12.00 (ISBN 0-919797-51-2). Herald Pr.
Ratzlaff, Erich. Ein Leben Fur Den Herrn. 171p. (Orig.). 1985. pap. 6.75 (ISBN 0-919797-37-7). Kindred Pr.
Redekop, Calvin. Strangers Become Neighbors. LC 80-13887. (Studies in Anabaptist & Mennonite History Ser.: No. 22). (Illus.). 312p. 1980. 24.95x (ISBN 0-8361-1228-8). Herald Pr.
Redekop, Calvin W. The Old Colony Mennonites: Dilemmas of Ethnic Minority Life. LC 69-13192. (Illus.). 302p. 1969. 22.00x (ISBN 0-8018-1020-5). Johns Hopkins.
Rich, Elaine S. Mennonite Women: A Story of God's Faithfulness. LC 82-15452. 256p. 1983. pap. 9.95 (ISBN 0-8361-3311-0). Herald Pr.
Rindzinsky, Milka, tr. from English. Confesion de fe las Iglesias Menonitas. 32p. (Orig.). 1983. pap. 0.60x (ISBN 0-8361-1258-X). Herald Pr.
Ruth, John L. Conrad Grebel: Son of Zurich (Biography) LC 75-8829. 160p. 1975. 9.95 (ISBN 0-8361-1767-0). Herald Pr.
--Mennonite Identity & Literary Art. 72p. 1978. pap. 1.95 (ISBN 0-8361-1861-8). Herald Pr.
Schelbert, Leo. Swiss Migration to America: The Swiss Mennonites. Cordasco, Francesco, ed. LC 80-891. (American Ethnic Groups Ser.). 1981. lib. bdg. 38.50x (ISBN 0-405-13452-5). Ayer Co Pubs.
Seguy, J. Les Assemblees Anabaptistes-Mennonites de France. 1977. 64.00x (ISBN 90-279-7524-8). Mouton.
Shenk, Wilbert R., compiled by. Bibliography of Henry Venn's Printed Writings. (Mennonite Missionary Studies: Pt. 4). 100p. 1975. pap. 3.75x (ISBN 0-8361-1203-2). Herald Pr.
Smith, Tilman R. Boards: Purposes, Organization, Procedures. LC 78-62628. 64p. 1978. pap. 1.95 (ISBN 0-8361-1862-6). Herald Pr.
Smith, Willard H. Mennonites in Illinois, No. 24. LC 83-152. (Studies in Anabaptist & Mennonite History Ser.). 616p. 1983. 24.95x (ISBN 0-8361-1253-9). Herald Pr.
Toews, John B. Czars, Soviets & Mennonites. LC 81-71490. (Illus.). 221p. 1982. pap. 10.95 (ISBN 0-87303-064-8). Faith & Life.
Unrau, Ruth. Encircled: Stories of Mennonite Women. LC 86-80403. (Illus.). 352p. 1986. pap. 12.95 (ISBN 0-87303-114-8). Faith & Life.
Wenger, J. C., ed. They Met God: A Number of Conversion Accounts & Personal Testimonies of God's Presence & Leading in the Lives of Children. LC 64-15344. pap. 48.00 (ISBN 0-317-26611-X, 2025422). Bks Demand UMI.
Wiebe, Katie F. Who Are the Mennonite Brethern? LC 84-82049. 107p. (Orig.). 1984. pap. 5.95 (ISBN 0-919797-31-8). Kindred Pr.
--Women among the Brethren: Stories of Fifteen Mennonite Brethren & Krimmer Mennonite Brethren Women. LC 79-54802. 197p. (Orig.). 1979. pap. 6.95 (ISBN 0-935196-00-5). Kindred Pr.
Yoder, Edward. Edward: Pilgrimage of a Mind. Yoder, Ida, ed. & pref. by. (Illus.). 512p. 1985. 20.00 (ISBN 0-9614083-0-8). Yoder.

MENNONITES–BIBLIOGRAPHY

Giesbrecht, Herbert. The Mennonite Brethren Church: A Bibliographic Guide. 99p. (Orig.). 1983. pap. 7.95 (ISBN 0-919797-28-8). Kindred Pr.
Springer, Nelson & Klassen, A. J., eds. Mennonite Bibliography, 2 vols. LC 77-9105. 1977. 78.00x ea. Vol. 1 (ISBN 0-8361-1206-7). Vol. 2 (ISBN 0-8361-1207-5). Set. 147.50. Herald Pr.

MENNONITES–CATECHISM AND CREEDS

Erb, Paul. We Believe. LC 69-15831. 112p. (Orig.). 1969. pap. 3.95 (ISBN 0-8361-1587-2). Herald Pr.
Gallardo, Jose. The Way of Biblical Justice. LC 82-83386. (Mennonite Faith Ser.: Vol. 11). 80p. (Orig.). 1983. pap. 1.50 (ISBN 0-8361-3321-8). Herald Pr.
Harder, Helmut. Guide to Faith. LC 79-50682. 1979. pap. 3.95 (ISBN 0-87303-022-2). Faith & Life.
Kaufman, Milo. The Way of True Riches. LC 79-83505. (Mennonite Faith Ser: No. 6). 64p. 1979. pap. 1.50 (ISBN 0-8361-1885-5). Herald Pr.
Mennonite Church. Mennonite Confession of Faith. LC 63-22593. 32p. (Orig.). 1963. pap. 0.95 (ISBN 0-8361-1314-4). Herald Pr.

MENNONITES–DOCTRINAL AND CONTROVERSIAL WORKS

Brief Statement of Mennonite Doctrine. pap. 2.50 (ISBN 0-8361-1324-1). Herald Pr.
Burkholder, J. R. & Redekop, Calvin, eds. Kingdom, Cross, & Community. LC 76-29663. 312p. 1976. 14.95 (ISBN 0-317-37847-3). Herald Pr.
Detweiler, Richard C. Mennonite Statements on Peace. 80p. (Orig.). 1968. pap. 2.95 (ISBN 0-8361-1581-3). Herald Pr.
Fairfield, James G. All That We Are We Give. LC 77-14510. 192p. 1977. pap. 5.95 (ISBN 0-8361-1839-1). Herald Pr.
Lederach, Paul M. Teaching in the Congregation. LC 79-83594. (Mennonite Faith Ser: No. 7). 1979. pap. 1.50 (ISBN 0-8361-1886-3). Herald Pr.
--A Third Way. LC 80-26280. 152p. 1980. pap. 6.95 (ISBN 0-8361-1934-7). Herald Pr.
Waltner, James. This We Believe. LC 68-20281. 1968. pap. 5.95 (ISBN 0-87303-845-2). Faith & Life.
Wenger, J. C. The Book We Call the Bible. LC 79-89440. (Mennonite Faith Ser.: No. 8). 80p. 1980. pap. 1.50 (ISBN 0-8361-1908-8). Herald Pr.
--El Camino de la Paz. Casas, Arnoldo J., ed. Vilela, Ernesto S., tr. LC 79-89311. (Mennonite Faith Ser.: No. 4). (Span.). 1979. pap. 1.50x (ISBN 0-8361-1226-1). Herald Pr.
--El Camino de una Nueva Vida. Casas, Arnold J., ed. Vilela, Ernesto S., tr. LC 79-89310. (Mennonite Faith Ser.: No. 3). (Span.). 72p. 1979. pap. 1.50x (ISBN 0-8361-1224-5). Herald Pr.
--Como Surgieron los Menonitas. Casas, Arnold J., ed. Vilela, Ernesto S., tr. LC 79-89306. (Mennonite Faith Ser.: No. 1). (Span.). 72p. 1979. pap. 1.50x (ISBN 0-8361-1222-9). Herald Pr.
--Los Discipulos de Jesus. Casas, Arnoldo J., ed. Vilela, Ernesto S., tr. LC 79-89308. (Mennonite Faith Ser.: No. 5). (Span.). 72p. 1979. pap. 1.50x (ISBN 0-8361-1225-3). Herald Pr.
--A Faith to Live by. LC 79-89441. (Mennonite Faith Ser.: No. 9). 1980. pap. 1.50 (ISBN 0-8361-1909-6). Herald Pr.
--Que Creen los Menonitas. Casas, Arnoldo J., ed. Vilela, Ernesto S., tr. from Eng. LC 79-89307. (Mennonite Faith Ser.: No. 2). (Span.) 72p. 1979. pap. 1.50x (ISBN 0-8361-1223-7). Herald Pr.
--What Mennonites Believe, Vol. 2. LC 77-86338. 72p. 1977. pap. 1.50 (ISBN 0-8361-1833-2). Herald Pr.
Wenger, John C., ed. Complete Writings of Menno Simons: Circa 1496-1561. Verduin, Leonard, tr. LC 55-9815. 1104p. 1956. 35.00 (ISBN 0-8361-1353-5). Herald Pr.
Widmer, Pierre. Some People Are Throwing You Into Confusion. LC 83-82879. (Mennonite Faith Ser.: No. 14). 80p. 1984. pap. 1.50 (ISBN 0-8361-3358-7). Herald Pr.
Yoder, Edward. Estudios de Doctrina Christiana: Dios. Jesucristo, el Espiritu Santo, Pt. 1. 123p. 1973. pap. 0.60x (ISBN 0-8361-1190-7). Herald Pr.
Yoder, Marvin K. What We Believe about Children. LC 83-82878. (Mennonite Faith Ser.: No. 13). 72p. 1984. pap. 1.50 (ISBN 0-8361-3357-9). Herald Pr.

MENNONITES–HISTORY

Bender, Harold S. Conrad Grebel, c. 1498-1526: The Founder of the Swiss Brethren Sometimes Called Anabaptists. (Studies in Anabaptist & Mennonite History Ser.: No. 6). pap. 85.80 (ISBN 0-317-28810-5, 2020335). Bks Demand UMI.
Bender, Urie. Four Earthen Vessels. 320p. 1982. pap. 9.95x (ISBN 0-8361-1246-6). Herald Pr.
Dyck, C. J. An Introduction to Mennonite History. rev. ed. LC 81-1958. 400p. 1981. 12.95 (ISBN 0-8361-1955-X). Herald Pr.
Dyck, Cornelius J. From the Files of the MCC. LC 80-10975. (MCC Story Ser.: Vol. 1). 168p. 1980. pap. 3.95x (ISBN 0-8361-1229-6). Herald Pr.
--Responding to Worldwide Needs. LC 80-10975. (MCC Story Ser.: Vol. 2). 168p. 1980. pap. 3.95x (ISBN 0-8361-1230-X). Herald Pr.
--Witness & Service in North America. LC 80-10975. (MCC Story Ser.: Vol. 3). 1980. pap. 3.95x (ISBN 0-8361-1231-8). Herald Pr.
Ewert, David. Stalwart for the Truth: The Life & Legacy of A. H. Unruh. (Trailblazer Ser.). 148p. (Orig.). 1975. pap. 6.95 (ISBN 0-919797-18-0). Kindred Pr.
Falcon, Rafael. The Hispanic Mennonite Church in North America, 1932-1982. LC 85-30220. (Span.). 224p. 1986. 17.95x (ISBN 0-8361-1282-2). Herald Pr.
--La Iglesia Menonita Hispana en Norte America: 1932-1982. LC 85-61020. (Span.). 208p. 1985. 14.95x (ISBN 0-8361-1272-5). Herald Pr.
Fast, Heinhold. Quellen zur Geschichte der Taufer in der Schweiz, Vol. 2: Ostschweiz. (Ger.). 1974. 59.00x (ISBN 0-8361-1197-4). Herald Pr.
Glanville, Joan P. Not a Sparrow Shall Fall. 184p. (Orig.). 1984. pap. 6.35 (ISBN 0-919797-38-5). Kindred Pr.
Gleysteen, Jan. Mennonite Tourguide to Western Europe. LC 84-683. 340p. (Orig.). 1984. pap. 17.95 (ISBN 0-8361-3360-9). Herald Pr.
Goertz, Hans-Jurgen, ed. Umstrittenes Taufertum 1525-1975. 1975. 22.50x (ISBN 0-8361-1128-1). Herald Pr.
Hamm, Peter M. Continuity & Change among Canadian Mennonite Brethren. (Social Scientific Studies in Religion: Religion & Identity). 304p. 1986. 35.00 (ISBN 0-88920-189-7, Pub. by Wilfrid Laurier Canada). Humanities.
Harms, Orlando. Pioneer Publisher: The Life & Times of J. F. Harms. LC 84-82050. 116p. (Orig.). 1984. pap. 5.95 (ISBN 0-919797-33-4). Kindred Pr.
Hershberger, Guy F. War, Peace & Nonresistance. rev. ed. LC 53-7586. (Christian Peace Shelf Ser.). 375p. 1969. 15.95 (ISBN 0-8361-1449-3). Herald Pr.
Hertzler, Daniel, ed. Not by Might. LC 83-10831. 192p. (Orig.). 1983. pap. 9.95 (ISBN 0-8361-3342-0). Herald Pr.
Hess, Mahlon M. The Pilgrimage of Faith of Tanzania Mennonite Church, 1934-83. (Illus.). 176p. 1985. 5.00 (ISBN 0-9613368-2-X). E Mennonite Bd.
Horst, Samuel L. Mennonites in the Confederacy. LC 67-15991. 148p. 1967. 6.95 (ISBN 0-317-37856-2). Herald Pr.
--Mennonities in the Confederacy: A Study in Civil War Pacifism. LC 67-15991. (Illus.). 148p. 1967. 8.95x (ISBN 0-8361-1180-X). Herald Pr.
Hostetler, Beulah S. American Mennonites & Protestant Movements. (Studies in Anabaptist & Mennonnite History). 344p. 1987. 29.95x (ISBN 0-8361-1288-1). Herald Pr.
Juhnke, James C. A People of Two Kingdoms. new ed. LC 74-84697. (Mennonite Historical Ser.). (Illus.). 221p. 1975. 7.95 (ISBN 0-87303-662-X). Faith & Life.
Keller, Frank R. Preparation for Covenant Life. LC 79-53522. 1979. pap. 4.95x (ISBN 0-87303-018-4). Faith & Life.
MacMaster, Richard K. Land, Piety & Peoplehood. LC 84-15790. (Mennonite Experience in America Ser.: Vol. 1). 344p. (Orig.). 1984. pap. 12.00x (ISBN 0-8361-1261-X). Herald Pr.
MacMaster, Richard K., et al. Conscience in Crisis. LC 78-27530. (Studies in Anabapitst & Mennonite History: No. 20). 528p. 1979. 19.95x (ISBN 0-8361-1213-X). Herald Pr.
Meet the Mennonites. (Pennsylvania Dutch Books Ser.). (Illus.). 1961. 3.00 (ISBN 0-911410-05-8). Applied Arts.
Paetkau, Paul, et al. God-Man-Land. LC 78-55244. 1978. 5.25 (ISBN 0-87303-008-7). Faith & Life.
Pannabecker, Samuel F. Open Doors. LC 75-9417. (Mennonite Historical Ser.). (Illus.). 432p. 1975. 18.50 (ISBN 0-87303-636-0). Faith & Life.
Peters, George W. Foundations of Mennonite Brethren Missions. LC 83-72078. 262p. (Orig.). 1984. pap. 12.95 (ISBN 0-318-18902-X). Kindred Pr.
Redekop, Calvin W. The Old Colony Mennonites: Dilemmas of Ethnic Minority Life. LC 69-13192. pap. 80.50 (ISBN 0-317-08392-9, 2021737). Bks Demand UMI.
Redekop, John H. Two Sides, the Best of Personal Opinion, 1964-1984. 306p. (Orig.). 1984. pap. 9.95 (ISBN 0-919797-13-X). Kindred Pr.
Ruth, John L. Maintaining the Right Fellowship. LC 83-18579. (Anabaptist & Mennonite History Ser.: No. 26). 608p. 1984. 24.95x (ISBN 0-8361-1259-8). Herald Pr.
--Twas Seeding Time. LC 76-41475. 220p. 1976. pap. 5.95 (ISBN 0-8361-1800-6). Herald Pr.
Schlabach, Theron F. Gospel Versus Gospel. LC 79-15888. 352p. 1980. 17.95x (ISBN 0-8361-1220-2). Herald Pr.

Schmid, Walter & Von Murat, Leonhard. Quellen zur Geschichte der Taufer in der Schweiz, Vol. 1: Zurich. 428p. 1952. PLB 9.00x (ISBN 0-8361-1152-4). Herald Pr.
Smith, C. Henry. Story of the Mennonites. Krahn, Cornelius, ed. LC 81-65130. (Illus.). 589p. 1981. pap. 17.95 (ISBN 0-87303-069-9). Faith & Life.
Smith, Charles H. The Coming of the Russian Mennonites: An Episode in the Settling of the Last Frontier, 1874-1884. 18.25 (ISBN 0-8369-7123-X, 7957). Ayer Co Pubs.
Stucky, Solomon. For Conscience' Sake. LC 83-98283. 240p. (Orig.). pap. 9.95 (ISBN 0-8361-3333-1). Herald Pr.
Toews, J. B. The Mennonite Church in Zaire. 255p. (Orig.). 1978. pap. 3.00 (ISBN 0-919797-23-7). Kindred Pr.
Toews, John A. A History of the Mennonite Brethren Church: Pilgrims & Pioneers. LC 74-33718. 513p. (Orig.). 1975. pap. 13.95 (ISBN 0-318-18904-6). Kindred Pr.
--People of the Way. Dueck, A. J., et al, eds. 256p. 1981. 10.95 (ISBN 0-919797-15-6); pap. 7.95 (ISBN 0-919797-16-4). Kindred Pr.
Toews, John B. With Courage to Spare. 185p. (Orig.). 1978. pap. 4.95 (ISBN 0-919797-26-1); 7.95 (ISBN 0-919797-25-3). Kindred Pr.
Toews, Paul. Pilgrims & Strangers: Essays in Mennonite Brethren History. (Perspective on Mennonite Life & Thought Ser.: Vol. 1). 183p. (Orig.). 1977. pap. 5.95 (ISBN 0-919797-36-9). Kindred Pr.
Wenger, J. C. How Mennonites Came to Be. LC 77-86332. (Mennonite Faith Ser.: No. 1). 1977. pap. 1.50 (ISBN 0-8361-1832-4). Herald Pr.
Wenger, John C. Mennonite Church in America. LC 66-23903. (Mennonite History Vol. 2). 384p. 1967. 14.95x (ISBN 0-8361-1179-6). Herald Pr.
Wiens, A. K. & Wiens, Gertrude. Shadowed by the Great Wall: The Story of Kimmer Mennonite Brethren Missions in Inner Mongolia (1922-1949) LC 79-55686. 120p. (Orig.). 1979. pap. 3.95 (ISBN 0-935196-01-3). Kindred Pr.

MENNONITES–HYMNS

Brunk, J. D., ed. Church & Sunday School Hymnal with Supplement. LC 72-2053. 384p. (532 hymns & songs, & 50 german songs, words only, 1902; supplement 1911). 1902. 7.95x (ISBN 0-8361-1110-9). Herald Pr.
Coffman, S. F., ed. Church Hymnal. 536p. (657 hymns). 1927. 7.95x (ISBN 0-8361-1106-0). Herald Pr.
Hostetler, Lester & Yoder, Walter E., eds. Mennonite Hymnal. LC 69-18131. 1969. 7.50x (ISBN 0-87303-515-1). Faith & Life.

MENNONITES–JUVENILE LITERATURE

Smucker, Barbara C. Henry's Red Sea. LC 55-7810. (Christian Peace Shelf Ser.). (Illus.). 108p. 1955. 3.95 (ISBN 0-8361-1372-1). Herald Pr.

MENNONITES–MISSIONS

Barrett, Lois. The Vision & the Reality: The Story of Home Missions in the General Conference Mennonite Church. LC 83-80402. 339p. (Orig.). 1983. pap. 16.95 (ISBN 0-87303-079-6). Faith & Life.
Driver, John. Understanding the Atonement for the Mission of the Church. LC 86-3133. 288p. (Orig.). 1986. pap. 19.95 (ISBN 0-8361-3403-6). Herald Pr.
Juhnke, James C. A People of Mission: A History of General Conference Mennonite Overseas Missions. LC 78-74809. 1979. pap. 5.95 (ISBN 0-87303-019-2). Faith & Life.
Klassen, James R. Jimshoes in Vietman. LC 86-9801. (Illus.). 400p. (Orig.). 1986. pap. 14.95 (ISBN 0-8361-3412-5). Herald Pr.
Kraus, Norman C. Missions, Evangelism, & Church Growth. LC 80-10922. (Mennonite Central Committee Story Ser.). 176p. 1980. pap. 6.95 (ISBN 0-8361-1925-8). Herald Pr.
Toews, J. J. The Mennonite Brethren Mission in Latin America. 255p. (Orig.). 1975. pap. 3.00 (ISBN 0-318-18905-4). Kindred Pr.

MENNONITES–SOCIAL LIFE AND CUSTOMS

Denlinger, Martha. Real People. rev. ed. LC 74-16966. (Illus.). 96p. 1975. pap. 3.95 (ISBN 0-8361-1960-6). Herald Pr.
Dregni, Meredith S. Experiencing More with Less. LC 83-80954. 88p. (Orig.). 1983. pap. 4.95 (ISBN 0-8361-3334-X). Herald Pr.
Kaufman, Gordon D. Nonresistance & Responsibility, & Other Mennonite Essays. (Institute of Mennonite Studies: No. 5). 1979. pap. 7.95 (ISBN 0-87303-024-9). Faith & Life.
MacMaster, Richard K. Land, Piety & Peoplehood. LC 84-15790. (Mennonite Experience in America Ser.: Vol. 1). 344p. (Orig.). 1984. pap. 12.00x (ISBN 0-8361-1261-X). Herald Pr.
Redekop, Calvin W. The Old Colony Mennonites: Dilemmas of Ethnic Minority Life. LC 69-13192. pap. 80.50 (ISBN 0-317-08392-9, 2021737). Bks Demand UMI.
Stucky, Solomon. For Conscience' Sake. LC 83-98283. 240p. (Orig.). pap. 9.95 (ISBN 0-8361-3333-1). Herald Pr.

MENNONITES IN THE SOVIET UNION

Belk, Fred R. The Great Trek of the Russian Mennonites to Central Asia. LC 75-28340. (Studies in Anabaptist & Mennonite History: No. 18). pap. 63.00 (ISBN 0-317-26601-2, 2025418). Bks Demand UMI.
Friesen, P. M. The Mennonite Brotherhood in Russia (1789-1910) rev. ed. LC 78-52664. 1065p. 1980. 24.95 (ISBN 0-919797-19-9). Kindred Pr.
Harder, Geraldine G. When Apples Are Ripe. LC 73-160722. (Illus.). 224p. 1972. pap. 3.95 (ISBN 0-8361-1694-1). Herald Pr.
Smith, Charles H. The Coming of the Russian Mennonites: An Episode in the Settling of the Last Frontier, 1874-1884. 18.25 (ISBN 0-8369-7123-X, 7957). Ayer Co Pubs.
Toews, John B. Lost Fatherland: The Story of the Mennonite Emigration from Soviet Russia, 1921-1927. LC 67-23294. (Studies in Anabaptist & Mennonite History: No. 12). pap. 65.50 (ISBN 0-317-26609-8, 2025421). Bks Demand UMI.

MENTAL DEPRESSION

see Depression, Mental

MENTAL HEALING

see also Christian Science; Mind and Body; New Thought

Addington, Jack E. Secret of Healing. 204p. 1979. pap. 7.95 (ISBN 0-911336-80-X). Sci of Mind.
Althouse, Lawrence. Rediscovering the Gift of Healing. 2nd ed. 144p. 1983. pap. 5.95 (ISBN 0-87728-604-3). Weiser.
Baars, Conrad W. & Terruwe, Anna A. Psychic Wholeness & Healing: Using All the Powers of the Human Psyche. LC 81-4964. 245p. (Orig.). 1981. pap. 8.95 (ISBN 0-8189-0410-0). Alba.
Bartow, Donald W. The Adventures of Healing: How to Use New Testament Practices & Receive New Testament Results. 3rd, rev. ed. 204p. 1981. pap. 11.95 (ISBN 0-938736-19-1). Life Enrich.
Beierle, Herbert L. Quiet Healing Zone. 1980. 10.00 (ISBN 0-940480-10-7). U of Healing.
Bibb, Benjamin O. & Weed, Joseph J. Amazing Secrets of Psychic Healing. 1976. pap. 5.95 (ISBN 0-13-023762-0). P-H.
Blomgren, David K. Prophetic Gatherings in the Church. (Illus.). 100p. 1979. pap. 8.95 (ISBN 0-914936-36-0). Bible Temple.
Caleron, Eduardo, et al. Eduardo el Curandero: The Words of a Peruvian Healer. (Illus.). 200p. 1982. 20.00 (ISBN 0-913028-94-0); pap. 7.95 (ISBN 0-913028-95-9). North Atlantic.
Cayce, H. L. Gifts of Healing. 1976. pap. 1.95 (ISBN 0-87604-070-9). ARE Pr.
Challoner, H. K. The Path of Healing. LC 76-3660. 175p. 1976. pap. 5.25 (ISBN 0-8356-0480-2, Quest). Theos Pub Hse.
--Path of Healing. 10.50 (ISBN 0-8356-5227-0). Theos Pub Hse.
Cooke, Ivan. Healing by the Spirit. 1955. pap. 7.95 (ISBN 0-85487-039-3). De Vorss.
Curtiss, Harriette & Homer, F. Four-Fold Health. 1936. 4.95 (ISBN 0-87516-304-1). De Vorss.
Davis, Creath. Lord, If I Ever Needed You, It's Now! 138p. Date not set. pap. 5.95 (ISBN 0-8010-2968-6). Baker Bk.
Demaray, Donald E. Laughter, Joy, & Healing. 160p. 1987. pap. 7.95 (ISBN 0-8010-2969-4). Baker Bk.
Drakeford, John W. The Awesome Power of the Healing Thought. LC 80-70915. 1981. 8.95 (ISBN 0-8054-5294-X). Broadman.
Erickson, Milton H., et al. Healing in Hypnosis. Rossi, Ernest L. & Sharp, Florence A., eds. 1984. 19.95 (ISBN 0-8290-0739-3). New Horizon NJ.
Evensen, Ken L. Healing Love: The Inner Power of All Things. 9.95 (ISBN 0-533-04807-9). Vantage.
Fillmore, Charles. Christian Healing. 1909. 5.95 (ISBN 0-87159-017-4). Unity School.
Finkelstein, Adrian. Your Past Lives & the Healing Process. 233p. (Orig.). 1985. pap. 9.95x (ISBN 0-87418-001-5). Coleman Pub.
--Your Past Lives & the Healing Process. 233p. (Orig.). 1985. pap. 9.95x. A Finkelstein.
Fricker, E. G. God Is My Witness: The Story of the World-Famous Healer. LC 76-50557. 1977. pap. 2.75 (ISBN 0-8128-7068-9). Stein & Day.
Gross, Ralph. Praise the Lord & Rub It Out. (Illus.). 30p. (Orig.). 1981. pap. 5.00 (ISBN 0-686-32010-7). Karma Pub.
Hagin, Kenneth E. Laying on of Hands. 1980. pap. 0.50 mini bk. (ISBN 0-89276-250-0). Hagin Ministries.
Hall, Manly P. Mysticism & Mental Healing. pap. 2.50 (ISBN 0-89314-336-7). Philos Res.
Harris, Anastas. Journal of Holistic Health: Vol. VI. (Illus.). 144p. 1981. pap. 12.00 (ISBN 0-939410-07-9). Mandala Holistic.
Hudson, T. J. A New System of Mental Therapeutics & the Phenomena of Spiritism. (Illus.). 171p. 1986. 187.65 (ISBN 0-89920-138-5). Am Inst Psych.
Johnson, Tom. Your Healing Is Today. 5th ed. 64p. 1986. pap. 4.95 (ISBN 0-941992-07-1). Los Arboles Pub.
Judd, Wayne. Healing: Faith or Fraud. (Uplook Ser.). 1978. pap. 0.99 (ISBN 0-8163-0199-9, 08303-0). Pacific Pr Pub Assn.
Keshavadas, Satguru S. Healing Techniques of the Holy East. LC 80-50447. (Illus.). 116p. (Orig.). 1980. pap. 3.95 (ISBN 0-931290-30-9). Vishwa.
Khan, Inayat. The Development of Spiritual Healing. 3rd ed. LC 78-65080. 112p. pap. 4.95 (ISBN 0-900217-15-4, Pub. by Sufi Pub Co England). Hunter Hse.
--Healing & the Mind World. (Sufi Message of Hazrat Inayat Khan Ser.: Vol. 4). 288p. 1979. 14.95 (ISBN 90-6077-952-5, Pub. by Servire BV Netherlands). Hunter Hse.
King, Serge. Imagineering for Health. LC 80-53949. 211p. (Orig.). 1981. pap. 6.95 (ISBN 0-8356-0546-9, Quest). Theos Pub Hse.
Kligman, Gail. Calus: Symbolic Transformation in Romanian Ritual. LC 80-21372. (Chicago Originals Ser.). (Illus.). 240p. 1981. lib. bdg. 14.00x (ISBN 0-226-44221-7). U of Chicago Pr.
Leuser, David V. How to Send Healing Energy: Diccionari Enciclopedic D'abast Universal, 8 vols. (Catalan.). 3500p. 1974. Set. 300.00 (ISBN 84-345-3560-2, S-50517). French & Eur.
Linn, Sr. Mary J., et al. Healing the Dying. LC 79-53111. 128p. 1979. pap. 3.95 (ISBN 0-8091-2212-X). Paulist Pr.
Linn, Matthew L. & Linn, D. Healing of Memories: Prayers & Confession-Steps to Inner Healing. LC 74-17697. 112p. (Orig.). 1974. pap. 3.95 (ISBN 0-8091-1854-8). Paulist Pr.
Lorrance, Arleen. Why Me? How to Heal What's Hurting You. LC 77-88151. 186p. 1982. 6.95 (ISBN 0-916192-19-9). L P Pubns.
MacNutt, Francis. The Power to Heal. LC 77-77845. 256p. 1977. pap. 3.95 (ISBN 0-87793-133-X). Ave Maria.
Maloney, George A. Broken but Loved: Healing Through Christ's Power. LC 81-1802. 126p. (Orig.). 1981. pap. 6.95 (ISBN 0-8189-0411-9). Alba.
Mann, Warner. The Healing Power of Inversion Thinking from Soul to Body. LC 85-91344. (Metaphysics for Everyone Ser.: No. 1). (Illus.). 250p. (Orig.). 1986. 14.95 (ISBN 0-9615973-0-5); pap. 9.95 (ISBN 0-9615973-1-3). Cos Sci Orange.
Masters, Roy. The Satin Principle. LC 78-78158. 1978. pap. 6.50 (ISBN 0-933900-05-8). Foun Human Under.
Meek, George W., ed. Healers & the Healing Process. LC 77-5251. (Illus., Orig.). 1977. pap. 6.75 (ISBN 0-8356-0498-5, Quest). Theos Pub Hse.
Paramananda, Swami. Spiritual Healing. 4th ed. 1975. pap. 3.50 (ISBN 0-911564-10-1). Vedanta Ctr.
Ponder, Catherine. The Healing Secrets of the Ages. rev. ed. LC 67-26503. 278p. 1985. pap. 6.95 (ISBN 0-87516-550-8). De Vorss.
Probstein, Bobbie. Return to Center. LC 85-70723. (Illus.). 256p. (Orig.). 1985. pap. 9.95 (ISBN 0-87516-554-0). De Vorss.
Puryear, Meredith. Healing Through Meditation & Prayer. 1978. pap. 5.95 (ISBN 0-87604-104-7). ARE Pr.
Rivers, Gloria R. Cosmic Consciouness: The Highway to Wholeness. Cramer, Owen, ed. (Orig.). 1987. pap. text ed. 12.00 (ISBN 0-918341-01-9). Temple Pubns.
Rush, James E. Toward a General Theory of Healing. LC 80-8264. (Illus.). 314p. (Orig.). 1982. lib. bdg. 25.75 (ISBN 0-8191-1880-X); pap. text ed. 13.50 (ISBN 0-8191-1881-8). U Pr of Amer.
Self Healing Yoga & Destiny. 1983. 4.95 (ISBN 0-943358-06-X). Aurora Press.
Shealy, C. Norman & Myss, Caroline M. The Creation of Health: The Merger of Traditional Medical Diagnosis with Clairvoyant Insight. 270p. 1987. 14.95 (ISBN 0-913299-40-5). Stillpoint.
Smith, Cushing. I Can Heal Myself & I Will. new ed. LC 62-14344. 315p. 1980. pap. 7.95 (ISBN 0-8119-0384-2). Fell.
Society of Metaphysicians Staff, ed. Etheric Heliang. 12.00x (ISBN 0-317-43573-6, Pub. by Soc of Metaphysicians). State Mutual Bk.
Syllabus, University of Healing. 1982. 1.00. U of Healing.
Tapscott, Betty. Inner Healing Through Healing of Memories. 1975. pap. 4.95 (ISBN 0-917726-29-4). Hunter Bks.
Towne, William E. Health & Wealth from Within. 157p. 1981. pap. 9.00 (ISBN 0-89540-081-2, SB-081). Sun Pub.
Viloldo, Alberto & Krippner, Stanley. Healing States. (Illus.). 224p. 1987. pap. 8.95 (ISBN 0-671-63202-7, Fireside) (ISBN 0-671-60240-3). S&S.
Wagner, James K. Blessed to Be a Blessing. LC 80-52615. 144p. (Orig.). 1980. pap. 5.95x (ISBN 0-8358-0410-0). Upper Room.
Walkenstein, Eileen. Your Inner Therapist. LC 83-19842. 128p. 1983. pap. 8.95 (ISBN 0-664-26005-5, A Bridgebooks Publication). Westminster.
Weldon, John & Levitt, Zola. Psychic Healing. 1982. pap. 5.95 (ISBN 0-8024-6446-7). Moody.
Whipple, Leander E. Philosophy of Mental Healing. 234p. 1981. pap. 13.50 (ISBN 0-89540-110-X, SB-110). Sun Pub.
White Eagle. Heal Thyself. 1962. 3.95 (ISBN 0-85487-015-6). De Vorss.
--Spiritual Unfoldment One. 1942. 6.95 (ISBN 0-85487-012-1). De Vorss.
--Spiritual Unfoldment Two. 1969. 6.95 (ISBN 0-85487-001-6). De Vorss.
--Sunrise. 1958. 3.95 (ISBN 0-85487-016-4). De Vorss.
Wolf, William. Healers, Gurus, Spiritual Guide. LC 76-2180. 1969. pap. 6.50 (ISBN 0-933900-07-4). Foun Human Under.
Young, Alan. Spiritual Healing: Miracle or Mirage? LC 81-82932. 280p. (Orig.). 1982. pap. 7.95 (ISBN 0-87516-460-9). De Vorss.

MENTAL PRAYER

see Meditation

MENTALLY ILL–RELIGIOUS LIFE

Ahlem, Lloyd. Help for Families of the Mentally Ill. LC 12-2820. (Trauma Bks.: Ser. 2). 1983. pap. 2.75 (ISBN 0-570-08257-9). Concordia.

MERCERSBURG THEOLOGY

Maxwell, Jack M. Worship & Reformed Theology: The Liturgical Lessons of Mercersburg. LC 75-45492. (Pittsburgh Theological Monographs: No. 10). 1976. pap. 12.00 (ISBN 0-915138-12-3). Pickwick.

MERCY DEATH

see Euthanasia

MERCY SEAT

see Ark of the Covenant

MERLO, THECLA, 1894-1964

Daughters Of St. Paul. Woman of Faith. (Illus.). 1965. 3.00 (ISBN 0-8198-0179-8). Dghtrs St Paul.

MERTON, THOMAS, 1915-1968

Baker, James T. Thomas Merton: Social Critic. LC 76-132827. 184p. 1971. 17.00x (ISBN 0-8131-1238-9). U Pr of Ky.
Cashen, Richard A. Solitude in the Thought of Thomas Merton. (Cistercian Studies: No. 40). 208p. 1981. 15.50 (ISBN 0-87907-840-5); pap. 5.50 (ISBN 0-87907-940-1). Cistercian Pubns.
Dell'Isola, Frank. Thomas Merton: A Bibliography. rev. ed. LC 74-79148. (Serif Ser.: No. 31). 200p. 1975. 13.50x (ISBN 0-87338-156-4). Kent St U Pr.
Finley, James. Merton's Palace of Nowhere. LC 78-58738. 160p. 1978. pap. 3.95 (ISBN 0-87793-159-3). Ave Maria.
Forest, James H. Thomas Merton: A Pictorial Biography. LC 80-82249. (Illus.). 112p. (Orig.). 1980. pap. 5.95 (ISBN 0-8091-2284-7). Paulist Pr.
Furlong, Monica. Merton: A Biography. LC 84-48218. (Illus.). 368p. 1985. pap. 8.95 (ISBN 0-06-063078-7, RD 529, HarpR). Har-Row.
Grayston, Donald. Thomas Merton: The Development of a Spiritual Theologian. LC 84-27299. (Toronto Studies in Theology: Vol. 20). 225p. 1985. 49.95x (ISBN 0-88946-758-7). E Mellen.
Hart, Patrick, ed. The Legacy of Thomas Merton. (Cistercian Studies: No. 92). 1985. 25.95 (ISBN 0-87907-892-8); pap. 7.95 (ISBN 0-87907-992-4). Cistercian Pubns.
--The Message of Thomas Merton. (Cistercian Studies: No. 42). (Illus.). 1981. 15.95 (ISBN 0-87907-842-1); pap. 5.50 (ISBN 0-87907-942-8). Cistercian Pub.
Hawkins, Anne O. Archetypes of Conversion: The Spiritual Autobiographies of St. Augustine, John Bunyan, & Thomas Merton. LC 83-46156. 192p. 1985. 25.00 (ISBN 0-8387-5079-6). Bucknell U Pr.
Higgins, John J. Thomas Merton on Prayer. 200p. 1975. pap. 3.95 (ISBN 0-385-02813-X, Im). Doubleday.
Kramer, Victor A. Thomas Merton. (United States Authors Ser.: No. 462). 1984. lib. bdg. 17.95 (ISBN 0-8057-7402-5, Twayne). G K Hall.
Labrie, Ross. The Art of Thomas Merton. LC 79-1341. 188p. 1979. pap. 9.95x (ISBN 0-912646-55-1). Tex Christian.
Leclercq, Jean, intro. by. Thomas Merton on St. Bernard. (Cistercian Studies: No. 9). 1980. 13.95 (ISBN 0-87907-809-X); pap. 4.95 (ISBN 0-87907-909-6). Cistercian Pubns.
Lentfoehr, Sr. Therese. Words & Silence: On the Poetry of Thomas Merton. LC 78-21475. 1979. 12.50 (ISBN 0-8112-0712-9); pap. 4.95 (ISBN 0-8112-0713-7, NDP472). New Directions.

Merton, Thomas. The Hidden Ground of Love: Letters on Religious Experience & Social Concern. Shannon, William H., ed. LC 84-26045. 684p. 1985. 27.95 (ISBN 0-374-16995-0). FS&G.
--The Seven Storey Mountain. LC 78-7109. 429p. 1978. pap. 7.95 (ISBN 0-15-680679-7, Harv). HarBraceJ.
--The Seven Storey Mountain. 1978. Repr. lib. bdg. 32.00x (ISBN 0-88254-843-3, Octagon). Hippocrene Bks.
--The Seven Storey Mountain. LC 85-6375. 784p. 1985. pap. 19.95 (ISBN 0-8027-2497-3). Walker & Co.
Mott, Michael. The Seven Mountains of Thomas Merton. LC 84-10944. 1984. 24.95 (ISBN 0-395-31324-4). HM.
--The Seven Mountains of Thomas Merton. 1986. pap. 12.95 (ISBN 0-395-40451-7). HM.
Mulhearn, Timothy, ed. Getting It All Together: The Heritage of Thomas Merton. 1984. pap. 4.95 (ISBN 0-89453-380-0). M Glazier.
Nouwen, Henri J. Thomas Merton: Contemplative Critic. LC 80-8898. 176p. 1981. pap. 6.95 (ISBN 0-06-066324-3, RD 357, HarpR). Har-Row.
Palmer, Parker J. In the Belly of a Paradox: The Thought of Thomas Merton. LC 78-71769. 1979. pap. 2.50x (ISBN 0-87574-224-6). Pendle Hill.
Patnaik, Deba, ed. Geography of Holiness: The Photography of Thomas Merton. LC 80-18604. 1980. 17.50 (ISBN 0-8298-0401-3). Pilgrim NY.
Shannon, William H. Thomas Merton's Dark Path. rev. ed. 260p. 1987. pap. 8.95 (ISBN 0-374-52019-4). FS&G.
Sussman, Cornelia & Sussman, Irving. Thomas Merton. LC 80-924. 176p. 1980. pap. 3.95 (ISBN 0-385-17172-2, Im). Doubleday.
Woodcock, George. Thomas Merton Monk & Poet: A Critical Study. 200p. 1978. 7.95 (ISBN 0-374-27635-8); pap. 3.95 (ISBN 0-374-51487-9). FS&G.

MESSALLINA, VALERIE–FICTION

Graves, Robert. Claudius the God. 1977. pap. 4.95 (ISBN 0-394-72537-9, Vin). Random.

MESSIAH

Here are entered general works on the conception of a messiah. Works dealing with prophecies in the Old Testament concerning a messiah are entered under Messiah–Prophecies. Works identifying Jesus Christ with the Messiah are entered under Jesus Christ–Messiahship.
see also Superman

Chwolsohn, D. Die Ssabier und der Ssabismus, 2 Vols. 1856. 85.00 (ISBN 0-384-09053-2). Johnson Repr.
Cresson, Warder. The Key of David: David the True Messiah. Davis, Moshe, ed. LC 77-70671. (America & the Holy Land Ser.). (Illus.). 1977. Repr. of 1852 ed. lib. bdg. 26.50x (ISBN 0-405-10239-9). Ayer Co Pubs.
Gratus, Jack. The False Messiahs: Prophets of the Millennium. LC 75-29890. 284p. 1976. 10.95 (ISBN 0-8008-2588-8). Taplinger.
Greenstone, Julius H. The Messiah Idea in Jewish History. LC 70-97284. 347p. 1972. Repr. of 1906 ed. lib. bdg. 22.50x (ISBN 0-8371-2606-1, GRMI). Greenwood.
Kac, Arthur W. Messianic Hope. pap. 4.95 (ISBN 0-8010-5362-5). Baker Bk.
Levey, Samson H. The Messiah: An Aramoic Interpretation. 1974. 20.00x (ISBN 0-87820-402-4, Pub. by Anti-Defamation League). Ktav.
McConkie, Bruce R. The Millennial Messiah. LC 81-19599. 726p. 1982. 17.95 (ISBN 0-87747-896-1). Deseret Bk.
Neusner, Jacob. Messiah in Context: Israel's History & Destiny in Formative Judaism. LC 83-20542. (Foundations of Judaism Ser.). 304p. 1984. 26.95 (ISBN 0-8006-0716-3, 1-716). Fortress.
Robinson, John M. Pagan Christs. 1967. 5.95 (ISBN 0-8216-0136-9). Univ Bks.
Schatz, Elihu A. Proof of the Accuracy of the Bible. LC 73-10726. (Illus.). xxvi, 740p. 1973. 15.00x (ISBN 0-8246-0161-0). Jonathan David.
Scholem, Gershom. The Messianic Idea in Judaism: And Other Essays on Jewish Spirituality. LC 70-130212. 384p. 1972. pap. 8.95 (ISBN 0-8052-0362-1). Schocken.
Shank, Robert. Until: The Coming of Messiah & His Kingdom. LC 81-72098. 520p. 1982. pap. 11.95 (ISBN 0-911620-04-4). Westcott.
Silver, Abba H. History of Messianic Speculation in Israel from the First Through the Seventeenth Centuries. 11.75 (ISBN 0-8446-2937-5). Peter Smith.

MESSIAH–PROPHECIES

Fruchtenbaum, Arnold G. Footsteps of the Messiah: A Study of the Sequence of Prophetic Events. (Illus.). 468p. 1982. 20.00 (ISBN 0-914863-02-9). Ariel Pr CA.
Hengstenberg, E. W. Christology of the Old Testament. Arnold, T. K., tr. from Ger. LC 77-129739. (Kregel Reprint Library). 716p. 1988. pap. 16.95 (ISBN 0-8254-2812-2). Kregel.
Lindsay, Gordon. The Key to Israel's Future-The Forgotten Covenant. 1.95 (ISBN 0-89985-191-6). Christ Nations.
--Messiah Witness-Israel's Destiny & Coming Deliverer. 0.95 (ISBN 0-89985-187-8). Christ Nations.
Patai, Raphael. The Messiah Texts. 1979. pap. 7.95 (ISBN 0-380-46482-9, 46482-9). Avon.
Smith, James E. What the Bible Says about the Promised Messiah. (What the Bible Says Ser.). 530p. 1984. 13.95 (ISBN 0-89900-095-9). College Pr Pub.
Tuckett, Christopher, ed. The Messianic Secret. LC 83-5499. (Issues in Religion & Theology Ser.). 176p. 1983. pap. 7.95 (ISBN 0-8006-1767-3). Fortress.

MESSIANIC CULTS

see Nativistic Movements

MESSIANISM, AMERICAN

Cherry, C. God's New Israel: Religious Interpretations of American Destiny. 1971. pap. 23.95 (ISBN 0-13-357335-4). P-H.
Merk, Federick & Merk, Lois B. Manifest Destiny & Mission in American History: A Reinterpretation. LC 82-25146. ix, 265p. 1983. Repr. lib. bdg. 35.00x (ISBN 0-313-23844-8, MERM). Greenwood.
Moorhead, James H. American Apocalypse: Yankee Protestants & the Civil War, 1860-1869. LC 77-14360. 1978. 32.00x (ISBN 0-300-02152-6). Yale U Pr.
Weinberg, Albert K. Manifest Destiny: A Study of Nationalist Expansionism in American History. LC 75-41293. Repr. of 1935 ed. 41.50 (ISBN 0-404-14706-2). AMS Pr.
Wilson, Ernest T. The Messianic Psalms. pap. 3.95 (ISBN 0-87213-963-8). Loizeaux.

METAMORPHOSIS (IN RELIGION, FOLK-LORE, ETC.)

see also Witchcraft

Walsingham, Thomae. De Archana Deorum. Van Kluyve, Robert A., ed. LC 67-31120. pap. 63.00 (ISBN 0-317-26876-7, 2023463). Bks Demand UMI.

METAPHOR

Keach, Benjamin. Preaching from the Types & Metaphors of the Bible. LC 78-165059. (Kregel Reprint Library). 1038p. 1975. 31.95 (ISBN 0-8254-3008-9). Kregel.
MacCormac, Earl R. Metaphor & Myth in Science & Religion. LC 75-23941. pap. 46.80 (2052207). Bks Demand UMI.

METAPHYSICS

see also Absolute, the; Cosmology; God; Ontology; Substance (Philosophy); Values

Aivanhov, Omraam M. Cosmic Moral Laws. 2nd ed. (Complete Works: Vol. 12). 294p. (Orig.). 1984. pap. 9.95 (ISBN 2-85566-112-9). Prosveta USA.
--The Key to the Problems of Existence. rev. ed. (Complete Works: Vol. 11). (Illus.). 263p. (Orig.). 1985. pap. 9.95 (ISBN 2-85566-111-0). Prosveta USA.
--Know Thyself: Jnani Yoga. (Complete Works: Vol. 17). (Illus.). 271p. 1981. pap. 9.95 (ISBN 2-85566-162-5). Prosveta USA.
--Life. (Complete Works: Vol. 5). (Illus.). 266p. 1978. pap. 9.95 (ISBN 2-85566-108-0). Prosveta USA.
--Love & Sexuality, Pt. I. (Complete Works: Vol. 14). (Illus.). 250p. 1976. pap. 9.95 (ISBN 2-85566-114-5). Prosveta USA.
--The Mysteries of Yesod. (Complete Works: Vol. 7). (Illus.). 217p. (Orig.). 1982. pap. 9.95 (ISBN 2-85566-109-9). Prosveta USA.
--A New Earth: Methods, Exercises, Formulas, Prayers. (Complete Works: Vol. 13). (Illus.). 232p. (Orig.). 1982. pap. 9.95 (ISBN 2-85566-113-7). Prosveta USA.
--On the Art of Teaching from the Initiatic Point of View. (Complete Works: Vol. 29). (Illus.). 245p. 1981. pap. 9.95 (ISBN 2-85566-142-0). Prosveta USA.
Anderson, James F. Introduction to the Metaphysics of St. Thomas Aquinas. LC 53-6515. 1969. pap. 6.50 (ISBN 0-89526-970-8). Regnery Bks.
Aune, Bruce. Metaphysics: The Elements. LC 85-2540. xiv, 235p. 1985. 25.00 (ISBN 0-8166-1412-1); pap. 12.95 (ISBN 0-8166-1414-8). U of Minn Pr.
Bancroft, Anne. Origins of the Sacred. 240p. 1987. pap. 12.95 (ISBN 1-85063-028-3, 30283, Ark Paperbks). Methuen Inc.
Beasley-Murray, Stephen. Towards a Metaphysics of the Sacred. LC 82-8288. (Special Studies: No. 8). viii, 110p. 1982. pap. 7.95 (ISBN 0-86554-038-1). NABPR.
Bennett, John G. Existence. 1977. 4.50 (ISBN 0-900306-40-8, Pub. by Coombe Springs Pr). Claymont Comm.
--The Foundations of Moral Philosophy, Vol. 2. (Dramatic Universe Ser.). 12.95 (ISBN 0-900306-42-4, Pub. by Coombe Springs Pr). Claymont Comm.
--The Foundations of Natural Philosophy, Vol. 1. (The Dramatic Universe Ser.). 29.95 (ISBN 0-900306-39-4, Pub. by Coombe Springs Pr). Claymont Comm.
--Talks on Beelzebub's Tales. 1977. 6.95 (ISBN 0-900306-36-X, Pub. by Coombe Springs Pr). Claymont Comm.
Berdiaev, Nikolai A. The Beginning & the End. French, R. M., tr. from Russian. LC 76-6083. 1976. Repr. of 1952 ed. lib. bdg. 35.00x (ISBN 0-8371-8837-7, BEBE). Greenwood.
Bergson, Henri. Creative Evolution. Mitxhell, Arthur, tr. LC 83-19859. 460p. 1984. pap. text ed. 13.50 (ISBN 0-8191-3553-4). U Pr of Amer.
--Study in Metaphysics. LC 61-10604. 1961. pap. 5.00 (ISBN 0-8022-0107-5). Philos Lib.
Bharata Krsna Tirthaji Maharaj. Vedic Metaphysics. 1978. Repr. 16.95 (ISBN 0-89684-337-8). Orient Bk Dist.
Burton, Asa. Essays on Some of the First Principles of Metaphysicks, Ethicks, & Theology. LC 73-4839. (History of Psychology Ser.). 432p. 1973. Repr. of 1824 ed. lib. bdg. 60.00x (ISBN 0-8201-1114-7). Schol Facsimiles.
Butchvarov, Panayot. Being Qua Being: A Theory of Identity, Existence & Predication. LC 78-13812. 288p. 1979. 22.50x (ISBN 0-253-13700-4). Ind U Pr.
Carey, Ken. Notes to My Children: A Simplified Metaphysics. 170p. 1987. pap. 8.95 (ISBN 0-913299-36-7, Dist. by NAL). Stillpoint.
--The Starseed Transmissions. 95p. 1986. pap. 6.95 (ISBN 0-913299-29-4, Dist. by NAL). Stillpoint.
--Terra Christa. (Illus.). 237p. 1986. pap. 9.95 (ISBN 0-913299-31-6, Dist. by NAL). Stillpoint.
--Vision. 90p. 1986. pap. 6.95 (ISBN 0-913299-30-8, Dist. by NAL). Stillpoint.
Chaney, Earlyne. The Masters & Astara. 2nd ed. (Illus.). 100p. 1982. pap. 8.95 (ISBN 0-918936-13-6). Astara.
Clayton, William R. Matter & Spirit. LC 80-81694. 136p. 1981. 9.95 (ISBN 0-8022-2368-0). Philos Lib.
Corey, Arthur. Behind the Scenes with the Metaphysicians. 7.50 (ISBN 0-87516-014-X). De Vorss.
DeRocco, Jovan. Legend of the Truant Tree. (Illus.). 112p. 1982. 6.50 (ISBN 0-682-49804-1). Exposition Pr FL.
Deutsch, Eliot. Humanity & Divinity: An Essay in Comparative Metaphysics. LC 76-128081. 1970. 14.00x (ISBN 0-87022-190-6). UH Pr.
Diggs, Bernard J. Love & Being: An Investigation into the Metaphysics of St. Thomas Aquinas. 180p. 1947. 6.75 (ISBN 0-913298-45-X). S F Vanni.
Dodds, James E. The Gentleman from Heaven. 123p. 1962. Repr. of 1948 ed. 3.50 (ISBN 0-87516-464-1). De Vorss.
Donato, Sri. The Unicorn. Morningland Publications, Inc., ed. (Illus.). 207p. (Orig.). 1981. pap. 10.00 (ISBN 0-935146-16-4). Morningland.
Donato, Sri & Donato, Gopi G. Oneness, Vol. III. Morningland Publications, Inc., ed. 167p. 1981. pap. 7.95 spiral bdg. (ISBN 0-935146-58-X). Morningland.
Flamma, Thomas. Metaphysics, a Bridge to ECKANKAR. LC 81-80177. 232p. 1981. pap. 3.95 (ISBN 0-914766-65-1, 0193). IWP Pub.
Genequand, C. F. The Metaphysics of Ibn Rushd: Averroes. LC 83-15428. (Studies in Islamic Philosophy & Science). write for info. cancelled (ISBN 0-88206-059-7). Caravan Bks.
Gunn, Giles, ed. New World Metaphysics: Readings on the Religious Meaning of the American Experience. 1981. pap. text ed. 10.95x (ISBN 0-19-502874-0). Oxford U Pr.
Gurudas. Flower Essences & Vibrational Healing. 2nd ed. 314p. 1985. pap. 12.95 (ISBN 0-914732-09-9). Bro Life Inc.
Hakim, K. A. Metaphysics of Rumi. 1959. 3.95x (ISBN 0-87902-061-X). Orientalia.
Hall, Manly P. Soul in Egyptian Metaphysics. pap. 2.50 (ISBN 0-89314-355-3). Philos Res.
--Visions & Metaphysical Experiences. pap. 2.50 (ISBN 0-89314-378-2). Philos Res.
Harmon, Frances A. The Social Philosophy of the St. Louis Hegelians. LC 75-3159. 1976. Repr. of 1943 ed. 20.00 (ISBN 0-404-59164-7). AMS Pr.
Hartshorne, Charles. Aquinas to Whitehead: Seven Centuries of Metaphysics of Religion. LC 76-5156. (Aquinas Lectures Ser.). 1976. 7.95 (ISBN 0-87462-141-0). Marquette.
Hegel, Georg W. The Metaphysics of the Jewish, the Aegyptian & the Assyrian Spirit. (Illus.). 177p. 1981. 67.85 (ISBN 0-89266-280-8). Am Classical Coll Pr.
Heidegger, Martin. What Is a Thing? Barton, W. B. & Deutsch, Vera, trs. from Ger. 320p. 1985. pap. text ed. 8.75 (ISBN 0-8191-4545-9). U Pr of Amer.
Houlgate, Stephen. Hegel, Nietzsche & the Criticism of Metaphysics. 304p. 1987. 39.50 (ISBN 0-521-32255-3). Cambridge U Pr.
Ichazo, Oscar. Between Metaphysics & Protoanalysis: A Theory for Analyzing the Human Psyche. Bleibtreu, John, ed. LC 82-70811. 120p. 1982. 15.95 (ISBN 0-916554-05-8); pap. 11.95 (ISBN 0-916554-06-6). Arica Inst Pr.
Kant, Immanuel. Grounding for the Metaphysics of Morals. Ellington, James W., tr. from Ger. LC 80-28839. (HPC Philosophical Classics Ser.). 80p. 1981. lib. bdg. 16.50 (ISBN 0-915145-01-4); pap. text ed. 3.45 (ISBN 0-915145-00-6). Hackett Pub.
--Metaphysical Knowledge & Transcendental Problems. (Illus.). 167p. 1985. Repr. 89.55 (ISBN 0-89901-200-0). Found Class Reprints.
Kappeler, Max. Metaphysics & Science in Christian Science. (Orig.). 1985. pap. 3.50 (ISBN 0-942958-11-X). Kappeler Inst Pub.
Kaufmann, Ronald G. Armadeus Prophecy & Teaching in the New Ages, Bk. 2. 155p. (Orig.). 1987. pap. 12.95 (ISBN 0-940539-02-0). Heridonius.
Kraus, Elizabeth M. The Metaphysics of Experience: A Companion to Whitehead's "Process & Reality". LC 78-70564. xiv, 190p. 1979. 22.50 (ISBN 0-8232-1038-3); pap. 9.00 (ISBN 0-8232-1039-1). Fordham.
Krolick, Sanford. Recollective Resolve: A Phenomenological Understanding of Time & Myth. 160p. 1987. 24.95 (ISBN 0-86554-248-1, MUP H-214). Mercer Univ Pr.
Leichtman, Robert R. Yogananda Returns. (From Heaven to Earth Ser.). 104p. (Orig.). 1981. pap. 3.50 (ISBN 0-89804-066-3). Ariel OH.
Linthorst, Ann T. Thus Saith the Lord: Giddyap: Metapsychiatric Commentaries on Human Experience & Spiritual Growth. 106p. (Orig.). 1986. pap. 11.00 (ISBN 0-913105-18-X). PAGL Pr.
MacCregor, Geddes, ed. Immortality & Human Destiny. 256p. 21.95 (ISBN 0-913757-45-4); pap. 12.95 (ISBN 0-913757-46-2). Paragon Hse.
Mahadevan, T. M., ed. Spiritual Perspectives: Essays in Mysticism & Metaphysics. 303p. 1975. lib. bdg. 12.00 (ISBN 0-89253-021-9). Ind-US Inc.
Manning, Al G. The Miraculous Laws of Universal Dynamics. 1964. pap. 5.95 (ISBN 0-317-46046-3). Pan Ishtar.
Maritain, Jacques. Distinguer Pour Unir: Les Degres du Savoir. 8th ed. 946p. 1959. 32.50 (ISBN 0-686-56350-6). French & Eur.
Matthews, Caitlin. Mabon & the Mysteries of Britain. 256p. 1987. pap. 11.95 (ISBN 1-85063-052-6, 30526, Ark Paperbks). Methuen Inc.
Nobo, Jorge L. Whitehead's Metaphysics of Extension & Solidarity. (Philosophy Ser.). 544p. (Orig.). 1986. 49.50x (ISBN 0-88706-261-X); pap. 24.50x (ISBN 0-88706-262-8). State U NY Pr.
Norman, Ruth E. Bridge to Heaven. 1969. 8.95 (ISBN 0-932642-10-1). Unarius Pubns.
--Keys to the Universe & the Mind. (Tesla Speaks Ser.: Vol. 11). (Illus.). 1977. 12.50 (ISBN 0-932642-34-9). Unarius Pubns.
--Mars Underground Cities Discovered. (Tesla Speaks Ser.: Vol. 12). (Illus.). 1977. 7.95 (ISBN 0-932642-35-7); pap. 6.95 (ISBN 0-932642-46-2). Unarius Pubns.
Norman, Ruth E., et al. The Masters Speak, 2 vols. (Tesla Speaks Ser.: No. 8). (Illus.). 1975. 8.95 ea.; Vol. 1. (ISBN 0-932642-30-6); Vol. 2. (ISBN 0-932642-29-2). Unarius Pubns.
Odin, Steve. Process Metaphysics & Hua-Yen Buddhism: A Critical Study of Cumulative Penetration vs. Interpretation. LC 81-9388. 256p. 1982. 44.50 (ISBN 0-87395-568-4); pap. 16.95 (ISBN 0-87395-569-2). State U NY Pr.
O'Leary, Joseph S. Questioning Back: The Overcoming of Metaphysics in Christian Tradition. 224p. 1985. cancelled (ISBN 0-8245-0675-8). Crossroad NY.
Olliver, C. W. An Analysis of Magic & Witchcraft: A Retrospective Introduction to the Study of Modern Metaphysics. 244p. 1985. Repr. of 1928 ed. Set. lib. bdg. 100.00 (ISBN 0-89984-775-7). Century Bookbindery.
Owens, Joseph. An Elementary Christian Metaphysics. LC 84-23888. 399p. 1985. pap. text ed. 12.95 (ISBN 0-268-00916-3, 85-09168, Dist. by Harper & Row). U of Notre Dame Pr.
Owens, Joseph C. Saint Thomas & the Future of Metaphysics. (Aquinas Lecture). 1957. 7.95 (ISBN 0-87462-122-4). Marquette.
Palmer, Melba P. Are You Ready? 81p. (Orig.). 1984. pap. 7.95 (ISBN 0-942494-88-1). Coleman Pub.
Peck, Paul L. Basic Spiritual Metaphysics. LC 78-61984. 1978. 14.50 (ISBN 0-87881-079-X). Mojave Bks.
--Footsteps along the Path. rev. ed. (Spiritual Metaphysics: Freeways to Divine Awareness Ser.). 164p. (Orig.). 1982. pap. 7.95 (ISBN 0-941600-01-7). Harmony Pr.

--Freeway to Health. (Spiritual Metaphysics: Freeways to Divine Awareness Ser.). 264p. (Orig.). 1982. pap. 7.95 (ISBN 0-941600-04-1). Harmony Pr.
--Freeway to Human Love. (Spiritual Metaphysics: Freeways to Divine Awareness Ser.). 264p. (Orig.). 1982. pap. 7.95 (ISBN 0-941600-06-8). Harmony Pr.
--Freeway to Personal Growth. (Spiritual Awareness: Freeways to Divine Awareness Ser.). 264p. (Orig.). 1982. pap. 7.95 (ISBN 0-941600-07-6). Harmony Pr.
--Freeway to Work & Health. (Spiritual Metaphysics: Freeways to Divine Awareness Ser.). 264p. (Orig.). 1982. pap. 7.95 (ISBN 0-941600-05-X). Harmony Pr.
--Inherit the Kingdom. rev. ed. (Spiritual Metaphysics: Freeways to Divine Awareness Ser.). (Orig.). 1982. pap. 7.95 (ISBN 0-941600-02-5). Harmony Pr.
--Intermediate Spiritual Metaphysics. LC 78-61985. (Spiritual Metaphysics Ser.: Vol. 2). 1979. 15.95 (ISBN 0-87881-081-1); pap. 13.50 (ISBN 0-87881-082-X). Mojave Bks.
--Milestones of the Way. rev. ed. (Spiritual Metaphysics: Freeways to Divine Awareness Ser.). 250p. (Orig.). 1982. pap. 7.95 (ISBN 0-941600-03-3). Harmony Pr.
Perrin, Stuart. The Mystical Ferryboat. (The Metaphysics Ser.). 121p. (Orig.). 1987. 12.95 (ISBN 0-943920-67-1); pap. price not set (ISBN 0-943920-64-7). Metamorphous Pr.
Prior, William J. Unity & Development in Plato's Metaphysics. LC 85-5073. 202p. 1985. 24.95 (ISBN 0-8126-9000-1). Open Court.
Ross, Stephen D. Transition to an Ordinal Metaphysics. 162p. 1980. 44.50x (ISBN 0-87395-434-3); pap. 16.95x (ISBN 0-87395-435-1). State U NY Pr.
Rowan, John. The Horned God. 160p. 1987. pap. 13.95 (ISBN 0-7102-0674-7, 06747, Ark Paperbks). Methuen Inc.
Rucker, Ruby, et al. The Fourth Dimension: A Guided Tour of Higher Universes. (Illus.). 228p. 1985. pap. 8.95 (ISBN 0-395-39388-4). HM.
Russell, Marjorie H. Oneness of All Life. 160p. 1984. 5.95 (ISBN 0-87159-123-5). Unity School.
Sabzavari, Hadi Ibn Mahdi. The Metaphysics of Haji Mulla Hadi Sabzavari. Izutsu, Toshihiku & Mohaghegh, Mehdi, trs. from Persian. LC 76-18174. 248p. 1977. lib. bdg. 35.00x (ISBN 0-88206-011-2). Caravan Bks.
Samuel, William. The Child Within Us Lives! 412p. 1986. 24.95 (ISBN 0-938747-01-0); pap. 15.95 (ISBN 0-938747-00-2). Mntn Brook Pubns.
Schuon, Frithjof. From the Divine to the Human: Survey of Metaphyisics & Epistemology. LC 82-50333. (The Library of Traditional Wisdom). 156p. 1982. pap. 7.00 (ISBN 0-941532-01-1). Wrld Wisdom Bks.
--Survey of Metaphysics & Esoterism. Polit, Gustavo, tr. from Fr. LC 86-13261. (The Library of Traditional Wisdom). Orig. Title: Resume de Metaphysique Integral Sur les Traces de la Religion Perenne. 224p. (Orig.). 1986. pap. 12.00 (ISBN 0-941532-06-2). Wrld Wisdom Bks.
Shastra, M. N. Hindu Metaphysics. 247p. 1978. Repr. of 1904 ed. text ed. 15.00 (ISBN 0-89684-121-9, Pub. by Cosmo Pubns India). Orient Bk Dist.
Singh, Balbir. Hindu Metaphysics. 256p. 1986. text ed. 25.00x (ISBN 0-391-03408-1). Humanities.
Slesinski, Robert. Pavel Florensky: A Metaphysics of Love. LC 83-27130. 256p. 1984. pap. text ed. 12.95 (ISBN 0-88141-032-2). St Vladimirs.
Spencer, Barbara H. The Book of Mag. 202p. pap. 7.95 (ISBN 0-942494-40-7). Coleman Pub.
Stahl, John. The World Union Company. 60p. 1980. pap. 5.00 (ISBN 0-318-21734-1). Evanescent Pr.
Strawson, P. F. Individuals: An Essay in Descriptive Metaphysics. 1964. pap. 12.95x (ISBN 0-416-68310-X, NO. 2535). Methuen Inc.
Thomas, James. I Am That I Am: A Metaphysical Course on Consciousness. (Illus.). 168p. 1984. 14.95x (ISBN 0-931290-90-2); pap. 6.95x (ISBN 0-931290-91-0). Alchemy Bks.
Thompson, Robert A. & Thompson, Louise S. Egoshell. 280p. 1986. 22.95 (ISBN 0-87975-365-X). Prometheus Bks.
Twitchell, Paul. Anitya. (Illus.). 1969. 5.95 (ISBN 0-914766-01-5). IWP Pub.
--Coins of Gold. 1972. 5.95 (ISBN 0-914766-02-3). IWP Pub.
--Dialogues with the Master. 1970. pap. 5.95 (ISBN 0-914766-78-3). IWP Pub.
--Drums of ECK. 1970. pap. 3.95 (ISBN 0-914766-04-X). IWP Pub.
--The ECK Vidya: The Ancient Science of Prophecy. LC 75-306773. 237p. 1972. 5.95 (ISBN 0-914766-89-9). IWP Pub.
--The Far Country. 1971. pap. 5.95 (ISBN 0-914766-91-0). IWP Pub.
--The Shariyat-Ki-Sugmad. 1971. Vol. 1 1970. kivar bdg. 7.95 (ISBN 0-914766-13-9); Vol. 2 1971. 7.95 (ISBN 0-914766-14-7). IWP Pub.
--Stranger by the River. 176p. 1970. pap. 5.95 (ISBN 0-914766-16-3). IWP Pub.
--Way of Dharma. 1970. pap. 3.95 (ISBN 0-914766-18-X). IWP Pub.
Ulery, Lloyd K. The Far Journey Through Life, Love & Eternity. LC 77-91280. 185p. 1978. 7.95 (ISBN 0-930984-01-3). Psychic Bks.
Urban, Wilbur M. The Intelligible World: Metaphysics & Value. LC 76-51208. 1977. Repr. of 1929 ed. lib. bdg. 26.75x (ISBN 0-8371-9437-7, URIW). Greenwood.
Van Hook, John E. Systematic Philosophy: An Overview of Metaphysics Showing the Development from the Greeks to the Contemporaries with Specified Directions & Projections. (Illus.). 1979. 8.50 (ISBN 0-682-49398-8, University). Exposition Pr FL.
Wagner, Melinda B. Metaphysics in Midwestern America. LC 83-2158. 241p. 1983. 20.00x (ISBN 0-8142-0346-9). Ohio St U Pr.
Wallack, F. Bradford. The Epochal Nature of Process in Whitehead's Metaphysics. LC 79-22898. 1980. 44.50x (ISBN 0-87395-404-1); pap. 16.95 (ISBN 0-87395-454-8). State U NY Pr.
Wellek, Rene, ed. James Burnett Monboddo (1714-1799) Antient Metaphysics, 6 Vol., 1779-99. LC 75-11236. (British Philosophers & Theologians of the 17th & 18th Centuries Ser.). 1977. lib. bdg. 46.00 (ISBN 0-8240-1789-7). Garland Pub.
Wells, Norman. Metaphysical Disputation, XXXI, De Ento Finito, on Finite Being. cancelled. Marquette.
Wendell, Leilah. The Book of Infinite Possibilities. 55p. (Orig.). 1987. pap. 4.50 (ISBN 0-89540-169-X). Sun Pub.
Wescott, Juanita. Magic & Music: The Language of the Gods Revealed. LC 85-71700. (Illus.). 145p. (Orig.). 1983. pap. 7.95 (ISBN 0-913407-00-3). Abbetira Pubns.
White Eagle. The Living Word of St. John. new ed. 208p. 1979. pap. 13.95 (ISBN 0-85487-044-X). De Vorss.
Wilbur, James B. Spinoza's Metaphysics: Essays in Critical Appreciation. (Philosophia Spinozae Perennis Ser.: No. 1). 170p. 1976. pap. text ed. 19.00 (ISBN 90-232-1361-0, Pub. by Van Gorcum Holland). Longwood Pub Group.
Wippel, John F. Metaphysical Themes in Thomas Aquinas. LC 82-7296. (Studies in Philosophy & the History of Philosophy: Vol. 10). 294p. 1984. 31.95x (ISBN 0-8132-0578-6). Cath U Pr.
--The Metaphysical Thought of Godfrey of Fontaines: A Study in Late Thirteenth-Century Philosophy. LC 80-16900. 413p. 1981. 31.95x (ISBN 0-8132-0556-5). Cath U Pr.

METAPSYCHOLOGY
see Psychical Research

METHOD OF WORK
see Work

METHODISM
see also Camp-Meetings; Perfection

Brewer, Earl D. Continuation or Transformation? The Involvement of United Methodism in Social Movements & Issues. (Into our Third Century Ser.). 128p. (Orig.). 1982. pap. 4.95 (ISBN 0-687-09623-5). Abingdon.
Dearing, Trevor. Wesleyan & Tractarian Worship. LC 66-72190. 1966. text ed. 15.00x (ISBN 0-8401-0531-2). A R Allenson.
Dengler, Sandy. Susanna Wesley: Servant of God. (Preteen Biographies Ser.). (YA) 1987. pap. text ed. 3.95 (ISBN 0-8024-8414-X). Moody.
Gill, Frederick C. The Romantic Movement & Methodism: A Study of English Romanticism & the Evangelical Revival. 1978. Repr. of 1937 ed. lib. bdg. 25.00 (ISBN 0-8492-4910-4). R West.
Green, Richard. Anti-Methodist Publications Issued During the 18th Century. LC 71-83701. 175p. 1974. Repr. of 1902 ed. lib. bdg. 22.50 (ISBN 0-8337-1436-8). B Franklin.
Hassing, Arne. Religion & Power: The Case of Methodism in Norway. (Jesse Lee Prize Ser.). (Illus.). 300p. 1980. 15.00 (ISBN 0-915466-03-1). United Meth Archives.
Lacy, Donald C. Methodist Mass. 1984. 2.95 (ISBN 0-89536-977-X, 7533). CSS of Ohio.
Meeks, M. Douglas, ed. The Future of the Methodist Theological Traditions. 224p. 1985. pap. 9.95 (ISBN 0-687-13868-X). Abingdon.
Moore, M. H. Sketches of the Pioneers of Methodism in North Carolina & Virginia. 314p. 1977. Repr. of 1884 ed. 8.95 (ISBN 0-87921-039-7). Attic Pr.
Norwood, Frederick A., ed. Sourcebook of American Methodism. 683p. (Orig.). 1982. 20.95 (ISBN 0-687-39140-7). Abingdon.
Peters, John L. Christian Perfection & American Methodism. 1985. pap. 9.95 (ISBN 0-310-31241-8, 17043P). Zondervan.
Roberts, B. T. Why Another Sect? (The Higher Christian Life Ser.). 321p. 1985. lib. bdg. 40.00 (ISBN 0-8240-6441-0). Garland Pub.
Rowe, Kenneth E. Methodist Union Catalog: Pre-1976 Imprints, Vol. V:G-Haz. LC 75-33190. 371p. 1981. 29.00 (ISBN 0-8108-1454-4). Scarecrow.
Rowe, Kenneth E., ed. Methodist Union Catalog: Pre-1976 Imprints, 20 vols, Vol. I, A-bj. LC 75-33190. 438p. 1975. 29.00 (ISBN 0-8108-0880-3). Scarecrow.
Rupp, Gordon, et al. The People Called Methodist. LC 84-72360. (Pan-Methodist Lectures). 96p. (Orig.). 1985. DR016B. pap. 3.95 (ISBN 0-88177-016-7). Discipleship Res.
Sano, Roy I. From Every Nation Without Number: Racial & Ethnic Diversity in United Methodism. LC 81-20610. (Into Our Third Century Ser.). (Orig.). 1982. pap. 3.95 (ISBN 0-687-13642-3). Abingdon.
Shepherd, T. B. Methodism & the Literature of the 18th Century. LC 68-4718. (Studies in Comparative Literature, No. 35). 1969. Repr. of 1940 ed. lib. bdg. 75.00x (ISBN 0-8383-0680-2). Haskell.
Simpson, Matthew. Encyclopedia of Methodism, 2 vols. 1977. lib. bdg. 250.00 (ISBN 0-8490-1766-1). Gordon Pr.
Watson, Philip S., ed. The Message of the Wesleys: A Reader of Instruction & Devotion. 270p. 1983. pap. 9.95 (ISBN 0-310-75031-8, 17027P). Zondervan.
Williams, John P. Social Adjustment in Methodism. LC 76-177639. (Columbia University. Teachers College. Contributions to Education: No. 765). Repr. of 1938 ed. 22.50 (ISBN 0-404-55765-1). AMS Pr.
Wolcott, Carolyn & Wolcott, Leonard. We Go Forward: Stories of United Methodist Pathmakers. LC 83-73225. 72p. pap. 5.25 (ISBN 0-88177-008-6, DR008B). Discipleship Res.

METHODISM-HISTORY

Baker, Frank. From Wesley to Asbury: Studies in Early American Methodism. LC 75-39454. xiv, 223p. 1976. 22.50 (ISBN 0-8223-0359-0). Duke.
Baker, George C., Jr. Introduction to the History of Early New England Methodism. LC 70-95393. 1969. Repr. of 1941 ed. 16.00 (ISBN 0-404-00466-0). AMS Pr.
Barr. Early Methodist under Persecution. pap. 4.95 (ISBN 0-686-23582-7). Schmul Pub Co.
Bilhartz, Terry O., ed. Francis Asbury's America: An Album of Early American Methodism. LC 83-18275. 128p. 1984. (Pub. by F. Asbury Pr); pap. 6.95 (ISBN 0-310-44791-7, 18275). Zondervan.
Connor, Elizabeth. Methodist Trail Blazer: Philip Gatch. rev. ed. LC 76-101704. (Illus.). 260p. pap. 12.00 smythsewn (ISBN 0-914960-51-2). Academy Bks.
Daniels, W. H. Illustrated History of Methodism. 1977. lib. bdg. 75.00 (ISBN 0-8490-2036-0). Gordon Pr.
Ferguson, Charles W. Methodists & the Making of America. 480p. 1983. 17.95 (ISBN 0-89015-424-4); pap. 12.95 (ISBN 0-89015-405-8). Eakin Pr.
Hayes, A. J. & Gowland, D. A. Scottish Methodism in the Early Victorian Period: The Scottish Correspondence of the Reverend Jabez Bunting, 1800-1857. 143p. 1981. 20.00x (ISBN 0-85224-412-6, Pub. by Edinburgh U Pr Scotland). Columbia U Pr.
Hayes, A. J. & Gowland, D. A., eds. Scottish Methodism in the Early Victorian Period: The Scottish Correspondence of the Rev. Jabez Bunting 1800-57. 1981. 40.00x (ISBN 0-85224-412-6, Pub. by Edinburgh Univ England). State Mutual Bk.
Hempton, David. Methodism & Politics in British Society, 1750-1850. LC 84-51419. 276p. 1984. 27.50x (ISBN 0-8047-1269-7). Stanford U Pr.
Jones, Charles E. Perfectionist Persuasion: The Holiness Movement & American Methodism, 1867-1936. LC 74-13766. (ATLA Monograph: No. 5). (Illus.). 262p. 1974. 22.50 (ISBN 0-8108-0747-5). Scarecrow.
Lee, Umphrey. Historical Backgrounds of Early Methodist Enthusiasm. LC 31-18047. (Columbia University. Studies in the Social Sciences: No. 339). Repr. of 1931 ed. 17.50 (ISBN 0-404-51339-5). AMS Pr.
Ludwig, Charles. Francis Asbury. 1984. pap. 6.95 (ISBN 0-88062-024-2). Mott Media.
McCulloh, Gerald O. Ministerial Education in the American Methodist Movement. LC 80-69028. (An Informed Ministry Ser.: 200 Years of American Methodist Thought). 342p. (Orig.). 1980. pap. 3.95 (ISBN 0-938162-00-4). United Meth Educ.
McEllhenney, John G. Proclaiming Grace & Freedom: The Story of United Methodism in America. (Orig.). 1982. pap. 7.95 (ISBN 0-687-34323-2). Abingdon.
Mays, Lois B. History of Folkston, Ga. Methodist Church. 37p. 1984. 3.25 (ISBN 0-9601606-1-2). Okefenokee Pr.
Nottingham, Elizabeth K. Methodism & the Frontier: Indiana Proving Ground. LC 41-19465. Repr. of 1941 ed. 7.00 (ISBN 0-404-04798-X). AMS Pr.
Phinney, William R., et al, eds. Thomas Ware, a Spectator at the Christmas Conference: A Miscellany on Thomas Ware & the Christmas Conference. LC 84-70457. (Illus.). 320p. (Orig.). 1984. pap. 8.95 smythsewn (ISBN 0-914960-48-2). Academy Bks.
Porter, Robert, ed. Emigrants at Worship: One Hundred & Twenty-Five Years of Chisago Lake Methodism. (Illus.). 85p. (Orig.). 1983. pap. 8.75 (ISBN 0-933565-02-X). Porter Pub Co.
Repass, Mary E. Faith Within the Hills. (Heritage Group Ser.). (Illus.). 1873. text ed. 15.00 (ISBN 0-940502-03-8). Foxhound Ent.
Steelman, Robert B. What God Has Wrought: A History of the Southern New Jersey Conference of the United Methodist Church. LC 86-70275. 368p. (Orig.). 1986. text ed. 12.50x (ISBN 0-914960-60-1); pap. text ed. 10.00x (ISBN 0-914960-56-3). Academy Bks.
Thrall, Homer S. A Brief History of Methodism in Texas. 304p. 1977. Repr. of 1889 ed. 9.95 (ISBN 0-87921-042-7). Attic Pr.
Ward, William R., Jr. Faith in Action: A History of Methodism in the Empire State 1784-1984. LC 86-70533. (Illus.). 324p. (Orig.). 1986. text ed. 12.50x (ISBN 0-914960-62-8); pap. text ed. 10.00x (ISBN 0-914960-58-X). Academy Bks.
Watson, David L. Early Methodist Class Meetings. 240p. (Orig.). pap. 10.95 (ISBN 0-88170-175-0, DR017B). Discipleship Res.
Werner, Julia S. The Primitive Methodist Connexion: Its Background & Early History. LC 84-40161. (Illus.). 352p. 1985. text ed. 35.00x (ISBN 0-299-09910-5). U of Wis Pr.
West, Anson D. A History of Methodism in Alabama. LC 83-19053. (Illus.). 840p. 1984. Repr. of 1893 ed. 30.00 (ISBN 0-87152-380-9). Reprint.
Wilder, Franklin. The Methodist Riots: The Testing of Charles Wesley. (Illus.). 160p. 1982. 8.95 (ISBN 0-89962-236-4). Todd & Honeywell.
Williams, William H. The Garden of American Methodism: The Delmarva Peninsula, 1769-1820. (Illus.). xiv, 225p. 1984. 25.00 (ISBN 0-8420-2227-9). Scholarly Res Inc.

METHODIST CHURCH

Abbey, Merrill R. The Epic of United Methodist Preaching: A Profile in American Social History. 216p. (Orig.). 1983. lib. bdg. 26.75 (ISBN 0-8191-3691-3); pap. text ed. 12.25 (ISBN 0-8191-3692-1). U Pr of Amer.
Allen, Charles L. Meet the Methodists: An Introduction to the United Methodist Church. 96p. 1986. pap. 3.50 (ISBN 0-687-24650-4). Abingdon.
Baldwin, Lewis V. Invisible Strands in African Methodism: A History of the African Union Methodist Protestant & Union American Methodist Episcopal Churches, 1805-1980. LC 83-15039. (ATLA Monographs: No. 19). (Illus.). 306p. 1983. 27.50 (ISBN 0-8108-1647-4). Scarecrow.
Bishop, John. Methodist Worship: In Relation to Free Church Worship. rev. ed. LC 75-20379. xvii, 173p. 1976. lib. bdg. 6.95 (ISBN 0-89177-001-1). Scholars Studies.
Byrne, Donald E. No Foot of Land: Folklore of American Methodist Itinerants. LC 75-1097. (ATLA Monograph: No. 6). (Illus.). 370p. 1975. 22.50 (ISBN 0-8108-0798-X). Scarecrow.
Chiles, Robert E. Theological Transition in American Methodism, 1790-1935. LC 83-16666. 238p. 1983. pap. text ed. 11.25 (ISBN 0-8191-3551-8). U Pr of Amer.
Davey, Cyril. John Wesley & the Methodists. 49p. (Orig.). 1986. 6.95 (ISBN 0-687-20434-8). Abingdon.
Gowland, D. A. Methodist Secessions. 192p. 1979. 40.00 (ISBN 0-7190-1335-6, Pub. by Manchester Univ Pr). Longwood Pub Group.
Heidinger, James V., II, ed. Basic United Methodist Beliefs: (An Evangelical View) 128p. 1986. pap. 4.95 (ISBN 0-917851-01-3). Forum Script.
Heitzenrater, Richard, ed. Methodist Conference Minutes & Traveling Preachers: 1773-1794. LC 79-51893. Date not set. pap. 9.25 (ISBN 0-914960-18-0). Academy Bks.
Hickman, Hoyt L. United Methodist Altars: A Guide for the Local Church. 96p. 1984. pap. 6.95 (ISBN 0-687-42985-4). Abingdon.
Holifield, E. Brooks. Health & Medicine & the Methodist Tradition. 176p. 1986. 17.95x (ISBN 0-8245-0792-4). Crossroad NY.
Johnston, Lyle. The Dubuque District - A History: The United Methodist Church. (Illus.). 128p. (Orig.). 1979. pap. 2.95 (ISBN 0-9616365-1-3). Grt Plains Emporium.
--The Mason City District - A History: The United Methodist Church. (Illus.). 109p. (Orig.). 1984. pap. 6.50 (ISBN 0-9616365-2-1). Grt Plains Emporium.
--The Ottumwa District - A History: The United Methodist Church. (Illus.). 118p. (Orig.). 1986. pap. 6.50 (ISBN 0-9616365-3-X). Grt Plains Emporium.

--The Sioux City District - A History: The United Methodist Church. (Illus.). 90p. (Orig.). 1978. pap. 1.95 (ISBN 0-9616365-0-5). Grt Plains Emporium.
Keysor, Charles W. Our Methodist Heritage. LC 84-80824. 174p. pap. 3.95 (ISBN 0-917851-00-5). Good News KY.
Langford, Thomas A. Practical Divinity: Theology in the Wesleyan Tradition. 304p. (Orig.). 1983. pap. 9.95 (ISBN 0-687-33326-1). Abingdon.
Lyles, Jean C. A Practical Vision of Christian Unity. LC 81-15032. (Into Our Third Century Ser.). 96p. (Orig.). 1982. pap. 3.95 (ISBN 0-687-33330-X). Abingdon.
McClain, William B. Black People in the Methodist Church: Whither Thou Goest? 160p. (Orig.). 1986. pap. 8.95 (ISBN 0-687-03588-0). Abingdon.
McKenzie, Donald A. More Notices from Methodist Papers 1830-1857. 424p. 1986. lib. bdg. 22.00 (ISBN 0-912606-29-0). Hunterdon Hse.
Morrow, Ralph E. Northern Methodism & Reconstruction. ix, 269p. 1956. 5.00 (ISBN 0-87013-018-8). Mich St U Pr.
Norwood, John H. The Schism in the Methodist Episcopal Church, 1844. LC 76-10284. (Perspectives in American Hist. Ser.: No. 33). 255p. 1976. Repr. of 1923 ed. lib. bdg. 25.00x (ISBN 0-87991-357-6). Porcupine Pr.
Nye, John. Between the Rivers: A History of United Methodism in Iowa. LC 86-80106. (Illus.). 350p. 1986. 12.95x (ISBN 0-9616298-0-0); pap. 10.95 (ISBN 0-9616298-1-9). IA Conf Com Arch.
Posey, Walter B. The Development of Methodism in the Old Southwest: 1783-1824. LC 73-18408. (Perspectives in American History Ser.: No. 19). (Illus.). 1974. Repr. of 1933 ed. lib. bdg. 22.50x (ISBN 0-87991-339-8). Porcupine Pr.
Ramsden, William E. The Church in a Changing Society. LC 79-24274. (Into Our Third Century Ser.). (Orig.). 1980. pap. 4.95 (ISBN 0-687-08250-1). Abingdon.
Rogers, Kristine M. & Rogers, Bruce A. Paths to Transformation: A Study of the General Agencies of the United Methodist Church. LC 81-17565. (Into Our Third Century Ser.). 96p. (Orig.). 1982. pap. 3.50 (ISBN 0-687-30094-0). Abingdon.
Rowe, Kenneth E., ed. Methodist Union Catalog: Pre-1976 Imprints, Vol. VI: He-I. LC 75-33190. 360p. 1985. 29.00 (ISBN 0-8108-1725-X). Scarecrow.
--Methodist Union Catalog: Pre-1976 Imprints, Vol. 3, Che-Dix. LC 75-33190. 431p. 1978. 29.00 (ISBN 0-8108-1067-0). Scarecrow.
--United Methodist Studies: Basic Bibliographies. 40p. (Orig.). 1982. pap. 2.00 (ISBN 0-687-43109-3). Abingdon.
Rupp, Gordon, et al. The People Called Methodist. LC 84-72360. (Pan-Methodist Lectures). 96p. (Orig.). 1985. DR016B. pap. 3.95 (ISBN 0-88177-016-7). Discipleship Res.
Schwartz, Charles D. & Schwartz, Ouida D. A Flame of Fire: The Story of Troy Annual Conference. LC 82-70624. (Illus.). 376p. (Orig.). 1982. pap. text ed. 15.00x (ISBN 0-914960-38-5). Academy Bks.
Shockley, Grant S., et al. Black Pastors & Churches in United Methodism. 1976. pap. 1.00 (ISBN 0-89937-005-5). Ctr Res Soc Chg.
Snyder, Howard A. & Runyon, Daniel V. The Divided Flame: Wesleyans & the Charismatic Renewal. Ruark, James, ed. 128p. 1986. pap. 6.95 (ISBN 0-310-75181-0, 17082P). Zondervan.
Stokes, Mack B. Major United Methodist Beliefs. rev. & enl. ed. LC 77-173955. 128p. (Orig.). 1971. pap. 2.00 (ISBN 0-687-22923-5). Abingdon.
Towlson, Clifford W. Moravian & Methodist. LC 57-3559. 1957. 20.00x (ISBN 0-8401-2387-6, 8401-2387-6). A R Allenson.
Towne, Ruth W. From These Beginnings: A History of the First United Methodist Church Kirksville, Missouri. 100p. 1984. pap. 6.00 (ISBN 0-9613631-0-X). Journal Printing.
Tuell, Jack M. The Organization of the United Methodist Church. rev. ed. 176p. 1985. pap. 7.95 (ISBN 0-687-29445-2). Abingdon.
Waltz, Alan K. Images of the Future. LC 79-25028. (Into Our Third Century Ser.). (Orig.). 1980. pap. 3.95 (ISBN 0-687-18689-7). Abingdon.
Washburn, Paul. An Unfinished Church: A Brief History of the Union of the Evangelical United Brethern Church & the Methodist Church. 176p. 14.95 (ISBN 0-687-01378-X). Abingdon.
Wearmouth, Robert F. Methodism & the Working-Class Movements of England 1800-1850. LC 73-139523. 1972. Repr. of 1937 ed. 29.50x (ISBN 0-678-00829-9). Kelley.
Wesley, John. Sunday Services of the Methodists in North America. 144p. (Orig.). 1984. pap. 4.95 (ISBN 0-687-40632-3). Abingdon.
--Works of John Wesley, 14 vols. Set. 249.50 (ISBN 0-8010-9616-2). Baker Bk.
Will, Herman, Jr. A Will for Peace: Peace Action in the United Methodist Church: A History. 300p. 9.95 (CS1007). General Board.
Willimon, William H. & Wilson, Robert L. Rekindling the Flame: Strategies for a Vital United Methodism. 128p. 1987. 9.95 (ISBN 0-687-35932-5). Abingdon.

METHODIST CHURCH–BIOGRAPHY

Cole, Charles E., ed. Something More Than Human: Biographies of Leaders in American Methodist Higher Education. LC 85-51267. (Illus.). 256p. 1986. 7.95 (ISBN 0-938162-04-7). United Meth Educ.
Fiester, Mark. Look for Me in Heaven: The Life of John Lewis Dyer. LC 80-14913. (Illus.). 400p. 1980. 19.95 (ISBN 0-87108-564-X). Pruett.
Heitzenrater, Richard P., ed. Diary of an Oxford Methodist: Benjamin Ingham, 1733-34. xvi, 304p. 1985. 37.50 (ISBN 0-8223-0595-X). Duke.
Holder, Ray. The Mississippi Methodists, Seventeen Ninety-Nine to Nineteen Eighty-Three: A Moral People "Born of Conviction". Date not set. 11.95 (ISBN 0-9612932-0-9); pap. 8.95 (ISBN 0-9612932-1-7). Maverick Prints.
Simpson, Robert D., ed. American Methodist Pioneer: The Life & Journals of the Rev. Freeborn Garrettson 1752-1827. LC 83-72532. (Illus.). 444p. 1983. text ed. 25.00 (ISBN 0-914960-49-0). Academy Bks.
Spellman, Norman W. Growing a Soul: The Story of A. Frank Smith. LC 78-20876. 1979. 17.95x (ISBN 0-87074-171-3). SMU Press.

METHODIST CHURCH–CLERGY

Bauman, Mark K. Warren Akin Candler: The Conservative As Idealist. LC 80-22230. 290p. 1981. 20.00 (ISBN 0-8108-1368-8). Scarecrow.
Connor, Elizabeth. Methodist Trail Blazer: Philip Gatch. rev. ed. LC 76-101704. (Illus.). 260p. pap. 12.00 smythsewn (ISBN 0-914960-51-2). Academy Bks.
Hunt, Richard A. & Hunt, Joan A. Called to Minister. LC 81-22796. (Into Our Third Century Ser.). (Orig.). 1982. pap. 3.95 (ISBN 0-687-04560-6). Abingdon.
Phinney, William R., et al, eds. Thomas Ware, a Spectator at the Christmas Conference: A Miscellany on Thomas Ware & the Christmas Conference. LC 84-70457. (Illus.). 320p. (Orig.). 1984. pap. 8.95 smythsewn (ISBN 0-914960-48-2). Academy Bks.
Shockley, Grant S., et al. Black Pastors & Churches in United Methodism. 1976. pap. 1.00 (ISBN 0-89937-005-5). Ctr Res Soc Chg.
Simpson, Robert D., ed. American Methodist Pioneer: The Life & Journals of the Rev. Freeborn Garrettson 1752-1827. LC 83-72532. (Illus.). 444p. 1983. text ed. 25.00 (ISBN 0-914960-49-0). Academy Bks.

METHODIST CHURCH–DOCTRINAL AND CONTROVERSIAL WORKS

Carter, Charles W. & Thompson, Duane R, eds. Contemporary Wesleyan Theology, 2 vols. 1200p. 1986. Set. 39.95 (ISBN 0-310-45650-9, 11626). Zondervan.
Colaw, Emerson. Beliefs of United Methodist Christian. 3rd ed. (Orig.). pap. 3.95 (ISBN 0-88177-025-6, DRO25B). Discipleship Res.
Green, Richard. Anti-Methodist Publications Issued During the 18th Century. LC 71-83701. 175p. 1974. Repr. of 1902 ed. lib. bdg. 22.50 (ISBN 0-8337-1436-8). B Franklin.
Stokes, Mack B. Major United Methodist Beliefs. rev. & enl. ed. LC 77-173955. 128p. (Orig.). 1971. pap. 2.00 (ISBN 0-687-22923-5). Abingdon.
Whitefield, George. George Whitefield's Journals. (Illus., Orig.). 1985. pap. 14.95 (ISBN 0-85151-482-0). Banner of Truth.

METHODIST CHURCH–EDUCATION

Carr, John & Carr, Adrienne. Experiment in Practical Christianity: Leader's Guide. rev. ed. 96p. 1985. manual 6.95 (ISBN 0-88177-028-0, DRO28B). Discipleship Res.
--Experiment in Practical Christianity: Participant's Guide. 104p. (Orig.). 1985. pap. 6.95 (ISBN 0-88177-027-2, DRO27B). Discipleship Res.
Cole, Charles E., ed. Something More Than Human: Biographies of Leaders in American Methodist Higher Education. LC 85-51267. (Illus.). 256p. 1986. 7.95 (ISBN 0-938162-04-7). United Meth Educ.

METHODIST CHURCH–HYMNS

Rogal, Samuel J. Guide to the Hymns & Tunes of American Methodism. LC 85-27114. (Music Reference Collection Ser.: No. 7). 337p. 1986. lib. bdg. 45.00 (ISBN 0-313-25123-1, RGH/). Greenwood.
Wesley, John. The Works of John Wesley: A Collection of Hymns for the Use of the People Called Methodists, Vol. 7. Hilderbrandt, Franz & Beckerlegge, Oliver A., eds. (Oxford Edition of the Works of John Wesley Ser.). (Illus.). 1984. 86.00x (ISBN 0-19-812529-1). Oxford U Pr.

METHODIST CHURCH–MISSIONS

Davey, Cyril J. March of Methodism. 1952. 5.95 (ISBN 0-8022-0345-0). Philos Lib.
Shaw, Barnabas. Memorials of South Africa. LC 71-109358. Repr. of 1840 ed. cancelled (ISBN 0-8371-3737-3, SMS&, Pub. by Negro U Pr). Greenwood.

METHODIST CHURCH–SERMONS

Gillingham, E. Leonard. Dealing with Conflict. LC 81-20662. 144p. 1982. 8.75 (ISBN 0-687-10329-0). Abingdon.
Hinson, William H. Solid Living in a Shattered World. 160p. 1985. 8.95 (ISBN 0-687-39048-6). Abingdon.
Payne, Daniel A. Sermons & Addresses, 1853-1891. LC 70-38458. (Religion in America, Ser. 2). 1972. 19.00 (ISBN 0-405-04079-2). Ayer Co Pubs.
Wesley, John. The New Birth. Oden, Thomas C., ed. LC 83-48460. 128p. 1984. 10.45 (ISBN 0-06-069312-6, HarpR). Har-Row.

METHODIST EPISCOPAL CHURCH

De Swarte, Carolyn G. & Dayton, Donald, eds. The Defense of Women's Rights to Ordination in the Methodist Episcopal Church. (Women in American Protestant Religion Series 1800-1930). 230p. 1987. lib. bdg. 35.00 (ISBN 0-8240-0654-2). Garland Pub.
Duvall, Sylvanus M. Methodist Episcopal Church & Education up to 1869. LC 79-176735. (Columbia University. Teachers College. Contributions to Education: No. 284). Repr. of 1928 ed. 22.50 (ISBN 0-404-55284-6). AMS Pr.
Hagood, L. M. Colored Man in the Methodist Episcopal Church. facs. ed. LC 77-149868. (Black Heritage Library Collection Ser). 1890. 19.50 (ISBN 0-8369-8631-8). Ayer Co Pubs.
Hagood, Lewis M. Colored Man in the Methodist Episcopal Church. LC 73-111577. Repr. of 1890 ed. cancelled (ISBN 0-8371-4602-X, HCM&, Pub. by Negro U Pr). Greenwood.
Harris, William L. Constitutional Powers of the General Conference: With a Special Application to the Subject of Slave Holding. facs. ed. LC 74-146265. (Black Heritage Library Collection Ser). 1860. 12.25 (ISBN 0-8369-8740-3). Ayer Co Pubs.
Jones, Donald G. The Sectional Crisis & Northern Methodism: A Study in Piety, Political Ethics & Civil Religion. LC 78-9978. 349p. 1979. lib. bdg. 22.50 (ISBN 0-8108-1175-8). Scarecrow.
Scott, Orange. Grounds of Secession from the M. E. Church. LC 71-82219. (Anti-Slavery Crusade in America Ser). 1969. Repr. of 1848 ed. 14.00 (ISBN 0-405-00659-4). Ayer Co Pubs.
Short, Roy H. The Episcopal Leadership Role in United Methodism. 224p. 1985. text ed. 9.95 (ISBN 0-687-11965-0). Abingdon.
Williams, John P. Social Adjustment in Methodism. LC 76-177639. (Columbia University. Teachers College. Contributions to Education: No. 765). Repr. of 1938 ed. 22.50 (ISBN 0-404-55765-1). AMS Pr.

METHODIST EPISCOPAL CHURCH–MISSIONS

Lee, Daniel & Frost, Joseph H. Ten Years in Oregon. LC 72-9457. (The Far Western Frontier Ser.). (Illus.). 348p. 1973. Repr. of 1844 ed. 24.50 (ISBN 0-405-04985-4). Ayer Co Pubs.

METHODIST EPISCOPAL CHURCH, SOUTH–HISTORY

Farish, Hunter D. Circuit Rider Dismounts, a Social History of Southern Methodism 1865-1900. LC 77-87534. (American Scene Ser). 1969. Repr. of 1938 ed. 45.00 (ISBN 0-306-71450-7). Da Capo.
Finley, James B. Sketches of Western Methodism: Biographical, Historical & Miscellaneous Illustrative of Pioneer Life. LC 79-83419. (Religion in America, Ser. 1). 1969. Repr. of 1954 ed. 30.00 (ISBN 0-405-00244-0). Ayer Co Pubs.
Hammond, Edmund J. Methodist Episcopal Church in Georgia. 1935. 10.00 (ISBN 0-88289-286-X). Pelican.
Jones, John G. Methodism in Mississippi, 2 Vols. in 1. 25.00 (ISBN 0-87511-592-6). Claitors.
Walker, Clarence E. A Rock in a Weary Land: The African Methodist Episcopal Church During the Civil War & Reconstruction. LC 81-11743. 188p. 1981. 22.50x (ISBN 0-8071-0883-9). La State U Pr.

METHODIST PUBLISHING HOUSE, NASHVILLE

Pilkington, James P. Methodist Publishing House: A History, Vol. 1. LC 68-21894. (Illus.). 1968. 8.25 (ISBN 0-687-26700-5). Abingdon.

METHODIUS, SAINT, ABP. OF MORAVIA, d. 885

The Apostles of the Slavs. 56p. 1985. pap. 3.95 (ISBN 1-55586-972-6). US Catholic.
Dvornik, Francis. Legendes de Constantin et de methode vues de Byzance. (Russian Ser: No. 12). 1969. Repr. of 1933 ed. 35.00 (ISBN 0-87569-009-2). Academic Intl.

METHODOLOGY

Feyerabend, Paul. Against Method. (Illus.). 1978. pap. 7.95 (ISBN 0-8052-7008-6, Pub by NLB). Schocken.

MEXICAN AMERICANS

Here are entered works on American citizens of Mexican descent or works concerned with Mexican American minority groups.

Brophy, A. Blake. Foundlings on the Frontier: Racial & Religious Conflict in Arizona Territory, 1904-1905. LC 79-187824. (Southwest Chronicles). 129p. 1972. pap. 3.95 (ISBN 0-8165-0319-2). U of Ariz Pr.
Cortes, Carlos E., ed. Church Views of the Mexican American. LC 73-14198. (The Mexican American Ser.). (Illus.). 58p. 1974. Repr. 45.00x (ISBN 0-405-05672-9). Ayer Co Pubs.
Falcon, Rafael. The Hispanic Mennonite Church in North America, 1932-1982. LC 85-30220. (Span.). 224p. 1986. 17.95x (ISBN 0-8361-1282-2). Herald Pr.
Mosqueda, Lawrence J. Chicanos, Catholicism & Political Ideology. 228p. (Orig.). 1986. lib. bdg. 24.50 (ISBN 0-8191-5318-4); pap. text ed. 12.75 (ISBN 0-8191-5319-2). U Pr of Amer.
Stevens-Arroyo, Antonio, ed. Prophets Denied Honor: An Anthology on the Hispanic Church in the U. S. LC 79-26847. 397p. (Orig.). 1982. pap. 12.95 (ISBN 0-88344-395-3). Orbis Bks.

MEXICAN ART

see Art, Mexican

MEXICO–HISTORY–CONQUEST, 1519-1540

Braden, C. S. Religious Aspects of the Conquest of Mexico. 1976. lib. bdg. 59.95 (ISBN 0-8490-2510-9). Gordon Pr.
Braden, Charles S. Religious Aspects of the Conquest of Mexico. LC 74-181914. Repr. of 1930 ed. 37.50 (ISBN 0-404-00925-5). AMS Pr.
Gomara, Francisco Lopez de. Cortes: The Life of the Conqueror of Mexico by His Secretary, Francisco Lopez de Gomara. Simpson, Lesley B., ed. & tr. LC 64-13474. 1964. pap. 5.95 (ISBN 0-520-00493-0, CAL 126). U of Cal Pr.
Leon-Portilla, Miguel. Broken Spears: The Aztec Account of the Conquest of Mexico. (Illus.). 1962. pap. 7.95x (ISBN 0-8070-5499-2, BP230). Beacon Pr.
Wagner, H. R. Rise of Fernando Cortes. (Cortes Society). 1944. 51.00 (ISBN 0-527-19733-5). Kraus Repr.

MEXICO–RELIGION

Church Wealth in Mexico: A Study of the Juzgado de Capellanias in the Archbishopric of Mexico, 1800-1856. LC 67-18310. (Cambridge Latin American Studies: No. 2). pap. 37.30 (ISBN 0-317-26021-9, 2024431). Bks Demand UMI.
Ingham, John M. Mary, Michael, & Lucifer: Folk Catholicism in Central Mexico. (Latin American Monographs: No. 69). (Illus.). 228p. 1986. text ed. 25.00x (ISBN 0-292-75089-7). U of Tex Pr.
Reville, Albert. The Native Religions of Mexico & Peru: Hibbert Lectures. Wicksteed, Phillip H., tr. LC 77-27167. 224p. 1983. Repr. of 1884 ed. 29.50 (ISBN 0-404-60405-6). Ams Pr.

MEXICO–SOCIAL LIFE AND CUSTOMS

Lafaye, Jacques. Quetzalcoatl & Guadalupe: The Formation of Mexican National Consciousness, 1531-1813. Keen, Benjamin, tr. from Fr. LC 75-20889. 1976. lib. bdg. 26.00x (ISBN 0-226-46794-5). U of Chicago Pr.

MI-LA RAS-PA, 1038-1122

De Jong, J. W., ed. Mi la Ras Pa'i Rnam Thar: Texte Tibetian De la Vie De Milarepa. (Indo-Iranian Monographs: No. 4). 1959. 22.00x (ISBN 90-2790-052-3). Mouton.

MICHAEL, ARCHANGEL

St. Michael & the Angels. LC 82-62040. Orig. Title: The Precious Blood & the Angels. 133p. 1983. pap. 3.50 (ISBN 0-89555-196-9). TAN Bks Pubs.

MICHELANGELO (BUONARROTI, MICHELANGELO), 1475-1564

Buonarroti, Michelangelo. Michelangelo: A Record of His Life As Told in His Own Letters & Papers. Carden, Robert W., tr. 1976. lib. bdg. 59.95 (ISBN 0-8490-2256-8). Gordon Pr.
Chastel, Andre, intro. by. The Vatican Frescoes of Michelangelo, 2 vols. Rosenthal, Raymond, tr. from Fr. LC 80-66646. (Illus.). 528p. 1980. ltd. ed. 7500.00 (ISBN 0-89659-158-1). Abbeville Pr.
Count Gobineau, Arthur. The Renaissance Savonarola. Levy, Oscar, ed. Cohen, Paul V., tr. (Fr., Illus.). 349p. 1986. Repr. of 1913 ed. lib. bdg. 75.00 (ISBN 0-89760-264-1). Telegraph Bks.

De Tolnay, Charles Q. Michelangelo, 6 vols. Incl. Vol. 1. The Youth of Michelangelo. 1969. 90.00x (ISBN 0-691-03858-9); Vol. 2. The Sistine Ceiling. 1969. 90.00x (ISBN 0-691-03856-2); Vol. 3. The Medeci Chapel. 1970. 90.00 (ISBN 0-691-03854-6); Vol. 4. The Tomb of Julius Two. 1970. 91.50x (ISBN 0-691-03857-0); Vol. 5. The Final Period. 1970. 90.00x (ISBN 0-691-03855-4); Vol. 6. Michelangelo, Architect. 68.00x (ISBN 0-691-03853-8); Michelangelo: Sculpter-Painter-Architect. (One vol. condensation). 52.50 (ISBN 0-691-03876-7); pap. 20.50 (ISBN 0-691-00337-8). Princeton U Pr.

Einem, Herbert Von. Michelangelo. 2nd ed. 1973. 43.00x (ISBN 0-416-15140-X, NO. 2183). Methuen Inc.

Gladden, Washington. Witnesses of the Light. facs. ed. LC 77-84307. (Essay Index Reprint Ser). 1903. 17.75 (ISBN 0-8369-1081-8). Ayer Co Pubs.

Grimm, H. Life of Michaelangelo, 2 vols. 200.00 (ISBN 0-8490-0533-7). Gordon Pr.

Grimm, Herman F. Life of Michael Angelo, 2 Vols. Bunnett, Fanny E., tr. Repr. of 1900 ed. Set. lib. bdg. 48.00x (ISBN 0-8371-2750-5, GRMA). Greenwood.

--Life of Michael Angelo, 2 Vols. 45.00x (ISBN 0-403-00399-7). Scholarly.

Hartt, Frederick, ed. Michelangelo. (Library of Great Painters). 1965. 45.00 (ISBN 0-8109-0299-0). Abrams.

Heuzinger, Lutz. Michelangelo. (Illus.). 96p. (Orig.). 1982. pap. 13.95 (ISBN 0-935748-43-1). Scala Books.

Hibbard, Howard. Michelangelo. LC 74-6576. (Icon Editions). (Illus.). 348p. 1975. 20.00i (ISBN 0-06-433323-X, HarpT); (HarpT). Har-Row.

Hupka, Robert. Michelangelo: Pieta. (Illus.). 96p. 1975. pap. 6.95 (ISBN 0-517-52414-7). Crown.

Mancusi-Ungaro, Harold R., Jr. Michelangelo: The Bruges Madonna & the Piccolomini Altar. LC 70-151582. (College Ser.: No. 11). (Illus.). Repr. of 1971 ed. 45.60 (ISBN 0-8357-9387-7, 2013192). Bks Demand UMI.

Phillips, Evelyn M. The Illustrated Guidebook to the Frescoes in the Sistine Chapel. (Illus.). 124p. 1981. Repr. of 1901 ed. 69.85 (ISBN 0-89901-029-6). Found Class Reprints.

Seymour, Charles, Jr., ed. & intro. by. Michelangelo: The Sistine Chapel Ceiling. (Critical Studies in Art History). (Illus.). 243p. 1972. pap. 7.95x (ISBN 0-393-09889-3). Norton.

Wilde, Johannes. Michelangelo: Six Lectures by Johannes Wilde. Shearman, John & Hirst, Michael, eds. (Oxford Studies in the History of Art & Architecture). (Illus.). 1979. pap. 13.95x (ISBN 0-19-817346-6). Oxford U Pr.

Wilson, Charles H. Life & Works of Michelangelo Buonarroti. Repr. of 1876 ed. 65.00 (ISBN 0-686-19837-9). Ridgeway Bks.

MIDDLE AGE

see also Aging; Old Age

Bianchi, Eugene C. On Growing Older. 176p. 1985. pap. 9.95 (ISBN 0-8245-0700-2). Crossroad NY.

Burg, Elizabeth. Midlife: Triumph-Not Crisis. 96p. (Orig.). 1986. pap. 4.50 (ISBN 0-914544-63-2). Living Flame Pr.

Clinebell, Howard J. Growth Counseling for Mid-Years Couples. Stone, Howard W., ed. LC 76-7863. (Creative Pastoral Care & Counseling Ser.). 1977. pap. 0.50 (ISBN 0-8006-0558-6, 1-558). Fortress.

Geddes, Jim. The Better Half of Life. (Orig.). 1987. pap. 7.95 (ISBN 0-8054-5732-1). Broadman.

Hickman, Martha W. The Growing Season. LC 80-68983. 128p. (Orig.). 1980. pap. 4.50x (ISBN 0-8358-0411-9). Upper Room.

McClelland, W. Robert. Chance to Dance: Risking a Spiritually Mature Life. Lambert, Herbert, ed. LC 85-18987. 128p. (Orig.). 1986. pap. 8.95 (ISBN 0-8272-0449-3). CBP.

Smith, Richard K. Forty-Nine & Holding. LC 75-11179. (Illus.). 1975. 10.00 (ISBN 0-89430-023-7). Palos Verdes.

Sterner, John. Growing Through Mid-Life Crises. 112p. 1985. 8.95 (ISBN 0-570-04220-8, 15-2181). Concordia.

MIDDLE AGES

see also Architecture, Medieval; Art, Medieval; Church History–Middle Ages, 600-1500; Civilization, Medieval; Renaissance; Science, Medieval

Allen, Judson B. Friar as Critic: Literary Attitudes in the Later Middle Ages. LC 77-123037. 1971. 11.50x (ISBN 0-8265-1158-9). Vanderbilt U Pr.

Baldwin, John W. The Scholastic Culture of the Middle Ages: 1000-1300. LC 70-120060. (Civilization & Society Ser). 192p. 1971. pap. 8.95x (ISBN 0-669-62059-9). Heath.

Bark, William C. Origins of the Medieval World. 1958. 15.00x (ISBN 0-8047-0513-5); pap. 5.95x (ISBN 0-8047-0514-3). Stanford U Pr.

Bartlett, Bede. Social Theories of the Middle Ages, Twelve Hundred to Twelve-Fifty. 1976. lib. bdg. 59.95 (ISBN 0-8490-2619-9). Gordon Pr.

Bishop, Morris. Middle Ages. abr. ed. LC 70-95728. 1970. pap. 7.95 (ISBN 0-07-005466-5). McGraw.

Cairns, Trevor. Middle Ages. (Cambridge Introduction to the History of Mankind Ser.: Bk. 4). (Illus.). 1971. 8.95 (ISBN 0-521-07726-5). Cambridge U Pr.

Caples, C. B., et al. A Medieval Miscellany. (Rice University Studies: Vol. 62, No. 2). (Illus.). 120p. (Orig.). 1976. pap. 10.00x (ISBN 0-89263-228-3). Rice Univ.

Church, R. W. The Beginning of the Middle Ages. 1977. lib. bdg. 59.95 (ISBN 0-8490-1484-0). Gordon Pr.

Coulton, George G. Life in the Middle Ages. Cambridge U Pr.

Crump, C. G. & Jacob, E. F., eds. Legacy of the Middle Ages. (Legacy Ser.). (Illus.). 1926. 32.50x (ISBN 0-19-821907-5). Oxford U Pr.

Cutts, Edward L. Scenes & Characters of the Middle Ages. LC 77-23575. 1977. Repr. of 1922 ed. lib. bdg. 45.00 (ISBN 0-89341-160-4). Longwood Pub Group.

Emerton, Ephraim. An Introduction to the Study of the Middle Ages (375-814) 1978. Repr. of 1900 ed. lib. bdg. 35.00 (ISBN 0-8482-0713-0). Norwood Edns.

Hauck, Karl, ed. Fruehmittelaterliche Studien, Vol. 11. (Illus.). 1977. 89.60x (ISBN 3-11-007076-6). De Gruyter.

Hearnshaw, Fossey J., ed. Medieval Contributions to Modern Civilization. LC 66-25917. 1966. Repr. of 1921 ed. 18.00x (ISBN 0-8046-0198-4, Pub. by Kennikat). Assoc Faculty Pr.

Heer, Friedrick. Medieval World: Europe Eleven Hundred to Thirteen Fifty. 1964. pap. 5.95 (ISBN 0-451-62542-0, ME2165, Ment). NAL.

Hodges, George. Saints & Heroes to the End of the Middle Ages. facsimile ed. LC 67-26749. (Essay Index Reprint Ser.). (Illus.). 268p. 1982. Repr. of 1911 ed. lib. bdg. 19.00 (ISBN 0-8290-0526-9). Irvington.

Hoyt, Robert S., ed. Life & Thought in the Early Middle Ages. LC 67-15065. (Illus.). 1968. pap. 1.95 (ISBN 0-8166-0464-9, MP11). U of Minn Pr.

Huizinga, J. Waning of the Middle Ages. LC 54-4529. pap. 5.95 (ISBN 0-385-09288-1, A42, Anch). Doubleday.

Jones, L. W., ed. Classical & Mediaeval Studies in Honor of Edward Kennard Rand, Presented upon the Completion of His Fortieth Year of Teaching. facs. ed. LC 68-57312. (Essay Index Reprint Ser). 1938. 21.50 (ISBN 0-8369-0312-9). Ayer Co Pubs.

Laistner, Max L. Intellectual Heritage of the Early Middle Ages. 1966. lib. bdg. 24.00x (ISBN 0-88254-852-2, Octagon). Hippocrene Bks.

Lucas, Angela. Women in the Middle Ages: Religion, Marriage & Letters. LC 82-42578. 215p. 1984. 11.95 (ISBN 0-312-88744-2). St Martin.

Lyon, Bryce, ed. High Middle Ages, One Thousand to Thirteen Hundred. LC 64-21207. (Orig.). 1964. pap. text ed. 13.95 (ISBN 0-02-919480-6). Free Pr.

Rand, Edward K. Founders of the Middle Ages. 1928. pap. 7.95 (ISBN 0-486-20369-7). Dover.

Southern, Richard W. Making of the Middle Ages. (Illus.). 1953. pap. 8.95x 1961 (ISBN 0-300-00230-0, Y46). Yale U Pr.

Townsend, W. J. The Great Schoolmen of the Middle Ages. 1977. lib. bdg. 39.95 (ISBN 0-8490-1903-6). Gordon Pr.

Zbozny, Frank T., ed. Annuale Mediaevale, Vol. 18. 1978. pap. text ed. 13.50x (ISBN 0-391-01220-7). Humanities.

MIDDLE AGES–HISTORY

see also Civilization, Medieval; Crusades; Europe–History–476-1492; Holy Roman Empire; Migrations of Nations; Monasticism and Religious Orders

Adams, G. B. Civilization During the Middle Ages. 75.00 (ISBN 0-87968-873-4). Gordon Pr.

Benson, Robert L. The Bishop-Elect: A Study in Medieval Ecclesiastical Office. LC 65-17130. pap. 115.00 (ISBN 0-317-07842-9, 2010535). Bks Demand UMI.

Birt, David. The Murder of Becket. (Resource Units: Middle Ages, 1066-1485 Ser.). (Illus.). 24p. 1974. pap. text ed. 12.95 10 copies & tchr's guide (ISBN 0-582-39376-0). Longman.

Bolton, Brenda. Medieval Reformation. (Foundations of Medieval History). (Illus.). 112p. 1983. text ed. 22.50x (ISBN 0-8419-0879-6); pap. text ed. 14.75x (ISBN 0-8419-0835-4). Holmes & Meier.

Brown, R. Allen. The Origins of Modern Europe: The Medieval Heritage of Western Civilization. LC 72-11597. 1973. pap. 7.95x (ISBN 0-88295-705-8). Harlan Davidson.

The Cambridge Medieval History, 9 vols. Incl. Vol. 1. The Christian Roman Empire & the Foundation of the Teutonic Kingdoms. 85.50 (ISBN 0-521-04532-0); Vol. 2. The Rise of the Saracens & the Foundation of the Western Empire; Vol. 3. Germany & the Western Empire. 85.00 (ISBN 0-521-04534-7); Vol. 4, Pt. 1. The Byzantine Empire. 2nd ed. Hussey, J. M. & Nicol, D. M., eds. 1966. 120.50 (ISBN 0-521-04535-5); Vol. 4, Pt. 2. Government Church & Civilization. 80.00 (ISBN 0-521-04536-3); Vol. 5. Contest of Empire & Papacy. 112.00 (ISBN 0-521-04537-1); Vol. 6. Victory of the Papacy. 112.50 (ISBN 0-521-04538-X); Vol. 7. Decline of the Empire & Papacy. 112.50 (ISBN 0-521-04539-8); Vol. 8. The Close of the Middle Ages. Cambridge U Pr.

Clifford, Alan. The Middle Ages. Yapp, Malcolm, et al, eds. (World History Ser.). (Illus.). 1980. lib. bdg. 6.95 (ISBN 0-89908-028-6); pap. text ed. 2.45 (ISBN 0-89908-003-0). Greenhaven.

Davidson, Audrey E. The Quasi-Dramatic St. John Passions from Scandinavia & Their Medieval Background. (Early Drama, Art & Music Monograph: No. 3). (Illus.). viii, 135p. 1981. pap. 8.95 (ISBN 0-918720-14-1). Medieval Inst.

Davison, Ellen S. Forerunners of Saint Francis & Other Studies. Richards, Gertrude R., ed. LC 77-85270. Repr. of 1927 ed. 49.50 (ISBN 0-404-16120-0). AMS Pr.

DiPaolo-Healey, Antonette, ed. The Old English Vision of St. Paul. LC 77-89928. 1978. 11.00x (ISBN 0-910956-76-6, SAM 2); pap. 5.00x (ISBN 0-910956-62-6). Medieval Acad.

Drew, Katherine F. & Lear, Floyd S., eds. Perspectives in Medieval History. LC 63-20902. Repr. of 1963 ed. 26.30 (ISBN 0-8357-9653-1, 2015753). Bks Demand UMI.

Emerton, Ephraim. An Introduction to the Study of the Middle Ages: 375-814. 1979. Repr. of 1895 ed. lib. bdg. 30.00 (ISBN 0-8495-1325-1). Arden Lib.

Falco, Giorgio. The Holy Roman Republic: A Historic Profile of the Middle Ages. Kent, K. V., tr. from Italian. LC 80-19696. Orig. Title: La Santa Romana Republica. 336p. 1980. Repr. of 1965 ed. lib. bdg. 42.50x (ISBN 0-313-22395-5, FAHR). Greenwood.

Garnier, H. L' Idee du Juste Prix Chez les Theologiens et Cannonistes du Moyen Age. LC 79-122228. (Fr.). 164p. 1973. Repr. of 1900 ed. lib. bdg. 20.50 (ISBN 0-8337-1286-1). B Franklin.

Geankoplos, Deno J. Byzantine East & Latin West: Two Worlds of Christendom in Middle Ages & Renaissance. LC 76-20685. (Illus.). xii, 206p. 1976. Repr. of 1966 ed. 17.50 (ISBN 0-208-01615-5, Archon). Shoe String.

Helmold Priest Of Bosau. Chronicle of the Slavs. Tschan, Francis J., tr. 1967. lib. bdg. 29.00x (ISBN 0-374-98018-7, Octagon). Hippocrene Bks.

Hoyt, Robert S. & Chodorow, Stanley. Europe in the Middle Ages. 3rd ed. (Illus.). 707p. 1976. text ed. 25.95 (ISBN 0-15-524712-3, HC). HarBraceJ.

Islam & the Medieval West: Aspects of Intercultural Relations. LC 79-18678. 1979. 44.50x (ISBN 0-87395-409-2); pap. 16.95x (ISBN 0-87395-455-6). State U NY Pr.

Keen, Maurice. Pelican History of Medieval Europe. 1969. pap. 5.95 (ISBN 0-14-021085-7, Pelican). Penguin.

LeClercq, Jean, et al. The Spirituality of the Middle Ages. (A History of Christian Spirituality Ser.: Vol. 2). 616p. 1982. pap. 14.95 (ISBN 0-8164-2373-3, HarpR). Har-Row.

McGarry, Daniel D. Medieval History & Civilization. (Illus.). 896p. 1976. text ed. write for info. (ISBN 0-02-379100-4). Macmillan.

McNeill, William H. & Houser, Schuyler O., eds. Medieval Europe. (Oxford Readings in World History Ser: Vol. 8). 1971. pap. 7.95x (ISBN 0-19-501312-3). Oxford U Pr.

Mundy, John H., et al. Essays in Medieval Life & Thought. LC 65-25472. 1955. 18.00 (ISBN 0-8196-0159-4). Biblo.

Powell, James M. Anatomy of a Crusade, Twelve Thirteen to Twelve Twenty-One. (Middle Ages Ser.). (Illus.). 336p. 1986. text ed. 34.95x (ISBN 0-8122-8025-3). U of Pa Pr.

Powicke, Frederick M. Ways of Medieval Life & Thought. LC 64-13394. (Illus.). 1949. 12.00 (ISBN 0-8196-0137-3). Biblo.

Previte-Orton, C. W. Outlines of Medieval History. 2nd ed. LC 64-25837. 1916. 12.00 (ISBN 0-8196-0147-0). Biblo.

Previte-Orton, C. W., ed. The Shorter Cambridge Medieval History, 2 vols. Incl. Vol. 1. The Later Roman Empire to the Twelfth Century. (Illus.). 644p. 74.50 (ISBN 0-521-20962-5); pap. 23.95 (ISBN 0-521-09976-5); Vol. 2. The Twelfth Century to the Renaissance. (Illus.). 558p. 74.50 (ISBN 0-521-20963-3); pap. 23.95 (ISBN 0-521-09977-3). (Medieval History Ser). 1975. pap. 18.95 ea. Set. 135.00 (ISBN 0-521-05993-3); Set. pap. 39.50 (ISBN 0-521-08758-9). Cambridge U Pr.

Riley-Smith, Louise & Riley-Smith, Jonathan. The Crusades: Idea & Reality, 1095-1274. (Documents in Medieval History). 208p. 1981. pap. text ed. 17.95 (ISBN 0-7131-6348-8). E Arnold.

Sellery, G. C. & Krey, A. C. Medieval Foundations of Western Civilization. LC 68-24116. (World History Ser., No. 48). (Illus.). 1968. Repr. 74.95x (ISBN 0-8383-0926-7). Haskell.

Shannon, Albert C. The Medieval Inquisition. 168p. 1983. 15.00 (ISBN 0-9612336-0-5, 83-72869); pap. 10.00 (ISBN 0-9612336-1-3). Augustinian Coll Pr.

Swanson, R. N. Universities, Academics & the Great Schism. LC 78-56764. (Cambridge Studies in Medieval Life & Thought: 3rd Ser., No. 12). 1979. 49.50 (ISBN 0-521-22127-7). Cambridge U Pr.

Syme, Ronald. Some Arval Brethren. 1980. 36.00x (ISBN 0-19-814831-3). Oxford U Pr.

Taylor, Charles H., ed. Anniversary Essays in Mediaeval History, by Students of Charles Homer Haskins: Presented on His Completion of Forty Years of Teaching. facs. ed. LC 67-30194. (Essay Index Reprint Ser). 1929. 22.00 (ISBN 0-8369-0155-X). Ayer Co Pubs.

Tierney, Brian & Painter, Sidney. Western Europe in the Middle Ages, 300-1475. 4th ed. 1982. text ed. 24.00 (ISBN 0-394-33060-9, RanC). Random.

Vitalis, Orderic. Ecclesiastical History of Orderic Vitalis, Vol. 6, Books 11, 12, 13. Chibnall, Marjorie, ed. & tr. 1978. text ed. 84.00x (ISBN 0-19-822242-4). Oxford U Pr.

Wall, James T. From the Law of Moses to the Magna Carta: Essays in Ancient & Medieval History. LC 79-66236. 1979. pap. text ed. 9.50 (ISBN 0-8191-0801-4). U Pr of Amer.

Wattenbach, W., ed. Die Chronik Fredegars und der Frankenkoenige, die Lebensbeschreibungen des Abtes Columban, der Bischoefe Arnulf, Leodegar und Eligius, der Koenigin Balthilde. 2nd ed. Abel, Otto, tr. (Die Geschichtschreiber der Deutschen Vorzeit Ser: Vol. 11). (Ger.). pap. 19.00 (ISBN 0-384-00104-1). Johnson Repr.

Wilks, Michael. The Problem of Sovereignty in the Later Middle Ages: The Papal Monarchy with Augustinus Triumphus & the Publicists. (Cambridge Studies in Medieval Life & Thought New: Vol. 9). pap. 158.30 (ISBN 0-317-09407-6, 2013890). Bks Demand UMI.

Wood, Charles T. The Quest for Eternity: Manners & Morals in the Age of Chivalry. LC 82-40476. (Illus.). 172p. 1983. pap. 8.00x (ISBN 0-87451-259-X). U Pr of New Eng.

MIDDLE AGES–JUVENILE LITERATURE

Cairns, Trevor, ed. Barbarians, Christians, & Muslims. LC 73-20213. (Cambridge Introduction to History Ser.). (Illus.). 104p. 1975. PLB 10.95 (ISBN 0-8225-0803-6). Lerner Pubns.

MIDDLEHAM, YORK, ENGLAND–COLLEGIATE CHURCH

Atthill, William L., ed. Documents Relating to the Foundation & Antiquities of the Collegiate Church of Middleham in the County of York. LC 70-161702. (Camden Society, London. Publications, First Ser.: No. 38). Repr. of 1847 ed. 19.00 (ISBN 0-404-50138-9). AMS Pr.

--Documents Relating to the Foundation & Antiquities of the Collegiate Church of Middleham, County of York. (Camden Society Ser.: Vol. 38). 19.00 (ISBN 0-384-02270-7). Johnson Repr.

MIDDLETON, THOMAS, d. 1627

Heinemann, Margot. Puritanism & Theatre: Thomas Middleton & Opposition Drama Under the Early Stuarts. LC 79-14991. (Past & Present Publications Ser.). 309p. 1982. 34.50 (ISBN 0-521-22602-3); pap. 13.95 (ISBN 0-521-27052-9). Cambridge U Pr.

Johansson, B. Religion & Superstition in the Plays of Ben Johnson & Thomas Middleton. (Essays & Studies on English Language & Literature: Vol. 7). pap. 28.00 (ISBN 0-8115-0205-8). Kraus Repr.

MIDRASH

see also Tannaim

The Complete Set of Midrash Rabba: Hebrew & English, 18 vols. 395.00 (ISBN 0-87559-160-4). Shalom.

Freehof, Lillian S. Bible Legends: An Introduction to Midrash. rev. ed. Schwartz, Howard, ed. 1987. pap. text ed. 6.95 (ISBN 0-8074-0357-1). UAHC.

--Bible Legends: An Introduction to Midrash. Schwartz, Howard, ed. (YA) Date not set. pap. text ed. 6.95 (ISBN 0-8074-0357-1). UAHC.

Freeman, Gordon M. The Heavenly Kingdom: Aspects of Political Thought in the Talmud & Midrash. 196p. (Orig.). 1986. lib. bdg. 24.75 (ISBN 0-8191-5139-4, Co-pub. by Ctr Jewish Comm Studies); pap. text ed. 11.75 (ISBN 0-8191-5140-8). U Pr of Amer.

Hartman, Geoffrey. Midrash & Literature. LC 85-17898. 424p. 1986. 28.50 (ISBN 0-300-03453-9). Yale U Pr.

Maftechoth Hamidrash Rabba: Keys to the Midrash Rabba. 35.00 (ISBN 0-87559-159-0). Shalom.

Midrash Bamidbar Rabba: Numbers Rabba, Hebrew & English, 4 vols. 80.00 (ISBN 0-87559-153-1). Shalom.

Midrash Devorim Rabba: Deuteronomy, Hebrew & English. 20.00 (ISBN 0-87559-154-X). Shalom.

Midrash Eicha Rabba: Lamentation Rabba, Hebrew & English. 20.00 (ISBN 0-87559-157-4). Shalom.

Midrash Esther Rabba & Midrash Ruth Rabba: Hebrew & English. 20.00 (ISBN 0-87559-155-8). Shalom.

Midrash Koheleth Rabba: Ecclesiastes Rabba, Hebrew & English. 20.00 (ISBN 0-87559-158-2). Shalom.

Midrash Shemoth Rabba: Exodus Rabba, Hebrew & English, 2 vols. 40.00 (ISBN 0-87559-151-5). Shalom.

Midrash Shirashirim Rabba: Songs of Rabba, Hebrew & English. 20.00 (ISBN 0-87559-156-6). Shalom.

Midrash Vayikra Rabba: Leviticus Rabba, Hebrew & English, 2 vols. 40.00 (ISBN 0-87559-152-3). Shalom.

Neusner, Jacob. Comparative Midrash: The Plan & Program of Genesis Rabbah & Leviticus Rabbah. (Brown Judaic Studies). 1986. 27.95 (ISBN 0-89130-958-6, 14-01-11); pap. 22.95 (ISBN 0-89130-959-4). Scholars Pr GA.

--Genesis & Judaism: The Perspective of Genesis Rabbah, an Analytical Anthology. 1985. 28.95 (ISBN 0-89130-940-3, 14-01-08); pap. 22.95 (ISBN 0-89130-941-1). Scholars Pr GA.

--Genesis Rabbah: The Judaic Commentary to the Book of Genesis, Vol. II. 1985. 34.95 (ISBN 0-89130-933-0, 14-01-05); pap. 29.55 (ISBN 0-89130-934-9). Scholars Pr GA.

--Genesis Rabbah: The Judaic Commentary to the Book of Genesis, Vol. III. 1985. 33.95 (ISBN 0-89130-935-7, 14-01-06); pap. 28.55 (ISBN 0-89130-936-5). Scholars Pr GA.

--Genesis Rabbah: The Judaic Commentary to the Book of Genesis, Vol. 1. 1985. 35.75 (ISBN 0-89130-931-4, 14-01-04); pap. 26.75 (ISBN 0-89130-932-2). Scholars Pr GA.

--Midrash in Context. LC 83-5705. 240p. 1983. 23.95 (ISBN 0-8006-0708-2, 1-708). Fortress.

Strack, Hermann L. Introduction to the Talmud & Midrash. LC 59-7191. (Temple Books). 1969. pap. text ed. 8.95x (ISBN 0-689-70189-6, T10). Atheneum.

MIDRASH–TRANSLATIONS INTO ENGLISH

The Complete Set of Midrash Rabba: Hebrew & English, 18 vols. 395.00 (ISBN 0-87559-160-4). Shalom.

Jacobson, David C. Modern Midrash: The Retelling of Traditional Jewish Narratives by Twentieth-Century Hebrew Writers. (SUNY Series in Modern Jewish Literature & Culture). 208p. 1986. 34.50x (ISBN 0-88706-323-3); pap. 10.95x (ISBN 0-88706-325-X). State U NY Pr.

Lauterbach, Jacob Z., intro. by. & tr. from Heb. Mekilta De-Rabbi Ishmael, 3 vols. LC 75-40823. (JPS Library of Jewish Classics). 808p. 1976. pap. 19.95 (ISBN 0-8276-0078-X, 382). Jewish Pubns.

Maftechoth Hamidrash Rabba: Keys to the Midrash Rabba. 35.00 (ISBN 0-87559-159-0). Shalom.

Midrash Bamidbar Rabba: Numbers Rabba, Hebrew & English, 4 vols. 80.00 (ISBN 0-87559-153-1). Shalom.

Midrash Devorim Rabba: Deuteronomy, Hebrew & English. 20.00 (ISBN 0-87559-154-X). Shalom.

Midrash Eicha Rabba: Lamentation Rabba, Hebrew & English. 20.00 (ISBN 0-87559-157-4). Shalom.

Midrash Esther Rabba & Midrash Ruth Rabba: Hebrew & English. 20.00 (ISBN 0-87559-155-8). Shalom.

Midrash Koheleth Rabba: Ecclesiastes Rabba, Hebrew & English. 20.00 (ISBN 0-87559-158-2). Shalom.

Midrash Shemoth Rabba: Exodus Rabba, Hebrew & English, 2 vols. 40.00 (ISBN 0-87559-151-5). Shalom.

Midrash Shirashirim Rabba: Songs of Rabba, Hebrew & English. 20.00 (ISBN 0-87559-156-6). Shalom.

Midrash Vayikra Rabba: Leviticus Rabba, Hebrew & English, 2 vols. 40.00 (ISBN 0-87559-152-3). Shalom.

Montefiore, C. G. & Loewe, H., eds. A Rabbinic Anthology. LC 73-91340. 1970. pap. 16.95 (ISBN 0-8052-0442-3). Schocken.

MIGNE, JACQUES PAUL, 1800-1875

Garnier, Freres. Catalogue General des Ouvrages Edites Par l'Abbe Migne. LC 71-168926. 1967. Repr. of 1885 ed. 22.50 (ISBN 0-8337-2386-3). B Franklin.

MIGRATIONS OF NATIONS

see also Jews–Migrations

Cairns, Trevor. Barbarians, Christians & Muslims. LC 69-11024. (Cambridge Introduction to the History of Mankind Ser.: Bk. 3). 1970. 8.95 (ISBN 0-521-07360-X). Cambridge U Pr.

MILITARY RELIGIOUS ORDERS

see also Hospitalers; Templars

Harnack, Adolf. Militia Christi: The Christian Religion & the Military in the First Three Centuries. Gracie, David M., tr. from Ger. LC 81-43089. Tr. of Militia Christi: Die christliche Religion und der Soldatenstand in den ersten drei Jahrhunderten. 112p. 1981. 3.00 (ISBN 0-8006-0673-6, 1-673). Fortress.

MILLENNIUM

see also Dispensationalism; Second Advent

Barkun, Michael. Disaster & the Millennium. LC 86-5979. 256p. 1986. pap. text ed. 12.95x (ISBN 0-8156-2392-5). Syracuse U Pr.

Bettis, Joseph & Johannesen, S. K., eds. The Return of the Millennium. LC 83-82671. 247p. 1984. pap. 11.95 (ISBN 0-913757-02-0). Rose Sharon Pr.

Bettis, Joseph & Johannesen, Stanley, eds. The Return of the Millennium. LC 83-82671. 232p. (Orig.). pap. 11.95 (ISBN 0-913757-02-0, Pub. by New Era Bks.). Paragon Hse.

Blodgett, Ralph. Millennium. (Outreach Ser.). 1981. pap. 1.25 (ISBN 0-8163-0398-3). Pacific Pr Pub Assn.

Bryant, M. Darrol & Dayton, Donald W., eds. Coming Kingdom: Essays in American Millennialism & Eschatology. LC 83-82211. xii, 258p. 1984. text ed. 15.95 o. p. (ISBN 0-913757-01-2, Pub. by New Era Bks); pap. text ed. 11.95 (ISBN 0-913757-00-4, Pub. by New Era Bks). Paragon Hse.

Burridge, Kenelm. New Heaven, New Earth: A Study of Millenarian Activities. (Pavilion Ser.). 198p. 1969. pap. text ed. 12.95x (ISBN 0-631-11950-7). Basil Blackwell.

Clouse, Robert G. The Meaning of the Millennium. 212p. 1978. pap. 5.95 (ISBN 0-88469-099-7). BMH Bks.

Clouse, Robert G., ed. The Meaning of the Millennium: Four Views. 1977. pap. 7.95 (ISBN 0-87784-794-0). Inter-Varsity.

Doan, Ruth A. The Miller Heresy, Millenialism, & Amercian Culture. 270p. 1987. price not set (ISBN 0-87722-481-1). Temple U Pr.

Erickson, Millard J. Contemporary Options in Eschatology: A Study of the Millennium. LC 77-89406. 1977. 9.95 (ISBN 0-8010-3262-8). Baker Bk.

Feinberg, Charles. Millennialism: The Two Major Views. 1985. 12.95 (ISBN 0-88469-166-7). BMH Bks.

Garrett, Clarke. Respectable Folly: Millenarians and the French Revolution in France and England. LC 74-24378. 252p. 1975. 26.00x (ISBN 0-8018-1618-1). Johns Hopkins.

Gilpin, W. Clark. The Millenarian Piety of Roger Williams. LC 78-20786. 1979. lib. bdg. 19.00x (ISBN 0-226-29397-1). U of Chicago Pr.

Harrison, John F. The Second Coming: Popular Millenarianism 1780-1850. 1979. 32.00x (ISBN 0-8135-0879-7). Rutgers U Pr.

Hopkins, Samuel. A Treatise on the Millennium. LC 70-38450. (Religion in America, Series 2). 162p. 1972. Repr. of 1793 ed. 14.00 (ISBN 0-405-04070-9). Ayer Co Pubs.

Lindsay, Gordon. The Millennium. (Revelation Ser.). 1.25 (ISBN 0-89985-048-0). Christ Nations.

Ryrie, Charles C. Basis of the Premillennial Faith. 1954. pap. 4.95 (ISBN 0-87213-741-4). Loizeaux.

Schwartz, Hillel. Knaves, Fools, Madmen & That Subtile Effluvium: A Study of the Opposition to the French Prophets in England, 1706-1710. LC 78-1692. (University of Florida Social Sciences Monographs: No. 62). 1978. pap. 5.50 (ISBN 0-8130-0505-1). U Presses Fla.

Thomas, L. R. Does the Bible Teach Millennialism. pap. 2.50 (ISBN 0-685-36796-7). Reiner.

Weber, Timothy P. Living in the Shadow of the Second Coming: American Premillennialism, 1875-1982. rev. & enl. ed. xiv, 306p. 1987. pap. 12.95 (ISBN 0-226-87732-9). U of Chicago Pr.

Weinstein, Donald. Savonarola & Florence: Prophecy & Patriotism in the Renaissance. LC 76-113013. Repr. of 1970 ed. 102.80 (ISBN 0-8357-9511-X, 2015484). Bks Demand UMI.

MILLER, WILLIAM, 1795-1861

Bliss, Sylvester. Memoirs of William Miller. LC 72-134374. Repr. of 1853 ed. 30.00 (ISBN 0-404-08422-2). AMS Pr.

Nichol, Francis D. The Midnight Cry: A Defense of William Miller & the Millerites. LC 72-8249. Repr. of 1944 ed. 36.00 (ISBN 0-404-11003-7). AMS Pr.

White, James. Sketches of the Christian Life & Public Labors of William Miller. LC 70-134376. Repr. of 1875 ed. 27.50 (ISBN 0-404-08424-9). AMS Pr.

MILTON, JOHN, 1608-1674

Ames, Percy. Milton Memorial Lectures 1909. LC 65-15895. (Studies in Milton, No. 22). 1969. Repr. of 1909 ed. lib. bdg. 49.95x (ISBN 0-8383-0501-6). Haskell.

Ames, Percy W. Milton Memorial Lectures. 1974. Repr. 32.50 (ISBN 0-8274-2738-7). R West.

Bailey, John C. Milton. LC 73-12210. 1973. lib. bdg. 17.50 (ISBN 0-8414-3218-X). Folcroft.

Barnes, C. L. Parallels in Dante & Milton. LC 74-3180. 1917. lib. bdg. 12.50 (ISBN 0-8414-9926-8). Folcroft.

Beers, Henry A. Milton's Tercentenary. LC 73-39421. Repr. of 1910 ed. 7.50 (ISBN 0-404-00725-2). AMS Pr.

--Milton's Tercentenary. LC 73-9747. 1910. lib. bdg. 8.50 (ISBN 0-8414-3168-X). Folcroft.

Belloc, Hilaire. Milton. LC 78-100142. Repr. of 1935 ed. lib. bdg. 24.75x (ISBN 0-8371-3248-7, BEMI). Greenwood.

Berry, W. Grinton. John Milton. LC 73-10007. 1909. lib. bdg. 17.50 (ISBN 0-8414-3150-7). Folcroft.

Blake, William. Milton. Russell, A. & Maclagan, E., eds. LC 73-16264. 1907. lib. bdg. 15.00 (ISBN 0-8414-3345-3). Folcroft.

Campbell, Oscar J., et al. Studies in Shakespeare, Milton & Donne. McCartney, Eugene S., ed. LC 78-93244. (University of Michigan Publications: Vol. 1). 235p. 1970. Repr. of 1925 ed. 20.00x (ISBN 0-87753-020-3). Phaeton.

Candy, Hugh C. Milton: The Individualist in Metre. 1930. lib. bdg. 7.50 (ISBN 0-8414-3630-4). Folcroft.

Chambers, R. W. Poets & Their Critics: Langland & Milton. 1942. lib. bdg. 10.00 (ISBN 0-685-10478-8). Folcroft.

Channing, William. Character & Writings of John Milton. 1826. lib. bdg. 8.50 (ISBN 0-8414-3465-4). Folcroft.

Channing, William E. Remarks on the Character & Writings of John Milton. 3rd ed. LC 72-966. Repr. of 1828 ed. 12.50 (ISBN 0-404-01448-8). AMS Pr.

Charlesworth, Arthur R. Paradise Found. LC 72-91109. 1973. 10.00 (ISBN 0-8022-2104-1). Philos Lib.

Cooke, John. John Milton: 1608-1674. LC 74-5138. 1973. Repr. of 1908 ed. lib. bdg. 10.00 (ISBN 0-8414-3549-9). Folcroft.

Courthope, W. J. Essays on Milton. 1908. lib. bdg. 10.00 (ISBN 0-8414-3599-5). Folcroft.

Crump, Galbraith M. The Mystical Design of "Paradise Lost". 194p. 1975. 18.00 (ISBN 0-8387-1519-2). Bucknell U Pr.

Curry, Walter C. Milton's Ontology, Cosmogony & Physics. LC 57-5833. (Illus.). 226p. 1957. pap. 6.00x (ISBN 0-8131-0102-6). U Pr of Ky.

Daiches, David. Milton. (Orig.). 1966. pap. 4.95x (ISBN 0-393-00347-7, Norton Lib). Norton.

Darbishire, Helen. Milton's Paradise Lost. LC 74-3031. 1951. lib. bdg. 15.00 (ISBN 0-8414-3750-5). Folcroft.

Darbishire, Helen, ed. Early Lives of Milton. LC 77-144967. (Illus.). 1971. Repr. of 1932 ed. 49.00x (ISBN 0-403-00935-9). Scholarly.

DiSalvo, Jackie. War of Titans: Blake's Critique of Milton & the Politics of Religion. LC 82-11136. 403p. 1983. 38.95x (ISBN 0-8229-3804-9). U of Pittsburgh Pr.

Dobbins, Austin C. Milton & the Book of Revelation: The Heavenly Cycle. LC 73-22715. (Studies in the Humanities: No. 7). 176p. 1975. o. p. 12.50 (ISBN 0-8173-7320-9); pap. 4.95 (ISBN 0-8173-7321-7). U of Ala Pr.

Edmonds, Cyrus R. John Milton: A Biography. LC 72-194753. 1851. lib. bdg. 20.00 (ISBN 0-8414-3886-2). Folcroft.

Ferry, Anne D. Milton & the Miltonic Dryden. LC 68-25608. 1968. 16.50x (ISBN 0-674-57576-8). Harvard U Pr.

Fletcher, H. Use of the Bible in Milton's Prose. LC 75-95425. (Studies in Milton, No. 22). 1970. Repr. of 1929 ed. lib. bdg. 39.95x (ISBN 0-8383-0974-7). Haskell.

Fletcher, Harris F. Milton Studies in Honor of Harris Francis Fletcher. LC 74-16488. 1974. Repr. of 1961 ed. lib. bdg. 30.00 (ISBN 0-8414-4247-9). Folcroft.

--Milton's Semitic Studies. LC 74-18236. 1973. lib. bdg. 27.50 (ISBN 0-8414-4249-5). Folcroft.

--Use of the Bible in Milton's Prose. 1973. lib. bdg. 59.95 (ISBN 0-87968-014-8). Gordon Pr.

French, J. Milton, ed. Life Records of John Milton, 1608-1674, 5 Vols. LC 66-20024. 2368p. 1966. Repr. of 1958 ed. Set. 150.00x (ISBN 0-87752-039-9). Gordian.

Garnett, Richard. Life of John Milton. LC 77-112638. Repr. of 1890 ed. 10.00 (ISBN 0-404-02686-9). AMS Pr.

--Life of John Milton. 1890. lib. bdg. 9.75 (ISBN 0-8414-4638-5). Folcroft.

--Prose of Milton. 1894. Repr. 20.00 (ISBN 0-8274-3214-3). R West.

Gertsch, Alfred. Der Steigende Ruhm Miltons. Repr. of 1927 ed. 54.00 (ISBN 0-384-18230-5). Johnson Repr.

Good, John W. Studies in the Milton Tradition. LC 73-144619. Repr. of 1915 ed. 16.00 (ISBN 0-404-02862-4). AMS Pr.

--Studies in the Milton Tradition. Repr. of 1915 ed. 22.00 (ISBN 0-384-19150-9). Johnson Repr.

Grace, William J. Ideas in Milton. LC 68-12290. 1969. Repr. of 1968 ed. 6.95x (ISBN 0-268-00126-X). U of Notre Dame Pr.

Grierson, Herbert. Criticism & Creation. LC 73-733. 1949. lib. bdg. 17.50 (ISBN 0-8414-1603-6). Folcroft.

Hall, William C. Milton & His Sonnets. LC 73-4268. 1973. lib. bdg. 12.50 (ISBN 0-8414-2071-8). Folcroft.

Hamilton, G. Rostrevor. Hero or Fool. LC 70-98995. (Studies in Milton, No. 22). 1970. pap. 19.95x (ISBN 0-8383-0038-3). Haskell.

--Hero or Fool: A Study of Milton's Satan. LC 74-16136. 1944. lib. bdg. 17.50 (ISBN 0-8414-4860-4). Folcroft.

Hamilton, John A. The Life of John Milton, Englishman. LC 74-16133. 1974. Repr. lib. bdg. 9.50 (ISBN 0-8414-4874-4). Folcroft.

Hamilton, W. Douglas. Original Papers Illustrative of the Life & Writings of John Milton. LC 76-29043. 1859. lib. bdg. 25.00 (ISBN 0-8414-4935-X). Folcroft.

Hamilton, William D., ed. Original Papers Illustrative of the Life & Writings of John Milton. (Camden Society, London. Publications, First Ser.: No. 75). Repr. of 1859 ed. 28.00 (ISBN 0-404-50175-3). AMS Pr.

--Original Papers Illustrative of the Life & Writings of John Milton. 1859. 28.00 (ISBN 0-384-21220-4). Johnson Repr.

Harris, W. Melville. John Milton: Puritan, Patriot, Poet. LC 77-3593. lib. bdg. 5.00 (ISBN 0-8414-4919-8). Folcroft.

Hartwell, Kathleen. Lactantius & Milton. LC 74-17014. (Studies in Milton, No. 22). 1974. lib. bdg. 46.95x (ISBN 0-8383-1743-X). Haskell.

Hayley, William. The Life of Milton. LC 76-26849. Repr. of 1796 ed. lib. bdg. 45.00 (ISBN 0-8414-4739-X). Folcroft.

--Life of Milton. LC 78-122485. 1970. Repr. of 1796 ed. 50.00x (ISBN 0-8201-1081-7). Schol Facsimiles.

Herford, C. H. Dante & Milton. 1924. lib. bdg. 10.00 (ISBN 0-8414-5044-7). Folcroft.

Hieatt, A. Kent. Chaucer, Spenser, Milton: Mythopoeic Continuities & Transformations. (Illus.). 336p. 1975. 25.00x (ISBN 0-7735-0228-9). McGill-Queens U Pr.

Hillis, Newell D. Great Men As Prophets of a New Era. facs. ed. LC 68-16939. (Essay Index Reprint Ser). 1968. Repr. of 1922 ed. 15.00 (ISBN 0-8369-0541-5). Ayer Co Pubs.

Hunter, Joseph. Milton, A Sheaf of Gleanings. LC 76-26898. 1850. lib. bdg. 12.50 (ISBN 0-8414-4737-3). Folcroft.

Hunter, William. Milton on the Nature of Man. LC 76-48905. 1946. lib. bdg. 12.50 (ISBN 0-8414-4908-2). Folcroft.

Hunter, William B., Jr., et al. Bright Essence: Studies in Milton's Theology. LC 74-161485. 1971. 14.95x (ISBN 0-87480-061-7). U of Utah Pr.

Hunter, Wm. Bridges. Milton on the Nature of Man. 1978. Repr. of 1946 ed. lib. bdg. 15.00 (ISBN 0-8492-1186-7). R West.

Hutchinson, F. Milton & the English Mind. LC 74-7187. (Studies in Milton, No. 22). 1974. lib. bdg. 49.95x (ISBN 0-8383-1906-8). Haskell.

Hutchinson, F. E. Milton & the English Mind. LC 74-28171. 1946. Repr. lib. bdg. 17.50 (ISBN 0-8414-4897-3). Folcroft.

Ivimey, Joseph. John Milton: His Life & Times, Religious & Political Opinions. LC 72-190658. 1833. lib. bdg. 37.50 (ISBN 0-8414-5069-2). Folcroft.

Jenks, Tudor. In the Days of Milton. LC 76-170812. Repr. of 1905 ed. 19.45 (ISBN 0-404-03559-0). AMS Pr.

Keightley, Thomas. An Account of the Life, Opinions, & Writings of John Milton. LC 73-11332. 1855. Repr. lib. bdg. 49.50 (ISBN 0-8414-2222-2). Folcroft.

Kerrigan, William. The Prophetic Milton. LC 74-6118. Repr. of 1974 ed. 74.30 (ISBN 0-8357-9813-5, 2016964). Bks Demand UMI.

Kranidas, Thomas, ed. New Essays on Paradise Lost. LC 72-82463. 1969. pap. 4.95x (ISBN 0-520-01902-4, CAMPUS51). U of Cal Pr.

Larson, Martin A. Modernity of Milton. LC 76-23120. 1927. lib. bdg. 7.95 (ISBN 0-8414-5800-6). Folcroft.

--Modernity of Milton: A Theological & Philosophical Interpretation. LC 76-124764. Repr. of 1927 ed. 18.75 (ISBN 0-404-03880-8). AMS Pr.

Lawson, McEwan. Master John Milton of the Citie of London. LC 72-10632. 1973. Repr. lib. bdg. 12.50 (ISBN 0-8414-0725-8). Folcroft.

Lijegren, Sten. Studies in Milton. LC 67-30816. (Studies in Milton, No. 22). 1969. Repr. of 1918 ed. lib. bdg. 75.00x (ISBN 0-8383-0718-3). Haskell.

Liljegren, Sten B. Studies in Milton. 1918. lib. bdg. 20.00 (ISBN 0-8414-5707-7). Folcroft.

Macaulay, Rose. Milton. LC 74-7050. (Studies in Milton, No. 22). 1974. lib. bdg. 75.00x (ISBN 0-8383-1911-4). Haskell.

MacCaffrey, Isabel G. Paradise Lost As Myth. LC 59-9282. 1959. 15.00x (ISBN 0-674-65450-1). Harvard U Pr.

Mackail, John W. Bentley's Milton. LC 73-7628. 1973. lib. bdg. 15.00 (ISBN 0-8414-2343-1). Folcroft.

Manuel, M. Seventeenth Century Critics & Biographers of Milton. LC 77-23430. 1962. lib. bdg. 19.50 (ISBN 0-8414-6184-8). Folcroft.

Marsh, John F. Papers Connected with the Affairs of Milton & His Family. LC 74-22180. 1974. Repr. of 1851 ed. lib. bdg. 15.00 (ISBN 0-8414-5959-2). Folcroft.

Martin, John R. Portrait of John Milton at Princeton. LC 61-14263. (Illus.). 42p. 1961. 7.50 (ISBN 0-87811-006-2). Princeton Lib.

Martin, L. C. Thomas Warton & the Early Poems of Milton. LC 77-9907. 1934. lib. bdg. 9.50 (ISBN 0-8414-6096-5). Folcroft.

Martyn, Carlos. Life & Times of John Milton. LC 76-39970. 1976. Repr. of 1866 ed. lib. bdg. 37.50 (ISBN 0-8414-6009-4). Folcroft.

Masson, David. Life of John Milton: Narrated in Connection with the Political, Literary & Ecclesiastical History of His Time, 7 vols. Set. 117.25 (ISBN 0-8446-1303-7); 16.75 ea. Peter Smith.

--Three Devils: Luther's, Milton's & Goethe's. LC 72-193946. 1874. lib. bdg. 20.00 (ISBN 0-8414-6495-2). Folcroft.

Masterman, J. Howard. The Age of Milton. 1906. Repr. lib. bdg. 15.00 (ISBN 0-8414-6453-7). Folcroft.

Milton, John. Catalogue of an Exhibition Commemorative of the Tercentenary of the Birth of John Milton. Repr. of 1909 ed. lib. bdg. 20.00 (ISBN 0-8414-6620-3). Folcroft.

--Complete Poetry of John Milton. Shawcross, John T., ed. LC 72-150934. 1971. pap. 8.95 (ISBN 0-385-02351-0, Anch). Doubleday.

--On the Morning of Christ's Nativity: Milton's Hymn with Illustrations by William Blake. Keynes, Geoffrey, ed. LC 77-22296. (Illus.). Repr. of 1923 ed. lib. bdg. 12.50 (ISBN 0-8414-9917-9). Folcroft.

--Portraits, Prints & Writings of John Milton. LC 73-15855. 1908. lib. bdg. 17.50 (ISBN 0-8414-6060-4). Folcroft.

Mordell, Albert. Dante & Other Waning Classics. LC 68-8219. 1969. Repr. of 1915 ed. 18.50x (ISBN 0-8046-0322-7, Pub. by Kennikat). Assoc Faculty Pr.

Morris, Edward E. Milton: Tractate of Education. LC 73-13795. 1895. Repr. lib. bdg. 12.50 (ISBN 0-8414-6000-0). Folcroft.

Mulryan, John, ed. Milton & the Middle Ages. LC 81-694400. 192p. 1982. 22.50 (ISBN 0-8387-5036-2). Bucknell U Pr.

Mutschmann, H. Secret of John Milton. LC 72-194771. 1925. lib. bdg. 15.00 (ISBN 0-8414-6694-7). Folcroft.

Myers, Ernest, ed. Selected Prose Writings of John Milton. 1973. Repr. of 1904 ed. lib. bdg. 20.00 (ISBN 0-8414-6695-5). Folcroft.

Myers, Robert M. Handel, Dryden & Milton. 1956. lib. bdg. 32.50 (ISBN 0-8414-6129-5). Folcroft.

Nelson, James G. The Sublime Puritan: Milton & the Victorians. LC 74-8794. (Illus.). 209p. 1974. Repr. of 1963 ed. lib. bdg. 24.75x (ISBN 0-8371-7586-0, NESP). Greenwood.

Osgood, Charles G. Classical Mythology of Milton's English Poems. LC 64-8180. 198p. 1964. Repr. of 1900 ed. 17.50x (ISBN 0-87752-080-1). Gordian.

--Classical Mythology of Milton's English Poems. LC 65-15902. (Studies in Comparative Literature, No. 35). 1969. Repr. of 1900 ed. lib. bdg. 75.00x (ISBN 0-8383-0603-9). Haskell.

Patrick, J. Max & Sundell, Roger H. Milton & the Art of Sacred Song. LC 78-65014. 248p. 1979. 32.50x (ISBN 0-299-07830-2). U of Wis Pr.

Pattison, Mark. Milton. Morley, John, ed. LC 68-58393. (English Men of Letters). Repr. of 1887 ed. lib. bdg. 12.50 (ISBN 0-404-51725-0). AMS Pr.

--Milton. 1896. Repr. 12.00 (ISBN 0-8274-2735-2). R West.

Plotkin, Frederick. Milton's Inward Jerusalem: "Paradise Lost" & the Ways of Knowing. LC 76-159468. (Studies in English Literature: No. 72). 155p. 1971. text ed. 17.60x (ISBN 0-686-22493-0). Mouton.

Racine, Louis. Life of Milton. LC 74-16189. 1930. lib. bdg. 17.00 (ISBN 0-8414-7258-0). Folcroft.

Radzinowicz, Mary Ann. Toward Samson Agonistes: The Growth of Milton's Mind. LC 77-85559. 1978. 50.00x (ISBN 0-691-06357-5). Princeton U Pr.

Raleigh, Walter A. Milton. LC 67-13336. 1967. Repr. of 1900 ed. 17.00 (ISBN 0-405-08873-6). Ayer Co Pubs.

--Milton. 1973. 10.00 (ISBN 0-8274-1323-8). R West.

Reesing, John. Milton's Poetic Art: A Mask, Lycidas, & Paradise Lost. LC 68-17632. Repr. of 1968 ed. 55.50 (ISBN 0-8357-9166-1, 2017011). Bks Demand UMI.

Richmond, Hugh M. The Christian Revolutionary: John Milton. 1974. 32.50x (ISBN 0-520-02443-5). U of Cal Pr.

Riggs, William G. The Christian Poet in Paradise Lost. 1972. 30.00x (ISBN 0-520-02081-2). U of Cal Pr.

Robertson, John G. Milton's Fame on the Continent. Repr. of 1908 ed. lib. bdg. 8.50 (ISBN 0-8414-7462-1). Folcroft.

Rudrum, Alan, ed. John Milton. LC 71-127553. (Modern Judgement Ser). 1978. pap. text ed. 2.50 (ISBN 0-87695-100-0). Aurora Pubs.

Saillens, E. Les Sonnets Anglais et Italians De Milton. LC 74-12230. 1930. lib. bdg. 28.50 (ISBN 0-8414-7784-1). Folcroft.

Sampson, Alden. Studies in Milton & an Essay on Poetry. LC 71-126686. 1970. Repr. of 1913 ed. 24.00 (ISBN 0-404-05555-9). AMS Pr.

Saurat, D. Milton, Man & Thinker. LC 76-121151. (Studies in Milton, No. 22). 1970. Repr. of 1925 ed. lib. bdg. 49.95x (ISBN 0-8383-1093-1). Haskell.

Saurat, Denis. Milton: Man & Thinker. LC 73-153352. Tr. of La Pensee De Milton. Repr. of 1925 ed. 24.50 (ISBN 0-404-05565-6). AMS Pr.

Scherpbier, H. Milton in Holland. LC 76-41928. 1933. lib. bdg. 30.00 (ISBN 0-8414-7580-6). Folcroft.

Schultz, H. Milton & Forbidden Knowledge. (MLA RFS). 1955. 22.00 (ISBN 0-527-80600-5). Kraus Repr.

Seldin, Mariam. Monarch Notes on Milton's Paradise Lost. (Orig.). pap. 3.50 (ISBN 0-671-00513-8). Monarch Pr.

Senior, H. L. John Milton: The Supreme Englishman. lib. bdg. 15.50 (ISBN 0-8414-8126-1). Folcroft.

Sensabaugh, George. Milton in Early America. LC 79-14332. 322p. 1979. 32.50x (ISBN 0-87752-180-8). Gordian.

Sewell, Arthur. A Study in Milton's Christian Doctrine. LC 67-26661. xiii, 214p. 1967. Repr. of 1939 ed. 22.50 (ISBN 0-208-00416-5, Archon). Shoe String.

Sherburn, George. The Early Popularity of Milton's Minor Poems. LC 73-14758. 1974. Repr. of 1919 ed. lib. bdg. 8.50 (ISBN 0-8414-7647-0). Folcroft.

Shumaker, W. Unpremeditated Verse Feeling & Perception in Milton's Paradise Lost. 1967. 26.00x (ISBN 0-691-06134-3). Princeton U Pr.

Simmonds, James D., ed. Milton Studies, Vol. III. LC 69-12335. (Milton Studies). 1971. 32.95x (ISBN 0-8229-3218-0). U of Pittsburgh Pr.

--Milton Studies, Vol. II. LC 69-12335. (Milton Studies). 1970. 32.95x (ISBN 0-8229-3194-X). U of Pittsburgh Pr.

--Milton Studies, Vol. V. LC 69-12335. (Milton Studies). 1973. 32.95x (ISBN 0-8229-3272-5). U of Pittsburgh Pr.

--Milton Studies, Vol. VI. LC 69-12335. (Milton Studies). 1974. 32.95x (ISBN 0-8229-3288-1). U of Pittsburgh Pr.

--Milton Studies, Vol. VIII. LC 69-12335. (Milton Studies). 1975. 39.95x (ISBN 0-8229-3310-1). U of Pittsburgh Pr.

--Milton Studies, Vol. IX. LC 69-12335. (Milton Studies). 1976. 32.95x (ISBN 0-8229-3329-2). U of Pittsburgh Pr.

Skeat, Walter W. John Milton's Epitaphium Damonis. LC 75-44069. 1933. lib. bdg. 15.00 (ISBN 0-8414-7644-6). Folcroft.

Sotheby, S. L. Ramblings in the Elucidation of the Autograph of Milton. 1974. Repr. of 1861 ed. lib. bdg. 100.00 limited ed. (ISBN 0-8414-8008-7). Folcroft.

Stevens, David H. Milton Papers. LC 75-176438. Repr. of 1927 ed. 5.00 (ISBN 0-404-06262-8). AMS Pr.

--Milton Papers. LC 76-27340. 1927. lib. bdg. 12.00 (ISBN 0-8414-7615-2). Folcroft.

Symmons, Charles. Life of John Milton. 3rd ed. LC 71-128979. 1970. Repr. of 1822 ed. 25.50 (ISBN 0-404-06325-X). AMS Pr.

Thompson, Elbert. Essays on Milton. LC 72-195123. 1910. lib. bdg. 30.00 (ISBN 0-8414-8044-3). Folcroft.

Todd, H. J. Some Account of the Life & Writings of John Milton. LC 77-22935. 1826. lib. bdg. 49.50 (ISBN 0-8414-8637-9). Folcroft.

Toland, John. Life of John Milton. LC 76-40068. 1761. lib. bdg. 30.00 (ISBN 0-8414-8619-0). Folcroft.

Trent, William P. John Milton: A Short Study of His Life & Works. LC 71-177572. Repr. of 1899 ed. 12.00 (ISBN 0-404-06523-6). AMS Pr.

--John Milton: A Short Study of His Life & Work. LC 72-187004. 1899. lib. bdg. 30.00 (ISBN 0-8414-8430-9). Folcroft.

Tuckwell, W. Lycidas: A Monograph. LC 77-22476. 1911. lib. bdg. 10.00 (ISBN 0-8414-8588-7). Folcroft.

Verity, A. W. Milton's Ode on the Morning of Christ's Nativity, L'allegro, Il Penseroso, & Lycidas. LC 73-12943. 1974. Repr. of 1931 ed. lib. bdg. 22.50 (ISBN 0-8414-9150-X). Folcroft.

Visiak, E. H. Animus Against Milton. 1945. lib. bdg. 12.50 (ISBN 0-8414-9173-9). Folcroft.

Warner, Rex. John Milton. LC 72-12371. Repr. of 1949 ed. lib. bdg. 12.50 (ISBN 0-8414-9389-8). Folcroft.

Werblowsky, Raphael J. Lucifer & Prometheus: A Study of Milton's Satan. LC 79-153359. Repr. of 1952 ed. 7.50 (ISBN 0-404-06906-1). AMS Pr.

Williamson, George C. Milton. LC 75-19089. 1975. Repr. of 1905 ed. lib. bdg. 15.00 (ISBN 0-88305-757-3). Norwood Edns.

--Milton Tercentenary: The Portraits, Prints & Writings of John Milton. LC 72-194902. 1973. lib. bdg. 18.50 (ISBN 0-8414-9743-5). Folcroft.

Woodberry, George E. Great Writers. facs. ed. LC 67-30236. (Essay Index Reprint Ser). 1907. 14.50 (ISBN 0-8369-1008-7). Ayer Co Pubs.

Woodhouse, A. S. The Heavenly Muse: A Preface to Milton. Maccallum, Hugh R., ed. LC 79-185724. 1972. 35.00x (ISBN 0-8020-5247-9). U of Toronto Pr.

--Milton the Poet. LC 73-785. 1955. lib. bdg. 10.00 (ISBN 0-8414-1606-0). Folcroft.

Woodhull, Marianna. Epic of Paradise Lost. LC 72-194899. 1907. lib. bdg. 12.50 (ISBN 0-8414-9501-7). Folcroft.

Woods, M. A. Characters of Paradise Lost. LC 72-6863. 1908. lib. bdg. 27.50 (ISBN 0-8414-0133-0). Folcroft.

MILTON, JOHN, 1608-1674–CONCORDANCES

Bradshaw, John. A Concordance to the Poetical Works of John Milton. LC 77-13457. 1977. Repr. of 1894 ed. lib. bdg. 20.00 (ISBN 0-89341-452-2). Longwood Pub Group.

--A Concordance to the Poetical Works of John Milton. LC 70-144894. 412p. 1972. Repr. of 1894 ed. 27.00 (ISBN 0-403-00833-6). Scholarly.

Cleveland, Charles D. Complete Concordance to the Poetical Works of John Milton. LC 76-57784. 1867. lib. bdg. 38.50 (ISBN 0-8414-3459-X). Folcroft.

Cooper, L., ed. Concordance of the Latin, Greek, & Italian Poems of John Milton. Repr. of 1923 ed. 18.00 (ISBN 0-527-19440-9). Kraus Repr.

Ingram, William & Swain, Kathleen M., eds. Concordance to Milton's English Poetry. 1972. 135.00x (ISBN 0-19-811138-X). Oxford U Pr.

Lockwood, Laura E. Lexicon to the English Poetical Works of John Milton. LC 68-56596. (Bibliography & Reference Ser: No. 323). 1968. Repr. of 1907 ed. 32.00 (ISBN 0-8337-2132-1). B Franklin.

MILTON, JOHN, 1608-1674–KNOWLEDGE AND LEARNING

Babb, Lawrence. Moral Cosmos of Paradise Lost. 1970. 7.50 (ISBN 0-87013-154-0). Mich St U Pr.

Bailey, Margaret L. Milton & Jakob Boehme. LC 65-15885. (Studies in Comparative Literature, No. 35). 1969. Repr. of 1914 ed. lib. bdg. 39.95x (ISBN 0-8383-0505-9). Haskell.

Curry, Walter C. Milton's Ontology, Cosmogony & Physics. LC 57-5833. (Illus.). 226p. 1957. pap. 6.00x (ISBN 0-8131-0102-6). U Pr of Ky.

Fletcher, Harris F. Milton's Rabbinical Readings. LC 67-30701. 344p. 1967. Repr. of 1930 ed. 29.50x (ISBN 0-87752-034-8). Gordian.

--Milton's Rabbinical Readings. LC 67-22303. 344p. 1967. Repr. of 1930 ed. 29.50 (ISBN 0-208-00335-5, Archon). Shoe String.

--Milton's Semitic Studies & Some Manifestations of Them in His Poetry. LC 66-29575. 155p. 1966. Repr. of 1926 ed. 14.50x (ISBN 0-87752-035-6). Gordian.

--Use of the Bible in Milton's Prose. 1973. lib. bdg. 59.95 (ISBN 0-87968-014-8). Gordon Pr.

Frye, Roland M. Milton's Imagery & the Visual Arts: Iconographic Tradition in the Epic Poems. LC 77-24541. 1978. 83.00x (ISBN 0-691-06349-4). Princeton U Pr.

Warren, William F. Universe As Pictured in Milton's Paradise Lost. LC 73-12894. 1915. lib. bdg. 15.00 (ISBN 0-8414-9418-5). Folcroft.

MILTON, JOHN, 1608-1674–PARADISE LOST

Addison, Joseph. Criticisms on Paradise Lost. (Works of Joseph Addison Ser.). 200p. 1985. Repr. of 1892 ed. lib. bdg. 29.00 (ISBN 0-932051-91-X, Pub. by Am Repr Serv). Am Biog Serv.

Babb, Lawrence. Moral Cosmos of Paradise Lost. 1970. 7.50 (ISBN 0-87013-154-0). Mich St U Pr.

Berry, Boyd M. Process of Speech: Puritan Religious Writing & Paradise Lost. LC 75-36933. pap. 80.00 (ISBN 0-317-41618-9, 2025830). Bks Demand UMI.

Blondel, Jacques. Milton Poete De la Bible Dans le Paradis Perdu. LC 73-13668. 1959. lib. bdg. 12.50 (ISBN 0-8414-3252-X). Folcroft.

Broadbent, John. Introduction to Paradise Lost. (Milton for Schools & Colleges Ser.). (Illus.). 1971. 34.50 (ISBN 0-521-08068-1); pap. 11.95 (ISBN 0-521-09639-1). Cambridge U Pr.

Cann, Christian. A Scriptural & Allegorical Glossary to Milton's Paradise Lost. 1978. Repr. of 1828 ed. lib. bdg. 35.00 (ISBN 0-8495-0807-X). Arden Lib.

--Scriptural & Allegorical Glossary to Milton's Paradise Lost. Repr. of 1828 ed. 32.50 (ISBN 0-8414-0566-2). Folcroft.

Carter, George. The Story of Milton's Paradise. 1909. lib. bdg. 15.00 (ISBN 0-8414-1590-0). Folcroft.

Cohen, Kitty. The Throne & the Chariot: Studies in Milton's Hebraism. (Studies in English Literature: No. 97). 1975. text ed. 23.20x (ISBN 0-686-22628-3). Mouton.

Condee, Ralph W. Milton's Theories Concerning Epic Poetry. LC 77-861. 1977. lib. bdg. 8.50 (ISBN 0-8414-3421-2). Folcroft.

Considerations on Milton's Early Reading & the Prima Stamina of His Paradise Lost. 59.95 (ISBN 0-87968-933-1). Gordon Pr.

Crump, Galbraith M., ed. Approaches to Teaching Milton's Paradise Lost. LC 85-21390. (Approaches to Teaching World Literature Ser.: No. 10). 175p. 1986. 30.00x (ISBN 0-87352-493-4); pap. text ed. 16.50x (ISBN 0-87352-494-2). Modern Lang.

Davies, Stevie. Images of Kinship in "Paradise Lost". Milton's Politics & Christian Liberty. LC 82-17485. 256p. 1983. text ed. 21.00x (ISBN 0-8262-0392-2). U of Mo Pr.

Douglas, John. Milton on Plagiary; Or a Detection of the Forgeries. LC 72-187954. Repr. of 1756 ed. lib. bdg. 10.00 (ISBN 0-8414-0508-5). Folcroft.

Fish, Stanley E. Surprised by Sin: The Reader in Paradise Lost. 1971. pap. 9.95 (ISBN 0-520-01897-4, CAL228). U of Cal Pr.

Frye, Northrop. The Return of Eden: Five Essays on Milton's Epics. 1975. 15.00x (ISBN 0-8020-1353-8). U of Toronto Pr.

Gurteen, S. Humphreys. Epic of the Fall of Man. LC 65-15879. (Studies in Comparative Literature, No. 35). 1969. Repr. of 1896 ed. lib. bdg. 75.00x (ISBN 0-8383-0561-X). Haskell.

Hayley, William. Life of Milton. LC 78-122485. 1970. Repr. of 1796 ed. 50.00x (ISBN 0-8201-1081-7). Schol Facsimiles.

Himes, John A. A Study of Milton's Paradise Lost. LC 76-17888. 1976. lib. bdg. 42.00 (ISBN 0-8414-4841-8). Folcroft.

Hunter, G. K. Paradise Lost. (Critical Library). 232p. 1980. text ed. 24.95x (ISBN 0-04-800004-3). Allen Unwin.

Jacobus, Lee A. Sudden Apprehension: Aspects of Knowledge in Paradise Lost. (Studies in English Literature: No. 94). 225p. 1976. text ed. 27.20x (ISBN 90-2793-253-0). Mouton.

Kirkconnell, Watson. Celestial Cycles: The Theme of Paradise Lost in World Literature with Translations of the Major Analogues. LC 67-30308. 701p. 1967. Repr. of 1952 ed. 47.50x (ISBN 0-87752-058-5). Gordian.

Knott, John R., Jr. Milton's Pastoral Vision: An Approach to "Paradise Lost". LC 79-145576. 1971. text ed. 15.00x (ISBN 0-226-44846-0). U of Chicago Pr.

Kranidas, Thomas, ed. New Essays on Paradise Lost. LC 72-82463. 1969. pap. 4.95x (ISBN 0-520-01902-4, CAMPUS51). U of Cal Pr.

Lewis, Clive S. Preface to Paradise Lost. 1942. pap. 7.95x (ISBN 0-19-500345-4). Oxford U Pr.

Lieb, Michael. The Dialectics of Creation: Patterns of Birth & Regeneration in "Paradise Lost". LC 71-76047. 272p. 1970. 17.50x (ISBN 0-87023-049-2). U of Mass Pr.

Marilla, E. L. The Central Problem of Paradise Lost: The Fall of Man. (Essays & Studies on English Language & Literature: Vol. 15). pap. 15.00 (ISBN 0-8115-0213-9). Kraus Repr.

Marilla, Esmond L. Central Problem of Paradise Lost. 1953. lib. bdg. 12.00 (ISBN 0-8414-6200-3). Folcroft.

Martindale, Charles. John Milton & the Transformation of Ancient Epic. LC 86-3408. 254p. 1986. 28.50x (ISBN 0-389-20624-5). B&N Imports.

Massey, William. Remarks upon Milton's Paradise Lost. LC 77-4961. 1751. lib. bdg. 30.00 (ISBN 0-8414-6194-5). Folcroft.

Merrill, Thomas F. Epic God-Talk: Paradise Lost & the Grammar of Religious Language. LC 85-29385. 140p. 1986. lib. bdg. 18.95x (ISBN 0-89950-194-X). McFarland & Co.

Milton, John. Milton's "Paradise Lost.". new ed. Bentley, Richard, ed. LC 74-5237. Repr. of 1732 ed. 67.50 (ISBN 0-404-11537-3). AMS Pr.

--Milton's Paradise Lost, 3 Vols. Verity, A. W., ed. LC 72-4906. 1921. lib. bdg. 120.00 (ISBN 0-8414-0012-1). Folcroft.

--Paradise Lost. Elledge, Scott, ed. (Critical Editions Ser). 546p. 1975. 19.95 (ISBN 0-393-04406-8); pap. 8.95x (ISBN 0-393-09230-5). Norton.

--Paradise Lost. (Modern Critical Interpretations--Seventeenth & Eighteenth Century British Literature Ser.). 1987. 19.95 (ISBN 0-87754-421-2). Chelsea Hse.

--Paradise Lost, Bks. 3 & 4. Potter, L. J. & Broadbent, J., eds. LC 75-36681. (Milton for Schools & Colleges Ser.). 200p. 1976. pap. 8.95x (ISBN 0-521-21150-6). Cambridge U Pr.

--Paradise Lost, Bks. 5 & 6. Hodge, R. I. & MacCaffrey, I., eds. LC 75-8314. (Milton for Schools & Colleges Ser). (Illus.). 176p. 1975. pap. text ed. 8.95 (ISBN 0-521-20796-7). Cambridge U Pr.

--Paradise Lost, Bks. 7 & 8. Aers, D. & Radzinowics, Mary Ann, eds. LC 77-181884. (Milton for Schools & Colleges Ser.). 200p. 1974. pap. text ed. 8.95 (ISBN 0-521-20457-7). Cambridge U Pr.

--Paradise Lost, Bks. 9 & 10. Evans, J. M., ed. LC 72-87438. (Milton for Schools & Colleges). 208p. 1973. 8.95 set (ISBN 0-521-20067-9). Cambridge U Pr.

Mutschmann, H. Further Studies Concerning the Origin of Paradise Lost. LC 77-24899. lib. bdg. 10.00 (ISBN 0-8414-6211-9). Folcroft.

Mutschmann, Heinrich. Studies Concerning the Origins of Milton's Paradise Lost. LC 79-163459. (Studies in Milton, No. 22). 1971. Repr. of 1924 ed. lib. bdg. 39.95x (ISBN 0-8383-1324-8). Haskell.

--Studies Concerning the Origins of Milton's Paradise Lost. 1924. Repr. 15.00 (ISBN 0-8274-3532-0). R West.

Orchard, Thomas N. Astronomy of Milton's Paradise Lost. LC 68-4178. (Studies in Milton, No. 22). (Illus.). 1969. Repr. of 1896 ed. lib. bdg. 75.00x (ISBN 0-8383-0672-1). Haskell.

Patrick, John M. Milton's Conception of Sin As Developed in Paradise Lost. 1930. Repr. 25.00 (ISBN 0-8274-2740-9). R West.

Rajan, Balachandra, ed. Paradise Lost: A Tercenenary Tribute. LC 77-429833. pap. 38.50 (ISBN 0-317-27001-X, 2023659). Bks Demand UMI.

Richardson, Jonathan & Richardson, Jonathan, Jr. Explanatory Notes & Remarks on Milton's Paradise Lost. LC 77-174317. Repr. of 1734 ed. 37.50 (ISBN 0-404-05298-3). AMS Pr.

Seaman, John E. Moral Paradox of Paradise Lost. LC 74-135665. (Studies in English Literature: Vol. 61). 1971. text ed. 17.00x (ISBN 90-2791-715-9). Mouton.

Smith, Eric. Some Versions of the Fall: The Myth of the Fall of Man in English Literature. LC 75-185025. (Illus.). 1973. 22.95x (ISBN 0-8229-1107-8). U of Pittsburgh Pr.

Stein, Arnold. The Art of Presence: The Poet & Paradise Lost. 1977. 30.95x (ISBN 0-520-03167-9). U of Cal Pr.

Stevens, Paul. Imagination & the Presence of Shakespeare in Paradise Lost. LC 85-40378. 256p. 1985. text ed. 32.50x (ISBN 0-299-10420-6). U of Wis Pr.

Swaim, Kathleen. Before & After the Fall: Contrasting Modes in "Paradise Lost". LC 85-28925. 312p. 1986. lib. bdg. 27.50X (ISBN 0-87023-504-4). U of Mass Pr.

Verity, A. W., ed. Milton's Paradise Lost. 1974. Repr. of 1921 ed. lib. bdg. 47.50 (ISBN 0-685-45197-6). Folcroft.

Waldock, A. J. Paradise Lost & Its Critics. 11.50 (ISBN 0-8446-1463-7). Peter Smith.

Warren, William F. Universe As Pictured in Milton's Paradise Lost. LC 73-12894. 1915. lib. bdg. 15.00 (ISBN 0-8414-9418-5). Folcroft.

--Universe As Pictured in Milton's Paradise Lost: An Illustrated Study for Personal & Class Use. LC 68-59037. (Illus.). 80p. 1968. Repr. of 1915 ed. 10.00x (ISBN 0-87752-117-4). Gordian.

Weber, Burton J. Construction of Paradise Lost. LC 72-132483. (Literary Structures Ser.). 218p. 1971. 12.50x (ISBN 0-8093-0488-0). S Ill U Pr.

Wilding, M. Milton's Paradise Lost. (Sydney Studies in Literature Ser.). 1969. 15.00x (ISBN 0-424-05850-2, Pub. by Sydney U Pr). Intl Spec Bk.

Wilkes, Gerald A. The Thesis of Paradise Lost. LC 76-28374. 1976. Repr. of 1961 ed. lib. bdg. 20.00 (ISBN 0-8414-9514-9). Folcroft.

Woodhull, Marianna. Epic of Paradise Lost: Twelve Essays. LC 68-57833. 386p. 1968. Repr. of 1907 ed. 32.50x (ISBN 0-87752-124-7). Gordian.

MILTON, JOHN, 1608-1674–PARADISE REGAINED

Frye, Northrop. The Return of Eden: Five Essays on Milton's Epics. 1975. 15.00x (ISBN 0-8020-1353-8). U of Toronto Pr.

Frye, Roland M. Milton's Imagery & the Visual Arts: Iconographic Tradition in the Epic Poems. LC 77-24541. 1978. 83.00x (ISBN 0-691-06349-4). Princeton U Pr.

Meadowcourt, Richard. Milton's Paradise Regained: Two Eighteenth-Century Critiques, 2 vols. in 1. Wittreich, Joseph A., Jr., ed. LC 76-161937. 1971. Repr. of 1732 ed. 50.00x (ISBN 0-8201-1087-6). Schol Facsimiles.

Milton, John. Paradise Regained, A Poem, in Four Books. LC 73-9863. Repr. of 1795 ed. lib. bdg. 50.00 (ISBN 0-8414-5950-9). Folcroft.

Weber, Burton J. Wedges & Wings: The Patterning of Paradise Regained. LC 74-20703. (Literary Structure Ser.). 144p. 1975. 10.00x (ISBN 0-8093-0673-5). S Ill U Pr.

MILTON, JOHN, 1608-1674–RELIGION AND ETHICS

Acton, Henry. Religious Opinions & Example of Milton, Locke, & Newton. LC 71-158223. Repr. of 1833 ed. 11.50 (ISBN 0-404-00283-8). AMS Pr.

Barker, Arthur E. Milton & the Puritan Dilemma, 1641-1660. LC 58-3195. 1942. 30.00x (ISBN 0-8020-5025-5); pap. 8.50 o. p. (ISBN 0-8020-6306-3). U of Toronto Pr.

Charlesworth, Arthur R. Paradise Found. LC 72-91109. 1973. 10.00 (ISBN 0-8022-2104-1). Philos Lib.

Empson, William. Milton's God. LC 80-40109. 320p. 1981. pap. 18.95 (ISBN 0-521-29910-1). Cambridge U Pr.

--Milton's God. LC 78-14409. 1978. Repr. of 1961 ed. lib. bdg. 27.50x (ISBN 0-313-21021-7, EMMG). Greenwood.

Knight, G. Wilson. Chariot of Wrath: The Message of John Milton to Democracy at War. LC 72-196540. 1942. lib. bdg. 20.00 (ISBN 0-8414-5589-9). Folcroft.

Knight, George W. Chariot of Wrath. 1978. Repr. of 1942 ed. lib. bdg. 25.00 (ISBN 0-8495-3012-1). Arden Lib.

McLachlan, Herbert. The Religious Opinions of Milton, Locke & Newton. LC 74-20740. 1974. Repr. of 1941 ed. lib. bdg. 35.00 (ISBN 0-8414-5930-4). Folcroft.

Muldrow, George M. Milton & the Drama of the Soul: A Study of the Theme of the Restoration of Man in Milton's Later Poetry. LC 76-89796. (Studies in English Literature: Vol. 51). 1970. text ed. 23.20x (ISBN 90-2790-530-4). Mouton.

O'Keeffe, Timothy J. Milton & the Pauline Tradition: A Study of Theme & Symbolism. LC 80-5842. 356p. (Orig.). 1982. PLB 32.25 (ISBN 0-8191-2453-2); pap. text ed. 15.75 (ISBN 0-8191-2454-0). U Pr of Amer.

Palacios, Miguel A. Islam & the Divine Comedy. 295p. 1968. Repr. of 1926 ed. 30.00x (ISBN 0-7146-1995-7, F Cass Co). Biblio Dist.

Patrides, C. A. Milton & the Christian Tradition. LC 79-10846. xvi, 302p. 1979. Repr. 28.00 (ISBN 0-208-01821-2, Archon). Shoe String.

Rowse, A. L. Milton the Puritan: Portrait of a Mind. 298p. 1985. pap. text ed. 12.50 (ISBN 0-8191-4778-8). U Pr of Amer.

Sewell, Arthur. Study in Milton's Christian Doctrine. LC 72-193159. 1939. lib. bdg. 25.00 (ISBN 0-8414-8118-0). Folcroft.

--A Study in Milton's Christian Doctrine. LC 67-26661. xiii, 214p. 1967. Repr. of 1939 ed. 22.50 (ISBN 0-208-00416-5, Archon). Shoe String.

Sims, James H. & Ryken, Leland, eds. Milton & Scriptural Tradition: The Bible into Poetry. LC 83-16781. 192p. 1984. text ed. 19.50x (ISBN 0-8262-0427-9). U of MO Pr.

Wittreich, Joseph A., Jr. Visionary Poetics: Milton's Tradition & His Legacy. LC 78-52569. (Illus.). 324p. 1979. 29.95 (ISBN 0-87328-101-2). Huntington Lib.

Wood, Louis A. Form & Origin of Milton's Antitrinitarian Conception. LC 72-191655. 1911. lib. bdg. 15.00 (ISBN 0-8414-0833-5). Folcroft.

MILTON, JOHN, 1608-1674–SAMSON AGONISTES

Kreipe, Christian E. Milton's Samson Agonistes. LC 76-10958. (Ger.). 1926. lib. bdg. 20.00 (ISBN 0-8414-5458-2). Folcroft.

--Milton's Samson Agonistes. 59.95 (ISBN 0-8490-0638-4). Gordon Pr.

Low, Anthony. The Blaze of Noon: A Reading of "Samson Agonistes". LC 74-1484. 236p. 1974. 28.00x (ISBN 0-231-03842-9). Columbia U Pr.

Radzinowicz, Mary Ann. Toward Samson Agonistes: The Growth of Milton's Mind. LC 77-85559. 1978. 50.00x (ISBN 0-691-06357-5). Princeton U Pr.

Visiak, E. H. Milton Agonistes. (Studies in Milton, No. 22). 1970. pap. 39.95x (ISBN 0-8383-0102-9). Haskell.

--Milton's Agonistes: A Metaphysical Criticism. LC 77-9361. 1922. lib. bdg. 12.50 (ISBN 0-8414-9187-9). Folcroft.

MILTON, JOHN, 1608-1674–SOURCES

Fletcher, Harris F. The Use of the Bible in Milton's Prose. Repr. of 1929 ed. 15.00. Johnson Repr.

Harding, David P. Milton & the Renaissance Ovid. LC 76-47466. 1977. Repr. of 1946 ed. lib. bdg. 17.50 (ISBN 0-8414-4941-4). Folcroft.

Mutschmann, H. Further Studies Concerning the Origin of Paradise Lost. LC 77-24899. lib. bdg. 10.00 (ISBN 0-8414-6211-9). Folcroft.

MIND

see Psychology

MIND AND BODY

see also Consciousness; Mental Healing; Self; Temperament

Almaas, A. H. The Void: A Psychodynamic Investigation of the Relationship Between Mind & Space. LC 85-82559. 175p. (Orig.). 1986. pap. 8.00 (ISBN 0-936713-00-3). Almaas Pubns.

Ashbrook, James B. The Human Mind & the Mind of God: Theological Promise in Brain Research. (Illus.). 408p. (Orig.). 1985. lib. bdg. 30.75 (ISBN 0-8191-4225-5); pap. text ed. 17.75 (ISBN 0-8191-4226-3). U Pr of Amer.

Atkinson, William W. Mind Power: The Secret of Mental Magic. limited ed. limited ed. 9.00 (ISBN 0-911662-27-8). Yoga.

Bacik, James J. Apologetics & the Eclipse of Mystery: Mystagogy According to Karl Rahner. LC 80-123. 192p. 1980. 15.00 (ISBN 0-268-00592-3); pap. 6.95 (ISBN 0-268-00593-1). U of Notre Dame Pr.

Ducasse, C. J. Critical Examination of the Belief in a Life after Death. 336p. 1974. pap. 39.50x spiral (ISBN 0-398-03037-5). C C Thomas.

--Nature, Mind & Death. (Paul Carus Lecture Ser.). 533p. 1951. 19.95 (ISBN 0-87548-102-7). Open Court.

Hartman, Edwin. Substance, Body & Soul: Aristotelian Investigations. LC 77-71984. 1977. text ed. 34.50x (ISBN 0-691-07223-X). Princeton U Pr.

Hislop, John S. My Baba & I. LC 85-61733. 1985. pap. 6.30 (ISBN 0-9600958-8-8). Birth Day.

Kappeler, Max. Compendium for the Study of Christian Science: No. 4, Mind. 35p. 1951. pap. 3.50 (ISBN 0-85241-058-1). Kappeler Inst Pub.

Leichtman, Robert R. & Japikse, Carl. Books of Light. (Illus.). 160p. (Orig.). 1986. pap. 3.95 (ISBN 0-89804-049-3). Ariel OH.

Leland, Charles G. The Mystic Will. 1976. Repr. of 1907 ed. 6.00 (ISBN 0-911662-58-8). Yoga.

Lovejoy, Arthur O. Revolt Against Dualism. 2nd ed. (Paul Carus Lecture Ser.). 420p. 1960. 21.95 (ISBN 0-87548-106-X); pap. 8.95 (ISBN 0-87548-107-8). Open Court.

Mayer, Fred S. Why Two Worlds: Relation of Physical to Spiritual Realities. LC 78-134425. Repr. of 1934 ed. 21.00 (ISBN 0-404-08465-6). AMS Pr.

Reed, Sampson. Observations on the Growth of the Mind Including GENIUS. 5th ed. LC 72-4971. (The Romantic Tradition in American Literature Ser.). 110p. 1972. Repr. of 1859 ed. 18.00 (ISBN 0-405-04641-3). Ayer Co Pubs.

Sandweiss, Samuel H. Spirit & the Mind. 1985. pap. 6.30 (ISBN 0-9600958-9-6). Birth Day.

Shaner, David E. The Bodymind Experience in Japanese Buddhism: A Phenomenological Study of Kukai & Dogen. (Series in Buddhist Studies). 202p. 1986. 44.50x (ISBN 0-88706-061-7); pap. 14.95x (ISBN 0-88706-062-5). State U NY Pr.

Swami Muktananda. Mystery of the Mind. LC 81-50159. (Illus.). 64p. (Orig.). 1983. pap. 3.95 (ISBN 0-914602-70-5). SYDA Found.

Takpo Tashi Namgyal. Mahamudra: The Quintessance of Mind & Meditation. Lhalungpa, Lobsang P., tr. from Tibetan. LC 85-27963. (Orig.). 1986. pap. 25.00 (ISBN 0-87773-360-0). Shambhala Pubns.

Yuasa, Yasuo. The Body: Toward an Eastern Mind-Body Theory. Kasulis, Thomas P., ed. (Buddhist Studies). 256p. 1987. 39.50x (ISBN 0-88706-469-8); pap. 14.95 (ISBN 0-88706-468-X). State U NY Pr.

MIND-CURE

see Christian Science; Mental Healing; Mind and Body

MINDSZENTY, JOZSEF, CARDINAL, 1892-

Vecsey, Joseph & Schlafly, Phyllis. Mindszenty the Man. LC 72-93906. 1972. 2.00 (ISBN 0-934640-04-1). Pere Marquette.

MINHAGIM

see Jews–Rites and Ceremonies

MINIATURES (ILLUMINATION OF BOOKS AND MANUSCRIPTS)

see Illumination of Books and Manuscripts

MINISTERIAL RESPONSIBILITY

Kelly, George A., ed. Catholic Ministries in Our Times. 1981. 4.00 (ISBN 0-8198-1400-8); pap. 3.00 (ISBN 0-8198-1401-6). Dghtrs St Paul.

Pollitt, Christopher. Manipulating the Machine: Changing the Pattern of Ministerial Departments, 1960-83. 296p. 1984. text ed. 29.95x (ISBN 0-04-351064-7). Allen Unwin.

MINISTERS OF RELIGIOUS EDUCATION

see Directors of Religious Education

MINISTERS OF THE GOSPEL

see Clergy

MINISTRY

see Church Work; Clergy–Office; Pastoral Theology

MINISTRY, COFFEE HOUSE

see Coffee House Ministry

MINISTRY, URBAN

see City Clergy

MINOR PROPHETS

see Prophets

MINORESSES

see Poor Clares

MINORITIES

see also Jews–Diaspora; Race Relations

Janowsky, Oscar I. Jews & Minority Rights, 1898-1919. LC 33-31678. (Columbia University. Studies in the Social Sciences: No. 384). Repr. of 1933 ed. 24.50 (ISBN 0-404-51384-0). AMS Pr.

MIRACLE-PLAYS

see Mysteries and Miracle-Plays

MIRACLES

see also Holy Wells; Jesus Christ–Miracles; Modernist-Fundamentalist Controversy; Saints–Legends; Shrines; Supernatural

Bachelder, Robert S. Mystery & Miracle. 1983. 3.00 (ISBN 0-89536-606-1, 1340). CSS of Ohio.

Bailey, Keith M. The Children's Bread: Divine Healing. LC 77-83941. 1977. kivar cover 5.95 (ISBN 0-87509-233-0). Chr Pubns.

Bales, James D. Miracles or Mirages? 1956. 3.00 (ISBN 0-88027-010-1). Firm Foun Pub.

Basinger, David & Basinger, Randall. Philosophy & Miracle: The Contemporary Debate. LC 86-12766. (Problems in Contemporary Philosophy Ser.: No. 2). 130p. 1986. 39.95 (ISBN 0-88946-327-1). E Mellen.

Brewer, E. Cobham. The Dictionary of Miracles, 2 vols. (Illus.). 337p. 1986. Repr. of 1882 ed. Set. 217.50 (ISBN 0-89901-263-9). Found Class Reprints.

--A Dictionary of Miracles, Imitative, Realistic, & Dogmatic. LC 66-29783. 1966. Repr. of 1885 ed. 50.00x (ISBN 0-8103-3000-8). Gale.

Brewer, Ebenezer. A Dictionary of Miracles. 75.00 (ISBN 0-8490-0040-8). Gordon Pr.

Britten, Emma. Nineteenth Century Miracles. 1977. lib. bdg. 59.95 (ISBN 0-8490-2348-3). Gordon Pr.

Brown, Colin. Miracles & the Critical Mind. LC 83-16600. 432p. 1984. 19.95 (ISBN 0-8028-3590-2). Eerdmans.

Brown, William N. The Indian & Christian Miracles of Walking on the Water. LC 78-72381. Repr. of 1928 ed. 16.50 (ISBN 0-404-17243-1). AMS Pr.

Buntain, Mark, et al. Miracle in the Mirror. LC 81-70999. (Illus.). 155p. 1982. pap. 3.50 (ISBN 0-87123-352-5, 210352). Bethany Hse.

Burns, R. M. The Great Debate on Miracles: From Joseph Glanvill to David Hume. LC 78-75197. 300p. 1981. 28.50 (ISBN 0-8387-2378-0). Bucknell U Pr.

Calkin, Ruth H. Lord, It Keeps Happening...& Happening. LC 83-91404. 112p. 1984. pap. 2.95 (ISBN 0-8423-3823-3). Tyndale.

Chambers, Joseph E. Micacles, My Father's Delight. 136p. (Orig.). text ed. 8.95 (ISBN 0-87148-585-0); pap. 6.95 (ISBN 0-87148-586-9). Pathway Pr.

Collins, J. H. Ten Miracles. 1975. pap. 0.50 (ISBN 0-8198-0479-7). Dghtrs St Paul.

A Course in Miracles. LC 76-20363. 1975. Set Of 3 Vols. incl. text, tchrs' manual wkbk. 40.00 (ISBN 0-9606388-0-6). Found Inner Peace.

Course in Miracless. LC 76-20363. 1985. pap. text ed. 25.00 (ISBN 0-9606388-2-2). Found Inner Peace.

De Vries, Jan. Do Miracles Exist? 176p. 1986. 39.75x (ISBN 1-85158-029-8, Pub. by Mainstream Scotland); pap. 24.75x (ISBN 1-85158-030-1). State Mutual Bk.

Dye, Harold E. A Daily Miracle. (Orig.). 1986. pap. 3.25 (ISBN 0-8054-5026-2). Broadman.

Findeisen, Barbara. A Course in Miracles Concordance. 457p. 15.00 (ISBN 0-942494-45-8). Coleman Pub.

Fox, George. George Fox's Book of Miracles. Cadbury, Henry J., ed. LC 73-735. 161p. 1973. Repr. of 1948 ed. lib. bdg. 16.50x (ISBN 0-374-92825-8, Octagon). Hippocrene Bks.

Galloway, Dale E. Expect a Miracle. 1982. pap. 4.95 (ISBN 0-8423-0822-9). Tyndale.

Geisler, Norman L. Miracles & Modern Thought. 208p. (Orig.). 1982. pap. 7.95 (ISBN 0-310-44681-3, 12560P). Zondervan.
Gregorius, Saint Les Livres des Miracles & Autres Opuscules, 4 Vols. 1863. Set. 149.00 (ISBN 0-384-19888-0); 38.00 ea.; pap. 32.00 ea.; Set. pap. 125.00 (ISBN 0-384-19889-9). Johnson Repr.
Hagin, Kenneth, Jr. Is Your Miracle Passing You By? 1985. mini bk. 0.50 (ISBN 0-89276-718-9). Hagin Ministries.
Hayes, Norvel. The Gift of Working of Miracles. 1980. pap. 0.75 (ISBN 0-89274-371-9). Harrison Hse.
Hunter, Charles & Hunter, Frances. Impossible Miracles. 1976. pap. 4.95 (ISBN 0-917726-05-7). Hunter Bks.
Jividen, Jimmy. Miracles: From God or Men. 288p. 1987. 9.95 (ISBN 0-915547-93-7). Abilene Christ U.
Johnston, Francis. Fatima: The Great Sign. LC 80-54423. 1980. Repr. of 1979 ed. 5.00 (ISBN 0-89555-163-2). Tan Bks Pubs.
Kee, Howard C. Miracle in the Early Christian World: A Study in Sociohistorical Method. LC 83-40004. 304p. 1983. 30.00x (ISBN 0-300-03008-8); pap. 9.95 (ISBN 0-300-03632-9, Y-570). Yale U Pr.
Keller, Ernst & Keller, Marie-Luise. Miracles In Dispute: A Continuing Debate. 256p. pap. 8.95 (ISBN 0-317-31482-3, 30-1012-259). Fortress.
Kelsey, Morton. The Age of Miracles. LC 78-74095. 80p. 1979. pap. 2.45 (ISBN 0-87793-169-0). Ave Maria.
King, Barbara. What Is a Miracle? 61p. 1981. pap. 3.00 (ISBN 0-317-20876-4). CSA Pr.
Koch, Dietrich-Alex. Die Bedeutung der Wundererzaehlungen fuer die Christologie des Markusevangeliums. (Beiheft 42 zur Zeitschrift fuer die neutestamentliche Wissenschaft Ser.). 217p. 1975. 44.40x (ISBN 3-11-004783-7). De Gruyter.
Kole, Andre & Janssen, Al. Miracles or Magic? rev. ed. 1987. pap. 5.95 (ISBN 0-89081-579-8). Harvest Hse.
Kuhlman, Kathryn. I Believe in Miracles. 1975. pap. 2.25 (ISBN 0-515-05858-0). Jove Pubns.
Kvamme, Rodney A. Miracles Today. 96p. (Orig.). 1986. pap. 4.95 (ISBN 0-570-04439-1). Concordia.
Laurentin, Rene. Miracles in El Paso. (Illus.). 135p. 1982. pap. 6.95 (ISBN 0-89283-150-2). Servant.
Lecanu, A. F. Dictionnaire des Propheties et des Miracles, 2 vols. Migne, J. P., ed. (Nouvelle Encyclopedie Theologique Ser.: Vols. 24-25). (Fr.). 1246p. Repr. of 1852 ed. lib. bdg. 159.00x (ISBN 0-89241-268-2). Caratzas.
Lewis, C. S. Miracles. 1978. pap. 3.95 (ISBN 0-02-086760-3, Collier). Macmillan.
Lindsay, Gordon. The Miracles of Divine Discipline, Vol. 7. (Miracles in the Bible Ser.). 0.95 (ISBN 0-89985-184-3). Christ Nations.
MacDonald, George. The Miracles of Our Lord. Hein, Rolland, ed. LC 79-22261. (Wheaton Literary Ser.). 166p. 1980. pap. 6.95 (ISBN 0-87788-547-8). Shaw Pubs.
McInerny, Ralph. Miracles: A Catholic View. LC 86-61141. 153p. (Orig.). 1986. pap. 6.95 (ISBN 0-87973-540-6). Our Sunday Visitor.
McKenna, Briege & Libersat, Henry. Miracles Do Happen. 170p. (Orig.). 1987. pap. 4.95 (ISBN 0-89283-316-5). Servant.
Menendez, Josefa. The Way of Divine Love. LC 79-112493. 504p. 1972. pap. 12.00 (ISBN 0-89555-030-X). TAN Bks Pubs.
Miracles De Nostre Dame Par Personnages, 8 Vols. 1876-1893. Set. 265.00 (ISBN 0-384-39105-2); pap. 28.00 ea.; Set. pap. 220.00 (ISBN 0-685-13516-0). Johnson Repr.
Oliveira, Joseph De. Jacinta, Flower of Fatima. 192p. 1972. pap. 3.95 (ISBN 0-911988-45-9). AMI Pr.
Pickett, Toni. Miracles. 1983. 5.95 (ISBN 0-8062-2201-8). Carlton.
Praeder, Susan M. Miracle Stories in Christian Antiquity. LC 86-45909. 288p. 1987. pap. 22.95 (ISBN 0-8006-2115-8, 1-2115). Fortress.
Remus, Harold. Pagan-Christian Conflict over Miracle in the Second Century. LC 83-6729. (Patristic Monograph: No. 10). xiii, 371p. 1983. pap. 11.00 (ISBN 0-915646-09-9). Phila Patristic.
Rev. Gene Ulses. The Wisdom of the Lord: Homilies for Weekdays & Feast Days. LC 86-60910. 254p. (Orig.). 1986. 12.95 (ISBN 0-87973-512-0, 512). Our Sunday Visitor.
Robertson, Pat & Proctor, William. Beyond Reason: How Miracles Can Change Your Life. LC 84-61470. 192p. 1984. 12.95 (ISBN 0-688-02214-6). Morrow.
--Beyond Reason: How Miracles Can Change Your Life. (Religion Ser.). 176p. 1986. pap. 3.50 (ISBN 0-553-25415-4). Bantam.
Sanford, Agnes. The Healing Power of the Bible. LC 83-48999. 1984. pap. 6.95 (ISBN 0-06-067053-3, RD 520, HarpR). Har-Row.
Shelly, Bruce. The Miracle of Anne. 90p. 1974. pap. 4.50 (ISBN 0-911336-55-9). Sci of Mind.
Singh, Tara. Commentaries on A Course in Miracles. LC 86-18350. (Orig.). 1986. 16.95 (ISBN 1-55531-015-X); pap. 12.95 (ISBN 1-55531-016-8). Life Action Pr.
--A Course in Miracles - A Gift for All Mankind. LC 86-12073. (Orig.). 1986. 12.95 (ISBN 1-55531-013-3); pap. 7.95 (ISBN 1-55531-014-1). Life Action Pr.
--Dialogues on A Course in Miracles. LC 86-82912. (Orig.). 1987. 19.95 (ISBN 1-55531-130-X); pap. 14.95 (ISBN 1-55531-131-8). Life Action Pr.
--Our Story of Bringing a Course in Miracles into Application. (Orig.). Date not set. price not set (ISBN 1-55531-127-X); pap. price not set (ISBN 1-55531-128-8). Life Action Pr.
Spurgeon, Charles H. Sermons on the Miracles. Cook, Charles T, ed. 256p. 1977. Repr. of 1958 ed. limp bk. 5.95 (ISBN 0-551-05576-6). Attic Pr.
Summers, Georgianna. Night of Miracles. 1982. pap. 4.95 (ISBN 0-89536-552-9, 1411). CSS of Ohio.
Theissen, Gerd. The Miracle Stories of the Early Christian Tradition. Riches, John, ed. McDonagh, Francis, tr. LC 82-48546. 416p. 1983. 29.95 (ISBN 0-8006-0700-7). Fortress.
Wagner, Petti. Murdered Heiress, Living Witness. LC 84-80413. 211p. (Orig.). 1984. pap. 6.95 (ISBN 0-910311-09-9). Huntington Hse Inc.
Wapnick, Gloria & Wapnick, Kenneth. Awaken from the Dream: A Presentation of a Course in Miracles. 125p. (Orig.). 1987. pap. 10.00 (ISBN 0-933291-04-3). Foun Miracles.
Wapnick, Kenneth. The Fifty Miracle Principles of "A Course in Miracles". 153p. (Orig.). 1985. pap. 8.00 (ISBN 0-933291-02-7). Foun Miracles.
--Glossary: Index for "A Course in Miracles." 255p. (Orig.). 1982. 16.00. Foun Miracles.
--Glossary-Index for "A Course in Miracles". 2nd, enl. ed. 312p. 1986. text ed. 16.00 (ISBN 0-933291-03-5). Foun Miracles.
--A Talk Given on "A Course in Miracles". 2nd ed. 55p. 1985. pap. 4.00 (ISBN 0-933291-00-0). Foun Miracles.
Ward, Benedicta. Miracles & the Medieval Mind: Theory, Record, & Event, 1000 to 1215. LC 81-23106. (Middle Ages Ser.). (Illus.). 300p. 1982. 29.95x (ISBN 0-8122-7836-4). U of Pa Pr.
Warfield, B. B. Counterfeit Miracles. 1976. pap. 6.95 (ISBN 0-85151-166-X). Banner of Truth.
Whitcomb, John C., Jr. Does God Want Christians to Perform Miracles Today? 1979. pap. 1.00 (ISBN 0-88469-016-4). BMH Bks.
Wise, Robert L. When There Is No Miracle. LC 77-89394. 176p. 1978. pap. 4.95 (ISBN 0-8307-0582-1, 5408008); study guide o.p. 1.39 (ISBN 0-8307-0651-8, 6101518). Regal.

MISHNAH

Albeck, Chanoch. Einfuehrung in die Mischna. (Studia Judaica, 6). 493p. 1971. 33.60x (ISBN 3-11-006429-4). De Gruyter.
Avery-Peck, Alan J. Mishnah's Division of Agriculture: A History & Theology of Seder Zeriam. (Brown Judaic Studies). 1985. 39.25 (ISBN 0-89130-888-1, 14-00-79); pap. 32.25 (ISBN 0-89130-889-X). Scholars Pr GA.
Bokser, Baruch M. Post Mishnaic Judaism in Transition: Samuel in Berakhot & the Beginnings of Gemara. LC 80-19702. (Brown Judaic Studies). 543p. 1980. 19.50 (ISBN 0-89130-432-0, 14 00 17); pap. 15.00 (ISBN 0-89130-433-9). Scholars Pr GA.
Cohen, Shaye J. From the Maccabees to the Mishnah. Meeks, Wayne A., ed. LC 86-28077. (Library of Early Christianity: Vol. 7). 252p. 1987. 20.95 (ISBN 0-664-21911-X). Westminster.
Eilberg-Schwartz, Howard. The Human Will in Judaism: The Mishnah's Philosophy of Intention. (Brown Judaic Studies). 164p. 1986. 31.95 (ISBN 0-89130-938-1, 14-01-03). Scholars Pr GA.
Elmslie, W. A., ed. The Mishna of Idolatry Aboda Zara. (Texts & Studies Ser.: No. 1, Vol. 8, Pt. 2). pap. 19.00 (ISBN 0-8115-1709-8). Kraus Repr.
Fishman, Priscilla. Learn Mishnah Notebook. 128p. 1983. pap. 3.50x (ISBN 0-87441-369-9). Behrman.
Gersh, Harry & Platzner, Robert S. Mishnah, the Oral Law. 64p. 1984. pap. 2.95 (ISBN 0-87441-390-7); tchr's 6.95 (ISBN 0-317-15397-8). Behrman.
Goldworm, Hersh. Mishnah-Moed, Vol. 2. (Artscroll Mishnah Ser.). 416p. 1981. 16.95 (ISBN 0-89906-254-7); pap. 13.95 (ISBN 0-89906-255-5). Mesorah Pubns.
Hoffmann, David. The First Mishna & the Controversies of the Tannaim. Forchheimer, Paul, tr. from German. Incl. The Highest Court in the City of Sanctuary. LC 77-98683. 1977. 12.50 (ISBN 0-87203-072-5). Hermon.
Mandelbaum, Irving J. A History of the Mishnaic Law of Agriculture: Kilayim. Neusner, Jacob, ed. LC 81-1462. (Brown Judaic Studies Ser.: No. 26). 1981. pap. text ed. 18.00 (ISBN 0-89130-465-7, 14 00 26). Scholars Pr GA.
Neusner, Jacob. Ancient Israel after Catastrophe: The Religious World View of the Mishnah. LC 82-15972. 82p. 1983. pap. 8.95x (ISBN 0-8139-0980-5). U Pr of Va.
--Form-Analysis & Exegesis: A Fresh Approach to the Interpretation of Mishnah. 224p. 1981. 22.50 (ISBN 0-8166-0984-5); pap. 9.95x (ISBN 0-8166-0985-3). U of Minn Pr.
--From Mishnah to Scripture: The Problem of the Unattributed Saying. LC 84-10527. (Brown Judaic Studies). 135p. 1984. 20.95 (ISBN 0-89130-759-1, 14 00 67); pap. 13.95 (ISBN 0-89130-749-4). Scholars Pr GA.
--Judaism: The Evidence of the Mishnah. LC 80-26080. xx, 420p. 1981. 25.00x (ISBN 0-226-57617-5); pap. 15.95 (ISBN 0-226-57619-1). U of Chicago Pr.
--Learn Mishnah. LC 78-5482. (Illus.). 1978. pap. 4.95x (ISBN 0-87441-310-8). Behrman.
--The Memorized Torah: The Mnemonic System of the Mishnah. (Brown Judaic Studies). 1985. 22.95 (ISBN 0-89130-866-0, 14-00-96); pap. 17.95 (ISBN 0-89130-867-9). Scholars Pr GA.
Newman, Louis E. The Sanctity of the Seventh Year: A Study of Mishnah Tractate Shebiit. LC 83-8683. (Brown Judaic Studies). 276p. 1983. pap. 12.00 (ISBN 0-89130-630-7, 14 00 44). Scholars Pr GA.
Rosner. Maimonides' Commentary on the Mishnah. cancelled (ISBN 0-87306-083-0). Feldheim.
Rosner, Fred. Maimonides' Commentary on Mishnah Sanhedrin. LC 81-51800. 224p. 1981. 14.95 (ISBN 0-87203-099-7). Hermon.
Weingreen, Jacob. From Bible to Mishna: The Continuity of Tradition. LC 75-37728. 250p. 1976. text ed. 27.00x (ISBN 0-8419-0249-6). Holmes & Meier.

MISSALS

see also Catholic Church–Liturgy and Ritual–Missal; Illumination of Books and Manuscripts

Daughters of St Paul. My Massbook. 1978. plastic bdg. 2.00 (ISBN 0-8198-0361-8); pap. 1.25 (ISBN 0-8198-0362-6). Dghtrs St Paul.
The New Saint Joseph Sunday Missal & Hymnal. complete ed. (Illus., References, Calendar, Bold Sense-Lines, Two Color Ordinary, Perpetual). red flexible vinyl 9.25 (ISBN 0-89942-820-7, 820/09); green cloth, colored edges 10.95 (ISBN 0-89942-819-3, 820/22-GN); black cloth hard bdg. 10.95 (ISBN 0-89942-818-5, 820/22-B); brown flexible bdg., colored edges 11.95 (ISBN 0-89942-817-7, 820/10-BN); white durocoat, marriage cert, gold edges 12.95 (ISBN 0-89942-816-9, 820/51W); dlx. white sim. pearl, gold edges 15.00 (ISBN 0-89942-815-0, 820/82W). Catholic Bk Pub.
New...Saint Joseph Children's Missal. (Illus.). black leatherette, hard bd. 2.25 (ISBN 0-89942-806-1, 806/67-B); white leatherette, hard bd. 2.25 (ISBN 0-89942-805-3, 806/67-W); black soft simulated lea., colored edges 2.50 (ISBN 0-89942-804-5, 806/42-B); white soft simulated lea., colored edges 2.50 (ISBN 0-89942-803-7, 806/42-W); dlx. black sim. pearl, gold edges 8.95 (ISBN 0-89942-802-9, 806/82B); dlx. white sim. pearl, gold edges 8.95 (ISBN 0-89942-801-0, 806/82W). Catholic Bk Pub.
Vatican Two Sunday Missal. 1974. 8.75 (ISBN 0-8198-0513-0); pap. 5.95 (ISBN 0-8198-0514-9); gold edge bonded leather 14.95 (ISBN 0-8198-0515-7); genuine leather 18.95 (ISBN 0-8198-0516-5). Dghtrs St Paul.
Vatican Two Weekday Missal. 1975. red edge 18.50 (ISBN 0-8198-0497-5); bonded leather, gold edge 24.95 (ISBN 0-8198-0498-3); genuine leather 29.95 (ISBN 0-8198-0499-1). Dghtrs St Paul.

MISSIOLOGY

see Missions–Theory

MISSION OF THE CHURCH

Here are entered works on the chief objective and responsibility of the church as viewed in its entirety. Works on missionary work are entered under Missions.

see also Church and the World; Missions

Anderson, Gerald & Stransky, Thomas, eds. Mission Trends: Liberation Theologies in North America & Europe, No. 4. LC 78-70827. 1978. pap. 3.95 (ISBN 0-8028-1709-2). Eerdmans.
Braaten, Carl E. The Flaming Center: A Theology of the Christian Mission. LC 76-62605. pap. 44.00 (2026958). Bks Demand UMI.
Collins, Sheila D. & Collins, John A. In Your Midst: Perspectives on Christian Mission. (Orig.). 1980. pap. 3.25 (ISBN 0-377-00101-5). Friend Pr.
Costas, Orlando E. The Integrity of Mission: The Inner Life & Outreach of the Church. LC 79-1759. 1979. pap. 5.95 (ISBN 0-06-061586-9, RD 235, HarpR). Har-Row.
Davis, Warren B. & Cromie, Richard M. The Future Is Now. 110p. (Orig.). 1984. pap. 6.00 (ISBN 0-914733-03-6). Desert Min.
Escobar, Samuel & Driver, John. Christian Mission & Social Justice. LC 78-6035. (Mennonite Missionary Study Ser.: No. 5). 112p. 1978. pap. 4.95 (ISBN 0-8361-1855-3). Herald Pr.
Gatti, Enzo. Rich Church-Poor Church? O'Connell, Matthew, tr. from It. LC 74-77432. Orig. Title: Couli che Sa Il Dolore Dell'uomo. 138p. (Orig.). 1974. 4.95 (ISBN 0-88344-437-2). Orbis Bks.
Getz, Gene A. Sharpening the Focus of the Church. 360p. 1984. pap. 8.95 (ISBN 0-89693-393-8). Victor Bks.
Glasser, Arthur F. & McGavran, Donald A. Contemporary Theologies of Mission. 320p. (Orig.). 1983. pap. 12.95 (ISBN 0-8010-3790-5). Baker Bk.
Guder, Darrell L. Be My Witnesses: The Church's Mission, Message, & Messengers. LC 85-10129. 256p. (Orig.). 1985. pap. 10.95 (ISBN 0-8028-0051-3). Eerdmans.
Halverson, Richard C. A Living Fellowship. 195p. 1985. pap. 5.95 (ISBN 0-310-25781-6, Pub. by Pyranee). Zondervan.
Hesselgrave, David J. Communicating Christ Cross-Culturally. 1978. 12.95 (ISBN 0-310-36691-7, 11157P). Zondervan.
Hodges, Melvin L. The Indigenous Church. rev. ed. 160p. 1976. pap. 2.95 (ISBN 0-88243-527-2, 02-0527). Gospel Pub.
Hopewell, James F., et al. Ministry & Mission: Theological Reflections for the Life of the Church. Taylor, Barbara B., ed. 192p. (Orig.). 1985. pap. 9.95x (ISBN 0-935311-00-9). Post Horn Pr.
Hopkins, Paul A. What Next in Mission? LC 77-21776. 122p. 1977. pap. 3.95 (ISBN 0-664-24143-3). Westminster.
Killinger, John. Steeple People & the World: Planning for Mission Through the Church. (Orig.). 1977. pap. 2.50 (ISBN 0-377-00059-0). Friend Pr.
McConkey, Dale. Goal Setting: A Guide to Achieving the Church's Mission. (Administration for Churches Ser.). 1978. pap. 3.95 (ISBN 0-8066-1651-2, 10-2558). Augsburg.
McMullen, Eleanor & Sonnenfeld, Jean. Go-Groups: Gearing up for Reaching Out. (Orig.). 1977. pap. 2.50 (ISBN 0-377-00060-4). Friend Pr.
National Conference of Catholic Bishops Staff. To the Ends of the Earth: A Pastoral Statement on World Mission. 40p. (Orig.). pap. 3.95 (ISBN 1-55586-112-1). US Catholic.
Pluth, Alphonsus & Koch, Carl. The Catholic Church: Our Mission in History. (Illus.). 330p. (Orig.). 1985. pap. text ed. 11.00x (ISBN 0-88489-161-5); teaching manual 18.95x (ISBN 0-88489-162-3). St Mary's.
Ramseyer, Robert L. Mission & the Peace Witness. LC 79-16738. (Christian Peace Shelf Ser.: No. 7). 144p. 1979. pap. 6.95 (ISBN 0-8361-1896-0). Herald Pr.
Scherer, James A. Gospel, Church, & Kingdom: Comparative Studies in World Mission Theology. 256p. (Orig.). 1987. pap. 14.95 (ISBN 0-8066-2280-6, 10-2828). Augsburg.
Spears, W. Eugene Jr. The Church on Assignment. LC 84-15541. 1985. pap. 3.25 (ISBN 0-8054-5011-4). Broadman.
Stott, John R. Christian Mission in the Modern World. LC 75-21455. 128p. (Orig.). 1976. pap. 5.95 (ISBN 0-87784-485-2). Inter-Varsity.
Thung, Mady A. The Precarious Organisation: Sociological Explorations of the Church's Mission & Structure. (Religion & Society Ser.: No. 5). 1976. text ed. 22.00 (ISBN 0-686-22627-5). Mouton.
Webber, Robert E. Common Roots: A Call to Evangelical Maturity. 256p. 1982. pap. 7.95 (ISBN 0-310-36631-3, 12205P). Zondervan.

MISSION SERMONS

see Missions–Sermons

MISSIONARIES

Abrahams, Doug. Doug: Man & Missionary. 1983. pap. 3.95 (ISBN 0-85363-151-4). OMF Bks.
Adams, Carl & McElhaney, Dolly. Born with a Mission. Wallace, Mary H., ed. (Illus.). 240p. 1981. pap. 5.95 (ISBN 0-912315-15-6). Word Aflame.
Ahonen, Lauri. Missions Growth: A Case Study on Finnish Free Foreign Missions. LC 84-12636. 96p. (Orig.). 1984. pap. 5.95 (ISBN 0-87808-335-9). William Carey Lib.
Allen, Catherine. The New Lottie Moon Story. LC 79-52336. 1980. 9.95 (ISBN 0-8054-6319-4). Broadman.
Barkman, Betty. Anna. 171p. (Orig.). 1985. pap. 6.65 (ISBN 0-919797-10-5). Kindred Pr.
Beals, Paul A. A People for His Name: A Church-Based Mission Strategy. LC 84-73488. (Illus.). 248p. (Orig.). 1985. pap. text ed. 9.95X (ISBN 0-87808-336-7). William Carey Lib.
Beeching, Jack. Open Path: Christian Missionaries, 1515-1914. LC 80-21270. (Illus.). 350p. 1982. 19.95 (ISBN 0-915520-37-0); pap. 10.95 (ISBN 0-915520-53-2). Ross-Erikson.

Bennett, Adrian A. Missionary Journalist in China: Young J. Allen & His Magazines, 1860-1883. LC 81-19761. (Illus.). 336p. 1983. 28.00x (ISBN 0-8203-0615-0). U of Ga Pr.

Blessitt, Arthur. Arthur-Peacemaker. LC 85-71322. (Orig.). 1986. pap. 5.00 (ISBN 0-934461-02-3, BP603). Blessitt Pub.

Bolton, Leonard. China Call. LC 83-82301. 256p. 1984. pap. text ed. 4.95 (ISBN 0-88243-509-4, 02-0509). Gospel Pub.

Buffam, C. John. The Life & Times of an MK. LC 84-27482. (Mission Candidate Aids Ser.). 224p. (Orig.). 1985. pap. 9.95 (ISBN 0-87808-198-4). William Carey Lib.

Chan, Silas. A Biographical Sketch of G. Campbell Morgan. (Chinese.). 1984. pap. write for info. (ISBN 0-941598-21-7). Living Spring Pubns.

Christopher, Kenneth. The Merry Missionary: A Story About Philip Neri. (Stories About Christian Heroes Ser.). (Illus.). 32p. pap. 1.95 (ISBN 0-03-056876-5, HarpR). Har-Row.

Clifford, James. Person & Myth: Maurice Leenhardt in the Melanesian World. LC 81-4509. (Illus.). 320p. 1982. 35.00x (ISBN 0-520-04247-6). U of Cal Pr.

Coleman, Bernard & LaBud, Verona. Masinaigans: The Little Book. (Illus.). 368p. 1972. 10.00 (ISBN 0-686-05025-8). North Central.

Coleman, Gary. A Member Missionary? Hey...I Can Do That! LC 83-80527. 79p. 1983. pap. 4.95 (ISBN 0-88290-220-2). Horizon-Utah.

Collins, Marjorie A. Manual for Missionaries on Furlough. LC 72-92747. 1978. pap. 4.45 (ISBN 0-87808-119-4). William Carey Lib.

Conn, Harvie M., ed. Reaching the Unreached: The Old-New Challenge. 192p. 1985. 8.95 (ISBN 0-8010-2508-7). Baker Bk.

Coole, Arthur B. A Trouble Shooter for God in China. (Illus.). 1976. 20.00 (ISBN 0-912706-05-8). M Akers.

Craven, Rulon G. The Effective Missionary. LC 82-1471. 106p. 1982. 6.95 (ISBN 0-87747-898-8). Deseret Bk.

Crawford, David & Crawford, Leona. Missionary Adventures in the South Pacific. LC 67-15137. 1967. 5.50 (ISBN 0-8048-0403-6). C E Tuttle.

Creegan, Charles C. & Goodnow, Josephine A. Great Missionaries of the Church. facsimile ed. LC 73-37522. (Essay Index Reprint Ser). Repr. of 1895 ed. 24.50 (ISBN 0-8369-2541-6). Ayer Co Pubs.

Danielson, Edward E. Missionary Kid, MK. rev. ed. LC 84-12655. (Mission Candidate Aids Ser.). (Illus.). 104p. 1985. pap. 5.95 (ISBN 0-87808-745-1). William Carey Lib.

Darst, Mrs. H. W. Missions in the Mountains. (Illus.). 116p. 1979. pap. 2.50 (ISBN 0-89114-085-9). Baptist Pub Hse.

DeNevi, Don & Moholy, Noel. Junipero Serra: The Illustrated Story of the Franciscan Founder of California's Missions. LC 84-47718. (Illus.). 256p. 1985. 14.45 (ISBN 0-06-061876-0, HarpR). Har-Row.

Donnelly, Joseph P. Pierre-Gibault, Missionary, Seventeen Thirty-Seven to Eighteen Hundred Two. LC 77-156371. 1971. 8.95 (ISBN 0-8294-0203-9). Loyola.

Drury, Clifford M. Marcus & Narcissa Whitman & the Opening of Old Oregon. (Illus.). 911p. 1986. pap. 21.84 (ISBN 0-914019-08-2). Pacif NW Natl Pks.

Duggar, John W. Girl with a Missionary Heart. (Illus.). 104p. 1975. pap. 1.95 (ISBN 0-89114-074-3). Baptist Pub Hse.

Eddy, George S. Pathfinders of the World Missionary Crusade. facs. ed. LC 76-84304. (Essay Index Reprint Ser). 1945. 20.25 (ISBN 0-8369-1127-X). Ayer Co Pubs.

Eklund, Emmet E. Peter Fjellstedt: Missionary Mentor to Three Continents. LC 83-71472. (Augustana Historical Society Publication Ser.: No. 30). 197p. 1983. 20.00x (ISBN 0-910184-30-5). Augustana.

Elliot, Betsy R. How to Help a Missionary. 32p. (Orig.). 1984. pap. 0.75 (ISBN 0-87784-069-5). Inter-Varsity.

Engelhardt, Zephyrin. Missions & Missionaries of California, 4 Vols. (Illus.). lib. bdg. 185.00 (ISBN 0-87821-019-9). Milford Hse.

Filbeck, David. Social Context & Proclamation: A Socio-Cognitive Study in Proclaiming the Gospel Cross-Culturally. LC 84-28539. (Illus.). 192p. 1985. pap. text ed. 8.95X (ISBN 0-87808-199-2). William Carey Lib.

Fink, Benjamin. Life of John Kline. 7.95 (ISBN 0-87178-516-1). Brethren.

Fox, Donald S. The White Fox of Andhra. 216p. 1978. 6.95 (ISBN 0-8059-2432-9). Dorrance.

Freeman, Nona. The Adventures of Bug & Me. Clanton, Charles, ed. 128p. (Orig.). 1977. pap. 4.95 (ISBN 0-912315-28-8). Word Aflame.

--Bug & Nona on the Go. Clanton, Charles, ed. LC 86-9845. 176p. (Orig.). 1979. pap. 4.95 (ISBN 0-912315-27-X). Word Aflame.

--Shoutin' on the Hills. LC 85-22521. (Illus.). 320p. (Orig.). 1985. pap. 6.95 (ISBN 0-912315-94-6). Word Aflame.

Friesen, Abraham. P. M. Friesen & His History: Understanding Mennonite Brethren Beginnings. (Perspective on Mennonite Life & Thought Ser.: Vol. 2). 176p. (Orig.). 1979. pap. 5.95 (ISBN 0-318-18906-2). Kindred Pr.

Frizen, Edwin L., ed. Christ & Caesar in Christian Missions. Coggins, Wade T. LC 79-17124. (Orig.). 1979. pap. 5.95 (ISBN 0-87808-169-0). William Carey Lib.

Fuller, Millard. Bokotola. LC 77-1277. 1978. pap. 5.95 (ISBN 0-8329-1179-8). New Century.

Furlow, Elaine. Love with No Strings: The Human Touch in Christian Social Ministries. Hullum, Everett, ed. (The Human Touch Photo-Text Ser.: Volume IV). (Illus.). 1977. 6.95 (ISBN 0-937170-15-1). Home Mission.

Garrand, Victor. Augustine Laure, S. J., Missionary to the Yakimas. 36p. 1977. 8.00_o.s.i (ISBN 0-87770-176-8); pap. 5.95 (ISBN 0-87770-187-3). Ye Galleon.

Hare, Eric B. Fulton's Footprints in Fiji. 1985. pap. 5.95 (ISBN 0-8163-0583-8). Pacific Pr Pub Assn.

Hayden, Eric W. Traveller's Guide to Spurgeon Country. 1974. pap. 1.95 (ISBN 0-686-10527-3). Pilgrim Pubns.

Hefley, James & Hefley, Marti. Prisoners of Hope. LC 76-28840. 1976. 6.95 (ISBN 0-87509-122-9); pap. 3.95 (ISBN 0-87509-123-7). Chr Pubns.

Henery, Charles R., ed. Beyond the Horizon. 96p. (Orig.). 1986. pap. 4.30 (ISBN 0-88028-055-7). Forward Movement.

Hiebert, Paul G. Anthropological Insights for Missionaries. 280p. 1987. pap. 13.95 (ISBN 0-8010-4291-7). Baker Bk.

Hodges, Melvin L. The Indigenous Church & the Missionary: A Sequel to the Indigenous Church. LC 77-14519. 1978. pap. 2.95 (ISBN 0-87808-151-8). William Carey Lib.

Howard, David M. Moving Out: The Story of Student Initiative in World Missions. 80p. 1984. pap. 2.95 (ISBN 0-87784-565-4). Inter-Varsity.

--What Makes a Missionary. (Orig.). 1987. pap. 5.95 (ISBN 0-8024-5204-3). Moody.

Hunter, J. H. Beside All Waters. 245p. 1964. 3.95 (ISBN 0-87509-050-8). Chr Pubns.

Kane, J. Herbert. The Making of a Missionary. 160p. 1975. pap. 5.95 (ISBN 0-8010-5481-8). Baker Bk.

Kenney, Betty Jo. The Missionary Family. LC 83-6572. (Mission Candidate Aids Ser.). 120p. 1983. pap. 5.95 (ISBN 0-87808-193-3). William Carey Lib.

Kerr, James L. Wilfred Grenfell, His Life & Work. LC 73-21177. 1977. lib. bdg. 22.50x (ISBN 0-8371-6068-5, KEWG). Greenwood.

Kizer, Kathryn W. The Harley Shields: Alaskan Missionaries. LC 84-5821. (Meet the Missioanry Ser.). 1984. 5.50 (ISBN 0-8054-4285-5, 4242-85). Broadman.

Koll, Elsie. The Golden Thread: Diary of Mrs. Elsie Koll, Missionary to China. Scales, John L., ed. (Illus.). 180p. (Orig.). 1982. pap. 4.95 (ISBN 0-942504-00-3). Overcomer Pr.

Kulp, Mary A. No Longer Strangers: A Biogrpahy of H. Stover Kulp. LC 68-4439. pap. 47.00 (ISBN 0-317-28389-8, 2022413). Bks Demand UMI.

Lantry, Eileen E. Dark Night, Brilliant Star. (Daybreak Ser.). 112p. 1981. pap. 2.89 (ISBN 0-8163-0397-5). Pacific Pr Pub Assn.

Laveille, E. Life of Father De Smet, S. J. Eighteen Hundred One to Eighteen Seventy-Three. Lindsay, Marian, tr. (Loyola Request Reprint Ser.). 398p. 1981. Repr. of 1915 ed. 8.95 (ISBN 0-8294-0372-8). Loyola.

Lee, Amy. Throbbing Drums: The Story of James H. Robinson. (Orig.). 1968. pap. 0.95 (ISBN 0-377-84141-2). Friend Pr.

Livingstone, David. Missionary Travels & Researches in South Africa. LC 72-5439. (Select Bibliographies Reprint Ser.). 1972. Repr. of 1857 ed. 52.00 (ISBN 0-8369-6918-9). Ayer Co Pubs.

Livingstone, W. P. Mary Slessor of Calabar. LC 83-9286. 352p. 1984. 7.95 (ISBN 0-310-27451-6, 9286P, Clarion class). Zondervan.

Lockerbie, Jeannie. By Ones & By Twos: Single & Double Missionaries. LC 83-7272. (Mission Candidate Aids Ser.). 96p. 1983. pap. 4.95 (ISBN 0-87808-194-1). William Carey Lib.

Lutz, Lorry. Destined for Royalty: A Brahmin Priest's Search for Truth. LC 85-22681. 152p. (Orig.). 1986. pap. 5.95 (ISBN 0-87808-202-6, WCL202-6). William Carey Lib.

McCants, Sr. Dorothea O., ed. They Came to Louisiana: Letters of a Catholic Mission, 1854-1882. LC 72-96258. (Illus.). Repr. of 1970 ed. 72.80 (ISBN 0-8357-9392-3, 2020997). Bks Demand UMI.

McGaw, Francis. John Hyde. 64p. 1986. pap. 3.50. Bethany Hse.

Maclear, George F. Apostles of Mediaeval Europe. LC 72-624. (Essay Index Reprint Ser.). Repr. of 1869 ed. 21.50 (ISBN 0-8369-2803-2). Ayer Co Pubs.

McMinn, Tom. The Caudills: Courageous Missionaries. LC 81-70474. (Meet the Missionary Ser.). 1982. 5.50 (ISBN 0-8054-4277-4, 4242-77). Broadman.

Metzler, James F. From Saigon to Shalom. LC 84-9313. (Mennonite Missionary Study Ser.: No. 11). 144p. (Orig.). 1985. pap. 7.95 (ISBN 0-8361-3379-X). Herald Pr.

Mickelson, Einar H. God Can. (Illus.). 301p. 1966. 2.50 (ISBN 0-87509-086-9). Chr Pubns.

Milner, Clyde A., II & O'Neil, Floyd A., eds. Churchmen & the Western Indians, 1820-1920. LC 85-40477. (Illus.). 272p. 1985. 19.95 (ISBN 0-8061-1950-0). U of Okla Pr.

Missionary Heroes, 2 vols. pap. 3.95 ea. Schmul Pub Co.

Morrison, James H. Missionary Heroes of Africa. LC 79-89010. Repr. of 1922 ed. 22.50x (ISBN 0-8371-1738-0, MOM&, Pub. by Negro U Pr). Greenwood.

Morton, Daniel O. Memoir of Rev. Levi Parsons: Late Missionary to Palestine. Davis, Moshe, ed. (America & the Holy Land Ser.). 1977. Repr. of 1824 ed. lib. bdg. 33.00x (ISBN 0-405-10271-2). Ayer Co Pubs.

Moshe, Beth. Judaism's Truth versus the Missionaries. 354p. 1987. 14.95 (ISBN 0-8197-0515-2). Bloch.

Mueller, John T. Great Missionaries to China. LC 73-38329. (Biography Index Reprint Ser). Repr. of 1947 ed. 12.75 (ISBN 0-8369-8124-3). Ayer Co Pubs.

--Great Missionaries to the Orient. LC 78-38330. (Biography Index Reprint Ser). Repr. of 1948 ed. 14.75 (ISBN 0-8369-8125-1). Ayer Co Pubs.

Muggeridge, Malcolm. Something Beautiful for God: Mother Teresa of Calcutta. 1977. pap. 3.50 (ISBN 0-385-12639-5, Im). Doubleday.

Murray, Andrew & Choy, Leona. Key to the Missionary Problem. (Orig.). 1980. pap. 3.95 (ISBN 0-87508-401-X). Chr Lit.

Nida, Eugene A. Customs & Cultures: Anthropology for Christian Missions. 2nd ed. LC 54-8976. (Applied Cultural Anthropology Ser.). 306p. 1975. Repr. of 1954 ed. 7.95x (ISBN 0-87808-723-0). William Carey Lib.

Odom, Martha. The Making of a Missionary. Woolsey, Raymond H., ed. 128p. (Orig.). 1985. pap. 5.95 (ISBN 0-8280-0289-4). Review & Herald.

Oliver, Caroline. Western Women in Colonial Africa. LC 81-24194. (Contributions in Comparative Colonial Studies: No. 12). xv, 201p. 1982. lib. bdg. 29.95 (ISBN 0-313-23388-8, OWA/). Greenwood.

Pierson, Robert H. Here Comes Adventure. Wheeler, Gerald, ed. (Banner Ser.). (Illus.). 192p. (Orig.). 1984. pap. 5.95 (ISBN 0-8280-0244-4). Review & Herald.

Reed, Lyman E. Preparing Missionaries for Intercultural Communication. LC 84-23060. (Illus.). 224p. (Orig.). 1985. pap. text ed. 6.95x (ISBN 0-87808-438-X). William Carey Lib.

Rives, Elsie. The Shoemakers: God's Helpers. LC 86-4148. (Meet the Missionary Ser.). 1986. pap. 5.50 (ISBN 0-8054-4328-2). Broadman.

Romb, Anselm. Man of Peace: Casimir Michael Cypher, OFM Conv: His Meaning in Life Was Found in Death. (Illus.). 67p. (Orig.). 1985. pap. 3.75 (ISBN 0-913382-17-5, 105-42). Prow Bks-Franciscan.

Russell, H. Africa's Twelve Apostles. 1980. 6.95 (ISBN 0-8198-0702-8); pap. 5.50 (ISBN 0-8198-0703-6). Dghtrs St Paul.

Schmitt, Robert C. The Missionary Censuses of Hawaii. (Pacific Anthropological Records: No. 20). 50p. pap. 5.00 (ISBN 0-910240-66-3). Bishop Mus.

Scotish Missions Promotion. St. Andrews Seven. (Orig.). 1985. pap. 5.95 (ISBN 0-85151-428-6). Banner of Truth.

Shaw, John. Travels in England: A Ramble with the City & Town Missionaries. LC 84-48282. (The Rise of Urban Britain Ser.). 393p. 1985. 50.00 (ISBN 0-8240-6284-1). Garland Pub.

Shenk, Wilbert R. Henry Venn: Missionary Statesman. LC 82-18779. 192p. (Orig.). 1983. pap. 2.49 (ISBN 0-88344-181-0). Orbis Bks.

Sigal, Gerald. The Jew & the Christian Missionary: A Jewish Response to Missionary Christianity. 1981. 20.00x (ISBN 0-87068-886-3). Ktav.

Smith, Edwin W. Great Lion of Bechuanaland: The Life and Times of Roger Price, Missionary. LC 57-36876. 1957. text ed. 20.00x (ISBN 0-8401-2210-1). A R Allenson.

Soldier of God. 1.00. Paulist Pr.

Spence, Jonathan D. The Memory Palace of Matteo Ricci. (Nonfiction Ser.). 368p. 1985. pap. 7.95 (ISBN 0-14-008098-8). Penguin.

Stafford, Tim. The Friendship Gap: Reaching Out Across Cultures. LC 84-6725. 152p. (Orig.). 1984. pap. 5.95 (ISBN 0-87784-975-7). Inter-Varsity.

Stone, Clara R., ed. Library Manual for Missionaries. LC 79-116205. (Illus., Orig.). 1979. pap. 4.95 (ISBN 0-686-31591-X). Assn Chr Libs.

Taylor, Hudson. Hudson Taylor. 2nd ed. 160p. 1987. pap. 3.50 (ISBN 0-87123-951-5). Bethany Hse.

Taylor, Hudson & Thompson, Phyllis. God's Adventurer. (Illus.). 1978. pap. 2.50 (ISBN 9971-83-777-3). OMF Bks.

Thompson, Mollie. Of Caesar's Household. Clanton, Charles, ed. 232p. (Orig.). 1978. pap. 4.95 (ISBN 0-912315-29-6). Word Aflame.

Thompson, R. E. & Thompson, Ella. Missionary Discipleship: The Story of R. E. & Ella Thompson. (Illus.). 42p. (Orig.). 1982. pap. 3.95 (ISBN 0-942726-00-6). Missionary Intern.

Tiltman, Marjorie. God's Adventurers. facs. ed. LC 68-16979. (Essay Index Reprint Ser.). 1933. 18.00 (ISBN 0-8369-0945-3). Ayer Co Pubs.

Tucker, Ruth. From Jerusalem to Irian Jaya: A Biographical History of Christian Missions. 1986. pap. 14.95 (ISBN 0-310-45931-1, 12723P). Zondervan.

Tuttle, Daniel S. Missionary to the Mountain West: The Reminiscences of Episcopal Bishop Daniel S. Tuttle, 1866-1886. 509p. 1987. Repr. of 1906 ed. 20.00 (ISBN 0-87480-305-5). U of Utah Pr.

Vester, Bertha H. Our Jerusalem: An American Family in the Holy City, 1881-1949. Davis, Moshe, ed. LC 77-70752. (America & the Holy Land Ser.). 1977. Repr. of 1950 ed. lib. bdg. 30.00x (ISBN 0-405-10296-8). Ayer Co Pubs.

Welch, Herbert. Men of the Outposts: The Romance of the Modern Christian Movement. facs. ed. LC 69-17594. (Essay Index Reprint Ser). 1937. 16.50 (ISBN 0-8369-1162-8). Ayer Co Pubs.

Wendland, E. H. Dear Mr. Missionary. 1978. pap. 4.95 (ISBN 0-8100-0035-0, 12N1714). Northwest Pub.

Wilson, J. Christy, Jr. Today's Tentmakers. 1979. pap. 5.95 (ISBN 0-8423-7279-2). Tyndale.

Wyker, Bertha P. Spanning the Decades: A Spiritual Pilgrimage. (Illus.). 224p. 1981. 8.50 (ISBN 0-682-49746-0). Exposition Pr FL.

Zhizn' Valaamskago Monakha Germana (Aljaskinskago)-Amerikanskago Missionjera. Tr. of The Life of the Valaam Monk Herman (of Alaska)-Missionary to America. 24p. pap. 1.00 (ISBN 0-317-29192-0). Holy Trinity.

MISSIONARIES–APPOINTMENT, CALL, AND ELECTION

Bacon, Daniel W. Who Me? A Missionary? 1985. pap. 1.25 (ISBN 9971-972-32-8). OMF Bks.

Carrigan, Ana. Salvador Witness: The Life & Calling of Jean Donovan. 320p. 1984. 16.95 (ISBN 0-671-47992-X). S&S.

Hunter, J. H. Beside All Waters. 245p. 1964. 3.95 (ISBN 0-87509-050-8). Chr Pubns.

McCloskey, Michael. The Formative Years of the Missionary College of Santa Cruz of Queretaro: 1683-1733. (Monograph Ser.). 1955. 10.00 (ISBN 0-88382-051-X). AAFH.

Morgan, Helen. Who'd Be a Missionary. 1972. pap. 1.50 (ISBN 0-87508-365-X). Chr Lit.

--Who'd Stay a Missionary. 1972. pap. 1.50 (ISBN 0-87508-366-8). Chr Lit.

MISSIONARIES–CORRESPONDENCE, REMINISCENCES, ETC.

Arnez, John A., intro. by. Slovenian Letters by Missionaries in America, 1851-1874. (Studia Slovenica Special Ser.: No.4). 230p. 1984. pap. 11.00 (ISBN 0-318-01454-8). Studia Slovenica.

Austin, Althea. First Impressions: From the Diary of Althea Austin. 1984. 6.95 (ISBN 0-533-05806-6). Vantage.

Barnard, Laura B. & Hill, Georgia. Touching the Untouchables. 224p. 1985. pap. 6.95 (ISBN 0-8423-7296-2). Tyndale.

Bliss, Eugene F., ed. Diary of David Zeisberger: A Missionary Among the Indians of Ohio, 2 vols. LC 73-108557. 1972. Repr. of 1885 ed. 59.00x (ISBN 0-403-00253-2). Scholarly.

Brooks, Cyril. Grace Triumphant: Autobiography. 266p. (Orig.). 1985. pap. 9.95 (ISBN 0-937396-66-4). Walterick Pubs.

Carrigan, Ana. Salvador Witness: The Life & Calling of Jean Donvan. 320p. 1986. pap. 3.95 (ISBN 0-345-32984-8). Ballantine.

Cinquin, Emmanuelle. To Share with God's Poor: Sister among the Outcasts. LC 83-47735. (Illus.). 458p. 1983. pap. 5.95 (ISBN 0-06-061392-0, RD-485, HarpR). Har-Row.

Collins, Jodie. Codeword: Catherine. 240p. (Orig.). 1984. pap. 6.95 (ISBN 0-8423-0301-4). Tyndale.

Crandall, Faye E. Into the Copper River Valley. 1983. 9.95 (ISBN 0-8062-2025-2). Carlton.

Crider, Virginia. Allegheny Gospel Trails. (Illus.). 1971. 7.50 (ISBN 0-87813-502-2). Christian Light.

Dean, Elizabeth. Carrie-Ambassador at Large. rev. ed. (Illus.). 269p. 1984. pap. 4.95 (ISBN 0-930033-00-0). Christ Life Revivals.

De Smet, Pierre J. Life, Letters & Travels of Father Pierre Jean de Smet, 4 vols. LC 75-83418. (Religion in America Ser. I). 1969. Repr. of 1905 ed. 88.00 set (ISBN 0-405-00237-8); Vols. 1-2. 22.00 ea. Vol. 1 (ISBN 0-405-00238-6). Vol. 2 (ISBN 0-405-00239-4). Vols. 3-4. 22.00 ea. Vol. 3 (ISBN 0-405-00240-8). Vol. 4 (ISBN 0-405-00241-6). Ayer Co Pubs.

Dodge, Ralph E. The Revolutionary Bishop: Who Saw God at Work in Africa. LC 85-29092. (Illus.). 216p. (Orig.). 1986. pap. 7.95 (ISBN 0-87808-203-4, WCL203-4). William Carey Lib.

Elliot, Jim. The Journals of Jim Elliot. Elliot, Elisabeth, ed. 416p. 1978. 7.95 (Power Bks). Revell.

--The Journals of Jim Elliot. Elliot, Elisabeth, ed. 416p. 1983. pap. 7.95 (ISBN 0-8007-5147-7, Power Bks). Revell.

Eyer, Mary S. He Restoreth My Soul. LC 82-1363. 98p. 1982. 6.95 (ISBN 0-87747-908-9). Deseret Bk.

Gamblin, Eleanor & Morehouse, Joyce M. The Sparrow's Song. Wallace, Mary H., ed. 192p. (Orig.). 1984. pap. 5.95 (ISBN 0-912315-68-7). Word Aflame.

Godwin, Don & Godwin, Vi. Faith vs. Fear. 257p. 1986. pap. 7.95 (ISBN 0-317-52284-1). Christian Pub.

Hind, Carolyn S. Whither Thou Goest. LC 85-51991. (Illus.). 192p. 1985. 12.50 (ISBN 0-936029-00-5). Western Bk Journ.

Horn, Siegfried. Promise Deferred. Wheeler, Gerald, ed. 96p. 1987. pap. price not set (ISBN 0-8280-0380-7). Review & Herald.

Hyland, Judy. In the Shadow of the Rising Sun. LC 84-12303. 128p. (Orig.). 1984. pap. 5.95 (ISBN 0-8066-2091-9, 10-3260). Augsburg.

Jorden, Paul J. & Adair, James R. Surgeon on Safari. (Living Bks.). 192p. (Orig.). 1985. pap. 3.95 (ISBN 0-8423-6686-5). Tyndale.

Knapp, Doug, et al. Thunder in the Valley. (Orig.). 1986. pap. 6.95 (ISBN 0-8054-6342-9). Broadman.

LaBerge, Agnes N. What God Hath Wrought. Dayton, Donald W., ed. (The Higher Christian Life Ser.). 127p. 1985. 20.00 (ISBN 0-8240-6425-9). Garland Pub.

Leonard, Harry, ed. J. N. Andrews: The Man & the Mission. xii, 355p. (Orig.). 1985. pap. 11.95 (ISBN 0-943872-91-X). Andrews Univ Pr.

McDowell, Catherine, ed. Letters from the Ursuline 1852-1853. LC 77-85460. 1978. boxed 20.00 (ISBN 0-911536-69-8); 18.00. Trinity U Pr.

Mild, Frieda H. The Potter's Clay. 160p. 1984. 10.50 (ISBN 0-89962-356-5). Todd & Honeywell.

Mole, Winifred A. So Dear to Me. 1985. 11.95 (ISBN 0-533-06486-4). Vantage.

Morley, Lewis H. Now It Can Be Told. Wallace, Mary H., ed. LC 84-126606. (Illus.). 251p. (Orig.). 1983. pap. 5.95 (ISBN 0-912315-11-3). Word Aflame.

Murray, Dorothy G. Sister Anna: God's Captive to Set Others Free. 175p. (Orig.). 1983. pap. 7.95 (ISBN 0-87178-796-2). Brethren.

Murray, Tom. A Higher Call. 1984. 12.95 (ISBN 0-533-06032-X). Vantage.

Narayan, R. K. My Dateless Diary. 1960. pap. 3.25 (ISBN 0-86578-118-4). Ind-US Inc.

Smith, John C. From Colonialism to World Community: The Church's Pilgrimage. LC 82-12138. 334p. 1982. pap. 8.95 (ISBN 0-664-24452-1, Pub. by Geneva Press). Westminster.

Thompson, Mollie. When You're in You're Out. LC 86-10977. (Illus.). 192p. (Orig.). 1986. pap. 5.95 (ISBN 0-932581-50-1). Word Aflame.

Tinsley, William K. Seadog. 270p. 1986. 9.95 (ISBN 0-936637-00-5); pap. 6.95 (ISBN 0-936637-01-3). Living Stone Pubs.

Van Ess, Dorothy. Pioneers in the Arab World. 1974. pap. 4.95 (ISBN 0-8028-1585-5). Eerdmans.

Whitman, Narcissa. My Journal. 2nd ed. 74p. 1985. 7.50 (ISBN 0-87770-348-5); pap. 4.95; pap. 9.95. Ye Galleon.

Whitman, Narcissa P. The Letters of Narcissa Whitman. 245p. 1986. 14.95 (ISBN 0-87770-386-8). Ye Galleon.

Wilkinson, Larry & Wilkinson, Dorcas. Gifts from Korea. 1983. pap. 7.00 (ISBN 0-8309-0376-3). Herald Hse.

MISSIONARIES–JUVENILE LITERATURE

Barrett, Marsha. Vena Aguillard: Woman of Faith. LC 82-73664. (Meet the Missionary Ser.). 1983. 5.50 (ISBN 0-8054-4281-2, 4242-81). Broadman.

Bostrom, Alice. David Livingstone, Missionary to Africa. (Children's Missionary Library: Bk. 7). (Illus.). 32p. (Orig.). 1982. pap. 1.50 (ISBN 0-89323-027-8). Bible Memory.

Brown, Pam. It Was Always Africa. LC 86-2240. (YA) 1986. pap. 4.95 (ISBN 0-8054-4335-5). Broadman.

Butler, Mary & Butler, Trent. The John Allen Moores: Good News in War & Peace. LC 85-6656. (Meet the Missionary Ser.). 1985. 5.50 (ISBN 0-8054-4295-2, 4242-95). Broadman.

Carter, Virginia B. I'm Going to Be a Missionary. (Orig.). 1978. pap. 2.95 (ISBN 0-89036-103-7). Hawkes Pub Inc.

Chamberlain, Eugene. Loyd Corder: Traveler for God. LC 82-73663. (Meet the Missionary Ser.). 1983. 5.50 (ISBN 0-8054-4284-7, 4242-84). Broadman.

Heath, Lou. Ed Taylor: Father of Migrant Missions. LC 81-70911. (Meet the Missionary Ser.). 1982. 5.50 (ISBN 0-8054-4278-2, 4242-78). Broadman.

Hollaway, Lee. The Donald Orrs: Missionary Duet. LC 82-732666. (Meet the Missionary Ser.). 1983. 5.50 (ISBN 0-8054-4283-9, 4242-83). Broadman.

Howard, Mildred T. These Are My People. (Illus.). 152p. (Orig.). 1984. pap. 5.95 (ISBN 0-89084-242-6). Bob Jones Univ Pr.

Human, Johnnie. Finlay & Julia Graham: Missionary Partners. LC 86-4148. (Meet the Missionary Ser.). 1986. 5.50 (ISBN 0-8054-4327-4). Broadman.

Irland, Nancy B. No More Alphabet Soup. Van Dolson, Bobbie J., ed. LC 83-3303. (A Banner Bk.). 128p. (Orig.). 1984. pap. 5.95 (ISBN 0-8280-0165-0). Review & Herald.

Lathem, Judy. Hattie Gardner: Determined Adventurer. LC 81-70909. (Meet the Missionary Ser.). 1982. 5.50 (ISBN 0-8054-4280-4, 4242-80). Broadman.

McElrath, William N. Oz & Mary Quick: Taiwan Teammates. LC 84-2962. (Meet the Missionary Ser.). 1984. pap. 5.50 (ISBN 0-8054-4287-1, 4242-87). Broadman.

Massey, Barbara. Virginia Wingo: Teacher & Friend. LC 82-73665. (Meet the Missionary Ser.). 1983. 5.50 (ISBN 0-8054-4282-0, 4242-82). Broadman.

Monsell, Helen A. Her Own Way: The Story of Lottie Moon. LC 82-71443. 1982. pap. 4.50 (ISBN 0-8054-4319-3, 4243-19). Broadman.

Olmstead, Nan. Ladybug & Country Preacher. LC 84-29264. 1985. pap. 3.95 (ISBN 0-8054-4297-9). Broadman.

Ryan, Roberta. The George Lozuks: Doers of the Word. LC 85-6615. (Meet the Missionary Ser.). 1985. 5.50 (ISBN 0-8054-4293-6, 4242-93). Broadman.

Timyan, Janis, illus. A Happy Day for Ramona & Other Missionary Stories for Children. (Illus., Orig.). Date not set. pap. price not set (ISBN 0-87509-392-2). Chr Pubns.

--The Pink & Green Church & Other Missionary Stories for Children. (Illus.). Date not set. pap. price not set (ISBN 0-87509-393-0). Chr Pubns.

Wallace, Mary H. Profiles of Pentecostal Missionaries. LC 86-15919. (Illus.). 352p. (Orig.). 1986. pap. 6.95 (ISBN 0-932581-00-5). Word Aflame.

Wendell, Belew M. Ken Prickett: Man of Joy. LC 85-6208. (Meet the Missionary Ser.). 1985. 5.50 (ISBN 0-8054-4296-0, 4242-96). Broadman.

Zook, Mary R. Little Missionaries. 184p. (YA) 1979. 6.75 (ISBN 0-686-30764-X). Rod & Staff.

MISSIONARIES–VOCATION

see Missionaries–Appointment, Call, and Election

MISSIONARIES, ANGLO-SAXON

Glunz, Hans. Britannien und Bibeltext. Repr. of 1930 ed. 16.00 (ISBN 0-384-18950-4). Johnson Repr.

Renner, Louis L. Father Tom of the Artic. LC 85-71951. (Illus.). 176p. (Orig.). 24.95 (ISBN 0-8323-0445-X); pap. 10.95 (ISBN 0-8323-0443-3). Binford-Metropolitan.

--The Knom: Father Jim Poole Story. LC 85-71950. (Illus.). 184p. (Orig.). 1985. pap. 8.95 (ISBN 0-8323-0444-1). Binford-Metropolitan.

MISSIONARIES, BRITISH

Bawden, C. R. Shamans, Lamas & Evangelicals: The English Missionaries in Siberia. (Illus.). 400p. 1985. 50.00x (ISBN 0-7102-0064-1). Methuen Inc.

Bocking, Ronald. History of the London Missionary Society. 256p. 1986. 59.00x (ISBN 0-317-54254-0, Pub. by Elmcrest UK). State Mutual Bk.

The English Missionaries in Sweden & Finland. (Church Historical Society, London, Ser.: No. 27). Repr. of 1937 ed. 55.00 (ISBN 0-8115-3151-1). Kraus Repr.

Mackay, A. M. A. M. Mackay: Pioneer Missionary of the Church of the Missionary Society of Uganda. (Illus.). 485p. 1970. Repr. of 1890 ed. 35.00x (ISBN 0-7146-1874-8, F Cass Co). Biblio Dist.

Oddie, G. A. Social Protest in India: British Protestant Missionaries & Social Reforms, Eighteen Fifty to Nineteen Hundred. 1979. 17.50x (ISBN 0-8364-0195-6). South Asia Bks.

Sargent, John. Life & Letters of Henry Martyn. 496p. 1985. pap. 6.95 (ISBN 0-85151-468-5). Banner of Truth.

Wright, Louis B. Religion & Empire. 1965. lib. bdg. 18.50x (ISBN 0-374-98816-1, Octagon). Hippocrene Bks.

MISSIONARIES, IRISH

Glunz, Hans. Britannien und Bibeltext. Repr. of 1930 ed. 16.00 (ISBN 0-384-18950-4). Johnson Repr.

McDowell, Catherine, ed. Letters from the Ursuline 1852-1853. LC 77-85460. 1978. boxed 20.00 (ISBN 0-911536-69-8); 18.00. Trinity U Pr.

Murray, Tom. A Higher Call. 1984. 12.95 (ISBN 0-533-06032-X). Vantage.

MISSIONARY STORIES

Ascent to the Tribes. 1956. pap. 3.95 (ISBN 0-85363-136-0). OMF Bks.

Bagley, Val C. Mission Mania: A Cartoonist's View of the Best Two Years of Life. (Illus.). 98p. (Orig.). 1980. pap. 3.95 (ISBN 0-88290-140-0). Horizon Utah.

Bentley-Taylor, David. Java Saga. Orig. Title: Weathercocks Reward. 1975. pap. 2.25 (ISBN 0-85363-100-X). OMF Bks.

Cammack, Phyllis. Missionary Moments. LC 66-30364. (Illus.). 134p. 1966. 3.50 (ISBN 0-913342-09-2). Barclay Pr.

Dumas, Edith B. The Least of These. 128p. 1982. 7.95 (ISBN 0-89962-261-5). Todd & Honeywell.

Fraser, J. O. & Allbutt, Mary E., eds. Prayer of Faith. pap. 1.00 (ISBN 0-85363-106-9). OMF Bks.

Holder, Philip. Captain Mahjong. 1976. pap. 2.40 (ISBN 0-85363-113-1). OMF Bks.

Hoste, D. E. If I Am to Lead. 1968. pap. 0.90 (ISBN 0-85363-068-2). OMF Bks.

Kendrick, Bv. Ben. Battle for Yanga. LC 80-20643. 127p. 1980. pap. 3.95 (ISBN 0-87227-074-2). Reg Baptist.

Kirkpatrick, Charles. Cow in the Clinic & Other Missionary Stories from Around the World. 1977. pap. 4.95 (ISBN 0-89367-016-2). Light & Life.

Kuhn, Isobel. In the Arena. 1960. pap. 3.95 (ISBN 9971-972-19-0). OMF Bks.

--Nests Above the Abyss. pap. 3.95 (ISBN 9971-83-817-6). OMF Bks.

--Stones of Fire. 1951. pap. 3.95 (ISBN 9971-972-00-X). OMF Bks.

Lane, Denis. God's Powerful Weapon. 1977. pap. 1.25 (ISBN 9971-972-21-2). OMF Bks.

Lyall, Leslie. Three of China's Mighty Men. pap. 3.95 (ISBN 0-340-25561-7). OMF Bks.

Lyall, Leslie T. A Passion for the Impossible. 1965. pap. 2.40 (ISBN 0-85363-115-8). OMF Bks.

Marcus, Sophia. The Potato Man. Wheeler, Gerald, ed. (Banner Ser.). 128p. (Orig.). 1986. pap. 6.50 (ISBN 0-8280-0309-2). Review & Herald.

Mathews, R. Arthur. Born for Battle. 3rd ed. 1980. pap. 2.95 (ISBN 0-85363-143-3). OMF Bks.

Muira, Ayako. Shiokari Pass. 1968. 4.95 (ISBN 9971-972-23-9). OMF Bks.

Nielson, Larry. How Would You Like to See the Slides of My Mission? A Tasteful Collection of Missionary Humor. LC 80-82708. (Illus.). 158p. (Orig.). 1980. pap. 4.95 (ISBN 0-88290-153-2, 2040). Horizon Utah.

Nightingale, Ken. One Way Through the Jungle. pap. 2.50 (ISBN 0-85363-107-7). OMF Bks.

Sanders, J. Oswald. Best That I Can Be. 1976. pap. 1.95 (ISBN 9971-83-873-7). OMF Bks.

Stickly, Caroline. Broken Snare. 1975. pap. 3.75 (ISBN 0-85363-102-6). OMF Bks.

Wendland, E. H. Dear Mr. Missionary. 1978. pap. 4.95 (ISBN 0-8100-0035-0, 12N1714). Northwest Pub.

White, Paul. Alias Jungle Doctor: An Autobiography. (Illus.). 236p. 1977. pap. 6.95 (ISBN 0-85364-205-2). Attic Pr.

MISSIONS

see also Bible–Publication and Distribution; Church Growth; Communication (Theology); Evangelistic Work; Language Question in the Church; Missionaries; Salvation Army; Spanish Missions of California; Spanish Missions of New Mexico; Spanish Missions of the Southwest

also subdivision Missions under names of churches, denominations, religious orders, etc. e.g. Church of England–Missions; Jesuits–Missions; Lutheran Church–Missions; Spanish Missions of California

Allen, Roland. The Compulsion of the Spirit: A Roland Allen Reader. Long, Charles H. & Paton, David, eds. 160p. 1983. pap. 3.70 (ISBN 0-88028-025-5). Forward Movement.

--Missionary Methods: St. Paul's or Our's? 1962. pap. 5.95x (ISBN 0-8028-1001-2). Eerdmans.

Anderson, Gerald & Stransky, Thomas, eds. Mission Trends: Faith Meets Faith, No. 5. LC 81-80983. 320p. (Orig.). 1981. pap. 4.95 (ISBN 0-8091-2356-8). Paulist Pr.

Anderson, Gerald H. & Stansky, Thomas. Missions Trends, No. 2. LC 75-29836. 1975. pap. 3.95 (ISBN 0-8028-1624-X). Eerdmans.

Anderson, Gerald H. & Stranskey, Thomas F. Mission Trends: "Evangelization", No. 2. LC 75-29836. (Mission Trend Ser.). 288p. 1976. pap. 4.95 (ISBN 0-8091-1900-5). Paulist Pr.

Anderson, Gerald H. & Stransky, Thomas F., eds. Mission Trends: Crucial Issues in Mission Today, No. 1. LC 74-81222. (Mission Trend Ser.). (Orig.). 1974. pap. 4.95 (ISBN 0-8091-1843-2). Paulist Pr.

--Mission Trends: Faith Meets Faith, No. 5. (Mission Trends Ser.). 320p. (Orig.). 1981. pap. 3.95 (ISBN 0-8028-1821-8). Eerdmans.

Barrett, Kate W. Some Practical Suggestions on the Conduct of a Rescue Home: Including Life of Dr. Kate Waller Barrett. facsimile ed. LC 74-3928. (Women in America Ser.). Orig. Title: Fifty Years Work with Girls. 186p. 1974. Repr. of 1903 ed. 20.00x (ISBN 0-405-06075-0). Ayer Co Pubs.

Bartlett, Samuel C. Historical Sketches of the Missions of the American Board. LC 78-38436. (Religion in America, Ser. 2). 210p. 1972. Repr. of 1972 ed. 21.00 (ISBN 0-405-04057-1). Ayer Co Pubs.

Bassham, Rodger C. Mission Theology, Nineteen Forty Eight to Nineteen Seventy-Five: Years of Worldwide Creative Tension--Ecumenical, Evangelical & Roman Catholic. LC 79-17116. 1980. 10.95 (ISBN 0-87808-330-8). William Carey Lib.

Bauer, Arthur O. Being in Mission: A Resource for the Local Church & Community. 1987. pap. 4.95. Friend Pr.

--Making Mission Happen. 1974. pap. 4.50 (ISBN 0-377-00019-1). Friend Pr.

Bavinck, J. H. Introduction to the Science of Missions. 1977. pap. 5.95 (ISBN 0-8010-0600-7). Baker Bk.

Bavinck, John H. Introduction to Science of Missions. 1960. pap. 5.95 (ISBN 0-87552-124-X). Presby & Reformed.

Beals, Paul A. A People for His Name: A Church-Based Mission Strategy. LC 84-73488. (Illus.). 248p. (Orig.). 1985. pap. text ed. 9.95X (ISBN 0-87808-336-7). William Carey Lib.

Bolle, Jeff, ed. Lay Mission Handbook. 100p. binder 20.00 (ISBN 0-318-21725-2). Intl Liaison.

Bolton, Herbert E. Wider Horizons of American History. 1967. pap. 5.95x (ISBN 0-268-00301-7). U of Notre Dame Pr.

Braun, J. R. Is This My Neighbor? The Union Gospel Mission. (Illus.). 60p. (Orig.). 1980. pap. text ed. 8.95 (ISBN 0-933656-08-4). Trinity Pub Hse.

Cabat, Erni. Father Eusebio Francisco Kino & His Missions of the Pimeria Alta: The Side Altars, Bk. I. Polzer, Charles W., ed. Prezelski, Carmen V., tr. LC 82-50219. (Illus.). 36p. (Orig.). 1982. pap. 5.00 (ISBN 0-915076-06-3). SW Mission.

Cabat, Erni & Polzer, Charles W. Father Eusebio Francisco Kino & His Missions of the Pimeria Alta: Bk. II, The Main Altars, Book II. Prezelski, Carmen V., tr. LC 82-50219. (Illus.). 36p. (Orig.). 1983. pap. 5.00 (ISBN 0-915076-08-X). SW Mission.

Camp Farthest Out Staff. Roots & Fruits of the Camp Farthest Out. 1980. 3.95 (ISBN 0-910924-89-9). Macalester.

Chambers, Oswald. So Send I You. 1973. pap. 2.95 (ISBN 0-87508-138-X). Chr Lit.

Colligan, John, et al. Mission & Ministry: A Vision for the Church. LC 83-62365. 84p. (Orig.). 1983. pap. text ed. 3.95 (ISBN 0-911905-07-3). Past & Mat Rene Ctr.

Collins, Marjorie A. Manual for Today's Missionary: From Recruitment to Retirement. rev. ed. LC 85-27603. (Mission Candidate Aids Ser.). 400p. 1986. pap. 9.95x (ISBN 0-87808-204-2, WCL204-2). William Carey Lib.

Conn, Harvie M. Eternal Word & Changing Worlds: Theology, Anthropology & Mission in Trialogue. 336p. 1984. pap. 10.95 (ISBN 0-310-45321-6, 11647P). Zondervan.

Conn, Harvie M., ed. Reaching the Unreached: The Old-New Challenge. 192p. 1985. 8.95 (ISBN 0-8010-2508-7). Baker Bk.

Conn, Harvie M. & Rowen, Samuel F., eds. Missions & Theological Education in World Perspective. LC 84-72527. 484p. (Orig.). 1984. pap. text ed. 11.95 (ISBN 0-930957-00-8). Assocs Urbanus.

Crawley, Winston. Global Mission. LC 85-3752. 1985. 11.95 (ISBN 0-8054-6340-2). Broadman.

Davids, Richard C. Man Who Moved a Mountain. LC 75-99609. (Illus.). 270p. 1972. pap. 5.95 (ISBN 0-8006-1237-X, 1-1237). Fortress.

Davies, John D. The Faith Abroad. (Faith & the Future Ser.). 163p. 1984. 24.95x (ISBN 0-631-13183-3); pap. 8.95x (ISBN 0-631-13221-X). Basil Blackwell.

DiGangi, Mariano. I Believe in Mission. 1979. pap. 2.95 (ISBN 0-87552-255-6). Presby & Reformed.

Dubose, Francis M., ed. Classics of Christian Missions. LC 78-53147. 1979. pap. 12.95 (ISBN 0-8054-6313-5). Broadman.

Dwight, Henry Otis, et al, eds. Encyclopedia of Missions: Descriptive, Historical, Biographical, Statistical. 2nd ed. LC 74-31438. 851p. 1975. Repr. of 1904 ed. 80.00x (ISBN 0-8103-3325-2). Gale.

Elkins, Phillip W. Church Sponsored Missions. 1974. pap. 3.00 (ISBN 0-88027-003-9). Firm Foun Pub.

Elsbree, Oliver W. The Rise of the Missionary Spirit in America 1790-1815. LC 79-13028. (Perspectives in American History Ser.: No. 55). 1980. Repr. of 1928 ed. 22.50x (ISBN 0-87991-376-2). Porcupine Pr.

Episcopal Church Center. The Work You Give Us to Do: A Mission Study. 179p. (Orig.). 1982. pap. 4.95 (ISBN 0-8164-7116-9, HarpR); study guide 1.25 (ISBN 0-8164-7117-7). Har-Row.

Fairbank, John K., ed. The Missionary Enterprise in China & America. LC 74-82191. (Studies in American-East Asian Relations: No. 6). 442p. 1974. text ed. 25.00x (ISBN 0-674-57655-1). Harvard U Pr.

Filbeck, David. Social Context & Proclamation: A Socio-Cognitive Study in Proclaiming the Gospel Cross-Culturally. LC 84-28539. (Illus.). 192p. 1985. pap. text ed. 8.95X (ISBN 0-87808-199-2). William Carey Lib.

Flanagan, Padraig, ed. A New Missionary Era. LC 81-9595. 192p. (Orig.). 1982. pap. 2.49 (ISBN 0-88344-331-7). Orbis Bks.

Flood, Robert G. & Jenkins, Jerry B. Teaching the Word, Reaching the World. 1985. text ed. 14.95 (ISBN 0-8024-8567-7). Moody.

Franklin, Karl, ed. & intro. by. Current Concerns of Anthropologists & Missionaries. LC 86-81558. (International Museum of Cultures Ser.: No. 22). 174p. (Orig.). 1987. pap. text ed. 14.00 (ISBN 0-88312-176-X); microfiche (3) 6.00 (ISBN 0-88312-259-6). Summer Inst Ling.

Gambill, Sandra & Ashley, Clara. Missions Studies: Taiwan. pap. 1.00 (ISBN 0-89114-123-5). Baptist Pub Hse.

Gatti, Enzo. Rich Church-Poor Church? O'Connell, Matthew, tr. from It. LC 74-77432. Orig. Title: Couli che Sa Il Dolore Dell'uomo. 138p. (Orig.). 1974. 4.95 (ISBN 0-88344-437-2). Orbis Bks.

Gehris, Paul & Gehris, Kathy. The Teaching Church: Active in Mission. 80p. 1987. pap. 5.95 (ISBN 0-8170-1080-7). Judson.

Gilliland, Dean S. Pauline Theology & Mission Practice. 304p. 1983. pap. 12.95 (ISBN 0-8010-3788-3). Baker Bk.

Gordon, Adoniram J. Holy Spirit in Missions. pap. 2.25 (ISBN 0-87509-094-X). Chr Pubns.

Gration, John. Steps to Getting Overseas. 38p. (Orig.). 1986. pap. 1.95 (ISBN 0-87784-203-5). Inter-Varsity.

Gribble, Mercedes & Friedmann, Hope. Two Hundred Rooms in the Inn: The Story of Providence Mission Homes. LC 83-15367. (Illus.). 112p. (Orig.). 1983. pap. 3.95 (ISBN 0-87808-195-X). William Carey Lib.

Griffiths, Michael. Get Your Church Involved in Missions. 1972. pap. 1.00 (ISBN 9971-83-784-6). OMF Bks.

Gurganus, George P., ed. Guidelines for World Evangelism. 1977. 11.95 (ISBN 0-89112-040-8, Bibl Res Pr). Abilene Christ U.

Harrison, William P. Gospel Among the Slaves. LC 70-168249. Repr. of 1893 ed. 27.50 (ISBN 0-404-00263-3). AMS Pr.

Hesselgrave, David J. Planting Churches Cross-Culturally. 1980. pap. 12.95 (ISBN 0-8010-4219-4). Baker Bk.

Hilbert, Frances F. & Paul, G. Case Studies in Missions. 1987. pap. 7.95 (ISBN 0-8010-4308-5). Baker Bk.

Hinson, William H. A Place to Dig In. 1987. 10.95t (ISBN 0-687-31549-2). Abingdon.

Hughes, Amelia. Missions Studies: Bolivia. 32p. (Orig.). 1982. pap. text ed. 1.00 (ISBN 0-89114-109-X). Baptist Pub Hse.

Hulbert, Terry C. World Missions Today. LC 78-68233. 96p. 1979. pap. text ed. 4.95 (ISBN 0-910566-16-X); Perfect bdg. instr's. guide 5.95 (ISBN 0-910566-28-3). Evang Tchr.

Kane, J. Herbert. The Christian World Mission: Today & Tomorrow. 240p. 1981. 13.95 (ISBN 0-8010-5426-5). Baker Bk.

--Life & Work on the Mission Field. LC 80-65010. 1980. 16.95 (ISBN 0-8010-5406-0). Baker Bk.

Kendall, R. T. Once Saved, Always Saved. (Orig.). 1985. pap. 3.95 (ISBN 0-8024-6064-X). Moody.

Lacroix & De Djunkovskoy, E. Dictionnaire des Missions Catholiques, 2 vols. Migne, J. P., ed. (Troisieme et Derniere Encyclopedie Theologique Ser.: Vols. 59-60). (Fr.). 1545p. Repr. of 1864 ed. lib. bdg. 197.50x (ISBN 0-89241-325-5). Caratzas.

Lees, W. C. Second Thoughts on Missions. 1965. pap. 0.95 (ISBN 0-87508-908-9). Chr Lit.

Lewis, Gladys S. On Earth As It Is... LC 83-70006. (Orig.). 1983. pap. 6.50 (ISBN 0-8054-6332-1). Broadman.

Lewis, Karen. From Arapesh to Zuni: A Book of Bibleless Peoples. (Illus.). 31p. 1986. pap. text ed. 4.95 (ISBN 0-938978-07-1). Wycliffe Bible.

Loew, M. R. Mission to the Poorest. 184p. 1984. pap. 7.95 (ISBN 0-7220-5524-2). Chr Classics.

Loewen, Jacob A. Culture & Human Values: Christian Intervention in Anthropological Perspective. Smalley, William A., ed. LC 75-12653. (Applied Cultural Anthropology Ser.). 443p. (Orig.). 1975. pap. 10.95x (ISBN 0-87808-722-2). William Carey Lib.

Lum, Ada. A Hitchhiker's Guide to Missions. LC 84-19149. 144p. 1984. pap. 5.95 (ISBN 0-87784-328-7). Inter-Varsity.

McBeth, Leon. Hombres Claves En las Misiones. Orig. Title: Men Who Made Missions. 128p. 1980. pap. 3.75 (ISBN 0-311-01070-9). Casa Bautista.

MacDonald, Allan J. Trade, Politics & Christianity in Africa & the East. LC 77-89007. Repr. of 1916 ed. lib. bdg. cancelled (ISBN 0-8371-1755-0, MAT&, Pub. by Negro U Pr). Greenwood.

McGavran, Donald A. How Churches Grow. (Orig.). 1965. pap. 6.95 (ISBN 0-377-40011-4). Friend Pr.

--Momentous Decisions in Missions Today. 1984. pap. 11.95 (ISBN 0-8010-6176-8). Baker Bk.

McGee, Gary B. This Gospel...Shall Be Preached: A History & Theology of Assemblies of God Foreign Missions to 1959. LC 86-80015. 288p. (Orig.). 1986. pap. 8.95 (ISBN 0-88243-511-6, 02-0511). Gospel Pub.

Matthews, Reginald L. Missionary Administration in the Local Church. 1972. 3.95 (ISBN 0-87227-002-5); pap. 2.95 (ISBN 0-87227-011-4). Reg Baptist.

Mellis, Charles J. Committed Communities: Fresh Streams for World Missions. LC 76-53548. 1976. pap. 5.95 (ISBN 0-87808-426-6). William Carey Lib.

Missions: A Family Affair, Leader's Guide. (Orig.). 1985. pap. text ed. 3.95 (ISBN 0-934688-20-6). Great Comm Pubns.

Missions Strategy of the Local Church. 10p. 1976. pap. 2.95 (ISBN 0-912552-14-X). Missions Adv Res Com Ctr.

Mott, John R., et al. Student Mission Power: Report of the First International Convention of the Student Volunteer Movement for Foreign Missions, 1891. LC 79-92013. 1979. pap. 6.95 (ISBN 0-87808-736-2). William Carey Lib.

Murray, Andrew & Choy, Leona. Key to the Missionary Problem. (Orig.). 1980. pap. 3.95 (ISBN 0-87508-401-X). Chr Lit.

Nelson, Marlin L., ed. Readings in Third World Missions: A Collection of Essential Documents. LC 76-45803. 1976. pap. 6.95x (ISBN 0-87808-319-7). William Carey Lib.

Nevius, John. Planting & Development of Missionary Churches. 1974. pap. 2.45 (ISBN 0-87552-346-3). Presby & Reformed.

Older, Mrs. Fremont. California Missions & Their Romances. 314p. 1983. Repr. of 1938 ed. lib. bdg. 50.00 (ISBN 0-89987-620-X). Darby Bks.

Parvin, Earl. Missions U. S. A. (Orig.). 1985. pap. text ed. 14.95 (ISBN 0-8024-5975-7). Moody.

Patterson, Frank W. A Short History of Christian Missions. 176p. 1985. pap. 15.95 (ISBN 0-311-72663-1). Casa Bautista.

Pomerville, Paul. The Third Force in Missions. 196p. 1986. pap. 9.95 (ISBN 0-913573-15-9). Hendrickson MA.

Powles, Cyril & Nelson, Rob. Mission Impossible-Unless... (Orig.). 1973. pap. 2.95 (ISBN 0-377-03009-0). Friend Pr.

Provost, James H., ed. Church As Mission. (Permanent Seminar Studies: No. 2). 288p. 1984. pap. 8.00 (ISBN 0-943616-24-7). Canon Law Soc.

Sao Paulo, Brazil Mission Team. Steps into the Mission Field. 1978. 5.95 (ISBN 0-88027-019-5). Firm Foun Pub.

Schindler, Robert & Schindler, Marian. Mission Possible. 168p. 1984. pap. 5.95 (ISBN 0-88207-618-3). Victor Bks.

Scott, Jack B. Missions: A Family Affair. 1985. pap. 4.95 (ISBN 0-934688-15-X). Great Comm Pubns.

Seamands, J. T. Tell It Well. 236p. (Orig.). 1981. pap. 6.95 (ISBN 0-8341-0684-1). Beacon Hill.

Shenk, Wilbert. Anabaptism & Mission. LC 84-12863. (Missionary Study: No. 10). 264p. (Orig.). 1984. pap. 12.95 (ISBN 0-8361-3367-6). Herald Pr.

Shenk, Wilbert R., ed. Mission Focus: Current Issues. LC 80-15686. pap. 122.00 (ISBN 0-317-26607-1, 2025420). Bks Demand UMI.

Simonet, Andre. Apostles for Our Time: Thoughts on Apostolic Spirituality. Bouchard, M. Angeline, tr. from Fr. LC 77-8537. 1977. pap. 4.95 (ISBN 0-8189-0354-6). Alba.

Skoglund, Herbert H. The World Seen. LC 85-80101. 120p. (Orig.). 1985. pap. 3.95 (ISBN 0-935797-18-1). Harvest IL.

Smith, Bertha. Our Lost World. LC 80-68537. 1981. pap. 4.95 (ISBN 0-8054-6324-0). Broadman.

Smith, John C. From Colonialism to World Community: The Church's Pilgrimage. LC 82-12138. 334p. 1982. pap. 8.95 (ISBN 0-664-24452-1, Pub. by Geneva Press). Westminster.

Stamoolis, James J. Eastern Orthodox Mission Theology Today. LC 85-15596. 208p. (Orig.). 1986. pap. 18.95 (ISBN 0-88344-215-9). Orbis Bks.

Starkes, M. Thomas. The Foundation for Missions. LC 80-67460. 1981. pap. 5.50 (ISBN 0-8054-6325-9). Broadman.

--Toward a Theology of Missions. 1984. pap. 5.95 (ISBN 0-89957-055-0). AMG Pubs.

Starling, Allan, ed. Seeds of Promise: World Consultation on Frontier Missions, Edinburgh '80. LC 81-69488. (Illus.). 272p. (Orig.). 1981. pap. 8.95 (ISBN 0-87808-186-0). William Carey Lib.

Stoesz, Samuel J. Church & Missions Alive. 1975. pap. 2.50 (ISBN 0-87509-068-0); leaders guide 0.95 (ISBN 0-87509-069-9). Chr Pubns.

Stransky, Thomas & Anderson, Gerald H., eds. Mission Trends: Liberation Theologies, No. 4. LC 78-70827. (Mission Trend Ser.). 304p. 1979. pap. 4.95 (ISBN 0-8091-2185-9). Paulist Pr.

Truman, George, et al. Narrative of a Visit to the West Indies: In 1840 & 1841. facsimile ed. LC 71-38027. (Black Heritage Library Collection). Repr. of 1844 ed. 15.25 (ISBN 0-8369-8993-7). Ayer Co Pubs.

Vierow, Duain W. On the Move with the Master: A Daily Devotional Guide on World Mission. LC 76-57679. 1977. 4.95 (ISBN 0-87808-155-0). William Carey Lib.

Vincent, M. R. Vincent's Word Studies in th New Testament, 4 vols. 2720p. 49.95 (ISBN 0-917006-30-5). Hendrickson MA.

Warren, Max. I Believe in the Great Commission. (I Believe Ser.). 1976. pap. 4.95 (ISBN 0-8028-1659-2). Eerdmans.

Weninger, Franz X. Die Heilige Mission, & Praktische Winke fur Missionaire. 65.00 (ISBN 0-405-10865-6, 11862). Ayer Co Pubs.

White, Mrs. Bob. Unto the Uttermost. (Illus.). 80p. 1977. pap. 1.00 (ISBN 0-89114-079-4). Baptist Pub Hse.

Wicks, Doug, ed. Forget the Pith Helmet: Perspectives on the Missionary Experience. (Orig.). 1984. pap. 6.95 (ISBN 0-8024-3266-2). Moody.

Wilson, Otto & Barratt, Robert S. Fifty Years' Work with Girls, 1883-1933: A Story of the Florence Crittenton Homes. LC 74-1717. (Children & Youth Ser.: Vol. 12). (Illus.). 513p. 1974. Repr. of 1933 ed. 44.00x (ISBN 0-405-05992-2). Ayer Co Pubs.

Winter, Ralph, frwd. by. I Will Do a New Thing: The Story of the U. S. Center for World Mission. rev. ed. LC 78-66367. Orig. Title: Once More Around Jericho. 320p. 1987. pap. 4.95 (ISBN 0-87808-201-8). William Carey Lib.

MISSIONS–BIBLICAL TEACHING

see also Kerygma

Barnard, Laura B. Biblical Basis of Missions. 32p. 1973. pap. 1.50 (ISBN 0-89265-100-8). Randall Hse.

Devadutt, Vinjamuri E. Bible & the Faiths of Men. (Orig.). 1967. pap. 1.25 (ISBN 0-377-37011-8). Friend Pr.

Goerner, H. Cornell. All Nations in God's Purpose. LC 78-50360. 1979. pap. 4.95 (ISBN 0-8054-6312-7). Broadman.

Means, Frank K. All Nations in God's Purpose: A Study Guide. LC 83-21073. 1984. pap. 4.25 (ISBN 0-8054-6334-8). Broadman.

Peters, George. A Biblical Theology of Missions. LC 72-77952. 384p. 1972. 11.95 (ISBN 0-8024-0706-4). Moody.

Senior, Donald & Stuhlmueller, Carroll. The Biblical Foundations for Mission. LC 82-22430. 384p. (Orig.). 1983. 12.50 (ISBN 0-88344-046-6); pap. 14.95 (ISBN 0-88344-047-4). Orbis Bks.

MISSIONS–BIBLIOGRAPHY

Ericson, Jack T., ed. Missionary Society of Connecticut Papers, 1759-1948: A Guide to the Microform Edition. 49p. 1976. pap. 15.00 (ISBN 0-667-00289-8). Microfilming Corp.

Horvath, David G., ed. Papers of the American Home Missionary Society, 1816 (1826-1894) 1936: A Guide to the Microfilm Edition. 94p. 1975. pap. 50.00 (ISBN 0-88455-994-7). Microfilming Corp.

Missionary Research Library. New York Dictionary Catalog of the Missionary Research Library, 17 vols. 1968. Set. 1680.00 (ISBN 0-8161-0778-5, Hall Library). G K Hall.

MISSIONS–EDUCATIONAL WORK

Schipani, Daniel S. El Reino de Dios y el Ministerio Educativo de la Iglesia. (Span.). 213p. 1984. pap. 5.50 (ISBN 0-89922-232-3). Edit Caribe.

Stone, Frank A. Academies for Anatolia: A Study of the Rationale, Program & Impact of the Educational Institutions Sponsored by the American Board in Turkey: 1830-1980. (Illus.). 384p. 1984. lib. bdg. 32.75 (ISBN 0-8191-4064-3). U Pr of Amer.

Terry, Robert H. Light in the Valley: The McCurdy Mission School Story. LC 84-50388. (Illus.). 148p. (Orig.). 1984. pap. 9.95 (ISBN 0-86534-051-X). Sunstone Pr.

MISSIONS–HISTORY

Eddy, George S. Pathfinders of the World Missionary Crusade. facs. ed. LC 76-84304. (Essay Index Reprint Ser). 1945. 20.25 (ISBN 0-8369-1127-X). Ayer Co Pubs.

Fear, Leona K. New Ventures-Free Methodist Missions Nineteen Sixty to Nineteen Seventy-Nine. (Orig.). 1979. pap. 1.50 (ISBN 0-89367-036-7). Light & Life.

Filbeck, David. The First Fifty Years. LC 80-65966. 336p. 1980. pap. cancelled (ISBN 0-89900-060-6). College Pr Pub.

Kane, J. Herbert. Global View of Christian Missions. 1971. 19.95 (ISBN 0-8010-5308-0). Baker Bk.

Karotempel, Sebastian. Albizuri Among the Lyngams: A Brief History of the Catholic Mission Among the Lyngams on North East India. 1986. 17.50x (ISBN 0-8364-1569-8, Pub. by KL Mukhopadhyay). South Asia Bks.

Kverndal, Roald. Seamen's Missions: Their Origins & Early Growth. LC 85-25508. (Illus.). 936p. 1987. text ed. 29.95x (ISBN 0-87808-440-1, WCL440-1); pap. text ed. cancelled (ISBN 0-87808-439-8, WCL439-8). William Carey Lib.

Kyle, John E., compiled by. The Unfinished Task. LC 84-11727. 1984. pap. 6.95 (ISBN 0-8307-0983-5, 5418342). Regal.

Lacordaire, Henry D. Henri Dominique Lacordaire: Essay on the Re-establishment in France of the Order of Preachers. Tugwell, Simon, ed. (Dominican Sources). 70p. 1983. pap. 4.00 (ISBN 0-9511202-1-2). Parable.

McBeth, Leon. Hombres Claves En las Misiones. Orig. Title: Men Who Made Missions. 128p. 1980. pap. 3.75 (ISBN 0-311-01070-9). Casa Bautista.

Mangham, Evelyn. Great Missionaries in a Great Work. Schroeder, E. H., ed. (Illus.). 85p. 1970. pap. 1.75 (ISBN 0-87509-091-5). Chr Pubns.

Motte, Mary & Lang, Joseph R., eds. Mission in Dialogue: The Sedos Research Seminar on the Future of Mission. LC 82-2258. 704p. (Orig.). 1982. 35.00 (ISBN 0-88344-332-5). Orbis Bks.

Murray, Andrew & Choy, Leona. Key to the Missionary Problem. (Orig.). 1980. pap. 3.95 (ISBN 0-87508-401-X). Chr Lit.

Neill, Stephen. History of Christian Missions. (History of the Church Ser.: Vol. 6). (Orig.). 1964. pap. 5.95 (ISBN 0-14-020628-0, Pelican). Penguin.

--The Pelican History of the Church: A History of the Christian Missions, Vol. 6. 512p. 1987. pap. 6.95 (ISBN 0-14-022736-9, Pelican). Penguin.

Pardington, G. P. Twenty-Five Wonderful Years, Eighteen Eighty-Nine to Nineteen Fourteen: A Popular Sketch of the Christian & Missionary Alliance. Dayton, Donald W., ed. (The Higher Christian Life Ser.). 238p. 1985. 30.00 (ISBN 0-8240-6435-6). Garland Pub.

Smalley, William A., ed. Readings in Missionary Anthropology II. 2nd rev. enl. ed. LC 78-6009. (Applied Cultural Anthropology Ser.). 1978. pap. text ed. 13.95x (ISBN 0-87808-731-1). William Carey.

Tracy, Joseph, et al, eds. History of American Missions to the Heathens from Their Commencement to the Present Time. LC 35-32346. (American Studies). 1970. Repr. of 1840 ed. 45.00 (ISBN 0-384-23460-7). Johnson Repr.

Tucker, Ruth. From Jerusalem to Irian Jaya: A Biographical History of Christian Missions. 1986. pap. 14.95 (ISBN 0-310-45931-1, 12723P). Zondervan.

MISSIONS–JUVENILE LITERATURE

Butler, Mary & Butler, Trent. The John Allen Moores: Good News in War & Peace. LC 85-6656. (Meet the Missionary Ser.). 1985. 5.50 (ISBN 0-8054-4295-2, 4242-95). Broadman.

Missions, Basic: Questions & Answers. (Teaching Bks.). (Illus.). 10p. (Orig.). 1970. pap. text ed. 2.95 (ISBN 0-86508-156-5). BCM Intl Inc.

Taylor, Richard K. A Peace Ministry in Practice. (YA) 1986. pap. 3.95 (ISBN 0-697-02205-6). Wm C Brown.

MISSIONS–SERMONS

To the Ends of the Earth: A Pastoral Statement on the Missions. 1987. pap. 3.95 (ISBN 1-55586-112-1). US Catholic.

MISSIONS–STUDY AND TEACHING

Grunlan, Stephen A. & Mayers, Marvin K. Cultural Anthropology: A Christian Perspective. 1979. 9.95 (ISBN 0-310-36321-7, 11280P). Zondervan.

Kauffman, Richard A. Pilgrimage in Mission: Leader's Guide. 60p. 1983. pap. 4.95x (ISBN 0-8361-1260-1). Herald Pr.

MISSIONS–THEORY

Brock, Charles. The Principles & Practice of Indigenous Church Planting. 1981. pap. 4.25 (ISBN 0-8054-6328-3). Broadman.

Danielou, Jean. Salvation of the Nations. 1962. pap. 1.25x (ISBN 0-268-00244-4). U of Notre Dame Pr.

DuBose, Francis M. God Who Sends. LC 83-70002. 1983. 10.95 (ISBN 0-8054-6331-3). Broadman.

Liao, David. The Unresponsive: Resistant or Neglected? The Hakka Chinese in Taiwan Illustrate the Homogeneous Unit Principle. LC 73-175494. 1979. pap. 5.95 (ISBN 0-87808-735-4). William Carey Lib.

Pentecost, Edward C. Issues in Missiology. LC 82-70467. 192p. 1982. 11.95 (ISBN 0-8010-7071-6). Baker Bk.

Peters, George. A Biblical Theology of Missions. LC 72-77952. 384p. 1972. 11.95 (ISBN 0-8024-0706-4). Moody.

Scott, Waldron. Karl Barth's Theology of Mission. Bockmuehl, Klaus, ed. (World Evangelical Fellowship: Outreach & Identity Theological Monograph). 40p. 1978. pap. 1.95 (ISBN 0-87784-541-7). Inter-Varsity.

Tippett, Alan R. Introduction to Missiology. LC 86-9605. 300p. (Orig.). 1987. pap. text ed. 15.95x (ISBN 0-87808-206-9, WCL206-9). William Carey Lib.

To the Ends of the Earth: A Pastoral Statement on the Missions. 1987. pap. 3.95 (ISBN 1-55586-112-1). US Catholic.

Webster, Douglas. Yes to Mission. LC 66-72166. 1966. text ed. 6.00x (ISBN 0-8401-2703-0). A R Allenson.

MISSIONS–AFRICA

Aubin, Pierre & Cotter, George. Agencies for Project Assistance: Sources of Support for Small Church & or Lay Sponsored Projects in Africa, Asia, Latin America & the Pacific. 2nd ed. (Illus.). 330p. 1984. pap. 50.00 (ISBN 0-913671-03-7). Mission Proj Serv.

Brookes, Edgar H. & Vandenbosch, Amry. The City of God & the City of Man in Africa. LC 64-13998. (Illus.). 144p. 1964. 12.00x (ISBN 0-8131-1091-2). U Pr of Ky.

Buhlmann, Walbert. The Missions on Trial. Dolan, A. P., tr. from Fr. & Ger. LC 78-23922. Orig. Title: Missions prozess in Addis Abeba. 160p. (Orig.). 1979. pap. 2.98 (ISBN 0-88344-316-3). Orbis Bks.

Campbell, Penelope. Maryland in Africa: The Maryland State Colonization Society, 1831-1857. LC 75-131058. pap. 68.00 (ISBN 0-317-41903-X, 2025915). Bks Demand UMI.

Hastings, Adrian. Church & Mission in Modern Africa. LC 67-30321. (Orig.). 1967. 25.00 (ISBN 0-8232-0770-6). Fordham.

Imam Alhaji Obaba Muhammadu. The African Islamic Mission. 38p. (Orig.). 1982. pap. 1.00 (ISBN 0-916157-04-0). African Islam Miss Pubns.

Johnston, James. Missionary Landscapes in the Dark Continent. LC 72-3911. (Black Heritage Library Collection Ser.). Repr. of 1892 ed. 16.00 (ISBN 0-8369-9100-1). Ayer Co Pubs.

Keim, Curtis A. & Brown, Howard. Missions in Africa: Relevant or Relic? A Conference. (African Humanities Ser.). 89p. (Orig.). 1980. pap. text ed. 5.00 (ISBN 0-941934-30-6). Indiana Africa.

Kendrick, V. Ben. Buried Alive for Christ & Other Missionary Stories. LC 78-14984. 1978. pap. 3.95 (ISBN 0-87227-061-0). Reg Baptist.

Kenya Mission Team. Church Planting, Watering & Increasing in Kenya. Humble, B. J., ed. (Illus.). 130p. 1981. pap. 2.95 (ISBN 0-88027-002-0). Firm Foun Pub.

Markowitz, Marvin D. Cross & Sword: The Political Role of Christian Missions in the Belgian Congo, 1908-1960. LC 75-170209. (Publications Ser.: No. 114). 1973. 13.50x (ISBN 0-8179-1141-3). Hoover Inst Pr.

Mole, Winifred A. So Dear to Me. 1985. 11.95 (ISBN 0-533-06486-4). Vantage.

Mondini, A. G. Africa or Death. (Illus.). 1964. 5.00 (ISBN 0-8198-0007-4). Dghtrs St Paul.

Morrison, James H. Missionary Heroes of Africa. LC 79-89010. Repr. of 1922 ed. 22.50x (ISBN 0-8371-1738-0, MOM&, Pub. by Negro U Pr). Greenwood.

Oduyoye, Mercy A. Hearing & Knowing: Theological Reflections on Christianity in Africa. LC 85-29873. 176p. (Orig.). 1986. pap. 9.95 (ISBN 0-88344-258-2). Orbis Bks.

Richardson, James. Narrative of a Mission to Central Africa: 1850-1851, 2 vols. (Illus.). 704p. 1970. Repr. of 1853 ed. 95.00x set (ISBN 0-7146-1848-9, BHA-01848, F Cass Co). Biblio Dist.

Schmelzenbach, Elmer & Parrott, Leslie. Sons of Africa. 217p. 1979. 8.95 (ISBN 0-8341-0601-9). Beacon Hill.

Schon, James F. & Crowther, Samuel. Journals of the Rev. James Frederick Schon & Mr. Samuel Crowther Who with the Sanction of Her Majesty's Government; Accompanied the Expedition Up the Niger in 1841 on Behalf of the Church Missionary Society. 2nd ed. 394p. 1970. 37.50x (ISBN 0-7146-1877-2, F Cass Co). Biblio Dist.

Van Horne, John C., ed. & intro. by. Religious Philanthropy & Colonial Slavery: The American Correspondence of the Associates of Dr. Bray, 1717-1777. LC 84-2766. (Blacks in the New World Ser.). 400p. 1985. 29.95 (ISBN 0-252-01142-2). U of Ill Pr.

Westermann, Diedrich. Africa & Christianity. LC 74-15102. (Duff Lectures, 1935). Repr. of 1937 ed. 24.50 (ISBN 0-404-12151-9). AMS Pr.

Williams, Lima L. Walking in Missionary Shoes. 1986. pap. 14.95 (ISBN 0-87162-417-6, D8750). Warner Pr.

Williams, Walter L. Black Americans & the Evangelization of Africa, 1877-1900. LC 81-69830. 282p. 1982. text ed. 32.50x (ISBN 0-299-08920-7). U of Wis Pr.

MISSIONS–AFRICA, CENTRAL

Arnot, Frederick S. Garenganze or Seven Years' Pioneer Mission Work in Central Africa. 2nd, rev. ed. (Illus.). 276p. 1969. 29.50x (ISBN 0-7146-1860-8, BHA 01860, F Cass Co). Biblio Dist.

Bowen, T. J. Adventures & Missionary Labours in Several Countries in the Interior of Africa from 1849-1856. 2nd rev. ed. 359p. 1968. Repr. of 1857 ed. 32.50x (ISBN 0-7146-1863-2, F Cass Co). Biblio Dist.

Fuller, Millard. Bokotola. LC 77-1277. 1978. pap. 5.95 (ISBN 0-8329-1179-8). New Century.

Jack, James W. Daybreak in Livingstonia: The Story of the Livingstonia Mission, British Central Africa. rev. ed. LC 79-77204. (Illus.). Repr. of 1900 ed. cancelled (ISBN 0-8371-1308-3, JAL&, Pub. by Negro U Pr). Greenwood.

Linden, Ian & Linden, Jane. Church & Revolution in Rwanda. LC 76-58329. 295p. 1977. text ed. 39.50x (ISBN 0-8419-0305-0, Africana). Holmes & Meier.

Wendland, E. H. Of Other Gods & Other Spirits. 1977. pap. 4.95 (ISBN 0-8100-0034-2, 12-1711). Northwest Pub.

MISSIONS–AFRICA, EAST

Beidelman, T. O. Colonial Evangelism: A Socio-Historical Study of an East African Mission at the Grassroots. LC 81-47771. (Midland Bks. Ser.: No. 278). (Illus.). 296p. 1982. 29.95x (ISBN 0-253-31386-4); pap. 12.50x (ISBN 0-253-20278-7). Ind U Pr.

Gregory, John W. Foundation of British East Africa. LC 78-88412. Repr. of 1901 ed. cancelled (ISBN 0-8371-1727-5, GRB&, Pub. by Negro U Pr). Greenwood.

Healey, Joseph G. A Fifth Gospel: The Experience of Black Christian Values. LC 80-25033. (Illus.). 220p. (Orig.). 1981. pap. 3.98 (ISBN 0-88344-013-X). Orbis Bks.

Knapp, Doug, et al. Thunder in the Valley. (Orig.). 1986. pap. 6.95 (ISBN 0-8054-6342-9). Broadman.

Macdonald, Duff. Africana, or, the Heart of Heathen Africa, 2 Vols. LC 70-82058. (Illus.). Repr. of 1882 ed. 14.50x (ISBN 0-8371-1523-X, MAA&, Pub. by Negro U Pr). Greenwood.

Pringle, M. A. Journey in East Africa: Towards the Mountains of the Moon. new ed. LC 72-3957. (Black Heritage Library Collection Ser.). Repr. of 1886 ed. 27.50 (ISBN 0-8369-9105-2). Ayer Co Pubs.

Tucker, Alfred R. Eighteen Years in Uganda & East Africa. LC 77-106884. Repr. of 1911 ed. cancelled (ISBN 0-8371-3280-0, TUU&, Pub. by Negro U Pr). Greenwood.

MISSIONS–AFRICA, SOUTH

Livingston, David. Missionary Travels & Researches in South Africa. LC 5-15250. 1971. Repr. of 1857 ed. 62.00 (ISBN 0-384-32983-7). Johnson Repr.

Moffat, Robert. Missionary Labours & Scenes in Southern Africa. (Landmarks in Anthropology Ser). (Illus.). 1969. Repr. of 1842 ed. 32.00 (ISBN 0-384-39470-1). Johnson Repr.

Philip, John. Researches in South Africa, 2 vols. LC 77-82065. (Illus.). Repr. of 1828 ed. 33.00x (ISBN 0-8371-3855-8, PHR&). Greenwood.

Shaw, Barnabas. Memorials of South Africa. LC 71-109358. Repr. of 1840 ed. cancelled (ISBN 0-8371-3737-3, SMS&, Pub. by Negro U Pr). Greenwood.

MISSIONS–AFRICA, WEST

Barrow, Alfred. Fifty Years in Western Africa. LC 79-92739. Repr. of 1900 ed. cancelled (ISBN 0-8371-2193-0, BAW&, Pub. by Negro U Pr). Greenwood.

Hening, Mrs. E. F. History of the African Mission of the Protestant Episcopal Church in the United States. facsimile ed. LC 77-173608. (Black Heritage Library Collection). Repr. of 1849 ed. 20.75 (ISBN 0-8369-8900-7). Ayer Co Pubs.

Scott, Anna M. Day Dawn in Africa: Or Progress of the Protestant Episcopal Mission at Cape Palmas, West Africa. LC 69-18659. (Illus.). Repr. of 1858 ed. cancelled (ISBN 0-8371-5091-4, SCD&, Pub. by Negro U Pr). Greenwood.

MISSIONS–ALASKA

Aaron Ladner Lindsley: Founder of Alaska Missions. (Shorey Historical Ser.). 9p. pap. 2.25 (ISBN 0-8466-0050-1, S50). Shorey.

Crandall, Faye E. Into the Copper River Valley. 1983. 9.95 (ISBN 0-8062-2025-2). Carlton.

Savage, Alma H. Dogsled Apostles. facs. ed. LC 68-55857. (Essay Index Reprint Ser). 1942. 18.00 (ISBN 0-8369-0851-1). Ayer Co Pubs.

MISSIONS–ASIA

Aubin, Pierre & Cotter, George. Agencies for Project Assistance: Sources of Support for Small Church & or Lay Sponsored Projects in Africa, Asia, Latin America & the Pacific. 2nd ed. (Illus.). 330p. 1984. pap. 50.00 (ISBN 0-913671-03-7). Mission Proj Serv.

Chase, Barbara H. & Man, Martha L., eds. Spirit & Struggle in Southern Asia. 105p. (Orig.). 1986. pap. 5.95 (ISBN 0-377-00157-0). Friend Pr.

Hyatt, Irwin T., Jr. Our Ordered Lives Confess. (American-East Asian Relations Ser.: No. 8). 1976. 20.00x (ISBN 0-674-64735-1). Harvard U Pr.

Mathews, Basil J., ed. East & West: Conflict or Cooperation. facs. ed. LC 67-26764. (Essay Index Reprint Ser). 1936. 14.25 (ISBN 0-8369-0694-2). Ayer Co Pubs.

Meersman, Achilles. The Franciscans in the Indonesian Archipelago, 1300-1775. 1967. pap. 49.50x (ISBN 0-317-27470-8). Elliots Bks.

Mueller, John T. Great Missionaries to the Orient. LC 78-38330. (Biography Index Reprint Ser). Repr. of 1948 ed. 14.75 (ISBN 0-8369-8125-1). Ayer Co Pubs.

Wagner, C. Peter, et al. Unreached Peoples, Eighty-One. (Orig.). 1981. pap. 8.95 (ISBN 0-89191-331-9). Cook.

MISSIONS–AUSTRALIA

Hughes, Amelia. Missions Studies: Australia. (Illus.). 32p. (Orig.). 1984. pap. 1.00 (ISBN 0-89114-117-0). Baptist Pub Hse.

Mole, Winifred A. So Dear to Me. 1985. 11.95 (ISBN 0-533-06486-4). Vantage.

Perez, Eugene. Kalumburu: The Benedictine Mission & the Aborigines 1908-1975. (Illus.). 1978. pap. 15.00x (ISBN 0-9596887-0-6, Pub. by U of W Austral Pr). Intl Spec Bk.

Wright, Don. Mantle of Christ: A History of the Sydney Central Methodist Mission. (Illus.). 179p. 1985. text ed. 25.00x. U of Queensland Pr.

MISSIONS–BAHAMAS

Davis, Kortright. Mission for Caribbean Change. (IC-Studies in the Intercultural History of Christianity: Vol. 28). 300p. 1982. pap. 32.10 (ISBN 3-8204-5732-1). P Lang Pubs.

MISSIONS–BOLIVIA

Smith, W. Douglas. Toward Continuous Misson: Strategizing for the Evangelization of Bolivia. LC 77-21490. 1978. pap. 4.95 (ISBN 0-87808-321-9). William Carey Lib.

MISSIONS–BRAZIL

Barnes, Vera F. Miles Beyond in Brazil. 3.50 (ISBN 0-87509-104-0); pap. 2.00 (ISBN 0-87509-105-9). Chr Pubns.

Beasley, Mrs. Jim. Missions Studies: Brazil. (Illus.). 32p. (Orig.). 1985. pap. 1.00 (ISBN 0-89114-155-3). Baptist Pub Hse.

Edwards, Fred E. The Role of the Faith Mission: A Brazilian Case Study. LC 79-152406. (Illus.). 76p. 1971. pap. 3.45 (ISBN 0-87808-406-1). William Carey Lib.

Steven, Hugh. To the Ends of the Earth. 2nd ed. 142p. 1986. pap. 3.10 (ISBN 0-938978-31-4). Wycliffe Bible.

MISSIONS–BURMA

Andrews, C. W. Memoire of Mrs. Ann R. Page. De Swarte, Carolyn G. & Dayton, Donald, eds. (Women in American Protestant Religion Series 1800-1930). 95p. 1987. lib. bdg. 25.00 (ISBN 0-8240-0657-7). Garland Pub.

Hare, Eric B. Fullness of Joy. 1985. pap. 5.95 (ISBN 0-8163-0586-2). Pacific Pr Pub Assn.

Tegenfeldt, Herman. A Century of Growth: The Kachin Baptist Church of Burma. LC 74-4415. 540p. 1974. 10.95 (ISBN 0-87808-416-9). William Carey Lib.

MISSIONS–CANADA

Brasseur De Bourbourg, E. Ch. Histoire de Canada, de Son Eglise et De Ses Missions. (Canadiana Avant 1867: No. 4). 1968. 44.40x (ISBN 90-2796-333-9). Mouton.

Faraud, Henri J. Dix-Huit Ans Chez Les Sauvages: Voyages Et Missions De Monseigneur Henry Faraud. Repr. of 1866 ed. 28.00 (ISBN 0-384-15135-3). Johnson Repr.

Marsden, Joshua. The Narrative of a Mission to Nova Scotia, New Brunswick & the Somers Islands. Repr. of 1816 ed. 25.00 (ISBN 0-384-35430-0). Johnson Repr.

Pritchett, John P. Black Robe & Buckskin. 1960. 12.95x (ISBN 0-8084-0063-0); pap. 8.95 (ISBN 0-8084-0064-9). New Coll U Pr.

Tache, Alexandre A. Vingt Annees De Missions Dans le Nord-Ouest De L'amerique. (Canadiana Before 1867 Ser). (Fr). Repr. of 1866 ed. 18.00 (ISBN 0-384-59425-5). Johnson Repr.

--Vingt Annees De Missions Dans le Nord-Ouest De L'amerique Par Mgr. Alex. Tache Eveque De Saint-Boniface (Montreal, 1866) (Canadiana Avant 1867: N0. 21). 1970. 16.80x (ISBN 90-2796-343-6). Mouton.

MISSIONS–CHINA

Aylward, Gladys. La Pequena Gran Mujer en la China. Orig. Title: Little Woman in China. (Span.). 160p. 1974. pap. 3.50 (ISBN 0-8254-1048-7). Kregel.

Barr, Pat. To China With Love: The Lives & Times of Protestant Missionaries in China, 1860-1900. 1972. 16.95 (ISBN 0-436-03355-0, Pub. by Secker & Warburg UK). David & Charles.

Bohr, Paul R. Famine in China & the Missionary: Timothy Richard As Relief Administrator & Advocate of National Reform, 1876-1884. LC 72-75828. (East Asian Monographs Ser: No. 48). (Illus.). 1972. pap. 11.00x (ISBN 0-674-29425-4). Harvard U Pr.

Carlson, Ellsworth C. The Foochow Missionaries, 1847-1880. LC 72-97832. (East Asian Monographs Ser: No. 51). 1973. pap. 20.00x (ISBN 0-674-30735-6). Harvard U Pr.

Cohen, Paul A. China & Christianity: The Missionary Movement & the Growth of Chinese Antiforeignism, 1860-1870. LC 63-19135. (East Asian Ser: No. 11). (Illus.). 1963. 27.50x (ISBN 0-674-11701-8). Harvard U Pr.

Covell, Ralph. W. A. P Martin: Pioneer of Progress in China. LC 77-13321. Repr. of 1978 ed. 59.10 (ISBN 0-8357-9133-5, 2012723). Bks Demand UMI.

Crawley, Winston. Partners Across the Pacific. LC 85-29088. 1986. pap. 4.95 (ISBN 0-8054-6341-0). Broadman.

Dunne, George H. Generation of Giants. 1962. 19.95 (ISBN 0-268-00109-X). U of Notre Dame Pr.

Edwards, E. H. Fire & Sword in Shansi: The Story of the Martyrdom of Foreigners & Chinese Christians. LC 74-111738. (American Imperialism: Viewpoints of United States Foreign Policy, 1898-1941). 1970. Repr. of 1903 ed. 21.00 (ISBN 0-405-02014-7). Ayer Co Pubs.

Fairbank, John K., ed. The Missionary Enterprise in China & America. LC 74-82191. (Studies in American-East Asian Relations: No. 6). 442p. 1974. text ed. 25.00x (ISBN 0-674-57655-1). Harvard U Pr.

Forster, Roger T. & Marston, V. Paul. God's Strategy in Human History. Tseng, Chen C., tr. from Eng. (Chinese.). 1986. write for info. (ISBN 0-941598-92-6); pap. write for info. (ISBN 0-941598-09-8). Living Spring Pubns.

Forsythe, Sidney A. An American Missionary Community in China, 1895-1905. LC 70-178077. (East Asian Monographs Ser: No. 43). 1971. pap. 11.00x (ISBN 0-674-02626-8). Harvard U Pr.

Gamblin, Eleanor & Morehouse, Joyce M. The Sparrow's Song. Wallace, Mary H., ed. 192p. (Orig.). 1984. pap. 5.95 (ISBN 0-912315-68-7). Word Aflame.

Goforth, Rosalind. Goforth of China. 384p. 1969. pap. 4.95 (ISBN 0-87123-181-6, 200181). Bethany Hse.

Greene, Ruth A. Hsiang-Ya Journal. LC 76-28526. Repr. of 1977 ed. 36.70 (2011504). Bks Demand UMI.

Gulick, Edward V. Peter Parker & the Opening of China. LC 73-82628. (Harvard Studies in American-East Asian Relations: No. 3). 228p. 1974. text ed. 17.50x (ISBN 0-674-66326-8). Harvard U Pr.

Head, William. Yenan: Colonel Peterkin's Dixie Mission to China. 1986. write for info. (ISBN 0-89712-175-9). Documentary Pubns.

Hsiang, Paul Stanislaus. The Catholic Missions in China During the Middle Ages: 1294-1368, No. 37. (Studies in Sacred Theology, Second Series). 57p. 1983. Repr. of 1949 ed. 12.00x (ISBN 0-939738-32-5). Zubal Inc.

Hunter, Jane. The Gospel of Gentility: American Women Missionaries in Turn-of-the Century-China. LC 83-16668. 352p. 1984. 27.50x (ISBN 0-300-02878-4). Yale U Pr.

Koll, Elsie. The Golden Thread: Diary of Mrs. Elsie Koll, Missionary to China. Scales, John L., ed. (Illus.). 180p. (Orig.). 1982. pap. 4.95 (ISBN 0-942504-00-3). Overcomer Pr.

Latourette, Kenneth S. History of Christian Missions in China. LC 66-24721. 1967. Repr. of 1929 ed. 22.50x (ISBN 0-8462-0992-6). Russell.

Liu Kwang-Ching, ed. American Missionaries in China: Papers from Harvard Seminars. LC 66-31226. (East Asian Monographs Ser: No. 21). 1966. pap. 11.00x (ISBN 0-674-02600-4). Harvard U Pr.

Medhurst, W. H. China: Its State & Prospects with Special Reference to the Spread of the Gospel. LC 72-79833. (The China Library Ser.). 1972. Repr. of 1842 ed. 42.00 (ISBN 0-8420-1379-2). Scholarly Res Inc.
Mensendiek, C. William. Not Without Struggle. (Illus.). 236p. 1986. 16.95 (ISBN 0-8298-0586-9). Pilgrim NY.
Mueller, John T. Great Missionaries to China. LC 73-38329. (Biography Index Reprint Ser). Repr. of 1947 ed. 12.75 (ISBN 0-8369-8124-3). Ayer Co Pubs.
Park, Polly, ed. To Save Their Heathen Souls: Voyage to & Life in Foochow, China, Based on Wentworth Diaries & Letters, 1854-1858. (Pittsburgh Theological Monographs: New Ser. 9). (Illus., Orig.). 1984. pap. 10.00 (ISBN 0-915138-66-2). Pickwick.
Rabe, Valentin H. The Home Base of American China Missions, 1880-1920. (Harvard East Asian Monographs: Vol. 75). 1978. 21.00x (ISBN 0-674-40581-1). Harvard U Pr.
Ricci, Matteo. The True Meaning of the Lord of Heaven. Lancashire, Douglas & Hu Kuo-chen, Peter, trs. Malatesta, Edward J., ed. LC 84-80944. (Jesuit Primary Sources in English Translations Series I: No. 6). (Eng. & Chinese., Illus.). 300p. 1985. 39.00 (ISBN 0-912422-78-5); smyth sewn 34.00 (ISBN 0-912422-77-7). Inst Jesuit.
Smith, Bertha. Go Home & Tell. LC 65-10342. (Orig.). 1964. pap. 5.50 (ISBN 0-8054-7202-9). Broadman.
Taylor, Alice H. Rescued from the Dragon. 199p. (Orig.). 1982. pap. 5.25 (ISBN 0-89367-078-2). Light & Life.
Varg, Paul A. Missionaries, Chinese & Diplomats. LC 76-30301. 1977. Repr. lib. bdg. 23.00x (ISBN 0-374-98071-3, Octagon). Hippocrene Bks.
West, Philip. Yenching University & Sino-Western Relations, 1916-1952. (East Asian Ser.: No. 85). 1976. 18.50x (ISBN 0-674-96569-8). Harvard U Pr.
Widmer, Eric. The Russian Ecclestastical Mission in Peking During the Eighteenth Century. (East Asian Monographs: No. 69). 1976. 21.00x (ISBN 0-674-78129-5). Harvard U Pr.
Wu, Chao-Kwang. The International Aspect of the Missionary Movement in China. LC 75-41300. (Johns Hopkins University. Studies in Historical & Political Science: Extra Volumes; New Ser.: No. 11). Repr. of 1930 ed. 18.50 (ISBN 0-404-14708-9). AMS Pr.
Wyker, Bertha P. Spanning the Decades: A Spiritual Pilgrimage. (Illus.). 224p. 1981. 8.50 (ISBN 0-682-49746-0). Exposition Pr FL.

MISSIONS–COLOMBIA

Thompson, Mollie. When You're in You're Out. LC 86-10977. (Illus.). 192p. (Orig.). 1986. pap. 5.95 (ISBN 0-932581-50-1). Word Aflame.

MISSIONS–CONGO

Bently, W. Holman. Pioneering on the Congo, 2 Vols. (Landmarks in Anthropology Ser). 1970. Repr. of 1900 ed. Set. lib. bdg. 85.00 (ISBN 0-384-03943-X). Johnson Repr.
Rodeheaver, Homer A. Singing Black. LC 72-1681. Repr. of 1936 ed. 12.50 (ISBN 0-404-08330-7). AMS Pr.

MISSIONS–EAST (FAR EAST)

Richter, Julius. History of Protestant Missions in the Near East. LC 79-133822. Repr. of 1910 ed. 29.50 (ISBN 0-404-05331-9). AMS Pr.

MISSIONS–ECUADOR

Elliot, Elisabeth. Through Gates of Splendor. 1981. 3.95 (ISBN 0-8423-7151-6). Tyndale.

MISSIONS–ETHIOPIA

Bakke, Johnny. Evangelical Ministry in Ethiopia: The Ethiopian Evangelical Church Mekana Yesus. (Studia Missionalia Upsaliensia). 96p. 1987. text ed. price not set (ISBN 0-391-03544-4, Pub. by Solum Verlag). Humanities.
Collins, Jodie. Codeword Catherine. 384p. cancelled (ISBN 0-8423-0302-2). Tyndale.

MISSIONS–EUROPE

Brother Andrew, et al. God's Smuggler. (Illus.). 224p. 1968. pap. 2.95 (ISBN 0-8007-8016-7, Spire Bks); pap. 0.79 (ISBN 0-8007-8501-0, Spire Comics). Revell.
Koop, Allen V. American Evangelical Missionaries in France, 1945-1975. (Illus.). 220p. (Orig.). 1986. lib. bdg. 27.00 (ISBN 0-8191-5204-8); pap. text ed. 13.50 (ISBN 0-8191-5205-6). U Pr of Amer.
Maclear, George F. Apostles of Mediaeval Europe. LC 72-624. (Essay Index Reprint Ser.). Repr. of 1869 ed. 21.50 (ISBN 0-8369-2803-2). Ayer Co Pubs.
Sherrill, J., et al. God's Smuggler. 1968. pap. 2.95 (ISBN 0-451-13254-8, AE3254, Sig). NAL.

MISSIONS–FIJI ISLANDS

Fischer, Edward. Fiji Revisited: A Columbian Father's Memories of Twenty-Eight Years in the Islands. LC 81-5365. (Illus.). 1981. 10.95 (ISBN 0-8245-0097-0). Crossroad NY.
Murray, Thomas. Pitcairn's Island. LC 72-281. (World History Ser., No. 48). 1972. Repr. of 1860 ed. lib. bdg. 52.95x (ISBN 0-8383-1410-4). Haskell.

MISSIONS–FINLAND

The English Missionaries in Sweden & Finland. (Church Historical Society, London, Ser.: No. 27). Repr. of 1937 ed. 55.00 (ISBN 0-8115-3151-1). Kraus Repr.
Oppermann, Charles J. English Missionaries in Sweden & Finland. LC 38-16784. (Church Historical Society Ser.: No. 26). 1937. 17.50x (ISBN 0-281-00240-1). A R Allenson.

MISSIONS–GABON

Klein, Carol M. We Went to Gabon. 1974. pap. 2.95 (ISBN 0-87509-151-2). Chr Pubns.

MISSIONS–INDIA

Anderson, Emma D. & Campbell, Mary J. In the Shadow of the Himalayas: A Historical Narrative of the Missions of the United Presbyterian Church of North America as Conducted in the Punjab, India 1855-1940. 373p. 1983. Repr. of 1942 ed. lib. bdg. 45.00 (ISBN 0-89987-042-2). Darby Bks.
Barnard, Laura B. & Hill, Georgia. Touching the Untouchables. 224p. 1985. pap. 6.95 (ISBN 0-8423-7296-2). Tyndale.
Carmichael, Amy. Gold Cord. 1957. pap. 5.95 (ISBN 0-87508-068-5). Chr Lit.
--Mimosa. 1958. pap. 2.95 (ISBN 0-87508-074-X). Chr Lit.
Chase, Barbara H. & Man, Martha L., eds. Spirit & Struggle in Southern Asia. 105p. (Orig.). 1986. pap. 5.95 (ISBN 0-377-00157-0). Friend Pr.
Doig, Desmond. Mother Teresa: Her Work & Her People. LC 75-39857. (Illus.). 176p. 1980. pap. 11.95 (ISBN 0-06-061941-4, RD336, HarpR). Har-Row.
Ingham, Kenneth. Reformers in India, 1793-1833: An Account of the Work of Christian Missionaries on Behalf of Social Reform. LC 73-16425. xi, 150p. 1973. Repr. of 1956 ed. lib. bdg. 17.00x (ISBN 0-374-94112-2, Octagon). Hippocrene Bks.
Karotemprel, Sebastian. Albizuri Among the Lyngams: A Brief History of the Catholic Mission Among the Lyngams on North East India. 1986. 17.50x (ISBN 0-8364-1569-8, Pub. by KL Mukhopadhyay). South Asia Bks.
Muggeridge, Malcolm. Something Beautiful for God. 312p. 1985. pap. 8.95 (ISBN 0-8027-2474-4). Walker & Co.
Murthy, B. Srinivasa. Mother Teresa & India. LC 82-80522. (Illus.). 144p. (Orig.). 1983. pap. 6.95x (ISBN 0-941910-00-8). Long Beach Pubns.
Neill, Stephen. A History of Christianity in India 1707-1858. (Illus.). 592p. 1985. 79.50 (ISBN 0-521-30376-1). Cambridge U Pr.
Nixon, E. Anna. A Century of Planting: A History of the American Friends Mission in India. LC 85-72070. (Illus.). 493p. (Orig.). 1985. 16.95x (ISBN 0-913342-55-6); pap. 11.95 (ISBN 0-913342-54-8). Barclay Pr.
Pennington, M. Basil. Monastic Journey to India. 144p. (Orig.). 1982. pap. 9.95 (ISBN 0-8164-2398-9, HarpR). Har-Row.
Puthenpurakal, Joseph. Baptist Missions in Nagaland. 1984. 22.50x (ISBN 0-8364-1138-2, Pub. by Mukhopadhyaya). South Asia Bks.
Schutte, Josef F. Valignano's Mission Principles for Japan: Vol. I (1573-1582), Pt. I - The Problem (1573-1580) Coyne, John J., tr. from Ger. LC 78-69683. (Modern Scholarly Studies About the Jesuits, in English Translations, Ser. II: No. 3). (Illus.). xxiv, 428p. 1980. 14.00 (ISBN 0-912422-36-X); pap. 12.00 smyth sewn (ISBN 0-912422-35-1). Inst Jesuit.

MISSIONS–INDONESIA

Bentley-Taylor, David. Java Saga. Orig. Title: Weathercocks Reward. 1975. pap. 2.25 (ISBN 0-85363-100-X). OMF Bks.

MISSIONS–IRAN

Wilson, Samuel G. Persian Life & Customs. 3rd ed. LC 76-178305. Repr. of 1900 ed. 24.50 (ISBN 0-404-06996-7). AMS Pr.

MISSIONS–ISLANDS OF THE PACIFIC

Aubin, Pierre & Cotter, George. Agencies for Project Assistance: Sources of Support for Small Church & or Lay Sponsored Projects in Africa, Asia, Latin America & the Pacific. 2nd ed. (Illus.). 330p. 1984. pap. 50.00 (ISBN 0-913671-03-7). Mission Proj Serv.
Miller, Char, ed. Missions & Missionaries in the Pacific. LC 85-5074. (Symposium Ser.: Vol. 14). 136p. 1985. 19.95x (ISBN 0-88946-705-6). E Mellen.

MISSIONS–ISRAEL

Davis, Moshe, ed. Holy Land Missions & Missionaries: An Original Anthology. LC 77-70703. (America & the Holy Land Ser.). (Illus.). 1977. lib. bdg. 20.00x (ISBN 0-405-10259-3). Ayer Co Pubs.
Morton, Daniel O. Memoir of Rev. Levi Parsons: Late Missionary to Palestine. Davis, Moshe, ed. (America & the Holy Land Ser.). 1977. Repr. of 1824 ed. lib. bdg. 33.00x (ISBN 0-405-10271-2). Ayer Co Pubs.

MISSIONS–JAMAICA

Phillippo, James M. Jamaica: Its Past & Present State. LC 70-109998. (Illus.). Repr. of 1843 ed. 23.75x (ISBN 0-8371-4132-X, PIA&, Pub. by Negro U Pr). Greenwood.

MISSIONS–JAPAN

Boardman, Robert. A Higher Honor. 197p. 1986. pap. 7.95 (ISBN 0-89109-552-7). NavPress.
Bollinger, Edward E. The Cross & the Floating Dragon: The Gospel in the Ryukyu. LC 82-23540. (Illus.). 368p. 1983. pap. 10.95 (ISBN 0-87808-190-9). William Carey Lib.
Fischer, Edward. Japan Journey: The Columban Fathers in Nippon. LC 84-14228. 208p. 1984. pap. 9.95 (ISBN 0-8245-0656-1). Crossroad NY.
Hughes, Amelia. Missions Studies: Japan. pap. 1.00 (ISBN 0-89114-113-8). Baptist Pub Hse.
Laures, John. Catholic Church in Japan: A Short History. Repr. of 1954 ed. lib. bdg. 22.50x (ISBN 0-8371-2974-5, LACC). Greenwood.
Mensendiek, C. William. Not Without Struggle. (Illus.). 236p. 1986. 16.95 (ISBN 0-8298-0586-9). Pilgrim NY.
Schutte, Josef F. Valignano's Mission Principles for Japan: Vol. I (1573-1582), Pt. I - The Problem (1573-1580) Coyne, John J., tr. from Ger. LC 78-69683. (Modern Scholarly Studies About the Jesuits, in English Translations, Ser. II: No. 3). (Illus.). xxiv, 428p. 1980. 14.00 (ISBN 0-912422-36-X); pap. 12.00 smyth sewn (ISBN 0-912422-35-1). Inst Jesuit.

MISSIONS–KAFFRARIA

Gibson, Alan G. Eight Years in Kaffraria, 1882-1890. LC 79-82052. (Illus.). Repr. of 1891 ed. cancelled (ISBN 0-8371-1573-6, GIK&, Pub. by Negro U Pr). Greenwood.

MISSIONS–KOREA

Fisher, James E. Democracy & Mission Education in Korea. LC 70-176773. (Columbia University. Teachers College. Contributions to Education Ser.: No. 306). Repr. of 1928 ed. 22.50 (ISBN 0-404-55306-0). AMS Pr.
Wilkinson, Larry & Wilkinson, Dorcas. Gifts from Korea. 1983. pap. 7.00 (ISBN 0-8309-0376-3). Herald Hse.

MISSIONS–LAOS

Menger, Matt. Valley of Mekong. 1970. 4.95 (ISBN 0-685-79412-1); pap. 3.95 (ISBN 0-685-79413-X). Guild Bks.
Menger, Matt J. In the Valley of the Mekong. LC 79-115966. 1970. pap. 3.95 (ISBN 0-686-18632-X). Oblate.

MISSIONS–LATIN AMERICA

Aubin, Pierre & Cotter, George. Agencies for Project Assistance: Sources of Support for Small Church & or Lay Sponsored Projects in Africa, Asia, Latin America & the Pacific. 2nd ed. (Illus.). 330p. 1984. pap. 50.00 (ISBN 0-913671-03-7). Mission Proj Serv.
Carrigan, Ana. Salvador Witness: The Life & Calling of Jean Donvan. 320p. 1986. pap. 3.95 (ISBN 0-345-32984-8). Ballantine.
Costello, Gerald M. Mission to Latin America: The Successes & Failures of a Twentieth-Century Crusade. LC 78-12974. 319p. (Orig.). 1979. pap. 2.49 (ISBN 0-88344-312-0). Orbis Bks.
Materne, Yves, ed. Indian Awakening in Latin America. 1980. pap. 5.95 (ISBN 0-377-00097-3). Friend Pr.
Nouwen, Henri J. Love in Fearful Land: A Guatemalan Story. LC 85-71913. (Illus.). 120p. (Orig.). 1985. pap. 5.95 (ISBN 0-87793-294-8). Ave Maria.

MISSIONS–LIBERIA

Camphor, Alexander P. Missionary Story Sketches: Folk-Lore from Africa. facsimile ed. LC 79-173603. (Black Heritage Library Collection). Repr. of 1909 ed. 20.00 (ISBN 0-8369-8915-5). Ayer Co Pubs.
Christy, David. Ethiopia: Her Gloom & Glory. LC 73-75550. Repr. of 1857 ed. 22.50x (ISBN 0-8371-1016-5, CHR&, Pub. by Negro U Pr). Greenwood.
Freeman, Nona. Box 44, Monrovia. Wallace, Mary H., ed. (Illus.). 224p. 1983. pap. 5.95 (ISBN 0-912315-09-1). Word Aflame.

MISSIONS–MADAGASCAR

Gow, Bonar A. Madagascar & the Protestant Impact. LC 78-11216. (Dalhousie African Studies). 256p. 1980. text ed. 49.50x (ISBN 0-8419-0463-4, Africana). Holmes & Meier.
--Madagascar & the Protestant Impact: The Work of the British Missions, 1818-95. (Dalhousie African Studies Ser.). pap. 71.00 (ISBN 0-317-27749-9, 2025229). Bks Demand UMI.

MISSIONS–MALAWI

Linden, Ian & Linden, Jane. Catholics, Peasants & Chewa Resistance in Nyasaland, 1889-1939. 1974. 38.50x (ISBN 0-520-02500-8). U of Cal Pr.
McCracken, J. Politics & Christianity in Malawi 1875-1940. LC 76-27905. (Cambridge Commonwealth Ser.). (Illus.). 1977. 49.50 (ISBN 0-521-21444-0). Cambridge U Pr.

MISSIONS–MEXICO

Barnes, Vera F. Daybreak Below the Border. 1975. Repr. 2.50 (ISBN 0-87509-078-8). Chr Pubns.
Gambill, Sandra & Ashley, Clara. Missions Studies: Mexico. pap. 1.00 (ISBN 0-89114-095-6). Baptist Pub Hse.
Robertson, Tomas. Baja California & Its Missions. (Illus.). 1978. pap. 3.95 (ISBN 0-910856-66-4). La Siesta.
Weddle, Robert S. San Juan Bautista: Gateway to Spanish Texas. (Illus.). 485p. 1968. 24.50x (ISBN 0-292-73306-2). U of Tex Pr.

MISSIONS–NEAR EAST

Abu-Ghazaleh, Adnan. American Missions in Syria. 120p. (Orig.). 1985. 16.95 (ISBN 0-915597-26-8); pap. 8.95 (ISBN 0-915597-25-X). Amana Bks.
Burnet, David S. & Davis, Moshe, eds. The Jerusalem Mission: Under the Direction of the American Christian Missionary Society. (America & the Holy Land Ser.). 1977. Repr. of 1853 ed. lib. bdg. 26.50x (ISBN 0-405-10233-X). Ayer Co Pubs.
Richter, Julius. History of Protestant Missions in the Near East. LC 79-133822. Repr. of 1910 ed. 29.50 (ISBN 0-404-05331-9). AMS Pr.

MISSIONS–NEW GUINEA

Bromilow, William E. Twenty Years Among Primitive Papuans. LC 75-32800. Repr. of 1929 ed. 31.50 (ISBN 0-404-14103-X). AMS Pr.
Hall, Clarence. Miracle on the Sepik. 2nd ed. (Illus.). 100p. 1980. pap. 3.95. Full Gospel.

MISSIONS–NIGERIA

Ajayi, J. F. Christian Missions in Nigeria, Eighteen Forty-One to Eighteen Ninety-One: The Making of a New Elite. 1965. 19.95 (ISBN 0-8101-0038-X). Northwestern U Pr.
Ayandele, Emmanuel A. Missionary Impact on Modern Nigeria, 1842-1914. (Ibadan History Ser.). 1967. pap. text ed. 17.50x (ISBN 0-582-64512-3). Humanities.
Helser, Albert D. Education of Primitive People. LC 75-97403. Repr. of 1934 ed. cancelled (ISBN 0-8371-2651-7, HPP&, Pub. by Negro U Pr). Greenwood.
Kulp, Mary A. No Longer Strangers: A Biogrpahy of H. Stover Kulp. LC 68-4439. pap. 47.00 (ISBN 0-317-28389-8, 2022413). Bks Demand UMI.
Linden, Ian. Emirs & Evangelicals. 1986. 29.50x (ISBN 0-7146-3146-9, BHA-03146, F Cass Co). Biblio Dist.

MISSIONS–NORTH AMERICA

Humphreys, David. Historical Account of the Incorporated Society for the Propagation of the Gospel in Foreign Parts - to the Year 1728. LC 75-83426. (Religion in America, Ser. 1). 1969. Repr. of 1730 ed. 21.00 (ISBN 0-405-00251-3). Ayer Co Pubs.
Toepperwein, Emilie & Toepperwein, Fritz. The Missions of San Antonio. pap. text ed. 1.50 (ISBN 0-910722-12-9). Highland Pr.

MISSIONS–OCEANICA

Boutilier, James A., et al, eds. Mission, Church, & Sect in Oceania. (Asao Monograph: No. 6). (Illus.). 514p. 1984. lib. bdg. 38.25 (ISBN 0-8191-3837-1, Assoc Soc Anthro Oceania); pap. text ed. 20.75 (ISBN 0-8191-3838-X, Assoc Soc Anthro Oceania). U Pr of Amer.
Gunson, Niel. Messengers of Grace: Evangelical Missionaries in the South Seas 1797-1860. (Illus.). 1978. 49.95x (ISBN 0-19-550517-4). Oxford U Pr.

MISSIONS–PERU

Wight, Maxine C. A Story About Light. LC 79-14691. 1979. 1.99 (ISBN 0-8309-0236-8). Herald Hse.

MISSIONS–PHILIPPINE ISLANDS

Baily, Michael. Small Net in a Big Sea: The Redemptorists in the Philippines, 1905-1929. (Illus.). 8.00x (ISBN 0-686-24529-6, San Carlos Pubns); pap. 5.00x (ISBN 0-686-24530-X). Cellar.
Gambill, Sandra & Ashley, Clara. Missions Studies: The Philippines. (Vacation Bible School Ser.). (Illus.). 32p. (Orig.). 1981. pap. 1.00 (ISBN 0-89114-105-7). Baptist Pub Hse.

MISSIONS–RHODESIA

Dodge, Ralph E. The Revolutionary Bishop: Who Saw God at Work in Africa. LC 85-29092. (Illus.). 216p. (Orig.). 1986. pap. 7.95 (ISBN 0-87808-203-4, WCL203-4). William Carey Lib.
Embree, Esther. Now Rings the Bell. (Illus.). 1978. pap. 2.95 (ISBN 0-89367-023-5). Light & Life.
Rotberg, Robert I. Christian Missionaries & the Creation of Northern Rhodesia, 1880-1924. 1965. 30.50x (ISBN 0-691-03009-X). Princeton U Pr.

MISSIONS–SOLOMON ISLANDS

Laracy, Hugh. Marists & Melanesians: A History of Catholic Missions in the Solomon Islands. 222p. 1976. text ed. 15.00x (ISBN 0-8248-0361-2). UH Pr.

MISSIONS–SOUTH AMERICA

Holland, Clifton L., ed. World Christianity: Central America & the Caribbean. LC 79-89819. 1981. pap. 15.00 (ISBN 0-912552-36-0). Missions Adv Res Comm Ctr.
Rippy, J. Fred & Nelson, Jean T. Crusaders of the Jungle. LC 76-123495. 1971. Repr. of 1936 ed. 31.50x (ISBN 0-8046-1382-6, Pub. by Kennikat). Assoc Faculty Pr.

Stoll, David. Fishers of Men or Founders of Empire: The Wycliffe Bible Translators in Latin America. (Illus.). 352p. 1983. 29.50x (ISBN 0-86232-111-5, Pub. by Zed Pr England); pap. 10.75 (ISBN 0-86232-112-3, Pub. by Zed Pr England). Humanities.

MISSIONS–SOVIET UNION

Bawden, C. R. Shamans, Lamas & Evangelicals: The English Missionaries in Siberia. (Illus.). 400p. 1985. 50.00x (ISBN 0-7102-0064-1). Methuen Inc.

Smirnoff, Eugene. Russian Orthodox Missions. pap. 8.95 (ISBN 0-686-01299-2). Eastern Orthodox.

MISSIONS–SRI LANKA

Chase, Barbara H. & Man, Martha L., eds. Spirit & Struggle in Southern Asia. 105p. (Orig.). 1986. pap. 5.95 (ISBN 0-377-00157-0). Friend Pr.

MISSIONS–SWEDEN

The English Missionaries in Sweden & Finland. (Church Historical Society, London, Ser.: No. 27). Repr. of 1937 ed. 55.00 (ISBN 0-8115-3151-1). Kraus Repr.

Oppermann, Charles J. English Missionaries in Sweden & Finland. LC 38-16784. (Church Historical Society Ser.: No. 26). 1937. 17.50x (ISBN 0-281-00240-1). A R Allenson.

MISSIONS–SYRIA

Abu-Ghazaleh, Adnan. American Missions in Syria. 120p. (Orig.). 1985. 16.95 (ISBN 0-915597-26-8); pap. 8.95 (ISBN 0-915597-25-X). Amana Bks.

MISSIONS–TANGANYIKA

Hore, Edward C. Missionary to Tanganyika: 1877-1888. Wolf, James B., ed. 200p. 1971. 28.50x (ISBN 0-7146-2605-8, F Cass Co). Biblio Dist.

MISSIONS–TONGA ISLANDS

Tremblay, Edward. When You Go to Tonga. (Illus.). 1954. 3.25 (ISBN 0-8198-0173-9). Dghtrs St Paul.

MISSIONS–UNITED STATES

Abell, Aaron I. The Urban Impact on American Protestantism, 1865-1900. x, 275p. 1962. Repr. of 1943 ed. 22.50 (ISBN 0-208-00587-0, Archon). Shoe String.

Ahlborn, Richard E. The San Antonio Missions: Edward Everett & the American Occupation, 1847. LC 85-71971. (Illus.). 62p. 1985. pap. 6.95 (ISBN 0-88360-076-5). Amon Carter.

Appleby, Jerry. Missions Have Come Home to America. 120p. 1986. pap. 3.95 (ISBN 0-8341-1132-2). Beacon Hill.

Archibald, Robert R. An Economic History of the California Missions. (Monograph). 1977. 25.00 (ISBN 0-88382-063-3). AAFH.

Arnez, John A., intro. by. Slovenian Letters by Missionaries in America, 1851-1874. (Studia Slovenica Special Ser.: No.4). 230p. 1984. pap. 11.00 (ISBN 0-318-01454-8). Studia Slovenica.

Barton, Bruce W. The Tree at the Center of the World: The Story of the California Missions. LC 79-26434. (Illus., Orig.). 1980. lib. bdg. 19.95 (ISBN 0-915520-30-3); pap. 12.95 (ISBN 0-915520-29-X). Ross-Erikson.

Beaver, R. Pierce, ed. American Missions in Bicentennial Perspective. LC 77-7569. 1977. pap. 10.95 (ISBN 0-87808-153-4). William Carey Lib.

Berkhofer, Robert F. Salvation & the Savage: An Analysis of Protestant Missions & American Indian Response, 1787-1862. LC 77-22857. 1977. Repr. of 1965 ed. lib. bdg. 22.50x (ISBN 0-8371-9745-7, BESSA). Greenwood.

Bolton, Herbert E. Fray Juan Crespi, Missionary Explorer on the Pacific Coast, 1769-1774. LC 78-158616. Repr. of 1927 ed. 29.50 (ISBN 0-404-01838-6). AMS Pr.

Cabat, Erni & Polzer, Charles W. Father Eusebio Francisco Kino & His Missions of the Pimeria Alta: Facing the Missions, Bk. II. Prezelski, Carmen V., tr. LC 82-50219. (Illus.). 36p. 1983. pap. 5.00 (ISBN 0-915076-09-8). SW Mission.

Chaney, Charles L. Birth of Missions in America. LC 75-26500. 352p. 1976. pap. 7.95 (ISBN 0-87808-146-1). William Carey Lib.

Cochran, Alice C. Miners, Merchants & Missionaries: The Roles of Missionaries & Pioneer Churches in the Colorado Gold Rush & Its Aftermath, 1858-1870. LC 80-16895. (ATLA Monographs: No. 15). x, 287p. 1980. 21.00 (ISBN 0-8108-1325-4). Scarecrow.

Company for Promoting & Propagation of the Gospel of Jesus Christ in New England: The Ledger for the Years 1650-1660 & the Record Book of Meetings Between 1656 & 1686. Repr. of 1920 ed. 23.50 (ISBN 0-8337-4481-X). B Franklin.

Durham, Jackie. In Search of Energy. Pennington, Celeste, ed. (Home Mission Study). (Illus., Orig.). 1984. pap. 1.75 (ISBN 0-937170-27-5). Home Mission.

Engelhardt, Zephyrin. Mission Santa Ines. LC 85-23977. (Missions & Missionaries of California Ser.). (Illus.). 202p. (Orig.). 1986. 16.50 (ISBN 0-87461-063-X); pap. 7.50 (ISBN 0-87461-062-1). McNally & Loftin.

--Missions & Missionaries of California, 4 Vols. (Illus.). lib. bdg. 185.00 (ISBN 0-87821-019-9). Milford Hse.

Ericson, Jack T., ed. Missionary Society of Connecticut Papers, 1759-1948: A Guide to the Microform Edition. 49p. 1976. pap. 15.00 (ISBN 0-667-00289-8). Microfilming Corp.

Foster, Lee. Beautiful California Missions. Shangle, Robert D., ed. LC 78-102341. (Illus.). 72p. 1986. pap. 8.95 (ISBN 0-915796-22-8). Beautiful Am.

Foster, Nancy H. The Alamo & Other Texas Missions to Remember. LC 84-647. (Illus.). 96p. (Orig.). 1984. pap. 9.95x (ISBN 0-88415-033-X, Lone Star Bks). Gulf Pub.

Furlow, Elaine, et al. Light upon the Land. (Home Mission Study). 110p. (Orig.). 1984. pap. 2.85 (ISBN 0-937170-28-3). Home Mission.

Gallagher, Neil. Don't Go Overseas until You've Read This Book. LC 77-2643. 128p. 1977. pap. 5.95 (ISBN 0-87123-105-0, 210105). Bethany Hse.

Gannon, Michael V. Cross in the Sand: The Early Catholic Church in Florida, 1513-1870. LC 83-10498. 1965. pap. 12.00 (ISBN 0-8130-0776-3). U Presses Fla.

Geary, Gerald J. The Secularization of the California Missions (1810-1846) LC 73-3572. (Catholic University of America. Studies in American Church History: No. 17). Repr. of 1934 ed. 26.00 (ISBN 0-404-57767-9). AMS Pr.

Hind, Carolyn S. Whither Thou Goest. LC 85-51991. (Illus.). 192p. 1985. 12.50 (ISBN 0-936029-00-5). Western Bk Journ.

Horvath, David G., ed. Papers of the American Home Missionary Society, 1816 (1826-1894) 1936: A Guide to the Microfilm Edition. 94p. 1975. pap. 50.00 (ISBN 0-88455-994-7). Microfilming Corp.

Kessell, John L. The Missions of New Mexico Since 1776. LC 79-4934. (Illus.). 320p. 1980. 45.00x (ISBN 0-8263-0514-8). U of NM Pr.

Kocher, Paul. Alabado, a Story of Old California. 1978. 6.95 (ISBN 0-8199-0689-1). Franciscan Herald.

Kuykendall, John W. Southern Enterprize: The Work of National Evangelical Societies in the Antebellum South. LC 81-23723. (Contributions to the Study of Religion Ser.: No. 7). xv, 188p. 1982. lib. bdg. 29.95 (ISBN 0-313-23212-1, KSE/). Greenwood.

Lanning, John T. Spanish Missions of Georgia. (Illus.). 1971. Repr. of 1935 ed. 39.00 (ISBN 0-403-00803-4). Scholarly.

McCoy, Isaac. History of Baptist Indian Missions. LC 19-11605. 1970. Repr. of 1840 ed. 36.00 (ISBN 0-384-36590-6). Johnson Repr.

McLoughlin, William G. Cherokees & Missionaries, 1789-1839. LC 83-11759. 375p. 1984. 35.00x (ISBN 0-300-03075-4). Yale U Pr.

Martin, Carol O. Exploring the California Missions: Activity Cards. Margolin, Malcolm, ed. (Illus.). 94p. (Orig.). 1984. pap. 7.95 (ISBN 0-318-18397-8). Bay Area CA.

Montgomery, R. G., et al. Franciscan Awatovi: The Excavation & Conjectural Reconstruction of a Seventeenth Century Spanish Mission. (Harvard University Peabody Museum of Archaeology & Ethnology Papers). 1949. 24.00 (ISBN 0-527-01292-0). Kraus Repr.

Morfi, Fray J. History of Texas, Sixteen Seventy-Three to Seventeen Seventy-Nine, 2 pts. Castaneda, Carlos E., ed. LC 67-24718. (Quivira Society Publications Ser.: Vol. 6). 1967. Repr. of 1935 ed. 34.00 (ISBN 0-405-19053-0). Ayer Co Pubs.

Mylar, Isaac L. Early Days at the Mission San Juan Bautista. (Illus.). 208p. 1986. pap. 9.95 (ISBN 0-317-44751-3). Panorama West.

Nestorova, Tatyana. American Missionaries among the Bulgarians: 1858-1912. 160p. 1987. text ed. 20.00 (ISBN 0-88033-114-3, 218). East Eur Quarterly.

Nolan, James L. Discovery of the Lost Art Treasures of California's First Mission. Pourade, Richard F., ed. LC 78-73173. (Illus.). 128p. 1978. 20.00 (ISBN 0-913938-20-3). Copley Bks.

O'Rourke, Thomas P. The Franciscan Missions in Texas (1690-1793) LC 73-3559. (Catholic University of America. Studies in American Church History: No. 5). Repr. of 1927 ed. 19.50 (ISBN 0-404-57755-5). AMS Pr.

Roberts, Helen M. Mission Tales: Stories of the Historic California Missions: Missions San Diego, San Luis Rey, San Juan Capistrano, Vol. 1. LC 62-11254. (Illus.). 91p. 1962. 5.95x (ISBN 0-87015-244-0). Pacific Bks.

--Mission Tales: Stories of the Historic California Missions: Missions San Gabriel, San Fernando Rey, San Buenaventura, Vol. 2. LC 62-11254. (Illus.). 92p. 1962. 5.95x (ISBN 0-87015-245-9). Pacific Bks.

--Mission Tales: Stories of the Historic California Missions: Missions Santa Barbara, Santa Ines, Purisima, Vol. 3. LC 62-11254. (Illus.). 95p. 1962. 5.95x (ISBN 0-87015-246-7). Pacific Bks.

--Mission Tales: Stories of the Historic California Missions: Missions San Luis Obispo, San Miguel, San Antonio, Vol. 4. LC 62-11254. (Illus.). 92p. 1962. 5.95x (ISBN 0-87015-247-5). Pacific Bks.

--Mission Tales: Stories of the Historic California Missions: Missions Soledad, San Carlos, San Juan Bautista, Vol. 5. LC 62-11254. (Illus.). 88p. 1962. 5.95x (ISBN 0-87015-248-3). Pacific Bks.

Robinson, Alfred. Life in California Before the Conquest. LC 68-30553. (American Scene Ser). (Illus.). 1969. Repr. of 1846 ed. lib. bdg. 39.50 (ISBN 0-306-71142-7). Da Capo.

Salpointe, J. B. Soldiers of the Cross. 1977. Repr. of 1898 ed. lib. bdg. 24.95x (ISBN 0-89712-063-9). Documentary Pubns.

Schiwetz, E. M. Six Spanish Missions in Texas: A Portfolio of Paintings. Memorial ed. (Illus.). 1984. 60.00 (ISBN 0-292-77597-0). U of Tex Pr.

Six Missions of Texas. (Illus.). 1965. 15.95 (ISBN 0-87244-002-8). Texian.

Stumme, Wayne, ed. Bible & Mission: Biblical Foundations & Working Models for Congregational Ministry. LC 86-22167. (Mission in the U. S. A. Series). 208p. (Orig.). 1986. pap. 10.95 (ISBN 0-8066-2237-7, 10-0705). Augsburg.

Taraval, Sigismundo. Indian Uprising in Lower California, 1734-1737. LC 79-137296. Repr. of 1931 ed. 24.00 (ISBN 0-404-06337-3). AMS Pr.

Temple, Sydney. The Carmel Mission, from Founding to Rebuilding. LC 79-57168. (Illus.). 176p. 1980. pap. 5.95 (ISBN 0-913548-71-5, Valley Calif). Western Tanager.

Tuttle, Daniel S. Missionary to the Mountain West: The Reminiscences of Episcopal Bishop Daniel S. Tuttle, 1866-1886. 509p. 1987. Repr. of 1906 ed. 20.00 (ISBN 0-87480-305-5). U of Utah Pr.

Wissel, Joseph. The Redemptorist on the American Missions, 3 vols. In 2. 115.00 (ISBN 0-405-10867-2). Ayer Co Pubs.

MISSIONS–VIETNAM

Boardman, Elizabeth J. The Phoenix Trip: Notes on a Quaker Mission to Haiphong. LC 84-72319. (Illus.). 192p. 1985. pap. 9.95 (ISBN 0-914064-22-3). Celo Pr.

Borri, Christoforo. Cochin-China: Containing Many Admirable Rarities of That Countrey. LC 71-25710. (English Experience Ser.: No. 223). 1970. Repr. of 1633 ed. 9.50 (ISBN 90-221-0223-8). Walter J Johnson.

MISSIONS–WEST INDIES

Latimer, James. Foundations of the Christian Missions in the British, French & Spanish West Indies. 1984. 10.95 (ISBN 0-533-05875-9). Vantage.

Underhill, Edward B. West Indies: Their Social & Religious Condition. LC 73-107525. Repr. of 1862 ed. 24.75x (ISBN 0-8371-3772-1, UWI&). Greenwood.

MISSIONS–ZAMBIA

International Missionary Council - Department of Social & Economic Research & Council. Modern Industry & the African. 2nd ed. Davis, J. Mearle, ed. LC 67-24749. 1961. Repr. of 1932 ed. 37.50x (ISBN 0-678-05042-2). Kelley.

Ragsdale, John P. Protestant Mission Education in Zambia: Eighteen Eighty to Nineteen Fifty-Four. LC 85-40505. 192p. 1986. 26.50x (ISBN 0-941664-09-0). Susquehanna U Pr.

MISSIONS, CITY

see City Missions

MISSIONS, FOREIGN

Allen, Roland. The Spontaneous Expansion of the Church. 1962. pap. 4.95 (ISBN 0-8028-1002-0). Eerdmans.

Davey, Cyril J. March of Methodism. 1952. 5.95 (ISBN 0-8022-0345-0). Philos Lib.

Hill, Patricia R. The World Their Household: The American Women's Foreign Mission Movement & Cultural Transformation, 1870-1920. (Women & Culture Ser.). 300p. 1985. text ed. 19.50x (ISBN 0-472-10055-6). U of Mich Pr.

Hutchinson, William R. Errand to the World: American Protestant Thought & Foreign Missions. 216p. 1987. lib. bdg. 24.95x (ISBN 0-226-36257-4). U of Chicago Pr.

Mott, John R. The Evangelization of the World in This Generation. LC 76-38457. (Religion in America, Ser. 2). 258p. 1972. Repr. of 1900 ed. 17.00 (ISBN 0-405-04078-4). Ayer Co Pubs.

Steiner, Zara, ed. The Times Survey of the Foreign Ministries of the World. (Illus.). 1982. 87.50x (ISBN 0-930466-37-3). Meckler Pub.

Strong, William E. Story of the American Board: An Account of the First Hundred Years of the American Board for Foreign Missions. LC 79-83443. (Religion in America Ser.). 1969. Repr. of 1910 ed. 26.50 (ISBN 0-405-00277-7). Ayer Co Pubs.

MISSIONS, HOME

see also City Missions

Gunstone, Don & Gunstone, Gail. Home Fellowship Meetings: Creative Ideas. 47p. 1986. pap. 3.25 (ISBN 0-914936-99-9). Bible Temple.

Horvath, David G., ed. Papers of the American Home Missionary Society, 1816 (1826-1894) 1936: A Guide to the Microfilm Edition. 94p. 1975. pap. 50.00 (ISBN 0-88455-994-7). Microfilming Corp.

Tanner, William G. From Sea to Shining Sea. LC 86-9609. 1986. pap. 4.95 (ISBN 0-8054-5667-8). Broadman.

MISSIONS, INDIAN

see Indians of North America–Missions; Indians of South America–Missions

MISSIONS, MEDICAL

see also Missions to Lepers

Greene, Ruth A. Hsiang-Ya Journal. LC 76-28526. Repr. of 1977 ed. 36.70 (2011504). Bks Demand UMI.

Jorden, Paul J. & Adair, James R. Surgeon on Safari. (Living Bks.). 192p. (Orig.). 1985. pap. 3.95 (ISBN 0-8423-6686-5). Tyndale.

Krimsky, Joseph. Pilgrimage & Service. Davis, Moshe, ed. LC 77-70712. (America & the Holy Land Ser.). 1977. Repr. of 1919 ed. lib. bdg. 17.00x (ISBN 0-405-10261-5). Ayer Co Pubs.

Schweitzer, Albert. On the Edge of the Primeval Forest & More from the Primeval Forest: Experiences & Observations of a Doctor in Equatorial Africa. LC 75-41244. (Illus.). 1976. Repr. of 1948 ed. 18.50 (ISBN 0-404-14598-1). AMS Pr.

Seaton, Ronald S. & Seaton, Edith B. Here's How: Health Education by Extension. LC 76-40599. 1976. pap. 3.95 (ISBN 0-87808-150-X). William Carey Lib.

Seel, David J. Challenge & Crisis in Missionary Medicine. LC 79-16015. (Illus.). 1979. pap. 3.95 (ISBN 0-87808-172-0). William Carey Lib.

Stirling, Leader. Tanzanian Doctor. LC 78-316167. pap. 38.50 (ISBN 0-317-26454-0, 2023860). Bks Demand UMI.

White, Ellen G. Counsels on Health & Instruction to Medical Missionary Workers. 1951. deluxe ed. 10.95 (ISBN 0-8163-0114-X, 03561-8). Pacific Pr Pub Assn.

--Medical Ministry. 1963. deluxe ed. 8.95 (ISBN 0-8163-0158-1, 13370-2). Pacific Pr Pub Assn.

Wilkinson, Larry & Wilkinson, Dorcas. Gifts from Korea. 1983. pap. 7.00 (ISBN 0-8309-0376-3). Herald Hse.

MISSIONS TO ITALIANS

Cordasco, Francesco, ed. Protestant Evangelism among Italians in America. LC 74-17943. (Italian American Experience Ser.). (Illus.). 276p. 1975. Repr. 21.00x (ISBN 0-405-06414-4). Ayer Co Pubs.

MISSIONS TO JEWS

see also Converts from Judaism

Burnet, David S. & Davis, Moshe, eds. The Jerusalem Mission: Under the Direction of the American Christian Missionary Society. (America & the Holy Land Ser.). 1977. Repr. of 1853 ed. lib. bdg. 26.50x (ISBN 0-405-10233-X). Ayer Co Pubs.

Endelman, Todd M., ed. Jewish Apostasy in the Modern World. 300p. 1987. 34.50 (ISBN 0-8419-1029-4). Holmes & Meier.

Fleischner, Eva. Judaism in German Christian Theology since 1945: Christianity & Israel Considered in Terms of Mission. LC 75-22374. (ATLA Monograph: No. 8). 205p. 1975. 17.50 (ISBN 0-8108-0835-8). Scarecrow.

Grob, Gerald, ed. A Course of Lectures on the Jews: By Ministers of the Established Church in Glasgow. LC 76-46095. (Anti-Movements in America). 1977. lib. bdg. 37.50x (ISBN 0-405-09968-1). Ayer Co Pubs.

MISSIONS TO LEPERS

Dutton, Charles J. The Samaritans of Molokai. facsimile ed. (Select Bibliographies Reprint Ser). Repr. of 1932 ed. 23.50 (ISBN 0-8369-5733-4). Ayer Co Pubs.

Farrow, John. Damien the Leper. 1954. pap. 3.95 (ISBN 0-385-02918-7, D3, Im). Doubleday.

MISSIONS TO MORMONS

Bailey, Jack S. Inside a Mormon Mission. 190p. pap. 3.95 (ISBN 0-89036-076-6). Hawkes Pub Inc.

MISSIONS TO MUSLIMS

Addison, James T. The Christian Approach to the Moslem. LC 76-158227. (BCL Ser.: No. II). Repr. of 1942 ed. 24.50 (ISBN 0-404-00294-3). AMS Pr.

Marsh, C. R. Share Your Faith with a Muslim. LC 75-15883. 1975. pap. 4.50 (ISBN 0-8024-7900-6). Moody.

MITHAN

see Gayal

MITHRAISM
see also Zoroastrianism
Cumont, Franz. The Mysteries of Mithra. 2nd ed. McCormack, Thomas J., tr. (Illus., Fr). 1911. pap. 5.95 (ISBN 0-486-20323-9). Dover.
--Mysteries of Mithra. (Illus.). 14.00 (ISBN 0-8446-1926-4). Peter Smith.
Speidel, Michael P. Mithras-Orion: Greek Hero & Roman Army God. (Illus.). 56p. 1980. pap. text ed. 19.95 (ISBN 90-04-06055-3). Humanities.
Wynne-Tyson, Esme. Mithras. 1985. 50.00x (ISBN 0-900000-79-1, Pub. by Centaur Bks). State Mutual Bk.

MITRA (HINDU DEITY)
Thieme, Paul. Mitra & Aryaman. (Connecticut Academy of Arts & Sciences Transaction: Vol. 41). 1967. 18.00 (ISBN 0-208-01104-8). Shoe String.

MITSVOT
see Commandments (Judaism)

MIXED MARRIAGE
see Marriage, Mixed

MO TI, fl. 400 B.C.
Yi-Pac, Mei. Motse, the Neglected Rival of Confucius. LC 73-892. (China Studies). (Illus.). xi, 222p. 1973. Repr. of 1934 ed. 20.75 (ISBN 0-88355-084-9). Hyperion Conn.

MODERN PHILOSOPHY
see Philosophy, Modern

MODERNISM
see also Fundamentalism
Kolb, David. The Critique of Pure Modernity: Hegel, Heidegger, & After. LC 85-24510. 334p. 1987. lib. bdg. 25.00 (ISBN 0-226-45031-7). U of Chicago Pr.
Mathews, Shailer. Faith of Modernism. LC 71-108117. Repr. of 1924 ed. 17.50 (ISBN 0-404-04266-X). AMS Pr.
Streeter, Burnett H. Foundations: A Statement of Christian Belief in Terms of Modern Thought by 70 Oxford Men. facs. ed. (Essay Index Reprint Ser). 1912. 20.50 (ISBN 0-8369-2189-5). Ayer Co Pubs.

MODERNISM–CATHOLIC CHURCH
see also Americanism (Catholic Controversy)
Carmody, John T. & Carmody, Denise L. Contemporary Catholic Theology. rev. ed. LC 84-48213. 256p. 1985. pap. 9.95 (ISBN 0-06-061316-5, HarpR). Har-Row.
Daly, Gabriel. Transcendence & Immanence: A Study in Catholic Modernism & Integralism. 1980. 37.50x (ISBN 0-19-826652-9). Oxford U Pr.
Hutchison, William R. The Modernist Impulse in American Protestantism. (Illus.). 384p. 1976. 22.50x (ISBN 0-674-58058-3). Harvard U Pr.
Lilley, Alfred L. Modernism: A Record & Review. LC 75-102575. 1970. Repr. of 1908 ed. 25.00x (ISBN 0-8046-0735-4, Pub. by Kennikat). Assoc Faculty Pr.
Loisy, Alfred F. My Duel with the Vatican: The Autobiography of a Catholic Modernist. Boynton, Richard W., tr. 1968. Repr. of 1924 ed. lib. bdg. 22.50 (ISBN 0-8371-0148-4, LODV). Greenwood.
Reardon, Bernard M., ed. Roman Catholic Modernism. 1970. 20.00x (ISBN 0-8047-0750-2). Stanford U Pr.
Ruthler, George W. Beyond Modernity: Reflections of a Post-Modern Catholic. LC 86-82636. 227p. (Orig.). 1986. pap. 11.95 (ISBN 0-89870-135-X). Ignatius Pr.
Wilhelm, Anthony. Christ among Us: A Modern Presentation of the Catholic Faith for Adults. 4th, rev. ed. LC 84-48465. 480p. 1985. pap. 6.95 (ISBN 0-06-069417-3, HarpR). Har-Row.

MODERNIST-FUNDAMENTALIST CONTROVERSY
see also Fundamentalism
Glick, Thomas, compiled by. Darwinism in Texas. LC 72-185614. (Illus.). 38p. 1972. 7.00 (ISBN 0-87959-032-7). U of Tex H Ransom Ctr.
Pope Pius X. On the Doctrine of the Modernists. 1973. pap. 0.50 (ISBN 0-8198-0248-4). Dghtrs St Paul.
Walker, K. R., ed. The Evolution-Creation Controversy Perspectives on Religion, Philosophy, Science & Education: A Handbook. (Paleontological Society Special Publications Ser.). (Illus.). 155p. pap. 6.50 (ISBN 0-931377-00-5). U of Tenn Geo.

MODESTUS, d. 634 or 635
Baumstark, Anton. Die Modestianischen und Die Konstantinischen Bauten Am Heiligen Grabe Zu Jerusalem. Repr. of 1915 ed. 15.00 (ISBN 0-384-03585-X). Johnson Repr.

MOEHLER, JOHANN ADAM, 1796-1838
Fitzer, Joseph. Moehler & Baur in Controversy Eighteen Thirty-Two to Thirty-Eight: Romantic-idealist Assesment of the Reformation & Counter-Reformation. LC 74-77619. (American Academy of Religion. Studies in Religion). 1974. 9.95 (ISBN 0-88420-111-2, 010007). Scholars Pr GA.

MOHAMMED, THE PROPHET, 570-632
Abbott, Nabia. Aishah: The Beloved of Mohammed. LC 73-6264. (The Middle East Ser.). Repr. of 1942 ed. 18.00 (ISBN 0-405-05318-5). Ayer Co Pubs.
Abdullah. The Prophet's Speech at Tabuk. abr. ed. 16p. (Orig.). 1984. pap. 1.00 (ISBN 0-916157-02-4). African Islam Miss Pubns.
Ahmad, G. Sayings of Muhammad. 8.25 (ISBN 0-87902-036-9). Orientalia.
Ahmad, Ghazi. Sayings of Muhammad. pap. 2.00 (ISBN 0-686-18342-8). Kazi Pubns.
Alladin, Bilzik. Story of Mohammad the Prophet. (Illus.). 1979. 7.25 (ISBN 0-89744-139-7). Auromere.
Al-Majilisi, Muhammad B. The Life & Religion of Muhammad. Merrick, James, tr. 463p. 1987. pap. 19.95 (ISBN 0-7103-0216-9, 02169, Kegan Paul). Methuen Inc.
Andrae, Tor. Mohammed: The Man & His Faith. facsimile ed. Menzel, Theophil, tr. LC 79-160954. (Select Bibliographies Reprint Ser). Repr. of 1936 ed. 19.00 (ISBN 0-8369-5821-7). Ayer Co Pubs.
Azzam, Abd-Al-Rahman. Eternal Message of Muhammad. 1964. 9.50 (ISBN 0-8159-5401-8). Devin.
Balquir, Allama Muhammad Al-Majlisi. The Life & Religion of Muhammad, 3 vols, Vol. 2. Merrick, J. L., tr. from Persian. Tr. of Hiyat al-Qulub. 483p. 1982. 35.00x (ISBN 0-317-39115-1, Pub. by Luzac & Co Ltd). State Mutual Bk.
Bermann, Richard A. The Mahdi of Allah: The Story of the Dervish, Mohammed Ahmed. John, Robin, tr. LC 80-1935. Repr. of 1932 ed. 36.00 (ISBN 0-404-18955-5). AMS Pr.
Bey, E. Mohammed. 336p. 1985. 50.00x (ISBN 0-317-39181-X, Pub. by Luzac & Co Ltd). State Mutual Bk.
Bodley, Ronald V. Messenger: The Life of Mohammed. LC 70-92296. Repr. of 1946 ed. lib. bdg. 35.00x (ISBN 0-8371-2423-9, BOTM). Greenwood.
Bucke, Richard M. Buddha, Mohammed, Bacon, Whitman & Others & the Theory of Cosmic Consciousness, 2 vols. (Illus.). 291p. 1986. Set. 237.50 (ISBN 0-89901-269-8). Found Class Reprints.
Chattapadhyaya. Muhammad, the Prophet of Islam. 1981. 1.25 (ISBN 0-686-97878-1). Kazi Pubns.
Chirri, Mohamad J. The Brother of the Prophet Mohammad: The Imam Ali, 2 vols, Vol. II. LC 79-127838. 400p. 1982. 15.00 (ISBN 0-942778-00-6). Islamic Ctr.
Cook, Michael. Muhammad. (Past Masters Ser.). (Illus.). 1983. 13.95x (ISBN 0-19-287606-6); pap. 4.95 (ISBN 0-19-287605-8). Oxford U Pr.
Cragg, Kenneth. Muhammad & the Christian: A Question of Response. 192p. (Orig.). 1984. pap. 8.95 (ISBN 0-88344-349-X). Orbis Bks.
Dashti, Ali. Twenty Three Years: A Study of the Prophetic Career of Mohammad. Bagley, F. R., tr. from Persian. 224p. 1985. 17.50 (ISBN 0-04-297048-2). Allen Unwin.
De Boulainvilliers, H. The Life of Mahomet. Luzac & Co. Ltd. Staff, ed. 400p. 1985. 60.00 (ISBN 0-317-39040-6, Pub. by Luzac & Co Ltd). State Mutual Bk.
Dermenghem, Emile. Muhammad & the Islamic Tradition. Watt, Jean M., tr. from Fr. LC 81-47412. (Spiritual Masters Ser.). (Illus.). 192p. 1981. 18.95 (ISBN 0-87951-130-3). Overlook Pr.
Friedlander, Ira, ed. Submission Sayings of the Prophet Muhammad. 1977. pap. 5.95 (ISBN 0-06-090592-1, CN592, PL). Har-Row.
Ghazi, A. Our Prophet, Vol. II. 1981. 3.50 (ISBN 0-686-97846-3). Kazi Pubns.
Gibbon, Edward. Mahomet & the Political Theory of the Arab Empire, 2 vols. (Illus.). 328p. 1984. Repr. of 1901 ed. 217.85 set (ISBN 0-89901-181-0). Found Class Reprints.
Hashim, A. S. Life of Prophet Muhammad-I. (Islamic Books for Children: Bk. 4). pap. 4.95 (ISBN 0-686-18410-6); pap. 45.00 entire ser. (ISBN 0-686-18411-4). Kazi Pubns.
--Life of Prophet Muhammad-II. (Islamic Books for Children: Bk 5). pap. 4.95 (ISBN 0-686-18408-4); pap. 45.00 entire ser. (ISBN 0-686-18409-2). Kazi Pubns.
Haykal, M. H. The Life of Muhammad. Faruqi, R. I., tr. LC 76-3060. 1976. 15.95 (ISBN 0-89259-002-5); pap. 12.95. Am Trust Pubns.
Hosain, S. Who Was Muhammad? pap. 3.50 (ISBN 0-686-18418-1). Kazi Pubns.
Hussain, F. Wives of the Prophet. 9.50 (ISBN 0-686-18463-7). Kazi Pubns.
Hussain, S. A. Sayings of Muhammad, the Last Prophet. pap. 1.25 (ISBN 0-686-18340-1). Kazi Pubns.
Irving, Washington. Mahomet & His Successors, 2 Vols. 1983. Repr. of 1868 ed. lib. bdg. 200.00 set (ISBN 0-89987-405-3). Darby Bks.
Ishaq, I. The Life of Muhammad: A Translation of Ishaq's Sirat Rasul Allah. Guillaume, A., intro. by. 1979. pap. text ed. 24.95x (ISBN 0-19-636034-X). Oxford U Pr.
Ismail, V. Muhammad: The Last Prophet. 8.50 (ISBN 0-686-83579-4). Kazi Pubns.
Khan, Muhammad Z. Muhammad: Seal of the Prophets. 1980. pap. 10.50 (ISBN 0-7100-0610-1). Methuen Inc.
Khan, S. A. Essays on the Life of Muhammad. 1968. 27.00x (ISBN 0-87902-172-1). Orientalia.
Lings, Martin. Muhammad. LC 83-49. 349p. 1983. 24.95 (ISBN 0-89281-046-7). Inner Tradit.
Malik, Fida H. Wives of the Prophet. 185p. (Orig.). 1981. pap. 5.75 (ISBN 0-686-31657-6) (ISBN 0-88004-005-X). Sunwise Turn.
Margoliouth, David S. Mohammed & the Rise of Islam. LC 73-14455. Repr. of 1905 ed. 30.00 (ISBN 0-404-58273-7). AMS Pr.
--Mohammed & the Rise of Islam. LC 73-38361. (Select Bibliographies Reprint Ser.). Repr. of 1905 ed. 34.00 (ISBN 0-8369-6778-X). Ayer Co Pubs.
Margoliuth, David S. Mohammed. LC 79-2875. 151p. 1981. Repr. of 1939 ed. 23.00 (ISBN 0-8305-0044-8). Hyperion Conn.
Muir, William. The Life of Mohammad from Original Sources. new rev. ed. Weir, Thomas H., ed. LC 78-180366. Repr. of 1923 ed. 57.50 (ISBN 0-404-56306-6). AMS Pr.
Nasr, S. H. Muhammad: Man of Allah. 61p. 1982. 20.00x (ISBN 0-317-39130-5, Pub. by Luzac & Co Ltd). State Mutual Bk.
Nasr, Seyyed H. Muhammed: Man of Allah. 61p. (Orig.). 1986. pap. text ed. 9.95 (ISBN 0-7103-0154-5). Methuen Inc.
Pitts, Joseph. A Faithful Account of the Religion & Manners of the Mahometans. 284p. Repr. of 1738 ed. text ed. 62.10x (ISBN 0-576-03333-2). Gregg Intl.
Pool, S. L. Orations of Mohammad. pap. 2.00 (ISBN 0-686-18347-9). Kazi Pubns.
Prayers of Mohammad. (With arabic text). pap. 16.50 (ISBN 0-686-18346-0). Kazi Pubns.
Price, David. Mahommedan History, 3 vols. Orig. Title: Chronological Retrospect or the Principal Events of Mahommedan History. (Illus.). 2291p. 1984. Repr. of 1811 ed. Set. text ed. 400.00x (ISBN 0-86590-393-X, Inter India Pubns Delhi). Apt Bks.
Qazi, M. A. Miracles of Prophet Muhammad. pap. 3.50 (ISBN 0-686-18629-X). Kazi Pubns.
Quaraishi, M. Tariq, ed. Some Aspects of Prophet Muhammad's Life. LC 83-71409. 89p. (Orig.). Date not set. pap. 4.50 (ISBN 0-89259-045-9). Am Trust Pubns.
Rahman, A. Muhammad as a Military Leader. pap. 12.50 (ISBN 0-317-46107-9). Kazi Pubns.
Rehman, A. Muhammad the Educator. pap. 15.00 (ISBN 0-686-18433-5). Kazi Pubns.
Rodinson, Maxime. Muhammad. Carter, Anne, tr. LC 69-20189. 1980. pap. 9.95 (ISBN 0-394-73822-5). Pantheon.
Sawar, G. Muhammad the Holy Prophet. pap. 14.50 (ISBN 0-686-18432-7). Kazi Pubns.
Schimmel, Annemarie. And Muhammad Is His Messenger: The Veneration of the Prophet in Islamic Piety. LC 84-17374. (Studies in Religion). (Illus.). xii, 377p. 1985. 32.00x (ISBN 0-8078-1639-6); pap. 9.95x (ISBN 0-8078-4128-5). U of NC Pr.
Shariati, Ali. The Visage of Muhammad. 28p. (Orig.). 1979. pap. 1.25 (ISBN 0-318-03828-5). Book-Dist-Ctr.
Siddiqui, A. H. Life of Muhammad. 15.50 (ISBN 0-686-18307-X). Kazi Pubns.
Siddiqui, N. Muhammad the Benefactor of Humanity. pap. 9.50 (ISBN 0-686-18434-3). Kazi Pubns.
Tabatabai, Muhammad. Muhammad in the Mirror of Islam. Chittick, William, tr. from Persian. 21p. 1979. pap. 1.00 (ISBN 0-941722-18-X). Book-Dist-Ctr.
Townsend, Meredith. Mahommed "the Great Arabian". 86p. 1981. Repr. of 1912 ed. lib. bdg. 20.00 (ISBN 0-89984-454-5). Century Bookbindery.
Watt, W. Montgomery. Muhammad at Medina. 1981. Repr. of 1956 ed. 39.95x (ISBN 0-19-577307-1). Oxford U Pr.
--Muhammad: Prophet & Statesman. 1961. pap. 7.95 (ISBN 0-19-881078-4). Oxford U Pr.

MOHAMMEDANISM
see Islam

MOHAMMEDANS
see Muslims

MOJICA, JOSE, 1895-
De Jesus, Gonzalo. Fray Jose de Guadalupe Mojica: Mi Guia y Mi Estrella. (Illus.). 100p. 1976. 2.00 (ISBN 0-8199-0570-4). Franciscan Herald.
Mojica, Fray Jose G. I, a Sinner. 1962. 5.95 (ISBN 0-685-10968-2, L38305). Franciscan Herald.

MOLINA, LUIS DE, 1535-1600
Smith, Gerard. Freedom in Molina. 1966. 2.25 (ISBN 0-8294-0070-2). Loyola.

MOLOKAI
Farrow, John. Damien the Leper. 1954. pap. 3.95 (ISBN 0-385-02918-7, D3, Im). Doubleday.

MOLOKANS
Young, Pauline V. Pilgrims of Russian-Town: The Community of Spiritual Christian Jumpers in America. LC 66-27375. (Illus.). 1967. Repr. of 1932 ed. 9.00x (ISBN 0-8462-1001-0). Russell.

MONACHISM
see Monasticism and Religious Orders

MONARCHIANISM
Weisser, Thomas H. Three Persons from the Bible: Or Babylon. (Illus.). 44p. pap. 2.00 (ISBN 0-317-17477-0). Tom Weisser.

MONASTERIES
see also Abbeys; Convents and Nunneries; Monasticism and Religious Orders; Priories; Secularization
Bastin, Dom P. La Charterhouse Du Mont St. Jean Baptiste Pres de Fribourg en Brisgau, 1345-1782. Hogg, James, ed. (Analecta Cartusiana Ser.: No. 76). (Orig.). 1984. pap. 25.00 (ISBN 3-7052-0112-3, Pub. by Salzburg Studies). Longwood Pub Group.
Beckford, William. Recollections of an Excursion to the Monasteries of Alcobaca & Batalha. 27.50 (ISBN 0-87556-541-7). Saifer.
Beltrutti, Giorgio & Hogg, James. La Certosa Di Pesio. Hogg, James, ed. (Analecta Cartusiana Ser.: No. 73). 50p. (Orig.). 1979. pap. 25.00 (ISBN 3-7052-0108-5, Pub. by Salzburg Studies). Longwood Pub Group.
Birks, Walter & Gilbert, R. A. The Treasure of Montsegur. (Crucible Ser.). 176p. 1987. pap. 9.95 (ISBN 0-85030-424-5). Inner Tradit.
Birt, David. The Monastery. (Resource Units: Middle Ages, 1066-1485 Ser.). (Illus.). 1974. pap. text ed. 12.95x 10 copies & tchr's guide (ISBN 0-582-39380-9). Longman.
Braunfels, Wolfgang. Monasteries of Western Europe: The Architecture of the Orders. LC 73-2472. (Illus.). 263p. 1973. 55.50 (ISBN 0-691-03896-1); pap. 19.95 (ISBN 0-691-00313-0). Princeton U Pr.
Charukov, Georgy. Bulgarian Monasteries: Monuments of History, Culture & Art. 1981. 89.00x (ISBN 0-569-08507-1, Pub. by Collets UK). State Mutual Bk.
Cheney, Christopher R. Episcopal Visitation of Monasteries in the Thirteenth Century. 2nd, rev. ed. xxxi, 192p. 1983. lib. bdg. 25.00x (ISBN 0-87991-638-9). Porcupine Pr.
Curzon, Robert. Visits to Monasteries in the Levant. 400p. 1983. pap. 11.95 (ISBN 0-686-46958-5, 021260104X). Hippocrene Bks.
De Montrond, M. Dictionnaire des Abbayes et Monasteres ou Histoire Des Establissements Religieux. Migne, J. P., ed. (Troisieme et Derniere Encyclopedie Theologique Ser.: Vol. 16). (Fr.). 614p. Repr. of 1856 ed. lib. bdg. 81.00x (ISBN 0-89241-299-2). Caratzas.
Dickinson, John C. Monastic Life in Medieval England. LC 78-25804. (Illus.). 1979. Repr. of 1961 ed. lib. bdg. 24.75x (ISBN 0-313-20774-7, DIML). Greenwood.
DuPont, Philippe. Guigues Du Pont: Traite Sur la Contemplation, 2 vols. Hogg, James, ed. (Analecta Cartusiana Ser.: No. 72). (Orig.). 1984. pap. 50.00 (ISBN 3-7052-0107-7, Pub. by Salzburg Studies). Longwood Pub Group.
Forsyth, George H. & Weitzmann, Kurt. The Monastery of Saint Catherine at Mount Sinai: The Church & Fortress of Justinian: Plates. LC 68-29257. (Illus.). 236p. 1973. 65.00 (ISBN 0-472-33000-4). U of Mich Pr.
Gomez, Ildefonso M. & Hogg, James. La Cartuja de el Paular. Hogg, James, ed. (Analecta Cartusiana Ser.: No. 77). 100p. (Orig.). 1982. pap. 25.00 (ISBN 3-7052-0113-1, Pub. by Salzburg Studies). Longwood Pub Group.
Hocquard, Gaston, et al. Collectanea Cartusiensa, No. 1. Hogg, James, ed. (Analecta Cartusiana Ser.: No. 82-1). (Fr., Illus.). 1980. pap. 25.00 (ISBN 3-7052-0119-0, Pub. by Salzburg Studies). Longwood Pub Group.
Hoffman, Brunhilde. Die Aufhebung der Kartause Gaming. Hogg, James, ed. (Analecta Cartusiana Ser: No. 58). (Ger.). 120p. (Orig.). 1981. pap. 25.00 (ISBN 3-7052-0084-4, Pub. by Salzburg Studies). Longwood Pub Group.
Hogg, James. As Cartuxas de Portugal. Hogg, James, ed. (Analecta Cartusiana Ser.: No. 69). Tr. of The Charterhouses of Portugal. (Ger. Span. & Port., Illus.). 145p. (Orig.). 1984. pap. 25.00 (ISBN 3-7052-0101-8, Pub. by Salsburg Studies). Longwood Pub Group.
--La Cartuja de Aula Dei. Hogg, James, ed. (Analecta Cartusiana Ser.: No. 70). (Orig.). 1982. pap. 25.00 (ISBN 3-7052-0103-4, Pub. by Salzburg Studies). Longwood Pub Group.
--La Cartuja de la Conception. Hogg, James, ed. (Analecta Cartusiana Ser.). Tr. of The Charterhouse of the Conception. (Span.). 44p. (Orig.). 1980. pap. 25.00 (ISBN 3-7052-0105-0, Pub. by Salzburg Studies). Longwood Pub Group.
--La Cartuja de las Fuentes. Hogg, James, ed. (Anaalecta Cartusiana Ser.). Tr. of The Charterhouse of las Fuentes. (Ital., Illus.). 52p. (Orig.). 1980. pap. 25.00 (ISBN 3-7052-0104-2, Pub. by Salzburg Studies). Longwood Pub Group.
--La Cartuja de Miraflores. Hogg, James, ed. (Analecta Cartusiana Ser.: No. 79). Tr. of The Charterhouse of MiraFlores. (Span., Illus., Orig.). 1979. pap. 25.00 (ISBN 3-7052-0116-6, Pub. by Salzburg Studies). Longwood Pub Group.

--La Cartuja de Miraflores: Introduction, Vol. 1. Hogg, James, ed. (Analecta Cartusiana Ser.: No. 79). (Orig.). 1986. pap. 25.00 (ISBN 3-7052-0115-8, Pub. by Salzburg Studies). Longwood Pub Group.

--La Certosa Di Firenze. Hogg, James, ed. (Analecta Cartusiana Ser.: No. 66). Tr. of The Charterhouse of Florence. (Ital., Illus.). 110p. (Orig.). 1979. pap. 25.00 (ISBN 3-7052-0097-6, Pub. by Salzburg Studies). Longwood Pub Group.

--The Charterhouse of Padula: Introduction. Hogg, James, ed. (Analecta Cartusiana: No. 54). (Orig.). 1986. pap. 25.00 (ISBN 3-7052-0074-7, Pub. by Salzburg Studies). Longwood Pub Group.

--The Charterhouse of Pavia, 2 vols. Hogg, James, ed. (Analecta Cartusiana Ser.: No. 52). (Orig.). 1986. pap. 50.00 (ISBN 3-7052-0072-0, Pub. by Salzburg Studies). Longwood Pub Group.

--Les Charterhouses de Montrieux et XXX de la verne. Hogg, James, ed. (Analecta Cartusiana Ser.: No. 75). (Orig.). 1986. pap. 25.00 (ISBN 3-7052-0111-5, Pub. by Salzburg Studies). Longwood Pub Group.

--The Charterhouses of Aragon: Introduction, Vol. 1. (Analecta Carusiana Ser.: No. 70-1). (Orig.). 1986. pap. 25.00 (ISBN 3-7052-0102-6, Pub. by Salzburg Studies). Longwood Pub Group.

--The Charterhouses of Basel, Cologne, Konz (Trier) & Roermond. Hogg, James, ed. (Analecta Cartusiana Ser.: No. 62). (Orig.). 1986. pap. 25.00 (ISBN 3-7052-0090-9, Pub. by Salzburg Studies). Longwood Pub Group.

--The Charterhouses of Naples & Capri. Hogg, James, ed. (Analecta Cartusiana Ser.: No. 57-2). (Illus.). 175p. 1978. pap. 25.00 (ISBN 3-7052-0083-6, Pub. by Salzburg Studies). Longwood Pub Group.

--The Charterhouses of Padula, Parma, Ferrara & Bologna. Hogg, James, ed. (Analecta Cartusiana Ser.: No. 53). (Orig.). 1986. pap. 25.00 (ISBN 3-7052-0073-9, Pub. by Salzburg Studies). Longwood Pub Group.

--The Charterhouses of Seitz, Gairach, Freudenthal & Pletriach. Hogg, James, ed. (Analecta Cartusiana Ser.: No. 56). (Orig.). 1985. pap. 25.00 (ISBN 3-7052-0081-X, Pub. by Salzburg Studies). Longwood pub Group.

--The Charterhouses of Tuscany, 3 vols. Hogg, James, ed. (Analecta Cartusiana Ser.: No. 60). (Orig.). 1986. pap. 25.00 (ISBN 3-7052-0088-7, Pub. by Salzburg Studies). Longwood Pub Group.

--The Charterhouses of Vedana & Schnals, With a Supplement on the Montelli & Venice. Hogg, James, ed. (Analecta Cartusiana Ser.: No. 50). (Orig.). 1985. pap. 25.00 (ISBN 3-7052-0070-4, Pub. by Salzburg Studies). Longwood Pub Group.

--The Charterhouses of Villeneuve Les Avignon, Mougeres, Toulouse & Ste-Croix-en-Jarez. Hogg, James, ed. (Analecta Cartusiana Ser.: No. 63). (Orig.). 1986. pap. 25.00 (ISBN 3-7052-0091-7, Pub. by Salzburg Studies). Longwood Pub Group.

--The Chaterhouse of Padula: Album. Hogg, James, ed. (Analecta Cartusiana Ser.: No. 54). (Illus.). 210p. (Orig.). 1978. pap. 25.00 (ISBN 3-7052-0075-5, Pub. by Salzburg Studies). Longwood Pub Group.

--The Chaterhouse of Rome. Hogg, James, ed. (Analecta Cartusiana Ser.: No. 78). (Illus.). 55p. (Orig.). 1984. pap. 25.00 (ISBN 3-7052-0114-X, Pub. by Salzburg Studies). Longwood Pub Group.

--The Chaterhouses of Naples & Capri Album, Vol. 1. Hogg, James, ed. (Analecta Cartusiana Ser.: No. 57-1). (Orig.). 1985. pap. 25.00 (ISBN 3-7052-0082-8, Pub. by Salzburg Studies). Longwood Pub Group.

--La Grande Chartreuse, et les Chartreuses de Portes Selignac et Pierre Chatel. (Analecta Cartusiana: No. 61). (Orig.). 1984. pap. 85.00 (ISBN 3-7052-0089-5, Pub. by Salzburg Studies). Longwood Pub Group.

--Mount Grace Charterhouse & Late English Medieval Spirituality: John Norton, Vol. 3. (Analecta Cartusiana Ser.: No. 64-3). (Orig.). 1987. pap. 25.00 (ISBN 3-7052-0094-1, Pub. by Salzburg Studies). Longwood Pub Group.

--Mount Grace Charterhouse & Late Medieval English Spirituality, Vol. 2. (Analecta Cartusiana Ser.: No. 64-2). 144p. (Orig.). 1978. pap. 25.00 (ISBN 3-7052-0093-3, Pub. by Salzburg Studies). Longwood Pub Group.

--Mount Grace Charterhouse & Late Medieval English Spirituality: Richard Methley, Vol. 1. (Analecta Cartusiana Ser.: No. 64-1). (Orig.). 1987. pap. 25.00 (ISBN 3-7052-0092-5, Pub. by Salzburg Studies). Longwood Pub Group.

Hogg, James & Brauer, Wilhelm. Collectanea Cartusiensia, No. 3. Hogg, James, ed. (Analecta Cartusiana Ser.: No. 82-3). (Lat. & Ger.). 120p. (Orig.). 1980. pap. 25.00 (ISBN 3-7052-0121-2, Pub. by Salzburg Studies). Longwood Pub Group.

Hogg, James & Ellis, Roger. The Contemplative Life in England: Carthusians, Bridgettines, Benedictines, 2 Vols. Hogg, James, ed. (Analecta Cartusiana Ser.: No. 68). (Orig.). 1985. pap. 50.00 (ISBN 3-7052-0100-X, Pub. by Salzburg Studies). Longwood Pub Group.

Hogg, James & Hogg, James. Collectanea Cartusiensia, No. 6. (Analecta Cartusiana Ser.: No. 82-6). (Orig.). 1985. pap. 25.00 (ISBN 3-7052-0124-7, Pub. by Salzburg Studies). Longwood Pub Group.

Hogg, James, ed. Los Cartujos, Hoy: Una Vida Para la Vida de la Iglesia. (Analecta Cartusiana Ser.: No. 81). 110p. (Orig.). 1980. pap. 25.00 (ISBN 3-7052-0118-2, Pub. by Salzburg Studies). Longwood Pub Group.

--Collectanea Cartusiensia, No. 4. (Analecta Cartusiana Ser.: No. 82-4). (Orig.). 1985. pap. 25.00 (ISBN 3-7052-0122-0, Pub. by Salzburg Studies). Longwood Pub Group.

--Collectanea Cartusiensia, No. 5. (Analecta Cartusiana Ser.: No. 82-5). (Orig.). 1985. pap. 25.00 (ISBN 3-7052-0123-9, Pub. by Salzburg Studies). Longwood Pub Group.

--Collectanea Cartusiensia, No. 7. (Analecta Cartusiana Ser.: No. 82-7). (Orig.). 1986. pap. 25.00 (ISBN 3-7052-0125-5, Pub. by Salzburg Studies). Longwood Pub Group.

--Collectanea Cartusiensia, No. 8. (Analecta Cartusiana Ser.: No. 82-8). (Orig.). 1987. pap. 25.00 (ISBN 3-7052-0126-3, Pub. by Salzburg Studies). Longwood Pub Group.

--Collectanea Cartusiensia, No. 9. (Analecta Cartusiana Ser.: No. 82-9). (Orig.). 1987. pap. 25.00 (ISBN 3-7052-0127-1, Pub. by Salzburg Studies). Longwood Pub Group.

--Die Kartauser In Osterreich, Vol. 2. Wharton, Janet, tr. (Analecta Cartusiana Ser.: No. 83-2). (Ger. Ital. & Eng., Illus.). 308p. (Orig.). 1981. pap. 25.00 (ISBN 3-7052-0129-8, Pub. by Salzburg Studies). Longwood Pub Group.

--Kartausermystik und Mystiker, Vol. 1. (Analecta Cartusiana Ser.: No. 55-1). 238p. (Orig.). 1981. pap. 25.00 (ISBN 0-317-40525-X, Pub. by Salzburg Studies). Longwood Pub Group.

--Kartausermystik und Mystiker, Vol. 2. (Analecta Cartusiana Ser.: No. 55-2). 226p. (Orig.). 1981. pap. 25.00 (ISBN 3-7052-0077-1, Pub. by Salzburg Studies). Longwood Pub Group.

--Kartausermystik und Mystiker, Vol. 3. (Analecta Cartusiana Ser.: No. 55-3). 198p. 1982. pap. 25.00 (ISBN 3-7052-0078-X, Pub. by Salzburg Studies). Longwood Pub Group.

--Kartausermystik und Mystiker, Vol. 4. (Analecta Cartusiana Ser.: No. 55-4). 172p. (Orig.). 1982. pap. 25.00 (ISBN 3-7052-0079-8, Pub. by Salzburg Studies). Longwood Pub Group.

--Kartausermystik und Mystiker, Vol. 5. (Analecta Cartusiana Ser.: No. 55-5). 103p. (Orig.). 1982. pap. 25.00 (ISBN 3-7052-0080-1, Pub. by Salzburg Studies). Longwood Pub Group.

Hogg, James, et al. Die Kartauser In Osterreich, Vol. 1. Hogg, James, ed. (Analecta Cartusiana Ser.: No. 83-1). (Ger.). 236p. (Orig.). 1980. pap. 25.00 (ISBN 3-7052-0128-X, Pub. by Salzburg Studies). Longwood Pub Group.

Holy Trinity Monastry: A History. (Illus.). 47p. 1983. pap. 1.00 (ISBN 0-317-30446-1). Holy Trinity.

Jelinek, Heienrich. Die Kartause Gaming. Hogg, James, ed. (Analecta Cartusiana Ser.: No. 58-2). (Ger., Illus.). 175p. 1981. pap. 25.00 (ISBN 3-7052-0085-2, Pub. by Salzburg Studies). Longwood Pub Group.

Jordanville: A Portrait of Holy Trinity Monastery. 1985. pap. 5.00 (ISBN 0-317-30449-6). Holy Trinity.

Kontsevich, I. M. Optina Pustin' i jeja vremja. Tr. of Optina Hermitage & It's Time. (Illus.). 604p. 1970. 25.00 (ISBN 0-317-29246-3); pap. 20.00 (ISBN 0-317-29247-1). Holy Trinity.

Leoncini, Giovanni. La Certosa Di Firenze: Nei Suoi Rapporti con L'Architettura Certosina. Hogg, James, ed. (Analecta Cartusiana Ser.: No. 71). (Ital., Illus.). 231p. (Orig.). 1979. pap. 25.00q (ISBN 3-7052-0106-9, Pub. by Salzburg Studies). Longwood Pub Group.

Little, Bryan. Abbeys & Priories of England & Wales. LC 79-213. (Illus.). 216p. 1979. text ed. 34.50x (ISBN 0-8419-0485-5). Holmes & Meier.

Matthew, Donald. The Norman Monasteries & Their English Possessions. LC 78-26293. (Oxford Historical Ser.). 1979. Repr. of 1962 ed. lib. bdg. 24.75x (ISBN 0-313-20847-6, MANM). Greenwood.

Midmer, Roy. English Mediaeval Monasteries, 1066-1540. LC 79-53097. 394p. 1980. 27.00x (ISBN 0-8203-0488-3). U of Ga Pr.

Moorman, John R. Medieval Franciscan Houses. Marcel, George, ed. (History Ser.: No. 4). 1983. 40.00 (ISBN 0-318-00515-8). Franciscan Inst.

Morrison, Barrie M. Lalmai, a Cultural Center of Early Bengal: An Archaeological Report & Historical Analysis. LC 74-9892. (Publications on Asia of the School of International Studies: No. 24). (Illus.). 160p. 1974. 18.50x (ISBN 0-295-95342-X). U of Wash Pr.

Obshchje-zhitel'naya Sarovskaja Pustin' Tr. of The Sarov Monastery. (Illus.). 241p. pap. 10.00 (ISBN 0-317-29243-9). Holy Trinity.

O'Connell, Patrick F. Collectanea Cartusiensia, No. 2. Hogg, James, ed. (Analecta Cartusiana Ser.: No. 82-2). (Fr. & Ger.). 118p. (Orig.). 1980. pap. 25.00 (ISBN 3-7052-0120-4, Pub. by Salzburg Studies). Longwood Pub Group.

Paganuzzi, P. N. Visoko-Dechanskaja Lavra na Kosovje Polje (v Serbii) Tr. of The Visoko-Dechansky Monastery at Kosova Polija (in Serbia) 1976. pap. 1.00 (ISBN 0-317-30331-7). Holy Trinity.

Plante, Julian G. Austrian Monasteries, Part 1: Gottweig, Heiligenkreuz, Herzogenburg,...Seitenstetten, & Wilhering. (Checklists of Manuscripts Microfilmed for the Hill Monastic Manuscript Library Ser.: Vol. I). iv, 52p. (Orig.). 1967. pap. 10.00 (ISBN 0-940250-26-8). Hill Monastic.

--Austrian Monasteries, Part 2: Admont, Altenburg,..."Osterreichische Nationalbibliothek, Universitatsbibliothek, Wilten, Zwettl. (Checklists of Manuscripts Microfilmed for the Hill Monastic Manuscript Library Ser.: Vol. I). viii, 296p. 1974. pap. 20.00 (ISBN 0-940250-27-6). Hill Monastic.

Reeves, Marjorie. The Medieval Monastery: Then & There Ser. (Illus.). 90p. (Orig.). 1980. pap. text ed. 4.75 (ISBN 0-582-20372-4). Longman.

Rossman, Heribert. Bibliographie Zur Geschichte Des Karatauser-Spirit-Ualitat: Im Deutschen Sprachraum Und Nachbargebieten. Hogg, James, ed. (Analecta Cartusiana Ser.: No. 67). (Orig.). 1987. pap. 25.00 (ISBN 3-7052-0099-2, Pub. by Salzburg Studies). Longwood Pub Group.

Rossmann, Heribert. Bibliographie Zur Geschichte Des Kartauser-Ordens: Im Deutschen Sprachraum Und Nachbargebieten. Hogg, James, ed. (Analecta Cartusiana Ser.: No. 67). (Orig.). 1987. pap. 25.00 (ISBN 3-7052-0098-4, Pub. by Salzburg Studies). Longwood Pub Group.

Rozanow, Gora Z. Cultural Heritage of Jasna Gora. (Illus.). 1977. 14.00 (ISBN 0-912728-44-2). Newbury Bks.

Sechi, Antonietta A. La Certosa Di Trisulti Da Innocenzo III: Al Concilio Di Costanza 1204-1414. Hogg, James, ed. (Analecta Cartusiana Ser.). (Ital.). 197p. (Orig.). 1981. pap. 25.00 (ISBN 3-7052-0109-3, Pub. by Salzburg Studies). Longwood Pub Group.

Thompson, A. Hamilton. English Monasteries. LC 78-3738. 1974. Repr. of 1913 ed. lib. bdg. 17.50 (ISBN 0-8414-8646-8). Folcroft.

Unstead, R. J. Monasteries. (Junior Reference Ser.). (Illus.). 1961. 10.95 (ISBN 0-7136-1043-3). Dufour.

White, L. T., Jr. Latin Monasticism in Norman Sicily. 1967. Repr. of 1938 ed. 9.00x (ISBN 0-910956-12-X). Medieval Acad.

Zouche, Robert C. Visits to Monasteries in the Levant. LC 80-2200. Repr. of 1916 ed. 45.00 (ISBN 0-404-18989-X). AMS Pr.

MONASTIC AND RELIGIOUS LIFE

see also Asceticism; Celibacy; Hermits; Perfection (Catholic); Spiritual Direction; Superiors, Religious; Vows

Alberione, James. Christ, Model & Reward of Religious. 1964. 5.00 (ISBN 0-8198-0023-6); pap. 4.00. Dghtrs St Paul.

Bale, John. The First Two Partes of the Acts or Unchaste Examples of the Englyshe Votaryes. LC 79-84086. (English Experience Ser.: No. 906). 540p. 1979. Repr. of 1560 ed. lib. bdg. 40.00 (ISBN 90-221-0906-2). Walter J Johnson.

Balla, Mother Ignatius. Our Continuing Yes. 1973. pap. 2.00 (ISBN 0-8198-0243-3). Dghtrs St Paul.

Becoming Christ. 4.95 (ISBN 0-87193-127-3). Dimension Bks.

Beyer, Jean. Religious Life or Secular Institute. 1970. pap. 2.75 (ISBN 0-8294-0319-1, Pub. by Gregorian U Pr). Loyola.

Boyd, Anne. Life in a Fifteenth Century Monastery. LC 76-22452. (Cambridge Topic Bks). (Illus.). 1978. PLB 8.95 (ISBN 0-8225-1208-4). Lerner Pubns.

Cummings, Charles. Monastic Practices. pap. 7.95 (ISBN 0-87907-975-4). Cistercian Pubns.

Cushing, Richard J. Meditations for Religious. 1959. 3.00 (ISBN 0-8198-0102-X). Dghtrs St Paul.

Cussianovich, Alejandro. Religious Life & the Poor: Liberation Theology Perspectives. Drury, John, tr. from Sp. LC 78-16740. Orig. Title: Desde los Pobres de la Tiera. 168p. (Orig.). 1979. pap. 1.74 (ISBN 0-88344-429-1). Orbis Bks.

Daughters Of St. Paul. Religious Life in the Light of Vatican 2. (Orig.). 4.00 (ISBN 0-8198-0132-1). Dghtrs St Paul.

Dondero, John P. & Frary, Thomas D. New Pressures, New Responses in Religious Life. LC 76-26585. 1979. pap. 5.95 (ISBN 0-8189-0332-5). Alba.

Doyle, Stephen C. Covenant Renewal in Religious Life: Biblical Reflections. 140p. 1976. 6.95 (ISBN 0-8199-0585-2). Franciscan Herald.

Edwards, Bruce & Fudge, Edward. A Journey Toward Jesus. 1.50 (ISBN 0-686-12687-4). E Fudge.

Fudge, Edward. Christianity Without Ulcers. pap. 5.00 (ISBN 0-686-12686-6). E Fudge.

Gambari, Elio. Updating of Religious Formation. LC 75-98171. 1969. pap. 2.00 (ISBN 0-8198-0168-2). Dghtrs St Paul.

Gasquet, Cardinal. Monastic Life in the Middle Ages. 59.95 (ISBN 0-8490-0657-0). Gordon Pr.

Grandaur, Georg, ed. & tr. Leben Des Abtes Eigil Von Fulda und der Aebtissin Hathumoda Von Gandersheim Nebst der Uebertragung Des Hl. Liborius und Des Hl. Vitus. (Ger). pap. 10.00 (ISBN 0-384-19640-3). Johnson Repr.

Han-ung Yang, et al, eds. The Hye Ch'o Diary: Memoir of the Pilgrimage to the Five Regions of India. (Religions of Asia Ser.). 118p. 1984. 20.00 (ISBN 0-89581-024-7). Asian Human Pr.

Hogg, James. Mount Grace Charterhouse & Late English Medieval Spirituality: John Norton, Vol. 3. (Analecta Cartusiana Ser.: No. 64-3). (Orig.). 1987. pap. 25.00 (ISBN 3-7052-0094-1, Pub. by Salzburg Studies). Longwood Pub Group.

--Mount Grace Charterhouse & Late Medieval English Spirituality, Vol. 2. (Analecta Cartusiana Ser.: No. 64-2). 144p. (Orig.). 1978. pap. 25.00 (ISBN 3-7052-0093-3, Pub. by Salzburg Studies). Longwood Pub Group.

--Mount Grace Charterhouse & Late Medieval English Spirituality: Richard Methley, Vol. 1. (Analecta Cartusiana Ser.: No. 64-1). (Orig.). 1987. pap. 25.00 (ISBN 3-7052-0092-5, Pub. by Salzburg Studies). Longwood Pub Group.

Jenkins, Claude. The Monastic Chronicler & the Early School of St. Albans: A Lecture. LC 74-19113. 1974. Repr. of 1922 ed. lib. bdg. 20.00 (ISBN 0-8414-5320-9). Folcroft.

Kiesling, Christopher. Celibacy, Prayer & Friendship: A Making-Sense-Out-of-Life Approach. LC 77-25084. 1978. pap. 7.95 (ISBN 0-8189-0365-1). Alba.

Kolmer, Elizabeth. Religious Women in the United States: A Survey of the Literature from 1950 to 1983. (Consecrated Life Studies Ser.: Vol. 4). 1984. pap. 6.95 (ISBN 0-89453-445-9). M Glazier.

Lackener, Bede K. The Eleventh-Century Background of Citeaux. LC 70-152484. (Cistercian Studies: No. 8). xxii, 305p. 1972. 7.50 (ISBN 0-87907-808-1). Cistercian Pubns.

Lackner, Bede K., ed. Stephen of Sawley: Treatises. O'Sullivan, Jeremiah F., tr. 1984. 24.95 (ISBN 0-87907-636-4). Cistercian Pubns.

Leclercq, Jean. Love of Learning & Desire for God: A Study of Monastic Culture. 3rd ed. LC 60-53004. x, 282p. 1985. pap. 10.00 (ISBN 0-8232-0407-3). Fordham.

McDonnell, Thomas P., ed. A Thomas Merton Reader. LC 74-29. 600p. 1974. pap. 6.50 (ISBN 0-385-03292-7, Im). Doubleday.

McNamee, Fintan, ed. Helping Disturbed Religious. O'Doherty, E. F. (Synthesis Ser.). pap. 0.75 (ISBN 0-8199-0393-0, L38268). Franciscan Herald.

Main, John. Letters from the Heart: Christian Monasticism & the Renewal of Community. 1982. pap. 6.95 (ISBN 0-8245-0444-5). Crossroad NY.

Maloney, George. Inscape: God at the Heart of the Matter. 1978. pap. 4.95 (ISBN 0-87193-095-1). Dimension Bks.

Manning, Brennan. The Wisdom of Accepted Tenderness. casebound 5.95 (ISBN 0-87193-110-9); pap. 4.95. Dimension Bks.

Merton, Thomas. The Silent Life. 178p. 1975. pap. 6.95 (ISBN 0-374-51281-7). FS&G.

--The Silent Life. 1983. 12.75 (ISBN 0-8446-5986-X). Peter Smith.

--Thoughts in Solitude. 1983. 14.50 (ISBN 0-8446-5989-4). Peter Smith.

Mohler, James A. Heresy of Monasticism. LC 76-148683. 1971. 5.95 (ISBN 0-8189-0183-7). Alba.

Monasticon Praemonstratense, Vol. 1. 274p. 1983. 99.20 (ISBN 3-11-008917-3). De Gruyter.

Monks of New Skete. Monastic Typicon. 49p. (Orig.). 1980. pap. 10.00 (ISBN 0-9607924-6-5). Monks of New Skete.

Nouwen, Henri J. M. The Genesee Diary: Report from a Trappist Monastery. LC 75-38169. 192p. 1976. 9.95 (ISBN 0-385-11368-4). Doubleday.

O'Reilly, James. Lay & Religious States of Life. LC 76-43048. 1977. pap. text ed. 0.75 (ISBN 0-685-81233-2). Franciscan Herald.

Panikkar, Raimundo, et al. Blessed Simplicity: The Monk as Universal Archetype. 224p. (Orig.). 1982. 17.95 (ISBN 0-8164-0531-X, HarpR). Har-Row.

Pennington, M. Basil. Place Apart: Monastic Prayer & Practice for Everyone. LC 81-43566. 168p. 1985. pap. 5.95 (ISBN 0-385-19706-3, Im). Doubleday.

Ridick, Joyce. Treasures in Earthen Vessels: The Vows, a Wholistic Approach. LC 84-2817. 166p. 1984. pap. 9.95 (ISBN 0-8189-0467-4). Alba.

Robertson, Frederick W. Sermons on Religion & Life. 332p. 1981. Repr. of 1906 ed. lib. bdg. 15.00 (ISBN 0-89984-437-5). Century Bookbindery.

Rousseau, Phillip. Ascetics, Authority, & the Church in the Age of Jerome & Cassian. (Historical Monographs). 1978. 39.95x (ISBN 0-19-821870-2). Oxford U Pr.

Salmon, Pierre. The Abbot in Monastic Tradition. Lavoie, Claire, tr. from Fr. LC 78-158955. (Cistercian Studies: No. 14). Tr. of L Abbe' dans la Tradition Monastique. 148p. 1972. 9.95 (ISBN 0-87907-814-6). Cistercian Pubns.

Schellenberger, Bernadin. Nomad of the Spirit: Reflections of a Young Monastic. 112p. 1981. 8.95 (ISBN 0-8245-0075-X). Crossroad NY.

Schlink, Basilea. Let Me Stand at Your Side. 1975. 2.95 (ISBN 3-87209-614-1). Evang Sisterhood Mary.

Theophane The Monk. Tales of a Magic Monastery. LC 81-9765. (Illus.). 96p. 1981. pap. 8.95 (ISBN 0-8245-0085-7). Crossroad NY.

Unstead, R. J. Monasteries. (Junior Reference Ser.). (Illus.). 1961. 10.95 (ISBN 0-7136-1043-3). Dufour.

Van Kaam, Adrian. On Being Involved. 2.95 (ISBN 0-87193-039-0). Dimension Bks.

--The Vowed Life. 19.95 (ISBN 0-87193-040-4). Dimension Bks.

Westley, Frances. The Complex Forms of the Religious Life: A Durkheimian View of New Religious Movements. LC 83-4579. (AAR Academy Ser.). 210p. 1983. 13.50 (ISBN 0-89130-626-9, 01 01 45). Scholars Pr GA.

William of St. Thierry. The Nature & Dignity of Love. Elder, E. R., ed. Davis, Thomas X., tr. from Lat. (Cistercian Fathers Ser.: No. 30). Orig. Title: De natura et dignitate amoris. 1981. 13.95 (ISBN 0-87907-330-6). Cistercian Pubns.

Willis, Elbert. Who Is Responsible for Sickness. 1978. 1.25 (ISBN 0-89858-010-2). Fill the Gap.

Wolff, Y, ed. A Guide to Monastic Communities in the Northeast. 1984. pap. 2.50 (ISBN 0-317-39519-X). St Bedes Pubns.

Wolter, Allan B. Living in God's Love. 172p. 1958. pap. 1.75 (ISBN 0-8199-0059-1, L38375). Franciscan Herald.

Ziavras, Charles E. The Monastery. LC 85-81279. (Illus.). 1985. 12.95 (ISBN 0-915940-05-1); pap. 4.95 (ISBN 0-915940-06-X). Ithaca Pr MA.

Zumkeller, Adolar. Augustine's Ideal of the Religious Life. xii, 468p. 1986. 40.00 (ISBN 0-8232-1105-3); pap. 20.00 (ISBN 0-8232-1106-1). Fordham.

MONASTIC AND RELIGIOUS LIFE OF WOMEN

see also Asceticism; Celibacy; Monasticism and Religious Orders for Women; Nuns; Perfection (Catholic); Vows

Alcock, John. Spousage of a Virgin to Christ. LC 74-80158. (English Experience Ser.: No. 638). (Illus.). 19p. 1974. Repr. of 1496 ed. 3.50 (ISBN 90-221-0638-1). Walter J Johnson.

Christ, Carol. Diving Deep & Surfacing: Women Writers on Spiritual Quest. 2nd, rev. ed. LC 86-70552. 157p. 1986. pap. 8.95 (ISBN 0-8070-6351-7, BP 722). Beacon Pr.

Colli, Carlo. The Spirit of Mornese. 198p. (Orig.). 1982. pap. 4.95 (ISBN 0-89944-064-9, P-064-9). Don Bosco Multimedia.

Daughters of St Paul. Blessed Kateri Takakwitha: Mohawk Maiden. 1980. 3.75 (ISBN 0-8198-1100-9); pap. 2.25 (ISBN 0-8198-1101-7). Dghtrs St Paul.

Dubay, Thomas. Dawn of a Consecration. 1964. 4.00 (ISBN 0-8198-0034-1). Dghtrs St Paul.

Horstmann, C., ed. Prose Lives of Women Saints of Our Contrie of England. (EETS, OS Ser.: No.86). Repr. of 1886 ed. 45.00 (ISBN 0-527-00082-5). Kraus Repr.

Kolmer, Elizabeth. Religious Women in the United States: A Survey of the Literature from 1950 to 1983. (Consecrated Life Studies Ser.: Vol. 4). 1984. pap. 6.95 (ISBN 0-89453-445-9). M Glazier.

Mary Francis, Sr. Right to Be Merry. LC 73-6850. 1973. pap. 6.50 (ISBN 0-8199-0506-2). Franciscan Herald.

Miller, Page P. A Claim to New Roles. LC 85-2249. (ATLA Monograph Ser.: No. 22). 253p. 1985. 17.50 (ISBN 0-8108-1809-4). Scarecrow.

Monaco, Frank. They Dwell in Monasteries. (Illus.). 80p. (Orig.). 1982. pap. 7.95 (ISBN 0-8164-2409-8, HarpR). Har-Row.

Morgan, John H. Women Priests: An Emerging Ministry in the Episcopal Church (1960 to 1980) 185p. (Orig.). 1985. pap. 12.95x (ISBN 0-932269-48-6). Wyndham Hall.

Randour, Mary L. Women's Psyche, Women's Spirit: The Reality of Relationships. LC 86-17180. 240p. 1987. 25.00x (ISBN 0-231-06250-8). Columbia U Pr.

MONASTIC VOCATION

see Vocation (In Religious Orders, Congregations, etc.)

MONASTICISM AND RELIGIOUS ORDERS

see also Benedictines; Carthusians; Cistercians; Cluniacs; Dominicans; Franciscans; Friars; Hospitalers; Jesuits; Monasteries; Monastic and Religious Life; Novitiate; Recollets (Franciscan); Retreats; Superiors, Religious; Trappists; Vocation (In Religious Orders, Congregations, etc.); Vows

Ahlborn, Richard E. The Penitente Moradas of Abiquiu. LC 85-43242. (Illus.). 52p. 1986. pap. 3.95x (ISBN 0-87474-253-6). Smithsonian.

Archbishop Averky Taushev. O Monashistvje. Tr. of On Monasticism. 46p. pap. 2.00 (ISBN 0-317-29064-9). Holy Trinity.

Archpriest John Vostorgov. O Monashestvje. Tr. of On Monasticism. 48p. 1969. pap. 2.00 (ISBN 0-317-29004-5). Holy Trinity.

Armstrong, Regis J. & Brady, Ignatius C., eds. Francis & Clare: The Complete Works. (Classics of Western Spirituality Ser.). 1983. pap. 8.95 (ISBN 0-8091-2446-7). Paulist Pr.

Bharati, Agahananda. The Ochre Robe: An Autobiography. 2nd ed. 300p. 1980. 14.95 (ISBN 0-915520-40-0); pap. 7.95 (ISBN 0-915520-28-1). Ross-Erikson.

Bland, C. C., tr. The Autobiography of Guibert: Abbot of Nogent-Sous-Coucy. 1979. Repr. of 1925 ed. lib. bdg. 30.00 (ISBN 0-8482-0140-X). Norwood Edns.

Boulding, Maria, ed. A Touch of God: Eight Monastic Journeys. LC 82-24055. 1983. pap. 7.95x (ISBN 0-932506-26-7). St Bedes Pubns.

Brianchianinov, Ignatius. Prinoshenije Sovremennomu Monashestvu, Vol. 5. Tr. of An Offering to Contemporary Monasticism. 354p. 20.00 (ISBN 0-317-28966-7); pap. 15.00 (ISBN 0-317-28967-5). Holy Trinity.

Brooke, Odo. Studies in Monastic Theology. (Cistercian Studies Ser.: No. 37). 1980. 8.95 (ISBN 0-87907-837-5). Cistercian Pubns.

Campbell, Stephanie, ed. As We Seek God: International Reflections on Contemporary Benedictine Monasticism. (Cistercian Studies Ser.: No. 70). 1983. pap. 7.95 (ISBN 0-87907-868-5). Cistercian Pubns.

Capps, Walter. The Monastic Impulse. LC 82-14866. 224p. 1982. 10.95 (ISBN 0-8245-0490-9). Crossroad NY.

Cary-Elwes, Columbia. Law, Liberty & Love. 1950. 5.00 (ISBN 0-8159-6104-9). Devin.

Chapman, John. Saint Benedict & the Sixth Century. LC 79-109719. 239p. 1972. Repr. of 1929 ed. lib. bdg. 22.50x (ISBN 0-8371-4209-1, CHSB). Greenwood.

Corbett, Julian. Monk. facsimile ed. LC 72-154148. (Select Bibliographies Reprint Ser). Repr. of 1889 ed. 18.00 (ISBN 0-8369-5764-4). Ayer Co Pubs.

Cowdrey, H. E. Popes, Monks & Crusaders. (No. 27). 400p. 1983. 40.00 (ISBN 0-907628-34-6). Hambledon Press.

Daniel, E. Randolph. Abbot Joachim of Fiore Liber De Concordia Noui Ac Veteris Testamenti. LC 82-73832. 455p. 18.00 (ISBN 0-87169-738-6). Am Philos.

English Benedictine Congregation Members & Rees, Daniel. Consider Your Call. (Cistercian Studies Ser.: No. 20). 447p. 1980. 17.95 (ISBN 0-87907-820-0). Cistercian Pubns.

Erasmus, Desiderius. De Contemptu Mundi. Paynell, Thomas, tr. LC 67-18715. 1967. 30.00x (ISBN 0-8201-1016-7). Schol Facsimiles.

Faricy, Robert. The End of the Religious Life. 96p. 1983. pap. 6.95 (ISBN 0-86683-690-X, HarpR). Har-Row.

Fry, Timothy, et al, eds. RB Nineteen-Eighty: The Rule of St. Benedict in Latin & English with Notes & Thematic Index. abr. ed. LC 81-12434. xii, 198p. 1981. pap. 8.95 (ISBN 0-8146-1243-1). Liturgical Pr.

Goldfrank, David, ed. The Monastic Rule of Losif Volotsky. 1983. pap. 14.95 (ISBN 0-87907-936-3). Cistercian Pubns.

Guigo II. Guigo II: The Ladder of Monks & Twelve Meditations. Colledge, Edmund & Walsh, James, trs. (Cistercian Studies: No. 48). (Illus.). 1981. pap. write for info. (ISBN 0-87907-748-4). Cistercian Pubns.

Herold, Sr. Duchesne. New Life: Preparation of Religious for Retirement. LC 73-76987. 168p. 1973. pap. 5.50 (ISBN 0-87125-007-1). Cath Health.

Johnson, Penelope. Prayer, Patronage, & Power: The Abbey of la Trinite, Vendome, 1032-1187. (Illus.). 224p. 1981. 30.00x (ISBN 0-8147-4162-2). NYU Pr.

Kingsley, Rose G. The Order of St. John of Jerusalem: Past & Present. LC 76-29842. Repr. of 1918 ed. 27.50 (ISBN 0-404-15422-0). AMS Pr.

Kraus, Dorothy & Kraus, Henry. The Hidden World of the Misericords. LC 75-10869. (Illus.). 192p. 1975. 20.00 (ISBN 0-8076-0804-1). Braziller.

McCoy, Adam D. Holy Cross: A Century of Anglican Monasticism. 1987. 29.95. Morehouse.

Merton, Thomas. The Climate of Monastic Prayer. (Cistercian Studies: No. 1). 154p. 1973. Repr. of 1969 ed. 7.95 (ISBN 0-87907-801-4). Cistercian Pubns.

--The Silent Life. 1983. 12.75 (ISBN 0-8446-5986-X). Peter Smith.

Moffitt, John, ed. New Charter for Monasticism. 1970. 17.95x (ISBN 0-268-00433-1). U of Notre Dame Pr.

Mohler, James A. Heresy of Monasticism. LC 76-148683. 1971. 5.95 (ISBN 0-8189-0183-7). Alba.

Monasticism: A Historical Overview. (Word & Spirit Ser.: Vol. VI). 1984. pap. 7.00 (ISBN 0-932506-33-X). St Bedes Pubns.

Monks of New Skete Staff. Exaltation of the Holy Cross. Reverend Laurence Mancuso, tr. from Gr. & Church Slavonic. (Liturgical Music Series I: Great Feasts: Vol. 4). 60p. 1986. pap. text ed. 15.00 (ISBN 0-935129-05-7). Monks of New Skete.

Muller, Max, ed. Sacred Books of China: Text of Taoism, 2 vols. lib. bdg. 250.00 (ISBN 0-87968-298-1). Krishna Pr.

Murphy, Sr. M. Gertrude. Saint Basil & Monasticism. LC 70-144661. Repr. of 1930 ed. 14.75 (ISBN 0-404-04543-X). AMS Pr.

Noble Piety & Reformed Monasticism. 166p. pap. 8.95 (ISBN 0-87907-864-2). Cistercian Pubns.

Pennington, M. B., ed. One Yet Two: Monastic Tradition East & West. LC 75-26146. (Cistercian Studies Ser.: No. 29). 1976. 14.95 (ISBN 0-87907-800-6). Cistercian Pubns.

Prebish, Charles S. Buddhist Monastic Discipline: The Sanskrit Pratimoksa Sutras of the Mahasamghikas & Mulasarvastivadins. LC 74-10743. (Institute for Advanced Study of World Religions Ser.). 1975. 22.50x (ISBN 0-271-01171-8). Pa St U Pr.

Sheils, W. J., ed. Monks, Hermits & the Ascetic Tradition. (Studies in Church History: Vol. 22). 500p. 1985. 45.00x (ISBN 0-631-14351-3). Basil Blackwell.

Skudlarek, William, ed. The Continuing Quest for God: Monastic Spirituality in Tradition & Transition. LC 81-23614. x, 302p. (Orig.). 1982. pap. 8.95 (ISBN 0-8146-1235-0). Liturgical Pr.

Sophrony, Archimandrite. The Monk of Mount Athos: Staretz Silouan 1866-1938. LC 61-4333. 124p. 1975. pap. 4.95 (ISBN 0-913836-15-X). St Vladimirs.

Tettemer, John. I Was a Monk. LC 73-89888. pap. 1.25 (ISBN 0-8356-0300-8, Quest). Theos Pub Hse.

Veilleux, Armand, tr. Pachomian Koinonia I: The Life of St. Pachomius. (Cistercian Studies: No. 45). (Gr.). 524p. 1981. pap. 12.95 (ISBN 0-87907-945-2). Cistercian Pubns.

Weisgerber, Charles A. Psychological Assessment of Candidates for a Religious Order. LC 77-91649. 1969. pap. 2.95 (ISBN 0-8294-0019-2). Loyola.

White, L. T., Jr. Latin Monasticism in Norman Sicily. 1967. Repr. of 1938 ed. 9.00x (ISBN 0-910956-12-X). Medieval Acad.

Wishart, Alfred W. A History of Monks & Monasteries. 1977. lib. bdg. 59.95 (ISBN 0-8490-1980-X). Gordon Pr.

Wynne, Edward A. Traditional Catholic Religious Orders. 224p. 1987. 24.95 (ISBN 0-88738-129-4). Transaction Bks.

MONASTICISM AND RELIGIOUS ORDERS–BIBLIOGRAPHY

Constable, Giles. Medieval Monasticism: A Select Bibliography. LC 75-42284. 1976. 20.00x (ISBN 0-8020-2200-6). U of Toronto Pr.

MONASTICISM AND RELIGIOUS ORDERS–COMMON LIFE

English Benedictine Congregation Members & Rees, Daniel. Consider Your Call. (Cistercian Studies Ser.: No. 20). 447p. 1980. 17.95 (ISBN 0-87907-820-0). Cistercian Pubns.

Van Corstanje, Auspicius. Covenant with God's Poor. 3.95 (ISBN 0-8199-0014-1). Franciscan Herald.

MONASTICISM AND RELIGIOUS ORDERS–DICTIONARIES

De Montrond, M. Dictionnaire des Abbayes et Monasteres ou Histoire Des Etablissements Religieux. Migne, J. P., ed. (Troisieme et Derniere Encyclopedie Theologique Ser.: Vol. 16). (Fr.). 614p. Repr. of 1856 ed. lib. bdg. 81.00x (ISBN 0-89241-299-2). Caratzas.

Helyot, P. Dictionnaires des Ordres Religieux ou Historie des Ordres Monastiques, Religieux et Militaires, 4 vols. Migne, J. P., ed. (Encyclopedie Theologique Ser.: Vols. 20-23). (Fr.). 2724p. Repr. of 1859 ed. lib. bdg. 347.50x (ISBN 0-89241-239-9). Caratzas.

MONASTICISM AND RELIGIOUS ORDERS–EARLY CHURCH, ca. 30-600

Chadwick, Owen. John Cassian. 2nd ed. 1968. 32.50 (ISBN 0-521-04607-6). Cambridge U Pr.

Colledge, Edmund & Walsh, James. Guigo II: The Ladder of Monks & Twelve Meditations. 14.95; pap. 6.00 (ISBN 0-87907-948-7). Cistercian Pubns.

Hausherr, I. Penthos. 24.95 (ISBN 0-87907-853-7); pap. 7.95 (ISBN 0-87907-953-3). Cistercian Pubns.

Lausaic History: Palladius. Budge, E. A., tr. 1977. pap. 5.95 (ISBN 0-686-19350-4). Eastern Orthodox.

Ryan, John. Irish Monasticism: Origins & Early Development. 520p. 1986. 60.00x (ISBN 0-7165-2374-4, Pub. by Irish Academic Pr Ireland). Biblio Dist.

The Sayings of the Desert Fathers. (Cistercian Studies: No. 59). pap. 7.95 (ISBN 0-87907-859-6). Cistercian Pubns.

MONASTICISM AND RELIGIOUS ORDERS–EAST

Jnanatmananda, Swami. Invitation to Holy Company. Dey, J. N., tr. from Bengali. (Illus.). 1979. pap. 2.95 (ISBN 0-87481-491-X). Vedanta Pr.

Mendelson, E. Michael. Sangha & State in Burma: A Study of Monastic Sectarianism & Leadership. Ferguson, John P., ed. LC 75-13398. (Illus.). 416p. 1975. 42.50x (ISBN 0-8014-0875-X). Cornell U Pr.

Syrtsov, V. L. The Insurrection of the Old-Ritualist Monks at the Solovetsk Monastery in the Seventeenth Century. 316p. Repr. of 1888 ed. text ed. 33.12 (ISBN 0-576-99180-5, Pub. by Gregg Intl Pubs England). Gregg Intl.

MONASTICISM AND RELIGIOUS ORDERS–JUVENILE LITERATURE

Caselli, Giovanni. A Medieval Monk. LC 86-70451. (The Everyday Life of Ser.). (Illus.). 30p. 1986. 9.95 (ISBN 0-87226-105-0). P Bedrick Bks.

MONASTICISM AND RELIGIOUS ORDERS–MIDDLE AGES, 600-1500

Alcock, T. The Life of Samuel of Kalamon. 144p. 1983. pap. text ed. 35.00x (ISBN 0-85668-219-5, Pub. by Aris & Phillips UK). Humanities.

Cairns, Trevor, ed. Life in a Medieval Monastery. (Cambridge Introduction to World History Ser.). (Illus.). 48p. Date not set. pap. 4.95 (ISBN 0-521-33724-0). Cambridge U Pr.

Costumes of Religious Orders of the Middle Ages. 300p. 1984. pap. 35.00 (ISBN 0-87556-491-7). Saifer.

Davison, Ellen S. Forerunners of Saint Francis & Other Studies. Richards, Gertrude R., ed. LC 77-85270. Repr. of 1927 ed. 49.50 (ISBN 0-404-16120-0). AMS Pr.

Dickinson, John C. Monastic Life in Medieval England. LC 78-25804. (Illus.). 1979. Repr. of 1961 ed. lib. bdg. 24.75x (ISBN 0-313-20774-7, DIML). Greenwood.

Gasquet, Francis A. Monastic Life in the Middle Ages, 1792-1806. facs. ed. LC 76-137377. (Select Bibliographies Reprint Ser). 1922. 16.00 (ISBN 0-8369-5578-1). Ayer Co Pubs.

Gregoire, Reginald, et al. The Monastic Realm. LC 85-43046. (Illus.). 288p. 1985. 75.00 (ISBN 0-8478-0664-2). Rizzoli Intl.

Jerome, Saint. Vitas Patrum: The Lyff of the Olde Auncyent Fathers Hermytes. Caxton, W., tr. LC 77-7409. (English Experience Ser.: No. 874). 1977. Repr. of 1495 ed. lib. bdg. 99.00 (ISBN 90-221-0874-0). Walter J Johnson.

Lawrence, C. H. Medieval Monasticism: Forms of Religious Life, Western Europe in the Middle Ages. 288p. 1984. pap. text ed. 12.95 (ISBN 0-582-49186-X). Longman.

Montalembert, Charles, pseud. The Monks of the West from St. Benedict to St. Bernard, 6 vols. LC 3-11386. Repr. of 1896 ed. Set. 195.00 (ISBN 0-404-04410-7). Vol. 1 (ISBN 0-404-04411-5). Vol. 2 (ISBN 0-404-04412-3). Vol. 3 (ISBN 0-404-04413-1). Vol. 4 (ISBN 0-404-04414-X). Vol. 5 (ISBN 0-404-04415-8). Vol. 6 (ISBN 0-404-04416-6). AMS Pr.

Rodley, Lyn. Cave Monasteries of Byzantine Cappadocia. (Illus.). 284p. 1986. 79.50 (ISBN 0-521-26798-6). Cambridge U Pr.

Southern, Richard W. Saint Anselm & His Biographer: A Study of Monastic Life & Thought, 1059c-1130. (Birkbeck Lectures: 1959). pap. 101.30 (ISBN 0-317-09510-2, 2022473). Bks Demand UMI.

Szittya, Penn R. The Antifraternal Tradition in Medieval Literature. LC 85-43316. (Illus.). 320p. 1986. text ed. 40.00x (ISBN 0-691-06680-9). Princeton U Pr.

Vaughan, Richard, tr. from Lat. The Chronicles of Matthew Paris: Monastic Life in the Thirteenth Century. LC 83-40602. 286p. 1985. 25.00 (ISBN 0-312-13452-5). St Martin.

Zeibig, Hartmann, ed. Urkundenbuch Des Stiftes Klosterneuburg Bis Zum Ende Des Vierzehnten Jahrhunderts. (Ger). Repr. of 1857 ed. 62.00 (ISBN 0-384-29875-3). Johnson Repr.

MONASTICISM AND RELIGIOUS ORDERS–RULES

Ancren Riwle: A Treatise on the Rules & Duties of Monastic Life. 1853. 55.00 (ISBN 0-685-13344-3). Johnson Repr.

Benedict, Saint Rule of Saint Benedict. Gasquet, Cardinal, tr. LC 66-30730. (Medieval Library). (Illus.). 130p. 1966. Repr. of 1926 ed. 18.50x (ISBN 0-8154-0022-5). Cooper Sq.

Eberle, Luke, tr. from Latin. & The Rule of the Master: Regula Magistri. LC 77-3986. (Cistercian Studies Ser: No. 6). 1977. 12.95 (ISBN 0-87907-806-5). Cistercian Pubns.

Flood, David & Matura, Thadee. The Birth of a Movement. LaChance, Paul & Schwartz, Paul, trs. 168p. 1975. 6.95 (ISBN 0-8199-0567-4). Franciscan Herald.

Havener, Ivan, et al, trs. Early Monastic Rules: The Rules of the Fathers & the Regula Orientalis. LC 82-51. 88p. (Orig.). 1982. pap. 5.95 (ISBN 0-8146-1251-2). Liturgical Pr.

Mork, Wulston. The Benedictine Way. 1987. pap. write for info. (ISBN 0-932506-48-8). St Bedes Pubns.

Morton, James, ed. Ancren Riwle, a Treatise on the Rules & Duties of Monastic Life from a Semi-Saxon MS. of the Thirteenth Century. LC 72-158250. (Camden Society, London. Publications, First Series: No. 1). Repr. of 1853 ed. 55.00 (ISBN 0-404-50157-5). AMS Pr.

Morton, James, tr. Nuns' Rule or the Ancrew Riwle. LC 66-23314. (Medieval Library). Repr. of 1926 ed. 17.50x (ISBN 0-8154-0155-8). Cooper Sq.

Poultney, James W. The Bronze Tables of Iguvium. (APA Philological Monographs). 37.50 (ISBN 0-89130-745-1, 40-00-18). Scholars Pr GA.

St. Cormac, Bishop of Munster. The Rule of St. Cormac: Irish Monastic Rules. (Vol. III). pap. 1.50 (ISBN 0-317-11386-0). Eastern Orthodox.

Tolkien, J. R., ed. Ancrene Wisse: English Text of the Ancrene Riwle. (Early English Text Society Ser.). 1962. 19.95x (ISBN 0-19-722249-8). Oxford U Pr.

Van der Looy, H. Rule for a New Brother. 1985. pap. 4.95 (ISBN 0-87243-138-X). Templegate.

MONASTICISM AND RELIGIOUS ORDERS–VOWS

see Vows

MONASTICISM AND RELIGIOUS ORDERS–EGYPT

Bell, David N., tr. & intro. by. Besa: The Life of Shenoute. (Cistercian Studies: No. 73). 1983. pap. 11.95 (ISBN 0-87907-873-1). Cistercian Pubns.

Budge, A. E., tr. from Syriac. The Paradise of the Fathers, 2 vols. (Illus.). 1984. Set. pap. 25.00 (ISBN 0-913026-56-5). Vol. 1, 386 pp. Vol. 2, 352 pp. St Nectarios.

Pachomius, St. History of the Monks at Tabenna. pap. 1.95 (ISBN 0-686-05644-2). Eastern Orthodox.

Veilleux, Armand. Pachomian Koinonia III. Instructions, Letters & Other Writings, No. 47. (Cistercian Studies). 1983. 26.95 (ISBN 0-87907-847-2); pap. 10.00 (ISBN 0-87907-947-9). Cistercian Pubns.

Ward, Benedicta & Russell, Norman, trs. from Gr. The Lives of the Desert Fathers: The Historia Monachorum in Aegypto. (Cistercian Studies: No. 34). 1981. 17.95 (ISBN 0-87907-834-0); pap. 8.95 (ISBN 0-87907-934-7). Cistercian Pubns.

MONASTICISM AND RELIGIOUS ORDERS–EUROPE

Leyser, Henrietta. Hermits & the New Monasticism: A Study of Religious Communities in Western Europe, 1000-1150. LC 83-40611. 131p. 1984. 25.00 (ISBN 0-312-36999-9). St Martin.

MONASTICISM AND RELIGIOUS ORDERS–FRANCE

Chaix, Gerald. Reforme et Contre-Reforme Catholiques Recherches Sur la Chartreuse de Cologne au XVI Siecle. Hogg, James, ed. (Analecta Cartusiana Ser.: No. 80,1-3). (Fr.). 1119p. (Orig.). 1981. pap. 85.00 (ISBN 3-7052-0117-4, Pub. by Salzburg Studies). Longwood Pub Group.

Chateaubriand, Rene de & Guyard, Marius Francois. Vie de Rance. 3.95 (ISBN 0-686-54375-0). French & Eur.

De Sainte Marthe, Denis. Gallia Christiana, 16 vols. 12462p. Repr. of 1715 ed. text ed. 1863.00x (ISBN 0-576-78556-3, Pub. by Gregg Intl Pubs England). Gregg Intl.

Hunt, Noreen, ed. Cluniac Monasticism in the Central Middle Ages. x, 248p. 1971. 25.00 (ISBN 0-208-01247-8, Archon). Shoe String.

Matthew, Donald. The Norman Monasteries & Their English Possessions. LC 78-26293. (Oxford Historical Ser.). 1979. Repr. of 1962 ed. lib. bdg. 24.75x (ISBN 0-313-20847-6, MANM). Greenwood.

Ultee, Maarten. The Abbey of St. Germain des Pres in the Seventeenth Century. LC 81-2265. (Illus.). 224p. 1981. text ed. 24.50x (ISBN 0-300-02562-9). Yale U Pr.

MONASTICISM AND RELIGIOUS ORDERS–GERMANY

Zeibig, Hartmann, ed. Urkundenbuch Des Stiftes Klosterneuburg Bis Zum Ende Des Vierzehnten Jahrhunderts. (Ger). Repr. of 1857 ed. 62.00 (ISBN 0-384-29875-3). Johnson Repr.

MONASTICISM AND RELIGIOUS ORDERS–GREAT BRITAIN

Bedford, William K. The Order or the Hospital of St. John of Jerusalem. LC 76-29831. Repr. of 1902 ed. 31.25 (ISBN 0-404-15412-3). AMS Pr.

Boyd, Anne. The Monks of Durham. LC 74-14438. (Introduction to the History of Mankind Ser). (Illus.). 48p. 1975. text ed. 4.95 (ISBN 0-521-20647-2). Cambridge U Pr.

Dickinson, John C. Monastic Life in Medieval England. LC 78-25804. (Illus.). 1979. Repr. of 1961 ed. lib. bdg. 24.75x (ISBN 0-313-20774-7, DIML). Greenwood.

Fish, Simon. A Supplicacyon for the Beggers. LC 72-5989. (English Experience Ser.: No. 515). 16p. 1973. Repr. of 1529 ed. 6.00 (ISBN 90-221-0515-6). Walter J Johnson.

Gasquet, Francis A. English Monastic Life. fascimile ed. LC 77-157336. (Select Bibliographies Reprint Ser.). Repr. of 1904 ed. 32.00 (ISBN 0-8369-5796-2). Ayer Co Pubs.

--English Monastic Life. LC 76-118470. 1971. Repr. of 1904 ed. 29.50x (ISBN 0-8046-1219-6, Pub. by Kennikat). Assoc Faculty Pr.

--Henry the Eighth & the English Monasteries, 2 vols. LC 74-39467. (Select Bibliography Reprint Ser.). 1972. Repr. of 1888 ed. 56.75 (ISBN 0-8369-9905-3). Ayer Co Pubs.

King, Edwin J. The Grand Priory of the Order of the Hospital of St. John of Jerusalem in England: A Short History. LC 76-29826. Repr. of 1924 ed. 28.00 (ISBN 0-404-15420-4). AMS Pr.

Knowles, David. Monastic Order in England. 2nd ed. 1963. 89.50 (ISBN 0-521-05479-6). Cambridge U Pr.

--Religious Orders in England. Incl. Vol. 1. The Old Orders. 1948. 57.50 (ISBN 0-521-05480-X); Vol. 2. End of the Middle Ages. 1955. 67.50 (ISBN 0-521-05481-8); pap. 22.95 (ISBN 0-521-29567-X); Vol. 3. The Tudor Age. Knowles, David. 1979. 72.50 (ISBN 0-521-05482-6); pap. 24.95 (ISBN 0-521-29568-8). Cambridge U Pr.

Little, Bryan. Abbeys & Priories of England & Wales. LC 79-213. (Illus.). 216p. 1979. text ed. 34.50x (ISBN 0-8419-0485-5). Holmes & Meier.

Matthew, Donald. The Norman Monasteries & Their English Possessions. LC 78-26293. (Oxford Historical Ser.). 1979. Repr. of 1962 ed. lib. bdg. 24.75x (ISBN 0-313-20847-6, MANM). Greenwood.

Rees, William. A History of the Order of St. John of Jerusalem in Wales & on the Welsh Border: Including an Account of the Templars. LC 76-29839. (Illus.). Repr. of 1947 ed. 26.50 (ISBN 0-404-15427-1). AMS Pr.

Wright, Thomas. Three Chapters of Letters Relating to the Suppression of Monasteries. 37.00 (ISBN 0-384-69545-0). Johnson Repr.

Wright, Thomas, ed. Three Chapters of Letters Relating to the Suppression of Monasteries. LC 72-74268. (Camden Society, London. Publications First Ser.: No. 26). Repr. of 1843 ed. 37.00 (ISBN 0-404-50126-5). AMS Pr.

MONASTICISM AND RELIGIOUS ORDERS–IRELAND

Burke, Thomas. Hibernia Dominicana, Sive Historia Provinciae: Hiberniae Ordinis Praedicatorum. 966p. Repr. of 1762 ed. text ed. 124.20x (ISBN 0-576-78541-5, Pub. by Gregg Intl Pubs England). Gregg Intl.

Hanson, William G. The Early Monastic Schools of Ireland, Their Missionaries, Saints & Scholars. 1927. 18.00 (ISBN 0-8337-4580-8). B Franklin.

Monastic Rules of Ireland. pap. 1.50 (ISBN 0-686-05654-X). Eastern Orthodox.

Ryan, John. Irish Monasticism: Origins & Early Development. 520p. 1986. 60.00x (ISBN 0-7165-2374-4, Pub. by Irish Academic Pr Ireland). Biblio Dist.

MONASTICISM AND RELIGIOUS ORDERS–JAPAN

Berlin, Charles. Studies in Jewish Bibliography, History & Literature: In Honor of I. Edward Kiev. 1971. 50.00x (ISBN 0-87068-143-5). Ktav.

Collcutt, Martin. Five Mountains: The Rinzai Zen Monastic Institution in Medieval Japan. (Harvard East Asian Monograph: Vol. 85). (Illus.). 450p. 1980. 27.50x (ISBN 0-674-30497-7). Harvard U Pr.

MONASTICISM AND RELIGIOUS ORDERS–NEAR EAST

Alcock, T. The Life of Samuel of Kalamon. 144p. 1983. pap. text ed. 35.00x (ISBN 0-85668-219-5, Pub. by Aris & Phillips UK). Humanities.

Carrithers, Michael. Forest Monks of Sri Lanka: An Anthropological & Historical Study. (Illus.). 1983. 34.50x (ISBN 0-19-561389-9). Oxford U Pr.

MONASTICISM AND RELIGIOUS ORDERS–PALESTINE

Russell, Norman, tr. The Lives of the Desert Fathers. 192p. 1981. 40.00x (ISBN 0-264-66581-3, Pub. by Mowbrays Pub Div). State Mutual Bk.

MONASTICISM AND RELIGIOUS ORDERS, BUDDHIST

see also Koan

Bunnag, Jane. Buddhist Monk, Buddhist Layman: A Study of Urban Monastic Organisation in Central Thailand. LC 72-86420. (Cambridge Studies in Social Anthropology: No. 6). (Illus.). 230p. 1973. 34.50 (ISBN 0-521-08591-8). Cambridge U Pr.

De Visser, Marinus W. The Arhats in China & Japan. LC 78-70136. Repr. of 1923 ed. 27.50 (ISBN 0-404-17406-X). AMS Pr.

Dutt, Nalinaksha. Early Monastic Buddhism. 1981. Repr. of 1971 ed. 12.50x (ISBN 0-8364-0815-2, Pub. by Mukhopadhyay). South Asia Bks.

Ikeda, Daisaku. The Human Revolution, Vol. 5. (Illus.). 250p. 1984. 13.95 (ISBN 0-8348-0198-1). Weatherhill.

Kakhun. Lives of Eminent Korean Monks: The Haedong Kosung Chon. Lee, Peter H., tr. LC 69-18037. (Harvard-Yenching Institute Studies: No. 25). 1969. pap. text ed. 7.00x (ISBN 0-674-53662-2). Harvard U Pr.

Lee, Kwan-Jo. Search for Nirvana. (Illus.). 124p. 1984. 24.00 (ISBN 0-8048-1417-1, Pub. by Seoul Intl Publishing House). C E Tuttle.

Prebish, Charles S. Buddhist Monastic Discipline: The Sanskrit Pratimoksa Sutras of the Mahasamghikas & Mulasarvastivadins. LC 74-10743. (Institute for Advanced Study of World Religions Ser.). 1975. 22.50x (ISBN 0-271-01171-8). Pa St U Pr.

Prip-Moller, J. Chinese Buddhist Monasteries: Their Plan & Its Function As a Setting for Buddhist Monastic Life. (Illus.). 400p. 1983. Repr. of 1937 ed. 100.00 (ISBN 0-295-96085-X). U of Wash Pr.

Suzuki, D. T. Introduction to Zen Buddhism. 1964. pap. 3.95 (ISBN 0-394-17474-7, B341, BC). Grove.

--Manual of Zen Buddhism. (Orig.). 1960. pap. 5.95 (ISBN 0-394-17224-8, E231, Ever). Grove.

Tambiah, Stanley J. The Buddhist Saints of the Forest & the Cult of Amulets: A Study in Charisma, Hagiography, Sectarianism & Millenial Buddhism. LC 83-15113. (Cambridge Studies in Social Anthropology: No. 49). (Illus.). 432p. 1984. 57.50 (ISBN 0-521-25984-3); pap. 18.95 (ISBN 0-521-27787-6). Cambridge U Pr.

Tanahashi, Kazuaki. Enku: Sculptor of a Hundred Thousand Buddhas. LC 81-50969. (Illus.). 176p. (Orig.). 1982. pap. 13.95 (ISBN 0-87773-212-4). Shambhala Pubns.

MONASTICISM AND RELIGIOUS ORDERS, ORTHODOX EASTERN

Carthach, St. The Monastic Rule of St. Carthach: St. Mochuda the Younger. pap. 1.50 (ISBN 0-686-05656-6). Eastern Orthodox.

Holy Transfiguration Monastery Staff. The Elder Joseph of Optina. LC 82-81456. 312p. (Orig.). 1985. pap. 10.50x (ISBN 0-913026-53-0). St Nectarios.

Murphy, Sr. M. Gertrude. Saint Basil & Monasticism. LC 70-144661. Repr. of 1930 ed. 14.75 (ISBN 0-404-04543-X). AMS Pr.

Pachomius, Saint Rule of St. Pachomius. Budge, E. A., tr. from Coptic. 1975. pap. 1.95 (ISBN 0-686-10939-2). Eastern Orthodox.

Patrinelis, Christos, et al. Stavronikita Monastery: History-Icons-Embroideries. (Illus.). 241p. 1974. 75.00 (ISBN 0-89241-076-0). Caratzas.

Robinson, N. F. Monasticism in the Orthodox Church. LC 72-131506. Repr. of 1916 ed. 18.50 (ISBN 0-404-05375-0). AMS Pr.

Skazanije o zhizni i Podvigakh Ieroskimanakha Parthenija, startsa Kievo-Petcherskoj-Lavri. Tr. of The Life & Labours of Hieroschemamonk Parthenius, Elder of the Kiev-Caves Monastery. 104p. pap. 4.00 (ISBN 0-317-29270-6). Holy Trinity.

MONASTICISM AND RELIGIOUS ORDERS FOR WOMEN

see also Convents and Nunneries; Monastic and Religious Life of Women; Nuns; Sisterhoods also names of orders, e.g. Sisters of Mercy

Daughters of St. Paul. The Daughters of St. Paul: 50 Years of Service in the U. S. A., 1932-1982. (Illus.). 295p. 1982. 15.00 (ISBN 0-8198-1805-4, MS0133). Dghtrs St Paul.

Ebaugh, Helen R. Out of the Cloister: A Study of Organizational Dilemmas. 177p. 1977. text ed. 12.50x (ISBN 0-292-76007-8). U of Tex Pr.

Eckenstein, Lina. Woman Under Monasticism. 59.95 (ISBN 0-8490-1318-6). Gordon Pr.

--Woman Under Monasticism: Chapters on Saint-Lore & Convent Life Between A. D. 500 & A. D. 1500. LC 63-11028. 1963. Repr. of 1896 ed. 10.00x (ISBN 0-8462-0363-4). Russell.

Hickey, Anne E. Women of the Roman Aristocracy As Christian Monastics. Miles, Margaret R., ed. LC 86-19242. (Studies in Religion: No. 1). 159p. 1986. 39.95 (ISBN 0-8357-1757-7). UMI Res Pr.

Ludlow, John M. Woman's Work in the Church. LC 75-33300. 1976. Repr. of 1866 ed. 14.95 (ISBN 0-89201-007-X). Zenger Pub.

Miller, Page P. A Claim to New Roles. LC 85-2249. (ATLA Monograph Ser.: No. 22). 253p. 1985. 17.50 (ISBN 0-8108-1809-4). Scarecrow.

Morton, James, ed. Ancren Riwle, a Treatise on the Rules & Duties of Monastic Life from a Semi-Saxon MS. of the Thirteenth Century. LC 72-158250. (Camden Society, London. Publications, First Series: No. 1). Repr. of 1853 ed. 55.00 (ISBN 0-404-50157-5). AMS Pr.

Morton, James, tr. Nuns' Rule or the Ancrew Riwle. LC 66-23314. (Medieval Library). Repr. of 1926 ed. 17.50x (ISBN 0-8154-0155-8). Cooper Sq.

Tolkien, J. R., ed. Ancrene Wisse: English Text of the Ancrene Riwle. (Early English Text Society Ser.). 1962. 19.95x (ISBN 0-19-722249-8). Oxford U Pr.

Zeller, Dom H. van. Glimpses. 260p. 1982. 5.00 (ISBN 0-8198-3027-5, SP0185); pap. 4.00 (ISBN 0-8198-3028-3). Dghtrs St Paul.

MONASTICISM AND RELIGIOUS ORDERS FOR WOMEN–BIOGRAPHY

Armstrong, Karen. Through the Narrow Gate. 288p. 1981. 12.95 (ISBN 0-312-80383-4). St Martin.

Code, Joseph B. Great American Foundresses. facs. ed. LC 68-20291. (Essay Index Reprint Ser). 1929. 21.50 (ISBN 0-8369-0319-6). Ayer Co Pubs.

Holy Transfiguration Monastery Staff. The Elder Joseph of Optina. LC 82-81456. 312p. (Orig.). 1985. pap. 10.50x (ISBN 0-913026-53-0). St Nectarios.

Walsh, James J., compiled by. These Splendid Sisters. LC 75-128326. (Essay Index Reprint Ser). 1927. 18.00 (ISBN 0-8369-1856-8). Ayer Co Pubs.

MONISM

see also Dualism; Idealism

Haeckel, Ernst. Riddle of the Universe at the Close of the 19th Century. LC 6403. 1900. 18.00x (ISBN 0-403-00117-X). Scholarly.

Ward, James J. Naturalism & Agnosticism: The Gifford Lectures Delivered Before the University of Aberdeen in 1896-1898, 2 Vols. in 1. 4th ed. Repr. of 1899 ed. 36.00 (ISBN 0-527-94500-5). Kraus Repr.

MONOTHEISM

Dietrich, Wendell S. Cohen & Troeltsch: Ethical Monotheistic Religion & Theory of Culture. (Brown Judaic Studies). 1986. text ed. 23.95 (ISBN 1-55540-017-5, 14-01-20); pap. 18.95 (ISBN 1-55540-018-3). Scholars Pr GA.

Fowler, William W. Roman Ideas of Deity in the Last Century Before the Christian Era. LC 75-102236. (Select Bibliographies Reprint Ser). 1914. 19.00 (ISBN 0-8369-5121-2). Ayer Co Pubs.

Freud, Sigmund. Moses & Monotheism. Jones, Katherine, ed. 1955. pap. 4.95 (ISBN 0-394-70014-7, V14, Vin). Random.

Goodman, Lenn E. Monotheism: A Philosophic Inquiry into the Foundations of Theology & Ethics. LC 79-24818. (Publications of the Oxford Centre for Postgraduate Hebrew Study). 228p. 1981. 22.50x (ISBN 0-86598-068-3). Allanheld.

Hack, Roy K. God in Greek Philosophy to the Time of Socrates. 1970. Repr. of 1931 ed. lib. bdg. 12.50 (ISBN 0-8337-1514-3). B Franklin.

Niebuhr, H. Richard. Radical Monotheism in Western Culture. pap. 5.95x (ISBN 0-06-131491-9, TB1491, Torch). Har-Row.

Tigay, Jeffrey H. You Shall Have No Other Gods: Israelite Religion in the Light of Hebrew Inscriptions. (Harvard Semitic Studies). 130p. 1987. 16.95 (ISBN 1-55540-063-9, 04-04-31). Scholars Pr GA.

MONT SAINT MICHEL, FRANCE

Adams, H. Mont-Saint-Michel & Chartres: A Study of 13th Century Unity. LC 81-47279. (Illus.). 448p. 1981. 40.00x (ISBN 0-691-03971-2); pap. 9.95x (ISBN 0-691-00335-1). Princeton U Pr.

Adams, Henry. Mont Saint Michel & Chartres. LC 36-27246. 397p. 1978. 18.95 (ISBN 0-910220-94-8). Berg.
Bazin, Germain. Mont-Saint-Michel. LC 75-24825. (Fr.). 1978. Repr. of 1933 ed. lib. bdg. 100.00 (ISBN 0-87817-190-8). Hacker.
Luce, Simeon, ed. Chronique Du Mont-Saint-Michel 1343-1468, 2 Vols. 1879-83. Set. 67.00 (ISBN 0-384-09010-9); Set. pap. 55.00 (ISBN 0-384-09011-7). Johnson Repr.
Rene-Jacques. Mont Saint-Michel. (Panorama Bks.). (Fr.). 62p. 3.95 (ISBN 0-685-23348-0). French & Eur.

MONTANISM

Labriolle, Pierre C. Les Sources de l'Histoire du Montanisme. LC 80-13175. (Heresies of the Early Christian & Medieval Era: Second Ser.). Repr. of 1913 ed. 42.00 (ISBN 0-404-16184-7). AMS Pr.

MONTESQUIEU, CHARLES LOUIS DE SECONDAT, BARON DE LA BREDE ET DE, 1689-1755

Carayon, Jean. Essai sur les rapports du pouvoir politique et du pouvoir religieux chez Montesquieu. LC 75-168919. (Fr.). 1973. Repr. of 1903 ed. lib. bdg. 15.00 (ISBN 0-8337-4024-5). B Franklin.
Jameson, Russell P. Montesquieu et l'Esclavage: Etude Sur les Origines De l'Opinion Antiesclavage En France Au Dix-Huitieme Siecle. LC 72-171409. (Research & Source Works Ser.: No. 859). (Fr.). 371p. (Philosophy & Religious History Monographs, No. 81). 1972. Repr. of 1911 ed. lib. bdg. 23.50 (ISBN 0-8337-4185-3). B Franklin.

MONUMENTAL THEOLOGY

see Bible–Antiquities; Christian Antiquities

MONUMENTS

see also Pyramids; Sepulchral Monuments; Tombs

Homage to Shravana Belgola. 1981. 35.00x (ISBN 0-8364-0761-X, Pub. by Marg India). South Asia Bks.
Kemp, Brian. Church Monuments. (Shire Album Ser.: No. 149). (Illus., Orig.). 1985. pap. 3.50 (ISBN 0-85263-768-3, Pub. by Shire Pubns England). Seven Hills Bks.
Parker, Richard B. & Sabin, Robin. The Islamic Monuments of Cairo: A Practical Guide. 3rd ed. Williams, Caroline, ed. 1986. pap. 12.50x (ISBN 977-424-036-7, Pub. by Am Univ Cairo Pr). Columbia U Pr.

MONUMENTS, SEPULCHRAL

see Sepulchral Monuments

MOODY, DWIGHT LYMAN, 1837-1899

Bailey, Faith C. D. L. Moody. (Golden Oldies Ser.). 1959. pap. 3.50 (ISBN 0-8024-0039-6). Moody.
Dengler, Sandy. D. L. Moody: God's Salesman. (Preteen Biography Ser.). (Orig.). 1986. pap. 3.50 (ISBN 0-8024-1786-8). Moody.
Fitt, A. P. Life of D. L. Moody. pap. 3.50 (ISBN 0-8024-4727-9). Moody.
Gericke, Paul. Crucial Experiences in the Life D. L. Moody. LC 78-7570. 72p. (Orig.). 1978. pap. 3.00 (ISBN 0-914520-12-1). Insight Pr.
Goodspeed, Edgar J. Full History of the Wonderful Career of Moody & Sankey, in Great Britain & America. LC 70-168154. (Illus.). Repr. of 1876 ed. 39.00 (ISBN 0-404-07227-5). AMS Pr.
Gundry, Stanley & Gundry, Patricia, eds. The Wit & Wisdom of D. L. Moody. (Direction Bks.). 78p. 1982. pap. 2.95 (ISBN 0-8010-3780-8). Baker Bk.
Gundry, Stanley N. Love Them In: The Proclamation Theology of D. L. Moody. 252p. 1982. pap. 8.95 (ISBN 0-8010-3783-2). Baker Bk.
Moody, W. R. The Life of Dwight L. Moody. (Heroes of the Faith Ser.). 508p. 1985. Repr. of 1900 ed. 6.95 (ISBN 0-916441-15-6). Barbour & Co.

MOON, SUN MYUNG

Bjornstad, James. Sun Myung Moon & the Unification Church. 160p. 1984. pap. 2.95 (ISBN 0-87123-301-0, 210301). Bethany Hse.
Chong Sun Kim. Reverend Sun Myung Moon. LC 78-52115. 1978. pap. text ed. 9.50 (ISBN 0-8191-0494-9). U Pr of Amer.
Duncan, Paul. Who Is Sun Myung Moon? 21p. (Orig.). 1981. pap. text ed. 1.25 (ISBN 0-87148-914-7). Pathway Pr.
Durst, Mose. To Bigotry, No Sanction: The Reverend Sun Myung Moon & the Unification Church. LC 84-60571. (Illus.). 196p. 1984. pap. 6.95 (ISBN 0-89526-829-9). Regnery Bks.
Fichter, Joseph H. The Holy Family of Father Moon. LC 84-82549. 155p. (Orig.). 1985. pap. 7.95 (ISBN 0-934134-13-8, Leaven Pr). Sheed & Ward MO.
Gullery, Jonathan G., ed. The Path of a Pioneer: The Early Days of Sun Myung Moon & the Unification Church. (Illus.). 88p. (Orig.). 1986. pap. 3.95 (ISBN 0-910621-50-0). HSA Pubns.
Horowitz, Irving L., ed. Science, Sin & Scholarship: The Politics of Reverend Moon & the Unification Church. 312p. 1978. pap. 7.95x (ISBN 0-262-58042-X). MIT Pr.
Lofland, John. Doomsday Cult: A Study of Conversion, Proselytization, & Maintenance of Faith. enl. ed. LC 77-23028. 1981. 29.00 (ISBN 0-8290-1111-0); pap. text ed. 12.95x (ISBN 0-8290-0095-X). Irvington.
Richardson, Herbert, ed. Constitutional Issues in the Case of Reverend Moon: Amicus Briefs Presented to the United States Supreme Court. 699p. 1984. pap. 19.95. Rose Sharon Pr.

MOON (IN RELIGION, FOLK-LORE, ETC.)

Harding, M. Esther. Woman's Mysteries. 1976. pap. 6.95 (ISBN 0-06-090525-5, CN525, PL). Har-Row.
Harley, Timothy. Moon Lore. 1976. Repr. 13.00x (ISBN 0-85409-828-3). Charles River Bks.
Manning, Al G. Moon Lore & Moon Magic. 1980. 14.95 (ISBN 0-13-600668-X). Pan Ishtar.
O'Neill, Eugene. Moon for the Misbegotten. LC 74-5218. 1974. pap. 2.95 (ISBN 0-394-71236-6, Vin). Random.
Rudhyar, Leyla Rael. The Lunation Process. pap. 3.95 (ISBN 0-943358-15-9). Aurora Press.
Rush, Anne K. Moon, Moon. 1976. pap. 7.95 (ISBN 0-394-73230-8). Random.

MOON WORSHIP

see Moon (In Religion, Folk-Lore, etc.)

MOORE, GEORGE EDWARD, 1873-1958–ETHICS

Cavarnos, Constantine. A Dialogue on G. E. Moore's Ethical Philosophy: Together with an Account of Three Talks with Moore on Diverse Philosophical Questions. LC 79-65479. 1979. 5.95 (ISBN 0-914744-43-7); pap. 2.95 (ISBN 0-914744-44-5). Inst Byzantine.
Regan, Tom. Bloomsbury's Prophet: G. E. Moore & the Development of His Moral Philosophy. 328p. 1986. 29.95 (ISBN 0-87722-446-3). Temple U Pr.
Rohatyn, Dennis. The Reluctant Naturalist: A Study of G.E. Moore's Principia Ethica. 150p. (Orig.). 1987. lib. bdg. 22.50 (ISBN 0-8191-5767-8); pap. text ed. 9.75 (ISBN 0-8191-5768-6). U Pr of Amer.
Soghoian, Richard J. The Ethics of G. E. Moore & David Hume: The Treatise as a Response to Moore's Refutation of Ethical Naturalism. LC 79-88306. 1979. pap. text ed. 9.50 (ISBN 0-8191-0774-3). U Pr of Amer.

MOORISH ARCHITECTURE

see Architecture, Islamic

MORAL EDUCATION

see also Christian Education; Religious Education

Berkowtiz, Marvin W. & Oser, Fritz, eds. Moral Education: International Perspectives. 472p. 1985. text ed. 45.00 (ISBN 0-89859-557-6). L Erlbaum Assocs.
Blackham, H. Moral & Religious Education in County Primary Schools. 6.00x (ISBN 0-85633-115-5, Pub. by NFER Nelson UK). Taylor & Francis.
Cochrane, Donald B. & Manley-Casimir, Michael, eds. Development of Moral Reasoning: Practical Approaches. LC 80-17141. 352p. 1980. 44.95 (ISBN 0-03-056209-0). Praeger.
Demaray, Kathleen. Instruye al Nino. Orig. Title: Train up a Child. (Span., Illus.). 24p. 1982. Spiral Wire Bound 5.95 (ISBN 0-89367-085-5). Light & Life.
Dreikurs, Rudolf. Character Education & Spiritual Values in an Anxious Age. (AAI Monograph Ser.: No. 1). 1971. pap. 2.00x (ISBN 0-918560-16-0). A Adler Inst.
Duska, Ronald & Whelan, Mariellen. Moral Development: A Guide to Piaget & Kohlberg. LC 75-20863. 136p. 1975. pap. 5.95 (ISBN 0-8091-1892-0). Paulist Pr.
Edwards, Carolyn P. Promoting Social & Moral Development in Young Children: Creative Approaches for the Classroom. (Early Childhood Education Ser.). 192p. 1986. text ed. 25.95x (ISBN 0-8077-2831-4); pap. text ed. 13.95x (ISBN 0-8077-2820-9). Tchrs Coll.
Hake, Edward. A Touchstone for This Time Present. LC 74-80182. (English Experience Ser.: No. 663). 96p. 1974. Repr. of 1574 ed. 7.00 (ISBN 90-221-0663-2). Walter J Johnson.
Hohlberg, L., ed. Meaning & Measurement of Moral Development. (Heinz Werner Lecture: No. 13). 1979. pap. 6.00 (ISBN 0-914206-18-4). Clark U Pr.
Horne, Herman H. Essentials of Leadership & Other Papers in Moral & Religious Education. LC 76-117808. (Essay Index Reprint Ser). 1931. 14.00 (ISBN 0-8369-1660-3). Ayer Co Pubs.
Isaacs, David. Character Building: A Guide for Parents & Teachers. Tr. of La Educacion de las Virtudes Humanas. 268p. (Orig.). 1984. write for info. (ISBN 0-906127-68-8, Pub. by Four Courts Pr Ireland); pap. 8.95 (ISBN 0-906127-67-X, Pub. by Four Courts Pr Ireland). Scepter Pubs.
Johnson, Henry C., Jr. The Public School & Moral Education. LC 80-20768. (The Education of the Public & the Public School Ser.). 96p. (Orig.). 1981. pap. 5.95 (ISBN 0-8298-0420-X). Pilgrim NY.
Knowles, Richard T. & McLean, George F., eds. Psychological Foundations of Moral Education & Character Development: An Integrated Theory of Moral Development. 374p. (Orig.). 1986. lib. bdg. 26.75 (ISBN 0-8191-5406-7, Pub. by The Council for Research in Values & Philosophy); pap. 14.50 (ISBN 0-8191-5407-5, Pub by The Council for Research in Values & Philosophy). U Pr of Amer.
Lande, Nathaniel & Slade, Afton. Stages: Understanding How You Make Your Moral Decisions. LC 78-195000. 1979. 10.00 (ISBN 0-06-250510-6, HarpR). Har-Row.
Lovasik, Lawrence G. Clean Love in Courtship. 1974. pap. 1.50 (ISBN 0-89555-095-4). TAN Bks Pubs.
McLean, George F. & Ellrod, Frederick E., eds. Act & Agent: Philosophical Foundations for Moral Education & Character Development. LC 86-1619. 412p. (Orig.). 1986. lib. bdg. 34.75 (ISBN 0-8191-5281-1, Pub. by Council for Research in Values & Philosophy); pap. text ed. 17.50 (ISBN 0-8191-5282-X). U Pr of Amer.
Orso, Kathryn W. Parenthood: A Commitment in Faith. LC 75-5219. 64p. (Orig.). 1975. pap. text ed. 2.95 (ISBN 0-8192-1198-2); tchr's ed. 3.75 (ISBN 0-8192-1204-0); wkbk. 3.95 (ISBN 0-8192-1199-0). Morehouse.
Parsons, Ramon M. La Moral en la Educacion. LC 83-10594. (Span.). 90p. 1984. write for info. (ISBN 0-8477-2746-7). U of PR Pr.
Piediscalzi, N., et al. Public Education Religion Studies: An Overview. Swyhart, B., ed. LC 76-26670. (American Academy of Religion. Section Papers). 1976. pap. 12.00 (ISBN 0-89130-082-1, 01-09-18). Scholars Pr GA.
Purcell, Royal. Ethics, Morality, & Mores. 177p. (Orig.). 1986. pap. 9.95 (ISBN 0-933189-01-X). Purcell Pub.
Rest, James R. Moral Development: Advances in Research & Theory. LC 86-21708. 241p. 1986. lib. bdg. 36.95 (ISBN 0-275-92254-5, C2254). Praeger.
Ryan, Kevin. Questions & Answers on Moral Education. LC 81-80011. (Fastback Ser.: No. 153). 1981. pap. 0.90 (ISBN 0-87367-153-8). Phi Delta Kappa.
Schulman, Michael & Mekler, Eva. Bringing up a Moral Child: A New Approach for Teaching Your Child to Be Kind, Just & Responsible. LC 84-18472. 1985. 19.95 (ISBN 0-201-16442-6); pap. 12.95 (ISBN 0-201-16443-4). Addison-Wesley.
Swami Vivekananda. Education. pap. 1.95 (ISBN 0-87481-451-0). Vedanta Pr.
Taylor, Monica, ed. Progress & Problems in Moral Education. 240p. 1975. 16.00x (ISBN 0-85633-069-8, Pub. by NFER Nelson UK). Taylor & Francis.
Tomlinson, Peter & Quinton, Margaret, eds. Values Across the Curriculum. LC 85-10389. 225p. 1986. 27.00x (ISBN 0-905273-75-3, Falmer Pr); pap. 15.00x (ISBN 0-905273-76-1). Taylor & Francis.
Wade, Francis C. Teaching & Morality. LC 63-17962. 1963. 2.95 (ISBN 0-8294-0080-X). Loyola.
Wilson, John. Discipline & Moral Education: A Survey of Public Opinion & Understanding. 160p. 1981. 22.00x (ISBN 0-85633-233-X, Pub. by NFER Nelson UK). Taylor & Francis.
Wilson, John & Cowell, Barbara. Dialogues on Moral Education. LC 83-4433. 170p. (Orig.). 1983. pap. 10.95 (ISBN 0-89135-035-7). Religious Educ.
Yulish, Stephen M. The Search for a Civic Religion: A History of the Character Education Movement in America, Eighteen Ninety to Nineteen Thirty-Five. LC 80-5619. 318p. 1980. lib. bdg. 27.75 (ISBN 0-8191-1173-2); pap. text ed. 13.75 (ISBN 0-8191-1174-0). U Pr of Amer.

MORAL JUDGMENT

see Judgment (Ethics)

MORAL PHILOSOPHY

see Ethics

MORAL THEOLOGY

see Christian Ethics

MORALITIES

see also Drama, Medieval; Mysteries and Miracle-Plays

Bevington, David M., ed. The Macro Plays. LC 72-3905. 1972. 50.00 (ISBN 0-384-34920-X). Johnson Repr.
Collins, Raymond F. Christian Morality: Biblical Foundations. LC 85-41020. 258p. 1987. pap. text ed. 10.95x (ISBN 0-268-00759-4, Dist. by Har-Row). U of Notre Dame Pr.
Eccles, Mark, ed. Macro Plays: The Castle of Perseverance, Wisdom, Mankind. (Early English Text Society Ser.). 1969. 17.95x (ISBN 0-19-722265-X). Oxford U Pr.
Happe, Peter, intro. by. Four Morality Plays. 1987. pap. 6.95 (ISBN 0-14-043119-5). Penguin.
Thompson, Elbert N. English Moral Plays. LC 70-131500. Repr. of 1910 ed. 7.00 (ISBN 0-404-06397-7). AMS Pr.

MORALITIES–HISTORY AND CRITICISM

Houle, Peter J. The English Morality & Related Drama: A Bibliographical Survey. LC 70-38714. xviii, 195p. 1972. 26.00 (ISBN 0-208-01264-8, Archon). Shoe String.
Hudson, Stephen D. Human Character & Morality: Reflections from the History of Ideas. 160p. 1986. 18.95 (ISBN 0-7102-0770-0, 07700). Methuen Inc.
MacKenzie, W. Roy. English Moralities from the Point of View of Allegory. LC 68-54172. (Studies in Drama, No. 39). 1969. Repr. of 1914 ed. lib. bdg. 49.95x (ISBN 0-8383-0592-X). Haskell.
Mackenzie, William R. English Moralities from the Point of View of Allegory. LC 66-29466. 278p. 1966. Repr. of 1914 ed. 25.00x (ISBN 0-87752-066-6). Gordian.
--The English Moralities from the Point of View of Allegory. (Harvard Studies in English). Repr. of 1914 ed. 23.00 (ISBN 0-384-34880-7). Johnson Repr.
Moore, E. Hamilton. English Miracle Plays & Moralities. LC 77-100517. Repr. of 1907 ed. 17.25 (ISBN 0-404-00598-5). AMS Pr.
Ossowska, M. Moral Norms: A Tentative Systemization. 264p. 1980. 47.00 (ISBN 0-444-85454-1, North-Holland). Elsevier.

MORALITIES, FRENCH

Fournier, Edouard, ed. Theatre Francais Avant La Renaissance, 1430-1550. 1965. Repr. of 1872 ed. 32.00 (ISBN 0-8337-1225-X). B Franklin.
Fraser, Theodore P. & Kopp, Richard L. The Moralist Tradition in France. LC 81-69245. 286p. (Orig.). 1982. text ed. 22.50x (ISBN 0-86733-017-1). Assoc Faculty Pr.

MORALITY AND RELIGION

see Religion and Ethics

MORALS

see Conduct of Life; Ethics

MORALS AND LAW

see Law and Ethics

MORALS AND LITERATURE

see Literature and Morals

MORALS AND WAR

see War and Morals

MORAVIANS

see also Bohemian Brethren

Bartos, F. M. The Hussite Revolution: Fourteen Twenty-Four to Fourteen Thirty-Seven. 256p. 1986. 25.00 (ISBN 0-88033-097-X). East Eur Quarterly.
Buchner, J. H. The Moravians in Jamaica. facsimile ed. LC 77-178470. (Black Heritage Library Collection Ser.). Repr. of 1854 ed. 17.50 (ISBN 0-8369-8918-X). Ayer Co Pubs.
Burkey, F. T., ed. The Brethren: Growth in Life & Thought. 1975. pap. 3.50x (ISBN 0-934970-00-9). Brethren Ohio.
Durnbaugh, Donald F. The Brethren in Colonial America. (Illus.). 659p. (YA) 1967. 15.95 (ISBN 0-87178-110-7). Brethren.
--The Church of the Brethren Yesterday & Today. Eller, David, ed. 192p. (Orig.). 1986. pap. 9.95 (ISBN 0-87178-151-4). Brethren.
--European Origins of the Brethren. 463p. 1958. 13.95 (ISBN 0-87178-256-1). Brethren.
Durnbaugh, Donald F., ed. Meet the Brethren. (Illus.). 120p. 1984. pap. 2.95 (ISBN 0-936693-11-8). Brethren Encyclopedia.
Durnbaugh, Hedwig. The German Hymnody of the Brethren, 1720-1903. Eberly, William R., ed. (Monograph). (Illus.). 336p. 1986. 25.00x (ISBN 0-936693-21-5). Brethren Encyclopedia.
Fliegel, Carl J., compiled by. Index to the Records of the Moravian Mission among the Indians of North America, 2 vols. 1407p. 1970. Set. 400.00 (ISBN 0-89235-018-0). Res Pubns CT.
Gollin, Gillian L. Moravians in Two Worlds: A Study of Changing Communities. LC 67-19653. 302p. 1967. 31.00x (ISBN 0-231-03033-9). Columbia U Pr.
Gray, Elma E. & Gray, Leslie R. Wilderness Christians: The Moravian Mission to the Delaware Indians. LC 72-84988. (Illus.). xiv, 354p. 1973. Repr. of 1956 ed. 22.00x (ISBN 0-8462-1701-5). Russell.
Griffin, Frances. Old Salem in Pictures. (Illus.). 64p. 1986. pap. 5.95 (ISBN 0-914875-10-8). Bright Mtn Bks.
Hamilton, John T. A History of the Church Known As the Moravian Church. LC 70-134379. Repr. of 1900 ed. 37.50 (ISBN 0-404-08427-3). AMS Pr.
Lehman, James H. The Old Brethren. LC 76-20274. (Illus.). 1976. pap. 2.45 (ISBN 0-87178-650-8). Brethren.
McKinnell, James. Now about Peace. (Orig.). 1971. pap. 1.50 (ISBN 0-87178-935-3). Brethren.
Rau, Albert G. & David, Hans T. Catalogue of Music by American Moravians, 1742-1842. LC 76-134283. Repr. of 1938 ed. 14.00 (ISBN 0-404-07206-2). AMS Pr.

Records of the Moravians in North Carolina, 11 vols. Incl. Vol. 1, 1752-1771. 511p. 1968. Repr. of 1925 ed; Vol. 2, 1752-1775. viii, 460p. 1968. Repr. of 1925 ed; Vol. 3, 1776-1779. viii, 513p. 1968. Repr. of 1926 ed; Vol. 4, 1780-1783. v, 471p. 1968. Repr. of 1930 ed; Vol. 5, 1784-1792. ix, 487p. 1970. Repr. of 1943 ed. 15.00x (ISBN 0-86526-060-5); Vol. 6, 1793-1808. x, 566p. 1970. Repr. of 1943 ed. 15.00x (ISBN 0-86526-061-3); Vol. 7, 1809-1822. x, 593p. 1970. Repr. of 1947 ed. 15.00x (ISBN 0-86526-062-1); Vol. 8, 1823-1837. Smith, Minnie J., ed. xi, 756p. 1954. 15.00x (ISBN 0-86526-063-X); Vol. 9, 1838-1847. Hamilton, Kenneth G., ed. xiii, 685p. 1964; Vol. 10, 1841-1851. Hamilton, Kenneth G., ed. xviii, 626p. 1966; Vol. 11, 1852-1879. Hamilton, Kenneth G., ed. xvi, 524p. 1969. 15.00x (ISBN 0-86526-066-4). (Illus.). NC Archives.

Ronk, A. T. History of Brethren Missionary Movements. LC 70-184490. 1971. pap. 2.25x (ISBN 0-934970-02-5). Brethren Ohio.

--History of the Brethren Church. LC 68-23554. 1968. 10.95x (ISBN 0-934970-03-3). Brethren Ohio.

Sappington, Roger. The Brethren in the New Nation. (Illus.). 1976. 13.95 (ISBN 0-87178-113-1). Brethren.

Sessler, John J. Communal Pietism Among Early American Moravians. LC 70-134387. Repr. of 1933 ed. 19.50 (ISBN 0-404-08430-3). AMS Pr.

Smith, Defost. Martyrs of the Oblong & Little Nine. 1948. 6.00 (ISBN 0-910294-11-9). Brown Bk.

Smith, Nathan D. Roots, Renewal & the Brethren. 152p. (Orig.). 1986. text ed. 12.95 (ISBN 0-932727-09-3); pap. 6.95 (ISBN 0-932727-08-5). Hope Pub Hse.

Towlson, Clifford W. Moravian & Methodist. LC 57-3559. 1957. 20.00x (ISBN 0-8401-2387-6, 8401-2387-6). A R Allenson.

MORAY JAMES STEWART, 1ST EARL OF, 1531-1570–FICTION

Lee, Maurice. James Stewart, Earl of Moray: A Political Study of the Reformation in Scotland. LC 73-104251. 1971. Repr. of 1953 ed. lib. bdg. 22.50x (ISBN 0-8371-3975-9, LEJS). Greenwood.

MORE, THOMAS, SIR, SAINT, 1478-1535

Chambers, R. W. Place of Saint Thomas More in English Literature & History. LC 65-15870. (English Biography Ser., No. 31). 1969. Repr. of 1937 ed. lib. bdg. 75.00x (ISBN 0-8383-0523-7). Haskell.

--The Saga & the Myth of Sir Thomas More. 1978. Repr. of 1927 ed. lib. bdg. 15.00 (ISBN 0-8495-0744-8). Arden Lib.

Chambers, Raymond W. Saga & Myth of Sir Thomas More. 1926. lib. bdg. 10.00 (ISBN 0-8414-3642-8). Folcroft.

Donner, Henry W. Introduction to Utopia. LC 78-94268. (Select Bibliographies Reprint Ser). 1946. 18.00 (ISBN 0-8369-5042-9). Ayer Co Pubs.

Fox, Alistair. Thomas More: History & Providence. LC 82-11178. 288p. 1985. pap. text ed. 10.95x (ISBN 0-300-03415-6, Y-536). Yale U Pr.

Guy, J. A. The Public Career of Sir Thomas More. LC 80-5391. 224p. 1980. 34.00x (ISBN 0-300-02546-7). Yale U Pr.

Gwynn, Stephen. Thomas Moore. LC 73-13838. 1905. Repr. lib. bdg. 15.00 (ISBN 0-8414-4448-X). Folcroft.

Hexter, Jack H. More's Utopia: The Biography of an Idea. LC 76-15177. (History of Ideas Ser.: No. 5). 1976. Repr. of 1952 ed. lib. bdg. 22.50x (ISBN 0-8371-8947-0, HEMU). Greenwood.

Heywood, Ellis. Il Moro: Ellis Heywood's Dialogue in Memory of Thomas More. Deakins, Roger L., tr. LC 75-184107. 176p. 1972. 12.50x (ISBN 0-674-58735-9). Harvard U Pr.

Hitchcock, Elsie V. & Chambers, R. W., eds. Harpsfield's Life of More. (EETS OS Ser.: Vol. 186). Repr. of 1931 ed. 40.00 (ISBN 0-8115-3377-8). Kraus Repr.

Hogrefe, Pearl. The Sir Thomas More Circle: A Program of Ideas & Their Impact on Secular Drama. LC 59-10553. 366p. 1959. 29.95 (ISBN 0-252-72653-7). U of Ill Pr.

Hollis, Christopher. Thomas More. 1934. Repr. 20.00 (ISBN 0-8274-3614-9). R West.

Jenkins, Claude. Sir Thomas More. 1935. Repr. 20.00 (ISBN 0-8274-3431-6). R West.

Kenny, Anthony. Thomas More. (Past Master Ser.). 1983. text ed. 13.95x (ISBN 0-19-287574-4); pap. 4.95 (ISBN 0-19-287573-6). Oxford U Pr.

Marc'hadour, Germain. The Bible in the Works of Thomas More, 2 vols. 1098p. 1969. Set. text ed. 127.50x (Pub. by B De Graaf Netherlands). Coronet Bks.

Maynard, Theodore. The Humanist As Hero: The Life of Sir Thomas More. 1971. Repr. of 1947 ed. 14.75x (ISBN 0-02-849040-1). Hafner.

More, Thomas. Sir Thomas More: Selected Letters. LC 61-14944. (The Yale Edition of the Works of St. Thomas More: Modernized Ser.). pap. 74.00 (ISBN 0-317-28285-9, 2022022). Bks Demand UMI.

More, St. Thomas, et al, eds. A Dialogue Concerning Heresies: Complete Works of St. Thomas More, Vol. 6, Pts. 1 & 2. LC 63-7949. (Illus.). 910p. 1981. Set. text ed. 87.00x (ISBN 0-300-02211-5). Yale U Pr.

Morison, Stanley. Likeness of Thomas More: An Iconographical Survey of Three Centuries. Barker, Nicolas, ed. (Illus.). 1964. 50.00 (ISBN 0-8232-0575-4). Fordham.

Munday, Anthony & Shakespeare, William. Sir Thomas More. LC 74-133715. (Tudor Facsimile Texts. Old English Plays: No. 65). Repr. of 1910 ed. 49.50 (ISBN 0-404-53365-5). AMS Pr.

Paul, Leslie. Sir Thomas More. facsimile ed. LC 75-128882. (Select Bibliographies Ser). Repr. of 1953 ed. 16.00 (ISBN 0-8369-5502-1). Ayer Co Pubs.

Quincentennial Essays on St. Thomas More: Selected Papers from the Thomas More College Conference. LC 78-67288. 14.95 (ISBN 0-932530-00-1). Albion NC.

Reynolds, Ernest E. Thomas More & Erasmus. LC 65-26739. x, 260p. 1966. 25.00 (ISBN 0-8232-0670-X). Fordham.

Roper, William. The Life of Sir Thomas More. pap. 6.95 (ISBN 0-87243-118-5). Templegate.

Sargent, Daniel. Thomas More. facs. ed. LC 71-119963. (Select Bibliographies Reprint Ser). 1933. 19.00 (ISBN 0-8369-5406-8). Ayer Co Pubs.

Stapleton. The Life & Illustrious Martyrdom of Sir Thomas More. LC 66-23617. 206p. 1984. 7.50 (ISBN 0-8232-0731-5). Fordham.

Sylvester, Richard S. & Harding, Davis P., eds. Two Early Tudor Lives. Incl. The Life & Death of Cardinal Wolsey. Cavendish, George; The Life of Sir Thomas More. Roper, William. xxi, 260p. 1962. pap. 8.95x (ISBN 0-300-00239-4, Y81). Yale U Pr.

Tyndale, William. An Answer to Sir Thomas More's Dialogue, the Supper of the Lord After the True Meaning of John 6 & or. 11. Repr. of 1850 ed. 31.00 (ISBN 0-384-62240-2). Johnson Repr.

MORE, THOMAS, SIR, SAINT, 1478-1535–DRAMA

Bolchazy, Ladislaus J., ed. A Concordance to the Utopia of St. Thomas More & a Frequency Word List. 388p. 1978. lib. bdg. 40.00x (ISBN 3-487-06514-2, Pub. by G Olms BRD). Coronet Bks.

Bolt, Robert. Man for All Seasons. 1962. 10.95 (ISBN 0-394-40623-0). Random.

--Man for All Seasons. 1966. pap. 2.95 (ISBN 0-394-70321-9, V321, Vin). Random.

MORGANTOWN, WEST VIRGINIA–FIRST CHRISTIAN CHURCH

Core, Earl L. Morgantown Disciples. (Illus.). 1960. 8.00 (ISBN 0-87012-024-7). McClain.

MORISCOS

Here are entered works on Muslims in Spain after about 1492 who were converted to Christianity by decree. Works on Muslims living in Spain under Christian protection before 1492 who did not convert to Christianity are entered under the heading Mudejares. Works including both Mudejares and Moriscos are entered under Moriscos.

Chejne, Anwar G. Islam & the West: The Moriscos. LC 82-703. 368p. 1983. 49.50 (ISBN 0-87395-603-6); pap. 19.95 (ISBN 0-87395-606-0). State U NY Pr.

Lea, Henry. Moriscos of Spain, Their Conversion & Expulsion. LC 68-26358. (Studies in Spanish Literature, No. 36). 1969. Repr. of 1901 ed. lib. bdg. 51.95x (ISBN 0-8383-0266-1). Haskell.

Lea, Henry C. Moriscos of Spain. LC 68-56783. 1968. Repr. of 1901 ed. 20.50 (ISBN 0-8337-4218-3). B Franklin.

--Moriscos of Spain: Their Conversion & Expulsion. 1968. Repr. of 1901 ed. lib. bdg. 23.50x (ISBN 0-8371-0141-7, LEMS). Greenwood.

MORMON TRAIL

Jones, Helen H. Over the Mormon Trail. LC 63-9706. (Frontiers of America Ser.). (Illus.). 128p. 1980. PLB 10.60 (ISBN 0-516-03354-9). Childrens.

Kimball, Stanley B. Discovering Mormon Trails. LC 79-53092. (Illus.). 1979. pap. 4.95 (ISBN 0-87747-756-6). Deseret Bk.

MORMONS AND MORMONISM

see also Book of Mormon; Church of Jesus Christ of Latter-Day Saints; Mountain Meadows Massacre, 1857; Utah Expedition, 1857-1858

Adams, George J. A Lecture on the Doctrine of Baptism for the Dead. new ed. (Orig.). 1983. pap. 1.00 (ISBN 0-942284-04-6). Restoration Re.

Allen, Edward J. The Second United Order among the Mormons. LC 73-38483. (Columbia University Studies in the Social Sciences: No. 419). Repr. of 1936 ed. 15.00 (ISBN 0-404-51419-7). AMS Pr.

Allen, James B. Trials of Discipleship: The Story of William Clayton, a Mormon. 416p. 1987. 22.95 (ISBN 0-252-01369-7). U of Ill Pr.

Andrew, Laurel B. The Early Temples of the Mormons: The Architecture of the Millennial Kingdom in the American West. LC 77-23971. (Illus.). 1978. 29.50 (ISBN 0-87395-358-4). State U NY Pr.

Arrington, Leonard J. & Bitton, Davis. Saints Without Halos: The Human Side of Mormon History. 168p. 1981. 10.95 (ISBN 0-941214-01-X). Signature Bks.

Backman, Milton V., Jr. Eyewitness Accounts of the Restoration. 1986. Repr. of 1983 ed. 10.95 (ISBN 0-87579-027-5). Deseret Bk.

Bagley, Pat. Treasures of Half-Truths. 100p. 1986. pap. 4.95 (ISBN 0-941214-47-8). Signature Bks.

Bahr, Howard M., et al. Life in Large Families: Views of Mormon Women. LC 82-45005. 264p. (Orig.). 1982. lib. bdg. 29.25 (ISBN 0-8191-2551-2); pap. text ed. 13.25 o. p. (ISBN 0-8191-2552-0). U Pr of Amer.

Bailey, F. My Summer in a Mormon Village. 59.95 (ISBN 0-8490-0692-9). Gordon Pr.

Barbour, Hugh. Margaret Fell Speaking. LC 76-4224. (Orig.). 1976. pap. 2.50x (ISBN 0-87574-206-8). Pendle Hill.

Barrett, Ivan J. Joseph Smith & the Restoration: A History of the LDS Church to 1846. rev. ed. LC 70-167990. (Illus.). 1973. pap. 9.95 (ISBN 0-8425-0672-1). Brigham.

Beach, Charles. The Not-So-Amazing Mormonism. (Truthway Ser.). 39p. 1981. pap. text ed. 1.25 (ISBN 0-87148-629-6). Pathway Pr.

Beier, Lucinda. Mormans, Jehovah's Witnesses & Christian Scientists. 1985. 13.00x (ISBN 0-7062-3880-X, Pub. by Ward Lock Educ Co Ltd). State Mutual Bk.

Bjornstad, James. Counterfeits at Your Door. LC 78-72864. 160p. 1979. pap. text ed. 2.95 (ISBN 0-8307-0610-0, S124254). Regal.

The Book of Mormon: It Begins with a Family. LC 83-73118. 270p. 1983. 8.95 (ISBN 0-87747-987-9). Deseret Bk.

Bradford, Mary L., ed. Mormon Women Speak. LC 82-62366. 1982. 9.95 (ISBN 0-913420-94-8). Olympus Pub Co.

Briggs, Kay. Most Quoted Scriptures. 417p. 1981. Repr. of 1980 ed. 11.95 (ISBN 0-934126-13-5). Randall Bk Co.

Bringhurst, Newell G. Saints, Slaves, & Blacks: The Changing Place of Black People Within Mormonism. LC 81-1093. (Contributions to the Study of Religion Ser.: No. 4). (Illus.). 256p. 1981. lib. bdg. 29.95 (ISBN 0-313-22752-7, BSB/). Greenwood.

Brooks, Juanita. Jacob Hamblin: Mormon Apostle to the Indians. LC 80-80395. (Illus.). 160p. 1980. pap. 6.95 (ISBN 0-935704-03-5). Howe Brothers.

Brooks, Juanita, ed. On the Mormon Frontier: The Diary of Hosea Stout, 2 Vols. 832p. 1982. Repr. of 1964 ed. 39.95 (ISBN 0-87480-214-8, SET). U of Utah Pr.

Brough, R. Clayton. His Servants Speak: Statements by Latter-day Saint Leaders on Contemporary Topics. LC 75-17101. 298p. 1975. 10.95 (ISBN 0-88290-054-4). Horizon Utah.

Call, William. The Trial of Faith: Discussions Concerning Mormonisn & Neo-Mormonism. 215p. (Orig.). Date not set. pap. write for info. (ISBN 0-916095-11-8). Pubs Pr UT.

Canfield, Anita. Self-Esteem for the Latter-Day Saint Woman. 2nd ed. 135p. 1983. 7.95 (ISBN 0-934126-15-1). Randall Bk Co.

Cannon, George Q. Writings from the "Western Standard". Repr. of 1864 ed. 25.00 (ISBN 0-404-01379-1). AMS Pr.

Card, Orson S. Saintspeak. 64p. (Orig.). 1981. pap. 3.95 (ISBN 0-941214-00-1). Signature Bks.

Christensen, Leon N. The Little Book: Why I Am a Mormon. 1976. 12.00 (ISBN 0-8283-1606-6). Branden Pub Co.

Clark, J. Reuben, Jr. Why the King James Version. LC 79-15008. (Classics in Mormon Literature Ser.). 535p. 1979. 7.95 (ISBN 0-87747-773-6). Deseret Bk.

Clayton, William. The Latter-Day Saints' Emigrants' Guide. Kimball, Stanley B. & Allen, James B., eds. LC 83-2473. (Illus.). vi, 111p. 1983. 12.95 (ISBN 0-935284-27-3). Patrice Pr.

--William Clayton's Journal: A Daily Record of the Journey of the Original Company of Mormon Pioneers from Nauveo, Illinois, to the Valley of the Great Salt Lake. LC 72-9435. (The Far Western Frontier Ser.). 380p. 1973. Repr. of 1921 ed. 26.50 (ISBN 0-405-04965-X). Ayer Co Pubs.

Codman, John T. Mormon Country. LC 70-134392. Repr. of 1874 ed. 18.25 (ISBN 0-404-08481-8). AMS Pr.

Coe, Jolene & Coe, Greg. The Mormon Experience: A Young Couple's Fascinating Journey to Truth. 176p. (Orig.). 1985. pap. 5.95 (ISBN 0-89081-486-4). Harvest Hse.

Coleman, Gary J. A Look at Mormonism. pap. 3.95 (ISBN 0-89036-142-8). Hawkes Pub Inc.

Cowan, Marvin W. Los Mormones: Sus Doctrinas Refutadas a la Luz De la Biblia. De La Fuente, Tomas, tr. from Eng. 160p. 1985. pap. 3.50 (ISBN 0-311-05763-2). Casa Bautista.

Cramer, Steven A. The Worth of a Soul. 127p. 1983. 7.95 (ISBN 0-934126-29-1). Randall Bk Co.

Creer, Leland H. Mormon Towns in the Region of the Colorado. Incl. The Activities of Jacob Hamblin in the Region of the Colorado. (Glen Canyon Ser.: Nos. 3-4). Repr. of 1958 ed. 20.00 (ISBN 0-404-60633-4). AMS Pr.

Crossfield, R. C. Book of Onias. LC 70-86503. 1969. 7.95 (ISBN 0-8022-2290-0). Philos Lib.

Crouch, Brodie. The Myth of Mormon Inspiration. 7.50 (ISBN 0-89315-158-0). Lambert Bk.

Crowther, Duane S. Gifts of the Spirit. LC 65-29176. 352p. 1983. 10.95 (ISBN 0-88290-210-5). Horizon Utah.

--Prophetic Warnings to Modern America. LC 77-87431. 415p. 1977. 12.95 (ISBN 0-88290-016-1). Horizon Utah.

Crowther, Jean D. Book of Mormon Puzzles & Pictures for Young Latter-Day Saints. LC 77-74495. (Books for LDS Children). (Illus.). 56p. 1977. pap. 4.95 (ISBN 0-88290-080-3). Horizon Utah.

Dalton, Lee. When the Brave Ones Cried. 176p. 1986. 8.95 (ISBN 0-88290-282-2). Horizon Utah.

Dean, Bessie. Let's Learn of God's Love. LC 79-89367. (Books for LDS Children). (Illus.). 64p. 1979. pap. 3.95 (ISBN 0-88290-124-9). Horizon Utah.

--Let's Learn the First Principles. LC 78-70366. (Books for LDS Children). (Illus.). 64p. 1978. pap. 3.95 (ISBN 0-88290-104-4). Horizon Utah.

--Let's Love One Another. LC 77-74492. (Books for Lds Children Ser.). (Illus.). 64p. 1978. pap. 3.95 (ISBN 0-88290-077-3). Horizon Utah.

Decker, Ed & Hunt, Dave. The God Makers. LC 83-82319. 192p. 1984. pap. 6.95 (ISBN 0-89081-402-3). Harvest Hse.

Divett, Robert T. Medicine & the Mormons: An Introduction to the History of Latter-day Saint Health Care. LC 81-84588. 230p. 1981. pap. 9.95 (ISBN 0-88290-194-X, 2050). Horizon Utah.

Dyer, William G. & Kunz, Phillip R. Effective Mormon Families. 1986. text ed. 9.95 (ISBN 0-87579-059-3). Deseret Bk.

Early Mormon Settlements in Nevada: Humpherys. 1981. 12.50 (ISBN 0-686-92671-4). Byzantine Pr.

Ellsworth, S. George, ed. Dear Ellen: Two Mormon Women & Their Letters. 92p. 1974. 12.00 (ISBN 0-941214-33-8). Signature Bks.

England, Eugene. Dialogues with Myself: Personal Essays on Mormon Experience. 205p. (Orig.). 1984. pap. 7.50 (ISBN 0-941214-21-4, Orion). Signature Bks.

England, Kathleen. Why We Are Baptized. LC 78-19180. (Illus.). 1978. 5.95 (ISBN 0-87747-893-7). Deseret Bk.

Enriquez, Edmund C. The Golden Gospel: A Pictorial History of the Restoration. (Illus.). 96p. 1981. pap. 5.95 (ISBN 0-88290-198-2). Horizon Utah.

Ericksen, Ephraim E. The Psychological & Ethical Aspects of Mormon Group Life. LC 75-310523. (A Bonneville Books Reprint Edition). pap. 30.80 (ISBN 0-317-41838-6, 2025900). Bks Demand UMI.

Etzenhouser, R. From Palmyra, New York, Eighteen Thirty to Independence, Missouri, Eighteen Ninety-Four. LC 73-134393. Repr. of 1894 ed. 29.50 (ISBN 0-404-08435-4). AMS Pr.

Evans, R. C. Forty Years in the Mormon Church: Why I Left It. 1976. Repr. of 1920 ed. 6.95 (ISBN 0-89315-054-1). Lambert Bk.

F. A. R. M. S. Staff. Book of Mormon Critical Text: A Tool for Scholarly Reference, 3 vols. LC 85-137843. (F. A. R. M. S. Critical Text Project). (Illus.). 1100p. (Orig.). 1986. Set. 55.00x (ISBN 0-934893-00-4, STF-84A); Vol. 3: Helaman - Moroni April 1987. pap. text ed. 20.00x (ISBN 0-934893-03-9). FARMS.

F. A. R. M. S. Staff, ed. Book of Mormon Critical Text: A Tool for Scholarly Reference, Vol. 1, I Nephi-Words of Mormon. rev., 2nd ed. (F. A. R. M. S. Critical Text Project Ser.: No. 4). (Illus.). 382p. 1986. Set of 3 Vols. 55.00 (ISBN 0-934893-07-1); pap. 20.00 (ISBN 0-934893-04-7). FARMS.

Fernandez, Domingo. El Mormonismo Revelacion Divina o Invencion Humana. 32p. 1984. pap. 1.00 (ISBN 0-311-05762-4). Casa Bautista.

Ferris, B. G. Mormons at Home. LC 70-134395. Repr. of 1856 ed. 24.00 (ISBN 0-404-08437-0). AMS Pr.

Fife, Austin & Fife, Alta. Saints of Sage & Saddle: Folklore Among the Mormons. 375p. 1980. pap. 14.95 (ISBN 0-87480-180-X). U of Utah Pr.

Flanders, Robert B. Nauvoo: Kingdom on the Mississippi. LC 65-19110. (Illus.). 374p. 1975. pap. 8.95 (ISBN 0-252-00561-9). U of Ill Pr.

Fluckiger, W. Lynn. Unique Advantages of Being a Mormon. pap. 3.95 (ISBN 0-89036-138-X). Hawkes Pub Inc.

Fox, Frank W. J. Reuben Clark: The Public Years. LC 80-17903. (J. Reuben Clark Three Vol. Ser.). (Illus.). 706p. 1980. 10.95 (ISBN 0-8425-1832-0). Brigham.

Francaviglia, Richard V. The Mormon Landscape: Existence, Creation & Perception of a Unique Image in the American West. LC 77-83791. (Studies in Social History: No. 2). (Illus.). 39.50 (ISBN 0-404-16020-4). AMS Pr.

Fraser, Gordon H. Is Mormonism Christian? 1977. pap. 3.95 (ISBN 0-8024-4169-6). Moody.

Gates, Susa Y. & Widtsoe, Leah D. The Life Story of Brigham Young. facsimile ed. LC 74-164602. (Select Bibliographies Reprint Ser). Repr. of 1930 ed. 24.00 (ISBN 0-8369-5886-1). Ayer Co Pubs.

Geer, Thelma. Mormonism & Me: A True Story. 1986. pap. 6.95 (ISBN 0-8024-5633-2). Moody.

--Mormonism, Mama & Me. 3rd, rev. ed. LC 81-146846. (Illus.). 228p. 1983. pap. 3.95 (ISBN 0-912375-00-0). Calvary Miss Pr.

--Mormonism, Mama, & Me. 1983. pap. 4.95 (ISBN 0-87508-192-4). Chr Lit.

Geer, Thelma, ed. Mormonism, Mama & Me. 4th ed. (Illus.). 252p. 1984. pap. 4.95 (ISBN 0-912375-01-9). Calvary Miss Pr.

Gerstner, John H. Teachings of Mormonism. pap. 1.95 (ISBN 0-8010-3719-0). Baker Bk.

Gibbons, Francis M. Heber J. Grant: Man of Steel, Prophet of God. LC 79-11649. 252p. 1979. 8.95 (ISBN 0-87747-755-8). Deseret Bk.

--John Taylor: Mormon Philosopher, Prophet of God. LC 84-73532. 312p. 1985. 10.95 (ISBN 0-87747-714-0). Deseret Bk.

Gottlieb, Robert & Wiley, Peter. America's Saints: The Rise of Mormon Power. LC 84-3304. 1984. 16.95 (ISBN 0-399-12924-3, Putnam). Putnam Pub Group.

Grant, J. M. J. M. Grant's Rigdon. 16p. (Orig.). 1984. pap. 1.95 (ISBN 0-942284-06-2). Restoration Re.

Green, N. W. Mormonism: Its Rise, Progress & Present Condition. LC 79-134401. Repr. of 1870 ed. 32.50 (ISBN 0-404-08445-1). AMS Pr.

Gruss, Edmond C. What Every Mormon Should Know. (Orig.). 1975. micro book 1.95 (ISBN 0-916406-34-2). Accent Bks.

Gunn, Rodger S. Mormonism: Challenge & Defense. 1979. pap. 8.95 (ISBN 0-89036-126-6). Hawkes Pub Inc.

Gunnison, John W. The Mormons: Or, Latter-Day Saints, in the Valley of the Great Salt Lake; a History of Their Rise & Progress, Peculiar Doctrines, Present Condition & Prospects, Derived from Personal Observation During a Residence Among Them. LC 70-38355. (Select Bibliographies Reprint Ser.). Repr. of 1852 ed. 16.00 (ISBN 0-8369-6772-0). Ayer Co Pubs.

Halverson, Sandy. Book of Mormon Activity Book: Creative Scripture Learning Experiences for Children 4-12. (Illus.). 80p. 1982. pap. 2.95 (ISBN 0-88290-188-5, 4521). Horizon Utah.

Hamilton, Charles M. & Cutrubus, C. Nina, eds. The Salt Lake Temple: A Monument to a People. (Illus.). 208p. 1983. write for info. (ISBN 0-913535-01-X); pap. write for info. (ISBN 0-913535-02-8); Ltd. Ed. 250.00 (ISBN 0-913535-00-1). Univ Servs Inc.

Hampshire, Annette P. Mormonism in Conflict: The Nauvoo Years. LC 84-27263. (Studies in Religion & Society: Vol. II). 350p. 1985. 59.95x (ISBN 0-88946-874-5). E Mellen.

Hansen, Klaus J. Mormonism & the American Experience. LC 80-19312. (History of American Religion Ser.). 224p. 1981. 15.00x (ISBN 0-226-31552-5). U of Chicago Pr.

--Mormonism & the American Experience. LC 80-19312. (Chicago History of American Religions Ser.). xx, 258p. 1983. pap. 8.50 (ISBN 0-226-31553-3). U of Chicago Pr.

Haslam, Gerald M. Clash of Cultures: The Norwegian Experience with Mormonism, 1842-1920. LC 83-49362. (American University Studies IX (History): Vol. 7). 350p. 1984. text ed. 39.80 (ISBN 0-8204-0179-X). P Lang Pubs.

Hawkes, John D. Book of Mormon Digest. 240p. 1966. pap. 4.95 (ISBN 0-89036-010-3). Hawkes Pub Inc.

Hector, Lee H. The Three Nephites: Substance & Significance of the Legend in Folklore. Dorson, Richard, ed. LC 77-70608. (International Folklore Ser.). 1977. Repr. of 1949 ed. lib. bdg. 14.00x (ISBN 0-405-10105-8). Ayer Co Pubs.

Heinerman, John & Shupe, Anson. The Mormon Corporate Empire: The Eye-Opening Report on the Church & Its Political & Financial Agenda. LC 85-47527. 352p. 1986. 19.95 (ISBN 0-8070-0406-5). Beacon Pr.

Hemingway, Donald W. Utah & the Mormons. (Illus.). 1979. pap. 2.50 (ISBN 0-686-30193-5). D W Hemingway.

Hemingway, Donald W., ed. Utah & the Mormons. (Travel Ser.). (Illus.). 32p. 1983. pap. write for info. (ISBN 0-938440-47-0). Colourpicture.

Hemmingway, Donald W. Gospel Themes. 90p. 1982. 3.95 (ISBN 0-934126-25-9). Randall Bk Co.

--Gospel Themes II. 71p. 1983. 3.95 (ISBN 0-934126-40-2). Randall Bk Co.

Hickman, Bill. Brigham's Destroying Angel. facsimile ed. LC 74-165642. (Select Bibliographies Reprint Ser). Repr. of 1904 ed. 18.00 (ISBN 0-8369-5951-5). Ayer Co Pubs.

Hillam, Ray C., ed. By the Hands of Wise Men: Essays on the U. S. Constitution. LC 79-13702. 1979. pap. text ed. 5.95 (ISBN 0-8425-1647-6). Brigham.

Hoekema, Anthony A. The Four Major Cults. 1963. 24.95 (ISBN 0-8028-3117-6). Eerdmans.

--Mormonism. 1974. pap. 2.95 (ISBN 0-8028-1491-3). Eerdmans.

Hullinger, Robert N., ed. Mormon Answer to Skepticism: Why Joseph Smith Wrote the Book of Mormon. LC 79-54055. 201p. (Orig.). 1980. pap. 14.95x (ISBN 0-915644-18-5). Clayton Pub Hse.

Hunt, Larry E. Frederick M. Smith: Saint as Reformer. LC 81-7213. 1982. Vol. 1. pap. 12.00 (ISBN 0-8309-0320-8); Vol. 2. 12.00 (ISBN 0-8309-0341-0). Herald Hse.

Jacobson, Jay. El Mormonismo Refutado. (Modern Doctrines Collection). 32p. 1984. Repr. of 1981 ed. 0.75 (ISBN 0-311-05030-1). Casa Bautista.

Jaussi, Laureen & Chaston, Gloria. Genealogical Records of Utah. LC 73-87713. 336p. 1974. 5.95 (ISBN 0-87747-507-5). Deseret Bk.

Kaiser, Edgar P. How to Respond to the Latter Day Saints. (The Response Ser.). 1977. 1.95 (ISBN 0-570-07680-3, 12-2669). Concordia.

Kendrick, Lionel. Scriptures to Success. 99p. 1983. 3.95 (ISBN 0-934126-42-9). Randall Bk Co.

Kern, Louis J. An Ordered Love: Sex Roles & Sexuality in Victorian Utopias--the Shakers, the Mormons, & the Oneida Community. LC 80-10763. xv, 430p. 1981. 27.00x (ISBN 0-8078-1443-1); pap. 9.95x (ISBN 0-8078-4074-2). U of NC Pr.

Kidder, Danuiel P. Mormonism & the Mormons. 59.95 (ISBN 0-8490-0674-0). Gordon Pr.

Kimball, Spencer W. My Beloved Sisters. LC 79-3620. 1979. 5.95 (ISBN 0-87747-798-1). Deseret Bk.

--President Kimball Speaks Out. LC 81-68861. 103p. 1981. 5.95 (ISBN 0-87747-881-3). Deseret Bk.

Kimball, Spencer W., et al. Prayer. 1977. pap. 1.95 (ISBN 0-87747-739-6). Deseret Bk.

Kirban, Salem. Mormonism. (Illus.). 1971. pap. 4.95 (ISBN 0-912582-13-8). Kirban.

Krueger, John R. An Analysis of the Names of Mormonism. 1979. pap. 3.00x (ISBN 0-911706-21-6). Selbstverlag.

Lautensach, Hermann. Das Mormoneniand Als Beispiel Eines Sozialgeographischen Raumes. Repr. of 1953 ed. 20.00 (ISBN 0-384-31640-9). Johnson Repr.

Le Grand Richards. A Marvelous Work & a Wonder. 424p. 14.00 (ISBN 0-87747-686-1); pap. 2.95 (ISBN 0-87747-614-4). Deseret Bk.

Leone, Mark P. Roots of Modern Mormonism. LC 78-25965. 1979. 17.50x (ISBN 0-674-77970-3). Harvard U Pr.

Lewis, Gordon. Bible, Christian & Latter Day Saints. pap. 1.25 (ISBN 0-8010-5567-9). Baker Bk.

Linn, W. A., et al. The Mormons & Mormonism, 15 vols. 1973. lib. bdg. 50.00 (ISBN 0-8490-0675-9). Gordon Pr.

Ludlow, Daniel H. Marking the Scriptures. 105p. (Orig.). 1980. pap. 4.95 (ISBN 0-87747-815-5). Deseret Bk.

Ludlow, Fitz H. Heart of the Continent. LC 74-134396. (Illus.). Repr. 35.45 (ISBN 0-404-08438-9). AMS Pr.

Lum, Dyer D. The Mormon Question in Its Economic Aspects. 1973. lib. bdg. 59.95 (ISBN 0-8490-0672-4). Gordon Pr.

Lythgoe, Dennis, et al. You're a Mormon Now: A Handbook for New Members of the Church of Jesus Christ of Latter-day Saints. 75p. (Orig.). 1983. pap. 6.95 (ISBN 0-913420-37-9). Olympus Pub Co.

McClintock, James. Mormon Settlement in Arizona. LC 78-134397. Repr. of 1921 ed. 27.00 (ISBN 0-404-08439-7). AMS Pr.

McElveen, Floyd. The Mormon Illusion. rev. ed. LC 76-57036. 1980. pap. text ed. 3.95 (ISBN 0-8307-0735-2, 5017807). Regal.

McMurrin, Sterling M. The Philosophical Foundations of Mormon Theology. 1959. pap. 4.95 (ISBN 0-87480-169-9). U of Utah Pr.

--The Theological Foundations of the Mormon Religion. LC 65-26131. 1965. pap. 9.95 (ISBN 0-87480-051-X). U of Utah Pr.

McNiff, William J. Heaven on Earth: A Planned Mormon Society. LC 72-8632. Repr. of 1940 ed. 14.00 (ISBN 0-404-11007-X). AMS Pr.

--Heaven on Earth: A Planned Mormon Society. LC 72-187474. (The American Utopian Adventure Ser.). 262p. 1973. Repr. of 1940 ed. lib. bdg. 27.50x (ISBN 0-87991-001-1). Porcupine Pr.

Marquardt, H. Michael. A Tanner Bibliography. 32p. pap. 3.00 (ISBN 0-942284-08-9). Restoration Re.

Marshal, Walter G. Through America: Nine Months in the United States. LC 73-13143. (Foreign Travelers in America, 1810-1935 Ser.). (Illus.). 490p. 1974. Repr. 32.00x (ISBN 0-405-05466-1). Ayer Co Pubs.

Martin, Walter. The Maze of Mormonism. LC 78-66067. (Orig.). 1979. pap. 6.95 (ISBN 0-88449-017-3, A424365). Vision Hse.

--Mormonism. 32p. 1968. pap. 2.95 (ISBN 0-87123-367-3, 210367). Bethany Hse.

Maxwell, Neal A. All These Things Shall Give Thee Experience. LC 79-26282. 144p. 1979. 7.95 (ISBN 0-87747-796-5). Deseret Bk.

Mayhew, Henry. Mormons: Or, Latter Day Saints. LC 71-134398. Repr. of 1852 ed. 24.75 (ISBN 0-404-08440-0). AMS Pr.

Mehew, Randall & Mehew, Karen. Gospel Basics Busy Book. 150p. 1980. 4.95 (ISBN 0-934126-11-9). Randall Bk Co.

Meirill Library Staff. Name Index to the Library of Congress Collection of Mormon Diaries. (Western Text Society Ser.: Vol. 1, No. 2). 391p. (Orig.). 1971. pap. 12.95 (ISBN 0-87421-045-3). Utah St U Pr.

Merrell, Karen D. Tithing. 22p. pap. 4.95 (ISBN 0-87747-560-1). Deseret Bk.

Miller, Ken. What the Mormons Believe: An Introduction to the Doctrines of the Church of Jesus Christ of Latter-Day Saints. LC 81-80958. 248p. 1981. 9.95 (ISBN 0-88290-177-X, 1040). Horizon Utah.

Miner, Caroline E. & Kimball, Edward L. Camilla. LC 80-69723. (Illus.). 1980. 8.95 (ISBN 0-87747-845-7). Deseret Bk.

Monson, Thomas S. Conference Classics. 59p. 1981. 4.95 (ISBN 0-87747-880-5). Deseret Bk.

--Pathway to Perfection. LC 73-886344. 328p. 1973. 6.95 (ISBN 0-87747-511-3). Deseret Bk.

Morey, Robert A. How to Answer a Mormon. 119p. (Orig.). 1983. pap. 3.95 (ISBN 0-87123-260-X, 210260). Bethany Hse.

Moss, Robert H. The Waters of Mormon. 176p. 1986. 9.95. Horizon Utah.

Mulder, William & Mortensen, A. Russell, eds. Among the Mormons: Historic Accounts by Contemporary Observers. LC 58-5825. xiv, 496p. 1973. (Bison). U of Nebr Pr.

Mulliken, Frances H. First Ladies of the Restoration. 1985. pap. 6.50 (ISBN 0-8309-0419-0). Herald Hse.

Nelson, Lowry. The Mormon Village: A Study in Social Origins. 59.95 (ISBN 0-8490-0673-2). Gordon Pr.

Newell, Linda K. & Avery, Valeen T. Mormon Enigma: Emma Hale Smith, Prophet's Wife, Elect Lady, Polygamy's Foe. LC 80-2400. (Illus.). 394p. 1984. 19.95 (ISBN 0-385-17166-8). Doubleday.

O'Dea, Thomas F. Mormons. LC 57-6984. 1964. pap. 10.00x (ISBN 0-226-61744-0, P162, Phoen). U of Chicago Pr.

Oviatt, Fern & Oviatt, Joan. Mormon Mind Puzzlers. 60p. 1983. 1.99 (ISBN 0-934126-30-5). Randall Bk Co.

Packer, Boyd K. Eternal Love. LC 73-88635. 22p. 1973. 1.50 (ISBN 0-87747-514-8). Deseret Bk.

Pearson, Carol L. A Lasting Peace. 110p. 1983. 7.95 (ISBN 0-934126-38-0). Randall Bk Co.

Pelham, R. W. A Shaker's Answer. 32p. 1981. pap. 1.50 (ISBN 0-937942-09-X). Shaker Mus.

Persuitte, David. Joseph Smith & the Origins of "The Book of Mormon". LC 84-42734. (Illus.). 303p. 1985. lib. bdg. 19.95x (ISBN 0-89950-134-6). McFarland & Co.

Pritt, Ann F. How to Make an L.D.S. Quiet Book. 38p. 1976. pap. 3.95 (ISBN 0-87747-116-9). Deseret Bk.

Reading, Lucile C. Shining Moments: Stories for Latter-day Saint Children. LC 85-1655. 158p. 1985. 6.95 (ISBN 0-87747-687-X). Deseret Bk.

Reel Index to the Microfilm Edition of Utah & the Mormons. 13p. 1982. 15.00. Res Pubns CT.

Remy, Jules & Brenchley, Julius. A Journey to Great Salt-Lake City, 2 vols. LC 75-134399. (Illus.). Repr. of 1861 ed. Set. 49.50 (ISBN 0-404-08441-9). Vol. 1 (ISBN 0-404-08442-7). Vol. 2 (ISBN 0-404-08443-5). AMS Pr.

Richards, LeGrand. Marvelous Work & a Wonder. 5.95 (ISBN 0-87747-161-4); pocket black leather o.p. 8.50 (ISBN 0-87747-163-0); pocket brown leather o.p. 11.95 (ISBN 0-87747-383-8). Deseret Bk.

Riegel, O. U. Crown of Glory: Life of J. J. Strang, Moses, of the Mormons. 1935. 59.50x (ISBN 0-685-69857-2). Elliots Bks.

Roberts, B. H. Outlines of Ecclesiastical History. LC 79-9744. 1979. 7.95 (ISBN 0-87747-748-5). Deseret Bk.

Robinson, Philip S. Sinners & Saints. LC 75-134400. Repr. of 1883 ed. 25.00 (ISBN 0-404-08444-3). AMS Pr.

Ropp, Harry L. The Mormon Papers. rev. ed. LC 77-2681. (Illus., Orig.). 1987. pap. 5.95 (ISBN 0-87784-469-0). Inter-Varsity.

Ruoff, Norman D., ed. The Writings of President Frederick M. Smith, Vol. 2. LC 78-6428. 1979. pap. 10.00 (ISBN 0-8309-0239-2). Herald Hse.

Scott, Latayne C. The Mormon Mirage. 276p. 1982. pap. 7.95 (ISBN 0-310-38911-9, 10450P). Zondervan.

Sealy, Shirley. Within My Heart. 168p. 1983. 7.95 (ISBN 0-934126-37-2). Randall Bk Co.

Shapiro, R. Gary. Exhaustive Concordance of the Book of Mormon, Doctrine & Covenants & Pearl of Great Peace. Orig. Title: Triple Concordance. 1977. 17.95 (ISBN 0-89036-085-5). Hawkes Pub Inc.

Shields, Steven. Divergent Paths of the Restoration: 1984 Supplement. (Orig.). Date not set. pap. cancelled (ISBN 0-942284-02-X). Restoration Re.

Shields, Steven L. The Restored Church. 16p. (Orig.). 1982. pap. 1.00 (ISBN 0-942284-01-1). Restoration Re.

Shipp, Richard C. Champions of Light. 118p. 1983. 7.95 (ISBN 0-934126-32-1). Randall Bk Co.

Shipps, Jan. Mormonism: The Story of a New Religious Tradition. LC 84-2672. (Illus.). 232p. 1985. 14.50 (ISBN 0-252-01159-7). U of Ill Pr.

Sill, Sterling W. Our World of Wonders. 96p. 1986. 7.95 (ISBN 0-88290-287-3). Horizon Utah.

Smith, Eliza R. Biography & Family Record of Lorenzo Snow. 1975. Repr. 15.00 (ISBN 0-914740-15-6). Western Epics.

Smith, Joseph. Doctrine & Covenants of the Church of Jesus Christ of Latter-Day Saints: Containing the Revelations Given to Joseph Smith, Jun, the Prophet, for the Building up of the Kingdom of God in the Last Days. Pratt, Orson, ed. LC 69-14082. 1971. Repr. of 1880 ed. lib. bdg. 29.75x (ISBN 0-8371-4101-X, SMCC). Greenwood.

Smith, Joseph F. Teachings of the Prophet Joseph Smith. LC 76-111624. 437p. 1977. pap. 2.50 (ISBN 0-87747-778-7). Deseret Bk.

--The Way to Perfection. 365p. 1972. 8.95 (ISBN 0-87747-300-5). Deseret Bk.

Smith, Joseph, Jr., tr. The Book of Mormon. LC 66-15423. 414p. 1973. pap. 4.00 (ISBN 0-8309-0273-2). Herald Hse.

Smith, William. A Proclamation: Eighteen Forty-Five. (Orig.). 1983. pap. 1.50 (ISBN 0-942284-03-8). Restoration Re.

Solomon, Dorothy A. In My Father's House. LC 84-11964. 312p. 1984. 17.95 (ISBN 0-531-09763-3). Watts.

Sondrup, Steven P., ed. Arts & Inspiration: Mormon Perspectives. LC 80-21927. (Illus.). 240p. 1980. pap. 7.95 (ISBN 0-8425-1845-2). Brigham.

Sorenson, John. An Ancient American Setting for the Book of Mormon. 400p. 1985. 14.95 (ISBN 0-87747-608-X). Deseret Bk.

Stewart, John J. Mormonism & the Negro. LC 78-52123. 92p. 1978. 5.50 (ISBN 0-88290-098-6). Horizon Utah.

Sturlaugson, Mary F. A Soul So Rebellious. 88p. 1980. 8.95 (ISBN 0-87747-841-4). Deseret Bk.

Talmage, James E. Articles of Faith. LC 80-22041. (Classics in Mormon Literature Edition Ser.). 537p. 1981. 9.95 (ISBN 0-87747-838-4). Deseret Bk.

--Great Apostasy. 6.95 (ISBN 0-87747-384-6). Deseret Bk.

--House of the Lord. 8.95 (ISBN 0-87747-112-6). Deseret Bk.

--Jesus the Christ. (Classics in Mormon Literature Ser.). 804p. 1982. 10.95 (ISBN 0-87747-903-8). Deseret Bk.

Taylor, Bill. A Tale of Two Cities: The Mormons-Catholics. 1981. pap. 5.50 (ISBN 0-933046-02-2). Little Red Hen.

Tingle, Donald S. Mormonism. rev. ed. (Viewpoints Ser.). 32p. 1987. pap. 1.95 (ISBN 0-8308-1103-6). Inter-Varsity.

Urrutia, Benjamin, ed. LDSF: Latter-Day Science Fiction, Vol. 2. 192p. (Orig.). 1985. pap. text ed. 4.95 (ISBN 0-9614960-0-2). Parables.

Vanderhoof, Elisha W. Historical Sketches of Western New York. LC 71-134434. Repr. of 1907 ed. 14.00 (ISBN 0-404-08476-1). AMS Pr.

Van Wagoner, Richard S. & Walker, Steven C. A Book of Mormons. 468p. 1982. 14.95 (ISBN 0-941214-06-0). Signature Bks.

Walker, John P., ed. Dale Morgan on Early Mormonism: Correspondence & a New History. 350p. 1986. 22.95 (ISBN 0-941214-36-2). Signature Bks.

Wallace, Arthur, compiled by. L. D. S. Children's Comments, Vol. 1. 60p. 1978. pap. 1.95x (ISBN 0-937892-03-3). LL Co.

Walton, H. Dyke. They Built with Faith: True Tales of God's Guidance in L.D.S. Chapel Building World-Wide. LC 79-89353. 125p. 1979. 5.95 (ISBN 0-88290-122-2). Horizon Utah.

Ward, Margery W., ed. A Frament: The Autobiography of Mary Jane Mount Tanner. 231p. 1980. 15.00 (ISBN 0-941214-38-9). Signature Bks.

Warenski, Marilyn. Patriarchs & Politics. (Illus.). 1978. 10.95 (ISBN 0-07-068270-4). McGraw.

Warner, Ross. Fulfillment of Book of Mormon Prophecies. 1975. pap. 4.95 (ISBN 0-89036-081-2). Hawkes Pub Inc.

Warren, Rod, illus. How Do Others See You? In an LDS Ward. (Illus., Orig.). 1977. pap. 2.95 (ISBN 0-89036-101-0). Hawkes Pub Inc.

Webb, Robert C. The Real Mormonism. LC 72-2971. Repr. of 1916 ed. 29.00 (ISBN 0-404-10736-2). AMS Pr.

Werner, Morris R. Brigham Young. LC 75-351. (The Radical Tradition in America Ser.). xvi, 478p. 1975. Repr. of 1925 ed. 32.50 (ISBN 0-88355-254-X). Hyperion Conn.

Whipple, Maurine. Giant Joshua. Repr. 12.50 (ISBN 0-914740-17-2). Western Epics.

White, O. Kendall, Jr. Mormon Neo-orthodoxy: A Crisis Theology. 250p. 1987. pap. 8.95 (ISBN 0-941214-52-4). Signature Bks.

Widtsoe, John A., ed. Discourses of Brigham Young. 497p. 14.95 (ISBN 0-87747-066-9). Deseret Bk.

A Woman's Choices: The Relief Society Legacy Lectures. LC 83-25517. 196p. 1984. 7.95 (ISBN 0-87747-999-2). Deseret Bk.

Young, Ann E. Wife Number Nineteen: The Story of a Life in Bondage, Being a Complete Expose of Mormonism, & Revealing the Sorrows, Sacrifices & Sufferings of Women in Polygamy. LC 72-2634. (American Women Ser: Images & Realities). (Illus.). 632p. 1972. Repr. of 1875 ed. 36.50 (ISBN 0-405-04488-7). Ayer Co Pubs.

MORMONS AND MORMONISM–FICTION

Ferris, B. G. Utah & the Mormons. LC 77-134394. Repr. of 1856 ed. 27.00 (ISBN 0-404-08436-2). AMS Pr.

Fisher, Vardis. Children of God. 1977. 12.95 (ISBN 0-918522-50-1). O L Holmes.

Gibson, Margaret W. Emma Smith: Elect Lady. LC 54-7910. 1954. pap. 8.00 (ISBN 0-8309-0256-2). Herald Hse.

Pratt, Parley P. Autobiography of Parley P. Pratt. Pratt, Parley P., Jr., pref. by. LC 85-10264. (Classics in Mormon Literature Ser.). (Illus.). 475p. 1985. 14.95 (ISBN 0-87747-740-X). Deseret Bk.

Switzer, Jennie B. Elder Northfield's Home; or, Sacrificed on the Mormon Altar. facsimile ed. LC 71-164576. (American Fiction Reprint Ser). Repr. of 1882 ed. 25.50 (ISBN 0-8369-7053-5). Ayer Co Pubs.

Weyland, Jack. First Day Forever & the Other Stories for LDS Youth. LC 80-82455. 120p. 1980. 7.95 (ISBN 0-88290-136-2, 2037). Horizon Utah.

Writers Program, Utah. Provo, Pioneer Mormon City. LC 73-3654. (American Guide Ser.). 1942. Repr. 11.50 (ISBN 0-404-57954-X). AMS Pr.

MORMONS AND MORMONISM–HISTORY

Ahmanson, John. Secret History: An Eyewitness Expose of the Rise of Mormonism. Archer, Gleason L., tr. from Danish. 1984. 9.95 (ISBN 0-8024-0277-1). Moody.

Alexander, Thomas G. Mormonism in Transition: The Latter-day Saints & Their Church, 1890-1930. LC 84-22164. (Illus.). 396p. 1986. 19.95 (ISBN 0-252-01185-6). U of Ill Pr.

Anderson, Einar. History & Beliefs of Mormonism. LC 81-13671. Orig. Title: Inside Story of Mormonism. 176p. 1981. pap. 6.95 (ISBN 0-8254-2122-5). Kregel.

Arrington, Leonard J. & Bitton, Davis. The Mormon Experience: A History of the Latter-Day Saints. LC 78-20561. (Illus.). 1979. 17.50 (ISBN 0-394-46566-0). Knopf.

--The Mormon Experience: A History of the Latter-Day Saints. LC 80-11843. (Illus.). 404p. 1980. pap. 5.95 (ISBN 0-394-74102-1, Vin). Random.

Barney, Garold D. Mormons, Indians & the Ghost Dance Religion of 1890. LC 85-29509. (Illus.). 258p. (Orig.). 1986. lib. bdg. 28.00 (ISBN 0-8191-5227-7); pap. text ed. 13.50 (ISBN 0-8191-5228-5). U Pr of Amer.

Barron, Howard H. Orson Hyde: Missionary, Apostle, Colonizer. LC 77-74490. (Illus.). 336p. 1977. 10.95 (ISBN 0-88290-076-5). Horizon Utah.

Barron, Howard H., ed. Of Everlasting Value, Vol. 1. (Orig.). 1978. pap. 5.95 (ISBN 0-89036-129-0). Hawkes Pub Inc.

Beecher, Maureen U. & Anderson, Lavina F., eds. Sisters in Spirit: Mormon Women in Historical & Cultural Perspective. 350p. 1987. 21.95 (ISBN 0-252-01411-1). U of Ill Pr.

Bitton, Davis & Beecher, Maureen U., eds. New Views of Mormon History: A Collection of Essays in Honor of Leonard J. Arrington. 1987. 25.00x (ISBN 0-87480-304-7). U of Utah Pr.

Brooks, Juanita. John Doyle Lee: Zealot, Pioneer Builder, Scapegoat. LC 84-12849. 406p. 1984. pap. 12.50 (ISBN 0-935704-21-3). Howe Brothers.

Bryson, Conrey. Winter Quarters. LC 86-2146. (Illus.). 191p. 1986. 9.95 (ISBN 0-87579-011-9). Deseret Bk.

Bush, Lester E. & Mauss, Armand L., eds. Neither White nor Black: Mormon Scholars Confront the Race Issue in a Universal Church. 250p. 1984. pap. 11.95 (ISBN 0-941214-22-2). Signature Bks.

Bushman, Claudia L., et al. Mormon Sisters: Women in Early Utah. LC 76-53854. (Illus.). 320p. 1980. pap. 9.95 (ISBN 0-913420-95-6). Olympus Pub Co.

Bushman, Richard L. Joseph Smith & the Beginnings of Mormonism. LC 84-2451. 270p. 1984. 17.95 (ISBN 0-252-01143-0). U of Ill Pr.

Cannon, Donald Q. & Cook, Lyndon W., eds. Far West Record. LC 82-23476. 318p. 1983. 10.95 (ISBN 0-87747-901-1). Deseret Bk.

Cannon, George Q. Life of Joseph Smith the Prophet. (Classics in Mormon Literature Ser.). 572p. 1986. Repr. of 1964 ed. 14.95 (ISBN 0-87747-148-7). Deseret Bk.

Cheesman, Paul R. & Hutchins, Barbara W. Pathways to the Past: A Guide to the Ruins of Mezo-America. LC 83-83236. 210p. 1984. pap. 8.95 (ISBN 0-88290-236-9). Horizon Utah.

Cleland, Robert G. & Brooks, Juanita, eds. A Mormon Chronicle: The Diaries of John D. Lee, 1848-1876, 2 vols. (Illus.). xxxii, 824p. 1955. Set. 39.95 (ISBN 0-87480-230-X). U of Utah Pr.

Cook, Lyndon W. Joseph Smith & the Law of Consecration. 100p. 1985. 8.95 (ISBN 0-910523-24-X). E B Grandin.

Cornwall, Rebecca & Arrington, Leonard J. Rescue of the Eighteen Fifty-Six Handcart Companies. Alexander, Thomas G., ed. (Charles Redd Monographs in Western History: No. 11). (Illus.). 59p. pap. 4.95 (ISBN 0-941214-04-4, Signature Bks). C Redd Ctr.

Corrill, John. Brief History of the Church of Christ of Latter Day Saints. 48p. (Orig.). 1983. pap. 1.95 (ISBN 0-942284-05-4). Restoration Re.

Davies, J. K. Mormon Gold: The Story of the Mormon Argonauts. 440p. (Orig.). 1984. pap. 12.95 (ISBN 0-913420-20-4). Olympus Pub Co.

Dyer, Alvin R. The Refiner's Fire. 8.95 (ISBN 0-87747-222-X). Deseret Bk.

Flake, Chad J., ed. A Mormon Bibliography, 1830-1930: Books, Pamphlets, Periodicals, & Broadsides Relating to the First Century of Mormonism. LC 74-22639. (Illus.). 1978. 80.00x (ISBN 0-87480-016-1). U of Utah Pr.

Foster, Lawrence. Religion & Sexuality: Three American Communal Experiments of the Nineteenth Century. 1981. 24.95x (ISBN 0-19-502794-9). Oxford U Pr.

Geddes, Joseph A. The United Order Among the Mormons (Missouri Phase) An Unfinished Experiment in Economic Organization. LC 72-8247. Repr. of 1924 ed. 19.50 (ISBN 0-404-11001-0). AMS Pr.

Gottlieb, Robert & Wiley, Peter. America's Saints: The Rise of Mormon Power. LC 85-24879. 288p. 1986. pap. 5.95 (ISBN 0-15-605658-5, Harv). HarBraceJ.

Gowans, Fred R. & Campbell, Eugene E. Fort Supply: Brigham Young's Green River Experiment. 1976. pap. 2.95 (ISBN 0-8425-0248-3). Brigham.

Grondahl, Calvin. Freeway to Perfection: A Collection of Mormon Cartoons. (Illus.). 96p. (Orig.). 1980. pap. 4.50 (ISBN 0-9606760-1-5). Sunstone Found.

Harrison, G. T. Mormonism, Now & Then. 357p. cancelled (ISBN 0-686-96149-8). Am Atheist.

Hartshorn, Leon R. Classic Stories from the Lives of Our Prophets. LC 73-155235. 384p. 1975. 9.95 (ISBN 0-87747-438-9). Deseret Bk.

Hill, Marvin S. & Rooker, C. Keith. The Kirtland Economy Revisited: A Market Critique of Sectarian Economics. LC 78-3848. (Studies in Mormon History: No. 3). (Illus.). 1977. pap. 4.95 (ISBN 0-8425-1230-6). Brigham.

Howe, Eber D. Mormonism Unvailed; or, a Faithful Account of That Singular Imposition & Delusion, from Its Rise to the Present Time. LC 72-2967. Repr. of 1834 ed. 32.50 (ISBN 0-404-10730-3). AMS Pr.

Jackson, Richard H., ed. The Mormon Role in the Settlement of the West. LC 78-24728. (Charles Redd Monographs in Western History Ser.: No. 9). (Illus.). 1978. pap. 6.95 (ISBN 0-8425-1321-3, Dist. by Signature Bks). C Redd Ctr.

Kimball, Stanley B. Heber C. Kimball: Mormon Patriarch & Pioneer. LC 80-21923. (Illus.). 345p. 1981. pap. 13.50 (ISBN 0-252-01299-2). U of Ill Pr.

Larson, Gustave O. Prelude to the Kingdom: Mormon Desert Conquest, a Chapter in American Cooperative Experience. LC 78-5694. 1978. Repr. of 1947 ed. lib. bdg. 25.75x (ISBN 0-313-20452-7, LAPK). Greenwood.

Launius, Roger D. Zion's Camp: Expedition to Missouri, 1834. 1984. pap. 14.00 (ISBN 0-8309-0385-2). Herald Hse.

LeSueur, Stephen C. The Eighteen Thirty-Eight Mormon War in Missouri. LC 86-16090. 256p. 1987. text ed. 24.00 (ISBN 0-8262-0626-3, 83-36349). U of Mo Pr.

Long, E. B. The Saints & the Union: Utah Territory During the Civil War. LC 80-16775. (Illus.). 292p. 1981. 22.50 (ISBN 0-252-00821-9). U of Ill Pr.

McClintock, James H. Mormon Settlement in Arizona. LC 85-8458. (Illus.). 384p. 1985. pap. 9.95 (ISBN 0-8165-0953-0). U of Ariz Pr.

Madsen, Brigham D., ed. A Forty-Niner in Utah with the Stansbury Exploration of Great Salt Lake: Letters & Journal of John Hudson, 1848-50. 227p. 1981. 22.50 (ISBN 0-941214-39-7). Signature Bks.

Morgan, Dale L. Dale Morgan on Early Mormonism: Correspondence & a New History. Walker, John P., ed. LC 86-60251. 414p. 1986. 20.95 (ISBN 0-941214-36-2). Signature Bks.

Mulder, William. The Mormons in American History. (The University of Utah Frederick William Reynolds Lecture Ser.: No. 21). 1981. pap. 4.95 (ISBN 0-87480-184-2). U of Utah Pr.

Nibley, Hugh. The World & the Profits: Mormanism & Earlt Christianity. 1987. 10.95 (ISBN 0-87579-078-X). Deseret Bk.

Petersen, Mark E. The Sons of Mosiah. 125p. 1984. 6.95 (ISBN 0-87747-297-1). Deseret Bk.

Quinn, D. Michael. Early Mormonism & the Magic World View. 250p. 1987. 14.95 (ISBN 0-941214-46-X). Signature Bks.

Reay, Lee. Incredible Passage: Through the Hole-in-the-Rock. Hechtle, Ranier, ed. (Illus.). 128p. (Orig.). 1981. 5.95 (ISBN 0-934826-05-6); pap. 4.50 (ISBN 0-934826-06-4). Meadow Lane.

Roberts, B. H. Comprehensive History of The Church of Jesus Christ of Latter-day Saints, 6 vols plus index. (Illus.). 1965. Vols. 1-6. 12.95 ea.; Vol. 1. (ISBN 0-8425-0299-8); Vol. 2. (ISBN 0-8425-0300-5); Vol. 3. (ISBN 0-8425-0301-3); Vol. 4. (ISBN 0-8425-0482-6); Vol. 5. (ISBN 0-8425-0304-8); Vol. 6. (ISBN 0-8425-0305-6); Index. 9.95 (ISBN 0-8425-0627-6). Brigham.

Roberts, B. H., intro. by. History of the Church, 7 vols. Incl. Vol. 1 (1820-1834) 511p. 1974 (ISBN 0-87747-074-X); Vol. 2 (1834-1837) 543p. 1974 (ISBN 0-87747-075-8); Vol. 3 (1834-1839) 478p (ISBN 0-87747-076-6); Vol. 4 (1839-1842) 620p (ISBN 0-87747-077-4); Vol. 5 (1842-1843) 563p (ISBN 0-87747-078-2); Vol. 6 (1843-1844) 641p (ISBN 0-87747-079-0); Vol. 7 (period 2, The Apostolic Interregnum) 640p (ISBN 0-87747-080-4). 15.95 ea.; index 15.95 (ISBN 0-87747-291-2). Deseret Bk.

Robison, Pamela. Alma. 90p. 1985. pap. 5.75 (ISBN 0-8309-0409-3). Herald Hse.

Shepherd, Gordon & Shepherd, Gary. A Kingdom Transformed: Themes in the Development of Mormonism. 320p. 1984. 19.95 (ISBN 0-87480-233-4). U of Utah Pr.

Shields, Steven L. Divergent Paths of the Restoration. 282p. 1982. 12.95 (ISBN 0-941214-48-6). Signature Bks.

--Divergent Paths of the Restoration: A History of the Latter Day Saint Movement. 3rd, rev., enlarged ed. LC 81-86304. (Illus.). 282p. 1982. 12.95 (ISBN 0-942284-00-3). Restoration Re.

Simmonds, A. J. The Gentile Comes to Cache Valley. LC 72-80615. 143p. 1976. 8.95. Utah St U Pr.

Sonne, Conway B. Ships, Saints, & Mariners: A Maritime Encyclopedia of Mormon Migration, 1830-1890. 256p. 1987. 19.50x (ISBN 0-87480-270-9). U of Utah Pr.

Sperry, Sidney B. Book of Mormon Chronology. pap. 1.00 (ISBN 0-87747-408-7). Deseret Bk.

Spurrier, Joseph H. Great Are the Promises unto the Isle of the Sea: The Church of Jesus Christ of Latter-Day Saints in the Hawaiian Islands. (Orig.). 1978. pap. 2.95 (ISBN 0-89036-114-2). Hawkes Pub Inc.

Stegner, Wallace. Mormon Country. LC 81-3410. x, 362p. 1981. 25.50x (ISBN 0-8032-4129-1); pap. 8.50 (ISBN 0-8032-9125-6, BB 778, Bison). U of Nebr Pr.

Stott, Clifford L. Search for Sanctuary: Brigham Young & the White Mountain Expedition. (American West Ser.: Vol. 19). (Illus.). 272p. 1984. 19.95 (ISBN 0-87480-237-7). U of Utah Pr.

Tanner, Jerald & Tanner, Sandra. Changing World of Mormonism. LC 79-18311. 1979. 16.95 (ISBN 0-8024-1234-3). Moody.

Taylor, Samuel W. Nightfall at Nauvoo. 1986. pap. 2.75 (ISBN 0-380-00247-7, 52696-4). Avon.

Van Wagoner, Richard S. Mormon Polygamy: A History. 275p. 1985. 19.95 (ISBN 0-941214-35-4). Signature Bks.

Wallace, Arthur. LDS Roots in Egypt. 63p. 1981. pap. 3.50x (ISBN 0-937892-08-4). LL Co.

Warenski, Marilyn. Patriarchs & Politics. (McGraw-Hill Paperbacks Ser.). 352p. 1980. pap. 6.95 (ISBN 0-07-068271-2). McGraw.

Wells, Merle W. Anti-Mormonism in Idaho, Eighteen Seventy-Two to Ninety-Two. LC 77-89975. (Studies in Mormon History Ser.: No. 4). 1978. pap. 7.95 (ISBN 0-8425-0904-6). Brigham.

Yorgason, Blaine M. & Yorgason, Brenton G. The Loftier Way. LC 85-70919. 143p. 1985. 8.95 (ISBN 0-87747-785-X). Deseret Bk.

MORMONS AND MORMONISM–HISTORY–SOURCES

Clark, Carol, ed. A Legacy Remembered: The Relief Society Magazine. (Illus.). 1982. 7.95 (ISBN 0-87747-926-7). Deseret Bk.

MORMONS AND MORMONISM–MISSIONS

Dennison, Mark A. Preparing for the Greatest Two Years of Your Life. pap. 3.95 (ISBN 0-89036-128-2). Hawkes Pub Inc.

Passantino, Robert, et al. Answers to the Cultist at Your Door. LC 80-83850. 1981. pap. 5.95 (ISBN 0-89081-275-6). Harvest Hse.

MORMONS AND MORMONISM–SERMONS

Burton, Alma P. Discourses of the Prophet Joseph Smith. LC 77-23977. 399p. 9.95 (ISBN 0-87747-067-7). Deseret Bk.

Hawkes, John D. Art of Achieving Success. 128p. 1971. pap. 2.95 (ISBN 0-89036-008-1). Hawkes Pub Inc.

Hyde, Orson. Speech of Elder Orson Hyde: 1845. 16p. (Orig.). 1986. pap. 1.95 (ISBN 0-942284-07-0). Restoration Re.

Russon, Robb. Letters to a New Elder: The Melchizedek Priesthood, Its Duty & Fulfillment. pap. 2.95 (ISBN 0-89036-144-4). Hawkes Pub Inc.

Sill, Sterling W. Christmas Sermons. LC 73-86165. 184p. 1973. 8.95 (ISBN 0-87747-503-2). Deseret Bk.

Smith, Joseph F. Gospel Doctrine. 553p. 1975. 10.95. Deseret Bk.

MORMONS AND MORMONISM–SONGS AND MUSIC

Cheney, Thomas E., ed. Mormon Songs from the Rocky Mountains: A Compilation of Mormon Folksong. 224p. 1968. pap. 9.95 (ISBN 0-87480-196-6). U of Utah Pr.

Sing with Me. 5.50 (ISBN 0-87747-362-5). Deseret Bk.

MORMONS AND MORMONISM IN MEXICO

Palmer, David S. In Search of Cumorah: New Evidences for the Book of Mormon from Ancient Mexico. LC 80-83866. (Illus.). 300p. 1981. 10.95 (ISBN 0-88290-169-9, 1063). Horizon Utah.

Tullis, F. LaMond. Mormonism in Mexico. (Illus.). 275p. 1987. 22.50 (ISBN 0-87421-130-1). Utah St U Pr.

MORRIS, SAMUEL, 1873-1893

Baldwin, Lindley. The March of Faith: Samuel Morris. 96p. 1969. pap. 2.95 (ISBN 0-87123-360-6, 200360). Bethany Hse.

--Samuel Morris. 96p. 1987. pap. 3.50 (ISBN 0-87123-950-7). Bethany Hse.

Stocker, Fern N. Sammy Morris: Believing in God's Power. (Guessing Bks.). (Orig.). 1986. pap. 3.95 (ISBN 0-8024-5443-7). Moody.

MORSE, JEDIDIAH, 1761-1826

Morse, James K. Jedidiah Morse: A Champion of New England Orthodoxy. LC 39-11247. Repr. of 1939 ed. 10.00 (ISBN 0-404-04504-9). AMS Pr.

Phillips, Joseph W. Jedidiah Morse & New England Congregationalism. 305p. 1983. 30.00x (ISBN 0-8135-0982-3). Rutgers U Pr.

MORTMAIN

Raban, S. Mortmain Legislation & the English Church, 1279-1500. LC 81-21685. (Cambridge Studies in Medieval Life & Thought: No. 17). (Illus.). 244p. 1982. 47.50 (ISBN 0-521-24233-9). Cambridge U Pr.

MORTUARY CUSTOMS

see Burial; Cremation; Funeral Rites and Ceremonies; Mourning Customs

MOSAIC LAW

see Jewish Law

MOSAICS

see also Mural Painting and Decoration

Avi-Yonah, Michael. The Art of Mosaics. LC 72-10793. (The Lerner Archaeology Ser.: Digging up the Past). (Illus.). 96p. 1975. PLB 8.95 (ISBN 0-8225-0828-1). Lerner Pubns.

Collet's Holdings, Ltd. Staff, ed. Early Russian Painting 11th to Early 13th Centuries: Mosaics, Frescoes & Icons. 308p. 1982. 125.00x (ISBN 0-317-39496-7, Pub. by Collets UK). State Mutual Bk.

Demus, Otto. Byzantine Mosaic Decoration: Aspects of Monumental Art in Byzantium. (Illus.). 162p. 1976. 25.00 (ISBN 0-89241-018-3). Caratzas.

DiFederico, Frank. The Mosaics of the National Shrine of the Immaculate Conception. (Illus.). 96p. 1981. 16.95 (ISBN 0-916276-09-0). Decatur Hse.

Harmon, Beatrice E. Mosaics. LC 74-144725. (Yale Ser. of Younger Poets: No. 18). Repr. of 1923 ed. 18.00 (ISBN 0-404-53818-5). AMS Pr.

Parlasca, Klans. Die Roemischen Mosaiken in Deutschland. (Illus.). 156p. 1970. Repr. of 1959 ed. 64.00x (ISBN 3-11-001212-X). De Gruyter.

Stephany, Konrad. Ludwig Schaffrath, Stained Glass & Mosaic. LC 77-79948. 1977. write for info. (ISBN 0-686-05497-0). C & R Loo.

Stern, Henri. Les Mosaiques De la Grande Mosquee De Cordoue. (Madrider Forschungen, Ser., Vol. 11). (Illus.). 55p. 1976. 64.00x (ISBN 3-11-002126-9). De Gruyter.

MOSES

Allis, Oswald T. The Five Books of Moses. 1977. pap. 5.95 (ISBN 0-8010-0108-0). Baker Bk.

Andre, G. Moses, the Man of God. 47p. pap. 1.95 (ISBN 0-88172-131-X). Believers Bkshelf.

Auerbach, Elias. Moses. Lehman, Israel O. & Barclay, R. A., trs. from Ger. LC 72-6589. 255p. 1975. text ed. 25.00x (ISBN 0-8143-1491-0). Wayne St U Pr.

Auld, A. Graeme. Joshua, Moses & the Land. 158p. 1981. 19.95 (ISBN 0-567-09306-9, Pub. by T & T Clark Ltd UK). Fortress.

Beegle, Dewey M. Moses, the Servant of Yahweh. LC 79-84558. 368p. 1972. pap. text ed. 8.95 (ISBN 0-933462-03-4). Pryor Pettengill.

Bock, Emil. Moses: From the Egyptian Mysteries to the Judges of Israel. 208p. (Orig.). 1986. pap. 12.95 (ISBN 0-89281-117-X). Inner Tradit.

Bork, Paul F. The World of Moses. LC 78-5022. (Horizon Ser.). 1978. pap. 5.95 (ISBN 0-8127-0166-6). Review & Herald.

Borne, Mortimer. Meet Moses: Fifty-Four Drawings in Color. LC 77-74180. (Illus.). 1981. 18.50 (ISBN 0-913870-39-0). Abaris Bks.

Campbell, Alexander & Haff, Gerry. Live with Moses. 90p. (Orig.). 1982. pap. 12.95 (ISBN 0-940754-13-4). Ed Ministries.

Cantleberry, Lillian. Moses: Prince, Servant, Prophet. 208p. (Orig.). 1985. pap. 7.95 (ISBN 0-570-03970-3, 12-3005). Concordia.

Chandler, Tertius. Moses & the Golden Age. (Illus.). 88p. 1986. 9.95 (ISBN 0-8059-3024-8). Dorrance.

Conner, Kevin. Tabernacle of Moses. 119p. 1974. 7.95 (ISBN 0-914936-08-5). Bible Temple.

Craig, Diana. The Young Moses. LC 84-50449. (Bible Stories Ser.). (Illus.). 24p. 1984. PLB 6.96 (ISBN 0-382-06797-5); 5.45 (ISBN 0-382-06946-3). Silver.

Freud, Sigmund. Moses & Monotheism. Jones, Katherine, ed. 1955. pap. 4.95 (ISBN 0-394-70014-7, V14, Vin). Random.

Gager, John G. Moses in Graeco-Roman Paganism. (SBL Monograph). 8.95 (ISBN 0-89130-323-5, 06-00-16). Scholars Pr GA.

Getz, Gene A. Moses: Moments of Glory...Feet of Clay. LC 75-23519. 160p. (Orig.). 1976. pap. 4.95 (ISBN 0-8307-0400-0, 5403200). Regal.

Glasson, T. Francis. Moses in the Fourth Gospel. LC 63-5666. (Studies in Biblical Theology: No. 40). 1963. pap. 10.00x (ISBN 0-8401-3040-6). A R Allenson.

Grant, Joan M. So Moses Was Born. 21.00 (ISBN 0-405-11791-4). Ayer Co Pubs.

Hamilton, James. Moses, the Man of God. 388p. 1985. Repr. lib. bdg. 14.75 (ISBN 0-86524-187-2, 8407). Klock & Klock.

Lindsay, Gordon. Moses & His Contemporaries. (Old Testament Ser.). 1.25 (ISBN 0-89985-133-9). Christ Nations.

--Moses & the Church in the Wilderness. (Old Testament Ser.). 1.25 (ISBN 0-89985-132-0). Christ Nations.

--Moses, The Deliverer. (Old Testament Ser.). 1.25 (ISBN 0-89985-131-2). Christ Nations.

--Moses the Lawgiver. (Old Testament Ser.: Vol. 10). pap. 1.25 (ISBN 0-89985-959-3). Christ Nations.

Maimonides, Moses. The Reason of the Laws of Moses. Townley, James, ed. LC 78-97294. 451p. 1975. Repr. of 1827 ed. lib. bdg. 22.50x (ISBN 0-8371-2618-5, MARL). Greenwood.

Mellinkoff, Ruth. The Horned Moses in Medieval Art & Thought. LC 77-85450. (California Studies in the History of Art: No. XIV). (Illus.). 1970. 40.00x (ISBN 0-520-01705-6). U of Cal Pr.

Meyer, F. B. Moses. 1972. pap. 4.50 (ISBN 0-87508-354-4). Chr Lit.

Moses. 1979. 0.75 (ISBN 0-8198-0586-6). Dghtrs St Paul.

Noerdlinger, Henry S. Moses & Egypt: The Documentation to the Motion Picture "the Ten Commandments". LC 56-12886. 202p. 1956. pap. 1.95 (ISBN 0-88474-007-2). U of S Cal Pr.

North, Gary. Moses & Pharaoh: Dominion Religion vs. Power Religion. 430p. 1985. pap. text ed. 12.50 (ISBN 0-930464-05-2). Inst Christian.

Ponder, Catherine. The Millionaire Moses. LC 77-71459. (The Millionaires of the Bible Ser.). 1977. pap. 5.95 (ISBN 0-87516-232-0). De Vorss.

Silver, Daniel J. Images of Moses. LC 82-70854. 1982. 16.95 (ISBN 0-465-03201-X). Basic.

Wellek, Rene, ed. The Divine Legation of Moses Demonstrated, 4 vols. 2nd ed. LC 75-11264. (British Philosophers & Theologians of the 17th & 18th Centuries Ser.: Vol. 62). 2259p. 1978. Set. lib. bdg. 204.00 (ISBN 0-8240-1813-3). Garland Pub.

Wildavsky, Aaron. The Nursing Father: Moses As a Political Leader. LC 83-1099. (Illus.). xi, 262p. 1984. text ed. 25.00 (ISBN 0-8173-0168-2); pap. text ed. 11.95 (ISBN 0-8173-0169-0). U of Ala Pr.

Wood, P. Moses: Founder of Preventive Medicine. 1976. lib. bdg. 59.95 (ISBN 0-8490-2285-1). Gordon Pr.

Young, William E. Moses: God's Helper. (BibLearn Ser.). (Illus.). 5.95 (ISBN 0-8054-4225-1, 4242-25). Broadman.

Zeligs, Dorothy F., ed. Moses: A Psychodynamic Study. 384p. 1986. 39.95 (ISBN 0-89885-236-6). Human Sci Pr.

MOSES–FICTION

Kayser, Rudolf. The Saints of Qumran: Stories & Essays on Jewish Themes. Zohn, Harry, ed. LC 76-20273. 188p. 1977. 18.00 (ISBN 0-8386-2024-8). Fairleigh Dickinson.

MOSES–JUVENILE LITERATURE

Barrett, Ethel. Moses. LC 82-16521. (Bible Biographies Ser.). 1982. pap. text ed. 2.50 (ISBN 0-8307-0772-7, 5811201). Regal.

Bracken, Carol, illus. The Baby Moses. (Tuck-A-Toy Bks.). (Illus.). 7p. 1985. 3.95 (ISBN 0-8407-6663-7). Nelson.

Craig, Diana. Moses & the Flight from Egypt. LC 84-50448. (Bible Stories Ser.). (Illus.). 24p. 1984. 5.45 (ISBN 0-382-06945-5); PLB 6.96 (ISBN 0-382-06797-5). Silver.

Diamond, Lucy. Moses, Prince & Shepherd. (Ladybird Ser). (Illus.). 1954. bds. 2.50 (ISBN 0-87508-850-3). Chr Lit.

Hodges. Moses & the Ten Plagues. (Arch Bks.). 24p. (Orig.). 1985. pap. 0.99 (ISBN 0-570-06190-3, 59-1291). Concordia.

Johnson, Sylvia A. Mosses. LC 83-17488. (Lerner Natural Science Bks.). (Illus.). 48p. 1983. PLB 12.95 (ISBN 0-8225-1482-6). Lerner Pubns.

Kramer, Janice. Princess & the Baby. (Arch Bks: Set 6). 1969. laminated bdg 0.99 (ISBN 0-570-06043-5, 59-1158). Concordia.

McKissack, Fredrick & McKissack, Patricia. Look What You've Done Now Moses! (Early Readers Ser.). (Illus.). 1984. 4.95 (ISBN 0-89191-839-6); pap. 2.95 (ISBN 0-89191-812-4). Cook.

Storr, Catherine, ed. Moses in the Wilderness. (People of the Bible Ser.). (Illus.). 32p. 1985. PLB 10.65 (ISBN 0-8172-2039-9). Raintree Pubs.

MOSES BEN MAIMON, 1135-1204

Baron, Salo W., ed. Essays on Maimonides. LC 79-160004. Repr. of 1941 ed. 24.50 (ISBN 0-404-00658-2). AMS Pr.

Burrell, David B. Knowing the Unknowable God: Ibn-Sina, Maimonides, Aquinas. LC 85-40600. 160p. 1986. text ed. 15.95x (ISBN 0-268-01225-3, 85-12253). U of Notre Dame Pr.

--Knowing the Unknowable God: Ibn-Sina, Maimonides, Aquinas. 130p. 1986. pap. text ed. 8.95x (ISBN 0-268-01226-1, Dist. by Harrow). U of Notre Dame Pr.

Chavel, C. B., tr. The Commandments of Maimonides, 2 vols. 305p. 1967. 35.00 (ISBN 0-900689-71-4); pap. 25.00. Soncino Pr.

Chavel, Charles B. Ramban: His Life & Teachings. LC 63-1543. pap. 5.95 (ISBN 0-87306-037-7). Feldheim.

Dienstag, J. I., ed. Studies in Maimonidean Medicine. (Texts, Studies & Translations in Maimonidean Thought & Scholarship: Vol.2). 35.00x (ISBN 0-87068-449-3). Ktav.

--Studies in Maimonides & Spinoza. (Texts, Studies & Translations in Maimonidean Thought & Scholarship: Vol. 3). 35.00x (ISBN 0-87068-330-6). Ktav.

Dienstag, Jacob I. Eschatology in Maimonidean Thought: Messianism, Resurrection, & the World to Come-Jacob I. LC 82-17303. cxx, 281p. 1982. 59.50x (ISBN 0-87068-706-9). Ktav.

--Maimonides & St. Thomas Aquinas. 1974. 39.50x (ISBN 0-87068-249-0). Ktav.

Efros, Israel I. Philosophical Terms in the Moreh Nebukim. LC 73-164764. (Columbia University. Oriental Studies: No. 22). Repr. of 1924 ed. 17.00 (ISBN 0-404-50512-0). AMS Pr.

Forchheimer, Paul. Maimonides' Commentary on Avoth. pap. 5.95 (ISBN 0-87306-332-5). Feldheim.

Ginzberg, Asher, et al. Maimonides Octocentennial Series, No. I-IV. (Jewish People; History, Religion, Literature Ser.). Repr. of 1935 ed. 15.00 (ISBN 0-405-05278-2). Ayer Co Pubs.

Goldman, Solomon. The Jew & the Universe. LC 73-2200. (The Jewish People; History, Religion, Literature Ser.). Repr. of 1936 ed. 23.50 (ISBN 0-405-05265-0). Ayer Co Pubs.

Haberman, Jacob. Maimonides & Aquinas: A Contemporary Appraisal. 25.00x (ISBN 0-87068-685-2). Ktav.

Hartman, David. Maimonides-Torah & Philosophic Quest. LC 76-6305. 288p. 1977. pap. 7.95 (ISBN 0-8276-0089-5, 392). Jewish Pubns.

Heschel, Abraham J. Maimonides. Neugroschel, Joachim, tr. from Ger. 273p. 1982. 15.00 (ISBN 0-374-19874-8); pap. 7.25 (ISBN 0-374-51759-2). FS&G.

Katz, Steven, ed. Maimonides: Selected Essays, Original Anthology. LC 79-7176. (Jewish Philosophy, Mysticism & the History of Ideas Ser.). 1980. lib. bdg. 51.50x (ISBN 0-405-12234-9). Ayer Co Pubs.

Letters of Maimonides. 1982. pap. 7.95 (ISBN 0-686-76539-7). Feldheim.

Maimonides Codex: The Laws of Moses Ben Maimon (1135-1204) (Jewish Legal System in Hebrew Ser.). 1982. 390.00x (ISBN 0-686-44755-7, Pub. by Collets (UK)). State Mutual Bk.

Maimonides, Moses. The Book of Women: The Code of Maimonides, Bk. 4. Klein, Isaac, ed. LC 49-9495. (Judaica Ser.: No. 19). 592p. 1972. 50.00x (ISBN 0-300-01438-4). Yale U Pr.

Maimonides, Moses & Twersky, Isadore. Introduction to the Code of Maimonides (Mishneh Torah) LC 79-10347. (Yale Judaica Ser.: No. XXII). 1980. 50.00x (ISBN 0-300-02319-7); pap. 11.95x (ISBN 0-300-02846-6). Yale U Pr.

Minkin, Jacob. The Teachings of Maimonides. 450p. 1987. Repr. of 1957 ed. 35.00 (ISBN 0-87668-953-5). Aronson.

Reines, Alvin J. Maimonides & Abravanel on Prophecy. 1971. 15.00x (ISBN 0-87820-200-5, Pub. by Hebrew Union). KTAV.

Rosner, Fred. Sex Ethics in the Writings of Moses Maimonides. LC 74-75479. 225p. 1974. 7.95x (ISBN 0-8197-0365-6). Bloch.

Roth, Norman D. Maimonides: Essays & Texts, 850th Anniversary. 1986. 10.00x (ISBN 0-942260-59-7). Hispanic Seminary.

Strauss, Leo. Persecution & the Art of Writing. LC 73-1407. 204p. 1973. Repr. of 1952 ed. lib. bdg. 19.75 (ISBN 0-8371-6801-5, STPA). Greenwood.

Twersky, Isadore. Maimonides Reader. LC 76-160818. pap. 9.95x (ISBN 0-87441-206-4). Behrman.

Yellin, David & Abrahams, Israel. Maimonides: His Life & Works. (The Judaic Studies Library: No. SHP 10). (Illus.). 240p. 1987. 12.95 (ISBN 0-87203-120-9); pap. 9.75 (ISBN 0-87203-121-7). Hermon.

MOSLEMS

see Muslims

MOSQUES

Cousens, H. The Architectural Antiquities of Western India. (Illus.). 1983. text ed. 34.00x. Coronet Bks.

Kuran, Aptullah. Mosque in Early Ottoman Architecture. LC 68-16701. (Publications of the Center for Middle Eastern Studies Ser). (Illus.). 1968. 25.00x (ISBN 0-226-46293-5). U of Chicago Pr.

Parshall, Phil. Beyond the Mosque. 312p. 1985. pap. 9.95 (ISBN 0-8010-7089-9). Baker Bk.

MOTAZILITES

see also Shiites

Ali ibn Isma'il, A. H., et al. Al ibanah 'an usul addiyanah. Klein, W. C., tr. (American Oriental Ser.: Vol. 19). 1940. 18.00 (ISBN 0-527-02693-X). Kraus Repr.

MOTHER AND CHILD

Bacher, June M. A Mother's Joy. 1984. pap. 6.95 (ISBN 0-8010-0852-2). Baker Bk.

Baker, Pat A. Mom, Take Time. 128p. 1976. pap. 3.95 (ISBN 0-8010-0857-3). Baker Bk.

Bernstein, Fred. The Jewish Mothers' Hall of Fame. LC 85-24541. (Illus.). 192p. 1986. pap. 6.95 (ISBN 0-385-23377-9, Dolp). Doubleday.

Hardin, Garrett. Mandatory Motherhood: The True Meaning of "Right to Live". LC 74-4880. 136p. 1974. 6.95 (ISBN 0-8070-2176-8). Beacon Pr.

Kollstedt, Paula L. Surviving the Crisis of Motherhood: Strategies for Caring for Your Child & Yourself. (Illus.). 117p. 1981. pap. 3.50 (ISBN 0-912228-91-1). St Anthony Mess Pr.

Lawrence, Bette. Mike: A Mother's Prayers. LC 84-21247. 64p. 1985. pap. 2.95 (ISBN 0-8006-1857-2, 1-1857). Fortress.

Lazarre, Jane. The Mother Knot. LC 85-47944. 210p. 1986. pap. 8.95 (ISBN 0-8070-6725-3, BP710). Beacon Pr.

Loeks, Mary F. Mom's Quiet Corner. (Comtempo Ser.). 1977. pap. 1.25 (ISBN 0-8010-5576-8). Baker Bk.

Maassen, Pierce. Motherhood. pap. 0.45 (ISBN 0-686-23476-6). Rose Pub MI.

Steiner, Rudolf. Prayers for Mothers & Children. 3rd. ed. Hersey, Eileen V. & Von Arnim, Christian, trs. from Ger. 76p. 1983. pap. 5.00 (ISBN 0-85440-195-4, Pub. by Steinerbooks). Anthroposophic.

MOTHER-GODDESSES

Bhattacharyya, N. N. Indian Mother Goddess. 2nd ed. 1977. 16.50x (ISBN 0-88386-736-2). South Asia Bks.

Kinsley, David. Hindu Goddesses: Visions of the Divine Feminine in the Hindu Religious Tradition. LC 84-28000. (Hermeneutics: Studies in the History of Religions). 1985. 35.00x (ISBN 0-520-05393-1). U of Cal Pr.

Linford, Marilyne. Is Anyone Out There Building Mother's Self Esteem? 1986. text ed. 8.95 (ISBN 0-87579-048-8). Deseret Bk.

Olson, Carl, ed. The Book of the Goddess, Past & Present: An Introduction to Her Religion. LC 82-23606. 275p. 1983. 14.95 (ISBN 0-8245-0566-2). Crossroad NY.

Preston, James J., ed. Mother Worship: Theme & Variations. LC 81-3336. (Studies in Religion). xxiv, 360p. 1982. text ed. 29.00x (ISBN 0-8078-1471-7). U of NC Pr.

--Mother Worship: Theme & Variations. (Studies in Religion). xxiv, 360p. 1983. pap. text ed. 9.95x (ISBN 0-8078-4114-5). U of NC Pr.

Sri Sarada Devi. The Gospel of the Holy Mother. 409p. 1986. pap. 7.50X (ISBN 0-8364-1667-8, Pub. by Mukhopadhyaya India). South Asia Bks.

Whitmont, Edward C. Return of the Goddess. 288p. 1986. pap. 9.50 (ISBN 0-8334-1002-4, Freedeeds Bks). Garber Comm.

MOTHERS

see also Grandparents

Arndt, Elise. A Mother's Touch. 156p. 1983. pap. 5.95 (ISBN 0-88207-101-7). Victor Bks.

Bacher, June Masters. A Mother's Joy. 128p. 1984. pap. 6.95 6x (ISBN 0-89081-415-5). Harvest Hse.

Haffey, Richard. Thank You, Mom. (Greeting Book Line Ser.). 24p. (Orig.). 1986. pap. 1.50 (ISBN 0-89622-306-X). Twenty-Third.

Hartshorn, Leon R. A Mother's Love. LC 80-81506. 76p. 1980. 5.95 (ISBN 0-88290-143-5). Horizon Utah.

Head, Diane. Come to the Waters. 96p. 1985. pap. 5.95 (ISBN 0-310-25941-X, 9586P). Zondervan.

Kitzinger, Sheila. Giving Birth: The Parents' Emotions in Childbirth. LC 77-2518. (Orig.). 1978. pap. 4.95 (ISBN 0-8052-0573-X). Schocken.

Lazarre, Jane. The Mother Knot. LC 85-47944. 210p. 1986. pap. 8.95 (ISBN 0-8070-6725-3, BP710). Beacon Pr.

Mall, E. Jane. A Mother's Gifts: A Book of Praise & Inspiration. LC 75-33082. pap. 15.00 (ISBN 0-8357-9017-7, 2016382). Bks Demand UMI.

Monsma, Hester. Devotions for Mothers. 30p. 1984. pap. 1.25 (ISBN 0-8010-2942-2). Baker Bk.

Radl, Shirley. Mother's Day Is over. 288p. 1987. 17.95 (ISBN 0-87795-864-5). Arbor Hse.

Sapone, Edith. To You Mom. (Illus.). 1961. 3.00 (ISBN 0-8198-0162-3); pap. 2.00 (ISBN 0-8198-0163-1). Dghtrs St Paul.

Shenk, Sara W. And Then There Were Three. LC 85-13936. 208p. (Orig.). 1985. pap. 8.95 (ISBN 0-8361-3398-6). Herald Pr.

Sjoo, Monica & Mor, Barbara. The Great Cosmic Mother. 1986. pap. 14.95 (ISBN 0-317-52386-4, PL 4115, HarpR). Har-Row.

Spencer, Anita. Mothers Are People Too: A Contemporary Analysis of Motherhood. 1984. pap. 5.95 (ISBN 0-8091-2616-8). Paulist Pr.

West, Marion B. Out of My Bondage. LC 76-5297. 128p. 1976. 5.50 (ISBN 0-8054-5144-7). Broadman.

MOTHERS–RELIGIOUS LIFE

Brenneman, H. G. Meditaciones para la Nueva Madre. 80p. 1982. Repr. of 1978 ed. 2.85 (ISBN 0-311-40032-9). Casa Bautista.

Brenneman, Helen G. Meditations for the Expectant Mother. LC 68-12025. (Illus.). 80p. (Orig.). 1968. 8.95 (ISBN 0-8361-1639-9); pap. 4.50 (ISBN 0-8361-1567-8). Herald Pr.

--Meditations for the New Mother. LC 53-7585. (Illus.). 78p. (Orig.). 1953. 8.95 (ISBN 0-8361-3400-1); pap. 4.50 (ISBN 0-8361-3399-4). Herald Pr.
Esway, Judy. Prayers of a Working Mother. (Getting Book Line Ser.). 32p. (Orig.). 1985. pap. 1.50 (ISBN 0-89622-269-1). Twenty-Third.
Garrison, Jayne. The Christian Working Mother's Handbook. 144p. 1986. pap. 7.95 (ISBN 0-8423-0258-1). Tyndale.
Hanes, Mari. The Child Within. 1983. pap. 2.95 (ISBN 0-8423-0219-0). Tyndale.
Hardison, Amy. How to Feel Great about Being a Mother. LC 86-29349. 1987. 8.95 (ISBN 0-87579-073-9). Deseret Bk.
Hebbelthwaite, Margaret. Motherhood & God. 144p. 1984. pap. 5.95 (ISBN 0-225-66384-8, HarpR). Har-Row.
Holmes, Deborah A. Survival Prayers for Young Mothers. 6.95 (ISBN 0-8042-2195-2). John Knox.
Johnson, Ruby E. From the Heart of a Mother. LC 82-8218. 1982. pap. 3.95 (ISBN 0-8024-5090-3). Moody.
Larson, Mobby. Prayers of a New Mother. (Greeting Book Line Ser.). 48p. (Orig.). 1985. pap. 1.50 (ISBN 0-89622-230-6). Twenty Third.
Loeks, Mary F. Good Morning, Lord: Devotions for Young Mothers. (Good Morning, Lord Ser.). 1977. 4.95 (ISBN 0-8010-5566-0). Baker Bk.
Marshall, Helen L. Bright Laughter-Warm Tears: Inspirational Thoughts for Mothers. 64p. 1985. pap. 3.95 (ISBN 0-8010-6195-4). Baker Bk.
Mattison, Judith. Prayers from a Mother's Heart. LC 74-14177. (Illus.). 96p. (Orig.). 1975. pap. 5.95 (ISBN 0-8066-1460-9, 10-5095). Augsburg.
Moody, D. L. Thoughts for the Quiet Hour. pap. 3.50 (ISBN 0-8024-8729-7). Moody.
O'Connor, Sarah H. The Nine Months Journey: A Christian Mother's Reflections on Pregnancy & Childbirth. 128p. (Orig.). 1984. pap. 6.95 (ISBN 0-687-28017-6). Abingdon.
Phillips, Sheree. Mothers: At the Heart of Life. 140p. (Orig.). 1985. pap. 4.95 (ISBN 0-89283-274-6, Pub. by Vine Books). Servant.
Rippey, Mari. It's Tough Being a Mother. 32p. 1983. pap. 2.95 (ISBN 0-8170-0995-7). Judson.
Rischer, Carol. Insights for Young Mothers. pap. 5.95 (ISBN 0-89081-485-6). Harvest Hse.
Steiner, Rudolf. Prayers for Mothers & Children. 3rd. ed. Hersey, Eileen V. & Von Arnim, Christian, trs. from Ger. 76p. 1983. pap. 5.00 (ISBN 0-85440-195-4, Pub. by Steinerbooks). Anthroposophic.
Tengbom, Mildred. Devotions for a New Mother. 127p. 1983. pap. 4.95 (ISBN 0-87123-294-4). Bethany Hse.
Tengbom, Mildren. Bible Readings for Mothers. (Bible Reading Ser.). 112p. (Orig.). 1987. pap. 3.95 (ISBN 0-8066-2249-0, 10-0692). Augsburg.

MOTHERS (IN RELIGION, FOLKLORE, ETC.)
see Mother-Goddesses; Women (In Religion, Folklore, etc.)

MOTHERS, UNMARRIED
see Unmarried Mothers

MOUNTAIN MEADOWS MASSACRE, 1857
Brooks, Juanita. Mountain Meadows Massacre. (Illus.). 342p. 1985. Repr. of 1963 ed. 18.95 (ISBN 0-8061-0549-6). U of Okla Pr.

MOURNING CUSTOMS
see also Funeral Rites and Ceremonies
Davidson, Glen W. Understanding Mourning: A Guide for Those Who Grieve. LC 84-14527. 112p. (Orig.). 1984. pap. 5.95 (ISBN 0-8066-2080-3, 10-6805). Augsburg.
Gorer, Geoffrey. Death, Grief, & Mourning. Kastenbaum, Robert, ed. LC 76-19573. (Death & Dying Ser.). (Illus.). 1977. Repr. of 1965 ed. lib. bdg. 24.50x (ISBN 0-405-09571-6). Ayer Co Pubs.
Hughes, Robert. A Trumpet in Darkness: Preaching to Mourners. LC 85-47719. (Fortress Resources for Preaching Ser.). 112p. 1985. pap. 5.95 (ISBN 0-8006-1141-1). Fortress.
Little, Geraldine C. Contrasts in Keening: Ireland. LC 82-60038. 50p. (Orig.). 1982. pap. 3.50 (ISBN 0-943710-00-6). Silver App Pr.
Pigman, C. W., III. Grief & English Renaissance Elegy. 192p. 1985. 29.95 (ISBN 0-521-26871-0). Cambridge U Pr.
Pike, Martha V. & Armstrong, Janice G. A Time to Mourn: Expressions of Grief in Nineteenth Century America. LC 80-15105. (Illus.). 192p. 1980. pap. 14.95 (ISBN 0-295-96325-5, Pub. by Museums at Stony Brook). U of Wash Pr.
Pollock, George. Mourning & Liberation. 1987. lib. bdg. price not set (ISBN 0-8236-3485-X). Intl Univs Pr.
Rosenblatt, Paul C., et al. Grief & Mourning in Cross-Cultural Perspective. LC 76-29270. (Comparative Studies Ser.). 242p. 1976. pap. 7.00x (ISBN 0-87536-334-2). HRAFP.
Spiro, Jack. A Time to Mourn. LC 67-30744. 160p. 1985. pap. text ed. 8.95 (ISBN 0-8197-0497-0). Bloch.
Stavsky, David. For Thou Art with Me: A Manual of Mourning. 1965. pap. 1.50 (ISBN 0-87306-093-8). Feldheim.

MOVEMENT, ECUMENICAL
see Ecumenical Movement

MOVING-PICTURES–MORAL AND RELIGIOUS ASPECTS
Adler, Mortimer J. Art & Prudence. Jowett, Garth S., ed. LC 77-11371. (Aspects of Film Ser.). 1978. Repr. of 1937 ed. lib. bdg. 59.50x (ISBN 0-405-11126-6). Ayer Co Pubs.
Campbell, Richard H. & Pitts, Michael R. The Bible on Film: A Checklist 1897-1980. LC 81-13560. 224p. 1981. 17.50 (ISBN 0-8108-1473-0). Scarecrow.
Dale, Edgar. Content of Motion Pictures. LC 77-124026. (Literature of Cinema Ser: Payne Fund Studies of Motion Pictures & Social Values). Repr. of 1935 ed. 17.00 (ISBN 0-405-01644-1). Ayer Co Pubs.
Friedman, Lester D. Hollywood's Image of the Jew. LC 81-70118. (Illus.). 408p. 1982. pap. 8.95 (ISBN 0-8044-6160-0). Ungar.
Lindsay, Gordon. Should Christians Attend Movies? 0.95 (ISBN 0-89985-007-3). Christ Nations.
Martin, Thomas M. Images & the Imageless: A Study in Religious Consciousness & Film. LC 79-57611. 200p. 1981. 18.50 (ISBN 0-8387-5005-2). Bucknell U Pr.
May, John R. & Bird, Michael, eds. Religion in Film. LC 81-23983. (Illus.). 232p. 1982. text ed. 17.95x (ISBN 0-87049-352-3); pap. text ed. 8.95x (ISBN 0-87049-368-X). U of Tenn Pr.
Tozer, A. H. Menace of the Religious Movie. 1974. pap. 1.00 (ISBN 0-915374-51-X, 51-X). Rapids Christian.

MOVING-PICTURES AND RELIGION
see Moving-Pictures–Moral and Religious Aspects

MUELLER, GEORGE, 1805-1898
Bailey, Faith C. George Mueller. 160p. 1980. pap. 3.50 (ISBN 0-8024-0031-0). Moody.
Harding, William H. The Life of George Muller. (Heroes of the Faith Ser.). 384p. 1985. Repr of 1914 ed. 6.95 (ISBN 0-916441-13-X). Barbour & Co.
Miller, Basil. George Mueller: Man of Faith. 160p. 1972. pap. 3.50 (ISBN 0-87123-182-4, 200182). Bethany Hse.
Muller, George. Autobiography of George Muller. Wayland, H. Lincoln, ed. (Giant Summit Books Ser.). 490p. 1981. pap. 11.95 (ISBN 0-8010-6105-9). Baker Bk.
--The Autobiography of George Muller. 300p. 1984. pap. 3.50 (ISBN 0-88368-159-5). Whitaker Hse.
Steer, Roger. George Muller: Delighted in God! rev. ed. LC 81-52600. 320p. 1981. pap. 3.95 (ISBN 0-87788-304-1). Shaw Pubs.
Tallach, John. God Made Them Great. 144p. 1982. pap. 5.45 (ISBN 0-85151-190-2). Banner of Truth.

MUHAMMADANS
see Muslims

MURAL PAINTING AND DECORATION
see also Mosaics
Balabanov, Kosta. Freske i Ikone u Makedoniji, iv-xv vek (Frescos & Icons in Macedonia, iv-xv Centory) 158p. 1983. 20.00 (ISBN 0-918660-26-2). Ragusan Pr.
Collet's Holdings, Ltd. Staff, ed. Early Russian Painting 11th to Early 13th Centuries: Mosaics, Frescoes & Icons. 308p. 1982. 125.00x (ISBN 0-317-39496-7, Pub. by Collets UK). State Mutual Bk.
Davidson, Bernice F. Raphael's Bible: A Study of the Vatican Logge. LC 84-43088. (College Art Association Monographs: Vol. 39). (Illus.). 198p. 1985. 30.00 (ISBN 0-271-00388-X). Pa St U Pr.
Howe, Eunice D. The Hospital of Santo Spirito & Pope Sixtus IV. LC 77-94698. (Outstanding Dissertations in the Fine Arts Ser.). (Illus.). 444p. 1978. lib. bdg. 52.00 (ISBN 0-8240-3230-6). Garland Pub.
Plugin, V. Frescoes of St. Demetrius' Cathedral. 44p. 1974. 25.00x (ISBN 0-569-08164-5, Pub. by Collets UK). State Mutual Bk.
Tintori, Leonetto & Meiss, Millard. The Painting of the Life of St. Francis in Assisi, with Notes on the Arena Chapel. LC 62-10308. pap. 55.50 (ISBN 0-317-10175-7, 2050842). Bks Demand UMI.

MUSIC–ANALYSIS, APPRECIATION
Godwin, Joscelyn. Music, Mysticism & Magic: A Source Book. 384p. 1986. text ed. 50.00 (ISBN 0-7102-0904-5, 0905W, Pub. by Routledge UK). Methuen Inc.
Hunter, Stanley A., ed. Music & Religion. LC 72-1615. Repr. of 1930 ed. 19.00 (ISBN 0-404-08316-1). AMS Pr.

MUSIC–SUNDAY-SCHOOLS
see Sunday-Schools–Hymns

MUSIC, AMERICAN
Billings, William. The Psalm Singer's Amusement. LC 73-5100. (Earlier American Music Ser.: Vol. 20). 104p. 1974. Repr. of 1781 ed. lib. bdg. 25.00 (ISBN 0-306-70587-7). Da Capo.
David, Hans T. Music of the Moravians in America from the Archives of the Moravian Church at Bethlehem Pa, 2 vols. Incl. Vol. 1. Ten Sacred Songs. Dencke, J., et al.; Vol. 2. Six Quintets. Peter, John F. write to C. F. Peters Corp., NY for prices (ISBN 0-685-22862-2). NY Pub Lib.
Hood, George. History of Music in New England, with Biographical Sketches of Reformers & Psalmists. (American Studies). 1970. Repr. of 1846 ed. 24.00 (ISBN 0-384-24140-9). Johnson Repr.
Ingalls, Jeremiah. The Christian Harmony. (Earlier American Music Ser.: Vol. 22). 230p. 1981. Repr. of 1805 ed. lib. bdg. 29.50 (ISBN 0-306-79617-1). Da Capo.
Kaufmann, Helen L. From Jehovah to Jazz: Music in America from Psalmody to the Present Day. facs. ed. LC 68-54352. (Essay Index Reprint Ser). 1968. Repr. of 1937 ed. 20.00 (ISBN 0-8369-0585-7). Ayer Co Pubs.
MacDougall, Hamilton C. Early New England Psalmody: An Historical Appreciation, 1620-1820. LC 79-87398. (Music Reprint Ser.). 1969. Repr. of 1940 ed. lib. bdg. 29.50 (ISBN 0-306-71542-2). Da Capo.
National Society of Colonial Dames of America. Church Music & Musical Life in Pennsylvania in the Eighteenth Century, 3 vols. in 4 pts. LC 79-38037. (Illus.). Repr. of 1926 ed. Set. 150.00 (ISBN 0-404-08090-1). AMS Pr.
Sonneck, Oscar G. Francis Hopkinson, the First American Poet-Composer, & James Lyon, Patriot, Preacher, Psalmodist. 2nd ed. LC 65-23393. (Music Reprint Ser.). 213p. 1966. Repr. of 1905 ed. lib. bdg. 32.50 (ISBN 0-306-70918-X). Da Capo.

MUSIC, BYZANTINE
Cavarnos, Constantine. Byzantine Sacred Music. 31p. 1981. pap. 1.00 (ISBN 0-914744-23-2). Inst Byzantine.
Conomos, Dimitri. Byzantine Hymnography & Byzantine Chant. Vaporis, N. M., intro. by. (Nicholas E. Kulukundis Lectures in Hellenism Ser.). 56p. (Orig.). 1984. pap. text ed. 4.00 (ISBN 0-917653-04-1). Hellenic Coll Pr.
Hatherly, S. G. Treatise on Byzantine Music. LC 77-75226. 1977. Repr. of 1892 ed. lib. bdg. 20.00 (ISBN 0-89341-071-3). Longwood Pub Group.
Tillyard, Henry J. Byzantine Music & Hymnography. LC 74-24242. Repr. of 1923 ed. 11.50 (ISBN 0-404-13116-6). AMS Pr.
Wellesz, Egon. History of Byzantine Music & Hymnography. 2nd ed. 1961. 49.95x (ISBN 0-19-816111-5). Oxford U Pr.

MUSIC, CHORAL
see Choral Music

MUSIC, HAWAIIAN
Emerson, Nathaniel B. Unwritten Literature of Hawaii; the Sacred Songs of the Hula. Repr. of 1909 ed. 39.00x (ISBN 0-403-03720-4). Scholarly.
Johnson, Rubellite K. Kumulipo: The Hawaiian Hymn of Creation. Holt, John D., ed. (Illus.). 1981. text ed. 19.95 (ISBN 0-914916-53-X); leather 100.00 (ISBN 0-914916-59-9). Topgallant.

MUSIC, HEBREW
see Music, Jewish

MUSIC, HINDU
Rudhyar, Dane. The Rebirth of Hindu Music. 112p. 1980. pap. 4.95 (ISBN 0-87728-448-2). Weiser.

MUSIC, INDIC
Henry, Edward. Chant the Names of God. (Illus.). 260p. 1984. 20.00 (ISBN 0-916304-65-5). SDSU Press.
Howard, Wayne. Samavedic Chant. LC 76-49854. (Illus.). 1977. 50.00x (ISBN 0-300-01956-4). Yale U Pr.
Leopold, Simon R. Spiritual Aspects of Indian Music. 1985. 22.50x (ISBN 0-8364-1258-3, Pub. by Sundeep). South Asia Bks.
Qureshi, Regula B. Sufi Music of India & Pakistan: Sound, Context & Meaning in Qawwali. (Cambridge Studies in Ethnomusicology). (Illus.). 300p. 1987. 69.50 (ISBN 0-521-26767-6); cassette 18.96 (ISBN 0-521-32598-6). Cambridge U Pr.
Tagore, Sourindo M. The Musical Scales of the Hindus. LC 74-24225. Repr. of 1884 ed. 21.50 (ISBN 0-404-12837-8). AMS Pr.
Tagore, Sourindo M., compiled by. Hindu Music, from Various Authors. 2nd ed. LC 74-24223. 1977. Repr. of 1882 ed. 35.00 (ISBN 0-404-12835-1). AMS Pr.
Vedas. Der Rig Veda, 4 pts. Ingalls, Daniel H., ed. LC 54-10046. (Oriental Ser: No. 33-35). Pts. 1-3. 1952 65.00x (ISBN 0-674-76965-1); Pt. 4. 1957 16.50x (ISBN 0-674-76967-8). Harvard U Pr.

MUSIC, JEWISH
Concise Encyclopedia of Jewish Music. 9.95 (ISBN 0-686-76494-3). Feldheim.
D'Allonnes, Olivier R. Musical Variations on Jewish Thought. Greenberg, Judith, tr. LC 83-15640. 169p. 1984. 12.95 (ISBN 0-8076-1091-7). Braziller.
Eisikovits, Max. Songs of the Martyrs: Hassidic Melodies of Maramures. LC 79-67624. 1980. pap. 7.95 (ISBN 0-87203-089-X). Hermon.
Fromm, Herbert. Herbert Fromm on Jewish Music: A Composers View. LC 78-60716. 1979. 10.00x (ISBN 0-8197-0465-2). Bloch.
Holde, Artur & Heskes, Irene, eds. Jews in Music: From the Age of Enlightenment to the Mid-Twentieth Century. rev. ed. LC 74-83942. 364p. 1974. 10.00 (ISBN 0-8197-0372-9). Bloch.
Idelsohn, Abraham Z. Jewish Music in Its Historical Development. LC 80-24235. (Illus.). xi, 535p. 1981. Repr. of 1948 ed. lib. bdg. 35.00 (ISBN 0-313-22749-7, IDJM). Greenwood.
--Jewish Music: In Its Historical Development. LC 67-25236. 1967. pap. 12.50 (ISBN 0-8052-0165-3). Schocken.
Karas, Joza. Music in Terezin Nineteen Forty-One to Nineteen Forty Five. LC 84-24411. (Illus.). 212p. 1985. 16.95x (ISBN 0-918728-34-7). Pendragon NY.
Marks, Paul F. Bibliography of Literature Concerning Yemenite-Jewish Music. LC 72-90431. (Detroit Studies in Music Bibliography Ser.: No. 27). 1973. pap. 2.00 (ISBN 0-911772-57-X). Info Coord.
Newsom, Carol. The Songs of the Sabbath Sacrifice: Edition, Translation, & Commentary. (Harvard Semitic Museum Ser.). 1985. 34.95 (ISBN 0-89130-837-7, 04-04-27). Scholars Pr GA.
Stainer, John. Music of the Bible. LC 74-100657. (Music Ser). (Illus.). 1970. Repr. of 1914 ed. lib. bdg. 32.50 (ISBN 0-306-71862-6). Da Capo.
Stevens, Joel & Olitzky, Kerry M. An Index to the Sound Recordings Collection of the American Jewish Arichives. 1980. 7.50x (ISBN 0-87820-009-6). Ktav.
Werner, Eric. A Voice Still Heard: The Sacred Songs of the Ashkenazic Jews. LC 75-26522. 1976. 32.50 (ISBN 0-271-01167-X). Pa St U Pr.

MUSIC, RELIGIOUS
see Church Music

MUSIC, SACRED
see Church Music

MUSIC, YIDDISH
see Music, Jewish

MUSIC AND RELIGION
see Religion and Music

MUSIC IN CHURCHES
see also Church Music; Psalmody; Religion and Music
Bay, Bill. The Liturgical Guitarist. 360p. 1980. spiral bdg. 9.95 (ISBN 0-89228-055-7). Impact Bks MO.
Flint, Tommy & Griffin, Neil. Gospel Guitar. 48p. 1976. wkbk 2.95 (ISBN 0-89228-018-2). Impact Bks MO.
Kurfees, M. C. Instrumental Music in Worship. 10.95 (ISBN 0-89225-106-9). Gospel Advocate.
Lutkin, Peter C. Music in the Church. LC 72-135722. Repr. of 1910 ed. 21.45 (ISBN 0-404-04069-1). AMS Pr.
Nelson, Edward W. Music & Worship. 176p. 1985. spiral bdg. 13.50 (ISBN 0-311-72642-9). Casa Bautista.
Routley, Erik. Church Music & the Christian Faith. LC 78-110219. 1979. 7.95 (ISBN 0-916642-11-9, Agape). Hope Pub.
Routley, Erik & Young, Carlton R. Music Leadership in the Church. 136p. 1985. pap. text ed. 6.95 (ISBN 0-916642-24-0). Agape IL.

MUSIC IN RELIGION
see Religion and Music

MUSIC OF THE SPHERES
see Harmony of the Spheres

MUSICIANS–CORRESPONDENCE, REMINISCENCES, ETC.
Anderson, Marian. My Lord, What a Morning: An Autobiography. 312p. Repr. of 1956 ed. lib. bdg. 39.00 (Pub. by Am Repr Serv). Am Biog Serv.

MUSICOLOGY
Anderson, Gordon A. Latin Compositions in the Sixth Fasciale of the Notre-Dame Manuscript Wolfenbuttel 1099. (Wissenschaftliche Abhandlungen-Musicological Studies Ser.: Vol. 24). Pt. 1. lib. bdg. 50.00 (ISBN 0-931902-02-9); Pt. 2. lib. bdg. 50.00 (ISBN 0-931902-03-7). Inst Mediaeval Mus.
Brockett, C. W. Antiphons, Responsories & other Chants from the Mozarabic Rite. (Wissenschaftliche Abhandlungen - Musicological Studies Ser.: No. 15). 300p. 1968. lib. bdg. 60.00 (ISBN 0-912024-85-2). Inst Mediaeval Mus.

Mattfeld, Victor. Georg Rhaw's Publications for Vespers. (Wissenschaftliche Abhandlungen-Musicological Studies: Vol. 11). 361p. 1967. lib. bdg. 30.00 (ISBN 0-912024-81-X). Inst Mediaeval Mus.

MUSLIM CIVILIZATION
see Civilization, Islamic

MUSLIM COUNTRIES
see Islamic Countries

MUSLIM ETHICS
see Islamic Ethics

MUSLIM MYSTICISM
see Mysticism–Islam

MUSLIM PAINTING
see Painting, Islamic

MUSLIM PHILOSOPHY
see Philosophy, Islamic

MUSLIM SECTS
see Islamic Sects

MUSLIM SOCIOLOGY
see Sociology, Islamic

MUSLIM THEOLOGY
see Islamic Theology

MUSLIM WOMEN
see Women, Muslim

MUSLIMISM
see Islam

MUSLIMS
see also Islamic Learning and Scholarship; Missions to Muslims

Abdullah. The Why & How of Burial & Death of a Muslim. (Illus.). 22p. (Orig.). 1985. pap. 1.50 (ISBN 0-916157-04-0). African Islam Miss Pubns.

Ahmad Ibn Yahya, Al-Baladuri. Origins of the Islamic State, 2 vols. Incl. Vol. 1. Hitti, Philip K., tr. Repr. of 1916 ed (ISBN 0-404-51694-7); Vol. 2. Murgotten, Francis C., tr. Repr. of 1924 ed (ISBN 0-404-51695-5). LC 76-82247. (Columbia University Studies in the Social Sciences: No. 163 & No. 163a). Set. 82.50 (ISBN 0-404-51163-5). AMS Pr.

Brown, Marguerite. Magnificent Muslims. LC 81-80056. 98p. 1981. 8.00 (ISBN 0-911026-10-X). New World Press NY.

Chejne, Anver. Ibn Hazm al Undalasi. 320p. (Orig.). 1982. 29.00x (ISBN 0-935782-03-6); pap. 19.95x (ISBN 0-935782-04-4). Kazi Pubns.

Cudsi, Alex & Dessouki, Ali E. Hillal, eds. Islam & Power in the Contemporary Muslim World. LC 81-47608. 208p. 1981. text ed. 25.00x (ISBN 0-8018-2697-7). Johns Hopkins.

Dayton, Edward & Wagner, C. Peter. Unreached Peoples '80. LC 79-57522. 1980. pap. 8.95 (ISBN 0-89191-837-X). Cook.

Diara, Agadem L. Islam & Pan-Africanism. LC 72-91318. (Illus.). 120p. 1973. pap. 3.75 (ISBN 0-913358-04-5). El-Shabazz Pr.

Donia, Robert J. Islam Under the Double Eagle: The Muslims of Bosnia & Hercegovina, 1878-1914. (East European Monographs: No. 78). 237p. 1981. 22.00x (ISBN 0-914710-72-9). East Eur Quarterly.

Gaudefroy-Demombynes, Maurice. Muslim Institutions. LC 84-12953. 216p. 1984. Repr. of 1950 ed. lib. bdg. 35.00x (ISBN 0-313-24287-9, GAMU). Greenwood.

Goldziher, Ignac. Muslim Studies. Stern, S. M., ed. & tr. Incl. Vol. 1. Muhammedanische Studien. LC 67-20745. 1967. 44.50 (ISBN 0-87395-234-0); Vol. 2. Hadith: The 'Traditions', Ascribed to Muhammed. LC 72-11731. 1972. State U NY Pr.

Hayes, K. H. Stories of Great Muslims. 4.75 (ISBN 0-686-18389-4). Kazi Pubns.

Hodkinson, Keith. Muslim Family Law: A Sourcebook. 401p. (Orig.). 1984. pap. 25.00 (ISBN 0-7099-1256-0, Pub. by Croom Helm Ltd). Methuen Inc.

Irving, J. B. Had You Been Born a Muslim. pap. 1.50 (ISBN 0-686-18471-8). Kazi Pubns.

Jones, Fraymond, Jr. & Kashaf Abdul Haq. Self Interpretation of All Religions. 80p. 1983. 8.95 (ISBN 0-89962-293-3). Todd & Honeywell.

Kettani, M. Ali. Muslim Minorities in the World Today. 267p. 1986. 56.00x (ISBN 0-7201-1802-6). Mansell.

--Muslim Minorities in the World Today. 267p. 1986. 56.00 (ISBN 0-7201-1802-6). Wilson.

Khan, Gazanfar A. & Sparroy, Wilfred. With the Pilgrims to Mecca: The Great Pilgrimage of A.H. 1319, A.D. 1902. LC 77-876447. Repr. of 1905 ed. 24.50 (ISBN 0-404-16417-X). AMS Pr.

Khan, M. Z. & Saleem, M. Umar the Great (Al-Farqu, 2 vols. 1970. Vol. 1. 12.50x (ISBN 0-87902-196-9); Vol. 2. 12.50x (ISBN 0-685-33011-7). Orientalia.

Kramer, Martin. Islam Assembled: The Advent of the Muslim Congresses. LC 84-21407. 280p. 1985. 30.00x (ISBN 0-231-05994-9). Columbia U Pr.

Kyani, A. S. Islam & Muslims in Red Regimes. pap. 4.50 (ISBN 0-686-18575-7). Kazi Pubns.

Leiden, Carl. The Conflict of Traditionalism & Modernism in the Muslim Middle East: A Symposium. LC 68-59178. pap. 40.50 (ISBN 0-317-08447-X, 2000823). Bks Demand UMI.

Morgan, Kenneth W., ed. Islam the Straight Path: Islam Interpreted by Muslims. LC 58-9807. pap. 115.80 (ISBN 0-317-08489-5, 2012383). Bks Demand UMI.

M. S. A. The Muslim Population of the World. pap. 1.00 (ISBN 0-686-18438-6). Kazi Pubns.

Nadawi, Abul H. Madha Khasira al-Alam bi-Inhtat al-Muslimin. 4th ed. (Arabic.). 432p. (Orig.). 1978. pap. 8.50x (ISBN 0-939830-14-0, Pub. by IIFSO Kuwait). New Era Pubns MI.

Nadwi, Abul H. Muslims in the West: The Message & the Mission. Murad, Khurram, ed. 191p. (Orig.). 1983. pap. 6.95x (ISBN 0-86037-130-1, Pub by Islamic Found UK). New Era Pubns MI.

Nu'man, Muhammad A. What Every American Should Know about Islam & the Muslims. 74p. (Orig.). 1985. pap. 5.00 (ISBN 0-933821-04-2). New Mind Prod.

Qazi, M. A. What's in a Muslim Name? pap. 3.50 (ISBN 0-686-18582-X). Kazi Pubns.

Shari'Ati, Ali. Hajj. Somayyah & Yaser, trs. 1984. pap. 5.95 (ISBN 0-686-78719-6). Mizan Pr.

Siddiqui, Zeba. Kareem & Fatimah. Quinlan, Hamid, ed. LC 82-70452. (Illus.). 50p. 1982. pap. 3.50 (ISBN 0-89259-032-7). Am Trust Pubns.

Wilson, S. G. Modern Movements among Moslems. 1977. lib. bdg. 59.95 (ISBN 0-8490-2270-3). Gordon Pr.

--Modern Movements among Moslems. LC 74-83190. (Islam & Mideast Ser.). 1976. Repr. of 1916 ed. 33.00 (ISBN 0-8420-1753-4). Scholarly Res Inc.

Zenkovsky, Serge A. Pan-Turkism & Islam in Russia. LC 60-5399. (Russian Research Center Studies: No. 36). 1960. 25.00x (ISBN 0-674-65350-5). Harvard U Pr.

MUSLIMS–WOMEN
see Women, Muslim

MUSLIMS IN AFRICA

Klein, Martin A. Islam & Imperialism in Senegal: Sine-Saloum, 1847-1914. 1968. 25.00x (ISBN 0-8047-0621-2). Stanford U Pr.

Trimingham, John S. Islam in West Africa. 1959. 29.95x (ISBN 0-19-826511-5). Oxford U Pr.

MUSLIMS IN ASIA

Ahmed, Rafiuddin. The Bengal Muslims, Eighteen Seventy-One to Nineteen Six: A Quest for Identity. (Illus.). 1981. 34.00x (ISBN 0-19-561260-4). Oxford U Pr.

Al-din, Minhaj. General History of Muhammadan Dynasties of Asia from 810 to 1260 AD, 2 vols. Raverty, H. C., tr. from Persian. Repr. of 1881 ed. Set. text ed. 77.50x. Coronet Bks.

Gowing, Peter G. Muslim Filipinos: Heritage & Horizon. (Illus.). 1979. pap. 11.00x (ISBN 0-686-25217-9, Pub. by New Day Pub). Cellar.

Long, David. The Hajj Today: A Survey of the Contemporary Pilgrimage to Makkah. (Illus.). 1979. 34.50 (ISBN 0-87395-382-7). State U NY Pr.

Rywkin, Michael. Moscow's Muslim Challenge: Soviet Central Asia. LC 81-14414. (Illus.). 232p. 1982. pap. 13.95 (ISBN 0-87332-262-2). M E Sharpe.

MUSLIMS IN CANADA

Waugh, E. H., et al, eds. The Muslim Community in North America. xii, 316p. 1983. pap. 15.00x (ISBN 0-88864-034-X, Pub. by Univ of Alta Pr Canada). U of Nebr Pr.

MUSLIMS IN CHINA

Chu, Wen-Djang. Moslem Rebellion in Northwest China, 1862-1878. (Central Asiatic Studies: No. 5). 1966. pap. text ed. 31.20x (ISBN 90-2790-017-5). Mouton.

Israeli, Raphael. Muslims in China: A Study in Cultural Confrontation. (Scandinavian Institute of Asian Studies: No. 29). 272p. 1981. pap. text ed. 17.50x (ISBN 0-391-00718-1, Pub. by Curzon Pr UK). Humanities.

MUSLIMS IN INDIA

Afaque, Khan M. Gandhian Approach to Communal Harmony: A Critical Study. 140p. 1986. 11.00 (ISBN 81-202-0163-9, Pub. by Ajanta). South Asia Bks.

Ahmad, Imtiaz, ed. Family, Kinship, & Marriage among the Muslims. LC 77-74484. 1977. 18.50x (ISBN 0-88386-757-5). South Asia Bks.

--Modernization & Social Change among Muslims in India. 1983. 28.00x (ISBN 0-88386-892-X). South Asia Bks.

--Ritual & Religion among Muslims in India. 1982. 20.00x (ISBN 0-8364-0852-7, Pub. by Manohar India). South Asia Bks.

Ahmad, Mohammad A. Traditional Education among Muslims: A Study of Some Aspects in Modern India. viii, 216p. 1986. text ed. 30.00x (ISBN 81-7018-259-X, Pub. by B R Pub Corp Delhi). Apt Bks.

Arnold, T. W. The Preachings of Islam. 467p. 1984. Repr. of 1913 ed. text ed. 50.00x (ISBN 0-86590-250-X, Pub. by Renaissance New Delhi). Apt Bks.

Baig, M. R. Muslim Dilemma in India. 1974. 7.50 (ISBN 0-7069-0311-0). Intl Bk Dist.

Datta, V. N. & Gleghorn, B. E., eds. A Nationalist Muslim & Indian Politics. LC 75-902114. 352p. 1974. 14.00 (ISBN 0-333-90023-5). South Asia Bks.

Engineer, Asghar A. Indian Muslims: A Study of Minority Problems in India. 1986. 28.00x (ISBN 81-202-0139-6, Pub. by Ajanta). South Asia Bks.

Gandhi, Rajmohan. Eight Lives: A Study of the Hindu-Muslim Encounter. 320p. 1986. 39.50x (ISBN 0-88706-196-6); pap. 14.95x (ISBN 0-88706-197-4). State U NY Pr.

Ghosh, S. K. Muslim Politics in India. 1986. 18.50 (ISBN 81-7024-070-0, Pub. by Ashish India). South Asia Bks.

Hardy, P. Muslims of British India. LC 77-184772. (South Asian Studies: No. 13). (Illus.). 300p. 1973. pap. 15.95 o. p. (ISBN 0-521-09783-5). Cambridge U Pr.

Hardy, Peter. The Muslims of British India. LC 77-184772. (Cambridge South Asian Studies: No. 13). pap. 79.30 (ISBN 0-317-27996-3, 2025585). Bks Demand UMI.

Ikram, S. M. History of Muslim Civilization in India. 25.50 (ISBN 0-317-46089-7). Kazi Pubns.

Jain, Naresh K., ed. Muslims in India: A Biographical Dictionary, Vol. II. 1984. 40.00x (ISBN 0-8364-1150-1, Pub. by Manohar India). South Asia Bks.

Jain, Sushila. Muslims & Modernization. 1986. 27.50x (ISBN 81-7033-009-2, Pub. by Rawat). South Asia Bks.

Jalal, Ayesha. The Sole Spokesman: Jinnah, the Muslim League & the Demand for Pakistan. (South Asian Studies: No. 31). (Illus.). 336p. 1985. 49.50 (ISBN 0-521-24462-5). Cambridge U Pr.

Karandikar, Maheshwar A. Islam in India's Transition to Modernity. 1972. lib. bdg. 35.00 (ISBN 0-8371-2337-2, KAI/). Greenwood.

Khurshid, Salman. At Home in India. x, 226p. 1987. text ed. 27.95 (ISBN 0-7069-3197-1, Pub. by Vikas India). Advent NY.

Miller, Roland. Mapilla Muslims of Kerala: A Study of Islamic Trends. LC 76-901758. 1976. 14.00x (ISBN 0-88386-080-5). South Asia Bks.

Oman, J. C. Brahmans, Theists & Muslims of India. 1973. 24.00 (ISBN 0-89684-371-8). Orient Bk Dist.

Robinson, Francis. Separatism among Indian Muslims: The Politics of the United Provinces' Muslims, 1860-1923. LC 73-93393. (Cambridge South Asian Studies: No. 16). pap. 121.80 (ISBN 0-317-26379-X, 2024521). Bks Demand UMI.

Roy, Shibani. The Dawoodi Bohras: An Anthropological Perspective. (Illus.). xv, 191p. 1984. text ed. 27.50x (ISBN 0-86590-324-7, Pub. by B R Publishing Corp). Apt Bks.

Satyaprakash. Muslims in India: A Bibliography of Their Religious, Socio-Economic & Political Literature. 1986. 34.00x (ISBN 0-8364-1558-2, Pub. by Indian Doc Serv India). South Asia Bks.

Shibany, Roy. Status of Muslim Women in North India. 1979. 21.00x (ISBN 0-8364-0353-3). South Asia Bks.

Smith, Wilfred C. Modern Islam in India: A Social Analysis. LC 70-179243. Repr. of 1946 ed. 17.00 (ISBN 0-404-54869-5). AMS Pr.

Srinivasau, Nirmala. Identity Crisis of Muslims: Profiles of Lucknow Youth. 140p. 1981. text ed. 15.00x (ISBN 0-391-02279-2, Pub. by Concept Pubs India). Humanities.

MUSLIMS IN THE UNITED STATES

Elkholy, Abdo A. The Arab Moslems in the United States. 1966. 12.95x (ISBN 0-8084-0052-5); pap. 8.95x (ISBN 0-8084-0053-3). New Coll U Pr.

Richardson, E. Allen. Islamic Cultures in North America. LC 81-2876. 84p. (Orig.). 1981. pap. 3.95 (ISBN 0-8298-0449-8). Pilgrim NY.

Waugh, E. H., et al, eds. The Muslim Community in North America. xii, 316p. 1983. pap. 15.00x (ISBN 0-88864-034-X, Pub. by Univ of Alta Pr Canada). U of Nebr Pr.

MUSSELMEN
see Muslims

MUSSULMANISM
see Islam

MUTAZILITES
see Motazilites

MYSTERIES (DRAMATIC)
see Mysteries and Miracle-Plays

MYSTERIES, RELIGIOUS
see also Cultus; Eleusinian Mysteries; Mother-Goddesses; Oracles; Rites and Ceremonies

Allan, John. Mysteries. (Book of Beliefs). 1981. 9.95 (ISBN 0-89191-477-3, 54775). Cook.

Angus, Samuel. The Mystery Religions & Christianity. 1977. lib. bdg. 59.95 (ISBN 0-8490-2314-9). Gordon Pr.

Bachelder, Robert S. Mystery & Miracle. 1983. 3.00 (ISBN 0-89536-606-1, 1340). CSS of Ohio.

Belanger, Mel. Ah, Sweet Mystery. (Illus.). 150p. (Orig.). 1983. pap. text ed. 5.00 (ISBN 0-9608146-8-X). Western Sun Pubns.

Brumfield, Allaire C. The Attic Festivals of Demeter & Their Relation to the Agricultural Year. Connor, W. R., ed. LC 80-2643. (Monographs in Classical Studies). 1981. lib. bdg. 29.00 (ISBN 0-405-14031-2). Ayer Co Pubs.

Douhet, J. Dictionnaire des Mysteres. Migne, J. P., ed. (Nouvelle Encyclopedie Theologique Ser.: Vol. 43). (Fr.). 788p. Repr. of 1854 ed. lib. bdg. 100.00x (ISBN 0-89241-282-8). Caratzas.

Eliade, Mircea. Myths, Dreams & Mysteries: The Encounter Between Contemporary Faiths & Archaic Realities. pap. 5.95x (ISBN 0-06-131943-0, TB 1943, Torch). Har-Row.

Francuch, Peter D. Major Ideas of the New Revelation. LC 84-51914. 266p. 1985. pap. 8.95 (ISBN 0-939386-08-9). TMH Pub.

Grant, James. The Mysteries of All Nations. LC 79-150243. 1971. Repr. of 1880 ed. 70.00x (ISBN 0-8103-3391-0). Gale.

Greeley, Andrew M. The Great Mysteries: An Essential Catechism. rev. ed. 192p. 1985. pap. 6.95 (ISBN 0-86683-871-6, HarpR). Har-Row.

Harrison, Jane E. Prolegomena to the Study of Greek Religion. facsimile ed. LC 75-10639. (Ancient Religion & Mythology Ser.). (Illus.). 1976. Repr. of 1922 ed. 57.50x (ISBN 0-405-07018-7). Ayer Co Pubs.

Iamblichus. On the Mysteries. Taylor, Thomas, tr. from Greek. LC 81-50200. (Secret Doctrine Reference Ser.). Tr. of Iamblichus on the Mysteries. 400p. 1984. Repr. of 1895 ed. 20.00 (ISBN 0-913510-51-3). Wizards.

Meyer, Marvin, ed. The Ancient Mysteries: A Sourcebook. LC 86-45022. (Illus.). 256p. (Orig.). 1986. 24.95 (ISBN 0-06-065577-1, HarpR); pap. 14.95 (ISBN 0-06-065576-3). Har-Row.

Myers, Edith. The Mysteries of the Rosary. (Illus.). 41p. 1977. Repr. of 1968 ed. 2.50 (ISBN 0-912414-13-8). Stella Maris Bks.

Nilsson, Martin P. The Dionysiac Mysteries of the Hellenistic & Roman Age. facsimile ed. LC 75-10643. (Ancient Religion & Mythology Ser.). (Illus.). 1976. Repr. of 1957 ed. 13.00x (ISBN 0-405-07261-9). Ayer Co Pubs.

Nottage, Isiah L. The Biblical Mysteries Revealed. 1984. 9.95 (ISBN 0-8062-2315-4). Carlton.

Prophet, Elizabeth C., ed. Mysteries of the Holy Grail: Archangel Gabriel. LC 83-51154. (Illus.). 430p. 1984. pap. 12.95 (ISBN 0-916766-64-0). Summit Univ.

Reitzenstein, Richard. The Hellenistic Mystery-Religions. Steely, John E., tr. from Ger. LC 77-12980. (Pittsburgh Theological Monographs: No. 15). Orig. Title: Die Hellenistischen Mysterienreligionen Nach Ihren Arundgedanken und Wirkungen. 1978. pap. text ed. 17.75 (ISBN 0-915138-20-4). Pickwick.

Wind, Edgar. Pagan Mysteries in the Renaissance. rev. ed. (Illus.). 1969. pap. 7.95 (ISBN 0-393-00475-9, Norton Lib). Norton.

MYSTERIES AND MIRACLE-PLAYS
see also Bible Plays; Drama, Medieval; Liturgical Drama; Moralities

Block, K. S., ed. Ludus Coventriae, Or, the Place Called Corpus Christi. (Early English Text Society Ser.). 1922. 26.00x (ISBN 0-19-722560-8). Oxford U Pr.

Browne, E. Martin, ed. Religious Drama, Vol. 2: 21 Medieval Mystery & Morality Plays. 17.75 (ISBN 0-8446-2793-3). Peter Smith.

Cawley, A. C., ed. Everyman & Medieval Miracle Plays. 10.95x (ISBN 0-460-10381-4, Evman). Biblio Dist.

--The Wakefield Pageants in the Towneley Cycle. (Old & Middle English Texts). 187p. 1975. pap. 10.95x (ISBN 0-06-491013-X, 06392). B&N Imports.

Collins, Fletcher, Jr., ed. Medieval Church Music-Dramas: A Repertory of Complete Plays. LC 75-33896. Repr. of 1976 ed. 128.50 (ISBN 0-8357-9809-7, 2013180). Bks Demand UMI.

Craig, Barbara. The Evolution of a Mystery Play: Le Sacrifice d'Abraham. 329p. 1983. 24.00 (ISBN 0-917786-30-0). Summa Pubns.

Davidson, Charles. Studies in the English Mystery Plays. LC 68-752. (Studies in Drama, No. 39). 1969. Repr. of 1892 ed. lib. bdg. 49.95x (ISBN 0-8383-0536-9). Haskell.

Fournier, Edouard, ed. Theatre Francais Avant La Renaissance, 1430-1550. 1965. Repr. of 1872 ed. 32.00 (ISBN 0-8337-1225-X). B Franklin.

Franklin, Alexander. Seven Miracle Plays. 1963. pap. 8.95x (ISBN 0-19-831391-8). Oxford U Pr.

Halverson, Marvin, ed. Religious Drama, Vol. 1: Five Plays. 11.25 (ISBN 0-8446-2792-5). Peter Smith.

--Religious Drama, Vol. 3. 11.25 (ISBN 0-8446-2794-1). Peter Smith.

Hone, William. Ancient Mysteries Described. LC 67-23905. (Illus.). 1969. Repr. of 1823 ed. 35.00x (ISBN 0-8103-3444-5). Gale.

Hopper, Vincent F. & Lahey, Gerald B., eds. Medieval Mysteries, Moralities & Interludes. LC 61-18362. 1962. pap. text ed. 5.95 (ISBN 0-8120-0135-4). Barron.
Hussey, Maurice, adapted by. Chester Mystery Plays. 2nd ed. 1975. pap. 3.50x (ISBN 0-87830-572-6). Theatre Arts.
King, Neil. Mystery & Morality. (Drama Ser.). pap. 8.95 (ISBN 0-7175-1231-2). Dufour.
Loomis, Roger S. & Wells, Henry W., eds. Representative Medieval & Tudor Plays. LC 77-111109. (Play Anthology Reprint Ser). 1942. 22.50 (ISBN 0-8369-8202-9). Ayer Co Pubs.
Manly, John M. Specimens of the Pre-Shakespearean Drama, 2 Vols. LC 67-18432. 1897. 20.00 (ISBN 0-8196-0200-0). Biblo.
Mysteres Provencaux Du XVe Siecle. Repr. of 1893 ed. 35.00 (ISBN 0-384-40753-6). Johnson Repr.
Rose, Martial, ed. Wakefield Mystery Plays. 1969. pap. 10.95x (ISBN 0-393-00483-X, Norton Lib). Norton.
Smith, Lucy T., ed. York Plays: The Plays Performed on the Day of Corpus Christi in the 14th, 15th, & 16th Centuries. LC 63-15180. (Illus.). 1963. Repr. of 1885 ed. 21.00x (ISBN 0-8462-0313-8). Russell.

MYSTERIES AND MIRACLE-PLAYS–BIBLIOGRAPHY

Coleman, Edward D. Bible in English Drama: An Annotated Bibliography. rev. ed. 1969. 25.00x (ISBN 0-87068-034-X). Ktav.
--Bible in English Drama: An Annotated List of Plays. 1969. 6.95 (ISBN 0-87104-021-2, Co-Pub by Ktav). NY Pub Lib.

MYSTERIES AND MIRACLE-PLAYS–HISTORY AND CRITICISM

Cargill, Oscar. Drama & Liturgy. LC 73-86272. 1969. Repr. of 1930 ed. lib. bdg. 17.00x (ISBN 0-374-91292-0, Octagon). Hippocrene Bks.
Carnahan, David H. Prologue in the Old French & Provencal Mystery. LC 68-55160. (Studies in French Literature, No. 45). 1969. Repr. of 1905 ed. lib. bdg. 46.95x (ISBN 0-8383-0519-9). Haskell.
Clarke, Sidney M. The Miracle Play in England. LC 65-15874. 1970. Repr. of 1897 ed. text ed. 75.00x (ISBN 0-8383-0529-6). Haskell.
Frank, Grace. Medieval French Drama. 1954. 34.95x (ISBN 0-19-815317-1). Oxford U Pr.
Gardiner, Harold C. Mysteries' End: An Investigation of the Last Days of the Medieval Religious Stage. LC 67-26652. (Yale Studies in English Ser.: No. 103). xiv, 139p. 1967. Repr. of 1946 ed. 21.50 (ISBN 0-208-00385-1, Archon). Shoe String.
Hein, Norvin. The Miracle Plays of Mathura. LC 75-99826. pap. 81.30 (ISBN 0-317-09863-2, 2022003). Bks Demand UMI.
Hone, William. Ancient Mysteries Described. LC 67-23905. (Illus.). 1969. Repr. of 1823 ed. 35.00x (ISBN 0-8103-3444-5). Gale.
--Ancient Mysteries Described. 59.95 (ISBN 0-8490-1426-3). Gordon Pr.
Lumiansky, R. M. & Mills, David. The Chester Mystery Cycle: Essays & Documents. LC 82-1838. viii, 339p. 1983. 40.00x (ISBN 0-8078-1522-5); essay "Music in the Cycle" by Richard Rastall incl. U of NC Pr.
McKean, Sr. M. Faith. Interplay of Realistic & Flamboyant Art Elements in the French Mysteres. LC 74-94196. (Catholic University of America Studies in Romance Languages & Literatures Ser: No. 60). Repr. of 1959 ed. 23.00 (ISBN 0-404-50360-8). AMS Pr.
Mathews, Godfrey W. Chester Mystery Plays. LC 77-4728. 1925. lib. bdg. 15.00 (ISBN 0-8414-6159-7). Folcroft.
Mills, David & Lumiansky, Robert, eds. The Chester Mystery Cycle: Commentary & Apparatus, Vol. II. (Early English Text Society Supplementary Ser.: No. 8). 1985. 34.50x (ISBN 0-19-722408-3). Oxford U Pr.
Moore, E. Hamilton. English Miracle Plays & Moralities. LC 77-100517. Repr. of 1907 ed. 17.25 (ISBN 0-404-00598-5). AMS Pr.
Neuss, Paula, ed. Aspects of Early English Drama. LC 83-21331. (Illus.). 176p. 1985. Repr. of 1983 ed. 42.50x (ISBN 0-389-20428-5, 07314). B&N Imports.
Prosser, Eleanor. Drama & Religion in the English Mystery Plays: A Re-Evaluation. 1961. 18.50x (ISBN 0-8047-0060-5). Stanford U Pr.

MYSTERIES AND MIRACLE-PLAYS, ENGLISH

Craig, Hardin. English Religious Drama of the Middle Ages. LC 78-6893. 1978. Repr. of 1968 ed. lib. bdg. 37.50x (ISBN 0-313-20496-9, CRER). Greenwood.
Neuss, Paula, ed. Aspects of Early English Drama. LC 83-21331. (Illus.). 176p. 1985. Repr. of 1983 ed. 42.50x (ISBN 0-389-20428-5, 07314). B&N Imports.

MYSTICAL BODY OF CHRIST

see Jesus Christ–Mystical Body

MYSTICAL THEOLOGY

see Mysticism; Mysticism–Catholic Church; Mysticism–Orthodox Eastern Church

MYSTICAL UNION

Here are entered works dealing with the indwelling of the Triune God, or of any person of the trinity, in the hearts of believers and conversely, works dealing with the union between man and the Triune God, especially between man and Jesus Christ. Works dealing with the church as the mystical body of Christ are entered under the heading Jesus Christ–Mystical Body.
see also Contemplation

Bernard de Clairvaux, St. On Loving God: Selections from Sermons by St. Bernard of Clairvaux. Martin, Hugh, ed. LC 79-8706. (A Treasury of Christian Bks.). 125p. 1981. Repr. of 1959 ed. lib. bdg. 22.50x (ISBN 0-313-20787-9, BEOL). Greenwood.
Blumenthal, Warren B. The Creator & Man. LC 80-5843. 139p. 1980. lib. bdg. 20.50 (ISBN 0-8191-1340-9); pap. text ed. 9.50 (ISBN 0-8191-1341-7). U Pr of Amer.
Branson, Robert. God's Word in Man's Language. 83p. (Orig.). 1980. pap. 2.75 (ISBN 0-8341-0659-0). Beacon Hill.
Bright, Bill. How to Be Filled with the Spirit. (Transferable Concepts Ser.). 58p. 1981. pap. 1.25 (ISBN 0-918956-90-0). Campus Crusade.
Chesterton, G. K. The Everlasting Man. 344p. 1981. Repr. of 1926 ed. lib. bdg. 20.00 (ISBN 0-89984-115-5). Century Bookbindery.
Cooper, Darien B. The Beauty of Beholding God. 168p. 1982. pap. 5.95 (ISBN 0-88207-350-8). Victor Bks.
Dalrymple, John. Toward the Heart of God. 108p. (Orig.). 1981. pap. 3.95 (ISBN 0-86683-602-0, HarpR). Har-Row.
Duckworth, Marion. The Strong Place. 1983. pap. 4.95 (ISBN 0-8423-6663-6). Tyndale.
Fandel, John. God's Breath in Man. LC 77-76604. 1977. pap. 1.50 (ISBN 0-87957-005-9). Roth Pub.
Fillmore, Cora D. Christ Enthroned in Man. 1981. 4.95. Unity School.
Foster, Genevieve & Hufford, David J. The World Was Flooded with Light: A Mystical Experience Remembered. LC 84-22013. 216p. 1985. 14.95 (ISBN 0-8229-3512-0). U of Pittsburgh Pr.
Gryn, Tom. Growing Closer to God. 100p. (Orig.). 1982. pap. 2.50 (ISBN 0-89283-160-X). Servant.
Guyon, Jeanne. Union with God. Edwards, Gene, ed. 117p. 1981. pap. 5.95 (ISBN 0-940232-05-7). Christian Bks.
Haught, John F. Religion & Self-Acceptance: A Study of the Relationship Between Belief in God & the Desire to Know. LC 80-5872. 195p. 1980. lib. bdg. 24.75 (ISBN 0-8191-1296-8); pap. text ed. 10.50 (ISBN 0-8191-1297-6). U Pr of Amer.
Huelsman, Richard J. Intimacy with Jesus: An Introduction. LC 82-60587. 1983. pap. 5.95 (ISBN 0-8091-2492-0). Paulist Pr.
Lane, Dermot A. The Experience of God: An Invitation to Do Theology. LC 81-80873. 96p. (Orig.). 1981. pap. 4.95 (ISBN 0-8091-2394-0). Paulist Pr.
Larsen, Norma C. His Everlasting Love, Vol. 2. LC 81-80956. 150p. 1981. 7.95 (ISBN 0-88290-182-6, 1062). Horizon Utah.
Linedecker, Clifford. God, the Unknown & the Country Music Singer. (Illus.). 200p. 1987. 17.95x (ISBN 0-938294-50-4); pap. 9.95x (ISBN 0-938294-51-2). Global Comm.
Maclennan, David A. He Restoreth. (Contempo Ser.). pap. 0.95 (ISBN 0-8010-6093-1). Baker Bk.
Malyala, Panduranga R. Interrelationship Between Atom-Body-Universe (Anda-Pinda-Brah Manda) Date not set. 1.99 (ISBN 0-938924-08-7). Sri Shirdi Sai.
Malz, Betty. Prayers That Are Answered. 1981. pap. 3.50 (ISBN 0-451-14948-3, Sig). NAL.
Marsh, Michael. Reaching Toward God. LC 81-81683. 27p. 1981. pap. 2.50x (ISBN 0-87574-237-8, 237). Pendle Hill.
Matthews, Anna M. God Answers Prayers. 96p. 1981. 8.95 (ISBN 0-89962-215-1). Todd & Honeywell.
Merrill, Dean. Another Chance: How God Overrides Our Big Mistakes. 160p. (Orig.). 1981. pap. 4.95 (ISBN 0-310-35331-9, 11325P). Zondervan.
Ogilvie, Lloyd. Congratulations - God Believes in You. 128p. 1980. 5.95 (ISBN 0-8499-2994-6). Word Bks.
Parrott, Bob W. Ontology of Humor. LC 81-80239. 96p. 1982. 10.95 (ISBN 0-8022-2387-7). Philos Lib.
Pink, George L. The Unity of One. 160p. 1982. 8.00 (ISBN 0-682-49838-6). Exposition Pr FL.
Porter, Alan. You've Really Got Me, God! (Direction Bks.). pap. 1.45 (ISBN 0-8010-7019-8). Baker Bk.
Richards, Lawrence O. How I Can Experience God. (Answers for Youth Ser.). 1980. pap. 4.95 (ISBN 0-310-38991-7, 18209P). Zondervan.
--Love Your Neighbour: A Woman's Workshop on Fellowship. (Woman's Workshop Ser.). 160p. (Orig.). 1981. pap. 3.95 (ISBN 0-310-43451-3, 18139P). Zondervan.
Rosage, David E. Listen to Him. 112p. (Orig.). 1981. pap. 3.50 (ISBN 0-89283-108-1). Servant.
Sales, Lorenzo. Jesus Appeals to the World. 1955. 5.95 (ISBN 0-8189-0069-5). Alba.
Schoenbrod, Gilbert A. The Anatomy of God & Man. (Illus.). 272p. 27.00 (ISBN 0-942494-02-4). Coleman Pub.
Snelling, George. The Divine Breakthrough. 92p. 1981. pap. 2.95 (ISBN 0-934142-01-7). Vancento Pub.
Talmadge, Virginia. Dear God Little Prayers to a Big God. 1981. cloth 3.25 (ISBN 0-86544-016-6). Salv Army Suppl South.
Weatherhead, Leslie D. Time for God. (Festival Ser.). 1981. pap. 1.75 (ISBN 0-687-42113-6). Abingdon.

MYSTICISM

see also Cabala; Christian Art and Symbolism; Contemplation; Devotion; Enthusiasm; Immanence of God; Perfection; Rosicrucians; Tantrism

Addison, Charles M. The Theory & Practice of Mysticism. 1977. lib. bdg. 59.95 (ISBN 0-8490-2742-X). Gordon Pr.
Aivanhov, Omraam M. The Second Birth. (Complete Works of O. M. Aivanhov: Vol. 1). 210p. 1981. pap. 9.50 (ISBN 0-87516-418-8). De Vorss.
Allen, James. The Life Triumphant. 112p. 1983. pap. 6.50 (ISBN 0-89540-125-8, SB-125). Sun Pub.
Almond, Philip C. Mystical Experience & Religious Doctrine: An Investigation of the Study of Mysticism in World Religions. (Religion & Reason: No. 26). 197p. 1982. text ed. 40.00 (ISBN 90-279-3160-7). Mouton.
Anquetil-Duperron, A. H. Zend-Avesta, Ouvrage de Zoroastre. Feldman, Burton & Richardson, Robert, eds. LC 78-60878. (Myth & Romanticism Ser.). 1984. lib. bdg. 240.00 (ISBN 0-8240-3550-X). Garland Pub.
Anzul, Dario. The Paintings of Mysticism & Violence in Full Colours of Dario Anzul. (Illus.). 97p. 1983. 225.75x (ISBN 0-86650-073-1). Gloucester Art.
Apuleius. Apuleius on the God of Socrates. Taylor, Thomas, tr. (Lat.). 1984. pap. 4.95 (ISBN 0-916411-25-7, Pub. by Alexandrian Pr). Holmes Pub.
Aristotelian Society for the Systematic Study of Philosophy Staff. Relativity, Logic & Mysticism: Proceedings, Supplementary Vol. 3. 14.00 (ISBN 0-384-50269-5); pap. 9.00. Johnson Repr.
Arraj, James. St. John of the Cross & Dr. C. G. Jung: Christian Mysticism in the Light of Jungian Psychology. LC 86-11315. 200p. (Orig.). 1986. pap. 11.95 (ISBN 0-914073-02-8). Tools for Inner.
Arseniew, Nicholas. Mysticism & the Eastern Church. 1977. lib. bdg. 59.95. Gordon Pr.
Aude, Sapere, ed. The Chaldean Oracles. LC 78-58111. 1978. 10.00 (ISBN 0-935214-02-X). Heptangle.
Bailey, Alice A. From Intellect to Intuition. 1973. 18.00 (ISBN 0-85330-008-9); pap. 7.00 (ISBN 0-85330-108-5). Lucis.
Balthasar, Hans Urs Von. A First Glance at Adrienne Von Speyr. Lawry, Antje & Englund, Sergia, trs. from Ger. LC 79-84879. Orig. Title: Erster Blick Auf Adrienne Von Speyr. 249p. (Orig.). 1981. pap. 9.95 (ISBN 0-89870-003-5). Ignatius Pr.
Bancroft, Anne. The Luminous Vision: Six Medieval Mystics & Their Teachings. 194p. 1983. text ed. 18.50x (ISBN 0-04-189001-9). Allen Unwin.
Baring-Gould, Sabine. Freaks of Fanaticism & Other Strange Events. LC 68-21754. 1968. Repr. of 1891 ed. 40.00x (ISBN 0-8103-3503-4). Gale.
Benedict, Clare M. St. Sharbel, Mystic of the East. 1977. 6.95 (ISBN 0-911218-11-4); pap. 3.45 (ISBN 0-911218-12-2). Ravengate Pr.
Bennett, John G. Creation. 1978. 5.95 (ISBN 0-900306-41-6, Pub. by Coombe Springs Pr). Claymont Comm.
--Witness. 1983. 8.95 (ISBN 0-934254-05-2). Claymont Comm.
Bernard, Helene. Great Women Initiates or the Feminine Mystic. Ziebel, Michelle, tr. from Fr. LC 84-50133. (Illus.). 151p. (Orig.). 1984. pap. 6.95 (ISBN 0-912057-36-X, G-650). AMORC.
Besant, Annie. Esoteric Christianity. 8th ed. 1966. 7.00 (ISBN 0-8356-7052-X). Theos Pub Hse.
Bharati, Agehananda. The Light at the Center: Context & Pretext of Modern Mysticism. 1976. lib. bdg. 11.95 (ISBN 0-915520-03-6); pap. 6.95 (ISBN 0-915520-04-4). Ross-Erikson.
Bjerregaard, C. H. The Inner Life. Incl. The Tao-Teh-King. 1977. lib. bdg. 49.00 (ISBN 0-8490-2061-1). Gordon Pr.
--Lectures on Mysticism & Nature Worship. 1977. lib. bdg. 59.95 (ISBN 0-8490-2138-3). Gordon Pr.
Boehme, Jacob. Jacob Boehme's "The Way to Christ". Stoudt, John J., tr. LC 78-13976. 1979. Repr. of 1947 ed. lib. bdg. 22.50x (ISBN 0-313-21075-6, BOTW). Greenwood.
Bowman, Mary Ann, compiled by. Western Mysticism: A Guide to the Basic Works. LC 78-18311. vi, 114p. 1979. pap. 9.00 (ISBN 0-8389-0266-9). ALA.
Braun, Eunice. The March of the Institutions: A Commentary on the Interdependence of Rulers & Learned. 112p. 9.95 (ISBN 0-85398-182-5); pap. 5.95 (ISBN 0-85398-183-3). G Ronald Pub.
Bulka, Reuven P., ed. Mystics & Medics: A Comparison of Mystical & Psychotherapeutic Encounters. LC 79-87593. 120p. 1979. pap. 12.95 (ISBN 0-87705-377-4). Human Sci Pr.
Butler, C. Western Mysticism: Neglected Chapters in the History of Religion. 69.95 (ISBN 0-87968-244-2). Gordon Pr.
Capps, Walter H. & Wright, Wendy M., eds. Silent Fire. LC 78-3366. (Forum Bk.). 1978. pap. 7.95x (ISBN 0-06-061314-9, RD 290, HarpR). Har-Row.
Capra, Fritjof. The Tao of Physics. 1977. pap. 4.95 (ISBN 0-553-26379-X). Bantam.
Carty, Charles M. Who Is Teresa Neumann? 1974. pap. 1.25 (ISBN 0-89555-093-8). TAN Bks Pubs.
Chaney, Robert. Mysticism: The Journey Within. LC 79-52959. 1979. softcover 12.50 (ISBN 0-918936-06-3). Astara.
Coleman, Thomas W. English Mystics of the Fourteenth Century. LC 74-109723. 1971. Repr. of 1938 ed. lib. bdg. 22.50x (ISBN 0-8371-4213-X, COEM). Greenwood.
Connolly, J. L. John Gerson: Reformer & Mystic. (Medieval Studies Ser.). (Illus.). Repr. of 1928 ed. lib. bdg. 44.00x (ISBN 0-697-00031-1). Irvington.
Corbin, Henry. Avicenna & the Visionary Recital. Trask, Willard R., tr. from French. (Dunquin Ser.: No. 13). 314p. 1980. pap. 14.50 (ISBN 0-88214-213-5). Spring Pubns.
Cox, Michael. Mysticism: The Direct Experience of God. 256p. 1984. pap. 9.95 (ISBN 0-85030-280-3). Newcastle Pub.
Coxhead, Nona. The Relevance of Bliss. 192p. 1986. pap. 6.95 (ISBN 0-312-67055-9). St Martin.
Crawford, Shirley O. Is God Dead Within You? 112p. 1981. 6.50 (ISBN 0-682-49789-4). Exposition Pr FL.
Crom, Scott. Obstacles to Mystical Experience. 1983. pap. 2.50x (ISBN 0-87574-132-0, 132). Pendle Hill.
Curtiss, H. A. & Curtiss, F. H. Gems of Mysticism. 83p. Date not set. pap. 5.00 (ISBN 0-89540-143-6, SB-143). Sun Pub.
Davison, William T. Mystics & Poets. 167p. 1980. Repr. of 1936 ed. lib. bdg. 32.50 (ISBN 0-8482-0639-8). Norwood Edns.
Dean, Stanley R. Psychiatry & Mysticism. LC 75-8771. (Illus.). 446p. 1975. 30.95x (ISBN 0-88229-189-0). Nelson-Hall.
Deikman, Arthur J. The Observing Self: Mysticism & Psychotherapy. LC 81-70486. 208p. 1983. pap. 8.95 (ISBN 0-8070-2951-3, BP 652). Beacon Pr.
De Jaegher, Paul, ed. An Anthology of Christian Mysticism. 1977. 7.95 (ISBN 0-87243-073-1). Templegate.
Drury, Nevill. Don Juan, Mescalito & Modern Magic: The Mythology of Inner Space. 256p. 1985. pap. 8.95 (ISBN 1-85063-015-1, Ark Paperbks). Methuen Inc.
--Encyclopedia of Mysticism & the Occult. LC 84-48215. (Illus.). 544p. (Orig.). 1985. 24.45 (ISBN 0-06-062093-5, HarpR); pap. 12.95 (ISBN 0-06-062094-3). Har-Row.
Dunlap, Knight. Mysticism, Freudianism & Scientific Psychology. facsimile ed. (Select Bibliographies Reprint Ser). Repr. of 1920 ed. 17.00 (ISBN 0-8369-5838-1). Ayer Co Pubs.
Dupre, Louis. The Deeper Life: A Meditation on Christian Mysticism. 128p. (Orig.). 1981. pap. 4.95 (ISBN 0-8245-0007-5). Crossroad NY.
Du Prel, Carl. The Philosophy of Mysticism, 2vols. in 1. Massey, C. C., tr. LC 75-36838. (Occult Ser.). 1976. Repr. of 1889 ed. 51.00x (ISBN 0-405-07951-6). Ayer Co Pubs.
--The Philosophy of Mysticism, 2 vols. 1977. lib. bdg. 250.00 (ISBN 0-8490-2434-X). Gordon Pr.
Dupuis, Charles. The Origin of All Religious Worship. Feldman, Burton & Richardson, Robert D., eds. LC 78-60897. (Myth & Romanticism Ser.). 1984. lib. bdg. 80.00 (ISBN 0-8240-3558-5). Garland Pub.
Dyson, W. H. Studies in Christian Mysticism. 1977. lib. bdg. 69.95 (ISBN 0-8490-2702-0). Gordon Pr.
Egan, Harvey D. Christian Mysticism. 300p. (Orig.). 1984. pap. 14.95 (ISBN 0-916134-63-6). Pueblo Pub Co.

--What Are They Saying about Mysticism? (WATSA Ser.). 128p. 1982. pap. 4.95 (ISBN 0-8091-2459-9). Paulist Pr.

Eustace, Cecil J. Infinity of Questions. facs. ed. LC 70-84356. (Essay Index Reprint Ser). 1946. 16.50 (ISBN 0-8369-1080-X). Ayer Co Pubs.

Fairweather, William. Among the Mystics. facs. ed. LC 68-20298. (Essay Index Reprint Ser.). 1936. 14.00 (ISBN 0-8369-0437-0). Ayer Co Pubs.

Faizi, A. Q. Milly: A Tribute to Amelia E. Collins. 52p. pap. 2.95 (ISBN 0-85398-074-8). G Ronald Pub.

Ferguson, John. Encyclopedia of Mysticism & Mystery Religions. (Crossroad Paperback Ser.). (Illus.). 228p. 1982. pap. 9.95 (ISBN 0-8245-0429-1). Crossroad NY.

Ferrara, J. A. Living Love. (Illus.). 142p. 1961. 9.45 (ISBN 0-933961-04-9). Mystic Jhamom.

Fisher, J. M. Mystic Gnosis. 1977. lib. bdg. 59.95 (ISBN 0-8490-2316-5). Gordon Pr.

Fortune, Dion, ed. The Esoteric Orders & Their Work. 144p. 1983. pap. 7.95 (ISBN 0-85030-310-9). Newcastle Pub.

Franklin, James C. Mystical Transformations: The Imagery of Liquids in the Work of Mechthild Von Magdeburg. LC 75-5248. 192p. 1976. 18.50 (ISBN 0-8386-1738-7). Fairleigh Dickinson.

Furse, Margaret L. Mysticism - Window on a World View: Introduction to Mysticism As a Pattern of Thought & Practice. LC 76-56816. Repr. of 1977 ed. 55.00 (ISBN 0-8357-9018-5, 2016384). Bks Demand UMI.

GAP Committee on Psychiatry & Religion. Mysticism: Spiritual Quest or Psychic Disorder, Vol. 9. LC 76-45931. (Report: No. 97). 1976. pap. 5.00 (ISBN 0-87318-134-4, Pub. by GAP). Brunner-Mazel.

Gardner, E. G. Dante & the Mystics: A Study of the Mystical Aspect of the Divina Commedia. LC 68-24952. (Studies in Italian Literature, No. 46). 1969. Repr. of 1913 ed. lib. bdg. 49.95x (ISBN 0-8383-0271-8). Haskell.

Gaynor, Frank. Dictionary of Mysticism. 211p. 1973. pap. 2.45 (ISBN 0-8065-0172-3). Citadel Pr.

Ghose, Sisirkumar. The Mystic As a Force for Change. rev. ed. LC 80-53954. 144p. 1980. pap. 4.75 (ISBN 0-8356-0547-7, Quest). Theos Pub Hse.

Giles, Herbert A., ed. & tr. from Chinese. Musings of a Chinese Mystic: Selections from the Philosophy of Chuang Tzu. 112p. Repr. of 1926 ed. text ed. 17.50x (ISBN 0-89644-497-X, Pub. by Chinese Matl Ctr). Coronet Bks.

Goldsmith, Joel S. Parenthesis in Eternity. LC 64-10368. 1963. pap. 11.95 (ISBN 0-06-063230-5, HarpR). Har-Row.

--Parenthesis in Eternity: Living the Mystical Life. LC 85-45354. 1986. pap. 11.95 (ISBN 0-06-063231-3, PL 4125, PL). Har-Row.

--Practicing the Presence. LC 58-7474. 1958. 11.95 (ISBN 0-06-063250-X, HarpR). Har-Row.

Graef, H. C. The Way of the Mystics. 1977. lib. bdg. 59.95 (ISBN 0-8490-2811-6). Gordon Pr.

Graham, R. B. A Brazilian Mystic: Life & Miracles of Antonio Conselheiro. 1976. lib. bdg. 59.95 (ISBN 0-87968-786-X). Gordon Pr.

Grant, Patrick. The Literature of Mysticism in Western Tradition. LC 83-5789. 200p. 1983. 22.50x (ISBN 0-312-48808-4). St Martin.

Grant, Patrick, ed. A Dazzling Darkness: An Anthology of Western Mysticism. (Orig.). 1985. pap. 9.95 (ISBN 0-8028-0088-2). Eerdmans.

Grierson, Francis. Modern Mysticism. 1977. lib. bdg. 59.95 (ISBN 0-8490-2271-1). Gordon Pr.

--Modern Mysticism. LC 77-102570. 1970. Repr. of 1899 ed. 22.50x (ISBN 0-8046-0730-3, Pub. by Kennikat). Assoc Faculty Pr.

Guerry, Herbert, ed. Philosophy & Mysticism. Dell.

Hall, Manly P. Mystical Christ. 10.95 (ISBN 0-89314-514-9). Philos Res.

Hanson, Virginia, ed. The Silent Encounter. LC 74-4168. 240p. (Orig.). 1974. pap. 4.75 (ISBN 0-8356-0448-9, Quest). Theos Pub Hse.

Happold, Frank C. Mysticism. (Orig.). 1963. pap. 6.95 (ISBN 0-14-020568-3, Pelican). Penguin.

Hartman, Sven S. & Edsman, C. M. Mysticism. (Illus.). 258p. (Orig.). 1970. pap. text ed. 16.95x (Pub. by Almqvist & Wiksell). Coronet Bks.

Hatcher, John. From the Auroral Darkness: The Life & Poetry of Robert Hayden. (Illus.). 368p. 23.50 (ISBN 0-85398-188-4); pap. 12.95 (ISBN 0-85398-189-2). G Ronald Pub.

Haywood, Harryl. Christian Mysticism. 59.95 (ISBN 0-87968-862-9). Gordon Pr.

Heard, Gerry C. Mystical & Ethical Experience. LC 84-29569. viii, 82p. 1985. 8.50 (ISBN 0-86554-149-3, MUP/H140). Mercer Univ Pr.

Heline, Corinne. Mystic Masonry & the Bible. pap. 1.00 (ISBN 0-87613-017-1). New Age.

Herman, E. The Meaning & Value of Mysticism. 3rd facsimile ed. LC 72-164607. (Select Bibliographies Reprint Ser.). Repr. of 1922 ed. 22.00 (ISBN 0-8369-5891-8). Ayer Co Pubs.

--The Meaning & Value of Mysticism. 1977. lib. bdg. 59.95 (ISBN 0-8490-2216-9). Gordon Pr.

Hodgson, Geraldine E. The Sanity of Mysticism. LC 76-11826. 1976. Repr. of 1926 ed. lib. bdg. 20.00 (ISBN 0-8414-4845-0). Folcroft.

Hofman, David. George Townshend, A Life of. (Illus.). 448p. 23.50 (ISBN 0-85398-126-4); pap. 12.95 (ISBN 0-85398-127-2). G Ronald Pub.

Hopkins, Emma C. High Mysticism. 368p. 1974. pap. 8.95 (ISBN 0-87516-198-7). De Vorss.

Hopkinson, Arthur W. Mysticism: Old & New. LC 77-118528. 1971. Repr. of 1946 ed. 21.50x (ISBN 0-8046-1151-3, Pub. by Kennikat). Assoc Faculty Pr.

Horne, James R. Beyond Mysticism. 158p. 1978. pap. text ed. 9.25x (ISBN 0-919812-08-2, Pub. by Wilfred Laurier Canada). Humanities.

Howard, Maude L. Myriam & the Mystic Brotherhood. 370p. 1981. pap. 20.00 (ISBN 0-89540-105-3, SB-105). Sun Pub.

Hunter, Irene, ed. American Mystical Verse. LC 79-116407. (Granger Index Reprint Ser). 1925. 19.00 (ISBN 0-8369-6148-X). Ayer Co Pubs.

Inge, William R. Mysticism in Religion. LC 76-15407. 1976. Repr. of 1948 ed. lib. bdg. 22.50x (ISBN 0-8371-8953-5, INMR). Greenwood.

--Studies of English Mystics. facs. ed. LC 69-17578. (Essay Index Reprint Ser). 1906. 15.00 (ISBN 0-8369-0081-2). Ayer Co Pubs.

Jae Jah Noh. Do You See What I See? LC 77-5255. (Orig.). 1977. pap. 3.95 (ISBN 0-8356-0499-3, Quest). Theos Pub Hse.

James, Joseph. The Way of Mysticism. 256p. 1981. pap. 14.50 (ISBN 0-89540-086-3, SB-086). Sun Pub.

--The Way of Mysticism: An Anthology. 1977. lib. bdg. 59.95 (ISBN 0-8490-2810-8). Gordon Pr.

Johnston, William. The Inner Eye of Love: Mysticism & Religion. LC 78-4428. 1978. pap. 6.95 (ISBN 0-06-064195-9, RD-349, HarpR). Har-Row.

--The Mirror Mind: Spirituality & Transformation. LC 80-8350. 192p. 1984. pap. 6.95 (ISBN 0-06-064206-8, RD 516, HarpR). Har-Row.

--Still Point: Reflections on Zen & Christian Mysticism. LC 75-95713. 1986. pap. 9.00 (ISBN 0-8232-0861-3). Fordham.

Jones, Rufus M. New Studies in Mystical Religion. 69.95 (ISBN 0-87968-102-0). Gordon Pr.

--Spiritual Reformers of the Sixteenth & Seventeenth Centuries. 1959. 11.25 (ISBN 0-8446-0161-6). Peter Smith.

Kakar, Sudhir. Shamans, Mystics, & Doctors: A Psychological Inquiry into India & Its Healing Traditions. LC 83-70654. 324p. 1983. pap. 10.95x (ISBN 0-8070-2903-3, BP 660). Beacon Pr.

Kalisch, Isidor. The Sepher Yezirah. 1984. write for info (ISBN 0-686-21219-3). Heptangle.

Katz, Steven T. Mysticism & Philosophical Analysis. 1978. 19.95x (ISBN 0-19-520010-1); pap. 8.95x (ISBN 0-19-520011-X). Oxford U Pr.

--Mysticism & Religious Traditions. 1983. 19.95x (ISBN 0-19-503313-2, 739); pap. 9.95 (ISBN 0-19-503314-0, GB). Oxford U Pr.

Kennedy, David G. Catholicism & the Mysticisms of the East. LC 86-62211. viii, 70p. (Orig.). 1986. pap. 4.95x (ISBN 0-934995-01-X). OLW Editions.

Kim, Hee-Jin. Dogen Kigen - Mystical Realist. LC 74-33725. (Association for Asian Studies Monograph: No. 29). 384p. 1975. pap. 8.95x (ISBN 0-8165-0513-6). U of Ariz Pr.

King, Thomas M. Teilhard's Mysticism of Knowing. 192p. 1981. 14.95 (ISBN 0-8164-0491-7, HarpR). Har-Row.

King, Ursula. Towards a New Mysticism: Teilhard de Chardin & Eastern Religions. 320p. 1980. (HarpR); pap. 8.95 (ISBN 0-8164-2327-X). Har-Row.

Krishnamurti, J. Exploration into Insight. LC 79-6651. 192p. (Orig.). 1980. pap. 7.95 (ISBN 0-06-064811-2, RD 326, HarpR). Har-Row.

Lang, Andrew. Magic & Religion. 59.95 (ISBN 0-8490-0576-0). Gordon Pr.

Leeming, David A. Flights: Readings in Magic, Mysticism, Fantasy & Myth. 388p. (Orig.). 1974. pap. text ed. 11.95 (ISBN 0-15-527556-9, HC). HarBraceJ.

Lejeune, Abbe P. An Introduction to the Mystical Life. 1977. lib. bdg. 59.95 (ISBN 0-8490-2070-0). Gordon Pr.

Lethaby, William. Architecture, Mysticism & Myth. LC 74-25316. (Illus.). 280p. 1975. 10.00 (ISBN 0-8076-0783-5). Braziller.

Levinsky, Sara A. A Bridge of Dreams: The Story of Paramananda, a Modern Mystic. LC 83-82698. (Illus.). 632p. (Orig.). 1984. pap. 12.95 (ISBN 0-89281-063-7, Lindisfarne Pr). Inner Tradit.

Lewis, H. Spencer. Self Mastery & Fate with the Cycles of Life. LC 55-16785. (Illus.). 253p. 1986. pap. 8.95 (ISBN 0-912057-45-9, G-657). AMORC.

L'Heureux, Mother Aloysius G. Mystical Vocabulary of Venerable Mere Marie De L'Incarnation & Its Problems. LC 72-94190. (Catholic University of America Studies in Romance Languages & Literatures Ser: No. 53). (Fr.). Repr. of 1956 ed. 24.00 (ISBN 0-404-50353-5). AMS Pr.

Livingstone, Alasdair. Mystical & Mythological Explanatory Works of Assyrian & Babylonian Scholars. 280p. 1986. 55.00x (ISBN 0-19-815462-3). Oxford U Pr.

Lohr, Andrew. Talks on Mystic Christianity. Challgren, Patricia & Crater, Mildred, eds. LC 84-90346. (Illus.). 152p. (Orig.). 1984. pap. 6.50 (ISBN 0-9613401-0-X). Fiery Water.

Lopez, Barry H. Desert Notes: Reflections in the Eye of a Raven. LC 76-6099. (Illus.). 96p. 1976. 6.95 (ISBN 0-8362-0661-4). Andrews McMeel Parker.

MacLagan, E. R. & Russell, A. G., eds. The Prophetic Books of William Blake: Jerusalem. 1979. Repr. of 1904 ed. lib. bdg. 35.00 (ISBN 0-8495-3510-7). Arden Lib.

McNamara, William. Earthy Mysticism: Contemplation & the Life of Passionate Presence. LC 82-33554. 128p. 1983. pap. 6.95 (ISBN 0-8245-0562-X). Crossroad NY.

Mahadevan, T. M., ed. Spiritual Perspectives: Essays in Mysticism & Metaphysics. 303p. 1975. lib. bdg. 12.00 (ISBN 0-89253-021-9). Ind-US Inc.

Malfitano, Gilbert J. The Seven Steps on How to Become a Mystic & Enjoy the Most Exhilirating Pleasure Available to Man on This Earth. (Illus.). 1979. deluxe ed. 47.50 (ISBN 0-930582-37-3). Gloucester Art.

Maloney, George. Invaded by God: Mysticism & the Indwelling Trinity. 1979. 5.95 (ISBN 0-87193-107-9). Dimension Bks.

Marechal, Joseph. Studies in the Psychology of the Mystics. LC 65-1694. 1964. lib. bdg. 12.95x (ISBN 0-87343-044-1). Magi Bks.

Massey, C. C. Thoughts of a Modern Mystic. 59.95 (ISBN 0-8490-1209-0). Gordon Pr.

Murray, Paul. The Mysticism Debate. 1978. 6.26 (ISBN 0-8199-0722-7). Franciscan Herald.

Mystic Jhamom Publishers Staff, ed. Is Man a Fress Agent Illustrations Booklet: Supplement. (Conversations with a Mystic Ser.: No. 1). 12p. 1985. pap. 1.75 (ISBN 0-933961-02-2). Mystic Jhamom.

Mystic Jhamom Staff, ed. Jhamom's Story of Creation. (Conversations Mystic Ser.: No. 3). (Illus.). 136p. 1986. pap. 9.95 (ISBN 0-933961-07-3). Mystic Jhamom.

--The Phenomena of Life. (Conversations with a Mystic Ser.: No. 4). (Illus.). 1986. pap. write for info. (ISBN 0-933961-09-X). Mystic Jhamom.

--The Phenomena of Life Illustrations Booklet: Supplement. (Conversations with a Mystic Ser.: No. 4). (Illus.). 24p. 1986. pap. write for info. (ISBN 0-933961-10-3). Mystic Jhamom.

Mystic Jhamon Editors. Is Man a Free Agent. (Conversations with a Mystic: No. 1). (Illus.). 128p. 1985. pap. 9.95 (ISBN 0-933961-01-4). Mystic Jhamom.

Nadzo, Stefan C. Take off Your Shoes. 120p. 1981. pap. 4.57 (ISBN 0-937226-01-7). Coleman Pub.

Newell, William L. Struggle & Submission: R. C. Zaehner on Mysticisms. LC 80-6295. 402p. 1981. lib. bdg. 29.25 (ISBN 0-8191-1696-3); pap. text ed. 15.25 (ISBN 0-8191-1697-1). U Pr of Amer.

Newhouse, Flower A. Prayers of a Mystic. Boult, Pamela, compiled by. & intro. by. LC 86-71083. 100p. (Orig.). 1986. pap. 6.00 (ISBN 0-910378-21-5). Christward.

Nichols, Lonnie J. God, the Universe & Self. LC 82-74521. 96p. 1983. pap. 4.50 (ISBN 0-87516-515-X). De Vorss.

Nicholson, D. H. The Mysticism of St. Francis of Assissi. 1977. lib. bdg. 59.95 (ISBN 0-8490-2319-X). Gordon Pr.

Nordau, Max. The Psychology of Mysticism, 2 Vols. 271p. 1985. Set. 249.50 (ISBN 0-89920-099-0). Am Inst Psych.

Norvell. Amazing Secrets of the Mystic East. cancelled 14.95 (ISBN 0-13-023754-X, Parker). P-H.

Otto, Rudolf. Mysticism East & West. Bracey, Bertha L. & Payne, Richenda C., trs. 289p. 1987. pap. 8.75 (ISBN 0-8356-0619-8). Theos Pub Hse.

Packull, Werner O. Mysticism & the Early South German-Austrian Anabaptist 1525-1531. LC 76-46557. (Studies in the Anabaptist & Mennonite History: No. 19). 296p. 1977. 19.95x (ISBN 0-8361-1130-3). Herald Pr.

Paelian, Frances. The Mystical Marriage of Science & Spirit. LC 81-70272. (Illus.). 200p. 1981. pap. 11.95 (ISBN 0-918936-11-X). Astara.

Parrinder, Geoffrey. Mysticism in the World's Religions. 1976. pap. text ed. 6.95 (ISBN 0-19-502185-1). Oxford U Pr.

Pascher, Josef. Der Konigsweg Zu Wiedergeburt und Vergottung Bei Philon Von Alexandreia. Repr. of 1931 ed. 22.00 (ISBN 0-384-45050-4). Johnson Repr.

Passmore, John. Perfectability of Man. LC 77-129625. 1970. 25.00x (ISBN 0-684-15521-4, ScribT). Scribner.

Peck, George. The Triple Way. LC 77-79824. 321p. (Orig.). 1977. pap. 2.50x (ISBN 0-87574-213-0). Pendle Hill.

Peers, E. Allison. The Mystics of Spain. 1977. lib. bdg. 59.95 (ISBN 0-8490-2322-X). Gordon Pr.

Pie, A., et al. Mystery & Mysticism. 1956. 5.95 (ISBN 0-8022-1988-8). Philos Lib.

Poole, Cecil A. Mysticism - the Ultimate Experience. LC 81-86628. 166p. 1982. 8.95 (ISBN 0-912057-33-5, G-647). AMORC.

Pruter, Karl. The Teachings of the Great Mystics. LC 85-13306. 118p. 1985. Repr. lib. bdg. 19.95x (ISBN 0-89370-595-0). Borgo Pr.

Rajneesh, Bhagwan Shree. Be Still & Know. Anurag, Ma Yoga, ed. (Question & Answer Ser.). (Illus.). 364p. (Orig.). 1981. pap. 13.95 (ISBN 0-88050-511-7). Chidvilas Found.

--Guest. Sudha, Ma Yoga, ed. LC 82-203740. (Kabir Ser.). (Illus.). 604p. (Orig.). 1981. pap. 15.95 (ISBN 0-88050-574-5). Chidvilas Found.

--Madman's Guide to Enlightenment. Maneesha, Ma Prem, ed. (Initiation Talks Ser.). (Illus.). 388p. (Orig.). 1980. pap. 18.95 (ISBN 0-88050-593-1). Chidvilas Found.

--Philosophia Perennis, Vol. 1. Anurag, Ma Yoga, ed. (Western Mystics Ser.). (Illus.). 392p. (Orig.). 1981. 19.95 (ISBN 0-88050-115-4); pap. 15.95 428p (ISBN 0-88050-615-6). Chidvilas Found.

--Philosophia Perennis, Vol. 2. Anurag, Ma Yoga, ed. (Western Mystics Ser.). (Illus.). 436p. (Orig.). 1981. pap. 15.95 (ISBN 0-88050-616-4). Chidvilas Found.

Ramacharaka, Yogi. Mystic Christianity. 8.00 (ISBN 0-911662-08-1). Yoga.

Regardie, Israel, et al. Mysticism, Psychology & Oedipus. LC 85-81908. 96p. (Orig.). 1986. pap. 6.95 (ISBN 0-941404-38-2). Falcon Pr AZ.

Reinhold, H. A. The Soul Afire: Revelations of the Mystics. 1977. Repr. of 1944 ed. 30.00 (ISBN 0-89984-099-X). Century Bookbindery.

Restivo, Sal. The Social Relations of Physics, Mysticism & Mathematics. (Pallas Paperbacks Ser.). 1985. pap. 14.95 (ISBN 90-277-2084-3, Pub. by Reidel Holland). Kluwer Academic.

Riccardo, Martin V. Mystical Consciousness: Exploring an Extraordinary State of Awareness. 1977. pap. 5.00 (ISBN 0-686-19170-6). MVR Bks.

Richmond, Olney H. The Mystic Test Book. (Orig.). 1983. pap. 9.95 (ISBN 0-87877-064-X). Newcastle Pub.

Riley, Isaac H. The Meaning of Mysticism. LC 75-26512. 1975. lib. bdg. 20.00 (ISBN 0-8414-7227-0). Folcroft.

Rivet, Mother Mary M. Influence of the Spanish Mystics on the Works of Saint Francis De Sales. LC 79-115355. (Catholic University of America. Studies in Romance Languages & Literatures: No. 22). Repr. of 1941 ed. 20.00 (ISBN 0-404-50322-5). AMS Pr.

Row, T. Subba. Consciousness & Immortality. (Sangam Texts Ser.). 96p. (Orig.). 1983. pap. 8.75 (ISBN 0-88695-012-0). Concord Grove.

Rowlands, Henry. Mona Antiqua Restaurata. Feldman, Burton & Richardson, Robert D., eds. LC 78-60894. (Myth & Romanticism Ser.: Vol. 21). 399p. 1979. lib. bdg. 80.00 (ISBN 0-8240-3570-4). Garland Pub.

Rufus, Jones M. Studies in Mystical Religion. 1978. Repr. of 1919 ed. lib. bdg. 45.00 (ISBN 0-8492-1257-X). R West.

Russell, Bertrand. Mysticism & Logic & Other Essays. 2nd ed. LC 81-119829. 168p. 1981. pap. 8.95x (ISBN 0-389-20135-9, 06657). B&N Imports.

Russell, George W. The Ascending Cycle. (Sangam Texts Ser.). 105p. (Orig.). 1983. pap. 8.75 (ISBN 0-88695-013-9). Concord Grove.

Savage, D. S. Mysticism & Aldous Huxley. LC 77-23247. 1947. lib. bdg. 12.50 (ISBN 0-8414-7805-8). Folcroft.

Schwarz, Jack. Human Energy Systems. (Illus.). 1980. pap. 7.95 (ISBN 0-525-47556-7, 0772-230). Dutton.

Sheiner, Ben. Intellectual Mysticism. LC 78-50531. (Illus.). 120p. 1978. 8.95 (ISBN 0-8022-2228-5). Philos Lib.

Shirley, Ralph. Occultists & Mystics of All Ages. 176p. 1974. pap. 2.95 (ISBN 0-8065-0419-6). Citadel Pr.

Singh, Khushwant. Gurus, Godman & Good People. (Illus.). 134p. 1975. text ed. 13.95x (ISBN 0-86125-087-7, Pub. by Orient Longman India). Apt Bks.

Smith, Margaret. An Early Mystic of Baghdad: A Study of the Life & Teaching of Harith B. Asad al-Muhasibi, A.D. 781-A.D. 857. LC 76-180379. Repr. of 1935 ed. 16.50 (ISBN 0-404-56324-4). AMS Pr.
--An Introduction to the History of Mysticism. 69.95 (ISBN 0-87968-437-2). Gordon Pr.
--The Way of the Mystics: The Early Christian Mystics & the Rise of the Sufis. 1978. pap. 6.95 (ISBN 0-19-519967-7). Oxford U Pr.
Spencer, Sidney. Mysticism in World Religion. 11.75 (ISBN 0-8446-0927-7). Peter Smith.
Sprietsma, Cargill. We Imperialists: Notes on Ernest Seilliere's "Philosophy of Imperialism". LC 70-176005. Repr. of 1931 ed. 16.50 (ISBN 0-404-06198-2). AMS Pr.
Staal, Frits. Exploring Mysticism: A Methodological Essay. LC 74-76391. (Center for South & Southeast Asia Studies). 1975. 42.00x (ISBN 0-520-02726-4); pap. 4.95 (ISBN 0-520-03119-9, CAL 313). U of Cal Pr.
Stace, W. T. Mysticism & Philosophy. 384p. 1987. pap. 10.95 (ISBN 0-87477-416-0). J P Tarcher.
Starcke, Walter. This Double Thread. 160p. 1969. 12.95 (ISBN 0-227-67738-2). Attic Pr.
Stavropoulos, C. Partakers of Divine Nature. 1976. pap. 4.95 (ISBN 0-937032-09-3). Light&Life Pub Co MN.
Steiner, Johannes. The Visions of Therese Newmann. LC 75-34182. 245p. 1976. pap. 5.95 (ISBN 0-8189-0318-X). Alba.
Steiner, Rudolf. Mysticism at the Dawn of the Modern Age. (Russian Language Ser.). 102p. 1985. pap. 7.00 (ISBN 0-89345-901-1, Steiner). Garber Comm.
--Mysticism at the Dawn of the Modern Age, Vol. 6. 2nd ed. Allen, Paul M., ed. Zimmer, Karl E., tr. from Ger. LC 60-15703. (The Major Writings of Rudolf Steiner in English Translation Ser.: The Centennial Edition). 256p. 1981. lib. bdg. 16.00 (ISBN 0-89345-026-X, Spiritual Sci Lib); pap. 9.50 (ISBN 0-89345-206-8, Steinerbks). Garber Comm.
Studies in Mysticism & Religion. cancelled (ISBN 0-686-76265-7). Feldheim.
Stutfield, Hugh E. Mysticism & Catholicism. 1977. lib. bdg. 59.95 (ISBN 0-8490-2318-1). Gordon Pr.
Suhrawardi, Shihabuddin Yahya. The Mystical & Visionary Treatises of Shihabuddin Yahya Suhrawardi. Thackston, W. H., Jr., tr. 1982. 16.95 (ISBN 0-900860-92-8, Pub. by Octagon Pr England). Ins Study Human.
Suzuki, Daisetz T. Mysticism: Christian & Buddhist. LC 75-31442. 214p. 1976. Repr. of 1957 ed. lib. bdg. 25.00x (ISBN 0-8371-8516-5, SUMY). Greenwood.
Tuckwell, James H. Religion & Reality. LC 77-118552. 1971. Repr. of 1915 ed. 25.00x (ISBN 0-8046-1177-7, Pub. by Kennikat). Assoc Faculty Pr.
Turnbul, Coulson. Sema-Kanda: Threshold Memories. 254p. Date not set. pap. 15.00 (ISBN 0-89540-131-2, SB-131). Sun Pub.
Underhill, Evelyn. The Essentials of Mysticism & Other Essays. LC 75-41277. Repr. of 1920 ed. 18.00 (ISBN 0-404-14620-1). AMS Pr.
--Mixed Pasture. facs. ed. LC 68-8501. (Essay Index Reprint Ser). 1933. 17.00 (ISBN 0-8369-0958-5). Ayer Co Pubs.
--Mysticism. 1955. pap. 12.95 (ISBN 0-452-00840-9, Mer). NAL.
--Mystics of the Church. 260p. 1975. 13.95 (ISBN 0-227-67820-6). Attic Pr.
--Practical Mysticism. 160p. 1986. pap. 5.95 (ISBN 0-89804-143-0). Ariel OH.
Upward, Allen. The Divine Mystery. LC 76-27214. 384p. 1977. lib. bdg. 12.95 (ISBN 0-915520-02-8); pap. 7.95 (ISBN 0-915520-01-X). Ross-Erikson.
Valiuddin, Mir. Love of God. (Orig.). 1979. pap. 9.95 (ISBN 0-900217-02-2, Pub. by Sufi Pub Co England). Hunter Hse.
Valla, Mary. The Mystical Way of Life. LC 74-14058. 176p. 1975. pap. 4.95 (ISBN 0-685-52237-7). De Vorss.
Vandana. Nama Japa: Prayer of the Name in the Hindu & Christian Traditions. 1985. pap. 10.00 (ISBN 0-8364-1509-4, Pub. by Bharatiya Vidya Bhavan). South Asia Bks.
Veysey, Laurence. The Communal Experience: Anarchist & Mystical Communities in Twentieth Century America. LC 78-55045. 1978. pap. 7.95X (ISBN 0-226-85458-2, P786, Phoen). U of Chicago Pr.
Voillaume, Rene, ed. Silent Pilgrimage to God: The Spirituality of Charles deFoucauld. Moiser, Jeremy, tr. from Fr. LC 74-32516. Orig. Title: Ce Sue Crojart Charles de Foucauld. 100p. (Orig.). 1977. pap. 4.95 (ISBN 0-88344-461-5). Orbis Bks.
Wainwright, William J. Mysticism. LC 81-50821. 264p. 1982. 40.00x (ISBN 0-299-08910-X). U of Wis Pr.
Waite, Arthur E. Raymund Lully: Christian Mystic. 69.95 (ISBN 0-87968-100-4). Gordon Pr.
Walker, David. God Is a Sea: The Dynamics of Christian Living. LC 81-8072. 144p. (Orig.). 1981. pap. 5.95 (ISBN 0-8189-0420-8). Alba.
Walsh, James, ed. Pre-Reformation English Spirituality. LC 65-12885. 1966. 20.00 (ISBN 0-8232-0655-6). Fordham.
Waters, Frank. Mexico Mystique: The Coming Sixth World of Consciousness. LC 74-18579. (Illus.). 326p. 1975. 13.95 (ISBN 0-8040-0663-6, SB). Ohio U Pr.
Watkin, Edward I. Poets & Mystics. facs. ed. LC 68-55862. (Essay Index Reprint Ser). 1953. 19.00 (ISBN 0-8369-0979-8). Ayer Co Pubs.
Watts, Alan W. This Is It. 1972. pap. 3.95 (ISBN 0-394-71904-2, Vin). Random.
The Way to the Kingdom. 2nd ed. 345p. 1972. pap. 6.00 (ISBN 0-87516-164-2). De Vorss.
Webb, James, ed. A Quest Anthology. LC 75-36916. (Occult Ser.). 1976. Repr. of 1976 ed. 46.50x (ISBN 0-405-07971-0). Ayer Co Pubs.
Weber, Renee. Dialogues with Scientists & Sages: The Search for Unity in Science & Mysticism. 288p. 1986. pap. 14.95 (ISBN 0-7102-0655-0, 06550, Pub. by Routledge UK). Methuen Inc.
Weiner, Herbert. Nine & One Half Mystics. 1986. pap. 8.95 (ISBN 0-02-068160-7, Collier). Macmillan.
Wells, Bruce. From Discontent: The Biography of a Mystic. (Illus.). 224p. 1985. 13.95 (ISBN 0-85398-206-6); pap. 5.95 (ISBN 0-85398-207-4). G Ronald Pub.
Wetherbee, Winthrop, ed. & tr. The Cosmographia of Bernardus Silvestris. LC 73-479. (Records of Civilization, Sources & Studies: Sources & Studies). 176p. 1973. 24.00x (ISBN 0-231-03673-6). Columbia U Pr.
Younghusband, Francis. Modern Mystics. 322p. 1970. 7.95 (ISBN 0-8216-0118-0). Univ Bks.
Younghusband, Francis E. Modern Mystics. facs. ed. LC 67-28774. (Essay Index Reprint Ser). 1935. 17.75 (ISBN 0-8369-1015-X). Ayer Co Pubs.
Zaehner, Robert C. Mysticism: Sacred & Profane. 1957. pap. 7.95x (ISBN 0-19-500229-6). Oxford U Pr.

MYSTICISM–MIDDLE AGES, 600-1500

Atkinson, Clarissa W. Mystic & Pilgrim: The "Book" & the World of Margery Kempe. LC 82-22219. 248p. (Orig.). 1983. 27.50x (ISBN 0-8014-1521-7); pap. text ed. 8.95x (ISBN 0-8014-9895-3). Cornell U Pr.
Boehme, Jacob. Of Heaven & Hell: A Dialogue Between Junius, a Scholar & Theophorus, His Master. 1986. pap. 3.95 (ISBN 0-916411-53-2). Sure Fire.
Bynum, Caroline W. Jesus As Mother: Studies in the Spirituality of the High Middle Ages. LC 81-13137. (Center for Medieval & Renaissance Studies. UCLA Publications: No. 16). 280p. 1982. pap. text ed. 7.95 (ISBN 0-520-05222-6, CAL 697). U of Cal Pr.
Cooper & Oakley. Masonry & Medieval Mysticism. pap. 9.25 (ISBN 0-8356-5301-3). Theos Pub Hse.
--Masonry & Medieval Mysticism. 12.95 (ISBN 0-8356-5309-9). Theos Pub Hse.
Gebhart, E. Mystics & Heretics in Italy at the End of the Middle Ages. 1977. lib. bdg. 59.95 (ISBN 0-8490-2321-1). Gordon Pr.
Hodgson, Phyllis, ed. The Cloud of Unknowing. (Analecta Cartusiana Ser.: No. 3). (Eng.). 234p. (Orig.). 1982. pap. 25.00 (ISBN 3-7052-0003-8, Pub by Salzburg Studies). Longwood Pub Group.
Hogg, James. The Latin Version of The Cloud of Unknowing. (Analecta Cartusiana Ser.: No. 120). (Orig.). 1988. pap. 25.00 (ISBN 0-317-42582-X, Pub. by Salzburg Studies). Longwood Pub Group.
Johnston, William. The Mysticism of the Cloud of Unknowing: A Modern Interpretation. LC 74-30738. (Religious Experience Ser.: Vol. 8). pap. 74.30 (2052172). Bks Demand UMI.
Johnston, William, ed. The Cloud of Unknowing & the Book of Privy Counselling. LC 73-79737. 200p. 1973. pap. 3.50 (ISBN 0-385-03097-5, Im). Doubleday.
Llewelyn, Robert, ed. Daily Readings from the Cloud of Unknowing. (Daily Readings Ser.). 1986. pap. 4.95 (ISBN 0-87243-149-5). Templegate.
--Julian: Woman of Our Day. 1987. pap. 6.95 (ISBN 0-89622-334-5). Twenty-Third.
Ozment, Steven E. Mysticism & Dissent: Religious Ideology & Social Protest in the Sixteenth Century. LC 72-91316. 272p. 1973. 33.00x (ISBN 0-300-01576-3). Yale U Pr.
Petry, Ray C., ed. Late Medieval Mysticism. LC 57-5092. (Library of Christian Classics). 420p. 1980. pap. 12.95 (ISBN 0-664-24163-8). Westminster.
Richard Of St. Victor, et al. Cell of Self-Knowledge. Gardner, E. G., ed. LC 66-25702. (Medieval Library). Repr. of 1926 ed. 17.50x (ISBN 0-8154-0188-4). Cooper Sq.
Szarmach, Paul E., ed. An Introduction to the Medieval Mystics of Europe. 368p. 1984. 44.50 (ISBN 0-87395-834-9); pap. 14.95x (ISBN 0-87395-835-7). State U NY Pr.
Walsh, James, ed. The Cloud of Unknowing. (Classics of Western Spirituality Ser.). 1981. 12.95 (ISBN 0-8091-0314-1); pap. 9.95 (ISBN 0-8091-2332-0). Paulist Pr.
Wolters, Clifton, tr. The Cloud of Unknowing & Other Works. (Classics Ser). 1978. pap. 3.95 (ISBN 0-14-044385-1). Penguin.

MYSTICISM–BUDDHISM

Govinda, L. Anagarika. Foundations of Tibetan Mysticism. (Illus.). 331p. 1969. pap. 7.95 (ISBN 0-87728-064-9). Weiser.
Suzuki, D. T. Mysticism: Christian & Buddhist. 160p. 1982. pap. 5.95 (ISBN 0-04-149053-3). Allen Unwin.

MYSTICISM–CATHOLIC CHURCH

Arintero, John G. Mystical Evolution, 2 vols. Aumann, Jordan, tr. from Sp. LC 78-62254. Orig. Title: La Evolucion Mistica. 1979. Set. pap. 24.00 (ISBN 0-89555-071-7); Vol. I. pap. (ISBN 0-89555-072-5); Vol. II. pap. (ISBN 0-89555-073-3). TAN Bks Pubs.
Bessieres, Albert. Wife, Mother & Mystic: Blessed Anna Maria Taigi. Newton, Douglas, ed. Rigby, Stephen, tr. from Fr. (Eng.). 1977. pap. 5.50 (ISBN 0-89555-058-X). TAN Bks Pubs.
Bonaventure, St. The Mind's Journey to God (Itinerarium Mentis Ad Deum) Cunningham, Lawrence S., tr. 1979. 6.95 (ISBN 0-8199-0765-0). Franciscan Herald.
De Caussade, Jean-Pierre. Abandonment to Divine Providence. LC 74-2827. 120p. 1975. pap. 3.50 (ISBN 0-385-02544-0, Im). Doubleday.
Franck, Sebastian. Sebastian Franck: Two Hundred Eighty Paradoxes or Wondrous Sayings. Furcha, E. J., tr. (Texts & Studies in Religion: 26). 562p. 1986. lib. bdg. 79.95 (ISBN 0-88946-814-1). E Mellen.
Godwin, George. The Great Mystics. LC 74-2430. (St. Paul, Plotinus, St. Augustine, St. Francis, St. Teresa, Martin Luther, Jacob Boehme, George Fox, Emanuel Swedenborg, William Blake). 1945. lib. bdg. 27.50 (ISBN 0-8414-4499-4). Folcroft.
Kempf, Nicolas. Tractatus de Mystica Theologia, Vol. 2. Hogg, James, ed. (Analecta Cartusiana Ser.: No. 9). (Lat. & Fr.). 574p. (Orig.). 1973. pap. 50.00 (ISBN 3-7052-0010-0, Pub by Salzburg Studies). Longwood Pub Group.
Lees, Rosemary A. The Negative Language of the Dionysian School of Mystical Theology: An Approach to the Cloud of Unknowing, 2 vols. Hogg, James, ed. (Analecta Cartusiana Ser.: No. 107). 549p. (Orig.). 1983. pap. 50.00 (ISBN 0-317-42591-9, Pub. by Salzburg Studies). Longwood Pub Group.
McNamara, William. Christian Mysticism: Psychotheology. LC 80-13139. 173p. 1981. 9.50 (ISBN 0-8199-0793-6). Franciscan Herald.
Mallory, Marilyn M. Christian Mysticism Transcending Techniques: A Theological Reflection on the Empirical Testing of the Teaching of St. John of the Cross. 320p. 1977. pap. text ed. 28.00 (ISBN 90-232-1535-4, Pub. by Van Gorcum Holland). Longwood Pub Group.
Maloney, George A. Indwelling Presence. 112p. (Orig.). 1985. pap. 4.50 (ISBN 0-914544-62-4). Living Flame Pr.
O'Connell, Patrick & Carty, Charles. The Holy Shroud & Four Visions: The Holy Shroud New Evidence Compared with the Visions of St. Bridget of Sweden, Maria d'Agreda, Anne Catherine Emmerich, & Teresa Neumann. (Illus.). 1974. pap. 1.50 (ISBN 0-89555-102-0). TAN Bks Pubs.
St. John of the Cross. Dark Night of the Soul. 1959. pap. 3.95 (ISBN 0-385-02930-6, D78, Im). Doubleday.
Suzuki, D. T. Mysticism: Christian & Buddhist. 160p. 1982. pap. 5.95 (ISBN 0-04-149053-3). Allen Unwin.
Teasdale, Wayne. Essays in Mysticism. 196p. 1982. pap. 8.95 (ISBN 0-941850-02-1). Sunday Pubns.
Teilhard De Chardin, Pierre. Hymn of the Universe. LC 65-10375. 1969. pap. 6.95x (ISBN 0-06-131910-4, TB1910, Torch). Har-Row.
--Hymne De L'univers. 1966. 13.95 (ISBN 0-685-11240-3). French & Eur.
Watkin, Edward I. Poets & Mystics. facs. ed. LC 68-55862. (Essay Index Reprint Ser). 1953. 19.00 (ISBN 0-8369-0979-8). Ayer Co Pubs.
Wilkinson, Peggy O. Finding the Mystic within You. 211p. (Orig.). 1985. pap. 4.95 (ISBN 0-914544-61-6). Living Flame Pr.

MYSTICISM–HINDUISM

see also Samadhi

Bhaktivedanta, Swami A. C. Easy Journey to Other Planets. LC 70-118080. (Illus.). 1970. pap. 1.95 (ISBN 0-912776-10-2). Bhaktivedanta.
Dasgupta, S. N. Hindu Mysticism. 1977. 12.95 (ISBN 0-8426-0929-6). Orient Bk Dist.
Jyotir Maya Nanda, Swami. Mysticism of Hindu Gods & Goddesses. (Illus.). 1974. pap. 3.99 (ISBN 0-934664-08-0). Yoga Res Foun.
Masson, J. Moussaieff. The Oceanic Feeling: The Origins of Religious Sentiment in Ancient India. (Studies of Classical India: No. 3). 228p. 1980. lib. bdg. 34.00 (ISBN 90-277-1050-3, Pub. by Reidel Holland). Kluwer Academic.
Oman, J. C. The Mystics, Ascetics & Saints of India: A Study of Sadhmaism with an Account of the Yogis, Sanyasis, Bairagis, & other Strange Hindu Sectarians. 308p. 1984. text ed. 38.50x (ISBN 0-89563-650-6). Coronet Bks.
Singh, Charu S. & Hogg, James. The Chariot of Fire: A Study of William Blake In the Light of Hindu Thought. (Romantic Reassessment Ser.). 194p. (Orig.). 1981. pap. 15.00 (ISBN 3-7052-0577-3, Pub. by Salzburg Studies). Longwood Pub Group.
Sircar, M. Hindu Mysticism According to the Upanisads. 1974. text ed. 19.00x. Coronet Bks.
Vandana. Nama Japa: Prayer of the Name in the Hindu & Christian Traditions. 1985. pap. 10.00 (ISBN 0-8364-1509-4, Pub. by Bharatiya Vidya Bhavan). South Asia Bks.

MYSTICISM–HISTORY

Beausobre, Isaac de. Histoire Critique de Manichee et du Manicheisme. Feldman, Burton & Richardson, Robert D., eds. LC 78-60880. (Myth & Romanticism Ser.). 1984. lib. bdg. 160.00 (ISBN 0-8240-3552-6). Garland Pub.
Chrisci, John. Mysticism: The Search for Ultimate Meaning. 78p. 1986. text ed. 17.50 (ISBN 0-8191-5609-4); pap. text ed. 7.75 (ISBN 0-8191-5610-8). U Pr of Amer.
Eckhart, Meister. Meister Eckhart: A Modern Translation. pap. 8.95x (ISBN 0-06-130008-X, TB8, Torch). Har-Row.
Fairweather, William. Among the Mystics. 150p. 1936. 4.95 (ISBN 0-567-02104-1, Pub. by T & T Clark Ltd UK). Fortress.
Gall, E. Mysticism Through the Ages. 59.95 (ISBN 0-8490-0697-X). Gordon Pr.
Herrera, Robert A. Lamps of Fire. 168p. (Orig.). 1986. pap. 7.95 (ISBN 0-932506-40-2). St Bedes Pubns.
Katsaros, Thomas & Kaplan, Nathaniel. The Western Mystical Tradition: An Intellectual History of Western Civilization, Vol. 1. 1969. 15.95x (ISBN 0-8084-0316-8); pap. 11.95x (ISBN 0-8084-0317-6). New Coll U Pr.
Louth, Andrew. The Origins of the Christian Mystical Tradition: From Plato to Denys. 1981. pap. text ed. 9.95x (ISBN 0-19-826668-5). Oxford U Pr.
Steiner, Rudolf. Mysticism at the Dawn of the Modern Age. (Russian Language Ser.). 102p. 1985. pap. 7.00 (ISBN 0-89345-901-1, Steiner). Garber Comm.
Swami Abhayananda. History of Mysticism. 464p. (Orig.). 1987. pap. 11.95 (ISBN 0-914557-04-1). Atma Bks.
Twenty-Five Days with Great Christian Mystics: A Journey into Practical Christianity. pap. 2.50 (ISBN 0-686-13933-X). Rorge Pub Co.
Wilder, Alexander. The Peculiar Mystical Rites of Ancient Peoples. (Illus.). 269p. 1984. 117.85x (ISBN 0-89266-451-7). AM Classical Coll Pr.

MYSTICISM–ISLAM

see also Sufism

Archer, John C. Mystical Elements in Mohammed. LC 80-26396. (Yale Oriental Ser. Researches: No. 11 Pt. 1; All Published). Repr. of 1924 ed. 22.50 (ISBN 0-404-60281-9). AMS Pr.
Boewering, Gerhard. The Mystical Vision of Existence in Classical Islam. (Studien zur Sprache, Geschichte und Kultur des islamischen Orients, Beihefte zur "der Islam"). 296p. 1979. text ed. 70.50x (ISBN 3-11-007546-6). De Gruyter.
Hall, Manly P. Mystics of Islam. pap. 3.95 (ISBN 0-89314-532-7). Philos Res.
Morewedge, Parviz, ed. Islamic Philosophy & Mysticism. LC 80-14364. (Studies in Islamic Philosophy & Science). 1981. 45.00x (ISBN 0-88206-302-2). Caravan Bks.
Mulla Sadra. The Wisdom of the Throne: An Introduction to the Philosophy of Mulla Sadra. Morris, James W., tr. from Arabic. LC 81-47153. (Princeton Library of Asian Translations). 300p. 1981. 34.50x (ISBN 0-691-06493-8). Princeton U Pr.
Nicholson, Reynold A. Studies in Islamic Mysticism. LC 78-73958. 1979. pap. 16.95 (ISBN 0-521-29546-7). Cambridge U Pr.
Rumi the Persian Mystic. 1970. 15.00 (ISBN 0-87902-185-3). Orientalia.
Smith, Margaret. An Early Mystic of Baghdad: A Study of the Life & Teaching of Harith B. Asad al-Muhasibi, A.D. 781-A.D. 857. LC 76-180379. Repr. of 1935 ed. 16.50 (ISBN 0-404-56324-4). AMS Pr.
--Rabi'a the Mystic & Her Fellow-Saints in Islam. 2nd ed. 256p. 1984. 37.50 (ISBN 0-521-26779-X); pap. 13.95 (ISBN 0-521-31863-7). Cambridge U Pr.

MYSTICISM–JUDAISM

Altmann, Alexander. Studies in Religious Philosophy & Mysticism. (New Reprints in Essay & General Literature Index Ser.). 1975. Repr. of 1969 ed. 24.25 (ISBN 0-518-10194-0). Ayer Co Pubs.

Aptowitzer, V. & Schwarz, A. Z. Abhandlungen zur Erinnerung an Hirsch Perez Chajes. LC 7-7163. (Jewish Philosophy, Mysticism & History of Ideas Ser.). 1980. Repr. of 1933 ed. lib. bdg. 60.00x (ISBN 0-405-12237-3). Ayer Co Pubs.

Ben Zion, Raphael, tr. from Hebrew. Anthology of Jewish Mysticism. 5.00 (ISBN 0-686-13334-X). Yesod Pubs.

Biale, David. Gershom Scholem: Kabbalah & Counter-History. 2nd ed. 240p. 1982. pap. text ed. 7.95x (ISBN 0-674-36332-9). Harvard U Pr.

Blumenthal, D. R. Understanding Jewish Mysticism: A Source Reader, No. I. (Library of Judaic Learning). Vol. II. 20.00x (ISBN 0-87068-334-9); pap. 9.95. Ktav.

Buber, Martin, et al. I & Thou. Kaufman, Walter & Smith, S. G., trs. LC 72-123845. (Hudson River Edition). 1970. 20.00 (ISBN 0-684-15575-3, ScribT); pap. 6.95 (ISBN 0-684-71725-5, ScribT). Scribner.

Cohen, Martin S. The Shiur Qomah: Liturgy & Theurgy in Pre-Kabbalistic Jewish Mysticism. 300p. (Orig.). 1983. lib. bdg. 27.50 (ISBN 0-8191-3272-1). U Pr of Amer.

Dan, Joseph. Jewish Mysticism & Jewish Ethics. LC 85-40358. 158p. 1986. 20.00x (ISBN 0-295-96265-8). U of Wash Pr.

Dan, Joseph & Talmage, Frank, eds. Studies in Jewish Mysticism. 25.00x (ISBN 0-915938-03-0). Ktav.

Greene, William B. The Blazing Star, with an Appendix Treating of the Jewish Kabbala. 1977. lib. bdg. 59.95 (ISBN 0-8490-1516-2). Gordon Pr.

Gutwirth, Israel. Kabbalah & Jewish Mysticism. LC 86-18693. 288p. 1986. 15.00 (ISBN 0-8022-2516-0). Philos Lib.

Jacobs, Louis. Jewish Ethics, Philosophy & Mysticism. LC 71-80005. (Chain of Tradition Ser). 1969. pap. 5.95x (ISBN 0-87441-012-6). Behrman.

--Jewish Mystical Testimonies. LC 76-46644. 1977. pap. 8.95 (ISBN 0-8052-0585-3). Schocken.

Jellinek, Adolph. Beitrage zur Geschichte der Kabbala. Katz, Steven, ed. LC 79-7138. (Jewish Philosophy, Mysticism, & History of Ideas Ser.). 1980. Repr. of 1852 ed. lib. bdg. 16.00x (ISBN 0-405-12264-0). Ayer Co Pubs.

Katz, Steven, ed. Studies by Samuel Horodezky: An Original Anthology. LC 79-51391. (Jewish Philosophy, Mysticism & History of Ideas Ser.). 1980. lib. bdg. 17.00x (ISBN 0-405-12233-0). Ayer Co Pubs.

Katz, Steven T., ed. Jewish Philosophy, Mysticism & History of Ideas Series, 50 bks. (Illus.). 1980. Set. lib. bdg. 2389.00x (ISBN 0-405-12229-2). Ayer Co Pubs.

Kaufman, William E. Journeys: An Introductory Guide to Jewish Mysticism. LC 80-69017. 1980. 12.50 (ISBN 0-8197-0482-2); pap. 7.95 (ISBN 0-686-77548-1). Bloch.

Scholem, Gersham G. Jewish Gnosticism, Merkabah Mysticism & Talmudic Tradition. 1960. 10.00x (ISBN 0-685-31427-8, Pub. by Jewish Theol Seminary). Ktav.

Scholem, Gershom. Major Trends in Jewish Mysticism. 3rd ed. LC 61-8991. 1961. pap. 8.95 (ISBN 0-8052-0005-3). Schocken.

--On Jews & Judaism in Crisis: Selected Essays. Dannhauser, Werner J., ed. LC 75-37010. 1978. 16.50 (ISBN 0-8052-3613-9). Schocken.

Schweid, ELiezer. Judaism & Mysticism According to Gershom Scholem: A Critical Analysis & Programmatic Discussion. Weiner, David A., tr. (Reprints & Translations). 1985. 22.95 (ISBN 0-89130-982-9, 00-07-09); pap. 16.95 (ISBN 0-89130-887-3). Scholars Pr Ga.

Weiss, Joseph. Studies in East European Jewish Mysticism. Goldstein, David, ed. (Littman Libray of Jewish Civilazation). 1985. 29.95x (ISBN 0-19-710034-1). Oxford U Pr.

Zion, Raphael Ben, tr. Anthology of Jewish Mysticism. 255p. 1984. pap. 6.95 (ISBN 0-910818-29-0). Judaica Pr.

MYSTICISM–ORTHODOX EASTERN CHURCH

Arseniev, Nicholas. Mysticism & the Eastern Church. 173p. 1979. pap. 7.95 (ISBN 0-913836-55-9). St Vladimirs.

Herman, Abbot. Blessed John, the Wonderworker. rev. ed. St. Herman of Alaska Brotherhood Staff, ed. (Illus.). 350p. 1987. pap. 15.00 (ISBN 0-938635-01-8). St Herman AK.

Isaac The Syrian. Mystical Writings of St. Isaac the Syrian. Wensinck, A. J., tr. from Syriac. 1977. pap. 6.95 (ISBN 0-686-19231-1). Eastern Orthodox.

Lossky, Vladimir. The Mystical Theology of the Eastern Church. LC 76-25448. Orig. Title: Essai sur la theologie mystique de L'eglise d'orient. 252p. 1976. pap. 8.95 (ISBN 0-913836-31-1). St Vladimirs.

Macarius, Saint Fifty Spiritual Homilies. 1974. Repr. of 1921 ed. 17.50 (ISBN 0-686-10200-2). Eastern Orthodox.

Monk of the Eastern Church. Orthodox Spirituality: An Outline of the Orthodox Ascetical & Mystical Tradition. 111p. 1978. pap. 4.95 (ISBN 0-913836-51-6). St Vladimirs.

Rahner, Hugo. Greek Myths & Christian Mystery. LC 79-156736. (Illus.). 1971. Repr. of 1963 ed. 18.00 (ISBN 0-8196-0270-1). Biblo.

Wisdom of the Desert Fathers. 1979. pap. 3.95 (ISBN 0-686-25228-4). Eastern Orthodox.

MYSTICISM–GERMANY

Boehme, Jakob. The Confessions. 69.95 (ISBN 0-87968-258-2). Gordon Pr.

Clark, James M. Great German Mystics: Eckhart, Tauler & Suso. LC 73-81493. 1970. Repr. of 1949 ed. 15.00x (ISBN 0-8462-1351-6). Russell.

MYSTICISM–GREAT BRITAIN

Bradley, Ritamary & Lagorio, Valerie M. The Fourteenth Century English Mystics: A Comprehensive Annotated Bibliography. LC 79-7922. (Garland Reference Library of the Humanities). 300p. 1981. lib. bdg. 36.00 (ISBN 0-8240-9535-9). Garland Pub.

Cholmeley, Katharine. Margery Kempe, Genius & Mystic. LC 78-7811. 1978. Repr. of 1947 ed. lib. bdg. 17.50 (ISBN 0-8414-0296-5). Folcroft.

Hodgson, Geraldine E. English Mystics. LC 73-13663. 1973. lib. bdg. 25.00 (ISBN 0-8414-4756-X). Folcroft.

--English Mystics. 1977. lib. bdg. 59.95 (ISBN 0-8490-1777-7). Gordon Pr.

Hollingworth, G. E. English Mystics. 1973. lib. bdg. 15.00 (ISBN 0-8414-5096-X). Folcroft.

Kempe, Margery, et al. The Cell of Self Knowledge: Seven Early English Mystical Treatises. Griffiths, John, ed. LC 81-126. (The Spiritual Classics Ser.). 128p. 1981. 8.95 (ISBN 0-8245-0082-2). Crossroad NY.

McCarthy, Adrian J. Studies in the English Mystics: Book to a Mother, No. 1. Hogg, James, ed. (Elizabethan & Renaissance Studies). 275p. (Orig.). 1981. pap. 15.00 (ISBN 3-7052-0742-3, Pub. by Salzburg Studies). Longwood Pub Group.

Molinari, Paolo. Julian of Norwich. LC 74-13160. 1974. Repr. of 1958 ed. lib. bdg. 32.50 (ISBN 0-8414-6168-6). Folcroft.

Sawyer, Michael E., compiled by. A Bibliographical Index of Five English Mystics: Richard Rolle, Julian of Norwich, The Author of the Cloud of Unknowing, Walter Hilton, Margery Kempe. LC 73-110788. 1978. 10.00 (ISBN 0-931222-09-5). Pitts Theolog.

Way, Robert, ed. The Wisdom of the English Mystics. LC 78-6435. 1978. pap. 3.75 (ISBN 0-8112-0700-5, NDP466). New Directions.

Wohrer, Franz K. Thomas Traherne's 'The Growth of a Mystic's Mind: A Study of the Evolution & the Phenomenology of Traherne's Mystical Consciousness. Hogg, James, ed. (Elizabethan & Renaissance Studies). 207p. (Orig.). 1982. pap. 15.00 (ISBN 3-7052-0747-4, Pub. by Salzburg Studies). Longwood Pub Group.

MYSTICISM–INDIA

see also Mandala

Balse, Mayah. Mystics & Men of Miracles in India. (Illus.). 1976. 5.95 (ISBN 0-913244-10-4). Hapi Pr.

Choudhary, K. P. Modern Indian Mysticism. 1981. 17.00x (ISBN 0-8364-0744-X, Pub. by Motilal Banarsidass). South Asia Bks.

Lakhani, M. P. Spiritualism & Mysticism. x, 119p. 1984. text ed. 20.00x (ISBN 0-86590-381-6, Pub. by Inter Pubns N Delhi). Apt Bks.

McGill, Ormond. Hypnotism & Mysticism of India. 2nd ed. (Illus.). 208p. 1979. Repr. of 1977 ed. text ed. 12.50 (ISBN 0-930298-01-2). Westwood Pub Co.

Masson, J. Moussaieff. The Oceanic Feeling: The Origins of Religious Sentiment in Ancient India. (Studies of Classical India: No. 3). 228p. 1980. lib. bdg. 34.00 (ISBN 90-277-1050-3, Pub. by Reidel Holland). Kluwer Academic.

Murphy, Paul E. Triadic Mysticism. 1986. 23.00X (ISBN 81-208-0010-9, Pub. by Motilal Banarsidass). South Asia Bks.

Rajneesh, Bhagwan Shree. The Beloved, 2 vols. Sudha, Ma Yoga, ed. LC 78-903022. (Baul Mystics Ser.). (Illus., Orig.). 1977. Vol. I, 324 pgs. 15.95 ea. (ISBN 0-88050-007-7). Vol. II, 288 pgs. 1978. Chidvilas Found.

Ramaiah, G. Sundara. A Philosophical Study of the Mysticism of Sankara. 1983. 12.00x (ISBN 0-686-88924-X, Pub. by KP Bagchi India). South Asia Bks.

Ranade, R. D. Mysticism in India: The Poet Saints of Maharashtra. LC 82-10458. (Illus.). 534p. 1982. 44.50x (ISBN 0-87395-669-9); pap. 12.95 (ISBN 0-87395-670-2). State U NY Pr.

Sircar, M. N. Mysticism in the Bhagavad-Gita. 1977. 12.00x (ISBN 0-686-22667-4). Intl Bk Dist.

Sridhara, Swami B. The Loving Search for the Lost Servant. Goswami, B. S. & Mahayogi, B. V., eds. (Illus.). 120p. 1987. pap. text ed. 9.95 (ISBN 0-940431-05-X). Guardian Devot Pr.

Vaswani, J. P. & Mirchandani, Jyoti. Temple Flowers. 182p. 1986. text ed. 25.00x (ISBN 0-317-43153-6, Pub. by Chopmen Pubs Singapore). Advent NY.

MYSTICISM–SPAIN

Clissold, Stephen. The Wisdom of the Spanish Mystics. (Wisdom Bks.). 3.95 (ISBN 0-8112-0663-7). New Directions.

Galilea, Segundo. The Future of Our Past: The Spanish Mystics Speak to Contemporary Spirituality. LC 85-71822. 96p. (Orig.). 1985. pap. 4.95 (ISBN 0-87793-296-4). Ave Maria.

Peers, E. A. Studies of the Spanish Mystics, 3 vols. 1977. lib. bdg. 300.00 (ISBN 0-8490-2706-3). Gordon Pr.

MYSTICISM IN LITERATURE

see also Occultism in Literature

Bose, Abinash C. Three Mystic Poets: A Study of W. B. Yeats, A. E. & Rabindrath Tagore. LC 72-187263. 1945. lib. bdg. 12.50 (ISBN 0-8414-2534-5). Folcroft.

Broers, B. C. Mysticism in the Neo-Romanticists. LC 68-767. (Studies in Comparative Literature: No. 35). 1969. Repr. of 1923 ed. text ed. 75.00x (ISBN 0-8383-0514-8). Haskell.

Davison, William T. Mystics & Poets. LC 77-924. 1977. lib. bdg. 25.00 (ISBN 0-8414-3680-0). Folcroft.

Foster, Ann T. Theodore Roethke's Meditative Sequences: Contemplation & the Creative Process. LC 85-3041. (Studies in Art & Religious Interpretation: Vol. 4). 210p. 1985. 49.95x (ISBN 0-88946-555-X). E Mellen.

Hodgson, P. The Orcherd of Syon & the English Mystical Tradition. (Sir Israel Gollancz Memorial Lectures in Old English). 1964. pap. 2.25 (ISBN 0-85672-264-2, Pub. by British Acad). Longwood Pub Group.

Hunter, Irene, ed. American Mystical Verse. LC 79-116407. (Granger Index Reprint Ser). 1925. 19.00 (ISBN 0-8369-6148-X). Ayer Co Pubs.

Inge, William R. Studies of English Mystics. facs. ed. LC 69-17578. (Essay Index Reprint Ser). 1906. 15.00 (ISBN 0-8369-0081-2). Ayer Co Pubs.

Itrat-Husain. The Mystical Element in the Metaphysical Poets of the Seventeenth Century. LC 66-23522. 1948. 15.00 (ISBN 0-8196-0177-2). Biblo.

Jones, Rufus M. Mysticism in Robert Browning. 1924. Repr. 15.00 (ISBN 0-8274-2784-0). R West.

Kennedy, David G. Incarnational Element in Hiltons Spirituality. Hogg, James, ed. (Elizabethan & Renaissance Studies). 312p. (Orig.). 1982. pap. 15.00 (ISBN 0-317-40146-7, Pub by Salzburg Studies). Longwood Pub Group.

Kortelling, Jacomina. Mysticism in Blake & Wordsworth. LC 68-2111. (Studies in Poetry, No. 38). 1969. Repr. of 1928 ed. lib. bdg. 39.95x (ISBN 0-8383-0577-6). Haskell.

McCarthy, Adrian J. Studies in the English Mystics: Book to a Mother, No. 1. Hogg, James, ed. (Elizabethan & Renaissance Studies). 275p. (Orig.). 1981. pap. 15.00 (ISBN 3-7052-0742-3, Pub. by Salzburg Studies). Longwood Pub Group.

Osmond, Percy H. Mystical Poets of the English Church. LC 72-5166. 1919. lib. bdg. 48.50 (ISBN 0-8414-6542-8). Folcroft.

Thompson, Elbert N. Mysticism in Seventeenth Century English Literature. LC 78-100788. 1970. pap. text ed. 39.95x (ISBN 0-8383-0076-6). Haskell.

Tuma, George W. The Fourteenth Century English Mystics: A Comparative Analysis, 2 vols. Hogg, James, ed. (Elizabethan & Renaissance Studies). 400p. (Orig.). 1977. pap. 30.00 (ISBN 0-317-40144-0, Pub. by Salzburg Studies). Longwood Pub Group.

Wright, Luella M. Literary Life of the Early Friends, 1650-1725. LC 32-25426. Repr. of 1932 ed. 19.50 (ISBN 0-404-07046-9). AMS Pr.

MYTH

see also Demythologization; Mythology

Bloomfield, Morton W., ed. Allegory, Myth, & Symbol. (Harvard English Studies: 9). 440p. 1982. text ed. 32.50x (ISBN 0-674-01640-8); pap. text ed. 10.95x (ISBN 0-674-01641-6). Harvard U Pr.

Bryant, Jacob. A New System, or, an Analysis of Ancient Mythology, 3 vols. Feldman, Burton & Richardson, Robert, eds. LC 78-60881. (Myth & Romanticism Ser.: Vol. 5). (Illus.). 1979. Set. lib. bdg. 240.00 (ISBN 0-8240-3554-2). Garland Pub.

Cassirer, Ernst. Language & Myth. Langer, Susanne K., tr. 1946. pap. 2.95 (ISBN 0-486-20051-5). Dover.

--Language & Myth. 13.50 (ISBN 0-8446-1820-9). Peter Smith.

--Myth of the State. 1961. pap. 8.95x (ISBN 0-300-00036-7, y33). Yale U Pr.

Colloquium on Myth in Literature, Bucknell & Susquehanna Universities, Mar. 21-2, 1974, et al. The Binding of Proteus: Perspectives on Myth & the Literary Process. McCune, Marjorie W. & Orbison, T. Tucker, eds. LC 76-49774. (Illus.). 352p. 1978. 28.50 (ISBN 0-8387-1708-X). Bucknell U Pr.

Day, Martin S. The Many Meanings of Myth. 574p. 1984. lib. bdg. 28.75 (ISBN 0-8191-3821-5); pap. text ed. 20.75 (ISBN 0-8191-3822-3). U Pr of Amer.

Dundes, Alan, ed. Sacred Narrative: Reading in the Theory of Myth. LC 83-17921. (Illus.). ix, 352p. 1984. 42.00x (ISBN 0-520-05156-4); pap. 11.95x (ISBN 0-520-05192-0, CAL 362). U of Cal Pr.

Ehrenreich, Paul. Die Allgemeine Mythologie und Ihre Ethnologischen Grundlagen. Bolle, Kees W., ed. LC 77-79125. (Mythology Ser.). 1978. Repr. of 1915 ed. lib. bdg. 34.50x (ISBN 0-405-10536-3). Ayer Co Pubs.

Eliade, Mircea. Myth & Reality. pap. 5.95x (ISBN 0-06-131369-6, TB1369, Torch). Har-Row.

Girardot, N. J. Myth & Meaning in Early Taoism: The Themes of Chaos (hun-tun) LC 81-21964. (Hermeneutics Studies in the History of Religions). (Illus.). 430p. 1983. 39.50x (ISBN 0-520-04330-8). U of Cal Pr.

Hansburg, Mary E. Myth, Faith & Hermeneutics. 85p. (Orig.). 1985. pap. 6.95x (ISBN 0-932269-23-0). Wyndham Hall.

Kelsey, Morton. Myth, History & Faith: The Re-Mythologizing of Christianity. LC 73-94216. 192p. 1974. pap. 5.95 (ISBN 0-8091-1827-0). Paulist Pr.

Leeming, David A. Flights: Readings in Magic, Mysticism, Fantasy & Myth. 388p. (Orig.). 1974. pap. text ed. 11.95 (ISBN 0-15-527556-9, HC). HarBraceJ.

Liebert, Arthur. Mythus und Kultur: Myth & Culture. Bolle, Kees W., ed. (Mythology Ser.). (Ger.). 1978. Repr. of 1925 ed. lib. bdg. 17.00x (ISBN 0-405-10549-5). Ayer Co Pubs.

Lowry, Shirley. Familiar Mysteries: The Truth in Myth. LC 80-27792. (Illus.). 1981. 25.00x (ISBN 0-19-502925-9). Oxford U Pr.

McLean, George F., ed. Myth & Philosophy. LC 72-184483. (Proceedings of the American Catholic Philosophical Association: Vol. 45). 1971. pap. 15.00 (ISBN 0-918090-05-9). Am Cath Philo.

Malinowski, Bronislaw. Myth in Primitive Psychology. LC 79-152394. 94p. 1972. Repr. of 1926 ed. text ed. 22.50x (ISBN 0-8371-5954-7, MMP&, Pub. by Negro U Pr). Greenwood.

Richardson, Robert D., Jr. Myth & Literature in the American Renaissance. LC 77-22638. 320p. 1978. 22.50x (ISBN 0-253-33965-0). Ind U Pr.

Steblin-Kamenskij, M. I. Myth. 165p. 1981. 15.50 (ISBN 0-89720-053-5); pap. 8.50 (ISBN 0-89720-054-3). Karoma.

Weisinger, Herbert. Agony & the Triumph: Papers on the Use & Abuse of Myth. x, 283p. 1964. 5.00 (ISBN 0-87013-081-1). Mich St U Pr.

MYTHOLOGY

see also Art and Mythology; Cultus; Demythologization; Fire (In Religion, Folk-Lore, etc.); Folk-Lore; Gods; Heroes; Mother-Goddesses; Myth; Religion, Primitive; Symbolism; Totemism

Ares, Jacques d' Encyclopedie de l'Esoterisme, 1: Mythologies. (Fr.). 232p. 1975. pap. 19.95 (ISBN 0-686-56898-2, M-6008). French & Eur.

Baring-Gould, S. Curious Myths of the Middle Ages. (Works of S. Baring-Gould Ser.). 254p. 1985. Repr. of 1867 ed. lib. bdg. 29.00 (ISBN 0-932051-19-7, Pub. by Am Repr Serv). Am Biog Serv.

Baring-Gould, Sabine. Curious Myths of the Middle Ages. 69.95 (ISBN 0-87968-261-2). Gordon Pr.

--Curious Myths of the Middle Ages. 1976. Repr. of 1867 ed. 69.00x (ISBN 0-403-06309-4, Regency). Scholarly.

Barnard, Mary. Mythmakers. LC 66-20061. 213p. 1979. 16.95 (ISBN 0-8214-0024-X); pap. 6.50 (ISBN 0-8214-0562-4). Ohio U Pr.

--The Mythmakers. LC 66-20061. 213p. 1986. 12.95 (ISBN 0-932576-36-2); pap. 6.95 (ISBN 0-932576-37-0). Breitenbush Bks.

Barthes, Roland. The Eiffel Tower & Other Mythologies. Howard, Richard, tr. from Fr. 152p. 1979. 9.95 (ISBN 0-8090-4115-4); pap. 5.25 (ISBN 0-8090-1391-6). Hill & Wang.

Beltz, Walter. God & the Gods: Myths of the Bible. Heinegg, Peter, tr. 272p. 1983. pap. 6.95 (ISBN 0-14-022192-1, Pelican). Penguin.

Bendix, Regina. Progress & Nostalgia: Silvester-Klausen in Urnasch, Switzerland. LC 84-28128. (UC Publications in Folklore & Mythology: Vol. 33). 1985. 21.00 (ISBN 0-520-09959-1). U of Cal Pr.

Biallas, Leonard J. Myths: Gods, Heroes & Saviors. 304p. (Orig.). 1986. pap. 9.95 (ISBN 0-89622-290-X). Twenty-Third.

Boas, Franz. Tsimshian Mythology Based on Texts Recorded by Henry W. Tate. (Landmarks in Anthropology Ser.). (Illus.). Repr. of 1916 ed. 60.00 (ISBN 0-384-04880-3). Johnson Repr.

Bolle, Kees W., ed. Mythology Series, 39 vols. (Illus.). 1978. Set. lib. bdg. 1807.50x (ISBN 0-405-10529-0); Set. lib. bdg. 669.00 (ISBN 0-405-18984-2). Ayer Co Pubs.

--Studies of A. J. Wensinck: An Original Arno Press Anthology. LC 77-82275. (Mythology Ser.). 1978. lib. bdg. 17.00x (ISBN 0-405-10567-3). Ayer Co Pubs.

Brailsford, Edward J. The Spiritual Sense in Sacred Legend. 288p. 1983. Repr. of 1910 ed. lib. bdg. 47.50 (ISBN 0-89987-957-8). Darby Bks.

Brinton, Daniel G. Religions of Primitive Peoples. LC 79-88423. Repr. of 1897 ed. 22.50x (ISBN 0-8371-1763-1, BRR&). Greenwood.

Bulfinch, Thomas. Bulfinch's Mythology. abr. ed. Fuller, Edmund, ed. 448p. 1959. pap. 4.50 (ISBN 0-440-30845-3, LE). Dell.

--Bulfinch's Mythology, 3 vols. Incl. Vol. 1. The Age of Fable. 408p. pap. 3.95 (ISBN 0-451-62444-0, ME2230); Vols 2 & 3. The Age of Chivalry & Legends of Charlemagne. 608p. pap. 3.95 (ISBN 0-451-62252-9, ME2252). (YA) pap. (Ment). NAL.

--Bulfinch's Mythology. 2nd rev. ed. LC 69-11314. (Illus.). 1970. 16.45i (ISBN 0-690-57260-3). T Y Crowell.

Burkert, Walter. Lore & Science in Ancient Pythagoreanism. Minar, Edwin L., Jr., tr. from Ger. LC 70-162856. (Illus.). 512p. 1972. 35.00x (ISBN 0-674-53918-4). Harvard U Pr.

Butler, E. M. The Myth of the Magus. 283p. 1982. Repr. of 1948 ed. lib. bdg. 65.00 (ISBN 0-89984-084-1). Century Bookbindery.

Campbell, Joseph. The Flight of the Wild Gander. LC 70-183820. 256p. 1972. pap. 7.50 (ISBN 0-89526-914-7). Regnery Bks.

--Hero with a Thousand Faces. rev. ed. LC 49-8590. (Bollingen Ser.: No. 17). (Illus.). 1968. 39.50 (ISBN 0-691-09743-7); pap. 9.95 (ISBN 0-691-01784-0). Princeton U Pr.

--The Inner Reaches of Outer Space: Metaphor As Myth & As Religion. LC 84-40776. (Illus.). 160p. 1986. 16.95 (ISBN 0-912383-09-7). Van der Marck.

--The Masks of God: Creative Mythology. (Illus.). 730p. 1970. pap. 7.95 (ISBN 0-14-004307-1). Penguin.

--The Masks of God: Occidental Mythology. (Illus.). 564p. 1976. pap. 7.95 (ISBN 0-14-004306-3). Penguin.

--The Masks of God: Oriental Mythology. (Illus.). 576p. 1970. pap. 7.95 (ISBN 0-14-004305-5). Penguin.

--The Masks of God: Primitive Mythology. (Illus.). 528p. 1976. pap. 7.95 (ISBN 0-14-004304-7). Penguin.

--The Masks of God 4: Creative Mythology. 1968. 19.95 (ISBN 0-670-46111-3). Viking.

Campbell, Joseph & Abadie, M. J. The Mythic Image. LC 79-166363. (Bollingen Series C). (Illus.). 560p. 1981. pap. 19.95 (ISBN 0-691-01839-1). Princeton U Pr.

Cassirer, Ernst. Philosophy of Symbolic Forms, Vol. 2, Mythical Thought. Manheim, Ralph, tr. 1955. pap. 11.95x (ISBN 0-300-00038-3, Y147). Yale U Pr.

Center for Learning Staff. World Literature I. 1985. pap. text ed. 34.95 (ISBN 0-697-02073-8). Wm C Brown.

--World Literature II. 1985. pap. text ed. 34.95 (ISBN 0-697-02074-6). Wm C Brown.

Clark, Glenn. God's Voice in the Folklore. 4.95 (ISBN 0-910924-06-6). Macalester.

Conacher, D. J. Aeschylus' "Prometheus Bound". A Literary Commentary. 128p. 1980. 25.00x (ISBN 0-8020-2391-6); pap. 8.50 (ISBN 0-8020-6416-7). U of Toronto Pr.

Connor, W. R., ed. Ancient Religion & Mythology, 32 vols. (Illus.). 1976. Set. 1039.00x (ISBN 0-405-07001-2). Ayer Co Pubs.

Cox, G. W. An Introduction to the Science of Comparative Mythology & Folklore. 69.95 (ISBN 0-8490-0420-9). Gordon Pr.

Cox, George W. An Introduction to the Science of Comparative Mythology & Folklore. 1976. lib. bdg. 59.95 (ISBN 0-8490-2071-9). Gordon Pr.

--A Manual of Mythology. LC 77-94556. 1979. Repr. of 1867 ed. lib. bdg. 30.00 (ISBN 0-89341-307-0). Longwood Pub Group.

--Tales of the Gods & Heroes. LC 77-94564. 1979. Repr. of 1895 ed. lib. bdg. 25.00 (ISBN 0-89341-309-7). Longwood Pub Group.

Creation Myths: Man's Introduction to the World. (Art & Imagination Ser.). (Illus.). 1977. pap. 10.95 (ISBN 0-500-81010-9). Thames Hudson.

Creuzer, Georg F. Symbolik und Mythologie der Alten Volker Besonders der Griechen, 6 vols. Bolle, Kees W., ed. LC 77-79119. (Mythology Ser.). (Ger., Illus.). 1978. Repr. of 1823 ed. lib. bdg. 325.00x (ISBN 0-405-10531-2). Ayer Co Pubs.

Davis, Hubert J. Myths & Legends of the Great Dismal Swamp. (Illus.). 112p. 1981. 7.50 (ISBN 0-930230-42-6). Johnson NC.

Davison, Peter, et al, eds. Content & Taste: Religion & Myth. LC 77-90615. (Literary Taste, Culture & Mass Communication: Vol. 7). 338p. 1978. lib. bdg. 47.00x (ISBN 0-85964-042-6). Chadwyck-Healey.

De Civrieux, Marc. Watunna: An Orinoco Creation Cycle. Guss, David, ed. LC 80-82440. (Illus.). 216p. 1980. 20.00 (ISBN 0-86547-002-2); pap. 12.50 (ISBN 0-86547-003-0). N Point Pr.

Detienne, Marcel. The Creation of Mythology. Cook, Margaret, tr. LC 85-24658. 192p. 1986. 25.00x (ISBN 0-226-14350-3); pap. 10.95x (ISBN 0-226-14348-1). U of Chicago Pr.

Doty, William G. Mythography: The Study of Myths & Rituals. LC 85-991. 384p. 1986. 28.50 (ISBN 0-8173-0269-7). U of Ala Pr.

Dumezil, Georges. Destiny of a King. Hiltebeitel, Alf, tr. 1973. 15.00x (ISBN 0-226-16975-8). U of Chicago Pr.

Eliade, Mircea. Myth & Reality. pap. 5.95x (ISBN 0-06-131369-6, TB1369, Torch). Har-Row.

--Myths, Dreams & Mysteries: The Encounter Between Contemporary Faiths & Archaic Realities. pap. 5.95x (ISBN 0-06-131943-0, TB 1943, Torch). Har-Row.

The Enchanted World: Fabled Lands. 1986. 16.95 (ISBN 0-8094-5253-7); lib. bdg. 22.60 (ISBN 0-8094-5254-5). Time-Life.

The Enchanted World: Fall of Camelot. 1986. 16.95 (ISBN 0-8094-5257-X); lib. bdg. 22.60 (ISBN 0-8094-5258-8). Time-Life.

The Enchanted World: Seekers & Saviors. 1986. 16.95 (ISBN 0-8094-5249-9); lib. bdg. 22.60 (ISBN 0-8094-5250-2). Time-Life.

Faber, George S. The Origin of Pagan Idolatry, 3 vols. Feldman, Burton & Richardson, Robert D., eds. LC 78-60891. (Myth & Romanticism Ser.). 1984. Set. lib. bdg. 240.00 (ISBN 0-8240-3559-3). Garland Pub.

Fahs, Sophia L. & Cobb, Alice. Old Tales for a New Day: Early Answers to Life's Eternal Questions. LC 80-84076. (Library of Liberal Religion). (Illus.). 1980. 11.95 (ISBN 0-87975-138-X); tchr's manual 9.95 (ISBN 0-87975-131-2). Prometheus Bks.

Feldman, Burton & Richardson, Robert D. The Rise of Modern Mythology, Sixteen Hundred Eighty to Eighteen Hundred Sixty. LC 71-135005. pap. 147.80 (2056249). Bks Demand UMI.

Fiske, John. Myths & Myth-Makers: Old Tales & Superstitions Interpreted by Comparative Mythology. LC 77-85618. 1977. Repr. of 1890 ed. lib. bdg. 30.00 (ISBN 0-89341-304-6). Longwood Pub Group.

Fortune, Dion. Winged Bull. 328p. (Orig.). 1980. pap. 6.95 (ISBN 0-87728-501-2). Weiser.

Frazer, James. The New Golden Bough. rev. ed. Gaster, Theodore, ed. 832p. 1975. pap. 5.95 (ISBN 0-451-62208-1, ME2208, Ment). NAL.

Frazer, James G. Golden Bough. rev., abr ed. 1985. pap. 10.95 (ISBN 0-02-095570-7, Collier). Macmillan.

Gimbutas, Marija. Goddesses & Gods of Old Europe, 7000 to 3500 B.C. Myths, Legends, & Cult Images. 1982. pap. 14.95 (ISBN 0-520-04655-2, CAL 565). U of Cal Pr.

Goodrich, Norma L. Ancient Myths. 256p. pap. 3.95 (ISBN 0-451-62361-4, Ment). NAL.

--Medieval Myths. rev. ed. 224p. (YA) 1977. pap. 3.95 (ISBN 0-451-62359-2, Ment). NAL.

Graves, Robert. The White Goddess: A Historical Grammar of Poetic Myth. rev. & enl. ed. 511p. 1966. pap. 9.95 (ISBN 0-374-50493-8). FS&G.

--The White Goddess (amended & enlarged edition) 1983. 16.50 (ISBN 0-8446-5983-5). Peter Smith.

Greenway, John. The Primitive Reader: An Anthology of Myths, Tales, Songs, Riddles, & Proverbs of Aboriginal Peoples Around the World. LC 65-21986. viii, 211p. Repr. of 1965 ed. 35.00x (ISBN 0-8103-5014-9). Gale.

Gruffydd, W. J. Folklore & Myth in the Mabinogion. LC 75-34083. 1958. lib. bdg. 15.00 (ISBN 0-8414-4522-2). Folcroft.

Guerber, H. A. Myths of Norsemen. 69.95 (ISBN 0-87968-280-9). Gordon Pr.

Hartland, Edwin S. Mythology & Folktales: Their Relation & Interpretation. LC 75-144519. (Popular Studies in Mythology, Romance & Folklore: No. 7). Repr. of 1900 ed. 5.50 (ISBN 0-404-53507-0). AMS Pr.

Heline, Corinne. Mythology & the Bible. 75p. pap. text ed. 4.50 (ISBN 0-933963-13-0). New Age Bible.

Hendricks, Rhoda A. Mythologies of the World: A Concise Encyclopedia. Shapiro, Max S., ed. (McGraw-Hill Paperbacks Ser.). 240p. 1981. pap. 5.95 (ISBN 0-07-056421-3). McGraw.

Hewitt, J. F. History & Chronology of the Myth-Making Age. LC 76-27523. (Illus.). 1976. Repr. of 1901 ed. lib. bdg. 60.00 (ISBN 0-89341-036-5). Longwood Pub Group.

Hodson. Concealed Wisdom in World Mythology. 13.50 (ISBN 0-8356-7556-4). Theos Pub Hse.

Hopkins, E. Washburn. Epic Mythology. 1974. Repr. 14.00 (ISBN 0-8426-0560-6). Orient Bk Dist.

Hungerford, Edward B. Shores of Darkness. 10.75 (ISBN 0-8446-2285-0). Peter Smith.

Jensen, Adolf E. & Bolle, Kees W., eds. Myth, Mensch & Umwelt. LC 77-79134. (Mythology Ser.). (Ger., Illus.). 1978. Repr. of 1950 ed. lib. bdg. 36.50x (ISBN 0-405-10544-4). Ayer Co Pubs.

Kauffman, Friedrich. Northern Mythology. LC 76-5464. 1976. Repr. of 1903 ed. lib. bdg. 17.50 (ISBN 0-8414-5524-4). Folcroft.

Kellett, Ernst E. Story of Myths. (Folklore & Society Ser). 1969. Repr. of 1927 ed. 20.00 (ISBN 0-384-29025-6). Johnson Repr.

Kerenyi, Karl. Goddesses of Sun & Moon: Circe, Aphrodite, Medea, Niobe. Stein, Murray, tr. from Ger. (Dunquin Ser.: No. 11). 84p. 1979. pap. 7.50 (ISBN 0-88214-211-9). Spring Pubns.

Kirk, G. S. Myth: Its Meaning & Functions in Ancient & Other Cultures. LC 72-628267. (Sather Classical Lectures: No. 40). 1970. pap. 8.95x (ISBN 0-520-02389-7, CAMPUS 94). U of Cal Pr.

Knight, Richard P. The Interpretation of Ancient, Strange Mythological Symbols. (Illus.). 137p. 1983. 147.75 (ISBN 0-89901-125-X). Found Class Reprints.

Koltuv, Barbara B. The Book of Lilith. (Illus.). 142p. (Orig.). 1986. pap. 9.95 (ISBN 0-89254-014-1). Nicolas-Hays.

Kramer, Samuel Noah, ed. Mythologies of the Ancient World. LC 60-13538. 1961. pap. 6.95 (ISBN 0-385-09567-8, A229, Anch). Doubleday.

Krappe, Alexandre H. Mythologie universelle: Universal Mythology. Bolle, Kees W., ed. LC 77-79135. (Mythology Ser.). 1978. Repr. of 1930 ed. lib. bdg. 36.50x (ISBN 0-405-10545-2). Ayer Co Pubs.

Kroeber, Alfred L. & Gifford, E. W. Karok Myths. Buzaljko, Grace, ed. LC 78-66022. 450p. 1980. 31.00 (ISBN 0-520-03870-3). U of Cal Pr.

Lang, Andrew. Custom & Myth. 2nd rev. ed. LC 68-59267. Repr. of 1885 ed. 11.00 (ISBN 0-404-03817-4). AMS Pr.

--Custom & Myth. (Illus.). 1977. Repr. of 1885 ed. 14.95x (ISBN 0-85409-969-7). Charles River Bks.

--Magic & Religion. Repr. of 1901 ed. lib. bdg. 22.50x (ISBN 0-8371-0933-7, LAMR). Greenwood.

--Modern Mythology. LC 68-54279. Repr. of 1897 ed. 16.75 (ISBN 0-404-03852-2). AMS Pr.

--Myth, Ritual & Religion, 2 Vols in 1. LC 68-54280. Repr. of 1906 ed. 35.00 (ISBN 0-404-03868-9). AMS Pr.

Langer, Fritz. Intellektualmythologie: Betrachtungen Uber das Wesen das Mythus und Die Mythologische Methode. Bolle, Kees W., ed. LC 77-79136. (Mythology Ser.). (Ger.). 1978. Repr. of 1916 ed. lib. bdg. 21.00x (ISBN 0-405-10546-0). Ayer Co Pubs.

Leach, Edmund, ed. Structural Study of Myth & Totenism. (Orig.). 1968. pap. 12.95 (ISBN 0-422-72530-7, NO.2287, Pub by Tavistock England). Methuen Inc.

Leeming, David A. Mythology: The Voyage of the Hero. 2nd ed. (Illus.). 370p. 1980. pap. text ed. 14.50 scp (ISBN 0-06-043942-4, HarpC); instr's manual avail. (ISBN 0-06-363950-5). Har-Row.

Lethbridge, T. C. The Legend of the Sons of God: A Fantasy. (Illus.). 126p. 1983. pap. 5.95 (ISBN 0-7100-9500-7). Methuen Inc.

Levi-Strauss, Claude. From Honey to Ashes: Introduction to a Science of Mythology, Vol. 2. Weightman, John & Weightman, Doreen, trs. LC 82-15965. 512p. 1973. pap. 13.00x (ISBN 0-226-47489-5). U of Chicago Pr.

--Myth & Meaning. LC 78-25833. 1979. pap. 3.95 (ISBN 0-8052-0622-1). Schocken.

--The Raw & the Cooked. (Science of Mythology Ser.). 1979. Repr. of 1970 ed. lib. bdg. 29.00x (ISBN 0-374-94953-0, Octagon). Hippocrene Bks.

--The Raw & the Cooked: Introduction to a Science of Mythology, Vol. 1. Weightman, John & Weightman, Doreen, trs. LC 82-15895. (Illus.). xiv, 388p. 1969. pap. 11.00x (ISBN 0-226-47487-9). U of Chicago Pr.

Levy-Bruhl, J. Primitives & the Supernatural. LC 73-4358. (Studies in Comparative Literature, No. 35). 1972. Repr. of 1935 ed. lib. bdg. 58.95x (ISBN 0-8383-1589-5). Haskell.

Lipps, Gottlob F. Mythenbildung und Erkenntnis: Eine Abhandlung Uber Die Grundlagen der Philosophie. Bolle, Kees W., ed. LC 77-79141. (Mythology Ser.). 1978. lib. bdg. 27.50x (ISBN 0-405-10550-9). Ayer Co Pubs.

Long, Haniel. Notes for a New Mythology: Pittsburgh Memoranda, 2 Vols. in 1. 1971. Repr. of 1926 ed. 27.00 (ISBN 0-384-33540-3). Johnson Repr.

Lopez, Barry H. Giving Birth to Thunder, Sleeping with His Daughter: Coyote Builds North America. LC 77-17395. 1978. 8.95 (ISBN 0-8362-0726-2). Andrews McMeel Parker.

Mabie, Hamilton W., ed. Myths Every Child Should Know: A Selection of the Classic Myths of All Times for Young People. (Illus.). 351p. 1986. Repr. of 1914 ed. lib. bdg. 40.00 (ISBN 0-8482-5040-0). Norwood Edns.

MacCormac, Earl R. Metaphor & Myth in Science & Religion. LC 75-23941. pap. 46.80 (2052207). Bks Demand UMI.

MacDonald, James. Religion & Myth. LC 74-82059. Repr. of 1893 ed. 22.50x (ISBN 0-8371-1550-7, MAR&, Pub. by Negro U Pr). Greenwood.

Mackenzie, D. Myths of Pre-Columbian America. 75.00 (ISBN 0-8490-0701-1). Gordon Pr.

Mannhardt, Wilhelm. Mythologische Forschungen Aus Dem Nachlasse, 2 vols. in 1. Bolle, Kees W., ed. LC 77-79142. (Mythology Ser.). (Ger.). 1978. Repr. of 1868 ed. lib. bdg. 38.50x (ISBN 0-405-10551-7). Ayer Co Pubs.

Middleton, John, ed. Gods & Rituals: Readings in Religious Beliefs & Practices. LC 75-44032. (Texas Press Sourcebooks in Anthropology Ser.: No. 6). 480p. 1976. pap. 11.50x (ISBN 0-292-72708-9). U of Tex Pr.

--Myth & Cosmos: Readings in Mythology & Symbolism. LC 75-43817. (Texas Press Sourcebooks in Anthropology: No. 5). 382p. 1976. pap. 9.95x (ISBN 0-292-75030-7). U of Tex Pr.

Miller, David L. The New Polytheism. 2nd, rev. ed. 148p. 1981. pap. 9.50 (ISBN 0-88214-314-X). Spring Pubns.

Mitrovic, George. Atlan Revisited: The War of the Gods. LC 84-90082. 156p. 1985. 11.95 (ISBN 0-533-06152-0). Vantage.

Monarch Notes on Mythology. (Orig.). pap. 3.50 (ISBN 0-671-00523-5). Monarch Pr.

Monter, William. Ritual, Myth & Magic in Early Modern Europe. LC 83-43136. (Illus.). viii, 184p. 1984. cloth 24.95x (ISBN 0-8214-0762-7). Ohio U Pr.

Mueller, Friedrich M. Selected Essays on Language, Mythology & Religion, 2 vols. LC 73-18814. Repr. of 1881 ed. 87.50 set (ISBN 0-404-11456-3). AMS Pr.

Muller, Friedrich Max. Comparative Mythology: An Essay. rev. ed. Dorson, Richard M., ed. LC 77-70612. (International Folklore Ser.). 1977. Repr. of 1909 ed. lib. bdg. 22.00x (ISBN 0-405-10111-2). Ayer Co Pubs.

Muller, Karl O. Introduction to a Scientific System of Mythology. Bolle, Kees W., ed. LC 77-79144. (Mythology Ser.). 1978. Repr. of 1844 ed. lib. bdg. 30.00x (ISBN 0-405-10553-3). Ayer Co Pubs.

Mus, Paul. Barabudur: Esquisse d'une histoire du bouddhisme fondee sur la critique archeologique des textes, 2 vols. in 1. Bolle, Kees W., ed. LC 77-79146. (Mythology Ser.). (Fr.). 1978. Repr. of 1935 ed. lib. bdg. 82.50x (ISBN 0-405-10555-X). Ayer Co Pubs.

Nicholson, Irene. Mexican & Central American Mythology. LC 84-45598. (The Library of the World's Myths & Legends). (Illus.). 144p. 1985. 18.95 (ISBN 0-87226-003-8). P Bedrick Bks.

Noble, Vicki. Motherpeace: A Way to the Goddess Through Myth, Art & Tarot. LC 82-47752. (Illus.). 240p. (Orig.). 1982. pap. 12.95 (ISBN 0-06-066300-6, CN4039, HarpR). Har-Row.

Nuttall, Zelia. Fundamental Principles of Old & New World Civilization. (HU PMP Ser.). 1901. 51.00 (ISBN 0-527-01190-8). Kraus Repr.

Olson, Alan M., ed. Myth, Symbol & Reality. LC 80-11617. 189p. 1982. pap. text ed. 7.95 (ISBN 0-268-01349-7). U of Notre Dame Pr.

Otto, Walter F. Gestez Urbild und Mythos. Bolle, Kees W., ed. LC 77-82281. (Mytholoy Ser.). (Ger.). 1978. Repr. of 1951 ed. lib. bdg. 17.00x (ISBN 0-405-10572-X). Ayer Co Pubs.

Palsson, Hermann, tr. Hrafnkel's Saga. (Classics Ser). 1971. pap. 4.95 (ISBN 0-14-044238-3). Penguin.

Peter, Lily. In the Beginning: Myths of the Western World. LC 82-20274. (Illus.). 96p. 1983. 19.00x (ISBN 0-938626-15-9); pap. 7.95 (ISBN 0-938626-18-3). U of Ark Pr.

Pettazzoni, Raffaele & Bolle, Kees W., eds. Miti E. Leggende: Myths & Legends, 4 vols. in 1. LC 77-79151. (Mythology Ser.). (Ital.). 1978. Repr. of 1959 ed. lib. bdg. 186.00x (ISBN 0-405-10560-6). Ayer Co Pubs.

Popular Studies in Mythology, Romance & Folklore, 15 vols. Repr. of 1908 ed. write for info. (ISBN 0-404-53500-3). AMS Pr.

Porteous, A. Forest Folklore, Mythology & Romance. 1977. lib. bdg. 59.95 (ISBN 0-8490-1858-7). Gordon Pr.

Puhvel, Jaan. Comparative Mythology. LC 86-20882. (Illus.). 304p. 1987. text ed. 29.50x (ISBN 0-8018-3413-9). Johns Hopkins.

Punke, Harold H. Mythology in American Education. 480p. 1981. pap. 14.75x (ISBN 0-8134-2136-5). Inter Print Pubs.

Radin, Paul. Literary Aspects of North American Mythology. 1979. Repr. of 1915 ed. lib. bdg. 15.50 (ISBN 0-8414-7304-8). Folcroft.

Raglan, FitzRoy. The Hero: A Study in Tradition, Myth, & Drama. LC 75-23424. 296p. 1975. Repr. of 1956 ed. lib. bdg. 45.00x (ISBN 0-8371-8138-0, RATH). Greenwood.

Reid, Doris F., ed. A Treasury of Edith Hamilton. LC 70-90989. 1969. 5.00 (ISBN 0-393-04313-4). Norton.

Richardson, Alan. Gate of Moon: Mythical & Magical Doorways to the Otherworld. 160p. 1984. pap. 9.95 (ISBN 0-85030-365-6). Newcastle Pub.

Robinson, Herbert S. & Wilson, Knox. Myths & Legends of All Nations. (Quality Paperback Ser.: No. 319). 244p. 1978. pap. 5.95 (ISBN 0-8226-0319-5). Littlefield.

Ross, Harriet, compiled by. Myths & Legends of Many Lands. new ed. (Illus.). 160p. 1984. PLB 7.95. Lion Bks.

Schneiderman, Leo. The Psychology of Myth, Folklore & Religion. LC 81-9471. 232p. 1981. text ed. 21.95x (ISBN 0-88229-659-0); pap. text ed. 10.95x (ISBN 0-88229-783-X). Nelson-Hall.

Schwab, Gustav. Gods & Heroes. LC 47-873. 1977. pap. 9.95 (ISBN 0-394-73402-5). Pantheon.

Sebeok, Thomas A., ed. Myth: A Symposium. LC 65-29803. (Midland Bks.: No. 83). 192p. 1955. pap. 4.95 (ISBN 0-253-20083-0). Ind U Pr.

Segal, Robert A. Joseph Campbell on Myth: An Introduction. LC 84-45374. (Reference Library on the Humanities). 125p. 1987. lib. bdg. 18.00 (ISBN 0-8240-8827-1). Garland Pub.

Sewell, H. & Bulfinch, Thomas. Book of Myths. LC 42-25450. (Illus.). 128p. 1969. 11.95 (ISBN 0-02-782280-X). Macmillan.

Sharpe, Kevin J. From Science to An Adequate Mythology. (Science, Religion & Society Ser.). 156p. (Orig.). 1984. pap. 11.95 (ISBN 0-86474-000-X, Pub. by Interface Press). ANZ Religious Pubns.

Siecke, Ernst. Drachenkampfe: Untersuchungen Sagenkunde, Vol. 1-pt. 1. Bolle, Kees W., ed. LC 77-79155. (Mythology Ser.). (Ger.). 1978. Repr. of 1907 ed. lib. bdg. 14.00x (ISBN 0-405-10564-9). Ayer Co Pubs.

Spence, L. The Gods of Mexico. 34.95 (ISBN 0-8490-0243-5). Gordon Pr.

Spence, Lewis. The Mythologies of Ancient Mexico & Peru. 80p. 1983. Repr. of 1907 ed. lib. bdg. 30.00 (ISBN 0-89987-949-7). Darby Bks.

--The Outlines of Mythology. LC 77-3223. 1977. Repr. of 1944 ed. lib. bdg. 17.50 (ISBN 0-8414-7803-1). Folcroft.

Sproul, Barbara C. Primal Myths: Creating the World. LC 78-4429. 1979. pap. 9.95x (ISBN 0-06-067501-2, HarpR, RD 230, HarpR). Har-Row.

Steiner, Rudolf. Ancient Myths: Their Meaning & Connection with Evolution. Cotterell, M., tr. from Ger. 1978. pap. 5.95 (ISBN 0-919924-07-7). Anthroposophic.

Toy, Crawford H. Introduction to the History of Religions. LC 76-126655. Repr. of 1913 ed. 27.50 (ISBN 0-404-06498-1). AMS Pr.

Tripp, Edward. Meridian Handbook of Classical Mythology. pap. 10.95 (ISBN 0-452-00785-2, Mer). NAL.

V. Haussig, Hans. Woerterbuch der Mythologie, Vol. 2. (Ger.). 1973. 175.00 (ISBN 3-12-909820-8, M-6979). French & Eur.

Vignoli, Tito. Myth & Science. 1976. lib. bdg. 59.95 (ISBN 0-8490-2323-8). Gordon Pr.

Watts, Alan W. Myth & Ritual in Christianity. (Illus.). 1968. pap. 9.95x (ISBN 0-8070-1375-7, BP301). Beacon Pr.

Watts, Alan W., ed. Patterns of Myth Series. Incl. Lord of the Four Quarters. Perry, John W; The Two Hands of God. Watts, Alan W; The Wisdom of the Serpent. Henderson, Joseph L. & Oakes, Maud.. Braziller.

Weigel, James, Jr. Mythology. 210p. 1973. pap. 3.95 (ISBN 0-8220-0865-3). Cliffs.

Welles, Marcia L. Arachne's Tapestry: The Transformation of Myth in Seventeenth-Century Spain. (Illus.). 220p. 1986. text ed. 22.50 (ISBN 0-939980-11-8). Trinity U Pr.

Welsch, Roger L. Omaha Tribal Myths & Tricksters Tales. LC 80-22636. x, 285p. 1981. 21.95 (ISBN 0-8040-0700-4, SB). Ohio U Pr.

Westman, Heinz. The Structure of Biblical Myths: The Ontogenesis of the Psyche. LC 83-19132. (Seminar Ser.: No. 16). v, 477p. (Orig.). 1983. pap. 18.50 (ISBN 0-88214-116-3). Spring Pubns.

Ziegler, Leopold. Gestaltwander der Gotter. Bolle, Kees W., ed. LC 77-79163. (Mythology Ser.). (Ger.). 1977. Repr. of 1920 ed. lib. bdg. 35.50x (ISBN 0-405-10571-1). Ayer Co Pubs.

MYTHOLOGY–BIBLIOGRAPHY

Law, Helen H. Bibliography of Greek Myth in English Poetry. LC 77-9519. 1955. lib. bdg. 15.00 (ISBN 0-8414-5827-8). Folcroft.

Zamora, Lois P., ed. The Apocalyptic Vision in America: Interdisciplinary Essays on Myth & Culture. LC 81-85524. 272p. 1982. 19.95 (ISBN 0-686-82270-6). Bowling Green Univ.

MYTHOLOGY–DICTIONARIES

Aubert, Henri. Diccionario de Mitologia. (Span.). 238p. 1961. 14.95 (ISBN 0-686-56710-2, S-33055). French & Eur.

Bell, Robert E. Dictionary of Classical Mythology: Symbols, Attributes, & Associations. LC 81-19141. 390p. 1982. 30.00 (ISBN 0-87436-305-5). ABC Clio.

Bonnerjea, Biren. Dictionary of Superstitions & Mythology. LC 69-17755. 1969. Repr. of 1927 ed. 43.00x (ISBN 0-8103-3572-7). Gale.

Bray, F. C. The World of Myths: A Dictionary of Universal Mythology. 75.00 (ISBN 0-8490-1335-6). Gordon Pr.

Cooper, William R. Archaic Dictionary. LC 73-76018. 688p. 1969. Repr. of 1876 ed. 75.00x (ISBN 0-8103-3885-8). Gale.

Cotterell, Arthur. A Dictionary of World Mythology. (Illus.). 256p. 1982. pap. 8.95 (ISBN 0-399-50619-5, Perigee). Putnam Pub Group.

Diccionario de la Mitologia Mundial. (Span.). 383p. 1971. 12.25 (ISBN 84-7166-165-9, S-12258). French & Eur.

Falcon, C., et al. Diccionario de la Mitologia Clasica. (Span.). 633p. 1980. pap. 25.00 (ISBN 84-206-1961-2, S-32723). French & Eur.

Gavalda, A. Diccionario Mitologico. (Span.). 900p. 29.95 (ISBN 0-686-92532-7, S-37663). French & Eur.

Gaytan, C. Diccionario Mitologico. (Span.). 3.75 (ISBN 0-686-56651-3, S-25775). French & Eur.

Gottschalk, Herbert. Lexikon der Mythologie der Eurpaeischen Voelker. (Ger.). 42.00 (ISBN 3-7934-1184-2, M-7246). French & Eur.

Grimal, Pierre. The Dictionary of Classical Mythology. 580p. 1985. 34.95x (ISBN 0-631-13209-0). Basil Blackwell.

Jobes, Gertrude. Dictionary of Mythology, Folklore & Symbols, 3 Vols. LC 61-860. 1759p. 1961. Vols. 1 & 2. 70.00 (ISBN 0-8108-0034-9); Vol. 3 index, 482 pgs. 35.00 (ISBN 0-8108-1697-0). Scarecrow.

Kravitz, David. Who's Who in Greek & Roman Mythology. 256p. 1977. (C N Potter Bks); pap. 5.95 (ISBN 0-517-52747-2). Crown.

Leach, ed. Funk & Wagnalls Standard Dictionary of Folklore, Mythology & Legend. LC 72-78268. (Funk & W Bk.). 23.00i (ISBN 0-308-40090-9). T Y Crowell.

Leach, Maria & Fried, Jerome, eds. Funk & Wagnall's Standard Dictionary of Folklore, Mythology, & Legends. 1984. pap. 29.95 (ISBN 0-06-250511-4, HarpR). Har-Row.

Lelama, Homero. Diccionario de Mitologia. (Span.). 364p. 1974. 44.95 (ISBN 0-686-56670-X, S-33075). French & Eur.

Migne, J. P., ed. Dictionnaire de Mythologie. (Troisieme et Derniere Encyclopedie Theologique Ser.: Vol. 10). (Fr.). 760p. Repr. of 1855 ed. lib. bdg. 96.50x (ISBN 0-89241-294-1). Caratzas.

Stapleton, Michael. The Concise Dictionary of Greek & Roman Mythology. LC 85-15101. (Orig.). 1986. pap. 4.95 (ISBN 0-87226-006-2). P Bedrick Bks.

Sykes, Egerton. Everyman's Dictionary of Non-Classical Mythology. rev. ed. (Everyman's Reference Library). (Illus.). 298p. 1977. Repr. of 1968 ed. 13.50x (ISBN 0-460-03010-8, Pub. by J. M. Dent England). Biblio Dist.

Thomas, Joseph. Universal Pronouncing Dictionary of Biography & Mythology, 2 Vols. 5th ed. LC 76-137298. Repr. of 1930 ed. Set. 225.00 (ISBN 0-404-06386-1). AMS Pr.

Walker, Barbara G. The Woman's Encyclopedia of Myths & Secrets. LC 83-47736. 1124p. (Orig.). 1983. 34.45 (ISBN 0-06-250926-8, HarpR); pap. 20.95 (ISBN 0-06-250925-X, CN 4066). Har-Row.

MYTHOLOGY–JUVENILE LITERATURE

see also subdivision Juvenile Literature under Mythology, Classical, Mythology, Greek, and similar headings.

Birrer, Cynthia & Birrer, William. Song to Demeter. LC 86-20895. (Illus.). 32p. 1987. 11.75 (ISBN 0-688-04040-3); PLB 11.88 (ISBN 0-688-04041-1). Lothrop.

Espeland, Pamela. The Story of Baucis & Philemon. LC 80-27674. (A Myth for Modern Children Ser.). (Illus.). 32p. 1981. PLB 6.95 (ISBN 0-87614-140-8). Carolrhoda Bks.

--Theseus & the Road to Athens. LC 80-27713. (Myths for Modern Children Ser.). (Illus.). 32p. 1981. PLB 6.95 (ISBN 0-87614-141-6). Carolrhoda Bks.

Evslin, Bernard, et al. The Greek Gods. 1972. pap. 2.25 (ISBN 0-590-06350-2, Schol Pap). Scholastic Inc.

Hadley, Eric & Hadley, Tessa. Legends of Earth, Air, Fire & Water. (Illus.). 32p. 1985. 10.95 (ISBN 0-521-26311-5). Cambridge U Pr.

Hamilton, Edith. Mythology. (Illus.). 1942. 15.45 (ISBN 0-316-34114-2). Little.

Homer. Odysseus & the Giants. Richardson, I. M., adapted by. LC 83-14233. (Tales from the Odyssey Ser.). (Illus.). 32p. 1984. PLB 9.79 (ISBN 0-8167-0009-5); pap. text ed. 2.50 (ISBN 0-8167-0010-9). Troll Assocs.

Ions, Veronica. Egyptian Mythology. (Library of the World's Myths & Legends). (Illus.). 144p. PLB 16.95 (ISBN 0-317-31011-9). Creative Ed.

Mabie, Hamilton W. Myths That Every Child Should Know. Repr. of 1905 ed. 20.00 (ISBN 0-89987-175-5). Darby Bks.

Naden, C. J., adapted by. Jason & the Golden Fleece. LC 80-50068. (Illus.). 32p. 1980. PLB 9.79 (ISBN 0-89375-360-2); pap. 2.50 (ISBN 0-89375-364-5). Troll Assocs.

--Pegasus, the Winged Horse. new ed. LC 80-50069. (Illus.). 32p. 1980. PLB 9.79 (ISBN 0-89375-361-0); pap. 2.50 (ISBN 0-89375-365-3). Troll Assocs.

--Perseus & Medusa. LC 80-50083. (Illus.). 32p. 1980. PLB 9.79 (ISBN 0-89375-362-9); pap. 2.50 (ISBN 0-89375-366-1). Troll Assocs.

--Theseus & the Minotaur. LC 80-50067. (Illus.). 32p. 1980. PLB 9.79 (ISBN 0-89375-363-7); pap. 2.50 (ISBN 0-89375-367-X). Troll Assocs.

Piggott, Juliet. Japanese Mythology. (Library of the World's Myths & Legends). (Illus.). 144p. PLB 16.95 (ISBN 0-317-31009-7). Creative Ed.

Pinsent, John. Greek Mythology. (Library of the World's Myths & Legends). (Illus.). 144p. PLB 16.95 (ISBN 0-317-31010-0). Creative Ed.

Ross, Harriet, compiled by. Heroes & Heroines of Many Lands. (Illus.). 160p. 1981. PLB 7.95 (ISBN 0-87460-214-9). Lion Bks.

Sylvester, Diane & Wiemann, Mary. Mythology, Archeology, Architecture. (Gifted & Talented Ser.). 112p. 1982. 8.95 (ISBN 0-88160-081-4, LW 901). Learning Wks.

Usher, Kerry. Heroes, Gods, & Emperors from Roman Mythology. LC 83-11085. (World Mythology Ser.). (Illus.). 132p. 1984. 15.95 (ISBN 0-8052-3880-8). Schocken.

World Book Staff, ed. Great Myths & Legends. LC 65-25105. (Childcraft-The How & Why Library). 310p. 1984. PLB write for info. (ISBN 0-7166-0684-4). World Bk.

Zimmerman. Dictionary of Classical Mythology. (YA) pap. 4.95 (ISBN 0-553-25776-5). Bantam.

MYTHOLOGY, AFRICAN

Abrahamsson, Hans. The Origin of Death: Studies in African Mythology. Kastenbaum, Robert, ed. LC 76-19555. (Death and Dying Ser.). 1977. Repr. of 1951 ed. lib. bdg. 23.50x (ISBN 0-405-09551-1). Ayer Co Pubs.

Ananikian, Mardiros H. Armenian Mythology & African Mythology. (Mythology of All Races Ser.: Vol. VII). Repr. of 1932 ed. 30.00x (ISBN 0-8154-0011-X). Cooper Sq.

Beier, Ulli. The Origin of Life & Death. (African Writers Ser.). 1966. pap. text ed. 4.50x (ISBN 0-435-90023-4). Heinemann Ed.

Knappert, Jan. Myths & Legends of the Swahili. (African Writers Ser.). 1970. pap. text ed. 5.00x (ISBN 0-435-90075-7). Heinemann Ed.

Luomala, K. Oceanic, American Indian, & African Myths of Snaring the Sun. (BMB Ser.). Repr. of 1940 ed. 11.00 (ISBN 0-527-02276-4). Kraus Repr.

Parrinder, Geoffrey. African Mythology. LC 85-22967. (Library of the World's Myths & Legends). (Illus.). 144p. 1986. 18.95 (ISBN 0-87226-042-9). P Bedrick Bks.

Pelton, Robert D. The Trickster in West Africa: A Study of Mythic Irony & Sacred Delight. LC 77-75396. (Hermeneutics: Studies in the History of Religions). 1980. 42.00x (ISBN 0-520-03477-5). U of Cal Pr.

Werner, Alice. Myths & Legends of Bantu. 289p. 1968. Repr. of 1933 ed. 30.00x (ISBN 0-7146-1735-0, F Cass Co). Biblio Dist.

--Myths & Legends of the Bantu. LC 78-63237. (The Folktale). (Illus.). Repr. of 1933 ed. 34.00 (ISBN 0-404-16176-6). AMS Pr.

MYTHOLOGY, ARMENIAN

Ananikian, Mardiros H. Armenian Mythology & African Mythology. (Mythology of All Races Ser.: Vol. VII). Repr. of 1932 ed. 30.00x (ISBN 0-8154-0011-X). Cooper Sq.

Sandalgian, Joseph. Histoire documentaire de l'Armenie, 2 Vols. LC 79-175431. 1917. Repr. of 1917 ed. Set. 70.00 (ISBN 0-404-05557-5). AMS Pr.

MYTHOLOGY, ASSYRO-BABYLONIAN

Enuma Elish. Le Poeme Babylonien de la Creation. LC 78-72734. (Ancient Mesopotamian Texts & Studies). Repr. of 1935 ed. 24.50 (ISBN 0-404-18173-2). AMS Pr.

Goetze, Albrecht. Old Babylonian Omen Texts. LC 79-3537. (Yale Oriental Series: Babylonian Texts: No. 10). (Illus.). 176p. Repr. of 1966 ed. 37.50 (ISBN 0-404-60265-7). AMS Pr.

King, Leonard W. Babylonian Religion & Mythology. LC 73-18854. (Illus.). Repr. of 1899 ed. 18.45 (ISBN 0-404-11352-4). AMS Pr.

--Babylonian Religion & Mythology. LC 77-94592. 1978. Repr. of 1899 ed. lib. bdg. 25.00 (ISBN 0-89341-311-9). Longwood Pub Group.

--Legends of Babylonia & Egypt in Relation to the Hebrew Tradition. LC 77-94593. 1979. Repr. of 1918 ed. lib. bdg. 20.00 (ISBN 0-89341-310-0). Longwood Pub Group.

Kinnier-Wilson, J. V. & Vanstiphout, Herman. The Rebel Lands: An Investigation into the Origins of Early Mesopotamian Mythology. LC 77-1272. (Oriental Publications Ser.: No. 29). (Illus.). 1979. 39.00 (ISBN 0-521-21469-6). Cambridge U Pr.

Livingstone, Alasdair. Mystical & Mythological Explanatory Works of Assyrian & Babylonian Scholars. 280p. 1986. 55.00x (ISBN 0-19-815462-3). Oxford U Pr.

MacKenzie, Donald A. Myths of Babylonia & Assyria. LC 77-94601. 1978. Repr. of 1915 ed. lib. bdg. 60.00 (ISBN 0-89341-315-1). Longwood Pub Group.

Radau, Hugo. Ninib, the Determiner of Fates from the Temple Library of Nippur. (Publications of the Babylonian Section, Ser. D: Vol. 5-2). (Illus.). x, 73p. 1910. bound 5.00xsoft (ISBN 0-686-11919-3). Univ Mus of U PA.

Spence, Lewis. Myths & Legends of Babylonia & Assyria. LC 77-167199. (Illus.). 414p. 1975. Repr. of 1916 ed. 53.00x (ISBN 0-8103-4089-5). Gale.

Wilson, J. Kinnier. The Legend of Etana. (Assyriology Ser.). (Illus.). 150p. 1985. pap. 36.00 (ISBN 0-86516-116-X). Bolchazy-Carducci.

MYTHOLOGY, AUSTRALIAN

Leenhardt, Maurice. Do Kamo: La Personne et le Mythe Dans le Monde Melanesien. Bolle, Kees W., ed. LC 77-79137. (Mythology Ser.). (Fr.). 1978. Repr. of 1971 ed. lib. bdg. 24.50x (ISBN 0-405-10547-9). Ayer Co Pubs.

Reed, A. W. Myths & Legends of Australia. LC 72-779. (Illus.). 1973. 7.50 (ISBN 0-8008-5463-2). Taplinger.

Wagner, Roy. Lethal Speech: Daribi Myth As Symbolic Obviation. LC 78-58049. (Symbol, Myth, & Ritual Ser). (Illus.). 272p. 1979. 27.50x (ISBN 0-8014-1193-9). Cornell U Pr.

Wirz, Paul. Die Marind-Anim Von Hollandischsud-Neu-Guinea, 2 vols. in 1. Bolle, Kees W., ed. (Mythology Ser.). (Ger.). 1978. Repr. of 1922 ed. lib. bdg. 54.00x (ISBN 0-405-10569-X). Ayer Co Pubs.

MYTHOLOGY, AUSTRALIAN (ABORIGINAL)

Levy-Bruel, Lucien. Primitive Mythology: The Mythic World of the Australian & Papuan Natives. Elliott, Brian, tr. LC 82-17332. 332p. 1984. text ed. 32.50 (ISBN 0-7022-1667-4). U of Queensland Pr.

MYTHOLOGY, BABYLONIAN

see Mythology, Assyro-Babylonian

MYTHOLOGY, BRAHMAN

see Mythology, Hindu; Vedas

MYTHOLOGY, BRITISH

see also Mythology, Welsh

Bett, Henry. English Myths & Traditions. (Illus.). 144p. 1980. Repr. of 1952 ed. lib. bdg. 17.50 (ISBN 0-8414-2921-9). Folcroft.

Gayley, Charles M. The Classic Myths in English Literature & Art. LC 77-6986. 1977. Repr. of 1911 ed. lib. bdg. 45.00 (ISBN 0-89341-163-9). Longwood Pub Group.

Jung, Emma & Von Franz, Marie-Louise. The Grail Legend. 452p. (Orig.). 1986. 27.50 (ISBN 0-938434-07-1); pap. 14.95 (ISBN 0-938434-08-X). Sigo Pr.

Spence, Lewis. The Minor Traditions of British Mythology. LC 72-84001. Repr. of 1948 ed. 31.00 (ISBN 0-405-08989-9). Ayer Co Pubs.

Squire, Charles. The Mythology of Ancient Britain & Ireland. LC 73-13769. 1974. Repr. of 1909 ed. lib. bdg. 17.50 (ISBN 0-8414-7650-0). Folcroft.

--Mythology of the British Islands. LC 77-94622. 1979. Repr. of 1905 ed. lib. bdg. 45.00 (ISBN 0-89341-306-2). Longwood Pub Group.

Westwood, Jennifer. Albion: A Guide to Legendary Britain. (Illus.). 448p. 1986. 18.95 (ISBN 0-88162-128-5). Salem Hse Pubs.

MYTHOLOGY, BUDDHIST

Halder, J. R. Early Buddhist Mythology. 1977. 15.00x (ISBN 0-88386-998-5). South Asia Bks.

MYTHOLOGY, CANAANITE

Gibson, John C. Canaanite Myths & Legends. (Illus.). 208p. 1978. 32.95 (ISBN 0-567-02351-6, Pub. by T & T Clark Ltd UK). Fortress.

L'Heureux, Conrad E. Rank among the Canaanite Gods: El, Baal, & the Raphaim. LC 79-15582. (Harvard Semitic Monographs: No. 21). 1979. 10.50 (ISBN 0-89130-326-X, 040021). Scholars Pr GA.

MYTHOLOGY, CELTIC

Davies, Edward. Celtic Researches, on the Origin, Traditions & Language, of the Ancient Britons. Feldman, Burton & Richardson, Robert D., eds. LC 78-60902. (Myth & Romanticism Ser.: Vol. 8). (Illus.). 1979. lib. bdg. 80.00 (ISBN 0-8240-3557-7). Garland Pub.

Loomis, Roger S. Celtic Myth & Arthurian Romance. LC 67-31638. (Arthurian Legend & Literature Ser., No. 1). 1969. Repr. of 1927 ed. lib. bdg. 75.00x (ISBN 0-8383-0586-5). Haskell.

McBain, Alexander. Celtic Mythology & Religion. LC 76-1877. 1976. Repr. of 1917 ed. lib. bdg. 28.50 (ISBN 0-8414-6043-4). Folcroft.

MacCana, Proinsias. Celtic Mythology. LC 84-45597. (The Library of the World's Myths & Legends). (Illus.). 144p. 1985. 18.95 (ISBN 0-87226-002-X). P Bedrick Bks.

MacCulloch, John A. Celtic Mythology & Slavic Mythology. Bd. with Machal, Jan. LC 63-19088. (Mythology of All Races Ser.: Vol. 3). (Illus.). 477p. Repr. of 1964 ed. 30.00x (ISBN 0-8154-0142-6). Cooper Sq.

--The Religion of the Ancient Celts. LC 77-4127. 1977. lib. bdg. 52.50 (ISBN 0-8414-5998-3). Folcroft.

MacKillop, James. Fionn Mac Cumhaill: Celtic Myth in English Literature. LC 85-22116. (Irish Studies). 256p. (Orig.). 1986. pap. text ed. 35.00x (ISBN 0-8156-2344-5); pap. 15.00x (ISBN 0-8156-2353-4). Syracuse U Pr.

O'Flaherty, Liam. The Ecstacy of Angus. 64p. 1978. Repr. of 1931 ed. 10.95 (ISBN 0-905473-18-3, Pub. by Wolfhound Pr Ireland). Irish Bks Media.

Rolleston, T. W. Myths & Legends of the Celtic Race. (Illus.). 457p. 1985. 14.95 (ISBN 0-8052-3996-0). Schocken.

Squire, Charles. Celtic Myth & Legend. LC 74-26575. (Newcastle Mythology Library: Vol. 1). 450p. 1975. pap. 6.95 (ISBN 0-87877-030-5). Newcastle Pub.

--Celtic Myth & Legend, Poetry & Romance. LC 80-53343. (Newcastle Mythology Library: Vol. 1). 450p. 1980. Repr. of 1975 ed. lib. bdg. 16.95x (ISBN 0-89370-630-2). Borgo Pr.

--Celtic Myth & Legend, Poetry & Romance. LC 77-6985. 1977. Repr. of 1910 ed. lib. bdg. 45.00 (ISBN 0-89341-164-7). Longwood Pub Group.

Symbols of Heraldry Explained. (Illus.). 112p. 1980. pap. 3.95 (ISBN 0-9502455-5-0, Pub. by Heraldic Art). Irish Bks Media.

MYTHOLOGY, CHINESE

Christie, Anthony. Chinese Mythology. LC 85-5975. (The Library of the World's Myths & Legends). (Illus.). 144p. 1985. 18.95 (ISBN 0-87226-015-1). P Bedrick Bks.

Mackenzie, Donald A. The Myths of China & Japan. LC 77-6878. 1977. Repr. of 1923 ed. lib. bdg. 45.00 (ISBN 0-89341-149-3). Longwood Pub Group.

Mayers, W. E. The Chinese Reader's Manual: A Handbook of Biographical, Historical, Mythological, & General Literary Reference. 70.00 (ISBN 0-87968-855-6). Gordon Pr.

Saunders, Tao T. Dragons, Gods & Spirits from Chinese Mythology. (World Mythologies Ser.). (Illus.). 132p. 1983. 16.95 (ISBN 0-8052-3799-2). Schocken.

Schneider, Laurence A. A Madman of Ch'u: The Chinese Myth of Loyalty & Dissent. LC 78-54800. (Center for Chinese Studies). 1980. 35.95x (ISBN 0-520-03685-9). U of Cal Pr.

Siou, Lily. Chi-Kung: The Art of Mastering the Unseen Life Force. LC 75-32212. 1975. 17.50 (ISBN 0-8048-1169-5). C E Tuttle.

Werner, E. T. A Dictionary of Chinese Mythology. LC 76-27521. 1976. Repr. of 1932 ed. lib. bdg. 60.00 (ISBN 0-89341-034-9). Longwood Pub Group.

--Myths & Legends of China. LC 71-172541. (Illus.). Repr. of 1922 ed. 33.00 (ISBN 0-405-09059-5, Pub. by Blom). Ayer Co Pubs.

--Myths & Legends of China. 2nd ed. (Illus.). 453p. 1984. pap. 15.00 (ISBN 9971-947-55-2, Pub. by Graham Brash Singapore). Three Continents.

MYTHOLOGY, CLASSICAL

see also Gods; Heroes; Mythology, Greek; Mythology, Roman

also names of mythological persons and objects

Alvarez, Octavio. The Celestial Brides: A Study in Mythology & Archaeology. LC 77-91208. (Illus.). 1978. 30.00 (ISBN 0-9601520-0-8). H Reichner.

Aycock, Wendell M. & Klein, Theodore M., eds. Classical Mythology in Twentieth-Century Thought & Literature. (Proceedings of the Comparative Literature Symposium, Vol. XI). (Illus.). 221p. (Orig.). 1980. pap. 12.00 (ISBN 0-89672-079-9). Tex Tech Univ Pr.

Bacon, Francis. De Sapientia Veterum, Repr. Of 1609 Ed. Bd. with The Wisedome of the Ancients. Gorges, Arthur, tr. Repr. of 1619 ed. LC 75-27863. (Renaissance & the Gods Ser.: Vol. 20). (Illus.). 1976. lib. bdg. 88.00 (ISBN 0-8240-2068-5). Garland Pub.

Baldini, Baccio. Discorso Sopra la Mascherata Della Genealogia Delg'Iddei, Repr. Of 1565 Ed. Bd. with Discorso Sopra Li Dei De'Gentili. Zucchi, Jacopo. Repr. of 1602 ed. LC 75-27852. (Renaissance & the Gods Ser.: Vol. 10). (Illus.). 1976. lib. bdg. 88.00 (ISBN 0-8240-2059-6). Garland Pub.

Barnard, Mary E. The Myth of Apollo & Daphne from Ovid to Quevedo. (Duke Monographs in Medieval & Renaissance Studies: No. 8). (Illus.). 190p. 1986. lib. bdg. 25.00 (ISBN 0-8223-0701-4). Duke.

Barthell, Edward E., Jr. Gods & Goddesses of Ancient Greece. LC 72-129664. 1981. 49.50 (ISBN 0-87024-165-6). U of Miami Pr.

Batman, Stephen. The Golden Booke of the Leaden Gods, Repr. Of 1577 Ed. Bd. with The Third Part of the Countess of Pembroke's Yvychurch. Fraunce, Abraham. Repr. of 1592 ed; The Fountaine of Ancient Fiction. Lynche, Richard. Repr. of 1599 ed. LC 75-27856. (Renaissance & the Gods Ser.: Vol. 13). (Illus.). 1976. lib. bdg. 88.00 (ISBN 0-8240-2062-6). Garland Pub.

Berens, E. M. The Myths & Legends of Ancient Greece & Rome. LC 77-91528. 1977. Repr. of 1880 ed. lib. bdg. 30.00 (ISBN 0-89341-029-2). Longwood Pub Group.

Blackwell, Thomas. Letters Concerning Mythology. LC 75-27887. (Renaissance & the Gods Ser.: Vol. 42). (Illus.). 1976. Repr. of 1748 ed. lib. bdg. 88.00 (ISBN 0-8240-2091-X). Garland Pub.

Boswell, Fred & Boswell, Jeanetta. What Men or Gods Are These? A Genealogical Approach to Classical Mythology. LC 80-13780. 324p. 1980. 27.50 (ISBN 0-8108-1314-9). Scarecrow.

Butterly, Daniel R. The Reckless Heart: Meleager & Atalanta. 64p. (Orig.). 1986. 25.00 (ISBN 0-86516-172-0); pap. 15.00 (ISBN 0-86516-173-9). Bolchazy-Carducci.

Cartari, Vincenzo. Le Imagini...Degli Dei. LC 75-27855. (Renaissance & the Gods Ser.: Vol. 12). (Illus.). 602p. 1976. Repr. of 1571 ed. lib. bdg. 88.00 (ISBN 0-8240-2061-8). Garland Pub.

Center for Learning Staff. Classical Literature. 1982. pap. text ed. 34.95 (ISBN 0-697-01884-9). Wm C Brown.

Comes, Natalis. Mythologiae. LC 75-27853. (Renaissance & the Gods Ser.: Vol. 11). (Illus.). 1976. Repr. of 1567 ed. lib. bdg. 88.00 (ISBN 0-8240-2060-X). Garland Pub.

Dall, Caroline H. Margaret & Her Friends; or, Ten Conversations with Margaret Fuller Upon the Mythology of the Greeks & Its Expression in Art. LC 72-4961. (The Romantic Tradition in American Literature Ser.). 166p. 1972. Repr. of 1895 ed. 18.00 (ISBN 0-405-04633-2). Ayer Co Pubs.

Du Choul, Guillaume. Discours de la Religion des Anciens Romains Illustre. LC 75-27851. (Renaissance & the Gods Ser.: Vol. 9). (Illus.). 1976. Repr. of 1556 ed. lib. bdg. 88.00 (ISBN 0-8240-2058-8). Garland Pub.

Eisner, Robert. The Road to Daulis: Psychoanalysis, Psychology & Classical Mythology. 284p. 1987. 32.50 (ISBN 0-8156-0210-3). Syracuse U Pr.

Feder, Lillian. Ancient Myth in Modern Poetry. LC 70-154994. 1972. 38.50x (ISBN 0-691-06207-2); pap. 11.50x (ISBN 0-691-01336-5). Princeton U Pr.

Godolphin, F. R., ed. & intro. by. Great Classical Myths. LC 64-10293. 7.95 (ISBN 0-394-60417-2). Modern Lib.

Grant, Michael. Myths of the Greeks & Romans. (Illus.). 1964. pap. 4.95 (ISBN 0-451-62267-7, ME2267, Ment). NAL.

Grant, Michael & Hazel, John. Gods & Mortals in Classic Mythology: Dictionary. 320p. 1985. 19.95 (ISBN 0-88029-036-6, Pub. by Dorset Pr). Hippocrene Bks.

Griffiths, J. G. The Conflict of Horus & Seth - A study in Ancient Mythology from Egyptian & Classical Sources. 194p. 1960. text ed. 19.95x (ISBN 0-85323-071-4, Pub. by Liverpool U Pr). Humanities.

Grimal, Pierre. The Dictionary of Classical Mythology. 580p. 1985. 34.95x (ISBN 0-631-13209-0). Basil Blackwell.

Guerber, H. A. Myths of Greece & Rome: Narrated with Special Reference to Literature & Art. 428p. 1985. Repr. of 1893 ed. 40.00 (ISBN 0-8495-2102-5). Arden Lib.

Harrison, Jane E. Myths of Greece & Rome. LC 76-46570. 1976. Repr. of 1927 ed. lib. bdg. 20.00 (ISBN 0-8414-4907-4). Folcroft.

Hendricks, Rhoda A., tr. & intro. by. Classical Gods & Heroes: Myths As Told by the Ancient Authors. 1974. pap. 7.95 (ISBN 0-688-05279-7). Morrow.

Henley, W. E., ed. The Golden Ass of Apuleius. Aldington, William, tr. from Lat. 249p. 1981. Repr. of 1893 ed. lib. bdg. 50.00 (ISBN 0-89984-233-X). Century Bookbindery.

Hope-Moncrieff, Ascott R. Classic Myth & Legend. LC 77-85616. 1977. Repr. of 1912 ed. lib. bdg. 45.00 (ISBN 0-89341-317-8). Longwood Pub Group.

Hough, Edith L. Sicily: The Fabulous Island. (Illus.). 1949. 4.00 (ISBN 0-8338-0027-2). M Jones.

Jacqueny, Mona G. The Golden Age Society & Other Studies. LC 77-87939. 183p. 1978. 12.00 (ISBN 0-8022-2219-6). Philos Lib.

Keightley, Thomas. Classical Mythology: The Myths of Ancient Greece & Italy. xviii, 507p. 1976. 25.00 (ISBN 0-89005-189-5). Ares.

Keuls, E. The Water Carriers in Hades: A Study of Catharsis Through Toil in Classical Antiquity. (Illus.). 179p. 1974. pap. text ed. 48.50 (Pub. by A. M. Hakkert). Coronet Bks.

King, William. Historical Account of Heathen Gods & Heroes Necessary for the Understanding of Ancient Poets. LC 64-18550. (Centaur Classics Ser.). (Illus.). 290p. 1965. 15.00x (ISBN 0-8093-0150-4). S Ill U Pr.

Kirkwood, G. M. Short Guide to Classical Mythology. 1960. pap. text ed. 10.95 (ISBN 0-03-008865-8, HoltC). H Holt & Co.

Marolles, Michel de. Tableaux Du Temple Des Muses, Repr. Of 1655 Ed. Bd. with Iconologia or Moral Problems. Ripa, Cesare. Repr. of 1709 ed. LC 75-27876. (Renaissance & the Gods Ser.: Vol. 31). (Illus.). 1976. lib. bdg. 80.00 (ISBN 0-8240-2080-4). Garland Pub.

Mayerson, Phil. Classic Mythology in Literature, Art, & Music. 1971. text ed. write for info. (ISBN 0-673-15690-7). Scott F.

Morford, Mark P. & Lenardon, Robert J. Classical Mythology. 3rd. ed. (Illus.). 644p. 1985. pap. text ed. 19.95x (ISBN 0-582-28541-0). Longman.

Nilsson, Martin P. The Mycenaean Origins of Greek Mythology. 16.50 (ISBN 0-8446-6208-9). Peter Smith.

Osgood, Charles G. Classical Mythology of Milton's English Poems. LC 64-8180. 198p. 1964. Repr. of 1900 ed. 17.50x (ISBN 0-87752-080-1). Gordian.

--Classical Mythology of Milton's English Poems. LC 65-15902. (Studies in Comparative Literature, No. 35). 1969. Repr. of 1900 ed. lib. bdg. 75.00x (ISBN 0-8383-0603-9). Haskell.

Ovid. Metamorphoseon. Pontanus, Jacobus, ed. LC 75-27868. (Renaissance & the Gods Ser.: Vol. 24). (Illus.). 1977. Repr. of 1618 ed. lib. bdg. 88.00 (ISBN 0-8240-2073-1). Garland Pub.

--Metamorphoses. Garth, et al, trs. LC 75-27884. (Renaissance & the Gods Ser.: Vol. 39). (Illus.). 1976. Repr. of 1732 ed. lib. bdg. 88.00 (ISBN 0-8240-2088-X). Garland Pub.

Pater, Walter. Cupid & Psyche. (Illus.). 48p. 1977. 9.95 (ISBN 0-571-11115-7). Faber & Faber.

Pomey, Antoine. The Pantheon. LC 75-27879. (Renaissance & the Gods Ser.: Vol. 34). (Illus.). 1976. Repr. of 1694 ed. lib. bdg. 88.00 (ISBN 0-8240-2083-9). Garland Pub.

Randall, Alice E. Sources of Spenser's Classical Mythology. 1896. Repr. 10.00 (ISBN 0-8274-3476-6). R West.

Seaton, J. A Reading of Vergil's "Georgics". 222p. 1983. lib. bdg. 33.00x (Pub. by A M Hakkert). Coronet Bks.

Seznec, Jean. The Survival of the Pagan Gods: The Mythological Tradition & Its Place in Renaissance Humanism & Art. Sessions, Barbara, tr. (Bollingen Ser.: Vol. 38). (Illus.). 108p. 1972. pap. 9.50x (ISBN 0-691-01783-2). Princeton U Pr.

Sienkewicz, Thomas J. Classical Gods & Heroes in the National Gallery of Art. LC 82-23818. (Illus.). 50p. (Orig.). 1983. pap. text ed. 9.75 (ISBN 0-8191-2967-4). U Pr of Amer.

Spence, Joseph. Polymetis. LC 75-27886. (Renaissance & the Gods Ser.: Vol. 41). (Illus.). 1976. Repr. of 1747 ed. lib. bdg. 88.00 (ISBN 0-8240-2090-1). Garland Pub.

Stapleton, Michael. The Illustrated Dictionary of Greek & Roman Mythology. LC 85-30692. (The Library of the World's Myths & Legends). (Illus.). 224p. 1986. 17.95 (ISBN 0-87226-063-1). P Bedrick Bks.

Starnes, DeWitt T. & Talbert, Ernest W. Classical Myth & Legend in Renaissance Dictionaries. LC 73-11753. (Illus.). 517p. 1973. Repr. of 1955 ed. lib. bdg. 42.50x (ISBN 0-8371-7086-9, STCM). Greenwood.

Tabeling, Ernst. Mater Larum: Zum Wesen der Larenreligion. facsimile ed. LC 75-10657. (Ancient Religion & Mythology Ser.). (Ger.). 1976. Repr. of 1932 ed. 12.00x (ISBN 0-405-07265-1). Ayer Co Pubs.

Tooke, Andrew. The Pantheon. LC 75-27880. (Renaissance & the Gods Ser.: Vol. 35). (Illus.). 1976. Repr. of 1713 ed. lib. bdg. 88.00 (ISBN 0-8240-2084-7). Garland Pub.

Vossius, Gerardus. Theologia Gentili, 3 vols. LC 75-27872. (Renaissance & the Gods Ser.: Vol. 28). (Illus.). 1976. Repr. of 1641 ed. Set. lib. bdg. 265.00 (ISBN 0-8240-2077-4). Garland Pub.

Wheeler, Charles F. Classical Mythology in the Plays, Masques, & Poems of Ben Jonson. LC 71-114234. 1970. Repr. of 1938 ed. 23.50 (ISBN 0-8046-1038-X, Pub. by Kennikat). Assoc Faculty Pr.

Whetstone, George. Promus & Cassandra, Pts. 1 & 2. (Tudor Facsimile Texts. Old English Plays: No. 52). Repr. of 1910 ed. 49.50 (ISBN 0-404-53352-3). AMS Pr.

Wolverton, Robert E. Outline of Classical Mythology. (Quality Paperback: No. 97). (Orig.). 1975. pap. 2.95 (ISBN 0-8226-0097-8). Littlefield.

Zimmerman. Dictionary of Classical Mythology. (YA) pap. 4.95 (ISBN 0-553-25776-5). Bantam.

MYTHOLOGY, CLASSICAL–DICTIONARIES

see Mythology–Dictionaries

MYTHOLOGY, CLASSICAL–JUVENILE LITERATURE

Benson, Sally. Stories of the Gods & Heroes. (Illus.). 1940. 12.95 (ISBN 0-8037-8291-8, 01258-370). Dial Bks Young.

Hawthorne, Nathaniel. Tanglewood Tales. (Classics Ser). (Illus.). 1968. pap. 1.25 (ISBN 0-8049-0175-9, CL-175). Airmont.

--Wonder Book. (Classics Ser.). pap. 1.25 (ISBN 0-8049-0118-X, CL-118). Airmont.

Kottmeyer, William A., et al. Greek & Roman Myths. 1962. pap. 7.96 (ISBN 0-07-033738-1). McGraw.

Weil, Lisl. Pandora's Box. LC 85-20128. (Illus.). 40p. 1986. 12.95 (ISBN 0-689-31216-4, Childrens Bk). Macmillan.

MYTHOLOGY, DANISH

see Mythology, Norse

MYTHOLOGY, EGYPTIAN

Armour, Robert. God & Myths of Ancient Egypt. 1986. pap. 15.00 (ISBN 977-424-113-4, Pub. by Am Univ Cairo Pr). Columbia U Pr.

Baines, J. Fecundity Figures: Egyptian Personification & the Iconology of a Genre. (Illus.). 200p. 1983. 60.00 (ISBN 0-85668-087-7, Pub. by Aris & Phillips UK). Humanities.

Budge, E. A. Gods of the Egyptians or Studies in Egyptian Mythology, 2 Vols. (Illus.). Set. 36.00 (ISBN 0-8446-0520-4). Peter Smith.

--The Gods of the Egyptians: Studies in Egyptian Mythology, 2 Vols. LC 67-28633. (Illus.). 1969. pap. 10.00 ea.; Vol. 1. pap. (ISBN 0-486-22055-9); Vol. 2. pap. (ISBN 0-486-22056-7). Dover.

Budge, E. Wallis. From Fetish to God in Ancient Egypt. LC 72-82206. (Illus.). Repr. of 1934 ed. 33.00 (ISBN 0-405-08317-3, Blom Pubns). Ayer Co Pubs.

Griffiths, J. G. The Conflict of Horus & Seth - A study in Ancient Mythology from Egyptian & Classical Sources. 194p. 1960. text ed. 19.95x (ISBN 0-85323-071-4, Pub. by Liverpool U Pr). Humanities.

Harris, Gerladine. Gods & Pharaohs from Egyptian Mythology. (World Mythologies Ser.). (Illus.). 132p. 1983. 15.95 (ISBN 0-8052-3802-6). Schocken.

Hooke, Samuel H. Middle Eastern Mythology. (Orig.). 1963. pap. 5.95 (ISBN 0-14-020546-2, Pelican). Penguin.

Ions, Veronica. Egyptian Mythology. rev. ed. LC 83-71478. (The Library of the World's Myths & Legends). (Illus.). 144p. 1983. 18.95 (ISBN 0-911745-07-6). P Bedrick Bks.

--Egyptian Mythology. (Library of the World's Myths & Legends). (Illus.). 144p. PLB 16.95 (ISBN 0-317-31011-9). Creative Ed.

Lanzone, R. V. Dizionario Di Mitologia Egizia, 3 vols. (Ital.). 1312p. 1974. 400.00x (ISBN 90-272-0931-6, 0932-4, 0933-2). Benjamins North Am.

--Dizzionario Di Mitologia Egizia, Vol. 4. xv, 205p. 1975. Repr. of 1881 ed. 80.00x (ISBN 90-272-0934-0). Benjamins North Am.

Lurker, Manfred. Gods & Symbols of Ancient Egypt: An Illustrated Dictionary. Clayton, Peter A., rev. by. (Illus.). 142p. 1984. pap. 9.95f (ISBN 0-500-27253-0). Thames Hudson.

Mackenzie, Donald A. Egyptian Myth & Legend. LC 76-27520. (Illus.). 1976. Repr. of 1907 ed. lib. bdg. 40.00 (ISBN 0-89341-033-0). Longwood Pub Group.

--Egyptian Myth & Legend. 454p. 1984. pap. cancelled (ISBN 0-89341-487-5). Longwood Pub Group.

Muller, W. Max. Egyptian Mythology & Indochinese Mythology. Bd. with Scott, James G. LC 63-19097. (Mythology of All Races Ser.: Vol. 12). (Illus.). Repr. of 1932 ed. 30.00x (ISBN 0-8154-0160-4). Cooper Sq.

Regency Press Ltd. Staff, ed. Secret of the Golden Hours. 112p. 1984. 40.00 (ISBN 0-7212-0656-5, Pub. by Regency Pr). State Mutual Bk.

Shorter, A. W. The Egyptian Gods: A Handbook. 1978. pap. 7.50 (ISBN 0-7100-0982-8). Methuen Inc.

Shorter, Alan W. The Egyptian Gods. (Mythology Library: Vol. 5). 300p. 1985. pap. 7.95 (ISBN 0-87877-082-8). Newcastle Pub.

--The Egyptian Gods: A Handbook. LC 85-26911. (Newcastle Mythology Library: Vol. 5). 300p. 1985. Repr. lib. bdg. 17.95x (ISBN 0-89370-682-5). Borgo Pr.

Steiner, Rudolf. Egyptian Myths & Mysteries. Macbeth, Norman, tr. from Ger. 1971. 15.00 (ISBN 0-910142-09-2); pap. 7.95 (ISBN 0-910142-10-6). Anthroposophic.

MYTHOLOGY, ESKIMO

Paul, Frances L. Kahtahah. LC 76-17804. (Illus., Orig.). 1976. pap. 7.95 (ISBN 0-88240-058-4). Alaska Northwest.

MYTHOLOGY, ESTONIAN

see Mythology, Finno-Ugrian

MYTHOLOGY, FINNO-UGRIAN

Holmberg, Uno. Finno-Ugric, Siberian Mythology. (Mythology of All Races Ser: Vol. Iv). (Illus.). Repr. of 1932 ed. 30.00x (ISBN 0-8154-0116-7). Cooper Sq.

MYTHOLOGY, GERMANIC

see also Mythology, Norse

Blumenberg, Hans. Work on Myth. Wallace, Robert M., tr. from Ger. (German Social Thought Ser.). 770p. 1985. text ed. 40.00x (ISBN 0-262-02215-X). MIT Pr.

Davidson, H. Ellis. Gods & Myths of Northern Europe. (Orig.). 1965. pap. 5.95 (ISBN 0-14-020670-1, Pelican). Penguin.

De La Saussaye, P. Chantepie. The Religion of the Teutons. LC 76-27519. 1976. Repr. of 1902 ed. lib. bdg. 50.00 (ISBN 0-89341-030-6). Longwood Pub Group.

Kauffmann, Friedrich. Northern Mythology. 1978. Repr. of 1903 ed. lib. bdg. 15.00 (ISBN 0-8495-3022-9). Arden Lib.

Lettsom, William N. The Nibelungenlied. LC 77-13811. 1977. lib. bdg. 45.00 (ISBN 0-8414-5830-8). Folcroft.

MacKenzie, Donald A. Teutonic Myth & Legend. LC 77-91530. 1978. Repr. of 1912 ed. lib. bdg. 50.00 (ISBN 0-89341-313-5). Longwood Pub Group.

Meyer, Richard M. Altgermanische Religionsgeschichte: History of Ancient Germanic Religion. Bolle, Kees W., ed. LC 77-79143. (Mythology Ser.). (Ger.). 1978. Repr. of 1910 ed. lib. bdg. 49.50x (ISBN 0-405-10552-5). Ayer Co Pubs.

Phillippson, Ernst A. Germanisches Heidentum Bei Den Angelsachsen. Repr. of 1929 ed. 20.00 (ISBN 0-384-46310-X). Johnson Repr.

Poser, Hans. Philosophie und Mythos. 1979. text ed. 35.20x (ISBN 3-11-007601-2). De Gruyter.

Sawyer, W. C. Teutonic Legends in the Nibelungen Lied & the Nibelungen Ring. 1976. lib. bdg. 59.95 (ISBN 0-8490-2736-5). Gordon Pr.

Stern, Herman I. The Gods of Our Fathers: A Study of Saxon Mythology. LC 77-85623. 1977. Repr. of 1898 ed. lib. bdg. 30.00 (ISBN 0-89341-303-8). Longwood Pub Group.

Wakefield, Ray M. Nibelungen Prosody. (De Proprietatibus Litterarum Ser.: No. 112). 1976. pap. 16.00x (ISBN 0-686-22366-7). Mouton.

Weston, Jessie L. The Legends of the Wagner Drama. LC 74-24255. Repr. of 1896 ed. 24.00 (ISBN 0-404-13132-8). AMS Pr.

MYTHOLOGY, GREEK

see also Cultus, Greek

Aldrich, Keith, tr. Apollodorus: The Library of Greek Mythology. 298p. 1975. 15.00x (ISBN 0-87291-072-5). Coronado Pr.

Allen, Blair H. Atlantis Trilogy. 1982. pap. 1.25 (ISBN 0-917458-09-5). Kent Pubns.

Apollodorus. Library, 2 Vols. (Loeb Classical Library: No. 121, 122). 13.95x ea. Vol. 1, Bks. 1-3 (ISBN 0-674-99135-4). Vol. 2 (ISBN 0-674-99136-2). Harvard U Pr.

Bacon, Francis. Wisedome of the Ancients. Gorges, A., tr. LC 68-54614. (English Experince Ser.: No. 1). 176p. 1968. Repr. of 1619 ed. 13.00 (ISBN 90-221-0001-4). Walter J Johnson.

Berens, E. M. The Myths & Legends of Ancient Greece & Rome. LC 77-91528. 1977. Repr. of 1880 ed. lib. bdg. 30.00 (ISBN 0-89341-029-2). Longwood Pub Group.

Boedeker, Deborah. Descent from Heaven: Images of Dew in Greek Poetry & Religion. (American Philological Association, American Classical Studies: No. 13). 154p. 1985. pap. 11.95 (ISBN 0-89130-807-5, 40 04 13). Scholars Pr GA.

Boer, Charles, tr. from Gr. The Homeric Hymns. rev. ed. (Dunquin Ser.: No. 10). vi, 182p. 1970. pap. 11.50 (ISBN 0-88214-210-0). Spring Pubns.

Bookidis, Nancy & Stroud, Ronald. Demeter & Persephone in Ancient Corinth. (Corinth Notes Ser.: No. 2). (Illus.). 32p. (Orig.). 1987. pap. 3.00. Am Sch Athens.

Bremmer, Jan & Graf, Fritz, eds. Interpretations of Greek Mythology. LC 86-20638. (Illus.). 304p. 1987. 28.50x (ISBN 0-389-20679-2). B&N Imports.

Brown, R. Semitic Influence in Hellenic Mythology. xvi, 228p. Repr. of 1898 ed. lib. bdg. 35.00x (ISBN 0-89241-206-2). Caratzas.

Brown, Robert. Semetic Influence in Hellenic Mythology. LC 65-27053. (Library of Religious & Philosophical Thought). 1966. Repr. of 1898 ed. lib. bdg. 25.00x (ISBN 0-678-09952-9, Reference Bk Pubs). Kelley.

--Semitic Influence in Hellenic Mythology. 19.00 (ISBN 0-405-10084-1, 14709). Ayer Co Pubs.

Brown, Robert F. Schelling's Treatise on "the Deities of Samothrace". A Translation & an Interpretation. LC 76-42239. (American Academy of Religion. Studies in Religion). 1977. pap. 9.95 (ISBN 0-89130-087-2, 010012). Scholars Pr GA.

Burgess, Eric. By Jupiter: Odysseys to a Giant. LC 82-4139. (Illus.). 192p. 1982. 26.50x (ISBN 0-231-05176-X). Columbia U Pr.

Burkert, Walter. Structure & History in Greek Mythology & Ritual. LC 78-62856. (Sather Classical Lectures Ser.: Vol. 47). 1980. 30.00x (ISBN 0-520-03771-5); pap. 9.95 (ISBN 0-520-04770-2, CAL 581). U of Cal Pr.

Butterworth, E. A. Some Traces of the Pre-Olympian World in Greek Literature & Myth. LC 85-21959. (Illus.). 1966. 44.25x (ISBN 3-11-005010-2). De Gruyter.

Canstantopoulos, E. Stories from Greek Mythology. (Illus.). 3.20 (ISBN 0-686-79632-2). Divry.

Carpenter, Thomas H. & Gula, Robert J. Mythology: Greek & Roman. (Illus.). 1977. pap. text ed. 6.95x (ISBN 0-88334-089-5). Ind Sch Pr.

Dall, Caroline H. Margaret & Her Friends; or, Ten Conversations with Margaret Fuller Upon the Mythology of the Greeks & Its Expression in Art. LC 72-4961. (The Romantic Tradition in American Literature Ser.). 166p. 1972. Repr. of 1895 ed. 18.00 (ISBN 0-405-04633-2). Ayer Co Pubs.

Downing, Christine. The Goddess: Mythological Images of the Feminine. 256p. 1984. pap. 9.95 (ISBN 0-8245-0624-3). Crossroad NY.

Duthie, Alexander. The Greek Mythology: A Reader's Handbook. 2nd ed. LC 78-12988. 1979. Repr. of 1949 ed. lib. bdg. 22.50x (ISBN 0-313-21077-2, DUGM). Greenwood.

Edwards, R. B. Kadmos the Phoenician: A Study in Greek Legends & the Mycenaen Age. xiv, 258p. 1979. pap. text ed. 67.50x (Pub. by A. M. Hakkert). Coronet Bks.

Espeland, Pamela. The Story of Cadmus. LC 80-66795. (Myths for Modern Children Ser.). (Illus.). 32p. 1980. PLB 6.95 (ISBN 0-87614-128-9). Carolrhoda Bks.

--The Story of King Midas. LC 80-66794. (Myths for Modern Children Ser.). (Illus.). 32p. 1980. PLB 6.95 (ISBN 0-87614-129-7). Carolrhoda Bks.

Flint, William W. Use of Myth to Create Suspense. (Studies in Comparative Literature, No. 35). 1970. pap. 24.95x (ISBN 0-8383-0030-8). Haskell.

Fontenrose, Joseph. Python: A Study of Delphic Myth & Its Origins. (California Library Reprint Ser.: No. 108). 637p. 1981. 40.00x (ISBN 0-520-04106-2); pap. 8.95 (ISBN 0-520-04091-0, CAL 449). U of Cal Pr.

Fortune, Dion. Goat-Foot God. (Orig.). 1980. pap. 7.95 (ISBN 0-87728-500-4). Weiser.

Geoghegan, Vincent. Reason & Eros: The Social Theory of Herbert Marcuse. 122p. 1981. pap. 6.75 (ISBN 0-86104-335-9, Pub. by Pluto Pr). Longwood Pub Group.

Gibson, Michael. Gods, Men & Monsters from the Greek Myths. LC 81-14542. (World Mythologies Ser.). (Illus.). 156p. 1982. 15.95 (ISBN 0-8052-3793-3). Schocken.

Godwin, William. The Pantheon: or, Ancient History of the Gods of Greece & Rome. Feldman, Burton & Richardson, Robert D., eds. LC 78-60886. (Myth & Romanticism Ser.). 1984. lib. bdg. 80.00 (ISBN 0-8240-3560-7). Garland Pub.

Gordon, R. L., ed. Myth, Religion & Society: Structuralist Essays by M. Detienne, L. Gernet, J. P. Vernant & P. Vidal-Naquet. (Illus.). 250p. 1982. text ed. 44.50 (ISBN 0-521-22780-1); pap. text ed. 15.95 (ISBN 0-521-29640-4). Cambridge U Pr.

Graves, Robert. Greek Myths. (Illus.). 244p. 1982. 25.00 (ISBN 0-385-17790-9). Doubleday.

--Greek Myths, 2 Vols. (Orig.). (YA) 1955. Vol. 1. pap. 4.95 (ISBN 0-14-020508-X, Pelican); Vol. 2. pap. 4.95 (ISBN 0-14-020509-8). Penguin.

Green, R. L. The Tale of Thebes. LC 76-22979. (Illus.). 1977. o. p. 14.95 (ISBN 0-521-21410-6); pap. 6.95 (ISBN 0-521-21411-4). Cambridge U Pr.

Grimal, Pierre. Dictionnaire de la Mythologie Grecque et Romaine. 5th ed. (Fr.). 612p. 1969. 59.95 (ISBN 0-686-57316-1, M-6299). French & Eur.

Gueber, H. A. The Myths of Greece & Rome. 1986. 27.50x (ISBN 0-245-56918-9, Pub. by Harrap Ltd England). State Mutual Bk.

Guerber, H. A. Myths of Greece & Rome: Narrated with Special Reference to Literature & Art. 428p. 1985. Repr. of 1893 ed. 40.00 (ISBN 0-8495-2102-5). Arden Lib.

Hamilton, Edith. Mythology. 336p. (YA) 1971. pap. 3.50 (ISBN 0-451-62523-4, Ment). NAL.

Harrison, Jane E. Prolegomena to the Study of Greek Religion. facsimile ed. LC 75-10639. (Ancient Religion & Mythology Ser.). (Illus.). 1976. Repr. of 1922 ed. 57.50x (ISBN 0-405-07018-7). Ayer Co Pubs.

Hathorn, Richmond. Greek Mythology. 1977. 22.00x (ISBN 0-8156-6048-0, Am U Beirut). Syracuse U Pr.

Hesiod. Hesoid: Theogony, Works & Days. Athanassakis, Apostolos N., tr. LC 83-6143. 184p. 1983. 20.00x (ISBN 0-8018-2998-4); pap. 6.95x (ISBN 0-8018-2999-2). Johns Hopkins.

Holme. Myths of Greece & Rome. 288p. 1981. pap. 18.95 (ISBN 0-14-005643-2). Penguin.

Hunger, H. Lexikon der Griechischen und Roemischen Mythologie. (Ger.). 452p. 1974. pap. 7.95 (ISBN 3-499-16178-8, M-7252). French & Eur.

Jones, Allen H. Essenes: The Elect of Israel & the Priests of Artemis. (Illus.). 146p. (Orig.). 1985. lib. bdg. 23.50 (ISBN 0-8191-4744-3); pap. text ed. 9.50 (ISBN 0-8191-4745-1). U Pr of Amer.

Keightley, Thomas. Classical Mythology: The Myths of Ancient Greece & Italy. xviii, 507p. 1976. 25.00 (ISBN 0-89005-189-5). Ares.

Kerenyi, C. The Gods of the Greeks. (Illus.). 1980. pap. 9.95 (ISBN 0-500-27048-1). Thames Hudson.

Kerenyi, Karl. Athene. Stein, Murray, tr. from Ger. (Dunquin Ser.: No. 9). 106p. (Orig.). 1978. pap. 7.50 (ISBN 0-88214-209-7). Spring Pubns.

Keuls, E. The Water Carriers in Hades: A Study of Catharsis Through Toil in Classical Antiquity. (Illus.). 179p. 1974. pap. text ed. 48.50 (Pub. by A. M. Hakkert). Coronet Bks.

Kingsley, Charles. The Heroes; or, Greek Fairy Tales. Repr. of 1882 ed. 20.00 (ISBN 0-686-20097-7). Quality Lib.

Kirk, G. S. The Nature of Greek Myths. LC 74-21683. 336p. 1975. 27.95 (ISBN 0-87951-031-5). Overlook Pr.

--Nature of Greek Myths. 1975. pap. 5.95 (ISBN 0-14-021783-5, Pelican). Penguin.

Kupfer, Grace H. Legends of Greece & Rome. 1911. 20.00 (ISBN 0-686-20105-1). Quality Lib.

Lefkowitz, Mary R. Women in Greek Myth. LC 86-7146. 164p. 1986. text ed. 22.50x (ISBN 0-8018-3367-1). Johns Hopkins.

Lines, Kathleen, ed. Faber Book of Greek Legends. 268p. 1973. 13.95 (ISBN 0-571-09830-4). Faber & Faber.

Lloyd-Jones, Hugh. The Justice of Zeus. 2nd ed. (Sather Classical Lectures: No. 41). 290p. 1983. pap. 8.95 (ISBN 0-520-04688-9). U of Cal Pr.

Low, Alice. The Macmillan Book of Greek Gods & Heroes. LC 85-7170. (Illus.). 192p. 1985. 15.95 (ISBN 0-02-761390-9). Macmillan.

MacKenzie, Donald A. Myths of Crete & Pre-Hellenic Europe. LC 76-27522. (Illus.). 1976. Repr. of 1918 ed. lib. bdg. 45.00 (ISBN 0-89341-035-7). Longwood Pub Group.

Nilsson, Martin P. The Mycenaean Origins of Greek Mythology. 16.50 (ISBN 0-8446-6208-9). Peter Smith.

--The Mycenaean Origins of Greek Mythology. (Sather Classical Lectures: Vol.80). 278p. 1983. pap. 7.95 (ISBN 0-520-05073-8, CAL 655). U of Cal Pr.

Otto, Walter F. The Homeric Gods: The Spiritual Significance of Greek Religion. 1978. Repr. of 1954 ed. lib. bdg. 24.00x (ISBN 0-88254-845-X, Octagon). Hippocrene Bks.

Pinsent, John. Greek Mythology. rev. ed. LC 83-71479. (The Library of the World's Myths & Legends). (Illus.). 144p. 1983. 18.95 (ISBN 0-911745-08-4). P Bedrick Bks.

--Greek Mythology. (Library of the World's Myths & Legends). (Illus.). 144p. PLB 16.95 (ISBN 0-317-31010-0). Creative Ed.

Powell, B. Athenian Mythology: Erichthonius & the Three Daughters of Cecrops. (Illus.). 90p. 1976. 15.00 (ISBN 0-89005-121-6). Ares.

Preller, Ludwig. Griechische Mythology. Bolle, Kees W., ed. LC 77-79153. (Mythology Ser.). (Ger.). 1978. lib. bdg. 62.00x (ISBN 0-405-10562-2). Ayer Co Pubs.

Rahner, Hugo. Greek Myths & Christian Mystery. LC 79-156736. (Illus.). 1971. Repr. of 1963 ed. 18.00 (ISBN 0-8196-0270-1). Biblo.

Richardson, Donald. Great Zeus & All His Children: Greek Mythology for Adults. 312p. 1984. 16.95 (ISBN 0-13-364950-4); pap. 7.95 (ISBN 0-13-364943-1). P-H.

Robert, Carl. Bild und Lied: Archaologische Beitrage Zur Geschichte der Griechischen Heldensage. facsimile ed. LC 75-10653. (Ancient Religion & Mythology Ser.). (Ger., Illus.). 1976. Repr. of 1881 ed. 20.00x (ISBN 0-405-07277-5). Ayer Co Pubs.

Rose, Herbert J. Handbook of Greek Mythology. 1959. pap. 7.95 (ISBN 0-525-47041-7, 0772-230). Dutton.

Ross, Harriet, compiled by. Myths of Ancient Greece. (Illus.). 160p. 1984. PLB 7.95 (ISBN 0-87460-383-8). Lion Bks.

Rouse, W. H. Gods, Heroes & Men of Ancient Greece. 192p. (YA) 1971. pap. 3.50 (ISBN 0-451-62366-5, Ment). NAL.

Ruskin, John. The Queen of the Air: A Study of the Greek Myths of Cloud & Storm. LC 78-58190. 1978. Repr. of 1869 ed. lib. bdg. 25.00 (ISBN 0-89341-322-4). Longwood Pub Group.

Sergent, Bernard. Homosexuality in Greek Myth. Goldhammer, Arthur, tr. from Fr. LC 85-73369. 360p. 1986. 21.95 (ISBN 0-8070-5700-2). Beacon Pr.

Simpson, Michael, tr. Gods & Heroes of the Greeks: The "Library" of Apollodorus. LC 75-32489. (Illus.). 320p. 1976. pap. 10.95x (ISBN 0-87023-206-1). U of Mass Pr.

Slater, Philip E. Glory of Hera: Greek Mythology & the Greek Family. LC 68-24373. 540p. 1985. pap. 14.95x (ISBN 0-8070-5795-9, BPA12, Pub. by Ariadne Bks). Beacon Pr.

Spretnak, Charlene. Lost Goddesses of Early Greece: A Collection of Pre-Hellenic Myths. LC 84-45068. 132p. 1984. pap. 6.95 (ISBN 0-8070-1345-5, BP682). Beacon Pr.

Vernant, Jean P. Myth & Thought Among the Greeks. 400p. 1983. 29.95x (ISBN 0-7100-9544-9). Methuen Inc.

Warner, Rex. The Stories of the Greeks. 480p. 1978. 15.00 (ISBN 0-374-27056-2); pap. 9.95 (ISBN 0-374-50728-7). FS&G.

--Vengeance of the Gods. 192p. 1955. 3.50 (ISBN 0-87013-009-9). Mich St U Pr.

Weitzmann, Kurt. Greek Mythology in Byzantine Art. LC 84-4849. (Illus.). 380p. 1984. text ed. 95.00 (ISBN 0-691-03574-1). Princeton U Pr.

West, M. L. The Hesiodic Catalogue of Women: Its Nature, Structure & Origins. (Illus.). 1985. 24.95x (ISBN 0-19-814034-7). Oxford U Pr.

Weston, Jessie L. The Legends of the Wagner Drama: Studies in Mythology & Romance. LC 76-22354. 1976. Repr. of 1903 ed. lib. bdg. 35.00 (ISBN 0-89341-003-9). Longwood Pub Group.

Wilson, J. V. The Legend of Etana. 140p. 1985. pap. text ed. 44.00 (ISBN 0-85668-258-6, Pub. by Aris & Phillips UK). Humanities.

Wittkowski, Wolfgang. Heinrich Von Kleist: Amphithryon Materialien zur Rezeption und Interpretation. 1978. 40.40x (ISBN 3-11-006988-1). De Gruyter.

MYTHOLOGY, GREEK–JUVENILE LITERATURE

Asimov, Isaac. Words from the Myths. (Illus.). 224p. 1961. 12.95 (ISBN 0-395-06568-2). HM.

--Words from the Myths. (Illus.). 144p. 1969. pap. 2.50 (ISBN 0-451-14097-4, Sig). NAL.

Coolidge, Olivia. Greek Myths. (Illus.). 256p. 1949. 13.95 (ISBN 0-395-06721-9). HM.

D'Aulaire, Ingri & D'Aulaire, Edgar P. D'Aulaires' Book of Greek Myths. LC 62-15877. (Illus.). 1962. 17.95a (ISBN 0-385-01583-6); PLB o. p. (ISBN 0-385-07108-6); pap. 10.95 (ISBN 0-385-15787-8). Doubleday.

Dolch, Edward W. & Dolch, M. P. Greek Stories. (Pleasure Reading Ser.). 176p. 1955. PLB 6.57 (ISBN 0-8116-2607-5). Garrard.

Evslin, Bernard, et al. The Greek Gods. (Illus.). 120p. 1984. pap. 2.25 (ISBN 0-590-33456-5, Point). Scholastic Inc.

--Heroes & Monsters of Greek Myth. (Illus.). 112p. 1984. pap. 2.25 (ISBN 0-590-33457-3, Point). Scholastic Inc.

Graves, Robert. Greek Gods & Heroes. 125p. pap. 2.50 (ISBN 0-440-93221-1, LFL). Dell.

Green, R. L. The Tale of Thebes. LC 76-22979. (Illus.). 1977. o. p. 14.95 (ISBN 0-521-21410-6); pap. 6.95 (ISBN 0-521-21411-4). Cambridge U Pr.

Green, Roger L. Tales of Greek Heroes. (Orig.). 1974. pap. 2.95 (ISBN 0-14-030119-4, Puffin). Penguin.

Kingsley, Charles. The Heroes. (Facsimilie Classics Ser.). (Illus.). 224p. 1980. 8.95 (ISBN 0-8317-4448-0, Mayflower Bks). Smith Pubs.

--The Heroes of Greek Fairy Tales for My Children. 1889. Repr. lib. bdg. 15.00 (ISBN 0-8414-5578-3). Folcroft.

McDermott, Gerald. Sun Flight. LC 79-5067. (Illus.). 40p. 1980. 10.95 (ISBN 0-02-765610-1, Four Winds). Macmillan.

Proctor, Percy M. Star Myths & Stories: From Andromeda to Virgo. (Illus.). 1972. 8.50 (ISBN 0-682-47470-3, Banner). Exposition Pr FL.

Richardson, I. M. Prometheus & the Story of Fire. LC 82-15979. (Illus.). 32p. 1983. PLB 9.79 (ISBN 0-89375-859-0); pap. text ed. 2.50 (ISBN 0-89375-860-4). Troll Assocs.

Stephanides Brothers. Greek Mythology, 6 vols. (Series A.). (Eng.). Set. 50.00x (ISBN 0-916634-25-6). Double M Pr.

Swinburne, Laurence & Swinburne, Irene. Ancient Myths: The First Science Fiction. LC 77-10915. (Myth, Magic & Superstition Ser.). (Illus.). 1977. PLB 14.65 (ISBN 0-8172-1042-3). Raintree Pubs.

MYTHOLOGY, HAWAIIAN

Beckwith, Martha W. Hawaiian Mythology. LC 70-97998. 1977. pap. 10.95 (ISBN 0-8248-0514-3). UH Pr.

Emerson, Nathaniel B. Pele & Hiiaka: A Myth from Hawaii. LC 75-35190. Repr. of 1915 ed. 29.50 (ISBN 0-404-14218-4). AMS Pr.

McBride, L. R. Kahuna: Versatile Mystics of Old Hawaii. pap. 4.25 (ISBN 0-912180-18-8). Petroglyph.

Melville, Leinani. Children of the Rainbow: The Religions, Legends & Gods of Pre-Christian Hawaii. LC 69-17715. (Illus.). 1969. pap. 5.95 (ISBN 0-8356-0002-5, Quest). Theos Pub Hse.

Westervelt, W. D. Legends of Gods & Ghosts from Hawaiian Mythology. 1977. lib. bdg. 59.95 (ISBN 0-8490-2147-2). Gordon Pr.

MYTHOLOGY, HINDU

Bhaktivedanta, Swami A. C. Easy Journey to Other Planets. LC 70-118080. (Illus.). 1970. pap. 1.95 (ISBN 0-912776-10-2). Bhaktivedanta.

--Prahlad, Picture & Story Book. LC 72-2032. (Illus.). 1973. pap. 2.95 (ISBN 0-685-47513-1). Bhaktivedanta.

Brahma Purana. (Ancient India Tradition & Mythology Ser.: Vol. 34). 241p. 1985. 18.50 (ISBN 0-317-46524-4, Pub. by Motilal Banarsidass India). Orient Bk Dist.

Coomaraswamy, A. K. & Noble, M. E. Myths of the Hindus & Buddhists. (Illus.). 15.25 (ISBN 0-8446-1896-9). Peter Smith.

Coomaraswamy, Ananda K. & Nivedita, Sr. Myths of the Hindus & Buddhists. (Illus.). 400p. pap. 6.95 (ISBN 0-486-21759-0). Dover.

Courtright. Ganesa: Lord of Obstacles, Lord of Beginnings. 1985. 29.95x (ISBN 0-19-503572-0). Oxford U Pr.

Dandekar, R. N. The Age of Guptas & Other Essays. 1982. 30.00 (ISBN 0-8364-0916-7, Pub. by Ajanta). South Asia Bks.

Devata (an Essay on Indian Mythology), by a Recluse of Vindhyachala. LC 73-3811. (Sacred Books of the Hindus: No. 19). Repr. of 1917 ed. 29.00 (ISBN 0-404-57819-5). AMS Pr.

Dimmitt, Cornelia, ed. Classical Hindu Mythology: A Reader in the Sanskrit Puranas. Van Buitenen, J. A., tr. LC 77-92643. 388p. 1978. 34.95 (ISBN 0-87722-117-0); pap. 12.95x (ISBN 0-87722-122-7). Temple U Pr.

Dumezil, Georges. Deesses Latines et Mythes Vediques. Bolle, Kees W., ed. LC 77-79121. (Mythology Ser.). (Fr.). 1978. Repr. of 1956 ed. lib. bdg. 17.00x (ISBN 0-405-10533-9). Ayer Co Pubs.

Feys, J. Sri Aurobindo's Treatment of Hindu Myth. 1984. 7.50x (ISBN 0-8364-1109-9, Pub. by Mukhopadhyay India). South Asia Bks.

Hale, Edward W. Asura in Early Vedic Religion. 275p. 1986. 16.00 (ISBN 81-208-0061-3, Pub. by Motilal Banarsidass). South Asia Bks.

Harshananda, Swami. Hindu Gods & Goddesses. (Illus., Orig.). 1985. pap. 4.25 (ISBN 0-87481-522-3, Pub. by Ramakrishna Math Madras India). Vedanta Pr.

Henry, Victor. La Magie dans L'Inde Antique: Paris, 1904. LC 78-74261. (Oriental Religions Ser.: Vol. 5). 325p. 1980. lib. bdg. 40.00 (ISBN 0-8240-3903-3). Garland Pub.

Hillebrandt, Alfred. Vedic Mythology, Vol. I. rev. 2nd ed. Sarma, Sreeramula R., tr. from Ger. Tr. of Vedische Mythologie. 472p. 1980. text ed. 22.00 (ISBN 0-89684-098-0, Pub. by Motilal Banarsidass India). Orient Bk Dist.

Hopkins, E. Washburn. Epic Mythology. rev. ed. LC 76-75358. 1968. Repr. of 1915 ed. 18.00 (ISBN 0-8196-0228-0). Biblo.

The Kaliya: King of Serpents. LC 79-4669. (Childhood Pastimes of Krishna). (Illus.). pap. 4.00 (ISBN 0-89647-009-1). Bala Bks.

MacDonell, Arthur A. Vedic Mythology. 69.95 (ISBN 0-87968-153-5). Gordon Pr.

Maurice, Thomas. The History of Hindostan. Feldman, Burton & Richardson, Robert D., eds. LC 78-60888. (Myth & Romanticism Ser.). 1984. lib. bdg. 240.00 (ISBN 0-8240-3566-6). Garland Pub.

Neve, Felix. An Essay on the Myth of the Rbhus. Davanc, G. V., tr. from Fr. 370p. 1985. 42.50 (ISBN 81-202-0150-7, Pub. by Ajanta). South Asia Bks.

O'Flaherty, Wendy, tr. Hindu Myths. (Classics Ser.). 360p. 1975. pap. 5.95 (ISBN 0-14-044306-1). Penguin.

O'Flaherty, Wendy D. Dreams, Illusion, & Other Realities. LC 83-17944. (Illus.). xvi, 366p. 1986. pap. 13.95 (ISBN 0-226-61855-2). U of Chicago Pr.

Phillips, Stephen H. Aurobindo's Philosophy of Brahman. xii, 200p. 1986. 30.64 (ISBN 90-04-07765-0, Pub. by E J Brill). Heinman.

Rele, V. G. Human Mind Power: Secrets of the Vedic Gods. 136p. 1983. pap. text ed. 5.95x (ISBN 0-86590-231-3, Pub. by Taraporevala India). Apt Bks.

Shastri, J. L., ed. Brahma Purana, Pt. I. (Ancient Tradition & Mythology Ser.: Vol. 33). 240p. 1985. 18.50 (ISBN 81-208-0003-6, Pub. by Motilal Banarsidass India). Orient Bk Dist.

Shulman, David D. Tamil Temple Myths: Sacrifice & Divine Marriage in the South Indian Saiva Tradition. LC 79-17051. 1980. 45.00x (ISBN 0-691-06415-6). Princeton U Pr.

MYTHOLOGY, HUNGARIAN

see Mythology, Finno-Ugrian

MYTHOLOGY, INDIAN (AMERICAN INDIAN)

see Indians–Religion and Mythology; Indians of Central America–Religion and Mythology; Indians of Mexico–Religion and Mythology; Indians of North America–Religion and Mythology; Indians of South America–Religion and Mythology

MYTHOLOGY, INDIC

Bhattacharji, Sukumari. The Indian Theogony: Comparative Study of Indian Mythology from the Vedas to the Puranas. rev. ed. 1978. Repr. of 1970 ed. 18.50x (ISBN 0-8364-0160-3). South Asia Bks.

Dange, S. S. The Bhagavata Purana: Mytho-Social Study. LC 84-900334. 1984. 28.50x (ISBN 0-8364-1132-3, Pub. by Ajanta). South Asia Bks.

Gangadharan, N., tr. from Sanskirt. Agnipurana, 4 pts, Pt. III. (Ancient Indian Tradition & Mythology: Vol. 29). 210p. 1986. 18.50 (ISBN 81-208-0174-1, Pub. by Motilal Banarsidass India). Orient Bk Dist.

Hertel, J. The Panchatantra. lib. bdg. 79.95 (ISBN 0-87968-523-9). Krishna Pr.

Holland, Barron, compiled by. Popular Hinduism & Hindu Mythology: An Annotated Bibliography. LC 79-7188. 1979. lib. bdg. 45.00 (ISBN 0-313-21358-5, HPH/). Greenwood.

Imam, S. M. Scenes from Indian Mythology. 2nd ed. 1975. pap. 1.50 (ISBN 0-89684-347-5). Orient Bk Dist.

Macdonell, A. A. Vedic Mythology. 1974. Repr. 15.50 (ISBN 0-8426-0674-2). Orient Bk Dist.

Moor, Edward. The Hindu Pantheon. Feldman, Burton & Richardson, Robert D., eds. LC 78-60887. (Myth & Romanticism Ser.). 1984. lib. bdg. 80.00 (ISBN 0-8240-3567-4). Garland Pub.

Naravane, V. S. A Dictionary of Indian Mythology. 350p. Date not set. text ed. price not set (ISBN 0-7069-2463-0, Vikas India). Advent NY.

Nivedita, Sr. Siva & Buddha. pap. 0.50 (ISBN 0-87481-116-3). Vedanta Pr.

O'Flaherty, Wendy D. Dreams, Illusion, & Other Realities. LC 83-17944. (Illus.). xvi, 366p. 1986. pap. 13.95 (ISBN 0-226-61855-2). U of Chicago Pr.

Oppert, Gustav. On the Original Inhabitants of Bharatavarsa or India. Bolle, Kees W., ed. (Mythology Ser.). 1978. Repr. of 1893 ed. lib. bdg. 55.00x (ISBN 0-405-10557-6). Ayer Co Pubs.

Shastri, J. L. Puranas: Ancient Indian Tradition & Mythology. 1978-82. Shiva Purana: 4 Vols. 60.00 (ISBN 0-89581-343-2); Bhagavata Purana: 5 Vols. 75.00 (ISBN 0-89581-536-2); Linga Purana: 2 Vols. 45.00 (ISBN 0-89581-537-0); Garuda Purana: 3 Vols. 45.00 (ISBN 0-89581-538-9); Narada Purana: 5 Vols. 75.00 (ISBN 0-89581-539-7). Asian Human Pr.

Venkatacharaya, T., ed. Sriharicarita Mahakavya of Srihari Padmanabhasastrin. 11.50 (ISBN 0-8356-7322-7). Theos Pub Hse.

MYTHOLOGY, INDO-EUROPEAN

see also Soma

Aiyangar, Narayan. Essays on Indo-Aryan Mythology. 656p. 1986. Repr. 34.00X (ISBN 0-8364-1712-7, Pub. by Manohar India). South Asia Bks.

Dumezil, Georges. Horace et les Curiaces. Bolle, Kees W., ed. (Mythology Ser.). (Fr.). 1978. Repr. of 1942 ed. lib. bdg. 17.00x (ISBN 0-405-10534-7). Ayer Co Pubs.

Gubernatis, Angelo De. Zoological Mythology, 2 Vols. LC 68-58904. 1968. Repr. of 1872 ed. Set. 56.00x (ISBN 0-8103-3527-1). Gale.

Oosten, Jarich G. The War of the Gods: The Social Code in Indo-European Mythology. (International Library of Anthropology). 240p. 1985. 32.50x (ISBN 0-7102-0289-X). Methuen Inc.

Polome, Edgar C., ed. Essays in Honor of Karl Kerenyi. (Journal of Indo-European Studies Monographs: No. 4). (Illus.). 144p. (Orig.). 1984. pap. 30.00x (ISBN 0-941694-20-8). Inst Study Man.

Tilcomb, Shara E. Aryan Sun-Myths: The Origin of Religions. LC 78-31508. 1979. Repr. of 1889 ed. lib. bdg. 20.00 (ISBN 0-89341-323-2). Longwood Pub Group.

Titcomb, Sarah E. Aryan Sun-Myths: The Origin of Religions. 1977. lib. bdg. 59.95 (ISBN 0-8490-1456-5). Gordon Pr.

MYTHOLOGY, IRISH

Coghlan, Ronan. Pocket Dictionary of Irish Myth & Legend. (Pocket Bk.). (Illus.). 96p. (Orig.). 1985. pap. 3.95 (ISBN 0-86281-152-X, Pub. by Appletree Pr). Irish Bks Media.

Cousins, H. James. Irish Mythology. 59.95 (ISBN 0-8490-0425-X). Gordon Pr.

Gantz, Jeffrey. Early Irish Myths & Sagas. (Pengiun Classic Ser.). 1982. pap. 4.95 (ISBN 0-14-044397-5). Penguin.

--Early Irish Myths & Sagas. 250p. 1985. 14.95 (ISBN 0-88029-038-2, Pub. by Dorset Pr). Hippocrene Bks.

Kavanagh, Peter. Irish Mythology: A Dictionary. (Illus.). 150p. (Hand Set & Printed). 100.00 (ISBN 0-914612-00-X). Kavanagh.

Squire, Charles. The Mythology of Ancient Britain & Ireland. LC 73-13769. 1974. Repr. of 1909 ed. lib. bdg. 17.50 (ISBN 0-8414-7650-0). Folcroft.

MYTHOLOGY, JAPANESE

Davis, F. Hadland. Myths & Legends of Japan. (Illus.). 1978. Repr. of 1912 ed. lib. bdg. 45.00 (ISBN 0-8495-1008-2). Arden Lib.

Ferguson, John C. Chinese Mythology. Bd. with Japanese Mythology. Anesaki, Masaharu. LC 63-19093. (Mythology of All Races Ser.: Vol. 8). (Illus.). Repr. of 1932 ed. 30.00x (ISBN 0-8154-0068-3). Cooper Sq.

Mackenzie, Donald A. The Myths of China & Japan. LC 77-6878. 1977. Repr. of 1923 ed. lib. bdg. 45.00 (ISBN 0-89341-149-3). Longwood Pub Group.

Piggott, Juliet. Japanese Mythology. rev. ed. LC 83-71480. (The Library of the World's Myths & Legends). (Illus.). 144p. 1983. 18.95 (ISBN 0-911745-09-2). P Bedrick Bks.

--Japanese Mythology. (Library of the World's Myths & Legends). (Illus.). 144p. PLB 16.95 (ISBN 0-317-31009-7). Creative Ed.

MYTHOLOGY, JEWISH

Graves, Robert & Patai, Raphael. Hebrew Myths. 1966. pap. 5.95 (ISBN 0-07-024125-2). McGraw.

Kushner, Lawrence. Honey from The Rock: Ten Gates of Jewish Mysticism. LC 77-7832. 160p. 1983. pap. 7.95 (ISBN 0-06-064904-6, RD/442, HarpR). Har-Row.

Shapiro, Rabbi R. ALEF-Bet: A Primer for a Davenen Universe. (Illus.). 70p. 1983. pap. 9.95 (ISBN 0-911511-00-8). ENR Word.

MYTHOLOGY, LAPPISH

see Mythology, Finno-Ugrian

MYTHOLOGY, MAGYAR

see Mythology, Finno-Ugrian

MYTHOLOGY, NEAR EASTERN

see Mythology, Oriental

MYTHOLOGY, NORSE

Anderson, R. B. Norse Mythology or the Religion of Our Forefathers. LC 77-6879. 1977. Repr. of 1891 ed. lib. bdg. 25.00 (ISBN 0-89341-147-7). Longwood Pub Group.

Branston, Brian. Gods & Heroes from Viking Mythology. LC 81-14540. (World Mythologies Ser.). (Illus.). 156p. 1982. 15.95 (ISBN 0-8052-3794-1). Schocken.

Bugge, Sophus. Home of the Eddic Poems. Schofield, William H., tr. LC 74-144524. (Grimm Library: No. 11). Repr. of 1899 ed. 21.00 (ISBN 0-404-53554-2). AMS Pr.

Craigie, William A. Religion of Ancient Scandinavia. facsimile ed. LC 74-99657. (Select Bibliographies Reprint Ser). 1906. 14.50 (ISBN 0-8369-5086-0). Ayer Co Pubs.

Crossley-Holland, Kevin. The Norse Myths. 1981. pap. 7.95 (ISBN 0-394-74846-8). Pantheon.

Davidson, H. Ellis. Gods & Myths of Northern Europe. (Orig.). 1965. pap. 5.95 (ISBN 0-14-020670-1, Pelican). Penguin.

Davidson, H. R. Gods & Myths of Northern Europe. 250p. 1986. pap. 3.00 (ISBN 0-317-53026-7). Noontide.

--Scandinavian Mythology. LC 85-22895. (The Library of the World's Myths & Legends). (Illus.). 144p. 1986. 18.95 (ISBN 0-87226-041-0). P Bedrick Bks.

De La Saussaye, P. Chantepie. The Religion of the Teutons. LC 76-27519. 1976. Repr. of 1902 ed. lib. bdg. 50.00 (ISBN 0-89341-030-6). Longwood Pub Group.

Dumezil, Georges. Gods of the Ancient Northmen. Haugen, Einar, ed. & tr. (Center for the Study of Comparative Folklore & Mythology, UCLA Ser.: No. 3). 1974. 34.00x (ISBN 0-520-02044-8); pap. 8.95 (ISBN 0-520-03507-0, CAL 371). U of Cal Pr.

Ellis, Hilda R. Road to Hell: A Study of the Conception of the Dead in Old Norse Literature. LC 68-23286. (Illus.). 1968. Repr. of 1943 ed. lib. bdg. 22.50x (ISBN 0-8371-0070-4, ELRH). Greenwood.

Faraday, Lucy W. Edda I: The Divine Mythology of the North, 2: The Heroic Mythology of the North, 2 Vols. in 1. (Popular Studies in Mythology, Romance & Folklore: Nos. 12 & 13). Repr. of 1902 ed. 11.00 (ISBN 0-404-53512-7). AMS Pr.

Hollander, Lee M., tr. from Norse. The Poetic Edda. rev. ed. 375p. 1986. pap. 12.95 (ISBN 0-292-76499-5). U of Tex Pr.

Kauffmann, Friedrich. Northern Mythology. 1978. Repr. of 1903 ed. lib. bdg. 15.00 (ISBN 0-8495-3022-9). Arden Lib.

--Northern Mythology. 106p. 1980. Repr. of 1903 ed. lib. bdg. 15.00 (ISBN 0-89987-450-9). Darby Bks.

Lindow, John. Myths & Legends of the Vikings. (Illus.). 1980. pap. 2.95 (ISBN 0-88388-071-7). Bellerophon Bks.

--Scandinavian Mythology: An Annotated Bibliography. LC 82-49170. (Folklore Ser.). 200p. 1986. lib. bdg. 25.00 (ISBN 0-8240-9173-6). Garland Pub.

MacCulloch, John A. Eddic Mythology. LC 63-19087. (Mythology of All Races Ser.: Vol. 2). (Illus.). Repr. of 1932 ed. 30.00x (ISBN 0-8154-0143-4). Cooper Sq.

Munch, Peter A. Norse Mythology, Legends of Gods & Heroes. Hustvedt, Sigurd B., tr. LC 74-112002. 1970. Repr. of 1926 ed. 23.75 (ISBN 0-404-04538-3). AMS Pr.

Pigott, Grenville. A Manual of Scandinavian Mythology: Containing a Popular Account of the Two Eddas & of the Religion of Odin. Bolle, Kees W., ed. LC 77-79152. (Mythology Ser.). 1978. Repr. of 1839 ed. lib. bdg. 27.50x (ISBN 0-405-10561-4). Ayer Co Pubs.

Sturluson, Snorri. The Prose Edda of Snorri Sturluson: Tales from Norse Mythology. Young, Jean I., tr. 1964. pap. 5.95x (ISBN 0-520-01232-1, CAMPUS55). U of Cal Pr.

Titchenell, Elsa-Brita. The Masks of Odin: Wisdom of the Ancient Norse. LC 85-40652. (Illus.). 316p. 1985. 15.00 (ISBN 0-911500-72-3); pap. 8.00 (ISBN 0-911500-73-1). Theos U Pr.

Turville-Petre, E. O. Myth & Religion of the North. LC 75-5003. (Illus.). 340p. 1975. Repr. of 1964 ed. lib. bdg. 49.75x (ISBN 0-8371-7420-1, TUMR). Greenwood.

MYTHOLOGY, NORSE–JUVENILE LITERATURE

Colum, Padraic. The Children of Odin. 1920. 40.00 (ISBN 0-686-18157-3). Havertown Bks.

Crossley-Holland, Kevin. Axe-Age, Wolf-Age: A Selection for Children from the Norse Myths. (Illus.). 128p. 1985. 11.95 (ISBN 0-233-97688-4). Andre Deutsch.

D'Aulaire, Ingri & D'Aulaire, Edgar P. Norse Gods & Giants. LC 67-19109. (Illus.). 160p. 1967. write for info. (ISBN 0-385-04908-0); o. p. 14.95 (ISBN 0-385-07235-X). Doubleday.

Davidson, H. R. Scandinavian Mythology. LC 85-22895. (The Library of the World's Myths & Legends). (Illus.). 144p. 1986. 18.95 (ISBN 0-87226-041-0). P Bedrick Bks.

MYTHOLOGY, ORIENTAL

see also Mythology, Semitic

Cadet, J. M. Ramakien: The Thai Epic. LC 70-128685. (Illus.). 256p. 1970. 35.00 (ISBN 0-87011-134-5). Kodansha.

Christesen, Barbara. Myths of the Orient. LC 77-22199. (Myth, Magic & Superstition). (Illus.). 1977. PLB 14.65 (ISBN 0-8172-1043-1). Raintree Pubs.

Gorres, Joseph. Mythengeschichte der Asiatischen Welt: Mit einen Anhang: Beitrage aus den Heidelberger Jahrbuchern. Bolle, Kees W., ed. (Mythology Ser.). (Ger.). 1978. Repr. of 1935 ed. lib. bdg. 54.00x (ISBN 0-405-10538-X). Ayer Co Pubs.

Gray, John. Near Eastern Mythology. LC 84-45599. (The Library of the World's Myths & Legends). (Illus.). 144p. 1985. 18.95 (ISBN 0-87226-004-6). P Bedrick Bks.

Keith, A. Berriedale. Indian Mythology & Iranian Mythology. Bd. with Carnoy, Albert J. LC 63-19091. (Mythology of All Races Ser.: Vol. 6). (Illus.). Repr. of 1932 ed. 30.00x (ISBN 0-8154-0126-4). Cooper Sq.

MYTHOLOGY, POLYNESIAN

Alpers, Antony. The World of the Polynesians Seen Through Their Myths & Legends, Poetry, & Art. (New Zealand Classics Ser.). (Illus.). 432p. 1986. 10.95 (ISBN 0-19-558142-3). Oxford U Pr.

Andersen, Johannes C. The Maori Tohunga & His Spirit World. LC 75-35224. Repr. of 1948 ed. 20.00 (ISBN 0-404-14403-9). AMS Pr.

--Myths & Legends of the Polynesians. LC 75-35170. (Illus.). Repr. of 1931 ed. 43.50 (ISBN 0-404-14200-1). AMS Pr.

Anderson, Johannes E. Myths & Legends of the Polynesians. LC 69-13509. (Illus.). 1969. Repr. of 1928 ed. 37.50 (ISBN 0-8048-0414-1). C E Tuttle.

Best, Elsdon. Maori Religion & Mythology. LC 75-35236. Repr. of 1924 ed. 45.00 (ISBN 0-404-14412-8). AMS Pr.

Buck, Peter H. Anthropology & Religion. LC 72-121753. viii, 96p. 1970. Repr. of 1939 ed. 16.00 (ISBN 0-208-00950-7, Archon). Shoe String.

Dixon, Roland B. Oceanic Mythology, Vol. 9. LC 63-19094. (Mythology of All Races Ser). (Illus.). 1964. Repr. of 1932 ed. 30.00x (ISBN 0-8154-0059-4). Cooper Sq.

Gifford, E. W. Tongan Myths & Tales. (BMB). Repr. of 1924 ed. 25.00 (ISBN 0-527-02111-3, BMB, NO. 8). Kraus Repr.

Gill, William W. Myths & Songs from the South Pacific. Dorson, Richard M., ed. LC 77-70596. (International Folklore Ser.). 1977. Repr. of 1876 ed. lib. bdg. 25.50x (ISBN 0-405-10095-7). Ayer Co Pubs.

Grey, George. Polynesian Mythology & Ancient Traditional History of the New Zealanders As Furnished by Their Priests & Chiefs. LC 75-35253. Repr. of 1906 ed. 20.50 (ISBN 0-404-14425-X). AMS Pr.

Shortland, Edward. Maori Religion & Mythology. LC 75-35268. Repr. of 1882 ed. 22.50 (ISBN 0-404-14437-3). AMS Pr.

Williamson, Robert W. Religion & Social Organization in Central Polynesia. Piddington, Ralph, ed. LC 75-35218. Repr. of 1937 ed. 38.00 (ISBN 0-404-14241-9). AMS Pr.

--Religious & Cosmic Beliefs of Central Polynesia, 2 vols. LC 75-35220. Repr. of 1933 ed. Set. 87.50 (ISBN 0-404-14300-8). AMS Pr.

MYTHOLOGY, ROMAN

Berens, E. M. The Myths & Legends of Ancient Greece & Rome. LC 77-91528. 1977. Repr. of 1880 ed. lib. bdg. 30.00 (ISBN 0-89341-029-2). Longwood Pub Group.

Carpenter, Thomas H. & Gula, Robert J. Mythology: Greek & Roman. (Illus.). 1977. pap. text ed. 6.95x (ISBN 0-88334-089-5). Ind Sch Pr.

Dumezil, Georges. Deesses Latines et Mythes Vediques. Bolle, Kees W., ed. LC 77-79121. (Mythology Ser.). (Fr.). 1978. Repr. of 1956 ed. lib. bdg. 17.00x (ISBN 0-405-10533-9). Ayer Co Pubs.

Godwin, William. The Pantheon: or, Ancient History of the Gods of Greece & Rome. Feldman, Burton & Richardson, Robert D., eds. LC 78-60886. (Myth & Romanticism Ser.). 1984. lib. bdg. 80.00 (ISBN 0-8240-3560-7). Garland Pub.

Green, Miranda J. The Gods of Roman Britain. (Shire Archeaology Ser.: No. 34). (Illus.). 64p. (Orig.). 1983. pap. 5.95 (ISBN 0-85263-634-2, Pub. by Shire Pubns England). Seven Hills Bks.

Grimal, Pierre. Dictionnaire de la Mythologie Grecque et Romaine. 5th ed. (Fr.). 612p. 1969. 59.95 (ISBN 0-686-57316-1, M-6299). French & Eur.

Gueber, H. A. The Myths of Greece & Rome. 1986. 27.50x (ISBN 0-245-56918-9, Pub. by Harrap Ltd England). State Mutual Bk.

Guerber, H. A. Myths of Greece & Rome: Narrated with Special Reference to Literature & Art. 428p. 1985. Repr. of 1893 ed. 40.00 (ISBN 0-8495-2102-5). Arden Lib.

Holme. Myths of Greece & Rome. 288p. 1981. pap. 18.95 (ISBN 0-14-005643-2). Penguin.

Keightley, Thomas. Classical Mythology: The Myths of Ancient Greece & Italy. xviii, 507p. 1976. 25.00 (ISBN 0-89005-189-5). Ares.

Kupfer, Grace H. Legends of Greece & Rome. 1911. 20.00 (ISBN 0-686-20105-1). Quality Lib.

McDermott, Gerald. Daughter of Earth: A Roman Myth. LC 82-23585. (Illus.). 32p. 1984. 15.00 (ISBN 0-385-29294-5). Delacorte.

Perowne, Stewart. Roman Mythology. LC 84-6446. (The Library of the World's Myths & Legends). (Illus.). 144p. 1984. 18.95 (ISBN 0-911745-56-4). P Bedrick Bks.

Preller, Ludwig. Romische Mythologie: Roman Mythology. Bolle, Kees W., ed. LC 77-79154. (Mythology Ser.). (Ger.). 1978. Repr. of 1865 ed. lib. bdg. 53.00x (ISBN 0-405-10563-0). Ayer Co Pubs.

Roscher, Wilhelm & Hillman, James. Pan & the Nightmare: Two Essays. (Dunquin Ser.: No. 4). lxiii, 88p. 1972. pap. 8.50 (ISBN 0-88214-204-6). Spring Pubns.

Sanders, Henry A., ed. Roman History & Mythology. Repr. of 1910 ed. 37.00 (ISBN 0-384-38804-3). Johnson Repr.

Small, Jocelyn P. Cacus & Marsyas in Etrusco-Roman Legend. LC 82-47614. (Princeton Monographs in Art & Archaeology: No. 45). (Illus.). 208p. 1982. 31.50x (ISBN 0-691-03562-8). Princeton U Pr.

Usher, Kerry. Heroes, Gods, & Emperors from Roman Mythology. LC 83-11085. (World Mythology Ser.). (Illus.). 132p. 1984. 15.95 (ISBN 0-8052-3880-8). Schocken.

MYTHOLOGY, SCANDINAVIAN

see Mythology, Norse

MYTHOLOGY, SEMITIC

see also Mythology, Assyro-Babylonian; Mythology, Jewish

Brown, Robert. Semitic Influence in Hellentic Mythology. 19.00 (ISBN 0-405-10084-1, 14709). Ayer Co Pubs.

Graves, Robert & Patai, Raphael. Hebrew Myths. 1966. pap. 5.95 (ISBN 0-07-024125-2). McGraw.

Hooke, Samuel H. Middle Eastern Mythology. (Orig.). 1963. pap. 5.95 (ISBN 0-14-020546-2, Pelican). Penguin.

Langdon, Stephen H. Semitic Mythology. LC 63-19090. (Mythology of All Races Ser.: Vol. 5). (Illus.). Repr. of 1932 ed. 30.00x (ISBN 0-8154-0133-7). Cooper Sq.

Maier, Walter A., III. Aserah: Extrabiblical Evidence. (Harvard Semitic Monographs). 274p. 1987. 21.95 (ISBN 1-55540-046-9, 04-00-37). Scholars Pr GA.

MYTHOLOGY, SIBERIAN

Holmberg, Uno. Finno-Ugric, Siberian Mythology. (Mythology of All Races Ser: Vol. Iv). (Illus.). Repr. of 1932 ed. 30.00x (ISBN 0-8154-0116-7). Cooper Sq.

Sartakov, S. Siberian Stories. 607p. 1979. 9.45 (ISBN 0-8285-1621-9, Pub. by Progress Pubs USSR). Imported Pubns.

MYTHOLOGY, SLAVIC

Oinas, Felix J. Essays on Russian Folklore & Mythology. (Illus.). 183p. (Orig.). 1985. pap. 12.95 (ISBN 0-89357-148-2). Slavica.

Ralston, W. R. Songs of the Russian People: As Illustrative of Slavonic Mythology & Russian Social Life. LC 77-132444. (Studies in Music, No. 42). 1970. Repr. of 1872 ed. lib. bdg. 69.95x (ISBN 0-8383-1224-1). Haskell.

Warner, Elizabeth. Heroes, Monsters & Other Worlds from Russian Mythology. LC 85-10750. (Illus.). 132p. 1986. 15.95 (ISBN 0-8052-4007-1). Schocken.

MYTHOLOGY, SUMERIAN

Kinnier-Wilson, J. V. & Vanstiphout, Herman. The Rebel Lands: An Investigation into the Origins of Early Mesopotamian Mythology. LC 77-1272. (Oriental Publications Ser.: No. 29). (Illus.). 1979. 39.00 (ISBN 0-521-21469-6). Cambridge U Pr.

Kramer, Samuel N. Sumerian Mythology. (Illus.). 1972. pap. 10.95x (ISBN 0-8122-1047-6, Pa Paperbks). U of Pa Pr.

MYTHOLOGY, SWEDISH

see Mythology, Norse

MYTHOLOGY, VEDIC

see Mythology, Hindu; Vedas

MYTHOLOGY, VOGUL

see Mythology, Finno-Ugrian

MYTHOLOGY, WELSH

Guest, Charlotte. The Mabinogion. (Illus.). 504p. 1978. pap. 9.95 (ISBN 0-89733-000-5). Academy Chi Pubs.

Newstead, Helaine. Bran the Blessed in Arthurian Romance. LC 40-4360. Repr. of 1939 ed. 14.50 (ISBN 0-404-04687-8). AMS Pr.

Owen, William. The Cambrian Biography; or Historical Notices of Celebrated Men Among the Ancient Britons. Feldman, Burton & Richardson, Robert, eds. LC 78-60896. (Myth & Romanticism Ser.: Vol. 20). (Illus.). 1979. lib. bdg. 80.00 (ISBN 0-8240-3569-0). Garland Pub.

MYTHOLOGY IN ART

see Art and Mythology

MYTHOLOGY IN LITERATURE

Bush, Douglas. Pagan Myth & Christian Tradition in English Poetry. LC 68-8639. (Memoirs Ser.: Vol. 72). 1968. 5.00 (ISBN 0-87169-072-1). Am Philos.

Euripides. Hippolytus in Drama & Myth. Sutherland, Donald, tr. LC 60-13112. vi, 124p. 1960. pap. 4.50x (ISBN 0-8032-5195-5, BB 103, Bison). U of Nebr Pr.

Feder, Lillian. Ancient Myth in Modern Poetry. LC 70-154994. 1972. 38.50x (ISBN 0-691-06207-2); pap. 11.50x (ISBN 0-691-01336-5). Princeton U Pr.

Fisch, Harold. A Remembered Future: A Study in Literary Mythology. LC 83-48899. 208p. 1985. 22.50x (ISBN 0-253-35003-4). Ind U Pr.

Franklin, H. Bruce. The Wake of the Gods: Melville's Mythology. 1963. pap. 16.95x (ISBN 0-8047-0137-7). Stanford U Pr.

Gould, Eric. Mythical Intentions in Modern Literature. LC 81-47132. 304p. 1981. 30.50 (ISBN 0-691-06482-2). Princeton U Pr.

Greenway, John L. The Golden Horns: Mythic Imagination & the Nordic Past. LC 74-30676. 232p. 1977. 20.00x (ISBN 0-8203-0384-4). U of Ga Pr.

Hughes, Richard E. The Lively Image: Four Myths in Literature. 1975. pap. text ed. 12.00 (ISBN 0-316-38034-2). Little.

Hunger, H. Lexikon der Griechischen und Roemischen Mythologie. (Ger.). 452p. 1974. pap. 7.95 (ISBN 3-499-16178-8, M-7252). French & Eur.

Luke, Helen. The Inner Story: Myth & Symbol in the Bible & Literature. 112p. 1982. 8.95 (ISBN 0-8245-0443-7). Crossroad NY.

MacKillop, James. Fionn Mac Cumhaill: Celtic Myth in English Literature. LC 85-22116. (Irish Studies). 256p. (Orig.). 1986. pap. text ed. 35.00x (ISBN 0-8156-2344-5); pap. 15.00x (ISBN 0-8156-2353-4). Syracuse U Pr.

Norton, Daniel S. & Rushton, Peters. Classical Myths in English Literature. Repr. of 1952 ed. lib. bdg. 39.75x (ISBN 0-8371-2440-9, NOCM). Greenwood.

Slochower, Harry. Mythopoesis: Mythic Patterns in the Literary Classics. LC 96-11337. (Waynebooks Ser: No. 35). 363p. 1970. 29.95x (ISBN 0-8143-1395-7); pap. text ed. 9.95x (ISBN 0-8143-1511-9). Wayne St U Pr.

Stillman, Peter R. Introduction to Myth. 1977. pap. text ed. 9.25x (ISBN 0-8104-5890-X). Boynton Cook Pubs.

Strelka, Joseph P., ed. Literary Criticism & Myth. LC 79-15111. (Yearbook of Comparative Criticism Ser.: Vol. 9). 1980. text ed. 25.00x (ISBN 0-271-00225-5). Pa St U Pr.

Vickery, John B. Robert Graves & the White Goddess. LC 70-183363. Repr. of 1972 ed. 29.50 (ISBN 0-8357-9713-9, 2011899). Bks Demand UMI.

Wetzels, Walter D., ed. Myth & Reason: A Symposium. LC 72-3096. (Germanic Languages Symposium Ser). 206p. 1973. 9.95x (ISBN 0-292-75003-X). U of Tex Pr.

Whitman, Cedric H. Euripides & the Full Circle of Myth. LC 74-81676. (Loeb Classical Monographs Ser). 176p. 1974. text ed. 11.00x (ISBN 0-674-26920-9). Harvard U Pr.

MYTHS

see Mythology

N

NAAMAN (BIBLICAL CHARACTER)

Diamond, Lucy. Naaman & the Little Maid. (Ladybird Ser). (Illus.). 1959. bds. 2.50 (ISBN 0-87508-852-X). Chr Lit.

NANAK, 1ST GURU OF THE SIKHS, 1469-1538

Singh, Khushwant, ed. & tr. Hymns of Guru Nanak. Repr. of 1969 ed. cancelled (ISBN 0-8364-0302-9, Orient Longman). South Asia Bks.

Singh, Mala. The Story of Guru Nanak. (Illus.). 1979. 6.25 (ISBN 0-89744-138-9). Auromere.

Wylam, P. Guru Nanak. (Illus.). 1979. pap. 4.00 (ISBN 0-89744-154-0). Auromere.

NANTES, EDICT OF

see Edict of Nantes

NASORAEANS

see Mandaeans

NATION OF ISLAM

see Black Muslims

NATIONALISM-JEWS

see also Zionism

Jacobs, Louis. Jewish Thought Today. LC 73-116679. (Chain of Tradition Ser). (Illus.). 1970. pap. 5.95x (ISBN 0-87441-014-2). Behrman.

Janowsky, Oscar I. Jews & Minority Rights, 1898-1919. LC 33-31678. (Columbia University. Studies in the Social Sciences: No. 384). Repr. of 1933 ed. 24.50 (ISBN 0-404-51384-0). AMS Pr.

Simon, Leon. Studies in Jewish Nationalism. LC 75-6458. (The Rise of Jewish Nationalism & the Middle East Ser.). xi, 174p. 1975. Repr. of 1920 ed. 19.80 (ISBN 0-88355-343-0). Hyperion Conn.

NATIONALISM AND RELIGION

see also Buddhism and State; Church and State; Islam and State; Jews–Election, Doctrine of; Religion and Language; Religion and State; War and Religion

Baron, Salo W. Modern Nationalism & Religion. facs. ed. LC 79-134050. (Essay Index Reprint Ser). 1947. 19.50 (ISBN 0-8369-2142-9). Ayer Co Pubs.

Cogan, Morton. Imperialism & Religion: Assyria, Judah & Israel in the Eighth & Seventh Centuries B.C.E. LC 73-83723. (Society of Biblical Literature. Monograph). 1974. 13.50 (ISBN 0-89130-330-8, 060019); pap. 9.95 (ISBN 0-89130-331-6, 00-06-19). Scholars Pr GA.

Guterman, Simeon L. Religious Toleration & Persecution in Ancient Rome. LC 70-104269. 160p. Repr. of 1951 ed. lib. bdg. 22.50x (ISBN 0-8371-3936-8, GURT). Greenwood.

Hudson, Winthrop S. Nationalism & Religion in America: Concepts of American Identity & Mission. 12.00 (ISBN 0-8446-0711-8). Peter Smith.

Liebman, Charles S. & Don-Yehiya, Eliezer. Civil Religion in Israel: Traditional Judaism & Political Culture in the Jewish State. LC 82-17427. 270p. 1983. 27.50x (ISBN 0-520-04817-2). U of Cal Pr.

Smith, Wilfred C. Modern Islam in India: A Social Analysis. LC 70-179243. Repr. of 1946 ed. 17.00 (ISBN 0-404-54869-5). AMS Pr.

Von der Mehden, Fred R. Religion & Nationalism in Southeast Asia: Burma, Indonesia, & the Philippines. (Illus.). 272p. 1963. pap. 7.95 (ISBN 0-299-02944-1). U of Wis Pr.

NATIVE RACES

Howitt, William. Colonization & Christianity: A Popular History of the Treatment of the Natives by the Europeans in All Their Colonies. LC 70-76856. Repr. of 1838 ed. 22.75x (ISBN 0-8371-1162-5, HOC&, Pub. by Negro U Pr). Greenwood.

MacDonald, Allan J. Trade, Politics & Christianity in Africa & the East. LC 77-89007. Repr. of 1916 ed. lib. bdg. cancelled (ISBN 0-8371-1755-0, MAT&, Pub. by Negro U Pr). Greenwood.

NATIVISM

Hughes, John & Breckinridge, John. A Discussion: Is the Roman Catholic Religion Inimical to Civil or Religious Liberty? Is the Presbyterian Religion Inimical to Civil or Religious Liberty? LC 76-122167. (Civil Liberties in American History Ser). 1970. Repr. of 1836 ed. lib. bdg. 75.00 (ISBN 0-306-71979-7). Da Capo.

NATIVISTIC MOVEMENTS

see also Ghost Dance

Ahlberg, Sture. Messianic Movements: A Comparative Analysis of the Sabbatians, the People's Temple & the Unification Church. 128p. (Orig.). pap. text ed. 19.00x (ISBN 91-22-00787-3, Pub. by Almqvist & Wiksell). Coronet Bks.

Daneel, M. L. Zionism & Faith-Healing in Rhodesia: Aspects of African Independent Churches. V. A. February Communications, tr. from Dutch. (Illus.). 1970. pap. 6.00x (ISBN 90-2796-278-2). Mouton.

Desroche, Henri, et al. Dieux D'hommes: Dictionnaire Des Messianismes & Millenarismes De L'ere Chretienne. 1969. 30.40x (ISBN 90-2796-415-7). Mouton.

How to Respond to the Cults. 1977. 1.75 (ISBN 0-570-07682-X, 12-2654). Concordia.

Shovers, Aaron H. Visions of Peace: The Story of the Messianic Expectation. LC 81-86206. 237p. (Orig.). 1985. pap. 12.75 (ISBN 0-9613613-0-1); wkbk. 8.75 (ISBN 0-9613613-1-X). Three Dimensional.

Williams, Francis E. The Vailala Madness & the Destruction of Native Ceremonies in the Gulf Division. LC 75-35166. (Territory of Papua. Anthropological Report: No. 4). Repr. of 1923 ed. 20.00 (ISBN 0-404-14180-3). AMS Pr.

NATIVITY OF CHRIST

see Jesus Christ–Nativity

NATURAL LAW

see also Ethics; Political Ethics

Battaglia, Anthony. Toward a Reformulation of Natural Law. 1981. 14.95 (ISBN 0-8164-0490-9, HarpR). Har-Row.

Hegel, G. W. Philosophy of Right. Knox, T. M., tr. 1942. 37.50x (ISBN 0-19-824128-3); pap. 10.95x (ISBN 0-19-500276-8). Oxford U Pr.

Johnson, Harold J. The Medieval Tradition of Natural Law. LC 86-31126. (Studies in Medieval Culture: No. 22). Date not set. price not set (ISBN 0-918720-81-8). Medieval Inst.

Kaplan, Morton A. Justice, Human Nature, & Political Obligation. LC 76-8145. 1976. 18.95 (ISBN 0-02-916890-2). Free Pr.

Maritain, Jacques. Rights of Man & Natural Law. LC 74-150416. 120p. 1971. Repr. of 1943 ed. 17.50x (ISBN 0-87752-146-8). Gordian.

Villafranca, Anthony L. The Theory of Sin & the Equilibrium Between the Emotional & the Rational in Man. (Illus.). 104p. 1986. 88.50 (ISBN 0-89266-568-8). Am Classical Coll Pr.

NATURAL RELIGION

see Natural Theology

NATURAL RIGHTS

see Natural Law

NATURAL THEOLOGY

see also Analogy (Religion); Creation; Philosophical Theology; Philosophy of Nature; Religion and Science; Theodicy

Banks, Natalie N. The Golden Thread. 1979. pap. 5.00 (ISBN 0-85330-127-1). Lucis.

Bushnell, Horace. Nature & the Supernatural As Together Constituting the One System of God. LC 70-39569. Repr. of 1858 ed. 29.50 (ISBN 0-404-01246-9). AMS Pr.

Currey, Cecil B. Reason & Revelation: John Duns Scotus on Natural Theology. LC 77-9614. (Synthesis Ser.). 1977. pap. 0.75 (ISBN 0-8199-0717-0). Franciscan Herald.

Derham, William. Physico-Theology: A Demonstration of the Being & Attributes of God, from His Works of Creation. Egerton, Frank N., 3rd, ed. LC 77-74212. (History of Ecology Ser.). 1978. Repr. of 1716 ed. lib. bdg. 37.50 (ISBN 0-405-10383-2). Ayer Co Pubs.

Greene, John C. Darwin & the Modern World View. LC 61-15489. (Rockwell Lectures Ser.). 152p. 1973. pap. text ed. 6.95x (ISBN 0-8071-0062-5). La State U Pr.

Hartshorne, Charles. A Natural Theology for Our Time. LC 66-14722. 145p. 1967. pap. 9.95 (ISBN 0-87548-239-2). Open Court.

Holloway, Maurice R. Introduction to Natural Theology. LC 59-6522. 1959. text ed. 19.95x (ISBN 0-89197-244-7). Irvington.
Hume, David. Dialogues Concerning Natural Religion. Smith, Norman K., ed. 1947. pap. 8.40 scp (ISBN 0-672-60404-3, LLA174). Bobbs.
--Dialogues Concerning Natural Religion. Aiken, Henry D., ed. (Library of Classics Ser: No. 5). pap. text ed. 5.95x (ISBN 0-02-846180-0). Hafner.
--Dialogues Concerning Natural Religion: Text & Critical Essays. Pike, Nelson, ed. LC 77-132933. (Text & Critical Essays Ser). (Orig.). 1970. pap. write for info. (ISBN 0-02-358440-8, TC6). Macmillan.
--The Natural History of Religion & Dialogues Concerning Natural Religion. Colver, A. Wayne & Price, Vladimir, eds. 1976. 49.95x (ISBN 0-19-824379-0). Oxford U Pr.
--A Treatise of Human Nature, 2 vols. Green, T. H. & Grose, T. H., eds. 1025p. 1981. Repr. of 1898 ed. lib. bdg. 200.00 (ISBN 0-89987-377-4). Darby Bks.
Joyce, George H. Principles of Natural Theology. LC 79-170829. Repr. of 1923 ed. 37.45 (ISBN 0-404-03609-0). AMS Pr.
Klubertanz, George P. & Holloway, Maurice R. Being & God: Introduction to the Philosophy of Being & to Natural Theology. LC 63-15359. 1963. 39.50x (ISBN 0-89197-045-2); pap. text ed. 19.95x (ISBN 0-89197-674-4). Irvington.
LeMahieu, D. L. The Mind of William Paley: A Philosopher & His Age. LC 75-22547. xiv, 215p. 1976. 18.50x (ISBN 0-8032-0865-0). U of Nebr Pr.
Lincoln, Bruce. Priests, Warriors & Cattle: A Study in the Ecology of Religions. LC 78-68826. (Hermeneutics: Studies in the History of Religions Ser.). 240p. 1981. 37.95x (ISBN 0-520-03880-0). U of Cal Pr.
Mahan, Asa. The Science of Natural Theology. LC 75-3273. Repr. of 1867 ed. 27.50 (ISBN 0-404-59261-9). AMS Pr.
Mather, Cotton. Christian Philosopher: A Collection of the Best Discoveries in Nature, with Religious Improvements. LC 68-29082. 1968. Repr. of 1721 ed. 45.00x (ISBN 0-8201-1033-7). Schol Facsimiles.
Mueller, Friedrich M. Natural Religion. LC 73-18810. (Gifford Lectures: 1888). Repr. of 1889 ed. 44.50 (ISBN 0-404-11450-4). AMS Pr.
--Physical Religion. LC 73-18811. (Gifford Lectures: 1890). Repr. of 1891 ed. 34.00 (ISBN 0-404-11451-2). AMS Pr.
Ray, John. The Wisdom of God Manifested in the Works of the Creation: Heavenly Bodies, Elements, Meteors, Fossils, Vegetables, Animals. Egerton, Frank N., 3rd, ed. LC 77-74250. (History of Ecology Ser.). 1978. Repr. of 1717 ed. lib. bdg. 40.00x (ISBN 0-405-10419-7). Ayer Co Pubs.
Robb, J. Wesley. The Reverent Skeptic. LC 79-83609. 238p. 1979. 12.50 (ISBN 0-8022-2245-5). Philos Lib.
Rose, P. L. Bodin & the Great God of Nature: The Moral & Religious Universe of a Judaiser. 200p. (Orig.). 1980. pap. text ed. 48.50x (Pub. by Droz Switzerland). Coronet Bks.
The Science of Religion. pap. 9.95 (ISBN 0-937134-16-3). Amrita Found.
Smithline, Arnold. Natural Religion in American Literature. 1966. 11.95x (ISBN 0-8084-0227-7); pap. 7.95x (ISBN 0-8084-0228-5). New Coll U Pr.
Stokes, George G. Natural Theology. LC 77-27232. (Gifford Lectures: 1891). Repr. of 1891 ed. 30.00 (ISBN 0-404-60452-8). AMS Pr.
Taylor, Alfred E. Faith of a Moralist, 2 Vols. in 1. LC 37-23815. (Gifford Lectures 1926-1928). 1968. Repr. of 1937 ed. 41.00 (ISBN 0-527-89062-6). Kraus Repr.
Temple, William. Nature, Man & God. LC 77-27190. (Gifford Lectures Ser.: 1932-33, 1933-34). 1979. Repr. of 1935 ed. 54.50 (ISBN 0-404-60493-5). AMS Pr.
Tindal, Matthew. Christianity As Old Creation of the Gospel. Wellek, Rene, ed. LC 75-11256. (British Philosophers & Theologians of the 17th & 18th Centuries Ser.). 1976. lib. bdg. 51.00 (ISBN 0-8240-1806-0). Garland Pub.
Torrance, Thomas F. The Ground & Grammar of Theology. LC 79-21429. 180p. 1980. 13.95x (ISBN 0-8139-0819-1). U Pr of Va.
Wallace, Robert. Various Prospects of Mankind, Nature & Providence. LC 69-19550. 1969. Repr. of 1761 ed. 39.50x (ISBN 0-678-00491-9). Kelley.
Ward, J. Naturalism & Agnosticism: The Gifford Lectures Delivered Before the University of Aberdeen in 1896-1898, 2 Vols. in 1. 4th ed. Repr. of 1899 ed. 36.00 (ISBN 0-527-94500-5). Kraus Repr.
Wilkins, John. Of the Principles & Duties of Natural Religion: Two Books. Repr. of 1693 ed. 35.00 (ISBN 0-384-68500-5). Johnson Repr.
Willey, Basil. Religion of Nature. LC 76-40105. 1957. lib. bdg. 12.50 (ISBN 0-8414-9506-8). Folcroft.
Wollaston, William. The Religion of Nature Delineated. Wellek, Rene, ed. LC 75-11267. (British Philosophers & Theologians of the 17th & 18th Centuries Ser.). 1978. Repr. of 1722 ed. lib. bdg. 51.00 (ISBN 0-8240-1816-8). Garland Pub.

NATURE–PHILOSOPHY
see Philosophy of Nature

NATURE–RELIGIOUS INTERPRETATIONS
Abrecht, Paul. Faith, Science, & the Future. LC 79-7035. pap. 60.00 (2026942). Bks Demand UMI.
Glacken, Clarence J. Traces on the Rhodian Shore: Nature & Culture in Western Thought from Ancient Times to the End of the Eighteenth Century. LC 67-10970. 1973. pap. 15.50x (ISBN 0-520-03216-0, CAMPUS 170). U of Cal Pr.
Hendry, George S. Theology of Nature. LC 79-27375. 258p. 1980. pap. 13.95 (ISBN 0-664-24305-3). Westminster.
Keller, Phillip. Wonder O' the Wind. 1986. 7.95 (ISBN 0-8499-3061-8). Word Bks.
Owens, Virginia S. Wind River Winter: How the World Dies. 288p. 1987. pap. 10.95 (ISBN 0-310-45861-7). Zondervan.
Persson, Norma J. God & Nature: A Book of Devotions for Christians Who Love Wildlife. 240p. 1984. pap. 6.95 (ISBN 0-13-357559-4). P-H.
Pois, Robert A. National Socialism & the Religion of Nature. LC 85-27615. 208p. 1986. 27.50 (ISBN 0-312-55958-5). St Martin.
Stewart, Claude Y., Jr. Nature in Grace: A Study in the Theology of Nature. LC 83-8196. xx, 318p. 1983. pap. 21.50 (ISBN 0-86554-068-3, P08). Mercer Univ Pr.
Walker, Raymond B. Beside Still Waters. LC 75-32601. (Illus.). 1975. 12.50 (ISBN 0-8323-0264-3). Binford-Metropolitan.
Wollaston, William. The Religion of Nature Delineated, 1724 & Related Commentaries. LC 74-1469. 1974. 45.00x (ISBN 0-8201-1127-9). Schol Facsimiles.

NATURE (IN RELIGION, FOLK-LORE, ETC.)
see also Nature Worship
Clarkson, Margaret. All Nature Sings. 160p. (Orig.). 1986. pap. 5.95 (ISBN 0-8028-0225-7). Eerdmans.
Feliks, Yehuda. Nature & Man in the Bible. 294p. 1981. 25.00 (ISBN 0-900689-19-6). Soncino Pr.
Glacken, Clarence J. Traces on the Rhodian Shore: Nature & Culture in Western Thought from Ancient Times to the End of the Eighteenth Century. LC 67-10970. 1973. pap. 15.50x (ISBN 0-520-03216-0, CAMPUS 170). U of Cal Pr.

NATURE, LAW OF
see Natural Law

NATURE, PHILOSOPHY OF
see Philosophy of Nature

NATURE WORSHIP
see also Anthropomorphism; Phallicism; Sun-Worship
Bjerregaard, C. H. Lectures on Mysticism & Nature Worship. 1977. lib. bdg. 59.95 (ISBN 0-8490-2138-3). Gordon Pr.
Frazer, James G. The Worship of Nature. LC 73-21271. (Gifford Lectures: 1924-25). Repr. of 1926 ed. 41.50 (ISBN 0-404-11427-X). AMS Pr.
Mitchell, John. The Earth Spirit: Its Ways, Shrines & Mysteries. 1976. pap. 5.95 (ISBN 0-380-01154-9, 26880). Avon.

NDEMBU (AFRICAN TRIBE)
Turner, Victor. The Forest of Symbols: Aspects of Ndembu Ritual. LC 67-12308. (Illus.). 417p. 1970. pap. 12.95x (ISBN 0-8014-9101-0, CP101). Cornell U Pr.

NEAR EAST–ANTIQUITIES
Aubrey, John. Remaines of Gentilisme & Judaisme, Sixteen Hundred Eighty-Six to Eighty-Seven. Britten, James, ed. (Folk-Lore Society, London, Monograph Ser.: Vol. 4). pap. 29.00 (ISBN 0-8115-0501-4). Kraus Repr.
Flinder, Alexander. Secrets of the Bible Seas: An Underwater Archaeologist in the Holy Land. (Illus.). 192p. 1986. 17.95 (ISBN 0-7278-2047-8). Salem Hse Pubs.
Nebenzahl, Kenneth. Maps of the Holy Land: Images of Terra Sancta Through Two Millennia. LC 86-675055. (Illus.). 164p. 1986. 55.00 (ISBN 0-89659-658-3). Abbeville Pr.
Pearson, H. F., et al. Preliminary Report on the Synagogue at Dura-Europos. (Illus.). 1936. pap. 49.50x (ISBN 0-686-51290-1). Elliots Bks.
Pritchard, James B., ed. Ancient Near East in Pictures with Supplement. 2nd ed. Incl. Ancient Near Eastern Texts Relating to the Old Testament with Supplement. 3rd ed. Set. text ed. 60.50x ea. (ISBN 0-691-03503-2, 035032T); pictures 66.25x (032024T). 1969. deluxe ed. 68.50x ea. (ISBN 0-691-03502-4); Set. 126.75x (ISBN 0-686-66606-2). Princeton U Pr.
Schous, Gerald P. The Extramural Sanctuary of Demeter & Persephone at Cyrene, Libya, Final Reports: Volume II: The East Greek, Island, & Laconian Pottery. White, Donald, ed. (University Museum Monograph: No. 56). (Illus.). xxi, 121p. 1986. 45.00 (ISBN 0-934718-55-5). Univ Mus of U PA.

NEAR EAST–CIVILIZATION
Garsoian, Nina & Mathews, Thomas, eds. East of Byzantium: Syria & Armenia in the Formative Period. LC 82-9665. (Dumbarton Oaks Symposium). (Illus.). 266p. 1982. 35.00x (ISBN 0-88402-104-1). Dumbarton Oaks.
Goedicke, Hans & Roberts, J. J., eds. Unity & Diversity: Essays in the History, Literature, & Religion of the Ancient Near East. LC 74-24376. (Johns Hopkins University Near Eastern Studies). pap. 60.00 (ISBN 0-317-11301-1, 2016572). Bks Demand UMI.
Gorelick, L. & Williams-Forte, E., eds. Ancient Seals & the Bible. (Occasional Papers on the Near East: Vol. 2, Issue 1). (Illus.). 84p. 1984. pap. 13.00x (ISBN 0-89003-045-6). Undena Pubns.
Jurji, Edward J. The Middle East, Its Religion & Culture. LC 72-9809. 159p. 1973. Repr. of 1956 ed. lib. bdg. 22.50x (ISBN 0-8371-6597-0, JUME). Greenwood.

NEAR EAST–DESCRIPTION AND TRAVEL
Davis, Moshe, ed. Holy Land Missions & Missionaries: An Original Anthology. LC 77-70703. (America & the Holy Land Ser.). (Illus.). 1977. lib. bdg. 20.00x (ISBN 0-405-10259-3). Ayer Co Pubs.
Littell, Franklin H. A Pilgrim's Interfaith Guide to the Holy Land. (Illus.). 84p. 1982. 7.95 (ISBN 9-65220-030-1, Carta Pub Israel). Hippocrene Bks.
Nebenzahl, Kenneth. Maps of the Holy Land: Images of Terra Sancta Through Two Millennia. LC 86-675055. (Illus.). 164p. 1986. 55.00 (ISBN 0-89659-658-3). Abbeville Pr.

NEAR EAST–RELIGION
Arberry, Arthur J. Religion in the Middle East, 2 Vols. LC 68-21187. (Illus.). 1969. Set. 105.00 (ISBN 0-521-07400-2). Vol. 1. 62.50 (ISBN 0-521-20543-3); Vol. 2. 59.50 (ISBN 0-521-20544-1). Cambridge U Pr.
Caldarola, Carlo, ed. Religion & Societies: Asia & the Middle East. (Religion & Society: No. 22). 688p. 1982. text ed. 73.75 (ISBN 90-279-3259-X); Pub. 1984. pap. 29.50 (ISBN 3-11-010021-5). Mouton.
Curtis, Michael, ed. Religion & Politics in the Middle East. LC 81-52445. (Westview Special Studies on the Middle East). 406p. 1982. pap. 14.95x (ISBN 0-86531-388-1). Westview.
Frankfort, Henri. Cylinder Seals, A Documentary Essay on the Art & Religion of the Ancient Near East. 427p. Repr. of 1939 ed. text ed. 74.52x (ISBN 0-576-19456-5). Gregg Intl.
Goedicke, Hans & Roberts, J. J., eds. Unity & Diversity: Essays in the History, Literature, & Religion of the Ancient Near East. LC 74-24376. (Johns Hopkins University Near Eastern Studies). pap. 60.00 (ISBN 0-317-11301-1, 2016572). Bks Demand UMI.
It Is No Dream. LC 78-51766. 1978. pap. 4.95 (ISBN 0-915540-21-5). Friends Israel-Spearhead Pr.
Joseph, John. Muslim-Christian Relations & Inter-Christian Rivalries in the Middle East: The Case of the Jacobites in an Age of Transition. LC 82-870. 320p. 1983. 49.50x (ISBN 0-87395-600-1); pap. 19.95 (ISBN 0-87395-601-X). State U NY Pr.
Jurji, Edward J. The Middle East, Its Religion & Culture. LC 72-9809. 159p. 1973. Repr. of 1956 ed. lib. bdg. 22.50x (ISBN 0-8371-6597-0, JUME). Greenwood.
Kim, Young O. World Religions I: Near & Middle Eastern Religions. 2nd, rev. ed. 275p. 1982. pap. 5.75 (ISBN 0-910621-36-5). HSA Pubns.
Lindenberger, James M. The Aramaic Proverbs of Ahiqar. LC 82-18000. (Near Eastern Studies). 384p. 1983. text ed. 38.00x (ISBN 0-8018-2797-3). Johns Hopkins.
Nijim, Basheer K., ed. American Church Politics & the Middle East. (Monograph: No. 15). 156p. (Orig.). 1982. pap. 7.50 (ISBN 0-937694-53-3). Assn Arab-Amer U Grads.

NEBULAR HYPOTHESIS
see also Cosmogony; Creation
Kant, Immanuel. Kant's Cosmogony. Hastie, W., ed. 1971. Repr. 25.00 (ISBN 0-384-28575-9). Johnson Repr.
Numbers, Ronald L. Creation by Natural Law: Laplace's Nebular Hypothesis in American Thought. LC 76-45810. 196p. 1977. 22.50x (ISBN 0-295-95439-6). U of Wash Pr.

NEHEMIAH
Barber, Cyril J. Nehemiah & the Dynamics of Effective Leadership. LC 76-22567. 1976. pap. 3.95 (ISBN 0-87213-021-5). Loizeaux.
Campbell, Donald K. Nehemiah: Man in Charge. 1979. pap. 4.95 (ISBN 0-88207-781-3). Victor Bks.
Engle, Paul. The Governor Drove Us up the Wall: A Guide to Nehemiah. 1985. pap. text ed. 4.95 (ISBN 0-934688-11-7); pap. text ed. 3.95 leader's guide (ISBN 0-934688-13-3). Great Comm Pubns.
Getz, Gene A. Nehemiah: A Man of Prayer & Persistence. LC 80-53102. 1981. pap. 4.95 (ISBN 0-8307-0778-6, 5414500). Regal.
Lindsay, Gordon. Ezra & Nehemiah & the Return from Babylon. (Old Testament Ser.). 1.25 (ISBN 0-89985-154-1). Christ Nations.

NEMEA, GREECE
Hill, Bert H. Temple of Zeus at Nemea. rev., suppl. ed. Williams, Charles, ed. LC 67-102135. (Illus.). 1966. portfolio 22.00x (ISBN 0-87661-921-9). Am Sch Athens.

NEO-CONFUCIANISM
Chan, Wing-Tsit, ed. Chu Hsi & Neo-Confucianism. LC 85-24532. (Illus.). 672p. 1986. 30.00x (ISBN 0-8248-0961-0). UH Pr.
Chan, Wing-Tsit, tr. from Chinese. Neo-Confucian Terms Explained: The Pei-hsi tzu-i. LC 86-5427. (Neo-Confucian Studies Ser.). 288p. 1986. 35.00x (ISBN 0-231-06384-9). Columbia U Pr.
Chan, Wing Tstit, tr. Reflections on Things at Hand: The Neo-Confucian Anthology. LC 65-22548. (Records of Civilization Sources Studies). 441p. 1967. 38.00x (ISBN 0-231-02819-9); pap. 16.00x (ISBN 0-231-06037-8). Columbia U Pr.
Chang, Carsun. The Development of Neo-Confucian Thought. LC 77-8338. 1977. Repr. of 1957 ed. lib. bdg. 26.75x (ISBN 0-8371-9693-0, CHDN). Greenwood.
--The Development of Neo-Confucian Thought, Vol. 1. 1957. pap. 10.95x (ISBN 0-8084-0105-X); 14.95x (ISBN 0-8084-0104-1). New Coll U Pr.
Ch'ien, Edward T. Chiao Hung & the Restructuring of Neo-Confucianism in the Late Ming. (Neo-Confucian Studuies). 328p. 1986. 29.00 (ISBN 0-231-06022-X). Columbia U Pr.
De Bary, W. Theodore, ed. The Unfolding of Neo-Confucianism. LC 74-10929. (Neo-Confucian Series & Studies in Oriental Culture: No. 10). 593p. 1975. 38.00x (ISBN 0-231-03828-3); pap. 18.50x (ISBN 0-231-03829-1). Columbia U Pr.
De Bary, W. Theodore & Bloom, Irene, eds. Principle & Practicality: Essays in Neo-Confucianism & Practical Learning. LC 78-11530. (Neo-Confucian Series & Studies in Oriental Culture). 1979. 38.00x (ISBN 0-231-04612-X); pap. 19.00x (ISBN 0-231-04613-8). Columbia U Pr.
De Bary, William T. Neo-Confucian Orthodoxy & the Learning of the Mind-&-Heart. LC 81-3809. (Neo-Confucian Studies). 267p. 1986. pap. 15.00x (ISBN 0-231-05229-4). Columbia U Pr.
De Bary, William T. & Haboush, Jahyun K., eds. The Rise of Neo-Confucianism in Korea. 512p. 1985. 40.00x (ISBN 0-231-06052-1). Columbia U pr.
Huang, Hsiu-Chi. Lu Hsiang-Shan: A 12th Century Chinese Idealist Philosopher. LC 75-39028. (China Studies: from Confucius to Mao Ser.). (Illus.). 116p. 1976. Repr. of 1944 ed. 18.15 (ISBN 0-88355-384-8). Hyperion-Conn.
Liu, James T. Ou-yang Hsiu: An Eleventh-Century Neo-Confucianist. 1967. 18.50x (ISBN 0-8047-0262-4). Stanford U Pr.
Nosco, Peter, ed. Confucianism & Tokugawa Culture. LC 83-43086. 360p. 1984. 32.50x (ISBN 0-691-07286-8). Princeton U Pr.
Taylor, Rodney L. The Cultivation of Sagehood As a Religious Goal in Neo-Confucianism: A Study of Selected Writings of Kao P'an-Lung (1562-1626) LC 78-18685. 1978. pap. 10.25 (01-01-22). Scholars Pr GA.
Yang Ming, Wang. Instructions for Practical Living & Other Neo-Confucian Writings. Chan, Wing tsit, tr. from Chinese. 358p. 1985. pap. 14.00x (ISBN 0-231-06039-4). Columbia U Pr.

NEOPLATONISM
Armstrong, A. H. An Introduction to Ancient Philosophy. 3rd ed. LC 81-3731. (Quality Paperback Ser.: No. 418). 260p. 1981. pap. 7.45 (ISBN 0-8226-0418-3). Littlefield.
De Pauley, William C. The Candle of the Lord: Studies in the Cambridge Platonists. (Church Historical Society, London, New Ser.: No. 28). pap. 23.00 (ISBN 0-8115-3152-X). Kraus Repr.
Elsas, Christoph. Neuplatonische und gnostische Weltablehnung in der Schule Plotins. (Religionsgeschichtliche Versuche und Vorarbeiten Ser., Vol. 34). 1975. 45.60 (ISBN 3-11-003941-9). De Gruyter.
Finamore, John. Iamblichus & the Theory of the Vehicle of the Soul. (APA-American Classical Studies). 1985. pap. 12.95 (ISBN 0-89130-883-0, 40-04-14). Scholars Pr GA.

Goudard, Sr. M. Lucien. Etude Sur les Epistres Morales D'Honore D'Urfe. LC 70-94204. (Catholic University of America Studies in Romance Languages & Literatures Ser: No. 8). (Fr). Repr. of 1933 ed. 21.00 (ISBN 0-404-50308-X). AMS Pr.

Greive, Hermann. Studien zum juedischen Neuplatonismus: Die Religionsphilosophie des Abraham Ibn Ezra. (Studia Judaica Vol. 7). 225p. 1973. 35.60x (ISBN 3-11-004116-2). De Gruyter.

Katz, Steven, ed. Jewish Neo-Platonism: Selected Essays. An Original Anthology. LC 79-7178. (Jewish Philosophy, Mysticism & History of Ideas Ser.). 1980. lib. bdg. 48.50x (ISBN 0-405-12236-5). Ayer Co Pubs.

Lamberton, Robert. Homer the Theologian: Neoplatonist Allegorical Rading & the Growth of the Epic Tradition. LC 85-1184. (Transformation of the Classical Heritage Ser.: No. 9). 375p. 1986. text ed. 40.00x (ISBN 0-520-05437-7). U of Cal Pr.

O'Meara, Dominic J. Neoplatonism & Christian Thought. LC 81-5272. (Neoplatonism: Ancient & Modern Ser.). 270p. 1981. 44.50x (ISBN 0-87395-492-0); pap. 14.95x (ISBN 0-87395-493-9). State U NY Pr.

Wilder, Alexander. New Platonism & Alchemy. (Secret Doctrine Reference Ser). 1975. pap. 3.00 (ISBN 0-913510-18-1). Wizards.

NEO-SCHOLASTICISM

Brezik, Victor B., ed. One Hundred Years of Thomism: Aeterni Patris & Afterwards - A Symposium. LC 85-14986. 210p. pap. text ed. 9.95 (ISBN 0-9605456-0-3). U of Notre Dame Pr.

--Thomistic Papers, No. I. LC 85-18508. 176p. 1983. text ed. 20.95 (ISBN 0-268-01850-2); pap. text ed. 10.95 (ISBN 0-268-01851-0). U of Notre Dame Pr.

Miethe, Terry L. & Bourke, Vernon J., eds. Thomistic Bibliography, 1940-1978. LC 80-1195. xxii, 318p. 1980. lib. bdg. 45.00 (ISBN 0-313-21991-5, MTH/). Greenwood.

NEO-THOMISM

see Neo-Scholasticism

NEPAL

Bernier, Ronald M. The Temples of Napal: An Introductory Survey. (Illus.). 247p. 1970. text ed. 27.50x. Coronet Bks.

NESTORIAN CHURCH

D'Mar Shimun, Surma. Assyrian Church Customs & the Murder of Mar Shimun. Wigram, W. A., ed. (Illus.). 128p. 1983. pap. 5.00 (ISBN 0-931428-02-5). Vehicle Edns.

Stewart, John. Nestorian Missionary Enterprise. LC 78-63172. (Heresies of the Early Christian & Medieval Era: Second Ser.). Repr. of 1928 ed. 46.50 (ISBN 0-404-16187-1). AMS Pr.

Tregelles, Samuel P., tr. Gesenius' Hebrew & Chaldee Lexicon. (Reference Set). 919p. 1982. Repr. of 1979 ed. 24.95 (ISBN 0-915134-70-5). Mott Media.

Vine, Aubrey R. The Nestorian Churches. LC 78-63173. (Heresies of the Early Christian & Medieval Era: Second Ser.). Repr. of 1937 ed. 31.50 (ISBN 0-404-16188-X). AMS Pr.

NESTORIANS

see also Nestorian Church

Abramowski, Luise & Goodman, Allan E., eds. Nestorian Collection of Christological Texts, 2 vols. Incl. Vol. 1. Syriac Text. 59.50 (ISBN 0-521-07578-5); Vol. 2. Introduction, Translation & Indexes. 49.50 (ISBN 0-521-08126-2). LC 77-130904. (Oriental Publications Ser.: No. 18, 19). 1972. Cambridge U Pr.

Emhardt, William C. & Lamsa, G. M. Oldest Christian People. LC 71-126651. Repr. of 1926 ed. 14.50 (ISBN 0-404-02339-8). AMS Pr.

Joseph, John B. The Nestorians & Their Muslim Neighbors, A Study of Western Influence on Their Relations. LC 61-7417. (Princeton Studies on the Near East). pap. 74.30 (ISBN 0-317-08465-8, 2000553). Bks Demand UMI.

Montgomery, James A., ed. History of Yaballaha III. 1967. lib. bdg. 14.00x (ISBN 0-374-95814-9, Octagon). Hippocrene Bks.

Westcott, William W. The Chaldean Oracles Attributed to Zoroaster. pap. 5.95 (ISBN 0-916411-16-8). Sure fire.

NESTORIUS, PATRIARCH OF CONSTANTINOPLE, fl. 428

Bethune-Baker, J. F. Nestorius & His Teaching. 1908. 20.00 (ISBN 0-527-07500-0). Kraus Repr.

Loofs, Richard. Nestorius & His Place in the History of the Christian Doctrine. LC 75-1225. 1975. Repr. of 1914 ed. 18.50 (ISBN 0-8337-4903-X). B Franklin.

NEUMANN, JOHN NEPOMUCENE, BP. 1811-1860

Hindman, Jane F. An Ordinary Saint, John Neumann. 1977. pap. 1.95 (ISBN 0-88479-004-5). Arena Lettres.

Rush, Alfred C., ed. Autobiography of St. John Neumann. 1977. 3.50 (ISBN 0-8198-0384-7); pap. 2.50 (ISBN 0-8198-0385-5). Dghtrs St Paul.

NEUMANN, THERESA

Carty, Charles M. Who Is Teresa Neumann? 1974. pap. 1.25 (ISBN 0-89555-093-8). TAN Bks Pubs.

Steiner, Johannes. Therese Neumann. LC 66-27536. (Illus.). 1967. pap. 5.95 (ISBN 0-8189-0144-6). Alba.

NEW CHURCH

see New Jerusalem Church

NEW ENGLAND–BIOGRAPHY

Mather, Cotton. Magnalia Christi Americana: Or the Ecclesiastical History of New England. Cunningham, Raymond J., ed. LC 75-12340. (Milestones of Thought Ser). 1971. pap. 5.95x (ISBN 0-8044-6478-2). Ungar.

Stout, Harry S. The New England Soul: Preaching & Religious Culture in Colonial New England. LC 85-29853. 352p. 1986. 29.95x (ISBN 0-19-503958-0). Oxford U Pr.

NEW ENGLAND–CHURCH HISTORY

Backus, Isaac. History of New England. LC 76-83410. (Religion in America, Ser. 1). 1969. Repr. of 1871 ed. 54.00 (ISBN 0-405-00231-9). Ayer Co Pubs.

Bacon, Leonard. The Genesis of the New England Churches. LC 74-38435. (Religion in America, Ser. 2). 510p. 1972. Repr. of 1874 ed. 32.00 (ISBN 0-405-04056-3). Ayer Co Pubs.

Conforti, Joseph A. Samuel Hopkins & the New Divinity Movement: Calvinism, the Congregational Ministry, & Reform in New England Between the Great Awakenings. LC 80-28268. pap. 62.30 (ISBN 0-317-08398-8, 2020840). Bks Demand UMI.

Earle, Alice M. Sabbath in Puritan New England. 335p. 1969. Repr. of 1891 ed. 20.00 (ISBN 0-87928-005-0). Corner Hse.

Fleming, Sanford. Children & Puritanism: The Place of Children in the Life & Thought of the New England Churches, 1620-1847. LC 70-89178. (American Education: Its Men, Institutions & Ideas Ser). 1969. Repr. of 1933 ed. 15.00 (ISBN 0-405-01416-3). Ayer Co Pubs.

Hall, David D. The Faithful Shepherd: A History of the New England Ministry in the Seventeenth Century. LC 72-81326. (Institute for Early American History & Culture Ser.). xvi, 301p. 1972. 27.50x (ISBN 0-8078-1193-9). U of NC Pr.

Lechford, Thomas. Plain Dealing: Or News from New England. 1969. Repr. of 1867 ed. 19.00 (ISBN 0-384-31985-8). Johnson Repr.

Mansur, Ina. A New England Church: Its First Hundred Years. LC 74-76868. (Illus.). 256p. 1974. 10.95 (ISBN 0-87027-139-3); pap. 5.95 (ISBN 0-87027-140-7). Cumberland Pr.

Marini, Stephen A. Radical Sects of Revolutionary New England. LC 81-6913. 224p. 1982. text ed. 16.50x (ISBN 0-674-74625-2). Harvard U Pr.

Mather, Cotton. Magnalia Christi Americana, or the Ecclesiastical History of New-England from the Year 1620, Unto the Year 1698, 7 Bks. LC 74-141092. (Research Library of Colonial Americana). (Illus.). 1971. Repr. of 1702 ed. Set. 58.00 (ISBN 0-405-03297-8). Ayer Co Pubs.

--Magnalia Christi Americana: Or the Ecclesiastical History of New England. Cunningham, Raymond J., ed. LC 75-12340. (Milestones of Thought Ser). 1971. pap. 5.95x (ISBN 0-8044-6478-2). Ungar.

Morse, James K. Jedidiah Morse: A Champion of New England Orthodoxy. LC 39-11247. Repr. of 1939 ed. 10.00 (ISBN 0-404-04504-9). AMS Pr.

Riegler, Gordon A. The Socialization of the New England Clergy Eighteen Hundred to Eighteen Sixty. LC 79-13027. (Perspectives in American History Ser.: No. 37). 187p. 1980. Repr. of 1945 ed. lib. bdg. 25.00x (ISBN 0-87991-361-4). Porcupine Pr.

Slafter, Edmund F. & Slafter, Edmund F., eds. John Checkley, or, Evolution of Religious Tolerance in Massachusetts, 2 vols. (Prince Soc. Pubns: Nos. 22 & 23). 1966. 39.00 (ISBN 0-8337-0553-9). B Franklin.

Stauffer, Vernon. New England & the Bavarian Illuminati. LC 66-27153. 1967. Repr. of 1918 ed. 8.50x (ISBN 0-8462-0953-5). Russell.

Walker, Williston. Ten New England Leaders. LC 76-83445. (Religion in America Ser). 1969. Repr. of 1901 ed. 28.00 (ISBN 0-405-00278-5). Ayer Co Pubs.

Winslow, Ola E. Meetinghouse Hill, Sixteen Thirty to Seventy Eighty-Three. 1972. pap. 2.95x (ISBN 0-393-00632-8, Norton Lib). Norton.

NEW ENGLAND–HISTORY–COLONIAL PERIOD, ca. 1600-1775

Adair, John. Founding Fathers: The Puritans in England & America. 314p. 1982. 24.95x (ISBN 0-460-04421-4, Pub. by J M Dent England). Biblio Dist.

Brown, J. Pilgrim Fathers of New England & Their Puritan Successors. 4th ed. (Illus.). Repr. of 1920 ed. 39.00 (ISBN 0-527-12050-2). Kraus Repr.

Cobbett, Thomas. Civil Magistrate's Power in Matters of Religion Modestly Debated, London, 1653. LC 74-141104. (Research Library of Colonial Americana). 1972. Repr. of 1653 ed. 24.50 (ISBN 0-405-03318-4). Ayer Co Pubs.

Company for the Propagation of the Gospel in New England & the Parts Adjacent in America, London. Some Correspondence Between the Governors & Treasurers of the New England Company in London & the Commissioners of the United Colonies in America, the Missionaries of the Company & Others Between the Years 1657 & 1712. Ford, John W., ed. LC 73-126413. (Research & Source Works: No. 524). 1970. Repr. of 1896 ed. lib. bdg. 29.50 (ISBN 0-8337-1185-7). B Franklin.

Mather, Cotton. Magnalia Christi Americana: Or the Ecclesiastical History of New England. Cunningham, Raymond J., ed. LC 75-12340. (Milestones of Thought Ser). 1971. pap. 5.95x (ISBN 0-8044-6478-2). Ungar.

Neal, Daniel. The History of New-England... to the Year of Our Lord, 1700, 2 vols. LC 75-31125. Repr. of 1747 ed. Set. 64.00 (ISBN 0-404-13760-1). AMS Pr.

Rumsey, Peter L. Acts of God & the People, 1620-1730. Miles, Margaret R., ed. LC 86-19292. (Studies in Religion: No. 2). 182p. 1986. 39.95 (ISBN 0-8357-1761-5). UMI Res Pr.

Wilson, Robert J., III. The Benevolent Deity: Ebenezer Gay & the Rise of Rational Religion in New England, 1669-1787. LC 83-3657. (Illus.). 320p. 1984. 26.00x (ISBN 0-8122-7891-7). U of Pa Pr.

NEW ENGLAND–INTELLECTUAL LIFE

Bercovitch, Sacvan. The Puritan Origins of the American Self. LC 74-29713. 272p. 1975. pap. 9.95x (ISBN 0-300-02117-8). Yale U Pr.

Lowance, Mason I, Jr. The Language of Canaan: Metaphor & Symbol in New England from the Puritans to the Transcendentalists. LC 79-21179. 1980. 22.50x (ISBN 0-674-50949-8). Harvard U Pr.

Morison, Samuel E. The Intellectual Life of Colonial New England. LC 79-20246. 1980. Repr. of 1956 ed. lib. bdg. 24.75x (ISBN 0-313-22032-8, MOIL). Greenwood.

NEW ENGLAND–SOCIAL LIFE AND CUSTOMS

Lowell, James R. Among My Books. LC 75-126666. 1970. 11.50 (ISBN 0-404-04039-X). AMS Pr.

Morgan, E. S. Puritan Family. 14.75 (ISBN 0-8446-2609-0). Peter Smith.

Morgan, Edmund S., ed. Puritan Family: Religion & Domestic Relations in 17th-Century New England. rev. ed. pap. 6.95x (ISBN 0-06-131227-4, TB1227, Torch). Har-Row.

NEW ENGLAND THEOLOGY

Fleming, Sanford. Children & Puritanism: The Place of Children in the Life & Thought of the New England Churches, 1620-1847. LC 70-89178. (American Education: Its Men, Institutions & Ideas Ser). 1969. Repr. of 1933 ed. 15.00 (ISBN 0-405-01416-3). Ayer Co Pubs.

Foster, Frank H. Modern Movement in American Theology. facs. ed. LC 76-86751. (Essay Index Reprint Ser). 1939. 14.50 (ISBN 0-8369-1131-8). Ayer Co Pubs.

McKinsey, Elizabeth R. The Western Experiment: New England Transcendentalists in the Ohio Valley. LC 72-83467. (Essays in History & Literature Ser.). 80p. 1973. pap. 4.95x (ISBN 0-674-95040-2). Harvard U Pr.

NEW ENGLAND TRANSCENDENTALISM

see Transcendentalism (New England)

NEW FRANCE–DISCOVERY AND EXPLORATION

Sagard-Theodat, Gabriel. Long Journey to the Country of the Hurons. Wrong, George M., ed. Langton, H. H., tr. LC 68-28613. 1968. Repr. of 1939 ed. lib. bdg. 29.25x (ISBN 0-8371-3861-2, SAJC). Greenwood.

NEW JERUSALEM CHURCH

Field, G. Memoirs, Incidents, Reminiscences of the Early History of the New Church in Michigan, Indiana, Illinois, & Adjacent States, & Canada. LC 70-134423. 1972. Repr. of 1879 ed. 27.00 (ISBN 0-404-08463-X). AMS Pr.

Keller, Helen. My Religion: Large Print Edition. LC 74-11645. 1979. 4.75 (ISBN 0-87785-158-1). Swedenborg.

Meyers, Mary A. A New World Jerusalem: The Swedenborgian Experience in Community Construction. LC 82-11997. (Contributions in American Studies: No. 65). (Illus.). xiii, 217p. 1983. lib. bdg. 29.95 (ISBN 0-313-23602-X, MNJ/). Greenwood.

Science & Philosophy in the Light of the New Church. (Words for the New Church Ser.: Vols. IV-VI). 289p. 1976. Repr. of 1879 ed. 7.00 (ISBN 0-915221-24-1). Swedenborg Sci Assn.

Swedenborg, Emanuel. Four Leading Doctrines of the New Church. LC 71-134426. Repr. of 1882 ed. 21.00 (ISBN 0-404-08466-4). AMS Pr.

Words in Swedenborg & Their Meanings in Modern English. 54p. 1985. pap. 2.75 (ISBN 0-910557-13-6). Acad New Church.

NEW JERUSALEM CHURCH–DOCTRINAL AND CONTROVERSIAL WORKS

James, Henry, Sr. Tracts for the New Times: No. 1 Letter to a Swedenborgian. LC 72-916. (The Selected Works of Henry James, Sr.: Vol. 9). 1983. Repr. of 1847 ed. 24.50 (ISBN 0-404-10089-9). AMS Pr.

Keller, Helen. My Religion. LC 74-11654. 1972. pap. 2.95 (ISBN 0-87785-103-4); Span. ed. leatherette o.s.i. 5.00 (ISBN 0-87785-114-X). Swedenborg.

Mayer, Fred S. Why Two Worlds: Relation of Physical to Spiritual Realities. LC 78-134425. Repr. of 1934 ed. 21.00 (ISBN 0-404-08465-6). AMS Pr.

Reed, Sampson. Observations on the Growth of the Mind Including GENIUS. 5th ed. LC 72-4971. (The Romantic Tradition in American Literature Ser.). 110p. 1972. Repr. of 1859 ed. 18.00 (ISBN 0-405-04641-3). Ayer Co Pubs.

Sechrist, Alice S., ed. Dictionary of Bible Imagery. LC 79-63409. 1972. 3.95 (ISBN 0-87785-118-2). Swedenborg.

Swedenborg, Emanuel. Divine Love & Wisdom. LC 75-37094. student ed. 12.00 (ISBN 0-87785-056-9). Swedenborg.

--Divine Love & Wisdom. Dole, George, tr. LC 85-50918. 1986. pap. 6.95 (ISBN 0-87785-129-8). Swedenborg.

--Four Doctrines. LC 67-1465. 1971. student ed. 12.00 (ISBN 0-87785-063-1); pap. 2.95 (ISBN 0-87785-064-X). Swedenborg.

--Miscellaneous Theological Works. LC 76-46143. 1970. cancelled (ISBN 0-87785-071-2); student ed. 12.00 (ISBN 0-87785-070-4). Swedenborg.

--Posthumous Theological Works, 2 vols. LC 38-24293. 634p. Vol. 1. Set. cancelled (ISBN 0-87785-078-X); student ed. 12.00 ea. Vol. 1 (ISBN 0-87785-073-9). Vol. 2 (ISBN 0-87785-074-7). Set. 24.00 (ISBN 0-87785-075-5). Swedenborg.

NEW SOUTH WALES–RELIGION

Phillips, Walter. Defending "A Christian Country". Churchmen & Society in New South Wales in the 1880's & After. (Illus.). 332p. 1982. text ed. 39.95 (ISBN 0-7022-1539-2). U of Queensland Pr.

Waldersee, James. Catholic Society in New South Wales 1788-1860. (Illus.). 348p. 1974. 31.00x (ISBN 0-424-06460-X, Pub. by Sydney U Pr). Intl Spec Bk.

NEW TESTAMENT GREEK

see Greek Language, Biblical

NEW THOUGHT

see also Jesus Christ–New Thought Interpretations; Psychology, Applied

Addington, Jack & Addington, Cornelia. The Perfect Power Within You. new ed. LC 73-87712. 167p. 1973. pap. 4.95 (ISBN 0-87516-179-0). De Vorss.

Addington, Jack E. Psychogenesis: Everything Begins in the Mind. LC 79-145391. 1971. 10.95 (ISBN 0-396-06334-9). Dodd.

Allen, James. As a Man Thinketh. pap. 1.00 (ISBN 0-87516-000-X). De Vorss.

--As a Man Thinketh. 1959. 3.95 (ISBN 0-399-12829-8, G&D). Putnam Pub Group.

--As a Man Thinketh. 4.95 (ISBN 0-529-05908-8, F12); pap. 2.95 (ISBN 0-529-05906-1, D6). World Bible.

--As You Thinketh: Update & Revision of James Allen's Classic "As a Man Thinketh". rev. ed. 88p. 1984. pap. 5.95 (ISBN 0-914295-03-9). Top Mtn Pub.

Andersen, Uell S. Magic in Your Mind. pap. 7.00 (ISBN 0-87980-089-5). Wilshire.

--Secret of Secrets. pap. 7.00 (ISBN 0-87980-134-4). Wilshire.

Behrend, Genevieve. Your Invisible Power. 1921. pap. 2.75 (ISBN 0-87516-004-2). De Vorss.

Bristol, C. & Sherman, H. TNT: The Power Within You. 1954. pap. 4.95 (ISBN 0-13-922674-5). P-H.

Curtis, Donald. Your Thoughts Can Change Your Life. pap. 7.00 (ISBN 0-87980-179-4). Wilshire.

Ellsworth, Paul. Direct Healing. LC 83-3920. 1983. lib. bdg. 15.95x (ISBN 0-89370-658-2). Borgo Pr.

Fox, Emmet. Alter Your Life. 1950. 12.45 (ISBN 0-06-062850-2, HarpR). Har-Row.

--Around the Year with Emmet Fox. LC 58-13248. 1958. 12.45 (ISBN 0-06-062870-7, HarpR). Har-Row.

--Find & Use Your Inner Power. 1941. 11.60 (ISBN 0-06-062890-1, HarpR). Har-Row.

--Make Your Life Worthwhile. LC 83-48456. 256p. 1984. pap. 7.95 (ISBN 0-06-062913-4, RD 508, HarpR). Har-Row.

--Power Through Constructive Thinking. 1940. 12.45 (ISBN 0-06-062930-4, HarpR). Har-Row.

--Stake Your Claim. LC 52-11683. 1952. 8.95 (ISBN 0-06-062970-3, HarpR). Har-Row.
--The Ten Commandments. LC 53-8369. 1953. 12.45 (ISBN 0-06-062990-8, HarpR). Har-Row.
Goldsmith, Joel. Beyond Words & Thoughts. 6.00 (ISBN 0-8216-0041-9). Univ Bks.
--Conscious Union with God. 6.00 (ISBN 0-8216-0050-8). Univ Bks.
Goldsmith, Joel S. Art of Meditation. LC 56-13258. 1957. 12.45 (ISBN 0-06-063150-3, HarpR). Har-Row.
--Art of Spiritual Healing. LC 59-14532. 1959. 11.45 (ISBN 0-06-063170-8, HarpR). Har-Row.
--The Contemplative Life. 212p. 1976. pap. 5.95 (ISBN 0-8065-0523-0). Citadel Pr.
--Living the Infinite Way. rev. ed. LC 61-9646. 1961. 11.45 (ISBN 0-06-063190-2, HarpR). Har-Row.
--The Mystical I. Sinkler, Lorraine, ed. LC 73-149745. 1971. 10.45 (ISBN 0-06-063195-3, HarpR). Har-Row.
--Parenthesis in Eternity. LC 64-10368. 1963. pap. 11.95 (ISBN 0-06-063230-5, HarpR). Har-Row.
--Thunder of Silence. LC 61-7340. 1961. 12.45 (ISBN 0-06-063270-4, HarpR). Har-Row.
--The World Is New. LC 62-7953. 1978. 8.95 (ISBN 0-06-063291-7, HarpR). Har-Row.
Holmes, Ernest. The Basic Ideas of Science of Mind. 96p. 1957. pap. 4.50 (ISBN 0-911336-23-0). Sci of Mind.
--Creative Ideas. Kinnear, Willis H., ed. 96p. 1964. pap. 4.50 (ISBN 0-911336-00-1). Sci of Mind.
--Creative Mind & Success. 1947. 10.95 (ISBN 0-396-02070-4). Dodd.
--Discover a Richer Life. Kinnear, Willis H., ed. 96p. 1961. pap. 4.50 (ISBN 0-911336-27-3). Sci of Mind.
--Effective Prayer. Kinnear, Willis H., ed. 52p. 1966. pap. 4.50 (ISBN 0-911336-02-8). Sci of Mind.
--Freedom from Stress. Kinnear, Willis H., ed. 96p. 1964. pap. 4.50 (ISBN 0-911336-30-3). Sci of Mind.
--Freedom to Live. Kinnear, Willis H., ed. 96p. 1969. pap. 4.50 (ISBN 0-911336-35-4). Sci of Mind.
--How to Use the Science of Mind. 1950. 8.95 (ISBN 0-396-03212-5). Dodd.
--Journey into Life. Kinnear, Willis H., ed. 88p. 1967. pap. 5.50 (ISBN 0-911336-05-2). Sci of Mind.
--Keys to Wisdom. Kinnear, Willis H., ed. 96p. 1965. pap. 5.50 (ISBN 0-911336-06-0). Sci of Mind.
--Know Yourself! Kinnear, Willis H., ed. 96p. (Orig.). 1970. pap. 4.50 (ISBN 0-911336-36-2). Sci of Mind.
--The Larger Life. Kinnear, Willis H., ed. 84p. 1969. pap. 5.50 (ISBN 0-911336-07-9). Sci of Mind.
--Living Without Fear. Kinnear, Willis H., ed. 96p. 1962. pap. 4.50 (ISBN 0-911336-28-1). Sci of Mind.
--Observations. Kinnear, Willis H., ed. 64p. 1968. pap. 5.50 (ISBN 0-911336-12-5). Sci of Mind.
--The Power of an Idea. Kinnear, Willis H., ed. 96p. 1965. pap. 4.50 (ISBN 0-911336-31-1). Sci of Mind.
--Science of Mind. rev. & enl. ed. 17.95 (ISBN 0-396-02069-0). Dodd.
--Ten Ideas That Make a Difference. Kinnear, Willis H., ed. 96p. 1966. pap. 4.50 (ISBN 0-911336-32-X). Sci of Mind.
--Think Your Troubles Away. Kinnear, Willis H., ed. 96p. 1963. pap. 4.50 (ISBN 0-911336-29-X). Sci of Mind.
--This Thing Called Life. 1947. 8.95 (ISBN 0-396-02851-9). Dodd.
--Thoughts Are Things. Kinnear, Willis H., ed. 96p. 1967. pap. 4.50 (ISBN 0-911336-33-8). Sci of Mind.
--Words That Heal Today. 1948. 10.95 (ISBN 0-396-03093-9). Dodd.
Holmes, Ernest & Hornaday, William H. Help for Today. 256p. 1969. pap. 7.50 (ISBN 0-911336-03-6). Sci of Mind.
Holmes, Ernest & Kinnear, Willis. Practical Application of Science of Mind. 96p. 1958. pap. 4.50 (ISBN 0-911336-24-9). Sci of Mind.
Holmes, Ernest & Kinnear, Willis H. It Can Happen to You. 96p. 1959. pap. 4.50 (ISBN 0-911336-25-7). Sci of Mind.
Hornaday, William H. & Ware, Harlan. Your Aladdin's Lamp. 288p. 1979. pap. 8.50 (ISBN 0-911336-75-3). Sci of Mind.
Kinnear, Willis. Thirty Day Mental Diet. 144p. 1965. pap. 7.95 (ISBN 0-911336-20-6). Sci of Mind.
Larson, Martin. New Thought: The Revolt Against Orthodoxy. 352p. cancelled (ISBN 0-8159-6317-3). Devin.
Larson, Martin A. New Thought or a Modern Religious Approach: The Philosophy of Health, Happiness & Prosperity. LC 84-7637. 475p. 1985. 19.95 (ISBN 0-8022-2464-4). Philos Lib.
Lighton, Merle. Addict to Yearning: Inspirational Philosophy & Religion. 1952. 5.00 (ISBN 0-910892-00-8, 910892). Lighton Pubns.
Mary. You Are God. 1955. pap. 4.95 (ISBN 0-87516-057-3). De Vorss.
Murphy, Joseph. Amazing Laws of Cosmic Mind Power. 1965. pap. 4.95 (ISBN 0-13-023804-X, Reward). P-H.
--Infinite Power for Richer Living. 1969. pap. 4.95 (ISBN 0-13-464396-8, Reward). P-H.
--Living Without Strain. 157p. 1973. pap. 3.95 (ISBN 0-87516-187-1). De Vorss.
--Pray Your Way Through It. 171p. 1973. pap. 4.00 (ISBN 0-87516-190-1). De Vorss.
--Prayer Is the Answer. 190p. 1973. pap. 5.00 (ISBN 0-87516-189-8). De Vorss.
Nimick, John A. Be Still & Know. LC 67-11989. 1967. 7.95 (ISBN 0-8022-1222-0). Philos Lib.
Parker, Gail T. Mind Cure in New England: From the Civil War to World War I. LC 72-92704. 209p. 1973. 18.00x (ISBN 0-87451-073-2). U Pr of New Eng.
Skarin, Annalee. Celestial Song of Creation. 1962p. pap. 5.95 (ISBN 0-87516-090-5). De Vorss.
--Man Triumphant. 1966p. pap. 5.95 (ISBN 0-87516-091-3). De Vorss.
--Secrets of Eternity. 1960. pap. 5.95 (ISBN 0-87516-092-1). De Vorss.
--Temple of God. pap. 5.95 (ISBN 0-87516-093-X). De Vorss.
--To God the Glory. pap. 5.95 (ISBN 0-87516-094-8). De Vorss.
--Ye Are Gods. 343p. 1973. pap. 5.95 (ISBN 0-87516-344-0). De Vorss.
Trine, Ralph W. In Tune with the Infinite. LC 72-125594. 1970. pap. 4.95 (ISBN 0-672-51349-8). Bobbs.
Troward, Thomas. Creative Process in the Individual. rev. ed. 10.95 (ISBN 0-396-02064-X). Dodd.
--Dore Lectures on Mental Science. 1909. 9.95 (ISBN 0-396-02063-1). Dodd.
--Edinburgh Lectures on Mental Science. 1909. 9.95 (ISBN 0-396-02062-3). Dodd.
Werber, Eva B. Journey with the Master. 1950. pap. 3.25 (ISBN 0-87516-103-0). De Vorss.
--Quiet Talks with the Master. 1936. pap. 3.25 (ISBN 0-87516-104-9). De Vorss.
Wolhorn, Herman. Emmet Fox's Golden Keys to Successful Living. LC 76-62930. 1977. 10.84 (ISBN 0-06-069670-2, HarpR). Har-Row.

NEW YORK (N.Y.)–CHURCHES

Bayley, James R. A Brief Sketch of the Early History of the Catholic Church on the Island of New York. LC 77-359171. (Monograph Ser.: No. 29). 1973. Repr. of 1870 ed. 8.50x (ISBN 0-930060-09-1). US Cath Hist.
Bennett, William H. Catholic Footsteps in Old New York: A Chronicle of Catholicity in the City of New York from 1524 to 1808. LC 77-359169. (Monograph Ser.: No. 28). 1973. Repr. of 1909 ed. 10.00x (ISBN 0-930060-08-3). US Cath Hist.
Campbell, Helen. Darkness & Daylight: Or, Lights & Shadows of New York Life: A Pictorial Record of Personal Experiences by Day & Night in the Great Metropolis with Hundreds of Thrilling Anecdotes & Incidents. LC 76-81511. 1969. Repr. of 1895 ed. 48.00x (ISBN 0-8103-3566-2). Gale.
Carthy, Mary P. Old St. Patrick's: New York's First Cathedral. (Monograph Ser.: No. 23). (Illus.). 1947. 10.00x (ISBN 0-930060-05-9). US Cath Hist.
Competitive Designs for the Cathedral of St. John the Divine in New York City. (Architecture & Decorative Art Ser.). 57p. 1982. Repr. lib. bdg. 95.00 (ISBN 0-306-76139-4). Da Capo.
Dolan, Jay P. The Immigrant Church: New York's Irish & German Catholics. LC 75-12552. pap. 59.30 (ISBN 0-317-08406-2, 2019817). Bks Demand UMI.
Messiter, Arthur. History of the Choir & Music of Trinity Church. LC 72-137317. Repr. of 1906 ed. 21.45 (ISBN 0-404-04313-5). AMS Pr.

NEW YORK (N.Y.)–FIVE POINTS MISSION

Ladies Of The Mission. Old Brewery & the New Mission House at the Five Points. LC 72-112563. (Rise of Urban America). (Illus.). 1970. Repr. of 1854 ed. 26.50 (ISBN 0-405-02461-4). Ayer Co Pubs.

NEW YORK (STATE)–CHURCH HISTORY

Kreider, Harry J. Lutheranism in Colonial New York. LC 78-38452. (Religion in America, Ser. 2). 184p. 1972. Repr. of 1942 ed. 13.00 (ISBN 0-405-04072-5). Ayer Co Pubs.
Lindsley, James Elliott. This Planted Vine: A Narrative History of the Episcopal Diocese of New York. LC 84-47588. (Illus.). 320p. 1984. 24.50 (ISBN 0-06-015347-4, HarpT). Har-Row.
Orange County Genealogical Society. Diagram & List of Goshen Presbyterian Church Pews, 1796. 1986. pap. text ed. 0.50 (ISBN 0-937135-02-X). Orange County Genealog.
Taylor, Mary C. A History of the Foundations of Catholicism in Northern New York. LC 77-359034. (Monograph Ser.: No. 32). (Illus.). 13.50x (ISBN 0-930060-12-1). US Cath Hist.
Zwierlein, Frederick K. Religion in the New Netherland, 1623-1664. LC 72-120851. (Civil Liberties in American History Ser.). 1971. Repr. of 1910 ed. lib. bdg. 39.50 (ISBN 0-306-71960-6). Da Capo.

NEW YORK (STATE)–HISTORY–COLONIAL PERIOD, ca. 1600-1775

Zwierlein, Frederick K. Religion in the New Netherland, 1623-1664. LC 72-120851. (Civil Liberties in American History Ser.). 1971. Repr. of 1910 ed. lib. bdg. 39.50 (ISBN 0-306-71960-6). Da Capo.

NEWMAN, JOHN HENRY, CARDINAL, 1801-1890

Allenson, Robert D., compiled by. John Henry Newman, 1801-1890: A Preliminary Register of Editions from 1818 to 1890. 1976. pap. text ed. 5.00x (ISBN 0-8401-0050-7, Aleph Pr). A R Allenson.
Barry, William. Cardinal Newman. 1973. Repr. of 1904 ed. 20.00 (ISBN 0-8274-1797-7). R West.
Blehl, Vincent F. John Henry Newman: A Bibliograhical Catalogue of His Writings. LC 77-12141. 148p. 1978. 20.00x (ISBN 0-8139-0738-1). U Pr of Va.
Capuchin, Zeno. John Henry Newman: His Inner Life. LC 86-81424. 340p. (Orig.). 1987. 29.95 (ISBN 0-89870-149-X); pap. 12.95 (ISBN 0-89870-112-0). Ignatius Pr.
Chadwick, Owen. Newman. (Past Masters Ser.). 1983. 13.95x (ISBN 0-19-287568-X); pap. 4.95 (ISBN 0-19-287567-1). Oxford U Pr.
Coulson, John & Allchin, Arthur M., eds. The Rediscovery of Newman: An Oxford Symposium. LC 68-84451. 1967. text ed. 15.00x (ISBN 0-8401-0458-8). A R Allenson.
Culler, Arthur D. The Imperial Intellect. LC 55-8700. Repr. of 1955 ed. lib. bdg. 22.50x (ISBN 0-8371-7683-2, CUII). Greenwood.
D'Arcy, Martin C. The Nature of Belief. facsimile ed. (Select Bibliographies Reprint Ser). Repr. of 1931 ed. 21.00 (ISBN 0-8369-5930-2). Ayer Co Pubs.
Dessain, Charles S. John Henry Newman. 2nd ed. 1971. 17.50x (ISBN 0-8047-0778-2). Stanford U Pr.
Donald, Gertrude. Men Who Left the Movement. facs. ed. LC 67-23207. (Essay Index Reprint Ser). 1933. 20.00 (ISBN 0-8369-0385-4). Ayer Co Pubs.
Earnest, James D. & Tracey, Gerard. John Henry Newman: An Annotated Bibliography of His Tract & Pamphlet Collection. LC 84-48069. (Reference Library of Social Science). 600p. 1984. lib. bdg. 78.00 (ISBN 0-8240-8958-8). Garland pub.
Garraghan, Gilbert J. Prose Studies in Newman. 1915. Repr. 25.00 (ISBN 0-8274-3216-X). R West.
Hutton, Richard H. Cardinal Newman. LC 75-30029. Repr. of 1891 ed. 21.00 (ISBN 0-404-14033-5). AMS Pr.
Leslie, Shane. Studies in Sublime Failure. LC 70-117817. (Essay Index Reprint Ser). 1932. 20.00 (ISBN 0-8369-1670-0). Ayer Co Pubs.
Martin, Brian W. John Henry Newman: His Life & Work. (Illus.). 1982. 22.50x (ISBN 0-19-520387-9). Oxford U Pr.
May, J. Lewis. Cardinal Newman. 1945. Repr. lib. bdg. 20.00 (ISBN 0-8414-6605-X). Folcroft.
Moody, John. John Henry Newman. 1946. Repr. 20.00 (ISBN 0-8482-5070-2). Norwood Edns.
Newman, Jay. The Mental Philosophy of John Henry Newman. 224p. 1986. pap. 22.95x (ISBN 0-88920-186-2, Pub. by Wilfrid Laurier Canada). Humanities.
Newman, John H. The Letters & Diaries of John Henry Cardinal Newman: Consulting the Laity, January 1859-June 1861, Vol. 19. 38.50x (ISBN 0-19-920051-3). Oxford U Pr.
--The Letters & Diaries of John Henry Cardinal Newman: Ealing, Trinity, Oriel, February 1801 to December 1826, Vol. I. Ker, Ian & Gornall, Thomas, eds. 1978. 52.00x (ISBN 0-19-920102-1). Oxford U Pr.
--The Letters & Diaries of John Henry Cardinal Newman: The Oxford Movement, July 1833 to December 1834, Vol. IV. Ker, Ian & Gornall, Thomas, eds. 1980. 55.00x (ISBN 0-19-920112-9). Oxford U Pr.
--The Letters & Diaries of John Henry Newman: A Cardinal's Apostolate, October 1881-December 1884, Vol. 30. Dessain, Charles S., ed. 1976. 47.00x (ISBN 0-19-920060-2). Oxford U Pr.
--The Letters & Diaries of John Henry Newman: New Bearings, January 1832 to June 1833, Vol. 3. Ker, Ian & Gornall, Thomas, eds. 1979. 52.00x (ISBN 0-19-920109-9). Oxford U Pr.
--The Letters & Diaries of John Henry Newman: Standing Firm Amid Trials, July 1861-December 1863, Vol. 20. 38.50x (ISBN 0-19-920052-1). Oxford U Pr.
--The Letters & Diaries of John Henry Newman: The Cardinalate, January 1878-September 1881, Vol. 29. Dessain, Charles S. & Gornall, Thomas, eds. 1976. 47.00x (ISBN 0-19-920059-9). Oxford U Pr.
--The Letters & Diaries of John Henry Newman: The Last Years, January 1885 to August 1890, Vol.31. Dessain, Charles S. & Gornall, Thomas, eds. 1977. 52.00x (ISBN 0-19-920083-1). Oxford U Pr.
--The Letters & Diaries of John Henry Newman: Tutor of Oriel, January 1827 to December 1831, Vol. II. Ker, Ian & Gornall, Thomas, eds. 1979. 55.00x (ISBN 0-19-920108-0). Oxford U Pr.
--The Letters & Diaries of John Henry Newman, Vols. 27 & 28. Dessain, Stephen & Gornall, Thomas, eds. Incl. Vol. 27. Controversy with Gladstone, January 1874-December 1875 (ISBN 0-19-920057-2); Vol. 28. Fellow of Trinity, January 1876-December 1878 (ISBN 0-19-920058-0). 1975. 38.50x ea. Oxford U Pr.
--A Packet of Letters: A Selection from the Correspondence of John Henry Newman. Suggs, Joyce, intro. by. LC 82-4444. (Illus.). 1983. 19.95x (ISBN 0-19-826442-9). Oxford U Pr.
Newman, Cardinal John H. Characteristics from the Writings of John Henry Newman. LC 76-45366. 1976. Repr. of 1875 ed. lib. bdg. 49.50 (ISBN 0-8414-5813-8). Folcroft.
O'Connell, Daniel M. A Cardinal Newman Prayerbook: Kindly Light. 352p. 1985. pap. 14.95 (ISBN 0-87193-220-2). Dimension Bks.
Powell, Jouett L. Three Uses of Christian Discourse in John Henry Newman. LC 75-29423. (American Academy of Religion. Dissertation Ser.). 1975. pap. 9.95 (ISBN 0-89130-042-2, 010110). Scholars Pr GA.
Robbins, William. Newman Brothers: An Essay in Comparative Intellectual Biography. LC 66-4976. (Illus.). 1966. 15.00x (ISBN 0-674-62200-6). Harvard U Pr.
Ryan, John K. & Benard, Edmond, eds. American Essays for the Newman Centennial. LC 47-30528. pap. 64.50 (ISBN 0-317-07851-8, 2005379). Bks Demand UMI.
Sarolea, Charles. Cardinal Newman. 174p. 1980. Repr. of 1908 ed. lib. bdg. 30.00 (ISBN 0-89987-759-1). Darby Bks.
Sencourt, Robert. The Life of Newman. 1973. Repr. of 1948 ed. 30.00 (ISBN 0-8274-1085-9). R West.
Sugg, Joyce. Snapdragon: The Story of John Henry Newman. LC 81-85242. (Illus.). 192p. 1982. pap. 3.95 (ISBN 0-87973-653-4, 653). Our Sunday Visitor.
Tristram, Henry. The Living Thoughts of Cardinal Newman. 167p. 1983. Repr. of 1948 ed. lib. bdg. 25.00 (ISBN 0-8495-5218-4). Arden Lib.
Ward, Wilfred. The Life of John Henry Newman Based on His Private Journals & Correspondence, 2 vols. 1912. Repr. 50.00 (ISBN 0-8274-2889-8). R West.
Ward, Wilfrid P. Last Lectures. facs. ed. LC 67-26793. (Essay Index Reprint Ser). 1918. 22.50 (ISBN 0-8369-0976-3). Ayer Co Pubs.
Weatherby, Harold L. Cardinal Newman in His Age: His Place in English Theology & Literature. LC 72-1347. 320p. 1973. 16.50x (ISBN 0-8265-1182-1). Vanderbilt U Pr.
Weaver, Mary J., ed. Newman & the Modernists. (Resources in Religion Ser.: Vol. 1). 232p. (Orig.). 1986. lib. bdg. 25.75 (ISBN 0-8191-4687-0, College Theo Soc); pap. text ed. 12.25 (ISBN 0-8191-4688-9). U Pr of Amer.
Whyte, Alexander. Newman: An Appreciation. 1973. Repr. of 1901 ed. 30.00 (ISBN 0-8274-0570-7). R West.
Woodfield, Malcom, ed. R. H. Hutton, Critic & Theologian: The Writings of R. H. Hutton on Newman, Arnold, Tennyson, Wordsworth & George Eliot. 240p. 42.00 (ISBN 0-19-818564-2). Oxford U Pr.
Yearley, Lee H. The Ideas of Newman: Christianity & Human Religiosity. LC 77-13894. 1978. 22.50x (ISBN 0-271-00526-2). Pa St U Pr.

NEWSPAPERS

Bowen, Francis A. How to Produce a Church Newspaper... & Other Ways Churches Communicate. (Illus.). 1974. 5.00 (ISBN 0-9602830-1-3). F A Bowen.
Spurgeon, C. H. The Bible & the Newspaper. 1973. pap. 2.50 (ISBN 0-686-09104-3). Pilgrim Pubns.

NEWTON, JOHN, 1725-1807

McLachlan, Herbert. The Religious Opinions of Milton, Locke & Newton. LC 74-20740. 1974. Repr. of 1941 ed. lib. bdg. 35.00 (ISBN 0-8414-5930-4). Folcroft.
Newton, John. Letters of John Newton. 1976. pap. 3.95 (ISBN 0-85151-120-1). Banner of Truth.

--Out of the Depths. LC 80-85340. (Shepherd Illustrated Classics Ser.). (Illus.). 1981. pap. 5.95 (ISBN 0-87983-243-6). Keats.

NGONDE (AFRICAN TRIBE)

Wilson, Monica. For Men & Elders: Change in the Relations of Generations & of Men & Women Among the Nyakyusa-Ngonde People, 1875-1971. LC 77-4203. 208p. 1978. 35.00x (ISBN 0-8419-0313-1, Africana). Holmes & Meier.

NICAEA, COUNCIL OF, 325

Haase, Felix A. Die Koptischen Quellen Zum Konzil Von Nicaa. 12.00 (ISBN 0-384-20630-1). Johnson Repr.

NICARAGUA–CHURCH HISTORY

Cabestrero, Teofilo. Ministers of God, Ministers of the People: Testimonies of Faith from Nicaragua. Barr, Robert R., tr. from Span. LC 83-6306. Orig. Title: Ministros De Dios, Ministros Del Pueblo. (Illus.). 160p. (Orig.). 1983. pap. 6.95 (ISBN 0-88344-335-X). Orbis Bks.

--Revolutionaries for the Gospel: Testimonies of Fifteen Christians in the Nicaraguan Government. Berryman, Phillip, tr. from Spanish. LC 85-25865. Tr. of Revolucionarios por el Evangelico. 176p. (Orig.). 1986. pap. 9.95 (ISBN 0-88344-406-2). Orbis Bks.

McGinnis, James. Solidarity with the People of Nicaragua. LC 84-27202. (Illus.). 192p. (Orig.). 1985. pap. 7.95 (ISBN 0-88344-448-8). Orbis Bks.

Randall, Margaret. Christians in the Nicaraguan Revolution. (Illus.). 240p. (Orig.). 1984. 15.95 (ISBN 0-919573-14-2, Pub. by New Star Bks BC); pap. 7.95 (ISBN 0-919573-15-0, Pub. by New Star Bks BC). Left Bank.

NICENE CREED

Bull, George. Harmony on Justification, Defense of the Nicene Creed, Judgement of the Catholic Church, 5 vols. LC 71-39556. (Library of Anglo-Catholic Theology: No. 4). Repr. of 1855 ed. Set. 150.00 (ISBN 0-404-52070-7). AMS Pr.

MacGregor, Geddes. The Nicene Creed, Illumined by Modern Thought. LC 80-19348. pap. 40.80 (ISBN 0-317-20013-5, 2023220). Bks Demand UMI.

Metropolitan Emilianos Timiadis. The Nicene Creed: Our Common Faith. LC 82-71826. 128p. (Orig.). 1983. pap. 7.95 (ISBN 0-8006-1653-7, 1-1653). Fortress.

Novak, Michael. Confession of a Catholic. LC 85-20367. 232p. 1986. pap. text ed. 12.25 (ISBN 0-8191-5023-1). U Pr of Amer.

Szarnicki, Zygmunt V. Faith Leads to Salvation: The Truths of the Nicene Creed. 137p. (Orig.). 1984. pap. 9.95 (ISBN 0-939332-08-6). J Pohl Assocs.

NICEPHORUS, SAINT, PATRIARCH OF CONSTANTINOPLE

Alexander, Paul J. The Patriarch Nicephorus of Constantinople: Ecclesiastical Policy & Image Worship in the Byzantine Empire. LC 78-63177. (Heresies Ser.: No. II). Repr. of 1958 ed. 42.50 (ISBN 0-404-16195-2). AMS Pr.

Jenkins, R. J., ed. & tr. Nicholas I, Patriarch of Constantinople: Letters. LC 74-28930. (Dumbarton Oaks Texts: Vol. 2). 668p. 1973. 45.00x (ISBN 0-88402-039-8). Dumbarton Oaks.

Westerink, L. G., ed. Nicholas I, Patriarch of Constantinople: Miscellaneous Writings. LC 80-70736. (Dumbarton Oaks Texts: Vol. 6). 160p. 1981. 28.00x (ISBN 0-88402-089-4). Dumbarton Oaks.

NICHIREN, 1222-1282

Anesaki, Masharu. Nichiren: The Buddhist Prophet. 1916. 11.25 (ISBN 0-8446-1029-1). Peter Smith.

NICHOLAS, SAINT, BP. OF MYRA

Jones, Charles W. Saint Nicholas of Myra, Bari & Manhattan: Biography of a Legend. LC 77-51487. 1978. lib. bdg. 36.00x (ISBN 0-226-40699-7). U of Chicago Pr.

McKnight, George H. Saint Nicholas: His Legend & His Role in the Christmas Celebration & Other Popular Customs. (Illus.). 153p. 1974. Repr. of 1917 ed. 15.95 (ISBN 0-87928-051-4). Corner Hse.

NICHOLAS, SAINT, BP. OF MYRA–JUVENILE LITERATURE

Krasovec, Bernice. A Legend of Saint Nicholas. (Illus.). 48p. 1985. 5.95 (ISBN 0-89962-467-7). Todd & Honeywell.

NICOLAUS CUSANUS, CARDINAL, 1401-1464

Berschin, Walter. Greek Letters & the Latin Middle Ages: From Jerome to Nicholas of Cusa. Frakes, Jerold C., tr. from Ger. Tr. of Griechisch-lateinisches mittelater von Hieronymus zu Nikolaus von Kues. 1987. price not set (ISBN 0-8132-0606-5). Cath U Pr.

Bett, Henry. Nicholas of Cusa. LC 76-1131. (Great Medieval Churchmen Ser). x, 210p. 1976. Repr. of 1932 ed. lib. bdg. 17.50x (ISBN 0-915172-05-4). Richwood Pub.

Biechler, James E. The Religious Language of Nicholas of Cusa. LC 75-23096. (American Academy of Religion, Dissertation Ser.). 240p. 1975. pap. 10.25 (ISBN 0-89130-021-X, 01 01 08). Scholars Pr GA.

Hopkins, Jasper. A Concise Introduction to the Philosophy of Nicholas of Cusa. 3rd ed. LC 85-72432. xii, 194p. 1986. text ed. 20.00x (ISBN 0-938060-32-5). Banning Pr.

--Nicholas of Cusa on God as Not-other: A Translation & an Appraisal of De Li Non Aliud. 2nd ed. LC 82-73976. ix, 179p. 1983. text ed. 20.00x (ISBN 0-938060-26-0). Banning Pr.

--Nicholas of Cusa on Learned Ignorance: A Translation & an Appraisal of De Docta Ignorantia. 2nd ed. LC 80-82907. ix, 205p. 1985. text ed. 23.00x (ISBN 0-938060-30-9); pap. text ed. 10.00x (ISBN 0-938060-27-9). Banning Pr.

--Nicholas of Cusa's Debate with John Wenck: A Translation & an Appraisal of De Ignota Litteratura & Apologia Doctae Ignorantiae. 2nd ed. LC 80-82908. viii, 119p. 1984. text ed. 23.00x (ISBN 0-938060-31-7). Banning Pr.

Yockey, James F. Mediations with Nicolas of Cusa. (Illus.). 144p. (Orig.). 1987. pap. 6.95 (ISBN 0-939680-40-8). Bear & Co.

NIEBUHR, HELMUT RICHARD, 1894-

Davies, D. R. Reinhold Niebuhr: Prophet from America. facs. ed. (Select Bibliographies Reprint Ser). 1945. 13.00 (ISBN 0-8369-5324-X). Ayer Co Pubs.

Diefenthaler, Jon. H. Richard Niebuhr: A Lifetime of Reflections on the Church & the World. 144p. (Orig.). 1986. 24.95 (ISBN 0-86554-214-7, MUP-H193); pap. 9.95 (ISBN 0-86554-235-X, MUP-P33). Mercer Univ Pr.

Fowler, James W. To See the Kingdom: The Theological Vision of H. Richard Niebuhr. LC 85-17878. 304p. 1985. pap. text ed. 13.75 (ISBN 0-8191-4938-1). U Pr of Amer.

Grant, C. David. God the Center of Value: Value Theory in the Theology of H. Richard Niebuhr. LC 84-40232. 185p. 1984. 16.95x (ISBN 0-912646-92-6). Tex Christian.

Hoedemaker, Libertus. The Theology of H. Richard Niebuhr. LC 78-139271. 1979. pap. 6.95 (ISBN 0-8298-0186-3). Pilgrim NY.

Irish, Jerry A. The Religious Thought of H. Richard Niebuhr. LC 83-6202. pap. 32.30 (2027155). Bks Demand UMI.

Kliever, Lonnie. H. Richard Niebuhr. LC 77-92452. (Makers of the Modern Theological Mind Ser.). 1978. 8.95 (ISBN 0-8499-0078-6, 0078-6). Word Bks.

Ramsey, Paul. Faith & Ethics: The Theology of H. Richard Niebuhr. 11.25 (ISBN 0-8446-2778-X). Peter Smith.

NIEBUHR, REINHOLD, 1892-1971

Bingham, June. Courage to Change: An Introduction to the Life & Thought of Reinhold Niebuhr. Repr. of 1961 ed. lib. bdg. 27.50x (ISBN 0-678-02766-8). Kelley.

Chrystal, William G., ed. Young Reinhold Niebuhr: The Early Writings - 1911 to 1931. rev. ed. 256p. 1982. pap. 8.95 (ISBN 0-8298-0607-5). Pilgrim NY.

Eckardt, A. Roy. For Righteousness' Sake: Contemporary Moral Philosophies. 1987. 29.95 (ISBN 0-253-32241-3). Ind U Pr.

Harries, Richard, ed. Reinhold Niebuhr & the Issues of Our Time. 216p. (Orig.). 1986. pap. 9.95 (ISBN 0-8028-0232-X). Eerdmans.

Kegley, Charles W., ed. Reinhold Niebuhr: His Religious, Social & Political Thought. rev. ed. LC 82-22531. 448p. (Orig.). 1984. pap. 11.95 (ISBN 0-8298-0616-4). Pilgrim NY.

King, Rachel H. Omission of the Holy Spirit from Reinhold Niebuhr's Theology. LC 64-13324. 209p. 1964. 6.95 (ISBN 0-8022-0865-7). Philos Lib.

Landon, Harold R., ed. Reinhold Niebuhr: A Prophetic Voice in Our Time. (Essay Index Reprint Ser.). Repr. of 1962 ed. 11.00 (ISBN 0-518-10150-9). Ayer Co Pubs.

Patterson, Bob E. Reinhold Niebuhr. LC 76-46783. (Makers of the Modern Theological Mind Series). 1977. 8.95 (ISBN 0-87680-508-X). Word Bks.

Plaskow, Judith. Sex, Sin & Grace: Women's Experience & the Theologies of Reinhold Niebuhr & Paul Tillich. LC 79-5434. 1980. pap. text ed. 11.25 (ISBN 0-8191-0882-0). U Pr of Amer.

Reinitz, Richard. Irony & Consciousness: American Historiography & Reinhold Niebuhr's Vision. LC 77-92574. 232p. 23.50 (ISBN 0-8387-2062-5). Bucknell U Pr.

Robertson, D. B. Reinhold Niebuhr's Works: A Bibliography. LC 83-16840. 282p. 1984. lib. bdg. 25.50 (ISBN 0-8191-3592-5); pap. text ed. 12.75 (ISBN 0-8191-3593-3). U Pr of Amer.

Scott, Nathan A., Jr. Reinhold Niebuhr. (Pamphlets on American Writers Ser: No. 31). (Orig.). 1963. pap. 1.25x (ISBN 0-8166-0305-7, MPAW31). U of Minn Pr.

Scott, Nathan A., Jr., ed. Legacy of Reinhold Niebuhr. LC 74-30714. xxiv, 124p. 1975. 10.00X (ISBN 0-226-74297-0). U of Chicago Pr.

Vaughan, Judith. Sociality, Ethics, & Social Change: A Critical Appraisal of Reinhold Niebuhr's Ethics in the Light of Rosemary Radford Ruether's Works. annual LC 83-1293. 228p. (Orig.). 1983. text ed. 26.00 (ISBN 0-8191-3100-8); pap. text ed. 12.50 (ISBN 0-8191-3101-6). U Pr of Amer.

Wurth, G. Niebuhr. (Modern Thinkers Ser.). 1960. pap. 1.50 (ISBN 0-87552-586-5). Presby & Reformed.

NIETZSCHE, FRIEDRICH WILHELM, 1844-1900

Antosik, Stanley J. The Question of Elites: An Essay on the Cultural Elitism of Nietzche, George & Hesse. (New York University Ottendorfer Series, Neue Folge: Vol. 11). 204p. 1978. 22.75 (ISBN 3-261-03102-6). P Lang Pubs.

Bernstein, John A. Nietzsche's Moral Philosophy. LC 85-46001. 1987. 32.50 (ISBN 0-8386-3283-1). Fairleigh Dickinson.

Del Caro, Adrian. Dionysian Aesthetics: The Role of Destruction in Creation as Reflected in the Life & Works of Friedrich Nietzsche. (European University Studies: Series 20, Philosophy: Vol. 69). 157p. 1980. 20.65 (ISBN 3-8204-6819-6). P Lang Pubs.

Deudon, Eric H. Nietzsche en France: L'antichristianisme et la Critique, 1891-1915. LC 81-43820. 176p. (Orig.). 1982. lib. bdg. 27.50 o. p. (ISBN 0-8191-2339-0); pap. text ed. 11.75 (ISBN 0-8191-2340-4). U Pr of Amer.

Dionne, James R. Pascal & Nietzche: Etude Historique & Comparee. LC 74-3300. (Fr.). 1976. lib. bdg. 18.00 (ISBN 0-89102-032-2). B Franklin.

Djuric, Mihailo. Nietzsche und Die Metaphysik. (Monographien und Texte zur Nietsche-Forschung: Band 16). (Ger.). viii, 326p. 1985. 61.60x (ISBN 3-11-010169-6). De Gruyter.

Geffre, Claude & Jossua, Jean-Pierre, eds. Nietzsche & Christianity, Vol. 145. (Concilium 1981). 128p. (Orig.). 1981. pap. 6.95 (ISBN 0-8164-2312-1, HarpR). Har-Row.

Houlgate, Stephen. Hegel, Nietzsche & the Criticism of Metaphysics. 304p. 1987. 39.50 (ISBN 0-521-32255-3). Cambridge U Pr.

Hubbard, Stanley. Nietzche und Emerson. LC 80-2538. Repr. of 1958 ed. 25.50 (ISBN 0-404-19264-5). AMS Pr.

Knight, G. Wilson. Christ & Nietzsche. 1948. lib. bdg. 17.50 (ISBN 0-8414-5590-2). Folcroft.

--Christ & Nietzsche: An Essay in Poetic Wisdom. 1982. 17.00 (ISBN 0-8495-3135-7). Arden Lib.

Magnus, Bernd. Nietzsche's Existential Imperative. LC 77-9864. (Studies in Phenomenology & Existential Philosophy Ser.). 256p. 1978. 20.00x (ISBN 0-253-34062-4). Ind U Pr.

Mistry, Freny. Nietzsche & Buddhism. (Monographien und Texte zur Nietzsche-Forschung, Vol. 6). 211p. 1981. 43.25 (ISBN 3-11-008305-1). De Gruyter.

Natoli, Charles M. Nietzsche & Pascal on Christianity. LC 83-49020. (American University Studies V (Philosophy): Vol. 3). 200p. (Orig.). 1984. pap. text ed. 24.25 (ISBN 0-8204-0071-8). P Lang Pubs.

Newell, William L. The Secular Magi: Marx, Nietzsche, & Freud on Religion. 264p. (Orig.). 1986. pap. 13.95 (ISBN 0-8298-0579-6). Pilgrim NY.

Norris, Margot. Beasts of the Modern Imagination: Darwin, Nietzsche, Kafka, & Lawrence. LC 84-21320. 256p. 1985. text ed. 26.50x (ISBN 0-8018-3252-7). Johns Hopkins.

Ouden, Bernard D. Essays on Reason, Will, Creativity, & Time: Studies in the Philosophy of Friedrich Nietzsche. LC 82-45042. 124p. (Orig.). 1982. PLB 23.75 o. p. (ISBN 0-8191-2449-4); pap. text ed. 9.50 (ISBN 0-8191-2450-8). U Pr of Amer.

Schacht, Richard. Nietzsche. (Arguments of the Philosophers Ser.). 560p. 1983. 35.00x (ISBN 0-7100-9191-5); pap. 17.50 (ISBN 0-7102-0544-9). Methuen Inc.

NIGERIA–RELIGION

Gilliland, Dean S. African Religion Meets Islam: Religious Change in Northern Nigeria. 250p. (Orig.). 1986. lib. bdg. 24.50 (ISBN 0-8191-5634-5); pap. text ed. 12.75 (ISBN 0-8191-5635-3). U Pr of Amer.

Hackett, Rosalind I., ed. New Religious Movements in Nigeria. LC 86-31080. (African Studies: Vol. 5). 1987. 59.95 (ISBN 0-88946-180-5). E Mellen.

Hambly, W. D. Serpent Worship in Africa - the Ovimbundu of Angola: Culture Areas of Nigeria. (Chicago Field Museum of Natural History Fieldiana Anthropology Ser). Repr. of 1935 ed. 51.00 (ISBN 0-527-01881-3). Kraus Repr.

Johnston, Geoffrey. Of God & Maxim Guns: Presbyterianism in Nigeria, 1846-1966, Vol. 8. 270p. 1987. pap. 17.50 (ISBN 0-88920-180-3, Pub. by Wilfrid Laurier Canada). Humanities.

Kraft, Marguerite G. Worldview & Communication of the Gospel. LC 78-10196. (Illus.). 1978. pap. 7.95 (ISBN 0-87808-324-3). William Carey Lib.

Lubeck, Paul M. Islam & Urban Labor in Northern Nigeria: The Making of a Muslim Working Class. (African Studies Ser.: No. 52). (Illus.). 368p. Date not set. 49.50 (ISBN 0-521-30942-5). Cambridge U Pr.

Omoyajowo, Akin. Diversity in Unity: The Development & Expansion of the Cherubim & Seraphim Church in Nigeria. LC 83-21706. 126p. (Orig.). 1984. lib. bdg. 22.00 (ISBN 0-8191-3655-7). U Pr of Amer.

Paden, John N. Religion & Political Culture in Kano. LC 74-153548. 1973. 46.50x (ISBN 0-520-02020-0). U of Cal Pr.

NIPPUR

Chiera, E. Lists of Personal Names from the Temple School of Nippur: A Syllabary of Personal Names. (Publications of the Babylonian Section: Vol. 11-1). (Illus.). 88p. 1916. soft bound 10.50x (ISBN 0-686-11923-1). Univ Mus of U PA.

--Lists of Personal Names from the Temple School of Nippur: Lists of Akkadian Personal Names. (Publications of the Babylonian Section: Vol. 11-2). (Illus.). 85p. 1916. soft bound 10.50x (ISBN 0-686-11924-X). Univ Mus of U PA.

Chiera, Edward. Lists of Personal Names from the Temple School of Nippur: Lists of Sumerian Personal Names. LC 17-5006. (University of Pennsylvania, University Museum, Publications of the Babylonian Section: Vol. 11, No. 3). pap. 34.00 (ISBN 0-317-28537-8, 2052027). Bks Demand UMI.

Clay, A. T. Documents from the Temple Archives of Nippur Dated in the Reigns of Cassite Rulers with Incomplete Dates. (Publications of the Babylonian Section, Ser. A: Vol. 15). (Illus.). xii, 68p. 1906. soft bound 12.00x (ISBN 0-686-11914-2). Univ Mus of U PA.

Clay, Albert T. Documents from the Temple Arhcives of Nippur Dated in the Reigns of Cassite Rulers. LC 13-1106. (University of Pennsylvania, The Museum, Publications of the Babylonian Section: Vol. 2, No. 2). pap. 27.00 (ISBN 0-317-28572-6, 2052022). Bks Demand UMI.

Gibson, McGuire. Excavations at Nippur. LC 75-9054. (Oriental Institute Communications Ser.: No. 22). 1976. pap. 15.00x (ISBN 0-226-62339-4). U of Chicago Pr.

Gibson, McGuire, et al. Excavations at Nippur: Twelfth Season. LC 78-59117. (Oriental Institute Communications Ser.: No. 23). (Illus.). 1978. pap. 22.00x (ISBN 0-918986-22-2). Oriental Inst.

Hilprecht, Hermann V. Mathematical Metrological & Chronological Tablets from the Temple Library of Nippur. LC 8-33648. (University of Pennsylvania, Babylonian Expedition, Series A: Cuneiform Texts: Vol. 20, Pt. 1). pap. 33.80 (ISBN 0-317-28568-8, 2052019). Bks Demand UMI.

McCown, Donald E. & Haines, Richard C. Nippur One: Temple of Enlil, Scribal Quarter & Soundings. LC 66-17104. (Illus.). 1967. 10.00 (ISBN 0-226-55688-3, OIP78). U of Chicago Pr.

Radau, Hugo. Ninib, the Determiner of Fates from the Temple Library of Nippur. (Publications of the Babylonian Section, Ser. D: Vol. 5-2). (Illus.). x, 73p. 1910. bound 5.00xsoft (ISBN 0-686-11919-3). Univ Mus of U PA.

NIRVANA

Arundale. Nirvana. 7.50 (ISBN 0-8356-7537-8). Theos Pub Hse.

Carus, Paul. Karma Nirvana: Two Buddhist Tales. LC 73-82781. (Illus.). 160p. 1973. 15.95 (ISBN 0-87548-249-X); pap. 6.95 (ISBN 0-87548-359-3). Open Court.

--Nirvana: A Story of Buddhist Psychology. 93p. 1913. 1.95 (ISBN 0-317-40415-6). Open Court.

Evans-Wentz, W. Y., ed. Tibetan Book of the Great Liberation. 1954. 24.95x (ISBN 0-19-501437-5). Oxford U Pr.

--Tibetan Book of the Great Liberation. (Illus.). 1968. pap. 9.95 (ISBN 0-19-500293-8). Oxford U Pr.

Rajneesh, Bhagwan Sri. Nirvana: The Last Nightmare. Rajneesh Foundation, ed. (Illus.). 278p. (Orig.). 1981. pap. 8.95 (ISBN 0-914794-37-X). Wisdom Garden Bks.

Stcherbatsky, Theodore. The Conception of Buddhist Nirvana. 408p. 1979. pap. 6.95 (ISBN 0-87728-427-X). Weiser.

NOAH

Abbay, Ellen. Noah Takes Two. LC 85-80406. 1985. 9.95 (ISBN 0-9615015-0-2). Kudzu.

Allen, Don C. The Legend of Noah: Renaissance Rationalism in Art, Science, & Letters. LC 49-49065. (Reprint of Studies in Language & Literature Ser.: Vol. 33, No. 3-4, 1949). (Illus.). 1963. pap. 8.95 (ISBN 0-252-72516-6). U of Ill Pr.

Fant, Louie J., Jr. Noah. new ed. (Illus.). 14p. 1973. pap. text ed. 5.00 (ISBN 0-917002-70-9). Joyce Media.

Hutton, Warwick. Noah & the Great Flood. LC 77-3217. (Illus.). 32p. 1977. 8.95 (ISBN 0-689-50098-X, McElderry Bk). Macmillan.

Ife, Elaine & Sutton, Rosalind, eds. Noah & the Ark. (Now You Can Read Stories from the Bible Ser.). (Illus.). 24p. 1985. 2.50 (ISBN 0-8407-5390-X). Nelson.

Lindsay, Gordon. Enoch & Noah, Patriarchs of the Deluge. (Old Testament Ser.). 1.25 (ISBN 0-89985-125-8). Christ Nations.

Petersen, Mark E. Noah & the Flood. LC 82-14947. 97p. 1982. 6.95 (ISBN 0-87747-935-6). Deseret Bk.

Thompson, Don. Captain Noah. (Rainy Day Survival Bk.: No. 1). (Illus.). 32p. pap. 0.99 (ISBN 0-87123-696-6, 220696). Bethany Hse.

Truitt. Noah & God's Promise. (Arch Bks.). 24p. (Orig.). 1985. pap. 0.99 (ISBN 0-570-06193-8, 59-1294). Concordia.

Wengrov, Charles. Tales of Noah & the Ark. (Biblical Ser.). (Illus.). 1969. 4.00 (ISBN 0-914080-23-7). Shulsinger Sales.

NOAH'S ARK

Berlitz, Charles. The Lost Ship of Noah: In Search of the Ark at Ararat. (Illus.). 224p. 1986. 17.95 (ISBN 0-399-13182-5, Perigee). Putnam Pub Group.

Burman, Ben L. Children of Noah. 5.00 (ISBN 0-685-02658-2). Taplinger.

Cartwright, Ann & Cartwright, Reg. Norah's Ark. (Illus.). 32p. 1984. PLB 11.97 (ISBN 0-671-52540-9). Messner.

Cummings, Violet. Has Anybody Really Seen Noah's Ark? 416p. 1982. pap. 8.95 (ISBN 0-89051-086-5). Master Bks.

Hollyer, Belinda. Noah & the Ark. LC 84-50450. (Bible Stories Ser.). (Illus.). 24p. 1984. PLB 6.96 (ISBN 0-382-06793-2); pap. 5.45 (ISBN 0-382-06942-0). Silver.

Hutton, Warwick. Noah & the Great Flood. LC 77-3217. (Illus.). 32p. 1977. 8.95 (ISBN 0-689-50098-X, McElderry Bk). Macmillan.

Ife, Elaine & Sutton, Rosalind, eds. Noah & the Ark. (Now You Can Read Stories from the Bible Ser.). (Illus.). 24p. 1985. 2.50 (ISBN 0-8407-5390-X). Nelson.

Irwin, James B. & Unger, Monte. More Than an Ark on Ararat. LC 85-4157. 1985. 6.95 (ISBN 0-8054-5018-1). Broadman.

Meyer, Nathan M. Noah's Ark, Pitched & Parked. pap. 4.00 (ISBN 0-88469-039-3). BMH Bks.

Montgomery, John W. Quest for Noah's Ark. LC 74-21993. (Illus.). 384p. 1972. pap. 4.95 (ISBN 0-87123-477-7, 200477). Bethany Hse.

Noah & the Ark: In Arabic. (MacDonald Educational Ser.). (Illus.). 3.50x (ISBN 0-86685-212-3). Intl Bk Ctr.

Noorbergen, Rene. Noah's Ark Found! The End of the Search. Golbitz, Pat, ed. LC 86-33162. (Illus.). 192p. 1987. 14.95 (ISBN 0-688-06456-6). Morrow.

Simons, John & Ward, Kay. Noah & His Great Ark. Ward, Kay, ed. (Bible Stories for Today Ser.). (Illus.). 16p. (Orig.). 1987. pap. text ed. 2.50 (ISBN 0-937039-00-4). Sun Pr FL.

Spier, Peter. Noah's Ark. 48p. 1981. pap. 4.95 (ISBN 0-385-17302-4, Zephyr). Doubleday.

Teeple, Howard M. The Noah's Ark Nonsense. LC 78-53529. (Truth in Religion Ser.: No. 1). 156p. 1978. 10.00 (ISBN 0-914384-01-5). Religion & Ethics.

Wengrov, Charles. Tales of Noah & the Ark. (Biblical Ser.). (Illus.). 1969. 4.00 (ISBN 0-914080-23-7). Shulsinger Sales.

Williams-Ellis, Virginia. Noah's Ark. (Board Bks.). (Illus.). 10p. 1984. 2.95 (ISBN 0-8249-8079-4). Ideals.

Yeatman, Linda. Noah's Ark. (Press-Out Model Bk.). (Illus.). 12p. 1984. 6.95 (ISBN 0-698-20598-7, Coward). Putnam Pub Group.

NONCONFORMISTS, RELIGIOUS

see Dissenters, Religious

NON-RESISTANCE TO EVIL

see Evil, Non-Resistance to

NONVIOLENCE

see also Pacifism

Culliton, Joseph T. Non-Violence-Central to Christian Spirituality: Perspectives from Scriptures to the Present. LC 82-7964. (Toronto Studies in Theology: Vol. 8). 312p. 1982. 49.95x (ISBN 0-88946-964-4). E Mellen.

Gregg, Richard B. A Discipline for Non-Violence. 1983. pap. 2.50x (ISBN 0-87574-011-1, 011). Pendle Hill.

Hinshaw, Cecil E. Nonviolent Resistance. 1983. pap. 2.50x (ISBN 0-87574-088-X, 088). Pendle Hill.

Jewish Peace Fellowship, ed. Roots of Jewish Nonviolence. 1984. lib. bdg. 79.95 (ISBN 0-87700-628-8). Revisionist Pr.

Lakey, George. Non-Violent Action: How it Works. 1983. pap. 2.50x (ISBN 0-87574-129-0, 129). Pendle Hill.

Seeger, Daniel A. The Seed & the Tree: Reflections on Non-Violence. (Orig.). 1986. pap. 2.50x (ISBN 0-87574-269-6). Pendle Hill.

Trocme, Andre. Jesus & the Nonviolent Revolution. Shenk, Michel, tr. from Fr. LC 73-9934. (Christian Peace Shelf Ser.). 216p. 1974. pap. 12.95 (ISBN 0-8361-3320-X). Herald Pr.

Vanderhaar, Gerard A. Christians & Nonviolence in the Nuclear Age: Scripture, the Arms Race & You. 128p. 1982. pap. 5.95 (ISBN 0-89622-162-8). Twenty-Third.

Young, Mildred B. Another Will Gird You: A Message to the Society of Friends. 1983. pap. 2.50 (ISBN 0-87574-109-6, 109). Pendle Hill.

NORMANDY-HISTORY-MEDIEVAL PERIOD

Chibnall, Marjorie, ed. The Ecclesiastical History of Orderic Vitalis, Vol. 1. (Oxford Medieval Texts Ser.). (Illus.). 1981. 98.00x (ISBN 0-19-822243-2). Oxford U Pr.

Ordericus Vitalis. Ecclesiastical History of England & Normandy, 4 Vols. Forrester, T., tr. LC 68-57872. (Bohn's Antiquarian Library Ser). Repr. of 1856 ed. Set. 115.00 (ISBN 0-404-50040-4). AMS Pr.

Ordericus, Vitalis. Historiae Ecclesiasticae Libri Tredecim, 5 Vols. Le Prevost, A., ed. Set. 240.00 (ISBN 0-384-43511-4); Set. pap. 210.00 (ISBN 0-384-43512-2). Johnson Repr.

Strayer, Joseph R. Administration of Normandy Under Saint Louis. LC 72-171362. Repr. of 1932 ed. 16.00 (ISBN 0-404-06297-0). AMS Pr.

NORMANS

Ordericus Vitalis. Ecclesiastical History of England & Normandy, 4 Vols. Forrester, T., tr. LC 68-57872. (Bohn's Antiquarian Library Ser). Repr. of 1856 ed. Set. 115.00 (ISBN 0-404-50040-4). AMS Pr.

Ordericus, Vitalis. Historiae Ecclesiasticae Libri Tredecim, 5 Vols. Le Prevost, A., ed. Set. 240.00 (ISBN 0-384-43511-4); Set. pap. 210.00 (ISBN 0-384-43512-2). Johnson Repr.

NORTH, JOHN WESLEY

Stonehouse, Merlin. John Wesley North & the Reform Frontier. LC 65-15075. pap. 73.00 (ISBN 0-317-29473-3, 2055921). Bks Demand UMI.

NORTH CAROLINA-SOCIAL CONDITIONS

Bode, Frederick A. Protestantism & the New South: North Carolina Baptists & Methodists in Political Crisis, 1894-1903. LC 75-1289. 171p. 1975. 15.00x (ISBN 0-8139-0597-4). U Pr of Va.

Kelly, Kent. State of North Carolina vs Christian Liberty. 112p. (Orig.). 1978. pap. 2.95 (ISBN 0-9604138-3-9). Calvary Pr.

Pope, Liston. Millhands & Preachers: A Study of Gastonia. (Studies in Religious Education: No. 15). (Illus.). 1965. pap. 11.95x (ISBN 0-300-00182-7). Yale U Pr.

NORTHERN BUDDHISM

see Mahayana Buddhism

NORTHERN IRELAND-RELIGION

Farrell, Michael. Arming the Protestants: The Formation of the Ulster Special Constabulary & the Royal Ulster Constabulary, 1920-1927. 274p. (Orig.). 1983. pap. 15.00 (ISBN 0-86104-705-2, Pub by Pluto Pr). Longwood Pub Group.

McGuinness, Frank. Observe the Sons of Ulster Marching Towards the Somme. (Orig.). 1986. pap. 8.95 (ISBN 0-571-14611-2). Faber & Faber.

Nelson, Sarah. Ulster's Uncertain Defenders: Protestant Political, Paramilitary & Community Groups & the Northern Ireland Conflict. (Irish Studies). 206p. 1984. text ed. 32.00x (ISBN 0-8156-2316-X). Syracuse U Pr.

NORWAY-CHURCH HISTORY

Hauglid, R. Norwegian Stave Churches. (Illus.). 1977. 22.00x (ISBN 8-2090-0937-0, N497). Vanous.

Molland, Einar. Church Life in Norway: 1800-1950. Harris, Kaasa, tr. LC 78-2711. 1978. Repr. of 1957 ed. lib. bdg. 22.50 (ISBN 0-313-20342-3, MOCL). Greenwood.

Undset, Sigrid. Saga of Saints. facs. ed. Ramsden, E. C., tr. LC 68-22952. (Essay Index Reprint Ser). 1968. Repr. of 1934 ed. 20.00 (ISBN 0-8369-0959-3). Ayer Co Pubs.

Willson, Thomas B. History of the Church & State in Norway: From the 10th to the 16th Century. LC 72-145376. (Illus.). 1971. Repr. of 1903 ed. 49.00x (ISBN 0-403-01280-5). Scholarly.

NORWEGIANS IN THE UNITED STATES

Kaasa, Harris & Rosholt, Malcolm, trs. Pioneer Churchman: The Narrative & Journal of J. W. C. Dietrichson, 1844-1850. Nelson, Clifford, ed. 265p. 1973. 9.00 (ISBN 0-87732-053-5). Norwegian-Am Hist Assn.

Lindberg, Duane R. Men of the Cloth & the Social-Cultural Fabric of the Norwegian Ethnic Community in North Dakota. Cordasco, Francesco, ed. LC 80-877. (American Ethnic Groups Ser.). 1981. lib. bdg. 38.00x (ISBN 0-405-13438-X). Ayer Co Pubs.

Tjossem, Wilmer L. Quaker Sloopers: From the Fjords to the Prairies. LC 84-80195. 80p. 1984. pap. 8.95 (ISBN 0-913408-85-9). Friends United.

NOTHING (PHILOSOPHY)

see also Ontology

Novak, Michael. Experience of Nothingness. 1971. pap. 5.95x (ISBN 0-06-131938-4, TB 1938, Torch). Har-Row.

NOVENAS

Cassidy, Norma C. Favorite Novenas & Prayers. LC 72-91456. 144p. 1972. pap. 3.95 (ISBN 0-8091-1761-4, Deus). Paulist Pr.

Franciscan Friars of Marytown Staff, ed. Kolbe Novena in Honor of the Immaculate Conception & Novena in Honor of St. Maximilin Kolbe. (Illus.). 31p. 1983. pap. 0.50 (ISBN 0-913382-14-0, 105-38). Prow Bks-Franciscan.

Hickey, Mary E., tr. from Fr. Novena of Confidence & Thanksgiving to the Sorrowful & Immaculate Heart of Mary. (Illus.). 20p. 1962. pap. 0.25 (ISBN 0-913382-21-3, 107-2). Prow Bks-Franciscan.

Lacy, C. Rosary Novenas. 1974. pap. 1.00 (ISBN 0-02-645810-1). Macmillan.

Rosary Novenas. 1.80. Benziger Pub Co.

Thirty Favorite Novenas. 31p. 1975. pap. 0.40 (ISBN 0-89555-105-5). TAN Bks Pubs.

NOVITIATE

Lynch, Joseph H. Simoniacal Entry into Religious Life, 1000 to 1260: A Social, Economic, & Legal Study. LC 76-22670. (Illus.). 286p. 1976. 15.00x (ISBN 0-8142-0222-5). Ohio St U Pr.

NOYES, JOHN HUMPHREY, 1811-1886

Jacoby, John E. Two Mystic Communities in America. LC 75-326. (The Radical Tradition in America Ser). 104p. 1975. Repr. of 1931 ed. 15.00 (ISBN 0-88355-230-2). Hyperion Conn.

Nelson, Truman. God in Love: The Sexual Revolution of John Humphrey Noyes. write for info (ISBN 0-393-01636-6). Norton.

Noyes, George W., ed. John Humphrey Noyes: The Putney Community. (Illus.). 1931. 30.00x (ISBN 0-8156-8059-7). Syracuse U Pr.

--Religious Experience of John Humphrey Noyes. 1923. 15.00x (ISBN 0-8156-8060-0). Syracuse U Pr.

Noyes, John H. Religious Experience of John Humphrey Noyes, Founder of the Oneida Community. facsimile ed. Noyes, George W., ed. (Select Bibliographies Reprint Ser). Repr. of 1923 ed. 26.50 (ISBN 0-8369-5750-4). Ayer Co Pubs.

Parker, Robert A. A Yankee Saint: John Humphrey Noyes & the Oneida Community. LC 75-187456. (The American Utopian Adventure Ser.). 322p. 1973. Repr. of 1935 ed. lib. bdg. 27.50x (ISBN 0-87991-009-7). Porcupine Pr.

--A Yankee Saint: John Humphrey Noyes & the Oneida Community. LC 73-2570. (Illus.). 332p. 1973. Repr. of 1935 ed. 29.50 (ISBN 0-208-01319-9, Archon). Shoe String.

NOYON, FRANCE-NOTRE-DAME (CATHEDRAL)

Seymour, Charles, Jr. Notre-Dame of Noyon in the Twelfth Century: A Study in the Early Development of Gothic Architecture. (Illus.). 1968. pap. 3.95x (ISBN 0-393-00464-3, Norton Lib). Norton.

NUCLEAR ENERGY-MORAL AND RELIGIOUS ASPECTS

see also Nuclear Warfare-Moral and Religious Aspects

Aukerman, Dale. Darkening Valley. 1981. pap. 8.95 (ISBN 0-8164-2295-8, HarpR). Har-Row.

Eastham, Scott T. Nucleus: Reconnecting Science & Religion in the Nuclear Age. LC 86-22265. 223p. (Orig.). 1986. pap. 9.95 (ISBN 0-939680-31-9). Bear & Co.

Grannis, J. Christopher, et al. The Risk of the Cross: Christian Discipleship in the Nuclear Age. 128p. (Orig.). 1981. pap. 5.95 (ISBN 0-8164-2305-9, HarpR). Har-Row.

Hessel, Dieter T., ed. Energy Ethics: A Christian Response. (Orig.). 1979. pap. 4.25 (ISBN 0-377-00094-9). Friend Pr.

Hollenbach, David. Nuclear Ethics: A Christian Moral Argument. 112p. 1983. pap. 3.95 (ISBN 0-8091-2546-3). Paulist Pr.

Kamen, Martin D. Radiant Science, Dark Politics: A Memoir of the Nuclear Age. 1987. pap. 8.95 (ISBN 0-520-05897-6). U of Cal Pr.

Nelkin, Dorothy & Pollak, Michael. The Atom Besieged: Extraparliamentary Dissent in France & Germany. (Illus.). 256p. 1981. 30.00x (ISBN 0-262-14034-9); pap. 8.95 (ISBN 0-262-64021-X). MIT Pr.

O'Neill, Ana M. Etica Para la Era Atomica. facsimile ed. 10.00 (ISBN 0-8477-2815-3); pap. 9.00 (ISBN 0-8477-2807-2). U of PR Pr.

Pope John Center Staff. Technological Powers & the Person: Nuclear Energy & Reproductive Technology. Lossing, Larry D. & Bayer, Edward J., eds. (Illus.). 370p. (Orig.). 1983. pap. 15.95 (ISBN 0-935372-12-1). Pope John Ctr.

Shrader-Frechette, K. S. Nuclear Power & Public Policy: The Social & Ethical Problems of Fission Technology. (Pallas Paperbacks Ser.: No. 15). 220p. 1980. lib. bdg. 20.00 (ISBN 90-277-1054-6, Pub. by Reidel Holland); pap. 10.50 (ISBN 90-277-1080-5). Kluwer Academic.

Unger, Georg. Spiritual Science & the New Nature Forces: The Nuclear Dilemma. Thomas, Nick, tr. 28p. 1981. pap. 2.95 (ISBN 0-88925-063-4, Pub. by Steiner Book Centre Canada). Anthroposophic.

NUCLEAR WARFARE-MORAL AND RELIGIOUS ASPECTS

Augsburger & Curry. Nuclear Arms: Two Views on World Peace. 1987. 14.95 (ISBN 0-8499-0576-1). Word Bks.

Barrs, Jerram. Who Are the Peacemakers? The Christian Case for Nuclear Deterrence. LC 83-62684. 60p. 1983. pap. 2.95 (ISBN 0-89107-307-8, Crossway Bks). Good News.

Blake, Nigel & Pole, Kay, eds. Objections to Nuclear Defence: Philosophers on Deterrence. 208p. (Orig.). 1984. pap. 11.95x (ISBN 0-7102-0249-0). Methuen Inc.

Bollen, Peter D. Nuclear Voices: A Book of Quotations & Perspectives. LC 85-60616. (Illus.). 250p. (Orig.). 1985. pap. 6.95x (ISBN 0-9611350-1-8). Hillside Bks.

Castelli, Jim. Bishops & the Bomb: Waging Peace in a Nuclear Age. LC 82-48706. 288p. 1983. pap. 7.95 (ISBN 0-385-18760-2, IM). Doubleday.

Chapman, G. Clarke. Facing the Nuclear Heresy. Eller, David, ed. 224p. (Orig.). 1986. pap. 9.95 (ISBN 0-87178-225-1). Brethren.

Child, James. Nuclear War: The Moral Dimension. (Studies in Social Philosophy & Policy: No. 6). 150p. 1986. 16.95 (ISBN 0-912051-09-4); pap. 8.95 (ISBN 0-912051-10-8). Soc Phil Pol.

Child, James E., ed. Nuclear War: The Moral Dimension. 160p. (Orig.). 1985. 16.95 (ISBN 0-912051-04-3, Dist. by Transaction Bks); pap. 8.95 (ISBN 0-912051-05-1). Soc Phil Pol.

The Cross & the Bomb. 1985. pap. 29.00x (ISBN 0-317-39053-8, Pub by Mowbrays Pub Div). State Mutual Bk.

Davidson, Donald L. Nuclear War & the American Churches: Ethical Positions on Modern Warfare. 200p. 1983. 21.50x (ISBN 0-86531-706-2). Westview.

Davis, Howard, ed. Ethics & Defence: Power & Responsibility in the Nuclear Age. 224p. 1987. text ed. 39.95 (ISBN 0-631-15174-5); pap. text ed. 19.95 (ISBN 0-631-15175-3). Basil Blackwell.

Dougherty, James E. The Bishops & Nuclear Weapons: The Catholic Pastoral Letter on War & Peace. LC 84-2994. 255p. 1984. 22.50 (ISBN 0-208-02051-9, Archon Bks). Shoe String.

Dresner, Samuel H. God, Man & Atomic War. 6.95 (ISBN 0-87677-007-3). Hartmore.

Dwyer, Judith A., ed. The Catholic Bishops & Nuclear War: A Critique & Analysis of the Pastoral, the Challenge of Peace. 120p. 1984. pap. 6.50 (ISBN 0-87840-409-0). Georgetown U Pr.

Fisher, David. Morality & the Bomb: An Ethical & Assessment of Nuclear Deterrence. LC 85-2210. 136p. 1985. 25.00 (ISBN 0-312-54784-6). St Martin.

Fisher, Phyllis K. Los Alamos Experience. (Illus.). 240p. 1985. 12.95 (ISBN 0-87040-623-X, Dist. by Harper & Row). Japan Pubns USA.

Flynn, Eileen P. My Country Right or Wrong? Selective Conscientious Objection in the Nuclear Age. 1985. pap. 3.95 (ISBN 0-317-18110-6). Loyola.

Freund, Ronald. What One Person Can Do to Help Prevent Nuclear War. 2nd ed. 144p. 1983. pap. 5.95 (ISBN 0-89622-192-X). Twenty-Third.

Gilpin, Robert G., Jr. American Scientists & Nuclear Weapons Policy. 1962. 37.00x (ISBN 0-691-07501-8). Princeton U Pr.

Grinspoon, Lester, ed. & intro. by. The Long Darkness: Psychological & Moral Perspectives on Nuclear Winter. LC 85-40986. 224p. 1986. text ed. 25.00 (ISBN 0-300-03663-9); pap. 7.95 (ISBN 0-300-03664-7, YF-31). Yale U Pr.

Grossinger, Richard & Hough, Lindy, eds. Nuclear Strategy & the Code of the Warrior: Faces of Mars & Shiva in the Crisis of Human Survival. (Io Ser.: No. 33). 320p. (Orig.). 1984. 25.00 (ISBN 0-938190-50-4); pap. 12.95 (ISBN 0-938190-49-0). North Atlantic.

Hardin, Russell, et al, eds. Nuclear Deterrence: Ethics & Strategy. LC 85-8423. viii, 396p. 1985. 25.00x (ISBN 0-226-31702-1); pap. 10.95 (ISBN 0-226-31704-8). U of Chicago Pr.

Heller, Agnes & Feher, Ferenc. Doomsday or Deterence? On the Antinuclear Issue. 192p. 1986. 35.00 (ISBN 0-87332-368-8); pap. 12.95 (ISBN 0-87332-369-6). M E Sharpe.

Ibuse, Masuji. Black Rain. 304p. 1985. pap. 3.95 (ISBN 0-553-24988-6). Bantam.

Jones, John D. & Griesbach, Marc F. Just War Theory in the Nuclear Age. LC 85-6092. 236p. (Orig.). 1985. lib. bdg. 25.50 (ISBN 0-8191-4659-5); pap. text ed. 10.75 (ISBN 0-8191-4660-9). U Pr of Amer.

Katz, Milton S. Ban the Bomb: A History of SANE, the Committee for a SANE Nuclear Policy, 1957-1985. LC 85-24824. (Contributions in Political Science Ser.: No. 147). (Illus.). 230p. 1986. lib. bdg. 35.00 (ISBN 0-313-24167-8, KBB/). Greenwood.

Kaufman, Gordon D. Theology for a Nuclear Age. 78p. 1985. 12.95 (ISBN 0-664-21400-2); pap. 8.95 (ISBN 0-664-24628-1). Westminster.

Lefever, Ernest W. & Hunt, E. Stephen, eds. The Apocalyptic Premise: Nuclear Arms Debated. LC 82-18315. 429p. 1982. 22.00 (ISBN 0-89633-062-1); pap. 14.00 (ISBN 0-89633-063-X). Ethics & Public Policy.

Lifton, Robert J. & Humphrey, Nicholas, eds. In a Dark Time. LC 84-10816. 154p. (Orig.). 1984. 15.00 (ISBN 0-674-44538-4); pap. 5.95 (ISBN 0-674-44539-2). Harvard U Pr.

Lutz, Charles P. & Folk, Jerry L. Peaceways: Sixteen Christian Perspectives on Security in a Nuclear Age. LC 83-70500. 224p. (Orig.). 1983. pap. 10.95 (ISBN 0-8066-2006-4, 10-4904). Augsburg.

Marciano, Teresa & Sussman, Marvin B., eds. Families & the Prospect of Nuclear Attack-Holocaust. LC 86-18320. (Marriage & Family Review Ser.: Vol. 10, No. 2). 1986. pap. 22.95 (ISBN 0-86656-374-1). Haworth Pr.

Mische, Patricia M. Star Wars & the State of Our Souls: Deciding the Future of Planet Earth. 122p. (Orig.). 1985. pap. 4.95 (ISBN 0-86683-450-8, HarpR). Har-Row.

Mumford, Lewis. The Human Way Out. 1983. pap. 2.50x (ISBN 0-87574-097-9, 097). Pendle Hill.

Norman, Edward R. & English, Raymond. Ethics & Nuclear Arms: European & American Perspectives. LC 85-10304. 1985. pap. 7.00 (ISBN 0-89633-095-8). Ethics & Public Policy.

Paul, Ellen F., et al, eds. Nuclear Rights-Nuclear Wrongs. LC 85-26711. 248p. 1986. text ed. 24.95x (ISBN 0-631-14964-3). Basil Blackwell.

Russell, Bertrand. Common Sense & Nuclear Warfare. LC 68-54291. Repr. of 1959 ed. 18.00 (ISBN 0-404-05465-X). AMS Pr.

Sawyer, Peter, ed. Domesday Book: A Reassessment. 224p. 1985. 49.95 (ISBN 0-7131-6440-9). E Arnold.

Sider, Ronald J. & Taylor, Richard K. Nuclear Holocaust & Christian Hope: A Book for Christian Peacemakers. 360p. 1983. pap. 6.95 (ISBN 0-8091-2512-9). Paulist Pr.

Stein, Walter. Nuclear Weapons & Christian Conscience. 165p. (Orig.). 1981. pap. 6.75 (ISBN 0-85036-112-5, Pub. by Merlin Pr UK). Longwood Pub Group.

Velikhov, Y., et al. The Night after: Climatic & Biological Consequences of a Nuclear War. 165p. 1985. 8.95 (ISBN 0-8285-3110-2, Pub. by Mir Pubs USSR). Imported Pubns.

Weeramantry, C. G. Nuclear Weapons & Scientific Responsibility. 225p. 1986. 25.00 (ISBN 0-89341-542-1, Pub. by Longwood Academic). Longwood Pub Group.

Zars, Belle, et al, eds. Education & the Threat of Nuclear War. (Reprint Ser.: No. 18). 166p. 1985. pap. 9.95x (ISBN 0-916690-20-2). Harvard Educ Rev.

NUER (AFRICAN TRIBE)

Crazzolara, J. P. Zur Gesellschaft & Religion der Nueer. 1953. 46.00 (ISBN 0-384-10150-X). Johnson Repr.

Evans-Pritchard, Edward E. Kinship & Marriage among the Nuer. (Illus.). 1951. 32.50x (ISBN 0-19-823104-0). Oxford U Pr.

--Nuer Religion. (Illus.). 1956. 10.95x (ISBN 0-19-874003-4). Oxford U Pr.

NULLITY OF MARRIAGE

see Marriage–Annulment

NUMBERS IN THE BIBLE

Davis, John J. Biblical Numerology. (Orig.). 1968. pap. 4.50 (ISBN 0-8010-2813-2). Baker Bk.

--Biblical Numerology. pap. 4.95 (ISBN 0-88469-063-6). BMH Bks.

Grant, F. W. Witness the Witness of Arithmetic to Christ. 64p. 1980. pap. 2.25 (ISBN 0-87213-272-2). Loizeaux.

Kistler, Don, ed. The Arithmetic of God, Vol. 1. 187p. (Orig.). 1976. pap. 3.95x (ISBN 0-940532-00-X). AOG.

Thiele, Edwin R. The Mysterious Numbers of the Hebrew Kings. New rev. ed. 256p. 1984. pap. 11.95 (ISBN 0-310-36011-0, 10116P). Zondervan.

Vannah, Joanne M. Number Sense. 1985. 4.95 (ISBN 0-8062-2451-7). Carlton.

Wenham, Gordon J. Numbers. Wiseman, D. J., ed. LC 81-11806. (Tyndale Old Testament Commentaries Ser.). 240p. 1981. 12.95 (ISBN 0-87784-891-2); pap. 6.95 (ISBN 0-87784-254-X). Inter-Varsity.

NUNS

see also Ex-Nuns

Brown, Judith C. Immodest Acts: The Life of a Lesbian Nun in Renaissance Italy. (Studies in the History of Sexuality). 221p. 1985. 14.95 (ISBN 0-19-503675-1). Oxford U Pr.

Corrigan, Felicitas. The Nun, the Infidel, & the Superman: The Remarkable Friendships of Dame Laurentia McLachlan. LC 84-52822. (Illus.). viii, 152p. 1985. 14.95 (ISBN 0-226-11589-5). U of Chicago Pr.

Ericson, Donald E. The Portuguese Letters: Love Letters of a Nun to a French Officer. 2nd ed. LC 86-71957. 78p. 1986. pap. 5.95 (ISBN 0-9617271-0-1). Bennett-Edwards.

Ewens, Mary. The Role of the Nun in Nineteenth Century America. 36.50 (ISBN 0-405-10828-1). Ayer Co Pubs.

Hackel, Sergei. Pearl of Great Price: The Life of Mother Maria Skobtsova 1891-1945. rev. ed. LC 81-21356. 192p. 1982. pap. 6.95 (ISBN 0-913836-85-0). St Vladimirs.

Holloway, Marcella. Should You Become a Sister? 1978. pap. 1.50 (ISBN 0-89243-073-7, 29553). Liguori Pubns.

Monk, Maria & Grob, Gerald. Awful Disclosures by Marcia Monk of the Hotel Dieu Nunnery of Montrial. LC 76-46089. (Anti-Movements in America Ser.). 1977. lib. bdg. 29.00 (ISBN 0-405-09962-2). Ayer Co Pubs.

Moore, Sr. Mary E. And I Married the Son of a King. 185p. 1979. pap. 6.95 (ISBN 0-8059-2688-7). Dorrance.

Murphy, Paul I. & Arlington, R. Rene. La Popessa. LC 82-61880. (Illus.). 296p. (Orig.). 1983. 16.50 (ISBN 0-446-51258-3). Warner Bks.

Neal, Marie A. Catholic Sisters in Transition: From the 1960's to the 1980's. (Consecrated Life Studies Ser.: Vol. 2). 1984. pap. 7.95 (ISBN 0-89453-444-0). M Glazier.

Sanchez, Julio. The Community of the Holy Spirit: A Movement of Change in a Covent of Nuns in Puerto Rico. 190p. (Orig.). 1984. lib. bdg. 25.25 (ISBN 0-8191-3367-1); pap. text ed. 11.75 (ISBN 0-8191-3368-X). U Pr of Amer.

Shin, Nan. Diary of a Zen Nun. LC 85-27576. (Illus.). 192p. 1986. 15.95 (ISBN 0-525-24408-5, 01549-460). Dutton.

Target, C. M. The Nun in the Concentration Camp. 1974. pap. 1.60 (ISBN 0-08-017611-9). Pergamon.

Upton, Elizabeth. Secrets of a Nun: My Own Story. LC 84-14828. 264p. 1985. 16.95 (ISBN 0-688-04187-6). Morrow.

--Secrets of a Nun: My Own Story. 1987. pap. write for info. (ISBN 0-449-21127-4, Crest). Fawcett.

Walter, Alicia E. Catarina Lutero, Monja Liberada. 1984. 3.50 (ISBN 0-915644-26-6). Clayton Pub Hse.

Wedmore, S. Delphine. The Woman Who Couldn't Be Stopped. LC 86-61680. (Illus.). 515p. (Orig.). 1986. pap. 10.50 (ISBN 0-9616887-0-X). Sisters Christ Charity.

Wong, Mary G. Nun: A Memoir. LC 82-47656. 416p. 1983. 15.95 (ISBN 0-15-167739-5). HarBraceJ.

--Nun-A Memoir: An Intimate Account of One Women's Years in the Covent & Her Eventual Return to the World. LC 84-47611. 416p. 1984. pap. 8.95 (ISBN 0-06-091188-3, CN 1188, PL). Har-Row.

NUTRITION

see also Food

Aivanhov, Omraam M. The Yoga of Nutrition. (Izvor Collection Ser.: Vol. 204). 130p. pap. 4.95 (ISBN 0-911857-03-6). Prosveta USA.

Ali, Shahrazad. How Not to Eat Pork: Or Life Without the Pig. LC 85-70171. (Illus.). 120p. (Orig.). 1985. pap. 5.95 (ISBN 0-933405-00-6). Civilized Pubns.

Aschwanden, Richard J. & Aschwanden, Maria. A Time of Personal Regeneration. Aschwanden, Charles R., ed. 60p. 1984. pap. 3.40x (ISBN 0-913071-00-5, TX1-202-40). Rama Pub Co.

Barniak, Carl K. The Food of Angels. 96p. (Orig.). 1984. pap. 4.95 (ISBN 0-9613803-0-6). Barniak Pubns.

Gang, Miriam & Gang, Arthur. The Gang's Weigh. 88p. (Orig.). 1986. pap. 9.95 (ISBN 0-941850-24-2). Sunday Pubns.

Holmes, Marjorie. God & Vitamins. 368p. 1982. pap. 3.50 (ISBN 0-380-56994-9, 68536-1). Avon.

Rosenbaum, Ernest, et al. Nutrition for the Cancer Patient. (Orig.). 1980. pap. 7.95 (ISBN 0-915950-38-3). Bull Pub.

Steiner, Rudolf. Nutrition & Health. Hahn, Gladys, tr. from Ger. Tr. of Die Schoepfung der Welt und des Menschen. Erdenleben und Stennenwirken. (Illus.). 35p. 1987. pap. 3.95 (ISBN 0-88010-182-2). Anthroposophic.

Swope, Mary R. Are You Sick & Tired? 176p. (Orig.). 1984. pap. 3.95 (ISBN 0-88368-149-8). Whitaker Hse.

NYGREN, ANDERS, BP., 1890-

Hall, Thor. Anders Nygren. (Makers of the Modern Theological Mind Ser.). 1978. 8.95 (ISBN 0-8499-0098-0). Word Bks.

--Anders Nygren. 230p. 1984. pap. text ed. 8.95 (ISBN 0-8499-3004-9, 3004-9). Word Bks.

O

OATHS

see also Vows

Arnstein, Walter L. The Bradlaugh Case: Atheism, Sex, & Politics among the Late Victorians. LC 83-6814. (Illus.). 384p. 1984. text ed. 30.00x; pap. text ed. 13.50x (ISBN 0-8262-0417-1). U of Mo Pr.

Giesey, Ralph. If Not, Not: The Oath of the Aragonese & the Legendary Laws of the Sobrarbe. LC 67-21023. 1968. 30.50 (ISBN 0-691-05128-3). Princeton U Pr.

Stewart, George R. Year of the Oath. LC 77-150422. (Civil Liberties in American History Ser). 1971. Repr. of 1950 ed. lib. bdg. 22.50 (ISBN 0-306-70103-0). Da Capo.

OBEDIENCE

Beecher, Willard & Beecher, Marguerite. The Sin of Obedience. 88p. (Orig.). 1982. pap. 4.75 (ISBN 0-942350-00-6). Beecher Found.

Boesak, Allan. Walking on Thorns: The Call to Christian Obedience. 80p. (Orig.). 1984. pap. 4.95 (ISBN 0-8028-0041-6). Eerdmans.

Cary-Elwes, Columbia. Law, Liberty & Love. 1950. 5.00 (ISBN 0-8159-6104-9). Devin.

Chrysostomos, Archimandrite & Ambrosios, Hieromonk. Obedience. Young, Alexey & Derugin, Vladimir, eds. (Themes in Orthodox Patristic Psychology Ser.: Vol. 2). 90p. (Orig.). 1984. text ed. write for info. (ISBN 0-916586-88-X); pap. text ed. write for info. (ISBN 0-916586-31-6). Holy Cross Orthodox.

Gardiner, Stephen. Obedience in Church & State: Three Political Tracts. Janelle, Pierre, ed. LC 68-19272. 1968. Repr. of 1930 ed. lib. bdg. 22.50x (ISBN 0-8371-0081-X, GABW). Greenwood.

Hulshizer, S. J. Obedience. 69p. pap. 3.95 (ISBN 0-88172-156-5). Believers Bkshelf.

La Boetie, Etienne. The Politics of Obedience: The Discourse of Voluntary Servitude. Kurz, Harry, tr. from Fr. Tr. of De la Servitude Volontaire. 88p. 1975. 19.95 (ISBN 0-919618-58-8, Dist. by U of Toronto Pr); pap. 9.95 (ISBN 0-919618-57-X, Dist. by U of Toronto Pr). Black Rose Bks.

Miller, Arthur. The Obedience Experiments: A Case Study of Controversy in Social Science. LC 85-25723. 305p. 1986. 35.00 (ISBN 0-275-92012-7, C2012). Praeger.

Murray, Andrew. The Blessings of Obedience. Orig. Title: School of Obedience; Believer's Secret of Obedience. 107p. 1984. pap. text ed. 3.50 (ISBN 0-88368-155-2). Whitaker Hse.

--La Escuela de la Obediencia. Orig. Title: The School of Obedience. (Span.). 128p. 1984. pap. 3.25 (ISBN 0-317-14852-4). Kregel.

OBERAMMERGAU

Swidler, Leonard & Sloyan, Gerard S., eds. The Oberammergau Passionsspiel Nineteen Eighty-Four. 104p. pap. 5.00 (ISBN 0-686-95110-7). ADL.

OBERLIN COLLEGE

Fletcher, Robert S. History of Oberlin College: From Its Foundation Through the Civil War, 2 vols. in 1. LC 75-165716. (American Education Ser, No. 2). 1971. Repr. of 1943 ed. 60.50 (ISBN 0-405-03705-8). Ayer Co Pubs.

OBESITY

Thomas, Ann. God's Answer to Overeating. (Aglow Bible Study Basic Ser.). 64p. 1975. 2.95 (ISBN 0-932305-36-9, 4220-7). Aglow Pubns.

OBJECT-TEACHING

see also Children's Sermons

Biller, Tom A. & Biller, Martie. Simple Object Lessons for Children. (Object Lesson Ser.). 160p. 1980. pap. 4.95 (ISBN 0-8010-0793-3). Baker Bk.

Bringman, Dale. A Star Is Born. (Orig.). 1987. pap. price not set (ISBN 0-89536-881-1, 7867). CSS of Ohio.

Classen, David J. Object Lessons for a Year. 112p. 1986. pap. 4.95 (ISBN 0-8010-2514-1). Baker Bk.

Connelly, H. W. Forty-Seven Object Lessons for Youth Programs. (Object Lesson Ser). (YA) 1964. pap. 3.95 (ISBN 0-8010-2314-9). Baker Bk.

Cross, Luther. Object Lessons for Children. (Object Lesson Ser). (Illus., Orig.). 1967. pap. 3.95 (ISBN 0-8010-2315-7). Baker Bk.

Dean, Bessie. Let's Go to Church. LC 76-3995. (Books for Lds Children Ser.). (Illus.). 63p. 1976. pap. 3.95 (ISBN 0-88290-062-5). Horizon Utah.

Hendricks, William C. & Den Bleyker, Merle. Object Lessons from Sports & Games. (Object Lessons Ser). 126p. 1975. pap. 3.95 (ISBN 0-8010-4134-1). Baker Bk.

Mocko, George P. Lord, Empower Us! Sherer, Michael L., ed. (Orig.). 1987. pap. 2.75 (ISBN 0-89536-851-X, 7810). CSS of Ohio.

Morentz, Jim & Morentz, Doris. Children's Object Lesson Sermons Based on the New Common Lectionary: Year C. 112p. (Orig.). 1985. pap. 6.95 (ISBN 0-687-06498-8). Abingdon.

Runk, Wesley. What Color Is Your Balloon? (Orig.). 1987. pap. price not set (ISBN 0-89536-883-8, 7869). CSS of Ohio.

Runk, Wesley T. On Jesus' Team. Sherer, Michael L., ed. (Orig.). 1986. pap. 5.25 (ISBN 0-89536-809-9, 6838). CSS of Ohio.

Trull, Joe E. Forty Object Sermons for Children. (Object Lesson Ser.). 96p. 1975. pap. 3.95 (ISBN 0-8010-8831-3). Baker Bk.

OBSEQUIES

see Funeral Rites and Ceremonies

OCCASIONAL SERMONS

Here are entered works containing sermons preached on special days or for special occasions, e.g. Christmas, Easter, dedications, anniversaries, etc. Single sermons or works containing sermons of one kind only, are entered under the specific subject, e.g. christmas Sermons.

Dennis, Mildred. Short Talks for Special Occasions, Bk. 1. 64p. 1987. pap. 2.95 (ISBN 0-87403-069-2, 2880). Standard Pub.

--Short Talks for Special Occasions, Bk. 2. 64p. 1987. pap. 2.95 (ISBN 0-87403-070-6, 2881). Standard Pub.

Wood, Charles R., ed. Sermon Outlines for Special Days & Occasions. 64p. 1970. pap. 2.95 (ISBN 0-8254-4006-8). Kregel.

OCCASIONAL SERVICES

Tharp, Zeno C., ed. Minister's Guide for Special Occasions. Repr. 7.95 (ISBN 0-87148-553-2). Pathway Pr.

OCCULTISM IN LITERATURE

see also Mysticism in Literature

Banta, Martha. Henry James & the Occult: The Great Extension. LC 72-75386. Repr. of 1972 ed. 54.60 (ISBN 0-8357-9215-3, 2013010). Bks Demand UMI.

Bloom, Clive. The Occult Experience & the New Criticism: Daemonism, Sexuality & the Hidden in Literature. LC 86-10963. 160p. 1987. 27.50x (ISBN 0-389-20646-6). B&N Imports.

Friedman, Susan S. Psyche Reborn: The Emergence of H. D. LC 80-8378. (Illus.). 352p. 1981. 22.50x (ISBN 0-253-37826-5). Ind U Pr.

Saurat, Denis. Literature & Occult Traditions. LC 68-759. (Studies in Comparative Literature, No. 35). 1969. Repr. of 1930 ed. lib. bdg. 49.95x (ISBN 0-8383-0617-9). Haskell.

--Literature & the Occult Tradition. Bolton, D., tr. LC 65-27133. 1930. Repr. 23.00x (ISBN 0-8046-0405-3, Pub. by Kennikat). Assoc Faculty Pr.

Senior, John. Way Down & Out: The Occult in Symbolist Literature. LC 68-23326. (Illus.). 1968. Repr. of 1959 ed. lib. bdg. 22.50x (ISBN 0-8371-0218-9, SESL). Greenwood.

Sinnett, A. P. Tennyson an Occultist. LC 72-2102. (Studies in Tennyson, No. 27). 1972. Repr. of 1920 ed. lib. bdg. 46.95x (ISBN 0-8383-1485-6). Haskell.

OCCUPATIONS AND BUSY WORK

see Creative Activities and Seatwork

OCKHAM, WILLIAM, d. ca. 1349

Boehner, Philotheus & Buytaert, Eligius M. Collected Articles on Ockham. (Philosophy Ser). 1958. 23.00 (ISBN 0-686-11542-2). Franciscan Inst.

Boehner, Philotheus, ed. The Tractatus De Successivis Attributed to William Ockham. (Philosophy Ser). 1944. 8.00 (ISBN 0-686-11531-7). Franciscan Inst.

Boehner, Philotheus, et al, eds. Guillelmi de Ockham: Opera Philosophica, Vol. 1, Summa Philosophica. 1974. 52.00 (ISBN 0-686-11530-9). Franciscan Inst.

Brown, Stephen F., ed. Guillelmi de Ockham: Scriptum in Librum Primum Sententiarum, Ordinatio, Opera Theologica, Vol. 2, Distinctiones Secunda et Tertia. 1970. 37.00 (ISBN 0-686-11529-5). Franciscan Inst.

Buescher, Gabriel. The Eucharistic Teaching of William Ockham. (Theology Ser). 1974. Repr. of 1950 ed. 10.00 (ISBN 0-686-11585-6). Franciscan Inst.

Gal, Gedeon, ed. Guillelmi de Ockham: Scriptum in Librum Primum Sententiarum, Ordinatio, Opera Theologica, Vol. 1, Prologues et Distinctio Prima. 1967. 35.00 (ISBN 0-686-11528-7). Franciscan Inst.

Goddu, A. The Physics of William of Ockham. (Studies und Texte zur Geistesgeschichte des Mittelalters: No. 16). 310p. 1984. text ed. 50.00x (ISBN 90-04-06912-7, Pub. by EJ Brill Holland). Humanities.

Menges, Matthew C. The Concept of Univocity Regarding the Predication of God & Creature According to William Ockham. (Philosophy Ser.). 1952. 8.00 (ISBN 0-686-11539-2). Franciscan Inst.

Ryan, John J. The Nature, Structure, & Function of the Church in William of Ockham. LC 78-2891. (American Academy of Religion: Studies in Religion, 16). 1979. pap. 9.95 (ISBN 0-89130-230-1, 1010016). Scholars Pr GA.

Wey, Joseph C., ed. Guillelmi de Ockham: Quodlibeta Septem, Ordinatio, Opera Theologica, Vol. 9. 1980. 50.00 (ISBN 0-686-28122-5). Franciscan Inst.

William of Ockham. The Power of the Mind in the Philosophy of William of Ockham. (Illus.). 137p. 1986. 117.50 (ISBN 0-89920-132-6). Am Inst Psych.

O'CONNOR, FLANNERY

Feeley, Kathleen. Flannery O'Connor: Voice of the Peacock. 2nd ed. LC 76-163958. xviii, 198p. 1982. pap. 9.00 (ISBN 0-8232-1093-6). Fordham.

Fitzgerald, Sally, ed. The Habit of Being: Letters of Flannery O'Connor. LC 79-23319. 1980. pap. 10.95 (ISBN 0-394-74259-1, Vin). Random.

Friedman, Melvin J. The Added Dimension: The Art of Mind of Flannery O'Connor. 2nd ed. LC 66-11070. xviii, 263p. 1977. pap. 9.00 (ISBN 0-8232-0711-0). Fordham.

Gentry, Marshall B. Flannery O'Connor's Religion of the Grotesque. LC 85-20267. 216p. 1986. 22.50x (ISBN 0-87805-285-2). U Pr of Miss.

Golden, Robert & Sullivan, Mary C. Flannery O'Connor & Caroline Gordon: A Reference Guide. 1977. lib. bdg. 28.50 (ISBN 0-8161-7845-3, Hall Reference). G K Hall.

McFarland, Dorothy T. Flannery O'Connor. LC 74-78443. (Literature and Life Ser.). 141p. 1976. 14.95x (ISBN 0-8044-2609-0). Ungar.

O'Connor, Flannery. The Habit of Being. Fitzgerald, Sally, ed. & intro. by. LC 78-11559. 639p. 1979. 15.00 (ISBN 0-374-16769-9). FS&G.

Orvell, Miles. Invisible Parade: The Fiction of Flannery O'Connor. LC 72-91132. 246p. 1975. 27.95 (ISBN 0-87722-023-9). Temple U Pr.

OEDIPUS

Money-Kyrle, Roger E. Meaning of Sacrifice. Repr. of 1930 ed. 17.00 (ISBN 0-384-39690-9). Johnson Repr.

Velikovsky, Immanuel. Oedipus & Akhnaton: Myth & History. LC 60-7886. 1960. 11.95 (ISBN 0-385-00529-6). Doubleday.

OEDOGONIACEAE

Hirn, K. E. Monographie & Iconographie der Oedogoniaceen. (Illus.). 1960. pap. 95.00x (ISBN 3-7682-7056-4). Lubrecht & Cramer.

OFFICE, ECCLESIASTICAL

see Clergy–Office

OLD AGE

see also Aged; Aging; Middle Age

Andrews, Elsie M. Facing & Fulfilling the Later Years. LC 68-16318. (Orig.). 1968. pap. 2.50x (ISBN 0-87574-157-6). Pendle Hill.

Glas, Norbert. Fulfillment of Old Age. Easton, Stewart, tr. from Fr. Tr. of Lichtvolles Alter. 141p. 1987. pap. 9.95 (ISBN 0-88010-161-X). Anthroposophic.

Hess, Bartlett & Hess, Margaret. Never Say Old. 156p. 1984. pap. 5.95 (ISBN 0-89693-375-X). Victor Bks.

Simmons, Leo W. The Role of the Aged in Primitive Society. LC 78-103998. (Illus.). 317p. 1970. Repr. of 1945 ed. 28.00 (ISBN 0-208-00824-1, Archon). Shoe String.

Smith, Bert K. Aging in America. LC 72-6232. 256p. 1973. pap. 5.95 (ISBN 0-8070-2769-3, BP502). Beacon Pr.

Wisloff, Fredrik. The Evening of Life. LC 66-12386. pap. 35.00 (2027868). Bks Demand UMI.

Worth, Richard. You'll Be Old Someday, Too. LC 85-29419. 128p. 1986. lib. bdg. 11.90 (ISBN 0-531-10158-4). Watts.

OLD CATHOLIC CHURCH

Mathew, Arnold H., tr. Old Catholic Missal & Ritual. LC 73-84708. Repr. of 1909 ed. 27.45 (ISBN 0-404-01949-8). AMS Pr.

Pruter, Karl. A History of the Old Catholic Church. LC 85-13418. 76p. 1985. Repr. lib. bdg. 19.95x (ISBN 0-89370-594-2). Borgo Pr.

Pruter, Karl & Melton, J. Gordon. The Old Catholic Sourcebook. LC 83-47610. 254p. 1983. 39.00 (ISBN 0-8240-9111-6). Garland Pub.

OLD ORDER AMISH

see Amish

OLDCASTLE, SIR JOHN, called LORD COBHAM, d. 1417

Bale, John. Select Works of John Bale, Bishop of Ossory. 51.00 (ISBN 0-384-03135-8). Johnson Repr.

OLDHEIM, SAINT, BP. OF SHERBORNE, 640-709

Duckett, Eleanor S. Anglo-Saxon Saints & Scholars. x, 484p. 1967. Repr. of 1947 ed. 35.00 (ISBN 0-208-00200-6, Archon). Shoe String.

OLIPHANT, LAURENCE, 1829-1888

Oliphant, Margaret. Memoir of the Life of Laurence Oliphant & of Alice Oliphant, His Wife. LC 75-36915. (Occult Ser.). 1976. Repr. of 1892 ed. 32.00x (ISBN 0-405-07970-2). Ayer Co Pubs.

Schneider, Herbert & Lawton, George. Prophet & a Pilgrim. LC 78-134433. (Illus.). Repr. of 1942 ed. 36.50 (ISBN 0-404-05610-5). AMS Pr.

OLMECS

Luckert, Karl W. Olmec Religion: A Key to Middle America & Beyond. LC 75-12869. (The Civilization of the American Indian: Vol. 137). (Illus.). 200p. 1976. 14.95x (ISBN 0-8061-1298-0). U of Okla Pr.

OMENS

see also Oracles; Signs and Symbols

Clay, Albert T. Epics, Hymns, Omens & Other Texts. LC 78-63519. (Babylonian Records in the Library of J. Pierpont Morgan: 4). Repr. of 1923 ed. 30.00 (ISBN 0-404-60124-3). AMS Pr.

Forester, Bruce. Signs & Omens. 256p. 1984. 15.95 (ISBN 0-396-08392-7). Dodd.

Signs & Wonders Today. 1983. Repr. 4.95 (ISBN 0-88419-189-3). Creation Hse.

Wasserzug, Dr. G. Signs & Wonders. 1.95 (ISBN 0-686-12836-2). Midnight Call.

ONE-PARENT FAMILY

see Single-Parent Family

ONEIDA COMMUNITY

see also Perfection

Daily Journal of Oneida Community, 5 vols. in 1. LC 74-32539. (American Utopian Adventure Ser.). (Illus., Vols. 1-3, bd. with the O.C. daily, vols. 4-5). 1975. Repr. of 1868 ed. lib. bdg. 95.00x (ISBN 0-87991-032-1). Porcupine Pr.

De Maria, Richard. Communal Love at Oneida: A Perfectionist Vision of Authority, Property & Sexual Order. LC 78-60958. (Texts & Studies in Religion: Vol. 2). xiii, 248p. 1978. soft cover 19.95x (ISBN 0-88946-986-5). E Mellen.

DeMaria, Richard. Communal Love at Oneida: A Perfectionist Vision of Authority, Property & Sexual Order. 2nd. ed. LC 78-60958. (Texts & Studies in Religion: Vol. 2). 248p. 1983. 49.95x (ISBN 0-88946-988-1). E Mellen.

Eastlake, A. The Oneida Community. 69.95 (ISBN 0-8490-0769-0). Gordon Pr.

Eastman, Hubbard. Noyesism Unveiled. LC 72-134402. Repr. of 1849 ed. 30.00 (ISBN 0-404-08446-X). AMS Pr.

Estlake, Allan. The Oneida Community: A Record of an Attempt to Carry Out the Principles of Christian Unselfishnes & Scientific Race-Improvement. LC 72-4179. Repr. of 1900 ed. 11.50 (ISBN 0-404-10758-3). AMS Pr.

Foster, Lawrence. Religion & Sexuality: Three American Communal Experiments of the Nineteenth Century. 1981. 24.95x (ISBN 0-19-502794-9). Oxford U Pr.

Jacoby, John E. Two Mystic Communities in America. LC 75-326. (The Radical Tradition in America Ser). 104p. 1975. Repr. of 1931 ed. 15.00 (ISBN 0-88355-230-2). Hyperion Conn.

Oneida Community. Bible Communism. LC 76-187475. (The American Utopian Adventure Ser.). 128p. 1973. Repr. of 1853 ed. lib. bdg. 17.50x (ISBN 0-87991-015-1). Porcupine Pr.

--Bible Communism: A Compilation from the Annual Reports & Other Publications of the Oneida Association & Its Branches. LC 72-2978. Repr. of 1853 ed. 8.50 (ISBN 0-404-10742-7). AMS Pr.

--Hand-book of the Oneida Community, with a Sketch of Its Founder, & an Outline of Its Constitution & Doctrines, 3 vols in 1. Incl. Hand-Book of the Oneida Community, Containing a Brief Sketch of Its Present Condition, Internal Economy & Leading Principles; Mutual Criticism. LC 72-2977. Repr. of 1876 ed. 23.50 (ISBN 0-404-10741-9). AMS Pr.

Parker, Robert A. A Yankee Saint: John Humphrey Noyes & the Oneida Community. LC 75-187456. (The American Utopian Adventure Ser.). 322p. 1973. Repr. of 1935 ed. lib. bdg. 27.50x (ISBN 0-87991-009-7). Porcupine Pr.

--A Yankee Saint: John Humphrey Noyes & the Oneida Community. LC 73-2570. (Illus.). 332p. 1973. Repr. of 1935 ed. 29.50 (ISBN 0-208-01319-9, Archon). Shoe String.

Rich, Jane K. & Blake, Nelson M., eds. A Lasting Spring: Jessie Catherine Kinsley, Daughter of the Oneida Community. LC 82-19200. (York State Bks.). (Illus.). 300p. (Orig.). 1983. 32.00x (ISBN 0-8156-0183-2); pap. 14.95 (ISBN 0-8156-0176-X). Syracuse U Pr.

Robertson, C. N. Oneida Community Profiles. (Illus.). 1977. 10.00x (ISBN 0-8156-0140-9). Syracuse U Pr.

Robertson, Constance N. Oneida Community: The Breakup, 1876 - 1881. LC 72-38405. (New York State Studies). (Illus.). 330p. 1972. 14.95x (ISBN 0-8156-0086-0). Syracuse U Pr.

ONONDAGA LANGUAGE

Hale, Horatio E., ed. Iroquois Book of Rites. LC 74-83458. (Library of Aboriginal American Literature: No. 2). Repr. of 1883 ed. 30.00 (ISBN 0-404-52182-7). AMS Pr.

ONTOLOGY

see also Absolute, the; Demythologization; Existentialism; Identity; Metaphysics; Nothing (Philosophy); Philosophical Anthropology; Philosophy; Substance (Philosophy)

Brown, Barry F. Accidental Being: A Study in the Metaphysics of St. Thomas Aquinas. LC 85-15653. 440p. (Orig.). 1985. lib. bdg. 32.75 (ISBN 0-8191-4886-5); pap. text ed. 19.50 (ISBN 0-8191-4887-3). U Pr of Amer.

Buber, Martin, et al. I & Thou. Kaufman, Walter & Smith, S. G., trs. LC 72-123845. (Hudson River Edition). 1970. 20.00 (ISBN 0-684-15575-3, ScribT); pap. 6.95 (ISBN 0-684-71725-5, ScribT). Scribner.

Coe, David K. Angst & the Abyss: The Hermeneutics of Nothingness. (Academic Ser.). 1985. 17.95 (ISBN 0-89130-862-8, 01-01-49); pap. 11.95 (ISBN 0-89130-863-6). Scholars Pr GA.

Daniels, Charles B., et al. Towards an Ontology of Number Mind & Sign. (Scots Philosophical Monographs: Vol. 10). 200p. 1986. 29.95x (ISBN 0-391-03397-2, Pub. by Aberdeen U Scotland); pap. 12.50 (ISBN 0-391-03398-0, Pub. by Aberdeen U Scotland). Humanities.

De Saint-Martin, Louis-Claude. Of Errors & Truth. Vadenais, Philip & Vadenais, Antoinette, trs. from Fr. LC 86-63353. 435p. (Orig.). 1987. pap. write for info. (ISBN 0-912057-47-5, G-651). AMORC.

Deutsch, Eliot. On Truth: An Ontological Theory. LC 79-12754. 1979. text ed. 14.00x (ISBN 0-8248-0615-8). UH Pr.

Feldstein, Leonard C. The Dance of Being: Man's Labyrinthe Rhythms, the Natural Ground of the Human. LC 77-75799. xvi, 302p. 1979. 30.00 (ISBN 0-8232-1032-4). Fordham.

Henke, Peter. Vor Dem Nichts. (Theologischo Bibliothek Toepelmann: Vol. 34). (Illus.). 1978. 26.80 (ISBN 3-11-007254-8). De Gruyter.

Klubertanz, George P. & Holloway, Maurice R. Being & God: Introduction to the Philosophy of Being & to Natural Theology. LC 63-15359. 1963. 39.50x (ISBN 0-89197-045-2); pap. text ed. 19.95x (ISBN 0-89197-674-4). Irvington.

Lango, John. Whitehead's Ontology. LC 78-171184. 1972. 34.50x (ISBN 0-87395-093-3). State U NY Pr.

McInerny, Ralph. Being & Predication: Thomistic Interpretations. (Studies in Philosophy & the History of Philosophy: Vol. 16). 1986. 36.95 (ISBN 0-8132-0612-X). Cath U Pr.

Marcel, Gabriel. Being & Having: An Existentialist Diary. 11.25 (ISBN 0-8446-2528-0). Peter Smith.

Moore, Jared S. Rifts in the Universe: A Study of the Historic Dichotomies & Modalities of Being. 1927. 29.50x (ISBN 0-686-51303-7). Elliots Bks.

Munk, Arthur W. A Synoptic Approach to the Riddle of Existence. LC 77-818. 264p. 1977. 15.00 (ISBN 0-87527-165-0). Fireside Bks.

Neville, Robert C. God the Creator: On the Transcendence & Presence of God. LC 68-13128. (Illus.). 1968. 12.50x (ISBN 0-226-57641-8). U of Chicago Pr.

Nobo, Jorge L. Whitehead's Metaphysics of Extension & Solidarity. (Philosophy Ser.). 544p. (Orig.). 1986. 49.50x (ISBN 0-88706-261-X); pap. 24.50x (ISBN 0-88706-262-8). State U NY Pr.

Owens, Joseph. An Interpretation of Existence. LC 84-23805. 162p. 1985. pap. text ed. 7.95 (ISBN 0-268-01157-5, 85-11578, Dist. by Harper & Row). U of Notre Dame Pr.

Pico Della Mirandola, Giovanni. On the Dignity of Man. Wallis, Charles G., et al, trs. Bd. with On Being & Unity; Heptaplus. LC 65-26540. 1965. pap. 7.87 scp (ISBN 0-672-60483-3, LLA227). Bobbs.

Steiner, Rudolf. Man's Being, His Destiny & World Evolution. 3rd ed. McArthur, Erna & Riggins, William, trs. from Ger. 123p. (Orig.). 1984. pap. 7.95 (ISBN 0-88010-090-7). Anthroposophic.

Stoops, John A. Religious Values in Education. LC 67-25689. 1967. text ed. 4.95x (ISBN 0-8134-0950-0, 950). Inter Print Pubs.

Thatcher, Adrian. The Ontology of Paul Tillich. (Oxford Theological Monographs). 1978. text ed. 29.95x (ISBN 0-19-826715-0). Oxford U Pr.

Theunissen, Michael. The Other: Studies in the Social Ontology of Husserl, Heidegger, Sartre & Buber. Macann, Christopher, tr. from Ger. LC 83-16267. (Studies in Contemporary German Social Thought). 429p. 1984. text ed. 45.00x (ISBN 0-262-20048-1). MIT Pr.

Tillich, Paul. Courage to Be. (Terry Lectures Ser.). 1952. pap. 6.95 (ISBN 0-300-00241-6, Y11). Yale U Pr.

Wells, Norman. Metaphysical Disputation, XXXI, De Ento Finito, on Finite Being. cancelled. Marquette.

Wilkes, James. The Gift of Courage. LC 81-11507. 108p. 1981. pap. 6.95 (ISBN 0-664-24394-0). Westminster.

ORACLES

see also Delphian Oracle; Sibyls

Alexander, Paul J. The Oracle of Baalbek: The Tiburtine Sibyl in Greek Dress. LC 75-27113. (Dumbarton Oaks Studies: Vol. 10). (Illus.). 151p. 1967. 12.00x (ISBN 0-88402-020-7). Dumbarton Oaks.

Booker, John. The Dutch Oracle. (Illus.). 224p. 1981. pap. 5.95 (ISBN 0-931116-01-5). Ralston-Pilot.

Terry, Milton S., tr. from Gr. The Sibylline Oracles. new ed. LC 72-176141. Repr. of 1899 ed. 21.45 (ISBN 0-404-06362-4). AMS Pr.

Vandenberg, Philipp. The Mystery of the Oracles: World Famous Archaeologists Reveal the Best Kept Secrets of Antiquity. Unwin, George, tr. (Illus.). 288p. 1982. 14.95 (ISBN 0-02-621590-X). Macmillan.

Ward, Charles A. Oracles of Nostradamus. 400p. 1981. pap. 22.00 (ISBN 0-89540-084-7, SB-084). Sun Pub.

Westcott, William W., ed. Chaldean Oracles. 1984. pap. 5.95 (ISBN 0-916411-16-8, Pub. by Alexandrian Pr). Holmes Pub.

ORAL LAW (JUDAISM)

see Tradition (Judaism)

ORAL TRADITION (JUDAISM)

see Tradition (Judaism)

ORDER OF ST. CLARE

see Poor Clares

ORDER OF THE EASTERN STAR

Bell. Eastern Star. 8.95x (ISBN 0-685-21937-2). Wehman.

Voorhis, Harold V. The Eastern Star: The Evolution from a Rite to an Order. 138p. 1986. Repr. of 1954 ed. text ed. 6.95 (ISBN 0-88053-306-4, S-300). Macoy Pub.

ORDER OF THE EASTERN STAR–RITUAL

Adams, Ruth. One Little Candle. 4th ed. 206p. 1981. Repr. of 1966 ed. text ed. 6.50 (ISBN 0-88053-314-5, S-251). Macoy Pub.

Adams, Ruth, et al. Gathered Memories. 152p. 1985. pap. 5.00 (ISBN 0-88053-308-0, S-76). Macoy Pub.

Alexander, J. L. Memorable Ceremonies & Poems: Including Material from "Along the Story Trail". 192p. 1986. Repr. of 1928 ed. 5.50 (ISBN 0-88053-302-1, S-109). Macoy Pub.

Bell, F. A. Eastern Star Ritual. 5.50 (ISBN 0-685-19473-6). Powner.

Cooley, Doris H., ed. Ritual of Music. 12p. 1968. pap. text ed. 1.00 (ISBN 0-88053-318-8, S-79). Macoy Pub.

Daughters of the Sphinx Ritual. 3.50 (ISBN 0-685-19471-X). Powner.

Gibbany, Etta M. Star Beams. 24p. 1958. pap. 1.50 (ISBN 0-88053-323-4, S-304). Macoy Pub.

Hansen, Vee & Shaw, Opal. Macoy's Short Addresses for Matron: Forty-Five Sentiments. 28p. 1975. pap. 1.50 (ISBN 0-88053-329-3, S-83). Macoy Pub.

Hansen, Vee, et al. Macoy's Short Addresses & Ceremonies for Matron's Use. 24p. 1983. pap. 1.50 (ISBN 0-88053-330-7). Macoy Pub.

Meekins, Inez P. Old Dominion Addresses & Ceremonies. 70p. 1975. Repr. of 1972 ed. softcover 1.00 (ISBN 0-88053-312-9, S-417). Macoy Pub.

Voorhis, Harold V. The Eastern Star: The Evolution from a Rite to an Order. 138p. 1986. Repr. of 1954 ed. text ed. 6.95 (ISBN 0-88053-306-4, S-300). Macoy Pub.

ORDERS, ANGLICAN

see Anglican Orders

ORDERS, MAJOR

see Bishops; Clergy

ORDERS, MONASTIC

see Monasticism and Religious Orders

ORDINALIA

Longsworth, Robert M. Cornish Ordinalia: Religion & Dramaturgy. LC 67-22869. 1967. 12.50x (ISBN 0-674-17200-0). Harvard U Pr.

ORDINATION

see also Priesthood

Cox, Robert G. Do You Mean Me, Lord? The Call to the Ordained Ministry. LC 85-8785. 116p. 1985. pap. 8.95 (ISBN 0-664-24668-0). Westminster.

Ellard, G. Ordination Anointings in the Western Church Before 1000 A. D. (Med Acad of Amer Pubns). 1932. 18.00 (ISBN 0-527-01688-8). Kraus Repr.

Hersey, Herman. Preparation for Ordination. 1981. pap. 1.95 (ISBN 0-89265-069-9). Randall Hse.

McEachern, Alton H. Set Apart for Service. LC 79-5114. 1980. 7.50 (ISBN 0-8054-2537-3). Broadman.

Packard, Russell C. Come, Journey with Me: A Personal Story of Conversion & Ordination. LC 84-24356. 208p. (Orig.). 1984. pap. 8.00 (ISBN 0-89571-021-8). Affirmation.

Reynolds, Roger E. The Ordinals of Christ from Their Origins to the Twelfth Century. 1978. 55.00x (ISBN 3-11-007058-8). De Gruyter.

Stendahl, Krister. The Bible & the Role of Women: A Case Study in Hermeneutics. Reumann, John, ed. Sander, Emilie T., tr. LC 66-25262. (Facet Bks). 64p. 1966. pap. 3.95 (ISBN 0-8006-3030-0, 1-3030). Fortress.

Warkentin, Marjorie. Ordination: A Biblical-Historical View. LC 82-8908. pap. 53.00 (ISBN 0-317-30166-7, 2025348). Bks Demand UMI.

Watts, J. Wash. Ordination of Baptist Ministers. pap. 1.50 (ISBN 0-8054-9404-9). Broadman.

ORDINATION OF WOMEN

Canham, Elizabeth. Pilgrimage to Priesthood. 128p. (Orig.). 1985. pap. 9.95 (ISBN 0-8164-2492-6, 8603, HarpR). Har-Row.

Ide, Arthur F. God's Girls: Ordination of Women in the Early Christian & Agnostic Churches. (Illus.). 185p. (Orig.). 1986. pap. 8.95 (ISBN 0-934667-01-2). Tangelwuld.

Maitland, Sara. A Map of the New Country: Women & Christianity. LC 82-13142. 218p. 1983. pap. 8.95 (ISBN 0-7100-9301-2). Methuen Inc.

Malone, David M. The Church Cannot Ordain Women to the Priesthood. 1978. 0.75 (ISBN 0-8199-0724-3). Franciscan Herald.

Stendahl, Krister. The Bible & the Role of Women: A Case Study in Hermeneutics. Reumann, John, ed. Sander, Emilie T., tr. LC 66-25262. (Facet Bks). 64p. 1966. pap. 3.95 (ISBN 0-8006-3030-0, 1-3030). Fortress.

ORGAN–INSTRUCTION AND STUDY

Andrews, Mildred & Riddle, Pauline. Church Organ Method. 123p. 1973. pap. 15.00 (ISBN 0-8258-0050-1, 04904). Fischer Inc NY.

Buck, Dudley. Illustrations in Choir Accompaniment. LC 79-137316. Repr. of 1892 ed. 18.00 (ISBN 0-404-01145-4). AMS Pr.

ORGAN MUSIC

Barrett, Philip. The Organs & Organists of the Cathedral Church of St. Thomas of Canterbury at Portsmouth. 1975. Repr. of 1968 ed. 39.00x (ISBN 0-317-43672-4, Pub. by City of Portsmouth). State Mutual Bk.

Bender, Jan. Organ Improvisation for Beginners. LC 75-2934. (Illus.). 71p. 1975. bds. 8.25 (ISBN 0-570-01312-7, 99-1229). Concordia.

Coleman, Henry. Church Organist. 2nd ed. 1968. 9.75 (ISBN 0-19-322100-4). Oxford U Pr.

Lovelace, Austin C. The Organist & Hymn Playing. rev. ed. LC 81-80265. (Illus.). 61p. 1981. pap. 5.95 (ISBN 0-916642-16-X). Hope Pub.

ORGANIZATIONS

see Associations, Institutions, etc.

ORIENT AND OCCIDENT

see East and West

ORIENTAL MYTHOLOGY

see Mythology, Oriental

ORIENTAL PHILOSOPHY

see Philosophy, Oriental

ORIENTAL STUDIES

see also Egyptology; Philosophy, Comparative

Cassuto, U. Biblical & Oriental Studies: Bible, Vol. 1. Abrahams, Israel, tr. from Hebrew. (Illus.). 298p. 1973. text ed. 29.95x (Pub. by Magnes Pr Israel). Humanities.

--Biblical & Oriental Studies: Bible & Ancient Oriental Texts, Vol. 2. Abrahams, Israel, tr. from Hebrew. 286p. 1975. text ed. 35.00x (Pub. by Magnes Pr Israel). Humanities.

Mueller, Hans-Peter, ed. Bibel und Alter Orient: Altorientische Beitrage zum Alten Testament von Wolfram von Soden. (Beihefte zur Zeitschrift fur die Alttestamentliche Wissenschaft Ser.: Band 162). xii, 224p. 1985. 50.50x (ISBN 3-11-010091-6). De Gruyter.

ORIGEN

Bigg, Charles. Christian Platonists of Alexandria: Eight Lectures. LC 75-123764. Repr. of 1886 ed. 27.50 (ISBN 0-404-00799-6). AMS Pr.

Burghardt, W. J., et al, eds. Origen, Prayer, Exhortation to Martyrdom. LC 78-62467. (ACW Ser.: No. 19). 261p. 1954. 14.95 (ISBN 0-8091-0256-0). Paulist Pr.

--Origen, the Song of Songs: Commentary & Homilies. LC 57-11826. (ACW Ser.: No. 26). 491p. 1957. 14.95 (ISBN 0-8091-0261-7). Paulist Pr.

Caspary, Gerard E. Politics & Exegesis: Origen & the Two Swords. LC 77-71058. 1979. 42.00x (ISBN 0-520-03445-7). U of Cal Pr.

Cox, Claude E. Hexaplaric Materials Preserved in the Armenian Version. (Septuagint & Cognate Studies). 1986. text ed. 12.95 (ISBN 1-55540-028-0, 06-04-21); pap. 9.95 (ISBN 1-55540-029-9). Scholars Pr GA.

Cox, Patricia. Biography in Late Antiquity: A Quest for the Holy Man. LC 82-4946. (The Transformation of the Classical Heritage Ser.: Vol. 5). 208p. 1983. text ed. 30.00x (ISBN 0-520-04612-9). U of Cal Pr.

De Faye, Eugene. Origen & His Work. LC 78-16959. 1926. 27.50 (ISBN 0-8414-3684-3). Folcroft.

Drewery, Benjamin. Origen & the Doctrine of Grace. LC 61-19395. 1960. text ed. 17.50x (ISBN 0-8401-0579-7). A R Allenson.

Eros & Psyche: Studies in Plato, Plotinus & Origen. LC 66-627. (Phoenix Supplementary Ser.: No. 6). pap. 63.50 (ISBN 0-317-08094-6, 2019201). Bks Demand UMI.

ORIGIN OF MAN

see Man–Origin

ORIGINAL SIN

see Sin, Original

ORPHEUS

Linforth, Ivan M. The Arts of Orpheus. LC 72-9296. (The Philosophy of Plato & Aristotle Ser.). Repr. of 1941 ed. 24.50 (ISBN 0-405-04847-5). Ayer Co Pubs.

Taylor, Thomas. Hymns of Orpheus. Bd. with Concerning the Beautiful, Plotinus. 15.00 (ISBN 0-89314-415-0). Philos Res.

Warden, John, ed. Orpheus, the Metamorphoses of a Myth. LC 82-189058. pap. 63.50 (2026404). Bks Demand UMI.

ORTHODOX EASTERN CHURCH

Allen, Joseph J., ed. Orthodox Synthesis: The Unity of Theological Thought. 231p. (Orig.). 1981. pap. 8.95 (ISBN 0-913836-84-2). St Vladimirs.

Baker, Derek, ed. The Orthodox Churches & the West. (Studies in Church History Ser.: Vol. 13). 350p. 1976. 45.00x (ISBN 0-631-17180-0). Basil Blackwell.

Brianchaninov, Ignatius. Three Essays: On Reading the Gospel, on Reading the Holy Fathers, on Shunning Reading of Books Containing False Teachings. pap. 0.25 (ISBN 0-686-16365-6). Eastern Orthodox.

Budge, E. A. Apophthegmata Patrum. 150p. 1975. pap. 5.95 (ISBN 0-686-10938-4). Eastern Orthodox.

Cassian, St. John. Teachings of St. John Cassian. pap. 4.95 (ISBN 0-686-05665-5). Eastern Orthodox.

Cavarnos, Constantine. The Future Life According to Orthodox Teaching. Auxentios, Hieromonk & Chrysostomos, Archimandrite, trs. from Gr. 100p. (Orig.). 1985. pap. 6.50 (ISBN 0-911165-06-1). Ctr Trad Orthodox.

--Modern Orthodox Saints: St. Nikephoros of Chios, Vol. 4. 2nd, rev. ed. LC 86-82207. (Illus.). 124p. 1986. pap. 4.95 (ISBN 0-914744-74-7). Inst Byzantine.

--Orthodox Iconography. LC 77-74606. (Illus.). 76p. 1977. pap. 4.50 (ISBN 0-914744-37-2). Inst Byzantine.

Chesterton, G. K. Orthodoxy. 160p. 1973. pap. 3.50 (ISBN 0-385-01536-4, Im). Doubleday.

Chitty, Derwas J. The Desert a City. 222p. 1977. pap. 8.95 (ISBN 0-913836-45-1). St Vladimirs.

Chrysostom, John. St. John Chrysostom on the Priesthood. 160p. 1977. pap. 4.95 (ISBN 0-913836-38-9). St Vladimirs.

Chrysostomos & Auxentios, Hieromonk. Contemporary Traditionalist Orthodox Thought. 80p. (Orig.). 1986. pap. 5.00 (ISBN 0-911165-07-X). Ctr Trad Orthodox.

Chrysostomos, Archimandrite & Ambrosios, Hieromonk. Obedience. Young, Alexey & Derugin, Vladimir, eds. (Themes in Orthodox Patristic Psychology Ser.: Vol. 2). 90p. (Orig.). 1984. text ed. write for info. (ISBN 0-916586-88-X); pap. text ed. write for info. (ISBN 0-916586-31-6). Holy Cross Orthodox.

Colliander, Tito. The Way of the Ascetics. 130p. Repr. of 1960 ed. cancelled 5.95 (ISBN 0-913026-22-0). St Nectarios.

Coniaris, A. M. Introducing the Orthodox Church. 1982. pap. 7.95. Light&Life Pub Co MN.

--Making God Real in the Orthodox Christian Home. 1977. pap. 5.95 (ISBN 0-937032-07-7). Light&Life Pub Co MN.

--Orthodoxy: A Creed for Today. 1972. pap. 7.95 (ISBN 0-937032-19-0). Light&Life Pub Co MN.

Constantelos, Demetrios J. Understanding the Greek Orthodox Church: Its Faith, History & Practice. 214p. 1982. (HarpR); pap. 9.95 (ISBN 0-8164-2367-9). Har-Row.

Constantelos, Demetrios J., intro. by. Orthodox Theology & Diakonia: Trends & Prospects. 398p. 1981. 24.95 (ISBN 0-916586-79-0); pap. 17.95 (ISBN 0-916586-80-4). Hellenic Coll Pr.

Constantine, Archimandrite. Antichrist, Orthodoxy or Heterodoxy. pap. 0.25 (ISBN 0-686-11505-8). Eastern Orthodox.

Cronk, George. The Message of the Bible: An Orthodox Christian Perspective. LC 82-7355. 293p. (Orig.). 1982. pap. 8.95 (ISBN 0-913836-94-X). St Vladimirs.

Dabovich, Sebastian. True Church of Christ. pap. 0.25 (ISBN 0-686-11506-6). Eastern Orthodox.

Dawes, Elizabeth & Baynes, Norman H., trs. from Greek. Three Byzantine Saints. 275p. 1977. pap. 8.95 (ISBN 0-913836-44-3). St Vladimirs.

Ellis, Jane. The Russian Orthodox Church: A Contemporary History. LC 85-45884. 700p. 1986. 39.95x (ISBN 0-253-35029-8). Ind U Pr.

Eterovich, Adam S. Orthodox Church Directory of the United States. 1968. softcover 5.00 (ISBN 0-88247-126-0). Ragusan Pr.

Fortescue, Adrian. The Orthodox Eastern Church. 3rd facsimile ed. LC 70-179520. (Select Bibliographies Reprint Ser). Repr. of 1920 ed. 26.50 (ISBN 0-8369-6649-X). Ayer Co Pubs.

--Orthodox Eastern Church. (Illus.). 1969. 25.50 (ISBN 0-8337-1217-9). B Franklin.

Fry, Barbara, et al, eds. Eastern Churches Review, Vols. I-X, 1966-1978. 2000p. 1985. pap. text ed. 80.00x (ISBN 0-89370-095-9). Borgo Pr.

Gavin, Frank S. Some Aspects of Contemporary Greek Orthodox Thought. LC 73-133818. Repr. of 1923 ed. 29.00 (ISBN 0-404-02687-7). AMS Pr.

Harakas, S. Something Is Stirring in World Orthodoxy. 1978. pap. 3.25 (ISBN 0-937032-04-2). Light&Life Pub Co MN.

Harakas, S. S. Contemporary Moral Issues Facing the Orthodox Christian. 1982. pap. 6.95 (ISBN 0-937032-24-7). Light&Life Pub Co MN.

Hopko, T., et al. God & Charity: Images of Eastern Orthodox Theology, Spirituality & Practice. Costa, Francis D., ed. LC 79-3027. (Pan-Am Books). 103p. (Orig.). 1979. pap. text ed. 3.95 (ISBN 0-916586-34-0). Holy Cross Orthodox.

Hopko, Thomas. All the Fulness of God: Essays on Orthodoxy, Ecumenism & Modern Society. LC 82-5454. 188p. (Orig.). 1982. pap. 7.95 (ISBN 0-913836-96-6). St Vladimirs.

Khomiakov, Alexei S. The Church Is One. (Illus.). 1980. pap. 1.25x (ISBN 0-913026-23-9). St Nectarios.

Koulomzin, Sophie. Our Church & Our Children. LC 75-20215. 158p. 1975. pap. 6.95 (ISBN 0-913836-25-7). St Vladimirs.

Lossky, Vladimir. Orthodox Theology: An Introduction. LC 78-1853. 137p. 1978. pap. 5.95 (ISBN 0-913836-43-5). St Vladimirs.

Makrakis, Apostolos. The City of Zion-The Human Society in Christ, i.e., the Church Built Upon a Rock. Orthodox Christian Educational Society, ed. Cummings, Denver, tr. from Hellenic. 109p. 1958. pap. 4.00x (ISBN 0-938366-16-5). Orthodox Chr.

--The Holy Orthodox Church. Orthodox Christian Educational Society, ed. Lisney, M. I. & Krick, L., trs. from Hellenic. 298p. (Orig.). 1980. pap. 7.95x (ISBN 0-938366-34-3). Orthodox Chr.

--Memoir of the Nature of the Church of Christ. Orthodox Christian Educational Society, ed. Cummings, Denver, tr. from Hellenic. 175p. 1947. 4.75x (ISBN 0-938366-21-1). Orthodox Chr.

--The Orthodox Definition of Political Science. Orthodox Christian Educational Society, ed. Cummings, Denver, tr. from Hellenic. 163p. 1968. pap. 4.00x (ISBN 0-938366-31-9). Orthodox Chr.

Metropolitan Philip Saliba & Allen, Joseph J. Out of the Depths Have I Cried: Thoughts on Incarnational Theology in the Eastern Christian Experience. LC 79-18611. (Illus., Orig.). 1979. pap. 4.95 (ISBN 0-916586-32-4). Holy Cross Orthodox.

Meyendorff, et al. The Primacy of Peter. 134p. 1963. 7.95 (ISBN 0-913836-20-6). St Vladimirs.

Meyendorff, John. The Byzantine Legacy in the Orthodox Church. LC 82-797. 268p. (Orig.). 1982. pap. 8.95 (ISBN 0-913836-90-7). St Vladimirs.

--Living Tradition. LC 78-2031. 202p. 1978. pap. 7.95 (ISBN 0-913836-48-6). St Vladimirs.

--The Orthodox Church: Its Past & Its Role in the World Today. LC 81-4978. 258p. 1981. pap. 8.95 (ISBN 0-913836-81-8). St Vladimirs.

--St. Gregory Palamas & Orthodox Spirituality. (Illus.). 184p. pap. 7.95 (ISBN 0-913836-11-7). St Vladimirs.

Neale, John M. A History of the Holy Eastern Church, 5 vols. LC 74-144662. Repr. of 1850 ed. Set. 215.00 (ISBN 0-404-04670-3). AMS Pr.

--Voices from the East: Documents of the Present State & Working of the Oriental Church. LC 75-173069. Repr. of 1859 ed. 18.00 (ISBN 0-404-04659-2). AMS Pr.

Nissiotis, N. Interpreting Orthodoxy. 1980. pap. 2.95 (ISBN 0-937032-23-9). Light&Life Pub Co MN.

Nykanen, Marita & Williams, Esther, trs. from Finnish. The Faith We Hold: Archbishop Paul. LC 80-10404. 96p. 1980. pap. 4.95 (ISBN 0-913836-63-X). St Vladimirs.

O'Callaghan, P. O. An Eastern Orthodox Response to Evangelical Claims. 1984. pap. 2.95 (ISBN 0-937032-35-2). Light&Life Pub Co MN.

Orthodox Eastern Church-Synod of Jerusalem. Acts & Decrees of the Synod of Jerusalem, 1672. pap. 1.95 (ISBN 0-686-05637-X). Eastern Orthodox.

Orthodox Spirituality. pap. 0.25 (ISBN 0-686-05392-3). Eastern Orthodox.

Palassis, Neketas S., ed. St. Nectarios Orthodox Conference. LC 80-53258. 176p. (Orig.). 1981. pap. 15.00x (ISBN 0-913026-14-X). St Nectarios.

Pargoire, Jules. Eglise Byzantine De 527 a 847. 1971. Repr. of 1905 ed. lib. bdg. 26.00 (ISBN 0-8337-2672-2). B Franklin.

Platon. Orthodox Doctrine of the Apostolic Eastern Church: A Compendium of Christian Theology. LC 70-81772. Repr. of 1857 ed. 18.50 (ISBN 0-404-05058-1). AMS Pr.

Pruter, Karl. Directory of Autocephalous Anglican, Catholic, & Orthodox Bishops. 3rd ed. LC 86-34289. 53p. 1986. lib. bdg. 19.95x (ISBN 0-89370-528-4). Borgo Pr.

Ridding, Laura, ed. Travels of Macarius: Extracts from the Diary of the Travels of Macarius, Patriarch of Antioch. LC 77-115577. (Russia Observed Ser). 1971. Repr. of 1936 ed. 12.00 (ISBN 0-405-03089-4). Ayer Co Pubs.

Schmemann, Alexander. Church, World, Mission. LC 79-27597. 227p. 1979. pap. 7.95 (ISBN 0-913836-49-4). St Vladimirs.

Scupoli, Lorenzo. Unseen Warfare. 280p. 1978. pap. 8.95 (ISBN 0-913836-52-4). St Vladimirs.

Semenoff-Tian-Chansky, Alexander. Father John of Kronstadt: A Life. 160p. 1979. pap. 7.95 (ISBN 0-913836-56-7). St Vladimirs.

Smirnoff, Eugene. Russian Orthodox Missions. pap. 8.95 (ISBN 0-686-01299-2). Eastern Orthodox.

Sokoloff, D. Archpriest. Manual of the Orthodox Church's Divine Services. 172p. (Orig.). 1975. pap. 6.00 (ISBN 0-317-30302-3). Holy Trinity.

Symeon of Thessalonike. A Treatise on Prayer: An Explanation of the Services of the Orthodox Church. Vaporis, N. M., intro. by. Simmons, H. L., tr. from Gr. (The Archbishop Iakovos Library of Ecclesiastical & Historical Sources: No. 9). Orig. Title: Peri Theias Kai Hieras Proseuches. (Orig.). 1984. 12.95; pap. text ed. 7.95 (ISBN 0-917653-05-X). Hellenic Coll Pr.

Synaxis: The Journal of Orthodox Theology, Vol. 2. 1977. pap. 4.00x (ISBN 0-913026-88-3). St Nectarios.

Taft, Robert F., ed. The Oriental Orthodox Churches in the United States. 32p. 1986. pap. 2.95 (ISBN 1-55586-987-4). US Catholic.

Taylor, John. Icon Painting. LC 78-25925. (The Mayflower Gallery Ser.). (Illus.). 1979. 12.50 (ISBN 0-8317-4813-3, Mayflower Bks); pap. 6.95 (ISBN 0-8317-4814-1). Smith Pubs.

Trempelas, Panagiotes N. The Autocephaly of the Metropolia in America. Bebis, George S., tr. Stephanopoulos, Robert G., ed. 80p. 1974. pap. 2.50 (ISBN 0-916586-00-6). Holy Cross Orthodox.

Tsirpanlis, Constantine N., ed. Orthodox-Unification Dialogue. LC 80-54586. (Conference Ser.: No. 8). (Illus.). x, 139p. (Orig.). 1981. pap. text ed. 7.95 (ISBN 0-932894-08-9, Pub. by New Era Bks). Paragon Hse.

Vaporis, N. M, ed. Byzantine Fellowship Lectures, No. One, No. 1. (Illus.). 1974. pap. 2.95 (ISBN 0-916586-02-2). Holy Cross Orthodox.

Ware, Timothy. Orthodox Church. (Orig.). 1963. pap. 5.95 (ISBN 0-14-020592-6, Pelican). Penguin.

Winkler, Gabriele. Prayer Attitude in the Eastern Church. 1978. pap. 1.45 (ISBN 0-937032-01-8). Light&Life Pub Co MN.

Znoskovo-Borovsky, Mitrophan. Pravoslavije, Rimo-Katolichestvo, Protenstatizm i Sektantstvo. Tr. of Orthodoxy, Roman-Catholicism, Protenstatism & Sectarianism. 156p. 1972. pap. text ed. 5.00 (ISBN 0-317-30254-X). Holy Trinity.

ORTHODOX EASTERN CHURCH–HISTORY

see also Schism–Eastern and Western Church

Basil, Saint St. Basil the Great on The Forty Martyrs of Sebaste, Paradise, & the Catholic Faith. 1979. pap. 3.95 (ISBN 0-686-25227-6). Eastern Orthodox.

Cavarnos, Constantine. Modern Orthodox Saints: St. Methodia of Kimolos, Vol. 9. (Illus.). 123p. 1987. 8.95 (ISBN 0-914744-75-5); pap. 5.95 (ISBN 0-914744-76-3). Inst Byzantine.

Hussey, J. M. The Orthodox Church in the Byzantine Empire. (History of the Christian Church Ser.). 320p. 1986. 59.00x (ISBN 0-19-826901-3). Oxford U Pr.

Joannes, Damascenus. On Holy Images. Allies, Mary H., tr. from Greek. 1977. pap. 2.95 (ISBN 0-686-19232-X). Eastern Orthodox.

Miller, E. C., Jr. Toward a Fuller Vision: Orthodoxy & the Anglican Experience. LC 84-61015. 188p. (Orig.). 1984. pap. 7.95 (ISBN 0-8192-1351-9). Morehouse.

Orthodox Eastern Church. Synod of Sixteen Seventy-Two: Acts & Decrees of the Jerusalem Synod Held Under Dositheus, Containing the Confession Published Name of Cyril Lukaris. Robertson, J. N., tr. LC 78-81769. 1969. Repr. of 1899 ed. 18.50 (ISBN 0-404-03567-1). AMS Pr.

Papadopoullos, Theodore H. Studies & Documents Relating to the History of the Greek Church & People Under Turkish Domination. LC 78-38759. Repr. of 1952 ed. 27.50 (ISBN 0-404-56314-7). AMS Pr.

Polyzoides, G. History & Teachings of the Eastern Greek Orthodox Church. (Illus.). 96p. 4.00 (ISBN 0-686-83964-1). Divry.

Rabbath, Antoine. Documents Inedits Pour Servir a l'Histoire Du Christianisme En Orient, 2 Vols. LC 72-174293. Repr. of 1911 ed. Set. lib. bdg. 95.00 (ISBN 0-404-05202-9). AMS Pr.

St. Nectarios Press, ed. New Martyrs of the Turkish Yoke. Papadopulos, Leonidas, et al, trs. from Gr. LC 84-50974. 400p. (Orig.). 1985. pap. 12.50x (ISBN 0-913026-57-3); pap. 15.00x after January 1986. St Nectarios.

Schmemann, Alexander. Historical Road of Eastern Orthodoxy. LC 77-12074. 343p. 1977. pap. 8.95 (ISBN 0-913836-47-8). St Vladimirs.

Tradition in the Eastern Orthodox Church. pap. 0.35 (ISBN 0-686-16369-9). Eastern Orthodox.

Williams, George, tr. Orthodox Church of the East in the Eighteenth Century. LC 73-131028. Repr. of 1868 ed. 21.00 (ISBN 0-404-06977-0). AMS Pr.

ORTHODOX EASTERN CHURCH–HYMNS

Bogolepov, Alexander. Orthodox Hymns of Christmas, Easter, & Holy Week. LC 65-16177. 78p. 1965. pap. 1.95 (ISBN 0-913836-02-8). St Vladimirs.

Lungu, N., et al. A Guide to the Music of the Eastern Orthodox Church. Apostola, Nicholas K., tr. from Rumanian. Orig. Title: Gramatica Muzicii Psaltice. (Illus.). 180p. (Orig.). 1984. pap. 15.00 (ISBN 0-917651-00-6). Holy Cross Orthodox.

Neale, John M. Hymns of the Eastern Church. LC 77-131029. Repr. of 1862 ed. 17.95 (ISBN 0-404-04666-5). AMS Pr.

Von Gardner, Johann. Russian Church Singing: Orthodox Worship & Hymnography, Vol. I. LC 79-27480. 146p. 1980. pap. 7.95 (ISBN 0-913836-59-1). St Vladimirs.

ORTHODOX EASTERN CHURCH–LITURGY AND RITUAL

Budge, E. A. Sayings of the Fathers. 1975. pap. 5.95 (ISBN 0-686-10941-4). Eastern Orthodox.

Cabasilas, Nicholas. Commentary on the Divine Liturgy. Hussey, J. M. & McNulty, P. A., trs. from Greek. LC 62-53410. 120p. 1977. pap. 6.95 (ISBN 0-913836-37-0). St Vladimirs.

Coniaris, A. M. Where Moth & Rust Do Not Consume. 1983. pap. 5.95 (ISBN 0-937032-30-1). Light&Life Pub Co MN.

Conomos, Dimitri E. The Late Byzantine & Slavonic Communion Cycle: Liturgy & Music. LC 84-12176. (Dumbarton Oaks Studies: Vol. 21). (Illus.). 222p. 1985. 25.00x (ISBN 0-88402-134-3). Dumbarton Oaks.

Cyril Of Jerusalem, Saint St. Cyril of Jerusalem on the Sacraments. 83p. 1977. pap. 4.95 (ISBN 0-913836-39-7). St Vladimirs.

Dabovich, Sebastian. Holy Orthodox Church: Its Ritual, Services, & Sacraments. 1898. pap. 2.95 (ISBN 0-686-00253-9). Eastern Orthodox.

Drillock, David & Erickson, John, eds. The Divine Liturgy. 368p. 1982. text ed. 30.00 (ISBN 0-913836-95-8); pap. 20.00 (ISBN 0-913836-93-1). St Vladimirs.

Father Benedict. The Daily Cycle of Services of the Orthodox Church: An Historical Synopsis. 30p. (Orig.). 1986. pap. 4.95x (ISBN 0-936649-09-7, TX 1-781-934). St Anthony Orthodox.

Gerostergios, Asterios. On the Divine Liturgy: Orthodox Homilies, Vol. 1. Kantiotes, Augoustinos N., tr. LC 85-81949. (Illus.). 274p. 1986. 13.95 (ISBN 0-914744-72-0). Inst Byzantine.

Harakas, S. Living the Liturgy. 1974. pap. 4.95 (ISBN 0-937032-17-4). Light&Life Pub Co MN.

Harrilchak, Paul N. The Divine Liturgy of the Great Church with Melodies for Congregational Sin. (Illus.). x, 221p. (Orig.). 1984. 15.00x (ISBN 0-930055-00-4). Holy Trinity Ortho.

Holy Transfiguration Monastery, tr. from Greek. The Lamentations: From the Matins of Holy & Great Saturday. 65p. (Orig.). 1981. pap. 4.95x (ISBN 0-913026-51-4). St Nectarios.

Hopko, T., et al. God & Charity: Images of Eastern Orthodox Theology, Spirituality & Practice. Costa, Francis D., ed. LC 79-3027. (Pan-Am Books). 103p. (Orig.). 1979. pap. text ed. 3.95 (ISBN 0-916586-34-0). Holy Cross Orthodox.

Kantiotes, Angoustinos N. On the Divine Liturgy: Orthodox Homilies, Vol. 2. Gerostergios, Asterios, tr. (Illus.). 285p. 1986. 14.95 (ISBN 0-914744-73-9). Inst Byzantine.

King, Archdale A. Rites of Eastern Christendom, 2 Vols. LC 70-142246. Repr. of 1948 ed. Set. 125.00 (ISBN 0-404-03677-5). Vol. 1 (ISBN 0-404-03678-3). Vol. 2 (ISBN 0-404-03679-1). AMS Pr.

King, John G. Rites & Ceremonies of the Greek Church in Russia. LC 73-126673. Repr. of 1772 ed. 34.50 (ISBN 0-404-03692-9). AMS Pr.

Kucharek, Casimir. The Sacramental Mysteries: A Byzantine Approach. 416p. 1976. 15.75 (ISBN 0-911726-17-9); pap. 12.75 laminated (ISBN 0-911726-25-X). Alleluia Pr.

Ledkovsky, Boris. Great Vespers. (Music Ser.). 218p. 1976. pap. 10.00 (ISBN 0-913836-26-5). St Vladimirs.

Light is Life: Eastern Rite Religious Emblem Record. 1980. pap. 1.60 (ISBN 0-8395-3011-0, 3011). BSA.

Littledale, Richard F. Offices from the Service Books of the Holy Eastern Church. LC 77-133819. 1970. Repr. of 1863 ed. 24.50 (ISBN 0-404-03996-0). AMS Pr.

Makrakis, Apostolos. Catechesis of the Orthodox Church. rev. ed. Orthodox Christian Educational Society, ed. 239p. 1969. pap. text ed. 5.00x (ISBN 0-938366-14-9). Orthodox Chr.

Mancuso, Laurence. A Prayerbook. (New Skete). (Illus.). 720p. 1976. 35.00x (ISBN 0-9607924-3-0). Monks of New Skete.

Mancuso, Laurence, tr. from Slavonic & Gr. A Service Book. (New Skete). (Illus.). 214p. 1978. 20.00x (ISBN 0-9607924-4-9). Monks of New Skete.

Moore, Lazarus. Sacred Tradition in the Orthodox Church. 1984. pap. 2.95 (ISBN 0-937032-34-4). Light&Life Pub Co MN.

Mother Mary & Archimandrite Kallistos Ware, trs. The Festal Menaion. 248p. 1977. pap. 10.95 (ISBN 0-571-11137-8). Faber & Faber.

Nestorian Church. Liturgy & Ritual: The Liturgy of the Holy Apostles Adai & Mari. LC 79-131032. Repr. of 1893 ed. 14.50 (ISBN 0-404-03997-9). AMS Pr.

Orthodox Eastern Church. The General Menaion, or the Book of Services Common to the Festivals of Our Lord Jesus Christ, of the Holy Virgin, & of the Different Orders of Saints. Orloff, Nicholas, tr. from Old Slavonic. pap. 15.00 (ISBN 0-686-25551-8). Eastern Orthodox.

--Offices of the Oriental Church. LC 73-79805. Repr. of 1884 ed. 16.75 (ISBN 0-404-00874-7). AMS Pr.

Polyzoides, G. What We See & Hear in a Greek Eastern Orthodox Church. 92p. 4.00 (ISBN 0-686-83965-X). Divry.

Raya, Joseph & Vinck, Jose D. Musical Setting for the Liturgy of St. John Chrysostom. (Illus.). 44p. 1971. pap. 2.00 (ISBN 0-911726-05-5). Alleluia Pr.

Schmemann, Alexander. Introduction to Liturgical Theology. LC 66-69197. 170p. 1966. pap. 9.95 (ISBN 0-913836-18-4). St Vladimirs.

Shann, G. V. Book of the Needs of the Holy Orthodox Church. LC 77-82258. 1969. Repr. of 1894 ed. 19.45 (ISBN 0-404-05951-1). AMS Pr.

--Euchology: A Manual of Prayers of the Holy Orthodox Church. LC 75-82260. 1969. Repr. of 1891 ed. 32.50 (ISBN 0-404-05952-X). AMS Pr.

Shorter Catechism of the Orthodox Church. pap. 0.50 (ISBN 0-686-05664-7). Eastern Orthodox.

Vaporis, Nomikos M., ed. Mikron Euchologion: An Orthodox Prayer Book. Gelsinger, Michael, tr. from Greek. & pref. by. LC 77-77642. 288p. 1977. 18.95 (ISBN 0-916586-09-X). Holy Cross Orthodox.

Ware, K. Communion & Intercommunion. 1980. pap. 1.95 (ISBN 0-937032-20-4). Light&Life Pub Co MN.

ORTHODOX EASTERN CHURCH–MISSIONS

Puhalo, Lazar. Missionary Handbook. 49p. (Orig.). 1985. pap. text ed. 3.00 (ISBN 0-911523-00-6). Synaxis Pr.

Stamoolis, James J. Eastern Orthodox Mission Theology Today. LC 85-15596. 208p. (Orig.). 1986. pap. 18.95 (ISBN 0-88344-215-9). Orbis Bks.

ORTHODOX EASTERN CHURCH–MYSTICISM

see Mysticism–Orthodox Eastern Church

ORTHODOX EASTERN CHURCH–PRAYER-BOOKS AND DEVOTIONS

A Manual of Eastern Orthodox Prayer. 2nd ed. pap. text ed. 3.95 (ISBN 0-88141-012-8). St Vladimirs.

ORTHODOX EASTERN CHURCH–RELATIONS–ANGLICAN COMMUNION

Istavridis, Vasil T. Orthodoxy & Anglicanism. LC 67-79982. 1966. 15.00x (ISBN 0-8401-1183-5). A R Allenson.

Overbeck, J. J. Catholic Orthodoxy & Anglo-Catholicism. LC 76-81771. Repr. of 1866 ed. 10.00 (ISBN 0-404-04839-0). AMS Pr.

ORTHODOX EASTERN CHURCH–RELATIONS–CATHOLIC CHURCH

see also Schism–Eastern and Western Church

Anthimos. Reply of the Orthodox Church to Roman Catholic Overtures on Reunion. rev., enl. ed. 64p. 1986. pap. 2.00 (ISBN 0-913026-62-X). St Nectarios.

Chrysostomos, Archimandrite. Orthodoxy & Papism. Williams, Theodore M., ed. LC 82-73693. 70p. 1982. pap. 4.50 (ISBN 0-911165-00-2). Ctr Trad Orthodox.

Encyclical Epistle of the One Holy Catholic & Apistolic Church: Being a Reply to the Epistle of Pius IX to the Easterns. pap. 2.50 (ISBN 0-686-05641-8). Eastern Orthodox.

Halecki, Oscar. From Florence to Brest, Fourteen Thirty-Nine to Fifteen Ninety-Six. 2nd ed. LC 68-26103. 456p. 1968. 35.00 (ISBN 0-208-00702-4, Archon). Shoe String.

Makrakis, Apostolos. The Innovations of the Roman Church. 82p. (Orig.). 1966. pap. 3.75x (ISBN 0-938366-39-4). Orthodox Chr.

Metropolitan Philaret of Moscow. Comparison of the Differences in the Doctrines of Faith Between the Eastern & Western Churches. Pinkerton, Robert, tr. from Rus. 1974. pap. 1.25 (ISBN 0-686-10206-1). Eastern Orthodox.

Norden, Walter. Papsttum Und Byzanz: Das Problem Ihrer Wiedervereinigung Bis Zum Untergange Des Byzantinischen Reichs (1453) 1903. 40.50 (ISBN 0-8337-2571-8). B Franklin.

ORTHODOX EASTERN CHURCH–RELATIONS–PROTESTANT CHURCHES

Confession of Dositheus. pap. 1.95 (ISBN 0-686-05640-X). Eastern Orthodox.

Makrakis, Apostolos. An Orthodox-Protestant Debate. Cummings, Denver, tr. 101p. 1949. pap. 3.25x (ISBN 0-938366-37-8). Orthodox Chr.

Mastrantonis, George. Augsburg & Constantinople: The Correspondence Between Patriarch Jeremiah II & the Tubingen Theologians. 424p. 1981. 22.95 (ISBN 0-916586-81-2); pap. 14.95 (ISBN 0-916586-82-0). Hellenic Coll Pr.

Spoer, Hans H. Aid for Churchmen, Episcopal & Orthodox. LC 71-79152. Repr. of 1930 ed. 12.50 (ISBN 0-404-06197-4). AMS Pr.

ORTHODOX EASTERN CHURCH–SERMONS

Bitzer, Heinrich, ed. Light on the Path: Daily Scripture Readings in Hebrew & Greek. 400p. (Orig.). 1982. pap. 9.95 (ISBN 0-8010-0822-0). Baker Bk.

Coniaris, A. Gems from the Sunday Gospel Lessons in the Orthodox Church, Vol. II. pap. 5.95 (ISBN 0-937032-13-1). Light&Life Pub Co MN.

Coniaris, A. M. Eighty Talks for Orthodox Young People. 1975. pap. 4.95 (ISBN 0-937032-16-6). Light&Life Pub Co MN.

Gerostergios, Asterios. On the Divine Liturgy: Orthodox Homilies, Vol. 1. Kantiotes, Augoustinos N., tr. LC 85-81949. (Illus.). 274p. 1986. 13.95 (ISBN 0-914744-72-0). Inst Byzantine.

St. Cyril, Bishop of Jerusalem. Five Instructions on the Sacraments. 1974. pap. 1.25 (ISBN 0-686-10197-9). Eastern Orthodox.

ORTHODOX EASTERN CHURCH, GREEK

Anatolius of Mohilew & Mstislaw. Greek Orthodox Faith: Scriptural Presentation. Bjerring, Nicholas, tr. from Rus. 1974. pap. 1.00 (ISBN 0-686-10205-3). Eastern Orthodox.

Batalden, Stephen K. Catherine II's Greek Prelate: Eugenios Voulgaris in Russia, 1771-1806. (East European Monographs: No. 115). 197p. 1983. 26.00x (ISBN 0-88033-006-6). East Eur Quarterly.

Chirban, John T., ed. Marriage & the Family Medicine, Psychology & Religion: New Directions, New Integrations. (Series on Medicine, Psychology & Religion). (Illus.). 94p. (Orig.). 1983. pap. text ed. 4.95 (ISBN 0-916586-63-4). Holy Cross Orthodox.

Chrysostomos, Archimandrite, et al. The Old Calendar Orthodox Church of Greece. 116p. 1985. pap. 4.50 (ISBN 0-911165-05-3). Ctr Trad Orthodox.

Every, George. Byzantine Patriarchate, Four Hundred Fifty-One to Twelve Hundred Four. 2nd rev. ed. LC 78-63340. (The Crusades & Military Orders: Second Ser.). Repr. of 1962 ed. 27.50 (ISBN 0-404-17015-3). AMS Pr.

Frazee, Charles A. Orthodox Church in Independent Greece 1821-52. LC 69-10488. 1969. 42.50 (ISBN 0-521-07247-6). Cambridge U Pr.

Han, Nathan E. A Parsing Guide to the Greek New Testament. LC 77-158175. 496p. 1971. pap. 17.95 (ISBN 0-8361-1653-4). Herald Pr.

Harakas, Stanley S. Let Mercy Abound: Social Concern in the Greek Orthodox Church. 188p. 1983. text ed. 18.95 (ISBN 0-686-90967-4); pap. text ed. 12.95 (ISBN 0-686-90968-2). Holy Cross Orthodox.

Kalomiros, Alexander. Against False Union. 2nd ed. Gabriel, George, tr. from Greek. (Illus., Orig.). 1979. pap. 2.50x (ISBN 0-913026-20-4). St Nectarios.

King, John G. Rites & Ceremonies of the Greek Church in Russia. LC 73-126673. Repr. of 1772 ed. 34.50 (ISBN 0-404-03692-9). AMS Pr.

Macris, George P. The Orthodox Church & the Ecumenical Movement During the Period 1920-1969. (Illus.). 196p. (Orig.). 1986. pap. 12.50 (ISBN 0-913026-74-3). St Nectarios.

Meyendorff, John. Byzantine Theology: Historical Trends & Doctrinal Themes. 2nd, rev. ed. LC 72-94167. viii, 243p. 1983. pap. 9.00 (ISBN 0-8232-0967-9). Fordham.

Moskos, C. C., Jr. & Papajohn, J. C. Greek Orthodox Youth Today. Vaporis, N. M., intro. by. (Saints Peter & Paul Youth Ministry Lectures Ser.). 56p. (Orig.). 1983. pap. 3.00 (ISBN 0-916586-56-1). Holy Cross Orthodox.

Palmer, G. E. & Sherrard, Philip, trs. The Philokalia, Vol. 1: The Complete Text Compiled By St. Nikodimos of the Holy Mountain & St. Markarios of Corinth, Vol. 1. 384p. 1983. pap. 10.95 (ISBN 0-571-13013-5). Faber & Faber.

Papadopoullos, Theodore H. Studies & Documents Relating to the History of the Greek Church & People Under Turkish Domination. LC 78-38759. Repr. of 1952 ed. 27.50 (ISBN 0-404-56314-7). AMS Pr.

Payne, Robert. The Holy Fire. LC 79-27594. 328p. 1980. pap. 8.95 (ISBN 0-913836-61-3). St Vladimirs.

Polyzoides, M. Catechism of Eastern Greek Orthodox Church. 96p. 4.00 (ISBN 0-686-79625-X). Divry.

Scourby, Alice. Third Generation Greek Americans: A Study of Religious Attitudes. Cordasco, Francesco, ed. LC 80-893. (American Ethnic Groups Ser.). lib. bdg. 16.00x (ISBN 0-405-13454-1). Ayer Co Pubs.

Tsirpanlis, Constance N. Greek Patristic Theolgy, Vol. 1: Eleven Studies in Eastern Orthodox Doctrine Spirituality. 170p. 1979. pap. 9.95 (ISBN 0-686-36327-2). EO Pr.

Vaporis, Nomikos M., ed. The Holy Gospel. 245p. 1979. 95.00 (ISBN 0-916586-25-1). Holy Cross Orthodox.

--Post-Byzantine Ecclesiastical Personalities. LC 78-11037. 111p. 1978. pap. 3.95 (ISBN 0-916586-30-8). Holy Cross Orthodox.

Ware, Timothy. Eustratios Argenti: Study of the Greek Church under Turkish Rule. 1974. Repr. of 1964 ed. 12.50 (ISBN 0-686-10203-7). Eastern Orthodox.

ORTHODOX EASTERN CHURCH, RUSSIAN

Anderson, Paul B. People, Church & State in Modern Russia. LC 79-5204. 240p. 1980. Repr. of 1944 ed. 23.00 (ISBN 0-8305-0058-8). Hyperion Conn.

Archbishop Vitaly Maximenko. Motivi Moijej Zhizni. Tr. of Motives of My Life. 205p. 1955. pap. 7.00 (ISBN 0-317-29054-1). Holy Trinity.

Archimandrite Anthony Yamshcikov, ed. Sovremennost' v svjetje Slova Bozhija - Slove i Rechi Arkiepiskopa Averkija, 4 vols. Tr. of Comtemporaneity in Light of the Word of God - the Works & Writings of Archbishop Averky. 2100p. 1976. 89.00 (ISBN 0-317-29057-6); pap. 69.00 (ISBN 0-317-29058-4). Holy Trinity.

Bogolepov, Alexander. Church Reforms in Russia, 1905-1918. 59p. 1966. pap. 1.95 (ISBN 0-913836-01-X). St Vladimirs.

Brianchianinov, Ignatius. The Arena. Archimandrite Lazarus Moore, tr. from Rus. 300p. (Orig.). 1982. 15.00 (ISBN 0-88465-009-X); pap. 10.00 (ISBN 0-88465-011-1). Holy Trinity.

Brotherhood of St. Herman of Alaska Staff. St. Herman Calendar of Orthodox Saints. pap. 5.00 (ISBN 0-686-05410-5). Eastern Orthodox.

Fireside, Harvey. Icon & Swastika: The Russian Orthodox Church Under Nazi & Soviet Control. LC 70-123567. (Harvard University, Russian Research Center Studies: Vol. 62). pap. 67.00 (ISBN 0-317-08921-8, 2021595). Bks Demand UMI.

Gagarin, Jean X. Russian Clergy. LC 70-131035. Repr. of 1872 ed. 21.00 (ISBN 0-404-02666-4). AMS Pr.

Garrett, Paul D. St. Innocent: Apostle to America. LC 79-19634. 345p. 1979. pap. 8.95 (ISBN 0-913836-60-5). St Vladimirs.

Grabbe, George. Dogmat Tserkvi v Sovrjemjennom Mire. Tr. of The Dogma of the Church in the Modern World. 1975. pap. 1.50 (ISBN 0-317-30381-3). Holy Trinity.

Heard, Albert F. Russian Church & Russian Dissent. LC 70-127907. Repr. of 1887 ed. 24.50 (ISBN 0-404-03198-6). AMS Pr.

Khrapovitsky, Antony. Confession. Birchall, Christopher, tr. from Rus. LC 74-29537. 100p. (Orig.). 1975. pap. 3.00 (ISBN 0-88465-005-7). Holy Trinity.

King, John G. Rites & Ceremonies of the Greek Church in Russia. LC 73-126673. Repr. of 1772 ed. 34.50 (ISBN 0-404-03692-9). AMS Pr.

Lzhe-Pravoslavije na podjomje. Tr. of False-Orthodoxy on the Rise. 212p. 1954. pap. 7.00 (ISBN 0-317-30370-8). Holy Trinity.

Metropolitan Panteleimon. Pravoslavije i Inoslavnija Khristijanskija Ispovjedanija. Tr. of Orthodoxy & Other Christian Faiths. 1950. pap. 0.55 (ISBN 0-317-30259-0). Holy Trinity.

Nikiforoff-Volgin, V. Zemlja Imjeninnitsa. Tr. of The Feast of the Land. 182p. 1960. pap. 6.00 (ISBN 0-317-30418-6). Holy Trinity.

Pitirim, Monseigneur, et al. The Orthodox Church of Russia: A Millennial Celebration. LC 82-6933. (Illus.). 320p. 1982. 65.00 (ISBN 0-86565-029-2). Vendome.

Platon. Orthodox Doctrine of the Apostolic Eastern Church. 1973. 5.00 (ISBN 0-686-05409-1). Eastern Orthodox.

--Present State of the Greek Church in Russia. LC 75-131031. Repr. of 1815 ed. 21.50 (ISBN 0-404-05059-X). AMS Pr.

Protopresbyter Michael Pomazansky. Pravosavnoje Dogmaticheskoje Bogoslovije. Tr. of Orthodox Dogmatic Theology. 280p. 1963. pap. text ed. 20.00 (ISBN 0-317-29309-5). Holy Trinity.

Rodzianko, M. The Truth about the Russian Church Abroad. Hilko, Michael P., tr. from Rus. LC 74-29321. (Illus.). 48p. (Orig.). 1975. pap. 1.50 (ISBN 0-88465-004-9). Holy Trinity.

Saint John Kronstadt. Misli o Bogosluzhenii Pravoslavnoi Tserkvi. Tr. of Thoughts on the Divine Services of the Orthdox Church. 141p. 1954. 5.00 (ISBN 0-317-28907-1). Holy Trinity.

Schmemann, Alexander, ed. Ultimate Questions: An Anthology of Modern Russian Religious Thought. 310p. 1977. pap. 8.95 (ISBN 0-913836-46-X). St Vladimirs.

Skhi-Igumen, John. Christ Is in Our Midst: Letters from a Russian Monk. Williams, Esther, tr. from Rus. LC 80-10530. 168p. (Orig.). 1980. pap. 4.95 (ISBN 0-913836-64-8). St Vladimirs.

Smirnoff, Peter. Instruction in God's Law. 1974. pap. 5.00 (ISBN 0-686-10199-5). Eastern Orthodox.

Theophan the Recluse. O Pravoslavii s Predestereshenijami ot Pogreshenij Protiv Hego. Tr. of On Orthodoxy with Warning Against Apostasy from It. 202p. 1962. pap. 7.00 (ISBN 0-317-28919-5). Holy Trinity.

Ware, Kallistos T. Orthodox Way. 196p. 1979. pap. 4.95 (ISBN 0-913836-58-3). St Vladimirs.

Zernov, Nicholas. Moscow, the Third Rome. 2nd ed. LC 76-149664. Repr. of 1938 ed. 12.50 (ISBN 0-404-07075-2). AMS Pr.

Zernov, Nicolas. The Russians & Their Church. 196p. 1977. pap. 6.95 (ISBN 0-913836-36-2). St Vladimirs.

Znamensky, G. A. Azbuka Pravoslavnago Vjerouchenija. Tr. of The Alphabet of the Orthodox Faith. 80p. pap. text ed. 3.00 (ISBN 0-317-29292-7). Holy Trinity.

ORTHODOX EASTERN CHURCH, RUSSIAN–HISTORY

Batalden, Stephen K. Catherine II's Greek Prelate: Eugenios Voulgaris in Russia, 1771-1806. (East European Monographs: No. 115). 197p. 1983. 26.00x (ISBN 0-88033-006-6). East Eur Quarterly.

Curtiss, John S. The Russian Church & the Soviet State, 1917-1950. 1953. 11.75 (ISBN 0-8446-1141-7). Peter Smith.

Freeze, Gregory L. The Parish Clergy in Nineteenth-Century Russia: Crisis, Reform, Counter-Reform. LC 82-61361. 552p. 1983. 52.50x (ISBN 0-691-05381-2). Princeton U Pr.

--The Russian Levites: Parish Clergy in the Eighteenth Century. (Russian Research Center Studies: 78). 1977. 22.50x (ISBN 0-674-78175-9). Harvard U Pr.

Gardner, Johann v. Bogosluzhebncje Penije Russkoj Pravoslavnoj Tserkvi: Suschnost' Sistema I Istoria: Liturgical Chant of the Russian Orthodox Church: Its Essence, Structure & History, Vol. 1. LC 77-77086. (Rus., Illus., Orig.). 1979. text ed. 30.00 (ISBN 0-88465-008-1); pap. text ed. 25.00 (ISBN 0-686-50014-8). Holy Trinity.

--Bogosluzhebnoje Penije Russkoj Pravoslavnoj Tserkvi: Istorija, Vol. 2. LC 77-77086. Tr. of Liturgical Chant of the Russian Orthodox Church; History. (Illus.). 1981. text ed. 30.00 (ISBN 0-88465-010-3); pap. text ed. 25.00 (ISBN 0-317-30384-8). Holy Trinity.

Hale, Charles. Russian Missions in China & Japan. 1974. pap. 1.50 (ISBN 0-686-10198-7). Eastern Orthodox.

Kontsevich, I. M. Optina Pustin' i jeja vremja. Tr. of Optina Hermitage & It's Time. (Illus.). 604p. 1970. 25.00 (ISBN 0-317-29246-3); pap. 20.00 (ISBN 0-317-29247-1). Holy Trinity.

Nichols, Robert L. & Stavrou, Theofanis G., eds. Russian Orthodoxy under the Old Regime. LC 78-3196. 1978. 16.50 (ISBN 0-8166-0846-6); pap. text ed. 8.95x (ISBN 0-8166-0847-4). U of Minn Pr.

Pisoma Arkhiepiskopa Theophana Poltavskago i Perejaslavskago. Tr. of The Letters of Archbishop Theophan of Poltava & Pereyeslav. 76p. 1974. pap. 4.00 (ISBN 0-317-29047-9). Holy Trinity.

Pospielovsky, Dimitry. The Russian Church under the Soviet Regime. 533p. Set. 18.95 (ISBN 0-88141-033-0); Vol. I, 248 pgs. 9.95 (ISBN 0-88141-015-2); Vol. II, 285 pgs. 9.95 (ISBN 0-88141-016-0). St Vladimirs.

Pushkarev, Sergei. Rol' Pravoslavnoi Tserkvi V Istorii Rosii: The Role of the Orthodox Church in Russian History. Protoierei, pref. by. LC 85-80831. (Rus.). 125p. 1985. 9.50 (ISBN 0-911971-13-0). Effect Pub.

Smirnoff, Eugene. Russian Orthodox Missions. pap. 8.95 (ISBN 0-686-01299-2). Eastern Orthodox.

Talberg, N. D. K Sorokaljetiju pagubnago evlogijanskago raskola. Tr. of The Fortieth Anniversary of the Ruinous Evlogian Schism. 128p. 1966. pap. 4.00 (ISBN 0-317-30373-2). Holy Trinity.

Variorum, ed. Polynj Pravoslavnyj Bogoslavskij Enciklopediceskij. 1240p. 1971. 75.00x (ISBN 0-902089-08-0). State Mutual Bk.

ORTHODOX EASTERN CHURCH, SERBIAN

Vrga, Djuro J. & Fahey, Frank J. Changes & Socio-Religious Conflict in an Ethnic Minority Group: The Serbian Orthodox Church in America. LC 74-31771. 1975. softcover 8.00 (ISBN 0-88247-335-2). Ragusan Pr.

ORTHODOX EASTERN MONASTICISM AND RELIGIOUS ORDERS

see Monasticism and Religious Orders, Orthodox Eastern

ORTHODOX JUDAISM

see also Jewish Sects

Associations of Orthodox Jewish Scientists Staff. Proceedings, Vol. 3 & 4. Rosner, Fred, ed. 248p. 1976. pap. 9.95 (ISBN 0-87306-074-1). Feldheim.

Bernstein, Saul. The Renaissance of the Torah Jew. 1986. text ed. 20.00x (ISBN 0-88125-090-2). Ktav.

Bulka, Rueven P., ed. Dimensions of Orthodox Judaism. LC 83-260. 471p. 1983. 25.00x (ISBN 0-87068-894-4). Ktav.

Heilman, Samuel C. The People of the Book: Drama, Felloship, & Religion. LC 82-13369. x, 338p. 1987. pap. text ed. price not set (ISBN 0-226-32493-1). U of Chicago Pr.

--The People of the Book: Drama, Fellowship, & Religion. LC 82-13369. 264p. 1983. lib. bdg. 25.00x (ISBN 0-226-32492-3). U of Chicago Pr.

--Synagogue Life: A Study in Symbolic Interaction. LC 75-36403. 1976. 12.95x (ISBN 0-226-32488-5); pap. 9.95x (ISBN 0-226-32490-7, P824, Phoen). U of Chicago Pr.

Helmreich, William N. The World of the Yeshiva: An Intimate Portrait of Orthodox Jewry. LC 81-67440. 424p. 1986. pap. 14.95x (ISBN 0-300-03715-5). Yale U Pr.

Liberles, Robert. Religious Conflict in Social Context: The Resurgence of Orthodox Judaism in Frankfurt Am Main, 1838-1877. LC 84-27981. (Contributions to the Study of Religion Ser.: No. 13). xvi, 297p. 1985. lib. bdg. 29.95 (ISBN 0-313-24806-0, LRX/). Greenwood.

OSIRIS

Budge, E. Wallis. Osiris & the Egyptian Resurrection, 2 vols. LC 72-81534. (Illus.). 906p. 1973. Vol. 1. pap. 7.95 (ISBN 0-486-22780-4); Vol. 2. pap. 7.95 (ISBN 0-486-22781-2). Dover.

--Osiris & the Egyptian Resurrection, 2 vols. (Illus.). 30.50 (ISBN 0-8446-4715-2). Peter Smith.

Cook. Osiris. 1979. Repr. of 1931 ed. 12.50 (ISBN 0-89005-287-5). Ares.

OSTRAKA

Hayes, William C. Ostraka & Name Stones from the Tomb of Sen-Mut (No. 71) at Thebes: Metropolitan Museum of Art Publications in Reprint. LC 76-168406. (Illus.). 136p. 1972. Repr. of 1942 ed. 22.00 (ISBN 0-405-02239-5). Ayer Co Pubs.

Winlock, Herbert E., et al. The Monastery of Epiphanius at Thebes: Metropolitan Museum of Art Egyptain Expedition Publications, Vols. 3 & 4, 2 vols. LC 72-168413. (The Metropolitan Museum of Art Publication in Reprint Ser.). 1926. 88.00 set (ISBN 0-405-02249-2). Ayer Co Pubs.

OSTWALD, WILHELM, 1853-1932

Slosson, Edwin E. Major Prophets of To-Day. facs. ed. LC 68-8493. (Essay Index Reprint Ser.). 1914. 20.00 (ISBN 0-8369-0882-1). Ayer Co Pubs.

OTFRID VON WEISSENBURG, 9TH CENTURY

Bork, Hans. Chronologische Studien Zu Otfrids Evangelienbuch. 27.00 (ISBN 0-685-02224-2); pap. 22.00 (ISBN 0-685-02225-0). Johnson Repr.

Bossert, Gustav. Quellen zur Geshichte der Wiedertaufer. 90.00 (ISBN 0-384-05276-2); pap. 84.00 (ISBN 0-384-05275-4). Johnson Repr.

Mackenzie, Donald A. Otfrid Von Weissenburg: Narrator or Commentator. (Stanford University. Stanford Studies in Language & Literature: Vol. 6, Pt. 3). Repr. of 1946 ed. 18.00 (ISBN 0-404-51812-5). AMS Pr.

OTTERBEIN, PHILIP WILLIAM, 1726-1813

Core, Arthur C. Otterbein (Philip William) 1968. 4.00 (ISBN 0-687-30917-4); pap. 2.25 (ISBN 0-687-30918-2). Abingdon.

OTTOMAN EMPIRE

see Turkey

OU-YANG, HSIU, 1007-1072

Liu, James T. Ou-yang Hsiu: An Eleventh-Century Neo-Confucianist. 1967. 18.50x (ISBN 0-8047-0262-4). Stanford U Pr.

OUSPENSKY, PETER DEMIANOVICH, 1878-1947

Da Silva, Andrew J. Do from the Octave of Man Number Four: The Awakening & Crisis, Vol. 1. Sajkovic, Olivera, ed. LC 85-71128. 128p. 1985. 12.00 (ISBN 0-9614941-0-7). Borderline NY.

Nicoll, Maurice. Psychological Commentaries on the Teaching of Gurdjieff & Ouspensky, Vol. 1. LC 83-25194. 371p. (Orig.). 1984. pap. 15.95 (ISBN 0-87773-269-8). Shambhala Pubns.

--Psychological Commentaries on the Teachings of Gurdjieff & Ouspensky, Vol. 2. LC 83-25194. 404p. (Orig.). 1984. pap. 18.95 (ISBN 0-87773-270-1). Shambhala Pubns.

--Psychological Commentaries on the Teachings of Gurdjieff & Ouspensky, Vol. 3. LC 83-25194. 447p. (Orig.). 1984. pap. 11.95 (ISBN 0-87773-271-X). Shambhala Pubns.

Reyner, J. H. Ouspensky: The Unsung Genius. 115p. 1982. 14.95 (ISBN 0-04-294122-9). Allen Unwin.

OVIMBUNDU

Hambly, W. D. Serpent Worship in Africa - the Ovimbundu of Angola: Culture Areas of Nigeria. (Chicago Field Museum of Natural History Fieldiana Anthropology Ser). Repr. of 1935 ed. 51.00 (ISBN 0-527-01881-3). Kraus Repr.

OWEN, JOHN, 1616-1683

Toon, Peter. God's Statesman: The Life & Work of John Owen. 208p. 1971. 9.95 (ISBN 0-85364-133-1). Attic Pr.

OXFORD MOVEMENT

see also Anglo-Catholicism

Chadwick, Owen, ed. The Mind of the Oxford Movement. 1961. 18.50x (ISBN 0-8047-0342-6). Stanford U Pr.

Church, R. W. The Oxford Movement: Twelve Years 1833-1845. 1979. Repr. of 1891 ed. lib. bdg. 35.00 (ISBN 0-8482-7569-1). Norwood Edns.

Dawson, Christopher H. The Spirit of the Oxford Movement. LC 75-30020. Repr. of 1934 ed. 16.50 (ISBN 0-404-14025-4). AMS Pr.

Donald, Gertrude. Men Who Left the Movement. facs. ed. LC 67-23207. (Essay Index Reprint Ser). 1933. 20.00 (ISBN 0-8369-0385-4). Ayer Co Pubs.

Faber, Geoffrey. Oxford Apostles. 467p. 1974. 7.95 (ISBN 0-571-10495-9). Faber & Faber.

--Oxford Apostles: A Character Study of the Oxford Movement. 1979. Repr. of 1933 ed. lib. bdg. 35.00 (ISBN 0-8482-3953-9). Norwood Edns.

Faber, Geoffrey C. Oxford Apostles: A Character Study of the Oxford Movement. LC 75-30022. Repr. of 1933 ed. 34.50 (ISBN 0-404-14027-0). AMS Pr.

Hutchison, William G. The Oxford Movement: Being a Selection from the Tracts for the Times. (Victorian Age Ser). 1906. Repr. 20.00 (ISBN 0-8482-4421-4). Norwood Edns.

Jay, Elisabeth. The Evangelical & Oxford Movements. LC 82-9605. (Cambridge English Prose Texts Ser.). 232p. 1983. 34.50 (ISBN 0-521-24403-X); pap. 13.95 (ISBN 0-521-28669-7). Cambridge U Pr.

Morse-Boycott, Desmond L. Lead, Kindly Light. LC 70-107728. (Essay Index Reprint Ser). 1933. 16.00 (ISBN 0-8369-1529-1). Ayer Co Pubs.

Newsome, David H. Wilberforces & Henry Manning: The Parting of Friends. LC 67-2. (Illus.). 1966. 30.00x (ISBN 0-674-95280-4, Belknap Pr). Harvard U Pr.

Rowell, Geoffrey, ed. Tradition Renewed: The Oxford Movement Conference Papers. (Princeton Theological Monograph Ser.: No. 3). (Orig.). 1986. pap. 30.00 (ISBN 0-915138-82-4). PickWick.

Seebohm, Frederick. The Oxford Reformers. Incl. Oxford Wit & Humour. 1914. Repr. 20.00 (ISBN 0-8274-3094-9). R West.

Tennyson, G. B. Victorian Devotional Poetry: The Tractarian Mode. LC 80-14416. 1980. text ed. 18.50x (ISBN 0-674-93586-1). Harvard U Pr.

Walsh, Walter. Secret History of the Oxford Movement. LC 73-101915. Repr. of 1898 ed. 25.00 (ISBN 0-404-06819-7). AMS Pr.

--The Secret History of the Oxford Movement. 1977. lib. bdg. 59.95 (ISBN 0-8490-2583-4). Gordon Pr.

Walworth, Clarence A. The Oxford Movement in America. LC 77-150436. (Monograph Ser.: No. 30). (Illus.). 1974. Repr. of 1895 ed. 12.00x (ISBN 0-930060-10-5). US Cath Hist.

Ward, Wilfrid. The Oxford Movement. (Victorian Age Ser). 20.00 (ISBN 0-8482-6908-X). Norwood Edns.

Ward, Wilfrid P. William George Ward & the Oxford Movement. LC 75-29625. Repr. of 1889 ed. 41.75 (ISBN 0-404-14043-2). AMS Pr.

OXFORD UNIVERSITY CHRIST CHURCH–HISTORY

Shaw, James B. Drawings by Old Masters at Christ Church, Oxford, 2 vols. (Illus.). 1976. 150.00x (ISBN 0-19-817323-7). Oxford U Pr.

P

PACIFISM

see also Evil, Non-Resistance To; Peace

Allen, Devere. Fight for Peace, 2 vols. LC 74-147439. (Library of War & Peace; Histories of the Organized Peace Movement). 1972. Set. lib. bdg. 92.00 (ISBN 0-8240-0228-8); lib. bdg. 38.00 ea. Garland Pub.

Brock, Peter. Pioneers of a Peaceable Kingdom: The Quaker Peace Testimony from the Colonial Era to the First World War. 1970. pap. 12.95x (ISBN 0-691-00573-7). Princeton U Pr.

Brown, Dale W. Biblical Pacifism: A Peace Church Perspective. 176p. 1985. pap. 8.95 (ISBN 0-87178-108-5). Brethren.

Chatfield, Charles. Kirby Page & the Social Gospel: Pacifist & Socialist Aspects. LC 70-147695. (Library of War & Peace: Documentary Anthologies). 1976. lib. bdg. 46.00 (ISBN 0-8240-0451-5). Garland Pub.

Dymond, Jonathan. Inquiry into the Accordancy of War with the Principles of Christianity. LC 79-147432. (Library of War & Peace; Proposals for Peace: a History). 1973. lib. bdg. 46.00 (ISBN 0-8240-0222-9). Garland Pub.

First American Peace Movement. Incl. War Inconsistent with the Religion of Jesus Christ. Dodge, David L; Lawfulness of War for Christians Examined. Mott, James; Solemn Review of the Custom of War. Worcester, Noah. LC 73-147428. (Library of War & Peace; Proposals for Peace: a History). 1973. lib. bdg. 46.00 (ISBN 0-8240-0220-2). Garland Pub.

Gara, Larry. War Resistance in Historical Perspective. 1983. pap. 2.50x (ISBN 0-87574-171-1, 171). Pendle Hill.

Gregg, Richard B. Pacifist Program. 1983. pap. 2.50x (ISBN 0-686-43957-0, 005). Pendle Hill.

Hamilton, Wallace. Clash by Night. 1983. pap. 2.50x (ISBN 0-87574-023-5, 023). Pendle Hill.

Hershberger, Guy F. War, Peace & Nonresistance. rev. ed. LC 53-7586. (Christian Peace Shelf Ser.). 375p. 1969. 15.95 (ISBN 0-8361-1449-3). Herald Pr.

Hirst, Margaret E. The Quakers in Peace & War: An Account of Their Peace Principles & Practice. LC 73-137545. (Peace Movement in America Ser). 560p. 1972. Repr. of 1923 ed. lib. bdg. 32.95x (ISBN 0-89198-073-3). Ozer.

Hixon, Robert. Lawrie Tatum: Indian Agent. LC 81-81684. 28p. 1981. pap. 2.50x (ISBN 0-87574-238-6, 238). Pendle Hill.

Lind, Millard. Respuesta a La Guerra. Orig. Title: Answer to War. 188p. 1963. pap. 1.50x (ISBN 0-8361-1149-4). Herald Pr.

Morey, Robert A. When Is It Right to Fight? 160p. (Orig.). 1985. pap. 4.95 (ISBN 0-87123-810-1, 210810). Bethany Hse.

Muste, A. J. Non-Violence in an Aggressive World. LC 76-137551. (Peace Movement in America Ser). 220p. 1972. Repr. of 1940 ed. lib. bdg. 15.95x (ISBN 0-89198-081-4). Ozer.

--Of Holy Disobedience. LC 52-1568. (Orig.). 1952. pap. 2.50x (ISBN 0-87574-064-2). Pendle Hill.

--War is the Enemy. 1983. pap. 2.50x (ISBN 0-87574-015-4, 015). Pendle Hill.

--The World Task of Pacifism. 1983. pap. 2.50x (ISBN 0-87574-013-8, 013). Pendle Hill.

Nuttall, Geoffrey. Christian Pacifism in History. pap. 1.25 (ISBN 0-912018-13-5). World Without War.

Robinson, Jo Ann. A. J. Muste: Pacifist & Prophet. Mather, Eleanore P., ed. LC 81-80219. 31p. 1981. pap. 2.50x (ISBN 0-87574-235-1, 235). Pendle Hill.

Sundberg, Gunnar. Toward Pacifism. 1983. pap. 2.50x (ISBN 0-87574-056-1, 056). Pendle Hill.

Yoder, John H. Nevertheless. LC 75-170197. (Christian Peace Shelf Ser.). 144p. 1972. pap. 4.95 (ISBN 0-8361-1661-5). Herald Pr.

--The Politics of Jesus. 176p. 1972. pap. 7.95 (ISBN 0-8028-1485-9). Eerdmans.

Young, Mildred B. Participation in Rural Life. 1983. pap. 2.50x (ISBN 0-87574-019-7, 019). Pendle Hill.

Young, Wilmer J. Visible Witness. 1983. pap. 2.50x (ISBN 0-87574-118-5, 118). Pendle Hill.

PACKARD, FREDERICK ADOLPHUS, 1794-1867

Culver, Raymond B. Horace Mann & Religion in the Massachusetts Public Schools. LC 72-89168. (American Education: Its Men, Institutions & Ideas, Ser. 1). 1969. Repr. of 1929 ed. 17.00 (ISBN 0-405-01406-6). Ayer Co Pubs.

PADUA–MADONNA DELL'ARNE (CHAPEL)

Stubblebine, James, ed. Giotto: The Arena Chapel Frescoes. LC 67-17689. (Critical Studies in Art History Ser). (Illus.). 1969. pap. text ed. 7.95x (ISBN 0-393-09858-3, NortonC). Norton.

Tintori, Leonetto & Meiss, Millard. The Painting of the Life of St. Francis in Assisi, with Notes on the Arena Chapel. LC 62-10308. pap. 55.50 (ISBN 0-317-10175-7, 2050842). Bks Demand UMI.

PAGANISM

Adler, Margot. Drawing down the Moon: Witches, Druids, Goddess-Worshippers, & Other Pagans in America Today. rev. & enl. ed. LC 86-70551. 608p. 1987. pap. 14.95 (ISBN 0-8070-3253-0, BP 723). Beacon Pr.

Benton, Richard A. Spoken Pangasinan. LC 79-152457. (University of Hawaii, Honolulu. Pacific & Asian Linguistics Institute). pap. 160.00 (ISBN 0-317-10118-8, 2017214). Bks Demand UMI.

Burghardt, W. J., et al, eds. Arnobius of Sicca, the Case Against the Pagans, Vol. 1. (ACW Ser.: No. 7). 372p. 1949. 13.95 (ISBN 0-8091-0248-X). Paulist Pr.

--Arnobius of Sicca, the Case Against the Pagans, Vol. 2. LC 78-62458. (ACW Ser.: No. 8). 659p. 1949. 11.95 (ISBN 0-8091-0249-8). Paulist Pr.

--Firmicus Maternus, the Error of the Pagan Religions. (Ancient Christian Writers Ser.: No. 37). 1970. 11.95 (ISBN 0-8091-0039-8). Paulist Pr.

Carpenter, Edward. Pagan & Christian Creeds. 59.95 (ISBN 0-8490-0794-1). Gordon Pr.

Condon, R. J. Our Pagan Christmas. 12p. 1982. pap. 1.00 (ISBN 0-911826-47-5). Am Atheist.

Drachman, A. Atheism In Pagan Antiquity. 178p. 1977. 12.50 (ISBN 0-89005-201-8). Ares.

Ellspermann, Gerald L. The Attitude of the Early Christian Latin Writers Toward Pagan Literature & Learning. 295p. 1984. Repr. of 1949 ed. 45.00x (ISBN 0-939738-26-0). Zubal Inc.

Fitch, Ed & Renee, Janine. Magical Rites from the Crystal Well. Weschcke, Carl L., ed. LC 83-80134. (Practical Magick Ser.). (Illus.). 166p. 1984. pap. 9.95 (ISBN 0-87542-230-6, L-230). Llewellyn Pubns.

Fox, Robin L. Pagans & Christians. 1987. 35.00 (ISBN 0-394-55495-7). Knopf.

Garnier, J. Worship of the Dead: The Origin & Nature of Pagan Idolatry & Its Bearing Upon the Early History of Egypt & Babylonia. LC 77-85617. 1977. Repr. of 1904 ed. lib. bdg. 50.00 (ISBN 0-89341-300-3). Longwood Pub Group.

Geffcken, J. The Last Days of Greco-Roman Paganism. (Europe in the Middle Ages Selected Studies: Vol. 8). 344p. 1978. 74.50 (ISBN 0-444-85005-8, North-Holland). Elsevier.

Gorham, Melvin. The Pagan Bible. 296p. 1982. 8.95 (ISBN 0-914752-22-7). Sovereign Pr.

Halliday, W. R. The Pagan Background of Christianity. 59.95 (ISBN 0-8490-0795-X). Gordon Pr.

Hillgarth, J. N., ed. Christianity & Paganism, Three Hundred Fifty to Seven Hundred Fifty: The Conversion of Western Europe. rev. ed. LC 85-1154. (Middle Ages Ser.). 160p. 1986. lib. bdg. 25.00 (ISBN 0-8122-7993-X); pap. 10.95 (ISBN 0-8122-1213-4). U of Pa Pr.

Howells, William. The Heathens Primitive Man & His Religions. 302p. pap. text ed. 9.95 (ISBN 0-88133-240-2). Sheffield Wisc.

Huttman, Maude A. Establishment of Christianity & the Proscription of Paganism. LC 15-703. (Columbia University. Studies in the Social Sciences: No. 147). Repr. of 1914 ed. 18.50 (ISBN 0-404-51147-3). AMS Pr.

Inman, Thomas. Ancient, Pagan & Modern Christian Symbolism. LC 77-6998. Repr. of 1884 ed. lib. bdg. 25.00 (ISBN 0-89341-301-1). Longwood Pub Group.

MacFarlane, Katherine N. Isidore of Seville on the Pagan Gods, Vol. 70, Pt. 3. 1980. 6.00 (ISBN 0-87169-703-3). Am Philos.

MacMullen, Ramsay. Paganism in the Roman Empire. LC 80-54222. 384p. 1981. 30.00x (ISBN 0-300-02655-2); pap. text ed. 8.95x (ISBN 0-300-02984-5). Yale U Pr.

Madden, Sr. Mary. The Pagan Divinities & Their Worship As Depicted in the Work of St. Augustine. 59.95 (ISBN 0-8490-0796-8). Gordon Pr.

Molnar, Thomas. The Pagan Temptation. 208p. (Orig.). 1987. pap. 11.95 (ISBN 0-8028-0262-1). Eerdmans.

Skeat, Walter W. & Blagden, Charles O. Pagan Races of the Malay Peninsula, 2 vols. new ed. (Illus.). 1966. 95.00x set (ISBN 0-7146-2027-0, F Cass Co). Biblio Dist.

Slater, Herman, ed. A Book of Pagan Rituals, Vol. 1. 1978. pap. 9.95 (ISBN 0-87728-348-6). Weiser.

Toland, John. Letters to Serena. Wellek, Rene, ed. LC 75-11259. (British Philosophers & Theologians of the 17th & 18th Centuries: Vol. 58). 295p. 1976. Repr. of 1704 ed. lib. bdg. 51.00 (ISBN 0-8240-1809-5). Garland Pub.

Wedeck, Harry E. & Baskin, Wade. Dictionary of Pagan Religions. 324p. 1973. pap. 3.95 (ISBN 0-8065-0386-6). Citadel Pr.

Weigall, Arthur. The Paganism in Our Christianity. 69.95 (ISBN 0-87968-149-7). Gordon Pr.

Wilson, Thomas. St. Paul & Paganism. 1977. lib. bdg. 59.95 (ISBN 0-8490-2560-5). Gordon Pr.

Wind, Edgar. Pagan Mysteries in the Renaissance. (Illus.). 1958. 75.00x (ISBN 0-686-83672-3). Elliots Bks.

PAGEANTS

see also Mysteries and Miracle-Plays

Gardner, John C. The Construction of the Wakefield Cycle. LC 74-5191. (Literary Structures Ser.). 173p. 1974. 8.95x (ISBN 0-8093-0668-9). S Ill U Pr.

Mueller, Robert. For People Just Like Us. Sherer, Michael L., ed. (Orig.). 1986. pap. 3.75 (ISBN 0-89536-834-X, 6848). CSS of Ohio.

PAIN

see also Suffering

Bakan, David. Disease, Pain & Sacrifice: Toward a Psychology of Suffering. 1971. pap. 3.95x (ISBN 0-8070-2971-8, BP394). Beacon Pr.

Fichter, Joseph H. Religion & Pain: The Spiritual Dimensions of Health Care. 128p. 1981. 9.95 (ISBN 0-8245-0102-0). Crossroad NY.

Lewis, C. S. The Problem of Pain. 1978. pap. 3.95 (ISBN 0-02-086850-2, Collier). Macmillan.

Woods, B. W. Christians in Pain: Perspectives on Suffering. 176p. 1982. pap. 4.95 (ISBN 0-8010-9652-9). Baker Bk.

PAINTED GLASS

see Glass Painting and Staining

PAINTING–HISTORY

see also painting, Italian, and similar headings

Bernen, Satia & Bernen, Robert. A Guide to Myth & Religion in European Painting 1270-1700. LC 72-96070. 288p. 1973. 8.95 (ISBN 0-8076-0683-9). Braziller.

PAINTING, DECORATIVE

see Mural Painting and Decoration

PAINTING, EUROPEAN

Bernen, Satia & Bernen, Robert. A Guide to Myth & Religion in European Painting 1270-1700. LC 72-96070. 288p. 1973. 8.95 (ISBN 0-8076-0683-9). Braziller.

PAINTING, FLEMISH

Roosen-Runge, Heinz. The Rolin-Madonna of Jan Van Eyck. (Illus.). 56p. 1973. pap. 9.75 (ISBN 0-8390-0125-8). Abner Schram Ltd.

PAINTING, INDIC

Welch, Stuart C. & Beach, Milo C. Gods, Thrones, & Peacocks: Northern Indian Painting from Two Traditions; Fifthteenth to Nineteenth Centuries. LC 74-27422. (Asia Society Ser.). (Illus.). 1979. Repr. of 1965 ed. lib. bdg. 33.00x (ISBN 0-405-06570-1). Ayer Co Pubs.

PAINTING, ISLAMIC

Arnold, Thomas W. Painting in Islam. (Illus.). 16.25 (ISBN 0-8446-1553-6). Peter Smith.

PAINTING, ITALIAN

see also Painting, Renaissance

Geiger, Gail. The Carafa Chapel, Renaissance Art in Rome. (Sixteenth Century Essays & Studies Ser.: Vol. V). (Illus.). 210p. 1985. smyth sewn 50.00x (ISBN 0-940474-05-0). Sixteenth Cent.

Meiss, Millard. Painting in Florence & Siena after the Black Death: The Arts, Religion & Society in the Mid-Fourteenth-Century. 1976. 37.00x (ISBN 0-691-03919-4); pap. 9.95x (ISBN 0-691-00312-2). Princeton U Pr.

PAINTING, MEDIEVAL

Berenson, Bernard. Studies in Medieval Painting. LC 73-153884. (Graphic Art Ser.). (Illus.). 148p. 1971. Repr. of 1930 ed. lib. bdg. 39.50 (ISBN 0-306-70292-4). Da Capo.

Lavin, Irving & Plummer, John, eds. Studies in Late Medieval & Renaissance Painting in Honor of Millard Meiss. LC 75-27118. 550p. 1978. 200.00x set (ISBN 0-8147-4963-1); Vol. I (ISBN 0-8147-5001-X); Vol. II (ISBN 0-8147-4978-X). NYU Pr.

PAINTING, MUSLIM

see Painting, Islamic

PAINTING, RELIGIOUS

see Christian Art and Symbolism

PAINTING, RENAISSANCE

Lavin, Irving & Plummer, John, eds. Studies in Late Medieval & Renaissance Painting in Honor of Millard Meiss. LC 75-27118. 550p. 1978. 200.00x set (ISBN 0-8147-4963-1); Vol. I (ISBN 0-8147-5001-X); Vol. II (ISBN 0-8147-4978-X). NYU Pr.

PAINTING, RUSSIAN

Collet's Holdings, Ltd. Staff, ed. Early Russian Painting 11th to Early 13th Centuries: Mosaics, Frescoes & Icons. 308p. 1982. 125.00x (ISBN 0-317-39496-7, Pub. by Collets UK). State Mutual Bk.

Lazarer, V. N. Novgorodian Icon-Painting. (Illus.). 40.00 (ISBN 0-912729-00-7). Newbury Bks.

Plugin, V. Frescoes of St. Demetrius' Cathedral. 44p. 1974. 25.00x (ISBN 0-569-08164-5, Pub. by Collets UK). State Mutual Bk.

PAINTINGS

Anzul, Dario. The Paintings of Mysticism & Violence in Full Colours of Dario Anzul. (Illus.). 97p. 1983. 225.75x (ISBN 0-86650-073-1). Gloucester Art.

PAINTINGS, ASIAN

Wray, Elizabeth, et al. Ten Lives of the Buddha: Siamese Temple Paintings & Jataka Tales. LC 73-179982. (Illus.). 156p. 1972. 20.00 (ISBN 0-8348-0067-5). Weatherhill.

PAINTINGS, DUTCH

Francis, Anne F. Hieronimus Bosch: The Temptation of Saint Anthony. (Illus.). 1980. 15.00 (ISBN 0-682-48910-7, University). Exposition Pr FL.

PAINTINGS, ITALIAN

Passavant, Anthony C. A Highly Informative History of the Renaissance Period of Italian Painting. (Illus.). 117p. 1984. pap. 23.75 (ISBN 0-86650-128-2). Gloucester Art.

PAINTINGS, JAPANESE

Rosenfield, John M. & Ten Grotenhuis, Elizabeth. Journey of the Three Jewels: Japanese Buddhist Paintings from Western Collections. LC 79-15072. (Illus.). 1979. 19.95 (ISBN 0-87848-054-4). Asia Soc.

PAINTINGS, MAORI

Simmons, David. Whakairo: Maori Tribal Art. (Illus.). 1985. 34.95x (ISBN 0-19-558119-9). Oxford U Pr.

PALAMAS, GREGORIUS, ABP. OF THESSALONICA, 1296-1359

Meyendorff, John. A Study of Gregory Palamas. LC 65-56528. 245p. 1964. 12.95 (ISBN 0-913836-14-1). St Vladimirs.

PALESTINE

see also Israel;

also names of cities, regions, etc. in Palestine

Arab Office, London Staff. The Future of Palestine. LC 75-12167. (The Rise of Jewish Nationalism & the Middle East Ser.). 166p. 1976. Repr. of 1947 ed. 16.50 (ISBN 0-88355-229-9). Hyperion Conn.

Chissin, Chaim. A Palestine Diary. 1976. 10.00 (ISBN 0-685-82598-1). Herzl Pr.

Clark, W. Joseph. The Holy Land. LC 86-61593. 204p. (Orig.). 1986. pap. 7.95 (ISBN 0-87973-546-5, 546). Our Sunday Visitor.

Davies, W. D. The Gospel & the Land: Early Christianity & Jewish Territorial Doctrine. LC 72-82228. 1974. 32.50x (ISBN 0-520-02278-5). U of Cal Pr.

Duff, E. Gordon, ed. Information for Pilgrims Unto the Holy Land. LC 78-63464. Repr. of 1893 ed. 16.50 (ISBN 0-404-16536-2). AMS Pr.

Esco Foundation For Palestine Inc. Palestine: A Study of Jewish, Arab, & British Policies, 2 Vols. LC 47-2569. Repr. of 1947 ed. Set. 192.00 (ISBN 0-527-27750-9). Kraus Repr.

Frischwasser-Ra' Anan, H. F. The Frontiers of a Nation. LC 75-6433. (The Rise of Jewish Nationalism & the Middle East Ser.). 168p. 1976. Repr. of 1955 ed. 18.15 (ISBN 0-88355-320-1). Hyperion Conn.

Gafni, Shlomo S. & Van der Heyden, A. The Glory of the Holy Land. LC 81-17054. (Illus.). 256p. 1982. o. p. 21.95 (ISBN 0-521-24612-1). Cambridge U Pr.

Halpern, Ben. Idea of the Jewish State. rev. ed. LC 71-89969. (Middle Eastern Studies: No. 3). (Illus.). 1969. 30.00x (ISBN 0-674-44201-6). Harvard U Pr.

Holy Land. (Panorama Bks.). (Fr., Illus.). 3.95 (ISBN 0-685-11233-0). French & Eur.

Ibn Al-Firkah & Ibrahim ibn Abd Al-Rahman. Palestine: Mohammedan Holy Land. Matthews, Charles, ed. LC 78-63568. (Yale Oriental Ser. Researches: No. 24). Repr. of 1949 ed. 34.50 (ISBN 0-404-60324-6). AMS Pr.

Lindsay, Gordon. Fire over the Holy Land. 1.25 (ISBN 0-89985-185-1). Christ Nations.

Mehdi, M. T. Peace in Palestine. LC 75-43266. 1976. pap. 8.00 (ISBN 0-911026-08-8). New World Press NY.

Pedlow, J. C. Windows on the Holy Land. (Illus.). 150p. 1980. pap. 8.95 (ISBN 0-227-67839-7). Attic Pr.

Schlink, Basilea. The Holy Land Today. rev. ed. 1975. 4.50 (ISBN 3-87209-610-9). Evang Sisterhood Mary.

Talmage, Thomas. Talmage on Palestine: Series of Sermons. Davis, Moshe, ed. LC 77-70747. (America & the Holy Land Ser.). 1977. Repr. of 1890 ed. lib. bdg. 17.00x (ISBN 0-405-10293-3). Ayer Co Pubs.

PALESTINE–ANTIQUITIES

see also Bible–Antiquities; Dead Sea Scrolls

Albright, William F. Archaeology of Palestine. rev. ed. 11.25 (ISBN 0-8446-0003-2). Peter Smith.

Chiat, Marilyn. Handbook of Synagogue Architecture. LC 81-9419. (Brown Judiac Studies). 1982. pap. 20.00 (ISBN 0-89130-524-6, 14-00-29). Scholars Pr GA.

Cole, Dan P. Shechem I: Middle Bronze IIB Pottery. (Excavation Reports of the American Schools of Oriental Research). xiv, 203p. 1984. text ed. 30.00 (ISBN 0-89757-047-2, Dist.by Eisenbrauns). Am Sch Orient Res.

Conder, Claude R. The Survey of Western Palestine, 3 vols. Palmer, E. H. & Besant, Walter, eds. LC 78-63331. (The Crusades & Military Orders: Second Ser.). (Illus.). Repr. of 1883 ed. Set. 110.00 (ISBN 0-404-17010-2). AMS Pr.

Cook, S. A. The Religion of Ancient Palestine in the Light of Archaeology. (British Academy, London, Schweich Lectures on Biblical Archaeology Series, 1925). pap. 28.00 (ISBN 0-8115-1267-3). Kraus Repr.

De Hass, Frank S. Buried Cities Recovered: Explorations in Bible Lands. Davis, Moshe, ed. LC 77-70774. (America & the Holy Land). (Illus.). 1977. lib. bdg. 40.00x (ISBN 0-405-10242-9). Ayer Co Pubs.

FitzGerald, G. M. Sixth Century Monastery at Beth-Shan (Scythopolis) (Publications of the Palestine Section Ser.: Vol. 4). (Illus.). xiv, 66p. 1939. 18.75 (ISBN 0-686-24094-4). Univ Mus of U.

Kenyon, Kathleen M. Archaeology in the Holy Land. 4th ed. (Illus.). 1979. 10.95x (ISBN 0-393-01285-9). Norton.

Kyle, Melvin G. Explorations at Sodom: Story of Ancient Sodom in the Light of Modern Research. Davis, Moshe, ed. LC 77-70715. (America & the Holy Land Ser.). (Illus.). 1977. Repr. of 1928 ed. lib. bdg. 12.00x (ISBN 0-405-10304-2). Ayer Co Pubs.

Lapp, Nancy L., ed. The Tale of the Tell: Archaeological Studies by Paul W. Lapp. LC 75-5861. (Pittsburgh Theological Monographs: No. 5). 1975. pap. text ed. 9.25 (ISBN 0-915138-05-0). Pickwick.

Macalister, Robert A. A Century of Excavation in Palestine. Davis, Moshe, ed. LC 77-70720. (America & the Holy Land Ser.). (Illus.). 1977. Repr. of 1925 ed. lib. bdg. 32.00x (ISBN 0-405-10265-8). Ayer Co Pubs.

Negev, Avraham, ed. Archaeological Encyclopedia of the Holyland. LC 79-92775. (Illus.). 356p. 1980. Repr. of 1974 ed. 9.95 (ISBN 0-89961-004-8). SBS Pub.

Pritchard, James B. Palestinian Figurines in Relation to Certain Goddesses Known Through Literature. (American Oriental Ser.: Vol. 24). 1943. 11.00 (ISBN 0-527-02698-0). Kraus Repr.

Warren, Charles & Conder, Claude R. The Survey of Western Palestine. LC 78-63371. (The Crusades & Military Orders: Second Ser.). Repr. of 1884 ed. 41.50 (ISBN 0-404-17047-1). AMS Pr.

Yadin, Yigael. Hazor: The Head of All Those Kingdoms, Joshua 11: 10 with a Chapter on Israelite Megiddo. 210p. 1979. 40.00x (ISBN 0-19-725925-1). State Mutual Bk.

PALESTINE–DESCRIPTION AND TRAVEL

Babcock, Maltbie D. Letters from Egypt & Palestine. Davis, Moshe, ed. LC 77-70662. (America & the Holy Land Ser.). (Illus.). 1977. Repr. of 1902 ed. lib. bdg. 19.00x (ISBN 0-405-10223-2). Ayer Co Pubs.

Baedeker, Karl. Baedeker's Historical Palestine. (Baedeker's Handbooks for Traveler's Ser.). (Illus.). 240p. 1985. Repr. of 1930 ed. 19.95 (ISBN 0-88254-699-6). Hippocrene Bks.

Bartlett, Samuel C. From Egypt to Palestine: Through Sinai, the Wilderness & the South Country: History of the Israelites. Davis, Moshe, ed. LC 77-70668. (America & the Holy Land Ser.). (Illus.). 1977. Repr. of 1879 ed. lib. bdg. 43.00x (ISBN 0-405-10227-5). Ayer Co Pubs.

Bludau, August. Die Pilgerreise der Aetheria. pap. 22.00 (ISBN 0-384-04760-2). Johnson Repr.

Bolitho, Hector. Beside Galilee. 206p. 1981. Repr. of 1933 ed. lib. bdg. 25.00 (ISBN 0-89987-076-7). Darby Bks.

Buhiery, Marwan, ed. The Splendor of the Holy Land. LC 77-5503. 1979. deluxe ed. 500.00x (ISBN 0-88206-019-8). Caravan Bks.

Burckhardt, John L. Travels in Syria & the Holy Land. LC 77-87614. (Illus.). 720p. 1983. Repr. of 1822 ed. 76.50 (ISBN 0-404-16437-4). AMS Pr.

Chase, Thornton. In Galilee. Facsimile reprint ed. (Illus.). 98p. 1985. Repr. of 1921 ed. 7.95 (ISBN 0-933770-38-3). Kalimat.

Chateaubriand, Rene de & Mourot, Jean. Itineraire De Paris a Jerusalem. 448p. 1968. 3.50 (ISBN 0-686-54365-3). French & Eur.

Davis, Moshe, ed. Pioneer Settlement in the Twenties: An Original Anthology. LC 77-70699. (America & the Holy Land Ser.). 1977. lib. bdg. 20.00x (ISBN 0-405-10250-X). Ayer Co Pubs.

Dehoney, Wayne. An Evangelical's Guidebook to the Holy Land. LC 73-85698. pap. 9.95 (ISBN 0-8054-5701-1). Broadman.

Ellis, Henry, ed. Pylgrymage of Sir Richard Guylforde to the Holy Land, A. D. 1506. LC 75-166023. (Camden Society, London. Publications, First Ser.: No. 51). Repr. of 1851 ed. 19.00 (ISBN 0-404-50151-6). AMS Pr.

Field, Frank M. Where Jesus Walked: Through the Holy Land with the Master. Davis, Moshe, ed. LC 77-70681. (America & the Holy Land Ser.). (Illus.). 1977. Repr. of 1951 ed. lib. bdg. 20.00x (ISBN 0-405-10244-5). Ayer Co Pubs.

Fosdick, Harry E. A Pilgrimage to Palestine. Davis, Moshe, ed. LC 77-70688. (America & the Holy Land Ser.). 1977. Repr. of 1927 ed. lib. bdg. 30.00x (ISBN 0-405-10247-X). Ayer Co Pubs.

Frankl, Ludwig A. The Jews in the East, 2 vols. Beaton, P., tr. LC 78-97278. 1975. Repr. of 1859 ed. Set. lib. bdg. 28.50x (ISBN 0-8371-2596-0, FRJE). Greenwood.

Fulton, John. Beautiful Land: Palestine: Historical, Geographical & Pictorial. Davis, Moshe, ed. LC 77-70694. (America & the Holy Land Ser.). (Illus.). 1977. Repr. of 1891 ed. lib. bdg. 52.00x (ISBN 0-405-10248-8). Ayer Co Pubs.

Geyer, Paul, ed. Itinera Hierosolymitana, Saeculi 3-8. (Corpus Scriptorum Ecclesiasticorum Latinorum Ser: Vol. 39). Repr. of 1898 ed. 40.00 (ISBN 0-384-18270-4). Johnson Repr.

Gordon, Benjamin L. New Judea: Jewish Life in Modern Palestine & Egypt. Davis, Moshe, ed. LC 77-70697. (America & the Holy Land Ser.). (Illus.). 1977. Repr. of 1919 ed. lib. bdg. 30.00x (ISBN 0-405-10251-8). Ayer Co Pubs.

Kallen, Horace M. Frontiers of Hope. Davis, Moshe, ed. LC 77-70711. (America & the Holy Land Ser.). 1977. Repr. of 1929 ed. lib. bdg. 37.50x (ISBN 0-405-10260-7). Ayer Co Pubs.

Krimsky, Joseph. Pilgrimage & Service. Davis, Moshe, ed. LC 77-70712. (America & the Holy Land Ser.). 1977. Repr. of 1919 ed. lib. bdg. 17.00x (ISBN 0-405-10261-5). Ayer Co Pubs.

Kyle, Melvin G. Explorations at Sodom: Story of Ancient Sodom in the Light of Modern Research. Davis, Moshe, ed. LC 77-70715. (America & the Holy Land Ser.). (Illus.). 1977. Repr. of 1928 ed. lib. bdg. 12.00x (ISBN 0-405-10304-2). Ayer Co Pubs.

Kyngeston, Richard. Expeditions to Prussia & the Holy Land Made by Henry Earl of Derby. Smith, L. T., ed. 1965. Repr. of 1894 ed. 27.00 (ISBN 0-384-30775-2). Johnson Repr.

Le Strange, Guy, tr. Palestine under the Moslems. LC 70-180356. Repr. of 1890 ed. 47.50 (ISBN 0-404-56288-4). AMS Pr.

Mader, Andreas E. Altchristliche Basiliken und Lokaltraditionen in Sudjudaa. pap. 19.00 (ISBN 0-384-35000-3). Johnson Repr.

Morris, Robert. Freemasonry in the Holy Land: Handmarks of Hiram's Builders. Davis, Moshe, ed. LC 77-70731. (America & the Holy Land Ser.). (Illus.). 1977. Repr. of 1872 ed. lib. bdg. 46.50x (ISBN 0-405-10270-4). Ayer Co Pubs.

Prime, William C. Tent Life in the Holy Land. Davis, Moshe, ed. LC 77-70734. (America & the Holy Land Ser.). (Illus.). 1977. Repr. of 1857 ed. lib. bdg. 38.50x (ISBN 0-405-10278-X). Ayer Co Pubs.

Pylgrymage of Sir Richard Guylforde to the Holy Land A. D. 1506. 1851. 19.00 (ISBN 0-384-48440-9). Johnson Repr.

Ritter, K. Comparative Geography of Palestine & the Sinaitic Peninsula, 4 Vols. LC 68-26367. (Reference Ser., No. 44). 1969. Repr. of 1865 ed. Set. lib. bdg. 159.95x (ISBN 0-8383-0180-0). Haskell.

Ritter, Karl. The Comparative Geography of Palestine, 4 vols. 1865. Set. 65.00x (ISBN 0-403-03564-3). Scholarly.

--Comparative Geography of Palestine & the Sinaitic Peninsula, 4 Vols. Gage, William L., tr. LC 69-10151. 1969. Repr. of 1866 ed. Set. lib. bdg. 71.00x (ISBN 0-8371-0638-9, RISP). Greenwood.

Schaff, Philip. Through Bible Lands: Notes on Travel in Egypt, the Desert, & Palestine. Davis, Moshe, ed. LC 77-70740. (America & the Holy Land Ser.). 1977. Repr. of 1878 ed. lib. bdg. 30.00x (ISBN 0-405-10286-0). Ayer Co Pubs.

Sneersohn, Haym Z. Palestine & Roumania: A Description of the Holy Land & the Past & Present State of Roumania & the Roumanian Jews. Davis, Moshe, ed. LC 77-70745. (America & the Holy Land Ser.). 1977. Repr. of 1872 ed. lib. bdg. 17.00x (ISBN 0-405-10291-7). Ayer Co Pubs.

Timberlake, Henry. A True & Strange Discourse of the Travailes of Two English Pilgrimes. LC 74-80228. (English Experience Ser.: No. 699). 28p. 1974. Repr. of 1603 ed. 3.50 (ISBN 90-221-0699-3). Walter J Johnson.

Wright, Thomas, ed. Early Travels in Palestine. LC 77-84863. (Bohn's Antiquarian Library). Repr. of 1848 ed. 31.50 (ISBN 0-404-50026-9). AMS Pr.

PALESTINE–HISTORICAL GEOGRAPHY

Smith, George A. Historical Geography of the Holy Land. 13.25 (ISBN 0-8446-2956-1). Peter Smith.

Wright, Thomas, ed. Early Travels in Palestine. LC 77-84863. (Bohn's Antiquarian Library). Repr. of 1848 ed. 31.50 (ISBN 0-404-50026-9). AMS Pr.

PALESTINE–HISTORY

see also Bible–History of Biblical Events; Bible–History of Contemporary Events, etc.; Crusades; Judaism–History

American Jewish Historical Society Staff, et al. The Palestine Question in American History. American Historical Association, ed. 14.00 (ISBN 0-405-11521-0). Ayer Co Pubs.

Cogan, Morton. Imperialism & Religion: Assyria, Judah & Israel in the Eighth & Seventh Centuries B.C.E. LC 73-83723. (Society of Biblical Literature. Monograph). 1974. 13.50 (ISBN 0-89130-330-8, 060019); pap. 9.95 (ISBN 0-89130-331-6, 00-06-19). Scholars Pr GA.

Cohen, Richard I., ed. Vision & Conflict in the Holy Land. LC 85-1972. 350p. 1985. 29.95 (ISBN 0-312-84967-2). St Martin.

Davis, Moshe. America & the Holy Land Series, 72 vols. (Illus.). 1977. Repr. lib. bdg. 2212.50 (ISBN 0-405-10220-8). Ayer Co Pubs.

Eckenstein, Lina. A History of the Sinai. LC 78-63461. (The Crusades & Military Orders: Second Ser.). Repr. of 1921 ed. 22.50 (ISBN 0-404-16533-8). AMS Pr.

Friedman, Isaiah. Germany, Turkey, & Zionism, 1897-1918. 1977. 59.00x (ISBN 0-19-822528-8). Oxford U Pr.

Frith, Francis. Egypt & the Holy Land in Historic Photographs: Seventy-Seven Views. Van Haaften, Julia, ed. 112p. 1981. pap. 7.95 (ISBN 0-486-24048-7). Dover.

Gibbons, John. Road to Nazareth: Through Palestine Today. LC 77-180339. Repr. of 1936 ed. 26.00 (ISBN 0-404-56264-7). AMS Pr.

Handy, Robert T., ed. The Holy Land in American Protestant Life, 1800 to 1948: A Documentary History. LC 79-1052. (Illus.). 1980. lib. bdg. 22.00x (ISBN 0-405-13466-5). Ayer Co Pubs.

Honor, Leo L. Sennacherib's Invasion of Palestine. LC 26-20926. (Columbia University. Contributions to Oriental History & Philology: No. 12). Repr. of 1926 ed. 15.00 (ISBN 0-404-50542-2). AMS Pr.

Hunt, Edward D. Holy Land Pilgramage in the Later Roman Empire, AD 312-460. 1982. 47.00x (ISBN 0-19-826438-0); pap. 13.50x (ISBN 0-19-826449-6). Oxford U Pr.

Hyamson, Albert M. Palestine: A Policy. LC 75-6438. (The Rise of Jewish Nationalism & the Middle East Ser). 214p. 1975. Repr. of 1942 ed. 20.35 (ISBN 0-88355-325-2). Hyperion Conn.

The Jewish Agency for Palestine: The Jewish Plan for Palestine. Repr. of 1947 ed. 77.00 (ISBN 3-601-00327-9). Kraus Repr.

Kaganoff, Nathan M., ed. Guide to America-Holy Land Studies: Vol. 1, American Presence. LC 79-8575. (Illus.). 1980. lib. bdg. 22.00x (ISBN 0-405-12755-3). Ayer Co Pubs.

Kedourie, Elie & Haim, Sylvia G., eds. Palestine & Israel in the Nineteenth & Twentieth Centuries. (Illus.). 286p. 1982. 39.50x (ISBN 0-7146-3121-3, F Cass Co). Biblio Dist.

Lorch, Netanel. One Long War. 1976. 8.00 (ISBN 0-685-82597-3). Herzl Pr.

McCullough, W. Stewart. The History & Literature of Palestinian Jews from Cyrus to Herod 550 BC-4 BC. LC 74-80889. 1975. 25.00x (ISBN 0-8020-5317-3); pap. 9.50 (ISBN 0-8020-6324-1). U of Toronto Pr.

Ma'Oz, Moshe, ed. Studies on Palestine During the Ottoman Period. 582p. 1975. text ed. 40.00x (Pub. by Magnes Pr Israel). Humanities.

Moo, Douglas J. The Old Testament in the Gospel Passion Narratives. xii, 468p. 1983. text ed. 29.95x (ISBN 0-907459-28-5, Pub. by Almond Pr England); pap. text ed. 17.95x (ISBN 0-907459-29-3). Eisenbrauns.

Nir, Yeshayahu. The Bible & the Image: The History of Photography in the Holy Land, 1839-1899. LC 84-21997. (Illus.). 1985. 39.95 (ISBN 0-8122-7981-6). U of Pa Pr.

Paton, Lewis B. The Early History of Syria & Palestine. LC 79-2878. (Illus.). 302p. 1981. Repr. of 1901 ed. 28.50 (ISBN 0-8305-0046-4). Hyperion Conn.

Regan, Geoffrey B. Israel & the Arabs: Cambridge Introduction to the History of Mankind. (Illus.). 48p. 1984. pap. 4.95 (ISBN 0-521-27580-6). Cambridge U Pr.

Rowley, Gwyn, ed. Israel into Palestine. LC 83-22167. 198p. 1983. 31.00x (ISBN 0-7201-1674-0). Mansell.

Samuel, Maurice. Harvest in the Desert. LC 82-985. 316p. 1982. Repr. lib. bdg. 27.50x (ISBN 0-313-23354-3, SAHA). Greenwood.

Shehaden, Raja. Samed. 172p. 1984. pap. 9.95 (ISBN 0-531-09839-7). Watts.

Wilson, Robert R. Prophecy & Society in Ancient Israel. LC 78-14677. 336p. 1980. 11.95 (ISBN 0-8006-1814-9, 1-1814). Fortress.

PALESTINE–JUVENILE LITERATURE

Bamberger, David. A Young Person's History of Israel. Mandelkern, Nicholas, ed. (Illus.). 150p. (Orig.). 1985. pap. 6.95 (ISBN 0-87441-393-1). Behrman.

PALESTINE–RELIGION

Bliss, Frederick J. Religions of Modern Syria & Palestine. LC 76-39454. Repr. of 1912 ed. 20.00 (ISBN 0-404-00897-6). AMS Pr.

Cook, S. A. The Religion of Ancient Palestine in the Light of Archaeology. (British Academy, London, Schweich Lectures on Biblical Archaeology Series, 1925). pap. 28.00 (ISBN 0-8115-1267-3). Kraus Repr.

Cook, Stanley A. The Religion of Ancient Palestine. 122p. 1921. 0.95 (ISBN 0-317-40429-6). Open Court.

Higgens, Elford. Hebrew Idolatry & Superstition. 1971. Repr. of 1893 ed. 19.50x (ISBN 0-8046-1150-5, Pub. by Kennikat). Assoc Faculty Pr.

PALESTINE–SOCIAL LIFE AND CUSTOMS

Gilbertson, Merrill T. Way It Was in Bible Times. LC 59-10759. (Illus.). 1959. pap. 6.95 (ISBN 0-8066-1442-0, 10-7000). Augsburg.

Granqvist, Hilma N. Birth & Childhood Among the Arabs. LC 72-9643. Repr. of 1947 ed. 36.00 (ISBN 0-404-57447-5). AMS Pr.

PALI LITERATURE

Bode, Mabel H. The Pali Literature of Burma. LC 77-87008. Repr. of 1909 ed. 15.00 (ISBN 0-404-16796-9). AMS Pr.

Johansson, Rune E. Pali Buddhist Texts. 160p. 1982. 30.00x (ISBN 0-7007-0063-3, Pub. by Curzon England). State Mutual Bk.

--Pali Buddhist Texts Explained to the Beginner. 1981. pap. 12.00 (ISBN 0-8364-0329-0, Pub. by Curzon Pr). South Asia Bks.

PALLOTTI VINCENZO, SAINT, 1795-1850

Gaynor, John S. Life of St. Vincent Pallotti. 1980. 4.00 (ISBN 0-8198-4401-2); pap. 3.00 (ISBN 0-8198-4402-0). Dghtrs St Paul.

PALMA, MAJORCA–CATHEDRAL

Cram, R. A. Folio. 1932. 22.00 (ISBN 0-527-01687-X). Kraus Repr.

PAN (DEITY) IN LITERATURE

Baker, Dorothy Z. Mythic Masks in Self-Reflexive Poetry: A Study of Pan & Orpheus. LC 85-16468. (Studies in Comparative Literature Ser.: No. 62). x, 186p. 1986. 20.00x (ISBN 0-8078-7062-5). U of NC Pr.

PAN-ISLAMISM

see Panislamism

PANISLAMISM

see also Mahdi

Gibb, Hamilton A., ed. Whither Islam? A Survey of Modern Movements in the Moslem World. LC 73-180338. Repr. of 1932 ed. 27.00 (ISBN 0-404-56263-9). AMS Pr.

Kedourie, Elie & Haim, Sylvia G., eds. Zionism & Arabism in Palestine & Israel. 266p. 1982. text ed. 37.50x (ISBN 0-7146-3169-8, F Cass Co). Biblio Dist.

Narayan, B. K. Pan-Islamism. 232p. 35.00X (ISBN 0-317-52149-7, Pub. by S Chand Mutual). State Mutual Bk.

Slater, Samuel. Keynes Schumpeter & the Effort to Save Capitalism from Total Collapse. (Illus.). 137p. 1984. 93.00x (ISBN 0-86654-134-9). Inst Econ Finan.

Unity of the Muslim World. 1.00 (ISBN 0-686-18622-2). Kazi Pubns.

PANNENBERG, WOLFHART, 1928-

McKenzie, David. Wolfhart Pannenberg & Religious Philosophy. LC 80-8171. 169p. 1980. lib. bdg. 25.00 (ISBN 0-8191-1314-X); pap. text ed. 11.25 (ISBN 0-8191-1315-8). U Pr of Amer.

Olive, Don. Wolfhart Pannenberg. 120p. 1984. pap. text ed. 8.95 (ISBN 0-8499-3003-0, 3003-0). Word Bks.

PANTHEISM

see also Advaita; Deism; Immanence of God; Monotheism; Theism

Hunt, John. Pantheism & Christianity. LC 78-102573. 1970. Repr. of 1884 ed. 25.50 (ISBN 0-8046-0733-8, Pub. by Kennikat). Assoc Faculty Pr.

Johnstone, Parker L. Pantheism Is Heresy. 208p. 1982. cloth 7.95 (ISBN 0-917802-05-5). Theoscience Found.

Lanman, Charles. Beginnings of Hindu Pantheism. 35.00 (ISBN 0-87968-719-3). Gordon Pr.

McFarland, Thomas. Coleridge & the Pantheist Tradition. 1969. 48.00x (ISBN 0-19-811664-0). Oxford U Pr.

Picton, J. Allanson. Pantheism. 96p. 1914. 0.95 (ISBN 0-317-40425-3). Open Court.

Schopenhauer, Arthur. Pantheism & the Christian System. (Illus.). 119p. 1987. 117.50 (ISBN 0-89266-588-2). Am Classical Coll Pr.

Toland, John. Pantheisticon. Wellek, Rene, ed. LC 75-11260. (British Philosophers & Theologians of the 17th & 18th Centuries: Vol. 59). 1977. Repr. of 1751 ed. lib. bdg. 51.00 (ISBN 0-8240-1810-9). Garland Pub.

PAPACY

see also Apostolic Succession; Catholic Church; Church–Foundation; Popes

Anderson, John D. & Kennan, Elizabeth T., trs. Bernard of Clairvaux: Consideration: Advice to a Pope. LC 75-27953. (Cistercian Fathers Ser.: No. 37). 1976. 5.00 (ISBN 0-87907-137-0). Cistercian Pubns.

Buschkuhl, Matthias. Great Britain & the Holy See 1746-1870. (Illus.). 260p. 1982. text ed. 40.00x (ISBN 0-7165-0290-9, Pub. by Irish Academic Pr Ireland). Biblio Dist.

Cardinale, H. E. Orders of Knighthood, Awards & the Holy See: A Historical Juridical & Practical Compendium. 3rd, rev., enl. ed. 1985. text ed. 55.00x (ISBN 0-905715-26-8). Humanities.

Hislop, Alexander. The Two Babylons. 9.95 (ISBN 0-87213-330-3). Loizeaux.

Holmes, Derek J. The Papacy in the Modern World Nineteen Fourteen to Nineteen Seventy. LC 81-65110. 275p. 1981. 14.95 (ISBN 0-8245-0047-4). Crossroad NY.

Korn, Frank J. From Peter to John Paul II. LC 80-65721. 300p. (Orig.). 1980. pap. 5.50 (ISBN 0-8189-1161-1, 161, Pub. by Alba Bks). Alba.

Lund, Candida, ed. If I Were Pope. 1987. 11.95 (ISBN 0-88347-187-6). Thomas More.

Miller, Michael. What Are They Saying about Papal Primacy? (WATSA Ser.). 128p. 1983. pap. 4.95 (ISBN 0-8091-2501-3). Paulist Pr.

Millheim, John E. Let Rome Speak for Herself. LC 82-16616. 1982. pap. 3.95. Reg Baptist.

Morrissey, Gerard. Defending the Papacy. 96p. (Orig.). 1984. pap. 4.95 (ISBN 0-931888-15-8). Christendom Pubns.

O'Reilly, Sean. Our Name Is Peter. LC 77-380. 155p. 1977. 5.95 (ISBN 0-8199-0666-2). Franciscan Herald.

Pole, Reginald. De Summo Pontifice. 330p. Repr. of 1569 ed. text ed. 62.10 (ISBN 0-576-99123-6, Pub. by Gregg Intl Pubs England). Gregg Intl.

Poliakov, Leon. Jewish Barbers & the Holy See: From the Thirteenth to the Seventeenth-Century. Kochan, Miriam, tr. from Fr. (Littman Library of Jewish Civilization). 288p. 1977. 29.00x (ISBN 0-19-710028-7). Oxford U Pr.

PAPACY–HISTORY

see also Roman Question; Schism, the Great Western, 1378-1417

Abdel-Massih, Ernest. The Life & Miracles of Pope Kirillos VI. 139p. (Orig.). 1982. pap. text ed. 3.00 (ISBN 0-932098-20-7). St Mark Coptic Orthodox.

Barraclough, Geoffrey. The Medieval Papacy. (Library of World Civilization). (Illus.). 1979. pap. text ed. 7.95x (ISBN 0-393-95100-6). Norton.

Barstow, Anne L. Married Priests & the Reforming Papacy: The 11th Century Debates. LC 82-7914. (Texts & Studies in Religion: Vol. 12). 288p. 1982. 49.95x (ISBN 0-88946-987-3). E Mellen.

Camp, R. L. Papal Ideology of Social Reform: A Study in Historical Development, 1878-1967. 1969. 30.00 (ISBN 9-0040-4317-9). Heinman.

Chadwick, Owen. Catholicism & History. LC 77-77740. 1978. 24.95 (ISBN 0-521-21708-3). Cambridge U Pr.

--The Popes & European Revolution. (Oxford History of the Christian Church Ser.). 1981. 84.00x (ISBN 0-19-826919-6). Oxford U Pr.

Cheve, C. F. Dictionnaire des Papes ou Histoire Complete des tous les Souvenirs Pontifes. Migne, J. P., ed. (Troisieme et Derniere Encyclopedie Theologique Ser.: Vol. 32). (Fr.). 706p. Repr. of 1857 ed. lib. bdg. 90.00x (ISBN 0-89241-311-5). Caratzas.

Cowdrey, H. E. The Age of Abbot Desiderius: Montecassino, the Papacy & the Normans in the Eleventh & Early Twelfth Centuries. 1983. 55.00x (ISBN 0-19-821939-3). Oxford U Pr.

Creighton, Mandell. History of the Papacy from the Great Schism to the Sack of Rome, 6 Vols. rev. ed. LC 74-77897. Repr. of 1897 ed. Set. 165.00 (ISBN 0-404-01870-X); 27.50 ea. AMS Pr.

DiFranco, Anthony. Pope John Paul II: Bringing Love to a Troubled World. LC 82-23618. (Taking Part Ser.). (Illus.). 48p. 1983. PLB 8.95 (ISBN 0-87518-241-0). Dillon.

Dionne, J. Robert. The Papacy & the Church: A Study of Praxis & Reception in Ecumenical Perspective. LC 85-9319. 524p. 1987. 29.95 (ISBN 0-8022-2494-6). Philos Lib.

Grigulevich, I. Papado Siglo XX. 354p. 1982. 5.95 (ISBN 0-8285-2323-1, Pub. by Progress Pubs USSR). Imported Pubns.

Grisar, Hartmann. History of Rome & the Popes in the Middle Ages, 3 vols. LC 70-154115. Tr. of Geschichte Roms und der Papste Immittelater. (Illus.). Repr. of 1912 ed. Set. 120.00 (ISBN 0-404-09370-1). AMS Pr.

Hertling, Ludwig. Communio: Church & Papacy in Early Christianity. Wicks, Jared, tr. from Ger. LC 75-38777. (Orig.). 1972. pap. 2.95 (ISBN 0-8294-0212-8). Loyola.

Holmes, J. Derek. The Triumph of the Holy See: A Short History of the Papacy in the Nineteenth Century. LC 78-18616. (Illus.). viii, 306p. 1978. 21.95x (ISBN 0-915762-06-4). Patmos Pr.

Housley, Norman. The Avignon Papacy & the Crusades, Thirteen Five to Thirteen Seventy-Eight. 450p. 1986. 55.00x (ISBN 0-19-821957-1). Oxford U Pr.

Kent, Peter. The Pope & the Duce. 1981. 26.00 (ISBN 0-312-63024-7). St Martin.

Korn, Frank J. Country of the Spirit: Vatican City. (Illus.). 139p. 1982. pap. 7.00 (ISBN 0-8198-1415-6, MS0214). Dghtrs St Paul.

--From Peter to John Paul II. LC 80-65721. 300p. (Orig.). 1980. pap. 5.50 (ISBN 0-8189-1161-1, 161, Pub. by Alba Bks). Alba.

Lunt, W. E. Financial Relations of the Papacy with England to 1327. 1967. Repr. of 1939 ed. 20.00X (ISBN 0-910956-13-8). Medieval Acad.

--Financial Relations of the Papacy with England, 1327-1534. 1962. 25.00X (ISBN 0-910956-48-0). Medieval Acad.

McCabe, Joseph. Crises in the History of the Papacy. 1977. lib. bdg. 59.95 (ISBN 0-8490-1684-3). Gordon Pr.

Magnuson, Torgil. Rome in the Age of Bernini, Vol. II: From the Election of Innocent X to the Death of Innocent XI. Adler, Nancy, tr. from Swedish. (Illus.). 420p. 1986. 39.95 (ISBN 0-391-03448-0, Pub. by Humanities Press & Almgrist & Wiksell). Humanities.

Maras, Raymond J. Innocent XI, Pope of Christian Unity. (The Church & the World Ser.). xiv, 356p. 1984. 42.85x (ISBN 0-317-52635-9); lib. bdg. 42.85x. Cross Cultural Pubns.

Marcel, Raymond, et al. Builders & Humanists: The Renaissance Popes As Patrons of the Arts. (Illus.). 1966. pap. 8.00 (ISBN 0-914412-20-5). Inst for the Arts.

Maycock, A. L. The Papacy. 1928. 10.00 (ISBN 0-8414-6607-6). Folcroft.

Milman, Henry H. History of Latin Christianity, 9 Vols. LC 71-172734. Repr. of 1887 ed. Set. lib. bdg. 145.00 (ISBN 0-404-04360-7). AMS Pr.

Murphy, Paul I. & Arlington, R. Rene. La Popessa. 432p. 1985. pap. 3.95 (ISBN 0-446-32817-0). Warner Bks.

Norden, Walter. Papsttum Und Byzanz: Das Problem Ihrer Wiedervereinigung Bis Zum Untergange Des Byzantinischen Reichs (1453) 1903. 40.50 (ISBN 0-8337-2571-8). B Franklin.

Pennington, Kenneth. Pope & Bishops: A Study of the Papal Monarchy in the Twelfth & Thirteenth Centuries. LC 83-21799. (The Middle Ages Ser.). 227p. 1984. 31.50x (ISBN 0-8122-7918-2). U of Pa Pr.

Popes of the 20th Century. 2.50 (ISBN 0-8198-5811-0); 1.50 (ISBN 0-8198-5812-9). Dghtrs St Paul.

Poussin, J. C. & Garnier, J. C. Dictionnaire de la Tradition Pontificale, Patristique et Conciliaire, 2 vols. Migne, J. P., ed. (Troisieme et Derniere Encyclopedie Theologique Ser.: Vol. 12-13). (Fr.). 1464p. Repr. of 1855 ed. lib. bdg. 186.00x (ISBN 0-89241-296-8). Caratzas.

Reinerman, Alan J. Austria & the Papacy in the Age of Metternich: Between Conflict & Cooperation, 1809-1830. LC 79-774. (Vol. 1). 254p. 1979. 27.95x (ISBN 0-8132-0548-4). Cath U Pr.

Ridley, Francis A. The Papacy & Fascism: The Crisis of the 20th Century. LC 72-180422. (Studies in Fascism, Ideology & Practice). Repr. of 1937 ed. 24.50 (ISBN 0-404-56156-X). AMS Pr.

Riezler, Sigmund. Die Literarischen Widersacher der Paepste Zur Zeit Ludwig Des Baiers. 336p. 1874. Repr. 25.50 (ISBN 0-8337-2994-2). B Franklin.

Setton, Kenneth M. The Papacy & the Levant, Twelve Hundred Four to Fifteen Seventy-One, Vol. Two: The Fifteenth Century. LC 75-25476. (Memoirs Ser.: Vol. 127). (Illus.). 1978. 40.00 (ISBN 0-87169-127-2). Am Philos.

--The Papacy & the Levant Twelve Hundred Four to Fifteen Seventy-One Vol I: The Thirteenth & Fourteenth Centuries. LC 75-25476. (Memoirs Ser.: Vol. 114). 1976. 35.00 (ISBN 0-87169-114-0). Am Philos.

Shannon, Albert C. The Popes & Heresy in the Thirteenth Century. LC 78-63192. (Heresies of the Early Christian & Medieval Era: Second Ser.). Repr. of 1949 ed. 31.00 (ISBN 0-404-16228-2). AMS Pr.

Shotwell, James T. & Loomis, Louis R., eds. See of Peter. 1965. lib. bdg. 49.00x (ISBN 0-374-97391-1, Octagon). Hippocrene Bks.

Symonds, Henry E. The Church Universal & the See of Rome: A Study of the Relations Between the Episcopate & the Papacy up to the Schism Between East & West. (Church Historical Society London N. S. Ser.: No. 36). pap. 60.00 (ISBN 0-8115-3159-7). Kraus Repr.

Thomson, J. A. Popes & Princes Fourteen Seventeen to Fifteen Seventeen: Politics & Polity in Late Medieval Church. (Early Modern Europe Today Ser.). 256p. 1980. text ed. 10.00 (ISBN 0-04-901027-1). Allen Unwin.

Tomasello, Andrew. Music & Ritual at Papal Avignon, 1309-1403. Buelow, George, ed. LC 83-18296. (Studies in Musicology: No. 75). 314p. 1983. 49.95 (ISBN 0-8357-1493-4). UMI Res Pr.

Ullmann, Walter. A Short History of the Papacy in the Middle Ages. 1974. pap. 16.95x (ISBN 0-416-74970-4, NO. 2562). Methuen Inc.

Vaillancourt, Jean-Guy. Papal Power: A Study of Vatican Control Over Lay Catholic Elites. 375p. 1980. 24.95x (ISBN 0-520-03733-2). U of Cal Pr.

Von Le Fort, Gertrud. The Pope from the Ghetto: The Legend of the Family of Pier Leone. Bonacina, Conrad R., tr. 330p. 1981. Repr. of 1935 ed. lib. bdg. 15.00 (ISBN 0-89984-205-4). Century Bookbindery.

Von Ranke, Leopold. History of the Popes: Their Church & State, 3 vols. 1205p. 1986. Repr. of 1901 ed. lib. bdg. 150.00 (ISBN 0-8495-4730-X). Arden Lib.

Walsh, Michael. An Illustrated History of the Popes: St. Peter to John Paul II. (Illus.). 256p. 1980. 19.95 (ISBN 0-312-40817-X). St Martin.

Wigginton, Peter. Popes of Vatican Council II. 329p. 1983. 15.00 (ISBN 0-8199-0828-2). Franciscan Herald.

Winter, Michael M. Saint Peter & the Popes. LC 78-21507. 1979. Repr. of 1960 ed. lib. bdg. cancelled (ISBN 0-313-21158-2, WISP). Greenwood.

PAPACY–HISTORY–SOURCES

Giles, Edward, ed. Documents Illustrating Papal Authority, A.D. 96-454. LC 78-59023. 1979. Repr. of 1952 ed. 28.00 (ISBN 0-88355-696-0). Hyperion Conn.

Loomis, Louise R., tr. Book of the Popes. 1965. lib. bdg. 19.50x (ISBN 0-374-95093-8, Octagon). Hippocrene Bks.

PAPAL DOCUMENTS

see also Encyclicals, Papal; Letters, Papal

Abbott, Walter M., ed. The Documents of Vatican II. pap. cancelled (ISBN 0-686-19062-9, EC-101). US Catholic.

Daughters of St. Paul, ed. Dimensions of the Priesthood. new ed. 1973. 5.75 (ISBN 0-8198-0253-0); pap. 4.50 (ISBN 0-8198-0254-9). Dghtrs St Paul.

Girard, Raphael. Esotericism of the Popol Vuh. LC 78-74712. (Illus.). 1979. 14.00 (ISBN 0-911500-13-8); pap. 8.50 (ISBN 0-911500-14-6). Theos U Pr.

Morneau, Robert F. Themes & Theses of Six Recent Papal Documents: A Commentary. 160p. (Orig.). 1985. pap. 5.95 (ISBN 0-8189-0482-8). Alba.

Padberg, John W., ed. Documents of the Thirty-First & Thirty-Second General Congregations of the Society of Jesus: An English Translation of the Official Latin Texts of the General Congregations & of the Accompanying Papal Documents. LC 77-70881. (Jesuit Primary Sources in English Translation: No. 2). 608p. 1977. pap. 6.00 smyth sewn (ISBN 0-912422-26-2). Inst Jesuit.

Walsh, Michael & Davies, Brian, eds. Proclaiming Justice & Peace: Documents from John XXIII to John Paul II. 370p. 1985. 16.95 (ISBN 0-89622-239-X); pap. 12.95 (ISBN 0-89622-236-5). Twenty Third.

Wurth, Elmer P. Papal Documents Relating to the New China, 1937-1984. 193p. (Orig.). 1985. pap. 10.00 (ISBN 0-88344-403-8). Orbis Bks.

PAPAL ENCYCLICALS

see Encyclicals, Papal

PAPAL INFALLIBILITY

see Popes–Infallibility

PAPAL LETTERS

see Letters, Papal

PAPAL SCHISM

see Schism, the Great Western, 1378-1417

PAPAL STATES

Noble, Thomas F. X. The Republic of St. Peter: The Birth of the Papal State, 680-825. LC 83-21870. (The Middle Ages Ser.). (Illus.). 416p. 1984. 36.95x (ISBN 0-8122-7917-4); pap. 14.95. U of Pa Pr.

PAPER WORK–JUVENILE LITERATURE

Westphal, Arnold C. Fold 'n Cut Surprise Sermonetes, No. 2. 1968. 4.95 (ISBN 0-915398-01-X). Visual Evangels.

--Gospel Magic with Homemade Stuff & Things, No. 1. 1972. pap. 4.95 (ISBN 0-915398-09-5). Visual Evangels.

--Happy Surprise Junior Objectalks. 1978. 4.95 (ISBN 0-915398-11-7). Visual Evangels.

--Paper Tearing Bible Talks, No. 4. 1970. pap. 4.95 (ISBN 0-915398-03-6). Visual Evangels.

--Paper Tearing Evangels, No. 8. 1975. pap. 4.95 (ISBN 0-915398-07-9). Visual Evangels.

--Paper Tearing Gospel Illustrations, No. 3. 1969. pap. 4.95 (ISBN 0-915398-02-8). Visual Evangels.

--Paper Tearing Trick Talks, No. 1. 1967. pap. 4.95 (ISBN 0-915398-00-1). Visual Evangels.

--Surprise Paper Tearing Talks, No. 9. 1976. pap. 4.95 (ISBN 0-915398-08-7). Visual Evangels.

--Trick Paper Tears with Gospel Truth, No. 10. 1977. pap. 4.95 (ISBN 0-915398-10-9). Visual Evangels.

PAPYRI, EGYPTIAN

see Egyptian Language–Papyri; Manuscripts (Papyri)

PARABLES

see also Bible–Parables; Fables; Jesus Christ–Parables

Bailey, James. Sermons from the Parables. 128p. (Orig.). 1981. pap. 2.95 (ISBN 0-8341-0730-9). Beacon Hill.

Burlingame, E. W. Buddhist Parables. 59.95 (ISBN 0-87968-803-3). Gordon Pr.

Butterworth, Nick. Parables, 4 vols. (Illus.). 1986. 6.95 ea. Vol. 1: The House on the Rock (ISBN 0-88070-146-3). Vol. 2: The Lost Sheep (ISBN 0-88070-147-1). The Two Sons (ISBN 0-88070-145-5) (ISBN 0-88070-148-X). Multnomah.

Castagnola, Lawrence. Parables for Little People. LC 86-62628. (Illus.). 101p. (Orig.). 1982. pap. 5.56 (ISBN 0-89390-034-6); pap. text ed. 7.95. Resource Pubns.

Eberhart, E. T. Burnt Offerings: Parables for Twentieth Century Christians. LC 77-23158. 1977. pap. 3.95 (ISBN 0-687-04375-1). Pilgrim Hse.

Feldman, Asher. The Parables & Similes of the Rabbis, Agricultural & Pastoral. LC 75-23127. 1975. Repr. of 1927 ed. lib. bdg. 27.50 (ISBN 0-8414-4229-0). Folcroft.

Flood, Edmund. More Parables For Now. 4.95 (ISBN 0-87193-192-3). Dimension Bks.

Gregory, Christelle E. Creative Parables for Christian Teachers. LC 86-62626. 100p. 1987. pap. 9.95 (ISBN 0-89390-096-6). Resource Pubns.

Heineman, Benno. The Maggid of Dubno & His Parables. rev ed. 1978. 11.95 (ISBN 0-87306-156-X). Feldheim.

Hunter, Archibald M. Interpreting the Parables. LC 61-5122. 126p. 1976. pap. 5.95 (ISBN 0-664-24746-6). Westminster.

--The Parables Then & Now. LC 72-170113. 128p. 1972. pap. 5.95 (ISBN 0-664-24940-X). Westminster.

Jyotir Maya Nanda, Swami. Yoga Mystic Stories & Parables. (Illus.). 1974. pap. 3.99 (ISBN 0-934664-24-2). Yoga Res Foun.

Keshavadas, Satguru S. Stories & Parables. (Illus.). 100p. 1979. 6.50 (ISBN 0-533-03818-9). Vishwa.

Klemp, Harold. Book of ECK Parables, Vol. 1. (Illus.). 265p. (Orig.). 1986. pap. 8.95 (ISBN 0-88155-046-9). IWP Pub.

Manning, Brennan. The Parable of Willie Juan. 1985. 2.95 (ISBN 0-87193-162-1). Dimension Bks.

Norman, Ernest L. The Anthenium. 1964. 4.95 (ISBN 0-932642-13-6). Unarius Pubns.

--The Elysium. (Illus.). 1956. 4.95 (ISBN 0-932642-14-4). Unarius Pubns.

Osborne, Denis. The Andromedans & Other Parables of Science & Faith. LC 78-18550. (Illus.). 1978. pap. 2.50 (ISBN 0-87784-600-6). Inter-Varsity.

Park, Thelma. The House of Neh. (Illus.). 178p. (Orig.). 1986. pap. 9.95 (ISBN 1-55630-023-9). Brentwood Comm.

Patte, Daniel, ed. Semiology & Parables: Exploration of the Possibilities Offered by Structuralism for Exegesis. Papers of the Vanderbilt University Conference, May 15-17, 1975. LC 76-20686. (Pittsburgh Theological Monographs: No. 9). 1976. pap. 9.95 (ISBN 0-915138-11-5). Pickwick.

Reeve, Pamela. Parables by the Sea. LC 77-6209. (Illus.). 1976. gift ed. o.p. 5.95 (ISBN 0-930014-10-3); pap. 5.95 (ISBN 0-930014-11-1). Multnomah.

Rogahn, Kenneth & Schoedel, Walter. Parables from the Cross. 1981. pap. 5.95 (ISBN 0-570-03847-2, 12-2950). Concordia.

Saint-Exupery, Saint Antoine De. The Wisdom of the Sands. Gilbert, Stuart, tr. from Fr. LC 79-15938. 1979. pap. 10.95 (ISBN 0-226-73372-6, P826). U of Chicago Pr.

Spener, Philip J. Pia Desideria. Tappert, Theodore G., ed. & tr. LC 64-12995. 1964. pap. 5.95 (ISBN 0-8006-1953-6, 1-1953). Fortress.

Spurgeon, Charles H. Sermons on the Parables. Cook, Charles T, ed. 256p. 1977. Repr. of 1958 ed. limp bk. 5.95 (ISBN 0-551-05574-X). Attic Pr.

Suter, David W. Tradition & Composition in the Parables of Enoch. LC 79-17441. (Society of Biblical Literature. Dissertation Ser.: No. 47). 1979. pap. 9.95 (ISBN 0-89130-336-7, 060147). Scholars Pr GA.

Twitchell, Paul. Eckankar: La Clave de los Mondos Secretos. 1978. pap. 5.95 (ISBN 0-88155-029-9). IWP Pub.

Via, Dan O., Jr. The Parables: Their Literary & Existential Dimension. LC 67-11910. 232p. 1974. pap. 6.95 (ISBN 0-8006-1392-9, 1-1392). Fortress.

Worcester, William F. The Language of Parable. LC 76-6008. 1976. pap. 4.00 (ISBN 0-87785-155-7). Swedenborg.

Young, Norman. Rebuke & Challenge: The Point of Jesus' Parables. Coffen, Richard W., ed. 96p. (Orig.). 1985. pap. 6.95 (ISBN 0-8280-0286-X). Review & Herald.

PARACLETE

see Holy Spirit

PARADISE

Kloss, Jethro. Back to Eden. authorized ed. LC 81-82411. 702p. 1984. pap. 9.95. World Wide OR.

--Back to Eden: Authorized Kloss Family Edition. rev. ed. (Illus.). 724p. 1985. pap. 3.50 (ISBN 0-940676-00-1). Back to Eden.

Marsella, Elena M. Quest for Eden. LC 66-16172. 275p. 1966. 8.95 (ISBN 0-8022-1063-5). Philos Lib.

PARADISE IN LITERATURE AND ART

Kirkpatrick, R. Dante's Paradiso & the Limitations of Modern Criticism. LC 77-80839. 1978. 39.50 (ISBN 0-521-21785-7). Cambridge U Pr.

Lindenbaum, Peter. Changing Landscapes: Anti-Pastoral Sentiment in the English Renaissance. LC 85-24546. 264p. 1986. 27.50x (ISBN 0-8203-0835-8). U of GA Pr.

Spalding, John H. The Kingdom of Heaven As Seen by Swedenborg. LC 72-8245. Repr. of 1916 ed. 18.00 (ISBN 0-404-11006-1). AMS Pr.

PARAGUAY–HISTORY

Graham, Robert B. Vanished Arcadia: Being Some Account of the Jesuits in Paraguay. LC 68-25238. (Studies in Spanish Literature, No. 36). 1969. Repr. of 1901 ed. lib. bdg. 50.95x (ISBN 0-8383-0949-6). Haskell.

PARAPLEGIA

Eareckson, Joni & Estes, Steve. A Step Further. 192p. 1982. pap. 3.95 (ISBN 0-310-23972-9, 12008P). Zondervan.

Eareckson, Joni & Musser, Joe. Joni. (Illus.). 256p. 1980. pap. 3.95 (ISBN 0-310-23982-6, 12009P). Zondervan.

--Joni. 1976 (12563L). kivar, large print o.p. 7.95 (ISBN 0-310-23967-2); pap. 6.95 (ISBN 0-310-23961-3, 12005P). Zondervan.

PARAPSYCHOLOGY

see Psychical Research

PARENT AND CHILD

see also Adolescence; Fathers; Mother and Child; Mothers; Single-Parent Family; Youth

Ahrens, Herman C., Jr. Life with Your Parents. (Looking Up Ser.). 24p. 1983. pap. 1.25 booklet (ISBN 0-8298-0667-9). Pilgrim NY.

Arledge, Byron W. Laugh with Your Teenager. 128p. 1985. pap. 4.95 (ISBN 0-8423-2102-0). Tyndale.

Arnold, L. Eugene & Estreicher, Donna G. Parent-Child Group Therapy: Building Self-Esteem in a Cognitive-Behavioral Group. LC 84-40723. 288p. 1985. 29.00 (ISBN 0-669-09934-1). Lexington Bks.

Baden, Robert. How to Understand Your Parents & Maybe Like the Ones You Love. 1987. pap. 4.95 (ISBN 0-570-04467-7). Concordia.

Barber, Virginia & Skaggs, Merrill M. The Mother Person. LC 76-48850. 1977. pap. 7.95 (ISBN 0-8052-0565-9). Schocken.

Barr, Debbie. Caught in the Crossfire. 288p. (Orig.). 1985. pap. 8.95 (ISBN 0-310-28561-5, 12083P). Zondervan.

Biegert, John E. Mirando Hacia Arriba en Medio de la Enfermedad: (Looking Up...While Lying Down) (Looking Up Ser.). (Span.). 24p. (Orig.). 1983. pap. 1.25 booklet (ISBN 0-8298-0663-6). Pilgrim NY.

Blair, Maury & Brendel, Doug. Maury, Hijo Del Dolor. Araujo, Juan S., tr. from Eng. Tr. of Maury, Wednesday's Child. (Span.). 144p. 1986. pap. 3.75 (ISBN 0-88113-204-7). Edit Betania.

Bradshaw, Charles. You & Your Teen. (Family Ministry Ser.). (Illus.). 54p. 1985. pap. text ed. 19.95 (ISBN 0-89191-950-3). Cook.

Campbell. How to Really Love Your Teenager. LC 81-51515. 1982. 4.95 (ISBN 0-88207-274-9). Victor Bks.

Campbell, D. Ross. How to Really Love Your Child. LC 77-89470. 132p. 1977. pap. 4.95 (ISBN 0-88207-751-1). Victor Bks.

Campion, Michael & Zehr, Wilmer. Especially for Parents. (When Was the Last Time Ser.). (Illus.). 112p. 1978. pap. 5.95 (ISBN 0-87123-137-9, 210137). Bethany Hse.

Carlson, Lee W., ed. Christian Parenting. 80p. 1984. pap. 6.95 (ISBN 0-8170-1072-6). Judson.

Chemnitz, Martin. Justification: The Chief Article of Christian Doctrine. Preus, J. A., tr. 200p. 1986. 16.95 (ISBN 0-570-04227-5, 15-2186). Concordia.

Chrysostom, St. John. Duties of Parents & Children to One Another. pap. 0.25 (ISBN 0-686-17310-4). Eastern Orthodox.

Craig, Sidney D. Raising Your Child, Not by Force But by Love. LC 72-10436. 192p. 1982. pap. 6.95 (ISBN 0-664-24413-0). Westminster.

Cross, Luther S. Growing in Faith: Devotions for Parent-Child Interaction. 32p. (Orig.). 1984. pap. 2.95 (ISBN 0-8066-2070-6, 23-1606). Augsburg.

Gallagher, Maureen, ed. Christian Parenting Handbook. 2.95 (ISBN 0-8091-2262-6). Paulist Pr.

Gaulke, Earl H. You Can Have a Family Where Everybody Wins. LC 75-23574. 104p. 1975. pap. 3.50 (ISBN 0-570-03723-9, 12-2625). Concordia.

Gordon, Sol & Gordon, Judith. Raising a Child Conservatively in a Sexually Permissive World. 224p. 1986. pap. 7.95 (ISBN 0-671-62797-X, Fireside). S&S.

Hickman, Martha H. Waiting & Loving: Thoughts Occasioned by the Illness & the Death of a Parent. LC 83-51399. 160p. (Orig.). 1984. pap. 5.95 (ISBN 0-8358-0483-6). Upper Room.

Jones, Elizabeth B. Let the Children Come. 112p. 1980. pap. 2.95 (ISBN 0-8010-5102-9). Baker Bk.

Keane, Bil. At Home with the Family Circus. LC 72-11667. (Illus.). 64p. (Orig.). 1973. pap. 1.00 (ISBN 0-8170-0598-6). Judson.

Kern, Mary M. Be a Better Parent. LC 79-9098. 160p. 1979. pap. 6.95 (ISBN 0-664-24271-5). Westminster.

Kesler, Jay, ed. Parents & Teenagers. 696p. 1984. pap. 16.95 (ISBN 0-88207-817-8). Victor Bks.

Ketterman, Grace H. The Complete Book of Baby & Child Care. rev. & updated ed. 560p. 1981. 18.95 (ISBN 0-8007-1421-0); pap. 8.95 (ISBN 0-8007-1515-2). Revell.

Lein, Laura & O'Donnell, Lydia. Children. LC 84-7543. (Choices: Guides for Today's Woman Ser.: Vol. 9). 120p. 1984. pap. 6.95 (ISBN 0-664-24550-1). Westminster.

Leman, Kevin. Parenthood Without Hassles-Well, Almost. LC 78-656211. 144p. 1982. pap. 2.95 (ISBN 0-89081-304-3). Harvest Hse.

Lenz, Friedel. Celebrating the Festivals with Children. Tr. of Mit Kindren Feste feiern. 20p. (Orig.). 1986. pap. 3.95 (ISBN 0-88010-151-2). Anthroposophic.

Mueller, Charles S. Thank God I Have a Teenager. LC 84-24363. 128p. (Orig.). 1985. pap. 5.95 (ISBN 0-8066-2126-5, 10-6239). Augsburg.

Neff, Pauline. Tough Love: How Parents Can Deal with Drug Abuse. 160p. 1984. pap. 7.50 (ISBN 0-687-42407-0). Abingdon.

Nethery, Susan. A Mother Shares: Meditations on Parenting. 128p. 1981. 5.95 (ISBN 0-8010-6736-7). Baker Bk.

Oraker, James & Meredith, Char. Almost Grown: A Christian Guide for Parents of Teenagers. LC 78-20585. 192p. 1982. pap. 6.95 (ISBN 0-06-066398-7, RD 380, HarpR). Har-Row.

Orr, Bill & Lutzer, Erwin. If I Could Change My Mom & Dad. 128p. 1983. pap. 3.50 (ISBN 0-8024-0174-0). Moody.

Orso, Kathryn W. Parenthood: A Commitment in Faith. LC 75-5219. 64p. (Orig.). 1975. pap. text ed. 2.95 (ISBN 0-8192-1198-2); tchr's ed. 3.75 (ISBN 0-8192-1204-0); wkbk. 3.95 (ISBN 0-8192-1199-0). Morehouse.

Pipe, Virginia E. Live & Learn with Your Teenager. LC 85-18451. (Family Life Ser.). 160p. 1985. pap. 6.95 (ISBN 0-8170-1069-6). Judson.

Pitts, David. How in the World Do I Get Along With My Parents? 40p. 1982. pap. 0.95 (ISBN 0-88144-046-9). Christian Pub.

Radl, Shirley. Mother's Day Is over. 288p. 1987. 17.95 (ISBN 0-87795-864-5). Arbor Hse.

Richards, Lawrence O. The Word Parents Handbook. 1983. 9.95 (ISBN 0-8499-0328-9). Word Bks.

Riddell, Carole & Wallingford, Kay. Helpful Hints for Fun-filled Parenting. LC 84-2056. 128p. 1984. pap. 6.95 spiral (ISBN 0-8407-5880-4). Nelson.

Roberts, Peg. Devotions for New Parents. 85p. 1984. 4.95 (ISBN 0-8010-7727-3). Baker Bk.

Ross, Bette M. Our Special Child. rev. ed. 256p. 1984. pap. 8.95 (ISBN 0-8007-1230-7). Revell.

Sears, William. Christian Parenting & Child Care. 544p. 1985. 19.95 (ISBN 0-8407-5422-1). Nelson.

Smith, Harold I. You & Your Parents: Strategies for Building an Adult Relationship. 176p. (Orig.). 1987. pap. 8.95 (ISBN 0-8066-2267-9, 10-7407). Augsburg.

Udo de Haes, Daniel. The Young Child: Creative Living with Two to Four Year Olds. Blaxland de Lange, Simon & Blaxland de Lange, Paulamaria, trs. from Dutch. 90p. (Orig.). 1986. pap. 10.95 (ISBN 0-88010-169-5). Anthroposophic.

Walsh, David. Growing up Together: A Spiritual Perspective for Parents of Adolescents. 124p. (Orig.). 1980. pap. 2.50 (ISBN 0-912228-73-3). St Anthony Mess Pr.

White, John. Parents in Pain. LC 78-24760. 1979. pap. 7.95 (ISBN 0-87784-582-4); study guide 1.95 (ISBN 0-87784-492-5). Inter-Varsity.

Wilczak, Paul F., ed. Parenting. LC 78-69758. (Marriage & Family Living in Depth Bk.). 1978. pap. 2.45 (ISBN 0-87029-138-6, 20220-0). Abbey.

Wright, Norman & Johnson, Rex. Building Positive Parent-Teen Relationships: Teacher's Guide. LC 78-56980. 1978. pap. 9.95 (ISBN 0-89081-148-2); transparencies & repro masters incl. Harvest Hse.

PARENT EDUCATION

Lanstrom, Edith. Christian Parent Burnout. LC 12-2979. (Continued Applied Christianity Ser.). 1983. pap. 2.95 (ISBN 0-570-03897-9). Concordia.

Narramore, S. Bruce. Help! I'm a Parent. 1972. pap. 6.95 (ISBN 0-310-30321-4). Zondervan.

Wilson, Earl D. Empty Nest: Life after the Kids Leave Home. (Family Ministry Ser.). 96p. 1986. pap. 19.95 (ISBN 0-89191-969-4). Cook.

PARENTS WITHOUT PARTNERS

see Single-Parent Family

PARIS–COLLEGE DE L'AVE MARIA

Gabriel, Astrik L. Student Life in Ave Maria College, Medieval Paris. (Mediaeval Studies Ser.: No. 14). (Illus.). 1955. 26.95 (ISBN 0-268-00265-7). U of Notre Dame Pr.

PARIS–NOTRE-DAME

Gillerman, Dorothy. The Cloture of Notre-Dame & Its Role in the 14th Century Choir Program. LC 76-23623. (Outstanding Dissertations in the Fine Arts - 2nd Series - Medieval). (Illus.). 292p. 1977. Repr. of 1973 ed. lib. bdg. 69.00 (ISBN 0-8240-2693-4). Garland Pub.

PARISH BOARDS

see Parish Councils

PARISH COUNCILS

Broderick, Robert C. Parish Council Handbook. 1968. pap. 2.25 (ISBN 0-8199-0083-4, L38623). Franciscan Herald.

A Day in the Life of a DRE. 36p. 1977. 3.60 (ISBN 0-318-20612-9). Natl Cath Educ.

Fransen, Paul. Effective Church Councils: Leadership Styles & Decision Making in the Church. (Administration Series for Churches). 56p. (Orig.). 1985. pap. 3.95 (ISBN 0-8066-2198-2, 10-2023). Augsburg.

McConnell, Theodore A. Finding a Pastor: The Search Committee Handbook. 72p. (Orig.). 1985. pap. 4.95 (ISBN 0-86683-493-1, HarpR). Har-Row.

Rademacher, William J. Answers for Parish Councillors. LC 81-51429. 1981. pap. 6.95 (ISBN 0-89622-134-2). Twenty-Third.

PARISH GROUP WORK

see Church Group Work

PARISH HOUSES

see also Church Work; Churches

DeMena, Henry F. How to Increase Parish Income. 144p. 1982. pap. 12.95 (ISBN 0-89622-160-1). Twenty-Third.

Knoche, Vikki. Parish the Thought. 1984. pap. 4.95 (ISBN 0-8163-0560-9). Pacific Pr Pub Assn.

LeFevre, Perry & Schroeder, W. Widick, eds. Pastoral Care & Liberation Praxis: Studies in Personal & Social Transformation. (Studies in Ministry & Parish Life). 112p. 1986. text ed. 18.95x (ISBN 0-913552-31-3); pap. text ed. 8.95x (ISBN 0-913552-32-1). Exploration Pr.

PARISH-IN-ELMET, ENGLAND

Colman, T. S. History of the Parish of Barwick-In-Elmet in the County of York. 1908. 34.00 (ISBN 0-384-09565-8). Johnson Repr.

PARISH LIBRARIES

see Libraries, Church

PARISH MANAGEMENT

see Church Management

PARISH REGISTERS

see Registers of Births, Deaths, Marriages, etc.

PARISH SCHOOLS

see Church Schools

PARISHES

see also Parish Councils; Pastoral Theology

Anderson, William A. RCIA: A Total Parish Process. 1986. pap. 12.95 (ISBN 0-697-02200-5). Wm C Brown.

Ashbee, Charles R., ed. Parish of Bromley-By-Bow. LC 73-138270. (London County Council. Survey of London: No. 1). Repr. of 1900 ed. 74.50 (ISBN 0-404-51651-3). AMS Pr.

Bausch, William J. The Christian Parish: Whispers of the Risen Christ. 232p. 1981. pap. 7.95 (ISBN 0-89622-146-6). Twenty-Third.

Boyak, Kenneth. A Parish Guide to Adult Initiation. LC 79-91001. 112p. (Orig.). 1980. pap. 4.95 (ISBN 0-8091-2282-0). Paulist Pr.

Broderick, Robert C. Your Parish - Where the Action Is. 1974. pap. 2.25 (ISBN 0-8199-0486-4). Franciscan Herald.

Byers, David, ed. The Parish in Transition: Proceedings of a Conference on the American Catholic Parish. 120p. 1986. pap. 8.95 (ISBN 1-55586-967-X). US Catholic.

Downs, Thomas. The Parish As Learning Community. LC 78-70816. 128p. 1979. pap. 3.95 (ISBN 0-8091-2172-7). Paulist Pr.

Fagan, Harry. Empowerment: Skills for Parish Social Action. LC 79-52106. 64p. 1979. pap. 4.95 (ISBN 0-8091-2210-3). Paulist Pr.

Geaney, Dennis J. & Sokol, Dolly. Parish Celebrations: A Reflective Guide for Liturgy Planning. (Orig.). 1983. pap. 5.95 (ISBN 0-89622-190-3). Twenty-Third.

Ingle, E. Parish Institutions of Maryland, with Illustrations from Parish Records. 1973. pap. 9.00 (ISBN 0-384-25740-2). Johnson Repr.

Kavanagh, Peter. Savage Rock: Inniskeen, the History of a Parish. LC 78-58360. 1978. 20.00. Kavanagh.

Kilian, Sabbas. Theological Models for the Parish. LC 76-42986. 1977. 5.95 (ISBN 0-8189-0337-6). Alba.

Lyons, Mark. The Good Parishioner. 1983. 4.50 (ISBN 0-8199-0830-4). Franciscan Herald.

The National Inventory of Parish Catechetical Programs. pap. cancelled (ISBN 0-686-15370-7, V-590). US Catholic.

O'Brien, J. Stephen, ed. Gathering God's People: Signs of a Successful Parish. LC 81-85241. 264p. (Orig.). 1982. pap. 7.95 (ISBN 0-87973-656-9, 656). Our Sunday Visitor.

Parish Life in the United States, Final Report to the Bishops of the United States by the Parish Project, November, 1982. 90p. 1983. pap. 7.50 (ISBN 1-55586-876-2). US Catholic.

The Parish Self-Study Guide. 97p. 1982. pap. 7.95 (ISBN 1-55586-842-8). US Catholic.

Prior, David. Parish Renewal at the Grassroots. 1987. 12.95 (ISBN 0-310-38370-6). Zondervan.

Quinn, Bernard. The Small Rural Parish. LC 79-56508. (Orig.). 1980. pap. 3.50x (ISBN 0-914422-11-1). Glenmary Res Ctr.

Schaller, Lyle E. Survival Tactics in the Parish. LC 76-54751. (Orig.). 1977. pap. 8.75 (ISBN 0-687-40757-5). Abingdon.

Sweetser, Thomas P. Successful Parishes: How They Meet the Challenge of Change. 204p. 1983. pap. 9.95 (ISBN 0-86683-694-2, HarpR). Har-Row.

Walters, Thomas P., ed. Handbook for Parish Evaluation. (Orig.). 1984. pap. 10.95 (ISBN 0-8091-2587-0). Paulist Pr.

Weiss, Ed. The Parent, the Parish, & the Catholic School. 1986. 6.60 (ISBN 0-318-20566-1). Natl Cath Educ.

Wells, Guy F. Parish Education in Colonial Virginia. LC 71-89252. (American Education: Its Men, Institutions & Ideas, Ser. 1). 1969. Repr. of 1923 ed. 11.00 (ISBN 0-405-01490-2). Ayer Co Pubs.

PARISHES–CANADA

Desautels, Joseph. Manuel des cures pour le bon Gouvernement Temporel Des Paroisses et des Fabriques dans le Bas-Canada. 1864. 24.00 (ISBN 0-384-11480-6). Johnson Repr.

PARISHES–GREAT BRITAIN

Godfrey, Walter H., ed. Parish of Chelsea, Pt. 1. LC 71-138271. (London County Council. Survey of London: No. 2). Repr. of 1909 ed. 74.50 (ISBN 0-404-51652-1). AMS Pr.

Liu, Tai. Puritan London: A Study of Religion & Society in the City Parishes. LC 85-40534. 256p. 1986. 38.50x (ISBN 0-87413-283-5, Pub. by U Delaware Pr). Assoc Univ Prs.

London County Council. The Parishes of Christ Church & All Saints & the Liberties of Norton Folgate & the Old Artillery Ground. LC 74-6547. (London County Council. Survey of London: No. 27). Repr. of 1957 ed. 74.50 (ISBN 0-404-51677-7). AMS Pr.

--Survey of London: The Parish of St. Mary Lambeth. Pt. 2, Southern Area. LC 74-6546. Repr. of 1956 ed. 74.50 (ISBN 0-404-51676-9). AMS Pr.

Macdonald, Alexander, ed. Reports on the State of Certain Parishes in Scotland. LC 79-175588. (Maitland Club, Glasgow. Publications: No. 34). Repr. of 1835 ed. 24.50 (ISBN 0-404-53003-6). AMS Pr.

Reddan, Minnie & Clapham, Alfred W. The Church of St. Helen, Bishopsgate, Pt. 1. LC 74-6179. (London County Council Survey of London: No. 9). Repr. of 1924 ed. 74.50 (ISBN 0-404-51659-9). AMS Pr.

Redstone, Lilian J., ed. Parish of All Hallows, Pt. 1. LC 74-138273. (London County Council. Survey of London: No. 12). Repr. of 1929 ed. 74.50 (ISBN 0-404-51662-9). AMS Pr.

Trotter, E. Seventeenth Century Life in the Country Parish. 242p. 1968. Repr. of 1919 ed. 28.50x (ISBN 0-7146-1363-0, F Cass Co). Biblio Dist.

PARKER, THEODORE, 1810-1860

Chadwick, John W. Theodore Parker: Preacher & Reformer. LC 72-144939. 1971. Repr. of 1900 ed. 39.00x (ISBN 0-403-00925-1). Scholarly.

Collins, Robert E. Theodore Parker: American Transcendentalist: A Critical Essay & a Collection of His Writings. LC 73-9593. 277p. 1973. 17.50 (ISBN 0-8108-0641-X). Scarecrow.

Commager, H. S. Theodore Parker: Yankee Crusader. 11.25 (ISBN 0-8446-1884-5). Peter Smith.

Commager, Henry S. Theodore Parker. 1982. pap. 6.45 (ISBN 0-933840-15-2). Unitarian Univ.

Myerson, Joel. Theodore Parker: A Descriptive Bibliography. LC 81-43354. 238p. 1981. lib. bdg. 33.00 (ISBN 0-8240-9279-1). Garland Pub.

Radicalism in Religion, Philosophy, & Social Life: Four Papers from the Boston Courier for 1858. LC 72-1804. (Black Heritage Library Collection Ser.). Repr. of 1858 ed. 10.50 (ISBN 0-8369-9052-8). Ayer Co Pubs.

Reville, Albert. The Life & Writings of Theodore Parker. 59.95 (ISBN 0-8490-0525-6). Gordon Pr.

Weiss, John. Life & Correspondence of Theodore Parker. LC 70-83446. (Religion in America, Ser. 1). 1969. Repr. of 1864 ed. 52.00 (ISBN 0-405-00279-3). Ayer Co Pubs.

--Life & Correspondence of Theodore Parker, 2 Vols. facs. ed. LC 69-16854. (Select Bibliographies Reprint Ser). 1863. 52.00 (ISBN 0-8369-5018-6). Ayer Co Pubs.

--Life & Correspondence of Theodore Parker, 2 Vols. LC 76-106987. (American Public Figures Ser). 1864. Set. lib. bdg. 95.00 (ISBN 0-306-71874-X). Da Capo.

--Life & Correspondence of Theodore Parker, Minister of the Twenty-Eighth Congregational Society, Boston. LC 74-97443. Repr. of 1864 ed. 42.00x (ISBN 0-8371-2723-8, WEQ&, Pub. by Negro U Pr). Greenwood.

PAROCHIAL LIBRARIES

see Libraries, Church

PAROCHIAL SCHOOLS

see Church Schools

PARSEES

see also Avesta; Zoroastrianism

Haug, Martin. The Parsis. 427p. 1978. Repr. of 1878 ed. 25.00 (ISBN 0-89684-157-X). Orient Bk Dist.

Hinnells, John. Zoroastrianism & the Parsis. 1985. 13.00x (ISBN 0-7062-3973-3, Pub. by Ward Lock Educ Co Ltd). State Mutual Bk.

Karaka, Dosabhai F. History of the Parsis, 2 vols. LC 74-21259. Repr. of 1884 ed. Set. 70.00 (ISBN 0-404-12812-2). AMS Pr.

Moulton, James H. Treasure of the Magi: A Story of Modern Zoroastrianism. LC 73-173004. Repr. of 1917 ed. 21.75 (ISBN 0-404-04508-1). AMS Pr.

PART-SONGS

De La Rue, Pierre. Magnificat Quinti Toni. Davison, Nigel, ed. LC 65-26095. (Penn State Music Series, No. 8). 19p. 1965. pap. 3.00x (ISBN 0-271-73081-1). Pa St U Pr.

Palestrina, Giovanni P. Ten Four-Part Motets for the Church's Year. Harman, Alec, tr. (Lat. & Eng.). 1964. 9.95 (ISBN 0-19-353332-4). Oxford U Pr.

PASCAL, BLAISE, 1623-1662

Barker, John C. Strange Contrarieties: Pascal in England During the Age of Reason. (Illus.). 352p. 1976. 20.00x (ISBN 0-7735-0188-6). McGill-Queens U Pr.

Baudin. Etudes Historiques et Critiques sur la Philosophie de Pascal, 3 tomes. Incl. Tome I. Pascal et Descartes. 11.95 (ISBN 0-685-34021-X); Tome II. Pascal, les Libertins et les Jansenites. 22.50 (ISBN 0-685-34022-8); Tome III. Pascal et la Casuistique. 11.50 (ISBN 0-685-34023-6). (Coll. Etre et Penser). French & Eur.

Cruickshank, John. PASCAL: Pensees. (Critical Guides to French Texts Ser.: No. 23). 79p. 1983. pap. 3.95 (ISBN 0-7293-0154-0, Pub. by Grant & Cutler). Longwood Pub Group.

Davidson, Hugh M. The Origins of Certainty: Means & Meanings in Pascal's "Pensees". LC 78-12768. 1979. lib. bdg. 16.00x (ISBN 0-226-13716-3). U of Chicago Pr.

Davidson, Hugh M. & Dube, Pierre H., eds. A Concordance to Pascal's "Pensees". LC 75-16808. (Cornell Concordances Ser.). 1488p. 1975. 85.00x (ISBN 0-8014-0972-1). Cornell U Pr.

De Sainte-Beuve, Charles-Augustin. Port-Royal, 3 tomes. 1953-1955. Set. 79.95 (ISBN 0-685-11502-X). French & Eur.

Dionne, James R. Pascal & Nietzche: Etude Historique & Comparee. LC 74-3300. (Fr.). 1976. lib. bdg. 18.00 (ISBN 0-89102-032-2). B Franklin.
Duclaux, Mary. Portrait of Pascal. 1927. Repr. 25.00 (ISBN 0-8274-3188-0). R West.
Hubert, Marie L. Pascal's Unfinished Apology. LC 70-153272. 165p. 1973. Repr. of 1952 ed. 21.50 (ISBN 0-8046-1699-X, Pub. by Kennikat). Assoc Faculty Pr.
Kummer, Irene. Blaise Pascal: Das Heil Im Widerspruch. 1978. 56.80x (ISBN 3-11-007253-X). De Gruyter.
MacKenzie, Charles S. Pascal's Anguish & Joy. LC 73-77404. 272p. 1973. 12.95 (ISBN 0-8022-2117-3). Philos Lib.
Maggioni, Sr. M. Julie. Pensees of Pascal: A Study in Baroque Style. LC 79-94181. (Catholic University of America Studies in Romance Languages & Literature Ser: No. 39). Repr. of 1950 ed. 25.00 (ISBN 0-404-50339-X). AMS Pr.
Melzer, Sara E. Discourses of the Fall: A Study of Pascal's Pensees. LC 85-24519. 128p. 1986. text ed. 22.95x (ISBN 0-520-05540-3). U of Cal Pr.
Miel, Jan. Pascal & Theology. LC 75-93822. 216p. 1970. 19.50x (ISBN 0-8018-1101-5). Johns Hopkins.
Mordell, Albert. Dante & Other Waning Classics. LC 68-8219. 1969. Repr. of 1915 ed. 18.50x (ISBN 0-8046-0322-7, Pub. by Kennikat). Assoc Faculty Pr.
Mortimer, Ernest. Blaise Pascal: The Life & Work of a Realist. 1979. Repr. of 1959 ed. lib. bdg. 25.00 (ISBN 0-8414-6341-7). Folcroft.
Pascal, Blaise. The Thoughts, Letters, & Opuscules of Blaise Pascal. 1978. Repr. of 1864 ed. lib. bdg. 35.00 (ISBN 0-8492-2094-7). R West.
Paul, C. Kegan. The Thoughts of Blaise Pascal: Translated from the Text of M. Auguste Molinier. 1978. Repr. of 1888 ed. 30.00 (ISBN 0-8492-2095-5). R West.
Rescher, Nicholas. Pascal's Wager: A Study of Practical Reasoning in Philosophical Theology. LC 84-40820. 176p. 1985. text ed. 19.95 (ISBN 0-268-01556-2, 85-15561). U of Notre Dame Pr.
Russell, Olga W. Humor in Pascal. 1977. 8.95 (ISBN 0-8158-0343-5). Chris Mass.
St. Cyres, Viscount. Pascal. 1909. Repr. 25.00 (ISBN 0-8274-3103-1). R West.
Saint-Beuve. Port Royal, 3 vols. Vol. 1. 37.50 (ISBN 0-686-56564-9); Vol. 2. 37.50 (ISBN 0-686-56565-7); Vol. 3. 35.95 (ISBN 0-686-56566-5). French & Eur.
Stewart, H. F. Blaise Pascal. 1973. Repr. of 1942 ed. 6.00 (ISBN 0-8274-1623-7). R West.
--The Holiness of Pascal. 1977. lib. bdg. 59.95 (ISBN 0-8490-2015-8). Gordon Pr.
Stewart, Hugh F. Blaise Pascal. LC 77-16601. 1977. Repr. of 1942 ed. lib. bdg. 12.50 (ISBN 0-8414-7801-5). Folcroft.
Waterman, Mina. Voltaire, Pascal & Human Destiny. LC 70-120676. 1970. Repr. lib. bdg. 14.50x (ISBN 0-374-98279-1, Octagon). Hippocrene Bks.
Webb, C. J. Pascal's Philosophy of Religion. Repr. of 1929 ed. 12.00 (ISBN 0-527-94918-3). Kraus Repr.

PASCHAL MYSTERY

Hamman, Adelbert. Paschal Mystery: Ancient Liturgical & Patristic Texts. Halton, Thomas, ed. LC 78-77646. Orig. Title: Mystere De Paques. 1969. 5.95 (ISBN 0-8189-0108-X). Alba.
Hennessey, Augustine. The Paschal Mystery: Core Grace in the Life of the Christian. (Synthesis Ser.). 37p. 1977. pap. 0.75 (ISBN 0-8199-0707-3). Franciscan Herald.
Sedgwick, Timothy F. Sacramental Ethics: Paschal Identity & the Christian Life. LC 86-45925. 128p. 1987. pap. text ed. 7.95 (ISBN 0-8006-1965-X, 1-1965). Fortress.

PASCUA PASSION-PLAY

Painter, Muriel T. A Yaqui Easter. LC 74-153706. 40p. 1971. pap. 3.95 (ISBN 0-8165-0168-8). U of Ariz Pr.

PASSION-MUSIC

Reed, Will L., ed. Treasury of Easter Music & Music for Passiontide. 1963. 12.95 (ISBN 0-87523-142-X). Emerson.
Smith, Oswald J. Pasion por las Almas. Orig. Title: Passion for Souls. (Span.). 208p. 1985. pap. 4.25 (ISBN 0-8254-1672-8). Kregel.

PASSION-PLAYS

see also Mysteries and Miracle-Plays; Passion-Music

Blackburn, Henry. Art in the Mountains: Story of the Passion Play. LC 77-94544. 1979. Repr. of 1870 ed. lib. bdg. 20.00 (ISBN 0-89341-178-7). Longwood Pub Group.
Edwards, Robert. The Montecassino Passion & the Poetics of Medieval Drama. LC 75-22655. 1977. 36.50x (ISBN 0-520-03102-4). U of Cal Pr.
Foote, Samuel. A Treatise on the Passions, So Far As They Regard the Stage. LC 72-144608. Repr. of 1747 ed. 11.50 (ISBN 0-404-02448-3). AMS Pr.
The Northern Passion: Pt. I: Four Parallel Texts. (EETS, OS Ser.: No. 145). Repr. of 1912 ed. 20.00 (ISBN 0-527-00141-4). Kraus Repr.

PASSIONS

see Emotions

PASSOVER

Adler, David A. Passover Fun Book: Puzzles, Riddles, Magic & More. (Bonim Fun-to-Do Bk.). (Illus.). 1978. saddlewire bdg. 3.95 (ISBN 0-88482-759-3, Bonim Bks). Hebrew Pub.
--A Picture Book of Passover. LC 81-6983. (Illus.). 32p. 1982. reinforced bdg. 10.95 (ISBN 0-8234-0439-0); pap. 5.95 (ISBN 0-8234-0609-1). Holiday.
The Amsterdam Passover Haggadah, 1695. (Illus.). 1984. 80.00 (ISBN 0-915361-06-X, 09837-0, Dist. by Watts); leather bdg. 125.00 (09844-3). Adama Pubs Inc.
Bin-Nun, Judy & Cooper, Nancy. Pesach: A Holiday Funtext. (Illus.). 32p. (Orig.). 1983. pap. text ed. 5.00 (ISBN 0-8074-0161-7, 101310). UAHC.
Birnbaum, Philip. The Birnbaum Haggadah. (Illus.). 160p. 1976. 5.95 (ISBN 0-88482-908-1); pap. 3.95 (ISBN 0-88482-912-X). Hebrew Pub.
Blank, Richard. A Christian Passover Celebration. 1981. 2.95 (ISBN 0-89536-477-8, 0317). CSS of Ohio.
Blau, Esther & Deitsch, Cyrel, eds. Spice & Spirit of Kosher-Passover Cooking. LC 77-72116. (Lubavitch Women's Organization Ser.). 1981. 7.95 (ISBN 0-317-14690-4). Lubavitch Women.
Bronstein, Herbert, ed. A Passover Haggadah. (Illus.). 1974. 79.00 set (ISBN 0-916694-66-6); lib. bdg. 27.50 (ISBN 0-916694-06-2); pap. 9.95 (ISBN 0-916694-05-4). Central Conf.
Central Conference of American Rabbis Staff. A Passover Haggadah. rev. ed. Baskin, Leonard, ed. & illus. (Illus.). 124p. 1978. pap. 14.95 (ISBN 0-14-004871-5). Penguin.
Chanover, Hyman & Chanover, Alice. Pesah Is Coming. (Holiday Series of Picture Story Books). (Illus.). 1956. 5.95 (ISBN 0-8381-0713-3, 10-713). United Syn Bk.
--Pesah Is Here. (Holiday Series of Picture Story Books). (Illus.). 1956. 5.95 (ISBN 0-8381-0714-1). United Syn Bk.
Dov ben Khayyim. The Telling: A Loving Hagadah for Passover (Non-Sexist, Yet Traditional) rev. ed. (Illus.). 48p. 1984. pap. 4.00 (ISBN 0-9612500-0-3). Rakhamim Pubns.
Elias, Joseph. The Haggadah. (The Art Scroll Mesorah Ser.). 224p. 1977. 10.95 (ISBN 0-89906-150-8); pap. 7.95 (ISBN 0-89906-151-6). Mesorah Pubns.
Fredman, Ruth G. The Passover Seder: Afikoman in Exile. 1981. 22.00x (ISBN 0-8122-7788-0). U of Pa Pr.
--The Passover Seder: Afikoman in Exile. 192p. 19.00 (ISBN 0-686-95143-3). ADL.
Galbreath, Naomi. The Story of Passover for Children. (Illus.). 32p. pap. 2.95 (ISBN 0-8249-8084-0). Ideals.
Gaster, Theodor H. Passover, Its History & Tradition. LC 83-22678. (Illus.). 102p. 1984. Repr. of 1949 ed. lib. bdg. 22.50x (ISBN 0-313-24372-7, GAPA). Greenwood.
Geller, Norman. Color Me Kosher for Passover. (Illus.). 23p. 1985. pap. 1.00 (ISBN 0-915753-06-5). N Geller Pub.
--David's Seder. (Illus.). 16p. 1983. pap. 4.95 (ISBN 0-915753-01-4). N Geller Pub.
Goodman, Philip, ed. Passover Anthology. LC 61-11706. (Illus.). 196p. 1961. 14.95 (ISBN 0-8276-0019-4, 250). Jewish Pubns.
Greenberg, Sidney, ed. New Model Seder. pap. 1.95 (ISBN 0-87677-058-8). Prayer Bk.
Greenfeld, Howard. Passover. LC 77-13910. (Illus.). 32p. 1978. 6.95 (ISBN 0-03-039921-1). H Holt & Co.
Hacohen, Menachem. The Haggadah of Legends & Customs. (Illus.). 128p. 1987. 29.95 (ISBN 0-915361-78-7, Dist. by Watts). Adama Pubs Inc.
Halper, Roe. Passover Haggadah. (Illus.). 40p. (Orig.). 1986. pap. 5.00 (ISBN 0-916326-03-9). Bayberry Pr.
Hynes, Arleen. Passover Meal. LC 76-187207. 64p. 1972. pap. 2.50 (ISBN 0-8091-1653-7). Paulist Pr.
Interreligious Haggadah. write for info. ADL.
Kafra. The Illuminated Haggadah. (Illus.). 27.50 (ISBN 0-87306-078-4). Feldheim.
Kaplan, Aryeh, tr. & intro. by. The MeAm Lo'ez Haggadah. 216p. pap. 6.45 (ISBN 0-940118-24-6). Maznaim.
Kaplan, Aryeh, tr. The Passover Haggadah. (MeAm Lo'ez Ser.). 288p. sephardic 11.95 (ISBN 0-940118-23-8). Maznaim.
Kolatch, Alfred J. Fun-In-Learning about Passover. LC 74-175489. (Illus.). 1972. pap. 3.95 (ISBN 0-8246-0133-5). Jonathan David.
Kustanowitz, Shulamit & Foont, Ronnie. A First Haggadah. LC 98-11598. (Illus.). 64p. 1980. 6.95 (ISBN 0-88482-766-6). Hebrew Pub.
Lipson, Eric-Peter. Passover Haggadah: A Messianic Celebration. LC 85-82168. (Illus.). 128p. 1986. 10.95 (ISBN 0-9616148-0-3). JFJ Pub.
Mackintosh, Sam. Passover Seder for Christian Families. 32p. 1984. pap. 2.95 (ISBN 0-89390-057-5). Resource Pubns.
Mordell, Klein, ed. Passover. 128p. pap. 4.50 (ISBN 0-686-95142-5). ADL.
New Jewish Agenda, ed. The Shalom Seders. 128p. 1984. pap. 12.95 (ISBN 0-531-09840-0). Watts.
New Jewish Agenda, compiled by. The Shalom Seders: Three Passover Haggadahs. LC 83-25857. (Illus.). 128p. 1984. pap. 12.95 (ISBN 0-915361-03-5, 09747-1, Dist. by Watts). Adama Pubs Inc.
Passover. 64p. (Orig.). 1986. 20.95 (ISBN 0-86683-778-7, HarpR); pap. 10.95 (ISBN 0-86683-778-7). Har-Row.
Rakov, Lois E. My First Haggadah. new ed. (Illus.). 1978. 3.95 (ISBN 0-87243-075-8). Templegate.
Raphael, Chaim. Memoirs of a Special Case. rev. ed. LC 62-9548. 208p. 1985. 12.95 (ISBN 0-940646-16-1); pap. 7.95 (ISBN 0-940646-17-X). Rossel Bks.
Raphael, Chaim, tr. The Passover Haggadah. LC 78-52362. (Illus.). 1978. pap. 3.95 (ISBN 0-87441-312-5). Behrman.
Regelson, Abraham, tr. The Deluxe Haggadah. 1961. velour bound 30.00 (ISBN 0-914080-34-2). Shulsinger Sales.
--The Haggadah-Kleinman. 1965. pap. 1.99 (ISBN 0-914080-33-4). Shulsinger Sales.
Rosen, Anne, et al. Family Passover. LC 79-89298. 64p. 1980. 6.95 (ISBN 0-8276-0169-7, 452). Jewish Pubns.
Rosen, Ceil & Rosen, Moishe. Christ in the Passover. LC 77-10689. 1978. pap. 4.95 (ISBN 0-8024-1392-7). Moody.
Rousso, Nira. The Passover Gourmet. (Illus.). 192p. 1987. 19.95 (ISBN 0-915361-66-3, Dist. by Watts). Adama Pubs Inc.
Rudin, Jacob. Haggadah for Children. 1973. 2.25x (ISBN 0-8197-0032-0). Bloch.
Scherman, Nosson, tr. The Family Haggadah. (Artscroll Mesorah Ser.). 96p. (Orig.). 1981. pap. 2.75 (ISBN 0-89906-178-8). Mesorah Pubns.
Segal, Judah B. Hebrew Passover from the Earliest Times to A.D. 70. 1963. 24.95x (ISBN 0-19-713529-3). Oxford U Pr.
Shevilei Hahagadah. 1980. 5.00 (ISBN 0-686-46793-0). T Black.
Silver, Arthur M. Passover Haggadah: The Complete Seder. 1980. 10.95 (ISBN 0-932232-06-X). Menorah Pub.
Simon, Norma. My Family Seder. (Festival Series of Picture Story Books). (Illus.). 1961. plastic cover 4.50 (ISBN 0-8381-0710-9, 10-710). United Syn Bk.
--Passover. LC 65-11644. (Holiday Ser.). (Illus.). 1965. PLB 12.89 (ISBN 0-690-61094-7, Crowell Jr Bks). HarpJ.
Stern, Chaim. Gates of Freedom: A Passover Haggadah. LC 81-84191. (Illus.). 130p. 1986. pap. 6.95 (ISBN 0-940646-21-8). Rossel Bks.
--Gates of Freedom: A Passover Haggadah. 1986. pap. 6.95 (ISBN 0-317-42655-9). Shapolsky Pubs.
Union Haggadah. 1977. Repr. of 1923 ed. 4.75 (ISBN 0-916694-08-9). Central Conf.
Wengrov, Charles. The Story of Passover. (Holiday Ser.). (Illus.). 1965. pap. 1.50 (ISBN 0-914080-54-7). Shulsinger Sales.
Zwerin, Raymond A. & Marcus, Audrey F. But This Night Is Different. (Illus.). 48p. 1981. text ed. 7.95x (ISBN 0-8074-0032-7, 102561). UAHC.

PASTORAL COUNSELING

Here are entered works on the clergyman as the counselor.

see also Counseling; Pastoral Medicine; Pastoral Psychology; Telephone in Church Work

Aaen, Bernhard. No Appointment Needed. Van Dolson, Bobbie J., ed. 128p. 1981. pap. 5.95 (ISBN 0-8280-0025-5). Review & Herald.
Adams, J. What about Nouthetic Counseling? 1976. pap. 2.50 (ISBN 0-87552-064-2). Presby & Reformed.
Adams, Jay E. Capacitado para Orientar. Orig. Title: Competent to Counsel. (Span.). 328p. 1981. pap. 7.95 (ISBN 0-8254-1000-2). Kregel.
--Christian Counselor's Casebook. (Companion Vol. to Christian Counselor's Manual). 1976. pap. 5.95 (ISBN 0-8010-0075-0). Baker Bk.
--Christian Counselor's Casebook. 223p. 1974. pap. 7.95 (ISBN 0-87552-012-X). Presby & Reformed.
--The Christian Counselor's Casebook. (A Jay Adams Library). 224p. 1986. pap. 7.95 (ISBN 0-310-51161-5, 12128). Zondervan.
--Christian Counselor's Manual. 490p. 1973. 19.95 (ISBN 0-87552-013-8). Presby & Reformed.
--The Christian Counselor's Manual: The Practice of Nouthetic Counseling. (Jay Adams Library). 496p. 1986. 16.95 (ISBN 0-310-51150-X, 12127). Zondervan.
--Christian Counselor's Wordbook. 1981. pap. 1.95 (ISBN 0-8010-0172-2). Baker Bk.
--Competent to Counsel. 1977. pap. 6.95 (ISBN 0-8010-0047-5). Baker Bk.
--Competent to Counsel: Introduction to Nouthetic Counseling. Smith, Michael, ed. (A Jay Adams Library). 320p. 1986. 15.95 (ISBN 0-310-51140-2, 12126). Zondervan.
--Coping with Counseling Crises. 98p. 1976. pap. 2.95 (ISBN 0-87552-018-9). Presby & Reformed.
--Essays on Counseling. (A Jay Adams Library). 288p. 1986. pap. 9.95 (ISBN 0-310-51171-2, 1219P). Zondervan.
--Helps for Counselors. (Orig.). 1980. pap. 2.95 (ISBN 0-8010-0156-0). Baker Bk.
--Insight & Creativity in Christian Counseling: An Antidote to Rigid & Mechanical Approaches. (A Jay Adams Library). 144p. 1986. pap. 6.95 (ISBN 0-310-51131-3, 12125P). Zondervan.
--Journal of Pastoral Practice, Vol. 1, No. 1 - Winter, 1977. 1977. pap. 3.50 (ISBN 0-8010-0116-1). Baker Bk.
--The Language of Counseling & the Christian Counselor's WordBook. (A Jay Adams Library). 160p. 1986. pap. 7.95 (ISBN 0-310-51061-9, 12118P). Zondervan.
--Lectures on Counseling. 281p. 1977. kivar 4.50 (ISBN 0-87552-041-3). Presby & Reformed.
--Lectures on Counseling. (A Jay Adams Library). 288p. 1986. pap. 9.95 (ISBN 0-310-51121-6, 12124P). Zondervan.
--Shepherding God's Flock: A Handbook on Pastoral Ministry, Counseling, & Leadership. (A Jay Adams Library). 544p. 1986. pap. 14.95 (ISBN 0-310-51071-6, 12119P). Zondervan.
--Solving Marriage Problems. 132p. 1983. pap. 5.95 (ISBN 0-87552-081-2). Presby & Reformed.
--Solving Marriage Problems: Biblical Solutions for Christian Counselors. (A Jay Adams Library). 144p. 1986. pap. 6.95 (ISBN 0-310-51081-3, 12120P). Zondervan.
--Update on Christian Counseling, 2 vols. (A Jay Adams Library). 288p. 1986. pap. 9.95 (ISBN 0-310-51051-1, 12117P). Zondervan.
--Update on Christian Counseling, Vol. 1. pap. 3.50 (ISBN 0-8010-0153-6). Baker Bk.
--Update on Christian Counseling, Vol. 1. 1979. pap. 3.50 (ISBN 0-87552-062-6). Presby & Reformed.
--Use of Scripture in Counseling. 1975. pap. 2.95 (ISBN 0-87552-063-4). Presby & Reformed.
Adams, Jay E., ed. Journal of Practical Practice, Vol. IV, No. 2. 1980. pap. 5.00 (ISBN 0-87552-032-4). Presby & Reformed.
Aldridge, Marion D. The Pastor's Guidebook: A Manual for Worship. LC 83-70213. 1984. 9.95 (ISBN 0-8054-2312-5). Broadman.
Anderson, Douglas A. New Approaches to Family Pastoral Care. LC 79-8898. (Creative Pastoral Care & Counseling Ser.). pap. 24.00 (2029614). Bks Demand UMI.
Anderson, Herbert. The Family & Pastoral Care. Browining, Don S., ed. LC 83-48914. (Theology & Pastoral Care Ser.). 128p. pap. 7.95 (ISBN 0-8006-1728-2, 1-1728). Fortress.
Archpriest Mitrophan Znosko-Borovsky. Iz Missionersko-pastirskoj dejatel'nosti na Nivje Khristovoj v Emigratsii. Tr. of From My Missionary-Pastoral Activities in Christ's Field in the Immigration. 320p. 1985. pap. 12.00 (ISBN 0-317-29117-3). Holy Trinity.
Arnold, Eberhard. God's Revolution: The Witness of Eberhard Arnold. Hutterian Society of Brothers & Yoder, John H., eds. LC 83-62952. 230p. 1984. pap. 8.95 (Pub. by Paulist Pr). Plough.
Arnold, Heini. Freiheit Von Gedankensunden Nur Christus Bricht Den Fluch. LC 73-20198. (Ger.). 118p. 1973. text ed. 3.50. Plough.
Augsburger, David W. Pastoral Counseling Across Cultures. LC 86-13343. 408p. 1986. 21.95 (ISBN 0-664-21272-7). Westminster.
--When Caring Is Not Enough: Resolving Conflicts Through Fair Fighting. LC 83-80999. (Caring Enough Ser.: No. 4). 196p. (Orig.). 1983. pap. 5.95 (ISBN 0-8361-3343-9). Herald Pr.
Backus, William. Telling the Truth to Troubled People. 256p. (Orig.). 1985. pap. 6.95 (ISBN 0-87123-811-X, 210811). Bethany Hse.
Baker, Benjamin S. Shepherding the Sheep. LC 82-73531. 1983. 8.95 (ISBN 0-8054-2543-8). Broadman.
Bassett, William T. Counseling the Childless Couple. LC 63-14722. (Successful Pastoral Counseling Ser.). pap. 34.80 (2026938). Bks Demand UMI.
Bausch, William J. Ministry: Traditions, Tensions, Transitions. LC 81-86345. 192p. 1982. pap. 7.95 (ISBN 0-89622-153-9). Twenty-Third.

Benner, David G. Baker Encyclopedia of Psychology. 1376p. 1985. text ed. 39.95 (ISBN 0-8010-0865-4). Baker Bk.

Bennett, G. F. When They Ask for Bread: Pastoral Care & Counseling. LC 77-15743. 1978. 8.95 (ISBN 0-8042-1159-0). John Knox.

Bergendoff, Conrad L. Pastoral Care for Alcoholism: An Introduction. 36p. 1981. pap. 1.95 (ISBN 0-89486-123-9). Hazelden.

Betancourt, Esdras, ed. Manual Comprensivo de Sicologia Pastoral. (Span.). 168p. 1980. pap. 4.95 (ISBN 0-87148-580-X). Pathway Pr.

Black, R. L. The Church of God of Prophecy: Pastor. 1977. 4.25 (ISBN 0-934942-29-3). White Wing Pub.

Bobgan, Martin & Bobgan, Deidre. How to Counsel from Scripture. 1985. pap. 8.95 (ISBN 0-8024-0373-5). Moody.

Borchert, Gerald L. & Lester, Andrew D., eds. Spiritual Dimensions of Pastoral Care: Witness to the Ministry of Wayne E. Oates. LC 84-19581. 152p. (Orig.). 1985. pap. 11.95 (ISBN 0-664-24562-5). Westminster.

Bradford, Lyle. Building Relationships Through Pastoral Visitation. 64p. 1984. pap. 4.95 (ISBN 0-8170-1006-8). Judson.

Brand, Ralph. Simplified Techniques of Counseling. 132p. 1972. pap. 2.50 (ISBN 0-89114-049-2). Baptist Pub Hse.

Brien, Robert C. You Are What You Think: Basic Issues in Pastoral Counseling. 182p. (Orig.). 1986. pap. 5.95 (ISBN 0-87227-102-1). Reg Baptist.

Britsch, R. Lanier & Olson, Terrance D., eds. Counseling: A Guide to Helping Others, Vol. 2. LC 83-72396. 335p. 1985. 9.95 (ISBN 0-87747-737-X). Deseret Bk.

Brother Bernard Seif. Images of God: Religious Beliefs Given Life Through Counseling, Spiritual Direction, & Prayer. 1987. 7.95 (ISBN 0-533-07239-5). Vantage.

Brown, J. Paul. Counseling with Senior Citizens. LC 64-15217. (Successful Pastoral Counseling Ser.). pap. 36.00 (2027174). Bks Demand UMI.

Brown, Raymond K. Reach Out to Singles: A Challenge to Ministry. LC 79-15495. 192p. 1979. pap. 7.95 (ISBN 0-664-24270-7). Westminster.

Browning, Don S. The Moral Context of Pastoral Care. LC 76-5858. 144p. 1983. pap. 8.95 (ISBN 0-664-24483-1). Westminster.

--Religious Ethics & Pastoral Care. LC 83-5589. (Theology & Pastoral Care Ser.). 128p. 1983. pap. 7.95 (ISBN 0-8006-1725-8, 1-1725). Fortress.

Calhoun, Gerald J. Pastoral Companionship: Ministry with Seriously Ill Persons & Their Families. 180p. (Orig.). 1986. pap. 8.95 (ISBN 0-8091-2753-9). Paulist Pr.

Campbell, Alastair V. Rediscovering Pastoral Care. LC 81-7547. 132p. 1981. pap. 7.95 (ISBN 0-664-24381-9). Westminster.

Cannell, Marian. Caregiver's Handbook. 1986. 46.50 (ISBN 0-939273-00-4). Caregiving Resc.

Capps, Donald. Life Cycle Theory & Pastoral Care. LC 83-5585. (Theology & Pastoral Care Ser.). 128p. 1983. pap. 7.95 (ISBN 0-8006-1726-6, 1-1726). Fortress.

--Pastoral Counseling & Preaching: A Quest for an Integrated Ministry. LC 80-18502. 156p. 1980. pap. 8.95 (ISBN 0-664-24342-8). Westminster.

Clarke, Rita-Lou. Pastoral Care of Battered Women. LC 86-5604. 132p. (Orig.). 1986. pap. 7.95 (ISBN 0-664-24015-1). Westminster.

Clebsch, William & Jaekle, Charles. Pastoral Care in Historical Perspective. LC 84-451130. 344p. 1983. Repr. of 1975 ed. 30.00x (ISBN 0-87668-717-6). Aronson.

Clements, William M. Care & Counseling of the Aging. Clinebell, Howard J. & Stone, Howard W., eds. LC 78-54547. (Creative Pastoral Care & Counseling Ser). 96p. 1979. pap. 4.50 (ISBN 0-8006-0561-6, 1-561). Fortress.

Clinebell, Charlotte H. Counseling for Liberation. Clineball, Howard J. & Stone, Howard W., eds. LC 75-36447. (Creative Pastoral Care & Counseling Ser). 96p. (Orig.). 1976. pap. 4.50 (ISBN 0-8006-0555-1, 1-555). Fortress.

Clinebell, Howard. Basic Types of Pastoral Care & Counseling. 464p. 1984. 17.95 (ISBN 0-687-02492-7). Abingdon.

Clinebell, Howard J. Growth Counseling for Mid-Years Couples. LC 76-7863. (Creative Pastoral Care & Counseling Ser.). pap. 24.00 (2029607). Bks Demand UMI.

Cobb, John B., Jr. Theology & Pastoral Care. Clinebell, Howard J. & Stone, Howard W., eds. LC 76-7862. (Creative Pastoral Care & Counseling Ser.). 96p. 1977. pap. 4.50 (ISBN 0-8006-0557-8, 1-557). Fortress.

Collins, Gary. Innovations in Counseling (RCC) 224p. 1986. 12.95 (ISBN 0-8499-0510-9). Word Bks.

--Orientacion Sicologica Eficaz. Blanch, Miguel, tr. from Eng. Tr. of Effective Counseling. (Span.). 206p. 1979. pap. 4.75 (ISBN 0-89922-136-X). Edit Caribe.

--Personalidades Quebrantadas. Flores, Jose, tr. from Eng. LC 78-62403. Tr. of Fractured Personalities. (Span.). 215p. 1978. pap. 4.95 (ISBN 0-89922-116-5). Edit Caribe.

Collins, Gary R. Christian Counseling. 1980. pap. 13.95 (ISBN 0-8499-2889-3). Word Bks.

Colston, Lowell G. Pastoral Care with Handicapped Persons. Clinebell, Howard J. & Stone, Howard W., eds. LC 77-15229. (Creative Pastoral Care & Counseling Ser). 96p. (Orig.). 1978. pap. 4.50 (ISBN 0-8006-0560-8, 1-560). Fortress.

Corr, Finbarr M. From the Wedding to the Marriage. 1987. 6.95 (ISBN 0-533-07038-4). Vantage.

Crabb, Jr. & Lawrence, J. Effective Biblical Counseling. 1986. 9.95 (ISBN 0-88469-187-X). BMH Bks.

--Encouragement. 1986. 9.95 (ISBN 0-88469-199-3). BMH Bks.

Crabb, Lawrence J., Jr. Basic Principles of Biblical Counseling. 160p. 1975. 9.95 (ISBN 0-310-22560-4, 10159). Zondervan.

--Basic Principles of Biblical Counseling. 1986. 9.95 (ISBN 0-88469-186-1). BMH Bks.

--Effective Biblical Counseling: A Model for Helping Caring Christians Become Capable Counselors. 1977. 10.95 (ISBN 0-310-22570-1, 10173). Zondervan.

Demaray, Donald. Near Hurting People: The Pastoral Ministry of Robert Moffat Fine. (Illus.). 1978. pap. 3.50 (ISBN 0-89367-024-3). Light & Life.

Detwiler-Zapp, Diane & Dixon, William C. Lay Caregiving. LC 81-66519. (Creative Pastoral Care & Counseling Ser.). 1982. pap. 4.50 (ISBN 0-8006-0567-5, 1-567). Fortress.

Deuink, James W. The Ministry of the Christian School Guidance Counselor. (Illus.). 175p. (Orig.). 1984. pap. 6.60 (ISBN 0-89084-273-6). Bob Jones Univ Pr.

DeVille, Jard. Pastor's Handbook on Interpersonal Relationships. 145p. 1986. pap. 8.95 (ISBN 0-8010-2961-9). Baker Bk.

Dittes, James E. When Work Goes Sour. 120p. (Orig.). 1987. pap. 6.95 (ISBN 0-664-24045-3). Westminster.

Drakeford, John W. Counseling for Church Leaders. LC 61-12412. 1961. 9.25 (ISBN 0-8054-2405-9). Broadman.

Draper, Edgar. Psychiatry & Pastoral Care. LC 65-23861. (Successful Pastoral Counseling Series). pap. 34.50 (2026894). Bks Demand UMI.

Duffy, Regis A. A Roman Catholic Theology of Pastoral Care. LC 83-48006. (Theology & Pastoral Care Ser.). 128p. 1983. pap. 7.95 (ISBN 0-8006-1727-4, 1-1727). Fortress.

Duncombe, Alice E. Handbook for Telephone Ministry. Rev. ed. 7.95 (ISBN 0-89985-110-X). Christ Nations.

Dunn, Frank G. Building Faith in Families: Using the Sacraments in Pastoral Ministry. 160p. (Orig.). 1987. pap. 8.95 (ISBN 0-8192-1394-2). Morehouse.

Dunn, Jerry G. God Is for the Alcoholic. Tr. of Deus e a Favor do Alcoolatra. 1986. write for info. (ISBN 0-8297-1610-6). Life Pubs Intl.

Fairchild, Roy W. Finding Hope Again: A Pastor's Guide to Counseling Depressed Persons. LC 79-2988. 160p. 1980. 9.45 (ISBN 0-06-062325-X, HarpR). Har-Row.

Fenn, Carl. The Church & the Disabled. 1985. pap. 5.00 (ISBN 0-8309-0414-X). Herald Hse.

Fortunato, John. Embracing the Exile: Healing Journeys of Gay Christians. 156p. (Orig.). 1984. pap. 7.95 (ISBN 0-8164-2637-6, 6338, HarpR). Har-Row.

Fowler, James W. Faith Development & Pastoral Care. LC 86-45904. 128p. 1987. pap. 7.95 (ISBN 0-8006-1739-8). Fortress.

George, Malcom F. Introduction to Christian Counseling. (Parchment Psychology Ser.). 64p. 1975. pap. 2.25 (ISBN 0-88428-038-1). Parchment Pr.

Gerkin, Charles V. The Living Human Document: Re-Visioning Pastoral Counseling in a Hermeneutical Mode. 224p. 1984. pap. 10.95 (ISBN 0-687-22372-5). Abingdon.

Ghezzi, Bert & Kinzer, Mark. Emotions As Resources: A Biblical & Pastoral Perspective. 110p. 1983. pap. 6.95 (ISBN 0-89283-158-8). Servant.

Gilbert, Marvin G. & Brock, Raymond T., eds. The Holy Spirit & Counseling: Theology & Theory. 248p. 1985. pap. 12.95 (ISBN 0-913573-41-8). Hendrickson MA.

Giles, James E. Pastoral Care & Counselling. pap. text ed. 10.95 (ISBN 0-311-72535-X). Casa Bautista.

Grant, Brian W. Reclaiming the Dream: Marriage Counseling in the Parish Context. 176p. (Orig.). 1986. pap. 9.95 (ISBN 0-687-35729-2). Abingdon.

Green, Calvin C. Counseling: With the Pastor & CPE Student in Mind. 1984. 12.95 (ISBN 0-533-05923-2). Vantage.

Haas, Harold I. Pastoral Counseling with People in Distress. LC 77-99316. 1969. pap. 6.95 (ISBN 0-570-03794-8, 12-2776). Concordia.

Hamilton, James D. Ministry of Pastoral Counseling. (Source Books for Ministers Ser). 1972. pap. 5.95 (ISBN 0-8010-4069-8). Baker Bk.

Hart, Archibald. Counseling the Depressed. 224p. 1987. 12.95 (ISBN 0-8499-0582-6). Word Bks.

Hartbauer, Roy E. Pastoral Care of the Handicapped. LC 82-74357. (Illus.). xvi, 183p. 1983. pap. 11.95 (ISBN 0-943872-87-1). Andrews Univ Pr.

Haugh, Kenneth & McKay, William J. Christian Caregiving: A Way of Life, Leaders Guide. LC 86-10931. 128p. (Orig.). 1986. pap. 8.95 (ISBN 0-8066-2224-5, 10-1104). Augsburg.

Hazelip, Harold. Questions People Ask Ministers Most. 1986. pap. 3.95 (ISBN 0-8010-4302-6). Baker Bk.

Hiltner, Seward. Pastoral Counseling. rev. ed. (Series AF). 1969. pap. 9.95 (ISBN 0-687-30317-6, Apex). Abingdon.

Hoff, Paul. Le Pasteur & la Cure d'Ame. Tr. of The Pastor As a Counselor. (Fr.). 240p. 1986. pap. 4.10 (ISBN 0-8297-0692-5). Life Pubs Intl.

Hoffman, John C. Ethical Confrontation in Counseling. LC 78-11799. 1979. lib. bdg. 10.50x (ISBN 0-226-34785-0). U of Chicago Pr.

Holifield, E. Brooks. A History of Pastoral Care in America: From Salvation to Self-Realization. 416p. (Orig.). 1983. pap. 16.95 (ISBN 0-687-17249-7). Abingdon.

Holinger, Paul C. Pastoral Care for Severe Emotional Disorders: Principles of Diagnosis & Treatment. LC 83-18670. 145p. 1985. text ed. 24.95x (ISBN 0-8290-1509-4). Irvington.

Howe, Reuel L. Miracle of Dialogue. 1963. pap. 6.95 (ISBN 0-86683-886-4, SP9, HarpR). Har-Row.

Hulme, William E. Pastoral Care & Counseling: Using the Unique Resources of the Christian Tradition. LC 80-67806. 160p. (Orig.). 1981. pap. 9.95 (ISBN 0-8066-1869-8, 10-4896). Augsburg.

Hurding, Roger F. Restoring the Image: An Introduction to Christian Caring & Counselling. 128p. 1986. pap. 6.50 (ISBN 0-85364-268-0). Attic Pr.

Huskey, Hyrum H., Jr. Counseling Skills for Church Leadership. 1980. pap. 6.00 (ISBN 0-8309-0295-3). Herald Hse.

Irwin, Paul B. The Care & Counseling of Youth in the Church. Clinebell, Howard J. & Stone, Howard W., eds. LC 74-26334. (Creative Pastoral Care & Counseling Ser.). 96p. 1975. pap. 4.50 (ISBN 0-8006-0552-7, 1-552). Fortress.

Jackson, Edgar. Parish Counseling. LC 84-45066. 221p. 1983. 25.00x (ISBN 0-87668-672-2). Aronson.

Jackson, Gordon E. Pastoral Care & Process Theology. LC 81-40159. 266p. (Orig.). 1981. lib. bdg. 29.75 (ISBN 0-8191-1710-2); pap. text ed. 12.75 (ISBN 0-8191-1711-0). U Pr of Amer.

Jakobcic, Cathy. Prayer Room Counselor's Handbook. 47p. 1983. pap. 2.25 (ISBN 0-88144-015-9). Christian Pub.

Johnson, Douglas W. Ministry with Young Couples: A Pastor's Planbook. 128p. (Orig.). 1985. pap. 6.95 (ISBN 0-687-27043-X). Abingdon.

Johnson, Emmett V. Work of the Pastoral Relations Committee. 128p. 1983. pap. 4.95 (ISBN 0-8170-0984-1). Judson.

Jones, James A. Counseling Principles for Christian Leaders. 5.95 (ISBN 0-89137-534-1). Quality Pubns.

Kaplan, Steven K. & Schoeneberg, Lynn A. New Approaches in Pastoral Counseling. 1987. text ed. 19.95 (ISBN 0-8290-1806-9). Irvington.

Kelley, Walter R. Clergy Say the Dardnest Things: Or How to Speak "Clergy-ese". (Illus.). 200p. (Orig.). 1987. pap. text ed. write for info. (ISBN 0-937071-01-3). Pyramid Designs Pr.

Kelsey, Morton T. Prophetic Ministry: The Psychology & Spirituality of Pastoral Care. 258p. 1982. 12.95 (ISBN 0-8245-0441-0). Crossroad NY.

Keyes, Paul T. Pastoral Presence & the Diocesan Priest. LC 78-22009. 142p. 1978. pap. 4.95 (ISBN 0-89571-004-8). Affirmation.

Kline, Donald L. One Flesh. 1985. 4.95 (ISBN 0-89536-730-0, 5814). CSS of Ohio.

Koehler, Walter J. Counseling & Confession. 1982. pap. 7.50 (ISBN 0-570-03849-9, 12-2804). Concordia.

Larsen, John A. When a Member of the Family Needs Counseling. LC 79-51274. (When Bk.). (Illus.). 1979. pap. 2.45 (ISBN 0-87029-147-5, 20234-1). Abbey.

Leas, Speed & Kittlaus, Paul. The Pastoral Counselor in Social Action. Clinebell, Howard J. & Stone, Howard W., eds. LC 80-8059. (Creative Pastoral Care & Counseling Ser.). 96p. (Orig.). 1981. pap. 4.50 (ISBN 0-8006-0565-9, 1-565). Fortress.

Lee, Ronald R. Clergy & Clients: The Practice of Pastoral Psychotherapy. 1980. 10.95 (ISBN 0-8164-0115-2, HarpR). Har-Row.

Lefebure, Marcus, ed. Conversation on Counseling Between a Doctor & a Priest. 2nd ed. 128p. pap. 6.95 (ISBN 0-317-31445-9) (ISBN 0-317-31446-7). Fortress.

--Conversations on Counselling. 126p. 1985. pap. 10.95 (ISBN 0-567-29120-0, Pub. by T&T Clark Ltd UK). Fortress.

--Human Experience & the Art of Counselling. 160p. 1985. pap. 9.95 (ISBN 0-567-29121-9, Pub. by T&T Clark Ltd UK). Fortress.

Lefevre, Perry & Schroeder, W. Widick, eds. Spiritual Nurture & Congregational Development. (Studies in Ministry & Parish Life). 186p. 1984. text ed. 19.95x (ISBN 0-913552-20-8); pap. text ed. 8.95x (ISBN 0-913552-23-2). Exploration Pr.

Leon, Jorge A. Psicologia Pastoral para Todos los Cristianos. LC 76-43121. (Span.). 181p. (Orig.). 1976. pap. 5.95 (ISBN 0-89922-020-7). Edit Caribe.

Lester, Andrew D. Pastoral Care with Children in Crisis. LC 84-21901. 144p. (Orig.). 1985. pap. 9.95 (ISBN 0-664-24598-6). Westminster.

Loyola College, Pastoral & Counseling Faculty. Pastoral Counseling. (Illus.). 352p. 1982. 29.67 (ISBN 0-13-652867-8). P-H.

MacDonald, W. G. Prison & Pastoral Letters. 96p. 1967. pap. 0.75 (ISBN 0-88243-792-5, 02-0792). Gospel Pub.

Mack, Wayne. Homework Manual for Biblical Counseling: Family & Marital Problems, Vol. 2. 1980. pap. 3.95 (ISBN 0-87552-357-9). Presby & Reformed.

--Homework Manual for Biblical Counseling: Personal & Interpersonal Problems, Vol. 1. 1979. pap. 5.50 (ISBN 0-87552-356-0). Presby & Reformed.

Malgo, Wim. Biblical Counseling. 4.95 (ISBN 0-937422-18-5). Midnight Call.

Malony, H. Newton. Clergy Malpractice. Needham, Thomas L. & Southaud, Samuel, eds. LC 85-31466. 192p. (Orig.). 1986. pap. 12.95 (ISBN 0-664-24591-9). Westminster.

Martin, Grant. Counseling in Cases of Family Violence & Abuse. 192p. 1987. 12.95 (ISBN 0-8499-0587-7). Word Bks.

Mason, Robert L., et al. The Clergyman & the Psychiatrist: When to Refer. LC 77-22597. 248p. 1978. 20.95x (ISBN 0-88229-260-9). Nelson-Hall.

Metcalfe, J. C. Bible & Counselling. 1966. pap. 2.95 (ISBN 0-87508-911-9). Chr Lit.

Miller, William R. & Jackson-Miller, Kathleen A. Practical Psychology for Pastors. (Illus.). 400p. 1985. 30.95 (ISBN 0-13-692807-2). P-H.

Mitchell, Kenneth R. & Anderson, Herbert. All Our Losses, All Our Griefs: Resources for Pastoral Care. LC 83-19851. 180p. (Orig.). 1983. pap. 8.95 (ISBN 0-664-24493-9). Westminster.

More Than "I Do". Pastor's Resource Book for Premarital Counseling. (Orig.). 1983. pap. 4.95 (ISBN 0-8341-0865-8). Beacon Hill.

Mundfrom, Gerald F. The Depressed Christian. 115p. (Orig.). 1983. 2.50 (ISBN 0-318-19335-3). Mercy & Truth.

--Purged. 175p. Date not set. 5.00 (ISBN 0-318-19336-1). Mercy & Truth.

Murphy, Carol. The Ministry of Counseling. 1983. pap. 2.50x (ISBN 0-87574-067-7, 067). Pendle Hill.

Murphy-O'Connor, Jerome. Becoming Human Together: The Pastoral anthropology of St. Paul. (Good News Studies: Vol. 2). 224p. 1982. pap. 8.95 (ISBN 0-89453-075-5). M Glazier.

Narramore, Clyde M. Counseling Youth. new ed. 128p. (Orig.). 1974. pap. 5.95 (ISBN 0-310-29891-1, 12229P). Zondervan.

--Psychology of Counseling. 13.95 (ISBN 0-310-29930-6, 10409). Zondervan.

Oates, Wayne E. Introduction to Pastoral Counseling. 1959. 14.95 (ISBN 0-8054-2404-0). Broadman.

--Pastoral Care & Counseling in Grief & Separation. Clinebell, Howard J. & Stone, Howard W., eds. LC 75-13048. (Creative Pastoral Care & Counseling Ser.). 96p. 1976. pap. 4.50 (ISBN 0-8006-0554-3, 1-554). Fortress.

--Pastoral Counseling. LC 73-19719. 240p. 1982. pap. 8.95 (ISBN 0-664-24405-X). Westminster.

--Pastor's Handbook, Vol. 1. LC 79-28639. (Christian Care Bks.). 120p. 1980. pap. 7.95 (ISBN 0-664-24300-2). Westminster.

Oates, Wayne E. & Oates, Charles E. People in Pain: Guidelines for Pastoral Care. LC 85-5403. 152p. 1985. pap. 8.95 (ISBN 0-664-24674-5). Westminster.

O'Connor, Brian P., et al, eds. The Pastoral Role in Caring for the Dying & Bereaved: Pragmatic & Ecumenical. LC 86-545. (Foundation of Thanatology Ser.: Vol. 7). 245p. 1986. lib. bdg. 39.95 (ISBN 0-275-92153-0, C2153). Praeger.

Oden, Thomas C. Crisis Ministries. 224p. 1985. 19.95 (ISBN 0-8245-0709-6). Crossroad NY.

Pastoral Care Office, Reorganized Church of Jesus Christ of Latter Day Saints. Visiting: A Pastoral Care Ministry. 186p. (Orig.). 1985. pap. 10.25 (ISBN 0-8309-0429-8). Herald Hse.

Patton, John. Pastoral Counseling: A Ministry of the Church. 240p. (Orig.). 1983. pap. 12.95 (ISBN 0-687-30314-1). Abingdon.

Pazhayatil, Harshajan. Counseling & Health Care. LC 76-29068. 385p. 1977. pap. 8.00 (ISBN 0-8199-0623-9). Franciscan Herald.

Peterseon, Evelyn H. Who Cares? A Handbook of Christian Counselling. 181p. 1982. pap. text ed. 6.95 (ISBN 0-85364-272-9). Attic Pr.

Peterson, Eugene H. Working the Angles: A Trigonometry for Pastoral Work. 266p. (Orig.). 1987. pap. 7.95 (ISBN 0-8028-0265-6). Eerdmans.

Peterson, Evelyn. Who Cares? A Handbook of Christian Counselling. LC 82-60447. (Illus.). 192p. 1982. pap. 7.95 (ISBN 0-8192-1317-9). Morehouse.

Peterson, Thomas D. Epoxy Epistles: Letters That Stick. Sherer, Michael L., ed. (Orig.). 1987. pap. 3.95 (ISBN 0-89536-868-4, 7827). CSS of Ohio.

Platt, Nancy V. Pastoral Care to the Cancer Patient. 100p. 1980. pap. 9.75x (ISBN 0-398-04051-6). C C Thomas.

Premoe, Deborah & Premoe, David. Multiple Faith Relationships. (Pastoral Care Office Pamphlet Ser.). 84p. 1984. pap. text ed. 5.00 (ISBN 0-8309-0390-9). Herald Hse.

Propst, Rebecca L. Psychotherapy in a Religious Framework. LC 86-27582. 208p. 1987. text ed. 29.95 (ISBN 0-89885-350-8). Human Sci Pr.

Quesnell, John Q. The Message of Christ & the Counselor. (Synthesis Ser). 1975. 2.00 (ISBN 0-8199-0534-8). Franciscan Herald.

Ramshaw, Elaine. Ritual & Pastoral Care. LC 85-45487. (Theology and Pastoral Care Ser.). 128p. 1987. pap. 7.95 (ISBN 0-8006-1738-X). Fortress.

Sandford, John & Sandford, Paula. The Transformation of the Inner Man. LC 82-72007. 432p. 1986. pap. 6.95 (ISBN 0-932081-13-4). Victory Hse.

Schroeder, Theodore W. Pastor's Counseling Manual for Ministry to Those Who Must Sustain a Loved One in Crisis. 1981. pap. 2.75 (ISBN 0-570-08250-1, 12YY2922). Concordia.

Seamands, David A. Healing of Memories. 156p. 1985. text ed. 11.95 (ISBN 0-89693-532-9); pap. 6.95 (ISBN 0-89693-169-2). Victor Bks.

Smith, Harold I. Pastoral Care for Single Parents. 158p. 1982. pap. 3.95 (ISBN 0-8341-0782-1). Beacon Hill.

Soulen, Richard N. Care for the Dying. LC 74-19968. 120p. 1975. pap. 6.50 (ISBN 0-8042-1098-5). John Knox.

Spurgeon, C. H. Words of Counsel for Christian Workers. 160p. 1985. pap. 2.95. Pilgrim Pubns.

Stone, Howard W. The Caring Church: A Guide for Lay Pastoral Care. LC 82-48415. 116p. (Orig.). 1983. pap. 6.95 (ISBN 0-06-067695-7, RD420, HarpR). Har-Row.

--Crisis Counseling. Clinebell, Howard J., ed. LC 75-13047. (Creative Pastoral Care & Counseling Ser.). 96p. (Orig.). 1976. pap. 5.95 (ISBN 0-8006-0553-5, 1-553). Fortress.

--Using Behavioral Methods in Pastoral Counseling. Clinebell, Howard J. & Stone, Howard E., eds. LC 79-2287. (Creative Pastoral Care & Counseling Ser.). 96p. 1980. pap. 0.50 (ISBN 0-8006-0563-2, 1-563). Fortress.

Stone, James, ed. And He Gave Some Pastors Teachers. 324p. (Orig.). 1986. pap. text ed. 9.95 (ISBN 0-934942-61-7, 4052). White Wing Pub.

Strom, Kay M. Helping Women in Crisis: A Handbook for People-Helpers. 208p. 1986. pap. 7.95 (ISBN 0-310-33641-4, 11716P). Zondervan.

Switzer, David L. The Minister as Crisis Counselor. rev. ed. 304p. 1986. pap. 13.95 (ISBN 0-687-26954-7). Abingdon.

Tapley, William. Happily Ever after Is No Accident. Sherer, Michael L., ed. (Orig.). 1987. pap. 2.75 leaders guide (ISBN 0-89536-862-5, 7821); pap. 3.45 couples bk. (ISBN 0-89536-863-3, 7822). CSS of Ohio.

Teikmanis, Arthur L. Preaching & Pastoral Care. LC 64-23551. pap. 36.00 (2026863). Bks Demand UMI.

Ter Linden, Nico. In the Lord's Boarding House: Stories of Caring for Others. Mitchell, Kenneth R., tr. from Dutch. 128p. (Orig.). 1985. pap. text ed. 7.95 (ISBN 0-687-18971-3). Abingdon.

A Theology of Christian Counseling: More Than Redemption. (A Jay Adams Library). 1986. pap. 11.95 (ISBN 0-310-51101-1, 12122P). Zondervan.

Thrasher, Kenneth. The Complex Ministry of Rural Pastorate. 1984. pap. 5.95 (ISBN 0-89957-054-2). AMG Pubs.

Tobin, Eamon. Help for Making Difficult Decisions. 32p. 1987. pap. 1.50 (ISBN 0-89243-267-5). Liguori Pubns.

Trobisch, Walter. I Loved a Girl. LC 75-12281. 128p. 1975. pap. 6.95 (ISBN 0-06-068443-7, RD 352, HarpR). Har-Row.

Turner, F. Bernadette. God-Centered Therapy. 1968. pap. 4.95 (ISBN 0-8315-0182-0). Speller.

Underwood, Ralph L. Empathy & Confrontation in Pastoral Care. LC 85-47722. (Theology & Pastoral Care Ser.). 128p. 1986. pap. 7.50 (ISBN 0-8006-1737-1). Fortress.

Van Kaam, Adrian. The Art of Existential Counseling. 6.95 (ISBN 0-87193-044-7). Dimension Bks.

Vaughan, Richard P. Basic Skills for Christian Counselors: An Introduction for Pastoral Ministers. 192p. (Orig.). 1987. pap. 8.95 (ISBN 0-8091-2857-8). Paulist Pr.

Virgo, Leslie, ed. First Aid in Pastoral Care. 220p. 1986. pap. 9.95 (ISBN 0-567-29122-7, Pub. by T & T Clark Ltd UK). Fortress.

Ward, Waylon O. The Bible in Counseling. 1977. pap. 12.95 (ISBN 0-8024-0623-8). Moody.

Watts, P. Mark. Living Through Your Separation or Divorce. Sherer, Michael L., ed. (Orig.). 1987. pap. 2.25 (ISBN 0-89536-864-1, 7823). CSS of Ohio.

Wicks, Robert J., et al. Clinical Handbook of Pastoral Counseling. 592p. (Orig.). 1985. 22.95 (ISBN 0-8091-0350-8); pap. 14.95 (ISBN 0-8091-2687-7). Paulist Pr.

Williams, R. T. Pastor & People. pap. 2.95 (ISBN 0-686-12898-2). Schmul Pub Co.

Wimberly, Edward P. Pastoral Counseling & Spiritual Values: A Black Point of View. LC 81-10918. 176p. (Orig.). 1982. pap. 7.75 (ISBN 0-687-30336-2). Abingdon.

Wynn, J. C. Family Therapy in Pastoral Ministry. LC 81-47840. 192p. 1982. 12.00 (ISBN 0-06-069703-2, HarpR). Har-Row.

PASTORAL COUNSELING (JUDAISM)

Faber, Heije. Pastoral Care in the Modern Hospital. De Waal, Hugo, tr. LC 70-168632. 160p. 1972. 10.95 (ISBN 0-664-20922-X). Westminster.

Katz, Robert L. Pastoral Care & the Jewish Tradition: Empathic Process & Religious Counseling. LC 84-47925. (Theology & Pastoral Care Ser.). 128p. 1984. pap. 7.95 (ISBN 0-8006-1731-2). Fortress.

Kemp, Charles F. The Caring Pastor: An Introduction to Pastoral Counseling in the Local Church. LC 85-3994. (Orig.). 1985. pap. 9.95 (ISBN 0-687-35548-6). Abingdon.

McKenzie, John G. Nervous Disorders & Religion: A Study of Souls in the Making. LC 79-8719. 183p. 1981. Repr. of 1951 ed. lib. bdg. 22.50x (ISBN 0-313-22192-8, MCND). Greenwood.

Rothstein, Joseph, ed. Meeting Life's Challenges with Pastoral Counseling. 1986. 14.95 (ISBN 0-533-06612-3). Vantage.

PASTORAL MEDICINE

Catholic Health Association Staff. The Ministry of Healing: Readings in the Catholic Health Care Ministry. LC 81-12201. 120p. 1981. pap. 7.50 (ISBN 0-686-85771-2). Cath Health.

Dayringer, Richard, ed. Pastor & Patient. LC 80-70247. 240p. 1981. 25.00x (ISBN 0-87668-437-1). Aronson.

Faber, Heije. Pastoral Care in the Modern Hospital. De Waal, Hugo, tr. LC 70-168632. 160p. 1972. 10.95 (ISBN 0-664-20922-X). Westminster.

Fath, Gerald. Health Care Ministries. 2nd ed. LC 80-12620. 1980. pap. 8.50 (ISBN 0-87125-061-6). Cath Health.

Hesch, John B. Clinical Pastoral Care for Hospitalized Children & Their Families. 224p. 1987. pap. 9.95 (ISBN 0-8091-2871-3). Paulist Pr.

McGeehan, Jude J. Ministry to the Sick & Dying. (Synthesis Ser.). 1981. 1.75 (ISBN 0-8199-0836-3). Franciscan Herald.

O'Connor, Brian P., et al, eds. The Pastoral Role in Caring for the Dying & Bereaved: Pragmatic & Ecumenical. LC 86-545. (Foundation of Thanatology Ser.: Vol. 7). 245p. 1986. lib. bdg. 39.95 (ISBN 0-275-92153-0, C2153). Praeger.

Pastoral Care of the Sick: Rites of Anointing & Viaticum. 1983. deluxe ed. 19.95; text ed. 13.95 (ISBN 0-8146-1287-3). Liturgical Pr.

Patterson, Robert. Pastoral Health Care: Understanding the Church's Healing Ministers. LC 83-1948. 30p. 1983. pap. 0.90 (ISBN 0-87125-080-2). Cath Health.

Pazhayatil, Harshajan. Counseling & Health Care. LC 76-29068. 385p. 1977. pap. 8.00 (ISBN 0-8199-0623-9). Franciscan Herald.

Ramshaw, Elaine. Ritual & Pastoral Care. LC 85-45487. (Theology and Pastoral Care Ser.). 128p. 1987. pap. 7.95 (ISBN 0-8006-1738-X). Fortress.

Smith, David H. Health & Medicine in Anglican Tradition. 140p. 1986. 15.95x (ISBN 0-8245-0716-9). Crossroad NY.

Steiner, Rudolf. Pastoral Medicine. Hahn, Gladys, tr. from Ger. Tr. of Pastoral-Medizinischer Kurs. 1987. 20.00 (ISBN 0-88010-250-0); pap. 9.95 (ISBN 0-88010-253-5). Anthroposophic.

Ter Linden, Nico. In the Lord's Boarding House: Stories of Caring for Others. Mitchell, Kenneth R., tr. from Dutch. 128p. (Orig.). 1985. pap. text ed. 7.95 (ISBN 0-687-18971-3). Abingdon.

Weil, Andrew. Health & Healing: Understanding Conventional & Alternative Medicine. 1983. 13.95 (ISBN 0-395-34430-1). HM.

Wheelock, Robert D. Policies & Procedures for the Pastoral Care Department. LC 76-9660. 1977. pap. 4.00 (ISBN 0-87125-036-5). Cath Health.

PASTORAL OFFICE AND WORK

see Pastoral Theology

PASTORAL PRAYERS

Here are entered works containing the formal or general prayers used in public worship.

Aelred of Rievaulx. Treatises & the Pastoral Prayer. pap. 5.00 (ISBN 0-87907-902-9). Cistercian Pubns.

Currie, David M. Come, Let Us Worship God: A Handbook of Prayers for Leaders of Worship. LC 77-6808. 132p. 1977. softcover 4.25 (ISBN 0-664-24757-1). Westminster.

Dubois, W. E. B. Prayers for Dark People. Aptheker, Herbert, ed. LC 80-12234. 88p. 1980. lib. bdg. 12.00x (ISBN 0-87023-302-5); pap. 6.95 (ISBN 0-87023-303-3). U of Mass Pr.

McNulty, James F. Words of Power. LC 83-2514. 226p. (Orig.). 1983. pap. 8.95 (ISBN 0-8189-0442-9). Alba.

Morgan, Campbell G. The Westminister Pulpits, 10 vols. 1983. Set. deluxe ed. 99.95 (ISBN 0-8010-6155-5). Baker Bk.

Spurgeon, C. H. Pastor in Prayer. 192p. Date not set. pap. write for info. Pilgrim Pubns.

PASTORAL PSYCHOLOGY

see also Pastoral Counseling; Pastoral Medicine

Arnold, William V. Introduction to Pastoral Care. LC 81-16092. 222p. 1982. pap. 10.95 (ISBN 0-664-24400-9). Westminster.

Augsburger, David W. Anger & Assertiveness in Pastoral Care. Clinebell, Howard J. & Stone, Howard W., eds. LC 78-14660. (Creative Pastoral Care & Counseling Ser.). 96p. 1979. pap. 0.50 (ISBN 0-8006-0562-4, 1-562). Fortress.

--Pastoral Counseling Across Cultures. LC 86-13343. 408p. 1986. 21.95 (ISBN 0-664-21272-7). Westminster.

Batson, Horace W. & Batson, Gary, eds. Overcoming Stress: Everything You Ever Need to Know! 100p. (Orig.). 1987. pap. 9.95 (ISBN 0-938503-00-6). Welstar Pubns.

Benner, David G. Baker Encyclopedia of Psychology. 1376p. 1985. text ed. 39.95 (ISBN 0-8010-0865-4). Baker Bk.

Bier, W. C., ed. Human Life: Problems of Birth, of Living, & of Dying. LC 77-71939. (Pastoral Psychology Ser.: No. 9). 1977. 20.00 (ISBN 0-8232-1025-1). Fordham.

--Personality & Sexual Problems in Pastoral Psychology. LC 62-16224. (Pastoral Psychology Ser: No. 1). xvi, 256p. 1964. 20.00 (ISBN 0-8232-0585-1). Fordham.

--Privacy: A Vanishing Value? LC 79-56138. (Pastoral Psychology Ser.: No. 10). xiv, 398p. 1980. 25.00 (ISBN 0-8232-1044-8). Fordham.

Bier, William C., ed. Woman in Modern Life. LC 68-20626. (Pastoral Psychology Ser.: No. 5). x, 278p. 1968. 20.00 (ISBN 0-8232-0800-1). Fordham.

Capps, Donald. Pastoral Care: A Thematic Approach. LC 78-15093. (Illus.). 162p. 1979. softcover 8.95 (ISBN 0-664-24222-7). Westminster.

Cavanagh, Michael E. The Effective Minister. 160p. (Orig.). 1986. 14.95 (ISBN 0-06-254210-9, HarpR). Har-Row.

Goldbrunner, Josef. Realization: The Anthropology of Pastoral Care. 1966. 18.95 (ISBN 0-268-00227-4). U of Notre Dame Pr.

Kelsey, Morton. Christianity As Psychology: The Healing Power of the Christian Message. LC 85-22864. 114p. (Orig.). 1986. pap. 7.95 (ISBN 0-8066-2194-X, 10-1184). Augsburg.

Lee, Ronald R. Clergy & Clients: The Practice of Pastoral Psychotherapy. 1980. 10.95 (ISBN 0-8164-0115-2, HarpR). Har-Row.

McKee, William. How to Reach Out to Inactive Catholics: A Practical Parish Program. 40p. 1982. pap. 6.95 (ISBN 0-89243-155-5). Liguori Pubns.

McKenzie, John G. Nervous Disorders & Religion: A Study of Souls in the Making. LC 79-8719. 183p. 1981. Repr. of 1951 ed. lib. bdg. 22.50x (ISBN 0-313-22192-8, MCND). Greenwood.

Malony, H. Newton. Clergy Malpractice. Needham, Thomas L. & Southaud, Samuel, eds. LC 85-31466. 192p. (Orig.). 1986. pap. 12.95 (ISBN 0-664-24591-9). Westminster.

Mason, Robert L., et al. The Clergyman & the Psychiatrist: When to Refer. LC 77-22597. 248p. 1978. 20.95x (ISBN 0-88229-260-9). Nelson-Hall.

Meier, Paul D., et al. Introduction to Psychology & Counseling: Christian Perspectives & Applications. LC 82-70462. 432p. 1982. 21.95 (ISBN 0-8010-6128-8). Baker Bk.

New York Academy Of Medicine. Ministry & Medicine in Human Relations. facs. ed. Galdston, Iago, ed. LC 77-142682. (Essay Index Reprint Ser). 1955. 17.00 (ISBN 0-8369-2120-8). Ayer Co Pubs.

Oates, Wayne E. The Christian Pastor. Rev. 3rd ed. LC 82-4933. 298p. 1982. pap. 9.95 (ISBN 0-664-24372-X). Westminster.

--Pastor's Handbook, Vol. II. LC 79-28639. (Christian Care Bks.). 120p. 1980. pap. 7.95 (ISBN 0-664-24330-4). Westminster.

--The Religious Care of the Psychiatric Patient. LC 78-18454. 252p. 1978. 13.95 (ISBN 0-664-21365-0). Westminster.

Polcino, Anna, ed. Intimacy: Issues of Emotional Living in an Age of Stress for Clergy & Religious. LC 78-104617. 1978. pap. 5.00 (ISBN 0-89571-003-X). Affirmation.

Propst, Rebecca L. Psychotherapy in a Religious Framework. LC 86-27582. 208p. 1987. text ed. 29.95 (ISBN 0-89885-350-8). Human Sci Pr.

Pruyser, Paul W. The Minister As Diagnostician: Personal Problems in Pastoral Perspective. LC 76-8922. 144p. 1976. pap. 7.95 (ISBN 0-664-24123-9). Westminster.

Randall, Robert L. Putting the Pieces Together: Guidance from a Pastoral Psychologist. 80p. (Orig.). 1986. pap. 4.95 (ISBN 0-8298-0583-4). Pilgrim NY.

Rassieur, Charles L. The Problem Clergymen Don't Talk About. LC 75-40306. 156p. 1976. pap. 5.95 (ISBN 0-664-24790-3). Westminster.

Stokes, Allison. Ministry after Freud. (Illus.). 256p. 1985. pap. 10.95 (ISBN 0-8298-0569-9). Pilgrim NY.

Swain, Bernard F. Liberating Leadership: Practical Styles of Pastoral Ministry. 96p. (Orig.). 1986. pap. 6.95 (ISBN 0-86683-483-4, HarpR). Har-Row.

Tournier, Paul. The Person Reborn. LC 75-12283. 256p. 1975. (HarpR); pap. 1.95 (ISBN 0-06-068377-5, RD-327). Har-Row.

PASTORAL THEOLOGY

see also Church Attendance; Church Work; City Clergy; Clergy; Communication (Theology); Pastoral Counseling; Pastoral Medicine; Pastoral Psychology; Visitations (Church Work)

Adams, J. Journal of Pastoral Practice, Vol. I, No. 2. 1978. 3.50 (ISBN 0-87552-024-3). Presby & Reformed.

Adams, Jay E. Communicating with Twentieth Century Man. 41p. 1979. pap. 1.95 (ISBN 0-87552-008-1). Presby & Reformed.

--Journal of Pastoral Practice, Vol. IV, No. II. pap. 5.00 (ISBN 0-8010-0169-2). Baker Bk.

--Journal of Pastoral Practice, Vol. V, No. 1. 1981. pap. 5.00 (ISBN 0-87552-035-9). Presby & Reformed.

--Journal of Pastoral Practice, Vol. IV, No. 1. 1979. 5.00 (ISBN 0-87552-031-6). Presby & Reformed.

--Journal of Pastoral Practice, Vol. V, No.1. 1981. pap. 5.00 (ISBN 0-8010-0178-1). Baker Bk.

--Journal of Pastoral Practice, Vol. I, No. 2. 1977. pap. 3.50 (ISBN 0-8010-0125-0). Baker Bk.

--Journal of Pastoral Practice, Vol. V, No. 2. 1981. pap. 5.00 (ISBN 0-87552-036-7). Presby & Reformed.

--Journal of Pastoral Practice, Vol. V, No. 2 1981. pap. 5.00 (ISBN 0-8010-0183-8). Baker Bk.

--Journal of Pastoral Practice, Vol. IV, No. 3. 1981. pap. 5.00 (ISBN 0-87552-033-2). Presby & Reformed.

--Journal of Pastoral Practice, Vol. V, No 3. 1982. pap. 5.00 (ISBN 0-8010-0186-2). Baker Bk.

--Journal of Pastoral Practice, Vol. IV, No. 4. 1981. pap. 5.00 (ISBN 0-87552-034-0). Presby & Reformed.

--Shepherding God's Flock: A Handbook on Pastoral Ministry, Counseling, & Leadership. (A Jay Adams Library). 544p. 1986. pap. 14.95 (ISBN 0-310-51071-6, 12119P). Zondervan.

--Shepherding God's Flock: Pastoral Leadership, Vol. III. 1975. pap. 4.75 (ISBN 0-87552-057-X). Presby & Reformed.

Anderson, Ray S. Theological Foundations for Ministry. LC 78-13613. 1978. pap. 8.95 (ISBN 0-8028-1776-9). Eerdmans.

Arnold, William V. Introduction to Pastoral Care. LC 81-16092. 222p. 1982. pap. 10.95 (ISBN 0-664-24400-9). Westminster.

Augsburger, David W. Pastoral Counseling Across Cultures. LC 86-13343. 408p. 1986. 21.95 (ISBN 0-664-21272-7). Westminster.

Barclay, Mark. Seven Bible Ways to Properly Relate to Your Pastor. 32p. 1982. pap. 2.25 (ISBN 0-88144-024-8). Christian Pub.

Bausch, William J. The Christian Parish: Whispers of the Risen Christ. 232p. 1981. pap. 7.95 (ISBN 0-89622-146-6). Twenty-Third.

Beall, James L. & Barber, Marjorie. Your Pastor, Your Shepherd. LC 77-77579. 1977. pap. 4.95 (ISBN 0-88270-216-5). Bridge Pub.

Biebel, David B. & Lawrence, Howard W., eds. Pastors Are People Too. LC 86-3835. 205p. (Orig.). 1986. pap. 5.95 (ISBN 0-8307-1102-3, 5418654). Regal.

Biersdorf, John E. Healing of Purpose: God's Call to Discipleship. 192p. (Orig.). 1985. pap. 11.95 (ISBN 0-687-16741-8). Abingdon.

Boff, Clodovis. Feet-on-the-Ground Theology: Pastoral Ministry in Western Brazil. Berryman, Phillip, tr. from Port. 288p. (Orig.). 1987. 19.95 (ISBN 0-88344-579-4); pap. 8.95 (ISBN 0-88344-554-9). Orbis Bks.

Borchert, Gerald L. & Lester, Andrew D., eds. Spiritual Dimensions of Pastoral Care: Witness to the Ministry of Wayne E. Oates. LC 84-19581. 152p. (Orig.). 1985. pap. 11.95 (ISBN 0-664-24562-5). Westminster.

Boshtchanovsky, Basil. Uroki po Pastirskomu Bogosloviju. Tr. of Studies in Pastoral Theology. 100p. 1961. pap. text ed. 5.00 (ISBN 0-317-30267-1). Holy Trinity.

Brister, C. W. El Cuidado Pastoral De la Iglesia. Tinao, D., et al, trs. Orig. Title: Pastoral Care in the Church. (Span.). 226p. 1982. pap. 5.50 (ISBN 0-311-42040-0). Casa Bautista.

--Pastoral Care in the Church. LC 64-19497. 1977. pap. 6.00 (ISBN 0-06-061051-4, RD 222, HarpR). Har-Row.

Browning, Don S. The Moral Context of Pastoral Care. LC 76-5858. 144p. 1983. pap. 8.95 (ISBN 0-664-24483-1). Westminster.

Brueggemann, Walter. The Prophetic Imagination. LC 78-54546. 128p. 1978. pap. 5.95 (ISBN 0-8006-1337-6, 1-1337). Fortress.

C & MA Home Department Board Staff. The Pastor's Handbook. 102p. 3.95 (ISBN 0-87509-118-0). Chr Pubns.

Calian, Carnegie S. Today's Pastor in Tomorrow's World. Rev. ed. LC 82-7114. 164p. 1982. pap. 8.95 (ISBN 0-664-24426-2). Westminster.

Campbell, Alastair V. Professionalism & Pastoral Care. LC 84-48710. (Theology & Pastoral Care Ser.). 128p. 1985. pap. 7.95 (ISBN 0-8006-1733-9, 1-1733). Fortress.

Capon, Robert F. An Offering of Uncles: The Priesthood of Adam & the Shape of the World. (The Crossroad Paperback Ser.). 192p. 1982. pap. 5.95 (ISBN 0-8245-0422-4). Crossroad NY.

Capps, Donald. Pastoral Care: A Thematic Approach. LC 78-15093. (Illus.). 162p. 1979. softcover 8.95 (ISBN 0-664-24222-7). Westminster.

--Pastoral Care & Hermeneutics. LC 84-47909. (Theology & Pastoral Care Ser.). 128p. 1984. pap. 7.95 (ISBN 0-8006-1732-0). Fortress.

Cardinal Joseph Bernardin. The Ministry of Service. 40p. 1986. pap. 1.25 (ISBN 0-8146-1485-X). Liturgical Pr.

Chambers, Oswald. Workmen of God. 1965. pap. 2.95 (ISBN 0-87508-131-2). Chr Lit.

Chemitz, Martin. Ministry, Word, & Sacraments: An Enchiridion. Poellot, Luther, tr. 1981. pap. 17.50 (ISBN 0-570-03295-4, 15-2730). Concordia.

Churches Alive, Inc. Staff. Growing by Discipling Pastor's Handbook. rev. ed. (Illus.). 150p. 1980. pap. text ed. 9.95 (ISBN 0-934396-09-4). Churches Alive.

--Growth Group Leader's Guide. rev. ed. LC 80-52536. (Illus.). 110p. 1980. pap. 7.95 (ISBN 0-934396-10-8). Churches Alive.

Cobb, John B., Jr. Theology & Pastoral Care. Clinebell, Howard J. & Stone, Howard W., eds. LC 76-7862. (Creative Pastoral Care & Counseling Ser.). 96p. 1977. pap. 4.50 (ISBN 0-8006-0557-8, 1-557). Fortress.

Colligan, John & Colligan, Kathleen. Evenings for Parish Ministers: Leader's Guide. LC 84-60266. 53p. (Orig.). 1984. pap. text ed. 2.95 (ISBN 0-911905-20-0); wkbk. 1.95 (ISBN 0-911905-16-2). Past & Mat Rene Ctr.

Colligan, John, et al. Mission & Ministry: A Vision for the Church. LC 83-62365. 84p. (Orig.). 1983. pap. text ed. 3.95 (ISBN 0-911905-07-3). Past & Mat Rene Ctr.

The Continuing Formation of Priests (Growing in Wisdom, Age & Grace) 44p. 1984. pap. 2.50 (ISBN 1-55586-954-8). US Catholic.

Cothen, Joe H. Equipped for Good Work: A Guide for Pastors. LC 80-37964. 336p. 1981. 14.95 (ISBN 0-88289-271-1). Pelican.

Criswell, W. A. Criswell's Guidebook for Pastors. LC 79-7735. 1980. 12.95 (ISBN 0-8054-2536-5). Broadman.

Davie, Peter. Pastoral Care & the Parish. 102p. 1984. 24.95x (ISBN 0-631-13225-2); pap. 8.95x (ISBN 0-631-13226-0). Basil Blackwell.

Dobbins, Gaines S. Ministering Church. LC 60-9530. 1960. 9.95 (ISBN 0-8054-2505-5). Broadman.

Duncombe, Alice E. Handbook for Telephone Ministry. Rev. ed. 7.95 (ISBN 0-89985-110-X). Christ Nations.

Emswiler, James P. & Moore, Joseph. Handbook for Peer Ministry. LC 81-84351. 128p. (Orig.). 1982. pap. 4.95 (ISBN 0-8091-2427-0). Paulist Pr.

Fenhagen, James C. More Than Wanderers: Spiritual Disciplines for Christian Ministry. 1985. pap. 7.95 (ISBN 0-86683-978-X, HarpR). Har-Row.

--Mutual Ministry: New Vitality for the Local Church. 1986. 7.95 (ISBN 0-8164-0332-5, HarpR). Har-Row.

Forrester, Duncan B. Theology & Practice. 1986. 32.00x (Pub. by Hesketh UK). State Mutual Bk.

Gedde, Palmer. One Plus One Equals. Kujath, Mentor, ed. 1979. pap. 4.95 (ISBN 0-8100-0103-9, 12-1712). Northwest Pub.

Gerkin, Charles V. Widening the Horizons: Pastoral Responses to a Fragmented Society. LC 86-7832. 154p. (Orig.). 1986. pap. 11.95 (ISBN 0-664-24037-2). Westminster.

Gibbons, Sherry, et al. Evenings of Joy & Inspiration for Parish Leaders. LC 83-62197. 64p. (Orig.). 1983. pap. text ed. 2.95 (ISBN 0-911905-08-1). Past & Mat Rene Ctr.

Hall, David D. The Faithful Shepherd: A History of the New England Ministry in the Seventeenth Century. 320p. 1974. pap. 3.45x (ISBN 0-393-00719-7, Norton Lib). Norton.

--The Faithful Shepherd: A History of the New England Ministry in the Seventeenth Century. LC 72-81326. (Institute for Early American History & Culture Ser.). xvi, 301p. 1972. 27.50x (ISBN 0-8078-1193-9). U of NC Pr.

Hall, Douglas J. God & Human Suffering: An Excercise in the Theology of the Cross. LC 86-7964. 224p. 1986. text ed. 16.95 (ISBN 0-8066-2223-7, 10-2640). Augsburg.

Hamilton, Neill Q. Maturing in the Christian Life: A Pastor's Guide. LC 83-20661. 192p. (Orig.). 1984. pap. 10.95 (ISBN 0-664-24515-3). Westminster.

Haugh, Kenneth & McKay, William J. Christian Caregiving: A Way of Life, Leaders Guide. LC 86-10931. 128p. (Orig.). 1986. pap. 8.95 (ISBN 0-8066-2224-5, 10-1104). Augsburg.

Heft, James. John XXII & Papal Taching Authority. (Texts & Studies in Religion: Vol. 27). 282p. 1986. lib. bdg. 49.95x (ISBN 0-88946-815-X). E Mellen.

Hesch, John B. Clinical Pastoral Care for Hospitalized Children & Their Families. 224p. 1987. pap. 9.95 (ISBN 0-8091-2871-3). Paulist Pr.

Hightower, J. A., Jr. El Cuidado Pastoral: Desde la Cuna Hasta la Tumba. Morales, Edgar, tr. from Eng. Tr. of Caring for Folks from Birth to Death. (Span.). 192p. (Orig.). 1986. pap. 5.75 (ISBN 0-311-11045-2). Casa Bautista.

Hills. Pastoral Theology. kivar 6.95 (ISBN 0-686-12899-0). Schmul Pub Co.

Hiscox, Edward T. Star Book for Ministers. rev. ed. 1967. 7.95 (ISBN 0-8170-0167-0). Judson.

Holifield, E. Brooks. A History of Pastoral Care in America: From Salvation to Self-Realization. 416p. (Orig.). 1983. pap. 16.95 (ISBN 0-687-17249-7). Abingdon.

Holmes, Urban T., III. Ministry & Imagination. 288p. 1981. pap. 5.50 (ISBN 0-8164-2351-2, HarpR). Har-Row.

--Spirituality for Ministry. LC 81-47839. 244p. 1982. 14.45 (ISBN 0-06-064008-1, HarpR). Har-Row.

Hulme, William E., et al, eds. Pastors in Ministry: Guidelines for Seven Critical Issues. LC 85-1213. 176p. (Orig.). 1985. pap. 9.95 (ISBN 0-8066-2159-1, 10-4898). Augsburg.

Hulse, Erroll. Billy Graham: The Pastor's Dilemma. pap. 2.50 (ISBN 0-685-61833-1). Reiner.

Hutton, Samuel W. Minister's Service Manual. 1964. 8.95 (ISBN 0-8010-4035-3). Baker Bk.

Hyde, Clark. To Declare God's Forgiveness: Toward a Pastoral Theology of Reconciliation. LC 84-60626. 188p. (Orig.). 1984. pap. 8.95 (ISBN 0-8192-1348-9). Morehouse.

Johanson, Gregory J., ed. Pastoral Care Issues in the Pulpit. 1984. 7.50 (ISBN 0-89536-621-5, 1630). CSS of Ohio.

Kemp, Charles F. Reflections: Fifty Years of Pastoral Ministry. (Orig.). pap. 9.95 (ISBN 0-937689-04-1). Chisum Pub.

--Reflections: 50 Years of Pastoral Ministry. 150p. (Orig.). 1986. pap. 9.95 (ISBN 0-318-20075-9). Chisum Pub.

Kent, Homer A., Jr. Pastoral Epistles. 320p. 1982. pap. 10.95 (ISBN 0-88469-075-X). BMH Bks.

Kent, Homer A., Sr. The Pastor & His Work. pap. 8.95 (ISBN 0-88469-079-2). BMH Bks.

Killinger, John. The Tender Shepherd. 208p. (Orig.). 1985. pap. 9.95 (ISBN 0-687-41242-0). Abingdon.

Kloppenburg, Bonaventure. Pastoral Practice & the Paranormal. Smith, David, tr. from Span. 1979. 8.95 (ISBN 0-685-92509-9). Franciscan Herald.

LeFevre, Perry & Schroeder, W. Widick, eds. Pastoral Care & Liberation Praxis: Studies in Personal & Social Transformation. (Studies in Ministry & Parish Life). 112p. 1986. text ed. 18.95x (ISBN 0-913552-31-3); pap. text ed. 8.95x (ISBN 0-913552-32-1). Exploration Pr.

Malcomson, William L. How to Survive in the Ministry. 88p. 1982. pap. 4.95 (ISBN 0-8170-0964-7). Judson.

Marsan, Jules. Pastorale Dramatique en France a la Fin du Seizieme & Au Commencement du Dix-Septieme Siecle. LC 79-159703. (Research & Source Works Ser.: No. 745). (Illus.). 1971. Repr. of 1905 ed. lib. bdg. 32.50 (ISBN 0-8337-4254-X). B Franklin.

Mead, Daniel L. & Allen, Darrel J. Ministry by Objectives. LC 78-59182. (Evangelical Leadership Preparation Ser.). 80p. 1978. pap. 3.95 (ISBN 0-910566-84-4). Evang Tchr.

Miller, Kenneth R. & Wilson, Mary E. The Church That Cares. LC 85-14786. 96p. 1985. pap. 6.95 (ISBN 0-8170-1087-4). Judson.

Miller, Paul M. Servant of God's Servants: The Work of a Christian Minister. LC 63-15499. (The Conrad Grebel Lectures: 1963). pap. 59.00 (ISBN 0-317-26613-6, 2025423). Bks Demand UMI.

Mitchell, Nathan. Mission & Ministry: History & Theology in the Sacrament of Order. (Message of the Sacraments Ser.: Vol. 6). 1982. text ed. 16.95 (ISBN 0-89453-396-7); pap. 12.95 (ISBN 0-89453-292-8). M Glazier.

Moore, Robert L., ed. Sources of Vitality in American Church Life. LC 78-71065. (Studies in Ministry & Parish Life). 1978. text ed. 13.95x (ISBN 0-913552-14-3). Exploration Pr.

New Parish Ministries: Series 2. 248p. 1984. pap. 8.95 (ISBN 0-86683-839-2, HarpR). Har-Row.

Nouwen, Henri J. Creative Ministry. LC 73-139050. 1971. pap. 3.50 (ISBN 0-385-12616-6, Im). Doubleday.

--The Living Reminder: Service & Prayer in Memory of Jesus Christ. 80p. 1981. pap. 4.95 (ISBN 0-86683-915-1, HarpR). Har-Row.

Nunez, Emilio A. Reflexion Pastoral: El Pastor y Su Ministerio. Orig. Title: Pastoral Reflection. (Span.). Date not set. pap. 6.50 (ISBN 0-8254-1515-2). Kregel.

Oates, Wayne E. The Christian Pastor. Rev. 3rd ed. LC 82-4933. 298p. 1982. pap. 9.95 (ISBN 0-664-24372-X). Westminster.

--Pastor's Handbook, Vol. II. LC 79-28639. (Christian Care Bks.). 120p. 1980. pap. 7.95 (ISBN 0-664-24330-4). Westminster.

--The Religious Care of the Psychiatric Patient. LC 78-18454. 252p. 1978. 13.95 (ISBN 0-664-21365-0). Westminster.

Oden, Thomas C. Care of Souls in the Classic Tradition. LC 83-48912. (Theology & Pastoral Care Ser.). pap. 7.95 (ISBN 0-8006-1729-0, 1-729). Fortress.

--Pastoral Theology: Essentials of Ministry. LC 82-47753. 456p. (Orig.). 1983. 15.95 (ISBN 0-06-066353-7, RD 415, HarpR). Har-Row.

Olsen, Charles M. Cultivating Religious Growth Groups. LC 83-27328. (The Pastor's Handbook Ser.: Vol. 3). 118p. (Orig.). 1984. pap. 7.95 (ISBN 0-664-24617-6). Westminster.

Pastirskoje Sovjeshchjanije 1969. Tr. of Pastoral Conference 1969. 95p. 1969. pap. 3.00 (ISBN 0-317-30274-4). Holy Trinity.

Pastoral Care Office. Empowered to Care. 1980. pap. 9.00 (ISBN 0-8309-0291-0). Herald Hse.

Pastoral Pointers: Contribution by Thirteen Church of God Ministers. 1976. pap. 2.95 (ISBN 0-87148-686-5). Pathway Pr.

Patton, John. Is Human Forgiveness Possible? A Pastoral Care Perspective. 192p. (Orig.). 1985. pap. 10.95 (ISBN 0-687-19704-X). Abingdon.

Pinson. The Local Church in Ministry. LC 73-75629. 7.50 (ISBN 0-8054-6304-6). Broadman.

Poling, James N. & Miller, Donald E. Foundations for a Practical Theology of Ministry. 192p. 1985. pap. 9.95 (ISBN 0-687-13340-8). Abingdon.

Polocino, Anna. The Adventure of Affirming: Reflections on Healing & Ministry. LC 86-8005. 111p. (Orig.). 1986. pap. 7.95 (ISBN 0-89571-030-7). Affirmation.

Pruyser, Paul W. The Minister As Diagnostician: Personal Problems in Pastoral Perspective. LC 76-8922. 144p. 1976. pap. 7.95 (ISBN 0-664-24123-9). Westminster.

Rigby, Peter. Persistent Pastoralists: Nomadic Societies in Transition. 208p. 1985. 26.25x (ISBN 0-86232-226-X, Pub. by Zed Pr England); pap. 9.95 (ISBN 0-86232-227-8, Pub. by Zed Pr England). Humanities.

Rocker, Dolore & Pierre, Kenneth J. Shared Ministry: An Integrated Approach to Leadership & Service. (Illus.). 245p. (Orig.). 1984. pap. 18.95 (ISBN 0-88489-158-5). St Mary's.

Sampson, Tom S. Only by Grace: A Candid Look at the Life of a Minister. Lambert, Herbert, ed. LC 85-29916. 144p. (Orig.). 1986. pap. 9.95 (ISBN 0-8272-2707-8). CBP.

Schaller, Lyle E. It's a Different World! The Challenge for Today's Pastor. 240p. 1987. pap. 10.95 (ISBN 0-687-19729-5). Abingdon.

--The Pastor & the People: Building a New Partnership for Effective Ministry. LC 72-8567. 176p. (Orig.). 1973. pap. 7.95 (ISBN 0-687-30136-X). Abingdon.

--Survival Tactics in the Parish. LC 76-54751. (Orig.). 1977. pap. 8.75 (ISBN 0-687-40757-5). Abingdon.

Schoun, Benjamin D. Helping Pastors Cope: A Psycho-social Support System for Pastors. viii, 259p. 1982. pap. 9.95 (ISBN 0-943872-86-3). Andrews Univ Pr.

Schuetze, Armin W. & Habezk, Irwin J. The Shepherd Under Christ. LC 74-81794. 1974. text ed. 14.95 (ISBN 0-8100-0046-6, 15N0351). Northwest Pub.

Segler, Franklin M. Broadman Minister's Manual. LC 68-26920. 1968. 9.95 (ISBN 0-8054-2307-9). Broadman.

--Theology of Church & Ministry. LC 60-14146. 1960. bds. 11.95 (ISBN 0-8054-2506-3). Broadman.

Shelly, Judith A. Caring in Crisis: Bible Studies for Helping People. LC 78-13878. 1979. pap. 4.95 (ISBN 0-87784-563-8). Inter-Varsity.

Shelly, Judith Allen. Spiritual Care Workbook. 1978. pap. 5.95 (ISBN 0-87784-507-7). Inter-Varsity.

Shelp, Earl E. & Sunderland, Ronald H. The Pastor As Servant. 112p. (Orig.). 1986. pap. 8.95 (ISBN 0-8298-0580-X). Pilgrim NY.

Shelp, Earl E. & Sutherland, Ronald H., eds. The Pastor As Prophet. 172p. 1985. pap. 9.95 (ISBN 0-8298-0547-8). Pilgrim NY.

Skelton, Eugene A. The Ministry of the Small Group Leader. 48p. 1986. pap. 1.25 (ISBN 0-8146-1487-6). Liturgical Pr.

Snyder, Ross, ed. Openings into Ministry. LC 77-92707. (Studies in Ministry & Parish Life). 1977. 13.95x (ISBN 0-913552-10-0); pap. 5.95x (ISBN 0-913552-11-9). Exploration Pr.

Stowe, W. McFerrin. If I Were a Pastor. 112p. (Orig.). 1983. pap. 6.50 (ISBN 0-687-18655-2). Abingdon.

Stratman, Gary D. Pastoral Preaching: Timeless Truth for Changing Needs. 112p. (Orig.). 1983. pap. 8.75 (ISBN 0-687-30139-4). Abingdon.

Swain, Bernard F. Liberating Leadership: Practical Styles of Pastoral Ministry. 96p. (Orig.). 1986. pap. 6.95 (ISBN 0-86683-483-4, HarpR). Har-Row.

Switzer, David L. The Minister as Crisis Counselor. rev. ed. 304p. 1986. pap. 13.95 (ISBN 0-687-26954-7). Abingdon.

Thayer, Nelson S. Spirituality & Pastoral Care. LC 84-48716. (Theology & Pastoral Care Ser.). 128p. 1985. pap. 7.95 (ISBN 0-8006-1734-7, 1-1734). Fortress.

A Theology of Christian Counseling: More Than Redemption. (A Jay Adams Library). 1986. pap. 11.95 (ISBN 0-310-51101-1, 12122P). Zondervan.

Thiessen, John C. Pastoring the Smaller Church. kivar 6.95 (ISBN 0-310-36901-0). Zondervan.

Tidball, Derek J. Skillful Shepherds: An Introduction to Pastoral Theology. 1986. pap. 12.95 (ISBN 0-310-44631-7). Zondervan.

To Teach as Jesus Did. 57p. 1972. pap. 2.95 (ISBN 1-55586-063-X). US Catholic.

Trotter, W. Five Letters on Worship & Ministry. 39p. pap. 0.60 (ISBN 0-88172-128-X). Believers Bkshelf.

Walrath, Douglas A. Leading Churches Through Change. LC 79-4456. (Creative Leadership Ser.). 1979. pap. 6.95 (ISBN 0-687-21270-7). Abingdon.

Willimon, William H. Worship As Pastoral Care. rev. ed. LC 79-894. 1979. 11.95 (ISBN 0-687-46388-2). Abingdon.

Zaitsev, Konstantine. Pastirskoje Bogoslovije, 2 Vols. Tr. of Pastoral Theology. 478p. 1960. pap. text ed. 16.00 (ISBN 0-317-30273-6). Holy Trinity.

Zimmerman, Thomas F., et al, eds. And He Gave Pastors. LC 78-50485. 500p. 1978. text ed. 12.95 (ISBN 0-88243-460-8, 02-0460). Gospel Pub.

PASTORAL THEOLOGY–ANGLICAN COMMUNION

Edwards, O. C., et al. Anglican Theology & Pastoral Care. Griffiss, James, ed. 160p. (Orig.). 1985. pap. 8.95 (ISBN 0-8192-1364-0). Morehouse.

Elmen, Paul, ed. The Anglican Moral Choice. LC 82-62391. 274p. (Orig.). 1983. pap. 10.95 (ISBN 0-8192-1322-5). Morehouse.

Neill, Stephen. Anglicanism. 4th ed. 1977. pap. 10.95x (ISBN 0-19-520033-0). Oxford U Pr.

Smith, David H. Health & Medicine in Anglican Tradition. 140p. 1986. 15.95x (ISBN 0-8245-0716-9). Crossroad NY.

Toon, Peter. The Anglican Way: Evangelical & Catholic. LC 83-60934. 96p. 1983. pap. 5.95 (ISBN 0-8192-1330-6). Morehouse.

PASTORAL THEOLOGY–CATHOLIC CHURCH

Bausch, William J. The Christian Parish: Whispers of the Risen Christ. 232p. 1981. pap. 7.95 (ISBN 0-89622-146-6). Twenty-Third.

Burrell, David B. & Kane, Franzita, eds. Evangelization in the American Context. LC 76-22403. 1976. pap. 2.95x (ISBN 0-268-00902-3). U of Notre Dame Pr.

Houtart, Francois. Sociology & Pastoral Work. pap. 1.50 (ISBN 0-8199-0133-4, L38828). Franciscan Herald.

Kern, Walter. Pastoral Ministry with Disabled Persons. LC 84-24619. 248p. 1985. pap. 6.95 (ISBN 0-8189-0472-0). Alba.

Mathis, Marcian & Bonner, Dismas, eds. Pastoral Companion. 14th ed. 1976. 17.50 (ISBN 0-8199-0084-2, L38625). Franciscan Herald.

National Conference of Catholic Bishops Staff. Together, a New People: Pastoral Statement on Migrants & Refugees. 40p. (Orig.). 1987. pap. 3.95 (ISBN 1-55586-147-4). US Catholic.

Nolan, Hugh J., ed. Pastoral Letters of the United States Catholic Bishops, 1975-1983, Vol. IV. 616p. 1984. pap. 24.95 (ISBN 1-55586-875-4). US Catholic.

--Pastoral Letters of the United States Catholic Bishops, 1962-1974, Vol. III. 511p. 1984. pap. 24.95 (ISBN 1-55586-870-3). US Catholic.

--Pastoral Letters of the United States Catholic Bishops, 1941-1961, Vol. II. 271p. 1984. pap. 24.95 (ISBN 1-55586-885-1). US Catholic.

--Pastoral Letters of the United States Catholic Bishops, 1792-1940, Vol. I. 487p. 1984. pap. 24.95 (ISBN 1-55586-880-0). US Catholic.

Pastoral Constitution on the Church in the Modern World (Gaudium et Spes) 138p. 1965. pap. 3.95 (ISBN 1-55586-015-X). US Catholic.

Pastoral Formation & Pastoral Field Edcation in the Catholic Seminary. 84p. 1985. pap. 4.95 (ISBN 1-55586-936-X). US Catholic.

A Pastoral Statement on the Catholic Charismatic Renewal. 48p. 1984. pap. 2.25 (ISBN 1-55586-931-9). US Catholic.

Rahner, Karl, ed. Pastoral Mission of the Church. LC 76-57341. (Concilium Ser.: Vol. 3). 192p. 7.95 (ISBN 0-8091-0108-4). Paulist Pr.

Schillebeeckx, Edward. Church with a Human Face: New & Expanded Theology of Ministry. Bowden, John, tr. 400p. 1985. 19.95 (ISBN 0-8245-0693-6). Crossroad NY.

Shorter, Aylward. African Culture & the Christian Church: An Introduction to Social & Pastoral Anthropology. LC 73-79481. pap. 60.30 (ISBN 0-317-26684-5, 2025114). Bks Demand UMI.

Sweet, Henry. King Alfred's West-Saxon Version of Gregory's Pastoral Care. 1979. Repr. of 1871 ed. lib. bdg. 200.00 (ISBN 0-8492-8102-4). R West.

PASTORAL THEOLOGY–CHURCH OF ENGLAND

see Pastoral Theology–Anglican Communion

PASTORAL THEOLOGY–HANDBOOKS, MANUALS, ETC.

Bolinder, Garth, et al. What Every Pastor Needs to Know about Music, Youth, & Education. (Leadership Library). 192p. 1986. 9.95 (ISBN 0-917463-09-9). Chr Today.

Fry, Malcolm C. & Crowson, Milton. The Ministry of Ushering: Leader's Guide. 1980. pap. 2.50 (ISBN 0-89265-066-4). Randall Hse.

Hobbs, James R. Pastor's Manual. 1940. 8.95 (ISBN 0-8054-2301-X). Broadman.

Perry, Lloyd M. & Lias, Edward J. Manual of Pastoral Problems & Procedures. 8.95 (ISBN 0-8010-7063-5). Baker Bk.

Steinbron, Melvin J. Can the Pastor Do It Alone. 1987. pap. 7.95 (ISBN 0-8307-1171-6, 5418925). Regal.

Sugden, Howard F. & Wiersbe, Warren W. Confident Pastoral Leadership. (Orig.). 1977. pap. 6.95 (ISBN 0-8024-1598-9). Moody.

Tibbetts, Orlando L. The Minister's Handbook. 224p. 1986. 9.95 (ISBN 0-8170-1088-2). Judson.

PASTORS

see Clergy; Priests

PATARINES

Baring-Gould, Sabine. Freaks of Fanaticism & Other Strange Events. LC 68-21754. 1968. Repr. of 1891 ed. 40.00x (ISBN 0-8103-3503-4). Gale.

PATRIARCHS (BIBLE)

Ponder, Catherine. The Millionaires of Genesis. (The Millionaires of the Bible Ser.). 1976. pap. 4.95 (ISBN 0-87516-215-0). De Vorss.

Storr, Catherine. Abraham & Isaac. LC 84-18076. (People of the Bible Ser.). (Illus.). 32p. 1985. PLB 10.65 (ISBN 0-8172-1994-3). Raintree Pubs.

Thompson, Thomas L. The Historicity of the Patriarchal Narratives: The Quest for the Historical Abraham. LC 72-76042. (Beiheft 133 zur Zeitschrift fuer die alttestamentliche Wissenschaft). 1974. 57.00x (ISBN 3-11-004096-4). De Gruyter.

Von Wellnitz, Marcus. Christ & the Patriarchs: New Light from Apocryphal Literature & Tradition. LC 80-83035. 400p. 1980. 9.95 (ISBN 0-88290-164-8, 2045). Horizon Utah.

Westermann, Claus. The Promises to the Fathers: Studies on the Patriarchal Narratives. LC 79-7395. pap. 51.80 (2027191). Bks Demand UMI.

Wiseman, D. J. & Millard, A. R., eds. Essays on the Patriarchal Narratives. 1983. text ed. 17.50x (ISBN 0-931464-13-7); pap. 9.95 (ISBN 0-931464-12-9). Eisenbrauns.

PATRIARCHY

see Family

PATRICK, SAINT, 373?-463?

Burg, J. B. The Place of St. Patrick in History & His Life. 59.95 (ISBN 0-8490-0839-5). Gordon Pr.

Bury, John B. The Life of St. Patrick: His Place in History. facsimile ed. LC 79-175691. (Select Bibliographies Reprint Ser). Repr. of 1905 ed. 24.50 (ISBN 0-8369-6606-6). Ayer Co Pubs.

Corfe, T. St. Patrick & Irish Christianity. LC 73-75862. (Cambridge Introduction to the Hoistory of Mankind Ser.). 48p. 1973. 4.95 (ISBN 0-521-20228-0). Cambridge U Pr.

Corfe, Tom. St. Patrick & Irish Christianity. LC 78-56811. (Cambridge Topic Bks). (Illus.). 1978. PLB 8.95 (ISBN 0-8225-1217-3). Lerner Pubns.

Cushing, Richard C. St. Patrick & the Irish. 1963. 3.50 (ISBN 0-8198-6824-8); pap. 2.00 (ISBN 0-8198-6827-2). Dghtrs St Paul.

Czarnowski, Stefan. Le Culte Des Heros et Ses Conditions Sociales. LC 74-25745. (European Sociology Ser.). 472p. 1975. Repr. 35.50x (ISBN 0-405-06500-0). Ayer Co Pubs.

De Breffny, Brian. In the Steps of St. Patrick. (Illus.). 1982. 9.98 (ISBN 0-500-24110-4). Thames Hudson.

Hanson, R. P. The Life & Writings of the Historical St. Patrick. 144p. 1983. 11.95 (ISBN 0-8164-0523-9, HarpR). Har-Row.

Harney, Martin. Legacy of St. Patrick. 1972. 3.50 (ISBN 0-8198-4407-1); pap. 2.25 (ISBN 0-8198-4408-X). Dghtrs St Paul.

Patrick, Saint Confession of St. Patrick. pap. 1.95 (ISBN 0-686-25547-X). Eastern Orthodox.

Patrick, Saint & Fiacc, Saint Writings of St. Patrick, with the Metrical Life of St. Patrick. pap. 2.95 (ISBN 0-686-25558-5). Eastern Orthodox.

Picard, J. M. & De Pontlarcy, Y. Saint Patrick's Purgatory. 78p. 1985. pap. 7.00 (ISBN 0-912414-44-8). Lumen Christi.

Stokes, Whitley, ed. Tripartite Life of St. Patrick, with Other Documents Related to the Saint with Translation & Indexes, 2 vols. (Rolls Ser.: No. 89). Repr. of 1888 ed. Set. 88.00 (ISBN 0-8115-1165-0). Kraus Repr.

Thompson, E. A. Who Was St. Patrick? LC 85-14624. (Illus.). 192p. 1986. 21.95 (ISBN 0-312-87084-1). St Martin.

Tripartite Life of St. Patrick. pap. text ed. 3.95 (ISBN 0-686-25557-7). Eastern Orthodox.

The Works of Saint Patrick: Saint Secundius Hymn on St. Patrick. (Ancient Christian Writers Ser.: No. 17). 10.95. Paulist Pr.

PATRIOTISM

Van Hoeven, James W. Piety & Patriotism. 1976. pap. 4.95 (ISBN 0-8028-1663-0). Eerdmans.

PATRISTICS

see Fathers of the Church

PATRONAGE, ECCLESIASTICAL

Curtis, Lewis P. Chichester Towers. LC 66-21514. (Illus.). Repr. of 1966 ed. 32.50 (ISBN 0-8357-1319-9, 2013199). Bks Demand UMI.

Schmidt, Steffen W., et al. Friends, Followers & Factions: A Reader in Political Clientelism. LC 73-93060. 1977. 48.50x (ISBN 0-520-02696-9); pap. 12.95x (ISBN 0-520-03156-3, CAMPUS 167). U of Cal Pr.

Warren, Ann K. Anchorites & Their Patrons in Medieval England. LC 84-24091. 1985. 42.00x (ISBN 0-520-05278-1). U of Cal Pr.

PAUL 2ND, POPE, 1443-1513

Paul Of Venice. Logica Magna of Paul of Venice, Part 1, Fascicule 1. Kretzmann, Norman, ed. (British Academy Ser.). 1979. text ed. 98.00x (ISBN 0-19-725980-4). Oxford U Pr.

PAUL 6TH, POPE, 1897-1978

O'Reilly, Sean. Our Name Is Peter. LC 77-380. 155p. 1977. 5.95 (ISBN 0-8199-0666-2). Franciscan Herald.

Paul Sixth, Pope Ecclesiam Suam. pap. 0.50 (ISBN 0-8091-5035-2). Paulist Pr.

Pope Paul VI. Humanae Vitae. 2nd, rev. ed. Caligari, Marc, tr. from Lat. 1983. pap. 1.95 (ISBN 0-89870-000-0). Ignatius Pr.

PAUL, SAINT, APOSTLE

Arbuckle, Gwendolyne & Wolcott, Carolyn. Paul: Adventurer for Christ. (Illus.). 96p. (Orig.). 1984. pap. 5.50 (ISBN 0-687-30487-3). Abingdon.

Barclay, William. The Mind of St. Paul. LC 75-9310. 256p. 1975. pap. 8.95 (ISBN 0-06-060471-9, RD110, HarpR). Har-Row.

Baring-Gould, S. A Study of St. Paul: His Character & Opinions. 1977. lib. bdg. 59.95 (ISBN 0-8490-2712-8). Gordon Pr.

Barnes, Arthur S. Christianity at Rome in the Apostolic Age. LC 72-114462. (Illus.). 1971. Repr. of 1938 ed. lib. bdg. 55.00x (ISBN 0-8371-4760-3, BACR). Greenwood.

Beker, J. Christian. Paul the Apostle: The Triumph of God in Life & Thought. LC 79-8904. 468p. 1980. pap. 14.95 (ISBN 0-8006-1811-4). Fortress.

Black, David A. Paul, Apostle of Weakness: Astheneia & Its Cognates in the Pauline Literature. LC 83-49515. (American University Studies VII (Theology & Religion): Vol. 3). 340p. (Orig.). 1984. pap. text ed. 27.00 (ISBN 0-8204-0106-4). P Lang Pubs.

Booth, A. E. Ministry of Peter, John & Paul. 1982. pap. 1.25 (ISBN 0-88172-004-6). Believers Bkshelf.

Bornkamm, Gunther. Paul. Stalker, D. M., tr. from Ger. LC 70-85068. 1971. short disc 15.95xi (ISBN 0-06-060933-8, HarpR). Har-Row.

Bratcher, Robert G. A Translator's Guide to Paul's Letters to Timothy & to Titus. LC 83-4823. (Helps for Translators Ser.). viii, 138p. 1983. softcover 2.30x (ISBN 0-8267-0190-6, 08781, Pub. by United Bible). Am Bible.

Bratcher, Robert G. & Nida, Eugene A. A Translator's Handbook on Paul's Letters to the Colossians & to Philemon. (Helps for Translators Ser.). 149p. soft cover 3.30x (ISBN 0-8267-0145-0, 08529, Pub. by United Bible). Am Bible.

Bruce, F. F. Jesus & Paul: Places They Knew. 128p. 1983. Repr. of 1981 ed. 12.95 (ISBN 0-8407-5281-4). Nelson.

--Paul & His Converts. rev. ed. LC 85-19764. 155p. 1985. pap. 5.95 (ISBN 0-87784-593-X). Inter-Varsity.

--Paul: Apostle of the Heart Set Free. LC 77-26127. 1978. 20.95 (ISBN 0-8028-3501-5). Eerdmans.

Bunyan, John. Paul's Departure & Crown. pap. 0.95 (ISBN 0-685-19839-1). Reiner.

Caird, George B. Paul's Letters from Prison (Elphesians, Phillipians, Colossians, Philemon) in the Revised Standard Edition. (New Clarendon Bible). (Orig.). 1976. pap. text ed. 18.95x (ISBN 0-19-836920-4). Oxford U Pr.

Campbell, James M. Paul the Mystic. 1977. lib. bdg. 59.95 (ISBN 0-8490-2415-3). Gordon Pr.

Chadwick, Edward W. Pastoral Teaching of Paul. LC 84-7123. 416p. 1984. 11.95 (ISBN 0-8254-2325-2). Kregel.

Christensen, Chuck & Christensen, Winnie. Paul: Thirteenth Apostle. (Fisherman Bible Studyguide Ser.). 64p. (Orig.). 1987. pap. 2.95 (ISBN 0-87788-652-0). Shaw Pubs.

Conybeare, W. J. & Howson, J. S. Life & Epistles of St. Paul. 1949. 16.95 (ISBN 0-8028-8086-X). Eerdmans.

--The Life & Epistles of St. Paul. 1977. lib. bdg. 59.95 (ISBN 0-8490-2160-X). Gordon Pr.

Cunningham, Philip A. The Apostle Paul: Male Chauvinist or Proponent of Equality? 24p. (Orig.). 1986. pap. 4.25 (ISBN 0-937997-03-X). Hi-Time Pub.

--Jewish Apostle to the Gentiles: Paul As He Saw Himself. 112p. (Orig.). 1986. pap. 5.95 (ISBN 0-89622-302-7). Twenty-Third.

Daughters of St. Paul. St. Paul: A Good Friend of Jesus. 1980. 2.50 (ISBN 0-8198-6811-6); pap. 1.75 (ISBN 0-8198-6810-8). Dghtrs St Paul.

Davies, W. D. Jewish & Pauline Studies. LC 82-48620. 432p. 1983. text ed. 29.95 (ISBN 0-8006-0694-9). Fortress.

--Paul & Rabbinic Judaism: Some Rabbinic Elements in Pauline Theology. LC 80-8049. 448p. 1980. pap. 14.95 (ISBN 0-8006-1438-0, 1-1438). Fortress.

Deissman, Adolph. Paul: A Study in Social & Religious History. Wilson, William W., tr. 1958. 12.75 (ISBN 0-8446-1965-5). Peter Smith.

Dennison, William D. Paul's Two-Age Construction & Apologetics. LC 85-20272. 144p. (Orig.). 1986. lib. bdg. 19.50 (ISBN 0-8191-5011-8); pap. text ed. 8.75 (ISBN 0-8191-5012-6). U Pr of Amer.

Doohan, Helen. Leadership in Paul. (Good News Studies Ser.: Vol. 11). 1984. pap. 7.95 (ISBN 0-89453-435-1). M Glazier.

Drane, John. Paul: An Illustrated Documentary on the Life & Writings. LC 76-62918. (Illus.). 1977. pap. text ed. 9.95 (ISBN 0-06-062065-X, RD 208, HarpR). Har-Row.

Drew, George. St. Paul. 60p. (Orig.). 1984. pap. 6.95 (ISBN 0-940754-22-3). Ed Ministries.

Dyet, James T. Paul: Apostle of Steel & Velvet. 3rd. ed. LC 76-9579. 1976. pap. 3.50 (ISBN 0-916406-30-X). Accent Bks.

Easwaran, Eknath. Love Never Faileth: The Inspiration of St. Francis, St. Augustine, St. Paul & Mother Teresa. (Illus.). 208p. (Orig.). 1985. 15.00 (ISBN 0-915132-31-1); pap. 8.00 (ISBN 0-915132-32-X). Nilgiri Pr.

Ellis, Peter F. Seven Pauline Letters. LC 82-15252. (Orig.). 1982. pap. 8.95 (ISBN 0-8146-1245-8). Liturgical Pr.

Farrar, F. W. The Life & Work of St. Paul. 1980. 2 vol. set 43.95 (ISBN 0-86524-055-8, 8402). Klock & Klock.

Giordani, Igino. St. Paul Apostle & Martyr. (Obelisk Ser.). 1961. 8.00 (ISBN 0-8198-0138-0); pap. 7.00 (ISBN 0-8198-0139-9). Dghtrs St Paul.

Glover, Terrot R. Springs of Hellas. LC 74-122878. (Essay & General Literature Index Reprint Ser). 1971. Repr. of 1945 ed. 21.00x (ISBN 0-8046-1333-8, Pub. by Kennikat). Assoc Faculty Pr.

Goodwin, Frank J. Harmony of the Life of St. Paul. 1951. pap. 8.95 (ISBN 0-8010-3797-2). Baker Bk.

Grant, Michael. Saint Paul. (Crossroad Paperback Ser.). 256p. pap. 7.95 (ISBN 0-686-85826-3). Crossroad NY.

--Saint Paul. 272p. 1976. 5.95 (ISBN 0-684-14682-7, ScribT); pap. 5.95 (ISBN 0-684-17746-3). Scribner.

Grollenberg, Lucas. Paul. Bowden, John, tr. LC 78-14372. 186p. 1979. pap. 4.50 (ISBN 0-664-24234-0). Westminster.

Hagin, Kenneth. Paul's Revelation: The Gospel of Reconciliation. 1983. pap. 0.50 mini bk. (ISBN 0-89276-261-6). Hagin Ministries.

Hagner, Donald & Harris, Murray, eds. Pauline Studies: Essays Presented to Prof. F. F. Bruce on His 70th Birthday. LC 80-16146. 336p. 1981. 19.95 (ISBN 0-8028-3531-7). Eerdmans.

Hengel, Martin. Between Jesus & Paul. LC 83-48003. 256p. 1983. pap. 14.95 (ISBN 0-8006-1720-7). Fortress.

Hightower, James E., Jr. Illustrating Paul's Letter to the Romans. LC 84-7074. 1984. pap. 5.95 (ISBN 0-8054-2251-X). Broadman.

Hock, Ronald F. The Social Context of Paul's Ministry: Tentmaking & Apostleship. LC 79-7381. 112p. 1980. 8.95 (ISBN 0-8006-0577-2, 1-577). Fortress.

Howard, George. Paul: Crisis in Galatia: A Study in Early Christian Theology. LC 77-84002. (Society for New Testament Studies Monographs: No. 35). pap. 31.50 (ISBN 0-317-29375-3, 2024478). Bks Demand UMI.

Hughes, Don. Paul's Thorn. (Orig.). 1977. pap. 0.75 (ISBN 0-89274-047-7, HH-047). Harrison Hse.

Hultgren, Arland J. Paul's Gospel & Mission: The Outlook from His Letter to the Romans. LC 85-4430. 176p. 1985. pap. 9.95 (ISBN 0-8006-1871-8). Fortress.

Jewett, Robert. A Chronology of Paul's Life. LC 78-54553. 176p. 1979. 14.95 (ISBN 0-8006-0522-5, 1-522). Fortress.

Johnson, Hubert R. Who Then Is Paul? Chevy Chase Manuscripts Staff, ed. LC 80-1406. 272p. 1981. lib. bdg. 28.25 (ISBN 0-8191-1364-6); pap. text ed. 10.00 (ISBN 0-8191-1365-4). U Pr of Amer.

Kallas, James. Story of Paul. LC 66-19206. (Orig.). 1966. pap. 6.95 (ISBN 0-8066-0608-8, 10-6055). Augsburg.

Kasemann, Ernst. Perspectives on Paul. LC 79-157540. pap. 45.80 (2029296). Bks Demand UMI.

Keck, Leander E. Paul & His Letters. Krodel, Gerhard, ed. LC 78-54554. (Proclamation Commentaries, The New Testament Witnesses for Preaching). 144p. 1979. pap. 4.95 (ISBN 0-8006-0587-X, 1-587). Fortress.

Kennedy, H. A. St. Paul & the Mystery Religions. 1977. lib. bdg. 59.95 (ISBN 0-8490-2561-3). Gordon Pr.

Landgraf, Arthur. Commentarius Cantabrigiensis in Epistolas Pauli e Schola Petri Abaelardi, 3 vols. Incl. Vol. 1. In Epistolam Ad Romanos. 223p. 1937. 17.95 (ISBN 0-268-00133-2); Vol. 2. In Epistolam Ad Corinthios Iam et Iiam, Ad Galatas et Ad Ephesios. 1223p. 1960. 17.95 (ISBN 0-268-00134-0); Vol. 3. In Epistolam ad Philippenses, ad Colossenses, ad Thessalonicenses Primam et Secundam, ed Timotheam Priman et Secundam, ad Titum et Philemonem. 447p. 1944. 17.95 (ISBN 0-268-00132-4). (Mediaeval Studies Ser.: No. 2). U of Notre Dame Pr.

Lapide, Cornelius A. The Personality of St. Paul. 1959. 3.50 (ISBN 0-8198-5802-1); pap. 2.25 (ISBN 0-8198-5803-X). Dghtrs St Paul.

Lapide, Pinchas & Stuhlmacher, Peter. Paul: Rabbi & Apostle. Denef, Lawrence W., tr. LC 84-23482. 80p. (Orig.). 1984. pap. 5.95 (ISBN 0-8066-2122-2, 10-4903). Augsburg.

Levy, Rosalie M. The Man in Chains, St. Paul. 1951. 4.00 (ISBN 0-8198-4704-6); pap. 3.00 (ISBN 0-8198-4705-4). Dghtrs St Paul.

Lincoln, Andrew T. Paradise Now & Not Yet. LC 80-41024. (Society for the New Testament Studies Monographs: No. 43). 240p. 1981. 44.50 (ISBN 0-521-22944-8). Cambridge U Pr.

Lindsay, Gordon. Paul & Silas Evangelize Greece. (Acts in Action Ser.: Vol. 4). pap. 1.25 (ISBN 0-89985-965-8). Christ Nations.

--Paul Before the Sanhedrin. (Acts in Action Ser.: Vol. 5). pap. 1.25 (ISBN 0-89985-966-6). Christ Nations.

The Living Thoughts of St. Paul. 2nd ed. 4.76 (ISBN 0-02-659680-6, 65968). Benziger Pub Co.

Lohfink, Gerhard. The Conversion of Saint Paul: Narrative & History in Acts. Malina, Bruce J., ed. & tr. 156p. 1976. 5.95 (ISBN 0-8199-0572-0). Franciscan Herald.

Longenecker, Richard N. Ministry & Message of Paul. (Contemporary Evangelical Perspective Ser). 1971. kivar 6.95 (ISBN 0-310-28341-8, 12234P). Zondervan.

Luedemann, Gerd. Paul, Apostle to the Gentiles: Studies in Chronology. Jones, Stanley F., tr. from Ger. LC 83-48919. 320p. 1984. 29.95 (ISBN 0-8006-0714-7, 1-714). Fortress.

Lyons, George. Pauline Autobiography: Toward a New Understanding. (Society of Biblical Literature Dissertation Ser.). 1985. 23.50 (ISBN 0-89130-730-3, 06-01-73); pap. 15.50 (ISBN 0-89130-765-6). Scholars Pr GA.

MacDonald, Dennis R. The Legend & the Apostle: The Battle for Paul in Story & Canon. LC 82-21953. 144p. (Orig.). 1983. pap. 9.95 (ISBN 0-664-24464-5). Westminster.

Madsen, Norman P. St. Paul: The Apostle & His Letters. LC 85-62816. 165p. (Orig.). 1986. pap. 6.95 (ISBN 0-87973-589-9, 598). Our Sunday Visitor.

Maritain, Jacques. The Living Thoughts of Saint Paul. 135p. 1983. Repr. of 1942 ed. lib. bdg. 20.00 (ISBN 0-8495-3946-3). Arden Lib.

Marrow, Stanley B. Paul, His Letters & Theology: An Introduction to Paul's Epistles. 288p. (Orig.). 1986. pap. 9.95 (ISBN 0-8091-2744-X). Paulist Pr.

Meeks, Wayne A. The First Urban Christians: The Social World of the Apostle Paul. LC 82-8447. (Illus.). 296p. 1982. 30.00x (ISBN 0-300-02876-8). Yale U Pr.

--The First Urban Christians: The Social World of the Apostle Paul. LC 82-8447. 312p. 1984. pap. 9.95 (ISBN 0-300-03244-7, Y-503). Yale U Pr.

Meinardus, Otto F. St. Paul in Ephesus & the Cities of Galatia & Cyprus. LC 78-51246. (In the Footsteps of the Saints Ser.). (Illus.). 160p. 1979. 17.50 (ISBN 0-89241-071-X); pap. 6.95 (ISBN 0-89241-044-2). Caratzas.

--St. Paul in Greece. LC 78-51244. (In the Footsteps of the Saints Ser.). 160p. 1979. 17.50 (ISBN 0-89241-072-8); pap. 6.95 (ISBN 0-89241-045-0). Caratzas.

--St. Paul's Last Journey. LC 78-51247. (In the Footsteps of the Saints Ser.). (Illus.). 160p. 1979. 17.50 (ISBN 0-686-85764-X); pap. 6.95 (ISBN 0-89241-073-6). Caratzas.

Meyer, F. B. Paul. 1968. pap. 4.50 (ISBN 0-87508-348-X). Chr Lit.

Montefiore, Claude G. Judaism & St. Paul. LC 73-2222. (The Jewish People; History, Religion, Literature Ser.). Repr. of 1914 ed. 23.50 (ISBN 0-405-05284-7). Ayer Co Pubs.

Morgan, W. The Religion & Theology of Paul. 272p. 1917. 9.95 (ISBN 0-567-02200-5, Pub. by T & T Clark Ltd UK). Fortress.

Morton, H. V. In the Steps of St. Paul. (Illus.). 440p. 1986. Repr. of 1936 ed. lib. bdg. 45.00 (ISBN 0-89984-770-6). Century Bookbindery.

Munck, Johannes. Paul & the Salvation of Mankind. LC 60-5412. 1977. pap. 8.95 (ISBN 0-8042-0373-3). John Knox.

Orr, William F. & Walther, James S. Corinthians I. LC 75-42441. (Anchor Bible Ser.: Vol. 32). 1976. 18.00 (ISBN 0-385-02853-9). Doubleday.

Paul. 1979. 0.75 (ISBN 0-8198-0590-4). Dghtrs St Paul.

Paul the Missionary. 64p. Date not set. pap. 2.95 (ISBN 0-9609302-0-5). L Imperio.

Peterson, Mark E. The Teachings of Paul. LC 84-70647. 120p. 1984. 6.95 (ISBN 0-87747-843-0). Deseret Bk.

Pfleiderer, Otto. Lectures on the Influence of the Apostle Paul on the Development of Christianity. Smith, J. Frederick, tr. LC 77-27166. (Hibbert Lectures: 1885). Repr. of 1885 ed. 29.00 (ISBN 0-404-60406-4). AMS Pr.

Phipps, William E. Encounter Through Questioning Paul: A Fresh Approach to the Apostle's Life & Letters. LC 82-17580. (Illus.). 114p. (Orig.). 1983. lib. bdg. 24.25 (ISBN 0-8191-2785-X); pap. text ed. 9.50 (ISBN 0-8191-2786-8). U Pr of Amer.

--Paul Against Supernaturalism. LC 85-19228. 177p. 1986. 17.95 (ISBN 0-8022-2501-2). Philos Lib.

Picirilli, Robert. Pauline Writings Notes. 1967. pap. 2.95 (ISBN 0-89265-001-X). Randall Hse.

Picirilli, Robert E. Paul the Apostle. (Orig.). 1986. pap. 7.95 (ISBN 0-8024-6325-8). Moody.

--Paul the Apostle. 1986. pap. 7.95 (ISBN 0-89265-117-2). Randall Hse.

Pollock, John. Apostle. Orig. Title: Man Who Shook the World. 244p. 1972. pap. 7.95 (ISBN 0-88207-233-1). Victor Bks.

--The Apostle: A Life of Paul. 312p. 1985. 11.95 (ISBN 0-89693-368-7). Victor Bks.

Raisanen, Heikki. Paul & the Law. 332p. 1986. pap. 19.95 (ISBN 0-8006-1915-3, 1-1915). Fortress.

--Paul & the Law. 330p. 1983. lib. bdg. 67.50x (ISBN 3-16-144629-1, Pub. by J C B Mohr BRD). Coronet Bks.

Ramsay, William M. St. Paul the Traveller & Roman Citizen. (William M. Ramsay Library Ser.). 1979. pap. 14.95 (ISBN 0-8010-7613-7). Baker Bk.

Richardson, P. & Hurd, J. From Jesus to Paul: Studies in Honour of Francis Wright Beare. 256p. 1984. pap. text ed. 16.50x (ISBN 0-88920-138-2, Pub. by Wilfrid Laurier Canada). Humanities.

Robinson, Benjamin W. The Life of Paul. 1918. 20.00 (ISBN 0-8414-7468-0). Folcroft.

--Life of Paul. 2nd ed. LC 18-19810. (Midway Reprint Ser). 1973. pap. 16.00x (ISBN 0-226-72261-9). U of Chicago Pr.

Rostron, S. Nowell. The Christology of St. Paul. 1977. lib. bdg. 59.95 (ISBN 0-8490-1620-7). Gordon Pr.

Sabatier, A. The Apostle Paul: A History of the Development of the Doctrine of St. Paul. 1977. lib. bdg. 59.95 (ISBN 0-8490-1442-5). Gordon Pr.

Sanders, E. P. Paul & Palestinian Judaism: A Comparison of Patterns of Religion. LC 76-62612. 648p. 1977. pap. 19.95 (ISBN 0-8006-1899-8, 1-1899). Fortress.

Sanders, J. O. Paul the Leader. LC 83-62737. 192p. 1984. pap. 5.95 (ISBN 0-89109-515-2). NavPress.

Sanders, J. Oswald. Pablo, el Lider. Tr. of Paul the Leader. (Span.). 208p. 1986. pap. 3.50 (ISBN 0-8297-0760-3). Life Pubs Intl.

--Paulo, o Lider. Orig. Title: Paul the Leader. (Port.). 1986. write for info. (ISBN 0-8297-0756-5). Life Pubs Intl.

Schatzman, Siegfried. A Pauline Theology of Charismata. 150p. 1986. pap. 7.95 (ISBN 0-913573-45-0). Hendrickson MA.

Schillebeeckx, Edward. Paul the Apostle. (Illus.). 128p. 1983. 14.95 (ISBN 0-8245-0574-3). Crossroad NY.

Schoder, Raymond V., tr. from Gr. & intro. by. Paul Wrote from the Heart. (Gr. & Eng.). 64p. 1987. 24.50 (ISBN 0-86516-181-X). Bolchazy-Carducci.

Seeley, Burns K. Meditations on St. Paul. Coniker, Jerome F., ed. LC 82-72201. (Living Meditation & Prayerbook Ser.). (Illus.). 270p. (Orig.). 1982. pap. text ed. 5.00 (ISBN 0-932406-06-8). AFC.

--Reflections on St. Paul. Coniker, Jerome F., ed. LC 82-72202. (Living Meditation & Prayerbook Ser.). (Illus.). 270p. (Orig.). 1982. pap. text ed. 5.00 (ISBN 0-932406-07-6). AFC.

Segundo, Juan L. The Humanist Christology of Paul: Jesus of Nazareth Yesterday & Today, Vol. 3. Drury, John, tr. from Span. LC 86-8480. 256p. (Orig.). 1986. pap. 14.95 (ISBN 0-88344-221-3). Orbis Bks.

Selby, Donald J. Toward the Understanding of St. Paul. 1962. ref. ed. 26.67 (ISBN 0-13-925693-8). P-H.

Selden, Edward G. In the Time of Paul. 1900. 10.00 (ISBN 0-8414-8134-2). Folcroft.

Smith, David, ed. The Life & Letters of Saint Paul. 1977. lib. bdg. 69.95 (ISBN 0-8490-2161-8). Gordon Pr.

Smyth, Bernard T. Paul: Mystic & Missionary. LC 80-14041. 191p. (Orig.). 1980. pap. 3.98 (ISBN 0-88344-380-5). Orbis Bks.

Snider, Theodore M. The Continuity of Salvation: A Study of Paul's Letter to the Romans. LC 84-42602. 200p. 1984. lib. bdg. 18.95x (ISBN 0-89950-126-5). McFarland & Co.

Soards, Marion J. Thinking about Paul: His Life, Letters, & Theology. 224p. (Orig.). 1987. pap. 8.95 (ISBN 0-8091-2864-0). Paulist Pr.

Soards, Marion L. The Apostle Paul: An Introduction to His Writings & Teaching. 1987. pap. 8.95. Paulist Pr.

Stalker, James. Vida de San Pablo. (Span.). 160p. 1973. pap. 3.50 (ISBN 0-89922-025-8). Edit Caribe.

Stalker, James A. The Life of St. Paul. (Stalker Trilogy Ser.). 176p. 1984. pap. 5.95 (ISBN 0-310-44181-1, 12617P). Zondervan.

St Jerome. St. Paul the First Hermit: His Life by St. Jerome. Shewring, Walter, ed. Hawkins, tr. from Lat. 48p. 1987. 1.50 (ISBN 0-916375-07-2). Press Alley.

Tabor, James. Things Unutterable: Paul's Ascent to Paradise in Its Greco-Roman, Judaic & Early Christian Contexts. LC 86-18924. (Studies in Judaism Ser.). 166p. (Orig.). 1986. lib. bdg. 23.50 (ISBN 0-8191-5643-4, Pub. by Studies in Judaism); pap. text ed. 11.50 (ISBN 0-8191-5644-2, Pub. by Studies in Judaism). U Pr of Amer.

Tasker, G. P. Saint Paul & His Gospel. 87p. 1982. pap. 1.00 (ISBN 0-686-36256-X). Faith Pub Hse.

Taylor, Mendell L. Every Day with Paul. 1978. 6.95 (ISBN 0-8341-0529-2). Beacon Hill.

Thompson, William. Paul & His Message for Life's Journey. 160p. 1986. pap. 9.95 (ISBN 0-8091-2824-1). Paulist Pr.

Tucker, Iva J. Paul: The Missionary. (BibLearn Ser.). (Illus.). 5.95 (ISBN 0-8054-4228-6, 4242-28). Broadman.

Van Til, Cornellius. Paul at Athens. 1959. pap. 0.95 (ISBN 0-87552-493-1). Presby & Reformed.

Von Loewenich, Walther. Paul: His Life & Work. 1960. text ed. 7.50x (ISBN 0-8401-1421-4). A R Allenson.

Weiss, Herold. Paul of Tarsus. 175p. (Orig.). 1986. pap. 9.95 (ISBN 0-943872-92-8). Andrews Univ Pr.

Whiteley, D. E. The Theology of St. Paul. 2nd ed. 312p. 1975. pap. 14.95x (ISBN 0-631-16430-8). Basil Blackwell.

--The Theology of St. Paul. 312p. 1967. 45.00x (ISBN 0-631-15710-7). Basil Blackwell.

Wilson, Thomas. St. Paul & Paganism. 1977. lib. bdg. 59.95 (ISBN 0-8490-2560-5). Gordon Pr.

Youngblood, Ronald. Esaie, Commentaire Biblique, (Themes from Isaiah) (Fr.). 1986. write for info. (ISBN 0-8297-0607-0). Life Pubs Intl.

PAUL, SAINT, APOSTLE–JUVENILE LITERATURE

Barrett, Ethel. Paul. LC 81-51740. (Bible Biography Ser.). 128p. 1981. pap. text ed. 1.95 (ISBN 0-8307-0767-0, 5810701). Regal.

Storr, Catherine. St. Peter & St. Paul. LC 84-18078. (People of the Bible Ser.). (Illus.). 32p. 1985. PLB 10.65 (ISBN 0-8172-1998-6). Raintree Pubs.

PAULICIANS

Garsoian, N. G. Paulician Heresy: A Study of the Origin & Development of Paulicianism in Armenia & the Eastern Provinces of the Byzantine Empire. (Publications in Near & Middle East Ser.: No. 6). 1967. text ed. 32.80x (ISBN 90-2790-096-5). Mouton.

Gilliland, Dean S. Pauline Theology & Mission Practice. 304p. 1983. pap. 12.95 (ISBN 0-8010-3788-3). Baker Bk.

PAULUS DIACONUS, 720-797

Schroll, Sr. M. Alfred. Benedictine Monasticism As Reflected in the Warnefrid-Hildemar Commentaries on the Rule. LC 77-140026. (Columbia University. Studies in the Social Sciences: No. 478). Repr. of 1941 ed. 20.00 (ISBN 0-404-51478-2). AMS Pr.

PAUPERISM

see Poor

PEACE

see also Pacifism; Peace Societies

Addams, Jane. Peace & Bread in Time of War. LC 75-137524. (Peace Movement in America Ser). 269p. 1972. Repr. of 1922 ed. lib. bdg. 18.95x (ISBN 0-89198-051-2). Ozer.

Alexander, Horace. Everyman's Struggle for Peace. 1983. pap. 2.50x (ISBN 0-87574-074-X, 074). Pendle Hill.

Alt, Franz. Peace Is Possible: The Politics of the Sermon on the Mount. Neugroschel, Joachim, tr. from Ger. LC 84-23499. 136p. 1985. 12.95 (ISBN 0-8052-3969-3). Schocken.

Arnett, Ronald C. Dwell in Peace. 156p. (Orig.). 1980. pap. 7.95 (ISBN 0-87178-199-9). Brethren.

Bhikshu Hung Ju & Bhikshu Hung Yo. Three Steps, One Bow. (Illus.). 160p. (Orig.). 1976. pap. 5.00 (ISBN 0-917512-18-9). Buddhist Text.

Boulding, Kenneth E. & Mayer, Milton. Mayer Boulding Dialogue on Peace Research. Murphy, Carol, ed. LC 67-23313. (Orig.). 1967. pap. 2.50x (ISBN 0-87574-153-3). Pendle Hill.

Brinton, Howard H. Sources of the Quaker Peace Testimony. 1983. pap. 2.50x (ISBN 0-87574-027-8, 027). Pendle Hill.

Bunyan, John. Exhortation to Unity & Peace. pap. 0.95 (ISBN 0-685-00744-8). Reiner.

Burnham, Kenneth E. God Comes to America: Father Divine & the Peace Mission Movement. 167p. 1979. 16.95x (ISBN 0-931186-01-3). Lambeth Pr.

Butler, Geoffrey. Studies in Statecraft. LC 79-110899. 1970. Repr. of 1920 ed. 17.00x (ISBN 0-8046-0882-2, Pub. by Kennikat). Assoc Faculty Pr.

Canadian Christian Movement for Peace Staff. Work & Co-Creation. Huntly, Alyson, et al, eds. (People Living for Justice Ser.). 160p. 1983. pap. text ed. 29.95 (ISBN 0-697-01921-7). Wm C Brown.

Carlson, Don, ed. Peace Trek: Reclaiming Our Future. Comstock, Craig. (Illus.). 300p. (Orig.). 1985. pap. 19.95 (ISBN 0-317-19166-7). Ark Comm Inst.

Carlson, Don & Comstock, Craig, eds. Citizen Summitry: Keeping the Peace When It Matters Too Much to Be Left to Politicians. (Illus.). 336p. 1986. pap. 10.95 (ISBN 0-87477-406-3). J P Tarcher.

Carlson, Don & Comstock, Craig K., eds. Citizen Summitry. (Ark Reflections: No. 1). (Illus.). 396p. 1986. 11.95 (ISBN 0-934325-01-4). Ark Comm Inst.

--Making the Shift to Peace. (Ark Reflections: No. 2). 368p. 1986. 14.95 (ISBN 0-934325-02-2). Ark Comm Inst.

Carmody, John. The Quiet Imperative: Meditations on Justice & Peace Based on Readings from the New Testament. 176p. (Orig.). 1986. pap. 6.95 (ISBN 0-8358-0518-2). Upper Room.

Chakravarty, Amiya. The Indian Testimony. 1983. pap. 2.50x (ISBN 0-87574-072-3, 072). Pendle Hill.

Cochrane, Arthur C. The Mystery of Peace. 224p. 1985. pap. 11.95 (ISBN 0-87178-695-8). Brethren.

Culver, Robert D. The Peacemongers. Carpenter, Mark, ed. 160p. 1985. pap. 5.95 (ISBN 0-8423-4789-5). Tyndale.

Curti, Merle E. American Peace Crusade, Eighteen Fifteen to Eighteen Sixty. 1965. lib. bdg. 18.50x (ISBN 0-374-91976-3, Octagon). Hippocrene Bks.

Dodge, David L. War Inconsistent with the Religion of Jesus Christ. LC 75-137540. (Peace Movement in America Ser). xxiv, 168p. 1972. Repr. of 1905 ed. lib. bdg. 15.95x (ISBN 0-89198-067-9). Ozer.

Dunn, Frederick S. War & the Minds of Men. LC 79-131371. xvi, 115p. 1971. Repr. of 1950 ed. 15.00 (ISBN 0-208-00945-0, Archon). Shoe String.

Elizondo, Virgil & Greinacher, Norbert, eds. Church & Peace. (Concilium 1983: Vol. 164). 128p. (Orig.). 1983. pap. 6.95 (ISBN 0-8164-2444-6, HarpR). Har-Row.

Eller, Vernard. War & Peace from Genesis to Revelation. LC 80-26280. (Christian Peace Shelf Ser.). 232p. 1981. pap. 9.95 (ISBN 0-8361-1947-9). Herald Pr.

Emmons, Viva. Roots of Peace. LC 73-78911. (Orig.). 1969. pap. 1.75 (ISBN 0-8356-0505-1, Quest). Theos Pub Hse.

Erdahl, Lowell O. Pro-Life, Pro-Peace: Life Affirming Alternatives to Abortion, War, Mercy Killing, & the Death Penalty. LC 86-3552. 160p. (Orig.). 1986. pap. 8.95 (ISBN 0-8066-2209-1, 10-5240). Augsburg.

Fellers, Pat. Peace-ing It Together: Peace & Justice Activities for Youth. (The Learning Connection Ser.). 160p. (Orig.). 1984. pap. 9.95 (ISBN 0-86683-836-8, 8440, HarpR). Har-Row.

Ferrero, Guglielmo. Peace & War. facs. ed. Pritchard, B., tr. LC 69-18927. (Essay Index Reprint Ser). 1933. 18.00 (ISBN 0-8369-0041-3). Ayer Co Pubs.

Friedrich, Carl J. Inevitable Peace. Repr. of 1948 ed. lib. bdg. 22.50x (ISBN 0-8371-2397-6, FRIN). Greenwood.

Fuchs, Harald. Augustin und der Antike Friendensgedanke. LC 72-147669. (Library of War & Peace; Relig. & Ethical Positions on War). 1973. lib. bdg. 46.00 (ISBN 0-8240-0427-2). Garland Pub.

Gagiati, Annie. Peace Where Is It? LC 73-91996. 1974. pap. 1.95 (ISBN 0-8198-0507-6). Dghtrs St Paul.

Geyer, Alan. Idea of Disarmament, Rethinking the Unthinkable. 256p. 1985. 11.95. Brethren.

Gooddard, Harold C. Atomic Peace. 1983. pap. 2.50x (ISBN 0-87574-057-X, 057). Pendle Hill.

Gorbachev, Mikail S. The Coming Century of Peace. Richardson, Stewart, ed. 304p. 1986. 17.95 (ISBN 0-931933-22-6). Richardson & Steirman.

Grimke, Thomas S. Address on the Truth, Dignity, Power & Beauty of the Principles of Peace, & on the Unchristian Character & Influence of War & the Warrior. LC 72-137542. (Peace Movement in America Ser). 56p. 1972. Repr. of 1832 ed. lib. bdg. 11.95x (ISBN 0-89198-070-9). Ozer.

Hemmenway, John. The Apostle of Peace: Memoir of William Ladd. LC 70-137544. 272p. 1972. Repr. of 1872 ed. lib. bdg. 20.95x (ISBN 0-89198-072-5). Ozer.

Hershberger, Guy F. War, Peace & Nonresistance. rev. ed. LC 53-7586. (Christian Peace Shelf Ser.). 375p. 1969. 15.95 (ISBN 0-8361-1449-3). Herald Pr.

Hills, Christopher. Christ-Yoga of Peace: Proposal for a World Peace Center. 156p. 1970. 4.00 (ISBN 0-916438-01-5). Univ of Trees.

Holmes, John H. New Wars for Old. LC 71-147623. (Library of War & Peace; Non-Resis. & Non-Vio.). 1972. lib. bdg. 46.00 (ISBN 0-8240-0398-5). Garland Pub.

Kant, Immanuel. Perpetual Peace. Beck, Lewis W., tr. LC 57-3588. 1957. pap. 3.56 scp (ISBN 0-672-60227-X, LLA54). Bobbs.

--Perpetual Peace. 59.95 (ISBN 0-8490-0815-8). Gordon Pr.

Leaders of the Christian Church Staff & Teegarden, Kenneth L. Seeking God's Peace in a Nuclear Age. Osborn, Ronald, ed. LC 85-7836. 96p. (Orig.). 1985. pap. 2.50 (ISBN 0-8272-3422-8). CBP.

Let There Be Peace on Earth. (Chrysalis Bk). 128p. (Orig.). 1986. pap. 7.95 (ISBN 0-916349-00-4). Amity Hous Inc.

Long, Edward L., Jr. Peace Thinking in a Warring World. LC 83-14675. 118p. 1983. pap. 6.95 (ISBN 0-664-24503-X). Westminster.

McNeal, Patricia F. The American Catholic Peace Movement, 1928-1972. 32.00 (ISBN 0-405-10840-0, 11820). Ayer Co Pubs.
Mathis, Mary E. A Scriptural Treasury of Peace. 1981. pap. 0.40 (ISBN 0-570-08352-4, 12-2932). Concordia.
Mehdi, M. T. Peace in Palestine. LC 75-43266. 1976. pap. 8.00 (ISBN 0-911026-08-8). New World Press NY.
Mendl, Wolf. The Study of War As a Contribution to Peace. (Orig.). 1983. pap. 2.50x (ISBN 0-87574-247-5, 247). Pendle Hill.
Musto, Ronald G. The Catholic Peace Tradition. LC 86-12494. 464p. (Orig.). 1986. pap. 21.95 (ISBN 0-88344-263-9). Orbis Bks.
National Study Conference of the Churches on a Just & Durable Peace 1st Ohio Wesleyan University 1942. A Basis for the Peace to Come. McConnell, Francis J., ed. 9.75 (ISBN 0-8369-7277-5, 8076). Ayer Co Pubs.
Obold, Ruth. Prepare for Peace, Pt. I. (Illus.). 40p. 1986. 6.25 (ISBN 0-87303-116-4). Faith & Life.
--Prepare for Peace, Pt. II. (Illus.). 48p. 1986. 6.25 (ISBN 0-87303-117-2). Faith & Life.
--Prepare for Peace, Pt. III. (Illus.). 55p. (YA) 1986. 6.25 (ISBN 0-87303-118-0). Faith & Life.
Peace Education Council & Sister Loretta Carey. Directions for Justice-Peace Education in the Catholic Elementary School. 44p. 1985. 4.80 (ISBN 0-318-20608-0). Natl Cath Educ.
Reid, Charles J., Jr., ed. Peace in a Nuclear Age: The Bishops' Pastoral Letter in Perspective. 1986. 44.95 (ISBN 0-8132-0624-3). Cath U Pr.
Satchidanada, Sri Swami. Peace is Within Our Reach. LC 85-14384. 96p. (Orig.). 1985. pap. 4.95 (ISBN 0-932040-29-2). Integral Yoga Pubns.
Schnitzler, Arthur. Some Day Peace Will Return: Notes on War & Peace. Weiss, Robert O., tr. from Ger. LC 78-15807. 1971. 8.50 (ISBN 0-8044-2803-4). Ungar.
Shannon, Thomas A. What Are They Saying about Peace & War? (WATSA Ser.). 128p. 1983. pap. 4.95 (ISBN 0-8091-2499-8). Paulist Pr.
Thoughts on Love & Peace: To Commemorate the Visit of Pope John Paul II, India, 1986. 104p. (YA) 1986. text ed. 12.95x (ISBN 0-7069-3059-2, Pub. by Vikas India). Advent NY.
True, Michael. Homemade Social Justice: Teaching Peace & Justice in the Home. 2nd ed. 168p. 1983. pap. 5.95 (ISBN 0-89622-202-0). Twenty-Third.
Ullmann, Richard K. The Dilemmas of a Reconciler. 1983. pap. 2.50x (ISBN 0-87574-131-2, 131). Pendle Hill.
Van Impe, Rexella. Satisfied...A Promise of Peace in a Troubled World. 142p. 1984. pap. 4.95 (ISBN 0-934803-15-3). J Van Impe.
Ware, Henry. Memoirs of the Reverend Noah Worcester, D. D. LC 78-137557. (Peace Movement in America Ser). xii, 155p. 1972. Repr. of 1844 ed. lib. bdg. 14.95x (ISBN 0-89198-088-1). Ozer.
Words of Peace. (Words of... Ser.). (Illus.). 48p. 1983. 3.95 (ISBN 0-8407-5340-3). Nelson.
World Conference on Religion & Peace Staff. Religions for Human Dignity & World Peace: Unabridged Proceedings of the World Conference on Religion & Peace, 4th. Taylor, John B. & Gebhardt, Gunther, eds. 469p. 1986. pap. write for info. (ISBN 2-88235-000-7). World Confer Rel & Peace.
Yarrow, C. H. Quaker Experiences in International Conciliation. LC 78-7415. 1978. 25.00x (ISBN 0-300-02260-3). Yale U Pr.
Yoder, Perry B. Shalom: The Bible's Word for Salvation, Justice & Peace. LC 86-82879. 161p. 1987. pap. 14.95 (ISBN 0-87303-120-2). Faith & Life.

PEACE (THEOLOGY)

Allen, James. From Passion to Peace. 64p. 1981. pap. 4.50 (ISBN 0-89540-077-4, SB-077). Sun Pub.
Beery, Angilee. So What Is Peace. 1971. pap. 1.50 (ISBN 0-87178-934-5). Brethren.
Brown, Dale W. Biblical Pacifism: A Peace Church Perspective. 176p. 1985. pap. 8.95 (ISBN 0-87178-108-5). Brethren.
Byers, David, ed. In the Name of Peace: Collective Statements of the United States Catholic Bishops on War & Peace, 1919-1980. 121p. 1983. pap. 8.95 (ISBN 1-55586-861-4). US Catholic.
Cohen, Alan. The Peace That You Seek. (Illus.). 195p. (Orig.). 1985. pap. 5.95 (ISBN 0-910367-35-3, 157). A Cohen.
Detweiler, Richard C. Mennonite Statements on Peace. 80p. (Orig.). 1968. pap. 2.95 (ISBN 0-8361-1581-3). Herald Pr.
Enz, Jacob J. The Christian & Warfare: The Old Testament, War & the Christian. (Christian Peace Shelf Ser.). 104p. 1972. pap. 2.95 (ISBN 0-8361-1684-4). Herald Pr.
Ferguson, John. War & Peace in the World's Religions. 1978. pap. 5.95 (ISBN 0-19-520074-8). Oxford U Pr.
Flournoy, Richard L., et al. One Hundred Ways to Obtain Peace: Overcoming Anxiety. (Life Enrichment Ser.). 1986. pap. 4.95 (ISBN 0-8010-3528-7). Baker Bk.
Ford, J. Massyngbaerd. My Enemy Is My Guest. LC 84-5812. 192p. 1984. pap. 9.95 (ISBN 0-88344-348-1). Orbis Bks.
Friesen, Ivan & Frieson, Rachel. How Do You Decide? (Shalom Ser.: No. 6). (Illus.). 16p. pap. 0.50 (ISBN 0-8361-1975-4). Herald Pr.
Gerlach, Barbara. The Things That Make for Peace: Biblical Meditations. (Illus.). 64p. (Orig.). 1983. pap. 4.95 (ISBN 0-8298-0664-4). Pilgrim NY.
Gordon, Haim & Grob, Leonard, eds. Education for Peace: Testimonies from World Religions. LC 86-31083. 224p. (Orig.). 1987. pap. 14.95 (ISBN 0-88344-359-7). Orbis Bks.
Heckman, Shirley J. Visions of Peace. LC 83-16522. 75p. (Orig.). 1984. pap. 5.95 (ISBN 0-377-00140-6). Friend Pr.
Johnson, David M., ed. Justice & Peace Education: Models for College & University Faculty. LC 85-25808. 256p. (Orig.). 1986. pap. 16.95 (ISBN 0-88344-247-7). Orbis Bks.
Klassen, William. Love of Enemies: The Way to Peace. LC 84-47927. (Overtures to Biblical Theology Ser.). 176p. 1984. pap. 8.95 (ISBN 0-8006-1539-5). Fortress.
Kury, Zaher P. From a Gun to a Flower. (Illus.). 352p. (Orig.). 1985. pap. 13.50 (ISBN 0-9615041-0-2). Unity Pr.
Leaders of the Christian Church Staff & Teegarden, Kenneth L. Seeking God's Peace in a Nuclear Age. Osborn, Ronald, ed. LC 85-7836. 96p. (Orig.). 1985. pap. 2.50 (ISBN 0-8272-3422-8). CBP.
Lenski, Lois. Sing for Peace. 16p. 1985. pap. 1.50 (ISBN 0-8361-3396-X). Herald Pr.
McIntyre, Michael, et al. Peaceworld. (Illus., Orig.). 1976. pap. 2.50 (ISBN 0-377-00054-X). Friend Pr.
Malgo, Wim. One Thousand Years Peace...A Utopia? 3.95 (ISBN 0-937422-11-8). Midnight Call.
National Conference of Catholic Bishops. The Challenge of Peace: God's Promise & Our Response. 116p. (Orig.). 1983. pap. 1.95 (ISBN 1-555868-63-0). US Catholic.
The Non Role of Religion in Peace or How to Convince a Woman to Kill Her Child or Have It Killed by Others. (Analysis Ser.: No. 6). 1982. pap. 10.00 (ISBN 0-686-42841-2). Inst Analysis.
O'Brien, David J. & Shannon, Thomas A., eds. Renewing the Earth: Catholic Documents on Peace, Justice & Liberation. LC 76-52008. 1977. pap. 6.95 (ISBN 0-385-12954-8, Im). Doubleday.
Peachey, J. Lorne. How to Teach Peace to Children. 32p. (Orig.). 1981. pap. 1.45 (ISBN 0-8361-1969-X). Herald Pr.
Peachey, Paul, ed. Peace, Politics, & the People of God. LC 85-45490. 208p. 1986. pap. 12.95 (ISBN 0-8006-1898-X). Fortress.
Pollock, Algernon J. La Paz con Dios. 2nd ed. Mahecha, Alberto, ed. Bautista, SAra, tr. from Eng. (La Serie Diamante). Tr. of Peace With God. (Span., Illus.). 48p. 1982. pap. 0.85 (ISBN 0-942504-09-7). Overcomer Pr.
Richardson, Beth, ed. Seasons of Peace. 72p. (Orig.). 1986. pap. 3.95 (ISBN 0-8358-0548-4). Upper Room.
Scully, Michael. The Best of This World. 416p. (Orig.). 1987. lib. bdg. 32.50 (ISBN 0-8191-5605-1, Pub. by IEA); pap. text ed. 19.75 (ISBN 0-8191-5606-X). U Pr of Amer.
Sider, Ronald J. & Brubaker, Darrel J., eds. Preaching on Peace. LC 82-10958. 96p. 1982. pap. 0.50 (ISBN 0-8006-1681-2). Fortress.
Yoder, John H. He Came Preaching Peace. LC 85-5474. 152p. (Orig.). 1985. pap. 8.95 (ISBN 0-8361-3395-1). Herald Pr.

PEACE OF MIND

Brandt, Henry R. The Struggle for Inner Peace. rev. ed. 136p. 1984. pap. 4.95 (ISBN 0-88207-245-5). Victor Bks.
Haggai, John E. How to Win Over Worry. 1967. pap. 3.95 (ISBN 0-310-25712-3, 9740P). Zondervan.
Murphy, Joseph. Peace Within Yourself. 300p. 1972. pap. 6.50 (ISBN 0-87516-188-X). De Vorss.
Pendleton, Winston K. How to Stop Worrying-Forever. LC 66-19811. 80p. 1975. Repr. of 1966 ed. 4.95 (ISBN 0-88289-083-2). Pelican.
Rubin, Theodore I. Reconciliations: Inner Peace in an Age of Anxiety. 1983. pap. 3.50 (ISBN 0-425-06312-7). Berkley Pub.
Subramuniya. The Clear White Light. (On the Path Ser.). (Illus.). 1979. pap. 2.00 (ISBN 0-87516-350-5). De Vorss.
Swindoll, Charles R. For Those Who Hurt. LC 77-4594. (Illus.). 1977. pap. 3.95 (ISBN 0-930014-13-8). Multnomah.
Tillich, Paul. Courage to Be. (Terry Lectures Ser.). 1952. pap. 6.95 (ISBN 0-300-00241-6, Y11). Yale U Pr.

PEACE SOCIETIES

Canadian Christian Movement for Peace Staff, et al. Christian Movement for Peace: Militarism & Hope. Huntly, Alyson & Morin, James, eds. 208p. 1983. pap. 29.95 (ISBN 0-697-01919-5). Wm C Brown.
Curti, Merle E. American Peace Crusade, Eighteen Fifteen to Eighteen Sixty. 1965. lib. bdg. 18.50x (ISBN 0-374-91976-3, Octagon). Hippocrene Bks.
Geaney, Dennis J. The Prophetic Parish: A Center for Peace & Justice. 144p. (Orig.). 1983. pap. 6.95 (ISBN 0-86683-807-4, HarpR). Har-Row.
Hancock, Thomas. Principles of Peace: Exemplified by the Conduct of the Society of Friends in Ireland, 1798. LC 70-147620. (Library of War & Peace; Non-Resis. & Non-Vio.). lib. bdg. 46.00 (ISBN 0-8240-0377-2). Garland Pub.

PEACEMAKING

see Reconciliation

PEALE, NORMAN VINCENT, 1898-

Peale, Norman V. Norman Vincent Peale's Treasury of Courage & Confidence. 256p. 1985. pap. 3.50 (ISBN 0-515-08329-1). Jove Pubns.
Peale, Norman Vincent. The True Joy of Positive Living. 480p. 1985. pap. 16.95 (ISBN 0-8027-2503-1). Walker & Co.

PEASANTS' WAR, 1524-1525

see also Anabaptists

Schapiro, Jacob S. Social Reform & the Reformation. LC 74-127456. (Columbia University Studies in the Social Sciences: No. 90). 1970. Repr. of 1909 ed. 16.50 (ISBN 0-404-51090-6). AMS Pr.

PELAGIANISM

Augustinus, Aurelius. De Peccatorum Meritis et Remissione et de Baptismo Parvulorum, Ad Marcellinum Liber Tres, Bk. 3. Urba, C. F. & Zycha, I., eds. (Corpus Scriptorum Ecclesiasticorum Latinorum Ser: Vol. 60). 50.00 (ISBN 0-384-02490-4). Johnson Repr.
Warfield, Benjamin B. Studies in Tertullian & Augustine. Repr. of 1930 ed. lib. bdg. 29.00x (ISBN 0-8371-4490-6, WATT). Greenwood.

PELAGIUS

Donovan, Joseph P. Pelagius & the Fifth Crusade. LC 76-29822. Repr. of 1950 ed. 29.00 (ISBN 0-404-15416-6). AMS Pr.
Evans, Robert F. Four Letters of Pelagius: On the Grounds for Authenticity of 4 of the 20 Works Ascribed by De Plinval to Pelagius. LC 68-11594. 1968. text ed. 12.00x (ISBN 0-685-00379-5). A R Allenson.
Ferguson, John. Pelagius: A Historical & Theological Study. LC 77-84700. Repr. of 1956 ed. 27.00 (ISBN 0-404-16107-3). AMS Pr.

PELE (GODDESS)

McBride, L. R. Pele, Volcano Goddess of Hawaii. (Illus.). 1968. pap. 3.25 (ISBN 0-912180-11-0). Petroglyph.

PENANCE

see also Absolution; Church Discipline; Confession; Fasting; Forgiveness of Sin; Penitentials; Repentance

Barry, David W. Ministry of Reconciliation: Modern Lessons from Scripture & Sacrament. LC 75-4630. 129p. (Orig.). 1975. pap. 2.95 (ISBN 0-8189-0317-1). Alba.
Brennan, Patrick J. Penance & Reconciliation. (Guidelines for Contemporary Catholics Ser.). (Orig.). 1986. pap. 7.95 (ISBN 0-88347-195-7). Thomas More.
Burghardt, W. J., et al, eds. Tertullian, Treatise on Penance: On Penitence & on Purity. LC 58-10746. (Ancient Christian Writers Ser.: No. 28). 138p. 1959. 12.95 (ISBN 0-8091-0150-5). Paulist Pr.
Champlin, Joseph M. & Haggerty, Brian A. Together in Peace for Children. LC 76-26348. (Illus.). 72p. 1976. 1.50 (ISBN 0-87793-119-4). Ave Maria.
Dallen, James. The Reconciling Community: The Rite of Penance. (Reformed Rites of the Catholic Church Ser.: Vol. III). 400p. (Orig.). 1986. pap. 17.50 (ISBN 0-916134-76-8). Pueblo Pub Co.
Hamelin, Leonce. Reconciliation in the Church. O'Connell, Matthew J., tr. from Fr. LC 80-29328. Orig. Title: La Reconciliation en Eglise. 111p. 1980. pap. text ed. 5.50 (ISBN 0-8146-1215-6). Liturgical Pr.
Hellwig, Monika. Sign of Reconciliation & Conversion: The Sacrament of Penance for Our Times. (Message of the Sacraments Ser.: Vol. 4). 1982. 13.95 (ISBN 0-89453-394-0); pap. 8.95 (ISBN 0-89453-272-3). M Glazier.
Holmberg, Kathleen. Our First Penance: Celebrating God's Forgiving Love. Fischer, Carl, ed. 1986. dupl. masterbk 9.95 (ISBN 0-89837-108-2). Peter Li.
Kelly, George. Sacrament of Penance & Reconciliation. (Synthesis Ser). 96p. 1976. 0.75 (ISBN 0-8199-0701-4). Franciscan Herald.
Kelly, George, ed. The Sacrament of Penance in Our Time. 1976. 4.00 (ISBN 0-8198-0455-X). Dghtrs St Paul.
Lea, Henry C. History of Auricular Confession & Indulgences in the Latin Church, 3 Vols. LC 68-19287. 1968. Repr. of 1896 ed. lib. bdg. 67.25x (ISBN 0-8371-0140-9, LEHC). Greenwood.
Leichner, Jeannine T. Making Things Right: The Sacrament of Reconciliation. (Illus.). 62p. (Orig.). 1980. pap. 3.50 (ISBN 0-87973-351-9, 351). Our Sunday Visitor.
Munoz, Hector. Will You Hear My Confession? How to Make a Good Examination of Conscience & a Good Confession. Bair, Robert, tr. from Span. LC 82-20597. 162p. 1983. pap. 6.95 (ISBN 0-8189-0439-9). Alba.
Orsy, Ladislas. Evolving Church & the Sacrament of Penance. 1974. 6.95 (ISBN 0-87193-072-2). Dimension Bks.
Penance & Reconciliation in the Church. (Liturgy Documentary Ser.: No. 7). 96p. (Orig.). 1986. pap. 5.95 (ISBN 1-55586-104-0). US Catholic.
Reconciliation & Penance. 144p. 1984. pap. 3.95 (ISBN 1-55586-951-3). US Catholic.
Rite of Penance. pocket ed. 3.95 (ISBN 0-89942-128-8, 128/04). Catholic Bk Pub.
Rite of Penance. large ed. 160p. (Large, Two-Color Type). 8.50 (ISBN 0-89942-528-3, 528/22). Catholic Bk Pub.
Scanlan, Michael. The Power in Penance. 64p. 1972. pap. 0.95 (ISBN 0-87793-092-9). Ave Maria.
Schroeder, Frederick & Meyers, Craig. The Potential for Spiritual Direction in the New Rite of Penance. 1.85 (ISBN 0-89942-530-5, 530/04). Catholic Bk Pub.
Tobin, Eamon. The Sacrament of Penance: Its Past & Its Meaning for Today. 32p. (Orig.). 1984. pap. 1.50 (ISBN 0-89243-199-7). Liguori Pubns.
Twigg, Blanche. Penance: God's Gift for Forgiveness. (Illus.). 64p. 1974. pap. 2.50 (ISBN 0-912228-15-6). St Anthony Mess Pr.

PENANCE–HISTORY

Marshall, Nathaniel. Penitential Discipline of the Primitive Church. LC 74-172846. (Library of Anglo-Catholic Theology: No. 13). Repr. of 1844 ed. 27.50 (ISBN 0-404-52105-3). AMS Pr.

PENITENCE

see Repentance

PENITENTIALS

McNeill, John T. & Gamer, Helena M. Medieval Handbooks of Penance. 1965. lib. bdg. 40.00x (ISBN 0-374-95548-4, Octagon). Hippocrene Bks.
Oakley, Thomas P. English Penitential Discipline & Anglo-Saxon Law in Their Joint Influence. LC 71-82243. (Columbia University. Studies in the Social Sciences: No. 242). Repr. of 1923 ed. 20.00 (ISBN 0-404-51242-9). AMS Pr.
Weigle, Marta. Brothers of Light, Brothers of Blood: The Penitentes of the Southwest. 1st ed. LC 75-21188. pap. 82.00 (ISBN 0-317-27139-3, 2024680). Bks Demand UMI.

PENN, WILLIAM, 1644-1718

Beatty, Edward C. William Penn As Social Philosopher. 1972. lib. bdg. 24.50x (ISBN 0-374-90506-1, Octagon). Hippocrene Bks.
Brailsford, Mabel R. Making of William Penn. facs. ed. LC 77-124227. (Select Bibliographies Reprint Ser.). 1930. 22.00 (ISBN 0-8369-5416-5). Ayer Co Pubs.
Bronner, Edwin B. William Penn: 17th Century Founding Father. LC 75-32728. (Illus.). 36p. (Orig.). 1975. pap. 2.50x (ISBN 0-87574-204-1). Pendle Hill.
--William Penn's Holy Experiment; the Founding of Pennsylvania Sixteen Eighty-One to Seventeen Hundred & One. LC 78-5882. (Illus.). 306p. 1978. Repr. of 1963 ed. lib. bdg. 22.50x (ISBN 0-313-20432-2, BRWP). Greenwood.
Comfort, William W. William Penn & Our Liberties. (Illus.). 146p. 1976. pap. 3.00 (ISBN 0-941308-02-2). Religious Soc Friends.
Dobree, Bonamy. William Penn, Quaker & Pioneer. LC 78-15258. 1978. Repr. of 1932 ed. lib. bdg. 35.00 (ISBN 0-8414-3790-4). Folcroft.
--William Penn, Quaker & Pioneer. 346p. 1983. Repr. of 1932 ed. lib. bdg. 35.00 (ISBN 0-8492-4227-4). R West.
Hull, William I. William Penn. facsimile ed. LC 78-179525. (Select Bibliographies Reprint Ser). Repr. of 1937 ed. 32.00 (ISBN 0-8369-6654-6). Ayer Co Pubs.
Janney, Samuel M. The Life of William Penn: With Selections from His Correspondence & Autobiography. facsimile ed. LC 74-130555. (Select Bibliographies Reprint Ser.). Repr. of 1851 ed. 24.00 (ISBN 0-8369-5528-5). Ayer Co Pubs.
McDermott, F. William Penn, Thomas Gray & an Account of the Historical Associations of Stoke Poges. 1973. Repr. of 1930 ed. lib. bdg. 25.00 (ISBN 0-8414-6026-4). Folcroft.

Proud, Robert. The History of Pennsylvania, 2 Vols. LC 66-25101. 1967. Repr. of 1797 ed. 20.00 ea. Vol. 1 (ISBN 0-87152-031-1). Vol. 2 (ISBN 0-87152-032-X). Set. 40.00 (ISBN 0-87152-305-1). Reprint.

Reason, Joyce. Quaker Cavalier: William Penn. 1971. pap. 2.95 (ISBN 0-87508-618-7). Chr Lit.

Soderlund, Jean R. & Dunn, Richard S., eds. William Penn & the Founding of Pennsylvania, 1680-1684: A Documentary History. (Illus.). 380p. 1983. 26.50x (ISBN 0-8122-7862-3); pap. 10.95x (ISBN 0-8122-1131-6). U of Pa Pr.

Tolles, Frederick & Alderfer, Gordon E., eds. The Witness of William Penn. 1980. Repr. of 1957 ed. lib. bdg. 18.50x (ISBN 0-374-97950-2, Octagon). Hippocrene Bks.

Vining, Elizabeth G. William Penn: Mystic. LC 74-95891. (Orig.). 1969. pap. 2.50x (ISBN 0-87574-167-3, 167). Pendle Hill.

Weems, Mason L. The Life of William Penn. LC 75-31139. Repr. of 1822 ed. 17.50 (ISBN 0-404-13613-3). AMS Pr.

PENNSYLVANIA–BOUNDARIES–VIRGINIA

Smith, William H. St. Clair Papers: The Life & Public Services of Arthur St. Clair, 2 Vols. facs. ed. LC 77-117894. (Select Bibliographies Reprint Ser). 1881. Set. 62.00 (ISBN 0-8369-5347-9). Ayer Co Pubs.

PENNSYLVANIA–DESCRIPTION AND TRAVEL

Agnew, Daniel. History of the Region of Pennsylvania North of the Ohio & West of the Allegheny River. LC 75-146371. (First American Frontier Ser). 1971. Repr. of 1887 ed. 16.00 (ISBN 0-405-02821-0). Ayer Co Pubs.

Beatty, Charles. Journal of a Two-Months Tour, with a View to Promoting Religion. LC 72-108459. 1768. 25.00x (ISBN 0-403-00456-X). Scholarly.

Cazenove, Theophile. Cazenove Journal, 1794: A Journey Through New Jersey & Pennsylvania. Kelsey, Rayner W., ed. (Haverford Coll. Studies: No. 13). 1922. 17.50x (ISBN 0-686-17388-0). R S Barnes.

Foulke, Arthur T. Picture-Book for Proud Lovers of Danville, Montour County & Riverside, PA. LC 75-32061. (Illus.). 320p. 1976. 15.00 (ISBN 0-8158-0334-6). Chris Mass.

PENNSYLVANIA–HISTORY

Agnew, Daniel. History of the Region of Pennsylvania North of the Ohio & West of the Allegheny River. LC 75-146371. (First American Frontier Ser). 1971. Repr. of 1887 ed. 16.00 (ISBN 0-405-02821-0). Ayer Co Pubs.

Proud, Robert. The History of Pennsylvania, 2 Vols. LC 66-25101. 1967. Repr. of 1797 ed. 20.00 ea. Vol. 1 (ISBN 0-87152-031-1). Vol. 2 (ISBN 0-87152-032-X). Set. 40.00 (ISBN 0-87152-305-1). Reprint.

Rauman, Richard. For the Reputation of Truth: Politics, Religion, & Conflict Among the Pennsylvanian Quakers, 1750-1800. LC 79-143626. pap. 70.00 (ISBN 0-317-39712-5, 2025828). Bks Demand UMI.

Ressler, Martin E., et al. Lancaster County Churches in the Revolutionary War Era. Harrison, Matthew W., Jr., ed. LC 76-21210. (Illus.). 96p. 1976. pap. 3.50 (ISBN 0-915010-11-9, Co-Pub by Lancaster County Bicentennial Committee). Sutter House.

Ruth, John L. Twas Seeding Time. LC 76-41475. 220p. 1976. pap. 5.95 (ISBN 0-8361-1800-6). Herald Pr.

Thompson, Thomas R. Chris: A Biography of Christian C. Sanderson. LC 73-84422. (Illus.). 420p. 1973. 12.95 (ISBN 0-8059-1899-X). Dorrance.

Walker, Joseph E., ed. Pleasure & Business in Western Pennsylvania: The Journal of Joshua Gilpin, 1809. LC 75-623536. (Illus.). 156p. 1975. 9.00 (ISBN 0-911124-78-0). Pa Hist & Mus.

Wister, Sally. Sally Wister's Journal: A True Narrative Being a Quaker Maiden's Account of Her Experiences with Officers of the Continental Army, 1777-1778. Myers, Albert C., ed. LC 73-78039. (Eyewitness Accounts of the American Revolution Ser., No. 2). 1969. Repr. of 1902 ed. 16.00 (ISBN 0-405-01169-5). Ayer Co Pubs.

PENNSYLVANIA DUTCH

see Pennsylvania Germans

PENNSYLVANIA GERMANS

see also Mennonites;

also names of specific handicrafts for books on Pennsylvania German work in a special field, e.g. illumination of books and manuscripts

Buffington, Albert F., et al. Something for Everyone, Something for You: Essays in Memoriam Albert Franklin Buffington, Vol. 14. (Illus.). 1980. 25.00 (ISBN 0-911122-41-9). Penn German Soc.

Costabel, Eva D. The Pennsylvania Dutch. LC 86-3334. (Illus.). 48p. 1986. 14.95 (ISBN 0-689-31281-4, Children Bk). Macmillan.

Eshleman, H. Frank. Historic Background & Annals of the Swiss & German Pioneer Settlers of Southeastern Pennsylvania & of Their Remote Ancestors. LC 77-86809. 386p. 1982. Repr. of 1917 ed. 20.00 (ISBN 0-8063-0105-8). Genealog Pub.

Glatfelter, Charles H. Pastors & People: German & Lutheran Reformed Churches in the Pennsylvania Field, 1717-1793, Vol. II, The History. LC 80-83400. (Penn. German Ser.: Vol. 15). (Illus.). 25.00 (ISBN 0-911122-44-3). Penn German Soc.

Mercer, Henry C. The Bible in Iron. 3rd ed. (Illus.). 356p. 1961. pap. 15.00 (ISBN 0-910302-01-4). Bucks Co Hist.

Neff, Larry M. & Weiser, Frederick S., eds. The Account Book of Conrad Weiser: Berks County, Pennsylvania, 1746-1760. LC 81-84666. (Sources & Documents of the Pennsylvania Germans Ser.: No. 6). (Illus.). 1981. 15.00 (ISBN 0-911122-43-5). Penn German Soc.

Sachse, Julius F. German Pietists of Provincial Pennsylvania, 1694-1708. LC 70-134384. (Communal Societies Ser.). Repr. of 1895 ed. 32.50 (ISBN 0-404-07204-6). AMS Pr.

Weiser, Frederick S., tr. Records of Pastoral Acts at Emanual Lutheran Church (Known in the Eighteen Century as the Warwick Congregation, Near Brickerville, Elizabeth Township, Lancaster County) 1743-1799. (Sources & Documents Ser.: No. 8). 229p. 1983. pap. 15.00 (ISBN 0-911122-47-8). Penn German Soc.

PENTECOST

Bagiackas, Joseph. The Future Glory. LC 83-70962. 130p. (Orig.). 1983. pap. 3.95 (ISBN 0-943780-02-0, 8020). Charismatic Ren Servs.

Ball, John T. Barefoot in the Palace. 1985. 6.25 (ISBN 0-89536-748-3, 5854). CSS of Ohio.

Breton, Thierry. The Pentecost Project. LC 86-33730. 1987. 17.95 (ISBN 0-8050-0380-0). H Holt & Co.

Brice, Joseph. Pentecost. 6.95 (ISBN 0-686-12901-6). Schmul Pub Co.

Brokhoff, Barbara. Trouble on the Mountain! Sherer, Michael L., ed. (Orig.). 1986. pap. 6.25 (ISBN 0-89536-825-0, 6834). CSS of Ohio.

Brown, Schuyler & Saliers, Don E. Pentecost Three. Actemeier, Elizabeth, et al, eds. LC 79-7377. (Proclamation Ser.: No. 2). 64p. 1982. pap. 3.75 (ISBN 0-8006-4099-3, 1-4099). Fortress.

Brumback, Carl. What Meaneth This? a Pentecostal Answer to a Pentecostal Question. 352p. 1947. pap. 4.95 (ISBN 0-88243-626-0, 02-0624). Gospel Pub.

Chinn, Edward. Questions of the Heart. (Orig.). 1987. pap. price not set (ISBN 0-89536-877-3, 7863). CSS of Ohio.

Christenson, Larry. Speaking in Tongues. LC 97-5595. 1968. pap. 3.95 (ISBN 0-87123-518-8, 200518). Bethany Hse.

Clement, Arthur J. Pentecost Or Pretense. 1981. pap. 7.95 (ISBN 0-8100-0118-7, 12N1718). Northwest Pub.

Conn, Charles W. Pillars of Pentecost. 148p. 1979. 6.95 (ISBN 0-87148-681-4). Pathway Pr.

Corbett, W. J. Pentecost & the Chosen One. 240p. 1987. 14.95 (ISBN 0-385-29549-9). Delacorte.

Deal, William S. All about Pentacost. 1983. pap. 3.95 (ISBN 0-318-18716-7). Crusade Pubs.

Edwards, O. C., Jr. & Taylor, Gardner C. Pentecost 3. Achtemeier, Elizabeth, et al, eds. LC 79-7377. (Proclamation 2: Aids for Interpreting the Lessons of the Church Year, Ser. C). 64p. (Orig.). 1980. pap. 3.75 (ISBN 0-8006-4084-5, 1-4084). Fortress.

Elbert, Paul. Essays on Apostolic Themes. 252p. 1985. 14.95 (ISBN 0-913573-14-0). Hendrickson MA.

Ford, J. Massyngberd. Pentecostal Experience. LC 72-116869. 64p. (Orig.). 1970. pap. 1.95 (ISBN 0-8091-1655-3). Paulist Pr.

Gaffin, Richard B. Perspectives on Pentecost. 1979. pap. 3.95 (ISBN 0-87552-269-6). Presby & Reformed.

Gee, Donald. A New Discovery. Orig. Title: Pentecost. 96p. 1932. pap. 1.00 (ISBN 0-88243-569-8, 02-0569). Gospel Pub.

Hamilton, Ronald R. Reluctant Followers: A Chosen People? Sherer, Michael L., ed. (Orig.). 1986. pap. 6.25 (ISBN 0-89536-824-2, 6833). CSS of Ohio.

Harms, Paul. Seek Good, Not Evil (That You May Live) 1985. 6.25 (ISBN 0-89536-754-8, 5860). CSS of Ohio.

Harrington, Daniel J. Pentecost Two: Proclamation 3B. LC 84-18756. (Proclamation Ser.). 64p. 1985. pap. 3.75 (ISBN 0-8006-4107-8, 1-4107). Fortress.

Howard, Virgil P. Pentecost 1. LC 84-18756. (Proclamation 3 A). 64p. 1987. pap. 3.75 (ISBN 0-8006-4122-1, 1-4122). Fortress.

Hubbard, David A. Pentecost One: Proclamation 3B. LC 84-18756. (Proclamation Ser.). 64p. 1985. pap. 3.75 (ISBN 0-8006-4106-X, 1-4106). Fortress.

Keck, Leander E. & Hobbie, Francis W. Pentecost One. LC 79-7377. (Proclamation 2: Aids for Interpreting the Lessons of the Church Year, Series B). 64p. 1982. pap. 3.75 (ISBN 0-8006-4089-6, 1-4089). Fortress.

Kee, Howard C. & Gomes, Peter J. Pentecost One. Achtemeier, Elizabeth, et al, eds. LC 79-7377. (Proclamation 2: Aids for Interpreting the Lessons of the Church Year, Ser. C). 64p. 1980. pap. 3.75 (ISBN 0-8006-4081-0, 1-4081). Fortress.

Kelderman, Duane. The Gentle Whisper. 1985. 6.25 (ISBN 0-89536-752-1, 5858). CSS of Ohio.

Kemper, R. W. The Pentecost Cycle. LC 12-2965. 1982. pap. 7.95 (ISBN 0-570-03872-3). Concordia.

Kirby, Wallace. If Only... 1985. 6.25 (ISBN 0-89536-753-X, 5859). CSS of Ohio.

Lacy, Donald C. Healing Echoes: Values for Christian Unity. Sherer, Michael L., ed. (Orig.). 1986. pap. 6.25 (ISBN 0-89536-826-9, 6835). CSS of Ohio.

Macleod, Donald. Know the Way, Keep the Truth, Win the Life. (Orig.). 1987. pap. price not set (ISBN 0-89536-872-2, 7858). CSS of Ohio.

Mann, Leonard. Life-Size Living. Sherer, Michael L., ed. (Orig.). 1986. pap. 6.25 (ISBN 0-89536-820-X, 6829). CSS of Ohio.

Miller, Patrick D., Jr. Pentecost 2. LC 84-18756. (Proclamation 3 A). 64p. 1987. pap. 3.75 (ISBN 0-8006-4123-X). Fortress.

Mocko, George. Good God, Where in the World Are You? (Orig.). 1987. pap. price not set (ISBN 0-89536-878-1, 7864). CSS of Ohio.

Murray, Andrew. The Believer's Full Blessing of Pentecost. 112p. 1984. pap. 3.95 (ISBN 0-87123-597-8). Bethany Hse.

--Full Blessing of Pentecost. 1965. pap. 2.95 (ISBN 0-87508-376-5). Chr Lit.

--In Search of Spiritual Excellence. Orig. Title: The Full Blessing of Pentecost. 125p. 1984. pap. text ed. 3.50 (ISBN 0-88368-163-3). Whitaker Hse.

Patt, Richard W. Partners in the Impossible. 1984. 4.95 (ISBN 0-89536-678-9, 4854). CSS of Ohio.

Peck, George. Pentecost 3. LC 84-18756. (Proclamation 3 A). 64p. 1987. pap. 3.75 (ISBN 0-8006-4124-8, 1-4124). Fortress.

Pentecost: God's Answer for the Occult. pap. 2.00 (ISBN 0-911866-77-9). Advocate.

Peterson, Thomas. Doing Something by Doing Nothing. 1985. 6.25 (ISBN 0-89536-747-5, 5853). CSS of Ohio.

Prescott, Roger. The Promise of Life. 1984. 4.75 (ISBN 0-89536-683-5, 4859). CSS of Ohio.

Prince, Derek. From Jordan to Pentecost, Bk. III. (Foundation Ser.). pap. 2.95 (ISBN 0-934920-02-8, B-12). Derek Prince.

--Purposes of Pentecost. (Foundation Ser.: Bk. IV). 1965-66. pap. 3.95 (ISBN 0-934920-03-6). Derek Prince.

Radecke, Mark. In Christ: A New Creation. Sherer, Michael L., ed. (Orig.). 1986. pap. 6.25 (ISBN 0-89536-821-8, 6830). CSS of Ohio.

Rahner, Karl. The Spirit in the Church. 1979. pap. 3.95 (ISBN 0-8245-0399-6). Crossroad NY.

Ranaghan, Kevin & Ranaghan, Dorothy. Catholic Pentecostals Today. rev. ed. LC 83-70963. 196p. 1983. pap. 4.95 (ISBN 0-943780-03-9, 8039). Charismatic Ren Servs.

Robinson, James. A Cup Running Over. (Orig.). 1987. pap. price not set (ISBN 0-89536-873-0, 7859). CSS of Ohio.

Rogers, John B., Jr. Pentecost Three: Proclamation 3B. LC 84-18756. (Proclamation Ser.). 64p. 1985. pap. 3.75 (ISBN 0-8006-4108-6, 1-4108). Fortress.

Rueter, Alvin. The Freedom to Be Wrong. 1985. 6.25 (ISBN 0-89536-749-1, 5855). CSS of Ohio.

Skaballanovitch, M. Pjatidesjatnitsa. Tr. of Pentacost. 176p. pap. 6.00 (ISBN 0-317-29163-7). Holy Trinity.

Smith, Warren T. Journey in Faith. 1984. 5.50 (ISBN 0-89536-679-7, 4855). CSS of Ohio.

Thulin, Richard L. The Caller & the Called. Sherer, Michael L, ed. (Orig.). 1986. pap. 6.25 (ISBN 0-89536-819-6, 6828). CSS of Ohio.

Tiede, David L. & Kavanagh, Aidan. Pentecost 1. Achtemeier, Elizabeth, et al, eds. LC 79-7377. (Proclamation 2: Aids for Interpreting the Lessons of the Church Year, Ser. A). 64p. (Orig.). 1981. pap. 3.75 (ISBN 0-8006-4096-9, 1-4096). Fortress.

Turner, William H. Pentecost & Tongues. pap. 3.50 (ISBN 0-911866-83-3). Advocate.

Valliere, Paul. Holy War & Pentecostal Peace. 176p. (Orig.). 1983. pap. 9.95 (ISBN 0-8164-2481-0, HarpR). Har-Row.

Wedel, Alton. The Word Today. 1984. 5.25 (ISBN 0-89536-684-3, 4860). CSS of Ohio.

Weekley, James. Tilted Haloes. (Orig.). 1987. pap. price not set (ISBN 0-89536-871-4, 7857). CSS of Ohio.

Zelle, Donald. Wind Through the Valleys. (Orig.). 1987. pap. price not set (ISBN 0-89536-876-5, 7862). CSS of Ohio.

PENTECOST FESTIVAL

see also Shavu'Oth (Feast of Weeks)

Feather, Nevin & Collins, Myrtle. Come Holy Spirit. 1986. 4.75 (ISBN 0-89536-790-4, 6808). CSS of Ohio.

Furnish, Victor P. & Thulin, Richard L. Pentecost 3. Achtemeier, Elizabeth, et al, eds. LC 79-7377. (Proclamation 2: Aids for Interpreting the Lessons of the Church Year, Ser. A). 64p. (Orig.). 1981. pap. 3.75 (ISBN 0-8006-4098-5, 1-4098). Fortress.

Minear, Paul S. & Adams, Harry B. Pentecost 2. Achtemeier, Elizabeth, et al, eds. LC 79-7377. (Proclamation 2: Aids for Interpreting the Lessons of the Church Year, Ser. A). 64p. (Orig.). 1981. pap. 3.75 (ISBN 0-8006-4097-7, 1-4097). Fortress.

PENTECOSTAL CHURCHES

see also Church of God

Campbell, Joe E. Pentecostal Holiness Church. pap. 6.00 (ISBN 0-911866-55-8). Advocate.

Dayton, Donald W., ed. The Sermons of Charles F. Parham. (The Higher Christian Life Ser.). 261p. 1985. lib. bdg. 35.00 (ISBN 0-8240-6413-5). Garland Pub.

--Seven "Jesus Only" Tracts. (The Higher Christian Life Ser.). 379p. 1985. lib. bdg. 45.00 (ISBN 0-8240-6414-3). Garland Pub.

--Three Early Pentecostal Tracts. (The Higher Christian Life Ser.). 441p. 1985. 55.00 (ISBN 0-8240-6415-1). Garland Pub.

--The Work of T. B. Barratt. (The Higher Christian Life Ser.). 435p. 1985. 55.00 (ISBN 0-8240-6404-6). Garland Pub.

Dayton, Donald W. & Robeck, Cecil M., eds. Witness to Pentecost: The Life of Frank Bartleman. (The Higher Christian Life Ser.). 439p. 1985. 55.00 (ISBN 0-8240-6405-4). Garland Pub.

D'Epinay, Christian L. Haven of the Masses: A Study of the Pentecostal Movement in Chile. Sandle, Marjorie, tr. (World Studies of Churches in Mission). 1969. pap. 4.95 (ISBN 0-377-82931-5, Pub. by Lutterworth England). Friend Pr.

Faupel, David W. The American Pentecostal Movement: A Bibliographic Essay. LC 76-361994. (Occasional Bibliographic Papers of the B. L. Fisher Library: No. 2). 56p. 1972. 3.00 (ISBN 0-914368-01-X). Asbury Theological.

Fauss, O. F. What God Hath Wrought: The Complete Works of O. F. Fauss. Wallace, Mary H., ed. (Illus.). 300p. (Orig.). 1985. pap. 6.95 (ISBN 0-912315-84-9). Word Aflame.

Fleisch, Paul. Die Moderne Gemeinschaftsbewegung in Deutschland. Dayton, Donald W., ed. (The Higher Christian Life Ser.). 605p. 1985. 75.00 (ISBN 0-8240-6419-4). Garland Pub.

Fletcher, William c. Soviet Charismatics: The Pentecostals in the U. S. S. R. (American University Studies VII (Theology & Religion): Vol. 9). 287p. 1985. text ed. 25.15 (ISBN 0-8204-0226-5). P Lang Pubs.

Geffre, Claude, et al, eds. Different Theologies, Common Responsibilities. (Concilium Ser.: Vol. 171). 116p. 1984. pap. 6.95 (ISBN 0-567-30051-X, Pub. by T & T Clark Ltd Uk). Fortress.

Gerlach, Luther P. & Hine, Virginia H. People, Power, Change: Movements of Social Transformation. LC 70-109434. 1970. pap. 9.63 scp (ISBN 0-672-60613-5). Bobbs.

King, Joseph H. From Passover to Pentecost. pap. 3.95 (ISBN 0-911866-57-4). Advocate.

Kinzie, Frederick E. & Kinzie, Vera D. Strength Through Struggle. Stewart, James, ed. & intro. by. LC 86-1645. (Illus.). 350p. (Orig.). 1986. pap. 6.95 (ISBN 0-912315-98-9). Word Aflame.

Knight, Cecil B. Pentecostal Worship. 1974. pap. 3.95 (ISBN 0-87148-684-9). Pathway Pr.

Lemons, Frank W. Our Pentecostal Heritage. 174p. 1963. pap. 4.95 (ISBN 0-87148-653-9). Pathway Pr.

Poloma, Margaret M. The Charismatic Movement: Is There a New Pentecost? (Social Movements Past & Present Ser.). 304p. 1987. pap. 9.95 (ISBN 0-8057-9721-1, Twayne). G K Hall.

Schwartz, Gary. Sect Ideologies & Social Status. LC 72-120598. 1970. 18.00x (ISBN 0-226-74216-4). U of Chicago Pr.

Speaks, R. L. The Prelude to Pentecost. 200p. 1985. 11.95 (ISBN 0-682-40229-X). Exposition Pr FL.

Synan, Vinson. The Holiness-Pentecostal Movement. 1972. pap. 9.95 (ISBN 0-8028-1728-9). Eerdmans.

Tomlinson, A. J. The Last Great Conflict. (The Higher Christian Life Ser.). 219p. 1985. lib. bdg. 30.00 (ISBN 0-8240-6446-1); pap. 8.95 (ISBN 0-317-14532-0, 1925). Garland Pub.

Vaughn, Lou E. Brush Arbor Birthright. LC 86-80089. (Illus.). 160p. (Orig.). 1986. pap. 3.95 (ISBN 0-88243-483-7, 02-0483). Gospel Pub.

Walsh, Vincent M. Prepare My People. 100p. (Orig.). (YA) 1986. pap. text ed. 5.00 (ISBN 0-943374-13-8). Key of David.
Whittaker, Colin C. Seven Pentecostal Pioneers. LC 84-73310. 224p. 1985. Repr. of 1983 ed. 5.95 (ISBN 0-88243-545-0, 02-0545). Gospel Pub.
Williams, Melvin D. Community in a Black Pentecostal Church: An Anthropological Study. 202p. 1984. pap. 8.95x (ISBN 0-88133-049-3). Waveland Pr.
--Community in a Black Pentecostal Church: An Anthropological Study. LC 74-5108. pap. 53.50 (ISBN 0-317-42278-2, 2024332). Bks Demand UMI.
Womack, David. The Wellsprings of the Pentecostal Movement. 96p. 1968. pap. 1.50 (ISBN 0-88243-628-7, 02-0628). Gospel Pub.
Wood, Laurence W. Pentecostal Grace. Burgess, Harold, ed. 1980. pap. 8.95 (ISBN 0-310-75041-5, 17028P). Zondervan.

PENTECOSTALISM
see also Jesus People

Achtemeier, Paul J. Pentecost Three. LC 84-18756. (Proclamation Three C Ser.). 64p. 1986. pap. 3.75 (1-4132). Fortress.
Anderson, Robert M. Vision of the Disinherited: The Making of American Pentecostalism. 1979. 24.95x (ISBN 0-19-502502-4). Oxford U Pr.
Babcox, Neil. A Search for Charismatic Reality: One Man's Pilgrimage. LC 84-25506. 160p. 1985. pap. 5.95 (ISBN 0-88070-085-8). Multnomah.
Baker, Elizabeth V. Chronicles of a Faith Life. (The Higher Christian Life Ser.). 270p. 1984. 35.00 (ISBN 0-8240-6403-8). Garland Pub.
Bales, James D. Pentecostalism in the Church. pap. 2.95 (ISBN 0-89315-204-8). Lambert Bk.
Bartleman, Frank. Azusa Street. LC 80-82806. 1980. pap. 5.95 (ISBN 0-88270-439-7). Bridge Pub.
Bernard, David K. The New Birth. Wallace, Mary H., ed. 346p. (Orig.). 1984. pap. 6.95 (ISBN 0-912315-77-6). Word Aflame.
Black, R. L. Discerning the Body. 98p. (Orig.). 1984. pap. 3.95 (ISBN 0-934942-42-0, 1264). White Wing Pub.
Borsch, Frederick H. Pentecost One. LC 84-18756. (Proclamation Three C Ser.). 64p. 1986. pap. 3.75 (ISBN 0-8006-4130-2, 1-4130). Fortress.
Brandt, Robert L. Pentecostal Promise. (Charismatic Bks.). 47p. 1972. pap. 0.69 (ISBN 0-88243-920-0, 02-0920). Gospel Pub.
Cagle, Paul R., Jr. & Wallace, Mary H. The Curtain of Time. (Illus., Orig.). 1984. pap. 6.95 (ISBN 0-912315-76-8). Word Aflame.
Campbell, David. The Eternal Sonship: A Refutation According to Adam Clarke. (Illus.). 95p. (Orig.). 1977. pap. 1.95 (ISBN 0-912315-44-X). Word Aflame.
Chalfant, William B., ed. Ancient Champions of Oneness. Rev. ed. (Illus.). 156p. 1982. pap. 5.95 (ISBN 0-912315-41-5). Word Aflame.
Chambers, Calvin H. In Spirit & in Truth: Charismatic Worship & the Reformed Tradition. 168p. 1980. 7.95 (ISBN 0-8059-2686-0). Dorrance.
Chantry, Walter. Signs of the Apostles. 1979. pap. 3.95 (ISBN 0-85151-175-9). Banner of Truth.
Christenson, Larry, ed. Welcome, Holy Spirit: A Study of Charismatic Renewal in the Church. 400p. (Orig.). 1987. pap. 16.95 (ISBN 0-8066-2273-3, 10-7021). Augsburg.
Clanton, A. L. The Pentecostal Home: Study Guide. 80p. (Orig.). 1978. pap. 1.00 (ISBN 0-912315-43-1). Word Aflame.
Clanton, Arthur L. United We Stand. (Illus.). 207p. 1970. pap. 5.95 (ISBN 0-912315-42-3). Word Aflame.
Culpepper, R. Alan. Pentecost Two. LC 84-18756. (Proclamation Three C Ser.). 64p. 1986. pap. 3.75 (ISBN 0-8006-4131-0, 1-4131). Fortress.
Culpepper, Robert H. Evaluating the Charismatic Movement: A Theology & Biblical Appraisal. 192p. 1987. pap. text ed. 6.95 (ISBN 0-913029-17-3). Stevens Bk Pr.
Dallimore, Arnold. Forerunner of the Charismatic Movement. (Orig.). 1983. pap. 7.95 (ISBN 0-8024-0286-0). Moody.
DiOrio, Ralph A. & Gropman, Donald. The Man Beneath the Gift: The Story of My Life. LC 80-17619. (Illus.). 239p. 1981. 9.95 (ISBN 0-688-03740-2); pap. 7.95 (ISBN 0-688-00795-3). Morrow.
DuPlessis, David. A Man Called Mr. Pentecost. LC 76-53322. 1977. pap. 5.95 (ISBN 0-88270-184-3). Bridge Pub.
Du Plessis, David. Simple & Profound. 1986. pap. 7.95 (ISBN 0-941478-51-3). Paraclete Pr.
Edgar, Thomas R. Miraculous Gifts: Are They for Today? 384p. 1983. 11.95 (ISBN 0-87213-133-5). Loizeaux.
Ewart, Frank J. The Phenomenon of Pentecost. 208p. (Orig.). 1947. pap. 4.95 (ISBN 0-912315-32-6). Word Aflame.
Flora, Cornelia B. Pentecostalism in Colombia: Baptism by Fire & Spirit. LC 74-4974. 288p. 1976. 26.50 (ISBN 0-8386-1578-3). Fairleigh Dickinson.
Foster, Fred J. Their Story: Twentieth Century Pentecostals. Wallace, Mary H., ed. LC 86-26718. (Illus.). 192p. 1983. pap. 4.95 (ISBN 0-912315-05-9). Word Aflame.
Gardiner, George E. The Corinthian Catastrophe. LC 74-75106. 64p. 1975. pap. 2.95 (ISBN 0-8254-2708-8). Kregel.
Glazier, Stephen D., ed. Perspectives on Pentecostalism: Case Studies from the Caribbean & Latin America. LC 80-7815. 207p. 1980. lib. bdg. 25.25 (ISBN 0-8191-1071-X); pap. text ed. 12.25 (ISBN 0-8191-1072-8). U Pr of Amer.
Goss, Ethel E. The Winds of God. 2nd ed. (Illus.). 288p. 1958. pap. 5.95 (ISBN 0-912315-26-1). Word Aflame.
Graham, Billy. The Holy Spirit. 1978. 3.95 (ISBN 0-8499-4153-9). Word Bks.
Gray, David F. Questions Pentecostals Ask. Bernard. David, ed. LC 86-26784. 304p. (Orig.). 1986. pap. 6.95 (ISBN 0-932581-07-2). Word Aflame.
Haney, Kenneth F. Latter Day Shepherds & Sheepfolds. Wallace, Mary, ed. (Illus.). 78p. 1984. pap. 4.50 (ISBN 0-912315-72-5). Word Aflame.
Harrell, David E., Jr. All Things Are Possible: The Healing & Charismatic Revivals in Modern America. LC 75-1937. (Midland Bks.: No. 221). (Illus.). 320p. 1976. 20.00x (ISBN 0-253-10090-9); pap. 8.95x (ISBN 0-253-20221-3). Ind U Pr.
Hills, A. M. Holiness & Power for the Church & the Ministry. Dayton, Donald W., ed. (The Higher Christian Life Ser.). 386p. 1984. 50.00 (ISBN 0-8240-6422-4). Garland Pub.
--Pentacostal Light. 2.95 (ISBN 0-686-27775-9). Schmul Pub Co.
Hodges, Melvin L. A Theology of the Church & Its Mission: A Pentecostal Perspective. LC 76-20892. 1977. 6.95 (ISBN 0-88243-605-8, 02-0605); pap. 3.95 (ISBN 0-88243-607-4, 02-0607). Gospel Pub.
Huggett, Joyce. The Joy of Listening to God. LC 86-27689. 240p. (Orig.). 1987. pap. 6.95 (ISBN 0-87784-729-0). Inter-Varsity.
Hughes, Ray H. Pentecostal Preaching. LC 81-84606. 159p. (Orig.). 1981. pap. text ed. 5.95 (ISBN 0-87148-711-X). Pathway Pr.
Hunter, Harold D. Spirit-Baptism: A Pentecostal Alternative. LC 83-10500. 322p. (Orig.). 1983. lib. bdg. 28.50 (ISBN 0-8191-3323-X); pap. text ed. 14.50 (ISBN 0-8191-3324-8). U Pr of Amer.
Hutcheson, Richard G., Jr. Mainline Churches & the Evangelicals. LC 80-84648. 192p. (Orig.). 1981. pap. 9.95 (ISBN 0-8042-1502-2). John Knox.
Jones, Charles E. A Guide to the Study of the Pentecostal Movement, 2 Vols, Vol. 1. Pts. 1 & 2; Vol. 2 pts 3 &4; index. LC 82-10794. (ATLA Bibliography Ser.: No. 6). 1249p. 1983. Set. 82.50 (ISBN 0-8108-1583-4). Scarecrow.
Kinnaman, Gary D. And Signs Shall Follow. 1987. pap. 6.95 (Chosen Bks). Revell.
Knott, Ron. Trophies of Heaven. Wallace, Mary, ed. LC 86-26649. 160p. 1986. pap. 5.95 (ISBN 0-932581-06-4). Word Aflame.
Koch, Martha & Koch, Roy. My Personal Pentecost. LC 77-79229. 296p. 1977. pap. 4.95 (ISBN 0-8361-1816-2). Herald Pr.
Kosicki, George W. & Farrell, Gerald J. The Spirit & the Bride Say, "Come!". Mary's Role in the New Pentecost. 112p. pap. 3.95 (ISBN 0-911988-41-6). AMI Pr.
Letis, Theodore P. Martin Luther & Charismatic Ecumenism. (Orig.). 1979. pap. 1.95 (ISBN 0-936592-00-1). Reformation Res.
Lilly, Fred. Word Gifts: Keys to Charismatic Power. 100p. (Orig.). 1984. pap. 2.95 (ISBN 0-89283-182-0). Servant.
Lindsay, Gordon. Charismatic Ministry. 3.25 (ISBN 0-89985-122-3). Christ Nations.
MacArthur, John. The Charismatics. 1980. pap. 6.95 (ISBN 0-310-28491-0, 12645P). Zondervan.
McDonnell, Kilian. Presence, Power, Praise: Documents on Charismatic Renewal: National Documents, Vol. 2. LC 79-26080. 568p. 1980. 20.00 (ISBN 0-8146-1189-3). Liturgical Pr.
McDonnell, Kilian, ed. Presence, Power, Praise; Documents on Charismatic Renewal: International Documents, Vol. 3. LC 79-26080. 306p. 1980. 15.00 (ISBN 0-8146-1065-X). Liturgical Pr.
--Presence, Power, Praise: Documents on Charismatic Renewal: National Documents, Vol. 1. LC 79-26080. 696p. 1980. 20.00 (ISBN 0-8146-1066-8). Liturgical Pr.
McGuire, Meredith B. Pentecostal Catholics: Power, Charisma, & Order in a Religious Movement. 270p. 1982. 29.95 (ISBN 0-87722-235-5). Temple U Pr.
Martin, David & Mullen, Peter, eds. Strange Gifts: A Guide to Charismatic Renewal. 208p. 1984. 24.95x (ISBN 0-631-13357-7); pap. 9.95x (ISBN 0-631-13592-8). Basil Blackwell.
Martin, Ralph. Hungry for God: Practical Help in Personal Prayer. LC 74-4830. 168p. 1974. pap. 6.50 (ISBN 0-385-09534-1). Doubleday.
Mills, Watson E. Charismatic Religion in Modern Research: A Bibliography. Scholer, David M., ed. LC 85-127327. (National Association of Baptist Professors of Religion Bibliographic Ser.: No. 1). viii, 178p. 1985. text ed. 14.50 (ISBN 0-86554-143-4, MUP/M010). Mercer Univ Pr.
Morgan, Nell & Chambers, Catherine. Preserving the Pentecostal Lady. Wallace, Mary H., ed. LC 86-28067. (Illus.). 134p. 1980. pap. 4.95 (ISBN 0-912315-50-4). Word Aflame.
Morley, Lewis H. Now It Can Be Told. Wallace, Mary H., ed. LC 84-126606. (Illus.). 251p. (Orig.). 1983. pap. 5.95 (ISBN 0-912315-11-3). Word Aflame.
Paris, Arthur E. Black Pentecostalism: Southern Religion in an Urban World. LC 81-16169. 192p. 1982. lib. bdg. 17.50x (ISBN 0-87023-353-X). U of Mass Pr.
A Pastoral Statement on the Catholic Charismatic Renewal. 48p. 1984. pap. 2.25 (ISBN 1-55586-931-9). US Catholic.
Poloma, Margaret M. The Charismatic Movement: Is There a New Pentecost? (Social Movements: Past & Present Ser.). 1982. lib. bdg. 18.95 (ISBN 0-8057-9701-7, Twayne). G K Hall.
Preston, Daniel. The Era of A. J. Tomlinson. 206p. (Orig.). 1984. pap. 6.95 (ISBN 0-934942-41-2, 1925). White Wing Pub.
Pruitt, Rhonda R. Flames of Fire: Biographical Accounts of Pentecost Through the Centuries. (Orig.). pap. text ed. write for info. Faith Print.
Quebedeaux, Richard. The New Charismatics II: How a Christian Renewal Movement Became a Part of the American Religious Mainstream. LC 82-48417. 228p. 1983. pap. 8.95 (ISBN 0-06-066723-0, RD379, HarpR). Har-Row.
Reeves, Kenneth V. The Rivers of Living Water. (Illus.). 78p. (Orig.). 1980. pap. 3.00 (ISBN 0-912315-65-2). Word Aflame.
Reynolds, Ralph V. Truth Shall Triumph. 9th ed. 111p. 1983. pap. 2.95 (ISBN 0-912315-07-5). Word Aflame.
Rivera, Roberto A., ed. El Nacimiento del Mesias. (Span.). 172p. 1983. pap. 4.95 (ISBN 0-87148-308-4). Pathway Pr.
Roebling, Karl. Pentecostal Origins & Trends Early & Modern. 3rd, rev. ed. LC 85-63631. 112p. 8.95 (ISBN 0-942910-12-5). Paragon-Dynapress.
Segraves, Judy. Come on into My House. Wallace, Mary, ed. (Illus.). 90p. (Orig.). 1985. pap. 4.95 (ISBN 0-912315-87-3). Word Aflame.
Smelser, Georgia. OMA. LC 85-31579. (Illus.). 254p. (Orig.). 1981. pap. 5.95 (ISBN 0-912315-16-4). Word Aflame.
Snyder, Howard A. & Runyon, Daniel V. The Divided Flame: Wesleyans & the Charismatic Renewal. Ruark, James, ed. 128p. 1986. pap. 6.95 (ISBN 0-310-75181-0, 17082P). Zondervan.
Sullivan, Francis A. Charisms & Charismatic Renewal: A Biblical & Theological Study. 182p. 1982. pap. 8.95 (ISBN 0-89283-121-9). Servant.
Synan, Vinson. Aspects of Pentecostal-Charismatic Origins. LC 75-2802. 1975. 6.95 (ISBN 0-88270-111-8); pap. 6.95. Bridge Pub.
Trigg, Joseph W. & Sachs, William L. Of One Body: Renewal Movements in the Church. LC 86-2788. 168p. (Orig.). 1986. pap. 9.95 (ISBN 0-8042-0677-5). John Knox.
Tugwell, Simon. Did You Receive the Spirit? rev. ed. 144p. 1982. pap. 6.95 (ISBN 0-87243-108-8). Templegate.
United Pentecostal Church Int. & Hall, J. L., eds. Symposium on Oneness Pentecostalism 1986. LC 86-19024. (Orig.). pap. 7.95 (ISBN 0-932581-03-X). Word Aflame.
Wallace, Mary H. It's Real. (Illus.). 224p. (Orig.). 1981. pap. 5.95 (ISBN 0-912315-17-2). Word Aflame.
--Pioneer Pentecostal Women. (Pioneer Pentecostal Women Ser.: Vol. 1). (Illus.). 272p. (Orig.). 1983. pap. 5.95 (ISBN 0-912315-18-0). Word Aflame.
--Pioneer Pentecostal Women. LC 85-20981. (Pioneer Pentecostal Women: Vol. II). (Illus.). 288p. (Orig.). 1981. pap. 5.95 (ISBN 0-912315-19-9). Word Aflame.
--Profiles of Pentecostal Missionaries. LC 86-15919. (Illus.). 352p. (Orig.). 1986. pap. 6.95 (ISBN 0-932581-00-5). Word Aflame.
--Profiles of Pentecostal Preachers, Vol. II. LC 84-51290. (Illus.). 398p. (Orig.). 1984. pap. 6.95 (ISBN 0-912315-71-7). Word Aflame.
Wallace, Mary H., ed. Profiles of Pentecostal Preachers, Vol. I. LC 84-51290. (Illus.). 281p. (Orig.). 1983. pap. 5.95 (ISBN 0-912315-63-6). Word Aflame.
Walsh, Vincent M. Gathering the Fragments. 64p. 1980. pap. 1.00 (ISBN 0-943374-01-4). Key of David.
--A Key to Charismatic Renewal in the Catholic Church. LC 74-82238. 286p. 1974. pap. 6.00 (ISBN 0-686-32791-8). Key of David.
--Key to the Catholic Pentecostal Renewal, Vol. 2. 232p. 1985. pap. 8.00 (ISBN 0-943374-12-X). Key of David.
--Lead My People. 104p. 1980. pap. 4.00 (ISBN 0-943374-02-2). Key of David.
Warner, Wayne E. & Warner, Wayne E. The Woman Evangelist: The Life & Times of Charismatic Evangelist Maria B. Woodworth-Etter. LC 86-11854. (Studies in Evangelicalism: No. 8). (Illus.). 354p. 1986. 32.50 (ISBN 0-8108-1912-0). Scarecrow.
Wiens, Grace. Unto You & to Your Children. (Illus.). 229p. (Orig.). 1976. pap. 5.95 (ISBN 0-912315-10-5). Word Aflame.
Willoughby, David. What Time Is It? Clanton, Arthur L., ed. 126p. 1974. 3.95 (ISBN 0-912315-49-0). Word Aflame.
Winky-Lotz, H. I Owe My Life to Jesus -- You Also? An Autobiography Charismatic. (Illus.). 210p. 1986. 10.95 (ISBN 0-936112-00-X); pap. 6.50 (ISBN 0-936112-01-8). Willyshe Pub.
Yadon, Loren A. From an Acorn to an Oak. (Illus.). 89p. 1978. pap. 4.95 (ISBN 0-912315-46-6). Word Aflame.

PEOPLE, SINGLE
see Single People

PEOPLE'S TEMPLE

Ahlberg, Sture. Messianic Movements: A Comparative Analysis of the Sabbatians, the People's Temple & the Unification Church. 128p. (Orig.). pap. text ed. 19.00x (ISBN 91-22-00787-3, Pub. by Almqvist & Wiksell). Coronet Bks.
Hall, John R. Gone from the Promised Land: Jonestown As American Cultural History. 435p. 1987. 29.95 (ISBN 0-88738-124-3). Transaction Bks.
Levi, Ken, ed. Violence & Religious Commitment: Implications of Jim Jones's People's Temple Movement. LC 81-83147. (Illus.). 224p. 1982. 24.50x (ISBN 0-271-00296-4). Pa St U Pr.
Rose, Stephen. Jesus & Jim Jones. LC 79-17285. (Orig.). 1979. 8.95 (ISBN 0-8298-0379-3); pap. 6.95 (ISBN 0-8298-0373-4). Pilgrim NY.
Temple of the People Publications Staff. From the Mountain Top, Vol. 3. 144p. 1985. 11.25 (ISBN 0-933797-02-8). Halcyon Bk.
Weightman, Judith M. Making Sense of the Jonestown Suicides: A Sociological History of Peoples Temple. LC 83-21999. (Studies in Religion & Society: Vol. 7). 240p. 1984. 49.95x (ISBN 0-88946-871-0). E Mellen.

PERCY, THOMAS, BP. OF DROMORE, 1729-1811

Harp, Richard L. Thomas Percy's 'Life of Dr. Oliver Goldsmith' Hogg, James, ed. (Romantic Reassessment Ser.). 205p. (Orig.). 1976. pap. 15.00 (ISBN 3-7052-0507-2, Pub. by Salzburg Studies). Longwood Pub Group.
Percy, Bishop. Bishop Percy's Folio Manuscript Ballards & Romances, 3 vols. Hales, John W., et al, eds. LC 67-23962. 1866p. 1968. Repr. of 1868 ed. 210.00x (ISBN 0-8103-3409-7). Gale.
Willinsky, Margarete. Bischof Percy's Bearbeitung Der Volksballaden Und Kunstgedichte Seines Folio-Manuskriptes. Repr. of 1932 ed. 19.00 (ISBN 0-384-68615-X). Johnson Repr.
Wood, Harriet H. & Brooks, Cleanth, eds. The Correspondence of Thomas Percy & John Pinkerton: The Percy Letters, Vol. 8. LC 84-2916. 160p. 1985. text ed. 25.00x (ISBN 0-300-03344-3). Yale U Pr.

PERFECTION

Bogart, John L. Orthodox & Heretical Perfectionism in the Johannine Community As Evident in the First Epistle of John. LC 77-5447. (Society of Biblical Literature. Dissertation Ser.). 1977. pap. 9.95 (ISBN 0-89130-138-0, 060133). Scholars Pr GA.
Brunner, August. New Creation: Towards a Theology of the Christian Life. 143p. 1956. 10.00 (ISBN 0-8022-0189-X). Philos Lib.
Chambers, Oswald. If Thou Wilt Be Perfect. 1962. pap. 2.95 (ISBN 0-87508-113-4). Chr Lit.
Greathouse, William M. From the Apostles to Wesley. 124p. 1979. pap. 3.50 (ISBN 0-8341-0588-8). Beacon Hill.
LaRondelle, Hans K. Perfection & Perfectionism: A Dogmatic-Ethical Study of Biblical Perfection & Phenomenal Perfectionism. (Andrews University Monographs, Studies in Religion: Vol. III). vii, 364p. pap. 9.95 (ISBN 0-943872-02-2). Andrews Univ Pr.
MacArthur, John, Jr. Perfect Love. (John MacArthur's Bible Studies). 1985. pap. 3.50 (ISBN 0-8024-5110-1). Moody.
Milosh, Joseph E. The Scale of Perfection & the English Mystical Tradition. LC 66-22857. pap. 56.50 (ISBN 0-317-07863-1, 2010975). Bks Demand UMI.
Murray, Andrew. How to Be Perfect. 144p. 1982. pap. text ed. 3.50 (ISBN 0-88368-113-7). Whitaker Hse.

Omar, H. A. The Paragon of Human Perfection. 85p. 1984. 21.00x (ISBN 0-7212-0566-6, Pub. by Regency Pr). State Mutual Bk.

Peters, John L. Christian Perfection & American Methodism. 1985. pap. 9.95 (ISBN 0-310-31241-8, 17043P). Zondervan.

Warfield, Benjamin B. Studies in Perfectionism. 1958. 12.95 (ISBN 0-87552-528-8). Presby & Reformed.

Wesley, et al. Christian Perfection. 6.95 (ISBN 0-686-12854-0). Schmul Pub Co.

PERFECTION (CATHOLIC)

see also Monastic and Religious Life; Monastic and Religious Life of Women

Birdsong, Robert E. Paths to Human Perfection. (Aquarian Academy Supplementary Lecture: No. 3). 1979. pap. 0.75 (ISBN 0-917108-26-4). Sirius Bks.

Mason, Sr. M. Elizabeth. Active Life & Contemplative Life: A Study of the Concepts from Plato to the Present. Ganss, George E., ed. 1961. pap. 5.95 (ISBN 0-87462-418-5). Marquette.

St. Teresa of Avila. Way of Perfection. pap. 4.95 (ISBN 0-385-06539-6, D176, Im). Doubleday.

Scupoli, Lawrence. The Spiritual Combat. LC 78-61668. (The Spiritual Masters Ser.). 256p. 1978. pap. 4.95 (ISBN 0-8091-2158-1). Paulist Pr.

Warfield, B. B. Perfectionism. 12.95 (ISBN 0-8010-9587-5). Baker Bk.

PERFECTION (PHILOSOPHY)

Alioto, Joseph L., et al, eds. Teilhard de Chardin: In Quest of the Perfection of Man. LC 72-9596. 290p. 1973. 24.50 (ISBN 0-8386-1258-X). Fairleigh Dickinson.

Birdsong, Robert E. Paths to Human Perfection. (Aquarian Academy Supplementary Lecture: No. 3). 1979. pap. 0.75 (ISBN 0-917108-26-4). Sirius Bks.

Hartshorne, Charles. The Logic of Perfection & Other Essays in Neoclassical Metaphysics. LC 61-11286. 351p. 1973. pap. 8.95 (ISBN 0-87548-037-3). Open Court.

Hodson. Pathway of Perfection. 2.50 (ISBN 0-8356-7018-X). Theos Pub Hse.

Nicholson, R. A. The Sufi Doctrine of the Perfect Man. 1984. pap. 3.95 (ISBN 0-916411-48-6, Near Eastern). Holmes Pub.

Passmore, John. Perfectability of Man. LC 77-129625. 1970. 25.00x (ISBN 0-684-15521-4, ScribT). Scribner.

PERFECTIONISTS

see Oneida Community

PERICOPES

see Lectionaries

PERMISSIVE WILL OF GOD

see Theodicy

PERPETUA, SAINT

Robinson, J. A., ed. The Passion of S. Perpetua. (Texts & Studies Ser.: No. 1, Vol. 1,Pt. 2). pap. 13.00 (ISBN 0-8115-1680-6). Kraus Repr.

PERSECUTION

see also Inquisition; Jews–Persecutions; Liberty of Conscience; Martyrdom; Martyrs; Religious Liberty

also names of sects persecuted, e.g. Albigenses, Waldenses

Belouino, P. Dictionnaire General et Complet des Persecutions, 2 vols. Migne, J. P., ed. (Nouvelle Encyclopedie Theologique Ser.: Vols. 4-5). (Fr.). 1468p. Repr. of 1851 ed. lib. bdg. 186.50x (ISBN 0-89241-255-0). Caratzas.

Burr, George L. Persecution & Liberty: Essays in Honor of George Lincoln Burr. facs. ed. LC 68-26467. (Essay Index Reprint Ser). 1968. Repr. of 1931 ed. 17.50 (ISBN 0-8369-0783-3). Ayer Co Pubs.

De Groot, J. J. Sectarianism & Religious Persecution in China: A Page in the History of Religions, 2 vols. 872p. 1972. Repr. of 1903 ed. 60.00x (ISBN 0-7165-2034-6, Pub. by Irish Academic Pr Ireland). Biblio Dist.

Dengler, Sandy. To Die in the Queen of Cities: A Story of the Christian Courage & Love in the Face of Roman Persecution. 256p. 1986. pap. 6.95 (ISBN 0-8407-5996-7). Nelson.

Forbush, W. B., ed. Fox's Book of Martyrs. 11.95 (ISBN 0-310-24390-4, 9636); pap. 6.95 (ISBN 0-310-24391-2, 9636P). Zondervan.

Foxe, John. Acts & Monuments, 8 Vols. Cattley, S. R. & Townsend, George, eds. LC 79-168132. Repr. of 1849 ed. Set. 400.00 (ISBN 0-404-02590-0). AMS Pr.

Kleinig, John. Ethical Issues in Psychosurgery. (Studies in Applied Philosophy: No. 1). (Illus.). 176p. 1985. text ed. 19.95x (ISBN 0-04-170032-5); pap. text ed. 7.95x (ISBN 0-04-170033-3). Allen Unwin.

Ladany, L. The Catholic Church in China. LC 87-23. (Perspectives on Freedom Ser.: No. 7). (Orig.). 1987. pap. 5.00 (ISBN 0-932088-12-0). Freedom Hse.

Lange, Martin & Iblacker, Reinhold, eds. Witnesses of Hope: The Persecution of Christians in Latin America. Jerman, William E., tr. from Ger. LC 81-38378. Orig. Title: Christenverfolgung in SudAmerica: Zeugen du Hoffnung. Tr. of Christenverfalgung in Sudamerica: Zeugen der Hoffreung. 176p. (Orig.). 1981. pap. 6.95 (ISBN 0-88344-759-2). Orbis Bks.

Lesbaupin, Ivo. Blessed Are the Persecuted: Christian Life in the Roman Empire, A.D. 64-313. Barr, Robert R., tr. from Port. Tr. of A Bem-Aventuranca da Persecucion & La Bienaventuranza de la Persecution. 112p. (Orig.). 1987. 16.95 (ISBN 0-88344-562-X); pap. 7.95 (ISBN 0-88344-561-1). Orbis Bks.

Marongiu, Pietro & Newman, Graeme. Vengeance: The Fight Against Injustice. 176p. 1987. 27.50. Rowman.

Musurillo, Herbert. The Acts of the Christian Martyrs: Text & Translations. (Oxford Early English Texts Ser). 1972. 52.00x (ISBN 0-19-826806-8). Oxford U Pr.

Popov, Haralan. Tortured for His Faith. pap. 3.95 (ISBN 0-310-31262-0, 18070P). Zondervan.

Saint Victor Of Vita. Historia Persecutionis Africanae Provinciae. (Corpus Scriptorum Ecclesiasticorum Latinorum Ser.: Vol. 7). 1881. 30.00 (ISBN 0-384-64540-2). Johnson Repr.

Sheils, W. J., ed. Persecution & Toleration. (Studies in Church History: Vol. 21). 500p. 1984. 45.00x (ISBN 0-631-13601-0). Basil Blackwell.

Sinishta, Gjon. The Fulfilled Promise: A Documentary Account of Religious Persecution in Albania. LC 76-57433. (Illus.). 253p. (Orig.). pap. 10.00 (ISBN 0-317-18715-5). Albanian Cath Info.

Wright, William, tr. A Briefe Relation of the Persecution Lately Made Against the Catholike Christians in Japonia, Taken Out of the Annuall Letters of the Soc. of Jesus. LC 75-26238. (English Experience Ser.: No. 159). 1969. Repr. of 1619 ed. 35.00 (ISBN 90-221-0159-2). Walter J Johnson.

PERSEPOLIS

Bowman, Raymond A. Aramaic Ritual Texts from Persepolis. LC 65-55148. (Oriental Institute Pubns. Ser: No. 91). 1970. 35.00x (ISBN 0-226-62194-4). U of Chicago Pr.

Oriental Institute Staff. Persepolis & Ancient Iran. LC 76-7942. 1976. 55.00 (ISBN 0-226-69493-3, Chicago Visual Lib); 1 color & 11 black-&-white fiches incl. U of Chicago Pr.

PERSEVERANCE (THEOLOGY)

see also Assurance (Theology); Sanctification

Johnson, Ann D. The Value of Determination: The Story of Helen Keller. 2nd ed. LC 76-54762. (Valuetales Ser). (Illus.). 1976. 7.95 (ISBN 0-916392-07-4, Dist. by Oak Tree Pubns.). Value Comm.

Marshall, I. Howard. Kept by the Power of God. LC 74-23996. 288p. 1975. pap. 8.95 (ISBN 0-87123-304-5, 210304). Bethany Hse.

Shank, Robert. Life in the Son: A Study of the Doctrine of Perseverance. LC 59-15488. 380p. 1960. 8.95 (ISBN 0-911620-01-X). Westcott.

Swindoll, Charles R. Three Steps Forward, Two Steps Back. 320p. 1985. pap. 11.95 (ISBN 0-8027-2506-6). Walker & Co.

PERSIAN LITERATURE–AVESTAN

see Avesta

PERSIAN LITERATURE–TRANSLATIONS INTO ENGLISH

Gottheil, Richard J., intro. by. Persian Literature (Comprising of the Shan Nameth, the Rubaiyat, the Divan & the Gulistan, 2 vols. 1986. Repr. of 1900 ed. Set. PLB 150.00 (ISBN 0-89760-246-3). Telegraph Bks.

Nicholson, Reynold A., tr. Translations of Eastern Poetry & Prose. Repr. of 1922 ed. lib. bdg. 22.50 (ISBN 0-8371-2301-1, NIEP). Greenwood.

PERSONAL DEVELOPMENT

see Personality; Success

PERSONAL EFFICIENCY

see Success

PERSONALISM

see also Idealism

Brightman, Edgar S. Studies in Personalism. Steinkraus, Warren & Beck, Robert, eds. (Signature Series of Philosophy & Religion). Date not set. 16.00 (ISBN 0-86610-067-9). Meridian Pub.

Brightman, Edgar S., ed. Personalism in Theology. LC 75-3088. (Philosophy in America Ser.). Repr. of 1943 ed. 24.50 (ISBN 0-404-59086-1). AMS Pr.

Deats, Paul & Robb, Carol S., eds. The Boston Personalist Tradition in Philosophy, Social Ethics, & Theology. (Illus.). xiv, 295p. 1986. text ed. 28.95 (ISBN 0-86554-177-9, MUP-H167). Mercer Univ Pr.

Knudson, Albert C. Philosophy of Personalism: A Study in the Metaphysics of Religion. LC 27-21477. 1968. Repr. of 1927 ed. 26.00 (ISBN 0-527-51600-7). Kraus Repr.

PERSONALITY

see also Ego (Psychology); Identity (Psychology); Personalism; Self; Soul

Belgum, David. Religion & Personality in the Spiral of Life. LC 79-66478. 1979. pap. text ed. 14.25 (ISBN 0-8191-0832-4). U Pr of Amer.

Burton, Richard F. Personal Narrative of a Pilgrimage to Al-Madinah & Meccah, 2 Vols. Burton, Isabel, ed. Set. 28.50 (ISBN 0-8446-1781-4). Peter Smith.

Derstine, Gerald. Destined to Mature. 144p. (Orig.). 1984. pap. 3.50 (ISBN 0-88368-147-1). Whitaker Hse.

Duckworth, John, et al, eds. Identity Search. (Pacesetter Ser.). 64p. 1987. tchr's. ed. 7.95. Cook.

Dumont, Theron. Art & Science of Personal Magnetism. 8.00 (ISBN 0-911662-38-3). Yoga.

Giles, James E. La Psicologia y el Ministerio Cristiano. 384p. 1982. Repr. of 1978 ed. 3.20 (ISBN 0-311-42059-1). Casa Bautista.

Jackson, Edgar N. Group Counseling: Dynamic Possibilities for Small Groups. LC 73-91167. (Orig.). 1969. pap. 2.95 (ISBN 0-8298-0053-0). Pilgrim NY.

Jamison, Kaleel. The Nibble Theory & the Kernel of Power. LC 83-63112. 74p. (Orig.). 1984. 4.95 (ISBN 0-8091-2621-4); pap. 3.95 (ISBN 0-8091-2621-4). Paulist Pr.

Jonassen, Christen T. Value Systems & Personality in a Western Civilization: Norwegians in Europe & America. LC 83-11391. 400p. 1984. 25.00x (ISBN 0-8142-0347-7). Ohio St U Pr.

Keating, Dr. Charles J. Who We Are Is How We Pray: Matching Personality & Spirituality. 144p. (Orig.). 1987. 13.95 (ISBN 0-89622-292-6); pap. 7.95 (ISBN 0-89622-321-3). Twenty-Third.

Khan, Inayat. The Art of Personality. (Sufi Message of Hazrat Inayat Khan Ser.: Vol. 3). 256p. 1979. 14.95 (ISBN 90-6077-570-8, Pub. by Servire BV Netherlands). Hunter Hse.

Laird, John. Idea of the Soul. LC 76-107811. (Select Bibliographies Reprint Ser). 1924. 18.00 (ISBN 0-8369-5207-3). Ayer Co Pubs.

MacDougall, Mary K. Happiness Now. 178p. 1971. 5.95 (ISBN 0-87159-053-0). Unity School.

Micks, Marianne H. Our Search for Identity: Humanity in the Image of God. LC 81-70592. 176p. 1982. pap. 1.00 (ISBN 0-8006-1627-8). Fortress.

Moore, Donald. Improving Your Christian Personality. 61p. 1984. pap. 2.25 (ISBN 0-88144-037-X). Christian Pub.

Neumann, Erich. Origins & History of Consciousness. Hull, R. F., tr. (Bollingen Ser.: Vol. 42). (Illus.). 1954. pap. 9.95 (ISBN 0-691-01761-1). Princeton U Pr.

Pote, Lawrence. Acceptance. pap. 1.50 (ISBN 0-8010-7050-3). Baker Bk.

Schuller, Robert H. Move Ahead with Possibility Thinking. 224p. 1973. pap. 2.95 (ISBN 0-8007-8105-8, Spire Bks). Revell.

Sill, Sterling W. The Law of the Harvest. 392p. 1980. 10.95 (ISBN 0-88290-142-7). Horizon Utah.

Vinck, Jose D. The Yes Book. 1976. pap. 3.75 (ISBN 0-685-77499-6). Franciscan Herald.

--The Yes Book: An Answer to Life (a Manual of Christian Existentialism) LC 77-190621. 200p. 1972. 12.75 (ISBN 0-911726-12-8); pap. 8.75 (ISBN 0-911726-11-X). Alleluia Pr.

Webb, Clement C. Divine Personality & Human Life: Being the Gifford Lectures Delivered in the University of Aberdeen in the Years 1918 & 1919, Second Course. facsimile ed. LC 77-37917. (Select Bibliographies Reprint Ser.). Repr. of 1920 ed. 21.00 (ISBN 0-8369-6754-2). Ayer Co Pubs.

--God & Personality: Being the Gifford Lectures Delivered in the University of Aberdeen in the Years 1918 & 1919. facsimile ed. LC 76-164632. (Select Bibliographies Reprint Ser.). Repr. of 1919 ed. 20.00 (ISBN 0-8369-5916-7). Ayer Co Pubs.

Wojtyla, Cardinal Karol. The Acting Person. Potocki, Andrzej, tr. (Analecta Husserliana Ser.: No. 10). 1979. lib. bdg. 29.50 (ISBN 90-277-0969-6, Pub. by Reidel Holland); pap. 15.95 (ISBN 90-277-0985-8, Pub. by Reidel Holland). Kluwer Academic.

PERSONS, SINGLE

see Single People

PERU–RELIGION

Pike, Fredrick B. The Politics of the Miraculous in Peru: Haya de la Torre & the Spiritualist Tradition. LC 85-1162. (Illus.). xviii, 391p. 1986. 32.50x (ISBN 0-8032-3672-7). U of Nebr Pr.

Reville, Albert. The Native Religions of Mexico & Peru: Hibbert Lectures. Wicksteed, Phillip H., tr. LC 77-27167. 224p. 1983. Repr. of 1884 ed. 29.50 (ISBN 0-404-60405-6). Ams Pr.

PETER, SAINT, APOSTLE

Barnes, Arthur S. Christianity at Rome in the Apostolic Age. LC 72-114462. (Illus.). 1971. Repr. of 1938 ed. lib. bdg. 55.00x (ISBN 0-8371-4760-3, BACR). Greenwood.

Bender, Harold S. & Horsch, John. Menno Simons su Vida y Escritos. Palomeque, Carmen, tr. 160p. 1979. 4.95x (ISBN 0-8361-1218-0). Herald Pr.

Blackwell, Muriel. Peter: The Prince of Apostles. (BibLearn Ser.). (Illus.). 5.95 (ISBN 0-8054-4227-8, 4242-27). Broadman.

Booth, A. E. Ministry of Peter, John & Paul. 1982. pap. 1.25 (ISBN 0-88172-004-6). Believers Bkshelf.

Briscoe, Jill. Byttook or Crook: The Life of Peter. 192p. 1987. 12.95 (ISBN 0-8499-0561-3). Word Bks.

Chevrot, Georges. Simon Peter. 223p. 1980. pap. 4.95x (ISBN 0-933932-43-X). Scepter Pubs.

Gill, David. Peter the Rock: Extraordinary Lessons from an Ordinary Man. LC 86-7383. 192p. (Orig.). 1986. pap. 6.95 (ISBN 0-87784-609-X). Inter-Varsity.

Hare, D. S. Story of Peter the Fisherman. (Ladybird Ser). 1970. 2.50 (ISBN 0-87508-867-8). Chr Lit.

Jung-Inglesis, E. M. Saint Peter's. (Illus.). 64p. (Orig.). 1980. pap. 12.50 (ISBN 0-935748-15-6). Scala Books.

Lindsay, Gordon. Peter Escapes From Prison. (Acts in Action Ser.: Vol. 3). pap. 1.25 (ISBN 0-89985-964-X). Christ Nations.

MacDuff, John R. The Footsteps of St. Peter. 648p. 1982. lib. bdg. 24.25 Smythe Sewn (ISBN 0-86524-149-X, 8406). Klock & Klock.

Martin, Hugh. Simon Peter. 1984. pap. 5.45 (ISBN 0-85151-427-8). Banner of Truth.

Meyer, F. B. Peter. 1968. pap. 4.50 (ISBN 0-87508-349-8). Chr Lit.

Pennington, M. Basil. In Peter's Footsteps: Learning to Be a Disciple. LC 85-1541. 144p. 1985. 12.95 (ISBN 0-385-19398-X). Doubleday.

Shotwell, James T. & Loomis, Louis R., eds. See of Peter. 1965. lib. bdg. 49.00x (ISBN 0-374-97391-1, Octagon). Hippocrene Bks.

Thomas, W. H. The Apostle Peter: His Life & Writings. LC 84-1493. 304p. 1984. pap. 9.95 (ISBN 0-8254-3823-3). Kregel.

Walsh, John E. Bones of St. Peter: Fascinating Account of the Search for the Apostle's Body. LC 80-2883. (Illus.). 216p. 1985. 7.95 (ISBN 0-385-15039-3, Im). Doubleday.

Winter, Michael M. Saint Peter & the Popes. LC 78-21507. 1979. Repr. of 1960 ed. lib. bdg. cancelled (ISBN 0-313-21158-2, WISP). Greenwood.

PETER, SAINT, APOSTLE–FICTION

Douglas, Lloyd C. Big Fisherman. 1948. 15.95 (ISBN 0-395-07630-7). HM.

Storr, Catherine. St. Peter & St. Paul. LC 84-18078. (People of the Bible Ser.). (Illus.). 32p. 1985. PLB 10.65 (ISBN 0-8172-1998-6). Raintree Pubs.

PETER, SAINT, APOSTLE–JUVENILE LITERATURE

Barrett, Ethel. Peter. LC 81-52942. (Bible Biography Ser.). 128p. (Orig.). 1982. pap. text ed. 1.95 (ISBN 0-8307-0768-9, 5810809). Regal.

Johnson, Irene L. The Apostle Peter & His Writing. 48p. (Orig.). 1983. pap. 2.50 (ISBN 0-87239-672-X, 2772). Standard Pub.

Lalo, Laurent. Peter & the First Christians. LC 84-42946. (Illus.). 24p. 1985. 4.95 (ISBN 0-88070-084-X). Multnomah.

PETER 1ST, THE GREAT, EMPEROR OF RUSSIA, 1672-1725

Baker, Nina B. Peter the Great. (Illus.). 310p. 1943. 10.95 (ISBN 0-8149-0263-4). Vanguard.

Cracraft, James. The Church Reform of Peter the Great. 1971. 27.50x (ISBN 0-8047-0747-2). Stanford U Pr.

Graham, Stephen. Peter the Great: A Life of Peter I of Russia. LC 75-138241. (Illus.). 1971. Repr. of 1950 ed. lib. bdg. 39.75x (ISBN 0-8371-5598-3, GRPG). Greenwood.

Voltaire. Russia under Peter the Great. Jenkins, M. F., tr. LC 81-72050. 340p. 1983. 35.00 (ISBN 0-8386-3148-7). Fairleigh Dickinson.

Von Storcksburg Staehlin, Jakob. Original Anecdotes of Peter the Great, Collected from the Conversation of Several Persons of Distinction at Petersburg & Moscow. LC 74-115587. (Russia Observed, Series I). 1970. Repr. of 1788 ed. 21.00 (ISBN 0-405-03064-9). Ayer Co Pubs.

PETERBOROUGH CATHEDRAL

Chronicon Petroburgense. 1849. 24.00 (ISBN 0-384-08985-2). Johnson Repr.

Giles, John A., ed. Chronicon Angliae Petriburgense. 1966. Repr. of 1845 ed. 24.00 (ISBN 0-8337-1342-6). B Franklin.

Sandler, Lucy F. The Peterborough Psalter in Brussels & Other Fenland Manuscripts. (Illus.). 1974. 49.00x (ISBN 0-19-921005-5). Oxford U Pr.

PETIT, ADOLPHE, 1822-1914

Enrody, Ladislaus. Hope Unlimited. 1962. 2.50 (ISBN 0-8198-0060-0); pap. 1.50 (ISBN 0-8198-0061-9). Dghtrs St Paul.

PETRUS LOMBARDUS, BP. OF PARIS, 12TH CENTURY

Rogers, Elizabeth F. Peter Lombard & the Sacramental System. 250p. 1976. Repr. of 1927 ed. lib. bdg. 19.50x (ISBN 0-915172-22-4). Richwood Pub.

PETRUS THOMASIUS, SAINT, 1305-1366

Bridges, Geoffrey G. Identity & Distinction in Petrus Thomae. (Philosophy Ser). 1959. 10.00 (ISBN 0-686-11544-9). Franciscan Inst.

Hooper, Sr. M. Rachel & Buytaert, Eligius M., eds. Petrus Thomae, O. F. M. Quodlibet. (Text Ser). 1957. 10.00 (ISBN 0-686-11556-2). Franciscan Inst.

PEYOTISM

Aberle, David F. The Peyote Religion among the Navaho. 2nd ed. LC 82-2562. (Illus.). 454p. 1982. lib. bdg. 35.00x (ISBN 0-226-00082-6); pap. text ed. 15.00x (ISBN 0-226-00083-4). U of Chicago Pr.

Anderson, Edward F. Peyote: The Divine Cactus. LC 79-20173. 248p. 1980. pap. 9.95 (ISBN 0-8165-0613-2). U of Ariz Pr.

Huxley, Aldous. Doors of Perception. Bd. with Heaven & Hell. pap. 5.95 (ISBN 0-06-090007-5, CN7, PL). Har-Row.

--Doors of Perception. 1970. pap. 3.95 (ISBN 0-06-080171-9, P171, PL). Har-Row.

LaBarre, Weston. The Peyote Cult. 4th ed. LC 75-19425. (Illus.). xix, 296p. 1975. 27.50 (ISBN 0-208-01456-X, Archon). Shoe String.

McAllester, David P. Peyote Music. pap. 19.00 (ISBN 0-384-36490-X). Johnson Repr.

Petrullo, Vincenzo. The Diabolic Root: A Study of Peyotism, the New Indian Religion, Among the Delawares. 185p. 1975. Repr. of 1934 ed. lib. bdg. 18.00x (ISBN 0-374-96411-4, Octagon). Hippocrene Bks.

Stewart, Omer C., ed. Peyotism in the West: A Historical & Cultural Perspective. (Anthropological Papers: No. 108). (Illus.). 168p. (Orig.). 1984. pap. 17.50x (ISBN 0-87480-235-0). U of Utah Pr.

PHALLICISM

see also Sex and Religion

Brown, Sanger. Sex Worship & Symbolism: An Interpretation. LC 72-9624. Repr. of 1922 ed. 27.50 (ISBN 0-404-57419-X). AMS Pr.

Dulaure, Jacques-Antoine. The Gods of Generation. LC 72-9635. Tr. of De Divinites Generatrices. Repr. of 1934 ed. 42.00 (ISBN 0-404-57433-5). AMS Pr.

Goodland, Roger. A Bibliography of Sex Rites & Customs. LC 72-9839. Repr. of 1931 ed. 42.50 (ISBN 0-404-57445-9). AMS Pr.

Knight, Richard P. Worship of Priapus. LC 73-76829. (Illus.). 300p. 1974. Repr. of 1786 ed. 25.00 (ISBN 0-8216-0207-1). Univ Bks.

Pesek-Marous, Georgia. The Bull: A Religious & Secular History of Phallus Worship & Male Homosexuality. (Illus.). 185p. (Orig.). 1984. pap. 9.95 (ISBN 0-916453-01-4). Tau Pr.

Stone, Lee A. The Story of Phallicism, with Other Essays on Related Subjects by Eminent Authorities. LC 72-9682. Repr. of 1927 ed. 49.50 (ISBN 0-404-57500-5). AMS Pr.

Vanggaard, Thorkil. Phallos: A Symbol & Its History in the Male World. LC 72-80553. (Illus.). 266p. 1972. text ed. 22.50 (ISBN 0-8236-4135-X); pap. text ed. 17.95 (ISBN 0-8236-8192-0, 24135). Intl Univs Pr.

Westropp, H. M. Ancient Symbol Worship: Phallic Idea. 59.95 (ISBN 0-87968-633-2). Gordon Pr.

PHANTOMS

see Apparitions

PHARISEES

see also Qumran Community; Zealots (Jewish Party)

Coleman, William. The Pharisees' Guide To Total Holiness. LC 82-4551. 147p. 1982. 8.95 (ISBN 0-87123-473-4, 210473); pap. 4.95 (ISBN 0-87123-472-6, 210472). Bethany Hse.

Deady, Matthew P. Pharisee Among Philistines: The Diary of Judge Matthew P. Deady, 1871-1892, 2 vols. Clark, Malcolm, Jr., intro. by. LC 74-75363. (Illus.). 702p. 1975. 27.95 (ISBN 0-87595-046-9); deluxe ed. 30.00 (ISBN 0-686-96825-5); pap. 19.95 (ISBN 0-87595-080-9). Oregon Hist.

Neusner, Jacob. From Politics to Piety: The Emergence of Pharisaic Judaism. pap. 9.95 (ISBN 0-87068-677-1). Ktav.

Rivkin, Ellis. A Hidden Revolution: The Pharisee's Search for the Kingdom Within. LC 78-17180. 1978. 13.95 (ISBN 0-687-16970-4). Abingdon.

Umen, Samuel. Pharisaism & Jesus. LC 62-20875. 1962. 5.00 (ISBN 0-8022-1752-4). Philos Lib.

PHENOMENOLOGY

see also Existentialism

Brockelman, Paul. Time & Self: Phenomenological Explorations. (AAR Studies in Religion). 1985. 17.95 (ISBN 0-89130-779-6, 01-00-39); pap. 10.95 (ISBN 0-89130-780-X). Scholars Pr GA.

Detweiler, Robert. Story, Sign, & Self: Phenomenology & Structuralism As Literary-Critical Methods. Beardslee, William A., ed. LC 76-9713. (Semeia Studies). 240p. 1978. pap. 9.95 (ISBN 0-8006-1505-0, 1-1505). Fortress.

Dumery, Henry. Phenomenology & Religion: Structures of the Christian Institution. Barrett, Paul, tr. LC 73-94443. (Hermeneutics Series: Studies in the History of Religion). 1975. 27.50x (ISBN 0-520-02714-0). U of Cal Pr.

Hodgson, Shadworth H. & Nathanson, Maurice. The Metaphysic of Experience, 4 vols. LC 78-66730. (Phenomenology Ser.). 858p. 1980. lib. bdg. 233.00 (ISBN 0-8240-9564-2). Garland Pub.

Husserl, Edmund. Crisis of European Sciences & Transcendental Phenomenology: An Introduction to Phenomenological Philosophy. Carr, David, tr. LC 77-82511. (Studies in Phenomenology & Existential Philosophy Ser). 1970. 28.95 (ISBN 0-8101-0255-2); pap. 11.95 (ISBN 0-8101-0458-X). Northwestern U Pr.

Ihde, Don. Hermeneutic Phenomenology: The Philosophy of Paul Ricoeur. (Studies in Phenomenology & Existential Philosophy). 1971. 20.95 (ISBN 0-8101-0347-8); pap. 11.95 (ISBN 0-8101-0611-6). Northwestern U Pr.

Kainz, Howard P. Hegel's Phenomenology, Part II: The Evolution of Ethical & Religious Consciousness to the Absolute Standpoint. LC 82-22444. xii, 211p. 1983. text ed. 23.95x (ISBN 0-8214-0677-9); pap. 12.95x (ISBN 0-8214-0738-4). Ohio U Pr.

Kobler, John F. Vatican II & Phenomenology. 1986. lib. bdg. 37.50 (ISBN 90-247-3193-3, Pub. by Martinus Nijhoff Netherlands). Kluwer-Academic.

Laffoucriere. Le Destin De la Pensee et, la Mort De Dieu, Selon Heidegger. (Phaenomenologica Ser: No. 24). 1968. lib. bdg. 29.00 (ISBN 90-247-0255-0, Pub. by Martinus Nijhoff Netherlands). Kluwer Academic.

Laycock, Steven W. & Hart, James G., eds. Essays in Phenomenological Theology. 204p. (Orig.). 1986. 44.50x (ISBN 0-88706-164-8); pap. 14.95x (ISBN 0-88706-165-6). State U NY Pr.

McCown, Joe. Availability: Gabriel Marcel & the Phenomenology of Human Openness. LC 77-22358. (American Academy of Religion. Studies in Religion: No. 14). 1978. pap. 9.95 (ISBN 0-89130-144-5, 010014). Scholars Pr GA.

Van Der Leeuw, Gerardus. Religion in Essence & Manifestation, 2 vols. 26.50 set (ISBN 0-8446-1457-2). Peter Smith.

Westphal, Merold, ed. Method & Speculation in Hegel's Phenomenology. 137p. 1982. text ed. 15.00x (ISBN 0-391-02336-5, Pub. by Harvester Pr UK). Humanities.

Wojtyla, Cardinal Karol. The Acting Person. Potocki, Andrzej, tr. (Analecta Husserliana Ser.: No. 10). 1979. lib. bdg. 29.50 (ISBN 90-277-0969-6, Pub. by Reidel Holland); pap. 15.95 (ISBN 90-277-0985-8, Pub. by Reidel Holland). Kluwer Academic.

PHILANTHROPY

see Charities; Endowments

PHILIPPINE ISLANDS–CHURCH HISTORY

Hefley, Marti. Assignment in the Philippines: Dramatic Accounts from Jared & Marilee Barker. (Orig.). 1984. pap. 7.95 (ISBN 0-8024-0265-8). Moody.

Schumacher, John N. Revolutionary Clergy: The Filipino Clergy & the Nationalist Movement, 1850-1903. 306p. 1982. (Pub. by Ateneo De Manila U Pr Philippines); pap. 17.50. Cellar.

Yatco, Nicomedes T. Jesus Christ for Today's Filipino. 124p. (Orig.). 1984. pap. 6.50x (ISBN 971-10-0053-9, Pub. by New Day Philipines). Cellar.

PHILO JUDAEUS

Belkin, Samuel. Philo & the Oral Law: The Philonic Interpretation of Biblical Law. (Harvard Semitic Ser.: Vol. 11). Repr. of 1940 ed. 25.00 (ISBN 0-384-03795-X). Johnson Repr.

Bigg, Charles. Christian Platonists of Alexandria: Eight Lectures. LC 75-123764. Repr. of 1886 ed. 27.50 (ISBN 0-404-00799-6). AMS Pr.

Gookenough, Erwin R. An Introduction to Philo Judaeus. 2nd ed. (Brown Classics in Judaica Ser.). 194p. 1986. pap. text ed. 12.75 (ISBN 0-8191-5335-4). U Pr of Amer.

Pascher, Josef. Der Konigsweg Zu Wiedergeburt und Vergottung Bei Philon Von Alexandreia. Repr. of 1931 ed. 22.00 (ISBN 0-384-45050-4). Johnson Repr.

Philo. Philonis Alexandrini in Flaccum. Connor, W. R., ed. LC 78-18570. (Greek Texts & Commentaries Ser.). 1979. Repr. of 1939 ed. lib. bdg. 17.00x (ISBN 0-405-11414-1). Ayer Co Pubs.

Sandmel, Samuel. Philo of Alexandria: An Introduction. 1979. pap. 9.95 (ISBN 0-19-502515-6). Oxford U Pr.

Winston, David & Dillon, John. Two Treatises of Philo of Alexandria: A Commentary on De Gigantibus & Quod Deus Sit Immutabilis. LC 82-786. (Brown Judaic Studies). 416p. 1983. pap. 15.00 (ISBN 0-89130-563-7, 14 00 25). Scholars Pr GA.

Wolfson, Harry A. Philo: Foundations of Religious Philosophy in Judaism, Christianity & Islam, 2 vols. rev. ed. LC 47-30635. 1962. Set. 55.00x (ISBN 0-674-66450-7). Harvard U Pr.

PHILOSOPHERS

Dunham, James H. Religion of Philosophers. facs. ed. LC 78-80386. (Essay Index Reprint Ser). 1947. 21.50 (ISBN 0-8369-1059-1). Ayer Co Pubs.

Eight Jewish Philosophers. 1982. 12.95 (ISBN 0-686-76505-2). Feldheim.

Hall, Manly P. Twelve World Teachers. pap. 6.50 (ISBN 0-89314-816-4). Philos Res.

Jaspers, Karl. Socrates, Buddha, Confucius & Jesus: Taken from Vol. 1 of the Great Philosophers. Manheim, Ralph, tr. 1966. pap. 3.95 (ISBN 0-15-683580-0, Harv). HarBraceJ.

Kierkegaard, Soren. Diary of Soren Kierkegaard. Rohde, Peter P., ed. 1971. pap. 2.75 (ISBN 0-8065-0251-7). Citadel Pr.

Kuklick, Bruce. Churchmen & Philosophers: From Jonathan Edwards to John Dewey. LC 84-19579. 352p. 1985. 30.00 (ISBN 0-300-03269-2). Yale U Pr.

Macauley, Richard M. The Medieval Philosophers from St. Augustine to St. Anselm. (Illus.). 196p. 1984. 88.85 (ISBN 0-89266-483-5). Am Classical Coll Pr.

Mahan, Asa. Autobiography - Intellectual, Moral & Spiritual. LC 75-3269. Repr. of 1882 ed. 30.00 (ISBN 0-404-59257-0). AMS Pr.

Powys, Llewelyn. Rats in the Sacristy. facs. ed. LC 67-30226. (Essay Index Reprint Ser). 1937. 17.00 (ISBN 0-8369-0798-1). Ayer Co Pubs.

Reyner, J. H. Ouspensky: The Unsung Genius. 115p. 1982. 14.95 (ISBN 0-04-294122-9). Allen Unwin.

Robinson, Daniel S. Crucial Issues in Philosophy. 1955. 6.95 (ISBN 0-8158-0177-7). Chris Mass.

Wu, Kuang-ming. Chuang Tzu: World Philosopher at Play. (AAR Studies in Religion). 12.95 (ISBN 0-89130-537-8, 01-00-26). Scholars Pr GA.

PHILOSOPHERS–GREAT BRITAIN

Edward, Herbert. First Baron Herbert of Cherbury. Wellek, Rene, ed. (British Philosophers & Theologians of the 17th & 18th Centuries Ser.). 1979. 51.00 (ISBN 0-8240-1779-X). Garland Pub.

Lowe, Victor. Alfred North Whitehead: The Man & His Work, Vol. 1: 1861-1910. LC 84-15467. 392p. 1985. 27.50 (ISBN 0-8018-2488-5). Johns Hopkins.

PHILOSOPHICAL ANTHROPOLOGY

see also Humanism; Man (Theology); Mind and Body

Cabanis, Pierre J. On the Relations Between the Physical & Moral Aspects of Man, Vol. I. Saidi, Margaret D., tr. LC 80-21694. pap. 112.00 (ISBN 0-317-08229-9, 2019949). Bks Demand UMI.

Coe, David K. Angst & the Abyss: The Hermeneutics of Nothingness. (Academic Ser.). 1985. 17.95 (ISBN 0-89130-862-8, 01-01-49); pap. 11.95 (ISBN 0-89130-863-6). Scholars Pr GA.

Gale, Rodney. The Natural Path to Genuine Lasting Happiness. 1976. 6.50 (ISBN 0-533-02131-6). H R Gale.

Hammes, John A. Humanistic Psychology: A Christian Interpretation. LC 76-110448. 224p. 1971. 49.50 (ISBN 0-8089-0650-X, 791865). Grune.

Hickok, Laurens P. Humanity Immortal: Or, Man Tried, Fallen & Redeemed. LC 75-3180. Repr. of 1872 ed. 25.00 (ISBN 0-404-59183-3). AMS Pr.

LeFevre, Perry. Understandings of Man. LC 66-10432. 186p. 1966. pap. 6.95 (ISBN 0-664-24678-8). Westminster.

McCarthy, Donald G. & Bayer, Edward J. A Handbook on Critical Life Issues. 230p. (Orig.). 1982. pap. 9.95 (ISBN 0-935372-10-5). Pope John Ctr.

Macquarrie, John. In Search of Humanity: A Theological & Philosophical Approach. LC 82-22077. 288p. 1983. 16.95 (ISBN 0-8245-0564-6). Crossroad NY.

Murphy, Carol R. Man: The Broken Image. LC 68-30960. (Orig.). pap. 2.50x (ISBN 0-87574-158-4). Pendle Hill.

Teilhard De Chardin, Pierre. Energie Humaine. 1962. 18.95 (ISBN 0-685-11160-1). French & Eur.

--Future of Man. (Orig.). 1969. pap. 7.95 (ISBN 0-06-090496-8, CN496, PL). Har-Row.

--Phenomene Humain. (Coll. Points). 1955. pap. 6.25 (ISBN 0-685-11491-0). French & Eur.

--Phenomenon of Man. pap. 7.95 (ISBN 0-06-090495-X, CN495, PL). Har-Row.

Webb, C. J. Divine Personality & Human Life. (Gifford Lectures Delivered in the University of Aberdeen in 1918&1919, Second Course Ser.). Repr. of 1920 ed. 17.00 (ISBN 0-527-94900-0). Kraus Repr.

Weiss, Paul. Man's Freedom. LC 67-23318. (Arcturus Books Paperbacks). 335p. 1967. pap. 8.95x (ISBN 0-8093-0277-2). S Ill U Pr.

Wojtyla, Cardinal Karol. The Acting Person. Potocki, Andrzej, tr. (Analecta Husserliana Ser.: No. 10). 1979. lib. bdg. 29.50 (ISBN 90-277-0969-6, Pub. by Reidel Holland); pap. 15.95 (ISBN 90-277-0985-8, Pub. by Reidel Holland). Kluwer Academic.

PHILOSOPHICAL THEOLOGY

Adams, James L. The Prophethood of All Believers. Beach, George K., ed. LC 85-73368. 324p. 1986. 25.00 (ISBN 0-8070-1602-0). Beacon Pr.

Clark, Gordon H. Religion, Reason & Revelation, No. 13. 2nd, rev. ed. (Trinity Papers). 251p. 1986. pap. 7.95 (ISBN 0-940931-13-3). Trinity Found.

Creel, Richard E. Divine Impassibility: An Essay in Philosophical Theology. 300p. 1985. 39.50 (ISBN 0-521-30317-6). Cambridge U Pr.

Foster, Michael B. Mystery & Philosophy. LC 79-8721. (The Library of Philosophy & Theology). 96p. 1980. Repr. of 1957 ed. lib. bdg. 24.75x (ISBN 0-313-20792-5, FOMP). Greenwood.

Kant, Immanuel. Lectures on Philosophical Theology. Wood, Allen W. & Clark, Gertrude M., trs. from Ger. LC 78-58034. 192p. 1986. pap. text ed. 7.95x (ISBN 0-8014-9379-X). Cornell U Pr.

Laycock, Steven W. & Hart, James G., eds. Essays in Phenomenological Theology. 204p. (Orig.). 1986. 44.50x (ISBN 0-88706-164-8); pap. 14.95x (ISBN 0-88706-165-6). State U NY Pr.

Long, Eugene T. Existence, Being & God: An Introduction to the Philosophical Theology of John Mcquarrie. LC 84-16566. 144p. 1985. 17.95 (ISBN 0-913729-02-7); pap. 10.95 (ISBN 0-913729-08-6). Paragon Hse.

Maxwell, Mary. Human Evolution: A Philosophical Anthropology. 288p. 1984. 38.00x (ISBN 0-231-05946-9, King's Crown Paperbacks); pap. 18.00x (ISBN 0-231-05947-7). Columbia U Pr.

Morris, Thomas V. Anselmian Explorations: Essays in Philosophical Theology. LC 86-40239. 264p. 1987. text ed. 28.95 (ISBN 0-268-00616-4). U of Notre Dame Pr.

Oliver, Harold H. Relatedness: Essays in Metaphysics & Theology. LC 84-1152. xvi, 178p. 1984. 14.50 (ISBN 0-86554-141-8, MUP/H132). Mercer Univ Pr.

Rajneesh, Bhagwan S. Mystic Experience. Prem, Ma A., ed. Diddee, Dolly, tr. 543p. 1977. text ed. 25.00 (ISBN 0-89684-292-4, Pub. by Motilal Banarsidass India). Orient Bk Dist.

Ross, James F. Philosophical Theology. 366p. 1982. pap. 7.95 (ISBN 0-8290-1764-X). Irvington.

Wicksteed, Philip H. The Reactions Between Dogma & Philosophy Illustrated from the Works of St. Thomas Aquinas. LC 77-27153. (Hibbert Lectures: 1916). Repr. of 1920 ed. 57.50 (ISBN 0-404-60418-8). AMS Pr.

Wink, Walter. Unmasking the Powers: The Invisible Forces That Determine Human Existence. LC 85-45480. 224p. 1986. pap. 12.95 (ISBN 0-8006-1902-1, 1-1902). Fortress.

PHILOSOPHY

see also Belief and Doubt; Christianity–Philosophy; Consciousness; Cosmology; Creation; Dualism; Ethics; Fate and Fatalism; Free Will and Determinism; Gnosticism; God; Good and Evil; Hedonism; Humanism; Idealism; Ideology; Metaphysics; Mind and Body; Monism; Mysticism; Neoplatonism; Ontology; Pantheism; Philosophical Theology; Personalism; Platonists; Positivism; Psychology; Rationalism; Reality; Scholasticism; Self (Philosophy); Skepticism; Soul; Transcendentalism; Will

Abbot, Francis E. Scientific Theism. LC 75-3012. (Philosophy in America Ser.). Repr. of 1885 ed. 27.50 (ISBN 0-404-59004-7). AMS Pr.

Ala Maudoodi, Abul. Come Let Us Change This World. 4th ed. Siddique, Kaukab, intro. by. & tr. from Urdu. 151p. 1983. pap. 2.00 (ISBN 0-942978-05-6). Am Soc Ed & Rel.

American Catholic Philosophical Association Staff. Ethics & Other Knowledge: Proceedings, Vol. 31. 1957. 18.00 (ISBN 0-384-14760-7). Johnson Repr.

Andronis, Constantine. Apostolos Makrakis--An Evaluation of Half a Century. 369p. (Orig.). 1966. pap. 4.00x (ISBN 0-938366-33-5). Orthodox Chr.

Anthony, Dick, et al, eds. Spiritual Choices, the Problem of Recognizing Authentic Paths to Inner Transformation: The Problem of Recognizing Authentic Paths to Inner Transformation. 448p. 1986. 24.95 (ISBN 0-913729-14-0); pap. 12.95 (ISBN 0-913729-19-1). Paragon Hse.

Athanasius. Contra Gentes & De Incarnatione. Thomas, Robert W., ed. (Oxford Early Christian Texts Ser). 1971. 45.00x (ISBN 0-19-826801-7). Oxford U Pr.

Bailey, Foster. Running God's Plan. 190p. (Orig.). 1972. pap. 5.00 (ISBN 0-85330-128-X). Lucis.

Bailey, Liberty H. The Holy Earth. 59.95 (ISBN 0-8490-0369-5). Gordon Pr.

Bascom, John. Science, Philosophy & Religion. LC 75-3041. Repr. of 1871 ed. 36.00 (ISBN 0-404-59039-X). AMS Pr.

Benjamin, Harry. Everyone's Guide to Theosophy. 1969. 8.50 (ISBN 0-8356-5079-0). Theos Pub Hse.

Bodin, J. Selected Writings on Philosophy, Religion & Politics. Rose, Paul L., ed. xiv, 94p. (Orig.). 1980. pap. text ed. 18.50x (Pub. by Droz Switzerland). Coronet Bks.

Boehme, Jakob. Works of Jakob Boehme, 4 vols. 1974. lib. bdg. 1500.00 (ISBN 0-87968-465-8). Gordon Pr.

Browne, Peter. Things Divine & Supernatural Conceived by Analogy with Things Natural & Human. Wellek, Rene, ed. LC 75-11203. (British Philosophers & Theologians of the 17th & 18th Centuries: Vol. 9). 1976. Repr. of 1733 ed. lib. bdg. 51.00 (ISBN 0-8240-1758-7). Garland Pub.

Brunton, Paul. The Notebooks of Paul Brunton, Vol. 3: Part 1, Practices for the Quest; Part 2, Relax & Retreat. Cash, Paul & Smith, Timothy, eds. LC 86-81030. 392p. 1986. smyth-sewn bdg, acid-free 22.50 (ISBN 0-943914-15-9, Dist. by Kampmann & Co); pap. 12.50 smyth-sewn bdg, acid free (ISBN 0-943914-16-7, Dist. by Kampmann & Co). Larson Pubns Inc.

Buber, Martin. Meetings. Friedman, Maurice, ed. & tr. from Ger. LC 73-82780. 123p. 1973. 9.95 (ISBN 0-87548-085-3). Open Court.

--The Way of Response: Selections from His Writings. Glatzer, Nahum N., ed. LC 66-26977. 1971. pap. 5.95 (ISBN 0-8052-0292-7). Schocken.

Cavell, Stanley. The Claim of Reason: Wittgenstein, Skepticism, Morality, & Tragedy. 1979. pap. 11.95 (ISBN 0-19-503195-4). Oxford U Pr.

Chadwick, Henry, ed. Boethius: The Consolations of Music, Logic, Theology, & Philosophy. 1981. text ed. 47.00x (ISBN 0-19-826447-X). Oxford U Pr.

Clymer, R. Swinburne. La Filosofia del Fuego. Morel, Hector V., tr. Tr. of The Philosophy of Fire. (Span.). 190p. (Orig.). 1980. pap. 5.95 (ISBN 0-932785-54-9). Philos Pub.

Comte, Auguste. The Catechism of Positive Religion. 3rd ed. Congreve, Richard, tr. LC 72-77053. 1973. Repr. of 1891 ed. lib. bdg. 35.00x (ISBN 0-678-00910-4). Kelley.

Conway, Anne. The Principles of the Most Ancient & Modern Philosophy. 1982. 35.00 (ISBN 90-247-2671-9, Pub. by Martinus Nijhoff Netherlands). Kluwer Academic.

Cornford, F. M. From Religion to Philosophy. A Study of the Origins of Western Speculation. 275p. 1979. text ed. o. p. (ISBN 0-391-01238-X); pap. text ed. 12.50x (ISBN 0-391-01239-8). Humanities.

Cournand, Andre & Levy, Maurice. Shaping the Future: Gaston Berger & the Concept of Prospective. LC 72-78388. (Current Topics of Contemporary Thought Ser.). 314p. 1973. 72.75 (ISBN 0-677-12550-X). Gordon & Breach.

Crosby, Nina E. & Marten, Elizabeth H. Discovering Philosophy. (Illus.). 72p. (Orig.). 1980. pap. 5.95 (ISBN 0-914634-81-X). DOK Pubs.

Cudworth, Ralph. A Treatise Concerning Eternal & Immutable Morality. Wellek, Rene, ed. LC 75-11214. (British Philosophers & Theologians of the 17th & 18th Centuries Ser.: Vol. 17). 1976. Repr. of 1731 ed. lib. bdg. 51.00 (ISBN 0-8240-1768-4). Garland Pub.

DeBenedictis, Matthew M. The Social Thought of Saint Bonaventure: A Study in Social Philosophy. LC 73-138108. 276p. 1946. Repr. lib. bdg. 22.50x (ISBN 0-8371-5684-X, DESB). Greenwood.

De Chardin, Teilhard. Building the Earth. 7.95 (ISBN 0-87193-078-1). Dimension Bks.

--Le Groupe Zoologique Humain, Structure et Directions Evolutives. (Coll. les Savants et le Monde Ser.). pap. 6.95 (ISBN 0-685-36591-3). French & Eur.

Dodds, James E. The Gentleman from Heaven. 123p. 1962. Repr. of 1948 ed. 3.50 (ISBN 0-87516-464-1). De Vorss.

Dooyeweerd, Herman. In the Twilight of Western Thought. 1960. pap. 3.95 (ISBN 0-934532-09-5). Presby & Reformed.

Ducasse, C. J. Nature, Mind & Death. (Paul Carus Lecture Ser.). 533p. 1951. 19.95 (ISBN 0-87548-102-7). Open Court.

Dunne, John S. The Way of All the Earth: Experiments in Truth & Religion. LC 78-1575. 1978. text ed. 19.95x (ISBN 0-268-01927-4); pap. 7.95 (ISBN 0-268-01928-2). U of Notre Dame Pr.

Erasmus. Enchiridion of Erasmus. Himelick, Raymond, tr. 16.50 (ISBN 0-8446-0614-6). Peter Smith.

Fabry, Joseph B., et al, eds. Logotherapy in Action. LC 79-51917. 379p. 1979. 19.95 (ISBN 0-317-06212-3). Inst Logo.

Ferm, Vergilius. Philosophy Beyond the Classroom. 411p. 1974. 12.95 (ISBN 0-8158-0314-1). Chris Mass.

Findhorn Community. The Findhorn Garden. 1976. pap. 10.95 (ISBN 0-06-090520-4, CN520, PL). Har-Row.

Flew, Antony. God: A Critical Enquiry. 210p. 1984. pap. 8.95 (ISBN 0-87548-371-2). Open Court.

Friedlander, Saul, et al, eds. Visions of Apocalypse: End or Rebirth? 272p. 1985. text ed. 28.50x (ISBN 0-8419-0673-4); pap. text ed. 15.50x (ISBN 0-8419-0755-2). Holmes & Meier.

Gabirol, Solomon I. Fountain of Life. pap. 1.45 (ISBN 0-685-19402-7, 104, WL). Citadel Pr.

Gandhi, M. K. All Men Are Brothers. (Modern Classics of Peace Ser). pap. 7.95 (ISBN 0-912018-15-1). World Without War.

Gautama. Gautama: The Nyaya Philosophy. Junankar, N. S., tr. from Sanskrit. 1978. 25.50 (ISBN 0-89684-002-6, Pub. by Motilal Banarsidass India). Orient Bk Dist.

Gelwick, Richard. Way of Discovery: An Introduction to the Thought of Michael Polanyi. 1977. pap. 4.95 (ISBN 0-19-502193-2). Oxford U Pr.

Goldmann, Lucien. The Philosophy of the Enlightenment: The Burgess & the Enlightenment. Maas, Henry, tr. from Fr. 1973. 17.50x (ISBN 0-262-07060-X). MIT Pr.

Gomperz, Heinrich. Philosophical Studies by Heinrich Gomperz. Robinson, Daniel S., ed. 1953. 9.50 (ISBN 0-8158-0100-9). Chris Mass.

Guerry, Herbert, ed. Philosophy & Mysticism. Dell.

Habermas, Jurgen. Theory & Practice. Viertel, John, tr. from Ger. LC 72-6227. 320p. 1973. pap. 10.95x (ISBN 0-8070-1527-X, BP489). Beacon Pr.

Haydon, Albert E. Biography of the Gods. LC 74-37848. (Essay Index Reprint Ser.). Repr. of 1941 ed. 19.00 (ISBN 0-8369-2595-5). Ayer Co Pubs.

Heyd, David. Supererogation: Its Status in Ethical Theory. LC 81-15476. (Cambridge Studies in Philosophy). 180p. 1982. 37.50 (ISBN 0-521-23935-4). Cambridge U Pr.

Honer, Stanley M. & Hunt, Thomas C. Invitation to Philosophy: Issues & Options. 4th ed. 272p. 1981. pap. text ed. write for info. (ISBN 0-534-00997-2). Wadsworth Pub.

Horkheimer, Max & Adorno, Theodor W. Dialectic of Enlightenment. Cumming, John, tr. from Ger. LC 77-167870. 1975. pap. 9.95x (ISBN 0-8264-0093-0, Continuum). Continuum.

Horowitz, Irving L. Philosophy, Science & the Sociology of Knowledge. LC 76-27756. 1976. Repr. of 1961 ed. lib. bdg. 22.50x (ISBN 0-8371-9051-7, HOPS). Greenwood.

Hudson, W. D., ed. Is-Ought Question. LC 79-106390. (Controversies in Philosophy Ser). 1970. 12.95 (ISBN 0-312-43715-3). St Martin.

Hume, David. Of Miracles. LC 85-11410. 60p. 1985. pap. 4.95 (ISBN 0-912050-72-1). Open Court.

Hutchison, John A. Living Options in World Philosophy. LC 76-46489. 323p. 1977. 16.00x (ISBN 0-8248-0455-4). UH Pr.

James, William. The Will to Believe & Human Immortality. pap. 5.95 (ISBN 0-486-20291-7). Dover.

--Will to Believe & Other Essays in Popular Philosophy & Human Immortality. 15.75 (ISBN 0-8446-2313-X). Peter Smith.

Jung, Carl G. & Kerenyi, Carl. Essays on a Science of Mythology: The Myths of the Divine Child & the Mysteries of Eleusis. rev. ed. (Bollingen Ser.: Vol. 22). 1963. pap. 6.95 (ISBN 0-691-01756-5). Princeton U Pr.

Kierkegaard, Soren. Christian Discourses. Lowrie, W., tr. 1971. pap. 10.50x (ISBN 0-691-01973-8). Princeton U Pr.

--Either-Or, 2 Vols. Lowrie, W., tr. 1944. Vol 1. pap. 7.95 (ISBN 0-691-01976-2); Vol. 2. pap. 7.95x (ISBN 0-691-01977-0). Princeton U Pr.

Kilmer, Aline M. Hunting a Hair Shirt: And Other Spiritual Adventures. LC 76-39123. (Essay Index Reprint Ser.). Repr. of 1923 ed. 14.00 (ISBN 0-8369-2697-8). Ayer Co Pubs.

Klemke. Studies in the Philosophy of Kierkegaard. 1976. pap. 16.00 (ISBN 90-247-1852-X, Pub. by Martinus Nijhoff Netherlands). Kluwer Academic.

Koestler, Arthur. The God That Failed. Crossman, Richard H., ed. LC 81-85867. 1982. pap. 7.50 (ISBN 0-89526-867-1). Regnery Bks.

Krishnamurti, Jiddu. Think on These Things. 1970. pap. 4.95 (ISBN 0-06-080192-1, P192, PL). Har-Row.

Law, Edmund. An Enquiry into the Ideas of Space & Time. Wellek, Rene, ed. LC 75-11230. (British Philosophers & Theologians of the 17th & 18th Century: Vol. 31). 1976. Repr. of 1734 ed. lib. bdg. 51.00 (ISBN 0-8240-1783-8). Garland Pub.

Legge, James, tr. I Ching. 1969. pap. 4.95 (ISBN 0-553-26002-2). Bantam.

Lokhande, Ajit. Tukarama, His Person & His Religion: A Relio-Historical, Phenomenological & Typological Enquiry. (European University Studies: Series 20, Philosophy: Vol. 22). 210p. 1976. 23.50 (ISBN 3-261-02009-1). P Lang Pubs.

Lorbeer, Floyd I. Philosophy of Light: An Introductory Treatise. 259p. 1981. pap. 15.00 (ISBN 0-89540-102-9, SB-102). Sun Pub.

Lovin, Robin W. Christian Faith & Public Choices: The Social Ethics of Barth, Brunner, & Bonhoeffer. LC 83-48922. 192p. 1984. pap. 10.95 (ISBN 0-8006-1777-0, 1-1777). Fortress.

McInerny, Ralph. Rhyme & Reason: St. Thomas & Modes of Discourse. LC 81-80234. (Aquinas Lecture Ser.). 84p. 1981. 7.95 (ISBN 0-87462-148-8). Marquette.

Marcuse, Herbert. From Luther to Popper: Studies in Critical Philosophy. 236p. 1984. pap. 7.95 (ISBN 0-8052-7196-1, Pub. by NLB England). Schocken.

Maritain, Jacques. On the Church of Christ: The Person of the Church & Her Personnel. Evans, Joseph W., tr. from Fr. LC 73-11559. Orig. Title: De l'Eglise Du Christ. (Eng. & Fr.). 352p. 1973. text ed. 24.95 (ISBN 0-268-00519-2); pap. text ed. 8.95x (ISBN 0-268-00525-7). U of Notre Dame Pr.

Matczak, Sebastian A. Karl Barth on God: Our Knowledge of the Divine Existence. LC 62-15994. 358p. 1962. 7.25 (ISBN 0-912116-06-4). Learned Pubns.

Mayer, Fred S. Why Two Worlds: Relation of Physical to Spiritual Realities. LC 78-134425. Repr. of 1934 ed. 21.00 (ISBN 0-404-08465-6). AMS Pr.

Mayne, Zachary. Two Dissertations Concerning Sense, & the Immagination, with an Essay on Consciousness. Wellek, Rene, ed. LC 75-11234. (British Philosophers & Theologians of the 17th & 18th Centuries: Vol. 35). 1976. Repr. of 1728 ed. lib. bdg. 51.00 (ISBN 0-8240-1787-0). Garland Pub.

Merton, Thomas. No Man Is an Island. 264p. 1983. Repr. of 1955 ed. lib. bdg. 21.00 (ISBN 0-88254-872-7, Octagon). Hippocrene Bks.

--The Sign of Jonas. 362p. 1983. Repr. of 1953 ed. lib. bdg. 30.00 (ISBN 0-88254-871-9, Octagon). Hippocrene Bks.

Miller, Mitchell H., Jr. Plato's "Parmenides". The "Conversion" of the Soul. LC 85-43301. 264p. 1986. 30.00x (ISBN 0-691-07303-1). Princeton U PR.

Montague, William P. Belief Unbound. 1930. 13.50x (ISBN 0-686-83485-2). Elliots Bks.

Munitz, Milton K. Space, Time & Creation: Philosophical Aspects of Scientific Cosmology. 2nd ed. 11.75 (ISBN 0-8446-5908-8). Peter Smith.

Newman, Jeremiah. Conscience Versus Law. 260p. 1972. 5.95 (ISBN 0-8199-0433-3). Franciscan Herald.

Nietzsche, Friedrich. The Antichrist & Twilight of the Gods. 1974. 100.00 (ISBN 0-87968-210-8). Gordon Pr.

Nishitani, Keiji. Religion & Nothingness. Bragt, Jan Van, tr. from Japanese. LC 81-4084. 366p. 1982. 35.95x (ISBN 0-520-04329-4); pap. 10.95x (ISBN 0-520-04946-2, CAL 634). U of Cal Pr.

Oppenheimer, Oscar. God & Man. LC 79-64099. 1979. pap. text ed. 11.25 (ISBN 0-8191-0753-0). U Pr of Amer.

Panorelli, Dora. The Ultimate Relationship. 1985. 8.95 (ISBN 0-8062-2454-1). Carlton.

Pierrakos, Eva. Guide Lectures for Self-Transformation. LC 85-134343. 216p. (Orig.). 1985. 12.95 (ISBN 0-9614777-0-9); pap. 7.95 (ISBN 0-9614777-1-7). Pathwork Pr.

Prince, Derek. Philosophy, the Bible & the Supernatural. 1969. pap. 0.10 (ISBN 0-934920-22-2, B71). Derek Prince.

Ramanathan, P. The Western Approach to the Law & the Prophets of the Ancient World. (Illus.). 188p. 1984. 88.95 (ISBN 0-89920-113-X). Am Inst Psych.

Restivo, Sal. The Social Relations of Physics, Mysticism & Mathematics. 1983. lib. bdg. 49.50 (ISBN 90-277-1536-X, Pub. by Reidel Holland). Kluwer Academic.

Ricoeur, Paul. The Reality of the Historical Past. LC 84-60012. (Aquinas Lecture Ser.). 51p. 1984. 7.95 (ISBN 0-87462-152-6). Marquette.

Rotenstreich, Nathan. Practice & Realization. 1979. lib. bdg. 29.00 (ISBN 90-247-2112-1, Pub. by Martinus Nijhoff Netherlands). Kluwer Academic.

Schopenhauer, Arthur. Religion: A Dialogue, & Other Essays. 3rd ed. Saunders, T. Bailey, tr. LC 72-488. (Essay Index Reprint Ser.). Repr. of 1891 ed. 13.00 (ISBN 0-8369-2820-2). Ayer Co Pubs.

--Religion: A Dialogue, & Other Essays. Saunders, T. Bailey, tr. LC 72-11305. 140p. 1973. Repr. of 1899 ed. lib. bdg. 25.00x (ISBN 0-8371-6652-7, SCRE). Greenwood.

Shestov, Lev. In Job's Balances: On the Sources of the Eternal Truths. Coventry, Camilla & Macartney, C. A., trs. from Ger. LC 73-92902. (Eng.). l, 379p. 1975. 20.00x (ISBN 0-8214-0143-2, 82-81461). Ohio U Pr.

Sikora, R. I. & Barry, Brian, eds. Obligations to Future Generations. LC 78-5495. (Philosophical Monographs: Second Annual Ser.). 272p. 1978. 14.95 (ISBN 0-87722-132-4); pap. 12.95 (ISBN 0-87722-128-6). Temple U Pr.

Slote, Michael. Common-Sense Morality & Consequentialism. (International Library of Philosophy). 160p. 1985. 24.95x (ISBN 0-7102-0309-8). Methuen Inc.

Stace, W. T. Mysticism & Philosophy. 1960. text ed. 17.50x (ISBN 0-333-08274-5). Humanities.

Steiner, Rudolf. Philosophy, Cosmology & Religion: Ten Lectures. Easton, Stewart C., et al, eds. 180p. (Orig.). 1984. 16.00 (ISBN 0-88010-109-1); pap. 9.95 (ISBN 0-88010-110-5). Anthroposophic.

Swami Vivekananda. Lectures from Colombo to Almora. pap. 8.95 (ISBN 0-87481-171-6). Vedanta Pr.

Swedenborg, Emmanuel. On the Means Which Conduce to True Philosophy & on the True Philosopher. Clissold, Augustus, tr. from Lat. 42p. pap. 1.00 (ISBN 0-915221-15-2). Swedenborg Sci Assn.

Taimni, I. K. Man, God & the Universe. LC 74-4167. (Illus.). 447p. 1974. pap. 3.45 (ISBN 0-8356-0447-0, Quest). Theos Pub Hse.

Teilhard De Chardin, Pierre. Comment Je Crois. 15.50 (ISBN 0-685-36585-9). French & Eur.

--Etre Plus. 12.50 (ISBN 0-685-36589-1). French & Eur.

--Images et Paroles. 32.95 (ISBN 0-685-36592-1). French & Eur.

--Je m'explique. 13.50 (ISBN 0-685-36593-X). French & Eur.

--Le Milieu Divin. 8.95 (ISBN 0-685-36583-2). French & Eur.

--Le Phenomene Humain. 15.95 (ISBN 0-685-36581-6). French & Eur.

--La Place de L'homme dans la Nature. 15.95 (ISBN 0-685-36584-0). French & Eur.

Toland, John. A Collection of Several Pieces, 2 vols. Wellek, Rene, ed. LC 75-11258. (British Philosophers & Theologians of the 17th & 18th Centuries: Vol. 57). 1976. Repr. of 1726 ed. Set. lib. bdg. 101.00 (ISBN 0-8240-1808-7). Garland Pub.

Trismegistus, Hermes. The Divine Pymander. Randolph, J., tr. 129p. 1972. Repr. of 1889 ed. 6.00 (ISBN 0-911662-48-0). Yoga.

Turner, Dean. Commitment to Care: An Integrated Philosophy of Science, Education, & Religion. LC 77-78421. 1977. 12.50 (ISBN 0-8159-5216-3). Devin.

Van Der Poel, Cornelius J. The Integration of Human Values. 5.95 (ISBN 0-87193-004-8). Dimension Bks.

Van Kaam, Adrian, et al. The Participant Self, 2 vols. pap. 4.95 (ISBN 0-87193-045-5). Dimension Bks.

Werner, Karl. Psychologie und Erkenntnisslehre D. Johannes Bonaventura. (Ger.). 70p. 1973. Repr. of 1876 ed. lib. bdg. 18.50 (ISBN 0-8337-3739-2). B Franklin.

Williams, Bernard. Ethics & the Limits of Philosophy. 248p. 1985. 17.50 (ISBN 0-674-26857-1). Harvard U Pr.

Wilm, Emil C., ed. Studies in Philosophy & Theology. LC 75-3078. Repr. of 1922 ed. 17.00 (ISBN 0-404-59079-9). AMS Pr.

Wilson, Robert A. Prometheus Rising. LC 83-81665. 280p. 1983. pap. 7.95 (ISBN 0-941404-19-6). Falcon Pr Az.

Wood, Robert E. Martin Buber's Ontology: An Analysis of I & Thou. LC 73-82510. (Studies in Phenomenology & Existential Philosophy). 160p. 1969. 19.95 (ISBN 0-8101-0256-0); pap. 10.95 (ISBN 0-8101-0650-7). Northwestern U Pr.

Wysinger, Voss E. The Celestial Democracy. LC 66-24014. 149p. 1966. lib. bdg. 16.95 (ISBN 0-914002-01-5); text ed. 16.95 (ISBN 0-914002-02-3); pap. text ed. 14.00 (ISBN 0-686-36904-1). Wysinger Pub.

Young, Warren C. Christian Approach to Philosophy. (Twin Brook Ser.). 1973. pap. 9.95 (ISBN 0-8010-9904-8). Baker Bk.

PHILOSOPHY–ADDRESSES, ESSAYS, LECTURES

Bolingbroke, Henry Viscount. The Philosophical Works, 5 vols. Wellek, Rene, ed. LC 75-11198. (British Philosophers & Theologians of the 17th & 18th Centuries: Vol. 5). 1976. Repr. of 1777 ed. Set. lib. bdg. 231.00 (ISBN 0-8240-1754-4); lib. bdg. 254.00. Garland Pub.

Boulden, James. I Am All. (Illus.). 72p. 1982. pap. 2.95 (ISBN 0-87516-481-1). De Vorss.

Buber, Martin. Meetings. Friedman, Maurice, ed. & tr. from Ger. LC 73-82780. 123p. 1973. 9.95 (ISBN 0-87548-085-3). Open Court.

Burthogge, Richard. An Essay upon Reason & the Nature of Spirits. LC 75-11204. (British Philosophers & Theologians of the 17th & 18th Centuries: Vol. 10). 1976. Repr. of 1694 ed. lib. bdg. 51.00 (ISBN 0-8240-1759-5). Garland Pub.

Collins, Anthony. A Discourse on the Grounds & Reasons of the Christian Religion. Wellek, Rene, ed. LC 75-11212. (British Philosophers & Theologians of the 17th & 18th Centuries: Vol. 15). 1976. Repr. of 1724 ed. lib. bdg. 51.00 (ISBN 0-8240-1766-8). Garland Pub.

DiLustre, Tawny. A Compilation of Thoughts, I Think?! 104p. 1985. 6.95 (ISBN 0-8059-2962-2). Dorrance.

Dominican Fathers of the Province of St. Joseph, ed. The Maritain Volume of "The Thomist", Dedicated to Jacques Maritain on the Occasion of His 60th Anniversary. LC 77-92509. (Essay Index in Reprint Ser.). 1978. Repr. 24.50x (ISBN 0-8486-3003-3). Roth Pub Inc.

Drane, James F. The Possibility of God. (Quality Paperback Ser.: No. 321). 194p. 1976. pap. 3.50 (ISBN 0-8226-0321-7). Littlefield.

Gomperz, Heinrich. Philosophical Studies by Heinrich Gomperz. Robinson, Daniel S., ed. 1953. 9.50 (ISBN 0-8158-0100-9). Chris Mass.

Hartshorne, Charles. The Logic of Perfection & Other Essays in Neoclassical Metaphysics. LC 61-11286. 351p. 1973. pap. 8.95 (ISBN 0-87548-037-3). Open Court.

Henry, Caleb S. Moral & Philosophical Essays. LC 75-3178. Repr. of 1839 ed. 10.50 (ISBN 0-404-59181-7). AMS Pr.

Heschel, Abraham J. The Insecurity of Freedom: Essays on Human Existence. LC 66-16293. 320p. 1985. pap. 7.95 (ISBN 0-8052-0361-3). Schocken.

Hotema, Hilton. Kingdom of Heaven. 45p. 1960. pap. 8.95 (ISBN 0-88697-030-X). Life Science.

Jay, Lynn & Jay, Steve. A Glimpse into Reality. LC 81-71020. 144p. (Orig.). 1982. pap. 5.25 (ISBN 0-87516-475-7). De Vorss.

Kuhlewind, Georg. Stages of Consciousness: Meditations on the Boundaries of the Soul. St. Goar, Maria, tr. from Ger. 144p. (Orig.). 1985. pap. 8.95 (ISBN 0-89281-065-3, Lindisfarne Pr). Inner Tradit.

Lewis, Ralph, ed. The Immortalized Words of the Past. LC 85-63539. 300p. (Orig.). 1986. pap. 9.95 (ISBN 0-912057-42-4, G-654). AMORC.

Machiavelli, Niccolo. Machiavelli's Thoughts on the Management of Men. (Illus.). 119p. 1982. 107.50 (ISBN 0-89266-364-2). Am Classical Coll Pr.

Montaigne, Michel de & La Boetie, Etienne de. Discours de la Servitude Volontaire ou le Contr'un. 90p. 1947. 12.50 (ISBN 0-686-54775-6). French & Eur.

--Les Essais, 4 vols. 1974. Set. 500.00 (ISBN 0-686-54776-4). French & Eur.

Needham, Joseph. Moulds of Understanding: A Pattern of Natural Philosophy. LC 75-37252. 320p. 1976. 27.50 (ISBN 0-312-54950-4). St Martin.

Reese, William L. & Freeman, Eugene, eds. Process & Divinity: The Hartshorne Festschrift. LC 64-13547. 644p. 1964. 32.95 (ISBN 0-87548-054-3). Open Court.

Reid, Thomas. Essays on the Active Powers of Man. Wellek, Rene, ed. LC 75-11251. (British Philosophers & Theologians of the 17th & 18th Centuries: Vol. 50). 1977. Repr. of 1788 ed. lib. bdg. 51.00 (ISBN 0-8240-1802-8). Garland Pub.

Rescher, Nicholas. Essays in Philosophical Analysis. LC 82-45160. (Illus.). 438p. 1982. pap. text ed. 17.75 (ISBN 0-8191-2459-1). U Pr of Amer.

Robinson, Daniel S. Crucial Issues in Philosophy. 1955. 6.95 (ISBN 0-8158-0177-7). Chris Mass.

Rosenstock-Huessy, Eugen. I Am an Impure Thinker. 1970. 10.00 (ISBN 0-912148-03-9); pap. 6.95 (ISBN 0-912148-04-7). Argo Bks.

Seth Pringle Pattison, Andrew. Philosophical Radicals & Other Essays. 1907. 23.50 (ISBN 0-8337-4388-0). B Franklin.

Smith, Norman K. Credibility of Divine Existence. Porteous, A. J., et al, eds. 1969. 27.50 (ISBN 0-312-17185-4). St Martin.

Szekely, Edmond B. Talks by Edmond Bordeaux Szekely. 48p. 1972. pap. 2.95 (ISBN 0-89564-067-8). IBS Intl.

Thompson, Walter R. Dialogue on Science, Psychology & God. LC 67-17638. 1967. 6.00 (ISBN 0-8022-1717-6). Philos Lib.

Vlastos, Gregory, ed. Plato Two: Ethics, Politics, & Philosophy of Art & Religion; a Collection of Critical Essays. LC 77-19103. (Modern Studies in Philosophy). 1978. text ed. 16.95 (ISBN 0-268-01530-9); pap. text ed. 8.95x (ISBN 0-268-01531-7). U of Notre Dame Pr.

White, Morton G. Religion, Politics, & the Higher Learning: A Collection of Essays. LC 82-1013. x, 140p. 1982. Repr. of 1959 ed. lib. bdg. 22.50x (ISBN 0-313-23480-9, WHRE). Greenwood.

Wittgenstein, Ludwig. Wittgenstein: Lectures & Conversations on Aesthetics, Psychology, & Religious Belief. Barrett, Cyril, ed. 1967. pap. 3.50 (ISBN 0-520-01354-9, CAL83). U of Cal Pr.

PHILOSOPHY–BIBLIOGRAPHY

Dolan, Walter. The Classical World Bibliography of Philosophy, Religion, & Rhetoric. LC 76-52512. (Library of Humanities Reference Bks.: No. 95). 396p. 1978. lib. bdg. 51.00 (ISBN 0-8240-9878-1). Garland Pub.

PHILOSOPHY–BIOGRAPHY

see Philosophers

PHILOSOPHY–COLLECTED WORKS

Berkeley, George. Berkeley's Philosophical Writings. Armstrong, David M., ed. (Orig.). 1965. pap. 5.95 (ISBN 0-02-064170-2, Collier). Macmillan.

--Philosophical Writings. Jessop, T. E., ed. LC 69-13823. Repr. of 1953 ed. lib. bdg. 22.50x (ISBN 0-8371-1056-4, BEPW). Greenwood.

Buber, Martin. Writings of Martin Buber. Herberg, Will, ed. (Orig.). pap. 8.95 (ISBN 0-452-00616-3, F616, Mer). NAL.

Burleigh, John S., ed. Augustine: Earlier Writings. LC 53-13043. (Library of Christian Classics). 410p. 1979. softcover 8.95 (ISBN 0-664-24162-X). Westminster.

Descartes, Rene. Oeuvres et Lettres: Avec: Discours de la Methode. 1424p. 1937. 42.95 (ISBN 0-686-55676-3). French & Eur.

--Philosophical Essays: Discourse on Method; Meditations; Rules for the Direction of the Mind. Lafleur, Laurence J., tr. LC 63-16951. (Orig.). 1964. pap. 7.87 scp (ISBN 0-672-60292-X, LLA99). Bobbs.

--Philosophical Works, 2 Vols. Haldane, E. S. & Ross, G. R., eds. 1967. Vol. 2. 57.50 (ISBN 0-521-06944-0); Vol. 1. pap. 14.95 (ISBN 0-521-09416-X); Vol. 2. pap. 14.95 (ISBN 0-521-09417-8). Cambridge U Pr.

--Philosophical Writings. Anscombe, Elizabeth & Geach, Peter T., eds. Anscombe, Elizabeth & Geach, Peter T., trs. LC 79-171798. 1971. pap. 7.20 scp (ISBN 0-672-61274-7, LLA198). Bobbs.

--Principes de la Philosophie, Vol. 1. 3rd ed. 158p. 1970. 9.95 (ISBN 0-686-55678-X). French & Eur.

Gassendi, Pierre. Selected Works. Brush, Craig B., tr. 1972. Repr. 45.00 (ISBN 0-384-17685-2). Johnson Repr.

Lachs, John, ed. Animal Faith & Spiritual Life: Previously Unpublished & Uncollected Writings by George Santayana with Critical Essays on His Thought. LC 67-20665. (Century Philosophy Ser.). 1967. 39.50x (ISBN 0-89197-607-8). Irvington.

Leibniz, Gottfried W. & Parkinson, G. H. Leibniz Philosophical Writings. Morris, Mary, tr. from Ger. (Rowman & Littlefield University Library). 270p. 1973. 13.50x (ISBN 0-87471-659-4). Rowman.

More, Henry. A Collection of Several Philosophical Writings, 2 vols. 2nd ed. Wellek, Rene, ed. LC 75-11238. (British Philosophers & Theologians of the 17th & 18th Centuries Ser.). 839p. 1978. Set. lib. bdg. 101.00 (ISBN 0-8240-1790-0). Garland Pub.

Reagan, Charles E. & Stewart, David, eds. The Philosophy of Paul Ricoeur: An Anthology of His Work. LC 77-75444. 1978. pap. 11.95x (ISBN 0-8070-1517-2, BPA15, Pub. by Ariadne Bks). Beacon Pr.

Ridley, Gustave. From Boredom to Bliss. Campbell, Jean, ed. (Illus.). 160p. (Orig.). 1983. pap. 8.95 (ISBN 0-9610544-0-9). Harmonious Pr.

St. Thomas Aquinas. Selected Writings of St. Thomas Aquinas. Goodwin, Robert P., tr. Incl. The Principles of Nature; On Being & Essence; On the Virtues in General; On Free Choice. LC 65-26529. (Orig.). 1965. pap. 4.24 scp (ISBN 0-672-60469-8, LLA217). Bobbs.

Spinoza, Benedict. Theologico-Political Treatise: Political Treatise. Elwes, R. H., tr. pap. text ed. 6.95 (ISBN 0-486-20249-6). Dover.

Spinoza, Benedict D. Works of Spinoza, 2 Vols. Elwes, tr. Set. 29.50 (ISBN 0-8446-2986-3). Peter Smith.

Taylor, John. Collected Works. 600.00 (ISBN 0-87968-899-8). Gordon Pr.

PHILOSOPHY–HISTORY

Bregman, Jay. Synesius of Cyrene: Philosopher-Bishop. LC 81-10293. (The Transformation of the Classical Heritage Ser.: Vol. II). 1982. 33.00x (ISBN 0-520-04192-5). U of Cal Pr.

Copleston, Frederick. History of Philosophy, 9 vols. Incl. Vol. 1. Greece & Rome (ISBN 0-8091-0065-7); Vol. 2. Medieval Philosophy - Augustine to Scotus (ISBN 0-8091-0066-5); Vol. 3. Ockham to Suarez (ISBN 0-8091-0067-3); Vol. 4. Descartes to Leibniz (ISBN 0-8091-0068-1); Vol. 5. Hobbes to Hume (ISBN 0-8091-0069-X); Vol. 6. Wolff to Kant (ISBN 0-8091-0070-3); Vol. 7. Fichte to Nietzsche (ISBN 0-8091-0071-1); Vol. 8. Bentham to Russell (ISBN 0-8091-0072-X); Vol. 9. Maine de Bira to Sartre. 1976 (ISBN 0-8091-0196-3). Vols. 1-9. 19.95 ea. Paulist Pr.

Gay, Peter. The Enlightenment: An Interpretation-the Rise of Modern Paganism, Vol. 1. 1977. pap. 10.95x (ISBN 0-393-00870-3, N870, Norton Lib). Norton.

Issawi, Charles. An Arab Philosophy of History: Selections from the Prolegomena of Ibn Khaldun of Tunis (1332-1406) LC 86-29199. xiv, 192p. 1986. 9.95 (ISBN 0-87850-056-1). Darwin Pr.

Jaspers, Karl. Socrates, Buddha, Confucius & Jesus: Taken from Vol. 1 of the Great Philosophers. Manheim, Ralph, tr. 1966. pap. 3.95 (ISBN 0-15-683580-0, Harv). HarBraceJ.

Lyons, John D. & Nichols, Stephen G., Jr., eds. Mimesis: From Mirror to Method, Augustine to Descartes. LC 82-40340. (Illus.). 287p. 1982. 25.00x (ISBN 0-87451-244-1). U Pr of New Eng.

Oakley, Francis. Omnipotence, Covenant & Order: An Excursion in the History of Ideas from Abelard to Leibniz. LC 83-45945. 168p. 1984. 18.50x (ISBN 0-8014-1631-0). Cornell U Pr.

Perrier, Joseph L. Revival of Scholastic Philosophy in the Nineteenth Century. LC 9-10966. Repr. of 1909 ed. 17.50 (ISBN 0-404-04994-X). AMS Pr.

Ryan, John K., ed. Studies in Philosophy & the History of Philosophy, Vol. 4. LC 61-66336. Repr. of 1969 ed. 59.50 (ISBN 0-8357-9057-6, 2017279). Bks Demand UMI.

Szekely, Edmond B. The Evolution of Human Thought. (Illus.). 44p. 1971. pap. 2.50 (ISBN 0-89564-062-7). IBS Intl.

Tillyard, Eustace M. Elizabethan World Picture. 1959. pap. 3.16 (ISBN 0-394-70162-3, Vin). Random.

Trismegistus, Hermes. The Seven Golden Chapters of Hermes. 1984. pap. 2.95 (ISBN 0-916411-82-6, Pub by Alchemical Pr). Holmes Pub.

Wolfson, Harry A. Studies in the History of Philosophy & Religion, Vol. II. Twersky, Isadore & Williams, George H., eds. 1977. 40.00x (ISBN 0-674-84766-0). Harvard U Pr.

Zubiri, Xavier. Nature, History, God. Fowler, Thomas B., Jr., tr. from Span. LC 80-1355. 441p. 1981. lib. bdg. 31.25; pap. text ed. 17.75. U Pr of Amer.

PHILOSOPHY–INTRODUCTIONS

Hopkins, Jasper. A Concise Introduction to the Philosophy of Nicholas of Cusa. 3rd ed. LC 85-72432. xii, 194p. 1986. text ed. 20.00x (ISBN 0-938060-32-5). Banning Pr.

Wallace, William A. The Elements of Philosophy: A Compendium for Philosophers & Theologians. LC 77-1527. 1977. pap. 10.95 (ISBN 0-8189-0345-7). Alba.

PHILOSOPHY–STUDY AND TEACHING

Gilson, Etienne. History of Philosophy & Philosophical Education. (Aquinas Lecture). 1947. 7.95 (ISBN 0-87462-112-7). Marquette.

PHILOSOPHY, AMERICAN

see also Mercersburg Theology; Messianism, American

Abbot, Francis E. Scientific Theism. LC 75-3012. (Philosophy in America Ser.). Repr. of 1885 ed. 27.50 (ISBN 0-404-59004-7). AMS Pr.

Ames, Van Meter. Zen & American Thought. 1978. Repr. of 1962 ed. lib. bdg. 26.50 (ISBN 0-313-20066-1, AMZA). Greenwood.

Barrett, William. Death of the Soul. LC 82-45317. 192p. 1986. 16.95 (ISBN 0-385-15965-X, Anchor Pr). Doubleday.

Cherry, C. God's New Israel: Religious Interpretations of American Destiny. 1971. pap. 23.95 (ISBN 0-13-357335-4). P-H.

Jesuit Philosophical Association Of The Eastern States. Phases of American Culture. facs. ed. LC 69-17579. (Essay Index Reprint Ser). 1942. 14.00 (ISBN 0-8369-0021-9). Ayer Co Pubs.

Miller, Perry G. Errand into the Wilderness. LC 56-11285. 1956. 15.00x (ISBN 0-674-26151-8, Belknap Pr); pap. 6.95x (ISBN 0-674-26155-0). Harvard U Pr.

--Nature's Nation. LC 67-17316. 1967. 20.00x (ISBN 0-674-60550-0, Belknap Pr). Harvard U Pr.

Numbers, Ronald L. Creation by Natural Law: Laplace's Nebular Hypothesis in American Thought. LC 76-45810. 196p. 1977. 22.50x (ISBN 0-295-95439-6). U of Wash Pr.

Riley, Isaac W. American Thought from Puritanism to Pragmatism & Beyond: A Greenwood Archival Edition. 2nd ed. Repr. of 1923 ed. lib. bdg. 65.00x (ISBN 0-8371-2391-7, RIAT). Greenwood.

Riley, Woodbridge. American Thought from Puritanism to Pragmatism. 11.75 (ISBN 0-8446-1385-1). Peter Smith.

Sandeen, Ernest R. & Hale, Frederick, eds. American Religion & Philosophy: A Guide to Information Sources. LC 73-17562. (American Studies Information Guide: Vol. 5). 1978. 62.00x (ISBN 0-8103-1262-X). Gale.

Weinstein, Michael A. The Wilderness & the City: American Classical Philosophy As a Moral Quest. LC 82-4769. 176p. 1982. lib. bdg. 17.50x (ISBN 0-87023-375-0). U of Mass Pr.

Wentz, Richard E. The Saga of the American Soul. LC 80-5598. 163p. 1980. pap. text ed. 9.50 (ISBN 0-8191-1150-3). U Pr of Amer.

White, Morton. Science & Sentiment in America: Philosophical Thought from Jonathan Edwards to John Dewey. 1972. 25.00x (ISBN 0-19-501519-3). Oxford U Pr.

White, Morton, ed. Documents in the History of American Philosophy: From Jonathan Edward to John Dewey. 1972. pap. text ed. 13.95x (ISBN 0-19-501555-X). Oxford U Pr.

PHILOSOPHY, ANCIENT

see also Gnosticism; Manichaeism; Neoplatonism; Platonists; Stoics

Afnan, Ruhi. Zoroaster's Influence on Anaxagoras, the Greek Tragedians & Socrates. LC 68-18733. 161p. 1969. 6.95 (ISBN 0-8022-2250-1). Philos Lib.

--Zoroaster's Influence on Greek Thought. LC 64-20423. 1965. 8.95 (ISBN 0-8022-0011-7). Philos Lib.

Annas, Julia, ed. Oxford Studies in Ancient Philosophy, Vol. 2. 1984. text ed. 39.95x (ISBN 0-19-824769-9); pap. text ed. 16.95x (ISBN 0-19-824768-0). Oxford U Pr.

Armstrong, A. H. An Introduction to Ancient Philosophy. 3rd ed. LC 81-3731. (Quality Paperback Ser.: No. 418). 260p. 1981. pap. 7.45 (ISBN 0-8226-0418-3). Littlefield.

Benjamin, A. & Hackstaff, L. H. On Free Choice of the Will: Augustine. 1964. pap. text ed. write for info. (ISBN 0-02-308030-2). Macmillan.

Boman, Thorleif. Hebrew Thought Compared with Greek. Moreau, Jules L., tr. from Ger. 1970. pap. 6.95 (ISBN 0-393-00534-8, Norton Lib). Norton.

Brumbaugh, Robert S. The Philosophers of Greece. LC 81-9120. (Illus.). 274p. 1981. 34.50x (ISBN 0-87395-550-1); pap. 8.95x (ISBN 0-87395-551-X). State U NY Pr.

Caird, Edward. Evolution of Theology in the Greek Philosophers, 2 Vols in 1. LC 4-16272. (Gifford Lectures 1900-1902). 1968. Repr. of 1904 ed. 46.00 (ISBN 0-527-14130-5). Kraus Repr.

--Evolution of Theology in the Greek Philosophers, the Gifford Lectures, 1900-1902, 2 Vols. 1968. 39.00x (ISBN 0-403-00116-1). Scholarly.

Casaubon, Meric. The Golden Book of Marcus Aurelius. 1979. Repr. of 1906 ed. lib. bdg. 12.50 (ISBN 0-8482-7564-0). Norwood Edns.

Cavarnos, Constantine. The Classical Theory of Relations. LC 75-2659. 116p. 1975. pap. 3.75 (ISBN 0-914744-28-3). Inst Byzantine.

--The Holy Mountain. 2nd ed. LC 73-84103. (Illus.). 172p. 1977. pap. 6.50 (ISBN 0-914744-38-0). Inst Byzantine.

Cicero. Nature of the Gods. McGregor, Horace C., tr. (Classics Ser.). 280p. (Orig.). 1972. pap. 6.95 (ISBN 0-14-044265-0). Penguin.

Cornford, Francis M., ed. Greek Religious Thought from Homer to the Age of Alexander. LC 79-98637. (Library of Greek Thought: No. 2). Repr. of 1923 ed. 21.50 (ISBN 0-404-01734-7). AMS Pr.

Depew, David J., ed. The Greeks & the Good Life. 280p. lib. bdg. 25.00 (ISBN 0-937622-00-1); pap. text ed. 7.95 (ISBN 0-937622-01-X). CSU Fullerton.

Dvornik, Francis. Early Christian & Byzantine Political Philosophy: Origins & Background, 2 vols. LC 67-4089. (Dumbarton Oaks Studies: Vol. 9). 975p. 1966. 50.00x (ISBN 0-88402-016-9). Dumbarton Oaks.

Freeman, Kathleen. God, Man & State. LC 79-101039. 1969. Repr. of 1952 ed. 27.50x (ISBN 0-8046-0705-2, Pub. by Kennikat). Assoc Faculty Pr.

--God, Man & State: Greek Concepts. Repr. of 1952 ed. lib. bdg. 27.50x (ISBN 0-8371-2821-8, FRGM). Greenwood.

Geer, Russell. Letters, Principal Doctrines, & Vatican Sayings: Epicurus. 1964. pap. text ed. write for info. (ISBN 0-02-341200-3). Macmillan.

Hack, Roy K. God in Greek Philosophy to the Time of Socrates. 1970. Repr. of 1931 ed. lib. bdg. 12.50 (ISBN 0-8337-1514-3). B Franklin.

Jaeger, Werner W. The Theology of the Early Greek Philosophers: The Gifford Lectures, 1936. Robinson, Edward S., tr. LC 79-9940. vi, 259p. 1980. Repr. of 1947 ed. lib. bdg. 55.00x (ISBN 0-313-21262-7, JATH). Greenwood.

Lomperis, Timothy. Hindu Influence on Greek Philosophy. 1985. 9.00x (ISBN 0-8364-1311-3). South Asia Bks.

Paramananda, Swami. Plato & Vedic Idealism. (Orig.). 1924. 4.50 (ISBN 0-911564-15-2). Vedanta Ctr.

Pegis, Anton C. Saint Thomas & the Greeks. (Aquinas Lecture). 1939. 7.95 (ISBN 0-87462-103-8). Marquette.

Polka, Brayton. The Dialectic of Biblical Critique: Interpretation & Existence. LC 84-26216. 192p. 1986. 25.00 (ISBN 0-312-19874-4). St Martin.

Randall, John H. Hellenistic Ways of Deliverance & the Making of the Christian Synthesis. LC 74-137339. 1970. 28.00x (ISBN 0-231-03327-3). Columbia U Pr.
Robertson, W. On Christian Doctrine: Augustine. 1958. pap. text ed. write for info. (ISBN 0-02-402150-4). Macmillan.
Scott, Walter, ed. & tr. Hermetica: The Ancient Greek & Latin Writings Which Contain Religious or Philosophic Teachings Ascribed to Hermes Trismegistus, 4 vols. LC 85-8198. 1985. Vol 1; 549p. pap. 15.95 (ISBN 0-87773-338-4); Vol. 2; 482p. pap. 15.95 (ISBN 0-87773-339-2); Vol. 3; 632p. pap. 17.95 (ISBN 0-87773-340-6); Vol. 4; 576p. pap. 17.95 (ISBN 0-87773-341-4). Shambhala Pubns.
Tarrant, Harold. Scepticism or Platonism: The Philosophy of the Fourth Academy. (Cambridge Classical Studies). 192p. 1985. 39.50 (ISBN 0-521-30191-2). Cambridge U Pr.
Taylor, Thomas. Sallust on the Gods & the World & Other Works. 12.50 (ISBN 0-89314-401-0). Philos Res.
Vernant, Jean P. Myth & Thought Among the Greeks. 400p. 1983. 29.95x (ISBN 0-7100-9544-9). Methuen Inc.
Wolfson, Harry A. Studies in the History of Philosophy & Religion, Vol. I. Twersky, Isadore & Williams, George H., eds. LC 72-86385. 640p. 1973. 40.00x (ISBN 0-674-84765-2). Harvard U Pr.

PHILOSOPHY, ARAB

see also Philosophy, Islamic

Issawi, Charles. An Arab Philosophy of History: Selections from the Prolegomena of Ibn Khaldun of Tunis (1332-1406) LC 86-29199. xiv, 192p. 1986. 9.95 (ISBN 0-87850-056-1). Darwin Pr.
Kaufmann, David. Die Sinne: Beitrage Zur Geschichte der Physiologie und Psychologie Im Ittelalter Aus Hebraischen und Arabisch En Quellen. Katz, Steven, ed. LC 79-7141. (Jewish Philosophy, Mysticism & History of Ideas Ser.). 1980. Repr. of 1884 ed. lib. bdg. 17.00x (ISBN 0-405-12267-5). Ayer Co Pubs.
Munk, Salomon. Melanges Philosophie Juive et Arabe. Katz, Steven, ed. LC 79-7148. (Jewish Philosophy, Mysticism & History of Ideas Ser.). 1980. Repr. of 1927 ed. lib. bdg. 51.50x (ISBN 0-405-12278-0). Ayer Co Pubs.

PHILOSOPHY, BRITISH

Anderson, Fulton H., ed. The New Organon: Bacon. 1960. pap. text ed. write for info. (ISBN 0-02-303380-0). Macmillan.
Collier, Arthur. Clavis Universalis: New Inquiry after Truth, Being a Demonstration of the Non-Existence or Impossibility of an External World. Wellek, Rene, ed. LC 75-11208. (British Philosophers & Theologians of the 17th & 18th Centuries Ser.). 150p. 1978. lib. bdg. 51.00 (ISBN 0-8240-1763-3). Garland Pub.
Collins, Anthony. A Disclosure on Free-Thinking. LC 75-11209. (British Philosophers & Theologians of the 17th & 18th Centuries Ser.). 395p. 1976. lib. bdg. 51.00 (ISBN 0-8240-1764-1). Garland Pub.
Evans, G. Rosemary. Anselm & Talking About God. 1978. 29.95x (ISBN 0-19-826647-2). Oxford U Pr.
Ferguson, Adam. Institutes of Moral Philosophy. 2nd rev. ed. LC 75-11219. (British Philosophers & Theologians of the 17th & 18th Centuries Ser.: Vol. 22). 1978. Repr. of 1773 ed. lib. bdg. 51.00 (ISBN 0-8240-1773-0). Garland Pub.
Glanvill, Joseph. Scepsis Scientifics: Or Confest Ignorance, the Way to Science, 2 vols. in 1. Wellek, Rene, ed. LC 75-11222. (British Philosophers & Theologians of the 17th & 18th Centuries Ser.). 330p. 1978. lib. bdg. 51.00 (ISBN 0-8240-1776-5). Garland Pub.
Glanville, Joseph. Some Discourse, Sermons & Remains. Wellek, Rene, ed. LC 75-11221. (British Philosophers & Theologians of the 17th & 18th Centuries Ser.). 1979. lib. bdg. 51.00 (ISBN 0-8240-1775-7). Garland Pub.
Grant, Patrick. Six Modern Authors & Problems of Belief. LC 79-14511. 175p. 1979. text ed. 28.50x (ISBN 0-06-492515-3). B&N Imports.
Lowde, James. Disclosure Concerning the Nature of Man, 1694. LC 75-11233. (British Philosophers & Theologians in the 17th & 18th Century Ser.). 271p. 1979. lib. bdg. 51.00 (ISBN 0-8240-1786-2). Garland Pub.
Patrides, C. A. & Wittreich, Joseph A., Jr., eds. The Apocalypse in English Renaissance Thought & Literature. LC 84-71281. 452p. (Orig.). 1985. 52.00x (ISBN 0-8014-1648-5); pap. 19.95x (ISBN 0-8014-9893-7). Cornell U Pr.
Ray, John. The Wisdom of God Manifested in the Works of the Creation. LC 75-11250. (British Philosophers & Theologians in the 17th & 18th Century Ser.). 247p. 1979. lib. bdg. 51.00 (ISBN 0-8240-1801-X). Garland Pub.
Wiley, Margaret L. Subtle Knot: Creative Scepticism in Seventeenth-Century England. LC 68-54994. (Illus.). 1968. Repr. of 1952 ed. lib. bdg. 22.50x (ISBN 0-8371-0753-9, WISK). Greenwood.

PHILOSOPHY, BUDDHIST

see also Buddhist Logic; Philosophy, Indic

Barrington, E. The Great Teachings of the Buddha, 2 vols. (Illus.). 211p. 1986. Set. 147.50 (ISBN 0-89901-273-6). Found Class Reprints.
Chang Chung-Yuan, ed. The Original Teachings of Ch'an Buddhism. LC 82-48003. (Grove Press Eastern Philosophy & Religion Ser.). 320p. 1982. pap. 9.95 (ISBN 0-394-62417-3, E813, Ever). Grove.
Cleary, Thomas, tr. The Flower Ornament Scripture: A Translation of the Avatamsaka Sutra, Vol. 1. LC 83-2370. 703p. 1984. 40.00 (ISBN 0-87773-767-3, 53690-8). Shambhala Pubns.
Conze, Edward. Buddhist Thought in India. 1967. pap. 8.95 (ISBN 0-472-06129-1, 129, AA). U of Mich Pr.
Coomaraswamy, Ananda K. Hinduism & Buddhism. LC 78-138215. 1971. Repr. of 1943 ed. lib. bdg. 22.50x (ISBN 0-8371-5570-3, COHB). Greenwood.
Eckel, Malcolm D. Jnanagarbha's Commentary on the Distinction Between the Two Truths. (Buddhist Studies). 196p. (Orig.). 1986. 39.50x (ISBN 0-88706-301-2); pap. 12.95x (ISBN 0-88706-302-0). State U NY Pr.
Graumann, Nicholas S. A Representational Outline of the Philosophy of Buddhism. (Illus.). 151p. 1982. 77.85 (ISBN 0-89266-331-6). Am Classical Coll Pr.
Guenther, H. V. Philosophy & Psychology in the Abhidharma. 2nd rev. ed. 1974. 18.00 (ISBN 0-87773-048-2). Orient Bk Dist.
Herman, A. L. An Introduction to Buddhist Thought: A Philosophic History of Indian Buddhism. (Illus.). 480p. (Orig.). 1984. lib. bdg. 35.75 (ISBN 0-8191-3594-1); pap. text ed. 13.50 (ISBN 0-8191-3595-X). U Pr of Amer.
Hopkins, Jeffrey & Klein, Ann. Compassion in Tibetan Buddhism. 2nd ed. Napper, Elizabeth, ed. LC 80-85453. 263p. 1980. pap. 10.95 (ISBN 0-937938-04-1). Snow Lion.
Inada, Kenneth K. Guide to Buddhist Philosophy. (Reference Books - Area Studies: Area Studies). 1985. lib. bdg. 45.00 (ISBN 0-8161-7899-2). G K Hall.
Inada, Kenneth K. & Jacobson, Nolan P. Buddhism & American Thinkers. 182p. 1983. 39.50 (ISBN 0-87395-753-9); pap. 14.95 (ISBN 0-87395-754-7). State U NY Pr.
Kalupahana, David J. Buddhist Philosophy: A Historical Analysis. LC 75-20040. 210p. 1976. (Eastwest Ctr); pap. 4.95x (ISBN 0-8248-0392-2). UH Pr.
--Nagarjuna: The Philosophy of the Middle Way. (Buddhist Studies). 488p. 1986. 49.50x (ISBN 0-88706-148-6); pap. 19.95 (ISBN 0-88706-149-4). State U NY Pr.
--A Path of Righteousness: Dhammapada-An Introductory Essay, Together with the Pali Text, English Translation with Commentary. LC 86-9088. (Eng. & Pali.). 234p. (Orig.). 1986. lib. bdg. 24.75 (ISBN 0-8191-5365-6); pap. text ed. 12.50 (ISBN 0-8191-5366-4). U Pr of Amer.
Katz, Nathan, ed. Buddhist & Western Psychology. LC 82-12325. 300p. (Orig.). 1983. pap. 15.00 (ISBN 0-87773-758-4, Prajna). Shambhala Pubns.
Kitaro, Nishida. Last Writings: Nothingness & the Religious Worldview. Dilworth, David A., tr. 176p. 1987. text ed. 18.00x (ISBN 0-8248-1040-6). UH Pr.
Kohli, S. S. Critical Study of Adigranth. 1976. Repr. 12.50 (ISBN 0-89684-038-7). Orient Bk Dist.
Lalwani, K. C. Dasavaikalika Sutra. 1973. 8.95 (ISBN 0-89684-192-8). Orient Bk Dist.
McGovern, William M. A Manual of Buddhist Philosophy. LC 78-70097. Repr. of 1923 ed. 27.50 (ISBN 0-404-17346-2). AMS Pr.
Maitreya, Sthiramati. Madhyantavibhagatika: An Analysis of the Middle Path & the Extremes. Friedman, David L., tr. from Sanskrit. 154p. 1984. Repr. of 1937 ed. lib. bdg. 19.50x (ISBN 0-88181-004-5). Canon Pubns.
Miyamoto, Shoson. The Buddhist Philosophy of the Middle Way. 1983. cancelled 9.95x (ISBN 0-914910-07-8). Buddhist Bks.
Myo-Bong, Master & Hye-Am Choi. Gateway to Patriarchal Son (Zen) Venerable Master Hye-Am's Dharma Talks. Myo-Bong, Master, tr. from Chinese & Korean. LC 86-50754. (Chinese Korean & Eng.). 450p. (Orig.). 1986. 18.00 (ISBN 0-938647-01-6). Western Son Acad.
Myo-Bong Master. Gateway to Zen (Ch'an) Hye-Am Choi, ed. LC 86-50750. (Chinese Korean & Eng.). 355p. (Orig.). 1986. 18.00 (ISBN 0-938647-00-8). Western Son Acad.
Piatigorsky, Alexander. The Buddhist Philosophy of Thought: Essays in Interpretation. LC 82-3987. 240p. 1984. text ed. 24.50x (ISBN 0-389-20266-5, 07084). B&N Imports.
Revelation in Indian Thought: A Festschrift in Honor of Professor T. R. V. Murti. Coward, Harold, ed. LC 77-71192. 1977. 25.00 (ISBN 0-913546-52-6). Dharma Pub.
Rexroth, Kenneth, ed. The Buddhist Writings of Lafcadio Hearn. LC 77-2496. 312p. 1977. lib. bdg. 12.95 (ISBN 0-915520-05-2). Ross-Erikson.
Rinbochay, Lati. Mind in Tibetan Buddhism. Napper, Elizabeth, ed. LC 86-3799. 172p. (Orig.). 1980. lib. bdg. 12.95 cancelled (ISBN 0-937938-03-3); pap. 10.95 (ISBN 0-937938-02-5). Snow Lion.
Sayama, Mike. Samadhi: Self Development in Zen, Swordsmanship, & Psychotherapy. (Transpersonal & Humanistic Psychology). 147p. 1985. 34.50x (ISBN 0-88706-146-X); pap. 10.95 (ISBN 0-88706-147-8). State U NY Pr.
Sivananda, Swami. Divine Nectar. 2nd rev. ed. 1976. pap. 14.00 (ISBN 0-89684-196-0). Orient Bk Dist.
Sogen, Yamakami. Systems of Buddhist Thought. 385p. Repr. of 1912 ed. text ed. 28.50x (ISBN 0-89644-474-0, Pub. by Chinese Matl Ctr). Coronet Bks.
Takakusu, J. Essentials of Buddhist Philosophy. 3rd ed. 1975. Repr. 8.50 (ISBN 0-8426-0826-5). Orient Bk Dist.
--Essentials of Buddhist Philosophy. 2nd ed. Chan, W. & Moore, Charles A., eds. (Illus.). Repr. of 1949 ed. text ed. 14.00x. Coronet Bks.
Tiwari, Kapil N. Dimensions of Renunciation in Advaita Vedanta. 1977. 12.95 (ISBN 0-89684-195-2). Orient Bk Dist.
Tripitaka Master Hua, commentary by. Dharma Flower Sutra, Vol. VI. Buddhist Text Translation Society, tr. from Chinese. (Illus.). 161p. (Orig.). 1980. pap. 8.00 (ISBN 0-917512-65-0). Buddhist Text.
--Dharma Flower Sutra, Vol. V. Buddhist Text Translation Society, tr. from Chinese. (Illus.). 200p. (Orig.). 1980. pap. 8.00 (ISBN 0-917512-64-2). Buddhist Text.
Tulku, Tarthang. Time, Space & Knowledge: A New Vision. LC 77-19224. (Illus.). 1977. 14.95 (ISBN 0-913546-08-9); pap. 10.95 (ISBN 0-913546-09-7). Dharma Pub.
Verdu, Alfonso. Early Buddhist Philosophy in the Light of the Four Noble Truths. 220p. 1986. 22.50X (ISBN 0-317-53523-4, Pub. by Motilal Banarsidass). South Asia Bks.

PHILOSOPHY, BYZANTINE

Cavarnos, Constantine. A Dialogue Between Bergson, Aristotle, & Philologos. 3rd. enl. ed. 100p. 1986. pap. 4.95 (ISBN 0-914744-77-1). Inst Byzantine.
Dvornik, Francis. Early Christian & Byzantine Political Philosophy: Origins & Background, 2 vols. LC 67-4089. (Dumbarton Oaks Studies: Vol. 9). 975p. 1966. 50.00x (ISBN 0-88402-016-9). Dumbarton Oaks.

PHILOSOPHY, CHINESE

see also Neo-Confucianism

Anthony, Carol K. The Philosophy of the I Ching. LC 81-69537. 160p. 1981. pap. 6.50 (ISBN 0-9603832-1-2). Anthony Pub Co.
Beck, L. A. The Story of Confucius & of the Other Great Chinese Mystics, 3 vols. (Illus.). 241p. 1986. Set. 187.75 (ISBN 0-89901-274-4). Found Class Reprints.
Brown, B. The Essence of Chinese Wisdom. (Illus.). 227p. 1986. 117.50 (ISBN 0-89901-279-5). Found Class Reprints.
Carus, Paul, ed. Yin Chih Wen: The Tract of the Quiet Way. Suzuki, Teitaro & Carus, Paul, trs. from Chinese. 52p. 1950. pap. 0.95 (ISBN 0-87548-245-7). Open Court.
Chuang Tzu. Chuang Tzu: Mystic, Moralist, & Social Reformer. 2nd rev. ed. Giles, Herbert A., tr. LC 70-38059. (BCL Ser.: No. II). Repr. of 1926 ed. 44.50 (ISBN 0-404-56915-3). AMS Pr.
Confucius. Analects. Waley, Arthur, tr. 1966. pap. 4.95 (ISBN 0-394-70173-9, V173, Vin). Random.
--Sayings of Confucius. Ware, James R., tr. (Orig.). pap. 2.95 (ISBN 0-451-62168-9, Ment). NAL.
Field, Stephen, tr. from Chinese. Tian Wen: A Chinese Book of Origins. LC 86-12737. 128p. (Orig.). 1986. 22.95 (ISBN 0-8112-1010-3); pap. 8.95 (ISBN 0-8112-1011-1, NDP624). New Directions.
Garvy, John W., Jr. Yin & Yang: Two Hands Clapping. Liebermann, Jeremiah, ed. (Five Phase Energetics Ser.: No. 2). (Illus.). 1985. pap. 3.00 (ISBN 0-943450-01-2). Wellbeing Bks.
Giles, Herbert A., ed. & tr. from Chinese. Musings of a Chinese Mystic: Selections from the Philosophy of Chuang Tzu. 112p. Repr. of 1926 ed. text ed. 17.50x (ISBN 0-89644-497-X, Pub. by Chinese Matl Ctr). Coronet Bks.
Hall, Fitzedward, ed. Vishnu Purana. Wilson, Horace M., tr. from Sanskrit. LC 74-78004. (Secret Doctrine Reference Ser.). 2150p. Date not set. lib. bdg. 95.00 (ISBN 0-913510-14-9). Wizards.
Hsun Tzu. Hsun Tzu: Basic Writings. Watson, Burton, tr. LC 63-20340. (Translations from Oriental Classics Ser.). (Orig.). 1963. pap. 10.00x (ISBN 0-231-08607-5). Columbia U Pr.
Legge, James. I Ching: Book of Changes. 449p. 1983. pap. 7.95 (ISBN 0-8065-0458-7). Citadel Pr.
Legge, James, tr. The Ch'un Ts'ew with the Tso Chuen, 4 vols, Vol. 4. (Chinese Classics Ser.). (Chinese & Eng.). 1983. Repr. of 1893 ed. 25.00x (ISBN 0-89986-356-6); 95.00x (ISBN 0-89986-352-3). Oriental Bk Store.
--The Sho King, or the Book of Historical Documents, 4 vols, Vol. 2. (Chinese Classics Ser.). (Chinese & Eng.). 1983. Repr. of 1893 ed. 25.00x (ISBN 0-89986-354-X); Set. 95.00x (ISBN 0-89986-352-3). Oriental Bk Store.
Liang Chi-Chao. History of Chinese Political Thought. LC 70-100526. Repr. of 1930 ed. 17.50 (ISBN 0-404-03985-5). AMS Pr.
Loewe, Michael. Chinese Ideas of Life & Death. 240p. 1982. China Stands Up - see attached. text ed. 25.00x (ISBN 0-04-180001-X). Allen Unwin.
--Ways to Paradise: The Chinese Quest for Immortality. (Illus.). 1979. text ed. 34.00x (ISBN 0-04-181025-2). Allen Unwin.
Mencius. Works of Mencius. Legge, James, tr. 15.75 (ISBN 0-8446-0331-7). Peter Smith.
Munro, Donald J., ed. Individualism & Holism: The Confucian & Taoist Philosophical Perspectives. (Michigan Monographs in Chinese Studies: No. 52). 399p. 1985. 25.00 (ISBN 0-89264-057-X); pap. 12.50 (ISBN 0-89264-058-8). U of Mich Ctr Chinese.
Palmer, Martin, tr. from Chinese. T'ung Shu. LC 85-2520. (Illus.). 240p. 1986. pap. 7.95 (ISBN 0-87773-346-5, 74221-4, Dist. by Random). Shambhala Pubns.
Schmidt, Paul F. Buddhist Meditation on China. LC 84-81398. (Illus.). 74p. 1984. lib. bdg. 15.00 (ISBN 0-912998-06-7); pap. 6.00 (ISBN 0-912998-07-5). Hummingbird.
Schwartz, Benjamin I. The World of Thought in Ancient China. (Illus.). 456p. 1985. text ed. 27.50x (ISBN 0-674-96190-0, Belknap Pr). Harvard U Pr.
Tsung-Hsi, Huang. The Records of Ming Scholars. Ching, Julia & Fang, Chaoying, eds. LC 86-27257. 688p. 1987. text ed. 27.00x (ISBN 0-8248-1028-7). UH Pr.
Wang Kung-Hsing. Chinese Mind. LC 68-23336. 1968. Repr. of 1946 ed. lib. bdg. 22.50x (ISBN 0-8371-0260-X, WACM). Greenwood.
Watson, Burton, ed. & tr. Basic Writings of Mo Tzu, Hsun Tzu, & Han Fei Tzu. LC 67-16170. (Records of Civilization, Sources & Studies: No. 74). 1967. 20.00x (ISBN 0-231-02515-7). Columbia U Pr.
Watts, Alan W. Nature, Man & Woman. LC 58-8266. 1970. pap. 3.95 (ISBN 0-394-70592-0, V592, Vin). Random.
Williams, Wells S. China, Chinese Philosophers & Confucianism. (Illus.). 137p. 1982. Repr. of 1883 ed. 73.45 (ISBN 0-89901-059-8). Found Class Reprints.
Yang Ming, Wang. Instructions for Practical Living & Other Neo-Confucian Writings. Chan, Wing tsit, tr. from Chinese. 358p. 1985. pap. 14.00x (ISBN 0-231-06039-4). Columbia U Pr.

PHILOSOPHY, CHRISTIAN

Corrie ten Boom. Jesus Is Victor. 288p. 1984. pap. 6.95 (ISBN 0-8007-5176-0, Power Bks). Revell.
McIntire, C. T., ed. The Legacy of Herman Dooyeweerd: Reflections on Critical Philosophy in the Christian Tradition. (Illus.). 198p. (Orig.). 1986. lib. bdg. 25.25 (ISBN 0-8191-5033-9, Pub. by Inst Christ Stud); pap. text ed. 12.00 (ISBN 0-8191-5034-7). U Pr of Amer.

PHILOSOPHY, COMPARATIVE

Here are entered works on the comparison of the philosophies of the East and the West.

Corbin, Henry. The Concept of Comparative Philosophy. Russell, Peter, tr. from Fr. (Orig.). 1985. pap. 3.95 (ISBN 0-933999-29-1). Phanes Pr.
Coward, Harold C. Jung & Eastern Thought. (Series in Transpersonal & Humanistic Philosophy). 229p. 1985. 39.50 (ISBN 0-88706-052-8); pap. 12.95 (ISBN 0-88706-051-X). State U NY Pr.
De Groot, Jeanne L. Man & Mind. ix, 441p. 1985. text ed. 45.00x (ISBN 0-8236-3087-0). Intl Univs Pr.
Hutchison, John A. Living Options in World Philosophy. LC 76-46489. 323p. 1977. 16.00x (ISBN 0-8248-0455-4). UH Pr.
Levy, Zelev. Between Yafeth & Shem: On the Relationship Between Jewish & General Philosophy. (American University Studies V-Philosophy: Vol. 21). 262p. 1986. text ed. 23.50 (ISBN 0-8204-0373-3). P Lang Pubs.

Lomperis, Timothy. Hindu Influence on Greek Philosophy. 1985. 9.00x (ISBN 0-8364-1311-3). South Asia Bks.

Scharfstein, Ben-Ami, ed. Philosophy East-Philosophy West: A Critical Comparison of Indian, Chinese, Islamic & European Philosophy. 1978. 25.00x (ISBN 0-19-520064-0). Oxford U Pr.

Watts, Alan W. The Meaning of Happiness: The Quest for Freedom of the Spirit in Modern Psychology & the Wisdom of the East. 1979. pap. 6.95 (ISBN 0-06-090676-6, CN 676, PL). Har-Row.

PHILOSOPHY, EAST INDIAN

see Philosophy, Indic

PHILOSOPHY, EUROPEAN

Derenbourg, Joseph. Essai Sur L'Histoire et la Geographie de la Palestine, D'Apres les Autres Sources Rabbiniques. Premiere Partie, Hisoire Depuis Cyrun Jusqu' a Adrien. 490p. Repr. of 1867 ed. text ed. 99.36x (ISBN 0-576-80155-0). Gregg Intl.

PHILOSOPHY, FRENCH

Betts, C. J. Early Deism in France. 1984. lib. bdg. 53.50 (ISBN 90-247-2923-8, Pub. by Martinus Nijhoff Netherlands). Kluwer Academic.

Crocker, Lester G. An Age of Crisis: Man & World in Eighteenth Century French Thought. LC 59-14233. (Goucher College Ser.). Repr. of 1959 ed. 129.00 (ISBN 0-8357-9260-9, 2011983). Bks Demand UMI.

De Saint-Martin, Louis-Claude. Of Errors & Truth. Vadenais, Philip & Vadenais, Antoinette, trs. from Fr. LC 86-63353. 435p. (Orig.). 1987. pap. write for info. (ISBN 0-912057-47-5, G-651). AMORC.

Descartes, Rene. Oeuvres, 11 tomes. Adam & Tannery, eds. Incl. Tome I. Correspondance (Avril 1622-Fevrier 1638) 36.95 (ISBN 0-685-34212-3); Tome II. Correspondance (Mars 1638 - Decembre 1639) 32.95 (ISBN 0-685-34213-1); Tome III. Correspondance (Janvier 1640-Juin 1643) 37.95 (ISBN 0-685-34214-X); Tome IV. Correspondance (Juillet 1643-Avril 1647) 37.95 (ISBN 0-685-34215-8); Tome V. Correspondance (Mai 1647 - Fevrier 1650) 36.95 (ISBN 0-685-34216-6); Tome VI. Discours de la Methode et Essais. 32.95 (ISBN 0-685-34217-4); Tome VII. Meditationes de Prima Philosophia. 27.95 (ISBN 0-685-34218-2); Tome VIII, Pt. 1. Principia Philosophiae. 15.95 (ISBN 0-685-34219-0); Tome VIII, Pt. 2. Epistola ad Voetium, Lettre Apologetique, Notas in Programma. 20.95 (ISBN 0-685-34220-4); Tome IX, Pt. 1. Meditations. 12.95 (ISBN 0-685-34221-2); Tome IX, Pt. 2. Principes. 14.95 (ISBN 0-685-34222-0); Tome X. Physico-Mathematica, Compendium Musicae, Regulea ad Directionem Ingenii, Recherche de la Verite, Supplement a la Correspondance. 37.95 (ISBN 0-685-34223-9); Tome XI. Le Monde, Description du Corps Humain, Passions de l'Ame, Anatomica, Varia. 37.95 (ISBN 0-685-34224-7). French & Eur.

Fecher, Charles A. Philosophy of Jacques Maritain. LC 70-90705. Repr. of 1953 ed. lib. bdg. 22.50x (ISBN 0-8371-2287-2, FEJM). Greenwood.

Kingston, Frederick T. French Existentialism, a Christian Critique. LC 61-925. pap. 59.30 (ISBN 0-317-08761-4, 2014272). Bks Demand UMI.

Leighton, Walter L. French Philosophers-New England Transcendentalism. LC 68-19289. 1968. Repr. of 1908 ed. lib. bdg. 22.50x (ISBN 0-8371-0143-3, LEPT). Greenwood.

Maritain, Jacques. Le Payson de Garonne: Un Vieux Laic s'Interroge a propos du Temps Present. 19.95 (ISBN 0-685-34274-3). French & Eur.

Pascal, Blaise. Pensees. (Univers des Lettres). pap. 2.50 (ISBN 0-685-34246-8). French & Eur.

--Pensees. Desgranges, ed. (Coll. Prestige). 16.95 (ISBN 0-685-34245-X). French & Eur.

Perkins, J. A. The Concept of the Self in the French Enlightenment. 162p. (Orig.). 1969. pap. text ed. 24.50x (Pub. by Droz Switzerland). Coronet Bks.

Reagan, Charles E. & Stewart, David, eds. The Philosophy of Paul Ricoeur: An Anthology of His Work. LC 77-75444. 1978. pap. 11.95x (ISBN 0-8070-1517-2, BPA15, Pub. by Ariadne Bks). Beacon Pr.

Vartanian, Aram. Diderot & Descartes: A Study of Scientific Naturalism in the Enlightment. LC 75-18406. (History of Ideas Series: No. 6). 336p. 1975. Repr. of 1953 ed. lib. bdg. 22.50x (ISBN 0-8371-8337-5, VADD). Greenwood.

PHILOSOPHY, GERMAN

Buber, Martin. Meetings. Friedman, Maurice, ed. & tr. from Ger. LC 73-82780. 123p. 1973. 9.95 (ISBN 0-87548-085-3). Open Court.

Eckermann, Willigis. Der Physikkommentar Hugolins von Orvieto Oesa: Ein Beitrag zur Erkenntnislehre des spaetmittelalterlichen Augustinismus. (Spaetmittelalter und Reformation, Vol. 5). 160p. 1972. 23.60x (ISBN 3-11-003714-9). De Gruyter.

Feuerbach, Ludwig. Thoughts on Death & Immortality: From the Pages of a Thinker, along with an Appendix of Theological Satirical Epigrams, Edited by One of His Friends. Massey, James A., tr. from Ger. LC 80-25259. 263p. 1980. 33.00x (ISBN 0-520-04051-1); pap. 6.95 (ISBN 0-520-04062-7, CAL 486). U of Cal Pr.

Heine, Heinrich. Religion & Philosophy in Germany. Snodgrass, John, tr. from Ger. 210p. (Orig.). 1986. 29.50x (ISBN 0-88706-282-2); pap. 9.95 (ISBN 0-88706-283-0). State U NY Pr.

Helten, William L. Van, ed. Die Altostniederfraenkischen Psalmenfragmente: Die Lipsius'schen Glossen & Die Altsuedmittelfraenkischen Psalmenfragmente. 222p. 1970. 30.00 (ISBN 0-384-22230-7). Johnson Repr.

Jaspers, Karl. Man in the Modern Age. LC 75-41155. Repr. of 1933 ed. 28.50 (ISBN 0-404-14558-2). AMS Pr.

Loader, Jamer A. Polar Structures in the Book of Qohelet. (Beihefte aur Zeitschrift fuer die alttestamentliche Wissenschaft). 150p. 1979. text ed. 32.75x (ISBN 3-11-007636-5). De Gruyter.

Luther, Martin. Luthers Werke, 4 vols. (Ger.). 1920p. 1982. Set. pap. 67.50 (ISBN 3-11-008942-4). De Gruyter.

Nietzsche, Friedrich. The Dawn of Day. 1974. 100.00 (ISBN 0-87968-204-3). Gordon Pr.

--A Nietzsche Reader. Hollingdale, R. J., tr. from Ger. (Classics Ser.). (Orig.). 1978. pap. 4.95 (ISBN 0-14-044329-0). Penguin.

--Nietzsche, Werke, Kritische Gesamtausgabe, Sect. 8, Vol. 1: Nachgelassene Fragmente, Herbst 1885 bis Herbst 1887. Colli, Giorgio & Montinari, Mazzino, eds. (Ger.). viii, 360p. 1974. 28.20x (ISBN 3-11-004741-1). De Gruyter.

Peake, A. S., et al. Germany in the Nineteenth Century. facs. ed. LC 67-30189. (Manchester University Publications Historical Ser.: No. 24). 1915. 15.00 (ISBN 0-8369-0472-9). Ayer Co Pubs.

Poser, Hans. Philosophie und Mythos. 1979. text ed. 35.20x (ISBN 3-11-007601-2). De Gruyter.

Schonborn, Johann P. Von. Die Psalmen Des Koniglichen Propheten Davids. xl, 872p. Repr. of 1658 ed. 62.00. Johnson Repr.

PHILOSOPHY, GREEK

see Philosophy, Ancient

PHILOSOPHY, HINDU

see also Advaita; Dharma; Maya (Hinduism); Philosophy, Buddhist; Philosophy, Indic; Yoga

Amritachandra. Purushartha-Siddhyupaya (Jaina-Pravachana-Rahasya-Kosha) Prasada, Ajit, ed. & tr. LC 73-3838. (The Sacred Books of the Jainas: No. 4). Repr. of 1933 ed. 22.50 (ISBN 0-404-57704-0). AMS Pr.

Aurobindo, Sri. The Future Evolution of Man. Saint-Hilaire, P. B., ed. 157p. 1982. pap. 2.95 (ISBN 0-89071-323-5, Pub. by Sri Aurobindo Ashram India). Matagiri.

--Ideal of the Karmayogin. 170p. Date not set. 7.00 (ISBN 0-317-17429-0). Auromere.

--The Life Divine. 1112p. 1982. 19.50 (ISBN 0-89071-301-4, Pub. by Sri Aurobindo Ashram India); pap. 15.00 (ISBN 0-89071-300-6, Pub. by Sri Aurobindo Ashram India). Matagiri.

--The Mother, with Letters on the Mother & Translations of Prayers & Meditations. 500p. 1982. 11.95 (ISBN 0-89071-311-1, Pub. by Sri Aurobindo Ashram India); pap. 8.95 (ISBN 0-89071-310-3, Pub. by Sri Aurobindo Ashram India). Matagiri.

--The Problem of Rebirth. 186p. 1983. 7.50 (ISBN 0-89071-305-7, Pub. by Sri Aurobindo Ashram India); pap. 5.50 (ISBN 0-89071-304-9, Pub. by Sri Aurobindo Ashram India). Matagiri.

--The Riddle of This World. 98p. 1984. pap. 1.25 (ISBN 0-89071-306-5, Pub. by Sri Aurobindo Ashram India). Matagiri.

--Santan Dharma Ka Mahatva: (Uttarpara Speech) 14p. 3.00 (ISBN 0-317-17480-0). Auromere.

--The Supramental Manifestation on Earth. 108p. 1980. pap. 2.25 (ISBN 0-89071-307-3, Pub. by Sri Aurobindo Ashram India). Matagiri.

--The Synthesis of Yoga. 899p. 1984. 16.75 (ISBN 0-89071-313-8, Pub. by Sri Aurobindo Ashram India); pap. 12.50 (ISBN 0-89071-312-X, Pub. by Sri Aurobindo Ashram India). Matagiri.

--Thoughts & Glimpses. 30p. 1973. pap. 0.60 (ISBN 0-89071-308-1, Pub. by Sri Aurobindo Ashram India). Matagiri.

--The Yoga & Its Objects. 33p. 1984. pap. 0.75 (ISBN 0-89071-314-6, Pub. by Sri Aurobindo Ashram India). Matagiri.

Babineau, Edmour J. Love of God & Social Duty in the Ramcaritmanas. 1979. 13.95 (ISBN 0-89684-050-6, Pub. by Motilal Banarsidass India). Orient Bk Dist.

Badarayana. Brahma Sutra: The Philosophy of Spiritual Life. Radhakrishnan, S., tr. LC 68-21330. 1968. Repr. of 1960 ed. lib. bdg. 37.25x (ISBN 0-8371-0291-X, BABS). Greenwood.

Bernard, Theos. Hindu Philosophy. LC 68-21323. 1968. Repr. of 1947 ed. lib. bdg. 22.50x (ISBN 0-8371-0311-8, BEHP). Greenwood.

--Hindu Philosophy. 1981. Repr. of 1947 ed. 14.00x (ISBN 0-8364-0765-2, Pub. by Motilal Banarsidass). South Asia Bks.

Bhashycharaya, Pundit M. Catechism of the Visishtadwaita Philosophy. Robb, R. I., ed. (Secret Doctrine Reference Ser.). (Orig.). 1986. pap. 4.00 (ISBN 0-913510-56-4). Wizards.

Bose, Ram C. Hindu Philosophy. 420p. 1986. Repr. 28.00X (ISBN 0-8364-1757-7, Pub. by Manohar India). South Asia Bks.

Brabazon, Francis. The Word at World's End. 88p. 1971. 5.95 (ISBN 0-940700-04-2); pap. 3.45 (ISBN 0-940700-03-4). Meher Baba Info.

Bruteau, Beatrice. Evolution Toward Divinity. LC 73-16198. 260p. 1974. 10.00 (ISBN 0-8356-0216-8). Theos Pub Hse.

Coomaraswamy, Ananda K. Hinduism & Buddhism. LC 78-138215. 1971. Repr. of 1943 ed. lib. bdg. 22.50x (ISBN 0-8371-5570-3, COHB). Greenwood.

Crawford, S. Cromwell. The Evolution of Hindu Ethical Ideals. (Asian Studies at Hawaii: No. 28). 197p. 1982. pap. text ed. 14.00x (ISBN 0-8248-0782-0). UH Pr.

Das Goswami, Satsvarupa. Prabhupada Nectar, Bk. 2. Dasi, Bimala, ed. 145p. pap. 4.99 (ISBN 0-911233-23-7). Gita Nagari.

--Prabhupada Nectar, Vol. 4. Bimala dasi, ed. 160p. 1985. pap. text ed. 2.00 (ISBN 0-911233-29-6). Gita Nagari.

Das Goswami, Satvarupa. Prabhupada Nectar, Vol. 5. Bimala dasi, ed. 160p. 1986. pap. text ed. 4.00 (ISBN 0-911233-31-8). Gita Nagari.

Dash, Vaidya B. Handbook of Ayurveda. 221p. (Orig.). 1983. 28.00 (ISBN 0-317-17437-1, Pub. by Cultural Integration). Auromere.

Degler, Lois. Man & God. LC 74-28943. (Illus.). 1975. pap. 3.00 (ISBN 0-930422-04-X). Dennis-Landman.

Devendra Gani. Davva-Samgaha (Dravya-Samgaha) Goshal, Sarat C., ed. & intro. by. LC 73-3835. Repr. of 1917 ed. 27.50 (ISBN 0-404-57701-6). AMS Pr.

--Gommatsara Jiva-Kanda (the Soul) Jaini, Rai B., ed. & intro. by. LC 73-3839. Repr. of 1927 ed. 48.00 (ISBN 0-404-57705-9). AMS Pr.

--Gommatsara Karma-Kanda, Pts. 1 & 2. Jaini, Rai B. & Ji, Brachmachari S., eds. LC 73-3840. Repr. of 1927 ed. Set. 72.50 (ISBN 0-404-57712-1). AMS Pr.

The Dharam Shastra: Hindu Religious Codes, 6 vols. Incl. Vol. I. 267p. 1978 (ISBN 0-89684-137-5); Vol. II. 230p. 1979 (ISBN 0-89684-138-3); Vol. III. 309p. 1979 (ISBN 0-89684-139-1); Vol. IV. 187p. 1979 (ISBN 0-89684-140-5); Vol. V. 438p. 1979 (ISBN 0-89684-141-3); Vol. VI. 222p. 1979 (ISBN 0-89684-142-1). Repr. of 1908 ed. 100.00 set (ISBN 0-686-77519-8, Pub. by Cosmo Pubns India). Orient Bk Dist.

Donato, Sri. The Day of Brahma. Morningland Publications, Inc., ed. (Illus.). 377p. 1981. pap. 10.00 (ISBN 0-935146-20-2). Morningland.

Gandhi, M. K. Delhi Diary: Daily Talks at Prayer Meetings, 1947-1948. 426p. 1982. 7.50 (ISBN 0-934676-56-9). Greenlf Bks.

Gotama. The Nyaya Sutras of Gotama. Satisa Chandra Vidyabhusana, tr. LC 73-3795. (Sacred Books of the Hindus: No. 8). Repr. of 1913 ed. 29.00 (ISBN 0-404-57808-X). AMS Pr.

Greenlees. Gospel of Guru Granth Sahib. 8.95 (ISBN 0-8356-7132-1). Theos Pub Hse.

Gunabhadra Acharya. Atmanushasana (Discourse to the Soul) Jaini, Rai B., ed. & tr. LC 73-3841. (Sacred Books of the Jainas: No. 7). Repr. of 1928 ed. 18.00 (ISBN 0-404-57707-5). AMS Pr.

Haug, Martin, ed. & tr. The Aitareya Brahmanam of Rigveda: Containing the Earliest Speculations of the Brahmans on the Meaning of the Sacrificial Prayers, & on the Origin, Performance & Sense of the Rites of the Vedic Religion. LC 73-3830. (Sacred Books of the Hindus: Extra Vol. 4). Repr. of 1922 ed. 27.50 (ISBN 0-404-57848-9). AMS Pr.

Jain, Pratibha. Gandhian Ideas, Social Movements & Creativity. 1986. 32.00x (ISBN 81-7033-007-6, Pub. by Rawat). South Asia Bks.

Keith, Arthur B. The Religion & Philosophy of the Veda & Upanishads, 2 vols. LC 71-109969. Repr. of 1925 ed. lib. bdg. 34.00x (ISBN 0-8371-4475-2, KEVU). Greenwood.

Kumarappa, Bharatan. Realism & Illusionism in Hinduism. xvi, 356p. 1986. Repr. text ed. 40.00x (ISBN 81-7047-012-9, Pub. by Mayur Pubns India). Apt Bks.

LeMaitre, Solange. Ramakrishna & the Vitality of Hinduism. Markmann, Charles L., tr. from Fr. LC 68-54059. (The Overlook Spiritual Masters Ser.). (Illus.). 244p. 1986. pap. 9.95 (ISBN 0-87951-241-5). Overlook Pr.

Lomperis, Timothy. Hindu Influence on Greek Philosophy. 1985. 9.00x (ISBN 0-8364-1311-3). South Asia Bks.

Mahadevan, T. M. Superimposition in Advaita Vedanta. 80p. 1985. text ed. 20.00x (ISBN 0-86590-570-3, Pub. by Sterling Pubs India). Apt Bks.

Mallik, G. N. Philosophy of Vaisnava Religion. 59.95 (ISBN 0-8490-0829-8). Gordon Pr.

Malyala, Panduranga R. Upanayanam (Thread Marriage) (Illus.). 20p. 1983. pap. text ed. 2.00 (ISBN 0-938924-15-X). Sri Shirdi Sai.

Mother. The Sunlit Path. 194p. 1984. pap. 4.95 (ISBN 0-89071-318-9, Pub. by Sri Aurobindo Ashram India). Matagiri.

Muktananda, Swami. A Book for the Mind. 40p. (Orig.). 1976. pap. 1.75 (ISBN 0-685-99448-1). SYDA Found.

--God Is with You. (Illus.). 40p. (Orig.). 1978. pap. 1.75 (ISBN 0-914602-57-8). SYDA Found.

Nisargadatta Maharaj. Prior to Consciousness: Talks with Sri Nisargadatta Maharaj. Dunn, Jean, ed. LC 85-71544. ix, 159p. (Orig.). pap. 9.95 (ISBN 0-317-19710-X). Acorn NC.

Oberoi, A. S. Support of the Shaken Sangat: Meetings with Three Masters. Perkins, Russell, ed. LC 84-50911. (Illus.). 256p. (Orig.). 1984. pap. 15.00 (ISBN 0-89142-043-6). Sant Bani Ash.

Pandey, Raj B. Hindu Sanskaras. 1976. Repr. 25.00 (ISBN 0-8426-0853-2). Orient Bk Dist.

Potter, Karl H., ed. Advaita Vedanta Up to Samkara & His Pupils: Encyclopedia of Indian Philosophies, Vol. 3. LC 77-8558. 648p. 1982. 63.00x (ISBN 0-691-07182-9). Princeton U Pr.

Prabhavananda, Swami. Religion in Practice. 6.95 (ISBN 0-87481-016-7). Vedanta Pr.

--Spiritual Heritage of India. LC 63-10517. 1979. pap. 8.95 (ISBN 0-87481-035-3). Vedanta Pr.

--Vedic Religion & Philosophy. 3.95 (ISBN 0-87481-411-1). Vedanta Pr.

Radhakrishnan, S. Hindu View of Life. (Unwin Paperbacks Ser.). 92p. 1980. pap. 4.95 (ISBN 0-04-294115-6). Allen Unwin.

Rajneesh, Acharya. The Mysteries of Life & Death. Bisen, Malini, tr. from Hindi. 1978. pap. 3.50 (ISBN 0-89684-045-X, Pub. by Motilal Banarsidass India). Orient Bk Dist.

Ramacharaka, Yogi. Philosophies & Religions of India. 8.00 (ISBN 0-911662-05-7). Yoga.

Ramanuja Research Society. Vishishtadvaita: Philosophy & Religion. 273p. 1975. 10.75 (ISBN 0-88253-683-4). Ind-US Inc.

Rammohun Roy, R. The English Works of Raja Ramohun Roy. Ghose, Jogendra C., ed. LC 75-41220. Repr. of 1906 ed. 49.50 (ISBN 0-404-14738-0). AMS Pr.

Rolland, Romain. Life of Ramakrishna. 5.95 (ISBN 0-87481-080-9). Vedanta Pr.

Saksena, S. K. Nature of Consciousness in Hindu Philosophy. 2nd ed. 1971. 5.95 (ISBN 0-89684-284-3). Orient Bk Dist.

Saraydarian, Torkom. Five Great Mantrams of the New Age. LC 73-39431. 1975. pap. 2.00 (ISBN 0-911794-19-0). Aqua Educ.

--Flame of Beauty, Culture, Love, Joy. LC 80-67681. 1980. pap. 10.00 (ISBN 0-911794-02-6). Aqua Educ.

--Hierarchy & the Plan. LC 75-39432. 1975. pap. 2.00 (ISBN 0-911794-20-4). Aqua Educ.

--Legend of Shamballa. LC 76-12895. 1976. 12.00 (ISBN 0-911794-40-9); pap. 10.00 (ISBN 0-911794-41-7). Aqua Educ.

--Triangles of Fire. LC 77-82155. 1977. pap. 3.00 (ISBN 0-911794-35-2). Aqua Educ.

--The Unusual Court. LC 77-86720. 1979. pap. 4.00 (ISBN 0-911794-44-1). Aqua Educ.

Schweitzer, Albert. Indian Thought & Its Development. 1962. 11.00 (ISBN 0-8446-2893-X). Peter Smith.

Seader, Ruth, ed. The Teachings of Kirpal Singh, 3 vols. Vol. I, The Holy Path, 104 pp. 3.00 (ISBN 0-318-03046-2); Vol. III, The New Life, 200 pp. 3.50 (ISBN 0-318-03047-0); One-Volume Ed., 474 pp. 7.95 (ISBN 0-318-03048-9). Sant Bani Ash.

Seal, Brajendranath. The Positive Sciences of the Ancient Hindus. 313p. 1986. Repr. 19.00x (ISBN 0-8364-1575-2, Pub. by Motilal Banarsidass). South Asia Bks.

Singh, Ajaib. The Jewel of Happiness: The Sukhmani of Guru Arjan. Perkins, Russell & Perkins, Judith, eds. Bagga, Raaj K., tr. LC 84-50910. (Illus.). 384p. (Orig.). 1984. pap. 15.00 (ISBN 0-89142-042-8). Sant Bani Ash.

Singh, Balbir. Hindu Metaphysics. 256p. 1986. text ed. 25.00x (ISBN 0-391-03408-1). Humanities.

Singh, Kirpal. Baba Jaimal Singh: His Life & Teachings. (Illus.). 168p. 3.00 (ISBN 0-318-03045-4). Sant Bani Ash.

Sri Hanumaan Chaaleesa. 2.00 (ISBN 0-938924-22-2). Sri Shirdi Sai.

Stcherbatsky, T. Buddhist Logic, 2 Vols. 1958. Repr. of 1932 ed. Set. text ed. 74.00x (ISBN 90-2790-060-4). Mouton.

Stcherbatsky, Theodore. Buddhist Logic, 2 vols. 1930. pap. text ed. 8.95 ea.; Vol. 1. pap. text ed. (ISBN 0-486-20955-5); Vol. 2. pap. text ed. (ISBN 0-486-20956-3). Dover.

Subramuniya. Gems of Wisdom. (Illus.). 234p. 1973. 7.00 (ISBN 0-87516-346-7); pap. 5.00 (ISBN 0-87516-345-9). De Vorss.

Swami Bhaktivedanta. Sri Isopanisad: Discovering the Original Person. 1985. 7.95; pap. 2.95 (ISBN 0-89213-138-1). Bhaktivedanta.

Swami Muktananda. In the Company of a Siddha: Interviews & Conversations with Swami Muktananda. rev. ed. LC 78-65085. 192p. 1978. 5.95. SYDA Found.

Swami Nikhilananda, compiled by. Vivekananda: The Yogas & Other Works. LC 53-7534. (Illus.). 1018p. includes biography 19.95 (ISBN 0-911206-04-3). Ramakrishna.

Swami Vivekananda. Complete Works of Swami Vivekananda, 8 vols. pap. 55.00x (ISBN 0-87481-176-7). Vedanta Pr.

--Teachings of Swami Vivekananda. 1971. pap. 3.95 (ISBN 0-87481-134-1). Vedanta Pr.

The Mother. The Lesson of Life. 180p. 1985. pap. 5.25 (ISBN 0-89071-322-7, Pub. by Sri Aurobindo Ashram India). Matagiri.

Vasu, Srisa Chandra, tr. The Gheranda Samhita. LC 73-3804. (Sacred Books of the Hindus: 15, Pt. 2). Repr. of 1914 ed. 14.50 (ISBN 0-404-57836-5). AMS Pr.

--The Vedanta Sutras of Badarayana with the Commentary of Baladeva. LC 73-3790. (Sacred Books of the Hindus: Vol. 5). Repr. of 1912 ed. 57.50 (ISBN 0-404-57805-5). AMS Pr.

PHILOSOPHY, INDIC

see also Philosophy, Buddhist; Philosophy, Hindu

Alanahally, Shrikrishna. The Woods. Taranath, Rajeeve, tr. from Kannada. Orig. Title: Kaadu. 112p. 1979. pap. 2.95 (ISBN 0-86578-091-9). Ind-US Inc.

Anand, Kewal K. Indian Philosophy: The Concept of Karma. 396p. 1982. 34.95 (ISBN 0-940500-91-4, Pub by Bharatiya Vidya Prakashan India). Asia Bk Corp.

Aurobindo. Life Companion Paperback Supplement Series. (Life Companion Ser.). 1339p. (Orig.). 1984. pap. 39.25 (ISBN 0-89744-013-7, Pub. by Madanlal Himatsinghlea). Auromere.

--Sri Aurobindo Life Companion Library. (Life Companion Ser.). 4522p. 1984. Repr. of 1979 ed. 111.85 (ISBN 0-317-19956-0, Pub. by Mandanlal Himatsinghlea). Auromere.

Aurobindo, Sri. The Durga Stotra. 31p. (Orig.). 1982. pap. 5.00 (ISBN 0-89744-235-0). Auromere.

--Life Divine. (Life Companion Library Bible Paper Ser.). 1112p. 1983. Repr. of 1949 ed. deluxe ed. 24.95 (ISBN 0-89744-008-0); write for info. Auromere.

--Sri Aurobindo Birth Centenary Library: Complete Writings of Sri Aurobindo, 30 vols. 1979. Set. 300.00x (ISBN 0-89744-964-9); lib. bdg. 400.00x (ISBN 0-89744-965-7). Auromere.

Aurobindo, Sri & Mother. The Hierachy of Minds. Sobel, Prem & Sobel, Jyoti, eds. 174p. 1984. pap. 5.50 (ISBN 0-89071-324-3, Pub. by Sri Aurobindo Ashram India). Matagiri.

Baba, Bangali. The Yogasutra of Patanjali: With Commentary of Vyasa. 115p. 1982. 12.95 (ISBN 81-208-0154-7, Pub. by Motilal Banarsidass India); pap. 9.95 (ISBN 81-208-0155-5, Pub. by Motilal Banarsidass India). Orient Bk Dist.

Baba, Meher. Sparks of the Truth: From the Dissertations of Meher Baba. Deshmukh, C. D., ed. (Illus.). 96p. (Orig.). 1971. pap. 2.95 (ISBN 0-913078-02-6). Sheriar Pr.

Baba, Meher, et al. Meher Baba Journal, Vol. 1, No. 6. Patterson, Elizabeth C., ed. (Illus.). 68p. 1972. pap. 2.50x (ISBN 0-913078-10-7). Sheriar Pr.

--Meher Baba Journal, Vol. 1, No. 7. Patterson, Elizabeth C., ed. (Illus.). 68p. 1972. pap. 2.50x (ISBN 0-913078-11-5). Sheriar Pr.

Bahadur, K. P. The Wisdom of Saankhya. LC 78-901698. (The Wisdom of India Ser.: Vol. 2). 222p. 1977. 9.25 (ISBN 0-89684-469-2). Orient Bk Dist.

--The Wisdom of Vaisheshika. (The Wisdom of India Ser.: Vol. 4). 207p. 1979. 10.50 (ISBN 0-89684-470-6). Orient Bk Dist.

Barua, Benimadhab. A History of Pre-Buddhistic Indian Philosophy. 1981. Repr. of 1921 ed. 28.50x (ISBN 0-8364-0800-4, Pub. by Motilal Banarsidass). South Asia Bks.

Batchelor, Stephen. Alone with Others. Rosset, Hannelore, ed. LC 82-21054. (Grove Press Eastern Philosophy & Religion Ser.). 144p. 1983. pap. 5.95 (ISBN 0-394-62457-2, E843, Ever). Grove.

Betty, L. Stafford. Vadiraja's Refutation of Sankara's Non-Dualism: Clearing the Way for Theism. 1978. 9.95 (ISBN 0-89684-001-8). Orient Bk Dist.

Bose, D. N. The Yoga Vasistha Ramayana. rev. ed. 1984. Repr. of 1954 ed. 12.50x (ISBN 0-8364-1181-1, Pub. by Mukhopadhyaya India). South Asia Bks.

Chairanya, Krishna. Freedom & Transcendence. 1983. 28.00x (ISBN 0-8364-0953-1, Pub. by Manohar India). South Asia Bks.

Chakrabarti, Kisor K. The Logic of Gotama. LC 77-13853. (Society for Asian & Comparative Philosophy Monograph: No. 5). 168p. 1978. pap. text ed. 7.00x (ISBN 0-8248-0601-8). UH Pr.

Chakraborty, Bhaktivenode. Platonic Bearings in Rabindranath. 1986. 9.00x (ISBN 0-8364-1580-9, Pub. by KP Bagchi India). South Asia Bks.

Chari, S. M. Advaita & Visistadvaita. 2nd ed. 1976. 11.95 (ISBN 0-8426-0886-9). Orient Bk Dist.

Chaudhury, Sukomal. Analytical Study of the Abhidharmakosa. 1983. 18.00x (ISBN 0-8364-1017-3, Pub. by Mukhopadyaya). South Asia Bks.

Christanand, M. The Philosophy of Indian Monotheism. 1979. 12.00x (ISBN 0-8364-0558-7, Pub. by Macmillan India). South Asia Bks.

Conversations: The Mother. 133p. 1973. pap. 1.75 (ISBN 0-89071-246-8). Matagiri.

Debate Study Group & Tharchin, Sermey G., eds. Logic & Debate Tradition of India, Tibet & Mongolia: History, Reader & Sources. 281p. (Orig.). 1979. pap. 9.50 (ISBN 0-918753-00-7, Pub by Rashi Gempil Ling). Mahayana.

Desai, Yogi A. The Wisdom of the Body. Sarasohn, Lisa, ed. (Illus.). 40p. (Orig.). 1984. pap. 2.00 (ISBN 0-940258-13-7). Kripalu Pubns.

Devaraja, N. K. The Mind & Spirit of India. 1967. 5.95 (ISBN 0-89684-281-9). Orient Bk Dist.

Dhawan, Y. P. Beyond the Guru. 227p. 1980. pap. 4.25 (ISBN 0-86578-060-9). Ind-US Inc.

Flowers & Their Messages. rev. ed. 308p. Date not set. pap. 32.50 (ISBN 0-89744-990-8, Pub. by Sri Aurobindo Ashram Trust India). Auromere.

Free John, Da. The Method of the Siddhas. rev. ed. LC 78-53869. (Illus.). 364p. 1978. pap. 9.95 (ISBN 0-913922-44-7). Dawn Horse Pr.

Gandhi, M. K. & Tagore, Rabindranath. Tagore-Gandhi Controversy. Prabhu, R. K., ed. 155p. (Orig.). 1983. pap. 2.00 (ISBN 0-934676-52-6). Greenlf Bks.

Ghosh, Oroon K. Science, Society & Philosophy: A New Radical Humanist Approach. 1986. 28.00x (ISBN 0-8364-1563-9, Pub. by Ajanta). South Asia Bks.

Goudriaan, Teun. Maya, Divine & Human. 1979. 26.00x (ISBN 0-685-95754-3). South Asia Bks.

Herman, A. L. The Problem of Evil & Indian Thought. 1976. 13.95 (ISBN 0-8426-0991-1). Orient Bk Dist.

Herzberger, Radhika. An Essay in the Development of Fifth & Sixth Century Indian Thought. 1986. lib. bdg. 64.00 (ISBN 90-277-2250-1, Pub. by Reidel Holland). Kluwer Academic.

Jha, Ganganatha. The Prabhakara School of Purva Mimamsa. 2nd, rev. ed. 1978. 12.50 (ISBN 0-89684-016-6, Pub. by Motilal Banarsidass India). Orient Bk Dist.

Johnston, E. H. Early Samkhya. 1974. Repr. 5.95 (ISBN 0-8426-0684-X). Orient Bk Dist.

Kangle, R. P. The Kautiliya Arthasastra, 3 pts. 1986. Repr. of 1965 ed. Set. 75.00 (Pub. by Motilal Banarsidass). Pt. 1 (ISBN 81-208-0039-7). Pt. 2. 36.00 (ISBN 81-208-0040-0); Pt. 3. 46.00 (ISBN 81-208-0024-9). South Asia Bks.

Kar, Bijayananda. Indian Philosophy: An Analytical Study. 1986. 17.00x (ISBN 0-317-44233-3, Pub. by Ajanta). South Asia Bks.

Keith, Arthur B. Indian Logic & Atomism: An Exposition of the Nyaya & Vaicesika Systems. lib. bdg. 79.95 (ISBN 0-87968-529-8). Krishna Pr.

Keshavadas, Satguru S. Cosmic Meditations. (Illus.). 22p. (Orig.). 1974. pap. 1.99 (ISBN 0-942508-08-4). Vishwa.

--Cosmic Shakti Kundalini: The Universal Mother. LC 76-11347. (Illus.). 112p. (Orig.). 1976. pap. 3.50 (ISBN 0-942508-04-1). Vishwa.

--Essence of Bhagavad Gita & Bible. LC 80-50446. (Illus.). 303p. 1982. pap. 30.00 (ISBN 0-942508-00-9); pap. 15.00 (ISBN 0-942508-01-7). Vishwa.

--Garland of Prayers. (Illus.). 30p. (Orig.). 1975. pap. 1.99 (ISBN 0-942508-03-3). Vishwa.

--Gayatri: The Highest Meditation. LC 78-69857. (Illus.). 164p. 1978. 6.50 (ISBN 0-533-03188-5). Vishwa.

--Liberation from Karma & Rebirth. (Illus.). 164p. (Orig.). 1970. pap. 3.50 (ISBN 0-942508-02-5). Vishwa.

--Life & Teaching of Satguru Sant Keshavadas. LC 77-81277. (Illus.). 150p. (Orig.). 1977. pap. 3.50 (ISBN 0-942508-12-2). Vishwa.

--The Purpose of Life. LC 78-50754. (Illus.). 112p. 1978. 5.95 (ISBN 0-533-03147-8). Vishwa.

--Ramayana at a Glance. (Illus.). 184p. (Orig.). 1978. pap. 3.50 (ISBN 0-942508-11-4). Vishwa.

--Sadguru Speaks. (Illus.). 96p. (Orig.). 1975. pap. 3.50 (ISBN 0-942508-06-8). Vishwa.

--Self-Realization. (Illus.). 131p. (Orig.). 1976. pap. 3.50 (ISBN 0-942508-11-4). Vishwa.

--This Is Wisdom. (Illus.). 96p. (Orig.). 1975. pap. 3.50 (ISBN 0-942508-07-6). Vishwa.

Kuppuswamy, B. Elements of Ancient Indian Psychology. 305p. 1986. text ed. 30.00x (ISBN 0-7069-2620-X, Pub. by Vikas India); pap. text ed. 10.95x (ISBN 0-7069-2620-X, Pub. by Vikas India). Advent NY.

Lal, Basant K. Contemporary Indian Philosophy. xxi, 345p. 1986. 15.00 (ISBN 81-208-0260-8, Pub. by Motilal Banarsidass). South Asia Bks.

Larson, Gerald J. & Bhattacharya, Ram Shankar, eds. Samkhya: A Dualist Tradition in Indian Philosophy. LC 85-43199. (Encyclopedia of Indian Philosophies: Vol. 4). 800p. 1987. 75.00x (ISBN 0-691-07301-5). Princeton U Pr.

Matilal, Bimal K. Language & Reality: An Introduction to Indian Philosophical Studies. 450p. 1986. 31.00X (ISBN 0-317-53529-3, Pub. by Motilal Banarsidass). South Asia Bks.

--Logic, Language & Reality: An Introduction to Indian Philosophical Studies. 447p. 1985. 29.50 (ISBN 81-208-0008-7, Pub. by Motilal Banarsidass India). Orient Bk Dist.

--Perception & Inference: An Essay on Classical Indian Theories of Knowledge. 350p. 1986. 65.00x (ISBN 0-19-824625-0). Oxford U Pr.

Michael, Aloysius. Radhakrishna on Hindu Moral Life & Action. 1979. 17.50x (ISBN 0-8364-0334-7). South Asia Bks.

Pandit, M. P. The Teaching of Sri Aurobindo. (Illus., Orig.). 1978. pap. 3.50 (ISBN 0-89744-982-7, Pub. by Bharatiya Vidya Bhavan India). Auromere.

Prasad, Ram Chandra. Rajneesh: The Mystic of Feeling. 2nrev. ed. 1978. 10.95 (ISBN 0-89684-023-9, Pub. by Motilal Banarsidass India). Orient Bk Dist.

Puligandla, R. The Fundamentals of Indian Philosophy. LC 85-20195. 364p. 1985. pap. text ed. 14.75 (ISBN 0-8191-4891-1). U Pr of Amer.

Purdom, C. B. The God-Man: The Life, Journeys & Work of Meher Baba with an Interpretation of His Silence & Spiritual Teaching. LC 72-175960. (Illus.). 464p. 1971. 9.95 (ISBN 0-913078-03-4). Sheriar Pr.

Radhakrishnan, S. Indian Religions. (Orient Paperbacks Ser.). 196p. 1981. pap. 3.95 (ISBN 0-86578-084-6); 8.95 (ISBN 0-86578-117-6). Ind-US Inc.

--Living with a Purpose. 136p. 1982. 9.00 (ISBN 0-86578-204-0); pap. 4.25 (ISBN 0-86578-137-0). Ind-US Inc.

Rajneesh, Bhagwan S. Hammer on the Rock: A Darshan Diary. (Illus.). 464p. 1979. pap. 8.95 (ISBN 0-394-17090-3, E730, Ever). Grove.

--The Rajneesh Upanishad. Ma Deva Sarito, ed. 1032p. 1986. pap. 9.95 (ISBN 3-907757-00-9). Rajneesh Neo-Sannyas Intl.

--Wings of Love & Random Thought. 1979. pap. 4.50 (ISBN 0-89684-031-X, Pub. by Motilal Barnarsidass India). Orient Bk Dist.

Raju, P. T. Spirit, Being & Self. (Studies in Indian & Western Philosophy). 285p. 1982. 29.95 (ISBN 0-940500-98-1, Pub. by S. Asian Pubs India). Asia Bk Corp.

--Structural Depths of Indian Thought. (Philosophy Ser.). 600p. 1985. 49.50x (ISBN 0-88706-139-7); pap. 24.50x (ISBN 0-88706-140-0). State U NY Pr.

Reddy, V. Narayan. The East West Understanding of Man. 320p. 1985. text ed. 40.00x (ISBN 0-86590-704-8, Pub. by B R Pub Corp India). Apt Bks.

Riepe, Dale M. The Naturalistic Tradition in Indian Thought. LC 82-9185. xii, 308p. 1982. Repr. of 1961 ed. lib. bdg. 35.00x (ISBN 0-313-23622-4, RINA). Greenwood.

Sen, Debabrata. The Concept of Knowledge: Indian Theories. 1985. 24.00x (ISBN 0-8364-1398-9, Pub. by KP Bagchi India). South Asia Bks.

Sri Aurobindo. Glossary of Terms in Sri Aurobindo's Writings. 1978. 10.00 (ISBN 0-89071-271-9). Matagiri.

--Light for Students: Compiled from the Writings of Sri Aurobindo & the Mother. 1984. pap. 3.50 (ISBN 0-89071-272-7). Matagiri.

--Sri Aurobindo & the Mother on Education. 6th, Special ed. 1978. pap. 16.00 (ISBN 0-89744-955-X). Auromere.

Srinivasachari, P. N. Philosophy of Bhedabheda. 6.95 (ISBN 0-8356-7253-0). Theos Pub Hse.

Srivastava, Rama S. Contemporary Indian Philosophy. 1983. text ed. 24.00x. Coronet Bks.

Thakar, Vimala. Totality in Essence. 132p. 1986. pap. 7.00 (ISBN 81-208-0048-6, Pub. by Motilal Banarsidass India). Orient Bk Dist.

The Mother. Flowers & Their Messages. (Illus.). 308p. 1985. pap. 14.95 (ISBN 0-89071-282-4). Matagiri.

Vijay, ed. How to Bring up a Child. (Illus.). 1985. pap. 3.50 (ISBN 0-89071-334-0, Pub. by Sri Aurobindo Ashram India). Matagiri.

Vyasa. Bhagavata, Srimad. Tapasyananda, Swami, tr. from Sanskrit. 1983. Vol. 1, 455p. 25.00x ea. (ISBN 0-87481-516-9). Vol. 2, 492p (ISBN 0-87481-517-7). Vol. 3, 447p (ISBN 0-87481-518-5). Vol. 4 (ISBN 0-87481-519-3). Vedanta Pr.

Warrier, A. G. God in Advaita. 1977. text ed. 15.00x (ISBN 0-8426-1047-2). Verry.

Wayman, Alex. Yoga of the Guhyasamajatantra. 1977. 28.00 (ISBN 0-89684-003-4, Pub. by Motilal Banarsidass India). Orient Bk Dist.

Werner, Karel. Yoga & Indian Philosophy. 1977. 11.00 (ISBN 0-8426-0900-8, Pub. by Motilal Banarsidass India). Orient Bk Dist.

--Yoga & Indian Philosophy. 1979. 12.50x (ISBN 0-8364-0479-3). South Asia Bks.

Woods, James H. Yoga-System of Patanjali. 1977. Repr. 19.50 (ISBN 0-89684-272-X, Pub. by Motilal Banarsidass India). Orient Bk Dist.

Yoga Unveiled, Part 1. 1977. 16.50 (ISBN 0-8426-1031-6, Pub. by Motilal Banarsidass India). Orient Bk Dist.

PHILOSOPHY, ISLAMIC

see also Islamic Ethics

Abd al-Rahman al Jami. The Precious Pearl: Al-Durrah Al-Fakhirah. Heer, Nicholas L., tr. from Arabic. LC 78-126071. 1979. 29.50 (ISBN 0-87395-379-7). State U NY Pr.

Abdul Fattah Rashid Hamid. Self Knowledge & Spiritual Yearning. Quinlan, Hamid, ed. LC 82-70348. (Illus.). 116p. 1982. pap. 4.00 (ISBN 0-89259-027-0). Am Trust Pubns.

Al-Ghazali. On the Duties of Brotherhood. 7.95 (ISBN 0-686-83895-5). Kazi Pubns.

Al-Qibrisi, Shaykh N. Mercy Oceans: Teachings of Maulana Abdullah al-Faiza ad-Daghestani. 190p. (Orig.). 1980. pap. 4.75x (ISBN 0-939830-11-6, Pub. by Leon). New Era Pubns MI.

Al-Tahafut, Tahafut. Averroes's, 2 vols. in 1. Van Den Bergh, S., tr. 593p. 1985. Repr. of 1978 ed. 60.00x (ISBN 0-317-39039-2, Pub. by Luzac & Co Ltd). State Mutual Bk.

Ansari, F. R. Through Science & Philosophy to Religion. pap. 1.25 (ISBN 0-686-18536-6). Kazi Pubns.

Ar-Razi, Al-Kulayni. Al-Kafi: The Book of Divine Proof, No. I. Rizvi, S. Muhammad, tr. from Arabic. LC 85-52242. 90p. (Orig.). 1985. pap. 12.00 (ISBN 0-940368-64-1). Tahrike Tarsile Quran.

--Al-Kafi: The Book of Divine Proof, No. V. Rizvi, S. Muhammad, tr. from Arabic. LC 85-52242. 80p. (Orig.). 1985. pap. 12.00 (ISBN 0-940368-67-6). Tahrike Tarsile Quran.

--Al-Kafi: The Book of Reason & Ignorance. Rizvi, S. Muhammad, tr. from Arabic. LC 85-52263. 72p. (Orig.). 1985. pap. 12.00 (ISBN 0-940368-63-3). Tahrike Tarsile Quran.

Banisadr, Abolhassan. The Fundamental Principles & Precepts of Islamic Government. Ghanoonparvar, Mohammed R., tr. from Persian. LC 81-82634. (Iran-e NO Literary Collection Ser.). 120p. (Orig.). 1981. pap. 5.95 (ISBN 0-939214-01-6). Mazda Pubs.

Bazargan, Mehdi. The Inevitable Victory. Yousefi, Mohammad, tr. from Persian. 35p. 1979. pap. 1.25x (ISBN 0-941722-03-1). Book-Dist-Ctr.

Boer, Tjitze J. De. The History of Philosophy in Islam. LC 70-131638. 216p. 1903. Repr. 39.00x (ISBN 0-403-00525-6). Scholarly.

Davidson, Herbert. Proofs for Eternity, Creation, & the Existence of God in Medieval Islamic & Jewish Philosophy. (Studies in Northeast Culture & Society: Vol. 7). 500p. 1985. write for info. (ISBN 0-89003-180-0); pap. 62.00x (ISBN 0-89003-181-9). Undena Pubns.

Fakhry, Majid. A History of Islamic Philosophy. 2nd ed. LC 81-21781. 450p. 1983. 29.50x (ISBN 0-231-05532-3). Columbia U Pr.

--A History of Islamic Philosophy. 2nd ed. (Studies in Oriental Culture: No. 5). 394p. 1987. pap. text ed. 16.00 (ISBN 0-231-05533-1). Columbia U Pr.

Genequand, C. F. The Metaphysics of Ibn Rushd: Averroes. LC 83-15428. (Studies in Islamic Philosophy & Science). write for info. cancelled (ISBN 0-88206-059-7). Caravan Bks.

Greenlees. Gospel of Islam. 7.25 (ISBN 0-8356-7158-5). Theos Pub Hse.

Guttmann, Jacob. Die Religionsphilosophischen Lehren des Isaak Abravanel. Katz, Steven, ed. LC 79-7134. (Jewish Philosophy, Mysticism & History of Ideas Ser.). 1980. Repr. of 1916 ed. lib. bdg. 14.00x (ISBN 0-405-12260-8). Ayer Co Pubs.

Hooker, M. B., ed. Islam in South East Asia. 272p. 1983. text ed. 39.95x (ISBN 0-686-46644-6, Pub. by EJ Brill Holland). Humanities.

Hourani, George F., ed. Essays on Islamic Philosophy & Science. LC 74-13493. 1974. 49.50 (ISBN 0-87395-224-3). State U Ny Pr.

Kerr, Malcolm H., ed. An Islamic Tradition & Its Problems. LC 80-53523. (Giorgio Levi Della Vida Conference: Vol. 7). 140p. (Orig.). 1983. pap. 18.50x (ISBN 0-89003-069-3). Undena Pubns.

Leaman, Oliver. An Introduction to Medieval Islamic Philosophy. 224p. 1985. 34.50 (ISBN 0-521-24707-1); pap. 12.95 (ISBN 0-521-28911-4). Cambridge U Pr.

Malik, Imam & Din, M. R. Muwata. 25.50 (ISBN 0-686-83588-3). Kazi Pubns.

Marmura, Michael E., ed. Islamic Theology & Philosophy: Studies in Honor of George F. Hourani. 344p. 1983. 49.50 (ISBN 0-87395-746-6); pap. 18.95 (ISBN 0-87395-747-4). State U NY Pr.

Mohamed. The Philosophical Essence of Islam. (The Essential Library of the Great Philosophies). (Illus.). 143p. 1985. 117.50 (ISBN 0-317-19583-2). Am Inst Psych.

Molana-al-Moazam Hazrat Shah & Maghsoud Sadegh-ibn-Mohammad Angha. Al Rasa'El. 146p. (Orig.). 1986. lib. bdg. 22.50 (ISBN 0-8191-5331-1); pap. text ed. 10.25 (ISBN 0-8191-5332-X). U Pr of Amer.

Morewedge, Parviz, ed. Islamic Philosophy & Mysticism. LC 80-14364. (Studies in Islamic Philosophy & Science). 1981. 45.00x (ISBN 0-88206-302-2). Caravan Bks.

Mutahhari, Ayatullah M. Fundamentals of Islamic Thought: God, Man & the Universe. Algar, Hamid, ed. Campbell, R., tr. (Comtemporary Islamic Thought Perian Ser.). Orig. Title: Per. 231p. (Orig.). 1985. 19.95 (ISBN 0-933782-14-4); pap. 8.95 (ISBN 0-933782-15-2). Mizan Pr.

--Social & Historical Change: An Islamic Perspective. Algar, Hamid, ed. Campbell, R., tr. from Persian. (Contemporary Islamic Thought, Persian Ser.). 156p. 1986. 18.95 (ISBN 0-933782-18-7); pap. 7.95 (ISBN 0-933782-19-5). Mizan Pr.

Ngah, Nor bin. Kitab Jawi: Islamic Thought of the Malay Muslim Scholars. 64p. (Orig.). 1982. pap. text ed. 7.50x (ISBN 9971-902-48-6, Pub. by Inst Southeast Asian Stud). Gower Pub Co.

Niazi, Kausar. Towards Understanding Islam. 232p. (Orig.). 1981. pap. 12.50 (ISBN 0-88004-009-2). Sunwise Turn.

Qutb, Muhammad. Islam: The Misunderstood Religion. Tr. of Shubuhat haul al-Islam. 199p. (Orig.). 1977. pap. 5.95 (ISBN 0-939830-05-1, Pub. by IIFSO Kuwait). New Era Pubns MI.

--Shubuhat Haul al-Islam. (Arabic.). 203p. (Orig.). 1977. pap. 4.75x (ISBN 0-939830-15-9, Pub. by IIFSO Kuwait). New Era Pubns MI.

Rahman, Fazlur. Islam. 2nd ed. LC 78-68547. 1979. pap. 9.95 (ISBN 0-226-70281-2, P806, Phoen). U of Chicago Pr.

--The Philosophy of Mulla Sadra Shirazi. LC 75-31693. 1976. 39.50x (ISBN 0-87395-300-2). State U NY Pr.

--Prophecy in Islam: Philosophy & Orthodoxy. LC 78-66082. (Midway Reprints Ser.). 1979. pap. text ed. 9.00x (ISBN 0-226-70282-0). U of Chicago Pr.

Rumi, Jalalu'ddin. The Mathnawi of Jalalu'ddin Rumi, 3 vols. Nicholson, R. A., tr. from Persian. 1444p. 1985. 175.00x (ISBN 0-317-39128-3, Pub. by Luzac & Co Ltd). State Mutual Bk.

Sabzavari, Hadi Ibn Mahdi. The Metaphysics of Haji Mulla Hadi Sabzavari. Izutsu, Toshihiku & Mohaghegh, Mehdi, trs. from Persian. LC 76-18174. 248p. 1977. lib. bdg. 35.00x (ISBN 0-88206-011-2). Caravan Bks.

Saeed, M. Studies in Muslim Philosophy. 12.00 (ISBN 0-686-18601-X). Kazi Pubns.

Saeeed, M. A Dictionary of Muslim Philosophy. 14.50 (ISBN 0-686-18370-3). Kazi Pubns.

Sartain, E. M. Jajal Al-Din Al-Suywti, 2 vols. Incl. Vol. 1. Biography & Background. 230p. 44.50 (ISBN 0-521-20547-6); Vol. 2. Al-Tahadduth bini'mat allah. 370p. 52.50 (ISBN 0-521-20546-8). LC 74-82226. (Oriental Publications Ser.: Nos. 23 & 24). 1975. Set. 86.00 (ISBN 0-521-20633-2). Cambridge U Pr.

Shariati, Ali. Culture & Ideology. Marjani, Fathollah, tr. from Persian. 23p. 1980. pap. 1.00x (ISBN 0-941722-12-0). Book-Dist-Ctr.

--From Where Shall We Begin & Machine in the Captivity of Machinism. Marjani, Fathollah, tr. from Persian. 51p. 1980. pap. 1.95x (ISBN 0-941722-10-4). Book-Dist-Ctr.

--Hajj. 2nd ed. Behzadnia, A., tr. from Persian. 162p. 1978. pap. 4.95 (ISBN 0-941722-09-0). Book-Dist-Ctr.

Shehadi, Fadlou. Metaphysics in Islamic Philosophy. LC 81-18069. 1983. 35.00x (ISBN 0-88206-049-X). Caravan Bks.

Sheikh, M. Saeed. Islamic Philosophy. 1982. 16.95 (ISBN 0-900860-50-2, Pub. by Octagon Pr England). Ins Study Human.

--Studies in Muslim Philosophy. 248p. (Orig.). 1981. pap. 11.75 (ISBN 0-88004-008-4). Sunwise Turn.

Sherif, Mohamed A. Ghazali's Theory of Virtue. LC 71-38000. 200p. 1975. 44.50 (ISBN 0-87395-206-5). State U NY Pr.

Siddiqui, A. H. Islam & Remaking of Humanity. 14.95 (ISBN 0-686-83885-8); pap. 9.95 (ISBN 0-686-83886-6). Kazi Pubns.

--Philosophical Interpretation of History. 14.95 (ISBN 0-686-83884-X). Kazi Pubns.

Stern, et al. Islamic Philosophy & the Classical Tradition. 549p. 1972. 100.00x (ISBN 0-317-39094-5, Pub. by Luzac & Co Ltd). State Mutual Bk.

Wolfson, Harry A. Repercussions of the Kalam in Jewish Philosophy. LC 78-9798. 1979. 18.50x (ISBN 0-674-76175-8). Harvard U Pr.

PHILOSOPHY, JAPANESE

Franck, Frederick. The Buddha Eye: An Anthology of the Kyoto School. 256p. 1982. 14.95 (ISBN 0-8245-0410-0). Crossroad NY.

Fujisawa, Chikao. Zen & Shinto: The Story of Japanese Philosophy. LC 78-139133. 92p. Repr. of 1959 ed. lib. bdg. 22.50x (ISBN 0-8371-5749-8, FUZS). Greenwood.

Kitaro, Nishida. Last Writings: Nothingness & the Religious Worldview. Dilworth, David A., tr. 176p. 1987. text ed. 18.00x (ISBN 0-8248-1040-6). UH Pr.

Suzuki, D. T. Zen & Japanese Culture. (Bollingen Ser.: Vol. 64). (Illus.). 1959. 52.00x (ISBN 0-691-09849-2); pap. 10.95x (ISBN 0-691-01770-0). Princeton U Pr.

PHILOSOPHY, JEWISH

see also Hasidism

Abraham, B. Hayya. The Meditation of the Sad Soul. Wigoder, Geoffrey, tr. (The Littman Library of Jewish Civilization Ser.). 1969. 14.50x (ISBN 0-19-710018-X). Oxford U Pr.

Abravanal, Isaac. Principles of Faith (Rosh Amanah) (Littman Library of Jewish Civilization). 272p. 1982. 26.00x (ISBN 0-19-710045-7). Oxford U Pr.

Altmann, Alexander. Studies in Religious Philosophy & Mysticism. (New Reprints in Essay & General Literature Index Ser.). 1975. Repr. of 1969 ed. 24.25 (ISBN 0-518-10194-0). Ayer Co Pubs.

Appel, Gersion. A Philosophy of Mizvot. pap. 11.95x (ISBN 0-87068-250-4). Ktav.

Aptowitzer, V. & Schwarz, A. Z. Abhandlungen zur Erinnerung an Hirsch Perez Chajes. LC 7-7163. (Jewish Philosophy, Mysticism & History of Ideas Ser.). 1980. Repr. of 1933 ed. lib. bdg. 60.00x (ISBN 0-405-12237-3). Ayer Co Pubs.

Bar-On, A. Zvie, ed. On Shumuel Hugo Bergman's Philosophy. 134p. 1986. pap. 19.95x (ISBN 90-6203-947-2, Pub. by Rodopi Holland). Humanities.

Berkovits, Eliezer. Major Themes in Modern Philosophies of Judaism. 1974. 25.00x (ISBN 0-87068-264-4); pap. 11.95. Ktav.

Blau, Joseph L. The Story of Jewish Philosophy. 8.95x (ISBN 0-87068-174-5). Ktav.

Boman, Thorleif. Hebrew Thought Compared with Greek. Moreau, Jules L., tr. from Ger. 1970. pap. 6.95 (ISBN 0-393-00534-8, Norton Lib). Norton.

Borowitz, Eugene B. Choices in Modern Jewish Thought. 352p. 1983. pap. text ed. 9.95x (ISBN 0-87441-343-5). Behrman.

Brann, M. & Elbogen, I. Festschrift zu Israel Lewy's Siebzigstem Geburtstag. Katz, Steven, ed. LC 79-7157. (Jewish Philosophy, Mysticism & the History of Ideas Ser.). (Ger. & Hebrew.). 1980. Repr. of 1911 ed. lib. bdg. 51.50x (ISBN 0-405-12242-X). Ayer Co Pubs.

Buber, Martin. Good & Evil. 1984. 19.75 (ISBN 0-8446-6121-X). Peter Smith.

--I & Thou. 13.50 (ISBN 0-8446-6219-4). Peter Smith.

--To Hallow This Life: An Anthology. Trapp, Jacob, ed. LC 73-11862. 174p. 1974. Repr. of 1958 ed. lib. bdg. 22.50x (ISBN 0-8371-7096-6, BUHL). Greenwood.

Cohen, Boaz & Katz, Steven, eds. Saadia Anniversary Volume. LC 79-7168. (Jewish Philosophy, Mysticism & History of Ideas Ser.). 1980. Repr. of 1943 ed. lib. bdg. 28.50x (ISBN 0-405-12244-6). Ayer Co Pubs.

Cohen, Hermann. Hermann Cohen's Judische Schriften, 3 vols. Katz, Steven, ed. LC 79-7128. (Jewish Philosophy, Mysticism & History of Ideas Ser.). 1980. Repr. of 1924 ed. lib. bdg. 103.50x (ISBN 0-405-12245-4). Ayer Co Pubs.

Davidson, Herbert. Proofs for Eternity, Creation, & the Existence of God in Medieval Islamic & Jewish Philosophy. (Studies in Northeast Culture & Society: Vol. 7). 500p. 1985. write for info. (ISBN 0-89003-180-0); pap. 62.00x (ISBN 0-89003-181-9). Undena Pubns.

Efros, Israel I. Ancient Jewish Philosophy. 1976. pap. 5.95x (ISBN 0-8197-0014-2). Bloch.

--Problem of Space in Jewish Medieval Philosophy. LC 77-164765. (Columbia University. Oriental Studies: No. 11). Repr. of 1917 ed. 14.75 (ISBN 0-404-50501-5). AMS Pr.

--Problem of Space in Jewish Medieval Philosophy. facsimile ed. lib. bdg. 37.50x (ISBN 0-697-00037-0); pap. 7.95 (ISBN 0-89197-904-2). Irvington.

Eight Jewish Philosophers. 1982. 12.95 (ISBN 0-686-76505-2). Feldheim.

Eisler, Moritz. Vorlesungen ueber die Juedischen Philosophen des Mittelalters, 3vols in 2. 1965. Repr. of 1884 ed. 39.50 (ISBN 0-8337-4086-5). B Franklin.

Finkelstein, Louis & Katz, Steven, eds. Rab Saadia Gaon: Studies in His Honor. LC 79-7169. (Jewish Philosophy, Mysticism & History of Ideas Ser.). 1980. Repr. of 1944 ed. lib. bdg. 19.00x (ISBN 0-405-12250-0). Ayer Co Pubs.

Formstecher, Salomon. Die Religion des Geistes. Katz, Steven, ed. LC 79-7129. (Jewish Philosophy, Mysticism & History of Ideas Ser.). 1980. Repr. of 1841 ed. lib. bdg. 40.00x (ISBN 0-405-12251-9). Ayer Co Pubs.

Franck, Adolph. The Kabbalah or the Religious Philosophy of the Hebrews. LC 73-2199. (The Jewish People; History, Religion, Literature Ser.). Repr. of 1926 ed. 30.00 (ISBN 0-405-05264-2). Ayer Co Pubs.

Gershom, Levi B. The Wars of the Lord: Immortality of the Soul, Vol. I: Book 1. Feldman, Seymour, tr. from Hebrew. 256p. 1984. 23.95 (ISBN 0-8276-0220-0, 605). Jewish Pubns.

Glatzer, Nahum N., ed. Modern Jewish Thought: A Source Reader. LC 76-9139. 1976. pap. 7.50 (ISBN 0-8052-0542-X). Schocken.

Goldman, Solomon. The Jew & the Universe. LC 73-2200. (The Jewish People; History, Religion, Literature Ser.). Repr. of 1936 ed. 23.50 (ISBN 0-405-05265-0). Ayer Co Pubs.

Guttman, Julius. Philosophies of Judaism: The History of Jewish Philosophy from Biblical Times to Franz Rosenzweig. LC 63-11875. 560p. 1973. pap. 13.50 (ISBN 0-8052-0402-4). Schocken.

Herring, Basil. Joseph Ibn Kaspi's Gevia' Kesef: A Study in Medieval Jewish Philosophical Bible Commentary. 1982. 35.00x (ISBN 0-87068-716-6). Ktav.

Heschel, Abraham J. God in Search of Man: Philosophy of Judaism. 437p. 1987. Repr. of 1955 ed. 30.00 (ISBN 0-87668-955-1). Aronson.

Hirsch, Samuel. Die Religionsphilosophie der Juden. Katz, Steven, ed. LC 79-7136. (Jewish Philosophy, Mysticism & History of Ideas Ser.). 1980. Repr. of 1842 ed. lib. bdg. 74.50x (ISBN 0-405-12262-4). Ayer Co Pubs.

Jacobs, Louis. Jewish Ethics, Philosophy & Mysticism. LC 71-80005. (Chain of Tradition Ser). 1969. pap. 5.95x (ISBN 0-87441-012-6). Behrman.

Jewish Philosophy. 1982. 15.95 (ISBN 0-686-76523-0). Feldheim.

Joel, Manuel. Beitrage zur Geschichte der Philosophie. Katz, Steven, ed. LC 79-7140. (Jewish Philosophy, Mysticism & History of Ideas Ser.). 1980. Repr. of 1876 ed. lib. bdg. 51.50x (ISBN 0-405-12266-7). Ayer Co Pubs.

Jung, Leo. Love & Life. LC 79-87873. 84p. 1979. 7.50 (ISBN 0-8022-2355-9). Philos Lib.

Kane, Israel. In Quest of the Truth: A Survey of Medieval Jewish Thought. LC 84-90191. 77p. 1985. 8.95 (ISBN 0-533-06243-8). Vantage.

Katz, Steven, ed. Jewish Neo-Platonism: Selected Essays. An Original Anthology. LC 79-7178. (Jewish Philosophy, Mysticism & History of Ideas Ser.). 1980. lib. bdg. 48.50x (ISBN 0-405-12236-5). Ayer Co Pubs.

--Medieval Jewish Philosophy: Original Anthology. LC 79-7177. (Jewish Philosophy, Mysticism & the History of Ideas Ser.). (Ger., Eng., Ital, Fr. Span.). 1980. lib. bdg. 44.00x (ISBN 0-405-12235-7). Ayer Co Pubs.

--Saadiah Gaon: Selected Essays: An Original Anthology. LC 79-7171. (Jewish Philosophy, Mysticism & History of Ideas Ser.). 1980. lib. bdg. 34.50x (ISBN 0-405-12230-6). Ayer Co Pubs.

--Selected Writings of Julius Guttmann: An Original Anthology. LC 79-7175. (Jewish Philosophy, Mysticism & History of Ideas Ser.). 1980. lib. bdg. 34.50x (ISBN 0-405-12232-2). Ayer Co Pubs.

Katz, Steven T. The Jewish Philosophers. LC 75-7590. (Illus.). 300p. 1975. 10.95x (ISBN 0-8197-0387-7); pap. 8.95x (ISBN 0-8197-0010-X). Bloch.

Katz, Steven T., ed. Collected Papers of Jacob Guttmann: An Original Anthology. LC 79-7172. (Jewish Philosophy, Mysticism & History of Ideas Ser.). 1980. lib. bdg. 40.00x (ISBN 0-405-12231-4). Ayer Co Pubs.

--Jewish Philosophy, Mysticism & History of Ideas Series, 50 bks. (Illus.). 1980. Set. lib. bdg. 2389.00x (ISBN 0-405-12229-2). Ayer Co Pubs.

Kaufman, William E. Contemporary Jewish Philosophies. 290p. 1986. pap. text ed. 12.25 (ISBN 0-8191-5092-4). U Pr of Amer.

Kaufmann, David. Gesammelte Schriften, 3 vols. Katz, Steven, ed. LC 79-7143. (Jewish Philosophy, Mysticism & the History of Ideas Ser.). (Ger.). 1980. Repr. of 1915 ed. Set. lib. bdg. 120.00x (ISBN 0-405-12268-3); lib. bdg. 40.00x ea. Vol. 1 (ISBN 0-405-12269-1). Vol. 2 (ISBN 0-405-12270-5). Vol. 3 (ISBN 0-405-12271-3). Ayer Co Pubs.

--Die Sinne: Beitrage Zur Geschichte der Physiologie und Psychologie Im Ittelalter Aus Hebraischen und Arabisch En Quellen. Katz, Steven, ed. LC 79-7141. (Jewish Philosophy, Mysticism & History of Ideas Ser.). 1980. Repr. of 1884 ed. lib. bdg. 17.00x (ISBN 0-405-12267-5). Ayer Co Pubs.

--Studien uber Salomon Ibn Gabirol. Katz, Steven, ed. LC 79-7144. (Jewish Philosophy, Mysticism & the History of Ideas Ser.). (Ger. & Hebrew.). 1980. Repr. of 1899 ed. lib. bdg. 14.00x (ISBN 0-405-12272-1). Ayer Co Pubs.

Kayserling, Meyer. Judischen Frauen in der Geschichte, Literatur und Kunst. Katz, Steven, ed. (Jewish Philosophy, Mysticism & the History of Ideas Ser.). 1980. Repr. of 1879 ed. lib. bdg. 21.50x (ISBN 0-405-12273-X). Ayer Co Pubs.

Lasker, Daniel J. Jewish Philosophical Polemics Against Christianity in the Middle Ages. 320p. 15.00 (ISBN 0-686-95177-8). ADL.

Lazaroff, Allan. The Theology of Abraham Bibago: A Defense of the Divine Will, Knowledge, & Providence in Fifteenth-Century Spanish-Jewish Philosophy. LC 77-10611. (Judaic Studies Ser.). 192p. 1981. text ed. 17.50 (ISBN 0-8173-6906-6). U of Ala Pr.

Lazarus, M. & Winter, Jakob. Die Ethnik des Judenthums, 2 vols. LC 79-7146. (Jewish Philosophy, Mysticism & History of Ideas Ser.). 1980. Repr. of 1911 ed. Set. lib. bdg. 80.00x (ISBN 0-405-12276-4). Ayer Co Pubs.

Levy, Zelev. Between Yafeth & Shem: On the Relationship Between Jewish & General Philosophy. (American University Studies V-Philosophy: Vol. 21). 262p. 1986. text ed. 23.50 (ISBN 0-8204-0373-3). P Lang Pubs.

Lewy, Hans, et al, eds. Three Jewish Philosophers: Philo, Saadya, Gaon, Jehuda, Halevi. LC 60-9081. 1969. pap. text ed. 7.95x (ISBN 0-689-70126-8, T6). Atheneum.

Macdonald, Duncan B. Hebrew Philosophical Genius. LC 65-18819. 1965. Repr. of 1936 ed. 7.50x (ISBN 0-8462-0688-9). Russell.

Maimonides, Moses. Guide for the Perplexed. Friedlander, M., tr. 1904. pap. 6.95 (ISBN 0-486-20351-4). Dover.

--Guide for the Perplexed: Morah Nevochim. (Heb, & Eng). 37.50 (ISBN 0-87559-079-9). Shalom.

--Guide of the Perplexed, 2 vols. Pines, Shlomo, tr. LC 62-18113. 1963. 25.00x ea.; Vol. 1. (ISBN 0-226-50232-5). Vol. 2 (ISBN 0-226-50233-3). U of Chicago Pr.

Midrash: The Search for a Contemporary Past. pap. 3.00 (ISBN 0-686-96071-8); discussion leader's guide 2.00 (ISBN 0-686-99696-8). United Syn Bk.

Morgan, Michael L. & Fackenheim, Emil, eds. The Jewish Thought of Emil Fackenheim: A Reader. LC 87-2116. 400p. 1987. 39.95X (ISBN 0-8143-1820-7); pap. 15.95X (ISBN 0-8143-1821-5). Wayne St U Pr.

Munk, S. Philosophy & Philosophical Authors of the Jews: A Historical Sketch with Explanatory Notes. Kalisch, Isidor, tr. (Reprints in Philosophy Ser.). Repr. of 1881 ed. lib. bdg. 26.50 (ISBN 0-697-00012-5). Irvington.

--Philosophy & Philosophical Authors of the Jews: A Historical Sketch With Explanatory Notes. Kalisch, Isidor, tr. (Reprints in Philosophy Ser.). 1986. pap. text ed. 6.95x (ISBN 0-8290-1881-6). Irvington.

Munk, Salomon. Melanges Philosophie Juive et Arabe. Katz, Steven, ed. LC 79-7148. (Jewish Philosophy, Mysticism & History of Ideas Ser.). 1980. Repr. of 1927 ed. lib. bdg. 51.50x (ISBN 0-405-12278-0). Ayer Co Pubs.

Nachman of Breslov. Les Contes. Regnot, Franz, tr. from Yiddish. Tr. of Sippurey Ma'asioth. (Fr.). 180p. (Orig.). 1981. pap. 7.00 (ISBN 0-930213-22-X). Breslov Res Inst.

--The Gems of Rabbi Nachman. Rosenfeld, Tzvi A., ed. Kaplan, Ayreh, tr. from Hebrew. (Illus.). 186p. (Orig.). 1980. pap. 2.00 (ISBN 0-930213-10-6). Breslov Res Inst.

--Hitbodedouth: Ou La Porte du Ciel. Besancon, Its'hak, adapted by. (Fr.). 110p. (Orig.). 1982. pap. 2.00 (ISBN 0-930213-27-0). Breslov Res Inst.

Nachman of Breslov & Nathan of Breslov. Azamra (I Will Sing) Greenbaum, Avraham, tr. from Hebrew. 64p. (Orig.). 1984. pap. 1.50 (ISBN 0-930213-11-4). Breslov Res INst.

--Courage! Tr. of Meshivat Nefesh. 119p. (Orig.). 1983. pap. 3.00 (ISBN 0-930213-23-8). Breslov Res Inst.

Nathan of Breslov. Advice. Greenbaum, Avraham, tr. from Hebrew. LC 83-70202. Tr. of Likutey Etzot. 522p. 1983. 13.00 (ISBN 0-930213-04-1). Breslov Res Inst.

Neumark, David. Geschichte der Judischen Philosophie des Mittelalters, 3 vols. Katz, Steven, ed. LC 79-7149. (Jewish Philosophy, Mysticism & History of Ideas Ser.). 1980. Repr. of 1928 ed. Set. lib. bdg. 120.00x (ISBN 0-405-12279-9); lib. bdg. 40.00x ea. Vol. 1 (ISBN 0-405-12280-2). Vol. 2, Pt. 1 (ISBN 0-405-12281-0). Vol. 2, Pt. 2 (ISBN 0-405-12282-9). Ayer Co Pubs.

Neusner, Jacob. Tzedakah: Can Jewish Philanthropy Buy Jewish Survival? Altshuler, David, ed. (Basic Jewish Ideas Ser.). 160p. 1982. pap. 7.95 (ISBN 0-940646-07-2). Rossel Bks.

Novak, David & Samuelson, Norbert, eds. Creation & the End of Days - Judaism & Scientific Cosmology: Proceedings of the 1984 Meeting of the Academy for Jewish Philosophy. LC 86-19062. 336p. (Orig.). 1986. 26.75 (ISBN 0-8191-5524-1, Pub. by Studies in Judaism); pap. text ed. 14.50 (ISBN 0-8191-5525-X, Pub. by Studies in Judaism). U Pr of Amer.

Pakuda, Bahya I. The Book of Direction to the Duties of the Heart. Mansoor, Menahem, et al, trs. from Arabic. (Littman Library of Jewish Civilization). 1973. 43.00x (ISBN 0-19-710020-1). Oxford U Pr.

Pearl, Chaim. The Medieval Jewish Mind. LC 76-184221. 208p. 1973. 8.95 (ISBN 0-87677-043-X). Hartmore.

Petuchowski, Jacob, ed. New Perspectives on Abraham Geiger. pap. 2.50x (ISBN 0-87820-201-3, Pub. by Hebrew Union College Press). Ktav.

Rosenthal, Erwin I. & Katz, Steven, eds. Saadya Studies: In Commemoration of the One Thousandth Anniversary of the Death of R. Saadya Gaon. LC 79-7170. (Jewish Philosophy, Mysticism & History of Ideas Ser.). 1980. Repr. of 1943 ed. lib. bdg. 25.50x (ISBN 0-405-12284-5). Ayer Co Pubs.

Sabsovich, Katherine. Adventures in Idealism: A Personal Record of the Life of Professor Sabsovich. facsimile ed. LC 74-29520. (Modern Jewish Experience Ser.). (Illus.). 1975. Repr. of 1922 ed. 23.50x (ISBN 0-405-06745-3). Ayer Co Pubs.

Sirat, Colette. A History of Jewish Philosophy in the Middle Ages. 476p. 1985. 59.50 (ISBN 0-521-26087-6). Cambridge U Pr.

Steinheim, Salomon L. Die Offenbarung nach dem Lehrbegriffe der Synagoge, 4 vols. Katz, Steven, ed. LC 79-7151. (Jewish Philosophy, Mysticism & History of Ideas Ser.). 1980. Repr. of 1865 ed. Set. lib. bdg. 160.00x (ISBN 0-405-12286-1); lib. bdg. 40.00x ea. Vol. 2 (ISBN 0-405-12288-8). Vol. 3 (ISBN 0-405-12220-9). Vol. 4 (ISBN 0-405-12221-7). Ayer Co Pubs.

Stitskin, Leon D. Jewish Philosophy: A Study in Personalism. 1976. 15.00x (ISBN 0-685-84458-7). Bloch.

Strauss, Leo. Philosophy & Law: Essays Toward the Understanding of Maimonides His Predecessors. Baumann, Fred, tr. from Ger. Tr. of Philosophie und Gesetz. 120p. 1987. 18.95 (ISBN 0-8276-0273-1). Jewish Pubns.

A Time to Be Born, a Time to Die. pap. 3.50 (ISBN 0-686-96060-2); discussion Leader's guide 2.00 (ISBN 0-686-99692-5). United Syn Bk.

Twersky, I. Studies in Jewish Law & Philosophy. 39.50x (ISBN 0-87068-335-7). Ktav.

Twersky, Isadore, ed. Studies in Medieval Jewish History & Literature. LC 79-11588. (Judaic Monographs: No. 2). 1979. text ed. 25.00x (ISBN 0-674-85192-7). Harvard U Pr.

Twersky, Isadore & Septimus, Bernard, eds. Jewish Thought in the Seventeenth Century. (Harvard Judaic Texts & Studies: VI). 425p. 1986. text ed. 25.00x (ISBN 0-674-47465-1); pap. text ed. 12.50x (ISBN 0-674-47466-X). Harvard U Pr.

Wolfson, Harry A. Repercussions of the Kalam in Jewish Philosophy. LC 78-9798. 1979. 18.50x (ISBN 0-674-76175-8). Harvard U Pr.

PHILOSOPHY, MEDIEVAL

see also Scholasticism; Thomists

Davidson, Herbert. Proofs for Eternity, Creation, & the Existence of God in Medieval Islamic & Jewish Philosophy. (Studies in Northeast Culture & Society: Vol. 7). 500p. 1985. write for info. (ISBN 0-89003-180-0); pap. 62.00x (ISBN 0-89003-181-9). Undena Pubns.

Efros, Israel I. Problem of Space in Jewish Medieval Philosophy. LC 77-164765. (Columbia University. Oriental Studies: No. 11). Repr. of 1917 ed. 14.75 (ISBN 0-404-50501-5). AMS Pr.

--Problem of Space in Jewish Medieval Philosophy. facsimile ed. lib. bdg. 37.50x (ISBN 0-697-00037-0); pap. 7.95 (ISBN 0-89197-904-2). Irvington.

Eisler, Moritz. Vorlesungen ueber die Juedischen Philosophen des Mittelalters, 3vols in 2. 1965. Repr. of 1884 ed. 39.50 (ISBN 0-8337-4086-5). B Franklin.

Erasmus, Desiderius. The Critical Writing by Desiderius Erasmus on the Spiritual Conditions of His Times & the Psychological Impulses Motivating the Actions of Men. (Illus.). 123p. 1984. 89.45 (ISBN 0-89920-106-7). Am Inst Psych.

Gilson, Etienne H. The Philosophy of St. Thomas Aquinas. facsimile ed. Elrington, G. A., ed. Bullough, Edward, tr. from Fr. LC 70-157337. (Select Bibliographies Reprint Ser). Repr. of 1937 ed. 26.50 (ISBN 0-8369-5797-0). Ayer Co Pubs.

Hill, Ida T. Medieval Humanist: Michael Akominatos. LC 73-3164. 48p. 1974. Repr. of 1923 ed. lib. bdg. 14.00 (ISBN 0-8337-3497-0). B Franklin.

Hyman, Arthur & Walsh, James J., eds. Philosophy in the Middle Ages: The Christian, Islamic & Jewish Traditions. 2nd ed. LC 82-23337. 816p. (Orig.). 1983. lib. bdg. 30.00 (ISBN 0-915145-81-2); pap. text ed. 15.00x (ISBN 0-915145-80-4). Hackett Pub.

Jones, John D., tr. Pseudo-Dionysius Aeropagite: The Divine Names & Mystical Theology. (Mediaeval Philosophical Texts in Translation: No. 21). 320p. 24.95 (ISBN 0-87462-221-2). Marquette.

Kane, Israel. In Quest of the Truth: A Survey of Medieval Jewish Thought. LC 84-90191. 77p. 1985. 8.95 (ISBN 0-533-06243-8). Vantage.

Kelly, William J. Karl Rahner, S. J., Theology & Discovery: Essays in Honor of Karl Rahner, S. J. 320p. 24.95 (ISBN 0-87462-521-1). Marquette.

Macauley, Richard M. The Medieval Philosophers from St. Augustine to St. Anselm. (Illus.). 196p. 1984. 88.85 (ISBN 0-89266-483-5). Am Classical Coll Pr.

McInerny, Ralph M. History of Western Philosophy: Philosophy from St. Augustine to Ockham. LC 63-20526. 1970. 12.00x (ISBN 0-268-00417-X). U of Notre Dame Pr.

Maimonides, Moses. Guide for the Perplexed. Friedlander, M., tr. 1904. pap. 6.95 (ISBN 0-486-20351-4). Dover.

--Guide for the Perplexed. 2nd ed. 16.00 (ISBN 0-8446-2512-4). Peter Smith.

--Guide for the Perplexed: Morah Nevochim. (Heb, & Eng). 37.50 (ISBN 0-87559-079-9). Shalom.

--Guide of the Perplexed, 2 vols. Pines, Shlomo, tr. LC 62-18113. 1963. 25.00x ea.; Vol. 1. (ISBN 0-226-50232-5). Vol. 2 (ISBN 0-226-50233-3). U of Chicago Pr.

Malloy, Michael P. Civil Authority in Medieval Philosophy: Lombard, Aquinas & Bonaventure. LC 85-3210. 240p. (Orig.). 1985. lib. bdg. 26.25 (ISBN 0-8191-4582-3); pap. text ed. 12.25 (ISBN 0-8191-4583-1). U Pr of Amer.

Marenbon, John. Early Medieval Philosophy Four Eighty to Eleven Fifty: An Introduction. 224p. 1983. 19.95x (ISBN 0-7100-9405-1). Methuen Inc.

Parr, Roger P. Matthieu de Vendome, ars Versificatoria. Robb, James, ed. LC 80-84768. 1981. pap. 9.95 (ISBN 0-87462-222-0). Marquette.

Pegis, Anton C. Saint Thomas & the Greeks. (Aquinas Lecture). 1939. 7.95 (ISBN 0-87462-103-8). Marquette.

Pico della Mirandola, Giovanni. On the Imagination. Caplan, Harry, tr. & notes by. LC 72-113063. (Lat. & Eng.). ix, 102p. Repr. of 1930 ed. lib. bdg. 22.50x (ISBN 0-8371-4703-4, PIOI). Greenwood.

Rudavsky, Tamar, ed. Divine Omniscience & Omnipotence in Medieval Philosophy. 1984. lib. bdg. 54.00 (ISBN 90-277-1750-8, Pub. by Reidel Holland). Kluwer Academic.

Smally, Beryl. Studies in Medieval Thought & Learning from Abelard to Wyclif. (Illus.). 455p. 1982. 45.00 (ISBN 0-9506882-6-6). Hambledon Press.

Tallon, Andrew. Personal Becoming: In Honor of Karl Rahner. 188p. pap. 19.95 (ISBN 0-686-65691-1). Marquette.

Twersky, Isadore, ed. Studies in Medieval Jewish History & Literature. LC 79-11588. (Judaic Monographs: No. 2). 1979. text ed. 25.00x (ISBN 0-674-85192-7). Harvard U Pr.

Van Den Boogaard, Nico H. J. Autour De 1300: Etudes de Philologie et de Literature Medievales. (Faux Titre: Vol. 21). (Fr., Illus.). 288p. 1985. pap. text ed. 45.00 (ISBN 90-6203-518-3, Pub. by Editions Rodopi). Humanities.

Wells, Norman J., tr. Francis Suarez: On the Essence of Finite Being as Such, on the Existence of the Essence & Their Distinction. (Mediaeval Philosophical Texts in Translation). 250p. 1983. pap. 24.95 (ISBN 0-87462-224-7). Marquette.

Wicksteed, Philip H. Dante & Aquinas. LC 79-153489. (Studies in Dante, No. 9). 1971. Repr. of 1913 ed. lib. bdg. 49.95x (ISBN 0-8383-1240-3). Haskell.

Wippel, John F. & Wolter, Allen B., eds. Medieval Philosophy: From St. Augustine to Nicholas of Cusa. LC 69-10043. 1969. pap. text ed. 14.95 (ISBN 0-02-935650-4). Free Pr.

Wolfson, Harry A. Studies in the History of Philosophy & Religion, Vol. I. Twersky, Isadore & Williams, George H., eds. LC 72-86385. 640p. 1973. 40.00x (ISBN 0-674-84765-2). Harvard U Pr.

PHILOSOPHY, MODERN

see also Enlightenment; Evolution; Existentialism; Humanism, Religious; Neo-Scholasticism; Phenomenology; Philosophy, Renaissance; Positivism; Semantics (Philosophy); Transcendentalism

also philosophy, french and similiar headings

Becker, Carl L. Heavenly City of the Eighteenth-Century Philosophers. (Storrs Lectures Ser.). 1932. pap. 6.95x (ISBN 0-300-00017-0, Y5). Yale U Pr.

Boutroux, Emile. Science & Religion in Contemporary Philosophy. LC 70-102563. 1970. Repr. of 1909 ed. 33.50x (ISBN 0-8046-0723-0, Pub. by Kennikat). Assoc Faculty Pr.

Deats, Paul & Robb, Carol S., eds. The Boston Personalist Tradition in Philosophy, Social Ethics, & Theology. (Illus.). xiv, 295p. 1986. text ed. 28.95 (ISBN 0-86554-177-9, MUP-H167). Mercer Univ Pr.

Edman, Irwin. Contemporary & His Soul. LC 66-25907. Repr. of 1931 ed. 18.50x (ISBN 0-8046-0129-1, Pub. by Kennikat). Assoc Faculty Pr.

Fielding-Hall, A. The Theory of the World Soul. (Illus.). 161p. 1985. Repr. of 1910 ed. 88.85 (ISBN 0-89901-235-3). Found Class Reprints.

Hazard, Paul. European Thought in the Eighteenth Century: From Montesquieu to Lessing. 16.50 (ISBN 0-8446-2226-5). Peter Smith.

Husserl, Edmund. Crisis of European Sciences & Transcendental Phenomenology: An Introduction to Phenomenological Philosophy. Carr, David, tr. LC 77-82511. (Studies in Phenomenology & Existential Philosophy Ser). 1970. 28.95 (ISBN 0-8101-0255-2); pap. 11.95 (ISBN 0-8101-0458-X). Northwestern U Pr.

Kaufmann, Walter. Critique of Religion & Philosophy. 1979. pap. 13.50x (ISBN 0-691-02001-9). Princeton U Pr.

Klocker, Harry R., ed. Thomism & Modern Thought. LC 62-9414. 1962. 32.50x (ISBN 0-89197-451-2). Irvington.

Kopp, Sheldon. The Way Out Is the Way In. 224p. Date not set. 13.95 (ISBN 0-87477-413-6). J P Tarcher.

Leland, Dorothy, ed. Husserl, Heidegger, Sartre, Merleau-Ponty: Phenomenology & the Problem of Intentionality. 640p. (Orig.). 1987. lib. bdg. 35.00 (ISBN 0-87220-005-1); pap. text ed. 19.50 (ISBN 0-87220-004-3). Hackett Pub.

Maritain, Jacques. Theonas. facs. ed. LC 74-84325. (Essay Index Reprint Ser). 1933. 17.25 (ISBN 0-8369-1095-8). Ayer Co Pubs.

Paul, Leslie A. Meaning of Human Existence. LC 73-148642. 1971. Repr. of 1949 ed. lib. bdg. 22.50x (ISBN 0-8371-6008-1, PAHE). Greenwood.

Rockwood, Raymond O., ed. Carl Becker's Heavenly City Revisited. LC 68-11256. xxxii, 227p. 1968. Repr. of 1958 ed. 23.00 (ISBN 0-208-00421-1, Archon). Shoe String.

Schweitzer, Albert. Thoughts for Our Times. Anderson, Erica, ed. (Illus.). 64p. 1981. Repr. of 1975 ed. 3.95 (ISBN 0-8298-0448-X). Pilgrim NY.

Seth Pringle Pattison, Andrew. Philosophical Radicals & Other Essays. 1907. 23.50 (ISBN 0-8337-4388-0). B Franklin.

Urban, Wilbur M. The Intelligible World: Metaphysics & Value. LC 76-51208. 1977. Repr. of 1929 ed. lib. bdg. 26.75x (ISBN 0-8371-9437-7, URIW). Greenwood.

Wachterhauser, Brice R., ed. Hermeneutics & Modern Philosophy. 536p. (Orig.). 1986. 49.50x (ISBN 0-88706-295-4); pap. 16.95x (ISBN 0-88706-296-2). State U NY Pr.

PHILOSOPHY, MODERN–18TH CENTURY

see also Enlightenment

Collier, Arthur. Clavis Universalis: New Inquiry after Truth, Being a Demonstration of the Non-Existence or Impossibility of an External World. Wellek, Rene, ed. LC 75-11208. (British Philosophers & Theologians of the 17th & 18th Centuries Ser.). 150p. 1978. lib. bdg. 51.00 (ISBN 0-8240-1763-3). Garland Pub.

Glanville, Joseph. Some Discourse, Sermons & Remains. Wellek, Rene, ed. LC 75-11221. (British Philosophers & Theologians of the 17th & 18th Centuries Ser.). 1979. lib. bdg. 51.00 (ISBN 0-8240-1775-7). Garland Pub.

Harari, Josue V. Scenarios of the Imaginary: Theorizing the French Englightenment. LC 86-24247. 240p. 1987. text ed. 24.95x (ISBN 0-8014-1842-9). Cornell U Pr.

PHILOSOPHY, MODERN–20TH CENTURY

Hoffer, Eric. Before the Sabbath. LC 78-69626. 1979. 11.45i (ISBN 0-06-011914-4, HarpT). Har-Row.

International Philosophy Year Conferences, Brockport. Contemporary Philosophic Thought: Proceedings, 4 vols. Kiefer, Howard E. & Munitz, Milton K., eds. Incl. Vol. 1. Language, Belief, & Metaphysics. LC 69-14643. 21.50x (ISBN 0-87395-151-4); Vol. 2. Mind, Science, & History. LC 69-14642. 49.50 (ISBN 0-87395-052-6); Vol. 3. Perspectives in Education, Religion, & the Arts. LC 69-14641. 33.50x (ISBN 0-87395-153-0); Vol. 4. Ethics & Social Justice. LC 69-14640. 49.50x (ISBN 0-87395-054-2). 1970. State U NY Pr.

Maquarrie, John. Twentieth Century Religion Thought: The Frontiers of Philosophy & Theology, 1900-1980. rev. ed. 429p. 1981. pap. text ed. write for info. (ISBN 0-02-374500-2, Pub. by Scribner). Macmillan.

Santayana, George. Interpretations of Poetry & Religion. 11.25 (ISBN 0-8446-0893-9). Peter Smith.

PHILOSOPHY, MORAL

see Ethics

PHILOSOPHY, MUSLIM

see Philosophy, Islamic

PHILOSOPHY, ORIENTAL

see also Philosophy, Buddhist; Philosophy, Chinese; Philosophy, Comparative; Philosophy, Hindu; Philosophy, Japanese

Agni Yoga. 5th ed. (Agni Yoga Ser.). 1980. Index 12.00 (ISBN 0-933574-04-5). Agni Yoga Soc.

Al-Ghazzali. Alchemy of Happiness. 1964. 3.75x (ISBN 0-87902-055-5). Orientalia.

--Confessions of Al-Ghazzali. Watt, W. M., tr. 3.25x (ISBN 0-87902-059-8). Orientalia.

--Foundations of the Articles of Faith. 1969. 7.50x (ISBN 0-87902-058-X). Orientalia.

--Mishkat Al-Anwar: A Niche for Lights. 1952. 4.25x (ISBN 0-87902-051-2). Orientalia.

--Mysteries of Fasting. 1970. 3.50x (ISBN 0-87902-052-0). Orientalia.

--Mysteries of Purity. 1966. 4.50x (ISBN 0-87902-053-9). Orientalia.

--On Divine Predicates & Their Attributes. 1970. 6.50x (ISBN 0-87902-057-1). Orientalia.

--Some Moral & Religious Teachings. 4.50x (ISBN 0-87902-056-3). Orientalia.

--Tahafut Al-Falasifah. 8.25x (ISBN 0-87902-054-7). Orientalia.

Aum. (Agni Yoga Ser.). 1982. Repr. of 1959 ed. Index 12.00 (ISBN 0-933574-12-6). Agni Yoga Soc.

Brotherhood. (Agni Yoga Ser.). 1982. Repr. of 1962 ed. Index 12.00 (ISBN 0-933574-13-4). Agni Yoga Soc.

Fiery World. Incl. (Agni Yoga Ser.: Vol. I). 1982. Repr. of 1969 ed. Index 12.00 (ISBN 0-933574-09-6); (Vol. II). 1978. Repr. of 1946 ed. softcover 12.00 (ISBN 0-933574-10-X); (Agni Yoga Ser.: Vol. III). 1980. Repr. of 1948 ed. flexible cover. 12.00 (ISBN 0-933574-11-8). Agni Yoga Soc.

Heart. rev. ed. (Agni Yoga Ser.). 1980. Repr. of 1975 ed. index 12.00 (ISBN 0-933574-08-8). Agni Yoga Soc.

Hua, Ellen K. Wisdom from the East: Meditations, Reflections, Proverbs & Chants. LC 73-21886. (Illus.). 128p. (Orig.). 1974. pap. 3.00 (ISBN 0-87407-202-6, FP2). Thor.

Infinity I. (Agni Yoga Ser.). 1980. Repr. of 1956 ed. index 12.00 (ISBN 0-933574-05-3). Agni Yoga Soc.

Infinity II. (Agni Yoga Ser.). 1980. Repr. of 1957 ed. index 12.00 (ISBN 0-933574-06-1). Agni Yoga Soc.

Kim, Yong C. Oriental Thought: An Introduction to the Philosophical & Religious Thought of Asia. (Quality Paperback Ser.: No. 365). 144p. 1981. pap. 4.95 (ISBN 0-8226-0365-9). Littlefield.

Kim, Yong Choon. Oriental Thought: An Introduction to the Philosophical & Religious Thought of Asia. LC 80-39672. 144p. 1981. Repr. of 1973 ed. 11.50x (ISBN 0-8476-6972-6). Rowman.

Kundakunda Acharya. Niyamsara (the Perfect Law) Sain, Uggar, tr. & intro. by. LC 73-3844. (Sacred Books of the Jainas: No. 9). Repr. of 1931 ed. 18.00 (ISBN 0-404-57709-1). AMS Pr.

--Samayasara (the Soul Essence) Jaini, Rai B., tr. & commentaries by. LC 73-3843. (Sacred Books of the Jainas: No. 8). Repr. of 1930 ed. 25.00 (ISBN 0-404-57708-3). AMS Pr.

Letters of Helena Roerich, Vol. I. 1979. Repr. of 1954 ed. flexible cover 16.00 (ISBN 0-933574-14-2). Agni Yoga Soc.

Ramacharaka, Yogi. The Hindu Yogi Science of Breath. 88p. 1905. pap. text ed. 5.95 (ISBN 0-88697-047-4). Life Science.

Watt, W. M. Faith & Practice of Al-Ghazzali. 1967. 5.75x (ISBN 0-87902-060-1). Orientalia.

PHILOSOPHY, RENAISSANCE

Mahoney, Edward P., ed. Philosophy & Humanism: Renaissance Essays in Honor of Paul Oskar Kristeller. LC 75-42285. 624p. 1976. 65.00 (ISBN 0-231-03904-2). Columbia U Pr.

Wilcox, Donald J. In Search of God & Self: Renaissance & Reformation Thought. (Illus.). 401p. 1987. pap. text ed. 12.95 (ISBN 0-88133-276-3). Waveland Pr.

PHILOSOPHY, ROMAN

see Philosophy, Ancient

PHILOSOPHY, RUSSIAN

Berdyaev, Nicolas. Origin of Russian Communism. 1960. pap. 8.95 (ISBN 0-472-06034-1, 34, AA). U of Mich Pr.

Godoretzky, N. T. The Humiliated Christ in Modern Russian Thought. 59.95 (ISBN 0-8490-0376-8). Gordon Pr.

PHILOSOPHY AND RELIGION

see also Christianity–Philosophy; Faith and Reason; Philosophical Theology; Religion–Philosophy

Ahlstrom, Sydney E. & Mullin, Robert B. The Scientific Theist: A Life of Francis Ellingwood Abbot. 208p. 1987. 29.95 (ISBN 0-86554-236-8). Mercer Univ Pr.

Alexander, Hartley B. God & Man's Destiny: Inquiries into the Metaphysical Foundations of Faith. LC 75-3017. 1976. Repr. of 1936 ed. 16.50 (ISBN 0-404-59010-1). AMS Pr.

Allen, Hope E. Writings Ascribed to Richard Rolle Hermit of Hampole & Materials for His Biography. 568p. 1981. Repr. of 1927 ed. lib. bdg. 125.00 (ISBN 0-89987-023-6). Darby Bks.

Baba, Meher, et al. Meher Baba Journal, Vol. 1, No. 9. Patterson, Elizabeth C., ed. (Illus.). 1973. pap. 2.50x (ISBN 0-913078-13-1). Sheriar Pr.

--Meher Baba Journal, Vol. 1, No. 10. Patterson, Elizabeth C., ed. (Illus.). 1973. pap. 2.50x (ISBN 0-913078-14-X). Sheriar Pr.

Becker, Carl L. Heavenly City of the Eighteenth-Century Philosophers. (Storrs Lectures Ser.). 1932. pap. 6.95x (ISBN 0-300-00017-0, Y5). Yale U Pr.

Beredene, Jocelyn. What Difference Did the Deed of Christ Make? 1979. pap. 1.50 (ISBN 0-88010-103-2). Anthroposophic.

Besant, Annie. Yoga: The Hatha Yoga & Raja Yoga of India. 73p. 1974. pap. 7.95 (ISBN 0-88697-035-0). Life Science.

Bixler, Julius S. Religion in the Philosophy of William James. LC 75-3049. Repr. of 1926 ed. 24.50 (ISBN 0-404-59046-2). AMS Pr.

Blood, Benjamin P. The Philosophy of Justice Between God & Man. LC 75-3056. Repr. of 1851 ed. 20.50 (ISBN 0-404-59054-3). AMS Pr.

Bockl, George. How to Find Something Big to Live for: A Spirital Odyssey. 193p. (Orig.). 1984. pap. 7.95 (ISBN 0-942494-83-0). Coleman Pub.

Boethius. The Consolation of Philosophy. Green, Richard H., tr. LC 62-11788. 1962. pap. 5.44 scp (ISBN 0-672-60273-3, LLA86). Bobbs.

--Consolation of Philosophy. Buchanan, James J., ed. LC 57-8649. (Milestones of Thought Ser.). 7.00 (ISBN 0-8044-5149-4); pap. 3.95 (ISBN 0-8044-6057-4). Ungar.

Bonhoeffer, Dietrich. Act & Being. 192p. 1983. Repr. of 1962 ed. 18.50 (ISBN 0-88254-869-7, Octagon). Hippocrene Bks.

Bradish, Norman C. John Sergeant: A Forgotten Critic of Descartes & Locke. 65p. 1929. 6.95 (ISBN 0-87548-363-1). Open Court.

Bradshaw, Marion J. Philosophical Foundations of Faith. LC 78-99248. Repr. of 1941 ed. 10.00 (ISBN 0-404-00968-9). AMS Pr.

Brown, C. C. Philosophy of Hope. 1972. 2.95 (ISBN 0-9600378-0-2); pap. 2.00 (ISBN 0-9600378-3-7). C C Brown Pub.

Brown, Colin. Philosophy & the Christian Faith. LC 68-58083. (Orig.). 1969. pap. 9.95 (ISBN 0-87784-712-6). Inter-Varsity.

Bubacz, Bruce. St. Augustine's Theory of Knowledge: A Contemporary Analysis. LC 81-18754. (Texts & Studies in Religion: Vol. 11). 248p. 1982. 39.95x (ISBN 0-88946-959-8). E Mellen.

Buber, Martin. Eclipse of God: Studies in the Relation Between Religion & Philosophy. 1979. pap. text ed. 7.95x (ISBN 0-391-00902-8). Humanities.

Burger, Harald. Zeit und Ewigkeit: Studien zum Wortschatz der Geistlichen Texte des Alt-und Fruehmittelhochdeutschen. LC 74-174177. (Studia Linguistica Germanica: Vol. 6). 1972. 34.00x (ISBN 3-11-003995-8). De Gruyter.

Carus, Paul. God: An Enquiry & a Solution. 253p. 1943. 15.95 (ISBN 0-87548-223-6); pap. 6.95 (ISBN 0-87548-224-4). Open Court.

--Point of View. Cook, Catherine E., ed. (Illus.). 227p. 1927. 16.95 (ISBN 0-87548-268-6). Open Court.

Cassara, Ernest. Hosea Ballou: The Challenge to Orthodoxy. LC 81-40859. 236p. 1982. lib. bdg. 27.75 (ISBN 0-8191-2271-8); pap. text ed. 12.50 (ISBN 0-8191-2272-6). U Pr of Amer.

Clark, Gordon H. Dewey. (Modern Thinkers Ser.). 1960. pap. 2.00 (ISBN 0-87552-582-2). Presby & Reformed.

Clift, Wallace B. Jung & Christianity: The Challenge of Reconciliation. LC 81-17395. 192p. 1983. pap. 8.95 (ISBN 0-8245-0552-2). Crossroad NY.

Cohen, Alan. If We Only Have Love. (Illus., Orig.). 1984. pap. 2.00 (ISBN 0-942494-86-5). Coleman Pub.

Cook, David. Thinking about Faith: An Introductory Guide to Philosophy & Religion. 1986. pap. 8.95 (ISBN 0-310-44131-5). Zondervan.

Cooper, Barry. Michel Foucault: An Introduction to the Study of His Thought. LC 82-8260. (Studies in Religion & Society: Vol. 2). 176p. 1982. 39.95x (ISBN 0-88946-867-2). E Mellen.

Cornold, W. The Yoga of Yama. 64p. 1970. pap. 4.95 (ISBN 0-88697-041-5). Life Science.

DeBurgh, W. G. From Morality to Religion. LC 70-102568. 1970. Repr. of 1938 ed. 31.50x (ISBN 0-8046-0728-1, Pub. by Kennikat). Assoc Faculty Pr.

De Burgh, W. G. From Morality to Religion. 352p. 1985. Repr. of 1938 ed. lib. bdg. 85.00 (ISBN 0-89984-042-6). Century Bookbindery.

De Pauley, William C. Candle of the Lord. facsimile ed. LC 75-107693. (Essay Index Reprint Ser). 1937. 16.00 (ISBN 0-8369-1496-1). Ayer Co Pubs.

De Unamuno, Miguel. Tragic Sense of Life. 14.00 (ISBN 0-8446-3100-0). Peter Smith.

Dillett, Eric S. What Is Man? 80p. 1985. 6.50 (ISBN 0-682-40254-0). Exposition Pr FL.

Dixon, W. Macneile. The Human Situation. 75.00 (ISBN 0-87968-062-8). Gordon Pr.

Dunham, James H. Religion of Philosophers. facs. ed. LC 78-80386. (Essay Index Reprint Ser). 1947. 21.50 (ISBN 0-8369-1059-1). Ayer Co Pubs.

Earle, William, et al, eds. Christianity & Existentialism. (Studies in Phenomenology & Existential Philosophy). 1963. pap. 7.95 (ISBN 0-8101-0084-3). Northwestern U Pr.

Edman, Irwin. Contemporary & His Soul. LC 66-25907. Repr. of 1931 ed. 18.50x (ISBN 0-8046-0129-1, Pub. by Kennikat). Assoc Faculty Pr.

Edwards, Jonathan. Treatise on Grace & Other Posthumous Published Writings Including Observations on the Trinity. Helm, Paul, ed. 141p. 1971. 13.95 (ISBN 0-227-67739-0). Attic Pr.

Fabry, Joseph B., et al, eds. Logotherapy in Action. LC 79-51917. 379p. 1979. 19.95 (ISBN 0-317-06212-3). Inst Logo.

Fasching, Darrell J. The Thought of Jacques Ellul: A Systematic Exposition. LC 81-22529. (Toronto Studies in Theology: Vol. 7). 272p. 1982. 49.95x (ISBN 0-88946-961-X). E Mellen.

Friedlander, Saul, et al, eds. Visions of Apocalypse: End or Rebirth? 272p. 1985. text ed. 28.50x (ISBN 0-8419-0673-4); pap. text ed. 15.50x (ISBN 0-8419-0755-2). Holmes & Meier.

Gaskin, J. C. The Quest for Eternity: An Outline of the Philosophy of Religion. (Pelican Ser.). 192p. 1984. pap. 5.95 (ISBN 0-14-022538-2). Penguin.

Geffre, Claude & Jossua, Jean-Pierre, eds. Nietzsche & Christianity, Vol. 145. (Concilium 1981). 128p. (Orig.). 1981. pap. 6.95 (ISBN 0-8164-2312-1, HarpR). Har-Row.

Gill, Jerry H. Philosophy & Religion: Some Contemporary Perspectives. LC 68-54894. pap. 95.50 (ISBN 0-317-08950-1, 2003459). Bks Demand UMI.

Glanvill, Joseph. Essays on Several Important Subjects in Philosophy & Religion. Repr. of 1676 ed. 32.00 (ISBN 0-384-18880-X). Johnson Repr.

Gopi Krishna. The Inner World. 12p. 1978. pap. 3.95 (ISBN 0-88697-001-6). Life Science.

--To Those Concerned Citizens. (Illus.). 16p. 1978. pap. 3.95 (ISBN 0-88697-002-4). Life Science.

Gossman, Lionel. Orpheus Philologus Bachofen versus Mommsen on the Study of Antiquity. 90p. 1983. 8.00 (ISBN 0-87169-735-1). Am Philos.

Gross, Darwin. The Atom. 130p. (Orig.). 1984. pap. 3.95 (ISBN 0-931689-01-5). SOS Pub OR.

Guttmann, Yitzhak J. On the Philosophy of Religion. Herman, David V., tr. from Hebrew. 134p. 1976. text ed. 25.00x (Pub. by Magnes Pr Israel). Humanities.

Gyatso, Geshe K. Clear Light of Bliss. Landaw, Jonathan, ed. Norbu, Tenzin, tr. from Tibetan. (Wisdom Advanced Book: Blue Ser.). (Illus.). 264p. (Orig.). 1982. pap. 10.95 (ISBN 0-86171-005-3, Pub. by Wisdom Pubns). Great Traditions.

Hall, Manly P. The Secret Teachings of All Ages: An Encyclopedic Outlines of Masonic, Hermetic, Quabbalistic & Rosicrucian Symbolical Philosophy. (Illus.). 1978. pap. 24.95 (ISBN 0-89314-540-8). Philos Res.

Harris, Errol E. Revelation Through Reason: Religion in the Light of Science & Philosophy. 1958. 39.50x (ISBN 0-317-27547-X). Elliots Bks.

Hasime, Tanabe. Philosophy As Metanoetics. 224p. 1987. text ed. 40.00 (ISBN 0-520-05490-3). U of Cal Pr.

Hegel, G. W. Lectures on the Philosophy of Religion. Hodgson, Peter, ed. Incl. Vol. 1. Introduction & the Concept of Religion. 1984. lib. bdg. 50.00x (ISBN 0-520-04676-5); Vol. 3. The Consumate Religion. 1985. lib. bdg. 45.00x (ISBN 0-520-05514-4); Vol. II. Determinate Religion. Hegel, G. W. Hodgson, Peter C., ed. & tr. 816p. 1987. text ed. 50.50 (ISBN 0-520-05513-6). LC 83-9132. 450p. U of Cal Pr.

Heide, Della M. The Covenant Renewed. 176p. 1983. pap. 7.95 (ISBN 0-317-04516-4). Coleman Pub.

Herring, Basil. Joseph Ibn Kaspi's Gevia' Kesef: A Study in Medieval Jewish Philosophical Bible Commentary. 1982. 35.00x (ISBN 0-87068-716-6). Ktav.

Hotema, Hilton. Cosmic Science of the Ancient Masters. 2nd ed. 32p. 1960. pap. 8.95 (ISBN 0-88697-031-8). Life Science.

--Kingdom of Heaven. 45p. 1960. pap. 8.95 (ISBN 0-88697-030-X). Life Science.

--Secret of Regeneration. Orig. Title: The Science of Human Regeneration (Postgraduate Orthopathy) (Illus.). 900p. 1963. pap. 59.95 (ISBN 0-88697-019-9). Life Science.

Hutchison, John A. Living Options in World Philosophy. LC 76-46489. 323p. 1977. 16.00x (ISBN 0-8248-0455-4). UH Pr.

Huxley, Aldous. Perennial Philosophy. 1970. pap. 7.95 (ISBN 0-06-090191-8, CN191, PL). Har-Row.

Huxley, Aldous L. Perennial Philosophy. LC 76-167362. (Essay Index Reprint Ser.). Repr. of 1945 ed. 25.50 (ISBN 0-8369-2773-7). Ayer Co Pubs.

Jaeger, Werner. Humanism & Theology. (Aquinas Lecture). 1943. 7.95 (ISBN 0-87462-107-0). Marquette.

James, William. Varieties of Religious Experience. LC 37-27013. 1936. 6.95 (ISBN 0-394-60463-6). Modern Lib.

--The Varieties of Religious Experience. (The Works of William James). (Illus.). 728p. 1985. text ed. 45.00x (ISBN 0-674-93225-0). Harvard U Pr.

Jehan, L. F. Dictionnaire de Philosophie Catholique, 3 vols. Migne, J. P., ed. (Troisieme et Derniere Encyclopedie Theologique Ser.: Vols. 50-52). (Fr.). 2047p. Repr. of 1864 ed. lib. bdg. 260.00x (ISBN 0-89241-321-2). Caratzas.

Kant, Immanuel. Religion Within Limits or Reason Alone. pap. 8.95x (ISBN 0-06-130067-5, TB67, Torch). Har-Row.

Kidd, James W., ed. Philosophy, Psychology & Spirituality. LC 83-80836. 87p. (Orig.). 1984. pap. text ed. 9.95 (ISBN 0-910727-05-8). Golden Phoenix.

Knudson, Albert C. Philosophy of Personalism: A Study in the Metaphysics of Religion. LC 27-21477. 1968. Repr. of 1927 ed. 26.00 (ISBN 0-527-51600-7). Kraus Repr.

Kolenda, Konstantin. Religion Without God. LC 76-19349. (Skeptic's Bookshelf Ser.). 125p. 1976. 13.95 (ISBN 0-87975-066-9). Prometheus Bks.

Kuklick, Bruce. Churchmen & Philosophers: From Jonathan Edwards to John Dewey. LC 84-19579. 352p. 1985. 30.00 (ISBN 0-300-03269-2). Yale U Pr.

Kuntz, Paul G. & Kuntz, Marion L. Jacob's Ladder & the Tree of Life: Concepts of Hierarchy & the Great Chain of Being. (American University Studies V-Philosophy: Vol. 14). 444p. 1987. text ed. 40.00 (ISBN 0-8204-0233-8). P Lang Pubs.

Locke, John. Reasonableness of Christianity & a Discourse of Miracles. Ramsey, I. T., ed. 1958. pap. 6.95x (ISBN 0-8047-0341-8). Stanford U Pr.

Lotze, H. Outlines of the Philosophy of Religion: Dictated Portions of the Lectures of Hermann Lotze. Ladd, G., ed. LC 11-24754. Repr. of 1885 ed. 20.00 (ISBN 0-527-58550-5). Kraus Repr.

Luft, Eric, ed. & tr. Hegel, Hinrichs & Schleiermacher on Feeling & Reason in Religion: The Texts of Their 1821-22 Debate. LC 87-5550. (Studies in German Thought & History: Volume 3). 544p. 1987. lib. bdg. 79.95 (ISBN 0-88946-352-2). E Mellen.

McCarthy, Vincent A. Quest for a Philosophical Jesus: Christianity & Philosophy in Rousseau, Kant, Hegel, & Schelling. xv, 240p. 1986. 28.95 (ISBN 0-86554-210-4, MUP-H190). Mercer Univ Pr.

MacGregor, Geddes. The Gospels As a Mandala of Wisdom. 224p. (Orig.). 1982. pap. 6.50 (ISBN 0-8356-0554-X, Quest). Theos Pub Hse.

McLean, George F. & Dougherty, Jude P., eds. Philosophy & Christian Theology. (Proceedings of the American Catholic Philosophical Association: Vol. 44). 1970. pap. 15.00 (ISBN 0-918090-04-0). Am Cath Philo.

McMurrin, Sterling M. Religion, Reason, & Truth: Historical Essays in the Philosophy of Religion. 1982. 24.95 (ISBN 0-87480-203-2). U of Utah Pr.

Maidens, Melinda, ed. Religion, Morality & "the New Right". 224p. 1982. 24.95x (ISBN 0-87196-639-5). Facts on File.

Maimonides. Ethical Writings of Maimonides. (Philosophy & Religion Ser.). 182p. (Orig.). 1983. pap. 4.50 (ISBN 0-486-24522-5). Dover.

Maquarrie, John. Twentieth Century Religion Thought: The Frontiers of Philosophy & Theology, 1900-1980. rev. ed. 429p. 1981. pap. text ed. write for info. (ISBN 0-02-374500-2, Pub. by Scribner). Macmillan.

Marti, Fritz. Religion, Reason & Man. LC 74-9353. 127p. 1974. 7.50 (ISBN 0-87527-141-3). Green.

Masaryk, Thomas G. Modern Man & Religion. facsimile ed. LC 74-107816. (Select Bibliographies Reprint Ser). 1938. 24.50 (ISBN 0-8369-5216-2). Ayer Co Pubs.

Masaryk, Tomas G. Modern Man & Religion. Kennedy, H. E., et al, trs. LC 78-109783. viii, 320p. Repr. of 1938 ed. lib. bdg. 22.50x (ISBN 0-8371-4273-3, MAMR). Greenwood.

Mehl, Roger. Imagenes Del Hombre. Benlliure, Felix, tr. from Fr. Orig. Title: Images Del'homme. 64p. 1980. pap. 1.35 (ISBN 0-311-05051-4). Casa Bautista.

Monti, Joseph E. Who Do You Say That I Am? LC 83-82023. (Orig.). 1984. pap. 4.95 (ISBN 0-8091-2598-6). Paulist Pr.

Morin, F. Dictionnaire de Philosophie et de Theologie Scolastiques, 2 vols. Migne, J. P., ed. (Troisieme et Derniere Encyclopedie Theologique Ser.: Vols. 21-22). (Fr.). 1496p. Repr. of 1865 ed. lib. bdg. 190.00x (ISBN 0-89241-304-2). Caratzas.

Muccie, Frank J., Jr. I & the Father Are One. 180p. 1982. pap. 7.95 (ISBN 0-938520-01-6). Edenite.

Natoli, Charles M. Nietzsche & Pascal on Christianity. LC 83-49020. (American University Studies V (Philosophy): Vol. 3). 200p. (Orig.). 1984. pap. text ed. 24.25 (ISBN 0-8204-0071-8). P Lang Pubs.

Nee, Watchman. Love One Another. Kaung, Stephen, tr. (Basic Lesson Ser.: Vol. 6). 1975. 5.50 (ISBN 0-935008-09-8); pap. 4.25 (ISBN 0-935008-10-1). Christian Fellow Pubs.

Newlin, Claude M. Philosophy & Religion in Colonial America. LC 68-23317. 1968. Repr. of 1962 ed. lib. bdg. cancelled (ISBN 0-8371-0184-0, NEPR). Greenwood.

Nielsen, Kai. An Introduction to the Philosophy of Religion. LC 82-16843. 200p. 1983. 22.50x (ISBN 0-312-43310-7). St Martin.

Nietzsche, Friedrich. The Antichrist & Twilight of the Gods. 1974. 100.00 (ISBN 0-87968-210-8). Gordon Pr.

Nishitani, Keiji. Religion & Nothingness. Bragt, Jan Van, tr. from Japanese. LC 81-4084. 366p. 1982. 35.95x (ISBN 0-520-04329-4); pap. 10.95x (ISBN 0-520-04946-2, CAL 634). U of Cal Pr.

Noonan, John T., Jr., et al, eds. The Role & Responsibility of the Moral Philosopher: Proceedings, Vol. 56. LC 81-69068. 214p. 1983. pap. 15.00 (ISBN 0-918090-16-4). Am Cath Philo.

Oman, John W. The Natural & the Supernatural. LC 79-39696. (Select Bibliographies Reprint Ser.). 1972. Repr. of 1931 ed. 20.75 (ISBN 0-8369-9941-X). Ayer Co Pubs.

Palmer, G. E. & Sherrard, Philip, trs. The Philokalia, Vol. 1: The Complete Text Compiled By St. Nikodimos of the Holy Mountain & St. Markarios of Corinth, Vol. 1. 384p. 1983. pap. 10.95 (ISBN 0-571-13013-5). Faber & Faber.

Palmer, Melba P. Are You Ready? 81p. (Orig.). 1984. pap. 7.95 (ISBN 0-942494-88-1). Coleman Pub.

Patterson, David. Faith & Philosophy. LC 81-43469. 162p. (Orig.). 1982. pap. text ed. 10.50 (ISBN 0-8191-2651-9). U Pr of Amer.

Peacocke, Arthur. Intimations of Reality: Critical Realism in Science & Religion. LC 84-40357. (The Mendenhall Lectures). 96p. 1984. text ed. 10.95 (ISBN 0-268-01155-9, 85-11552); pap. text ed. 4.95 (ISBN 0-268-01156-7, 85-11560). U of Notre Dame Pr.

Penelhum, Terence. God & Skepticism. 1983. lib. bdg. 34.95 (ISBN 90-277-1550-5, Pub. by Reidel Holland). Kluwer Academic.

Pratt, James B. Adventures in Philosophy & Religion. LC 75-3323. Repr. of 1931 ed. 16.00 (ISBN 0-404-59319-4). AMS Pr.

Price, Richard. A Free Discussion of the Doctrine of Materialism and Philosophical Necessity, 1778. Wellek, Rene, ed. LC 75-11247. (British Philosophers & Theologians of the 17th & 18th Centuries Ser.). 1978. lib. bdg. 51.00 (ISBN 0-8240-1798-6). Garland Pub.

Ramanuja Research Society. Vishishtadvaita: Philosophy & Religion. 273p. 1975. 10.75 (ISBN 0-88253-683-4). Ind-US Inc.

Randall, John H., Jr. The Role of Knowledge in Western Religion. 160p. 1986. pap. text ed. 10.75 (ISBN 0-8191-5167-X). U Pr of Amer.

Rashdall, Hastings. Philosophy & Religion: Six Lectures Delivered at Cambridge. Repr. of 1910 ed. lib. bdg. 22.50x (ISBN 0-8371-3025-5, RAPR). Greenwood.

Reese, William L. Dictionary of Philosophy & Religion: Eastern & Western Thought. text ed. 29.95x 648p. 1980 (ISBN 0-391-00688-6); pap. text ed. 19.95x 644p. 1981 (ISBN 0-391-00941-9). Humanities.

Rolle, Richard. The Mending of Life: Being an Anonymous Version of about A. D. 1400 from the De Emendatione Vitae of Richard Rolle of Hampole. 95p. 1981. Repr. of 1913 ed. lib. bdg. 30.00 (ISBN 0-89987-374-X). Darby Bks.

Rowe, William L. & Wainwright, William J., eds. Philosophy of Religion: Selected Readings. 489p. 1973. pap. text ed. 16.95 (ISBN 0-15-570580-6, HC). HarBraceJ.

Roy, Rustrum. Experimenting with Truth: The Fusion of Religion with Technology Needed for Humanity's Survival. (The Hibbert Lectures: 1979). (Illus.). 228p. 1981. 32.00 (ISBN 0-08-025820-4); pap. 10.00 (ISBN 0-08-025819-0). Pergamon.

Rust, Eric C. Religion, Revelation & Reason. LC 81-2760. vi, 192p. 1981. 14.50x (ISBN 0-86554-006-3). Mercer Univ Pr.

Sandoz, Ellis, ed. Eric Voegelin's Thought: A Critical Appraisal. LC 81-43591. xv, 208p. 1982. 24.75 (ISBN 0-8223-0465-1). Duke.

Santayana, George. The Life of Reason: Reason in Religion, Vol. 3. 288p. 1982. pap. 5.95 (ISBN 0-486-24253-6). Dover.

Scheler, Max F. On the Eternal in Man. Noble, Bernard, tr. LC 72-6599. 480p. 1972. Repr. of 1960 ed. 35.00 (ISBN 0-208-01280-X, Archon). Shoe String.

Scholz, Heinrich. Religionsphilosophie. rev. ed. (Ger.). xi, 332p. 1974. Repr. of 1922 ed. 36.80x (ISBN 3-11-002217-6). De Gruyter.

Schwanktfeld, Kurt W. The Hegel-Kierkegaard Cosmology of the Spirit. (Illus.). 103p. 1984. 87.85 (ISBN 0-89266-497-5). Am Classical Coll Pr.

Science, Philosophy & Religion. 559p. 1985. Repr. of 1942 ed. lib. bdg. 85.00 (ISBN 0-8492-3208-2). R West.

Seth Pringle Pattison, Andrew. Philosophical Radicals & Other Essays. 1907. 23.50 (ISBN 0-8337-4388-0). B Franklin.

Seton-Sears, Julia. Key to Health, Wealth, & Love. 32p. 1976. pap. 4.95 (ISBN 0-88697-025-3). Life Science.

Shestov, Lev. Potestas Clavium. Martin, Bernard, tr. LC 67-24282. 1968. 15.00x (ISBN 0-8214-0040-1). Ohio U Pr.

Simonson, Harold P. Radical Discontinuities: American Romanticism & Christian Consciousness. LC 81-72051. 180p. 1983. 24.50 (ISBN 0-8386-3159-2). Fairleigh Dickinson.

Smart, Ninian. A Dialogue of Religions. LC 79-8730. (The Library of Philosophy & Theology). 142p. 1981. Repr. of 1960 ed. lib. bdg. 22.50x (ISBN 0-313-22187-1, SMDR). Greenwood.

--The Philosophy of Religion. 1979. pap. 7.95x (ISBN 0-19-520139-6). Oxford U Pr.

Smith, John E. Reason & God: Encounters of Philosophy with Religion. LC 77-13887. 1978. Repr. of 1961 ed. lib. bdg. 22.50x (ISBN 0-8371-9867-4, SMRG). Greenwood.

Steiner, Rudolf. Truth & Knowledge: Introduction to "Philosophy of Spiritual Activity", Vol. 14. 2nd ed. Allen, Paul M., ed. Stebbing, Rita, tr. from Ger. LC 81-51762. (The Major Writings of Rudolf Steiner in English Translation Ser.). 112p. 1981. Repr. of 1963 ed. lib. bdg. 10.00 (ISBN 0-89345-008-1, Spiritual Sci Lib). Garber Comm.

Stirling, James H. Philosophy & Theology. LC 77-27233. (Gifford Lectures: 1890). 1978. Repr. of 1890 ed. 39.00 (ISBN 0-404-60451-X). AMS Pr.

Taylor, A. E. The Faith of the Moralist: Gifford Lectures Delivered in the University of St. Andrews, 1926-1928, 2 vols. 1977. Repr. of 1932 ed. Set. lib. bdg. 50.00 (ISBN 0-8482-2663-1). Norwood Edns.

Taylor, Alfred E. Faith of a Moralist, 2 Vols. in 1. LC 37-23815. (Gifford Lectures 1926-1928). 1968. Repr. of 1937 ed. 41.00 (ISBN 0-527-89062-6). Kraus Repr.

Turner, John E. Essentials in the Development of Religion. LC 70-102587. 1970. Repr. of 1934 ed. 24.50x (ISBN 0-8046-0747-8, Pub. by Kennikat). Assoc Faculty Pr.

Tyrrell, Bernard J. Bernard Lonergan's Philosophy of God. LC 73-22205. pap. 54.00 (ISBN 0-317-29698-1, 2022063). Bks Demand UMI.

Unamuno, Miguel. Tragic Sense of Life. Flitch, J. Crawford, tr. 1921. pap. 6.00 (ISBN 0-486-20257-7). Dover.

Vezzosi, Antonio F. I Scrittori De'Chierici Regolari Detti Teatini. 1030p. Date not set. Repr. of 1780 ed. text ed. 165.60x (ISBN 0-576-72811-X, Pub. by Gregg Intl Pubs England). Gregg Intl.

Vos, Geerhardus. The Kingdom of God & the Church. 1972. pap. 3.50 (ISBN 0-87552-502-4). Presby & Reformed.

Webb, C. J. God & Personality. (Gifford Lectures Delivered in the University of Aberdeen in 1918 & 1919 First Course). Repr. of 1918 ed. 17.00 (ISBN 0-527-94906-X). Kraus Repr.

Webb, Clement C. Divine Personality & Human Life: Being the Gifford Lectures Delivered in the University of Aberdeen in the Years 1918 & 1919, Second Course. facsimile ed. LC 77-37917. (Select Bibliographies Reprint Ser.). Repr. of 1920 ed. 21.00 (ISBN 0-8369-6754-2). Ayer Co Pubs.

Wei, Henry. The Guiding Light of Lao Tzu. LC 81-53011. 234p. (Orig.). 1982. 12.95 (ISBN 0-8356-0562-0, Quest); pap. 6.95 (ISBN 0-8356-0558-2, Quest). Theos Pub Hse.

Whitehead, Alfred N. An Enquiry Concerning the Principles of Natural Knowledge. (Western Philosophy & Religion Ser.). 207p. 1982. pap. 5.95 (ISBN 0-486-24343-5). Dover.

Wilson, Colin. Religion & the Rebel. Rev. ed. 352p. 1984. pap. 9.95 (ISBN 0-88162-050-5). Salem Hse Pubs.

Wilson, John. Philosophy & Religion: The Logic of Religious Belief. LC 78-14000. 1979. Repr. of 1961 ed. lib. bdg. 24.75x (ISBN 0-313-20738-0, WIPH). Greenwood.

Wolfson, Harry A. Religious Philosophy: A Group of Essays. LC 61-16696. 1961. 17.50x (ISBN 0-674-75900-1, Belknap Pr). Harvard U Pr.

Yandell, Keith. Christianity & Philosophy. LC 83-14226. (Studies in a Christian World View: Vol. 2). 284p. 1984. pap. 12.95 (ISBN 0-8028-1964-8). Eerdmans.

Yoder, Robert S. Judgement unto Victory. 1983. 6.75 (ISBN 0-8062-1964-5). Carlton.

PHILOSOPHY AND SCIENCE

see Science–Philosophy

PHILOSOPHY IN LITERATURE

see also Existentialism in Literature

Edge, Henry T., et al. Mirrors of the Hidden Wisdom: Threads of Theosophy in Literature - I. (Study Ser.: No. 7). 122p. 1981. pap. 5.95 (ISBN 0-913004-42-1). Point Loma Pub.

Kolenda, Konstantin. Philosophy in Literature: Metaphysical Darkness & Ethical Light. LC 81-7979. 250p. 1982. 28.75x (ISBN 0-389-20224-X). B&N Imports.

Von Goethe, J. W. & Steiner, Rudolf. The Fairy Tale of the Green Snake & the Beautiful Lily. 2nd ed. LC 78-73644. 72p. (Orig.). 1981. pap. 3.50 (ISBN 0-89345-203-3, Steinerbks). Garber Comm.

PHILOSOPHY OF HISTORY

see History–Philosophy

PHILOSOPHY OF NATURE

see also Cosmology; Natural Theology; Nature–Religious Interpretations

Beckett, L. C. Movement & Emptiness. 1969. pap. 1.45 (ISBN 0-8356-0414-4, Quest). Theos Pub Hse.

Bonifazi, Conrad. A Theology of Things. LC 76-7549. 1976. Repr. of 1967 ed. lib. bdg. 22.50x (ISBN 0-8371-8838-5, BOTT). Greenwood.

Hotema, Hilton. Cosmic Science of the Ancient Masters. 2nd ed. 32p. 1960. pap. 8.95 (ISBN 0-88697-031-8). Life Science.

James, William. The Varieties of Religious Experience: A Study in Human Nature. Marty, Martin, ed. (Penguin American Library). 1982. pap. 4.95 (ISBN 0-14-039034-0). Penguin.

Rouner, Leroy S., ed. On Nature. LC 84-7502. (Boston University Studies in Philosophy & Religion: Vol. 6). 224p. 1984. text ed. 20.95 (ISBN 0-268-01499-X, 85-14994). U of Notre Dame Pr.

Willey, Basil. Religion of Nature. LC 76-40105. 1957. lib. bdg. 12.50 (ISBN 0-8414-9506-8). Folcroft.

Williamson, Jack V. Natures Religion. 6.95 (ISBN 0-8062-2425-8). Carlton.

PHOTIUS, d. 892

Gerostergios, Asterios. St. Photios the Great. LC 80-82285. (Illus.). 125p. 1980. 8.50 (ISBN 0-914744-50-X); pap. 5.50 (ISBN 0-914744-51-8). Inst Byzantine.

Mango, Cyril, tr. The Homilies of Photius, Patriarch of Constantinople. (Dumbarton Oaks Studies: Vol. 3). 327p. (LC A58-6068). 1958. 20.00x (ISBN 0-88402-003-7). Dumbarton Oaks.

PHYSICIANS–BIOGRAPHY

Abramson, Ruth. Benjamin: Journey of a Jew. (The Life-Cycle Bookshelf Ser.). (Orig.). 1987. pap. 10.00 (ISBN 0-933771-02-9). Alpha Pub Co.

Hartmann, Heinz. Once a Doctor, Always a Doctor: The Memoirs of a German-Jewish Immigrant Physician. 130p. Date not set. 18.95 (ISBN 0-87975-342-0). Prometheus Bks.

Hes, Hindle S. Jewish Physicians in the Netherlands 1600-1940. 248p. 1980. pap. text ed. 14.50 (ISBN 0-317-51979-4, Pub. by Van Gorcum Holland). Longwood Pub Group.

Koren, Nathan, ed. Jewish Physicians: A Biographical Index. 275p. 1973. 25.00 (ISBN 0-87855-184-0). Transaction Bks.

PICTURE-WRITING, INDIAN

Brinton, Daniel G., ed. The Lenape & Their Legends. LC 77-102641. (Library of Aboriginal American Literature Ser.: No. 5). Repr. of 1884 ed. 30.00 (ISBN 0-404-52185-1). AMS Pr.

Olum, Walam. The Lenape & Their Legends. Brinton, Daniel G., tr. LC 74-108462. 262p. 1973. Repr. of 1884 ed. 29.00 (ISBN 0-403-00449-7). Scholarly.

PIERRE LE VENERABLE, 1092-1156

Peter The Venerable. Letters of Peter the Venerable, 2 Vols. Constable, Giles, ed. LC 67-10086. (Historical Studies: No. 78). 1967. Set. 55.00x (ISBN 0-674-52775-5). Harvard U Pr.

PIERRE DE DREUX, DUKE OF BRITTANY, 13TH CENTURY

Painter, Sidney. Scourge of the Clergy: Peter of Dreux, Duke of Brittany. LC 76-96188. 1970. Repr. of 1937 ed. lib. bdg. 16.00x (ISBN 0-374-96175-1, Octagon). Hippocrene Bks.

PIETISM

see also Evangelicalism

Carpenter, Delburn. The Radical Pietists. LC 72-13586. (Illus.). 19.00 (ISBN 0-404-11008-8). AMS Pr.

Erb, Peter C., ed. The Pietists: Selected Writings. (Classics of Western Spirituality Ser.). 1983. 13.95 (ISBN 0-8091-0334-6); pap. 9.95 (ISBN 0-8091-2509-9). Paulist Pr.

Haeusermann, Friederich & Breymayer, Reinhard, eds. Die Lehntafel der Prinzessin Antonia, 2 Vol. (Texte Zur Geschichte Des Pietismus: Sec. 7, Vol. 1). 1977. 112.00x (ISBN 3-11-004130-8). De Gruyter.

McCardle, Arthur W. Friedrich Schiller & Swabian Pietism. (American University Studies I-Germanic Languages & Literature: Vol. 36). 236p. 1986. text ed. 40.65 (ISBN 0-8204-0196-X). P Lang Pubs.

Sachse, Julius F. German Pietists of Provincial Pennsylvania, 1694-1708. LC 70-134384. (Communal Societies Ser.). Repr. of 1895 ed. 32.50 (ISBN 0-404-07204-6). AMS Pr.

PIETY

Bayly, Lewis. The Practice of Piety: Directing a Christian How to Walk, That He May Please God. LC 75-31081. Repr. of 1718 ed. 34.50 (ISBN 0-404-13500-5). AMS Pr.

Bourghei, S. R., et al. Piety. Tavakoli, Amir, tr. from Persian. 1980. pap. 1.00 (ISBN 0-318-03827-7). Book-Dist-Ctr.

Lundin, Roger & Noll, Mark, eds. Voices from the Heart: Four Centuries of American Piety. 416p. 1987. 19.95 (ISBN 0-8028-3633-X). Eerdmans.

Van Hoeven, James W. Piety & Patriotism. 1976. pap. 4.95 (ISBN 0-8028-1663-0). Eerdmans.

PIKE, JAMES ALBERT, BP., 1913-1969

Morris, Frederick M. Bishop Pike: Ham, Heretic, or Hero. LC 67-28381. pap. 20.00 (ISBN 0-317-08443-7, 2012934). Bks Demand UMI.

PILATE, PONTIUS, 1ST CENTURY

Maier, Paul L. Pontius Pilate. 1981. pap. 3.95 (ISBN 0-8423-4852-2). Tyndale.

PILGRIMS (NEW PLYMOUTH COLONY)

see also Brownists

Bacon, Leonard. The Genesis of the New England Churches. LC 74-38435. (Religion in America, Ser. 2). 510p. 1972. Repr. of 1874 ed. 32.00 (ISBN 0-405-04056-3). Ayer Co Pubs.

Blaxland, G. Cuthbert. Mayflower Essays: On the Story of the Pilgrim Fathers, As Told in Governor Bradford's Ms. History of the Plimoth Plantation. LC 78-39713. (Essay Index Reprint Ser.). Repr. of 1896 ed. 13.00 (ISBN 0-8369-2748-6). Ayer Co Pubs.

Bradford, William. Of Plymouth Plantation: The Pilgrims in America. 18.00 (ISBN 0-8446-1718-0). Peter Smith.

--Of Plymouth Plantation: 1620-1647. Morison, Samuel E., ed. (The American Past Ser). (Illus.). (YA) 1952. 19.95 (ISBN 0-394-43895-7). Knopf.

Brown, Elizabeth M., et al, eds. Pilgrims & Their Times. rev. ed. (Illus.). 32p. 1973. pap. 2.50 (ISBN 0-87534-121-7). Highlights.

Brown, J. Pilgrim Fathers of New England & Their Puritan Successors. 4th ed. (Illus.). Repr. of 1920 ed. 39.00 (ISBN 0-527-12050-2). Kraus Repr.

Cushing, John D. Laws of the Pilgrims. 1978. facsimile ed. 8.50 (ISBN 0-940628-00-7). Pilgrim Soc.

Dexter, Henry M. & Dexter, Morton. The England & Holland of the Pilgrims. LC 77-90433. (Illus.). 673p. 1978. Repr. of 1906 ed. 28.50 (ISBN 0-8063-0794-3). Genealog Pub.

Forman, Charles C. Four Early Bibles in Pilgrim Hall. (Pilgrim Society Notes: No. 9). 1959. 1.00 (ISBN 0-940628-17-1). Pilgrim Soc.

Gay, David. Voyage to Freedom: Story of the Pilgrim Fathers. pap. 5.45 (ISBN 0-85151-384-0). Banner of Truth.

Gies, Frances. The Knight in History. LC 84-47571. (Illus.). 192p. 1984. 16.45 (ISBN 0-06-015339-3, HarpT). Har-Row.

Lawrence, Henry W. The Not Quite Puritans: Some Genial Follies & Peculiar Frailities of Our Revered New England Ancestors. (Illus.). 1975. Repr. of 1928 ed. 40.00x (ISBN 0-8103-3993-5). Gale.

Plooij, D. Pilgrim Fathers from a Dutch Point of View. LC 71-100509. Repr. of 1932 ed. 8.50 (ISBN 0-404-05065-4). AMS Pr.

Plooij, Daniel. Pilgrim Fathers from a Dutch Point of View. LC 79-131801. 1970. Repr. of 1932 ed. 7.00x (ISBN 0-403-00688-0). Scholarly.

Saxby, Trevor J. Pilgrims of a Common Life. LC 86-27043. 208p. (Orig.). 1987. pap. 17.95 (ISBN 0-8361-3426-5). Herald Pr.

Sherman, Ruth W. & Wakefield, Robert S. Plymouth Colony Probate Guide: Where to Find Wills & Related Data for 800 People of Plymouth Colony, 1620-1691. LC 83-2362. (Plymouth Colony Research Group Ser.: No.2). xxi, 167p. 1983. 21.00x (ISBN 0-910233-01-2). Plymouth Col.

Steele, Ashbel. Chief of the Pilgrims: Or, the Life & Time of William Brewster. facs. ed. LC 72-133535. (Select Bibliographies Reprint Ser). (Illus.). 1857. 23.50 (ISBN 0-8369-5567-6). Ayer Co Pubs.

Twain, Mark. Plymouth Rock & the Pilgrims: And Other Salutary Opinions. Neider, Charles, ed. LC 84-47603. 320p. 1984. 19.45i (ISBN 0-06-015353-9, HarpT). Har-Row.

Usher, Roland G. The Pilgrims & Their History. (Illus.). 310p. 1977. Repr. of 1918 ed. 20.00 (ISBN 0-87928-082-4). Corner Hse.

Young, Alexander. Chronicles of the Pilgrim Fathers of the Colony of Plymouth, 1602-1625. LC 78-87667. (Law, Politics & History Ser). 1971. Repr. of 1841 ed. lib. bdg. 42.50 (ISBN 0-306-71760-3). Da Capo.

PILGRIMS (NEW PLYMOUTH COLONY)–JUVENILE LITERATURE

Bains, Rae. Pilgrims & Thanksgiving. LC 84-2686. (Illus.). 32p. 1985. PLB 7.59 (ISBN 0-8167-0222-5); pap. text ed. 1.95 (ISBN 0-8167-0223-3). Troll Assocs.

Payne, Elizabeth. Meet the Pilgrim Fathers. (Step-up Books Ser). (Illus.). 1966. PLB 5.99 (ISBN 0-394-90063-4, BYR). Random.

Siegel, Beatrice. A New Look at the Pilgrims: Why They Came to America. LC 76-57060. (Illus.). 96p. 1987. Repr. of 1977 ed. o. p. 5.95 (ISBN 0-8027-6291-3); PLB 12.85 (ISBN 0-8027-6292-1). Walker & Co.

Smith, E. Brooks & Meredith, Robert. The Coming of the Pilgrims. 1964. 11.45 (ISBN 0-316-80048-1). Little.

PILGRIMS AND PILGRIMAGES

see also Holy Wells; Saints; Shrines

Bartlett, Robert M. The Pilgrim Way. LC 70-172790. 384p. 1971. 15.00 (ISBN 0-8298-0222-3). Pilgrim NY.

Bhardwaj, Surinder M. Hindu Places of Pilgrimage in India: A Study in Cultural Geography. LC 73-174454. (Center for South & Southeast Asia Studies, U.C. Berkeley). (Illus.). 1973. 42.50x (ISBN 0-520-02135-5); pap. 8.95 (ISBN 0-520-04951-9, CAL 621). U of Cal Pr.

Birks, J. S. Across the Savannas to Mecca: The Overland Pilgrimage Route from West Africa. (Illus.). 161p. 1978. 29.50x (ISBN 0-7146-6005-1, F Cass Co). Biblio Dist.

Bludau, August. Die Pilgerreise der Aetheria. pap. 22.00 (ISBN 0-384-04760-2). Johnson Repr.

Brackenridge, Hugh H. & Freneau, Philip. Father Bombo's Pilgrimage to Mecca, 1770. Bell, Michael D., ed. LC 75-5391. (Illus.). 129p. 1975. 10.00 (ISBN 0-87811-020-8). Princeton Lib.

Brother John of Taize. The Pilgrim God: A Biblical Journey. (Orig.). 1985. pap. 12.95 (ISBN 0-912405-18-X). Pastoral Pr.

Bunyan, John. Pilgrim's Progress. 1975. 14.95 (ISBN 0-685-52821-9). Reiner.

Burton, Richard F. Personal Narrative of a Pilgrimage to Al-Madinah & Meccah, 2 Vols. (Illus.). 1893. Vol. 1. pap. 8.95 (ISBN 0-486-21217-3). Vol. 2. pap. 8.95 (ISBN 0-486-21218-1). Dover.

--Personal Narrative of a Pilgrimage to Al-Madinah & Meccah, 2 Vols. Burton, Isabel, ed. Set. 28.50 (ISBN 0-8446-1781-4). Peter Smith.

Capgrave, John. Ye Solace of Pilgrimes. Mills, C. A., ed. LC 78-63453. (The Crusades & Military Orders: Second Ser.). Repr. of 1911 ed. 25.00 (ISBN 0-404-16375-0). AMS Pr.

De Sivry, L. Dictionnaire Geographique, Historique, Descriptif, Archeologique des Pelegrinages, 2 vols. Migne, J. P., ed. (Encyclopedie Theologique Ser.: Vols. 43-44). (Fr.). 1328p. Repr. of 1851 ed. lib. bdg. 169.00x (ISBN 0-89241-248-8). Caratzas.

Dexter, W. Mr. Pickwick's Pilgrimages. 59.95 (ISBN 0-8490-0645-7). Gordon Pr.

Doyle, Stephen. The Pilgrim's New Guide to the Holy Land. 1985. pap. 7.95 (ISBN 0-89453-440-8). M Glazier.

Eck, Diana L. Banaras: City of Light. LC 81-48134. (Illus.). 1982. 25.00 (ISBN 0-394-51971-X). Knopf.

Ediger, Max. A Vietnamese Pilgrimage. LC 78-53650. (Illus.). 1978. pap. 5.25 (ISBN 0-87303-007-9). Faith & Life.

Ellis, Henry, ed. Pylgrymage of Sir Richard Guylforde to the Holy Land, A. D. 1506. LC 75-166023. (Camden Society, London. Publications, First Ser.: No. 51). Repr. of 1851 ed. 19.00 (ISBN 0-404-50151-6). AMS Pr.

Field, Frank M. Where Jesus Walked: Through the Holy Land with the Master. Davis, Moshe, ed. LC 77-70681. (America & the Holy Land Ser.). (Illus.). 1977. Repr. of 1951 ed. lib. bdg. 20.00x (ISBN 0-405-10244-5). Ayer Co Pubs.

Fosdick, Harry E. A Pilgrimage to Palestine. Davis, Moshe, ed. LC 77-70688. (America & the Holy Land Ser.). 1977. Repr. of 1927 ed. lib. bdg. 30.00x (ISBN 0-405-10247-X). Ayer Co Pubs.

French, Reginald M., tr. from Rus. Way of a Pilgrim. (Illus.). 242p. 1974. (HarpR); pap. 7.95 (ISBN 0-86683-898-8, SP18). Har-Row.

Gaudefroy-Demombynes, Maurice. Le Pelerinage a la Mekke: Etude D'histoire Religieuse. LC 77-10690. (Studies in Islamic History: No. 7). viii, 332p. 1978. Repr. of 1923 ed. lib. bdg. 35.00x (ISBN 0-87991-456-4). Porcupine Pr.

Gavriilova, Alexandra. Zapiski Palomnitsi. Tr. of Diary of a Pilgrim. 175p. (Orig.). 1968. pap. 6.00 (ISBN 0-317-30250-7). Holy Trinity.

Geyer, Paul, ed. Itinera Hierosolymitana, Saeculi 3-8. (Corpus Scriptorum Ecclesiasticorum Latinorum Ser: Vol. 39). Repr. of 1898 ed. 40.00 (ISBN 0-384-18270-4). Johnson Repr.

Glover, Terrot R. Life & Letters in the Fourth Century. LC 68-10923. 1968. Repr. of 1901 ed. 11.00x (ISBN 0-8462-1065-7). Russell.

Higgins, Paul L. Pilgrimages: A Guide to the Holy Places of Europe for Today's Traveler. 146p. 1984. 12.95 (ISBN 0-13-676163-1); pap. 5.95 (ISBN 0-13-676155-0). P-H.

Jacobs, Donald R. Pilgrimage in Mission. LC 83-306. 168p. 1983. pap. 6.50 (ISBN 0-8361-3324-2). Herald Pr.

Jha, Makhan, ed. Dimensions of Pilgrimage: An Anthropoligical Appraisal (Based on the Transactions of a World Symposium of Pilgrimage) (Illus.). xvi, 180p. 1986. text ed. 45.00x (ISBN 81-210-0007-6, Pub. by Inter India Pubns N Delhi). Apt Bks.

John Paul II, Pope. Pilgrimage of Peace: John Paul II in Ireland & the United States. (Illus.). 175p. 1980. 17.50 (ISBN 0-374-23307-1); pap. 9.95 (ISBN 0-374-51578-6). FS&G.

Johnson, Sarah B. Hadji in Syria: Three Years in Jerusalem. Davis, Moshe, ed. LC 77-70708. (America & the Holy Land Ser.). (Illus.). 1977. Repr. of 1858 ed. lib. bdg. 26.50x (ISBN 0-405-10258-5). Ayer Co Pubs.

Khalifa, Saida M. The Fifth Pillar: The Story of a Pilgrimage to Mecca & Medina. 1977. 7.50 (ISBN 0-682-48772-4). Exposition Pr FL.

Kinnara Inc. Pilgrimage. (Illus., Orig.). 1977. pap. 4.95 (ISBN 0-89346-011-7). Heian Intl.

Lacueva, Francisco. Mi Camino de Damasco. Orig. Title: My Way from Damascus. (Span.). 112p. 1982. pap. 2.75 (ISBN 0-8254-1426-1). Kregel.

Lamartine, Alphonse de. A Pilgrimage to the Holy Land. LC 78-14368. 1978. Repr. of 1838 ed. 75.00x (ISBN 0-8201-1323-9). Schol Facsimiles.

Long, David. The Hajj Today: A Survey of the Contemporary Pilgrimage to Makkah. (Illus.). 1979. 34.50 (ISBN 0-87395-382-7). State U NY Pr.

Malhotra, S. S. Gangaotri & Gaumukh: A Trek to the Holy Source. 1984. 12.50x (ISBN 0-8364-1175-7, Pub. by Allied India). South Asia Bks.

Marechal, Paul. Dancing Madly Backwards: A Journey into God. (The Crossroad Paperback Ser.). 128p. 1982. pap. 5.95 (ISBN 0-8245-0408-9). Crossroad NY.

Mauro, Phillip. God's Pilgrims. 192p. 1969. pap. 3.00 (ISBN 0-87509-090-7). Chr Pubns.

Mokashi, D. B. Palkhi: An Indian Pilgrimage. Engblom, Philip C., tr. 160p. 1987. 34.50x (ISBN 0-88706-461-2); pap. 10.95x (ISBN 0-88706-462-0). State U NY Pr.

Morinis, E. Alan, ed. Pilgrimage in the Hindu Tradition: A Case Study of West Bengal. (Illus.). 1984. 34.95x (ISBN 0-19-561412-7). Oxford U Pr.

Munro, Eleanor. On Glory Roads: A Pilgrims Book about Pilgrimages. LC 86-50231. (Illus.). 286p. 1987. pap. 17.95 (ISBN 0-500-24127-9). Thames Hudson.

Odell, Catherine. On Pilgrimage with Father Ralph Diorio: Following the Footpaths of Faith through the Holyland, Rome & Lourdes. LC 85-7083. (Illus.). 192p. 1986. 16.95 (ISBN 0-385-19908-2). Doubleday.

Ogier VIII. The Holy Jerusalem Voyage of Ogier VIII, Seigneure D'anglure. Browne, Roland A., tr. LC 75-4773. (Illus.). 163p. 1975. 10.00 (ISBN 0-8130-0513-2). U Presses Fla.

Palliere, Aime. The Unknown Sanctuary. Wise, Louise W., tr. LC 79-150294. 243p. 1985. pap. 8.95x (ISBN 0-8197-0498-9). Bloch.

Pilgrimages to Rome & Beyond: A Guide to the Holy Places of Southern Europe for Today's Traveler. 1985. pap. 7.95. S&S.

A Pilgrim's Guide to Planet Earth. LC 85-11046. 320p. 1985. Repr. of 1981 ed. lib. bdg. 19.95x (ISBN 0-89370-888-7). Borgo Pr.

Pochin-Mould, Daphne. Irish Pilgrimage. 1957. 12.95 (ISBN 0-8159-5816-1). Devin.

Pope John Paul II At the United Nations. pap. 4.95 (E. 80.1.8); pap. 4.95 (ISBN 92-1-100166-8). UN.

Pope John Paul II. Germany-Pilgrimage of Unity & Peace. 1981. 6.00 (ISBN 0-8198-3013-5); pap. 5.00 (ISBN 0-8198-3014-3). Dghtrs St Paul.

Porter, A. Kingsley. Romanesque Sculpture of the Pilgrimage Roads, 10 Vols. in 3. LC 67-4262. (Illus.). 1986. Repr. of 1923 ed. 250.00 set (ISBN 0-87817-020-0). Hacker.

Roos, Richard. Christwalk. 208p. (Orig.). 1985. pap. 7.95 (ISBN 0-8091-2667-2). Paulist Pr.

Scheuerman, Richard D. Pilgrims on the Earth. 165p. 1976. 12.00 (ISBN 0-87770-128-8). Ye Galleon.

Sheridan, John V. Tourist in His Footsteps. LC 79-53024. (Presence Ser., Vol. 1). (Orig.). 1979. pap. 2.95 (ISBN 0-89003-034-0). Undena Pubns.

Statler, Oliver. Japanese Pilgrimage. (Illus.). 352p. 1985. pap. 9.95 (ISBN 0-688-04834-X, Quill). Morrow.

Turner, Victor & Turner, Edith. Image & Pilgrimage in Christian Culture. LC 77-25442. (Lectures on the History of Religions Ser.). 1978. 25.00x (ISBN 0-231-04286-8). Columbia U Pr.

Tylenda, Joseph N., tr. & intro. by. A Pilgrim's Journey: The Autobiography of Ignatius of Loyola. 1985. pap. 8.95 (ISBN 0-89453-468-8). M Glazier.

Works, John A., Jr. Pilgrims in a Strange Land: Hausa Communities in Chad. LC 76-23138. 1976. 32.00x (ISBN 0-231-03976-X). Columbia U Pr.

PINCKNEY, THOMAS, 1750-1828

Cross, Jack L. London Mission: The First Critical Years. x, 180p. 1969. 6.00 (ISBN 0-87013-128-1). Mich St U Pr.

PIO DA PIETRELCINA, FATHER

Capuchin, John A. Padre Pio. 1983. 9.50 (ISBN 0-8199-0864-9). Franciscan Herald.

Carty, Charles M. Padre Pio: The Stigmatist. (Illus.). 1971. pap. 8.50 (ISBN 0-89555-054-7, 115). TAN Bks Pubs.

Parente, Pascal P. City on a Mountain - Padre Pio. Orig. Title: Padre Pio. 154p. 1968. pap. 3.50 (ISBN 0-911988-35-1). AMI Pr.

Ruffin, C. Bernard. Padre Pio: The True Story. LC 81-81525. (Illus.). 348p. (Orig.). 1982. pap. 8.95 (ISBN 0-87973-673-9, 673). Our Sunday Visitor.

Schug, John A. A Padre Pio Profile. (Orig.). 1987. pap. 4.95 (ISBN 0-932506-56-9). St Bedes Pubns.

White, Laura C., tr. Who Is Padre Pio? (Illus.). 44p. 1974. pap. 1.00 (ISBN 0-89555-101-2). TAN Bks Pubs.

PIUS 5TH, POPE, 1504-1572

Anderson, Robin. St. Pius V - A Brief Account of His Life, Times, Virtues & Miracles. LC 78-55637. 1978. pap. 2.50 (ISBN 0-89555-068-7). TAN Bks Pubs.

PIUS 6TH, POPE, 1717-1799

Olf, Lillian. Their Name Is Pius. LC 74-107729. (Essay Index Reprint Ser). 1941. 27.50 (ISBN 0-8369-1768-5). Ayer Co Pubs.

PIUS 7TH, POPE, 1742-1823

O'Dwyer, Margaret M. The Papacy in the Age of Napoleon & the Restoration: Pius VII, 1800-1823. 296p. (Orig.). 1985. lib. bdg. 24.00 (ISBN 0-8191-4825-3); pap. text ed. 12.75 (ISBN 0-8191-4826-1). U Pr of Amer.

Olf, Lillian. Their Name Is Pius. LC 74-107729. (Essay Index Reprint Ser). 1941. 27.50 (ISBN 0-8369-1768-5). Ayer Co Pubs.

PIUS 9TH, POPE, 1792-1878

Coppa, Frank J. Pope Pius IX. (World Leaders Ser.). 1979. lib. bdg. 15.95 (ISBN 0-8057-7727-X, Twayne). G K Hall.

Olf, Lillian. Their Name Is Pius. LC 74-107729. (Essay Index Reprint Ser). 1941. 27.50 (ISBN 0-8369-1768-5). Ayer Co Pubs.

PIUS 10TH, SAINT, POPE, 1835-1914

Olf, Lillian. Their Name Is Pius. LC 74-107729. (Essay Index Reprint Ser). 1941. 27.50 (ISBN 0-8369-1768-5). Ayer Co Pubs.

Smit, John. Saint Pius the Tenth. 1965. 4.00 (ISBN 0-8198-0140-2); pap. 3.00 (ISBN 0-8198-0141-0). Dghtrs St Paul.

PIUS 11TH, POPE, 1857-1939

Anderson, Robin. Between Two Wars: The Story of Pope Pius XI. 1978. 7.95 (ISBN 0-8199-0687-5). Franciscan Herald.

Bruehl, Charles P. The Pope's Plan for Social Reconstruction. 10.00 (ISBN 0-8159-6507-9). Devin.

Olf, Lillian. Their Name Is Pius. LC 74-107729. (Essay Index Reprint Ser). 1941. 27.50 (ISBN 0-8369-1768-5). Ayer Co Pubs.

PIUS 12TH, POPE, 1876-1958

O'Carroll, Michael. Pius XII: Greatness Dishonoured. 252p. 1980. 10.00 (ISBN 0-912414-41-3). Lumen Christi.

Taylor, Myron, ed. Wartime Correspondence: Between President Roosevelt & Pope Pius 12th. (FDR & the Era of the New Deal Ser). 1975. Repr. of 1947 ed. lib. bdg. 22.50 (ISBN 0-306-70709-8). Da Capo.

PIUS 12TH, POPE, 1876-1958–DRAMA

Hochhuth, Rolf. The Deputy. Winston, Richard & Winston, Clara, trs. from Ger. 1963. pap. 7.95 (ISBN 0-394-17125-X, B154, BC). Grove.

PLACE, FRANCIS, 1771-1854

Wallas, Graham. Life of Francis Place. 1898. 21.00 (ISBN 0-8337-3674-4). B Franklin.

PLAIN CHANT

see Chants (Plain, Gregorian, etc.)

PLAINSONG

see Chants (Plain, Gregorian, etc.)

PLATO, 427?-347 B.C.

Davison, William T. Mystics & Poets. LC 77-924. 1977. lib. bdg. 25.00 (ISBN 0-8414-3680-0). Folcroft.

Despland, Michel. The Education of Desire: Plato & the Philosophy of Religion. 400p. 1985. 25.00 (ISBN 0-8020-6524-4). U of Toronto Pr.

Eckstein, Jerome. The Deathday of Socrates: Living, Dying & Immortality-The Theater of Ideas in Plato's "Phaedo". 1981. 17.95 (ISBN 0-914366-19-X); pap. 12.95 (ISBN 0-914366-20-3). Vanguard.

Eros & Psyche: Studies in Plato, Plotinus & Origen. LC 66-627. (Phoenix Supplementary Ser.: No. 6). pap. 63.50 (ISBN 0-317-08094-6, 2019201). Bks Demand UMI.

Feibleman, James K. Religious Platonism. LC 78-161628. 236p. Repr. of 1959 ed. lib. bdg. 22.50x (ISBN 0-8371-6184-3, FERP). Greenwood.

Franck, Adolf. The Kabbalah & the Philosophy of Plato. (Illus.). 81p. 1986. 98.85 (ISBN 0-89901-288-4). Found Class Reprints.

Greville, Brooke R. The Nature of Truth, It's Union & Unity with the Soule. 210p. Repr. of 1640 ed. text ed. 33.12x (ISBN 0-576-02144-X, Pub. by Gregg Intl Pubs England). Gregg Intl.

Griswold, Charles L., Jr. Self-Knowledge in Plato's Phaedrus. LC 86-5506. 328p. 1986. text ed. 29.50x (ISBN 0-300-03594-2). Yale U Pr.

Gysi, Lydia. Platonism & Cartesianism in the Philosophy of Ralph Cudworth. 163p. 1962. 14.35 (ISBN 3-261-00648-X). P Lang Pubs.

Harris, W. T. The Mythology of Plato & Dante & the Future Life. (The Essential Library of the Great Philosophers). (Illus.). 107p. 1983. Repr. of 1896 ed. 71.85 (ISBN 0-89901-091-1). Found Class Reprints.

Jaspers, Karl. Plato & Augustine: Taken from Vol. 1 of the Great Philosophers. Manheim, Karl, tr. LC 67-38117. Orig. Title: Great Philosophers, Vol 1 (Pt. 2) 1966. pap. 4.95 (ISBN 0-15-672035-3, Harv). HarBraceJ.

Miller, Mitchell H., Jr. Plato's "Parmenides". The "Conversion" of the Soul. LC 85-43301. 264p. 1986. 30.00x (ISBN 0-691-07303-1). Princeton U PR.

More, P. E. Religion of Plato. (Greek Tradition: Vol. 1). Repr. of 1921 ed. 22.00 (ISBN 0-527-64950-3). Kraus Repr.

Morrow, Glenn R. & Dillion, John M. Proclus' Commentary on Plato's "Parmenides". LC 85-43302. 712p. 1986. text ed. 80.00x (ISBN 0-691-07305-8). Princeton U Pr.

Novak, David. Suicide & Morality: The Theories of Plato, Aquinas & Kant & Their Relevance for Suicidology. LC 75-37543. x, 136p. 1976. lib. bdg. 7.50 (ISBN 0-685-69079-2). Scholars Studies.

O'Connell, Robert J. An Introduction to Plato's Metaphysics. LC 84-73309. xii, 235p. 1985. pap. 6.25 (ISBN 0-8232-1132-0). Fordham.

Paramananda, Swami. Plato & Vedic Idealism. (Orig.). 1924. 4.50 (ISBN 0-911564-15-2). Vedanta Ctr.

Post, Levi A. The Vatican Plato & Its Relations. (APA Philological Monographs). 22.50 (ISBN 0-89130-704-4, 40-00-04). Scholars Pr GA.

Prior, William J. Unity & Development in Plato's Metaphysics. LC 85-5073. 202p. 1985. 24.95 (ISBN 0-8126-9000-1). Open Court.

Proclus. The Platonic Theology, Vol. II: Bks IV-VI. rev. ed. Navon, Robert, ed. Taylor, Thomas, tr. from Gr. LC 84-52789. (Great Works of Philosophy: Vol. II). Tr. of The Six Books of Proclus on the Theology of Plato. 292p. 1986. text ed. 35.00 (ISBN 0-933601-05-0); pap. text ed. 22.50 (ISBN 0-933601-06-9). Selene Bks.

--The Platonic Theology: Vol. 1 - Books I-III. Rev. ed. Navon, Robert, ed. Taylor, Thomas, tr. from Greek. (Great Works of Philosophy Ser.: Vol. I). xxvi, 222p. 1985. text ed. 35.00 (ISBN 0-9609866-7-7); pap. text ed. 22.50 (ISBN 0-9609866-6-9). Selene Bks.

Rexine, John E. Religion in Plato & Cicero. LC 68-28581. 72p. Repr. of 1959 ed. lib. bdg. 22.50x (ISBN 0-8371-0198-0, RERP). Greenwood.

Robertson, W. On Christian Doctrine: Augustine. 1958. pap. text ed. write for info. (ISBN 0-02-402150-4). Macmillan.

Solmsen, Friedrich. Plato's Theology. 1942. 24.00 (ISBN 0-384-56600-6). Johnson Repr.

Tobin, Thomas H. Timaios of Locri, on the Nature of the World & the Soul. (Society of Biblical Literature, Texts & Translations Ser.: No. 26). 1985. 14.95 (ISBN 0-89130-767-2, 06 02 26); pap. 9.95 (ISBN 0-89130-742-7). Scholars Pr GA.

Versenyi, Laszlo. Holiness & Justice: An Interpretation of Plato's "Euthyphro". LC 81-43830. 164p. 1982. lib. bdg. 26.75 (ISBN 0-8191-2316-1); pap. text ed. 11.50 (ISBN 0-8191-2317-X). U Pr of Amer.

Vlastos, Gregory, ed. Plato Two: Ethics, Politics, & Philosophy of Art & Religion; a Collection of Critical Essays. LC 77-19103. (Modern Studies in Philosophy). 1978. text ed. 16.95 (ISBN 0-268-01530-9); pap. text ed. 8.95x (ISBN 0-268-01531-7). U of Notre Dame Pr.

Voegelin, Eric. Order & History, 4 vols. Incl. Vol. 1. Israel & Revelation. LC 56-11670. xxvi, 534p. 1956 (ISBN 0-8071-0818-9); Vol. 2. The World of the Polis. LC 57-11670. xvii, 390p. 1957 (ISBN 0-8071-0819-7); Vol. 3. Plato & Aristotle. LC 57-11670. xviii, 384p. 1957 (ISBN 0-8071-0820-0); Vol. 4. The Ecumenic Age. LC 56-11670. 1974 (ISBN 0-8071-0081-1). 19.95 ea. La State U Pr.

PLATONISTS

see also Neoplatonism

Miles, Leland. John Colet & the Platonic Tradition. LC 60-16716. 258p. 1961. 11.95 (ISBN 0-87548-005-5); pap. 6.95 (ISBN 0-87548-006-3). Open Court.

Patrides, C. A. Cambridge Platonists. (Stratford-Upon-Avon Library). 1969. 25.00x (ISBN 0-674-09125-6). Harvard U Pr.

Tarrant, Harold. Scepticism or Platonism: The Philosophy of the Fourth Academy. (Cambridge Classical Studies). 192p. 1985. 39.50 (ISBN 0-521-30191-2). Cambridge U Pr.

PLAYS, CHRISTMAS

see Christmas Plays

PLAYS, MEDIEVAL

see Drama, Medieval; Moralities; Mysteries and Miracle-Plays

PLOTINUS, d. 270 A.D.

Atkinson, M. J., ed. A Commentary on Plotinus: Emnead. (Classical & Philosophical Monographs: Vol. 1). 1983. 47.50x (ISBN 0-19-814719-8). Oxford U Pr.

Cox, Patricia. Biography in Late Antiquity: A Quest for the Holy Man. LC 82-4946. (The Transformation of the Classical Heritage Ser.: Vol. 5). 208p. 1983. text ed. 30.00x (ISBN 0-520-04612-9). U of Cal Pr.

Deck, John N. Nature, Contemplation, & the One: A Study in the Philosophy of Plotinus. LC 67-98055. pap. 36.30 (ISBN 0-317-08774-6, 2014184). Bks Demand UMI.

Eros & Psyche: Studies in Plato, Plotinus & Origen. LC 66-627. (Phoenix Supplementary Ser.: No. 6). pap. 63.50 (ISBN 0-317-08094-6, 2019201). Bks Demand UMI.

The Essential Plotinus: Representative Treatises from The Enneads. O'Brien, Elmer, tr. 236p. 1975. lib. bdg. 15.00 (ISBN 0-915144-10-7); pap. 4.95 (ISBN 0-915144-09-3). Hackett Pub.

Henry, P. Plotin & l'Occident: Firmicus Maternus, Marius Victorinus, Saint Augustin, et Macrobe. (Classical Studies Ser.). (Fr.). Repr. of 1934 ed. lib. bdg. 39.50x (ISBN 0-697-00039-7). Irvington.

Inge, W. R. The Religious Philosophy of Plotinus & Some Modern Philosophies of Religion. 1977. lib. bdg. 59.95 (ISBN 0-8490-2513-3). Gordon Pr.

Inge, William R. Philosophy of Plotinus: The Gifford Lectures at St. Andrews, 1917-1918, 2 Vols. 3rd ed. LC 68-8740. (Illus.). 1968. Repr. of 1929 ed. Set. lib. bdg. 67.50x (ISBN 0-8371-0113-1, INPP). Greenwood.

Marien, Bert. Bibliografica Critica Degli Studi Plotiniani: Con rassegna della loro recensioni. Cilento, V., ed. (Classical Studies Ser.). (Ital.). Repr. of 1949 ed. lib. bdg. 47.00x (ISBN 0-697-00043-5). Irvington.

Mead, G. R. Plotinus. 1983. pap. 5.95 (ISBN 0-916411-01-X, Pub. by Alexandrian Pr). Holmes Pub.

Plotinus. Opera: Enneades IV-V, Vol II. Schwyzer, H. R. & Henry, Paul, eds. (Oxford Classical Texts). 1977. 24.95x (ISBN 0-19-814582-9). Oxford U Pr.

--Plotinus: Essay on the Beautiful. Taylor, Thomas, tr. 1984. pap. 5.95 (ISBN 0-916411-86-9, Pub. by Alexandrian Pr). Holmes Pub.

Tripolitis, Antonia. The Doctrine of the Soul in the Thought of Plotinus & Origen. LC 76-16321. 1977. 6.95 (ISBN 0-87212-061-9). Libra.

Turnbull, Grace R., ed. The Essence of Plotinus: Extracts from the Six Enneads & Porphyry's Life of Plotinus. Mackenna, Stephen, tr. LC 76-40320. 1976. Repr. of 1934 ed. lib. bdg. 37.50x (ISBN 0-8371-9054-1, TUEP). Greenwood.

PLYMOUTH BRETHREN

Darby, J. N. Letters of J. N. Darby, 3 vols. Set. 18.95 (ISBN 0-88172-061-5); 6.95 ea. Believers Bkshelf.

Steele, Daniel. A Substitute for Holiness, Or Antinomianism Revived. (The Higher Christian Life Ser.). 370p. 1985. lib. bdg. 45.00 (ISBN 0-8240-6445-3). Garland Pub.

PNEUMA (WORD)

Bullinger, Ethelbert W. Word Studies on the Holy Spirit. LC 85-7631. 232p. 1985. pap. 7.95 (ISBN 0-8254-2246-9). Kregel.

PNEUMATOLOGY (THEOLOGY)

see Spirit

POETRY–COLLECTIONS

see also the poetry of specific nationalities, e.g. English poetry

Berrigan, Daniel. We Die Before We Live: Talking with the Very Ill. 160p. 1980. 11.95 (ISBN 0-8164-0462-3, HarpR). Har-Row.

Erasmus, Desiderius. The Praise of Folly. Miller, Clarence H., intro. by. LC 78-13575. 1979. text ed. 25.00 (ISBN 0-300-02279-4); pap. 7.95x (ISBN 0-300-02373-1). Yale U Pr.

Furnivall, Frederick J., ed. Political, Religious & Love Poems. 348p. 1981. Repr. of 1866 ed. lib. bdg. 75.00 (ISBN 0-89987-276-X). Darby Bks.

Kwiatkowski, Diana, ed. The Poet Pope. 67p. 1981. 9.50 (ISBN 0-933906-16-1); pap. 4.50 (ISBN 0-933906-15-3). Gusto Pr.

Levy, D. A., et al. Zen Concrete & Etc. (Illus.). 100p. 1987. pap. 10.00 (ISBN 0-941160-04-1). Ghost Pony Pr.

Parry, Betty, ed. The Unicorn & the Garden. LC 78-64531. (Illus.). 1978. perfect bdg. 10.00 (ISBN 0-915380-04-8). Word Works.

Pine, Edward, ed. The Pauline Muses. 355p. 1981. Repr. of 1947 ed. lib. bdg. 25.00 (ISBN 0-8495-4395-9). Arden Lib.

Reddy, T. J. Poems in One Part Harmony. 60p. 1980. pap. 4.00 (ISBN 0-932112-07-2). Carolina Wren.

Sachs, Michael. Die Religiose Poesie der Juden in Spanien. Katz, Steven, ed. LC 79-7150. (Jewish Philosophy, Mysticism & History of Ideas Ser.). 1980. Repr. of 1901 ed. lib. bdg. 37.00x (ISBN 0-405-12285-3). Ayer Co Pubs.

Schwartz, Howard & Rudolf, Anthony, eds. Voices Within the Ark. 1983. pap. 15.95 (ISBN 0-380-76109-2, 80119). Avon.

Trungpa, Chogyam. The Rain of Wisdom. Nalanda Translation Committee, tr. from Tibetan. LC 80-51130. Tr. of Bka'-Rgyud Mgur-Mtsho. 384p. 1985. pap. 18.95 (ISBN 0-87773-345-7, 73972-8). Shambhala Pubns.

White, Roger. Another Song, Another Season: Poems & Portrayals. 184p. 1979. cloth o.p. 4.00 (ISBN 0-85398-087-X); pap. 8.95 (ISBN 0-85398-088-8). G Ronald Pub.

Whitman, Ruth. An Anthology of Modern Yiddish Poetry. LC 66-25551. 141p. 1979. pap. 4.95 (ISBN 0-686-29291-X). Workmen's Circle.

POLAND–HISTORY

Dobroszycki, Lucjan & Kirshenblatt-Gimblett, Barbara. Image Before My Eyes: A Photographic History of Jewish Life in Poland, 1864-1939. LC 75-35448. (Illus.). 1977. 29.95 (ISBN 0-8052-3607-4). Schocken.

Heller, Celia. On the Edge of Destruction: Jews in Poland Between the Two World Wars. LC 76-22646. (Illus.). 1977. 36.00x (ISBN 0-231-03819-4). Columbia U Pr.

Pollard, Alfred F. Jesuits in Poland. LC 76-116799. (Studies in Philosophy, No. 40). 1970. Repr. of 1902 ed. lib. bdg. 39.95x (ISBN 0-8383-1041-9). Haskell.

Pomian-Srzednicki, Maciej. Religious Changes in Contemporary Poland: Secularization & Politics. (International Library of Sociology). 227p. 1982. 27.95x (ISBN 0-7100-9245-8). Methuen Inc.

Rebhun, Joseph. God & Man in Two Worlds. 1985. lib. bdg. 16.95 (ISBN 0-9614162-1-1). OR Pub.

Ringelblum, Emmanuel. Polish-Jewish Relations During the Second World War. Allon, Dafna, et al, trs. LC 76-1394. 330p. 1976. 35.00x (ISBN 0-86527-155-0). Fertig.

Tazbir, Janusz. A State Without Stakes: Religious Toleration in Reformation Poland. Jordan, A. T., tr. (Library of Polish Studies: Vol. 3). text ed. 4.00 (ISBN 0-917004-05-1). Kosciuszko.

POLARITY (IN RELIGION, FOLK-LORE, ETC.)

see also Blessing and Cursing; Good and Evil; Joy and Sorrow

Jehan, L. F. Dictionnaire des Controverses Historiques. Migne, J. P., ed. (Troisieme et Derniere Encyclopedie Theologique Ser.: Vol. 66). (Fr.). 698p. Repr. of 1866 ed. lib. bdg. 90.00x (ISBN 0-89241-329-8). Caratzas.

POLEMICS (THEOLOGY)

see Apologetics

POLITICAL DISABILITIES (GREAT BRITAIN)

see Catholic Emancipation; Dissenters, Religious–England

POLITICAL ETHICS

Bonino, Jose M. Toward a Christian Political Ethics. LC 82-48541. 144p. 1983. pap. 6.95 (ISBN 0-8006-1697-9, 1-1697). Fortress.

Fenton, Geoffrey. A Forme of Christian Pollicie. LC 78-38180. (English Experience Ser.: No. 454). 424p. 1972. Repr. of 1574 ed. 42.00 (ISBN 90-221-0454-0). Walter J Johnson.

Horwitz, Robert H., ed. The Moral Foundations of the American Republic. 3rd ed. LC 85-17772. (Kenyon Public Affairs Conference Center Ser.). xii, 347p. 1986. 25.00x (ISBN 0-8139-1081-1); pap. 5.95x (ISBN 0-8139-1082-X). U Pr of Va.

Mosse, George L. The Holy Pretence. LC 68-14552. 1968. 23.50x (ISBN 0-86527-099-6). Fertig.

Niebuhr, Reinhold. Moral Man & Immoral Society: A Study in Ethics & Politics. 1932. pap. 9.95 (ISBN 0-684-71857-X, ScribT). Scribner.

Russell, Bertrand. Human Society in Ethics & Politics. 1954. text ed. 18.50x (ISBN 0-04-172004-0). Allen Unwin.

St. Thomas Aquinas. Aquinas on Politics & Ethics. Sigmund, Paul e., ed. (Norton Critical Edition Ser.). pap. write for info. (ISBN 0-393-95243-6). Norton.

Srisang, Koson. Perspectives on Political Ethics: An Ecumenical Inquiry. 196p. 1983. pap. 8.95 (ISBN 0-87840-407-4). Georgetown U Pr.

POLITICAL SCIENCE–EARLY WORKS TO 1700

Fenton, Geoffrey. A Forme of Christian Pollicie. LC 78-38180. (English Experience Ser.: No. 454). 424p. 1972. Repr. of 1574 ed. 42.00 (ISBN 90-221-0454-0). Walter J Johnson.

Hill, Henry B., tr. Political Testament of Cardinal Richelieu: The Significant Chapters & Supporting Selections. (Illus.). 148p. 1961. 15.00x (ISBN 0-299-02420-2); pap. 8.95x (ISBN 0-299-02424-5). U of Wis Pr.

St. Thomas Aquinas. Political Ideas of St. Thomas Aquinas. Bigongiari, Dino, ed. (Library of Classics Ser.: No. 15). 1973. pap. text ed. 7.95x (ISBN 0-02-840380-0). Hafner.

Saint Augustine. Political Writings of St. Augustine. Paolucci, Henry, ed. 358p. pap. 5.95 (ISBN 0-89526-941-4). Regnery Bks.

Tomas, Andrew. Mirage of the Ages: A Critique of Christianity. 152p. 1983. 9.00 (ISBN 0-682-49999-4). Exposition Pr FL.

POLITICAL SCIENCE–HISTORY–INDIA

Coomaraswamy, Ananda K. Spiritual Authority & Temporal Power in the Indian Theory of Government. (Amer Oriental Soc Ser.). 1942. pap. 16.00 (ISBN 0-527-02696-4). Kraus Repr.

POLITICAL SCIENCE–HISTORY–ISLAMIC COUNTRIES

Evans-Pritchard, Edward E. The Political System of the Anuak of the Anglo-Egyptian Sudan. LC 74-15036. (London School of Economics & Political Science Monographs on Social Anthropology: No. 4). Repr. of 1940 ed. 27.50 (ISBN 0-404-12041-5). AMS Pr.

POLITICAL SCIENCE–HISTORY–UNITED STATES

Berlin, William S. On the Edge of Politics: The Roots of Jewish Political Thought in America. (Contributions in Political Science Ser.: No. 14). 1978. lib. bdg. 29.95x (ISBN 0-313-20422-5, BEP/). Greenwood.

Bishirjian, Richard. The Nature of Public Philosophy. LC 82-20170. 62p. 1983. pap. text ed. 4.75 (ISBN 0-8191-2861-9). U Pr of Amer.

Power, M. Susan. Before the Convention: Religion & the Founders. LC 84-12004. 268p. (Orig.). 1984. lib. bdg. 26.25 (ISBN 0-8191-4133-X); pap. text ed. 13.25 (ISBN 0-8191-4134-8). U Pr of Amer.

POLITICS AND CHRISTIANITY

see Christianity and Politics

POLITICS AND RELIGION

see Religion and Politics

POLYGAMY

see also Mormons and Mormonism

Badawi, G. A. Polygamy in Islamic Law. pap. 1.00 (ISBN 0-686-18440-8). Kazi Pubns.

Deer, John. Bigamy, Polygamy & Polyandry: A Comprehensive Bibliography. 108p. (Orig.). 1986. pap. 11.95 (ISBN 0-940519-08-9). Res Discover Pubns.

Hitchens, Robert J. Multiple Marriage: A Study of Polygamy in Light of the Bible. LC 86-72269. 160p. (Orig.). 1987. pap. 6.95 (ISBN 0-9617379-1-3). Doulos Pubs.

Solomon, Dorothy A. In My Father's House. LC 84-11964. 312p. 1984. 17.95 (ISBN 0-531-09763-3). Watts.

Van Wagoner, Richard S. Mormon Polygamy: A History. 275p. 1985. 19.95 (ISBN 0-941214-35-4). Signature Bks.

Young, Ann E. Wife Number Nineteen: The Story of a Life in Bondage, Being a Complete Expose of Mormonism, & Revealing the Sorrows, Sacrifices & Sufferings of Women in Polygamy. LC 72-2634. (American Women Ser: Images & Realities). (Illus.). 632p. 1972. Repr. of 1875 ed. 36.50 (ISBN 0-405-04488-7). Ayer Co Pubs.

POLYNESIA

Buck, Peter H. Anthropology & Religion. LC 72-121753. viii, 96p. 1970. Repr. of 1939 ed. 16.00 (ISBN 0-208-00950-7, Archon). Shoe String.

Coppell, William & Flores, Bess, eds. Bibliography of the Cook Islands. 1982. cancelled. Inst Polynesian.

POLYNESIA–SOCIAL LIFE AND CUSTOMS

Buck, Peter H. Anthropology & Religion. LC 72-121753. viii, 96p. 1970. Repr. of 1939 ed. 16.00 (ISBN 0-208-00950-7, Archon). Shoe String.

Handy, E. S. Polynesian Religion. (Bayard Dominick Expedition Publication Ser: No. 12). Repr. of 1927 ed. 56.00 (ISBN 0-527-02137-7). Kraus Repr.

Williamson, Robert W. Religion & Social Organization in Central Polynesia. Piddington, Ralph, ed. LC 75-35218. Repr. of 1937 ed. 38.00 (ISBN 0-404-14241-9). AMS Pr.

--Religious & Cosmic Beliefs of Central Polynesia, 2 vols. LC 75-35220. Repr. of 1933 ed. Set. 87.50 (ISBN 0-404-14300-8). AMS Pr.

POOR

see also Charities; Population

Benjamin, Dick & Richardson, Jim. Remember the Poor. 1982. pap. 1.75 (ISBN 0-911739-26-2). Abbott Loop.

Pilgrim, Walter E. Good News to the Poor: Wealth & Poverty in Luke-Acts. LC 81-65653. 208p. (Orig.). 1981. pap. 10.95 (ISBN 0-8066-1889-2, 10-2807). Augsburg.

Sider, Ronald J. Cry Justice: The Bible Speaks on Hunger & Poverty. LC 80-82133. 224p. 1980. pap. 3.95 (ISBN 0-8091-2308-8). Paulist Pr.

Tuckerman, Joseph. On the Elevation of the Poor: A Selection from His Reports As Minister at Large in Boston. LC 79-137190. (Poverty U. S. A. Historical Record Ser). 1971. Repr. of 1874 ed. 15.00 (ISBN 0-405-03128-9). Ayer Co Pubs.

POOR CLARES

Koester, Camilla. Into This Land: Centennial History of the Cleveland Poor Clare Monastery of the Blessed Sacrament. LC 80-83390. (Illus.). 274p. 1981. 8.95 (ISBN 0-934906-28-9). R J Liederbach.

Mary Francis, Sr. Right to Be Merry. LC 73-6850. 1973. pap. 6.50 (ISBN 0-8199-0506-2). Franciscan Herald.

POOR PRIESTS

see Lollards

POOR SOULS IN PURGATORY, PRAYERS FOR THE

see Prayers for the Dead

POPES

see also Conciliar Theory; Papacy

Anderson, Robin. Between Two Wars: The Story of Pope Pius XI. 1978. 7.95 (ISBN 0-8199-0687-5). Franciscan Herald.

Bander, Peter. The Prophecies of St. Malachy & St. Columbkille. 3rd ed. 1979. pap. text ed. 6.95x (ISBN 0-901072-10-9). Humanities.

Baum, Gregory. The Priority of Labor: A Commentary on "Laborem Exercens", Encyclical Letter of Pope John Paul II. 112p. 1982. pap. 5.95 (ISBN 0-8091-2479-3). Paulist Pr.

Campano, Giovanni. Antonio: Opera Omnia. 608p. 1495. Repr. of 1495 ed. text ed. 99.36 (ISBN 0-576-72225-1, Pub. by Gregg Intl Pubs England). Gregg Intl.

Carrere, Jean. The Pope: An Analysis of the Office of the Pope & the Roman Church & City. 1977. lib. bdg. 59.95 (ISBN 0-8490-2453-6). Gordon Pr.

Cowdrey, H. E. Popes, Monks & Crusaders. (No. 27). 400p. 1983. 40.00 (ISBN 0-907628-34-6). Hambledon Press.

Daughters of St. Paul. Karol from Poland. write for info. Dghtrs St Paul.

Degrelle, Leon. Letter to the Pope on His Visit to Auschwitz. 1982. lib. bdg. 59.95 (ISBN 0-87700-346-7). Revisionist Pr.

De Syrmia, Edmond. At the Head of Nations: The Rise of the Papal & Princely House of Odescalchi. LC 76-44029. (Illus.). 116p. 1978. 10.00 (ISBN 0-914226-05-3). Cyclopedia.

Halliwell, William J. The Style of Pope St. Leo the Great, No. 59. (Patristic Studies). 114p. 1984. 26.00x (ISBN 0-939738-25-2). Zubal Inc.

Isho, Anan. Stories of the Holy Fathers, 2 vols. Budge, E. A., tr. 1980. Set. lib. bdg. 125.00 (ISBN 0-8490-3195-8). Gordon Pr.

The Jewish Problem as Dealt with by the Popes. 1982. lib. bdg. 59.95 (ISBN 0-87700-344-0). Revisionist Pr.

Kelly, J. N. The Oxford Dictionary of Popes. LC 85-15599. 450p. 1986. 24.95 (ISBN 0-19-213964-9). Oxford U Pr.

Kuhner, Hans. Dictionnaire des Papes. (Fr.). pap. 6.95 (ISBN 0-686-56856-7, M-6634). French & Eur.

Loomis, Louise R., tr. Book of the Popes. 1965. lib. bdg. 19.50x (ISBN 0-374-95093-8, Octagon). Hippocrene Bks.

McCabe, Joseph. The Pope & the Italian Jackal. 31p. pap. cancelled (ISBN 0-911826-88-2). Am Atheist.

--The Pope Helps Hitler to World Power. 30p. pap. cancelled (ISBN 0-911826-87-4). Am Atheist.

Macdonald, Allan J. Hildebrand: A Life of Gregory the Seventh. (Great Medieval Churchmen Ser.). 254p. 1977. Repr. of 1932 ed. lib. bdg. 17.50x (ISBN 0-915172-26-7). Richwood Pub.

Maras, Raymond J. Innocent XI, Pope of Christian Unity. (The Church & the World Ser.). xiv, 356p. 1984. 42.85x (ISBN 0-317-52635-9); lib. bdg. 42.85x. Cross Cultural Pubns.

O'Dwyer, Margaret M. The Papacy in the Age of Napoleon & the Restoration: Pius VII, 1800-1823. 296p. (Orig.). 1985. lib. bdg. 24.00 (ISBN 0-8191-4825-3); pap. text ed. 12.75 (ISBN 0-8191-4826-1). U Pr of Amer.

Pope John Paul II. The Far East Journey of Peace & Brotherhood. write for info. Dghtrs St Paul.

Sullivan, George. Pope John Paul II: The People's Pope. LC 83-40395. (Illus.). 120p. 1984. 11.95 (ISBN 0-8027-6523-8). Walker & Co.

Thibault, Paul R. Pope Gregory XI: The Failure of Tradition. 252p. 1986. lib. bdg. 26.50 (ISBN 0-8191-5462-8); pap. text ed. 12.75 (ISBN 0-8191-5463-6). U Pr of Amer.

Walsh, James J. The Popes & Science. 1977. lib. bdg. 59.95 (ISBN 0-8490-2454-4). Gordon Pr.

POPES–HISTORY

see Papacy–History

POPES–INFALLIBILITY

see also Catholic Church–Infallibility; Conciliar Theory

Empie, Paul C., et al, eds. Teaching Authority & Infallibility in the Church, No. 6. LC 79-54109. (Lutherans & Catholics in Dialogue). 352p. (Orig.). 1979. pap. 8.95 (ISBN 0-8066-1733-0, 10-6222). Augsburg.

Makrakis, Apostolos. A Scriptural Refutation of the Pope's Primacy. Cummings, Denver, tr. from Hellenic. 171p. (Orig.). 1952. pap. 3.75x (ISBN 0-938366-40-8). Orthodox Chr.

Ryan, Alvan, ed. Newman & Gladstone: The Vatican Decrees. 1962. 13.95 (ISBN 0-268-00190-1). U of Notre Dame Pr.

Tekippe, Terry J., ed. Papal Infallibility: An Application of Lonergan's Theological Method. LC 82-23837. 416p. (Orig.). 1983. lib. bdg. 34.50 (ISBN 0-8191-2995-X); pap. text ed. 17.75 o. p. (ISBN 0-8191-2996-8). U Pr of Amer.

Tierney, B. Origins of Papal Infallibility 1150-1350. 1972. 45.00. Heinman.

POPES–PRIMACY

see also Bishops; Councils and Synods

Empie, Paul C., et al, eds. Papal Primacy & the Universal Church. LC 74-83329. 1974. pap. 7.95 (ISBN 0-8066-1450-1, 10-4870). Augsburg.

Makrakis, Apostolos. A Scriptural Refutation of the Pope's Primacy. Cummings, Denver, tr. from Hellenic. 171p. (Orig.). 1952. pap. 3.75x (ISBN 0-938366-40-8). Orthodox Chr.

POPES–TEMPORAL POWER

see also Church and State; Roman Question

Friedlander, Saul. Pius XII & the Third Reich. LC 80-12830. 238p. 1980. Repr. of 1966 ed. lib. bdg. 21.50x (ISBN 0-374-92930-0, Octagon). Hippocrene Bks.

POPISH PLOT, 1678

Greene, Douglas, ed. Diaries of the Popish Plot. LC 77-938. 1977. 50.00x (ISBN 0-8201-1288-7). Schol Facsimiles.

Hibbard, Caroline M. Charles I & the Popish Plot. LC 81-23075. ix, 342p. 1983. 30.00x (ISBN 0-8078-1520-9). U of NC Pr.

McHenry, Robert, ed. Contexts: Absalom & Achitophel. LC 84-24160. (Contexts Ser.: No. 3). (Illus.). xiv, 296p. 1986. lib. bdg. 29.50 (ISBN 0-208-01845-X, Archon Bks). Shoe String.

POPULATION

see also Birth Control

also subdivision Population under names of countries, cities, etc., e.g. United States–Population

Bayles, Michael D. Morality & Population Policy. LC 79-23965. 208p. 1980. 15.75 (ISBN 0-8173-0032-5); pap. text ed. 7.50 (ISBN 0-8173-0033-3). U of Ala Pr.

Callahan, Daniel. Ethics & Population Limitation. LC 78-155736. 45p. (Orig.). 1971. pap. text ed. 3.95 (ISBN 0-87834-002-5). Population Coun.

Clark, Colin. The Myth of Over-Population. 133p. 1975. pap. 3.50 (ISBN 0-912414-26-X). Lumen Christi.

--Population. 30p. 1974. pap. 0.50 (ISBN 0-912414-19-7). Lumen Christi.
Hardin, Garrett, ed. Population, Evolution, & Birth Control: A Collection of Controversial Ideas. 2nd ed. LC 69-16921. (Biology Ser.). (Illus.). 386p. 1969. pap. text ed. 13.95x (ISBN 0-7167-0670-9). W H Freeman.
Reining, Priscilla & Tinker, Irene, eds. Population: Dynamics, Ethics & Policy. 1975. pap. 19.00 (ISBN 0-12-586751-4). Acad Pr.
Wogaman, Philip J., ed. Population Crisis & Moral Responsibility. 1973. 15.00 (ISBN 0-8183-0146-5). Pub Aff Pr.

PORNOGRAPHY
Gallagher, Neil. The Porno Plague. LC 77-21992. (Illus.). 256p. 1977. pap. 5.95 (ISBN 0-87123-231-6, 210231). Bethany Hse.
Kirk, Jerry. The Mind Polluters. 224p. 1985. pap. 6.95 (ISBN 0-8407-5965-7). Nelson.
Mishan, E. J. Making the World Safe for Pornography. LC 73-83001. 262p. 1973. 1.95 (ISBN 0-912050-41-1, Library Pr). Open Court.

PORNOGRAPHY–RELIGIOUS ASPECTS
Minnery, Tom, ed. Pornography: A Human Tragedy. 350p. 1986. pap. 14.95 (ISBN 0-8423-4947-2). Tyndale.
Tanner, Paul A. Call to Righteousness. 1984. pap. 0.75 (ISBN 0-87162-404-4, D3012). Warner Pr.

PORT ROYAL
Clark, Ruth. Strangers & Sojourners at Port Royal. 1972. lib. bdg. 26.00x (ISBN 0-374-91664-0, Octagon). Hippocrene Bks.
De Sainte-Beuve, Charles-Augustin. Port-Royal, 3 tomes. 1953-1955. Set. 79.95 (ISBN 0-685-11502-X). French & Eur.
Pascal, Blaise. Les Provinciales. 1966. 4.95 (ISBN 0-686-54852-3). French & Eur.
Saint-Beuve. Port Royal, 3 vols. Vol. 1. 37.50 (ISBN 0-686-56564-9); Vol. 2. 37.50 (ISBN 0-686-56565-7); Vol. 3. 35.95 (ISBN 0-686-56566-5). French & Eur.

POSITIVISM
see also Agnosticism; Idealism
Harrison, Frederic. Positive Evolution of Religion. facs. ed. LC 74-142641. (Essay Index Reprint Ser). 1913. 18.00 (ISBN 0-8369-2053-8). Ayer Co Pubs.
Schuller, Robert H. Discover Freedom. (Orig.). 1978. pap. 1.25 (ISBN 0-89081-155-5). Harvest Hse.
--Discover How Tou Can Turn Activity into Energy. (Orig.). 1978. pap. 1.25 (ISBN 0-89081-135-0). Harvest Hse.
--Discover Self-Love. (Orig.). 1978. pap. 1.25 (ISBN 0-89081-134-2). Harvest Hse.
--Discover Your Possibilities. (Orig.). 1980. pap. 3.95 (ISBN 0-89081-214-4). Harvest Hse.

POSSESSION, DEMONIAC
see Demoniac Possession

POSTEL, GUILLAUME, 1510-1581
Bouwsma, William J. Concordia Mundi: The Career & Thought of Guillaume Postel, 1510-1581. LC 57-8622. (Historical Monographs Ser: No. 33). 1957. 22.50x (ISBN 0-674-15950-0). Harvard U Pr.
Butler, Geoffrey. Studies in Statecraft. LC 79-110899. 1970. Repr. of 1920 ed. 17.00x (ISBN 0-8046-0882-2, Pub. by Kennikat). Assoc Faculty Pr.

POTSHERDS (OSTRAKA)
see Ostraka

POVERTY
see also Charities; Poor
Hartman, Robert H., ed. Poverty & Economic Justice: A Philosophical Approach. 1984. pap. 10.95 (ISBN 0-8091-2597-8). Paulist Pr.
Paget, Wilkes M. Poverty, Revolution & the Church. 142p. (Orig.). 1982. pap. text ed. 10.95 (ISBN 0-85364-285-0). Attic Pr.
Stegemann, Wolfgang. The Gospel & the Poor. Elliott, Dietlinde, tr. from Ger. LC 83-48915. 80p. 1984. pap. 3.95 (ISBN 0-8006-1783-5, 1-1783). Fortress.
Tuckerman, Joseph. On the Elevation of the Poor: A Selection from His Reports As Minister at Large in Boston. LC 79-137190. (Poverty U. S. A. Historical Record Ser). 1971. Repr. of 1874 ed. 15.00 (ISBN 0-405-03128-9). Ayer Co Pubs.
Ward, Barbara. World Poverty, Can It Be Solved. pap. 0.75 (ISBN 0-8199-0394-9, L39010). Franciscan Herald.

POVERTY (VIRTUE)
Dubay, Thomas. Happy Are You Poor. 5.95 (ISBN 0-87193-141-9). Dimension Bks.
George, Augustine, et al. Gospel Poverty: Essays in Biblical Theology. Guinan, Michael D., tr. LC 76-44548. 167p. 1977. 6.95 (ISBN 0-8199-0610-7). Franciscan Herald.
Sill, Sterling W. The Power of Poetry. LC 83-83267. 141p. 1984. 7.95 (ISBN 0-88290-238-5). Horizon Utah.

POWER (THEOLOGY)
see also Authority (Religion)
Campolo, Anthony, Jr. The Power Delusion. 168p. 1983. pap. 5.95 (ISBN 0-88207-292-7). Victor Bks.
Edwards, F. Henry. The Power That Worketh in Us. 1987. pap. 16.00 (ISBN 0-8309-0481-6). Herald Hse.
McCarthy, Estelle & McCarthy, Charles. The Power Picture. (Orig.). 1973. pap. 1.95 (ISBN 0-377-03031-7). Friend Pr.
Migliore, Daniel L. The Power of God. LC 82-20037. (Library of Living Faith Ser.: Vol. 8). 116p. (Orig.). 1983. pap. 5.95 (ISBN 0-664-24454-8). Westminster.
Sherwood, John R. & Wagner, John C. Sources & Shapes of Power. LC 80-28125. (Into Our Third Century Ser.). (Orig.). 1981. pap. 3.95 (ISBN 0-687-39142-3). Abingdon.
Tassell, Paul. Pathways to Power: Keys That Open Doors. LC 83-9576. 1983. pap. 3.95 (ISBN 0-87227-093-9). Reg Baptist.

POWERS (THEOLOGY)
see Spirits

PRAISE
Carothers, Merlin R. Answers to Praise. 169p. (Orig.). 1972. pap. 4.95 (ISBN 0-943026-07-5). Carothers.
--The Bible on Praise. 32p. (Orig.). 1981. pap. 2.25 (ISBN 0-943026-03-2). Carothers.
--Bringing Heaven into Hell. 120p. (Orig.). 1976. pap. 4.95 (ISBN 0-943026-10-5). Carothers.
--Power in Praise. 143p. 1972. pap. 4.95 (ISBN 0-943026-01-6). Carothers.
--Praise Works. 161p. (Orig.). 1973. pap. 4.95. Carothers.
--Prison to Praise. 106p. (Orig.). 1970. pap. 2.95 (ISBN 0-943026-02-4). Carothers.
--Prison to Praise: Giant Print. 106p. (Orig.). 1970. pap. 3.95 (ISBN 0-943026-08-3). Carothers.
--Victory on Praise Mountain. 175p. (Orig.). 1979. pap. 4.95 (ISBN 0-943026-04-0). Carothers.
--Walking & Leaping. 129p. (Orig.). 1974. pap. 4.95 (ISBN 0-943026-05-9). Carothers.
Collingridge, Ruth & Sekowsky, JoAnne. Introduction to Praise. (Workbook Ser.). (Orig.). 1981. pap. 4.95 (ISBN 0-930756-60-6, 581001). Aglow Pubns.
Cornwall, Judson. Let Us Praise: A Prominent Charismatic Leader Tells How & Why to Praise God. LC 73-75957. 1973. pap. 4.95 (ISBN 0-88270-039-1). Bridge Pub.
Gossett, Don. I'm Sold on Being Bold. 1979. pap. 2.25 (ISBN 0-88368-085-8). Whitaker Hse.
--Praise Avenue. 128p. 1976. pap. 3.50 (ISBN 0-88368-059-9). Whitaker Hse.
--There's Dynamite in Praise. rev. ed. 1974. pap. 3.50 (ISBN 0-88368-048-3). Whitaker Hse.
Haas, James E. Praise the Lord! LC 74-80388. 1974. pap. 3.95 (ISBN 0-8192-1176-1). Morehouse.
Herbert, Janet. ABC's of Praise. (Sparkler Bks.). (Illus.). 32p. 1986. plastic comb bdg. 2.95 (ISBN 0-89191-926-0, 59261, Chariot Bks). Cook.
Larson, Muriel. Praise Every Day. 135p. 1984. 10.95 (ISBN 0-910311-11-0). Huntington Hse Inc.
Osbeck, Kenneth W. Junior's Praise. LC 57-1012. 184p. 1981. 5.95x (ISBN 0-8254-3400-9). Kregel.
Swanson, James R. & Tanner, Don. The Invincible Power of Praise. LC 86-19151. (Illus.). 64p. 1986. pap. 2.95 (ISBN 0-88005-004-7). Uplift Bks.

PRAJNAPARAMITAS
Conze, Edward. The Short Prajnaparamita Texts. 217p. 1973. 35.00x (ISBN 0-317-39153-4, Pub. by Luzac & Co Ltd). State Mutual Bk.
Obermiller, E. The Doctrine of Prajna-Paramita As Exposed in the Abhisamayalamkara of Maitreya. 153p. 1984. Repr. of 1932 ed. lib. bdg. 19.50x (ISBN 0-88181-002-9). Canon Pubns.

PRAYER
see also Contemplation; Devotional Exercises; Meditation; Prayers; Retreats
Abhishiktananda. Prayer. LC 73-600. 88p. 1973. pap. 3.95 (ISBN 0-664-24973-6). Westminster.
Agape Ministries Staff. Prayer Life. (Orig.). 1984. pap. 3.50 (ISBN 0-89274-346-8). Harrison Hse.
Aglow Editors. Aglow Prayer Diary I. 226p. 1982. 10.95 (ISBN 0-930756-70-3). Aglow Pubns.
Al-Abidin, Zayn. Supplication: Makarim al-Akhlaq. Chittick, William C., tr. 30p. 1984. pap. 3.95 (ISBN 0-940368-45-5). Tahrike Tarsile Quran.
Alberione, James. Pray Always. 1966. 4.00 (ISBN 0-8198-0126-7); pap. 3.00 (ISBN 0-8198-0127-5). Dghtrs St Paul.
Allen, Charles L. All Things Are Possible Through Prayer. 1984. pap. 2.95 (ISBN 0-515-08808-0, PV072). Jove Pubns.
--All Things Are Possible Through Prayer. o. p. 7.95 (ISBN 0-8007-0007-4); pap. 2.95 (ISBN 0-8007-8000-0, Spire Bks). Revell.
Allen, Charles L. & Rice, Helen S. The Prayerful Heart. 160p. (Orig.). 1981. pap. 5.95 (ISBN 0-8007-5073-X, Power Bks). Revell.
Appleton, George, ed. The Oxford Book of Prayer. 416p. 1985. 22.95 (ISBN 0-19-213222-9). Oxford U Pr.
Austin, Bill. How to Get What You Pray For. LC 83-50970. 160p. 1984. pap. 4.95 (ISBN 0-8423-1473-3); leader's guide 2.95 (ISBN 0-8423-1474-1). Tyndale.
Azcar. How to Talk Directly with God. 51p. 1977. pap. 1.95 (ISBN 0-931865-05-0). Psychegenics.
Baelz, Peter. Does God Answer Prayer? (Illus.). 122p. (Orig.). 1983. pap. 6.95 (ISBN 0-87243-117-7). Templegate.
Baker, Pat & Marshall, Mary R. More Simulation Games. (Youth Work Guide Ser.). (Illus.). 88p. (Orig.). 1977. pap. 7.95 (ISBN 0-85819-194-6, Pub. by JBCE). ANZ Religious Pubns.
Barth, Karl. Prayer. 2nd ed. Saliers, Don E., ed. Terrien, Sara F., tr. from German. LC 84-25782. 96p. 1985. pap. 7.95 (ISBN 0-664-24626-5). Westminster.
Bedford, Stewart. Prayer Power & Stress Management. pap. 6.95 (ISBN 0-935930-05-1). A & S Pr.
Bennett, Rita. How to Pray for Inner Healing for Yourself & Others. 126p. (Orig.). 1983. pap. 5.95 (ISBN 0-8007-5126-4, Power Bks). Revell.
Bergan, Jacqueline & Schwan, S. Marie. Birth. (Take & Receive Ser.). (Illus.). 154p. (Orig.). 1985. pap. 6.95 (ISBN 0-88489-170-4). St Mary's.
--Forgiveness: A Guide for Prayer. (Take & Receive Ser.). 200p. (Orig.). 1985. pap. 6.95 (ISBN 0-88489-169-0). St Mary's.
--Love: A Guide for Prayer. (Take & Receive Ser.). 96p. (Orig.). 1984. pap. 5.95 (ISBN 0-88489-168-2). St Mary's.
Berrigan, Daniel. Beside the Sea of Glass: The Song of the Lamb. (Classic Prayer Ser.). (Illus.). 112p. 1978. pap. 2.50 (ISBN 0-8164-2174-9, HarpR). Har-Row.
Berry, MaryAnn. Answered Prayer. 28p. (Orig.). 1985. 4.95 (ISBN 0-9614947-0-0); pap. 2.50 (ISBN 0-9614947-1-9). First Love Min.
Bewes, Richard. Talking about Prayer. LC 80-7781. 128p. (Orig.). 1980. pap. 2.95 (ISBN 0-87784-465-8). Inter-Varsity.
Biehl, Bobb & Hagelganz, James W. Praying: How to Start & Keep Going. LC 80-54003. 128p. 1981. pap. 2.50 (ISBN 0-8307-0781-6, 5016900). Regal.
Bisagno, John. Power of Positive Praying. 1965. pap. 3.50 (ISBN 0-310-21212-X, 9238). Zondervan.
--The Secret of Positive Praying. Ruark, Jim, ed. 128p. 1986. pap. 3.95 (ISBN 0-310-21152-2, 9239). Zondervan.
Bisagno, Juan. El Poder De la Oracion Tenaz. De Lerin, Olivia S. D., tr. from Eng. Orig. Title: The Power of Positive Praying. (Span.). 96p. 1983. pap. 2.15 (ISBN 0-311-40029-9). Casa Bautista.
Blanchard, Charles A. Getting Things from God. (Classic Elective Ser.: No. 1). 168p. 1985. pap. 5.95 (ISBN 0-89693-520-5); pap. 0.95. Victor Bks.
Bloom, Anthony. Beginning to Pray. LC 70-169613. 128p. 1982. pap. 4.95 (ISBN 0-8091-1509-3). Paulist Pr.
Bloom, Anthony & LeFebvre, George. Courage to Pray. 3rd ed. Livingstone, Dinah, tr. from Fr. 123p. (Orig.). pap. text ed. 4.95 (ISBN 0-88141-031-4). St Vladimirs.
Bloom, Metropolitan A. Living Prayer. 1975. pap. 6.95 (ISBN 0-87243-054-5). Templegate.
Blume, Judy. Are You There God? It's Me, Margaret. 156p. 1986. pap. 2.50 (ISBN 0-440-90419-6, LFL). Dell.
Boase, Leonard S. Prayer of Faith. 1985. Repr. 5.95 (ISBN 0-8294-0493-7). Loyola.
Bodenstedt, Mary I. Praying the Life of Christ. Hogg, James, ed. (Analecta Cartusiana Ser.: No. 15). 184p. (Orig.). 1983. pap. 25.00 (ISBN 3-7052-0017-8, Pub by Salzburg Studies). Longwood Pub Group.
Boesak, Allan A. & Villa-Vicencio, Charles, eds. When Prayer Makes News. 192p. (Orig.). 1986. pap. 10.95 (ISBN 0-664-24035-6). Westminster.
Boone, Tom & Boone, Edna. Prayer & Action. 1974. pap. 1.25x (ISBN 0-8358-0309-0). Upper Room.
Booty, John E. Three Anglican Divines on Prayer: Jewel, Andrewes & Hooker. vii, 48p. (Orig.). 1978. pap. 3.00 (ISBN 0-936384-00-X). Cowley Pubns.
Boros, Ladislaus. Christian Prayer. 1976. 5.95 (ISBN 0-8245-0208-6). Crossroad NY.
Borst, James. Contemplative Prayer: A Guide for Today's Catholic. 1979. pap. 1.50 (ISBN 0-89243-106-7). Liguori Pubns.
Bounds, E. M. The Essentials of Prayer. (Direction Bks Ser.). 1979. pap. 3.95 (ISBN 0-8010-0756-9). Baker Bk.
--The Necessity of Prayer. (Direction Bks). 144p. 1976. pap. 2.95 (ISBN 0-8010-0659-7). Baker Bk.
--The Necessity of Prayer. 144p. 1984. pap. 3.50 (ISBN 0-88368-139-0). Whitaker Hse.
--Obtaining Answers to Prayer. 144p. 1984. pap. 3.50 (ISBN 0-88368-142-0). Whitaker Hse.
--The Possibilities of Prayer. (Direction Bks). 1979. pap. 3.95 (ISBN 0-8010-0757-7). Baker Bk.
--Power Through Prayer. 112p. 1983. pap. text ed. 2.95 (ISBN 0-88368-117-X). Whitaker Hse.
--Power Through Prayer. (Moody Classics Ser.). 1985. pap. text ed. 3.50 (ISBN 0-8024-6729-6). Moody.
--Prayer & Praying Men. (Direction Bks). 1977. pap. 3.95 (ISBN 0-8010-0721-6). Baker Bk.
--Reality of Prayer. (Direction Bks). 1978. pap. 3.50 (ISBN 0-8010-0739-9). Baker Bk.
--A Treasury of Prayer. LC 53-9865. 192p. 1981. pap. 5.95 (ISBN 0-87123-543-9, 210543). Bethany Hse.
--The Weapon of Prayer. (Direction Bks.). 57p. 1975. pap. 3.95 (ISBN 0-8010-0634-1). Baker Bk.
Bounds, Edward M. Power Through Prayer. (Direction Bks). 1972. pap. 3.95 (ISBN 0-8010-0584-1). Baker Bk.
--Power Through Prayer. pap. 2.95 (ISBN 0-310-21612-5, 9237). Zondervan.
--Purpose in Prayer. (Direction Bks). 1978. pap. 3.95 (ISBN 0-8010-0738-0). Baker Bk.
Boylan, Eugene D. Difficulties in Mental Prayer. 128p. 1984. pap. 5.95 (ISBN 0-87061-105-4). Chr Classics.
Bradshaw, Paul F. Daily Prayer in the Early Church: A Study of the Origins & Early Development of the Divine Office. 1982. 26.00x (ISBN 0-19-520394-1); pap. 9.95x (ISBN 0-19-520395-X). Oxford U Pr.
Brandt, Leslie F. Book of Christian Prayer: Gift Edition. rev. ed. LC 73-88603. 160p. 1980. 8.95 (ISBN 0-8066-1751-9, 10-0786). Augsburg.
Breault, William. A Voice over the Water. LC 84-73051. 128p. (Orig.). 1985. pap. 4.95 (ISBN 0-87793-281-6). Ave Maria.
Bremond, Henri. Prayer & Poetry: Contribution to Poetical Theory. LC 72-188148. 1927. lib. bdg. 25.00 (ISBN 0-8414-9825-3). Folcroft.
Breton, Valentine. Life & Prayer. 189p. 1960. 5.95 (ISBN 0-933932-21-9). Scepter Pubs.
Brians, Pearl. Prayer Changes My Life. large print ed. 23p. 1985. pap. 4.00 (ISBN 0-914009-35-4). VHI Library.
Briggs, Edward C. A Pilgrim's Guide to Prayer. (Orig.). 1987. pap. 3.25 (ISBN 0-8054-8156-7). Broadman.
Briscoe, Jill. Hush, Hush. 1978. pap. 5.95 (ISBN 0-310-21831-4, 9258P). Zondervan.
Brooks, Keith L. How to Pray. (Teach Yourself the Bible Ser.). 1961. pap. 2.75 (ISBN 0-8024-3708-7). Moody.
Brown, Bob W. It's Been One of Those Days, Lord. 144p. (Orig.). 1985. pap. 2.95 (ISBN 0-310-28912-2, 12773P). Zondervan.
Bryant, David. With Concerts of Prayer. LC 84-17916. 1985. pap. 6.95 (ISBN 0-8307-0975-4, 5418295). Regal.
Burghardt, W. J., et al, eds. Origen, Prayer, Exhortation to Martyrdom. LC 78-62467. (ACW Ser.: No. 19). 261p. 1954. 14.95 (ISBN 0-8091-0256-0). Paulist Pr.
Burrows, Ruth. Guidelines for Mystical Prayer. 5.95 (ISBN 0-87193-134-6). Dimension Bks.
Bush, Bernard J. Living in His Love: Essays on Prayer & Christian Living. LC 78-11809. 115p. 1978. pap. 3.95 (ISBN 0-89571-005-6). Affirmation.
Butler, B. C. Prayer: An Adventure in Living. (Ways of Prayer Ser.: Vol. 10). 8.95 (ISBN 0-89453-431-9); pap. 4.95 (ISBN 0-89453-302-9). M Glazier.
Buttrick, George A. Prayer in Life: Life in Prayer. 1976. pap. 0.85x (ISBN 0-8358-0346-5). Upper Room.
Campbell, Will & Campbell, Bonnie. God on Earth: The Lord's Prayer for Our Time. (Illus.). 128p. 1983. pap. 12.95 (ISBN 0-8245-0586-7). Crossroad NY.
Capps, Charles. Releasing the Ability of God Through Prayer. 159p. 1978. pocketbook 3.50 (ISBN 0-89274-075-2). Harrison Hse.
Caprio, Betsy. Experiments in Prayer. (Illus.). 192p. 1973. pap. 5.95 (ISBN 0-87793-054-6). Ave Maria.
Carberry, John. Reflections & Prayers for Visits with Our Eucharistic King. pap. 0.50 (ISBN 0-8198-0315-4). Dghtrs St Paul.
Carlson, G. Raymond. Prayer & the Christian's Devotional Life. LC 80-83522. (Radiant Life Ser.). 128p. (Orig.). 1981. 2.50 (ISBN 0-88243-878-6, 02-0878); teacher's ed. 3.95 (ISBN 0-88243-190-0, 32-0190). Gospel Pub.
Carretto, Carlo. The Desert in the City. (The Crossroad Paperback Ser.). 112p. 1982. pap. 4.95 (ISBN 0-8245-0423-2). Crossroad NY.
Carse, James P. The Silence of God: Meditations on Prayer. 128p. 1985. 11.95 (ISBN 0-02-521490-X). Macmillan.
--The Silence of God: Meditations on Prayer. 120p. 1987. pap. 4.95 (ISBN 0-02-084270-8, Collier). Macmillan.

Carter, Edward, ed. Prayer Perspectives. LC 86-28675. 108p. (Orig.). 1987. pap. 5.95 (ISBN 0-8189-0513-1). Alba.

Cassidy, Sheila A. A Prayer for Pilgrims: A Book about Prayer for Ordinary People. (The Crossroad Paperback Ser.). 192p. 1982. pap. 6.95 (ISBN 0-8245-0420-8). Crossroad NY.

Caulfield, Sean. The Experience of Praying. LC 79-92428. 88p. 1980. 3.95 (ISBN 0-8091-2358-4). Paulist Pr.

Chadwick, Samuel. Path of Prayer. 1963. pap. 2.95 (ISBN 0-87508-095-2). Chr Lit.

Champlin, Joseph M. Behind Closed Doors: A Handbook on How to Pray. 240p. (Orig.). 1984. pap. 8.95 (ISBN 0-8091-2637-0). Paulist Pr.

Chariton, Igumen. The Art of Prayer. Kadloubovsky, Palmer, tr. 288p. 1966. 26.95 (ISBN 0-571-06899-5). Faber & Faber.

Charles, Pierre. Prayer for All Times. Waterfield, Robin, tr. from Fr. Tr. of La Priere du Toutes Les Heures. 157p. 1983. pap. 5.95 (ISBN 0-87061-090-2). Chr Classics.

Chervokas, John. Pinstripe Prayers: Or How to Talk to God While Pursuing Mammon. 48p. (Orig.). 1984. pap. 2.95 (ISBN 0-86683-874-0, 7457, HarpR). Har-Row.

Cho, Paul Y. & Manzano, R. Whitney. Prayer: Key to Revival. 224p. 1984. 9.95 (ISBN 0-8499-0453-6, 0453-6). Word Bks.

Cihlar, Many. Misticos en Oracion. AMORC Staff, tr. from Eng. (Span.). 59p. (Orig.). 1982. pap. 7.00 (ISBN 0-912057-82-3, GS-509). AMORC.

Clapp, Steve, ed. Prayer & the Christian Life: C-4 Devotional Journal II. (The C-4 Journals Ser.). 126p. (Orig.). 1982. pap. 6.00 (ISBN 0-317-11522-7). C-Four Res.

Clark, Glenn. I Will Lift up Mine Eyes. 1937. pap. 7.95 (ISBN 0-06-061393-9, RP518, HarpR). Har-Row.

--Living Prayer. 1980. pap. 0.50 (ISBN 0-910924-88-0). Macalester.

--Lord's Prayer. pap. 0.50 (ISBN 0-910924-08-2). Macalester.

Clark, Keith. Make Space, Make Symbols. LC 78-73826. (Illus.). 112p. 1979. pap. 2.95 (ISBN 0-87793-173-9). Ave Maria.

Cobb, John B., Jr. To Pray or Not to Pray. 1974. pap. 1.25x (ISBN 0-8358-0310-4). Upper Room.

Coburn, John. A Life to Live - a Way to Pray. 160p. (Orig.). 1973. pap. 5.95 (ISBN 0-8164-2079-3, SP80, HarpR). Har-Row.

Coburn, John B. Prayer & Personal Religion. LC 57-5397. (Layman's Theological Library). 96p. 1957. pap. 4.95 (ISBN 0-664-24005-4). Westminster.

--Prayer & Personal Religion. LC 85-10477. 160p. 1985. pap. 8.95 (ISBN 0-8027-2509-0). Walker & Co.

Collier, Robert. Prayer Works. 1950. pap. 3.95 (ISBN 0-910140-04-9). C & R Anthony.

Cook, Charles, ed. Daily Meditations for Prayer. Gift Ed. 9.95 (ISBN 0-89107-160-1). Good News.

Cornish, Patty Jo. The Prayer Primer: A Philosophy Book. Quintero, Roberto, ed. LC 84-81741. 68p. (Orig.). pap. 5.95 (ISBN 0-9613717-0-6). Hilltop Hse.

Cranor, Phoebe. Is Anybody Listening When I Pray? LC 79-27475. 112p. (Orig.). 1980. pap. 3.95 (ISBN 0-87123-200-6, 210200). Bethany Hse.

Cronin, Gaynell & Cronin, Jim. Prayer. 1980. pap. 7.55 (ISBN 0-88479-032-0). Arena Lettres.

Cunningham, Agnes. Prayer: Personal & Liturgical. (Message of the Fathers of the Church Ser.: Vol. 16). 1985. 12.95 (ISBN 0-89453-356-8); pap. 8.95 (ISBN 0-89453-327-4). M Glazier.

Curran, Dolores. Family Prayer. rev. ed. 136p. (Orig.). 1983. pap. text ed. 5.95 (ISBN 0-86716-014-4). St Anthony Mess Pr.

Dalrymple, John. Simple Prayer. (Ways of Prayer Ser.: Vol. 9). 118p. 1984. pap. 4.95 (ISBN 0-89453-301-0). M Glazier.

Daly, Gabriel. Asking the Father: A Study of the Prayer of Petition. (Ways of Prayer Ser.: Vol. 4). 1982. 8.95 (ISBN 0-89453-428-9); pap. 5.95 (ISBN 0-89453-277-4). M Glazier.

Daughters of St. Paul. Moments for Prayer. plastic bdg. 1.00 (ISBN 0-8198-0277-8); pap. 0.40 (ISBN 0-8198-0278-6). Dghtrs St Paul.

--My Favorite Prayers & Reflections. 1973. plastic bdg. 5.00 (ISBN 0-8198-0276-X). Dghtrs St Paul.

Davidson, Graeme J. & Macdonald, Mary. Anyone Can Pray: A Guide to Methods of Christian Prayer. LC 82-62921. 208p. (Orig.). 1983. pap. 7.95 (ISBN 0-8091-2542-0). Paulist Pr.

Day, Albert E. An Autobiography of Prayer. 1979. pap. 3.95x (ISBN 0-8358-0384-8). Upper Room.

Deason, Dee & Deason, Velma. World Outreach Intercessory Prayer Warriors. 1983. pap. 2.50 (ISBN 0-910709-40-8). PTL Repro.

DeHaan, Richard W. Pray: God Is Listening. 80p. (Orig.). 1980. pap. 2.50 (ISBN 0-310-23542-1). Zondervan.

Deitering, Carolyn. Actions, Gestures & Bodily Attitudes. LC 80-51058. 1980. pap. 10.95 (ISBN 0-89390-021-4). Resource Pubns.

Delbene, Ron & Montgomery, Herb. Breath of Life: Discovering Your Breath Prayer. 108p. (Orig.). 1981. pap. 3.95 (ISBN 0-86683-639-X, HarpR). Har-Row.

De Liguori, Alphonse. How to Converse Continually & Familiarly with God. Aubin, tr. 2.95 (ISBN 0-8198-0062-7). Dghtrs St Paul.

Demaray, Donald. How Are You Praying? 176p. (Orig.). 1985. pap. 5.95 (ISBN 0-310-23841-2, 6801P). Zondervan.

De Sola, Carla. The Spirit Moves: A Handbook of Dance & Prayer. Adams, Doug, ed. & intro. by. LC 77-89743. (Illus.). 152p. 1986. pap. 9.95 (ISBN 0-941500-38-1). Sharing Co.

Devas, Dominic. Treatise on Prayer & Meditation. Repr. of 1926 ed. lib. bdg. 25.00 (ISBN 0-8495-1026-0). Arden Lib.

Deweese, Charles W. Prayer in Baptist Life. LC 85-21301. 1986. pap. 4.95 (ISBN 0-8054-6941-9). Broadman.

DeWelt, Don & Baird, John. What the Bible Says about Fasting. LC 79-57087. (What the Bible Says Ser.). 1984. 13.95 (ISBN 0-89900-077-0). College Pr Pub.

Diefenbach, Gabriel. Common Mystic Prayer. 1978. 2.50 (ISBN 0-8198-0527-0); pap. 1.95 (ISBN 0-8198-0528-9). Dghtrs St Paul.

Dodd, Robert V. Praying the Name of Jesus. 96p. (Orig.). 1985. pap. 4.95 (ISBN 0-8358-0514-X). Upper Room.

--Your Church's Ministry of Prayer. 1981. 3.00 (ISBN 0-89536-476-X, 2501). CSS of Ohio.

Doherty, John. Praying in the Home. 2nd. ed. LC 83-61212. 54p. 1984. pap. text ed. 1.95 (ISBN 0-911905-04-9). Past & Mat Rene Ctr.

Donne, John. The Prayers of John Donne. Umbach, Herbert H., ed. (Orig.). 1962. 11.95x; pap. 7.95x (ISBN 0-8084-0252-8). New Coll U Pr.

Duewel, Wesley L. Touch the World Through Prayer. 240p. 1986. pap. 3.95 (ISBN 0-310-36271-7, 17093P). Zondervan.

Dufresne, Ed. Praying God's Word. 96p. (Orig.). 1983. pap. 2.75 (ISBN 0-89274-276-3). Harrison Hse.

Dull, Elaine & Sekowsky, Jo Anne. Teach Us to Pray. (Aglow Bible Study Book Enrichment). 64p. 1980. pap. 2.95 (ISBN 0-930756-49-5, 522002). Aglow Pubns.

Dunnam, Maxie D. Workbook of Intercessory Prayer. LC 78-65617. 1979. pap. 4.50x (ISBN 0-8358-0382-1). Upper Room.

--The Workbook of Living Prayer. 1975. 4.50x (ISBN 0-8358-0323-6). Upper Room.

Ecclestone, Alan. A Staircase for Silence. 158p. 1977. pap. 6.50 (ISBN 0-232-51364-3). Attic Pr.

Edwards, F. Henry. Meditation & Prayer. LC 79-23708. 1980. pap. 12.00 (ISBN 0-8309-0271-6). Herald Hse.

Eims, LeRoy. Prayer: More Than Words. LC 82-61301. 162p. 1983. pap. 3.95 (ISBN 0-89109-493-8). NavPress.

Enjoy the Lord. 3.50 (ISBN 0-318-02213-3). Chrstphrs NY.

Faith's Prayer Sequence. 1979. 1.25 (ISBN 0-89858-029-3). Fill the Gap.

Fancy, Robert & Rooney, Lucy. The Contemplative Way of Prayer: Deepening Your Life with God. 112p. (Orig.). 1986. pap. 4.95 (ISBN 0-89283-308-4). Servant.

Faricy, Robert. Praying for Inner Healing. LC 79-92857. 94p. (Orig.). 1979. pap. 3.95 (ISBN 0-8091-2250-2). Paulist Pr.

Faricy, Robert S. J. Praying. 120p. 1980. pap. 3.50 (ISBN 0-03-056661-4, HarpR). Har-Row.

Farrell, Edward. Can You Drink This Cup? pap. 4.95 (ISBN 0-87193-179-6). Dimension Bks.

Fenelon, et al. A Guide to True Peace, or the Excellency of Inward & Spiritual Prayer. LC 78-78157. 1979. pap. 6.95x (ISBN 0-87574-905-4). Pendle Hill.

Ferris, Theodore P. Prayers. 1981. 6.95 (ISBN 0-8164-0483-6, HarpR). Har-Row.

Ffrench-Beytagh, Gonville. A Glimpse of Glory. 128p. 1987. pap. 7.95 (ISBN 0-8091-2903-5). Paulist Pr.

Fillmore, Charles & Fillmore, Cora. Teach Us to Pray. 1976. 5.95 (ISBN 0-87159-152-9). Unity School.

Finkel, Asher & Frizzell, Lawrence. Standing Before God: Studies on Prayer in Scripture & in Essays in Honor of John M. Oesterreicher. 1981. 39.50x (ISBN 0-87068-708-5). Ktav.

Finney, Charles. Principles of Devotion. rev. ed. Parkhurst, Louis, ed. 288p. 1987. pap. 6.95 (ISBN 0-87123-873-X). Bethany Hse.

Fitts, Bob. When You Pray - Things Happen. LC 82-82018. 144p. 1982. 2.95 (ISBN 0-89221-089-3). New Leaf.

Fosdick, Harry E. The Meaning of Prayer. 1982. pap. 2.95 (ISBN 0-687-23960-5, Festival). Abingdon.

--The Meaning of Prayer. LC 76-50560. 1976. Repr. of 1946 ed. lib. bdg. 18.50 (ISBN 0-8414-4159-6). Folcroft.

Foulks, Frances, ed. La Oracion Eficaz. Tr. of Effectual Prayer. (Span.). 160p. 5.95 (ISBN 0-87159-089-1). Unity School.

Fourth Day Guide: A Book of Prayers for Christian Pilgrims. 1969. wrps. 3.50x (ISBN 0-686-09495-6). Cellar.

Francis, Mary. How to Pray. 84p. 1985. 1.50 (ISBN 0-8199-0931-9). Franciscan Herald.

Freeman, James D. Prayer: The Master Key. 1975. 5.95 (ISBN 0-87159-128-6). Unity School.

Friedman, Greg. It Begins with Friendship: A Fresh Approach to Prayer. 73p. (Orig.). 1984. pap. text ed. 3.95 (ISBN 0-86716-038-1). St Anthony Mess Pr.

Fromer, Margaret & Keyes, Sharrel. Let's Pray Together: Studies in Prayer. LC 74-76160. (Fisherman Bible Studyguide Ser.). 63p. 1974. saddle-stitched 2.95 (ISBN 0-87788-801-9). Shaw Pubs.

Gallen, John, ed. Christians at Prayer. LC 76-22407. 1977. text ed. 14.95x (ISBN 0-268-00718-7). U of Notre Dame Pr.

--Christians at Prayer. LC 76-22407. (Liturgical Studies). 1977. pap. text ed. 5.95 (ISBN 0-268-00719-5). U of Notre Dame Pr.

Garrotto, Alfred J. Christians & Prayer. (Orig.). 1980. pap. text ed. 4.95 (ISBN 0-03-056981-8, HarpR). Har-Row.

Gaspard, Perry A. The Basic Principles of Prayer. 1984. pap. 2.00 (ISBN 0-931867-07-X). Abundant Life Pubns.

--The Different Kinds of Prayer. 88p. 1984. pap. text ed. 3.00 (ISBN 0-931867-08-8). Abundant Life Pubns.

Gawle, Barbara. How to Pray: Discovering Spiritual Growth Through Prayer. (Illus.). 204p. 1984. pap. 6.95 (ISBN 0-13-430463-2). P-H.

Getz, Gene. Praying for One Another. 132p. 1982. pap. 5.50 (ISBN 0-88207-351-6). Victor Bks.

Gibson, Elsie. Honest Prayer. LC 80-39570. 120p. (Orig.). 1981. pap. 7.95 (ISBN 0-664-24348-7). Westminster.

Gift of Prayer. (Gifts of Gold Ser.). 1971. 4.95 (ISBN 0-88088-623-4). Peter Pauper.

Gipson, Leland F. How to Use the Tremendous Power of Creative Prayer. LC 80-85276. 114p. (Orig.). 1981. pap. 2.95 (ISBN 0-9605014-0-1). Levada.

Godshall, C. David. Prayers in Dialogue B: (Con-Luth) 1984. 7.95 (ISBN 0-89536-692-4, 4869). CSS of Ohio.

Goldsmith, Joel S. The Altitude of Prayer. Sinkler, Lorainne, ed. LC 74-25082. 160p. 1975. 9.45 (ISBN 0-06-063171-6, HarpR). Har-Row.

Gordon, S. D. Quiet Talks on Prayer. (S. D. Gordon Library). 1980. pap. 4.95 (ISBN 0-8010-3754-9). Baker Bk.

Green, Thomas H. Darkness in the Marketplace. LC 81-67559. 128p. (Orig.). 1981. pap. 3.95 (ISBN 0-87793-230-1). Ave Maria.

--Opening to God: A Guide to Prayer. LC 77-83197. 144p. 1977. pap. 3.95 (ISBN 0-87793-136-4). Ave Maria.

--When the Well Runs Dry: Prayer Beyond the Beginnings. LC 79-52404. 176p. (Orig.). 1979. pap. 4.95 (ISBN 0-87793-182-8). Ave Maria.

Griffin, Emilie. Clinging: The Experience of Prayer. LC 83-48989. 96p. 1984. 11.95 (ISBN 0-06-063461-8); 11.45i. Har-Row.

Groeschel, Benedict J. Listening at Prayer. 80p. (Orig.). 1984. 4.95 (ISBN 0-8091-2582-X). Paulist Pr.

Groff, Warren F. Prayer: God's Time & Ours! 144p. (Orig.). 1984. pap. 6.95 (ISBN 0-87178-714-8). Brethren.

Grou, Jean-Nicholas. How to Pray. Dalby, Joseph, tr. 154p. 1982. pap. 6.95 (ISBN 0-227-67485-5). Attic Pr.

Gruen, Ernest J. Touching the Heart of God. (Orig.). 1986. pap. 3.95 (ISBN 0-88368-175-7). Whitaker Hse.

Guest, John. Only a Prayer Away. 140p. (Orig.). 1985. pap. 6.95 (ISBN 0-89283-273-8, Pub. by Vine Books). Servant.

Gurbachan Singh Talib. Japuji: The Immortal Prayer-Chant. 1977. 7.00x (ISBN 0-88386-967-5). South Asia Bks.

Guyon, Madame. Experiencing God Through Prayer. (Experiencing the Depths of Jesus Christ Ser.). 176p. 1984. pap. text ed. 3.50 (ISBN 0-88368-153-6). Whitaker Hse.

Hagin, Kenneth E. The Art of Intercession. 1980. pap. 3.50 (ISBN 0-89276-503-8). Hagin Ministries.

--Prayer Secrets. 2nd ed. 1983. pap. 1.00 (ISBN 0-89276-005-2). Hagin Ministries.

Hakenewerth, Quentin. The Prayer of Faith. 76p. (Orig.). 1969. pap. 1.75 (ISBN 0-9608124-3-1). Marianist Com Ctr.

Hall, Douglas J. When You Pray: Thinking Your Way Into God's World. 176p. 1987. pap. 9.95 (ISBN 0-8170-1105-6). Judson.

Hall, Manly P. Cabalistic Keys to Prayer. pap. 2.50 (ISBN 0-89314-308-1). Philos Res.

--Value of Prayer in Psychological Integration. pap. 2.50 (ISBN 0-89314-366-9). Philos Res.

Hall, Robert B. & Hall, Marjorie W. Prayer, Responding to God. 1985. pap. 5.95 (ISBN 0-318-04676-8). Episcopal Ctr.

Hallesby, O. Prayer. LC 75-2846. 176p. 1975. pap. 3.95 (ISBN 0-8066-1473-0, 10-5067). Augsburg.

Harakas, Stanley. Melody of Prayer: How to Personally Experience the Divine Liturgy. pap. 1.95 (ISBN 0-686-27068-1). Light&Life Pub Co MN.

Hardon, Reverend John. Theology of Prayer. 1979. 3.75 (ISBN 0-8198-7311-X); pap. 2.50 (ISBN 0-8198-7312-8). Dghtrs St Paul.

Harries, Richard. Prayer & the Pursuit of Happiness. 160p. (Orig.). 1985. pap. 6.95 (ISBN 0-8028-0089-0). Eerdmans.

Harrington, Wilfrid. The Bible's Ways of Prayer. 164p. (Orig.). 1981. pap. 5.95 (ISBN 0-89453-182-4, Pub. by Dominican Pubns Ireland). M Glazier.

Hartley, Jan. Family Ideas for Prayers. (Together with God Ser.). (Illus.). 80p. (Orig.). 1984. pap. 5.95 (ISBN 0-85819-495-3, Pub. by JBCE). ANZ Religious Pubns.

Hassel, David J. Dark Intimacy: Hope for Those in Difficult Prayer Experiences. 176p. (Orig.). 1986. pap. 8.95 (ISBN 0-8091-2818-7). Paulist Pr.

--Radical Prayer. 160p. 1983. 5.95 (ISBN 0-8091-2649-4). Paulist Pr.

Hatchett, Marion J. The Making of the First American Book of Common Prayer. 224p. 1982. 19.95 (ISBN 0-8164-0512-3, HarpR). Har-Row.

Hayford, Jack. Prayer Is Invading the Impossible. LC 77-71684. 1977. pap. 4.95 (ISBN 0-88270-218-1). Bridge Pub.

--Prayerpath. 80p. (Orig.). 1987. mass 2.95, (ISBN 0-8423-4964-2). Tyndale.

Hayford, Jack W. La Oracion Invade Lo Imposible. Carrodeguas, Angel, ed. Oyola, Eliezer, tr. from Span. Orig. Title: Prayer Is Invading the Impossible. 160p. 1985. pap. text ed. 2.95 (ISBN 0-8297-1457-X). Life Pubs Intl.

Hays, Edward. Secular Sanctity. rev. ed. LC 84-81954. (Illus.). 176p. 1984. pap. 7.95 (ISBN 0-939516-05-5). Forest Peace.

Heard, Gerald. Ten Questions on Prayer. LC 51-10133. (Orig.). 1951. pap. 2.50x (ISBN 0-87574-058-8, 058). Pendle Hill.

Helldorfer, Martin C. Prayer: A Guide When Troubled. LC 85-13561. (Illus.). 88p. (Orig.). 1985. pap. 7.95 (ISBN 0-89571-024-2). Affirmation.

Herman, E. Creative Prayer. 1985. pap. 2.00 (ISBN 0-88028-049-2). Forward Movement.

Hesch, John B. Prayer & Meditation for Middle School Kids. 144p. (Orig.). 1985. pap. 7.95 (ISBN 0-8091-2723-7). Paulist Pr.

Heschel, Abraham J. Quest for God: A Journey into Prayer & Symbolism. (Crossroad Paperback Ser.). 176p. 1982. pap. 7.95 (ISBN 0-8245-0436-4). Crossroad NY.

Higgins, John J. Thomas Merton on Prayer. 200p. 1975. pap. 3.95 (ISBN 0-385-02813-X, Im). Doubleday.

Hobe, Phyllis, ed. The Wonder of Prayer. LC 82-8317. (Small Wonders Ser.). (Illus.). 112p. (Orig.). 1982. pap. 4.95 (ISBN 0-664-26002-0, A Bridgebooks Publication). Westminster.

Hoffman, Marlin A. The Power of Prayer & Fasting. 2.50 (ISBN 0-89137-535-X). Quality Pubns.

Hole, Helen G. Prayer: The Cornerstone. LC 62-19073. (Orig.). 1962. pap. 2.50x (ISBN 0-87574-123-1). Pendle Hill.

Holland, Leo. Images of God. LC 84-72318. (Illus.). 112p. (Orig.). 1985. pap. 4.95 (ISBN 0-87793-276-X). Ave Maria.

Hollings, Michael. Enfolded by Christ: An Encouragement to Pray. Orig. Title: Day by Day. 128p. 1976. pap. 2.95 (ISBN 0-914544-10-1). Living Flame Pr.

Holmes, Ernest. Effective Prayer. Kinnear, Willis H., ed. 52p. 1966. pap. 4.50 (ISBN 0-911336-02-8). Sci of Mind.

Hoover, Mab G. In My Upstairs Room. 96p. (Orig.). 1982. pap. 2.95 (ISBN 0-310-35632-6, 11272P). Zondervan.

Hubbard, David A. The Practice of Prayer. 91p. 1983. pap. 2.95 (ISBN 0-87784-393-7). Inter-Varsity.

Huck, Gabe. A Book of Family Prayer. 1979. 9.95 (ISBN 0-8164-0415-1, HarpR); pap. 9.95 (ISBN 0-8164-2486-1). Har-Row.

Huck, Gabe & Klenicki, Leon, eds. Spirituality & Prayer, Jewish & Christian Understandings (Stimulus Bk.) LC 82-62966. 200p. (Orig.). 1983. pap. 7.95 (ISBN 0-8091-2538-2). Paulist Pr.

Huegel, F. J. Secretos de la Oracion. Orig. Title: Secrets of Prayer. (Span.). 1984. pap. 3.25 (ISBN 0-8254-1323-0). Kregel.

Huelsman. Pray: Moderator's Manual: An Introduction to the Spiritual Life for Busy People. LC 76-2449. 168p. 1976. pap. 7.95 (ISBN 0-8091-1975-7). Paulist Pr.

Huelsman, Richard J. Pray: An Introduction to the Spiritual Life for Busy People. LC 76-24449. (Participants Handbook). 136p. 1976. pap. 4.95 (ISBN 0-8091-1976-5). Paulist Pr.

Huffman, Walter. The Prayer of the Faithful: Understanding & Creatively Using the Prayer of the Church. 80p. (Orig.). 1986. pap. 5.95 (ISBN 0-8066-2230-X, 10-5079). Augsburg.

Hughes, R. Kent. Abba Father: The Lord's Pattern for Prayer. LC 85-72920. 128p. 1986. pap. 5.95 (ISBN 0-89107-377-9, Crossway Bks). Good News.

Hunter, W. Bingham. The God Who Hears. LC 86-7268. 250p. (Orig.). 1986. pap. 6.95 (ISBN 0-87784-604-9). Inter-Varsity.

Huntington, Wm. The Kingdom of Heaven Taken by Prayer. pap. 2.50 (ISBN 0-686-48162-3). Reiner.

Hutchinson, Gloria. Six Ways to Pray from Six Great Saints. (Illus.). 152p. 1982. pap. text ed. 4.95 (ISBN 0-86716-007-1). St Anthony Mess Pr.

Ingram, Kristen. Quiet Time with God. 96p. 1984. pap. 3.95 (ISBN 0-8170-1026-2). Judson.

International Partners in Prayer. Prayer Seminar-Workshop Workbook. 11p. 1984. pap. 2.50 (ISBN 0-917593-02-2, Pub. by Intl Partners). Prosperity & Profits.

International Partners in Prayers. International Partners in Prayer Triumpeting News: Packet of Past Issues. 6p. 1984. pap. 0.50 (ISBN 0-917593-04-9, Pub. by Intl Partners). Prosperity & Profits.

Ironside, H. A. Holy Spirit: Mission of, & Praying in. pap. 2.95 (ISBN 0-87213-366-4). Loizeaux.

Irwin, Kevin W. Liturgy, Prayer & Spirituality. 1984. pap. 9.95 (ISBN 0-8091-2560-9). Paulist Pr.

Jessey, Cornelia. The Prayer of Cosa: Praying in the Way of Francis of Assisi. (Orig.). 1985. pap. 5.95 (ISBN 0-86683-936-4, AY8512, HarpR). Har-Row.

Job, Reuben & Shawchuck, Norman. A Guide to Prayer for Ministers & Other Servants. LC 83-80409. 400p. (Orig.). 1983. pap. 21.95 bible bdg. (ISBN 0-8358-0460-7). Upper Room.

Job, Rueben P. & Shawchuck, Norman. A Guide to Prayer. 432p. 1987. pap. 11.95 (ISBN 0-8358-0559-X). Upper Room.

Johnian, Mona. Renewing Your Mind. (Orig.). 1986. pap. text ed. 3.95 (ISBN 0-88368-182-X). Whitaker Hse.

Johnstone, Patrick. Operation World: A Day-to-Day Guide to Praying for the World. 4th ed. 502p. Date not set. pap. 5.95 (ISBN 0-87808-211-5). William Carey Lib.

Jungmann, Josef. Christian Prayer Through the Centuries. LC 78-61729. Orig. Title: Christliches Beten. 176p. 1978. pap. 3.95 (ISBN 0-8091-2167-0). Paulist Pr.

Kaam, Adrian van & Muto, Susan. Practicing the Prayer of Presence. 7.95 (ISBN 0-87193-174-5). Dimension Bks.

Kappeler, Max. The Spiritual Principle of Prayer. 26p. 1969. pap. 3.50 (ISBN 0-85241-077-8). Kappeler Inst Pub.

Kaukola, Olavi. The Riches of Prayer. Hillila, Bernhard, tr. LC 85-47716. 80p. 1986. pap. 3.95 (ISBN 0-8006-1861-0). Fortress.

Keating, Dr. Charles J. Who We Are Is How We Pray: Matching Personality & Spirituality. 144p. (Orig.). 1987. 13.95 (ISBN 0-89622-292-6); pap. 7.95 (ISBN 0-89622-321-3). Twenty-Third.

Kelly, Faye L. Prayer in Sixteenth Century England. LC 66-64090. (U of Fla. Humanities Monographs: No. 22). 1966. pap. 3.50 (ISBN 0-8130-0127-7). U Presses Fla.

Kelman, Stuart. Prayer Transparencies. 32p. (Orig.). 1982. 29.95x (ISBN 0-686-81835-0). Arbit.

Kiesling, Christopher. Celibacy, Prayer & Friendship: A Making-Sense-Out-of-Life Approach. LC 77-25084. 1978. pap. 7.95 (ISBN 0-8189-0365-1). Alba.

Kimball, Spencer W., et al. Prayer. LC 77-15521. 1977. 8.95 (ISBN 0-87747-657-8). Deseret Bk.

Kimmel, Jo. Steps to Prayer Power. (Festival Bks.). 1976. pap. 5.95 (ISBN 0-687-39339-6). Abingdon.

Klug, Ronald. My Prayer Journal. LC 12-2964. 1982. pap. 3.95 (ISBN 0-570-03871-5). Concordia.

Kon, Abraham. Prayer. 12.95x (ISBN 0-900689-05-6). Bloch.

Kovats, Alexandra. Prayer: A Discovery of Life. (Nazareth Bks). 128p. 1983. pap. 4.95 (ISBN 0-86683-714-0, AY8361, HarpR). Har-Row.

Kreeft, Peter. Prayer: The Great Conversation-Straight Answers to Tough Questions about Prayer. 164p. (Orig.). 1985. pap. 6.95 (ISBN 0-89283-218-5). Servant.

Krosnicki, Thomas A. Ancient Patterns in Modern Prayer. LC 74-172790. (Catholic University of America. Studies in Christian Antiquity Ser.). pap. 79.30 (2029516). Bks Demand UMI.

Krutza, William J. Prayer: The Vital Link. 96p. 1983. pap. 3.95 (ISBN 0-8170-0986-8). Judson.

Kupferle, Mary L. The Light Will Dawn. LC 77-91310. 1978. 5.95 (ISBN 0-87159-087-5). Unity School.

Lake, Russell W. Thank God for Prayer. LC 83-50397. 293p. 1983. 5.95 (ISBN 0-87159-159-6). Unity School.

Landstrom, Elsie H. Friends, Let Us Pray. LC 79-146679. (Orig.). 1970. pap. 2.50x (ISBN 0-87574-174-6, 174). Pendle Hill.

Langford, Thomas. Prayer & the Common Life. LC 83-51396. 96p. (Orig.). 1984. pap. 3.95 (ISBN 0-8358-0473-9). Upper Room.

Leech, Kenneth. True Prayer: An Invitation to Christian Spirituality. LC 80-8358. 208p. 1981. 12.00 (ISBN 0-06-065227-6, HarpR). Har-Row.

LeFevre, Perry. Radical Prayer: Contemporary Interpretations. LC 82-72097. 100p. 1982. text ed. 13.95x (ISBN 0-913552-18-6); pap. text ed. 5.95x (ISBN 0-913552-19-4). Exploration Pr.

--Understandings of Prayer. LC 81-11622. 212p. 1981. pap. 10.95 (ISBN 0-664-24382-7). Westminster.

Lekeux, Martial. The Art of Prayer. Oligny, Paul J., tr. LC 59-14706. pap. 78.50 (ISBN 0-317-28176-3, 2022570). Bks Demand UMI.

Lewis, C. S. Letters to Malcolm: Chiefly on Prayer. LC 64-11536. 124p. 1973. pap. 3.95 (ISBN 0-15-650880-X, Harv). HarBraceJ.

Liguori, Alphonsus. Praying to God As a Friend. 48p. 1987. pap. text ed. 1.50 (ISBN 0-89243-264-0). Liguori Pubns.

Line, Francis & Line, Helen. Our Road to Prayer. 1974. pap. 1.25x (ISBN 0-8358-0305-8). Upper Room.

Link, Julie, ed. Kneeling Christian. 112p. 1986. pap. 5.95 (ISBN 0-310-33491-8, 6659P, Clarion Class). Zondervan.

Link, Mark. You: Prayer for Beginners & Those Who Have Forgotten How. LC 76-41584. 1976. pap. 2.95 (ISBN 0-913592-78-1). Argus Comm.

Linn, Matthew & Linn, Dennis. Prayer Course for Healing Life's Hurts: Book. 128p. 1983. pap. 5.95 (ISBN 0-8091-2522-6). Paulist Pr.

Linn, Matthew & Linn, Dennis, eds. Deliverance Prayer: Experiential, Psychological & Theological Approaches. LC 81-82334. 256p. (Orig.). 1981. pap. 6.95 (ISBN 0-8091-2385-1). Paulist Pr.

Llewelyn, Robert. All Shall Be Well: The Spirituality of Julian of Norwich for Today. 160p. 1985. pap. 7.95 (ISBN 0-8091-2668-0). Paulist Pr.

Lundstrom, Lowell. How You Can Pray with Power & Get Results. 272p. 1984. pap. text ed. 3.50 (ISBN 0-88368-151-X). Whitaker Hse.

MacArthur, John, Jr. Jesus' Pattern of Prayer. LC 81-3947. 200p. 1981. 5.95 (ISBN 0-8024-4962-X). Moody.

McDonald, Hope. Descubramos Como Orar. Coleman, F. G., tr. from Eng. Tr. of Discovering How to Pray. (Span.). 128p. 1982. pap. 3.20 (ISBN 0-311-40040-X). Casa Bautista.

MacDonald, Hope. Discovering How to Pray. 160p. 1976. pap. 2.95 (ISBN 0-310-28512-7, 10050P). Zondervan.

McDonald, Julie J. A Diary of Personal Prayer. Liffring-Zug, Joan, ed. & illus. (Illus.). 96p. (Orig.). 1986. pap. 9.95. Penfield.

McHugh, Dorothea H. A Personal Pathway to Prayer. LC 85-51408. 104p. 1985. 6.95 (ISBN 0-938232-90-8, Dist. by Baker & Taylor). Winston-Derek.

M'Intyre, David M. Hidden Life of Prayer. 96p. 1962. pap. 2.50 (ISBN 0-87123-214-6, 200214). Bethany Hse.

Mack, Wayne. How to Pray Effectively. (Christian Growth Ser.). 1977. pap. 2.95 (ISBN 0-87552-331-5). Presby & Reformed.

McKenna, Megan & Ducote, Darryl. Sacraments, Liturgy & Prayer. LC 78-71531. (Followers of the Way Ser.: Vol. 5). 221p. 1979. 22.50 (ISBN 0-8091-9546-1); cassette 7.50 (ISBN 0-8091-7670-X). Paulist Pr.

Mackintosh, Carlos H. La Oracion y los Cultos de Oracion. 2nd ed. Daniel, Roger P., ed. Bautista, Sara, tr. from Eng. (La Serie Diamante). Tr. of Prayer & the Prayer Meeting. (Span., Illus.). 40p. 1982. pap. 0.85 (ISBN 0-942504-08-9). Overcomer Pr.

MacLachlan, Lewis. Commonsense about Prayer. 141p. 1965. pap. 2.95 (ISBN 0-227-67653-X). Attic Pr.

--How to Pray for Healing. 112p. 1977. pap. 2.95 (ISBN 0-227-67486-3). Attic Pr.

--Intelligent Prayer. 104p. 1965. pap. 3.50 (ISBN 0-227-67496-0). Attic Pr.

MacNutt, Francis. Praying for Your Unborn Child. (Illus.). 144p. 1987. 12.95 (ISBN 0-385-23281-0). Doubleday.

Mains, David. Praying More Effectively. (Chapel Talks Ser.). 64p. 1.75 (ISBN 0-89191-261-4, 52613). Cook.

Malgo, Wm. Called to Pray. 3.95 (ISBN 0-937422-19-3). Midnight Call.

--Prayer & Revival. 4.95 (ISBN 0-937422-12-6). Midnight Call.

Maloney, George. The Breath of the Mystic. 8.95 (ISBN 0-87193-058-7). Dimension Bks.

--Centering on the Lord Jesus: The Whole Person at Prayer. (Ways of Prayer Ser.: Vol. 3). 1982. 8.95 (ISBN 0-89453-427-0). M Glazier.

Maloney, George A. Prayer of the Heart. LC 80-69095. 208p. (Orig.). 1981. pap. 3.95 (ISBN 0-87793-216-6). Ave Maria.

Mann, Stella T. Change Your Life Through Prayer. 1971. pap. 3.95 (ISBN 0-87516-053-0). De Vorss.

--How to Live in the Circle of Prayer & Make Your Dreams Come True. (Illus.). 180p. 1975. pap. 4.95 (ISBN 0-87516-206-1). De Vorss.

Marshall, Catherine. Adventures in Prayer. 1980. pap. 2.25 (ISBN 0-345-27210-2). Ballantine.

--Adventures in Prayer. (Illus.). 120p. 1976. pap. 2.95 (ISBN 0-8007-8269-0, Spire Bks). Revell.

Martin, Fay C. Availing Prayer. 120p. pap. 1.00 (ISBN 0-686-29098-4). Faith Pub Hse.

Massey, James E. Spiritual Disciplines: Growth Through the Practice of Prayer, Fasting, Dialogue, & Worship. rev. ed. Allison, Joseph D., ed. 112p. 1985. pap. 4.95 (ISBN 0-310-37151-1, 12410P). Zondervan.

Members of Community at Taize, France, ed. Praise God: Common Prayer at Taize. LC 76-47437. 1977. 16.95x (ISBN 0-19-519915-4). Oxford U Pr.

Michael, Chester P. & Norrisey, Marie C. Prayer & Temperament: Different Prayer Forms for Different Personality Types. 192p. (Orig.). 1984. pap. 5.95 (ISBN 0-940136-01-5). Open Door Inc.

Michaelle. Yoga & Prayer. Cumming, Diane, tr. pap. 6.50 (ISBN 0-87061-059-7). Chr Classics.

Mitchell, Curtis C. Praying Jesus' Way. 160p. 1977. 10.95 (ISBN 0-8007-0843-1). Revell.

Mitchell, Leonel L. Praying Shapes Believing: A Theological Commentary on the Book of Common Prayer. 220p. 1985. 17.95 (ISBN 0-86683-494-X, HarpR). Har-Row.

--The Way We Pray. 96p. (Orig.). 1984. pap. 1.35 (ISBN 0-88028-039-5). Forward Movement.

Moffet, Ruth. DU'A, on Wings of Prayer. rev. ed. Brown, Keven, ed. 96p. 1984. 11.95 (ISBN 0-87961-142-1); pap. 5.95 (ISBN 0-87961-143-X). Naturegraph.

Montapert, Alfred A. Pray to Win! A Blueprint for Success. LC 86-73037. 235p. 1986. perfect bdg. 4.95 (ISBN 0-9603174-4-9). Bks of Value.

--Pray to Win: A Blueprint for Success. pap. 4.95 (ISBN 0-9603174-4-9, Pub. by Bks of Value). Borden.

Moody, D. L. Prevailing Prayer. pap. 3.50 (ISBN 0-8024-6814-4). Moody.

More, Hannah. The Spirit of Prayer: From the Works of Hannah More. Link, Julie, ed. 144p. 1986. pap. 5.95 (ISBN 0-310-43641-9, 10272, Clarion Class). Zondervan.

Morgan, G. Campbell. Practice of Prayer. (Morgan Library). pap. 3.95 (ISBN 0-8010-5896-1). Baker Bk.

Morneau, Robert F. Discovering God's Presence. LC 80-18590. 188p. (Orig.). 1980. pap. 3.95 (ISBN 0-8146-1197-4). Liturgical Pr.

Morris, Danny E. Any Miracle God Wants to Give. 1974. pap. 1.25x (ISBN 0-8358-0314-7). Upper Room.

Morrison, Jim. American Prayer. 1983. pap. 8.95x (ISBN 0-915628-46-5). Zeppelin.

Mother Angelica. Living Prayer. 126p. (Orig.). 1985. pap. 4.95 (ISBN 0-89283-280-0). Servant.

Mrozinski, Ronald. Franciscan Prayer Life. 1983. 12.50 (ISBN 0-8199-0795-2). Franciscan Herald.

Muck, Terry. Liberating the Leader's Prayer Life. 160p. 1985. 9.95 (ISBN 0-8499-0549-4, 0549-4). Word Bks.

Muck, Terry C. Liberating the Leader's Prayer Life. (Leadership Library). 176p. 1985. 9.95 (ISBN 0-917463-05-6). Chr Today.

Mueller, Geo. God Answers Prayer. pap. 2.95 (ISBN 0-686-27009-6). Schmul Pub Co.

Mueller, George. Answers to Prayer. (Moody Classics Ser.). 1984. pap. 3.50 (ISBN 0-8024-0565-7). Moody.

Mullens, Leonard. Lord Teach Us to Pray. 1963. pap. 1.00 (ISBN 0-686-75248-1). Firm Foun Pub.

Muller, Michael. Prayer-the Key to Salvation. LC 85-52207. 226p. 1985. pap. 5.00 (ISBN 0-89555-287-6). Tan Bks Pubs.

Murphy, Joseph. How to Pray with a Deck of Cards. pap. 0.75 (ISBN 0-87516-335-1). De Vorss.

--How to Use the Power of Prayer. pap. 1.50 (ISBN 0-87516-275-4). De Vorss.

Murray, Andrew. The Inner Life. 1980. pap. 2.95 (ISBN 0-310-29752-4). Zondervan.

--The Ministry of Intercessory Prayer. rev. ed. LC 81-18011. 1981. pap. 3.95 (ISBN 0-87123-353-3, 210353). Bethany Hse.

--Prayer Life. (Andrew Murray Ser.). pap. 3.50 (ISBN 0-8024-6806-3). Moody.

--The Prayer Life. 160p. 1981. pap. 3.50 (ISBN 0-88368-102-1). Whitaker Hse.

--The Secret of Believing Prayer. LC 80-69320. 80p. 1980. pap. 3.50 (ISBN 0-87123-528-5, 200528). Bethany Hse.

--Secret of United Prayer. (Secret Ser.). (Orig.). 1980. pap. 1.95 (ISBN 0-87508-394-3). Chr Lit.

--With Christ in the School of Prayer. 288p. 1981. pap. 3.50 (ISBN 0-88368-106-4). Whitaker Hse.

--With Christ in the School of Prayer. 288p. 1983. pap. 5.95 (ISBN 0-310-29771-0, 10527P, Clarion Class). Zondervan.

Myers, Warren & Myers, Ruth. Pray: How to Be Effective in Prayer. LC 83-61679. 204p. 1984. pap. 5.95 (ISBN 0-89109-510-1). NavPress.

Nee, Watchman. Let Us Pray. Kaung, Stephen, tr. from Chinese. 1977. pap. 2.50 (ISBN 0-935008-26-8). Christian Fellow Pubs.

--The Prayer Ministry of the Church. Kaung, Stephen, tr. 1973. pap. 2.75 (ISBN 0-935008-30-6). Christian Fellow Pubs.

Neel, Peg. How to Pray According to God's Word. 72p. 1982. pap. 2.25 (ISBN 0-88144-004-3, CPS-004). Christian Pub.

Nemeck, Francis K. & Coombs, Marie T. Contemplation. (Ways of Prayer Ser.: Vol. 5). 151p. 1982. 8.95 (ISBN 0-89453-429-7); pap. 5.95 (ISBN 0-89453-276-6). M Glazier.

Nieman, Charles. Prayer: An Invitation from God. 140p. (Orig.). 1983. pap. text ed. 4.95 (ISBN 0-914307-03-7, Dist. by Harrison Hse). Word Faith.

Nilus of Sinai. Selected Texts on Prayer. pap. 0.25 (ISBN 0-317-11390-9). Eastern Orthodox.

Nouwen, Henri J. Behold the Beauty of the Lord: Praying with Icons. LC 86-72698. (Illus.). 80p. (Orig.). 1987. spiral binding 7.95 (ISBN 0-87793-356-1). Ave Maria.

--With Open Hands. LC 71-177600. (Illus.). 160p. 1972. pap. 3.95 (ISBN 0-87793-040-6). Ave Maria.

Nye, Naomi S. Different Ways to Pray. LC 79-5470. 1980. pap. 6.95 (ISBN 0-932576-04-4). Breitenbush Bks.

O'Brien, Gene & O'Brien, Judith T. Couples Praying: A Special Intimacy. 132p. 1986. pap. 3.95 (ISBN 0-8091-2816-0). Paulist Pr.

O'Collins, Gerald. A Month with Jesus. pap. 2.95 (ISBN 0-87193-097-8). Dimension Bks.

Ogilvie, LLoyd J. Praying with Power. LC 83-17742. 1983. 8.95 (ISBN 0-8307-0854-5, 5110309). Regal.

O'Hair, Madalyn. O'Hair on Prayer. 12p. (Orig.). 1980. saddle stiched 1.00 (ISBN 0-910309-30-2). Am Atheist.

Olsen, Kermit. First Steps in Prayer. pap. 2.50 (ISBN 0-910924-49-X). Macalester.

On the Holy Spirit & on Prayer. LC 81-9305. (Word & Spirit Ser.: Vol. 3). (Orig.). 1981. pap. 6.00 (ISBN 0-932506-15-1). St Bedes Pubns.

Parker, W. & St. Johns, E. Prayer Can Change Your Life. 1974. pap. 2.95 (ISBN 0-346-12137-X). Cornerstone.

Parker, William & St. Johns, Elaine. Prayer Can Change Your Life. 270p. 1983. pap. 4.95 (ISBN 0-13-694786-7, Reward). P-H.

Paterson, Eugene H. Earth & Altar: The Community of Prayer in a Self-Bound Society. 180p. (Orig.). 1985. pap. 5.95 (ISBN 0-8091-2732-6). Paulist Pr.

Paterson, John. How to Pray Together. pap. 0.75 (ISBN 0-87784-119-5). Inter-Varsity.

Pennington, Basil. Challenges in Prayer. (Ways of Prayer Ser.: Vol. 1). 1982. 8.95 (ISBN 0-89453-425-4); pap. 4.95 (ISBN 0-89453-275-8). M Glazier.

Pennington, M. Basil. Centered Living: The Way of Centering Prayer. LC 85-27474. (Illus.). 216p. 1986. 15.95 (ISBN 0-385-23186-5). Doubleday.

Penn-Lewis, Jessie. Prayer & Evangelism. 1962. pap. 2.95 (ISBN 0-87508-952-6). Chr Lit.

Peterson, Alan W., illus. Truth the Poet Sings. (Illus.). 220p. 1984. 5.95 (ISBN 0-87159-160-X). Unity School.

Pevarnik, Carrie & Chaney, Robert. Psalms: Prayer Power for Your Problems. LC 78-58146. (Illus.). 1978. pap. 9.95 (ISBN 0-918936-05-5). Astara.

Phelps, Austin. The Still Hour. 1979. pap. 3.45 (ISBN 0-85151-202-X). Banner of Truth.

Phillips, E. Lee. Prayer for Our Day. LC 81-82349. 156p. 1982. pap. 4.95 (ISBN 0-8042-2583-4). John Knox.

Polese, Richard, compiled by. Prayers of the World. 62p. 1987. pap. 5.00 (ISBN 0-943734-00-2). Ocean Tree Bks.

Ponder, Catherine. The Prospering Power of Prayer. 80p. 1983. pap. 3.00 (ISBN 0-87516-516-8). De Vorss.

Popoff, Peter. Three Steps to Answered Prayer. Tanner, Don, ed. LC 81-70342. 92p. 1981. pap. 2.00 (ISBN 0-938544-10-1). Faith Messenger.

Poslusney, Venard. Attaining Spiritual Maturity for Contemplation (According to St. John of the Cross) (Orig.). 1973. pap. 1.50 (ISBN 0-914544-04-7). Living Flame Pr.

--Union with the Lord in Prayer: Beyond Meditation to Affective Prayer, Aspiration & Contemplation. (Illus., Orig.). 1973. pap. 1.50 (ISBN 0-914544-03-9). Living Flame Pr.

Postema, Donald H. Space for God, Study & Practice of Spirituality & Prayer. LC 83-15504. 180p. 1983. pap. 9.95 (ISBN 0-933140-46-0). CRC Pubns.

Powell, John. He Touched Me: My Pilgrimage of Prayer. 1974. pap. 2.75 (ISBN 0-913592-47-1). Argus Comm.

Praktikos. Evagrius Ponticus. Bamberger, John E., tr. from Gr. & Syriac. LC 76-152483. (Cistercian Studies: No. 4). xciv, 88p. 1970. pap. 4.00 (ISBN 0-87907-804-9). Cistercian Pubns.

Prater, Arnold. Learning to Pray. 144p. (Orig.). 1986. pap. 6.50 (ISBN 0-687-21330-4). Abingdon.

Prayer of St. Patrick. pap. 1.00 (ISBN 0-686-18721-0). Eastern Orthodox.

Prayer: Selections from the Writings of the Holy Fathers. pap. 2.95 (ISBN 0-317-11391-7). Eastern Orthodox.

Praying to Get Results. 2nd ed. 1983. pap. 1.00 (ISBN 0-89276-013-3). Hagin Ministries.

Praying with Christ: A Holy Hour. 128p. 1981. pap. 1.95 (ISBN 0-8146-1244-X). Liturgical Pr.

Preston, John. The Saints Daily Exercise. LC 76-57409. (English Experience Ser.: No. 824). 1977. Repr. of 1629 ed. lib. bdg. 16.00 (ISBN 90-221-0824-4). Walter J Johnson.

Price, E. W. Acts in Prayer. LC 74-15278. 1974. pap. 0.95 (ISBN 0-8054-9209-7). Broadman.

Pronzato, Alessandro. Meditation on the Sand. LC 82-24513. (Ital.). 104p. (Orig.). 1983. pap. 5.95 (ISBN 0-8189-0457-7). Alba.

Protopresbyer Michael Pomazansky. V Mire Molitvi. Tr. of Prayer in the World. 148p. 1957. pap. 5.00 (ISBN 0-317-29096-7). Holy Trinity.

Purkiser, W. T. A Primer on Prayer. (Christian Living Ser.). 32p. (Orig.). 1987. pap. write for info. (ISBN 0-8341-1191-8). Beacon Hill.

Rahner, Karl & Metz, Johann B. The Courage to Pray. 112p. (Orig.). 1980. pap. 3.95 (ISBN 0-8245-2024-6). Crossroad NY.

Ramsey, Michael. Be Still & Know: A Study in the Life of Prayer. 128p. (Orig.). 1983. pap. 6.95 (ISBN 0-8164-2473-X, HarpR). Har-Row.

Regardie, Israel. Energy, Prayer & Relaxation. LC 82-83292. 80p. 1982. pap. 5.95 (ISBN 0-941404-02-1). Falcon Pr Az.

Religious Education Staff. The Spirit Alive in Prayer: Spirit Masters. 1979. 9.95 (ISBN 0-697-01699-4). Wm C Brown.

Reutemann, Charles. Let's Pray: Fifty Services for Praying Communities. LC 75-197. 1975. pap. 5.95 (ISBN 0-9600824-1-7). St Marys.

Rhymes, Douglas A. Through Prayer to Reality. LC 74-81813. 1976. pap. 3.95 (ISBN 0-88489-088-0). St Mary's.

Richards, H. M., Jr. Faith & Prayer. (Uplook Ser.). 32p. 1971. pap. 0.79 (ISBN 0-8163-0071-2, 06010-3). Pacific Pr Pub Assn.

Rinker, Rosalind. Prayer: Conversing with God. pap. 3.50 (ISBN 0-310-32092-5, 10716P). Zondervan.

Roberts, Howard W. Learning to Pray. LC 82-74296. 1984. pap. 4.95 (ISBN 0-8054-5195-1). Broadman.

Roberts, Kenneth J. Pray It Again, Sam. Ruskin, Anna Marie, ed. LC 83-61243. 116p. (Orig.). 1983. pap. 3.95 (ISBN 0-9610984-0-6). Pax Tapes.

Roberts, William P. Touchstones for Prayer. 98p. 1983. pap. text ed. 2.95 (ISBN 0-86716-023-3). St Anthony Mess Pr.

Rosage, David E. Follow Me: A Pocket Guide to Daily Scriptural Prayer. 240p. 1982. pap. 3.95 (ISBN 0-89283-168-5). Servant.

--Praying with Scripture in the Holy Land: Daily Meditations with the Risen Jesus. 184p. (Orig.). 1977. pap. 3.95 (ISBN 0-914544-14-4). Living Flame Pr.

--Speak, Lord, Your Servant Is Listening. 1977. pap. 2.95 (ISBN 0-89283-046-8). Servant.

Rowlett, Martha G. In Spirit & in Truth: A Guide to Praying. LC 82-50944. 112p. 1983. pap. 5.95 (ISBN 0-8358-0448-8). Upper Room.

Saliers, Don E. The Soul in Paraphrase: Prayer & the Religious Affections. 160p. 1980. 8.95 (ISBN 0-8164-0121-7, HarpR). Har-Row.

Sanders, J. Oswald. Effective Prayer. pap. write for info. (ISBN 0-8024-0781-1). Moody.

--Effective Prayer. 1961. pap. 1.00 (ISBN 9971-83-818-4). OMF Bks.

--Prayer Power Unlimited. (Moody Press Electives Ser.). (Orig.). 1984. pap. 3.95 (ISBN 0-8024-6675-3); pap. 2.50 leader's guide (ISBN 0-8024-6676-1). Moody.

Sangster, W. E. Teach Me to Pray. 1959. pap. 1.50x (ISBN 0-8358-0125-X). Upper Room.

Saphir, Adolph. Our Lord's Pattern for Prayer. LC 84-9710. (Adolph Saphir Study Ser.). 432p. 1984. pap. 11.95 (ISBN 0-8254-3748-2). Kregel.

Savary, Louis M. & Berne, Patricia H. Prayerways: For Those Who Feel Discouraged or Distraught, Frightened or Frustrated, Angry or Anxious, Powerless or Purposeless, Over-Extended or Under-Appreciated, Burned Out or Just Plain Worn Out. LC 80-7737. 176p. 1984. pap. 7.95 (ISBN 0-06-067064-9, RD 526, HarpR). Har-Row.

Schlink, Basilea. Praying Our Way Through Life. 32p. 1970. pap. 0.95 (ISBN 0-87123-455-6, 260455). Bethany Hse.

--The Weapon of Prayer. 1974. Gift ed. 0.95 (ISBN 3-87209-658-3). Evang Sisterhood Mary.

Schlitzer, Albert L. Prayerlife of the Church. 1962. 7.95x (ISBN 0-268-00214-2). U of Notre Dame Pr.

Schmidt, Joseph. Praying Our Experience. (Illus.). 56p. (Orig.). 1980. pap. 1.95 (ISBN 0-88489-113-5). St Mary's.

Schreck, Nancy & Leach, Maureen. Surrender: A Guide to Prayer. (Take & Receive Ser.). 165p. (Orig.). 1986. pap. 6.95t (ISBN 0-88489-171-2). St Mary's.

Scroggie, W. Graham. How to Pray. rev. ed. LC 80-8076. (W. Graham Scroggie Library). 112p. 1981. pap. 4.50 (ISBN 0-8254-3736-9). Kregel.

Shaw, Thomas, ed. Ways to Pray. LC 84-71180. (Sermon Ser.: No. 4). 92p. (Orig.). 1984. pap. 5.00 (ISBN 0-936384-19-0). Cowley Pubns.

Shedd, Charlie & Shedd, Martha. Praying Together: Making Marriage Last. 128p. 1987. pap. 5.95 (ISBN 0-310-43291-X). Zondervan.

Sheen, Fulton J. The World's Great Love: The Prayer of the Rosary. (Illus.). 1978. pap. 4.95 (ISBN 0-8164-2182-X, HarpR). Har-Row.

Shepherd, J. Barrie. Diary of Daily Prayer. LC 74-14176. 136p. (Orig.). 1975. pap. 5.95 (ISBN 0-8066-1459-5, 10-1900). Augsburg.

Sherman, Harold. How to Use the Power of Prayer. 192p. 1985. 5.95 (ISBN 0-87159-061-1). Unity School.

Sherrer, Quin. How to Pray for Your Children. (Book Ser.). 112p. 1986. pap. 5.95 (ISBN 0-932305-33-4, 531022). Aglow Pubns.

Shoemaker, Helen S. The Magnificent Promise: The Unifying Power of Prayer. 128p. (Orig.). 1985. pap. 6.95 (ISBN 0-687-22904-9). Abingdon.

--The Secret of Effective Prayer. LC 67-19306. 1976. pap. 1.95 (ISBN 0-87680-869-0, 91004, Key Word Bks). Word Bks.

Shorter, Aylward. Prayer in the Religious Traditions of Africa. 1975. pap. 7.95 (ISBN 0-19-519848-4). Oxford U Pr.

Simcox, Carroll E. Prayer: The Divine Dialog. LC 84-28930. 108p. (Orig.). 1985. pap. 4.95 (ISBN 0-87784-527-1). Inter-Varsity.

Simler, Joseph. Catechism of Mental Prayer. LC 84-51901. 69p. 1985. pap. 1.50 (ISBN 0-89555-256-6). Tan Bks Pubs.

Simpson, A. B. Life of Prayer. 122p. 1975. pap. 2.50 (ISBN 0-87509-164-4). Chr Pubns.

Singh, Kirpal. Prayer: Its Nature & Technique. 4th ed. LC 81-50727. (Illus.). 149p. 1982. pap. 5.95 (ISBN 0-918224-10-1). Sawan Kirpal Pubns.

Smith, Chuck. Effective Prayer Life. LC 78-27511. 96p. 1980. pap. 1.95 (ISBN 0-936728-03-5). Word for Today.

Smith, Joyce M. Learning to Talk with God. 1976. pap. 2.95 (ISBN 0-8423-2140-3). Tyndale.

Sproul, R. C. Effective Prayer. 96p. 1984. 2.50 (ISBN 0-8423-0735-4). Tyndale.

Stanley, Charles. Handle with Prayer. 120p. 1982. pap. 4.95 (ISBN 0-88207-309-5). Victor Bks.

Steere, Douglas V. Prayer in the Contemporary World. LC 80-82942. 32p. pap. 2.50x (ISBN 0-87574-907-0). Pendle Hill.

Steindl-Rast, David. Gratefulness, the Heart of Prayer: An Approach to Life in Fullness. 144p. 1984. pap. 7.95 (ISBN 0-8091-2628-1). Paulist Pr.

Steiner, Rudolf. Prayer. 1966. pap. 2.00 (ISBN 0-910142-30-0). Anthroposophic.

Stern, Chaim, ed. Gates of Prayer. 1978. Gift edition. 25.00 (ISBN 0-916694-69-0). Central Conf.

Stone, James. How to Have a Powerful Prayer Life. (How To Ser.). 73p. (Orig.). 1985. pap. 2.50 (ISBN 0-934942-50-1, 2467). White Wing Pub.

Stough, Richard H. Dial-A-Prayer. (Orig.). 1983. pap. 4.50 (ISBN 0-937172-44-8). JLJ Pubs.

Strauss, Lehman. Sense & Nonsense about Prayer. 128p. 1974. 4.95 (ISBN 0-8024-7700-3). Moody.

--Sense & Nonsense about Prayer. 1976. pap. 3.95 (ISBN 0-8024-7702-X). Moody.

Taylor, Jack R. The Hallelujah Factor. 180p. 1983. 8.95 (ISBN 0-8054-5531-0). Broadman.

--Prayer: Life's Limitless Reach. LC 77-73984. 1977. 8.95 (ISBN 0-8054-5258-3). Broadman.

Thomas, David M., ed. Prayer in the Home. LC 81-69503. (Marriage & Family Living in Depth Bk.). 1981. pap. 2.45 (ISBN 0-87029-180-7, 20250-7). Abbey.

Tileston, Mary W. Great Souls at Prayer. 366p. 1980. Repr. of 1898 ed. 9.50 (ISBN 0-227-67474-X). Attic Pr.

Torkington, Rayner. Peter Calvay -- Hermit: A Personal Rediscovery of Prayer. LC 80-13188. 107p. (Orig.). 1980. pap. 3.95 (ISBN 0-8189-0404-6). Alba.

Torrey, R. A. How to Pray. 112p. 1983. pap. text ed. 3.50 (ISBN 0-88368-133-1). Whitaker Hse.

--How to Pray. Chen, Fu H., tr. (Chinese.). 1986. pap. write for info. (ISBN 0-941598-31-4). Living Spring Pubns.

--Power & Peace in Prayer. (One Evening Christmas Classic Ser.). 1976. pap. 2.50 (ISBN 0-89107-019-2). Good News.

Torrey, R. A. & Davis, J. E. Como Orar. 96p. 1985. Repr. of 1984 ed. 2.00 (ISBN 0-311-40001-9). Casa Bautista.

Torrey, Reuben A. How to Pray. (Moody Classics Ser.). 1984. pap. 3.50 (ISBN 0-8024-3709-5). Moody.

--The Power of Prayer. 192p. 1971. pap. 3.95 (ISBN 0-310-33312-1, 10907P). Zondervan.

Townsend, Ralph. Faith, Prayer & Devotion. (Faith & the Future Ser.). 123p. 1984. cloth 24.95x (ISBN 0-631-13189-2); pap. 8.95x (ISBN 0-631-13232-5). Basil Blackwell.

Tritton, Frederick J. The Discipline of Prayer. 1983. pap. 2.50x (ISBN 0-87574-042-1, 042). Pendle Hill.

Troeger, Thomas H. Rage! Reflect. Rejoice! Praying with the Psalmists. LC 77-22755. 96p. 1977. pap. 3.95 (ISBN 0-664-24293-6). Westminster.

Tugwell, Simon. Prayer: Living with God. 1980. pap. 7.95 (ISBN 0-87243-100-2). Templegate.

Turner, F. Bernadette. Prosperity & the Healing Power of Prayer. LC 83-21276. (Illus.). 166p. 1984. pap. 6.95 (ISBN 0-13-731324-1). P-H.

Tuttle, Robert G. Help Is on the Way: Overcoming Barriers to Spirit-Assisted Prayer. LC 83-80412. 128p. (Orig.). 1983. pap. 4.95 (ISBN 0-8358-0461-5). Upper Room.

Usher, Charles H. Prayer Life. 1967. pap. 1.50 (ISBN 0-87508-545-8). Chr Lit.

Valentine, Ferdinand. Art & Technique of Prayer. (Overview Studies: No. 9). 1969. pap. 0.50x (ISBN 0-87343-049-2). Magi Bks.

Van Breemen, Peter G. Called by Name. 9.95 (ISBN 0-87193-094-3). Dimension Bks.

Vanderwall, Francis W. Water in the Wilderness: Paths of Prayer. 1985. pap. 5.95 (ISBN 0-8091-2680-X). Paulist Pr.

Van Zeller, Hubert. Ideas for Prayer. 1973. pap. 3.95 (ISBN 0-87243-046-4). Templegate.

--Patterns for Prayer. 128p. 1983. pap. 5.95 (ISBN 0-87243-124-X). Templegate.

--Prayer & the Will of God. 1978. 4.95 (ISBN 0-87243-084-7). Templegate.

Vaswig, William L. I Prayed, He Answered. LC 77-72457. 1977. pap. 5.95 (ISBN 0-8066-1589-3, 10-3189). Augsburg.

Vincent, Mary C. The Life of Prayer & the Way to God. LC 81-21257. (Illus.). 96p. (Orig.). 1982. pap. 3.50 (ISBN 0-932506-11-9). St Bedes Pubns.

Von Balthasar, Hans U. Prayer. Harrison, Graham, tr. from Ger. LC 85-82172. Orig. Title: Das Betrachtende Gebet. 311p. 1986. pap. 10.95 (ISBN 0-89870-074-4). Ignatius Pr.

Von Speyr, Adrienne. World of Prayer. Harrison, Graham, tr. from Ger. LC 84-80904. Tr. of Die Welt des Gebetes. 311p. (Orig.). 1985. pap. 10.95 (ISBN 0-89870-033-7). Ignatius Pr.

Wade, David L. Prayers of Confession: Series B. (Orig.). 1987. pap. price not set (ISBN 0-89536-885-4, 7871). CSS of Ohio.

Walker, Lucille. What to Do When You Pray. LC 78-60948. 181p. 1983. pap. text ed. 6.95 (ISBN 0-87148-920-1). Pathway Pr.

Wallace, Mary H., compiled by. God Answers Prayer. LC 85-22484. (Illus.). 368p. (Orig.). 1986. pap. 6.95 (ISBN 0-912315-90-3). Word Aflame.

Wallis, Arthur. Pray in the Spirit. 1970. pap. 2.95 (ISBN 0-87508-561-X). Chr Lit.

Walsh, James, tr. A Letter of Private Direction. 1979. pap. 5.95 (ISBN 0-87243-083-9). Templegate.

Ward, Harvey. Miracle of Prayer: Operation Esther. Floyd, Diane & Kinnaird, Judith, eds. LC 87-70021. 128p. 1987. pap. 5.95 (ISBN 0-89221-146-6). New Leaf.

Ward, J. Neville. The Use of Praying. 1977. 10.95x (ISBN 0-19-520106-X); pap. 5.95 (ISBN 0-19-519959-6). Oxford U Pr.

Weatherhead, Leslie D. A Private House of Prayer. (Festival Bks). 1979. pap. 2.95 (ISBN 0-687-34220-1). Abingdon.

Webb, Lance. The Art of Personal Prayer. 1977. 3.95x (ISBN 0-8358-0365-1). Upper Room.

Webber, Robert E. The Book of Family Prayer. 288p. 1986. 17.95 (ISBN 0-8407-5479-5). Nelson.

Weil, Louis. Gathered to Pray: Understanding Liturgical Prayer. LC 86-17413. (Parish Life Sourcebooks Ser.: No. 3). 148p. (Orig.). 1986. pap. 6.95 (ISBN 0-936384-35-2). Cowley Pubns.

Wells, Albert. As Touching the Holy. (Direction Bks.). (Orig.). 1980. pap. 2.45 (ISBN 0-8010-9637-5). Baker Bk.

Welsh, Evan. A Touch of Heaven Here. 96p. 1985. pap. 3.95 (ISBN 0-8423-7294-6). Tyndale.

Whiston, Charles. Instructions in the Life of Prayer. 2nd ed. 96p. 1985. pap. 1.50 (ISBN 0-88028-046-8). Forward Movement.

White, John. Daring to Draw Near: People in Prayer. LC 77-6554. (Orig.). 1977. pap. 5.95 (ISBN 0-87784-788-6). Inter-Varsity.

--Prayer. 1984. pap. 0.75 (ISBN 0-87784-067-9). Inter-Varsity.

White Eagle. Prayer in the New Age. 112p. 1984. Repr. of 1957 ed. 5.95 (ISBN 0-85487-064-4, Pub. by White Eagle Pub). De Vorss.

Whitman, Virginia. Excitement of Answered Prayer. (Direction Bks). pap. 3.95 (ISBN 0-8010-9617-0). Baker Bk.

Whitsett, Dan D. Does Prayer Make a Difference? (Prayers in My Life Ser.: Ser. I). 1974. pap. 1.25x (ISBN 0-8358-0312-0). Upper Room.

Wiersbe, Warren W. Listen! Jesus Is Praying. 1982. pap. 4.95 (ISBN 0-8423-2167-5); leader's guide 2.95 (ISBN 0-8423-2168-3). Tyndale.

Wilkerson, Ralph. God's Power Through Prayer. Countryman, Marsha, ed. 300p. 1985. leatherbound 19.95 (ISBN 0-937347-02-7). J Countryman Pubs.

Willis, Elbert. Praying the Right Way. 1977. 1.25 (ISBN 0-89858-011-0). Fill the Gap.

Wilson, Jim. Growth in Prayer. 74p. 1969. pap. 2.95 (ISBN 0-227-67475-8). Attic Pr.

Winkler, Gabriele. Prayer Attitude in the Eastern Church. 1978. pap. 1.45 (ISBN 0-937032-01-8). Light&Life Pub Co MN.

Wise, Charles C., Jr. Mind Is It: Meditation, Prayer, Healing, & the Psychic. LC 77-82923. 191p. (Orig.). 1978. pap. 3.75 (ISBN 0-917023-02-1). Magian Pr.

Wolmarans, Theo. Praying in the Spirit. 56p. (Orig.). 1985. 4.95 (ISBN 0-914307-50-9). Word Faith.

Womens Anglow Staff. The Ministry of Prayer. (Cornerstone Ser.). 32p. 1983. pap. 2.00 (ISBN 0-930756-77-0, 533008). Aglow Pubns.

The Wonders of the Holy Name. 1976. pap. 1.50x (ISBN 0-932104-01-0). St George Pr.

Wood, Barry. Questions Christians Ask about Prayer & Intercession. 160p. (Orig.). 1984. pap. 5.95 (ISBN 0-8007-5177-9, Power Bks). Revell.

Wood, Ernest. An Introduction to the Science of Prayer. 2nd ed. 1980. pap. text ed. 1.95 (ISBN 0-918980-08-9). St Alban Pr.

Worth, Grant A. Do Your Prayers Bounce off the Ceiling? LC 81-17411. 68p. 1982. 6.95 (ISBN 0-87747-895-3). Deseret Bk.

Wright, Norman. Self-Talk, Prayer & Imagery in Counseling (RCC) 192p. 1986. 12.95 (ISBN 0-8499-0585-0). Word Bks.

Zodhiates, Spiros. Why Pray? LC 82-71266. (Luke Trio Ser.). 1982. pap. 5.95 (ISBN 0-89957-554-4). AMG Pubs.

PRAYER–BIBLICAL TEACHING

Anderson, Joseph. Prayerbook Hebrew Teacher's Guide. Simon, Ethelyn & Kelman, Victoria, eds. (Orig.). 1985. pap. text ed. 4.95 (ISBN 0-939144-10-7). EKS Pub Co.

Bright, Bill. How to Pray. (Transferable Concepts Ser.). 63p. 1981. pap. 1.25 (ISBN 0-918956-96-X). Campus Crusade.

Clements, Ronald E. In Spirit & in Truth: Insights from Biblical Prayers. LC 85-228. 264p. 1985. pap. 9.95 (ISBN 0-8042-0071-8). John Knox.

Cornwell, Malcolm. Formed by His Word: Patterns of Scriptural Prayer. (Orig.). 1978. pap. 2.95 (ISBN 0-914544-20-9). Living Flame Pr.

Donehoo, Paris. Prayer in the Life of Jesus. (Orig.). 1984. pap. 3.95 (ISBN 0-8054-5101-3). Broadman.

Elliff, Thomas D. Praying for Others. LC 79-52341. 1979. pap. 3.95 (ISBN 0-8054-5273-7). Broadman.

Evans, Colleen T. Give Us This Day Our Daily Bread: Asking for & Sharing Life's Necessities. 160p. 1982. pap. 3.50 (ISBN 0-687-14743-3). Abingdon.

International Partners in Prayer. Biblical References to Prayer. 15p. 1984. pap. 1.75 (ISBN 0-917593-03-0, Pub. by Intl Partners). Prosperity & Profits.

McDonnell, Rea. Prayer Pilgrimage Through Scripture. LC 83-82025. (Orig.). 1984. pap. 6.95 (ISBN 0-8091-2601-X). Paulist Pr.

Madsen, Norman P. Lord, Teach Us to Pray. LC 83-61890. 96p. (Orig.). 1983. pap. 3.95 (ISBN 0-87973-611-9, 611). Our Sunday Visitor.

Martin, George. To Pray As Jesus. 1978. pap. 2.50 (ISBN 0-89283-054-9). Servant.

My Prayer Book. 235p. 1983. 4.50 (ISBN 0-570-03059-5, 06-1184). Concordia.

O'Donoghue, Noel D. The Holy Mountain: Approaches to the Mystery of Prayer. 9.95 (ISBN 0-89453-430-0); pap. 6.95 (ISBN 0-89453-300-2). M Glazier.

St. Teresa of Avila. The Life of Prayer. Houston, James M., ed. LC 83-12185. (Classics of Faith & Devotion). 1983. 11.95 (ISBN 0-88070-022-X). Multnomah.

Stedman, Ray C. Talking to My Father: What Jesus Teaches on Prayer. LC 84-20783. (Authentic Christianity Bks.). 184p. 1985. pap. 6.95 (ISBN 0-88070-075-0). Multnomah.

Tileston, Mary W., ed. Great Souls at Prayer. Large Print ed. 1983. 16.95 (ISBN 0-87983-343-2). Keats.

Wenger, J. C. The Prayer Veil in Scripture & History. 31p. 1964. pap. 1.50 (ISBN 0-8361-1501-5). Herald Pr.

PRAYER–EARLY WORKS TO 1800

Hand, Thomas A. Augustine on Prayer. rev. ed. (Orig.). 1986. pap. 3.95 (ISBN 0-89942-171-7, 171-04). Catholic BK Pub.

Trexler, Richard C. The Christian at Prayer: An Illustrated Prayer Manual Attributed to Peter the Chanter. (Medieval & Renaissance Texts & Studies: Vol. 44). (Illus.). 1987. 25.00 (ISBN 0-86698-027-X). Medieval & Renaissance NY.

PRAYER–JUVENILE LITERATURE

see also Children–Prayer-Books and Devotions

Bennett, Marian. House Full of Prayers. (Surprise Bks.). (Illus.). 14p. (Orig.). 1982. pap. 4.95 (ISBN 0-87239-563-4, 2709). Standard Pub.

Brooks, Sandra. I Can Pray to God. LC 82-80031. (Happy Day Bks.). (Illus.). 24p. (Orig.). 1982. pap. 1.59 (ISBN 0-87239-540-5, 3586). Standard Pub.

Chandler, Linda S. When I Talk to God. LC 84-4967. (Illus.). 1984. 5.95 (ISBN 0-8054-4291-X, 4242-91). Broadman.

Davidson, Alice J. Prayers & Graces. (Alice in Bibleland Ser.). 32p. 1986. 4.95 (ISBN 0-8378-5078-9). Gibson.

Fitzgerald. Rainbow. (Dear God Kids Ser.). Date not set. 3.95 (ISBN 0-671-50681-1). S&S.

Fox, Robert J. A Prayer Book for Young Catholics. LC 82-81318. 168p. 1982. pap. 5.50 Leatherette (ISBN 0-87973-370-5, 370). Our Sunday Visitor.

Geller, Norman. Talk to God...I'll Get the Message: Catholic Version. (Illus.). 23p. 1983. pap. 4.95 (ISBN 0-915753-03-0). N Geller Pub.

--Talk to God...I'll Get the Message: Jewish Version. (Illus.). 23p. 1983. pap. 4.95 (ISBN 0-915753-02-2). N Geller Pub.

--Talk to God...I'll Get the Message: Protestant Version. (Illus.). 23p. 1983. pap. 4.95 (ISBN 0-915753-04-9). N Geller Pub.

Gompertz, Helen. First Prayers. (Illus.). 32p. 1983. 5.95 (ISBN 0-8170-1013-0). Judson.

Groth, J. L. Prayer: Learning How to Talk to God. LC 56-1395. (Concept Books Series Four). 1983. pap. 3.95 (ISBN 0-570-07799-0). Concordia.

Guttschuss, Heather. Growing More Like Jesus. 128p. 1985. pap. 6.95 (ISBN 0-8163-0486-6). Pacific Pr Pub Assn.

Hague, Michael. A Child's Book of Prayers. LC 85-8380. (Illus.). 32p. 1985. 11.95 (ISBN 0-03-001412-3). H Holt & Co.

Hein, Lucille E. I Can Make My Own Prayers. LC 72-154026. (Illus.). 1971. 3.95 (ISBN 0-8170-0528-5). Judson.

Hillman, Priscilla, illus. Merry-Mouse Book of Prayers & Graces. LC 82-45497. (Balloon Bks.). (Illus.). 32p. 1983. 4.95 (ISBN 0-385-18337-2). Doubleday.

Kelling, Furn F. Prayer Is... (Illus.). 1979. 5.95 (ISBN 0-8054-4256-1, 4242-56). Broadman.

Kepes, Joanne L. I Believe: The Creed. 1981. 9.95 (ISBN 0-89837-067-1, Pub. by Pflaum Pr). Peter Li.

Merrell, Karen D. Prayer. 23p. 4.95 (ISBN 0-87747-562-8). Deseret Bk.

Nijsse, Marinus. Through Troubled Waters. (Children's Summit Bks.). pap. 1.95 (ISBN 0-8010-6728-6). Baker Bk.

Prayer: How to Talk to God. (Teaching Bks.). (Illus.). 1970. pap. text ed. 2.95 (ISBN 0-86508-153-0). BCM Intl Inc.

Prayers for a Small Child. LC 83-16050. (Knee-High Bks.). (Illus.). 24p. 1984. PLB 4.99 (ISBN 0-394-96281-8, BYR); 3.95 (ISBN 0-394-86281-3). Random.

Stuckey, Debra K. God Made Prayer. (God Made Ser.). (Illus.). 24p. 1985. 4.95 (ISBN 0-570-04117-1, 56-1528). Concordia.

Thiry, Joan. Creative Prayer. 1981. 9.95 (ISBN 0-89837-068-X, Pub. by Pflaum Pr). Peter Li.

Todd, Sharon. Adventures at Nameless Valley Ranch. Van Dolson, Bobbie J., ed. 96p. 1981. pap. 5.95 (ISBN 0-8280-0032-8). Review & Herald.

Touching Incidents & Remarkable Answers to Prayer. 135p. pap. 1.00 (ISBN 0-686-29172-7). Faith Pub Hse.

PRAYER–SERMONS

De Sales, Francis. The Sermons of St. Francis de Sales on Prayer. Fiorelli, Lewis, ed. Visitation Nuns, tr. LC 84-52310. 51p. 1985. pap. 3.00 (ISBN 0-89555-258-2). Tan Bks Pubs.

Ford, W. Herschel. Simple Sermons on Prayer. 88p. 1985. pap. 3.50 (ISBN 0-8010-3520-1). Baker Bk.

Howington, Nolan P. The Vigil of Prayer. (Orig.). 1987. pap. 4.95 (ISBN 0-8054-1505-X). Broadman.

Spurgeon, C. H. Only a Prayer Meeting. 1976. pap. 4.25 (ISBN 0-686-09106-X). Pilgrim Pubns.

Wynne, Edward J., Jr. & Thompson, Henry O., eds. Prayer for Today's People: Sermons on Prayer by Carl Michalson (1915-1965) LC 82-17583. 88p. (Orig.). 1983. lib. bdg. 23.50 (ISBN 0-8191-2771-X); pap. text ed. 8.75 (ISBN 0-8191-2772-8). U Pr of Amer.

PRAYER (JUDAISM)

Bokser, Ben Z., tr. from Hebrew. The Prayer Book. 430p. 1983. pap. text ed. 11.95 (ISBN 0-87441-372-9). Behrman.

Cone, Molly. First I Say the Shema. (Shema Primary Ser: No. 1). (Illus., Orig.). 1971. pap. text ed. 5.00 (ISBN 0-8074-0134-X, 101081). UAHC.

Goldstein, Rose. Time to Pray. LC 72-91792. 10.00 (ISBN 0-87677-141-X). Hartmore.

Heinemann, Joseph. Prayer in the Talmud: Forms & Patterns. (Studia Judaica: Vol. 9). 1977. 61.00 (ISBN 3-11-004289-4). De Gruyter.

Heschel, Abraham J. Man's Quest for God: Studies in Prayer & Symbolism. LC 54-10371. 1954. 5.95 (ISBN 0-684-13582-5, ScribT). Scribner.

Hoffman, Lawrence A. The Canonization of the Synagogue Service. LC 78-62972. 245p. 1986. pap. 12.95 (ISBN 0-268-00756-X). U of Notre Dame Pr.

Jacobs, Louis. Hasidic Prayer. LC 72-86765. (Littman Library of Jewish Civilization). 1978. pap. 4.95 (ISBN 0-8052-0604-3). Schocken.

Kon, Abraham. Prayer. 277p. 1971. 9.95 (ISBN 0-900689-05-6). Soncino Pr.

Munk, Elie. The World of Prayer, 2 vols. 19.95 set (ISBN 0-87306-080-6); Vol. 1. 9.50 (ISBN 0-87306-081-4); Vol. 2. 11.50 (ISBN 0-87306-082-2). Feldheim.

--The World of Prayer. Biberfeld, Henry & Oschry, Leonard, trs. from Ger. Orig. Title: Die Welt der Gebete. 1978. pap. 10.95 (ISBN 0-87306-170-5). Feldheim.

Petuchowski, Jakob J., ed. Understanding Jewish Prayer. 1972. pap. 7.95x (ISBN 0-87068-186-9). Ktav.

Spiegel, Marcia C. & Kremsdorf, Deborah L., eds. Women Speak To God: The Prayers & Poems of Jewish Women. LC 86-51498. 100p. (Orig.). 1987. pap. 9.98 (ISBN 0-9608054-6-X). Womans Inst-Cont Jewish Ed.

Union Prayerbook, 2 vols. 1977. Vol. 1. 10.00 (ISBN 0-916694-09-7); Vol. 2. 10.00 (ISBN 0-916694-10-0); pulpit ed. 15.00 (ISBN 0-686-67882-6). Central Conf.

Weiss, Avraham. Women's Prayer Groups: A Halakhic Analysis. 1987. pap. 8.95 (ISBN 0-88125-126-7). Ktav.

PRAYER, MENTAL

see Meditation

PRAYER-BOOKS

see also Church of England–Book of Common Prayer; Hours, Books of; Liturgies; Protestant Episcopal Church in the U. S. A.–Book of Common Prayer;

also subdivision Prayer-Books and Devotions under religious denominations, and classes of persons, etc. for whose use the prayers are intended, e.g. Lutheran Church–Prayer-Books and Devotions; family–Prayer-Books and Devotions

Alberione, James. Queen of Apostles Prayerbook. 7.50 (ISBN 0-8198-0266-2); plastic bdg. 6.00 (ISBN 0-8198-0267-0). Dghtrs St Paul.

Albrecht, Earl. Altar Prayer Workbook B: (Common-Luth) 1984. 7.75 (ISBN 0-89536-688-6, 4865). CSS of Ohio.

Anderson, Joseph, et al. Prayerbook Hebrew the Easy Way. 2nd ed. Simon, Ethelyn, ed. 1985. pap. text ed. 14.95 (ISBN 0-939144-12-3). EKS Pub Co.

Atkinson, Clifford W. A Lay Reader's Guide to the Book of Common Prayer. 1981. pap. 3.95 (ISBN 0-8192-1222-9). Morehouse.

Baillie, John. A Diary of Private Prayer. 1979. pap. 3.95 (ISBN 0-684-16323-3, ScribT). Scribner.

Barclay, William. Guide to Daily Prayer. LC 62-11473. 1974. pap. 6.95 (ISBN 0-06-060401-8, RD75, HarpR). Har-Row.

Bemmel, John V. A Get Well Prayer Book. (Greeting Book Line Ser.). 48p. (Orig.). 1985. pap. 1.50 (ISBN 0-89622-231-4). Twenty Third.

Bibliotheca Press Research Division Staff, ed. On This Day We Will Pray: Prayers for Sunday Through Saturday. 7p. 1986. pap. 1.75 (ISBN 0-939476-19-3, Pub. by Biblio Pr GA). Prosperity & Profits.

Bitney, James. Bright Intervals: Prayers for Paschal People. 96p. 1982. pap. 5.95 (ISBN 0-86683-669-1, HarpR). Har-Row.

Bodo, Murray. Song of the Sparrow: Meditations & Poems to Pray by. (Illus.). 187p. (Orig.). 1976. pap. 3.95 (ISBN 0-912228-26-1). St Anthony Mess Pr.

Brown, Allen W. The Inner Fire. rev. ed. 1984. pap. 1.95 (ISBN 0-88028-033-6). Forward Movement.

Carney, Mary Lou. A Month of Mondays: Poems & Prayers for the Monday Morning Homemaker Blues. 112p. (Orig.). 1984. pap. 5.95 (ISBN 0-687-27164-9). Abingdon.

Castle, Tony. The New Book of Christian Prayers. 364p. 1986. 17.95 (ISBN 0-8245-0781-9). Crossroad NY.

Celebrate God's Mighty Deeds: Child Prayerbook. 1971. 1.95 (ISBN 0-8091-6502-3). Paulist Pr.

Christian Prayer. (Two Color Sight-Saving Type, Ribbon Markers). maroon bdg., colored edges 22.50 (ISBN 0-89942-406-6, 406/10); annual guide 1.00 (ISBN 0-686-14264-0, 406G); vinyl case o.s.i. 1.95 (ISBN 0-686-14265-9, 406C). Catholic Bk Pub.

Coniker, Jerome F. Devotions & Prayers in Honor of St. Joseph. (Living Meditation & Prayer Bklt. Library). (Illus.). 34p. (Orig.). 1978. pap. text ed. 2.50 (ISBN 0-932406-04-1). AFC.

--Peaceful Seed Living, Vols. 1 & 2. 2nd ed. LC 78-66369. (Living Meditation & Prayerbook Ser.). (Illus.). 156p. 1981. pap. text ed. 3.00 ea. (ISBN 0-932406-00-9). AFC.

--Prayers & Recommended Practices. 2nd ed. LC 78-66374. (Living Meditation & Prayerbook Ser.). (Illus.). 91p. pap. text ed. 3.00 (ISBN 0-932406-01-7). AFC.

Cook, Anna. Powerful Petite Prayers. 3rd ed. LC 85-52398. (Illus.). 112p. 1986. pap. 4.95 (ISBN 0-936029-02-1). Western Bk Journ.

Cook, Walter L. Table Prayers for the Family Circle. 96p. (Orig.). 1982. pap. 3.45 (ISBN 0-8010-2471-4). Baker Bk.

Cushman, Ralph S., compiled by. Pocket Prayer Book: Large-Type Edition. 1977. 5.00x (ISBN 0-8358-0361-9). Upper Room.

Daughters of St Paul. My Prayer Book. 1978. plastic bdg. 2.00 (ISBN 0-8198-0359-6); pap. 1.25 (ISBN 0-8198-0360-X). Dghtrs St Paul.

De la Cruz Aymes, Maria, et al. Growing with the Bread of Life & My Mass Book. (Sacrament Program Ser.). 72p. 1985. pap. text ed. 3.30 (ISBN 0-8215-2370-8); tchr's. ed. 4.50 (ISBN 0-8215-2372-4); Parent Pack (10 booklets) 5.04 (ISBN 0-8215-2376-7). Sadlier.

Doberstein, John W., ed. Minister's Prayer Book: An Order of Prayers & Readings. LC 85-16212. 512p. 1986. 12.95 (ISBN 0-8006-0760-0, 1-760). Fortress.

Dollen, Charles. Prayer Book of the Saints. LC 84-60749. 1984. pap. 6.95 (ISBN 0-87973-717-4, 717). Our Sunday Visitor.

Eisler, Colin & Corbett, Patricia. The Prayer Book of Michelino Da Besozzo. LC 81-68186. (Illus.). 1981. 50.00 (ISBN 0-8076-1016-X). Braziller.

Falla, Terry, ed. Be Our Freedom, Lord: Responsive Prayers & Readings for Contemporary Worship. 376p. (Orig.). 1985. pap. 11.95 (ISBN 0-8028-0014-9). Eerdmans.

Fittipaldi, Silvio. How to Pray Always: Without Always Praying. LC 85-80599. (Orig.). 1985. pap. 2.95 (ISBN 0-89243-237-3). Liguori Pubns.

Fox, Robert J. A World at Prayer. LC 78-74623. 1979. pap. 3.95 (ISBN 0-87973-633-X). Our Sunday Visitor.

Franke, Merle G. Lord, Where Are You? I'm Hip-Deep in Alligators. 1985. 4.95 (ISBN 0-89536-740-8, 5824). CSS of Ohio.

Galley, Howard, ed. The Prayer Book Office. 800p. 1980. 39.95 (ISBN 0-8164-0370-8, HarpR). Har-Row.

Gilmour, Peter. Praying Together. LC 77-91623. (Illus.). 1978. pap. 1.95 (ISBN 0-88489-097-X); leader's manual 1.00 (ISBN 0-88489-120-8). St Mary's.

Gold, Avie. Hoshanos. (Art Scroll Mesorah Ser.). 160p. 1980. 11.95 (ISBN 0-89906-162-1); pap. 8.95 (ISBN 0-89906-163-X). Mesorah Pubns.

Harsley, F., ed. Eadwine's Canterbury Psalter from Ms of Trinity College. (EETS, OS Ser.: No. 92). Repr. of 1889 ed. 50.00 (ISBN 0-527-00091-4). Kraus Repr.

Hatchett, Marion. Commentary on the American Prayer Book. 608p. 1981. 32.50 (ISBN 0-8164-0206-X, HarpR). Har-Row.

Heiman, Carrie J. The Nine-Month Miracle. (Illus.). 144p. (Orig.). 1986. pap. 4.95 (ISBN 0-89243-250-0). Liguori Pubns.

Hostetter, B. David. Psalms & Prayers for Congregational Participation: Series C (Common Consensus Lectionary) 1985. 7.75 (ISBN 0-89536-770-X, 5865). CSS of Ohio.

Hubbard, Bede, ed. Companion on Life's Journey: A Book of Prayers & Readings. 260p. 1986. pap. 9.95 (ISBN 0-8146-1550-3). Liturgical Pr.

Huck, Gabe. A Book of Family Prayer. 1979. 9.95 (ISBN 0-8164-0415-1, HarpR); pap. 9.95 (ISBN 0-8164-2486-1). Har-Row.

Hurley, Dermot, ed. Everyday Prayer Book with the Order of Mass. 208p. 1984. pap. 1.95 (ISBN 0-225-66273-6, HarpR). Har-Row.

Innis, Pauline, ed. Prayer & Power in the Capital: With Prayers of the Presidents. LC 82-156801. (Illus.). 120p. 1982. 10.00 (ISBN 0-941402-02-9). Devon Pub.

International Partners in Prayer. Index to Prayer Books, Pamphlets, Etc. 50p. 1984. pap. 2.50 (ISBN 0-917593-01-4, Pub. by Intl Partners). Prosperity & Profits.

International Partners to Prayer. Starting a Prayer Bank: Deposits & Withdrawals. 1985. pap. text ed. 1.00 (ISBN 0-917593-09-X, Pub. by Intl Partners). Prosperity & Profits.

Isler, Betty. Thank You for My Grandchild. 1983. pap. 4.95 (ISBN 0-570-03915-0, 12-2850). Concordia.

John Paul II, Pope Day by Day With Pope John Paul II. 1982. pap. 6.95 (ISBN 0-8091-2458-0). Paulist Pr.

Johnson, Lois W. Songs for Silent Moments: Prayers for Daily Living. LC 79-54115. 128p. (Orig.). 1980. pap. 4.95 (ISBN 0-8066-1765-9, 10-5851). Augsburg.

Kaplan, Mordecai M. & Kohn, Eugene, eds. Sabbath Prayerbook. LC 57-9678. 573p. 1979. 11.50 (ISBN 0-935457-32-1). Reconstructionist Pr.

Kaplan, Mordecai M., et al, eds. High Holiday Prayerbook: Rosh Hashanah, Vol. 1. 360p. 1948. 9.00 (ISBN 0-935457-29-1). Reconstructionist Pr.

--High Holiday Prayerbook: Yom Kippur, Vol. 2. 597p. 1948. 13.00 (ISBN 0-935457-30-5). Reconstructionist Pr.

Kirk, James G. When We Gather: A Book of Prayers for Worship, Year A. LC 83-14221. (Illus.). 142p. 1983. pap. 8.95 (ISBN 0-664-24505-6, A Geneva Press Publication). Westminster.

--When We Gather: A Book of Prayers for Worship, Year C. LC 83-14221. (Illus.). 142p. 1985. pap. 8.95 (ISBN 0-664-24652-4, A Geneva Press Publication). Westminster.

Kohn, Eugene, ed. Festival Prayerbook. LC 57-13301. 547p. 1958. 10.00 (ISBN 0-935457-28-3). Reconstructionist Pr.

Kolb, Erwin. A Prayer Primer. 1982. pap. 4.25 (ISBN 0-570-03843-X, 12-2946). Concordia.

Littlehales, H., ed. The Prymer, or Lay Folks Prayer Book, Pts. 1 & 2. (EETS, OS Ser.: No. 109). Repr. of 1897 ed. Set. 18.00 (ISBN 0-527-00108-2). Kraus Repr.

Luke the Physician. On Trial: Being a Summary of Eyewitness Reports Concerning the Early Church. LC 82-60668. (Illus.). 120p. 1982. pap. 3.25 (ISBN 0-87973-648-8, 648). Our Sunday Visitor.

Luther, Martin. Devotions & Prayers of Martin Luther: 52 One-Page Meditations & Prayers on the Psalms. 1978. pap. 2.95 (ISBN 0-8010-5582-2). Baker Bk.

McCarter, P. Kyle, Jr. Samuel One: Volume Eight, a New Translation with Introduction & Commentary. LC 79-7201. (Anchor Bible Ser.). 1980. 20.00 (ISBN 0-385-06760-7). Doubleday.

Mancuso, Laurence. A Prayerbook. (New Skete). (Illus.). 720p. 1976. 35.00x (ISBN 0-9607924-3-0). Monks of New Skete.

Mantenach, Janaan & Pfeifer, Carl J. Living Water: Prayers of Our Heritage. LC 78-58965. (Illus.). 128p. 1978. pap. 3.95 (ISBN 0-8091-2128-X). Paulist Pr.

Mother Immaculata. Consecration & the Spirit of Carmel. LC 82-72203. (Living Meditation & Prayerbook Ser.). (Illus.). 270p. (Orig.). 1985. pap. text ed. 6.00 (ISBN 0-932406-08-4). AFC.

The New Haggadah. Rev. ed. 1978. pap. 4.95 (ISBN 0-935457-31-3). Reconstructionist Pr.

Oosterhuis, Huub. Your Word Is Near. Smith, N. D., tr. from Dutch. LC 68-20848. 192p. 1968. pap. 4.95 (ISBN 0-8091-1775-4, Deus). Paulist Pr.

Pappas, Michael G. Sweet Dreams for Little Ones. (Illus.). 64p. (Orig.). 1982. pap. 6.95 (ISBN 0-86683-641-1, AY8156, HarpR). Har-Row.

Parmisano, Stan. Come to the Mountain: The Comtemporary Experience of Prayer. LC 86-70254. 96p. (Orig.). 1986. pap. 4.95 (ISBN 0-87793-337-5). Ave Maria.

Prayer Book. 368p. (Orig.). 1979. 10.00 (ISBN 0-317-30304-X). Holy Trinity.

Prayers for Everyone. (Illus.). 16p. 1982. pap. 0.99 (ISBN 0-86683-653-5, AY8232, HarpR). Har-Row.

Prayers for Home & School. (Illus.). 16p. 1982. pap. 0.99 (ISBN 0-86683-652-7, AY8231, HarpR). Har-Row.

Preparation for Total Consecration. pap. 2.00 (ISBN 0-910984-10-7). Montfort Pubns.

Pullan, Leighton. The History of the Book of Common Prayer. LC 77-15663. 1901. 20.00 (ISBN 0-8414-6848-6). Folcroft.

Rahner, Karl & Metz, Johann B. The Courage to Pray. 112p. (Orig.). 1980. pap. 3.95 (ISBN 0-8245-2024-6). Crossroad NY.
Reflections on the Jesus Prayer. 1985. 3.95 (ISBN 0-87193-070-6). Dimension Bks.
Richards, Lawrence O. The Believer's Prayer Book. 1986. pap. 2.50 (ISBN 0-310-43602-8, 18213P). Zondervan.
Rosage, David E. Speak, Lord, Your Servant Is Listening. 1977. pap. 2.95 (ISBN 0-89283-046-8). Servant.
Seagren, Daniel R. Uncommon Prayers: For Young Adults at Work. 3.50 (ISBN 0-8010-8129-7). Baker Bk.
Seeley, Burns K. Meditations on St. John. Coniker, Jerome F. & Francis, Dale, eds. LC 81-65808. (Living Meditation & Prayerbook Ser.). (Illus.). 245p. (Orig.). 1981. pap. text ed. 5.00 (ISBN 0-932406-03-3). AFC.
Sheen, Fulton J. The Way of the Cross: Giant Print Edition. rev. ed. (Illus.). 64p. 1982. pap. 2.50 (ISBN 0-87973-659-3, 659); roncote pocket-size 2.50 (ISBN 0-87973-660-7, 660). Our Sunday Visitor.
Showalter, G. H. & Cox, Frank L. A Book of Prayers. 1940. pap. 1.00 (ISBN 0-88027-063-2). Firm Foun Pub.
Sinclair, Keith V. Prieres en Ancien Francais. LC 78-137. 208p. 1978. 35.00 (ISBN 0-208-01741-0, Archon). Shoe String.
Singer, S. Prayer Book. Repr. of 1962 ed. 10.95x (ISBN 0-8197-0057-6). Bloch.
Skold, Betty W. I'm Glad You're Open Weekdays: Everyday Prayers to the God Who Works Between Sundays. LC 85-3923. 112p. (Orig.). 1985. pap. 5.95 (ISBN 0-8066-2129-X, 10-3201). Augsburg.
Snyder, Bernadette M. The Kitchen Sink Prayer Book. 96p. 1984. pap. 3.25 (ISBN 0-89243-217-9). Liguori Pubns.
Sorenson, Jane. Time Out for God. 64p. 1985. pap. 2.50 (ISBN 0-87239-895-1, 2825). Standard Pub.
--Time Out for God, No. 2. 64p. 1985. pap. 2.50 (ISBN 0-87239-896-X, 2826). Standard Pub.
Spurgeon, C. H. C. H. Spurgeon's Prayers. 192p. Date not set. pap. price not set. Pilgrim Pubns.
Strode, Muriel. My Little Book of Prayer. 73p. 1942. pap. 1.95 (ISBN 0-87548-237-6). Open Court.
Stroud, Marion. Our Baby: The First Five Years. (Illus.). 48p. 1986. 11.95 (ISBN 0-7459-1119-6). Lion USA.
Swami Karunananda Ma, ed. Lotus Prayer Book. LC 86-10384. 224p. (Orig.). 1986. pap. 9.95 (ISBN 0-932040-33-0). Integral Yoga Pubns.
Thank You for the World. (Illus.). 16p. 1982. pap. 0.99 (ISBN 0-86683-655-1, AY8234, HarpR). Har-Row.
Thank You Prayers. (Illus.). 16p. 1982. pap. 0.99 (ISBN 0-86683-654-3, AY8233, HarpR). Har-Row.
Tompkins, Iverna. TLC Prayer Network Training Manual. Green, Shirlee & Stultz, Roberta, eds. write for info. tchr's. manual (ISBN 0-9611260-3-5). I Tompkins.
Wickham, Legg J. Breviarium Romanum a Francisco Cardinali: Quignonio Editum. 262p. Repr. of 1888 ed. text ed. 49.68x (ISBN 0-576-99727-7, Pub. by Gregg Intl Pubs England). Gregg Intl.
Worshipbook: Services. deluxe ed. 10.00 (ISBN 0-664-21287-5). Westminster.
Zimmerman, Leander M. Prayers, for All People, for All Occasions. pap. 2.00 (2027877). Bks Demand UMI.

PRAYER GROUPS

see also Prayer-Meetings

Holmes, Urban T. Praying with the Family of God: Leader Guide. 1980. pap. 3.95 (ISBN 0-03-049551-2, HarpR). Har-Row.
International Partners in Prayer. Prayer Seminar-Workshop Workbook. 11p. 1984. pap. 2.50 (ISBN 0-917593-02-2, Pub. by Intl Partners). Prosperity & Profits.
International Partners in Prayer Staff. Prayer Movements: An International Directory. 20p. Date not set. pap. 3.00 (ISBN 0-917593-00-6, Pub. by Intl Partners). Prosperity & Profits.
International Partners in Prayers. International Partners in Prayer Triumpeting News: Packet of Past Issues. 6p. 1984. pap. 0.50 (ISBN 0-917593-04-9, Pub. by Intl Partners). Prosperity & Profits.
Linn, Dennis M., et al. Praying with One Another for Healing. 1984. pap. 4.95 (ISBN 0-8091-2619-2). Paulist Pr.
Murray, Andrew. Secret of United Prayer. (Secret Ser.). (Orig.). 1980. pap. 1.95 (ISBN 0-87508-394-3). Chr Lit.
Russell, Marjorie. The Arcadia Story. LC 85-40651. 265p. 1985. pap. 9.95 (ISBN 0-938232-83-5, Dist. by Baker & Taylor Co.). Winston-Derek.
St. Romain, Philip. How to Form a Christian Growth Support Group. 48p. (Orig.). 1985. pap. 2.95 (ISBN 0-89243-242-X). Liguori Pubns.

PRAYER-MEETINGS

see also Prayer Groups

Brians, Pearl. Prayer Meeting at Our House. large print ed. 25p. 1985. pap. 4.00 (ISBN 0-914009-33-8). VHI Library.
Doty, Harry. Prayer Meetings. LC 78-10622. 1979. pap. 6.00 (ISBN 0-8309-0228-7). Herald Hse.
Mackintosh, Carlos H. La Oracion y los Cultos de Oracion. 2nd ed. Daniel, Roger P., ed. Bautista, Sara, tr. from Eng. (La Serie Diamante). Tr. of Prayer & the Prayer Meeting. (Span., Illus.). 40p. 1982. pap. 0.85 (ISBN 0-942504-08-9). Overcomer Pr.

PRAYERS

see also Bible–Prayers; Children–Prayer-Books and Devotions; Grace at Meals; Hours, Books of; Lord's Prayer; Meditations; Pastoral Prayers; Prayer; Rosary;
also subdivision Prayer-Books and Devotions under religious denominations, classes of persons, etc., e.g. Catholic Church–Prayer-Books and Devotions

Abd Allah Ansarti, Khwajih. Munajat: The Intimate Prayers. Morris, Lawrence & Sarfeh, Rustam, trs. from Fari. LC 75-30173. (Eng. & Persian.). 1975. 7.50 (ISBN 0-917220-00-5). Khaneghah & Maktab.
Adams, Jay E. Prayers for Troubled Times. 1979. pap. 1.50 (ISBN 0-87552-067-7). Presby & Reformed.
Alberione, James. Lord, Teach Us to Pray. Daughters of St. Paul, tr. from Ital. 295p. 1982. 4.00 (ISBN 0-8198-4422-5, SP0408); pap. 3.00 (ISBN 0-8198-4423-3). Dghtrs St Paul.
Albrecht, Earl. Altar Prayer Workbook A. rev. ed. Sherer, Michael L., ed. 1986. 7.75 (ISBN 0-89536-812-9, 6841). CSS of Ohio.
Allchin, A. M. & Waal, Esther de, eds. Daily Readings from Prayers & Praises in the Celtic Tradition. 1987. pap. 4.95 (ISBN 0-87243-151-7). Templegate.
Alleman, Herman & Scovil, Elizabeth R. Prayers for Boys & Prayers for Girls. 3.95x. Nelson.
Amlaw, Mary. From Praying Never to Praying Always. 100p. (Orig.). 1985. pap. 5.95 (ISBN 0-916134-69-5). Pueblo Pub Co.
Appleton, George. Prayers from a Troubled Heart. LC 83-48010. 64p. 1983. pap. 3.50 (ISBN 0-8006-1711-8, 1-1711). Fortress.
Arbour, Basil. Time Out: Prayers for Busy People. 96p. 1984. pap. 3.95 (ISBN 0-86683-828-7, HarpR). Har-Row.
Atkinson, James, ed. Daily Readings with Martin Luther. 1987. pap. 4.95 (ISBN 0-87243-157-6). Templegate.
Aurobindo, tr. from Fr. Prayers & Meditations. rev. ed. 380p. (Orig.). 1979. pap. 16.00 (ISBN 0-89744-998-3, Sri Aurobindo Ashram Trust India); text ed. 21.00 (ISBN 0-89744-219-9). Auromere.
Bahaullah. Prayers & Meditations. Effendi, Shoghi, tr. 1978. 14.95 (ISBN 0-900125-39-X). Baha'i.
Bahaullah & Bab. O God, Guide Me: A Selection of Prayers Revealed. (Illus.). 1986. pap. 4.75 (ISBN 0-87743-202-3). Baha'i.
Baillie, John. A Diary of Private Prayer. 136p. 1978. 8.95 (ISBN 0-684-30997-1, ScribT). Scribner.
Baird, Coleen. Seven Days & Prayer. (Illus.). 1980. pap. 2.95 (ISBN 0-87747-802-3). Deseret Bk.
Barclay, William. Everyday Prayers. LC 60-5326. 160p. 1981. pap. 6.95 (ISBN 0-06-060411-5, RD 361, HarpR). Har-Row.
Bartow, Donald W. Ministry of Prayer. 3rd ed. 165p. 1983. pap. 7.95 (ISBN 0-938736-22-1). LIFE ENRICH.
Beck, Norman. Scripture Notes A. rev. ed. Sherer, Michael L., ed. 1986. pap. 9.95 (ISBN 0-89536-808-0, 6837). CSS of Ohio.
Becon, Thomas. Prayers & Others Pieces of Thomas Becon, Chaplain to Archbishop Cranmer. Repr. of 1844 ed. 55.00 (ISBN 0-384-03730-5). Johnson Repr.
Beilenson, John, ed. Prayers for Inner Strength. (Illus.). 64p. 1986. 5.95 (ISBN 0-88088-468-1, 884681). Peter Pauper.
Bennett, Dennis. How to Pray for the Release of the Holy Spirit. 1985. pap. 3.95 (ISBN 0-88270-593-8). Bridge Pub.
Bjorge, James R. Forty Ways to Say Thank You, Lord. LC 80-67802. 96p. (Orig.). 1981. pap. 5.95 (ISBN 0-8066-1864-7, 102361). Augsburg.
Blackwood, Andrew W. Prayers for All Occasions. (Pocket Pulpit Library). pap. 3.95 (ISBN 0-8010-0923-5). Baker Bk.
Boelhower, Gary, et al. Let Us Give Thanks: Meal Prayers for All Occasions. 42p. (Orig.). 1986. pap. 3.00 (ISBN 0-937997-04-8). Hi-Time Pub.
Boelhower, Gary J. Sacred Times, Timeless Seasons. (Illus.). 76p. 1986. pap. 6.95 (ISBN 0-937997-05-6). Hi-Time Pub.
Bonhoeffer, Dietrich. Prayers from Prison. Hampe, Johann C., tr. from Ger. LC 77-15228. Tr. of Von guten Machten. 1978. pap. 4.95 (ISBN 0-8006-1334-1, 1-1334). Fortress.
Book of Common Worship. 406p. 1978. maroon softcover 4.95 (ISBN 0-664-24331-2); green softcover 4.95 (ISBN 0-664-24332-0). Westminster.
Bootz, John, ed. The Book of Common Prayer. LC 75-29330. 1976. 24.95 (ISBN 0-918016-58-4). Folger Bks.
Bornhoeft, Theodore P. Prayers Responsively: Responsive Prayers for the Three-Year Lectionary. 1984. pap. 8.95 (ISBN 0-570-03922-3, 12-2861). Concordia.
Botz, Paschal, et al. Prayers Before & after Communion. 24p. 1981. pap. 0.50 (ISBN 0-8146-1213-X). Liturgical Pr.
Bradford, John. Writings of John Bradford...Martyr, 1555, 2 Vols. Repr. of 1853 ed. Set. 92.00 (ISBN 0-384-05440-4). Johnson Repr.
Brandt, Leslie F. Book of Christian Prayer. LC 73-88603. 96p. (Orig.). 1974. pap. 4.95 (ISBN 0-8066-1406-4, 10-0785). Augsburg.
Briffa, Salvino. That I May See: A Prayerful Discovery Through Imagination. 140p. 1986. 6.95 (ISBN 0-87193-251-2). Dimension Bks.
Brokering, Herbert F., ed. Luthers Prayers. Kistler, Charles E., tr. LC 67-25366. 1967. lea. bdg. 7.95 (ISBN 0-8066-0721-1, 10-4231). Augsburg.
Brooke, Avery. Plain Prayers for a Complicated World. 124p. 1983. 5.95 (ISBN 0-8164-0501-8, HarpR); pap. 2.95 (ISBN 0-8164-2428-4). Har-Row.
Bull, Henry, ed. Christian Prayers & Holy Meditations. 1842. 21.00 (ISBN 0-384-06285-7). Johnson Repr.
Cadram, Glenna & Grubbs, Sylvia. The Potter & the Clay. 1986. pap. 9.95 (ISBN 0-87162-446-X). Warner Pr.
Calkin, Ruth H. Tell Me Again, Lord, I Forget. (Living Bks.). 160p. (Orig.). 1986. 3.50 (ISBN 0-8423-6990-2). Tyndale.
Carr, Jo & Sorley, Imogene. Bless This Mess & Other Prayers. (Festival Books). 1976. pap. 3.25 (ISBN 0-687-03618-6). Abingdon.
--Plum Jelly & Stained Glass & Other Prayers. 1981. pap. 2.50 (ISBN 0-687-31660-X, Festival). Abingdon.
Carter, Edward. Jesus, I Want to Talk with You: Contemporary Prayers. LC 73-75617. (Illus.). 1977. pap. 1.95 (ISBN 0-8189-1142-5, Pub. by Alba Bks). Alba.
Cassidy, Norma C. Favorite Novenas & Prayers. LC 72-91456. 144p. 1972. pap. 3.95 (ISBN 0-8091-1761-4, Deus). Paulist Pr.
Chautard, Jean-Baptiste. The Soul of the Apostolate. 1977. pap. 6.00 (ISBN 0-89555-031-8). TAN Bks Pubs.
Chavis, Benjamin F., Jr. Psalms from Prison. 192p. 1983. 10.95 (ISBN 0-8298-0661-X); pap. 7.95 (ISBN 0-8298-0666-0). Pilgrim NY.
Chervokas, John. Pinstripe Prayers: Or How to Talk to God While Pursuing Mammon. 48p. (Orig.). 1984. pap. 2.95 (ISBN 0-86683-874-0, 7457, HarpR). Har-Row.
Chirri, Imam Mohamad Jawad. The Five Daily Prayers. 24p. Date not set. pap. 3.00 (ISBN 0-317-52360-0). Islamic Ctr.
Cho, Paul Y. & Manzano, R. Whitney. La Oracion - Clave del Avivamiento. Araujo, Juan S., tr. from Eng. Tr. of Prayer - Key to Revival. (Span.). 128p. 1987. pap. 3.95 (ISBN 0-88113-241-1). Edit Betania.
Christian Prayer. (Two Color Sight-Saving Type, Ribbon Markers). maroon bdg., colored edges 22.50 (ISBN 0-89942-406-6, 406/10); annual guide 1.00 (ISBN 0-686-14264-0, 406G); vinyl case o.s.i. 1.95 (ISBN 0-686-14265-9, 406C). Catholic Bk Pub.
Church of Scotland - Committee on Public Worship & Aids to Devotion. Prayers for Contemporary Worship. 1977. pap. 4.95x (ISBN 0-7152-0351-7). Outlook.
--Prayers for Sunday Services. 1980. pap. 6.95x (ISBN 0-7152-0456-4). Outlook.
Church of Scotland - General Assembly - Committee On Public Worship And Aids To Devotion. Prayers for the Christian Year. 2nd ed. 172p. 1952. 10.95x (ISBN 0-19-145602-0). Oxford U Pr.
Church of Scotland, the Woman's Guild Staff. Let's Choose Our Worship: Prayers for Women's Meetings. 1980. pap. 1.65 (ISBN 0-7152-0461-0). Outlook.
Cihlar, Many. Misticos en Oracion. AMORC Staff, tr. from Eng. (Span.). 59p. (Orig.). 1982. pap. 7.00 (ISBN 0-912057-82-3, GS-509). AMORC.
Clark, Mary E. Thy Kingdom Come. 1.77 (ISBN 0-8091-9315-9). Paulist Pr.
Coburn, John. A Life to Live - a Way to Pray. 160p. (Orig.). 1973. pap. 5.95 (ISBN 0-8164-2079-3, SP80, HarpR). Har-Row.
Coleman, William V. Prayer-Talk: Casual Conversations with God. LC 82-74085. 112p. (Orig.). 1983. pap. 3.95 (ISBN 0-87793-265-4). Ave Maria.
Collier, Robert. Prayer Works! 4.95 (ISBN 0-912576-01-4). R Collier.
Colquhoun, Frank. Family Prayers. 80p. 1984. pap. 1.35 (ISBN 0-88028-040-9). Forward Movement.
Colquhoun, Frank, ed. Prayers for Every Occasion. Orig. Title: Parish Prayers. 445p. 1974. Repr. of 1967 ed. kivar 14.95 (ISBN 0-8192-1280-6). Morehouse.
Craghan, John. The Psalms: Prayers for the Ups, Downs & In-Betweens of Life: A Literary Experiential Approach. (Background Bks.: Vol. 2). 1985. pap. 7.95 (ISBN 0-89453-439-4). M Glazier.
Crowther, Jean D. A Mother's Prayer. 14p. 1978. pap. 1.00 (ISBN 0-88290-099-4). Horizon Utah.
Cumming, John & Burns, Paul, eds. Prayers for Our Times. 144p. 1983. 10.95 (ISBN 0-8245-0071-7); pap. 6.95 (ISBN 0-8245-0107-1). Crossroad NY.
Cummings, J. T. & Moll, H. Prayers for College Students. LC 12-2962. 1982. pap. 4.95 (ISBN 0-570-03869-3). Concordia.
Curtiss, Harriete & Homer, F. Potent Prayers. 1976p. pap. 1.00 (ISBN 0-87516-362-9). De Vorss.
Daughters of St. Paul. Prayers for Young Adults. 1985. 4.00 (ISBN 0-8198-5822-6). Dghtrs St Paul.
Daytime Prayer from the Liturgy of the Hours. 521p. pap. 6.95 (ISBN 1-55586-577-1, V-577). US Catholic.
Decker, Ed & Hunt, Dave. Los Fabricantes de Dioses. Powell, Adriana, tr. from Eng. Tr. of The Godmakers. (Span.). 240p. 1987. pap. 4.95 (ISBN 0-88113-088-5). Edit Betania.
De Foucauld, Charles. Come, Let Us Sing a Song Unknown. 2.95 (ISBN 0-87193-080-3). Dimension Bks.
Dering, Edward. M. Derings Workes: More at Large Than Ever Hath Heer-to-Fore Been Printed, 3 pts. LC 74-38171. (English Experience Ser.: No. 448). 692p. 1972. Repr. of 1597 ed. 95.00 (ISBN 90-221-0448-6). Walter J Johnson.
Didion, Joan. A Book of Common Prayer. 288p. 1983. pap. 3.95 (ISBN 0-671-49589-5). PB.
Di Nola, Alfonso, ed. Prayers of Man. 1960. 27.95 (ISBN 0-8392-1152-X). Astor-Honor.
Di Orio, Ralph A. Healing Love. LC 86-1572. 216p. 1987. 14.95 (ISBN 0-385-23694-8). Doubleday.
Doerffler, Alfred. Open the Meeting with Prayer. LC 55-7442. 1955. 3.50 (ISBN 0-570-03147-8, 12-2531). Concordia.
Dollen, Charles. Prayers for the Third Age: A Devotion for Mature Catholics. LC 85-60889. 200p. (Orig.). 1985. pap. 7.95 (ISBN 0-87973-837-5, 837). Our Sunday Visitor.
Donne, John. The Prayers of John Donne. Umbach, Herbert H., ed. (Orig.). 1962. 11.95x; pap. 7.95x (ISBN 0-8084-0252-8). New Coll U Pr.
Doughty, W. L., ed. The Prayers of Susanna Wesley. 80p. 1984. pap. 3.95 (ISBN 0-310-36351-9, 12368P, Clarion Class). Zondervan.
Drescher, Sandra. Dear Jesus, Love Sandy. 112p. 1982. pap. 3.95 (ISBN 0-310-44841-7, 18235P); gift ed. o. p. cancelled 7.95 (ISBN 0-310-44840-9). Zondervan.
Dubois, W. E. B. Prayers for Dark People. Aptheker, Herbert, ed. LC 80-12234. 88p. 1980. lib. bdg. 12.00x (ISBN 0-87023-302-5); pap. 6.95 (ISBN 0-87023-303-3). U of Mass Pr.
Duncan, Denis. The Way of Love: A Thought & a Prayer a Day at a Time. LC 81-15925. 96p. 1982. Westminster.
Eastman, Dick. No Easy Road: Inspirational Thoughts on Prayer. new ed. (Direction Bks.). 1973. pap. 2.50 (ISBN 0-8010-3259-8). Baker Bk.
Ed Dufresne Ministries. Praying God's Word. 1979. pap. 1.50 (ISBN 0-89274-126-0). Harrison Hse.
Eddy, Mary B. & Carpenter, Gilbert C., eds. Watches, Prayers, Arguments. 100p. 1985. pap. 12.00 (ISBN 0-930227-01-8). Pasadena Pr.
Elliot, Elisabeth. Notes on Prayer. 1982. pap. 0.95 (ISBN 0-89107-254-3). Good News.
Elliott, Douglas. As You Recover. 32p. 1984. pap. 1.25 (ISBN 0-8010-3414-0). Baker Bk.
Ellul, Jacques. Prayer & Modern Man. Hopkins, C. Edward, tr. from Fr. 192p. 1973. pap. 6.95 (ISBN 0-8164-2081-5, HarpR). Har-Row.
Die Ernsthafte Christenpflicht. 251p. 1924. 5.95x (ISBN 0-8361-1141-9). Herald Pr.
Fandel, John. A Morning Answer. 1984. pap. 3.35 (ISBN 0-88028-041-7). Forward Movement.
Farrell, Edward. Prayer Is a Hunger. 4.95 (ISBN 0-87193-031-5). Dimension Bks.
Fauth, Roy D. Prayers for All Reasons. 1980. 3.50 (ISBN 0-89536-448-4, 1642). CSS of Ohio.
Ferris, Theodore P. Prayers. 1981. 6.95 (ISBN 0-8164-0483-6, HarpR). Har-Row.

Fiensy, David A. Prayers Alleged to Be Jewish: An Examination of the Constitutiones Apostolorum. (Brown Judaic Studies). 1985. 29.95 (ISBN 0-89130-795-8, 14-00-65); pap. 21.95 (ISBN 0-89130-796-6). Scholars Pr GA.
Foulks, Frances W. Effectual Prayer. 1979. 5.95 (ISBN 0-87159-031-X). Unity School.
Fritz, Patricia. We Praise You, O Lord! 2.95 (ISBN 0-8091-2518-8). Paulist Pr.
George, Denise & George, Timothy. Dear Unborn Child. LC 83-71714. 1984. pap. 4.95 (ISBN 0-8054-5658-9). Broadman.
Geres, Paul. Prayers for Impossible Days. Hjelm, Ingalill H., tr. from Fr. LC 75-36442. 64p. 1976. pap. 2.95 (ISBN 0-8006-1214-0, 1-1214). Fortress.
Godshall, C. David. Prayers in Dialogue. (Common & Lutheran Ser. C). 1985. 7.95 (ISBN 0-89536-759-9, 5866). CSS of Ohio.
--Prayers in Dialogue: Series A. rev. ed. Sherer, Michael L., ed. 1986. pap. 7.95 (ISBN 0-89536-813-7, 6842). CSS of Ohio.
Golden Treasury of Psalms & Prayers. 5.95 (ISBN 0-88088-242-5). Peter Pauper.
Gompertz, Helen. My Book of Prayers. (Illus.). 32p. 1986. pap. 3.95 (ISBN 0-8170-1104-8). Judson.
Grant, Gi-Gi. Thirty-Three Prayers. 1986. 6.95 (ISBN 0-533-05468-0). Vantage.
Green, Thomas. Weeds among the Wheat: Discernment: Where Prayer & Action Meet. LC 84-70663. 208p. (Orig.). 1984. pap. 4.95 (ISBN 0-87793-318-9). Ave Maria.
Greene, Barbara & Gollancz, Victor, eds. God of a Hundred Names: Prayers & Meditations from Many Faiths & Cultures. 304p. 1985. pap. 7.95 (ISBN 0-575-03645-1, Pub. by Gollancz England). David & Charles.
Greene, Carol. I Am One: Prayers for Singles. LC 85-23015. 112p. (Orig.). 1985. pap. 5.95 (ISBN 0-8066-2186-9, 10-3191). Augsburg.
Grenier, M. Special Day Prayers for the Very Young Child. LC 56-1719. 1983. 7.95 (ISBN 0-570-04076-0). Concordia.
Hagin, Kenneth E. Prevailing Prayer to Peace. 2nd ed. 1973. pap. 2.50 (ISBN 0-89276-071-0). Hagin Ministries.
Hard, Larry. Contemporary Altar Prayers, Vol. 7. 1983. 5.95 (ISBN 0-89536-576-6, 0383). CSS of Ohio.
Harrison, Helen R. Values to Cherish. (Orig.). 1978. pap. 4.50 (ISBN 0-87881-071-4). Mojave Bks.
Harrison, Russell F. More Brief Prayers for Bread & Cup. Lambert, Herbert, ed. LC 86-6076. 80p. (Orig.). 1986. pap. 4.95 (ISBN 0-8272-2319-6). CBP.
Hasbrouck, Hypatia. Handbook of Positive Prayer. 160p. 1984. 5.95 (ISBN 0-87159-051-4). Unity School.
Hayes, Bernard. Who Is This God You Pray To. 96p. (Orig.). 1981. pap. 2.95 (ISBN 0-914544-41-1). Living Flame Pr.
Hayes, Helen. A Gathering of Hope. 222p. 1985. pap. 7.95 large print ed. (ISBN 0-8027-2467-1). Walker & Co.
Hayford, Jack. Prayer Is Invading the Impossible. (Epiphany Bks.). 160p. 1983. pap. 2.50 (ISBN 0-345-30467-5). Ballantine.
Hays, Edward. Prayers for the Servants of God. (Illus.). 144p. (Orig.). 1980. pap. 6.95 (ISBN 0-939516-03-9). Forest Peace.
Herbert, George. The Temple: Sacred Poems & Private Ejaculations. 6th ed. LC 72-5489. (Select Bibliographies Reprint Ser.). 1972. Repr. of 1882 ed. 18.00 (ISBN 0-8369-6915-4). Ayer Co Pubs.
Hicks, Roy H. Praying Beyond God's Ability. 96p. 1977. 2.95 (ISBN 0-89274-052-3). Harrison Hse.
Hilburn, May S. One Hundred Short Prayers. 4th ed. 100p. 1983. pap. 3.50 softcover (ISBN 0-88053-313-7). Macoy Pub.
Hill, Robert. The Pathway to Prayer & Pietie. LC 74-28864. (English Experience Ser.: No. 744). 1975. Repr. of 1613 ed. 26.50 (ISBN 90-221-0744-2). Walter J Johnson.
Hinton, Pat C. Prayer after Nine Rainy Days & Other Family Prayers. 1978. pap. 4.95 (ISBN 0-86683-626-8, HarpR). Har-Row.
Hintz, Debra T. Prayer Services for Parish Meetings. (Illus.). 96p. (Orig.). 1983. pap. 9.95 (ISBN 0-89622-170-9). Twenty-Third.
Hoagland, Victor. Prayers: For Daily & Occasional Use. pap. 1.45 (ISBN 0-8091-5158-8). Paulist Pr.
Hobe, Phyllis. Your Personal Handbook of Prayer. LC 83-3475. 256p. 1983. 11.95 (ISBN 0-664-27007-7, A Bridgebooks Publication). Westminster.
--Your Personal Handbook of Prayer. LC 83-3475. 256p. 1987. 11.95 (A Bridgebooks Publication). Westminster.
Hollings, Michael, ed. Daily Readings with St. Therese of Lisieux. 1987. pap. 4.95 (ISBN 0-87243-154-1). Templegate.
Holmes, Deborah A. Survival Prayers for Young Mothers. 6.95 (ISBN 0-8042-2195-2). John Knox.
Holmes, Marjorie. Lord, Let Me Love: A Marjorie Holmes Treasury. LC 77-26516. 1978. 12.95 (ISBN 0-385-14093-2, Galilee). Doubleday.
Hostetter, B. David. Psalms & Prayers for Congregational Participation: Series A. 1983. 7.75 (ISBN 0-89536-639-8, 1633). CSS of Ohio.
--Psalms & Prayers for Congregational Participation: Series B (Common Consensus Lectionary) 1984. 7.75 (ISBN 0-89536-694-0, 4871). CSS of Ohio.
Hunter, Frances. Hot Line to Heaven. 1978. pap. 3.25 (ISBN 0-87162-117-7). Hunter Bks.
Jasper, Ronald, et al. Everyday Prayer. 1978. pap. 5.95 (ISBN 0-916134-34-2). Pueblo Pub Co.
Jennings, Theodore W. Life As Worship: Prayer & Praise in Jesus' Name. LC 82-7283. pap. 37.80 (ISBN 0-317-30146-2, 2025329). Bks Demand UMI.
Johnson, John R. Liturgy for the Free Church. LC 86-18782. 176p. 1986. lib. bdg. 19.95x (ISBN 0-89370-527-6). Borgo Pr.
Johnson, Samuel. Doctor Johnson's Prayers. LC 76-25954. 1976. Repr. of 1947 ed. lib. bdg. 17.50 (ISBN 0-8414-8580-1). Folcroft.
--Dr. Johnson's Prayers. Trueblood, Elton, ed. 88p. 1980. pap. 2.50 (ISBN 0-932970-17-6). Prinit Pr.
Jones, Gwyn. Three Poetical Prayer-Makers of the Island of Britain. (Warton Lectures on English Peotry). 9p. 1981. pap. 3.00 (ISBN 0-85672-356-8, Pub. by British Acad). Longwood Pub Group.
Judd, Judy, ed. Prayers & Reading for Worship. 1987. pap. 12.50 (ISBN 0-8309-0478-6). Herald Hse.
Kadel, William H. Prayers for Every Need. pap. 4.95 (ISBN 0-8042-2496-X). John Knox.
Kelly, Kelly B. Bread for the Eating. 121p. (Orig.). 1982. pap. 3.50 (ISBN 0-914544-39-X). Living Flame Pr.
Kenseth, Arnold & Unsworth, Richard P. Prayers for Worship Leaders. LC 77-15249. 132p. (Orig.). 1978. pap. 5.95 (ISBN 0-8006-1331-7, 1-1331). Fortress.
Keshavadas, Satguru S. Cosmic Hymns & Prayers. (Illus.). 174p. (Orig.). 1982. pap. text ed. 10.00 (ISBN 0-942508-13-0). Vishwa.
Kikkert, Lois. Prayers for the Seasons. 1.50 (ISBN 0-8091-9306-X). Paulist Pr.
--Prayers to a God of Surprises. 1.50 (ISBN 0-8091-9327-2). Paulist Pr.
Kirk, James G. When We Gather: A Book of Prayers for Worship, Year B. LC 83-14221. (Illus.). 144p. 1984. pap. 8.95 (ISBN 0-664-24553-6). Geneva Pr.
Kirvan, John. Our Heritage Is the Lord. new ed. 1980. 5.95 (ISBN 0-03-047661-5, HarpR). Har-Row.
Klenck, Robert H. Words Fitly Spoken: Reflections & Prayers. LC 79-13449. 1979. 10.95 (ISBN 0-934878-35-8, 07764-1, Dist. by W.W. Norton). Dembner Bks.
Klug, Ron. Bible Readings on Prayer. LC 85-28979. 112p. (Orig.). 1986. pap. 3.95 (ISBN 0-8066-2189-3, 10-0690). Augsburg.
Klug, Ron & Klug, Lyn. Family Prayers. LC 79-50081. 1979. pap. 4.95 (ISBN 0-8066-1708-X, 10-2258). Augsburg.
Koch, Sr. M. Pierre. Analysis of the Long Prayers in Old French Literature with Special Reference to the Biblical Creed Narrative Prayers. LC 70-94168. (Catholic University of America Studies in Romance Languages & Literatures Ser: No. 19). Repr. of 1940 ed. 24.00 (ISBN 0-404-50319-5). AMS Pr.
Krutza, Willlam J. Let's All Pray Together. 128p. 1984. pap. 3.95 (ISBN 0-8170-1024-6). Judson.
Lamb, Shirley. Washing & Dressing Prayers with Jesus. 1983. pap. 1.50 (ISBN 0-910709-41-6). PTL Repro.
Lang, J. David. Devotion for Every Day. (Illus.). pap. cancelled (ISBN 0-87239-230-9, 2099). Standard Pub.
Larrick, Nancy. Tambourines! Tambourines to Glory! Prayers & Poems. LC 81-23158. (Illus.). 122p. 1982. 8.95 (ISBN 0-664-32689-7). Westminster.
Larson, Mobby. Prayers of a New Mother. (Greeting Book Line Ser.). 48p. (Orig.). 1985. pap. 1.50 (ISBN 0-89622-230-6). Twenty Third.
Leen, Edward. Progress Through Mental Prayer. 1978. pap. 2.45 (ISBN 0-88479-012-6). Arena Lettres.
LeFevre, Perry D., ed. Prayers of Kierkegaard. LC 56-11000. (Midway Reprint Ser.). 1956. pap. 14.00x (ISBN 0-226-47059-8). U of Chicago Pr.
Lelen, J. M. Pray the Rosary. (Illus., Purse-Size). blue bdg. 0.60 (ISBN 0-89942-040-0, 40/05). Catholic Bk Pub.
Lesser, Isaac. The Pentateuch-Haftaroth & Sabeth Prayers: Hebrew with English. 22.50 (ISBN 0-317-00457-3). Shalom.
Lindsay, Gordon. The Art of Successful Praying. (School of Prayer Ser.). 1.25 (ISBN 0-89985-079-0). Christ Nations.
--Increase Your Prayer Power Tenfold. (School of Prayer Ser.). 1.25 (ISBN 0-89985-080-4). Christ Nations.
--Prayer & Fasting. (School of Prayer Ser.). 1.75 (ISBN 0-89985-076-6). Christ Nations.
--Prayer That Moves Mountains. (School of Prayer Ser.). 2.50 (ISBN 0-89985-078-2). Christ Nations.
--Praying to Change the World, 2 vols. (School of Prayer Ser.). 2.95 ea. Vol. 1 (ISBN 0-89985-956-9). Vol. 2 (ISBN 0-89985-957-7). Christ Nations.
Llewelyn, Robert & Moss, Edward, eds. Daily Readings with William Law. 1987. pap. 4.95 (ISBN 0-87243-153-3). Templegate.
Loder, Ted. Guerrillas of Grace: Prayers for the Battle. 2nd ed. LC 84-26096. (Illus.). 133p. (Orig.). 1984. pap. 9.95 (ISBN 0-931055-04-0). LuraMedia.
Lovasik, Lawrence G. I Believe in God: The Apostles' Creed. (Saint Joseph Picture Bks.). (Illus.). flexible bdg. 0.95 (ISBN 0-89942-276-4, 276). Catholic Bk Pub.
Lyons, H. P. Praying Our Prayers. 1976. 4.95 (ISBN 0-8199-0598-4). Franciscan Herald.
McCord, David. Let Us Pray. 64p. 1986. pap. 2.95 (ISBN 0-87403-099-4, 3025). Standard Pub.
McDonald, Julie J. Good Graces: Table Prayers. Liffring-Zug, Joan, et al, eds. (Illus.). 64p. (Orig.). 1986. pap. 7.95. Penfield.
McGiffert, Arthur C., Jr. Public Prayers. LC 83-83269. (Studies in Ministry & Parish Life). 44p. 1984. pap. 2.50x (ISBN 0-913552-24-0). Exploration Pr.
McKenzie, John L. Mastering the Meaning of the Bible. 140p. 1986. 4.95 (ISBN 0-87193-252-0). Dimension Bks.
Macleod, Donald. Princeton Pulpit Prayers. 112p. (Orig.). 1987. prayerbook 9.95 (ISBN 0-941850-21-8). Sunday Pubns.
McNally, Thomas & Storey, William G., eds. Lord Hear Our Prayer. LC 78-67423. (Illus.). 1978. 5.95 (ISBN 0-87793-163-1). Ave Maria.
Malyala, Pandurangarao. Daily Prayers. (Illus., Orig.). 1984. pap. 2.00 (ISBN 0-938924-24-9). Sri Shirdi Sai.
Mattison, Judith. Who Will Listen to Me? Prayer Thoughts for High School Girls. LC 77-72450. (Illus.). 1977. pap. 3.95 (ISBN 0-8066-1596-6, 10-7085). Augsburg.
Mazza, Enrico. The Eucharistic Prayers of the Roman Catholic Church. O'Connell, Matthew J., tr. from Ital. 380p. (Orig.). 1986. pap. 19.50 (ISBN 0-916134-78-4). Pueblo Pub Co.
Merton, Thomas. Contemplative Prayer. 1971. pap. 3.50 (ISBN 0-385-09219-9, Im). Doubleday.
Micklem, Nathaniel. Prayers & Praises. 1982. pap. 3.95x (ISBN 0-7152-0541-2). Outlook.
Miller, William A. Conversations. LC 80-54283. 96p. 1980. pap. 3.50 (ISBN 0-934104-04-2). Woodland.
The Minature Book of Hours. 480p. 250.00 (ISBN 0-8115-0905-2). Kraus Repr.
Montefiore, C. G. Ancient Jewish & Greek Consolation. LC 75-184052. 86p. 1973. text ed. 7.95 (ISBN 0-87677-045-6). Hartmore.
Morgan, John. You Can't Manage Alone: Practical Prayers for Conscientious Managers. 272p. 1986. gift ed. 12.95 (ISBN 0-310-33608-2). Zondervan.
Morgan, John S. & Philp, J. R. You Can't Manage Alone. 256p. (Orig.). 1985. pap. 4.95 (ISBN 0-310-33602-3, 12766P). Zondervan.
Morneau, Robert F. Mantras for the Evening. LC 82-83587. (Illus.). 116p. (Orig.). 1982. pap. text ed. 4.95 (ISBN 0-8146-1269-5). Liturgical Pr.
--Mantras for the Morning: An Introduction to Holistic Prayer. LC 81-1085. (Illus.). 120p. 1981. pap. 4.95 (ISBN 0-8146-1210-5). Liturgical Pr.
--Trinity Sunday Revisted. LC 79-25097. 96p. 1980. pap. 3.50 (ISBN 0-8146-1084-6). Liturgical Pr.
Mother Teresa of Calcutta. Life in the Spirit: Reflections, Meditations, & Prayers. LC 82-48938. 128p. 1983. 10.45i (ISBN 0-06-066021-X, HarpR). Har-Row.
Mother Teresa of Calcutta & Roger of Taize. Meditations on the Way of the Cross. (Illus.). 64p. (Orig.). 1987. pap. 5.95 (ISBN 0-8298-0585-0). Pilgrim NY.
Moynahan, Michael. God of Seasons. LC 79-93127. 1980. pap. text ed. 4.95 (ISBN 0-89390-019-2). Resource Pubns.
Moynahan, Michael E. God of Untold Tales. LC 79-64823. 1979. pap. 4.95 (ISBN 0-89390-009-5). Resource Pubns.
Murphy, Joseph. Quiet Moments with God. pap. 2.00 (ISBN 0-87516-276-2). De Vorss.
Murray, Andrew. The Believer's School of Prayer. rev. ed. LC 82-4401. 201p. 1982. pap. 3.95 (ISBN 0-87123-195-6, 210195). Bethany Hse.
Myers, Rawley. Lent: A Journey to Resurrection Prayers & Reflections for the Penitential Season. LC 83-63084. 192p. 1984. pap. 5.95 (ISBN 0-87973-605-4). Our Sunday Visitor.
Noffke, Suzanne, ed. Prayers of Catherine of Siena. LC 82-60746. 288p. 1983. pap. 9.95 (ISBN 0-8091-2508-0). Paulist Pr.
Nommensen, B. P. Comfort for the Sick. rev. ed. 1976. pap. 5.00 (ISBN 0-8100-0011-3, 06N0553). Northwest Pub.
Norden, John. A Pensive Mans Practise. LC 77-171776. (English Experience Ser.: No. 401). 192p. 1971. Repr. of 1584 ed. 18.50 (ISBN 90-221-0401-X). Walter J Johnson.
--Progress of Piety. Repr. of 1847 ed. 21.00 (ISBN 0-384-41910-0). Johnson Repr.
Nouwen, Henri J. Cry for Mercy: Prayers from the Genesee. LC 80-2563. (Illus.). 175p. 1983. pap. 6.95 (ISBN 0-385-17508-6, Im). Doubleday.
Oglesby, Stuart R. Prayers for All Occasions. 180p. 1983. pap. 5.95 (ISBN 0-8042-2485-4). John Knox.
Original Publications, tr. from Span. Helping Yourself With Selected Prayers. pap. 3.95 (ISBN 0-942272-01-3). Original Pubns.
Ortmayer, Roger. Sing & Pray & Shout Hurray. 1974. pap. 2.75 (ISBN 0-377-00004-3). Friend Pr.
Panj Sura: Collection of 5 Famous Prayers. 4.50 (ISBN 0-686-18594-3). Kazi Pubns.
Pawelzik, Fritz. I Sing Your Praise All the Day Long. (Illus., Orig.). 1967. pap. 1.50 (ISBN 0-377-37221-8). Friend Pr.
Payne, Alfred C. A University at Prayer. LC 86-14613. (Illus.). 1987. 13.95x (ISBN 0-9617635-0-7). VA Tech Educ Found.
Pennington, M. Basil. Centering Prayer: Renewing an Ancient Christian Prayer Form. LC 82-45077. 256p. 1982. pap. 4.50 (ISBN 0-385-18179-5, Im). Doubleday.
--Pocket Book of Prayers. LC 85-12936. 192p. 1986. pap. 4.50 (ISBN 0-385-23298-5, Im). Doubleday.
--Prayertimes: Morning-Midday-Evening. LC 87-4212. 168p. 1987. pap. 3.95 (ISBN 0-385-24061-9, Im). Doubleday.
Phifer, Kenneth G. A Book of Uncommon Prayer. LC 82-50945. 128p. 1983. pap. 5.95 (ISBN 0-8358-0451-8). Upper Room.
Phillips, E. Lee. Prayers for Worship. 148p. 1985. pap. 4.95 (ISBN 0-8010-7090-2). Baker Bk.
Porto, Humberto & Schlesinger, Hugo. Prayers of Blessing & Praise for All Occasions. Leipsiger, Michael, tr. from Port. Tr. of Dialogando com Deus. 128p. 1987. 9.95 (ISBN 0-89622-311-6). Twenty-Third.
Poslusney, Venard. Prayer of Love: The Art of Aspiration. 128p. (Orig.). 1975. pap. 2.95 (ISBN 0-914544-06-3). Living Flame Pr.
Prayers for All Occasions. 1951. 0.95 (ISBN 0-88028-006-9). Forward Movement.
Prayers New & Old. 1937. 1.25 (ISBN 0-88028-005-0). Forward Movement.
Prayers of Mohammad. (With arabic text). pap. 16.50 (ISBN 0-686-18346-0). Kazi Pubns.
Prayers of the Orthodox Church. pap. 1.00 (ISBN 0-317-11389-5). Eastern Orthodox.
Prince, Derek. Praying for the Government. 1970. pap. 1.50 (ISBN 0-934920-11-7, B-20). Derek Prince.
--Shaping History Through Prayer & Fasting. 1973. 9.95 (ISBN 0-934920-23-0, B-24); pap. 5.95 (ISBN 0-686-12766-8, B-25). Derek Prince.
Private Prayers, Put Forth by Authority During the Reign of Queen Elizabeth. 1851. 51.00 (ISBN 0-384-47970-7). Johnson Repr.
Quezada, Adolfo. A Desert Place. (Illus.). 96p. (Orig.). 1982. pap. 2.95 (ISBN 0-914544-40-3). Living Flame Pr.
Rahman, A. Utility of Prayers. pap. 3.50 (ISBN 0-686-18590-0). Kazi Pubns.
Rahner, Karl. Prayers for a Lifetime. 256p. 1984. 12.95 (ISBN 0-8245-0678-2). Crossroad NY.
--Prayers for a Lifetime. 256p. 1986. pap. 8.95 (ISBN 0-317-42453-X). Crossroad NY.
Rauschenbusch, Walter. For God & the People. LC 77-8615. 1977. lib. bdg. 22.00 (ISBN 0-8414-7332-3). Folcroft.
--Prayers of the Social Awakening. LC 77-8615. 1909. 22.00 (ISBN 0-8414-7332-3). Folcroft.
Redding, David A., et al. The Prayers I Love. LC 78-17798. (Illus., Orig.). 1978. pap. 6.95 (ISBN 0-89407-025-8). Strawberry Hill.
Reutemann, Charles. Let's Pray Two. LC 82-60612. (Illus.). 224p. (Orig.). 1982. pap. 6.95 (ISBN 0-88489-148-8). St Mary's.
Revell, Peter. Fifteenth-Century English Prayers & Meditations: A Bibliography of Manuscripts Preserved at the British Museum Library. LC 75-6579. (Reference Library of Humanities: Vol. 19). 150p. 1975. lib. bdg. 28.00 (ISBN 0-8240-1098-1). Garland Pub.
Richards, Lawrence O. Believer's Promise Book. 80p. (Orig.). 1984. pap. 2.50 (ISBN 0-310-43462-9, 18144P). Zondervan.
Robertson, John M. Perdonado. Lumpuy, Luis B., tr. from Eng. Orig. Title: Pardoned. (Span., Illus.). 64p. 1985. pap. 0.95 (ISBN 0-8297-0909-6). Life Pubs Intl.

Rogahn, Kenneth W. Begin with Prayer: Prayers & Devotional Outlines for Church Meetings. 112p. 1985. 6.95 (ISBN 0-570-03962-2, 15-2178). Concordia.

Rosage, David E. Linger with Me: Moments Aside with Jesus. 212p. (Orig.). 1979. pap. 3.95 (ISBN 0-914544-29-2). Living Flame Pr.

Ryder, Andrew. Prayer: The Eastern Tradition. (Orig.). 1983. pap. 2.95 (ISBN 0-914544-47-0). Living Flame Pr.

Sabbath, Linda. The Radiant Heart. 1986. Repr. of 1985 ed. 4.95 (ISBN 0-87193-003-X). Dimension Bks.

St. John of Kronstadt. On Prayer. (Orig.). 1985. pap. 3.00 (ISBN 0-317-30263-9). Holy Trinity.

St. Romain, Philip. Praying the Daily Gospels: A Guide to Meditation. LC 84-71186. 248p. (Orig.). 1984. pap. 5.95 (ISBN 0-87793-314-6). Ave Maria.

Savage, Robert C. Pocket Praise. (Pocket Ser.). 176p. 1985. pap. 2.95 (ISBN 0-8423-4931-6). Tyndale.

--Pocket Prayers: Seven Hundred & Seventy-Seven Bible Ways to Pray. 1982. pap. 2.95 (ISBN 0-8423-4849-2). Tyndale.

Schreivogel, Paul A. Small Prayers for Small Children. LC 76-135226. (Illus.). 32p. 1980. pap. 3.95 (ISBN 0-8066-1804-3, 10-5836). Augsburg.

Schroeder, L. Celebrate-While We Wait. (Illus.). 1977. pap. 4.95 (ISBN 0-570-03052-8, 6-1177). Concordia.

Scroggie, W. Graham. Paul's Prison Prayers. LC 80-8077. (W. Graham Scroggie Library). 78p. 1981. pap. 4.50 (ISBN 0-8254-3737-7). Kregel.

Seagren, Daniel R. Uncommon Prayers for Couples. 1980. pap. 3.95 (ISBN 0-8010-8173-4). Baker Bk.

See, Maura, ed. Daily Readings with St. Augustine. 1987. pap. 4.95 (ISBN 0-87243-152-5). Templegate.

Shad, A. R. Prescribed Islamic Prayers. pap. 5.50 (ISBN 0-686-18593-5). Kazi Pubns.

Shaikh Muhammad Sarwar. Arabic Alphabet & Daily Prayer. 34p. 1981. pap. 3.00 (ISBN 0-941724-07-7). Islamic Seminary.

Shepherd, Massey H., Jr. Companion of Prayer for Daily Living. LC 78-62063. 1978. pap. 3.95 kivar (ISBN 0-8192-1230-X). Morehouse.

Shiner, Margaret. Good Morning, Lord: Prayers & Promises for Teens. (Good Morning, Lord Ser.). 96p. 1976. 4.95 (ISBN 0-8010-8079-7). Baker Bk.

Shree Rudram: Namakam & Chamakam. 96p. (Orig.). 1978. pap. 3.50 (ISBN 0-914602-64-0). SYDA Found.

Siddiqui, A. H. Prayers of the Prophet with Arabic Text. pap. 2.00 (ISBN 0-686-18345-2). Kazi Pubns.

Simons, Thomas G. Blessings for God's People: A Book of Blessings for All Occasions. LC 82-62045. 112p. (Orig.). 1983. pap. 5.95 (ISBN 0-87793-264-6). Ave Maria.

Skold, Betty W. The Kids Are Gone, Lord, but I'm Still Here: Prayers for Mothers. LC 80-67801. 96p. (Orig.). 1981. pap. 5.95 (ISBN 0-8066-1863-9, 10-3703). Augsburg.

--Lord, I Need an Answer: Story Devotions for Girls. LC 81-52279. 112p. (Orig.). 1982. pap. 3.95 (ISBN 0-8066-1911-2, 10-4099). Augsburg.

Smuck, Harold V. I Do Not Climb This Mountain Alone. (Illus.). 48p. (Orig.). 1985. pap. 3.00 (ISBN 0-913408-88-3). Friends United.

Snowden, Rita. Prayers in Later Life. 1981. pap. 3.50 (ISBN 0-8358-0435-6). Upper Room.

Snyder, Bernadet M. Dear God, I Have This Terrible Problem: A Housewife's Secret Letters. 96p. 1983. pap. 2.95 (ISBN 0-89243-188-1). Liguori Pubns.

Snyder, Bernadette M. Everyday Prayers for Everyday People. LC 83-63165. 132p. 1984. pap. 4.95 (ISBN 0-87973-604-6, 604). Our Sunday Visitor.

--More Graham Crackers, Galoshes, & God. LC 85-80929. 96p. (Orig.). 1985. pap. 2.95 (ISBN 0-89243-243-8). Liguori Pubns.

Sorenson, Stephen W. Lord, I Want to Know You Better: Story Devotions for Boys. LC 81-52280. 112p. (Orig.). 1982. pap. 3.95 (ISBN 0-8066-1912-0, 10-4103). Augsburg.

Speckner, Killian. The Prayers of Father Killian. 384p. 1986. pap. 8.95 (ISBN 0-941478-56-4). Paraclete Pr.

Spell, Leonard, Sr. House of Prayer for All Nations. 174p. 1986. 12.95x (ISBN 0-9615439-1-4, 133997); pap. 9.95x (ISBN 0-9615439-2-2). Spell Assoc.

Spiess, Margaret B. Hold Me Steady, Lord: And Other Prayers for Mothers. 112p. 1986. text ed. 7.95 (ISBN 0-8010-8266-8). Baker Bk.

Stevenson, Robert Louis. The Book of Selected Prayers by Robert Louis Stevenson. Rev. ed. (Illus.). 99p. 1982. 47.85 (ISBN 0-89901-066-0). Found Class Reprints.

--Prayers Written at Vailima. xi, 61p. 1973. 40.00 (ISBN 0-317-11648-7). Dawsons.

--Selected Prayers by Robert Louis Stevenson. (Illus.). 1980. Repr. of 1904 ed. 39.75 (ISBN 0-89901-004-0). Found Class Reprints.

Storey, William G. Praise Him: A Prayerbook for Today's Christian. 224p. (Orig.). 1973. pap. 2.95 (ISBN 0-87793-056-2). Ave Maria.

Stravinskas, Peter M. Prayer Book of the Bible: Reflection on the Old Testament. LC 83-63171. 160p. 1984. pap. 5.95 (ISBN 0-87973-606-2, 606). Our Sunday Visitor.

Stuhlmueller, Carroll. The Psalms. (Read & Pray Ser.). 1979. 1.75 (ISBN 0-8199-0631-X). Franciscan Herald.

Sullivan, Daniel & Andrews, Judy. Sunday Scriptures. 4.95 (ISBN 0-8091-9336-1). Paulist Pr.

Supplementary Prayers & Readings for the High Holidays. 216p. 1960. pap. 6.00 (ISBN 0-935457-34-8). Reconstructionist Pr.

Supplementary Prayers for the Pilgramage Festivals: Sukkot & Simhat Torah, Vol. 2. 1956. pap. 3.50 (ISBN 0-935457-36-4). Reconstructionist Pr.

Supplementary Prayers for the Pilgrimage Festivals: Pesah & Shavuot, Vol. 1. 95p. 1956. pap. 3.00 (ISBN 0-935457-35-6). Reconstructionist Pr.

Table Graces for the Family. rev. ed. 128p. 1984. 4.95 (ISBN 0-8407-5369-1). Nelson.

Talib, Ali I. Supplications. Chittick, William C., tr. LC 84-52746. 63p. 1985. pap. 4.95 (ISBN 0-940368-46-3). Tahrike Tarsile Quran.

Thorne, Leo S. Prayers from Riverside. 120p. (Orig.). 1983. pap. 5.95 (ISBN 0-8298-0643-1). Pilgrim NY.

Thurman, Howard. The Centering Moment. LC 80-67469. 1980. pap. 6.95 (ISBN 0-913408-64-6). Friends United.

Travnikar, Rock. The Blessing Cup. 64p. (Orig.). 1979. pap. 2.25 (ISBN 0-912228-60-1). St Anthony Mess Pr.

Treinen, Sylvester. An Adventure in Prayer. 16p. (Orig.). 1983. pap. 30.00 pkg. of 100 (ISBN 0-8146-1331-4). Liturgical Pr.

Tugwell, Simon. Prayer in Practice. 1980. pap. 7.95 (ISBN 0-87243-099-5). Templegate.

Turner, Dean. Krinkle Nose: A Prayer of Thanks. LC 77-78424. 1978. 6.95 (ISBN 0-8159-6002-6). Devin.

Uboldi, Gian L., illus. A Book of Prayers. (Illus.). 192p. 1981. 4.95 (ISBN 0-87973-667-4, 667). Our Sunday Visitor.

Van Corstanje, Auspicius. Saint Francis Prayer Book. 1978. pap. 2.50 (ISBN 0-8199-0693-X). Franciscan Herald.

Vaswig, William L. At Your Word, Lord. LC 81-52272. 128p. (Orig.). 1982. pap. 5.95 (ISBN 0-8066-1904-X, 10-0498). Augsburg.

Ward, Benedicta, tr. Prayers & Meditations of St. Anselm. (Classics Ser.). 1979. pap. 5.95 (ISBN 0-14-044278-2). Penguin.

Ward, Mae Y. The Seeking Heart: Prayer Journal of Mae Yoho Ward. Ward, Don, ed. LC 84-23836. 144p. (Orig.). 1985. pap. 7.95 (ISBN 0-8272-3420-1). CBP.

White Eagle. Prayer in the New Age. 1957. 3.95 (ISBN 0-85487-041-5). De Vorss.

Wiles, G. P. Paul's Intercessory Prayers. (Society for New Testament Studies Monographs: No. 24). 360p. 1974. 59.50 (ISBN 0-521-20274-4). Cambridge U Pr.

Willis, Elbert. Prayer for Guidance. 1977. 1.25 (ISBN 0-89858-012-9). Fill the Gap.

--Prayer for Patient Waiting. 1977. 1.25 (ISBN 0-89858-002-1). Fill the Gap.

--Praying the Right Way. 1977. 1.25 (ISBN 0-89858-011-0). Fill the Gap.

--Private Praise. 1977. 1.25 (ISBN 0-89858-009-9). Fill the Gap.

Wood, Arthur S., ed. Daily Readings with John Wesley. 1987. pap. 4.95 (ISBN 0-87243-158-4). Templegate.

Wood, Robert. A Thirty-Day Experiment in Prayer. LC 78-65160. 1978. pap. 3.75 (ISBN 0-8358-0380-5). Upper Room.

Word Ministries, Inc. Prayers That Avail Much. 110p. (Orig.). 1980. pap. 3.95 (ISBN 0-89274-116-3). Harrison Hse.

Wurmbrand, Richard. One Hundred Prison Meditations. 1984. pap. 2.95 (ISBN 0-88270-577-6). Bridge Pub.

Yatiswarananda, Swami, tr. from Sanskrit. Universal Prayers. (Sanskrit & Eng.). 3.95 (ISBN 0-87481-443-X). Vedanta Pr.

Young, Helen. Children Won't Wait: A Parent's Prayer. 1985. gift ed. 6.95 (ISBN 0-915720-83-3). Brownlow Pub Co.

Ziad, Kumail I. Du'A-E-Kumail. Mardi, N. Hussein, tr. from Arabic. 35p. Date not set. pap. 2.95 (ISBN 0-940368-75-7). Tahrike Tarsile Quran.

Ziegler, Edward K. Prayers for Public Worship. Eller, David, ed. 1986. pap. 3.95. Brethren.

Zundel, Veronica, ed. Eerdmans' Book of Famous Prayers. (Illus.). 126p. 1984. 12.95 (ISBN 0-8028-3593-7). Eerdmans.

PRAYERS, PASTORAL

see Pastoral Prayers

PRAYERS, TABLE

see Grace at Meals

PRAYERS FOR CHILDREN

see Children–Prayer-Books and Devotions

PRAYERS FOR THE DEAD

Levine, Stephen. Meetings at the Edge: Conversations with the Grieving & the Dying, the Healing & the Healed. LC 82-45931. 264p. 1984. pap. 7.95 (ISBN 0-385-18786-6, Anchor Pr). Doubleday.

Scherman, Nosson. Kaddish. (Art Scroll Mesorah Ser.). 64p. 1980. 6.95 (ISBN 0-89906-160-5). Mesorah Pubns.

PRAYERS FOR YOUTH

see Youth–Prayer-Books and Devotions

PRAYERS IN THE PUBLIC SCHOOLS

see Religion in the Public Schools

PREACHING

see also Bible–Homiletical Use; Communication (Theology); Homiletical Illustrations; Sermons

Abbey, Merrill R. Communication in Pulpit & Parish. LC 72-14329. 238p. 1980. pap. 8.50 (ISBN 0-664-24312-6). Westminster.

Achtemeier, Elizabeth. Creative Preaching: Finding the Words. LC 80-16890. (Abingdon Preacher's Library). 128p. (Orig.). 1980. pap. 6.95 (ISBN 0-687-09831-9). Abingdon.

--Preaching As Theology & Art. 144p. 1984. pap. 8.75 (ISBN 0-687-33828-X). Abingdon.

Adams, Jay E. Preaching to the Heart. 40p. 1983. pap. 1.75 (ISBN 0-87552-080-4). Presby & Reformed.

--Preaching with Purpose. 1983. pap. 6.95 (ISBN 0-87552-078-2). Presby & Reformed.

--Preaching with Purpose: The Urgent Task of Homiletics. (A Jay Adams Library). 160p. 1986. pap. 7.95 (ISBN 0-310-51091-0, 12121P). Zondervan.

Alan Of Lille. The Art of Preaching. Evans, Gillian R., tr. (Cistercian Fathers Ser.: No. 23). (Lat., Orig.). 1981. pap. 13.95 (ISBN 0-87907-923-1). Cistercian Pubns.

Allen, Kring. The Paradox of Preaching. (Illus.). 104p. (Orig.). 1986. pap. 9.95 (ISBN 1-55630-018-2). Brentwood Comm.

Allen, R. Earl & Gregory, Joel. Southern Baptist Preaching Today. 1987. pap. 11.95 (ISBN 0-8054-5714-3). Broadman.

Allen, Ronald J. Our Eyes Can Be Opened: Preaching the Miracle Stories of the Synoptic Gospels Today. LC 81-43679. 146p. 1983. pap. text ed. 9.50 (ISBN 0-8191-2671-3). U Pr of Amer.

Apostolon, Billy. Preach the Word. (Sermon Outline Ser.). 1978. pap. 2.50 (ISBN 0-8010-0039-4). Baker Bk.

Archbishop Averky Taushev. Rukovodstvo po Gomiletikje. Tr. of Handbook for Homiletics. 110p. 1961. pap. text ed. 5.00 (ISBN 0-317-30276-0). Holy Trinity.

Asquith, Glenn H. Renewed Power for Preaching. 128p. 1983. pap. 3.95 (ISBN 0-8170-1003-3). Judson.

Aycock, Don, ed. Preaching with Purpose & Power: Selected E. Y. Mullins Lectures on Preaching. LC 81-22388. vi, 314p. 1982. 15.95 (ISBN 0-86554-027-6, MUP-H27). Mercer Univ Pr.

Aycock, Don M. The E. Y. Mullins Lectures on Preaching with Reference to the Aristotelian Triad. LC 79-6080. 113p. 1980. text ed. 20.50 (ISBN 0-8191-0981-9); pap. text ed. 9.25 (ISBN 0-8191-0982-7). U Pr of Amer.

--Heralds to a New Age: Preaching for the Twenty-First Century. 228p. 1985. 11.95 (ISBN 0-87178-352-5). Brethren.

Barnhart, Phil. More Seasonings for Sermons. 1985. 6.25 (ISBN 0-89536-723-8, 5807). CSS of Ohio.

--Still More Seasonings for Sermons, Vol. 3. 1986. 7.50 (ISBN 0-89536-787-4, 6805). CSS of Ohio.

Barry, James C., ed. Preaching in Today's World. LC 83-24021. (Orig.). 1984. pap. 6.50 (ISBN 0-8054-2113-0). Broadman.

Barth, Karl. Karl Barth: Preaching Through the Christian Year. McTavish, John B. & Wells, Harold G., eds. 288p. 1978. 11.95 (ISBN 0-567-29052-2, Pub. by T&T Clark Ltd UK). Fortress.

Bartlett, Gene E. Postscript to Preaching: After Forty Years, How Will I Preach Today? 88p. 1981. pap. 3.95 (ISBN 0-8170-0909-4). Judson.

Baumann, J. Daniel. An Introduction to Contemporary Preaching. 1972. 14.95 (ISBN 0-8010-0572-8). Baker Bk.

Baxter, Batsell B. Speaking for the Master. pap. 4.95 (ISBN 0-8010-0588-4). Baker Bk.

Beatty, David. He That Wins Souls Is Wise. 1982. pap. 0.75 (ISBN 0-88144-005-1, CPS-005). Christian Pub.

Beecher, Henry W. Yale Lectures on Preaching. 1976. Repr. of 1872 ed. 39.00x (ISBN 0-403-06546-1, Regency). Scholarly.

--Yale Lectures on Preaching. (The Works of Henry Ward Beecher Ser.). vii, 359p. Repr. of 1873 ed. lib. bdg. 29.00 (ISBN 0-932051-02-2, Pub. by Am Repr Serv). Am Biog Serv.

Bell, Foster & Bell, Darlene. Queener: The Man Behind the Preaching. 1976. pap. 2.95 (ISBN 0-934942-13-7). White Wing Pub.

Berkley, James D. Preaching to Convince. 192p. 1986. 9.95 (ISBN 0-8499-0577-X). Word Bks.

Berkley, Jim, ed. Preaching to Convince. (Leadership Library). 175p. 1986. 9.95 (ISBN 0-917463-11-0). Chr Today.

Best, Ernest. From Text to Sermon: Responsible Use of the New Testament in Preaching. LC 77-79584. 1978. 8.95 (ISBN 0-8042-0245-1). John Knox.

Biddle, Perry, Jr. Lectionary Preaching Workbook B: Series II. (Orig.). 1987. pap. price not set (ISBN 0-89536-879-X, 7865). CSS of Ohio.

Boden, Evan H. Guide for the Lay Preacher. 1979. pap. 2.95 (ISBN 0-8170-0836-5). Judson.

Booth, William. How to Preach. 84p. (Orig.). 1979. pap. 3.95 (ISBN 0-89216-026-8). Salv Army Suppl South.

Braga, James. Como Preparar Mensajes. Orig. Title: How to Prepare Bible Messages. (Port.). 1986. write for info. (ISBN 0-8297-1609-2). Life Pubs Intl.

Broadus, J. A. Tratado Sobre la Predicacion. Barocio, Ernesto, tr. Orig. Title: On the Preparation & Delivery of Sermons. 336p. 1985. pap. 5.50 (ISBN 0-311-42034-6). Casa Bautista.

Brokhoff, John. Preaching the Parables: Series B. (Orig.). 1987. pap. price not set (ISBN 0-89536-880-3, 7866). CSS of Ohio.

Brown, Henry C., Jr., et al. Steps to the Sermon. LC 63-19068. 1963. 12.95 (ISBN 0-8054-2103-3). Broadman.

Brownlow, Leroy. A Time to Laugh - or Grandpa Was a Preacher. 1973. gift ed. 6.95 (ISBN 0-915720-11-6). Brownlow Pub Co.

Buerlein, Homer K. How to Preach More Powerful Sermons. LC 85-26378. 140p. (Orig.). 1986. pap. 10.95 (ISBN 0-664-24683-4). Westminster.

Burghardt, Walter J. Sir, We Would Like to See Jesus: Homilies from a Hilltop. LC 82-60589. 1983. pap. 8.95 (ISBN 0-8091-2490-4). Paulist Pr.

Burke, John. Gospel Power: Toward the Revitalization of Preaching. LC 77-14517. 1978. pap. 4.95 (ISBN 0-8189-0359-7). Alba.

Burke, John, ed. A New Look at Preaching. (Good News Studies Ser.: Vol. 7). 1983. pap. 6.95 (ISBN 0-89453-336-3). M Glazier.

Capps, Donald. Pastoral Counseling & Preaching: A Quest for an Integrated Ministry. LC 80-18502. 156p. 1980. pap. 8.95 (ISBN 0-664-24342-8). Westminster.

Carl, William J., II. Preaching Christian Doctrine. LC 83-48923. pap. 8.95 (ISBN 0-8006-1788-6). Fortress.

Carroll, Thomas K. Preaching the Word. (Message of the Fathers of the Church Ser.: Vol. 11). 15.95 (ISBN 0-89453-351-7); pap. 9.95 (ISBN 0-89453-322-3). M Glazier.

Catherwood, Christopher, ed. Martyn Lloyd-Jones: Chosen by God. LC 86-70463. 288p. (Orig.). 1986. pap. 7.95 (ISBN 0-89107-404-X, Crossway Bks). Good News.

Caudill, R. Paul. Mountain Preacher, Vol. 3. LC 84-71992. 1986. pap. 3.00 (ISBN 0-938980-05-X). Blue Ridge.

Champlin, Joseph M. Messengers of God's Word: A Handbook for Lectors. 1983. pap. 4.95 (ISBN 0-8091-2484-X). Paulist Pr.

Chartier, Myron R. Preaching As Communication: An Interpersonal Perspective. LC 80-21304. (Abingdon Preacher Library). 128p. (Orig.). 1981. pap. 6.95 (ISBN 0-687-33826-3). Abingdon.

Cothen, Joe H. Equipped for Good Work: A Guide for Pastors. LC 80-37964. 336p. 1981. 14.95 (ISBN 0-88289-271-1). Pelican.

Cox, James W. Preaching: A Comprehensive Approach to the Design & Delivery of Sermons. LC 84-48214. 320p. 1985. 18.45 (ISBN 0-06-061600-8, HarpR). Har-Row.

Cox, James W. & Cox, Patricia P., eds. Twentieth Century Pulpit, Vol. II. LC 77-21997. 1981. pap. 9.95 (ISBN 0-687-42716-9). Abingdon.

Crabtree, T. T. The Zondervan Nineteen Eighty-Seven Pastor's Annual: A Planned Preaching Program for the Year. (Pastor's Annual Ser.). 384p. 1986. 12.95 (ISBN 0-310-22701-1, 11384P). Zondervan.

--Zondervan Pastor's Annual 1988: A Planned Preaching Program. rev. ed. Smith, M., ed. (Zondervan Pastor's Annuals). 384p. 1987. Repr. of 1968 ed. price not set (ISBN 0-310-22711-9). Zondervan.

Craddock, Fred B. Preaching. 224p. 1985. 16.95 (ISBN 0-687-33636-8). Abingdon.

Craddock, Fred B., et al. Preaching the New Common Lectionary: Year B: Lent, Holy Week, Easter, 2 vols. 256p. (Orig.). 1984. Vol. 2, 256 pgs. pap. 9.95 (ISBN 0-687-33846-8); Vol. 3, 304 pgs. pap. 11.95 (ISBN 0-687-33847-6). Abingdon.

--Preaching the New Common Lectionary: Year C-Advent, Christmas, Epiphany. 176p. (Orig.). 1985. pap. 9.50 (ISBN 0-687-33848-4). Abingdon.

Crane, J. D. Manual para Predicadores Laicos. 122p. 1983. pap. 2.10 (ISBN 0-311-42039-7). Casa Bautista.
Culpepper, R. Alan. One, Two, Three, John. Hayes, John, ed. LC 85-42821. (Preaching Guides). 132p. 1985. pap. 6.95 (ISBN 0-8042-3248-2). John Knox.
Dabney, Robert L. On Preaching. 1979. 11.95 (ISBN 0-85151-290-9). Banner of Truth.
Davis, H. Grady. Design for Preaching. LC 58-5749. (Orig.). 1958. 9.95 (ISBN 0-8006-0806-2, 1-806). Fortress.
Drakeford, John W. Humor in Preaching. 160p. 1986. pap. 6.95 (ISBN 0-310-20121-7). Zondervan.
Duncan, George B. Preacher among the Prophets. 176p. 1985. pap. 5.95 (ISBN 0-930577-00-0). N Burleson.
Eaton, Arthur W. The Famous Mather Byles: Noted Boston Tory Preacher, Poet, & Wit 1707-1788. facsimile ed. LC 74-165626. (Select Bibliographies Reprint Ser). Repr. of 1914 ed. 33.00 (ISBN 0-8369-5933-7). Ayer Co Pubs.
Edwards, O. C. The Living & Active Word: A Way to Preach from the Bible Today. 166p. 1975. 1.50 (ISBN 0-8164-0265-5, HarpR). Har-Row.
Edwards, O. C., Jr. Elements of Homiletic. LC 84-157333. 110p. (Orig.). 1982. pap. 7.95 (ISBN 0-916134-55-5). Pueblo Pub CO.
Eggold, Henry J. Preaching Is Dialogue. 144p. 1980. pap. 5.95 (ISBN 0-8010-3358-6). Baker Bk.
Evans, William. How to Prepare Sermons. 1964. 9.95 (ISBN 0-8024-3725-7). Moody.
Fakes, Dennis. Points with Punch. 1982. pap. 5.00 (ISBN 0-89536-534-0, 1616). CSS of Ohio.
Fant, Clyde. Preaching for Today. 1977. pap. 8.95 (ISBN 0-06-062332-2, RD-204, HarpR). Har-Row.
Farmer, Herbert H. Servant of the Word. LC 64-20405. 128p. (Orig.). 1964. pap. 3.95 (ISBN 0-8006-4001-2, 1-4001). Fortress.
Finley, James F. Wake up & Preach. LC 85-26667. 111p. (Orig.). 1986. pap. 5.95 (ISBN 0-8189-0492-5). Alba.
Fitzgerald, George. A Practical Guide to Preaching. LC 79-67742. 160p. (Orig.). 1980. pap. 5.95 (ISBN 0-8091-2281-2). Paulist Pr.
Fletcher, John. Portrait of a Preacher. 8.95 (ISBN 0-686-12902-4). Schmul Pub Co.
Foege, Richard H. Stewardship Preaching: Series C. 56p. (Orig.). 1985. pap. 4.95 (ISBN 0-8066-2152-4, 10-6003). Augsburg.
Foley, N. Nadine, intro. by. Preaching & the Non-Ordained: An Interdisciplinary Study. 1983. pap. 6.95 (ISBN 0-8146-1291-1). Liturgical Pr.
Freeman, Harold. Variety in Biblical Preaching. 192p. 1986. 12.95 (ISBN 0-8499-0562-1). Word Bks.
Fudge, Edward. Preaching with Power. pap. 2.00 (ISBN 0-686-12680-7). E Fudge.
Fulfilled in Your Hearing (The Homily in the Sunday Assembly) 48p. 1982. pap. 2.95 (ISBN 1-55586-850-9). US Catholic.
Fuller, Reginald H. Preaching the Lectionary: The Word of God for the Church Today. rev. ed. 672p. 1984. pap. 16.95 (ISBN 0-8146-1351-9). Liturgical Pr.
Gibble, Kenneth L. The Preacher as Jacob: A Paradigm for Pulpit Ministry. 144p. (Orig.). 1985. pap. 8.95 (ISBN 0-8164-2633-3, AY8587, HarpR). Har-Row.
Gibbs, A. P. The Preacher & His Preaching. 16.95 (ISBN 0-937396-31-1); pap. 10.95 (ISBN 0-937396-30-3). Walterick Pubs.
Gonzalez, Justo L. & Gonzalez, Catherine G. Liberation Preaching: The Pulpit & the Oppressed. LC 79-27858. (Abingdon Preacher's Library). 1980. pap. 6.95 (ISBN 0-687-21700-8). Abingdon.
Gravrock, Mark. Stewardship Preaching. (Ser. B). 56p. (Orig.). 1984. pap. 4.95 (ISBN 0-8066-2076-5, 10-6002). Augsburg.
Hall, Thor. The Future Shape of Preaching. LC 77-157537. pap. 40.00 (2026899). Bks Demand UMI.
Hamsher, Paul. Pulpit Preparation. (Orig.). 1981. pap. 5.95 (ISBN 0-937172-29-4). JLJ Pubs.
Haney, William R. From the Backwoods to Bethel. Jones, Amos, Jr., ed. LC 84-50332. 95p. (Orig.). 1985. pap. cancelled. Sunday School.
Hayes, John, ed. John Fred Craddock. (Knox Preaching Guide Ser.). 1983. pap. 6.95 (ISBN 0-8042-3236-9). John Knox.
Hazelton, Roger. Graceful Courage: A Venture in Christian Humanism. LC 84-48706. 128p. 1985. pap. 4.95 (ISBN 0-8006-1850-5, 1-1850). Fortress.
Hoefler, Richard C. Creative Preaching & Oral Writing. 1978. 7.95 (ISBN 0-89536-349-6, 0342). CSS of Ohio.
Holland, DeWitte T. The Preaching Tradition: A Brief History. LC 80-16339. (Abingdon Preacher's Library). 128p. (Orig.). 1980. pap. 6.95 (ISBN 0-687-33875-1). Abingdon.
Horne, Chevis F. Dynamic Preaching. LC 82-70871. (Orig.). 1983. pap. 6.95 (ISBN 0-8054-2110-6). Broadman.
Hostetler, Michael J. Introducing the Sermon: The Art of Compelling Beginnings. 96p. 1986. pap. 5.95 (ISBN 0-310-30741-4, 10570P). Zondervan.
Howard, J. Grant. Creativity in Preaching. Ruark, J., ed. (Craft of Preaching Ser.). 112p. 1987. pap. price not set (ISBN 0-310-26251-8). Zondervan.
Hughes, Robert. A Trumpet in Darkness: Preaching to Mourners. LC 85-47719. (Fortress Resources for Preaching Ser.). 112p. 1985. pap. 5.95 (ISBN 0-8006-1141-1). Fortress.
Hunter, Archibald M. Preaching the New Testament. LC 81-19482. pap. 39.00 (ISBN 0-317-30145-4, 2025328). Bks Demand UMI.
Hutchinson, Warner. The Oral Roberts Scrapbook. LC 78-58611. 1978. pap. 5.95 (ISBN 0-448-16259-8). Brown Bk.
Jabusch, Willard F. The Person in the Pulpit: Preaching as Caring. LC 79-28812. (Abingdon Preacher's Library). (Orig.). 1980. pap. 5.95 (ISBN 0-687-30784-8). Abingdon.
Jensen, Richard A. Telling the Story: Variety & Imagination in Preaching. LC 79-54113. 190p. (Orig.). 1979. pap. 9.95 (ISBN 0-8066-1766-7, 10-6232). Augsburg.
Jones, Bob. How to Improve Your Preaching. 2nd ed. 151p. 1964. pap. 3.95 (ISBN 0-89084-141-1). Bob Jones Univ Pr.
Jones, G. Curtis. One Thousand Illustrations for Preaching & Teaching. 1986. pap. 9.95 (ISBN 0-8054-2249-8). Broadman.
Jones, Ilion T. Principles & Practice of Preaching. LC 56-7761. 1974. pap. 7.75 (ISBN 0-687-34061-6). Abingdon.
Jones, Ralph H. Charles Albert Tindley: Prince of Preachers. 192p. 1982. pap. 8.95 (ISBN 0-687-06325-6). Abingdon.
Kaiser, Walter C., Jr. Old Testament in Contemporary Preaching. 1973. pap. 6.95 (ISBN 0-8010-5331-5). Baker Bk.
Keck, Leander E. The Bible in the Pulpit: The Renewal of Biblical Preaching. LC 77-12015. 1978. pap. 8.95 (ISBN 0-687-03160-5). Abingdon.
Kelly, W. Preaching to the Spirits in Prison. pap. 4.75 (ISBN 0-88172-105-0). Believers Bkshelf.
Kemper, Deane A. Effective Preaching: A Manual for Students & Pastors. LC 84-20880. 142p. (Orig.). 1985. pap. 10.95 (ISBN 0-664-24595-1). Westminster.
Killinger, John. Fundamentals of Preaching. LC 84-47926. 224p. 1985. pap. 9.95 (ISBN 0-8006-1796-7, 1-1796). Fortress.
Killinger, John, ed. Experimental Preaching. LC 72-8419. Repr. of 1973 ed. 33.30 (ISBN 0-8357-9006-1, 2009067). Bks Demand UMI.
Kinlaw, Dennis F. Preaching in the Spirit. 1985. pap. 6.95 (ISBN 0-310-75091-1, 17036P). Zondervan.
Koller, Charles W. Expository Preaching Without Notes Plus Sermons Preached Without Notes. 1962. 10.95 (ISBN 0-8010-5301-3). Baker Bk.
Kroll, Woodrow M. Prescription for Preaching. 1980. 11.95 (ISBN 0-8010-5409-5). Baker Bk.
Lewis, Ralph L. Inductive Preaching: Activities Guidbook. 32p. 1983. pap. 3.95 (ISBN 0-9608180-2-2). Asbury Theological.
--Persuasive Preaching Today. 276p. 1982. Repr. of 1979 ed. 6.95 (ISBN 0-9608180-0-6). Asbury Theological.
Lewis, Ralph L. & Lewis, Gregg. Inductive Preaching: Helping People Listen. LC 83-70321. 224p. 1983. pap. 6.95 (ISBN 0-89107-287-X, Crossway Bks). Good News.
Liptak, David Q. Preaching the Saints As Models. 1983. pap. 8.95 (ISBN 0-941850-10-2). Sunday Pubns.
Lischer, Richard. A Theology of Preaching: The Dynamics of the Gospel. LC 81-1470. (Abingdon Preacher's Library). (Orig.). 1981. pap. 6.95 (ISBN 0-687-41570-5). Abingdon.
Liscner, Richard, ed. Theories of Preaching: Selected Readings in the Nomiletical Tradition. 384p. 1987. pap. 30.00 (ISBN 0-939464-46-2); pap. 15.95 (ISBN 0-939464-45-4). Labyrinth Pr.
Litfin, Duane & Robinson, Haddon, eds. Recent Homiletical Thought: A Bibliography, 1966-1979. LC 82-72135. 296p. 1983. 16.95 (ISBN 0-8010-5613-6). Baker Bk.
Lloyd-Jones, D. Martyn. Preaching & Preachers. 325p. 1972. 15.95 (ISBN 0-310-27870-8, 10573). Zondervan.
Logan, Samuel T., Jr., ed. The Preacher & Preaching: Reviving the Art in the Twentieth Century. 480p. 1986. 16.95 (ISBN 0-87552-294-7). Presby & Reformed.
Lowry, Eugene. The Homiletical Plot: The Sermon As Narrative Art Form. LC 79-92074. 100p. (Orig.). 1980. pap. 6.95 (ISBN 0-8042-1652-5). John Knox.
Lowry, Eugene L. Doing Time in the Pulpit. 112p. (Orig.). pap. 6.95 (ISBN 0-687-11034-3). Abingdon.
Lundquist, Carl, et al. Proclaim the Good News: Essays in Honor of Gordon G. Johnson. Magnuson, Norris, ed. LC 86-80862. 244p. (Orig.). 1986. pap. 4.95 (ISBN 0-935797-24-6). Harvest IL.
Lybrand, R. E., Jr. Home Is a Four-Letter Word. 1985. 5.95 (ISBN 0-89536-719-X, 5803). CSS of Ohio.
McEachern, Alton H. Dramatic Monologue Preaching. LC 82-82953. 1984. pap. 4.50 (ISBN 0-8054-2111-4). Broadman.
McKibbens, Thomas R., Jr. The Forgotten Heritage: A Lineage of Great Baptist Preaching. (Orig.). 1986. 27.95 (ISBN 0-86554-179-5, MUP-H169); pap. 18.95 (ISBN 0-86554-186-8, MUP-P18). Mercer Univ Pr.
McLaughlin, Raymond W. Ethics of Persuasive Preaching. 1978. 9.95 (ISBN 0-8010-6051-6). Baker Bk.
McNulty, Frank J. Preaching Better. 1985. pap. 8.95 (ISBN 0-8091-2682-6). Paulist Pr.
Mann, Jacob. The Bible As Read & Preached in the Old Synagogue, Vol. 1. rev. ed. (Library of Biblical Studies). 1970. 59.50x (ISBN 0-87068-083-8). Ktav.
Marcel, Pierre Ch. Relevance of Preaching. (Notable Books on Preaching). 1977. pap. 2.95 (ISBN 0-8010-6037-0). Baker Bk.
Marcoux, Paul & LoCigno, Joseph P., eds. Reading, Preaching & Celebrating the Word. pap. 9.95 (ISBN 0-941850-00-5). Sunday Pubns.
Markquart, Edward F. Quest for Better Preaching: Resources for Renewal in the Pulpit. LC 85-13500. 240p. (Orig.). 1985. pap. 10.95 (ISBN 0-8066-2170-2, 10-5349). Augsburg.
Marty, Martin E. The Word: People Participating in Preaching. LC 83-16611. 112p. 1984. pap. 3.95 (ISBN 0-8006-1778-9, 1-1778). Fortress.
Mast, Russel. Preach the Word. LC 68-28782. 1968. pap. 1.25 (ISBN 0-87303-680-8). Faith & Life.
Merrill, Dean & Shelley, Marshall, eds. Fresh Ideas for Preaching, Worship & Evangelism. (Fresh Ideas Ser.). 155p. 1984. pap. 6.95 (ISBN 0-917463-00-5). Chr Today.
Mitchell, Carnell C., Jr. Speaking in Church Made Simple. 1985. pap. 3.95 (ISBN 0-8054-3431-3). Broadman.
Moore, Oscar. Preachers: You Asked for It. pap. 2.00 (ISBN 0-911866-79-5). Advocate.
Moore, T. M. Making God's Good News Known. (Orig.). 1985. pap. text ed. 4.95 (ISBN 0-934688-18-4); pap. text ed. 3.95 leader's guide (ISBN 0-934688-19-2). Great Comm Pubns.
Morentz, Jim & Morentz, Doris. Minister's Annual: Preaching in 1987. 432p. 1986. 9.95 (ISBN 0-687-26990-3). Abingdon.
--Minister's Annual: Preaching in 1988. 496p. 1987. 12.95 (ISBN 0-687-26991-1). Abingdon.
Morneau, Robert F. Principles of Preaching. 1983. pap. 6.95 (ISBN 0-941850-11-0). Sunday Pubns.
Muehl, William. Why Preach? Why Listen? LC 86-45216. 96p. 1986. pap. 4.95 (ISBN 0-8006-1928-5, 1-1928). Fortress.
Newton, Joseph F. Some Living Masters of the Pulpit: Studies in Religious Personality. facsimile ed. LC 71-152203. (Essay Index Reprint Ser). Repr. of 1923 ed. 18.00 (ISBN 0-8369-2287-5). Ayer Co Pubs.
Nichols, J. Randall. Building the Word: The Dynamics of Communication & Preaching. LC 79-3590. 176p. 1980. 10.00 (ISBN 0-06-066109-7, HarpR). Har-Row.
Noyce, Gaylord. The Art of Pastoral Conversation. LC 81-82350. 128p. 1982. pap. 3.99 (ISBN 0-8042-1131-0). John Knox.
O'Donnell, J. D. The Preacher & His Preaching. 1974. pap. 3.95 (ISBN 0-89265-018-4). Randall Hse.
Osborne, Roy F. Great Preachers of Today. 212p. 1966. case bound 11.95 (ISBN 0-89112-207-9, Bibl Res Pr). Abilene Christ U.
Oxnam, Garfield B. Preaching in a Revolutionary Age. facsimile ed. LC 75-142687. (Essay Index Reprint Ser). Repr. of 1944 ed. 18.00 (ISBN 0-8369-2421-5). Ayer Co Pubs.
Parker, Joseph. Preaching Through the Bible, 14 vols. 189.50 (ISBN 0-8010-7032-5). Baker Bk.
Parkhurst, Charles H. Pulpit & the Pew. 1913. 39.50x (ISBN 0-686-83717-7). Elliots Bks.
Peck, John M. Father Clark: Or, The Pioneer Preacher. 285p. 1986. pap. text ed. 6.95x (ISBN 0-8290-1901-4). Irvington.
Perry, Lloyd M. Manual for Biblical Preaching. pap. 12.95 (ISBN 0-8010-7047-3). Baker Bk.
--Predicacion Biblica para el Mundo Actual. Carrodeguas, Angel A., tr. from Eng. Orig. Title: Biblical Preaching for Today's World. (Span.). 176p. 1986. pap. 4.95 (ISBN 0-8297-0957-6). Life Pubs Intl.
Pittenger, Norman. Preaching the Gospel. LC 83-62716. 108p. (Orig.). 1984. pap. 5.95 (ISBN 0-8192-1340-3). Morehouse.
Pitt-Watson. A Primer for Preachers. 112p. 1987. 5.95 (ISBN 0-8010-7096-1). Baker Bk.
Pitt-Watson, Ian. Preaching: A Kind of Folly. LC 77-21983. 120p. 1978. pap. 3.95 (ISBN 0-664-24181-6). Westminster.
Preacher's Homiletic Library, 14 vols. Set. 189.50 (ISBN 0-8010-6916-5). Baker Bk.
Prescott, Roger. The Second Mile. 1985. 4.95 (ISBN 0-89536-739-4, 5823). CSS of Ohio.
Radecke, Mark W. In Many & Various Ways. 1985. 5.75 (ISBN 0-89536-721-1, 5806). CSS of Ohio.
Rahner, Karl, ed. Renewal of Preaching. LC 68-22795. (Concilium Ser.: Vol. 33). 204p. 7.95 (ISBN 0-8091-0126-2). Paulist Pr.
Ratzinger, Joseph C. Dogma & Preaching. O'Connell, Matthew J., tr. 1983. 9.95 (ISBN 0-8199-0819-3). Franciscan Herald.
Roberts, Oral. The Call. 1982. pap. 1.25 (ISBN 0-380-01078-X, 10678). Avon.
Rosato, Philip. The Spirit as Lord. 240p. 1981. 20.95 (ISBN 0-567-09305-0, Pub. by T&T Clark Ltd UK). Fortress.
Rossow, Francis. Preaching the Creative Gospel Creatively. 1983. pap. 8.95 (ISBN 0-570-03917-7, 12-2856). Concordia.
Rothwell, Mel-Thomas. Preaching Holiness Effectively. 160p. 1982. pap. 4.95 (ISBN 0-8341-0784-8). Beacon Hill.
Rust, Eric C. The Word & Words: Towards a Theology of Preaching. LC 82-8032. xii, 131p. 1982. 10.95 (ISBN 0-86554-055-1, MUP-H36). Mercer Univ Pr.
Saint Augustine. On Christian Doctrine. Robertson, D. W., Jr., tr. LC 58-9956. 1958. pap. 7.20 scp (ISBN 0-672-60262-8). Bobbs.
Sanders, James A. God Has a Story Too: Biblical Sermons in Context. LC 77-15244. 160p. 1979. pap. 6.95 (ISBN 0-8006-1353-8, 1-1353). Fortress.
Schultz, Kathleen, et al, eds. The Radical Preacher's Sermon Book. (Illus.). 96p. 1983. pap. 4.00 (ISBN 0-9612114-0-7). Inst People's Church.
Scott, Bernard B. The Word of God in Words: Reading & Preaching the Gospels. LC 85-5227. (Fortress Resources for Preaching). 96p. 1985. pap. 4.95 (ISBN 0-8006-1142-X). Fortress.
Sermonic Pictures of a Preacher's Soul. 1981. pap. 4.95 (ISBN 0-933184-32-8). Flame Intl.
Shannon, Robert & Shannon, J. Michael. Expository Preaching. 128p. (Orig.). 1982. pap. 5.95 (ISBN 0-87239-605-3, 3020). Standard Pub.
Shetler, Sanford G. Preacher of the People. LC 81-13387. 288p. 1982. 16.95x (ISBN 0-8361-1247-4); pap. 13.95x (ISBN 0-8361-1248-2). Herald Pr.
Sleeth, Ronald E. God's Word & Our Words: Basic Homiletics. LC 85-23777. 120p. (Orig.). 1986. pap. 7.95 (ISBN 0-8042-1577-4). John Knox.
--Persuasive Preaching. LC 55-8527. viii, 96p. 1981. pap. 4.95 (ISBN 0-943872-81-2). Andrews Univ Pr.
Sloyan, Gerard. Rejoice & Take It Away: Sunday Preaching from the Scriptures, 2 vols. 1984. 15.00 (ISBN 0-89453-381-9). M Glazier.
Sloyan, Gerard S. Worshipful Preaching. LC 83-48911. (Fortress Resources for Preaching Ser.). 80p. 1984. pap. 3.95 (ISBN 0-8006-1781-9, 1-1781). Fortress.
Smith, J. Alfred. Preach On! LC 84-8439. 1984. pap. 4.95 (ISBN 0-8054-2112-2). Broadman.
Smith, Kelly M. Social Crisis Preaching. LC 84-6656. x, 125p. 1984. 9.95x (ISBN 0-86554-111-6, MUP/H106); pap. 9.95 (ISBN 0-86554-246-5, MUP-P38). Mercer Univ Pr.
Spurgeon, C. H. Eccentric Preachers. 1978. pap. 3.25 (ISBN 0-686-00496-5). Pilgrim Pubns.
Staack, Hagen. Lectionary Preaching Workbook on the Psalms. (Ser. C). 1982. 14.25 (ISBN 0-89536-573-1, 1263). CSS of Ohio.
Steimle, Edmund A., et al. Preaching the Story. LC 78-14675. 208p. 1980. 9.95 (ISBN 0-8006-0538-1, 1-538). Fortress.
Stevenson, Dwight E. & Diehl, Charles F. Reaching People from the Pulpit: A Guide to Effective Sermon Delivery. (Notable Books on Preaching). 1978. pap. 4.50 (ISBN 0-8010-8133-5). Baker Bk.
Stott, John R. Preacher's Portrait in the New Testament. 1964. pap. 4.95 (ISBN 0-8028-1191-4). Eerdmans.
Sweazey, George E. Preaching the Good News. 368p. 1976. 24.95 (ISBN 0-13-694802-2). P-H.
Terry, John R. Powerful Points for Preaching. 150p. 1982. pap. 4.95 (ISBN 0-933704-44-5). Dawn Pr.
Thompson, William D. Preaching Biblically: Exegesis & Interpretation. (Abingdon Preacher's Library). (Orig.). 1981. pap. 6.95 (ISBN 0-687-33840-9). Abingdon.
Tripp, Bramwell. Big Themes in Small Portions. 121p. (Orig.). 1984. pap. 2.95 (ISBN 0-89216-054-3). Salvation Army.
Tugwell, Simon. The Way of the Preacher. (Orig.). 1979. pap. 7.95 (ISBN 0-87243-093-6). Templegate.
Turner, J. J. Practical Sermons That Motivate. pap. 2.95 (ISBN 0-89315-211-0). Lambert Bk.

Turner, R. Edward. Proclaiming the Word: The Concept of Preaching in the Thought of Ellen G. White. (Andrews University Monographs, Studies in Religion: Vol. XII). x, 183p. 1980. pap. 3.95 (ISBN 0-943872-12-X). Andrews Univ Pr.

Walker, Alan. Standing Up to Preach. LC 83-72736. 84p. (Orig.). 1983. pap. 3.95 (ISBN 0-88177-005-1, DR005B). Discipleship Res.

Wallace, James A. Preaching Through the Saints. LC 82-7745. 80p. 1982. pap. 2.50 (ISBN 0-8146-1271-7). Liturgical Pr.

Warlick, Harold C., Jr. The Rarest of These Is Hope. 1985. 7.50 (ISBN 0-89536-743-2, 5826). CSS of Ohio.

Warren, Thomas B. & Elkins, Garland, eds. God Demands Doctrinal Preaching. 1978. pap. 9.00 (ISBN 0-934916-32-2). Natl Christian Pr.

Waznak, Robert. Sunday after Sunday: Preaching the Homily as a Story. LC 82-62922. 128p. (Orig.). 1983. pap. 4.95 (ISBN 0-8091-2540-4). Paulist Pr.

Welsh, Clement. Preaching in a New Key. LC 74-5268. 192p. 1974. 5.95 (ISBN 0-8298-0273-8). Pilgrim NY.

White, D. M. Predicacion Expositiva. Estrello, Francisco E., tr. Orig. Title: The Excellence of Exposition. 160p. 1982. Repr. of 1980 ed. 3.75 (ISBN 0-311-42061-3). Casa Bautista.

White, Douglas M. The Excellence of Exposition: Practical Procedure in Expository Preaching. 1977. 4.95 (ISBN 0-87213-939-5). Loizeaux.

Wiersbe, Warren & Perry, Lloyd M. The Wycliffe Handbook of Preaching & Preachers. 1984. 18.95 (ISBN 0-8024-0328-X). Moody.

Wiersbe, Warren & Wiersbe, David. Elements of Preaching. 96p. 1986. pap. 2.95 (ISBN 0-8423-0757-5). Tyndale.

Wiersbe, Warren W. Listening to the Giants. 1979. 14.95 (ISBN 0-8010-9618-9). Baker Bk.

--Walking with the Giants: A Minister's Guide to Good Reading & Great Preaching. LC 76-22989. 304p. 1976. 14.95 (ISBN 0-8010-9578-6). Baker Bk.

Willimon, William H. Integrative Preaching: The Pulpit at the Center. LC 80-39628. (Abingdon Preacher's Library). 112p. (Orig.). 1981. pap. 6.95 (ISBN 0-687-19129-7). Abingdon.

--Preaching & Leading Worship. LC 83-26021. (The Pastor's Handbooks Ser.: Vol. 1). 116p. (Orig.). 1984. pap. 7.95 (ISBN 0-664-24616-8). Westminster.

Wilson, Jim. Go Preach the Kingdom Heal the Sick. 127p. 1979. pap. text ed. 2.95 (ISBN 0-227-67659-9). Attic Pr.

Young, Henry J., ed. Preaching the Gospel. LC 75-36449. pap. 23.80 (2026828). Bks Demand UMI.

PREACHING-HISTORY

see also Kerygma

Brastow, Lewis O. Representative Modern Preachers. facs. ed. LC 68-57306. (Essay Index Reprint Ser). 1904. 20.00 (ISBN 0-8369-0101-0). Ayer Co Pubs.

Crew, P. Mack. Calvinist Preaching & Iconoclasm in the Netherlands, 1544-1569. LC 77-77013. (Studies in Early Modern History). 1978. 37.50 (ISBN 0-521-21739-3). Cambridge U Pr.

Dargan, Edwin C. History of Preaching, 2 Vols. 1965. lib. bdg. 47.00 (ISBN 0-8337-0772-8). B Franklin.

DeWelt, Don. If You Want to Preach. 2nd ed. LC 56-13226. 1964. pap. 3.95 (ISBN 0-89900-111-4). College Pr Pub.

Elliott, Emory. Power & the Pulpit in Puritan New England. 256p. 1975. 27.00x (ISBN 0-691-07206-X). Princeton U Pr.

Gotaas, Mary C. Bossuet & Vieira. LC 75-128929. (Catholic Univ. of American Studies in Romance Lang. & Lit. Ser.: No. 46). Repr. of 1953 ed. 21.00 (ISBN 0-404-50346-2). AMS Pr.

Herr, Alan F. Elizabethan Sermon. LC 77-75996. 1969. Repr. of 1940 ed. lib. bdg. 16.50x (ISBN 0-374-93838-5, Octagon). Hippocrene Bks.

Ianucci, R. J. Treatment of the Capital Sins. LC 70-140024. (Catholic University Studies in German: No. 17). Repr. of 1942 ed. 21.00 (ISBN 0-404-50237-7). AMS Pr.

Jenkins, R. B. Henry Smith: England's Silver-Tongued Preacher. LC 83-878. vi, 131p. 1983. 10.95 (ISBN 0-86554-077-2, H64). Mercer Univ Pr.

Jones, Edgar D. American Preachers of Today: Intimate Appraisals of Thirty-Two Leaders. facsimile ed. LC 76-156667. (Essay Index Reprint Ser). Repr. of 1933 ed. 19.00 (ISBN 0-8369-2279-4). Ayer Co Pubs.

--Royalty of the Pulpit. LC 79-134105. (Essay Index Reprint Ser). 1951. 27.50 (ISBN 0-8369-1979-3). Ayer Co Pubs.

Kiessling, Elmer C. Early Sermons of Luther & Their Relation to the Pre-Reformation Sermon. LC 75-171064. Repr. of 1935 ed. 21.50 (ISBN 0-404-03669-4). AMS Pr.

Macartney, Clarence E. Six Kings of the American Pulpit. facsimile ed. LC 75-152192. (Essay Index Reprint Ser). Repr. of 1942 ed. 16.00 (ISBN 0-8369-2323-5). Ayer Co Pubs.

Morris, R., ed. The Blickiling Homilies, Pts. I-III. (EETS OS Ser.: Vols. 58 & 63, 73). 1874. 28.00 (ISBN 0-8115-3354-9). Kraus Repr.

Oliver, Robert T. History of Public Speaking in America. LC 78-13428. 1978. Repr. of 1965 ed. lib. bdg. 47.50 (ISBN 0-313-21152-3, OLPS). Greenwood.

Pipes, William H. Say Amen Brother, Old-Time Negro Preaching: A Study in American Frustration. LC 73-111585. Repr. of 1951 ed. 22.50x (ISBN 0-8371-4611-9, PSA&, Pub. by Negro U Pr). Greenwood.

Skinner, Craig. Teaching Ministry of the Pulpit: Its History, Theology, Psychology & Practice for Today. 1979. pap. 6.95 (ISBN 0-8010-8165-3). Baker Bk.

Smith, Hilary D. Preaching in the Spanish Golden Age: A Study of Some Preachers of the Reign of Philip III. (Modern Language & Literature Monographs). 1979. 29.95x (ISBN 0-19-815532-8). Oxford U Pr.

Steel, David. Preaching Through the Year. LC 80-82191. 168p. 1980. pap. 1.79 (ISBN 0-8042-1801-3). John Knox.

Stout, Harry S. The New England Soul: Preaching & Religious Culture in Colonial New England. LC 85-29853. 352p. 1986. 29.95x (ISBN 0-19-503958-0). Oxford U Pr.

Turnbull, Ralph G. Dargan's History of Preaching, Vol. III. 12.95 (ISBN 0-8010-8819-4). Baker Bk.

Wiersbe, Warren W. Listening to the Giants. 1979. 14.95 (ISBN 0-8010-9618-9). Baker Bk.

PREACHING FRIARS

see Dominicans

PRECEPTS (JUDAISM)

see Commandments (Judaism)

PRECISIANS

see Puritans

PREDELLAS

see Altarpieces

PREDESTINATION

see also Election (Theology); Free Will and Determinism

Augustine, Saint Presdestinacion of Saintes. Bd. with Perserveraunce Unto Thende. LC 68-54611. (English Experience Ser.: No. 32). Repr. of 1556 ed. 20.00 (ISBN 90-221-0032-4). Walter J Johnson.

Boettner, Loraine. Reformed Doctrine of Predestination. 1932. 7.95x (ISBN 0-87552-129-0). Presby & Reformed.

Calvin, John. On God & Man. Strothmann, F. W., ed. LC 56-7500. (Milestones of Thought Ser.). 1965. o.p 6.00 (ISBN 0-8044-5214-8); pap. 3.95 (ISBN 0-8044-6073-6). Ungar.

Clark, Gordon H. Biblical Predestination. 1969. pap. 4.95 (ISBN 0-87552-137-1). Presby & Reformed.

Ess, Josef Von. Zwischen Hadit und Theologie: Studien Zum Entstehen Praedestinatianischer Ueberlieferung. LC 73-91809. (Studien Zur Sprache, Geschichte und Kultur Des Islamischen Orients, N.F. Vol. 7). (Ger.). 1974. 53.20x (ISBN 3-11-004290-8). De Gruyter.

Fletcher, George. Predestination. pap. 0.50 (ISBN 0-686-64389-5). Reiner.

Gerstner, John H. Predestination Primer. 1981. pap. 2.50 (ISBN 0-88469-145-4). BMH Bks.

Jewett, Paul K. Election & Predestination. 184p. (Orig.). 1985. pap. 8.95 (ISBN 0-8028-0090-4). Eerdmans.

St. Thomas Aquinas. Providence & Predestination: Questions 5 & 6 of "Truth". Mulligan, Robert W., tr. 154p. 1961. pap. 5.95 (ISBN 0-89526-937-6). Regnery Bks.

William Of Ockham. Predestination, God's Foreknowledge & Future Contingents. 2nd ed. Kretzmann, Norman & Adams, Marilyn M., trs. LC 82-23317. 146p. 1983. 19.50 (ISBN 0-915144-14-X); pap. text ed. 4.95x (ISBN 0-915144-13-1). Hackett Pub.

PREDICADORES

see Dominicans

PREJUDICES AND ANTIPATHIES

see also Antisemitism

Bettelheim, Bruno & Janowitz, Morris B. Social Change & Prejudice. LC 64-11214. 1964. 18.95 (ISBN 0-02-903480-9). Free Pr.

PREMANANDA, SWAMI

Prabhavananda, Swami, tr. Memories of a Loving Soul. (Orig.). 1968. pap. 4.95 (ISBN 0-87481-015-9). Vedanta Pr.

PREMARITAL COUNSELING

see Marriage Counseling

PRESBYTERIAN CHURCH

see also names of specific branches of the Presbyterian Church, e.g. Presbyterian Church in the U. S.

Bayley, Robert G. The Healing Ministry of the Local Church. 32p. 1983. 1.95 (ISBN 0-934421-03-X). Presby Renewal Pubns.

Bradford, Brick. Releasing the Power of the Holy Spirit. 32p. 1983. 1.95x (ISBN 0-934421-00-5). Presby Renewal Pubns.

Bradford, Brick, ed. Healing for the Homosexual. 64p. 1983. 1.95 (ISBN 0-934421-06-4). Presby Renewal Pubns.

Dove Songs. 88p. 1983. 1.95 (ISBN 0-934421-07-2). Presby Renewal Pubns.

Ellis, Dorsey D. Look unto the Rock: A History of the Presbyterian Church, in West Virginia from 1719 to 1974. LC 82-60889. (Illus.). 372p. (Orig.). 1982. pap. 14.95 (ISBN 0-9609076-0-2). McClain.

Fickett, John D. Confess It, Possess It: Faith's Formula? 40p. 1984. 1.95 (ISBN 0-934421-04-8). Presby Renewal Pubns.

Gray, Joan S. & Tucker, Joyce C. Presbyterian Polity for Church Officers. LC 86-2797. 228p. (Orig.). 1986. pap. 7.95 (ISBN 0-8042-1406-9). John Knox.

Pinnell, Lois M. French Creek Presbyterian Church. (Illus.). 1971. 10.00 (ISBN 0-87012-110-3). McClain.

Prince, Harold B., compiled by. A Presbyterian Bibliography. LC 83-10116. (ATLA Bibliography Ser.: No. 8). 466p. 1983. pap. 35.00 (ISBN 0-8108-1639-3). Scarecrow.

Pursey, Barbara. The Gifts of the Holy Spirit. 40p. 1984. 1.95 (ISBN 0-934421-02-1). Presby Renewal Pubns.

Whalen, William J. Reaching Out to the Presbyterians & the Reformed with Heart & Mind. (Reaching Out to...Ser.). 32p. 1984. pap. 1.50 (ISBN 0-89243-208-X). Liguori Pubns.

Wise, Robert L. Healing of the Past. 40p. 1984. 2.00 (ISBN 0-318-04134-0). Presby Renewal Pubns.

Wright, Paul S. The Presbyterian Elder. rev. ed. 64p. (Orig.). 1986. pap. 4.95 saddle stapled (ISBN 0-664-24014-3). Westminster.

PRESBYTERIAN CHURCH-CATECHISMS AND CREEDS

Clark, Gordon H. What Do Presbyterians Believe? 1965. pap. 6.95 (ISBN 0-87552-140-1). Presby & Reformed.

Lingle, Walter L. & Kuykendall, John W. Presbyterians, Their History & Beliefs. LC 77-15750. 1978. pap. 5.95 (ISBN 0-8042-0985-5). John Knox.

Williamson, G. I. The Shorter Catechism: A Study Manual, 2 vols. Vol. 1. pap. 4.50 (ISBN 0-87552-539-3); Vol. 2. pap. 4.50 (ISBN 0-87552-540-7). Presby & Reformed.

PRESBYTERIAN CHURCH-CLERGY-CORRESPONDENCE, REMINISCENCES, ETC.

Buechner, Frederick. The Sacred Journey. 224p. 1984. pap. 8.95 large print ed. (ISBN 0-8027-2479-5). Walker & Co.

Elson, Edward. Wide Was His Parish. 320p. 1986. 12.95 (ISBN 0-8423-8205-4). Tyndale.

PRESBYTERIAN CHURCH-DOCTRINAL AND CONTROVERSIAL WORKS

Clark, Gordon H. What Do Presbyterians Believe? 1965. pap. 6.95 (ISBN 0-87552-140-1). Presby & Reformed.

Hodge, Charles. Systematic Theology, 3 Vols. 1960. Set. 49.95 (ISBN 0-8028-8135-1). Eerdmans.

Ward, William B. Toward Responsible Discipleship. LC 61-7078. (Orig.). 1961. pap. 2.50 (ISBN 0-8042-4049-3); leader's guide o.p. 1.00 (ISBN 0-8042-4050-7). John Knox.

PRESBYTERIAN CHURCH-HISTORY

Boyd, Lois A. & Brackenridge, R. Douglas. Presbyterian Women in America: Two Centuries of a Quest for Status. LC 82-15845. (Contributions to the Study of Religion: No. 9). 416p. 1983. lib. bdg. 35.00 (ISBN 0-313-23678-X, BOY/). Greenwood.

Brackenridge, R. Douglas & Garcia-Treto, Francisco O. Iglesia Presbiteriana: A History of Presbyterians & Mexican Americans in the Southwest. LC 74-76777. (Illus.). 262p. 1974. 8.00 (ISBN 0-911536-53-1). Trinity U Pr.

Coleman, Michael C. Presbyterian Missionary Attitudes Toward American Indians, 1837-1893. LC 85-7496. (Illus.). 1985. 25.00x (ISBN 0-87805-278-X). U Pr of Miss.

Gear, Felix B. Our Presbyterian Belief. LC 79-23421. 90p. (Orig.). 1980. pap. 6.95 (ISBN 0-8042-0676-7). John Knox.

Johnston, Geoffrey. Of God & Maxim Guns: Presbyterianism in Nigeria, 1846-1966, Vol. 8. 270p. 1987. pap. 17.50 (ISBN 0-88920-180-3, Pub. by Wilfrid Laurier Canada). Humanities.

Lingle, Walter L. & Kuykendall, John W. Presbyterians, Their History & Beliefs. LC 77-15750. 1978. pap. 5.95 (ISBN 0-8042-0985-5). John Knox.

Loetscher, Lefferts A. A Brief History of the Presbyterians: With a New Chapter by George Laird Hunt. 4th ed. LC 83-21652. 224p. 1984. pap. 4.95 (ISBN 0-664-24622-2). Westminster.

McIlvain, James W. Early Presbyterianism in Maryland. Bd. with The Study of History in Germany & France. Fredericq, Paul. Leonard, Henrietta, tr. from Fr.. (Johns Hopkins University Studies in Historical & Political Science, 8: No. 5,6). Repr. of 1890 ed. 15.00 (ISBN 0-384-16755-1). Johnson Repr.

Pierson, Paul E. A Younger Church in Search of Maturity: Presbyterianism in Brazil from 1910-1959. LC 73-89596. 306p. 1974. 8.00 (ISBN 0-911536-49-3). Trinity U Pr.

Vander-Velde, Lewis G. Presbyterian Churches & the Federal Union 1861-1869. LC 32-30007. (Historical Studies: No. 33). 1932. 35.00x (ISBN 0-674-70151-8). Harvard U Pr.

PRESBYTERIAN CHURCH-HYMNS

The Hymnal. 7.95 (ISBN 0-664-10033-3). Westminster.

PRESBYTERIAN CHURCH-LITURGY AND RITUAL

Bower, Peter C. Handbook for the Common Lectionary. 300p. (Orig.). 1987. pap. 10.95 (ISBN 0-664-24048-8, A Geneva Press Publication). Westminster.

Gear, Felix B. Our Presbyterian Belief. LC 79-23421. 90p. (Orig.). 1980. pap. 6.95 (ISBN 0-8042-0676-7). John Knox.

Office of Worship for the Presbyterian Church (U. S. A.) & the Cumberland Presbyterian Church Station. Christian Marriage. (Supplemental Liturgical Resource Ser.: 3). 120p. (Orig.). 1986. pap. 7.95 (ISBN 0-664-24033-X). Westminster.

Office of Worship for the Presbyterian Church (U. S. A.) & the Cumberland Presbyterian Church. The Funeral: A Service of Witness to the Resurrection. (Supplemental Liturgical Resource Ser.: 4). 120p. (Orig.). 1986. pap. write for info. (ISBN 0-664-24034-8). Westminster.

PRESBYTERIAN CHURCH-MEMBERSHIP

Sherrill, Lewis J. & Sherrill, Helen H. Becoming a Christian. 1943. pap. 1.49 (ISBN 0-8042-1548-0). John Knox.

PRESBYTERIAN CHURCH-SERMONS

Davis, Ron L. Gold in the Making. LC 83-21931. 160p. 1984. pap. 5.95 (ISBN 0-8407-5869-3). Nelson.

Gossip, A. J. Experience Worketh Hope. (A Scholar As Preacher Ser.). 208p. 1945. 10.95 (ISBN 0-567-04423-8, Pub. by T & T Clark Ltd UK). Fortress.

Newbold, Robert T., Jr., ed. Black Preaching: Select Sermons in the Presbyterian Tradition. LC 77-4015. 180p. 1977. softcover 5.65 (ISBN 0-664-24323-1). Westminster.

Sanders, James A. God Has a Story Too: Biblical Sermons in Context. LC 77-15244. 160p. 1979. pap. 6.95 (ISBN 0-8006-1353-8, 1-1353). Fortress.

Scott, W. A. Wedge of Gold. 1974. pap. 3.95 (ISBN 0-685-52824-3). Reiner.

Stewart, James S. The Gates of New Life. (The Scholar As Preacher Ser.). 262p. 1976. pap. text ed. 11.95 (ISBN 0-567-24426-1, Pub. by T & T Clark Ltd UK). Fortress.

--The Strong Name. (The Scholar As Preacher Ser.). 268p. 1940. 12.95 (ISBN 0-567-04427-0, Pub. by T & T Clark Ltd UK). Fortress.

PRESBYTERIAN CHURCH IN THE U. S.

Gray, Joan S. & Tucker, Joyce C. Presbyterian Polity for Church Officers. LC 86-2797. 228p. (Orig.). 1986. pap. 7.95 (ISBN 0-8042-1406-9). John Knox.

Marshall, James W. Presbyterian Churches in Alabama 1811-1936: Sketches of Churches, Outposts, & Preaching Points in the Synod of Alabama, Pt. I: Abbeville-Butler, & Megargel. Foreman, Kenneth J., Jr., ed. (Illus.). 519p. (Orig.). 1985. 29.95 (ISBN 0-935883-01-0); pap. 14.95 (ISBN 0-935883-00-2); With computer-readable disk. 69.95 (ISBN 0-935883-02-9). Cooling Spring.

Prince, Harold B., compiled by. A Presbyterian Bibliography. LC 83-10116. (ATLA Bibliography Ser.: No. 8). 466p. 1983. pap. 35.00 (ISBN 0-8108-1639-3). Scarecrow.

Thompson, Ernest T. Presbyterian in the South. LC 63-19121. (Presbyterian Historical Society. Publication Ser.: Vol. 13). Vol. 1. pap. 157.30 (2027295); Vol. 2. pap. 132.00; Vol. 3. pap. 159.00. Bks Demand UMI.

Weeks, Louis. Kentucky Presbyterians. LC 83-8372. 228p. 1983. 8.95 (ISBN 0-8042-0920-0); after Sept. 1, 1983 9.95 (ISBN 0-686-46122-3). John Knox.

White, Alvin D. History of the Cross Creek Presbyterian Church. 1969. 6.00 (ISBN 0-87012-040-9). McClain.

PRESBYTERIAN CHURCH IN THE U. S. A.

see also United Presbyterian Church in the U. S. a.

Bower, Peter C. Handbook for the Common Lectionary. 300p. (Orig.). 1987. pap. 10.95 (ISBN 0-664-24048-8, A Geneva Press Publication). Westminster.

Briggs, Charles A. Inaugural Address & Defense, Eighteen Ninety-One to Eighteen Ninety-Three. LC 70-38442. (Religion in America, Ser. 2). 336p. 1972. Repr. of 1972 ed. 22.00 (ISBN 0-405-04062-8). Ayer Co Pubs.

Buxbaum, Melvin H. Benjamin Franklin & the Zealous Presbyterians. LC 74-14932. 320p. 1974. 28.75x (ISBN 0-271-01176-9). Pa St U Pr.

Rogers, Jack. Presbyterian Creeds: A Guide to the Book of Confessions. LC 84-22001. 252p. (Orig.). 1985. pap. 8.95 (ISBN 0-664-24627-3). Westminster.

Thompson, Ernest T. Presbyterian in the South. LC 63-19121. (Presbyterian Historical Society. Publication Ser.: Vol. 13). Vol. 1. pap. 157.30 (2027295); Vol. 2. pap. 132.00; Vol. 3. pap. 159.00. Bks Demand UMI.

PRESBYTERIAN CHURCH IN THE U. S. A.–EDUCATION

Sherrill, Lewis J. Presbyterian Parochial Schools, 1846-1870. LC 74-89234. (American Education: Its Men, Institutions & Ideas, Ser. 1). 1969. Repr. of 1932 ed. 11.50 (ISBN 0-405-01471-6). Ayer Co Pubs.

PRESBYTERIAN CHURCH IN THE U. S. A.–HISTORY

Foote, William H. Sketches of North Carolina. 3rd ed. 593p. 1965. 12.00. Synod NC Church.

History of the Organization of the First Presbyterian Church of Durham, Greene County, N. Y. (Illus.). 1976. pap. 2.00 (ISBN 0-685-69663-4). Hope Farm.

Marshall, James W. Presbyterian Churches in Alabama 1811-1936: Sketches of Churches, Outposts, & Preaching Points in the Synod of Alabama, Pt. I: Abbeville-Butler, & Megargel. Foreman, Kenneth J., Jr., ed. (Illus.). 519p. (Orig.). 1985. 29.95 (ISBN 0-935883-01-0); pap. 14.95 (ISBN 0-935883-00-2); With computer-readable disk. 69.95 (ISBN 0-935883-02-9). Cooling Spring.

Minutes of the Presbyterian Church in America: 1706-1788. Date not set. text ed. price not set (ISBN 0-685-84634-2). Presby Hist.

Pope, Earl. New England Calvinism & the Disruption of the Presbyterian Church. Kuklick, Bruce, ed. (American Religious Thought of the 18th & 19th Centuries Ser.). 400p. 1987. lib. bdg. 50.00 (ISBN 0-8240-6969-2). Garland Pub.

Predmore, Helen R. Chester, N.Y. Presbyterian Church: A History. LC 73-89297. (Illus.). 377p. 1975. 9.45 (ISBN 0-912526-11-4). Lib Res.

Presbyterian Church In The United States Of America. Records of the Presbyterian Church in the United States of America, 1706-1788. LC 75-83434. (Religion in America, Ser. 1). 1969. Repr. of 1904 ed. 30.00 (ISBN 0-405-00259-9). Ayer Co Pubs.

Rudolph, L. C. Hoosier Zion: The Presbyterians in Early Indiana. LC 62-8261. (Yale Publications in Religion Ser.: No. 5). (Illus.). pap. 49.00 (ISBN 0-317-09434-3, 2009008). Bks Demand UMI.

Smith, Frank J. History of the PCA: Continuing Church Movement. 260p. 1985. 20.00 (ISBN 0-9612862-1-0). R E F Typesetting Pub.

Smylie, James H. American Presbyterians: A Pictorial History. 1985. write for info. (ISBN 0-664-24679-6). Westminster.

Taylor, William W. & Smith, Thomas A., Sr. A History of the Chartiers Hill United Presbyterian Church of Canonsburg, Pennsylvania. 1975. write for info. (ISBN 0-87012-210-X). McClain.

Thompson, Robert E. History of the Presbyterian Churches in the U. S. (American Church History Ser). Repr. of 1895 ed. 22.00 (ISBN 0-8337-3935-2). B Franklin.

Trinterud, Leonard J. Forming of an American Tradition. facs. ed. LC 78-124262. (Select Bibliographies Reprint Ser). 1949. 26.50 (ISBN 0-8369-5450-5). Ayer Co Pubs.

PRESBYTERIAN CHURCH SOUTH

see Presbyterian Church in the U. S.

PRESBYTERIANISM

Anderson, Emma D. & Campbell, Mary J. In the Shadow of the Himalayas: A Historical Narrative of the Missions of the United Presbyterian Church of North America as Conducted in the Punjab, India 1855-1940. 373p. 1983. Repr. of 1942 ed. lib. bdg. 45.00 (ISBN 0-89987-042-2). Darby Bks.

Bancroft, Richard. Dangerous Positions & Proceedings. LC 74-38147. (English Experience Ser.: No. 427). 192p. 1972. Repr. of 1593 ed. 28.50 (ISBN 90-221-0427-3). Walter J Johnson.

Blomgren, David K. Prophetic Gatherings in the Church. (Illus.). 100p. 1979. pap. 8.95 (ISBN 0-914936-36-0). Bible Temple.

Currell, R. G. & Hurlbut, E. P. The Ruler of the Kings on the Earth: A Clear Look at Amillennialism for the Lay Person. 126p. 1983. pap. 4.95 (ISBN 0-87552-211-4). Presby & Reformed.

Gerstner, John H. The Problem of Pleasure. 1983. pap. 1.50 (ISBN 0-87552-275-0). Presby & Reformed.

Marston, George W. Tongues Then & Now. 1983. pap. 2.95 (ISBN 0-87552-288-2). Presby & Reformed.

Parker, Harold M., Jr., compiled by. Bibliography of Published Articles on American Presbyterianism, 1901-1980. LC 85-7987. (Bibliographies & Indexes in Religious Studies: No. 4). xv, 261p. 1985. lib. bdg. 37.50 (ISBN 0-313-24544-4, PBP/). Greenwood.

Weeks, Louis. To Be a Presbyterian. 96p. (Orig.). 1983. pap. 4.95 (ISBN 0-8042-1880-3). John Knox.

PRESBYTERS

see Elders (Church Officers)

PRESENTS

see Gifts

PRESTON, JENNET, d. 1612

Potts, Thomas. Potts' Discovery of Witches in the County of Lancaster. Repr. of 1745 ed. 31.00 (ISBN 0-384-47430-6). Johnson Repr.

PRESTON, JOHN, 1587-1628

Morgan, Irvonwy. Prince Charles's Puritan Chaplain, John Preston. LC 58-3992. 1957. 10.00x (ISBN 0-8401-1648-9). A R Allenson.

PRETENDERS

see Impostors and Imposture

PRIDE AND VANITY

Prynne, William. The Unlovelinesse of Love-Lockes. LC 76-57410. (English Experience Ser.: No. 825). 1977. Repr. of 1628 ed. lib. bdg. 10.50 (ISBN 90-221-0825-2). Walter J Johnson.

PRIESTESSES

see Priests

PRIESTHOOD

see also Episcopacy; Jesus Christ–Priesthood; Priesthood, Universal; Priests

Basic Scheme for Priestly Training: Sacred Congregation for Catholic Education. 1973. pap. 0.50 (ISBN 0-8198-0251-4). Dghtrs St Paul.

Chrysostom, John. St. John Chrysostom on the Priesthood. 160p. 1977. pap. 4.95 (ISBN 0-913836-38-9). St Vladimirs.

Cole, Clifford A., ed. The Priesthood Manual. rev. ed. LC 81-7220. 1985. 15.00 (ISBN 0-8309-0420-4). Herald Hse.

Cox, Robert G. Do You Mean Me, Lord? The Call to the Ordained Ministry. LC 85-8785. 116p. 1985. pap. 8.95 (ISBN 0-664-24668-0). Westminster.

DiNunzio, Sylvester L. The Priesthood & Humanity. 1984. 8.50 (ISBN 0-8062-2379-0). Carlton.

Hemesath, Caroline. From Slave to Priest. 1974. 6.95 (ISBN 0-8199-0468-6). Franciscan Herald.

Hickes, George. Two Treatises on the Christian Priesthood, 3 Vols. (Library of Anglo-Catholic Theology: No. 9). Repr. of 1848 ed. Set. 87.50 (ISBN 0-404-52100-2). AMS Pr.

Hickey, Raymond. A Case for an Auxiliary Priesthood. LC 81-16950. 160p. (Orig.). 1982. pap. 1.99 (ISBN 0-88344-021-0). Orbis Bks.

Kimball, Spencer W., et al. Priesthood. LC 81-5394. 170p. 1981. 8.95 (ISBN 0-87747-859-7). Deseret Bk.

Laity, Edward. Priesthood, Old & New. 1980. 2.25 (ISBN 0-86544-012-3). Salv Army Suppl South.

Larkin, Ernest E. & Broccolo, Gerald T., eds. Spiritual Renewal of the American Priesthood. 1973. pap. 2.75 (ISBN 1-55586-230-6, V-230). US Catholic.

Lauder, Robert E. The Priest as a Person: A Philosophy of Priestly Existence. LC 81-3665. 144p. (Orig.). 1981. pap. 5.00 (ISBN 0-89571-013-7). Affirmation.

McGinnity, Gerard. Christmen: Experience of Priesthood Today. 94p. 1986. pap. 7.95 (ISBN 0-87061-124-0). Chr Classics.

Mohler, James A. The Origin & Evolution of the Priesthood. 137p. 1976. pap. 3.95 (ISBN 0-8189-0342-2). Alba.

Moloney, Francis J. A Life of Promise: Poverty, Chastity & Obedience. (Consecrated Life Studies Ser.: Vol. 1). 1983. 8.95 (ISBN 0-89453-370-3). M Glazier.

Norden, Eduard. Aus Altromischen Priesterbuchern. facsimile ed. LC 75-10644. (Ancient Religion & Mythology Ser.). (Ger.). 1976. Repr. of 1939 ed. 23.50x (ISBN 0-405-07019-5). Ayer Co Pubs.

Report of the Bishops' Ad Hoc Committee for Priestly Life & Ministry: Authority, Maturity, Ministry, Scholarship. pap. cancelled (ISBN 0-686-18990-6, V-295). US Catholic.

Stockums, Wilhelm. The Priesthood. 242p. 1982. pap. 7.00 (ISBN 0-89555-170-5). TAN Bks Pubs.

Tierney, Terence. Should You Become a Priest? 64p. (Orig.). (YA) 1975. pap. 1.50 (ISBN 0-89243-020-6, 29530). Liguori Pubns.

Wuerl, Donald W. The Catholic Priesthood Today. 164p. 1976. 6.95 (ISBN 0-8199-0591-7). Franciscan Herald.

PRIESTHOOD, UNIVERSAL

see also Church Membership

Howington, Nolan P. A Royal Priesthood. LC 85-22376. 1986. pap. 4.95 (ISBN 0-8054-1622-6). Broadman.

Lyons, Bob E. Kingdom of Priests. LC 77-92990. 160p. 1984. pap. text ed. 5.95 (ISBN 0-87148-478-1). Pathway Pr.

Vanhoye, Albert. Old Testament Priests & the New Priest. Orchard, Bernard, tr. from Fr. LC 85-2171. (Studies in Scripture: Vol. II). Tr. of Pretres anciens, pretre nouveau selon le nouveau testament. 1986. pap. 24.95 (ISBN 0-932506-38-0). St Bedes Pubns.

PRIESTS

see also Clergy; Priesthood; also subdivision Clergy under church bodies, e.g. Catholic Church–Clergy; Church of England–Clergy

Arnal, Oscar L. Priests in Working Class Blue: The History of the Worker-Priests, (1943-1954) 248p. (Orig.). 1986. pap. 11.95 (ISBN 0-8091-2831-4). Paulist Pr.

Baars, Conrad W. How to Treat & Prevent the Crisis in the Priesthood. 1972. pap. 0.75 (ISBN 0-8199-0399-X). Franciscan Herald.

Barstow, Anne L. Married Priests & the Reforming Papacy: The 11th Century Debates. LC 82-7914. (Texts & Studies in Religion: Vol. 12). 288p. 1982. 49.95x (ISBN 0-88946-987-3). E Mellen.

Craig, James D. & Hill, Donald E., eds. How to Start a Home Cell Ministry. 1st ed. 32p. 1981. pap. 7.95 includes cassettes (ISBN 0-88151-019-X). Lay Leadership.

Custodio, Sidney & Dudley, Cliff. Love-Hungry Priest. LC 82-61308. 192p. (Orig.). 1983. pap. 2.95 (ISBN 0-89221-099-0). New Leaf.

De Saint Pierre, Michel. The New Priests. 209p. 1966. pap. 1.95 (ISBN 0-912414-18-9). Lumen Christi.

Doolittle, H. D. Priest & A Dead Priestess Speaks. (Illus.). 38p. 1983. 90.00x (ISBN 0-914742-79-5). Copper Canyon.

Duryea, John S. & Bartlett, Oso. Alive into the Wilderness: The Story of An Excommunicated Priest. (Illus.). 300p. (Orig.). 1984. pap. 9.50 (ISBN 0-9606288-3-5). Coastlight Pr.

Elchaninov, Alexander. The Diary of a Russian Priest. 2nd ed. Ware, Kallistos T., ed. LC 82-16795. (Illus.). 225p. (Orig.). 1982. pap. 8.95 (ISBN 0-88141-000-4). St Vladimirs.

Fleure, H. F. & Peake, Harold. Priests & Kings. (Corridors of Time Ser.: No. 4). 1927. 29.50x (ISBN 0-686-83710-X). Elliots Bks.

Griffin, James A. The Priestly Heart. LC 83-26611. 149p. (Orig.). 1984. pap. 6.95 (ISBN 0-8189-0460-7). Alba.

Griffith, Earle G. The Pastor As God's Minister. LC 76-50694. 1978. 7.95 (ISBN 0-87227-054-8). Reg Baptist.

Landtman, Gunnar. Origin of the Inequality of the Social Classes. LC 68-56332. (Illus.). 1968. Repr. of 1938 ed. lib. bdg. 22.50x (ISBN 0-8371-0522-6, LASC). Greenwood.

Laurance, John D. Priest as Type of Christ: The Leader of the Eucharist in Salvation History According to Cyprian of Carthage. LC 84-47539. (American University Studies VII (Theology & Religion): Vol. 5). 245p. (Orig.). 1984. 37.25 (ISBN 0-8204-0117-X). P Lang Pubs.

Marney, Carlyle. Priests to Each Other. 125p. 1985. pap. 6.95 (ISBN 0-913029-06-8). Stevens Bk Pr.

Merwick, Donna. Boston Priests, Eighteen Forty-Eight to Nineteen Ten: A Study in Social & Intellectual Change. LC 72-79309. 288p. 1973. 17.50x (ISBN 0-674-07975-2). Harvard U Pr.

Morales, Phyllis S. Fray Angelico Chavez: A Bibliography of His Published Writings (1925-1978) LC 77-73462. 1980. 15.00 (ISBN 0-89016-035-X). Lightning Tree.

Myers, Rawley. Journal of a Parish Priest. LC 81-82022. 144p. (Orig.). 1982. pap. 3.75 (ISBN 0-87973-675-5, 675). Our Sunday Visitor.

Odens, Peter R. Father Garces: The Maverick Priest. (Illus.). 1980. pap. 3.50 (ISBN 0-9609484-3-0). P R Odens.

Quinn, Bernard. Distribution of Catholic Priests in the United States: 1971. 1975. pap. 3.50x (ISBN 0-914422-04-9). Glenmary Res Ctr.

Rosmini, Antonio. Talks to Priests. Ingoldsby, Mary F., tr. from Ital. LC 82-61099. Tr. of Confrerenze Sui Doveri Ecclesiastici. 368p. 1983. 18.00 (ISBN 0-911782-43-5). New City.

Sanchez, Pedro. Memories of the Life of the Priest Don Antonio Jose Martinez. De Aragon, Ray J., tr. LC 78-51462. (Span. & Eng.). 1978. 12.00 (ISBN 0-89016-044-9); pap. 6.95 (ISBN 0-89016-045-7). Lightning Tree.

Schillebeeckx, Edward & Metz, Johann B., eds. The Right of the Community to a Priest: New Concilium 1980, No. 133. 128p. 1980. pap. 5.95 (ISBN 0-8164-2275-3, HarpR). Har-Row.

Schmidt, Marilee. Could I Be a Teacher. 1985. 2.95 (ISBN 0-8100-0200-0, 16N0782). Northwest Pub.

Schlitzer, Albert L. Prayerlife of the Church. 1962. 7.95x (ISBN 0-268-00214-2). U of Notre Dame Pr.

Schmidt, Marilee. Could I Be a Pastor. 1985. 2.95 (ISBN 0-8100-0199-3, 16N0781). Northwest Pub.

Sheen, Fulton J. Those Mysterious Priests. 1979. pap. 10.00 (ISBN 0-385-08102-2). Lumen Christi.

Stendahl, Brita. The Force of Tradition: A Case Study of Women Priests in Sweden. LC 84-48713. (Illus.). 208p. 1985. pap. 14.95 (ISBN 0-8006-1808-4, 1-1808). Fortress.

Suarez, Federico. About Being a Priest. 229p. 1979. 7.00 (ISBN 0-912414-27-8). Lumen Christi.

Tchizhiv, P. M. Otjets Ioann Kronshtadtsky. Tr. of Father John of Kronstadt. 192p. 1958. pap. 8.00 (ISBN 0-317-29203-X). Holy Trinity.

Terwilliger, Robert E. & Holmes, Urban T. To Be a Priest: Perspectives on Vocation & Ordination. 192p. (Orig.). 1975. pap. 4.95 (ISBN 0-8164-2592-2, 8164-2592-2, HarpR). Har-Row.

Tormey, John C. Priests Are Only Human. LC 73-15083. (Illus.). 128p. 1974. pap. 1.25 (ISBN 0-8189-1114-X, Pub. by Alba Bks). Alba.

Walsh, James J., compiled by. These Splendid Priests. facs. ed. LC 68-29252. (Essay Index Reprint Ser). 1968. Repr. of 1926 ed. 17.00 (ISBN 0-8369-0973-9). Ayer Co Pubs.

PRIESTS, ASSYRO-BABYLONIAN

Lindl, Ernest. Das Priester und Beamtentum der Altbabylonischen Kontrakte. Repr. of 1913 ed. 37.00 (ISBN 0-384-32780-X). Johnson Repr.

PRIESTS, BUDDHIST

Norbu, Thinley. A Brief Fantasy History of a Himalayan. LC 84-29754. (Orig.). Date not set. pap. 10.00 (ISBN 0-9607000-1-3). Jewel Pub Hse.

PRIESTS, JEWISH

Rabbinical Assembly Mahzor. 12.00 (ISBN 0-686-96025-4). United Syn Bk.

Vanhoye, Albert. Old Testament Priests & the New Priest. Orchard, Bernard, tr. from Fr. LC 85-2171. (Studies in Scripture: Vol. II). Tr. of Pretres anciens, pretre nouveau selon le nouveau testament. 1986. pap. 24.95 (ISBN 0-932506-38-0). St Bedes Pubns.

PRIESTS, JEWISH–VESTMENTS

Slemming, Charles W. These Are the Garments. 1963. pap. 2.95 (ISBN 0-87508-507-5). Chr Lit.

PRIESTS IN LITERATURE

see Clergy in Literature

PRIMACY OF JESUS CHRIST

see Jesus Christ–Primacy

PRIMACY OF THE POPE

see Popes–Primacy

PRIMITIVE LITERATURE

see Folk Literature

PRIMITIVE RELIGION

see Religion, Primitive

PRINCETON THEOLOGICAL SEMINARY–BIOGRAPHY

Kerr, Hugh T., ed. Sons of the Prophets: Leaders in Protestantism from Princeton Seminary. 1963. 26.50x (ISBN 0-691-07136-5). Princeton U Pr.

PRIORIES

Nichols, John. Some Account of the Alien Priories, & of Such Lands As They Are Known to Have Possessed in England & Wales, 2 Vols. in 1. LC 72-173079. Repr. of 1786 ed. 47.50 (ISBN 0-404-04689-4). AMS Pr.

Thorold, Henry. Collins Guide to Cathedrals, Abbeys & Priories of England & Wales. (Illus.). 332p. 1987. 24.95 (ISBN 0-00-217241-0). Salem Hse Pubs.

Wright, Geoffrey N. Discovering Abbeys & Priories. (Discovery Ser.: No. 57). (Illus.). 1985. pap. 4.50 (ISBN 0-85263-454-4, Pub. by Shire Pubns England). Seven Hills Bks.

PRISONERS–PERSONAL NARRATIVES

How, Nehemiah. A Narrative of the Captivity of Nehemiah How. 59.95 (ISBN 0-8490-0708-9). Gordon Pr.

Popov, Haralan. Tortured for His Faith. pap. 3.95 (ISBN 0-310-31262-0, 18070P). Zondervan.

Winters, Ted & Janssen, Al. Lifer. (Living Books). 320p. 1985. pap. 3.95 (ISBN 0-8423-2142-X). Tyndale.

PRIVILEGIUM FORI

Tiemann, William H. & Bush, John C. The Right to Silence: Privileged Clergy Communication & the Law. 256p. (Orig.). 1983. pap. 11.95 (ISBN 0-687-36315-2). Abingdon.

PROCESS THEOLOGY

Cauthen, Kenneth. Process Ethics: A Constructive System. LC 84-16662. (Toronto Studies in Theology: Vol. 18). 365p. 1985. 59.95x (ISBN 0-88946-764-1). E Mellen.

Cobb, John B., Jr. Process Theology As Political Theology. LC 82-1845. 174p. (Orig.). 1982. pap. 8.95 (ISBN 0-664-24417-3). Westminster.

Cobb, John B., Jr. & Griffin, David R. Process Theology: An Introductory Exposition. LC 76-10352. 192p. 1976. pap. 8.95 (ISBN 0-664-24743-1). Westminster.

Counsins, Ewert H. Process Thought on the Eve of the Twenty-First Century. 50p. (Orig.). 1985. pap. 3.95x (ISBN 0-932269-25-7). Wyndham Hall.

Garvey, Edwin C. Process Theology & Secularization. 21p. 1972. pap. 0.75 (ISBN 0-912414-14-6). Lumen Christi.

Gruenler, Royce G. The Inexhaustible God: Biblical Faith & the Challenge of Process Theism. 176p. 1983. pap. 11.95 (ISBN 0-8010-3794-8). Baker Bk.

Jackson, Gordon E. Pastoral Care & Process Theology. LC 81-40159. 266p. (Orig.). 1981. lib. bdg. 29.75 (ISBN 0-8191-1710-2); pap. text ed. 12.75 (ISBN 0-8191-1711-0). U Pr of Amer.
Lee, Jung Y. The Theology of Change: A Christian Concept of God in an Eastern Perspective. LC 78-16745. 155p. (Orig.). 1979. pap. 5.95 (ISBN 0-88344-492-5). Orbis Bks.
Mann, Lester. On the Trail of Process. 592p. 1979. 46.00 (ISBN 0-8089-1137-6, 792678). Grune.
Neville, Robert C. Creativity & God: A Challenge to Process Theology. 192p. 1980. 12.95 (ISBN 0-8164-0120-9, HarpR). Har-Row.
Odin, Steve. Process Metaphysics & Hua-Yen Buddhism: A Critical Study of Cumulative Penetration vs. Interpretation. LC 81-9388. 256p. 1982. 44.50 (ISBN 0-87395-568-4); pap. 16.95 (ISBN 0-87395-569-2). State U NY Pr.
Pittenger, Norman. Catholic Faith in a Process Perspective. LC 81-9615. 160p. (Orig.). 1981. pap. 1.74 (ISBN 0-88344-091-1). Orbis Bks.
Progoff, Ira. The White Robed Monk. 3rd, rev. & enl. ed. LC 79-1553. (Entrance Meditation Ser.). 111p. 1983. pap. 3.95 (ISBN 0-87941-007-8); pap. 11.50 incl. cassette. Dialogue Hse.
Suchocki, Marjorie. God-Christ-Church: A Practical Approach to Process Theology. 224p. 1982. pap. 10.95 (ISBN 0-8245-0464-X). Crossroad NY.
Trethowan, Illtyd. Process Theology & the Christian Tradition. LC 84-26240. (Studies in Historical Theology). 122p. 1985. 11.95 (ISBN 0-932506-36-4). St Bedes Pubns.
Williams. Essays in Process Theology. 24.95 (ISBN 0-317-46805-7); pap. 12.95 (ISBN 0-317-46806-5). Exploration Pr.
Williams, Daniel D. Essays in Process Theology. LeFevre, Perry, ed. LC 84-82337. 342p. 1985. text ed. 24.95x (ISBN 0-913552-25-9); pap. text ed. 12.95x (ISBN 0-913552-26-7). Exploration Pr.

PROGRAMS, DEDICATION
see Dedication Services

PROGRESS
see also Science and Civilization; Social Change
Dawson, Christopher H. Progress & Religion, an Historical Enquiry. LC 79-104266. Repr. of 1929 ed. lib. bdg. 27.50x (ISBN 0-8371-3917-1, DAPR). Greenwood.
Frankel, Charles. Faith of Reason. LC 71-86277. 1969. Repr. of 1948 ed. lib. bdg. 17.00x (ISBN 0-374-92850-9, Octagon). Hippocrene Bks.
Macmurray, John, ed. Some Makers of the Modern Spirit: A Symposium. facs. ed. LC 68-22926. (Essay Index Reprint Ser). Repr. of 1933 ed. 16.25 (ISBN 0-8369-0658-6). Ayer Co Pubs.
Teilhard De Chardin, Pierre. Avenir De L'homme. 1959. 21.50 (ISBN 0-685-11021-4). French & Eur.
--Future of Man. (Orig.). 1969. pap. 7.95 (ISBN 0-06-090496-8, CN496, PL). Har-Row.

PROGRESS AND CHRISTIANITY
see Christianity and Progress

PROMETHEUS
Johnson, Michael J. Prometheus Reborn. LC 76-52144. 1977. 7.95 (ISBN 0-87212-073-2). Libra.
Kerenyi, C. Prometheus: Archetypal Image of Human Existence. 1963. 50.00 (ISBN 0-8274-3210-0). R West.
Kerenyi, Carl. Archetypal Images in Greek Religion, 5 vols. Manheim, R., tr. Incl. Vol. 1. Prometheus: Archetypal Image of Human Existence. 1963; Vol. 2. Dionysos: Archetypal Image of Industructible Life. 1975; Vol. 3. Asklepios: Archetypal Image of the Physician's Existence. 1959. 37.00x (ISBN 0-691-09703-8); Vol. 4. Eleusis: Archetypal Image of Mother & Daughter. 1967; Vol. 5. Zeus & Hera-Archetypal Image of Father, Husband & Wife. Holme, tr. 1975. (Bollingen Ser.: Vol. 65). Princeton U Pr.

PROPAEDEUTICS (THEOLOGY)
see Theology–Methodology

PROPERTY, CHURCH
see Church Property

PROPHECY (CHRISTIANITY)
Allis, Oswald T. Prophecy & the Church. 1977. pap. 5.95 (ISBN 0-8010-0110-2). Baker Bk.
--The Unity of Isaiah: A Study in Prophecy. 1974. pap. 4.50 (ISBN 0-8010-0111-0). Baker Bk.
Archbishop Averky Taushev. Provozvjestnik Karl Bozhijej Russkomy Narodu. Tr. of The Prophet of the Wrath of God upon the Russian People. 30p. 1968. pap. 1.00 (ISBN 0-317-29066-5). Holy Trinity.
Aune, David E. Prophecy in Early Christianity & the Ancient Mediterranean World. 400p. 1983. 29.95 (ISBN 0-8028-3584-8). Eerdmans.
Baron, David. Types, Psalms & Prophecies. 1981. lib. bdg. 14.00 (ISBN 0-86524-077-9, 9511). Klock & Klock.
Bechtel, Faythelma. God's Marvelous Gifts. (Christian Day School Ser.). 1982. 13.75x (ISBN 0-87813-920-6). Christian Light.
Blenkinsopp, Joseph. A History of Prophecy in Israel: From the Settlement in the Land to the Hellenistic Period. LC 83-10178. 288p. (Orig.). 1983. pap. 16.95 (ISBN 0-664-24479-3). Westminster.
Brians, Charline, ed. Spirit of Prophecy, Vol. I & II. large print ed. 27p. 1984. pap. 5.00 (ISBN 0-9608650-3-9). VHI Library.
Carter, Mary E. Edgar Cayce on Prophecy. 208p. 1968. pap. 3.50 (ISBN 0-446-32712-3). Warner Bks.
Cheetham, Erika. The Further Prophecies of Nostradamus Nineteen Eighty Five & Beyond. 256p. (Orig.). 1985. pap. 6.95 (ISBN 0-399-51121-0, Perigee). Putnam Pub Group.
Crowther, Duane S. The Prophecies of Joseph Smith. LC 83-80664. 413p. 1873. 10.95 (ISBN 0-88290-221-0). Horizon-Utah.
Dasbach, Fernando L. The Father Has Come. 113p. 1981. 10.00 (ISBN 0-686-28999-4). Regenbogen-Verlag.
DeHaan, M. R. The Jew & Palestine in Prophecy. 1978. pap. 5.95 (ISBN 0-310-23381-X, 9497P). Zondervan.
DuPont, Yves. Catholic Prophecy. (Eng.). 1977. pap. 2.50 (ISBN 0-89555-015-6). TAN Bks Pubs.
Eggstein, Kurt. The Prophet Jakob Lorber Predicts Coming Catastrophies & the True Christianity. Schuck, Marjorie M., ed. Meuss, A. R., tr. from Ger. LC 85-51354. 480p. 1985. pap. 12.00 (ISBN 0-934616-40-X). Valkyrie Pub Hse.
Ellis, E. Earle. Prophecy & Hermeneutics in Early Christianity: New Testament Essays. 306p. 1978. lib. bdg. 54.00x. Coronet Bks.
Feiring, Evolyn B. Concatenation: Enoch's Prophecy Fulfilling! Hebrew-Christian Metaphysics Supported by Modern Science. LC 72-96989. 5.00x (ISBN 0-9603386-0-8); pap. 2.00x (ISBN 0-9603386-1-6). Rocky Mtn Bks.
Flores, Jose. Profecia y Carisma, Que de las Lenguas? Orig. Title: Prophecy & Charisma. (Span.). 68p. 1974. pap. 2.25 (ISBN 0-8254-1238-2). Kregel.
Green, Joel B. How to Read Prophecy. LC 84-12838. 150p. (Orig.). 1984. pap. 6.95 (ISBN 0-87784-936-6). Inter-Varsity.
Gromacki, Robert G. Are These the Last Days? LC 75-42165. 1975. pap. 3.50 (ISBN 0-87227-019-X). Reg Baptist.
Gularte, Frank & Richardson, Jim. Prophecy. pap. 2.95 (ISBN 0-911739-23-8). Abbott Loop.
Hagin, Kenneth E. The Gift of Prophecy. 1969. pap. 1.00 (ISBN 0-89276-015-X). Hagin Ministries.
--Seven Steps for Judging Prophecy. 1982. pap. 1.00 (ISBN 0-89276-024-9). Hagin Ministries.
Haines, Leland M. The Unfolding Plan of Redemption. 1982. 3.50 (ISBN 0-87813-517-0). Christian Light.
Hall, Henry R. A. D. Nineteen Ninety-One: The Genesis of Holocaust. (Prophetic Ser.). 375p. (Orig.). 1985. pap. 4.95 (ISBN 0-930351-01-0). Spirit Prophecy.
Hall, Robert B. Anyone Can Prophesy. 1977. pap. 3.95 (ISBN 0-686-23219-4). Episcopal Ctr.
Hartsaw, John W. End Time-God's Glory. 112p. 1982. 6.50 (ISBN 0-682-49848-3). Exposition Pr FL.
Henson, H. H. The Liberty of Prophesying: With Its Just Limits & Temper Considered with Reference to the Circumstances of the Modern Church. 1910. 39.50x (ISBN 0-686-51411-4). Elliots Bks.
Hill, David. New Testament Prophecy. LC 79-16707. (New Foundations Theological Library). 260p. (Peter Toon & Ralph Martin series editors). 1980. 6.49 (ISBN 0-8042-3702-6). John Knox.
Huber, Elaine C. Women & the Authority of Inspiration: A Reexamination of Two Prophetic Movements from a Contemporary Feminist Perspective. LC 85-15823. 262p. (Orig.). 1985. lib. bdg. 27.75 (ISBN 0-8191-4903-9); pap. text ed. 13.75 (ISBN 0-8191-4904-7). U Pr of Amer.
Kirban, Salem. Charts on Prophecy. 1982. pap. 14.92 (ISBN 0-912582-39-1). Kirban.
Leckey, Dolores R. Laity Stirring the Church: Prophetic Questions. LC 86-45213. (Laity Exchange Ser.). 128p. pap. 6.95 (ISBN 0-8006-1659-6, 1-1659). Fortress.
Lindsay, Gordon. Red China in Prophecy. (Prophecy Ser.). 2.25 (ISBN 0-89985-059-6). Christ Nations.
--Signs of the Times in the Heavens. (Prophecy Ser.). 1.25 (ISBN 0-89985-062-6). Christ Nations.
Lumby, J. R., ed. Bernardus de Cura Rei Familiaris: Early Scottish Prophecies, Etc. (EETS OS Ser.: Vol. 42). pap. 15.00 (ISBN 0-8115-3351-4). Kraus Repr.
McKeever, Jim. Coming Climax of History. 1983. 6.95 (ISBN 0-86694-099-5). Omega Pubns OR.
--The Coming Climax of History. 324p. 1983. 15.95 (ISBN 0-86694-098-7). Omega Pubns OR.
Macpherson, Ian. God's Plan for This Planet. LC 76-51001. 96p. 1977. pap. 1.25 (ISBN 0-88243-517-5, 02-0517, Radiant Bks). Gospel Pub.
Malgo, Wim. Twentieth Century Handwriting on the Wall. 4.95 (ISBN 0-686-12823-0). Midnight Call.
Maseroni, Robert S. The Gift of Prophecy, No. 8. 1983. 0.80 (ISBN 0-89536-632-0, 0740). CSS of Ohio.
Overholt, Thomas W. Prophecy in Cross Cultural Perspective: A Sourcebook for Biblical Researchers. (Society of Biblical Literature Ser.). 1985. pap. 26.95 (ISBN 0-89130-901-2, 06-03-17). Scholars Pr GA.
Powell, Ivor C. What in the World Will Happen Next? LC 85-7579. 176p. (Orig.). 1985. pap. 5.95 (ISBN 0-8254-3524-2). Kregel.
Richards, Larry. Tomorrow Today. 132p. 1986. pap. 4.95 (ISBN 0-89693-505-1). Victor Bks.
Roebling, Karl. Prophecy from Here to Two Thousand. 144p. 1983. pap. 4.95 (ISBN 0-942910-06-0). Paragon DynaPress.
Sandford, John & Sandford, Paula. Elijah Task. LC 77-82331. 252p. (Orig.). 1986. pap. 5.95 (ISBN 0-932081-11-8). Victory Hse.
Sauer, Val J., Jr. The Eschatology Handbook: The Bible Speaks to Us about Endtimes. (Illus.). 180p. (Orig.). 1981. pap. 3.99 (ISBN 0-8042-0066-1). John Knox.
Stephenson, James. Prophecy on Trial. 1984. 10.50 (ISBN 0-317-03380-8). Lucis.
Taber, William. The Prophetic Stream. LC 84-61291. (Orig.). 1984. pap. 2.50x (ISBN 0-87574-256-4). Pendle Hill.
Tan, Paul L. The Interpretation of Prophecy. 4th ed. LC 73-85613. 1979. Repr. 8.95 (ISBN 0-932940-01-3). Assurance Pubs.
Thurston, Mark A. Visions & Prophecies for a New Age. (Illus.). 228p. 1981. pap. 6.95 (ISBN 0-87604-136-5). ARE Pr.
Vandeman, G. Showdown in the Middle East. (Stories That Win Ser.). pap. 1.25 (ISBN 0-8163-0392-4). Pacific Pr Pub Assn.
Van Impe, Jack. Everything You Always Wanted to Know about Prophesy. 61p. 1980. pap. 1.95 (ISBN 0-934803-11-0). J Van Impe.
Walvoord, John F. Prophetic Trilogy: The Nations in Prophecy, the Church in Prophecy, Israel in Prophecy. pap. 15.85 (ISBN 0-310-34148-5, 17051P00687415X). Zondervan.
Warner, D. S. & Riggle, H. M. The Cleansing of the Sanctuary. 541p. Repr. 5.50 (ISBN 0-686-29145-X). Faith Pub Hse.
Wilkerson, David. The Vision. 144p. 1974. pap. 3.50 (ISBN 0-8007-8150-3, Spire Bks). Revell.
Wilmot, John. Inspired Principles of Prophetic Interpretation. pap. 10.95 (ISBN 0-686-48168-2). Reiner.
Woodrow, Ralph. His Truth Is Marching On! Advanced Studies on Prophecy in the Light of History. (Illus.). 1977. pap. 4.95 (ISBN 0-916938-03-4). R Woodrow.
Wright, Bonnie L., et al. A Prophet Crying in the Wilderness. Donohue, John & Turowski, Diane, eds. 164p. 1986. pap. 6.98 (ISBN 0-9616309-0-6). Mountain Movers.
Yandian, Bob. End Time Prophecy. 15p. 1983. wkbk. 3.95 (ISBN 0-914307-15-0, Dist. by Harrison Hse). Word Faith.
Yocum, Bruce. Prophecy. (Orig.). 1976. pap. 4.95 (ISBN 0-89283-029-8). Servant.
Yohn, Rick. What Every Christian Should Know about Bible Prophecy. LC 81-85895. 80p. (Orig.). 1982. pap. 3.95 (ISBN 0-89081-311-6, 3116). Harvest Hse.
Young, Robert D. Religious Imagination: God's Gift to Prophets & Preachers. LC 78-26843. 176p. 1979. pap. 6.95 (ISBN 0-664-24239-1). Westminster.

PROPHETISTIC MOVEMENTS
see Nativistic Movements

PROPHETS
see also Sibyls;
also various subdivisions concerning prophets of the Bible in the Bible listings
Ackland, Donald F. Day by Day with the Prophets. LC 82-82950. 1983. pap. 4.95 (ISBN 0-8054-5193-5). Broadman.
Ali-Nadawi, Abul H. Prophet's Stories. Quinlan, Hamid, ed. El-Helbawy, Kamal, tr. from Arabic. LC 82-70453. Tr. of Qasas An Nabiyin. (Illus.). 200p. (Orig.). Date not set. pap. 5.00 (ISBN 0-89259-038-6). Am Trust Pubns.
Aubert, Roger. Prophets in the Church. LC 68-57877. (Concilium Ser.: Vol. 37). 160p. 1964. 7.95 (ISBN 0-8091-0120-3). Paulist Pr.
Barack, Nathan A. God Speaks Naturally: An Organic Perspective on the Prophets. LC 83-7836. 242p. 1983. 12.50 (ISBN 0-8246-0299-4). Jonathan David.
Baring-Gould, S. Legends of the Patriarchs & Prophets & Other Old Testament Characters. LC 74-9741. 1872. lib. bdg. 42.00 (ISBN 0-8414-3205-8). Folcroft.
Bergren, Victor. The Prophets & the Law. 15.00x (ISBN 0-87820-403-2, Pub. by Hebrew Union College Press). Ktav.
Bevan, Edwyn R. Sibyls & Seers. 1979. Repr. of 1928 ed. lib. bdg. 39.50 (ISBN 0-8495-0510-0). Arden Lib.
Blank, Sheldon. Understanding the Prophets. 144p. 1983. pap. text ed. 4.00 (ISBN 0-8074-0250-8, 382755). UAHC.
Boice, James M. Ordinary Men Called by God: Abraham, Moses, & David. 160p. 1982. pap. 5.95 (ISBN 0-88207-224-2). Victor Bks.
Bradford, Gamaliel. A Prophet of Joy. facsimile ed. LC 77-179506. (Select Bibliographies Reprint Ser.). Repr. of 1920 ed. 17.00 (ISBN 0-8369-6635-X). Ayer Co Pubs.
Brengle, Samuel L. Ancient Prophets & Modern Problems. 1978. pap. 3.95 (ISBN 0-86544-000-X). Salv Army Suppl South.
Brickner, Balfour & Vorspan, Albert. Searching the Prophets for Values. 1981. 6.95 (ISBN 0-8074-0047-5). UAHC.
Bright, John. Covenant & Promise: The Prophetic Understanding of the Future in Pre-Exilic Israel. LC 76-13546. 208p. 1976. 10.00 (ISBN 0-664-20752-9). Westminster.
Brueggemann, Walter. The Prophetic Imagination. LC 78-54546. 128p. 1978. pap. 5.95 (ISBN 0-8006-1337-6, 1-1337). Fortress.
Bukhari, Sohail, tr. Abuzar. 200p. 1985. pap. 9.00 (ISBN 0-941724-35-2). Islamic Seminary.
Burman, Madeleine L. Code of the Prophets. LC 84-90888. (Illus.). 100p. (Orig.). 1984. 9.95x (ISBN 0-9613283-0-4); pap. 6.95x. M L Burman.
Butler, P. T. Minor Prophets: The Prophets of the Decline: Hosea-Jonan. LC 79-1493. (Bible Study Textbook). 1968. 15.90 (ISBN 0-317-03548-7). College Pr Pub.
Coffman, James B. Commentary on the Minor Prophets, Vol. 3. (Commmentary Ser.). 322p. 1983. cancelled 10.95 (ISBN 0-88027-107-8). Firm Foun Pub.
Conn, Charles W. Poets & Prophets of Israel. 1981. 5.25 (ISBN 0-87148-707-1); pap. 4.25 (ISBN 0-87148-708-X). Pathway Pr.
Cornhill, Carl H. The Prophets of Israel: Popular Sketches from Old Testament History. 1977. Repr. of 1913 ed. lib. bdg. 30.00 (ISBN 0-8482-3453-7). Norwood Edns.
Crowther, Duane S. The Prophecies of Joseph Smith. LC 83-80664. 413p. 1873. 10.95 (ISBN 0-88290-221-0). Horizon-Utah.
Culleton, R. Gerald. The Prophets & Our Times. 1974. pap. 6.00 (ISBN 0-89555-050-4). TAN Bks Pubs.
Dehlvi, A. M. The Finality of Prophethood. pap. 1.25 (ISBN 0-686-18424-6). Kazi Pubns.
Dickinson, George T. Jeremiah: The Iron Prophet. (Horizon Ser.). 1978. pap. 5.95 (ISBN 0-8127-0183-6). Review & Herald.
Drew, George. The Prophets Speak to Our Time. 62p. (Orig.). 1981. pap. 6.95 (ISBN 0-940754-09-6). Ed Ministries.
Frost, Stanley B. Patriarchs & Prophets. 232p. 1963. 10.00 (ISBN 0-7735-0010-3). McGill-Queens U Pr.
Gokak, Vinayak K. Narahari: Prophet of New India. 298p. 1972. pap. 7.95 (ISBN 0-317-20882-9). CSA Pr.
Goodman, Hannah G. Story of Prophecy. LC 65-24925. 1965. 5.95x (ISBN 0-87441-017-7). Behrman.
Graham, William A. Divine Word & Prophetic Word in Early Islam: A Reconsideration of the Sources, with Special Reference to the Divine Saying or Hadith Qudsi. (Religion & Society Ser.). 1977. text ed. 37.50x (ISBN 90-279-7612-0). Mouton.
Hakim, K. A. The Prophet & His Message. 8.50 (ISBN 0-686-18422-X). Kazi Pubns.
Hall, Clarence W. Samuel Logan Brengle: Portrait of a Prophet. 1978. Repr. of 1933 ed. 3.95 (ISBN 0-86544-006-9). Salv Army Suppl South.
Hamilton, Edith. Spokesmen for God. 1962. pap. 3.95 (ISBN 0-393-00169-5, Norton Lib). Norton.
Harrison, William H. Mother Shipton Investigated. LC 77-3412. 1977. Repr. of 1881 ed. lib. bdg. 17.00 (ISBN 0-8414-4911-2). Folcroft.
Hashim, A. S. Stories of Some of the Prophets, Vol. I. (Islamic Books for Children: Bk. 8). pap. 4.95 (ISBN 0-686-18402-5); pap. 45.00 entire series (ISBN 0-686-18403-3). Kazi Pubns.
--Stories of Some of the Prophets, Vol II. (Islamic Books for Children: Bk. 9). pap. 4.95 (ISBN 0-686-18400-9); pap. 45.00 entire series (ISBN 0-686-18401-7). Kazi Pubns.
Heschel, Abraham J. Prophets, 2 vols. Vol. 1, 1969. pap. 6.95x (ISBN 0-06-131421-8, TB1421, Torch); Vol. 2, 1971. pap. 7.95x (ISBN 0-06-131557-5, TB1557, Torch). Har-Row.
Ibn'Arabi. Wisdom of the Prophets. Burckardt, Titus, tr. 1976. pap. write for info. (ISBN 0-685-67327-8). Weiser.
Koch, Klaus. The Prophets, Volume Two: The Babylonian & Persian Period. LC 79-8894. 224p. 1984. pap. 10.95 (ISBN 0-8006-1756-8, 1-1756). Fortress.

Lecanu, A. F. Dictionnaire des Propheties et des Miracles, 2 vols. Migne, J. P., ed. (Nouvelle Encyclopedie Theologique Ser.: Vols. 24-25). (Fr.). 1246p. Repr. of 1852 ed. lib. bdg. 159.00x (ISBN 0-89241-268-2). Caratzas.

Lindblom, J. Prophecy in Ancient Israel. LC 63-907. 480p. 1962. 17.95 (ISBN 0-8006-0916-6, 1-916). Fortress.

Lindblom, Johannes. Prophecy in Ancient Israel. LC 63-907. pap. 120.00 (2029298). Bks Demand UMI.

Lindsay, Gordon. Apostles, Prophets & Governments. 1.50 (ISBN 0-89985-121-5). Christ Nations.

--False Christs, False Prophets. (Prophecy Ser.). 1.95 (ISBN 0-89985-054-5). Christ Nations.

--The Minor Prophets: Hosea, Joel, Amos, Obadiah, Jonah, Micah. (Old Testament Ser.). 1.25 (ISBN 0-89985-156-8). Christ Nations.

--The Minor Prophets: Nahum, Habakkuk, Zephaniah, Haggai. Zechariah, Malachi. (Old Testament Ser.). 1.25 (ISBN 0-89985-157-6). Christ Nations.

Lods, Adolphe. Prophets & the Rise of Judaism. Hooke, S. H., tr. LC 77-109772. (Illus.). 1971. Repr. of 1937 ed. lib. bdg. 25.75x (ISBN 0-8371-4262-8, LOPR). Greenwood.

McMinn, Tom. Prophets: Preachers for God. (BibLearn Ser.). (Illus.). 1979. 5.95 (ISBN 0-8054-4250-2, 4242-50). Broadman.

Maloney, George. Listen, Prophets! 5.95 (ISBN 0-87193-059-5). Dimension Bks.

Masters, Edgar L. The Blood of Prophets. 59.95 (ISBN 0-87968-761-4). Gordon Pr.

Moloney, F. J. Disciples & Prophets. 240p. 1981. 12.95 (ISBN 0-8245-0049-0). Crossroad NY.

Nadvi, A. H. Only a Prophet Could Do It. pap. 1.00 (ISBN 0-686-18429-7). Kazi Pubns.

--Tales of the Prophets. pap. 2.50 (ISBN 0-686-18388-6). Kazi Pubns.

Norquist, Marilyn. How to Read & Pray the Prophets. (Handbook of the Bible Ser.). (Orig.). 1980. pap. 1.50 (ISBN 0-89243-122-9, 44900). Liguori Pubns.

Nurbakhsh, Jawad. Traditions of the Prophet, Vol. 2. Lewisohn, Leonard & Graham, Terry, trs. 1984. pap. 6.00x (ISBN 0-933546-10-6). KhaniQahi-Nimatullahi-Sufi.

Osen, James L. Prophet & Peacemaker: The Life of Adolphe Monod. (Illus.). 420p. 1984. lib. bdg. 32.25 (ISBN 0-8191-3825-8); pap. text ed. 17.75 (ISBN 0-8191-3826-6). U Pr of Amer.

Overholt, Thomas W. Prophecy in Cross Cultural Perspective: A Sourcebook for Biblical Researchers. (Society of Biblical Literature Ser.). 1985. pap. 26.95 (ISBN 0-89130-901-2, 06-03-17). Scholars Pr GA.

Prophets--Nevi'im: A New Translation of the Holy Scriptures According to the Traditional Hebrew Text. LC 77-87245. 930p. 1978. 10.95 (ISBN 0-8276-0096-8, 55). Jewish Pubns.

Ramsay, William M. Four Modern Prophets: Walter Rauschenbusch, Martin Luther King, Jr., Gustavo Gutierrez, Rosemary Radford Ruether. LC 86-45351. 108p. (Orig.). 1986. pap. 6.95 (ISBN 0-8042-0811-5). John Knox.

Raza, M. S. Introducing the Prophets. 1970. 5.00x (ISBN 0-87902-184-5). Orientalia.

Reid, David P. What Are They Saying about the Prophets? LC 80-80869. 112p. (Orig.). 1980. pap. 3.95 (ISBN 0-8091-2304-5). Paulist Pr.

Robinson, George L. Twelve Minor Prophets. 5.95 (ISBN 0-8010-7669-2). Baker Bk.

Robinson, Henry W. Inspiration & Revelation in the Old Testament. LC 78-9891. 1979. Repr. of 1946 ed. lib. bdg. 24.75x (ISBN 0-313-21068-3, ROIR). Greenwood.

Rowley, Harold H. Prophecy & Religion in Ancient China & Israel. LC 56-12074. 1956. 12.00x (ISBN 0-8401-2059-1). A R Allenson.

St. John, Robert. Tongue of the Prophets. pap. 7.00 (ISBN 0-87980-166-2). Wilshire.

Sawyer, John F. Prophecy & Prophets of the Old Testament. 1987. pap. 8.95. Oxford U Pr.

Seilhamer, Frank H. Prophets & Prophecy: Seven Key Messengers. LC 76-62603. pap. 23.80 (2027878). Bks Demand UMI.

Sharafuddin, Sadruddin. Ammar Yasir. Haq, M. Fazal, tr. Orig. Title: Halif al-Makhzum. 264p. 1985. pap. 9.00 (ISBN 0-941724-40-9). Islamic Seminary.

Siddiqui, A. H. Prophethood in Islam. pap. 4.95 (ISBN 0-686-18344-4). Kazi Pubns.

Slosson, Edwin E. Six Major Prophets. facsimile ed. LC 71-167421. (Essay Index Reprint Ser). Repr. of 1917 ed. 23.00 (ISBN 0-8369-2571-8). Ayer Co Pubs.

Smart, Ninian & Purnananda, Swami. Prophet of the New Hindu Age: The Life & Times of Archarya Pranavananda. (Illus.). 256p. 1985. 15.00 (ISBN 0-04-922032-2); pap. 9.50 (ISBN 0-04-922033-0). Allen Unwin.

Smith, John M. Prophets & Their Times. rev ed. Irwin, William A., ed. LC 25-6864. 1941. 20.00x (ISBN 0-226-76356-0). U of Chicago Pr.

Smith, W. Robertson. Prophets of Israel & Their Place in History to the Close of the Eighth Century B. C. 1979. Repr. of 1895 ed. lib. bdg. 50.00 (ISBN 0-8495-4905-1). Arden Lib.

Smith, William R. The Prophets of Israel. (Social Science Classics Ser.). 446p. text ed. cancelled (ISBN 0-87855-700-8); pap. text ed. cancelled (ISBN 0-686-68060-X). Transaction Bks.

--The Prophets of Israel: And Their Place in History to the Close of the Eighth Century, B.C. LC 77-87666. 504p. Repr. of 1907 ed. 47.50 (ISBN 0-404-16403-X). AMS Pr.

Stevens-Arroyo, Antonio, ed. Prophets Denied Honor: An Anthology on the Hispanic Church in the U. S. LC 79-26847. 397p. (Orig.). 1982. pap. 12.95 (ISBN 0-88344-395-3). Orbis Bks.

Van Buskirk, William R. Saviors of Mankind. LC 71-86790. (Essay Index Reprint Ser.). 1929. 32.00 (ISBN 0-8369-1432-5). Ayer Co Pubs.

Von Rad, Gerhard. The Message of the Prophets. Stalker, D. M., tr. from Ger. LC 72-183633. 288p. 1972. pap. 10.95xi (ISBN 0-06-068929-3, RD45, HarpR). Har-Row.

Wiesel, Elie. Five Biblical Portraits. LC 81-40458. vii, 157p. 1983. pap. 4.95 (ISBN 0-268-00962-7, 85-09622). U of Notre Dame Pr.

Wifall, Walter. Israel's Prophets: Envoys of the King. (Biblical Booklets). 1975. pap. 1.25 (ISBN 0-8199-0521-6). Franciscan Herald.

Willis, John T. My Servants the Prophets, Vol. 4. (Way of Life Ser.: No. 119). 1982. pap. 3.95 (ISBN 0-89112-119-6, Bibl Res Pr). Abilene Christ U.

Wolff, Hans W. Confrontations with Prophets. LC 82-48585. 80p. 1983. pap. 4.25 (ISBN 0-8006-1702-9). Fortress.

Wood, Leon J. Prophets of Israel. LC 79-50172. 1979. 16.95 (ISBN 0-8010-9607-3). Baker Bk.

Young, Edward J. My Servants the Prophets. 1952. pap. 8.95 (ISBN 0-8028-1697-5). Eerdmans.

Zimmerman, Dean. Living Prophet. 1974. pap. 2.95 (ISBN 0-89036-041-3). Hawkes Pub Inc.

PROPOSED RELIGIONS

see Religions (Proposed, Universal, etc.)

PROSE (LITURGY)

see Sequences (Liturgy)

PROSELYTES AND PROSELYTING

Carmel, Abraham. So Strange My Path. LC 64-17487. 1977. pap. 5.95 (ISBN 0-8197-0066-5). Bloch.

Cresson, Warder. The Key of David: David the True Messiah. Davis, Moshe, ed. LC 77-70671. (America & the Holy Land Ser.). (Illus.). 1977. Repr. of 1852 ed. lib. bdg. 26.50x (ISBN 0-405-10239-9). Ayer Co Pubs.

Eichhorn, David M. Conversion to Judaism: A History & Analysis. 1966. 12.50x (ISBN 0-87068-019-6). Ktav.

Mayer, Egon. Becoming Jewish. 40p. (Orig.). Date not set. pap. price not set. Am Jewish Comm.

Rosenbloom, Joseph R. Conversion to Judaism: From the Biblical Period to the Present. 20.00x (ISBN 0-87820-113-0). Ktav.

PROSPER OF AQUITAINE

Burghardt, W. J., et al, eds. St. Prosper of Aquitaine, the Call of All Nations. (Ancient Christian Writers Ser.: No. 14). 250p. 1952. 10.95 (ISBN 0-8091-0253-6). Paulist Pr.

PROSTITUTION

see also Sexual Ethics

Pivar, David J. Purity Crusade: Sexual Morality & Social Control, 1868-1900. LC 70-179650. (Contributions in American History Ser.: No. 23). 308p. 1973. lib. bdg. 29.95 (ISBN 0-8371-6319-6, PPC/). Greenwood.

PROTESTANT CHURCHES

see also Protestantism;

also names of Protestant denominations, e.g. Lutheran Church

Abell, Aaron I. The Urban Impact on American Protestantism, 1865-1900. x, 275p. 1962. Repr. of 1943 ed. 22.50 (ISBN 0-208-00587-0, Archon). Shoe String.

Anderson, William K., ed. Protestantism. facs. ed. LC 69-18918. (Essay Index Reprint Ser). 1944. 17.50 (ISBN 0-8369-1018-4). Ayer Co Pubs.

Berkhofer, Robert F. Salvation & the Savage: An Analysis of Protestant Missions & American Indian Response, 1787-1862. LC 77-22857. 1977. Repr. of 1965 ed. lib. bdg. 22.50x (ISBN 0-8371-9745-7, BESSA). Greenwood.

Bollen, J. D. Protestantism & Social Reform in New South Wales 1890-1910. (Illus.). 200p. 1972. 20.00x (ISBN 0-522-84023-X, Pub. by Melbourne U Pr). Intl Spec Bk.

Bouyer, Louis. Orthodox Spirituality & Protestant & Anglican Spirituality. (A History of Christian Spirituality Ser.: Vol. 3). 232p. 1982. pap. 9.95 (ISBN 0-8164-2374-1, HarpR). Har-Row.

Bower, William C., ed. Church at Work in the Modern World. facs. ed. LC 67-26717. (Essay Index Reprint Ser.). 1935. 18.00 (ISBN 0-8369-0231-9). Ayer Co Pubs.

Brauer, Jerald C. Protestantism in America: A Narrative History. rev. ed. LC 66-12686. 320p. 1972. Westminster.

Carey, George. A Tale of Two Churches: Can Protestants & Catholics Get Together? LC 84-28858. 180p. (Orig.). 1985. pap. 5.95 (ISBN 0-87784-972-2). Inter-Varsity.

Carter, Paul A. The Decline & Revival of the Social Gospel: Social & Political Liberalism in American Protestant Churches, 1920-1940. 2nd ed. LC 70-122413. xxvi, 265p. 1971. Repr. of 1956 ed. 27.50 (ISBN 0-208-01083-1, Archon). Shoe String.

Chaney, Charles L. Birth of Missions in America. LC 75-26500. 352p. 1976. pap. 7.95 (ISBN 0-87808-146-1). William Carey Lib.

Cordasco, Francesco, ed. Protestant Evangelism among Italians in America. LC 74-17943. (Italian American Experience Ser.). (Illus.). 276p. 1975. Repr. 21.00x (ISBN 0-405-06414-4). Ayer Co Pubs.

Dillenberger, John & Welch, Claude. Protestant Christianity. 340p. 1976. pap. text ed. write for info. (ISBN 0-02-330470-7, Pub. by Scribner). Macmillan.

Durasoff, Steve. The Russian Protestants: Evangelicals in the Soviet Union. LC 72-76843. (Illus.). 312p. 1969. 27.50 (ISBN 0-8386-7465-8). Fairleigh Dickinson.

Ernst, Eldon. Moment of Truth for Protestant America: Interchurch Campaigns Following World War I. LC 74-16567. (American Academy of Religion. Dissertation Ser.). 1974. pap. 9.95 (010103). Scholars Pr GA.

Forell, George W. The Protestant Faith. LC 74-26341. 320p. 1975. pap. 9.95 (ISBN 0-8006-1095-4, 1-1095). Fortress.

Forsythe, Sidney A. An American Missionary Community in China, 1895-1905. LC 70-178077. (East Asian Monographs Ser: No. 43). 1971. pap. 11.00x (ISBN 0-674-02626-8). Harvard U Pr.

Garrison, Winfred E. March of Faith: The Story of Religion in America Since 1865. LC 79-138112. 1971. Repr. of 1933 ed. lib. bdg. 22.50x (ISBN 0-8371-5688-2, GAMF). Greenwood.

Gunson, Niel. Messengers of Grace: Evangelical Missionaries in the South Seas 1797-1860. (Illus.). 1978. 49.95x (ISBN 0-19-550517-4). Oxford U Pr.

Handy, Robert T. A Christian America: Protestant Hopes & Historical Realities. 2nd & enl. ed. 1983. 27.00x (ISBN 0-19-503386-8); pap. 10.95x (ISBN 0-19-503387-6). Oxford U Pr.

Harper, Howard V. Profiles of Protestant Saints. LC 67-24071. 1968. 9.95 (ISBN 0-8303-0037-6). Fleet.

Hudson, Winthrop S. American Protestantism. LC 61-15936. (Chicago History of American Civilization Ser). 1961. pap. 4.95x (ISBN 0-226-35803-8, CHAC10). U of Chicago Pr.

LaRuffa, Anthony L. San Cipriano: Life in a Puerto Rican Community. LC 73-136765. (Library of Anthropology Ser.). (Illus.). 166p. 1971. 44.00 (ISBN 0-677-03470-9). Gordon & Breach.

Loescher, Frank S. The Protestant Church & the Negro, a Pattern of Segregation. LC 76-135601. 159p. 1972. Repr. of 1948 ed. text ed. cancelled (ISBN 0-8371-5193-7, LPC&, Pub. by Negro U Pr). Greenwood.

McWilliams, Warren. The Passion of God: Divine Suffering in Contemporary Protestant Theology. 208p. 1985. text ed. 16.50 (ISBN 0-86554-158-2, MUP H148). Mercer Univ Pr.

MARC, ed. Directory: North American Protestant Schools & Professors of Mission. 220p. pap. 6.60 (ISBN 0-912552-37-9). Missions Adv Res Com Ctr.

Miller, Robert M. American Protestantism & Social Issues, 1919-1939. LC 77-22031. 1977. Repr. of 1958 ed. lib. bdg. 26.75x (ISBN 0-8371-9777-5, MIAM). Greenwood.

Miscitelli, Peter. Savonarola, Protestantism & the Church of Rome, 2 vols. (Illus.). 247p. 1985. Set. 187.50 (ISBN 0-89901-230-2). Found Class Reprints.

A Request Presented to the King of Spayn by the Inhabitants of the Lowe Countreyes, Protesting That They Will Live According to the Reformation of the Gospell. LC 71-26044. (English Experience Ser.: No. 266). 1970. Repr. of 1578 ed. 7.00 (ISBN 90-221-0266-1). Walter J Johnson.

Roof, Wade C. Community & Commitment: Religious Plausibility in a Liberal Protestant Church. 278p. 1978. 28.00 (ISBN 0-444-99038-0). Elsevier.

Schaff, Philip. The Principles of Protestantism. Thompson, Bard & Bricker, George H., eds. 1964. pap. 6.95 (ISBN 0-8298-0348-3). Pilgrim NY.

Shanahan, William O. German Protestants Face the Social Question: The Conservative Phase, 1815-1871. 1954. 22.95 (ISBN 0-268-00110-3). U of Notre Dame Pr.

Troeltsch, Ernst. Protestantism & Progress: The Significance of Protestantism for the Rise of the Modern World. LC 86-45221. (Fortress Texts in Modern Theology Ser.). 112p. 1986. pap. 8.95 (ISBN 0-8006-3200-1). Fortress.

Ward, Marcus. Protestant Christian Churches. 1985. 13.00x (ISBN 0-7062-3597-5, Pub. by Ward Lock Educ Co Ltd). State Mutual Bk.

Willems, Emilio. Followers of the New Faith: Culture Change & the Rise of Protestantism in Brazil & Chile. LC 67-27517. 1967. 16.50x (ISBN 0-8265-1106-6). Vanderbilt U Pr.

Zaits, Kyrill Archpriest. Missionary Conversations with Protestant Sectarians. 49p. (Orig.). 1985. pap. 2.00 (ISBN 0-317-30291-4). Holy Trinity.

PROTESTANT CHURCHES–RELATIONS–CATHOLIC CHURCH

Arnstein, Walter L. Protestant vs. Catholic in Mid-Victorian England: Mr. Newdegate & the Nuns. LC 81-11451. 272p. text ed. 20.00x (ISBN 0-8262-0354-X). U of Mo Pr.

Tavard, George H. Holy Writ or Holy Church: The Crisis of the Protestant Reformation. LC 78-17085. 1978. Repr. of 1959 ed. lib. bdg. 22.75x (ISBN 0-313-20584-1, TAHO). Greenwood.

Underwood, Kenneth W. Protestant & Catholic. LC 72-9051. (Illus.). 484p. 1973. Repr. of 1957 ed. lib. bdg. 22.50x (ISBN 0-8371-6567-9, UNPC). Greenwood.

Zaits, Kyrill Archpriest. Missionary Conversations with Protestant Sectarians. 49p. (Orig.). 1985. pap. 2.00 (ISBN 0-317-30291-4). Holy Trinity.

PROTESTANT DISSENTERS

see Dissenters, Religious

PROTESTANT EPISCOPAL CHURCH IN THE U. S. A.

see also Anglo-Catholicism

Benton, Angelo Ames. The Church Cyclopaedia: A Dictionary of Church Doctrine, History, Organization & Ritual, & Containing Original Articles on Special Topics, Written Expressly for This Work by Bishops, Presbyters, & Laymen. LC 74-31499. 810p. 1975. Repr. of 1883 ed. 65.00x (ISBN 0-8103-4204-9). Gale.

Bernardin, Joseph B. Introduction to the Episcopal Church. rev ed. (Orig.). 1978. pap. 4.95 (ISBN 0-8192-1231-8). Morehouse.

Brewer, Clifton H. History of Religious Education in the Episcopal Church to 1835. LC 73-89152. (American Education Its Men, Institutions & Ideas, Ser. 1). 1969. Repr. of 1924 ed. 16.00 (ISBN 0-405-01390-6). Ayer Co Pubs.

Carlozzi, Carl G. The Episcopal Way. 1977. pap. text ed. 4.95x (ISBN 0-8192-4073-7); tchrs ed. 4.95x (ISBN 0-8192-4074-5). Morehouse.

Cushman, Joseph D., Jr. Goodly Heritage, the Episcopal Church in Florida, 1821-1892. LC 65-28693. (Illus.). 1965. 7.50 (ISBN 0-8130-0054-8). U Presses Fla.

--Sound of Bells: The Episcopal Church in South Florida, 1892-1969. LC 75-30946. (Illus.). 1976. 15.00 (ISBN 0-8130-0518-3). U Presses Fla.

Davies-Rodgers, Ellen. Heirs Through Hope: The Episcopal Diocese of West Tennessee. LC 83-50733. 1983. 30.00 (ISBN 0-317-05919-X). Plantation.

--The Romance of the Episcopal Church in West Tennessee. 12.00 (ISBN 0-685-84991-0). Plantation.

Edwards, O. C. The Living & Active Word: A Way to Preach from the Bible Today. 166p. 1975. 1.50 (ISBN 0-8164-0265-5, HarpR). Har-Row.

The Episcopal Church Annual. LC 46-33254. 1987. 22.50 (ISBN 0-8192-3015-4). Morehouse.

Gray, William B. & Gray, Betty. Episcopal Church Welcomes You: An Introduction to Its History, Worship & Mission. rev. ed. LC 73-17898. 168p. 1974. (HarpR); pap. 3.95 (ISBN 0-8164-2087-4). Har-Row.

Krumm, John M. Why Choose the Episcopal Church? 160p. 1974. pap. 1.35 (ISBN 0-88028-030-1). Forward Movement.

M'Cheyne, Robert M. Bethany. 1974. pap. 1.65 (ISBN 0-685-52814-6). Reiner.

Meade, William. Old Churches, Ministers & Families of Virginia, 2 vols. Bd. with Digested Index & Genealogical Guide. Wise, Jennings C. Repr. of 1910 ed. LC 65-28854. 1100p. 1978. Repr. of 1857 ed. Set. 50.00 (ISBN 0-8063-0238-0). Genealog Pub.

Prichard, Robert W., ed. Readings from the History of the Episcopal Church. 192p. (Orig.). 1986. pap. 14.95 (ISBN 0-8192-1383-7). Morehouse.

Ross, Robert W. So It Was True: The American Protestant Press & the Nazi Persecution of the Jews. 374p. pap. 9.95 (ISBN 0-686-95052-6). ADL.

Sydnor, William. Looking at the Episcopal Church. LC 80-81103. 142p. (Orig.). 1981. pap. 5.95 (ISBN 0-8192-1279-2). Morehouse.

Wood, Richard H. A Cyclopedic Dictionary of Ecclesiastical Terms According to the Use of the Episcopal Church. 1984. 10.95 (ISBN 0-8062-2141-0). Carlton.

PROTESTANT EPISCOPAL CHURCH IN THE U. S. A.–BOOK OF COMMON PRAYER

Carlozzi, Carl G. The Episcopal Way. 1977. pap. text ed. 4.95x (ISBN 0-8192-4073-7); tchrs ed. 4.95x (ISBN 0-8192-4074-5). Morehouse.

Morning Prayer & the Psalter: Large Type Edition. 1981. pap. 12.95 (ISBN 0-8192-1284-9). Morehouse.

Shepherd, Massey H. Oxford American Prayer Book Commentary. 1950. 27.50 (ISBN 0-19-501202-X). Oxford U Pr.

PROTESTANT EPISCOPAL CHURCH IN THE U. S. A.–CLERGY

Boyd, Malcolm. Gay Priests: An Inner Journey. 208p. 1986. 14.95 (ISBN 0-312-31797-2). St Martin.

Donovan, Mary S. A Different Call: Women's Ministries in the Episcopal Church. 216p. (Orig.). 1986. text ed. 19.95 (ISBN 0-8192-1396-9). Morehouse.

PROTESTANT EPISCOPAL CHURCH IN THE U. S. A.–DOCTRINAL AND CONTROVERSIAL WORKS

Pike, James A. & Pittenger, W. Norman. Faith of the Church. 224p. (Orig.). 1951. pap. 1.00 (ISBN 0-8164-2019-X, SP3, HarpR). Har-Row.

Wilson, Frank E. Faith & Practice. rev. ed. (Orig.). 1961. pap. 7.95 (ISBN 0-8192-1082-X). Morehouse.

PROTESTANT EPISCOPAL CHURCH IN THE U. S. A.–HISTORY

Atwater, George P. The Episcopal Church: Its Message for Today. rev ed. 1978. pap. 4.95 (ISBN 0-8192-1244-X). Morehouse.

Caswall, Henry. America, & the American Church. LC 77-83413. (Religion in America Ser). 1969. Repr. of 1839 ed. 21.00 (ISBN 0-405-00234-3). Ayer Co Pubs.

Dalcho, Frederick. An Historical Account of the Protestant Episcopal Church, in South Carolina, from the First Settlement of the Province, to the War of the Revolution. LC 71-38445. (Religion in America, Ser. 2). 180p. 1972. Repr. of 1820 ed. 42.00 (ISBN 0-405-04064-4). Ayer Co Pubs.

Davies-Rodgers, Ellen. The Holy Innocents: The Story of a Historic Church & Country Parish. (Illus.). 12.00 (ISBN 0-685-84990-2). Plantation.

Dawley, Powel M. Our Christian Heritage: Revised & Expanded. 4th ed. LC 78-62062. 1978. pap. 5.50 (ISBN 0-8192-1243-1); leader's guide 3.95x (ISBN 0-8192-4086-9). Morehouse.

Gregg, Edward. The Protestant Succession in International Politics, 1710-1716. (Outstanding Theses from the London School of Economics & Political Science Ser.). 475p. 1987. lib. bdg. 75.00 (ISBN 0-8240-1918-0). Garland Pub.

Hughes, Leonard V., Jr. St. George's Episcopal Church, Germantown, Tennessee: The First Twenty Years. Russell, James D., ed. LC 83-50804. (Illus.). 224p. 1984. 6.00 (ISBN 0-9613533-0-9). St Georges Episcopal.

Lindsley, James Elliott. This Planted Vine: A Narrative History of the Episcopal Diocese of New York. LC 84-47588. (Illus.). 320p. 1984. 24.50 (ISBN 0-06-015347-4, HarpT). Har-Row.

Manross, William W. Episcopal Church in the United States, 1800-1840: A Study in Church Life. LC 38-38020. (Columbia University. Studies in the Social Sciences: No. 441). Repr. of 1938 ed. 21.00 (ISBN 0-404-51441-3). AMS Pr.

Mullin, Robert B. Episcopal Vision-American Reality: High Church Theology & Social Thought in Evangelical America. 1986. 20.00 (ISBN 0-300-03487-3). Yale U Pr.

Phillips, Charles H. The History of the Colored Methodist Episcopal Church in America: Comprising Its Organization, Subsequent Developments & Present Status. LC 73-38459. (Religion in America, Ser. 2). 252p. 1972. Repr. of 1898 ed. 17.00 (ISBN 0-405-04080-6). Ayer Co Pubs.

Schaff, Philip. The Principle of Protestantism: Chambersburg, PA 1845. Kuklick, Bruce, ed. Bd. with What Is Church History? Philadelphia, PA 1846. 215p. (American Religious Thought of the 18th & 19th Centuries Ser.). 343p. 1987. lib. bdg. 50.00. Garland Pub.

Simeone, William E. The Episcopal Church in Alaska: A Catalog of Photographs from the Archives & Historical Collections of the Episcopal Church. (Alaska Historical Commission Studies in History: No. 19). 152p. (Orig.). 1981. pap. text ed. 8.00 (ISBN 0-943712-08-4); microfiche 4.50 (ISBN 0-943712-07-6). Alaska Hist.

PROTESTANT EPISCOPAL CHURCH IN THE U. S. A.–LITURGY AND RITUAL

Altar Service of the Protestant Episcopal Church. write for info. Oxford U Pr.

General Episcopal Synod. The Holy Eucharist, Longer Form & Other Services. rev. ed. 44p. 1986. pap. 1.50 (ISBN 0-935461-12-4). St Alban Pr CA.

Smith, Martin L. Reconciliation: Preparing for Confession in the Episcopal Church. LC 85-21271. 121p. (Orig.). 1985. pap. 8.95 (ISBN 0-936384-30-1). Cowley Pubns.

PROTESTANT EPISCOPAL CHURCH IN THE U. S. A.–MISSIONS

Hening, Mrs. E. F. History of the African Mission of the Protestant Episcopal Church in the United States. facsimile ed. LC 77-173608. (Black Heritage Library Collection). Repr. of 1849 ed. 20.75 (ISBN 0-8369-8900-7). Ayer Co Pubs.

Scott, Anna M. Day Dawn in Africa: Or Progress of the Protestant Episcopal Mission at Cape Palmas, West Africa. LC 69-18659. (Illus.). Repr. of 1858 ed. cancelled (ISBN 0-8371-5091-4, SCD&, Pub. by Negro U Pr). Greenwood.

PROTESTANT EPISCOPAL CHURCH IN THE U. S. A.–SERMONS

Brooks, Phillips. Selected Sermons. facs. ed. Scarlett, William, ed. LC 79-142610. (Essay Index Reprint Ser). 1949. 19.50 (ISBN 0-8369-2146-1). Ayer Co Pubs.

Hamilton, Charles G. You Can't Steal First Base. LC 74-164909. 1972. 6.95 (ISBN 0-8022-2057-6). Philos Lib.

PROTESTANT REFORMATION

see Reformation

PROTESTANT SECTS

see Protestant Churches

PROTESTANTISM

see also Evangelicalism; Protestant Churches; Reformation

Alves, Rubem. Protestantism & Repression: A Brazilian Case Study. Drury, John, tr. from Portuguese. LC 82-3594. Tr. of Protestantismo e repressao. 256p. (Orig.). 1985. pap. 11.95 (ISBN 0-88344-098-9). Orbis Bks.

Anderson, William K., ed. Protestantism. facs. ed. LC 69-18918. (Essay Index Reprint Ser). 1944. 17.50 (ISBN 0-8369-1018-4). Ayer Co Pubs.

Bailey, Kenneth K. Southern White Protestantism in the Twentieth Century. 15.50 (ISBN 0-8446-1035-6). Peter Smith.

Bowen, Kurt. Protestants in a Catholic State: Ireland's Privileged Minority. 240p. 1983. 27.50x (ISBN 0-7735-0412-5). McGill-Queens U Pr.

Bowman, Derek. Life into Autobiography: A Study of Goethe's "Dichtung und Wahrheit". (Germanic Studies in America: Vol. 5). 162p. 1972. 19.60 (ISBN 3-261-00311-1). P Lang Pubs.

Brown, Robert M. Spirit of Protestantism. (YA) 1961. pap. 8.95 (ISBN 0-19-500724-7). Oxford U Pr.

Cobb, John B., Jr. Living Options in Protestant Theology: A Survey of Methods. 336p. 1986. pap. text ed. 14.75 (ISBN 0-8191-5488-1). U Pr of Amer.

Collinson, Patrick. Godly People: Essays on English Protestantism & Puritanism. (No. 23). 634p. 1983. 40.00 (ISBN 0-907628-15-X). Hambledon Press.

Colwell, Stephen. New Themes for the Protestant Clergy. LC 71-83417. (Religion in America, Ser. 1). 1969. Repr. of 1851 ed. 32.00 (ISBN 0-405-00243-2). Ayer Co Pubs.

Dorner, Isaak A. History of Protestant Theology, 2 Vols. LC 72-133823. Repr. of 1871 ed. Set. 87.50 (ISBN 0-404-02147-6). AMS Pr.

Dunstan, J. Leslie, ed. Protestantism. LC 61-15497. (Great Religions of Modern Man Ser). 1961. 8.95 (ISBN 0-8076-0161-6). Braziller.

Durnbaugh, Donald F. The Believers' Church. LC 85-7599. 328p. (Orig.). 1985. pap. 12.95x (ISBN 0-8361-1271-7). Herald Pr.

Fanfani, Amintore. Catholicism, Protestantism & Capitalism. LC 78-38251. (The Evolution of Capitalism Ser.). 234p. 1972. Repr. of 1935 ed. 23.50 (ISBN 0-405-04119-5). Ayer Co Pubs.

Ferm, Virgiulius. Protestant Credo. 1953. 5.95 (ISBN 0-8022-0494-5). Philos Lib.

Finkelstein, et al. Religions of Democracy. 1941. 9.50 (ISBN 0-8159-6708-X). Devin.

Fishman, Hertzel. American Protestantism & a Jewish State. LC 72-3746. (Schaver Publication Fund for Jewish Studies Ser). 250p. 1973. 24.95x (ISBN 0-8143-1481-3). Wayne St U Pr.

Flew, Robert N. & Davies, Rupert E., eds. The Catholicity of Protestantism: Being a Report Presented to His Grace the Archbishop of Canterbury by a Group of Free Churchmen. LC 80-29108. 159p. 1981. Repr. of 1950 ed. lib. bdg. 22.50x (ISBN 0-313-22825-6, FLCAT). Greenwood.

Gerrish, B. A. The Old Protestantism & the New: Essays on the Reformation Heritage. LC 82-2730. 400p. 1983. lib. bdg. 38.00x (ISBN 0-226-28869-2). U of Chicago Pr.

Gollwitzer, Helmut. An Introduction to Protestant Theology. Cairns, David, tr. LC 82-4798. 236p. 1982. pap. 12.95 (ISBN 0-664-24415-7). Westminster.

Heron, Alasdair I. A Century of Protestant Theology. LC 80-17409. 240p. 1980. pap. 9.95 (ISBN 0-664-24346-0). Westminster.

Hughley, Neal. Trends in Protestant Social Idealism. LC 74-167359. (Essay Index Reprint Ser.). Repr. of 1948 ed. 18.00 (ISBN 0-8369-2771-0). Ayer Co Pubs.

Kelling, Hans-Wilhelm. The Idolatry of Poetic Genius in German Goethe Criticism. (European University Studies: Series 1, German Language & Literature: Vol. 27). 200p. 1970. pap. 9.80 (ISBN 3-261-00026-0). P Lang Pubs.

Kemper, Robert G. Kind Words for Our Kind of Faith. 144p. (Orig.). 1986. pap. 8.95 (ISBN 0-8298-0738-1). Pilgrim NY.

Kerr, Hugh. Protestantism. LC 76-16065. (World Religions Ser.). 1979. pap. text ed. 6.95 (ISBN 0-8120-0665-8). Barron.

Kittel, Helmuth. Evangelische Religionspaedagogik. (Ger). 1970. 23.20x (ISBN 3-11-002654-6). De Gruyter.

Loewen, Harry. Goethe's Response to Protestantism. (Canadian Studies in German Language & Literature: Vol. 7). 168p. 1972. pap. 19.60. P Lang Pubs.

McWilliams, Warren. The Passion of God: Divine Suffering in Contemporary Protestant Theology. 208p. 1985. text ed. 16.50 (ISBN 0-86554-158-2, MUP H148). Mercer Univ Pr.

Marty, Martin E. Protestantism in the United States: Righteous Empire. 2nd ed. 320p. 1986. text ed. write for info. (ISBN 0-02-376500-3). Macmillan.

Michaelsen, Robert S. & Roof, Wade C. Liberal Protestantism. 200p. (Orig.). 1986. pap. 11.95 (ISBN 0-8298-0584-2). Pilgrim NY.

Murray, Iain H. The Puritan Hope. 1975. pap. 5.95 (ISBN 0-85151-037-X). Banner of Truth.

Nash, Arnold S., ed. Protestant Thought in the Twentieth Century: Whence & Whither? LC 78-5860. 1978. Repr. of 1951 ed. lib. bdg. 22.50x (ISBN 0-313-20484-5, NAPT). Greenwood.

North American Protestant Ministries Overseas. Mission Handbook. 13th ed. 1986. write for info. World Vision Intl.

Pratt, Henry J. Liberalization of American Protestantism: A Case Study in Complex Organizations. LC 74-38837. 345p. 1972. 24.95 (ISBN 0-8143-1475-9). Wayne St U Pr.

Reardon, Bernard M., ed. Liberal Protestantism. 1968. 18.50x (ISBN 0-8047-0647-6). Stanford U Pr.

Roof, Wade C. Community & Commitment: Religious Plausibility in a Liberal Protestant Church. LC 77-16329. 288p. pap. 10.95 (ISBN 0-8298-0669-5). Pilgrim NY.

Rotenberg, Mordechai. Damnation & Deviance: The Protestant Ethic & the Spirit of Failure. LC 77-18432. 1978. 12.95 (ISBN 0-02-927490-7). Free Pr.

Sanders, Thomas G. Protestant Concepts of Church & State. 19.50 (ISBN 0-8446-6185-6). Peter Smith.

Seebohm, Frederic. The Era of the Protestant Revolution. 1902. 25.00 (ISBN 0-8495-6274-0). Arden Lib.

Senn, Frank C., ed. Protestant Spiritual Traditions. 288p. (Orig.). 1986. pap. 9.95 (ISBN 0-8091-2761-X). Paulist Pr.

Stark, Rodney & Foster, Bruce D. Wayward Shepards: Prejudice & the Protestant Clergy. 130p. pap. 6.95 (ISBN 0-686-95186-7). ADL.

Tillich, Paul. Protestant Era. abr ed. Adams, James L., tr. 1957. pap. 7.00x (ISBN 0-226-80342-2, P19, Phoen). U of Chicago Pr.

Toon, Peter. Protestants & Catholics: A Guide to Understanding the Differences. 160p. (Orig.). 1984. pap. 5.95 (ISBN 0-89283-188-X). Servant.

Vallee, L. Dictionnaire du Protestantisme. Migne, J. P., ed. (Troisieme et Derniere Encyclopedie Theologique Ser.: Vol. 36). (Fr.). 692p. Repr. of 1858 ed. lib. bdg. 88.00x (ISBN 0-89241-315-8). Caratzas.

Warfield, B. B. Counterfeit Miracles. 1976. pap. 6.95 (ISBN 0-85151-166-X). Banner of Truth.

Weber, Max. Protestant Ethic & the Spirit of Capitalism. rev. ed. 1977. pap. 8.95 (ISBN 0-684-16489-2, ScribT). Scribner.

--The Protestant Ethic & the Spirit of Capitalism. 1984. 15.50 (ISBN 0-8446-6118-X). Peter Smith.

Westmeier, Karl-Wilhelm. Reconciling Heaven & Earth: The Transcendental Enthusiasm & Growth of an Urban Protestant Community, Bogota, Colombia. (Studies in the Intercultural History of Christianity: Vol. 41). 462p. 1986. text ed. 34.00 (ISBN 3-261-03547-1). P Lang Pubs.

Znoskovo-Borovsky, Mitrophan. Pravoslavije, Rimo-Katolichestvo, Protenstatizm i Sektantstvo. Tr. of Orthodoxy, Roman-Catholicism, Protenstatism & Sectarianism. 156p. 1972. pap. text ed. 5.00 (ISBN 0-317-30254-X). Holy Trinity.

PROTESTANTISM–HISTORY

Balbani, Niccolo. Newes from Italy of a Second Moses or, the Life of Galeacius Carracciolus the Noble Marquese of Vico. Crashaw, W., tr. LC 79-84085. (English Experience Ser.: No. 905). 92p. 1979. Repr. of 1608 ed. lib. bdg. 10.00 (ISBN 90-221-0905-4). Walter J Johnson.

Becon, Thomas. The Demaundes of Holy Scripture, with Answers to the Same. LC 79-84087. (English Experience Ser.: No.907). 116p. 1979. Repr. of 1577 ed. lib. bdg. 9.00 (ISBN 90-221-0907-0). Walter J Johnson.

Bodo, John R. Protestant Clergy & Public Issues, Eighteen Twelve to Eighteen Forty-Eight. LC 79-12849. (Perspectives in American History Ser: No. 52). 1980. Repr. of 1954 ed. lib. bdg. 27.50x (ISBN 0-87991-854-3). Porcupine Pr.

Brown, Colin. Jesus in European Protestant Thought, 1778-1860. (Studies in Historical Theology: Vol. 1). 380p. 1985. lib. bdg. 35.00x (ISBN 0-939464-18-7). Labyrinth Pr.

Coverdale, M., tr. from Dutch. The Original & Sprynge of All Sectes & Orders by Whome, Wha or Where (Sic) They Beganne. LC 79-84127. (English Experience Ser.: No. 946). (Eng.). 140p. 1979. Repr. of 1537 ed. lib. bdg. 11.50 (ISBN 90-221-0946-1). Walter J Johnson.

Davies, S. L. Peace, Print & Protestantism, Fourteen Fifty to Fifteen Eighty. 1976. 24.50x (ISBN 0-8464-0706-X). Beekman Pubs.

Ferm, Robert L., ed. Issues in American Protestantism: A Documentary History from the Puritans to the Present. 15.25 (ISBN 0-8446-2052-1). Peter Smith.

Fletcher, Charles R. Gustavus Adolphus & the Struggle of Protestantism for Existence. LC 73-14441. (Heroes of the Nations Ser.). Repr. of 1892 ed. 30.00 (ISBN 0-404-58260-5). AMS Pr.

Green, Robert W., ed. Protestantism & Capitalism & Social Science: The Webster Thesis Controversy. 2nd ed. (Problems in American Civilization Ser). 1973. pap. text ed. 5.50 (ISBN 0-669-81737-6). Heath.

Hutchison, William R. The Modernist Impulse in American Protestantism. (Illus.). 1982. pap. 9.95x (ISBN 0-19-503084-2). Oxford U Pr.

Jacobus, Verheiden. The History of the Moderne Protestant Divines, Containing Their Parents, Countries, Education, with Register of Their Writings. Lupton, D., tr. from Latin. LC 79-84142. (English Experience Ser.: No. 959). 400p. 1979. Repr. of 1637 ed. lib. bdg. 28.00 (ISBN 90-221-0959-3). Walter J Johnson.

Kington-Oliphant, Thomas L. Rome & Reform, 2 Vols. LC 76-118541. 1971. Repr. of 1902 ed. Set. 47.50x (ISBN 0-8046-1165-3, Pub. by Kennikat). Assoc Faculty Pr.

Martin, Marie-Louise. Kimbangu: An African Prophet & His Church. Moore, D. M., tr. LC 75-45371. pap. 55.50 (ISBN 0-317-08451-8, 2012735). Bks Demand UMI.

Piepkorn, Arthur C. Profiles in Belief, Vol. 2: Protestantism. LC 76-9971. 1978. 30.00 (ISBN 0-06-066582-3, HarpR). Har-Row.

The Proceedings of the Grisons in the Year 1618. LC 78-171760. (English Experience Ser.: No. 383). 94p. Repr. of 1619 ed. 14.00 (ISBN 90-221-0383-8). Walter J Johnson.

Ribuffo, Leo. The Old Christian Right: The Protestant Far Right from the Great Depression to the Cold War. 277p. 1983. 29.95 (ISBN 0-87722-297-5). Temple U Pr.

Rolte, J., tr. Palatinate-a Full Declaration of the Faith & Ceremonies Professed in the Dominions of Prince Fredericke, 5. Prince Elector Palatine. LC 79-84129. (English Experience Ser.: No. 947). 208p. 1979. Repr. of 1614 ed. lib. bdg. 20.00 (ISBN 90-221-0947-X). Walter J Johnson.

Welch, Claude. Protestant Thought in the Nineteenth Century, Vol. 1: 1799 to 1870. LC 72-75211. Repr. of 1972 ed. 84.00 (ISBN 0-8357-9459-8, 2013200). Bks Demand UMI.

--Protestant Thought in the Nineteenth Century: Volume 1, 1799-1870. LC 72-75211. 335p. 1986. Repr. 25.00x (ISBN 0-300-01535-6). Yale U Pr.

--Protestant Thought in the Nineteenth Century: Volume 2, 1870-1914. LC 72-75211. 328p. 1985. 25.00x (ISBN 0-300-03369-9). Yale U Pr.

Zwingli, Ulrich. The Acconmpt Rekenynge & Confession of the Faith of Huldrik Zwinglius. Cotsforde, Thomas, tr. from Latin. LC 79-84148. (The English Experience: No. 964). Orig. Title: Swinglische Bekenntuis. 156p. 1979. Repr. of 1555 ed. lib. bdg. 11.50 (ISBN 90-221-0964-X). Walter J Johnson.

PROTESTANTISM, EVANGELICAL

see Evangelicalism

PROTESTANTS IN ENGLAND

Clebsch, William A. England's Earliest Protestants, 1520-1535. LC 80-15226. (Yale Publications in Religion: No. 11). xvi, 358p. 1980. Repr. of 1964 ed. lib. bdg. 22.50x (ISBN 0-313-22420-X, CLEE). Greenwood.

Collinson, Patrick. The Religion of Protestants: The Church in English Society 1559-1625. 1982. pap. 15.95x (ISBN 0-19-820053-6). Oxford U Pr.
Huntley, Frank L. Bishop Joseph Hall & Protestant Meditation in Seventeenth-Century England: A Study, with Texts of the Art of Divine Meditation (1606) & Occasional Meditations (1633) (Medieval & Renaissance Texts & Studies: 1). (Illus.). 234p. (Orig.). 1981. 15.00 (ISBN 0-86698-000-8); pap. 9.00 (ISBN 0-86698-005-9). Medieval.
Pettegree, Andrew. Foreign Protestant Communities in Sixteenth-Century London. (Historical Monographs). 280p. 1987. 49.50 (ISBN 0-19-822938-0). Oxford U Pr.
Scott, Thomas. The Interpreter, Wherein Three Principal Terms of State Are Clearly Unfolded. LC 74-80194. (English Experience Ser.: No. 673). 1974. Repr. of 1624 ed. 3.50 (ISBN 90-221-0281-5). Walter J Johnson.

PROTESTANTS IN FRANCE

Kelly, Caleb G. French Protestantism, Fifteen Fifty-Nine to Fifteen Sixty-Two. LC 78-63967. (Johns Hopkins University. Studies in the Social Sciences, 1918: No. 36 4). Repr. of 1918 ed. 24.50 (ISBN 0-404-61213-X). AMS Pr.
Kingdon, R. M. Geneva & the Consolidation of the French Protestant Movement, 1564-1572: A Contribution to the History of Congregationalism, Presbyterianism, & Calvinist Resistance Theory. 244p. (Orig.). 1967. pap. text ed. 27.50x (Pub. by Droz Switzerland). Coronet Bks.
Marteilhe, Jean. The Memoirs of a Protestant Condemned to the Galleys of France for His Religion, 2 Vols. Goldsmith, Oliver, tr. 290p. 1983. Repr. of 1895 ed. Set. lib. bdg. 75.00 (ISBN 0-8495-2138-6). Arden Lib.

PROTESTANTS IN IRELAND

Dawe, Gerald & Longley, Edna, eds. Across a Roaring Hill: The Protestant Imagination in Modern Ireland. 242p. 1985. 16.50 (ISBN 0-85640-334-2, Pub. by Blackstaff Pr). Longwood Pub Group.
Nelson, Sarah. Ulster's Uncertain Defenders: Protestant Political, Paramilitary & Community Groups & the Northern Ireland Conflict. (Irish Studies). 206p. 1984. text ed. 32.00x (ISBN 0-8156-2316-X). Syracuse U Pr.

PROTESTANTS IN LATIN AMERICA

Alves, Rubem. Protestantism & Repression: A Brazilian Case Study. Drury, John, tr. from Portuguese. LC 82-3594. Tr. of Protestantismo e repressao. 256p. (Orig.). 1985. pap. 11.95 (ISBN 0-88344-098-9). Orbis Bks.
Costas, O., et al, eds. Hacia Una Teologia Evangelica Latinoamericana. 154p. 1984. pap. 3.95 (ISBN 0-89922-238-2). Edit Caribe.
Lalive D'Epinay, Christian. Religion, Dynamique Sociale et Dependance: Les Mouvements Protestants En Argentine et Au Chili. (Interaction Ser: L'homme et Son Environnementsocial, No. 4). (Fr., Illus.). 368p. 1976. pap. text ed. 36.40x (ISBN 90-2797-922-7). Mouton.
Lee, Elizabeth M. He Wears Orchids & Other Latin American Stories. LC 76-117327. (Biography Index Reprint Ser). 1951. 19.00 (ISBN 0-8369-8019-0). Ayer Co Pubs.
Nelson, Wilton M. Protestantism in Central America. 96p. (Orig.). 1984. pap. 4.95 (ISBN 0-8028-0024-6). Eerdmans.
--El Protestantismo en Centro America. (Span.). 102p. (Orig.). 1982. pap. 2.50 (ISBN 0-89922-211-0). Edit Caribe.
Sinclair, John H., ed. Protestantism in Latin America: A Bibliographical Guide. rev. ed. LC 73-12837. 1976. pap. text ed. 8.95x (ISBN 0-87808-126-7). William Carey Lib.

PROTESTANTS IN THE SOVIET UNION

Hebly, J. A. Protestants in Russia. Pott, John, tr. LC 76-149. pap. 48.00 (ISBN 0-317-08445-3, 2012741). Bks Demand UMI.

PROTESTANTS IN THE UNITED STATES

Bode, Frederick A. Protestantism & the New South: North Carolina Baptists & Methodists in Political Crisis, 1894-1903. LC 75-1289. 171p. 1975. 15.00x (ISBN 0-8139-0597-4). U Pr of Va.
Bodo, John R. Protestant Clergy & Public Issues, Eighteen Twelve to Eighteen Forty-Eight. LC 79-12849. (Perspectives in American History Ser: No. 52). 1980. Repr. of 1954 ed. lib. bdg. 27.50x (ISBN 0-87991-854-3). Porcupine Pr.
Cortes, Carlos E., ed. Protestantism & Latinos in the United States: An Original Anthology. LC 79-6266. (Hispanics in the United States Ser.). (Illus.). 1981. lib. bdg. 51.50x (ISBN 0-405-13173-9). Ayer Co Pubs.
Dickens, A. G. Lollards & Protestants in the Diocese of York. (No. 10). 280p. 1983. 27.00 (ISBN 0-907628-05-2); pap. 12.00 (ISBN 0-907628-06-0). Hambledon Press.
Giuseppi, Montague S. Naturalization of Foreign Protestants in the American & West Indian Colonies, Etc. LC 64-19759. 196p. 1979. Repr. of 1921 ed. 14.00 (ISBN 0-8063-0157-0). Genealog Pub.
Hale, Frederick. Trans-Atlantic Conservative Protestantism in the Evangelical Free & Mission Covenant Traditions. Scott, Franklyn D., ed. LC 78-15183. (Scandinavians in America Ser.). 1979. lib. bdg. 30.50x (ISBN 0-405-11638-1). Ayer Co Pubs.
Huggins, Nathan I. Protestants Against Poverty: Boston's Charities, 1870-1900. (Contributions in American History: No. 9). 1970. lib. bdg. 29.95 (ISBN 0-8371-3307-6, HUP/). Greenwood.
Hutchison, William R., ed. American Protestant Thought in the Liberal Era. LC 84-19614. 252p. 1985. pap. text ed. 10.75 (ISBN 0-8191-4336-7). U Pr of Amer.
Moore, R. Laurence. Religious Outsiders & the Making of Americans. 288p. 1986. text ed. 24.95x (ISBN 0-19-503663-8). Oxford U Pr.
Moorhead, James H. American Apocalypse: Yankee Protestants & the Civil War, 1860-1869. LC 77-14360. 1978. 32.00x (ISBN 0-300-02152-6). Yale U Pr.
Orozco, E. C. Republican Protestantism in Aztlan. LC 80-82906. 261p. 1980. 24.00x (ISBN 0-9606102-1-9); pap. 14.50x (ISBN 0-9606102-2-7). Petereins Pr.
Parker, T. V. American Protestantism. 1956. 7.95 (ISBN 0-8022-1264-6). Philos Lib.
Smith, Timothy. Revivalism & Social Reform: American Protestantism on the Eve of the Civil War. LC 80-8114. 272p. 1980. pap. text ed. 8.95x (ISBN 0-8018-2477-X). Johns Hopkins.
Szasz, Ferenc M. The Divided Mind of Protestant America, 1880-1930. LC 81-7597. 216p. 1982. text ed. 19.95 (ISBN 0-8173-0080-5). U of Ala Pr.

PROTESTANTS IN THE WEST INDIES

Giuseppi, Montague S. Naturalization of Foreign Protestants in the American & West Indian Colonies, Etc. LC 64-19759. 196p. 1979. Repr. of 1921 ed. 14.00 (ISBN 0-8063-0157-0). Genealog Pub.

PROVERBS

see also Aphorisms and Apothegms

Arnander, Primose & Skipwith, Ashkain. The Son of a Duck is a Floater: An Illustrated Book of Arab Proverbs. (Illus.). 90p. 1985. 7.95 (ISBN 0-905743-41-5, Pub. by Stacey Intl UK). Humanities.
Arnot, William. Studies in Proverbs. LC 78-6014. (Reprint Library). Orig. Title: Laws From Heaven for Life on Earth. 584p. 1986. pap. 14.95 (ISBN 0-8254-2123-3). Kregel.
Ayalti, Hanan J., ed. Yiddish Proverbs. LC 49-11135. (Illus., Bilingual). 1963. pap. 4.75 (ISBN 0-8052-0050-9). Schocken.
Baz, Petros D. Dictionary of Proverbs. (Orig.). pap. 1.85 (ISBN 0-685-19399-3, 108, WL). Citadel Pr.
Bohn, Henry G. Polyglot of Foreign Proverbs. LC 68-55796. (Bohn's Antiquarian Library Ser.). Repr. of 1857 ed. 12.50 (ISBN 0-404-50004-8). AMS Pr.
Bohn, Henry G., ed. Polyglot of Foreign Proverbs - with English Translations. LC 67-23915. (Polyglot Ser.). 1968. Repr. of 1857 ed. 40.00x (ISBN 0-8103-3197-7). Gale.
Bryant, Margaret M. Proverbs & How to Collect Them. (Publications of the American Dialect Society: No. 4). 25p. 1945. pap. 2.35 (ISBN 0-8173-0604-8). U of Ala Pr.
Burton, Richard F. Wit & Wisdom from West Africa: A Book of Proverbial Philosophy, Idioms, Enigmas, & Laconisms. LC 77-79952. 1969. Repr. of 1865 ed. 16.00 (ISBN 0-8196-0243-4). Biblo.
Castle, Tony, ed. The New Book of Christian Quotations. LC 82-25253. 272p. 1983. pap. 9.95 (ISBN 0-8245-0551-4). Crossroad NY.
Drake, Marsha. The Proverbs Thirty-One Lady & Other Impossible Dreams. LC 84-6453. 192p. (Orig.). 1984. pap. 5.95 (ISBN 0-87123-595-1, 210595). Bethany Hse.
Du Castel, Christine. The Morale Proberbes of Christyne. LC 73-25783. (English Experience Ser.: No. 241). 8p. 1970. Repr. of 1478 ed. 14.00 (ISBN 90-221-0241-6). Walter J Johnson.
Erasmus, Desiderius. Erasmus on His Times: A Shortened Version of the Adages of Erasmus. Phillips, Margaret M., ed. 1967. pap. 9.95 (ISBN 0-521-09413-5). Cambridge U Pr.
--Proverbs or Adages. Taverner, Richard, tr. LC 55-11634. 1977. Repr. of 1569 ed. 35.00x (ISBN 0-8201-1232-1). Schol Facsimiles.
--Proverbs or Adagies with Newe Addicions, Gathered Out of the Chiliades of Erasmus. LC 73-264117. (English Experience Ser.: No. 124). 1969. Repr. of 1539 ed. 13.00 (ISBN 90-221-0124-X). Walter J Johnson.
Fulton, Ginger A. When I'm a Mommy: A Little Girl's Paraphrase of Proverbs 31. (Illus.). 1984. pap. 2.95 (ISBN 0-8024-0367-0). Moody.
Kogos, Fred. One Thousand One Yiddish Proverbs. 1970. 5.95 (ISBN 0-8065-0013-1). Citadel Pr.
Larousse. Larousse Dictionnaire des Proverbs, Sentences et Maximes. 37.50 (ISBN 0-317-45655-5). French & Eur.
McCormick, Malachi. Yiddish Proverbs: A Collection. (Proverbs of the World Ser.). (Illus.). 60p. (Orig.). 1982. pap. text ed. 12.50 (ISBN 0-943984-02-5). Stone St Pr.
MacDonald, William. Enjoying the Proverbs. 1982. pap. 4.00 (ISBN 0-937396-23-0). Walterick Pubs.
--Listen, My Son. Rev. ed. pap. 3.00 (ISBN 0-937396-23-0). Walterick Pubs.
McLellan, Vern. Proverbs For People. LC 82-83841. (Illus.). 1983. pap. 3.25 (ISBN 0-89081-326-4). Harvest Hse.
Mieder, Wolfgang. The P-H Encyclopedia of World Proverbs. LC 85-12345. 582p. 1986. 34.95 (ISBN 0-13-695586-X). P-H.
Proverbs, Promises & Principles. pap. 3.25 (ISBN 0-89081-460-0). Harvest Hse.
Robert. Dictionnaire de Proverbes & Dictons. 45.00 (ISBN 0-317-45633-4). French & Eur.
Simpson, J. A., ed. The Concise Oxford Dictionary of Proverbs. (Paperback Reference Ser.). 1983. pap. 6.95 (ISBN 0-19-281880-5). Oxford U Pr.
Thomas, Barbara J. Proverbs II. 56p. (Orig.). 1985. pap. 5.95 (ISBN 0-9616788-0-1). Landsberry Pr.
Turner, Charles W. Studies in Proverbs: Wise Words in a Wicked World. (Contemporary Discussion Ser.). 1977. pap. 3.50 (ISBN 0-8010-8815-1). Baker Bk.
Vaughan, Henry H. Welsh Proverbs with English Translations. LC 68-17945. (Eng. & Welsh.). 1969. Repr. of 1889 ed. 43.00x (ISBN 0-8103-3205-1). Gale.
Whiting, B. J. Proverbs in the Earlier English Drama. LC 70-86290. 1969. Repr. of 1938 ed. lib. bdg. 34.50x (ISBN 0-374-98513-8, Octagon). Hippocrene Bks.
Yandian, Bob. Proverbs. 1985. pap. 6.95 (ISBN 0-89274-386-7). Harrison Hse.

PROVERBS–BIBLIOGRAPHY

Mieder, Wolfgang. International Bibliography of Explanatory Essays on Individual Proverbs & Proverbial Expressions: German Language & Literature. (European University Studies Ser.: No.1, Vol. 191). 146p. 1977. pap. 18.25 (ISBN 3-261-02932-3). P Lang Pubs.

PROVIDENCE AND GOVERNMENT OF GOD

see also Trust in God

Baker, Sanna A. Who's a Friend of the Water-Spurting Whale? (Illus.). 1987. 7.95 (ISBN 0-89191-587-7). Cook.
Billheimer, Paul. The Mystery of God's Providence. 1983. pap. 3.95 (ISBN 0-8423-4664-3). Tyndale.
Brengle, Samuel. God As Strategist. (Illus.). 64p. 1978. pap. 1.50 (ISBN 0-89216-017-9). Salvation Army.
Bruce, Alexander B. The Providential Order of the World. LC 77-27225. (Gifford Lectures: 1897). 1978. Repr. of 1897 ed. 37.50 (ISBN 0-404-60455-2). AMS Pr.
Clymer, R. Swinburne. La Ley Divina: La Senda Hacia la Maestria. (Span., Orig.). 1972. pap. 6.95 (ISBN 0-932785-55-7). Philos Pub.
Geisler, Norman L. The Roots of Evil. (Christian Free University Curriculum Ser.). 1978. pap. 4.95 (ISBN 0-310-35751-9, 12655P). Zondervan.
Gillquist, Peter. Designed for Holiness: God's Plan to Shape & Use You for His Kingdom. rev. ed. 210p. 1986. pap. 5.95 (ISBN 0-89283-286-X). Servant.
Giroux, Paul L. God's Plan for the Human Race. 1980. 5.00 (ISBN 0-682-49270-1). Exposition Pr FL.
Goodenough, Daniel W. Providence & Free Will in Human Actions. 132p. 1986. pap. 5.95 (ISBN 0-915221-63-2). Swedenborg Sci Assn.
Gooding, David. Un Reino Inconmovible. Orig. Title: An Unshakeable Kingdom. (Span.). 196p. 1983. pap. 4.95 (ISBN 0-8254-1275-7). Kregel.
Henry, Carl F. God, Revelation & Authority: God Who Speaks & Shows, Vols. 3, 4, 5 & 6. 1979. Vol. 3. 24.95 (ISBN 0-8499-0091-3); Vol. 4. 24.95 (ISBN 0-8499-0126-X); Vol. 5. 24.95 (ISBN 0-8499-0320-3); Vol. 6. 24.95 (ISBN 0-8499-0333-5). Word Bks.
Hick, John H. Evil & the God of Love. rev. ed. LC 76-62953. 1977. pap. 6.95 (ISBN 0-06-063902-4, RD219, HarpR). Har-Row.
Hunt, Don. What the Bible Says about the Unfolded Plan of God. LC 81-82988. (What the Bible Says Ser.). 500p. 1981. 13.95 (ISBN 0-89900-084-3). College Pr Pub.
Keck, Saundria. God Made Me. LC 86-17572. (Bible & Me Ser.). 1987. 5.95 (ISBN 0-8054-4173-5). Broadman.
Kempe, Janice. Listening to God: Lessons from Everyday Places. (Orig.). 1985. pap. 2.95 (ISBN 0-310-34822-6, 12748P). Zondervan.
Lane, Denis. When God Guides. 1984. pap. 3.95 (ISBN 9971-972-16-6). OMF Bks.
Lewis, C. S. The Problem of Pain. 1978. pap. 3.95 (ISBN 0-02-086850-2, Collier). Macmillan.
Light, Mary. God: Incidences or Divine Providence. 1975. pap. 1.00 (ISBN 0-910924-69-4). Macalester.
Lindsay, Gordon. God's Master Key to Prosperity. 1.95 (ISBN 0-89985-001-4). Christ Nations.
--God's Plan of the Ages. (Prophecy Ser.). 5.00 (ISBN 0-89985-056-1). Christ Nations.
Lovett, C. S. Does God Condemn Those Who Never Hear the Gospel? 1963. pap. 2.95 (ISBN 0-938148-19-2). Personal Christianity.
Mains, Karen & Mains, David. Parenting Us: How God Does It. 96p. 1986. pap. 3.50 (ISBN 0-87788-669-5). Shaw Pubs.
Marxhausen, Evelyn. When God Laid Down the Law. LC 59-1259. (Arch Bk.). 1981. pap. 0.99 (ISBN 0-570-06142-3). Concordia.
Migliore, Daniel L. The Power of God. LC 82-20037. (Library of Living Faith Ser.: Vol. 8). 116p. (Orig.). 1983. pap. 5.95 (ISBN 0-664-24454-8). Westminster.
Murray, Andrew. School of Obedience. (Andrew Murray Ser.). pap. 3.50 (ISBN 0-8024-7627-9). Moody.
Nee, Watchman. God's Work. Kaung, Stephen, tr. 1974. pap. 2.25 (ISBN 0-935008-20-9). Christian Fellow Pubs.
Ogilvie, Lloyd J. If God Cares, Why Do I Still Have Problems? 208p. 1985. 12.95 (ISBN 0-8499-0454-4, 0454-4). Word Bks.
Pink, Arthur W. Attributes of God. pap. 3.95 (ISBN 0-8010-6989-0). Baker Bk.
Ruppert, Hoover. God Will See You Through. 1976. pap. 0.75x (ISBN 0-8358-0351-1). Upper Room.
Russell, Robert A. God Works Through You. 1977. pap. 3.95 (ISBN 0-87516-217-7). De Vorss.
St. John Vianney. Thoughts of the Cure d'Ars. LC 84-50404. 79p. 1984. pap. 1.50 (ISBN 0-89555-240-X). TAN Bks Pubs.
Saint-Jure, Jean B. & De La Colombiere, Claude. Trustful Surrender to Divine Providence: The Secret of Peace & Happiness. LC 83-50252. 139p. 1983. pap. 3.00 (ISBN 0-89555-216-7). TAN Bks Pubs.
Showalter, Lester. Investigating God's Orderly World, Bk 2. (YA) 1975. write for info. (ISBN 0-686-11144-3); tchr's. ed. avail. (ISBN 0-686-11145-1). Rod & Staff.
Spurgeon, C. H. God's Providence. pap. 0.75 (ISBN 0-685-00749-9). Reiner.
Stark, Tom & Stark, Joan. Guidance & God's Will. (Fisherman Bible Studyguide). 60p. 1978. saddle stitch 2.50 (ISBN 0-87788-324-6). Shaw Pubs.
Swedenborg, Emanuel. Divine Providence. LC 74-30441. 1974. trade ed. o.p. 10.00 (ISBN 0-87785-060-7); student ed. 12.00 (ISBN 0-87785-059-3); pap. 3.95 (ISBN 0-87785-061-5). Swedenborg.
Tennis, Diane. Is God the Only Reliable Father. LC 84-20899. 118p. (Orig.). 1985. pap. 7.95 (ISBN 0-664-24594-3). Westminster.
Terstegge, Georgiana. Providence As "Idee-Maitresse" in the Works of Bossuet. LC 73-128931. (Catholic University of America. Studies in Romance Languages & Literature: No. 43). 1970. Repr. of 1948 ed. 29.00 (ISBN 0-404-50334-9). AMS Pr.
Tomczak, Larry. Divine Appointments. 168p. (Orig.). 1986. pap. 5.95 (ISBN 0-89283-261-4, Pub. by Vine Books). Servant.

PRUDENTIUS CLEMENS, AURELIUS

Meritt, Herbert D., ed. Old English Prudentius Glosses at Boulogne-Sur-Mer. LC 58-7843. (Stanford University. Stanford Studies in Language & Literature: No. 16). Repr. of 1959 ed. 24.00 (ISBN 0-404-51826-5). AMS Pr.
Shoham, S. Giora. Rebellion, Creativity & Revelation. Cherns, Albert, intro. by. 320p. 1986. 29.95 (ISBN 0-905927-61-3). Transaction Bks.
Smith, Macklin. Prudentius 'Psychomachia' A Re-examination. LC 75-37192. 1976. 30.50x (ISBN 0-691-06299-4). Princeton U Pr.

PRYNNE, WILLIAM, 1600-1669

Davison, Peter, ed. Theatrum Redivivum, 17 vols. Repr. 535.00 (ISBN 0-384-59985-0). Johnson Repr.
Gardiner, Samuel R., ed. Documents Relating to the Proceedings Against William Prynne, in 1634 & 1637. Repr. of 1877 ed. 27.00 (ISBN 0-384-17635-6). Johnson Repr.

PSALMODY

Here are entered works on the singing of Psalms in public worship.

see also Church Music; Hymns; Music in Churches

Benbow, Doras R. Lantern in the Moonlight. (Illus.). 1974. lib. bdg. 3.00 (ISBN 0-931611-06-7); pap. 1.50. D R Benbow.
Berry, Diana L. The Psalms in Rhyme, Vol. I. LC 86-80658. 104p. (Orig.). 1986. pap. 6.95 (ISBN 0-931637-01-5). Ferndale Hse.
Blaiklock, E. M., commentary by. Living Waters: Psalms for Your Quiet Time with God. (Illus.). 256p. 1985. Repr. 10.95 (ISBN 0-687-22378-4). Abingdon.
Chittister, Joan & Kownacki, Mary L. Psalm Journal. LC 85-50308. 104p. (Orig.). 1985. pap. 6.95 (ISBN 0-934134-28-6, Leaven Pr). Sheed & Ward MO.

Finney, Theodore M., ed. James Warrington: Short Titles of Books, Relating to or Illustrating the History & Practice of Psalmody in the United States,1620-1820. LC 70-18250. (Bibliographia Tripotamopolitana: No.1). 1970. 6.00x (ISBN 0-931222-00-1). Pitts Theolog.
Halliburton, Warren J. & Katz, William L. American Majorities & Minorities: A Syllabus of United States History for Secondary Schools. 6.95 (ISBN 0-405-18855-2, 19424). Ayer Co Pubs.
MacDougall, Hamilton C. Early New England Psalmody: An Historical Appreciation, 1620-1820. LC 79-87398. (Music Reprint Ser.). 1969. Repr. of 1940 ed. lib. bdg. 29.50 (ISBN 0-306-71542-2). Da Capo.
Meyer, Frederick B. The Shepherd Psalm. (Large Print Christian Classics Ser.). (Illus.). 1984. large print 9.95 (ISBN 0-87983-361-0). Keats.
Opatz, Patricia G. Nobody Says "Please" in the Psalms. 72p. (Orig.). 1984. pap. 2.95 (ISBN 0-8146-1326-8). Liturgical Pr.
Philips, John. Exploring the Psalms, Vol. 3. 318p. 1986. 14.95 (ISBN 0-87213-686-8). Loizeaux.
Pratt, Waldo S. Music of the French Psalter of 1562. LC 40-4909. Repr. of 1939 ed. 15.00 (ISBN 0-404-05119-7). AMS Pr.
Smith, Carleton S., ed. Psalmody in Seventeenth Century America: Series 1, the Ainsworth Psalter. price on application (ISBN 0-685-18958-9, Dist. by C. F. Peters Corp). NY Pub Lib.
Tully, Mary Jo. Psalms: Faith Songs for the Faith-Filled. 96p. 1982. pap. 3.50 (ISBN 0-697-01824-5). Wm C Brown.
Twenty-Third Psalm. (The Inspirational Library Ser.). 24p. 3.95 (ISBN 0-8326-2005-X, 3252). World Bible.
Voznesensky, J. Obshchjedostupnija Chtenija o Tserkovnom Peniji. Tr. of Popular Readings in Church Singing. 48p. 1969. pap. 2.00 (ISBN 0-317-30383-X). Holy Trinity.
Wippler, M. Gonzalez, ed. New Revised Sixth & Seventh Books of Moses & the Magical Use of the Psalms. pap. 6.95 (ISBN 0-942272-02-1). Original Pubns.

PSALMS (MUSIC)

Abbey, Hermione, ed. Three Psalm Tunes by Thomas Tallis. 16p. (Orig.). 1982. pap. 2.50 (ISBN 0-939400-02-2). RWS Bks.
Alexander, Dorsey & Alexander, Joyce. Psalm One Hundred Four. 32p. (Calligraphy & Illus.). 1978. pap. 5.00 (ISBN 0-912020-19-9). Turtles Quill.
Allen, Ronald B. Lord of Song: The Messiah Revealed in the Psalms. LC 85-21693. (Living Theology Bks.). 1985. pap. 7.95 (ISBN 0-88070-129-3). Multnomah.
Appel, Richard G. The Music of the Bay Psalm Book: Ninth Edition (1698) LC 75-34880. (I.S.A.M. Monographs: No. 5). 44p. (Orig.). 1975. pap. 4.00 (ISBN 0-914678-04-3). Inst Am Music.
Baron, David. Types, Psalms & Prophecies. 1981. lib. bdg. 14.00 (ISBN 0-86524-077-9, 9511). Klock & Klock.
Barrett, James E. The Psalmnary: Gradual Psalms for Cantor & Congregation. 196p. 1982. incl. binder 24.00 (ISBN 0-942466-04-7); 21.00 (ISBN 0-942466-03-9). Hymnary Pr.
Brandt, Leslie. Psalms-Now. LC 73-78108. 1973. 8.50 (ISBN 0-570-03230-X, 15-2125). Concordia.
Brueggemann, Walter. The Message of the Psalms: A Theological Commentary. LC 84-21734. (Augsburg Old Testament Studies). 224p. (Orig.). 1984. pap. 11.95 (ISBN 0-8066-2120-6, 10-4370). Augsburg.
Bruntz, Nelle L. Contemporary Psalms. (Illus.). 64p. 1984. 4.50 (ISBN 0-938462-13-X). Green Leaf Ca.
Chamberlain, Gary, tr. Psalms for Singing: Twenty-Six Psalms with Musical Settings for Congregation & Choir. LC 84-50778. 141p. (Orig.). 1984. pap. 7.50 (ISBN 0-8358-0495-X). Upper Room.
Cox, Samuel. The Pilgrim Psalms: An Exposition of the Songs of Degrees. 255p. 1983. lib. bdg. 9.50 (ISBN 0-86524-159-7, 1903). Klock & Klock.
Crawford, Richard L. Andrew Law, American Psalmodist. (Music Ser.). (Illus.). xix, 424p. 1981. Repr. of 1968 ed. lib. bdg. 42.50 (ISBN 0-306-76090-8). Da Capo.
Earles, Brent D. Psalms for Graduates. 5.95 (ISBN 0-8010-3426-4). Baker Bk.
Feuer, A. C. Tehillim: Psalms, 2 vols. 1985. 39.95 (ISBN 0-317-38548-8); pap. 29.95 (ISBN 0-317-38549-6). Mesorah Pubns.
Fever, Avrohom C. Tehillim (Psalms, 3 vols. Incl. Vol. 1. Psalms 1-30. 368p. 1977. (ISBN 0-89906-050-1); pap. (ISBN 0-89906-051-X); Vol. 2. Psalms 31-55. 352p. 1978. (ISBN 0-89906-052-8); pap. (ISBN 0-89906-053-6); Vol. 3. Psalms 56-85. 384p. 1979. (ISBN 0-89906-054-4); pap. (ISBN 0-89906-055-2). (Art Scroll Tanach Ser.). 15.95 ea.; pap. 12.95 ea. Mesorah Pubns.
Gaebelein, Arno C. Psalms. 1939. 10.95 (ISBN 0-87213-222-6). Loizeaux.
Gelineau, Joseph. Psalms: A Singing Version. 256p. 1968. pap. 3.95 (ISBN 0-8091-1669-3, Deus). Paulist Pr.
Goldsmith, Joel S. Secret of the Twenty-Third Psalm. 1972. pap. 1.50 (ISBN 0-87516-140-5). De Vorss.
Gutierrez, Rolando C. El Mensaje de los Salmos en Nuestro Contexto Tomo I. 160p. 1984. Repr. of 1979 ed. 5.95 (ISBN 0-311-04023-3). Casa Bautista.
Hostetter, B. David. Psalms & Prayers for Congregational Participation: Series B (Common Consensus Lectionary) 1984. 7.75 (ISBN 0-89536-694-0, 4871). CSS of Ohio.
Kidner, D. Psalms One - Seventy-Two. LC 75-23852. 1973. 12.95 (ISBN 0-87784-868-8); pap. 6.95 (ISBN 0-87784-264-7). Inter-Varsity.
Koeblitz, Roy E. The Psalms: A New Version. LC 85-63357. 208p. 1986. 12.95 (ISBN 0-936187-11-5). Palm Pub Co.
Kroeger, Karl & Crawford, Richard, eds. The Complete Works of William Billings, Vol. III: The Psalm-Singer's Amusement, the Suffolk Harmony, & Independent Publications. (Illus.). 456p. 1986. text ed. 50.00x (ISBN 0-8139-1130-3, Pub. by American Musicological Society-Colonial Society MA). U Pr of Va.
Kyes, Robert L., ed. The Old Low Franconian Psalms & Glosses. LC 69-15843. pap. 42.50 (ISBN 0-317-09363-0, 2051048). Bks Demand UMI.
Mayer, Harry, ed. Modern Reader's Book of Psalms. (Black & Gold Lib). 1968. 6.95 (ISBN 0-87140-879-1, Co-Pub with Tudor). Liveright.
Miller, Patrick D., Jr. Interpreting the Psalms. LC 85-16258. 176p. 1986. pap. 10.95 (ISBN 0-8006-1896-3). Fortress.
Morris, Henry. Amostra de Salmos. Orig. Title: Sampling the Psalms. (Port.). 1986. write for info. (ISBN 0-8297-0698-4). Life Pubs Intl.
--Psaumes Choisis. Tr. of Sampling the Psalms. (Fr.). 192p. 1986. pap. 3.50 (ISBN 0-8297-0697-6). Life Pubs Intl.
Murphy, Joseph. Songs of God. LC 79-52353. (Orig.). 1979. pap. 6.00 (ISBN 0-87516-379-3). De Vorss.
National Council of Churches Staff. Inclusive-Language Psalms. 144p. (Orig.). 1987. pap. 7.95 (ISBN 0-8298-0747-0). Pilgrim NY.
Ogilvie, Lloyd J. Caer en la Grandeza. Lievano, M. Francisco, tr. from Eng. Orig. Title: Falling into Greatness. (Span.). 190p. 1985. pap. 4.95 (ISBN 0-8297-0702-6). Life Pubs Intl.
Peeters, Flor. Jubilate Deo Omnis Terra: Psalm 99, Score & Brass Parts Accompaniment 1954. pap. 20.00 (ISBN 0-317-09824-1, 2003407). Bks Demand UMI.
Perti, Giacomo Antonio. Laudate Pueri. Berger, Jean, ed. LC 65-26097. (Penn State Music Series, No. 10). 35p. 1965. pap. 4.00x (ISBN 0-271-73075-7). Pa St U Pr.
Phillips, John. Exploring the Psalms, Vol. 4. 1987. 14.95 (ISBN 0-87213-687-6). Loizeaux.
--Exploring the Psalms, Vol. 5. 1987. 14.95 (ISBN 0-87213-688-4). Loizeaux.
--Exploring the Psalms: Vol. II, 42-72. 288p. 1986. 14.95 (ISBN 0-87213-685-X). Loizeaux.
--Exploring the Psalms: Volume 1 (Psalms 1-41) 318p. 1985. 14.95 (ISBN 0-87213-684-1). Loizeaux.
Pratt, Waldo S. The Music of the Pilgrims: A Description of the Psalm-Book Brought to Plymouth in Sixteen Twenty. 1980. lib. bdg. 59.00 (ISBN 0-8490-3180-X). Gordon Pr.
Robinson, Haddon. The Good Shepherd: Reflections on Psalm 23. 1987. pap. 1.95 (ISBN 0-8024-6688-5). Moody.
Sitting for the Psalms: A Historical Study. (Church Historical Society, London, New Ser.: No. 6). Repr. of 1931 ed. 20.00 (ISBN 0-8115-3130-9). Kraus Repr.
Spurgeon, Charles H. Psalms. Fuller, David O., ed. LC 76-12085. 704p. 1977. kivar 14.95 (ISBN 0-8254-3714-8). Kregel.
Sullivan, Francis. Tragic Psalms. 1987. pap. 5.95. Pastoral Pr.
Sullivan, Francis P. Lyric Psalms: Half a Psalter. (Illus.). 192p. (Orig.). 1983. pap. 5.95 (ISBN 0-9602378-8-7). Pastoral Pr.
Theophan the Recluse. Psalom 118. Tr. of Psalm 118. 496p. 22.00 (ISBN 0-317-28925-X); pap. 17.00 (ISBN 0-317-28926-8). Holy Trinity.
Wakeman, Frank M. Psalms in Song for the White Cavalry. 3rd ed. (Illus.). 1979. 5.00 (ISBN 0-910840-19-9). Kingdom.
Weisheit, Eldon. The Psalms for Children: Series B. LC 84-18562. 128p. (Orig.). 1984. pap. 6.95 (ISBN 0-8066-2096-X, 10-5304). Augsburg.
--The Psalms for Children: Sixty Object Lessons. LC 83-70510. (Series A). 128p. (Orig.). 1983. pap. 6.95 (ISBN 0-8066-2016-1, 10-5303). Augsburg.
Whedon Commentary: Psalms. boards 13.95 (ISBN 0-686-27779-1). Schmul Pub Co.
White, R. E. A Christian Handbook to the Psalms. 224p. (Orig.). 1984. pap. 7.95 (ISBN 0-8028-0031-9). Eerdmans.
Wilson, Ernest T. The Messianic Psalms. pap. 3.95 (ISBN 0-87213-963-8). Loizeaux.
Zerr, Bonaventure. Psalms: A New Translation. 8.95 (ISBN 0-8091-2218-9). Paulist Pr.
Zlotowitz, Meir. Shir Hashirim-Song of Songs. (The Art Scroll Tanach Ser.). 224p. 1977. 11.95 (ISBN 0-89906-008-0); pap. 8.95 (ISBN 0-89906-009-9). Mesorah Pubns.

PSALTERS

Abbot, John & Bamberger, Eudes. The Abbey Psalter: The Book of Psalms Used by the Trappist Monks of Genesee Abbey. LC 81-80871. 368p. 1981. 24.95 (ISBN 0-8091-0316-8). Paulist Pr.
Altbauer, Mosha & Lunt, Horace G., eds. An Early Slavonic Psalter from Rus' Vol. 1: Phoreproduction. LC 78-59967. (Harvard Ukrainian Research Institute, Sources & Documents Ser.). 1979. text ed. 15.00x (ISBN 0-674-22310-1). Harvard U Pr.
Anderson, Fred R. Singing Psalms of Joy & Praise. LC 86-1550. 78p. (Orig.). 1986. pap. 5.95 ea. (ISBN 0-664-24696-6). Westminster.
Buchtal, Hugo. The Miniatures of the Paris Psalter: A Study in Middle Byzantine Painting. (Warburg Institute Studies: Vol. 2). Repr. of 1938 ed. 88.00 (ISBN 0-8115-1379-3). Kraus Repr.
Glass, Henry A. Story of the Psalters. LC 72-1635. Repr. of 1888 ed. 18.50 (ISBN 0-404-08308-0). AMS Pr.
Gould, Karen. The Psalter & Hours of Yolande of Soissons. LC 78-55888. 1978. 11.00x (ISBN 0-910956-78-2, SAM4); pap. 5.00x (ISBN 0-910956-64-2). Medieval Acad.
Keefer, Sarah L. The Old English Metrical Psalter: An Annotated Set of Collation Lists with the Psalter Glosses. LC 79-7920. (Garland Reference Library of the Humanities). 200p. 1979. lib. bdg. 36.00 (ISBN 0-8240-9538-3). Garland Pub.
Kimmens, A. C., ed. The Stowe Psalter. LC 78-23622. (Toronto Old English Ser.). 1979. 47.50x (ISBN 0-8020-2201-4). U of Toronto Pr.
Merton, Thomas. Bread in the Wilderness. LC 82-23864. 180p. 1986. pap. 5.95 (ISBN 0-8006-1912-9, 1-1912). Fortress.
Monks of New Skete, tr. from Ancient Languages. The Psalter. 286p. 1984. 39.50x (ISBN 0-9607924-5-7). Monks of New Skete.
Office of Worship for the Presbyterian Church (U. S. A.) & Cumberland Presbyterian Church. A Psalm Sampler. LC 85-753089. (Illus.). 48p. 1986. pap. 4.95 ea. (ISBN 0-664-24681-8). Westminster.
The Psalter. 3.50 (ISBN 0-8164-0311-2, HarpR). Har-Row.
Sandler, Lucy F. The Peterborough Psalter in Brussells & Other Fenland Manuscripts. (Illus.). 1974. 49.00x (ISBN 0-19-921005-5). Oxford U Pr.
--The Psalter of Robert de Lisle. (Harvey Miller Publication Ser.). (Illus.). 1983. 105.00x (ISBN 0-19-921028-4). Oxford U Pr.
Wilson, Gerald H. The Editing of the Hebrew Psalter. (Society of Biblical Literature Disseration Ser.: No. 76). 1985. pap. 11.50 (ISBN 0-89130-728-1). Scholars Pr GA.
Wright, William A. The Hexaplar Psalter, Being the Book of Psalms in Six English Versions. 395p. Repr. of 1911 ed. lib. bdg. 63.00X (Pub. by G Olms BRD). Coronet Bks.

PSYCHAGOGY

see Psychology, Applied

PSYCHE (GODDESS) LITERATURE

Apuleius. Cupid & Psyche. Balme, M. G. & Morwood, J. H., eds. (Illus.). 1976. pap. 6.95x (ISBN 0-19-912047-1). Oxford U Pr.
Goldwert, Marvin. Psyche & History. 85p. (Orig.). 1985. pap. 6.95x (ISBN 0-932269-41-9). Wyndham Hall.
Hanson, Karen. The Self Imagined: Philosophical Reflections on the Social Character of Psyche. 160p. 1986. 26.95 (ISBN 0-7102-0559-7, 05597). Methuen Inc.
Richardson, I. M. The Adventures of Eros & Psyche. LC 82-16057. (Illus.). 32p. 1983. PLB 9.79 (ISBN 0-89375-861-2); pap. text ed. 2.50 (ISBN 0-89375-862-0). Troll Assocs.

PSYCHIATRY AND RELIGION

see also Psychoanalysis and Religion

Frankl, Victor. The Unconscious God. 1976. pap. 5.95 (ISBN 0-671-22426-3, Touchstone Bks). S&S.
Frankl, Viktor. The Unconscious God. 1985. pap. 3.50 (ISBN 0-671-54728-3). WSP.
GAP Committee on Psychiatry & Religion. The Psychic Function of Religion in Mental Illness & Health, Vol. 6. LC 62-2872. (Report: No. 67). 1968. pap. 5.00 (ISBN 0-87318-092-5, Pub. by GAP). Brunner-Mazel.
Gerber, Isreal J. Job on Trial: A Book for Our Time. 217p. 1982. 14.95 (ISBN 0-318-01102-6). E P Press.
Hora, Thomas. God in Psychiatry. (Discoures in Metapsychistry Ser.). 35p. 1984. pap. 4.00 (ISBN 0-913105-06-6). PAGL Pr.
James, William. Varieties of Religious Experience. pap. 4.50 (ISBN 0-451-62486-6, ME2069, Ment). NAL.
Kew, Clifton E. & Kew, Clinton J. Therapist Responds. LC 79-171467. 1972. 6.95 (ISBN 0-8022-2070-3). Philos Lib.
Lovinger, Robert J. Working with Religious Issues in Therapy. LC 84-6198. 328p. 1984. 30.00x (ISBN 0-87668-727-3). Aronson.
Mairet, Philip. Christian Essays in Psychiatry. 1957. 7.95 (ISBN 0-8022-1038-4). Philos Lib.
Murphy, Carol. Religion & Mental Illness. 1983. pap. 2.50x (ISBN 0-87574-082-0, 082). Pendle Hill.
Peck, M. Scott. People of the Lie: The Hope for Healing Human Evil. LC 83-13631. 269p. 1983. 15.95 (ISBN 0-671-45492-7). S&S.
--People of the Lie: The Hope for Healing Human Evil. 1985. pap. 7.95 (ISBN 0-671-52816-5, Touchstone Bks). S&S.
--The Road Less Traveled. 448p. 1985. pap. 16.95 (ISBN 0-8027-2498-1). Walker & Co.
Robinson, Lillian H. Psychiatry & Religion: Overlapping Concerns (Clinical Insights Monograph) LC 85-28728. 192p. 1986. pap. text ed. 12.00x (ISBN 0-88048-099-8, 48-099-8). Am Psychiatric.
Ryder, Lew. Why J. R.? A Psychiatrist Discusses the Villain of Dallas. LC 82-82836. 153p. (Orig.). 1983. pap. 4.95 (ISBN 0-910311-02-1). Huntington Hse Inc.
Sayama, Mike. Samadhi: Self Development in Zen, Swordsmanship, & Psychotherapy. (Transpersonal & Humanistic Psychology). 147p. 1985. 34.50x (ISBN 0-88706-146-X); pap. 10.95 (ISBN 0-88706-147-8). State U NY Pr.
Sipe, A. W. & Rowe, Clarence J., eds. Psychiatry, Ministry, & Pastoral Counseling. rev ed. Orig. Title: Psychiatry, the Clergy, & Pastoral Counseling. 384p. 1984. pap. 12.95 (ISBN 0-8146-1324-1). Liturgical Pr.
Spero, Moshe H., ed. Psychotherapy of the Religious Patient. 250p. 1985. 32.75 (ISBN 0-398-05058-9). C C Thomas.
Tournier, Paul. The Violence Within. 2nd ed. LC 78-3139. 208p. 1982. pap. 6.95 (ISBN 0-06-068295-7, RD376, HarpR). Har-Row.
Wilkes, James. The Gift of Courage. LC 81-11507. 108p. 1981. pap. 6.95 (ISBN 0-664-24394-0). Westminster.

PSYCHICAL RESEARCH

see also Apparitions; Mind and Body; Psychology, Religious

Berger, I. K. Everybody's Guide to Paradise. 204p. 1986. pap. 29.00x (ISBN 0-7212-0776-6, Pub. by Regency Pr). State Mutual Bk.
Blackmore, Susan. The Adventures of a Parapsychologist. 250p. 1986. 19.95 (ISBN 0-87975-360-9). Prometheus Bks.
Bordner, Marie S. Marvels & Mysteries. 96p. (Orig.). 1986. pap. 4.95 (ISBN 0-912661-09-7). Woodsong Graph.
Cayce, Hugh L. Venture Inward: Edgar Cayce's Story & the Mysteries of the Unconscious Mind. LC 85-42772. 256p. 1985. pap. 4.95 (ISBN 0-06-250131-3, HarpR). Har-Row.
Coates, Sanford E. Psychical Research & Spiritualism. (Illus.). 1980. deluxe ed. 69.75 (ISBN 0-89920-006-0). Am Classical Coll Pr.
Cooke, Grace & Cooke, Ivan. The Light in Britain. (Illus.). 1971. pap. 5.95 (ISBN 0-85487-056-3). De Vorss.
Crossley, Alan. Jesus Psychi Super Star. 64p. 1984. 29.00x (ISBN 0-7212-0683-2, Pub. by Regency Pr). State Mutual Bk.
De Jim, Strange. Visioning. LC 79-66208. (Illus.). 112p. (Orig.). 1979. pap. 5.95 (ISBN 0-9605308-0-0). Ash-Kar Pr.
Dhiegh, Khigh, ed. The Golden Oracle: The Ancient Chinese Way to Prosperity. LC 82-18471. (Illus.). 176p. 1983. 15.95 (ISBN 0-668-05661-4); pap. 8.95 (ISBN 0-668-05913-3). Arco.
Harrold, Robert. Cassadaga: An Inside Look at the South's Oldest Psychic Community with True Experiences of People Who Have Been There. (Illus.). 1979. pap. 4.95 (ISBN 0-916224-49-X). Banyan Bks.
Heline, Corinne. Occult Anatomy & the Bible. 1985. pap. 9.95 (ISBN 0-87613-093-7). New Age.
Hill, John L. The Enlightened Society. LC 86-40403. 278p. (Orig.). 1987. pap. 7.95 (ISBN 0-8356-0615-5). Theos Pub Hse.
Hudson, Jay T. New Discoveries into the Realm of Psychic Phenomena. (Illus.). 129p. 1983. 85.85 (ISBN 0-89920-065-6). Am Inst Psych.
Karagulla, Shafica. Breakthrough to Creativity. 12.95 (ISBN 0-87516-034-4). De Vorss.
Kearns, Thomas F. The Art of the Mystic: The Master Course in Spiritual & Psychic Development. Paterson, Kathy, ed. (Illus.). 160p. (Orig.). 1986. pap. 9.95 (ISBN 0-935251-00-6). Manchurch.
Kurtz, Paul. The Transcendental Temptation: A Critique of Religion & the Paranormal. 450p. 1986. 18.95 (ISBN 0-87975-362-5). Prometheus Bks.
Mystic Jhamom Staff, ed. Why? Psychic Development & How! (Conversations with a Mystic Ser.: No. 2). (Illus.). 176p. 1985. pap. 11.75 (ISBN 0-933961-05-7). Mystic Jhamom.

Oppenheim, Janet. The Other World: Spiritualism & Physical Research in England, 1850-1914. (Illus.). 580p. 1985. 44.50 (ISBN 0-521-26505-3). Cambridge U Pr.
Probstein, Bobbie. Return to Center. LC 85-70723. (Illus.). 256p. (Orig.). 1985. pap. 9.95 (ISBN 0-87516-554-0). De Vorss.
Stone, Peter C. The First Book of the Lamb. 110p. 1987. 15.00 (ISBN 0-934469-01-6). Gabriel Pr CA.
--The Second Book of the Lamb. 233p. 1987. 22.00 (ISBN 0-934469-02-4). Gabriel Pr CA.
Summer Rain, Mary. Spirit Song. Friedman, Robert, ed. LC 85-15894. 200p. (Orig.). 1985. pap. 7.95 (ISBN 0-89865-405-X, Unilaw). Donning Co.
Weilgart, W. John. AUI, Language of Space: Logos of Love, Pentecostal Peace, & Health Thru Harmony, Creation & Truth. 4th ed. (Illus.). 350p. 1979. pap. 11.95 (ISBN 0-912038-08-X). Cosmic Comm.

PSYCHOANALYSIS AND RELIGION

Beit-Hallahmi, Benjamin. Psychoanalysis & Religion. 1978. lib. bdg. 27.50 (ISBN 0-8482-7374-5). Norwood Edns.
Boeschemeyer, Uwe. Die Sinnfrage in Psychotherapie und Theologie: Die Existenzanalyse und Logotherapie Viktor E. Frankls aus theologischer Sicht. (Theologische Bibliothek Toepelmann Ser.: Vol. 32). 1977. 22.80x (ISBN 3-11-006727-7). De Gruyter.
De Luca, Anthony J. Freud & Future Religious Experience. (Quality Paperback Ser: No. 330). 263p. 1977. pap. 4.95 (ISBN 0-8226-0330-6). Littlefield.
Egenter, Richard & Matussek, Paul. Moral Problems & Mental Health. 1967. 4.95 (ISBN 0-8189-0095-4). Alba.
Fromm, Erich. Psychoanalysis & Religion. (Terry Lectures Ser.). 1950. pap. 5.95 (ISBN 0-300-00089-8, Y12). Yale U Pr.
Fuller, Andrew R. Psychology & Religion: Eight Points of View. 2nd ed. 286p. 1986. pap. text ed. 9.75 (ISBN 0-8191-5336-2). U Pr of Amer.
Gay, Volney P. Reading Freud: Psychology, Neurosis, & Religion. LC 83-2917. (AAR Studies in Religion). 142p. 1983. pap. 8.25 (ISBN 0-89130-613-7, 01 00 32). Scholars Pr GA.
Homans, Peter. Theology After Freud: An Interpretive Inquiry. LC 76-84162. 1970. 29.50x (ISBN 0-672-51245-9); pap. text ed. 16.95x (ISBN 0-8290-1399-7). Irvington.
Kakar, Sudhir. The Inner World: A Psycho-Analytic Study of Childhood & Society in India. 2nd ed. (Illus.). 1981. pap. text ed. 8.95x (ISBN 0-19-561508-5). Oxford U Pr.
Klein, Dennis B. Jewish Origins of the Psychoanalytic Movement: With a New Preface. 224p. 1985. pap. 8.95 (ISBN 0-226-43960-7). U of Chicago Pr.
Kung, Hans. Freud & the Problem of God. Quinn, Edward, tr. LC 78-25581. (Terry Lecture Ser.). 136p. 1980. 19.50 (ISBN 0-300-02350-2, Y-237); pap. 5.95 (ISBN 0-300-02597-1). Yale U Pr.
Lovinger, Robert J. Working with Religious Issues in Therapy. LC 84-6198. 328p. 1984. 30.00x (ISBN 0-87668-727-3). Aronson.
McMlelland, David C. Psychoanalysis & Religious Mysticism. 1983. pap. 2.50x (ISBN 0-87574-104-5, 104). Pendle Hill.
Masson, J. Moussaieff. The Oceanic Feeling: The Origins of Religious Sentiment in Ancient India. (Studies of Classical India: No. 3). 228p. 1980. lib. bdg. 34.00 (ISBN 90-277-1050-3, Pub. by Reidel Holland). Kluwer Academic.
Meissner, W. W. Life & Faith: Psychoanalytic Perspectives on Religious Experience. 302p. 1987. 19.95 (ISBN 0-87840-429-5); pap. 11.95. Georgetown U Pr.
--Psychoanalysis & Religious Experience. 1984. 27.50 (ISBN 0-317-13715-8). Yale U Pr.
--Psychoanalysis & Religious Experience. LC 83-51296. 272p. 1986. pap. 9.95x (ISBN 0-300-03751-1, Y-599). Yale U Pr.
Ostow, Mortimer. Psychoanalysis & Judaism. 1982. 25.00x (ISBN 0-87068-713-1). Ktav.
Peck, M. Scott. The Road Less Traveled. 448p. 1985. pap. 16.95 (ISBN 0-8027-2498-1). Walker & Co.
Rollins, Wayne G. Jung & the Bible. LC 82-48091. 156p. 1983. pap. 10.95 (ISBN 0-8042-1117-5). John Knox.
Rubenstein, Richard L. The Religious Imagination: A Study in Psychonalysis & Jewish Theology. LC 85-15825. (Brown Classics in Judaica Ser.). 276p. 1985. pap. text ed. 12.50 (ISBN 0-8191-4539-4). U Pr of Amer.
Stein, Murray & Moore, Robert, eds. Jung's Challenge to Contemporary Religion. 175p. 1987. pap. 14.95 (ISBN 0-933029-09-8). Chiron Pubns.
Stern, E. Mark, ed. Psychotherapy & the Religiously Committed Patient. LC 84-25276. (The Psychotherapy Patient Ser.: Vol. 1, No. 3). 158p. 1985. text ed. 19.95 (ISBN 0-86656-394-6); pap. text ed. 14.95 (ISBN 0-86656-396-2). Haworth Pr.

PSYCHOLOGY

see also Belief and Doubt; Consciousness; Emotions; Ideology; Interpersonal Relations

Abraham, Kurt. Introduction to the Seven Rays. LC 86-80170. 108p. (Orig.). 1986. pap. 6.95 (ISBN 0-9609002-2-5). Lampus Pr.
Ajaya, Swami. Yoga Psychology: A Practical Guide to Meditation. rev. ed. LC 76-374539. 115p. 1976. pap. 5.95 (ISBN 0-89389-052-9). Himalayan Pubs.
Arnold, Heini. Man, the Image of God & Modern Psychology. 14p. 1973. pap. 1.25 (ISBN 0-87486-176-4). Plough.
Baudouin, Charles. Power Within Us. facs. ed. LC 68-16905. (Essay Index Reprint Ser). 1923. 15.00 (ISBN 0-8369-0176-2). Ayer Co Pubs.
Cavanagh, Michael E. Make Your Tomorrow Better: A Psychological Resource for Singles, Parents & the Entire Family. LC 80-80638. 360p. (Orig.). 1980. pap. 9.95 (ISBN 0-8091-2293-6). Paulist Pr.
Dorsey, John M. Psychology of Ethics. 261p. 1974. 18.95 (ISBN 0-8143-1639-5). Wayne St U Pr.
Dunlap, Knight. Mysticism, Freudianism & Scientific Psychology. facsimile ed. (Select Bibliographies Reprint Ser). Repr. of 1920 ed. 17.00 (ISBN 0-8369-5838-1). Ayer Co Pubs.
Eisner, Robert. The Road to Daulis: Psychoanalysis, Psychology & Classical Mythology. 284p. 1987. 32.50 (ISBN 0-8156-0210-3). Syracuse U Pr.
Far West Editions. Material for Thought, No. 8. LC 79-56899. 88p. 1979. pap. 2.95 (ISBN 0-914480-05-7). Far West Edns.
Haimowitz, Morris L. & Haimowitz, Natalie R. Suffering Is Optional! The Myth of the Innocent Bystander. LC 77-72839. (Illus.). 1977. pap. 6.00 (ISBN 0-917790-01-4). Haimowoods.
Halevi, Z'ev Ben Shimon. Kabbalah & Psychology. (Illus.). 260p. (Orig.). 1986. pap. 12.50 (ISBN 0-87728-671-X). Weiser.
Holmes, Ernest. Know Yourself! Kinnear, Willis H., ed. 96p. (Orig.). 1970. pap. 4.50 (ISBN 0-911336-36-2). Sci of Mind.
Husserl, Edmund. Crisis of European Sciences & Transcendental Phenomenology: An Introduction to Phenomenological Philosophy. Carr, David, tr. LC 77-82511. (Studies in Phenomenology & Existential Philosophy Ser). 1970. 28.95 (ISBN 0-8101-0255-2); pap. 11.95 (ISBN 0-8101-0458-X). Northwestern U Pr.
Jackins, Harvey. Is Death Necessary? 1970. pap. 0.50 (ISBN 0-911214-22-4). Rational Isl.
Jackson, Edgar N. Group Counseling: Dynamic Possibilities for Small Groups. LC 73-91167. (Orig.). 1969. pap. 2.95 (ISBN 0-8298-0053-0). Pilgrim NY.
Koteskey, Ronald L. General Psychology for Christian Counselors. 308p. (Orig.). 1983. pap. 11.95 (ISBN 0-687-14044-7). Abingdon.
Laurie, Sanders, et al. Centering: Your Guide to Inner Growth. 299p. 1983. 6.95 (ISBN 0-89281-050-5, Destiny Bks). Inner Tradit.
Leahey, Thomas H. & Leahey, Grace E. Psychology's Occult Doubles: Psychology & the Problem of Pseudoscience. LC 82-24635. 296p. 1983. lib. bdg. 25.95x (ISBN 0-88229-717-1). Nelson-Hall.
Miller, David L. The New Polytheism. 2nd, rev. ed. 148p. 1981. pap. 9.50 (ISBN 0-88214-314-X). Spring Pubns.
Murphy, Carol R. The Available Mind. LC 73-94186. (Orig.). 1974. pap. 2.50x (ISBN 0-87574-193-2). Pendle Hill.
Narayananda, Swami. The Primal Power in Man: The Kundalini Shakti Yoga. 155p. 1971. pap. 11.95 (ISBN 0-88697-027-X). Life Science.
New York Academy Of Medicine. Ministry & Medicine in Human Relations. facs. ed. Galdston, Iago, ed. LC 77-142682. (Essay Index Reprint Ser). 1955. 17.00 (ISBN 0-8369-2120-8). Ayer Co Pubs.
Popoff, Irmis B. Gurdjieff Group Work with Wilhem Nyland. (Illus.). 80p. 1983. pap. 4.95 (ISBN 0-87728-580-2). Weiser.
Reuman, Robert E. Walls: Physical & Psychological. LC 66-24444. (Orig.). pap. 2.50x (ISBN 0-87574-147-9). Pendle Hill.
Sachdeva, I. P. Yoga & Depth Psychology. 269p. 1978. 16.95x (ISBN 0-317-12334-3, Pub. by Motilal Banarsi). Asia Bk Corp.
Vitz, Paul C. Psychology As Religion: The Cult of Self-Worship. 192p. 1977. pap. 5.95 (ISBN 0-8028-1696-7). Eerdmans.

PSYCHOLOGY, APPLIED

Here are entered general works on the application of psychology in various fields such as industry, advertising, military life. Works on applied psychology intended as guides to successful personal development are entered under such headings as Success and Personality.

see also Counseling; Interpersonal Relations; Pastoral Psychology; Peace of Mind; Security (Psychology)

Bloodworth, Venice. Key to Yourself. 1986. pap. 4.95 (ISBN 0-87516-296-7). De Vorss.
Germain, Walter M. Magic Power of Your Mind. pap. 7.00 (ISBN 0-87980-093-3). Wilshire.
Hadfield, J. A. Psychology & Morals. 245p. 1980. Repr. of 1926 ed. lib. bdg. 30.00 (ISBN 0-8492-5282-2). R West.
Peale, Norman V. Power of Positive Thinking. 1954. pap. 9.95 (ISBN 0-13-686402-3). P-H.
--Power of Positive Thinking. 224p. 1966. pap. 3.50 (ISBN 0-8007-8033-7, Spire Bks). Revell.
Widutis, Florence. Yours Is the Power. LC 57-9315. 1978. pap. 4.95 (ISBN 0-87516-245-2). De Vorss.

PSYCHOLOGY, CLERICAL

see Pastoral Psychology

PSYCHOLOGY, PASTORAL

see Pastoral Psychology

PSYCHOLOGY, PRACTICAL

see Psychology, Applied

PSYCHOLOGY, RELIGIOUS

see also Bible–Psychology; Enthusiasm; Experience (Religion); Miracles; Pastoral Psychology; Psychology, Applied; Religion and Geography

Abbot, Francis E. The Way Out of Agnosticism: Or the Philosophy of Free Religion. LC 75-3014. (Philosophy in America Ser.). Repr. of 1890 ed. 20.00 (ISBN 0-404-59008-X). AMS Pr.
Abdu, Hani R. Christian Psychology. 288p. 1981. 11.00 (ISBN 0-682-49643-X). Exposition Pr FL.
Adler, Gerard, et al, eds. The Collected Works of C. G. Jung: Psychology & Religion - West & East, No. 11. 2nd ed. Hull, R. F., tr. (Bollingen Ser.: No. 20). 1969. 45.50 (ISBN 0-691-09772-0). Princeton U Pr.
Alpert, Nancy L. Religion & Psychology: A Medical Subject Analysis & Research Index with Bibliography. LC 83-71657. 150p. 1985. 34.50 (ISBN 0-88164-034-4); pap. 26.50 (ISBN 0-88164-035-2). ABBE Pubs Assn.
Amsel. Judaism & Psychology. pap. 5.95 (ISBN 0-87306-064-4). Feldheim.
Amsel, Avrohom. Rational Irrational Man: Torah Psychology. 1976. pap. 7.95 (ISBN 0-87306-129-2). Feldheim.
Argyle, Michael & Beit-Hallahmi, Benjamin. Social Psychology of Religion. 1975. 25.00x (ISBN 0-7100-7997-4); pap. 10.95X (ISBN 0-7100-8043-3). Methuen Inc.
Arraj, James. St. John of the Cross & Dr. C. G. Jung: Christian Mysticism in the Light of Jungian Psychology. LC 86-11315. 200p. (Orig.). 1986. pap. 11.95 (ISBN 0-914073-02-8). Tools for Inner.
Baudouin, Charles. Suggestions & Autosuggestions. 1978. Repr. of 1920 ed. lib. bdg. 49.00 (ISBN 0-8495-0350-7). Arden Lib.
Baum, Gregory, ed. Religion & Alienation: A Theological Reading of Sociology. LC 75-28652. 304p. 1976. pap. 9.95 (ISBN 0-8091-1917-X). Paulist Pr.
Benner, David G., ed. Psychotherapy in Christian Perspective. 300p. 1987. pap. price not set (ISBN 0-8010-0942-1). Baker Bk.
Boff, Leonardo & Boff, Clodovis. Liberation Theology: From Dialogue to Confrontation. 120p. (Orig.). 1986. pap. 8.95 (ISBN 0-86683-528-8, HarpR). Har-Row.
Boisen, Anton T. Exploration of the Inner World: A Study of Mental Disorder and Religious Experience. 1971. pap. 12.95x (ISBN 0-8122-1020-4, Pa Paperbks). U of Pa Pr.
Boisen, Anton T. & Leary, John. Religion in Crisis & Custom: A Sociological & Psychological Study. LC 72-10977. 271p. 1973. Repr. of 1955 ed. lib. bdg. 22.50x (ISBN 0-8371-6642-X, BORC). Greenwood.
Bolt, Martin & Myers, David G. The Human Connection. LC 83-20420. 168p. (Orig.). 1984. pap. 6.95 (ISBN 0-87784-913-7). Inter-Varsity.
Booth, Howard J. Edwin Diller Starbuck: Pioneer in the Psychology of Religion. LC 80-5731. 304p. 1981. pap. text ed. 15.50 (ISBN 0-8191-1703-X). U Pr of Amer.
Bourguignon, Erika, ed. Religion, Altered States of Consciousness, & Social Change. LC 72-8448. (Illus.). 399p. 1973. 12.50 (ISBN 0-8142-0167-9). Ohio St U Pr.
Boyden Howes, Elizabeth. Intersection & Beyond, Vol. II. LC 86-3067. 200p. (Orig.). 1986. pap. 8.50 (ISBN 0-917479-07-6). Guild Psy.
Brigham, Amariah. Observations on the Influence of Religion upon the Health & Physical Welfare of Mankind, 1835: Remarks on the Influence of Mental Cultivation & Mental Excitement Upon Health, 2 vols. in 1. LC 73-17271. (History of Psychology Ser.). 1973. 55.00x (ISBN 0-8201-1125-2). Schol Facsimiles.
Brightman, Edgar S. Personality & Religion. LC 75-3084. (Philosophy in America Ser.). Repr. of 1934 ed. 20.00 (ISBN 0-404-59083-7). AMS Pr.
Brown, L. B. Advances in the Psychology of Religion. (International Series in Experimental Social Psychology: Vol. 11). (Illus.). 236p. 1985. 27.50 (ISBN 0-08-027948-1, Pub by PPL). Pergamon.
--The Psychology of Religious Belief. 1987. 48.00 (ISBN 0-12-136355-4); pap. 24.00 (ISBN 0-12-136356-2). Acad Pr.
Browning, Don S. Religious Thought & the Modern Psychologies: A Critical Conversation in the Theology of Culture. LC 86-45205. 288p. 1986. 22.50 (ISBN 0-8006-0784-8). Fortress.
Bulka, Reuven P. & Spero, Moshe H. A Psychology-Judaism Reader. (Illus.). 338p. 1982. pap. 27.00x (ISBN 0-398-04582-8). C C Thomas.
Bynum, Caroline W., et al, eds. Gender & Religion: On the Complexity of Symbols. LC 86-47552. 296p. 1986. 25.00 (ISBN 0-8070-1008-1). Beacon Pr.
Byrnes, Joseph F. The Psychology of Religion. LC 84-47854. 320p. 1984. 24.95x (ISBN 0-02-903580-5). Free Pr.
Capps, Donald, et al. Encounter with Erikson: Historical Interpretation & Religious Biography. LC 76-44434. (American Academy of Religion, Formative Contemporary Thinkers Ser.: No. 2). 1977. pap. 13.50 (010402). Scholars Pr GA.
Capps, Donald, et al, eds. Psychology of Religion: A Guide to Information Sources. LC 73-17530. (Philosophy & Religion Information Guide Ser.: Vol. 1). vii, 380p. 1976. 62.00x (ISBN 0-8103-1356-1). Gale.
Caputi, Natalino. Guide to the Unconscious. LC 83-24620. 172p. (Orig.). 1984. pap. 14.95 (ISBN 0-89135-042-X). Religious Educ.
Chirban, John T., ed. Marriage & the Family Medicine, Psychology & Religion: New Directions, New Integrations. (Series on Medicine, Psychology & Religion). (Illus.). 94p. (Orig.). 1983. pap. text ed. 4.95 (ISBN 0-916586-63-4). Holy Cross Orthodox.
Chrysostomos, Bishop. Repentance. (Themes in Orthodox Patristic Psychology Ser.: Vol. III). 75p. (Orig.). 1986. pap. 5.00 (ISBN 0-911165-09-6). Ctr Trad Orthodox.
Clift, Jean & Clift, Wallace. Symbols of Transformation in Dreams. 144p. 1986. pap. 9.95 (ISBN 0-8245-0727-4). Crossroad NY.
Coe, George A. The Psychology of Religion. LC 75-3113. Repr. of 1916 ed. 40.00 (ISBN 0-404-59109-4). AMS Pr.
--The Psychology of Religion. Repr. of 1916 ed. 25.00 (ISBN 0-89987-046-5). Darby Bks.
Collins, Gary R. Psychology & Theology. LC 81-588. 160p. (Orig.). 1981. pap. 7.50 (ISBN 0-687-34830-7). Abingdon.
Crapps, Robert W. An Introduction to the Psychology of Religion. 384p. 1986. text ed. 49.95 (ISBN 0-86554-194-9); pap. text ed. 24.95 (ISBN 0-86554-195-7). Mercer Univ Pr.
Davenport, Frederick M. Primitive Traits in Religious Revivals. LC 72-163669. Repr. of 1905 ed. 15.00 (ISBN 0-404-01929-3). AMS Pr.
--Primitive Traits in Religious Revivals. LC 68-58053. Repr. of 1905 ed. cancelled (ISBN 0-8371-0378-9, DAR&). Greenwood.
Drakeford, J. W. Psicologia y Religion. 384p. 1980. pap. 8.95 (ISBN 0-311-46035-6, Edit Mundo). Casa Bautista.
Drakeford, John W. Psychology in Search of a Soul. LC 64-15096. 1964. 11.95 (ISBN 0-8054-6701-7). Broadman.
Faber, Heije. Psychology of Religion. LC 75-43721. 348p. 1976. 13.95 (ISBN 0-664-20748-0). Westminster.
Farnsworth, Kirk E. Integrating Psychology & Theology: Elbows Together but Hearts Apart. LC 81-40100. 94p. 1982. lib. bdg. 23.50 (ISBN 0-8191-1851-6); pap. text ed. 8.25 (ISBN 0-8191-1852-4). U Pr of Amer.
Ferder, Fran. Words Made Flesh: Scripture, Psychology & Human Communication. LC 85-73255. 184p. (Orig.). 1986. pap. 5.95 (ISBN 0-87793-331-6). Ave Maria.
Ferm, Vergilius T., ed. Religion in Transition. facs. ed. LC 68-29204. (Essay Index Reprint Ser). 1937. 15.50 (ISBN 0-8369-0074-X). Ayer Co Pubs.
Freud, Sigmund. The Future of an Illusion. Strachey, James, ed. 1975. 10.95 (ISBN 0-393-01120-8); pap. 2.95 (ISBN 0-393-00831-2). Norton.

--Moses & Monotheism. Jones, Katherine, ed. 1955. pap. 4.95 (ISBN 0-394-70014-7, V14, Vin). Random.

Fromm, Erich. Psychoanalysis & Religion. (Terry Lectures Ser.). 1950. pap. 5.95 (ISBN 0-300-00089-8, Y12). Yale U Pr.

Frost, Christopher J. Religious Melancholy or Psychological Depression: Some Issues Involved in Relating Psychology & Religion As Illustrated in a Study of Elie Wiesel. 274p. (Orig.). 1985. lib. bdg. 27.75 (ISBN 0-8191-4496-7); pap. text ed. 13.50 (ISBN 0-8191-4497-5). U Pr of Amer.

Fuller, Andrew R. Psychology & Religion: Eight Points of View. 143p. 1977. pap. text ed. 8.75 (ISBN 0-8191-0143-5). U Pr of Amer.

--Psychology & Religion: Eight Points of View. 2nd ed. 286p. 1986. pap. text ed. 9.75 (ISBN 0-8191-5336-2). U Pr of Amer.

Gawryn, Marvin. Reaching High: The Psychology of Spiritual Living. LC 80-24306. 200p. 1981. 11.95 (ISBN 0-938380-00-1); pap. 7.95 (ISBN 0-938380-01-X). Highreach Colorado.

Gay, Volney P. Freud on Ritual: Reconstruction & Critique. LC 79-11385. (American Academy of Religion, Dissertation Ser.: No. 26). 1979. 14.00 (ISBN 0-89130-282-4, 010126); pap. 9.95 (ISBN 0-89130-301-4). Scholars Pr Ga.

Godin, Andre. Psycological Dynamics of Religious Experience. Turton, Mary, tr. from Fr. Orig. Title: Psychologie des Experiences Religieuses. 279p. 1985. pap. 13.95 (ISBN 0-89135-039-X). Religious Educ.

Gorman, Margaret, ed. Psychology & Religion: A Reader. pap. 11.95 (ISBN 0-8091-2684-2). Paulist Pr.

Greenburg, Samuel A. & Gilkey, Helen L. Guests in My House, Bk. 1. 212p. 1984. 10.95 (ISBN 0-533-05727-2). Vantage.

Hall, Manly P. Psychology of Religious Ritual. pap. 2.50 (ISBN 0-89314-347-2). Philos Res.

Heaney, John J. Psyche & Spirit. rev. ed. 1984. pap. 10.95 (ISBN 0-8091-2610-9). Paulist Pr.

Heisig, James W. Imago Dei: A Study of C. G. Jung's Psychology of Religion. LC 77-74405. 256p. 1978. 26.50 (ISBN 0-8387-2076-5). Bucknell U Pr.

Hendricks, Gay & Weinhold, Barry. Transpersonal Approaches to Counseling & Psychotherapy. 199p. 1982. pap. text ed. 12.95 (ISBN 0-89108-112-7). Love Pub Co.

Heuscher, Julius E. A Psychiatric Study of Myths & Fairy Tales: Their Origins, Meaning & Usefulness. 2nd ed. (Illus.). 440p. 1974. 23.75x (ISBN 0-398-02851-6). C C Thomas.

Homans, Peter, ed. Dialogue Between Theology & Psychology. LC 68-16698. (Essays in Divinity Ser: Vol. 3). 1968. 25.00x (ISBN 0-226-35110-6). U. of Chicago Pr.

Hooker, Douglas. The Healthy Personality & the Christian Life. 1977. 10.95 (ISBN 0-8158-0351-6). Chris Mass.

Inayat Khan, Hazrat. Spiritual Dimensions of Psychology. LC 80-54830. (Collected Works of Hazrat Inayat Khan Ser.). 256p. (Orig.). 1981. 7.95 (ISBN 0-930872-24-X, 1012P). Omega Pr NM.

James, William. Varieties of Religious Experience. LC 37-27013. 1936. 6.95 (ISBN 0-394-60463-6). Modern Lib.

--Varieties of Religious Experience. pap. 4.50 (ISBN 0-451-62486-6, ME2069, Ment). NAL.

--The Varieties of Religious Experience. (The Works of William James). (Illus.). 728p. 1985. text ed. 45.00x (ISBN 0-674-93225-0). Harvard U Pr.

--The Varieties of Religious Experience: A Study in Human Nature. Marty, Martin, ed. (Penguin American Library). 1982. pap. 4.95 (ISBN 0-14-039034-0). Penguin.

Johansson, Rune. The Dynamic Psychology of Early Buddhism. (Scandinavian Institute of Asian Studies Monographs: No. 37). (Illus.). 1979. pap. text ed. 15.00x (ISBN 0-7007-0114-1). Humanities.

Jones, Stanton L., ed. Psychology & the Christian Faith: An Introductory Reader. 1986. pap. 11.95 (ISBN 0-8010-5217-3). Baker Bk.

Jung, C. G. Psychology & Western Religion. LC 84-42548. (Bollingen Ser.). (Illus.). 312p. (Orig.). 1984. pap. 8.95x (ISBN 0-691-01862-6). Princeton U Pr.

Jung, Carl G. Psychology & Religion. (Terry Lecture Ser.). 1938. pap. 5.95 (ISBN 0-300-00137-1, Y14). Yale U Pr.

Kallstad, T. Psychological Studies on Religious Man. 252p. 1978. pap. text ed. 22.00x (ISBN 91-554-0801-X, Pub. by Almqvist & Wiksell). Coronet Bks.

Kane, Thomas A. Happy Are You Who Affirm. LC 80-26834. (Illus.). 184p. 1980. pap. 5.00 (ISBN 0-89571-010-2). Affirmation.

Kelsey, Morton. Christianity As Psychology: The Healing Power of the Christian Message. LC 85-22864. 114p. (Orig.). 1986. pap. 7.95 (ISBN 0-8066-2194-X, 10-1184). Augsburg.

Kidd, James W., ed. Philosophy, Psychology & Spirituality. LC 83-80836. 87p. (Orig.). 1984. pap. text ed. 9.95 (ISBN 0-910727-05-8). Golden Phoenix.

McComas, Henry C. Psychology of Religious Sects. LC 70-172763. Repr. of 1912 ed. 20.00 (ISBN 0-404-04107-8). AMS Pr.

McDargh, John. Psychoanalytic Object Relations Theory & the Study of Religion: On Faith & the Imaging of God. 296p. 1983. lib. bdg. 28.50 (ISBN 0-8191-3510-0); pap. text ed. 12.75 (ISBN 0-8191-3511-9). U Pr of Amer.

McDonough, Reginald. Keys to Effective Motivation. LC 77-26532. 1979. pap. 4.25 (ISBN 0-8054-3226-4). Broadman.

Mackey, James. The Religious Imagination. 256p. 1986. 17.50x (ISBN 0-85224-512-2, Pub. by Edinburgh U Pr Scotland). Columbia U Pr.

Malony, H. Newton. Wholeness & Holiness: Readings in the Psychology, Theology of Mental Health. 304p. (Orig.). 1983. pap. 12.95 (ISBN 0-8010-6147-4). Baker Bk.

Malony, H. Newton, ed. Is There a Shrink in the Lord's House? How Psychologists Can Help the Church. LC 86-81513. (Orig.). 1986. pap. 12.00 (ISBN 0-9609928-4-7). Integ Pr.

Marechal, Joseph. Studies in the Psychology of the Mystics. LC 65-1694. 1964. lib. bdg. 12.95x (ISBN 0-87343-044-1). Magi Bks.

Martin, Luther H. & Goss, James, eds. Essays on Jung & the Study of Religion. LC 85-17865. 214p. (Orig.). 1986. lib. bdg. 29.50 (ISBN 0-8191-4923-3); pap. text ed. 12.75 (ISBN 0-8191-4924-1). U Pr of Amer.

Masson, J. Moussaieff. The Oceanic Feeling: The Origins of Religious Sentiment in Ancient India. (Studies of Classical India: No. 3). 228p. 1980. lib. bdg. 34.00 (ISBN 90-277-1050-3, Pub. by Reidel Holland). Kluwer Academic.

Meadow, Mary J. & Kahoe, Richard D. Psychology of Religion: Religion in Individual Lives. 488p. 1984. text ed. 22.50 scp (ISBN 0-06-044411-8, HarpC). Har-Row.

Meyer, Donald. The Positive Thinkers: Religion As Pop Psychology from Mary Baker Eddy to Oral Roberts. 1980. 15.95 (ISBN 0-394-51029-1); pap. 5.95 (ISBN 0-394-73899-3). Pantheon.

Miller, David L. Three Faces of God: Traces of the Trinity in Literature & Life. LC 85-45493. 176p. 1986. pap. 11.95 (ISBN 0-8006-1895-5, 1-1895). Fortress.

Miller, William A. You Count-You Really Do! LC 76-27078. 1976. pap. 5.95 (ISBN 0-8066-1569-9, 10-7420). Augsburg.

Morningstar, Jim. Spiritual Psychology: A New Age Course for Body, Mind & Spirit. 2nd ed. (Illus.). 119p. 1981. pap. 10.00 (ISBN 0-9604856-0-0). Transform Inc.

Murphy, Robert, Jr. Psychotherapy Based on Human Longing. LC 60-14173. (Orig.). 1960. pap. 2.50x (ISBN 0-87574-111-8, 111). Pendle Hill.

Myers, David C. The Human Puzzle: Psychological Research & Christian Belief. LC 77-15873. 1978. pap. 8.95x (ISBN 0-06-065558-5, RD 265, HarpR). Har-Row.

Narramore, Bruce S. & Carter, John. The Integration of Psychology & Theology: An Introduction. (Rosemead Ser.). (Orig.). 1979. pap. 8.95 (ISBN 0-310-30341-9, 11190P). Zondervan.

Ostow, Mortimer & Scharfstein, Ben-Ami. The Need to Believe: The Psychology of Religion. 1969. pap. text ed. 19.95 (ISBN 0-8236-8159-9, 23520). Intl Univs Pr.

Paloutzian, Raymond F. Invitation to the Psychology of Religion. 1983. pap. text ed. 13.50x (ISBN 0-673-15343-6). Scott F.

Peatling, John H. Religious Education in a Psychological Key. LC 81-8678. 439p. (Orig.). 1981. pap. 14.95 (ISBN 0-89135-027-6). Religious Educ.

Philp, Howard L. Freud & Religious Belief. LC 72-12635. 140p. 1974. Repr. of 1956 ed. lib. bdg. 22.50x (ISBN 0-8371-6682-9, PHFR). Greenwood.

Pratt, James B. The Psychology of Religious Belief. LC 75-3326. (Philosophy of America Ser.). Repr. of 1907 ed. 34.00 (ISBN 0-404-59321-6). AMS Pr.

--The Religious Consciousness: A Psychological Study. 1971. Repr. of 1920 ed. 21.95x (ISBN 0-02-850350-3). Hafner.

Reik, Theodor. Dogma & Compulsion. LC 72-9369. 332p. 1973. Repr. of 1951 ed. lib. bdg. 45.00x (ISBN 0-8371-6577-6, REDC). Greenwood.

Rizzuto, Ana-Maria. The Birth of the Living God: A Psychoanalytic Study. LC 78-10475. (Illus.). 246p. 1981. pap. 8.50x (ISBN 0-226-72102-7). U of Chicago Pr.

Rosik, Christopher H. & Malony, H. Newton, eds. The Nineteen Eighty-Three Travis Papers in the Integration of Psychology & Theology. 1986. pap. 10.00 (ISBN 0-9609928-5-5). Integ Pr.

Rowland, Roy V. The Psychological Search for God. (Illus.). 1980. 44.75 (ISBN 0-89920-003-6). Am Inst Psych.

Ruble, Richard, ed. Christian Perspectives on Psychology. LC 75-15956. 147p. 1975. pap. text ed. 14.95x (ISBN 0-8422-0456-3). Irvington.

Rudin, Josef. Psychotherapy & Religion. Bailey, Paul C. & Reinecke, Elisabeth, trs. LC 68-12291. 1968. pap. 7.95x (ISBN 0-268-00226-6). U of Notre Dame Pr.

Savelle, Jerry. A Right Mental Attitude. 138p. (Orig.). 1981. pap. 3.25 (ISBN 0-89274-159-7). Harrison Hse.

Schneiderman, Leo. The Psychology of Myth, Folklore & Religion. LC 81-9471. 232p. 1981. text ed. 21.95x (ISBN 0-88229-659-0); pap. text ed. 10.95x (ISBN 0-88229-783-X). Nelson-Hall.

Siirala, Aarne. The Voice of Illness. 225p. 1981. Repr. of 1964 ed. 49.95 (ISBN 0-88946-995-4). E Mellen.

Spero, Moshe H. Judaism & Psychology: Halakhic Perspectives. 25.00x (ISBN 0-87068-693-3). Ktav.

Sullivan, John. Carmelite Studies II: Carmel & Psychology. LC 82-1091. 320p. pap. 6.95x (ISBN 0-935216-00-6). ICS Pubns.

Symington, Thomas A. Religious Liberals & Conservatives: A Comparison of Those Who Are Liberal in Their Religious Thinking & Those Who Are Conservative. LC 70-177727. (Columbia University. Teachers College. Contributions to Education: No. 640). Repr. of 1935 ed. 22.50 (ISBN 0-404-55640-X). AMS Pr.

Thouless, R. H. An Introduction to the Psychology of Religion. 3rd ed. LC 76-184142. 160p. 1972. pap. 10.95 (ISBN 0-521-09665-0). Cambridge U Pr.

Thouless, Robert H. An Introduction to the Psychology of Religion. 286p. 1980. Repr. of 1925 ed. lib. bdg. 25.00 (ISBN 0-89987-802-4). Darby Bks.

Tisdale, John R., ed. Growing Edges in the Psychology of Religion. LC 79-20116. 350p. 1980. text ed. 24.95x (ISBN 0-88229-338-9); pap. text ed. 12.95x (ISBN 0-88229-748-1). Nelson-Hall.

Tournier, Paul. The Strong & the Weak. LC 63-8898. 252p. 1976. pap. 6.95 (ISBN 0-664-24745-8). Westminster.

Turner, John E. Essentials in the Development of Religion. LC 70-102587. 1970. Repr. of 1934 ed. 24.50x (ISBN 0-8046-0747-8, Pub. by Kennikat). Assoc Faculty Pr.

Ulanov, Ann & Ulanov, Barry. Religion & the Unconscious. LC 75-16302. 288p. 1975. 13.95 (ISBN 0-664-20799-5). Westminster.

--Religion & the Unconscious. 2nd ed. LC 75-16302. 288p. 1985. pap. 14.95 (ISBN 0-664-24657-5). Westminster.

Van Belzen, J. A. & Van Der Lans, J. M., eds. Proceedings of the Third Symposium on the Psychology of Religion in Europe: Current Issues in the Psychology of Religion. (Amsterdam Studies in Theology Ser.). 292p. 1986. pap. text ed. 65.00 (ISBN 90-6203-758-5, Pub. by Rodopi Holland). Humanities.

Vande Kemp, Hendrika. Psychology & Theology in Western Thought, 1672-1965: A Historical & Annotated Bibliography. LC 82-49045. (Bibliographies in the History of Psychology & Psychiatry Ser.). (Orig.). 1984. lib. bdg. 75.00 (ISBN 0-527-92779-1). Kraus Intl.

Van Leeuwen, Mary S. The Sorcerer's Apprentice: A Christian Looks at the Changing Face of Psychology. 144p. (Orig.). 1982. pap. 7.95 (ISBN 0-87784-398-8). Inter-Varsity.

Wicks, Robert J. Availability, the Problem & the Gift. LC 85-62868. 144p. (Orig.). 1986. pap. 5.95 (ISBN 0-8091-2767-9). Paulist Pr.

Wieman, Henry N. & Westcott-Wieman, Regina. Normative Psychology of Religion. 564p. 1986. Repr. of 1935 ed. lib. bdg. 95.00 (ISBN 0-89984-538-X). Century Bookbindery.

Wilbur, Ken. A Sociable God. LC 82-15241. (New Press Ser.). 176p. 1982. 12.95 (ISBN 0-07-070185-7). McGraw.

Wilson, Earl D. The Undivided Self: Bringing Your Whole Life in Line with God's Will. LC 83-6189. 191p. (Orig.). 1983. pap. 5.95 (ISBN 0-87784-842-4). Inter-Varsity.

Winquist, Charles, ed. The Archaeology of the Imagination. (JAAR Thematic Studies). 1981. pap. 11.95 (ISBN 0-89130-679-X, 01-24-82). Scholars Pr GA.

Woodward, Luther E. Relations of Religious Training & Life Patterns to the Adult Religious Life. LC 71-177627. (Columbia University. Teachers College. Contributions to Education: No. 527). Repr. of 1932 ed. 22.50 (ISBN 0-404-55527-6). AMS Pr.

Yungblut, John. Seeking Light in the Darkness of the Unconscious. LC 77-71933. (Orig.). 1977. pap. 2.50x (ISBN 0-87574-211-4). Pendle Hill.

Zeligs, Dorothy F. Psychoanalysis & the Bible: A Study in Depth of Seven Leaders. LC 73-85071. 1973. 15.95x (ISBN 0-8197-0360-5). Bloch.

Zielinski, Stanislaw. Psychology & Silence. Bassuk, Daniel, ed. LC 75-7413. (Illus.). 32p. (Orig.). 1975. pap. 2.50x (ISBN 0-87574-201-7). Pendle Hill.

PSYCHOLOGY AND RELIGION

see Psychology, Religious

PUBLIC LAW (CANON LAW)

see Canon Law; Catholic Church–Government

PUBLIC RELATIONS–CHURCHES

see also Advertising–Churches

Williams, Barbara. Public Relations Handbook for Your Church. 112p. 1985. pap. 5.95 (ISBN 0-8170-1050-5). Judson.

PUBLIC WORSHIP

see also Church Attendance; Liturgics; Pastoral Prayers; Prayer-Meetings; Ritual; Worship Programs; Young People'S Meetings (Church Work)

Baynes, Richard W. God's OK-You're OK? Perspective on Christian Worship. LC 79-67440. 96p. (Orig.). 1981. pap. 2.25 (ISBN 0-87239-382-8, 40088). Standard Pub.

Beachy, Alvin J. Worship As Celebration of Covenant & Incarnation. LC 68-57497. 1968. pap. 2.00 (ISBN 0-87303-940-8). Faith & Life.

Coffin, Henry S. The Public Worship of God: A Source Book. 16.00 (ISBN 0-8369-7272-4, 8071). Ayer Co Pubs.

Ducey, Michael H. Sunday Morning: Aspects of Urban Ritual. LC 76-25342. 1977. 17.00 (ISBN 0-02-907640-4). Free Pr.

Kendrick, Graham. Learning to Worship As a Way of Life. 214p. 1985. pap. 4.95 (ISBN 0-87123-863-2, 210863). Bethany Hse.

Lawson, LeRoy. The Family of God: The Meaning of Church Membership. LC 80-53497. 64p. (Orig.). 1981. pap. 1.50 (ISBN 0-87239-432-8, 39970). Standard Pub.

Pegram, Don R. Great Churches-Today's Essentials. 1982. pap. 1.25 (ISBN 0-89265-083-4). Randall Hse.

Webber, Robert E. Worship Old & New. 256p. 1982. 11.95 (ISBN 0-310-36650-X, 12207); pap. 9.95 (ISBN 0-310-36651-8, 12207P). Zondervan.

Willimon, William H. The Service of God. 240p. 1983. pap. 11.50 (ISBN 0-687-38094-4). Abingdon.

PULPIT PRAYERS

see Pastoral Prayers

PUPPETS AND PUPPET-PLAYS

Bivens, Ruth. Aunt Ruth's Puppet Scripts, Bk. I. (Orig.). 1986. pap. 19.95 (ISBN 0-89265-096-6). Randall Hse.

Cheasebro, Margaret. Puppet Scripts by the Month. 1985. pap. 4.95 (ISBN 0-8054-7524-9). Broadman.

Christy, James. The Puppet Ministry. 78p. 1978. 2.50 (ISBN 0-8341-0532-2). Beacon Hill.

Faust, David & Faust, Candy. Puppet Plays with a Point. rev. ed. 160p. 1979. pap. 7.95 (ISBN 0-87239-248-1, 3364). Standard Pub.

Garsee, Lee. New Dimensions in Puppet Ministry. 1983. pap. 5.95 (ISBN 0-89137-607-0). Quality Pubns.

Harp, Grace. Handbook of Christian Puppetry. LC 83-73204. 128p. (Orig.). 1984. pap. 5.95 plastic comb bdg. (ISBN 0-89636-125-X). Accent Bks.

Irving, Lynn. Pocketful of Puppets: Poems for Church School. Keller, Merily H., ed. (Puppetry in Education ser.). (Illus.). 48p. (Orig.). 1982. 11.50; pap. 7.50 (ISBN 0-931044-05-7). Renfro Studios.

Marsh, Fredda. Putting It All Together in a Puppet Ministry. LC 77-91674. 144p. 1978. pap. text ed. 6.95 (ISBN 0-88243-578-7, 02-0578). Gospel Pub.

Reynolds, Joyce. Puppet Shows That Reach & Teach Children, 3 vols. LC 73-185586. (Illus.). 1974. Vol. 1. pap. 3.50 (ISBN 0-88243-740-2, 02-0740); Vol. 2. pap. 3.50 (ISBN 0-88243-741-0, 02-0741); Vol. 3. pap. 3.50 (ISBN 0-88243-744-5, 02-0744). Gospel Pub.

Robertson, Everett, ed. Puppet Scripts for Use at Church. LC 78-72843. 1979. pap. 6.95 (ISBN 0-8054-7516-8). Broadman.

--Using Puppetry in the Church. LC 78-72842. 1979. pap. 6.95 (ISBN 0-8054-7517-6). Broadman.

Roden, Shelly. When Puppets Talk, Everybody Listens. LC 78-55265. 72p. 1978. pap. 4.95 (ISBN 0-88207-266-8). Victor Bks.

Shoemaker, Mary E. Meanwhile, Back at the Flock: A Christmas Puppet Play. (Orig.). 1980. pap. 1.85 (ISBN 0-937172-09-X). JLJ Pubs.

Sylwester, R. The Puppet & the Word. LC 12-2966. 1982. pap. 4.95 (ISBN 0-570-03873-1). Concordia.

Sylwester, Roland. Teaching Bible Stories More Effectively with Puppets. (Illus.). 64p. 1976. pap. 3.95 (ISBN 0-570-03731-X, 12-2633). Concordia.

Tickle, Phyllis. Tobias & the Angels. 96p. (Orig.). 1982. pap. text ed. 2.95 (ISBN 0-918518-23-7). St Luke TN.

PURANAS

Bhaktivedanta Swami. Srimad Bhagavatam: 11th Canto, Vol. 5. 1985. 12.95 (ISBN 0-89213-126-8). Bhaktivedanta.

Bhavisya Purana. write for info. Asian Human Pr.

Das Goswami, Hridayananda. Srimad Bhagavatam. 12.95 (ISBN 0-89213-129-2). Bhaktivedanta.

Devi Bhagavata. Date not set. cancelled. Asian Human Pr.

Hazra, R. C. Studies in the Puranic Records on Hindu Rites & Customs. 2nd ed. 1975. 28.00 (ISBN 0-8426-0965-2). Orient Bk Dist.

Shastri, J. L. Puranas: Ancient Indian Tradition & Mythology. 1978-82. Shiva Purana: 4 Vols. 60.00 (ISBN 0-89581-343-2); Bhagavata Purana: 5 Vols. 75.00 (ISBN 0-89581-536-2); Linga Purana: 2 Vols. 45.00 (ISBN 0-89581-537-0); Garuda Purana: 3 Vols. 45.00 (ISBN 0-89581-538-9); Narada Purana: 5 Vols. 75.00 (ISBN 0-89581-539-7). Asian Human Pr.

Shastri, J. L., tr. Siva Purana, Vol. 1. cancelled (ISBN 0-89581-343-2). Asian Human Pr.

--Siva Purana, Vol. 2. cancelled (ISBN 0-89581-475-7). Asian Human Pr.

--Siva Purana, Vol. 3. cancelled (ISBN 0-89581-476-5). Asian Human Pr.

--Siva Purana, Vol. 4. cancelled (ISBN 0-89581-476-5). Asian Human Pr.

Sheridan, Daniel P. The Advaitic Theism of the Bhagavata Purana. 1986. 14.00 (ISBN 81-208-0179-2, Pub. by Motilal Banarsidass). South Asia Bks.

Tagare, G. V., tr. Bhagavata Purana, Vol. 9. cancelled (ISBN 0-89581-480-3). Asian Human Pr.

--Bhagavata Purana, Vol. 10. cancelled (ISBN 0-89581-481-1). Asian Human Pr.

--Bhagavata Purana, Vol. 11. cancelled (ISBN 0-89581-482-X). Asian Human Pr.

--Narada Purana, Vol. 15. write for info. (ISBN 0-89581-539-7). Asian Human Pr.

--Skanda Purana. Date not set. cancelled. Asian Human Pr.

--Vayu Purana. write for info. Asian Human Pr.

PURGATORY

see also Future Life; Future Punishment; Indulgences; Prayers for the Dead

Arendzen, J. P. Purgatory & Heaven. (Canterbury Ser.). 1972. pap. 2.00 (ISBN 0-89555-045-8). TAN Bks Pubs.

Harley, Marta P. A Revelation of Purgatory by an Unknown, 15th Century Woman Visionary: Introduction, Critical Text & Translation. (Studies in Women & Religion: Vol. 18). 160p. 1986. lib. bdg. 49.95x (ISBN 0-88946-531-2). E Mellen.

Jeanroy, A. & Vignaux, A., eds. Voyage Au Purgatoire De Saint Patrice, Visions De Tindale & De Saint Paul. Repr. of 1903 ed. 21.00 (ISBN 0-384-64950-5). Johnson Repr.

Kreider, Alan. English Chantries: The Road to Dissolution. LC 78-12453. (Harvard Historical Studies: No. 97). 1979. 22.50x (ISBN 0-674-25560-7). Harvard U Pr.

Le Goff, Jacques. The Birth of Purgatory. Goldhammer, Arthur, tr. from Fr. LC 83-1108. (Illus.). 448p. 1984. 25.00 (ISBN 0-226-47082-2). U of Chicago Pr.

LeGoff, Jacques. The Birth of Purgatory. Goldhammer, Arthur, tr. LC 83-1108. (Illus.). x, 430p. 1986. pap. 13.95 (ISBN 0-226-47083-0). U of Chicago Pr.

More, Thomas. The Supplycacyon of Soulys: Agaynst the Supplycacyon of Beggars. LC 72-220. (English Experience Ser.: No. 353). 88p. 1971. Repr. of 1529 ed. 14.00 (ISBN 90-221-0353-6). Walter J Johnson.

Rastell, John. A Critical Edition of John Rastell's "The Pastyme of People" & " A New Book of Purgatory". Gertiz, Albert J. & Orgel, Stephen, eds. (The Renaissance Imagination Ser.). 509p. 1985. lib. bdg. 28.00 (ISBN 0-8240-5459-8). Garland Pub.

Schouppe, F. X. Purgatory--Explained by the Lives & Legends of the Saints. LC 86-50579. 427p. (Orig.). 1986. pap. 5.00 (Pulp Pocketbook (ISBN 0-89555-301-5). Tan Bks Pubs.

Shouppe, F. X. Purgatory: Explained by the Lives & Legends of the Saints. LC 79-112489. 1973. pap. 8.50 (ISBN 0-89555-042-3). TAN Bks Pubs.

PURIM (FEAST OF ESTHER)

Chaikin, Miriam. Make Noise, Make Merry: The Story & Meaning of Purim. LC 82-12926. (Illus.). 96p. 1983. 11.95 (ISBN 0-89919-424-9, Pub. by Clarion); pap. 4.95. Ticknor & Fields.

Goodman, Philip, ed. Purim Anthology. (Illus.). 525p. 1949. 7.50 (ISBN 0-8276-0022-4, 248). Jewish Pubns.

Greenfeld, Howard. Purim. LC 82-3058. (Illus.). 32p. 1983. 9.95 (ISBN 0-03-061478-3). H Holt & Co.

Rosenberg, A. J. Megillath Esther. 86p. 1985. pap. 6.95 (ISBN 0-900689-97-8). Soncino Pr.

Silverman, Morris & Neusner, Jacob. Complete Purim Service. pap. 2.95 (ISBN 0-87677-064-2). Prayer Bk.

Simon, Norma. Happy Purim Night. (Festival Series of Picture Story Books). (Illus.). plastic cover 4.50 (ISBN 0-8381-0706-0, 10-706). United Syn Bk.

--Purim Party. (Festival Series of Picture Story Books). (Illus.). 1959. plastic cover 4.50 (ISBN 0-8381-0707-9). United Syn Bk.

Stuhlman, Daniel D. My Own Pesah Story. (My Own Holiday Stories: No. 2). (Illus., Orig.). 1981. Personalized Version. pap. 3.95x (ISBN 0-934402-09-4); Trade Version. pap. 3.00 (ISBN 0-934402-10-8); Seder cards 1.50 (ISBN 0-934402-11-6). BYLS Pr.

Wengrov, Charles. The Story of Purim. (Holiday Ser.). (Illus.). 1965. pap. 1.50 (ISBN 0-914080-53-9). Shulsinger Sales.

PURITANS

see also Brownists; Calvinism; Church of England; Congregationalism; Pilgrims (New Plymouth Colony); Presbyterianism

Abbott, Lyman, et al. The New Puritanism: During the Semi-Centennial Celebration of Plymouth Church, N.Y., 1847-1897. LC 70-39672. (Essay Index Reprint Ser.). 19.00 (ISBN 0-8369-2732-X). Ayer Co Pubs.

Adair, John. Founding Fathers: The Puritans in England & America. 314p. 1982. 24.95x (ISBN 0-460-04421-4, Pub. by J M Dent England). Biblio Dist.

Ames, William. A Fresh Suit Against Human Ceremonies in God's Worship. 886p. Repr. of 1633 ed. 82.80x (ISBN 0-576-99734-X, Pub. by Gregg Intl Pubs England). Gregg Intl.

--Technometry. Gibbs, Lee W., tr. from Lat. LC 78-65117. (Haney Foundation Ser.). (Illus.). 1979. 31.50x (ISBN 0-8122-7756-2). U of Pa Pr.

Annesley, Samuel. Puritan Sermons, Sixteen Fifty-Nine To Sixteen Eighty-Nine Being the Morning Exercises at Cripplegate, St. Giles in the Fields & in Southwark: By 75 Ministers of the Gospel in or Near London, with Notes & Translations by James Nichols, 6 vols. Nichols, James, ed. 4200p. 1981. Set. lib. bdg. 120.00 (ISBN 0-940033-19-4). R O Roberts.

Babbage, Stuart B. Puritanism & Richard Bancroft. LC 63-2799. (Church Historical Society Ser.: No. 84). 1962. 20.00x (ISBN 0-8401-5084-9). A R Allenson.

Bacon, Leonard. The Genesis of the New England Churches. LC 74-38435. (Religion in America, Ser. 2). 510p. 1972. Repr. of 1874 ed. 32.00 (ISBN 0-405-04056-3). Ayer Co Pubs.

Bailyn, Bernard. The Apologia of Robert Keayne: The Self-Portrait of a Puritan Merchant. 11.25 (ISBN 0-8446-0470-4). Peter Smith.

Ball, Bryan W. The English Connection: The Puritan Roots of Seventh-Day Adventist Belief. 252p. 1981. text ed. 17.50 (ISBN 0-227-67844-3). Attic Pr.

Baltzell, E. Digby. Puritan Boston & Quaker Philadelphia. LC 81-70494. 585p. 1982. pap. 12.95x (ISBN 0-8070-5415-1, BP 638). Beacon Pr.

Barcovitch, Sacvan, ed. Aspects of Puritan Religious Thought: Library, Vol. VI. LC 83-12782. (Library of American Puritan Writings). 728p. 1984. Repr. 57.50 (ISBN 0-404-60806-X). AMS Pr.

Bardsley, C. W. Curiosities of Puritan Nomenclature. (The International Library of Names). 252p. Repr. of 1880 ed. text ed. cancelled (ISBN 0-8290-1239-7). Irvington.

Baynes, Paul. The Diocesans Tryall. 102p. Repr. of 1621 ed. text ed. 33.12x (ISBN 0-576-99736-6, Pub. by Gregg Intl Pubs England). Gregg Intl.

Bercovitch, S. The American Puritan Imagination. LC 73-94136. 256p. 1974. 39.50 (ISBN 0-521-20392-9); pap. 14.95 (ISBN 0-521-09841-6). Cambridge U Pr.

Bercovitch, Sacvan. The Puritan Origins of the American Self. LC 74-29713. 272p. 1975. pap. 9.95x (ISBN 0-300-02117-8). Yale U Pr.

Bercovitch, Sacvan, ed. The American Puritan Imagination: Essays in Revaluation. LC 73-94136. pap. 68.30 (2027269). Bks Demand UMI.

Berryman, Charles. From Wilderness to Wasteland: The Trial of the Puritan God in the American Imagination. (National University Publications, Literary Criticism Ser.). 1979. 21.50x (ISBN 0-8046-9235-1, Pub. by Kennikat). Assoc Faculty Pr.

Boston, Thomas. The Complete Works of the Late Rev. Thomas Boston, Ettrick: Including His Memoirs, Written by Himself, 12 vols. M'Millan, Samuel, ed. (Puritan Library). (Illus.). 1980. Repr. of 1853 ed. Set. lib. bdg. 225.00 (ISBN 0-940033-00-3). R O Roberts.

Bradshaw, William. English Puritanisme & Other Works. 326p. text ed. 62.10 (ISBN 0-576-99738-2, Pub. by Gregg Intl Pub England). Gregg Intl.

Brown, John. The English Puritans. 1978. Repr. of 1910 ed. lib. bdg. 20.00 (ISBN 0-8495-0434-1). Arden Lib.

--The English Puritans. LC 73-12821. 1910. lib. bdg. 22.50 (ISBN 0-8414-3235-X). Folcroft.

--The Pilgrim Fathers of New England. 352p. 1970. 4.95 (ISBN 0-686-09112-4). Pilgrim Pubns.

Byington, Ezra H. The Puritan As a Colonist & Reformer. LC 75-31115. Repr. of 1899 ed. 34.50 (ISBN 0-404-13601-X). AMS Pr.

--The Puritan in England & New England: With a Chapter on Witchcraft in New England. 4th & enl. ed. LC 70-183241. (Research & Source Works Ser). (Illus.). 457p. 1972. Repr. of 1900 ed. lib. bdg. 29.50 (ISBN 0-8337-4017-2). B Franklin.

Caldwell, Patricia. The Puritan Conversion Narrative: The Beginnings of American Expression. LC 82-22772. (Cambridge Studies in American Literature & Culture). 192p. 1983. 21.95 (ISBN 0-521-25460-4). Cambridge U Pr.

--The Puritan Conversion Narrative: The Beginnings of American Expression. 224p. 1985. pap. 12.95 (ISBN 0-521-31147-0). Cambridge U Pr.

Church of England Staff. A Parte of a Register, Contayninge Sundrie Memorable Matters, Written by Diuers Godly & Learned in Our Time, Which Stande for the Reformation of Our Church. LC 72-5981. (English Experience Ser.: No. 509). 1973. Repr. of 1593 ed. 67.00 (ISBN 90-221-0509-1). Walter J Johnson.

Cliffe, J. T. The Puritan Gentry: The Great Puritan Families of Early Stuart England. 300p. 1984. 25.00x (ISBN 0-7102-0007-2). Methuen Inc.

Cobbett, Thomas. Civil Magistrate's Power in Matters of Religion Modestly Debated, London, 1653. LC 74-141104. (Research Library of Colonial Americana). 1972. Repr. of 1653 ed. 24.50 (ISBN 0-405-03318-4). Ayer Co Pubs.

Cohen, Charles. God's Caress: The Psychology of Puritan Religious Experience. 336p. 1986. text ed. 29.95x (ISBN 0-19-503973-4). Oxford U Pr.

Collinson, Patrick. The Elizabethan Puritan Movement. (Library Reprints Ser.). 528p. 1982. 60.00x (ISBN 0-416-34000-8, NO. 3701). Methuen Inc.

--Godly People: Essays on English Protestantism & Puritanism. (No. 23). 634p. 1983. 40.00 (ISBN 0-907628-15-X). Hambledon Press.

Conkin, Paul K. Puritans & Pragmatists: Eight Eminent American Thinkers. LC 75-34730. (Midland Bks.: No. 197). 512p. 1976. 20.00x (ISBN 0-253-34720-3); pap. 6.95x (ISBN 0-253-20197-7). Ind U Pr.

Cotton, John. Bloudy Tenent, Washed, & Made White in the Bloud of the Lambe. LC 78-141105. (Research Library of Colonial Americana). 1972. Repr. of 1647 ed. 34.00 (ISBN 0-405-03319-2). Ayer Co Pubs.

--Christ the Fountaine of Life, Or, Sundry Choyce Sermons on Part of the Fifth Chapter of the First Epistle of St. John. LC 75-141107. (Research Library of Colonial Americana). 1971. Repr. of 1651 ed. 24.50 (ISBN 0-405-03321-4). Ayer Co Pubs.

Cragg, Gerald R. Puritanism in the Period of the Great Persecution, 1660-1688. LC 76-143557. 1971. Repr. of 1957 ed. 16.00x (ISBN 0-8462-1578-0). Russell.

Daly, Robert. God's Altar: The World & the Flesh in Puritan Poetry. LC 77-76182. 1978. 23.00x (ISBN 0-520-03480-5). U of Cal Pr.

Davenport, John. Letters of John Davenport, Puritan Divine. Calder, Isabel M., ed. 1937. 65.00x (ISBN 0-685-69794-0). Elliots Bks.

Eliot, John. Christian Commonwealth: Or, the Civil Policy of the Rising Kingdom of Jesus Christ. LC 77-141110. (Research Library of Colonial Americana). 1972. Repr. of 1659 ed. 18.00 (ISBN 0-405-03323-0). Ayer Co Pubs.

Elliott, Emory. Power & the Pulpit in Puritan New England. 256p. 1975. 27.00x (ISBN 0-691-07206-X). Princeton U Pr.

Ellis, George E. Puritan Age & Rule in the Colony of the Massachusetts Bay, 1629-1685. LC 75-122838. (Research & Source Ser.: No. 522). 1970. Repr. of 1888 ed. lib. bdg. 32.00 (ISBN 0-8337-1054-0). B Franklin.

Emerson, Everett. Puritanism in America. (World Leaders Ser.). 1977. lib. bdg. 12.50 (ISBN 0-8057-7692-3, Twayne). G K Hall.

Erikson, Kai T. Wayward Puritans: A Study in the Sociology of Deviance. LC 66-16140. (Deviance & Criminology Ser.). 228p. 1968. pap. text ed. write for info. (ISBN 0-02-332200-4). Macmillan.

Fenner, Dudley. A Short Treatise of Lawfull & Unlawfull Recreations. LC 77-6740. (English Experience Ser.: No. 870). 1977. Repr. of 1590 ed. lib. bdg. 3.50 (ISBN 90-221-0870-8). Walter J Johnson.

Fleming, Sanford. Children & Puritanism: The Place of Children in the Life & Thought of the New England Churches, 1620-1847. LC 70-89178. (American Education: Its Men, Institutions & Ideas Ser). 1969. Repr. of 1933 ed. 15.00 (ISBN 0-405-01416-3). Ayer Co Pubs.

Flynn, John S. Influence of Puritanism. LC 72-102569. 1970. Repr. of 1920 ed. 23.00x (ISBN 0-8046-0729-X, Pub. by Kennikat). Assoc Faculty Pr.

Forrer, Richard. Theodicies in Conflict: A Dilemma in Puritan Ethics & Nineteenth-Century American Literature. LC 85-27220. (Contributions to the Study of Religion: No. 17). 302p. 1986. lib. bdg. 37.95 (ISBN 0-313-25191-6, FTS/). Greenwood.

Foster, Stephen. Their Solitary Way: The Puritan Social Ethic in the First Century of Settlement in New England. LC 76-151573. (Yale Historical Publications Miscellany Ser.: No. 94). pap. 59.50 (ISBN 0-317-29587-X, 2021997). Bks Demand UMI.

Frere, Walter H. Puritan Manifestoes. 1907. 20.50 (ISBN 0-8337-4119-5). B Franklin.

Gura, Philip F. A Glimpse of Sion's Glory. Incl. 1984. 30.00x (ISBN 0-8195-5095-7); Puritan Radicalism in New England,1620-1660. (Illus.). 399p. 1986. pap. 12.95 (ISBN 0-8195-6154-1). 1984. 30.00. Wesleyan U Pr.

Gurnall, William. The Christian in Complete Armour. 1979. 26.95 (ISBN 0-85151-196-1). Banner of Truth.

Hall, Michael. The Last American Puritan: The Life of Increase Mather. 1987. 35.00 (ISBN 0-8195-5128-7). Wesleyan U Pr.

Haller, William. Elizabeth One & the Puritans. LC 64-7541. 1965. pap. 3.95 (ISBN 0-918016-24-X). Folger Bks.

--Liberty & Reformation in the Puritan Revolution. LC 54-6482. 410p. 1955. pap. 14.00x (ISBN 0-231-08547-8). Columbia U Pr.

--The Rise of Puritanism. LC 57-10117. 479p. 1972. pap. 14.95x (ISBN 0-8122-1048-4, Pa Paperbks). U of Pa Pr.

Hambrick-Stowe, Charles E. The Practice of Piety: Puritan Devotional Disciplines in Seventeenth Century New England. LC 81-19806. (Published for the Institute of Early American History & Culture, Williamsburg, Virginia Ser.). xvi, 298p. 1986. pap. 10.95x (ISBN 0-8078-4145-5). U of Nc Pr.

Heimert, Alan & Delbanco, Nicholas, eds. The Puritans in America: A Narrative Anthology. 456p. 1985. text ed. 25.00x (ISBN 0-674-74065-3); pap. text ed. 7.95x (ISBN 0-674-74066-1). Harvard U Pr.

Henson, Herbert H. Puritanism in England. LC 70-185944. 294p. 1973. Repr. of 1912 ed. 23.50 (ISBN 0-8337-4177-2). B Franklin.

Herget, Winfried, ed. Studies in New England Puritanism. 240p. 1983. 28.95. P Lang Pubs.

Hooker, Thomas. Application of Redemption, by the Effectual Work of the Word, & the Spirit of Christ, for the Bringing Home of Lost Sinners to God. LC 70-141111. (Research Library of Colonial Americana). 1972. Repr. of 1657 ed. 37.50 (ISBN 0-405-03324-9). Ayer Co Pubs.

--Christian's Two Chief Lessons, Viz. Selfe Deniall, & Selfe Tryall. LC 74-14112. (Research Library of Colonial Americana). 1972. Repr. of 1640 ed. 34.50 (ISBN 0-405-03325-7). Ayer Co Pubs.

--Survey of the Summe of Church-Discipline Wherein the Way of the Congregational Churches of Christ in New England Is Warranted & Cleared, by Scripture & Argument. LC 78-141113. (Research Library of Colonial Americana). 1971. Repr. of 1648 ed. 40.00 (ISBN 0-405-03326-5). Ayer Co Pubs.

Howard, Leon. Essays on Puritans & Puritanism. Barbour, James & Quirk, Thomas, eds. LC 85-28878. 221p. 1986. 19.95 (ISBN 0-8263-0877-5). U of NM Pr.

Howell, Roger, Jr. Puritans & Radicals in North England: Essays on the English Revolution. LC 84-10411. 226p. (Orig.). 1984. lib. bdg. 24.25 (ISBN 0-8191-4013-9); pap. text ed. 12.25 (ISBN 0-8191-4014-7). U Pr of Amer.

Hunt, William. The Puritan Moment: The Coming of Revolution in an English County. (Harvard Historical Studies: No. 102). (Illus.). 384p. 1983. text ed. 36.00x (ISBN 0-674-73903-5). Harvard U Pr.

--The Puritan Moment: The Coming of Revolution in an English County. (Harvard Historical Studies: No. 102). 384p. 1985. pap. text ed. 8.95x (ISBN 0-674-73904-3). Harvard U Pr.

Kawashima, Yasuhide. Puritan Justice & the Indian: White Man's Law in Massachusetts, 1630-1763. (Illus.). xii, 258p. 1984. 35.00x (ISBN 0-8195-5068-X). Wesleyan U Pr.

Kendall, Ritchie D. The Drama of Dissent: The Radical Poetics of Nonconformity, 1380-1590. LC 86-1289. (Studies in Religion). 286p. 1986. 27.50x (ISBN 0-8078-1700-7). U of NC Pr.

Kibbey, Ann. The Interpretation of Material Shapes in Puritanism: A Study of Rhetoric, Prejudice & Violence. (Cambridge Studies in American Literature & Culture). (Illus.). 256p. 1986. 27.95 (ISBN 0-521-26509-6). Cambridge U Pr.

Knappen, Marshall M. Tudor Puritanism: A Chapter in the History of Idealism. LC 39-10082. 1965. pap. 3.45x (ISBN 0-226-44627-1, P194, Phoen). U of Chicago Pr.

Lake, Peter. Moderate Puritans & the Elizabethan Church. LC 81-17052. 345p. 1982. 57.50 (ISBN 0-521-24010-7). Cambridge U Pr.

Leites, Edmund. The Puritan Conscience & Modern Sexuality. LC 85-20198. 208p. 1986. 17.50 (ISBN 0-300-03490-3). Yale U Pr.

Leverenz, David. The Language of Puritan Feeling: An Exploration in Literature, Psychology, & Social History. 1980. 32.00x (ISBN 0-8135-0882-7). Rutgers U Pr.

Little, David. Religion, Order, & Law: A Study in Pre-Revolutionary England. LC 84-2611. 270p. 1984. pap. text ed. 11.00x (ISBN 0-226-48546-3). U of Chicago Pr.

Liu, Tai. Puritan London: A Study of Religion & Society in the City Parishes. LC 85-40534. 256p. 1986. 38.50x (ISBN 0-87413-283-5, Pub. by U Delaware Pr). Assoc Univ Prs.

Loane, Marcus L. Makers of Puritan History. (Canterbury Bks). Orig. Title: Pioneers of Religious Freedom. 240p. 1980. pap. 6.95 (ISBN 0-8010-5593-8). Baker Bk.

McGiffert, Michael, ed. God's Plot: The Paradoxes of Puritan Piety, Being the Autobiography & Journal of Thomas Shepard. LC 71-181364. (Commonwealth Ser.: Vol. 1). (Illus.). 264p. 1972. 20.00x (ISBN 0-87023-100-6). U of Mass Pr.

Mackie, J. D. Cavalier & Puritan. 1930. Repr. 10.00 (ISBN 0-8482-5082-6). Norwood Edns.

Maly-Schlatter, Florence. Puritan Element in Victorian Fiction. LC 72-195449. 1940. lib. bdg. 20.00 (ISBN 0-8414-5974-6). Folcroft.

Mather, Cotton. Manuductio Administerium, Directions for a Candidate of the Ministry. LC 75-41190. Repr. of 1938 ed. 17.25 (ISBN 0-404-14685-6). AMS Pr.

--Ratio Disciplinae Fratrum Novanglorum: A Faithful Account of the Discipline Professed & Practised, in the Churches of New-England. LC 71-141114. (Research Library of Colonial Americana). 1971. Repr. of 1726 ed. 23.50 (ISBN 0-405-03327-3). Ayer Co Pubs.

Mather, Increase & Stoddard, Solomon. Increase Mather Vs. Solomon Stoddard: Two Puritan Tracts. LC 72-141117. (Research Library of Colonial Americana). 1971. Repr. of 1700 ed. 17.00 (ISBN 0-405-03328-1). Ayer Co Pubs.

Mather, Richard. Church Covenant: Two Tracts. LC 75-141115. (Research Library of Colonial Americana). 1972. Repr. of 1643 ed. 23.50 (ISBN 0-405-03329-X). Ayer Co Pubs.

Middlekauff, Robert. The Mathers: Three Generations of Puritan Intellectuals, 1596-1728. LC 79-140912. 1971. pap. 7.95 (ISBN 0-19-502115-0). Oxford U Pr.

Miller, Perry. American Puritans: Their Prose & Poetry. 1959. 21.75 (ISBN 0-8446-2596-5). Peter Smith.

Miller, Perry & Johnson, T. H. Puritans: A Sourcebook of Their Writings, 2 Vols. Set. 38.50 (ISBN 0-8446-2593-0). Vol. 2. Peter Smith.

Miller, Perry & Johnson, Thomas H., eds. Puritans: A Sourcebook of Their Writings, 2 vols. (Orig.). Vol. 1. pap. 8.95x (ISBN 0-06-131093-X, TB1093, Torch); Vol. 2. pap. 8.95x (ISBN 0-06-131094-8, TB1094, Torch). Har-Row.

Montgomery, Michael S., compiled by. American Puritan Studies: An Annotated Bibliography of Dissertations, 1882-1981. LC 84-6553. (Bibliographies & Indexes in American History Ser.: No. 1). xxii, 419p. 1984. lib. bdg. 49.95 (ISBN 0-313-24237-2, MON/). Greenwood.

Morgan, E. S. Puritan Family. 14.75 (ISBN 0-8446-2609-0). Peter Smith.

Morgan, Edmund S. The Puritan Family: Religion & Domestic Relations in Seventeenth-Century New England. LC 80-18819. x, 196p. 1980. Repr. of 1966 ed. lib. bdg. 29.75x (ISBN 0-313-22703-9, MOPFA). Greenwood.

--Visible Saints: The History of a Puritan Idea. LC 63-9999. 168p. 1965. pap. 6.95x (ISBN 0-8014-9041-3). Cornell U Pr.

Morgan, Edmund S., ed. Puritan Family: Religion & Domestic Relations in 17th-Century New England. rev. ed. pap. 6.95x (ISBN 0-06-131227-4, TB1227, Torch). Har-Row.

Morgan, John. Godly Learning: Puritan Attitudes Towards Reason, Learning, & Education, 1560-1640. 378p. 1986. 49.50 (ISBN 0-521-23511-1) (ISBN 0-317-39807-5). Cambridge U Pr.

Mosse, George L. The Holy Pretence. LC 68-14552. 1968. 23.50x (ISBN 0-86527-099-6). Fertig.

Murray, Iain H. The Puritan Hope. 1975. pap. 5.95 (ISBN 0-85151-037-X). Banner of Truth.

Myers, Aaron M. Representation & Misrepresentation of the Puritan in Elizabethan Drama. LC 76-20654. 1976. Repr. of 1931 ed. lib. bdg. 27.50 (ISBN 0-8414-6141-4). Folcroft.

Neal, Daniel. History of the Puritans, 3 vols. 1979. 54.95 (ISBN 0-86524-011-6, 9401). Klock & Klock.

Oberholzer, Emil, Jr. Delinquent Saints: Disciplinary Action in the Early Congregational Churches of Massachusetts. LC 70-76660. (Columbia University. Studies in the Social Sciences: No. 590). Repr. of 1956 ed. 14.50 (ISBN 0-404-51590-8). AMS Pr.

Oliver, Peter. The Puritan Commonwealth. LC 75-31127. Repr. of 1856 ed. 41.50 (ISBN 0-404-13606-0). AMS Pr.

Ormerod, Oliver. The Picture of a Puritane: Or, a Relation of the Opinions - of the Anabaptists in Germanie, & of the Puritanes in England. LC 74-28879. (English Experience Ser.: No. 757). 1975. Repr. of 1605 ed. 9.50 (ISBN 90-221-0757-4). Walter J Johnson.

Perry, Ralph B. Puritanism & Democracy. 688p. 1944. 19.50 (ISBN 0-8149-0180-8). Vanguard.

Pope, Robert G. Half-Way Covenant: Church Membership in Puritan New England. Repr. of 1969 ed. 63.30 (ISBN 0-8357-9500-4, 2011473). Bks Demand UMI.

Porter, H. C., ed. Puritanism in Tudor England. LC 75-145532. (History in Depth Ser). xvi, 312p. 1971. 17.95x (ISBN 0-87249-222-2); pap. 7.95x (ISBN 0-87249-223-0). U of SC Pr.

Puritan Personal Writings: Autobiographies & Other Writings, Vol. 8. LC 78-270. (American Puritan Writings Ser.). 240p. 1982. 67.50 (ISBN 0-404-60808-6). AMS Pr.

Puritan Personal Writings: Diaries, Vol. 7. LC 78-269. (American Puritan Writings Ser.). 1982. 67.50 (ISBN 0-404-60807-8). AMS Pr.

Randall, Daniel R. A Puritan Colony in Maryland. LC 78-63763. (Johns Hopkins University. Studies in the Social Sciences. Fourth Ser. 1886: 6). Repr. of 1886 ed. 11.50 (ISBN 0-404-61031-5). AMS Pr.

Reinitz, R. Tensions in American Puritanism. LC 70-100325. (Problems in American History Ser.). pap. 52.00 (ISBN 0-8357-9991-3, 2019292). Bks Demand UMI.

Rogers, Richard & Ward, Samuel. Two Elizabethan Puritan Diaries. Knappen, Marshall M., ed. 1933. 11.75 (ISBN 0-8446-1387-8). Peter Smith.

Rose, Elliot. Cases of Conscience: Alternatives Open to Recusants & Puritans under Elizabeth I & James I. LC 74-76947. pap. 68.50 (2027243). Bks Demand UMI.

Rowse, A. L. Milton the Puritan: Portrait of a Mind. 298p. 1985. pap. text ed. 12.50 (ISBN 0-8191-4778-8). U Pr of Amer.

Rumsey, Peter L. Acts of God & the People, 1620-1730. Miles, Margaret R., ed. LC 86-19292. (Studies in Religion: No. 2). 182p. 1986. 39.95 (ISBN 0-8357-1761-5). UMI Res Pr.

Ryken, Leland. Wordly Saints: The Puritans As They Really Were. 272p. 1986. 18.95 (ISBN 0-310-32500-5). Zondervan.

Sasek, Lawrence A. Literary Temper of the English Puritans. Repr. of 1961 ed. lib. bdg. 22.50x (ISBN 0-8371-2333-X, SAEP). Greenwood.

Schoffler, Herbert. Anfange Des Puritanismus. Repr. of 1932 ed. 16.00 (ISBN 0-384-54220-4). Johnson Repr.

Scott, Thomas. The Interpreter, Wherein Three Principal Terms of State Are Clearly Unfolded. LC 74-80194. (English Experience Ser.: No. 673). 1974. Repr. of 1624 ed. 3.50 (ISBN 90-221-0281-5). Walter J Johnson.

Seaver, Paul S. The Puritan Lectureships: The Politics of Religious Dissent, 1560-1662. LC 71-93497. 1970. 30.00x (ISBN 0-8047-0711-1). Stanford U Pr.

--Wallington's World: A Puritan Artisan in Seventeenth-Century London. LC 84-40447. 272p. 1985. 29.50x (ISBN 0-8047-1267-0). Stanford U Pr.

Selement, George. Keepers of the Vineyard: The Puritan Ministry & Collective Culture in Colonial New England. 128p. (Orig.). 1984. lib. bdg. 22.00 (ISBN 0-8191-3876-2); pap. text ed. 9.50 (ISBN 0-8191-3877-0). U Pr of Amer.

Seymour, Malcolm. Puritan Migration to Connecticut: The Saga of the Seymour Family, 1129-1746. LC 82-548. (Illus.). 136p. 1982. 29.50 (ISBN 0-914016-85-7). Phoenix Pub.

Simpson, Alan. Puritanism in Old & New England. LC 55-13637. (Walgreen Foundation Lecture Ser). 1961. pap. 4.00x (ISBN 0-226-75929-6, P66, Phoen). U of Chicago Pr.

Slater, Peter G. Children in the New England Mind: In Death & in Life. LC 77-7352. 248p. 1977. 27.50 (ISBN 0-208-01652-X, Archon). Shoe String.

Slotkin, Richard & Folsom, James K., eds. So Dreadful a Judgment: Puritan Responses to King Philip's War, 1676-1677. LC 77-14847. 1978. 27.00x (ISBN 0-8195-5027-2); pap. 13.00x (ISBN 0-8195-6058-8). Wesleyan U Pr.

Solberg, Winton U. Redeem the Time: The Puritan Sabbath in Early America. (Illus.). 1977. 25.00x (ISBN 0-674-75130-2). Harvard U Pr.

Solt, Leo F. Saints in Arms. LC 74-153355. (Stanford University. Stanford Studies in History, Economics & Political Science: No. 18). Repr. of 1959 ed. 19.00 (ISBN 0-404-50976-2). AMS Pr.

Sprunger, Keith. Dutch Puritanism. (Studies in the History of Christian Thought: Vol. 31). 485p. 1982. text ed. 90.00x (ISBN 90-04-06793-0, Pub. by E J Brill Holland). Humanities.

Sprunger, Keith L. The Learned Doctor William Ames: Dutch Backgrounds of English & American Puritanism. LC 77-175172. pap. 76.30 (ISBN 0-317-08400-3, 2020215). Bks Demand UMI.

Stannard, David E. The Puritan Way of Death: A Study in Religion, Culture & Social Change. LC 76-42647. (Illus.). 1977. 19.95x (ISBN 0-19-502226-2). Oxford U Pr.

--The Puritan Way of Death: A Study in Religion, Culture, & Social Change. LC 76-42647. (Illus.). 1977. pap. 8.95 (ISBN 0-19-502521-0). Oxford U Pr.

Stephenson, George M. The Puritan Heritage. LC 78-10512. 1978. Repr. of 1952 ed. lib. bdg. 22.50x (ISBN 0-313-20733-X, STPU). Greenwood.

Stoever, William K. A Faire & Easie Way to Heaven: Covenant Theology & Antinomianism in Early Massachusetts. LC 77-14851. 251p. 1978. 22.00x (ISBN 0-8195-5024-8). Wesleyan U Pr.

Thompson, Elbert N. Controversy Between the Puritans & the Stage. LC 76-176150. Repr. of 1903 ed. 21.50 (ISBN 0-404-06396-9). AMS Pr.

Vaughan, Alden T. & Clark, Edward W., eds. Puritans among the Indians: Accounts of Captivity & Redemption, 1676-1724. (John Harvard Library). 288p. 1986. pap. text ed. 7.95x (ISBN 0-674-73899-3, Belknap Pr). Harvard U Pr.

Von Rohr, John. The Covenant of Grace in Puritan Thought. (American Academy of Religion Studies in Religion). 240p. 1987. 18.95 (01-00-45); pap. 13.95. Scholars Pr Ga.

Wagner, Hans-Peter. Puritan Attitudes Towards Recreation in Early Seventeenth-Century New England, Vol. 17. (Mainzer Studien zur Internationalen Entwecklung). 273p. 1982. pap. 33.15 (ISBN 3-8204-7286-X). P Lang Pubs.

Waller, George M., ed. Puritanism in Early America. 2nd ed. (Problems in American Civilization Ser). 1973. pap. text ed. 5.95 (ISBN 0-669-82719-3). Heath.

White, Eugene E. Puritan Rhetoric: The Issue of Emotion in Religion. LC 76-181987. (Landmarks in Rhetoric & Public Address Ser.). 229p. 1972. 10.95x (ISBN 0-8093-0563-1). S Ill U Pr.

Whiting, Charles E. Studies in English Puritanism from the Restoration to the Revolution, 1660-1688. (Church Historical Society London, N. S. Ser.: No. 5). Repr. of 1931 ed. 95.00 (ISBN 0-8115-3129-5). Kraus Repr.

Whittingham, William. A Briefe Discourse of the Troubles Begonne at Franckford. LC 71-38228. (English Experience Ser.: No. 492). 210p. 1972. Repr. of 1574 ed. 13.00 (ISBN 90-221-0492-3). Walter J Johnson.

Wigglesworth, Michael. The Diary of Michael Wigglesworth, 1653 to 1657: The Conscience of a Puritan. Morgan, Edmund, ed. 11.25 (ISBN 0-8446-0808-4). Peter Smith.

Woodhouse, A. S., ed. & intro. by. Puritanism & Liberty: Being the Army Debates (1647-9) from the Clarke Manuscripts with Supplementary Documents. 634p. 1986. pap. 11.95x (ISBN 0-460-01057-3, Pub. by Evman England). Biblio Dist.

Zaret, David. The Heavenly Contract: Ideology & Organization in Pre-Revolutionary Puritanism. LC 84-16473. 192p. 1985. lib. bdg. 22.50x (ISBN 0-226-97882-6). U of Chicago Pr.

PURITY, RITUAL

see also Taboo

Douglas, Mary. Purity & Danger: An Analysis of the Concepts of Pollution & Taboo. 196p. 1984. pap. 6.95 (ISBN 0-7448-0011-0, Ark Paperbks). Methuen Inc.

Faris, N. A. The Mysteries of Purity. pap. 4.75 (ISBN 0-686-18614-1). Kazi Pubns.

Newton, Michael. The Concept of Purity at Quaram & in the Letters of Paul. (Society of New Testament Studies Monograph: No. 53). 180p. 1985. 32.50 (ISBN 0-521-26583-5). Cambridge U Pr.

PUZZLES–JUVENILE LITERATURE

Adler, David A. Bible Fun Book: Puzzles, Riddles, Magic, & More. (A Bonim Fun-to-Do Bk.). (Illus., Orig.). 1979. pap. 3.95 (ISBN 0-88482-769-0). Hebrew Pub.

Crowther, Jean D. Book of Mormon Puzzles & Pictures for Young Latter-Day Saints. LC 77-74495. (Books for LDS Children). (Illus.). 56p. 1977. pap. 4.95 (ISBN 0-88290-080-3). Horizon Utah.

Sattler, Helen. Bible Puzzle Trails. (Pelican Activity Ser.). 32p. 1977. pap. 0.89 (ISBN 0-8010-7900-4). Baker Bk.

PYRAMIDS

Capt, E. Raymond. The Great Pyramid Decoded. rev. ed. LC 78-101677. (Illus.). 96p. 1978. pap. 3.00 (ISBN 0-934666-01-6). Artisan Sales.

Edwards, I. E. S. The Pyramids of Egypt. 368p. 1987. 25.00 (ISBN 0-670-80153-4). Viking.

Fakhry, Ahmed. The Pyramids. 2nd ed. LC 61-8645. 272p. 1974. pap. 9.95 (ISBN 0-226-23473-8, P571, Phoen). U of Chicago Pr.

Gangstad, John E. Great Pyramid: Signs in the Sun (Pyramid Design & Prophecy: Second Advent) LC 76-24077. (Illus.). 200p. 1976. 1980-86 supplement 3.00 (ISBN 0-9603374-2-3). Di-Tri Bks.

Lewis, H. Spencer. Symbolic Prophecy of the Great Pyramid. 16th ed. LC 37-3808. 192p. 1982. 8.95 (ISBN 0-912057-13-0, G-514). AMORC.

Pace, Mildred M. Pyramids: Tombs for Eternity. (Illus.). 192p. 1981. 10.95 (ISBN 0-07-048054-0). McGraw.

Reiff, Stephanie A. Secrets of Tut's Tomb & the Pyramids. LC 77-22770. (Great Unsolved Mysteries). (Illus.). 1977. PLB 14.65 (ISBN 0-8172-1051-2). Raintree Pubs.

Seiss, Joseph. The Great Pyramid: A Miracle in Stone. LC 72-81590. (Illus.). 256p. 1973. pap. 5.00 (ISBN 0-89345-218-1, Steinerbks). Garber Comm.

Seiss, Joseph A. The Great Pyramid: A Miracle in Stone. LC 80-8341. (Harper's Library of Spiritual Wisdom). 256p. 1981. pap. 5.95i (ISBN 0-06-067211-0, CN4005, HarpR). Har-Row.

Smith, Warren. The Secret Forces of the Pyramids. 220p. 1975. pap. 1.75 (ISBN 0-89083-114-9). Zebra.

Smyth, Piazzi. Our Inheritance in the Great Pyramid, Vol. 8. LC 77-5284. (Illus.). 672p. 1980. Repr. of 1877 ed. lib. bdg. 45.00 (ISBN 0-89345-029-4, Spiritual Sci Lib). Garber Comm.

Wake, C. Staniland. The Origin & Significance of the Great Pyramid. 2nd ed. LC 73-84047. (Secret Doctrine Reference Ser.). (Illus.). 170p. 1980. pap. 6.00 (ISBN 0-913510-32-7). Wizards.

Weeks, John. Pyramids. (Cambridge Introduction to the History of Mankind Ser.). (Illus.). 1971. 5.95 (ISBN 0-521-07240-9). Cambridge U Pr.

--The Pyramids. LC 76-22457. (Cambridge Topic Bks.). (Illus.). 1977. PLB 8.95 (ISBN 0-8225-1209-2). Lerner Pubns.

PYRAMIDS–CURIOSA AND MISCELLANEA

Andersen, U. S. Secret Power of the Pyramids. 1977. pap. 7.00 (ISBN 0-87980-343-6). Wilshire.

David, A. R. The Pyramid Builders of Ancient Egypt: A Modern Investigation of Pharoah's Workforce. 258p. 1986. text ed. 34.95 (ISBN 0-7100-9909-6). Methuen Inc.

Lemesurier, Peter. The Great Pyramid Decoded. (YA) 1984. pap. 4.95 (ISBN 0-380-43034-7, 43034-7). Avon.

Mendelssohn, Kurt. The Riddle of Pyramids. (Illus.). 1986. 24.95f (ISBN 0-500-05015-5); pap. 12.95f (ISBN 0-500-27388-X). Thames Hudson.

Nicklin, J. Bernard. Testimony in Stone. 1961. 6.00 (ISBN 0-685-08818-9). Destiny.

Riffert, George R. Great Pyramid Proof of God. 1932. 8.00 (ISBN 0-685-08804-9). Destiny.

Schul, Bill & Pettit, Ed. Pyramids & the Second Reality. 1979. pap. 4.95 (ISBN 0-449-90008-8, Columbine). Fawcett.

--Secret Power of Pyramids. 1987. pap. 3.50 (ISBN 0-449-13986-7, GM). Fawcett.

Q

QUAKERS

see Friends, Society Of

QUEBEC (PROVINCE)–SOCIAL CONDITIONS

Riddell, Walter A. Rise of Ecclesiastical Control in Quebec. (Columbia University. Studies in the Social Sciences: No. 174). Repr. of 1916 ed. 17.50 (ISBN 0-404-51174-0). AMS Pr.

QUMRAN COMMUNITY

see also Dead Sea Scrolls

Brownlee, William H. The Midrash Pesher of Habakkuk. LC 76-30560. (Society of Biblical Literature Monograph). 220p. 1979. pap. 9.95 (ISBN 0-89130-147-X, 06 00 24). Scholars Pr GA.

Cross, Frank M. The Ancient Library of Qumran & Modern Biblical Studies. LC 76-29736. (The Haskell Lectures, 1956-57). (Illus.). 1976. Repr. of 1958 ed. lib. bdg. 22.50x (ISBN 0-8371-9281-1, CRAL). Greenwood.

Davies, Philip R. Qumran. (Cities of the Biblical World Ser.). 1983. pap. 6.95 (ISBN 0-8028-1034-9). Eerdmans.

Fritsch, Charles T. The Qumran Community: Its History & Scrolls. 1973. Repr. of 1956 ed. 18.00 (ISBN 0-8196-0279-5). Biblo.
Garnett, Paul. Salvation & Atonement in the Qumran Scrolls. 160p. 1977. pap. 24.00x (Pub. by J C B Mohr BRD). Coronet Bks.
Gilliam, Olive. Qumran & History: The Place of the Teachers in Religion. 3.95 (ISBN 0-533-01167-1). Vantage.
Kittel, Bonnie P. The Hymns of Qumran: Translation & Commentary. Kittel, Bonnie, tr. LC 80-11616. 1981. pap. 13.50 (ISBN 0-89130-397-9, 06 01 50). Scholars Pr GA.
Roth, Cecil. Dead Sea Scrolls: A New Historical Approach. 1966. pap. 3.95x (ISBN 0-393-00303-5, Norton Lib). Norton.
Scharlemann, Martin H. Qumran & Corinth. 1962. pap. 5.95x (ISBN 0-8084-0358-3). New Coll U Pr.
--Qumran & Corinth. 78p. 1962. write for info. Concordia Schl Grad Studies.
Schubert, Kurt. Dead Sea Community: Its Origin & Teachings. Doberstein, John W., tr. LC 73-15245. 178p. 1974. Repr. of 1959 ed. lib. bdg. 22.50x (ISBN 0-8371-7169-5, SCDS). Greenwood.
Vermes, Geza. The Dead Sea Scrolls: Qumran in Perspective. LC 80-2382. 240p. 1981. pap. 8.95 (ISBN 0-8006-1435-6, 1-1435). Fortress.

QUOTATIONS

see also Aphorisms and Apothegms; Proverbs

The Book of Bible Quotes. 272p. 1984. pap. 5.95 (ISBN 0-8407-5929-0). Nelson.
Cory, Lloyd, compiled by. Quotable Quotations. 400p. 1985. pap. 12.95 (ISBN 0-88207-823-2). Victor Bks.
Dawson, Samuel G. & MacArthur, Rod, eds. Handbook of Religious Quotations. 188p. (Orig.). 1987. pap. 5.95 (ISBN 0-938855-16-6). Gospel Themes Pr.
Holdcraft, Paul E. Snappy Bulletin Bits. LC 72-109673. pap. 20.00 (ISBN 0-8357-9027-4, 2016076). Bks Demand UMI.
Puritan Treasury of Quotations. pap. 6.45 (ISBN 0-85151-249-6). Banner of Truth.
Sumner, William G. Forgotten Man's Almanac: Rations of Common Sense from William Graham Sumner. Keller, A. G., ed. LC 70-141268. 1971. Repr. of 1943 ed. lib. bdg. 22.50x (ISBN 0-8371-5828-1, SUFM). Greenwood.
Watson, Lillian E. Light from Many Lamps. 1951. 15.95 (ISBN 0-671-42300-2). S&S.

R

RABBINICAL LITERATURE

see also Midrash

Attar, Chaim B. Light of Life: A Compendium of the Writings of Rabbi Chaim Ben Attar. 236p. 1986. pap. 9.95 (ISBN 0-87877-090-9). Newcastle Pub.
Bartolocci, Giulio & Imbonati, Carlo. Bibliotheca Magna Rabbinica & Biblio Latino-Hebrauca. 4440p. Date not set. Repr. of 1694 ed. text ed. 1242.00x (ISBN 0-576-72820-9, Pub. by Gregg Intl Pubs England). Gregg Intl.
Birnbaum, Philip, ed. The New Treasury of Judaism. 1977. 15.00 (ISBN 0-88482-410-1, Sanhedrin Pr); pap. 9.95 (ISBN 0-88482-411-X, Sanhedrin Pr). Hebrew Pub.
Hacohen, Menachem. The Haggadah of Legends & Customs. (Illus.). 128p. 1987. 29.95 (ISBN 0-915361-78-7, Dist. by Watts). Adama Pubs Inc.
Lieberman, Saul. Texts & Studies. 1973. 35.00x (ISBN 0-87068-210-5). Ktav.
Low, Leopold. Beitrage zur Judischen Alterthumskunde, 2 vols. 922p. Date not set. Repr. text ed. 149.04x (ISBN 0-576-80127-5, Pub. by Gregg Intl Pubs England). Gregg Intl.
Nachman of Breslov. Rabbi Nachman's Stories: Skazocnniji Histori Rabbi Nechman iz Bratzlav. Avni, Baruch, tr. from Hebrew & Rus. Tr. of Sippurey Maasiot. (Illus.). 332p. (Orig.). 1987. pap. 10.00 (ISBN 0-930213-29-7). Breslov Res Inst.
Nathan, Rabbi. Tzaddik. Greenbaum, Avraham, tr. from Hebrew. Orig. Title: Chayey Moharan. Date not set. price not set (ISBN 0-930213-17-3). Breslov Res Inst.
Petuchowski, Jakob J. Our Masters Taught Rabbinic Stories & Sayings. LC 82-9999. 160p. 1982. 10.95 (ISBN 0-8245-0521-2). Crossroad NY.
Rabbi Aryeh Kaplan. Unitl the Mashiach: The Life of Rabbi Nachman. Shapiro, Dovid, ed. 379p. 1986. text ed. 15.00 (ISBN 0-930213-08-4). Breslov Res Inst.
Rabbi Nachman of Breslov. The Aleph-Bet Book. Mykoff, Moshe, tr. from Hebrew & intro. by. Tr. of Sefer HaMiddot. 268p. 1986. text ed. 12.00 (ISBN 0-930213-15-7). Breslov Res Inst.
--Likutey Moharan, Vol. 1. Bergman, Simcha & Mykoff, Moshe, trs. from Hebrew. 213p. 1986. pap. text ed. 10.00 (ISBN 0-930213-76-9). Breslov Res Inst.
--TSOHAR. Greenbaum, Avraham, tr. from Hebrew. 64p. (Orig.). 1986. pap. text ed. 1.50 (ISBN 0-930213-26-2). Breslov Res Inst.
Rabbi Nachman. Le Tikoun Haklali. Dimermanas, Alon, tr. from Hebrew. (Fr.). 125p. 1986. pap. text ed. 3.00 (ISBN 0-930213-24-6). Breslov Res Inst.

RABBINICAL LITERATURE–HISTORY AND CRITICISM

Alon, Gedaliah. The Jews in Their Land in the Talmudic Age, Vol. 1. Gershon, Levi, tr. from Hebrew. 324p. 1980. text ed. 32.50x (ISBN 965-223-352-8, Pub. by Magnes Pr Israel). Humanities.
Aptowitzer, Victor. Das Schriftwort in der Rabbinischen Literatur. rev. ed. (Library of Biblical Studies Ser). 1970. 45.00x (ISBN 0-87068-005-6). Ktav.
Attar, Chaim ben Moshe. Light of Life: A Compendium of the Writings of Rabbi Chaim ben Moshe Attar. 160p. 1986. Repr. lib. bdg. 19.95x (ISBN 0-89370-690-6). Borgo Pr.
Dalman, Gustaf. Jesus Christ in the Talmud, Midrash, Zohar, & the Liturgy of the Synagogue. LC 73-2190. (The Jewish People; History, Religion, Literature Ser.). Repr. of 1893 ed. 11.00 (ISBN 0-405-05256-1). Ayer Co Pubs.
Daube, David. The New Testament & Rabbinic Judaism. LC 73-2191. (The Jewish People; History, Religion, Literature Ser.). Repr. of 1956 ed. 38.50 (ISBN 0-405-05257-X). Ayer Co Pubs.
Faur, Jose. Golden Doves with Silver Dots: Semiotics & Textuality in Rabbinic Tradition. LC 84-47967. (Jewish Literature & Culture Ser.). 256p. 1986. 27.50x (ISBN 0-253-32600-1). Ind U Pr.
Goldberg, Hillel. Israel Salanter: Text, Structure, Idea. 1982. 25.00x (ISBN 0-87068-709-3). Ktav.
Green, William S., ed. Persons & Institutions in Early Rabbinic Judaism. LC 79-20712. (Brown University, Brown Judaic Studies: No. 3). 1977. pap. 13.50 (ISBN 0-89130-131-3, 14 00 03). Scholars Pr GA.
Halperin, David. Merkabah in Rabbinic Literature. (American Oriental Ser.: Vol. 62). 1980. 14.00x (ISBN 0-940490-62-5). Am Orient Soc.
Heinemann, Joseph. Prayer in the Talmud: Forms & Patterns. (Studia Judaica: Vol. 9). 1977. 61.00 (ISBN 3-11-004289-4). De Gruyter.
Herford, R. Travers. Christianity in Talmud & Midsrah. Repr. of 1903 ed. 16.95x (ISBN 0-87068-479-5). Ktav.
Kadushin, Max. Rabbinic Mind. 3rd ed. LC 75-189016. 1972. 12.50 (ISBN 0-8197-0007-X). Bloch.
--Worship & Ethics: A Study in Rabbinic Judaism. LC 63-10586. 350p. 1975. pap. 8.95x (ISBN 0-8197-0011-8). Bloch.
--Worship & Ethics: A Study in Rabbinic Judaism. LC 77-18849. 1978. Repr. of 1964 ed. lib. bdg. cancelled (ISBN 0-313-20217-6, KAWE). Greenwood.
Montefiore, Claude G. Judaism & St. Paul. LC 73-2222. (The Jewish People; History, Religion, Literature Ser.). Repr. of 1914 ed. 23.50 (ISBN 0-405-05284-7). Ayer Co Pubs.
Nachman & Nathan. Mayim. Mykoff, Moshe, ed. 64p. (Orig.). 1987. pap. 1.50 (ISBN 0-930213-28-9). Breslov Res Inst.
Nachman of Breslov. Rabbi Nachman's Stories. Kaplan, Aryeh, tr. from Hebrew. LC 83-70201. Tr. of Sippurey Ma'asioth. 552p. 1983. 15.00 (ISBN 0-930213-02-5). Breslov Res Inst.
--Rabbi Nachman's Tikkun: The Comprehensive Remedy. Greenbaum, Avraham, tr. from Hebrew. 240p. 1984. 10.00 (ISBN 0-930213-06-8). Breslov Res Inst.
--Rabbi Nachman's Wisdom. Rosenfeld, Zvi A., ed. Kaplan, Aryeh, tr. from Hebrew. Tr. of Shevachay HaRan-Sichos HaRan. (Illus.). 510p. 1984. 14.00 (ISBN 0-930213-00-9); pap. 11.00 (ISBN 0-930213-01-7). Breslov Res Inst.
--Les Contes. Regnot, Franz, tr. from Yiddish. Tr. of Sippurey Ma'asioth. (Fr.). 180p. (Orig.). 1981. pap. 7.00 (ISBN 0-930213-22-X). Breslov Res Inst.
--The Gems of Rabbi Nachman. Rosenfeld, Tzvi A., ed. Kaplan, Ayreh, tr. from Hebrew. (Illus.). 186p. (Orig.). 1980. pap. 2.00 (ISBN 0-930213-10-6). Breslov Res Inst.
Nachman of Breslov & Nathan of Breslov. Restore My Soul. Greenbaum, Avraham, tr. from Hebrew. Tr. of Meshivat Nefesh. 128p. (Orig.). 1980. pap. 3.00 (ISBN 0-930213-13-0). Breslov Res Inst.
Nathan of Breslov. Advice. Greenbaum, Avraham, tr. from Hebrew. LC 83-70202. Tr. of Likutey Etzot. 522p. 1983. 13.00 (ISBN 0-930213-04-1). Breslov Res Inst.
Neusner, Jacob. Formative Judaism: Religious, Historical, & Literary Studies. (Brown Judaic Studies). (Fifth Series Revisioning the Written Records of a Nascent Religion). 1985. 29.95 (ISBN 0-89130-850-4, 14-00-91); pap. 21.95 (ISBN 0-89130-851-2). Scholars Pr Ga.
--The Integrity of Leviticus Rabbah: The Problem of the Autonomy of a Rabbinic Document. (Brown Judaic Studies). 1985. 25.95 (ISBN 0-89130-852-0, 14-00-93); pap. 21.50 (ISBN 0-89130-853-9). Scholars Pr Ga.
--Israel & Iran in Talmudic Times: A Political History. (Illus.). 266p. (Orig.). 1987. lib. bdg. 27.50 (ISBN 0-8191-5729-5, Pub. by Studies in Judaism); pap. text ed. 14.75 (ISBN 0-8191-5730-9). U Pr of Amer.
--Understanding Rabbinic Judaism: From Talmudic to Modern Times. 1974. pap. 11.95x (ISBN 0-685-56200-X). Ktav.
Oesterley, William O. A Short Survey of the Literature of Rabbinical & Medieval Judaism. LC 72-82352. 328p. 1973. Repr. of 1920 ed. lib. bdg. 24.50 (ISBN 0-8337-3944-1). B Franklin.
Priest, Ames. Governmental & Judicial Ethics in the Bible & Rabbinic Literature. 1980. 20.00x (ISBN 0-87068-697-6). Ktav.
Saldarini, Anthony J. Scholastic Rabbinism: A Literary Study of the Fathers According to Rabbi Nathan. LC 81-13564. (Brown Judaic Studies). 1982. pap. text ed. 12.00 (ISBN 0-89130-523-8, 14-00-14). Scholars Pr GA.

RABBIS

see also Jews–Biography; Pastoral Counseling (Judaism); Tannaim

Axelrad, Albert S. Meditations of a Maverick Rabbi. Whitfield, Stephen, ed. 256p. (Orig.). 1985. pap. 8.95 (ISBN 0-940646-12-9). Rossel Bks.
Berniker, Bernard. Great Rabbis. Gorr, Samuel, ed. (Illus.). 1978. 10.00 (ISBN 0-87306-144-6); portfolio ed. 10.00 (ISBN 0-87306-195-0). Feldheim.
Bernstein, Louis. Challenge & Mission. LC 82-60203. 272p. 1982. 13.95 (ISBN 0-88400-081-8). Shengold.
Blumenthal, David R., ed. And Bring Them Closer to Torah: The Life & Works of Rabbi Aaron H. Blumenthal. 235p. 1986. text ed. 9.95 (ISBN 0-88125-082-1). Ktav.
Bokser, Ben Zion, tr. Abraham Isaac Kook: The Lights of Penitance, Lights of Holiness. the Moral Principles. Essays, Letters & Poems. LC 78-70465. (Classics of Western Spirituality Ser.). 448p. 1978. 13.95 (ISBN 0-8091-0278-1); pap. 10.95 (ISBN 0-8091-2159-X). Paulist Pr.
CCAR Yearbook, 1889-1891, 3 vols. (Illus.). 1951. 10.00 (ISBN 0-916694-30-5). Central Conf.
Cowett, Mark. Birmingham's Rabbi: Morris Newfield & Alabama, 1895-1940. LC 85-20897. 379p. 1986. 22.50 (ISBN 0-8173-0284-0). U of Ala Pr.
Ehrmann, Naftali H. The Rav. Paritzky, Karen, tr. from Ger. Tr. of Der Rav. (Illus.). 1978. 7.95 (ISBN 0-87306-137-3); pap. 5.95. Feldheim.
Eisenstein, Ira & Kohn, Eugene, eds. Mordecai M. Kaplan: An Evaluation. 324p. 1952. 12.00 (ISBN 0-935457-11-9). Reconstructionist Pr.
Elkins, Dov P. God's Warriors: Dramatic Adventures of Rabbis in Uniform. LC 74-226. (Illus.). 92p. 1974. 7.95 (ISBN 0-8246-0168-8). Jonathan David.
Ginzberg, Louis. Students Scholars & Saints. LC 85-9089. (Brown Classics in Judaica Ser.). 312p. 1985. pap. text ed. 12.75 (ISBN 0-8191-4490-8). U Pr of Amer.
Gordon, Harold H. Chaplain on Wings. Zahavy, Zev, ed. LC 81-51749. (Illus.). 192p. 1981. 12.95 (ISBN 0-88400-075-3). Shengold.
Grade, Chaim. Rabbis & Wives. LC 83-5855. 320p. 1983. pap. 5.95 (ISBN 0-394-71647-7, Vin). Random.
Jaffe, Hirshel, et al. Why Me? Why Anyone? 256p. 1986. 15.95 (ISBN 0-312-87803-6, Pub. by Marek). St Martin.
Jung, Leo. The Path of a Pioneer: The Autobiography of Rabbi Leo Jung. 408p. 1980. 9.50 (ISBN 0-900689-51-X). Soncino Pr.
Kaganoff, Nathan M. & Urofsky, Melvin I., eds. Turn to the South: Essays on Southern Jewry. LC 78-9306. 205p. 1979. 10.95x (ISBN 0-8139-0742-X). U Pr of Va.
Katchen, Aaron L. Christian Hebraists & Dutch Rabbis: Seventeenth Century Apologetics & the Study of Maimonides' Mishneh Torah. (Harvard Judaic Texts & Studies: No. 3). 430p. 1985. text ed. 28.00x (ISBN 0-674-12865-6). Harvard U Ctr Jewish.
Klein, Nancy I. Heritage of Faith: Two Pioneers of Judaism in America. 16.95 (ISBN 0-88125-119-4). Ktav.
Landman, Leo. Rabbi Joseph H. Lookstein Memorial Volume. 1979. 35.00x (ISBN 0-87068-705-0). Ktav.
Marcus, Jacob R. & Peck, Abraham J. The American Rabbinate: A Century of Continuity & Change 1883-1983. 300p. 1985. text ed. 20.00x (ISBN 0-88125-076-7). Ktav.
Mechoulan, Henry & Nahon, Gerard, eds. Menasseh ben Israel: The Hope of Israel. (Litman Library of Jewish Civilzation). (Illus.). 224p. 37.00 (ISBN 0-19-710054-6). Oxford U Pr.
Mowshowitz, Israel. A Rabbi's Rovings. 385p. 1985. 20.00 (ISBN 0-88125-069-4). Ktav.
Neusner, Jacob. The Pharisees: Rabbinic Perspectives. LC 85-5783. (Studies in Ancient Judaism). 300p. (Orig.). 1985. pap. text ed. 19.95x (ISBN 0-88125-067-8). Ktav.
--Understanding Rabbinic Judaism: From Talmudic to Modern Times. 1974. pap. 11.95x (ISBN 0-685-56200-X). Ktav.
Porton, Gary G. Understanding Rabbinic Midrash. 1985. 14.95 (ISBN 0-88125-056-2). Ktav.
Rabbi Nachman of Breslov & Rabbi Nathan of Breslov. Rabbi Nachman De Breslov. Dimermanas, Alon, ed. (Illus.). 442p. 1986. text ed. 18.00 (ISBN 0-930213-19-X); pap. 15.00 (ISBN 0-930213-20-3). Breslov Res Inst.
Rabbi Mindy Avra Portnoy. Ima on the Bima: My Mommy is a Rabbi. LC 86-3023. (Illus.). 32p. 1986. 10.95 (ISBN 0-930494-54-7); pap. 4.95 (ISBN 0-930494-55-5). Kar Ben.
Rabbi's Manual. rev. ed. 1961. 7.50 (ISBN 0-916694-26-7). Central Conf.
Raz, Simcha. A Tzaddik in Our Time: Life & Times of Rav Aryeh Levin of Jerusalem, Celebrated Tzaddik of Jerusalem. Wengrov, Charles, tr. from Hebrew. Tr. of Ish Tzaddik Hayah. (Illus.). 1978. pap. 10.95 (ISBN 0-87306-986-2). Feldheim.
Rosenberg, Stuart E. The Real Jewish World: A Rabbi's Second Thoughts. LC 83-17455. 434p. 1984. 19.95 (ISBN 0-8022-2439-3). Philos Lib.
Rossini, Lillian M. Rabbi Letters, No. 1. (Illus.). 32p. 1986. 5.95 (ISBN 0-89962-506-1). Todd & Honeywell.
Saperstein, Marc. Decoding the Rabbis: A Thirteenth-Century Commentary on the Aggadah. LC 80-13166. (Judaic Monographs: No. 3). 298p. 1980. text ed. 20.00x (ISBN 0-674-19445-4). Harvard U Pr.
Schochet, Elijah Judah. Bach: Rabbi Joel Sirkes, His Life, Works & Times. 13.95 (ISBN 0-87306-031-8). Feldheim.
Septimus, Bernard. Hispano-Jewish Culture in Transition: The Career & Controversies of Ramah. LC 81-13275. (Harvard Judaic Monographs: No. 4). 192p. 1982. text ed. 20.00x (ISBN 0-674-39230-2). Harvard U Pr.
Sherwin, Byron L. Mystical Theology & Social Dissent: The Life & Works of Judah Loew of Prague. (Littman Library of Jewish Civilization). 256p. 1982. 24.95x (ISBN 0-19-710051-1). Oxford U Pr.
Stein, Joshua B. Claude G. Montefiore on the Ancient Rabbis: The Second Generation on Reform Judaism in Britain. LC 77-13194. (Brown University. Brown Judaic Studies: No. 4). 85p. 1977. pap. 9.00 (ISBN 0-89130-190-9, 140004). Scholars Pr GA.
Stevens, Elliot L., ed. CCAR Yearbook. Incl. Vol. 86. 1976. 1977. 15.00 (ISBN 0-916694-36-4); Vol. 88. 1978. Weber, Donald R., ed. 1979. 15.00 (ISBN 0-916694-58-5); Vol. 89. 1979. 1980. 15.00. Central Conf.
--Rabbinic Authority. 184p. 1982. 15.00 (ISBN 0-317-01466-8). Central Conf.
Stevens, Elliot L. & Weber, Donald A., eds. CCAR Yearbook: 1978, Vol. 88. 1979. 15.00 (ISBN 0-916694-58-5). Central Conf.
The Story of the Chofetz Chaim. (Illus.). 160p. 9.85 (ISBN 0-317-53891-8); pap. 7.15. Torah Umesorah.
Wanefsky, Joseph. Rabbi Isaac Jacob Reines: His Life & Thought. LC 79-118314. 181p. 1970. 6.95 (ISBN 0-8022-2349-4). Philos Lib.
Zeitlin, Joseph. Disciples of the Wise. LC 71-121517. (Essay Index Reprint Ser). 1945. 19.00 (ISBN 0-8369-1859-2). Ayer Co Pubs.

RABELAIS, FRANCOIS, ca. 1490-1553?

Febvre, Lucien. The Problem of Unbelief in the Sixteenth Century: The Religion of Rabelais. Gottlieb, Beatrice, tr. from Fr. (Illus.). 528p. 1982. text ed. 40.00x (ISBN 0-674-70825-3). Harvard U Pr.
--The Problem of Unbelief in the Sixteenth Century: The Religion of Rabelais. Gottlieb, Beatrice, tr. 552p. 1985. pap. 9.95x (ISBN 0-674-70826-1). Harvard U Pr.
Weinberg, Florence M. The Wine & the Will: Rabelais's Bacchic Christianity. LC 78-181450. Repr. of 1972 ed. 47.30 (2027593). Bks Demand UMI.

RABINOWITZ, SHALOM, 1859-1916

Aarons, Victoria. Author As Character in the Works of Sholom Aleichem. LC 84-22703. (Studies in Art & Religious Interpretation: Vol. 3). 192p. 1985. 39.95x (ISBN 0-88946-553-3). E Mellen.
Miron, Dan. Sholem Aleykhem: Person, Persona, Presence. LC 73-161969. (Uriel Weinreich Memorial Lecture Ser.: No.1). 45p. 1972. pap. 2.00 (ISBN 0-914512-02-1). Yivo Inst.
Samuel, Maurice. The World of Sholom Aleichem. LC 86-47697. 344p. 1986. pap. 9.95 (ISBN 0-689-70709-6, 343). Atheneum.

RACE

Samuels, Maurice. You Gentiles. pap. 3.00x (ISBN 0-911038-08-6). Noontide.

RACE PROBLEMS

see Race Relations

RACE RELATIONS
see also Church and Race Relations; Minorities
Bettelheim, Bruno & Janowitz, Morris B. Social Change & Prejudice. LC 64-11214. 1964. 18.95 (ISBN 0-02-903480-9). Free Pr.
Brown, Hubert L. Black & Mennonite. LC 76-44043. 112p. 1976. pap. 3.95 (ISBN 0-8361-1801-4). Herald Pr.
Kousser, J. Morgan & McPherson, James M. Region, Race & Reconstruction: Essays in Honor of C. Vann Woodward. 1982. 25.00x (ISBN 0-19-503075-3). Oxford U Pr.
Lincoln, Eric. Race, Religion, & the Continuing American Dilemma. (American Century Ser.). 304p. 1985. 17.95 (ISBN 0-8090-8016-8). FS&G.
MacDonald, Allan J. Trade, Politics & Christianity in Africa & the East. LC 77-89007. Repr. of 1916 ed. lib. bdg. cancelled (ISBN 0-8371-1755-0, MAT&, Pub. by Negro U Pr). Greenwood.
Race, Nation, Person: Total Aspects of the Race Problem. facs. ed. LC 70-128291. (Essay Index Reprint Ser). 1944. 25.50 (ISBN 0-8369-2019-8). Ayer Co Pubs.
Rudwick, Elliot. Race Riot at East St. Louis, July 2, 1917. LC 64-13634. (Studies in American Negro Life). 1972. pap. text ed. 3.95x (ISBN 0-689-70336-8, NL31). Atheneum.
Taylor, Richard. Friends & the Racial Crisis. LC 70-129552. (Orig.). pap. 2.50x (ISBN 0-87574-172-X). Pendle Hill.

RACE RELATIONS AND THE CHURCH
see Church and Race Relations

RADHAKRISHNAN, SARVEPALI, SIR, 1888-
Harris, Ishwar C. Radhakrishna: Profile of a Universalist. 1982. 17.50x (ISBN 0-8364-0778-4). South Asia Bks.
Minor, Robert N. Radhakrishnan: A Religious Biography. 178p. 1987. text ed. 34.50x (ISBN 0-88706-554-6); pap. 10.95x (ISBN 0-88706-555-4). State U NY Pr.

RADIO IN RELIGION
Davis, Lenwood & Hill, George H. Religious Broadcasting, Nineteen Twenty to Nineteen Eighty-Three: A Selectively Annotated Bibliography. (Reference Library of Social Science). 1984. lib. bdg. 40.00 (ISBN 0-8240-9015-2). Garland Pub.
Durfey, Thomas C. & Ferrier, James A. Religious Broadcast Management Handbook. 1986. pap. 14.95 (ISBN 0-310-39741-3). Zondervan.

RAHNER, KARL, 1904-
Carr, Anne. The Theological Method of Karl Rahner. LC 76-51639. (American Academy of Religion, Dissertation Ser.: No. 19). pap. 72.30 (ISBN 0-317-08410-0, 2017556). Bks Demand UMI.
King, J. Norman. The God of Forgiveness & Healing in the Theology of Karl Rahner. LC 81-40932. 100p. (Orig.). 1982. lib. bdg. 24.00 (ISBN 0-8191-2237-8); pap. text ed. 8.25 (ISBN 0-8191-2238-6). U Pr of Amer.
Kress, Robert. A Rahner Handbook. LC 81-85333. 118p. 1982. pap. 10.95 (ISBN 0-8042-0652-X). John Knox.
Rahner, Karl & Metz, Johann B. The Courage to Pray. 112p. (Orig.). 1980. pap. 3.95 (ISBN 0-8245-2024-6). Crossroad NY.
Rolwing, Richard J. A Philosophy of Revelation: According to Karl Rahner. LC 78-63067. 1978. pap. text ed. 8.50 (ISBN 0-8191-0609-7). U Pr of Amer.
Vass, George. Understanding Karl Rahner, 2 vols. (Orig.). 1985. Vol. 1, 153 pgs. pap. 12.50 (ISBN 0-87061-115-1); Vol. 2, 200 pgs. pap. 12.50 (ISBN 0-87061-116-X); Set. pap. 25.00 (ISBN 0-317-20726-1). Chr Classics.
Vorgrimler, Herbert. Understanding Karl Rahner: An Introduction to His Life & Thought. 176p. 1986. 14.95 (ISBN 0-8245-0790-8). Crossroad NY.
Weger, Karl-Heinz. Karl Rahner: An Introduction to His Theology. 1980. 10.95 (ISBN 0-8245-0324-4). Crossroad NY.

RAJASUYA
Heesterman, J. C. Ancient Indian Royal Consecration: The Rajasuya Described According to the Yajus Texts & Annotated. (Disputationes Rheno-Trajectinae Ser: No. 2). (Orig.). 1957. pap. text ed. 25.60x (ISBN 90-2790-028-0). Mouton.

RALL, HARRIS FRANKLIN, 1870-1964
McCutcheon, W. J. Essays in American Theology: The Life & Thought of Harris Franklin Rall. LC 72-190198. 350p. 1972. 15.00 (ISBN 0-8022-2085-1). Philos Lib.

RAMAKRISHNA, 1836-1886
Advaita Ashrama Staff, compiled by. Life of Sri Ramakrishna. 12.00 (ISBN 0-87481-077-9). Vedanta Pr.
Advaita Ashrama Staff, ed. Ramakrishna: A Biography in Pictures. (Illus.). 1976. 30.00x (ISBN 0-87481-167-8). Vedanta Pr.
Akhilananda, Swami. Modern Problems & Religion. pap. 9.00 (ISBN 0-8283-1146-3). Branden Pub Co.
Chakravarti, Sri S., ed. Hidden Treasure of the Gospel of Sri Ramakrishna. 1975. Repr. of 1907 ed. 6.25 (ISBN 0-685-58386-4). Ranney Pubns.
LeMaitre, Solange. Ramakrishna & the Vitality of Hinduism. Markmann, Charles L., tr. from Fr. LC 68-54059. (The Overlook Spiritual Masters Ser.). (Illus.). 244p. 1986. pap. 9.95 (ISBN 0-87951-241-5). Overlook Pr.
M, pseud. The Condensed Gospel of Sri Ramakrishna. 1979. pap. 4.95 (ISBN 0-87481-489-8). Vedanta Pr.
Mookerjee, Nanda, ed. Sri Ramakrishna in the Eyes of Brahma & Christian Admirers. LC 76-904430. 1976. 6.50x (ISBN 0-88386-791-5). South Asia Bks.
Mueller, Friedrich M. Ramakrishna, His Life & Sayings. LC 73-18812. Repr. of 1899 ed. 22.00 (ISBN 0-404-11452-0). AMS Pr.
Mukherji, Dhan G. The Face of Silence: A Biography of Rama Krishna. LC 85-22355. 264p. 1985. Repr. lib. bdg. 19.95x (ISBN 0-89370-584-5). Borgo Pr.
Ramakrishna, Swami. Tales from Ramakrishna. (Illus.). 54p. (Orig.). 1975. pap. 2.75 (ISBN 0-87481-152-X). Vedanta Pr.
Ramakrishnananda, Swami. Krishna: Pastoral & Kingmaker. pap. 2.25 (ISBN 0-87481-447-2). Vedanta Pr.
Ramakrishna's Disciples. Message of Our Master. pap. 1.95 (ISBN 0-87481-102-3). Vedanta Pr.
Ranganathananda, Swami. Ramakrishna Math & Mission: Its Ideals & Activities. (Illus.). pap. 1.00 (ISBN 0-87481-448-0). Vedanta Pr.
Rolland, Romain. Life of Ramakrishna. 5.95 (ISBN 0-87481-080-9). Vedanta Pr.
Satprakashananda, Swami. Sri Ramakrishna's Life & Message in the Present Age: With the Author's Reminiscences of Holy Mother & Some Direct Disciples. LC 75-46386. 208p. 1976. 6.00 (ISBN 0-916356-54-X). Vedanta Soc St Louis.
Shivananda, Swami. For Seekers of God: Spiritual Talks of Mahapurush Swami Shivananda. Vividishananda, Swami & Gambhirananda, Swami, trs. from Bengali. 186p. 1972. 10.00 (ISBN 0-87481-169-4); pap. 7.50 (ISBN 0-87481-130-9). Vedanta Pr.
Smarananda, Swami. The Story of Ramakrishna. (Illus., Orig.). 1976. pap. 2.25 (ISBN 0-87481-168-6). Vedanta Pr.
Swami Vivekananda. Ramakrishna & His Message. (Orig.). 1971. pap. 2.00 (ISBN 0-87481-126-0). Vedanta Pr.
--Ramakrishna As Swamiji Saw Him. (Orig.). 1970. pap. 1.00 (ISBN 0-87481-452-9). Vedanta Pr.
Tejasananda, Swami. Ramakrishna Movement: Its Ideal & Activities. (Illus.). pap. 3.95 (ISBN 0-87481-117-1). Vedanta Pr.
Whitmarsh, Katherine. A Concordance to the Gospel of Sri Ramakrishna. LC 85-50340. 640p. (Orig.). 1985. pap. text ed. 59.95x (ISBN 0-87481-042-6). Vedanta Pr.
Yogeshananda, Swami, compiled by. The Visions of Sri Ramakrishna. 150p. 1974. 2.75 (ISBN 0-87481-455-3). Vedanta Pr.

RAMAKRISHNANDA, SWAMI
Apurvananda, compiled by. Swami Vijananda: A Short Life. 173p. 1987. pap. 4.50 (ISBN 0-87481-547-9, Pub. by Ramakrishna Math Madras India). Vedanta Pr.
French, Harold W. The Swan's Wide Waters: Ramakrishna & Western Culture. new ed. LC 74-77657. (National University Publications Ser.). 214p. 1974. 23.50x (ISBN 0-8046-9055-3, Pub by Kennikat). Assoc Faculty Pr.
Niramayananda. Call of the Spirit: Conversion with Swami Akhandananda. 170p. 1987. pap. text ed. 3.50 (ISBN 0-87481-538-X, Pub. by Ramakrishna Math Madras India). Vedanta Pr.
Shankara. Sivananda Lahari of Sri Sankara. Tapasyananda, tr. from Sanskrit. 87p. 1987. pap. 2.25 (ISBN 0-87481-545-2, Pub. by Ramakrishna Math Madras India). Vedanta Pr.
Tapasyananda, Swami. Swami Ramakrishnananda: The Apostle of Sri Ramakrishna to the South. 276p. 1973. 2.50 (ISBN 0-87481-453-7). Vedanta Pr.

RAMANUJA
Lipner, Julius J. The Face of Truth: A Study of Meaning & Metaphysics in the Vedantic Theology of Ramanuja. 224p. 1986. 44.50x (ISBN 0-88706-038-2); pap. 18.95x (ISBN 0-88706-039-0). State U NY Pr.
Swami Vireshwarananda. Brahma Sutra Sri Bhasya. 1979. 10.00 (ISBN 0-87481-189-9). Vedanta Pr.

RAMAYANA
Antoine, Robert. Rama & the Bards: Epic Memory in the Ramayana. (Greybird Book). 114p. 1975. 12.00 (ISBN 0-88253-821-7); pap. 6.75 (ISBN 0-88253-822-5). Ind-US Inc.
Choudhary, Bani R. The Story of Ramayan. (Illus.). 1979. 7.50 (ISBN 0-89744-133-8). Auromere.
Dutt, Romesh C., tr. The Ramayana. Bd. with The Mahabharata. 1972. 12.95x (ISBN 0-460-00403-4, Evman). Biblio Dist.
Hopkins, E. Washburn. Epic Mythology. rev. ed. LC 76-75358. 1968. Repr. of 1915 ed. 18.00 (ISBN 0-8196-0228-0). Biblo.
Iyengar, K. Srinivasa. The Epic Beautiful: An English Verse Rendering of the Sundara Kanda of the Ramayana of Valmiki. 1986. 12.50x (ISBN 0-8364-1545-0, Pub. by National Sahitya Akademi). South Asia Bks.
Iyengar, K. Srinivasa, ed. Asian Variations in Ramayana. 1986. 14.00x (ISBN 0-8364-1571-X, Pub. by National Sahitya Akademi). South Asia Bks.
Mehta, Hansa. Prince of Ayodhya. (Nehru Library for Children). (Illus.). 1979. pap. 2.00 (ISBN 0-89744-178-8). Auromere.
Monier-Williams, M. Indian Epic Poetry: An Analysis of Ramayana. lib. bdg. 79.95 (ISBN 0-87968-547-6). Krishna Pr.
Raghavan, V., ed. The Ramayana Tradition in Asia. 1982. 18.00x (ISBN 0-8364-0899-3, Pub. by National Sahitya Akademi). South Asia Bks.
Rajagopalachari, C. Ramayana. 1979. pap. 5.95 (ISBN 0-89744-930-4). Auromere.
Sankalia, H. D. The Ramayana in Historical Perspective. 1983. 18.50x (ISBN 0-8364-0997-3, Pub. by Macmillan India). South Asia Bks.
Sitaramiah, V. Valmiki Ramayanan. 1982. Repr. 7.00x (ISBN 0-317-47015-9, Pub. by National Sahitya Akademi). South Asia Bks.
Smith, H. Daniel. Reading the Ramayana: A Bibliographic Guide for Students & College Teachers. Indian Variants on the Rama Theme in English Translations. (Foreign & Comparative Studies Program, South Asian Special Publications: No. 4). (Orig.). 1983. pap. text ed. 6.50x (ISBN 0-915984-87-3). Syracuse U Foreign Comp.
Valmiki. Ramayana. 3rd ed. Rajagopalachari, Chakravarti, ed. & tr. from Tamil. 320p. (Orig.). 1980. pap. 4.25 (ISBN 0-934676-17-8). Greenlf Bks.
Whaling, Frank. The Rise of the Religious Significance of Rama. 392p. 1980. text ed. 10.00 (ISBN 0-8426-1758-2). Verry.
Wurm, Alois. Character-Portrayals in the Ramayana of Valmiki. 1977. 30.00x (ISBN 0-686-22658-5). Intl Bk Dist.

RAMESES 2ND, KING OF EGYPT
Schmidt, John D. Ramesses II: A Chronological Structure of His Reign. LC 72-6558. (Near Eastern Studies). Repr. of 1973 ed. 56.00 (ISBN 0-8357-9282-X, 2011503). Bks Demand UMI.

RAMESES 6TH, KING OF EGYPT
Piankoff, A. & Rambova, N., eds. The Tomb of Ramesses VI, 2 vols. LC 54-5646. (Bollingen Ser.: No. 40). Vol. 1- Texts. pap. 145.80 (ISBN 0-317-28638-2, 2051348); Vol. 2- Plates. pap. 53.00 (ISBN 0-317-28639-0). Bks Demand UMI.

RAPHAEL (RAFFAELO SANZIO D'URBINO), 1483-1520
Davidson, Bernice F. Raphael's Bible: A Study of the Vatican Logge. LC 84-43088. (College Art Association Monographs: Vol. 39). (Illus.). 198p. 1985. 30.00 (ISBN 0-271-00388-X). Pa St U Pr.

RAPTURE (CHRISTIAN ESCHATOLOGY)
Biederwolf, William E. The Second Coming Bible Commentary. (Paperback Reference Library). 728p. 1985. pap. 17.95 (ISBN 0-8010-0887-5). Baker Bk.
Efird, James M. End-Times: Rapture, Antichrist, Mellennium. 96p. (Orig.). 1986. pap. 5.95 (ISBN 0-687-11787-9). Abingdon.
Kimball, William R. Rapture: A Question of Timing. 200p. (Orig.). pap. 5.95 (ISBN 0-89900-205-6). College Pr Pub.
--The Rapture: A Question of Timing. 1985. pap. 6.95 (ISBN 0-8010-5468-0). Baker Bk.
Lindsey, Hal. The Rapture: Truth or Consequences. 224p. (Orig.). 1985. pap. 3.95 (ISBN 0-553-26692-6). Bantam.
Yogananda, Paramhansa. Second Coming of Christ, Vol. II. LC 79-50352. 1984. pap. 12.95 (ISBN 0-937134-05-8). Amrita Found.

RAS SHAMRA
Montgomery, James A. & Harris, Zellig S. The Ras Shamra Mythological Texts. LC 36-2726. (American Philosophical Society. Philadelphia. Memoirs: Vol. 4). pap. 34.80 (ISBN 0-317-09878-0, 2000354). Bks Demand UMI.

RAS TAFARI MOVEMENT
Campbell, Horace. Rasta & Resistance: From Marcus Garvey to Walter Rodney. LC 85-73332. 240p. (Orig.). 1987. 32.95 (ISBN 0-86543-034-9); pap. 10.95 (ISBN 0-86543-035-7). Africa World.
Cashmore, Ernest. Rastaman: The Rastafarian Movement in England. (Counterpoint Ser.). 263p. 1983. pap. 9.95 (ISBN 0-04-301164-0). Allen Unwin.
Clarke, Peter B. Black Paradise: The Rastafarian Movement. 112p. 1986. pap. 11.95 (ISBN 0-85030-428-8). Newcastle Pub.
--Black Paradise: The Rastafarian Movement. 176p. 1986. lib. bdg. 19.95x (ISBN 0-8095-7021-1). Borgo Pr.
Myers, Trevor C. The Essence of Rastafari Nationalism & Black Economic Development. 1986. 10.00 (ISBN 0-533-06629-8). Vantage.
Williams, Kathy. The Rastafarians. 1985. 13.00x (ISBN 0-7062-4063-4, Pub. by Ward Lock Educ Co Ltd). State Mutual Bk.

RASKOLNIKS
Crummey, Robert O. Old Believers & the World of Antichrist: The Vyg Community & the Russian State, 1694-1855. LC 79-98121. (Illus.). 278p. 1970. 30.00x (ISBN 0-299-05560-4). U of Wis Pr.
Pascal, Pierre. Avvakum et les Debuts Du Raskol. (Etudes Sur L'histoire, L'economie et la Sociologie Des Pays Slaves Ser.: No. 8). 1969. pap. 35.60x (ISBN 90-2796-293-6). Mouton.

RASPUTIN, GRIGORII EFIMOVICH, 1871-1916
Fulop-Miller, Rene. Rasputin the Holy Devil. 1977. Repr. of 1928 ed. lib. bdg. 30.00 (ISBN 0-8414-4308-4). Folcroft.
Rasputin, Maria. My Father. 1970. 5.00 (ISBN 0-8216-0120-2). Univ Bks.

RASTAFARI MOVEMENT
see Ras Tafari Movement

RATIONALISM
see also Agnosticism; Atheism; Belief and Doubt; Deism; Empiricism; Enlightenment; Faith and Reason; Free Thought; Positivism; Reason; Skepticism; Theism
Feyerabend, Paul. Against Method. (Illus.). 1978. pap. 7.95 (ISBN 0-8052-7008-6, Pub by NLB). Schocken.
Hart, Hendrik & Van Der Hoeven, Johan, eds. Rationality in the Calvinian Tradition. LC 83-19672. (Christian Studies Today). 420p. (Orig.). 1984. lib. bdg. 32.25 (ISBN 0-8191-3616-6); pap. text ed. 16.75 (ISBN 0-8191-3617-4). U Pr of Amer.
McGiffert, A. C. Protestant Thought Before Kant. 11.25 (ISBN 0-8446-0204-3). Peter Smith.
Mansel, Henry L. Limits of Religious Thought Examined. LC 72-172840. Repr. of 1859 ed. 25.00 (ISBN 0-404-04182-5). AMS Pr.
Maultsby, Maxie C., Jr. Help Yourself to Happiness. LC 75-15057. 1975. pap. 9.95 (ISBN 0-917476-06-9). Inst Rational-Emotive.
Schluchter, Wolfgang. The Rise of Western Rationalism: Max Weber's Developmental History. Roth, Guenther, tr. from Ger. LC 81-2763. 300p. 1981. 24.50x (ISBN 0-520-04060-0); pap. 9.95 (ISBN 0-520-05464-4, CAL 747). U of Cal Pr.
Seckel, Al, ed. Bertrand Russell on God & Religion. 345p. pap. 12.95 (ISBN 0-87975-323-4). Prometheus Bks.
Sheriff, John K. The Good-Natured Man: The Evolution of a Moral Ideal, 1660-1800. LC 81-14758. 144p. 1982. text ed. 13.50 (ISBN 0-8173-0097-X). U of Ala Pr.
Stambaugh, Joan. The Real Is Not the Rational. (Buddhist Studies). 142p. (Orig.). 1986. 34.50 (ISBN 0-88706-166-4); pap. 10.95 (ISBN 0-88706-167-2). State U NY Pr.
Stein, Gordon, ed. An Anthology of Atheism & Rationalism. LC 80-81326. (The Skeptic's Bookshelf Ser.). 354p. 1984. pap. 15.95 (ISBN 0-87975-267-X). Prometheus Bks.
Suchla, Peter. Kritischer Rationalismus In Theologischer Pruefung. (European University Studies Series No. 23: Vol. 187). (Ger.). 443p. 1982. 41.60 (ISBN 3-8204-5828-X). P Lang Pubs.
Tindal, Matthew. Christianity As Old Creation of the Gospel. Wellek, Rene, ed. LC 75-11256. (British Philosophers & Theologians of the 17th & 18th Centuries Ser.). 1976. lib. bdg. 51.00 (ISBN 0-8240-1806-0). Garland Pub.
Toland, John. Christianity Not Mysterious. Wellek, Rene, ed. LC 75-11257. (The Philosophy of John Locke Ser.). 1978. lib. bdg. 46.00 (ISBN 0-8240-1807-9). Garland Pub.
Villafranca, Anthony L. The Theory of Sin & the Equilibrium Between the Emotional & the Rational in Man. (Illus.). 104p. 1986. 88.50 (ISBN 0-89266-568-8). Am Classical Coll Pr.
Wilson, Robert J., III. The Benevolent Deity: Ebenezer Gay & the Rise of Rational Religion in New England, 1669-1787. LC 83-3657. (Illus.). 320p. 1984. 26.00x (ISBN 0-8122-7891-7). U of Pa Pr.

READERS–BIBLE
Armstrong, Terry A., et al. Reader's Hebrew-English Lexicon of the Old Testament: Isaiah-Malachi, Vol. 3. 208p. 1985. 14.95 (ISBN 0-310-37010-8, 6293). Zondervan.
Baltz, Frederick. Bible Readings for Farm Living. LC 85-7421. 112p. (Orig.). 1985. pap. 3.95 (ISBN 0-8066-2164-8, 10-0688). Augsburg.
Brown, David, ed. Bible Wisdom for Modern Living: Arranged by Subject. 400p. 1986. 17.95 (ISBN 0-671-62545-4). S&S.
Daily Light on the Daily Path (NIV) 384p. 1981. 9.95 (ISBN 0-310-23110-8, 18027); pap. 5.95 (ISBN 0-310-23111-6). Zondervan.
An Inclusive-Language Lectionary: Readings for Year B. LC 84-7420. 256p. 1984. pap. 9.95 (ISBN 0-664-24564-1). Westminster.

Klug, Lyn. Bible Readings for Women. LC 85-7508. 112p. 1985. pap. 3.95 (ISBN 0-8066-2163-X, 10-0687). Augsburg.
Larson, Robert L. Bible Stories Reader. 1985. 8.95 (ISBN 0-533-06749-9). Vantage.
Lecourt, Nancy. Rainbow. (Books I Can Read). 32p. 1980. pap. 1.95 (ISBN 0-8127-0290-5). Review & Herald.
Miller, Graham. Treasury of His Promises. 386p. (Orig.). 1986. pap. 12.95 (ISBN 0-85151-472-3). Banner of Truth.
Miller, Ted, ed. The Story. 400p. 1986. 4.95 (ISBN 0-8423-6677-6). Tyndale.
Mills, W. Douglas. A Daily Lectionary: Scripture Readings for Every Day Based on the New Common Lectionary. 144p. (Orig.). 1986. pap. 6.95 (ISBN 0-8358-0517-4). Upper Room.
Morse, Joyce. Peter Sinks in the Water. (Books I Can Read). 32p. (Orig.). 1980. pap. 1.95 (ISBN 0-8127-0281-6). Review & Herald.
--Where Is Jesus? (Books I Can Read). 32p. 1980. pap. 1.95 (ISBN 0-8127-0280-8). Review & Herald.
National Council of Churches of Christ. An Inclusive Language Lectionary: Readings for Year B. 192p. (Orig.). 1984. pap. 8.95 (ISBN 0-8298-0719-5). Pilgrim NY.
Northrup, Melvin. Toby's Gift. (Books I Can Read). 32p. (Orig.). 1980. pap. 1.95 (ISBN 0-8127-0291-3). Review & Herald.
Plueddemann, Carol, ed. Great Passages of the Bible. (Fisherman Bible Studyguide Ser.). 64p. (Orig.). 1987. pap. 2.95 (ISBN 0-87788-332-7). Shaw Pubs.
Spatz, Jacob W. The Speaker's Bible. 2nd ed. 288p. 1986. pap. 10.00 (ISBN 0-938033-00-X). Alert Pubs.
Speck, S. L. & Riggle, H. M., eds. Bible Readings for Bible Students & for the Home & Fireside. 432p. 1902. 5.00 (ISBN 0-686-29102-6). Faith Pub Hse.
Taylor, Kenneth. The One-Year Bible. 1985. cloth 16.95 (ISBN 0-8423-2431-3); kivar 10.95 (ISBN 0-8423-2428-3). Tyndale.
Walvoord, John F. & Zuck, Roy B. The Bib Sac Reader. (Orig.). 1983. pap. 8.95 (ISBN 0-8024-0459-6). Moody.

REAL PRESENCE
see Transubstantiation

REALITY
see also Monism; Substance (Philosophy)
Beckett, L. C. Movement & Emptiness. 1969. pap. 1.45 (ISBN 0-8356-0414-4, Quest). Theos Pub Hse.
Bist, Umrao S. Jaina Theories of Reality & Knowledge. 1985. 6.50x (ISBN 0-8364-1362-8, Pub. by Eastern). South Asia Bks.
Butchvarov, Panayot. Being Qua Being: A Theory of Identity, Existence & Predication. LC 78-13812. 288p. 1979. 22.50x (ISBN 0-253-13700-4). Ind U Pr.
Charon, Jean E., ed. Spirit & Science: Reality & Imagination. (Illus.). 440p. 1987. 24.95 (ISBN 0-89226-027-0, Pub. by ICUS). Paragon Hse.
Culliton, Joseph T. A Processive World View for Pragmatic Christians. LC 75-3781. 302p. 1975. 13.95 (ISBN 0-8022-2170-X). Philos Lib.
Davis, Roy E. This Is Reality. 160p. 1983. pap. 3.95 (ISBN 0-317-20863-2). CSA Pr.
Dewey, Barbara. The Creating Cosmos. LC 85-70369. 128p. 1985. 16.95 (ISBN 0-933123-00-0). Bartholomew Bks.
Marcel, Gabriel. Mystery of Being, Vol. II: Faith & Reality. 198p. 1984. pap. text ed. 7.75 (ISBN 0-8191-3311-6). U Pr of Amer.
Navickas. Consciousness & Reality. 1976. pap. 37.00 (ISBN 90-247-1775-2, Pub. by Martinus Nijhoff Netherlands). Kluwer Academic.
Oman, John W. The Natural & the Supernatural. LC 79-39696. (Select Bibliographies Reprint Ser.). 1972. Repr. of 1931 ed. 20.75 (ISBN 0-8369-9941-X). Ayer Co Pubs.
Padmarajiah, Y. J. A Comparative Study of the Jaina Theories of Reality & Knowledge. 460p. 1986. 22.00 (ISBN 81-208-0036-2, Pub. by Motilal Banarsidass India). South Asia Bks.
Torrance, T. F. Reality & Evangelical Theology. LC 81-19811. 174p. 1982. pap. 8.95 (ISBN 0-664-24401-7). Westminster.
Woodman, Hugh M. The Ultimate Reality. LC 84-90244. 145p. 1985. 10.95 (ISBN 0-533-06292-6). Vantage.

REASON
see also Faith and Reason; Wisdom
Brunner, Emil. Revelation & Reason. 448p. 1984. pap. 14.95 (ISBN 0-913029-01-7). Stevens Bk Pr.
Casserley, J. V. Langmead. No Faith of My Own & Graceful Reason: The Contribution of Reason to Theology. 408p. 1984. pap. text ed. 16.75 (ISBN 0-8191-3793-6). U Pr of Amer.
Clark, Stephen R. From Athens to Jerusalem: The Love of Wisdom & the Love God. 1984. 29.95x (ISBN 0-19-824698-6); pap. 11.95x (ISBN 0-19-824697-8). Oxford U Pr.
Geoghegan, Vincent. Reason & Eros: The Social Theory of Herbert Marcuse. 122p. 1981. pap. 6.75 (ISBN 0-86104-335-9, Pub. by Pluto Pr). Longwood Pub Group.
Horkheimer, Max. Eclipse of Reason. LC 73-17887. 1973. pap. 12.95x (ISBN 0-8264-0009-4, Continuum). Continuum.
Kant, Immanuel. Critique of Pure Reason. 480p. 1986. Repr. of 1900 ed. lib. bdg. 75.00 (ISBN 0-8495-3103-9). Arden Lib.
Kenny, Anthony. Faith & Reason. LC 82-22187. (Bampton Lectures in America Ser.). 100p. 1983. 21.50 (ISBN 0-231-05488-2). Columbia U Pr.
Moreno, Francisco Jose. Between Faith & Reason: An Approach to Individual & Social Psychology. LC 76-56926. 1977. 20.00x (ISBN 0-8147-5416-3). NYU Pr.
Walker, Ralph C., ed. Kant on Pure Reason. (Illus.). 1982. pap. text ed. 7.95x (ISBN 0-19-875056-0). Oxford U Pr.
Wolterstorff, Nicholas. Reason Within the Bounds of Religion. 2nd ed. 168p. 1984. pap. 4.95 (ISBN 0-8028-1604-5). Eerdmans.

REASON AND FAITH
see Faith and Reason

REBIRTH
see Reincarnation

RECITATIONS
see also Schools–Exercises and Recreations
also subdivisions Exercise, Recitations, etc. under subjects, e.g. Schools–exercises, Recitations, etc.; Sunday-Schools–Exercises, Recitations, etc.
Kellogg, Alice M. Christmas Entertainments. facs. ed. LC 72-139764. (Granger Index Reprint Ser). 1897. 15.00 (ISBN 0-8369-6218-4). Ayer Co Pubs.
McNaught, Rosemond L., compiled by. Christmas Selections: For Readings & Recitations. facsimile ed. LC 74-38601. (Granger Index Reprint Ser.). Repr. of 1906 ed. 12.00 (ISBN 0-8369-6333-4). Ayer Co Pubs.
Spatz, Jacob W. The Speaker's Bible. 2nd ed. 288p. 1986. pap. 10.00 (ISBN 0-938033-00-X). Alert Pubs.

RECOLLETS (FRANCISCAN)
Le Clercq, Chretien. First Establishment of the Faith in New France, 2 Vols. LC 77-172312. Repr. of 1881 ed. Set. 67.50 (ISBN 0-404-03914-6). Vol. 1 (ISBN 0-404-03915-4). Vol. 2 (ISBN 0-404-03916-2). AMS Pr.
Sagard-Theodat, Gabriel. Long Journey to the Country of the Hurons. Wrong, George M., ed. Langton, H. H., tr. LC 68-28613. 1968. Repr. of 1939 ed. lib. bdg. 29.25x (ISBN 0-8371-3861-2, SAJC). Greenwood.

RECONCILIATION
Brennan, Patrick J. Penance & Reconciliation. (Guidelines for Contemporary Catholics Ser.). (Orig.). 1986. pap. 7.95 (ISBN 0-88347-195-7). Thomas More.
Buckley, Francis J. Reconciling. LC 81-68699. 96p. (Orig.). 1981. pap. 2.95 (ISBN 0-87793-237-9). Ave Maria.
Buzzard, Lynn & Buzzard, Juanita. Readiness for Reconciliation. 36p. (Orig.). 1982. wkbk 3.00 (ISBN 0-686-39857-2). Chr Concil Serv.
Cooke, Bernard. Reconciled Sinners: Healing Human Brokenness. 128p. (Orig.). 1986. pap. 4.95 (ISBN 0-89622-284-5). Twenty-Third.
Donaghy, John A. Peacemaking & the Community of Faith: A Handbook for Congregations. 2.95 (ISBN 0-8091-5181-2). Paulist Pr.
Drew, Naomi. Learning the Skills of Peacemaking. Lovelady, Janet, ed. 200p. (Orig.). 1987. pap. 17.95x (ISBN 0-915190-46-X). Jalmar Pr.
Fisher, Douglas. Peacemaking. homily bk. 1.50 (ISBN 0-8091-9321-3); group discussion guide 2.95 (ISBN 0-8091-9326-4); participants' bks. 1.00 (ISBN 0-8091-9341-8). Paulist Pr.
Gula, Richard M. To Walk Together Again: The Sacrament of Reconciliation. LC 83-82021. (Orig.). 1984. pap. 8.95 (ISBN 0-8091-2603-6). Paulist Pr.
Haessly, Jacqueline. Peacemaking: Family Activities for Peace & Justice. 2.95 (ISBN 0-8091-2269-3). Paulist Pr.
Jennings, Sr. Vivian. Valiant Woman: At the Heart of Reconciliation. LC 74-6037. 128p. 1974. 3.95 (ISBN 0-8189-0291-4). Alba.
Lachmund, Margarethe. With Thine Adversary in the Way: A Quaker Witness for Reconciliation. Kite, Florence, tr. LC 79-91957. (Orig.). pap. 2.50x (ISBN 0-87574-228-9). Pendle Hill.
Morrison, Mary. Re-Conciliation: The Hidden Hyphen. LC 74-24007. 24p. (Orig.). 1974. pap. 2.50x (ISBN 0-87574-198-3, 198). Pendle Hill.
O'Reilly, James. Reconciliation & Renewal. (Synthesis Ser). 36p. 1974. pap. 0.75 (ISBN 0-8199-0361-2). Franciscan Herald.
Reconciliation & Penance. 144p. 1984. pap. 3.95 (ISBN 1-55586-951-3). US Catholic.
St. Alphonsus de Liguori. Uniformity with God's Will. 1977. pap. 1.00 (ISBN 0-89555-019-9). TAN Bks Pubs.
Stair, Rolland. Be Reconciled. 48p. 1981. softcover 0.75 (ISBN 0-8146-1233-4). Liturgical Pr.
Stuhlmueller, Carroll. Reconciliation: A Biblical Call. (Biblical Booklets Ser). 68p. 1975. pap. 1.25 (ISBN 0-8199-0522-4). Franciscan Herald.
Umbreit, Mark. Crime & Reconciliation. 144p. (Orig.). 1985. pap. 7.95 (ISBN 0-687-09885-8). Abingdon.

RECONSTRUCTIONIST JUDAISM
Dinin, Samuel. Judaism in a Changing Civilization. LC 70-176722. (Columbia University. Teachers College. Contributions to Education: No. 563). Repr. of 1933 ed. 22.50 (ISBN 0-404-55563-2). AMS Pr.
Kaplan, Mordecai M. Judaism As a Civilization: Toward a Reconstruction of American-Jewish Life. LC 81-6057. 601p. 1981. 25.00 (ISBN 0-8276-0193-X, 474); pap. 12.95 (ISBN 0-8276-0194-8, 480). Jewish Pubns.

RECORDS OF BIRTHS, ETC.
see Registers of Births, Deaths, Marriages, etc.

RECREATION–STUDY AND TEACHING
see Recreation Leadership

RECREATION AS A PROFESSION
see Recreation Leadership

RECREATION LEADERSHIP
Bannerman, Glenn & Fakkema, Robert. Guide for Recreation Leaders. LC 74-28523. 120p. (Orig.). 1975. pap. 7.95 (ISBN 0-8042-2154-5). John Knox.
Kraus, Richard. Recreation Leadership Today. 1985. text ed. write for info. (ISBN 0-673-18140-5); instr's. manual & test items incl. Scott F.

RECREATIONS
see Games; Schools–Exercises and Recreations

RECTORS
see Clergy

RECUSANTS
see Catholics in England

REDEMPTION
see also Atonement; Salvation
Adams, Jay E. More Than Redemption. 350p. 1979. pap. 10.95 (ISBN 0-87552-039-1). Presby & Reformed.
Andreason, Neils-Erik. Rest & Redemption: A Study of the Biblical Sabbath. (Andrews University Monographs, Studies in Religion: Vol. XI). vii, 137p. 1978. pap. 3.95 (ISBN 0-943872-11-1). Andrews Univ Pr.
Anselm of Canterbury. Trinity, Incarnation, & Redemption: Theological Treatises. (Anselm Ser.: No. 6). 1974. 9.95 (ISBN 0-88946-008-6). E Mellen.
Boultwood, Alban. Christ in Us: Reflections on Redemption. LC 81-8371. 144p. (Orig.). 1981. pap. 5.50 (ISBN 0-8146-1234-2). Liturgical Pr.
Brunner, Emil. The Christian Doctrine of Creation & Redemption. Wyon, Olive, tr. LC 50-6821. (Dogmatic Ser.: Vol. 2). 396p. 1979. pap. 10.95 (ISBN 0-664-24248-0). Westminster.
Buchanan, George W. Revelation & Redemption. 1978. text ed. 29.50 (ISBN 0-915948-04-4). Bks Distinction.
Cave, Sydney. Redemption, Hindu & Christian: The Religious Quest of India. facsimile ed. LC 73-102230. (Select Bibliographies Reprint Ser). 1919. 24.50 (ISBN 0-8369-5115-8). Ayer Co Pubs.
Chambers, Oswald. Psychology of Redemption. 1955. pap. 2.95 (ISBN 0-87508-124-X). Chr Lit.
Coffman, James B. The Mystery of Redemption. 1976. 5.95 (ISBN 0-88027-089-6). Firm Foun Pub.
Gaspard, Perry A. Redeemed from the Curse. 64p. 1983. pap. 2.00 (ISBN 0-931867-03-7). Abundant Life Pubns.
The Gift of the Redemption. 55p. 1984. pap. 3.95 (ISBN 1-55586-925-4). US Catholic.
Graham, Billy. Paz con Dios. rev. & enl. ed. Tr. of Peace with God. (Span.). 220p. 1987. pap. 7.50 (ISBN 0-311-46109-3). Casa Bautista.
Haines, Leland M. The Unfolding Plan of Redemption. 1982. 3.50 (ISBN 0-87813-517-0). Christian Light.
Kilpatrick, T. B. The Redemption of Man. (Short Course Ser.). 200p. 1940. 6.95 (ISBN 0-567-08320-9, Pub. by T & T Clark Ltd UK). Fortress.
Moyd, Olin P. Redemption in Black Theology. LC 78-23816. 1979. soft cover 8.95 (ISBN 0-8170-0806-3). Judson.
Murray, John. Redemption: Accomplished & Applied. 1961. pap. 5.95 (ISBN 0-8028-1143-4). Eerdmans.
Pittenger, Norman. Freed to Love: A Process Interpretation of Redemption. 1987. pap. 8.95. Morehouse.
Ramm, Bernard L. God's Way Out. rev. ed. Stewart, Ed, ed. 214p. 1987. pap. 5.95 (ISBN 0-8307-1215-1, 5416514). Regal.
Roberts, Howard W. Redemptive Responses of Jesus. (Orig.). 1987. pap. 5.95 (ISBN 0-8054-5715-1). Broadman.
Robinson, H. P. Redemption, Conceived & Revealed. 3.95 (ISBN 0-911866-59-0); pap. 2.95 (ISBN 0-911866-89-2). Advocate.
Sauer, Erich. La Aurora de la Redencion del Mundo. Orig. Title: The Dawn of World Redemption. (Span.). 320p. 1967. pap. 7.95 (ISBN 0-8254-1652-3). Kregel.
The Story of Redemption. large print ed. 1980. pap. 7.95 (ISBN 0-8280-0058-1, 19654-3). Review & Herald.
Teasley, D. O. The Double Cure, or Redemption Twofold. 160p. pap. 1.50 large print (ISBN 0-686-29147-6). Faith Pub Hse.
Towner, W. Sibley. How God Deals with Evil. LC 76-24916. (Biblical Perspectives on Current Issues). 186p. 1976. softcover 4.95 (ISBN 0-664-24127-1). Westminster.
Westley, Dick. Redemptive Intimacy. LC 80-54810. 176p. 1981. pap. 5.95 (ISBN 0-89622-123-7). Twenty-Third.

REDEMPTIONISTS
see Trinitarians

REDUCING
Bilich, Marion. Weight Loss from the Inside Out: Help for the Compulsive Eater. LC 83-633. 192p. (Orig.). 1983. pap. 9.95 (ISBN 0-8164-2485-3, HarpR). Har-Row.
Chapian, Marie. Free to Be Thin. LC 79-15656. (Illus.). 192p. 1979. pap. 5.95 (ISBN 0-87123-560-9, 210560); study guide (No. 1) by Neva Coyle 64 pgs. 2.50 (ISBN 0-87123-163-8, 210163). Bethany Hse.
Food for Thought: Daily Meditations for Overeaters. (Hazelden Meditation Ser.). 1986. 6.50 (ISBN 0-317-46275-X). Har-Row.
Hill, Harold. How to Flip Your Flab-Forever. LC 79-64912. 1979. pap. 2.95 (ISBN 0-88270-377-3). Bridge Pub.
Kreml, Patricia B. Slim for Him. LC 78-53422. 1978. pap. 4.95 (ISBN 0-88270-300-5). Bridge Pub.
Lemieux, Joanne H. Diet Signs: Follow Your Horoscope to a Slimmer You. LC 82-16251. 1982. pap. 6.95 (ISBN 0-87491-491-4). Acropolis.

REFERENCE BOOKS
Schwarz, Richard, ed. Internationales Jahrbuch fuer interdisziplinaere Forschung, Vol. 1: 1974. Wissenschaft als interdisziplinaeres Problem. 1974. 44.00x (ISBN 3-11-004633-4). De Gruyter.

REFORM JUDAISM
Bial, Morrison D. Liberal Judaism at Home: The Practices of Modern Reform Judaism. rev. ed. 1971. pap. 5.00 (ISBN 0-8074-0075-0, 383110); tchrs'. guide 1.50 (ISBN 0-8074-0225-7, 203110). UAHC.
Borowitz, Eugene. Liberal Judaism. LC 83-17997. 468p. (Orig.). 1984. pap. 8.95 (ISBN 0-8074-0264-8, 306050). UAHC.
Borowitz, Eugene B. Reform Judaism Today. 800p. 1983. pap. text ed. 9.95x (ISBN 0-87441-364-8). Behrman.
CCAR Yearbook, 1889-1891, 3 vols. (Illus.). 1951. 10.00 (ISBN 0-916694-30-5). Central Conf.
Dever, William G. Gezer One: Preliminary Report of the 1964-1966 Seasons. 1971. 35.00x (ISBN 0-87820-300-1, Pub. by Hebrew Union). Ktav.
Eighty Seven Immortals. 1982. limited 900.00 (ISBN 0-384-14045-9). Johnson Repr.
Freehof, S. Reform Jewish Practice. 9.95x (ISBN 0-685-55600-X). Ktav.
Freehof, S. B. Reform Responsa for Our Time. 15.00x (ISBN 0-87820-111-4, HUC Pr). Ktav.
Freehof, Solomon B. Current Reform Responsa. 1969. 15.00x (ISBN 0-87820-102-5, Pub. by Hebrew Union). Ktav.
--Modern Reform Response. 1971. 15.00x (ISBN 0-87820-101-7, Pub. by Hebrew Union). Ktav.
Furman, Frida K. Beyond Yiddishkeit: The Struggle for Jewish Identity in a Reform Synagogue. (Anthropology & Judaic Studies). 152p. 1987. text ed. 29.50x (ISBN 0-88706-513-9); pap. 9.95x (ISBN 0-88706-514-7). State U NY Pr.
Kraut, Benny. From Reform Judaism to Ethical Culture: The Religious Evolution of Felix Adler. LC 79-14441. (Monographs: No. 5). 285p. 1979. 16.50x (ISBN 0-87820-404-0). Ktav.
Maslin, Simeon J., ed. Shaarei Mitzvah: Gates of Mitzvah. (Illus.). 1979. 9.95 (ISBN 0-916694-37-2); pap. 7.95 (ISBN 0-916694-53-4). Central Conf.
Plaut, W. Gunther. The Rise of Reform Judaism: A Sourcebook of Its European Origins. Incl. Growth of Reform Judaism: American & European Sources to 1948. 1965. 1963. 10.00 (ISBN 0-8074-0089-0, 382770, Pub. by World Union). UAHC.
Plaut, W. Gunther, ed. Growth of Reform Judaism: American & European Sources Until 1948. 1965. 10.00 (ISBN 0-8074-0086-6, 382780). UAHC.
Silverman, William B. Basic Reform Judaism. LC 69-15531. 308p. 1970. 15.00 (ISBN 0-8022-2332-X). Philos Lib.

REFORM OF THE CHURCH
see Church Renewal

REFORMATION

see also Anabaptists; Augsburg Confession; Calvinism; Church History–Modern Period, 1500- ; Counter-Reformation; Europe–History–1492-1648; Peasants' War, 1524-1525; Protestantism; Sixteenth Century; Theology, Doctrinal–History–16th Century; Trent, Council of 1545-1563

also names of religious sects, e.g. Huguenots, Hussites, Waldenses

Anjou, Lars A. The History of the Reformation in Sweden. Mason, Henry M., tr. from Swedish. LC 83-45598. Date not set. Repr. of 1859 ed. 62.50 (ISBN 0-404-19866-X). AMS Pr.

Armstrong, William P., ed. Calvin & the Reformation: Four Studies. (Twin Brooks Ser.). 1980. pap. 6.95 (ISBN 0-8010-2901-5). Baker Bk.

Arrowsmith, Richard S. The Prelude to the Reformation: A Study of English Church Life from the Age of Wycliffe to the Breach with Rome. LC 83-45573. Date not set. Repr. of 1923 ed. 30.00 (ISBN 0-404-19891-0). AMS Pr.

Aulen, Gustaf E. Reformation & Catholicity. Wahlstrom, Eric H., tr. from Swedish. LC 78-25981. 1979. Repr. of 1961 ed. lib. bdg. 22.50x (ISBN 0-313-20809-3, AURC). Greenwood.

Babington, J. A. Reformation. LC 71-118513. 1971. Repr. of 1901 ed. 28.75x (ISBN 0-8046-1135-1, Pub. by Kennikat). Assoc Faculty Pr.

Bainton, Roland. Reformation of the Sixteenth Century. 18.50 (ISBN 0-8446-1581-1). Peter Smith.

Bainton, Roland H. The Age of the Reformation. LC 83-25145. 192p. pap. 7.50 (ISBN 0-89874-736-8). Krieger.

--Reformation of the Sixteenth Century. enl. ed. LC 85-47516. (Illus.). 290p. 1985. pap. 9.95 (ISBN 0-8070-1301-3, BP697). Beacon Pr.

Baker, Derek, ed. Reform & Reformation: England & the Continent c.1500-c.1750. (Studies in Church History: Subsidia 2). (Illus.). 336p. 1980. 45.00x (ISBN 0-631-19270-0). Basil Blackwell.

Barth, Karl. The Knowledge of God & the Service of God According to the Teaching of the Reformation: Recalling the Scottish Confession of 1560. LC 77-27187. (Gifford Lectures: 1937-38). Repr. of 1939 ed. 30.00 (ISBN 0-404-60495-1). AMS Pr.

Beard, Charles. The Reformation of the Sixteenth Century in Its Relations to Modern Thought & Knowledge. new ed. LC 77-27168. (Hibbert Lectures: 1883). Repr. of 1927 ed. 47.50 (ISBN 0-404-60404-8). AMS Pr.

--The Reformation of the Sixteenth Century in Its Relation to Modern Thought & Knowledge. LC 80-12915. xxviii, 450p. 1980. Repr. of 1962 ed. lib. bdg. 37.50x (ISBN 0-313-22410-2, BERF). Greenwood.

Belloc, Hilaire. How the Reformation Happened. 12.00 (ISBN 0-8446-0483-6). Peter Smith.

Brandt, Geeraert. History of the Reformation & Other Ecclesiastical Transactions in, & about, the Low Countries, from the Beginning of the Eighth Century down to the End of the Famous Synod of Dort, 4 Vols. in 2. LC 70-130625. Repr. of 1733 ed. Set. 285.00 (ISBN 0-404-07960-1). AMS Pr.

Calvin, John & Sadoleto, Jacopo, eds. A Reformation Debate. 1976. pap. 4.95 (ISBN 0-8010-2390-4). Baker Bk.

Chadwick, Owen. Reformation, Vol. 3. (History of the Church Ser.). (Orig.). 1964. pap. 5.95 (ISBN 0-14-020504-7, Pelican). Penguin.

Cubitt, Heather. Luther & the Reformation. Reeves, Marjorie, ed. (Then & There Ser.). (Illus.). 96p. 1976. pap. text ed. 4.75 (ISBN 0-582-20542-5). Longman.

Cunningham, William. Reformers & the Theology of Reformation. 1979. 19.95 (ISBN 0-85151-013-2). Banner of Truth.

Cuthbertson, David. A Tragedy of the Reformation: Being the Authentic Narrative of the History & Burning of the "Christianismi Restitution", 1953, with a Succinct Account of the Theological Controversy Between Michael Servetus, Its Author, & the Reformer, John Calvin. LC 83-45608. Date not set. Repr. of 1912 ed. 20.00 (ISBN 0-404-19826-0). AMS Pr.

Dannenfeldt, Karl H. Church of the Renaissance & Reformation. LC 77-98300. (Church in History Ser). 1978. pap. 4.95 (ISBN 0-570-06271-3, 12-2726). Concordia.

D'Aubigne, Merle. History of the Reformation. (Religious Heritage Reprint Library). 1976. Repr. 18.95 (ISBN 0-8010-2859-0). Baker Bk.

--History of the Reformation of the Sixteenth-Century, 1 vol. 1986. pap. 18.95 (ISBN 0-8010-2962-7). Baker Bk.

--The Reformation in England, 2 vols. 1977. Vol. 1. pap. 13.95 (ISBN 0-85151-486-3); Vol. 2. pap. 13.95 (ISBN 0-85151-487-1); Set. o. p. 25.95 (ISBN 0-85151-488-X). Banner of Truth.

De Vio, Tommasso. Cajetan Responds: A Reader in Reformation Controversy. Wicks, Jared, ed. LC 77-22606. pap. 75.00 (2029507). Bks Demand UMI.

Dickens, A. G. Reformation & Society in Sixteenth Century Europe. (History of European Civilization Library). (Illus., Orig.). 1966. pap. text ed. 11.95 (ISBN 0-15-576455-1, HC). HarBraceJ.

Dickens, A. G., et al. The Reformation in Historical Thought. 456p. 1985. text ed. 33.50x (ISBN 0-674-75311-9). Harvard U Pr.

Durant, Will. Reformation. (Story of Civilization: Vol. 6). (Illus.). 1957. 29.95 (ISBN 0-671-61050-3). S&S.

Eire, Carlos M. War Against the Idols: The Reformation of Worship from Erasmus to Calvin. 320p. 1986. 37.50 (ISBN 0-521-30685-X). Cambridge U Pr.

Elton, Gelffrey R. Renaissance & Reformation, Thirteen Hundred to Sixteen Forty-Eight. 3rd ed. (Ideas & Institutions in Western Civilization: Vol. 3). 1976. pap. text ed. write for info. (ISBN 0-02-332840-1). Macmillan.

Emmerson, Walter L. Reformation & the Advent Movement. 224p. pap. 9.95 (ISBN 0-8280-0168-5). Review & Herald.

Erasmus. Christian Humanism & the Reformation: Selected Writings with the Life of Erasmus by Beatus Rhenanus. Olin, John C., ed. 11.25 (ISBN 0-8446-2035-1). Peter Smith.

Erasmus, Desiderius. The Historical Significance of Desiderius Erasmus in the Light of the Protestant Revolution & the Catholic Church As Revealed by His Most Famous Pronouncements, 2 vols. (Illus.). 396p. 1985. Set. 207.50. Am Classical Coll Pr.

Estep, William R. Renaissance & Reformation. 320p. (Orig.). pap. text ed. 21.95 (ISBN 0-8028-0050-5). Eerdmans.

Evans, G. R. The Language & Logic of the Bible: The Road to Reformation. 200p. 1985. 32.50 (ISBN 0-521-30548-9). Cambridge U Pr.

Fisher, George P. The Reformation. LC 83-45660. Date not set. Repr. of 1906 ed. 54.50 (ISBN 0-404-19810-4). AMS Pr.

Forde, Gerhard O. Justification by Faith: A Matter of Death & Life. LC 81-70663. 112p. 1982. pap. 5.95 (ISBN 0-8006-1634-0, 1-1634). Fortress.

Gerrish, Brian, ed. Reformatio Perennis: Essays on Calvin & the Reformation in Honor of Ford Lewis Battles. (Pittsburgh Theological Monograph Ser.: No. 32). 1981. pap. 15.00 (ISBN 0-915138-41-7). Pickwick.

Green, Lowell C. How Melanchthon Helped Luther Discover the Gospel: The Doctrine of Justification in the Reformation. 274p. 1980. 7.95 (ISBN 0-89890-010-7). Attic Pr.

Green, V. H. Renaissance & Reformation: A Survey of European History Between 1450 & 1660. 2nd ed. 462p. 1964. pap. text ed. 17.95 (ISBN 0-7131-5617-1). E Arnold.

Grimm, Harold J. The Reformation. LC 72-76717. (AHA Pamphlets: No. 403). 1972. pap. text ed. 1.50 (ISBN 0-87229-003-4). Am Hist Assn.

--The Reformation Era: 1500-1650. 2nd ed. (Illus.). 700p. 1973. text ed. write for info. (ISBN 0-02-347270-7, 34727). Macmillan.

Harbison, E. Harris. The Age of Reformation. LC 76-10816. (Development of Western Civilization Ser). (Illus.). 145p. (Orig.). (YA) 1955. 5.95x (ISBN 0-8014-9844-9). Cornell U Pr.

--The Age of Reformation. LC 82-2985. (The Development of Western Civilization Ser.). xiv, 145p. 1982. Repr. of 1955 ed. lib. bdg. 22.50x (ISBN 0-313-23555-4, HAAGR). Greenwood.

Hearnshaw, F. J., ed. The Social & Political Ideas of Some Great Thinkers of the Renaissance & the Reformation. LC 85-7662. 216p. 1985. lib. bdg. 39.75x (ISBN 0-313-23862-6, HREN). Greenwood.

Hillerbrand, Hans J. Men & Ideas in the Sixteenth Century. 130p. 1984. pap. text ed. 7.95x (ISBN 0-88133-080-9). Waveland Pr.

--The World of the Reformation. (Twin Brooks Ser.). 229p. 1981. pap. 6.95 (ISBN 0-8010-4248-8). Baker Bk.

The History of the Church, 10 Vols. 920p. 1980. complete set 595.00x (ISBN 0-8245-0318-X). Crossroad NY.

Hogg, James. Die Kartauser und die Reformation: Internationaler Kongress Vom 24 bis 27 1983, 2 vols. (Analecta Cartusiana Ser.: No. 108). 320p. (Orig.). 1984. pap. 50.00 (ISBN 0-317-42576-5, Pub. by Salzburg Studies). Longwood Pub Group.

Hulme, Edward M. The Renaissance, the Protestant Revolution & the Catholic Reformation in Continental Europe. LC 83-45662. Date not set. Repr. of 1915 ed. 62.50 (ISBN 0-404-19812-0). AMS Pr.

Jedin, Hubert & Dolan, John, eds. Reformation & Counter-Reformation. 1980. 59.50x (ISBN 0-686-95526-9). Crossroad NY.

Jensen, De Lamar. Reformation Europe: Age of Reform & Revolution. 480p. 1981. pap. text ed. 12.95 (ISBN 0-669-03626-9). Heath.

Kidd, Beresford J., ed. Documents Illustrative of the Continental Reformation. LC 83-45663. Date not set. Repr. of 1911 ed. 64.50 (ISBN 0-404-19813-9). AMS Pr.

Klassen, Peter. The Reformation. LC 79-54030. (Problems in Civilization Ser.). (Orig.). 1980. pap. text ed. 6.95x (ISBN 0-88273-408-3). Forum Pr IL.

Lacoste, Auguste. Henri Arnaud und die Waldenser. (Basler und Berner Studien zur historischen und systematischen: Vol. 47). 213p. 1982. 20.00 (ISBN 3-261-04890-5). P Lang Pubs.

Lawlor, Hugh J. The Reformation & the Irish Episcopate. 2nd ed. (Church Historical Society, London, Ser.: No. 11). Repr. of 1932 ed. 20.00 (ISBN 0-8115-3135-X). Kraus Repr.

Lindberg, Carter. The Third Reformation: Charismatic Movements & the Lutheran Tradition. LC 83-11371. x, 346p. 1983. 24.95 (ISBN 0-86554-075-6, MUP/H83). Mercer Univ Pr.

Lindberg, Carter, ed. Piety, Politics, & Ethics: Reformation Studies in Honor of George Wolfgang Forell. (Sixteenth Century Essays & Studies: Vol. III). (Illus.). 200p. 1984. smythe sewn 25.00x (ISBN 0-940474-03-4). Sixteenth Cent.

Lindsay, Thomas. History of the Reformation. (Illus.). 648p. 1908. 16.95 (ISBN 0-567-07212-6, Pub. by T & T Clark Ltd UK). Fortress.

Lindsay, Thomas M. A History of the Reformation, 2 vols. facsimile ed. LC 72-37893. (Select Bibliographies Reprint Ser). Repr. of 1907 ed. Set. 54.00 (ISBN 0-8369-6730-5). Ayer Co Pubs.

--A History of the Reformation, 2 vols. LC 83-45664. Date not set. Repr. of 1904 ed. Set. 105.00 (ISBN 0-404-19814-7). AMS Pr.

--The Reformation. Whyte, A. & Moffatt, J., eds. (Handbooks for Bible Classes & Private Students Ser.). 228p. 1889. pap. 6.95 (ISBN 0-686-70864-4, Pub. by T & T Clark Ltd UK). Fortress.

Loeschen, John R. The Divine Community: Trinity, Church, & Ethics in Reformation Theologies. (Sixteenth Century Essays & Studies Ser.: Vol. I). 238p. 1981. 25.00x (ISBN 0-940474-01-8). Sixteenth Cent.

Lucas, Henry S. The Renaissance & the Reformation. LC 83-45665. Date not set. Repr. of 1934 ed. 67.50 (ISBN 0-404-19815-5). AMS Pr.

Lytle, Guy F., ed. Reform & Authority in the Medieval & Reformation Church. LC 79-17380. pap. 87.80 (2029496). Bks Demand UMI.

McGrath, Alister E. The Intellectual Origins of the European Reformation. 272p. 1987. text ed. 39.95 (ISBN 0-631-15144-3). Basil Blackwell.

Mackinnon, James. Calvin & the Reformation. LC 83-45648. Date not set. Repr. of 1936 ed. 37.50 (ISBN 0-404-19841-4). AMS Pr.

--Luther & the Reformation, 4 vols. LC 83-45648. Date not set. Repr. of 1925 ed. Set. 157.50 (ISBN 0-404-19857-0). AMS Pr.

Major, J. Russell. Age of the Renaissance & Reformation: A Short History. LC 73-107245. (Orig.). 1970. pap. text ed. 5.50i (ISBN 0-397-47195-5). Har-Row.

Merle d'Aubigne, Jean H. History of the Reformation of the Sixteenth Century, 5 vols. White, H., tr. LC 83-45666. Date not set. Repr. of 1872 ed. Set. 225.00 (ISBN 0-404-19816-3). AMS Pr.

Merle d'Augbine, Jean H. History of the Reformation in Europe in the Time of Calvin, 8 vols. Cates, W. L., tr. LC 83-45624. Date not set. Repr. of 1873 ed. Set. 395.00 (ISBN 0-404-19842-2). AMS Pr.

Mills, Dorothy. Renaissance & Reformation Times. LC 83-45667. Date not set. Repr. of 1939 ed. 55.00 (ISBN 0-404-19817-1). AMS Pr.

Moore, John A. Anabaptist Portraits. LC 84-12769. 256p. (Orig.). 1984. pap. 9.95 (ISBN 0-8361-3361-7). Herald Pr.

Mosse, George L. The Reformation. rev. ed. LC 63-11339. (Berkshire Studies in History). 1969. pap. text ed. 10.95 (ISBN 0-03-082836-8, HoltE). H Holt & Co.

Nauert, Charles G., Jr. The Age of Renaissance & Reformation. LC 81-40034. 330p. 1982. lib. bdg. 30.25 (ISBN 0-8191-1861-3); pap. text ed. 12.75 (ISBN 0-8191-1862-1). U Pr of Amer.

New, John F. The Renaissance & Reformation: A Short History. 2nd ed. 201p. 1977. pap. text ed. 11.00 (ISBN 0-394-34199-6, RanC). Random.

Nugent, Donald. Ecumenism in the Age of the Reformation: The Colloquy of Poissy. LC 73-80026. (Historical Studies: No. 89). 296p. 1974. text ed. 20.00x (ISBN 0-674-23725-0). Harvard U Pr.

Oberman, H. A. Masters of the Reformation: Rival Roads to a New Ideology. Martin, D., tr. from German. 432p. 1981. 57.50 (ISBN 0-521-23098-5). Cambridge U Pr.

Oberman, Heiko A. The Dawn of the Reformation: Essays in Late Medieval & Early Reformation Thought. 352p. 1986. pap. 26.95 (ISBN 0-567-09371-9, Pub. by T & T Clark Ltd UK). Fortress.

Olin, John C. & Smart, James D., eds. Luther, Erasmus & the Reformation: A Catholic-Protestant Reappraisal. LC 82-15500. x, 150p. 1982. Repr. of 1969 ed. lib. bdg. 22.50x (ISBN 0-313-23652-6, OLLE). Greenwood.

Ozment, Steven. When Fathers Ruled: Family Life in Reformation Europe. LC 83-6098. (Illus.). 238p. 1983. text ed. 17.50x (ISBN 0-674-95120-4). Harvard U Pr.

Ozment, Steven E. The Reformation in the Cities: The Appeal of Protestantism to Sixteenth-Century Germany & Switzerland. LC 75-8444. 228p. 1975. 28.50x (ISBN 0-300-01898-3); pap. 7.95x (ISBN 0-300-02496-7). Yale U Pr.

Pauck, Wilhelm. From Luther to Tillich: The Reformers & Their Heirs. Pauck, Marion, ed. LC 84-48229. 144p. 1985. 19.45 (ISBN 0-06-066475-4, HarpR). Har-Row.

Quellen und Forschungen zur Reformationgeschichte, Vols. 1-23, Lacking Vols. 3 & 7. Set. 895.00 (ISBN 0-384-49010-7); Set. pap. 775.00 (ISBN 0-685-02139-4). Johnson Repr.

Reasons Four, Explaining the Reformed Perspective. 120p. (Orig.). 1981. pap. text ed. 4.10 (ISBN 0-933140-29-0); tchr's manual, 60pgs 4.10 (ISBN 0-933140-30-4). CRC Pubns.

Richmond, Hugh M. Puritans & Libertines: Anglo-French Literary Relations in the Reformation. 400p. 1981. 35.95x (ISBN 0-520-04179-8). U of Cal Pr.

Schaff, Philip. History of the Christian Church, 8 vols. Incl. Vol. 1. Apostolic Christianity. 17.95 (ISBN 0-8028-8047-9); Vol. 2. Ante-Nicene. 100-325. 17.95 (ISBN 0-8028-8048-7); Vol. 3. Nicene & Post-Nicene. 311-600. 17.95 (ISBN 0-8028-8049-5); Vol. 4. Medieval Christianity. 590-1073. 17.95 (ISBN 0-8028-8050-9); Vol. 5. Middle Ages. 1049-1294. 17.95 (ISBN 0-8028-8051-7); Vol. 6. Middle Ages. 1295-1517. 17.95 (ISBN 0-8028-8052-5); Vol. 7. German Reformation. 17.95 (ISBN 0-8028-8053-3); Vol. 8. Swiss Reformation. 17.95 (ISBN 0-8028-8054-1). 1960. Repr. 17.95 ea.; 143.60 (ISBN 0-8028-8046-0). Eerdmans.

Schwiebert, Ernest G. Luther & His Times: The Reformation from a New Perspective. (Illus.). 1950. 24.95 (ISBN 0-570-03246-6, 15-1164). Concordia.

Seebohm, Frederic. Era of the Protestant Revolution. LC 77-147114. Repr. of 1903 ed. 7.50 (ISBN 0-404-05695-4). AMS Pr.

--The Era of the Protestant Revolution. 1902. 25.00 (ISBN 0-8495-6274-0). Arden Lib.

Sessions, Kyle & Bebb, Phillip. Pietas et Societas, New Trends in Reformation Social History: Essays in Memory of Harold J. Grimm. (Sixteenth Century Essays & Studies: Vol. IV). (Illus.). 240p. 1985. Smyth Sewn 25.00x (ISBN 0-940474-04-2). Sixteenth Cent.

Simpler, Steven. Roland H. Bainton: An Examination of His Reformation Historiography. LC 85-21567. (Texts & Studies in Religion: Vol. 24). 266p. 1985. PLB 49.95x (ISBN 0-88946-812-5). E Mellen.

Spitz, Lewis W. The Protestant Reformation, Fifteen Seventeen to Fifteen Fifty-Nine: The Rise of Modern Europe. LC 83-48805. (Illus.). 448p. 1986. pap. 8.95 (ISBN 0-06-091277-4, PL 1277, PL). Har-Row.

--The Protestant Reformation 1517-1559. LC 83-48805. (The Rise of Modern Europe Ser.). (Illus.). 444p. 1984. 22.45i (ISBN 0-06-013958-7, HarpT). Har-Row.

--Renaissance & Reformation, 2 vols. Incl. Vol. 1. The Renaissance. LC 12-2759 (ISBN 0-570-03818-9); Vol. 2. The Reformation. LC 12-2760 (ISBN 0-570-03819-7). 1980. pap. 15.50 ea. Concordia.

Spitz, Lewis W., ed. Reformation: Basic Interpretations. 2nd ed. (Problems in European Civilization Ser.). 1972. pap. text ed. 5.95 (ISBN 0-669-81620-5). Heath.

Stone, Jean M. Reformation & Renaissance. LC 83-45670. (Illus.). Date not set. Repr. of 1904 ed. 76.50 (ISBN 0-404-19820-1). AMS Pr.

Strype, John. Annals of the Reformation & Establishment of Religion & Other Various Occurrences in the Church of England, 4 vols. in 7. 2nd ed. LC 66-20694. 1708-09. Repr. 255.00 (ISBN 0-8337-3444-X). B Franklin.

Tentler, T. Sin & Confession on the Eve of the Reformation. 1977. 46.50x (ISBN 0-691-07219-1). Princeton U Pr.

Thompson, Bard. Renaissance & Reformation. (Texts & Studies in Religion). (Orig.). write for info. (ISBN 0-88946-915-6). E Mellen.

Tonkin, John. The Church & the Secular Order in Reformation Thought. LC 73-143390. pap. 58.30 (ISBN 0-317-26653-5, 2025107). Bks Demand UMI.

Veith, Gene E., Jr. Reformation Spirituality: The Religion of George Herbert. LC 83-46176. 288p. 1985. 34.50 (ISBN 0-8387-5071-0). Bucknell U Pr.

Vogelstein, Ingeborg B. Johann Sleidan's Commentaries: Vantage Point of a Second Generation Lutheran. 176p. 1987. lib. bdg. 21.75 (ISBN 0-8191-5641-8); pap. text ed. 11.50 (ISBN 0-8191-5642-6). U Pr of Amer.

Whitney, James P. Reformation Essays. (Church Historical Society London N. S. Ser.: No. 38). Repr. of 1939 ed. 40.00 (ISBN 0-8115-3161-9). Kraus Repr.

Wickham, Legg J. Breviarium Romanum a Francisco Cardinali: Quignonio Editum. 262p. Repr. of 1888 ed. text ed. 49.68x (ISBN 0-576-99727-7, Pub. by Gregg Intl Pubs England). Gregg Intl.

Wilcox, Donald J. In Search of God & Self: Renaissance & Reformation Thought. (Illus.). 401p. 1987. pap. text ed. 12.95 (ISBN 0-88133-276-3). Waveland Pr.

Williams, George H. Radical Reformation. LC 62-7066. (Illus.). 960p. 1962. 24.95 (ISBN 0-664-20372-8). Westminster.

Wiswedel, Wilhelm. Bilder und Fuehrergestalten Aus Dem Taeufertum: Dritter Band ein Beitrag Zur Reformationsgeschichte Des Sechszehnten Jahrhunderts. (Ger.). 231p. 1952. pap. 2.00x (ISBN 0-8361-1154-0). Herald Pr.

REFORMATION–BIBLIOGRAPHY

Bainton, Roland H. & Gritsch, Eric W. Bibliography of the Continental Reformation: Materials Available in English. 2nd ed. LC 72-8216. ix, 220p. 1974. 24.50 (ISBN 0-208-01219-2, Archon). Shoe String.

Boehmer, Eduard. Bibliotheca Wiffeniana: Bibliotheca Wiffeniana: Spanish Reformers of Two Centuries from Fifteen Twenty, 3 Vols. 1964. Repr. of 1904 ed. Set. 62.00 (ISBN 0-8337-0330-7). B Franklin.

Booty, John E., ed. The Godly Kingdom of Tudor England: Great Books of the English Reformation. LC 81-80626. (Illus.). 288p. 1981. 15.95 (ISBN 0-8192-1287-3). Morehouse.

Crawford, James L. Catalogue of a Collection of 1500 Tracts by Martin Luther & His Contemporaries, 1511-1598. 1965. Repr. of 1903 ed. 32.00 (ISBN 0-8337-1001-X). B Franklin.

Ozment, Steven E., ed. Reformation Europe: A Guide to Research. 390p. 1982. 18.50x (ISBN 0-910345-01-5); pap. 13.50x (ISBN 0-686-82436-9). Center Reform.

Phillips, Leona R. Martin Luther & the Reformation: An Annotated Bibliography. 1985. lib. bdg. 79.95 (ISBN 0-8490-3242-3). Gordon Pr.

REFORMATION–BIOGRAPHY

Bainton, Roland H. Here I Stand: A Life of Martin Luther. (Festival Books). 1978. pap. 4.95 (ISBN 0-687-16894-5, Co-Pub. with NAL). Abingdon.

Baker, J. Wayne. Heinrich Bullinger & the Covenant: The Other Reformed Tradition. LC 80-14667. xxvi, 300p. 1980. 24.95x (ISBN 0-8214-0554-3). Ohio U Pr.

Belloc, Hilaire. Characters of the Reformation. facs. ed. LC 72-121449. (Essay Index Reprint Ser). 1936. 24.00 (ISBN 0-8369-1696-4). Ayer Co Pubs.

Bietenholz, Peter G. & Deutscher, Thomas B., eds. Contemporaries of Erasmus: A Biographical Register of the Renaissance & Reformation, Vol. 1 (A-E) (Illus.). 480p. 1985. 72.50x (ISBN 0-8020-2507-2). U of Toronto Pr.

Caccamo, Domenico. Eretici Italiani in Moravia, Polonia, Transilvania (1558-1611) LC 72-3474. (Corpus Reformatorum Italicorum & Biblioteca Ser.). (Lat. & Ital., Illus.). 286p. 1970. pap. 17.50 (ISBN 0-87580-511-6). N Ill U Pr.

Caponetto, Salvatore, ed. Benedetto Da Mantova: Il Beneficio Di Cristo. LC 72-3471. (Corpus Reformatorum Italicorum & Biblioteca Ser.). (Lat. & Ital., Illus.). 558p. 1972. 40.00 (ISBN 0-87580-035-1). N Ill U Pr.

Cory, David M. Faustus Socinus. LC 83-45606. Date not set. Repr. of 1932 ed. 28.50 (ISBN 0-404-19874-0). AMS Pr.

DeMolen, Richard L., ed. Leaders of the Reformation. LC 83-51423. 360p. 1984. 39.50 (ISBN 0-941664-05-8, Pub. Susquehanna U Pr). Assoc Univ Prs.

Ginzburg, Carlo, ed. I Costituti Di Don Pietro Manelfi. LC 72-3473. (Corpus Reformatorum Italicorum & Biblioteca Ser.). (Illus.). 101p. 1970. pap. 10.00 (ISBN 0-87580-510-8). N Ill U Pr.

Grimm, Harold J. Lazarus Spengler: A Lay Leader of the Reformation. LC 78-13508. (Illus.). 249p. 1979. 22.50x (ISBN 0-8142-0290-X). Ohio St U Pr.

Gritsch, Eric W. Martin - God's Court Jester: Luther in Retrospect. LC 83-48004. 304p. 1983. pap. 15.95 (ISBN 0-8006-1753-3, 1-1753). Fortress.

Rotondo, Antonio, ed. Camillo Renato: Opere, Documenti E Testimonianze. LC 72-3454. (Corpus Reformatorum Italicorum & Biblioteca Ser.). (Lat. & Ital., Illus.). 353p. 1968. 25.00 (ISBN 0-87580-034-3). N Ill U Pr.

Rumsey, Thomas R. Men & Women of the Renaissance & Reformation 1300-1600. 487p. (Orig.). 1981. pap. text ed. 10.95 (ISBN 0-686-81286-7). Ind Sch Pr.

Steinmetz, David C. Reformers in the Wings. (Twin Brooks Ser.). 240p. 1981. pap. 7.95 (ISBN 0-8010-8208-0). Baker Bk.

Tulloch, John. Leaders of the Reformation: Luther, Calvin et al. 34.95 (ISBN 0-8490-0492-6). Gordon Pr.

REFORMATION–EARLY MOVEMENTS

Here are entered works descriptive of reform movements preceding the Reformation.

see also Sects, Medieval

Abray, Lorna J. The People's Reformation: Magistrates, Clergy & Commons in Strasbourg, 1500-1598. LC 84-45805. 288p. 1985. text ed. 27.50x (ISBN 0-8014-1776-7). Cornell U Pr.

Bonnechose, Emile de. The Reformers Before the Reformation. Mackenzie, Campbell, tr. LC 78-63194. (Heresies of the Early Christian & Medieval Era: Second Ser.). Repr. of 1844 ed. 36.50 set (ISBN 0-404-16190-1). AMS Pr.

Ullmann, C. Reformers Before the Reformation in Germany & the Netherlands, 2 vols. 1977. lib. bdg. 200.00 (ISBN 0-8490-2507-9). Gordon Pr.

Workman, Herbert B. The Dawn of the Reformation, 2 vols. LC 77-85273. Repr. of 1902 ed. 65.00 set (ISBN 0-404-16170-7). AMS Pr.

Zimmermann, Gunter. Die Antwort Der Reformatoren Auf Die Zehntenfrage. (European University Studies Three: Vol. 164). 175p. 1982. 21.05 (ISBN 3-8204-5745-3). P Lang Pubs.

REFORMATION–SOURCES

Articles Agreed on in the National Synode of the Reformed Churches of France. LC 76-57381. (English Experience Ser.: No. 799). 1977. Repr. of 1623 ed. lib. bdg. 5.00 (ISBN 90-221-0799-X). Walter J Johnson.

Best, William. The Churches Plea for Her Right. LC 76-57357. (English Experience Ser.: No. 776). 1977. Repr. of 1635 ed. lib. bdg. 10.50 (ISBN 90-221-0776-0). Walter J Johnson.

Broughton, Richard. English Protestants Plea. LC 76-57380. (English Experience Ser.: No. 798). 1977. Repr. of 1621 ed. lib. bdg. 9.50 (ISBN 90-221-0798-1). Walter J Johnson.

Bucer, Martin. A Briefe Treatise Concerning the Burnynge of Bucer & Phagius at Cambridge. LC 76-57362. (English Experience Ser.: No. 780). 1977. Repr. of 1562 ed. lib. bdg. 14.00 (ISBN 90-221-0780-9). Walter J Johnson.

Burton, Henry. An Apology of Appeale: Also, an Epistle to the True Hearted Nobility. LC 76-57364. (English Experience Ser.: No. 782). 1977. Repr. of 1636 ed. lib. bdg. 5.00 (ISBN 90-221-0782-5). Walter J Johnson.

--For God & the King. LC 76-57365. (English Experience Ser.: No. 783). 1977. lib. bdg. 17.50 (ISBN 90-221-0783-3). Walter J Johnson.

Draxe, Thomas. Bibliotheca Scholastica Instructissima: Or a Treasure of Ancient Adagies. LC 76-57378. (English Experience Ser.: No. 796). 1977. Repr. lib. bdg. 24.00 (ISBN 90-221-0796-5). Walter J Johnson.

Heylin, Peter. A Briefe & Moderate Answer to H. Burton. LC 76-57389. (English Experience Ser.: No. 806). 1977. Repr. of 1637 ed. lib. bdg. 22.00 (ISBN 90-221-0806-6). Walter J Johnson.

Hillerbrand, Hans J., ed. Protestant Reformation. (Documentary History of Western Civilization Ser). (Orig.). 1968. pap. 7.95x (ISBN 0-06-131342-4, TB 1342, Torch). Har-Row.

--The Reformation: A Narrative History Related by Contemporary Observers & Participants. (Twin Brooks Ser). (Illus.). 1978. pap. 11.95 (ISBN 0-8010-4185-6). Baker Bk.

Klassen, William & Klaassen, Walter, eds. The Writings of Pilgrim Marpeck. LC 77-87419. (Classics of the Radical Reformation Ser.: No. 2). (Illus.). 608p. 1978. 24.95x (ISBN 0-8361-1205-9). Herald Pr.

Powell, Gabriel. The Catholikes Supplication Unto the King's Majestie, for Toleration of Catholike Religion in England. LC 76-57406. (English Experience Ser.: No. 822). 1977. lib. bdg. 6.00 (ISBN 90-221-0822-8). Walter J Johnson.

Sibthorpe, Robert. Apostolike Obedience: A Sermon. LC 76-57418. (English Experience Ser.: No. 831). 1977. Repr. of 1627 ed. lib. bdg. 6.00 (ISBN 90-221-0831-7). Walter J Johnson.

Spitz, Lewis W. Protestant Reformation. (Orig.). 1966. pap. 3.95x (ISBN 0-13-731638-0, Spec). P-H.

REFORMATION–CZECHOSLOVAK REPUBLIC

Gillett, Ezra H. The Life & Times of John Huss: The Bohemian Reformation of the Fifteenth Century, 2 vols. LC 77-85271. Repr. of 1863 ed. Set. 94.50 (ISBN 0-404-16150-2). AMS Pr.

Spinka, Matthew. John Hus: A Biography. LC 78-14366. (Illus.). 1978. Repr. of 1968 ed. lib. bdg. 37.50 (ISBN 0-313-21050-0, SPJH). Greenwood.

Zeman, Jarold K. The Hussite Movement & the Reformation in Bohemia, Moravia & Slovakia, 1350-1650: A Bibliographic Study Guide. 1977. 15.00 (ISBN 0-930042-00-X). Mich Slavic Pubns.

REFORMATION–ENGLAND

Baker, Derek, ed. Reform & Reformation: England & the Continent c.1500-c.1750. (Studies in Church History: Subsidia 2). (Illus.). 336p. 1980. 45.00x (ISBN 0-631-19270-0). Basil Blackwell.

Bancroft, Richard. Dangerous Positions & Proceedings. LC 74-38147. (English Experience Ser.: No. 427). 192p. 1972. Repr. of 1593 ed. 28.50 (ISBN 90-221-0427-3). Walter J Johnson.

Bowker, Margaret. The Henrician Reformation: The Diocese of Lincoln Under John Longland 1521-1547. LC 80-41655. (Illus.). 256p. 1981. 49.50 (ISBN 0-521-23639-8). Cambridge U Pr.

Broughton, Richard. English Protestants Plea. LC 76-57380. (English Experience Ser.: No. 798). 1977. Repr. of 1621 ed. lib. bdg. 9.50 (ISBN 90-221-0798-1). Walter J Johnson.

Bucer, Martin. A Briefe Treatise Concerning the Burnynge of Bucer & Phagius at Cambridge. LC 76-57362. (English Experience Ser.: No. 780). 1977. Repr. of 1562 ed. lib. bdg. 14.00 (ISBN 90-221-0780-9). Walter J Johnson.

Burnet, Gilbert. The History of the Reformation of the Church of England, 7 vols. rev. ed. LC 83-45575. Date not set. Repr. of 1865 ed. Set. 425.00 (ISBN 0-404-19893-7). Ams Pr.

Burton, Henry. An Apology of Appeale: Also, an Epistle to the True Hearted Nobility. LC 76-57364. (English Experience Ser.: No. 782). 1977. Repr. of 1636 ed. lib. bdg. 5.00 (ISBN 90-221-0782-5). Walter J Johnson.

--For God & the King. LC 76-57365. (English Experience Ser.: No. 783). 1977. lib. bdg. 17.50 (ISBN 90-221-0783-3). Walter J Johnson.

Butterworth, Charles C. The English Primers, Fifteen Twenty-Nine to Fifteen Forty-Five: Their Publication & Connection with the English Bible & the Reformation in England. 1970. lib. bdg. 26.00x (ISBN 0-374-91131-2, Octagon). Hippocrene Bks.

Collinson, Patrick. The Religion of Protestants: The Church in English Society 1559-1625. 1982. pap. 15.95x (ISBN 0-19-820053-6). Oxford U Pr.

Constant, Gustave L. The Reformation in England. Scantlebury, R. E., tr. LC 83-45576. Date not set. Repr. of 1934 ed. 85.00 (ISBN 0-404-19895-3). AMS Pr.

Dent, C. M. Protestant Reformers in Elizabethan England. (Oxford Theological Monographs). 1985. 39.95x (ISBN 0-19-826723-1). Oxford U Pr.

Dickens, A. G. Reformation Studies. 624p. 1983. 40.00 (ISBN 0-907628-04-4). Hambledon Press.

Dickens, Arthur G. English Reformation. LC 64-22987. (Fabric of British History Ser). 1968. pap. 8.95 (ISBN 0-8052-0177-7). Schocken.

Dickens, Arthur G. & Carr, Dorothy. Reformation in England to the Accession of Elizabeth 1. (Documents of Modern History Ser). (Orig.). 1968. pap. 11.95 (ISBN 0-312-66815-5). St Martin.

Draxe, Thomas. Bibliotheca Scholastica Instructissima: Or a Treasure of Ancient Adagies. LC 76-57378. (English Experience Ser.: No. 796). 1977. Repr. lib. bdg. 24.00 (ISBN 90-221-0796-5). Walter J Johnson.

Elton, G. R. Reform & Reformation: England, 1509-1558. LC 77-6464. (Harvard Paperback Ser.: No. 146, The New History of England). 1979. 27.50x (ISBN 0-674-75245-7); pap. 8.95x (ISBN 0-674-75248-1). Harvard U Pr.

Epistolae Tigurinae De Rebus Potissimum Ad Ecclesiae Anglicanae Reformationem Pertinentibus Conscriptae. 1848. 41.00 (ISBN 0-384-14505-1). Johnson Repr.

Firth, Katherine R. The Apocalyptic Tradition in Reformation Britain 1530-1645. (Historical Monographs). (Illus.). 1979. 45.00x (ISBN 0-19-821868-0). Oxford U Pr.

Fletcher, J. S. Reformation in Northern England. LC 71-118469. 1971. Repr. of 1925 ed. 23.50x (ISBN 0-8046-1218-8, Pub. by Kennikat). Assoc Faculty Pr.

Gairdner, James. English Church in the Sixteenth Century, from the Accession of Henry Eighth to the Death of Mary, 1509-1558. LC 72-168089. (History of the English Church Ser.: No. 4). Repr. of 1902 ed. 29.50 (ISBN 0-404-50754-9). AMS Pr.

--Lollardy & the Reformation in England: An Historical Survey, 4 Vols. 1965. Repr. of 1913 ed. 141.00 (ISBN 0-8337-1268-3). B Franklin.

Gasquet, Francis A. Eve of the Reformation. LC 75-118522. 1971. Repr. of 1900 ed. 35.00x (ISBN 0-8046-1144-0, Pub. by Kennikat). Assoc Faculty Pr.

George, Charles & George, Katherine. The Protestant Mind of the English Reformation, 1570-1640. LC 77-130746. pap. 116.00 (ISBN 0-317-08472-0, 2000986). Bks Demand UMI.

Gilman, Ernest B. Iconoclasm & Poetry in the English Reformation: Down Went Dragon. LC 85-28837. (Illus.). 240p. 1986. lib. bdg. 19.00x (ISBN 0-226-29382-3). U of Chicago Pr.

Hall, Louis B. The Perilous Vision of John Wyclif. LC 82-18890. 288p. 1983. lib. bdg. 23.95X (ISBN 0-8304-1006-6). Nelson-Hall.

Heylin, Peter. A Briefe & Moderate Answer to H. Burton. LC 76-57389. (English Experience Ser.: No. 806). 1977. Repr. of 1637 ed. lib. bdg. 22.00 (ISBN 90-221-0806-6). Walter J Johnson.

Jones, R. Tudur. The Great Reformation. LC 85-23930. 272p. 1986. pap. 9.95 (ISBN 0-87784-606-5). Inter-Varsity.

Karant-Nunn, Susan C. Luther's Pastors: The Reformation in the Ernestine Countryside. LC 79-51539. (Transactions Ser.: Vol. 69, Pt. 8). 1979. 8.00 (ISBN 0-87169-698-3). Am Philos.

Kreider, Alan. English Chantries: The Road to Dissolution. LC 78-12453. (Harvard Historical Studies: No. 97). 1979. 22.50x (ISBN 0-674-25560-7). Harvard U Pr.

Marti, Oscar A. Economic Causes of the Reformation in England. LC 83-45586. Date not set. Repr. of 1929 ed. 32.50 (ISBN 0-404-19904-6). AMS Pr.

Morison, Richard. An Exhortation to Styre All Englyshe Men to the Defense of Theyr Countreye. LC 79-38211. (English Experience Ser.: No. 476). 64p. 1972. Repr. of 1539 ed. 9.50 (ISBN 90-221-0476-1). Walter J Johnson.

--An Inuective Agenste Treason. LC 72-38212. (English Experience Ser.: No. 477). 104p. 1972. Repr. of 1539 ed. 9.50 (ISBN 90-221-0477-X). Walter J Johnson.

Nichols, John G., ed. Narrative of the Days of the Reformation, Chiefly from the Manuscripts of John Foxe the Martyrologist. Repr. of 1859 ed. 37.00 (ISBN 0-384-41460-5). Johnson Repr.

--Narrative of the Days of the Reformation. (Camden Society, London. Publications, First Ser.: No. 77). Repr. of 1859 ed. 37.00 (ISBN 0-404-50177-X). AMS Pr.

O'Day, Rosemary. The Debate on the English Reformation. 217p. 1986. text ed. 29.95 (ISBN 0-416-72670-4, 9794); pap. text ed. 9.95 (ISBN 0-416-72680-1, 9802). Methuen Inc.

Original Letters Relative to the English Reformation, 2 Vols. 1846-1847. Set. 61.00 (ISBN 0-384-43680-3). Johnson Repr.

Parker Society-London. Parker Society Publications, 55 Vols. Repr. of 1841 ed. Set. 2200.00 (ISBN 0-384-44880-1). Johnson Repr.

Pierce, William. Historical Introduction to the Marprelate Tracts: A Chapter in the Evolution of Religious & Civil Liberty in England. 1908. 23.50 (ISBN 0-8337-2762-1). B Franklin.

Pocock, Nicholas, ed. Troubles Connected with the Prayer Book of 1549. 1884. 27.00 (ISBN 0-384-47030-0). Johnson Repr.

Pollard, Albert F. Thomas Cranmer & the English Reformation, 1849-1556. LC 83-45587. Date not set. Repr. of 1927 ed. 42.50 (ISBN 0-404-19905-4). AMS Pr.

Porter, H. C. Reformation & Reaction in Tudor Cambridge. LC 77-179573. (Illus.). xv, 462p. 1972. Repr. of 1958 ed. 35.00 (ISBN 0-208-01228-1, Archon). Shoe String.

Powell, Gabriel. The Catholikes Supplication Unto the King's Majestie, for Toleration of Catholike Religion in England. LC 76-57406. (English Experience Ser.: No. 822). 1977. lib. bdg. 6.00 (ISBN 90-221-0822-8). Walter J Johnson.

Pruser, Friedrich. England und Die Schmalkaldener, 1535-1540. 34.00 (ISBN 0-384-48058-6); pap. 28.00 (ISBN 0-384-48057-8). Johnson Repr.

Scarisbrick, J. J. The Reformation & the English People. 214p. 1986. pap. text ed. 12.95x (ISBN 0-631-14755-1). Basil Blackwell.

Schoffler, Herbert. Anfange Des Puritanismus. Repr. of 1932 ed. 16.00 (ISBN 0-384-54220-4). Johnson Repr.

Sibthorpe, Robert. Apostolike Obedience: A Sermon. LC 76-57418. (English Experience Ser.: No. 831). 1977. Repr. of 1627 ed. lib. bdg. 6.00 (ISBN 90-221-0831-7). Walter J Johnson.

Smyth, Charles H. Cranmer & the Reformation under Edward VI. Repr. of 1926 ed. lib. bdg. 22.50x (ISBN 0-8371-4025-0, SMCR). Greenwood.

Thorpe, William. The Examinacions of Thorpe & Oldcastell. LC 74-28889. (English Experience Ser.: No. 766). 1975. Repr. of 1530 ed. 7.00 (ISBN 90-221-0766-3). Walter J Johnson.

Verkamp, Bernard J. The Indifferent Mean: Adiaphorism in the English Reformation to 1554. LC 77-13672. (Studies in the Reformation: Vol. 1). 1977. 15.00x (ISBN 0-8214-0387-7, Co-Pub by Wayne State). Ohio U Pr.

Visser, Derk, ed. Controversy & Conciliation: The Reformation & the Palatinate 1559 - 1583. (Pittsburgh Theological Monographs Ser.: No. 18). (Orig.). 1986. pap. 19.95 (ISBN 0-915138-73-5). Pickwick.

Walters, Henry B. London Churches at the Reformation: With an Account of Their Contents. (Church Historical Society London N. S. Ser.: No. 37). Repr. of 1939 ed. 95.00 (ISBN 0-8115-3160-0). Kraus Repr.

White, Helen C. Social Criticism in Popular Religious Literature of the Sixteenth-Century. 1965. lib. bdg. 20.50x (ISBN 0-374-98455-7, Octagon). Hippocrene Bks.

Wright, Thomas. Three Chapters of Letters Relating to the Suppression of Monasteries. 37.00 (ISBN 0-384-69545-0). Johnson Repr.

Wright, Thomas, ed. Three Chapters of Letters Relating to the Suppression of Monasteries. LC 72-74268. (Camden Society, London. Publications First Ser.: No. 26). Repr. of 1843 ed. 37.00 (ISBN 0-404-50126-5). AMS Pr.

REFORMATION–FRANCE

Articles Agreed on in the National Synode of the Reformed Churches of France. LC 76-57381. (English Experience Ser.: No. 799). 1977. Repr. of 1623 ed. lib. bdg. 5.00 (ISBN 90-221-0799-X). Walter J Johnson.

De Mornay, Charlotte A. Memoires, 2 vols. 1869. Set. 67.00 (ISBN 0-384-40148-1); Set. pap. 55.00 (ISBN 0-384-40149-X). Johnson Repr.

Greengrass, Mark. The French Reformation. 96p. 1987. pap. text ed. 7.95 (ISBN 0-631-14516-8). Basil Blackwell.

Jones, R. Tudur. The Great Reformation. LC 85-23930. 272p. 1986. pap. 9.95 (ISBN 0-87784-606-5). Inter-Varsity.

Stafford, William S. Domesticating the Clergy: The Inception of the Reformation in Strasbourg 1522-1524. LC 76-15567. (American Academy of Religion, Dissertation Ser.). 1976. pap. 9.95 (ISBN 0-89130-109-7, 010117). Scholars Pr GA.

REFORMATION–GERMANY

Beard, Charles. Martin Luther & the Reformation in Germany until the Close of the Diet of Worms. LC 83-45638. Date not set. Repr. of 1889 ed. 49.50 (ISBN 0-404-19822-8). AMS Pr.

Bezold, Friedrich. Geschichte der Deutschen Reformation. LC 79-149654. (BCL Ser. I). (Ger.). Repr. of 1890 ed. 37.50 (ISBN 0-404-00797-X). AMS Pr.

Birnbaum, Norman. Social Structure & the German Reformation. Zuckerman, Harriet & Merton, Robert K., eds. LC 79-8976. (Dissertation on Sociology Ser.). 1980. lib. bdg. 40.00x (ISBN 0-405-12952-1). Ayer Co Pubs.

Christensen, Carl C. Art & the Reformation in Germany. (Studies in the Reformation Ser.: Vol.2). (Illus.). 269p. 1981. 18.95x (ISBN 0-8214-0388-5, 82-82816, Co-Pub by Wayne State U Pr). Ohio U Pr.

Dickens, A. G. Reformation Studies. 624p. 1983. 40.00 (ISBN 0-907628-04-4). Hambledon Press.

Eells, Hastings. The Attitudes of Martin Bucer Toward the Bigamy of Philip of Hesse. LC 83-45611. Date not set. Repr. of 1924 ed. 32.50 (ISBN 0-404-19829-5). AMS Pr.

Evans, Austin P. Episode in the Struggle for Religious Freedom. LC 74-130618. Repr. of 1924 ed. 19.00 (ISBN 0-404-02357-6). AMS Pr.

Fehlauer, Adolph. Life & Faith of Martin Luther. 1981. pap. 5.95 (ISBN 0-8100-0125-X, 15N0376). Northwest Pub.

Grisar, Hartmann. Martin Luther: His Life & Work. Preuss, Arthur, ed. LC 71-137235. Repr. of 1930 ed. 29.50 (ISBN 0-404-02935-3). AMS Pr.

Hannemann, Manfred. The Diffusion of the Reformation in Southwestern Germany, 1518-1534. LC 75-14120. (Research Papers Ser.: No. 167). (Illus.). 1975. pap. 10.00 (ISBN 0-89065-074-8). U Chicago Dept Geog.

Hoffmeister, Gerhart. The Renaissance & Reformation in Germany: An Introduction. LC 77-5429. 1977. 25.00 (ISBN 0-8044-1391-6); pap. 9.95 (ISBN 0-8044-6272-0). Ungar.

Holborn, H. A History of Modern Germany, 3 vols. 1982. Vol. 1, The Reformation. 47.50 (ISBN 0-691-05357-X); pap. 10.50 (ISBN 0-691-00795-0); Vol. 2, 1648-1840. 60.50 (ISBN 0-691-05358-8); pap. 11.50 (ISBN 0-691-00796-9); Vol. 3, 1840-1945. 79.00 (ISBN 0-691-05359-6); pap. 13.95 (ISBN 0-691-00797-7); Set. 155.00; Set. pap. 27.50. Princeton U Pr.

Holborn, Hajo. Ulrich Von Hutten & the German Reformation. Bainton, Roland H., tr. LC 77-25067. (Yale Historical Publications Studies: No. XI). (Illus.). 1978. Repr. of 1937 ed. lib. bdg. 22.50x (ISBN 0-313-20125-0, HOUV). Greenwood.

Janssen, Johannes. History of the German People at the Close of the Middle Ages, 17 Vols. LC 67-104463. Repr. of 1925 ed. Set. 637.50 (ISBN 0-404-03570-1); 37.50 ea. AMS Pr.

Jones, R. Tudur. The Great Reformation. LC 85-23930. 272p. 1986. pap. 9.95 (ISBN 0-87784-606-5). Inter-Varsity.

Karant-Nunn, Susan C. Zwickau in Transition, Fifteen-Hundred to Fifteen Forty-Seven: The Reformation as an Agent of Change. 1987. 29.50x (ISBN 0-8142-0421-X). Ohio St U Pr.

Lacey, Thomas A. The Reformation & the People. LC 83-45583. Date not set. Repr. of 1929 ed. 22.00 (ISBN 0-404-19901-1). AMS Pr.

Moeller, Bernd. Imperial Cities & the Reformation. Midelfort, H. C. Erik & Edwards, Mark U., Jr., eds. 128p. (Orig.). 1982. pap. text ed. 5.95x (ISBN 0-939464-04-7). Labyrinth Pr.

Pascal, Roy. Social Basis of the German Reformation: Martin Luther & His Times. LC 68-30539. 1971. Repr. of 1933 ed. 25.00x (ISBN 0-678-00549-4). Kelley.

Pruser, Friedrich. England und Die Schmalkaldener, 1535-1540. 34.00 (ISBN 0-384-48058-6); pap. 28.00 (ISBN 0-384-48057-8). Johnson Repr.

Raitt, Jill, ed. Shapers of Religious Traditions in Germany, Switzerland, & Poland, Fifteen Sixty to Sixteen Hundred. LC 80-23287. 256p. 1981. text ed. 28.50x (ISBN 0-300-02457-6). Yale U Pr.

Russell, Paul A. Lay Theology in the Reformation: Popular Pamphleteers in Southwest Germany, 1521-1525. (Illus.). 303p. 1986. 39.50 (ISBN 0-521-30727-9). Cambridge U Pr.

Schapiro, Jacob S. Social Reform & the Reformation. LC 74-127456. (Columbia University Studies in the Social Sciences: No. 90). 1970. Repr. of 1909 ed. 16.50 (ISBN 0-404-51090-6). AMS Pr.

Scribner, R. The German Reformation. LC 85-19732. (Studies in European History). 88p. 1986. pap. text ed. 7.95x (ISBN 0-391-03362-X). Humanities.

Scribner, R. W. For the Sake of Simple Folk: Popular Propaganda for the German Reformation. (Cambridge Studies in Oral & Literate Culture: No. 2). (Illus.). 350p. 1981. Cambridge U Pr.

Staehelin, Ernst. Das Theologische Lebenswerk Johannes Oekolampads. 61.00 (ISBN 0-384-57419-X); pap. 55.00 (ISBN 0-384-57418-1). Johnson Repr.

Strauss, Gerald. Law, Resistance & the State: The Opposition to Roman Law in Reformation Germany. LC 85-43315. 312p. 1986. text ed. 34.50 (ISBN 0-691-05469-X). Princeton U Pr.

--Luther's House of Learning: Indoctrination of the Young in the German Reformation. LC 77-18705. pap. 101.30 (ISBN 0-317-20464-5, 2023003). Bks Demand UMI.

Ullmann, C. Reformers Before the Reformation in Germany & the Netherlands, 2 vols. 1977. lib. bdg. 200.00 (ISBN 0-8490-2507-9). Gordon Pr.

Vedder, H. C. The Reformation in Germany. 1977. lib. bdg. 59.95 (ISBN 0-8490-2506-0). Gordon Pr.

Von Schubert, Hans. Lazarus Spengler und Die Reformation in Nurnberg. 29.00 (ISBN 0-685-92689-3); pap. 28.00 (ISBN 0-384-54287-5). Johnson Repr.

Zeeden, Ernest W. The Legacy of Luther: Martin Luther & the Reformation in the Estimation of the German Lutherans from Luther's Death to the Beginning of the Age of Goethe. Bethell, Ruth M., tr. from Ger. LC 83-45685. Date not set. Repr. of 1954 ed. 30.00 (ISBN 0-404-19865-1). AMS Pr.

REFORMATION–ITALY

Collett, Barry. Italian Benedictine Scholars & the Reformation: The Congregation of Santa Giustina of Padua. (Historical Monographs). 300p. 1985. 48.00x (ISBN 0-19-822934-8). Oxford U Pr.

Cory, David M. Faustus Socinus. LC 83-45606. Date not set. Repr. of 1932 ed. 28.50 (ISBN 0-404-19874-0). AMS Pr.

Gilbert, O. & Whittaker, R. The Historical Meaning of Savonarola As a Religious, Moral & Political Prophet & the Progress of the Reformation in Italy. 189p. 1985. 88.45 (ISBN 0-89266-514-9). Am Classical Coll Pr.

Gleason, Elisabeth G. Reform Thought in Sixteenth Century Italy. Massey, James A., ed. LC 81-5648. (American Academy of Religion Texts & Translations Ser.). 1981. pap. text ed. 10.95 (ISBN 0-89130-498-3, 01-02-04). Scholars Pr GA.

Hallman, Barbara M. Italian Cardinals, Reform, & the Church As Property, 1492-1563. LC 84-8501. (Center for Medieval & Renaissance Studies, UCLA Publications: No. 22). 1985. 35.00x (ISBN 0-520-04937-3). U of Cal Pr.

Jones, R. Tudur. The Great Reformation. LC 85-23930. 272p. 1986. pap. 9.95 (ISBN 0-87784-606-5). Inter-Varsity.

McCrie, Thomas. History of the Progress & Suppression of the Reformation in Italy. LC 72-1006. Repr. of 1856 ed. 22.45 (ISBN 0-404-04118-3). AMS Pr.

Wallace, Eugene V. The History of the Reformation in Italy, 2 vols. (Illus.). 393p. 1987. Repr. of 1843 ed. Set. 189.75 (ISBN 0-89901-317-1). Found Class Reprints.

Yates, Frances A. Renaissance & Reform: The Italian Contribution. Trapp, J., ed. (Collected Essays Ser.: Vol. II). (Illus.). 288p. 1983. 31.50 (ISBN 0-7100-9530-9). Methuen Inc.

REFORMATION–POLAND

Fox, Paul. Reformation in Poland. LC 72-136395. Repr. of 1924 ed. 24.50 (ISBN 0-404-02544-7). AMS Pr.

--Reformation in Poland, Some Social & Economic Aspects. LC 71-104272. Repr. of 1924 ed. lib. bdg. 22.50x (ISBN 0-8371-3924-4, FORP). Greenwood.

Raitt, Jill, ed. Shapers of Religious Traditions in Germany, Switzerland, & Poland, Fifteen Sixty to Sixteen Hundred. LC 80-23287. 256p. 1981. text ed. 28.50x (ISBN 0-300-02457-6). Yale U Pr.

Tazbir, Janusz. A State Without Stakes: Religious Toleration in Reformation Poland. Jordan, A. T., tr. (Library of Polish Studies: Vol. 3). text ed. 4.00 (ISBN 0-917004-05-1). Kosciuszko.

Wotschke, Theodor. Geschichte Der Reformation in Polen. (Ger.). 34.00 (ISBN 0-384-69301-6); pap. 28.00 (ISBN 0-384-69300-8). Johnson Repr.

REFORMATION–SCOTLAND

Cowan, I. B., ed. Blast & Counterblast: Contemporary Writings on the Scottish Reformation. 76p. 1985. 22.00x (ISBN 0-317-39400-2, Pub. by Saltire Society). State Mutual Bk.

Cowan, Ian B. The Scottish Reformation. LC 82-5834. 256p. 1982. 25.00x (ISBN 0-312-70519-0). St Martin.

Cowan, Ian B. & Shaw, Duncan, eds. The Renaissance & Reformation in Scotland. 220p. 1983. 20.00x (ISBN 0-7073-0261-7, Scot Acad Pr). Longwood Pub Group.

Donaldson, G. The Scottish Reformation. 49.50 (ISBN 0-521-08675-2). Cambridge U Pr.

Fleming, David H., ed. The Reformation in Scotland, Causes, Characteristics, Consequences: Stone Lectures at Princeton Theological Seminary, 1907-1908. LC 83-45579. Date not set. Repr. of 1910 ed. 67.50 (ISBN 0-404-19897-X). AMS Pr.

Lee, Maurice. James Stewart, Earl of Moray: A Political Study of the Reformation in Scotland. LC 73-104251. 1971. Repr. of 1953 ed. lib. bdg. 22.50x (ISBN 0-8371-3975-9, LEJS). Greenwood.

McMillan, William. The Worship of the Scottish Reformed Church, 1550-1638: The Hastie Lectures in the University of Glasgow, 1930. LC 83-45585. Date not set. Repr. of 1931 ed. 35.00 (ISBN 0-404-19903-8). AMS Pr.

Walker, Ralph S. John Knox: Historia of the Reformation in Scotland. 72p. 1985. 22.00x (ISBN 0-85411-021-6, Pub. by Saltire Soc.). State Mutual Bk.

REFORMATION–SPAIN

McCrie, Thomas. History of the Progress & Suppression of the Reformation in Spain in the Sixteenth Century. LC 79-127433. Repr. of 1829 ed. 30.00 (ISBN 0-404-04117-5). AMS Pr.

Yoder, John H., ed. Textos Encogidoes de la Reforma Radical. (Span.). 500p. (Orig.). 1984. pap. 25.00 (ISBN 0-8361-1237-7). Herald Pr.

REFORMATION–SWITZERLAND

Baker, J. Wayne. Heinrich Bullinger & the Covenant: The Other Reformed Tradition. LC 80-14667. xxvi, 300p. 1980. 24.95x (ISBN 0-8214-0554-3). Ohio U Pr.

Blackburn, William M. William Farel & the Story of the Swiss Reform. Date not set. Repr. of 1865 ed. 40.00 (ISBN 0-404-19870-8). AMS Pr.

Epistolae Tigurinae De Rebus Potissimum Ad Ecclesiae Anglicanae Reformationem Pertinentibus Conscriptae. 1848. 41.00 (ISBN 0-384-14505-1). Johnson Repr.

Jackson, Samuel M. Huldrych Zwingli: The Reformer of German Switzerland. 2nd rev. ed. LC 75-170836. Repr. of 1901 ed. 24.50 (ISBN 0-404-03543-4). AMS Pr.

Jones, R. Tudur. The Great Reformation. LC 85-23930. 272p. 1986. pap. 9.95 (ISBN 0-87784-606-5). Inter-Varsity.

Raitt, Jill, ed. Shapers of Religious Traditions in Germany, Switzerland, & Poland, Fifteen Sixty to Sixteen Hundred. LC 80-23287. 256p. 1981. text ed. 28.50x (ISBN 0-300-02457-6). Yale U Pr.

Zurich Letters, 2 Vols. 1842-1845. 51.00 ea. (ISBN 0-384-71255-X). Johnson Repr.

Zwingli. Selected Writings. 1972. 9.95x (ISBN 0-8122-1049-2). U of Pa Pr.

REFORMED CHURCH

see also Calvinism

Brouwer, Arie R. Reformed Church Roots. write for info. (ISBN 0-685-62275-4). Reformed Church.

Dillenberger, John, ed. John Calvin: Selections from His Writings. LC 75-26875. (American Academy of Religion. Aids for the Study of Religion). 590p. 1975. pap. 10.95 (ISBN 0-89130-025-2, 010302). Scholars Pr GA.

Furcha, E., tr. Huldrych Zwingli Writings in Defense of the Reformed Faith: Writings in the Defense of the Reformed Faith, Vol. 1. (Pittsburgh Theological Monographs: No. 12). 1984. pap. 19.95 (ISBN 0-915138-58-1). Pickwick.

Gerrish, B. A. Tradition & the Modern World: Reformed Theology in the Nineteenth Century. LC 78-4982. 1978. lib. bdg. 20.00x (ISBN 0-226-28866-8). U of Chicago Pr.

Leith, John H. Introduction to the Reformed Tradition: A Way of Being the Christian Community. rev. ed. LC 81-5968. (Illus.). 253p. 1981. pap. 10.95 (ISBN 0-8042-0479-9). John Knox.

Old, Hughes O. Guides to the Reformed Tradition: Worship. Leith, John H. & Kuykendall, John W., eds. LC 83-19616. 194p. 1984. pap. 11.95 (ISBN 0-8042-3252-0). John Knox.

The Reformed Pulpit. 2.50 (ISBN 0-686-23482-0). Rose Pub MI.

Ridder, Herman. Membership in the Reformed Church. pap. 1.65 (ISBN 0-686-23484-7). Rose Pub MI.

Slack, Kenneth. The United Reformed Church. 1978. pap. 3.15 (ISBN 0-08-021414-2). Pergamon.

Vandenberge, Peter N. The Historical Directory of the Reformed Church in America. 1978. pap. 17.95 (ISBN 0-8028-1746-7). Eerdmans.

REFORMED CHURCH–CATECHISMS AND CREEDS

see also Heidelberg Catechism

Calvin, Jean. Catechisms or, Manner to Teach-Children the Christian Religion. LC 68-54624. (English Experience Ser.: No. 46). 168p. 1968. Repr. of 1556 ed. 14.00 (ISBN 90-221-0046-4). Walter J Johnson.

Miller, Allen O. & Osterhaven, M. Eugene, trs. Heidelberg Catechism. LC 62-20891. 1963. pap. 2.25 (ISBN 0-8298-0060-3). Pilgrim NY.

Williamson, G. I. The Shorter Catechism: A Study Manual, 2 vols. Vol. 1. pap. 4.50 (ISBN 0-87552-539-3); Vol. 2. pap. 4.50 (ISBN 0-87552-540-7). Presby & Reformed.

REFORMED CHURCH–DOCTRINAL AND CONTROVERSIAL WORKS

Berkhof, Louis. Summary of Christian Doctrine. 1939. pap. 5.95 (ISBN 0-8028-1513-8). Eerdmans.

Calvin, Jean. Aphorismes of Christian Religion or a Verie Compendious Abridgement of M. I. Calvins Institutions Set Forth by M I Piscator. Holland, H., tr. LC 73-6107. (English Experience Ser.: No. 575). 1973. Repr. of 1596 ed. 26.00 (ISBN 90-221-0575-X). Walter J Johnson.

Calvin, John. Institutes of the Christian Religion: Beveridge Translation, 2 Vols. 1953. Set. pap. 16.95 (ISBN 0-8028-8026-6). Eerdmans.

--On God & Man. Strothmann, F. W., ed. LC 56-7500. (Milestones of Thought Ser.). 1965. o.p 6.00 (ISBN 0-8044-5214-8); pap. 3.95 (ISBN 0-8044-6073-6). Ungar.

Hageman, Howard G. Lily Among the Thorns. 1978. write for info. (ISBN 0-916466-00-0). Reformed Church.

O'Malley, J. Steven. Pilgrimage of Faith: The Legacy of the Otterbeins. LC 73-5684. (ATLA Monograph: No. 4). 226p. 1973. 18.00 (ISBN 0-8108-0626-6). Scarecrow.

Phillips, Nancy V. & Van Andel, Mary T. Journeying Together: A Study on the Psalms. write for info. (ISBN 0-916466-03-5). Reformed Church.

Shoemaker, Dennis E. Heritage & Hope: A People of Hope. write for info. (ISBN 0-916466-04-3). Reformed Church.

United Reformed Church in England & Wales-the Doctrine & Worship Committee. A Book of Services. 1980. 8.95x (ISBN 0-7152-0446-7). Outlook.

Van Til, Cornelius. Defense of the Faith. 1967. pap. 6.95 (ISBN 0-87552-483-4). Presby & Reformed.

REFORMED CHURCH–SERMONS

Bullinger, Henry. The Decades of Henry Bullinger, Minister of the Church of Zurich, 4 vols. 1849-1851. Set. 144.00 (ISBN 0-384-06315-2). Johnson Repr.

Calvin, Jean. Certain Homilies Containing Profitable Admonition for This Time. LC 73-6108. (English Experience Ser.: No. 576). 120p. 1973. Repr. of 1553 ed. 8.00 (ISBN 90-221-0576-8). Walter J Johnson.

REFORMED CHURCH IN AMERICA

Dalenburg, Cornelia & De Groot, David. Sharifa. (THe Historical Series of the Reformed Church in America: Vol. 11). (Orig.). 1983. pap. 11.95 (ISBN 0-8028-1973-7). Eerdmans.

DeJong. The Dutch Reformed Church in the American Colonies. LC 78-17216. 1978. pap. 8.95 (ISBN 0-8028-1741-6). Eerdmans.

Evans, Thomas G. & Wright, Toblas A., eds. Baptisms from Sixteen Thirty-Nine to Eighteen Hundred in the Reformed Dutch Church, New York, 2 Vols. 1298p. 1968. Repr. of 1902 ed. 75.00 (ISBN 0-8398-0152-1). Parnassus Imprints.

Harmelink, Herman. Ecumenism & the Reformed Church. 1969. pap. 3.95 (ISBN 0-8028-1281-3). Eerdmans.

Holland Society of New York. Records of the Reformed Dutch Church of Albany, New York, 1683-1809. LC 78-54063. 922p. (Repr. of the 1904-1927 eds.). 1978. 38.50 (ISBN 0-8063-0808-7). Genealog Pub.

Peale, Norman Vincent. The True Joy of Positive Living. 480p. 1985. pap. 16.95 (ISBN 0-8027-2503-1). Walker & Co.

Purple, Samuel S. Records of the Dutch Reformed Church in New Amsterdam & New York. 50.00 (ISBN 0-8490-0936-7). Gordon Pr.

Versteeg, Dingman, tr. Records of the Reformed Dutch Church of New Paltz, New York. LC 77-77266. 269p. 1977. Repr. of 1896 ed. 15.00 (ISBN 0-8063-0772-2). Genealog Pub.

REFORMED CHURCH IN THE UNITED STATES

see also United Church of Christ

Bratt, James D. Dutch Calvinism in Modern America: A History of a Conservative Subculture. (Illus.). 368p. (Orig.). 1984. pap. 13.95 (ISBN 0-8028-0009-2). Eerdmans.

Harner, Nevin C. Factors Related to Sunday School Growth & Decline in the Eastern Synod of the Reformed Church in the U. S. LC 71-176839. (Columbia University. Teachers College. Contributions to Education Ser.: No. 479). Repr. of 1931 ed. 22.50 (ISBN 0-404-55479-2). AMS Pr.

Hinke, William J., ed. Life & Letters of the Rev. John Philip Boehm: Founder of the Reformed Church in Pennsylvania, 1683-1749. LC 71-38784. (Religion in America, Ser. 2). 572p. 1972. Repr. of 1916 ed. 35.00 (ISBN 0-405-04069-5). Ayer Co Pubs.

REFORMED DUTCH CHURCH IN AMERICA

see Reformed Church in America

REFORMED PROTESTANT DUTCH CHURCH IN NORTH AMERICA

see Reformed Church in America

REFORMERS

Aston, Margaret. Lollards & Reformers: Images & Literacy in Late Medieval Religion. 405p. 1984. 35.00 (ISBN 0-907628-03-6). Hambledon Press.

Carter, John F. American Messiahs by the Unofficial Observer. LC 68-26232. 1968. Repr. of 1935 ed. 21.50x (ISBN 0-8046-0010-4, Pub by Kennikat). Assoc Faculty Pr.

Connolly, J. L. John Gerson: Reformer & Mystic. (Medieval Studies Ser.). (Illus.). Repr. of 1928 ed. lib. bdg. 44.00x (ISBN 0-697-00031-1). Irvington.

Lotz, Philip H., ed. Founders of Christian Movements. LC 71-111843. (Essay Index Reprint Ser). 1941. 17.00 (ISBN 0-8369-1672-7). Ayer Co Pubs.

Parbury, Kathleen. Women of Grace: A Biographical Dictionary of British Women Saints, Martyrs & Reformers. 224p. 1985. 25.00x (ISBN 0-85362-213-2, Oriel). Methuen Inc.

Whitman, Alden, ed. American Reformers. LC 85-636. (Illus.). 944p. 1985. 75.00 (ISBN 0-8242-0705-X). Wilson.

REFUGEES

Bau, Iqnatius. This Ground Is Holy: Church Sanctuary & Central American Refugees. LC 84-60406. 304p. (Orig.). 1985. pap. 9.95 (ISBN 0-8091-2720-2). Paulist Pr.

Fein, Helen. Congregational Sponsorship of Indochinese Refugees in the United States, 1979-1981: Helping Beyond Borders: A Study of Collective Altruism. LC 85-45952. 168p. 1987. 26.50x (ISBN 0-8386-3279-3). Fairleigh Dickinson.

Kitagawa, Joseph M., ed. American Refugee Policy: Ethical & Religious Reflections. 192p. (Orig.). 1985. pap. 9.95 (ISBN 0-86683-955-0, AY8541, HarpR). Har-Row.

REFUGEES, JEWISH

see also Jews–Migrations

Berghahn, Marion. German-Jewish Refugees in England: The Ambiguities of Assimilation. LC 83-9802. 270p. 1984. 30.00 (ISBN 0-312-32571-1). St Martin.

Feingold, Henry L. The Politics of Rescue: The Roosevelt Administration & the Holocaust, 1938-1945. LC 75-127049. 1970. 40.00 (ISBN 0-8135-0664-6). Rutgers U Pr.

Friedman, Philip. Their Brothers' Keepers: The Christian Heroes & Heroines Who Helped the Oppressed Escape the Nazi Terror. LC 57-8773. 1978. pap. 8.95 (ISBN 0-8052-5002-6, Pub. by Holocaust Library). Schocken.

Friedman, Saul S. No Haven for the Oppressed: United States Policy Toward Jewish Refugees, 1938-1945. LC 72-2271. 315p. 1973. 25.00x (ISBN 0-8143-1474-0). Wayne St U Pr.

Heller, James E. Our Share of Morning. LC 73-5262. 360p. 1974. Repr. of 1961 ed. lib. bdg. 22.50x (ISBN 0-8371-6874-0, BUOS). Greenwood.

Prital, David. In Search of Self: The Soviet Jewish Intelligentsia & the Exodus. 282p. 1983. pap. text ed. 25.00x (ISBN 965-223-420-6, Pub. by Magnes Pr Israel). Humanities.

Strauss, Herbert, ed. Jewish Immigrants of the Nazi Period in the U. S. A, 6 Vols. Set. lib. bdg. 130.00 (ISBN 0-317-11838-2); Vol. 1. 35.00 (ISBN 3-598-08006-9). Vol. 2 (ISBN 3-598-08007-7). Vol. 3, Pt. 1 (ISBN 3-598-08008-5). Vol. 3, Pt. 2 (ISBN 3-598-08013-1). K G Saur.

REFUGEES, RELIGIOUS

Hockings, Paul, ed. Ancient Hindu Refugees: Badaga Social History 1550-1975. (Studies in Anthropology). 1980. text ed. 39.50x (ISBN 90-279-7798-4). Mouton.

REGENERATION (IN RELIGION, FOLK-LORE, ETC.)

see also Birth (In Religion, Folk-Lore, etc.)

Baxter, Richard. The Reformed Pastor. 1979. pap. 4.95 (ISBN 0-85151-191-0). Banner of Truth.

Pink, Arthur W. Regeneration. pap. 0.75 (ISBN 0-685-00735-9). Reiner.

REGISTERS OF BIRTHS, DEATHS, MARRIAGES, ETC.

see also Church Work–Forms, Blanks, etc.

Bell, James P. Our Quaker Friends of Ye Olden Time. LC 76-22486. (Illus.). 287p. 1976. Repr. of 1905 ed. 17.50 (ISBN 0-8063-0732-3). Genealog Pub.

Dabbs, Jack A. & Breitenkamp, Edward C. Records of Salem Lutheran Church, Brenham, Texas 1850-1940. LC 86-72575. (Illus.). 501p. 1986. 35.00 (ISBN 0-911494-10-3). Dabbs.

Helbron, Peter. Catholic Baptisms in Western Pennsylvania, 1799-1828: Father Peter Helbron's Greensburg Register. LC 84-73331. 123p. 1985. Repr. of 1915 ed. 12.50 (ISBN 0-8063-1113-4). Genealog Pub.

Historical Records Survey, WPA Staff. Inventory of the Roman Catholic Church Records of New Hampshire. 19p. 1985. pap. 3.50 (ISBN 0-935207-18-X). DanBury Hse Bks.

Mecenseffy, Grete. Tauferaktenband Osterreich III. (TAK Ser.: Vol. XIV). (Ger.). 795p. 1982. 105.00 (ISBN 0-8361-1265-2). Herald Pr.

Smith, George M. Hebron Church Register 1750-1825, Madison, Virginia, 2 vols. 1981. pap. 13.00 set (ISBN 0-917968-08-5). Shenandoah Hist.

Weiser, Frederick S., ed. & tr. Maryland German Church Records, Vol. 4: Evangelical Lutheran Church Baptisms, 1780-1811, Frederick, Maryland. 150p. (Orig.). 1987. pap. 20.00x (ISBN 0-913281-06-9). Noodle Doosey.

Wust, Klaus. Record of Hawksbill Church 1788-1850, Page County, Virginia. 1979. pap. 5.50 (ISBN 0-917968-06-9). Shenandoah Hist.

REIMS–NOTRE DAME (CATHEDRAL)

Pretzel, Ulrich. Fruhgeschichte Des Deutschen Reims. (Ger). 27.00 (ISBN 0-384-47740-2); pap. 22.00 (ISBN 0-685-02131-9). Johnson Repr.

Zemach, Harve. The Judge: An Untrue Tale. LC 79-87209. (Illus.). 48p. 1969. 14.95 (ISBN 0-374-33960-0). FS&G.

REINCARNATION

see also Anthroposophy; Karma; Soul

Abhedananda, Swami. Reincarnation. 2.95 (ISBN 0-87481-604-1). Vedanta Pr.

Atkinson, Linda. Have We Lived Before? (High Interest, Low Vocabulary Ser.). (Illus.). 112p. 1982. PLB 8.95 (ISBN 0-396-07999-7). Dodd.

Atkinson, William W. Reincarnation & Law of Karma. 8.00 (ISBN 0-911662-26-X). Yoga.

Besant, Annie. Reincarnation. 11th ed. 1975. 5.25 (ISBN 0-8356-7019-8). Theos Pub Hse.

Bhaktivedanta, A. C. Coming Back: The Science of Reincarnation. (Contemporary Vedic Library Ser.). (Illus.). 133p. 1982. 2.95 (ISBN 0-89213-114-4). Bhaktivedanta.

Brennan, J. H. Reincarnation Five Keys to Past Lives. (Paths to Inner Power Ser.). 1981. pap. 3.50 (ISBN 0-85030-275-7). Weiser.

Brownell, George B. Reincarnation. 153p. 1981. pap. 9.00 (ISBN 0-89540-107-X, SB-107). Sun Pub.

Butler, Chris. Reincarnation Explained. LC 83-61000. 288p. 1984. 12.95 (ISBN 0-88187-000-5). Science Identity.

Cavarnos, Constantine. The Future Life According to Orthodox Teaching. Auxentios, Hieromonk & Chrysostomos, Archimandrite, trs. from Gr. 100p. (Orig.). 1985. pap. 6.50 (ISBN 0-911165-06-1). Ctr Trad Orthodox.

Chaney, Robert G. Reincarnation: Cycle of Opportunity. LC 84-72387. (Adventures in Esoteric Learning Ser.). (Illus.). 56p. 1984. pap. 4.25 (ISBN 0-918936-13-6). Astara.

Chinmoy, Sri. Death & Reincarnation: Eternity's Voyage. LC 74-81308. (Illus.). 143p. (Orig.). 1974. pap. 3.95 (ISBN 0-88497-038-8). Aum Pubns.

Cooke, Grace & Cooke, Ivan. The Return of Arthur Conan Doyle. (Illus.). 1963. 9.95 (ISBN 0-85487-037-7). De Vorss.

Cooper, Irving S. Reincarnation: A Hope of the World. LC 79-11475. 1979. pap. 3.95 (ISBN 0-8356-0528-0, Quest). Theos Pub Hse.

Cranston, Sylvia & Williams, Carey. Reincarnation: A New Horizon in Science, Religion & Society. 1984. 16.95 (ISBN 0-517-55496-8, Harmony). Crown.

Crawford, Shirley O. Is God Dead Within You? 112p. 1981. 6.50 (ISBN 0-682-49789-4). Exposition Pr FL.

Dallison, Dennis. Yamamoto Returns: A True Story of Reincarnation. (Illus.). 200p. 1985. pap. 5.95 (ISBN 0-932642-98-5). Unarius Pubns.

Druffel, Ann & Marcotte, Armand. Past Lives Future Growth. (Inner Visions Ser.). (Orig.). 1987. pap. 12.95 (ISBN 0-917086-88-0). A C S Pubns Inc.

Ducasse, C. J. Critical Examination of the Belief in a Life after Death. 336p. 1974. pap. 39.50x spiral (ISBN 0-398-03037-5). C C Thomas.

Endemann, Carl T. Voyage into the Past: Continuous Life Through 35 Centuries. LC 81-81554. (Illus.). 1981. 9.95 (ISBN 0-931926-10-6). Alta Napa.

Finkelstein, Adrian. Your Past Lives & the Healing Process. 233p. (Orig.). 1985. pap. 9.95x (ISBN 0-87418-001-5). Coleman Pub.

--Your Past Lives & the Healing Process. 233p. (Orig.). 1985. pap. 9.95x. A Finkelstein.

Fisher, Joe. The Case for Reincarnation. 208p. 1985. pap. 3.95 (ISBN 0-553-24868-5). Bantam.

Fox, Emmet. Power Through Constructive Thinking. 1940. 12.45 (ISBN 0-06-062930-4, HarpR). Har-Row.

Freeman, James D. The Case for Reincarnation. 320p. 1986. 5.95 (ISBN 0-87159-021-2). Unity School.

Gandy, Tillie H. Of Cabbages & Kings. 1983. 6.50 (ISBN 0-8062-2138-0). Carlton.

Gandy, Tilly H. Ears to Hear. 1984. 6.95 (ISBN 0-8062-2293-X). Carlton.

--Ten True Tales of Reincarnation. 1984. 6.00 (ISBN 0-8062-2292-1). Carlton.

Geisler, Norman L. & Amano, J. Yutaka. The Reincarnation Sensation. 224p. 1986. pap. 6.95 (ISBN 0-8423-5404-2). Tyndale.

Green, Harry L. Echoes of Thunder. LC 80-66322. 167p. 1980. 10.95 (ISBN 0-936958-00-6); pap. 5.95 (ISBN 0-936958-01-4). Emerald Hse.

Guirdham, Arthur. Cathars & Reincarnation. LC 77-17012. (Illus.). 1978. pap. 3.75 (ISBN 0-8356-0506-X, Quest). Theos Pub Hse.

Hall, Manly P. Death to Rebirth. pap. 4.95 (ISBN 0-89314-395-2). Philos Res.

--Reincarnation: The Cycle of Necessity. 1978. 8.50 (ISBN 0-89314-519-X); pap. 4.95 (ISBN 0-89314-387-1). Philos Res.

--Research on Reincarnation. pap. 2.50 (ISBN 0-89314-349-9). Philos Res.

Head, Joseph & Cranston, S. L. Reincarnation: An East-West Anthology. LC 68-146. 1968. pap. 5.50 (ISBN 0-8356-0035-1, Quest). Theos Pub Hse.

--Reincarnation: the Phoenix Fire Mystery. 1977. 10.95 (ISBN 0-517-52893-2). Crown.

Hodson, Geoffrey. Reincarnation, Fact or Fallacy. rev. ed. LC 67-4405. 1967. pap. 2.95 (ISBN 0-8356-0046-7, Quest). Theos Pub Hse.

Hubbard, L. Ron. Have You Lived Before This Life? A Study of Death & Evidence of Past Lives. 1978. 42.87 (ISBN 0-88404-055-0). Bridge Pubns Inc.

Jyotir Maya Nanda, Swami. Death & Reincarnation. (Illus.). 1970. 6.99 (ISBN 0-934664-04-8). Yoga Res Foun.

Kostelanetz, Richard. Reincarnations. 1981. pap. 5.00 (ISBN 0-686-84602-8); signed 50.00 (ISBN 0-686-84603-6). Future Pr.

Lenz, Frederick. Lifetimes: True Accounts of Reincarnation. 224p. 1986. pap. 2.95 (ISBN 0-449-20908-3, Crest). Fawcett.

Lewis, H. Spencer. Las Mansiones del Alma. 16th ed. AMORC Staff, tr. from Eng. (Span., Illus.). 235p. 1981. pap. 7.00 (ISBN 0-912057-67-X, GS-511). AMORC.

--Mansions of the Soul. 19th ed. LC 30-34218. 1981. 11.95 (ISBN 0-912057-07-6, G-511). AMORC.

Lewis, Jim. Reincarnation & Translation. 31p. (Orig.). 1981. pap. 3.00 (ISBN 0-942482-02-6). Unity Church Denver.

Lewis, Spencer H. Mansions of the Soul. LC 30-34218. 338p. 1986. pap. 9.95 (ISBN 0-912057-43-2, G-655). AMORC.

Lodo, Venerable L. Bardo Teachings: The Way of Death & Rebirth. Clark, Nancy & Parke, Caroline M., eds. LC 82-21372. (Illus.). 76p. 1982. pap. text ed. 5.95 (ISBN 0-910165-00-9). KDK Pubns.

Loewe, Michael. Ways to Paradise: The Chinese Quest for Immortality. (Illus.). 1979. text ed. 34.00x (ISBN 0-04-181025-2). Allen Unwin.

Luria. Gates of Reincarnation. (Hebrew.). 200p. 1985. pap. 9.95 (ISBN 0-943688-49-3). Res Ctr Kabbalah.

MacGregor, Geddes. Reincarnation As a Christian Hope. LC 81-8013. (Library of Philosophy & Religion). 174p. 1982. 28.50x (ISBN 0-389-20220-7). B&N Imports.

Metz, Warren. Change of Face & Pace. LC 82-90982. 1983. 8.95 (ISBN 0-87212-165-8). Libra.

Miles, Eustace. Life after Life: The Theory of Reincarnation. 180p. 1985. pap. 10.00 (ISBN 0-89540-126-6, SB-126). Sun Pub.

Moore, Marcia & Douglas, Mark. Reincarnation, Key to Immortality. LC 67-19603. 1968. 10.00 (ISBN 0-912240-02-4). Arcane Pubns.

Morey, Robert A. Reincarnation & Christianity. LC 80-24497. 60p. 1980. pap. 2.95 (ISBN 0-87123-493-9, 210493). Bethany Hse.

The Next Life: Course XX, Lessons 173-82. (Illus.). 1976. pap. 11.00 (ISBN 0-87887-356-2). Church of Light.

Norman, Ruth & Spaegel, Charles. Principles & Practice of Past Life Therapy. (Illus.). 500p. 1984. 10.95 (ISBN 0-932642-79-9). Unarius Pubns.

Paramananda, Swami. Reincarnation & Immortality. 2nd ed. 1961. 4.50 (ISBN 0-911564-05-5). Vedanta Ctr.

Perkins, James S. Experiencing Reincarnation. LC 77-5249. (Illus.). 1977. pap. 4.95 (ISBN 0-8356-0500-0, Quest). Theos Pub Hse.

--Through Death to Rebirth. new ed. LC 61-13301. (Illus.). 124p. 1974. pap. 4.25 (ISBN 0-8356-0451-9, Quest). Theos Pub Hse.

Querido, Rene. Questions & Answers on Reincarnation & Karma. 1977. pap. 3.50 (ISBN 0-916786-18-8). St George Bk Serv.

Riley, Betty. A Veil Too Thin: Reincarnation Out of Control. LC 84-50090. 96p. 1984. pap. 2.95 (ISBN 0-911842-37-3). Valley Sun.

Risedorf, Gwen. Born Today, Born Yesterday: Reincarnation. LC 77-21406. (Myth, Magic & Superstition). (Illus.). 1977. PLB 14.65 (ISBN 0-8172-1045-8). Raintree Pubs.

Robillard, Edmond. Reincarnation: Illusion or Reality. LC 82-1638. 182p. (Orig.). 1982. pap. 5.95 (ISBN 0-8189-0432-1). Alba.

Rogo, D. Scott. The Search for Yesterday: A Critical Examination of the Evidence for Reincarnation. 288p. 1985. 22.95 (ISBN 0-13-797036-6); pap. 10.95 (ISBN 0-13-797028-5). P H.

Sharma, I. C. Cayce, Karma & Reincarnation. LC 81-23214. 186p. 1982. pap. 5.50 (ISBN 0-8356-0563-9, Quest). Theos Pub Hse.

Shelley, Violet M. Reincarnation Unnecessary. 1979. pap. 5.95 (ISBN 0-87604-112-8). ARE Pr.

Snyder, John. Reincarnation vs Resurrection. (Orig.). 1984. pap. 4.95 (ISBN 0-8024-0321-2). Moody.

Sri Aurobindo. The Problem of Rebirth. 1979. pap. 15.00 (ISBN 0-89744-913-4). Auromere.

Stearn, Jess. Yoga, Youth & Reincarnation. (Illus.). 352p. 1986. pap. 3.95 (ISBN 0-553-26057-X). Bantam.

Stein, Walter J. The Principle of Reincarnation. 1986. pap. 2.50 (ISBN 0-916786-85-4). St George Bk Serv.

Steiner, Rudolf. Reincarnation & Immortality. 3rd ed. LC 77-130817. 224p. 1970. pap. 5.00 (ISBN 0-89345-221-1, Steinerbks). Garber Comm.

--Reincarnation & Karma: Their Significance in Modern Culture. Osmond, D. S. & Davy, Charles, trs. (Ger.). 95p. 1977. pap. 6.50 (ISBN 0-919924-06-9, Pub. by Steiner Book Centre Canada). Anthroposophic.

Stroh, Luella. Aamot. 320p. (Orig.). 1987. pap. 9.95 (ISBN 0-939213-02-8). Oasis Bks.

Sutphen, Dick. Past Lives, Future Loves. 1982. pap. 3.50 (ISBN 0-671-54363-6). PB.

--Reincarnation-The Unanswered Questions. 100p. 1983. pap. 2.95 (ISBN 0-686-47947-5). Valley Sun.

Sutphen, Dick & Taylor, Lauren L. Past Life Therapy in Action. 100p. 1983. pap. 2.95 (ISBN 0-911842-32-2). Valley Sun.

Tingley, Katherine. Reincarnation. 72p. 1981. pap. 4.50 (ISBN 0-89540-111-8, SB-111). Sun Pub.

Van Auken, John. Born Again... & Again & Again: How Reincarnation Occurs, Why & What It Means to You. (Illus.). 144p. 1984. 12.95 (ISBN 0-917483-00-6). Innervision.

--Born Again & Again: How Reincarnation Occurs, Why & What It Means to You! LC 84-223300. (Illus.). 144p. (Orig.). 1985. pap. 8.95 (ISBN 0-917483-02-2). Innervision.

Van Den Tak, Richard. The Scientific Proof of the Existence of Reincarnation & Transmigration. (Illus.). 1981. 16.50 (ISBN 0-89962-015-9). Todd & Honeywell.

Wilson, Colin. Afterlife. 288p. 1987. 16.95 (ISBN 0-385-23765-0, Dolp). Doubleday.

Wolfe, Hal. Through the Eye of the Dove: One Man's Journey into Reincarnation. Date not set. pap. price not set. Dearen Pub.

Wright, Leoline L. Reincarnation. LC 74-18350. pap. 3.25 (ISBN 0-8356-0453-5, Quest). Theos Pub Hse.

Wright, Leoline L., et al. Reincarnation: A Lost Chord in Modern Thought. Small, Emmett & Todd, Helen, eds. (Theosophical Manual). 122p. 1975. pap. 3.25 (ISBN 0-8356-0453-5). Point Loma Pub.

Young, Robert & Young, Loy. Past Lives: The Key to Your Present Relationships: Introducing the Youngs' Past Life Regression Technique. Pellegrin, Mignonette, ed. LC 85-73214. (Illus.). 344p. (Orig.). 1985. pap. 19.95 (ISBN 0-936121-00-9). Draco Prod Pubns.

RELICS AND RELIQUARIES

see also Jesus Christ–Relics of the Passion; Miracles; Saints; Shrines

Cruz, Joan C. Relics. LC 84-60744. (Illus.). 352p. 1984. pap. 10.95 (ISBN 0-87973-701-8, 701). Our Sunday Visitor.

Geary, Patrick J. Furta Sacra: Thefts of Relics in the Central Middle Ages. LC 77-85538. 1978. 26.50 (ISBN 0-691-05261-1). Princeton U Pr.

Grandaur, Georg, ed. & tr. Leben Des Abtes Eigil Von Fulda und der Aebtissin Hathumoda Von Gandersheim Nebst der Uebertragung Des Hl. Liborius und Des Hl. Vitus. (Ger). pap. 10.00 (ISBN 0-384-19640-3). Johnson Repr.

RELIGION

see also Agnosticism; Atheism; Belief and Doubt; Cultus; Deism; Faith; Fetishism; Monotheism; Mysteries, Religious; Mysticism; Myth; Mythology; Natural Theology; Pantheism; Positivism; Psychology, Religious; Rationalism; Religions; Revelation; Satanism; Skepticism; Spiritual Life; Supernatural; Superstition; Syncretism (Religion); Theism; Theology; Theosophy; Worship

also subdivision Religion, or Religion and Mythology, under names of countries, races, peoples, etc., e.g. Egypt–Religion; Indians of North America–Religion and Mythology; also headings beginning with the word Religious

Ackermann, Robert J. Religion as Critique. LC 84-16471. 184p. 1985. lib. bdg. 20.00x (ISBN 0-87023-462-5); pap. 8.95x (ISBN 0-87023-463-3). U of Mass Pr.

Al-Ghazzali. Alchemy of Happiness. 1964. 3.75x (ISBN 0-87902-055-5). Orientalia.

--Confessions of Al-Ghazzali. Watt, W. M., tr. 3.25x (ISBN 0-87902-059-8). Orientalia.

--Mishkat Al-Anwar: A Niche for Lights. 1952. 4.25x (ISBN 0-87902-051-2). Orientalia.

--Mysteries of Fasting. 1970. 3.50x (ISBN 0-87902-052-0). Orientalia.

--Mysteries of Purity. 1966. 4.50x (ISBN 0-87902-053-9). Orientalia.

--On Divine Predicates & Their Attributes. 1970. 6.50x (ISBN 0-87902-057-1). Orientalia.

--Some Moral & Religious Teachings. 4.50x (ISBN 0-87902-056-3). Orientalia.

--Tahafut Al-Falasifah. 8.25x (ISBN 0-87902-054-7). Orientalia.

Allegro, John M. All Manner of Men. (Illus.). 186p. 1982. spiral bdg. 18.50x (ISBN 0-398-04575-5). C C Thomas.

Allen, Douglas. Structure & Creativity in Religion. (Religion & Reason Ser.: No. 14). 1978. 20.40x (ISBN 90-279-7594-9). Mouton.

Allport, Gordon W. Individual & His Religion. 1967. pap. 4.95 (ISBN 0-02-083130-7). Macmillan.

Alves, Rubem. What Is Religion? Vinzant, Don, tr. from Portugese. LC 83-19398. Orig. Title: O Que E Religiao. 96p. (Orig.). 1984. pap. 4.95 (ISBN 0-88344-705-3). Orbis Bks.

Arnold, Charlotte. Group Readings for the Church. (Paperback Program Ser.). (Orig.). 1975. pap. 1.95 (ISBN 0-8010-0065-3). Baker Bk.

Augustinus, Saint Aurelius. De Genesi ad Litteram Libri Duodecim Eiusdem Libri Capitula, Pt. 1. (Corpus Scriptorum Ecclesiasticorum Latinorum Ser: Vol. 28). 50.00 (ISBN 0-384-02485-8). Johnson Repr.

Badley, John H. Form & Spirit. LC 77-113347. (Essay & General Literature Index Reprint Ser). 1971. Repr. of 1951 ed. 19.50x (ISBN 0-8046-1398-2, Pub. by Kennikat). Assoc Faculty Pr.

Bahm, Archie J. World's Living Religions. (Arcturus Books Paperbacks). 384p. 1971. pap. 12.95x (ISBN 0-8093-0529-1). S Ill U Pr.

Barker, George. Thurgarton Church. 1969. write for info. (ISBN 0-685-01054-6, Pub. by Trigram Pr); signed ed. 100 copies 12.00 ea.; pap. 2.00 (ISBN 0-685-01056-2). Small Pr Dist.

Barnes, Harry E. The Twilight of Christianity. 75.00 (ISBN 0-87700-037-9). Revisionist Pr.

Barnes, Michael H. In the Presence of Mystery: An Introduction to the Study of Human Religiousness. 324p. (Orig.). 1984. pap. 9.95 (ISBN 0-89622-205-5). Twenty-Third.

Barron, Howard H., ed. Of Everlasting Value, Vol. 2. (Orig.). pap. 5.95 (ISBN 0-89036-130-4). Hawkes Pub Inc.

Bascom, John. Science, Philosophy & Religion. LC 75-3041. Repr. of 1871 ed. 36.00 (ISBN 0-404-59039-X). AMS Pr.

Bawa Muhaiyaddeen, M. R. The Guidebook to the True Secret of the Heart, Vol. 2. LC 75-44557. (Illus.). 232p. 1976. pap. 5.95 (ISBN 0-914390-08-2). Fellowship Pr PA.

Belanger, Merlyn. On Religious Maturity. LC 61-15238. 1962. 5.95 (ISBN 0-8022-0090-7). Philos Lib.

Bender, David L. & Leone, Bruno, eds. Religion & Human Experience: Opposing Viewpoints. LC 85-7660. 1981. 11.95 (ISBN 0-89908-333-1); pap. text ed. 6.95 (ISBN 0-89908-308-0). Greenhaven.

Bennett, Charles A. Dilemma of Religious Knowledge. LC 71-85986. (Essay & General Literature Index Reprint Ser). 1969. pap. text ed. 15.95x (ISBN 0-8046-0538-6, Pub. by Kennikat). Assoc Faculty Pr.

Bertram, Martin H., tr. Luther's Works, Vol. 23. LC 55-9893. 1958. 16.95 (ISBN 0-570-06423-6, 15-1765). Concordia.

Bettenson, Henry, ed. Documents of the Christian Church. 2nd ed. 1970. pap. 8.95 (ISBN 0-19-501293-3). Oxford U Pr.

Bixler, Julius S. Religion for Free Minds. LC 75-3048. (Philosophy in America Ser.). 1976. Repr. of 1939 ed. 18.00 (ISBN 0-404-59045-4). AMS Pr.

Bjerregaard, C. H. The Great Mother: A Gospel of the Eternally Feminine. 1977. lib. bdg. 59.95 (ISBN 0-8490-1900-1). Gordon Pr.

Bodin, J. Selected Writings on Philosophy, Religion & Politics. Rose, Paul L., ed. xiv, 94p. (Orig.). 1980. pap. text ed. 18.50x (Pub. by Droz Switzerland). Coronet Bks.

Booth, Catherine. Papers on Practical Religion. (Writings of Catherine Booth Ser.). 1986. Repr. of 1891 ed. deluxe ed. 4.95 (ISBN 0-86544-036-0). Salvation Army.

Bowker, John. The Religious Imagination & the Sense of God. 1978. text ed. 32.50x (ISBN 0-19-826646-4). Oxford U Pr.

Bowne, Borden P. The Essence of Religion. LC 75-3070. Repr. of 1910 ed. 34.50 (ISBN 0-404-59069-1). AMS Pr.

Braun, Herbert, et al. God & Christ: Existence & Province. Funk, Robert W. & Ebeling, Gerhard, eds. lib. bdg. 17.50x (ISBN 0-88307-042-1). Gannon.

Breaking the Devil's Hold. 1982. 1.25 (ISBN 0-89858-032-3). Fill the Gap.

Brownlow, Leroy. God, the Bible & Common Sense. 1978. pap. 2.50 (ISBN 0-915720-48-5). Brownlow Pub Co.

Buck, Peter H. Anthropology & Religion. 1939. 11.50x (ISBN 0-686-83471-2). Elliots Bks.

Bunyan, John. Reprobation Asserted. pap. 1.25 (ISBN 0-685-19841-3). Reiner.

Bush, Richard C., et al. Religious Word. 1982. text ed. write for info. (ISBN 0-02-317480-3). Macmillan.

Butler, J. Donald. The Language of Exixtence & Faith. LC 86-30549. 1987. 19.95 (ISBN 0-8022-2532-2). Philos Lib.

Butler, Joseph. The Analogy of Religion. 30.00 (ISBN 0-8274-1862-0). R West.

Caird, Edward. Evolution of Religion, 2 Vols. in 1. LC 1-17697. (Gifford Lectures 1890-1892). 1968. Repr. of 1893 ed. 46.00 (ISBN 0-527-14120-8). Kraus Repr.

Campbell, Murry M. Why Denominationalism? LC 84-90492. 140p. 1985. 10.00 (ISBN 0-533-06376-0). Vantage.

Caplow, Theodore, et al. All Faithful People: Change & Continuity in Middletown's Religion. LC 82-24759. x, 380p. 1983. 19.50 (ISBN 0-8166-1230-7). U of Minn Pr.

Carlton, Eric. Patterns of Belief, 2 vols. Incl. Vol. 1. Peoples & Religion. 130p. pap. 4.95 Vol. 1 (ISBN 0-04-377004-5); Vol. 2. Religions in Society. 140p. pap. 4.95 2 vols. each (ISBN 0-04-377005-3); pap. 4.95 Vol. 2. 1973. pap. 6.95 ea. Attic Pr.

Carmody & Carmody. Shamans, Prophets & Sages: A Concise Intro to World Religion. 1984. write for info. (ISBN 0-534-04263-5). Wadsworth Pub.

Carmody, Denise L. & Carmody, John. Religion: The Great Questions. 176p. 1983. pap. 11.95 (ISBN 0-8164-2476-4, HarpR). Har-Row.

Carre, E. G. Praying Hyde. LC 82-73972. 183p. 1983. pap. 4.95 (ISBN 0-88270-541-5). Bridge Pub.

Chalfant, H. Paul & Beckley, Robert E. Religion in Contemporary Society. 500p. 1986. text ed. 28.95 (ISBN 0-87484-691-9). Mayfield Pub.

Chesterton, G. K. The Everlasting Man. 280p. 1974. pap. 4.50 (ISBN 0-385-07198-1, Im). Doubleday.

Chiesa, Bruno. The Emergence of Hebrew Biblical Pointing, Vol. 1. (Judentum v. Umwelt Ser.: Vol. 1). 92p. 1979. pap. 17.70 (ISBN 3-8204-6419-0). P Lang Pubs.

Childbirth God's Way. 1982. 1.25 (ISBN 0-89858-027-7). Fill the Gap.

Cobb, John B., Jr. God & the World. LC 69-11374. 138p. 1969. pap. 5.95 (ISBN 0-664-24860-8). Westminster.

Colless, Brian & Donovan, Peter, eds. Religion in New Zealand Society. 216p. 1980. 17.95 (ISBN 0-567-09303-4, Pub. by T & T Clark Uk). Fortress.

Collier, Howard E. Experiment with a Life. (Orig.). 1953. pap. 2.500784485x (ISBN 0-87574-069-3). Pendle Hill.

Conference On The Scientific Spirit And Democratic Faith - 3rd. Science for Democracy. facs. ed. LC 70-121459. (Essay Index Reprint Ser.). 1946. 18.00 (ISBN 0-8369-1793-6). Ayer Co Pubs.

Conference On The Scientific Spirit And Democratic Faith-1st-New York-1943. Scientific Spirit & Democratic Faith. facs. ed. LC 72-121457. (Essay Index Reprint Ser). 1944. 14.00 (ISBN 0-8369-1872-X). Ayer Co Pubs.

Connolly, Myles. Mister Blue. pap. 3.50 (ISBN 0-385-02866-0, Im). Doubleday.

Conquest of the Mind. 1982. 3.50 (ISBN 0-89858-037-4). Fill the Gap.

Cooper, Douglas. Living in Our Finest Hour. Phillips, Max, ed. (RWD Ser.). 112p. 1982. pap. 4.95 (ISBN 0-8163-0465-3). Pacific Pr Pub Assn.

The Cord: Twenty-Five Year Index 1950-1975. 1977. 4.00 (ISBN 0-686-19080-7). Franciscan Inst.

Cornish, Graham. Religious Periodicals Directory. (Clio Periodicals Directories Ser.). 250p. 1986. lib. bdg. 89.00 (ISBN 0-87436-365-9). ABC-Clio.

Costello, Don. For Inner Peace & Strength. 1978. 4.00 (ISBN 0-8198-0380-4); pap. 3.00 (ISBN 0-8198-0381-2). Dghtrs St Paul.

Coulson, John. Religion & Imagination. 1981. 39.95x (ISBN 0-19-826656-1). Oxford U Pr.

Creel, Richard. Religion & Doubt: Toward a Faith of Your Own. 1977. write for info. (ISBN 0-13-771931-0). P-H.

Crone, Patricia & Cook, M. Hagarism: The Making of the Islamic World. LC 75-41714. 1980. pap. 14.95 (ISBN 0-521-29754-0). Cambridge U Pr.

Crosby, Donald A. Interpretive Theories of Religion. (Religion & Reason Ser.: No.20). 336p. 1981. 34.25x (ISBN 90-279-3039-2). Mouton.

Daniels, Madeline M. Living Your Religion in the Real World. LC 84-18209. 192p. 14.95 (ISBN 0-13-539016-8); pap. 6.95 (ISBN 0-13-539008-7). P-H.

Dasgupta, S. N. Religion & Rational Outlook. 1974. Repr. 9.95 (ISBN 0-8426-0661-0). Orient Bk Dist.

Daughters of St. Paul. Religion for the People of Today. LC 78-160576. (Illus.). 1971. pap. 1.25 (ISBN 0-8198-0345-6). Dghtrs St Paul.

Davids, Rhys. Vinaya Texts, 3 vols. lib. bdg. 300.00 (ISBN 0-87968-513-1). Krishna Pr.

Davis, J., ed. Religious Organization & Religious Experience. (ASA Monograph). 1982. 42.00 (ISBN 0-12-206580-8). Acad Pr.

Dawson, Christopher H. Progress & Religion, an Historical Enquiry. LC 79-104266. Repr. of 1929 ed. lib. bdg. 27.50x (ISBN 0-8371-3917-1, DAPR). Greenwood.

Deitrick, Bernard E. Know Your Neighbor's Faith. LC 83-7259. (Orig.). 1983. pap. 3.95x (ISBN 0-915324-19-9); pap. 3.00 members. CSLA.

Deux Redactions Du Roman Des Sept Sages De Rome. 1876. 28.00 (ISBN 0-384-54933-0); pap. 22.00 (ISBN 0-384-54923-3). Johnson Repr.

Dewey, John. Common Faith. (Terry Lectures Ser.). 1934. pap. 3.95x (ISBN 0-300-00069-3, Y18). Yale U Pr.

Directives for the Mutual Relations Between Bishops & Religions in the Church. pap. cancelled (ISBN 0-686-15367-7, V-591). US Catholic.

Dollinger, Johann J. Von. Lectures on the Reunion of the Churches. LC 74-131579. (Sources in the History of Interpretation: No. 2). 1973. 15.00x (ISBN 0-8401-0567-3). A R Allenson.

Drake, Durant. Problems of Religion: An Introductory Survey. LC 68-19268. Repr. of 1916 ed. lib. bdg. 22.50x (ISBN 0-8371-0062-3, DRPR). Greenwood.

Eastman, Roger, ed. The Ways of Religion. 608p. 1975. pap. text ed. 21.95 scp (ISBN 0-06-382595-3, CP, HarpC). Har-Row.

Edwards, Jonathan. Sinners in the Hands of an Angry God. pap. 0.50 (ISBN 0-685-00746-4). Reiner.

Eliade, Mircea. The Sacred & the Profane: The Nature of Religion. Trask, Willard, tr. LC 58-10904. 1968. pap. 4.95 (ISBN 0-15-679201-X, Harv). HarBraceJ.

--The Sacred & the Profane: The Nature of Religion. 1983. 13.75 (ISBN 0-8446-6080-9). Peter Smith.

--The Two & the One. Cohen, J. M., tr. LC 79-2268. 1979. pap. 7.00 (ISBN 0-226-20389-1, P811). U of Chicago Pr.

Ellwood, Robert S., Jr. Introducing Religion: From Inside & Outside. (Illus.). 240p. 1983. pap. text ed. write for info. (ISBN 0-13-477497-3). P-H.

Exposing Demon's Work. 1982. 1.25 (ISBN 0-89858-034-X). Fill the Gap.

Exposing the Devil's Work. 1982. 1.25 (ISBN 0-89858-033-1). Fill the Gap.

Findhorn Community. The Findhorn Garden. 1976. pap. 10.95 (ISBN 0-06-090520-4, CN520, PL). Har-Row.

Flinn, Frank K. & Hendricks, Tyler, eds. Religion in the Pacific Era. 244p. (Orig.). 1985. (Pub. by New Era Bks.); pap. text ed. 12.95 (ISBN 0-913757-19-5, Pub. by New Era Bks.). Paragon Hse.

Fosdick, Harry E. As I See Religion. LC 75-11835. 201p. 1975. Repr. of 1932 ed. lib. bdg. 45.00x (ISBN 0-8371-8142-9, FOAI). Greenwood.

Freud, Sigmund. The Future of an Illusion. Strachey, James, ed. 1975. 10.95 (ISBN 0-393-01120-8); pap. 2.95 (ISBN 0-393-00831-2). Norton.

Friedman, Maurice S. & Burke, T. Patrick. Searching in the Syntax of Things: Experiments in the Study of Religion. LC 70-171494. pap. 40.00 (2026864). Bks Demand UMI.

Fuller, J. F. C. Secret Wisdom of Qabalah. 1976. Repr. 7.00 (ISBN 0-911662-63-4). Yoga.

Gangel, Elizabeth & McDaniel, Elsiebeth. You Can Reach Families Through Their Babies. 64p. 1976. pap. 3.50 (ISBN 0-88207-140-8). Victor Bks.

Gilman, Charlotte P. His Religion & Hers: A Study of the Faith of Our Fathers & the Work of Our Mothers. LC 75-29509. (Pioneers of the Woman's Movement: An International Perspective Ser.). xi, 300p. 1976. Repr. of 1923 ed. 26.50 (ISBN 0-88355-377-5). Hyperion-Conn.

Glock, Charles Y. & Bellah, Robert N., eds. The New Religious Consciousness. LC 75-17295. 1976. 36.50x (ISBN 0-520-03083-4); pap. 11.95x (ISBN 0-520-03472-4, CAMPUS 329). U of Cal Pr.

Goitein, S. D., ed. Religion in a Religious Age. 10.00x (ISBN 0-87068-268-7, Pub. by an Academic Inst); pap. 8.95. Ktav.

Goldman, Ronald. Readiness for Religion. 1970. pap. 4.95 (ISBN 0-8164-2060-2, SP70, HarpR). Har-Row.

Goldsmith, Joel S. Beyond Words & Thoughts. 200p. 1974. pap. 4.95 (ISBN 0-8065-0447-1). Citadel Pr.

Goldstein, Eleanor C., ed. Religion, Vol. 1 (incl. 1978-1980 Supplements) (Social Issues Resources Ser.). 1981. 70.00 (ISBN 0-89777-021-8). Soc Issues.

--Religion, Vol. 2 (incl. 1981-1985 Supplements) 1986. 70.00 (ISBN 0-89777-053-6). Soc Issues.

Greeley, Andrew M. Religion: A Secular Theory. 144p. 1982. text ed. 19.95 (ISBN 0-02-912870-6); pap. text ed. 8.95x (ISBN 0-02-912880-3). Free Pr.

Grollman, Earl A., ed. Explaining Death to Children. LC 67-4891. 1969. pap. 8.95 (ISBN 0-8070-2385-X, BP317). Beacon Pr.

Gumbert, J. P. & De Haan, M. J., eds. Texts & Manuscripts: Litterae Textuales. (Illus.). 110p. 1972. 46.50 (ISBN 0-8390-0105-3). Abner Schram Ltd.

--Varia Codicologica: Litterae Textuales. (Illus.). 110p. 1972. 46.50 (ISBN 0-8390-0106-1). Abner Schram Ltd.

Gundry, D. W. Teacher & the World's Religions. 160p. 1968. 6.50 (ISBN 0-227-67456-1). Attic Pr.

Gurdjieff, G. I. Life Is Real Only Then, When "I Am". 177p. 1981. 17.50 (ISBN 0-525-14547-8, 01699-510). Dutton.

Habig, Marion A., ed. The Marian Era, Vol. 11. (Illus.). 132p. 1973. 6.95 (ISBN 0-8199-0215-2). Franciscan Herald.

Hale, J. Russell. Who Are the Unchurched? An Exploratory Study. LC 77-81922. 1977. pap. 2.00x (ISBN 0-914422-06-5). Glenmary Res Ctr.

Hall, Manly P. Dark Night of the Soul. pap. 2.50 (ISBN 0-89314-311-1). Philos Res.

--Four Seasons of the Spirit. pap. 2.50 (ISBN 0-89314-315-4). Philos Res.

--Great Books on Religion & Esoteric Philosophy. pap. 5.50 (ISBN 0-89314-821-0). Philos Res.

--Lord Giveth & Taketh. pap. 2.50 (ISBN 0-89314-330-8). Philos Res.

Hall, T. William, et al. Religion: An Introduction. LC 85-42777. 288p. (Orig.). 1986. pap. 14.45 (ISBN 0-06-063573-8, HarpR). Har-Row.

Halperin, D. A. Psychodynamic Perspectives on Religion, Sect & Cult. 416p. 1983. pap. text ed. 46.50 (ISBN 0-7236-7029-3). PSG Pub Co.

Hannay, James B. Symbolism in Relation to Religion. LC 79-118523. (Illus.). 1971. Repr. of 1915 ed. 28.50x (Pub by Kennikat). Assoc Faculty Pr.

Harrison, Frederic. Positive Evolution of Religion. facs. ed. LC 74-142641. (Essay Index Reprint Ser). 1913. 18.00 (ISBN 0-8369-2053-8). Ayer Co Pubs.

Hart, Ray L., ed. Trajectories in the Study of Religion: Addresses at the Seventy-Fifth Anniversary of the American Academy of Religion. (Studies in Religion & Theological Scholarship (American Academy of Religion)). 333p. 25.95 (ISBN 1-55540-064-7, 00-08-03). Scholars Pr GA.

Heschel, Abraham J. Man Is Not Alone: A Philosophy of Religion. 320p. 1976. pap. 8.95 (ISBN 0-374-51328-7). FS&G.

Hick, John. Philosophy of Religion. 3rd ed. 160p. 1983. pap. write for info. (ISBN 0-13-663906-2). P-H.

Hilliard, F. H. The Teacher & Religion. 191p. 1963. 7.95 (ISBN 0-227-67675-0). Attic Pr.

Hirschmann, Maria A. Are You Prepared? Hansi Shares How You Can Face the Future Without Fear. LC 79-90957. 64p. (Orig.). 1979. pap. 1.95 (ISBN 0-932878-06-7, HB-06). Hansi.

Hocking, William E. Living Religions & a World Faith. LC 75-3187. (Hibbert Lectures Ser. 1938). Repr. of 1940 ed. 28.50 (ISBN 0-404-59189-2). AMS Pr.

Hoffding, Harald. The Philosophy of Religion. facsimile ed. Meyer, B. E., tr. from Ger. LC 71-152987. (Select Bibliographies Reprint Ser). Repr. of 1906 ed. 24.50 (ISBN 0-8369-5739-3). Ayer Co Pubs.

Holy Scriptures. 1917. blue cloth o.p. 11.95 (ISBN 0-685-13294-3, 101); leatherette, black or white boxed o.p. 17.95 (ISBN 0-685-13295-1, 102, 103,); small leatherette, white, boxed o.p. 17.95 (ISBN 0-8276-0035-6, 105); Heb. & Eng., two vols. 35.00 (ISBN 0-686-76879-5, 125). Jewish Pubns.

Howlett, Duncan. The Critical Way in Religion. LC 80-7460. (Library of Liberal Religion). 360p. 1984. pap. 14.95 (ISBN 0-87975-266-1). Prometheus Bks.

Hummel, Charles. Tyranny of the Urgent. pap. 0.75 (ISBN 0-87784-128-4). Inter-Varsity.

Hunt, George W. John Updike & the Three Great Secret Things: Sex, Religion & Art. LC 80-23796. pap. 60.50 (ISBN 0-317-20577-3, 2023218). Bks Demand UMI.

Huxley, Julian S. Religion Without Revelation. LC 78-12065. 1979. Repr. of 1967 ed. lib. bdg. 24.75x (ISBN 0-313-21225-2, HURR). Greenwood.

Inter-Varsity Staff. First Mornings with God. pap. 0.75 (ISBN 0-87784-134-9). Inter-Varsity.

Interdisciplinary Symposium. Contemplative Community. LC 70-184548. (Cistercian Studies: No. 21). 1972. 7.50 (ISBN 0-87907-821-9). Cistercian Pubns.

James, William. Varieties of Religious Experience. LC 37-27013. 1936. 6.95 (ISBN 0-394-60463-6). Modern Lib.

--Varieties of Religious Experience. pap. 4.50 (ISBN 0-451-62486-6, ME2069, Ment). NAL.

--The Varieties of Religious Experience. (The Works of William James). (Illus.). 728p. 1985. text ed. 45.00x (ISBN 0-674-93225-0). Harvard U Pr.

Jarrett, R. H. It Works. 31st ed. 1976. pap. 1.00 (ISBN 0-87516-323-8). De Vorss.

Joad, Cyril E. The Present & Future of Religion. LC 77-109756. 310p. 1974. Repr. of 1930 ed. lib. bdg. 22.50x (ISBN 0-8371-4246-6, JOPF). Greenwood.

John Paul II, Pope Redeemer of Man. 103p. (Orig.). 1979. pap. 3.95 (ISBN 1-55586-003-6). US Catholic.

Johnson, F. Ernest, ed. Religion & the World Order. LC 68-26189. (Essay & General Literature Index Reprint Ser). 1969. Repr. of 1944 ed. 22.50x (ISBN 0-8046-0221-2, Pub. by Kennikat). Assoc Faculty Pr.

Johnson, R., et al. Critical Issues in Modern Religion. 1973. pap. write for info. (ISBN 0-13-193979-3). P-H.

Johnsson, William G. Hebrews. LC 79-92068. (Knox Preaching Guides Ser.). 98p. (Orig., John Hayes series editor). 1980. pap. 4.95. John Knox.

Johnston, William. The Inner Eye of Love: Mysticism & Religion. LC 78-4428. 1978. pap. 6.95 (ISBN 0-06-064195-9, RD-349, HarpR). Har-Row.

Johnstone, Parker L. Is God a Separate Being? LC 76-706635. 1977. cloth 7.95 (ISBN 0-917802-01-2). Theoscience Found.

Johnstone, Ronald L. Religion in Society: A Sociology of Religion. 2nd ed. (Illus.). 320p. 1983. text ed. write for info. (ISBN 0-13-773077-2). P-H.

Jones, Donald G., ed. Business, Religion & Ethics: Inquiry & Encounter. LC 82-14479. 288p. 1982. 25.00 (ISBN 0-89946-164-6); pap. text ed. 12.95 (ISBN 0-89946-166-2). Oelgeschlager.

Jones, Henry. A Faith That Enquires. LC 77-27211. (Gifford Lectures: 1920-21). Repr. of 1922 ed. 20.00 (ISBN 0-404-60466-8). AMS Pr.

Juvencus, C. Vettius. Evangeliorum Libri Quattuor. (Corpus Scriptorum Ecclesiasticorum Latinorum Ser: Vol. 24). 1891. 30.00 (ISBN 0-384-28270-9). Johnson Repr.

Kanfield, William L. Heaven Is Not That Far Away. LC 85-91401. 88p. 1986. 8.95 (ISBN 0-533-06917-3). Vantage.

Kasemann, Ernst, et al. Distinctive Protestant & Catholic Themes Reconsidered. Funk, Robert W. & Ebeling, Gerhard, eds. 1967. lib. bdg. 17.50x (ISBN 0-88307-161-4). Gannon.

Kauffman, Milo. Personal Work. 1940. pap. 2.00 (ISBN 0-87813-951-6). Christian Light.

Kaufmann, Walter. Critique of Religion & Philosophy. 1979. pap. 13.50x (ISBN 0-691-02001-9). Princeton U Pr.

Kazantzakis, Nikos. The Last Temptation of Christ. 1966. Translation 1971. pap. 9.95 (ISBN 0-671-21170-6, Touchstone Bks). S&S.

Keifer, Howard & Munitz, Milton, eds. Perspectives in Education, Religion, & the Arts. LC 69-14641. Repr. of 1970 ed. 82.70 (ISBN 0-8357-9596-9, 2010111). Bks Demand UMI.

Kellogg, Jean. Dark Prophets of Hope. LC 75-5697. 1975. pap. 5.95 (ISBN 0-8294-0243-8). Loyola.

Kenik, Helen A. Design for Kingship: The Deuteronomistic Narrative Technique in 1 Kings 3: 4-15. LC 82-21054. (SBL Dissertation Ser.). 258p. 1983. pap. 13.50 (ISBN 0-89130-605-6, 06 01 69). Scholars Pr GA.

Kirban, Salem. One Thousand. (Illus.). 1973. pap. 2.95 (ISBN 0-912582-09-X). Kirban.

--Your Last Goodbye. LC 70-87000. (Illus.). 1969. pap. 5.95 (ISBN 0-912582-06-5). Kirban.

Kite, Roger. What Do We Mean Religion? 1985. 19.00x (ISBN 0-7062-3906-7, Pub. by Ward Lock Educ Co Ltd). State Mutual Bk.

Kolakowski, Leszek. Religion. LC 81-85135. 1982. 22.50x (ISBN 0-19-520372-0). Oxford U Pr.

Kolstoe, John E. Consultation: A Universal Lamp of Guidance. 208p. 1985. 13.95 (ISBN 0-85398-186-8); pap. 7.95 (ISBN 0-85398-187-6). G Ronald Pub.

Krumbine, Miles H., ed. The Process of Religion: Essays in Honor of Dean Shailer Mathews. facsimile ed. LC 71-38776. (Essay Index Reprint Ser). Repr. of 1933 ed. 18.00 (ISBN 0-8369-2667-6). Ayer Co Pubs.

Kuenen, Abraham. National Religions & Universal Religions. LC 77-27169. (Hibbert Lectures Ser.: 1882). Repr. of 1882 ed. 34.00 (ISBN 0-404-60403-X). AMS Pr.

Kung, Hans & Schillebeeckx, Edward, eds. Concilium: Religion in the Eighties. (Concilium Ser.: Vols. 131-140). 128p. (Orig.). 1980. pap. 53.55 (ISBN 0-8164-2283-4, HarpR). Har-Row.

--Concilium: Religion in the Eighties. (Concilium Ser.: Vols. 151-160). 128p. (Orig.). 1982. pap. 62.55 (ISBN 0-8164-2392-X, HarpR). Har-Row.

LaHaye, Tim. Transformed Temperaments. 1971. pap. 5.95 (ISBN 0-8423-7306-3). Tyndale.

Lamont, S. Religion Inc. 1986. 49.75X (ISBN 0-245-54334-1, Pub. by Harrap Ltd England). State Mutual Bk.

Larner, Christina. Witchcraft & Religion: The Politics of Popular Belief. 256p. 1984. 29.95x (ISBN 0-631-13447-6). Basil Blackwell.

Larrabee, James, ed. Religion, BL-BX. LC 85-6863. (LC Cumulative Classification Ser.). 1000p. 1985. loose-leaf set 105.00 (ISBN 0-933949-11-1); vol. 1 0.00 (ISBN 0-933949-12-X); vol. 2 0.00 (ISBN 0-933949-13-8); fiche set 0.00 (ISBN 0-933949-15-4); fiche vol. 1 0.00 (ISBN 0-933949-16-2); fiche vol. 2 0.00 (ISBN 0-933949-17-0). Livia Pr.

Larson, Martin A. New Thought Religion. 2nd., rev. ed. LC 86-16947. 390p. 1987. 16.95 (ISBN 0-8022-2525-X); pap. 9.95 (ISBN 0-8022-2527-6). Philos Lib.

Lefebvre, Dom G. God Present. 1979. pap. 3.95 (ISBN 0-03-053436-4, HarpR). Har-Row.

Lehmann, Arthur C. & Myers, James E. Magic, Witchcraft, & Religion. (Illus.). 416p. 1985. pap. text ed. 22.95 (ISBN 0-87484-685-4). Mayfield Pub.

Lenin, Vladimir I. Acerca De la Religion. (Span.). 81p. 1976. pap. 1.45 (ISBN 0-8285-1359-7, Pub. by Progress Pubs USSR). Imported Pubns.

Lenning, Larry G. Blessing in Mosque & Mission. LC 80-25110. 176p. (Orig.). 1981. pap. 5.95 (ISBN 0-87808-433-9). William Carey Lib.

Leuba, James H. The Psychological Origin & the Nature of Religion. LC 78-1577. 17.00 (ISBN 0-8414-5837-5). Folcroft.

Lincoln, Bruce, ed. Religion, Rebellion, Revolution: An Interdisciplinary & Cross-Cultural Collection of Essays. LC 85-1992. 312p. 1985. 27.50 (ISBN 0-312-67061-3). St Martin.

Lindbeck, George A. The Nature of Doctrine: Religion & Theology in a Postliberal Age. LC 83-27332. 142p. 1984. 16.95 (ISBN 0-664-21829-6); pap. 9.95 (ISBN 0-664-24618-4). Westminster.

Link, Henry C. The Return to Religion. LC 77-17291. 1977. Repr. of 1937 ed. lib. bdg. 16.50 (ISBN 0-8414-5846-4). Folcroft.

Livingston, James C. Anatomy of the Sacred: An Introduction to Religion. 734p. 1987. text ed. write for info. (ISBN 0-02-371370-4). Macmillan.

Luther, Martin. Luther's Works: Lectures on Galatians, Vols. 26 & 27. Incl. Vol. 26. Pelikan, Jaroslav, ed. 1962; Vol. 27. Pelikan, Jaroslav, ed. Jungkuntz, Richard, tr. 1963. 16.95 (ISBN 0-570-06427-9, 15-1769). LC 55-9893. 16.95 (ISBN 0-570-06426-0, 15-1768). Concordia.

Lyall, Alfred C. Studies in Literature & History. facs. ed. LC 68-29227. (Essay Index Reprint Ser). 1968. Repr. of 1915 ed. 21.50 (ISBN 0-8369-0637-3). Ayer Co Pubs.

McClendon, James W., Jr. Understanding Religious Convictions. LC 74-34519. 256p. 1975. text ed. 16.95x (ISBN 0-268-01903-7); pap. 7.95x (ISBN 0-268-01904-5). U of Notre Dame Pr.

MacCormac, Earl R. Metaphor & Myth in Science & Religion. LC 75-23941. pap. 46.80 (2052207). Bks Demand UMI.

MacDonald, James. Religion & Myth. LC 74-82059. Repr. of 1893 ed. 22.50x (ISBN 0-8371-1550-7, MAR&, Pub. by Negro U Pr). Greenwood.

McDowell, Josh & Stewart, Don. Answers: Living Book Ser. 256p. (Orig.). 1986. 3.95 (ISBN 0-8423-0021-X). Tyndale.

McGaw, Francis A. Praying Hyde. 80p. 1970. pap. 2.95 (ISBN 0-87123-454-8, 200454). Bethany Hse.

Maki, Lillian. Education, Human Nature & Peace: A Scientific Look at Religion. rev. ed. 192p. 1985. 8.50 (ISBN 0-9617372-0-4). Maryatta Co.

Maltz, B. My Glimpse of Eternity. 128p. 3.50 (ISBN 0-8007-8363-8, Spire Bks). Revell.

Mandeville, Bernard. Free Thoughts on Religion, the Church, & National Happiness. LC 77-17171. 1981. Repr. of 1720 ed. lib. bdg. 60.00x (ISBN 0-8201-1300-X). Schol Facsimiles.

Marshall, John F. Sharing God's Love. LC 81-11794. 108p. 1981. pap. 5.95 (ISBN 0-8146-1068-4). Liturgical Pr.

Mascall, E. L. The Triune God: An Ecumenical Study. (Princeton Theological Monograph: No. 10). 1986. pap. 12.90 (ISBN 0-915138-96-4). Pickwick.

Maslow, Abraham H. Religions: Values & Peak Experiences. 1983. 13.25 (ISBN 0-8446-6070-1). Peter Smith.

Massion, J. C. & Lambin, H. R. Questions of Christians: Mark's Response, Vol. 1. LC 80-68045. 1980. pap. 2.75 (ISBN 0-914070-16-9). ACTA Found.

Matthews, S. Church: Learning about God's People. LC 56-1396. (Concept Books Series Four). 1983. pap. 3.95 (ISBN 0-570-08525-X). Concordia.

Matura, Thaddee. The Crisis of Religious Life. Lachance, Paul & Schwartz, Paul, trs. 1973. 4.95 (ISBN 0-8199-0453-8). Franciscan Herald.

Mensching, G. Structures & Patterns of Religion. Sharma, V. S. & Klimkeit, H. M., trs. 1976. 21.00 (ISBN 0-8426-0958-X). Orient Bk Dist.

Mikalson, Jon D. Athenian Popular Religion. LC 82-25616. x, 142p. 1983. 16.00x (ISBN 0-8078-1563-2). U of NC Pr.

Mims, Edwin. Great Writers As Interpreters of Religion. facsimile ed. LC 70-134116. (Essay Index Reprint Ser). Repr. of 1945 ed. 17.00 (ISBN 0-8369-1988-2). Ayer Co Pubs.

Mol, Hans. Meaning & Place: An Introduction to the Social Scientific Study of Religion. (Orig.). 1983. pap. 6.95 (ISBN 0-8298-0638-5). Pilgrim NY.

Monk, Robert, et al. Exploring Religious Meaning. 2nd ed. (Illus.). 1980. text ed. write for info. (ISBN 0-13-297515-7). P-H.

Moody. Religion of Soldier & Sailor. LC 45-3352. 1945. 8.50x (ISBN 0-674-75750-5). Harvard U Pr.

Moore, John A. Write for the Religion Market. LC 80-25607. 128p. 1981. 9.95 (ISBN 0-88280-084-1). ETC Pubns.

Moore, Ralph & Beach, Dan. Let Go of the Ring. (Religion Ser.). (Illus.). 150p. (Orig.). 1983. pap. 4.95 (ISBN 0-941018-10-5). Martin Pr CA.

Morrish, Ivor. Obeah, Christ, & Rastaman: Jamaica & Its Religion. 128p. 1982. 17.95 (ISBN 0-227-67831-1). Attic Pr.

Moseley, Rufus. Reverse Side of the Cross. pap. 0.65 ea. 2 for 1.00 (ISBN 0-910924-83-X). Macalester.

The Most High God. LC 82-90990. 1982. pap. 5.95 (ISBN 0-915540-30-4). Frnds Israel.

Muller, Friedrich M. Introduction to the Science of Religion. Bolle, Kees W., ed. LC 77-79145. (Mythology Ser.). 1978. lib. bdg. 32.00x (ISBN 0-405-10554-1). Ayer Co Pubs.

Murray, Andrew. Secret Abiding Presence. (Secret Ser.). (Orig.). 1979. pap. 1.95 (ISBN 0-87508-382-X). Chr Lit.

--Secret of Adoration. (Secret Ser.). (Orig.). 1979. pap. 1.95 (ISBN 0-87508-384-6). Chr Lit.

Murray, Andrew & Choy, Leona. Inner Chamber. (Orig.). 1980. pap. 2.50 (ISBN 0-87508-405-2). Chr Lit.

Muyskens, James L. The Sufficiency of Hope: Conceptual Foundations of Religion. (Philosophical Monographs: 3rd Annual Ser.). 186p. 1979. 27.95 (ISBN 0-87722-162-6). Temple U Pr.

Needleman, Jacob, et al. Religion for a New Generation. 2nd ed. Scott, Kenneth, ed. 576p. 1977. pap. text ed. write for info. (ISBN 0-02-385990-3). Macmillan.

Newhouse, Flower A., et al. Insights into Reality. 2nd ed. LC 75-36869. 1975. pap. 8.50 (ISBN 0-910378-10-X). Christward.

North, J. B. From Pentecost to the Present. LC 82-74538. 520p. (Orig.). 1983. 18.95 (ISBN 0-89900-230-7). College Pr Pub.

Novak, Michael. Ascent of the Mountain, Flight of the Dove: An Invitation to Religious Studies. rev. ed. LC 77-20463. 1978. pap. 5.95xi (ISBN 0-06-066322-7, RD 232, HarpR). Har-Row.

Oman, John W. The Natural & the Supernatural. LC 79-39696. (Select Bibliographies Reprint Ser.). 1972. Repr. of 1931 ed. 20.75 (ISBN 0-8369-9941-X). Ayer Co Pubs.

O'Toole, R. Religion: Classic Sociological Approaches. 1984. text ed. 12.95 (ISBN 0-07-548560-5). McGraw.

Otto, Rudolf. Idea of the Holy. 2nd ed. Harvey, John W., tr. 1950. pap. 8.95 (ISBN 0-19-500210-5). Oxford U Pr.

Palau, Luis. Walk on Water, Pete! LC 80-39955. 1974. pap. 2.95 (ISBN 0-930014-34-0). Multnomah.

Palmer, Martin. Faiths & Festivals. (Ward Lock Educational Ser.). 25.00x (ISBN 0-7062-4293-9, Pub. by Ward Lock Educ Co Ltd). State Mutual Bk.

Panzarella, Andrew. Religion & Human Experience. LC 73-87024. 1974. pap. 5.20x (ISBN 0-88489-058-9); tchr's. guide 3.00x (ISBN 0-88489-080-5). St Marys.

Parker, Theodore. A Discourse of Matters Pertaining to Religion. LC 72-4968. (Romantic Tradition in American Literature Ser.). 510p. 1972. Repr. of 1842 ed. 35.00 (ISBN 0-405-04639-1). Ayer Co Pubs.

Parkhurst, Charles H. Pulpit & the Pew. 1913. 39.50x (ISBN 0-686-83717-7). Elliots Bks.

Paterson, William P. The Nature of Religion. LC 77-27202. (Gifford Lectures: 1924-25). Repr. of 1926 ed. 47.50 (ISBN 0-404-60476-5). AMS Pr.

Paulson, Ivar. Old Estonian Folk Religion. LC 76-63029. (Uralic & Altaic Ser: Vol. 108). (Orig.). 1971. pap. text ed. 19.95x (ISBN 0-87750-154-8). Res Ctr Lang Semiotic.

Peguy, Charles. Oeuvres en Prose: 1909-1914. Peguy, M., ed. (Bibl. de la Pleiade). 1957. 42.95 (ISBN 0-685-01987-X). French & Eur.

Pennington, M. Basil. Jubilee: A Monk's Journal. LC 81-82336. 208p. (Orig.). 1981. 6.95 (ISBN 0-8091-2402-5). Paulist Pr.

Perkins, Pheme. Johannine Epistles. (New Testament Ser.: Vol. 21). 120p. 1980. 10.95 (ISBN 0-89453-209-X); pap. 6.95 (ISBN 0-89453-144-1). M Glazier.

Peters, Dory. My God Is Real. 1984. pap. 3.95 (ISBN 0-938612-08-5). Revival Press.

Pickering, W. S., ed. Durkheim on Religion. 1983. pap. 10.95x (ISBN 0-7100-9074-9). Methuen Inc.

Pipkin, Wayne H., tr. Huldrych Zwingli-Writings in Search of True Religion: Reformation, Pastoral & Eucharistic Writings, Vol. 2. (Pittsburgh Theological Monographs: No. 13). 1984. pap. 19.95 (ISBN 0-915138-59-X). Pickwick.

Pittenger, Norman. After Death-Life in God. 96p. 1980. 4.95 (ISBN 0-8164-0108-X, HarpR). Har-Row.

--Loving Says It All. 128p. 1978. 6.95 (ISBN 0-8298-0352-1). Pilgrim NY.

Pomian-Srzednicki, Maciej. Religious Changes in Contemporary Poland: Secularization & Politics. (International Library of Sociology). 227p. 1982. 27.95x (ISBN 0-7100-9245-8). Methuen Inc.

Prather, Hugh. There Is a Place Where You Are Not Alone. LC 80-912. 224p. 1980. pap. 6.95 (ISBN 0-385-14778-3, Dolp). Doubleday.

Pratt, James B. The Religious Consciousness: A Psychological Study. 1971. Repr. of 1920 ed. 21.95x (ISBN 0-02-850350-3). Hafner.

Price, Eugenia. What Really Matters. 160p. 1985. pap. 2.95 (ISBN 0-515-08989-3). Jove Pubns.

Promise of Deliverance in Time of Trouble. 1978. 1.25 (ISBN 0-89858-023-4). Fill the Gap.

Promise of Power to Serve. 1978. 1.25 (ISBN 0-89858-024-2). Fill the Gap.

Promise of Total Protection. 1978. 1.25 (ISBN 0-89858-022-6). Fill the Gap.

Protection by Angles. 1982. 3.50 (ISBN 0-89858-041-2). Fill the Gap.

Prozesky, Martin. Religion & Ultimate Well-Being: An Explanatory Theory. LC 84-3340. 224p. 1984. 22.50 (ISBN 0-312-67057-5). St Martin.

Qutb, S. Milestone. 1981. pap. 7.50 (ISBN 0-686-77426-4). Kazi Pubns.

Rimmer, C. Brandon. Religion in Shreds. LC 73-82861. pap. 1.25 (ISBN 0-88419-046-3, Co-Pub by Crection Hse). Aragorn Bks.

Romig, Robert E. Reasonable Religion: A Commonsense Approach. LC 84-42823. 200p. 1984. 18.95 (ISBN 0-87975-252-1). Prometheus Bks.

Roszak, Theodore. Unfinished Animal. 1977. pap. 5.95 (ISBN 0-06-090537-9, CN 537, PL). Har-Row.

Rupp, George. Christologies & Cultures: Toward a Typology of Religious Worldviews. (Religion & Reason Ser: No. 10). 269p. 1974. text ed. 23.75x (ISBN 90-2797-641-4). Mouton.

Russell, Robert A. Dry Those Tears. 133p. 1975. pap. 4.95 (ISBN 0-87516-203-7). De Vorss.

Ryle, J. C. Practical Religion: Being Plain Papers on Daily Duties, Experience Dangers, & Privileges of Professing Christianity. 334p. 1977. Repr. of 1959 ed. 12.95 (ISBN 0-227-67569-X). Attic Pr.

Ryle, John Charles. Knots Untied: Being Plain Statements on Some of the Weightier Matters of Christianity. 342p. 1977. Repr. of 1964 ed. 12.95 (ISBN 0-227-67511-8). Attic Pr.

Ryrie, Charles. Neo-Orthodoxy. 1978. pap. 2.50 (ISBN 0-937396-27-3). Walterick Pubs.

Samuel, Herbert L. A Century's Changes of Outlook. LC 77-7136. (Hibbert Lectures: 1953). Repr. of 1953 ed. 11.00 (ISBN 0-404-60432-3). AMS Pr.

Sandmel, Samuel. A Little Book on Religion: For People Who Are Not Religious. LC 75-1831. 1975. pap. 3.95 cancelled (ISBN 0-89012-002-1). Anima Pubns.

Sayer, Elisabeth. Be Ye Also Ready. LC 80-82065. (Orig.). 1980. pap. text ed. 3.50 (ISBN 0-932050-07-7). New Puritan.

Schleiermacher, Friedrich. On Religion: Speeches to Its Cultured Despisers. pap. 8.95x (ISBN 0-06-130036-5, TB36, Torch). Har-Row.

--On Religion: Speeches to Its Cultured Despisers. 18.25 (ISBN 0-8446-2878-6). Peter Smith.

Schmid, Georg. Principles of Integral Science of Religion. (Religion & Reason Ser.). 1979. text ed. 33.75 (ISBN 90-279-7864-6). Mouton.

Scott, Nathan A., Jr., ed. Legacy of Reinhold Niebuhr. LC 74-30714. xxiv, 124p. 1975. 10.00X (ISBN 0-226-74297-0). U of Chicago Pr.

Sellars, Roy W. Religion Coming of Age. LC 75-3362. Repr. of 1928 ed. 20.50 (ISBN 0-404-59359-3). AMS Pr.

Sharpe, K. J. & Ker, J. M., eds. Religion Nature: With Charles Birch & Others. (Illus.). 116p. (Orig.). 1984. pap. 11.95 (ISBN 0-9597672-0-7, Pub. by Auckland Univ Chaplaincy). ANZ Religious Pubns.

Sheehan, John. Religion & Cult. 240p. pap. 6.95 (ISBN 0-87462-446-0). Marquette.

Sheldon, Jean. Ribbon of Lies, Knife of Truth. McFarland, Ken, ed. (Harvest Ser.). 96p. 1982. pap. 3.95 (ISBN 0-8163-0449-1). Pacific Pr Pub Assn.

Siebert, Rudolf J. Horkheimer's Critical Sociology of Religion: The Relative & the Transcendent. LC 78-66280. 1979. pap. text ed. 9.50 (ISBN 0-8191-0688-7). U Pr of Amer.

Smart, Ninian. Religion & the Western Mind. 1986. 39.50 (ISBN 0-88706-382-9); pap. 12.95 (ISBN 0-88706-383-7). State U NY Pr.

--The Religious Experience of Mankind. 3rd ed. (Scribner Press Ser.). (Illus.). 656p. 1984. 30.00 (ISBN 0-684-18077-4, ScribT). Scribner.

--The Science of Religion & the Sociology of Knowledge: Some Methodological Questions. LC 72-12115. 176p. 1973. 20.00x (ISBN 0-691-07191-8); pap. 8.50x (ISBN 0-691-01997-5). Princeton U Pr.

Smith, Wilfred C. The Faith of Other Men. 144p. 1972. pap. 6.95x (ISBN 0-06-131658-X, TB1658, Torch). Har-Row.

Soderblom, Nathan. The Living God: Basal Forms of Personal Religion. LC 77-27196. (Gifford Lectures: 1931). Repr. of 1933 ed. 40.00 (ISBN 0-404-60485-4). AMS Pr.

Sperry, Willard L. The Paradox of Religion. LC 77-27146. (Hibbert Lectures: 1927). Repr. of 1927 ed. 20.00 (ISBN 0-404-60424-2). AMS Pr.

Sri Chinmoy. From the Source to the Source. (Orig.). 1978. pap. 8.00 (ISBN 0-88497-431-6). Aum Pubns.

--Kundalini: The Mother - Power. 2nd rev. ed. 1974. pap. 3.95 (ISBN 0-88497-104-X). Aum Pubns.

Stark, Rodney & Bainbridge, William S. The Future of Religion: Secularization, Revival & Cult Formation. LC 83-18221. (Illus.). 600p. 1985. pap. 40.00x (ISBN 0-520-04854-7); 14.95 (ISBN 0-520-05731-7, CAMPUS 406). U of Cal Pr.

Stedman, Ray C. What's This World Coming To? LC 86-6439. 1986. pap. 5.95 (ISBN 0-8307-1154-6, 5418825). Regal.

Storms, E. M. Should a Christian Be a Mason? LC 80-83598. (Orig.). 1980. pap. text ed. 2.50 (ISBN 0-932050-08-5). New Puritan.

Streng. Understanding Religious Life. 3rd ed. 1984. write for info. (ISBN 0-534-03699-6). Wadsworth Pub.

Streng, Frederick J., et al. Ways of Being Religious: Readings for a New Approach to Religion. (Illus.). 608p. 1973. 34.00 (ISBN 0-13-946277-5). P-H.

Studies in Mysticism & Religion. cancelled (ISBN 0-686-76265-7). Feldheim.

Synan, Joseph A. Shape of Things to Come. 1969. 3.95 (ISBN 0-911866-52-3); pap. 2.95 (ISBN 0-911866-90-6). Advocate.

Tafoya, Alfonso. Confrontation at Calvary. (Chapbooks Ser.). 1975. pap. 1.50x (ISBN 0-914140-06-X). Carpenter Pr.

Tagore, Rabindranath. The Religion of Man. LC 77-27145. (Hibbert Lectures: 1930). 248p. Repr. of 1931 ed. 27.50 (ISBN 0-404-60426-9). AMS Pr.

Teilhard De Chardin, Pierre. L' Apparition de L'homme. 21.50 (ISBN 0-685-36582-4). French & Eur.

Thomas, Keith. Religion & the Decline of Magic. 716p. 1975. pap. text ed. write for info. (ISBN 0-02-420200-2, Pub. by Scribner). Macmillan.

--Religion & the Decline of Magic. 736p. 1986. pap. 17.95 (ISBN 0-684-14542-1). Scribner.

Thurman, Howard. The Creative Encounter. LC 72-12773. 155p. 1972. pap. 6.95 (ISBN 0-913408-07-7). Friends United.

Tiele, Cornelis P. Elements of the Science of Religion, 2 vols. LC 77-27226. (Gifford Lectures: 1896, 1898). Repr. of 1899 ed. Set. 55.00 (ISBN 0-404-60480-3). AMS Pr.

Tillich, Paul. The Meaning of Health: Relation of Religion & Health. 2nd ed. 64p. 1981. 20.00 (ISBN 0-913028-87-8); pap. 7.95 (ISBN 0-913028-81-9). North Atlantic.

Tinsley, John. Tragedy: Irony & Faith. 75p. (Orig.). 1985. pap. 5.95x (ISBN 0-317-26992-5). Wyndham Hall.

Tozer, A. W. Ese Increible Cristiano. Bruchez, Dardo, tr. from Eng. (Span.). 135p. (Orig.). 1979. pap. 2.00 (ISBN 0-87509-269-1). Chr Pubns.

Tremmel, William C. Religion: What Is It? 2nd ed. 1984. pap. text ed. 17.95 (ISBN 0-03-062834-2). HR&W.

Tuckwell, James H. Religion & Reality. LC 77-118552. 1971. Repr. of 1915 ed. 25.00x (ISBN 0-8046-1177-7, Pub. by Kennikat). Assoc Faculty Pr.

Unger, Merrill F. Demons in the World Today. 1980. pap. 6.95 (ISBN 0-8423-0661-7). Tyndale.

Von Balthasar, Hans, et al. Two Say Why. 1973. pap. 1.75 (ISBN 0-8199-0434-1). Franciscan Herald.

Wallace, Anthony F. Religion: An Anthropological View. 1966. text ed. 16.00 (ISBN 0-394-30543-4, RanC). Random.

Waterhouse, Eric S. Modern Theories of Religion. 1977. lib. bdg. 59.95 (ISBN 0-8490-2272-X). Gordon Pr.

Waterman, Leroy. Religion Faces the World Crisis. 1943. 3.75x (ISBN 0-685-21800-7). Wahr.

Watt, W. M. Faith & Practice of Al-Ghazzali. 1967. 5.75x (ISBN 0-87902-060-1). Orientalia.

Wedgwood, James I. The Larger Meaning of Religion. 80p. 1981. pap. text ed. 3.00 (ISBN 0-918980-10-0). St Alban Pr.

Whitehead, Alfred N. Religion in the Making. pap. 5.95 (ISBN 0-452-00723-2, Mer). NAL.

Whittaker, Thomas. Priests, Philosophers & Prophets. LC 77-102589. 1970. Repr. of 1911 ed. 22.50x (ISBN 0-8046-0748-6, Pub. by Kennikat). Assoc Faculty Pr.

Wiberg, Glen V. Called to Be His People. (Illus.). 331p. 1970. pap. text ed. 5.00 (ISBN 0-910452-16-4). Covenant.

Wiebe, Paul. The Architecture of Religion: A Theoretical Essay. LC 84-8667. (Trinity University Monograph Series in Religion). 170p. 1984. text ed. 15.95 (ISBN 0-939980-07-X). Trinity U Pr.

Wilkes, Paul, ed. Merton: By Those Who Knew Him Best. LC 84-47824. (Illus.). 160p. 1984. 13.95 (ISBN 0-06-069416-5, HarpR). Har-Row.

Wilkins, Ronald J. The Religions of the World. rev. ed. (To Live Is Christ Ser.). 240p. 1984. pap. 5.95 (ISBN 0-697-01928-4); tchr's manual 5.00 (ISBN 0-697-01929-2); spirit masters 10.95 (ISBN 0-697-01730-3). Wm C Brown.

Williamson, Clark M. Has God Rejected His People? LC 81-12847. 192p. (Orig.). 1982. pap. 8.75 (ISBN 0-687-16649-7). Abingdon.

Williamson, Tom & Bellamy, Lin. Ley Lines in Question. (Illus.). 272p. 1984. 22.50 (ISBN 0-437-19205-9, Pub. by Worlds Work). David & Charles.

Wilson, John F. Public Religion in American Culture. 240p. 1979. lib. bdg. 24.95 (ISBN 0-87722-159-6). Temple U Pr.

--Religion: A Preface. (Illus.). 240p. 1982. pap. text ed. write for info. (ISBN 0-13-773192-2). P-H.

Winden, Hans-Willi. Wie Kam und Wie Kommt Es Zum Osterglauben? (Disputationes Theologicae: Vol. 12). (Ger.). 352p. 1982. 39.45 (ISBN 3-8204-5820-4). P Lang Pubs.

Winn, Dick. If God Won the War, Why Isn't It Over? McFarland, Ken, ed. (Harvest Ser.). 64p. 1982. pap. 4.95 (ISBN 0-8163-0467-X). Pacific Pr Pub Assn.

Wolf, Eric R., ed. Religion Power & Protest in Local Communities: The Northern Shore of the Mediterranean. LC 84-8407. (Religion & Society Ser.: No. 24). 287p. 1984. 65.00 (ISBN 3-11-009777-X). Mouton.

Wood, Herbert G. Living Issues in Religious Thought: From George Fox to Betrand Russell. facsimile ed. LC 67-22128. (Essay Index Reprint Ser.). 187p. 1967. Repr. of 1924 ed. lib. bdg. 13.50 (ISBN 0-8290-0489-0). Irvington.

World Conference on Religion & Peace, 3rd Assembly. Religion in the Struggle for World Community: Unabridged Proceedings. Jack, Homer A., ed. (Orig.). 1980. pap. 6.95 (ISBN 0-935934-05-7). World Confer Rel & Peace.

Wuthnow, Robert. Experimentation in American Religion: The New Mysticisms & Their Implications for the Churches. 1978. 31.00x (ISBN 0-520-03446-5). U of Cal Pr.

Wuthnow, Robert, ed. The Religious Dimension: New Directions in Quantitative Research. LC 79-6948. 1979. 29.95 (ISBN 0-12-766050-X). Acad Pr.

Wysinger, Voss E. The Celestial Democracy. LC 66-24014. 149p. 1966. lib. bdg. 16.95 (ISBN 0-914002-01-5); text ed. 16.95 (ISBN 0-914002-02-3); pap. text ed. 14.00 (ISBN 0-686-36904-1). Wysinger Pub.

Yerman, Ron. Religion: Innocent or Guilty. LC 85-90019. 180p. 1985. 11.95 (ISBN 0-533-06540-2). Vantage.

Yinger, J. Milton. Scientific Study of Religion. (Illus.). 1970. text ed. write for info. (ISBN 0-02-430900-1). Macmillan.

Yogananda, Paramahansa. Science of Religion. LC 81-52892. (Illus.). 102p. 1982. 6.00 (ISBN 0-87612-004-4); Span. ed. 1.50x (ISBN 0-87612-001-X); pap. 5.00x German ed. (ISBN 3-87041-225-9); pap. 3.50 English ed. (ISBN 0-87612-005-2). Self Realization.

--Science of Religion. (Dutch.). 1974. 6.50x (ISBN 90-202-45-465). Self Realization.

Zain, C. C. Evolution of Religion: Section 2, Lessons 133-40. (Illus.). 1976. pap. 9.95 (ISBN 0-87887-346-5). Church of Light.

Zwingli, Ulrich. Commentary on True & False Religion. Jackson, Samuel M. & Heller, Nevin, eds. viii, 415p. 1981. pap. 15.95 (ISBN 0-939464-00-4). Labyrinth Pr.

RELIGION–ADDRESSES, ESSAYS, LECTURES

Adams, James L. The Prophethood of All Believers. Beach, George K., ed. LC 85-73368. 324p. 1986. 25.00 (ISBN 0-8070-1602-0). Beacon Pr.

Alder, Felix. Creed & Deed: A Series of Discourses. LC 76-38430. (Religion in America Ser: 2). 254p. 1972. Repr. of 1877 ed. 17.00 (ISBN 0-405-04051-2). Ayer Co Pubs.

Alexander, Jon & Dimock, Giles, eds. Religion in Western Civilization Since the Reformation: Select Readings. 184p. 1983. pap. text ed. 6.75 (ISBN 0-8191-3391-4). U Pr of Amer.

Apczynski, John V., ed. Foundations of Religious Literacy. 186p. 1986. pap. text ed. 12.00 (ISBN 0-8191-5617-5, Pub. by College Theology Society). U Pr of Amer.

Arnold, Matthew. The Complete Prose Works of Matthew Arnold, 11 vols. Super, R. H., ed. Incl. Vol. 1. On the Classical Tradition. 282p. 1960. 19.95x (ISBN 0-472-11651-7); Vol. 2. Democratic Education. 430p. 1962. 19.95x (ISBN 0-472-11652-5); Vol. 3. Lectures & Essays in Criticism. 586p. 1962. 19.95x (ISBN 0-472-11653-3); Vol. 4. Schools & Universities on the Continent. 446p. 1964. 19.95x (ISBN 0-472-11654-1); Vol. 5. Culture & Anarchy. 580p. 1965. 19.95x (ISBN 0-472-11655-X); Vol. 6. Dissent & Dogma. 624p. 1967. 19.95x (ISBN 0-472-11656-8); Vol. 7. God & the Bible. 604p. 1970. 19.95x (ISBN 0-472-11657-6); Vol. 8. Essays Religious & Mixed. 576p. 1972. 19.95x (ISBN 0-472-11658-4); Vol. 9. English Literature & Irish Politics. 1973. 19.95x (ISBN 0-472-11659-2); Vol. 10. Philistinism in England & America. 1974. 19.95x (ISBN 0-472-11660-6); Vol. 11. The Last Word. 1976. 19.95x (ISBN 0-472-11661-4). LC 60-5018. U of Mich Pr.

Arrupe, Pedro. Challenge to Religious Life Today: Selected Letters & Addresses--1. Aixala, Jerome, ed. LC 79-87603. 310p. 1979. 7.00 (ISBN 0-912422-45-9); pap. 6.00 smyth sewn (ISBN 0-912422-44-0). Inst Jesuit.

Audi, Robert & Wainwright, William J., eds. Rationality, Religious Belief, & Moral Commitment: New Essays in the Philosophy of Religion. LC 85-48200. 352p. 1986. text ed. 42.50x (ISBN 0-8014-1856-9); pap. text ed. 12.95x (ISBN 0-8014-9381-1). Cornell U Pr.

Bales, James & Teller, Woosey. Bales Teller Debate. pap. 4.95 (ISBN 0-89315-018-5). Lambert Bk.

Baxter, Richard. The Practical Works of Richard Baxter. (Giant Summit Bks.). 1000p. 1981. pap. 14.95 (ISBN 0-8010-0804-2). Baker Bk.

Bianco, Enzo. Don Bosco's Lay Religious: Essays on the Salesian Brother, Pt. 1. Swain, Peter, tr. LC 84-72160. 75p. pap. 3.00 (ISBN 0-89944-078-9). Don Bosco Multimedia.

--Don Bosco's Lay Religious: Profiles in Courage, Pt. 2. Swain, Peter, tr. 101p. pap. 3.00 (ISBN 0-89944-079-7). Don Bosco Multimedia.

Biggar, Nigel, et al. Cities of Gods: Faith, Politics & Pluralism in Judaism, Christianity & Islam. LC 85-9879. (Contributions to the Study of Religion Ser.: No. 16). 253p. 1986. lib. bdg. 39.95 (ISBN 0-313-24944-X, BCG/). Greenwood.

Bonney, Charles C. World's Congress Addresses. 88p. 1900. pap. 6.95 (ISBN 0-912050-48-9). Open Court.

Buechner, Frederick. A Room Called Remember: Uncollected Pieces. LC 83-48457. 192p. 1984. 13.45 (ISBN 0-06-061163-4, HarpR). Har-Row.

Burns, et al. The Revival of Religion. 449p. 1984. Repr. of 1840 ed. 13.95 (ISBN 0-85151-435-9). Banner of Truth.

Davison, Peter, et al, eds. Content & Taste: Religion & Myth. LC 77-90615. (Literary Taste, Culture & Mass Communication: Vol. 7). 338p. 1978. lib. bdg. 47.00x (ISBN 0-85964-042-6). Chadwyck-Healey.

Dawson, Christopher H. Enquiries into Religion & Culture. facs. ed. LC 68-29200. (Essay Index Reprint Ser.). 1933. 24.50 (ISBN 0-8369-0367-6). Ayer Co Pubs.

DeLoach, Clarence, Jr., ed. The Faith Once Delivered. (Illus.). 170p. 1974. 6.95 (ISBN 0-88428-033-0). Parchment Pr.

Eagleson, John & Scharper, Philip J., eds. Puebla & Beyond. LC 79-24098. 370p. (Orig.). 1979. pap. 9.95 (ISBN 0-88344-399-6). Orbis Bks.

Ellwood, Robert S., Jr. Words of the World's Religion. 1977. pap. text ed. 24.33x (ISBN 0-13-965004-0). P-H.

Ellwood, Robert S., Jr., ed. Readings on Religion: From Inside & Outside. 1978. pap. text ed. write for info. (ISBN 0-13-760942-6). P-H.

Evans-Pritchard, E. E. Theories of Primitive Religion. LC 85-22003. (Sir D. Owens Evan Lectures, 1962). 138p. 1985. Repr. of 1965 ed. lib. bdg. 29.75x (ISBN 0-313-24978-4, EPTP). Greenwood.

Far West Editions. Material for Thought, No.7. LC 77-89507. 76p. 1977. pap. 2.50 (ISBN 0-914480-03-0). Far West Edns.

--Material for Thought, No. 9. LC 81-68048. 94p. 1981. pap. 3.95 (ISBN 0-914480-07-3). Far West Edns.

--Material for Thought, Vol.74 & 76, Nos. 7 & 8. Bound Vol. pap. 7.95 (ISBN 0-686-47075-3). Far West Edns.

--Material For Thought: Spring 1976. LC 73-94407. 1976. pap. 2.95 (ISBN 0-914480-02-2). Far West Edns.

--Material for Thought: 1970. 31p. 1970. pap. 0.50 (ISBN 0-686-47079-6). Far West Edns.

--Material for Thought: 1971. 47p. 1971. pap. 0.50 (ISBN 0-686-47081-8). Far West Edns.

--Material for Thought: 1972. 63p. 1972. pap. 0.50 (ISBN 0-686-47082-6). Far West Edns.

--Material for Thought: 1974. LC 73-94407. 114p. 1974. pap. 2.00 (ISBN 0-914480-01-4). Far West Edns.

Finney, Charles G. Lectures to Professing Christians. (The Higher Christian Life Ser.). 348p. 1985. lib. bdg. 45.00 (ISBN 0-8240-6418-6). Garland Pub.
Forell, George W., ed. & tr. from Ger. Zinzendorf: Nine Public Lectures on Important Subjects in Religion. LC 74-93784. 170p. 1973. text ed. 15.00 (ISBN 0-87745-036-6). U of Iowa Pr.
Garvey, John. The Prematurely Saved. 1986. pap. 8.95 (ISBN 0-87243-150-9). Templegate.
Gauvin, Marshall J. Case Against Religion. 500p. 10.00 (ISBN 0-318-19200-4). Truth Seeker.
Gillman, Neil. Gabriel Marcel on Religious Knowledge. LC 80-5061. 315p. 1980. text ed. 26.75 (ISBN 0-8191-1034-5); pap. text ed. 14.25 (ISBN 0-8191-1035-3). U Pr of Amer.
Giovio, Paolo. The Worthy Tract of Paulus Iovius. Daniel, Samuel, tr. LC 76-13497. 300p. 1976. Repr. of 1585 ed. lib. bdg. 50.00x (ISBN 0-8201-1272-0). Schol Facsimiles.
Gyatso, Geshe K. Clear Light of Bliss. Landaw, Jonathan, ed. Norbu, Tenzin, tr. from Tibetan. (Wisdom Advanced Book: Blue Ser.). (Illus.). 264p. (Orig.). 1982. pap. 10.95 (ISBN 0-86171-005-3, Pub. by Wisdom Pubns). Great Traditions.
Haffert, John M. Dear Bishop: Memoirs of the Author Concerning the History of the Blue Army. (Illus.). 352p. 1981. 8.95 (ISBN 0-911988-44-0); pap. 5.95 (ISBN 0-911988-42-4). AMI Pr.
Hall, T. William, ed. Introduction to the Study of Religion. LC 78-4427. (Orig.). 1978. pap. text ed. 10.95xi (ISBN 0-06-063572-X, RD 281, HarpR). Har-Row.
Hammond, Philip E. The Sacred in a Secular Age: Toward Revision in the Scientific Study of Religion. LC 84-16470. 380p. 1985. 37.50x (ISBN 0-520-05342-7); pap. 8.95 (ISBN 0-520-05343-5, CAL 726). U of Cal Pr.
Hansadutta. Fool's Paradise. LC 85-5839. (Illus.). 190p. (Orig.). 1985. pap. 5.95 (ISBN 0-933593-05-8). Hansa Pub.
Harrison, Stanley M. & Taylor, Richard C., eds. The Life of Religion: A Marquette University Symposium on the Nature of Religious Belief. 124p. (Orig.). 1986. lib. bdg. 22.50 (ISBN 0-8191-5558-6); pap. text ed. 8.75 (ISBN 0-8191-5559-4). U Pr of Amer.
Henry, Carl F. Christian Countermoves in a Decadent Culture. LC 86-5286. (Orig.). 1986. 9.95 (ISBN 0-88070-151-X). Multnomah.
Hodges, H. A. God Beyond Knowledge. Hudson, W. D., ed. LC 77-22634. (Library of Philosophy & Religion Ser). 182p. 1979. text ed. 28.50x (ISBN 0-06-492922-1). B&N Imports.
Ibish, Yusuf & Marculescu, Ileana, eds. Contemplation & Action in World Religions. LC 78-61504. (Rothko Chapel). 1979. pap. 4.95 (ISBN 0-295-95634-8). U of Wash Pr.
Inge, William R. Church in the World. facs. ed. LC 68-57324. (Essay Index Reprint Ser). 1927. 17.00 (ISBN 0-8369-0080-4). Ayer Co Pubs.
Ingersoll, Robert G. The Gods & Other Lectures. 69.95 (ISBN 0-87968-246-9). Gordon Pr.
Izard, Michel & Smith, Pierre, eds. Between Belief & Transgression: Structuralist Essays in Religion, History & Myth. Leavitt, John, tr. LC 81-16377. (Chicago Originals Ser.). (Illus.). 1982. lib. bdg. 20.00x (ISBN 0-226-38861-1). U of Chicago Pr.
James, William. Essays in Religion & Morality. LC 81-7040. (Illus.). 376p. text ed. 25.00x (ISBN 0-674-26735-4). Harvard U Pr.
Kedourie, Elie. The Crossman Confessions & Other Essays in Politics, History & Religion. 255p. 1985. 30.00x (ISBN 0-7201-1712-7). Mansell.
King-Farlow, John, ed. The Challenge of Religion Today: Essays on the Philosophy of Religion. LC 76-13492. 1976. pap. text ed. 6.95 (ISBN 0-88202-157-5). Watson Pub Intl.
Lateiner, Donald & Stephens, Susan, eds. Selected Papers of Lionel Pearson. LC 83-16485. (Homage Ser.). 282p. 1983. 14.95 (ISBN 0-89130-646-3, 00 16 04). Scholars Pr GA.
Lewis, C. S. The Seeing Eye & Other Selected Essays from Christian Reflections. 256p. 1986. pap. 3.50 (ISBN 0-345-32866-3). Ballantine.
Luccock, Halford E. Enter the Crocus. Hartman, Charles S., ed. LC 79-22592. 1980. 3.50 (ISBN 0-8298-0386-6). Pilgrim NY.
McNulty, James F. Words of Power. LC 83-2514. 226p. (Orig.). 1983. pap. 8.95 (ISBN 0-8189-0442-9). Alba.
Martin, David. The Dilemmas of Contemporary Religion. LC 78-17704. 1978. 20.00x (ISBN 0-312-21055-8). St Martin.
Marx, Karl & Engels, Friedrich. On Religion. LC 82-17032. (Classics in Religious Studies). 384p. 1982. Repr. of 1964 ed. 10.50x (ISBN 0-89130-599-8, 01 05 03). Scholars Pr GA.
Mill, John S. Essays on Ethics, Religion & Society. Robson, J. M., ed. (Collected Works of John Stuart Hill Ser.: Vol. 10). pap. 160.00 (ISBN 0-317-41695-2, 2055827). Bks Demand UMI.
Monfasani, John, ed. Collectanea Trapezuntiana: Texts, Documents & Bibliographies of George of Trebizond. LC 83-19366. (Medieval & Renaissance Texts & Studies: Vol. 25). 896p. 1984. 60.00 (ISBN 0-86698-060-1). Medieval & Renaissance NY.
Moon, Sun M. Science & Absolute Values: Ten Addresses by Sun Myung Moon. (Illus.). 139p. 1982. casebound 9.95 (ISBN 0-89226-023-8, Pub. by ICF Pr); pap. 5.95 (ISBN 0-89226-019-X). Paragon Hse.
Morris, Brian. Anthropological Studies of Religion: An Introductory Text. (Illus.). 384p. 1987. 42.50 (ISBN 0-521-32794-6); pap. 12.95 (ISBN 0-521-33991-X). Cambridge U Pr.
Mueller, Friedrich M. Lectures on the Science of Religion: With a Paper on Buddhist Nihilism, & a Translation of the Dhammapada or Path of Virtue. LC 73-18818. Repr. of 1872 ed. 15.00 (ISBN 0-404-11444-X). AMS Pr.
--Selected Essays on Language, Mythology & Religion, 2 vols. LC 73-18814. Repr. of 1881 ed. 87.50 set (ISBN 0-404-11456-3). AMS Pr.
Murphy, Carol R. Many Religions: One God. LC 66-30689. (Orig.). 1966. pap. 2.50x (ISBN 0-87574-150-9). Pendle Hill.
Murray, Gilbert. Stoic, Christian & Humanist. LC 75-99712. (Essay Index Reprint Ser.). 1940. 17.00 (ISBN 0-8369-1363-9). Ayer Co Pubs.
Needham, Joseph. Time the Refreshing River: Science, Religion & Socialism & Other Essays. 292p. 1986. 39.95 (ISBN 0-85124-429-7, Pub. by Spokesman UK); pap. 12.50 (ISBN 0-85124-439-4, Pub. by Spokesman UK). Humanities.
Nicoll, Maurice. The Mark. LC 84-22116. 216p. 1985. pap. 9.95 (ISBN 0-87773-315-5, 72998-6). Shambhala Pubns.
Nock, Arthur D. Essays on Religion & the Ancient World. Stewart, Zeph, ed. 1164p. 1986. Set. 98.00x (ISBN 0-19-814282-X). Oxford U Pr.
Pendleton, Nathaniel D. Selected Papers & Addresses. 251p. 1985. 7.00 (ISBN 0-910557-09-8). Acad New Church.
Plotkin, Frederick. Faith & Reason: Essays in the Religious & Scientific Imagination. LC 72-97937. 1970. 6.00 (ISBN 0-8022-2322-2). Philos Lib.
Rahner, Karl. Karl Rahner in Dialogue. 352p. 1986. 18.95 (ISBN 0-8245-0749-5). Crossroad NY.
Roboz, Steven, ed. The Holy Grail: From the Works of Rudolf Steiner. 2nd ed. 1984. pap. 4.75 (ISBN 0-919924-24-7, Steiner Bk Ctr). Anthroposophic.
Rouner, Leroy S., ed. Religious Pluralism. LC 84-7431. (Boston University Studies in Philosphy & Religion: Vol. 5). 256p. 1984. text ed. 22.95 (ISBN 0-268-01626-7, 85-16262). U of Notre Dame Pr.
Runzo, Joseph & Ihara, Graig K., eds. Religious Experience & Religious Belief: Essays in the Epistemology of Religion. LC 86-1614. 160p. 1986. lib. bdg. 23.50 (ISBN 0-8191-5292-7); pap. text ed. 10.75 (ISBN 0-8191-5293-5). U Pr of Amer.
Schopenhauer, Arthur. Religion: A Dialogue, & Other Essays. 3rd ed. Saunders, T. Bailey, tr. LC 72-488. (Essay Index Reprint Ser.). Repr. of 1891 ed. 13.00 (ISBN 0-8369-2820-2). Ayer Co Pubs.
--Religion: A Dialogue, & Other Essays. Saunders, T. Bailey, tr. LC 72-11305. 140p. 1973. Repr. of 1899 ed. lib. bdg. 25.00x (ISBN 0-8371-6652-7, SCRE). Greenwood.
Seckel, Al, ed. Bertrand Russell on God & Religion. 345p. pap. 12.95 (ISBN 0-87975-323-4). Prometheus Bks.
Sellars, Roy W. The Next Step in Religion: An Essay Toward the Coming Renaissance. LC 75-3360. Repr. of 1918 ed. 24.50 (ISBN 0-404-59358-5). AMS Pr.
Spurgeon, C. H. The Best of C. H. Spurgeon. 256p. 1986. pap. 6.95 (ISBN 0-8010-8267-6). Baker Bk.
Spurgeon, Charles H. Lectures to My Students. 2nd ed. 443p. 1980. pap. 9.95 (ISBN 0-310-32911-6, 10845P). Zondervan.
Stanford, Neal. I Do Windows. 48p. 1982. 6.00 (ISBN 0-682-49865-3). Exposition Pr FL.
Steiner, Rudolf. Philosophy, Cosmology & Religion: Ten Lectures. Easton, Stewart C., et al, eds. 180p. (Orig.). 1984. 16.00 (ISBN 0-88010-109-1); pap. 9.95 (ISBN 0-88010-110-5). Anthroposophic.
Swedenborg, Emanuel. Spiritual Diary of Emanuel Swedenborg, 6 vols. lib. bdg. 700.00 (ISBN 0-87968-560-3). Krishna Pr.
Taylor, Mark C., ed. Unfinished... Essays in Honor of Ray L. Hart. (JAAR Thematic Studies). 1981. pap. 13.50 (ISBN 0-89130-680-3, 01-24-81). Scholars Pr GA.
Thundy, Zacharias P., et al, eds. Religion in Dialogue: East & West Meet. 336p. (Orig.). 1985. lib. bdg. 29.75 (ISBN 0-8191-4466-5); pap. text ed. 14.75 (ISBN 0-8191-4467-3). U Pr of Amer.
Toussaint, Stanley D. & Dyer, Charles, eds. Essays in Honor of J. Dwight Pentecost. 1986. text ed. 15.95 (ISBN 0-8024-2381-7). Moody.
Townsend, Janice M. Joy Before Us. LC 81-7198. 1982. pap. 8.00 (ISBN 0-8309-0327-5). Herald Hse.
Von Rad, Gerhard. The Problem of the Hexateuch & Other Essays. 352p. pap. 15.95 (ISBN 0-317-31485-8, 30-1310-259). Fortress.
Wach, Joachim. Understanding & Believing: Essays. Kitagawa, Joseph M., ed. LC 75-31987. 204p. 1976. Repr. of 1968 ed. lib. bdg. 25.00x (ISBN 0-8371-8488-6, WAUB). Greenwood.
Watts, Alan W. Cloud Hidden, Whereabouts Unknown: A Mountain Journal. 1965. pap. 3.95 (ISBN 0-394-71999-9, Vin). Random.
Webb, James, ed. A Quest Anthology. LC 75-36916. (Occult Ser.). 1976. Repr. of 1976 ed. 46.50x (ISBN 0-405-07971-0). Ayer Co Pubs.

RELIGION–BIBLIOGRAPHY

Capps, Donald, et al, eds. Psychology of Religion: A Guide to Information Sources. LC 73-17530. (Philosophy & Religion Information Guide Ser.: Vol. 1). vii, 380p. 1976. 62.00x (ISBN 0-8103-1356-1). Gale.
Choquette, Diane, compiled by. New Religious Movements in the United States & Canada: A Critical Assessment & Annotated Bibliography. LC 85-9964. (Bibliographies & Indexes in Religious Studies Ser.: No. 5). i, 235p. 1985. lib. bdg. 39.95 (ISBN 0-313-23772-7, CRM/). Greenwood.
Dolan, Walter. The Classical World Bibliography of Philosophy, Religion, & Rhetoric. LC 76-52512. (Library of Humanities Reference Bks.: No. 95). 396p. 1978. lib. bdg. 51.00 (ISBN 0-8240-9878-1). Garland Pub.
Freudenberger, Elsie. Reference Works in the Field of Religion 1977-1985. (Orig.). 1986. pap. 15.00 (ISBN 0-87507-037-X). Cath Lib Assn.
Kennedy, James, Jr. Library Research Guide to Religion & Theology: Illustrated Search Strategy & Sources. 2nd Rev. ed. LC 73-90317. (Library Research Guides Ser.: No. 1). 1984. 19.50 (ISBN 0-87650-185-4); pap. 12.50 (ISBN 0-87650-184-6). Pierian.
Lippy, Charles H. Bibliography of Religion in the South. LC 85-13575. xvi, 498p. 1985. text ed. 49.95 (ISBN 0-86554-161-2, MUP-H151). Mercer Univ Pr.
Menendez, Albert J. Religious Conflict in America: A Bibliography. LC 84-48078. (Reference Library of Social Science). 500p. 1984. lib. bdg. 20.00 (ISBN 0-8240-8904-9). Garland Pub.
Mitros, Joseph F. Religions: A Select, Classified Bibliography. Matczak, Sebastian A., intro. by. LC 77-183042. (Philosophical Questions Ser.: No. 8). 350p. 1973. 45.00x (ISBN 0-912116-08-0). Learned Pubns.
R. R. Bowker Co. Staff, ed. Religious & Inspirational Books & Serials in Print 1987. 1700p. 1987. 89.00 (ISBN 0-8352-2320-5). Bowker.
Regazzi, John J. & Hines, Theodore C. A Guide to Indexed Periodicals in Religion. LC 75-22277. 328p. 1975. 20.00 (ISBN 0-8108-0868-4). Scarecrow.
Religious & Inspirational Books & Serials in Print, 1985. 1648p. 1985. 79.95x (ISBN 0-8352-2052-4). Bowker.
Sayre, John L. & Hamburger, Roberta, eds. Tools for Theological Research. rev. 7th ed. LC 85-11979. 120p. (Orig.). 1985. pap. 5.00x (ISBN 0-912832-22-3). Seminary Pr.
Thompson, Laurence G. Chinese Religion in Western Languages: A Comprehensive & Classified Bibliography of Publications in English, French, & German Through 1980. LC 84-24010. (Monograph of the Association for Asian Studies: No. XLI). 302p. 1985. HC Monograph 19.95x (ISBN 0-8165-0926-3). U of Ariz Pr.
Waardenburg, Jacques. Classical Approaches to the Study of Religion: Aims, Methods & Theories of Research, Pt. 2 Bibliography. (Religion & Reason Ser.: No. 4). 332p. 1974. text ed. 58.50 (ISBN 90-2797-971-5). Mouton.
Weborg, John. Where Is It Written? An Introductory, Annotated Bibliography in Spirituality. 1978. 0.75 (ISBN 0-8199-0739-1). Franciscan Herald.
Wiersbe, Warren W. A Basic Library for Bible Students. (Orig.). 1981. pap. 2.95 (ISBN 0-8010-9641-3). Baker Bk.

RELIGION–DICTIONARIES

Aubert, Roger & Van Cauwenberg. Dictionnaire d'Histoire et du Geographie Ecclesiastiques, 16 vols. (Fr.). Set. pap. 1795.00 (ISBN 0-686-56903-2, M-6014). French & Eur.
Aurelio, John. Gather Round: Christian Fairy Tales for All Ages. LC 81-84389. (Illus.). 128p. (Orig.). 1982. pap. 5.95 (ISBN 0-8091-2444-0). Paulist Pr.
Balbus, Joannes. Catholicon. 746p. 1460. text ed. 186.30x (ISBN 0-576-72240-5, Pub. by Greggg Intl Pubs England). Gregg Intl.
Barrett, David, ed. World Christian Encyclopedia: A Comparative Survey of Churches & Religions in the Modern World, A. D. 1900 to 2000. (Illus.). 1982. text ed. 165.00x (ISBN 0-19-572435-6). Oxford U Pr.
Blazquez, Jose M. Diccionario De las Religiones Prerromanas De Hispania. (Span.). 192p. 1975. pap. 9.95 (ISBN 84-7090-071-4, S-50058). French & Eur.
Blunt, John H. Dictionary of Sects, Heresies, Ecclesiastical Parties & Schools of Religious Thought. LC 74-9653. 1974. Repr. of 1874 ed. 75.00x (ISBN 0-8103-3751-7). Gale.
Brandon, S. G. F. Diccionario de Religiones Comparadas, 2 vols. (Span.). 1553p. 1975. Set. 49.95 (ISBN 8-4705-7188-5). French & Eur.
Broderick, Robert C., ed. The Catholic Encyclopedia. rev. ed. 612p. 1987. pap. 18.95 (ISBN 0-8407-5544-9). Nelson.
Bumpus, J. A. Dictionary of Ecclesiastical Terms. 75.00 (ISBN 0-8490-0034-3). Gordon Pr.
Bumpus, John S. Dictionary of Ecclesiastical Terms: Being a History & Explanation of Certain Terms Used in Architecture, Ecclesiology, Liturgiology, Music, Ritual, Cathedral, Constitution, Etc. LC 68-30653. 1969. Repr. of 1910 ed. 35.00x (ISBN 0-8103-3321-X). Gale.
Cattell, Ann. Dictionary of Esoteric Words. (Orig.). 1967. pap. 1.75 (ISBN 0-8065-0175-8, C205). Citadel Pr.
Crim, Keith, et al, eds. Abingdon Dictionary of Living Religions. LC 81-1465. 864p. 1981. 17.95 (ISBN 0-687-00409-8). Abingdon.
Dacio, Juan. Diccionario de los Papas. (Span.). 37.50 (ISBN 84-233-0112-5, S-50110). French & Eur.
Diccionario del Hogar Catolico. (Span.). 1180p. 1962. 17.95 (ISBN 84-261-0075-9, S-12259). French & Eur.
Eliade, Mircea, ed. Encyclopedia of Religion, 16 vols. 8000p. 1986. Set. reference 1100.00x (ISBN 0-02-909480-1). Macmillan.
Enciclopedia de Citas Morales y Religiosas. (Span.). 456p. 1976. 18.95 (ISBN 84-7228-251-1, S-50575). French & Eur.
Ferm, Vergilius. An Encyclopedia of Religion. LC 75-36508. 844p. 1976. Repr. of 1945 ed. lib. bdg. 55.00x (ISBN 0-8371-8638-2, FEEOR). Greenwood.
Ferm, Vergilius, ed. Encyclopedia of Religion. LC 62-18535. 86p. 1962. 19.95 (ISBN 0-8022-0490-2). Philos Lib.
Fern, Vergilus. Concise Dictionary of Religion. 1956. 7.95 (ISBN 0-8022-0488-0). Philos Lib.
Gentz, William H., ed. The Dictionary of Bible & Religion. (Illus.). 1152p. 1986. 26.95 (ISBN 0-687-10757-1). Abingdon.
Hoermann, Karl. Diccionario de Moral Cristiana. 2nd ed. (Span.). 704p. 1978. pap. 35.95 (ISBN 84-254-0966-7, S-50192). French & Eur.
--Diccionario De Moral Cristiana. 2nd ed. (Span.). 704p. 1978. 41.95 (ISBN 84-254-0967-5, S-50193). French & Eur.
Kauffman, Donald T. Baker's Concise Dictionary of Religion. (Paperback Reference Library). 446p. 1985. pap. 11.95 (ISBN 0-8010-5467-2). Baker Bk.
Kennedy, Richard. International Dictionary of Religion. LC 83-27209. (Illus.). 1984. 24.50x (ISBN 0-8245-0632-4). Crossroad NY.
--International Dictionary of Religion. 256p. 1986. pap. 12.95 (ISBN 0-8245-0733-9). Crossroad NY.
Konig. Diccionario De las Religiones. (Span.). 816p. 1977. 37.50 (ISBN 84-254-0358-8, S-50201). French & Eur.
Koning, Frederick. Diccionario de Demonologia. 3rd ed. (Span.). 1978. pap. 2.95 (ISBN 0-686-57362-5, S-50155). French & Eur.
Mathews, Shailer & Smith, Gerald B., eds. Dictionary of Religion & Ethics. LC 70-145713. 1971. Repr. of 1921 ed. 51.00x (ISBN 0-8103-3196-9). Gale.
Mead, Frank S., ed. The Encyclopedia of Religious Quotations. 540p. 1985. 16.95 (ISBN 0-8007-1410-5). Revell.
Meagher, Paul K., et al. The Encyclopedic Dictionary of Religion, 3 vols. LC 78-62029. 3815p. 1979. 69.95 (ISBN 0-9602572-3-3). Cath U Pr.
Mildenberger, Friedrich. Theorie der Theologie: Enzyklopaedie als Methodenlehre. (Ger.). 164p. 1972. 12.95 (ISBN 3-7668-0384-0, M-7094). French & Eur.
Neggers, Gladys. Vocabulario Culto. 2nd ed. (Span.). 168p. 1977. pap. 8.75 (ISBN 84-359-0034-7, S-50023). French & Eur.
Neill, S. E. Lexikon Zur Weltmission. (Ger.). 48.00 (ISBN 3-7974-0054-3, M-7190). French & Eur.
Obermayer, H. Kleines Stuttgarter-Bibellexikon. 3rd ed. (Ger.). 344p. 1976. 9.95 (ISBN 3-460-30053-1, M-7507, Pub. by Vlg. Katholisches Bibelwerk). French & Eur.
Rouillard, Dom P. Diccionario De los Santos De Cada Dia. (Span.). 472p. 1966. 15.75 (ISBN 84-281-0062-4, S-50020). French & Eur.

Vilaro, Josep, et al. Diccionario Religioso Para los Hombres De Hoy. (Span.). 260p. 1976. pap. 7.50 (ISBN 84-320-0273-9, S-50025). French & Eur.

Woerterbuch zum Religionsunterricht. (Ger.). 1976. 10.95 (ISBN 0-686-56606-8, M-6906). French & Eur.

RELIGION–HISTORIOGRAPHY

Baird, Robert D., ed. Methodological Issues in Religious Studies. LC 75-44170. (Orig.). 1976. lib. bdg. 14.95x (ISBN 0-914914-08-1); pap. text ed. 5.95x (ISBN 0-914914-07-3). New Horizons.

Blasi, Anthony J. A Phenomenological Transformation of the Social Scientific Study of Religion. LC 85-13303. (American University Studies VII: Theology & Religion: Vol. 10). 195p. 1985. text ed. 27.85 (ISBN 0-8204-0235-4). P Lang Pubs.

Tierney, Brian. Religion, Law & the Growth of Constitutional Thought, 1150-1650. LC 81-12265. 128p. 1982. 24.95 (ISBN 0-521-23495-6). Cambridge U Pr.

RELIGION–HISTORY

Allen, William O. Two Hundred Years: The History of the Society for Promoting Christian Knowledge, 1698-1898. LC 76-135171. (Research & Source Works Ser.: No. 622). 1971. Repr. of 1898 ed. 32.00 (ISBN 0-8337-0044-8). B Franklin.

Altizer, Thomas J. History As Apocalypse. LC 84-16289. (SUNY Series in Religion). 250p. 1985. 44.50 (ISBN 0-88706-013-7); pap. 16.95 (ISBN 0-88706-014-5). State U NY Pr.

Amatora, Sr. Mary. The Queen's Portrait: The Story of Guadalupe. LC 74-188442. 1972. 7.50 (ISBN 0-682-47468-1, Lochinvar); (Lochinvar). Exposition Pr FL.

Amort, Eusebio. Vetus Disciplina Canocorum Regularium & Saecularium ex Documentis Magna Parte Hucusque Ineditis a Temporibus Apostolicis ad Saeculum XVII. 1112p. 1747. text ed. 248.40x (ISBN 0-576-99833-8, Pub. by Gregg Intl Pubs England). Gregg Intl.

Arndt, Karl J. George Rapp's Successors & Material Heirs: 1847-1916. LC 76-147268. (Illus.). 445p. 1972. 45.00 (ISBN 0-8386-7889-0). Fairleigh Dickinson.

Arndt, Karl J. R. George Rapp's Harmony Society: 1785-1847. rev. ed. LC 72-147267. (Illus.). 713p. 1972. 45.00 (ISBN 0-8386-7888-2). Fairleigh Dickinson.

Bailey, Albert E. Gospel in Hymns. (Illus.). 1950. lib. rep. ed. 45.00x (ISBN 0-684-15554-0, PG104HHRE, ScribT). Scribner.

Baldwin, Leland D. The American Quest for the City of God. ix, 368p. 1981. 18.95x (ISBN 0-86554-016-0). Mercer Univ Pr.

Bales, James & Teller, Woosey. Bales Teller Debate. pap. 4.95 (ISBN 0-89315-018-5). Lambert Bk.

Brooke, Rosalind & Brooke, Christopher. Popular Religion in the Middle Ages. (Illus.). 1985. pap. 10.95 (ISBN 0-500-27381-2). Thames Hudson.

Browning, John & Morton, Richard. Religion in the Eighteenth Century. LC 79-17715. (McMaster University Eighteenth Century Studies). 145p. 1979. lib. bdg. 22.00 (ISBN 0-8240-4005-8). Garland Pub.

Bruce, Alexander B. The Training of the Twelve. LC 79-88121. (Shepherd Illustrated Classics). 1979. pap. 6.95 (ISBN 0-87983-206-1). Keats.

Bushman, Richard L., ed. The Great Awakening: Documents on the Revival of Religion, 1740-1745. (Institute of Early American History & Culture Ser.). xiv, 174p. 1970. 15.00x (ISBN 0-8078-1181-5). U of NC Pr.

Butterfield, Herbert. Herbert Butterfield on History. Winks, Robin W., ed. LC 83-49176. (History & Historiography Ser.). 204p. 1985. lib. bdg. 30.00 (ISBN 0-8240-6352-X). Garland Pub.

Carter, Jesse B. Religious Life of Ancient Rome. 270p. 1972. Repr. of 1911 ed. lib. bdg. 27.50x (ISBN 0-8154-0429-8). Cooper Sq.

Carus, Paul. Godward: A Record of Religious Progress. 26p. 1898. 0.95 (ISBN 0-317-40417-2). Open Court.

Chick, Jack T. Smokescreens. (Illus.). 93p. 1982. pap. 2.50 (ISBN 0-937958-14-X). Chick Pubns.

Connor, W. R., ed. Ancient Religion & Mythology, 32 vols. (Illus.). 1976. Set. 1039.00x (ISBN 0-405-07001-2). Ayer Co Pubs.

Conway, Robert S. Ancient Italy & Modern Religion. LC 77-27141. (Hibbert Lectures: 1932). Repr. of 1933 ed. 17.00 (ISBN 0-404-60428-5). AMS Pr.

Deal, William S. The March of Holiness Through the Centuries. 1978. pap. 2.50 (ISBN 0-686-05528-4). Crusade Pubs.

De Vries, Jan. Perspectives in the History of Religions. Bolle, Kees W., tr. & intro. by. LC 76-20154. 1977. pap. 3.65 (ISBN 0-520-03300-0, CAL 352). U of Cal Pr.

Dumezil, Georges. Camillus: A Study of Indo-European Religion As Roman History. Strutynski, Udo, ed. Aronowicz, Annette, et al, trs. from Fr. LC 80-36771. 250p. 1980. 24.00x (ISBN 0-520-02841-4). U of Cal Pr.

Eliade, Mircea. A History of Religious Ideas: From the Stone Age to the Eleusinian Mysteries, Vol. 1. Trask, Willard R., tr. from Fr. LC 77-16784. xviii, 490p. 1979. 25.00x (ISBN 0-226-20400-6); pap. 16.95 (ISBN 0-226-20401-4). U of Chicago Pr.

--History of Religious Ideas, Vol. II: From Gautama Buddha to the Triumph of Christianity. Trask, Willard, tr. from Fr. LC 77-16784. vi, 564p. 1982. 27.50x (ISBN 0-226-20402-2). U of Chicago Pr.

--A History of Religious Ideas, Vol. 3: From Muhammad to the Age of Reforms. Hiltebeitel, Alf & Apostolos-Cappadona, Diane, trs. LC 77-16784. xii, 352p. 1985. 27.50 (ISBN 0-226-20404-9). U of Chicago Pr.

--Ordeal by Labyrinth: Conversations with Claude-Henri Rocquet. Coltman, Derek, tr. from Fr. LC 81-21796. (Illus.). 1982. 17.50x (ISBN 0-226-20387-5). U of Chicago Pr.

--The Quest: History & Meaning in Religion. LC 68-19059. (Midway Reprint Ser.). xii, 180p. 1984. pap. text ed. 10.00x (ISBN 0-226-20386-7). U of Chicago Pr.

Erasmus. Inquistio De Fide: A Colloquy by Desiderius Erasmus Roterodamus, 1524. 2nd ed. Thompson, Craig, ed. LC 74-31476. xiii, 137p. 1975. Repr. of 1950 ed. 20.00 (ISBN 0-685-51693-8, Archon). Shoe String.

Frederick, John T. The Darkened Sky: Nineteenth-Century American Novelists & Religion. LC 69-14811. pap. 72.50 (ISBN 0-317-29688-4, 2022068). Bks Demand UMI.

Garrett, Arthur. The Noble Romans. LC 86-30240. 550p. 1987. 34.95 (ISBN 0-8022-2528-4). Philos Lib.

Garrison, Winfred E. March of Faith: The Story of Religion in America Since 1865. LC 79-138112. 1971. Repr. of 1933 ed. lib. bdg. 22.50x (ISBN 0-8371-5688-2, GAMF). Greenwood.

Gaustad, Edwin S. A Documentary History of Religion in America Since 1865, Vol. 2. (Illus.). 640p. 1983. pap. 19.95 (ISBN 0-8028-1874-9). Eerdmans.

--Religious History of America. 1974. pap. 10.95 (ISBN 0-06-063093-0, RD/66, HarpR). Har-Row.

Gay, Volney P. Reading Freud: Psychology, Neurosis, & Religion. LC 83-2917. (AAR Studies in Religion). 142p. 1983. pap. 8.25 (ISBN 0-89130-613-7, 01 00 32). Scholars Pr GA.

Gill, Rowland P., ed. Public Relations Are an Asset for Archives & Museums. (No. 6). 32p. (Orig.). 1985. pap. text ed. 5.15 (ISBN 0-910653-12-7, 8101-L). Archival Servs.

Gregory. Teaching of Saint Gregory: An Early Armenian Catechism. Thomson, Robert W., et al, trs. from Arm. LC 78-115482. (Armenian Texts & Studies: No. 3). 1971. 14.00x (ISBN 0-674-87038-7). Harvard U Pr.

Gregory, Timothy E. Vox Populi: Popular Opinion & Violence in the Religious Controversies of the Fifth Century A.D. LC 79-16885. 257p. 1979. 25.00x (ISBN 0-8142-0291-8). Ohio St U Pr.

Harrington, Norman W. Shaping of Religion in America. (Illus.). 168p. 1980. 29.95 (ISBN 0-937692-01-8). Queen Anne Pr.

Heline, Corinne. Twelve Labors of Hercules. (In the Zodiacal School of Life Ser.). pap. 2.50 (ISBN 0-87613-029-5). New Age.

Hinson, E. Glenn. The Evangelization of the Roman Empire: Identity & Adaptability. LC 81-11266. viii, 332p. 1981. 22.00 (ISBN 0-86554-244-9, MUP-P36). Mercer Univ Pr.

Hopwood, P. G. The Religious Experience of the Primitive Church Proir to the Influence of Paul. 1977. lib. bdg. 59.95 (ISBN 0-8490-2512-5). Gordon Pr.

Hutchison, John A. Paths of Faith. 3rd ed. (Illus.). 608p. 1981. 31.95x (ISBN 0-07-031532-9). McGraw.

Jacobsen, Thorkild. The Treasures of Darkness: A History of Mesoptamian Religon. LC 75-27576. (Illus.). 1976. pap. 9.95x (ISBN 0-300-02291-3). Yale U Pr.

Jameson, Anna B. The History of Our Lord As Exemplified in Works of Art; with That of His Type; St. John the Baptist; & Other Persons of the Old & New Testament, 2 vols. LC 92-167006. (Illus.). 1976. Repr. of 1890 ed. Set. 70.00x (ISBN 0-8103-4304-5). Gale.

Jay, Eric G. The Church: Its Changing Image Through Twenty Centuries. LC 79-92070. 1980. 12.95 (ISBN 0-8042-0877-8). John Knox.

Jungmann, Joseph A. The Mass of the Roman Rite: Its Origins and Development, 2 vols. Brunner, Francis A., tr. from German. 1050p. 1986. pap. 39.95 (ISBN 0-87061-129-1). Chr Classics.

Kippenberg, Hans G. Garizim und Synagoge: Traditionsgeschichtliche Untersuchungen zur samaritanischen Religion der aramaeischen Periode. (Religionsgeschichtliche Versuche und Vorarbeiten, 30). (Ger). 1971. 43.20x (ISBN 3-11-001864-0). De Gruyter.

Kitagawa, Joseph M., ed. The History of Religions: Retrospect & Prospect. 192p. 1985. 19.95x (ISBN 0-02-916490-7). Macmillan.

Klausner, Joseph. From Jesus to Paul. Stinespring, William, tr. from Hebrew. 1978. 15.95x (ISBN 0-932232-03-5); pap. 12.95 (ISBN 0-932232-04-3). Menorah Pub.

--Jesus of Nazareth: His Life, Times & Teaching. Danby, Herbert, tr. from Hebrew. 1978. 15.95x (ISBN 0-932232-01-9); pap. 12.95 (ISBN 0-932232-02-7). Menorah Pub.

Krodel, ed. & tr. from Ger. Luther's Works: Letters II, Vol. 49. LC 55-9893. 480p. 1972. 19.95 (ISBN 0-8006-0349-4, 1-349). Fortress.

Leuba, James H. The Psychological Origin & the Nature of Religion. 94p. 1980. Repr. of 1909 ed. lib. bdg. 17.50 (ISBN 0-8482-1622-9). Norwood Edns.

Lewis, John. Religions of the World Made Simple. rev. ed. (Made Simple Ser.). 1958. pap. 4.95 (ISBN 0-385-02276-X). Doubleday.

Lietzmann, Hans. Geschichte der Alten Kirche, 4 vols. in 1. 1220p. 1975. Repr. 79.20x (ISBN 3-11-004625-3). De Gruyter.

Lofthouse, William F. Israel after the Exile: Sixth & Fifth Centuries B. C. LC 78-10629. (Illus.). 1979. Repr. of 1928 ed. lib. bdg. 24.75x (ISBN 0-313-21008-X, LOIS). Greenwood.

Luibheid, Colm. Eusebius of Caesarea & the Arian Crisis. 136p. 1981. 22.50x (ISBN 0-7165-2277-2, BBA 03636, Pub. by Irish Academic Pr Ireland). Biblio Dist.

Mabee, Charles. Reimagining America: A Theological Critique of the American Mythos & Biblical Hermeneutics. LC 84-27335. xvi, 156p. 1985. 13.95 (ISBN 0-86554-148-5, MUP/H139). Mercer Univ Pr.

McCabe, Joseph. History's Greatest Liars. 176p. (YA) 1985. pap. 5.00. Am Atheist.

--Rationalist Encyclopaedia: A Book of Reference on Religion, Philosophy, Ethics, & Science. LC 79-164054. 1971. Repr. of 1948 ed. 51.00x (ISBN 0-8103-3754-1). Gale.

Macdonald, John. Samaritan Chronicle No. 2 (or, Sepher Ha-Yamim) from Joshua to Nebuchadnezzar. (Beiheft 107 zur Zeitschrift fuer die alttestamentliche Wissenschaft). 1969. 34.80 (ISBN 3-11-002582-5). De Gruyter.

McKivigan, John R. The War Against Proslavery Religion: Abolitionism & the Northern Churches, 1830-1865. LC 83-45933. 328p. 1984. 32.50x (ISBN 0-8014-1589-6). Cornell U Pr.

Macuch, Rudolf. Grammatik des Samaritanischen Hebraeisch. (Studia Samaritana 1). (Ger). 1969. 110.00x (ISBN 3-11-000133-0). De Gruyter.

Madhava, K. G. Religions in Coastal Karnataka: 1500-1763. (Illus.). 206p. 1985. text ed. 37.50x (ISBN 0-86590-585-1, Inter India Pubns Delhi). Apt Bks.

Mead, Sidney E. History & Identity. LC 78-26543. (American Academy of Religion. Studies in Religion: No. 19). 1979. 14.00 (ISBN 0-89130-274-3, 010019); pap. 9.95 (ISBN 0-89130-297-2). Scholars Pr GA.

Medlin, W. K. & Patrinelis, C. G. Renaissance Influences & Religious Reforms in Russia: Western & Post-Byzantine Impacts on Culture & Education, (16th-17th Centuries) 184p. (Orig.). 1970. pap. text ed. 22.00x (Pub. by Droz Switzerland). Coronet Bks.

The Millennium in America: From the Puritan Migration to the Civil War, 41 vols. Incl. Vol. 1. The Puritan Interpretation of Scripture. LC 78-67510 (ISBN 0-404-60901-5); Vol. 2. The Puritan Doctrine of the Last Judgment. LC 78-67512 (ISBN 0-404-60902-3); Vol. 3. The Puritan Vision of New Jerusalem. LC 78-67513 (ISBN 0-404-60903-1); Vol. 4. Increase Mather: Selected Works. LC 78-67514 (ISBN 0-404-60904-X); Vol. 5. Samuel Willard: Selected Works. LC 78-67515 (ISBN 0-404-60905-8); Vol. 6. Cotton Mather: Selected Works. LC 78-67516 (ISBN 0-404-60906-6); Vol. 7. Representative Writings of the Eighteenth Century: Scriptural Interpretations. LC 78-67517 (ISBN 0-404-60907-4); Representative Writings of the Eighteenth Century: Applications of Prophecy. LC 78-67518 (ISBN 0-404-60908-2); Vol. 9. The Earthquakes of the Apocalypse. LC 78-67519 (ISBN 0-404-60909-0); Vol. 10. Edwardsian Revivalism from the Great Awakening to the Revolution. LC 78-67520 (ISBN 0-404-60910-4); Vol. 11. Charles Chauncy. LC 78-67586 (ISBN 0-404-60911-2); Vol. 12. The French & Indian Wars. LC 78-67587 (ISBN 0-404-60912-0); Vol. 13. Sermons of the American Revolution. LC 78-67588 (ISBN 0-404-60913-9); Vol. 14. The Celebration of Nationhood. LC 78-67590 (ISBN 0-404-60914-7); Vol. 15. Loyalist Millenarians. LC 78-67591 (ISBN 0-404-60915-5); Vol. 16. Poems on the Rising Glory of America. LC 78-67592 (ISBN 0-404-60916-3); Vol. 17. Interpretations of the French Revolution. LC 78-67599 (ISBN 0-404-60917-1); Vols. 18 & 19, Pts. 1 & 2. Signs of the Times: The Late Eighteenth Century. LC 78-67595. Set. 115.00 (ISBN 0-404-60942-2). Vol. 18 (ISBN 0-404-60918-X). Vol. 19 (ISBN 0-404-60919-8); Vols. 20 & 21. Elhanan Winchester. LC 78-67596. Set. 115.00 (ISBN 0-404-60943-0). Vol. 20 (ISBN 0-404-60920-1). Vol. 21 (ISBN 0-404-60921-X); Vol. 22. Timothy Dwight: Selected Writings. LC 78-67598 (ISBN 0-404-60922-8). Vols. 1-17, & 22-41. write for info. ea.; Set. write for info. (ISBN 0-404-60900-7). AMS Pr.

The Millennium in America: From the Puritan Migration to the Civil War, 41 vols. Incl. Vol. 23. Representative Writings of the Early Nineteenth Century (1800-1839) LC 78-67600 (ISBN 0-404-60923-6); Vol. 24. The Garden of the West. LC 78-67601 (ISBN 0-404-60924-4); Vol. 25. Three Women Prophets: Harriet Livermore. LC 78-67603 (ISBN 0-404-60925-2); Vol. 26. Three Women Prophets: Phoebe Palmer. LC 78-67604 (ISBN 0-404-60926-0); Vol. 27. Three Women Prophets: Ellen Gould White. LC 78-67605 (ISBN 0-404-60927-9); Vol. 28. Allegorical Narratives. LC 78-67606 (ISBN 0-404-60928-7); Vol. 29, Pt. 1. Slavery & Abolition. LC 78-67607 (ISBN 0-404-60929-5); Vol. 30, Pt. 2. Slavery & Abolition. LC 78-67608 (ISBN 0-404-60930-9); Vol. 31. Millennial Optimism & Despair. LC 78-67610 (ISBN 0-404-60931-7); Vol. 32. Hymns to the Millennium. LC 78-67611 (ISBN 0-404-60932-5); Vol. 33. Millenarian Anthologies. LC 78-67612 (ISBN 0-404-60933-3); Vol. 34. Elias Smith: Selected Writings. LC 78-67613 (ISBN 0-404-60934-1); Vol. 35. Elias Boudinot. LC 78-67614 (ISBN 0-404-60935-X); Vol. 36. Ethan Smith: Selected Writings. LC 78-67615 (ISBN 0-404-60936-8); Vol. 37. Lyman Beecher: Selected Works. LC 78-67616 (ISBN 0-404-60937-6); Vol. 38. Millennial Debate: Owen vs. Campbell. LC 78-67618 (ISBN 0-404-60938-4); Vol. 39. George Duffield: Selected Works. LC 78-67619 (ISBN 0-404-60939-2); Vol. 40. William Miller: Selected Works. LC 78-67620 (ISBN 0-404-60940-6); Vol. 41. Representative Writings, 1840-1860. LC 78-67621 (ISBN 0-404-60941-4). Vols. 1-17 & 22-41. write for info.; Set. write for info. (ISBN 0-404-60900-7). AMS Pr.

Milward, Peter. Religious Controversies of the Elizabethan Age: A Survey of Printed Sources. LC 77-80038. xvi, 202p. 1977. 21.00x (ISBN 0-8032-0923-1). U of Nebr Pr.

Moore, George F. The Birth & Growth of Religion. LC 23-13669. (Morse Lectures Ser.). 1923. text ed. 10.00x (ISBN 0-8401-1643-8). A R Allenson.

Morris, Brian. Anthropological Studies of Religion: An Introductory Text. (Illus.). 384p. 1987. 42.50 (ISBN 0-521-32794-6); pap. 12.95 (ISBN 0-521-33991-X). Cambridge U Pr.

Moseley, James G. A Cultural History of Religion in America. LC 80-23609. (Contributions to the Study of Religion Ser.: No. 2). 216p. 1981. lib. bdg. 29.95 (ISBN 0-313-22479-X, MRA/). Greenwood.

Moseley, James G., ed. A Complex Inheritance. LC 75-8955. (American Academy of Religion. Dissertation Ser.). ix, 169p. 1975. pap. 9.95 (ISBN 0-89130-000-7, 010104). Scholars Pr GA.

Mozley, James F. John Foxe & His Book. LC 76-120651. 1970. Repr. of 1940 ed. lib. bdg. 18.50x (ISBN 0-374-95977-3, Octagon). Hippocrene Bks.

Muehlenberg, Ekkehard. Psalmenkommentare aus der Katenenueberlieferung, Vol. 1. LC 73-91808. (Patristische Texte und Studien, Band 15). (Ger.). 1974. 58.40x (ISBN 3-11-004182-0). De Gruyter.

Mueller, Friedrich M. Physical Religion. LC 73-18811. (Gifford Lectures: 1890). Repr. of 1891 ed. 34.00 (ISBN 0-404-11451-2). AMS Pr.

Murray-Aynsley, Harriet. Symbolism of the East & West. LC 74-118538. 1971. Repr. of 1900 ed. 25.50x (ISBN 0-8046-1162-9, Pub by Kennikat). Assoc Faculty Pr.

Neusner, Jacob & Frerichs, Ernest S., eds. Goodenough on the History of Religion & on Judaism. (Brown Judaic Studies). 168p. 1987. pap. 29.95 (ISBN 1-55540-062-0, 14-01-21). Scholars Pr GA.

Obelkevich, James, ed. Religion & the People, 800-1700. LC 78-7847. v, 336p. 1979. 30.00x (ISBN 0-8078-1332-X). U of NC Pr.

Painter, Desmond & Shepard, John. Religion. Yapp, Malcolm & Killinger, Margaret, eds. (World History Ser.). (Illus.). 32p. 1980. lib. bdg. 6.95 (ISBN 0-89908-145-2); pap. text ed. 2.45 (ISBN 0-89908-120-7). Greenhaven.

Parker, Kenneth L. The English Sabbath: A Study of Doctrine & Practice from the Reformation to the Civil War. (Illus.). 224p. Date not set. price not set (ISBN 0-521-30535-7). Cambridge U Pr.

Parrinder, Geoffrey. Introduction to Asian Religions. 1976. pap. 7.95 (ISBN 0-19-519858-1). Oxford U Pr.

Persons, Stow. Free Religion: An American Faith. 1947. 49.50x (ISBN 0-686-83554-9). Elliots Bks.

Pfleiderer, Otto. Philosophy & Development of Religion, 2 vols. LC 77-27229. (Gifford Lectures: 1894). Repr. of 1894 ed. Set. 65.00 (ISBN 0-404-60470-6). AMS Pr.

Phares, Ross. Bible in Pocket, Gun in Hand: The Story of Frontier Religion. LC 64-11375. viii, 182p. 1971. pap. 5.50 (ISBN 0-8032-5725-2, BB 524, Bison). U of Nebr Pr.

Phinney, William R., et al, eds. Thomas Ware, a Spectator at the Christmas Conference: A Miscellany on Thomas Ware & the Christmas Conference. LC 84-70457. (Illus.). 320p. (Orig.). 1984. pap. 8.95 smythsewn (ISBN 0-914960-48-2). Academy Bks.

Pope Gregory VII. The Epistolae Vagantes of Pope Gregory Seven. Cowdrey, H. E., ed. (Oxford Medieval Texts). (Eng. & Lat.). 1972. 42.00x (ISBN 0-19-822220-3). Oxford U Pr.

Porterfield, P. & Spradlin, W. W. The Search for Certainty. 290p. 1983. pap. 28.50 (ISBN 0-387-90889-7). Springer-Verlag.

Rast, Walter E. Tradition History & the Old Testament. Tucker, Gene M., ed. LC 70-171509. (Guides to Biblical Scholarship: Old Testament Ser.). 96p. (Orig.). 1972. pap. 4.50 (ISBN 0-8006-1460-7, 1-1460). Fortress.

Reville, Albert D. Lectures on the Origin & Growth of Religion as Illustrated by the Native Religions of Mexico & Peru. 1977. lib. bdg. 59.95 (ISBN 0-8490-2140-5). Gordon Pr.

Reynolds, Frank E. & Capps, Donald, eds. The Biographical Process: Studies in the History & Psychology of Religion. (Religion & Reason, Method & Theory in the Study & Interpretation of Religion: No. 11). 1976. text ed. 51.50x (ISBN 90-2797-522-1). Mouton.

Rordorf, Willy, et al. The Eucharist of the Early Christians. O'Connell, Matthew J., tr. from Fr. 1978. pap. 9.95 (ISBN 0-916134-33-4). Pueblo Pub Co.

Rudolph, L. C. & Endelman, Judith E. Religion in Indiana: A Guide to Historical Resources. LC 84-43186. 224p. 1986. 22.50x (ISBN 0-253-34960-5). Ind U Pr.

Salibi, Kamal. The Bible Came from Arabia. (Illus.). 224p. 1986. 18.95 (ISBN 0-224-02830-8, Pub. by Jonathan Cape). Salem Hse Pubs.

Salisbury, Joyce E. Iberian Popular Religion, Six Hundred B. C. to Seven Hundred A. D. Celts, Romans & Visigoths. (Texts & Studies in Religion: Vol. 20). 340p. 1985. 59.95x (ISBN 0-88946-809-5). E Mellen.

Sandifer, Kevin W. Introduction to Religious Archival Science. Gill, Rowland P., ed. 16p. (Orig.). 1985. students guide 3.50 (ISBN 0-910653-05-4, 8101-F). Archival Servs.

Schmidt, W. The Origin & Growth of Religion: Facts & Theories. Rose, H. J., tr. from Ger. LC 74-184909. xvi, 302p. 1972. Repr. of 1931 ed. lib. bdg. 22.50x (ISBN 0-8154-0408-5). Cooper Sq.

Schure, Edouard. The Great Initiates: A Study of the Secret History of Religions. LC 79-3597. (Harper Library of Spiritual Wisdom). (Fr.). 528p. 1980. pap. 9.95 (ISBN 0-06-067125-4, RD 400, HarpR). Har-Row.

Schure, Edward. Great Initiates: Secret History of Religions, Vol. 3. LC 61-8623. (Spiritual Science Library). 528p. 1982. Repr. of 1961 ed. lib. bdg. 23.00 (ISBN 0-89345-025-1, Spiritual Sci Lib). Garber Comm.

Severinghaus, Leslie R. Religions & History: A Textbook for the Enlightenment of 12th Graders in our Tax-Supported Public High Schools. 1985. 13.95 (ISBN 0-533-06577-1). Vantage.

Shea, John J. Religious Experiencing: William James & Eugene Gendlin. 156p. (Orig.). 1987. lib. bdg. 22.50 (ISBN 0-8191-6136-5); pap. text ed. 10.75 (ISBN 0-8191-6137-3). U Pr of Amer.

Stark, Rodney, ed. Religious Movements: Genesis, Exodus, & Numbers. LC 85-9539. (Sociology of Religion Ser.). 369p. 1986. 24.95 (ISBN 0-913757-43-8, Pub by New Era Bks); pap. 12.95 (ISBN 0-913757-44-6, Pub. by New Era Bks). Paragon Hse.

Sutherland, N. M. Princes, Politics & Religion, 1547-1589. (No. 31). 240p. 1984. 30.00 (ISBN 0-907628-44-3). Hambledon Press.

Thrower, James A. The Alternative Tradition: A Study of Unbelief in the Ancient World. (Religon & Society Ser.). 1979. 38.00 (ISBN 90-279-7997-9). Mouton.

Toy, Crawford H. Introduction to the History of Religions. LC 76-126655. Repr. of 1913 ed. 27.50 (ISBN 0-404-06498-1). AMS Pr.

Travers, Walter. A Supplication Made to the Privy Counsel. LC 76-57419. (English Experience Ser.: No. 833). 1977. Repr. of 1591 ed. lib. bdg. 5.00 (ISBN 90-221-0833-3). Walter J Johnson.

Turner, J. E. Essentials in the Development of Religion: A Philosophic & Psychological Study. 1979. Repr. of 1934 ed. lib. bdg. 35.00 (ISBN 0-8482-2730-1). Norwood Edns.

Vidler, Alec I. Church in an Age of Revolution. rev. ed. (History of the Church: Vol. 5). (Orig.). 1962. pap. 5.95 (ISBN 0-14-020506-3, Pelican). Penguin.

Viehmeyer, L. Allen. Tumultuous Years - Schwenkfelder Chronicles Fifteen Eighty to Seventeen Fifty: The Reports of Martin John, Jr. & Balthazar Hoffmann. 157p. (Orig.). 1980. pap. write for info. (ISBN 0-935980-00-8). Schwenkfelder Lib.

Vrijhof, Peter H. & Waardenburg, Jacques, eds. Official & Popular Religion. (Religion & Society Ser.). 1979. text ed. 38.00x (ISBN 0-686-27030-4). Mouton.

Warren, Thomas B. & Elkins, Garland, eds. Some Modern Sects, Cults, Movements & World Religions. 1981. 13.00 (ISBN 0-934916-46-2). Natl Christian Pr.

Webb, Lillian A. About My Father's Business: The Life of Elder Michaux. LC 80-24595. (Contributions in Afro-American & African Studies: No. 61). (Illus.). 232p. 1981. lib. bdg. 29.95 (ISBN 0-313-22261-4, WFB/). Greenwood.

Webber, Roger. Evolution of Belief. 89p. 1984. 8.95 (ISBN 0-533-05475-3). Vantage.

Wilcox, Donald J. In Search of God & Self: Renaissance & Reformation Thought. (Illus.). 401p. 1987. pap. text ed. 12.95 (ISBN 0-88133-276-3). Waveland Pr.

Wilkins, Ronald J. Religion in North America. (To Live Is Christ Ser.). 208p. 1984. pap. 5.75 (ISBN 0-697-01930-6); tchr's manual 4.95 (ISBN 0-697-01931-4); spirit masters 10.95 (ISBN 0-697-01735-4). Wm C Brown.

Winchell, Paul. God Two Thousand: Religion Without the Bible. LC 82-71878. 329p. 1982. 20.00 (ISBN 0-9608772-0-7). April Enterp.

Wolfson, Harry A. Studies in the History of Philosophy & Religion, Vol. II. Twersky, Isadore & Williams, George H., eds. 1977. 40.00x (ISBN 0-674-84766-0). Harvard U Pr.

Words & Objects: Towards a Dialogue Between Archaeology & History of Religion. (The Institute for Comparative Research in Human Culture, Oslo, Series LXX A Norwegian University Press Publication). 304p. 64.00 (ISBN 82-00-07751-9). Oxford U Pr.

RELIGION–PHILOSOPHY

see also Christianity–Philosophy; Knowledge, Theory of (Religion); Philosophical Theology; Philosophy and Religion

Abernethy, George L. & Langford, Thomas A., eds. Philosophy of Religion: A Book of Readings. 2nd ed. 1968. write for info. (ISBN 0-02-300150-X, 30015). Macmillan.

Adams, Robert M. The Virtue of Faith & Other Essays in Philosophical Theology. 256p. 1987. 29.95 (ISBN 0-19-504145-3); pap. 12.95 (ISBN 0-19-504146-1). Oxford U Pr.

Afnan, Ruhi M. Baha'u'llah & the Bab Confront Modern Thinkers: Spinoza: Concerning God, Bk. 2. LC 75-109166. 188p. 1977. 10.00 (ISBN 0-8022-2197-1). Philos Lib.

Alain, pseud. The Gods. Pevear, Richard, tr. from Fr. LC 74-8291. 192p. 1974. 8.95 (ISBN 0-8112-0547-9); pap. 3.95 (ISBN 0-8112-0548-7, NDP382). New Directions.

American Catholic Philosophical Association Staff. Role of the Christian Philosopher: Proceedings. 1958. 18.00. Johnson Repr.

Anscombe, G. E. Collected Philosophical Papers: Ethics, Religion & Politics, Vol. 3. LC 81-4315. 192p. 1981. 27.50x (ISBN 0-8166-1082-7); pap. 10.95x (ISBN 0-8166-1083-5). U of Minn Pr.

Arapura, J. G. Religion As Anxiety & Tranquillity: An Essay in Comparative Phenomenology of the Spirit. (Religion & Reason Ser.: No. 5). 1973. 19.00x (ISBN 90-2797-180-3). Mouton.

Arnett, Willard E. Religion & Judgment: An Essay on the Method & Meaning of Religion. LC 66-11680. (Century Philosophy Ser.). 1966. 39.50x (ISBN 0-89197-377-X). Irvington.

Arnett, Willard E., ed. Modern Reader in the Philosophy of Religion. LC 66-20470. (Century Philosophy Ser.). 1966. 39.50x (ISBN 0-89197-482-2); pap. text ed. 24.50x (ISBN 0-89197-483-0). Irvington.

Aubert, Roger. Le Problem de L'acte de Foi: Donnees Traditionnelles et Resultants des Controverses Recentes. 1978. Repr. of 1958 ed. lib. bdg. 85.00 (ISBN 0-8492-0092-X). R West.

Audi, Robert & Wainwright, William J., eds. Rationality, Religious Belief, & Moral Commitment: New Essays in the Philosophy of Religion. LC 85-48200. 352p. 1986. text ed. 42.50x (ISBN 0-8014-1856-9); pap. text ed. 12.95x (ISBN 0-8014-9381-1). Cornell U Pr.

Augustine, St. Retractations. (Fathers of the Church Ser.: Vol. 60). 451p. 1968. 17.95x (ISBN 0-8132-0060-1). Cath U Pr.

Barnhart, J. The Study of Religion & Its Meaning. 1977. 25.50x (ISBN 90-279-7762-3). Mouton.

Barnhart, J. E. Religion & the Challenge of Philosophy. (Quality Paperback Ser.: No. 291). 400p. (Orig.). 1975. pap. 5.95 (ISBN 0-8226-0291-1). Littlefield.

Bascom, John. A Philosophy of Religion: Or, the Rational Grounds of Religious Belief. LC 75-3037. Repr. of 1876 ed. 57.50 (ISBN 0-404-59035-7). AMS Pr.

Batson, Daniel C. & Ventis, W. Larry. The Religious Experience: A Social-Psychological Perspective. (Illus.). 1982. text ed. 29.95x (ISBN 0-19-503030-3); pap. text ed. 15.95x (ISBN 0-19-503031-1). Oxford U Pr.

Bellah, Robert N. Beyond Belief. LC 77-109058. 1976. pap. text ed. 7.95x (ISBN 0-06-060775-0, RD129, HarpR). Har-Row.

Bennett, Charles A. Dilemma of Religious Knowledge. LC 71-85986. (Essay & General Literature Index Reprint Ser). 1969. pap. text ed. 15.95x (ISBN 0-8046-0538-6, Pub. by Kennikat). Assoc Faculty Pr.

Berchman, Robert M. From Philo to Origen: Middle Platonism in Transition. (Brown Judaic Studies: No. 69). 370p. 1985. 29.95 (ISBN 0-89130-750-8, 14 00 69); pap. 25.95 (ISBN 0-89130-815-6). Scholars Pr GA.

Bergson, Henri. The Two Sources of Morality & Religion. LC 74-10373. 308p. 1974. Repr. of 1935 ed. lib. bdg. 25.00x (ISBN 0-8371-7679-4, BETS). Greenwood.

Bertocci, Peter A. Religion As Creative Insecurity. LC 73-1836. 128p. 1973. Repr. of 1958 ed. lib. bdg. 22.50x (ISBN 0-8371-6803-1, BECI). Greenwood.

Bodin, Jean. Colloquium of the Seven About Secrets of the Sublime. Daniels, Marion L., tr. from Lat. & intro. by. LC 73-2453. 480p. 1975. 63.00x (ISBN 0-691-07193-4). Princeton U Pr.

Bodkin, Maud. Studies of Type-Images in Poetry, Religion & Philosophy. LC 74-14665. 1951. lib. bdg. 15.00 (ISBN 0-8414-3273-2). Folcroft.

Bonner, Geraldian. St. Augustine of Hippo: Life & Controversies. LC 82-45807. 1985. Repr. of 1963 ed. 42.50 (ISBN 0-404-62376-X). AMS Pr.

Boodin, John E. Religion of Tomorrow. LC 75-3062. Repr. of 1943 ed. 14.00 (ISBN 0-404-59061-6). AMS Pr.

Bostrom, Christopher J. Philosophy of Religion. 1962. 42.50x (ISBN 0-685-69791-6). Elliots Bks.

Boulding, Kenneth E. Mending the World: Quaker Insights on the Social Order. LC 86-60283. 1986. pap. 2.50 (ISBN 0-87574-266-1). Pendle Hill.

Bouman, Herbert J., tr. Luther's Works, Vol. 16. 1968. 14.95 (ISBN 0-570-06416-3, 15-1758). Concordia.

Bradley, Andrew C. Ideals of Religion. LC 77-27218. (Gifford Lectures: 1907). Repr. of 1940 ed. 30.00 (ISBN 0-404-60463-3). AMS Pr.

Bradshaw, Marion J. Philosophical Foundations of Faith. LC 78-99248. Repr. of 1941 ed. 10.00 (ISBN 0-404-00968-9). AMS Pr.

Brightman, Edgar S. Philosophy of Religion. LC 72-95112. Repr. of 1940 ed. lib. bdg. 29.75x (ISBN 0-8371-2468-9, BRPR). Greenwood.

Brody, Baruch, ed. Readings in the Philosophy of Religion: An Analytic Approach. LC 73-20485. 608p. 1974. text ed. write for info. (ISBN 0-13-759340-6). P-H.

Bronstein, Daniel J. & Schulweis, Harold M., eds. Approaches to the Philosophy of Religion. facsimile ed. LC 77-93320. (Essay Index Reprint Ser). 1954. 33.00 (ISBN 0-8369-1344-2). Ayer Co Pubs.

Brown, Stuart, ed. Reason & Religion. LC 77-3115. 336p. 1977. pap. 12.95x (ISBN 0-8014-9166-5). Cornell U Pr.

Brunner, Heinrich E. The Philosophy of Religion from the Standpoint of Protestant Theology. LC 78-14106. 1979. Repr. of 1937 ed. 20.35 (ISBN 0-88355-779-7). Hyperion Conn.

Burch, George B. Alternative Goals in Religion: Love, Freedom, Truth. 1973. pap. 3.95 (ISBN 0-7735-0163-0). McGill-Queens U Pr.

Burke, Patrick. The Fragile Universe: An Essay in the Philosophy of Religions. LC 78-17885. (Library of Philosophy & Religion). 129p. 1979. text ed. 28.50x (ISBN 0-06-490776-7, 06373). B&N Imports.

Burke, Thomas P. The Reluctant Vision: An Essay in the Philosophy of Religion. LC 73-88354. pap. 35.50 (2026883). Bks Demand UMI.

Butler, Joseph. The Analogy of Religion. 3rd ed. 1986. lib. bdg. 25.00x (ISBN 0-935005-40-4); pap. text ed. 13.00x (ISBN 0-935005-41-2). Ibis Pub VA.

Cahn, Stephen M. & Shatz, David, eds. Contemporary Philosophy of Religion. 1982. pap. text ed. 9.95x (ISBN 0-19-503009-5). Oxford U Pr.

Caird, John. Introduction to the Philosophy of Religion. LC 75-113569. (BCL Ser. I). Repr. of 1901 ed. 12.50 (ISBN 0-404-01363-5). AMS Pr.

Carter, Lee. Lucifer's Handbook. LC 76-55893. 1977. pap. text ed. 5.95 (ISBN 0-918260-01-9). Acad Assoc.

Cerminara, Gina. Insights for the Age of Aquarius. LC 76-6173. 314p. 1976. pap. 6.95 (ISBN 0-8356-0483-7, Quest). Theos Pub Hse.

Charlesworth, James H., ed. Old Testament Pseudepigrapha: Expansions of the Old Testament & Legends, Wisdom & Philosophical Literature, Prayers, Psalms & Odes, Fragments of Lost Judeo-Hellenistic Words, Vol. II. 1056p. 1985. 40.00 (ISBN 0-385-18813-7). Doubleday.

Ch'u Chai & Chai, Winberg. Confucianism. LC 73-3977. 1974. pap. text ed. 5.50 (ISBN 0-8120-0303-9). Barron.

Clark, Gordon H. A Christian Philosophy of Education. 2nd, rev. ed. (Trinity Papers: No. 7). 250p. 1987. pap. 8.95 (ISBN 0-940931-20-6). Trinity Found.

Clark, Stephen R. The Mysteries of Religion: An Introduction to Philosophy through Religion. 288p. text ed. 45.00 (ISBN 0-631-13419-0); pap. text ed. 12.95 (ISBN 0-631-14295-9). Basil Blackwell.

Conger, George P. Ideologies of Religion. facsimile ed. LC 70-93329. (Essay Index Reprint Ser). 1940. 19.00 (ISBN 0-8369-1283-7). Ayer Co Pubs.

Cornish, Patty Jo. The Prayer Primer: A Philosophy Book. Quintero, Roberto, ed. LC 84-81741. 68p. (Orig.). pap. 5.95 (ISBN 0-9613717-0-6). Hilltop Hse.

Cox, William E. Why I Left Scofieldism. 1975. pap. 0.50 (ISBN 0-87552-154-1). Presby & Reformed.

Crom, Scott. Encounters with Transcendence: Confessions of a Religious Philosopher. (Orig.). 1986. 2.50 (ISBN 0-87574-267-X). Pendle Hill.

Crowe, Frederick E., ed. A Third Collection: Papers by Bernard J. F. Longergan, S. J. LC 84-61028. 272p. 1985. pap. 12.95 (ISBN 0-8091-0363-X); pap. 9.95 (ISBN 0-8091-2650-8). Paulist Pr.

Culverwel, Nathanael. An Elegant & Learned Discourse on the Light of Nature, 1652: Nathanael Culverwel (1618-1651) Wellek, Rene, ed. Bd. with Spiritual Opticks. LC 75-11215. (British Philosophers & Theologians of the 17th & 18th Centuries Ser.). 456p. 1978. lib. bdg. 51.00 (ISBN 0-8240-1769-2). Garland Pub.

Delaney, C. F., ed. Rationality & Religious Belief. LC 79-63359. (Studies in the Philosophy of Religion: No. 1). 1979. text ed. 12.95x (ISBN 0-268-01602-X, 85-16023); pap. text ed. 5.95x (ISBN 0-268-01603-8, 85-16031). U of Notre Dame Pr.

Delp, Paul S. The Life of Mind. LC 82-61238. (Illus.). 125p. (Orig., PB). 1983. pap. 10.00 (ISBN 0-935356-05-3). Mills Pub Co.

Despland, Michel. The Education of Desire: Plato & the Philosophy of Religion. 400p. 1985. 25.00 (ISBN 0-8020-6524-4). U of Toronto Pr.

Dewart, Leslie. Foundations of Belief. LC 69-17777. 1970. pap. 4.95 (ISBN 0-8164-2549-3, HarpR). Har-Row.

Dickason, C. Fred. Angels, Elect & Evil. 256p. 1975. pap. 6.95 (ISBN 0-8024-0222-4). Moody.

Drake, Durant. Problems of Religion: An Introductory Survey. LC 68-19268. Repr. of 1916 ed. lib. bdg. 22.50x (ISBN 0-8371-0062-3, DRPR). Greenwood.

Dunne, John S. The Reasons of the Heart: A Journey into Solitude & Back Again into the Human Circle. 1979. pap. 5.95 (ISBN 0-268-01606-2). U of Notre Dame Pr.

Durkheim, Emile. Elementary Forms of the Religious Life. Swain, Joseph W., tr. 1965. pap. text ed. 14.95 (ISBN 0-02-908010-X). Free Pr.

Edwards, Rem B. Reason & Religion: An Introduction to the Philosophy of Religion. LC 78-66278. 1979. pap. text ed. 12.50 (ISBN 0-8191-0690-9). U Pr of Amer.

Eikner, Allen V., ed. Religious Perspectives & Problems: An Introduction to the Philosophy of Religion. LC 80-67265. 368p. 1980. lib. bdg. 29.75 (ISBN 0-8191-1215-1); pap. text ed. 15.25 (ISBN 0-8191-1216-X). U Pr of Amer.

Eisenstein, Ira. What We Mean by Religion. Rev., 3rd ed. LC 57-14413. 173p. 1958. pap. 7.95 (ISBN 0-935457-06-2). Reconstructionist Pr.

Eliade, Mircea. A History of Religious Ideas, Vol. 3: From Muhammad to the Age of Reforms. Hiltebeiten, Alf & Apostolos-Cappadona, Diane, trs. LC 77-16784. xii, 352p. 1985. 27.50 (ISBN 0-226-20404-9). U of Chicago Pr.

--The Quest: History & Meaning in Religion. LC 68-19059. (Midway Reprint Ser.). xii, 180p. 1984. pap. text ed. 10.00x (ISBN 0-226-20386-7). U of Chicago Pr.

Eliade, Mircea & Tracy, David, eds. What Is Religion? An Inquiry for Christian Theology, Concilium 136. (New Concilium 1980). 128p. 1980. pap. 5.95 (ISBN 0-8164-2278-8, HarpR). Har-Row.

Ferm, Vergilius. What Can We Believe. 1952. 5.95 (ISBN 0-8022-0497-X). Philos Lib.

Feuerbach, Ludwig. Essence of Christianity. pap. 7.95x (ISBN 0-06-130011-X, TB11, Torch). Har-Row.

--Essence of Christianity. Eliot, George, tr. 1958. 18.25 (ISBN 0-8446-2055-6). Peter Smith.

Forell, George W. & Lehmann, Helmut T., eds. Luther's Works: Career of the Reformer II, Vol. 32. LC 55-9893. 1958. 19.95 (ISBN 0-8006-0332-X, 1-332). Fortress.

Frank, Erich. Philosophical Understanding & Religious Truth. LC 82-8476. 220p. 1982. pap. text ed. 11.75 (ISBN 0-8191-2510-5). U Pr of Amer.

Frank, S. L. The Unknowable: An Ontological Introduction to the Philosophy of Religion. Jakim, Boris, tr. from Russian. xxii, 313p. 1983. text ed. 26.95x (ISBN 0-8214-0676-0, 82-84440). Ohio U Pr.

Gandhi, M. K. My Religion. Kumarappa, B., ed. 178p. (Orig.). 1983. pap. 5.00 (ISBN 0-934676-54-2). Greenlf Bks.

Goldenberg, Naomi R. Changing of the Gods: Feminism & the End of Traditional Religions. LC 78-19602. 1979. pap. 7.95 (ISBN 0-8070-1111-8, BP600). Beacon Pr.

Grimm, Harold J. & Lehmann, Helmut T., eds. Luther's Works: Career of the Reformer I, Vol. 31. LC 55-9893. 1957. 19.95 (ISBN 0-8006-0331-1, 1-331). Fortress.

Hall, James. Knowledge, Belief, & Trancendence: Philosophical Problems in Religion. LC 82-21757. 254p. 1983. pap. text ed. 12.25 (ISBN 0-8191-2912-7). U Pr of Amer.

Hartshorne, Charles. The Logic of Perfection & Other Essays in Neoclassical Metaphysics. LC 61-11286. 351p. 1973. pap. 8.95 (ISBN 0-87548-037-3). Open Court.

Hegel, Georg W. Lectures on the Philosophy of Religion, 3 vols. Speirs, E. B. & Sanderson, J. B., trs. 1968. Repr. of 1895 ed. Set. text ed. 70.00x (ISBN 0-7100-6080-7). Humanities.

Herberg, Will, ed. Four Existentialist Theologians. LC 75-17472. 346p. 1975. Repr. of 1958 ed. lib. bdg. 29.75x (ISBN 0-8371-8303-0, HEFE). Greenwood.

Hick, John. Classical & Contemporary Readings in the Philosophy of Religion. 2nd ed. LC 75-98092. (Philosophy Ser). 1969. text ed. write for info. (ISBN 0-13-135269-5). P-H.

Hodge, Charles B., Jr. Onion Creek Philosophy. LC 79-87865. 1979. 6.95 (ISBN 0-89112-054-8, Bibl Res Pr). Abilene Christ U.

Hoffding, H. The Philosophy of Religion. 1977. lib. bdg. 59.95 (ISBN 0-8490-2435-8). Gordon Pr.

Hourani, G. F. On the Harmony of Religion & Philosophy. 128p. 1976. 25.00x (ISBN 0-317-39133-X, Pub. by Luzac & Co Ltd). State Mutual Bk.

Hubbeling, H. G. Principles of Philosophy of Religion. (Philosophia Religionis Ser.: Vol. 25). 280p. 1987. pap. 22.95 (ISBN 90-232-2272-5, Pub. by Van Gorcum Holland). Longwood Pub Group.

Hume, David. The Natural History of Religion. Root, H. E., ed. 1957. pap. 4.95x (ISBN 0-8047-0333-7). Stanford U Pr.

--The Natural History of Religion & Dialogues Concerning Natural Religion. Colver, A. Wayne & Price, Vladimir, eds. 1976. 49.95x (ISBN 0-19-824379-0). Oxford U Pr.

Huxley, Aldous. Perennial Philosophy. 1970. pap. 7.95 (ISBN 0-06-090191-8, CN191, PL). Har-Row.

Huxley, Aldous L. Perennial Philosophy. LC 76-167362. (Essay Index Reprint Ser.). Repr. of 1945 ed. 25.50 (ISBN 0-8369-2773-7). Ayer Co Pubs.

Inge, W. R. The Religious Philosophy of Plotinus & Some Modern Philosophies of Religion. 1977. lib. bdg. 59.95 (ISBN 0-8490-2513-3). Gordon Pr.

James, William. Varieties of Religious Experiences. 1961. pap. 3.95 (ISBN 0-02-085960-0, Collier). Macmillan.

Jones, Bruce, ed. Becoming Makers of Peace. 1987. pap. 7.00 (ISBN 0-8309-0476-X). Herald Hse.

Kanal, S. The Philosophy of Religion. 480p. 1984. text ed. 45.00x (ISBN 0-86590-272-0, Sterling Pubs India). Apt Bks.

Kaplan, Mordecai M. The Religion of Ethical Nationhood. 1970. pap. 11.50 (ISBN 0-935457-12-7). Reconstructionist Pr.

Kellenberger, J. The Cognitivity of Religion: Three Perspectives. LC 84-27999. 1985. 20.00x (ISBN 0-520-05383-4). U of Cal Pr.

Kierkegaard, Soren. For Self-Examination & Judge for Yourself. (American-Scandinavian Foundation Ser.). 1944. pap. 8.50x (ISBN 0-691-01952-5). Princeton U Pr.

--Philosophical Fragments, or a Fragment of Philosophy-Johannes Climacus, or De Omnibus Dubitandum Est, 2 bks. in 1 vol. Hong, Howard V. & Hong, Edna H., eds. LC 85-3420. (No. VII). 386p. 1985. text ed. 35.00x (ISBN 0-691-07273-6); pap. 7.95x (ISBN 0-691-02036-1). Princeton U Pr.

King-Farlow, J. & Christensen, W. N. Faith & the Life at Reason. LC 72-83376. 253p. 1973. lib. bdg. 36.00 (ISBN 90-277-0275-6, Pub. by Reidel Holland). Kluwer Academic.

Kohn, Eugene. Religious Humanism. LC 53-10661. 154p. 1953. pap. 8.95 (ISBN 0-935457-24-0). Reconstructionist Pr.

Kolakowski, Leszek. Religion: If There Is No God.. On God, the Devil, Sin & Other Worries of the So-Called Philosophy of Religion. Kermode, Frank, ed. 1982. pap. 7.95 (ISBN 0-19-520429-8). Oxford U Pr.

Lacey, Paul A. Leading & Being Led. LC 85-63379. (Orig.). 1985. pap. 2.50 (ISBN 0-87574-264-5). Pendle Hill.

Ladd, George T. The Philosophy of Religion, 2 vols. LC 75-3225. 1976. Repr. of 1905 ed. 82.50 set (ISBN 0-404-59221-X). AMS Pr.

Laird, John. Mind & Deity. LC 70-114424. 322p. 1970. Repr. of 1941 ed. 32.50 (ISBN 0-208-00937-X, Archon). Shoe String.

Lamb, Matthew L. History, Method, & Theology: A Dialectical Comparison of Wilhelm Dilthey's Critique of Historical Reason & Bernard Lonergan's Meta-Methodology. LC 78-18707. 1978. pap. 19.95_o.s. (ISBN 0-89130-238-7, 01-01-25). Scholars Pr GA.

Lee, Atkinson. Groundwork of the Philosophy of Religion. LC 46-19011. (Studies in Theology Ser: No. 48). 1946. text ed. 6.00x (ISBN 0-8401-6048-8). A R Allenson.

Lehman, Martin E. & Lehman, Helmut T., eds. Luther's Works: Word & Sacrament IV, Vol. 38. LC 55-9893. 1971. 19.95 (ISBN 0-8006-0338-9, 1-338). Fortress.

Levine, Israel. Faithful Rebels. LC 76-118533. 1971. Repr. of 1936 ed. 22.00x (ISBN 0-8046-1156-4, Pub. by Kennikat). Assoc Faculty Pr.

Levinson, Henry S. & Levering, Ralph. The Religious Investigations of William James. LC 80-26109. (Studies in Religion). xii, 316p. 1981. 27.50x (ISBN 0-8078-1468-7). U of NC Pr.

Lewisohn, Ludwig. Permanent Horizon. LC 73-117818. (Essay Index Reprint Ser). 1934. 19.00 (ISBN 0-8369-1811-8). Ayer Co Pubs.

Ling, Trevor. Buddha, Marx & God: Some Aspects of Religion in the Modern World. 2nd ed. 1979. 26.00 (ISBN 0-312-10679-3). St Martin.

Lisiero, Dario. People Ideology-People Theology: New Perspectives on Religious Dogma. 226p. 1980. 10.95 (ISBN 0-682-49664-2, Banner). Exposition Pr FL.

Luther's Works, Vol. 29. 1968. 13.95 (ISBN 0-570-06429-5, 15-1771). Concordia.

McLean, George F., ed. The Human Person. LC 80-66375. (Proceedings: Vol. 53). 1979. pap. 15.00 (ISBN 0-918090-13-X). Am Cath Philo.

--Immateriality. LC 79-88689. (Proceedings: Vol. 52). 1978. pap. 15.00 (ISBN 0-918090-12-1). Am Cath Philo.

MacMurray, John. Self As Agent. 1978. pap. text ed. 5.95x (ISBN 0-391-02043-9). Humanities.

--The Structure of Religious Experience. LC 73-122406. xi, 77p. 1971. Repr. of 1936 ed. 15.00 (ISBN 0-208-00958-2, Archon). Shoe String.

Macquarrie, John. Twentieth Century Religious Thought. LC 81-9349. 1981. pap. text ed. 18.95x (ISBN 0-684-17334-4). Scribner.

--Twentieth Century Religious Thought. 1983. 19.95 (ISBN 0-684-17333-6). Scribner.

Mahin, Mark. Sixty-Two Arguments That Justify a Bold New Creed. LC 85-71756. 225p. (Orig.). 1986. 17.95 (ISBN 0-931959-03-9); pap. 9.95 (ISBN 0-931959-04-7). Mindlifter Pr.

Mansel, Henry L. Limits of Religious Thought Examined. LC 72-172840. Repr. of 1859 ed. 25.00 (ISBN 0-404-04182-5). AMS Pr.

Martin, James A. Empirical Philosophies of Religion. LC 78-111850. (Essay Index Reprint Ser.). 1945. 17.00 (ISBN 0-8369-1618-2). Ayer Co Pubs.

Masaryk, Thomas G. Masaryk on Thought & Life. LC 78-135840. (Eastern Europe Collection Ser.). 1970. Repr. of 1938 ed. 16.00 (ISBN 0-405-02782-6). Ayer Co Pubs.

Mathis, Terry R. Against John Hick: An Examination of His Philosophy of Religion. 148p. (Orig.). 1985. lib. bdg. 22.00 (ISBN 0-8191-4512-2); pap. text ed. 9.25 (ISBN 0-8191-4513-0). U Pr of Amer.

Mill, John S. Three Essays on Religion. LC 76-130995. Repr. of 1874 ed. 23.45 (ISBN 0-404-04325-9). AMS Pr.

--Three Essays on Religion. Repr. of 1874 ed. lib. bdg. 37.50x (ISBN 0-8371-1986-3, MIER). Greenwood.

Miller, Ed L. God & Reason: A Historical Approach to Philosophical Theology. 224p. 1972. pap. text ed. write for info. (ISBN 0-02-381270-2). Macmillan.

Mitchell, Basil, ed. Philosophy of Religion. (Oxford Readings in Philosophy Ser). (Orig.). 1971. pap. text ed. 9.95x (ISBN 0-19-875018-8). Oxford U Pr.

Mohapatra, A. R. Philosophy of Religion: An Approach to World Religions. 208p. 1986. text ed. 27.50x (ISBN 81-207-0110-0, Pub. by Sterling Pubs India). Apt Bks.

Monasterio, Xavier O. To Be Human: An Introductory Experiment in Philosophy. 256p. (Orig.). 1985. pap. 7.95 (ISBN 0-8091-2704-0). Paulist Pr.

Monk, Robert C., et al. Exploring Religious Meaning. 3rd ed. Affleck, Bert & Yamori, Tetsuano, eds. (Illus.). 416p. 1987. pap. text ed. write for info. (ISBN 0-13-297524-6). P-H.

Montague, William P. Belief Unbound. LC 72-109630. (Select Bibliographies Reprint Ser). 1930. 15.00 (ISBN 0-8369-5239-1). Ayer Co Pubs.

Munson, Thomas N. The Challenge of Religion: A Philosophical Appraisal. LC 85-10297. 238p. 1985. text ed. 21.00x (ISBN 0-8207-0179-3); pap. text ed. 10.00x (ISBN 0-8207-0181-5). Duquesne.

Murray, Andrew. Secret of Brotherly Love. (Secret Ser.). (Orig.). 1980. pap. 1.95 (ISBN 0-87508-390-0). Chr Lit.

Nature of Religious Experience: Essays in Honor of Douglas Clyde Macintosh. facsimile ed. LC 78-152202. (Essay Index Reprint Ser). Repr. of 1937 ed. 16.00 (ISBN 0-8369-2286-7). Ayer Co Pubs.

Nee, Watchman. Gospel Dialogue. Kaung, Stephen, tr. 1975. 5.25 (ISBN 0-935008-21-7); pap. 4.00 (ISBN 0-935008-22-5). Christian Fellow Pubs.

Needleman, John, ed. The Sword of Gnosis: Metaphysics, Cosmology, Tradition, Symbolism. 448p. 1986. pap. 10.95 (ISBN 0-317-40557-8). Methuen Inc.

Neville, Robert C. God the Creator: On the Transcendence & Presence of God. LC 68-13128. (Illus.). 1968. 12.50x (ISBN 0-226-57641-8). U of Chicago Pr.

Norris, John. Treatises Upon Several Subjects. Wellek, Rene, ed. LC 75-11244. (British Philosophers & Theologians of the 17th & 18th Centuries Ser.). 1978. Repr. of 1698 ed. lib. bdg. 51.00 (ISBN 0-8240-1796-X). Garland Pub.

Ogden, Schubert M. The Reality of God. LC 66-20783. 1977. pap. 4.95xi (ISBN 0-06-066351-0, RD 241, HarpR). Har-Row.

O'Hear, Anthony. Experience, Explanation & Faith: An Introduction to the Philosophy of Religion. LC 83-15957. 266p. (Orig.). 1984. pap. 10.95 (ISBN 0-7100-9768-9). Methuen Inc.

Opton, Frank. Liberal Religion: Principles & Practices. LC 81-81129. (Library of Liberal Religion). 295p. 1981. 20.95 (ISBN 0-87975-155-X). Prometheus Bks.

Ormond, Alexander T. The Philosophy of Religion: Lectures Written for the Elliott Lectureship at the Western Theological Seminary. 195p. 1982. Repr. of 1922 ed. lib. bdg. 50.00 (ISBN 0-8495-4219-7). Arden Lib.

Pahl, Paul D., tr. Luther's Works, Vol. 6. LC 55-9893. 1969. 16.95 (ISBN 0-570-06406-6, 15-1748). Concordia.

Paley, William. Natural Theology. 1986. lib. bdg. 30.00x (ISBN 0-935005-61-7); pap. 15.00x (ISBN 0-935005-62-5). Ibis Pub VA.

Patterson, Robert L. Philosophy of Religion. LC 74-101130. 1970. 31.75 (ISBN 0-8223-0223-3). Duke.

Pelikan, Jaroslav, ed. Luther's Works, Vol. 21. LC 55-9893. 16.95 (ISBN 0-570-06421-X, 15-1763). Concordia.

Pfleiderer, O. The Philosophy of Religion on the Basis of Its History, 4 vols. in 2. Repr. of 1886 ed. Set. 72.00 (ISBN 0-527-03238-7). Kraus Repr.

Pfleiderer, Otto. Philosophy & Development of Religion, 2 vols. LC 77-27229. (Gifford Lectures: 1894). Repr. of 1894 ed. Set. 65.00 (ISBN 0-404-60470-6). AMS Pr.

Phillips, D. Z. Belief, Change & Forms of Life. (Library of Philosophy & Religion). 144p. 1986. text ed. 29.95x (ISBN 0-391-03385-9). Humanities.

Pojman, Louis P. Philosophy of Religion: An Anthology. King, Ken, ed. (Orig.). 1986. write for info. (ISBN 0-534-06672-0). Wadsworth Pub.

Poulain, Jacques. Logique & Religion: L'Atomisme Logique de L. Wittgenstein & la Possibilite des Propositions Religieuses. (Religion & Reason: No. 7). 1974. 18.40x (ISBN 90-2797-284-2). Mouton.

Proudfoot, Wayne. God & the Self: Three Types of Philosophy of Religion. LC 75-28983. 241p. 1976. 22.50 (ISBN 0-8387-1769-1). Bucknell U Pr.

Purtill, Richard. Thinking about Religion: A Philosophical Introduction to Religion. 1978. pap. text ed. write for info (ISBN 0-13-917724-8). P-H.

Quasem, Muhammad A. The Recitation & Interpretation of the Qur'an. 1979. 12.00 (ISBN 0-318-00410-0). Quasem.

Raabe, Paul J. The Scientific & Humorous Revelations of God. 2nd rev. ed. 1981. 4.00 (ISBN 0-682-49415-1). Exposition Pr FL.

Rajneesh, Bhagwan Shree. The Last Testament, Vol. I. Svadesh, Swami, et al, eds. LC 85-63289. (Interview Ser.). (Illus.). 832p. (Orig.). 1986. pap. 7.95x (ISBN 0-88050-250-9, 250-9). Chidvilas Found.

--The Rajneesh Bible, Vol. IV. LC 85-42539. (Illus.). 800p. (Orig.). 1987. pap. 9.95x (ISBN 3-907757-02-5). Chidvilas Found.

Ramm, Bernard. Varieties of Christian Apologetics. (Twin Brooks Ser.). pap. 5.95 (ISBN 0-8010-7610-2). Baker Bk.

Rebhun, Joseph. God & Man in Two Worlds. 1985. lib. bdg. 16.95 (ISBN 0-9614162-1-1). OR Pub.

Reischauer, August K. Nature & Truth of the Great Religions: Toward a Philosophy of Religion. LC 65-20612. 1966. 19.50 (ISBN 0-8048-0420-6). C E Tuttle.

Rosenzweig, Franz. The Star of Redemption. Hallo, William W., tr. from Ger. LC 84-40833. 464p. 1985. text ed. 30.00 (ISBN 0-268-01717-4, 85-17179); pap. text ed. 12.95 (ISBN 0-268-01718-2, 85-17187). U of Notre Dame Pr.

Rossner, John. Toward Recovery of the Primordial Tradition: Ancient Insights & Modern Discoveries, 2 bks, Vol. 1. Incl. Bk. 1. From Ancient Magic to Future Technology. LC 79-66892. 14.75 (ISBN 0-8191-0861-8); Bk. 2. Toward a Parapsychology of Religion: from Ancient Religion to Future Science. LC 79-66893. 14.25 (ISBN 0-8191-0862-6). 1979. U Pr of Amer.

Rowe, William. Philosophy of Religion: An Introduction. 207p. 1985. pap. text ed. write for info. (ISBN 0-8221-0208-0). Wadsworth Pub.

Royce, Josiah. The Religious Philosophy of Josiah Royce. Brown, Stuart G., ed. LC 76-4496. 239p. 1976. Repr. of 1952 ed. lib. bdg. 22.50x (ISBN 0-8371-8810-5, RORP). Greenwood.

--Sources of Religious Insight. LC 76-56454. 1977. Repr. lib. bdg. 20.00x (ISBN 0-374-96989-2, Octagon). Hippocrene Bks.

Runzo, Joseph & Ihara, Graig K., eds. Religious Experience & Religious Belief: Essays in the Epistemology of Religion. LC 86-1614. 160p. 1986. lib. bdg. 23.50 (ISBN 0-8191-5292-7); pap. text ed. 10.75 (ISBN 0-8191-5293-5). U Pr of Amer.

Rupp, George. Beyond Existentialism & Zen: Religion in a Pluralistic World. 1979. 14.95x (ISBN 0-19-502462-1). Oxford U Pr.

Ryrie, Charles. Neo-Orthodoxy. 1978. pap. 2.50 (ISBN 0-937396-27-3). Walterick Pubs.

Saher, P. J. Eastern Wisdom & Western Thought: A Comparative Study in the Modern Philosophy of Religion. LC 72-441621. pap. 73.50 (ISBN 0-317-09011-9, 2012165). Bks Demand UMI.

Scheler, Max F. On the Eternal in Man. Noble, Bernard, tr. LC 72-6599. 480p. 1972. Repr. of 1960 ed. 35.00 (ISBN 0-208-01280-X, Archon). Shoe String.

Schenke, Ludger. Glory & the Way of the Cross: The Gospel of St. Mark. Karris, Robert, ed. Scroggs, Robin, tr. (Herald Biblical Bklts). 1972. pap. 1.25 (ISBN 0-8199-0517-8). Franciscan Herald.

Schick, G. V., tr. Luther's Works: Genesis Chapters 21-25, Vol. 4. LC 55-9893. 1964. 16.95 (ISBN 0-570-06404-X, 15-1746). Concordia.

Schlink, Basilea. Why Doesn't God Intervene? Evangelical Sisterhood of Mary, tr. from Ger. 32p. 1982. pap. 0.50 (ISBN 3-87209-629-X). Evang Sisterhood Mary.

The Science of Religion. pap. 9.95 (ISBN 0-937134-16-3). Amrita Found.

Seth Pringle-Pattison, A. Studies in the Philosophy of Religion. LC 77-27204. (Gifford Lectures: 1923). Repr. of 1930 ed. 30.00 (ISBN 0-404-60474-9). AMS Pr.

Sheen, Fulton J. The Life of All Living. 1979. pap. 3.50 (ISBN 0-385-15458-5, Im). Doubleday.

Showalter, Lester. Investigating God's Orderly World, Bk. 1. (YA) 1970. write for info. (ISBN 0-686-05588-8); tchr's. ed. avail. (ISBN 0-686-05589-6). Rod & Staff.

Siebert, Rudolf J. The Critical Theory of Religion: The Frankfurt School from Universal Pragmatic to Political Theology. (Religion & Reason Ser.: Vol. 29). xvi, 722p. 1985. 112.00x (ISBN 0-89925-119-6). Mouton.

Slaate, Howard A. Contemporary Philosophies of Religion. LC 86-13148. 252p. (Orig.). 1986. pap. text ed. 14.50 (ISBN 0-8191-5492-X). U Pr of Amer.

Slesinski, Robert. Pavel Florensky: A Metaphysics of Love. LC 83-27130. 256p. 1984. pap. text ed. 12.95 (ISBN 0-88141-032-2). St Vladimirs.

Smith, Huston. Forgotten Truth: The Primordial Tradition. 1977. pap. 6.95x (ISBN 0-06-132054-4, TB 2054, Torch). Har-Row.

Smith, John E. Experience & God. 1968. 11.95x (ISBN 0-19-501207-0). Oxford U Pr.

--Religion & Empiricism. (Aquinas Lecture Ser.). 1967. 7.95 (ISBN 0-87462-132-1). Marquette.

Sparrow, Carroll M. Voyages & Cargoes. 1947. 3.00 (ISBN 0-685-09018-3). Dietz.

Spilka, Bernard, et al. The Psychology of Religion: An Empirical Approach. (Illus.). 400p. 1985. text ed. write for info. (ISBN 0-13-736398-2). P-H.

Spitz, Lewis W. & Lehmann, Helmut T., eds. Luther's Works: Career of the Reformer IV, Vol. 34. LC 55-9893. 1960. 19.95 (ISBN 0-8006-0334-6, 1-334). Fortress.

Stace, Walter T. Time & Eternity: An Essay in the Philosophy of Religion. Repr. of 1952 ed. lib. bdg. 22.50x (ISBN 0-8371-1867-0, STTE). Greenwood.

Starratt, Alfred B. Your Self, My Self & the Self of the Universe. LC 79-9971. (Illus.). 192p. 1979. 12.95 (ISBN 0-916144-38-0); pap. 4.95 (ISBN 0-916144-39-9). Stemmer Hse.

Stewart, D. Exploring the Philosophy of Religion. (Illus.). 1980. pap. text ed. write for info. (ISBN 0-13-297366-9). P-H.

Streeter, Burnett H. Buddha & the Christ. LC 72-102585. 1970. Repr. of 1932 ed. 29.50x (ISBN 0-8046-0745-1, Pub. by Kennikat). Assoc Faculty Pr.

Sullivan, John E. Ideas of Religion: A Prolegomenon to the Philosophy of Religion. LC 79-66230. 1979. pap. text ed. 12.25 (ISBN 0-8191-0808-1). U Pr of Amer.

Synan, Vinson. Old Time Power. 6.95 (ISBN 0-911866-67-1). Advocate.

Tchividjian, Gigi & Tchividjian, Stephan. Our Search for Serenity. 168p. 1983. pap. 5.95 (ISBN 0-8007-5151-5, Power Bks). Revell.

Temporini, Hildegard & Haase, Wolfgang, eds. Aufstieg und Niedergang der Roemischen Welt: Section 2, Principat. Incl. Vol. 13. Recht (Normen, Verbreitung, Materien) 1980. 200.00 (ISBN 3-11-008121-0); Vol. 14. Recht (Materien, Fortsetzung) 1982. 253.00 (ISBN 3-11-008122-9); Vol. 15. Recht (Methoden, Schulen, Einzelne Juristen) 1976. 184.00 (ISBN 3-11-006736-6); Vol. 16, Pt. 1. Religion (Heidentum: Romische Religion, Allgemeines) 1978. 200.00 (ISBN 3-11-006737-4); Vol. 16, Pt. 2. Religion (Heidentum: Romische Religion, Allgemeines FS) 1978. 226.00 (ISBN 3-11-007612-8); Vol. 17, Pt. 1. Religion (Heidentum: Romische Gotterkulte, Orientalische Kulte in der romischen Welt) 1981. 147.00 (ISBN 3-11-008468-6); Vol. 17, Pt. 2. Religion (Heidentum: Romische Gotterkulte, Orientalische Kulte in der romischen Welt, Fortsetzung) 1981. 190.00 (ISBN 3-11-008556-9); Vol. 17, Pt. 3. Religion (Heidentum: Romische Gotterkulte, Orientalische Kulte in der romischen Welt, Fortsetzung) 1984. 174.00 (ISBN 3-11-009521-1); Vol. 17, Pt. 4. Religion (Heidentum: Romische Gotterkulte, Orientalische Kulte in der romishcen Welt, Fortsetzung) 1984. 205.00 (ISBN 3-11-010213-7); Vol. 19, Pt. 1. Religion (Judentum: Allgemeines, palastinensisches Judentum) 1979. 210.00 (ISBN 3-11-007968-2); Vol. 19, Pt. 2. Religion (Judentum: Allgemeines, palastinensisches Judentum FS) 1979. 160.00 (ISBN 3-11-007969-0); Vol. 21, Pt. 1. Religion (Hellinistisches Judentum in romischer Zeit): Philon & Josephus. 1984. 210.00 (ISBN 3-11-008845-2); Vol. 21, Pt. 2. Religion (Hellinistisches Judentum in romischer Zeit): Philon & Josephus (Fortsetzung) 1984. 168.00 (ISBN 3-11-009522-X); Vol. 23, Pt. 1. Religion (Vorkonstantinisches Christentum: Verhaltnis zu romischem Staat und heidnischer Religion) 1979. 205.00 (ISBN 3-11-007822-8); Vol. 23, Pt. 2. Religion (Vorkonstantinisches Christentum: Verhaltnis zu romischen Staat und heidnischer Religion) 1980. 161.00 (ISBN 3-11-008016-8). (Ger.). De Gruyter.

Thomas, Owen C. William Temple's Philosophy of Religion. LC 61-4400. 1961. 10.00x (ISBN 0-8401-2330-2). A R Allenson.

Trillhaas, Wolfgang. Religionsphilosophie. 278p. 1972. 19.20x (ISBN 3-11-003868-4). De Gruyter.

Trueblood, David E. Philosophy of Religion. LC 75-31446. 324p. 1976. Repr. of 1957 ed. lib. bdg. 29.25x (ISBN 0-8371-8514-9, TRPHR). Greenwood.

Trueblood, Elton. Philosophy of Religion. (Twin Brooks Ser.). 1973. 12.95 (ISBN 0-8010-8813-5). Baker Bk.

Turner, J. E. Essentials in the Development of Religion: A Philosophic & Psychological Study. 1979. Repr. of 1934 ed. lib. bdg. 35.00 (ISBN 0-8482-2730-1). Norwood Edns.

Van Baal, T. & Van Beek, W. E. Symbols for Communication: An Introduction to the Anthropological Study of Religion. 2nd, rev. ed. (Studies of Developing Countries: No. 11). 272p. 1985. pap. 30.00 (ISBN 90-232-2074-9, Pub. by Van Gorcum Holland). Longwood Pub Group.

Van Der Leeuw, Gerardus. Religion in Essence & Manifestation, 2 vols. 26.50 set (ISBN 0-8446-1457-2). Peter Smith.

Von Hildebrand, Alice J. Introduction to a Philosophy of Religion. LC 79-139972. 1971. 6.95 (ISBN 0-8199-0426-0). Franciscan Herald.

Walker, Philip. Germinal & Zola's Philosophical & Religious Thought. (Purdue Univ. Monographs in Romance Languages: No. 14). 200p. (Orig.). pap. 28.00x (ISBN 90-272-1724-6). Benjamins North Am.

Walvoord, John F. Rapture Question. rev. enlarged ed. 1970. pap. 8.95 (ISBN 0-310-34151-5, 10978P). Zondervan.

Watts, Alan W. Nature, Man & Woman. LC 58-8266. 1970. pap. 3.95 (ISBN 0-394-70592-0, V592, Vin). Random.

--The Supreme Identity. 1972. pap. 4.95 (ISBN 0-394-71835-6, Vin). Random.

Weiss, Paul. God We Seek. LC 64-13476. 267p. 1964. 10.95x (ISBN 0-8093-0133-4). S Ill U Pr.

--God We Seek. LC 72-11838. (Arcturus Books Paperbacks). 268p. 1973. pap. 7.95x (ISBN 0-8093-0628-X). S Ill U Pr.

Westphal, Merold. God, Guilt & Death: An Existential Phenomenology of Religion. LC 83-48525. (Studies in Phenomenology & Existential Philosophy). 320p. 1987. 27.50x (ISBN 0-253-32586-2); pap. 9.95 (ISBN 0-253-32586-2). Ind U Pr.

Wiche, Donald. Religion & Truth. 295p. 1981. text ed. 44.50 (ISBN 90-279-3149-6). Mouton.

Wieman, Henry N. Religious Experience & Scientific Method. Repr. of 1926 ed. lib. bdg. 22.50x (ISBN 0-8371-4368-3, WIRE). Greenwood.

--Religious Experience & Scientific Method. (Arcturus Books Paperbacks). 387p. 1971. pap. 9.95x (ISBN 0-8093-0530-5). S Ill U Pr.

Wieman, Henry N. & Meland, Bernard E. American Philosophies of Religion. 370p. 1985. Repr. of 1936 ed. lib. bdg. 75.00 (ISBN 0-89984-539-8). Century Bookbindery.

Williamson, William B. Decisions in Philosophy of Religion. LC 85-42846. 407p. 1985. pap. 16.95 (ISBN 0-87975-295-5). Prometheus Bks.

Winquist, Charles, ed. The Archaeology of the Imagination. (JAAR Thematic Studies). 1981. pap. 11.95 (ISBN 0-89130-679-X, 01-24-82). Scholars Pr GA.

Wood, Forrest, Jr. Whiteheadian Thought as a Basis for a Philosophy of Religion. LC 86-9282. 110p. (Orig.). 1986. lib. bdg. 19.50 (ISBN 0-8191-5422-9); pap. text ed. 8.75 (ISBN 0-8191-5423-7). U Pr of Amer.

RELIGION–PSYCHOLOGY

see Psychology, Religious

RELIGION–QUOTATIONS, MAXIMS, ETC.

Carey, Floyd D. Teenagers Pocket Companion, No. 2. 1962. pap. 0.25 (ISBN 0-87148-828-0). Pathway Pr.

--Teenagers Pocket Companion, No. 3. 1962. pap. 0.25 (ISBN 0-87148-829-9). Pathway Pr.

Hart, Reed L. Key Thoughts for Talks. (Orig.). 1978. pap. 3.50 (ISBN 0-89036-105-3). Hawkes Pub Inc.

Havner, Vance. The Vance Havner Quotebook. 208p. 1986. 9.95 (ISBN 0-8010-4299-2). Baker Bk.

Lawson, James G. The World's Best Religious Quotations. 1979. Repr. lib. bdg. 35.00 (ISBN 0-8492-1610-9). R West.

McNulty, James F. Words of Power. LC 83-2514. 226p. (Orig.). 1983. pap. 8.95 (ISBN 0-8189-0442-9). Alba.

Negrin, S., ed. The Great Harmony: Teachings & Observations of the Way of the Universe. LC 77-77387. (Illus., Orig.). 1977. pap. 3.50 (ISBN 0-87810-033-4). Times Change.

Proctor, F. B. Treasury of Quotations on Religious Subjects. LC 76-15741. 832p. 1976. 21.95 (ISBN 0-8254-3500-5). Kregel.

Spurgeon, C. H. The Best of C. H. Spurgeon. 256p. 1986. pap. 6.95 (ISBN 0-8010-8267-6). Baker Bk.

RELIGION–STUDY AND TEACHING

see also Theology–Study and Teaching

Ballou, R. O., et al, eds. The Bible of the World. 1415p. 1980. pap. 5.50 (ISBN 0-380-01057-7, 17350). Avon.

Boucher, Therese. Becoming a Sensuous Catechist: Using the Arts in Religion Classes. (Illus.). 80p. 1984. pap. 5.95 (ISBN 0-89622-216-0). Twenty-Third.

Carr, Anne, et al. Academic Study of Religion, 1975: Public Schools Religion-Studies. LC 75-26653. (American Academy of Religion. Section Papers). 1975. pap. 9.95 (ISBN 0-89130-023-6, 01-09-17). Scholars Pr Ga.

Daughters of St Paul. Your Right to Be Informed. LC 68-59042. (Divine Master Ser.: Vol. 1). 1969. 7.95 (ISBN 0-8198-0518-1); pap. 6.50 (ISBN 0-8198-0519-X); teacher manual 8.50 (ISBN 0-8198-0520-3). Dghtrs St Paul.

Davis, Billie. Teaching to Meet Crisis Needs. LC 83-82815. 128p. (Orig.). 1984. pap. text ed. 2.95 (ISBN 0-88243-609-0, 02-0609). Gospel Pub.

De Witt, Roy L. Teaching from the Tabernacle. LC 86-60046. (Illus.). 168p. (Orig.). pap. 8.95 (ISBN 0-9616360-0-9). Revival Teach.

Eliade, Mircea & Kitagawa, Joseph. History of Religions: Essays in Methodology. LC 59-11621. 1959. 12.50x (ISBN 0-226-20394-8). U of Chicago Pr.

Enns, Herman. This We Believe, Leader's Guide. LC 78-130643. 1970. pap. 1.75 (ISBN 0-87303-846-0). Faith & Life.

Gorman, G. E., et al, eds. Theological & Religious Reference Materials: Practical Theology. LC 86-380. (Bibliographies & Indexes in Religious Studies: No. 7). 402p. 1986. lib. bdg. 49.95 (ISBN 0-313-25397-8, GPA/). Greenwood.

Hall, T. William, ed. Introduction to the Study of Religion. LC 78-4427. (Orig.). 1978. pap. text ed. 10.95xi (ISBN 0-06-063572-X, RD 281, HarpR). Har-Row.

Harris, Alan. Teaching Morality & Religion. 104p. 1975. 14.95x (ISBN 0-8464-1274-8). Beekman Pubs.

Hartshorne, Hugh & Lotz, Elsa. Case Studies of Present-Day Religions Teaching. (Educational Ser.). 1932. Repr. 15.00 (ISBN 0-8482-4454-0). Norwood Edns.

Honko, Lauro, ed. Science of Religion, Studies in Methodology. (Religion & Reason Ser.). 1979. text ed. 50.50x (ISBN 90-279-7854-9). Mouton.

Jastrow, Morris, Jr. The Study of Religion. Clebsch, William A., ed. LC 81-9184. (Classics & Reprints Series of the American Academy of Religion & Scholars Press). 1981. text ed. 10.95 (ISBN 0-89130-519-X, 01-05-01). Scholars Pr GA.

Kane, J. Herbert. Understanding Christian Missions. 16.95 (ISBN 0-8010-5344-7). Baker Bk.

Killgallon, James J., et al. La Vida en Cristo. Pascual, Manuel, tr. from Eng. LC 76-26451. 1978. pap. 2.25 (ISBN 0-914070-12-6). ACTA Found.

Kniker, Charles R. Teaching about Religion in the Public Schools. LC 84-62994. (Fastback Ser.: No. 224). 50p. (Orig.). 1985. pap. 0.90 (ISBN 0-87367-224-0). Phi Delta Kappa.

Kubo, Sakae. The Open Rapture. (Flame Ser.). 1978. pap. 0.99 (ISBN 0-8127-0170-4). Review & Herald.

Kurt, Rudolph. Historical Fundamentals & the Study of Religions. 180p. 1985. 17.95x (ISBN 0-02-927190-8). Macmillan.

Lockerbie, D. Bruce. Asking Questions: A Classroom Model for Teaching the Bible. Zimmerman, Diane, ed. LC 80-18198. (Orig.). 1980. pap. text ed. 5.95 (ISBN 0-915134-75-6). Mott Media.

Martin, Luther H. & Goss, James, eds. Essays on Jung & the Study of Religion. LC 85-17865. 214p. (Orig.). 1986. lib. bdg. 29.50 (ISBN 0-8191-4923-3); pap. text ed. 12.75 (ISBN 0-8191-4924-1). U Pr of Amer.

Ramsey, Paul. Study of Religion in Colleges & Universities. Wilson, John F., ed. LC 70-90957. 336p. 1970. 37.00x (ISBN 0-691-07161-6). Princeton U Pr.

Richards, Lawrence O. Sixty Nine Ways to Start a Study Group & Keep It Growing. 2nd ed. 144p. 1980. pap. 3.95 (ISBN 0-310-31981-1, 18138P). Zondervan.

Saia, Mary J., et al. Awakenings. (Education to Wonder Ser.: Pre-School Program). 1973. program director's handbook 3.50 (ISBN 0-8091-9075-3); tchr dev. handbook 3.50 (ISBN 0-8091-9074-5); tchr. guidebk. 4 yr. olds 6.95 (ISBN 0-8091-9071-0); tchr. guidebk. 5 yr. olds 6.95 (ISBN 0-8091-9072-9). parent-tchr. dev. kit 75.00 (ISBN 0-8091-9073-7); child-parent kit 4 yr. olds 5.95 (ISBN 0-8091-9077-X); child-parent kit 5 yr. olds 5.95 (ISBN 0-8091-9078-8). Paulist Pr.

Sharpe, Eric J. Understanding Religion. LC 82-25055. 160p. 1984. 19.95 (ISBN 0-312-83208-7). St Martin.

Swami Vivekananda. Education. pap. 1.95 (ISBN 0-87481-451-0). Vedanta Pr.

Tanner, Florice. The Mystery Teachings in World Religions. LC 73-8887. (A Quest Book Original Ser). 160p. (Orig.). 1973. pap. 2.45 (ISBN 0-8356-0439-X, Quest). Theos Pub Hse.

Thrower, James. Marxist-Leninist 'Scientific Atheism' & the Study of Religion & Atheism in the U. S. S. R. (Ger.). 500p. 1983. 78.00 (ISBN 90-279-3060-0). Mouton.

Turned On: A Cassette Programmed Multi-Media Design for the Training of Religious Teachers, Based on an Exploration of Youth Culture. kit 49.95 (ISBN 0-02-640530-X, 64053); coordinator's handbk only 5.40 (ISBN 0-02-640540-7); student-teacher workbk. only 3.00 (ISBN 0-02-640520-2). Benziger Pub Co.

Waardenburg, Jacques. Classical Approaches to the Study of Religion: Aims, Methods & Theories of Research: Part 1: Introduction & Anthology. LC 70-152082. (Religion & Reason Ser: No. 3). 742p. 1973. pap. text ed. 47.50x (ISBN 0-686-22556-2). Mouton.

--Reflections on the Study of Religion. (Religion & Reason Ser.: No. 15). 1978. text ed. 32.00 (ISBN 0-686-27034-7). Mouton.

Zuck, Roy B. & Getz, Gene A. Adult Education in the Church. LC 79-123154. 1970. pap. 15.95 (ISBN 0-8024-0468-5). Moody.

RELIGION, ASSYRO-BABYLONIAN

see Assyro-Babylonian Religion

RELIGION, COMPARATIVE

see Religions

RELIGION, MIXED

see Marriage, Mixed

RELIGION, PRIMITIVE

see also Ancestor Worship; Beads (In Religion, Folk-Lore, etc.); Birth (In Religion, Folk-Lore, etc.); Blood (In Religion, Folk-Lore, etc.); Body, Human (In Religion, Folk-Lore, etc.); Cats (In Religion, Folk-Lore, Etc.); Cultus; Dancing (In Religion, Folk-Lore, Etc.); Dead (In Religion, Folk-Lore, Etc.); Dogs (In Religion, Folk-Lore, Etc.); Fetishism; Fire (In Religion, Folk-Lore, Etc.); Fish (In Religion, Folk-Lore, Etc.); Gems (In Religion, Folk-Lore, Etc.); Horns (In Religion, Folk-Lore, etc.); Idols and Images; Indians of North America–Religion and Mythology; Initiations (In Religion, Folk-Lore, Etc.); Kings and Rulers (In Religion, Folk-Lore, Etc.); Moon (In Religion, Folk-Lore, Etc.); Nativistic Movements; Phallicism

also subdivisions Religion or Religion and mythology under names of ethnic groups, e.g. Indians of North America–Religion and Mythology

Andersen, Johannes C. The Maori Tohunga & His Spirit World. LC 75-35224. Repr. of 1948 ed. 20.00 (ISBN 0-404-14403-9). AMS Pr.

Attar, Farid Ud-Din. The Conference of the Birds: A Sufi Fable. Nott, C. S., tr. (Clear Light Ser). (Illus.). 147p. (Orig.). 1971. pap. 6.95 (ISBN 0-87773-031-8, 73001-1). Shambhala Pubns.

Banton, Michael, ed. Anthropological Approaches to the Study of Religion. 1968. pap. 13.95 (ISBN 0-422-72510-2, NO.2068, Pub. by Tavistock England). Methuen Inc.

Bastide, Roger. The African Religions of Brazil: Toward a Sociology of the Interpenetration of Civilizations. Sebba, Helen, tr. (Johns Hopkins Studies in Atlantic History & Culture Ser.). 1978. text ed. 45.00x (ISBN 0-8018-2056-1); pap. text ed. 14.95x (ISBN 0-8018-2130-4). Johns Hopkins.

Bell, John. Bell's New Pantheon, 2 vols. Feldman, Burton & Richardson, Robert D., eds. LC 78-60919. (Myth & Romanticism Ser.: Vol. 4). 809p. 1979. Set. lib. bdg. 160.00 (ISBN 0-8240-3553-4). Garland Pub.

Brinton, Daniel G. Religions of Primitive Peoples. LC 79-88423. Repr. of 1897 ed. 22.50x (ISBN 0-8371-1763-1, BRR&). Greenwood.

Buck, Peter H. Anthropology & Religion. LC 72-121753. viii, 96p. 1970. Repr. of 1939 ed. 16.00 (ISBN 0-208-00950-7, Archon). Shoe String.

Burkert, Walter. Homo Necans: Interpretationen altgriechischer Opferriten und Mythen. LC 72-83051. (Religionsgeschichtliche Versuche und Vorarbeiten: Vol. 32). 356p. 1972. 43.20x (ISBN 3-11-003875-7). De Gruyter.

Burl, Aubrey. Rites of the Gods. (Illus.). 272p. 1981. text ed. 26.50x (ISBN 0-460-04313-7, BKA 04660, Pub. by J M Dent England). Biblio Dist.

Burriss, Eli E. Taboo, Magic, Spirits: A Study of Primitive Elements in Roman Religion. LC 72-114489. x, 250p. Repr. of 1931 ed. lib. bdg. 22.50x (ISBN 0-8371-4724-7, BUTA). Greenwood.

Carmody, Denise L. The Oldest God: Archaic Religion Yesterday & Today. LC 80-25499. 192p. (Orig.). 1981. pap. 7.50 (ISBN 0-687-28813-4). Abingdon.

Cassirer, Ernst. Language & Myth. Langer, Susanne K., tr. 1946. pap. 2.95 (ISBN 0-486-20051-5). Dover.

--Language & Myth. 13.50 (ISBN 0-8446-1820-9). Peter Smith.

Collins, John J. Primitive Religion. (Quality Paperback Ser.: No. 342). 256p. 1978. pap. 4.95 (ISBN 0-8226-0342-X). Littlefield.

Dioszegi, V., ed. Popular Beliefs & Folklore Tradition in Siberia. (Uralic & Altaic Ser.: No. 57). 1968. text ed. 40.80x (ISBN 0-686-22621-6). Mouton.

Dulaure, Jacques-Antoine. The Gods of Generation. LC 72-9635. Tr. of De Divinites Generatrices. Repr. of 1934 ed. 42.00 (ISBN 0-404-57433-5). AMS Pr.

Dupre, Wilhelm. Religion in Primitive Cultures: A Study in Ethnophilosophy. (Religion & Reason: No. 9). 366p. 1975. text ed. 39.00x (ISBN 0-686-22610-0). Mouton.

Durkheim, Emile. Elementary Forms of the Religious Life. Swain, Joseph W., tr. 1965. pap. text ed. 14.95 (ISBN 0-02-908010-X). Free Pr.

Evans-Pritchard, E. E. Theories of Primitive Religion. LC 85-22003. (Sir D. Owens Evan Lectures, 1962). 138p. 1985. Repr. of 1965 ed. lib. bdg. 29.75x (ISBN 0-313-24978-4, EPTP). Greenwood.

Evans-Pritchard, Edward E. Theories of Primitive Religion. 1965. pap. 9.95x (ISBN 0-19-823131-8). Oxford U Pr.

Faber, George S. The Origin of Pagan Idolatry, 3 vols. Feldman, Burton & Richardson, Robert D., eds. LC 78-60891. (Myth & Romanticism Ser.). 1984. Set. lib. bdg. 240.00 (ISBN 0-8240-3559-3). Garland Pub.

Frazer, James G. The Worship of Nature. LC 73-21271. (Gifford Lectures: 1924-25). Repr. of 1926 ed. 41.50 (ISBN 0-404-11427-X). AMS Pr.

Gill, Sam. Beyond the "Primitive". Religions of Nonliterate Peoples. (Illus.). 200p. 1982. pap. 14.95 (ISBN 0-13-076034-X). P-H.

Godwin, Joscelyn. Mystery Religions: In the Ancient World. LC 81-47423. (Illus.). 180p. (Orig.). 1981. pap. 9.95 (ISBN 0-06-063140-6, CN4020, HarpR). Har-Row.

Goodland, Roger. A Bibliography of Sex Rites & Customs. LC 77-11605. 1977. Repr. of 1931 ed. lib. bdg. 60.00 (ISBN 0-89341-193-0). Longwood Pub Group.

Gorham, Melvin. Pagan Reality. 201p. 1970. pap. 5.00 (ISBN 0-914752-02-2). Sovereign Pr.

Green, Ronald M. Religious Reason: The Rational & Moral Basis of Religious Belief. 1978. text ed. 18.95x (ISBN 0-19-502388-9); pap. text ed. 7.95x (ISBN 0-19-502389-7). Oxford U Pr.

Hadfield, Percival. The Savage & His Totem. LC 75-32825. Repr. of 1938 ed. 20.00 (ISBN 0-404-14129-3). AMS Pr.

Howells, William. The Heathens Primitive Man & His Religions. 302p. pap. text ed. 9.95 (ISBN 0-88133-240-2). Sheffield Wisc.

James, Edwin O. The Beginnings of Religion: An Introductory & Scientific Study. 159p. 1973. Repr. of 1950 ed. lib. bdg. 22.50x (ISBN 0-8371-6706-X, JABE). Greenwood.

Jarrett, Emmett. God's Body. LC 75-8967. 32p. 1975. pap. 1.50 (ISBN 0-914610-05-8). Hanging Loose.

Jensen, Adolf E. Myth & Cult Among Primitive Peoples. LC 63-20909. 1963. 10.00x (ISBN 0-226-39823-4). U of Chicago Pr.

Keary, Charles F. Outlines of Primitive Belief among the Indo-European Races. LC 77-85620. 1977. Repr. of 1882 ed. lib. bdg. 50.00 (ISBN 0-89341-305-4). Longwood Pub Group.

Lang, Andrew. Custom & Myth. 2nd rev. ed. LC 68-59267. Repr. of 1885 ed. 11.00 (ISBN 0-404-03817-4). AMS Pr.

--Magic & Religion. Repr. of 1901 ed. lib. bdg. 22.50x (ISBN 0-8371-0933-7, LAMR). Greenwood.

--Myth, Ritual & Religion, 2 Vols in 1. LC 68-54280. Repr. of 1906 ed. 35.00 (ISBN 0-404-03868-9). AMS Pr.

Leach, Edmund R. Dialectic in Practical Religion. (Cambridge Papers in Social Anthropology: No. 5). 34.50 (ISBN 0-521-05525-3). Cambridge U Pr.

Le Roy, Alexander. Religion of the Primitives. Thompson, Newton, tr. LC 72-78769. Repr. of 1922 ed. cancelled (ISBN 0-8371-1400-4). Greenwood.

Leuven, J. V. Prehistoric Religion in Greece. (Illus.). 280p. 1987. lib. bdg. 72.00 (Pub. by A. M. Hakkert). Coronet Bks.

Lowie, Robert H. Primitive Religion. new ed. LC 75-114373. 1970. pap. 5.95 (ISBN 0-87140-209-2). Liveright.

Malefijt, Anne M. Religion & Culture: An Introduction to Anthropology of Religion. 1968. text ed. write for info. (ISBN 0-02-374920-2). Macmillan.

Marett, R. R. Faith, Hope & Charity in Primitive Religion. LC 72-80150. Repr. of 1932 ed. 22.00 (ISBN 0-405-08780-2, Pub. by Blom). Ayer Co Pubs.

Marett, Robert R. Faith, Hope & Charity in Primitive Religion. LC 77-27193. (Gifford Lectures: 1931-32). Repr. of 1932 ed. 15.00 (ISBN 0-404-60487-0). AMS Pr.

--The Threshold of Religion. LC 76-44755. Repr. of 1900 ed. 26.50 (ISBN 0-404-15950-8). AMS Pr.

Mayfair, Norman P. The Religious Practices of Primitive Peoples. (Illus.). 139p. 1980. deluxe ed. 67.75 (ISBN 0-89266-241-7). Am Classical Coll.

Middleton, John. Lugbara Religion: Ritual & Authority among East African People. LC 86-21889. (Illus.). 294p. 1987. pap. 14.95x (ISBN 0-87474-667-1). Smithsonian.

Mutahhari, Morteza. Religion & the World. Tawheedi, Mohammad S., tr. 44p. 1984. pap. 3.95 (ISBN 0-940368-34-X). Tahrike Tarsile Quran.

Parrinder, Geoffrey. African Traditional Religion. 3rd ed. LC 76-22490. (Illus.). 156p. 1976. Repr. of 1976 ed. lib. bdg. 25.00x (ISBN 0-8371-3401-3, PAF&, Pub. by Negro U Pr). Greenwood.

Radin, Paul. Primitive Religion: Its Nature & Origin. 1937. pap. text ed. 5.95 (ISBN 0-486-20393-X). Dover.

Radin, Pual. Primitive Religion. 15.25 (ISBN 0-8446-2775-5). Peter Smith.

Roheim, Geza. Eternal Ones of the Dream: Myth & Ritual, Dreams & Fantasies-Their Role in the Lives of Primitive Man. 1970. pap. text ed. 19.95 (ISBN 0-8236-8044-4, 021760). Intl Univs Pr.

--The Riddle of the Sphinx, or Human Origins. Money-Kryle, R., tr. 10.75 (ISBN 0-8446-5238-5). Peter Smith.

Schmidt, W. The Origin & Growth of Religion: Facts & Theories. Rose, H. J., tr. from Ger. LC 74-184909. xvi, 302p. 1972. Repr. of 1931 ed. lib. bdg. 22.50x (ISBN 0-8154-0408-5). Cooper Sq.

Shorter, Aylward. Prayer in the Religious Traditions of Africa. 1975. pap. 7.95 (ISBN 0-19-519848-4). Oxford U Pr.

Starhawk. The Spiral Dance: Rebirth of the Ancient Religion of the Goddess. (Orig.). 1979. pap. 10.95 (ISBN 0-06-067535-7, RD 301, HarpR). Har-Row.

Swanson, Guy E. Birth of the Gods: The Origin of Primitive Beliefs. 1960. pap. 4.95 (ISBN 0-472-06093-7, 93, AA). U of Mich Pr.

Throop, P. A. Criticism of the Crusade: A Study of Public Opinion & Crusade Propaganda. 59.95 (ISBN 0-87968-968-4). Gordon Pr.

Toland, John. Letters to Serena. Wellek, Rene, ed. LC 75-11259. (British Philosophers & Theologians of the 17th & 18th Centuries: Vol. 58). 295p. 1976. Repr. of 1704 ed. lib. bdg. 51.00 (ISBN 0-8240-1809-5). Garland Pub.

RELIGION, PROPOSED

see Religions (Proposed, Universal, etc.)

RELIGION, UNIVERSAL

see Religions (Proposed, Universal, Etc.)

RELIGION AND ART

see Art and Religion

RELIGION AND ASTRONAUTICS

Decard, Bob. The California Connection. 90p. (Orig.). 1986. pap. 6.95 (ISBN 0-9616620-1-8). Constellation Pr.

Irwin, James B., Jr. & Emerson, W. A. Un Astronauta y la Lumbrera de la Noche. 176p. 1981. Repr. of 1978 ed. 4.25 (ISBN 0-311-01066-0). Casa Bautista.

Perrin, Arnold. Out of Bondage. (Illus.). 52p. 1983. pap. 4.95 (ISBN 0-939736-45-4). Wings ME.

Schindler, David L., ed. Beyond Mechanism: The Universe in Recent Physics & Catholic Thought. 166p. (Orig.). 1986. lib. bdg. 22.75 (ISBN 0-8191-5357-5, Pub. by Communio Intl Cth Review); pap. text ed. 10.75 (ISBN 0-8191-5358-3). U Pr of Amer.

RELIGION AND COMMUNISM

see Communism and Religion

RELIGION AND CULTURE

see also Christianity and Culture

Bednarowski, Mary F. American Religion: A Cultural Perspective. LC 83-22895. (Illus.). 182p. 1984. pap. text ed. 17.00 (ISBN 0-13-029059-9). P-H.

Coward, Harold & Kawamura, Leslie, eds. Religion & Ethnicity. 181p. 1978. pap. text ed. 9.95 (ISBN 0-88920-064-5, Pub. by Wilfrid Laurier Canada). Humanities.

Coyle, Neva. Daily Thoughts on Living Free. LC 82-4495. 174p. (Orig.). 1982. pap. 4.95 (ISBN 0-87123-286-3, 210286). Bethany Hse.

Dawson, Christopher H. Religion & Culture. LC 77-27183. (Gifford Lectures Ser.: 1947). 232p. Repr. of 1948 ed. 27.50 (ISBN 0-404-60498-6). AMS Pr.

--Religion & the Rise of Western Culture. LC 77-27181. (Gifford Lectures: 1948-49). Repr. of 1950 ed. 26.50 (ISBN 0-404-60499-4). AMS Pr.

Dietrich, Wendell S. Cohen & Troeltsch: Ethical Monotheistic Religion & Theory of Culture. (Brown Judaic Studies). 1986. text ed. 23.95 (ISBN 1-55540-017-5, 14-01-20); pap. 18.95 (ISBN 1-55540-018-3). Scholars Pr GA.

Fallon, Timothy P. & Riley, Philip B., eds. Religion & Culture: Essays in Honor of Bernard Lonergan, S.J. 512p. 1987. 44.50x (ISBN 0-88706-289-X). State U NY Pr.

Gilkey, Langdon. Society & the Sacred: Toward a Theology of Culture in Decline. LC 81-9775. 225p. 1981. 14.95 (ISBN 0-8245-0089-X). Crossroad NY.

Gopi Krishna. To Those Concerned Citizens. (Illus.). 16p. 1978. pap. 3.95 (ISBN 0-88697-002-4). Life Science.

Greinacher, Norbert & Mette, Norbert, eds. Popular Religion. (Concilium Nineteen Eighty-Six Ser.). 120p. 1986. pap. 6.95 (ISBN 0-567-30066-8, Pub. by T & T Clark Ltd UK). Fortress.

Hartt, Julian N., ed. The Critique of Modernity: Theological Reflections on Contemporary Culture. (Virginia Lectures on Individual & Society). 160p. 1987. text ed. 16.95x (ISBN 0-8139-1118-4). U Pr of VA.

Horosz, William & Clements, Tad, eds. Religion & Human Purpose. 1987. lib. bdg. 64.50 (ISBN 90-247-3000-7, Pub. by Martinus Nijhoff Netherlands). Kluwer Academic.

Loos, Amandus W., ed. Religious Faith & World Culture. LC 71-128270. (Essay Index Reprint Ser). 1951. 20.00 (ISBN 0-8369-1976-9). Ayer Co Pubs.

May, John R., ed. The Bent World: Essays on Religion & Culture. LC 81-5801. (College Theology Society Annual Publications Ser.). 215p. 1979. 18.00 (ISBN 0-89130-503-3, 34 10 79). Scholars Pr GA.

--The Bent World: Essays on Religion & Culture. 224p. (Orig.). 1986. pap. 23.00 (ISBN 0-8191-5614-0, Pub. by College Theology Society). U Pr of Amer.

Meland, Bernard E. Faith & Culture. (Arcturus Books Paperbacks). 176p. 1972. lib. bdg. 7.00x (ISBN 0-8093-0591-7); pap. 2.45x (ISBN 0-8093-0571-2). S Ill U Pr.

Moltmann, Jurgen. On Human Dignity: Political Theology & Ethics. Meeks, M. Douglas, tr. from Ger. LC 83-48913. 240p. 1984. 15.95 (ISBN 0-8006-0715-5, 1-715). Fortress.

Panichas, George A. The Reverent Discipline: Essays in Literary Criticism & Culture. LC 73-15749. 488p. 1974. 29.95x (ISBN 0-87049-149-0). U of Tenn Pr.

Raschke, Carl A. The Bursting of New Wineskins: Reflection on Religion & Culture at the End of Affluence. LC 78-16604. (Pittsburgh Theological Monographs: No. 24). 1978. 10.75 (ISBN 0-915138-34-4). Pickwick.

Shairp, J. C. Culture & Religion in Some of Their Relations: The Literary Theory of Culture. 1978. Repr. of 1872 ed. lib. bdg. 30.00 (ISBN 0-8492-8044-3). R West.

Slater, Peter, ed. Religion & Culture in Canada. 568p. pap. text ed. 9.75x (ISBN 0-919812-06-6, Pub. by Wilfrid Laurier Canada). Humanities.

Smith, David L. Horace Bushnell: Selected Writings on Language, Religion & American Culture. LC 83-6678. (AAR Studies in Religion). 196p. 1984. pap. 9.75 (ISBN 0-89130-636-6, 01 00 33). Scholars Pr GA.

Taylor, Mark K. Beyond Explanation: Religious Dimensions in Cultural Anthropology. LC 85-13770. x, 262p. 1985. text ed. 24.50 (ISBN 0-86554-165-5, MUP-H155). Mercer Univ Pr.

Tylor, Edward. Religion in Primitive Culture. (Primitive Culture - Part 2). 18.75 (ISBN 0-8446-0946-3). Peter Smith.

Van Baal, T. & Van Beek, W. E. Symbols for Communication: An Introduction to the Anthropological Study of Religion. 2nd, rev. ed. (Studies of Developing Countries: No. 11). 272p. 1985. pap. 30.00 (ISBN 90-232-2074-9, Pub. by Van Gorcum Holland). Longwood Pub Group.

Wilson, John F. Public Religion in American Culture. 240p. 1981. pap. 9.95 (ISBN 0-87722-226-6). Temple U Pr.

RELIGION AND EDUCATION

see Church and Education

RELIGION AND ETHICS

see also Buddhist Ethics; Christian Ethics; Ethics, Jewish; Islamic Ethics

Bergson, Henri. The Two Sources of Morality & Religion. Audra, R. Ashley, tr. from Fr. LC 77-89762. 1977. pap. text ed. 8.95 (ISBN 0-268-01835-9). U of Notre Dame Pr.

Buber, Martin. Between Man & Man. 15.25 (ISBN 0-8446-6207-0). Peter Smith.

Butler, John. TV, Movies & Morality: A Guide for Catholics. LC 84-60753. 144p. 1984. pap. 6.95 (ISBN 0-87973-602-X, 602). Our Sunday Visitor.

Cooney, Timothy J. Telling Right from Wrong: What Is Moral, What Is Immoral & What Is Neither One Nor the Other. 158p. 1985. 18.95 (ISBN 0-87975-297-1). Prometheus Bks.

Curran, Charles E. Transition & Tradition in Moral Theology. LC 78-20877. 1979. text ed. 18.95x (ISBN 0-268-01837-5, Dist. by Har Row). U of Notre Dame Pr.

Dietrich, Wendell S. Cohen & Troeltsch: Ethical Monotheistic Religion & Theory of Culture. (Brown Judaic Studies). 1986. text ed. 23.95 (ISBN 1-55540-017-5, 14-01-20); pap. 18.95 (ISBN 1-55540-018-3). Scholars Pr GA.

Donagan, Alan. Theory of Morality. LC 76-25634. 1979. pap. 10.00x (ISBN 0-226-15567-6, P838, Phoen); 20.00x (ISBN 0-226-15566-8). U of Chicago Pr.

Eeningenburg, Dennis. Workbook on Morality: A Biblical View of Sexuality. 74p. (Orig.). 1981. pap. 4.95 (ISBN 0-8341-0717-1). Beacon Hill.

Evans, Donald. Faith, Authenticity, & Morality. 1980. 30.00x (ISBN 0-8020-5424-2). U of Toronto Pr.

Fox, James J. Religion & Morality: Their Nature & Mutual Relations. 334p. 1983. Repr. of 1899 ed. 20.00x (ISBN 0-939738-09-0). Zubal Inc.

Fries, Jakob F. Dialogues on Morality & Religion. Phillips, D. Z., et al, eds. LC 82-13787. (Values & Philosophical Inquiry Ser.). (Illus.). 268p. 1982. text ed. 28.95x (ISBN 0-389-20326-2). B&N Imports.

Guissani, Luigi. Morality: Memory & Desire. Whitehead, Kenneth D., tr. LC 86-80476. Tr. of Italian. 174p. 1986. pap. 8.95 (ISBN 0-89870-090-6). Ignatius Pr.

Hastings, A. W. & Hastings, E., eds. Important Moral Issues. 128p. 1966. pap. 6.95 (ISBN 0-567-22302-7, Pub. by T & T Clark Ltd UK). Fortress.

Helm, Paul, ed. Divine Commands & Morality. (Readings in Philosophy Ser.). 1981. pap. 9.95x (ISBN 0-19-875049-8). Oxford U Pr.

Kelly, Geffrey B. & Godsey, John D., eds. Ethical Responsibility: Bonhoeffer's Legacy to the Churches. LC 81-18823. (Toronto Studies in Theology: Vol. 6). 352p. 1982. 59.95x (ISBN 0-88946-960-1). E Mellen.

McCormick, Richard A. Ambiguity in Moral Choice. (Pere Marquette Theology Lectures). 1977. pap. 7.95 (ISBN 0-87462-505-X). Marquette.

McDonagh, Edna. Doing the Truth: The Quest for Moral Theology. LC 79-63361. 223p. 1980. pap. text ed. 6.95 (ISBN 0-268-00845-0). U of Notre Dame Pr.

Makari, Victor E. Ibn Taymiyyah's Ethics: The Social Factor. LC 81-1019. (AAR Academy Ser.). 246p. 1983. 17.95 (ISBN 0-89130-476-2, 01 01 34). Scholars Pr GA.

Mitchell, Basil. Morality: Religious & Secular. 176p. 1986. pap. 10.95x (ISBN 0-19-824928-4). Oxford U Pr.

Nelson, Paul. Narrative & Morality: A Theological Inquiry. LC 86-43034. 192p. 1987. 21.50x (ISBN 0-271-00485-1). Pa St U Pr.

Noonan, John T., Jr., et al, eds. The Role & Responsibility of the Moral Philosopher: Proceedings, Vol. 56. LC 81-69068. 214p. 1983. pap. 15.00 (ISBN 0-918090-16-4). Am Cath Philo.

Patterson, Ward. The Morality Maze. LC 81-14539. 128p. (Orig.). 1982. pap. 2.25 (ISBN 0-87239-478-6, 41010). Standard Pub.

Porter, Burton F. Deity & Morality-with Regard to the Naturalistic Fallacy. LC 68-16017. 1968. text ed. 7.95x (ISBN 0-04-100012-9). Humanities.

Priest, Ames. Governmental & Judicial Ethics in the Bible & Rabbinic Literature. 1980. 20.00x (ISBN 0-87068-697-6). Ktav.

Ratzinger, Joseph, et al. Principles of Christian Morality. Harrison, Graham, tr. from Ger. LC 85-82176. Orig. Title: Prinzipien Chrislicher Moral. 104p. (Orig.). 1986. pap. 6.95 (ISBN 0-89870-086-8). Ignatius Pr.

Sorley, William R. Moral Values & the Idea of God. LC 77-27215. (Gifford Lectures: 1914-15). 1978. Repr. of 1918 ed. 37.50 (ISBN 0-404-60465-X). AMS Pr.

Stark, Werner. Social Bond, an Investigation into the Bases of Law-Abidingness, Vol. IV: Safeguards of the Social Bond: Ethos & Religion. viii, 288p. 1983. 25.00 (ISBN 0-8232-1083-9); pap. 12.50 (ISBN 0-8232-1084-7). Fordham.

Thielicke, Helmut. Theological Ethics. LC 78-31858. Repr. of 1979 ed. 160.00 (2027550). Bks Demand UMI.

Warren, Thomas B. & Barnhart, Joe. Warren-Barnhart Debate on Ethics. 1981. pap. 13.00 (ISBN 0-934916-47-0). Natl Christian Pr.

Welch, D. Don. Law & Morality. LC 86-45195. 192p. 1987. pap. text ed. 14.95 (ISBN 0-8006-1974-9, 1-1974). Fortress.

Wood, Louis A. Form & Origin of Milton's Antitrinitarian Conception. LC 72-191655. 1911. lib. bdg. 15.00 (ISBN 0-8414-0833-5). Folcroft.

RELIGION AND GEOGRAPHY

see also Ecclesiastical Geography

Planhol, Xavier de. The World of Islam. 153p. 1959. pap. 8.95x (ISBN 0-8014-9830-9). Cornell U Pr.

RELIGION AND HUMOR

Adams, Doug. Humor in the American Pulpit from George Whitefield Through Henry Ward Beecher. rev. ed. 1981. 6.95 (ISBN 0-941500-10-1). Sharing Co.

Anderson, Dave & Wilcox, Tim. A Funny Thing Happened on the Way to Church. 1981. pap. 4.50 (ISBN 0-570-03834-0, 12YY2799). Concordia.

Armstrong, Wm. Benedictine Cartoons. (Armstrong Cartoon Ser.). (Illus., Orig.). 1973. pap. 1.00 (ISBN 0-913452-25-4). Jesuit Bks.

--Franciscan Cartoons. (Armstrong Cartoon Ser.). (Illus., Orig.). 1974. pap. 1.00 (ISBN 0-913452-24-6). Jesuit Bks.

Benson, Donald. Biblical Limericks, Old Testament Stories Re-versed. 1986. 6.95 (ISBN 0-345-33033-1). Ballantine.

Bonham, Tal. D. Humor: God's Gift. 1988. text ed. 9.95 (ISBN 0-8054-5720-8). Broadman.

Bonham, Tal D. The Treasury of Clean Church Jokes. LC 85-26837. 1986. pap. 3.50 (ISBN 0-8054-5719-4). Broadman.

Clower, Jerry. Let the Hammer Down. 1979. pap. 1.95 (ISBN 0-671-82626-3). PB.

Davis, Creath. Lord, If I Ever Needed You, It's Now! 138p. Date not set. pap. 5.95 (ISBN 0-8010-2968-6). Baker Bk.

Demaray, Donald E. Laughter, Joy, & Healing. 160p. 1987. pap. 7.95 (ISBN 0-8010-2969-4). Baker Bk.

Gregory, Dick. Dick Gregory's Bible Tales. 1978. pap. 2.95 (ISBN 0-06-080445-9, P 445, PL). Har-Row.

John, Da Free. The Dreaded Gom-Boo: Or the Imaginary Desease That Religion Seeks to Cure. LC 83-70401. 400p. (Orig.). 1983. pap. 9.95 (ISBN 0-913922-74-9). Dawn Horse Pr.

Naglee, David I. In Praise of More Folly. 208p. 1982. 10.00 (ISBN 0-682-49803-3, Banner). Exposition Pr FL.

Phelan, Paul J. With a Merry Heart. 353p. 1981. Repr. of 1943 ed. lib. bdg. 25.00 (ISBN 0-89760-710-4). Telegraph Bks.

Phillips, Bob. The World's Greatest Collection of Heavenly Humor. LC 81-82676. 192p. (Orig.). 1982. pap. text ed. 2.95 (ISBN 0-89081-297-7). Harvest Hse.

Samra, Cal. The Joyful Christ: The Healing Power of Humor. 1986. pap. 7.95 (ISBN 0-06-067032-0). Har-Row.

Stone, Jeff, et al. Growing up Catholic: An Infinitely Funny Guide for the Faithful, the Fallen & Everyone in Between. LC 83-25394. 144p. 1985. pap. 5.95 (ISBN 0-385-19240-1, Dolp). Doubleday.

Willimon, William H., ed. And the Laugh Shall be First: A Treasury of Religious Humor. 1986. pap. 12.95 (ISBN 0-687-01383-6). Abingdon.

RELIGION AND LANGUAGE

see also Language Question in the Church

Burke, Kenneth. The Rhetoric of Religion: Studies in Logology. 1970. pap. 9.95x (ISBN 0-520-01610-6, CAMPUS 341). U of Cal Pr.

Clark, Gordon H. Language & Theology. 1979. pap. 4.95 (ISBN 0-87552-141-X). Presby & Reformed.

Clarke, Bowman L. Language & Natural Theology. (Janua Linguarum, Ser. Minor: No. 47). (Orig.). 1966. pap. text ed. 18.00 (ISBN 90-2790-580-0). Mouton.

Crosby, Donald A. Horace Bushnell's Theory of Language: In the Context of Other Nineteenth-Century Philosophies of Language. (Studies in Philosophy: No. 22). 300p. 1975. text ed. 33.60x (ISBN 90-2793-044-9). Mouton.

Fenn, Richard K. Liturgies & Trials: The Secularization of Religious Language. LC 81-19250. 256p. 1982. 15.95 (ISBN 0-8298-0495-1). Pilgrim NY.

German, Terence J. Hamann on Language & Religion. (Oxford Theological Monographs). 1981. text ed. 34.95x (ISBN 0-19-826717-7). Oxford U Pr.

Heimbeck, Raeburne S. Theology & Meaning: A Critique of Metatheological Scepticism. LC 68-13146. 1969. 22.50x (ISBN 0-8047-0704-9). Stanford U Pr.

Johnson, Alfred M. A Bibliography of Semiological & Structural Studies of Religion. LC 79-110955. 1979. 10.00 (ISBN 0-931222-10-9). Pitts Theolog.

Lundeen, Lyman T. Risk & Retoric in Religion: Whitehead's Theory of language. LC 71-171501. pap. 72.00 (202868). Bks Demand UMI.

Santoni, Ronald E., ed. Religious Language & the Problem of Religious Knowledge. LC 68-27352. Repr. of 1968 ed. 95.50 (ISBN 0-8357-9238-2, 2017640). Bks Demand UMI.

Silva, Moises. Biblical Words & Their Meaning: An Introduction to Lexical Semantics. 1986. pap. 8.95 (ISBN 0-310-45671-1, 11630P). Zondervan.

Smith, Wilfred C. Belief & History. LC 75-50587. 138p. 1977. pap. 7.95x (ISBN 0-8139-1086-2). U Pr of Va.

Swinburne, Richard. The Coherence of Theism. (Clarendon Library of Logic & Philosophy). 1977. 42.00x (ISBN 0-19-824410-X). Oxford U Pr.

Winquist, Charles E. The Communion of Possibility. LC 75-859. (The Religions Quest Ser: Vol. 2). 160p. 1975. pap. text ed. 6.95x (ISBN 0-914914-04-9). New Horizons.

RELIGION AND LAW

Burstein, A. Religion, Cults & the Law. 2nd ed. (Legal Almanac Ser.: No. 23). 128p. 1980. 6.95 (ISBN 0-379-11133-0). Oceana.

Catholic Lawyer: 1955-1984, 1-29 vols. 696.00x (ISBN 0-686-89717-X). microfilm avail. Rothman.

Dengevin, K. The Idea of Justice in Christian Perspective. 1978. pap. 2.95 (ISBN 0-88906-102-5). Radix Bks.

Eidsmoe, John. Christian Legal Advisor. 1987. pap. 14.95 (ISBN 0-8010-3441-8). Baker Bk.

--Christianity & the Constitution. 442p. 1987. pap. price not set (ISBN 0-8010-3444-2). Baker Bk.

Fort, Timothy L. Law & Religion. LC 86-43082. 153p. 1987. pap. 13.95 (ISBN 0-89950-265-2). McFarland & Co.

Hayward, John. A Reporte of a Discourse Concerning Supreme Power in Affaires of Religion. LC 79-84116. (English Experience Ser.: No. 935). 64p. 1979. Repr. of 1606 ed. lib. bdg. 8.00 (ISBN 90-221-0935-6). Walter J Johnson.

International Commission of Jurists, Geneva. The Trial of Beyers Naude: Christian Witness & the Rule of Law. 1975. pap. 5.95 (ISBN 0-377-00057-4, Pub. by Search Pr England). Friend Pr.

Johnson, David M., ed. Justice & Peace Education: Models for College & University Faculty. LC 85-25808. 256p. (Orig.). 1986. pap. 16.95 (ISBN 0-88344-247-7). Orbis Bks.

Little, David. Religion, Order, & Law: A Study in Pre-Revolutionary England. LC 84-2611. 270p. 1984. pap. text ed. 11.00x (ISBN 0-226-48546-3). U of Chicago Pr.

McClain, Alva J. Law & Grace. pap. 1.75 (ISBN 0-88469-001-6). BMH Bks.

McMillan, Richard C., ed. Education, Religion, & the Supreme Court. LC 78-74196. (Special Studies: No. 6). iv, 129p. 1979. pap. 8.95 (ISBN 0-932180-05-1). NABPR.

Malbin, Michael J. Religion & Politics: The Intentions of the Authors of the First Amendment. 40p. 1978. pap. 3.25 (ISBN 0-8447-3302-4). Am Enterprise.

Miller, Robert T. & Flowers, Ronald B., eds. Toward Benevolent Neutrality: Church, State, & the Supreme Court. rev. ed. LC 82-81902. xi, 726p. 1982. 32.50x (ISBN 0-918954-28-2). Baylor Univ Pr.

--Toward Benevolent Neutrality: Church, State, & the Supreme Court. 3rd ed. LC 86-72072. 612p. 1987. 36.00x (ISBN 0-918954-44-4). Baylor Univ Pr.

Mooney, Christopher F. Public Virtue: Law & the Social Character of Religion. LC 85-41014. 192p. 1986. text ed. 22.95x (ISBN 0-268-01561-9). U of Notre Dame Pr.

Murdock, Kenneth B. Literature & Theology in Colonial New England. LC 78-104247. xi, 235p. Repr. of 1949 ed. lib. bdg. 22.50x (ISBN 0-8371-3990-2, MUCN). Greenwood.

O'Brien, Raymond C. Legal Education & Religious Perspective. LC 85-220822. (Illus.). 95p. Date not set. price not set. Cambridge U Pr.

Religion & the Law. 64p. 1975. pap. 1.00 (ISBN 0-686-47944-0). Amer Bar Assn.

Robillard, St. John A. Religion & the Law: Religious Liberty in Modern English Law. LC 83-197990. 224p. 1984. pap. 42.50 (ISBN 0-7190-0956-1, Pub. by Manchester Univ Pr). Longwood Pub Group.

St. John-Stevas, Norman. Life, Death & the Law: A Study of the Relationship Between Law & Christian Morals in the English & American Legal Systems. 375p. 1981. Repr. of 1961 ed. lib. bdg. 32.50x (ISBN 0-8377-1119-3). Rothman.

Schiblin, Richard. The Bible, the Church, & Social Justice. 64p. 1983. pap. 1.50 (ISBN 0-89243-187-3). Liguori Pubns.

Semonche, John E. Religion & Law in American History. LC 85-201489. (Church, State, & the First Amendment, a North Carolina Dialogue: No. 2). 125p. Date not set. price not set. U of NC Pr.

Shannon, Thomas & Manfra, Jo Ann. Law & Bioethics: Selected Cases. LC 81-80876. 448p. (Orig.). 1981. pap. 14.95 (ISBN 0-8091-2353-3). Paulist Pr.

Wake Forest University Law School. Law & Religion. 1985. 10.00 (ISBN 0-318-18444-3). Wake Forest Law.

Wilpert, P., ed. Antike und Orient im Mittelalter: Vortraege der Koelner Mediaevistentagungen 1956-1959. 2nd ed. (Miscellanea mediaevalia, 1). 274p. 1971. 33.60x (ISBN 3-11-002395-4). De Gruyter.

RELIGION AND LITERATURE

ApRoberts, Ruth. Arnold & God. LC 82-10847. 304p. 1983. text ed. 29.00x (ISBN 0-520-04747-8). U of Cal Pr.

Ault, Norman. The Poets' Life of Christ. 30.00 (ISBN 0-686-17669-3). Quaker City.

Averintsev, Sergei. Religya i Literatura: Religion & Literature. LC 81-4115. (Rus.). 140p. 1981. pap. 7.00 (ISBN 0-938920-02-2). Hermitage.

Barkway, Lunsden & Menzies, Lucy, eds. An Anthology of the Love of God: From the Writings of Evelyn Underhill. 220p. 1981. Repr. of 1953 ed. lib. bdg. 30.00 (ISBN 0-8495-0067-2). Arden Lib.

Bethell, Samuel L. Literary Outlook. LC 73-9787. 1943. lib. bdg. 15.00 (ISBN 0-8414-3145-0). Folcroft.

Bogdanos, Theodore. Pearl, Image of the Ineffable: A Study in Medieval Poetic Symbolism. LC 82-42783. 184p. 1983. 22.50x (ISBN 0-271-00339-1). Pa St U Pr.

Bregy, Katherine. Poets Chantry. LC 70-105766. 1970. Repr. of 1912 ed. 21.50x (ISBN 0-8046-1043-6, Pub. by Kennikat). Assoc Faculty Pr.

Brooke, Stopford A. Theology in the English Poets. 59.95 (ISBN 0-8490-1189-2). Gordon Pr.

Chapman, John J. Letters & Religion. 1977. Repr. 29.00x (ISBN 0-403-07361-8). Scholarly.

Crossan, John D. The Dark Interval: Towards a Theology of Story. 1975. pap. cancelled (ISBN 0-913592-52-8). Argus Comm.

Derrick, Christopher. Joy Without a Cause: Selected Essays of Christopher Derrick. 254p. 1979. pap. 5.95 (ISBN 0-89385-004-7). Sugden.

Forrer, Richard. Theodicies in Conflict: A Dilemma in Puritan Ethics & Nineteenth-Century American Literature. LC 85-27220. (Contributions to the Study of Religion: No. 17). 302p. 1986. lib. bdg. 37.95 (ISBN 0-313-25191-6, FTS/). Greenwood.

Gardner, Dame H. Religion & Literature. 1983. pap. text ed. 9.95x (ISBN 0-19-812824-X). Oxford U Pr.

Ghosh, Prabodh C. Poetry & Religion As Drama. 1979. Repr. of 1965 ed. lib. bdg. 25.00 (ISBN 0-8492-4940-6). R West.

Glicksberg, Charles I. Literature & Religion: A Study in Conflict. LC 77-23753. 1977. Repr. of 1960 ed. lib. bdg. 22.50x (ISBN 0-8371-9753-8, GLLR). Greenwood.

God & the Writer. 1953. pap. 10.00 (ISBN 0-527-01720-5, YFS 12). Kraus Repr.

Gunn, Giles. The Interpretation of Otherness: Literature Religion & the American Imagination. 1979. 24.95x (ISBN 0-19-502453-2). Oxford U Pr.

Hoffman, Frederick J. Imagination's New Beginning: Theology & Modern Literature. LC 67-12121. (Ward-Phillips Lecture Ser.: No. 1). 1967. pap. 1.95x (ISBN 0-268-00329-7). U of Notre Dame Pr.

Humphries, Jefferson. The Puritan & the Cynic: Moralists & Theorists in French Letters. 144p. 1986. 15.95 (ISBN 0-19-504180-1). Oxford U Pr.

Jarrett-Kerr, Martin. Studies in Literature & Belief. facsimile ed. LC 74-134101. (Essay Index Reprint Ser). Repr. of 1954 ed. 18.00 (ISBN 0-8369-1978-5). Ayer Co Pubs.

Jasper, David, ed. Images of Belief in Literature. LC 83-40170. 195p. 1984. 22.50 (ISBN 0-312-40920-6). St Martin.

--The Interpretation of Belief: Coleridge, Schleiermacher & Romanticism. LC 85-26204. 192p. 1986. 25.00x (ISBN 0-312-42401-9). St Martin.

Jay, Elisabeth. The Religion of the Heart: Anglican Evangelicalism & the Nineteenth-Century Novel. 1979. 49.00x (ISBN 0-19-812092-3). Oxford U Pr.

Kerr, Howard. Mediums, & Spirit Rappers, & Roaring Radicals: Spiritualism in American Literature, 1850-1900. LC 78-170964. pap. 67.80 (ISBN 0-317-41918-8, 2025919). Bks Demand UMI.

Kort, Wesley A. Narrative Elements & Religious Meanings. LC 75-15257. pap. 32.00 (2026873). Bks Demand UMI.

Labarge, Margaret W. Court, Church & Castle. (Illus.). 112p. 1972. pap. 3.25 (ISBN 0-88884-431-X, 56310-3, Pub. by Natl Mus Canada). U of Chicago Pr.

Luccock, Halford E. Contemporary American Literature & Religion. 300p. 1980. Repr. of 1934 ed. lib. bdg. 30.00 (ISBN 0-89984-324-7). Century Bookbindery.

Lynch, William F. Christ & Apollo: The Dimensions of the Literary Imagination. 224p. 1975. pap. 5.95x (ISBN 0-268-00712-8). U of Notre Dame Pr.

Lyttle, David. Studies in Religion in Early American Literature: Edwards, Poe, Channing, Emerson, Some Minor Transcendentalists, Hawthorne & Thoreau. 262p. (Orig.). 1984. lib. bdg. 28.50 (ISBN 0-8191-3499-6). U Pr of Amer.

Miller, David L. Three Faces of God: Traces of the Trinity in Literature & Life. LC 85-45493. 176p. 1986. pap. 11.95 (ISBN 0-8006-1895-5, 1-1895). Fortress.

Mulder, John R., ed. Religion & Literature: The Convergence of Approaches. (AAR Thematic Studies). pap. 8.95_o.s. (ISBN 0-89130-676-5, 01-24-72). Scholars Pr GA.

Paulson, Ronald. Book & Painting: Shakespeare, Milton, & the Bible. LC 82-2769. (Hodges Lectures Ser.). (Illus.). 248p. 1982. text ed. 23.50x (ISBN 0-87049-358-2). U of Tenn Pr.

Pinto, De Solo, et al. The Tree of Life: An Anthology. 1981. Repr. of 1929 ed. lib. bdg. 35.00 (ISBN 0-89984-390-5). Century Bookbindery.

Ralli, Augustus. Poetry & Faith. LC 76-16831. 1976. Repr. of 1951 ed. lib. bdg. 20.00 (ISBN 0-8414-7316-1). Folcroft.

Ruland, Vernon. Horizons of Criticism: An Assessment of Religious-Literary Options. LC 75-20162. pap. 68.80 (ISBN 0-317-29363-X, 2024203). Bks Demand UMI.

Sasek, Lawrence A. Literary Temper of the English Puritans. Repr. of 1961 ed. lib. bdg. 22.50x (ISBN 0-8371-2333-X, SAEP). Greenwood.

Schmerling, Hilda L. Finger of God: Religious Thought & Themes in Literature from Chaucer to Kafka. 1977. lib. bdg. 69.95 (ISBN 0-8490-1358-5). Gordon Pr.

Shea, Leo Martin. Lowell's Religious Outlook. 124p. 1983. Repr. of 1926 ed. 16.00x (ISBN 0-939738-13-9). Zubal Inc.

Short, Robert L. Something to Believe in. LC 75-36754. (Illus.). 1977. pap. 5.95i (ISBN 0-06-067381-8, RD 169, HarpR). Har-Row.

Sill, Sterling W. The Majesty of Books. LC 74-81407. 336p. 1974. 9.95 (ISBN 0-87747-532-6). Deseret Bk.

Smithline, Arnold. Natural Religion in American Literature. 1966. 11.95x (ISBN 0-8084-0227-7); pap. 7.95x (ISBN 0-8084-0228-5). New Coll U Pr.

Wiggins, James B., ed. Religion As Story. 218p. 1985. pap. text ed. 9.75 (ISBN 0-8191-4682-X). U Pr of Amer.

Wilder, Amos N. Theology & Modern Literature. LC 58-11556. pap. 39.30 (ISBN 0-317-10086-6, 2003002). Bks Demand UMI.

RELIGION AND MUSIC

see also Church Music; Music in Churches

Andre, Evelyn, compiled by. Sing & Be Joyful: Enjoying Music with Young Children. LC 79-14787. 1979. pap. 8.95 (ISBN 0-687-38550-4). Abingdon.

Bawa Muhaiyaddeen, M. R. Songs of God's Grace. LC 73-91016. (Illus.). 154p. 1974. pap. 4.95 (ISBN 0-914390-02-3). Fellowship Pr PA.

Georgiades, Thrysbulos. Music & Language: The Rise of Western Music Exemplified in Settings of the Mass. Gollner, Marie-Louise, tr. LC 82-4246. (Illus.). 150p. 1983. 29.95 (ISBN 0-521-23309-7); pap. 9.95 (ISBN 0-521-29902-0). Cambridge U Pr.

Irwin, Joyce, ed. Sacred Sound: Music in Religious Thought & Practice. LC 83-15390. (AAR Thematic Studies). 180p. 1984. 22.50 (ISBN 0-89130-655-2, 01 25 01). Scholars Pr GA.

Kylin, Helen. When Silence Becomes Singing. LC 84-61827. 32p. (Orig.). 1985. pap. 2.50x (ISBN 0-87574-258-0). Pendle Hill.

Nelson, Edward W. Music & Worship. 176p. 1985. spiral bdg. 13.50 (ISBN 0-311-72642-9). Casa Bautista.

Seay, Davin & Neely, Mary. Stairway to Heaven: The Spiritual Roots of Rock & Roll. 384p. 1986. pap. 9.95 (ISBN 0-345-33022-6, Pub. by Ballantine Epiphany). Ballantine.

Syverud, Genevieve W. This Is My Song of Songs. (Orig.). 1966. pap. 2.95 (ISBN 0-8066-0613-4, 11-9495). Augsburg.

Topp, Dale. Music in the Christian Community. LC 76-20471. Repr. of 1976 ed. 51.30 (ISBN 0-8357-9130-0, 2019340). Bks Demand UMI.

RELIGION AND NATIONALISM

see Nationalism and Religion

RELIGION AND PHILOSOPHY

see Philosophy and Religion

RELIGION AND POLITICS

see also Christianity and Politics

Baker, Tod A. & Steed, Robert P., eds. Religion & Politics in the South: Mass & Elite Perspectives. LC 83-21155. 208p. 1983. 29.95 (ISBN 0-03-069558-9, C0940). Praeger.

Balsiger, David W. Candidates Biblical Scoreboard. Balsiger, David W., intro. by. (Biblical News Ser., 1986: No. 1). 1986. 2.25 (ISBN 0-89921-015-5). Biblical News Serv.

Benson, Peter L. & Hill, Dorothy. Religion on Capitol Hill: Myths & Realities. LC 86-16434. (Illus.). 223p. 1986. pap. 8.95x (ISBN 0-19-504168-2). Oxford U Pr.

Bergessen, Albert. The Sacred & the Subversive: Political Witch-Hunts as National Rituals. LC 84-61370. (Society for Scientific Study of Religion Monograph: No. 4). 1984. pap. 5.50 (ISBN 0-932566-03-0). Soc Sci Stud Rel.

Edel, Wilbur. Defenders of the Faith: Religion & Politics from Pilgrim Fathers to Ronald Reagan. LC 87-2367. 280p. 1987. lib. bdg. 38.95 (ISBN 0-275-92662-1, C2662). Praeger.

Eidsmoe, John. God & Caesar: Christian Faith & Political Action. LC 84-71423. 226p. 1984. (Crossway Bks); pap. 7.95 (ISBN 0-89107-313-2). Good News.

Elipoulos, Nicholas C. Oneness of Politics & Religion. rev. ed. 169p. 1979. text ed. 6.95 (ISBN 0-9605396-3-8). Eliopoulos.

Elliott, Charles. Praying the Kingdom: Towards A Political Spirituality. 160p. (Orig.). 1986. pap. 6.95 (ISBN 0-8091-2820-9). Paulist Pr.

Farah, Nadia R. Religious Strife in Egypt: Crisis & Ideological Conflict in the Seventies. 144p. 1986. text ed. 42.00 (ISBN 2-88124-092-5). Gordon & Breach.

Fowler, Robert Booth. Religion & Politics in America. LC 84-20237. (Atla Monograph: No. 21). 365p. 1984. 25.00 (ISBN 0-8108-1752-7). Scarecrow.

Goldstein, Doris. Trial of Faith: Religion & Politics in Tocqueville's Thought. 144p. 1975. 21.00 (ISBN 0-444-99001-1). Elsevier.

Goldstein, Doris S. Trial of Faith: Religion & Politics in Tocqueville's. LC 75-4753. pap. 39.00 (2026263). Bks Demand UMI.

Hadden, Jeffrey K. & Shupe, Anson, eds. Prophetic Religions & Politics: Religion & the Political Order. 408p. 1986. 24.95 (ISBN 0-913757-63-2, Pub. by New Era Bks); pap. 12.95 (ISBN 0-913757-53-5, Pub. by New Era Bks). Paragon Hse.

Halsell, Grace. Prophecy & Politics: Militant Evangelists on the Road to Nuclear War. (Illus.). 256p. 1986. 14.95 (ISBN 0-88208-210-8). Lawrence Hill.

Hamada, Louis. God Loves the Arabs Too. Graves, Helen, ed. LC 85-40888. 174p. 1986. 13.95 (ISBN 1-55523-044-X); pap. 10.95 (ISBN 1-55523-000-8). Winston-Derek.

Hanus, Jerome J. & Schall, James V., eds. Studies on Religion & Politics. LC 86-9166. 120p. (Orig.). 1986. lib. bdg. 28.50 (ISBN 0-8191-5391-5); pap. text ed. 12.75 (ISBN 0-8191-5392-3). U Pr of Amer.

Heper, Metin & Israeli, Raphael, eds. Islam & Politics in the Modern Middle East. LC 84-40042. 131p. 1984. 25.00 (ISBN 0-312-43742-0). St Martin.

Hick, John. Problems of Religious Pluralism. LC 85-2505. 144p. 1985. 19.95 (ISBN 0-312-65154-6). St Martin.

Hinchliff, Peter B. Holiness & Politics. LC 83-1749. pap. 55.80 (ISBN 0-317-30143-8, 2025326). Bks Demand UMI.

Hinkelammert, Franz. The Ideological Weapons of Death: A Theological Critique of Capitalism. Berryman, Phillip, tr. from Span. LC 86-2557. Tr. of Las Armas Ideologicas de la Muerte. 320p. (Orig.). 1986. pap. 17.95 (ISBN 0-88344-260-4). Orbis Bks.

Holloway, Richard. The Sidelong Glance: Politics, Conflict & the Church. LC 86-13473. 86p. 1986. pap. 6.95 (ISBN 0-936384-40-9). Cowley Pubns.

Hood, Robert E. Contemporary Political Orders & Christ: Karl Barth's Christology & Political Praxis. (Pittsburgh Theological Monographs, New Ser.: 14). (Orig.). 1985. pap. 19.90 (ISBN 0-915138-56-5). Pickwick.

Irani, George E. The Papacy & the Middle East: The Role of the Holy See in the Arab-Israeli Conflict, 1962-1984. LC 85-41013. 224p. 1986. text ed. 22.95x (ISBN 0-268-01560-0). U of Notre Dame Pr.

Kaufman, Peter I. The Polytyque Churche: Religion & Early Tudor Political Culture. 208p. 1986. 24.95 (ISBN 0-86554-211-2, MUP-H191). Mercer Univ Pr.

Kauper, Paul G. Religion & the Constitution. LC 64-7898. pap. 36.80 (ISBN 0-317-29869-0, 2051881). Bks Demand UMI.

McBrien, Richard P. Caesar's Coin: Religion & Politics in America. 320p. 1987. 19.95 (ISBN 0-02-919720-1). Macmillan.

Maliszewski, Joan M., et al. Economic Justice for All: Study Guide, the American Bishops' Pastoral on Social Teaching & the U. S. Economy. 48p. (Orig.). 1987. pap. 1.95 (ISBN 0-8091-5201-0). Paulist Pr.

Merkl, Peter H., ed. Religion & Politics in the Modern World. Smart, Ninian. 296p. 1983. 37.50 (ISBN 0-8147-5389-2); pap. 12.50 (ISBN 0-8147-5393-0). NYU Pr.

Micklem, Nathaniel. The Theology of Politics. 10.75 (ISBN 0-8369-7119-1, 7953). Ayer Co Pubs.

Mooney, Christopher F. Public Virtue: Law & the Social Character of Religion. LC 85-41014. 192p. 1986. text ed. 22.95x (ISBN 0-268-01561-9). U of Notre Dame Pr.

Nelson-Pallmeyer, Jack. The Politics of Compassion: A Biblical Perspective on World Hunger, the Arms Race & U. S. Policy in Central America. LC 85-25809. 128p. (Orig.). 1986. pap. 8.95 (ISBN 0-88344-356-2). Orbis Bks.

O'Ferrall, F. Catholic Emancipation: Daniel O'Connell & the Birth of Irish Democracy. LC 85-14178. 350p. 1985. text ed. 38.50x (ISBN 0-391-03353-0). Humanities.

Rouner, Leroy S., ed. Civil Religion & Political Theology. LC 86-11242. (Boston University Studies in Philosophy & Religion: Vol. 8). 240p. 1986. text ed. 24.95x (ISBN 0-268-00757-8). U of Notre Dame Pr.

Rouse, John E., Jr., et al, eds. The Political Role of Religion on the U. S. (Special Study Ser.). 300p. 1985. pap. text ed. 24.50x (ISBN 0-8133-7030-2). Westview.

Rubenstein, Richard L., ed. The Worldwide Impact of Religion on Comtemporary Politics. 224p. 1987. 21.95 (ISBN 0-88702-203-0, Pub. by Wash Inst DC); pap. 12.95 (ISBN 0-88702-211-1, Pub.by Wash Inst DC). Paragon Hse.

St. John-Stevas, Norman. The Two Cities. 352p. 1984. 27.50 (ISBN 0-571-13083-6). Faber & Faber.

Schmitt, Carl. Political Theology: Four Chapters on the Concept of Sovereignity. Schwab, George, tr. from Ger. (German Social Thought Ser.). 75p. 1985. 15.00x (ISBN 0-262-19244-6). MIT Pr.

Sivan, Emmanuel. Radical Islam: Medieval Theology & Modern Politics. LC 84-20999. 224p. 1985. 20.00x (ISBN 0-300-03263-3). Yale U Pr.

Smith, Donald E., ed. Religion & Political Modernization. LC 73-86917. pap. 87.50 (ISBN 0-317-29714-7, 2022041). Bks Demand UMI.

Spretnak, Charlene. The Spiritual Dimension of Green Politics. LC 86-70255. 96p. (Orig.). 1986. pap. 4.95 (ISBN 0-939680-29-7). Bear & Co.

Stehlin, Stewart A. Weimar & the Vatican, 1919-1933. LC 83-42544. (Illus.). 512p. 1986. pap. 19.95x (ISBN 0-691-10195-7); text ed. 52.50x (ISBN 0-691-05399-5). Princeton U Pr.

Sutherland, Charles W. Disciples of Destruction. 325p. 1986. 22.95 (ISBN 0-87975-349-8). Prometheus Bks.

Voegelin, Erich. Political Religions. (TST Ser.: No. 23). 1986. 39.95x (ISBN 0-88946-767-6). E Mellen.

Wroblewski, Sergius. The July Secret: The Prohetic Meaning of Fatima about Russia & the Future of the Church. (Illus.). 90p. (Orig.). 1985. pap. 4.50 (ISBN 0-913382-15-9, 105-39). Prow Bks-Franciscan.

RELIGION AND PSYCHIATRY

see Psychiatry and Religion

RELIGION AND PSYCHOANALYSIS

see Psychoanalysis and Religion

RELIGION AND PSYCHOLOGY

see Psychology, Religious

RELIGION AND SCIENCE

see also Bible and Science; Creation; Evolution; Faith and Reason; Man–Origin; Modernist-Fundamentalist Controversy; Natural Theology; Nature–Religious Interpretations; Religion and Astronautics; Religion and Geography

Abrecht, Paul. Faith, Science, & the Future. LC 79-7035. pap. 60.00 (2026942). Bks Demand UMI.

Association of Orthodox Jewish Scientists. Proceedings. Set. cancelled (ISBN 0-87306-072-5); Vol. 1. 5.95 (ISBN 0-686-67018-3); Vol. 2. 6.95 (ISBN 0-87306-073-3). Feldheim.

Associations of Orthodox Jewish Scientists Staff. Proceedings, Vol. 3 & 4. Rosner, Fred, ed. 248p. 1976. pap. 9.95 (ISBN 0-87306-074-1). Feldheim.

Austin, William H. The Relevance of Natural Science to Theology. LC 75-43222. (Library of Philosophy & Religion). 132p. 1976. text ed. 28.50x (ISBN 0-06-490240-4, 06321). B&N Imports.

Barbour, Ian G. Issues in Science & Religion. 1971. pap. 8.95x (ISBN 0-06-131566-4, TB1566, Torch). Har-Row.

--Myths, Models, & Paradigms. LC 73-18690. 1976. pap. text ed. 6.95x (ISBN 0-06-060387-9, RD 183, HarpR). Har-Row.

Barker. Science & Religion: An Annotated Bibliography. 1986. lib. bdg. 40.00 (ISBN 0-8240-8762-3). Garland Pub.

Barnes, Ernest W. Scientific Theory & Religion. LC 77-27198. (Gifford Lectures: 1927-29). Repr. of 1933 ed. 42.50 (ISBN 0-404-60483-8). AMS Pr.

Barnes, Harry E. The Twilight of Christianity. 75.00 (ISBN 0-87700-037-9). Revisionist Pr.

Bender, David L. & Leone, Bruno, eds. Science & Religion: Opposing Viewpoints. LC 85-7641. 1981. 11.95 (ISBN 0-89908-334-X); pap. 6.95 (ISBN 0-89908-309-9). Greenhaven.

Bernstein, Richard. Beyond Objectivism & Relativism: Science, Hermeneutics, & Praxis. 320p. (Orig.). 1983. 28.95x (ISBN 0-8122-7906-9); pap. 10.95 (ISBN 0-8122-1165-0). U of Pa Pr.

Boutroux, Emile. Science & Religion in Contemporary Philosophy. Nield, Jonathan, tr. 1979. Repr. of 1909 ed. lib. bdg. 35.00 (ISBN 0-8495-0540-2). Arden Lib.

--Science & Religion in Contemporary Philosophy. LC 70-102563. 1970. Repr. of 1909 ed. 33.50x (ISBN 0-8046-0723-0, Pub. by Kennikat). Assoc Faculty Pr.

Bozeman, Theodore D. Protestants in an Age of Science: The Baconian Ideal & Antebellum Religious Thought. LC 76-25962. xv, 240p. 1977. 22.50x (ISBN 0-8078-1299-4). U of NC Pr.

Budhananda, Swami. Can One Be Scientific & Yet Spiritual? 114p. 1973. pap. 2.00 (ISBN 0-87481-145-7). Vedanta Pr.

Callahan, Daniel & Engelhardt, H. Tristram, Jr., eds. The Roots of Ethics. (The Hasting Center Series in Ethics). 464p. 1981. 35.00 (ISBN 0-306-40796-5, Plenum Pr). Plenum Pub.

Callahan, John D. Science & Christianity. 2nd ed. (Illus.). 120p. 1986. pap. 5.95 (ISBN 0-9615767-0-7). Callahan CA.

Capra, Fritjof. The Tao of Physics. 1977. pap. 4.95 (ISBN 0-553-26379-X). Bantam.

Carty, Charles M. Stigmata & Modern Science. 31p. 1974. pap. 0.65 (ISBN 0-89555-104-7). TAN Bks Pubs.

Clairmonte, Glenn. Truth to Tell. LC 78-66006. 1979. 5.95 (ISBN 0-87159-155-3). Unity School.

Clark, Gordon H. The Philosophy of Science & Belief in God. 2nd rev. ed. 125p. pap. 5.95 (ISBN 0-940931-18-4). Trinity Found.

Compton, Arthur H. Man's Destiny in Eternity. LC 75-117821. (Essay Index Reprint Ser). 1949. 19.00 (ISBN 0-8369-1762-6). Ayer Co Pubs.

Cotton, Edward H., ed. Has Science Discovered God: A Symposium of Modern Scientific Opinion. facs. ed. LC 68-8452. (Essay Index Reprint Ser). 1931. 21.50 (ISBN 0-8369-0340-4). Ayer Co Pubs.

Dankenbring, William F. The First Genesis: A New Case for Creation. LC 75-10841. (Illus.). 408p. 1975. 8.95 (ISBN 0-685-54180-0). Triumph Pub.

Davidheiser, Bolton. Evolution & Christian Faith. 1969. pap. 10.95 (ISBN 0-87552-251-3). Presby & Reformed.

Davies, Paul. God & the New Physics. 272p. 1984. pap. 7.95 (ISBN 0-671-52806-8, Touchstone Bks). S&S.

Davis, William H. Science & Christian Faith. LC 68-21524. (Way of Life Ser: No. 104). 1968. pap. 3.95 (ISBN 0-89112-104-8, Bibl Res Pr). Abilene Christ U.

De Candolle, Alphonse. Histiore Des Sciences et Des Savants Depuis Deux Siecles. Cohen, I. Bernard, ed. LC 80-2116. (Development of Science Ser.). (Illus.). 1981. lib. bdg. 50.00x (ISBN 0-405-13836-9). Ayer Co Pubs.

Eastham, Scott T. Nucleus: Reconnecting Science & Religion in the Nuclear Age. LC 86-22265. 223p. (Orig.). 1986. pap. 9.95 (ISBN 0-939680-31-9). Bear & Co.

Einstein, Albert. The World As I See It. 1979. pap. 2.95 (ISBN 0-8065-0711-X). Citadel Pr.

Eister, Allan W., ed. Changing Perspectives in the Scientific Study of Religion. LC 74-2092. 370p. 1974. 25.50 (ISBN 0-471-23476-1, Pub. by Wiley). Krieger.

Eliseo, Vivas L. Creation & Discovery. LC 81-85511. 460p. 1982. pap. 4.95 (ISBN 0-89526-952-X). Regnery Bks.

Esterer, Arnulf K. Towards a Unified Faith. LC 62-20870. 1963. 5.95 (ISBN 0-8022-0459-7). Philos Lib.

Eyring, Henry. Reflections of a Scientist. LC 83-7109. (Illus.). 101p. 1983. 7.95 (ISBN 0-87747-944-5). Deseret Bk.

Gange, Robert. Origins & Destiny: A Scientist Examines God's Handiwork. 192p. 1986. 12.95 (ISBN 0-8499-0447-1, 0447-1). Word Bks.

Gebhardt, Richard F. & Armstrong, Mark. Object Lessons from Science Experiments. (Object Lesson Ser.). 128p. 1987. pap. 5.95 (ISBN 0-8010-3811-1). Baker Bk.

Gerhart, Mary & Russell, Allan M. Metaphoric Process: The Creation of Scientific & Religious Understanding. LC 83-15614. 217p. 1984. 16.95x (ISBN 0-912646-82-9); pap. 10.95x (ISBN 0-912646-86-1). Tex Christian.

Gilkey, Langdon. Religion & the Scientific Future. LC 81-18934. (Reprints of Scholarly Excellence (ROSE)). xii, 193p. Repr. of 1970 ed. text ed. 13.95 (ISBN 0-86554-030-6, MUP-H21). Mercer Univ Pr.

Gillispie, Charles C. Genesis & Geology: A Study in the Relations of Scientific Thought, Natural Theology & Social Opinion in Great Britain, 1790-1850. LC 51-10449. (Historical Monographs Ser: No. 58). 1951. 22.50x (ISBN 0-674-34480-4). Harvard U Pr.

Glover, Elsa M. Science & Religion. 1987. 8.95 (ISBN 0-533-07048-1). Vantage.

Godfrey, Laurie R., ed. Scientists Confront Creationism. 352p. 1984. pap. 8.95 (ISBN 0-393-30154-0). Norton.

Greene, John C. Darwin & the Modern World View. LC 61-15489. (Rockwell Lectures Ser.). 152p. 1973. pap. text ed. 6.95x (ISBN 0-8071-0062-5). La State U Pr.

Haeckel, Ernst. Riddle of the Universe at the Close of the 19th Century. LC 6403. 1900. 18.00x (ISBN 0-403-00117-X). Scholarly.

Haldane, John B. Possible Worlds: And Other Papers. facsimile ed. LC 75-167351. (Essay Index Reprint Ser). Repr. of 1928 ed. 18.00 (ISBN 0-8369-2452-5). Ayer Co Pubs.

Hare, F. Kenneth, ed. The Experiment of Life: Science & Religion. 192p. 1983. 25.00x (ISBN 0-8020-2486-6); pap. 9.95 (ISBN 0-8020-6506-6). U of Toronto Pr.

Harm, Frederick R. How to Respond to the Science Religions. 1981. pap. 1.75 (ISBN 0-570-07686-2, 12-2787). Concordia.

Harris, Errol E. Revelation Through Reason: Religion in the Light of Science & Philosophy. 1958. 39.50x (ISBN 0-317-27547-X). Elliots Bks.

Haught, John F. The Cosmic Adventure: Science, Religion & the Quest for Purpose. LC 83-82026. (Orig.). 1984. pap. 7.95 (ISBN 0-8091-2599-4). Paulist Pr.

Heim, Karl. Christian Faith & Natural Science. 10.25 (ISBN 0-8446-0690-1). Peter Smith.

Heller, Michael. The World & the Word: Between Science & Religion. Kisiel, Adam C., tr. from Polish. LC 86-61668. (Philosophy in Science Library: Vol. 1). 184p. 1987. pap. 14.95 (ISBN 0-88126-724-4). Pachart Pub Hse.

Henry, Carl F., ed. Horizons of Science: Christian Scholars Speak Out. LC 77-7849. 1978. pap. 6.95xi (ISBN 0-06-063866-4, RD 240, HarpR). Har-Row.

Henry, Granville C., Jr. Logos: Mathematics & Christian Theology. LC 74-25529. 361p. 1976. 25.00 (ISBN 0-8387-1653-9). Bucknell U Pr.

Hills, Edward F. Space Age Science. 2nd ed. (Illus.). 50p. pap. 1.50 (ISBN 0-915923-02-5). Christian Res Pr.

Hoover, Stewart M. The Electronic Giant: A Critique of the Telecommunications Revolution from a Christian Perspective. LC 81-6083. pap. 42.80 (2029383). Bks Demand UMI.

Hopkins, Emma C. Scientific Christian Mental Practice. 1974. pap. 7.95 (ISBN 0-87516-199-5). De Vorss.

Horigan, James E. Chance or Design? LC 79-83605. 242p. 1979. 13.95 (ISBN 0-8022-2238-2). Philos Lib.

Hsu, Francis L. Exorcising the Trouble Makers: Magic, Science, & Culture. LC 83-5522. (Contributions to the Study of Religion Ser.: No. 11). (Illus.). xvi, 164p. 1983. lib. bdg. 29.95 (ISBN 0-313-23780-8, HET/). Greenwood.

Hurley, Mark J. The Church & Science. 167p. 1982. 6.00 (ISBN 0-8198-1420-2, MS0125); pap. 5.00 (ISBN 0-8198-1421-0). Dghtrs St Paul.

Hutton, Richard H. Aspect of Religious & Scientific Thought. 766p. Repr. of 1899 ed. text ed. 49.68x (ISBN 0-576-29209-5). Gregg Intl.

Huxley, Julian, et al. Science & Religion. facs. ed. LC 75-84336. (Essay Index Reprint Ser). 1931. 14.25 (ISBN 0-8369-1106-7). Ayer Co Pubs.

Huxley, Thomas H. Science & Hebrew Tradition: Essays. 1979. Repr. of 1894 ed. lib. bdg. 30.00 (ISBN 0-8495-2263-3). Arden Lib.

Jastrow, Robert. Two Faces of Reality. Date not set. 14.95 (ISBN 0-393-02400-8). Norton.

Jauncey, J. H. La Ciencia Retorna a Dios. Swenson, Ana M., tr. Moore, J. N. Tr. of Science Returns to God. (Span.). 110p. 1981. pap. 2.35 (ISBN 0-311-05004-2). Casa Bautista.

Johnstone, Parker L. Origin of the Universe, Life, Then Religion. 235p. 7.95 (ISBN 0-917802-20-9). Theoscience Found.

--Quandary of Life, Science & Religion. LC 82-83297. 212p. 1982. cloth 7.95 (ISBN 0-917802-04-7). Theoscience Found.

--A Religious Science Book. 212p. 1984. 7.95 (ISBN 0-917802-13-6). Theoscience Found.

Jones, James W. The Redemption of Matter: Towards the Rapprochment of Science & Religion. 154p. (Orig.). 1984. lib. bdg. 23.00 (ISBN 0-8191-3675-1); pap. text ed. 9.25 (ISBN 0-8191-3676-X). U Pr of Amer.

--The Texture of Knowledge: An Essay on Religion & Science. LC 80-69036. 112p. 1981. lib. bdg. 23.00 (ISBN 0-8191-1360-3); pap. text ed. 8.50 (ISBN 0-8191-1361-1). U Pr of Amer.

Joranson, Philip N. & Butigan, Ken, eds. Cry of the Environment: Rebuilding the Christian Creation Tradition. LC 84-72254. (Illus.). 476p. (Orig.). 1984. pap. 14.95 (ISBN 0-939680-17-3). Bear & Co.

Keller, Clifton & Appel, Jeanette. Science Activities for Christian Children. rev. ed. 112p. 1986. pap. 5.50 (ISBN 0-930192-15-X). Gazelle Pubns.

Khalifa, Rashad. The Computer Speaks: God's Message to the World. (Illus.). 250p. (Orig.). 1981. 9.50 (ISBN 0-934894-38-8). Islamic Prods.

Klotz, John W. Genes, Genesis & Evolution. rev. ed. 1970. pap. 17.95 (ISBN 0-570-03212-1, 12-2637). Concordia.

Le Conte, Joseph. Evolution: Its Nature Its Evidences, - Its Relation to Religious Thought. 2nd ed. 1897. 29.00 (ISBN 0-527-55700-5). Kraus Repr.

--Religion & Science. LC 75-3239. Repr. of 1874 ed. 21.50 (ISBN 0-404-59231-7). AMS Pr.

Lewis, Samuel L. Introduction to Spiritual Brotherhood: Science, Mysticism & the New Age. Klotz, Saadi, ed. (Bismillah Bks.: No. 3). (Illus.). 112p. (Orig.). 1981. pap. 4.50 (ISBN 0-915424-07-X). Sufi Islamia-Prophecy.

Lindsay, Alexander D. Religion, Science, & Society in the Modern World. facsimile ed. LC 70-37847. (Essay Index Reprint Ser). Repr. of 1943 ed. 12.00 (ISBN 0-8369-2604-8). Ayer Co Pubs.

Lunn, Arnold H. The Revolt Against Reason. LC 72-108396. xiv, 273p. Repr. of 1951 ed. lib. bdg. 22.50x (ISBN 0-8371-3819-1, LURA). Greenwood.

McDougall, William. Religion & the Sciences of Life: With Other Essays on Allied Topics. LC 70-39108. (Essay Index Reprint Ser.). Repr. of 1934 ed. 20.00 (ISBN 0-8369-2700-1). Ayer Co Pubs.

MacKay, Donald M. Human Science & Human Dignity. LC 79-2383. 1979. pap. 3.50 (ISBN 0-87784-461-5). Inter-Varsity.

Macmurray, John, ed. Some Makers of the Modern Spirit: A Symposium. facs. ed. LC 68-22926. (Essay Index Reprint Ser). Repr. of 1933 ed. 16.25 (ISBN 0-8369-0658-6). Ayer Co Pubs.

Madeley, Hulon M. The Other Revelation for Christians. (Illus.). 48p. 1985. 7.95 (ISBN 0-89962-434-0). Todd & Honeywell.

Marsh, Frank L. Life, Man & Time. 2nd ed. LC 66-21121. (Illus.). (YA) 1967. 8.95 (ISBN 0-911080-15-5). Outdoor Pict.

Martin, George V. Are There a Beginning & an End to Man's Existence? 1983. 8.95 (ISBN 0-533-05562-8). Vantage.

Maslow, Abraham H. Religions, Values, & Peak-Experiences. 1976. pap. 4.95 (ISBN 0-14-004262-8). Penguin.

Mathews, Shailer, et al. Contributions of Science to Religion. LC 79-117822. (Essay Index Reprint Ser). 1924. 27.50 (ISBN 0-8369-1763-4). Ayer Co Pubs.

Metz, Johannes B., ed. Evolving World & Theology. LC 67-25695. (Concilium Ser.: Vol. 26). 91p. 1967. 7.95 (ISBN 0-8091-0042-8). Paulist Pr.

Midgley, Mary. Evolution As a Religion: Strange Hopes & Stranger Fears. 192p. 1986. text ed. 33.00 (ISBN 0-416-39650-X, 9512); pap. text ed. 12.95 (ISBN 0-416-39660-7, 9513). Methuen Inc.

Millikan, Robert A. Evolution in Science & Religion. LC 72-85283. 104p. 1973. Repr. of 1927 ed. 21.50x (ISBN 0-8046-1702-3, Pub. by Kennikat). Assoc Faculty Pr.

Mitchell, Ralph. Einstein & Christ: A New Approach to the Defence of Christian Religion. (Theology & Science at the Frontiers of Knowledge Ser.: Vol. 5). 256p. 1986. 21.95 (ISBN 0-7073-0453-9, Pub. by Scot Acad Pr). Longwood Pub Group.

Morris, Henry M. Evolution & the Modern Christian. pap. 3.95 (ISBN 0-8010-5881-3). Baker Bk.

Morrison, J. H. Christian Faith & the Science of Today. 12.50 (ISBN 0-8414-6676-9). Folcroft.

Nebelsick, Harold. Theology & Science in Mutual Modification. 1981. text ed. 19.95x (ISBN 0-19-520273-2). Oxford U Pr.

Nebelsick, Harold P. Circles of God-Theology & Science from the Greeks to Copernicus. (Theology & Science at the Frontiers of Knowledge Ser.: Vol. 2). 312p. 1985. 24.00 (ISBN 0-7073-0448-2, Pub. by Scottish Academic Pr Scotland). Longwood Pub Group.

Nelson, Byron C. After Its Kind. rev. ed. (Illus.). 1967. pap. 5.95 (ISBN 0-87123-008-9). Bethany Hse.

Norman, Ruth. Science, Politics & the Great Deception, Religion. 530p. (Orig.). 1987. text ed. 14.95 (ISBN 0-932642-93-4). Unarius Pubns.

O'Reilly, Sean. Bioethics & the Limits of Science. 176p. (Orig.). 1980. pap. 9.95 (ISBN 0-931888-02-6, Chris. Coll. Pr.). Christendom Pubns.

Osler, Margaret J. & Farber, Paul L., eds. Religion, Science & Worldview: Essays in Honor of Richard S. Westfall. 320p. 1985. 49.50 (ISBN 0-521-30452-0). Cambridge U Pr.

Pannenberg, Wolfhart. Theology & the Philosophy of Science. McDonagh, Francis, tr. LC 76-20763. 464p. 1976. 17.50 (ISBN 0-664-21337-5). Westminster.

Patel, Ishwarbhai, ed. Sciences & the Vedas. 1986. 12.50X (ISBN 0-8364-1663-5, Pub. by Somaiya). South Asia Bks.

Patterson, Gordon N. Message from Infinity: A Space-Age Correlation of Science & Religion. (Illus.). 96p. 1984. 6.50 (ISBN 0-682-40149-8). Exposition Pr FL.

Paul, Harry W. The Edge of Contingency: French Catholic Reaction to Scientific Change from Darwin to Duhem. LC 78-11168. 1979. 15.00 (ISBN 0-8130-0582-5). U Presses Fla.

Paul, Iain. Science, Theology & Einstein. (Theology & Scientific Culture Ser.). 1982. 16.95x (ISBN 0-19-520378-X). Oxford U Pr.

Peacocke, A. R. Creation & the World of Science: The Bampton Lecturers. 1979. 22.50x (ISBN 0-19-826650-2). Oxford U Pr.

--Science & the Christian Experiment. 1971. pap. 8.95x (ISBN 0-19-213956-8). Oxford U Pr.

Peacocke, A. R., ed. The Sciences & Theology in the Twentieth Century. LC 81-14771. 309p. 1982. 25.00 (ISBN 0-268-01704-2). U of Notre Dame Pr.

Peacocke, Arthur R., ed. The Sciences & Theology in the Twentieth Century. LC 81-14771. 327p. 1986. pap. 12.95 (ISBN 0-268-01725-5). U of Notre Dame Pr.

Peterson, Roland. Everyone Is Right. 352p. (Orig.). 1986. pap. 12.95 (ISBN 0-87516-565-6). De Vorss.

Peukert, Helmut. Science, Action, & Fundamental Theology: Toward a Theology of Communicative Action. Bohman, James, tr. from Ger. (German Social Thought Ser.). 364p. 1984. text ed. 37.50x (ISBN 0-262-16095-1). MIT Pr.

Polkinghorne, John. One World: The Interaction of Science & Theology. 128p. 1987. 17.50 (ISBN 0-691-08459-9); pap. 7.95 (ISBN 0-691-02407-3). Princeton U Pr.

Pollard, W. G. Transcendence & Providence: Reflections of a Physicist & Priest. (Theology & Science at the Frontiers of Knowledge Ser.: Vol. 6). 146p. 1986. 17.00 (ISBN 0-7073-0486-5, Pub. by Scot Acad Pr). Longwood Pub Group.

Poppelbaum, Hermann. New Light on Heredity & Evolution. Macbeth, Norman, tr. 1977. pap. 6.95 (ISBN 0-916786-15-3). St George Bk Serv.

Priestley, Joseph. Disquisitions Relating to Matter & Spirit. LC 74-26285. (History, Philosophy & Sociology of Science Ser). 1975. Repr. 27.00x (ISBN 0-405-06612-0). Ayer Co Pubs.

Qamar, J. God's Existence & Contemporary Science. pap. 1.00 (ISBN 0-686-18452-1). Kazi Pubns.

Rahn, Carl. Science & the Religious Life. 1928. 39.50x (ISBN 0-685-69853-X). Elliots Bks.

Ramm, Bernard. Christian View of Science & Scripture. 1954. pap. 4.95 (ISBN 0-8028-1429-8). Eerdmans.

Ranganathananda, Swami. Science & Religion. 1979. pap. 3.75 (ISBN 0-87481-190-2). Vedanta Pr.

Reuterdahl, Arvid. Scientific Theism. 1926. 10.00 (ISBN 0-8159-6805-1). Devin.

Reynolds, Vernon & Tanner, Ralph E. The Biology of Religion. LC 82-6573. (Illus.). 321p. 1983. text ed. 31.95x (ISBN 0-582-30021-5). Longman.

Richardson, Alan. Science, History & Faith. LC 86-22863. 216p. 1986. Repr. of 1950 ed. lib. bdg. 39.75x (ISBN 0-313-25325-0, RISHF). Greenwood.

Rolston, Holmes, III. Science & Religion: A Critical Survey. 368p. 1986. 34.95 (ISBN 0-87722-437-4). Temple U Pr.

--Science & Religion: An Introduction. 200p. 1987. pap. text ed. 11.50 (ISBN 0-394-36327-2, RanC). Random.

Rosenstock-Huessy, Eugen. Applied Science of the Soul. 40p. 1984. pap. text ed. 3.95 (ISBN 0-910727-04-X). Golden Phoenix.

Roy, Rustrum. Experimenting with Truth: The Fusion of Religion with Technology Needed for Humanity's Survival. (The Hibbert Lectures: 1979). (Illus.). 228p. 1981. 32.00 (ISBN 0-08-025820-4); pap. 10.00 (ISBN 0-08-025819-0). Pergamon.

Russell, Bertrand. Religion & Science. 1961. pap. 8.95 (ISBN 0-19-500228-8). Oxford U Pr.

Russell, Colin A. Cross-Currents: Interaction Between Science & Faith. 272p. 1985. pap. 10.95 (ISBN 0-8028-0163-3). Eerdmans.

Santayana, George. Reason in Religion. 1983. 14.50 (ISBN 0-8446-5927-4). Peter Smith.

Sardar, Ziauddin, ed. The Touch of Midas: Science, Values & the Environment in Islam & the West. LC 83-22262. 253p. 1984. 38.50 (ISBN 0-7190-0974-X, Pub. by Manchester Univ Pr). Longwood Pub Group.

Schlesinger, G. Religion & Scientific Method. 1977. lib. bdg. 29.00 (ISBN 90-277-0815-0, Pub. by Reidel Holland); pap. 10.50 (ISBN 90-277-0816-9, Pub. by Reidel Holland). Kluwer Academic.

Schoen, Edward L. Religious Explanations: A Model from the Sciences. LC 84-24237. xiv, 226p. 1985. text ed. 24.75 (ISBN 0-8223-0616-6). Duke.

Schroeder, W. Widick. Cognitive Structures & Religious Research. xiii, 211p. 1971. 7.50 (ISBN 0-87013-150-8). Mich St U Pr.

Science & Philosophy in the Light of the New Church. (Words for the New Church Ser.: Vols. IV-VI). 289p. 1976. Repr. of 1879 ed. 7.00 (ISBN 0-915221-24-1). Swedenborg Sci Assn.

Science & Religion. 1982. pap. 3.95 (ISBN 0-686-76255-X). Feldheim.

Science, Philosophy & Religion. 559p. 1985. Repr. of 1942 ed. lib. bdg. 85.00 (ISBN 0-8492-3208-2). R West.

Seiss, Joseph A. The Gospel in the Stars. LC 72-86676. (Illus.). 1986. pap. 10.95 (ISBN 0-8254-3755-5). Kregel.

Shafer, Robert. Christianity & Naturalism: Essays in Criticism. LC 68-26206. 1969. Repr. of 1926 ed. 25.50x (ISBN 0-8046-0413-4, Pub. by Kennikat). Assoc Faculty Pr.

Singer, Charles. Religion & Science: Considered in Their Historical Relations. 78p. 1980. Repr. lib. bdg. 15.00 (ISBN 0-89987-756-7). Darby Bks.

Stace, Walter T. Religion & the Modern Mind. LC 80-24093. 285p. 1980. Repr. of 1952 ed. lib. bdg. 24.75x (ISBN 0-313-22662-8, STRM). Greenwood.

Stanesby, Derek. Science, Reason & Religion. 210p. 1985. 34.50 (ISBN 0-7099-3360-6, Pub. by Croom Helm Ltd). Methuen Inc.

Swimme, Brian. The Universe Is a Green Dragon: A Cosmic Creation Story. LC 84-72255. (Illus.). 173p. (Orig.). 1984. pap. 8.95 (ISBN 0-939680-14-9). Bear & Co.

Talbot, George. Philosophy & Unified Science. 1435p. 1982. Repr. of 1978 ed. 36.50 (ISBN 0-941524-18-3). Lotus Light.

Teilhard De Chardin, Pierre. Science et Christ. 1965. 14.50 (ISBN 0-685-11556-9). French & Eur.

Temple, Frederick. The Relations Between Religion & Science: Eight Lectures Preached Before the University of Oxford in Eighteen Eighty-Four on the Foundation of the Late Reverend John Bampton Ma. 264p. Repr. of 1884 ed. text ed. 41.40x (ISBN 0-576-29206-0, Pub. by Gregg Intl Pubs England). Gregg Intl.

Thakur, Shivesh C. Religion & Rational Choice. (Library of Philosophy & Religion). 132p. 1981. 29.50x (ISBN 0-389-20047-6). B&N Imports.

Thomson, Alexander. Tradition & Authority in Science & Theology. (Theology & Science at the Frontiers of Knowledge Ser.: Vol. 4). 160p. 1986. 17.00 (ISBN 0-7073-0452-0, Pub. by Scot Acad Pr). Longwood Pub Group.

Tiner, John H. When Science Fails. (Direction Bks). 1974. pap. 2.95 (ISBN 0-8010-8823-2). Baker Bk.

Torrance, T. F. Reality & Scientific Theology. (Theology & Science at the Frontiers of Knowledge Ser.: Vol. 1). 212p. 1985. 15.50 (ISBN 0-7073-0429-6, Pub. by Scottish Academic Pr Scotland). Longwood Pub Group.

Torrance, Thomas F. Christian Theology & Scientific Culture. 1981. text ed. 14.95x (ISBN 0-19-520272-4). Oxford U Pr.

--The Ground & Grammar of Theology. LC 79-21429. 180p. 1980. 13.95x (ISBN 0-8139-0819-1). U Pr of Va.

--Theological Science. 1969. pap. 7.95 (ISBN 0-19-520083-7). Oxford U Pr.

Twining, R. H. Science and Religion-Convergence or Collision. 136p. pap. 2.95 (ISBN 0-686-12939-3). Hiawatha Bondurant.

Van Baaren, T. P. & Driljvers, H. J., eds. Religion, Culture & Methodology: Papers of the Groningen Working-Group for the Study of Fundamental Problems & Methods of Science of Religion. 1973. text ed. 14.00x (ISBN 90-2797-249-4). Mouton.

Van Klaveren, Pieter. The Great Deception. 160p. 1985. 12.95 (ISBN 0-8059-2997-5). Dorrance.

Verbitsky, F. V. Religion & Science. 1959. pap. 1.00 (ISBN 0-317-30432-1). Holy Trinity.

Walsh, James J. Catholic Churchmen in Science, First Ser. facs. ed. LC 68-16985. (Essay Index Reprint Ser). 1906. 19.00 (ISBN 0-8369-0971-2). Ayer Co Pubs.

--Catholic Churchmen in Science. Third Ser. facs. ed. LC 67-22126. (Essay Index Reprint Ser). 1917. 19.00 (ISBN 0-8369-0972-0). Ayer Co Pubs.

Ward, J. Naturalism & Agnosticism: The Gifford Lectures Delivered Before the University of Aberdeen in 1896-1898, 2 Vols. in 1. 4th ed. Repr. of 1899 ed. 36.00 (ISBN 0-527-94500-5). Kraus Repr.

Webster, Gary. Wonders of Man. LC 57-6055. 1957. 3.50 (ISBN 0-685-42655-6, Pub. by Sheed). Guild Bks.

White, Lynn, Jr. Medieval Religion & Technology: Collected Essays. LC 77-83113. (Center for Medieval & Renaissance Studies, UCLA: Publication: No. 13). 1978. pap. 11.95x (ISBN 0-520-05896-8, CAMPUS 371). U of Cal Pr.

Whiteford Boyle, John E. Primers for the Age of Innerspace - I Beyond the Present Prospect: The Impact of the Twentieth Century Revolutions in Science on the Varieties of Ethical & Religious Experience. LC 76-44888. 9.95 (ISBN 0-917888-00-6). Wheat Forders.

Wieman, Henry N. Religious Experience & Scientific Method. 387p. 1971. Repr. of 1927 ed. lib. bdg. 11.95x (ISBN 0-8093-0537-2). S Ill U Pr.

--Religious Experience & Scientific Method. (Arcturus Books Paperbacks). 387p. 1971. pap. 9.95x (ISBN 0-8093-0530-5). S Ill U Pr.

Wilkins, Walter J. Science & Religious Thought: A Darwinism Case Study. Miles, Margaret R., ed. LC 86-24946. (Studies in Religion: No. 3). 224p. 1986. 39.95 (ISBN 0-8357-1778-X). UMI Res Pr.

Wilson, Clifford. The War of the Chariots. LC 78-55211. 1978. pap. 3.95 (ISBN 0-89051-050-4). Master Bks.

Windle, Bertram C. Science & Morals, & Other Essays. facsimile ed. LC 70-156731. (Essay Index Reprint Ser). Repr. of 1919 ed. 17.00 (ISBN 0-8369-2301-4). Ayer Co Pubs.

Wonderly, Daniel E. God's Time-Records in Ancient Sediments: Evidences of Long Time Spans in Earth's History. LC 77-85681. (Illus.). 258p. (Orig.). 1977. pap. 7.00 (ISBN 0-930402-01-4). Crystal MI.

RELIGION AND SCIENCE–HISTORY OF CONTROVERSY

see also Modernist-Fundamentalist Controversy

Carmell, Aryeh & Domb, Cyril, eds. Challenge. 1978. 14.95 (ISBN 0-87306-174-8); pap. 9.95 (ISBN 0-87306-165-9). Feldheim.

Carus, Paul. The Religion of Science. 3rd ed. 145p. 1913. 6.95 (ISBN 0-912050-68-3). Open Court.

Cosslett, Tess. Science & Religion in the Nineteenth Century. LC 83-7505. (Cambridge English Prose Texts Ser.). 225p. 1984. 42.50 (ISBN 0-521-24402-1); pap. 14.95 (ISBN 0-521-28668-9). Cambridge U Pr.

Dillenberger, John. Protestant Thought & Natural Science: A Historical Interpretation. LC 77-7200. 1977. Repr. of 1960 ed. lib. bdg. 22.75x (ISBN 0-8371-9670-1, DIPT). Greenwood.

Gebler, Karl Von. Galileo Galilei & the Roman Curia from Authentic Sources. Sturge, Jane, tr. LC 76-1124. 1977. Repr. of 1897 ed. lib. bdg. 28.50x (ISBN 0-915172-11-9). Richwood Pub.

Greene, John C. Darwin & the Modern World View. LC 61-15489. (Rockwell Lectures Ser.). 152p. 1973. pap. text ed. 6.95x (ISBN 0-8071-0062-5). La State U Pr.

Haber, Francis C. The Age of the World: Moses to Darwin. LC 77-13854. 1978. Repr. of 1959 ed. lib. bdg. 22.50x (ISBN 0-8371-9898-4, HAAW). Greenwood.

Hovenkamp, Herbert. Science & Religion in America, 1800-1860. LC 78-53332. 1978. 26.00x (ISBN 0-8122-7748-1). U of Pa Pr.

Kappeler, Max. Metaphysics & Science in Christian Science. (Orig.). 1985. pap. 3.50 (ISBN 0-942958-11-X). Kappeler Inst Pub.

Klaaren, Eugene M. Religious Origins of Modern Science: Belief in Creation in Seventeenth-Century Thought. LC 85-17804. 256p. 1985. pap. text ed. 12.75 (ISBN 0-8191-4922-5). U Pr of Amer.

Lau, Dicksen T. The New Religion & Relativity. LC 83-62038. 138p. (Orig.). 1983. pap. 5.95 (ISBN 0-9612000-0-6). Magnolia Bks.

Nelkin, Dorothy. The Creation Controversy: Science or Scripture in the Schools? LC 83-45954. 242p. 1984. pap. 9.95x (ISBN 0-8070-3155-0, BP 675). Beacon Pr.

Raven, Charles E. Natural Religion & Christian Theology: First & Second Series, 2 vols. LC 77-27176. (Gifford Lectures: 1951-52). Repr. of 1953 ed. Set. 37.50 (ISBN 0-404-60540-0). AMS Pr.

Russell, Bertrand. Religion & Science. 1961. pap. 8.95 (ISBN 0-19-500228-8). Oxford U Pr.

Shapiro, Barbara J. John Wilkins, Sixteen Fourteen to Sixteen Seventy-Two: An Intellectual Biography. LC 73-84042. 1969. 40.00x (ISBN 0-520-01396-4). U of Cal Pr.

Simpson, James Y. Landmarks in the Struggle Between Science & Religion. LC 75-118549. 1971. Repr. of 1925 ed. 26.50x (ISBN 0-8046-1174-2, Pub. by Kennikat). Assoc Faculty Pr.

White, Andrew D. History of the Warfare of Science with Theology in Christendon, 2 Vols. Set. 26.50 (ISBN 0-8446-3170-1). Peter Smith.

White, Edward A. Science & Religion in American Thought. LC 68-54307. (Stanford University. Stanford Studies in History, Economics, & Poltical Science: No. 8). Repr. of 1952 ed. 17.50 (ISBN 0-404-50972-X). AMS Pr.

RELIGION AND SEX

see Sex and Religion

RELIGION AND SOCIAL PROBLEMS

see Church and Social Problems; Judaism and Social Problems; Religion and Sociology

RELIGION AND SOCIAL STATUS

Goode, Erich. Social Class & Church Participation. Zuckerman, Harriet & Merton, Robert K., eds. LC 79-9001. (Dissertations on Sociology Ser.). 1980. lib. bdg. 22.00x (ISBN 0-405-12970-X). Ayer Co Pubs.

RELIGION AND SOCIETY

see Religion and Sociology

RELIGION AND SOCIOLOGY

Works limited to the Christian religion are entered under the heading Sociology, Christian, and related subjects referred to under that heading.

see also Church and Social Problems; Religion and Social Status; Sociology, Biblical; Sociology, Christian

Amjad-Ali, Charles & Pitcher, W. Alvin, eds. Liberation & Ethics: Essays in Religious Social Ethics in Honor of Gibson Winter. LC 83-73425. (Studies in Religion & Society). 233p. 1985. text ed. 24.95x (ISBN 0-913348-22-8). Ctr Sci Study.

Banton, Michael, ed. Anthropological Approaches to the Study of Religion. 1968. pap. 13.95 (ISBN 0-422-72510-2, NO.2068, Pub. by Tavistock England). Methuen Inc.

Barlow, Fred M. Timeless Truth for Twentieth Century Times. 123p. 1970. 3.25 (ISBN 0-87398-838-8, Pub. by Bibl Evang Pr). Sword of Lord.

Baum, Gregory, ed. Sociology & Human Destiny: Studies in Sociology, Religion & Society. 224p. 1980. 14.50 (ISBN 0-8164-0110-1, HarpR). Har-Row.

Beckford, James A. Cult Controversies: The Societal Response to the New Religious Movements. 336p. 1985. 39.95 (ISBN 0-422-79630-1, 9592, Pub. by Tavistock England); pap. 13.95 (ISBN 0-422-79640-9, 9593, Pub. by Tavistock England). Methuen Inc.

Beidelman, T. O. W. Robertson Smith & the Sociological Study of Religion. LC 73-87311. 1974. pap. 1.95x (ISBN 0-226-04160-3, P618, Phoen). U of Chicago Pr.

Bellah, Robert & Greenspahn, Frederick. Uncivil Religion: Interreligious Hostility in America. 256p. 1986. 16.95. Crossroad NY.

Bellah, Robert N. Beyond Belief: Essays on Religion in a Post-Traditional World. LC 77-109058. 1970. 8.95x (ISBN 0-06-060774-2, RD-129, HarpR). Har-Row.

Bellamy, Edward. Selected Writings on Religion & Society. Schiffman, Joseph, ed. LC 74-40. (The American Heritage Ser.: No. 11). 139p. 1974. Repr. of 1955 ed. lib. bdg. 22.50 (ISBN 0-8371-7359-0, BEWR). Greenwood.

Berger, Peter L. The Precarious Vision. LC 76-1981. 238p. 1976. Repr. of 1961 ed. lib. bdg. 22.50x (ISBN 0-8371-8657-9, BEPV). Greenwood.

--Sacred Canopy: Elements of a Sociological Theory of Religion. LC 67-19805. 1969. pap. 4.50 (ISBN 0-385-07305-4, Anch). Doubleday.

Binder, Louis R. Modern Religious Cults & Society. LC 77-113556. Repr. of 1933 ed. 10.00 (ISBN 0-404-00867-4). AMS Pr.

Blasi, Anthony J. & Cuneo, Michael W. Issues in the Sociology of Religion: A Bibliography. Chekki, Dan A., ed. (Bibliographies in Sociology-Reference Library of Social Science). 392p. 1986. 53.00 (ISBN 0-8240-8585-X). Garland Pub.

Boisen, Anton T. & Leary, John. Religion in Crisis & Custom: A Sociological & Psychological Study. LC 72-10977. 271p. 1973. Repr. of 1955 ed. lib. bdg. 22.50x (ISBN 0-8371-6642-X, BORC). Greenwood.

Bouman, Herbert J., tr. Law & Gospel: Selected Writings of C.F.W. Walther. 1981. 12.95 (ISBN 0-570-08275-7, 15-2733). Concordia.

Brauer, Jerald C., ed. The Lively Experiment Continued: Essays in Honor of Sidney E. Mead. 288p. 1987. 39.95 (ISBN 0-86554-264-3, H225). Mercer Univ Pr.

Brothers, Joan. Religious Institutions. (Aspects of Modern Sociology Ser.). 1971. pap. text ed. 6.95 (ISBN 0-582-48120-1). Humanities.

Brunkow, Robert de V., ed. Religion & Society in North America: An Annotated Bibliography. LC 82-24304. (Clio Bibliography Ser.: No. 12). 515p. 1983. lib. bdg. 68.25 (ISBN 0-87436-042-0). ABC-Clio.

Bryant, M. Darrol & Mataragnon, Rita H., eds. The Many Faces of Religion & Society. LC 84-26539. (God Ser.). 208p. (Orig.). 1985. 21.95 (ISBN 0-913757-20-9, Pub. by New Era Bks.); pap. 12.95 (ISBN 0-913757-21-7, Pub. by New Era Bks). Paragon Hse.

Caillois, Roger. Man & the Sacred. Barash, Meyer, tr. from Fr. LC 79-8709. 190p. 1980. Repr. of 1959 ed. lib. bdg. 22.50x (ISBN 0-313-22196-0, CAMS). Greenwood.

Caldarola, Carlo, ed. Religion & Societies: Asia & the Middle East. (Religion & Society: No. 22). 688p. 1982. text ed. 73.75 (ISBN 90-279-3259-X); Pub. 1984. pap. 29.50 (ISBN 3-11-010021-5). Mouton.

Cardwell, Jerry D. The Social Context of Religiosity. LC 80-67216. 174p. 1980. pap. text ed. 10.75 (ISBN 0-8191-1136-8). U Pr of Amer.

Chalfant, Paul H. & Beckley, Robert E. Religion in Contemporary Society. Palmer, C. Eddie, ed. 592p. 1981. Repr. text ed. 28.95 (ISBN 0-87484-691-9). Mayfield Pub.

Chamie, Joseph. Religion & Fertility: Arab Christian-Muslim Differentials. LC 80-19787. (ASA Rose Monograph). (Illus.). 176p. 1981. 29.95 (ISBN 0-521-23677-0); pap. 9.95 (ISBN 0-521-28147-4). Cambridge U Pr.

Christianica Center Staff. Rosario Biblico. (Illus.). 1980. 5.95 (ISBN 0-911346-04-X). Christianica.

Connor, John S. The Spiritual Import of Society. LC 85-91374. 208p. 1987. 10.95 (ISBN 0-533-06881-9). Vantage.

Crawford, S. Cromwell, ed. World Religions & Global Ethics. (Contemporary Discussion Ser.). 168p. 21.95 (ISBN 0-913757-57-8); pap. 12.95 (ISBN 0-913757-58-6). Paragon Hse.

Cross, Whitney R. The Burned-over District: The Social & Intellectual History of Enthusiastic Religion in Western New York, 1800-1850. 400p. 1982. pap. 9.95x (ISBN 0-8014-9232-7). Cornell U Pr.

Daly, Lloyd W. Iohannis Philoponi: De Vocabulis Quae Diversum Significatum Exhibent Secundum Differentiam Accentus. LC 81-72156. (Memoirs Ser.: Vol. 151). 1983. 20.00 (ISBN 0-87169-151-5). Am Philos.

Darrand, Tom C. & Shupe, Anson D. Metaphors of Social Control in a Pentecostal Sect. LC 83-9006. (Studies in Religion & Society: Vol. 6). 232p. 1984. 49.95x (ISBN 0-88946-870-2). E Mellen.

Davis, Richard H., ed. Religion & Aging: The Behavioral & Social Sciences Look at Religion & Aging. 84p. 1967. pap. 3.00 (ISBN 0-88474-009-9). U of S Cal Pr.

Desroche, Henri. Jacob & the Angel: An Essay in Sociologies of Religion. Savacool, John K., ed. & tr. from Fr. LC 72-77575. 196p. 1973. 15.00x (ISBN 0-87023-109-X). U of Mass Pr.

Dugan, Albert. The Masses Are Asses. 256p. (Orig.). 1987. pap. 9.95 (ISBN 0-89896-047-9). Larksdale.

Dwyer, Judith A., ed. Questions of Special Urgency: The Church in the Modern World Twenty Years after Vatican II. 200p. (Orig.). 1986. 17.95 (ISBN 0-87840-434-1); pap. 9.95 (ISBN 0-87840-425-2). Georgetown U Pr.

Eisenstadt, S. N., et al, eds. Orthodoxy, Heterodoxy & Dissent in India. LC 83-26910. (Religion & Society Ser.: No. 23). viii, 179p. 1984. 42.00x (ISBN 3-11-009659-5). Mouton.

Everett, J. Rutherford. Religion in Economics: A Study of John B. Clark, Richard T. Ely & Simon N. Patten. 1982. Repr. of 1946 ed. lib. bdg. 22.50x (ISBN 0-87991-866-7). Porcupine Pr.

Faber, Frederick W. The Creator & Creature. LC 78-66301. 1978. pap. 9.50 (ISBN 0-89555-076-8). TAN Bks Pubs.

Fry, P. Spirits of Protest. LC 75-20832. (Cambridge Studies in Social Anthropology: No. 14). 134p. 1976. 27.95 (ISBN 0-521-21052-6). Cambridge U Pr.

Furman, D. Religion & Social Conflicts in the U. S. A. 254p. 1985. 7.95 (ISBN 0-8285-2975-2, Pub. by Progress Pubs USSR). Imported Pubns.

Gilsenan, Michael. Saint & Sufi in Modern Egypt: An Essay in the Sociology of Religion. (Monographs in Social Anthropology). (Illus.). 1973. 42.00x (ISBN 0-19-823181-4). Oxford U Pr.

Gopi Krishna. To Those Concerned Citizens. (Illus.). 16p. 1978. pap. 3.95 (ISBN 0-88697-002-4). Life Science.

Granet, Marcel. The Religion of the Chinese People. Freedman, Maurice, tr. from Fr. 1977. pap. 5.95x (ISBN 0-06-131905-8, TB 1905, Torch). Har-Row.

Greeley, Andrew M. Unsecular Man. LC 85-2459. 297p. 1985. pap. 8.95 (ISBN 0-8052-0794-5). Schocken.

Hadden, Jeffrey K., ed. Religion in Radical Transition. 166p. 1973. 9.95 (ISBN 0-87855-070-4); pap. 3.95x (ISBN 0-87855-567-6). Transaction Bks.

Hadden, Jeffrey K. & Long, Theodore E., eds. Religion & Religiosity in America. LC 82-23605. (Studies in Honor of Joseph H. Fichter). 192p. 1983. 15.95 (ISBN 0-8245-0555-7). Crossroad NY.

Hargrove, Barbara. The Emerging New Class of Experts: Implications for Church & Society. 160p. (Orig.). 1986. pap. 8.95 (ISBN 0-8298-0578-8). Pilgrim NY.

--The Sociology of Religion: Classical & Contemporary Approaches. LC 79-50879. 1979. pap. text ed. 16.95x (ISBN 0-88295-211-0). Harlan Davidson.

Harvard University, Phillips Brooks House Association. Religion & Modern Life. LC 75-39104. (Essay Index Reprint Ser.). Repr. of 1927 ed. 21.00 (ISBN 0-8369-2713-3). Ayer Co Pubs.

Haver, Ted. Throw Away Society. 140p. (Orig.). 1986. pap. write for info. (ISBN 0-914981-13-7). Paradigm ID.

Herberg, Will. Protestant, Catholic, Jew: An Essay in American Religious Sociology. LC 83-9120. xvi, 310p. 1983. pap. 11.00x (ISBN 0-226-32734-5). U of Chicago Pr.

Hollway, Richard. Suffering, Sex & Other Paradoxes. 150p. 1985. 10.95 (ISBN 0-8192-1358-6). Morehouse.

Homan, Roger, compiled by. The Sociology of Religion: A Bibliographical Survey. LC 86-18471. (Bibliographies & Indexes in Religious Studies: No. 9). 309p. 1986. lib. bdg. 45.00 (ISBN 0-313-24710-2, HOS/). Greenwood.

Houtart, Francois. Sociology & Pastoral Work. pap. 1.50 (ISBN 0-8199-0133-4, L38828). Franciscan Herald.

Hubbard, Barbara M. Happy Birthday Planet Earth: The Instant of Co-Operation. (No. 1). (Illus.). 64p. (Orig.). 1986. pap. 6.00 perfect bdg. (ISBN 0-943734-08-8). Ocean Tree Bks.

Irving, T. B. Religion & Social Responsibility. pap. 1.00 (ISBN 0-686-18445-9). Kazi Pubns.

Johnson, Harry M., ed. Religious Change & Continuity: Sociological Perspectives. LC 79-83574. (Jossey-Bass Social & Behavioral Science Ser.). pap. 94.80 (2027756). Bks Demand UMI.

Jones, Rufus M. Social Law in the Spirtual World. (Studies in Human & Divine Inter-Relationship Ser.). 1978. Repr. of 1904 ed. lib. bdg. 25.00 (ISBN 0-8495-2731-7). Arden Lib.

Jordan, James B. The Sociology of the Church: Essays in Reconstruction. LC 86-80571. 320p. (Orig.). 1986. pap. 12.95 (ISBN 0-939404-12-5). Geneva Ministr.

Jung, Loyle S. Identity & Community: A Social Introduction to Religion. LC 79-87753. pap. 51.00 (2027156). Bks Demand UMI.

Le Bras, Gabriel. Etudes De Sociologie Religieuse: Studies in Religious Sociology, 2 vols. in one. LC 74-25763. (European Sociology Ser.). 824p. 1975. Repr. 59.50x (ISBN 0-405-06517-5). Ayer Co Pubs.

Lenski, Gerhard E. The Religious Factor: A Sociological Study of Religion's Impact on Politics, Economics, & Family Life. LC 77-1275. 1977. Repr. of 1961 ed. lib. bdg. 27.50x (ISBN 0-8371-9506-3, LERF). Greenwood.

Longenecker, Richard N. New Testament Social Ethics for Today. 128p. (Orig.). 1984. pap. 5.95 (ISBN 0-8028-1992-3). Eerdmans.

Luhmann, Niklas. Religious Dogmatics & the Evolution of Societies. Beyer, Peter, tr. LC 84-8976. (Studies in Religion & Society: Vol. 9). 192p. 1984. 49.95x (ISBN 0-88946-866-4). E Mellen.

MacGaffey, Wyatt. Religion & Society in Central Africa: The BaKongo of Lower Zaire. LC 85-31805. (Illus.). xii, 296p. 1986. lib. bdg. 45.00x (ISBN 0-226-50029-2); pap. text ed. 16.95 (ISBN 0-226-50030-6). U of Chicago Pr.

McGuire. Religion: The Social Context. 2nd ed. Fullerton, Sheryl, ed. 1986. pap. text ed. write for info. (ISBN 0-534-07242-9). Wadsworth Pub.

Marshall, Gordon. In Search of the Spirit of Capitalism: An Essay on Max Weber's Protestant Ethic Thesis. LC 81-18053. 233p. 1982. 26.50x (ISBN 0-231-05498-X); pap. 13.00x (ISBN 0-231-05499-8). Columbia U Pr.

--Presbyteries & Profits: Calvinism & the Development of Capitalism in Scotland, 1560 - 1707. 1980. 54.00x (ISBN 0-19-827246-4). Oxford U Pr.

Maston, T. B. Como Vivir en el Mundo de Hoy. Adams, Bob, tr. from Eng. Tr. of A World in Travail. (Span.). 224p. Date not set. pap. price not set (ISBN 0-311-46084-4). Casa Bautista.

Matthes, Joachim, et al, eds. The Annual Review of the Social Sciences of Religion, Vol. 3, 1979. 1979. pap. text ed. 26.00x (ISBN 0-686-27015-0). Mouton.

--The Annual Review of the Social Sciences of Religion, Vol. 1. 1977. pap. 23.20x (ISBN 90-279-7794-1). Mouton.

Menendez, Albert J. Religious Conflict in America: A Bibliography. LC 84-48078. (Reference Library of Social Science). 500p. 1984. lib. bdg. 20.00 (ISBN 0-8240-8904-9). Garland Pub.

Merton, Thomas. The Hidden Ground of Love: Letter on Religious Experience & Social Concerns. Shannon, William H., ed. 1986. pap. 14.95 (ISBN 0-374-51963-3). FS&G.

Mol, Hans. Meaning & Place: An Introduction to the Social Scientific Study of Religion. (Orig.). 1983. pap. 6.95 (ISBN 0-8298-0638-5). Pilgrim NY.

Mol, Hans, ed. Identity & Religion: International Cross-Cultural Approaches. LC 77-93700. (Sage Studies in International Sociology: Vol. 16). 246p. 1978. 28.00 (ISBN 0-8039-9890-2). Sage.

Mol, Hans J. Indentity & the Sacred. LC 76-27153. 1977. 22.50 (ISBN 0-02-921600-1). Free Pr.

Moore, Robert L. & Reynolds, Frank E., eds. Anthropology & the Study of Religion. LC 83-71781. (Studies in Religion & Society). 230p. 1984. text ed. 24.95x (ISBN 0-913348-20-1); pap. text ed. 11.95 (ISBN 0-913348-21-X). Ctr Sci Study.

National Conference on Religion & Race. Race: Challenge to Religion. Ahmann, Mathew, ed. LC 78-24276. 1979. Repr. of 1963 ed. lib. bdg. 22.50x (ISBN 0-313-20796-8, NCRA). Greenwood.

Neuhaus, Richard J. The Naked Public Square: Religion & Democracy in America. LC 84-6017. 288p. 1984. 16.95 (ISBN 0-8028-3588-0). Eerdmans.

Newman, Jay. Foundations of Religious Tolerance. 192p. 1982. 27.50x (ISBN 0-8020-5591-5); pap. 9.95 (ISBN 0-8020-6507-4). U of Toronto Pr.

Norbeck, E. Religion in Human Life: Anthropological Views. LC 73-7862. (Basic Anthropology Unit Ser.). 1974. pap. text ed. 9.95 (ISBN 0-03-091284-9, HoltC). H HOlt & Co.

Nottingham, Elizabeth K. Religion: A Sociological View. LC 81-40769. 348p. 1981. pap. text ed. 13.50 (ISBN 0-8191-1813-3). U Pr of Amer.

Novak, Michael. Ascent of the Mountain, Flight of the Dove: An Invitation to Religious Studies. rev. ed. LC 77-20463. 1978. pap. 5.95xi (ISBN 0-06-066322-7, RD 232, HarpR). Har-Row.

Ozment, Steven E. Mysticism & Dissent: Religious Ideology & Social Protest in the Sixteenth Century. LC 72-91316. 272p. 1973. 33.00x (ISBN 0-300-01576-3). Yale U Pr.

Paris, Peter J. The Social Teaching of the Black Churches. LC 84-47930. 176p. 1985. pap. 8.95 (ISBN 0-8006-1805-X, 1-1805). Fortress.

Patten, Simon. The Social Basis of Religion. (The Neglected American Economists Ser.). 1974. lib. bdg. 61.00 (ISBN 0-8240-1028-0). Garland Pub.

Patterson, Ward. Wonders in the Midst. LC 78-62709. 96p. (Orig.). 1979. pap. 2.25 (ISBN 0-87239-237-6, 40076). Standard Pub.

Pickering, W. S. Durkheim's Sociology of Religion: Themes & Theories. 576p. 1984. 45.00x (ISBN 0-7100-9298-9). Methuen Inc.

Rahner, Karl, ed. Pastoral Mission of the Church. LC 76-57341. (Concilium Ser.: Vol. 3). 192p. 7.95 (ISBN 0-8091-0108-4). Paulist Pr.

Roberts, Keith A. Religion in Sociological Perspective. 466p. 1984. 31.00x (ISBN 0-256-03127-4). Dorsey.

Ronan, Patrick J. Religion & Rural Life: A Mission Statement for the Religion & Rural Life Council of Rural America. 1982. 1.90 (ISBN 0-318-01734-2). Rural America.

Roof, Wade C. & McKinney, William. America Mainline Religion: Its Changing Shape of the Religious Establishment. 272p. 1987. text ed. 27.00 (ISBN 0-8135-1215-8); pap. text ed. 10.00 (ISBN 0-8135-1216-6). Rutgers U Pr.

Russell, Dora. The Religion of the Machine Age. 232p. 1985. 27.95 (ISBN 0-7100-9547-3). Methuen Inc.

Scherer, Ross P., ed. American Denominational Organization: A Sociological View. LC 80-13859. 378p. 1980. pap. 14.95x (ISBN 0-87808-173-9, Ecclesia). William Carey Lib.

Schluchter, Wolfgang. The Rise of Western Rationalism: Max Weber's Developmental History. Roth, Guenther, tr. from Ger. LC 81-2763. 300p. 1981. 24.50x (ISBN 0-520-04060-0); pap. 9.95 (ISBN 0-520-05464-4, CAL 747). U of Cal Pr.

Silvert, Kalman H., ed. Churches & States: The Religious Institution & Modernization. LC 67-22384. 224p. 1967. 7.50 (ISBN 0-910116-64-4). U Field Staff Intl.

Simmel, Georg. Sociology of Religion. Coser, Lewis A. & Powell, Walter W., eds. Rosenthal, Curt, tr. from Ger. LC 79-7021. (Perennial Works in Sociology Ser.). 1979. Repr. of 1959 ed. lib. bdg. 15.00x (ISBN 0-405-12120-2). Ayer Co Pubs.

Smith, Donald E. Religion, Politics & Social Change in the Third World. LC 73-143516. 1951. 14.95 (ISBN 0-02-929490-8); pap. text ed. 6.95 (ISBN 0-02-929460-6). Free Pr.

Stark, Rodney, ed. Religious Movements: Genesis, Exodus, & Numbers. LC 85-9539. (Sociology of Religion Ser.). 369p. 1986. 24.95 (ISBN 0-913757-43-8, Pub by New Era Bks); pap. 12.95 (ISBN 0-913757-44-6, Pub. by New Era Bks). Paragon Hse.

Stark, Werner. The Sociology of Religion: A Study of Christendom, 5 vols. Incl. Vol. 1. Established Religion. xii, 235p. 1967. 20.00 (ISBN 0-8232-0720-X); Vol. 2. Sectarian Religion. viii, 357p. 1967. 22.50 (ISBN 0-8232-0735-8); Vol. 3. The Universal Church. x, 454p. 1967. 25.00 (ISBN 0-8232-0760-9); Vol. 4. Types of Religious Man. xii, 340p. 1970. 22.50 (ISBN 0-8232-0855-9); Vol. 5. Types of Religious Culture. x, 453p. 1972. 25.00 (ISBN 0-8232-0935-0). LC 66-27652. Set (ISBN 0-8232-0719-6). Fordham.

Stoutzenberger, Joseph. The Christian Call to Justice & Peace. (Illus.). 250p. (Orig.). 1987. pap. text ed. 11.00 (ISBN 0-88489-180-1). St Mary's.

Swatos, William H., Jr. Faith of the Fathers: Science, Religion, & Reform in the Development of Early American Sociology. vi, 102p. 1985. pap. text ed. 6.95x (ISBN 0-932269-11-7). Wyndham Hall.

Swift, Louis J. The Early Fathers on War & Military Service. (Message of the Fathers of the Church Ser.: Vol. 19). 1984. 15.95 (ISBN 0-89453-359-2); pap. 9.95 (ISBN 0-89453-330-4). M Glazier.

Task Force on World Hunger. And He Had Compassion on Them: The Christian & World Hunger. (Illus.). 1979. pap. text ed. 3.50 (ISBN 0-933140-00-2). CRC Pubns.

Thompson, Kenneth. Beliefs & Ideologies. (Key Ideas Ser.). 150p. 1985. 19.95 (ISBN 0-85312-858-8, 9582, Pub. by Tavistock England); pap. 7.50 (ISBN 0-85312-859-6, 9583, Pub. by Tavistock England). Methuen Inc.

Towler, Robert. The Need for Certainty: A Sociological Study of Conventional Religion. 180p. 1985. 22.50x (ISBN 0-7100-9973-8). Methuen Inc.

Von Der Mehden, Fred. Religion & Modernization in Southeast Asia. 232p. 1986. text ed. 29.95x (ISBN 0-8156-2360-7); pap. text ed. 14.95x (ISBN 0-8156-2361-5). Syracuse U Pr.

Wach, Joachim. Sociology of Religion. 1944. 12.00x (ISBN 0-226-86707-2). U of Chicago Pr.

Wallis, Roy. Salvation & Protest: Studies of Social & Religious Movements. 1979. 26.00x (ISBN 0-312-69834-8). St Martin.

Weber, Max. Protestant Ethic & the Spirit of Capitalism. rev. ed. 1977. pap. 8.95 (ISBN 0-684-16489-2, ScribT). Scribner.

--Religion of China. 1968. 14.95 (ISBN 0-02-934440-9); text ed. 14.95 (ISBN 0-02-934450-6). Free Pr.

--Sociology of Religion. Fischoff, Ephraim, tr. 1964. pap. 10.95x (ISBN 0-8070-4193-9, BP189). Beacon Pr.

Weigel, George, Jr. Tranquillitas Ordinis: The Present Failure & Future Promise of American Catholic Thought on War & Peace. 416p. 1987. 27.50 (ISBN 0-19-504193-3). Oxford U Pr.

Westmeier, Karl-Wilhelm. Reconciling Heaven & Earth: The Transcendental Enthusiasm & Growth of an Urban Protestant Community, Bogota, Colombia. (Studies in the Intercultural History of Christianity: Vol. 41). 462p. 1986. text ed. 34.00 (ISBN 3-261-03547-1). P Lang Pubs.

Wilson, Bryan. Contemporary Transformations of Religion. 1976. pap. text ed. 7.95x (ISBN 0-19-875045-5). Oxford U Pr.

--Religion in Sociological Perspective. 1982. pap. 7.95x (ISBN 0-19-826664-2). Oxford U Pr.

Wilson, John F. Public Religion in American Culture. 240p. 1979. lib. bdg. 24.95 (ISBN 0-87722-159-6). Temple U Pr.

Wilson, Monica H. Religion & the Transformation of Society: A Study in Social Change in Africa. LC 73-134622. (The Scott Holland Memorial Lectures: 15; 1969). pap. 43.30 (ISBN 0-317-27081-8, 2024562). Bks Demand UMI.

Yinger, Milton J. Religion in the Struggle for Power: A Study in the Sociological Study of Religion. Zuckerman, Harriet & Merton, Robert K., eds. LC 79-9040. (Dissertations in Sociology Ser.). 1980. Repr. of 1946 ed. lib. bdg. 26.50x (ISBN 0-405-13007-4). Ayer Co Pubs.

RELIGION AND SPORTS

Holland, Leo. Twice the Challenge: Athlete & Christian. LC 86-80387. 128p. (Orig.). 1986. pap. 4.95 (ISBN 0-89243-251-9). Liguori Pubns.

Patterson, LeRoy. Good Morning, Lord: Devotions for Athletes. (Good Morning, Lord Ser.). 1979. 4.95 (ISBN 0-8010-7044-9). Baker Bk.

Ryan, Thomas. Wellness, Spirituality & Sports. LC 86-4923. 224p. 1986. pap. 8.95 (ISBN 0-8091-2801-2). Paulist Pr.

Warner, Gary. Competition. LC 79-51747. 1979. pap. 5.95 (ISBN 0-89191-074-3). Cook.

RELIGION AND STATE

see also Buddhism and State; Church and State; Islam and State; Nationalism and Religion

Algar, Hamid. Religion & State in Iran, 1785-1906: The Role of the 'Ulama in the Qajar Period. LC 72-79959. (Near Eastern Center, UCLA; Ca. Library Reprint Ser.: No. 106). 1980. 34.50x (ISBN 0-520-04100-3). U of Cal Pr.

Al-Yassini, Ayman. Religion & State in the Kingdom of Saudi Arabia. (WVSS on the Middle East Ser.). 190p. 1985. 30.00x (ISBN 0-8133-0058-4). Westview.

Anderson, Arthur L. Divided We Stand: Institutional Religion As a Reflection of Pluralism & Integration in America. LC 78-61582. 1978. pap. text ed. 9.95 (ISBN 0-8403-1935-5). Kendall-Hunt.

Aronoff, Myron J., ed. Religion & Politics. (Political Anthropology Ser.: Vol. III). 145p. 1983. 24.95 (ISBN 0-87855-459-9); pap. 12.95 (ISBN 0-87855-977-9). Transaction Bks.

Assault on the Bill of Rights: The Jewish Stake. LC 83-182603. 1983. 12.00. UAHC.

Avila, Rafael. Worship & Politics. Neely, Alan, tr. LC 81-38356. 144p. (Orig.). 1981. pap. 6.95 (ISBN 0-88344-714-2). Orbis Bks.

Banuazizi, Ali & Weiner, Myron, eds. The State, Religion, & Ethnic Politics: Afghanistan, Iran, & Pakistan. (Contemporary Issues in the Middle East Ser.). (Illus.). 464p. 1986. text ed. 35.00x (ISBN 0-8156-2385-2). Syracuse U Pr.

Berger, Peter L. Religion in a Revolutionary Society. (Bicentennial Lecture Ser.). 16p. 1974. pap. 1.00 (ISBN 0-8447-1306-6). Am Enterprise.

Berk, Stephen E. Calvinism vs. Democracy: Timothy Dwight & the Origins of American Evangelical Orthodoxy. LC 73-20053. xiv, 252p. 1974. 25.00 (ISBN 0-208-01419-5, Archon). Shoe String.

Birnbaum, Ervin. Politics of Compromise: State & Religion in Israel. LC 70-92557. 348p. 1970. 27.50 (ISBN 0-8386-7567-0). Fairleigh Dickinson.

Bjorkman, James. Fundamentalism, Revivalists & Violence in South Asia. LC 85-61080. 210p. 1987. 19.00 (ISBN 0-913215-06-6). Riverdale Co.

Clark, Juan. Religious Repression in Cuba. 115p. (Orig.). 1986. pap. 8.95 (ISBN 0-935501-04-5). U Miami N-S Ctr.

Cole, J. R. Roots of North Indian Shi'ism in Iran & Iraq: Religion & State in Awadh, 1722-1859. 340p. 1987. text ed. 38.00x (ISBN 0-520-05641-8). U of Cal Pr.

Cornwell, Peter. Church & the Nation: The Case for Disestablishment. (Faith & the Future Ser.). 160p. 1984. 24.95x (ISBN 0-631-13223-6); pap. 8.95x (ISBN 0-631-13224-4). Basil Blackwell.

Courlander, Harold & Bastien, Remy. Religion & Politics in Haiti. LC 66-26633. (Illus.). 1970. 3.95 (ISBN 0-911976-00-0). ICR.

Cox, Harvey. Religion in the Secular City: Toward a Post-Modern Theology. 320p. 1984. 16.95 (ISBN 0-671-45344-0). S&S.

Crockett, H. Dale. Focus on Watergate: An Examination of the Moral Dilemma of Watergate in the Light of Civil Religion. LC 81-16952. 126p. 1982. 10.95 (ISBN 0-86554-017-9, MUP-H17). Mercer Univ Pr.

Crone, Marie-Luise. Untersuchungen Zur Reichskirchenpolitik Lothars III, 1125-1137: Zwischen Reichskirchlicher Tradition Und Reformkurie. (European University Studies: No.3, Vol. 170). 398p. 1982. 40.55 (ISBN 3-8204-7019-0). P Lang Pubs.

Davis, Charles. Theology & Political Society. LC 80-40014. 180p. 1980. 27.95 (ISBN 0-521-22538-8). Cambridge U Pr.

Dawson, Christopher. Religion & the Modern State. 1977. Repr. lib. bdg. 20.00 (ISBN 0-8482-0547-2). Norwood Edns.

Drinan, Robert F. Religion, the Courts, & Public Policy. LC 78-6124. 261p. 1978. Repr. of 1963 ed. lib. bdg. 22.50x (ISBN 0-313-20444-6, DRRE). Greenwood.

Eddleman, H. Leo. Hail Mary, Are You Heeding the Blessed Virgin? In Defense of Public Schools. (Orig.). 1982. pap. 4.00 (ISBN 0-682-49899-8). Exposition Pr FL.

Edel, Wilbur. Defenders of the Faith: Religion & Politics from Pilgrim Fathers to Ronald Reagan. LC 87-2367. 280p. 1987. lib. bdg. 38.95 (ISBN 0-275-92662-1, C2662). Praeger.

Fenn, Richard K. The Spirit of Revolt: Anarchism & the Cult of Authority. LC 86-15430. 192p. 1986. 27.95x (ISBN 0-8476-7522-X). Rowman.

Floridi, Alexis. Moscow & the Vatican. 365p. 1986. 23.50 (ISBN 0-88233-647-9). Ardis Pubs.

Garver, Newton. Jesus, Jefferson & the Task of Friends. 1983. pap. 2.50x (ISBN 0-87574-251-3, 251). Pendle Hill.

Gremillion, Joseph, ed. Food-Energy & the Major Faiths. LC 77-17975. 302p. (Orig.). 1978. pap. 2.49 (ISBN 0-88344-138-1). Orbis Bks.

Hatfield, Mark, et al. Confessing Christ & Doing Politics. Skillen, James, ed. LC 80-71233. 100p. (Orig.). 1982. pap. 3.95 (ISBN 0-936456-02-7). Assn Public Justice.

Hayward, John. A Reporte of a Discourse Concerning Supreme Power in Affaires of Religion. LC 79-84116. (English Experience Ser.: No. 935). 64p. 1979. Repr. of 1606 ed. lib. bdg. 8.00 (ISBN 90-221-0935-6). Walter J Johnson.

Howe, Mark D. The Garden & the Wilderness: Religion & Government in American Constitutional History. (Phoenix Bks.). pap. 47.50 (ISBN 0-317-08469-0, 2020085). Bks Demand UMI.

Kelley, Dean M. Government Intervention in Religious Affairs, No. II. 200p. (Orig.). 1986. pap. 11.95 (ISBN 0-8298-0564-8). Pilgrim NY.

Knelman, F. H. Reagan, God & the Bomb. 350p. 1985. 19.95 (ISBN 0-87975-310-2). Prometheus Bks.

Lannoy, Richard. Speaking Tree: A Study of Indian Culture & Society. 1971. 32.50x (ISBN 0-19-501469-3). Oxford U Pr.

Lopatto, Paul. Religion & the Presidential Election. LC 84-26281. (American Political Parties & Elections Ser.). 192p. 1985. 34.95 (ISBN 0-03-001474-3, C0138). Praeger.

Myers, Robert J., ed. Religion & the State: The Struggle for Legitimacy & Power. LC 85-72100. (The Annals of the American Academy of Political & Social Science Ser.: Vol. 483). 1986. text ed. 15.00 (ISBN 0-8039-2538-7); pap. text ed. 7.95 (ISBN 0-8039-2539-5). Sage.

Pfeffer, Leo. Religion, State & the Burger Court. LC 84-43056. 310p. 1985. 23.95 (ISBN 0-87975-275-0). Prometheus Bks.

Reichley, A. James. Religion in American Public Life. LC 85-21312. 402p. 1985. 31.95 (ISBN 0-8157-7378-1); pap. 11.95 (ISBN 0-8157-7377-3). Brookings.

Rothenberg, Joshua. The Jewish Religion in the Soviet Union. 1971. 20.00x (ISBN 0-87068-156-7). Ktav.

Rubenstein, Richard. Reflections on Religion & Public Policy. (Monographs). 1984. 1.95 (ISBN 0-88702-002-X, Pub. by Wash Inst DC). Paragon Hse.

Schiff, Gary S. Tradition & Politics: The Religious Parties of Israel. LC 77-5723. 267p. 1977. 25.00x (ISBN 0-8143-1580-1). Wayne St U Pr.

Schonfield, Hugh J. The Politics of God. 2nd ed. LC 78-9024. (Illus.). 264p. 1978. pap. 9.95 (ISBN 0-916438-14-7). Univ of Trees.

Smith, Donald E. Religion, Politics & Social Change in the Third World. LC 73-143516. 1951. 14.95 (ISBN 0-02-929490-8); pap. text ed. 6.95 (ISBN 0-02-929460-6). Free Pr.

Sollmann, F. W. Religion & Politics. 1983. pap. 2.50x (ISBN 0-87574-014-6, 014). Pendle Hill.

Tierney, Brian. Religion, Law & the Growth of Constitutional Thought, 1150-1650. LC 81-12265. 128p. 1982. 24.95 (ISBN 0-521-23495-6). Cambridge U Pr.

Tracy, David. Religion in the Public Realm. 176p. 1987. 12.95 (ISBN 0-8245-0666-9). Crossroad NY.

Warenski, Marilyn. Patriarchs & Politics. (Illus.). 1978. 10.95 (ISBN 0-07-068270-4). McGraw.

Wilson, Charles R. Baptized in Blood: The Religion of the Lost Cause, 1865-1920. LC 80-126. 264p. 1980. 21.95x (ISBN 0-8203-0515-4); pap. 8.00x (ISBN 0-8203-0681-9). U of Ga Pr.

Wood, James E., Jr., ed. Religion & the State: Essays in Honor of Leo Pfeffer. 596p. 1985. 39.95x (ISBN 0-918954-29-0). Baylor Univ Pr.

RELIGION AND TEMPERANCE

see Temperance and Religion

RELIGION AND WAR

see War and Religion

RELIGION IN LITERATURE

see also Bible in Literature; Christianity in Literature; God in Literature; Jesus Christ-Drama; Jesus Christ-Fiction; Jesus Christ-Poetry; Literature and Morals; Religion and Literature; Religious Poetry; Theater-Moral and Religious Aspects

Adams, Henry H. English Domestic or Homiletic Tragedy: 1575-1642. LC 65-16225. Repr. of 1943 ed. 17.00 (ISBN 0-405-08178-2, Pub. by Blom). Ayer Co Pubs.

Anderson, Vincent P. Robert Browning As a Religious Poet: An Annotated Bibliography of the Crticism. LC 82-50407. 350p. 1984. 25.00X (ISBN 0-87875-221-8). Whitston Pub.

Bailey, Elmer J. Religious Thought in the Greater American Poets. facs. ed. LC 68-8436. (Essay Index Reprint Ser). 1968. Repr. of 1922 ed. 16.00 (ISBN 0-8369-0167-3). Ayer Co Pubs.

Benziger, James. Images of Eternity: Studies in the Poetry of Religious Vision, from Wordsworth to T. S. Eliot. LC 62-15007. (Arcturus Books Paperbacks). 333p. 1962. pap. 2.25 (ISBN 0-8093-0136-9). S Ill U Pr.

Brinkmeyer, Robert H., Jr. Three Catholic Writers of the Modern South. LC 84-19641. 1985. 20.00x (ISBN 0-87805-246-1). U Pr of Miss.

Brooke, Stopford A. Theology in the English Poets: Cowper, Coleridge, Wordsworth & Burns. 6th ed. LC 79-129367. Repr. of 1880 ed. 10.00 (ISBN 0-404-01116-0). AMS Pr.

Cottrell, Georgia M. Portrait of Christ in Poetry. (Contemporary Poets of Dorrance Ser.). 100p. 1983. 5.95 (ISBN 0-8059-2888-X). Dorrance.

Danielson, Dennis. Milton's Good God: A Study in Literary Theodicy. LC 81-15535. 272p. 1982. 39.50 (ISBN 0-521-23744-0). Cambridge U Pr.

Davis, James B. La Quete de Paul Gadenne: Une Morale pour Notre Epoque. (Fr.). 96p. 1979. 9.95 (ISBN 0-917786-18-1). Summa Pubns.

Detweiler, Robert. Four Spiritual Crises in Mid-Century American Fiction. facs. ed. LC 78-121461. (Essay Index Reprint Ser). 1964. 12.00 (ISBN 0-8369-1799-5). Ayer Co Pubs.

--Four Spiritual Crises in Mid-Century American Fiction. LC 64-63316. (University of Florida Humanities Monographs: No. 14). 1963. pap. 3.50 (ISBN 0-8130-0058-0). U Presses Fla.

Drummond, Andrew L. The Churches in English Fiction. 1950. 30.00 (ISBN 0-8495-6277-5). Arden Lib.

Eustace, C. J. Infinity of Questions: Studies in the Art of Religion & the Religion of Art in the Lives of Helen Foley, Katherine Mansfield, et al. 170p. 1946. 10.00 (ISBN 0-87556-595-6). Saifer.

Fairchild, Hoxie N. Religious Trends in English Poetry, 6 vols. Incl. Vol. 1. Protestantism & the Cult of Sentiment: 1700-1740 (ISBN 0-231-08821-3); Vol. 2. Religious Sentimentalism in the Age of Johnson: 1740-1780. 1942 (ISBN 0-231-08822-1); Vol. 3. Romantic Faith: 1780-1830. 1949 (ISBN 0-231-08823-X); Vol. 4. Christianity & Romanticism in the Victorian Era: 1830-1880. 1957 (ISBN 0-231-08824-8); Vol. 5. Gods of a Changing Poetry: 1880-1920. 1962 (ISBN 0-231-08825-6); Vol. 6. Valley of Dry Bones: 1920-1965. 1968 (ISBN 0-231-08826-4). LC 39-12839. 45.00x ea. Columbia U Pr.

Gildea, Sr. Marianna. Expressions of Religious Thought & Feeling in the Chansons De Geste. LC 75-94172. (Catholic University of America Studies in Romance Languages & Literatures Ser: No. 25). 1969. Repr. of 1943 ed. 30.00 (ISBN 0-404-50325-X). AMS Pr.

Grierson, Herbert J. Cross-Currents in Seventeenth Century English Literature: The World, the Flesh & the Spirit, Their Actions & Reactions. 1959. 11.25 (ISBN 0-8446-6247-X). Peter Smith.

Gunn, Giles. The Interpretation of Otherness: Literature Religion & the American Imagination. 1979. 24.95x (ISBN 0-19-502453-2). Oxford U Pr.

Happel, Stephen. Coleridge's Religious Imagination: Three Volume Set, 3 vol. set, No. 100. (Salzburg-Romantic Reassessment). 943p. 1983. Set. pap. text ed. 80.00x (ISBN 0-391-03042-6, Pub. by Salzburg Austria). Vol.1 (ISBN 0-391-03039-6). Vol.2 (ISBN 0-391-03040-X). Vol.3 (ISBN 0-391-03041-8). Humanities.

Harder, Johannes H. Observations on Some Tendencies of Sentiment & Ethics in 18th Century Poetry. LC 68-886. (Studies in Poetry, No. 38). 1969. Repr. of 1933 ed. lib. bdg. 49.95x (ISBN 0-8383-0564-4). Haskell.
Holroyd, Stuart. Emergence from Chaos. LC 73-167356. (Essay Index Reprint Ser.). Repr. of 1957 ed. 18.00 (ISBN 0-8369-2695-1). Ayer Co Pubs.
Killinger, John. The Fragile Presence: Transcendence in Modern Literature. LC 72-91520. pap. 44.00 (2026902). Bks Demand UMI.
Kort, Wesley A. Moral Fiber: Character & Belief in Recent American Fiction. LC 81-71389. 160p. 1982. pap. 1.00 (ISBN 0-8006-1624-3, 1-1624). Fortress.
Laifer, Miryam. Edmond Jabes: Un Judaisme Apres Dieu. (American University Studies II: Romance Languages & Literature: Vol. 39). 165p. 1986. pap. 33.70 (ISBN 0-8204-0283-4). P Lang Pubs.
Lamberton, Robert. Homer the Theologian: Neoplatonist Allegorical Rading & the Growth of the Epic Tradition. LC 85-1184. (Transformation of the Classical Heritage Ser.: No. 9). 375p. 1986. text ed. 40.00x (ISBN 0-520-05437-7). U of Cal Pr.
--Homer the Theologian: Neoplatonist Allegorical Reading & the Growth of the Epic Tradition, Vol. 10. Date not set. price not set. Oxford U Pr.
Luccock, Halford E. American Mirror: Social, Ethical & Religious Aspects of American Literature, 1930-1940. LC 75-156806. 300p. 1971. Repr. of 1940 ed. lib. bdg. 28.50x (ISBN 0-8154-0385-2). Cooper Sq.
--Contemporary American Literature & Religion. LC 73-111471. 1970. Repr. of 1934 ed. 20.50 (ISBN 0-404-00607-8). AMS Pr.
Mays, Benjamin E. Negro's God As Reflected in His Literature. LC 69-16578. (Illus.). Repr. of 1938 ed. 24.75x (ISBN 0-8371-1139-0, MAG&, Pub. by Negro U Pr). Greenwood.
Miller, David L. Three Faces of God: Traces of the Trinity in Literature & Life. LC 85-45493. 176p. 1986. pap. 11.95 (ISBN 0-8006-1895-5, 1-1895). Fortress.
Morton, A. L. The Everlasting Gospel. 1978. Repr. of 1958 ed. lib. bdg. 15.00 (ISBN 0-8495-3736-3). Arden Lib.
--Everlasting Gospel. (Studies in Blake, No. 3). 1958. pap. 39.95x (ISBN 0-8383-0098-7). Haskell.
O'Connor, Leo F. Religion in the American Novel: The Search for Belief, 1860-1920. LC 83-21842. 364p. (Orig.). 1984. lib. bdg. 31.00 (ISBN 0-8191-3683-2); pap. text ed. 14.50 (ISBN 0-8191-3684-0). U Pr of Amer.
O'Rourke, Brian. The Conscience of the Race: Sex & Religion in Irish & French Novels 1941-1973. 72p. 1980. 15.00x (ISBN 0-906127-22-X, BBA 03641, Pub. by Irish Academic Pr Ireland). Biblio Dist.
Pickering, Samuel, Jr. The Moral Tradition in English Fiction, 1785-1850. LC 74-12540. 194p. 1976. text ed. 16.00x (ISBN 0-87451-109-7). U Pr of New Eng.
Prickett, Stephen. Romanticism & Religion. LC 75-2254. 320p. 1976. 49.50 (ISBN 0-521-21072-0). Cambridge U Pr.
Prosser, Eleanor. Drama & Religion in the English Mystery Plays: A Re-Evaluation. 1961. 18.50x (ISBN 0-8047-0060-5). Stanford U Pr.
Reilly, Robert, ed. The Transcendent Adventure: Studies of Religion in Science Fiction-Fantasy. LC 84-542. (Contributions to the Study of Science Fiction & Fantasy Ser.: No. 12). x, 266p. 1985. lib. bdg. 35.00 (ISBN 0-313-23062-5, RET/). Greenwood.
Reynolds, David S. Faith in Fiction: The Emergence of Religious Literature in America. LC 80-20885. 304p. 1981. text ed. 25.00x (ISBN 0-674-29172-7). Harvard U Pr.
Rigney, Barbara H. Lilith's Daughters: Women & Religion in Contemporary Fiction. LC 81-70012. 136p. 1982. 17.50x (ISBN 0-299-08960-6). U of Wis Pr.
Routh, Harold V. God, Man & Epic Poetry: A Study in Comparative Literature, 2 Vols. LC 69-10152. (Illus.). 1968. Repr. of 1927 ed. lib. bdg. 37.50x (ISBN 0-8371-0206-5, ROEP). Greenwood.
Shaw, Robert B. The Call of God: The Theme of Vocation in the Poetry of Donne & Herbert. LC 81-66126. (Cowley Lectures). 123p. (Orig.). 1981. pap. 6.00 (ISBN 0-936384-04-2). Cowley Pubns.
Stock, R. D. The Holy & the Daemonic from Sir Thomas Browne to William Blake. LC 81-11974. (Illus.). 416p. 1981. 31.50 (ISBN 0-691-06495-4). Princeton U Pr.
Stratford, Philip. Faith & Fiction: Creative Process in Greene & Mauriac. 1964. pap. 9.95x (ISBN 0-268-00379-3). U of Notre Dame Pr.
Strong, Augustus H. American Poets & Their Theology. facs. ed. LC 68-26477. (Essay Index Reprint Ser). 1968. Repr. of 1916 ed. 21.50 (ISBN 0-8369-0910-0). Ayer Co Pubs.
Thorold, Algar. Six Masters in Disillusion. LC 75-113325. 1971. Repr. of 1909 ed. 21.50x (ISBN 0-8046-1364-8, Pub. by Kennikat). Assoc Faculty Pr.
Urang, Gunnar. Shadows of Heaven: Religion & Fantasy in the Writing of C. S. Lewis, Charles Williams & J. R. R. Tolkien. LC 73-153998. 208p. 1971. 7.95 (ISBN 0-8298-0197-9). Pilgrim NY.
Weales, Gerald C. Religion in Modern English Drama. LC 75-45367. 317p. 1976. Repr. of 1961 ed. lib. bdg. 24.75x (ISBN 0-8371-8735-4, WEME). Greenwood.
Wilder, Amos N. Spiritual Aspects of the New Poetry. facs. ed. LC 68-16988. (Essay Index Reprint Ser). 1940. 16.25 (ISBN 0-8369-0995-X). Ayer Co Pubs.
Windolph, F. Lyman. Selected Essays. LC 72-186116. 1972. 7.50 (ISBN 0-685-36105-5). Franklin & Marsh.

RELIGION IN POETRY

see Jesus Christ–Poetry; Religion in Literature

RELIGION IN THE PUBLIC SCHOOLS

Amundson, Kris. Religion in the Public Schools. 80p. (Orig.). 1986. pap. write for info. Am Assn Sch Admin.
Barr, David & Piediscalzi, Nicholas, eds. The Bible in American Education. LC 81-14436. (SBL The Bible in American Culture Ser.). 1982. 12.95 (ISBN 0-89130-538-6, 061205, Co-pub Fortress Pr). Scholars Pr GA.
Beggs, David W. America's Schools & Churches. LC 65-12279. pap. 60.30 (ISBN 0-317-28577-7, 2055190). Bks Demand UMI.
Bell, Sadie. Church, the State, & Education in Virginia. LC 78-89148. (American Education: Its Men, Institutions & Ideas Ser). 1969. Repr. of 1930 ed. 43.00 (ISBN 0-405-01385-X). Ayer Co Pubs.
Boles, Donald E. Bible, Religion & the Public Schools. 3rd ed. 408p. 1965. 8.95x (ISBN 0-8138-0200-8). Iowa St U Pr.
Brown, S. W. Secularization of American Education As Shown by State Legislation, State Constitutional Provisions & State Supreme Court Decisions. LC 70-176600. (Columbia University. Teachers College. Contributions to Education: No. 49). Repr. of 1912 ed. 22.50 (ISBN 0-404-55049-5). AMS Pr.
Burron, Arnold, et al. Classrooms in Crisis. LC 85-73068. 196p. (Orig.). 1986. pap. 7.95 (ISBN 0-89636-192-6). Accent Bks.
Carr, Anne, et al. Academic Study of Religion, 1975: Public Schools Religion-Studies. LC 75-26653. (American Academy of Religion. Section Papers). 1975. pap. 9.95 (ISBN 0-89130-023-6, 01-09-17). Scholars Pr Ga.
De Forest, Grant E. God in the American Schools: Religious Education in a Pluralistic Society. (Illus.). 1979. 49.50 (ISBN 0-89266-181-X). Am Classical Coll Pr.
Dolbeare, Kenneth M. & Hammond, Philip E. School Prayer Decisions: From Court Policy to Local Practice. LC 70-140461. 1971. 8.00x (ISBN 0-226-15515-3). U of Chicago Pr.
Donovan, Robert O. The Bible Back in Our Schools. LC 72-80782. 80p. 1972. pap. 2.50 (ISBN 0-913748-01-3). Orovan Bks.
Johnson, Alvin W. The Legal Status of Church-State Relationships in the United States with Special Reference to the Public Schools. ix, 332p. 1982. Repr. of 1934 ed. lib. bdg. 30.00x (ISBN 0-8377-0739-0). Rothman.
Laubach, John H. School Prayers. 1969. 9.00 (ISBN 0-8183-0206-2). Pub Aff Pr.
Lima, Tiago. Dios, Tu y la Escuela. Diaz, Alfredo, tr. (Dios, Tu y La Vida). 32p. (Orig.). 1974. pap. 0.95 (ISBN 0-311-46200-6). Casa Bautista.
Lowry, Charles W. To Pray or Not to Pray: A Handbook for Study of Recent Supreme Court Decisions & American Church-State Doctrine. 1969. enlarged ed. 6.00 (ISBN 0-87419-013-4, U Pr of Wash). Larlin Corp.
--To Pray or Not to Pray: A Handbook for Study of Recent Supreme Court Decisions & American Church-State Doctrine. (Special bicentennial facsimile of enlarged ed). 1978. 7.00 (ISBN 0-685-88420-1, U Pr of Wash). Larlin Corp.
McMillan, Richard C. Religion in the Public Schools: An Introduction. LC 84-9147. x, 301p. 1984. 21.95 (ISBN 0-86554-093-4, H85). Mercer Univ Pr.
Menendez, Albert J. School Prayer & Other Religious Issues in American Public Education: A Bibliography. LC 84-48756. (Reference Library of Social Science). 178p. 1985. lib. bdg. 20.00 (ISBN 0-8240-8775-5). Garland Pub.
Muir, William K., Jr. Prayer in the Public Schools: Law & Attitude Change. LC 67-28851. 1967. U of Chicago Pr.
O'Hair, Madalyn M. Atheist Epic: Bill Murray, the Bible & the Baltimore Board of Education. LC 71-88701. 316p. 1970. pap. 6.00 (ISBN 0-911826-01-7). Am Atheist.
Patton, John E. Case Against TM in the Schools. (Direction Bks.). 80p. 1976. pap. 1.45 (ISBN 0-8010-6957-2). Baker Bk.
Rugh, Charles E. Moral Training in the Public Schools. 203p. 1980. Repr. lib. bdg. 25.00 (ISBN 0-8492-7749-3). R West.
Spykman, Gordon, et al. Society, State, & Schools: A Case for Structural & Confessional Pluralism. 224p. (Orig.). 1981. pap. 9.95 (ISBN 0-8028-1880-3). Eerdmans.
Stallo, Johann B., et al. Bible in Public Schools. 2nd ed. LC 67-27464. (Law, Politics & History Ser). 1967. Repr. of 1870 ed. lib. bdg. 39.50 (ISBN 0-306-70963-5). Da Capo.

RELIGION OF HUMANITY

see Positivism

RELIGION OF THE FUTURE

see Religions (Proposed, Universal, etc.)

RELIGIONS

Here are entered works on the major world religions. Works on religious groups whose adherents recognize special teachings or practices which fall within the normative bounds of the major world religions are entered under Sects. Works on groups or movements whose system of religious beliefs or practices differs significantly from the major world religions and which are often gathered around a specific deity or person are entered under Cults.

see also Babism; Bahaism; Brahmanism; Buddhism; Christianity; Confucius and Confucianism; Cults; Druids and Druidism; Druses; Fetishism; Gnosticism; Gods; Hinduism; Humanism, Religious; Islam; Jains; Judaism; Lamaism; Mandaeans; Mythology; Paganism; Positivism; Religion; Sects; Shamanism; Shinto; Syncretism (Religion); Taoism; Yezidis; Zoroastrianism

Afnan, Ruhi. Great Prophets. 1960. 7.95 (ISBN 0-8022-0010-9). Philos Lib.
Amberley, John R. An Analysis of Religious Belief. LC 76-161318. (Atheist Viewpoint Ser.). 745p. 1972. Repr. of 1877 ed. 41.00 (ISBN 0-405-03621-3). Ayer Co Pubs.
--An Analysis of Religious Belief. 59.95 (ISBN 0-87968-619-7). Gordon Pr.
Anderson, J. N. The World's Religions. rev. ed. LC 75-26654. 1976. pap. 5.95 (ISBN 0-8028-1636-3). Eerdmans.
Archer, John C. Faiths Men Live by. facsimile ed. LC 79-156606. (Essay Index Reprint Ser). Repr. of 1934 ed. 25.50 (ISBN 0-8369-2266-2). Ayer Co Pubs.
Bach, Marcus. Major Religions of the World. 128p. 1984. pap. 4.95 (ISBN 0-87516-543-5). De Vorss.
Baird, Robert D. & Bloom, Alfred. Religion & Man: Indian & Far Eastern Religious Traditions. (Religion & Man: An Introduction, Pts. 2 & 3). 1972. pap. text ed. 14.95 scp (ISBN 0-06-040448-5, HarpC). Har-Row.
Barker, Eileen, ed. Of Gods & Men: New Religious Movements in the West. LC 83-23822. xiv, 347p. 1984. 26.50 (ISBN 0-86554-095-0, MUP/H87). Mercer Univ Pr.
Barley, L. M., et al. Religious Data: Recurrent Christian Sources, Non-Recurrent Christian Data, Judaism, Other Religions. (Reviews of U. K. Statistical Sources Ser.: No. 20). 635p. 1987. 86.50 (ISBN 0-08-034778-9). Pergamon.
Barton, George A. Religions of the World. LC 74-90469. Repr. of 1929 ed. lib. bdg. 22.50x (ISBN 0-8371-2216-3, BARW). Greenwood.
Baum, Gregory & Coleman, John, eds. New Religious Movements. (Concilium Ser. 1983: Vol. 161). 128p. (Orig.). 1983. pap. 6.95 (ISBN 0-8164-2441-1, HarpR); pap. 62.55 10 Volume Subscription (ISBN 0-8164-2453-5). Har-Row.
Beckford, James A. Religious Organization: A Trend Report & Bibliography Prepared for the International Sociological Association Under the Auspices of the International Committee for Social Science Documentation. (Current Sociology La Sociologie Contemporaine: Vol. 21, No. 2). 1973. pap. 11.60x (ISBN 90-2797-851-4). Mouton.
Besant. Seven Great Religions. 6.75 (ISBN 0-8356-7218-2). Theos Pub Hse.
Bhakti in Religions of the World: With Special Reference to Dr. Sri Bankey Behariji. 268p. 1987. text ed. 32.50x (ISBN 81-7018-371-5, Pub. by B R Pub Corp Delhi). Apt Bks.
Biezais, Haralds, ed. New Religions. 233p. (Orig.). 1975. pap. text ed. 18.50x (Pub. by Almqvist & Wiksell). Coronet Bks.
Binder, Louis R. Modern Religious Cults & Society. LC 77-113556. Repr. of 1933 ed. 10.00 (ISBN 0-404-00867-4). AMS Pr.
Boa, Kenneth. Cults, World Religions, & You. 1977. pap. 6.95 (ISBN 0-88207-752-X). Victor Bks.
Braswell, George W., Jr. Understanding World Religions. LC 81-65828. (Orig.). 1983. pap. 7.95 (ISBN 0-8054-6605-3). Broadman.
Braunthal, Alfred. Salvation & the Perfect Society: The Eternal Quest. LC 79-4705. 448p. 1979. lib. bdg. 25.00x (ISBN 0-87023-273-8). U of Mass Pr.
Braybrooke, Marcus. Inter-Faith Organizations 1893-1979: An Historical Directory. LC 79-91620. (Texts & Studies in Religion: Vol. 6). xiv, 228p. 1980. 49.95x (ISBN 0-88946-971-7). E Mellen.
Caird, Edward. Evolution of Religion, 2 Vols. in 1. LC 1-17697. (Gifford Lectures 1890-1892). 1968. Repr. of 1893 ed. 46.00 (ISBN 0-527-14120-8). Kraus Repr.
Cairns, Trevor, ed. Barbarians, Christians, & Muslims. LC 73-20213. (Cambridge Introduction to History Ser.). (Illus.). 104p. 1975. PLB 10.95 (ISBN 0-8225-0803-6). Lerner Pubns.
Carmody, Denise L. & Carmody, John T. Western Ways to the Center: An Introduction to Religions of the West. 272p. 1982. pap. text ed. write for info. (ISBN 0-534-01328-7). Wadsworth Pub.
Carmody, Dennis L. & Carmody, John T. Ways to the Center: An Introduction to World Religions. 432p. 1981. text ed. write for info. (ISBN 0-534-00890-9). Wadsworth Pub.
Carr, Anne, ed. Academic Study of Religion: Proceedings. LC 74-14212. (American Academy of Religion. Section Papers). Repr. of 1974 ed. 40.50 (ISBN 0-8357-9563-2, 2017552). Bks Demand UMI.
Catoir, John. World Religions: Beliefs Behind Today's Headlines. rev. ed. xxiii, 148p. pap. 5.00 (ISBN 0-317-46551-1). Chrstphrs NY.
Catoir, John T. World Religions: Beliefs Behind Today's Headlines. rev. ed. 160p. 1985. pap. 4.95 (ISBN 0-940518-04-X). Guildhall Pubs.
Champion, Selwyn G. The Eleven Religions & Their Proverbial Lore: A Comparative Study. 1979. Repr. of 1945 ed. lib. bdg. 30.00 (ISBN 0-8492-3856-0). R West.
--The Eleven Religions & Their Proverbial Lore: A Comparative Study. 340p. 1985. Repr. of 1945 ed. lib. bdg. 75.00 (ISBN 0-8492-4102-2). R West.
Chanler, Julie. His Messengers Went Forth. facs. ed. LC 77-148209. (Biography Index Reprint Ser.). (Illus.). 1948. 13.00 (ISBN 0-8369-8056-5). Ayer Co Pubs.
Clarke, Thomas J. People & Their Religions, Part One. (Literacy Volunteers of America Readers Ser.). 48p. (Orig.). 1983. pap. 1.95 (ISBN 0-8428-9609-0). Cambridge Bk.
--People & Their Religions, Part Two. (Literacy Volunteers of America Readers Ser.). 48p. (Orig.). 1983. pap. 1.95 (ISBN 0-8428-9610-4). Cambridge Bk.
Clemen, Carl C., et al. Religions of the World. facs. ed. LC 69-17570. (Essay Index Reprint Ser). 1931. 35.50 (ISBN 0-8369-0011-1). Ayer Co Pubs.
Cranston, Ruth. World Faith. facs. ed. LC 68-58782. (Essay Index Reprint Ser). 1949. 15.00 (ISBN 0-8369-0108-8). Ayer Co Pubs.
Cumont, Franz. Oriental Religions in Roman Paganism. 1911. pap. 5.95 (ISBN 0-486-20321-2). Dover.
Daly, Lloyd W. Iohannis Philoponi: De Vocabulis Quae Diversum Significatum Exhibent Secundum Differentiam Accentus. LC 81-72156. (Memoirs Ser.: Vol. 151). 1983. 20.00 (ISBN 0-87169-151-5). Am Philos.
Denny, Frederick M. & Taylor, Rodney L. The Holy Book in Comparative Perspective. LC 85-8473. (Studies in Comparative Religion). 244p. 1985. 19.95 (ISBN 0-87249-453-5). U of SC Pr.
Eliade, Mircea. Occultism, Witchcraft, & Cultural Fashion: Essays in Comparative Religions. LC 75-12230. 1978. pap. 9.00 (ISBN 0-226-20392-1, P755, Phoen). U of Chicago Pr.
--Patterns in Comparative Religion. pap. 9.95 (ISBN 0-452-00728-3, Mer). NAL.
--Patterns in Comparative Religion. 16.00 (ISBN 0-8446-6226-7). Peter Smith.
Ellwood, Robert S., Jr. Many Peoples, Many Faiths. 2nd ed. (Illus.). 416p. 1982. 27.95 (ISBN 0-13-556001-2). P-H.
--Religious & Spiritual Groups in Modern America. 352p. 1973. pap. 24.33 (ISBN 0-13-773309-7). P-H.
--Words of the World's Religion. 1977. pap. text ed. 24.33x (ISBN 0-13-965004-0). P-H.
Evans-Wentz, W. Y. Cuchama & Sacred Mountains. Waters, Frank & Adams, Charles L., eds. LC 81-8749. (Illus.). xxxii, 196p. 1982. 22.95 (ISBN 0-8040-0411-0, Pub. by Swallow). Ohio U Pr.
Faber, George S. The Origin of Pagan Idolatry, 3 vols. Feldman, Burton & Richardson, Robert D., eds. LC 78-60891. (Myth & Romanticism Ser.). 1984. Set. lib. bdg. 240.00 (ISBN 0-8240-3559-3). Garland Pub.
Fairchild, Johnson E., ed. Basic Beliefs: The Religious Philosophies of Mankind. 11.50x (ISBN 0-911378-03-0). Sheridan.
Farnell, Lewis R. Greece & Babylon: A Comparative Sketch of Mesopatamian, Anatolian, & Hellenic Religions. 1977. lib. bdg. 59.95 (ISBN 0-8490-1906-0). Gordon Pr.
Fausset, H. L'Anson. The Flame & the Light: Vedanta & Buddhism. 59.95 (ISBN 0-8490-0173-0). Gordon Pr.

Fellows, Ward J. Religions East & West. LC 78-27721. 1979. text ed. 31.95 (ISBN 0-03-019441-5, HoltC). H Holt & Co.

Ferm, Vergilius T., ed. Forgotten Religions. facs. ed. LC 70-128240. (Essay Index Reprint Ser). 1950. 22.00 (ISBN 0-8369-1922-X). Ayer Co Pubs.

--Religion in the Twentieth Century. Repr. of 1948 ed. lib. bdg. 22.50x (ISBN 0-8371-2290-2, FERT). Greenwood.

Friess, Horace L. & Schneider, Herbert W. Religion in Various Cultures. (Illus.). Repr. of 1932 ed. 24.00 (ISBN 0-384-16990-2). Johnson Repr.

Fu, Charles W. & Spiegler, Gerhard E., eds. Movements & Issues in World Religions: A Sourcebook & Analysis of Developments since 1945; Religion, Ideology, & Politics. LC 86-4634. 576p. 1987. lib. bdg. 75.00 (ISBN 0-313-23238-5, FUR). Greenwood.

Fugett, Albert F. Spokesman for the Devil. (Illus.). 165p. 1985. 14.95 (ISBN 0-9614870-0-3). Triple Seven.

Gaer, Joseph. What the Great Religions Believe. pap. 3.95 (ISBN 0-451-14320-5, AE1978, Sig). NAL.

Gardner, Hope C. & Gunnell, Sally. Teach Me in My Way: A Collection for L.D.S. Children. LC 80-84147. 1980. soft cover 5.95 (ISBN 0-913420-85-9). Olympus Pub Co.

Garvin, Harry. Literature, Arts & Religion. LC 80-70270. (Bucknell Review Ser.: Vol. 26, No. 2). (Illus.). 192p. 1982. 16.50 (ISBN 0-8387-5021-4). Bucknell U Pr.

Gates, Brian, ed. Afro-Caribbean Religions. 1985. 30.00x (ISBN 0-686-81323-5, Pub. by Ward Lock Educ Co Ltd). State Mutual Bk.

Ghai, O. P., ed. Unity in Diversity. 132p. 1986. text ed. 15.95x (ISBN 0-86590-762-5, Pub. by Sterling Pubs India). Apt Bks.

Gilbert, Arthur & Tarcov, Oscar. Your Neighbor Celebrates. 6.00x (ISBN 0-87068-364-0, Pub. by Friendly Hse). Ktav.

Gordis, Robert. Faith for Moderns. 2nd rev. ed. LC 76-136424. 1971. pap. 8.95x (ISBN 0-8197-0001-0, 10001). Bloch.

Gorham, Melvin. The Pagan Bible. 296p. 1982. 8.95 (ISBN 0-914752-22-7). Sovereign Pr.

Grant, Frederick C., ed. Hellenistic Religions: The Age of Syncretism. 1953. pap. 13.24 scp (ISBN 0-672-60342-X, LLA134). Bobbs.

Gregson, Vernon. Lonergan, Spirituality, & the Meeting of Religions. LC 85-3312. (College Theology Society-Studies in Religion: No. 2). 170p. (Orig.). 1985. lib. bdg. 24.50 (ISBN 0-8191-4619-6, Co-Pub by College Theo Soc); pap. text ed. 10.75 (ISBN 0-8191-4620-X). U Pr of Amer.

Guthrie, Gary D. The Wisdom Tree. 56p. (Orig.). Date not set. pap. price not set (ISBN 0-9612980-0-6). Gary Guthrie.

Hall, Manly P. E. A. Gordon - Pioneer in East-West Religious Understanding. pap. 2.50 (ISBN 0-89314-377-4). Philos Res.

Hawkridge, Emma. Wisdom Tree. LC 72-128257. (Essay Index Reprint Ser.). 1945. 33.00 (ISBN 0-8369-1881-9). Ayer Co Pubs.

Haydon, Albert E., ed. Modern Trends in World-Religions. facs. ed. LC 68-29214. (Essay Index Reprint Ser). 1934. 18.00 (ISBN 0-8369-0522-9). Ayer Co Pubs.

Hesselgrave, David J., ed. Dynamic Religious Movements: Case Studies of Rapidly Growing Religious Movement Around the World. 1978. 9.95 (ISBN 0-8010-4130-9). Baker Bk.

Heydt, Henry J. Comparison of World Religions. 1967. pap. 2.50 (ISBN 0-87508-241-6). Chr Lit.

Hick, John. Problems of Religious Pluralism. LC 85-2505. 144p. 1985. 19.95 (ISBN 0-312-65154-6). St Martin.

Holmes, Ernest. The Power of Belief. Kinnear, Willis H., ed. 96p. 1970. pap. 5.50 (ISBN 0-911336-13-3). Sci of Mind.

Hopfe, Lewis M. Religions of the World. 4th ed. 522p. 1987. pap. write for info. (ISBN 0-02-356930-1). Macmillan.

Hospital, Clifford G. Breakthrough: Insights of the Great Religious Discoverers. LC 85-5135. 208p. (Orig.). 1985. pap. 9.95 (ISBN 0-88344-206-X). Orbis Bks.

Hume, Robert E. The World's Living Religions. rev. ed. LC 58-12515. 335p. 1978. pap. text ed. write for info. (ISBN 0-02-358450-5, Pub. by). Macmillan.

Hume, Roberto E. Las Religiones Vivas. Beltroy, Manuel, tr. from Eng. Orig. Title: Living Religions of the World. (Span.). 320p. 1981. pap. 5.25 (ISBN 0-311-05758-6, Edit Mundo). Casa Bautista.

Hunt, Arnold D. & Crotty, Robert B. Ethics of World Religions. (Illus.). 1978. lib. bdg. 11.95 (ISBN 0-912616-74-1); pap. 6.95 (ISBN 0-912616-73-3). Greenhaven.

Hutchison, John A. Paths of Faith. 3rd ed. (Illus.). 608p. 1981. 31.95x (ISBN 0-07-031532-9). McGraw.

Jain, C. R. Confluence of Opposites or Scientific Comparative Study of Religions. 432p. 1975. Repr. 16.00 (Pub. by Messers Today & Tomorrows Printers & Publishers India). Scholarly Pubns.

--Key of Knowledge: The Key to Unlock the Mysteries of Important Religions of the World. 1012p. 1975. 35.00 (ISBN 0-88065-137-7, Pub. by Messers Today & Tomorrows Printers & Publishers India). Scholarly Pubns.

Jevons, Frank B. Comparative Religion. LC 76-57969. 1977. Repr. of 1913 ed. lib. bdg. 15.00 (ISBN 0-8414-5326-8). Folcroft.

Joudry, Patricia. Spirit River to Angels' Roost: Religions I Have Loved & Left. LC 76-22996. 1977. 12.95 (ISBN 0-912766-46-8). Tundra Bks.

Kim, Young O. World Religions, Vol. 1. LC 76-23739. 275p. 1982. pap. 8.95 (ISBN 0-318-11690-1). Rose Sharon Pr.

--World Religions, Vol. 2. LC 76-23739. 413p. 1982. pap. 10.95 (ISBN 0-318-11691-X). Rose Sharon Pr.

Kitagawa, Joseph M. Religions of the East. enl. ed. LC 60-7742. 352p. 1968. pap. 7.95 (ISBN 0-664-24837-3). Westminster.

Kramer, Kenneth. World Scriptures: An Introduction to Comparative Religion. LC 85-62933. 304p. 1986. pap. 12.95 (ISBN 0-8091-2781-4). Paulist Pr.

Langley, Myrtle. Religions. (Book of Beliefs Ser.). 1981. 9.95 (ISBN 0-89191-478-1, 54783). Cook.

Langley, Myrtle, et al. A Book of Beliefs. Alexander, P., ed. 192p. 1987. pap. 12.95 (ISBN 0-85648-504-7). Lion USA.

Legge, Francis. Forerunners & Rivals of Christianity, 2 vols. in 1. 19.00 (ISBN 0-8446-1280-4). Peter Smith.

Lessa, William A. & Vogt, Evon Z. Reader in Comparative Religion: An Anthropological Approach. 4th ed. 1979. pap. text ed. 27.50 scp (ISBN 0-06-043991-2, HarpC). Har-Row.

Lindbeck, George A. The Nature of Doctrine: Religion & Theology in a Postliberal Age. LC 83-27332. 142p. 1984. 16.95 (ISBN 0-664-21829-6); pap. 9.95 (ISBN 0-664-24618-4). Westminster.

McBeth, Leon. Strange New Religions. LC 76-47780. 1977. pap. 4.25 (ISBN 0-8054-1806-7). Broadman.

McDonald, Henry. The Ethics of Comparative Religion. LC 84-17370. 102p. (Orig.). 1985. lib. bdg. 19.75 (ISBN 0-8191-4304-9); pap. text ed. 7.75 (ISBN 0-8191-4305-7). U Pr of Amer.

McDowell, Josh & Stewart, Don. Understanding Non-Christian Religions. LC 81-86543. (Handbook of Today's Religion Ser.). 208p. 1982. pap. 6.95 (ISBN 0-86605-092-2, 402834). Heres Life.

--Understanding Secular Religions. 140p. 1982. pap. 6.95 (ISBN 0-86605-093-0). Here's Life.

Mahmoudi, Jalil. The Story As Told. rev. ed. LC 79-65925. (Illus.). 80p. (Orig.). 1980. pap. 4.95 (ISBN 0-933770-10-3). Kalimat.

Mark-Age. How to Do All Things: Your Use of Divine Power. LC 72-121118. 144p. 1970. pap. 5.00 (ISBN 0-912322-01-2). Mark-Age.

Marx, Herbert L., ed. Religions in America. (Reference Shelf Ser.). 1977. 8.00 (ISBN 0-8242-0608-8). Wilson.

Meade, F. H., et al. Religions of the World. 97p. 1985. 32.00x (ISBN 0-7157-2355-3, Pub by Holmes McDougall Ltd). State Mutual Bk.

Mehta, J L. India & the West: The Problem of Understanding-Selected Essays of J.L. Mehta. (Studies in World Religions: No. 4). 1985. 20.75 (ISBN 0-89130-826-1, 03 00 04); pap. 13.75 (ISBN 0-89130-827-X). Scholars Pr GA.

Merton, Thomas. Mystics & Zen Masters. 303p. 1986. pap. 8.95 (ISBN 0-374-52001-1). FS&G.

Milavec, Aaron. A Pilgrim Experiences the World's Religions: Discovering the Human Faces of the Hidden God. (Mellen Lives Ser.: Vol. 1). 96p. 1984. pap. 9.95x (ISBN 0-88946-010-8). E Mellen.

Mol, Hans, ed. & intro. by. Western Religion: A Country by Country Sociological Inquiry. (Religion & Reason Ser.: No. 2). (Illus.). 642p. 1972. text ed. 59.00x (ISBN 90-2797-004-1). Mouton.

Moore, Robert L. & Reynolds, Frank E., eds. Anthropology & the Study of Religion. LC 83-71781. (Studies in Religion & Society). 230p. 1984. text ed. 24.95x (ISBN 0-913348-20-1); pap. text ed. 11.95 (ISBN 0-913348-21-X). Ctr Sci Study.

Moosa, Matti. The Maronites in History. 350p. 1986. text ed. 35.00x (ISBN 0-8156-2365-8). Syracuse U Pr.

Mueller, Friedrich M. Anthropological Religion. LC 73-18822. (Gifford Lectures: 1891). 1975. Repr. of 1892 ed. 34.00 (ISBN 0-404-11428-8). AMS Pr.

Muhiyaddin, Mohammed A. A Comparative Study of the Religions of Today. 1984. 15.95 (ISBN 0-533-05963-1). Vantage.

Muller, Max. Chips from a German Workshop: Volume I: Essays on the Science of Religion. (Reprints & Translations). 1985. pap. 13.95 (ISBN 0-89130-890-3, 00-07-10). Scholars Pr GA.

Needleman, Jacob & Baker, George, eds. Understanding the New Religions. 1978. (HarpR); pap. 8.95 (ISBN 0-8164-2188-9). Har-Row.

Nielsen, Niels, et al, eds. Religions of the World. LC 81-51859. 688p. 1982. text ed. 28.95 (ISBN 0-312-67121-0); write for info. instructors manual. St Martin.

Nigosian, S. A. World Religions Series. (Comparative Religions Ser.). 1976. pap. text ed. 6.45 (ISBN 0-88343-688-4). McDougal-Littell.

Norbu, Tsampa Yeshe. Rasa Tantra: Blood Marriage, The Sacred Initiation, A Marriage of the Faiths of East & West. (Illus.). 36p. 1980. pap. 6.95 (ISBN 0-9609802-2-9). Life Science.

Noss, John B. & Noss, Davis S. Man's Religion. 7th ed. (Illus.). 608p. 1984. text ed. write for info. (ISBN 0-02-388470-3). Macmillan.

Oman, John W. The Natural & the Supernatural. LC 79-39696. (Select Bibliographies Reprint Ser.). 1972. Repr. of 1931 ed. 20.75 (ISBN 0-8369-9941-X). Ayer Co Pubs.

Pailin, David A. Attitudes to Other Religions: Comparative Religion in Seventeenth & Eighteenth-Century Britain. LC 83-20652. 368p. 1984. 49.00 (ISBN 0-7190-1065-9, Pub. by Manchester Univ Pr). Longwood Pub Group.

Palmer, A. Smythe. The Samson Saga & Its Place in Comparative Religion. 1977. lib. bdg. 59.95 (ISBN 0-8490-2565-6). Gordon Pr.

Panikkar, Raimundo. Intrareligious Dialogue. LC 78-58962. 136p. 1978. 6.95 (ISBN 0-8091-2728-8). Paulist Pr.

Parrinder, Edward G. Book of World Religions. (Illus.). 1967. 12.50 (ISBN 0-7175-0443-3). Dufour.

Parrinder, Geoffrey. Comparative Religion. LC 73-19116. 130p. 1975. Repr. of 1962 ed. lib. bdg. 45.00x (ISBN 0-8371-7301-9, PACR). Greenwood.

--Encounters in World Religions. 224p. 1987. 15.95 (ISBN 0-8245-0826-2). Crossroad NY.

--World Religions: From Ancient History to the Present. (Illus.). 224p. 1984. 29.95 (ISBN 0-87196-129-6). Facts on File.

Pastva, Mary L. Great Religions of the World. (Illus.). 251p. (Orig.). 1986. pap. text ed. 9.95x (ISBN 0-88489-175-5). St Mary's.

Perlmann, Moshe, ed. & tr. from Arabic. Ibn Kammuna's Examination of the Three Faiths: A Thirteenth-Century Essay in the Comparative Study of Religion. LC 73-102659. 1971. 32.00x (ISBN 0-520-01658-0). U of Cal Pr.

Pfister, Friedrich. Der Reliquienkult im Altertum, 2 vols. in 1. Incl. Vol. 1. Das Objekt des Reliquienkultes; Vol. 2. Die Reliquien als Kultobjekt: Geschichte des Reliquienkultes. (Ger.). xii, 686p. 1974. Repr. of 1909 ed. 76.00x (ISBN 3-11-002453-5). De Gruyter.

Platvoet, J. G. Comparing Religions: A Limitative Approach. (Religion & Reason Ser.: No. 24). xiv, 350p. 1982. 51.50x (ISBN 90-279-3170-4). Mouton.

Prado, Carlos G. Illusions of Faith: A Critique of Non-Credal Religion. (Orig.). 1980. pap. text ed. 9.95 (ISBN 0-8403-2176-7). Kendall-Hunt.

Pye, Michael & Morgan, Robert, eds. The Cardinal Meaning: Essays in Comparative Hermeneutics, Buddhism & Christianity. (Religion & Reason Ser: No. 6). 203p. 1973. text ed. 23.25x (ISBN 90-2797-228-1). Mouton.

Radhakrishnan, S. Eastern Religions & Western Thought. 2nd ed. 1975. pap. text ed. 10.95x (ISBN 0-19-560604-3). Oxford U Pr.

Rajneesh, Bhagwan S. The Rajneesh Bible, Vol. II. Rajneesh Academy Staff, ed. LC 85-42539. 839p. (Orig.). 1985. pap. 7.95x (ISBN 0-88050-201-0, 201-0). Chidvilas Found.

Rao, K. L. Mahatma Gandhi & Comparative Religion. 1979. 15.00x (ISBN 0-89684-034-4). South Asia Bks.

Reitzenstein, Richard. The Hellenistic Mystery-Religions. Steely, John E., tr. from Ger. LC 77-12980. (Pittsburgh Theological Monographs: No. 15). Orig. Title: Die Hellenistischen Mysterienreligionen Nach Ihren Arundgedanken und Wirkungen. 1978. pap. text ed. 17.75 (ISBN 0-915138-20-4). Pickwick.

Reyes, Benito F. The Essence of All Religions. 25p. 1983. pap. 3.00 (ISBN 0-939375-14-1). World Univ Amer.

Rice, Edward. Ten Religions of the East. LC 78-6186. (Illus.). 160p. 1978. 8.95 (ISBN 0-02-776210-6, Four Winds). Macmillan.

Richard, Lucien. What Are They Saying about Christ & World Religions? LC 81-80878. 96p. (Orig.). 1981. pap. 4.95 (ISBN 0-8091-2391-6). Paulist Pr.

Robbins, Thomas, et al, eds. Cults, Culture & the Law: Perspectives on New Religious Movements. (American Academy of Religion Studies in Religion: No. 36). 1985. 18.95 (ISBN 0-89130-832-6, 01 00 36); pap. 13.50 (ISBN 0-89130-833-4). Scholars Pr GA.

Robinson, John M. Pagan Christs. 1967. 5.95 (ISBN 0-8216-0136-9). Univ Bks.

Ross, Floyd H. & Hills, Tynette. Great Religions By Which Men Live. Orig. Title: Questions That Matter Most Asked by the World's Religions. 1977. pap. 2.50 (ISBN 0-449-30825-1, Prem). Fawcett.

Rossner, John. Towards Recovery of the Primordial Tradition: Ancient Insights & Modern Discoveries, Vol. II. LC 83-14753. (The Primordial Tradition in Contemporary Experience Ser.: Bk. 2). 152p. 1984. PLB 27.00 (ISBN 0-8191-3519-4); pap. 13.50 (ISBN 0-8191-3520-8). U Pr of Amer.

Ruland, Vernon. Eight Sacred Horizons: The Religious Imagination East & West. 240p. 1985. 19.95x (ISBN 0-317-18117-3). MacMillan.

Rupp, Israel D. The Religious Denominations in the United States: Their Past History, Present Condition, & Doctrines. LC 72-2943. Repr. of 1861 ed. 67.50 (ISBN 0-404-10709-5). AMS Pr.

Saltus, Edgar. Lords of the Ghostland: A History of the Ideal. LC 71-116003. Repr. of 1907 ed. 17.50 (ISBN 0-404-05539-7). AMS Pr.

Samartha, S. J., ed. Living Faith & Ultimate Goals: Salvation & World Religions. LC 75-7610. 119p. (Orig.). 1975. pap. 1.98 (ISBN 0-88344-297-3). Orbis Bks.

Schuon, Frithjof. The Transcendent Unity of Religions. Rev. ed. LC 84-239. 165p. 1984. pap. 7.95 (ISBN 0-8356-0587-6, Quest). Theos Pub Hse.

Schure, Edward. Krishna & Orpheus. 69.95 (ISBN 0-8490-0475-6). Gordon Pr.

Seeger, Elizabeth. Eastern Religions. LC 73-10206. (Illus.). 1973. 14.70 (ISBN 0-690-25342-7, Crowell Jr Bks). HarpJ.

Sharpe, Eric J. Comparative Religion: A History. LC 86-2380. 330p. 1987. 31.95 (ISBN 0-8126-9032-X); pap. 14.95 (ISBN 0-8126-9041-9). Open Court.

Sheils, W. J. & Wood, Diana, eds. Voluntary Religion, Vol 23. 544p. 1987. text ed. 49.95 (ISBN 0-631-15054-4). Basil Blackwell.

Slater, Robert H. World Religions & World Community. LC 63-9805. (Lectures on the History of Religions Ser.: No. 6). 1963. 28.00x (ISBN 0-231-02615-3). Columbia U Pr.

Small, Leonard R. No Other Name. 192p. 1966. 12.95 (ISBN 0-567-02257-9, Pub. by T & T Clark Ltd UK). Fortress.

Smart, Ninian. The Religious Experience of Mankind. 3rd ed. (Scribner Press Ser.). (Illus.). 656p. 1984. 30.00 (ISBN 0-684-18077-4, ScribT). Scribner.

--Worldviews: Crosscultural Explorations in Human Beliefs. (Illus.). 224p. 1983. 13.95 (ISBN 0-684-17811-7, ScribT). Scribner.

Smith, Huston. Religions of Man. pap. 7.95 (ISBN 0-06-090043-1, CN43, PL). Har-Row.

--Religions of Man. 1965. pap. 5.95 (ISBN 0-06-080021-6, P21, PL). Har-Row.

Starkes, M. Thomas. Today's World Religions. 1986. 10.95 (ISBN 0-937931-02-0); pap. 7.95. Global TN.

Stowe, David M. When Faith Meets Faith. rev. ed. 1972. pap. 2.95 (ISBN 0-377-37201-3). Friend Pr.

Swami Vivekananda, et al. Thus Spake Library: Teachings of Vivekananda, Ramakrishna, Sri Sarada Devi, Rama, Krishna, Buddha, Christ, Muhammad, Shankara & Guru Nanak. pap. 3.50 set 10 bklts (ISBN 0-87481-444-8). Vedanta Pr.

Thompson, Henry O., ed. The Global Congress of the World's Religions. LC 82-73565. (Conference Ser.: No. 15). (Orig.). 1982. pap. text ed. write for info. (ISBN 0-932894-15-1, Pub. by New Era Bks). Paragon Hse.

Tiwari, K. N. Comparative Religion. 1986. 14.00 (ISBN 81-208-0293-4, Pub. by Motilal Banarsidass). South Asia Bks.

Volney, C. F. A New Translation of Volney's Ruins, 2 vols. Feldman, Burton & Richardson, Robert D., eds. LC 78-60900. (Myth & Romanticism Ser.: Vol. 25). (Illus.). 1979. Set. lib. bdg. 160.00 (ISBN 0-8240-3574-7). Garland Pub.

Von Der Mehden, Fred. Religion & Modernization in Southeast Asia. 232p. 1986. text ed. 29.95x (ISBN 0-8156-2360-7); pap. text ed. 14.95x (ISBN 0-8156-2361-5). Syracuse U Pr.

Voss, Carl H. Living Religions of the World: Our Search for Meaning. (Library of Liberal Religion). 192p. 1977. pap. 6.95 (ISBN 0-87975-215-7). Prometheus Bks.

Wach, Joachim & Kitagawa, Joseph M. The Comparative Study of Religions. LC 58-9237. (Lectures on the History of Religions: No. 4). 1958. 30.00x (ISBN 0-231-02252-2); pap. 12.00x (ISBN 0-231-08528-1). Columbia U Pr.

Wallis, Roy. The Elementary Forms of the New Religious Life. LC 83-11092. (International Library of Sociology). 171p. 1984. 26.95x (ISBN 0-7100-9890-1). Methuen Inc.

Ward, Duren J. The Classification of Religions. 75p. 1909. pap. 0.95 (ISBN 0-317-40432-6). Open Court.

Whaling, Frank. World's Religious Traditions. 320p. (Orig.). 1986. pap. 14.95 (ISBN 0-8245-0747-9). Crossroad NY.

Whaling, Frank, ed. Contemporary Approaches to the Study of Religion, Vol. 1: The Humanities. LC 84-14807. (Religion & Reason Ser.: No. 27). 520p. 1984. 39.95x (ISBN 3-11-009834-2); Vol. 2: The Social Sciences, pgs.302. pap. 29.95 (ISBN 3-11-009836-9). Mouton.

Williams, George M. Freedom & Influence: The Role of Religion in American Society. 318p. 1985. write for info.; pap. write for info. (ISBN 0-915678-15-2). World Tribune Pr.

Wilson, John F. Religion: A Preface. (Illus.). 240p. 1982. pap. text ed. write for info. (ISBN 0-13-773192-2). P-H.

Wolfe, Rolland E. The Twelve Religions of the Bible. LC 82-20401. (Studies in the Bible & Early Christianity: Vol. 2). (Illus.). 440p. 1983. 69.95x (ISBN 0-88946-600-9). E Mellen.

RELIGIONS–BIBLIOGRAPHY

Adams, Charles J., ed. A Reader's Guide to the Great Religions. 2nd ed. LC 76-10496. 1977. 24.95 (ISBN 0-02-900240-0). Free Pr.

Ahrendts, Juergen, ed. Bibliographie zur alteuropaeischen Religionsgeschichte II, 1965-1969: Eine interdisziplinaere Auswahl von Literatur zu den Rand-und Nachfolgekulturen der Antike in Europa unter besonderer Beruecksichtigung der nichtchristlichen Religionen. LC 68-86477. (Arbeiten Zur Fruehmittelalterforschung: Vol. 5). xxvi, 591p. 1974. 59.20x (ISBN 3-11-003398-4). De Gruyter.

Eerdmans' Handbook to the World's Religions. (Illus.). 1982. 21.95 (ISBN 0-8028-3563-5). Eerdmans.

Glock, Charles & Bellah, Robert N., eds. The New Religious Consciousness. 391p. 29.50 (ISBN 0-686-95181-6); pap. 6.95 (ISBN 0-686-99471-X). ADL.

RELIGIONS–BIOGRAPHY

Capps, Donald, et al. Encounter with Erikson: Historical Interpretation & Religious Biography. LC 76-44434. (American Academy of Religion, Formative Contemporary Thinkers Ser.: No. 2). 1977. pap. 13.50 (010402). Scholars Pr GA.

Cornwell, Patricia D. A Time for Remembering: The Ruth Bell Graham Story. LC 82-48922. (Illus.). 320p. 1983. 13.45 (ISBN 0-06-061685-7, HarpR). Har-Row.

Crawford, S. Cromwell. Ram Mohan Roy: Social, Political & Religious Reform in 19th Century India. 288p. 1986. 22.95 (ISBN 0-913729-15-9). Paragon Hse.

Fraser, Amy S. The Hills of Home. (Illus.). 250p. 1973. pap. 8.95 (ISBN 0-7102-0540-6). Methuen Inc.

Gordon, Earnest B. Adoniram Judson Gordon. Dayton, Donald W., ed. (The Higher Christian Life Ser.). 386p. 1985. 55.00 (ISBN 0-8240-6421-6). Garland Pub.

Hillis, Dick. Not Made for Quitting. 144p. 1973. pap. 2.95 (ISBN 0-87123-396-7, 200396, Dimension Bks). Bethany Hse.

Lilipaly, Hendrik Th. Experiences with God & His Messengers: The Key to God's Kingdom. 1980. 6.00 (ISBN 0-682-49506-9). Exposition Pr FL.

Manton, Joseph. A View from the Steeple. LC 85-60519. 180p. (Orig.). 1985. pap. 7.95 (ISBN 0-87973-591-0, 591). Our Sunday Visitor.

Newbigin, Lesslie. Unfinished Agenda: An Autobiography. (Illus.). 280p. (Orig.). 1985. pap. 11.95 (ISBN 0-8028-0091-2). Eerdmans.

Poulos, George. Footsteps in the Sea: A Biography of Archbishop Athenagoras Cavadas. (Illus.). 186p. 1979. 7.95 (ISBN 0-916586-36-7); pap. 10.95 (ISBN 0-916586-35-9). Holy Cross Orthodox.

Rampa, T. Lobsang. The Rampa Story. pap. 2.95 (ISBN 0-552-11413-8). Weiser.

Sullivan, George. Pope John Paul II: The People's Pope. LC 83-40395. (Illus.). 120p. 1984. 11.95 (ISBN 0-8027-6523-8). Walker & Co.

Tsogyal, Yeshe. The Life & Liberation of Padmasambhava, 2 vols. Toussaint, G. C. & Douglas, Kenneth, trs. (Tibetan Translation Ser.). (Illus.). 1978. 60.00 set (ISBN 0-685-80849-1). Vol. I (ISBN 0-913546-18-6). Vol. II (ISBN 0-913546-20-8). Dharma Pub.

Van Buskirk, William R. Saviors of Mankind. LC 71-86790. (Essay Index Reprint Ser.). 1929. 32.00 (ISBN 0-8369-1432-5). Ayer Co Pubs.

Williams, Michael A., ed. Charisma & Sacred Biography. (JAAR Thematic Studies). 1982. 19.50 (ISBN 0-89130-681-1, 01-24-83). Scholars Pr GA.

Winebrenner, Jan. Steel in His Soul: The Dick Hillis Story. (Orig.). 1985. pap. 7.95 (ISBN 0-8024-2202-0). Moody.

RELIGIONS–DICTIONARIES

Ares, Jacques d' Encyclopedie De l'Esoterismelrisme, 2: Religions Non Chretiennes. Jacques D'ares. (Fr.). 244p. 1975. pap. 19.95 (ISBN 0-686-56899-0, M-6009). French & Eur.

Bertrand, F. M. Dictionnaire Universel, Historique et Comparatif des Toutes les Religions du Monde, 4 vols. Migne, J. P., ed. (Encyclopedie Theologique Ser.: Vols. 24-27). (Fr.). 2588p. Repr. of 1851 ed. lib. bdg. 329.50x (ISBN 0-89241-240-2). Caratzas.

Brandon, S. G. Dictionary of Comparative Religions. LC 76-11390. 1970. lib. bdg. 55.00 (ISBN 0-684-15561-3, ScribT). Scribner.

Canney, Maurice A. Encyclopaedia of Religions. LC 75-123370. 1970. Repr. of 1921 ed. 53.00 (ISBN 0-8103-3856-4). Gale.

Des Mas-Latrie, L. Dictionnaire de Statistique Religieuse. Migne, J. P., ed. (Nouvelle Encyclopedie Theologique Ser.: Vol. 9). (Fr.). 538p. Repr. of 1851 ed. lib. bdg. 69.00x (ISBN 0-89241-259-3). Caratzas.

Hill, Samuel S., ed. Encyclopedia of Religion in the South. LC 84-8957. viii, 878p. 1984. 60.00 (ISBN 0-86554-117-5, MUP/H97). Mercer Univ Pr.

Hinnells, John R., ed. The Facts on File Dictionary of Religions. LC 83-20834. 560p. 1984. 24.95x (ISBN 0-87196-862-2). Facts On File.

--The Penguin Dictionary of Religions. (Reference Ser.). 464p. 1984. pap. 7.95 (ISBN 0-14-051106-7). Penguin.

McDowell, Josh & Stewart, Don. Handbook of Today's Religions. 512p. 1983. 18.95 (ISBN 0-86605-121-X). Campus Crusade.

Mead, Frank S. & Hill, Samuel S. Handbook of Denominations in the United States. 8th ed. 400p. 1985. text ed. 10.95 (ISBN 0-687-16571-7). Abingdon.

Melton, J. Gordon, ed. Encyclopedia of American Religions. 2nd ed. 1200p. 1986. 165.00x (ISBN 0-8103-2133-5). Gale.

Parrinder, Geoffrey. A Dictionary of Non-Christian Religions. LC 73-4781. (Illus.). 320p. 1973. 10.95 (ISBN 0-664-20981-5). Westminster.

--Dictionary of Non-Christian Religions. 19.95 (ISBN 0-7175-0972-9). Dufour.

Zaehner, Robert C., ed. Concise Encyclopedia of Living Faiths. (Illus.). (YA) pap. 16.95x (ISBN 0-8070-1151-7, BP275). Beacon Pr.

RELIGIONS–HISTORY

Baird, Robert D. Category Formation & the History of Religions. (Religion & Reason Ser: No. 1). 178p. 1971. text ed. 20.50x (ISBN 90-2796-889-6). Mouton.

Baird, Robert D., ed. Methodological Issues in Religious Studies. LC 75-44170. (Orig.). 1976. lib. bdg. 14.95x (ISBN 0-914914-08-1); pap. text ed. 5.95x (ISBN 0-914914-07-3). New Horizons.

Brinton, Daniel G. Religions of Primitive Peoples. LC 79-88423. Repr. of 1897 ed. 22.50x (ISBN 0-8371-1763-1, BRR&). Greenwood.

Brown, Dale. Simulations on Brethren History. pap. 6.95 (ISBN 0-87178-794-6). Brethren.

Burrows, Millart. Founders of Great Religions: Being Personal Sketches of Famous Leaders. LC 72-13272. (Essay Index Reprint Ser.). Repr. of 1931 ed. 16.75 (ISBN 0-8369-8148-0). Ayer Co Pubs.

Burton, O. E. Study in Creative History. LC 71-105821. (Classics Ser). 1971. Repr. of 1932 ed. 26.00x (ISBN 0-8046-1197-1, Pub. by Kennikat). Assoc Faculty Pr.

Clemen, Carl C., et al. Religions of the World. facs. ed. LC 69-17570. (Essay Index Reprint Ser). 1931. 35.50 (ISBN 0-8369-0011-1). Ayer Co Pubs.

Cole, W. Owen. Five Religions in the Twentieth Century. LC 81-68724. (Illus.). 256p. 1981. pap. 11.95 (ISBN 0-8023-1272-1). Dufour.

Crone, Patricia & Cook, M. Hagarism: The Making of the Islamic World. LC 75-41714. 1980. pap. 14.95 (ISBN 0-521-29754-0). Cambridge U Pr.

Davenport, John. An Apologetical Reply to a Book Called: An Answer to the Unjust Complaint of W.B. (English Experience Ser.: No. 792). 1977. Repr. of 1636 ed. lib. bdg. 35.00 (ISBN 90-221-0792-2). Walter J Johnson.

Davis, Lola A. Towards a New World Religion. 256p. 1983. pap. 16.00 (ISBN 0-942494-77-6). Coleman Pub.

Drummond, Richard H. Unto the Churches: Jesus Christ, Christianity, & the Edgar Cayce Readings. 1978. pap. 7.95 (ISBN 0-87604-102-0). ARE Pr.

Eliade, Mircea. From Primitives to Zen: A Thematic Sourcebook in the History of Religions. LC 66-20775. 1978. 12.00 (ISBN 0-06-062134-6, RD 249, HarpR). Har-Row.

--A History of Religious Ideas: From the Stone Age to the Eleusinian Mysteries, Vol. 1. Trask, Willard R., tr. from Fr. LC 77-16784. xviii, 490p. 1979. 25.00x (ISBN 0-226-20400-6); pap. 16.95 (ISBN 0-226-20401-4). U of Chicago Pr.

Farnell, L. R. The Higher Aspects of Greek Religion. vii, 155p. 1977. 10.00 (ISBN 0-89005-206-9). Ares.

Farnell, Lewis R. Outline History of Greek Religion. 160p. (Orig.). 1986. 10.00 (ISBN 0-89005-025-2); pap. 10.00 (ISBN 0-89005-442-8). Ares.

Flaherty, Cornelia M. Go with Haste into the Mountains. 230p. (Orig.). 1984. 9.95 (ISBN 0-934318-42-5); pap. write for info. Falcon Pr MT.

Gaer, Joseph. How the Great Religions Began. LC 81-7764. 1981. pap. 6.95 (ISBN 0-396-08013-8). Dodd.

Hamilton, Bernard. Religion in the Medieval West. 224p. 1986. pap. text ed. 14.95 (ISBN 0-7131-6461-1). E Arnold.

Hill, Samuel S. The South & the North in American Religion. LC 80-234. (Mercer University Lamar Memorial Lecture Ser.: No. 23). 168p. 1980. 14.00x (ISBN 0-8203-0516-2). U of Ga Pr.

Jackson, Carl T. The Oriental Religious & American Thought: Nineteenth-Century Explorations. LC 80-25478. (Contributions in American Studies: No. 55). 296p. 1981. lib. bdg. 32.95 (ISBN 0-313-22491-9, JOR/). Greenwood.

Kellett, Ernest E. Short History of Religions. facsimile ed. LC 71-156671. (Essay Index Reprint Ser). Repr. of 1934 ed. 30.00 (ISBN 0-8369-2281-6). Ayer Co Pubs.

McAfee, Ward. A History of the World's Great Religions. 240p. (Orig.). 1983. lib. bdg. 27.00 (ISBN 0-8191-3394-9); pap. text ed. 12.25 (ISBN 0-8191-3395-7). U Pr of Amer.

Moore, George F. History of Religions, 2 vols. 19.95 ea. (Pub. by T & T Clark Ltd UK). Vol. 1, 1914, 654 pgs (ISBN 0-567-07202-9). Vol. 2, 1920, 568 pgs (ISBN 0-567-07203-7). Fortress.

Obelkevich, Jim & Roper, Lyndal. Disciplines of Faith. 512p. 1987. 55.00 (ISBN 0-7102-0750-6, Pub. by Routledge UK); pap. 25.00 (ISBN 0-7102-0993-2). Methuen Inc.

Parrinder, Geoffrey, ed. World Religions: From Ancient History to the Present. (Illus.). 528p. 1985. pap. 14.95 (ISBN 0-8160-1289-X). Facts on File.

Piepkorn, Arthur C. Profiles in Belief: The Religious Bodies of the United States & Canada, Vols. 3 & 4. Incl. Vol. 3. Holiness & Pentecostal Bodies; Vol. 4. Evangelical, Fundamental, & Other Christian Bodies. 1979. Set. 25.45i (ISBN 0-06-066581-5, HarpR). Har-Row.

Puech, Henri-Charles. Histoire des Religions, 3 vols. (Historique Ser.). Vols. 1 & 2. 59.95 ea.; Vol. 2. 69.95 (ISBN 0-686-56461-8). French & Eur.

Rupp, Israel D. He Pasa Ekklesia: An Original History of the Religious Denominations at Present Existing in the United States Containing Authentic Accounts of Their Rise, Progress, Statistics. 30.00 (ISBN 0-8369-7149-3, 7981). Ayer Co Pubs.

--The Religious Denominations in the United States: Their Past History, Present Condition, & Doctrines. LC 72-2943. Repr. of 1861 ed. 67.50 (ISBN 0-404-10709-5). AMS Pr.

Sandifer, Kevin W. A Layman's Look at Starting a Religious Archives. Hall, Renee, et al, eds. 48p. (Orig.). 1982. pap. text ed. 4.50 (ISBN 0-910653-00-3, 8101-A). Archival Servs.

Sanford, James H. Zen-Man Ikkyu. LC 81-5724. (Harvard Studies in World Religions). 1981. 18.00 (ISBN 0-89130-499-1, 030002); pap. 13.50 (ISBN 0-89130-500-9). Scholars Pr GA.

Shupe, Anson D., Jr. Six Perspectives on New Religions: A Case Study Approach. LC 81-9464. (Studies in Religion & Society: Vol. 1). 246p. 1981. 49.95x (ISBN 0-88946-983-0). E Mellen.

Smith, Hannah. Religious Fanaticism. Strachey, Ray, ed. & intro. by. LC 72-8252. Orig. Title: Group Movements of the Past & Experiments in Guidance. Repr. of 1928 ed. 21.50 (ISBN 0-404-11005-3). AMS Pr.

Toy, Crawford H. Introduction to the History of Religions. LC 76-126655. Repr. of 1913 ed. 27.50 (ISBN 0-404-06498-1). AMS Pr.

RELIGIONS–JUVENILE LITERATURE

Berger, Gilda. Religion. (A Reference First Bk.). 96p. 1983. PLB 9.40 (ISBN 0-531-04538-2). Watts.

Hamilton, Dorothy. Last One Chosen. LC 82-3150. (Illus.). 112p. (Orig.). 1982. pap. 3.95 (ISBN 0-8361-3306-4). Herald Pr.

Hofman, David. God & His Messengers. (Illus.). 1986. pap. 5.95 (ISBN 0-85398-049-7). G Ronald Pub.

Jones, Arthur. Illustrated Dictionary of World Religions. pap. 20.00 (ISBN 0-08-024176-X). Pergamon.

McGuire, Michael A. Father McGuire's New, Modern Catechism Know, Love, & Serve: The Holy Father, Our God-Given Supreme Teacher. LC 73-158919. (Know, Love, & Serve Catechisms Ser.). (Illus.). 222p. 1973. pap. 11.00 (ISBN 0-913382-43-4, 103-5). Prow Bks-Franciscan.

--Father McGuire's New, Modern Catechism Know, Love, & Serve, Bk. 1. LC 73-158919. (Know, Love & Serve Catechisms). (Illus.). 58p. 1971. pap. 5.25 (ISBN 0-913382-39-6, 103-1). Prow Bks-Franciscan.

--Father McGuire's New, Modern Catechism Know, Love, & Serve: Preparing for First Holy Communion, BK. 2. LC 73-158919. (Know, Love, & Serve Catechisms Ser.). (Illus.). 90p. 1971. pap. 6.50 (ISBN 0-913382-40-X, 103-2). Prow Bks-Franciscan.

--Father McGuire's New, Modern Catechism Know, Love, & Serve, Bk. 3. LC 73-158919. (Know, Love, & Serve Catechisms Ser.). (Illus.). 175p. 1972. pap. 9.50 (ISBN 0-913382-41-8, 103-3). Prow Bks-Franciscan.

--Father McGuire's New, Modern Catechism Know, Love, & Serve, Bk. 4. LC 73-158919. (Know, Love, & Serve Catechisms Ser.). (Illus.). 192p. 1973. pap. 10.00 (ISBN 0-913382-42-6, 103-4). Prow Bks-Franciscan.

Mangieri, Rose M. My Companion to Know, Love, & Serve. LC 73-158919. (Know, Love, & Serve Catechisms Ser.). (Illus.). 85p. (Orig.). 1977. pap. 5.50 (ISBN 0-913382-45-0, 103-7). Prow Bks-Franciscan.

Marshall, Catherine. Friends with God. (Illus.). 1972. pap. 1.95 (ISBN 0-380-01199-9, 52803-7). Avon.

Martin, John D. Living Together on God's Earth. (Christian Day School Ser.). 1974. 12.95x (ISBN 0-87813-915-X); tchr's. guide 19.65x (ISBN 0-87813-910-9). Christian Light.

Moore, Ruth N. The Sorrel Horse. LC 82-3136. 144p. (Orig.). 1982. pap. 3.95 (ISBN 0-8361-3303-X). Herald Pr.

Rice, Edward. American Saints & Seers: American-Born Religions & the Genius Behind Them. LC 81-15293. (Illus.). 240p. 1982. 11.95 (ISBN 0-02-775980-6, Four Winds). Macmillan.

Williamson, Nancy S. Inside & Occupied. LC 82-3139. 192p. (Orig.). 1982. pap. 9.95 (ISBN 0-8361-3304-8). Herald Pr.

RELIGIONS–RELATIONS

Coward, Harold. Pluralism: Challenge to World Religions. LC 84-14737. 144p. (Orig.). 1985. pap. 8.95 (ISBN 0-88344-710-X). Orbis Bks.

RELIGIONS (PROPOSED, UNIVERSAL, ETC.)

Bailey, Alice A. The Reappearance of the Christ. 1978. 18.00 (ISBN 0-85330-014-3); pap. 7.00 (ISBN 0-85330-114-X). Lucis.

Bennett, J. G. Works on Subud, 3 vols. 300.00 (ISBN 0-8490-1332-1). Gordon Pr.

Bromley, David G. & Hammond, Philip E., eds. The Future of New Religious Movements. 288p. 1987. 39.95 (ISBN 0-86554-237-6); pap. 19.95 (ISBN 0-86554-238-4). Mercer Univ Pr.

Clair, Frederic F. Ultimate Defense: A Practical Plan to Prevent Man's Self-Destruction. LC 59-6490. 1959. 3.30 (ISBN 0-8048-0606-3). C E Tuttle.

Hocking, William E. Living Religions & a World Faith. LC 75-3187. (Hibbert Lectures Ser. 1938). Repr. of 1940 ed. 28.50 (ISBN 0-404-59189-2). AMS Pr.

Johnson, Samuel. Oriental Religions & Their Relation to Universal Religion. 999p. Repr. of 1877 ed. text ed. 42.50x (ISBN 0-89644-558-5, Pub. by Chineses Matl Ctr). Coronet Bks.

Moreno, J. L. Words of the Father. 8.00 (ISBN 0-685-06817-X); pap. 6.00 (ISBN 0-685-06818-8). Beacon Hse.

Morris, Charles W. Paths of Life: Preface to a World Religion. LC 72-94732. 228p. 1973. pap. 2.25x (ISBN 0-226-53879-6, P541, Phoen). U of Chicago Pr.

Rofe, Husein. The Path of Subud. 69.95 (ISBN 0-8490-0805-0). Gordon Pr.

Sheils, W. J. & Wood, Diana, eds. Voluntary Religion, Vol. 23. 544p. 1987. text ed. 49.95 (ISBN 0-631-15054-4). Basil Blackwell.

RELIGIONS, COMPARATIVE

see Religions

RELIGIONS, UNIVERSAL

see Religions (Proposed, Universal, etc.)

RELIGIOUS AND ECCLESIASTICAL INSTITUTIONS

see also Mosques; Temples

Harrison, H. D. How to Start a Bible Institute. 1978. pap. 2.95 (ISBN 0-89265-051-6). Randall Hse.

Hite, Jordan, et al, eds. Religious Institutes, Secular Institutes, Societies of the Apostolic Life. (A Handbook on Canons Ser.: Nos. 573-746). 400p. 1985. pap. 22.50 (ISBN 0-8146-1403-5). Liturgical Pr.

Kerr, Hugh T., Jr., ed. Compend of the Institutes of the Christian Religion by John Calvin. 240p. 1964. pap. 8.95 (ISBN 0-664-24557-9). Westminster.

Reverend Mother Ruth. In Wisdom Thou Hast Made Them. Galanter, Patricia, ed. (Illus.). 141p. 1986. 15.95x (ISBN 0-937431-01-X). Adams Bannister Cox.

White, Jerry. The Church & the Parachurch: An Uneasy Marriage. LC 83-12125. (Critical Concern Ser.). 1983. 10.95 (ISBN 0-88070-018-1). Multnomah.

RELIGIOUS ART

see Cathedrals; Christian Art and Symbolism; Church Architecture; Idols and Images; Mosques; Temples;

also Art, Buddhist; Art, Gothic; Art, Medieval, and similar headings

RELIGIOUS ARTICLES

Dewhurst, C. Kurt, et al. Religious Folk Art in America: Reflections of Faith. (Illus.). 163p. 1983. 29.95 (ISBN 0-525-93300-X, 02908-870). Dutton.

De Winter, Patrick M. The Sacral Treasure of the Guelphs. LC 85-3820. (Illus.). 160p. 1985. pap. 14.95X (ISBN 0-910386-81-1, Pub. by The Cleveland Museum of Art). Ind U Pr.

Perlman, Alice. Torah Pointers in the Collection of the Judah L. Magnes Museum. (Illus.). 24p. (Orig.). 1987. pap. 4.95 (ISBN 0-943376-30-0). Magnes Mus.

Sussman, Varda. Ornamented Jewish Oil Lamps. (Illus.). 144p. 1982. pap. text ed. 55.00x (ISBN 0-85668-164-4, Pub. by Aris & Phillips UK). Humanities.

RELIGIOUS BELIEF

see Belief and Doubt; Faith

RELIGIOUS BIOGRAPHY

see also Christian Biography

Ahlstrom, Sydney E. & Mullin, Robert B. The Scientific Theist: A Life of Francis Ellingwood Abbot. 208p. 1987. 29.95 (ISBN 0-86554-236-8). Mercer Univ Pr.

Alberding, Faye V. Morrow & Miracles. (Illus.). 1983. 5.95 (ISBN 0-8062-2203-4). Carlton.

Anderson, Elizabeth Y. Faith in the Furnace. LC 84-72818. (Illus.). 1985. 10.00 (ISBN 0-9614002-0-X). E Y Anderson.

Arasteh, A. R. Rumi the Persian: Rebirth in Creativity & Love. 1970. 6.50x (ISBN 0-87902-043-1). Orientalia.

Archbishop Nikon Rklitsky, ed. Zhizneopisanie i Tvorenije Blazhennejshago Antonia, Mitropolita Kievskago i Galitzkago, v 17 tomakh, 17 vols. Tr. of The Life & Works of His Beatitude Anthony, Metropolitan of Kiev & Galitch. 6000p. 1971. pap. 200.00 (ISBN 0-317-29015-0). Holy Trinity.

Augur, Dorothy. Love's Old Song. 1984. pap. 6.95 (ISBN 0-89221-129-6, Pub. by Sonlife Intl). New Leaf.

Bayizian, Elise A. Mesrob Mashtotz: A Fifth Century Life. (Armenian Church Classics Ser.). (Illus.). 39p. (Orig.). 1984. pap. 4.00 (ISBN 0-934728-14-3). D O A C.

Bennett, John G. The Long Pilgrimage: The Life & Teaching of Shivapuri Baba. LC 81-66139. 191p. pap. 7.95 (ISBN 0-913922-54-4). Dawn Horse Pr.

Bershadsky, Luba & Millington, Ada. I Know His Touch. LC 83-72042. 192p. (Orig.). 1984. pap. 6.95 (ISBN 0-89107-299-3, Crossway Bks). Good News.

Bowden, Henry W. Dictionary of American Religious Biography. Gaustad, Edwin S., ed. LC 76-5258. (Orig.). 1976. lib. bdg. 45.00 (ISBN 0-8371-8906-3, BAR/). Greenwood.

Bowman, Billye G. Had I Known You Better, Lord I'd a Come Runnin' with a Bucket. Goodman, James, ed. 240p. (Orig.). 1986. pap. 10.00 (ISBN 0-89896-140-8, Linolean). Larksdale.

Buddhist Text Translation Society Staff, tr. from Chinese. Pictorial Biography of the Venerable Master Hsu Yun, Vol. 2. (Illus.). 236p. (Orig.). 1985. pap. 8.00 (ISBN 0-88139-116-6). Buddhist Text.

Campano, Giovanni. Antonio: Opera Omnia. 608p. 1495. Repr. of 1495 ed. text ed. 99.36 (ISBN 0-576-72225-1, Pub. by Gregg Intl Pubs England). Gregg Intl.

Carretto, Carlo. I Sought & I Found: My Experience of God & of the Church. Barr, Robert R., tr. from Ital. Tr. of Ho Cercato E. Ho Trovato. 144p. 1984. pap. 7.95 (ISBN 0-88344-202-7). Orbis Bks.

Cutler, William P. & Cutler, Julia P. Life, Journals & Correspondence of Rev. Manasseh Cutler, L.L.D, 2 vols. (Illus.). 1032p. 1987. Set. text ed. 40.00x (ISBN 0-8214-0859-3). Ohio U Pr.

Daughters of St. Paul. Heroes from Every Walk of Life. 1981. 5.00 (ISBN 0-8198-3303-7); pap. 4.00 (ISBN 0-8198-3304-5). Dghtrs St Paul.

Douie, Decima L. & Farmer, David H., eds. Magna Vita Sancti Hugonis: The Life of St. Hugh of Lincoln. (Medieval Texts Ser.). (Illus.). 1985. Vol. I. 45.00x (ISBN 0-19-822207-6); Vol. II. 45.00x (ISBN 0-19-822208-4). Oxford U Pr.

Durham, G. Homer. N. Eldon Tanner: His Life & Service. LC 82-9681. (Illus.). 370p. 1982. 9.95 (ISBN 0-87747-913-5). Deseret Bk.

Edwards, Dale. Founded Upon a Rock. 1977. pap. 3.95 (ISBN 0-89265-043-5). Randall Hse.

Egbert, Elaine. Hardly an Angel in Sight. Woolsey, Raymond H., ed. (Banner Ser.). 128p. (Orig.). 1987. pap. 6.50 (ISBN 0-8280-0369-6). Review & Herald.

Eitel, Alta W. Yon Mountain: A Doctor of Faith Walks with God. LC 85-90286. 101p. 1986. 10.95 (ISBN 0-533-06783-9). Vantage.

Ellis, William E. A "Man of Books & a Man of the People". E. Y. Mullins & the Crisis Moderate Southern Baptist Leadership. xi, 228p. 1985. text ed. 18.95 (ISBN 0-86554-175-2, MUP-H165). Mercer Univ Pr.

Etheridge, Myrna L. Fearing No Evil. (Illus.). 119p. (Orig.). 1984. pap. 5.00x (ISBN 0-937417-00-9). Etheridge Minist.

Field, Filip. W. Norman Cooper - a Prophet for Our Time. LC 79-52443. 1979. 7.50 (ISBN 0-87516-417-X); pap. 4.50 (ISBN 0-87516-372-6). De Vorss.

Fogelklou, Emilia. Reality & Radiance: Selected Autobiographical Works of Emilia Fogelklou. Lutz, Howard T., ed. & tr. from Swedish. 196p. (Orig.). 1986. pap. 10.95 (ISBN 0-913408-89-1). Friends United.

Forest, James H. Thomas Merton: A Pictorial Biography. LC 80-82249. (Illus.). 112p. (Orig.). 1980. pap. 5.95 (ISBN 0-8091-2284-7). Paulist Pr.

Fox, Robert J. Call of Heaven: Father Gino, Stigmatist. 2nd ed. (Illus.). 232p. pap. 5.95 (ISBN 0-931888-22-0). Christendom Pubns.

Gallagher, Joseph. Pain & the Privilege: Diary of a City Priest. LC 82-1766. 384p. 1983. pap. 7.95 (ISBN 0-385-19019-0, Im). Doubleday.

Gibbons, Francis M. David O. McKay: Apostle to the World, Prophet of God. LC 86-4564. (Illus.). 455p. 1986. 13.95 (ISBN 0-87579-036-4). Deseret Bk.

Hall, Manly P. Twelve World Teachers. pap. 6.50 (ISBN 0-89314-816-4). Philos Res.

Ham, Wayne & Ham, Marlene. My Million Faces. (World Religion Ser.). 74p. 1985. Set. pap. 3.00 (ISBN 0-8309-0415-8); Faces from India. pap. 3.00 (ISBN 0-8309-0416-6); Faces from the Orient. pap. 3.00 (ISBN 0-8309-0417-4); Faces from the Eternal. pap. 3.00 (ISBN 0-8309-0418-2). Herald Hse.

Hamre, James S. Georg Sverdrup: Educator, Theologian, Churchman. 194p. 1986. 15.00 (ISBN 0-87732-071-3). Norwegian-Am Hist Assn.

Harrison, Ted. Much Beloved Daughter: The Story of Florence Li. 110p. 1986. pap. 6.95 (ISBN 0-8192-1378-0). Morehouse.

Hembree, Ron. The Mark Buntain Story. LC 83-73187. 256p. 1984. pap. 3.95 (ISBN 0-87123-593-5, 200593). Bethany Hse.

Hildebrand, Henry. In His Loving Service. Mattson, Lloyd, frwd. by. 226p. (Orig.). 1985. pap. 6.95 (ISBN 0-942684-08-7). Camp Guidepts.

Hopkins, C. Howard. John R. Mott, Eighteen Sixty-Five to Nineteen Fifty-Five: A Biography. LC 79-15069. 22.50 (ISBN 0-8028-3525-2). Eerdmans.

Hospital, Clifford G. Breakthrough: Insights of the Great Religious Discoverers. LC 85-5135. 208p. (Orig.). 1985. pap. 9.95 (ISBN 0-88344-206-X). Orbis Bks.

Hyman, B. D. & Hyman, Jeremy. Narrow Is the Way. Golbitz, Pat, ed. LC 86-28588. 352p. 1987. 17.95 (ISBN 0-688-06345-4). Morrow.

Isichei, Elizabeth. Entirely for God. (Cistercian Studies: No. 43). 132p. 1980. pap. 11.95 (ISBN 0-87907-943-6). Cistercian Pubns.

Jung. Men of the Spirit. cancelled (ISBN 0-685-48594-3). Feldheim.

Kaiser, Grace. Dr. Frau. LC 86-81059. 168p. 1986. 14.95 (ISBN 0-934672-34-2). Good Bks PA.

King, Mike. The Mike King Story. LC 85-81940. (Illus.). 176p. (Orig.). 1985. 15.95 (ISBN 0-934672-33-4). Good Bks PA.

--The Mike King Story. LC 85-81940. (Illus.). pap. 5.95 (ISBN 0-934672-42-3). Good Bks PA.

Kulp, Kim. Yes. 144p. (Orig.). 1987. pap. 5.95 (ISBN 0-937947-03-2). Publius Pub.

Lappin, Peter. The Falcon & the Dove: The Story of Laura Vicuna. (Illus.). 180p. (YA) 1985. pap. 4.95 (ISBN 0-89944-067-3). Don Bosco Multimedia.

Leclercq, Jean, intro. by. Thomas Merton on St. Bernard. (Cistercian Studies: No. 9). 1980. 13.95 (ISBN 0-87907-809-X); pap. 4.95 (ISBN 0-87907-909-6). Cistercian Pubns.

Lejbowicz, Agnes. Omraam Mikhael Aivanhov: Master of the Great Universal White Brotherhood. (Testimonials Ser.). 115p. (Orig.). 1982. pap. 4.95 (ISBN 2-85566-191-9, Pub. by Prosveta France). Prosveta USA.

Lentfoehr, Sr. Therese. Words & Silence: On the Poetry of Thomas Merton. LC 78-21475. 1979. 12.50 (ISBN 0-8112-0712-9); pap. 4.95 (ISBN 0-8112-0713-7, NDP472). New Directions.

Luis Palau: Calling the Nations to Christ. Jenkins, Jerry B., as told to. (Illus.). 1983. pap. 4.95 (ISBN 0-8024-0461-8). Moody.

Lysaght, Moira. Father Theobald Matthew: Apostle of Temperance. 48p. 1984. 3.00 (ISBN 0-912414-42-1). Lumen Christi.

McCluney, Roalla. Outwit the Devil. 160p. (Orig.). 1987. pap. 6.95 (ISBN 0-89896-296-X, Linolean). Larksdale.

McGinn, Bernard. The Calabrian Abbott: Jaochim of Fiore in the History of Thought. 320p. 1985. 17.95 (ISBN 0-02-919550-0). Macmillan.

McGinn, Bernard, et al. Meister Eckhart: Teacher & Preacher. (Classics of Western Spirituality Ser.: Vol. 52). 448p. 1986. 15.95 (ISBN 0-8091-0377-X); pap. 12.95 (ISBN 0-8091-2827-6). Paulist Pr.

Mauro, Philip. More Than a Prophet: On John the Baptist. pap. 1.50 (ISBN 0-685-36794-0). Reiner.

Metzger, Charles R. The Silent River: A Pastoral Elegy in the Form of a Recollection of Arctic Adventure. (Illus.). xi, 161p. (Orig.). 1984. pap. 7.95x (ISBN 0-9613094-0-7). Omega LA.

Miles, Michael. Love Is Always. LC 86-2378. 320p. 1986. 17.95 (ISBN 0-688-06218-0). Morrow.

Miner, Caroline E. & Kimball, Edward L. Camilla. LC 80-69723. (Illus.). 1980. 8.95 (ISBN 0-87747-845-7). Deseret Bk.

Missionary Research Library. New York Dictionary Catalog of the Missionary Research Library, 17 vols. 1968. Set. 1680.00 (ISBN 0-8161-0778-5, Hall Library). G K Hall.

Murphy, Paul I. & Arlington, R. Rene. La Popessa. LC 82-61880. (Illus.). 296p. (Orig.). 1983. 16.50 (ISBN 0-446-51258-3). Warner Bks.

Murray, Iain H., ed. Diary of Kenneth Macrae. (Illus.). 535p. 1980. 19.95 (ISBN 0-85151-297-6). Banner of Truth.

Nester, Lois M. Lady of Faith. (Illus.). 112p. 1987. 7.95 (ISBN 0-8059-3040-X). Dorrance.

Niwano, Nikkyo. Lifetime Beginner: An Autobiography. Gage, Richard L., tr. from Japanese. Orig. Title: Shoshin Issho & Niwano Nikkyo Jiden. (Illus.). 344p. 1978. 14.95 (Pub. by Kosei Publishing Co). C E Tuttle.

--Shakyamuni Buddha: A Narrative Biography. rev. ed. Davis, Rebecca M., ed. Miyazaki, Kojiro, tr. from Japanese. LC 80-154779. Orig. Title: Bukkyo No Inochi Hokeyo. (Illus.). 128p. 1980. pap. 3.50 (ISBN 4-333-01001-2, Pub. by Kosei Publishing Co). C E Tuttle.

Omar, H. A. The Great Warriors. 1984. pap. 15.00x (ISBN 0-7212-0631-X, Pub. by Regency Pr). State Mutual Bk.

Paulk, Earl. The Provoker. Weeks, Trisha, ed. 400p. (Orig.). 1986. pap. 9.95 (ISBN 0-917595-09-2). K-Dimension.

Peterson, Owen. The Divine Discontent: The Life of Nathan S. S. Beman. (Illus.). xvii, 224p. 1985. text ed. 21.95 (ISBN 0-86554-170-1, MUP-H160). Mercer Univ Pr.

Pratt, Parley P. Autobiography of Parley P. Pratt. Pratt, Parley P., Jr., pref. by. LC 85-10264. (Classics in Mormon Literature Ser.). (Illus.). 475p. 1985. 14.95 (ISBN 0-87747-740-X). Deseret Bk.

Price, Eugenia. The Burden is Light: The Autobigraphy of a Transformed Pagan. 176p. pap. 2.95 (ISBN 0-8007-8583-5, Spire Bks). Revell.

Ramachandran. Sri Sankara Vijayam. 1977. pap. 2.25 (ISBN 0-89744-123-0, Pub. by Ganesh & Co. India). Auromere.

Rasooli, Jay M. & Allen, Cady H. Dr. Sa'eed of Iran: Kurdish Physician to Princes & Peasants, Nobles & Nomads. LC 57-13245. (Illus.). 192p. 1983. pap. 6.95 (ISBN 0-87808-743-5). William Carey Lib.

Reece, Colleen L. Comrades of the Trail. Wheeler, Gerald, ed. (Banner Ser.). 96p. (Orig.). 1987. pap. 6.50 (ISBN 0-8280-0355-6). Review & Herald.

Reid, Russell L. A Romance with Reality. 1983. 5.75 (ISBN 0-8062-2185-2). Carlton.

Sattler, Gary. God's Glory, Neighbor's Good: Francke's Biography & Sermons. 272p. 1982. pap. 8.95 (ISBN 0-910452-50-4). Covenant.

Scott, Ida B. My Hopes Were Shattered at Age Six: Read How God Blessed Me. 1981. 4.95 (ISBN 0-8062-1837-1). Carlton.

Sears, Lloyd C. Eyes of Jehovah: Life of James A. Harding. 8.50 (ISBN 0-89225-089-5). Gospel Advocate.

Seton, W. W. Some New Sources for the Life of Blessed Agnes of Bohemia. 184p. 1815. text ed. 33.12 (ISBN 0-576-99207-0, Pub. by Gregg Intl Pubs England). Gregg Intl.

Sharpe, Bertie W. Only God Cast out the Anti-Christ. 1983. 4.95 (ISBN 0-8062-2214-X). Carlton.

Sider, E. Morris. Messenger of Grace: A Biography of C. N. Hostetter Jr. LC 82-71583. 1982. cloth 7.95 (ISBN 0-916035-06-9); pap. 5.95 (ISBN 0-916035-07-7). Evangel Indiana.

Skinner, Craig. Lamplighter & Son. LC 82-82947. 1984. 13.95 (ISBN 0-8054-5705-4). Broadman.

Soper, Donald. Calling for Action: An Autobiographical Enquiry. LC 84-129410. (Illus.). 172p. 1985. 16.00 (ISBN 0-86051-265-7). Salem Hse Pubs.

Spink, Kathryn. A Universal Heart: The Life & Vision of Brother Roger of Taize. LC 86-45027. (Illus.). 192p. 1986. 14.95 (ISBN 0-06-067504-7, HarpR). Har-Row.

Steinberg, Jeff & Hefley, James C. Masterpiece in Progress. 288p. 1986. 11.95 (ISBN 0-8423-4194-3). Tyndale.

Sturlaugson, Mary F. A Soul So Rebellious. 88p. 1980. 8.95 (ISBN 0-87747-841-4). Deseret Bk.

Sullivan, Clayton. Called to Preach, Condemned to Survive: The Education of Clayton Sullivan. xiv, 237p. 1985. 19.95 (ISBN 0-86554-173-6, MUP-H163). Mercer Univ Pr.

Sussman, Cornelia & Sussman, Irving. Thomas Merton. LC 80-924. 176p. 1980. pap. 3.95 (ISBN 0-385-17172-2, Im). Doubleday.

Taylor, Horace M. Reminiscences of an Army Chaplain. LC 86-1472. Date not set. price not set. (ISBN 0-9617424-0-2). H M Taylor.

Triggs, Tony D. Founders of Religion. LC 82-60697. (In Profile Ser.). 64p. PLB 13.96 (ISBN 0-382-06676-6). Silver.

True, Michael. Justice Seekers Peace Makers: 32 Portraits in Courage. (Illus.). 160p. 1985. pap. 5.95 (ISBN 0-89622-212-8). Twenty Third.

Vail, Harley W. When Harley Heard from Heaven. LC 82-72633. 84p. 1982. pap. 2.95 (ISBN 0-9609096-0-5). Bethel Pub Or.

Vanderwerff, Corrine. An Arrow Returned. Woosley, Raymond H., ed. (Banner Ser.). 144p. (Orig.). 1987. pap. 6.50 (ISBN 0-8280-0364-5). Review & Herald.

Voskuil, Dennis. Mountains into Goldmines: Robert Schuller & the Gospel of Success. LC 83-1729. pap. 47.00 (ISBN 0-317-30165-9, 2025347). Bks Demand UMI.

Watts, Alan W. In My Own Way: An Autobiography. 1973. pap. 5.95 (ISBN 0-394-71951-4, Vin). Random.

White, Ellen G. Patriarchs & Prophets. 805p. 1958. deluxe ed. 9.95 (ISBN 0-8163-0038-0, 16082-0); pap. 5.95 (ISBN 0-8163-0039-9, 16083-8). Pacific Pr Pub Assn.

--Prophets & Kings. 752p. deluxe ed. 9.95 (ISBN 0-8163-0040-2, 16642-1); pap. 5.95 (ISBN 0-8163-0041-0, 16643-9). Pacific Pr Pub Assn.

Winkler, Kenneth D. Pilgrim of the Clear Light: The Biography of Dr. Walter Y. Evans-Wentz. Govinda A., intro. by. LC 81-70193. (Illus.). 140p. (Orig.). 1982. pap. 4.95 (ISBN 0-942058-00-3). Dawnfire.

Witt, Roselyn. W. Norman Cooper: A View of a Holy Man. LC 81-70657. 96p. 1982. 7.50 (ISBN 0-87516-492-7); pap. 4.50 (ISBN 0-87516-471-4). De Vorss.

Wolsted, Mabel E. Chosen Partners. 1983. 9.95 (ISBN 0-8062-1918-1). Carlton.

Zwalf, Wladimir. Buddism: Art & Faith. (Illus.). 300p. 1985. text ed. 45.00x (ISBN 0-02-934500-6). Macmillan.

RELIGIOUS BROADCASTING

see Radio in Religion

RELIGIOUS CEREMONIES

see Rites and Ceremonies

RELIGIOUS CORPORATIONS

see Corporations, Religious

RELIGIOUS DANCE, MODERN

Adams, Doug. Appropriating Australian Folk Dances into Sacred Dance. 1987. pap. 3.00 (ISBN 0-941500-45-4). Sharing Co.

--Changing Biblical Imagery & Artistic Identity in 20th Century Liturgical Dance. 1984. pap. 3.00 (ISBN 0-941500-31-4). Sharing Co.

--Sacred Dance with Senior Citizens in Churches, Convalescent Homes, & Retirement Homes. 1982. pap. 3.00 (ISBN 0-941500-27-6). Sharing Co.

Blessin, Ann M. Sacred Dance with Physically & Mentally Handicapped. Adams, Doug, ed. 1982. pap. 3.00 (ISBN 0-941500-28-4). Sharing Co.

Davies, J. G. & Van Zyl, P. A Shaker Dance Service Reconstucted. 1984. pap. 3.00 (ISBN 0-941500-34-9). Sharing Co.

Irwin, Kay. Primer of Prayer Gesture. 43p. 1977. pap. 3.00 (ISBN 0-941500-21-7). Sharing Co.

Mealy, Norman & Rock, Judith. Music, Dance & Religion: The Performing Arts in Worship. (Illus.). 192p. 1985. 15.95 (ISBN 0-13-607219-4); pap. 8.95 (ISBN 0-13-607201-1). P-H.

Packard, Dane. The Church Becoming Christ's Body: The Small Church's Manual of Dances for Holy Seasons. Adams, Doug, ed. 110p. (Orig.). 1985. pap. 7.95 (ISBN 0-941500-35-7). Sharing Co.

Phillippou, Margaret J. Transcendental Dancing. 1982. pap. 3.00 (ISBN 0-941500-29-2). Sharing Co.

Skidmore, Janet. Redemptive Dancing: Prayer Dance & Congregational Dance in the Life of the Contemporary Church. Adams, Doug, ed. pap. 2.50 (ISBN 0-941500-46-2). Sharing Co.

Taylor, Margaret & Adams, Doug. Hymns in Action for Everyone Nine to Ninety Dancing Today. 90p. 1985. pap. 7.95 (ISBN 0-941500-32-2). Sharing Co.

Winton-Henry, Cynthia. Leaps of Faith: Improvisational Dance in Worship & Education. Adams, Doug, ed. 1985. pap. 3.00 (ISBN 0-941500-33-0). Sharing Co.

Yates, Martha. Financing a Sacred Dance Choir. 56p. 1981. pap. 3.00 (ISBN 0-941500-19-5). Sharing Co.

RELIGIOUS DENOMINATIONS

see Religions; Sects;
also particular denominations and sects

RELIGIOUS DRAMA

see also Bible Plays; Christmas Plays; Easter–Drama; Liturgical Drama; Moralities; Mysteries and Miracle-Plays

Bates, Katharine L. The English Religious Drama. 1975. Repr. of 1911 ed. 30.00 (ISBN 0-8274-4103-7). R West.

Bennett, Gordon C. Acting Out Faith. Lambert, Herbert, ed. LC 86-6141. 160p. (Orig.). 1986. pap. 10.95 (ISBN 0-8272-0016-1). CBP.

--God Is My Fuehrer. (Orig.). 1970. pap. 1.50 (ISBN 0-377-80611-0). Friend Pr.

Berry, Joan P. What If...? 1985. 3.50 (ISBN 0-89536-729-7, 5813). CSS of Ohio.

Browne, E. Martin, ed. Religious Drama, Vol. 2: 21 Medieval Mystery & Morality Plays. 17.75 (ISBN 0-8446-2793-3). Peter Smith.

Council, Raymond. The One Who Made His Cross. 1986. 2.95 (ISBN 0-89536-793-9, 6811). CSS of Ohio.

Duckworth, John & Duckworth, Liz. The No-Frills Guide to Youth Group Drama. 64p. 1985. pap. 5.95 (ISBN 0-88207-574-8). Victor Bks.

Gibran, Kahlil. Lazarus & His Beloved. 64p. 1973. 5.95 (ISBN 0-8464-1165-2). Beekman Pubs.

Grimbol, William R. The Communion Clown Circle. 1985. 3.25 (ISBN 0-89536-734-3, 5818). CSS of Ohio.

Halverson, Marvin, ed. Religious Drama, Vol. 1: Five Plays. 11.25 (ISBN 0-8446-2792-5). Peter Smith.

--Religious Drama, Vol. 3. 11.25 (ISBN 0-8446-2794-1). Peter Smith.

Halvorson, Loren E. Grace at Point Zero. (Orig.). 1972. pap. 1.75 (ISBN 0-377-02111-3). Friend Pr.

Hatton, Thomas J. Joseph of Arimathea: An Easter Play. 1980. 4.25 (ISBN 0-89536-417-4, 1013). CSS of Ohio.

Henley, Gurden. He Is Risen Indeed! 1986. 3.50 (ISBN 0-89536-795-5, 6813). CSS of Ohio.

Huges, Robert D. Plays That'll Preach. LC 85-365. 1985. pap. 4.95 (ISBN 0-8054-6812-9). Broadman.

Irsch, Ed. As It Was Told: A Play for Christmas. 16p. (Orig.). 1980. pap. text ed. 3.75 (ISBN 0-89536-439-5, 0146). CSS of Ohio.

Janda, J. Julian: A Play Based on the Life of Julian of Norwich. 112p. (Orig.). 1984. pap. 6.95 (ISBN 0-8164-2632-5, 6464, HarpR). Har-Row.

Johnson, Albert. Best Church Plays: A Bibliography of Religious Drama. 11.25 (ISBN 0-8446-2328-8). Peter Smith.

Jones, Kathy. Acting for God. (Helping Hand Ser.). 48p. (YA) 1984. wkbk. 4.95 (ISBN 0-86653-236-6). Good Apple.

Joyce, Jon L. How to Use Chancel Drama Effectively. (Orig.). 1980. pap. 2.25 (ISBN 0-937172-00-6). JLJ Pubs.

Lee, Sharon. Grandfather Clock & Other Finger Plays, Word Rhythms, & Action Rhymes. (Illus.). 64p. 1984. pap. 5.95 (ISBN 0-86683-834-1, HarpR). Har-Row.

Meredith, Peter & Tailby, John, eds. The Staging of Religious Drama in Europe in the Middle Ages. Sleeman, Margaret & Ferrari, Raffaella, trs. (Early Drama, Art & Music Ser.). (Illus.). 301p. 1983. 24.95x (ISBN 0-918720-23-0). Medieval Inst.

--The Staging of Religious Drama in Europe in the Middle Ages. Sleeman, Margaret & Ferrari, Raffaella, trs. (Early Drama, Art & Music Ser.). (Illus.). 301p. 1983. pap. 14.95x (ISBN 0-918720-24-9). Medieval Inst.

Miller, Sarah H. Devotional Dramas for a Mission Witness. 1967. pap. 1.95 (ISBN 0-8054-9716-1). Broadman.

Miller, Sarah W. Devotional Dramas for the Christian Life. (Orig.). 1968. pap. 1.95 (ISBN 0-8054-9717-X). Broadman.

--A Variety Book of Puppet Scripts. LC 78-57276. 1978. pap. 4.50 (ISBN 0-8054-7515-X). Broadman.

Morey, Clinton R. The Denial: A Play for Lent. 1980. 3.95 (ISBN 0-89536-412-3, 0420). CSS of Ohio.

Mueller, Robert. For People Just Like Us. Sherer, Michael L., ed. (Orig.). 1986. pap. 3.75 (ISBN 0-89536-834-X, 6848). CSS of Ohio.

Nadasdy, Dean. Gospel Dramas: Twelve Plays for Worship in Lent & Other Seasons. LC 85-22886. 96p. (Orig.). 1985. pap. 4.95 (ISBN 0-8066-2185-0, 10-2829). Augsburg.

O'Gorman, Denis. Scriptual Dramas for Children. LC 77-70632. 232p. 1977. pap. 8.95 (ISBN 0-8091-2021-6). Paulist Pr.

Peele, George. Samples from the Love of King David & Fair Bethsabe: With Reference Portions of the Bible. Dreher, G. K., ed. LC 79-56834. 71p. (Orig.). 1980. pap. 4.95 (ISBN 0-9601000-2-4). Longshanks Bk.

Russ, Esther. The Eternal Echo of Easter: A Choral Drama. 1980. 4.50 (ISBN 0-89536-423-9, 0515). CSS of Ohio.

Sherer, Michael L., ed. Drama Anthology. (Orig.). 1987. pap. price not set (ISBN 0-89536-890-0, 7876). CSS of Ohio.

Smith, Judy G. Drama Through the Church Year. Zapel, Arthur L., ed. LC 84-61476. 164p. (Orig.). 1984. pap. 7.95 (ISBN 0-916260-26-7). Meriwether Pub.

Tiller, Howi. Asleep in the Light (A Musical for the Times) (Illus.). 41p. 1984. pap. text ed. 12.95 (ISBN 0-912315-79-2). Word Aflame.

Townsend, L., et al, eds. Parade of Plays I. 96p. 1986. pap. 5.95 (ISBN 0-89191-322-X). Cook.

Tozer, Tom. Amazing Grace & Her Incredible Place. 1984. 4.75 (ISBN 0-89536-706-8, 4802). CSS of Ohio.

Urfer, Pamela. Coming of Age in Judea: A Play about Young Jesus. 20p. (Orig.). 1983. pap. text ed. 3.95 (ISBN 0-912801-03-4). Creat Arts Dev.

--Five Short Plays about Jesus. 26p. (Orig.). 1983. pap. text ed. 3.95 (ISBN 0-912801-02-6). Creat Arts Dev.

--The Good-Wife. 40p. (Orig.). 1983. pap. text ed. 3.95 (ISBN 0-912801-01-8). Creat Arts Dev.

--Six Short Plays about Jesus. 35p. (Orig.). pap. text ed. 3.95 (ISBN 0-912801-07-7). Creat Arts Dev.

--Two Christmas Plays. 25p. (Orig.). pap. text ed. 3.95 (ISBN 0-912801-08-5). Creat Arts Dev.

Vaughn, Ruth. More Skits That Win. 1977. pap. 2.95 (ISBN 0-310-33671-6, 10942X). Zondervan.

Watson, Elizabeth W. Gift Wrap, Please. (Orig.). 1966. pap. 1.95 (ISBN 0-8054-9710-2). Broadman.

Wean, Ronald. One Must Die: Six-Week Lenten Drama Series. 1986. 6.50 (ISBN 0-89536-794-7, 6812). CSS of Ohio.

Whittaker, Violet. Puppet People Scripts. 1984. pap. 8.95 (ISBN 0-8010-9666-9). Baker Bk.

RELIGIOUS DRAMA–BIBLIOGRAPHY

Coleman, Edward D. Bible in English Drama: An Annotated Bibliography. rev. ed. 1969. 25.00x (ISBN 0-87068-034-X). Ktav.

--Bible in English Drama: An Annotated List of Plays. 1969. 6.95 (ISBN 0-87104-021-2, Co-Pub by Ktav). NY Pub Lib.

RELIGIOUS DRAMA–HISTORY AND CRITICISM

Baker, Donald C. & Murphy, J. L., eds. The Late Medieval Religious Plays of Bodleian Manuscripts Digby 133 & E Museo 160. (Early English Text Society Ser.). (Illus.). 1982. 37.50x (ISBN 0-19-722285-4). Oxford U Pr.

Ehrensperger, Harold A. & Lehrer, Stanley. Religious Drama: Ends & Means. LC 77-22986. (Illus.). 1977. Repr. of 1962 ed. lib. bdg. 32.50x (ISBN 0-8371-9744-9, EHRD). Greenwood.

Gibson, Arthur. The Silence of God: Creative Response to the Films of Ingmar Bergman. LC 81-18754. 171p. 1978. soft cover 9.95x (ISBN 0-88946-951-2). E Mellen.

Griffin, Nigel. Jesuit School Drama: Critical Literature. (Research Bibliographies & Checklists Ser.: 12). 54p. 1976. pap. 6.50 (ISBN 0-7293-0003-X, Pub. by Grant & Cutler). Longwood Pub Group.

Merchant, William M. Creed & Drama: An Essay in Religious Drama. LC 66-23222. pap. 31.80 (2027867). Bks Demand UMI.

Nagler, A. M. The Medieval Religious Stage: Shapes & Phantoms. LC 75-43328. (Illus.). 1976. 22.00x (ISBN 0-300-01986-6). Yale U Pr.

Raviez, Marilyn E. Early Colonial Religious Drama in Mexico: From Tzompantli to Golgotha. LC 77-157. pap. 68.30 (2029506). Bks Demand UMI.

Weales, Gerald C. Religion in Modern English Drama. LC 75-45367. 317p. 1976. Repr. of 1961 ed. lib. bdg. 24.75x (ISBN 0-8371-8735-4, WEME). Greenwood.

Wulff, Donna M. Drama as Mode of Religious Realization: The Vidaghamadhava of Rupa Gosvamin. (American Academy of Religion Academy Ser.: No. 43). 280p. 1985. 14.95 (ISBN 0-89130-608-0, 01 01 43). Scholars Pr GA.

RELIGIOUS DRAMA–PRESENTATION, ETC.

Parade of Plays for Your Church. 96p. pap. 5.95 (ISBN 0-317-47009-4, 33274, Chariot Bks). Cook.

RELIGIOUS EDUCATION

Here are entered works dealing with instruction in religion in school and private life, Cf. note under Church and Education.
see also Bible–Study; Christian Education; Confirmation–Instruction and Study; Discussion in Religious Education; Jewish Religious Education; Moral Education; Object-Teaching; Religion in the Public Schools; Sunday-Schools; Theology–Study and Teaching; Vacation Schools, Religious; Worship (Religious Education)

Aivanhov, Omraam M. Spiritual Alchemy. rev. ed. (Complete Works: Vol. 2). (Illus.). 205p. 1986. pap. 9.95 (ISBN 2-85566-371-7, Pub. by Prosveta France). Prosveta USA.

Arrington, French. Maintaining the Foundations. 1983. pap. 4.95 (ISBN 0-8010-0192-7). Baker Bk.

Autery & Holl. Help I Need a Bulletin Board. pap. 5.50 (ISBN 0-89137-621-6). Quality Pubns.

Barker, Kenneth. Religious Education, Catechesis & Freedom. LC 81-13962. 255p. (Orig.). 1981. pap. 12.95 (ISBN 0-89135-028-4). Religious Educ.

Barney, Kenneth D. Directions, Please. LC 82-82080. 128p. (Orig.). 1983. pap. 2.50 (ISBN 0-88243-856-5, 02-0856); tchr's. ed. 3.95 (ISBN 0-88243-197-8, 32-0197). Gospel Pub.

Bastide, Derek. Religious Education Five-Twelve. 27.00 (ISBN 1-85000-149-9, Falmer Press); pap. 14.00 (ISBN 1-85000-150-2). Taylor & Francis.

Betts, George H. The Curriculum of Religious Education. (Educational Ser.). 1924. Repr. 30.00 (ISBN 0-8482-7352-4). Norwood Edns.

Blazier, Kenneth D., ed. The Teaching Church at Work. 64p. 1980. pap. 3.50 (ISBN 0-8170-0879-9). Judson.

Boys, Mary C., ed. Ministry & Education in Conversation. LC 80-53204. 160p. (Orig.). 1981. pap. 6.95 (ISBN 0-88489-126-7). St Mary's.

Bright, Bill. How to Help Fulfill the Great Commission. (Transferable Concepts Ser.). 64p. 1981. pap. 1.25 (ISBN 0-918956-94-3). Campus Crusade.

Brokering, L. Thirty Six Creative Ideas for Children in the Church School. LC 12-2958. 1982. pap. 4.95 (ISBN 0-570-03865-0). Concordia.

Brown, Carolyn C. Developing Christian Education in a Smaller Church. LC 81-17563. (Griggs Educational Resources Ser.). 96p. (Orig.). 1982. pap. 7.75 (ISBN 0-687-10508-0). Abingdon.

Burgess, Harold W. An Invitation to Religious Education. LC 75-14980. 173p. 1975. lib. bdg. 12.95 (ISBN 0-89135-004-7); pap. 10.95 (ISBN 0-89135-019-5). Religious Educ.

Campus Crusade for Christ Staff. Discovery II. 1980. pap. 2.95 saddlestitched (ISBN 0-918956-63-3). Campus Crusade.

Christenson, Larry. Trinity Teacher Training Workshop Booklet. (Trinity Bible Ser.). 80p. 1975. pap. 2.95 (ISBN 0-87123-552-8, 240552). Bethany Hse.

Coe, George A. Social Theory of Religious Education. LC 78-89164. (American Education: Its Men, Institutions & Ideas, Ser. 1). 1969. Repr. of 1917 ed. 24.50 (ISBN 0-405-01402-3). Ayer Co Pubs.

Conn, Harvie M. & Rowen, Samuel F., eds. Missions & Theological Education in World Perspective. LC 84-72527. 484p. (Orig.). 1984. pap. text ed. 11.95 (ISBN 0-930957-00-8). Assocs Urbanus.

Craig, James D. Rejoice in the Lord. 32p. 1981. pap. 2.49 (ISBN 0-88151-018-1). Lay Leadership.

Crossan, John D. A Fragile Craft: The Work of Amos Niven Wilder. Richards, Kent, ed. LC 80-19755. 1981. pap. 8.95 (ISBN 0-89130-424-X, 06 11 03). Scholars Pr GA.

Curran, Dolores. Who, Me Teach My Child Religion? rev. ed. 156p. 1981. pap. 6.95 (HarpR). Har-Row.

Davidson, Robert. The Bible in Religious Education. 72p. 1980. pap. 5.00x (ISBN 0-905312-10-4, Pub. by Scot Acad Pr). Longwood Pub Group.

A Day in the Life of a DRE. 36p. 1977. 3.60 (ISBN 0-318-20612-9). Natl Cath Educ.

Discovery Class Leader's Guide. 4th ed. LC 83-71852. (Illus.). 82p. 1983. pap. text ed. 7.95 (ISBN 0-934396-38-8). Churches Alive.

Drinan, Robert F. Religion, the Courts, & Public Policy. LC 78-6124. 261p. 1978. Repr. of 1963 ed. lib. bdg. 22.50x (ISBN 0-313-20444-6, DRRE). Greenwood.

Eberhard, Arnold. Gemeinsamesleben-Wozu? (Ger.). 44p. 1978. pap. 2.50 (ISBN 3-87630-406-7, Pub. by Prasenz-Verlag, West Germany). Plough.

Eddleman, H. Leo. Hail Mary. rev. ed. 134p. 1983. pap. 4.00 (ISBN 0-682-40143-9). Exposition Pr FL.

Elias, John L. Psychology & Religious Education. 3rd ed. LC 83-7061. 154p. 1984. text ed. 11.50 (ISBN 0-89874-615-9). Krieger.

Enswiler, James P. The Religious Education Handbook: A Practical Parish Guide. LC 79-26008. 108p. (Orig.). 1980. pap. 4.95 (ISBN 0-8189-0398-8). Alba.

Evans, David M. The Pastor in a Teaching Church. 96p. 1983. pap. 4.95 (ISBN 0-317-00688-6). Judson.

Fairchild, James H. Oberlin: The Colony & the College. Dayton, Donald W., ed. (The Higher Christian Life Ser.). 377p. 1985. 45.00 (ISBN 0-8240-6416-X). Garland Pub.

Felderhof, M. C. Religious Education in a Pluralistic Society. 160p. 1985. pap. text ed. 18.95 (ISBN 0-340-35413-5). Princeton Bk Co.

Foster, Charles R. Teaching in the Community of Faith. 160p. (Orig.). 1982. pap. 8.75 (ISBN 0-687-41086-X). Abingdon.

Francis, Dorothy B. Promises & Turtle Shells: And Forty-Nine Other Object Lessons for Children. 112p. (Orig.). 1984. pap. 7.50 (ISBN 0-687-34337-2). Abingdon.

Gangel, Kenneth O. Building Leaders for Church Education. 1981. 21.95 (ISBN 0-8024-1592-X). Moody.

--The Church Education Handbook. 300p. 1985. pap. 9.95 (ISBN 0-89693-602-3). Victor Bks.

Giltner, Fern M., ed. Women's Issues in Religious Education. 190p. 1985. pap. 12.95 (ISBN 0-89135-051-9). Religious Educ.

Girzone, Joseph F. Who Will Teach Me? 61p. 1982. 6.00 (ISBN 0-911519-00-9). Richelieu Court.

Gordon, Haim & Grob, Leonard, eds. Education for Peace: Testimonies from World Religions. LC 86-31083. 224p. (Orig.). 1987. pap. 14.95 (ISBN 0-88344-359-7). Orbis Bks.

Grants for Religion & Religious Education. (Comsearch: Broad Topics Ser.). 1986. pap. text ed. 34.00 (ISBN 0-87954-172-5). Foundation Ctr.

Graves, William W. The Church Teaching & Training. Viertel, Weldon & Viertel, Joyce, eds. 152p. 1982. Repr. of 1975 ed. 11.50 (ISBN 0-311-72681-X, Carib Pubns). Casa Bautista.

Gulley, Hal & Gulley, Nadine. I Tell You Truly. LC 81-82218. 192p. 1983. pap. 4.95 (ISBN 0-89900-194-7). College Pr Pub.

Hartshorne, Hugh & Miller, J. Q. Community Organization in Religious Education. 1932. 49.50x (ISBN 0-686-51356-8). Elliots Bks.

Hassel, David J. City of Wisdom: A Christian View of the American University. 461p. 1983. 18.50 (ISBN 0-8294-0433-3). Loyola.

Hoekstra, Donald J. Adult Education in the Church. LC 85-17433. 109p. (Orig.). 1985. pap. 4.95 (ISBN 0-930265-14-9). CRC Pubns.

Horne, Herman H. Essentials of Leadership & Other Papers in Moral & Religious Education. LC 76-117808. (Essay Index Reprint Ser). 1931. 14.00 (ISBN 0-8369-1660-3). Ayer Co Pubs.

Inch, Morris A. Making the Good News Relevant: Keeping the Gospel Distinctive in Any Culture. 128p. 1986. pap. 8.95 (ISBN 0-8407-7540-7). Nelson.

Into the Christian Community: Religious Education with Disabled Persons. 115p. 1982. 6.35 (ISBN 0-686-40033-X). Natl Cath Educ.

Jennings, Kathryn. Beginning Special Religious Education Programs. (Special Education Newsletter Ser.: Vol. 2). 1980. 4.80 (ISBN 0-686-40038-0). Natl Cath Educ.

Jones, Bob. Cornbread & Caviar. (Illus.). 236p. 1985. 12.95 (ISBN 0-89084-305-8); pap. 8.95 (ISBN 0-89084-306-6). Bob Jones Univ Pr.

Jones, C. C. Religious Instruction of the Negroes in the United States. 1842. 23.00 (ISBN 0-527-46700-6). Kraus Repr.

Jones, Charles C. Religious Instruction of the Negroes in the United States. LC 73-82466. Repr. of 1842 ed. 22.50x (ISBN 0-8371-1645-7, JOI&). Greenwood.

Jones, G. Curtis. One Thousand Illustrations for Preaching & Teaching. 1986. pap. 9.95 (ISBN 0-8054-2249-8). Broadman.

Kinsler, F. Ross, ed. Ministry by the People: Theological Education by Extension. 348p. (Orig.). 1983. pap. 12.95 (ISBN 0-88344-334-1). Orbis Bks.

Kirk, Russell. The Assault on Religion. LC 86-656. 126p. 1986. lib. bdg. 19.00 (ISBN 0-8191-5294-3, Pub. by Ctr for Judical Studies); pap. text ed. 8.25 (ISBN 0-8191-5295-1). U Pr of Amer.

Lane, Dermot, ed. Religious Education & the Future. 240p. (Orig.). 1987. pap. 9.95 (ISBN 0-8091-2877-2). Paulist Pr.

Lang, Martin A. Acquiring Our Image of God: The Emotional Basis for Religious Education. LC 82-62968. 160p. (Orig.). 1983. pap. 6.95 (ISBN 0-8091-2537-4). Paulist Pr.

Lawler, Michael G. Raid on the Inarticulate: An Invitation to Adult Religion. LC 80-1438. 168p. 1980. pap. text ed. 9.50 (ISBN 0-8191-1186-4). U Pr of Amer.

Lee, Eva. Motivate with Bulletin Boards, No. 2. (Illus.). 48p. 1985. pap. 2.95 (ISBN 0-87239-919-2, 3289). Standard Pub.

Lee, James M. The Content of Religious Instruction: A Social Science Approach. LC 84-18255. 815p. (Orig.). 1985. pap. 14.95 (ISBN 0-89135-050-0). Religious Educ.
Lee, James M., ed. The Spirituality of the Religious Educator. 209p. (Orig.). 1985. pap. 12.95 (ISBN 0-89135-045-4). Religious Educ.
Lockerbie, D. Bruce. Asking Questions: A Classroom Model for Teaching the Bible. Zimmerman, Diane, ed. LC 80-18198. (Orig.). 1980. pap. text ed. 5.95 (ISBN 0-915134-75-6). Mott Media.
Lovett, C. S. Soul-Winning Classes Made Easy. 1962. pap. 2.95 tchr's. guide (ISBN 0-938148-12-5). Personal Christianity.
--Teach Dynamic Truths. 1973. pap. 5.95 tchr's. guide (ISBN 0-938148-14-1). Personal Christianity.
--Teach Them About Satan. 1970. pap. 5.45 tchr's guide (ISBN 0-938148-26-5). Personal Christianity.
McKenna, Gail T. Through the Year with the DRE: A Seasonal Guide for Christian Educators. 128p. (Orig.). 1987. pap. 7.95 (ISBN 0-8091-2860-8). Paulist Pr.
McKinney, Richard I. Religion in Higher Education among Negroes. 1945. 13.50x (ISBN 0-686-51299-5). Elliots Bks.
MARC, ed. Directory: North American Protestant Schools & Professors of Mission. 220p. pap. 6.60 (ISBN 0-912552-37-9). Missions Adv Res Com Ctr.
Matthews, Narvella. Man Heal Thyself. Graves, Helen, ed. LC 85-51970. 65p. 1986. 6.95 (ISBN 1-55523-004-0). Winston-Derek.
Mauck & Jenkins. Teaching Primaries Workbook. pap. 2.95 (ISBN 0-89137-432-9). Quality Pubns.
Mawdsley, R. & Permuth, S. Legal Problems of Religious & Private Schools. 1983. 9.95 (ISBN 0-318-02068-8). NOLPE.
Mayr, Marlene, ed. Modern Masters of Religious Education. LC 82-25009. 323p. (Orig.). 1983. pap. 14.95 (ISBN 0-89135-033-0). Religious Educ.
Meyer, F. B. The Secret of Guidance. Taniguchi, Ruth, tr. from Eng. (Chinese.). 1984. pap. write for info. (ISBN 0-941598-07-1). Living Spring Pubns.
Mills, Dick. The Four Loves. (Orig.). 1983. pap. 0.75 minibook (HH-287). Harrison Hse.
Monks of Solesmes, ed. Education. 1960. 8.50 (ISBN 0-8198-2300-7). Dghtrs St Paul.
Moran, Gabriel. Interplay: A Theory of Religion & Education. LC 80-53203. 125p. (Orig.). 1981. pap. 8.95 (ISBN 0-88489-125-9). St Mary's.
--Religious Education Development. (Images for the Future). 204p. 1983. pap. 12.95 (ISBN 0-86683-692-6, AY8272, HarpR). Har-Row.
Morgan, John. Godly Learning: Puritan Attitudes Towards Reason, Learning, & Education, 1560-1640. 378p. 1986. 49.50 (ISBN 0-521-23511-1) (ISBN 0-317-39807-5). Cambridge U Pr.
Mud Flower Collective. God's Fierce Whimsy: Christian Feminism & Theological Education. Heyward, Carter, ed. (Orig.). 1985. pap. 11.95 (ISBN 0-8298-0546-X). Pilgrim NY.
Nystrom, Carolyn. The Holy Spirit in Me. (Children's Bible Ser.). 32p. 1980. pap. 4.95 (ISBN 0-8024-5994-3). Moody.
O'Brien, Robert Y. Parish Adult Education in Five Practical Steps. 32p. 1985. pap. text ed. 1.50 (ISBN 0-89243-234-9). Liguori Pubns.
Orr, Dick & Bartlett, David L. Bible Journeys. 80p. 1980. pap. 4.95 (ISBN 0-8170-0898-5). Judson.
Ouellett, F. L' Etude des Religions dans les Ecoles: L'experience Americaine, Anglaise et Canadienne. (SR Editions Ser.: No. 7). (Fr.). 666p. 1985. pap. text ed. 20.50x (ISBN 0-88920-183-8, Pub. by Wilfrid Laurier Canada). Humanities.
Peatling, John H., ed. Annual Review of Research: Religious Education, Vol. 1. (Orig.). 1980. pap. 5.95 (ISBN 0-915744-23-6). Character Res.
--Annual Review of Research: Religious Education, Vol. 2. viii, 148p. (Orig.). 1981. pap. 6.95 (ISBN 0-915744-26-0). Character Res.
Peil, William. The Big Way. 1983. 1.00 (ISBN 0-89536-952-4, 7503). CSS of Ohio.
Potter, Henry C. Principles of Religious Education. (Educational Ser.). 1900. Repr. 10.00 (ISBN 0-8482-5585-2). Norwood Edns.
Powers, Elvin M. Building a Caring-Sharing Community of Believers. 128p. 1983. pap. 3.95 (ISBN 0-8341-0822-4). Beacon Hill.
Reed, Margaret C. The Church-Related Pre-School. 128p. 1985. pap. 7.95 (ISBN 0-687-08334-6). Abingdon.
Reichert, Richard J. A Learning Process for Religious Education. LC 74-14308. (Orig.). 1974. pap. 3.95 (ISBN 0-8278-0001-0, Pub. by Pflaum Pr). Peter Li.
Religious Education: Chicago, 1906-1955, Vols. 1-50. Repr. of 1955 ed. Set. lib. bdg. 2250.00 (ISBN 0-685-77259-4); lib. bdg. 45.00 ea. AMS Pr.
Renard, Pierre. The Solar Revolution & the Prophet. (Testimonials Ser.). (Illus.). 193p. (Orig.). 1980. pap. 9.95 (ISBN 2-85566-135-8, Pub. by Prosveta France). Prosveta USA.
Robinson, Peter S., ed. Foundation Guide for Religious Grant Seekers. LC 79-19006. (Scholars Press Handbooks in Humanities Ser.: No. 1). 1979. 10.50 (ISBN 0-89130-339-1, 001501); pap. 9.95 (ISBN 0-89130-340-5). Scholars Pr GA.
Rosen, Harold. Religious Education & Our Ultimate Committment: An Application of Henry Nelson Wieman's Philosophy of Creative Interchange. LC 84-19651. 196p. (Orig.). 1985. lib. bdg. 24.25 (ISBN 0-8191-4341-3, Unitarian Univ Assn); pap. text ed. 10.75 (ISBN 0-8191-4342-1, Unitarian Univ. Assn.). U Pr of Amer.
Sarno, Ronald A. Using Media in Religious Education. LC 86-33844. 230p. (Orig.). 1987. pap. 13.95 (ISBN 0-89135-058-6). Religious Educ.
Sealey, John. Religious Education: Philosophical Perspectives. Snelders, Philip & Wringe, Colin, eds. (Introductory Studies in the Philosophy of Education). 120p. 1985. text ed. 19.95x (ISBN 0-04-370130-2); pap. text ed. 7.95x (ISBN 0-04-370131-0). Allen Unwin.
Seymour, Jack L. & Miller, Donald E. Contemporary Approaches to Christian Education. LC 81-14899. 176p. (Orig.). 1982. pap. 8.75 (ISBN 0-687-09493-3). Abingdon.
Shafer, Carl. Excellence in Teaching with the Seven Laws: A Contemporary Abridgment of Gregory's Seven Laws of Teaching. 80p. 1985. pap. 4.95 (ISBN 0-8010-8261-7). Baker Bk.
Shannon, Foster H. The Green Leaf Bible Series, Year One. Rew, Lois J., ed. 1982. pap. 12.50 (ISBN 0-938462-06-7). Green Leaf CA.
Sherrill, Lou. Jovita Galan: Unselfish Teacher. LC 86-6110. (Meet the Missionary Ser.). 1986. 5.50 (ISBN 0-8054-4326-6). Broadman.
Spiker, Louis. Children Together. 128p. 1980. pap. 9.50 (ISBN 0-8170-0824-1). Judson.
Spurgen, C. H. Teaching Children. 1983. pap. 0.95 (ISBN 0-686-40816-0). Pilgrim Pubns.
Staton, Knofel. Check Your Discipleship. LC 81-9411. 116p. (Orig., Student's & instructor's ed. bnd. together). 1982. pap. 2.25 student ed. (ISBN 0-87239-424-7, 39991); instructor's ed. 2.50 (ISBN 0-87239-423-9, 39990). Standard Pub.
Steele, David. God Must Have a Sense of Humor, He Made Aadvarks & Orangutans..., & Me! LC 82-84780. (Illus., Orig.). 1983. pap. 6.00 (ISBN 0-937088-09-9). Illum Pr.
Stone, J. David & Keefauver, Larry. Friend to Friend: How You Can Help a Friend Through a Problem. LC 83-80942. (Illus.). 80p. (Orig.). 1983. pap. 5.95 (ISBN 0-936664-11-8). Group Bks.
Terry, Charles L., ed. Knowledge Without Goodness Is Dangerous: Moral Education in Boarding Schools. 2nd ed. LC 81-81105. 144p. (Orig.). 1981. pap. 6.95 (ISBN 0-939618-00-1). Phillips Exeter.
Thirty Five Handicraft Projects for Children. LC 12-2957. 1982. pap. 4.95 (ISBN 0-570-03864-2). Concordia.
Thompson, Norma H., ed. Religious Education & Theology. LC 81-17852. 254p. 1982. pap. 12.95 (ISBN 0-89135-029-2). Religious Educ.
Tidwell, Charles A. Educational Ministry of a Church. LC 81-68922. 1982. pap. 10.95 (ISBN 0-8054-3231-0). Broadman.
Troll, Christian W., ed. Religion & Religious Education. (Islam in India: Studies & Commentaries: Vol. 2). xxi, 315p. 1985. text ed. 40.00x (ISBN 0-7069-2751-6, Pub. by Vikas India). Advent NY.
Vander Lught, Henry. There's a New Day Coming. LC 83-81267. 160p. 1983. pap. 3.95 (ISBN 0-89081-389-2, Pub. by Radio B C). Harvest Hse.
Van Eijndhoven, J., ed. Religious Education of the Deaf. (Modern Approaches to the Diagnosis & Instruction of Multi-Handicapped Children Ser.: Vol. 11). 168p. 1973. text ed. 14.75 (ISBN 90-237-4111-0, Pub. by Swets & Zeitlinger Netherlands). Hogrefe Intl.
The Vocation & Spirituality of the DRE. 25p. 1980. 4.20 (ISBN 0-318-20610-2). Natl Cath Educ.
Vogel, Linda J. The Religious Education of Older Adults. LC 83-21109. 217p. (Orig.). 1984. pap. 12.95 (ISBN 0-89135-040-3). Religious Educ.
Wentz, Richard E. The Contemplation of Otherness. viii, 134p. 1984. 13.90x (ISBN 0-86554-135-3, MUP-H126). Mercer Univ Pr.
Whittemore, Lewis B. The Church & Secular Education. LC 78-17152. 1978. Repr. of 1960 ed. lib. bdg. 22.50 (ISBN 0-313-20540-X, WHCS). Greenwood.
Who Is the Master Omraam Mikhael Aivanhov. (Testimonials Ser.). (Illus.). 156p. (Orig.). 1982. pap. 9.00 (ISBN 2-85566-190-0, Pub. by Prosveta France). Prosveta USA.
Wilder, Amos N., ed. Liberal Learning & Religion. LC 77-86072. (Essay & General Literature Index Reprint Ser). 1969. Repr. of 1951 ed. 24.50x (ISBN 0-8046-0595-5, Pub. by Kennikat). Assoc Faculty Pr.
Willert, Albrecht. Religioese Existenz und Literarische Produktion. (Ger.). 316p. 1982. 43.70 (ISBN 3-8204-5994-4). P Lang Pubs.
Wilson, John B. & Natale, Samuel M. Education in Religious Understanding: A Report from the Foundation for Education in Religion & Morality. LC 86-28167. 86p. 1987. lib. bdg. 19.75 (ISBN 0-8191-5948-4); pap. text ed. 9.50 (ISBN 0-8191-5949-2). U Pr of Amer.
Woodward, Luther E. Relations of Religious Training & Life Patterns to the Adult Religious Life. LC 71-177627. (Columbia University. Teachers College. Contributions to Education: No. 527). Repr. of 1932 ed. 22.50 (ISBN 0-404-55527-6). AMS Pr.
Wulf, Dick. Find Yourself, Give Yourself. LC 83-61819. 162p. 1983. pap. 5.95 (ISBN 0-89109-496-2). NavPress.

RELIGIOUS EDUCATION–AUDIO-VISUAL AIDS

Cheasebro, Margaret. Puppet Scripts by the Month. 1985. pap. 4.95 (ISBN 0-8054-7524-9). Broadman.
Emswiler, Tom N., et al. A Complete Guide to Making the Most of Video in Religious Settings: How to Produce, Find, Use & Distribute Video in the Church & Synagogue. LC 85-50019. 128p. (Orig.). 1985. pap. 9.95 (ISBN 0-9606652-1-8). Wesley Found.
Frost, Marie H. Fifty-Two Primary Crafts. 48p. (Orig.). 1984. pap. 2.95 (ISBN 0-87239-726-2, 2106). Standard Pub.
Hack, John. How to Make Audiovisuals. rev. ed. LC 78-72847. 1980. pap. 5.95 (ISBN 0-8054-3427-5). Broadman.
Haggerty, Brian A. & Walters, Thomas P. We Receive the Spirit of Jesus Filmstrips. with guidebook & cassette 49.95 (ISBN 0-8091-7664-5). Paulist Pr.
Hart, Joanna. Fifty-Two Preschool Crafts. 48p. (Orig.). 1984. pap. 2.95 (ISBN 0-87239-725-4, 2105). Standard Pub.
Poganski, Donald J. Forty Object Lessons. LC 72-86233. 160p. 1973. pap. 4.50 (ISBN 0-570-03148-6, 12-2283). Concordia.
Rowland, Jacqueline. Fifty-Two Middler-Junior Crafts. 48p. (Orig.). 1984. pap. 2.95 (ISBN 0-87239-727-0, 2107). Standard Pub.
Russell, Susan. Fifty-Two Teen Crafts. 48p. (Orig.). 1984. pap. 2.95 (ISBN 0-87239-728-9, 2108). Standard Pub.
Stuart, Sally. All-Occasion Craft & Gift Book. (Illus.). 96p. (Orig.). 1984. pap. 5.95 (ISBN 0-87239-709-2, 2138). Standard Pub.

RELIGIOUS EDUCATION–BIBLIOGRAPHY

Clevenger, Ernest A., Jr. & Clevenger, Glenda W. Comprehensive Topical & Textual Lesson Commentary Index: 1922-1982. 4th ed. 114p. 1981. pap. text ed. 6.95 (ISBN 0-88428-019-5). Parchment Pr.
Hunt, Thomas C., et al. Religious Schools in America: A Selected Bibliography. LC 86-12118. (Reference Library of Social Science: Vol. 338). 416p. 1986. lib. bdg. 47.00 (ISBN 0-8240-8583-3). Garland Pub.
Pitts, V. Peter. Concept Development & the Development of the God Concept in the Child: A Bibliography. LC 77-70266. 1977. pap. 2.75 (ISBN 0-915744-07-4). Character Res.
Sandri-White, Alex. Guide to Religious Education. 7.95x (ISBN 0-685-22753-7). Aurea.

RELIGIOUS EDUCATION–DATA PROCESSING

Bedell, Kenneth. The Role of Computers in Religious Education. 144p. 1986. pap. 7.95 (ISBN 0-687-36540-6). Abingdon.
Clemans, E. V. Using Computers in Religious Education. 80p. 1986. pap. 6.95 (ISBN 0-687-43120-4). Abingdon.

RELIGIOUS EDUCATION–HISTORY

Adam, James. Religious Teachers of Greece. LC 72-2565. (Select Bibliographies Reprint Ser). 1972. Repr. of 1908 ed. 26.00 (ISBN 0-8369-6843-3). Ayer Co Pubs.
Grassi, Joseph A. Teaching the Way: Jesus, the Early Church & Today. LC 82-7054. 176p. 1982. lib. bdg. 26.75 (ISBN 0-8191-2501-6); pap. text ed. 11.50 (ISBN 0-8191-2502-4). U Pr of Amer.
Jordan, Louis H. Comparative Religion: Its Genesis & Growth. Kitagawa, Joseph M., ed. (SP-Reprints & Translations Ser.). 1986. pap. 19.50 (ISBN 1-55540-014-0, 00 07 11). Scholars Pr GA.
Kinlock, Tom F. Pioneers of Religious Education. facs. ed. LC 69-18929. (Essay Index Reprint Ser). 1939. 14.00 (ISBN 0-8369-0045-6). Ayer Co Pubs.
Mohler, James A. School of Jesus. new ed. LC 72-11835. 280p. 1973. 5.95 (ISBN 0-8189-0262-0). Alba.
Stewart, George, Jr. History of Religious Education in Connecticut to the Middle of the Nineteenth Century. LC 79-89238. (American Education: Its Men, Institutions & Ideas, Ser. 1). 1969. Repr. of 1924 ed. 17.00 (ISBN 0-405-01475-9). Ayer Co Pubs.
Ulich, Robert. History of Religious Education: Documents & Interpretations from the Judaeo-Christian Tradition. LC 68-29433. 1968. 30.00 (ISBN 0-8147-0420-4). NYU Pr.

RELIGIOUS EDUCATION–HOME TRAINING

see also Family–Religious Life

Adams, Jay E. Christian Living in the Home. 1972. pap. 3.95 (ISBN 0-87552-016-2). Presby & Reformed.
Brinkmann, William & Ditewig, William. Leading Our Children to God. LC 83-72992. (Illus.). 96p. (Orig.). 1984. pap. 4.95 (ISBN 0-87793-310-3). Ave Maria.
Fitzpatrick, Kathryn. Family Time, Faith Time, 3 Vols. (Illus.). 307p. (Orig.). 1982. Set. pap. text ed. 8.95 (ISBN 0-86716-030-6). St Anthony Mess Pr.
Guernsey, Dennis B. The Family Covenant: Students Manual. 113p. 1984. pap. text ed. 3.95 (ISBN 0-89191-843-4). Cook.
Hadaway, C. KIrk, et al. Home Cell Groups & House Churches. 1987. 9.95 (ISBN 0-8054-6944-3). Broadman.
Kobobel, Janet. The Family Covenant: Leaders Manual. 35p. 1984. tchr's ed. 10.95 (ISBN 0-89191-892-2). Cook.
Larson, Jim. Teaching Christian Values in the Family. (Illus.). 48p. 1982. pap. text ed. 29.95 (ISBN 0-89191-649-0). Cook.
Leonard, Joe, Jr. Planning Family Ministry: A Guide for the Teaching Church. 64p. 1982. pap. 3.95 (ISBN 0-8170-0971-X). Judson.
Sawin, Margaret M. Family Enrichment with Family Clusters. 1979. pap. 6.95 (ISBN 0-8170-0830-6). Judson.
Walsh, David. Growing up Together: A Spiritual Perspective for Parents of Adolescents. 124p. (Orig.). 1980. pap. 2.50 (ISBN 0-912228-73-3). St Anthony Mess Pr.

RELIGIOUS EDUCATION–PSYCHOLOGY

Goldman, Ronald. Religious Thinking from Childhood to Adolescence. 1968. pap. text ed. 6.95 (ISBN 0-8164-2061-0, SP53, HarpR). Har-Row.

RELIGIOUS EDUCATION–SERMONS

Aivanhov, Omraam M. New Light on the Gospels. (Izvor Collection: Vol. 217). (Orig.). 1985. pap. 4.95 (ISBN 2-85566-339-3, Pub. by Prosveta France). Prosveta USA.
Crane, Thomas F. The Exempla or Illustrative Stories from the Sermones: Vulgares off Jacques de Vitry. (Folk-Lore Society, London, Ser.: Vol. 26). pap. 35.00 (ISBN 0-8115-0512-X). Kraus Repr.

RELIGIOUS EDUCATION–TEACHER TRAINING

Here are entered works dealing with the systematic instruction of lay teachers to prepare them to give religious instruction.

see also Religious Education As a Profession

Adams, Jay E. Competent to Counsel. 309p. 1970. pap. 6.95 (ISBN 0-87552-017-0). Presby & Reformed.
Arndt, William. Fundamental Christian Beliefs. pap. text ed. 3.25 (ISBN 0-570-06324-8, 22-1144); pap. 3.75 guide (ISBN 0-570-06325-6, 22-1146); pap. tests 1.50 (ISBN 0-570-06362-0, 22-1145). Concordia.
Augustine, St. Christian Instruction, Admonition & Grace, The Christian Combat, Faith, Hope & Charity. LC 66-20314. (Fathers of the Church Ser.: Vol. 2). 494p. 1950. 34.95x (ISBN 0-8132-0002-4). Cath U Pr.
Blazier, Kenneth D. Workbook for Planning Christian Education. 48p. 1983. pap. 3.95 (ISBN 0-8170-0996-5). Judson.
Burns, Jim. Christian Growth Series Leader's Guide. 1986. 7.95 (ISBN 0-89081-555-0). Harvest Hse.
Bynum, Bill. Teaching Youth with Confidence. 48p. 1983. pap. 3.95 (ISBN 0-910566-41-0); seminar planbook 3.95 (ISBN 0-910566-42-9). Evang Tchr.
Clark, Robert E. Teaching Preschoolers with Confidence. 48p. 1983. pap. 3.95 (ISBN 0-910566-37-2); seminar planbook 3.95 (ISBN 0-910566-38-0). Evang Tchr.
Cove, Mary K. & Mueller, Mary L. Regarding Religious Education. LC 77-10873. 181p. (Orig.). 1977. pap. 8.95 (ISBN 0-89135-011-X). Religious Educ.
Evangelical Teacher Training Association. More Training When Meeting. 32p. 1982. pap. 2.95 (ISBN 0-317-02858-8); leader's planbook 3.95 (ISBN 0-910566-36-4). Evang Tchr.
--Video Seminar Planbook for Dynamic Bible Teaching. 64p. 1983. pap. 5.95 (ISBN 0-910566-60-7). Evang Tchr.

Fry, Malcolm C. Discipling & Developing: Teachers Guide. 1979. pap. 1.50 (ISBN 0-89265-062-1). Randall Hse.

Gangel, Kenneth O. Understanding Teaching. LC 68-24579. 96p. 1979. pap. text ed. 4.95 (ISBN 0-910566-14-3); Perfect bdg. instr's. guide 5.95 (ISBN 0-910566-26-7). Evang Tchr.

Garver. Watch Your Teaching: Home Study. pap. 4.95 (ISBN 0-935120-03-3). Christs Mission.

Gribbon, R. T. Students, Churches & Higher Education. 128p. 1981. pap. 6.95 (ISBN 0-8170-0931-0). Judson.

Griggs, Donald L. Teaching Teachers to Teach: A Basic Manual for Church Teachers. (Griggs Educational Resources Ser.). 1983. pap. 7.95 (ISBN 0-687-41120-3). Abingdon.

Hull, John, ed. New Directions in Religious Education. 226p. 1982. text ed. 24.50x (ISBN 0-905273-31-1, Falmer Pr); pap. 15.00x (ISBN 0-905273-30-3). Taylor & Francis.

Hyde, Floy. Protestant Leadership Education Schools. LC 70-176892. (Columbia University. Teachers College. Contributions to Education: No. 965). Repr. of 1950 ed. 22.50 (ISBN 0-404-55965-4). AMS Pr.

Jenkins, David. Teaching Children with Confidence. 48p. 1983. pap. 3.95 (ISBN 0-910566-39-9); seminar planbook 3.95 (ISBN 0-910566-40-2). Evang Tchr.

Klyver, F. H. Supervision of Student-Teachers in Religious Education. LC 79-176952. (Columbia University. Teachers College. Contributions to Education: No. 198). Repr. of 1925 ed. 22.50 (ISBN 0-404-55198-X). AMS Pr.

Loth, Paul E. Teaching Adults with Confidence. 48p. 1984. pap. 3.95 (ISBN 0-910566-43-7); seminar planbook 3.95 (ISBN 0-910566-44-5). Evang Tchr.

Mann, C. Stephen. The Message Delivered. 128p. (Orig.). 1973. pap. 2.50 (ISBN 0-8192-1143-5). Morehouse.

Robertson, Pat & Slosser, Bob. The Secret Kingdom: A Promise of Hope & Freedom in a World of Turmoil. LC 83-14268. 96p. 1983. 13.95 (ISBN 0-8407-5272-5). Nelson.

Rusbuldt, Richard E. Basic Teacher Skills: Handbook for Church School Teachers. 144p. 1981. pap. 5.95 (ISBN 0-8170-0919-1). Judson.

Rushdoony, Rousas J. The Institutes of Biblical Law. 1973. 24.00 (ISBN 0-87552-410-9). Presby & Reformed.

Swain, Dorothy G. Teach Me to Teach. pap. 4.95 (ISBN 0-8170-0316-9). Judson.

Thomsen, Helen S. The Message Delivered: Leader's Guide. (Orig.). 1973. pap. 2.50x (ISBN 0-8192-4048-6). Morehouse.

Whaling, Frank, ed. The World's Religious Traditions. 320p. 1984. 22.95 (ISBN 0-567-09353-0, Pub. by T&T Clark Ltd UK). Fortress.

RELIGIOUS EDUCATION–TEACHING METHODS

Benson, Clarence H. Teaching Techniques. rev. ed. 96p. 1983. pap. text ed. 4.95 (ISBN 0-910566-05-4); Perfect bdg. instr's. guide 5.95 (ISBN 0-910566-23-2). Evang Tchr.

Christy, James. The Puppet Ministry. 78p. 1978. 2.50 (ISBN 0-8341-0532-2). Beacon Hill.

Cove, Mary & Regan, Jane. Teaching Religion Effectively Program. 96p. 1982. pap. 3.50 (ISBN 0-697-01825-3); program manual 24.95 (ISBN 0-697-01826-1). Wm C Brown.

Dale, Daryl. Teaching Basics: Adult. (Illus.). 80p. (Orig.). 1985. pap. 2.00 (ISBN 0-87509-369-8). Chr Pubns.

--Teaching Basics: Junior. (Illus.). 73p. (Orig.). 1985. pap. 2.00 (ISBN 0-87509-359-0). Chr Pubns.

--Teaching Basics: Youth. (Illus.). 80p. (Orig.). 1985. pap. 2.00 (ISBN 0-87509-364-7). Chr Pubns.

Darkes, Anna S. How to Make & Use Overhead Transparencies. LC 77-7888. (Illus.). 1977. pap. 4.50 (ISBN 0-8024-3652-8). Moody.

Dixon, William C. Pointed Tales. LC 80-81102. 98p. (Orig.). 1980. pap. 5.95 (ISBN 0-8192-1270-9). Morehouse.

Edge, Findley B. Helping the Teacher. 1959. 10.95 (ISBN 0-8054-3403-8). Broadman.

--Teaching for Results. 1956. 10.95 (ISBN 0-8054-3401-1). Broadman.

Ford, Leroy. Pedagogia Ilustrada: Tomo I Principios Generales. Orig. Title: A Primer for Teachers & Leaders. (Illus.). 144p. 1982. pap. 3.95 (ISBN 0-311-11001-0, Edit Mundo). Casa Bautista.

Gangel, Kenneth O. Understanding Teaching. LC 68-24579. 96p. 1979. pap. text ed. 4.95 (ISBN 0-910566-14-3); Perfect bdg. instr's. guide 5.95 (ISBN 0-910566-26-7). Evang Tchr.

Gribbon, R. T. Students, Churches & Higher Education. 128p. 1981. pap. 6.95 (ISBN 0-8170-0931-0). Judson.

Grunze, Richard. Paul: An Example for Christian Teachers. 1979. pap. text ed. 3.50 (ISBN 0-8100-0108-X, 07N0740). Northwest Pub.

Hampton, Larry D. Commissioned to Communicate: Teacher's Guide. 1978. pap. 1.50 (ISBN 0-89265-056-7). Randall Hse.

--Pupil Profiles: Teacher's Guide. 1978. pap. 1.50 (ISBN 0-89265-057-5). Randall Hse.

Haystead, Wesley, ed. ICL Planbook--Early Childhood. 1978. pap. 1.65 (ISBN 0-8307-0670-4, 90-603-08). Regal.

Hersey, Herman. Faith for Today: Teacher's Guide. 1980. pap. 1.50 (ISBN 0-89265-067-2). Randall Hse.

ICL Planbook. Incl. Adult. Stewart, Ed, ed (ISBN 0-8307-0673-9, 99-603-09); Children. Haystead, Wesley, ed (ISBN 0-8307-0671-2, 91-603-02); Youth. Stewart, Ed, ed (ISBN 0-8307-0672-0, 97-603-18). 1978. pap. 1.65 ea. Regal.

Johnson, Kent L. Called to Teach: Ideas & Encouragement for Teachers in the Church. LC 83-72127. 128p. (Orig.). 1984. pap. 5.95 (ISBN 0-8066-2071-4, 10-0964). Augsburg.

Kemper, Frederick. Kirigami. 1979. pap. 4.95 (ISBN 0-570-03782-4, 12-2736). Concordia.

McCarthy, David S. Memo to a Weary Sunday School Teacher. LC 77-92877. 1978. pap. 3.95 (ISBN 0-8170-0807-1). Judson.

Malehor, Harold A. Over Two Hundred Ways to Improve Your Sunday School. 1982. pap. 5.95 (ISBN 0-570-03857-X, 12-2811). Concordia.

Manternach, Janaan & Pfeifer, Carl J. Creative Catechist. (Illus.). 144p. (Orig.). 1983. pap. text ed. 6.95 (ISBN 0-89622-169-5). Twenty-Third.

Owens, Joanne. The Unofficial Sunday School Teacher's Handbook. (Illus.). 240p. (Orig.). 1987. pap. 7.95 (ISBN 0-916260-42-9). Meriwether Pub.

Payne, Peggy. Teaching for Life-Changing Learning. (C. E. Ministries Ser.). 94p. (Orig.). 1984. pap. 3.50 (ISBN 0-89367-092-8). Light & Life.

Pearlman, Myer. Successful Sunday School Teaching. 112p. 1935. pap. 1.35 (ISBN 0-88243-606-6, 02-0606). Gospel Pub.

Rusbuldt, Richard E. Basic Teacher Skills: Handbook for Church School Teachers. 144p. 1981. pap. 5.95 (ISBN 0-8170-0919-1). Judson.

Sawyer, Kieran. Developing Faith. LC 78-72942. (Illus.). 152p. 1978. pap. text ed. 5.95 (ISBN 0-87793-164-X). Ave Maria.

Sherer, Michael L. Good News for Children. LC 80-65554. (Visual Messages on Epistle Texts, Ser. A). 128p. pap. 6.95 (ISBN 0-8066-1798-5, 10-2808). Augsburg.

Sisemore, John T. Blueprint for Teaching. LC 64-12413. 1964. 8.95 (ISBN 0-8054-3405-4). Broadman.

Skelly, Herbert & Skelly, Margaret. An Advent Event. (Illus.). 32p. (Orig.). 1973. pap. 3.25 (ISBN 0-8192-1148-6); kit 13.95 (ISBN 0-8192-1283-0). Morehouse.

Smith, Judy G. Teaching with Music Through the Church Year. 1979. pap. 7.95 (ISBN 0-687-41133-5). Abingdon.

Weisheit, Eldon. God's Promise for Children. LC 80-65554. (Visual Messages on Old Testament Texts, Ser. A). 128p. 1980. pap. 6.95 (ISBN 0-8066-1799-3, 10-2692). Augsburg.

RELIGIOUS EDUCATION–TEXT-BOOKS

see also Jesus Christ–Biography–Study; Vacation Schools, Religious–Text-Books

Baron, Henry. Touchstones, 4 vols. Incl. Vol. 1. Around Us (ISBN 0-8028-1532-4); Vol. 2. Within Us (ISBN 0-8028-1533-2); Vol. 3. Between Us (ISBN 0-8028-1534-0); Vol. 4. Above Us (ISBN 0-8028-1535-9). 1973. pap. 4.95 ea.; pap. 5.50 tchr's guide (ISBN 0-8028-1645-2). Eerdmans.

Bush, Marcella. The Community of God. (Illus.). 1975. pap. 3.75x (ISBN 0-8192-4057-5); tchr's guide 4.95x (ISBN 0-8192-4056-7). Morehouse.

Daughters of St. Paul. God's People on the Move. LC 68-59042. (Divine Master Ser.). pap. 2.50 (ISBN 0-8198-0348-0); rev. tchr's. manual 3.95 (ISBN 0-8198-0349-9). Dghtrs St Paul.

--Master Plan Revealed. (Divine Master Ser.). pap. 3.00 (ISBN 0-8198-0346-4); rev. project & discussion manual o.s.i. 3.95 (ISBN 0-8198-0347-2). Dghtrs St Paul.

--Really Living. LC 68-59042. (Divine Master Ser.). pap. 3.00 (ISBN 0-8198-0350-2); rev. tchr's. manual 3.95 (ISBN 0-8198-0351-0). Dghtrs St Paul.

Daughters of St. Paul, ed. Catechism of Modern Man. 3rd rev. ed. 1971. 7.95 (ISBN 0-8198-0015-5); pap. 6.95 (ISBN 0-8198-0016-3). Dghtrs St Paul.

De Angelis Bothwell, Sr. Mary. God Is Good. LC 73-5752. (Christ Our Life Ser.). (Illus.). 138p. 1986. pap. text ed. 4.20 (ISBN 0-8294-0537-2); 12.95 (ISBN 0-8294-0570-4). Loyola.

Fry, Malcolm C. Precepts for Practice. (Way of Life Ser.). 1971. pap. 3.95 (ISBN 0-89265-004-4, Free Will Baptist Dept); tchrs' guide 4.95 (ISBN 0-89265-005-2). Randall Hse.

Goodyear, Imogene, ed. Daily Bread, Nineteen Eighty-Six. 1985. pap. 7.50 (ISBN 0-8309-0407-7). Herald Hse.

Jiede, E. A. Living God's Word. 1947. pap. 2.25 (ISBN 0-570-03505-8, 14-1262). Concordia.

Kennedy, Richard. Basic Training. 100p. 1987. three-ring binder 12.95 (ISBN 0-89265-104-0). Randall Hse.

Marshall, Peter & Manuel, David. The Light & the Glory Study Guide. 1981. pap. 5.95 (ISBN 0-8007-1279-X); photo enrichment pack o.p. 12.50. Revell.

Partridge, Edmund. Church in Perspective: Standard Course for Layreaders. rev. ed. 1976. 5.95 (ISBN 0-8192-1210-5). Morehouse.

Perkins, Hal. Leadership Multiplication Books: Book A, World Vision. 30p. 1983. pap. 2.50 (ISBN 0-8341-0858-5); Set of 8 bks. pap. 19.95 (YD-1495). Beacon Hill.

--Leadership Multiplication Books: Book B, Knowing the Father. 30p. (Orig.). 1983. pap. 2.50 (ISBN 0-8341-0859-3); Set of 8 bks. pap. 19.95 (YD-1495). Beacon Hill.

--Leadership Multiplication Books: Book D, Following Jesus. 30p. (Orig.). (YA) 1983. pap. 2.50 (ISBN 0-8341-0860-7); Set of 8 bks. pap. 19.95 (YD-1495). Beacon Hill.

--Leadership Multiplication Books: Book E, Becoming Like Jesus. 30p. (Orig.). 1983. pap. 2.50 (ISBN 0-8341-0861-5); Set of 8 bks. pap. 19.95 (YD-1495). Beacon Hill.

--Leadership Multiplication Books: Book F, Making Leaders in Families. 30p. (Orig.). (YA) 1983. pap. 2.50 (ISBN 0-8341-0862-3); Set of 8 bks. pap. 19.95 (YD-1495). Beacon Hill.

--Leadership Multiplication Books: Book G, Making Leaders in the Church. 30p. (Orig.). (YA) 1983. pap. 2.50 (ISBN 0-8341-0866-6); Set of 8 bks. pap. 19.95 (YD-1495). Beacon Hill.

--Leadership Multiplication Books: Book H, Making Leaders in the World. 30p. (Orig.). (YA) 1983. pap. 2.50 (ISBN 0-8341-0867-4); Set of 8 bks. pap. 19.95 (YD-1495). Beacon Hill.

Schaeffer, Sue. Mine to Choose. LC 78-73144. 128p. 1979. 2.50 (ISBN 0-88243-553-1, 02-0553, Radiant Bks.); tchr's manual 2.50 (ISBN 0-88243-337-7, 02-0337). Gospel Pub.

Simons, George F. Faces & Facets: A Workbook for the Liturgical Celebrant. LC 77-78972. 1977. pap. 3.95 (ISBN 0-914070-11-8). ACTA Found.

Snyder, Graydon & Shaffer, Kenneth. Texts in Transit. (Orig.). 1976. pap. 2.95 (ISBN 0-685-61334-8). Brethren.

Spencer, Geoffrey. The Burning Bush. LC 74-84762. 1974. pap. 6.50 (ISBN 0-8309-0129-9). Herald Hse.

Stochl, Susan, et al, eds. Easter People, Grade 4: Remember. (The Easter People Ser). (Illus.). 1978. pap. text ed. 4.75 (ISBN 0-03-042801-7, HarpR); tchr's. manual 7.60 (ISBN 0-03-042796-7); activity pack 3.90 (ISBN 0-03-042911-0); parent book 2.25 (ISBN 0-03-042791-6). Har-Row.

Wilkins, Ronald J. Challenge! rev. ed. (To Live Is Christ Ser.). 1983. pap. 5.25 (ISBN 0-697-01850-4); tchr's. manual 5.95 (ISBN 0-697-01851-2); tests 10.95 (ISBN 0-697-01939-X). Wm C Brown.

--The Jesus Book: Extended Study. (To Live Is Christ Ser.). 168p. 1984. pap. 5.75 (ISBN 0-697-01917-9); tchrs. manual 5.00 (ISBN 0-697-01927-6); spirit master 10.95 (ISBN 0-697-01692-7). Wm C Brown.

RELIGIOUS EDUCATION–TEXTBOOKS–MORMON

Crowther, Jean D. Growing Up in the Church: Gospel Principles & Practices for Children. rev. ed. LC 67-25433. (Illus.). 84p. 1973. Repr. of 1965 ed. 6.95 (ISBN 0-88290-024-2). Horizon Utah.

RELIGIOUS EDUCATION–TEXT-BOOKS FOR CHILDREN

Barnhouse, Donald G. Teaching the Word of Truth. 1958. Repr. 5.95 (ISBN 0-8028-1610-X). Eerdmans.

Burgess, Beverly. Three Bears in the Ministry. 32p. (Orig.). 1982. pap. 3.98 (ISBN 0-89274-252-6). Harrison Hse.

Carver, Robert C. & Thiess, Susan. The Creator's World. 1978. 4.95x (ISBN 0-8192-4082-6); parent pupil packet 4.95x (ISBN 0-8192-4083-4). Morehouse.

Curley, Maureen. The Sacraments. (Children of the Kingdom Activities Ser.). 1975. 9.95 (ISBN 0-89837-019-1, Pub. by Pflaum Pr). Peter Li.

--The Ten Commandments. (Children of the Kingdom Activities Ser.). 1976. 9.95 (ISBN 0-89837-015-9, Pub. by Pflaum Pr). Peter Li.

Daughters of St. Paul. I Learn About Jesus. 1973. 5.50 (ISBN 0-8198-0246-8); pap. 4.00 (ISBN 0-8198-0247-6). Dghtrs St Paul.

--I Learn About Jesus: Projects & Activities for Pre-Schoolers. 1973. pap. 1.00 (ISBN 0-8198-0245-X). Dghtrs St Paul.

Geiger, Linda M. God Loves Me! 8 Lessons, Vol. 1. (Steps of Faith for Special Children Ser.). 1981. kit 19.95x (ISBN 0-86508-045-3); text ed. 4.95x (ISBN 0-86508-046-1). BCM Intl Inc.

Haas, Lois J. Tell Me How to Please God: 16 Lessons, Vol. 4. (Tiny Steps of Faith Ser.). 1974. complete kit 10.95 (ISBN 0-86508-020-8); text only 2.95 (ISBN 0-86508-021-6); color & action book 0.90 (ISBN 0-86508-022-4). BCM Intl Inc.

--Tell Me How to Trust God: 16 Lessons, Vol. 3. (Tiny Steps of Faith Ser.). 1970. complete kit 12.95 (ISBN 0-86508-017-8); text only 2.95 (ISBN 0-86508-018-6); color & action book 0.90 (ISBN 0-86508-019-4). BCM Intl Inc.

Hamilton, Joan K. Patterns. (Illus.). 1977. tchrs'. manual 5.25x (ISBN 0-8192-4078-8); parents' letters & pupils' leaflets package 5.75x (ISBN 0-8192-4077-X). Morehouse.

Jordan, Bernice C. Los Evangelios-Para que vino Jesus? 14 Lecciones, Tomo 2. (Pasos De Fe Ser.). (Span.). pap. text ed. 2.50 (ISBN 0-86508-411-4); figuras 8.95 (ISBN 0-86508-412-2). BCM Intl Inc.

--Los Evangelios-Quien es Jesus? 14 Lecciones, Tomo 1. (Pasos De Fe Ser.). (Span.). pap. text ed. 2.50 (ISBN 0-86508-409-2); figuras 8.95 (ISBN 0-86508-410-6). BCM Intl Inc.

--Los Hechos Epistolas-El Mar De la Vida: 14 Lecciones. (Pasos De Fe Ser.). (Span.). pap. text ed. 2.50 (ISBN 0-86508-415-7); figuras 8.95 (ISBN 0-86508-416-5). BCM Intl Inc.

Ligon, Ernest M. & Character Research Project Staff. Vicarious Sacrifice. Incl. Junior High Unit-Lesson Book. 2.00 (ISBN 0-915744-15-5); Junior High Unit-PLAN. 0.75 (ISBN 0-915744-17-1); Junior High Unit-Home Assignment Sheets. 0.75 (ISBN 0-915744-16-3). (Research Curriculum for Character Education Ser.). (Illus.). 1979. Character Res.

Malterner, Virginia M. Circles. (Illus.). 1977. tchrs'. manual 5.25x (ISBN 0-8192-4079-6); wkbk. 3.95x (ISBN 0-8192-4080-X); take-home cards packet 2.50x (ISBN 0-8192-4081-8). Morehouse.

Murphy, Elspeth C. Sometimes I Get Mad. (David & I Talk to God Ser.). 1981. pap. 2.95 (ISBN 0-89191-493-5, 54932). Cook.

--Sometimes I Have to Cry. (David & I Talk to God Ser.). (Illus.). 1981. pap. 2.95 (ISBN 0-89191-494-3, 54940). Cook.

--Sometimes I Need to Be Hugged. (David & I Talk to God Ser.). (Illus.). 1981. pap. 2.95 (ISBN 0-89191-492-7, 54924). Cook.

New God Cares for Us. 154p. 1980. pap. text ed. 4.20 (ISBN 0-8294-0303-5). Loyola.

Pearl, Patricia. Religious Books for Children: An Annotated Bibliography. (Orig.). 1983. pap. 5.95 (ISBN 0-915324-21-0); pap. 4.75 members. CSLA.

Van Der Veer, Andrew. Bible Lessons for Juniors, 4 bks. Incl. Bk. 1. Creation Through Moses. 2.95 (ISBN 0-8010-9253-1); Bk. 2. Kings & Prophets. 2.95 (ISBN 0-8010-9251-5); Bk. 3. The Life of Christ. 2.95 (ISBN 0-8010-9257-4); Bk. 4. The Early Church. 2.95 (ISBN 0-8010-9255-8). Baker Bk.

RELIGIOUS EDUCATION–TEXT-BOOKS FOR YOUNG PEOPLE

Aronin, Ben. The Secret of the Sabbath Fish. LC 78-63437. (Illus.). 1979. 5.95 (ISBN 0-8276-0110-7, 433). Jewish Pubns.

Baker, Eugene. What's Right? Buerger, Jane, ed. LC 80-17552. (Illus.). 112p. 1980. 5.95 (ISBN 0-89565-175-0, 4932). Standard Pub.

--Your Manners Are Showing. Buerger, Jane, ed. (Illus.). 112p. 1980. 5.95 (ISBN 0-89565-178-5, 4935). Standard Pub.

Berkhof, Louis. Summary of Christian Doctrine. 1939. pap. 5.95 (ISBN 0-8028-1513-8). Eerdmans.

Coleman, William. The Who, What, When, Where Book about the Bible. (Illus.). 1980. 11.95 (ISBN 0-89191-291-6). Cook.

Colina, Tessa. You & Me. Buerger, Jane, ed. (Illus.). 112p. 1980. 5.95 (ISBN 0-89565-179-3, 4936). Standard Pub.

Conn, Charles P. A Faith to Keep. LC 77-70783. pap. 1.99 (ISBN 0-87148-016-6). Pathway Pr.

Erb, Paul. We Believe. LC 69-15831. 112p. (Orig.). 1969. pap. 3.95 (ISBN 0-8361-1587-2). Herald Pr.

Fretz, Clarence Y. Story of God's People. (Christian Day School Ser). pap. 5.90x (ISBN 0-87813-900-1); tchrs. guide 6.95x (ISBN 0-87813-901-X). Christian Light.

Krabill, Russell. Beginning the Christian Life. 1958. pap. 2.95 (ISBN 0-8361-1312-8); (leader's guide) 4.95 (ISBN 0-8361-1313-6). Herald Pr.

McKenna, Megan & Ducote, Darryl. The Spirit in the Church. LC 78-71531. (Followers of the Way Ser.: Vol. 4). 1979. 22.50 (ISBN 0-8091-9545-3); cassette 7.50 (ISBN 0-8091-7669-6). Paulist Pr.

Murphy, Elspeth. Sometimes I Get Scared. (David & I Talk to God Ser.). (Illus.). 1980. pap. 2.95 (ISBN 0-89191-275-4). Cook.

--What Can I Say to You, God? (David & I Talk to God Ser.). (Illus.). 1980. pap. 2.95 (ISBN 0-89191-276-2). Cook.

--Where Are You, God? (David & I Talk to God Ser.). (Illus.). 1980. pap. 2.50 (ISBN 0-89191-274-6). Cook.

Pennock, Michael. Your Faith & You. rev. ed. LC 86-70575. (Ave Maria Press' High School Religion Text Programs Ser.). (Illus.). 320p. 1986. pap. text ed. 6.95 (ISBN 0-87793-334-0). Ave Maria.

RELIGIOUS EDUCATION–FRANCE

Elwell, Clarence E. Influence of the Enlightenment on the Catholic Theory of Religious Education in France, 1750-1850. LC 66-27064. 1967. Repr. of 1944 ed. 10.00x (ISBN 0-8462-0980-2). Russell.

RELIGIOUS EDUCATION–GERMANY

Helmreich, Ernst C. Religious Education in German Schools: An Historical Approach. LC 59-11509. 1959. 22.50x (ISBN 0-674-75850-1). Harvard U Pr.

Terry, W. Clinton, III. Teaching Religion: The Secularization of Religion Instruction in a West German School System. LC 80-5569. 208p. 1981. pap. text ed. 12.25 (ISBN 0-8191-1367-0). U Pr of Amer.

RELIGIOUS EDUCATION–GREAT BRITAIN

Blackham, H. Moral & Religious Education in County Primary Schools. 6.00x (ISBN 0-85633-115-5, Pub. by NFER Nelson UK). Taylor & Francis.

Burgess, Henry J. Enterprise in Education: The Story of the Work of the Established Church in the Education of the People Prior to 1870. LC 59-1586. 1958. text ed. 15.00x (ISBN 0-8401-0289-5). A R Allenson.

Fitzpatrick, T. A. Catholic Secondary Education in South-West Scotland Before 1972: Its Contributions to the Change in Status of the Catholic Community of the Area. (Illus.). 248p. 1986. 19.00 (ISBN 0-08-032439-8, Pub. by AUP). Pergamon.

RELIGIOUS EDUCATION AS A PROFESSION

see also Sunday-School Superintendents

White, Anne S. All in All. 128p. (Orig.). 1980. pap. 2.50 (ISBN 0-9605178-0-4). Victorious Ministry.

RELIGIOUS EDUCATION OF ADOLESCENTS

Campus Crusade Staff. Insights: Building a Successful Youth Ministry, Vol. I. (Insight Ser.). (Orig.). 1981. pap. text ed. 5.95 (ISBN 0-86605-017-5). Campus Crusade.

Chadwell, David. Christian Perspectives on Dating & Marriage. 1980. pap. 4.95 (ISBN 0-89137-523-6). Quality Pubns.

Curran, Dolores. In the Beginning There Were the Parents. 1978. pap. 4.95 (ISBN 0-03-042766-5, HarpR). Har-Row.

Norris, Docia W. Religious Science for Youth. pap. 1.50 (ISBN 0-87516-153-7). De Vorss.

Seely, Edward D. Teaching Early Adolescents Creatively: A Manual for Church School Teachers. 222p. 1971. Westminster.

RELIGIOUS EDUCATION OF ADULTS

Andersen, David W. & Brooker, Wendell. Expanding Your Church School Program: Planning Elective Classes for Adults. 88p. 1983. pap. 3.95 (ISBN 0-8170-1009-2). Judson.

Barnard, Tom. How to Grow an Adult Class. 88p. (Orig.). 1983. pap. 2.95 (ISBN 0-8341-0840-2). Beacon Hill.

Dale, Daryl. Teaching Basics: Adult. (Illus.). 80p. (Orig.). 1985. pap. 2.00 (ISBN 0-87509-369-8). Chr Pubns.

Dyet, James T. Getting Through to Adults. LC 79-53294. (Accent Teacher Training Ser.). (Orig.). 1980. pap. 4.95 (ISBN 0-89636-037-7). Accent Bks.

Elias, John L. The Foundations & Practice of Adult Religious Education. LC 81-19327. 312p. 1982. 18.50 (ISBN 0-89874-339-7). Krieger.

Leypoldt, Martha M. Learning Is Change. LC 70-144082. 1971. pap. 4.95 (ISBN 0-8170-0526-9). Judson.

Little, Lawrence C. Wider Horizons in Christian Adult Education. LC 62-14381. pap. 87.00 (ISBN 0-8357-9763-5, 2017871). Bks Demand UMI.

Long, Huey B. Adult Education in Church & Synagogue. LC 73-13292. (Ocassional Paper Ser.: No. 37). 1973. pap. 2.50 (ISBN 0-87060-061-3, OCP 37). Syracuse U Cont Ed.

McCollough, Charles. Heads of Heaven, Feet of Clay: Ideas & Stories for Adult Faith Education. 192p. (Orig.). 1983. pap. 11.95 (ISBN 0-8298-0693-8). Pilgrim NY.

McKenzie, Leon. The Religious Education of Adults. LC 81-19926. 256p. 1982. pap. 12.95 (ISBN 0-89135-031-4). Religious Educ.

Parent, Neil A., ed. Adult Learning & the Parish. 144p. 1985. pap. 6.95 (ISBN 0-697-02063-0). Wm C Brown.

Tighe, Jeanne & Szentkeresti, Karen. Rethinking Adult Religious Education: A Practical Parish Guide. 144p. (Orig.). 1986. pap. 9.95 (ISBN 0-8091-2829-2). Paulist Pr.

Wilbert, Warren N. Strategies Teaching Christian Adults. 280p. 1980. 12.95 (ISBN 0-8010-9668-5). Baker Bk.

Zuck, Roy B. & Getz, Gene A. Adult Education in the Church. LC 79-123154. 1970. pap. 15.95 (ISBN 0-8024-0468-5). Moody.

RELIGIOUS EDUCATION OF CHILDREN

see also Religious Education of Mentally Handicapped Children

Acheson, Edna L. The Construction of Junior Church School Curricula. LC 73-176503. Repr. of 1929 ed. 22.50 (ISBN 0-404-55331-1). AMS Pr.

Adcock, Mabel & Blackwell, Elsie. Creative Activities. (Illus.). 1984. 4.95 (ISBN 0-87162-011-1, D3195). Warner Pr.

Arnold, Eberhard. Children's Education in Community: The Basis of Bruderhof Education. Mow, Merrill, ed. LC 76-27728. 1976. pap. 3.25 (ISBN 0-87486-164-0). Plough.

Baptism, Penance, Eucharist, & Confirmation. 9.95 (ISBN 0-89837-020-5, PL306, Pub. by Pflaum). Peter Li.

Barber, Lucie W. The Religious Education of Preschool Children. LC 80-27623. 196p. (Orig.). 1981. pap. 12.95 (ISBN 0-89135-026-8). Religious Educ.

Beckman, Beverly. Shapes in God's World. LC 56-1462. 1984. 5.95 (ISBN 0-570-04094-9). Concordia.

--Sizes in God's World. 1984. 5.95 (ISBN 0-570-04095-7, 56-1463). Concordia.

Beechick, Ruth. Teaching Kindergarteners. LC 79-53295. (Accent Teacher Training Ser.). 192p. 1980. pap. 4.95 (ISBN 0-89636-038-5). Accent Bks.

--Teaching Primaries. LC 80-66723. (Accent Teacher Training Ser.). 128p. (Orig.). 1980. pap. 4.95 (ISBN 0-89636-054-7). Accent Bks.

Berenstain, Stan & Berenstain, Jan. How to Teach Your Children about God...Without Actually Scaring them out of Their Wits. 1984. pap. 3.95 (ISBN 0-345-29457-2). Ballantine.

Breeden, Terri. Teaching the Meaning of Church Ordinances to Children. (Orig.). 1986. pap. 5.95 (ISBN 0-89265-097-4). Randall Hse.

Brettschneider, Diana, et al. Twenty-Six Bible Programs for Preschoolers. 96p. 1987. tchr's wkbk. 8.95 (ISBN 0-87403-213-X, 3413). Standard Pub.

Brubaber, Zuck & Brubaker, Joanne. Childhood Education in the Church. rev., exp. ed. 1986. text ed. 24.95 (ISBN 0-8024-1251-3). Moody.

Brusselmans, Christiane & Wakin, Edward. Religion for Little Children: A Parent's Guide. LC 76-140110. 1977. pap. 6.95 (ISBN 0-87973-825-1). Our Sunday Visitor.

Children As Learners. (Christian Education Ministries Ser.). 1979. pap. 3.50 (ISBN 0-89367-029-4). Light & Life.

Cioni, Ray & Cioni, Sally. The Droodles Ten Commandments Storybook. (Droodles Adventure Ser.). (Illus.). 64p. 1983. text ed. 8.95 (ISBN 0-89191-636-9). Cook.

Coleman, Bill & Coleman, Patty. God's Own Child. rev. ed. 64p. 1983. Parent's Book. pap. text ed. 3.95x (ISBN 0-89622-188-1); Leader's Guide. wkbk. 1.00 (ISBN 0-89622-187-3). Twenty-Third.

Cone, Molly. About Belonging. (Shema Storybooks: No. 3). (Illus.). 64p. (Orig.). 1972. pap. 5.00 (ISBN 0-8074-0125-0, 101083). UAHC.

Costas, Orlando E. Comunicacion Por Medio de la Predicacion. (Span.). 255p. pap. 6.25 (ISBN 0-89922-021-5). Edit Caribe.

Dale, Daryl. Teaching Basics: Junior. (Illus.). 73p. (Orig.). 1985. pap. 2.00 (ISBN 0-87509-359-0). Chr Pubns.

DeWolf, Carol. Object Talks from A to Z. (Illus.). 64p. 1987. 5.95 (ISBN 0-87403-237-7, 2867). Standard Pub.

Dilley, Romilda. Silhouette Crafts. (Illus.). 24p. (YA) 1987. wkbk. 2.95 (ISBN 0-87403-238-5, 2148). Standard Pub.

Donin, Hayim H. To Raise a Jewish Child: A Guide for Parents. LC 76-7679. 1977. 15.95 (ISBN 0-465-08626-8). Basic.

Eager, George B. How to Succeed in Winning Children to Christ. 190p. 1979. pap. 3.95 (ISBN 0-9603752-0-1). Mailbox.

Fennema, Jack. Nurturing Children in the Lord. 1978. pap. 4.95 (ISBN 0-87552-266-1). Presby & Reformed.

Forehand, Mary A. Love Lives Here. (Orig.). 1975. pap. 1.95 (ISBN 0-377-00028-0). Friend Pr.

Freese, Doris. Children's Church: A Comprehensive How-to. LC 81-22426. 128p. 1982. pap. 6.95 (ISBN 0-8024-1250-5). Moody.

Gale, Elizabeth W. Children Together, Vol. 2. 128p. 1982. pap. 9.95 (ISBN 0-8170-0974-4). Judson.

Gestwicki, Ronald. Santa Claus: The Tooth Fairy & Other Stories - A Child's Introduction to Religion. Ashton, Sylvia, ed. LC 77-80276. 1977. 15.95 (ISBN 0-87949-108-6). Ashley Bks.

Gobbel, A. Roger & Huber, Phillip C. Creative Designs with Children at Worship. LC 80-82225. 96p. (Orig.). 1981. pap. 6.95 (ISBN 0-8042-1526-X). John Knox.

Goldman, Ronald. Readiness for Religion. 1970. pap. 4.95 (ISBN 0-8164-2060-2, SP70, HarpR). Har-Row.

Grabbe, George. Orthodox Christian Education of Children in Our Days. 30p. 1976. pap. 1.00x (ISBN 0-913026-17-4). St Nectarios.

Groomer, Vera. Good Friends Again: Two - Three. (Come Unto Me Ser.: Year 2, Bk. 3). 32p. 1980. pap. 1.65 (ISBN 0-8127-0272-7). Review & Herald.

--Growing Stronger: Two - Two. (Come Unto Me Ser.: Year 2, Bk. 2). 32p. 1980. pap. 1.65 (ISBN 0-8127-0271-9). Review & Herald.

--Obedience Brings Happiness. (Come Unto Me Ser.). 16p. 1979. pap. 1.65 (ISBN 0-8127-0251-4). Review & Herald.

--Quiet Because. (Come Unto Me Ser.). 1979. pap. 1.65 (ISBN 0-8127-0253-0). Review & Herald.

--Talking to My Friend Jesus: Two - Four. (Come Unto Me Ser.: Year 2, Bk. 4). 32p. 1980. pap. 1.65 (ISBN 0-8127-0273-5). Review & Herald.

Hand, Phyllis. Celebrate God & Country. (Celebrate Ser.). 144p. 1987. pap. 9.95 (ISBN 0-86653-390-7). Good Apple.

Hanna, Barbara & Hoover, Janet. Teaching Preschoolers. 3.95 (ISBN 0-89137-608-9). Quality Pubns.

Harlow, Joanne. Patterns & Instructions for a Child's Quiet Book. 27p. 1977. 3.50 (ISBN 0-317-03553-3). Randall Bk Co.

Helping Your Child Know Right from Wrong. LC 79-91138. (Redemptorist Pastoral Publication Ser.). 1980. pap. 2.95 (ISBN 0-89243-117-2, 39900). Liguori Pubns.

Hendricks, William L. A Theology for Children. LC 80-65539. 1980. 10.95 (ISBN 0-8054-1711-7). Broadman.

Hennig, David, compiled by. Good Stuff! (Good Stuff, Resources for Youth Leaders Ser.: Vol. 4). 160p. 1987. tchr's wkbk. 9.95 (ISBN 0-87403-216-4, 3416). Standard Pub.

Hilliard, Dick. The Lord Blesses Me. LC 78-61308. (Illus.). 1978. pap. 11.95 (ISBN 0-89390-005-2). Resource Pubns.

Hockett, Betty & Abbott, Grace. Life Changing Learning for Children: Resources That Work. (C. E. Ministries Ser.). 1977. pap. 3.50 (ISBN 0-89367-020-0). Light & Life.

I Believe in God. 52p. 1975. 3.60 (ISBN 0-686-29267-7). Natl Cath Educ.

Jahsmann, Allan H. Church Teaching Her Young. 1967. pap. text ed. 3.75 (ISBN 0-570-06330-2, 22-1287); teacher's guide 4.50 (ISBN 0-570-06331-0, 22-1289). Concordia.

Johnston, Dorothy G. & Abbas, Kathleen. Church Time for Children. LC 80-67855. 120p. (Orig.). 1981. 10.95 (ISBN 0-89636-056-3). Accent Bks.

Kniss, Lloy A. Practical Pointers for Training Your Child. 1975. pap. 2.75 (ISBN 0-87813-509-X). Christian Light.

Kotrba, Danella G. God's Helper. (Come Unto Me Ser.: Year 2, Bk. 1). 32p. 1980. pap. 1.65 (ISBN 0-8127-0211-5). Review & Herald.

Koulomzin, Sophie. Our Church & Our Children. LC 75-20215. 158p. 1975. pap. 6.95 (ISBN 0-913836-25-7). St Vladimirs.

Kraemer, Bonita. Rules Mean Happiness. (Come Unto Me Ser.). 1979. pap. 1.65 (ISBN 0-8127-0254-9). Review & Herald.

LeFever, Marlene D. Creative Teaching Methods. 320p. 1985. pap. 14.95 (ISBN 0-89191-760-8). Cook.

Leichner, Jeannine T. Making Things Right: The Sacrament of Reconciliation. (Illus.). 62p. (Orig.). 1980. pap. 3.50 (ISBN 0-87973-351-9, 351). Our Sunday Visitor.

Lelia, Mary. Leading the Little Ones to Mary. pap. 1.00 (ISBN 0-910984-13-1). Montfort Pubns.

Leppard, Lois G. Mandie & the Abandoned Mine. (Mandie Ser.). 144p. (Orig.). 1987. pap. 2.95 (ISBN 0-87123-932-9). Bethany Hse.

Lessin, Roy. How to Be Parents of Happy Obedient Children. 1978. 8.95 (ISBN 0-89728-003-2, 702120); pap. 4.95 (ISBN 0-686-67298-4). Omega Pubns OR.

Loukes, Harold. Readiness for Religion. LC 63-11818. (Orig.). 1963. pap. 2.50x (ISBN 0-87574-126-6). Pendle Hill.

MacKenthun, Carole & Dwyer, Paulinus. Gentleness. (Fruit of the Spirit Ser.). 48p. 1987. pap. 5.95 (ISBN 0-86653-395-8, SS879). Good Apple.

McMillan, Mary. God's ABC Zoo. 48p. 1987. pap. 5.95 (ISBN 0-86653-405-9, SS1802). Good Apple.

Mains, Karen B. & Mains, David. Tales of the Kingdom. (Illus.). 96p. 1983. 12.95 (ISBN 0-89191-560-5). Cook.

Mauck, Diane & Jenkins, Janet. Teaching Primaries. 4.50 (ISBN 0-89137-610-0); write for info. wkbk. (ISBN 0-89137-612-7). Quality Pubns.

Moore, Raymond & Moore, Dorothy. Home-Grown Kids. 253p. 1984. pap. text ed. 7.95 (ISBN 0-8499-3007-3, 3007-3). Word Bks.

--Homespun Schools. 1982. 9.95 (ISBN 0-8499-0326-2). Word Bks.

Murphy, Elspeth C. God Cares When I'm Disappointed. (God's Word in my Heart Ser.). (Illus.). 1983. 2.95 (ISBN 0-89191-725-X). Cook.

--God Cares When I'm Sorry. (God's Word in My Heart Ser.). (Illus.). 1983. 2.95 (ISBN 0-89191-724-1). Cook.

--God Cares When I'm Worried. LC 82-73572. (God's Word in My Heart Ser.). (Illus.). 1983. 2.95 (ISBN 0-89191-723-3). Cook.

Murray, Andrew. How to Raise Your Children for Christ. LC 75-29344. 288p. 1975. pap. 4.95 (ISBN 0-87123-224-3, 210224). Bethany Hse.

Nazigian, Arthur. Teach Them Diligently. 1986. pap. 2.95 (ISBN 0-8010-6747-2). Baker Bk.

Newman, Shirley. A Child's Introduction to the Early Prophets. LC 75-14052. (Illus.). 128p. 1975. 6.95x (ISBN 0-87441-244-7). Behrman.

Ng, David & Thomas, Virginia. Children in the Worshipping Community. LC 80-84655. (Illus.). 128p. (Orig.). 1981. pap. 7.95 (ISBN 0-8042-1688-6). John Knox.

Nyber, D. M. Help for Families with a Problem Child. LC 12-2822. (Trauma Bks.: Ser. 2). 1983. pap. 2.75 (ISBN 0-570-08259-5). Concordia.

Paul, James L., ed. The Exceptional Child: A Guidebook for Churches & Community Agencies. LC 82-16914. 176p. text ed. 22.00x (ISBN 0-8156-2287-2); pap. text ed. 12.95x (ISBN 0-8156-2288-0). Syracuse U Pr.

Pitts, V. Peter. Concept Development & the Development of the God Concept in the Child: A Bibliography. LC 77-70266. 1977. pap. 2.75 (ISBN 0-915744-07-4). Character Res.

Riehle, Mary C. & Ready, Dolores. Happy Together, 1977. rev. ed. 1977. pap. text ed. 4.95 (ISBN 0-86683-110-X, HarpR); tchr's. ed. 7.55 (ISBN 0-86683-113-4). Har-Row.

Runk, Wesley T. Object Lessons from the Bible. (Object Lessons Ser.). 96p. 1980. pap. 3.95 (ISBN 0-8010-7698-6). Baker Bk.

Sarwar, Shaikh M. Religious Teachings for Children, Bk. 1. 44p. pap. 5.00 (ISBN 0-941724-03-4). Islamic Seminary.

--Religious Teachings for Children, Bk. 2. 66p. pap. 5.00 (ISBN 0-941724-04-2). Islamic Seminary.

--Religious Teachings for Children, Bk. 3. 80p. pap. 5.00 (ISBN 0-941724-05-0). Islamic Seminary.

--Religious Teachings for Children, Bk. 4. 72p. 1981. pap. 5.00 (ISBN 0-941724-06-9). Islamic Seminary.

Set of Four Trauma Books. LC 12-2823. (Trauma Bks.: No. 2). 1983. Set. pap. 9.95 (ISBN 0-570-08260-9). Concordia.

Shoemaker, Kathryn E., illus. Children, Go Where I Send Thee: An American Spiritual. (Illus.). 32p. (Orig.). 1980. pap. 6.95 (ISBN 0-03-056673-8, HarpR). Har-Row.

Smalley, Gary. The Key to Your Child's Heart. 160p. 1984. 10.95 (ISBN 0-8499-0433-1, 0433-1). Word Bks.

Temple, Joe. Know Your Child. 1974. pap. 5.95 (ISBN 0-8010-8820-8). Baker Bk.

Toward Effective Parish Religious Education for Children & Young People. 108p. 1986. 14.00. Natl Cath Educ.

Vander Goot, Mary. Educating for Healthy Emotions: The Emotional Development of Children. 176p. (Orig.). 1987. pap. 8.95 (ISBN 0-8010-9303-1). Baker Bk.

Weber, Hans-Ruedi. Jesus & the Children: Biblical Resources for Study & Preaching. LC 79-87754. 1980. pap. 5.95 (ISBN 0-8042-1316-X). John Knox.

Westerhoff, John H., 3rd. Bringing up Children in the Christian Faith. 108p. (Orig.). 1980. pap. 4.95 (ISBN 0-86683-627-6, HarpR). Har-Row.

Wheatcroft, Anita L. Promises, 3 bks. (Illus.). 80p. (Orig.). 1973. Set. pap. 2.95x (ISBN 0-8192-4043-5); tchrs'. guide 4.50x (ISBN 0-8192-4044-3). Morehouse.

Winston Staff. Joy Five. rev. ed. (Joy Religion Ser.). (Illus.). 1978. pap. text ed. 5.87 (ISBN 0-86683-035-9, HarpR); tchr's. manual 8.95 (ISBN 0-03-041871-2). Har-Row.

Wyckoff, D. Campbell & Richter, Don, eds. Religious Education Ministry with Youth. LC 81-19239. 257p. (Orig.). 1982. pap. 12.95 (ISBN 0-89135-030-6). Religious Educ.

RELIGIOUS EDUCATION OF MENTALLY HANDICAPPED CHILDREN

Linam, Gail. God's Spring Gifts. (Illus., Orig.). 1980. pap. 3.25 (ISBN 0-8054-4157-3, 4142-57). Broadman.

RELIGIOUS EDUCATION OF PRE-SCHOOL CHILDREN

Archdiocese of Newark Staff. Growing in Faith with Your Child. Ivory, Thomas P., ed. Tr. of Cresciendo en Fe con su Nino. 48p. (Orig.). pap. 2.95 (ISBN 0-697-01693-5). Wm C Brown.

Barnett, Regina R. Create, Two. 31p. (Orig.). 1979. pap. text ed. 5.95 student work pad (ISBN 0-697-01705-2); tchrs.' manual 12.95 (ISBN 0-697-01706-0). Wm C Brown.

Beechick, Ruth. Teaching Preschoolers: It's Not Exactly Easy but Here Is How to Do It. LC 78-73252. (Accent Teacher Training Ser.). 1979. pap. 4.95 (ISBN 0-89636-019-9). Accent Bks.

Boardman, Lynda T. The Ministry of Teaching Toddlers. 92p. (Orig.). 1983. pap. 3.95 (ISBN 0-8341-0820-8). Beacon Hill.

--Tending & Teaching Babies. 83p. (Orig.). 1985. pap. 3.50 (ISBN 0-8341-1063-6). Beacon Hill.

Furfine, Sandy S. & Nowak, Nancy C. The Jewish Preschool Teachers Handbook. LC 81-67023. (Illus.). 132p. (Orig.). 1981. pap. 13.50 (ISBN 0-86705-004-7). AIRE.

Miller, Carol E. Teaching Toddlers. 1971. pap. 1.95 (ISBN 0-915374-22-6, 22-6). Rapids Christian.

Sauerman, Thomas H. & Schomaker, Linda, eds. Starting a Church-Sponsored Weekday Preschool Program: A Manual of Guidance. LC 80-14160. 128p. (Orig.). 1980. pap. 6.95 (ISBN 0-8006-1377-5, 1-1377). Fortress.

RELIGIOUS EDUCATION OF YOUNG PEOPLE

Boden, Robert. Teen Talks with God. 1980. pap. 3.50 (ISBN 0-570-03812-X, 12-2921). Concordia.

Boostrom, Paul. The Hostage Game: An Exciting Simulation Game for Junior High Youth Groups. (The Best of Young Teen Action Ser.). 32p. 1985. pap. 4.95 (ISBN 0-89191-382-3). Cook.

--That's Tough: Four Simulation Games on Christian Commitment for Junior High Youth Groups. (The Best of Young Teen Action Ser.). 32p. 1985. pap. 4.95 (ISBN 0-317-39454-1). Cook.

Bradshaw, Charles. You & Your Teen. (Family Ministry Ser.). (Illus.). 54p. 1985. pap. text ed. 19.95 (ISBN 0-89191-950-3). Cook.

Chenoweth, Linda. God's People: Nursery Leader's Guide. 64p. 1981. 2.95 (ISBN 0-686-74751-8). Westminster.

Collins, Gary R. Give Me a Break with Study Guide. 192p. 1982. pap. 5.95 (Power Bks). Revell.

Cumming, James T. & Moll, Hans G. And, God, What About...? 1980. 4.50 (ISBN 0-570-03806-5, 12-2915). Concordia.

Dale, Daryl. Teaching Basics: Youth. (Illus.). 80p. (Orig.). 1985. pap. 2.00 (ISBN 0-87509-364-7). Chr Pubns.

Finley, James. Your Future & You. LC 81-65228. (Illus.). 176p. (Orig.). 1981. pap. 4.50 (ISBN 0-87793-223-9); tchrs. ed. 2.25 (ISBN 0-87793-224-7). Ave Maria.

Griffin, Kathryn. Teaching Teens the Truth. LC 78-58567. 1978. pap. 4.95 (ISBN 0-8054-3425-9, 4234-25). Broadman.

Harder, Bertha F. Twelve Becoming: Leader's Guide for Juniors. new ed. (Illus.). 61p. 1973. pap. 2.00x (ISBN 0-87303-866-5). Faith & Life.

Johnson, Mary H. Where Our Lives Touch. 35p. (Orig.). 1985. pap. 3.00 (ISBN 0-914631-00-4). Questpr.

Kaiser, Eldor & Symmank, Leo. A New Start in Youth Ministry. 1980. pap. 4.95 (ISBN 0-570-03805-7, 12-2914). Concordia.

Mueller, Charles S. Getting Along: A Guide for Teenagers. LC 80-65546. 128p. (Orig.). 1980. pap. 4.95 (ISBN 0-8066-1791-8, 10-2545). Augsburg.

Perrone, Stephen P. & Spata, James P. Send in His Clowns. Zapel, Arthur L. & Pijanowski, Kathy, eds. (Illus.). 79p. (Orig.). 1985. pap. 7.95 (ISBN 0-916260-32-1). Meriwether Pub.

Sleeper, C. Freeman & Spivey, Robert A. The Study of Religion in Two-Year Colleges. LC 75-28158. (American Academy of Religion, Individual Volumes). 1975. pap. 8.95 (ISBN 0-89130-031-7, 010801). Scholars Pr GA.

Slover, Luella H. Ministry with Young Adults. 1980. pap. 4.00 (ISBN 0-8309-0283-X). Herald Hse.

Stone, J. David, ed. Catching the Rainbow: A Total Concept Youth Ministry. LC 81-12705. (The Complete Youth Ministries Handbook: Vol. II). 256p. (Orig.). 1981. pap. 19.95 (ISBN 0-687-04730-7); leadership training kit, includes book, 2 cassettes & leader's guide 24.95 (ISBN 0-687-04731-5). Abingdon.

Toward Effective Parish Religious Education for Children & Young People. 108p. 1986. 14.00. Natl Cath Educ.

Walker, Paul L. Counseling Youth. 112p. 1967. 5.25 (ISBN 0-87148-162-6); pap. 4.25 (ISBN 0-87148-163-4). Pathway Pr.

Zanzig, Thomas. Sharing the Christian Message: A Program Manual for Volunteer Catechists, Tenth Grade. 1977. pap. 9.95 (ISBN 0-88489-089-9); duplicating masters 6.95 (ISBN 0-88489-129-1). St Marys.

RELIGIOUS ETHICS

Augustine, St. Treatises on Various Moral Subjects. LC 65-18319. (Fathers of the Church Ser.: Vol. 16). 479p. 1952. 24.95x (ISBN 0-8132-0016-4). Cath U Pr.

Bridges, Horace J., ed. Aspects of Ethical Religion: Essays in Honor of Felix Adler. 1977. lib. bdg. 59.95 (ISBN 0-8490-1459-X). Gordon Pr.

Brightman, Edgar S. Religious Values. Repr. of 1925 ed. 29.00 (ISBN 0-527-11010-8). Kraus Repr.

Browning, Don S. Religious Ethics & Pastoral Care. LC 83-5589. (Theology & Pastoral Care Ser.). 128p. 1983. pap. 7.95 (ISBN 0-8006-1725-8, 1-1725). Fortress.

Brunt, John C. Promise & Present: Adventist Eschatology & Ethics. Coffen, Richard W., ed. 96p. 1987. pap. 5.95 (ISBN 0-8280-0386-6). Review & Herald.

Cauthen, Kenneth. Process Ethics: A Constructive System. LC 84-16662. (Toronto Studies in Theology: Vol. 18). 365p. 1985. 59.95x (ISBN 0-88946-764-1). E Mellen.

Chandler, Tertius. Godly Kings & Early Ethics. rev. ed. (Illus.). 220p. 1981. 24.00 (ISBN 0-9603872-4-2). Gutenberg.

Clair, Frederic F. Ultimate Defense: A Practical Plan to Prevent Man's Self-Destruction. LC 59-6490. 1959. 3.30 (ISBN 0-8048-0606-3). C E Tuttle.

Coleman, Lyman. Moral Issues: If Christ Is Lord. (Serendipity Ser.). (Orig.). 1981. pap. 4.95 leader's guide 64 pgs. (ISBN 0-687-37330-1); pap. 1.25 student's bk 32 pgs (ISBN 0-687-37331-X). Abingdon.

Gaffney, James. Newness of Life: A Modern Introduction to Catholic Ethics. LC 79-84404. 360p. 1979. pap. 6.95 (ISBN 0-8091-2202-2). Paulist Pr.

Guroian, Vigen. Incarnate Love: Essays in Orthodox Ethics. LC 86-40591. 208p. 1987. text ed. 22.95x (ISBN 0-268-01162-1, Dist. by Har-Row). U of Notre Dame Pr.

Gustafson, James M. Protestant & Roman Catholic Ethics: Prospects for Rapprochement. LC 77-21421. 1980. pap. 8.00x (ISBN 0-226-31108-2, P868); 15.00 (ISBN 0-226-31107-4). U of Chicago Pr.

Hastings, James, ed. The Encyclopedia of Religion & Ethics, 12 vols. 1926. Set. 599.95 (ISBN 0-567-06514-6, Pub. by T&T Clark Ltd Uk). Fortress.

Hick, John & Askari, Hasan. The Experience of Religious Diversity. 242p. 1985. text ed. 39.95 (ISBN 0-566-05020-X). Gower Pub Co.

Houlden. Ethics & the New Testament. 1977. pap. 6.95 (ISBN 0-19-519958-8). Oxford U Pr.

Lawler, Philip F. How Bishops Decide: An American Catholic Case Study. 45p. (Orig.). pap. 4.00 (ISBN 0-89633-101-6). Ethics & Public Policy.

Levy, Howard S. & Yang, F. S., trs. Chinese Monks & Nuns in a Sea of Sins: Short Stories. 1971. 15.00 (ISBN 0-686-01016-7). Oriental Bk Store.

Livingston, James. The Ethics of Belief. LC 74-18616. (American Academy of Religion. Studies in Religion). 1974. pap. 7.50 (ISBN 0-88420-121-X, 010009). Scholars Pr GA.

McClendon, James W., Jr. Ethics: Systematic Theology. 400p. 1986. 22.95 (ISBN 0-687-12015-2). Abingdon.

McDonald, Henry. The Ethics of Comparative Religion. LC 84-17370. 102p. (Orig.). 1985. lib. bdg. 19.75 (ISBN 0-8191-4304-9); pap. text ed. 7.75 (ISBN 0-8191-4305-7). U Pr of Amer.

Meilaender, Gilbert C. Friendship: A Study in Theological Ethics. LC 81-50459. 118p. 1981. text ed. 10.95 (ISBN 0-268-00956-2). U of Notre Dame Pr.

Montgomery, John W. Law Above the Law. LC 75-31395. 168p. 1975. pap. 3.95 (ISBN 0-87123-329-0, 200329). Bethany Hse.

Patterson, J. B. The Christmas Star Was Jesus Himself: A Theological Work Showing any Theological Value in the Miracle Side Is also Found in the Non-Miracle Side of the New Testament. 3rd ed. LC 84-71886. 238p. 1986. pap. 7.50x (ISBN 0-9613670-2-4). Christmas Star.

Swyhart, Barbara A. Bioethical Decision-making: Releasing Religion from the Spiritual. LC 75-13040. pap. 35.00 (2026973). Bks Demand UMI.

Tanenbaum, Marc H. Religious Values in an Age of Violence. (Pere Marquette Theology Lectures). 1976. 7.95 (ISBN 0-87462-508-4). Marquette.

Von Speyr, Adrienne. They Followed His Call. Leiva-Merikakis, Erasmo, tr. from Ger. LC 86-80294. Tr. of Sie Folgten Seinem Ruf. 137p. (Orig.). 1986. pap. 6.95 (ISBN 0-89870-100-7). Ignatius Pr.

Womer, Jan L. Morality & Ethics in Early Christianity. LC 86-45903. (Sources in Early Christian Thought Ser.). 144p. 1987. pap. 7.95 (ISBN 0-8006-1417-8). Fortress.

RELIGIOUS EXPERIENCE

see Experience (Religion)

RELIGIOUS FESTIVALS

see Fasts and Feasts

RELIGIOUS FREEDOM

see Religious Liberty

RELIGIOUS HISTORY

see Church History

RELIGIOUS HUMANISM

see Humanism, Religious

RELIGIOUS INSTITUTIONS

see Religious and Ecclesiastical Institutions

RELIGIOUS JOURNALISM

see Journalism, Religious

RELIGIOUS KNOWLEDGE, THEORY OF

see Knowledge, Theory of (Religion)

RELIGIOUS LIBERTY

see also Church and State; Liberty of Conscience; Nationalism and Religion; Persecution; Sunday Legislation

Alley, Robert, ed. James Madison on Religious Liberty. LC 85-42957. 343p. 1985. 19.95 (ISBN 0-87975-298-X). Prometheus Bks.

Assault on the Bill of Rights: The Jewish Stake. LC 83-182603. 1983. 12.00. UAHC.

Bainton, Roland H. Concerning Heretics. 1965. Repr. lib. bdg. 27.50x (ISBN 0-374-90323-9, Octagon). Hippocrene Bks.

Basnage De Beauval, Henry. Tolerance Des Religions. Repr. 20.00 (ISBN 0-384-03522-1). Johnson Repr.

Bates, M. Searle. Religious Liberty: An Inquiry. LC 77-166096. (Civil Liberties in American History Ser.). 1972. Repr. of 1945 ed. lib. bdg. 59.50 (ISBN 0-306-70235-5). Da Capo.

Bien, David D. The Calas Affair: Persecution, Toleration, & Heresy in Eighteenth-Century Toulouse. LC 78-12393. 1979. Repr. of 1960 ed. lib. bdg. cancelled (ISBN 0-313-21206-6, BICA). Greenwood.

Blakely, W. A., ed. American State Papers Bearing on Sunday Legislation. LC 79-122165. (Civil Liberties in American History Ser.). 1970. Repr. of 1911 ed. lib. bdg. 95.00 (ISBN 0-306-71973-8). Da Capo.

Borden, Morton. Jews, Turks, & Infidels. LC 83-19863. xii, 163p. 1984. 17.95x (ISBN 0-8078-1592-6). U of NC Pr.

Bosmajian, Haig A., ed. The Freedom of Religion. (The First Amendment in the Classroom Ser.: No. 2). 455p. 1987. text ed. 24.95 (ISBN 1-55570-002-0). Neal-Schuman.

Bradley, Gerard V. Church-State Relationships in America. LC 86-27149. (Contributions in Legal Studies). 1987. 29.85 (ISBN 0-313-25494-X, BYC). Greenwood.

Buckley, Thomas E. Church & State in Revolutionary Virginia, 1776-1787. LC 77-4283. xii, 217p. 1977. 17.95x (ISBN 0-8139-0692-X). U Pr of Va.

Burghardt, Walter J., ed. Religious Freedom, Nineteen Sixty-Five to Nineteen Seventy-Five: A Symposium on a Historic Document. LC 76-45938. 1977. pap. 2.95 (ISBN 0-8091-1993-5). Paulist Pr.

Burr, George L. Persecution & Liberty: Essays in Honor of George Lincoln Burr. facs. ed. LC 68-26467. (Essay Index Reprint Ser). 1968. Repr. of 1931 ed. 17.50 (ISBN 0-8369-0783-3). Ayer Co Pubs.

Burrell, David B. Exercises in Religious Understanding. LC 74-12566. pap. 63.30 (ISBN 0-317-26713-2, 2024366). Bks Demand UMI.

Buzzard, Lynn & Ericcson, Samuel. The Battle for Religious Liberty. (Issues & Insight Ser.). (Orig.). 1982. pap. 6.95 (ISBN 0-89191-552-4, 55525). Cook.

Carlyle, Alexander J. Christian Church & Liberty. LC 68-56734. (Research & Source Works Ser.: No. 214). 1968. Repr. of 1924 ed. 14.50 (ISBN 0-8337-0476-1). B Franklin.

Clark, Henry B., II. Freedom of Religion in America: Historical Roots, Philosophical Concepts, Contemporary Problems. 143p. 1982. pap. 6.95 (ISBN 0-87855-925-6). Transaction Bks.

Cobb, Sanford H. The Rise of Religious Liberty in America. 1978. pap. write for info. (ISBN 0-89102-115-9, Artemis). B Franklin.

--Rise of Religious Liberty in America: A History. LC 68-27517. 541p. 1968. Repr. of 1902 ed. 32.50x (ISBN 0-8154-0051-9). Cooper Sq.

--The Rise of Religious Liberty in America: A History. (American Studies). 1970. Repr. of 1902 ed. 30.00 (ISBN 0-384-09445-7). Johnson Repr.

Cole, Franklin P. They Preached Liberty. LC 76-26327. 1976. 5.95 (ISBN 0-913966-16-9, Liberty Pr); pap. 1.25 (ISBN 0-913966-20-7). Liberty Fund.

Cord, Robert L. Separation of Church & State: Historical Fact & Current Fiction. 307p. 1982. 19.95x (ISBN 0-931186-03-X). Lambeth Pr.

Curry, Thomas J. The First Freedoms: The Establishment of Freedom of Religion in America. 288p. 1986. text ed. 24.95x (ISBN 0-19-503661-1). Oxford U Pr.

Davies, Michael. Archbishop Lefebvre & Religious Liberty. 17p. 1980. pap. 1.00 (ISBN 0-89555-143-8). TAN Bks Pubs.

Edelby, Neophytos & Urresti, Teodoro-J., eds. Religious Freedom. LC 66-29260. (Concilium Ser.: Vol. 18). 191p. 7.95 (ISBN 0-8091-0124-6). Paulist Pr.

Glenn, Paul J. Apologetics. LC 80-51330. 303p. 1980. pap. 6.00 (ISBN 0-89555-157-8). TAN Bks Pubs.

Goldberg, George. Reconsecrating America. 160p. 1984. 9.95 (ISBN 0-8028-3607-0). Eerdmans.

Greene, Evarts B. Religion & the State: The Making & Testing of an American Tradition. LC 75-41122. Repr. of 1941 ed. 17.25 (ISBN 0-404-14548-5). AMS Pr.

Hanley, Thomas O. Their Rights & Liberties. 160p. 1984. 9.95 (ISBN 0-8294-0471-6). Loyola.

Helwys, Thomas. Objections Answered by Way of Dialogue, Wherein Is Proved That No Man Ought to Be Persecuted for His Religion. LC 73-6139. (English Experience Ser.: No. 603). 80p. 1973. Repr. of 1615 ed. 6.00 (ISBN 90-221-0603-9). Walter J Johnson.

Ives, J. Moss. Ark & the Dove: The Beginnings of Civil & Religious Liberties in America. LC 76-79200. (Illus.). 1969. Repr. of 1936 ed. 32.50x (ISBN 0-8154-0293-7). Cooper Sq.

James, Charles F. Documentary History of the Struggle for Religious Liberty in Virginia. LC 70-121101. (Civil Liberties in American History Ser). 1971. Repr. of 1900 ed. lib. bdg. 37.50 (ISBN 0-306-71977-0). Da Capo.

Kauper, Paul G. Religion & the Constitution. LC 64-7898. (Edward Douglass White Lectures). 1964. pap. 6.95x (ISBN 0-8071-0114-1). La State U Pr.

Kleinig, John. Ethical Issues in Psychosurgery. (Studies in Applied Philosophy: No. 1). (Illus.). 176p. 1985. text ed. 19.95x (ISBN 0-04-170032-5); pap. text ed. 7.95x (ISBN 0-04-170033-3). Allen Unwin.

Levy, Leonard W. The Establishment Clause: Religion & the First Amendment. LC 86-5417. 1986. 16.95 (ISBN 0-02-918750-8). Macmillan.

Lewin, Isaac. Towards International Guarantees for Religious Liberty. LC 81-52086. 128p. 7.95 (ISBN 0-88400-078-8). Shengold.

Liskofsky, Sidney. U. N. Declaration on the Elimination of Religious Intolerance & Discrimination. 20p. 1982. pap. 2.00 (ISBN 0-87495-041-4). Am Jewish Comm.

Merlin, Lester. Courage for a Cross: Six Stories About Growing up Christian in the U. S. S. R. 1987. pap. 3.95. Friend Pr.

Miller, Perry, et al. Religion & Freedom of Thought. facs. ed. LC 78-128296. (Essay Index Reprint Ser). 1954. 10.00 (ISBN 0-8369-2199-2). Ayer Co Pubs.

Miller, Robert T. & Flowers, Ronald B., eds. Toward Benevolent Neutrality: Church, State, & the Supreme Court. rev. ed. LC 82-81902. xi, 726p. 1982. 32.50x (ISBN 0-918954-28-2). Baylor Univ Pr.

Morgan, Richard E. The Supreme Court & Religion. LC 72-80077. 1972. 14.95 (ISBN 0-02-921970-1). Free Pr.

Noonan, John T. The Believer & the Powers That Are: Cases, History, & Other Data Bearing on the Relation of Religion & Government. LC 86-28440. 1987. 35.00 (ISBN 0-02-923161-2). Macmillan.

Paterson, James. The Liberty of the Press, Speech & Public Worship: Being Commentaries on the Liberty of the Subject & the Laws of England. xxxi, 568p. 1985. Repr. of 1880 ed. lib. bdg. 42.50x (ISBN 0-8377-1019-7). Rothman.

Paulson, Hank & Richardson, Don. Beyond the Wall. LC 81-84567. (Orig.). 1982. pap. 5.95 (ISBN 0-8307-0806-5, 5415708). Regal.

Pfeffer, L. Religious Freedom. Haiman, Franklyn S., ed. (To Protect These Rights Ser.). 192p. 1983. pap. 12.95 (ISBN 0-8442-6001-0, 6001-0, Passport Bks.). Natl Textbk.

Religious Liberty in Eastern Europe: A Test Case for Human Rights. pap. cancelled (ISBN 0-686-15372-3, B-122). US Catholic.

Richards, David A. Toleration & the Constitution. LC 86-2358. 288p. 1986. 29.95x (ISBN 0-19-504018-X). Oxford U Pr.

Rutland, Robert A. The First Amendment: The Legacy of George Mason. LC 85-2958. (Illus.). 208p. 1985. 15.00 (ISBN 0-913969-05-2, Pub. by G Mason U Pr). U Pr of Amer.

Shepherd, William C. Secure the Blessings of Liberty: American Constitutional Law & the New Religious Movement. LC 84-1347. (American Academy of Religion Studies in Religion: No. 35). 1984. 16.95 (ISBN 0-89130-733-8, 01-00-35); pap. 9.95 (ISBN 0-89130-824-5). Scholars Pr GA.

Swancara, Frank. Obstruction of Justice by Religion: A Treatise on Religious Barbarities of the Common Law, & a Review of Judicial Oppressions of the Non-Religious in the U. S. LC 70-139581. (Civil Liberties in American History Ser). (Illus.). 1971. Repr. of 1936 ed. lib. bdg. 32.50 (ISBN 0-306-71964-9). Da Capo.

Swidler, Leonard, ed. Religious Liberty & Human Rights in Nations & in Religions. 255p. (Orig.). 1986. pap. 9.95 (ISBN 0-931214-06-8). Ecumenical Phila.

Swomley, John M. Religious Liberty & the Secular State. 140p. 1987. 16.95x (ISBN 0-87975-373-0); pap. 10.95 (ISBN 0-87975-398-6). Prometheus Bks.

Thom, W. T. The Struggle for Religious Freedom in Virginia: The Baptists. Repr. of 1900 ed. 13.00 (ISBN 0-384-60163-4). Johnson Repr.

Thom, William T. The Struggle for Religious Freedom in Virginia. LC 78-63877. (Johns Hopkins University. Studies in the Social Sciences. Eighteenth Ser. 1900: 10-12). Repr. of 1900 ed. 11.50 (ISBN 0-404-61133-8). AMS Pr.

Torpey, William G. Judicial Doctrines of Religious Rights in America. LC 78-132289. (Civil Liberties in American History Ser). 1970. Repr. of 1948 ed. lib. bdg. 42.50 (ISBN 0-306-70067-0). Da Capo.

Underhill, Edwin B., ed. Tracts on Liberty of Conscience & Persecution. (Philosophy Monographs: No. 11). 1968. Repr. of 1846 ed. 29.50 (ISBN 0-8337-3594-2). B Franklin.

Whitehead, John W. The Freedom of Religious Expression in the Public High Schools. LC 83-72040. (Rutherford Institute Reports: No. 1). 64p. 1983. pap. 3.95 (ISBN 0-89107-295-0, Crossway Bks). Good News.

Williamson, Mabel. Have We No Rights? 1957. pap. 5.95 (ISBN 0-8024-3417-7). Moody.

Zwierlein, Frederick K. Religion in the New Netherland, 1623-1664. LC 72-120851. (Civil Liberties in American History Ser.). 1971. Repr. of 1910 ed. lib. bdg. 39.50 (ISBN 0-306-71960-6). Da Capo.

RELIGIOUS LIBERTY–FRANCE

Calvin, John. Concerning Scandals. Fraser, John W., tr. LC 78-8675. Repr. of 1978 ed. 24.90 (ISBN 0-8357-9126-2, 2012802). Bks Demand UMI.

Stankiewicz, W. J. Politics & Religion in Seventeenth-Century France. LC 76-2075. 269p. 1976. Repr. of 1960 ed. lib. bdg. 22.50x (ISBN 0-8371-8770-2, STPR). Greenwood.

RELIGIOUS LIBERTY–GERMANY

Duncan-Jones, Arthur S. The Struggle for Religious Freedom in Germany. LC 78-63664. (Studies in Fascism: Ideology & Practice). Repr. of 1938 ed. 34.00 (ISBN 0-404-16927-9). AMS Pr.

RELIGIOUS LIBERTY–GREAT BRITAIN

Furneaux, Philip. The Palladium of Conscience. LC 74-122161. (Civil Liberties in American History Ser). 267p. 1974. Repr. of 1773 ed. lib. bdg. 35.00 (ISBN 0-306-71972-X). Da Capo.

Jordan, W. K. The Development of Religious Toleration in England, 4 vols. Incl. Vol. 1. From the Beginning of the English Reformation to the Death of Queen Elizabeth (ISBN 0-8446-1251-0); Vol. 2. From the Accession of James One to the Convention of the Long Parliament; Vol. 3. From the Convention of the Long Parliament to the Restoration (ISBN 0-8446-1253-7); Vol. 4. Attainment of the Theory & Accommodations in Thought & Institutions (ISBN 0-8446-1254-5). 1932. 16.50 ea. Peter Smith.

Klein, Arthur J. Intolerance in the Reign of Elizabeth, Queen of England. LC 67-27614. 1968. Repr. of 1917 ed. 26.50x (ISBN 0-8046-0249-2, Pub. by Kennikat). Assoc Faculty Pr.

Seaton, Alexander A. The Theory of Toleration under the Later Stuarts. 1972. lib. bdg. 23.00x (ISBN 0-374-97233-8, Octagon). Hippocrene Bks.

Ward, Nathaniel. Simple Cobler of Aggawam in America. Zall, Paul M., ed. LC 69-19107. xviii, 81p. 1969. 7.50x (ISBN 0-8032-0188-5). U of Nebr Pr.

RELIGIOUS LIBERTY–SOVIET UNION

Alexeyeva, Ludmilla. Soviet Dissent: Contemporary Movements for National, Religious & Human Rights. Glad, John & Pearce, Carol, trs. from Rus. LC 84-11811. 1985. 35.00 (ISBN 0-8195-5124-4, Dist. by Harper). Wesleyan U Pr.

RELIGIOUS LIFE

see Christian Life; Monastic and Religious Life; Monastic and Religious Life of Women; also subdivision Religious Life under classes of persons, e.g. Family–Religious Life

RELIGIOUS LIFE (ISLAM)

Maududi, A. A. Islamic Way of Life. pap. 3.50 (ISBN 0-686-18496-3). Kazi Pubns.

Metcalf, Barbara D., ed. Moral Conduct & Authority: The Place of Adab in Sout h Asian Islam. LC 83-1361. 350p. 1984. text ed. 40.00x (ISBN 0-520-04660-9). U of Cal Pr.

RELIGIOUS LIFE (JUDAISM)

see Jewish Way of Life

RELIGIOUS LITERATURE

see also Bible As Literature; Buddhist Literature; Christian Literature; Hindu Literature; Language Question in the Church; Religious Drama; Religious Poetry; Sacred Books

Aivanhov, Omraam M. New Light on the Gospels. (Izvor Collection: Vol. 217). (Orig.). 1985. pap. 4.95 (ISBN 2-85566-339-3, Pub. by Prosveta France). Prosveta USA.

--Spiritual Alchemy. rev. ed. (Complete Works: Vol. 2). (Illus.). 205p. 1986. pap. 9.95 (ISBN 2-85566-371-7, Pub. by Prosveta France). Prosveta USA.

Ambrose, St. Seven Exegetical Works: Isaac, or the Soul, Death As a Good, Jacob & the Happy Life, Joseph, the Patriarchs, Flight from the World, the Prayer of Job & David. (Fathers of the Church Ser.: Vol. 65). 447p. 1972. 34.95x (ISBN 0-8132-0065-2). Cath U Pr.

Anderson, Margaret J. I Want the Truth. 96p. 1969. pap. 1.25 (ISBN 0-88243-531-0, 02-0531). Gospel Pub.

Apczynski, John. Foundations of Religious Literacy. LC 83-4453. (College Theology Society Annual Publications Ser.). 188p. 1983. pap. 10.50 (ISBN 0-89130-621-8, 34 10 82). Scholars Pr GA.

Archpriest Kyrill Zaits. Tserkov' Boga Ahivago, Stolp i Utverzhdjenije Istini. Tr. of The Church of the Living God, Piller & Affirmation of Truth. 92p. 1956. pap. 2.00 (ISBN 0-317-29113-0). Holy Trinity.

Arnold, Edward V. Rigveda. LC 73-139172. (Popular Studies in Mythology, Romance & Folklore: No. 9). Repr. of 1900 ed. 5.50 (ISBN 0-404-53509-7). AMS Pr.

Articles Agreed on in the National Synode of the Reformed Churches of France. LC 76-57381. (English Experience Ser.: No. 799). 1977. Repr. of 1623 ed. lib. bdg. 5.00 (ISBN 90-221-0799-X). Walter J Johnson.

Augustine, St. City of God, Bks. 8-16. LC 63-19613. (Fathers of the Church Ser.: Vol. 14). 567p. 1952. 27.95x (ISBN 0-8132-0014-8). Cath U Pr.

--The Happy Life & Other Works. (Fathers of the Church Ser.: Vol. 5). 450p. 1948. 22.95x (ISBN 0-8132-0005-9). Cath U Pr.

Ausmus, Harry J. Will Herberg: From Right to Right. LC 86-19357. (Studies in Religion). xx, 276p. 1987. 29.95x (ISBN 0-8078-1724-4). U of NC Pr.

Barney, Kenneth D. Fourth Watch of the Night. 96p. 1973. 1.50 (ISBN 0-88243-724-0, 02-0724). Gospel Pub.

--We Interrupt This Crisis. 63p. 1970. pap. 1.25 (ISBN 0-88243-704-6, 02-0704). Gospel Pub.

Barnhouse, Donald. Is Anybody Up There. LC 76-51734. 1977. 6.95 (ISBN 0-9606562-0-0, BT1102-B26). L Victor Pr.

Bawa Muhaiyaddeen, M. R. The Divine Luminous Wisdom That Dispels the Darkness God-Man Man-God. rev. ed. (Illus.). 288p. 1977. pap. 6.95 (ISBN 0-914390-11-2). Fellowship Pr PA.

Berger, Mike. Bittersweet: True Stories of Decisions That Shaped Eternal Paths. LC 80-81505. 124p. 1980. 6.95 (ISBN 0-88290-144-3). Horizon Utah.

Best, William. The Churches Plea for Her Right. LC 76-57357. (English Experience Ser.: No. 776). 1977. Repr. of 1635 ed. lib. bdg. 10.50 (ISBN 90-221-0776-0). Walter J Johnson.

Beyerlin, Walter, ed. Near Eastern Religious Texts Relating to the Old Testament. Bowden, John, tr. LC 77-28284. (Old Testament Library). (Illus.). 324p. 1978. 22.00 (ISBN 0-664-21363-4). Westminster.

Bialik, Hayyim N. Knight of Onions & Knight of Garlic. 55p. 1934. 4.95 (ISBN 0-88482-734-8). Hebrew Pub.

Birnbaum, Philip, tr. Selihot. 61p. 1952. pap. 1.95 (ISBN 0-88482-344-X). Hebrew Pub.

Bock, Fred & Leech, Bryan J., eds. Hymns for the Family of God. 1976. 7.95 (ISBN 0-89477-000-4, Dist. by Alexandria House); looseleaf 6.95 (ISBN 0-89477-002-0); pap. 7.95 (ISBN 0-89477-001-2). Paragon Benson.

Boruch, Behn. In the Beginning. 1958. 4.00 (ISBN 0-88482-727-5). Hebrew Pub.

--The Patriarchs. 28p. 1959. 3.95 (ISBN 0-88482-729-1). Hebrew Pub.

Boyd, Frank M. Ages & Dispensations. 112p. 1955. pap. 1.50 (ISBN 0-88243-463-2, 02-0463). Gospel Pub.

Brock, Raymond T. Into the Highways & Hedges. LC 61-18608. 1961. 1.25 (ISBN 0-88243-533-7, 02-0533). Gospel Pub.

Broughton, Richard. English Protestants Plea. LC 76-57380. (English Experience Ser.: No. 798). 1977. Repr. of 1621 ed. lib. bdg. 9.50 (ISBN 90-221-0798-1). Walter J Johnson.

Brown, Raphael, tr. Little Flower of St. Francis. 1971. pap. 5.50 (ISBN 0-385-07544-8, Im). Doubleday.

Brownlow, Leroy. With the Good Shepherd. 1969. gift ed. 6.95 (ISBN 0-915720-12-4). Brownlow Pub Co.

Burton, Henry. An Apology of Appeale: Also, an Epistle to the True Hearted Nobility. LC 76-57364. (English Experience Ser.: No. 782). 1977. Repr. of 1636 ed. lib. bdg. 5.00 (ISBN 90-221-0782-5). Walter J Johnson.

--For God & the King. LC 76-57365. (English Experience Ser.: No. 783). 1977. lib. bdg. 17.50 (ISBN 90-221-0783-3). Walter J Johnson.

Christian Periodical Index: Quarterlies, 1984. 10.00 (ISBN 0-318-01672-9). Assn Chr Libs.

Christian Publications, Inc. Staff, ed. Fifty-Two Visual Ideas for Opening Assemblies, 3 vols. 2.25 ea. Vol. 1 (ISBN 0-87509-271-3). Vol. 2 (ISBN 0-87509-272-1). Vol. 3 (ISBN 0-87509-273-X). Chr Pubns.

Church of Scotland, Committee on Public Worship & Aids to Devotion. The Book of Common Order. 1979. 8.95x (ISBN 0-7152-0391-6); leather 14.00 (ISBN 0-686-75148-5). Outlook.

Cumming, W. P., ed. The Revelations of Saint Birgitta. (EETS, OS Ser.: No. 178). Repr. of 1929 ed. 38.00 (ISBN 0-527-00175-9). Kraus Repr.

Cummings, Robert W. Unto You Is the Promise. pap. 0.79 (ISBN 0-88243-750-X, 02-0750). Gospel Pub.

Cyril Of Jerusalem, St. Catecheses Thirteen-Eighteen & Other Works, Vol. 2. (Fathers of the Church Ser.: Vol. 64). 1970. 14.95x (ISBN 0-8132-0064-4). Cath U Pr.

--Procatechesis, Catacheses One - Twelve. LC 68-55980. (Fathers of the Church Ser.: Vol. 61). 279p. 1969. 15.95x (ISBN 0-8132-0061-X). Cath U Pr.

Dalton, Robert C. Tongues Like As of Fire. 127p. 1945. pap. 1.25 (ISBN 0-88243-619-8, 02-0619). Gospel Pub.

David. The Trilogy of Armageddon. LC 85-90253. 138p. 1986. 10.95 (ISBN 0-533-06739-1). Vantage.

De Caussade, Jean-Pierre. The Joy of Full Surrender. (Living Library Ser.). 160p. 1986. pap. 5.95 (ISBN 0-941478-49-1). Paraclete Pr.

Delattre, Floris. La Literature De L'angleterre Puritaine 1603-1660. 1978. Repr. lib. bdg. 25.00 (ISBN 0-8492-0692-8). R West.

DePree, Gordon & DePree, Gladis. Faces of God. LC 80-14384. 128p. 1980. pap. 5.95 (ISBN 0-664-24350-9). Westminster.

Dewey, Melvil. Two Hundred (Religion) Class. LC 79-55849. 1980. Repr. saddlewire pap. 4.95 (ISBN 0-8054-3107-1). Broadman.

Dimont, Max I. Jews, God & History. 1972. pap. 4.95 (ISBN 0-451-14694-8, AE2181, Sig). NAL.

Donahue, Lois. Dear Moses: Letters to Saints & Other Prominent People. LC 84-60743. (Illus.). 104p. 1984. pap. 4.95 (ISBN 0-87973-699-2, 699). Our Sunday Visitor.

Draxe, Thomas. Bibliotheca Scholastica Instructissima: Or a Treasure of Ancient Adagies. LC 76-57378. (English Experience Ser.: No. 796). 1977. Repr. lib. bdg. 24.00 (ISBN 90-221-0796-5). Walter J Johnson.

Duck, Ruth C. Bread for the Journey: Resources for Worship Based on the New Ecumenical Lectionary. LC 81-5046. 96p. 1981. pap. 4.95 (ISBN 0-8298-0423-4). Pilgrim NY.

Duke, Paul D. Irony in the Fourth Gospel. LC 85-42822. 228p. 1985. pap. 11.95 (ISBN 0-8042-0242-7). John Knox.

Eugippius. Life of Saint Severin & Other Minor Works. LC 65-12908. (Fathers of the Church Ser: Vol. 55). 132p. 1965. 14.95x (ISBN 0-8132-0055-5). Cath U Pr.

Fields, Harvey J. With All Your Heart: Bechol Levavcha, 2 vols. (Illus.). 1977. Set. 10.00 (ISBN 0-8074-0197-8, 142611). UAHC.

Fischer, Gretl K. In Search of Jerusalem: Religion & Ethics in the Writings of A. M. Klein. LC 76-367083. pap. 66.50 (ISBN 0-317-26452-4, 2023858). Bks Demand UMI.

Frere, Walter H. Antiohonale Sarisburiense, 6 Vols. 115p. 1923. text ed. 310.50 (ISBN 0-576-28701-6, Pub. by Gregg Intl Pubs England). Gregg Intl.

Frodsham, Stanley H. With Signs Following. 188p. 1946. pap. 5.95 (ISBN 0-88243-635-X, 02-0635). Gospel Pub.

Furnivall, F. J., ed. The Gild of St. Mary & Other Documents. (EETS, ES Ser.: No. 114). Repr. of 1920 ed. 10.00 (ISBN 0-527-00316-6). Kraus Repr.

Gee, Donald. Fruitful or Barren? 90p. 1961. pap. 1.35 (ISBN 0-88243-502-7, 02-0502). Gospel Pub.

--Toward Pentecostal Unity. Orig. Title: All with One Accord. 62p. 1961. pap. 0.60 (ISBN 0-88243-689-9, 02-0689). Gospel Pub.

Golinkin, Noah. Shalom Aleichem. 77p. 1978. pap. 4.95x (ISBN 0-88482-696-1). Hebrew Pub.

Good, Mrs. Marvin. A Shepherd Boy. 1978. pap. 1.95 (ISBN 0-686-24054-5). Rod & Staff.

Greer, Rowan A., ed. Origen: Selected Writings. LC 79-84886. (Classics of Western Spirituality Ser.). 334p. 1979. 13.95 (ISBN 0-8091-0283-8); pap. 9.95 (ISBN 0-8091-2198-0). Paulist Pr.

Haldeman, I. M. Tabernacle, Priesthood & Offerings. 408p. 14.95 (ISBN 0-8007-0303-0). Revell.

Herbert, Frank. The God Makers. 1983. pap. 2.95 (ISBN 0-425-06388-7, Medallion). Berkley Pub.

Heylin, Peter. A Briefe & Moderate Answer to H. Burton. LC 76-57389. (English Experience Ser.: No. 806). 1977. Repr. of 1637 ed. lib. bdg. 22.00 (ISBN 90-221-0806-6). Walter J Johnson.

Hooker, Richard. The Answer of Mr. R. Hooker, to a Supplication to the Privie Counsell. LC 76-57390. (English Experience Ser.: No. 807). 1977. Repr. of 1612 ed. lib. bdg. 5.00 (ISBN 90-221-0807-4). Walter J Johnson.

Iberian Fathers Vol. 1: Marin of Braga, Paschasius, Leander. LC 70-80270. (Fathers of the Church Ser: Vol. 62). 254p. 1969. 14.95x (ISBN 0-8132-0062-8). Cath U Pr.

Iberian Fathers Vol. 2: Braulio of Saragossa, Fructuosus of Braga. LC 70-80270. (Fathers of the Church Ser: Vol. 63). 243p. 1969. 14.95x (ISBN 0-8132-0063-6). Cath U Pr.

Jerome, St. Homilies, Nos. 1-59. LC 64-13360. (Fathers of the Church Ser: Vol. 48). 430p. 1964. 23.95x (ISBN 0-8132-0048-2). Cath U Pr.

John Of Damascus, St. Selected Works. LC 56-792. (Fathers of the Church Ser: Vol. 37). 426p. 1958. 23.95x (ISBN 0-8132-0037-7). Cath U Pr.

Kadloubowsky, E. Early Fathers from the Philokalia. Palmer, G. E., tr. 454p. 1954. 18.95 (ISBN 0-571-03794-1). Faber & Faber.

--Writings from the Philokalia. Palmer, G. E., tr. (Illus.). 420p. 1951. 18.95 (ISBN 0-571-07062-0). Faber & Faber.

Karuna Jemal, Sophia. The Story of Joy. (Illus.). 1978. pap. 3.00 (ISBN 0-932286-00-3). Suratao.

Kippax, J. R. Churchyard Literature. 59.95 (ISBN 0-87968-870-X). Gordon Pr.

Kirban, Salem. Satan's Music Exposed. 1980. pap. 5.95 (ISBN 0-912582-35-9). Kirban.

Klassen, William, ed. The New Way of Jesus. LC 80-65049. 158p. 1980. pap. 7.95 (ISBN 0-87303-038-9). Faith & Life.

Kruckman, Herbert L. Joey Meets His People. 44p. 1940. 2.95 (ISBN 0-88482-732-1). Hebrew Pub.

Lacey, Thomas A., ed. The King's Book, or a Necessary Doctrine & Erudition for Any Christian Man, 1543. (Church Historical Society, London, N.S. Ser.: No. 10). Repr. of 1932 ed. 40.00 (ISBN 0-8115-3134-1). Kraus Repr.

Lactantius. Divine Institutes, Bks. 1-7. LC 64-18669. (Fathers of the Church Ser: Vol. 49). 495p. 1964. 29.95x (ISBN 0-8132-0049-0). Cath U Pr.

LaVigne, Ruth A. Special Messenger. 1978. 3.50 (ISBN 0-8198-0555-6); pap. 2.50 (ISBN 0-8198-0556-4). Dghtrs St Paul.

Lawler, Thomas C. & Burghart, Johannes, eds. The Octavius of Marcus Minucius Felix. Clarke, G. W., tr. from Latin. (Ancient Christian Writers Ser.: Vol. 39). 1974. 14.95 (ISBN 0-8091-0189-0). Paulist Pr.

Letteris, Meir H., ed. & tr. Megillat Esther: The Story of Esther. 1979. pap. 0.95 (ISBN 0-88482-583-3). Hebrew Pub.

Lindsell, Harold & Woodbridge, Charles J. A Handbook of Christian Truth. 352p. 1972. Repr. 13.95 (ISBN 0-8007-0129-1). Revell.

Little, J. M. The Gospel in the Last Days. LC 84-90258. 143p. 1985. 10.95 (ISBN 0-533-06299-3). Vantage.

Loukashevitch, Claudia. Sejatel. Tr. of The Sower. (Illus.). 462p. 1966. 20.00 (ISBN 0-317-30416-X); pap. 15.00 (ISBN 0-317-30417-8). Holy Trinity.

McClintock, John & Strong, James. Cyclopedia of Biblical, Theological, & Ecclesiastical Literature, 12 vols. 12400p. 1981. text ed. 395.00 (ISBN 0-8010-6123-7). Baker Bk.

Magie, Allan. Pets, People, Plagues. LC 79-19321. (Better Living Ser.). 1979. pap. 0.99 (ISBN 0-8127-0233-6). Review & Herald.

Mahfuz, Nagib. God's World: An Anthology of Short Stories. Abadir, Akef & Allen, Roger, trs. LC 73-79201. (Studies in Middle Eastern Literatures: No. 2). 1973. pap. 12.00x student ed. (ISBN 0-88297-031-3). Bibliotheca.

May, J. Lewis. An English Treasury of Religious Prose. 1977. Repr. of 1932 ed. 15.00 (ISBN 0-89984-062-0). Century Bookbindery.
Melito. On Pascha & Fragments. Hall, Stuart G., ed. (Oxford Early Christian Texts). 1979. text ed. 34.95x (ISBN 0-19-826811-4). Oxford U Pr.
Mensendiek, Mark. Grace to You. 20p. (Orig.). 1985. pap. 0.75 (ISBN 0-933643-22-5). Grace World Outreach.
Metropolitan Innocent of Moscow Staff. Ukazanije Puti v Tsarstvije Nebsnoje. Tr. of Indication of the Way Kingdom of Heaven. 59p. pap. 2.00 (ISBN 0-317-28978-0). Holy Trinity.
Metz, Johannes B. Poverty of Spirit. LC 68-31045. 56p. 1968. 2.95 (ISBN 0-8091-1924-2). Paulist Pr.
Miller, Keith. A Second Touch. LC 67-31340. 1982. 7.95 (ISBN 0-8499-0338-6, 80036). Word Bks.
Mitchell, Stephen, tr. & intro. by. The Book of Job. 176p. 1987. 22.50 (ISBN 0-86547-286-6); pap. 12.50 (ISBN 0-86547-270-X). N Point Pr.
Mittarelli, J. H. & Costadoni, A. Annales Camaldulenses Osb, 9 Vols. 6787p. 1773. text ed. 745.20x (ISBN 0-576-72247-2, Pub. by Gregg Intl Pubs England). Gregg Intl.
Mowlana Jalal ud-Din Mohammad Rumi. Masnavi, Vol. 1. Estelami, Mohammad, ed. (Mazda Special Persian Language Publications). (Persian.). 580p. 1987. lib. bdg. 25.00 (ISBN 0-939214-40-7). Mazda Pubs.
Moynahan, Michael E. How the Word Became Flesh: Story Dramas for Education & Worship. LC 80-54874. 1981. pap. 10.95 (ISBN 0-89390-029-X). Resource Pubns.
Murray, Andrew & Choy, Leona. Inner Chamber. (Orig.). 1980. pap. 2.50 (ISBN 0-87508-405-2). Chr Lit.
Murthy, B. Srinivasa, tr. from Sanskrit. The Bhagavad Gita: Translated with Introduction & Notes. LC 84-82433. 150p. 1985. pap. 9.95 (ISBN 0-941910-01-6). Long Beach Pubns.
Novatian: Writings. LC 73-9872. (Fathers of the Church Ser.: Vol. 67). 223p. 1974. 17.95x (ISBN 0-8132-0067-9). Cath U Pr.
Nutting, George L. & Nutting, Ruth S. The Angel World. 115p. (Orig.). 1985. pap. 2.95 (ISBN 0-9612266-1-7). Numard Bks.
Omer, Devorah. Path Beneath the Sea. 192p. 1969. 3.50 (ISBN 0-88482-744-5). Hebrew Pub.
Pak, Bo Hi. Truth Is My Sword. LC 78-74661. 110p. (Orig.). 1978. pap. 2.00 (ISBN 0-318-03063-2). HSA Pubns.
Parker, Marjorie. Bread from My Oven. (Quiet Time Bks). 128p. 1972. pap. 3.50 (ISBN 0-8024-0910-5). Moody.
Patrizi, Agostino P. Caeremoniale Romanum of Agostino Patrizi Piccolomini. 310p. 1516. text ed. 66.24x (ISBN 0-576-99434-0, Pub. by Gregg Intl Pubs England). Gregg Intl.
Pez, Bernhard. Bibliotheca Asctica Antiquo-Nova, 12 Vols. 6600p. 1740. text ed. 414.00x (ISBN 0-576-72814-4, Pub. by Gregg Intl Pubs England). Gregg Intl.
Powell, Gabriel. The Catholikes Supplication Unto the King's Majestie, for Toleration of Catholike Religion in England. LC 76-57406. (English Experience Ser.: No. 822). 1977. lib. bdg. 6.00 (ISBN 90-221-0822-8). Walter J Johnson.
Price, A. F. & Mou-Lam, trs. from Sanskrit & Chinese. The Diamond Sutra & the Sutra of Hui Neng. (The Clear Light Ser.). 190p. 1969. pap. 7.95 (ISBN 0-87773-005-9). Shambhala Pubns.
Ramakrishnananda, Swami. The Ancient Quest. 112p. pap. 1.00 (ISBN 0-87481-412-X). Vedanta Pr.
Ramos, Dominga D. Moncado. 1985. 9.75 (ISBN 0-8062-2452-5). Carlton.
Reece, Colleen L. The Other Nine. (Orig.). 1981. pap. 7.50 (ISBN 0-8309-0288-0). Herald Hse.
Renard, Pierre. The Solar Revolution & the Prophet. (Testimonials Ser.). (Illus.). 193p. (Orig.). 1980. pap. 9.95 (ISBN 2-85566-135-8, Pub. by Prosveta France). Prosveta USA.
Richards, Harold. Earthquake. LC 79-13559. (Flame Ser.). 1979. pap. 0.99 (ISBN 0-8127-0240-9). Review & Herald.
Riggs, Ralph M. So Send I You. 130p. 1965. 1.25 (ISBN 0-88243-587-6, 02-0587). Gospel Pub.
--The Spirit Himself. 210p. 1949. 5.50 (ISBN 0-88243-590-6, 02-0590). Gospel Pub.
--The Story of the Future. LC 67-31330. 1968. 2.95 (ISBN 0-88243-742-9, 02-0742). Gospel Pub.
Rittmayer, Jane F. Life, Time. 1st ed. pap. 31.80 (ISBN 0-317-26230-0, 2055572). Bks Demand UMI.
Roy, Cristina. Sunshine Country. 160p. (YA) 6.50 (ISBN 0-686-05594-2); pap. 4.35 (ISBN 0-686-05595-0). Rod & Staff.
Saint John Moschus. Trorenija Svatago Efrema Sirina, Vol. 1. Tr. of The Works of St. Works of Ephraim. 475p. 21.00 (ISBN 0-317-28899-7); pap. 16.00 (ISBN 0-317-28900-4). Holy Trinity.
Schneider, Claire. Inspirations Unlimited. 48p. (Orig.). 1985. pap. 4.95 (ISBN 0-9601982-2-9). Greenwood Hse.
Sibthorpe, Robert. Apostolike Obedience: A Sermon. LC 76-57418. (English Experience Ser.: No. 831). 1977. Repr. of 1627 ed. lib. bdg. 6.00 (ISBN 90-221-0831-7). Walter J Johnson.
Skaballanovitch, M. Uspenije Presvjatija Bogorodits. Tr. of The Dormition of the Mother of God. 114p. pap. 4.00 (ISBN 0-317-29164-5). Holy Trinity.
--Vozdvizhenije Tchestnago Krjesta Gospodnja. Tr. of The Exaltation of the Life Giving Cross. 173p. pap. 6.00 (ISBN 0-317-29152-1). Holy Trinity.
Speculum Christiani: A Middle English Religious Treatise of the 14th Century. (EETS OS: No. 182). Repr. of 1933 ed. 34.00 (ISBN 0-527-00179-1). Kraus Repr.
Speculum Sacerdotale. (EETS, OS Ser.: No. 200). Repr. of 1936 ed. 21.00 (ISBN 0-527-00200-3). Kraus Repr.
Stevens, Beulah F. Dear Georgia. LC 78-13546. 1979. pap. 0.75 (ISBN 0-8127-0204-2). Review & Herald.
Stott, John R. The Message of Second Timothy. LC 73-75890. (Bible Speaks Today Ser.). 144p. 1973. text ed. 5.95 (ISBN 0-87784-295-7). Inter-Varsity.
Stuart, G. On the Shores of the Infinite. pap. 4.95 (ISBN 0-910122-34-2). Amherst Pr.
Suelflow, August R. Religious Archives: An Introduction. LC 80-17159. (SAA Basic Archival Manual Ser.). 1980. pap. text ed. 7.00 (ISBN 0-931828-20-1). Soc Am Archivists.
Summers, JoAn. God's Little Animals: Easy Illustrations & Bible Parallels. (Illus.). 32p. 1969. pap. 1.95 (ISBN 0-88243-718-6, 02-0718). Gospel Pub.
Swedenborg, Emanuel. Arcana Coelestia (Heavenly Secrets, Vol. 1. pap. 3.95 (ISBN 0-87785-053-4). Swedenborg.
--Conjugal Love. Student ed. LC 79-93407. 12.00 (ISBN 0-87785-054-2). Swedenborg.
--Four Doctrines. LC 67-1465. 1971. student ed. 12.00 (ISBN 0-87785-063-1); pap. 2.95 (ISBN 0-87785-064-X). Swedenborg.
--Heaven & Hell. LC 77-93044. cancelled (ISBN 0-87785-167-0); student ed. 12.00 (ISBN 0-87785-066-6); pap. 5.95 (ISBN 0-87785-153-0). Swedenborg.
Taylor, Richard S. Disciplined Life Style. LC 80-65581. 96p. 1975. pap. 2.95 (ISBN 0-87123-110-7, Dimension Bks). Bethany Hse.
Thomas, J. D. Heaven's Window: Sequel to We Be Brethren. LC 74-28950. 159p. 1975. 11.95 (ISBN 0-89112-002-5, Bibl Res Pr). Abilene Christ U.
Thomson, S. H. The Writings of Robert Grosseteste, Bishop of Lincoln: 1235-1253. Repr. of 1940 ed. 29.00 (ISBN 0-527-89820-1). Kraus Repr.
Tishby, Isaiah, ed. The Wisdom of the Zohar, 3 vols. Goldstein, David, tr. (The Litman Library of Jewish Civilization). 2000p. 1986. Set. 198.00x (ISBN 0-19-710043-0). Oxford U Pr.
Townsend, John T. Midrash Tanhuma, 2 vols. 800p. 1987. price not set (ISBN 0-88125-087-2). Ktav.
Truett, George W. George W. Truett Library, 4 vols. 1980. Set. pap. 34.95 (ISBN 0-8054-2237-4). Broadman.
United Reformed Church in England & Wales-the Doctrine & Worship Committee. A Book of Services. 1980. 8.95x (ISBN 0-7152-0446-7). Outlook.
Van Pelt, Nancy. How to Develop Your Child's Character. (Better Living Ser.). 1979. pap. 0.99 (ISBN 0-8127-0232-8). Review & Herald.
Von Franz, Marie-Louise. Patterns of Creativity Mirrored in Creation Myths. (Seminar Ser: No. 6). 250p. 1972. pap. 15.00 (ISBN 0-88214-106-6). Spring Pubns.
Ward, C. M. This Child Shall Be Lent Unto the Lord. (Illus.). 32p. 1967. pap. 0.60 12 for 6.00 (ISBN 0-88243-822-0, 02-0822). Gospel Pub.
Wayman, Alex & Wayman, Hideko, trs. from Chinese. The Lion's Roar of Queen Srimala. 160p. 1974. 24.00x (ISBN 0-231-03726-0). Columbia U Pr.
Weidenschilling, J. M. Living with Luther. 1945. pap. text ed. 1.10 (ISBN 0-570-03523-6, 14-1155). Concordia.
Wells, Albert M., Jr., ed. Baker's Pocket Book of Religious Quotes. (Direction Bks.). 240p. 1976. pap. 2.95 (ISBN 0-8010-9575-1). Baker Bk.
Williams, Paul L., ed. Historicism & Faith: The Proceedings of the Fellowship of Catholic Scholars. LC 80-117742. 1980. pap. 5.95 (ISBN 0-937374-00-8). NE Bks.
Winn, Alison. Hello God. 1985. 3.95 (ISBN 0-87162-405-2, D4310). Warner Pr.
Wood, Phyllis A. This Time Count Me In. LC 80-15068. (A Hiway Book: A High Interest - Low Reading Level Book). 120p. 1980. 8.95 (ISBN 0-664-32665-X). Westminster.
Woodroffe, John. The Garland of Letters. 18.00 (ISBN 0-89744-112-5, Pub. by Ganesh & Co. India). Auromere.
The Works of William E. Channing, D.D. 1060p. 1982. Repr. of 1889 ed. lib. bdg. 100.00 (ISBN 0-8495-0959-9). Arden Lib.

RELIGIOUS LITERATURE (SELECTIONS: EXTRACTS, ETC.)

Amazing Grace. 1978. 4.95 (ISBN 0-8378-2014-6). Gibson.
Bell, Martin. Way of the Wolf: The Gospel in New Images. LC 77-120366. (Illus.). 128p. 1970. pap. 8.95 (ISBN 0-8164-0202-7, AY6445, HarpR); 2 records 8.95 ea. Har-Row.
Broadus, E. K. Thomas Fuller, Selections: With Essays by Charles Lamb, Leslie Stephen & Co. 1979. Repr. of 1928 ed. lib. bdg. 20.00 (ISBN 0-8492-3742-4). R West.
Burghardt, W. J., et al, eds. Tertullian, the Treatise Against Hermogenes. LC 56-13257. (Ancient Christian Writers Ser.: No. 24). 179p. 1956. 10.95 (ISBN 0-8091-0148-3). Paulist Pr.
Davies-Rogers, Ellen. A Tree Is Lighted. LC 84-90673. (Illus.). 1984. 5.00 (ISBN 0-317-19588-3). Plantation.
Doron, Pinchas. Interpretations of Difficult Passages in Rashi, Vol. I. (Hebrew.). 1985. text ed. 20.00x (ISBN 0-88125-080-5). Ktav.
Frost, S. E., Jr., ed. The Sacred Writings of the Worlds Great Religions. 416p. 1972. pap. 6.95 (ISBN 0-07-022520-6). McGraw.
Groeschel, Benedict J. Spiritual Passages. LC 82-17139. 176p. 1983. 12.95 (ISBN 0-8245-0497-6). Crossroad NY.
Jerome, St. Homilies, Nos. 60-96. LC 64-13360. (Fathers of the Church Ser: Vol. 57). 295p. 1966. 15.95x (ISBN 0-8132-0057-1). Cath U Pr.
Jessop, Augustus. Wise Words & Quaint Counsels of Thomas Fuller: Selected & Arranged with a Short Sketch of the Author's Life. 1979. Repr. of 1892 ed. lib. bdg. 45.00 (ISBN 0-8492-5602-X). R West.
John Chrysostom, St. Homilies on St. John 1-47. LC 57-1545. (Fathers of the Church Ser: Vol. 33). 485p. 1957. 25.95x (ISBN 0-8132-0033-4). Cath U Pr.
Johnson, Joe, compiled by. A Field of Diamonds. LC 73-87067. 12.95 (ISBN 0-8054-5133-1). Broadman.
Kratzmann, Gregory & Simpson, James, eds. Medieval English Religious & Ethical Literature. 224p. 1986. 37.50 (ISBN 0-85991-220-5, Pub. by Boydell & Brewer). Longwood Pub Group.
Marchand, Cecilia. Once upon a Rainbow. (Illus.). 128p. 1986. 8.95 (ISBN 0-89962-558-4). Todd & Honeywell.
Meir Bar-Am. The Fateful Mission. 180p. 1986. 9.95 (ISBN 0-87306-420-8); pap. 6.95 (ISBN 0-87306-421-6). Feldheim.
Mitchell, T. Crichton. Great Holiness Classics: The Wesley Century, Vol. 2. 504p. 1984. 21.95 (ISBN 0-8341-0910-7). Beacon Hill.
Prophet, Elizabeth C. & Prophet, Elizabeth, eds. Pearls of Wisdom 1971: Masters of the Far East-On the Pillars of Eternity, Vol. 14. LC 78-60619. 234p. 14.95 (ISBN 0-916766-31-4). Summit Univ.
St. John, Patricia. The Runaway. 1985. pap. 3.95 (ISBN 0-8024-9159-6). Moody.
St. Peter Chrysologos & St. Valerian. Selected Works. LC 65-27500. (Fathers of the Church Ser.: Vol. 17). 454p. 1953. 29.95x (ISBN 0-8132-0017-2). Cath U Pr.
Sider, E. Morris & Hostetler, Paul. Lantern in the Dawn: Selections from Writings of John E. Zercher. 1980. 6.95 (ISBN 0-916035-08-5). Evangel Indiana.
Smart, Ninian & Hecht, Richard, eds. Sacred Texts of the World: A Universal Anthology. LC 82-7375. 1982. 27.50x (ISBN 0-8245-0483-6). Crossroad NY.
Tertullian. Disciplinary, Moral & Ascetial Works. (Fathers of the Church Ser: Vol. 40). 495p. 1959. 34.95x (ISBN 0-8132-0040-7). Cath U Pr.
Wapnick, Kenneth. Glossary: Index for "A Course in Miracles. 255p. (Orig.). 1982. 16.00. Foun Miracles.
Wesley, John. The Works of John Wesley: (Letters II), 1740-1755, Vol. 26. Baker, Frank, ed. (The Oxford Edition of the Works of John Wesley Ser.). (Illus.). 1982. 45.00x (ISBN 0-19-812546-1). Oxford U Pr.
Zinn, Grover A., ed. Richard of St. Victor: The Twelve Patriarchs, the Mystical Ark Book, Three of the Trinity. LC 79-83834. (Classics of Western Spirituality Ser.). 448p. 1979. 13.95 (ISBN 0-8091-0241-2); pap. 7.95 (ISBN 0-8091-2122-0). Paulist Pr.

RELIGIOUS LITERATURE–AUTHORSHIP

see also Journalism, Religious

Aycock, Don M. & Goss, Leonard G. Writing Religiously. 1986. 13.95 (ISBN 0-8010-0210-9). Baker Bk.
Church of God Editorial Department. Manual for Editors & Writers. 1976. pap. 4.95 (ISBN 0-87148-568-0). Pathway Pr.
Cox, James H. Confessions of a Moonlight Writer: A Freelancer's Guide to the Church Market. LC 80-70315. 97p. (Orig.). 1982. pap. 5.95 (ISBN 0-939298-00-7). J M Prods.
Gentz, William H., ed. Religious Writer's Marketplace: The Definitive Sourcebook. rev. ed. LC 84-27691. 221p. 1985. pap. 17.95 (ISBN 0-89471-305-1). Running Pr.

RELIGIOUS LITERATURE–BIBLIOGRAPHY

see also Theology–Bibliography

Barber, Cyril J. The Minister's Library, Vol. 2. 1987. text ed. 23.95 (ISBN 0-8024-5299-X). Moody.
Elliot, Paula. Performing Arts Information, Nineteen Seventy-Five to Nineteen Eighty: A Bibliography of Reference Works. 1982. pap. 4.00. KSU.
Oudin, Casimir. Commentarius de Scriptoribus Ecclesiae Antiquis Illorumque Scriptis. 3296p. Date not set. Repr. of 1723 ed. text ed. 662.40x (ISBN 0-576-72229-4, Pub. by Gregg Intl Pubs England). Gregg Intl.
Religious Books, 1876-1982, 4 vol. set. 4389p. 1983. 225.00x (ISBN 0-8352-1602-0). Bowker.
Sandifer, Kevin. Religious Archives, a Complete Technical Look for the Layman. Gill, Rowland P., ed. 96p. (Orig.). 1985. pap. text ed. 5.50 (ISBN 0-910653-03-8, 8101-C). Archival Servs.
Scroggie, W. Graham. W. Graham Scroggie Library Series, 7 vols. 1981. pap. 28.00 (ISBN 0-8254-3740-7). Kregel.
Shutte, A. J. Printed Italian Vernacular Religious Books 1465-1550: A Finding List. 484p. (Orig.). 1983. pap. text ed. 65.00x (Pub. by Droz Switzerland). Coronet Bks.
Sieben, Hermann J. Voces: Eine Bibliographie zu Woertern und Begriffen aus der Patristik (1918-1978) (Bibliographia Patristica). 461p. 1979. text ed. 55.20x (ISBN 3-11-007966-6). De Gruyter.
Williams, William P. A Descriptive Catalogue of Seventeenth Century Religious Literature in the Kansas State University Library. LC 67-63307. (Libraries Bibliography Ser.: No. 3). 1966. 1.50 (ISBN 0-686-20809-9). KSU.
Wilson, John F. & Slavens, Thomas P., eds. Research Guide to Religious Studies. LC 81-22862. (Sources of Information in the Humanities Ser.). 199p. 1982. lib. bdg. 22.50x (ISBN 0-8389-0330-4). ALA.
Zernov, Nicholas, compiled by. Russian Emigre Authors: A Biographical Index & Bibliography of Their Works on Theology, Religious Philosophy, Church History & Orthodox Culture, 1921-1972. 1973. lib. bdg. 23.50 (ISBN 0-8161-1005-0). G K Hall.

RELIGIOUS LITERATURE–HISTORY AND CRITICISM

Ambrose, St. Hexameron Paradise, Cain & Abel. LC 77-81354. (Fathers of the Church Ser.: Vol. 42). 449p. 1961. 34.95x (ISBN 0-8132-0042-3). Cath U Pr.
Augustine, St. City of God, Bks. 17-22. LC 63-19613. (Fathers of the Church Ser.: Vol. 24). 461p. 1954. 27.95x (ISBN 0-8132-0024-5). Cath U Pr.
Basil, St. Exegetic Homilies. LC 63-12483. (Father of the Church Ser.: Vol. 46). 378p. 1963. 19.95x (ISBN 0-8132-0046-6). Cath U Pr.
Beckford, James A. Cult Controversies: The Societal Response to the New Religious Movements. 336p. 1985. 39.95 (ISBN 0-422-79630-1, 9592, Pub. by Tavistock England); pap. 13.95 (ISBN 0-422-79640-9, 9593, Pub. by Tavistock England). Methuen Inc.
Biezais, Haralds, ed. Religious Symbols & Their Functions. 178p. (Orig.). 1979. pap. text ed. 22.50 (ISBN 91-22-00199-9, Pub. by Almqvist & Wiksell). Coronet Bks.
Degeest, Achille. Saint Joseph Commentary on the Sunday Readings, 3 vols. 3.95 ea. Year A (ISBN 0-89942-341-8, 341/04). Year B (ISBN 0-89942-342-6, 342/04). Year C (ISBN 0-89942-343-4, 343/04). Catholic Bk Pub.
Farquhar, J. N. An Outline of Religious Literature of India. 1984. Repr. 30.00 (ISBN 0-89684-287-8). Orient Bk Dist.
Ficken, Carl. God's Story & Modern Literature: Reading Fiction in Community. LC 84-48705. 176p. 1985. pap. 9.95 (ISBN 0-8006-1823-8, 1-1823). Fortress.
Gersh, Harry. Sacred Books of the Jews. LC 68-17320. 1972. pap. 4.95 (ISBN 0-8128-1528-9). Stein & Day.
Justin Martyr, St. Complete Writings. (Fathers of the Church Ser.: Vol. 6). 486p. 1948. 34.95 (ISBN 0-8132-0006-7). Cath U Pr.
Lactantius. Minor Works. (Fathers of the Church Ser: Vol. 54). 1965. 15.95x (ISBN 0-8132-0054-7). Cath U Pr.
Lea, L. J., ed. Compendium of the Scriptures. 1951. pap. 10.00 (ISBN 0-8309-0253-8). Herald Hse.
Magistretti, Marco. Beroldus, Sive Ecclesiae Ambrosianae Mediolanensis Calendarium Et Ordines Saec XII. 294p. 1894. Repr. of 1894 ed. text ed. 66.24x (ISBN 0-576-99706-4, Pub. by Gregg Intl Pubs England). Gregg Intl.

Messbarger, Paul R. Fiction with a Parochial Purpose: Social Uses of American Catholic Literarture, 1884-1900. 1971. 11.95 (ISBN 0-87270-017-8). U of Notre Dame Pr.
Morris, Frank. The Divine Epic. LC 72-96118. 539p. 1973. pap. 5.00 (ISBN 0-913382-18-3, 101-18). Prow Bks-Franciscan.
Muir, Pearson M. Religious Writers of England. 1901. 20.00 (ISBN 0-8274-3264-X). R West.
Murphy, Roland E., ed. & intro. by. Medieval Exegesis of Wisdom Literature: Essays by Beryl Smalley. (Scholars Press Reprints & Translations Ser.). 1986. 13.95 (ISBN 1-55540-026-4, 00 07 16). Scholars Pr GA.
O'Donovan, Oliver. The Problem of Self-Love in Saint Augustine. LC 80-5397. 208p. 1980. text ed. 23.50x (ISBN 0-300-02468-1). Yale U Pr.
Salvian the Presbyter. Complete Writings. (Fathers of the Church Ser.: Vol. 3). 396p. 1947. 34.95x (ISBN 0-8132-0003-2). Cath U Pr.
Sargent, Michael G. James Grenehalgh As Textual Critic. Hogg, James, ed. (Analecta Cartusiana Ser.: No. 85/1&2). 589p. (Orig.). 1984. pap. 50.00 (ISBN 3-7052-0142-5, Pub. by Salzburg Studies). Longwood Pub Group.
Starks, Arthur E. Combined Concordances to the Scriptures. 1978. 33.00 (ISBN 0-8309-0255-4). Herald Hse.
Vielhauer, Philipp. Geschichte der urchristlichen Literatur: Einleitung in das Neue Testament, die Apokryphen und die Apostolischen Vaeter. 812p. 1981. 41.00x (ISBN 3-11-007763-9). De Gruyter.
Walsh, James, ed. Pre-Reformation English Spirituality. LC 65-12885. 1966. 20.00 (ISBN 0-8232-0655-6). Fordham.
White, Helen C. Social Criticism in Popular Religious Literature of the Sixteenth-Century. 1965. lib. bdg. 20.50x (ISBN 0-374-98455-7, Octagon). Hippocrene Bks.
--Tudor Books of Saints & Martyrs. LC 63-13741. pap. 73.00 (ISBN 0-317-07866-6, 2004164). Bks Demand UMI.
Willis, Lloyd A. Archaeology in Adventist Literature, 1937-1980. (Andrews University Seminary Doctoral Dissertation Ser.: Vol. 7). x, 670p. 1984. pap. 14.95 (ISBN 0-943872-39-1). Andrews Univ Pr.

RELIGIOUS LITERATURE–PUBLICATION AND DISTRIBUTION
see also Bible–Publication and Distribution
Gentz, William H., ed. Religious Writer's Marketplace: The Definitive Sourcebook. rev. ed. LC 84-27691. 221p. 1985. pap. 17.95 (ISBN 0-89471-305-1). Running Pr.
Smart, Ninian, et al. Nineteenth Century Religious Thought in the West, Vols. 2 & 3. 368p. Vol. 2, 08/1985. 49.50 (ISBN 0-521-22832-8); Vol. 3, 10/1985. 49.50 (ISBN 0-521-30114-9). Cambridge U Pr.

RELIGIOUS MUSIC
see Church Music

RELIGIOUS MYSTERIES
see Mysteries, Religious

RELIGIOUS NEWSPAPERS AND PERIODICALS
Lexau, Henry. A Treasury of Catholic Digest: Favorite Stories of Fifty Years, 1936-1986. LC 86-81597. 598p. 1986. 24.95 (ISBN 0-89870-115-5). Ignatius Pr.
Lippy, Charles H., ed. Religious Periodicals of the United States: Academic & Scholarly Journals. LC 85-9861. (Historical Guides to the World's Periodicals & Newspapers Ser.). 626p. 1986. lib. bdg. 65.00 (ISBN 0-313-23420-5, LRP/). Greenwood.
Lownethal, Rudolph. The Religious Periodical Press in China, 2 vols. (Illus.). 300p. Repr. of 1940 ed. Set. text ed. 45.50x (ISBN 0-89644-569-0, Pub. by Chinese Matl Ctr). Coronet Bks.
Wall, James, et al. A Century of the Century. 128p. (Orig.). 1987. pap. 8.95 (ISBN 0-8028-0180-3). Eerdmans.

RELIGIOUS NEWSPAPERS AND PERIODICALS–BIBLIOGRAPHY
Christian Periodical Index: Annual. 1982. cancelled. Assn Chr Libs.
Nelson, Barbara, ed. Christian Periodical Index. 88p. 3 yr. cumulative 45.00 (ISBN 0-318-17810-9); 10.00 ea. Assn Chr Libs.
Norton, Wesley. Religious Newspapers in the Old Northwest to 1861: A History, Bibliography, & Record of Opinion. LC 75-36983. xi, 196p. 1977. 12.50x (ISBN 0-8214-0193-9). Ohio U Pr.
Stroupe, Henry S. Religious Press in the South Atlantic States, 1802-1865. (Duke University. Trinity College Historical Socity. Historical Papers: No. 32). Repr. of 1956 ed. 24.50 (ISBN 0-404-51782-X). AMS Pr.

RELIGIOUS ORDERS
see Monasticism and Religious Orders

RELIGIOUS PAINTING
see Christian Art and Symbolism

RELIGIOUS POETRY
see also Hymns
Andre, Evelyn M. Places I Like to Be. LC 79-23964. (Illus.). 1980. 7.75g (ISBN 0-687-31540-9). Abingdon.
Armstrong, Karen, ed. Tongues of Fire: An Anthology of Religious & Poetic Experience. 444p. 1986. 19.95 (ISBN 0-670-80878-4). Viking.
Beaumont, Timothy, ed. Modern Religious Verse. (Pocket Poet Ser.). 1966. pap. 2.95 (ISBN 0-8023-9039-0). Dufour.
Bodo, Murray. Song of the Sparrow: Meditations & Poems to Pray by. (Illus.). 187p. (Orig.). 1976. pap. 3.95 (ISBN 0-912228-26-1). St Anthony Mess Pr.
Booth, Julianne. Bible Verses to Remember. 1982. pap. 2.95 (ISBN 0-570-04061-2, 56-1364). Concordia.
Bowers, R. H., ed. Three Middle English Religious Poems. LC 63-63267. (University of Florida Humanities Monographs: No. 12). 1963. pap. 3.50 (ISBN 0-8130-0025-4). U Presses Fla.
Braverman, Eric R. Psalms of the Rabbi Physician. (Illus.). 112p. (Orig.). 1986. pap. 9.95 (ISBN 1-55630-003-4). Brentwood Comm.
Bunyan, John. Pictorial Pilgrim's Progress. 1960. pap. 3.95 (ISBN 0-8024-0019-1). Moody.
--The Pilgrim's Progress. 1979. Repr. 19.95 (ISBN 0-85151-259-3). Banner of Truth.
--Pilgrim's Progress. (Moody Classics Ser.). 1984. pap. 3.95 (ISBN 0-8024-0012-4). Moody.
--Pilgrim's Progress. 256p. 1973. pap. 3.95 (ISBN 0-310-22142-0, 6610P). Zondervan.
--Pilgrim's Progress in Today's English. LC 64-25255. 1964. pap. 6.95 (ISBN 0-8024-6520-X). Moody.
Campbell, Lucile M. To God Be the Glory. (Orig.). 1981. pap. 1.95 (ISBN 0-9607114-0-6). L M Campbell.
Cardenal, Ernesto. Psalms. 96p. 1981. pap. 3.95 (ISBN 0-8245-0044-X). Crossroad NY.
Cardwell, Carolyn E., ed. My Heart Speaks to Thee, Vol. 1. (Illus.). 250p. 1985. pap. 8.45 (ISBN 0-916395-02-2, MH-1). Hieroglyphics.
--My Heart Speaks to Thee, Vol. 2. (Illus.). 250p. (Orig.). 1985. pap. 8.45 (ISBN 0-916395-05-7, MH-2). Hieroglyphics.
Chinmoy, Sri. The Golden Boat, 20 vols. (Illus.). 50p. (Orig.). 1974. pap. 3.00 ea. Aum Pubns.
Church, Elmer T. Walk with Me in White. LC 86-81184. 154p. 1986. perfect bdg. 9.95 (ISBN 0-318-21723-6). E T Church.
Denney, Reuel. In Praise of Adam. LC 61-18887. (Phoenix Poets Ser). 1961. pap. 1.50 (ISBN 0-226-14301-5, PP3, Phoen). U of Chicago Pr.
Duffy, John. Under the Goldwood Tree. 64p. 1982. 5.00 (ISBN 0-682-49869-6). Exposition Pr FL.
Eitel, Lorraine, compiled by. The Treasury of Christian Poetry. 192p. 1982. 12.95 (ISBN 0-8007-1291-9). Revell.
Enciclopedia de Poesia Evangelica. 3rd ed. (Span.). 365p. 1978. pap. 12.25 (ISBN 84-7228-037-3, S-50573). French & Eur.
Foster, Ellwood. Inspirationally Yours. LC 80-53330. 1984. 5.95 (ISBN 0-533-04843-5). Vantage.
Fremantle, Ann & Fremantle, Christopher. In Love with Love: One Hundred of the World's Greatest Spiritual Poems. LC 78-64360. (Spiritual Masters Ser.). 1978. pap. 2.95 (ISBN 0-8091-2136-0). Paulist Pr.
Frost, Gerhard E. Blessed Is the Ordinary. (Illus.). 96p. pap. 4.95 (ISBN 0-86683-606-3, HarpR). Har-Row.
Gallwey, Peter, ed. The Legend of St. Dismas & Other Poems. LC 83-82115. 126p. (Orig.). 1984. pap. 6.95 (ISBN 0-89870-034-5). Ignatius Pr.
Gans, Manfred, ed. Yeshiva Children Write Poetry: From the Heart We Sing. 6.95 (ISBN 0-914131-76-1, D43). Torah Umesorah.
Gilman, Arthur. Library of Religious Poetry. 59.95 (ISBN 0-8490-0521-3). Gordon Pr.
Grosseteste, Robert. Carmina Anglo-Normannica: Chasteau d'Amour, to Which Is Added La Vie de Saint-Marie Egyptienne & an English Version of the Chasteau d'Amour. Cooke, M., ed. 1852. 24.00 (ISBN 0-8337-1467-8). B. Franklin.
Hance, Lilian. Sowing & Reaping. 1981. 14.00x (ISBN 0-7223-1418-3, Pub. by A H Stockwell England). State Mutual Bk.
Harris, Daniel A. Inspirations Unbidden: The "Terrible Sonnets" of Gerard Manley Hopkins. LC 81-11497. 200p. 1982. 26.50x (ISBN 0-520-04539-4). U of Cal Pr.
Herbert, George. Bodleian Manuscript of George Herbert's Poems. LC 81-18454. 1984. 125.00x (ISBN 0-8201-1373-5). Schol Facsimiles.
Higginson, William J. Death Is, & Approaches to the Edge. (Xtras Ser.: No. 9). 48p. (Orig.). 1981. pap. 2.50 (ISBN 0-89120-019-3). From Here.
Hill, Caroline M., ed. The World's Great Religious Poetry. LC 70-137058. 836p. 1973. Repr. of 1938 ed. lib. bdg. 47.50x (ISBN 0-8371-5521-5, HIRP). Greenwood.
Hudson, Julius. Go Ask God. 1981. 4.75 (ISBN 0-8062-1827-4). Carlton.
Irving, Lynn. Pocketful of Puppets: Poems for Church School. Keller, Merily H., ed. (Puppetry in Education ser.). (Illus.). 48p. (Orig.). 1982. 11.50; pap. 7.50 (ISBN 0-931044-05-7). Renfro Studios.
Johnson, James Weldon. God's Trombones. (Poets Ser). 1976. pap. 4.95 (ISBN 0-14-042217-X). Penguin.
Jones, Mary H. Quaker Poets Past & Present. LC 75-7414. 32p. (Orig.). 1975. pap. 2.50x (ISBN 0-87574-202-5). Pendle Hill.
Kakonis, Tom E. & Scally, John, eds. We Have but Faith. LC 74-20434. 152p. 1975. 6.95 (ISBN 0-88498-023-5). Brevet Pr.
Kauffman, Donald T., compiled by. Baker's Pocket Treasury of Religious Verse. (Direction Bks.). 384p. 1980. pap. 4.95 (ISBN 0-8010-5417-6). Baker Bk.
Larrick, Nancy. Tambourines! Tambourines to Glory! Prayers & Poems. LC 81-23158. (Illus.). 122p. 1982. 8.95 (ISBN 0-664-32689-7). Westminster.
Lawson, James G., compiled by. The Best-Loved Religious Poems. 256p. 1981. 9.95 (ISBN 0-8007-0019-8). Revell.
Lee, Sharon. Grandfather Clock & Other Finger Plays, Word Rhythms, & Action Rhymes. (Illus.). 64p. 1984. pap. 5.95 (ISBN 0-86683-834-1, HarpR). Har-Row.
Lewis, Samuel L. The Jerusalem Trilogy. Meyer, Wali A., et al, eds. (Illus.). 336p. (Orig.). 1975. pap. 5.95 (ISBN 0-915424-03-7, Prophecy Pressworks). Sufi Islamia-Prophecy.
--Siva! Siva! Cresent & Heart: Selected Poetry of Murshid Samuel L. Lewis. (Bismillah Bks.: No. 1). (Illus.). 112p. (Orig.). 1980. pap. 3.50 (ISBN 0-915424-04-5). Sufi Islamia-Prophecy.
--Spiritual Dance & Walk: An Introduction from the Work of Murshid Samuel L. Lewis. 2nd, rev. ed. Jablonski, Moineddin, ed. (Illus.). 64p. (Orig.). 1978. pap. 4.50 (ISBN 0-915424-05-3, Prophecy Pressworks). Sufi Islamia-Prophecy.
McCaw, Mabel N. What God Can Do. LC 81-70865. 1982. 5.95 (ISBN 0-8054-4290-1, 4242-90). Broadman.
MacVeagh, Lincoln, ed. Poetry from the Bible. 180p. 1981. Repr. of 1925 ed. lib. bdg. 30.00 (ISBN 0-8495-3531-X). Arden Lib.
Merrifield, Fred, ed. Modern Religious Verse & Prose: An Anthology. LC 79-51964. (Granger Poetry Library). 1980. Repr. of 1925 ed. 32.50x (ISBN 0-89609-186-4). Roth Pub Inc.
Moeckel, Fred. None But a Child May Enter: Poetry. 80p. 1982. pap. 4.95 (ISBN 0-910452-49-0). Covenant.
Norman, Ruth, intro. by. Glowing Moments. 170p. (Orig.). 1982. pap. 4.95 (ISBN 0-932642-76-4). Unarius Pubns.
O'Connor, Francine M. Special Friends of Jesus: New Testament Stories. 64p. 1986. pap. 3.95 (ISBN 0-89243-255-1). Liguori Pubns.
Olds, Barbara M. Favorite Poems of Faith & Comfort. 1977. Repr. of 1947 ed. 25.00 (ISBN 0-89984-077-9). Century Bookbindery.
Overholt, James. From Tiny Beginnings. 64p. 1987. pap. 4.95 (ISBN 0-87178-296-0). Brethren.
Ozanam, Frederick. Franciscan Poets of the Thirteenth Century. LC 68-26288. 1969. Repr. of 1914 ed. 24.50x (ISBN 0-8046-0342-1). Assoc Faculty Pr.
Palmer, Jerry. One God. (Contemporary Poets of Dorrance Ser.). 88p. 1981. 4.95 (ISBN 0-8059-2789-1). Dorrance.
Pedrick, Jean. Saints. (Chapbook Ser.: No. 1). 40p. (Orig.). 1980. pap. 4.95 (ISBN 0-937672-00-9). Rowan Tree.
Prudentius. Poems, Vol. 2. LC 63-5499. (Fathers of the Church Ser: Vol. 52). 224p. 1965. 15.95x (ISBN 0-8132-0052-0). Cath U Pr.
Ramsey, Paul, ed. Contemporary Religious Poetry. 1987. pap. 7.95. Paulist Pr.
Rananujan, A. K., tr. from Tamil. Hymns for the Drowning: Poems for Vishnu by Nammalvar. LC 81-47151. (Princeton Library of Asian Translations). 145p. 1982. 23.50 (ISBN 0-691-06492-X); pap. 8.00 (ISBN 0-691-01385-3). Princeton U Pr.
Ray, Randolph, ed. One Hundred Great Religious Poems. LC 78-80378. (Granger Index Reprint Ser). 1951. 15.00 (ISBN 0-8369-6060-2). Ayer Co Pubs.
Ray, Sondra. Celebration of Breath. LC 83-1770. 192p. 1983. pap. 8.95 (ISBN 0-89087-355-0). Celestial Arts.
Rice, Helen S. Everyone Needs Someone: Poems of Love & Friendship. 80p. 1973. 8.95 (ISBN 0-8007-0966-7). Revell.
--Heart Gifts from Helen Steiner Rice. LC 68-28438. (Illus.). 96p. 1968. 8.95 (ISBN 0-8007-0133-X). Revell.
Salem, Luis. Rimas del Pesebre. LC 77-82265. (Span.). 86p. (Orig.). 1978. pap. 2.50 (ISBN 0-89922-118-1). Edit Caribe.
Shea, John. The Hour of the Unexpected. LC 77-73648. 1977. pap. 4.95 (ISBN 0-913592-85-4). Argus Comm.
Smith, Francis J. First Prelude. (Illus.). 64p. 1981. pap. 5.95 (ISBN 0-8294-0387-6). Loyola.
Solle, Dorothee. Of War & Love. Kimber, Robert & Kimber, Rita, trs. from Ger. LC 83-8252. Orig. Title: Im Hause Des Menschenfressers. 172p. (Orig.). 1983. pap. 7.95 (ISBN 0-88344-350-3). Orbis Bks.
Spiegelberg, Nancy & Purdy, Dorothy. Fanfare: A Celebration of Belief. LC 80-25519. (Illus., Orig.). 1981. pap. 6.95 (ISBN 0-930014-56-1). Multnomah.
Swami Muktananda. Mukteshwari, Vol. II. LC 79-101943. 188p. 1973. 6.00 (ISBN 0-914602-62-4). SYDA Found.
Swami Vivekananda. In Search of God & Other Poems. pap. 3.75 (ISBN 0-87481-121-X). Vedanta Pr.
Vanier, Jean. Tears of Silence. 3.95 (ISBN 0-87193-011-0). Dimension Bks.
Walsh, Chad. The Psalm of Christ: Forty Poems on the Twenty-Second Psalm. LC 82-5566. (Wheaton Literary Ser.). 74p. 1982. pap. 5.95 (ISBN 0-87788-700-4). Shaw Pubs.
Wharton, Michael. Time to Stop & Think, Vol. 1. 1981. 12.00x (ISBN 0-7223-1422-1, Pub. by A H Stockwell England). State Mutual Bk.
Williams, Rosa M., ed. Restoration: Our Philosophy Through Inspired Poems. LC 79-66586. 1980. (ISBN 0-9602366-1-9); pap. 6.50x. Sooty-Face.
Wones, David R. Sonnets for a Christian Year. (Illus.). 80p. (Orig.). 1987. pap. 4.95 (ISBN 0-936015-06-3). Pocahontas Pr.
Wood, Eileen C. Pure Thoughts. 1985. 5.95 (ISBN 0-533-06662-X). Vantage.
Yeshurun, Avoth. The Syrian-African Rift & Other Poems. Amichai, Yehuda & Mandelbaum, Allen, eds. Schimmel, Harold, tr. LC 80-13630. (Jewish Poetry Ser.). 160p. 1980. 11.95 (ISBN 0-8276-0181-6, 464); pap. 7.95 (ISBN 0-8276-0182-4, 463). Jewish Pubns.

RELIGIOUS POETRY (LATIN)
Dreves, Guido M., ed. Pia Dictamina, 7 Vols. 1893-1905. 60.00 ea. (ISBN 0-384-12950-1). Johnson Repr.
--Psalteria Rhythmica, 2 Vols. 1900-01. 60.00 ea. (ISBN 0-384-12960-9) (ISBN 0-384-12961-7). Johnson Repr.
Paulinus of Nola, Saint Sancti Pontii Meropii Pavlini Nolani Carmina. (Corpus Scriptorum Ecclesiasticorum Latinorum Ser: Vol. 30). Repr. of 1894 ed. 46.00 (ISBN 0-384-45185-3). Johnson Repr.
Stocklin, Ulrich V. Psalteria Wessofontana. Dreves, Guido M., ed. Repr. of 1902 ed. 60.00 (ISBN 0-384-58320-2). Johnson Repr.
--Udalricus Wessofontanus. Dreves, Guido M., ed. Repr. 60.00 (ISBN 0-384-58330-X). Johnson Repr.

RELIGIOUS POETRY–HISTORY AND CRITICISM
Diehl, Patrick S. The Medieval Religious Lyric: An Ars Poetria. LC 83-6557. 475p. 1984. text ed. 40.00x (ISBN 0-520-04673-0). U of Cal Pr.
Downey, David G. Modern Poets & Christian Teaching: Richard Watson Gilder, Edwin Markham, Edward Rowland Sill. 1973. Repr. of 1906 ed. 25.00 (ISBN 0-8274-1700-4). R West.
Hatfield, Edwin F. The Poets of the Church. LC 77-91533. 1977. Repr. of 1884 ed. lib. bdg. 45.00 (ISBN 0-89341-195-7). Longwood Pub Group.
Holroyd, Stuart. Emergence from Chaos. LC 73-167356. (Essay Index Reprint Ser.). Repr. of 1957 ed. 18.00 (ISBN 0-8369-2695-1). Ayer Co Pubs.
Lazear, Robert. Maestro de Dolores. (Span., Illus.). 342p. (Orig.). 1979. pap. 4.50 (ISBN 0-89922-138-6). Edit Caribe.
Lewalski, Barbara K. Protestant Poetics & the Seventeenth Century Religious Lyric. LC 78-70305. (Illus.). 536p. 1984. 47.50x (ISBN 0-691-06395-8); pap. 14.50x (ISBN 0-691-01415-9). Princeton U Pr.
Murray, Patrick, ed. Treasury of Irish Religious Verse. 1986. 17.95 (ISBN 0-8245-0776-2). Crossroad NY.
Musser, Benjamin F. Franciscan Poets. facs. ed. LC 67-26768. (Essay Index Reprint Ser). 1933. 17.25 (ISBN 0-8369-0732-9). Ayer Co Pubs.
Osmond, Percy H. Mystical Poets of the English Church. LC 72-5166. 1919. lib. bdg. 48.50 (ISBN 0-8414-6542-8). Folcroft.
Raspa, Anthony. The Emotive Image: Jesuit Poetics in the English Renaissance. LC 83-502. 173p. 1983. 19.50x (ISBN 0-912646-65-9). Tex Christian.
Salamon, Avrohon Y. Akdamus. (The Art Scroll Mesorah Ser.). 160p. 1978. 11.95 (ISBN 0-89906-154-0); pap. 8.95 (ISBN 0-89906-155-9). Mesorah Pubns.
Schroeder, M. J. Mary-Verse in "Meistergesang". (Catholic University Studies in German: No. 16). 1970. Repr. of 1942 ed. 30.00 (ISBN 0-404-50236-9). AMS Pr.

RELIGIOUS POETRY, AMERICAN

Broomell, Anna P. Poets Walk In. 1983. pap. 2.50x (ISBN 0-87574-077-4, 077). Pendle Hill.

Horder, W. G. Treasury of American Sacred Song. facs. ed. LC 74-76944. (Granger Index Reprint Ser). 1896. 18.00 (ISBN 0-8369-6019-X). Ayer Co Pubs.

Midgett, Andre, ed. Faces. (Campus Life Bks.). (Illus.). 160p. (Orig.). 1987. pap. 5.95 (ISBN 0-8423-0826-1). Tyndale.

Rice, Helen S. Someone Cares: The Collected Poems of Helen Steiner Rice. 128p. 1972. 12.95 (ISBN 0-8007-0524-6); large-print ed. 12.95 (ISBN 0-8007-0959-4). Revell.

Salvation Army Literary Staff, ed. It's Beautiful & Other Salvationist Verse. (Illus.). 105p. (Orig.). 1984. pap. 3.50 (ISBN 0-89216-052-7). Salvation Army.

RELIGIOUS POETRY, ANGLO-SAXON

Kennedy, Charles W., tr. Early English Christian Poetry. 1963. pap. 5.95 (ISBN 0-19-500246-6). Oxford U Pr.

RELIGIOUS POETRY, ENGLISH

Armstrong, O. V. & Armstrong, Helen, eds. Prayer Poems. facsimile ed. LC 72-86793. (Granger Index Reprint Ser). 1942. 16.00 (ISBN 0-8369-6094-7). Ayer Co Pubs.

Cattermole, Richard, ed. Sacred Poetry of the Seventeenth Century: Including the Whole of Giles Fletcher's Christ's Victory & Triumph, 2 vols. (Research & Source Works Ser.: No. 346). 1969. Repr. of 1835 ed. Set. 44.50 (ISBN 0-8337-0499-0). B Franklin.

Doughty, W. L. Studies in Religious Poetry of the Seventeenth Century: Essays on Henry Vaughn, Francis Quarles, Richard Crawshaw, John Davies, Henry More & Thomas Traherne. LC 68-26278. Repr. of 1946 ed. 21.00x (ISBN 0-8046-0113-5, Pub. by Kennikat). Assoc Faculty Pr.

Doyle, I. A., intro. by. The Vernon Manuscript: Bodleian Library MS. English Poet a.1. (Illus.). 704p. 1987. facsimile 695.00 (ISBN 0-85991-200-0, Pub. by Boydell & Brewer). Longwood Pub Group.

Ellsberg, Margaret. Created to Praise: The Language of Gerard Manley Hopkins. 160p. 1987. 15.95x (ISBN 0-19-504098-8). Oxford U Pr.

Farr, Edward, ed. Select Poetry, Chiefly Devotional, of the Reign of Queen Elizabeth, 2 Vols. 1845. Vol. 1. 41.00 (ISBN 0-384-15165-5); Vol. 2. 41.00 (ISBN 0-384-15166-3). Johnson Repr.

Horning, Mary E. Evidences of Romantic Treatment of Religious Elements in Late Eighteenth Century Minor Poetry, 1771-1800. LC 72-3719. (English Literature Ser., No. 33). 1972. Repr. of 1932 ed. lib. bdg. 29.95x (ISBN 0-8383-1542-9). Haskell.

Kennedy, Charles W. Early English Christian Poetry. 1977. lib. bdg. 59.95 (ISBN 0-8490-1739-4). Gordon Pr.

May, G. Lacey. English Religious Verse. 1937. lib. bdg. 8.50 (ISBN 0-8414-6604-1). Folcroft.

Patterson, Frank A. Middle English Penitential Lyric. LC 11-26002. Repr. of 1911 ed. 17.50 (ISBN 0-404-04908-7). AMS Pr.

Ross, Malcolm M. Poetry & Dogma. LC 78-86284. 1969. Repr. of 1954 ed. lib. bdg. 18.50x (ISBN 0-374-96973-6, Octagon). Hippocrene Bks.

Summers, Claude J. & Pebworth, Ted-Larry. Bright Shootes of Everlastingnesse: The Seventeenth-Century Religious Lyric. LC 86-16132. 208p. 1987. text ed. 24.00 (ISBN 0-8262-0618-2, 83-36265). U of Mo Pr.

White, L. B. English Sacred Poetry of the Olden Time. Repr. of 1864 ed. 25.00 (ISBN 0-89984-136-8). Century Bookbindery.

RELIGIOUS POETRY, ENGLISH–BIBLIOGRAPHY

Brown, Carleton & Robbins, Rossell H. Index of Middle English Verse. xix, 785p. 1943. 40.00x (ISBN 0-87352-017-3, Z2). Modern Lang.

RELIGIOUS POETRY, JAPANESE

Erickson, Lois J., tr. Songs from the Land of Dawn. facs. ed. LC 68-58828. (Granger Index Reprint Ser). 1949. 14.00 (ISBN 0-8369-6014-9). Ayer Co Pubs.

RELIGIOUS PSYCHOLOGY

see Psychology, Religious

RELIGIOUS RITES

see Rites and Ceremonies

RELIGIOUS SCULPTURE

see Christian Art and Symbolism

RELIGIOUS SOCIAL WORK

see Church Charities

RELIGIOUS SOCIOLOGY

see Religion and Sociology

RELIGIOUS SUPERIORS

see Superiors, Religious

RELIGIOUS TELEVISION

see Television in Religion

RELIGIOUS THOUGHT

see also Theology, Doctrinal–History

Adamnan, Saint. Vita Sancti Columbae. Reeves, William, ed. LC 79-174801. (Bannatyne Club, Edinburgh. Publications: No. 103). Repr. of 1857 ed. 45.00 (ISBN 0-404-52858-9). AMS Pr.

Aivanhov, Omraam M. New Light on the Gospels. (Izvor Collection: Vol. 217). (Orig.). 1985. pap. 4.95 (ISBN 2-85566-339-3, Pub. by Prosveta France). Prosveta USA.

Allen, Don C. Doubt's Boundless Sea. 1979. 25.50 (ISBN 0-405-10577-0). Ayer Co Pubs.

Avens, Roberts. The New Gnosis: Heidegger, Hillman, & Angels. LC 84-5297. 155p. (Orig.). 1984. 18.50 (ISBN 0-88214-328-X); pap. 12.50 (ISBN 0-88214-327-1). Spring Pubns.

Balchin, John. Citizens of Another Kingdom. 141p. 1986. pap. 4.95 (ISBN 0-89109-535-7). NavPress.

Basil, St. Ascetical Works. LC 50-10735. (Fathers of the Church Ser.: Vol. 9). 525p. 1950. 26.95x (ISBN 0-8132-0009-1). Cath U Pr.

Baum, Gregory & Coleman, John, eds. Neo-Conservatism: Social & Religious Phenomenon. (Concilium 1981 Ser.: Vol. 141). 128p. (Orig.). 1981. pap. 6.95 (ISBN 0-8164-2308-3, HarpR). Har-Row.

Brownlow, Leroy. Thoughts of Gold: Wisdom for Living from the Book of Proverbs. 1974. gift ed. 6.95 (ISBN 0-915720-13-2). Brownlow Pub Co.

Buechner, Frederick. Wishful Thinking: A Theological ABC. LC 72-9872. 128p. 1973. 12.45 (ISBN 0-06-061155-3, HarpR). Har-Row.

Bunk, Elie. Ascent to Harmony. 180p. 1987. 8.95 (ISBN 0-87306-407-0). Feldheim.

Camp, Norman. Pensando con Dios. Orig. Title: Thinking with God. (Span.). 128p. 1981. pap. 3.25 (ISBN 0-8254-1100-9). Kregel.

Carus, Paul. The Dawn of a New Religious Era. 131p. 1916. 1.95 (ISBN 0-317-40419-9). Open Court.

Crosson, Fred, ed. The Autonomy of Religious Belief: A Critical Inquiry. LC 81-50461. (Notre Dame Studies in the Philosophy of Religion: Vol. 2). 162p. 1982. pap. text ed. 6.95 (ISBN 0-268-00601-6). U of Notre Dame Pr.

Crosson, Frederick J. The Autonomy of Religious Belief: A Critical Inquiry. 160p. 1981. 14.95 (ISBN 0-268-00596-6). U of Notre Dame Pr.

Dillenberger, John. Protestant Thought & Natural Science: A Historical Interpretation. LC 77-7200. 1977. Repr. of 1960 ed. lib. bdg. 22.75x (ISBN 0-8371-9670-1, DIPT). Greenwood.

Fey, Harold E., ed. How My Mind Has Changed. 7.00 (ISBN 0-8446-2056-4). Peter Smith.

Frost, Gerhard E. Bless My Growing: For Parents, Teachers, & Others Who Learn. LC 74-77680. (Illus.). 96p. 1975. pap. 5.95 (ISBN 0-8066-1431-5, 10-0770). Augsburg.

Fryer, Alfred C. The Religious Thoughts of Some of Our Poets. 1911. Repr. 17.50 (ISBN 0-8274-3263-1). R West.

Ganz, Yaffa. The Gift That Grew. 1986. 8.95 (ISBN 0-87306-422-4). Feldheim.

Gonzalez, Justo L. A History of Christian Thought. rev. ed. 1987. Set. 59.95 (ISBN 0-687-17185-7). Abingdon.

Gun, Guneli. The Adventures of Huru on the Road to Baghdad. 352p. 1987. 19.95 (ISBN 0-89793-033-9). Hunter Hse.

Hazard, Paul. European Thought in the Eighteenth Century: From Montesquieu to Lessing. 16.50 (ISBN 0-8446-2226-5). Peter Smith.

Henry, Patrick, ed. Schools of Thought in the Christian Tradition. LC 84-47924. 208p. 1984. 19.95 (ISBN 0-8006-0730-9, 1-730). Fortress.

Heschel, Abraham J. Man Is Not Alone: A Philosophy of Religion. LC 74-169258. 306p. 1972. Repr. of 1951 ed. lib. bdg. 25.50x (ISBN 0-374-93879-2, Octagon). Hippocrene Bks.

Hiers, Richard H. Kingdom of God in the Synoptic Tradition. LC 70-630982. (U of Fla. Humanities Monograph Ser.: No. 33). Repr. of 1970 ed. 29.00 (ISBN 0-8357-9821-6, 2015531). Bks Demand UMI.

Inayat-Khan, F. Old Thinking, New Thinking. 2nd ed. 256p. 1985. cancelled. Hunter Hse.

Jacks, Lawrence P. Religious Perplexities. 3rd ed. LC 77-27149. (Hibbert Lectures: 1922). Repr. of 1923 ed. 20.00 (ISBN 0-404-60421-8). AMS Pr.

Jerome, St. Dogmatic & Polemical Works. (Fathers of the Church Ser: Vol. 53). 405p. 1965. 21.95x (ISBN 0-8132-0053-9). Cath U Pr.

Kim, Yong Choon. Oriental Thought: An Introduction to the Philosophical & Religious Thought of Asia. LC 80-39672. 144p. 1981. Repr. of 1973 ed. 11.50x (ISBN 0-8476-6972-6). Rowman.

Lawlor, Robert. Sacred Geometry: Philosophy & Practice. Purce, Jill, ed. LC 81-67703. (The Illustrated Library of Sacred Imagination Ser.). (Illus.). 96p. 1982. pap. 9.95 (ISBN 0-8245-0067-9). Crossroad NY.

Leonard, Ellen. George Tyrrell & the Catholic Tradition. 208p. 1982. pap. 9.95 (ISBN 0-8091-2424-6). Paulist Pr.

Lindskoog, Kathryn, ed. Around the Year with C. S. Lewis & His Friends. 384p. 1986. 12.95 (ISBN 0-8378-5126-2). Gibson.

Mansel, H. L. The Limits of Religious Thought. 5th ed. 1986. Repr. of 1870 ed. lib. bdg. 25.00X (ISBN 0-935005-46-3). Ibis Pub VA.

Nasr, Seyyed H., ed. Knowledge & the Sacred. 228p. 1982. 17.50 (ISBN 0-8245-0095-4). Crossroad NY.

Newell, William L. The Secular Magi: Marx, Nietzsche, & Freud on Religion. 264p. (Orig.). 1986. pap. 13.95 (ISBN 0-8298-0579-6). Pilgrim NY.

Pacini, David S. The Cunning of Modern Religious Thought. LC 86-45201. 192p. 1986. 16.95 (ISBN 0-8006-0786-4, 1-786). Fortress.

Ray, Bruce. Withhold Not Correction. pap. 3.45 (ISBN 0-8010-7687-0). Baker Bk.

Reardon, Bernard M. Religious Thought in the Nineteenth Century. (Orig.). 1966. 49.50 (ISBN 0-521-06049-4); pap. 16.95x (ISBN 0-521-09386-4). Cambridge U Pr.

Reardon, Bernard M., ed. Roman Catholic Modernism. 1970. 20.00x (ISBN 0-8047-0750-2). Stanford U Pr.

St. Augustine. Eighty-Three Different Questions. LC 81-2546. (Fathers of the Church Ser.: Vol. 70). 257p. 1982. 29.95x (ISBN 0-8132-0070-9). Cath U Pr.

Saint Augustine. The Essential Augustine. Bourke, Vernon J., commentary by. 274p. 1973. 15.00 (ISBN 0-915144-08-5); pap. text ed. 4.95 (ISBN 0-915144-07-7). Hackett Pub.

Short, Robert L. The Gospel from Outer Space. LC 82-48936. (Illus.). 128p. (Orig.). 1983. pap. 5.95 (ISBN 0-06-067376-1, CN4064, HarpR). Har-Row.

Slater, Peter. The Dynamics of Religion: Meaning & Change in Religious Traditions. LC 78-4426. 1978. pap. 6.95x (ISBN 0-685-53934-2, RD 280, HarpR). Har-Row.

Smart, Ninian. Religion & the Western Mind. 1986. 39.50 (ISBN 0-88706-382-9); pap. 12.95 (ISBN 0-88706-383-7). State U NY Pr.

--Worldviews. LC 82-16877. 190p. 1983. pap. 7.95x (ISBN 0-684-17812-5). Scribner.

Smith, Gerald B., ed. Religious Thought in the Last Quarter-Century. LC 71-107739. (Essay Index Reprint Ser). 1927. 12.00 (ISBN 0-8369-1583-6). Ayer Co Pubs.

Smith, Wilfred C. The Meaning & End of Religion. LC 77-20440. 1978. pap. 9.95 (ISBN 0-06-067465-2, RD 252, HarpR). Har-Row.

Soelle, Dorothee. Death by Bread Alone: Texts & Reflections on Religious Experience. Scheidt, David L., tr. from Ger. LC 77-78643. 168p. 1978. 2.00 (ISBN 0-8006-0514-4, 1-514). Fortress.

Sophrony, Archimandrite. Wisdom from Mount Athos: The Writings of Staretz Silouan, 1866-1938. 124p. 1974. pap. 5.95 (ISBN 0-913836-17-6). St Vladimirs.

Spinka, Matthew. Christian Thought: From Erasmus to Berdyaev. LC 78-11967. 1979. Repr. of 1962 ed. lib. bdg. 24.75x (ISBN 0-313-21122-1, SPCT). Greenwood.

Steele, D. Steele's Answers. 6.95 (ISBN 0-686-27781-3). Schmul Pub Co.

Steiner, Rudolf. From Buddha to Christ. Church, Gilbert, ed. Tr. of Das Esoterische Christentum & die geistige Fuehrung der Menschheit. 103p. 1987. pap. 5.95 (ISBN 0-88010-178-4). Anthroposophic.

Taylor, Robert R., Jr. A Review of "Shall We Splinter?". 1985. pap. 3.00 (ISBN 0-934916-08-X). Natl Christian Pr.

Thomas, Reuen. Leaders of Thought in the Modern Church. LC 72-8559. (Essay Index Reprint Ser.). 1972. Repr. of 1892 ed. 18.00 (ISBN 0-8369-7333-X). Ayer Co Pubs.

Tillyard, Eustace M. Elizabethan World Picture. 1959. pap. 3.16 (ISBN 0-394-70162-3, Vin). Random.

Wall, James M., ed. Theologians in Transition. 288p. 1981. 14.95 (ISBN 0-8245-0101-2); pap. 7.95 (ISBN 0-8245-0103-9). Crossroad NY.

Welch, John. Spiritual Pilgrims: Carl Jung & Teresa of Avila. LC 82-80164. 208p. 1982. 8.95 (ISBN 0-8091-2454-8). Paulist Pr.

Willey, Basil. Seventeenth Century Background: Studies in the Thought of the Age in Relation to Poetry & Religion. LC 34-21849. 1942. 31.00x (ISBN 0-231-01395-7). Columbia U Pr.

Williams, Daniel D. What Present-Day Theologians Are Thinking. rev. ed. LC 78-16410. 1978. Repr. of 1959 ed. lib. bdg. 22.50x (ISBN 0-313-20587-6, WIWP). Greenwood.

Wilson, Colin. Religion & the Rebel. LC 74-9134. 338p. 1974. Repr. of 1957 ed. lib. bdg. 27.50x (ISBN 0-8371-7596-8, WIRA). Greenwood.

RELIGIOUS THOUGHT–HISTORY

Boardman, George N. A History of New England Theology. Kuklick, Bruce, ed. (American Religious Thought of the 18th & 19th Centuries Ser.). 314p. 1987. lib. bdg. 45.00 (ISBN 0-8240-6955-2). Garland Pub.

Booth, Edward. Aristotelian Aporetic Ontology in Islamic & Christian Thinkers. LC 82-22068. (Cambridge Studies in Medieval Life & Thought: No. 20). 368p. 1984. 70.00 (ISBN 0-521-25254-7). Cambridge U Pr.

Bushnell, Horace. God in Christ: Hartford, 1849. Kuklick, Bruce, ed. (American Religious Thought of the 18th & 19th Centuries Ser.). 356p. 1987. lib. bdg. 50.00 (ISBN 0-8240-6964-1). Garland Pub.

Danielou, Alain. While the Gods Play. 352p. (Orig.). 1987. pap. 12.95 (ISBN 0-89281-115-3). Inner Tradit.

Earle, William, et al, eds. Christianity & Existentialism. (Studies in Phenomenology & Existential Philosophy). 1963. pap. 7.95 (ISBN 0-8101-0084-3). Northwestern U Pr.

Eliade, Mircea. A History of Religious Ideas, Vol. 2: From Gautama Buddha to the Triumph of Christianity. Trask, Willard R., tr. LC 77-16784. vi, 564p. 1984. pap. 15.95 (ISBN 0-226-20403-0). U of Chicago Pr.

Fisher, George P. Discussions in History & Theology. Kuklick, Bruce, ed. (American Religious Thought of the 18th & 19th Centuries Ser.). 565p. 1987. lib. bdg. 75.00 (ISBN 0-8240-6963-3). Garland Pub.

Foster, Frank H. A Genetic History of the New England Theology. Kuklick, Bruce, ed. (American Religious Thought of the 18th & 19th Centuries Ser.). 56p. 1987. lib. bdg. 75.00 (ISBN 0-8240-6956-0). Garland Pub.

Gregory Of Nyssa, St. Ascetical Works. LC 64-13360. (Fathers of the Church Ser: Vol. 58). 288p. 1967. 16.95x (ISBN 0-8132-0058-X). Cath U Pr.

Gronbech, Vilhelm. Religious Currents in the Nineteenth Century. Mitchell, P. M. & Paden, W. D., trs. from Danish. LC 72-11829. (Arcturus Bks. Paperbacks). 206p. 1973. lib. bdg. 7.00x (ISBN 0-8093-0629-8); pap. 2.45x (ISBN 0-8093-0630-1). S Ill U Pr.

Herr, William A. Catholic Thinkers in the Clear: Giants of Catholic Thought from Augustine to Rahner. LC 85-118829. (Basics of Christian Thought Ser.). 276p. 1985. 15.95 (ISBN 0-88347-179-5). Thomas More.

Hodge, Charles. Essays & Reviews: New York, 1879. Kuklick, Bruce, ed. (American Religious Thought of the 18th & 19th Centuries Ser.). 633p. 1987. lib. bdg. 85.00 (ISBN 0-8240-6966-8). Garland Pub.

Hort, Greta. Piers Plowman & Contemporary Religious Thought. (Church Historical Society, London, New Ser.: No. 29). Repr. of 1938 ed. 40.00 (ISBN 0-8115-3153-8). Kraus Repr.

Kippenberg, Hans G., ed. Struggles of Gods. LC 84-11501. (Religion & Reason Ser.: No. 31). vii, 296p. 1984. 34.95 (ISBN 90-279-3460-6). Mouton.

Kuklick, Bruce. Nathaniel Emmons: Works, 6 vols. (American Religious Thought of the 18th & 19th Centuries Ser.). 4935p. 1987. Set. lib. bdg. 620.00 (ISBN 0-8240-6952-8). Garland Pub.

McGiffert, A. C. Protestant Thought Before Kant. 11.25 (ISBN 0-8446-0204-3). Peter Smith.

Michalson, G. E. The Historical Dimensions of Rational Faith: The Role of History in Kant's Religious Thought. 1977. 12.25 (ISBN 0-8191-0308-X). U Pr of Amer.

Norton, Herman A. Religion in Tennessee, Seventeen Seventy-Seven to Nineteen Forty-Five. LC 81-1562. (Tennessee Three Star Ser.). (Illus.). 136p. 1981. pap. 3.50 (ISBN 0-87049-318-3). U of Tenn Pr.

Pope, Earl. New England Calvinism & the Disruption of the Presbyterian Church. Kuklick, Bruce, ed. (American Religious Thought of the 18th & 19th Centuries Ser.). 400p. 1987. lib. bdg. 50.00 (ISBN 0-8240-6969-2). Garland Pub.

Smart, Ninian, et al, eds. Nineteenth Century Religious Thought in the West, Vol. 1. 350p. 1985. 49.50 (ISBN 0-521-22831-X). Cambridge U Pr.

Smith, Henry B. Faith & Philosophy: New York, 1877. Kuklick, Bruce, ed. (American Religious Thought of the 18th & 19th Centuries Ser.). 496p. 1987. lib. bdg. 70.00 (ISBN 0-8240-6967-6). Garland Pub.

Tawney, Richard H. Religion & the Rise of Capitalism. 12.75 (ISBN 0-8446-1446-7). Peter Smith.

Taylor, Nathaniel W. Essays, Lectures, etc. Upon Select Topics in Revealed Theology: New York 1859. Kuklick, Bruce, ed. (American Religious Thought of the 18th & 19th Centuries Ser.). 480p. 1987. lib. bdg. 65.00 (ISBN 0-8240-6960-9). Garland Pub.

--Lectures on the Moral Government of God: New York, 1859, 2 vols. Kuklick, Bruce, ed. (American Religious Thought of the 18th & 19th Centuries Ser.). 840p. 1987. lib. bdg. 110.00 (ISBN 0-8240-6961-7). Garland Pub.

Tracy, David. Celebrating the Medieval Heritage: A Colloquy on the Thought of Aquinas & Bonaventura. 1978. pap. 8.95x (ISBN 0-226-81125-5). U of Chicago Pr.

Twitchell, Paul. Le Shariyat-Ki-Sugmad, Vol. 2. (Fr.). 189p. 1983. pap. 7.95 (ISBN 0-914766-72-4). IWP Pub.

Westcott, Brooke F. Essays in the History of Religious Thought in the West. LC 72-8480. (Essay Index Reprint Ser.). 1972. Repr. of 1891 ed. 24.50 (ISBN 0-8369-7338-0). Ayer Co Pubs.

RELIGIOUS THOUGHT–AFRICA

Cabrera, Lydia. La Regla Kimbisa del Santo Cristo del Buen Viaje. 2nd ed. (Coleccion del Chichereku en el Exilio Ser.). (Span.). 85p. 1986. pap. 6.95 (ISBN 0-89729-396-7). Ediciones.

Friedmann, Yohanan. Prophecy Continuous: Aspects of Ahmadi Religious Thoughts & Its Medieval Background. 370p. 1987. text ed. 35.00x. U of Cal Pr.

Van Binsbergen, Wim M. J. & Schoffeleers, J. Matthew, eds. Theoretical Explorations in African Religion. 330p. 1984. 49.95x (ISBN 0-7103-0049-2). Methuen Inc.

RELIGIOUS THOUGHT–FRANCE

Carayon, Jean. Essai sur les rapports du pouvoir politique et du pouvoir religieux chez Montesquieu. LC 75-168919. (Fr.). 1973. Repr. of 1903 ed. lib. bdg. 15.00 (ISBN 0-8337-4024-5). B Franklin.

Maritain, Raissa. Raissa's Journal. LC 72-95648. 1974. 12.95x (ISBN 0-87343-041-7). Magi Bks.

RELIGIOUS THOUGHT–GREAT BRITAIN

Hunt, John. Religious Thought in England from the Reformation to the End of the Last Century, 3 Vols. LC 72-153593. Repr. of 1873 ed. Set. 125.00 (ISBN 0-404-09480-5). AMS Pr.

Inge, William R. The Platonic Tradition in English Religious Thought. LC 77-8095. 1977. Repr. of 1926 ed. lib. bdg. 15.00 (ISBN 0-8414-5055-2). Folcroft.

McLachlan, Herbert. Religious Opinions of Milton, Locke & Newton. LC 74-173539. 1972. Repr. of 1941 ed. 12.00x (ISBN 0-8462-1623-X). Russell.

Routh, Harold V. Towards the Twentieth Century. facs. ed. LC 69-17587. (Essay Index Reprint Ser). 1937. 19.00 (ISBN 0-8369-0091-X). Ayer Co Pubs.

Shafer, Robert. Christianity & Naturalism: Essays in Criticism. LC 68-26206. 1969. Repr. of 1926 ed. 25.50x (ISBN 0-8046-0413-4, Pub. by Kennikat). Assoc Faculty Pr.

Stein, Gordon. Freethought in the United Kingdom & the Commonwealth: A Descriptive Bibliography. LC 80-1792. xxiii, 193p. 1981. lib. bdg. 39.95 (ISBN 0-313-20869-7, SFU/). Greenwood.

Webster, Graham. Celtic Religion in Roman Britain. LC 86-26532. (Illus.). 176p. 1987. 30.00 (ISBN 0-389-20686-5). B&N Imports.

White, Helen C. Social Criticism in Popular Religious Literature of the Sixteenth-Century. 1965. lib. bdg. 20.50x (ISBN 0-374-98455-7, Octagon). Hippocrene Bks.

Wiley, Margaret L. Subtle Knot: Creative Scepticism in Seventeenth-Century England. LC 68-54994. (Illus.). 1968. Repr. of 1952 ed. lib. bdg. 22.50x (ISBN 0-8371-0753-9, WISK). Greenwood.

Wood, Herbert G. Living Issues in Religious Thought, from George Fox to Bertrand Russell. facs. ed. LC 67-22128. (Essay Index Reprint Ser). 1924. 14.25 (ISBN 0-8369-1007-9). Ayer Co Pubs.

RELIGIOUS THOUGHT–GREECE

Cornford, Francis M., ed. Greek Religious Thought from Homer to the Age of Alexander. LC 79-98637. (Library of Greek Thought: No. 2). Repr. of 1923 ed. 21.50 (ISBN 0-404-01734-7). AMS Pr.

RELIGIOUS THOUGHT–INDIA

Chatterjee, Margaret. Gandhi's Religious Thought. LC 83-5841. 224p. 1984. text ed. 19.95x (ISBN 0-268-01009-9, 85-10091). U of Notre Dame Pr.

Dada. Towards the Unknown: The Journey into New-Dimensional Consciousness. LC 81-65123. (Illus.). 128p. (Orig.). 1981. pap. 8.00 (ISBN 0-930608-02-X). Dada Ctr.

Godwin, Shiri. Christian Social Thought in India, 1962-77. (Orig.). 1983. pap. 6.00 (ISBN 0-8364-0988-4, Pub. by Christian Lit Soc India). South Asia Bks.

Gunaratna, Henepola. The Path of Serenity & Insight. 1984. 22.50x (ISBN 0-8364-1149-8). South Asia Bks.

Maharshi, Ramana. The Spiritual Teaching of Ramana Maharshi. (Clear Light Ser). 112p. (Orig.). 1972. pap. 7.95 (ISBN 0-87773-024-5). Shambhala Pubns.

Prabhavananda, Swami. Spiritual Heritage of India. LC 63-10517. 1979. pap. 8.95 (ISBN 0-87481-035-3). Vedanta Pr.

RELIGIOUS THOUGHT–SOVIET UNION

Gorodetzky, Nadejda. The Humiliated Christ in Modern Russian Thought. LC 79-168159. Repr. of 1938 ed. 18.75 (ISBN 0-404-02883-7). AMS Pr.

RELIGIOUS THOUGHT–UNITED STATES

American Tract Society Staff. The American Tract Society Documents, Eighteen Twenty-Four to Nineteen Twenty-Five. LC 74-38434. (Religion in America, Ser. 2). 484p. 1972. Repr. of 1874 ed. 29.00 (ISBN 0-405-04055-5). Ayer Co Pubs.

Barcovitch, Sacvan, ed. Aspects of Puritan Religious Thought: Library, Vol. VI. LC 83-12782. (Library of American Puritan Writings). 728p. 1984. Repr. 57.50 (ISBN 0-404-60806-X). AMS Pr.

Boardman, George N. A History of New England Theology. Kuklick, Bruce, ed. (American Religious Thought of the 18th & 19th Centuries Ser.). 314p. 1987. lib. bdg. 45.00 (ISBN 0-8240-6955-2). Garland Pub.

Bushnell, Horace. Christ in Theology: Hartford, 1851. Kuklick, Bruce, ed. (American Religious Thought of the 18th & 19th Centuries Ser.). 348p. 1987. lib. bdg. 50.00 (ISBN 0-8240-6965-X). Garland Pub.

--God in Christ: Hartford, 1849. Kuklick, Bruce, ed. (American Religious Thought of the 18th & 19th Centuries Ser.). 356p. 1987. lib. bdg. 50.00 (ISBN 0-8240-6964-1). Garland Pub.

Carey, Patrick, ed. American Catholic Religious Thought. 1987. pap. 12.95. Paulist Pr.

Caskey, Marie. Chariot of Fire: Religion & the Beecher Family. LC 77-5291. (Historical Publications Ser.). (Illus.). 1978. 40.00x (ISBN 0-300-02007-4). Yale U Pr.

Clebsch, William A. American Religious Thought: A History. LC 73-82911. xii, 212p. 1985. pap. text ed. 10.00x (ISBN 0-226-10962-3). U of Chicago Pr.

Coffin, Henry S. Religion Yesterday & Today. facs. ed. LC 75-117769. (Essay Index Reprint Ser). 1940. 18.00 (ISBN 0-8369-1790-1). Ayer Co Pubs.

Fisher, George P. Discussions in History & Theology. Kuklick, Bruce, ed. (American Religious Thought of the 18th & 19th Centuries Ser.). 565p. 1987. lib. bdg. 75.00 (ISBN 0-8240-6963-3). Garland Pub.

Foster, Frank H. A Genetic History of the New England Theology. Kuklick, Bruce, ed. (American Religious Thought of the 18th & 19th Centuries Ser.). 56p. 1987. lib. bdg. 75.00 (ISBN 0-8240-6956-0). Garland Pub.

Friedmann, Yohanan. Prophecy Continuous: Aspects of Ahmadi Religious Thoughts & Its Medieval Background. 370p. 1987. text ed. 35.00x. U of Cal Pr.

Gibbons, James C. A Retrospect of Fifty Years, 2 vols. in 1. LC 79-38447. (Religion in America, Ser. 2). 720p. 1972. Repr. of 1916 ed. 47.50 (ISBN 0-405-04066-0). Ayer Co Pubs.

Hayden, Amos S. Early History of the Disciples in the Western Reserve, Ohio; with Biographical Sketches of the Principal Agents in Their Religious Movement. LC 76-38449. (Religion in America, Ser. 2). 480p. 1972. Repr. of 1875 ed. 32.00 (ISBN 0-405-04068-7). Ayer Co Pubs.

Hodge, Charles. Essays & Reviews: New York, 1879. Kuklick, Bruce, ed. (American Religious Thought of the 18th & 19th Centuries Ser.). 633p. 1987. lib. bdg. 85.00 (ISBN 0-8240-6966-8). Garland Pub.

Hood, Fred J. Reformed America: The Middle & Southern States, Seventeen Eighty-Three to Eighteen Thirty-Seven. LC 79-28834. 304p. 1980. 21.50 (ISBN 0-8173-0034-1). U of Ala Pr.

Hughes, John & Breckinridge, John. A Discussion: Is the Roman Catholic Religion Inimical to Civil or Religious Liberty? Is the Presbyterian Religion Inimical to Civil or Religious Liberty? LC 76-122167. (Civil Liberties in American History Ser). 1970. Repr. of 1836 ed. lib. bdg. 75.00 (ISBN 0-306-71979-7). Da Capo.

Kuklick, Bruce. Nathaniel Emmons: Works, 6 vols. (American Religious Thought of the 18th & 19th Centuries Ser.). 4935p. 1987. Set. lib. bdg. 620.00 (ISBN 0-8240-6952-8). Garland Pub.

Luker, Ralph. A Southern Tradition in Theology & Social Criticism, 1830-1930: The Religious Liberalism & Social Conservatism of James Warley Miles, William Porcher Dubose & Edgar Gardner Murphy. LC 84-8954. (Studies in American Religion: Vol. 11). 476p. 1984. 69.95x (ISBN 0-88946-655-6). E Mellen.

McLoughlin, William G. Revivals, Awakening, & Reform: An Essay on Religion & Social Change in America, 1607 to 1977. LC 77-27830. xvi, 240p. 1980. pap. 9.00x (ISBN 0-226-56092-9, P891, Phoen). U of Chicago Pr.

Miller, William L. The First Liberty: Religion & the American Republic. LC 85-40342. 416p. 1986. 24.95 (ISBN 0-394-53476-X). Knopf.

Nevin, John W. The Anxious Bench: Chambersburg, PA 1844. Kuklick, Bruce, ed. Bd. with The Mystical Presence (Philadelphia, PA 1846) 56p. (American Religious Thought of the 18th & 19th Centuries Ser.). 312p. 1987. lib. bdg. 45.00 (ISBN 0-8240-6970-6). Garland Pub.

Newlin, Claude M. Philosophy & Religion in Colonial America. LC 68-23317. 1968. Repr. of 1962 ed. lib. bdg. cancelled (ISBN 0-8371-0184-0, NEPR). Greenwood.

Norton, Herman A. Religion in Tennessee, Seventeen Seventy-Seven to Nineteen Forty-Five. LC 81-1562. (Tennessee Three Star Ser.). (Illus.). 136p. 1981. pap. 3.50 (ISBN 0-87049-318-3). U of Tenn Pr.

Park, Edwards A. Selected Essays. Kuklick, Bruce, ed. (American Religious Thought of the 18th & 19th Centuries Ser.). 367p. 1987. lib. bdg. 55.00 (ISBN 0-8240-6957-9). Garland Pub.

Pope, Earl. New England Calvinism & the Disruption of the Presbyterian Church. Kuklick, Bruce, ed. (American Religious Thought of the 18th & 19th Centuries Ser.). 400p. 1987. lib. bdg. 50.00 (ISBN 0-8240-6969-2). Garland Pub.

Rucker, Gilbert W. The Mystery of... America's Future... Destruction... Revealed! 1985. 6.95 (ISBN 0-8062-2440-1). Carlton.

Shea, William M. The Naturalists & the Supernatural: Studies in Horizon & an American Philosophy of Religion. LC 84-14686. xvi, 242p. 1984. 21.50 (ISBN 0-86554-116-7, MUP/H98). Mercer Univ Pr.

Shriver, Peggy L. The Bible Vote: Religion & the New Right. LC 81-7389. 170p. 1981. pap. 5.95 (ISBN 0-8298-0465-X). Pilgrim NY.

Smith, Henry B. Faith & Philosophy: New York, 1877. Kuklick, Bruce, ed. (American Religious Thought of the 18th & 19th Centuries Ser.). 496p. 1987. lib. bdg. 70.00 (ISBN 0-8240-6967-6). Garland Pub.

Taylor, Nathaniel W. Essays, Lectures, etc. Upon Select Topics in Revealed Theology: New York 1859. Kuklick, Bruce, ed. (American Religious Thought of the 18th & 19th Centuries Ser.). 480p. 1987. lib. bdg. 65.00 (ISBN 0-8240-6960-9). Garland Pub.

--Lectures on the Moral Government of God: New York, 1859, 2 vols. Kuklick, Bruce, ed. (American Religious Thought of the 18th & 19th Centuries Ser.). 840p. 1987. lib. bdg. 110.00 (ISBN 0-8240-6961-7). Garland Pub.

RELIGIOUS VACATION SCHOOLS

see Vacation Schools, Religious

RELIGIOUS VOCATION

see Vocation (In Religious Orders, Congregations, etc.)

REMARRIAGE

Bunny, Edmund. Of Divorce for Adulterie & Marrying Againe: That There Is No Sufficient Warrant So to Do. (English Experience Ser.: No. 781). 1977. Repr. of 1612 ed. lib. bdg. 20.00 (ISBN 90-221-0781-7). Walter J Johnson.

Ellisen, Stanley A. Divorce & Remarriage in the Church. 1977. pap. 5.95 (ISBN 0-310-35561-3, 11256P). Zondervan.

Hocking, David. Marrying Again: A Guide for Christians. 160p. 1983. 5.95 (ISBN 0-8007-5188-4, Power Bks). Revell.

Hoster, Helen K. To Love Again: Remarriage for the Christian. (Orig.). 1985. pap. 8.95 (ISBN 0-687-42187-X). Abingdon.

Joiner, E. Earl. A Christian Considers Divorce & Remarriage. LC 81-70411. 1983. pap. 5.95 (ISBN 0-8054-5427-6). Broadman.

Kelly, Kevin T. Divorce & Second Marriage: Facing the Challenge. 112p. 1983. pap. 6.95 (ISBN 0-8164-2471-3, HarpR). Har-Row.

Laney, J. Carl. The Divorce Myth. pap. 5.95 (ISBN 0-87123-892-6, 210892). Bethany Hse.

Martin, Norma & Levitt, Zola. Divorce, a Christian Dilemma. LC 76-45939. 168p. 1977. pap. 1.95 (ISBN 0-8361-1808-1). Herald Pr.

O'Brien, Judith T. & O'Brien, Gene. A Redeeming State: A Handbook-Leader's Guide for Couples Planning Remarriage in the Church. 1984. leader's guide pamphlet 2.95 (ISBN 0-8091-5183-9); pap. 3.95 handbook-pamphlet (ISBN 0-8091-5182-0). Paulist Pr.

Olson, Richard P. & Pia-Terry, Carole D. Help for Remarried Couples & Families. 160p. 1984. pap. 6.95 (ISBN 0-8170-0991-4). Judson.

Small, Dwight H. Remarriage & God's Renewing Grace. 184p. 1986. pap. 7.95 (ISBN 0-8010-8264-1). Baker Bk.

Steele & Ryrie. Meant to Last. 1983. 5.95 (ISBN 0-686-46323-4). Victor Bks.

Stewart, Ken. Divorce & Remarriage. 141p. (Orig.). 1984. pap. 4.95 (ISBN 0-89274-343-3). Harrison Hse.

Thomas, J. D. Divorce & Remarriage. (Way of Life Ser.: No.159). 1977. pap. 3.95 (ISBN 0-89112-159-5, Bibl Res Pr). Abilene Christ U.

Tracy, Jim. Divorce & Remarriage. (Illus.). 80p. (Orig.). 1986. pap. 9.95 (ISBN 1-55630-008-5). Brentwood Comm.

Twomey, Gerald S. When Catholics Marry Again: A Guide for the Divorced, Their Families & Those Who Minister to Them. 194p. (Orig.). 1982. pap. 7.95 (ISBN 0-86683-633-0, HarpR). Har-Row.

Warren, Thomas B. Three Hundred Charts You Can Use in Preaching, Teaching & Studying on Divorce & Remarriage. 1978. pap. 11.00looseleaf (ISBN 0-934916-29-2). Natl Christian Pr.

Warren, Thomas B. & Fuqua, E. C. Divorce & Remarriage: Are Non-Christians Amenable to the Law of Christ? 1977. pap. 6.00 (ISBN 0-934916-30-6). Natl Christian Pr.

Woodrow, Ralph. Divorce & Remarriage: What Does the Bible Really Say? LC 82-99960. (Illus.). 1982. pap. 4.95 (ISBN 0-916938-06-9). R Woodrow.

REMBRANDT, HARMENSZOON VAN RIJN, 1606-1669

Benesch, Otto. Rembrandt: Werk und Forschung. Repr. 17.00 (ISBN 0-384-03899-9). Johnson Repr.

Cundall, Joseph. The Life & Genius of Rembrandt. LC 77-94567. 1979. Repr. of 1867 ed. lib. bdg. 30.00 (ISBN 0-89341-235-X). Longwood Pub Group.

De Lint, J. G. Rembrandt. Repr. 20.00 (ISBN 0-8482-3695-5). Norwood Edns.

Haak, B. Rembrandt Drawings. Willems-Treeman, Elizabeth, tr. LC 76-10073. (Illus.). 1976. 22.50 (ISBN 0-87951-047-1). Overlook Pr.

--Rembrandt Drawings. Willems-Treeman, Elizabeth, tr. LC 76-10073. (Illus.). 1977. pap. 10.95 (ISBN 0-87951-051-X). Overlook Pr.

Hind, Arthur M. Catalogue of Rembrandt's Etchings 2 Vols. in 1. 2nd ed. LC 67-27456. (Graphic Art Ser). 1967. Repr. of 1923 ed. lib. bdg. 65.00 (ISBN 0-306-70977-5). Da Capo.

Longstreet, Stephen. More Drawings of Rembrandt. (Master Draughtsman Ser). 48p. treasure trove bdg. 10.95x (ISBN 0-87505-054-9); pap. 4.95 (ISBN 0-87505-207-X). Borden.

Michel, Emile. Rembrandt, 2 vols. 200.00 (ISBN 0-8490-0943-X). Gordon Pr.

Rea, Hope. Rembrandt Van Ryn. Repr. of 1903 ed. 20.00 (ISBN 0-8482-5893-2). Norwood Edns.

Rembrandt. Drawings of Rembrandt, 2 Vols. Slive, Seymour, ed. (Illus.). pap. 12.50 ea.; Vol. 1. pap. (ISBN 0-486-21485-0); Vol. 2. pap. (ISBN 0-486-21486-9). Dover.

Van Rijn, Rembrandt. Rembrandt: All the Etchings. LC 77-87012. (Illus.). 1977. (Pub. by Two Continents). Hippocrene Bks.

--Rembrandt Bible Drawings. LC 79-52975. (Fine Art Library). (Illus.). 64p. (Orig.). 1980. pap. 3.50 (ISBN 0-486-23878-4). Dover.

Van Rijn Rembrandt, Hermansz. Drawings of Rembrandt. Longstreet, Stephen, ed. (Master Draughtsman Ser). (Illus., Orig.). treasure trove bdg. 10.95x (ISBN 0-87505-029-8); pap. 4.95 (ISBN 0-87505-182-0). Borden.

RENAISSANCE

see also Civilization, Medieval; Humanism; Middle Ages; Sixteenth Century

Allen, Don C. Doubt's Boundless Sea. 1979. 25.50 (ISBN 0-405-10577-0). Ayer Co Pubs.

Bietenholz, Peter G. & Deutscher, Thomas B., eds. Contemporaries of Erasmus: A Biographical Register of the Renaissance & Reformation, Vol. 1 (A-E) (Illus.). 480p. 1985. 72.50x (ISBN 0-8020-2507-2). U of Toronto Pr.

Chatterton-Hill, Georges. The Sociological Value of Christianity. LC 83-45605. Date not set. Repr. of 1912 ed. 36.00 (ISBN 0-404-19873-2). AMS Pr.

Cowan, Ian B. & Shaw, Duncan, eds. The Renaissance & Reformation in Scotland. 220p. 1983. 20.00x (ISBN 0-7073-0261-7, Scot Acad Pr). Longwood Pub Group.

Elton, Gelffrey R. Renaissance & Reformation, Thirteen Hundred to Sixteen Forty-Eight. 3rd ed. (Ideas & Institutions in Western Civilization: Vol. 3). 1976. pap. text ed. write for info. (ISBN 0-02-332840-1). Macmillan.

Estep, William R. Renaissance & Reformation. 320p. (Orig.). pap. text ed. 21.95 (ISBN 0-8028-0050-5). Eerdmans.

Friedman, Jerome. The Most Ancient Testimony: Sixteenth-Century Christian-Hebraica in the Age of Renaissance Nostalgia. LC 82-18830. x, 279p. 1983. text ed. 26.95x (ISBN 0-8214-0700-7). Ohio U Pr.

Garber, Marjorie, ed. Cannibals, Witches, & Divorce: Estranging the Renaissance. LC 86-45472. (Selected Papers from the English Institute, 1985 New Ser.: No. 11). 256p. 1987. text ed. 19.50x (ISBN 0-8018-3405-8). Johns Hopkins.

Geankoplos, Deno J. Byzantine East & Latin West: Two Worlds of Christendom in Middle Ages & Renaissance. LC 76-20685. (Illus.). xii, 206p. 1976. Repr. of 1966 ed. 17.50 (ISBN 0-208-01615-5, Archon). Shoe String.

Gilbert, Felix. The Pope, His Banker & Venice. LC 80-13062. (Illus.). 167p. 1980. text ed. 12.50x (ISBN 0-674-68975-5). Harvard U Pr.

Green, V. H. Renaissance & Reformation: A Survey of European History Between 1450 & 1660. 2nd ed. 462p. 1964. pap. text ed. 17.95 (ISBN 0-7131-5617-1). E Arnold.

Hearnshaw, F. J., ed. The Social & Political Ideas of Some Great Thinkers of the Renaissance & the Reformation. LC 85-7662. 216p. 1985. lib. bdg. 39.75x (ISBN 0-313-23862-6, HREN). Greenwood.

Hulme, Edward M. The Renaissance, the Protestant Revolution & the Catholic Reformation in Continental Europe. LC 83-45662. Date not set. Repr. of 1915 ed. 62.50 (ISBN 0-404-19812-0). AMS Pr.

Kristeller, Paul O. Renaissance Thought: The Classic, Scholastic & Humanistic Strains. 15.50 (ISBN 0-8446-2405-5). Peter Smith.

Lucas, Henry S. The Renaissance & the Reformation. LC 83-45665. Date not set. Repr. of 1934 ed. 67.50 (ISBN 0-404-19815-5). AMS Pr.

Major, J. Russell. Age of the Renaissance & Reformation: A Short History. LC 73-107245. (Orig.). 1970. pap. text ed. 5.50i (ISBN 0-397-47195-5). Har-Row.

Nauert, Charles G., Jr. The Age of Renaissance & Reformation. LC 81-40034. 330p. 1982. lib. bdg. 30.25 (ISBN 0-8191-1861-3); pap. text ed. 12.75 (ISBN 0-8191-1862-1). U Pr of Amer.

New, John F. The Renaissance & Reformation: A Short History. 2nd ed. 201p. 1977. pap. text ed. 11.00 (ISBN 0-394-34199-6, RanC). Random.

Rumsey, Thomas R. Men & Women of the Renaissance & Reformation 1300-1600. 487p. (Orig.). 1981. pap. text ed. 10.95 (ISBN 0-686-81286-7). Ind Sch Pr.

Southern, R. W. Medieval Humanism: And Other Stories. (Illus.). 288p. 1984. pap. 12.95x (ISBN 0-631-13649-5). Basil Blackwell.

Spitz, Lewis W. Renaissance & Reformation, 2 vols. Incl. Vol. 1. The Renaissance. LC 12-2759 (ISBN 0-570-03818-9); Vol. 2. The Reformation. LC 12-2760 (ISBN 0-570-03819-7). 1980. pap. 15.50 ea. Concordia.

Steadman, John M. The Lamb & the Elephant: Ideal Imitation & the Context of Renaissance Allegory. LC 73-93874. 254p. 1974. 29.95 (ISBN 0-87328-062-8). Huntington Lib.

Stone, Jean M. Reformation & Renaissance. LC 83-45670. (Illus.). Date not set. Repr. of 1904 ed. 76.50 (ISBN 0-404-19820-1). AMS Pr.

Vickers, Brian, ed. Occult & Scientific Mentalities in the Renaissance. 432p. 1986. pap. 15.95 (ISBN 0-521-33836-0). Cambridge U Pr.

RENAISSANCE-EUROPE

see Renaissance

RENAISSANCE-FRANCE

Mahoney, Edward P., ed. Philosophy & Humanism: Renaissance Essays in Honor of Paul Oskar Kristeller. LC 75-42285. 624p. 1976. 65.00 (ISBN 0-231-03904-2). Columbia U Pr.

RENAISSANCE-GERMANY

Hoffmeister, Gerhart. The Renaissance & Reformation in Germany: An Introduction. LC 77-5429. 1977. 25.00 (ISBN 0-8044-1391-6); pap. 9.95 (ISBN 0-8044-6272-0). Ungar.

RENAISSANCE-ITALY

Count Gobineau, Arthur. The Renaissance Savonarola. Levy, Oscar, ed. Cohen, Paul V., tr. (Fr., Illus.). 349p. 1986. Repr. of 1913 ed. lib. bdg. 75.00 (ISBN 0-89760-264-1). Telegraph Bks.

D'Amico, John F. Renaissance Humanism in Papal Rome: Humanists & Churchmen on the Eve of the Reformation. LC 82-49059. (Studies in Historical & Political Science). 352p. 1983. text ed. 32.50x (ISBN 0-8018-2860-0). Johns Hopkins.

Gobineau, Arthur. The Renaissance, Savonarola - Cesare - Borgia -Julius II - Leo X - Michael Angelo. Levy, Oscar, ed. 349p. 1981. Repr. of 1903 ed. lib. bdg. 50.00 (ISBN 0-89984-235-6). Century Bookbindery.

Mahoney, Edward P., ed. Philosophy & Humanism: Renaissance Essays in Honor of Paul Oskar Kristeller. LC 75-42285. 624p. 1976. 65.00 (ISBN 0-231-03904-2). Columbia U Pr.

Mitchell, Bonner. Rome in the High Renaissance: The Age of Leo X. LC 72-9277. (Centers of Civilization Ser.: Vol. 33). 1973. 11.95x (ISBN 0-8061-1052-X). U of Okla Pr.

Stinger, Charles L. Humanism & the Church Fathers: Ambrogio Traversari (1386-1439) & the Revival of Patristic Theology in the Early Italian Renaissance. LC 76-21699. 1977. 49.50x (ISBN 0-87395-304-5). State U NY Pr.

Yates, Frances A. Renaissance & Reform: The Italian Contribution. Trapp, J., ed. (Collected Essays Ser.: Vol. II). (Illus.). 288p. 1983. 31.50 (ISBN 0-7100-9530-9). Methuen Inc.

RENAISSANCE PAINTING

see Painting, Renaissance

RENAISSANCE PHILOSOPHY

see Philosophy, Renaissance

RENAN, JOSEPH ERNEST, 1823-1890

Barry, William. Ernest Renan. 1905. Repr. 25.00 (ISBN 0-8274-3825-7). R West.

Chadbourne, Richard M. Ernest Renan. LC 67-25197. (Twayne's World Authors Ser.). 1968. lib. bdg. 17.95 (ISBN 0-8057-2754-X). Irvington.

Darmesteter. The Life of Ernest Renan. 1898. Repr. 25.00 (ISBN 0-8274-2884-7). R West.

Espinasse, Francis. Life of Ernest Renan. 1895. Repr. 20.00 (ISBN 0-8274-2925-8). R West.

Grant Duff, Mountstuart. Ernest Renan in Memoriam. 1893. Repr. 25.00 (ISBN 0-8274-2285-7). R West.

RENEWAL OF THE CHURCH

see Church Renewal

REORGANIZED CHURCH OF JESUS CHRIST OF LATTER-DAY SAINTS

Barrington, George. Use Even Me. 1983. pap. 10.00 (ISBN 0-8309-0375-5). Herald Hse.

Bonds of Sisterhood: A History of the RLDS Women's Organization, 1842-1983. 170p. 1985. pap. 9.75 (ISBN 0-8309-0401-8). Herald Hse.

Butterworth, F. Edward. Roots of the Reorganization: French Polynesia. LC 77-944. (Illus.). 1977. pap. 8.00 (ISBN 0-8309-0176-0). Herald Hse.

Cole, Clifford A., ed. The Priesthood Manual. rev. ed. LC 81-7220. 1985. 15.00 (ISBN 0-8309-0420-4). Herald Hse.

Davis, Inez S. Story of the Church. new ed. 1981. pap. 18.00 (ISBN 0-8309-0188-4). Herald Hse.

Draper, Maurice L., ed. Restoration Studies, Vol.1. 1980. pap. 13.00 (ISBN 0-8309-0292-9). Herald Hse.

Edwards, F. Henry. History of the Reorganized Church of Jesus Christ of Latter Day Saints Vol. 5: 1890-1902. 1969. 22.50 (ISBN 0-8309-0019-5). Herald Hse.

--History of the Reorganized Church of Jesus Christ of the Latter Day Saints, Vol. 8: 1926-1946. 1976. 22.50 (ISBN 0-8309-0157-4). Herald Hse.

Ham, Wayne. More Than Burnt Offerings. LC 78-17646. 1978. pap. 7.00 (ISBN 0-8309-0217-1). Herald Hse.

Holmes, Reed M. The Patriarchs. LC 78-1895. 1978. pap. 7.00 (ISBN 0-8309-0205-8). Herald Hse.

Judd, Peter A. & Cole, Clifford A. Distinctives: Yesterday & Today. 168p. 1983. pap. 10.50 (ISBN 0-8309-0378-X). Herald Hse.

Launius, Roger D. The Kirtland Temple: A Historical Narrative. 1986. pap. 12.50 (ISBN 0-8309-0449-2). Herald Hse.

Mulliken, Frances H. First Ladies of the Restoration. 1985. pap. 6.50 (ISBN 0-8309-0419-0). Herald Hse.

Reorganized Church of Jesus Christ of Latter Day Saints, Board of Publication Staff. Doctrine & Covenants. LC 78-134922. 1978. 14.00 (ISBN 0-8309-0204-X). Herald Hse.

Ruoff, Norman D., ed. Writings of President Frederick M. Smith, Vol. 1. LC 78-6428. 1978. pap. 10.00 (ISBN 0-8309-0215-5). Herald Hse.

Sarre, Winifred. Perce Judd: Man of Peace. (Illus.). 176p. 1983. pap. 10.00 (ISBN 0-8309-0377-1). Herald Hse.

Wellington, Paul A., ed. Rules & Resolutions, Nineteen Eighty. LC 74-84765. 1980. 10.00 (ISBN 0-8309-0136-1). Includes Supplements 1982, 1984 & 1986. Herald Hse.

Wight, Maxine C. A Story About Light. LC 79-14691. 1979. 1.99 (ISBN 0-8309-0236-8). Herald Hse.

REPENTANCE

see also Forgiveness of Sin; Penance

Barney, Kenneth D. Preparing for the Storm. LC 74-21021. 96p. 1975. pap. 1.25 (ISBN 0-88243-576-0, 02-0576). Gospel Pub.

Bradford, John. A Sermon of Repentance. LC 74-28835. (English Experience Ser.: No. 716). 1975. Repr. of 1553 ed. 6.00 (ISBN 90-221-0716-7). Walter J Johnson.

Burghardt, W. J., et al, eds. Tertullian, Treatise on Penance: On Penitence & on Purity. LC 58-10746. (Ancient Christian Writers Ser.: No. 28). 138p. 1959. 12.95 (ISBN 0-8091-0150-5). Paulist Pr.

Ephraem, Saint Repentance. pap. 1.95 (ISBN 0-686-18718-0). Eastern Orthodox.

Horton, Stanley M. It's Getting Late. LC 74-33869. 1975. pap. 1.25 (ISBN 0-88243-570-1, 02-0570). Gospel Pub.

Larson, Don & Larson, Joanie. Bought & Paid For. 1977. 5.95 (ISBN 0-89221-038-9); pap. 2.95 (ISBN 0-89221-051-6). New Leaf.

Law, Jerry L. The Fruits of Repentance. (Orig.). 1985. pap. 3.95 (ISBN 0-930875-00-1). Seed Life Pubns.

Prince, Derek. Repent & Believe. (Foundation Ser.: Bk. II). 1965-66. pap. 2.95 (ISBN 0-934920-01-X, B-11). Derek Prince.

Secret Joy of Repentance. 3.50 (ISBN 0-8198-6863-9); 2.25 (ISBN 0-8198-6864-7). Dghtrs St Paul.

Soloveitchik, Joseph D. Soloveitchik on Repentance. Peli, Pinchas, tr. 320p. 1984. 11.95 (ISBN 0-8091-2604-4). Paulist Pr.

Yedlicka, Leo C. Expressions of the Linguistic Area of Repentance & Remorse in Old French. LC 76-94175. (Catholic University of America Studies in Romance Languages & Literatures Ser: No. 28). 1969. Repr. of 1945 ed. 28.00 (ISBN 0-404-50328-4). AMS Pr.

REPTILES (IN RELIGION, FOLK-LORE, ETC.)

see Serpents (In Religion, Folk-Lore, etc.)

RESPONSA

Freehof, Solomon B. Contemporary Reform Response. 15.00x (ISBN 0-87820-108-4, Pub. by Hebrew Union College Press). Ktav.

Hurwitz, Simon. Responsa of Solomon Luria (Marharshal) Legal Decisions of the Famous Sixteenth-Century Sage. 2nd ed. LC 68-31710. 1969. 10.00 (ISBN 0-8197-0096-7). Bloch.

Klein, Isaac. Responsa & Halakhic Studies. 15.00x. Ktav.

RESTIF, NICHOLAS EDME, 1734-1806

Jacob, P. L., pseud. Bibliographie et Iconographie De Tous les Ouvrages De Restif De la Bretonne. 1971. Repr. of 1875 ed. lib. bdg. 32.50 (ISBN 0-8337-1817-7). B Franklin.

RESTORATION MOVEMENT (CHRISTIANITY)

Coyle, Neva. Restoration. 50p. (Orig.). 1985. saddlestitched 2.50 (ISBN 0-87123-851-9). Bethany Hse.

Leggett, Marshall. Introduction to the Restoration Ideal. 240p. 1986. pap. text ed. 7.95 (ISBN 0-87403-067-6, 3175). Standard Pub.

--Workbook for the Restoration Ideal. 96p. 1986. pap. 2.95 wkbk. (ISBN 0-87403-068-4, 3176). Standard Pub.

RESURRECTION

see also Future Life; Jesus Christ-Resurrection

Alves, Rubem. I Believe in the Resurrection of the Body. McCoy, L. M., tr. from Ger. & Port. LC 85-16246. 80p. 1986. pap. 4.95 (ISBN 0-8006-1885-8, 1-1885). Fortress.

Anderson, J. N. Evidence for the Resurrection. pap. 0.75 (ISBN 0-87784-124-1). Inter-Varsity.

Barth, Karl. The Resurrection of the Dead. Kastenbaum, Robert, ed. LC 76-19559. (Death and Dying Ser.). 1977. Repr. of 1933 ed. lib. bdg. 23.50x (ISBN 0-405-09555-4). Ayer Co Pubs.

Brengle, Samuel L. Resurrection Life & Power. 1978. Repr. of 1925 ed. 3.95 (ISBN 0-86544-005-0). Salv Army Suppl South.

Burghardt, W. J., et al, eds. Athenagoras, Embassy for the Christians, the Resurrection of the Dead. LC 56-11421. (Ancient Christian Writers Ser.: No. 23). 193p. 1956. 10.95 (ISBN 0-8091-0036-3). Paulist Pr.

Burt, Donald X. The Rush to Resurrection. 112p. 1985. pap. 5.95 (ISBN 0-8146-1440-X). Liturgical Pr.

Fishel, Kent & Rayds, John. Resurrection Evidences. (Cornerstone Ser.). 1985. pap. 2.95 (ISBN 0-310-46102-2, 12675P). Zondervan.

Goldfield, Lea N. An Inquiry into the Authenticity of Moses Maimonides' Treatise on Resurrection. 1985. text ed. 19.95x (ISBN 0-88125-088-0). Ktav.

Gresham, Charles R. What the Bible Says about Resurrection. LC 82-7411. (What the Bible Says Ser.). 351p. 1983. 13.95 (ISBN 0-89900-090-8). College Pr Pub.

Hanson, Richard S. Journey to Resurrection. 81p. (Orig.). 1986. pap. 4.95 (ISBN 0-8091-2737-7). Paulist Pr.

Harris, Murray J. Raised Immortal: Resurrection & Immortality in the New Testament. 320p. (Orig.). 1985. pap. 10.95 (ISBN 0-8028-0053-X). Eerdmans.

Ignoffo, Matthew. One Perfect Lover: A Story of the Resurrection. LC 86-60171. 200p. 1987. 14.95 (ISBN 0-89390-084-2). Resource Pubns.

Johnstone, Robert, ed. Samuel Butler on the Resurrection. 64p. Date not set. 9.95 (ISBN 0-901072-59-1). Dufour.

Kwak, Chung H., ed. Resurrection (Five) (Home Study Course Ser.). 40p. (Orig.). 1980. pap. 4.00 (ISBN 0-910621-14-4). HSA Pubns.

Ladd, George E. I Believe in the Resurrection. (I Believe). 160p. 1975. pap. 5.95 (ISBN 0-8028-1611-8). Eerdmans.

N. J. Insurrection - Resurrection. (Illus.). 1976. pap. 1.25 (ISBN 0-686-16521-7). Working Peoples Art.

Perkins, Pheme. Resurrection: New Testament Witness & Contemporary Reflection. LC 83-25473. 564p. 1984. 19.95 (ISBN 0-385-17256-7). Doubleday.

Pink, Arthur W. New Birth. pap. 0.50 (ISBN 0-685-00739-1). Reiner.

Prince, Derek. Resurrection of the Dead. (Foundation Ser.: Bk. VI). 1965-66. pap. 2.95 (ISBN 0-934920-05-2, B-15). Derek Prince.

Reesman, Richard T. Contributions of the Major Philosophers into the Problem of Body Resurrection & Personal Immortality. (Illus.). 117p. 1981. 61.85 (ISBN 0-89920-021-4). Am Inst Psych.

Rosner, Fred, tr. Moses Maimonides' Treatise on Resurrection. 12.50x (ISBN 0-87068-764-6); pap. 7.95. Ktav.

Sanders, Andrew. Charles Dickens, Resurrectionist. LC 81-21246. 1982. 26.00 (ISBN 0-312-13014-7). St Martin.

Sayers, Stanley E. The Nature of Things to Come. 1972. 7.95 (ISBN 0-88027-013-6). Firm Foun Pub.

Septimus, Bernard. Hispano-Jewish Culture in Transition: The Career & Controversies of Ramah. LC 81-13275. (Harvard Judiac Monographs: No. 4). 192p. 1982. text ed. 20.00x (ISBN 0-674-39230-2). Harvard U Pr.

Sheed, F. J. Death into Life: A Conversation. 1977. pap. 1.95 (ISBN 0-88479-005-3). Arena Lettres.

Snyder, John. Reincarnation vs Resurrection. (Orig.). 1984. pap. 4.95 (ISBN 0-8024-0321-2). Moody.

Spencer, Bonnell. They Saw the Lord: The Resurrection Appearances. LC 83-61765. 235p. 1983. pap. 8.95 (ISBN 0-8192-1332-2). Morehouse.

Walchars, John. Resurrection of Value. 176p. (Orig.). 1986. pap. 8.95 (ISBN 0-8245-0746-0). Crossroad NY.

Whitson, Robley E. The Resurrection Gospel. LC 85-51481. (Illus.). 48p. (Orig.). 1985. pap. text ed. 4.95x (ISBN 0-932269-55-9). Wyndham Hall.

RETABLES

see Altarpieces

RETREATS

Here are entered works dealing with periods of retirement for the purpose of meditation and spiritual development.

see also Meditations; Spiritual Exercises

Adams, Jay E. Four Weeks with God & Your Neighbor. 75p. 1978. pap. 2.50 (ISBN 0-87552-020-0). Presby & Reformed.

Burton, Laurel A. From Hiding to Healing. Sherer, Michael L., ed. (Orig.). 1987. pap. 2.75 participant bk. (ISBN 0-89536-860-9, 7819); pap. 2.25 leader's guide (ISBN 0-89536-861-7, 7820). CSS of Ohio.

Capon, Robert F. The Youngest Day: Nature & Grace on Shelter Island. LC 82-48414. (Illus.). 160p. 1983. 11.49 (ISBN 0-06-061309-2, HarpR). Har-Row.

Chiampi, Luke. Rebuild My Church. LC 72-87090. 105p. 1972. pap. 0.95 (ISBN 0-8199-0502-X). Franciscan Herald.

Clapp, Steve. Retreat Guide I. 20p. (Orig.). 1981. pap. 2.00 (ISBN 0-914527-04-5). C-Four Res.

--Retreat Guide II. (The C-4 Journals). 29p. (Orig.). 1982. pap. 2.00 (ISBN 0-914527-13-4). C-Four Res.

Colbeck, Kay & Harrell, Irene B. The Story of Singing Waters. (Orig.). 1987. pap. 7.00 (ISBN 0-915541-21-1). Star Bks Inc.

Collison, Kathleen & Webb, Warren. Forty-Eight Hours More or Less: A Retreat Resource. 111p. (Orig.). pap. 11.00 (ISBN 0-941988-03-1). K Q Assocs.

Cooney, Randy. Reaching, Touching, Teaching: How to Run Successful Days of Retreat. 1986. pap. 15.95 (ISBN 0-697-02199-8). Wm C Brown.

De Margerie, Bertrand. A Theological Retreat. 280p. 1977. 8.95 (ISBN 0-8199-0584-4). Franciscan Herald.

Doyle, Aileen A. Youth Retreats: Creating Sacred Space for Young People. (Illus.). 107p. 1986. spiral bdg. 12.95 (ISBN 0-88489-177-1). St Mary's.

Haas, Joseph S. The Northeast Retreat of 1759 & 1981. LC 81-90691. (Cathedral of the Beechwoods Ser.: No. 1). (Illus.). 148p. (Orig.). 1981. per copy 7.00 (ISBN 0-9605552-0-X). Haas Ent NH.

Harman, Shirley. Retreat Planning Made Easy: A Resource for Christian Retreats. 40p. (Orig.). pap. 4.95 (ISBN 0-8066-2155-9, 10-5488). Augsburg.

Kamstra, Doug. The Get-Away Book. (Good Things for Youth Leaders Ser.). 1984. pap. 5.95 (ISBN 0-8010-5459-1). Baker Bk.

Nelson, Virgil & Nelson, Lynn. Retreat Handbook. LC 75-23468. 128p. 1976. pap. 7.95 (ISBN 0-8170-0694-X). Judson.

Noon, Scott. Building a Fort in the Family Tree. 1984. 3.50 (ISBN 0-89536-703-3, 4884). CSS of Ohio.

Pastva, Mary L. The Catholic Youth Retreat Book: Everything You Need to Plan Prayer Experiences for a Day, an Evening, a Weekend. (Illus.). 87p. 1984. pap. 7.95 (ISBN 0-86716-032-2). St Anthony Mess Pr.

Plassmann, Thomas. The Upper Room: Retreat Readings for Priests. (Spirit & Life Ser). 1954. 4.50 (ISBN 0-686-11565-1). Franciscan Inst.

Reichter, Arlo, et al. The Group Retreat Book. LC 82-62532. (Illus.). 400p. (Orig.). 1983. pap. 15.95 (ISBN 0-936664-08-8). Group Bks.

Reimer, Sandy & Reimer, Larry. The Retreat Handbook. 192p. 1987. pap. 9.95. Morehouse.

Shawchuck, Norman, et al. How to Conduct a Spiritual Life Retreat. (Orig.). 1986. pap. 5.95 (ISBN 0-8358-0527-1, ICN 608805, Dist. by Abingdon Pr). Upper Room.

Target, George. Out of This World: A Guide to the Retreat Houses of Great Britain. 1985. 35.00x (ISBN 0-900873-67-1, Pub. by Bishopsgate Pr. Ltd); pap. 21.00x (ISBN 0-900873-73-6). State Mutual Bk.

RETRIBUTION

see Future Life; Future Punishment; Hell; Purgatory; Reward (Theology)

REVELATION

see also Apocalyptic Literature; Inner Light; Theophanies

Abraham, William J. Divine Revelation & the Limits of Historical Criticism. 1982. 29.95x (ISBN 0-19-826665-0). Oxford U Pr.

Anderson, Roy A. Unfolding the Revelation. LC 61-10884. (Dimension Ser.). 223p. 1961. pap. 6.95 (ISBN 0-8163-0027-5, 21400-7). Pacific Pr Pub Assn.

Baillie, John. The Idea of Revelation in Recent Thought. LC 56-8158. (Bantam Lectures in America Ser.). 151p. 1956. 23.00x (ISBN 0-231-02142-9); pap. 11.00x (ISBN 0-231-08554-0). Columbia U Pr.

Barnhouse, Donald G. Revelation: An Expositional Commentary. 1971. 14.95 (ISBN 0-310-20490-9); pap. 11.95 (ISBN 0-310-20491-7, 9760P). Zondervan.

Bavinck, Herman. Philosophy of Revelation. (Twin Brooks Ser.). 1980. pap. 7.95 (ISBN 0-8010-0767-4). Baker Bk.

Bea, Augustin. Word of God & Mankind. 1968. 6.50 (ISBN 0-8199-0149-0, L39003). Franciscan Herald.

Bevan, Edwyn R. Sibyls & Seers. 1979. Repr. of 1928 ed. lib. bdg. 39.50 (ISBN 0-8495-0510-0). Arden Lib.

Bowne, Borden P. The Christian Revelation. LC 75-3069. Repr. of 1898 ed. 20.00 (ISBN 0-404-59068-3). AMS Pr.

Brunner, Emil. Revelation & Reason. 448p. 1984. pap. 14.95 (ISBN 0-913029-01-7). Stevens Bk Pr.

Bullard, Rayford. Glimpses into Revelation. 5.95 (ISBN 0-911866-74-4). Advocate.

Coward, Parnell C. Revelation, Systematically Studied. 1983. pap. 6.95 (ISBN 0-87148-739-X). Pathway Pr.

Davis, Willard O. Evolution & Revelation. 6.95 (ISBN 0-88027-097-7). Firm Foun Pub.

De Waters, Lillian. Voice of Revelation. 5.95 (ISBN 0-686-05714-7). L De Waters.

Dhavamony, Mariasusai, et al. Revelation in Christianity & Other Religions. (Studia Missionalia: Vol. 20). (Eng., Fr., & Ital.). 1971. pap. 15.00 (ISBN 0-8294-0324-8, Pub. by Gregorian U Pr). Loyola.

Dulles, Avery. Models of Revelation. LC 82-45243. 360p. 1983. 16.95 (ISBN 0-385-17975-8). Doubleday.

--Models of Revelation. LC 82-45243. 360p. 1985. pap. 8.95 (ISBN 0-385-23235-7, Im). Doubleday.

Elder, Dorothy. Revelation: For a New Age. LC 81-65477. 320p. (Orig.). 1981. pap. 11.50 (ISBN 0-87516-446-3). De Vorss.

Engelzakis, Benedict. New & Old in God's Revelation. (Studies in Relations Between Spirit & Tradition in the Bible). 128p. 1982. text ed. 12.95 (ISBN 0-913836-89-3). St Vladimirs.

Farmer, Herbert H. Revelation & Religion: Studies in the Theological Interpretation of Religious Types. LC 77-27177. (Gifford Lectures: 1950). (Illus.). 256p. Repr. of 1954 ed. 31.00 (ISBN 0-404-60505-2). AMS Pr.

Fenwick, Agnes M. My Journey into God's Realm of Light. 1974. 3.50 (ISBN 0-682-47865-2). Exposition Pr FL.

Fichte, J. G. Fichte's Critique of All Revelation. Green, G. D., tr. LC 77-77756. 1978. 34.50 (ISBN 0-521-21707-5). Cambridge U Pr.

Hart, Ray. Unfinished Man & the Imagination: Toward an Ontology & a Rhetoric of Revelation. (Reprints & Translations Ser.). 1985. pap. text ed. 12.95 (ISBN 0-89130-937-3, 00-07-15). Scholars Pr GA.

Hellholm, David, ed. Apocalypticism in the Mediterranean World & the Near East: Proceedings of the International Colloquium. 889p. 1983. lib. bdg. 157.50x (ISBN 3-16-144460-4, Pub. by J C B Mohr BRD). Coronet Bks.

Hiral, Ange-Marie. The Revelations of Margaret of Cortona. (Spirit &Life Ser). 1952. 3.00 (ISBN 0-686-11562-7). Franciscan Inst.

Irion, J. Everett. Interpreting the Revelation with Edgar Cayce. 440p. 1982. 19.95 (ISBN 0-87604-137-3). ARE Pr.

Lahaye, Tim. Revelation-Illustrated & Made Plain. rev. ed. 456p. 1975. 7.95 (ISBN 0-310-26991-1, 18073P). Zondervan.

McConkie, Joseph F. Spirit of Revelation. LC 84-1705. 144p. 1984. 6.95 (ISBN 0-87747-990-9). Deseret Bk.

Maclean, Dorothy. To Hear the Angels Sing. 217p. (Orig.). 1983. pap. text ed. 7.00 (ISBN 0-936878-01-0). Lorian Pr.

Maurice, Frederick D. What Is Revelation? LC 76-173061. Repr. of 1859 ed. 37.50 (ISBN 0-404-04276-7). AMS Pr.

Moran, Gabriel. Theology of Revelation. 1968. pap. 5.95 (ISBN 0-8164-2567-1, HarpR). Har-Row.

Morris, Leon. I Believe in Revelation. (I Believe Ser.). 160p. 1976. pap. 6.95 (ISBN 0-8028-1637-1). Eerdmans.

Morrison. Morrison on James to Revelation. pap. 4.95 (ISBN 0-89957-563-3). AMG Pubs.

Murphy, Carol R. Revelation & Experience. LC 64-22765. (Orig.). pap. 2.50x (ISBN 0-87574-137-1). Pendle Hill.

Nee, Watchman. Aids to "Revelation". Kaung, Stephen, tr. 1983. pap. 2.75 (ISBN 0-935008-60-8). Christian Fellow Pubs.

Niebuhr, H. Richard. Meaning of Revelation. 1967. pap. 5.95 (ISBN 0-02-087750-1, Collier). Macmillan.

--The Meaning of Revelation. 1983. 14.00 (ISBN 0-8446-6033-7). Peter Smith.

Norris, Richard A. Understanding the Faith of the Church. (Church's Teaching Ser.: Vol. 4). 288p. 1979. 5.95 (ISBN 0-8164-0421-6, HarpR); pap. 3.95 (ISBN 0-8164-2217-6, Crossroad Bks); user guide .95 (ISBN 0-8164-2224-9). Har-Row.

Oppenheim, Michael. What Does Revelation Mean for the Modern Jew? LC 85-18929. (Symposium Ser.: Vol. 17). 152p. 1985. lib. bdg. 39.95x (ISBN 0-88946-708-0). E Mellen.

Outlaw, Stanley, et al. A Survey of the General Epistles & Revelation. 1976. pap. 2.95 (ISBN 0-89265-036-2). Randall Hse.

Reese, James M. Experiencing the Good News: The New Testament as Communication. (Good News Studies Ser.: Vol. 10). 1984. pap. 9.95 (ISBN 0-89453-448-3). M Glazier.

Robinson, Henry W. Inspiration & Revelation in the Old Testament. LC 78-9891. 1979. Repr. of 1946 ed. lib. bdg. 24.75x (ISBN 0-313-21068-3, ROIR). Greenwood.

Rolwing, Richard J. A Philosophy of Revelation: According to Karl Rahner. LC 78-63067. 1978. pap. text ed. 8.50 (ISBN 0-8191-0609-7). U Pr of Amer.

Rudhyar, Dane. White Thunder. 1976. pap. 3.50 (ISBN 0-916108-07-4). Seed Center.

Ryrie, Charles C. Apocalipsis (Comentario Biblico Portavoz) Orig. Title: Revelation (Everyman's Bible Commentary) (Span.). 128p. 1981. pap. 3.50 (ISBN 0-8254-1625-6). Kregel.

Schillebeeckx, Edward & Willems, Boniface, eds. Man As Man & Believer. LC 67-17789. (Concilium Ser.: Vol. 21). 188p. 7.95 (ISBN 0-8091-0093-2). Paulist Pr.

Sica, Joseph F. God So Loved the World. LC 81-40441. 120p. (Orig.). 1981. lib. bdg. 21.00 o. p. (ISBN 0-8191-1677-7); pap. text ed. 9.25 (ISBN 0-8191-1678-5). U Pr of Amer.

Smith, Chuck. What the World Is Coming To. LC 77-3186. 224p. 1980. pap. 1.95 (ISBN 0-936728-00-0). Word for Today.

Sri, Patricia. Revelations: As It Is. Moringland Publications Inc, ed. (Illus.). 635p. (Orig.). 1979. pap. 10.00 (ISBN 0-935146-08-3). Morningland.

Swedenborg, Emanuel. Arcana Coelestia (Heavenly Secrets) Student Edition, 12 vols. Incl. 12.00 ea. Vol. 1 (ISBN 0-87785-021-6). Vol. 2 (ISBN 0-87785-022-4). Vol. 3 (ISBN 0-87785-023-2). Vol. 4 (ISBN 0-87785-024-0). Vol. 5 (ISBN 0-87785-025-9). Vol. 6 (ISBN 0-87785-026-7); Vol. 7 (ISBN 0-87785-027-5). Vol. 8 (ISBN 0-87785-028-3). Vol. 9 (ISBN 0-87785-029-1). Vol. 10 (ISBN 0-87785-030-5). Vol. 11 (ISBN 0-87785-031-3). Vol. 12 (ISBN 0-87785-032-1). LC 63-1828. 1977. Set. 144.00 (ISBN 0-87785-033-X). Swedenborg.

Tatford, Frederick A. The Revelation. 656p. 1985. Repr. lib. bdg. 23.00 (ISBN 0-86524-186-4, 6602). Klock & Klock.

Thiemann, Ronald F. Revelation & Theology: The Gospel As Narrated Promise. LC 84-40822. 198p. 1987. pap. text ed. 9.95 (ISBN 0-268-01632-1, Dist. by Har-Row). U of Notre Dame Pr.

Tickle, John. The Book of Revelation: A Catholic Interpretation of the Apocalypse. 144p. 1983. pap. 3.95 (ISBN 0-89243-195-4). Liguori Pubns.

Warfield, Benjamin B. Inspiration & Authority of the Bible. 2nd ed. 1948. 12.95 (ISBN 0-87552-527-X). Presby & Reformed.

Watchman Nee. The Spirit of Wisdom & Revelation. Kaung, Stephen, tr. 1980. pap. 3.25 (ISBN 0-935008-48-9). Christian Fellow Pubs.

Watson, Sydney. Mark of the Beast. 256p. 1974. 5.95 (ISBN 0-8007-5199-X, Power Bks); (Spire Bks). Revell.

Wood, David. Genesis: The First Book of Revelations. 320p. 1985. 55.00x (ISBN 0-85936-180-2, Pub. by Chambers Green Ltd). State Mutual Bk.

REVELATION–HISTORY OF DOCTRINES

Fairweather, Alan M. The Word As Truth: A Critical Examination of the Christian Doctrine of Revelation in the Writings of Thomas Aquinas & Karl Barth. LC 78-26040. 1979. Repr. of 1944 ed. lib. bdg. cancelled (ISBN 0-313-20808-5, FAWT). Greenwood.

Latourelle, Rene. Theology of Revelation. LC 65-15734. 1966. pap. 12.95 (ISBN 0-8189-0143-8). Alba.

REVIVAL (RELIGION)

see Evangelistic Work

REVIVAL SERMONS

see Evangelistic Sermons

REVIVALISTS

see Evangelists

REVIVALS

see also Camp-Meetings; Enthusiasm; Evangelistic Work; Jesus People; Retreats

Bartleman, Frank. Another Wave of Revival. rev. ed. Meyers, John, ed. Orig. Title: Another Wave Rolls In. 176p. 1982. pap. text ed. 2.95 (ISBN 0-88368-111-0). Whitaker Hse.

Bell, Marion L. Crusade in the City: Revivalism in Nineteenth-Century Philadelphia. (Illus.). 1978. 22.50 (ISBN 0-8387-1929-5). Bucknell U Pr.

Bisagno, John R. Power of Positive Evangelism: How to Hold a Revival. LC 68-26912. 1968. pap. 3.95 (ISBN 0-8054-2503-9). Broadman.

Cairns, Earle E. An Endless Line of Splendor. 352p. 1986. text ed. 14.95 (ISBN 0-8423-0770-2). Tyndale.

Cleveland, Catherine C. The Great Revival in the West, 1797-1805. 11.25 (ISBN 0-8446-1117-4). Peter Smith.

Colton, Calvin. History & Character of American Revivals of Religion. LC 72-1008. Repr. of 1832 ed. 22.50 (ISBN 0-404-00018-5). AMS Pr.

Crawford, Dan R. Single Adults: Resource & Recipients for Revival. LC 85-7889. 1985. pap. 5.95 (ISBN 0-8054-3236-1). Broadman.

Davenport, F. M. Primitive Traits in Religious Revivals: A Study in Mental & Social Evolution. 1977. lib. bdg. 59.95 (ISBN 0-8490-2478-1). Gordon Pr.

Davenport, Frederick M. Primitive Traits in Religious Revivals. LC 72-163669. Repr. of 1905 ed. 15.00 (ISBN 0-404-01929-3). AMS Pr.

--Primitive Traits in Religious Revivals. LC 68-58053. Repr. of 1905 ed. cancelled (ISBN 0-8371-0378-9, DAR&). Greenwood.

Dieter, Melvin E. The Holiness Revival of the Nineteenth Century. LC 80-17259. (Studies in Evangelicalism: No. 1). 366p. 1980. 26.00 (ISBN 0-8108-1328-9). Scarecrow.

Finney, Charles G. Finney on Revival. Shelhamer, E. E., ed. 128p. 1974. pap. 3.50 (ISBN 0-87123-151-4, 200151). Bethany Hse.

--Revival Lectures. 544p. 15.95 (ISBN 0-8007-0272-7). Revell.

Harrell, David E., Jr. All Things Are Possible: The Healing & Charismatic Revivals in Modern America. LC 75-1937. (Midland Bks.: No. 221). (Illus.). 320p. 1976. 20.00x (ISBN 0-253-10090-9); pap. 8.95x (ISBN 0-253-20221-3). Ind U Pr.

Keller, Charles R. The Second Great Awakening in Connecticut. LC 68-26923. ix, 275p. 1968. Repr. of 1942 ed. 25.00 (ISBN 0-208-00662-1, Archon). Shoe String.

Koch, Kurt E. Revival Fires in Canada. LC 72-93352. 96p. 1975. pap. 2.95 (ISBN 0-8254-3015-1). Kregel.

Lloyd-Jones, D. Martyn. Revival. LC 86-72057. 320p. (Orig.). 1987. pap. 9.95 (ISBN 0-89107-415-5, Crossway Bks). Good News.

Maxson, Charles H. The Great Awakening in the Middle Colonies. 12.00 (ISBN 0-8446-1306-1). Peter Smith.

Murray, Robert H. Group Movements Throughout the Ages. LC 72-301. (Essay Index Reprint Ser.). Repr. of 1935 ed. 22.00 (ISBN 0-8369-2810-5). Ayer Co Pubs.

Randall, Max W. The Great Awakenings & the Restoration Movement. LC 82-74537. 442p. (Orig.). 1983. pap. 9.95 (ISBN 0-89900-229-3). College Pr Pub.

Rawlyk, G. A. Ravished by the Spirit: Religious Revivals, Baptists, & Henry Alline. 190p. 1984. 19.95x (ISBN 0-7735-0439-7); pap. 7.95 (ISBN 0-7735-0440-0). McGill-Queens U Pr.

Roberts, Richard O. Revival! 186p. 1982. pap. 6.95 (ISBN 0-8423-5575-8). Tyndale.

Smith, Timothy L. Revivalism & Social Reform: American Protestantism on the Eve of the Civil War. 11.25 (ISBN 0-8446-2960-X). Peter Smith.

Stark, Rodney & Bainbridge, William S. The Future of Religion: Secularization, Revival & Cult Formation. LC 83-18221. (Illus.). 600p. 1985. pap. 40.00x (ISBN 0-520-04854-7); 14.95 (ISBN 0-520-05731-7, CAMPUS 406). U of Cal Pr.

Sweet, William W. Revivalism in America. 1944. 12.75 (ISBN 0-8446-1430-0). Peter Smith.

Tracy, Joseph. Great Awakening: A History of the Revival of Religion in the Time of Edwards & Whitefield. LC 72-83444. (Religion in America Ser). 1969. Repr. of 1945 ed. 21.00 (ISBN 0-405-00280-7). Ayer Co Pubs.

Wesley, John. The Nature of Revival. rev. ed. Weakley, Clare, ed. 256p. 1987. pap. 6.95 (ISBN 0-87123-925-6). Bethany Hse.

Whittaker, Colin. Great Revivals. LC 85-72333. 224p. 1986. pap. 4.50 (ISBN 0-88243-522-1, 02-0522). Gospel Pub.

REVIVALS, ETHNIC

see Nativistic Movements

REVOLUTION (THEOLOGY)

Bruckberger, R. L. God & Politics. LC 78-190754. (Howard Greenfield Bk.). 1971. 9.95 (ISBN 0-87955-302-2). O'Hara.

Davies, John. Christians, Politics & Violent Revolution. LC 75-42517. pap. 56.00 (ISBN 0-317-26642-X, 2025118). Bks Demand UMI.

Hodgson, Peter C. Children of Freedom: Black Liberation in Christian Perspective. LC 74-76930. pap. 24.00 (2027866). Bks Demand UMI.

Khumayni, Ruh A. Islam & Revolution: Writings & Declarations of Imam Khomeini. Algar, Hamid, tr. LC 80-24032. 480p. 1981. 24.95 (ISBN 0-933782-04-7); pap. 11.95 (ISBN 0-933782-03-9). Mizan Pr.

Lindsay, Gordon. The Revolution & After. (Old Testament Ser.). 1.25 (ISBN 0-89985-152-5). Christ Nations.

Morris, William D. The Christian Origins of Social Revolt. LC 78-14133. 1979. Repr. of 1949 ed. 19.50 (ISBN 0-88355-805-X). Hyperion Conn.

Novitch, Miriam, ed. Sobibor: Martyrdom & Revolt. (Illus.). 168p. pap. 4.95 (ISBN 0-686-95087-9). ADL.

Wallis, Arthur. The Radical Christian. 160p. 1982. pap. 5.95 (ISBN 0-8007-5081-0, Power Bks). Revell.

Zuck, Lowell H., ed. Christianity & Revolution: Radical Christian Testimonies, 1520-1650. LC 74-25355. (Documents in Free Church History Ser.: No. 2). 324p. 1975. 29.95 (ISBN 0-87722-040-9); pap. 12.95 (ISBN 0-87722-044-1). Temple U Pr.

REVOLUTIONS

Kramer, Milton, ed. Shi'ism, Resistance & Revolution. 350p. 1986. 39.85 (ISBN 0-8133-0453-9). Westview.

Lincoln, Bruce, ed. Religion, Rebellion, Revolution: An Interdisciplinary & Cross-Cultural Collection of Essays. LC 85-1992. 312p. 1985. 27.50 (ISBN 0-312-67061-3). St Martin.

N. J. Insurrection - Resurrection. (Illus.). 1976. pap. 1.25 (ISBN 0-686-16521-7). Working Peoples Art.

Novak, Michael. Experience of Nothingness. 1971. pap. 5.95x (ISBN 0-06-131938-4, TB 1938, Torch). Har-Row.

Volney, C. F. A New Translation of Volney's Ruins, 2 vols. Feldman, Burton & Richardson, Robert D., eds. LC 78-60900. (Myth & Romanticism Ser.: Vol. 25). (Illus.). 1979. Set. lib. bdg. 160.00 (ISBN 0-8240-3574-7). Garland Pub.

REWARD (THEOLOGY)

Hodges, Zane C. Grace in Eclipse: A Study on Eternal Rewards. viii, 120p. (Orig.). 1985. pap. 4.95 (ISBN 0-9607576-3-5). Redencion Viva.

Savelle, Jerry. Fruits of Righteousness. 32p. (Orig.). 1980. pap. 1.95 (ISBN 0-89274-069-8). Harrison Hse.

RHODE ISLAND–HISTORY

Callender, John. Historical Discourse on the Civil & Religious Affairs of the Colony of Rhode Island. facs. ed. LC 79-150172. (Select Bibliographies Reprint Ser.). 1843. 18.00 (ISBN 0-8369-5685-0). Ayer Co Pubs.

Carpenter, Esther B. South County Studies: Of Some Eighteenth Century Persons, Places & Conditions. in That Portion of Rhode Island Called Narragansett. facsimile ed. LC 75-160961. (Select Bibliographies Reprint Ser). Repr. of 1924 ed. 21.00 (ISBN 0-8369-5829-2). Ayer Co Pubs.

Ernst, James E. Roger Williams: New England Firebrand. LC 76-90097. (BCL Ser.: I). Repr. of 1932 ed. 24.50 (ISBN 0-404-02355-X). AMS Pr.

Foster, Geraldine S. The Jews in Rhode Island: A Brief History. Conley, Patrick T., ed. (Rhode Island Ethnic Heritage Pamphlet Ser.). (Illus.). 48p. (Orig.). 1985. pap. 2.75 (ISBN 0-917012-80-1). RI Pubns Soc.

Gelenian, Ara A. The Armenians in Rhode Island: Ancient Roots to Present Experiences. Conley, Patrick T., ed. (Rhode Island Ethnic Heritage Ser.). (Illus.). 36p. (Orig.). 1985. pap. 2.75 (ISBN 0-917012-73-9). RI Pubns Soc.

Matthews, Margery I., et al. Churches of Foster: A History of Religious Life in Rural Rhode Island. (Illus.). 169p. (Orig.). 1978. pap. 5.00 (ISBN 0-917012-20-8). N Foster Baptist.

Straus, Oscar S. Roger Williams, the Pioneer of Religious Liberty. facs. ed. LC 76-137385. (Select Bibliographies Reprint Ser). 1936. 20.00 (ISBN 0-8369-5586-2). Ayer Co Pubs.

RICHARD 1ST, KING OF ENGLAND, 1157-1199

Archer, Thomas A. The Crusade of Richard I, 1189-92. LC 76-29828. Repr. of 1889 ed. 65.00 (ISBN 0-404-15408-5). AMS Pr.

Gibb, Christopher. Richard the Lionheart & the Crusades. (Life & Times Ser.). (Illus.). 64p. 1985. s&l 11.40 (ISBN 0-531-18011-5, Pub. by Bookwright Pr). Watts.

Sabatini, Rafael. Heroic Lives. facs. ed. LC 70-99648. (Essay Index Reprint Ser.). 1934. 19.50 (ISBN 0-8369-2071-6). Ayer Co Pubs.

RICHELIEU, ARMAND JEAN DU PLESSIS, CARDINAL, DUC DE, 1585-1642

Belloc, Hilaire. Richelieu: A Study. 1978. Repr. of 1929 ed. lib. bdg. 20.00 (ISBN 0-8495-0383-3). Arden Lib.

Belloc, Hilarie. Richelieu. 1935. Repr. 17.50 (ISBN 0-8274-3281-X). R West.

Bergin, Joseph. Cardinal Richelieu: Power & the Pursuit of Wealth. 352p. 1985. 30.00x (ISBN 0-300-03495-4). Yale U Pr.

Church, William F. Richelieu & Reason of State. LC 76-181518. 582p. 1972. 49.00x (ISBN 0-691-05199-2). Princeton U Pr.

--Richelieu & Reason of State. LC 76-181518. pap. 140.50 (ISBN 0-317-42020-8, 2025688). Bks Demand UMI.

Federn, Karl. Richelieu. LC 72-132440. (World History Ser., No. 48). 1970. Repr. of 1928 ed. lib. bdg. 38.95x (ISBN 0-8383-1222-5). Haskell.

Lodge, Richard. Richelieu. LC 77-112812. 1970. Repr. of 1896 ed. 23.00x (ISBN 0-8046-1079-7, Pub. by Kennikat). Assoc Faculty Pr.

Marvick, Elizabeth W. The Young Richelieu: A Psychoanalytic Approach to Leadership. LC 82-24754. (Orig.). 1983. 32.00x (ISBN 0-226-50904-4); pap. 14.00x (ISBN 0-226-50905-2). U of Chicago Pr.

Perkins, James B. Richelieu & the Growth of French Power. 359p. 1982. Repr. of 1900 ed. lib. bdg. 40.00 (ISBN 0-89984-826-5). Century Bookbindery.

Wedgwood, Cicely V. Richelieu & the French Monarchy. 1962. pap. 4.95 (ISBN 0-02-038240-5, Collier). Macmillan.

RIGHT AND WRONG

Mackie, J. L. Ethics: Inventing Right & Wrong. 1977. pap. 6.95 (ISBN 0-14-021957-9, Pelican). Penguin.

Mayo, Bernard. The Philosophy of Right & Wrong. 176p. 1986. 22.95 (ISBN 0-7102-0851-0, 08510); pap. 12.95 (ISBN 0-7102-0859-6, 08596). Methuen Inc.

RIGHT TO DIE

see also Euthanasia; Suicide

Ogg, Elizabeth. Facing Death & Loss. LC 85-51126. 106p. 1985. pap. 19.00 (ISBN 0-87762-423-2). Technomic.

Sherlock, Richard. Preserving Life: Public Policy & the Life Not Worth Living. LC 86-21347. 1987. 15.95 (ISBN 0-8294-0526-7). Loyola.

Society for the Right to Die. Handbook of Living Will Laws 1976-1980. rev. ed. Orig. Title: Handbook of Enacted Laws 1981 Handbook. 64p. pap. cancelled (ISBN 0-9613825-3-8). Soc Right to Die.

--Handbook of 1985 Living Will Laws. 128p. (Orig.). 1986. pap. 5.00x (ISBN 0-9613825-2-X). Soc Right to Die.

RIGHTS, NATURAL

see Natural Law

RIPLEY, GEORGE, 1802-1880

Frothingham, Octavius B. George Ripley. LC 75-101910. Repr. of 1883 ed. 24.50 (ISBN 0-404-02625-7). AMS Pr.

RIPON, TREATY OF, 1640

Borough, John. Notes of the Treaty Carried on at Ripon Between King Charles First & the Covenanters of Scotland, A. D. 1640. Bruce, John, ed. (Camden Society, London. Publications, First Ser.: No. 100). Repr. of 1869 ed. 19.00 (ISBN 0-404-50200-8). AMS Pr.

--Notes of the Treaty Carried on at Ripon Between King Charles First & the Covenanters of Scotland, A. D. 1640. 1869. 19.00 (ISBN 0-384-05145-6). Johnson Repr.

RITA DE CASCIA, SAINT, 1381-1457

Daughters of St. Paul. St. Rita of Cascia: Saint of the Impossible. LC 73-91992. 1973. 3.95 (ISBN 0-8198-0335-9). Dghtrs St Paul.

RITES AND CEREMONIES

see also Agape; Baptism; Birth (In Religion, Folk-Lore, etc.); Canonization; Confirmation; Cultus; Dancing (In Religion, Folk-Lore, etc.); Fasts and Feasts; Funeral Rites and Ceremonies; Initiations (In Religion, Folk-Lore, etc.); Marriage Customs and Rites; Mourning Customs; Mysteries, Religious; Ordination; Purity, Ritual; Ritual; Sacraments; Secret Societies; Taboo

also subdivision Ceremonies and Practices under subjects, e.g. Catholic Church–Ceremonies and Practice

Bateson, Gregory. Naven: A Survey of the Problems Suggested by a Composite Picture of the Culture of a New Guinea Tribe Drawn from Three Points of View. 2nd ed. (Illus.). 1958. 25.00x (ISBN 0-8047-0519-4); pap. 10.95 (ISBN 0-8047-0520-8). Stanford U Pr.

Brigham, Amariah. Observations on the Influence of Religion upon the Health & Physical Welfare of Mankind. LC 73-2389. (Mental Illness & Social Policy; the American Experience Ser.). Repr. of 1835 ed. 21.00 (ISBN 0-405-05197-2). Ayer Co Pubs.

Buckland, Raymond. Practical Candle-Burning Rituals. (Illus.). 189p. 1984. pap. 5.95 (ISBN 0-87542-048-6). Llewellyn Pubns.

Burl, Aubrey. Rites of the Gods. (Illus.). 272p. 1981. text ed. 26.50x (ISBN 0-460-04313-7, BKA 04660, Pub. by J M Dent England). Biblio Dist.

Crotty, Robert & Ryan, John B. Commentaries on the Readings of the Rites. (Orig.). 1982. pap. 12.95 (ISBN 0-916134-45-8). Pueblo Pub Co.

David, A. R. A Guide to Religious Ritual at Abydos. 182p. 1981. pap. text ed. 40.00x (ISBN 0-85668-060-5, Pub. by Aris & Phillips UK). Humanities.

DeGidio, Sandra. R. C. I. A: The Rites Revisited. 144p. (Orig.). 1984. pap. 7.95 (ISBN 0-86683-837-6, 8436, HarpR). Har-Row.

Edgar, James & Edgar, Ellen. A Chrismon Service. 20p. 1981. pap. text ed. 2.95 (ISBN 0-89536-500-6, 0341). CSS of Ohio.

Fischer, Balthasar. Signs, Words & Gestures. O'Connell, Matthew J., tr. from Ger. 1981. pap. 5.95 (ISBN 0-916134-48-2). Pueblo Pub Co.

Fisher, Constance L. Music & Dance: In the Worship Program of the Church. (Orig.). 1981. pap. 2.50 (ISBN 0-941500-20-9). Sharing Co.

Fitch, Ed & Renee, Janine. Magical Rites from the Crystal Well. Weschcke, Carl L., ed. LC 83-80134. (Practical Magick Ser.). (Illus.). 166p. 1984. pap. 9.95 (ISBN 0-87542-230-6, L-230). Llewellyn Pubns.

Fried, Martha N. & Fried, Morton H. Transitions: Four Rituals in Eight Cultures. 1980. 14.95 (ISBN 0-393-01350-2). Norton.

Gonzalez-Wippler, Migene. The Complete Book of Spells, Ceremonies, & Magic. (Illus.). 1977. 12.95 (ISBN 0-517-52885-1). Crown.

Grainger, Roger. The Language of the Rite. 192p. 1984. pap. 8.95 (ISBN 0-232-51246-9). Chr Classics.

Grimes, Ronald L. Research in Ritual Studies: A Programmatic Essay & Bibliography. LC 84-23474. (ATLA Bibliography Ser.: No. 14). 177p. 1985. 15.00 (ISBN 0-8108-1762-4). Scarecrow.

Heesterman, J. C. Ancient Indian Royal Consecration: The Rajasuya Described According to the Yajus Texts & Annotated. (Disputationes Rheno-Trajectinae Ser: No. 2). (Orig.). 1957. pap. text ed. 25.60x (ISBN 90-2790-028-0). Mouton.

James, Edwin O. Christian Myth & Ritual: A Historical Study. 11.25 (ISBN 0-8446-2307-5). Peter Smith.

Jules-Rosette, Bennetta. African Apostles: Ritual & Conversion in the Church of John Maranke. LC 75-8437. (Symbol, Myth & Ritual Ser.). (Illus.). 352p. 1975. 34.50x (ISBN 0-8014-0846-6). Cornell U Pr.

Kavanaugh, Aidan. Elements of Rite. LC 84-158728. 110p. (Orig.). 1982. pap. 7.95 (ISBN 0-916134-54-7). Pueblo Pub CO.

Kirk, Martha A. Mexican & Native American Dances in Christian Worship & Education. Adams, Doug, ed. (Orig.). 1981. pap. 3.00 (ISBN 0-941500-22-5). Sharing Co.

Lane, Christel. The Rites of Rulers: Ritual in Industrial Society-the Soviet Case. LC 80-41747. (Illus.). 338p. 1981. 57.50 (ISBN 0-521-22608-2); pap. 18.95 (ISBN 0-521-28347-7). Cambridge U Pr.

Lang, Andrew. Myth, Ritual & Religion, 2 Vols in 1. LC 68-54280. Repr. of 1906 ed. 35.00 (ISBN 0-404-03868-9). AMS Pr.

MacCormack, Sabine. Art & Ceremony in Late Antiquity. (The Transformation of the Classical Heritage Ser.: Vol. 1). (Illus.). 450p. 1981. 45.00x (ISBN 0-520-03779-0). U of Cal Pr.

MacLeod, Marian B. Dancing Through Pentecost: Dance Language for Worship from Pentecost to Thanksgiving. Adams, Doug, ed. (Orig.). 1981. pap. 3.00 (ISBN 0-941500-23-3). Sharing Co.

Meekins, Inez P. Meekins' Ceremonies. 48p. 1981. soft cover 3.00 (ISBN 0-88053-326-9). Macoy Pub.

Moore, Sally F. & Myerhoff, Barbara G., eds. Secular Ritual: A Working Definition of Ritual. 306p. 1977. text ed. 32.00 (ISBN 90-232-1457-9, Pub. by Van Gorcum Holland). Longwood Pub Group.

Nevins, Albert J. Called to Serve: A Guidebook for Altar Servers. LC 81-82546. 48p. 1981. pap. 13.95 pkg. of six (ISBN 0-87973-663-1, 663). Our Sunday Visitor.

Ode, James. Brass Instruments in Church Services. 1970. pap. 3.00 (ISBN 0-8066-1025-5, 11-9085). Augsburg.

Pfatteicher, Philip H. Commentary on the Occasional Services. LC 82-48542. 336p. 1983. 19.95 (ISBN 0-8006-0697-3, 1-1697). Fortress.

Regardie, Israel. Ceremonial Magic: A Guide to the Mechanism of Ritual. LC 86-18389. 176p. 1986. lib. bdg. 19.95x (ISBN 0-8095-7013-0). Borgo Pr.

Reik, Theodore. Ritual. pap. text ed. 19.95 (ISBN 0-8236-8269-2, 025840). Intl Univs Pr.

Rubel, Paula G. & Rosman, Abraham. Your Own Pigs You May Not Eat. LC 78-7544. (Illus.). 1978. lib. bdg. 30.00x (ISBN 0-226-73082-4). U of Chicago Pr.

Schieffelin, Edward L. The Sorrow of the Lonely & the Burning of the Dancers. LC 75-10999. (Illus.). 256p. 1975. pap. text ed. 9.95 (ISBN 0-312-74550-8). St Martin.

Shannon-Thornberry, Milo, ed. The Alternate Celebrations Catalogue. LC 82-3638. (Illus.). 192p. 1982. pap. 8.95 (ISBN 0-8298-0601-6). Pilgrim NY.

Shariati, Ali. Hajj. 2nd ed. Behzadnia, A., tr. from Persian. 162p. 1978. pap. 4.95 (ISBN 0-941722-09-0). Book-Dist-Ctr.

Taussig, Hal. The Lady of the Dance: A Movement Approach to the Biblical Figures of Wisdom in Worship & Education. (Orig.). 1981. pap. 2.50 (ISBN 0-941500-24-1). Sharing Co.

--New Categories for Dancing: The Old Testament. (Orig.). 1981. pap. 2.50 (ISBN 0-941500-25-X). Sharing Co.

Thompson, Robert. The Feasts of the Lord. pap. 5.95 (ISBN 0-89728-029-6, 645571). Omega Pubns OR.

Toy, Crawford H. Introduction to the History of Religions. LC 76-126655. Repr. of 1913 ed. 27.50 (ISBN 0-404-06498-1). AMS Pr.

Valeri, Valerio. Kingship & Sacrifice: Ritual & Society in Ancient Hawaii. Wissing, Paula, tr. from Hawaiian. LC 84-23991. (Fr. & Eng., Illus.). 392p. 1985. lib. bdg. 55.00x (ISBN 0-226-84559-1); pap. text ed. 22.50x (ISBN 0-226-84560-5). U of Chicago Pr.

Volkman, Toby A. Feasts of Honor: Ritual & Change in the Toraja Highlands. LC 84-16123. (Illinois Studies in Anthropology). (Illus.). 234p. 1985. pap. 21.50 (ISBN 0-252-01183-X). U of Ill Pr.

White, Nelson & White, Anne. Index & Reference Volume to the Lemegeton of Solomon (1979 White Transcription of Sloane 2731) LC 80-52052. 75p. (Orig.). 1980. pap. 15.00 (ISBN 0-939856-07-7). Tech Group.

--Selected Conjurations from the Lemegeton (& Other Sources) large type ed. LC 81-51403. 50p. (Orig.). 1981. pap. 10.00 (ISBN 0-939856-16-6). Tech Group.

White, Nelson & White, Anne, eds. Lemegeton, Clavicula Salomonis: Or the Complete Lesser Key of Solomon the King. rev ed. LC 79-91961. (Illus.). 130p. (Orig.). 1979. pap. 30.00 (ISBN 0-939856-06-9). Tech Group.

Williams, Francis E. The Vailala Madness & the Destruction of Native Ceremonies in the Gulf Division. LC 75-35166. (Territory of Papua. Anthropological Report: No. 4). Repr. of 1923 ed. 20.00 (ISBN 0-404-14180-3). AMS Pr.

Zaccaria, Francesco A. Bibliotheca Ritualis, 2 vols. in 3. 1964. Repr. of 1781 ed. Set. 106.00 (ISBN 0-8337-3913-1). B Franklin.

RITES AND CEREMONIES–INDIANS

see Indians of North America–Rites and Ceremonies

RITES AND CEREMONIES–JEWS

see Jews–Rites and Ceremonies

RITUAL

see also Liturgics; Liturgies; Rites and Ceremonies;

also subdivision Rituals under names of religions and religious denominations, e.g. Buddhism–rituals; and under the heading Secret societies, and names of specific secret societies

Abbott, J. Indian Ritual & Belief. Orig. Title: Keys of Power: A Study of Indian Religion & Ritual. 1985. Repr. of 1932 ed. 40.00x (ISBN 0-8364-1294-X, Pub. by Usha). South Asia Bks.

Ashcroft-Nowicki, Dolores. First Steps in Ritual: Safe, Effective Techniques for Experiencing the Inner Worlds. LC 86-18829. 176p. 1986. lib. bdg. 19.95x (ISBN 0-8095-7010-6). Borgo Pr.

Barth, Fredrik. Ritual & Knowledge among the Baktaman of New Guinea. LC 74-19572. (Illus.). pap. 74.00 (ISBN 0-317-11336-4, 2021979). Bks Demand UMI.

Collins, Patrick W. More Than Meets the Eye: Ritual & Parish Liturgy. LC 82-62920. 160p. (Orig.). 1983. pap. 6.95 (ISBN 0-8091-2539-0). Paulist Pr.

D'Aquili, Eugene G., et al. The Spectrum of Ritual: A Biogenetic Structural Analysis. LC 78-19015. 408p. 1979. 35.00x (ISBN 0-231-04514-X). Columbia U Pr.

Dean, Beryl. Embroidery in Religion & Ceremonial. (Illus.). 288p. 1985. pap. 16.50 (ISBN 0-7134-3325-6). Branford.

De Coppens, Peter R. The Nature & Use of Ritual. 1977. pap. text ed. 9.75 (ISBN 0-8191-0341-1). U Pr of Amer.

Farra, L. Genesis Seven. 1987. 8.95 (ISBN 0-533-07034-1). Vantage.

Gay, Volney P. Freud on Ritual: Reconstruction & Critique. LC 79-11385. (American Academy of Religion, Dissertation Ser.: No. 26). 1979. 14.00 (ISBN 0-89130-282-4, 010126); pap. 9.95 (ISBN 0-89130-301-4). Scholars Pr Ga.

Grainger, Roger. The Language of the Rite. 192p. 1984. pap. 8.95 (ISBN 0-232-51246-9). Chr Classics.

Grim, John A. The Shaman: Patterns of Siberian & Ojibway Healing. LC 83-47834. (Civilization of the American Indian Ser.: Vol. 165). (Illus.). 264p. 1983. pap. 19.95 (ISBN 0-8061-1809-1). U of Okla Pr.

Grimes, Ronald L. Beginnings in Ritual Studies. LC 81-40521. 312p. (Orig.). 1982. lib. bdg. 32.00 (ISBN 0-8191-2210-6); pap. text ed. 14.00 (ISBN 0-8191-2211-4). U Pr of Amer.

--Research in Ritual Studies: A Programmatic Essay & Bibliography. LC 84-23474. (ATLA Bibliography Ser.: No. 14). 177p. 1985. 15.00 (ISBN 0-8108-1762-4). Scarecrow.

Hamerton-Kelly, Robert G., ed. Violent Origins: Walter Burkert, Rene Girard, & Jonathan Z. Smith on Ritual Killing & Cultural Formation. LC 86-23009. 296p. 1987. 32.50x (ISBN 0-8047-1370-7). Stanford U Pr.

Highfield, A. C. Book of Celestial Images: Angelic & Godform Images in Ritual Magic. LC 86-16209. 192p. 1986. lib. bdg. 19.95 (ISBN 0-8095-7004-1). Borgo Pr.

Monter, William. Ritual, Myth & Magic in Early Modern Europe. LC 83-43136. (Illus.). viii, 184p. 1984. cloth 24.95x (ISBN 0-8214-0762-7). Ohio U Pr.

Paige, Karen E. & Paige, Jeffrey M. The Politics of Reproductive Ritual. 392p. 1981. 31.00x (ISBN 0-520-03071-0); pap. 8.95 (ISBN 0-520-04782-6, CAL 572). U of Cal Pr.

Ramshaw, Elaine. Ritual & Pastoral Care. LC 85-45487. (Theology and Pastoral Care Ser.). 128p. 1987. pap. 7.95 (ISBN 0-8006-1738-X). Fortress.

Roche de Coppens, Peter. The Nature & Use of Ritual for Spiritual Attainment. Rossner, John, ed. LC 85-10270. (Llewellyn's Spiritual Perspectives Ser.). (Illus.). 250p. (Orig.). 1985. pap. 9.95 (ISBN 0-87542-675-1, L-675). Llewellyn Pubns.

Sinding-Larsen, Staale. Iconography & Ritual: A Study of Analytical Perspectives. 260p. 1985. 30.00x (ISBN 82-00-07184-7). Oxford U Pr.

Tambiah, J. A Performative Approach to Ritual. (Radcliffe-Brown Lectures in Social Anthropology). 1978. pap. 3.75 (ISBN 0-85672-197-2, Pub. by British Acad). Longwood Pub Group.

Teish, Luisah. Jambalaya: The Natural Woman's Book of Personal Charms & Practical Rituals. LC 85-42793. (Illus.). 240p. 1985. 15.95 (ISBN 0-06-250860-1, HarpR). Har-Row.

Traube, Elizabeth G. Cosmology & Social Life: Ritual Exchange Among the Mambai of East Timor. (Illus.). 312p. 1987. text ed. 32.00x (ISBN 0-226-81149-2); pap. text ed. 14.95x (ISBN 0-226-81150-6). U of Chicago Pr.

Volkman, Toby A. Feasts of Honor: Ritual & Change in the Toraja Highlands. LC 84-16123. (Illinois Studies in Anthropology). (Illus.). 234p. 1985. pap. 21.50 (ISBN 0-252-01183-X). U of Ill Pr.

Wilson, David A. The Dance of the Rites. (Illus.). 156p. (Orig.). 1983. cancelled 13.00 (ISBN 0-934852-96-0); pap. 7.00 (ISBN 0-934852-27-8). Lorien Hse.

ROBBIA, LUCA DELLA, 1400-1482

Crutwell, Maud. Luca & Andrea Della Robbia. LC 79-155625. (Illus.). Repr. of 1902 ed. 29.50 (ISBN 0-404-01869-6). AMS Pr.

Pope-Hennessy, John. Luca della Robbia. LC 79-13566. (Illus.). 282p. 1980. 125.00x (ISBN 0-8014-1256-0). Cornell U Pr.

ROBERTSON, PAT

Eskelin, Neil. Pat Robertson: A Biography. 192p. (Orig.). 1987. pap. 7.95 (ISBN 0-910311-47-1). Huntington Hse Inc.

Robertson, Pat & Buckingham, Jamie. Shout It from the Housetops: The Story of the Founder of the Christian Broadcasting Network. LC 72-76591. 248p. 1972. pap. 3.95 (ISBN 0-88270-097-9). Bridge Pub.

ROBINSON, JOHN, 1575-1625

Burrage, Champlin, ed. Answer to John Robinson of Leyden by a Puritan Friend. (Harvard Theological Studies). 1920. pap. 15.00 (ISBN 0-527-01009-X). Kraus Repr.

George, Timothy F. John Robinson & the English Separatist Tradition. LC 82-14201. (National Association of Baptist Professors of Religion Dissertation Ser.: No. 1). ix, 263p. 1982. text ed. 18.50 (ISBN 0-86554-043-8, MUP-P006). Mercer Univ Pr.

--John Robinson & the English Separatist Tradition. (Dissertation Ser.: No. 1). ix, 263p. 1982. pap. 18.50 (ISBN 0-86554-043-8). NABPR.

Plooij, D. Pilgrim Fathers from a Dutch Point of View. LC 71-100509. Repr. of 1932 ed. 8.50 (ISBN 0-404-05065-4). AMS Pr.

ROCK-TOMBS

see Tombs

ROCKWELL, ORRIN PORTER, 1813-1878

Schindler, Harold. Orrin Porter Rockwell: Man of God, Son of Thunder. 2nd ed. (University of Utah Publications in the American West: Vol. 15). (Illus.). 1983. 24.95 (ISBN 0-87480-204-0). U of Utah Pr.

Van Alfen, Nicholas. Orrin Porter Rockwell, Mormon Frontier Marshall. 72p. pap. 3.95 (ISBN 0-87747-468-0). Deseret Bk.

ROCOCO ARCHITECTURE

see Architecture, Rococo

ROGERS, DALE EVANS

Rogers, Dale E. God in the Hard Times. LC 85-10479. 160p. 1985. pap. 8.95 (ISBN 0-8027-2516-3). Walker & Co.

ROLFE, FREDERICK WILLIAM, 1860-1913

Woolf, Cecil & Sewell, Brocard, eds. New Quests for Corvo: A Collection of Essays. 1961. 6.95 (ISBN 0-685-09185-6); pap. 3.00 (ISBN 0-685-09186-4). Dufour.

ROLLE, RICHARD, OF HAMPOLE, 1290-1349

Allen, Hope E. Writings Ascribed to Richard Rolle, Hermit of Hampole & Materials for His Biography. (MLA. MS Ser.). 1927. 44.00 (ISBN 0-527-01280-7). Kraus Repr.

Arntz, Mary Luke. Richard Rolle & de Holy Boke Gratia Dei: An Edition with Commentary. Hogg, James, ed. (Elizabethan & Renaissance Studies). 207p. (Orig.). 1981. pap. 15.00 (ISBN 3-7052-0743-1, Pub. by Salzburg Studies). Longwood Pub Group.

Boenig, Robert. Biblical Commentaries by Richard Rolle. Hogg, James, ed. (Elizabethan & Renaissance Studies). (Orig.). 1984. pap. 15.00 (ISBN 0-317-40122-X, Pub. by Salzburg Studies). Longwood Pub Group.

Daly, John P. An Edition of the Judica Me Deus of Richard Rolle. Hogg, James, ed. (Elizabethan & Renaissance Studies). (Orig.). 1984. pap. 15.00 (ISBN 0-317-40134-3, Pub by Salzburg Studies). Longwood Pub Group.

Horstman, C. Yorkshire Writers, Richard Rolle of Hampole, 2 vols. 1979. Repr. of 1895 ed. Set. lib. bdg. 400.00 (ISBN 0-8492-5264-4). R West.

Madigan, Mary F. The Passio Domini Theme in the Works of Richard Rolle: His Personal Contribution in Its Religeous Cultural, & Literary Context. Hogg, James, ed. (Elizabethan & Renaissance Studies). 347p. (Orig.). 1978. pap. 15.00 (ISBN 3-7052-0723-7, Pub. by Salzburg Studies). Longwood Pub Group.

Moyes, Malcolm. Richard Rolle's Expositio Super Novem Lectiones Mortuorum. Hogg, James, ed. (Elizabethan & Renaissance Studies). (Orig.). 1984. pap. 15.00 (ISBN 3-7052-0753-9, Pub. by Salzburg Studies). Longwood Pub Group.

Rolle, Richard. The Contra Amatores Mundi of Richard Rolle of Hampole. Theiner, Paul F., ed. LC 68-64641. 196p. 1983. Repr. of 1968 ed. lib. bdg. 19.95x (ISBN 0-89370-791-0). Borgo Pr.

--The Fire of Love & the Mending of Life. Comper, Francis M., ed. Misyn, Richard, tr. 1920. Repr. 25.00 (ISBN 0-8274-2346-2). R West.

ROMAN ANTIQUITIES

see Classical Antiquities; Rome (City)–Antiquities

ROMAN ARCHITECTURE

see Architecture, Roman

ROMAN CATHOLIC CHURCH

see Catholic Church

ROMAN CULTUS

see Cultus, Roman

ROMAN EMPERORS

Altmann, Walter. Die Romischen Grabaltare der Kaiserzeit. facsimile ed. LC 75-10626. (Ancient Religion & Mythology Ser.). (Ger., Illus.). 1975. Repr. of 1905 ed. 26.50x (ISBN 0-405-07002-0). Ayer Co Pubs.

Fears, J. R. Princeps a Diis Electus: The Divine Election of the Emperor as a Political Concept at Rome. 353p. 1977. 38.00x (ISBN 0-271-00474-6). Pa St U Pr.

Price, S. R. Rituals & Power: The Roman Imperial Cult in Asia Minor. (Illus.). 316p. 1986. pap. 14.95 (ISBN 0-521-31268-X). Cambridge U Pr.

Setton, Kenneth M. Christian Attitudes Towards the Emperor in the Fourth Century. LC 41-13567. (Columbia University. Studies in Social Sciences: No. 482). Repr. of 1941 ed. 20.00 (ISBN 0-404-51482-0). AMS Pr.

Taylor, Lily R. The Divinity of the Roman Emperor. LC 75-31647. xv, 296p. 1975. Repr. of 1931 ed. lib. bdg. 27.50x (ISBN 0-87991-606-0). Porcupine Pr.

Warmington, E. H., ed. Scriptores Historiae Augustae, 3 vols. Magie, D., tr. (Loeb Classical Library: No. 139-140, 263). (Lat. & Eng.). 13.95x ea.; Vol. 1. (ISBN 0-674-99154-0); Vol. 2. (ISBN 0-674-99155-9); Vol. 3. (ISBN 0-674-99290-3). Harvard U Pr.

ROMAN PHILOSOPHY

see Philosophy, Ancient

ROMAN QUESTION

Here are entered works dealing with the position of the Pope in relation to Italy.

Halperin, S. William. Separation of Church & State in Italian Thought from Cavour to Mussolini. LC 71-120623. 1970. Repr. lib. bdg. 15.00x (ISBN 0-374-93412-6, Octagon). Hippocrene Bks.

Halperin, Samuel W. Italy & the Vatican at War: A Study of Their Relations from the Outbreak of the Franco-Prussian War to the Death of Pius 9th. LC 68-57606. (Illus.). 1968. Repr. of 1939 ed. lib. bdg. 22.50x (ISBN 0-8371-0461-0, HAIV). Greenwood.

ROMANESQUE SCULPTURE

see Sculpture, Romanesque

ROMANTICISM

Abrams, M. H. Natural Supernaturalism: Tradition & Revolution in Romantic Literature. 550p. 1973. pap. 11.95 (ISBN 0-393-00609-3). Norton.

Addison, Agnes. Romanticism & the Gothic Revival. 204p. 1967. Repr. of 1938 ed. 17.50x (ISBN 0-87752-000-3). Gordian.

Greenberg, Martin. The Hamlet Vocation of Coleridge & Wordsworth. LC 85-18189. 232p. 1986. 22.50x (ISBN 0-87745-131-1). U of Iowa Pr.

Jasper, David, ed. The Interpretation of Belief: Coleridge, Schleiermacher & Romanticism. LC 85-26204. 192p. 1986. 25.00x (ISBN 0-312-42401-9). St Martin.

Prickett, Stephen. Romanticism & Religion. LC 75-2254. 320p. 1976. 49.50 (ISBN 0-521-21072-0). Cambridge U Pr.

Reardon, Bernard M. Religion in the Age of Romanticism: Studies in Early Nineteenth Century Thought. 320p. 1985. 39.50 (ISBN 0-521-30088-6); pap. 14.95 (ISBN 0-521-31745-2). Cambridge U Pr.

ROMANTICISM IN ART

Penny, Nicholas. Church Monuments in Romantic England. LC 76-58912. (Studies in British Art). (Illus.). 1977. 47.00x (ISBN 0-300-02075-9). Yale U Pr.

ROME–CIVILIZATION

Angus, S. The Environment of Early Christianity. 1977. lib. bdg. 59.95 (ISBN 0-8490-1778-5). Gordon Pr.

Angus, Samuel. The Environment of Early Christianity. facsimile ed. LC 75-157322. (Select Bibliographies Reprint Ser). Repr. of 1915 ed. 17.00 (ISBN 0-8369-5781-4). Ayer Co Pubs.

Durant, Will. Caesar & Christ: A History of Roman Civilization from Its Beginnings to A.D. 337. (Story of Civilization: Vol. 3). 1944. 29.95 (ISBN 0-671-11500-6). S&S.

Franzmann, Martin H. Romans. 288p. 1986. pap. 8.95 (ISBN 0-570-04426-X, 12-3036). Concordia.

Grenier, Albert. Roman Spirit in Religion, Thought & Art. Dobie, M. R., tr. LC 76-118639. (Illus.). 423p. 1970. Repr. of 1926 ed. lib. bdg. 32.50x (ISBN 0-8154-0330-5). Cooper Sq.

--The Roman Spirit in Religion, Thought & Art. (Illus.). 423p. 1986. Repr. of 1926 ed. lib. bdg. 100.00 (ISBN 0-89760-448-2). Telegraph Bks.

Palmer, Robert E. Roman Religion & Roman Empire: Five Essays. LC 73-89289. (Haney Foundation Ser.: No. 15). Repr. of 1974 ed. 36.40 (2055281). Bks Demand UMI.

Tucker, T. G. Life in the Roman World of Nero & St. Paul. 1924. 45.00 (ISBN 0-8274-3984-9). R West.

ROME–HISTORY–EMPIRE, 30 B.C.-476 A.D.

Benko, Stephen. Pagan Rome & the Early Christians. LC 83-48898. (Midland Books Ser.: no. 385). 192p. 1986. pap. 7.95x (ISBN 0-253-20385-6). Ind U Pr.

Croke, B. F. & Harris, J. D. Religious Conflict in Fourth Century Rome. (Sources in Ancient History Ser.). 139p. (Orig.). 1982. pap. 21.00x (ISBN 0-424-00091-1, Pub. by Sydney U Pr Australia). Intl Spec Bk.

Huttl, Willy. Antoninus Pius. LC 75-7326. (Roman History Ser.). (Ger.). 1975. Repr. 57.00x (ISBN 0-405-07089-6). Ayer Co Pubs.

MacMullen, Ramsay. Paganism in the Roman Empire. LC 80-54222. 384p. 1981. 30.00x (ISBN 0-300-02655-2); pap. text ed. 8.95x (ISBN 0-300-02984-5). Yale U Pr.

Warmington, E. H., ed. Scriptores Historiae Augustae, 3 vols. Magie, D., tr. (Loeb Classical Library: No. 139-140, 263). (Lat. & Eng.). 13.95x ea.; Vol. 1. (ISBN 0-674-99154-0); Vol. 2. (ISBN 0-674-99155-9); Vol. 3. (ISBN 0-674-99290-3). Harvard U Pr.

Westbury-Jones, John. Roman & Christian Imperialism. LC 78-118555. 1971. Repr. of 1939 ed. 28.00x (ISBN 0-8046-1180-7, Pub. by Kennikat). Assoc Faculty Pr.

ROME–RELIGION

Angus, S. The Religious Quests of the Graeco-Roman World. 1929. 30.00 (ISBN 0-686-20108-6). Quality Lib.

Appel, Georgius. De Romanorum Precationibus. facsimile ed. LC 75-10628. (Ancient Religion & Mythology Ser.). 1976. Repr. of 1909 ed. 18.00x (ISBN 0-405-07004-7). Ayer Co Pubs.

Armstrong, A. H., ed. Classical Mediterranean Spirituality. (World Spirituality Ser.). 499p. 1986. 49.50x (ISBN 0-8245-0764-9). Crossroad NY.

Bailey, Cyril. Phases in the Religion of Ancient Rome. LC 75-114460. 340p. 1972. Repr. of 1932 ed. lib. bdg. 22.50x (ISBN 0-8371-4759-X, BARA). Greenwood.

Barnes, Arthur S. Christianity at Rome in the Apostolic Age. LC 72-114462. (Illus.). 1971. Repr. of 1938 ed. lib. bdg. 55.00x (ISBN 0-8371-4760-3, BACR). Greenwood.

Benko, Stephen. Pagan Rome & the Early Christians. LC 83-48898. 192p. 1985. 20.00x (ISBN 0-253-34286-4). Ind U Pr.

Bouche-Leclercq, Auguste. Les Pontifes de L'Ancienne Rome: Etudes Historique sur les Institutions Religieuses de Rome. facsimile ed. LC 75-10630. (Ancient Religion & Mythology Ser.). (Fr.). 1976. Repr. of 1871 ed. 33.00x (ISBN 0-405-07006-3). Ayer Co Pubs.

Brown, Raymond E. & Meier, John. Antioch & Rome: New Testament Cradles of Catholic Christianity. 256p. 1983. pap. 5.95 (ISBN 0-8091-2532-3). Paulist Pr.

Burriss, Eli E. Taboo, Magic, Spirits: A Study of Primitive Elements in Roman Religion. LC 72-114489. x, 250p. Repr. of 1931 ed. lib. bdg. 22.50x (ISBN 0-8371-4724-7, BUTA). Greenwood.

Carter, Jesse B. Religious Life of Ancient Rome. 270p. 1972. Repr. of 1911 ed. lib. bdg. 27.50x (ISBN 0-8154-0429-8). Cooper Sq.

Cumont, Franz. Astrology & Religion among the Greeks & Romans. 1912. pap. 3.50 (ISBN 0-486-20581-9). Dover.

--The Mysteries of Mithra. 2nd ed. McCormack, Thomas J., tr. (Illus., Fr). 1911. pap. 5.95 (ISBN 0-486-20323-9). Dover.

--Mysteries of Mithra. (Illus.). 14.00 (ISBN 0-8446-1926-4). Peter Smith.

--Oriental Religions in Roman Paganism. 1911. pap. 5.95 (ISBN 0-486-20321-2). Dover.

--Oriental Religions in Roman Paganism. 14.00 (ISBN 0-8446-1925-6). Peter Smith.

De Marchi, Attilio. Il Culto Privato di Roma Antica, 2 vols. in 1. facsimile ed. LC 75-10641. (Ancient Religion & Mythology Ser.). (Ital., Illus.). 1976. Repr. 40.00x (ISBN 0-405-07011-X). Ayer Co Pubs.

De Rebecque, Constant & Benjamin, Henri. Dupolytheisme Romain: Considere dans ses rapports avec la philosophie grecque et la religion chertienne. Bolle, Kees W., ed. LC 77-79118. (Mythology Ser.). (Fr.). 1978. Repr. of 1833 ed. lib. bdg. 59.50 (ISBN 0-405-10530-4). Ayer Co Pubs.

Dill, S. Roman Society in the Last Century of Western Empire. 75.00 (ISBN 0-87968-060-1). Gordon Pr.

Dodds, E. R. Pagan & Christian in an Age of Anxiety: Some Aspects of Religious Experience from Marcus Aurelius to Constantine. 1970. pap. 5.95 (ISBN 0-393-00545-3, Norton Lib). Norton.

Du Choul, Guillaume. Discours de la Religion des Anciens Romains Illustre. LC 75-27851. (Renaissance & the Gods Ser.: Vol. 9). (Illus.). 1976. Repr. of 1556 ed. lib. bdg. 88.00 (ISBN 0-8240-2058-8). Garland Pub.

Dumezil, Georges. Archaic Roman Religion, 2 Vols. Krapp, Philip, tr. from Fr. LC 76-116981. 1971. Set. 45.00x (ISBN 0-226-16968-5). U of Chicago Pr.

Ferguson, John. The Religions of the Roman Empire. LC 71-110992. (Aspects of Greek & Roman Life Ser.). (Illus.). 296p. (Orig.). 1985. 29.95x (ISBN 0-8014-0567-X); pap. text ed. 8.95x (ISBN 0-8014-9311-0). Cornell U Pr.

Fowler, William W. Roman Ideas of Deity in the Last Century Before the Christian Era. LC 75-102236. (Select Bibliographies Reprint Ser). 1914. 19.00 (ISBN 0-8369-5121-2). Ayer Co Pubs.

Grenier, Albert. Roman Spirit in Religion, Thought & Art. Dobie, M. R., tr. LC 76-118639. (Illus.). 423p. 1970. Repr. of 1926 ed. lib. bdg. 32.50x (ISBN 0-8154-0330-5). Cooper Sq.

--The Roman Spirit in Religion, Thought & Art. (Illus.). 423p. 1986. Repr. of 1926 ed. lib. bdg. 100.00 (ISBN 0-89760-448-2). Telegraph Bks.

Henig, Martin. Religion in Roman Britain. LC 84-6914. 256p. 1984. 29.95 (ISBN 0-312-67059-1). St Martin.

Hinson, E. Glenn. The Evangelization of the Roman Empire: Identity & Adaptability. LC 81-11266. viii, 332p. 1981. 22.00 (ISBN 0-86554-244-9, MUP-P36). Mercer Univ Pr.

Kerenyi, Karoly. The Religion of the Greeks & Romans. LC 72-9823. (Illus.). 303p. 1973. Repr. of 1962 ed. lib. bdg. 24.75x (ISBN 0-8371-6605-5, KERG). Greenwood.

Laing, Gordon. Survivals of Roman Religion. LC 63-10280. (Our Debt to Greece & Rome Ser). 257p. 1963. Repr. of 1930 ed. 25.00x (ISBN 0-8154-0130-2). Cooper Sq.

Lewis, Martha W. The Official Priests of Rome under the Julio-Claudians: A Study of the Nobility from 44 B. C. to 68 A. D. LC 56-2111. (American Academy in Rome. Papers & Monographs: Vol. 16). pap. 48.00 (2026730). Bks Demand UMI.

Liebeschuetz, J. H. Continuity & Change in Roman Religion. 1979. text ed. 65.00x (ISBN 0-19-814822-4). Oxford U Pr.

Mancinelli, Fabrizio. Catacombs & Basilicas: The Early Christians in Rome. (Illus.). 65p. (Orig.). 1981. pap. 12.50 (ISBN 0-935748-13-X). Scala Books.

Massey, Michael. Roman Religion. Hodge, Peter, ed. (Aspects of Roman Life Ser.). 48p. (Orig.). 1979. pap. text ed. 4.40 (ISBN 0-582-21573-0). Longman.

Plutarch. The Roman Questions of Plutarch. facsimile ed. Rose, Herbert J., ed. LC 75-14267. (Ancient Religion & Mythology Ser.). 1976. Repr. of 1924 ed. 17.00x (ISBN 0-405-07272-4). Ayer Co Pubs.

Preibisch, P. Two Studies on the Roman Pontifices. LC 75-10647. (Ancient Religion & Mythology Ser.). 1976. 12.00x (ISBN 0-405-07271-6). Ayer Co Pubs.

Renan, Ernest. Lectures on the Influence of the Institutions, Thought & Culture of Rome, on Christianity & the Development of the Catholic Church. Beard, Charles, tr. LC 77-27170. (Hibbert Lectures: 1880). Repr. of 1898 ed. 24.50 (ISBN 0-404-60402-1). AMS Pr.

Rexine, John E. Religion in Plato & Cicero. LC 68-28581. 72p. Repr. of 1959 ed. lib. bdg. 22.50x (ISBN 0-8371-0198-0, RERP). Greenwood.

Segal, Alan F. Rebecca's Children: Judaism & Christianity in the Roman World. LC 85-17656. 216p. 1986. text ed. 20.00x (ISBN 0-674-75075-6). Harvard U Pr.

Smith, Robert C. & Lounibos, John, eds. Pagan & Christian Anxiety: A Response to E. R. Dodds. LC 83-27345. 248p. 1984. lib. bdg. 25.25 (ISBN 0-8191-3823-1); pap. text ed. 12.25 (ISBN 0-8191-3824-X). U Pr of Amer.

Strong, Eugenia. Apotheosis & after Life. facsimile ed. LC 78-103668. (Select Bibliographies Reprint Ser). 1915. 33.00 (ISBN 0-8369-5168-9). Ayer Co Pubs.

Von Domaszewski, Alfred. Abhandlungen Zur Romischen Religion. facsimile ed. LC 75-10633. (Ancient Religion & Mythology Ser.). (Ger., Illus.). 1976. Repr. of 1909 ed. 20.00x (ISBN 0-405-07008-X). Ayer Co Pubs.

--Die Religion Des Romischen Heeres. facsimile ed. LC 75-10634. (Ancient Religion & Mythology Ser.). (Ger., Illus.). 1976. Repr. of 1895 ed. 12.00 (ISBN 0-405-07012-8). Ayer Co Pubs.

Wagenvoort, Hendrik. Studies in Roman Literature, Culture & Religion. Commager, Steele, ed. LC 77-70817. (Latin Poetry Ser.: Vol. 31). 1978. lib. bdg. 40.00 (ISBN 0-8240-2981-X). Garland Pub.

Wardman, Alan. Religion & Statecraft among the Romans. LC 82-47928. pap. 55.80 (2026708). Bks Demand UMI.

Wissowa, Georg. Gesammelte Abhandlungen Zur Romischen Religions und Stadtgeschichte. facsimile ed. LC 75-10663. (Ancient Religion & Mythology Ser.). (Ger.). 1976. Repr. of 1904 ed. 25.50x (ISBN 0-405-07279-1). Ayer Co Pubs.

ROME (CITY)–ANTIQUITIES

Lanciani, Rodolfo. Pagan & Christian Rome. LC 67-23856. (Illus.). 1968. Repr. of 1892 ed. 27.50 (ISBN 0-405-08728-4, Blom Pubns). Ayer Co Pubs.

Toynbee, J. M. Death & Burial in the Roman World. Scullard, H. H., ed. LC 77-120603. (Aspects of Greek & Roman Life Ser). (Illus.). 336p. 1971. 35.00x (ISBN 0-8014-0593-9). Cornell U Pr.

ROME (CITY)–CHURCHES

Kirsch, Johann P. Roemischen Titelkirchen Im Altertum. 1918. 19.00 (ISBN 0-384-29614-9). Johnson Repr.

Phillips, Evelyn M. The Illustrated Guidebook to the Frescoes in the Sistine Chapel. (Illus.). 124p. 1981. Repr. of 1901 ed. 69.85 (ISBN 0-89901-029-6). Found Class Reprints.

ROME (CITY)–DESCRIPTION–GUIDEBOOKS

Rome & the Vatican in Color. (Sterling Travel Guide in Color Ser.). (Illus.). 140p. (Orig.). 1983. pap. 4.95 (ISBN 0-8069-1372-X). Sterling.

ROOD-LOFTS
see Church Architecture
ROSA OF LIMA, SAINT, 1586-1617
Kaye-Smith, Sheila. Quartet in Heaven. facs. ed. LC 75-136649. (Biography Index Reprint Ser.). 1952. 18.00 (ISBN 0-8369-8044-1). Ayer Co Pubs.
ROSAECRUCIANS
see Rosicrucians
ROSARY
Carberry, John. The Book of the Rosary. LC 83-62424. 120p. (Orig.). 1983. pap. 4.50 (ISBN 0-87973-610-0, 610). Our Sunday Visitor.
Christianica Center Staff. Scriptural Rosary. LC 64-66463. (Illus.). 1961. 5.95 (ISBN 0-911346-01-5). Christianica.
Cronin, Gaynell & Gaynell, Jim. The Rosary. 1978. 7.55 (ISBN 0-88479-018-5). Arena Lettres.
Daughters Of St. Paul. Sixteen Documents of Vatican Two. pap. 3.25 (ISBN 0-8198-0146-1). Dghtrs St Paul.
Daughters of St. Paul, compiled by. Scriptural Meditations on the Rosary. 1981. 3.50 (ISBN 0-8198-6814-0). Dghtrs St Paul.
De Monfort, St. Louis. The Secret of the Rosary. Barbour, Mary, tr. from Fr. 1976. pap. 1.00 (ISBN 0-89555-056-3). TAN Bks Pubs.
Dreves, Guido M., ed. Psalteria Rhythmica, 2 Vols. 1900-01. 60.00 ea. (ISBN 0-384-12960-9) (ISBN 0-384-12961-7). Johnson Repr.
Escriva de Balaguer, Josemaria. Holy Rosary. (Illus.). 49p. 1979. 5.95 (ISBN 0-933932-45-6); pap. 2.95 (ISBN 0-933932-44-8). Scepter Pubs.
Ferraro, John. Ten Series of Meditations on the Mysteries of the Rosary. (Illus., Orig.). 1964. 5.00 (ISBN 0-8198-0157-7); pap. 4.00 (ISBN 0-8198-0158-5). Dghtrs St Paul.
Habig, Marion A. Franciscan Crown Rosary. 1977. 3.00 (ISBN 0-8199-0605-0). Franciscan Herald.
Harrington, Wilfrid J. The Rosary: A Gospel Prayer. LC 75-44676. (Illus.). 160p. 1976. pap. 2.95 (ISBN 0-8189-1129-8, Pub. by Alba Bks). Alba.
Johnson, John S. The Rosary in Action. 1977. pap. 5.00 (ISBN 0-89555-023-7). TAN Bks Pubs.
Kepes, Joanne L. The Rosary. 1982. 9.95 (ISBN 0-89837-061-2, Pub. by Pflaum Pr). Peter Li.
Lelen, J. M. Pray the Rosary. (Illus., Purse-Size). blue bdg. 0.60 (ISBN 0-89942-040-0, 40/05). Catholic Bk Pub.
Llewelyn, Robert. A Doorway to Silence: The Contemplative Use of the Rosary. 96p. (Orig.). 1987. pap. 5.95 (ISBN 0-8091-2900-0). Paulist Pr.
Lovasik, Lawrence. Meditations on the Rosary. LC 82-72204. (Living Meditation & Prayerbook Ser.). (Illus.). 270p. (Orig.). 1985. pap. text ed. 5.00 (ISBN 0-932406-09-2). AFC.
Lovasik, Lawrence G. The Holy Rosary. (Saint Joseph Picture Bks.). (Illus.). flexible bdg. 0.95 (ISBN 0-89942-284-5, 284). Catholic Bk Pub.
Monks of Solesmes, ed. The Holy Rosary. 1980. 5.50 (ISBN 0-686-74345-8). Dghtrs St Paul.
Rosary Novenas. 1.80. Benziger Pub Co.
St. Louis De Montfort. Secret of the Rosary. pap. 1.00 (ISBN 0-910984-04-2). Montfort Pubns.
Seventeen Papal Documents on the Rosary. 1967. pap. 2.00 (ISBN 0-8198-0147-X). Dghtrs St Paul.
Von Balthasar, Hans Urs. The Threefold Garland: The World's Salvation in Mary's Prayer. Leiva-Merikakis, Erasmo, tr. from Ger. LC 81-83569. Tr. of Der Dreifache Kranz. 146p. (Orig.). 1982. pap. 7.95 (ISBN 0-89870-015-9). Ignatius Pr.
Ward, J. Neville. Five for Sorrow, Ten for Joy: A Consideration of the Rosary. rev. ed. LC 85-21318. xiii, 138p. 1985. pap. 6.95 (ISBN 0-936384-36-0). Cowley Pubns.
ROSATI, JOSEPH, BP., 1789-1843
Easterly, Frederick J. The Life of Rt. Rev. Joseph Rosati, D. M., First Bishop of St. Louis, 1789-1843. LC 73-3587. (Catholic University of America. Studies in American Church History: No. 33). Repr. of 1942 ed. 27.00 (ISBN 0-404-57783-0). AMS Pr.
ROSEGGER, PETER, 1843-1918
Sorg, Henry C. Rosegger's Religion. LC 78-140029. (Catholic University Studies in German Ser.: No. 11). 1970. Repr. of 1938 ed. 24.00 (ISBN 0-404-50231-8). AMS Pr.
ROSH HA-SHANAH
Bin-Nun, Judy & Einhorn, Franne. Rosh Hashana: A Holiday Funtext. (Illus.). 1978. pap. 5.00 (ISBN 0-8074-0010-6, 101300). UAHC.
Chaikin, Miriam. Sound the Shofar: The Story & Meaning of Rosh HaShanah & Yom Kippur. LC 86-2651. (Illus.). 96p. 1986. 13.95 (ISBN 0-89919-373-0, Pub. by Clarion); pap. 4.95 (ISBN 0-89919-427-3, Pub. by Clarion). Ticknor & Fields.
Friedman, Audrey M. & Zwerin, Raymond. High Holy Day Do It Yourself Dictionary. (Illus.). 32p. 1983. pap. 5.00 (ISBN 0-8074-0162-5, 101100). UAHC.
Goodman, Philip, ed. Rosh Hashanah Anthology. LC 74-105069. (Illus.). 379p. 1970. 10.95 (ISBN 0-8276-0023-2, 246). Jewish Pubns.
Simon, Norma. Rosh Hashanah. (Festival Series of Picture Story Books). (Illus.). 1961. plastic cover 4.50 (ISBN 0-8381-0700-1). United Syn Bk.
ROSICRUCIANS
Allen, Paul M., ed. A Christian Rosenkreutz Anthology, Vol. 10. 2nd, rev. ed. LC 68-13130. (Spiritual Science Library). (Illus.). 640p. 1981. Repr. of 1968 ed. lib. bdg. 65.00 (ISBN 0-89345-009-X, Steinerbks). Garber Comm.
Andrea, Raymond. The Technique of the Master. 12th ed. 174p. 1981. 7.95 (ISBN 0-912057-10-6, G-513). AMORC.
Bulwer-Lytton, Edward. Zanoni: A Rosicrucian Tale. 3rd ed. LC 78-157505. (Spiritual Fiction Publications: Vol. 1). 416p. 1985. cancelled (ISBN 0-8334-0000-2, Spiritual Fiction). Garber Comm.
--Zanoni: A Rosicrucian Tale, Vol. 4. LC 78-157505. (Spiritual Science Library). 412p. 1971. lib. bdg. 18.00 (ISBN 0-89345-014-6, Spiritual Sci Lib); pap. 11.50 (ISBN 0-89345-015-4, Steinerbks). Garber Comm.
Case, Paul F. The True & Invisible Rosicrucian Order. LC 85-3185. (Illus.). 352p. 1985. 22.50 (ISBN 0-87728-608-6). Weiser.
Cihlar, Many, compiled by. Mystics at Prayer. 19th ed. LC 36-17108. 57p. 1982. 7.95 (ISBN 0-912057-08-4, G-509). AMORC.
Clymer, R. Swinborne. The Rosicrucian Fraternity in America, 2 vols. 1935. 75.00 (ISBN 0-686-10446-3). Philos Pub.
Clymer, R. Swinburne. Book of Rosicruciae, 3 Vols. 1948. Set. 27.00 (ISBN 0-686-00809-X). Philos Pub.
--The Book of Rosicruciae, Vol. I. 286p. 1946. 9.95 (ISBN 0-932785-03-4). Philos Pub.
--Fraternitas Rosae Crucis. 1929. 9.95 (ISBN 0-932785-11-5). Philos Pub.
--Initiates & the People, 1928-1932, 5 vols. 1933. Repr. Set. 37.95 (ISBN 0-686-15595-5). Vol. I, 204 pp (ISBN 0-932785-18-2). Vol. II, 208 pp (ISBN 0-932785-19-0). Vol. III, 200 pp (ISBN 0-932785-20-4). Vol. IV, 192 pp (ISBN 0-932785-21-2). Vol. V, 207 pp (ISBN 0-932785-22-0). Philos Pub.
--Mysteries of Osiris: Egyptian Initiation. 287p. 1951. 8.95 (ISBN 0-932785-31-X). Philos Pub.
--The Rosy Cross: Its Teachings. 287p. 1965. 7.95 (ISBN 0-932785-43-3). Philos Pub.
Clymer, R. Swineburn & Morey, Grace K. Mystic Americanism or the Spiritual Heritage of America Revealed. 328p. 1975. 7.95 (ISBN 0-932785-33-6). Philos Pub.
Cooper-Oakley, Isabel. Comte de St. Germain. 15.95 (ISBN 0-7229-5146-9). Theos Pub Hse.
De Petri, Catharose. Golden Rosycross. Lectorium Rosicrucianum Staff, tr. from Dutch. Orig. Title: Het Goudew Rozenkruis. Date not set. pap. 8.00. Rosycross Pr.
--Seven Voices Speak. Lectorium Rosicrucianum, ed. Orig. Title: Zeven Stemmen Spreken. (Dutch.). 79p. Date not set. pap. 8.00. Rosycross Pr.
Earle, Alice M. Sun Dials & Roses of Yesterday. LC 79-75790. 1969. Repr. of 1902 ed. 37.00x (ISBN 0-8103-3830-0). Gale.
Gilbert, R. A. The Golden Dawn: Twilight of the Magicians. 128p. 1983. pap. 7.95 (ISBN 0-85030-278-1). Newcastle Pub.
Hall, Manly P. Codex Rosae Crucis - DOMA. 20.00 (ISBN 0-89314-404-5). Philos Res.
Hartman, Franz. Rosicrucian Symbols. 1983. 2.95 (ISBN 0-916411-15-X). Sure Fire.
Incognito, Magnus. Secret Doctrine of the Rosicrucians. 8.00 (ISBN 0-911662-30-8). Yoga.
Jennings, Hargrave. The Rosicrucians: Their Rites & Mysteries. 4th ed. LC 75-36845. (Occult Ser.). (Illus.). 1976. Repr. of 1907 ed. 36.50x (ISBN 0-405-07957-5). Ayer Co Pubs.
Lewis, H. Spencer. Manual Rosacruz. 8th ed. AMORC Staff, tr. from Eng. (Span., Illus.). 268p. (Orig.). 1981. pap. 8.00 (ISBN 0-912057-60-2, GS-508). AMORC.
--Preguntas y Respuestas Rosacruces: Con la historia completa de la Orden. 8th ed. AMORC Staff, tr. from Eng. (Span., Illus.). 231p. 1982. pap. 8.00 (ISBN 0-912057-61-0, GS-501). AMORC.
--Principios Rosacruces para el Hogar y los Negocios. 4th ed. AMORC Staff, tr. from Eng. (Span.). 210p. (Orig.). 1980. pap. 8.00 (ISBN 0-912057-76-9, GS-502). AMORC.
--La Profecia Simbolica de la Gran Piramide. 4th ed. AMORC Staff, tr. from Eng. (Span., Illus.). 167p. (Orig.). 1982. pap. 7.00 (ISBN 0-912057-70-X, GS-514). AMORC.
--Rosicrucian Manual. 28th ed. LC 78-104932. (Illus.). 214p. 1987. 8.95 (ISBN 0-912057-39-4, G-508). AMORC.
--Rosicrucian Principles for the Home & Business. 21st ed. LC 54-21694. 241p. 1981. 11.95 (ISBN 0-912057-04-1, G-502). AMORC.
--Rosicrucian Questions & Answers with Complete History. 16th ed. LC 65-14964. 358p. 1984. 12.50 (ISBN 0-912057-37-8, G-501). AMORC.
--The Secret Doctrines of Jesus. 19th ed. LC 37-22922. 237p. 1981. 10.95 (ISBN 0-912057-14-9, G-504). AMORC.
--Self Mastery & Fate with the Cycles of Life. 33rd ed. LC 55-16785. 253p. 1982. 11.95 (ISBN 0-912057-05-X, G-507). AMORC.
--A Thousand Years of Yesterday. 22nd ed. LC 20-9068. 156p. 1982. 8.95 (ISBN 0-912057-01-7, G-506). AMORC.
--La Vida Mistica de Jesus. 14th ed. AMORC Staff, tr. from Eng. (Span., Illus.). 234p. (Orig.). 1981. pap. 8.00 (ISBN 0-912057-63-7, GS 503). AMORC.
Lewis, Ralph. Mental Alchemy. 3rd ed. LC 79-66799. 270p. 1984. 11.95 (ISBN 0-912057-38-6, G-639). AMORC.
Lewis, Ralph, ed. The Immortalized Words of the Past. LC 85-63539. 300p. (Orig.). 1986. pap. 9.95 (ISBN 0-912057-42-4, G-654). AMORC.
Lewis, Ralph M. Behold the Sign. 12th ed. LC 44-30695. 1981. 7.95 (ISBN 0-912057-16-5, G521). AMORC.
--Cosmic Mission Fulfilled. 3rd ed. LC 66-25243. 364p. 1978. 12.50 (ISBN 0-912057-22-X, G-631). AMORC.
--Mision Cosmica Cumplida. 4th ed. AMORC Staff, tr. from Eng. (Span., Illus.). 403p. (Orig.). 1981. pap. 7.00 (ISBN 0-912057-73-4, GS-631). AMORC.
--A Traves del Ojo de la Mente. AMORC Staff, tr. from Eng. (Span.). 290p. (Orig.). 1983. pap. 8.00 (ISBN 0-912057-84-X, GS-646). AMORC.
Maier, Michael. Laws of the Fraternity of the Rosie Crosse (Themis Aurea) 12.50 (ISBN 0-89314-402-9). Philos Res.
Meyrinck, Gustav. Clockmaker. (Orig.). 1987. pap. 3.00. Rosycross Pr.
Poole, Cecil A. The Eternal Fruits of Knowledge. 3rd ed. LC 76-352583. 162p. 1978. 6.95 (ISBN 0-912057-27-0, G524). AMORC.
Pott, Constance M. Francis Bacon & His Secret Society. LC 71-174282. Repr. of 1891 ed. 32.50 (ISBN 0-404-05096-4). AMS Pr.
Randolph, Paschal B. After Death: The Immortality of Man. 272p. 1970. write for info. (ISBN 0-932785-00-X). Philos Pub.
--Ravalette: The Rosicrucian's Story. 283p. 1939. 7.95 (ISBN 0-932785-40-9). Philos Pub.
Reff, Theodore, ed. Exhibitions of the Rosicrucian Salon. (Modern Art in Paris 1855 to 1900 Ser.). 354p. 1981. lib. bdg. 53.00 (ISBN 0-8240-4730-3). Garland Pub.
Rosicrucian Foundation. The Brotherhood of the Rosy Cross. 76p. 1935. 5.95 (ISBN 0-932785-06-9). Philos Pub.
Secret Symbols of the Rosicrucians of the 16th & 17th Centuries. 1967. 20.00 (ISBN 0-912057-44-0). AMORC.
Sri Ramatherio, rev. by. Unto Thee I Grant. 32nd ed. LC 49-15007. 96p. 1979. 8.95 (ISBN 0-912057-02-5, G-505). AMORC.
Steiner, Rudolf. Rosicrucian Esotericism. Osmond, Dorothy S., tr. from Ger. 122p. 1978. 14.00 (ISBN 0-910142-78-5). Anthroposophic.
--Rosicrucianism & Modern Initiation: Mystery Centres of the Middle Ages. 3rd. ed. Adams, Mary, tr. 98p. 1982. pap. 9.95 (ISBN 0-85440-381-7, Pub by Steinerbooks). Anthroposophic.
--Theosophy of the Rosicrucian. Cotterell, Mabel & Osmond, D. S., trs. (Ger.). 168p. 1981. 15.95 (ISBN 0-85440-113-X, Pub. by Steinerbooks); pap. 11.95 (ISBN 0-85440-401-5). Anthroposophic.
Van Rijckenborgh, Jan. De Sen Mascavamiento. (Span.). 1987. pap. 5.00 (ISBN 8-439827-98-9). Rosycross Pr.
--Elementary Philosophy of the Modern Rosycross. 3rd ed. (Cornerstone Ser.: No. 5). Tr. of Elementaire Wijsbegeerte van het moderne Rozekruis. 207p. (Orig.). 1986. pap. 11.00 (ISBN 90-6732-004-8). Rosycross Pr.
--Ensenanza Elemental de la Rosacruz Moderna. (Span.). 1987. pap. 11.00 (ISBN 9-070196-80-8). Rosycross Pr.
--Light Over Tibet. 40p. (Orig.). 1987. pap. 1.75. Rosycross Pr.
--Mysterio de la Vide e de la Muerta. (Span.). 1987. pap. 2.00. Rosycross Pr.
--Mystery of Life & Death. Lectorium Rosicrucianum, tr. from Dutch. 50p. 1987. pap. 6.00. Rosycross Pr.
--Nuctemeron of Apollonius Tyana. (Dutch.). 125p. (Orig.). 1987. pap. 11.00. Rosycross Pr.
--Nueva Llamada. (Span.). 1987. pap. 1.50. Rosycross Pr.
--Secret of the Rosicrucian Brotherhood, 4 vols. Incl. Vol. 1. Call of Rosicrucian Brotherhood; Vol. 2. Confession of the Rosicrucian Brotherhood; Vol. 3. Alchemical Wedding of Christian Rosycross; Vol. 4. Alchemical Wedding of Christian Rosycross. Date not set. price not set. Rosycross Pr.
--Unmasking. 70p. 1987. pap. 3.00. Rosycross Pr.
Van Rijckenborgh, Jan & De Petri, Catharose. Fraternidade Shamballah. (Span.). 1987. pap. 11.00. Rosycross Pr.
--Lightgarment of the New Man. Tr. of Het Lichtkleed van de Niewe Mens. 100p. (Orig.). Date not set. pap. 11.00. Rosycross Pr.
--Universal Path. rev ed. (Cornerstone Ser.: No. 2). Tr. of Het Universele Pad. 99p. 1986. pap. 11.00 (ISBN 90-6732-007-2). Rosycross Pr.
Vaughan, Thomas. The Fraternity of the Rosy Cross. Waite, A. E., ed. 1983. pap. 5.95 (ISBN 0-916411-07-9, Pub. by Alchemical Pr). Holmes Pub.
Waite, Arthur E. Real History of the Rosicrucians, Vol. 20. LC 76-53632. (Spiritual Science Library). (Illus.). 456p. 1982. lib. bdg. 22.00 (ISBN 0-89345-018-9); pap. 14.00 (ISBN 0-89345-019-7). Garber Comm.
Weed, John K. Wisdom of the Mystic Masters. 1968. 10.95 (ISBN 0-13-961516-4, Reward); pap. 4.95 (ISBN 0-13-961532-6). P-H.
Westcott, W. W. Rosicrucian Thoughts on the Ever-Burning Lamps of the Ancients. 1986. pap. 2.95 (ISBN 0-916411-56-7). Sure Fire.
Wigston, W. F. Bacon, Shakespeare & the Rosicrucians. 59.95 (ISBN 0-87968-694-4). Gordon Pr.
Yates, Frances A. The Rosicrucian Enlightenment. (Illus.). 320p. 1986. pap. 7.95 (ISBN 0-7448-0051-X, 0051W, Ark Paperbks). Methuen Inc.
ROSY CROSS, ORDER OF THE
see Rosicrucians
ROUAULT, GEORGES, 1871-1958
Courthion, Pierre. Rouault. (Library of Great Painters). (Illus.). 1977. 45.00 (ISBN 0-8109-0459-4). Abrams.
Soby, James T. Georges Rouault: Paintings & Prints. LC 70-169317. (Museum of Modern Art Publications in Reprint). Repr. of 1947 ed. 24.50 (ISBN 0-405-01575-5). Ayer Co Pubs.
ROUSSEAU, JEAN JACQUES, 1712-1778
Lowell, James R. Among My Books. LC 75-126666. 1970. 11.50 (ISBN 0-404-04039-X). AMS Pr.
Maritain, Jacques. Three Reformers: Luther-Descartes-Rousseau. Repr. of 1950 ed. lib. bdg. 22.50x (ISBN 0-8371-2825-0, MATR). Greenwood.
RUBENS, PETER PAUL, SIR, 1577-1640
Adler, Wolfgang. Rubens: Landscapes. (A Harvey Miller Publication Ser.). (Illus.). 320p. 1982. 74.00x (ISBN 0-19-921027-6). Oxford U Pr.
Glen, Thomas L. Rubens & the Counter Reformation: Studies in His Religious Paintings Between 1609 & 1620. LC 76-23621. (Outstanding Dissertations in the Fine Arts Ser.). 1977. lib. bdg. 68.00 (ISBN 0-8240-2692-6). Garland Pub.
RUINS
see Excavations (Archaeology)
also subdivision Antiquities under names of countries, cities, etc. e.g. Rome–Antiquities
RUNNING
see also Jogging
Mayo, DeBarra. Runners' World Yoga, Bk. II. 180p. (Orig.). 1983. pap. 9.95 (ISBN 0-89037-274-8). Anderson World.
Paulk, Earl. Divine Runner. LC 78-71967. 142p. (Orig.). 1978. pap. 3.25 (ISBN 0-917595-00-9). K-Dimension.
Rohe, Fred. The Zen of Running. 1975. pap. 5.95 (ISBN 0-394-73038-0). Random.
RUPERT OF DEUTZ, 1070-1135
Van Engen, John. Rupert of Deutz. LC 82-40089. (Center for Medieval & Renaissance Studies, UCLA: Publication: No. 18). 1983. text ed. 34.50x (ISBN 0-520-04577-7). U of Cal Pr.
RURAL CHURCHES
see also Suburban Churches
O'Hara, Edwin V. The Church & the Country Community. 14.00 (ISBN 0-405-10846-X, 11849). Ayer Co Pubs.
Rother, Kathleen & Gosse, Carol A. National Catholic Rural Life Conference Idea Book for Small Town Churches. LC 76-2333. 106p. 1976. pap. 2.50x (ISBN 0-914422-05-7). Glenmary Res Ctr.
Wilkinson, Theodore S. Churches at the Testing Point: A Study in Rural Michigan. (World Council of Churches Studies in Mission). 1970. pap. 3.95 (ISBN 0-377-82021-0). Friend Pr.
RUSKIN, JOHN, 1819-1900
Downes, David A. Ruskin's Landscape of Beatitude. LC 83-48767. (American University Studies IV (English Language & Literature): Vol. 4). 247p. 1984. pap. text ed. 24.75 (ISBN 0-8204-0049-1). P Lang Pubs.
Farrar, Dean. Ruskin As a Religious Teacher. 1978. Repr. of 1904 ed. lib. bdg. 15.00 (ISBN 0-8495-1616-1). Arden Lib.
--Ruskin As a Religious Teacher. LC 73-2834. 1973. lib. bdg. 8.50 (ISBN 0-8414-1957-4). Folcroft.
Gibbs, Ellen & Gibbs, Mary. The Bible References of John Ruskin. 310p. 1973. Repr. of 1898 ed. 20.00 (ISBN 0-8274-0652-5). R West.

Gibbs, M. & Gibbs, E. The Bible References of John Ruskin. 59.95 (ISBN 0-87968-729-0). Gordon Pr.

Gladden, Washington. Witnesses of the Light. facs. ed. LC 77-84307. (Essay Index Reprint Ser). 1903. 17.75 (ISBN 0-8369-1081-8). Ayer Co Pubs.

McLaughlin, Elizabeth T. Ruskin & Gandhi. LC 72-3260. 202p. 1974. 20.00 (ISBN 0-8387-1086-7). Bucknell U Pr.

Quennell, Peter. John Ruskin: The Portrait of a Prophet. 1973. Repr. of 1949 ed. 35.00 (ISBN 0-8274-0472-7). R West.

Ruskin, John. The Bible References of John Ruskin. LC 77-13181. 1977. Repr. lib. bdg. 30.00 (ISBN 0-8414-4608-3). Folcroft.

Ward, May A. Prophets of the Nineteenth Century: Carlyle, Ruskin, Tolstoi. LC 76-7949. 1978. Repr. of 1900 ed. lib. bdg. 20.00 (ISBN 0-8414-9437-1). Folcroft.

Webb, Catherine. Lives of Great Men & Women: Charles Kingsley, John Ruskin, William Morris. 1911. Repr. 25.00 (ISBN 0-8274-2976-2). R West.

Whitehouse, John Howard. Ruskin: Prophet of the Good Life. LC 73-16263. 1948. lib. bdg. 12.50 (ISBN 0-8414-9491-6). Folcroft.

--Ruskin the Prophet & Other Centenary Studies. LC 73-11306. 1920. lib. bdg. 25.00 (ISBN 0-8414-9368-5). Folcroft.

Wihl, Gary. Ruskin & the Rhetoric of Infallibility. LC 85-5310. (Yale Studies in English: No. 194). 256p. 1985. 17.50x (ISBN 0-300-03321-4). Yale U Pr.

RUTH (BIBLICAL CHARACTER)

Barrett, Ethel. Ruth. LC 80-52961. (Bible Biography Ser.). 128p. 1980. pap. 1.95 (ISBN 0-8307-0764-6, 5810418). Regal.

Bob & Couchman, Win. Ruth & Jonah: People in Process. (Carpenter Studyguide). 80p. 1983. saddle-stiched member's handbk. 1.95 (ISBN 0-87788-736-5); leader's handbook 2.95 (ISBN 0-87788-737-3). Shaw Pubs.

Broch, Yitzhak I. The Book of Ruth. 1975. 7.95 (ISBN 0-87306-012-1); pap. 5.95. Feldheim.

Campbell, Edward F. Ruth. LC 74-18785. (Anchor Bible Ser.: Vol. 7). (Illus.). 216p. 1975. 14.00 (ISBN 0-385-05316-9). Doubleday.

Lindsay, Gordon. Ruth, The Gleaner, & the Boy Samuel. (Old Testament Ser.). 1.25 (ISBN 0-89985-137-1). Christ Nations.

Madison, Leslie. Redemption of Ruth. 96p. (Orig.). 1982. pap. 2.50 (ISBN 0-89323-038-3). Bible Memory.

Smith, Joyce M. Ruth: A Woman of Worth. 1979. pap. 2.50 (ISBN 0-8423-5810-2). Tyndale.

Storr, Catherine, as told by. Ruth's Story. (Peoples of the Bible Ser.). (Illus.). 32p. 1985. PLB 10.65 (ISBN 0-8172-2043-7). Raintree Pubs.

RUTH (BIBLICAL CHARACTER)–JUVENILE LITERATURE

Parris, Paula. Ruth: Woman of Courage. (BibLearn Ser.). (Illus.). 1977. bds. 5.95 (ISBN 0-8054-4229-4, 4242-29). Broadman.

S

SABBATH

Here are entered works on the concept of a day of rest, as defined in the Ten Commandments, particiularly works on Seventh-Day or Saturday observance. Works on First-Day or Sunday observance are entered under Sunday.

see also Sunday; Sunday Legislation

Anti-Sabbath Convention Staff. Proceedings of the Anti-Sabbath Convention, Melodeon, Boston. Parkhurst, Henry M., ed. LC 79-122662. 1971. Repr. of 1848 ed. 16.50x (ISBN 0-8046-1311-7, Pub. by Kennikat). Assoc Faculty Pr.

Brin, Ruth. The Shabbat Catalogue. 1971. 5.00x (ISBN 0-87068-636-4). Ktav.

Canright, D. M. El Adventismo Del Septimo Dia. Correa, F. G., tr. 1985. pap. 1.95 (ISBN 0-311-05601-6). Casa Bautista.

Dennison, James T., Jr. The Market Day of the Soul: The Puritan Doctrine of the Sabbath in England, 1532-1700. LC 83-6990. (Illus.). 188p. (Orig.). 1983. lib. bdg. 25.00 (ISBN 0-8191-3204-7); pap. text ed. 11.25 (ISBN 0-8191-3205-5). U Pr of Amer.

Dresner, Samuel H. Sabbath. 1970. pap. 2.95 (ISBN 0-8381-2114-4). United Syn Bk.

Edwards, Tilden. Sabbath Time: Understanding & Practice for Contemporary Christians. 144p. 1984. pap. 8.95 (ISBN 0-8164-0526-3, AY7883, HarpR). Har-Row.

Fernandez, Domingo. Por Que Guardamos el Domingo? 87p. 1984. pap. 2.00 (ISBN 0-311-05603-2). Casa Bautista.

Goldenberg, Robert. The Sabbath-Law of R. Meir. LC 78-14370. (Brown University. Brown Judaic Studies: No. 6). 1978. pap. 9.00 (ISBN 0-89130-249-2, 140006). Scholars Pr GA.

Greenberg, Sidney & Levine, Jonathan. Likrat Shabbat. LC 78-669313. 10.00 (ISBN 0-87677-076-6); large type ed. 14.95; 10.95. Prayer Bk.

Grunfeld, I. The Sabbath: A Guide to Its Understanding & Observance. 6.95; pap. 4.95 (ISBN 0-87306-099-7). Feldheim.

Heschel, Abraham J. The Sabbath. 118p. 1975. pap. 4.50 (ISBN 0-374-51267-1). FS&G.

Heylyn, Peter. The History of the Sabbath, 2 pts. LC 75-26002. (English Expericne Ser.: No. 150). 272p. 1969. Repr. of 1636 ed. 49.00 (ISBN 90-221-0150-9). Walter J Johnson.

Jordan, James B. Sabbath Breaking & the Death Penalty: A Theological Investigation. LC 86-80679. 109p. (Orig.). 1986. pap. 9.95 (ISBN 0-939404-13-3). Geneva Ministr.

Levy, Max. Der Sabbaath in England. Repr. of 1933 ed. 24.00 (ISBN 0-384-32425-8). Johnson Repr.

Lindsay, Gordon. The Seventh Day. 1.25 (ISBN 0-89985-116-9). Christ Nations.

Miller. Sabbath Shiurim. 1979. Vol. I. 12.00 (ISBN 0-87306-993-5); Vol. II. 12.00 (ISBN 0-686-67019-1). Feldheim.

Millgram, Abraham E., ed. Sabbath: The Day of Delight. (Illus.). 495p. 1944. 12.95 (ISBN 0-8276-0157-3, 247). Jewish Pubns.

Mishna Berurah: Laws of Shabbath, Section, 325-344, Sec. 325-344, Vol. 3-D. 1986. 17.95 (ISBN 0-87306-408-9); pap. 13.95 (ISBN 0-87306-409-7). Feldheim.

Moss, Rosalyn & Moss, David. An Invitation to Shabbat. (Illus.). 160p. 1981. cancelled (ISBN 0-89961-013-7); pap. cancelled (ISBN 0-89961-014-5). SBS Pub.

Newman, Louis E. The Sanctity of the Seventh Year: A Study of Mishnah Tractate Shebiit. LC 83-8683. (Brown Judaic Studies). 276p. 1983. pap. 12.00 (ISBN 0-89130-630-7, 14 00 44). Scholars Pr GA.

Parker, Kenneth L. The English Sabbath: A Study of Doctrine & Practice from the Reformation to the Civil War. (Illus.). 224p. Date not set. price not set (ISBN 0-521-30535-7). Cambridge U Pr.

Peli, Pinchas. Shabbat Shalom: A Renewed Encounter with the Sabbath. 120p. 1986. pap. 7.95 (ISBN 0-940646-37-4). Rossel Bks.

Rabbi Yehoshja Y. Neuwirth. Shemirath Sabbath. Grangewood, W., tr. from Hebrew. Tr. of Shemirath Sabbath Kehilchathah. 360p. 1984. 11.95 (ISBN 0-87306-298-1); pap. 8.95 (ISBN 0-87306-375-9). Feldheim.

Riggle, H. M. The Sabbath & the Lord's Day. 160p. pap. 1.50 (ISBN 0-686-29165-4). Faith Pub Hse.

The Sabbath Service. 1982. 15.00 (ISBN 0-686-76253-3). Feldheim.

Scherman, Nosson. Siddur: Sabbath Eve Service. 1980. 10.95 (ISBN 0-686-68764-7); pap. 7.95 (ISBN 0-686-68765-5). Mesorah Pubns.

--Zemiroth - Sabbath Songs. Zlotowitz, Meir, ed. (Artscroll Mesorah Ser.). 1979. 13.95 (ISBN 0-89906-156-7); pap. 10.95 (ISBN 0-89906-157-5). Mesorah Pubns.

Scriven, Charles W. Jubilee of the World: The Sabbath As a Day of Gladness. (Flame Ser.). 1978. pap. 0.99 (ISBN 0-8127-0188-7). Review & Herald.

Shabbat Manual. 1972. pap. 5.95 (ISBN 0-916694-54-2). Central Conf.

Sigal, Phillip. The Halakah of Jesus of Nazareth According to the Gospel of Matthew. 282p. (Orig.). 1986. lib. bdg. 23.75 (ISBN 0-8191-5210-2); pap. text ed. 13.25 (ISBN 0-8191-5211-0). U Pr of Amer.

Solberg, Winton U. Redeem the Time: The Puritan Sabbath in Early America. (Illus.). 1977. 25.00x (ISBN 0-674-75130-2). Harvard U Pr.

Watson, Cecilia. My Sabbath Fun Book. 1983. Bk. 1. pap. 4.95 ea. Bk. 2 (ISBN 0-8163-0463-7). Pacific Pr Pub Assn.

Webster, Hutton. Rest Days, the Christian Sunday, the Jewish Sabbath & Their Historical & Anthropological Prototypes. LC 68-58165. 1968. Repr. of 1916 ed. 48.00x (ISBN 0-8103-3342-2). Gale.

SABBATH–JUVENILE LITERATURE

Ashton, Leila M. It's Sabbath. (My Church Teaches Ser.). (Illus.). 1978. pap. 1.95 (ISBN 0-8127-0177-1). Review & Herald.

--Today Is Friday. (My Church Teaches Ser.). (Illus.). 1978. pap. 1.954 (ISBN 0-8127-0176-3). Review & Herald.

Chaikin, Miriam & Frampton, David. The Seventh Day: The Story of the Jewish Sabbath. LC 82-16987. (Illus.). 48p. (Orig.). 1983. pap. 4.95 (ISBN 0-8052-0743-0). Schocken.

Saypol, Judyth R. & Wikler, Madeline. Come Let Us Welcome Shabbat. LC 83-25638. (Illus.). 32p. 1978. pap. 2.95 (ISBN 0-930494-04-0). Kar Ben.

Simon, Norma. Every Friday Night. (Festival Series of Picture Story Booxs). (Illus.). plastic cover 4.50 (ISBN 0-8381-0708-7). United Syn Bk.

Wengrove, Charles. The Sabbath. (Illus.). 1960. pap. 0.99 (ISBN 0-914080-65-2). Shulsinger Sales.

SABBATH LEGISLATION

see also Sunday Legislation

Anti-Sabbath Convention Staff. Proceedings of the Anti-Sabbath Convention, Melodeon, Boston. Parkhurst, Henry M., ed. LC 79-122662. 1971. Repr. of 1848 ed. 16.50x (ISBN 0-8046-1311-7, Pub. by Kennikat). Assoc Faculty Pr.

SABIANS

see Mandaeans

SACRAMENTALS

see also Unction

Champlin, Joseph. Special Signs of Grace: The Seven Sacraments & Sacramentals. (Illus.). 160p. 1986. pap. 6.95 (ISBN 0-8146-1466-3). Liturgical Pr.

Guzie, Tad. The Book of Sacramental Basics. LC 81-83189. 160p. (Orig.). 1982. pap. 6.95 (ISBN 0-8091-2411-4). Paulist Pr.

Sacramentary. rev. ed. red cloth, colored edges 35.00 (ISBN 0-89942-022-2, 22/22). Catholic Bk Pub.

Sacramentary. large size ed. (Large Type). red cloth 59.00 (ISBN 0-89942-044-3, 44-02); lea., gold design, gold edges 85.00 (ISBN 0-89942-045-1, 44/13); protective jacket o.s.i. 1.50 (ISBN 0-686-14323-X, 44-CJ). Catholic Bk Pub.

Sacramentary for Sundays & Feastdays. (Extra Large Type). 25.00 (ISBN 0-89942-054-0, 54/02). Catholic Bk Pub.

Schanz, John P. Introduction to the Sacraments. 180p. (Orig.). 1983. pap. 9.95 (ISBN 0-916134-57-1). Pueblo Pub Co.

SACRAMENTS

see also Baptism; Confirmation; Extreme Unction; Lord's Supper; Marriage; Ordination; Penance; Sacred Meals

Borgen, Ole E. John Wesley on the Sacraments. 312p. 1986. pap. 12.95 (ISBN 0-310-75191-8, 17085P). Zondervan.

Brett, Laurence. Redeemed Creation: The Sacramentals Today. (Message of the Sacraments Ser.: Vol. 8). 10.95 (ISBN 0-89453-398-3); pap. 6.95 (ISBN 0-89453-234-0). M Glazier.

Browning, Robert L. & Reed, Roy A. The Sacraments in Religious Education & Liturgy: An Ecumenical Model. LC 84-27536. 313p. (Orig.). 1985. pap. 14.95 (ISBN 0-89135-044-6). Religious Educ.

Champlin, Joseph. Special Signs of Grace: The Seven Sacraments & Sacramentals. (Illus.). 160p. 1986. pap. 6.95 (ISBN 0-8146-1466-3). Liturgical Pr.

Coniaris, A. M. These Are the Sacraments. 1981. pap. 6.95 (ISBN 0-937032-22-0). Light&Life Pub Co MN.

Cowgill, Carol. Adult Confession: Conversion in Process. 80p. 1984. pap. 3.50 (ISBN 0-697-02030-4). Wm C Brown.

Curley, Maureen. The Sacraments. (Children of the Kingdom Activities Ser.). 1975. 9.95 (ISBN 0-89837-019-1, Pub. by Pflaum Pr). Peter Li.

Duffy, Regis. Real Presence: Worship, Sacraments, & Commitment. LC 81-47877. 192p. 1982. pap. 8.95 (ISBN 0-06-062105-2, RD 383, HarpR). Har-Row.

Farrell, Christopher & Artz, Thomas. The Sacraments Today: Their Meaning & Celebration. LC 78-69750. 1978. pap. 3.95 (ISBN 0-89243-087-7). Liguori Pubns.

Fearon, Mary & Hirstein, Sandra. Celebrating Our Sacraments. 1985. Boxed Set. 84.95 (ISBN 0-697-02066-5); program director's guide 4.95 (ISBN 0-697-02058-4); write for info. tchr's. guide & student leaflets. Wm C Brown.

Fitzpatrick, Kathryn. Sacraments: Twenty-Eight Family Times to Celebrate Life. (Family Time - Faith Time: A Home-Based Approach to Religious Education Ser.). (Illus.). 70p. (Orig.). 1982. pap. 3.50 (ISBN 0-86716-010-1). St Anthony Mess Pr.

Foley, Leonard. Signs of Love: The Sacraments of Christ. (Illus.). 1976. pap. 1.95 (ISBN 0-912228-32-6). St Anthony Mess Pr.

Grenz, Stanley J. The Baptist Congregation. 128p. 1985. pap. 7.95 (ISBN 0-8170-1083-1). Judson.

Hellwig, Monika. The Meaning of the Sacraments. 1.95 (ISBN 0-686-13702-7, Pub. by Pflaum Pr). Peter Li.

Israel, Martin. Healing As Sacrament: The Santification of the World. LC 84-72482. 116p. 1985. pap. 6.00 (ISBN 0-936384-23-9). Cowley Pubns.

Judd, Peter A. The Sacraments. LC 78-12776. 1978. pap. 7.00 (ISBN 0-8309-0225-2). Herald Hse.

Leadbeater. Science of the Sacraments. 18.95 (ISBN 0-8356-7126-7). Theos Pub Hse.

Lovasik, Lawrence G. The Seven Sacraments. (Saint Joseph Picture Bks.). (Illus.). flexible bdg 0.95 (ISBN 0-89942-278-0, 278). Catholic Bk Pub.

McKenna, Megan & Ducote, Darryl. Sacraments, Liturgy & Prayer. LC 78-71531. (Followers of the Way Ser.: Vol. 5). 221p. 1979. 22.50 (ISBN 0-8091-9546-1); cassette 7.50 (ISBN 0-8091-7670-X). Paulist Pr.

Marett, Robert R. Sacraments of Simple Folk. LC 77-27192. (Gifford Lectures: 1932-33). Repr. of 1933 ed. 28.00 (ISBN 0-404-60488-9). AMS Pr.

Morin, Jean. Commentarius Historicus de Disciplina in Administratione Sacramenti Poenitentiae. 1020p. Repr. of 1682 ed. text ed. 248.40x (ISBN 0-576-99723-4, Pub. by Gregg Intl Pubs England). Gregg Intl.

Newhouse, Flower A. The Meaning & Value of the Sacraments. LC 77-186123. 123p. 1971. 7.50 (ISBN 0-910378-07-X). Christward.

O'Connor, Francine & Boswell, Kathryn. ABC's of Faith, Bk. 4. (Illus.). 1981. pap. 1.95 (ISBN 0-89243-138-5). Liguori Pubns.

O'Neill, Colman. Sacramental Realism: A General Theory of the Sacraments. (Theology & Life Ser.: Vol. 2). 1983. 9.95 (ISBN 0-89453-297-9). M Glazier.

Overduin, Daniel. Reflections on the Sacraments. 1980. pap. 1.95 (ISBN 0-570-03816-2, 12-2784). Concordia.

Pennock, Michael. The Sacraments & You. LC 81-65227. (Illus.). 272p. 1981. pap. 5.50 (ISBN 0-87793-221-2); teachers ed. 2.95 (ISBN 0-87793-222-0). Ave Maria.

Pitt, Clifford S. Church, Ministry & Sacraments: A Critical Evaluation of the Thought of Peter Taylor Forsyth. LC 82-24817. 360p. (Orig.). 1983. lib. bdg. 31.25 (ISBN 0-8191-3027-3); pap. text ed. 15.75 (ISBN 0-8191-3028-1). U Pr of Amer.

Roberts, William P. Encounters with Christ: An Introduction to the Sacraments. 256p. (Orig.). 1985. pap. 8.95 (ISBN 0-8091-2707-5). Paulist Pr.

Ryan, Mary P. How Sacraments Celebrate Our Story. LC 78-53635. (Journeys Ser). 1978. pap. text ed. 6.00x (ISBN 0-88489-104-6); tchrs. guide 6.00x (ISBN 0-88489-108-9). St Mary's.

The Sacraments Today. 1979. leader's guide 2.95 (ISBN 0-89243-116-4); worksheets o.p. 1.50 (ISBN 0-89243-115-6). Liguori Pubns.

Seven Sacrements. 20p. 1980. pap. 7.55 (ISBN 0-88479-025-8). Arena Lettres.

Tesniere, A. The Adoration of the Blessed Sacrament. (Illus.). 288p. 1981. Repr. of 1902 ed. lib. bdg. 35.00 (ISBN 0-89984-461-8). Century Bookbindery.

Thompson, Robert. The Feasts of the Lord. pap. 5.95 (ISBN 0-89728-029-6, 645571). Omega Pubns OR.

Vaillancourt, Raymond. Toward a Renewal of Sacramental Theology. O'Connell, Matthew, tr. from Fr. LC 79-12621. 126p. 1979. pap. 4.50 (ISBN 0-8146-1050-1). Liturgical Pr.

Watkins, Keith. The Feast of Joy: Ministering the Lord's Supper in the Free Tradition. LC 77-525. 1977. pap. 1.50 (ISBN 0-8272-1006-X). CBP.

SACRAMENTS–CATHOLIC CHURCH

Bamonte, Louis J. Your Faith: Leader's Guide. 1978. tchr's ed 2.95 (ISBN 0-89243-085-0). Liguori Pubns.

Davies, Michael. Communion Under Both Kinds-an Ecumenical Surrender. 1980. pap. 1.00 (ISBN 0-89555-141-1). TAN Bks Pubs.

Dunne, Thomas A. Do This in Memory of Me. LC 81-67927. (Illus.). 237p. (Orig.). 1981. pap. text ed. 4.95x (ISBN 0-89944-056-8); tchr's manual 2.95x (ISBN 0-89944-057-6). Don Bosco Multimedia.

Dyckman, Katherine M. & Carroll, L. Patrick. Solitude to Sacrament. LC 82-252. 128p. (Orig.). 1982. pap. 2.95 (ISBN 0-8146-1255-5). Liturgical Pr.

Faber, Frederick W. The Blessed Sacrament. LC 78-66302. 1978. pap. 11.00 (ISBN 0-89555-077-6). TAN Bks Pubs.

Ganoczy, Alexandre. An Introduction to Catholic Sacramental Theology. 1984. pap. 8.95 (ISBN 0-8091-2568-4). Paulist Pr.

Glinsky, Vladimir. Confessionary Questions: A Preparation for the Sacrament of Penitence with Text of the Office. pap. 0.25 (ISBN 0-686-05391-5). Eastern Orthodox.

Gusmer, Charles W. And You Visited Me. (Studies in the Reformed Rites of the Catholic Church: Vol. VI). 160p. (Orig.). 1984. pap. 9.95 (ISBN 0-916134-61-X). Pueblo Pub Co.

Halligan, Nicholas. The Sacraments & Their Celebration. LC 85-23031. 284p. (Orig.). 1986. pap. 14.95 (ISBN 0-8189-0489-5). Alba.

International Committee on English in the Liturgy, tr. Rite of Funerals. blue cloth 8.50 (ISBN 0-89942-350-7, 350/22). Catholic Bk Pub.

McNamara, Kevin. Sacrament of Salvation. 1981. 9.50 (ISBN 0-8199-0806-1). Franciscan Herald.

Martos, Joseph. The Catholic Sacraments. (Message of the Sacraments Ser.: Vol 1). 13.95 (ISBN 0-89453-391-6); pap. 9.95 (ISBN 0-89453-227-8). M Glazier.

--Doors to the Sacred: A Historical Introduction to Sacraments in the Catholic Church. LC 82-45148. 552p. 1982. pap. 10.95 (ISBN 0-385-18180-9, Im). Doubleday.
Mathis, Marcian & Bonner, Dismas, eds. Pastoral Companion. 14th ed. 1976. 17.50 (ISBN 0-8199-0084-2, L38625). Franciscan Herald.
Merchant, Joan de & Gallagher, Merchant. A Closer Look at the Sacraments: A Study Guide for Catholic Adults. pap. 6.95 (ISBN 0-937997-00-5). Hi Time Pub.
Muller, Michael. Blessed Eucharist: Our Greatest Treasure. LC 79-112490. 1973. pap. 9.00 (ISBN 0-89555-040-7). TAN Bks Pubs.
O'Neill, Colman E. Meeting Christ in the Sacraments. LC 64-20111. 1964. pap. 3.95 (ISBN 0-8189-0090-3). Alba.
Osborne, Kenan B. The Christian Sacraments of Initiation, Baptism, Confirmation, Eucharist. 1987. pap. 12.95. Paulist Pr.
Rite of Baptism for Children. green cloth 8.50 (ISBN 0-89942-136-9, 136/22). Catholic Bk Pub.
Rite of Marriage. (Large Type, Two Colors, Homiletic Notes). red cloth 8.50 (ISBN 0-89942-238-1, 238/22). Catholic Bk Pub.
Sacraments & You. 2.50 (ISBN 0-8198-6866-3). Dghtrs St Paul.
Sadowy, Chester P. Benjamin Colman's "Some of the Glories of Our Lord & Saviour Jesus Christ," Exhibited in Twenty Sacramental Discourses (1928) 1979. lib. bdg. 35.00 (ISBN 0-8482-6210-7). Norwood Edns.
St. Cyril, Bishop of Jerusalem. Five Instructions on the Sacraments. 1974. pap. 1.25 (ISBN 0-686-10197-9). Eastern Orthodox.
Schlitzer, Albert L. Our Life in Christ. (University Theology Ser.: Vols. 1 & 2). 1962. Set. 12.95 (ISBN 0-268-00201-0). U of Notre Dame Pr.
Schroeder, Frederick & Meyers, Craig. The Potential for Spiritual Direction in the New Rite of Penance. 1.85 (ISBN 0-89942-530-5, 530/04). Catholic Bk Pub.
Stoutzenberger, Joseph. Celebrating Sacraments. Nagel, Stephan, ed. (Illus.). 240p. (Orig.). 1984. pap. text ed. 8.25x (ISBN 0-88489-159-3); teaching manual 12.00 (ISBN 0-88489-160-7); spiritmasters 18.95. St Mary's.
Summary of the Seven Sacraments. 2.75 (ISBN 0-8198-6858-2). Dghtrs St Paul.
Van Beeck, Frans J. Grounded in Love: Sacramental Theology in an Ecumenical Perspective. LC 81-40117. 162p. (Orig.). 1982. lib. bdg. 26.00 (ISBN 0-8191-2040-5); pap. text ed. 11.25 (ISBN 0-8191-2041-3). U Pr of Amer.
Worgul, George S. From Magic to Metaphor: A Validation of Christian Sacraments. 248p. 1986. pap. text ed. 11.75 (ISBN 0-8191-4983-7). U Pr of Amer.

SACRAMENTS–EARLY WORKS TO 1800
Hugh of St. Victor. Hugh of St. Victor: On the Sacraments of the Christian Faith. Deferrari, R. J., tr. (Eng.). 1976. Repr. of 1951 ed. 18.00x (ISBN 0-910956-32-4). Medieval Acad.

SACRAMENTS–HISTORY OF DOCTRINES
Feider, Paul A. The Sacraments: Encountering the Risen Lord. LC 85-73569. 128p. (Orig.). 1986. pap. 4.95 (ISBN 0-87793-327-8). Ave Maria.
Rogers, Elizabeth F. Peter Lombard & the Sacramental System. 250p. 1976. Repr. of 1927 ed. lib. bdg. 19.50x (ISBN 0-915172-22-4). Richwood Pub.
Wallace, Ronald S. Calvin's Doctrine of the Word & Sacraments. xii, 253p. 1982. pap. 12.95 (ISBN 0-939404-02-8). Geneva Ministr.

SACRAMENTS (CANON LAW)
Damiani Van Den Eynde & Odulphi Van Den Eynde, eds. Guidonis de Orchellis Tractatus de Sacramentis Ex Eius Summa de Sacramentis et Officiis Ecclesiae. (Text Ser). 1953. 11.00 (ISBN 0-686-11549-X). Franciscan Inst.
Edelby, Neophytos, et al, eds. Sacraments in Theology & Canon Law. LC 68-58308. (Concilium Ser.: Vol. 38). 191p. 1968. 7.95 (ISBN 0-8091-0132-7). Paulist Pr.
Liptak, David Q. The New Code & the Sacraments. 140p. 1983. pap. 7.95 (ISBN 0-941850-12-9). Sunday Pubns.

SACRAMENTS (LITURGY)
Hill, Brennan. Rediscovering the Sacraments: Approaches to the Sacrament. 126p. (Orig.). 1982. 3.95 (ISBN 0-8215-9882-1). Sadlier.
Sasse, Herman. We Confess: The Sacraments. (We Confess Ser.: Vol. II). 160p. 1985. 11.95 (ISBN 0-570-03982-7, 12-2899). Concordia.
Weil, Louis. Sacraments & Liturgy. 116p. 1984. 24.95x (ISBN 0-631-13192-2); pap. 6.95 (ISBN 0-631-13229-5). Basil Blackwell.

SACRED, THE
see Holy, The

SACRED BOOKS
see also names of individual books, e.g. Bible, Koran, Vedas; subdivision Sacred Books under names of religions, e.g. Buddhism–Sacred Books
Al-Arabi, Muhyiddin. The Seals of Wisdom. (Sacred Texts Ser.). (Illus., Orig.). 1983. pap. 8.75 (ISBN 0-88695-010-4). Concord Grove.
Chaudhury, Sukomal. Analytical Study of the Abhidharmakosa. 1983. 18.00x (ISBN 0-8364-1017-3, Pub. by Mukhopadyaya). South Asia Bks.
Denny, Frederick M. & Taylor, Rodney L. The Holy Book in Comparative Perspective. LC 85-8473. (Studies in Comparative Religion). 244p. 1985. 19.95 (ISBN 0-87249-453-5). U of SC Pr.
Frost, S. E., Jr., ed. The Sacred Writings of the World's Great Religions. 410p. 1983. Repr. of 1951 ed. lib. bdg. 40.00 (ISBN 0-89760-241-2). Telegraph Bks.
Hays, Edward. The Ethiopian Tattoo Shop. LC 83-82276. (Illus.). 184p. (Orig.). 1983. pap. 7.95 (ISBN 0-939516-06-3). Forest Peace.
Hoare, Frederick R. Eight Decisive Books of Antiquity. LC 73-99638. (Essay Index Reprint Ser). 1952. 19.50 (ISBN 0-8369-1414-7). Ayer Co Pubs.
Hospital, Clifford G. Breakthrough: Insights of the Great Religious Discoverers. LC 85-5135. 208p. (Orig.). 1985. pap. 9.95 (ISBN 0-88344-206-X). Orbis Bks.
Howard, George. The Teaching of Addai. LC 81-5802. (SBL Texts & Translations Ser.). 1981. pap. 13.50 (ISBN 0-89130-490-8, 060216). Scholars Pr GA.
Iyer, Raghavan, ed. The Jewel in the Lotus. 606p. (Orig.). 1983. pap. 19.75 (ISBN 0-88695-000-7). Concord Grove.
Jochai, Simeon B. In the Beginning. (Sacred Text Ser.). (Illus.). vii, 88p. 1983. pap. 8.75 (ISBN 0-88695-008-2). Concord Grove.
Morgan, Michael A. Sepher Ha-Razim: The Book of Mysteries. LC 82-25181. (Society of Biblical Literature Texts & Translations Ser.). 108p. 1983. pap. 10.95 (ISBN 0-89130-615-3, 06 02 25). Scholars Pr GA.
Muller, Max. Chips from a German Workshop: Volume I: Essays on the Science of Religion. (Reprints & Translations). 1985. pap. 13.95 (ISBN 0-89130-890-3, 00-07-10). Scholars Pr GA.
Muller, Max, ed. Sacred Books of the East, 50 vols. 1977-1980. Repr. of 1975 ed. Set. 630.00; 16.80 ea. (ISBN 0-89684-310-6). Orient Bk Dist.
Robicsek, Francis & Hale, Donald. The Maya Book of the Dead: The Ceramic Codex. LC 81-86395. (Illus.). 288p. 48.50 (ISBN 0-8061-9911-3). U of Okla Pr.
Sacred Books of the East. 457p. 1986. Repr. of 1900 ed. lib. bdg. 150.00 (ISBN 0-8495-5928-6). Arden Lib.
Saint Thomas. The Gospel According to Thomas. (Sacred Texts Ser.). Orig. Title: Coptic. vii, 88p. 1983. pap. 8.75 (ISBN 0-88695-005-8). Concord Grove.
Smart, Ninian & Hecht, Richard. Sacred Texts of the World. 496p. 1984. pap. 16.95 (ISBN 0-8245-0639-1). Crossroad NY.
Smart, Ninian & Hecht, Richard B., eds. Sacred Texts of the World: A Universal Anthology. (Illus.). 496p. 1987. pap. 17.00 (ISBN 0-8334-1001-6, Freedeeds Bks). Garber Comm.
Tzu, Lao. Tao Te Ching. (Sacred Texts Ser.). Orig. Title: Chinese. viii, 88p. 1983. pap. 8.75 (ISBN 0-88695-007-4). Concord Grove.
Valmiki. Return to Shiva. (Sacred Texts Ser.). viii, 88p. 1983. pap. 8.75 (ISBN 0-88695-006-6). Concord Grove.
Wilson, Epiphanius. Sacred Books of the East. 464p. 1986. Repr. 25.00X (ISBN 0-8364-1764-X, Pub. by Usha). South Asia Bks.
Wormhoudt, Arthur, tr. from Classical Arabic. Selections from the Quran. (Arab Translation Ser.: No. 51). 175p. 1981. pap. 6.50x (ISBN 0-916358-03-8). Wormhoudt.
Zarathustra. The Gathas of Zarathustra. (Sacred Texts Ser.). viii, 104p. 1983. pap. 8.75 (ISBN 0-88695-011-2). Concord Grove.

SACRED BOOKS (SELECTIONS, EXTRACTS, ETC.
Frost, S. E., Jr., ed. The Sacred Writings of the Worlds Great Religions. 416p. 1972. pap. 6.95 (ISBN 0-07-022520-6). McGraw.
Spangler, David. Emergence: The Rebirth of the Sacred. LC 83-7626. 160p. (Orig.). 1984. pap. 10.95 (ISBN 0-385-29311-9, Delta). Dell.
White, Nelson & White, Anne. Index to the Spirits Given in "Abramelin". 50p. (Orig.). 1981. pap. 8.00 (ISBN 0-939856-17-4). Tech Group.

SACRED HEART, DEVOTION TO
Allegra, Gabriel. Mary's Immaculate Heart: A Way of God. 156p. 1985. 9.50 (ISBN 0-8199-0875-4). Franciscan Herald.
Callahan, Annice. Karl Rahner's Spirituality of the Pierced Heart: A Reinterpretation of Devotion to the Sacred Heart. LC 84-29170. 198p. (Orig.). 1985. lib. bdg. 25.25 (ISBN 0-8191-4568-8); pap. text ed. 11.75 (ISBN 0-8191-4569-6). U Pr of Amer.
Crawley-Boevey, Mateo. Jesus Rey De Amor. (Span.). 1980. pap. 3.95 (ISBN 0-8198-3909-4). Dghtrs St Paul.
Haring, Bernard. Heart of Jesus: Symbol of Redeeming Love. 160p. 1983. pap. 4.25 (ISBN 0-89243-191-1). Liguori Pubns.
Kern, Walter. Updated Devotion to the Sacred Heart. LC 75-9277. (Illus.). 192p. 1975. pap. 2.95 (ISBN 0-8189-1124-7, Pub. by Alba Bks). Alba.
Larkin, Francis. Enthronement of the Sacred Heart. 1978. 6.95 (ISBN 0-8198-0529-7); pap. 4.95 (ISBN 0-8198-0530-0). Dghtrs St Paul.
Prevot, Andre. Love, Peace & Joy: Devotion to the Sacred Heart of Jesus According to St. Gertrude. LC 84-51822. 224p. 1985. pap. 4.00 (ISBN 0-89555-255-8). Tan Bks Pubs.
Ratzinger, Joseph. Behold the Pierced One. Tr. of Schauen auf den Durchbohrten. 128p. 1986. pap. 7.95 (ISBN 0-89870-087-6). Ignatius Pr.

SACRED LITERATURES
see Sacred Books

SACRED MEALS
see also Agape; Fasts and Feasts
Drower, Ethel S. Water into Wine: A Study of Ritual Idiom in the Middle East. LC 77-87663. Repr. of 1956 ed. 23.50 (ISBN 0-404-16401-3). AMS Pr.
Galavaris, George. Bread & the Liturgy: The Symbolism of Early Christian & Byzantine Bread Stamps. LC 75-98120. pap. 63.30 (ISBN 0-317-07859-3, 2015361). Bks Demand UMI.
Muccie, Frank J., Jr. Jesus Was a Vegetarian. 62p. pap. 1.95 (ISBN 0-938520-03-2). Edenite.

SACRED MINISTRY
see Clergy–Office

SACRED MUSIC
see Church Music

SACRED VOCAL MUSIC
see also Carols; Chants (Jewish); Chants (Plain, Gregorian, etc.); Choruses, Sacred; Christmas Music; Easter Music; Hymns; Masses; Passion-Music; Psalms (Music)
Arnold, Heini. May Thy Light Shine: Prayers. Hutterian Brethren, ed. LC 86-9387. (Illus.). 240p. 1986. 6.00 (ISBN 0-87486-199-3, BV245.A748 1986 242.80973). Plough.
Barwick, Steven, tr. Two Mexico City Choirbooks of 1717: An Anthology of Sacred Polyphony from the Cathedral of Mexico. LC 82-3047. 213p. 1982. 16.95x (ISBN 0-8093-1065-1). S Ill U Pr.
Carus, Paul. Sacred Tunes for the Consecration of Life. 48p. 1899. 0.95 (ISBN 0-317-40427-X). Open Court.
Curry, W. Lawrence, ed. Anthems for the Junior Choir, 5 bks. 1.50 ea. Westminster.
Davies, Walford & Ley, Henry G., eds. Church Anthem Book: One Hundred Anthems. rev. ed. 1959. 17.50x (ISBN 0-19-353106-2). Oxford U Pr.
Espina, Noni. Vocal Solos for Christian Churches: A Descriptive Reference of Solo Music for the Church Year. 3rd ed. LC 84-51398. 256p. 25.00 (ISBN 0-8108-1730-6). Scarecrow.
Foster, Myles B. Anthems & Anthem Composers. LC 76-125047. (Music Ser.). 1970. Repr. of 1901 ed. lib. bdg. 32.50 (ISBN 0-306-70012-3). Da Capo.
Le Huray, Peter, et al. Anthems for Men's Voices, 2 vols. Incl. Vol. 1. Altos, Tenors & Basses. 11.50x (ISBN 0-19-353234-4); Vol. 2. Tenors & Basses. 11.50x (ISBN 0-19-353235-2). 1965. Oxford U Pr.
Nordon, Hugo, tr. Chorale Harmonization in the Church Modes. 1974. pap. 3.75 (ISBN 0-8008-1516-5, Crescendo). Taplinger.
Patrick, J. Max & Sundell, Roger H. Milton & the Art of Sacred Song. LC 78-65014. 248p. 1979. 32.50x (ISBN 0-299-07830-2). U of Wis Pr.
Perti, Giacomo Antonio. Laudate Pueri. Berger, Jean, ed. LC 65-26097. (Penn State Music Series, No. 10). 35p. 1965. pap. 4.00x (ISBN 0-271-73075-7). Pa St U Pr.
Ryazhsky, A. Uchjebnik Tserkovnago Penija. Tr. of Textbook of Sacred Singing. 105p. 1966. pap. 5.00 (ISBN 0-317-30382-1). Holy Trinity.
A Sixteenth-Century Anthem Book: Twenty Anthems for Four Voices. 1960. 5.00 (ISBN 0-19-353406-1). Oxford U Pr.
Stephens, Evan. Eight Favorite Anthems. 1972. pap. 1.95 (ISBN 0-87747-350-1). Deseret Bk.

SACRIFICE
see also Atonement; Blood (In Religion, Folk-Lore, Etc.); Cultus; Votive Offerings
Altgeld, John P. The Cost of Something for Nothing. 59.95 (ISBN 0-87968-948-X). Gordon Pr.
Bourdillon, M. F. C. & Fortes, M. Sacrifices. 1980. 54.50 (ISBN 0-12-119040-4). Acad Pr.
Daly, Robert J. Christian Sacrifice: The Judaeo-Christian Background Before Origen. LC 78-12004. (Studies in Christian Antiquity: Vol. 18). 587p. 1978. 26.95x (ISBN 0-8132-0530-1). Cath U Pr.
--Origins of the Christian Doctrine of Sacrifices. LC 77-78628. pap. 40.00 (2026875). Bks Demand UMI.
Deane, John F. High Sacrifice. 61p. 1981. pap. text ed. 6.50x (ISBN 0-85105-382-3, Pub. by Dolmen Pr Ireland). Humanities.
Hubert, Henri & Mauss, Marcel. Sacrifice: Its Nature & Function. Halls, W. D., tr. LC 64-12260. 1964. pap. 11.00x (ISBN 0-226-35679-5). U of Chicago Pr.
Jukes, Andrew. The Law of the Offerings. LC 68-19198. 220p. 1976. pap. 6.95 (ISBN 0-8254-2957-9). Kregel.
Loeb, Edwin M. Blood Sacrifice Complex. LC 24-4020. (Amer Archaeology Association Memoirs Ser.). 1924. pap. 15.00 (ISBN 0-527-00529-0). Kraus Repr.
Money-Kyrle, Roger E. Meaning of Sacrifice. Repr. of 1930 ed. 17.00 (ISBN 0-384-39690-9). Johnson Repr.
Nee, Watchman. A Living Sacrifice. Kaung, Stephen, tr. (Basic Lesson Ser.: Vol. 1). 1972. 4.25 (ISBN 0-935008-07-1); pap. 2.75 (ISBN 0-935008-08-X). Christian Fellow Pubs.
Rusche, Franz. Blut, Leben und Seele, Ihr Verhaeltnis Nach Auffassung der Griechischen und Hellenistischen Antike, der Bibel und der Alten Alexandrinischen Theologen. Repr. of 1930 ed. 34.00 (ISBN 0-384-52515-6). Johnson Repr.
Siddiqui, M. I. Animal Sacrifice in Islam. pap. 2.75 (ISBN 0-686-63893-X). Kazi Pubns.
Slemming, Charles W. Thus Shalt Thou Serve. 1966. pap. 2.95 (ISBN 0-87508-508-3). Chr Lit.
Wadia, B. P. The Law of Sacrifice. (Sangam Texts). 135p. 1986. pap. 8.75 (ISBN 0-88695-023-6). Concord Grove.
Young, Frances M. Sacrificial Ideas in Greek Christian Writers. LC 78-61400. (Patristic Monograph: No. 5). 1979. pap. 10.00 (ISBN 0-915646-04-8). Phila Patristic.

SAINT CECILIA'S DAY–SONGS AND MUSIC
Handel, George F. Look Down, Harmonious Saint. Stevens, Denis, ed. LC 63-21369. (Penn State Music Series, No. 1). 22p. 1963. pap. 3.00x (ISBN 0-271-73079-X). Pa St U Pr.

SAINT-DENIS, FRANCE (BENEDICTINE ABBEY)
Crosby, Sumner M. The Royal Abbey of Saint-Denis from Its Beginnings to the Death of Suger 475-1151. LC 85-26464. 570p. 1987. text ed. 55.00 (ISBN 0-300-03143-2). Yale U Pr.

ST. FRANCIS, ORDER OF
see Franciscans

ST. JOHN'S CHRISTIANS
see Mandaeans

ST. PATRICK'S DAY
Barth, Edna. Shamrocks, Harps, & Shillelaghs: The Story of the St. Patrick's Day Symbols. LC 77-369. (Illus.). 96p. 1977. 9.95 (ISBN 0-395-28845-2, Clarion). HM.
Cantwell, Mary. Saint Patrick's Day. LC 67-10070. (Holiday Ser.). (Illus.). 1967. PLB 12.89 (ISBN 0-690-71673-7, Crowell Jr Bks). HarpJ.

SAINT-SIMON, CLAUDE HENRI, COMTE DE, 1760-1825
Butler, E. M. The Saint-Simonian Religion in Germany. 1968. Repr. of 1926 ed. 45.00x (ISBN 0-86527-177-1). Fertig.
Cofer, David B. Saint-Simonism in the Radicalism of Thomas Carlyle. (English Literature Ser., No. 33). 1970. pap. 39.95x (ISBN 0-8383-0017-0). Haskell.
Fournel, Henri. Bibliographie Saint-Simonienne: De 1802 au 31 December 1832. LC 70-131405. (Fr.). 130p. 1973. Repr. of 1833 ed. lib. bdg. 21.00 (ISBN 0-8337-1222-5). B Franklin.
Spitzer, Leo & Brody, Jules. Approaches Textuelles des "Memoires" de Saint-Simon. (Etudes Litteraires Francaise: No. 9). (Fr.). 107p. (Orig.). 1980. pap. 12.00 (ISBN 3-87808-888-4). Benjamins North Am.

SAINT VALENTINE'S DAY
Bulla, Clyde R. Saint Valentine's Day. LC 65-11643. (Holiday Ser.). (Illus.). 1965. PLB 12.89 (ISBN 0-690-71744-X, Crowell Jr Bks). HarpJ.
De Paola, Tomie. Things to Make & Do for Valentine's Day. (Things to Make & Do Ser.). (Illus.). 48p. 1976. PLB 8.90 (ISBN 0-531-01187-9). Watts.
Guilfoile, Elizabeth. Valentine's Day. LC 65-10086. (Holiday Bks.). (Illus.). 1965. PLB 7.56 (ISBN 0-8116-6556-9). Garrard.
Hopkins, Lee B., ed. Good Morning to You, Valentine. LC 75-11650. (Illus.). 32p. 1976. 11.95 (ISBN 0-15-232134-9, HJ). HarBraceJ.

SAINTS
see also Hagiography; Hermits; Martyrs; Shrines; also names of Saints, e.g. Teresa, Saint
Adair, James R. Saints Alive. facsimile ed. LC 76-117319. (Biography Index Reprint Ser). 1951. 18.00 (ISBN 0-8369-8011-5). Ayer Co Pubs.
Adair, John. The Pilgrim's Way: Shrines & Saints in Britain & Ireland. (Illus.). 1978. 12.98 (ISBN 0-500-25061-8). Thames Hudson.
Aelfric's Lives of Saints, Vol. I, Pts. I-II. (EETS OS Ser.: Vols. 76 & 82). Repr. of 1885 ed. 22.00 (ISBN 0-8115-3361-1). Kraus Repr.
Alphonsus, Mary. St. Rose of Lima. LC 81-86444. 304p. 1982. pap. 8.00 (ISBN 0-89555-172-1). TAN Bks Pubs.
Athanasius, Saint The Life of St. Anthony the Great. pap. 2.95 (ISBN 0-686-16367-2). Eastern Orthodox.

Athanassakis, Apostolos N. The Life of Pachomius. LC 84-4046. (Society of Biblical Literature. Texts & Translation-Early Christian Literature Ser.). 216p. 1975. pap. 14.25 (ISBN 0-89130-065-1, 06 02 07). Scholars Pr GA.

Attwater, Donald. Golden Book of Eastern Saints. facsimile ed. LC 72-156607. (Essay Index Reprint Ser). Repr. of 1938 ed. 18.00 (ISBN 0-8369-2267-0). Ayer Co Pubs.

--Names & Name-Days: A Dictionary of Catholic Christian Names in Alphabetical Order with Origins & Meanings. LC 68-30595. 1968. Repr. of 1939 ed. 40.00x (ISBN 0-8103-3108-X). Gale.

--The Penguin Dictionary of Saints. rev. ed. John, Catherine R., rev. by. 352p. 1984. pap. 7.95 (ISBN 0-14-051123-7). Penguin.

Auffray, A. Saint John Bosco. 393p. (Orig.). 1983. pap. 12.95 (ISBN 0-89944-060-6). Don Bosco Multimedia.

Baldwin, Robert F. The Healers. LC 85-62815. 175p. (Orig.). 1986. pap. 4.95 (ISBN 0-87973-836-7, 836). Our Sunday Visitor.

Ball, Ann. Modern Saints: Their Lives & Faces. LC 82-50357. (Illus.). 457p. 1983. pap. 10.00 (ISBN 0-89555-222-1). TAN Bks Pubs.

Bander, Peter. The Prophecies of St. Malachy. LC 74-125419. (Illus.). 1973. pap. 3.00 (ISBN 0-89555-038-5). TAN Bks Pubs.

Barlow, T. Edward. Living Saints Witness at Work. 1976. 6.00 (ISBN 0-8309-0153-1). Herald Hse.

Bedouelle, Guy. Saint Dominic: The Grace of the Word. (Illus.). 290p. (Orig.). 1987. pap. 11.95 (ISBN 0-89870-140-6). Ignatius Pr.

Bentley, James. A Calendar of Saints: The Lives of the Principal Saints of the Christian Year. (Illus.). 256p. 1987. 22.95 (ISBN 0-8160-1682-8). Facts on File.

Bhattacharya, Vivek. The Spirit of Indian Culture: Saints of India. 622p. 1980. 29.95 (ISBN 0-940500-40-X). Asia Bk Corp.

Bimler, Rich. Celebrating Saints. 80p. (Orig.). 1986. pap. 3.95 (ISBN 0-570-04440-5). Concordia.

Binet, Pere. The Divine Favors Granted to St. Joseph. LC 82-50590. 176p. 1983. pap. 3.00 (ISBN 0-89555-187-X). TAN Bks Pubs.

Brown, Judith G. I Sing a Song of the Saints of God. (Illus.). 32p. (Orig.). 1981. pap. 5.95 (ISBN 0-8164-2339-3, HarpR). Har-Row.

Burghardt, W. J. & Lawler, T. C., eds. St. Irenaeus: Proof of the Apostolic Preaching. LC 78-62503. (ACW Ser.: No. 16). 242p. 1952. 12.95 (ISBN 0-8091-0254-4). Paulist Pr.

Burghardt, W. J., et al, eds. St. Maximus the Confessor: The Ascetic Life, the Four Centuries on Charity. LC 55-8642. (ACW Ser.: No. 21). 293p. 1955. 13.95 (ISBN 0-8091-0258-7). Paulist Pr.

--St. Athanasius: The Life of St. Antony. LC 78-62454. (ACW Ser.: No. 10). 155p. 1950. 12.95 (ISBN 0-8091-0250-1). Paulist Pr.

--St. Prosper of Aquitaine, the Call of All Nations. (Ancient Christian Writers Ser.: No. 14). 250p. 1952. 10.95 (ISBN 0-8091-0253-6). Paulist Pr.

Butler, Alban. Lives of the Saints, 4 vols. Attwater, Thurston, ed. 1956. Set. 140.00 (ISBN 0-87061-045-7); Set. pap. 95.00 (ISBN 0-87061-137-2). Chr Classics.

Capgrave, J. Lives of St. Augustine & St. Gilbert of Sempringham. (EETS, OS Ser.: No. 140). Repr. of 1910 ed. 40.00 (ISBN 0-527-00137-6). Kraus Repr.

Catholic Church-Sacred Congregation of Divine Worship Staff. Celebrating the Saints. International Committee on English in the Liturgy, Confraternity of Christian Doctrine for the New American Bible, tr. from Latin. 1978. pap. 10.00 (ISBN 0-916134-30-X). Pueblo Pub Co.

Cavallini, Giuliana. St. Martin de Porres-Apostle of Charity. Holland, Caroline, tr. from It. LC 79-65530. (Cross & Crown Series of Spirituality). 1979. pap. 7.00 (ISBN 0-89555-092-X). TAN Bks Pubs.

Cavarnos, Constantine. Modern Orthodox Saints: St. Methodia of Kimolos, Vol. 9. (Illus.). 123p. 1987. 8.95 (ISBN 0-914744-75-5); pap. 5.95 (ISBN 0-914744-76-3). Inst Byzantine.

--Modern Orthodox Saints: Vol. 2-St. Macarios of Corinth. 2nd ed. LC 72-85116. (Illus.). 1977. pap. 4.50 (ISBN 0-914744-35-6). Inst Byzantine.

--Modern Orthodox Saints: Vol. 3-St. Nicodemos the Hagiorite. 2nd ed. LC 78-71478. (Illus.). 167p. 1979. 8.00 (ISBN 0-914744-41-0); pap. 4.50. Inst Byzantine.

--Modern Orthodox Saints: Vol. 6-St. Arsenios of Paros. LC 78-54384. (Illus.). 123p. 1978. 8.00 (ISBN 0-914744-39-9); pap. 4.50 (ISBN 0-914744-40-2). Inst Byzantine.

--Modern Orthodox Saints: Vol. 7-St. Nectarios of Aegina. LC 81-82963. (Illus.). 222p. 1981. 10.00 (ISBN 0-914744-53-4); pap. 7.00 (ISBN 0-914744-54-2). Inst Byzantine.

--Modern Orthodox Saints: Vol. 8, St. Savvas the New. LC 85-60117. (Illus.). 144p. 1985. 8.95 (ISBN 0-914744-62-3); pap. 5.95 (ISBN 0-914744-63-1). Inst Byzantine.

Cavarnos, Constantine, ed. Modern Orthodox Saints, Vol. 1: St. Cosmas Aitolos. 3rd. rev. & enl. ed. LC 85-80440. (Illus.). 118p. 1985. 8.95 (ISBN 0-914744-64-X); pap. 5.95 (ISBN 0-914744-65-8). Inst Byzantine.

Charlebois, Robert, et al. Saints for Kids by Kids. 80p. 1984. pap. 2.95 (ISBN 0-89243-223-3). Liguori Pubns.

Chervin, Ronda & Neill, Mary. God-Seekers. 212p. (Orig.). 1986. pap. 4.95 (ISBN 0-914544-65-9). Living Flame Pr.

Claret, Anthony M. The Autobiography of St. Anthony Mary Claret. LC 85-51661. 227p. 1985. pap. 8.00 (ISBN 0-89555-284-1). Tan Bks Pubs.

Clark, John D. Suffering & the Saints. Goodman, James, ed. 272p. (Orig.). 1987. pap. 9.95 (ISBN 0-89896-129-7, Linolean). Larksdale.

Colgrave, Bertram. The Earliest Saint's Lives Written in England. 1978. Repr. of 1958 ed. lib. bdg. 12.50 (ISBN 0-8495-0739-1). Arden Lib.

--Earliest Saints Lives Written in England. LC 72-193175. 1958. lib. bdg. 12.50 (ISBN 0-8414-2353-9). Folcroft.

Covannier, Henry. St. Francis De Sales. 1973. Repr. 5.00 (ISBN 0-8198-0512-2). Dghtrs St Paul.

Cruz, Joan C. The Incorruptibles. LC 77-93992. (Illus.). 1977. pap. 8.00 (ISBN 0-89555-066-0). TAN Bks Pubs.

Cushing, Richard C. St. Martin de Porres. LC 62-20203. (Illus.). 75p. 1981. 4.00 (ISBN 0-8198-6818-3, STO280); pap. 2.00 (ISBN 0-8198-6819-1). Dghtrs St Paul.

Dabovich, Sebastian. St. Panteleimon. pap. 0.25 (ISBN 0-686-01298-4). Eastern Orthodox.

D'Arcy, Mary R. The Saints of Ireland. 241p. 1985. pap. 9.95 (ISBN 0-9614900-0-4). Irish Am Cult.

Dawes, Elizabeth & Baynes, Norman H., trs. from Greek. Three Byzantine Saints. 275p. 1977. pap. 8.95 (ISBN 0-913836-44-3). St Vladimirs.

Dean, Bessie. Paul, God's Special Missionary. (Story Books to Color.). 72p. (Orig.). 1980. pap. 2.50 (ISBN 0-88290-152-4). Horizon Utah.

Delaney, John J. Dictionary of Saints. LC 79-7783. (Illus.). 648p. 1980. 24.95 (ISBN 0-385-13594-7). Doubleday.

Delany, Selden P. Married Saints. facs. ed. LC 69-17573. (Essay Index Reprint Ser). 1935. 18.00 (ISBN 0-8369-0071-5). Ayer Co Pubs.

Desmond, Cecelia. Blessed James Salomoni. 1970. 2.00 (ISBN 0-8198-0000-7); pap. 1.00 (ISBN 0-8198-0001-5). Dghtrs St Paul.

Dirvin, Joseph I. St. Catherine Laboure of the Miraculous Medal. LC 84-50466. 245p. 1984. pap. 7.50 (ISBN 0-89555-242-6). TAN Bks Pubs.

Doherty, Eddie. Wisdom's Fool. 4.95 (ISBN 0-910984-08-5); pap. 2.95 (ISBN 0-910984-09-3). Montfort Pubns.

Donaldson, James & Roberts, Alexander, trs. Martyrdom of St. Polycarp: The Encyclical Epistle of the Church at Smyrna Concerning the Martyrdom of the Holy Polycarp. pap. 1.50 (ISBN 0-317-11392-5). Eastern Orthodox.

Donde, Antoine. The Life, Death & Miracles of Saint Francois De Paule. (Printed Sources of Western Art Ser.). (Fr., Illus.). 258p. 1981. pap. 40.00 slipcase (ISBN 0-915346-64-8). A Wofsy Fine Arts.

Dooley, Kate. The Saints Book: Stories for Children. LC 80-82814. 48p. (Orig.). 1981. pap. 2.95 (ISBN 0-8091-6547-3). Paulist Pr.

Drake, Maurice. Saints & Their Emblems. (Illus.). 1971. Repr. of 1916 ed. lib. bdg. 24.50 (ISBN 0-8337-0902-X). B Franklin.

Dunne, William P. Is It a Saint's Name? 1977. pap. 1.25 (ISBN 0-89555-024-5). TAN Bks Pubs.

Elliott, Alison G. Roads to Paradise: Reading the Lives of the Early Saints. LC 86-40384. 272p. 1987. 27.50 (ISBN 0-87451-389-8). U Pr of New Eng.

Farmer, David H., ed. The Oxford Dictionary of Saints. 1978. pap. 8.95 (ISBN 0-19-283036-8). Oxford U Pr.

Father Benedict, ed. Wondrous Is God in His Saints. LC 85-63506. (Illus.). 190p. (Orig.). 1985. pap. 6.95 (ISBN 0-936649-00-3). St Anthony Orthodox.

Flaubert, Gustave. The Temptation of Saint Anthony. Mrosovsky, Kitty, tr. LC 80-70452. (Illus.). 288p. 1981. 29.95x (ISBN 0-8014-1239-0). Cornell U Pr.

Fox, Robert J. St. Louis Marie Grignon de Montfort: His Life As He Might Tell It. 20p. 1983. 1.00 (ISBN 0-911988-62-9). Ami Pr.

Fulop-Miller, Rene. Saints That Moved the World: Anthony, Augustine, Francis, Ignatius, Theresa. LC 72-13293. (Essay Index Reprint Ser.). Repr. of 1945 ed. 32.00 (ISBN 0-8369-8159-6). Ayer Co Pubs.

Garrett, Paul D. St. Innocent: Apostle to America. LC 79-19634. 345p. 1979. pap. 8.95 (ISBN 0-913836-60-5). St Vladimirs.

Gasnick, Roy M., compiled By. The Francis Book: A Celebration of the Universal Saint. (Illus.). 320p. 1980. (Collier); pap. 15.95 (ISBN 0-02-003200-5). Macmillan.

Goodier, Alban. Saints for Sinners. LC 70-99637. (Essay Index Reprint Ser.). 1930. 18.00 (ISBN 0-8369-1504-6). Ayer Co Pubs.

Gregorius I. Life & Miracles of Saint Benedict: Book Two of Dialogues. Zimmermann, Odo J. & Avery, Benedict R., trs. from Latin. LC 80-19624. xv, 87p. 1980. Repr. of 1949 ed. lib. bdg. 22.50x (ISBN 0-313-22766-7, GRLI). Greenwood.

Guenebault, L. J. Dictionnaire Iconographique des Figures Legendes et Actes des Saints. Migne, J. P., ed. (Encyclopedie Theologique Ser.: Vol. 45). (Fr.). 716p. Repr. of 1850 ed. lib. bdg. 91.00x (ISBN 0-89241-249-6). Caratzas.

Gumbley, Walter. Parish Priests among the Saints. facs. ed. LC 76-148214. (Biography Index Reprint Ser.). 1947. 15.00 (ISBN 0-8369-8061-1). Ayer Co Pubs.

Gunkel, Carroll R. They Met the Master: Sermons on Contemporary Saints. 1980. 4.50 (ISBN 0-89536-388-7, 2035). CSS of Ohio.

Habig, Marion. Franciscan Book of Saints. 988p. 1980. 30.00 (ISBN 0-8199-0751-0). Franciscan Herald.

Habig, Marion A., ed. English Omnibus of Sources: St. Francis of Assisi. new ed. 1977. 30.00 (ISBN 0-8199-0658-1). Franciscan Herald.

Hackel, Sergei. The Byzantine Saint. LC 83-8738. 245p. 1982. lib. bdg. 23.95x (ISBN 0-89370-081-9); pap. text ed. 15.95x (ISBN 0-7044-0451-6). Borgo Pr.

Hackel, Sergei, ed. The Byzantine Saint. (Illus.). 245p. (Orig.). 1981. pap. 6.95 (ISBN 0-7044-0451-6). St Vladimirs.

Hallick, Mary P. The Book of Saints. 1984. pap. 5.95 (ISBN 0-937032-31-X). Light&Life Pub Co MN.

Hamilton, Elizabeth. The Life of Saint Teresa of Avila. 190p. 1982. pap. 6.95 (ISBN 0-87061-089-9, Pub. by A Clarke Bks UK). Chr Classics.

Hayes, Zachary. The Hidden Center: Spirituality & Speculative Christology in St. Bonaventure. LC 80-84509. 240p. (Orig.). 1981. pap. 8.95 (ISBN 0-8091-2348-7). Paulist Pr.

Hedengren, Paul. In Defense of Faith: Assessing Arguments Against Latter-Day Saint Belief. 240p. (Orig.). 1985. pap. 14.95 (ISBN 0-915073-00-5). Bradford & Wilson.

Helms, Hal M., ed. Saints Alive! the Book. (Orig.). 1985. pap. 9.95 (ISBN 0-941478-44-0). Paraclete Pr.

Hindman, Jane F. An Ordinary Saint, John Neumann. 1977. pap. 1.95 (ISBN 0-88479-004-5). Arena Lettres.

Hodges, George. Saints & Heroes to the End of the Middle Ages. facsimile ed. LC 67-26749. (Essay Index Reprint Ser.). (Illus.). 268p. 1982. Repr. of 1911 ed. lib. bdg. 19.00 (ISBN 0-8290-0526-9). Irvington.

Hoever, H. Lives of the Saints. (Illus.). maroon cloth, colored edges 4.75 (ISBN 0-89942-870-3, 870/22). Catholic Bk Pub.

Hogan, Edmund. The Latin Lives of the Saints. LC 78-72684. (Royal Irish Academy. Todd Lecture Ser.: Vol. 5). Repr. of 1894 ed. 21.50 (ISBN 0-404-60565-6). AMS Pr.

Hogan, John G. Heralds of the King. LC 79-107714. (Essay Index Reprint Ser.). 1934. 17.00 (ISBN 0-8369-1516-X). Ayer Co Pubs.

Holtzclaw, Robert F. The Saints Go Marching In. rev. ed. LC 84-52751. (Illus.). 194p. (Orig.). 1984. write for info.; pap. 10.00 (ISBN 0-933144-00-8). Keeble Pr.

Holweck, Frederick G. Biographical Dictionary of the Saints. LC 68-30625. 1969. Repr. of 1924 ed. 75.00x (ISBN 0-8103-3158-6). Gale.

Hunt, Marigold. St. Patrick's Summer. 273p. 1950. 6.00 (ISBN 0-912414-24-3). Lumen Christi.

Jameson, Anna B. Sacred & Legendary Art, 2 Vols. LC 71-124594. Repr. of 1896 ed. 18.50 (ISBN 0-404-03551-5). AMS Pr.

Jones, Ernest. Geoffrey of Monmouth. LC 73-20320. 1944. Repr. lib. bdg. 20.00 (ISBN 0-8414-5283-0). Folcroft.

Jones, Franklin, ed. The Spiritual Instructions of Saint Seraphim of Sarov. LC 73-89308. 1973. pap. 3.95 (ISBN 0-913922-05-6). Dawn Horse Pr.

Judd, Peter & Lindgren, Bruce. An Introduction to the Saints Church. LC 75-35763. 1976. 14.00 (ISBN 0-8309-0154-X). Herald Hse.

Kalberer, Augustine. Lives of the Saints. (Illus.). 380p. 1976. 18.50 (ISBN 0-8199-0539-9). Franciscan Herald.

Keeler, Laura. Geoffrey of Monmouth & the Late Latin Chroniclers. LC 74-5455. 1946. Repr. lib. bdg. 27.50 (ISBN 0-8414-5493-0). Folcroft.

Kieckhefer, Richard. Unquiet Souls: Fourteenth Century Saints & Their Religious Milieu. LC 84-210. (Illus.). viii, 238p. 1987. pap. 10.95 (ISBN 0-226-43510-5). U of Chicago Pr.

Kleinz, John P. The "Who's Who" of Heaven: Saints for All Seasons. 220p. (Orig.). 1987. pap. 12.95 (ISBN 0-87061-136-4). Chr Classics.

Koehler, Lugmilla. Svjatoj Ioann (Pommer) Arkiepiskop Rihskij i Latvijskij. Tr. of St. John (Pommer) Archbishop of Riga & Latvia. (Illus.). 72p. 1985. pap. 3.00 (ISBN 0-317-29224-2). Holy Trinity.

Kolb, Robert. For All the Saints: Changing Perceptions of Martyrdom & Sainthood in the Lutheran Reformation. (Illus.). 192p. 1987. 29.95 (ISBN 0-86554-270-8, H233). Mercer Univ Pr.

Lappin, Peter. Dominic Savio: Teenage Saint. LC 54-11044. 1982. 2.75 (ISBN 0-89944-034-7, D Bosco Pubns); pap. 1.25 (ISBN 0-89944-033-9). Don Bosco Multimedia.

The Life of St. Alexis, the Man of God. 1985. pap. 1.50 (ISBN 0-317-30438-0). Holy Trinity.

Life of St. John the Almsgiver. pap. 1.25 (ISBN 0-317-11384-4). Eastern Orthodox.

The Life of St. Stanislaus Kosta, of the Society of Jesus, Patron of Novices. 1978. Repr. of 1850 ed. lib. bdg. 20.00 (ISBN 0-8495-0127-X). Arden Lib.

The Lives of St. Eugenia & St. Antipas. 1981. pap. 1.00 (ISBN 0-317-30436-4). Holy Trinity.

Lovasik, Lawrence G. Picture Book of Saints. (Illus.). 4.95 (ISBN 0-89942-235-7, 235-22). Catholic Bk Pub.

Lucas, E. V. At the Shrine of St. Charles. 1934. Repr. 25.00 (ISBN 0-8274-1898-1). R West.

McBride, Alfred. Saints Are People: Church History Through the Saints. 144p. (Orig.). 1981. pap. 4.50 (ISBN 0-697-01785-0). Wm C Brown.

McDonnell, Thomas P. Saints in Due Season. LC 83-60742. 196p. (Orig.). 1983. pap. 5.95 (ISBN 0-87973-623-2, 623). Our Sunday Visitor.

McGinley, Phyllis. Saint Watching. (The Crossroad Paperback Ser.). 256p. 1982. pap. 6.95 (ISBN 0-8245-0450-X). Crossroad NY.

Magee, William K. Bards & Saints. LC 76-8220. 1976. Repr. of 1906 ed. lib. bdg. 17.50 (ISBN 0-8414-3976-1). Folcroft.

Martindale, C. C. What Are Saints? Fourteen Studies in Sanctity. 1982. pap. 3.95 (ISBN 0-89453-270-7). M Glazier.

Martindale, Cyril C. What Are Saints: Fifteen Chapters in Sanctity. facs. ed. LC 68-16954. (Essay Index Reprint Ser). 1932. 13.75 (ISBN 0-8369-0681-0). Ayer Co Pubs.

Matthews, V. J. St. Philip Neri. LC 84-50406. 120p. 1984. pap. 3.00 (ISBN 0-89555-237-X). TAN Bks Pubs.

Mauriac, Francois. Sainte Marguerite de Cortone. pap. 5.95 (ISBN 0-685-34304-9). French & Eur.

Mead, Jude C. St. Paul of the Cross: A Source-Workbook in Paulacrucian Studies. 560p. 1983. pap. 12.95 (ISBN 0-89944-070-3). Don Bosco Multimedia.

Meschler, Maurice. Life of St. Aloysius Gonzaga: Patron of Christian Youth. LC 84-52294. 344p. 1985. pap. 7.00 (ISBN 0-89555-275-2). Tan Bks Pubs.

Miller, Molly. The Saints of Gwynedd. (Studies in Celtic History). 132p. 1979. 21.50x (ISBN 0-8476-6186-5). Rowman.

Monro, Margaret T. Book of Unlikely Saints. LC 77-107727. (Essay Index Reprint Ser.). 1943. 19.00 (ISBN 0-8369-1528-3). Ayer Co Pubs.

Montague, H. Patrick. The Saints & Martyrs of Ireland: Feast Days Calendar. (Illus.). 138p. Date not set. 15.95 (ISBN 0-86140-106-9); pap. 5.95 (ISBN 0-86140-107-7). Dufour.

Morrow, Danny R. Silhouette of a Saint: Albert Pepper. 1985. 4.95 (ISBN 0-86544-027-1). Salv Army Suppl South.

Mother Thais. Zhitija Russkikh Svatikh, v 2 tom, 2 vols. LC 82-81204. Tr. of The Lives of the Russian Saints. Vol. 1. pap. 10.00 (ISBN 0-88465-012-X); Vol. 2. pap. 13.00 (ISBN 0-88465-020-0). Holy Trinity.

Murphy, Frederick. Breviary Lives of the Saints: A Translation into English. 1979. pap. 1.00 (ISBN 0-8198-1108-4). Dghtrs St Paul.

Murray, John O. Little Lives of the Great Saints. LC 82-50593. 495p. 1985. pap. 12.00 (ISBN 0-89555-190-X). Tan Bks Pubs.

Nadejda Gorodetzky. Saint Tikhon of Zadonsk: Inspirer of Dostoevsky. LC 76-49919. 320p. 1977. pap. 8.95 (ISBN 0-913836-32-X). St Vladimirs.

Needham, G. I., ed. Lives of Three English Saints. rev. ed. 119p. 1979. pap. text ed. 7.95x (ISBN 0-85989-076-7, Pub. by U Exeter UK). Humanities.

Newland, Mary R. The Saint Book: For Parents, Teachers, Homilists, Storytellers & Children. (Illus.). 206p. 1979. pap. 8.95 (ISBN 0-8164-0210-8, 7480, HarpR). Har-Row.

--The Saint Book: For Parents, Teachers, Homilists, Storytellers & Children. 206p. (Orig.). 1985. pap. 8.95 (ISBN 0-86683-979-8, 7480, HarpR). Har-Row.

O'Leary, De Lacy E. The Saints of Egypt. (Church Historical Society, London, News Ser.: No. 27). Repr. of 1937 ed. 55.00 (ISBN 0-8115-3151-1). Kraus Repr.

Oppitz, Joseph. Autumn Memoirs of St. Alphonsus Liguori. 96p. 1986. pap. 3.95 (ISBN 0-89243-253-5). Liguori Pubns.

Papasogli, Giorgio. St. Teresa of Avila. LC 58-12223. 1973. Repr. 5.00 (ISBN 0-8198-0511-4). Dghtrs St Paul.

Parbury, Kathleen. Women of Grace: A Biographical Dictionary of British Women Saints, Martyrs & Reformers. 224p. 1985. 25.00x (ISBN 0-85362-213-2, Oriel). Methuen Inc.

Pastrovicchi, Angelo. Saint Joseph of Copertino. LC 79-91298. 135p. 1980. pap. 3.00 (ISBN 0-89555-135-7). TAN Bks Pubs.

Petin, L. M. Dictionnaire Hagiographique, 2 vols. Migne, J. P., ed. (Encyclopedie Theologique Ser.: Vols. 40-41). (Fr.). 1580p. Repr. of 1850 ed. lib. bdg. 240.00x (ISBN 0-89241-246-1). Caratzas.

Pierradrd, Pierre. Larousse Des Prenoms et Des Saints. (Fr.). 256p. 1976. 42.50 (ISBN 0-686-57079-0, M-6454). French & Eur.

Pierrard, Pierre. Dictionnaire des Prenoms et des Saints. (Fr.). 224p. 1975. pap. 6.95 (ISBN 0-686-56861-3, M-6639). French & Eur.

Prophet, Mark & Prophet, Elizabeth, eds. Pearls of Wisdom, 1978: Spoken by Elohim, Vol. 21. LC 79-66985. 513p. 1980. 14.95 (ISBN 0-916766-36-5). Summit Univ.

Puhalo, L. Lives of the Saints, Vols. 2. 1977. pap. 2.50x ea.; Vol. 2. (ISBN 0-913026-75-1); St Nectarios.

Raymond of Cupua. Saint Catherine of Siena. 30.00 (ISBN 0-89453-151-4). M Glazier.

Rex, Barbara. Saints & Innocents. 1972. 6.95 (ISBN 0-393-08664-X). Norton.

Royer, Fanchon. The Life of St. Anthony Mary Claret. LC 85-52248. 302p. (Orig.). 1985. pap. 8.00 (ISBN 0-89555-288-4). Tan Bks Pubs.

Rumbaut, Ruben D. John of God: His Place in the History of Psychiatry & Medicine. LC 77-91668. 1978. pap. 8.00 (ISBN 0-89729-198-0). Ediciones.

Rutten, Felix. Die Victorverehrung Im Christlichen Altertum. Repr. of 1936 ed. 15.00 (ISBN 0-384-52655-1). Johnson Repr.

St. Alexander Nevsky. pap. 0.50 (ISBN 0-686-05660-4). Eastern Orthodox.

St. John Ogilvie S.J., 1579-1615. 68p. 1979. 30.00x (Pub. by Third Eye Centre). State Mutual Bk.

St. Paisios the Great. 71p. 1983. pap. 3.00 (ISBN 0-317-30439-9). Holy Trinity.

St. Thomas Aquinas. St. Thomas Aquinas: Philosophical Texts. Gilby, Thomas, ed. xxiv, 406p. 1982. pap. 12.50x (ISBN 0-939464-06-3). Labyrinth Pr.

Saint Athanasius. Zhitie Prepodobnago Antonija Velikago. Tr. of The Life of St. Anthony the Great. 47p. pap. 2.00 (ISBN 0-317-29181-5). Holy Trinity.

Saint Dimitri Rostov. Zhitija Svjatikh v 12 tomov, 12 vols. Tr. of The Lives of the Saints. 10000p. Repr. of 1968 ed. 360.00 (ISBN 0-317-29175-0). Holy Trinity.

Saint John Bosco. St. Joseph Cafasso: Priest of the Gallows. LC 82-50979. Orig. Title: A Saint Speaks for Another Saint. 80p. 1983. pap. 2.00 (ISBN 0-89555-194-2). TAN Bks Pubs.

Saint John of Kronstadt. My Life in Christ. Goulaeff, E. E., tr. from Rus. LC 84-81775. 558p. 1984. 25.00 (ISBN 0-88465-018-9); pap. 20.00 (ISBN 0-88465-017-0). Holy Trinity.

Schamoni, Wilhelm. Face of the Saints. Fremantle, Anne, tr. LC 70-38328. (Biography Index Reprint Ser). Repr. of 1947 ed. 26.50 (ISBN 0-8369-8128-6). Ayer Co Pubs.

Schillebeeckx, Edward. Paul the Apostle. (Illus.). 128p. 1983. 14.95 (ISBN 0-8245-0574-3). Crossroad NY.

Schmalenberger, Jerry. Advent & Christmas Saints. 1984. 3.75 (ISBN 0-89536-685-1, 4861). CSS of Ohio.

Schneider, Albert. Communion with the Saints. 1983. 25.00 (ISBN 0-686-45785-4). Franciscan Herald.

Schouppe, F. X. Purgatory--Explained by the Lives & Legends of the Saints. LC 86-50579. 427p. (Orig.). 1986. pap. 5.00 (Pulp Pocketbook (ISBN 0-89555-301-5). Tan Bks Pubs.

Sell, Alan P. Saints: Visible, Orderly & Catholic: The Congregational Idea of the Church. (Princeton Theological Monograph Ser.: No. 7). (Orig.). 1986. pap. 15.00 (ISBN 0-915138-89-1). Pickwick.

Service to St. Tikhon of Kaluga. (Slavic.). pap. 5.00 (ISBN 0-686-16368-0). Eastern Orthodox.

Simi, Gino J. & Segreti, Mario M. St. Francis of Paola: God's Miracle Worker Supreme. LC 77-78097. 1977. pap. 4.50 (ISBN 0-89555-065-2). TAN Bks Pubs.

Skeat, W. W., ed. Aelfric's Lives of Saints, Vol. II, Pts. III-IV. (EETS OS Ser.: Vols. 94 & 114). Repr. of 1900 ed. 22.00 (ISBN 0-8115-3365-4). Kraus Repr.

Spiegelstein, Max. Paul, the Saint Who Ain't. 1980. 12.50 (ISBN 0-89962-017-5). Todd & Honeywell.

Spurgeon, C. H. Kingly Priesthood of the Saints. 1978. pap. 0.95 (ISBN 0-686-26195-X). Pilgrim Pubns.

--Sweet Comfort for Feeble Saints. 1978. pap. 0.95 (ISBN 0-686-28282-5). Pilgrim Pubns.

Sr. Vincent Regnault. St. Louise de Marillac: Servant of the Poor. LC 83-50058. 136p. 1984. pap. 3.50 (ISBN 0-89555-215-9). TAN Bks Pubs.

Stevens, Courtenay E. Sidonius Apollinaris & His Age. LC 78-21112. 1979. Repr. of 1933 ed. lib. bdg. 24.75x (ISBN 0-313-20850-6, STSA). Greenwood.

Sts. Cyril & Methodius. 1966. pap. 0.50 (ISBN 0-317-30441-0). Holy Trinity.

Subramanian, Anna A. Saints of India. (Illus.). 1978. pap. 3.25 (ISBN 0-87481-479-0). Vedanta Pr.

Svjelij Otrok; Sbornik Statej o Tsarevichje Mutchenikje Alekseje i drugikh Tsarstvennikh Mutchenikakh. Tr. of Bright Child; A Collection of Articles about the Prince-Martyr & Other Royal Martyrs. (Illus.). 105p. pap. 5.00 (ISBN 0-317-29229-3). Holy Trinity.

Taylor, John W. The Coming of the Saints. rev. ed. LC 85-71651. (Illus.). 272p. 1985. pap. 10.00 (ISBN 0-934666-19-9). Artisan Sales.

Tsirpanlis, Constance N. The Anthropology of Saint John of Damascus. 64p. 1980. pap. 3.00 (ISBN 0-686-36332-9). EO Pr.

Tylenda, Joseph N. Jesuit Saints & Martyrs. 503p. 1984. 15.95 (ISBN 0-8294-0447-3). Loyola.

Undset, Sigrid. Saga of Saints. facs. ed. Ramsden, E. C., tr. LC 68-22952. (Essay Index Reprint Ser). 1968. Repr. of 1934 ed. 20.00 (ISBN 0-8369-0959-3). Ayer Co Pubs.

Waddell, Helen. Desert Fathers. 1957. pap. 7.95 (ISBN 0-472-06008-2, 8, AA). U of Mich Pr.

Wallace, James A. Preaching Through the Saints. LC 82-7745. 80p. 1982. pap. 2.50 (ISBN 0-8146-1271-7). Liturgical Pr.

Walsh, Michael, ed. Butler's Lives of the Saints. LC 84-48781. 496p. 1985. 20.45 (ISBN 0-06-069251-0, HarpR). Har-Row.

Wirth, Morand. Don Bosco & the Salesians. DeBurgh, David, tr. from Italian. LC 82-72675. Orig. Title: Don Bosco e i Salesiani. 432p. (Orig.). 1982. pap. 10.95 (ISBN 0-89944-065-7). Don Bosco Multimedia.

Wright, John. The Saints Always Belong to the Present. Almagno, Stephen, pref. by. LC 84-80016. 221p. 1984. pap. 8.95 (ISBN 0-89870-047-7). Ignatius Pr.

Young, William, tr. St. Ignatius's Own Story. 1980. Repr. 3.95 (ISBN 0-8294-0359-0). Loyola.

Zander, Valentine. St. Seraphim of Sarov. LC 75-24136. Orig. Title: Seraphim of Sarov. 150p. 1975. pap. 6.95 (ISBN 0-913836-28-1). St Vladimirs.

Zekowski, Arlene & Berne, Stanley. Cardinals & Saints. LC 58-11713. (Illus.). 1958. 45.00 (ISBN 0-913844-10-1). Am Canadian.

Zhitije Prepodobnago Vasilia Novago i Videnije Grirorije, utchenika Ego. Tr. of The Life of St. Basil the New & the Vision of Gregory His Disciple. 125p. pap. 5.00 (ISBN 0-317-29188-2). Holy Trinity.

Zhitije Svjatago Pravednago Ioanna Kronshtatdskago Tchudotvortsa. Tr. of The Life of St. John the Miracle-worker of Kronstadt. 23p. 1964. pap. 1.00 (ISBN 0-317-29199-8). Holy Trinity.

SAINTS-CALENDAR

Daughters of St Paul. Saints for Young People for Every Day of the Year, Vol. 2. (Illus.). 6.00 (ISBN 0-8198-0647-1); pap. 4.50 (ISBN 0-8198-0648-X). Dghtrs St Paul.

Delaney, John J., ed. Saints for All Seasons. LC 77-81438. 1978. pap. 3.95 (ISBN 0-385-12909-2, Im). Doubleday.

Foley, Leonard, ed. Saint of the Day. (Illus.). 354p. 1981. text ed. 10.95 (ISBN 0-912228-96-2). St Anthony Mess Pr.

--Saint of the Day: A Life & Lesson for Each of the 173 Saints of the New Missal, Vol. 1. (Illus.). 1974. pap. 3.50 (ISBN 0-912228-16-4). St Anthony Mess Pr.

Levy, Rosalie. Heavenly Friends: A Saint for Each Day. 7.00 (ISBN 0-8198-0638-2); pap. 6.00 (ISBN 0-8198-0639-0). Dghtrs St Paul.

Murphy, Frederick J. Breviary Lives of the Saints, Vol. 1 Sept.- Jan., Vol. 2 Feb.-May. (Lat., Illus., Orig.). 1965. Vol. 1. pap. 2.50 (ISBN 0-8198-0012-0); Vol. 2. 3.50 (ISBN 0-8198-0013-9). Dghtrs St Paul.

SAINTS-CORRESPONDENCE, REMINISCENCES, ETC.

Adels, Jill H. Wisdom of the Saints: An Anthology of Voices. 288p. 1987. 16.95 (ISBN 0-19-504152-6). Oxford U Pr.

Alferirff, E. E., ed. Pisoma Tsarskoj Semji iz Zatotchenija. LC 73-91829. Tr. of Letters of the Tsar's Family from Captivity. (Illus.). 544p. 1974. 25.00 (ISBN 0-317-29225-0). Holy Trinity.

Aubry, Joseph, ed. The Spiritual Writings of St. John Bosco. Caselli, Joseph, tr. from Italian. LC 83-71820. Tr. of Giovanni Bosco, Scritti Spirituali. 412p. 1984. pap. 12.95 (ISBN 0-89944-049-5). Don Bosco Multimedia.

Clarke, Graeme W., ed. The Letters of St. Cyprian: Vol. 3, Letters 55-66. (ACW Ser.: No. 46). 352p. 1986. 24.95 (ISBN 0-8091-0369-9). Paulist Pr.

Clarke, John, tr. Saint Therese of Lisieux General Correspondence: Vol. I, 1877-1890. LC 81-6474. 700p. (Orig.). 1982. pap. 9.95x (ISBN 0-9600876-9-9). ICS Pubns.

Fox, Robert J. Saints & Heroes Speak. 512p. 1983. 7.95 (ISBN 0-911988-43-2). Ami Pr.

Ignacio Loyola. The Autobiography of St. Ignatius. lib. bdg. 59.95 (ISBN 0-87968-685-5). Gordon Pr.

John of the Cross. Dark Night of the Soul. Zimmerman, Benedict, tr. 246p. 1974. pap. 10.95 (ISBN 0-227-67807-9). Attic Pr.

Mark Of Ephesus, Saint Encyclical Letter of St. Mark of Ephesus. pap. 0.50 (ISBN 0-686-16366-4). Eastern Orthodox.

Paganuzzi, P. Pravda ob Ubijstvje Tsarskoj Semji. LC 80-84594. Tr. of The Truth About the Murder of the Royal Family. 234p. 1981. 15.00 (ISBN 0-317-29234-X); pap. 10.00 (ISBN 0-317-29235-8). Holy Trinity.

Paslanije Svatago Ignatija Aniokhiskago I Sviatago Polykarpa Smirnskago. Tr. of Letters of St. Ignatius of Anioch & of St.Polycarp of Smyrna. Repr. 2.00 (ISBN 0-317-28881-4). Holy Trinity.

St. Cyril of Alexandria. Letters, 1-50. (The Fathers of the Church: Vol. 76). 350p. 1987. 29.95x (ISBN 0-8132-0076-8). Cath U Pr.

St. Paul. The Writings of St. Paul. Meeks, Wayne, ed. (Critical Edition Ser). 1972. 12.95 (ISBN 0-393-04338-X); pap. 9.95x (ISBN 0-393-09979-2). Norton.

Schillebeeckx, Edward. Paul the Apostle. (Illus.). 128p. 1983. 14.95 (ISBN 0-8245-0574-3). Crossroad NY.

Vaporis, Nomikos M. Father Kosmas: The Apostle of the Poor. LC 77-77664. (Illus.). 164p. 1977. 7.95 (ISBN 0-916586-17-0); pap. 4.95 (ISBN 0-916586-10-3). Holy Cross Orthodox.

Veal, David L. Saints Galore. 160p. (Orig.). 1972. pap. 1.75 (ISBN 0-88028-009-3, 405). Forward Movement.

SAINTS-CULTUS

see also Mary, Virgin-Cultus

Brown, Peter. The Cult of the Saints: Its Rise & Function in Latin Christianity. LC 80-11210. xvi, 188p. 1982. pap. 7.95 (ISBN 0-226-07622-9, Phoen). U of Chicago Pr.

Hackel, Sergei, ed. The Byzantine Saint. (Illus.). 245p. (Orig.). 1981. pap. 6.95 (ISBN 0-7044-0451-6). St Vladimirs.

Perkins, Russell. The Impact of a Saint. LC 80-51959. 256p. 1980. pap. 7.50 (ISBN 0-89142-037-1). Sant Bani Ash.

Wilson, Stephen, ed. Saints & Their Cults: Studies in Religious Sociology, Folklore & History. 447p. 1986. pap. 19.95 (ISBN 0-521-31181-0). Cambridge U Pr.

SAINTS-INVOCATION

see Saints-Cultus

SAINTS-JUVENILE LITERATURE

Cartayne, Alice. Irish Saints for Boys & Girls. (Illus.). 96p. 1978. pap. 3.95 (ISBN 0-86167-018-3, Pub. by Educ Co of Ireland). Longwood Pub Group.

Curley, Ed. Saints for Young Christians. 1983. 9.95 (ISBN 0-89837-088-4, Pub. by Pflaum Pr). Peter Li.

De Santis, Zerlina. A Child's Story of Saints, Past & Present. 1979. 1.75 (ISBN 0-8198-0567-X); pap. 1.00 (ISBN 0-8198-0568-8). Dghtrs St Paul.

Lee, Frank. Bedtime Stories of the Saints, Bk. 2. 64p. (Orig.). 1980. pap. 1.95 (ISBN 0-89243-126-1). Liguori Pubns.

Nastick, Sharon. So You Think You've Got Problems: Twelve Stubborn Saints & Their Pushy Parents. LC 81-85454. (Illus.). 96p. (Orig.). 1982. pap. 3.95 (ISBN 0-87973-661-5, 661). Our Sunday Visitor.

Patterson, Yvonne. Doubting Thomas. (Arch Book Ser.: No. 18). 1981. pap. 0.99 (ISBN 0-570-06144-X, 59-1261). Concordia.

Puhalo, Lev. Lives of Saints for Young People, Vol. 1. 1975. pap. 2.50x (ISBN 0-913026-11-5). St Nectarios.

Scotti, Juliet & Linksman, Ricki. Kirpal Singh: The Story of a Saint. 2nd ed. LC 77-79840. (Children's Ser.: No. 1). (Illus.). 96p. 1982. pap. 4.95 (ISBN 0-918224-05-5). Sawan Kirpal Pubns.

Synge, Ursula. The Giant at the Ford & Other Legends of the Saints. LC 79-23020. (Illus.). 176p. 1980. 9.95 (ISBN 0-689-50168-4, McElderry Bk). Macmillan.

Twomey, Mark J. A Parade of Saints. LC 82-202387. (Illus.). 176p. 1983. 10.95 (ISBN 0-8146-1275-X). Liturgical Pr.

SAINTS-LEGENDS

Brodrick, James. Procession of Saints. LC 72-5436. (Biography Index Reprint Ser). 1972. Repr. of 1949 ed. 20.50 (ISBN 0-8369-8134-0). Ayer Co Pubs.

Delehaye, Hippolyte. The Legends of the Saints. LC 77-26797. 1907. 30.00 (ISBN 0-8414-3657-6). Folcroft.

Gerould, G. H. Saints' Legends. 59.95 (ISBN 0-8490-0987-1). Gordon Pr.

Gerould, Gordon H. Saints' Legends. 1980. Repr. of 1916 ed. lib. bdg. 37.00 (ISBN 0-8414-4627-X). Folcroft.

Henken, Elissa R. Traditions of the Welsh Saints. 200p. 1986. 37.50 (ISBN 0-85991-221-3, Pub. by Boydell & Brewer). Longwood Pub Group.

Keshavadas, Satguru S. Saints of India. 100p. (Orig.). 1975. pap. 3.50 (ISBN 0-942508-05-X). Vishwa.

Lang, David M., ed. Lives & Legends of the Georgian Saints. 179p. 1976. pap. 4.95 (ISBN 0-913836-29-X). St Vladimirs.

Metcalfe, W. M., ed. Legends of the Saints, in the Scottish Dialect of the Fourteenth Century, 3 Vols. 1896. Set. 140.00 (ISBN 0-384-32090-2). Johnson Repr.

Oliveira, Joseph De. Jacinta, Flower of Fatima. 192p. 1972. pap. 3.95 (ISBN 0-911988-45-9). AMI Pr.

Stanford, Gwendolyn C. Legende Doree Ou Legenda Aurea: The First Ten Chapters. LC 85-90222. 125p. 1986. 8.95 (ISBN 0-533-06725-1). Vantage.

Uitti, Karl D. Story, Myth & Celebration in Old French Narrative Poetry 1050-1200. LC 72-4048. 272p. 1973. 30.50x (ISBN 0-691-06242-0). Princeton U Pr.

SAINTS-VENERATION

see Saints-Cultus

SAINTS, ENGLISH

Adair, John. The Pilgrim's Way: Shrines & Saints in Britain & Ireland. (Illus.). 1978. 12.98 (ISBN 0-500-25061-8). Thames Hudson.

Gibbs, Margaret. Saints Beyond the White Cliffs: Stories of English Saints. facs. ed. LC 75-148211. (Biography Index Reprint Ser.). (Illus.). 1947. 20.00 (ISBN 0-8369-8058-1). Ayer Co Pubs.

Keep, David. St. Boniface & His World. (Illus.). 64p. 1979. pap. 4.50 (ISBN 0-85364-276-1). Attic Pr.

Reuter, Timothy, ed. The Greatest Englishman: Essays on St. Boniface & the Church at Crediton. 140p. 1980. text ed. 15.00 (ISBN 0-85364-277-X). Attic Pr.

Sladden, John C. Boniface of Devon: Apostle of Germany. 254p. 1980. text ed. 18.75 (ISBN 0-85364-275-3). Attic Pr.

Vince, John. Discovering Saints in Britain. (Discovering Ser.: No. 64). (Illus.). 64p. 1983. pap. 3.95 (ISBN 0-85263-449-8, Pub. by Shire Pubns England). Seven Hills Bks.

SAINTS, WOMEN

Bell, Rudolph M. Holy Anorexia. LC 85-8460. (Illus.). xii, 248p. 1985. 22.50 (ISBN 0-226-04204-9). U of Chicago Pr.

Benedictine Sisters of Clyde, Missouri Staff. St. Gertrude the Great: Herald of Divine Love. 1977. pap. 0.75 (ISBN 0-89555-026-1). TAN Bks Pubs.

Bridget. The Magnificent Prayers of Saint Bridget of Sweden. (Illus.). 19p. 1983. pap. 1.00 (ISBN 0-89555-220-5). TAN Bks Pubs.

Chavez, Jose. Santa Maria de Guadalupe. (Span.). 1963. pap. 2.00 (ISBN 0-8198-6825-6). Dghtrs St Paul.

Ghanananda, Swami & Steward-Wallace, John, eds. Women Saints of East & West. LC 79-65731. 1979. pap. 7.95 (ISBN 0-87481-036-1). Vedanta Pr.

Horstmann, C., ed. Prose Lives of Women Saints of Our Contrie of England. (EETS, OS Ser.: No.86). Repr. of 1886 ed. 45.00 (ISBN 0-527-00082-5). Kraus Repr.

Lappin, Peter. Halfway to Heaven. LC 80-68485. 265p. (Orig.). 1980. pap. 6.95 (ISBN 0-89944-052-5). Don Bosco Multimedia.

Smith, Margaret. Rabi'a the Mystic & Her Fellow-Saints in Islam. 2nd ed. 256p. 1984. 37.50 (ISBN 0-521-26779-X); pap. 13.95 (ISBN 0-521-31863-7). Cambridge U Pr.

Von Stamwitz, Alicia. Women of Valor: The Trials & Triumphs of Seven Saints. 64p. 1986. pap. 1.95 (ISBN 0-89243-258-6). Liguori Pubns.

SAINTS IN ART

Clement, Clara E. Saints in Art. LC 77-89303. 1976. Repr. of 1899 ed. 46.00x (ISBN 0-8103-3030-X). Gale.

De Bles, Arthur. How to Distinguish the Saints in Art by Their Costumes, Symbols & Attributes. LC 68-18018. 1975. Repr. of 1925 ed. 70.00x (ISBN 0-8103-4125-5). Gale.

Ridderbos, Bernhard. Saint & Symbol: Images of Saint Jerome in Early Italian Art. (Illus.). xv, 126p. 1984. pap. 18.00x (ISBN 90-6088-087-0, Pub. by Boumas Boekhuis Netherlands). Benjamins North AM.

Schamoni, Wilhelm. Face of the Saints. Fremantle, Anne, tr. LC 70-38328. (Biography Index Reprint Ser). Repr. of 1947 ed. 26.50 (ISBN 0-8369-8128-6). Ayer Co Pubs.

SAKTISM

see Shaktism

SALEM, MASSACHUSETTS

Bentley, William. The Diary of Rev. William Bentley: 1784-1819, 4 vols. 72.00 (ISBN 0-8446-1071-2). Set. Peter Smith.

Chamberlain, Samuel. Stroll Through Historic Salem. LC 78-79738. (Illus.). 1969. student ed. 9.95 (ISBN 0-8038-6689-5). Hastings.

Tolles, Bryant F., Jr. The John Tucker Daland House. LC 76-27382. (Historic House Booklet Ser.). 1978. 2.00 (ISBN 0-88389-065-8). Essex Inst.

Upham, Charles W. Salem Witchcraft, 2 Vols. LC 59-10887. (American Classics Ser.). (Illus.). 1959. 40.00 (ISBN 0-8044-1947-7). Ungar.

SALEM, MASSACHUSETTS–HISTORY

Adams, Herbert B. Village Communities of Cape Anne & Salem, from the Historical Collections of the Essex Institute. pap. 9.00 (ISBN 0-384-00334-6). Johnson Repr.

Boyer, Paul & Nissenbaum, Stephen. Salem Possessed: The Social Origins of Witchcraft. LC 73-84399. 320p. 1974. pap. 6.95x (ISBN 0-674-78526-6). Harvard U Pr.

Brown, David C. A Guide to the Salem Witchcraft Hysteria of 1692. LC 84-164658. (Illus.). 130p. (Orig.). 1984. pap. 5.95 (ISBN 0-9613415-0-5). D C Brown.

Cummings, A. L. & Fales, D. A., Jr. The Crowninshield-Bentley House. LC 76-16905. (Historic House Booklet Ser.: No. 2). 1976. 2.00 (ISBN 0-88389-060-7). Essex Inst.

Fritz, Jean. Early Thunder. LC 67-24217. (Illus.). 1967. 9.95 (ISBN 0-698-20036-5, Coward). Putnam Pub Group.

Gildrie, Richard P. Salem, Massachusetts, Sixteen Twenty-Six to Sixteen Eighty-Three: A Covenant Community. LC 74-20841. (Illus.). 187p. 1975. 20.00x (ISBN 0-8139-0532-X). U Pr of Va.

Hansen, Chadwick. Witchcraft at Salem. (Illus.). 252p. 1985. pap. 7.95 (ISBN 0-8076-1137-9). Braziller.

Kempfer, Lester L. The Salem Light Guard. LC 73-76068. (Illus.). 128p. 1973. 5.95 (ISBN 0-686-04916-0); pap. 3.95 (ISBN 0-686-04917-9). L Kempfer.

Mappen, Marc. Witches & Historians: Interpretations of Salem. LC 78-2579. (American Problem Studies). 126p. 1980. pap. 6.50 (ISBN 0-88275-653-2). Krieger.

Phillips, James D. Salem in the Eighteenth Century. LC 37-36381. (Illus.). 533p. 1969. Repr. of 1937 ed. 25.00 (ISBN 0-88389-017-8). Essex Inst.

Pynchon, William. The Diary of William Pynchon of Salem. Oliver, Fitch E., ed. LC 75-31131. Repr. of 1890 ed. 28.50 (ISBN 0-404-13608-7). AMS Pr.

Ward, Gerald W. The Assembly House. LC 76-16903. (Historic House Booklet Ser.: No. 3). 1976. 2.00 (ISBN 0-88389-061-5). Essex Inst.

--The Peirce-Nichols House. LC 76-16904. (Historic House Booklet Ser.: No. 4). 1976. 2.00 (ISBN 0-88389-062-3). Essex Inst.

SALESIANS

Serving the Salesian Family: A Resource Manual for Salesians. (Salesian Family Ser.). 88p. 1983. pap. 3.50 (ISBN 0-89944-076-2). Don Bosco Multimedia.

SALT LAKE CITY

Chandless, William. Visit to Salt Lake. LC 76-134391. Repr. of 1857 ed. 24.50 (ISBN 0-404-08434-6). AMS Pr.

Remy, Jules & Brenchley, Julius. A Journey to Great Salt-Lake City, 2 vols. LC 75-134399. (Illus.). Repr. of 1861 ed. Set. 49.50 (ISBN 0-404-08441-9). Vol. 1 (ISBN 0-404-08442-7). Vol. 2 (ISBN 0-404-08443-5). AMS Pr.

SALUS EXTRA ECCLESIAM

see Salvation outside the Catholic Church; Universalism

SALVATION

see also Assurance (Theology); Atonement; Covenants (Theology); Justification; Redemption; Repentance; Salvation outside the Catholic Church; Sanctification; Sin

Beall, James L. Laying the Foundation. LC 76-42084. 389p. 1976. pap. 5.95 (ISBN 0-88270-198-3). Bridge Pub.

Berry, R. L. Around Old Bethany. 83p. pap. 0.75 (ISBN 0-686-29097-6). Faith Pub Hse.

Blechschmidt, Meinulf. Der Leib und das Heil. (European University Studies: No. 23, Vol. 207). (Ger.). 435p. 1983. 22.10 (ISBN 3-261-03264-2). P Lang Pubs.

Bobosh, Theodore. Am I Saved? 1984. pap. 3.45 (ISBN 0-937032-38-7). Light&Life Pub Co MN.

Brandon, Samuel G., ed. The Saviour God: Comparative Studies in the Concept of Salvation Presented to Edwin Oliver James. LC 80-14924. xxii, 242p. 1980. Repr. of 1963 ed. lib. bdg. 24.75x (ISBN 0-313-22416-1, BRSG). Greenwood.

Brandt, Robert L. One Way. LC 77-75601. (Radiant Life Ser.). 128p. 1977. pap. 2.50 (ISBN 0-88243-909-X, 02-0909); teacher's ed 3.95 (ISBN 0-88243-179-X, 32-0179). Gospel Pub.

Braunthal, Alfred. Salvation & the Perfect Society: The Eternal Quest. LC 79-4705. 448p. 1979. lib. bdg. 25.00x (ISBN 0-87023-273-8). U of Mass Pr.

Brookes, James H. Salvation: The Way Made Plain. pap. 4.50 (ISBN 0-685-61831-5). Reiner.

Bunyan, John. Intercession of Christ. pap. 1.95 (ISBN 0-685-19835-9). Reiner.

--The Jerusalem Sinner Saved. pap. 3.25 (ISBN 0-685-88378-7). Reiner.

Byrum, E. E. The Secret of Salvation. 264p. pap. 2.50 (ISBN 0-686-29166-2). Faith Pub Hse.

Campbell, R. K. Things That Accompany Salvation. 40p. pap. 0.45 (ISBN 0-88172-013-5). Believers Bkshelf.

Cerdic Colloquium Staff. Liberation Theology & the Message of Salvation: Proceedings of the Cerdic Colloquium, 4th, Strasbourg, May 10-12, 1973. Metz, Rene & Schlick, Jean, eds. Gelzer, David G., tr. LC 78-7540. (Pittsburgh Theological Monographs: No. 20). 1978. pap. 8.75 (ISBN 0-915138-26-3). Pickwick.

Chafer, Lewis S. Salvation. 160p. 1972. pap. 5.95 (ISBN 0-310-22351-2, 6309P). Zondervan.

Cocoris, G. Michael. Lordship Salvation-Is It Biblical? 24p. (Orig.). 1983. pap. 1.25 (ISBN 0-9607576-2-7). Redencion Viva.

Cutting, Jorge. La Salvacion: Su Seguridad, Creteza y Gozo. 2nd ed. Daniel, Roger P., ed. Bautista, Sara, tr. from Eng. (La Serie Diamante). Tr. of Safety, Certainity & Enjoyment. (Span., Illus.). 48p. 1982. pap. 0.85 (ISBN 0-942504-05-4). Overcomer Pr.

Davis, Susan. Password to Heaven. (My Church Teaches Ser.). 32p. 1980. pap. 2.50 (ISBN 0-8127-0298-0). Review & Herald.

Deal, William S. How May I Know I Am Saved? 1973. pap. 0.60, 3 for 1.50, 5 for 2.50, 10 for 5.00 (ISBN 0-686-05834-8). Crusade Pubs.

DeCelles, Charles. The Unbound Spirit: God's Universal, Sanctifying Work. LC 85-20047. 367p. (Orig.). 1985. pap. 9.95 (ISBN 0-8189-0486-0). Alba.

Dent, Arthur. The Plaine Mans Path-Way to Heaven. LC 74-80173. (English Experience Ser.: No. 652). 430p. 1974. Repr. of 1601 ed. 29.00 (ISBN 90-221-0652-7). Walter J Johnson.

DiCrescenza, Frances. Annihilation or Salvation? 1986. 8.95 (ISBN 0-8062-2505-X). Carlton.

Dominy, Bert. God's Work of Salvation. LC 83-71264. (Layman's Library of Christian Doctrine Ser.). 1986. 5.95 (ISBN 0-8054-1638-2). Broadman.

Douty, Norman. Union with Christ. 10.95 (ISBN 0-685-36792-4). Reiner.

Duty, Guy. If Ye Continue. LC 82-2314. 192p. 1966. pap. 4.95 (ISBN 0-87123-243-X, 210243). Bethany Hse.

Edman, Irwin. Contemporary & His Soul. LC 66-25907. Repr. of 1931 ed. 18.50x (ISBN 0-8046-0129-1, Pub. by Kennikat). Assoc Faculty Pr.

Edwards, Denis. What Are They Saying about Salvation? 100p. 1986. pap. 4.95 (ISBN 0-8091-2793-8). Paulist Pr.

Field, Kent A. Test Your Salvation. 0.60 (ISBN 0-89137-531-7). Quality Pubns.

Friedman, Michael. Passages of Observation: A Guru's Guide to Salvation. Jacobsen, Liz, ed. (Illus.). 1983. pap. 4.95 (ISBN 0-912561-00-9). Counsel & Stress.

Gakpe-Ntrsi, Theodore. Church As a Sacrament of Salvation. 112p. 1987. 9.95 (ISBN 0-89962-577-0). Todd & Honeywell.

Gaspard, Perry A. Salvation. 1983. pap. 1.00 (ISBN 0-931867-00-2). Abundant Life Pubns.

Glaze, R. E., Jr. No Easy Salvation. LC 66-10708. 72p. 1984. pap. 4.00 (ISBN 0-914520-06-7). Insight Pr.

Grossman, Richard L. Salvation. (Literary Chapbook Ser.). 48p. 1977. pap. 3.00 (ISBN 0-916300-05-6). Gallimaufry.

Gunderson, Vivian D. Over the Cliff. 1974. pap. 1.75 (ISBN 0-915374-13-7, 13-7). Rapids Christian.

--Saved on Monday. 1964. pap. 1.75 (ISBN 0-915374-14-5, 14-5). Rapids Christian.

--The Wrong Road. 1964. pap. 1.75 (ISBN 0-915374-15-3, 15-3). Rapids Christian.

Hardon, John A. Salvation & Santification. 1978. 3.50 (ISBN 0-8198-0366-9); pap. 2.50 (ISBN 0-8198-0367-7). Dghtrs St Paul.

Hicks, Robert & Bewes, Richard. Salvation. (Understanding Bible Truth Ser.). (Orig.). 1981. pap. 0.95 (ISBN 0-89840-019-8). Heres Life.

Hole, F. B. Great Salvation. Daniel, R. P., ed. 72p. pap. 3.75 (ISBN 0-88172-142-5). Believers Bkshelf.

Hull, William E. The Christian Experience of Salvation. LC 84-20501. (Layman's Library of Christian Doctrine Ser.). 1987. 5.95 (ISBN 0-8054-1639-0). Broadman.

Jabay, Earl. The God-Players. LC 69-11637. 155p. 1970. pap. 5.95 (ISBN 0-310-26541-X, 9939P). Zondervan.

Jernigan. Salvation, Entire Sanctification. pap. 1.95 (ISBN 0-686-12907-5). Schmul Pub Co.

Koenig, F. Are You Really... Formed? pap. 0.60 (ISBN 0-88172-111-5). Believers Bkshelf.

Lassiter, Perry. Once Saved...Always Saved. new ed. LC 74-15289. 98p. 1975. pap. 3.75 (ISBN 0-8054-1931-4). Broadman.

Levinson, Henry S. Science, Metaphysics, & the Chance of Salvation: An Interpretation of the Thought of William James. LC 78-7383. 1978. pap. 9.95 (ISBN 0-89130-234-4, 01-01-24). Scholars Pr GA.

Lindsey, Hal. The Liberation of Planet Earth. 256p. 1976. pap. 3.95 (ISBN 0-553-25307-7). Bantam.

--There's a New World Coming. 320p. 1975. pap. 3.95 (ISBN 0-553-24555-4). Bantam.

Lloyd-Jones, Martyn. The Cross. 192p. 1986. pap. 6.95 (ISBN 0-89107-382-5, Crossway Bks). Good News.

Loudy, Aldai. The Gospel of Our Salvation. 122p. 1973. text ed. 4.00 (ISBN 0-910424-60-8). Concordant.

Lyonnet, Stanislas & Sabarin, Leopold. Sin Redemption & Sacrifice: A Biblical & Patristic Study. (Analecta Biblica: Vol. 48). (Eng.). 1971. pap. 22.00 (ISBN 88-7653-048-7, Biblical Inst. Press). Loyola.

MacArthur, John, Jr. The Tragedy of Rejecting Salvation. (John MacArthur's Bible Studies). (Orig.). 1986. pap. 3.50 (ISBN 0-8024-5346-5). Moody.

Marchbanks, John B. Great Doctrines Relating to Salvation. LC 73-123612. 1970. pap. 2.95 (ISBN 0-87213-640-X). Loizeaux.

Marshall, Alejandro & Bennett, Gordon H. La Salvacion y las Dudas de Algunas Personas. 2nd ed. Bautista, Sara, tr. from Span. (La Serie Diamante). Tr. of God's Way of Salvation. (Eng., Illus.). 36p. 1982. pap. 0.85 (ISBN 0-942504-01-1). Overcomer Pr.

Maududi, A. A. The Road to Salvation. pap. 1.00 (ISBN 0-686-18583-8). Kazi Pubns.

Maxwell, Neal A. We Will Prove Them Herewith. LC 82-1532. 132p. 1982. 6.95 (ISBN 0-87747-912-7). Deseret Bk.

Meyer, F. B. Saved & Kept. 1970. pap. 4.50 (ISBN 0-87508-350-1). Chr Lit.

Mirus, Jeffrey. The Divine Courtship: A History of Our Salvation. 183p. 1977. 7.95 (ISBN 0-931888-13-1). Christendom Pubns.

Moeller, Charles. Man & Salvation in Literature. Quinn, Charles U., tr. LC 77-122048. Orig. Title: L' Homme Moderne Devant le Salut. 208p. 1973. 11.95 (ISBN 0-268-00351-3); pap. 6.95x (ISBN 0-268-00489-7). U of Notre Dame Pr.

Nee, Watchman. The Spirit of Judgment. Fader, Herbert L., et al, eds. Kaung, Stephen, tr. from Chinese. 158p. (Orig.). 1984. pap. 3.25 (ISBN 0-935008-63-2). Christian Fellow Pubs.

Nettleton, David. Chosen to Salvation: Select Thoughts on the Doctrine of Election. LC 83-11062. 1983. pap. 5.95 (ISBN 0-87227-094-7). Reg Baptist.

Nies, Richard C. The Security of Salvation. LC 78-17523. (Waymark Ser.). 1978. pap. 2.50 (ISBN 0-8127-0187-9). Review & Herald.

Noyes, John H. Salvation from Sin. 59.95 (ISBN 0-8490-0990-1). Gordon Pr.

Okoroche, Cyril. The Meaning of Religious Conversion in Africa: The Case of the Igbo of Nigeria. 354p. 1987. text ed. 55.00x (ISBN 0-566-05030-7, Pub. by Gower Pub England). Gower Pub Co.

Ortiz, Joe. Saved? What Do You Mean Saved? A Journalist's Report on Salvation. Feldstein, Mark D., ed. (Illus.). 95p. (Orig.). 1983. pap. 4.95 (ISBN 0-912695-00-5). GBM Bks.

Palmer, Phobe. Full Salvation. pap. 4.95 (ISBN 0-686-27772-4). Schmul Pub Co.

Pink, A. W. A Fourfold Salvation. pap. 0.75 (ISBN 0-685-41831-6). Reiner.

--La Soberania De Dios. 3.50 (ISBN 0-85151-416-2). Banner of Truth.

Polan, Gregory J. In the Ways of Justice Toward Salvation. (American University Studies VII - Theology & Religion: Vol. 13). 360p. 1986. text ed. 46.00 (ISBN 0-8204-0280-X). P Lang Pubs.

Przybylski, Benno. Righteousness in Matthew & His World of Thought. LC 79-41371. (Society for New Testament Studies Monographs: No. 41). 240p. 1981. 32.50 (ISBN 0-521-22566-3). Cambridge U Pr.

Quasem, M. A. Salvation of the Soul & Islamic Devotion. 200p. (Orig.). 1984. pap. 12.95 (ISBN 0-7103-0033-6, Kegan Paul). Methuen Inc.

Rupp, E. Gordon & Watson, Philip S., eds. Luther & Erasmus: Free Will & Salvation. LC 76-79870. (Library of Christian Classics). 356p. 1978. softcover 10.95 (ISBN 0-664-24158-1). Westminster.

Russell, Letty M. Human Liberation in a Feminist Perspective: A Theology. LC 74-10613. 214p. 1974. pap. 8.95 (ISBN 0-664-24991-4). Westminster.

Salvation, Learning about God's Plan. (Teaching Bks.). (Illus.). 19p. (Orig.). 1974. pap. text ed. 2.95 (ISBN 0-86508-151-4). BCM Intl Inc.

Sawyer, John F. Semantics in Biblical Research: New Methods of Defining Hebrew Words for Salvation. LC 72-75901. (Studies in Biblical Theology, Second Ser.: No. 24). 1972. pap. text ed. 12.00x (ISBN 0-8401-3074-0). A R Allenson.

Shuler, John L. Wonders of Salvation. 1985. pap. 5.95 (ISBN 0-8163-0591-9). Pacific Pr Pub Assn.

Simpson, Albert B. Echoes of the New Creation. pap. 1.25 (ISBN 0-87509-010-9). Chr Pubns.

Smith, Kenneth L. The Last Warning. LC 79-53625. 1979. pap. 4.95 (ISBN 0-89412-030-1). Aegean Park Pr.

Soderholm, Marjorie. Explaining Salvation to Children. 8th ed. 1979. pap. 1.50 (ISBN 0-911802-13-4). Free Church Pubns.

--Salvation, Then What. 1968. pap. 1.75 (ISBN 0-911802-14-2). Free Church Pubns.

Spurgeon, C. H. All of Grace. 144p. 1981. pap. 2.95 (ISBN 0-88368-097-1). Whitaker Hse.

Stepping Heavenward. 1967. 0.50 (ISBN 0-686-05837-2). Crusade Pubs.

Stibbs, Alan M. So Great Salvation: The Meaning & Message of the Letter to the Hebrews. 118p. 1970. pap. 4.95 (ISBN 0-85364-102-1). Attic Pr.

Stob, Henry. Sin, Salvation & Service. (Orig.). 1984. pap. 2.95 (ISBN 0-933140-98-3). CRC Pubns.

Straub, Gerald T. Salvation for Sale: An Insider's View of Pat Robertson's Ministry. (Illus.). 300p. 1986. 18.95 (ISBN 0-87975-357-9). Prometheus Bks.

Strombeck, J. F. So Great Salvation. 26th ed. LC 81-85530. 160p. 1982. pap. 3.95 (ISBN 0-89081-215-2). Harvest Hse.

Thompson, Carroll J. The Miracle of Salvation. (Illus.). 178p. (Orig.). 1986. pap. 9.95 (ISBN 1-55630-010-7). Brentwood Comm.

Torrey, R. A., ed. Get Ready for Forever. 176p. 1984. pap. text ed. 3.50 (ISBN 0-88368-160-9). Whitaker Hse.

Van Impe, Jack. Great Salvation Themes. 215p. 1984. pap. 4.95 (ISBN 0-934803-06-4). J Van Impe.

Viladesau, Richard. Answering for Faith: Christ & the Human Search for Salvation. 1987. pap. 14.95. Paulist Pr.

Warner, D. S. Salvation, Present, Perfect, Now or Never. 63p. pap. 0.40 (ISBN 0-686-29138-7); pap. 1.00 3 copies (ISBN 0-686-29139-5). Faith Pub Hse.

Warren, Virgil. What the Bible Says about Salvation. LC 82-73345. (What the Bible Says Ser.). 640p. 1982. 13.95 (ISBN 0-89900-088-6). College Pr Pub.

Way of Salvation N. T. 1982. pap. 3.95 (ISBN 0-89225-220-0). Gospel Advocate.

Wilson, Ostis B. The Plan of Salvation. 64p. pap. 0.50 (ISBN 0-686-29160-3). Faith Pub Hse.

SALVATION–HISTORY OF DOCTRINES

Alderink, Larry J. Creation & Salvation in Ancient Orphism. LC 81-5772. (APA American Classical Studies Ser.). 1981. pap. 10.00 (ISBN 0-89130-502-5, 400408). Scholars Pr GA.

Bloesch, Donald G. Jesus Is Victor! Karl Barth's Doctrine of Salvation. LC 76-14360. Repr. of 1976 ed. 33.50 (ISBN 0-8357-9013-4, 2016373). Bks Demand UMI.

Boys, Mary C. Biblical Interpretation in Religious Education. LC 80-10249. 362p. (Orig.). 1980. pap. 10.95 (ISBN 0-89135-022-5). Religious Educ.

Criswell, W. A. Great Doctrines of the Bible, Vol. 5. 144p. 1985. 9.95 (ISBN 0-310-43930-2). Zondervan.

Horne, Charles. Doctrine of Salvation. 1984. pap. 5.95 (ISBN 0-8024-0424-3). Moody.

Rogers, Jack, et al. Case Studies in Christ & Salvation. LC 76-53765. 176p. 1977. pap. 7.95 (ISBN 0-664-24133-6). Westminster.

SALVATION (CATHOLIC CHURCH)

see Salvation; Salvation outside the Catholic Church

SALVATION ARMY

Booth, Catherine. Writings of Catherine Booth. 1101p. 1986. 19.95 (ISBN 0-86544-031-X). Salv Army Suppl South.

Booth, William. In Darkest England & the Way Out. 296p. 1984. Repr. of 1890 ed. 6.95 (ISBN 0-86544-024-7). Salv Army Suppl South.

Booth-Tucker, Frederick. The Salvation Army in America: Selected Reports, 1899-1903. LC 79-38439. (Religion in America, Ser. 2). 212p. 1972. Repr. of 1972 ed. 19.00 (ISBN 0-405-04060-1). Ayer Co Pubs.

Cedervall, David. Salvation Army Word Search Puzzles. 75p. (Orig.). 1985. pap. 1.65 (ISBN 0-89216-061-6). Salvation Army.

Exline, Barbara. Beyond the Battlefield. (Illus.). 78p. (Orig.). (YA) 1986. pap. 3.25 (ISBN 0-89216-063-2). Salvation Army.

Higgins, Edward J. Stewards of God. 1984. 3.25 (ISBN 0-86544-022-0). Salv Army Suppl South.

Holz, Ron. Heralds of Victory. (Illus.). 256p. (Orig.). 1986. 8.00 (ISBN 0-89216-068-3); pap. 5.00 (ISBN 0-89216-065-9). Salvation Army.

Huxley, Thomas H. Evolution & Ethics, & Other Essays. LC 70-8391. 334p. 1897. Repr. 49.00x (ISBN 0-403-00041-6). Scholarly.

McKinley, E. H. Somebody's Brother: A History of the Salvation Army Men's Social Service Department 1891-1985. LC 86-8604. (Studies in American Religion Ser.: Vol. 21). 264p. 1986. 9.95 (ISBN 0-88946-665-3). E Mellen.

McKinley, Edward H. Marching to Glory. 290p. pap. 4.95 (ISBN 0-86544-039-5). Salv Army Suppl South.

Sandall, Robert & Wiggins, Arch. The History of the Salvation Army, 6 vols. 2093p. (Orig.). 1979. pap. 10.00 set (ISBN 0-318-04018-2). Vol. 1 (ISBN 0-89216-030-6). Vol. 2 (ISBN 0-89216-031-4). Vol. 3 (ISBN 0-89216-032-2). Vol. 4 (ISBN 0-89216-033-0). Vol. 5 (ISBN 0-89216-034-9). Vol. 6 (ISBN 0-89216-035-7). Salvation Army.

Spence, Clark C. The Salvation Army Farm Colonies. LC 85-8763. 151p. 1985. 19.95x (ISBN 0-8165-0897-6). U of Ariz Pr.

Tripp, Bramwell, et al. Heritage of Holiness. 110p. 1977. pap. 3.50 (ISBN 0-89216-013-6). Salvation Army.

Waldron, John D. The Salvation Army & the Children. 135p. (Orig.). 1985. pap. 3.00 (ISBN 0-89216-060-8). Salvation Army.

--The Salvation Army & the Churches. 142p. (Orig.). 1986. pap. 3.95 (ISBN 0-89216-064-0). Salvation Army.

Yee, Check-Hung. For My Kinsmen's Sake. 1986. 15.00 (ISBN 0-89216-066-7). Salvation Army.

SALVATION IN LITERATURE

Haines, Victor Y. The Fortunate Fall of Sir Gawain: The Typology of Sir Gawain & the Green Knight. LC 80-5847. (Illus.). 240p. (Orig.). 1982. PLB 29.00 (ISBN 0-8191-2437-0); pap. text ed. 12.75 (ISBN 0-8191-2438-9). U Pr of Amer.

Satterlee, Allen. Notable Quotables (A Compendium of Quotes by Salvation Army Authors) 1985. 15.95 (ISBN 0-86544-028-X). Salv Army Suppl South.

SALVATION OUTSIDE THE CATHOLIC CHURCH

see also Universalism

Bainvel, S. J. Is There Salvation Outside the Catholic Church? LC 79-55461. 1979. pap. 1.50 (ISBN 0-89555-132-2). TAN Bks Pubs.

SAMADHI

Chakravarti, Sri S. Samadhi & Beyond. LC 74-79444. 1974. pap. 3.50 (ISBN 0-87707-135-7). Ranney Pubns.

Sadha, Mouni. Samadhi: The Superconsciousness of the Future. (Unwin Paperbacks). 1977. pap. 5.95 (ISBN 0-04-149039-8). Allen Unwin.

SAMARITANS

Bowman, John. The Samaritan Problem: Studies in the Relationship of Samaritanism, Judaism, & Early Christianity. Johnson, Alfred M., Jr., tr. from Ger. LC 75-20042. (Pittsburgh Theological Monographs: No. 4). 1975. pap. 8.75 (ISBN 0-915138-04-2). Pickwick.

Bowman, John, ed. & tr. Samaritans Documents Relating to Their History, Religion & Life. LC 77-4949. (Pittsburgh Original Texts & Translations Ser.: No. 2). 1977. pap. 11.50 (ISBN 0-915138-27-1). Pickwick.

Burt, Donald X. The Inn of the Samaritan. 96p. (Orig.). 1983. pap. 5.95 (ISBN 0-8146-1315-2). Liturgical Pr.

Gaster, M. The Samaritans: History, Doctrine & Literature. 1976. lib. bdg. 134.95 (ISBN 0-8490-2563-X). Gordon Pr.

--The Samaritans: Their History, Doctrines & Literature. (British Academy, London, Schweich Lectures on Biblical Archaeology Series, 1923). pap. 28.00 (ISBN 0-8115-1265-7). Kraus Repr.

Gaster, Moses. The Samaritan Oral Law & Ancient Traditions. LC 77-87609. Repr. of 1932 ed. 22.00 (ISBN 0-404-16433-1). AMS Pr.

Kippenberg, Hans G. Garizim und Synagoge: Traditionsgeschichtliche Untersuchungen zur samaritanischen Religion der aramaeischen Periode. (Religionsgeschichtliche Versuche und Vorarbeiten, 30). (Ger). 1971. 43.20x (ISBN 3-11-001864-0). De Gruyter.

Mead, G. R. S. Simon Magus. 1978. Repr. of 1892 ed. 10.00 (ISBN 0-89005-258-1). Ares.

Mills, John. Three Months' Residence at Nablus: And an Account of the Modern Samaritans. LC 77-87610. Repr. of 1864 ed. 25.50 (ISBN 0-404-16434-X). AMS Pr.

Thomson, J. The Samaritans: Their Testimony to the Religion of Israel. 1976. lib. bdg. 59.95 (ISBN 0-8490-2564-8). Gordon Pr.

SAMSON, ABBOT OF BURY ST. EDMUNDS, 1135-1211

Jocelin De Brakelond. Chronica Jocelini De Brakelonda. LC 17-17164. (Camden Society, London. Publications, First Series: No. 13). Repr. of 1840 ed. 19.00 (ISBN 0-404-50113-3). AMS Pr.

Jocelin De Brakelonda. Chronica Jocelini De Brakelonda, De Rebus Gestis Samsonis. 1840. 19.00 (ISBN 0-384-27530-3). Johnson Repr.

SAMSON, JUDGE OF ISRAEL

Andre, G. Gideon, Samson & Other Judges of Israel. (Let's Discuss It Ser.). pap. 1.95 (ISBN 0-88172-132-8). Believers Bkshelf.

Carus, Paul. The Story of Samson, & Its Place in the Religious Development of Mankind. 183p. 1907. 1.95 (ISBN 0-317-40420-2). Open Court.

Crenshaw, James L. Samson: A Secret Betrayed, A Vow Ignored. LC 77-15748. 173p. 1981. text ed. 9.95 (ISBN 0-86554-042-X, MUP-H01). Mercer Univ Pr.

Lindsay, Gordon. Jephthah & Samson. (Old Testament Ser.). 1.25 (ISBN 0-89985-136-3). Christ Nations.

Palmer, Abram S. Samson-Saga & Its Place in Comparative Religion. Dorson, Richard, ed. LC 77-70613. (International Folklore Ser.). 1977. Repr. of 1913 ed. lib. bdg. 23.50x (ISBN 0-405-10112-0). Ayer Co Pubs.

Small, Dwight H. No Rival Love. 201p. (Orig.). 1985. pap. 4.95 (ISBN 0-87508-495-8). Chr Lit.

SAMSON, JUDGE OF ISRAEL-JUVENILE LITERATURE

Kolbrek, Loyal & Larsen, Chris. Samson's Secret. (Arch Bks.: Set 8). (Orig.). 1970. pap. 0.99 (ISBN 0-570-06052-4, 59-1168). Concordia.

Storr, Catherine, as told by. Samson & Delilah. (People of the Bible). (Illus.). 32p. 1985. PLB 10.65 (ISBN 0-8172-2044-5). Raintree Pubs.

SAMSON, JUDGE OF ISRAEL-POETRY

Milton, John. Samson Agonistes. Prince, F. T., ed. 1957. pap. 7.95x (ISBN 0-19-831910-X). Oxford U Pr.

SAMUEL, THE PROPHET

Knapp, C. Samuel the Prophet. 6.95 (ISBN 0-88172-113-1). Believers Bkshelf.

Lindsay, Gordon. Ruth, The Gleaner, & the Boy Samuel. (Old Testament Ser.). 1.25 (ISBN 0-89985-137-1). Christ Nations.

--Samuel, the Prophet. (Old Testament Ser.). 1.25 (ISBN 0-89985-138-X). Christ Nations.

Meyer, F. B. Samuel. 1978. pap. 4.50 (ISBN 0-87508-339-0). Chr Lit.

Miller, Patrick D. & Roberts, J. J. M. The Hand of the Lord: A Reassessment of the "Ark Narrative" of Samuel. LC 76-48737. (The Johns Hopkins Near Eastern Studies). pap. 24.40 (ISBN 0-317-26633-0, 2010959). Bks Demand UMI.

Wengrov, Charles. Tales of the Prophet Samuel. (Biblical Ser.). (Illus.). 1969. 4.00 (ISBN 0-914080-22-9). Shulsinger Sales.

Whaley, Richie. Samuel: Prophet & Judge. (BibLearn Ser.). (Illus.). 1979. 5.95 (ISBN 0-8054-4242-1, 4242-42). Broadman.

SAN FRANCISCO-HISTORY

Levy, Harriet L. Nine-Twenty O'Farrell Street. facsimile ed. LC 74-29501. (Modern Jewish Experience Ser.). (Illus.). 1975. Repr. of 1947 ed. 23.50x (ISBN 0-405-06728-3). Ayer Co Pubs.

SAN LUIS OBISPO MISSION

Hoover, Robert L. & Costello, Julia G., eds. Excavations at Mission San Antonio, 1976-1978. (Monographs: No. XXVI). (Illus.). 221p. 1985. pap. 16.00 (ISBN 0-917956-48-6). UCLA Arch.

Jones, Thelma H. The Road to San Luis Rey. LC 73-87882. (Illus.). 1974. text ed. 5.00 (ISBN 0-912472-18-9). Miller Bks.

Seymour, Barbara. Portrait of a Place: San Luis Obispo. (Illus.). 120p. (Orig.). 1986. pap. 12.95 (ISBN 0-9617522-0-3). Garden Creek Pubns.

SAN SABA MISSION

Morrill, Sibley S. The Texas Cannibals, or, Why Father Serra Came to California. 28p. 1964. octavo wrappers 5.00 (ISBN 0-910740-04-6). Holmes.

SANCHEZ DE AREVALO RODRIGO, BISHOP, 1404-1470

Butler, Geoffrey. Studies in Statecraft. LC 79-110899. 1970. Repr. of 1920 ed. 17.00x (ISBN 0-8046-0882-2, Pub. by Kennikat). Assoc Faculty Pr.

SANCTIFICATION

see also Holiness; Mystical Union; Perfection; Perseverance (Theology)

Baker, William. Sanctification. 160p. 1986. pap. 6.95 (ISBN 0-310-35301-7, 11140P). Zondervan.

Berry, R. L. Adventures in the Land of Canaan. 128p. pap. 1.00 (ISBN 0-686-29096-8). Faith Pub Hse.

Byers, J. W. Sanctification. 96p. 0.75 (ISBN 0-686-29140-9). Faith Pub Hse.

Chambers, Oswald. Our Brilliant Heritage. 1965. pap. 2.95 (ISBN 0-87508-120-7). Chr Lit.

Finney, Charles & Parkhurst, Louis. Principles of Sanctification. rev. ed. 240p. 1986. pap. 5.95 (ISBN 0-87123-859-4). Bethany Hse.

Finney, Charles G. Sanctification. Allen, W. E., ed. 1963. pap. 2.50 (ISBN 0-87508-191-6). Chr Lit.

Hardon, John A. Salvation & Santification. 1978. 3.50 (ISBN 0-8198-0366-9); pap. 2.50 (ISBN 0-8198-0367-7). Dghtrs St Paul.

Hegre, T. A. Cross & Sanctification. LC 51-7866. Orig. Title: Three Aspects of the Cross. 288p. 1960. pap. 3.95 (ISBN 0-87123-067-4, 210067). Bethany Hse.

Key, Jeanette. Sanctification & the Christian. 1979. pap. 2.95 (ISBN 0-88027-049-7). Firm Foun Pub.

Lindstrom, Harold. Wesley & Sanctification. LC 83-17025. 256p. (Orig.). 1984. 8.95 (ISBN 0-310-75011-3, 17025P). Zondervan.

Maxwell, L. E. Born Crucified. (Moody Classic Ser.). 1984. pap. 3.95 (ISBN 0-8024-0038-8). Moody.

Sandford, John & Sandford, Paula. The Transformation of the Inner Man. LC 82-72007. 432p. 1986. pap. 6.95 (ISBN 0-932081-13-4). Victory Hse.

Simpson, A. B. Santificados por Completo-Wholly Sanctified. (Eng., Illus.). 136p. 1981. 2.50 (ISBN 0-87509-307-8). Chr Pubns.

Spurgeon, C. H. Sanctification. 1976. pap. 1.50 (ISBN 0-686-16844-5). Pilgrim Pubns.

Teasley, D. O. The Double Cure, or Redemption Twofold. 160p. pap. 1.50 large print (ISBN 0-686-29147-6). Faith Pub Hse.

Tyson, John R. Charles Wesley on Sanctification: A Biographical & Theological Study. 240p. 1986. pap. 10.95 (ISBN 0-310-75131-4, 17054P). Zondervan.

Wiersbe, Warren W. Be Right. LC 77-154327. 175p. 1977. pap. 5.95 (ISBN 0-88207-729-5). Victor Bks.

Zuesse, Evan M. Ritual Cosmos: The Sanctification of Life in African Religions. LC 79-13454. x, 256p. 1980. 21.95x (ISBN 0-8214-0398-2). Ohio U Pr.

SANFORD, AGNES MARY (WHITE)

Sanford, Agnes. Sealed Orders: The Autobiography of a Christian Mystic. LC 72-76592. 312p. 1972. (Pub. by Logos); pap. 7.95 (ISBN 0-88270-048-0). Bridge Pub.

SANHEDRIN

Tama, M. Diogene, tr. Transactions of the Parisian Sanhedrim. (Brown Classics in Judaica Ser.). 364p. 1985. pap. text ed. 15.25 (ISBN 0-8191-4488-6). U Pr of Amer.

SANKEY, IRA DAVID, 1840-1908

Goodspeed, Edgar J. Full History of the Wonderful Career of Moody & Sankey, in Great Britain & America. LC 70-168154. (Illus.). Repr. of 1876 ed. 39.00 (ISBN 0-404-07227-5). AMS Pr.

Sankey, Ira D. My Life & the Story of the Gospel Hymns & of Sacred Songs & Solos. LC 72-1682. Repr. of 1907 ed. 32.50 (ISBN 0-404-08332-3). AMS Pr.

SANSKRIT HYMNS

see Hymns, Sanskrit

SANSKRIT LITERATURE

Arya-Sura. The Gatnkamala: Or, Garland of Birth-Stories. Muller, F. Max, ed. Speyer, J. C., tr. from Sanskrit. LC 78-72371. Repr. of 1895 ed. 37.50 (ISBN 0-404-17218-0). AMS Pr.

Bhat, G. K. Theatric Aspects of Sanskrit Drama. 1985. 12.50x (ISBN 0-8364-1365-2, Pub. by Bhanarkar Oriental Inst). South Asia Bks.

Dayal, Har. The Bodhisattva Doctrine in Buddhist Sanskrit Literature. 1975. Repr. 22.50 (ISBN 0-89684-180-4). Orient Bk Dist.

Diskalkar, D. B. Selections from Sanskrit Inscriptions. 1977. 18.00x (ISBN 0-686-22673-9). Intl Bk Dist.

Gambhirananda, tr. from Sanskrit. Sruti Gita: The Song of the Srutis. 99p. 1982. pap. 4.95 (ISBN 0-87481-510-X). Vedanta Pr.

Heifetz, Hank. The Origin of the Young God: Kalidasa's Kumarasambhava. 1985. 30.00x (ISBN 0-520-05304-4). U of Cal Pr.

Madhavananda, tr. from Sanskrit. Uddhava Gita or Last Message of Sri Krishna. 425p. pap. 9.50 (ISBN 0-87481-211-9). Vedanta Pr.

Monier-Williams, Monier. Indian Wisdom. 575p. 1978. Repr. of 1893 ed. 21.00x (ISBN 0-89684-105-7, Pub. by Cosmo Pubns India). Orient Bk Dist.

Natha, Prana & Chaudhuri, J. B. Catalogue of the Library of the India Office: Vol. 2, Oriental Languages, Pt. 1, Sanskrit Books. Rev. ed. Napier, C. K., rev. by. 3149p. 1957. Repr. of 1938 ed. 45.00 (ISBN 0-7123-0612-9, Pub. by British Lib). Longwood Pub Group.

Poor, Laura E. Sanskrit & Its Kindred Literatures. LC 76-27525. 1976. Repr. of 1880 ed. lib. bdg. 35.00 (ISBN 0-89341-038-1). Longwood Pub Group.

Puranas, Brahmandapurana. The Adhyatma Ramayana. Nath, Lala B., tr. LC 73-3828. (Sacred Books of the Hindus: Extra Vol. 1). Repr. of 1913 ed. 25.00 (ISBN 0-404-57846-2). AMS Pr.

Sanskrit Mantras. 1977. 10.00x (ISBN 0-930736-03-6); cassett tape recording incl. (ISBN 0-685-32618-7). E W Cultural Ctr.

Sri Aurobindo. Essays on the Gita. (Life Companion Library). 763p. 1983. 21.95 (ISBN 0-89744-006-4). Auromere.

Swami Jyotir Maya Nanda. The Mystery of the Soul: Katha Upanishad. (Illus.). 1976. pap. 1.99 (ISBN 0-934664-07-2). Yoga Res Foun.

Swami Muktananda, tr. from Sanskrit. Shree Guru Gita. LC 81-51183. 128p. (Orig.). 1981. pap. 3.95 (ISBN 0-914602-73-X). SYDA Found.

Tyberg, Judith M. Sanskrit Keys to the Wisdom-Religion. 180p. 1976. pap. 5.00 (ISBN 0-913004-29-4). Point Loma Pub.

Venkatesananda, Swami. The Enlightened Living. 2nd ed. 1978. pap. 2.95 (ISBN 0-89684-038-7, Pub. by Motilal Banarsidass India). Orient Bk Dist.

Vijnanananda, Swami, tr. from Sanskrit. The Srimad Devi Bhagawatam, Pts. I & II. LC 75-985029. 1977. 55.00x (ISBN 0-89684-455-2). Orient Bk Dist.

Wilson, Epiphanius, intro. by. Hindu Literature: Comprising the Book of Good Counsels, Nala & Damayanti, Sakoontala, the Ramayan, & Poems of Toru Dutt. 467p. 1986. Repr. of 1900 ed. PLB 95.00 (ISBN 0-89760-654-X). Telegraph Bks.

SANSKRIT POETRY-HISTORY AND CRITICISM

Hueckstedt, Robert A. The Style of Bana: An Introduction to Sanskrit Prose Poetry. 228p. (Orig.). 1986. lib. bdg. 27.50 (ISBN 0-8191-4998-5); pap. text ed. 12.75 (ISBN 0-8191-4999-3). U Pr of Amer.

Lahiri, P. C. Concept of Riti & Guna in Sanskrit Poetics in Their Historical Development. xvi, 310p. 1974. 12.00x (ISBN 0-8364-0393-2). South Asia Bks.

SANSKRIT POETRY-TRANSLATIONS INTO ENGLISH

Bailly, Constantina R. Shaira Devotional Songs of Kashmir: A Translation & Study of Utpaladeva's Shivastotravali. (Kashmir Shaivism Ser.). 224p. 1987. 39.50x (ISBN 0-88706-492-2); pap. 12.95x (ISBN 0-88706-493-0). State U NY Pr.

Bhartrihari. Vairagya-Satakam: The Hundred Verses on Renunciation. (Sanskrit & Eng.). pap. 1.75 (ISBN 0-87481-070-1). Vedanta Pr.

Swami Jyotir Maya Nanda. The Way to Liberation: Moksha Dharma of Mahabharata, 2 vols. (Illus.). 1976. Ea. pap. 4.99 (ISBN 0-934664-11-0). Yoga Res Foun.

SANTA CLAUS

Giblin, James C. The Truth about Santa Claus. LC 85-47541. (Illus.). 96p. 1985. 11.70 (ISBN 0-690-04483-6, Crowell Jr Bks); PLB 11.89 (ISBN 0-690-04484-4). HarpJ.

Grimes, Bobbie M. The Parable of Jesus & Santa. LC 84-90331. (Illus.). 40p. 1984. 14.95 (ISBN 0-9613328-0-8). B & D Pub.

Mead, Margaret & Metraux, Rhoda. An Interview with Santa Claus. (Illus.). 1978. 4.95 (ISBN 0-8027-0620-7). Walker & Co.

Myra, Harold. Santa, Are You for Real? LC 77-23023. (Illus.). 6.95 (ISBN 0-8407-5122-2). Nelson.

SANTAYANA, GEORGE, 1863-1952

Santayana, George. The Intimate Analysis of a Lost Life, 2 vols. (Illus.). 285p. 1986. 147.55 (ISBN 0-86650-196-7). Gloucester Art.

SARACENIC ARCHITECTURE

see Architecture, Islamic

SARADA DEVI, 1853-1920

Gambhirananda, Swami. Holy Mother, Sri Sarada Devi. (Illus.). 8.95 (ISBN 0-87481-434-0). Vedanta Pr.

Mookerjee, Nanda, ed. Sri Sarada Devi: Consort of Sri Ramakrishna. 1978. 6.00x (ISBN 0-8364-0173-5). South Asia Bks.

Tapasyananda, Swami & Nikhilananda, Swami. Sarada Devi, the Holy Mother: Her Life & Conversations. (Illus.). 12.95 (ISBN 0-87481-435-9). Vedanta Pr.

SARCOPHAGI

see also Tombs

Gerke, Friedrich. Die Christlichen Sarkophage der vorkonstantinischen Zeit. (Studien Zur Spaetantiken Kunstgeschichte: Vol. 11). (Illus.). viii, 432p. 1978. Repr. of 1940 ed. 140.00x (ISBN 3-11-004999-6). De Gruyter.

Hanfmann, George M. The Season Sarcophagus in Dumbarton Oaks. LC 71-146800. (Dumbarton Oaks Studies: Vol. 2). (Illus.). 518p. 1951. Repr. 35.00x (ISBN 0-88402-001-0). Dumbarton Oaks.

--Season Sarcophagus in Dumbarton Oaks, 2 Vols. Repr. of 1951 ed. Set. 60.00 (ISBN 0-384-21290-5); 30.00 ea. Johnson Repr.

SARTRE, JEAN PAUL, 1905-1980

Anderson, Thomas C. The Foundation & Structure of Sartrean Ethics. LC 79-11762. x, 186p. 1979. 22.50x (ISBN 0-7006-0191-0). U Pr of KS.

Barnes, Hazel E. Sartre & Flaubert. LC 80-26872. x, 450p. 1982. pap. 10.95 (ISBN 0-226-03721-5, PHOEN). U of Chicago Pr.

Boni, Sylvain. The Self & the Other in the Ontologies of Sartre & Buber. LC 82-20130. 202p. (Orig.). 1983. lib. bdg. 27.50 (ISBN 0-8191-2852-X); pap. text ed. 12.50 (ISBN 0-8191-2853-8). U Pr of Amer.

Catalano, Joseph S. A Commentary of Jean-Paul Sartre's "Being & Nothingness". LC 79-21234. xvi, 240p. 1985. pap. text ed. 15.00x (ISBN 0-226-09699-8). U of Chicago Pr.

Greene, Norman N. Jean-Paul Sartre: The Existentialist Ethic. LC 80-12203. vii, 213p. 1980. Repr. of 1960 ed. lib. bdg. 22.50x (ISBN 0-313-22422-6, GRJP). Greenwood.

Kariuki, Joseph. The Possibility of Universal Moral Judgement in Existential Ethics: A Critical Analysis of the Phenomenology of Moral Experience According to Jean-Paul Sartre. (European University Studies: Series 20, Philosophy: Vol. 87). 363p. 1981. 37.95 (ISBN 3-261-04962-6). P Lang Pubs.

King, Thomas M. Sartre & the Sacred. LC 73-87304. xii, 196p. 1974. 17.00x (ISBN 0-226-43612-8). U of Chicago Pr.

Vargas, Mario. Entre Sartre y Camus. LC 81-68707. (Coleccion la Nave y el Puerto Ser.). 144p. 1981. pap. 5.50 (ISBN 0-940238-48-9). Ediciones Hura.

SATAN

see Devil

SATANISM

see also Demoniac Possession

Aranza, Jacob. Backward Masking Unmasked: Backward Satanic Messages of Rock & Roll Exposed. LC 83-80043. 118p. (Orig.). 1983. pap. 5.95 (ISBN 0-910311-04-8). Huntington Hse Inc.

Bainbridge, William S. Satan's Power: A Deviant Psychotherapy Cult. LC 77-80466. 1978. 33.00x (ISBN 0-520-03546-1). U of Cal Pr.

Barney, Kenneth D. The Longest War. LC 82-83915. 128p. (Orig.). 1984. pap. 2.50 (ISBN 0-88243-536-1, 02-0536). Gospel Pub.

Baskin, Wade. Dictionary of Satanism. 1972. pap. 3.95 (ISBN 0-8065-0292-4). Citadel Pr.

Brown, Rebecca. He Came to Set the Captives Free. 288p. (Orig.). 1986. pap. 7.50 (ISBN 0-937958-25-5). Chick Pubns.

Conway, Moncure D. Demonology & Devil-Lore, 2 vols. Set. 250.00 (ISBN 0-8490-0017-3). Gordon Pr.

Cristiani, Leon. Evidence of Satan in the Modern World. Rowland, Cynthia, tr. from Fr. (Eng.). 1977. pap. 5.50 (ISBN 0-89555-032-6). TAN Bks Pubs.

Cumbey, Constance. The Hidden Dangers of the Rainbow: The New Age Movement & Our Coming Age of Barbarism. LC 83-80044. 271p. (Orig.). 1983. pap. 6.95 (ISBN 0-910311-03-X). Huntington Hse Inc.

Godwin, Jeff. The Devil's Disciples. (Illus.). 352p. (Orig.). 1986. pap. 7.95 (ISBN 0-937958-23-9). Chick Pubns.

Jewett, Edward H. Diabolology: The Person & Kingdom of Satan. 1977. lib. bdg. 59.95 (ISBN 0-8490-1715-7). Gordon Pr.

King, Francis. Sexuality, Magic & Perversion. (Illus.). 1972. 6.95 (ISBN 0-8065-0289-4). Citadel Pr.

Kirban, Salem. Satan's Angels Exposed. 1980. pap. 5.95 (ISBN 0-912582-32-4). Kirban.

LaVey, Anton S. The Satanic Rituals. 1972. pap. 4.50 (ISBN 0-380-01392-4). Avon.

McCall, Thomas & Levitt, Zola. El Anticristo y el Santuario. Orig. Title: Satan in the Sanctuary. (Span.). 128p. 1983. pap. 3.25 (ISBN 0-8254-1474-1). Kregel.

Michelet, Jules. Satanism & Witchcraft. 352p. 1983. pap. 5.95 (ISBN 0-8065-0059-X, 89). Citadel Pr.

Nugent, Christopher. Masks of Satan: The Demonic in History. 216p. 1984. 22.50 (ISBN 0-89860-128-2, Sheed & Ward). Eastview.

Penn-Lewis, Jessie & Roberts, Evan. War on the Saints. 9th ed. 1986. Repr. of 1912 ed. 10.50 (ISBN 0-913926-02-7). T E Lowe.

Rhodes, H. T. The Satanic Mass. 254p. 1975. pap. 3.95 (ISBN 0-8065-0484-6). Citadel Pr.

Satan & Israel. Date not set. pap. 0.95 (ISBN 0-937408-13-1). GMI Pubns Inc.

Terry, Maury. The Ultimate Evil: An Investigation into America's Most Dangerous Satanic Cult. LC 86-29203. (Illus.). 432p. 1987. 17.95 (ISBN 0-385-23452-X, Dolp). Doubleday.

Warnke, Mike, et al. Satan-Seller. LC 79-94042. 204p. 1972. (Pub. by Logos); pap. 3.50 (ISBN 0-88270-096-0). Bridge Pub.

SATTLER, MICHAEL–FICTION

Augsburger, Myron S. Pilgrim Aflame. LC 67-15993. (Illus.). 288p. 1967. pap. 2.25 (ISBN 0-8361-1840-5). Herald Pr.

SAUDI ARABIA

Al-Yassini, Ayman. Religion & State in the Kingdom of Saudi Arabia. (WVSS on the Middle East Ser.). 190p. 1985. 30.00x (ISBN 0-8133-0058-4). Westview.

Blunt, Anne. Pilgrimage to Nejd, 2 vols. (Illus.). 1968. Repr. of 1881 ed. 85.00x (ISBN 0-7146-1979-5, F Cass Co). Biblio Dist.

SAUL, KING OF ISRAEL

Keller, W. Phillip. David II: The Shepherd King. 224p. 1986. 11.95 (ISBN 0-8499-0559-1). Word Bks.

Lindsay, Gordon. Saul & Jonathan. (Old Testament Ser.). 1.25 (ISBN 0-89985-140-1). Christ Nations.

--Saul, Israel's First King. (Old Testament Ser.). 1.25 (ISBN 0-89985-139-8). Christ Nations.

McCord, David. A Loser, a Winner, & a Wise-Guy: Saul, David & Solomon. LC 79-67438. 96p. 1980. pap. 2.25 (ISBN 0-87239-380-1, 40084). Standard Pub.

Petersen, Mark E. Three Kings of Israel. LC 80-36697. 179p. 1980. 6.95 (ISBN 0-87747-829-5). Deseret Bk.

Ridout, S. King Saul, Man after the Flesh. 8.50 (ISBN 0-88172-118-2). Believers Bkshelf.

Wengrov, Charles. Tales of King Saul. (Biblical Ser.). (Illus.). 1969. 4.00 (ISBN 0-914080-21-0). Shulsinger Sales.

SAVANNAH–FIRST BRYAN BAPTIST CHURCH

Simms, James M. First Colored Baptist Church in North America. LC 70-82074. (Illus.). Repr. of 1888 ed. 22.50x (ISBN 0-8371-1561-2, SIC&, Pub. by Negro U Pr). Greenwood.

SAVONAROLA, GIROLAMO MARIA FRANCESCO MATTEO, 1452-1498

Count Gobineau, Arthur. The Renaissance Savonarola. Levy, Oscar, ed. Cohen, Paul V., tr. (Fr., Illus.). 349p. 1986. Repr. of 1913 ed. lib. bdg. 75.00 (ISBN 0-89760-264-1). Telegraph Bks.

Gilbert, O. & Whittaker, R. The Historical Meaning of Savonarola As a Religious, Moral & Political Prophet & the Progress of the Reformation in Italy. 189p. 1985. 88.45 (ISBN 0-89266-514-9). Am Classical Coll Pr.

Gobineau, Joseph A. Golden Flower. facsimile ed. Redman, B. R., tr. LC 68-54347. (Essay Index Reprint Ser). 1924. 15.00 (ISBN 0-8369-0477-X). Ayer Co Pubs.

Hillis, Newell D. Great Men As Prophets of a New Era. facs. ed. LC 68-16939. (Essay Index Reprint Ser). 1968. Repr. of 1922 ed. 15.00 (ISBN 0-8369-0541-5). Ayer Co Pubs.

--Great Men As Prophets of a New Era. 1922. Repr. 20.00 (ISBN 0-8274-2445-0). R West.

Miscitelli, Peter. Savonarola, Protestantism & the Church of Rome, 2 vols. (Illus.). 247p. 1985. Set. 187.50 (ISBN 0-89901-230-2). Found Class Reprints.

Ridolfi, Roberto. The Life of Girolamo Savonarola. LC 76-8001. (Illus.). 1976. Repr. of 1959 ed. lib. bdg. 65.00x (ISBN 0-8371-8873-3, RIGS). Greenwood.

Steinberg, Ronald. Fra Girolamo Savonarola, Florentine Art & Renaissance Historiography. LC 76-8304. (Illus.). 151p. 1977. 14.00x (ISBN 0-8214-0202-1). Ohio U Pr.

Villari, P. Life & Times of Girolamo Savonarola. LC 68-25276. (World History Ser., No. 48). 1969. Repr. of 1888 ed. lib. bdg. 79.95x (ISBN 0-8383-0174-6). Haskell.

Villari, Pasquale. Studies, Historical & Critical. facs. ed. Villari, L., tr. LC 68-16983. (Essay Index Reprint Ser). 1968. Repr. of 1907 ed. 18.00 (ISBN 0-8369-0960-7). Ayer Co Pubs.

Villart, Pagquale. Life & Times of Girolamo Savonarola. Villari, Linda, tr. from Ital. (Illus.). 792p. 1985. Repr. of 1888 ed. lib. bdg. 85.00 (ISBN 0-89987-906-3). Darby Bks.

Weinstein, Donald. Savonarola & Florence: Prophecy & Patriotism in the Renaissance. LC 76-113013. Repr. of 1970 ed. 102.80 (ISBN 0-8357-9511-X, 2015484). Bks Demand UMI.

SAXONS

Earle, John. Facsimile of Some Leaves in Saxon Handwriting on Saint Swidhun. 1861. lib. bdg. 35.00 (ISBN 0-8414-3989-3). Folcroft.

SAYINGS

see Aphorisms and Apothegms; Proverbs; Quotations

SCANDINAVIA–RELIGION

Craigie, W. A. The Religion of Ancient Scandinavia. 59.95 (ISBN 0-8490-0939-1). Gordon Pr.

Davidson, Audrey E. The Quasi-Dramatic St. John Passions from Scandinavia & Their Medieval Background. (Early Drama, Art & Music Monograph: No. 3). (Illus.). viii, 135p. 1981. pap. 8.95 (ISBN 0-918720-14-1). Medieval Inst.

MacCulloch, John A. The Celtic & Scandinavian Religions. LC 72-11739. 180p. 1973. Repr. of 1948 ed. lib. bdg. 22.50x (ISBN 0-8371-6705-1, MCSR). Greenwood.

Turville-Petre, E. O. Myth & Religion of the North. LC 75-5003. (Illus.). 340p. 1975. Repr. of 1964 ed. lib. bdg. 49.75x (ISBN 0-8371-7420-1, TUMR). Greenwood.

SCHAFF, PHILIP, 1819-1893

Shriver, George H. Philip Schaff: Christian Scholar & Ecumenical Prophet. xii, 136p. 1987. 19.95 (ISBN 0-86554-234-1). Mercer Univ Pr.

Yrigoyen, Charles, Jr. & Bricker, George H, eds. Reformed & Catholic: Selected Theological Writings of Phillip Schaff. LC 79-17391. (Pittsburgh Original Texts & Translations Ser: No. 4). 1979. pap. text ed. 15.75 (ISBN 0-915138-40-9). Pickwick.

SCHEFFLER, JOHANN, 1624-1677

Carus, Paul, tr. Angelus Silesius. 174p. 1909. 1.95 (ISBN 0-317-40418-0). Open Court.

SCHELLING, FRIEDRICH WILHELM JOSEPH VON, 1775-1854

Brown, Robert F. Schelling's Treatise on "the Deities of Samothrace". A Translation & an Interpretation. LC 76-42239. (American Academy of Religion. Studies in Religion). 1977. pap. 9.95 (ISBN 0-89130-087-2, 010012). Scholars Pr GA.

O'Meara, Thomas F. Romantic Idealism & Roman Catholicism: Schelling & the Theologians. LC 81-40449. 240p. 1982. 25.00 (ISBN 0-268-01610-0). U of Notre Dame Pr.

SCHILLER, FERDINAND CANNING SCOTT, 1864-1937

Slosson, Edwin E. Six Major Prophets. facsimile ed. LC 71-167421. (Essay Index Reprint Ser). Repr. of 1917 ed. 23.00 (ISBN 0-8369-2571-8). Ayer Co Pubs.

SCHISM

Pluquet, F. A. Dictionnaire des Heresies des Erreurs et des Schismes, 2 vols. Migne, J. P., ed. (Encyclopedie Theologique Ser.: Vols. 11-12). (Fr.). 1374p. Repr. of 1847 ed. lib. bdg. 175.00x (ISBN 0-89241-235-6). Caratzas.

Talberg, N. D. K Sorokaljetiju pagubnago evlogijanskago raskola. Tr. of The Fortieth Anniversary of the Ruinous Evlogian Schism. 128p. 1966. pap. 4.00 (ISBN 0-317-30373-2). Holy Trinity.

SCHISM–EASTERN AND WESTERN CHURCH

Anthimos. Reply of the Orthodox Church to Roman Catholic Overtures on Reunion. rev., enl. ed. 64p. 1986. pap. 2.00 (ISBN 0-913026-62-X). St Nectarios.

Brehier, Louis. Schisme orientale du onzieme siecle. 1969. Repr. of 1899 ed. 25.50 (ISBN 0-8337-0363-3). B Franklin.

Conger, Yves M. After Nine Hundred Years: The Background of the Schism Between the Eastern & Western Churches. LC 78-6154. 1978. Repr. of 1959 ed. lib. bdg. 22.50x (ISBN 0-313-20493-4, COAN). Greenwood.

Makrakis, Apostolos. The Innovations of the Roman Church. 82p. (Orig.). 1966. pap. 3.75x (ISBN 0-938366-39-4). Orthodox Chr.

Runciman, Steven. The Eastern Schism. LC 78-63367. (The Crusades & Military Orders: Second Ser.). 200p. Repr. of 1956 ed. 24.50 (ISBN 0-404-16247-9). AMS Pr.

SCHISM, THE GREAT WESTERN, 1378-1417

Hogg, James. The Cartae of the Carthusian General Chapter of the Urbanist Observance During the Great Schism. (Analecta Cartusiana Ser.: No. 119). (Orig.). 1988. pap. 25.00 (ISBN 0-317-42562-5, Pub. by Salzburg Studies). Longwood Pub Group.

Jordan, George J. The Inner History of the Great Schism of the West, 1378-1417; a Problem in Church Unity. LC 72-80392. 216p. 1972. Repr. of 1930 ed. lib. bdg. 19.50 (ISBN 0-8337-4193-4). B Franklin.

Swanson, R. N. Universities, Academics & the Great Schism. LC 78-56764. (Cambridge Studies in Medieval Life & Thought: 3rd Ser., No. 12). 1979. 49.50 (ISBN 0-521-22127-7). Cambridge U Pr.

Symonds, Henry E. The Church Universal & the See of Rome: A Study of the Relations Between the Episcopate & the Papacy up to the Schism Between East & West. (Church Historical Society London N. S. Ser.: No. 36). pap. 60.00 (ISBN 0-8115-3159-7). Kraus Repr.

SCHLEIERMACHER, FRIEDRICH ERNST DANIEL, 1768-1834

Barth, Karl. The Theology of Schleiermacher. Bromiley, Geoffrey W., tr. 287p. 1982. 13.95 (ISBN 0-8028-3565-1). Eerdmans.

Brandt, Richard B. Philosophy of Schleiermacher: The Development of His Theory of Scientific & Religious Knowledge. LC 68-19265. 1968. Repr. of 1941 ed. lib. bdg. 27.00x (ISBN 0-8371-0027-5, BRPS). Greenwood.

Christian, C. W. Friedrich Schleiermacher. 157p. 1984. pap. text ed. 8.95 (ISBN 0-8499-3005-7, 3005-7). Word Bks.

Dilthey, Wilhelm. Leben Schleiermachers, 2 vols. Incl. Vol. 1, Pt. 1. 1768-1802. 3rd ed. Redeker, Martin, ed. xlvi, 567p. 1970. 48.00x (ISBN 3-11-006348-4); Vol. 1, Pt. 2. 1803-1807. Mulert, H., ed. xxiv, 251p. 1970. 24.00x (ISBN 3-11-006437-5); Vol. 2. Schleiermachers System als Philosophie und Theologie, 2 vols. in 1. Redeker, Martin, ed. lxxx, 811p. 1966. 72.00x (ISBN 3-11-001266-9). (Ger.). De Gruyter.

Gerrish, B. A. A Prince of the Church: Schleiermacher & the Beginnings of Modern Theology. LC 83-48924. 80p. 1984. pap. 4.95 (ISBN 0-8006-1787-8, 1-1787). Fortress.

Jasper, David, ed. The Interpretation of Belief: Coleridge, Schleiermacher & Romanticism. LC 85-26204. 192p. 1986. 25.00x (ISBN 0-312-42401-9). St Martin.

Schleiermacher, F. Aus Schleiermachers Leben, in Briefen, 4 vols. (Ger.). xxxvi, 2006p. 1974. Repr. of 1863 ed. 190.00x (ISBN 3-11-002261-3). De Gruyter.

Schleiermacher, Friedrich D. Kritische Gesamtausgabe: Fuenfte Abteilung (Briefwechsel & Biographische Dokumente) Briefwechsel, 1774-1796, Band 1. Arndt, Andreas & Virmond, Wolfgang, eds. (Illus.). lxxii, 489p. 1986. 120.00x (ISBN 3-11-008595-X). De Gruyter.

Schleiermacher, Friedrich E. Schleiermacher's Soliloques. Friess, Horace L., tr. LC 78-59040. 1984. Repr. of 1926 ed. 23.00 (ISBN 0-88355-712-6). Hyperion Conn.

Thiel, John E. God & World in Schleiermacher's Dialektik & Glaubenslehre, Vol. 43. (Basler und Berner Studien zur Historischen und Systematischen Theologie). xiv, 239p. 1981. pap. 28.15 (ISBN 3-261-04810-7). P Lang Pubs.

Williams, Robert R. Schleiermacher the Theologian: The Construction of the Doctrine of God. LC 77-78650. pap. 54.50 (2026892). Bks Demand UMI.

Wyman, Walter E., Jr. The Concept of Glaubenslehre: Ernst Troeltsch & the Theological Heritage of Schleiermacher. LC 83-4432. (American Academy of Religion, Academy Ser.). 276p. 1983. 14.95 (ISBN 0-89130-620-X, 01 01 44). Scholars Pr GA.

SCHOLASTICISM

see also Casuistry; Neo-Scholasticism; Philosophy, Medieval; Thomists

Fairweather, Eugene R., et al, eds. A Scholastic Miscellany: Anselm to Ockham. LC 56-5104. (Library of Christian Classics). 454p. 1982. pap. 11.95 (ISBN 0-664-24418-1). Westminster.

Klauder, Francis J. The Wonder of the Real: A Sketch in Basic Philosophy. rev., enlarged ed. LC 72-94706. (Illus.). 116p. 1973. 9.95 (ISBN 0-8158-0300-1). Chris Mass.

McLean, George F., ed. Scholasticism in the Modern World. (Proceedings of the American Catholic Philosophical Association: Vol. 40). 1966. pap. 15.00 (ISBN 0-918090-00-8). Am Cath Philo.

Maritain, Jacques. Art & Scholasticism & the Frontiers of Poetry. Evans, Joseph W., tr. from Fr. LC 74-13601. 240p. 1974. pap. 6.95x (ISBN 0-268-00557-5). U of Notre Dame Pr.

--Freedom & the Modern World. O'Sullivan, Richard, tr. LC 77-150414. 231p. 1971. Repr. of 1936 ed. 15.00x (ISBN 0-87752-147-6). Gordian.

--Scholasticism & Politics. LC 72-353. (Essay Index Reprint Ser.). Repr. of 1940 ed. 15.00 (ISBN 0-8369-2805-9). Ayer Co Pubs.

Morin, F. Dictionnaire de Philosophie et de Theologie Scolastiques, 2 vols. Migne, J. P., ed. (Troisieme et Derniere Encyclopedie Theologique Ser.: Vols. 21-22). (Fr.). 1496p. Repr. of 1865 ed. lib. bdg. 190.00x (ISBN 0-89241-304-2). Caratzas.

Panofsky, Erwin. Gothic Architecture & Scholasticism. (Illus.). pap. 7.95 (ISBN 0-452-00834-4, Mer). NAL.

Perrier, Joseph L. Revival of Scholastic Philosophy in the Nineteenth Century. LC 9-10966. Repr. of 1909 ed. 17.50 (ISBN 0-404-04994-X). AMS Pr.

Werner, Karl. Franz Suarez und Die Scholastik Des Letzen Jahrhunderts, 2 Vols. rev. ed. 1889. 50.50 (ISBN 0-8337-3731-7). B Franklin.

Worland, Stephen T. Scholasticism & Welfare Economics. 1967. 17.95 (ISBN 0-268-00246-0). U of Notre Dame Pr.

Wuellner, Bernard. Summary of Scholastic Principles. LC 56-10903. 1956. 1.50 (ISBN 0-8294-0084-2). Loyola.

SCHOLIA

see also Bible–Commentaries

Brock, Sebastian. Syriac Version of the Ps. Nonnos Mythological Scholia. LC 79-139712. (Oriental Publications: No. 20). 1971. 62.50 (ISBN 0-521-07990-X). Cambridge U Pr.

Mountford, J. F. The Scholia Bembina in Terentium. 140p. 1934. text ed. 41.40x (ISBN 0-576-72270-7, Pub. by Gregg Intl Pubs England). Gregg Intl.

SCHOOL ASSEMBLY

see Schools–Exercises and Recreations

SCHOOLS–EXERCISES AND RECREATIONS

see also Skits, Stunts, etc.

Brandling, Redvers. Christmas in the Primary School. (Ward Lock Educational Ser.). 1985. 29.00x (ISBN 0-7062-4068-5, Pub. by Ward Lock Educ Co Ltd). State Mutual Bk.

Kellogg, Alice M., ed. How to Celebrate Thanksgiving & Christmas. facs. ed. LC 76-139765. (Granger Index Reprint Ser). 1897. 15.00 (ISBN 0-8369-6219-2). Ayer Co Pubs.

SCHOOLS–OPENING EXERCISES

see Schools–Exercises and Recreations

SCHOOLS–RECREATIONS

see Schools–Exercises and Recreations

SCHOOLS, DENOMINATIONAL

see Church Schools

SCHOOLS, PAROCHIAL

see Church Schools

SCHWEITZER, ALBERT, 1875-1965

Berman, Edgar. In Africa With Schweitzer. 300p. 1986. 16.95 (ISBN 0-88282-025-7). New Horizon NJ.

Cousins, Norman. Albert Schweitzer's Mission: Healing & Peace. 1985. 16.95 (ISBN 0-393-02238-2). Norton.

Gollomb, Joseph. Albert Schweitzer: Genius in the Jungle. (Illus.). 149p. 1949. 10.95 (ISBN 0-8149-0308-8). Vanguard.

Griffith, Nancy S. & Person, Laura. Albert Schweitzer: An International Bibliography. 1981. lib. bdg. 47.00 (ISBN 0-8161-8531-X, Hall Reference). G K Hall.

Murry, J. Middleton. The Challenge of Schweitzer. LC 72-190328. Repr. of 1948 ed. lib. bdg. 20.00 (ISBN 0-8414-6171-6). Folcroft.

Roback, A. A., ed. The Albert Schweitzer Jubilee Book. LC 79-97392. (Illus.). 508p. Repr. of 1945 ed. lib. bdg. 24.50x (ISBN 0-8371-2670-3, ASJB). Greenwood.

Schweitzer, Albert. The Theology of Albert Schweitzer for Christian Inquirers. Mozley, E. N., ed. 1977. lib. bdg. 59.95 (ISBN 0-8490-2740-3). Gordon Pr.

SCHWEITZER, ALBERT, 1875-1965–JUVENILE LITERATURE

Johnson, Spencer. The Value of Dedication: The Story of Albert Schweitzer. LC 79-21805. (Value Tales Ser.). (Illus.). 1979. 7.95 (ISBN 0-916392-44-9, Dist. by Oak Tree Pubns.). Value Comm.

Schweitzer, Albert. Albert Schweitzer. Repath, Ann, ed. Winston, Richard & Winston, Clara, trs. (Living Philosophies Ser.). (Illus.). 32p. (YA) 1985. PLB 8.95 (ISBN 0-88682-013-8). Creative Ed.

SCHWENK FELDERS

Erb, Peter C. Schwenckfeld & Early Schwenkfeldianism. 428p. (Orig.). 1986. pap. 10.00 (ISBN 0-935980-05-9). Schwenkfelder Lib.

Meschter, W. Kyrel. Twentieth-Century Schwenkfelders: A Narrative History. 1984. pap. write for info (ISBN 0-935980-03-2). Schwenkfelder Lib.

Sommer, Fedor. The Iron Collar. Berky, Andrew S., tr. 261p. 1982. pap. 4.00 (ISBN 0-935980-01-6). Schwenkfelder Lib.

Weigelt, Horst. The Schwenkfelders in Silesia. Erb, Peter C., tr. from Ger. Tr. of Spiritualistische Tradition im Protestantismus. 1985. pap. 10.00 (ISBN 0-935980-04-0). Schwenkfelder Lib.

SCIENCE–EARLY WORKS TO 1800

see also Science, Medieval

Clayton, John. Reverend John Clayton: A Parson with a Scientific Mind. Berkeley, Edmund & Berkeley, Dorothy S., eds. LC 65-23459. (Virginia Historical Document: No. 6). (Illus.). 1965. 15.00x (ISBN 0-8139-0067-0). U Pr of Va.

Ray, John. The Wisdom of God Manifested in the Works of the Creation: Heavenly Bodies, Elements, Meteors, Fossils, Vegetables, Animals. Egerton, Frank N., 3rd, ed. LC 77-74250. (History of Ecology Ser.). 1978. Repr. of 1717 ed. lib. bdg. 40.00x (ISBN 0-405-10419-7). Ayer Co Pubs.

SCIENCE–MORAL ASPECTS

see Science and Ethics

SCIENCE–PHILOSOPHY

see also Semantics (Philosophy)

American Catholic Philosophical Association Staff. Philosophy & the Experimental Sciences: Proceedings, Vol. 26. 1952. 18.00 (ISBN 0-384-46400-9). Johnson Repr.

Antony, Judith. Where Time Becomes Space. 1978. 8.95 (ISBN 0-8199-0699-9). Franciscan Herald.

Ayres, C. E. Science - The False Messiah. Bd. with Holier Than Thou; The Way of the Righteous. LC 71-130660. 1973. Repr. of 1927 ed. 37.50x (ISBN 0-678-00774-8). Kelley.

Colloquium in the Philosophy of Science Staff. Induction, Physics, & Ethics: Proceedings of the Colloquium in the Philosophy of Science, Salzburg, 1969. Weingartner, P. & Zecha, G., eds. LC 78-118137. (Synthese Library: No. 31). 382p. 1970. lib. bdg. 39.50 (ISBN 90-277-0158-X, Pub. by Reidel Holland). Kluwer Academic.

Feyerabend, Paul. Against Method. (Illus.). 1978. pap. 7.95 (ISBN 0-8052-7008-6, Pub by NLB). Schocken.

Grene, Nails, ed. Spinoza & the Sciences. 1986. lib. bdg. 54.50 (ISBN 90-277-1976-4, Pub. by Reidel Holland). Kluwer-Academic.

Grof, Stanislav, ed. Ancient Wisdom & Modern Science. 360p. 1984. 39.50 (ISBN 0-87395-848-9); pap. 12.95x (ISBN 0-87395-849-7). State U NY Pr.

Haskell, Edward, ed. Full Circle: The Moral Force of Unified Science. LC 72-84271. (Current Topics of Contemporary Thought Ser.). (Illus.). 270p. (Orig.). 1972. 57.75 (ISBN 0-677-12480-5). Gordon & Breach.

Heisenberg, Werner. Tradition in Science. 160p. (Orig.). 1983. pap. 10.95 (ISBN 0-8164-2488-8, HarpR). Har-Row.

Heller, Michael. The World & the Word: Between Science & Religion. Kisiel, Adam C., tr. from Polish. LC 86-61668. (Philosophy in Science Library: Vol. 1). 184p. 1987. pap. 14.95 (ISBN 0-88126-724-4). Pachart Pub Hse.

Horstmann, Rolf-Peter, et al, eds. Transcendental Arguments & Science. (Synthese Library: No. 133). 1979. lib. bdg. 34.00 (ISBN 90-277-0963-7, Pub. by Reidel Holland); pap. 16.00 (ISBN 90-277-0964-5). Kluwer Academic.

Husserl, Edmund. Crisis of European Sciences & Transcendental Phenomenology: An Introduction to Phenomenological Philosophy. Carr, David, tr. LC 77-82511. (Studies in Phenomenology & Existential Philosophy Ser). 1970. 28.95 (ISBN 0-8101-0255-2); pap. 11.95 (ISBN 0-8101-0458-X). Northwestern U Pr.

Inge, W. R. Science & Ultimate Truth. 1978. lib. bdg. 12.50 (ISBN 0-8495-2603-5). Arden Lib.

International Colloquium on Philosophy, Science Theology in the Middle Ages, 1st, 1973. The Cultural Context of Medieval Learning: Proceedings, No.76. Murdock, John E. & Sylla, Edith D., eds. (Synthese Library: Boston Studies in the Philosophy of Science 26). ix, 540p. (Orig.). 1975. 68.50 (ISBN 90-277-0560-7, Pub. by Reidel Holland); pap. 39.50 (ISBN 90-277-0587-9, Pub. by Reidel Holland). Kluwer Academic.

Jardine, N. The Fortunes of Inquiry. (Clarendon Library of Logic & Philosophy). 204p. 36.00 (ISBN 0-19-824929-2). Oxford U Pr.

Laszlo, Ervin & Wilbur, James B., eds. Human Values & Natural Science. (Current Topics of Contemporary Thought Ser.: Vol. 4). 310p. 1970. 63.95 (ISBN 0-677-13960-8). Gordon & Breach.

Lunn, Arnold H. The Revolt Against Reason. LC 72-108396. xiv, 273p. Repr. of 1951 ed. lib. bdg. 22.50x (ISBN 0-8371-3819-1, LURA). Greenwood.

MacCormac, Earl R. Metaphor & Myth in Science & Religion. LC 75-23941. pap. 46.80 (2052207). Bks Demand UMI.

Macmurray, John, ed. Some Makers of the Modern Spirit: A Symposium. facs. ed. LC 68-22926. (Essay Index Reprint Ser). Repr. of 1933 ed. 16.25 (ISBN 0-8369-0658-6). Ayer Co Pubs.

Margenau, Henry. Thomas & the Physics of Nineteen Fifty-Eight: A Confrontation. (Aquinas Lecture). 1958. 7.95 (ISBN 0-87462-123-2). Marquette.

Millikan, Robert A. Evolution in Science & Religion. LC 72-85283. 104p. 1973. Repr. of 1927 ed. 21.50x (ISBN 0-8046-1702-3, Pub. by Kennikat). Assoc Faculty Pr.

Porterfield, P. & Spradlin, W. W. The Search for Certainty. 290p. 1983. pap. 28.50 (ISBN 0-387-90889-7). Springer-Verlag.

Pubek, Ronald E. The Metaphysical Imperative: A Critique of the Modern Approach to Science. LC 82-40244. 166p. (Orig.). 1983. lib. bdg. 26.00 (ISBN 0-8191-2663-2); pap. text ed. 11.25 (ISBN 0-8191-2664-0). U Pr of Amer.

Ratzsch, Del. Philosophy of Science. Evans, C. Stephen, ed. LC 86-178. (Contours of Christian Philosophy Ser.). 128p. (Orig.). 1986. pap. 6.95 (ISBN 0-87784-344-9). Inter-Varsity.

Science, Philosophy & Religion. 559p. 1985. Repr. of 1942 ed. lib. bdg. 85.00 (ISBN 0-8492-3208-2). R West.

Sherburne, Donald W., ed. A Key to Whitehead's "Process & Reality". LC 81-11661. 264p. 1981. pap. 10.00x (ISBN 0-226-75293-3). U of Chicago Pr.

Sparrow, Carroll M. Voyages & Cargoes. 1947. 3.00 (ISBN 0-685-09018-3). Dietz.

Stanesby, Derek. Science, Reason & Religion. 210p. 1985. 34.50 (ISBN 0-7099-3360-6, Pub. by Croom Helm Ltd). Methuen Inc.

Swedenborg, Emmanuel. The Principia: Or the First Princples of Natural Things, Vols. I & II. Clissold, Augustus, tr. from Lat. & intro. by. (Illus.). 1976. Repr. of 1846 ed. Set. 15.00 (ISBN 0-915221-20-9). Vol. I, 380p (ISBN 0-915221-37-3). Vol. II, 413p (ISBN 0-915221-38-1). Swedenborg Sci Assn.

Taimni. Science & Occultism. 6.95 (ISBN 0-8356-7501-7). Theos Pub Hse.

UNESCO Colloqium, 10th Anniversary of the Death of Albert Einstein & Teilhard De Charden. Science & Synthesis: An International Colloquium Organized by UNESCO on the Tenth Anniversary of the Death of Albert Einstein & Teilhard De Chardin. Crook, B. M., tr. LC 77-143044. 1971. 29.00 (ISBN 0-387-05344-1). Springer-Verlag.

Vartanian, Aram. Diderot & Descartes: A Study of Scientific Naturalism in the Enlightment. LC 75-18406. (History of Ideas Series: No. 6). 336p. 1975. Repr. of 1953 ed. lib. bdg. 22.50x (ISBN 0-8371-8337-5, VADD). Greenwood.

Voegelin, Eric. Science, Politics & Gnosticism. LC 68-14367. 128p. 4.95 (ISBN 0-89526-964-3). Regnery Bks.

SCIENCE, MEDIEVAL

International Colloquium on Philosophy, Science, & Theology in the Middle Ages, 1st, Boston, Sept. 1973. Boston Studies in the Philosophy of Science, Vol. 26: The Cultural Context of Medieval Learning, Proceedings. Murdoch, J. E. & Sylla, E. D., eds. LC 75-24997. (Synthese Library: No. 76). 566p. 1975. 68.50 (ISBN 90-277-0560-7, Pub. by Reidel Holland); pap. 39.50 (ISBN 90-277-0587-9). Kluwer Academic.

Langford, Jerome J. Galileo, Science & the Church. rev. ed. 1971. pap. 7.95x (ISBN 0-472-06173-9, 173, AA). U of Mich Pr.

Vickers, Brian, ed. Occult & Scientific Mentalities in the Renaissance. 432p. 1986. pap. 15.95 (ISBN 0-521-33836-0). Cambridge U Pr.

SCIENCE, MENTAL

see Psychology

SCIENCE, MORAL

see Ethics

SCIENCE AND CIVILIZATION

Here are entered works on the role of science in the history and development of civilization.

Aristotelian Society for the Systematic Study of Philosophy Staff. Science History & Theology: Proceedings, Suppl. 14. 13.00 (ISBN 0-384-54410-X); pap. 8.00 (ISBN 0-384-54411-8). Johnson Repr.

Bronowski, Jacob. Science & Human Values. rev. & enl. ed. Bd. with The Abacus & the Rose. (Illus.). 142p. 1972. pap. 3.50 (ISBN 0-06-080269-3, P269, PL). Har-Row.

Gore, G. The Scientific Basis of National Progress, Including That of Morality. 218p. 1970. Repr. of 1882 ed. 26.00x (ISBN 0-7146-2407-1, BHA-02407, F Cass Co). Biblio Dist.

Grof, Stanislav. East & West: Ancient Wisdom & Modern Science. (Broadside Ser.). 30p. 1985. pap. 2.95 (ISBN 0-931191-00-9). Rob Briggs.

Restivo, Sal. The Social Relations of Physics, Mysticism & Mathematics. 1983. lib. bdg. 49.50 (ISBN 90-277-1536-X, Pub. by Reidel Holland). Kluwer Academic.

Weber, Renee. Dialogues with Scientists & Sages: The Search for Unity in Science & Mysticism. 288p. 1986. pap. 14.95 (ISBN 0-7102-0655-0, 06550, Pub. by Routledge UK). Methuen Inc.

SCIENCE AND ETHICS

Becker, Lawrence C. On Justifying Moral Judgements. (International Library of Philosophy & Scientific Method). 199p. 1973. text ed. 19.95x (ISBN 0-7100-7524-3, Pub. by Routledge UK). Humanities.

Cattell, Raymond B. A New Morality from Science: Beyondism. 1973. 42.00 (ISBN 0-08-016956-2). Pergamon.

Davis, et al, eds. Contemporary Issues in Biomedical Ethics. LC 78-71406. (Contemporary Issues in Biomedicine, Ethics, & Society Ser.). 300p. 1979. 29.50 (ISBN 0-89603-002-4). Humana.

Glass, Hiram B. Science & Ethical Values. LC 81-13170. ix, 101p. 1981. Repr. of 1965 ed. lib. bdg. 22.50x (ISBN 0-313-23141-9, GLSE). Greenwood.

Gore, G. The Scientific Basis of National Progress, Including That of Morality. 218p. 1970. Repr. of 1882 ed. 26.00x (ISBN 0-7146-2407-1, BHA-02407, F Cass Co). Biblio Dist.

Graham, Loren R. Between Science & Values. LC 81-4436. 448p. 1981. 28.00 (ISBN 0-231-05192-1); pap. 14.00x (ISBN 0-231-05193-X). Columbia U Pr.

International Conference on the Unity of the Sciences, 2nd, Tokyo, Nov. 18-21, 1973. Modern Science & Moral Values: Proceedings. LC 75-306280. 608p. 1974. casebound smythesewn 20.00x (ISBN 0-89226-000-9, Pub. by ICF Pr). Paragon Hse.

Lappe, Marc & Morison, Robert S., eds. Ethical & Scientific Issues Posed by Human Uses of Molecular Genetics, Vol. 265. (Annals of the New York Academy of Sciences). 208p. 1976. 26.00x (ISBN 0-89072-019-3). NY Acad Sci.

Sardar, Ziauddin, ed. The Touch of Midas: Science, Values & the Environment in Islam & the West. LC 83-22262. 253p. 1984. 38.50 (ISBN 0-7190-0974-X, Pub. by Manchester Univ Pr). Longwood Pub Group.

Shannon, Thomas. Bioethics. 2nd ed. LC 76-18054. 646p. 1976. pap. 14.95 (ISBN 0-8091-1970-6). Paulist Pr.

Singer, Peter. The Expanding Circle: Ethics & Sociobiology. 190p. 1981. 10.95 (ISBN 0-374-15112-1). FS&G.

Teichler-Zallen, Doris & Clements, Colleen D. Science & Morality: New Directions in Bioethics. LC 80-8926. 320p. 1982. 29.00x (ISBN 0-669-04406-7); pap. text ed. 12.00x (ISBN 0-669-09808-6). Lexington Bks.

Walters, Leroy, ed. Bibliography of Bioethics, Vol. 7. 375p. 1981. 55.00 (ISBN 0-02-933770-4). Free Pr.

SCIENCE AND HISTORY

see Science and Civilization

SCIENCE AND RELIGION

see Religion and Science

SCIENCE AND SOCIETY

see Science and Civilization

SCIENTISTS

Gilpin, Robert G., Jr. American Scientists & Nuclear Weapons Policy. 1962. 37.00x (ISBN 0-691-07501-8). Princeton U Pr.

Proceedings of the Association of Orthodox Jewish Scientists, Vol. 6. 1982. pap. 9.95 (ISBN 0-87306-225-6). Feldheim.

Raistrick, Arthur. Quakers in Science & Industry. LC 68-18641. (Illus.). 1968. Repr. of 1950 ed. 35.00x (ISBN 0-678-05622-6). Kelley.

Walsh, James J. Catholic Churchmen in Science, First Ser. facs. ed. LC 68-16985. (Essay Index Reprint Ser). 1906. 19.00 (ISBN 0-8369-0971-2). Ayer Co Pubs.

--Catholic Churchmen in Science, Second Ser. facs. ed. LC 67-22126. (Essay Index Reprint Ser.). 1909. 19.00 (ISBN 0-8369-1387-6). Ayer Co Pubs.

--Catholic Churchmen in Science. Third Ser. facs. ed. LC 67-22126. (Essay Index Reprint Ser). 1917. 19.00 (ISBN 0-8369-0972-0). Ayer Co Pubs.

SCOTLAND–ANTIQUITIES

Chalmers, Patrick. Ancient Sculptured Monuments of the County of Angus. LC 72-1052. (Bannatyne Club, Edinburgh. Publications: No. 88). Repr. of 1848 ed. 145.00 (ISBN 0-404-52818-X). AMS Pr.

SCOTLAND–BIOGRAPHY

Barclay, William. William Barclay: A Spiritual Autobiography. LC 73-76528. 1977. pap. 1.50 (ISBN 0-8028-1667-3). Eerdmans.

Bonar, Andrew. Andrew Bonar Life & Diary. 535p. 1984. Repr. of 1893 ed. 14.95 (ISBN 0-85151-432-4). Banner of Truth.

Crone, Robert W. Covenanters Monuments of Scotland. 96p. 1984. 40.00x (ISBN 0-7212-0694-8, Pub. by Regency Pr). State Mutual Bk.

SCOTLAND–CHURCH HISTORY

Burns, et al. The Revival of Religion. 449p. 1984. Repr. of 1840 ed. 13.95 (ISBN 0-85151-435-9). Banner of Truth.

Burns, J. H. Scottish Churchmen & the Council of Basle. LC 64-7472. 1962. 15.00 (ISBN 0-8023-9034-X). Dufour.

Cairns, William T. Religion of Dr. Johnson. facsimile ed. LC 71-93324. (Essay Index Reprint Ser). 1946. 17.00 (ISBN 0-8369-1279-9). Ayer Co Pubs.

Crone, Robert W. Covenanters Monuments of Scotland. 96p. 1984. 40.00x (ISBN 0-7212-0694-8, Pub. by Regency Pr). State Mutual Bk.

Hayes, A. J. & Gowland, D. A. Scottish Methodism in the Early Victorian Period: The Scottish Correspondence of the Reverend Jabez Bunting, 1800-1857. 143p. 1981. 20.00x (ISBN 0-85224-412-6, Pub. by Edinburgh U Pr Scotland). Columbia U Pr.

Lumby, J. R., ed. Bernardus de Cura Rei Familiaris: Early Scottish Prophecies, Etc. (EETS OS Ser.: Vol. 42). pap. 15.00 (ISBN 0-8115-3351-4). Kraus Repr.

Lyall, Francis. Of Presbyters & Kings: Church & State in the Law of Scotland. 220p. 1980. 20.00 (ISBN 0-08-025715-1). Pergamon.

MacGregor, Malcolm B. The Sources & Literature of Scottish Church History. LC 76-1125. 260p. 1977. Repr. of 1934 ed. lib. bdg. 20.00x (ISBN 0-915172-10-0). Richwood Pub.

Mackenzie, Compton. Catholicism & Scotland. LC 75-118486. 1971. Repr. of 1936 ed. 23.50x (ISBN 0-8046-1235-8, Pub. by Kennikat). Assoc Faculty Pr.

McMillan, William. The Worship of the Scottish Reformed Church, 1550-1638: The Hastie Lectures in the University of Glasgow, 1930. LC 83-45585. Date not set. Repr. of 1931 ed. 35.00 (ISBN 0-404-19903-8). AMS Pr.

Pitcairne, Archibald. Babell. LC 75-174208. (Maitland Club, Glasgow. Publications Ser.: No. 6). Repr. of 1830 ed. 11.00 (ISBN 0-404-52931-3). AMS Pr.

Riesen, Richard A. Criticism & Faith in Late Victorian Scotland: A. B. Davidson, William Robertson Smith & George Adam Smith. LC 85-5388. 490p. (Orig.). 1985. lib. bdg. 30.50 (ISBN 0-8191-4655-2); pap. text ed. 18.75 (ISBN 0-8191-4656-0). U Pr of Amer.

Sanderson, Margaret H. Cardinal of Scotland - David Beaton 1494-1546. 324p. 1986. 39.95x (ISBN 0-85976-110-X, Pub. by John Donald Pub UK). Humanities.

Winzet, Ninian. Certane Tractatis for Reformatioun of Doctryne & Maneris in Scotland. LC 79-178311. (Maitland Club, Glasgow Publications: No. 33). Repr. of 1835 ed. 20.00 (ISBN 0-404-53001-X). AMS Pr.

Wodrow, Robert. Analecta, 4 Vols. LC 74-178318. (Maitland Club, Glasgow. Publications: No. 60). Repr. of 1843 ed. Set. 175.00 (ISBN 0-404-53051-6). AMS Pr.

SCOTLAND–CHURCH HISTORY–SOURCES

Chalmers, Patrick & Chalmers, John I., eds. Registrum Episcopatus Brechinensis, 2 Vols. LC 72-39524. (Bannatyne Club, Edinburgh. Publications: No. 102). Repr. of 1856 ed. Set. 110.00 (ISBN 0-404-52855-4). AMS Pr.

Church of Scotland Staff. Register of Ministers, Exhorters & Readers & of Their Stipends. LC 71-174310. (Maitland Club, Glasgow. Publications: No. 5). Repr. of 1830 ed. 15.00 (ISBN 0-404-52929-1). AMS Pr.

Innes, Cosmo, ed. Registrum De Dunfermelyn. LC 70-164810. (Bannatyne Club, Edinburgh. Publications: No. 74). Repr. of 1842 ed. 55.00 (ISBN 0-404-52793-0). AMS Pr.

--Registrum Episcopatus Glasguensis, 2 Vols. LC 70-168151. (Maitland Club, Glasgow. Publications: No. 61). Repr. of 1843 ed. Set. 95.00 (ISBN 0-685-05956-1). AMS Pr.

Innes, Cosmo, et al, eds. Origines Parochiales Scotiae, 2 Vols. in 3. LC 76-170804. (Bannatyne Club, Edinburgh. Publications: No. 97). Repr. of 1855 ed. 210.00 (ISBN 0-404-52850-3). AMS Pr.

Kelso Abbey. Liber S. Marie De Calchou, Registrum Abbacie Tironensis De Kelso, 1113-1567, 2 Vols. Innes, Cosmo, ed. LC 71-171552. Repr. of 1846 ed. 75.00 (ISBN 0-404-52805-8). AMS Pr.

Laing, David, ed. Original Letters Relating to the Ecclesiastical Affairs of Scotland, 2 Vols. LC 73-171637. (Bannatyne Club, Edinburgh. Publications: No. 92). Repr. of 1852 ed. 95.00 (ISBN 0-404-52833-3). AMS Pr.

--Registrum Cartarum Ecclesie Sancti Egidii De Edinburgh. LC 76-174803. (Bannatyne Club, Edinburgh. Publications: No. 105). Repr. of 1859 ed. 47.50 (ISBN 0-404-52860-0). AMS Pr.

--Registrum Domus De Soltre. LC 77-171638. (Bannatyne Club, Edinburgh. Publications: No. 109). Repr. of 1861 ed. 42.50 (ISBN 0-404-52863-5). AMS Pr.

Newbattle Abbey. Registrum S. Marie De Neubotle. Innes, Cosmo, ed. LC 74-173074. (Bannatyne Club, Edinburgh. Publications: No. 89). Repr. of 1849 ed. 42.50 (ISBN 0-404-52819-8). AMS Pr.

North Berwick Priory. Carte Monialium De Northberwic. Innes, Cosmo, ed. LC 74-173799. (Bannatyne Club, Edinburgh. Publications: No. 84). Repr. of 1847 ed. 27.50 (ISBN 0-404-52809-0). AMS Pr.

Paisley Abbey. Registrum Monasterii De Passelet. Innes, Cosmo, ed. LC 75-174311. (Maitland Club. Glasgow. Publications: No. 17). Repr. of 1832 ed. 52.50 (ISBN 0-404-52954-2). AMS Pr.

Scotland. Registrum Episcopatus Moraviensis. Innes, Cosmo N., ed. LC 71-172742. (Bannatyne Club, Edinburgh. Publications: No. 58). Repr. of 1837 ed. 47.50 (ISBN 0-404-52768-X). AMS Pr.

Thomson, Thomas, ed. Accounts of the Great Chamberlains of Scotland, 3 Vols. 1817-45. Set. 250.00 (ISBN 0-404-52810-4). AMS Pr.

SCOTLAND–HISTORY

Donovan, Robert K. No Popery & Radicalism: Opposition to Roman Catholic Relief in Scotland, 1778-1782. McNeill, Willaim H. & Stansky, Peter, eds. (Modern European History Ser.). 425p. 1987. lib. bdg. 65.00 (ISBN 0-8240-7804-7). Garland Pub.

Gunnin, Gerry C. John Wheatley, Catholic Socialism, & Irish Labour in the West of Scotland, 1906-1924. McNeil, William H. & Stansky, Peter, eds. (Modern European History Ser.). 375p. 1987. lib. bdg. 55.00 (ISBN 0-8240-7811-X). Garland Pub.

His Majesties Proclamation in Scotland with an Explanation of the Oath & Covenant. LC 74-80216. (English Experience Ser.: No. 692). 1974. Repr. of 1639 ed. 3.50 (ISBN 90-221-0692-6). Walter J Johnson.

Mackenzie, Agnes M. The Scotland of Queen Mary & the Religious Wars, 1513-1638. LC 75-41506. (Illus.). 404p. 1976. Repr. of 1957 ed. lib. bdg. 24.00x (ISBN 0-8371-8704-4, MASQ). Greenwood.

Melville, James. Diary. LC 70-172723. (Bannatyne Club, Edinburgh. Publications: No. 34). Repr. of 1829 ed. 32.50 (ISBN 0-404-52740-X). AMS Pr.

Rothes, John L. Relation of Proceedings Concerning the Affairs of the Kirk of Scotland. LC 79-174966. (Bannatyne Club, Edinburgh. Publications: No. 37). Repr. of 1830 ed. 28.00 (ISBN 0-404-52743-4). AMS Pr.

Sanderson, Margaret H. Cardinal of Scotland - David Beaton 1494-1546. 324p. 1986. 39.95x (ISBN 0-85976-110-X, Pub. by John Donald Pub UK). Humanities.

Sher, Richard B. Church & University in the Scottish Enlightenment: The Moderate Literati of Edinburgh. LC 85-17911. (Illus.). 1985. text ed. 47.50x (ISBN 0-691-05445-2). Princeton U Pr.

Somerville, Robert, ed. Scotia Pontificia: Papal Letters to Scotland Before the Pontificate of Innocent III, 1198 to 1216. 1981. 65.00x (ISBN 0-19-822433-8). Oxford U Pr.

Watson, John. The Scot of the Eighteenth Century. LC 76-47571. 1976. Repr. of 1907 ed. lib. bdg. 39.50 (ISBN 0-8414-9459-2). Folcroft.

SCOTLAND–RELIGION

Bruce, S. No Pope of Rome: Militant Protestantism in Modern Scotland. 270p. 1985. text ed. 35.00x (ISBN 0-906391-78-4, Pub. by Mainstream Pubs UK). Humanities.

Donovan, Robert K. No Popery & Radicalism: Opposition to Roman Catholic Relief in Scotland, 1778-1782. McNeill, Willaim H. & Stansky, Peter, eds. (Modern European History Ser.). 425p. 1987. lib. bdg. 65.00 (ISBN 0-8240-7804-7). Garland Pub.

Forrester, Duncan B. & Murray, Douglas M., eds. Studies in the History of Worship in Scotland. 190p. 1984. pap. 15.95 (ISBN 0-567-29349-1, Pub. by T&T Clark Ltd UK). Fortress.

Rankin, Eric. Cockburnspath: A Documentary History of a Border Parish. Bulloch, James, ed. (Illus.). 166p. 1981. 16.95 (ISBN 0-567-09316-6, Pub. by T&T Clark Ltd UK). Fortress.

Sanderson, Margaret H. Cardinal of Scotland - David Beaton 1494-1546. 324p. 1986. 39.95x (ISBN 0-85976-110-X, Pub. by John Donald Pub UK). Humanities.

SCROLLS

Maier, Johann. The Temple Scroll: An Introduction, Translation & Commentary. (No. 34). xii, 147p. 1985. text ed. 28.50x (ISBN 1-85075-003-3, Pub. by JSOT Pr England); pap. text ed. 13.50x (ISBN 1-85075-004-1). Eisenbrauns.

SCULPTURE–CHINA

Rhie, Marylin M. Fo-Kuang Ssu: Literary Evidences & Buddhist Images. LC 76-23690. (Outstanding Dissertations in the Fine Arts - Far Eastern). (Illus.). 1977. Repr. of 1970 ed. lib. bdg. 55.00 (ISBN 0-8240-2721-3). Garland Pub.

Sullivan, Michael. The Cave Temples of Maichishan. LC 69-15829. (Illus.). 1969. 70.00x (ISBN 0-520-01448-0). U of Cal Pr.

SCULPTURE–EGYPT

Winlock, Herbert E. Bas-Reliefs from the Temple of Rameses One at Abydos, 2 vols in 1. Incl. The Temple of Rameses One at Abydos. LC 72-2519. (Metropolitan Museum of Art Publications in Reprint). (Illus.). 1972. Repr. of 1937 ed. 20.00 (ISBN 0-685-32631-4). Ayer Co Pubs.

SCULPTURE–FRANCE

Forsyth, Ilene H. The Throne of Wisdom: Wood Sculptures of the Madonna in Romanesque France. LC 72-166372. pap. 77.30 (ISBN 0-317-41726-6, 2052061). Bks Demand UMI.

Forsyth, William H. Entombment of Christ: French Sculptures of the Fifteenth & Sixteenth Centuries. LC 70-99523. (Illus, Pub. for the Metropolitan Museum of Art). 1970. 22.50x (ISBN 0-674-25775-8). Harvard U Pr.

Katzenellenbogen, Adolf. Sculptural Programs of Chartres Cathedral. (Illus.). 1964. pap. 6.95x (ISBN 0-393-00233-0, Norton Lib). Norton.

SCULPTURE–GREAT BRITAIN

Chalmers, Patrick. Ancient Sculptured Monuments of the County of Angus. LC 72-1052. (Bannatyne Club, Edinburgh. Publications: No. 88). Repr. of 1848 ed. 145.00 (ISBN 0-404-52818-X). AMS Pr.

SCULPTURE–IRELAND

Porter, Arthur K. Crosses & Culture of Ireland. LC 68-56480. (Illus.). 1969. Repr. of 1931 ed. 33.00 (ISBN 0-405-08860-4, Pub. by Blom). Ayer Co Pubs.

SCULPTURE–JAPAN

Nishikawa, Kyotaro & Sano, Emily J. The Great Age of Japanese Buddhist Sculpture, AD 600-1300. LC 82-82805. (Illus.). 152p. (Orig.). 1982. 45.00 (ISBN 0-912804-07-6, Dist by U of Wash Pr); pap. 24.95 (ISBN 0-912804-08-4). Kimbell Art.

Saunders, E. Dale. Mudra: A Study of Symbolic Gestures in Japanese Buddhist Sculpture. (Bollingen Ser.: Vol. 58). (Illus.). 1960. 37.00x (ISBN 0-691-09796-8). Princeton U Pr.

Sugiyama, Jiro. Classic Buddhist Sculpture. LC 82-80738. (Japanese Arts Library: Vol. 11). (Illus.). 200p. 1982. 25.00 (ISBN 0-87011-529-4). Kodansha.

SCULPTURE–OCEANICA

Van Baaren, T. P. Korwars & Korwar Style: Art & Ancestor Worship in North-West New Guinea. (Art in Its Context, Studies in Ethno-Aesthetics, Museum Ser.: No. 2). (Illus.). 1968. 26.75x (ISBN 0-686-21795-0). Mouton.

SCULPTURE–UNITED STATES

Ahlborn, Richard. The Sculpted Saints of a Borderland Mission. LC 74-18171. (Illus.). 124p. 1974. pap. 7.50 (ISBN 0-915076-03-9). SW Mission.

Carmean, E. A., Jr., et al. The Sculpture of Nancy Graves: A Catalogue Raisonne. LC 86-29970. (Illus.). 192p. 1987. 50.00 (ISBN 0-933920-77-6, Dist. by Rizzoli); Museum Distribution Only. pap. 25.00 (ISBN 0-933920-78-4). Hudson Hills.

Combs, Diana W. Early Gravestone Art in Georgia & South Carolina. LC 85-1129. (Illus.). 256p. 1986. 35.00x (ISBN 0-8203-0788-2). U of Ga Pr.

Gillon, Edmund V., Jr. Early New England Gravestone Rubbings. (Illus., Orig.). 1966. pap. 7.95 (ISBN 0-486-21380-3). Dover.

Schultz, Douglas G. Eight Sculptors. LC 79-50457. (Illus.). 1979. pap. 6.50 (ISBN 0-914782-25-8). Buffalo Acad.

SCULPTURE, BAROQUE

Ahlborn, Richard. The Sculpted Saints of a Borderland Mission. LC 74-18171. (Illus.). 124p. 1974. pap. 7.50 (ISBN 0-915076-03-9). SW Mission.

SCULPTURE, GOTHIC

Hurtig, Judith W. Armored Gisant Before Fourteen Hundred. LC 78-74368. (Outstanding Dissertations in the Fine Arts, Fourth Ser.). 1979. lib. bdg. 63.00 (ISBN 0-8240-3956-4). Garland Pub.

Katzenellenbogen, Adolf E. The Sculptural Programs of Chartres Cathedral: Christ, Mary, Ecclesia. LC 59-14894. pap. 57.50 (ISBN 0-317-10764-X, 2007368). Bks Demand UMI.

SCULPTURE, GREEK

Hurry, J. B. Imhotep: The Egyptian God of Medicine. (Illus.). 120p. 1978. 12.50 (ISBN 0-89005-239-5). Ares.

SCULPTURE, HINDU

Desai, Devangana. Erotic Sculpture of India: A Socio-Cultural Study. (Illus.). 290p. 1984. text ed. 55.00x. Coronet Bks.

SCULPTURE, MEDIEVAL

see also Sculpture, Gothic; Sculpture, Romanesque

Porter, Arthur K. Crosses & Culture of Ireland. LC 68-56480. (Illus.). 1969. Repr. of 1931 ed. 33.00 (ISBN 0-405-08860-4, Pub. by Blom). Ayer Co Pubs.

SCULPTURE, RELIGIOUS

see Christian Art and Symbolism

SCULPTURE, RENAISSANCE

Forsyth, William H. Entombment of Christ: French Sculptures of the Fifteenth & Sixteenth Centuries. LC 70-99523. (Illus., Pub. for the Metropolitan Museum of Art). 1970. 22.50x (ISBN 0-674-25775-8). Harvard U Pr.

SCULPTURE, ROMAN

Spence, Joseph. Polymetis. LC 75-27886. (Renaissance & the Gods Ser.: Vol. 41). (Illus.). 1976. Repr. of 1747 ed. lib. bdg. 88.00 (ISBN 0-8240-2090-1). Garland Pub.

SCULPTURE, ROMANESQUE

Forsyth, Ilene H. The Throne of Wisdom: Wood Sculptures of the Madonna in Romanesque France. LC 72-166372. pap. 77.30 (ISBN 0-317-41726-6, 2052061). Bks Demand UMI.

O'Meara, Carra F. The Iconography of the Facade of Saint-Gilles-Du-Gard. LC 76-23668. (Outstanding Dissertations in the Fine Arts - Medieval). (Illus.). 352p. 1977. Repr. of 1975 ed. lib. bdg. 63.00 (ISBN 0-8240-2717-5). Garland Pub.

Porter, A. Kingsley. Romanesque Sculpture of the Pilgrimage Roads, 10 Vols. in 3. LC 67-4262. (Illus.). 1986. Repr. of 1923 ed. 250.00 set (ISBN 0-87817-020-0). Hacker.

Seidel, Linda. Romanesque Sculpture from the Cathedral of Saint-Etienne, Toulouse. LC 76-23646. (Outstanding Dissertations in the Fine Arts). (Illus.). 1977. Repr. of 1965 ed. lib. bdg. 63.00 (ISBN 0-8240-2729-9). Garland Pub.

Stoddard, Whitney S. The Facade of Saint-Gilles-du-Gard: Its Influence on French Sculpture. LC 72-3696. (Illus.). 341p. 1973. pap. 17.50 (ISBN 0-8195-6068-5). Wesleyan U Pr.

SEABURY, SAMUEL, BP., 1729-1796

Mitgang, Herbert. The Man Who Rode the Tiger: The Life of Judge Samuel Seabury. (Illus.). 1979. pap. 5.95 (ISBN 0-393-00922-X). Norton.

Rowthorn, Anne. Samuel Seabury: A Bicentennial Biography. 160p. 1983. 14.95 (ISBN 0-8164-0517-4, HarpR). Har-Row.

SECKER, THOMAS, ARCHBISHOP OF CANTERBURY, 1692-1768

Sykes, Norman. From Sheldon to Secker: Aspects of English Church History, 1660-1768. LC 59-2371. (The Ford Lectures: 1958). pap. 62.50 (ISBN 0-317-20808-X, 2024534). Bks Demand UMI.

SECOND ADVENT

see also Judgment Day; Millennium; Rapture (Christian Eschatology)

Abram, Victor P. Restoration of All Things. LC 62-18059. 1962. 4.00 (ISBN 0-910840-07-5). Kingdom.

Alderman, Paul R., Jr. God's Spotlight on Tomorrow: Seven Sevens Concerning the Return of Christ. 1960. pap. 1.25 (ISBN 0-87213-010-X). Loizeaux.

Bacci, Judy L. The Second Coming: Why Jesus Christ Became a Carpenter Instead of an Electrician. 110p. (Orig.). 1981. pap. 5.95 (ISBN 0-940002-00-0). Studio J Pub.

Bailey, K. M. Christ's Coming & His Kingdom. LC 80-70733. 175p. 1981. pap. 4.95 (ISBN 0-87509-296-9); Leader's Guide. 2.95 (ISBN 0-87509-309-4). Chr Pubns.

Bakker, Jim. Survival-Unite to Live. LC 80-84504. 1980. 7.95 (ISBN 0-89221-081-8). New Leaf.

Balyoz, Harold. Signs of Christ. LC 79-64608. 1979. 18.00 (ISBN 0-9609710-0-9). Altai Pub.

Biederwolf, William E. The Second Coming Bible Commentary. (Paperback Reference Library). 728p. 1985. pap. 17.95 (ISBN 0-8010-0887-5). Baker Bk.

Bloomfield, Arthur E. Signs of His Coming. LC 57-8724. 160p. 1962. pap. 4.95 (ISBN 0-87123-513-7, 210513). Bethany Hse.

Cambron, Mark. Come, Lord Jesus. pap. 1.45 (ISBN 0-686-12745-5). Grace Pub Co.

Carlson, Gertrude C. New Age. LC 85-90283. 252p. 1986. 13.95 (ISBN 0-533-06790-1). Vantage.

Carver, Everett I. When Jesus Comes Again. 1979. pap. 7.95 (ISBN 0-87552-159-2). Presby & Reformed.

Cutting, Jorge. La Venida del Senor. 2nd ed. Bennett, Gordon H., ed. Bautista, Sara, tr. from Eng. (La Serie Diamante). Tr. of The Lord's Coming. (Span., Illus.). 48p. 1982. pap. 0.85 (ISBN 0-942504-10-0). Overcomer Pr.

DeHaan, Martin R. Second Coming of Jesus. 1978. pap. 6.95 (ISBN 0-310-23461-1, 9498P). Zondervan.

Denslow, Jamin. The Day the Lion Roars. Graves, Helen, ed. LC 86-40284. 286p. (Orig.). 1987. pap. 8.95 (ISBN 1-55523-029-6). Winston-Derek.

Doan, Ruth A. The Miller Heresy, Millenialism, & Amercian Culture. 270p. 1987. price not set (ISBN 0-87722-481-1). Temple U Pr.

Eager, George B. Wake up World! Jesus Is Coming Soon! 40p. (Orig.). 1980. pap. 1.00 (ISBN 0-9603752-3-6). Mailbox.

Erdman, V. R. Signs of Christ's Second Coming. 29p. pap. 0.95 (ISBN 0-87509-130-X). Chr Pubns.

Gangstad, John E. Great Pyramid: Signs in the Sun (Pyramid Design & Prophecy: Second Advent) LC 76-24077. (Illus.). 200p. 1976. 1980-86 supplement 3.00 (ISBN 0-9603374-2-3). Di-Tri Bks.

Grier, W. J. The Momentous Event. 1976. pap. 2.95 (ISBN 0-85151-020-5). Banner of Truth.

Haldeman, I. M. Second Coming of Christ. 326p. 1986. 12.95 (ISBN 0-8254-2844-0). Kregel.

Jones, K. R. The New Government: Prophecies for Today. 1984. 16.95 (ISBN 0-533-05993-3). Vantage.

Kelly, William. The Second Coming. 375p. 6.25 (ISBN 0-88172-108-5). Believers Bkshelf.

Kwak, Chung H., ed. The Second Advent (6) (Home Study Course Ser.). 50p. (Orig.). 1980. pap. 4.00 (ISBN 0-910621-15-2). HSA Pubns.

Ladd, George E. Blessed Hope. 1956. pap. 6.95 (ISBN 0-8028-1111-6). Eerdmans.

Lindsay, Gordon. Forty Signs of the Soon Coming of Christ. (Prophecy Ser.). 1.95 (ISBN 0-89985-055-3). Christ Nations.

--The Rapture & the Second Coming of Christ. (Revelation Ser.). 1.25 (ISBN 0-89985-041-3). Christ Nations.

--The Second Coming of Christ. (Prophecy Ser.). 0.95 (ISBN 0-89985-061-8). Christ Nations.

Lovett, C. S. Jesus Is Coming-Get Ready Christian. 1969. pap. 4.25 (ISBN 0-938148-04-4). Personal Christianity.

MacKeeby, Margaret. Is Jesus Coming in a Flying Saucer? 1984. 8.95 (ISBN 0-533-05998-4). Vantage.

Malgo, Wim. Fifty Questions Most Frequently Asked about the Second Coming. 3.95 (ISBN 0-937422-04-5). Midnight Call.

Martin, Ralph. The Return of the Lord. 118p. (Orig.). 1983. pap. 4.95 (ISBN 0-89283-145-6). Servant.

Orchard, Richard E. Look Who's Coming. LC 74-33870. (Radiant Bks.). 128p. 1975. pap. 1.25 (ISBN 0-88243-541-8, 02-0541). Gospel Pub.

Rand, Howard B. Hour Cometh. 1966. 5.00 (ISBN 0-685-08805-7). Destiny.

Ray, Angeln. Angels Ascending & Descending. 176p. 1984. 12.95 (ISBN 0-915763-00-1). Starseed Pubns.

Redmond, Howard. A Philosophy of the Second Advent. Goss, Leonard G., ed. 160p. 1985. write for info. (ISBN 0-88062-070-6); pap. write for info. (ISBN 0-88062-067-6). Mott Media.

Redmond, Howard A. Philosophy of the Second Advent. 1986. text ed. 12.95 (ISBN 0-8010-7740-0). Baker Bk.

Reese, Alexander. Approaching Advent of Christ. LC 73-85374. 328p. 1975. 8.95 (ISBN 0-8254-3610-9). Kregel.

Riggle, H. M. Jesus Is Coming Again. 111p. pap. 1.00 (ISBN 0-686-29123-9). Faith Pub Hse.

Robinson, John A. Jesus & His Coming. 2nd ed. LC 79-14078. 192p. 1979. pap. 6.95 (ISBN 0-664-24278-2). Westminster.

Sanders, J. Oswald. Certainties of Christ's Coming. 128p. 1984. pap. 2.95 (ISBN 0-87788-111-1). Shaw Pubs.

Savoy, Gene. The Miracle of the Second Advent: The Emerging New Christianity. LC 84-81232. (Illus.). 68p. 1984. text ed. 14.50 (ISBN 0-936202-04-1). Intl Comm Christ.

Sayers, Stanley E. The Nature of Things to Come. 1972. 7.95 (ISBN 0-88027-013-6). Firm Foun Pub.

Scott, Jack B. Revelation Unfolded. pap. 2.95 (ISBN 0-8423-5510-3). Tyndale.

Silvestre, Lucio B. The End of the World, A.D. 2133. LC 83-90813. 233p. 1985. 12.95 (ISBN 0-533-05822-8). Vantage.

Steiner, Rudolf. The Reappearance of Christ in the Etheric. rev. ed. 190p. (Orig.). 1983. 14.00 (ISBN 0-88010-017-6); pap. 8.95 (ISBN 0-88010-016-8). Anthroposophic.

Taylor, G. F. Second Coming of Jesus. 3.95 (ISBN 0-911866-63-9); pap. 2.00 (ISBN 0-911866-62-0). Advocate.

Unopolus, James J. Scriptural Signs of the Second Coming. 1979. pap. 1.50 (ISBN 0-89036-072-3). Hawkes Pub Inc.

Venden, Morris. Return of Elijah. (Harv Ser.). 1983. pap. 4.50 (ISBN 0-8163-0453-X). Pacific Pr Pub Assn.

Walvoord, John F. The Blessed Hope & the Tribulation. (A Contemporary Evangelical Perspectives Ser.). 1976. kivar 5.95 (ISBN 0-310-34041-1, 10977P). Zondervan.

Weber, Timothy P. Living in the Shadow of the Second Coming: American Premillennialism, 1875-1982. rev. & enl. ed. xiv, 306p. 1987. pap. 12.95 (ISBN 0-226-87732-9). U of Chicago Pr.

White, John W. Re-Entry II. 1986. pap. 4.95 (ISBN 0-8010-9680-4). Baker Bk.

Yogananda, Paramhansa. Second Coming of Christ, Vol. II. LC 79-50352. 1984. pap. 12.95 (ISBN 0-937134-05-8). Amrita Found.

SECRET SOCIETIES

see also Mysteries, Religious
also names of societies, e.g. Freemasons, Rosicrucians

Daraul, Arkon. Secret Societies. 1983. Repr. of 1961 ed. 14.95 (ISBN 0-86304-024-1, Pub. by Octagon Pr England). Ins Study Human.

Hunt, George L. Secret Societies: Can a Christian Belong to Them & Still Honor Christ? pap. 1.50 (ISBN 0-87213-338-9). Loizeaux.

Macdonald, Fergus. The Catholic Church & the Secret Societies in the United States. LC 46-8049. (Monograph Ser.: No. 22). 1946. 12.50x (ISBN 0-930060-04-0). US Cath Hist.

Rongstad, James. How to Respond to the Lodge. (The Response Ser.). 1977. 1.95 (ISBN 0-570-07677-3, 12-2660). Concordia.

Sutton, Anthony C. The Secret Cult of the Order. 140p. (Orig.). 1984. pap. text ed. 9.95 (ISBN 0-914981-09-9). Res Pubns AZ.

Ward, J. S. The Hung Society: Or the Society of Heaven & Earth, 2 Vols. 1977. 35.00 (ISBN 0-89986-003-6). Oriental Bk Store.

SECTS

Here are entered works on religious groups whose adherents recognize special teachings or practices which fall within the normative bounds of the major world religions. Works on the major world religions are entered under Religions. Works on groups or movements whose system of religious beliefs or practices differs significantly from the major world religions and which are often gathered around a specific deity or person are entered under Cults.

see also Apostasy; Church History–Modern Period, 1500-; Corporations, Religious; Cults; Dissenters, Religious; Eastern Churches; Pentecostal Churches; Protestant Churches; Schism
also particular denominations and sects

Arrupe, Pedro. In Him Alone Is Our Hope: Texts on the Heart of Christ (1966-1983) Aixala, Jerome, ed. Ganss, G. E., et al, trs. from Span. LC 83-80037. (Selected Letters & Addresses of: IV). xvi, 180p. 1984. pap. 7.00 Smyth sewn (ISBN 0-912422-85-8); pap. 6.00 (ISBN 0-912422-87-4). Inst Jesuit.

Bales, James D. Soils & Seeds of Sectarianism. 1977. pap. 4.50 (ISBN 0-89315-264-1). Lambert Bk.

Barker, Eileen, ed. New Religious Movements: A Perspective for Understanding Society. LC 82-8263. (Studies in Religion & Society: Vol. 3). 440p. 1982. 69.95x (ISBN 0-88946-864-8). E Mellen.

Burrell, M. C. & Wright, J. S. Today's Sects. 4.50 (ISBN 0-8010-0855-7). Baker Bk.

Chesterton, G. K., et al. Twelve Modern Apostles & Their Creeds. facs. ed. LC 68-16982. (Essay Index Reprint Ser). 1926. 17.00 (ISBN 0-8369-0955-0). Ayer Co Pubs.

Daly, Lloyd W. Iohannis Philoponi: De Vocabulis Quae Diversum Significatum Exhibent Secundum Differentiam Accentus. LC 81-72156. (Memoirs Ser.: Vol. 151). 1983. 20.00 (ISBN 0-87169-151-5). Am Philos.

Doellinger, Johann J. Beitrage Zur Sektengenchichte des Mittelalter, 2 vols in 1. LC 91-26634. (Social Science Ser). (Ger). 1970. Repr. of 1890 ed. Set. lib. bdg. 57.50 (ISBN 0-8337-0880-5). B Franklin.

Durnbaugh, Donald F., ed. Every Need Supplied: Mutual Aid & Christian Community in Free Churches, 1525-1675. LC 73-94279. (Documents in Free Church History Ser.: No. 1). (Illus.). 258p. 1974. 19.95 (ISBN 0-87722-031-X). Temple U Pr.

Evenhouse, Bill. Reasons One, Sects & Cults with Non-Christian Roots. 120p. (Orig.). 1981. pap. text ed. 4.10 (ISBN 0-933140-23-1); tchr's manual, 61 pgs. 4.10 (ISBN 0-933140-24-X). CRC Pubns.

--Reasons Two, Sects & Cults with Christian Roots. (Orig.). 1981. pap. text ed. 4.10 (ISBN 0-933140-25-8); tchr's manual, 67 pgs. 4.10 (ISBN 0-933140-26-6). CRC Pubns.

Gerstner, John H. Theology of the Major Sects. (Twin Brooks Ser). 1960. pap. 6.95 (ISBN 0-8010-3656-9). Baker Bk.

Halperin, D. A. Psychodynamic Perspectives on Religion, Sect & Cult. 416p. 1983. pap. text ed. 46.50 (ISBN 0-7236-7029-3). PSG Pub Co.

Heath, Carl. Social & Religious Heretics in Five Centuries. LC 78-147622. (Library of War & Peace; Non-Resis. & Non-Vio.). 1972. lib. bdg. 46.00 (ISBN 0-8240-0397-7). Garland Pub.

Irvine, William C. Heresies Exposed. pap. 4.95 (ISBN 0-87213-401-6). Loizeaux.

Jones, Charles E. Guide to the Study of the Holiness Movement. LC 74-659. (ATLA Bibliography Ser.: No. 1). 946p. 1974. 57.50 (ISBN 0-8108-0703-3). Scarecrow.

McComas, Henry C. Psychology of Religious Sects. LC 70-172763. Repr. of 1912 ed. 20.00 (ISBN 0-404-04107-8). AMS Pr.

Melton, J. Gordon. Biographical Dictionary of American Cult & Sect Leaders. LC 83-48226. (Library of Social Sciences). 534p. 1986. lib. bdg. 39.95 (ISBN 0-8240-9037-3). Garland Pub.

Murray, Robert H. Group Movements Throughout the Ages. LC 72-301. (Essay Index Reprint Ser.). Repr. of 1935 ed. 22.00 (ISBN 0-8369-2810-5). Ayer Co Pubs.

Needleman, Jacob. New Religions. 276p. 1984. pap. 10.95 (ISBN 0-8245-0635-9). Crossroad NY.

Niebuhr, Richard H. The Social Sources of Denominationalism. 1984. 17.50 (ISBN 0-8446-6150-3). Peter Smith.

Patrick, Ted & Dulack, Tom. Let Our Children Go! 1977. pap. 2.25 (ISBN 0-345-28343-0). Ballantine.

Piepkorn, Arthur C. Profiles in Belief: the Religious Bodies of North America, Vol. 1: Roman Catholic, Old Catholic & Eastern Orthodox. LC 76-9971. 1977. 20.00 (ISBN 0-06-066580-7, HarpR). Har-Row.

Polsky, Michael. V Zashchitu Pravoslavnoj Vjeri ot Sektantov. Tr. of In Defence of Orthodoxy Against Sectarians. 1950. pap. 1.00 (ISBN 0-317-30261-2). Holy Trinity.

Porter, Jack N. Handbook of Cults, Sects, & Self-Realization Groups. 95p. (Orig.). 1982. pap. 6.95 (ISBN 0-932270-03-4). Spencer Pr.

Porter, Jack N. & Doress, Irvin. Kids in Cults: Why They Join, Why They Stay, Why They Leave. Rev. ed. 22p. (Orig.). 1982. pap. 2.95 (ISBN 0-932270-02-6). Spencer Pr.

Richardson, Herbert W., ed. New Religions & Mental Health: Understanding the Issues. (Symposium Ser.: Vol. 5). 240p. (Orig.). 1980. 39.95x (ISBN 0-88946-910-5). E Mellen.

Sheils, W. J. & Wood, Diana, eds. Voluntary Religion, Vol. 23. 544p. 1987. text ed. 49.95 (ISBN 0-631-15054-4). Basil Blackwell.

Sperry, Willard L., ed. Religion & Our Divided Denominations. facs. ed. LC 74-128315. (Essay Index Reprint Ser). 1945. 14.00 (ISBN 0-8369-2201-8). Ayer Co Pubs.

Stark, Rodney, ed. Religious Movements: Genesis, Exodus, & Numbers. LC 85-9539. (Sociology of Religion Ser.). 369p. 1986. 24.95 (ISBN 0-913757-43-8, Pub by New Era Bks); pap. 12.95 (ISBN 0-913757-44-6, Pub. by New Era Bks). Paragon Hse.

Vatican Secretariat for Promoting Christian Unity Staff. Sects or New Religious Movements: Pastoral Challenge. 24p. 1986. pap. 2.95 (ISBN 1-55586-100-8). US Catholic.

Whalen, William J. Separated Brethren. rev. ed. LC 79-83874. 1979. pap. 7.50 (ISBN 0-87973-829-4). Our Sunday Visitor.

Witt, James G., III. Deadly Deceptions. Fischer, William E., ed. (Illus.). 64p. (Orig.). 1987. pap. text ed. 2.95 (ISBN 0-938272-32-2); leaders guide 2.95. Wels Board.

SECTS–AFRICA

Hohensee, Donald W. Church Growth in Burundi. LC 76-54342. 1977. pap. 4.95 (ISBN 0-87808-316-2). William Carey Lib.

SECTS–CANADA

Mann, William E. Sect, Cult & Church in Alberta. rev. ed. LC 56-2838. 1972. 20.00x (ISBN 0-8020-5036-0). U of Toronto Pr.

SECTS–SOVIET UNION

Lane, Christel. Christian Religion in the Soviet Union: A Sociological Study. LC 77-801. 1978. 49.50 (ISBN 0-87395-327-4). State U NY Pr.

Znoskovo-Borovsky, Mitrophan. Pravoslavije, Rimo-Katolichestvo, Protenstatizm i Sektantstvo. Tr. of Orthodoxy, Roman-Catholicism, Protenstatism & Sectarianism. 156p. 1972. pap. text ed. 5.00 (ISBN 0-317-30254-X). Holy Trinity.

SECTS–UNITED STATES

see also Afro-American Churches

Bach, Marcus L. They Have Found a Faith. facsimile ed. LC 74-134049. (Essay Index Reprint Ser). Repr. of 1946 ed. 18.00 (ISBN 0-8369-2481-9). Ayer Co Pubs.

Braden, Charles S., ed. Varieties of American Religion. facsimile ed. LC 76-156616. (Essay Index Reprint Ser). Repr. of 1936 ed. 15.50 (ISBN 0-8369-2307-3). Ayer Co Pubs.

Braswell, George W., Jr. Understanding Sectarian Groups in America. 1986. pap. 10.95 (ISBN 0-8054-6607-X). Broadman.

Clark, Elmer T. The Small Sects in America. 11.75 (ISBN 0-8446-1862-4). Peter Smith.

Da Free John. The Way That I Teach. LC 77-94503. 1978. 10.95 (ISBN 0-913922-38-2); pap. 6.95 (ISBN 0-913922-34-X). Dawn Horse Pr.

Ellwood, Robert S., Jr. Religious & Spiritual Groups in Modern America. 352p. 1973. pap. 24.33 (ISBN 0-13-773309-7). P-H.

Fauset, Arthur H. Black Gods of the Metropolis, Negro Religious Cults of the Urban North. LC 73-120251. 1970. Repr. lib. bdg. 16.00x (ISBN 0-374-92714-6, Octagon). Hippocrene Bks.

--Black Gods of the Metropolis: Negro Religious Cults of the Urban North. LC 75-133446. 1971. pap. 9.95x (ISBN 0-8122-1001-8, Pa Paperbks). U of Pa Pr.

Hoekema, Anthony A. The Four Major Cults. 1963. 24.95 (ISBN 0-8028-3117-6). Eerdmans.

Lewis, Gordon R. Confronting the Cults. 1966. pap. 6.50 (ISBN 0-87552-323-4). Presby & Reformed.

Moore, Rebecca. The Jonestown Letters Correspondence of the Moore Family. LC 86-18192. (Studies in American Religion Ser.: Vol. 23). (Illus.). 398p. 1986. lib. bdg. 59.95 (ISBN 0-88946-667-X). E Mellen.

Pfeffer, Leo. Creeds in Competition: A Creative Force in American Culture. LC 78-2308. 1978. Repr. of 1958 ed. lib. bdg. 19.00x (ISBN 0-313-20349-0, PFCC). Greenwood.

Rosten, Leo, ed. Religions of America. LC 74-11705. 1975. pap. 11.95 (ISBN 0-671-21971-5, Touchstone Bks). S&S.

Starkes, M. Thomas. Confronting Popular Cults. LC 72-79177. 1972. pap. 4.25 (ISBN 0-8054-1805-9, 42-1805). Broadman.

Stephenson, George M. Religious Aspects of Swedish Immigration: A Study of Immigrant Churches. LC 69-18790. (American Immigration Collection Ser., No. 1). (Illus.). 1969. Repr. of 1932 ed. 22.50 (ISBN 0-405-00539-3). Ayer Co Pubs.

--Religious Aspects of Swedish Immigration. LC 71-137294. Repr. of 1932 ed. 14.00 (ISBN 0-404-06257-1). AMS Pr.

Van Baalen, Jan K. Chaos of Cults. 4th ed. rev. ed. 1962. 11.95 (ISBN 0-8028-3278-4). Eerdmans.

Whalen, William J. Minority Religions in America. rev. ed. LC 81-3664. 222p. (Orig.). 1981. pap. 7.95 (ISBN 0-8189-0413-5). Alba.

--Minority Religions in America. LC 79-38979. 312p. (Orig.). 1972. pap. 7.95 (ISBN 0-8189-0239-6). Alba.

SECTS, HINDU

see Hindu Sects

SECTS, ISLAMIC

see Islamic Sects

SECTS, JEWISH

see Jewish Sects

SECTS, MEDIEVAL

see also Reformation–Early Movements

Cohn, Norman. Pursuit of the Millennium. rev ed. 1970. pap. 11.95 (ISBN 0-19-500456-6). Oxford U Pr.

MacCulloch, J. Arnott. Medieval Faith & Fable. 1978. Repr. of 1932 ed. lib. bdg. 47.50 (ISBN 0-8492-1662-1). R West.

Moore, R. I. The Origins of European Dissent. 338p. 1985. pap. 12.95x (ISBN 0-631-14404-8). Basil Blackwell.

SECTS, MUSLIM

see Islamic Sects

SECTS, NATIVISTIC

see Nativistic Movements

SECTS, PROTESTANT

see Protestant Churches

SECULARISM

see also Agnosticism; Rationalism; Secularization (Theology)

Al-Naquib Al-Attas, Syed Muhammad. Islam, Secularism & the Philosophy of the Future. LC 84-26108. 239p. 1985. 31.00x (ISBN 0-7201-1740-2). Mansell.

Banks, J. A. Victorian Values: Secularism & the Smaller Family. 288p. 1981. 26.95x (ISBN 0-7100-0807-4). Methuen Inc.

Baxter, Ern, et al. Secular Humanism. 1986. pap. 2.95 (ISBN 0-8010-0936-7). Baker Bk.

Blamires, Harry. The Christian Mind. 1978. pap. 4.95 (ISBN 0-89283-049-2). Servant.

Colson, Charles, et al. Christianity in Conflict: The Struggle for Christian Integrity & Freedom in Secular Culture. Williamson, Peter S. & Perrotta, Kevin, eds. 180p. (Orig.). 1986. pap. 7.95 (ISBN 0-89283-292-4). Servant.

Gasquet, Francis A. Henry the Eighth & the English Monasteries, 2 vols. LC 74-39467. (Select Bibliography Reprint Ser.). 1972. Repr. of 1888 ed. 56.75 (ISBN 0-8369-9905-3). Ayer Co Pubs.

Harkness, Georgia E. The Modern Rival of Christian Faith: An Analysis of Secularism. LC 77-27000. 1978. Repr. of 1952 ed. lib. bdg. 20.50x (ISBN 0-313-20174-9, HAMR). Greenwood.

Hitchcock, James. What Is Secular Humanism? Why Humanism Became Secular & How It Is Changing Our World. (Illus.). 158p. 1982. pap. 6.95 (ISBN 0-89283-163-4). Servant.

Kurtz, Paul. A Secular Humanist Declaration. 40p. 1981. pap. 2.95 (ISBN 0-87975-149-5). Prometheus Bks.

Meland, Bernard E. Realities of Faith. 1962. pap. 2.25x (ISBN 0-912182-03-2). Seminary Co-Op.

Olan, Levi A. Prophetic Faith & the Secular Age. LC 82-2903. 168p. 1982. 15.00x (ISBN 0-87068-888-X). Ktav.

Panikkar, Raimundo. Worship & Secular Man: An Essay on the Liturgical Nature of Man. LC 72-93339. pap. 29.80 (ISBN 0-317-26670-5, 2025123). Bks Demand UMI.

Rice, Charles E. Beyond Abortion: The Origin & Future of the Secular State. 1978. 5.25 (ISBN 0-8199-0696-4). Franciscan Herald.

Sinha, V. K. Secularism in India. 1968. 6.25 (ISBN 0-89684-521-4). Orient Bk Dist.

Spann, J. Richard, ed. Christian Faith & Secularism. LC 70-86062. (Essay & General Literature Index Reprint Ser). 1969. Repr. of 1948 ed. 28.50x (ISBN 0-8046-0589-0, Pub. by Kennikat). Assoc Faculty Pr.

Szczesny, Gerhard. The Future of Unbelief. LC 60-1665. 1961. pap. 2.95 (ISBN 0-8076-0375-9). Braziller.

Tyabji, Badi-Ud Din. The Self in Secularism. 1971. 21.50x (ISBN 0-8046-8832-X, Pub. by Kennikat). Assoc Faculty Pr.

Woodbridge, John, et al, eds. Renewing Your Mind in a Secular World. (Orig.). 1985. pap. 6.95 (ISBN 0-8024-0384-0). Moody.

SECULARIZATION

Ausmus, Harry J. The Polite Escape: On the Myth of Secularization. xii, 189p. 1982. lib. bdg. 22.95x (ISBN 0-8214-0650-7, 82-84192). Ohio U Pr.

Lyon, David. The Steeple's Shadow: On the Myths & Realities of Secularization. 176p. (Orig.). 1987. pap. 9.95 (ISBN 0-8028-0261-3). Eerdmans.

Stark, Rodney & Bainbridge, William S. The Future of Religion: Secularization, Revival & Cult Formation. LC 83-18221. (Illus.). 600p. 1985. pap. 40.00x (ISBN 0-520-04854-7); 14.95 (ISBN 0-520-05731-7, CAMPUS 406). U of Cal Pr.

White, John. Flirting with the World: A Challenge to Loyalty. LC 81-21491. 156p. 1982. pap. 5.95 (ISBN 0-87788-156-1). Shaw Pubs.

SECULARIZATION (THEOLOGY)

see also Secularism

Aubert, Roger. Sacralization & Secularization. LC 76-96949. (Concilium Ser.: Vol. 47). 190p. 7.95 (ISBN 0-8091-0128-9). Paulist Pr.

Duquoc, Christian. Secularization & Spirituality. LC 76-103390. (Concilium Ser.: Vol. 49). 187p. 7.95 (ISBN 0-8091-0136-X). Paulist Pr.

Garvey, Edwin C. Process Theology & Secularization. 21p. 1972. pap. 0.75 (ISBN 0-912414-14-6). Lumen Christi.

Lynch, William F. Christ & Prometheus: A New Image of the Secular. LC 70-122046. 1970. 14.95 (ISBN 0-268-00431-5); pap. 4.95 (ISBN 0-268-00480-3). U of Notre Dame Pr.

Ong, Walter J. American Catholic Crossroads: Religious-Secular Encounters in the Modern World. LC 80-29660. xi, 160p. 1981. Repr. of 1959 ed. lib. bdg. 22.50x (ISBN 0-313-22467-6, ONAM). Greenwood.

Schlitzer, Albert L., ed. Spirit & Power of Christian Secularity. LC 75-75154. 1969. 12.95 (ISBN 0-268-00321-1). U of Notre Dame Pr.

Smith, Gary S. The Seeds of Secularization: Calvinism, Culture, & Pluralism in America, 1870-1915. 248p. (Orig.). 1985. pap. 14.95x (ISBN 0-8028-0058-0). Eerdmans.

Vahanian, Gabriel. The Death of God. LC 61-9962. 1961. 6.95 (ISBN 0-8076-0144-6). Braziller.

SECURITY (PSYCHOLOGY)

Bertocci, Peter A. Religion As Creative Insecurity. LC 73-1836. 128p. 1973. Repr. of 1958 ed. lib. bdg. 22.50x (ISBN 0-8371-6803-1, BECI). Greenwood.

SEE, HOLY

see Papacy; Popes

SEGREGATION–RELIGIOUS ASPECTS

Labbe, Dolores E. Jim Crow Comes to Church: The Establishment of Segregated Catholic Parishes in South Louisiana. 14.00 (ISBN 0-405-10838-9, 11845). Ayer Co Pubs.

Stevens, Richard J. Community Beyond Division: Chrisitan Life under South Africa's Apartheid System. 1984. 8.95 (ISBN 0-533-05729-9). Vantage.

SEIPEL, IGNAZ, 1876-1932

Von Klemperer, Klemens. Ignaz Seipel: Christian Statesman in a Time of Crisis. LC 77-166392. 420p. 1962. 49.50 (ISBN 0-691-05197-6). Princeton U Pr.

SELF

see also Consciousness; Ego (Psychology); Existentialism; Identity (Psychology); Mind and Body; Personality; Will

Culliton, Joseph T. Personal Presence: Its Effects on Honesty & Truthfulness. LC 85-6218. 202p. (Orig.). 1985. 24.50 (ISBN 0-8191-4661-7); pap. text ed. 10.75 (ISBN 0-8191-4662-5). U Pr of Amer.

Davies, Ann. This Is Truth about the Self. 3rd ed. 1984. 4.50 (ISBN 0-938002-03-1). Builders of Adytum.

Deikman, Arthur J. The Observing Self: Mysticism & Psychotherapy. LC 81-70486. 208p. 1983. pap. 8.95 (ISBN 0-8070-2951-3, BP 652). Beacon Pr.

Hocking, David L. Who Am I & What Difference Does It Make? LC 85-8810. (Living Theology Ser.). 1985. pap. 7.95 (ISBN 0-88070-102-1). Multnomah.

Kaam, Adrian van. Transcendent Self. 5.95 (ISBN 0-87193-180-X). Dimension Bks.

MacMurray, John. Self As Agent. 1978. pap. text ed. 5.95x (ISBN 0-391-02043-9). Humanities.

Strunk, Orlo, Jr. The Secret Self. LC 76-14780. Repr. of 1976 ed. 27.50 (ISBN 0-8357-9025-8, 2016404). Bks Demand UMI.

Vitz, Paul C. Psychology As Religion: The Cult of Self-Worship. 192p. 1977. pap. 5.95 (ISBN 0-8028-1696-7). Eerdmans.

Wagner, Maurice. The Sensation of Being Somebody. 256p. 1975. 8.95 (ISBN 0-310-33970-7, 15603P). Zondervan.

Wilson, Dora. The Self to the Self. 1983. pap. 2.50x (ISBN 0-87574-035-9, 035). Pendle Hill.

SELF (PHILOSOPHY)

Bennett, John G. Deeper Man. LC 84-73170. 254p. 1985. 8.95 (ISBN 0-934254-07-9). Claymont Comm.

Boni, Sylvain. The Self & the Other in the Ontologies of Sartre & Buber. LC 82-20130. 202p. (Orig.). 1983. lib. bdg. 27.50 (ISBN 0-8191-2852-X); pap. text ed. 12.50 (ISBN 0-8191-2853-8). U Pr of Amer.

Culliton, Joseph T. Personal Presence: Its Effects on Honesty & Truthfulness. LC 85-6218. 202p. (Orig.). 1985. 24.50 (ISBN 0-8191-4661-7); pap. text ed. 10.75 (ISBN 0-8191-4662-5). U Pr of Amer.

Dupre, Louis. Transcendent Selfhood: The Loss & Rediscovery of the Inner Life. 1976. 8.95 (ISBN 0-8164-0306-6, HarpR). Har-Row.

Kasulis, T. P. Zen Action-Zen Person. LC 80-27858. 192p. 1985. pap. text ed. 7.95x (ISBN 0-8248-1023-6). UH Pr.

Kenner, Dru A. My Friend Consider. LC 84-51459. 100p. (Orig.). 1985. pap. 4.95 (ISBN 0-930551-00-1). Vistara Pubns.

Peccorini, Francisco L. On to the World of "Freedom": A Kantian Meditation on Finite Selfhood. LC 82-40233. 370p. (Orig.). 1982. lib. bdg. 30.25 o. p. (ISBN 0-8191-2643-8); pap. text ed. 15.75 (ISBN 0-8191-2644-6). U Pr of Amer.

Perkins, J. A. The Concept of the Self in the French Enlightenment. 162p. (Orig.). 1969. pap. text ed. 24.50x (Pub. by Droz Switzerland). Coronet Bks.

Stack, George J. Kierkegaard's Existential Ethics. LC 75-16344. (Studies in Humanities: No. 16). 240p. 1977. 15.00 (ISBN 0-8173-6624-5); pap. 5.50 (ISBN 0-8173-6626-1). U of Ala Pr.

SELF-ACCEPTANCE

Cole-Whittaker, Terry. What You Think of Me Is None of My Business. 194p. (Orig.). 1982. pap. 9.95 (ISBN 0-86679-002-0). Oak Tree Pubns.

Fairbanks, Henry G. Towards Acceptance--the Ultimates: Aging, Pain, Fear & Death from an Integral Human View. 1986. pap. 8.95 (ISBN 0-8158-0433-4). Chris Mass.

SELF-ACTUALIZATION (PSYCHOLOGY)

Adams, Jay E. Ready to Restore. (Orig.). 1981. pap. 3.50 (ISBN 0-8010-0171-4). Baker Bk.

Baars, Conrad W. Born Only Once: The Miracle of Affirmation. 1977. pap. 4.00 (ISBN 0-8199-0700-6). Franciscan Herald.

Bloodworth, Venice. Key to Yourself. 1986. pap. 4.95 (ISBN 0-87516-296-7). De Vorss.

Ferrucci, Piero. What We May Be: Techniques for Psychological & Spiritual Growth. LC 81-51107. (Illus.). 256p. 1982. 6.95 (ISBN 0-87477-262-1). J P Tarcher.

Gelfond, Renee. Discover a New Beginning. LC 83-20079. (Illus.). 100p. (Orig.). 1983. pap. 6.95 (ISBN 0-914789-00-7). Serenity Hse.

Gold, E. J. The Human Biological Machine As a Transformational Apparatus. Lourie, Iven, pref. by. LC 85-60946. 176p. (Orig.). 1985. pap. 12.50 (ISBN 0-89556-046-1). Gateways Bks & Tapes.

Hardison, Amy. How to Feel Great about Being a Mother. LC 86-29349. 1987. 8.95 (ISBN 0-87579-073-9). Deseret Bk.

John-Roger. Dynamics of the Lower Self. LC 77-70406. 1976. pap. 5.00 (ISBN 0-914829-10-6). Baraka Bk.

Maultsby, Maxie C., Jr. Help Yourself to Happiness. LC 75-15057. 1975. pap. 9.95 (ISBN 0-917476-06-9). Inst Rational-Emotive.

Orr, Leonard & Ray, Sondra. Rebirthing in the New Age. LC 76-53337. 1978. pap. 9.95 (ISBN 0-89087-134-5). Celestial Arts.

Rowe, Stephen, ed. Living Beyond Crisis: Essays on Discovery & Being in the World. LC 80-18135. 261p. 1980. pap. 8.95 (ISBN 0-8298-0402-1). Pilgrim NY.

Schmelig, Leddy & Schmelig, Randolph. Steps in Self-Knowledge. LC 79-64038. 1979. 5.95 (ISBN 0-87159-144-8). Unity School.

Smyly, Glenn A. & Smyly, Barbara J. All in the Name of Love. 116p. 1986. 17.95 (ISBN 0-9616707-0-3); pap. 9.95 (ISBN 0-9616707-1-1). Alivening Pubns.

Tamiazzo, John. Love & Be Loved: A How-To Book. 176p. 1986. pap. 7.95 (ISBN 0-87877-087-9, Greenbriar Books). Newcastle Pub.

SELF-CONTROL

Backus, William. Finding the Freedom of Self-Control. 176p. (Orig.). 1987. pap. 5.95 (ISBN 0-87123-676-1). Bethany Hse.

Kelfer, Russell. Self-Control. (Living Studies). 240p. 1985. pap. 5.95 (ISBN 0-8423-5859-5); leader's guide 2.95 (ISBN 0-8423-5860-9). Tyndale.

MacKenthun, Carole & Dwyer, Paulinus. Self-Control. (Fruit of the Spirit Ser.). (Illus.). 48p. 1987. pap. 5.95 (ISBN 0-86653-396-6, SS878). Good Apple.

Snyder, Pam. A Life Styled by God: A Woman's Workshop on Spiritual Discipline for Weight Control. (Woman's Workshop Ser.). 112p. (Orig.). 1985. pap. 2.95 (ISBN 0-310-42791-6, 11378P). Zondervan.

Vohn, Rick. Getting Control of Your Inner Self. 176p. 1982. pap. 2.95 (ISBN 0-8423-0999-3). Tyndale.

SELF-DECEPTION

Faber, Frederick. Self-Deceit. 1983. pap. 2.50x (ISBN 0-87574-050-2, 050). Pendle Hill.

Weigel, Van B. Ostrich Christianity: Self-Deception in Popular Christianity. LC 85-17981. 254p. (Orig.). 1986. lib. bdg. 25.75 (ISBN 0-8191-4974-8); pap. text ed. 12.75 (ISBN 0-8191-4975-6). U Pr of Amer.

SELF-KNOWLEDGE, THEORY OF

Gasche, Rodolphe. The Tain of the Mirror. LC 86-4673. 384p. 1986. text ed. 25.00x (ISBN 0-674-86700-9). Harvard U Pr.

Halbritter, Irving J. How to Master the Miracle of Introspection for the Better Knowledge of Yourself, the Broader Dimensions of Your Intellectual Life & the Gaining of Maximal Success in Your Field of Endeavour. (Illus.). 136p. 1982. 69.75 (ISBN 0-89920-044-3). Am Inst Psych.

Marcel, Gabriel. Mystery of Being, Vol. I: Reflection & Mystery. 238p. 1984. pap. text ed. 8.50 (ISBN 0-8191-3310-8). U Pr of Amer.

Matsuo, Hosaku. The Logic of Unity: The Discovery of Zero & Emptiness in Prajanaparamita Thought. Inada, Kenneth K., tr. (Buddhist studies). 144p. 1987. 29.50 (ISBN 0-88706-391-8); pap. 9.95 (ISBN 0-88706-392-6). State U NY Pr.

Simone, R. Thomas & Sugarman, Richard I. Reclaiming the Humanities: The Roots of Self-Knowledge in the Greek & Biblical Worlds. 226p. (Orig.). 1986. lib. bdg. 25.75 (ISBN 0-8191-5093-2); pap. text ed. 9.75 (ISBN 0-8191-5094-0). U Pr of Amer.

Steiner, Rudolf. Road to Self Knowledge. 1975. 10.95 (ISBN 0-85440-290-X, Pub by Steinerbooks); pap. 6.95 o. p. (ISBN 0-85440-291-8). Anthroposophic.

Swami Muktananda. Reflections of the Self: Poems of Spiritual Life. LC 80-50391. (Illus.). 205p. (Orig.). 1980. pap. 5.95 (ISBN 0-914602-50-0). SYDA Found.

SELF-LOVE (THEOLOGY)

Adams, Jay. The Biblical View of Self-Esteem, Self-Love & Self-Image. 1986. pap. 5.95 (ISBN 0-89081-553-4). Harvest Hse.

Brownback, Paul. Danger of Self-Love. LC 82-12543. 1982. pap. 5.95 (ISBN 0-8024-2068-0). Moody.

Cernic, David & Longmire, Linda, eds. Know Thyself: Collected Readings on Identity. 1987. pap. 12.95 (ISBN 0-8091-2872-1). Paulist Pr.

Coleman, Lyman. Self Profile: The Me Nobody Knows. (Free University - Lay Academy in Christian Discipleship Ser.). (Orig.). 1981. pap. 4.95 leader's guide (ISBN 0-687-37346-8); pap. 1.25 (ISBN 0-687-37347-6). Abingdon.

Livingston, J. B. Love Yourself. 2.70 (ISBN 0-89137-421-3). Quality Pubns.

Manning, Brennan. Stranger to Self-Hatred. 6.95 (ISBN 0-87193-156-7). Dimension Bks.

O'Donovan, Oliver. The Problem of Self-Love in Saint Augustine. LC 80-5397. 208p. 1980. text ed. 23.50x (ISBN 0-300-02468-1). Yale U Pr.

Richardson, Edward. Love Yourself. 1970. pap. 1.50 (ISBN 0-89243-028-1, 28849). Liguori Pubns.

SELF-PERCEPTION

McDowell, Josh. Building Your Self-Image. (Living Bks.). Orig. Title: His Image...My Image. 192p. 1986. Repr. 3.95 (ISBN 0-8423-1395-8). Tyndale.

Miller, William A. You Count-You Really Do! LC 76-27078. 1976. pap. 5.95 (ISBN 0-8066-1569-9, 10-7420). Augsburg.

Olsen, Del. Made in God's Image. 128p. (Orig.). 1986. pap. 5.95 (ISBN 0-310-46381-5, 18382P). Zondervan.

Powell, John. Why Am I Afraid to Love? rev. ed. (Illus.). 120p. 1972. pap. 3.50 (ISBN 0-913592-03-X). Argus Comm.

--Why Am I Afraid to Tell You Who I Am? LC 70-113274. (Illus.). 168p. 1969. pap. 2.95 (ISBN 0-913592-02-1). Argus Comm.

Tangvald, Christine. Me, Myself & I. (I Am Special Bks.). (Illus.). 20p. 1985. 3.95 (ISBN 0-89191-925-2, 59253). Cook.

--My Own Special Body. (I Am Special Bks.). (Illus.). 20p. 1985. pap. 3.95 (ISBN 0-89191-903-1, 59030). Cook.

Wellman, Pat. Mirror, Mirror... Please Lie. 86p. (Orig.). 1984. pap. 3.50 (ISBN 0-8341-0931-X). Beacon Hill.

SELF-REALIZATION

Angell, James W. Seek It Lovingly. (Illus.). 1974. pap. 3.95 (ISBN 0-87516-184-7). De Vorss.

Baker, Martha. How to Survive & Live in Heaven on Earth. rev. ed. LC 81-4234. 165p. 1981. pap. 1.95 (ISBN 0-86663-763-X). Ide Hse.

Bingham, Mindy, et al. Challenges: A Young Man's Journal for Self-Awareness & Personal Planning. Greene, Barbara & Peters, Kathleen, eds. LC 84-70108. (Illus.). 240p. 1984. pap. 12.95 (ISBN 0-911655-24-7). Advocacy Pr.

Cole, Edwin L. The Potential Principle. 144p. (Orig.). 1984. pap. 3.95 (ISBN 0-88368-144-7). Whitaker Hse.

Geiger, Lura J. Inner Peace: Finding Serenity Within. 1987. pap. 34.50; cassette incl. LuraMedia.

Goldsmith, Joel S. Man Was Not Born to Cry. 1984. pap. 5.95 (ISBN 0-8065-0915-5). Citadel Pr.

Gray, William G. A Self Made by Magic. LC 76-15547. 198p. (Orig.). 1984. pap. 8.95 (ISBN 0-87728-556-X). Weiser.

LaViolette, Wesley. Wings Unfolding. LC 70-140225. 1971. 4.95 (ISBN 0-87516-040-9). De Vorss.

Lee, Dorothy. Valuing the Self: What We Can Learn from Other Cultures. (Illus.). 1986. pap. text ed. 6.95x (ISBN 0-88133-229-1). Waveland Pr.

Mahoney, James. Journey into Fullness. LC 73-91615. pap. 5.95 (ISBN 0-8054-5221-4). Broadman.

Manley, Stephen L. Journey into Wholeness. 96p. (Orig.). 1983. pap. 2.95 (ISBN 0-8341-0832-1). Beacon Hill.

Pictorial History of Self-Realization Fellowship. (Illus.). 80p. 1982. pap. 5.50 (ISBN 0-87612-196-2). Self Realization.

Taylor, Barbara. From Rejection to Acceptance. 1987. text ed. 8.95 (ISBN 0-8054-5045-9). Broadman.

Warner, Richard. Freedom, Enjoyment, & Happiness: An Essay on Moral Psychology. LC 86-19696. (Illus.). 208p. 1987. text ed. 19.95x (ISBN 0-8014-1977-8). Cornell U Pr.

Yogananda, Paramahansa. Man's Eternal Quest. LC 75-17183. (Illus.). 503p. 1982. pap. 5.50 (ISBN 0-87612-232-2). Self Realization.

Yukteswar, Swami Sri. Holy Science. LC 77-88199. (Illus.). 110p. 1984. 4.50 (ISBN 0-87612-051-6); 2nd Dutch ed. 6.50x (ISBN 90-202-4529-5); German ed. 6.00x (ISBN 3-87041-176-7); Japanese ed. 7.00x (ISBN 4-627-99950-X). Self Realization.

SELF-REALIZATION (RELIGION)

see Identification (Religion)

SELF-RESPECT

Abata, Russell M. How to Develop a Better Self-Image. LC 79-91440. (Orig.). 1980. pap. 2.95 (ISBN 0-89243-119-9, 41150). Liguori Pubns.

Adams, Jay. The Biblical View of Self-Esteem, Self-Love & Self-Image. 1986. pap. 5.95 (ISBN 0-89081-553-4). Harvest Hse.

Anderson, Esther & Kvindlog, Norma. Beyond Me: A Christ Centered Approach to Self-Esteem. 160p. 1987. pap. 5.95 (ISBN 0-8423-1310-9). Tyndale.

Birkey, Verna. You Are Very Special: A Biblical Guide to Self-Worth. 160p. 1977. pap. 5.95 (ISBN 0-8007-5032-2, Power Bks). Revell.

Bourgeous, Virginia. Quest for Love & Self-Esteem: New Insights from Psychology & Religion. LC 76-29301. (Illus.). 80p. (Orig.). 1976. pap. 5.95 (ISBN 0-88290-070-6). Horizon Utah.

Burwick, Ray. Self Esteem: You're Better Than You Think. 1983. pap. 5.95 (ISBN 0-8423-5865-X). Tyndale.

Caldwell, Louis O. You Can Develop a Positive Self-Image. (Christian Counseling Aids Ser.). pap. 1.25 (ISBN 0-8010-2503-6). Baker Bk.

Canfield, Anita. Self-Esteem for the Latter-Day Saint Woman. 2nd ed. 135p. 1983. 7.95 (ISBN 0-934126-15-1). Randall Bk Co.

Cerling, Chuck. Cleaning Out Your Mental Closet: Transforming Negative Emotions. 150p. 1987. pap. 9.95 (ISBN 0-87788-127-8). Shaw Pubs.

Chase, Betty N. How to Discipline & Build Self-Esteem in Your Child. 46p. 1983. pap. text ed. 19.95 (ISBN 0-89191-796-9). Cook.

Coleman, William. Bouncing Back: Finding Acceptance in the Face of Rejection. (Orig.). 1985. pap. 4.95 (ISBN 0-89081-455-4). Harvest Hse.

Dobson, James. Hide or Seek. expanded & updated ed. 192p. 1974. 11.95 (ISBN 0-8007-1070-3); pap. 6.95 (ISBN 0-8007-5146-9). Revell.

Earles, Brent D. You're Worth It! But Do You Believe It? 112p. 1985. pap. 5.95 (ISBN 0-8010-3427-2). Baker Bk.

Institute for Religious & Social Studies. Integrity & Compromise: Problems of Public & Private Conscience. facsimile ed. MacIver, R. M., ed. LC 76-167367. (Essay Index Reprints - Religion & Civilization Ser). Repr. of 1957 ed. 15.00 (ISBN 0-8369-2656-0). Ayer Co Pubs.

Jones, Cliff. Winning Through Integrity. 160p. 1985. 9.95 (ISBN 0-687-45604-5). Abingdon.

Keck, Saundria. God Made Me. LC 86-17572. (Bible & Me Ser.). 1987. 5.95 (ISBN 0-8054-4173-5). Broadman.

Mathis, Laura. The Road to Wholeness. 240p. 1986. pap. 6.95 (ISBN 0-8423-5674-6). Tyndale.

Miller, William A. You Count-You Really Do! LC 76-27078. 1976. pap. 5.95 (ISBN 0-8066-1569-9, 10-7420). Augsburg.

Olsen, Del. Made in God's Image. 128p. (Orig.). 1986. pap. 5.95 (ISBN 0-310-46381-5, 18382P). Zondervan.

Osborne, Cecil G. The Art of Learning to Love Yourself. 1976. 3.95 (ISBN 0-310-30572-1, 10475P). Zondervan.

Rochau, Dair. How to Raise Self Esteem. (Life Ser.). 1983. pap. 5.95 (ISBN 0-8163-0504-8). Pacific Pr Pub Assn.

Schuller, Robert H. Discover Self-Love. (Orig.). 1978. pap. 1.25 (ISBN 0-89081-134-2). Harvest Hse.

--Self-Esteem: The New Reformation. 144p. 1982. 3.95 (ISBN 0-8499-4172-5). Word Bks.

Smith, M. Blaine. One of a Kind: A Biblical View of Self-Acceptance. LC 84-574. 140p. 1984. pap. 3.95 (ISBN 0-87784-921-8). Inter-Varsity.

Taylor, Barbara. From Rejection to Acceptance. 1987. text ed. 8.95 (ISBN 0-8054-5045-9). Broadman.

Trobisch, Walter. The Complete Works of Walter Trobisch. 700p. 1987. 19.95 (ISBN 0-87784-524-7). Inter-Varsity.

Wagner, Maurice E. The Sensation of Being Somebody. 251p. 1985. pap. 8.95 (ISBN 0-310-33971-5). Zondervan.

Ward, Ruth M. Self Esteem: A Gift from God. 1984. pap. 7.95 (ISBN 0-8010-9664-2). Baker Bk.

Wright, H. Norman. Improving Your Self Image. LC 83-80119. 160p. (Orig.). 1983. pap. 4.95 (ISBN 0-89081-382-5). Harvest Hse.

SEMANTICS (PHILOSOPHY)

Burke, Kenneth. The Rhetoric of Religion: Studies in Logology. 1970. pap. 9.95x (ISBN 0-520-01610-6, CAMPUS 341). U of Cal Pr.

Clarke, Bowman L. Language & Natural Theology. (Janua Linguarum, Ser. Minor: No. 47). (Orig.). 1966. pap. text ed. 18.00 (ISBN 90-2790-580-0). Mouton.

Heimbeck, Raeburne S. Theology & Meaning: A Critique of Metatheological Scepticism. LC 68-13146. 1969. 22.50x (ISBN 0-8047-0704-9). Stanford U Pr.

Yolton, John W. Metaphysical Analysis. LC 68-88650. pap. 58.30 (ISBN 0-317-08857-2, 2014464). Bks Demand UMI.

SEMANTICS (RELIGION)

see Religion and Language

SEMINARIANS

Cothen, Joe H. Equipped for Good Work: A Guide for Pastors. LC 80-37964. 336p. 1981. 14.95 (ISBN 0-88289-271-1). Pelican.

Hemrick, Eugene F., et al. Seminarians in Theology: A National Profile. 128p. 1986. pap. 8.95 (ISBN 1-55586-978-5). US Catholic.

Hoge, Dean R., et al. Research on Men's Vocations to the Priesthood & the Religious Life. 104p. 1984. pap. 6.50 (ISBN 1-55586-904-1). US Catholic.

Kleinman, Sherryl. Equals Before God: Seminarians as Humanistic Professionals. LC 83-24208. 160p. 1984. lib. bdg. 15.00x (ISBN 0-226-43999-2). U of Chicago Pr.

Laborers for the Vineyard: Proceedings of a Conference on Church Vocations. 180p. 1984. pap. 7.50 (ISBN 1-55586-908-4). US Catholic.

Liturgical Formation in Seminaries: A Commentary. 120p. 1984. pap. 4.95 (ISBN 1-55586-917-3). US Catholic.

Potvin, Raymond H. Seminarians of the Eighties: A National Survey. 64p. 1986. 5.65 (ISBN 0-318-20579-3). Natl Cath Educ.

Spurgeon, Carlos M. Discursos a Mis Estudiantes. 352p. 1981. pap. 5.75 (ISBN 0-311-42006-0). Casa Bautista.

SEMINARIES, THEOLOGICAL

see Theological Seminaries

SEMITES

see also names of individual Semitic People, e.g. Arabs, Jews

Morgenstern, Julian. Rites of Birth, Marriage, Death, & Kindred Occasions Among the Semites. 1966. 20.00x (ISBN 0-87068-230-X). Ktav.

Ringgren, Helmer. Religions of the Ancient Near East. Sturdy, John, tr. LC 72-8587. (Illus.). 208p. 1972. 7.50 (ISBN 0-664-20953-X). Westminster.

Schaeffer, Henry. The Social Legislation of the Primitive Semites. LC 70-174369. Repr. of 1915 ed. 16.00 (ISBN 0-405-08929-5). Ayer Co Pubs.

SENEGAL

Behrman, Lucy. Muslim Brotherhoods & Politics in Senegal. LC 70-95918. 1970. 15.00x (ISBN 0-674-59490-8). Harvard U Pr.

Klein, Martin A. Islam & Imperialism in Senegal: Sine-Saloum, 1847-1914. 1968. 25.00x (ISBN 0-8047-0621-2). Stanford U Pr.

SENIOR CITIZENS

see Aged

SEPARATISM (RELIGION)

see Dissenters, Religious

SEPHARDIM

Angel, Marc D. The Rhythms of Jewish Living: The Sephardic Approach. LC 86-25993. 208p. 1987. 14.95 (ISBN 0-87203-125-X). Hermon.

Benardete, Mair Jose. Hispanic Culture & Character of the Sephardic Jews. 2nd rev. ed. 226p. 1981. 15.00 (ISBN 0-87203-100-4). Hermon.

Mehlman, Israel. Genozot Sefarim: Bibliographical Essays. 10.00 (ISBN 0-405-12617-4). Ayer Co Pubs.

Raphael, Chaim. The Road from Babylon: The Story of the Sephardic & Oriental Jews. LC 85-42587. (Illus.). 320p. 1986. 22.45i (ISBN 0-06-039048-4, C&M Bessie Bks). Har-Row.

Sephardim of England. cancelled (ISBN 0-686-76257-6). Feldheim.

SEPULCHERS

see Tombs

SEPULCHRAL MONUMENTS

see also Crosses; Pyramids; Tombs

Aries, Philippe. Images of Man & Death. Lloyd, Janet, tr. from Fr. LC 85-768. (Illus.). 271p. 1985. 35.00 (ISBN 0-674-44410-8). Harvard U Pr.

Cohen, Kathleen R. Metamorphosis of a Death Symbol: The Transi Tomb in the Late Middle Ages & the Renaissance. LC 78-138511. (California Studies in the History of Art: Vol. 15). 1974. 77.00x (ISBN 0-520-01844-3). U of Cal Pr.

Combs, Diana W. Early Gravestone Art in Georgia & South Carolina. LC 85-1129. (Illus.). 256p. 1986. 35.00x (ISBN 0-8203-0788-2). U of Ga Pr.

Dingley, Thomas. History from Marble, 2 Vols. LC 70-164834. (Camden Society, London. Publications, First Ser.: Nos. 94 & 97). Repr. of 1868 ed. Set. 74.00 (ISBN 0-404-50210-5). AMS Pr.

Gillon, Edmund V., Jr. Early New England Gravestone Rubbings. (Illus., Orig.). 1966. pap. 7.95 (ISBN 0-486-21380-3). Dover.

Hurtig, Judith W. Armored Gisant Before Fourteen Hundred. LC 78-74368. (Outstanding Dissertations in the Fine Arts, Fourth Ser.). 1979. lib. bdg. 63.00 (ISBN 0-8240-3956-4). Garland Pub.

Johnson, Martin C. The Churchyard Carvers' Art. 104p. 1986. 30.00x (ISBN 0-947939-00-8, Pub. by Elmcrest UK). State Mutual Bk.

Kleiner, Diana E. Roman Group Portraiture: The Funerary Reliefs of the Late Republic & Early Empire. LC 76-23634. (Outstanding Dissertations in the Fine Arts - 2nd Series - Ancient). (Illus.). 1977. Repr. lib. bdg. 76.00 (ISBN 0-8240-2703-5). Garland Pub.

Penny, Nicholas. Church Monuments in Romantic England. LC 76-58912. (Studies in British Art). (Illus.). 1977. 47.00x (ISBN 0-300-02075-9). Yale U Pr.

Portner, Balthasar. Die Agyptischen Totenstelen Als Zeugen Des Sozialen und Religiosen Lebens Ihrer Zeit. pap. 8.00 (ISBN 0-384-47040-8). Johnson Repr.

Suffling, Ernest R. English Church Brasses from the 13th to the 17th Century, a Manual for Antiquaries, Archaeologists & Collectors. LC 73-126133. (Illus.). 456p. 1970. Repr. of 1910 ed. 22.50 (ISBN 0-8063-0437-5). Genealog Pub.

Van Siclen, Charles C., III. Wall Scenes from the Tomb of Amenhotep (Huy) Governor of Bahria Oasis. (Illus.). ii, 46p. 1981. pap. text ed. 11.00x (ISBN 0-933175-00-0). Van Siclen Bks.

Watters, David, ed. Markers III: The Journal of the Association for Gravestone Studies. LC 81-642903. (Illus.). 162p. (Orig.). 1985. lib. bdg. 25.25 (ISBN 0-8191-4537-8); pap. text ed. 11.50 (ISBN 0-8191-4538-6). U Pr of Amer.

Wells, Peter S. The Emergence of an Iron Age Economy: The Mecklenburg Grave Groups from Hallstatt & Sticna: Mecklenburg Collection, Pt 3. LC 81-81958. (American School of Prehistoric Research Bulletins: No. 33). (Illus.). 256p. 1981. pap. 30.00x (ISBN 0-87365-536-2). Peabody Harvard.

SEQUENCES (LITURGY)

Blume, Clemens, ed. Thesauri Hymnologica Prosarium, 2 Vols in 3. (Illus.). Repr. of 1922 ed. 60.00 ea. Johnson Repr.

SERAFIM, SAINT, 1759-1833

Cavarnos, Constantine & Zeldin, Mary B. Modern Orthodox Saints: Vol. 5-St. Seraphim of Sarov. LC 80-80124. (Illus.). 167p. 1980. 9.00 (ISBN 0-914744-47-X); pap. 6.00 (ISBN 0-914744-48-8). Inst Byzantine.

Jones, Franklin, ed. The Spiritual Instructions of Saint Seraphim of Sarov. LC 73-89308. 1973. pap. 3.95 (ISBN 0-913922-05-6). Dawn Horse Pr.

Zander, Valentine. St. Seraphim of Sarov. LC 75-24136. Orig. Title: Seraphim of Sarov. 150p. 1975. pap. 6.95 (ISBN 0-913836-28-1). St Vladimirs.

SERAPHIM

see Angels

SERMON ON THE MOUNT

see also Beatitudes

Arnold, Eberhard. Salt & Light: Talks & Writings of the Sermon on the Mount. LC 77-1204. 1977. pap. 6.00 (ISBN 0-87486-170-5). Plough.

--Salt & Light: Talks & Writings on the Sermon on the Mount. LC 67-18009. 1967. 8.00 (ISBN 0-87486-105-5). Plough.

--Salt & Light: Talks & Writings on the Sermon on the Mount. rev. ed. Hutterian Brethren, ed. & tr. from Ger. 338p. 1986. pap. 6.00 (ISBN 0-87486-174-8). Plough.

Bauman, Clarence. The Sermon on the Mount: The Modern Quest for Its Meaning. x, 440p. 1985. 41.95 (ISBN 0-86554-113-2, MUP/H107). Mercer Univ Pr.

Betz, Hans D. Essays on the Sermon on the Mount. LC 84-47910. 192p. 1984. 24.95 (ISBN 0-8006-0726-0). Fortress.

Boice, James M. The Sermon on the Mount. LC 72-83882. 256p. 1972. 14.95 (ISBN 0-310-21510-2). Zondervan.

Bonhoeffer, Dietrich. Cost of Discipleship. 1963. pap. 5.95 (ISBN 0-02-083850-6, Collier). Macmillan.

--The Cost of Discipleship. 1983. 14.00 (ISBN 0-8446-5960-6). Peter Smith.

Brooks, Oscar S. The Sermon on the Mount: Authentic Human Values. 124p. (Orig.). 1985. lib. bdg. 22.00 (ISBN 0-8191-4740-0); pap. text ed. 8.75 (ISBN 0-8191-4741-9). U Pr of Amer.

Carson, D. A. Sermon on the Mount: An Evangelical Exposition of Matthew 5-7. LC 77-93260. 1978. 4.95 (ISBN 0-8010-2480-3). Baker Bk.

Chambers, Oswald. Studies in the Sermon on the Mount. 1973. pap. 2.95 (ISBN 0-87508-136-3). Chr Lit.

Cooper, Dale. Sermon on the Mount: A Study Guide. (Revelation Series for Adults). 1981. pap. text ed. 2.50 (ISBN 0-933140-22-3). CRC Pubns.

Davies, William. The Setting of the Sermon on the Mount. LC 64-630. pap. 140.80 (ISBN 0-317-26320-X, 2024449). Bks Demand UMI.

Davies, William D. Sermon on the Mount. (Orig.). 1966. pap. 9.95 (ISBN 0-521-09384-8, 384). Cambridge U Pr.

Donaldson, Terence L. Jesus on the Mountain: A Study in Matthean Theology. (JSNT Supplement Ser.: No. 8). 326p. 1985. text ed. 28.50x (ISBN 0-905774-74-4, Pub. by JSOT Pr England); pap. text ed. 13.50x (ISBN 0-905774-75-2, Pub. by JSOT Pr England). Eisenbrauns.

Duncan, Judith A., illus. The Sermon on the Mount: From the Translation Prepared at Cambridge in 1611 for King James I. LC 81-211201. (Illus.). 1978. 15.00 (ISBN 0-9606844-0-9). Mac Col MN.

Ferguson, Sinclair B. Kingdom Life in a Fallen World: Living out the Sermon on the Mount. (Christian Character Library). 224p. 1986. 8.95 (ISBN 0-89109-492-X). NavPress.

Fox, Emmet. El Sermon del Monte. Tr. of Sermon on the Mount. 1984. 5.95 (ISBN 0-87159-034-4). Unity School.

--Sermon on the Mount. 1934. 12.45 (ISBN 0-06-062950-9, HarpR). Har-Row.

Friedlander, Gerald. Jewish Sources of the Sermon on the Mount. 1976. lib. bdg. 59.95 (ISBN 0-8490-2102-2). Gordon Pr.

--Jewish Sources of the Sermon on the Mount. rev. ed. (Library of Biblical Studies). 1969. 14.95x (ISBN 0-87068-054-4). Ktav.

Gonsalves, Carol. Sermon on the Mountain. (Arch Bk. Supplement Ser.). 1981. pap. 0.99 (ISBN 0-570-06149-0, 59-1304). Concordia.

Gore, Charles. The Social Doctrine of the Sermon on the Mount. 59.95 (ISBN 0-8490-1063-2). Gordon Pr.

Guelich, Robert. The Sermon on the Mount. 448p. 1982. 19.95 (ISBN 0-8499-0110-3). Word Bks.

Hall, Manly P. Sermon on the Mount. pap. 2.50 (ISBN 0-89314-353-7). Philos Res.

Hendrickx, Herman. The Sermon on the Mount. (Commentary on the Synoptic Gospels Ser.). 228p. 1984. pap. 9.95 (ISBN 0-225-66399-6, 8526, HarpR). Har-Row.

Hunter, Archibald M. A Pattern for Life: An Exposition of the Sermon on the Mount. rev. ed. LC 66-11517. 128p. 1966. pap. 5.95 (ISBN 0-664-24687-7). Westminster.

Hutterian Society of Brothers, ed. & tr. Salz und Licht. (Ger.). 186p. 1982. pap. 4.95 (ISBN 3-87067-166-1, Pub. by Brendow-Verlag, West Germany). Plough.

Ishee, John A. Design for Living: The Sermon on the Mount. 36p. 1982. pap. 3.50 (ISBN 0-939298-07-4). J M Prods.

Jeremias, Joachim. Sermon on the Mount. Reumann, John, ed. Perrin, Norman, tr. from Ger. LC 63-17882. (Facet Bks.). (Orig.). 1963. pap. 2.50 (ISBN 0-8006-3002-5, 1-3002). Fortress.

Jones, E. Stanley. The Christ of the Mount. (Festival Ser.). 336p. 1981. pap. 2.45 (ISBN 0-687-06925-4). Abingdon.

Jordan, Clarence. Sermon on the Mount. 1970. pap. 4.95 (ISBN 0-8170-0501-3). Judson.

Kissinger, Warren S. Sermon on the Mount: A History of Interpretation & Bibliography. LC 75-29031. (ATLA Bibliography Ser.: No. 3). 309p. 1975. 22.50 (ISBN 0-8108-0843-9). Scarecrow.

Kodjak, Andreij. A Structural Analysis of the Sermon on the Mount. (Religion & Reasons Ser.: No. 34). (Illus.). x, 234p. 1986. lib. bdg. 54.50x (ISBN 0-89925-159-5). Mouton.

Lambrecht, Jan. The Sermon on the Mount: Proclamation & Exhortation. (Good News Studies: Vol. 14). 1985. pap. 12.95 (ISBN 0-89453-467-X). M Glazier.

Lapide, Pinchas. The Sermon on the Mount: Utopia or Program for Action? Swindler, Arlene, tr. from Ger. Tr. of DieBergpre digt-Utopie oder Program? 160p. (Orig.). 1986. pap. 9.95 (ISBN 0-88344-248-5, 85-29810). Orbis Bks.

Lloyd-Jones, D. Martyn. Studies in the Sermon on the Mount. 1984. 12.95 (ISBN 0-8028-0036-X). Eerdmans.

Lovett, C. S. Lovett's Lights on the Sermon on the Mount. 176p. (Orig.). 1985. pap. 5.45 (ISBN 0-938148-40-0). Personal Christianity.

McArthur, Harvey K. Understanding the Sermon on the Mount. LC 78-16404. 1978. Repr. of 1960 ed. lib. bdg. 22.50 (ISBN 0-313-20569-8, MCUS). Greenwood.

MacArthur, John, Jr. Kingdom Living Here & Now. LC 79-25326. 1980. pap. 5.95 (ISBN 0-8024-4562-4). Moody.

McEachern, Alton H. From the Mountain. LC 82-82948. (Orig.). 1983. pap. 4.95 (ISBN 0-8054-1529-7). Broadman.

Meyer, F. B. Inherit the Kingdom. 168p. 1985. pap. 5.95 (ISBN 0-89693-396-2). Victor Bks.

Miller, J. R. The Master's Blesseds: The Sermon on the Mount. pap. 1.50 (ISBN 0-685-88384-1). Reiner.

Miller, John W. Christian Way. new ed. LC 78-76622. (Christrian Peace Shelf Ser.). 104p. 1969. pap. 2.95 (ISBN 0-8361-1605-4). Herald Pr.

Paramhansa, Yogananda. Sermon on the Mount Interpreted by Paramhansa Yoganananda. LC 79-91531. 1980. pap. 8.95 (ISBN 0-937134-01-5). Amrita Found.

Pentecost, J. Dwight. El Sermon del Monte. Orig. Title: The Sermon on the Mount. (Span.). 1981. pap. 4.75 (ISBN 0-8254-1556-X). Kregel.

Perry, Jack. Light from Light. 208p. 1987. 11.95 (ISBN 0-310-23850-1). Zondervan.

Pink, Arthur W. Exposition on the Sermon on the Mount. 9.95 (ISBN 0-8010-7075-9). Baker Bk.

Prabhavananda, Swami. The Sermon on the Mount According to Vedanta. 1972. pap. 3.95 (ISBN 0-451-62509-9, ME2338, Ment). NAL.

--Sermon on the Mount According to Vedanta. LC 64-8660. 6.95 (ISBN 0-87481-002-7). Vedanta Pr.

Steiner, Rudolf. The Ten Commandments & the Sermon on the Mount. Solomon, Frieda, tr. from Ger. 44p. 1978. pap. 2.00 (ISBN 0-910142-79-3). Anthroposophic.

Stott, John R. The Message of the Semon on the Mount. LC 84-27763. (Bible Speaks Today Ser.). 1978. pap. 6.95 (ISBN 0-87784-296-5). Inter-Varsity.

--The Sermon on the Mount. (LifeGuide Bible Studies). 64p. 1987. pap. 2.95. Inter-Varsity.

Teed, Richard. Sermon on the Mount. 91p. pap. 2.75 (ISBN 0-87785-124-7). Swedenborg.

Thomas, Roger. Seek First His Kingdom. 144p. 1987. pap. price not set (ISBN 0-87403-210-5, 39960). Standard Pub.

Van Tilborg, Sjef. The Sermon on the Mount As an Ideological Intervention: A Reconstruction of Meaning. 324p. 1986. 30.00 (ISBN 90-232-2243-1, Pub. by Van Gorcum Holland). Longwood Pub Group.

Vaught, Carl G. The Sermon on the Mount: A Theological Interpretation. (Religious Studies). 192p. (Orig.). 1986. 34.50x (ISBN 0-88706-364-0); pap. 9.95x (ISBN 0-88706-365-9). State U NY Pr.

Warren, Thomas B. & Elkins, Garland, eds. Sermon on the Mount. 1982. 15.00 (ISBN 0-934916-00-4). Natl Christian Pr.

Wesley, John. The Nature of the Kingdom. Weakley, Clare, ed. 288p. 1986. pap. 6.95 (ISBN 0-87123-875-6, 210875). Bethany Hse.

Wilde, Gary, ed. Sermon on the Mount: Wisdom of the Kingdom. (Basic Bible Ser.). 96p. 1986. pap. 4.95 (ISBN 0-89191-521-4). Cook.

SERMON ON THE MOUNT–SERMONS

Coates, Thomas. The Sermon on the Mount for Today. LC 77-184. 1979. pap. 2.95x (ISBN 0-915644-13-4). Clayton Pub Hse.

Lloyd-Jones, D. M. El Sermon del Monte, Vol. 1. 1978. 4.75 (ISBN 0-85151-414-6). Banner of Truth.

Shinn, Roger L. Sermon on the Mount. LC 62-19785. 112p. (Orig.). 1984. pap. 3.95 (ISBN 0-8298-0120-0). Pilgrim NY.

Thielicke, Helmut. Life Can Begin Again: Sermons on the Sermon on the Mount. Doberstein, J. W., tr. from Ger. 224p. pap. 10.95 (ISBN 0-227-67854-0, Pub. by J Clarke UK). Attic Pr.

Wood, Charles R. Sermon Outlines from the Sermon on the Mount. LC 85-23734. 64p. (Orig.). 1986. pap. 2.95 (ISBN 0-8254-4032-7). Kregel.

SERMONS

see also Advent Sermons; Catechetical Sermons; Children'S Sermons; Christmas Sermons; Church Year Sermons; Communion Sermons; Evangelistic Sermons; Funeral Sermons; Holy-Week Sermons; Lenten Sermons; Occasional Sermons; Preaching; Wedding Sermons

also subdivision Sermons under special subjects, e.g. Beatitudes–Sermons; Easter–Sermons; Missions–Sermons

Adams, Jay. Sermon Analysis. LC 85-73072. (Pastor's Library). 224p. 1986. 17.95 (ISBN 0-89636-193-4). Accent Bks.

Annesley, Samuel. Puritan Sermons, Sixteen Fifty-Nine To Sixteen Eighty-Nine Being the Morning Exercises at Cripplegate, St. Giles in the Fields & in Southwark: By 75 Ministers of the Gospel in or Near London, with Notes & Translations by James Nichols, 6 vols. Nichols, James, ed. 4200p. 1981. Set. lib. bdg. 120.00 (ISBN 0-940033-19-4). R O Roberts.

Annesley, Samuel, et al. Puritan Sermons, 1659-1689, 6 vols. Nichols, James, ed. 4220p. 1981. Repr. of 1845 ed. lib. bdg. 120.00 set (ISBN 0-939464-07-1). Labyrinth Pr.

Appelman, Hyman. Seeds for Sermons. (Sermon Outline Ser.). 1980. pap. 2.50 (ISBN 0-8010-0026-2). Baker Bk.

Augsburg Sermons: Epistles. LC 77-72464. (Series A). 1977. 15.95 (ISBN 0-8066-1581-8, 10-0522). Augsburg.

Augsburg Sermons: Old Testament Lessons. LC 81-65654. (Series B). 256p. 1981. pap. 15.95 (ISBN 0-8066-1890-6, 10-0531). Augsburg.

Augsburg Sermons Two (Gospels - Series B) New Sermons on Gospel Texts. LC 84-72019. (Augsburg Sermon Ser.). 272p. (Orig.). 1984. kivar 15.95 (ISBN 0-8066-2095-1, 10-0534). Augsburg.

Augsburg Sermons Two Gospels: New Sermons on Gospel Texts. LC 82-70955. (Series C). 280p. (Orig.). 1982. pap. 15.95 (ISBN 0-8066-1930-9, 10-0532). Augsburg.

Augsburg Sermons, Two Gospels: New Sermons on Gospel Texts. LC 83-70509. (Series A). 280p. 1983. pap. 15.95 (ISBN 0-8066-2015-3, 10-0533). Augsburg.

Augustine, St. Commentary on the Lord's Sermon on the Mount with Seventeen Related Sermons. Bd. with Related Sermons. LC 63-18827. (Fathers of the Church Ser.: Vol. 11). 382p. 1951. 21.95x (ISBN 0-8132-0011-3). Cath U Pr.

Aycock, Don M. Heralds to a New Age: Preaching for the Twenty-First Century. 228p. 1985. 11.95 (ISBN 0-87178-352-5). Brethren.

Bailey, James. Sermons from the Parables. 128p. (Orig.). 1981. pap. 2.95 (ISBN 0-8341-0730-9). Beacon Hill.

Ball, John T. Barefoot in the Palace. 1985. 6.25 (ISBN 0-89536-748-3, 5854). CSS of Ohio.

Barnett, Joe R. Live, with Peace, Power & Purpose. Thomas, J. D., ed. (Twentieth Century Sermons Ser.). 1978. 11.95 (ISBN 0-89112-311-3, Bibl Res Pr). Abilene Christ U.

Barnhart, Phil. More Seasonings for Sermons. 1985. 6.25 (ISBN 0-89536-723-8, 5807). CSS of Ohio.

Barnhart, Phillip H. Seasonings for Sermons. 88p. (Orig.). 1980. pap. text ed. 6.25 (ISBN 0-89536-451-4, 1967). CSS of Ohio.

Barocio, Ernesto. Bosquejos de Sermones Selectos. 144p. 1986. pap. 5.95 (ISBN 0-311-43039-2). Casa Bautista.

Bartow, Charles L. The Preaching Moment: A Guide to Sermon Delivery. LC 80-12370. (Abingdon Preacher's Library). (Orig.). 1980. pap. 5.95 (ISBN 0-687-33907-3). Abingdon.

Beauchamp, Gary R. Sermons for Today. LC 80-70788. 1981. 11.95 (ISBN 0-89112-403-9, Bibl Res Pr). Abilene Christ U.

Beckett, Wendy M., tr. from Latin. John of Ford: Sermons on the Final Verses of the Song of Songs, IV. (Cistercian Fathers Ser.: No. 44). 1983. 24.95 (ISBN 0-87907-644-5). Cistercian Pubns.

--John of Ford: Sermons on the Final Verses of the Song of Songs, V (Sermons 62-82) (Cistercian Fathers Ser.: No. 45). 1983. 24.95 (ISBN 0-87907-645-3). Cistercian Pubns.

Benn, J. Solomon, III. Preaching from the Bible. (Resources for Black Ministries Ser.). 80p. (Orig.). 1981. pap. 2.45 (ISBN 0-8010-0801-8). Baker Bk.

Bernard Of Clairvaux. Bernard of Clairvaux: Sermons I on Conversion; Lenten Sermons on the Psalm "He Who Dwells". Said, Marie-Bernard, tr. (Cistercian Fathers Ser.: No. 25). (Lat.). 1982. 25.95 (ISBN 0-87907-125-7); pap. 7.00 (ISBN 0-87907-925-8). Cistercian Pubns.

--Sermons on the Song of Songs, Vol. 1. (Cistercian Fathers Ser.: No. 4). pap. 5.00 (ISBN 0-87907-704-2). Cistercian Pubns.

--Sermons on the Song of Songs, Vol. 4. (Cistercian Fathers Ser.: No. 40). 15.95. Cistercian Pubns.

Bess, C. W. Sermons for the Seasons. LC 84-23226. 1985. pap. 4.95 (ISBN 0-8054-2256-0). Broadman.

Blumhardt, Johann C. & Blumhardt, Christoph F. Thy Kingdom Come. Eller, Vernard, ed. LC 80-19328. (A Blumhardt Reader Ser.). 180p. 1980. text ed. 5.50 (ISBN 0-8028-3544-9, Pub. by Eerdmans). Plough.

Boesak, Allan. The Finger of God: Sermons on Faith & Socio-Political Responsibility. Randall, Peter, tr. from Afrikaans. LC 81-16943. Tr. of Die Vinger Van God. 112p. (Orig.). 1982. pap. 5.95 (ISBN 0-88344-135-7). Orbis Bks.

Bolding, Amy. Installation Services for All Groups. 1984. pap. 4.95 (ISBN 0-8010-0863-8). Baker Bk.

Bolton, Robert. A Discourse About the State of True Happinesse. LC 79-84089. (English Experience Ser.: No. 909). 184p. 1979. Repr. of 1611 ed. lib. bdg. 14.00 (ISBN 90-221-0909-7). Walter J Johnson.

Bonaventure, Saint Bonaventure, Rooted in Faith: Homilies to a Contemporary World. Schumacher, Marigwen, tr. from Lat. 1974. 5.95 (ISBN 0-8199-0465-1). Franciscan Herald.

Borras, Jose. El Inmenso Amor De Dios. (Span.). 96p. 1981. pap. 3.95 (ISBN 0-311-43038-4). Casa Bautista.

Braga, James. Como Preparar Mensajes Biblicos. Orig. Title: How to Prepare Bible Messages. Tr. of How to Prepare Bible Messages. (Span.). 320p. 1986. pap. 9.50 (ISBN 0-8254-1072-X). Kregel.

Brewer, Donald R. Dynamic Children's Sermons. (Orig.). 1984. pap. 3.95 (ISBN 0-937172-58-8). JLJ Pubs.

Brianchianinov, Ignatius. Asketitcheskaya Propovjed, Tom 4. Tr. of Ascetic Sermons. 537p. 25.00 (ISBN 0-317-28962-4); pap. 20.00 (ISBN 0-317-28963-2). Holy Trinity.

Brice, Eugene. Books That Bring Life, Vol. II. (Orig.). 1987. pap. price not set (ISBN 0-937462-05-5). Net Pr.

Broadus, John A. On the Preparation & Delivery of Sermons. 4th ed. Stanfield, Vernon L., rev. by. LC 78-20602. 1979. 7.95 (ISBN 0-06-061112-X, HarpR). Har-Row.

Brokhoff, Barbara. Trouble on the Mountain! Sherer, Michael L., ed. (Orig.). 1986. pap. 6.25 (ISBN 0-89536-825-0, 6834). CSS of Ohio.

Brokhoff, John. Advent & Event. 88p. (Orig.). 1980. pap. text ed. 3.25 (ISBN 0-89536-453-0, 0147). CSS of Ohio.

Bryson, Harold T. & Taylor, James C. Building Sermons to Meet People's Needs. LC 78-74962. 1980. 7.95 (ISBN 0-8054-2109-2). Broadman.

Budge, Ernest A., ed. Coptic Homilies in the Dialect of Upper Egypt. LC 77-3585. (Coptic Texts: Vol. 1). (Illus.). Repr. of 1910 ed. 50.00 (ISBN 0-404-11551-9). AMS Pr.

Buerlein, Homer K. How to Preach More Powerful Sermons. LC 85-26378. 140p. (Orig.). 1986. pap. 10.95 (ISBN 0-664-24683-4). Westminster.

Burghardt, Walter J. Tell the Next Generation: Homilies & Near Homilies. LC 79-91895. 240p. 1980. pap. 8.95 (ISBN 0-8091-2252-9). Paulist Pr.

Burns, William C. Revival Sermons. 205p. 1981. pap. 4.95 (ISBN 0-85151-316-6). Banner of Truth.

Butler, George P., ed. Best Sermons, Nineteen Forty-Nine to Nineteen Fifty. facsimile ed. LC 74-134065. (Essay Index Reprint Ser). Repr. of 1949 ed. 23.50 (ISBN 0-8369-2488-6). Ayer Co Pubs.

--Best Sermons, 1947. facsimile ed. LC 74-134065. (Essay Index Reprint Ser). Repr. of 1947 ed. 23.50 (ISBN 0-8369-2487-8). Ayer Co Pubs.

Caesarius Of Arles, St. Sermons, Nos. 81-186. LC 56-3628. (Fathers of the Church Ser.: Vol. 47). 495p. 1964. 25.95x (ISBN 0-8132-0047-4). Cath U Pr.

--Sermons, Nos. 187-238. LC 56-3628. (Fathers of the Church Ser.: Vol. 66). 303p. 1973. 17.95x (ISBN 0-8132-0066-0). Cath U Pr.

Calvin, John. Sermons on Ephesians. 1979. 19.95 (ISBN 0-85151-170-8). Banner of Truth.

Campbell, Richard D. Signs of a Lively Congregation. 1984. 3.95 (ISBN 0-89536-701-7, 4886). CSS of Ohio.

Carroll, B. H. Sermons. 1986. Repr. of 1893 ed. 19.50 (ISBN 0-317-47643-2). Church History.

Chappell, Clovis G. Chappell's Special Day Sermons. (Pocket Pulpit Library Ser.). 204p. 1983. pap. 4.50 (ISBN 0-8010-2383-1). Baker Bk.

--Sermons on Biblical Characters. (Pocket Pulpit Lib.). 192p. 1981. pap. 3.95 (ISBN 0-8010-2330-0). Baker Bk.

Cherry, Conrad, ed. Horace Bushnell: Sermons. LC 85-60410. (Sources of American Spirituality Ser.). 256p. (Orig.). 1985. 12.95 (ISBN 0-8091-0362-1). Paulist Pr.

Chinn, Edward. Questions of the Heart. (Orig.). 1987. pap. price not set (ISBN 0-89536-877-3, 7863). CSS of Ohio.

Clapp, Steve. Sermons on Shalom. 79p. (Orig.). 1982. pap. 8.00 (ISBN 0-914527-37-1). C-Four Res.

Collins, John J. Proverbs & Ecclesiastes. LC 79-92067. (Knox Preaching Guides Ser.). 117p. (Orig., John Hayes series editor). 1980. pap. 4.95 (ISBN 0-8042-3218-0). John Knox.

Cormier, Jay. Giving Good Homilies. LC 84-70383. 96p. 1984. pap. 3.95 (ISBN 0-87793-317-0). Ave Maria.

Coughlin, Charles E. Sermons, 2 vols. Set. 250.00 (ISBN 0-8490-1025-X). Gordon Pr.

Craddock, Fred B., et al, eds. Preaching the New Common Lectionary: Year C, Lent, Holy Week, Easter. 240p. (Orig.). 1986. pap. 9.95 (ISBN 0-687-33849-2). Abingdon.

Crane, James D. El Sermon Eficaz. 308p. 1986. pap. 4.50. Casa Bautista.

Crane, Thomas F. The Exempla or Illustrative Stories from the Sermones: Vulgares off Jacques de Vitry. (Folk-Lore Society, London, Ser.: Vol. 26). pap. 35.00 (ISBN 0-8115-0512-X). Kraus Repr.

Criswell, W. A. Expository Sermons on the Book of Daniel. 651p. 19.95 (ISBN 0-310-22800-X, 9461). Zondervan.

Crowell, Laura I. Speaking His Peace. 160p. 1985. pap. 8.95 (ISBN 0-8192-1359-4). Morehouse.

Cylwicki, Albert. If Today You Hear His Voice: Reflections on the Sunday Readings. LC 81-10966. 553p. (Orig.). 1981. pap. 12.95 (ISBN 0-8189-0418-6). Alba.

Davis, Earl C. Christ at the Door. LC 84-27441. 1985. pap. 5.95 (ISBN 0-8054-6249-X). Broadman.

Dayton, Donald W., ed. The Sermons of Charles F. Parham. (The Higher Christian Life Ser.). 261p. 1985. lib. bdg. 35.00 (ISBN 0-8240-6413-5). Garland Pub.

De Brand, Roy E. Children's Sermons for Special Occasions. LC 82-72228. (Orig.). 1983. pap. 3.95 (ISBN 0-8054-4927-2). Broadman.

Duke, Robert W. The Sermon As God's Word: Theologies for Preaching. LC 80-18094. (Abingdon Preacher's Library). 128p. (Orig.). 1980. pap. 6.95 (ISBN 0-687-37520-7). Abingdon.

Dunigan, Jack. How to Prepare Sermons. 1986. pap. 3.95 (ISBN 0-932943-02-0). Life Lines.

Eavey, C. B. Chapel Talks. (Pocket Pulpit Library). 120p. 1981. pap. 2.95 (ISBN 0-8010-3365-9). Baker Bk.

Eddy, Robert L. Minister's Saturday Night. LC 79-23819. (Orig.). 1980. pap. 6.95 (ISBN 0-8298-0382-3). Pilgrim NY.

Erbe, T. Mirk's Festial: A Collection of Homilies. (EETS ES Ser.: No. 96). Repr. of 1905 ed. 28.00 (ISBN 0-527-00296-8). Kraus Repr.

Escriva de Balaguer, Josemaria. Friends of God. Tr. of Amigos de Dios. 301p. 1981. 14.50 (ISBN 0-906138-03-5); deluxe ed. 24.00 (ISBN 0-906138-04-3); pap. 7.95 (ISBN 0-906138-02-7). Scepter Pubs.

Eslinger, Richard. Prepare in the Wilderness. 1984. 5.25 (ISBN 0-89536-680-0, 4856). CSS of Ohio.

Evans, Christmas. Sermons & Memoirs of Christmas Evans. LC 86-7108. 320p. 1986. Repr. 12.95 (ISBN 0-8254-2522-0). Kregel.

Fasol, Al. A Guide to Self-Improvement in Sermon Delivery. 128p. 1983. pap. 5.95 (ISBN 0-8010-3507-4). Baker Bk.

Ferris, Theodore P. This Is the Day: Selected Sermons. 2nd ed. LC 76-39640. 368p. 1980. pap. 10.00 (ISBN 0-911658-16-5). Yankee Bks.

Finney, Charles G. Principles of Holiness. LC 83-25769. 274p. 1984. pap. 5.95 (ISBN 0-87123-403-3, 210403). Bethany Hse.

Follette, John W. Broken Bread: Sermons & Poems. 216p. 1957. pap. 4.95 (ISBN 0-88243-474-8, 02-0474). Gospel Pub.

Ford, W. Herschel. Sermons You Can Preach. (Simple Sermon Ser.). 384p. 1983. pap. 10.95 (ISBN 0-310-46971-6). Zondervan.

--Simple Sermons for Saints & Sinners. 152p. 1986. pap. 3.95 (ISBN 0-8010-3522-8). Baker Bk.

--Simple Sermons for Special Days & Occasions. 140p. 1985. pap. 4.50 (ISBN 0-8010-3515-5). Baker Bk.

--Simple Sermons for Sunday Morning. 128p. 1986. pap. 3.95 (ISBN 0-8010-3523-6). Baker Bk.

--Simple Sermons for Time & Eternity. 120p. 1985. pap. 3.95 (ISBN 0-8010-3516-3). Baker Bk.

--Simple Sermons of Great Christian Doctrines. 138p. 1985. pap. 4.50 (ISBN 0-8010-3519-8). Baker Bk.

--Simple Sermons on Conversion & Commitment. (W. Herschel Ford Sermon Library). 128p. 1986. pap. 3.95 (ISBN 0-8010-3524-4). Baker Bk.

--Simple Sermons on Evangelistic Themes. 128p. 1986. pap. 3.95 (ISBN 0-8010-3525-2). Baker Bk.

--Simple Sermons on Grace & Glory. 92p. 1986. pap. 3.50 (ISBN 0-8010-3526-0). Baker Bk.

--Simple Sermons on Salvation & Service. 136p. 1986. pap. 4.50 (ISBN 0-8010-3527-9). Baker Bk.

Fox, Frederic E. Seven Sermons & One Eulogy As Preached in the Chapel of Princeton University from 1965 to 1980. Fox, Donald H., ed. LC 82-90693. 88p. (Orig.). 1982. pap. 5.95 (ISBN 0-910521-02-6). Fox Head.

Fraser, Mitchell W. English Pulpit Oratory from Andrews to Tillotson: A Study of Its Literary Aspects. 516p. 1982. Repr. of 1932 ed. lib. bdg. 85.00 (ISBN 0-89760-564-0). Telegraph Bks.

Fudge, Edward. Sermons That Demand a Decision. pap. 2.00 (ISBN 0-686-12681-5). E Fudge.

--Sermons That Strengthen. pap. 2.00 (ISBN 0-686-12682-3). E Fudge.

--Sermons to Grow on. pap. 2.00 (ISBN 0-686-12683-1). E Fudge.

--Simple Sermons That Demand a Decision. 2.00 (ISBN 0-686-12689-0). E Fudge.

--Simple Sermons That Say Something. pap. 2.00 (ISBN 0-686-12684-X). E Fudge.

--Sunday Night Sermons. pap. 2.00 (ISBN 0-686-12685-8). E Fudge.

Gataker, Thomas. A Sparke Towards the Kindling of Sorrow for Zion. LC 76-57382. (English Experience Ser.: No. 800). 1977. Repr. of 1621 ed. lib. bdg. 7.00 (ISBN 90-221-0800-7). Walter J Johnson.

Gilbert of Hoyland. Sermons on the Song of Songs, 3 vols, Vols. 1-3. Set. 30.00. Cistercian Pubns.

Gollwitzer, Helmut. The Way to Life. Cairns, David, tr. from Ger. Tr. of Wendung Zum Leben. 232p. 1981. 21.95 (ISBN 0-567-09322-0, Pub. by T&T Clark Ltd UK); pap. 11.95 (ISBN 0-567-29322-X). Fortress.

Goodall, Blake. The Homilies of St. John Chrysostom on the Letters of St. Paul to Titus & Philemon. (Univ. of California Publications in Classical Studies: Vol. 20). 1979. 19.95x (ISBN 0-520-09596-0). U of Cal Pr.

Graham, Billy. Paz con Dios. Muntz, Carrie, tr. from Eng. Orig. Title: Peace with God. 272p. 1981. pap. 3.75 (ISBN 0-311-43037-6). Casa Bautista.

Greene, Ralph L. Dynamic & Inspirational Sermons for Today. 128p. 1980. 7.95 (ISBN 0-89962-021-3). Todd & Honeywell.

Gregson, Stephen, ed. Arthur Oakman's Radio Sermons, Vol. 2. 193p. 1984. pap. 11.00 (ISBN 0-8309-0400-X). Herald Hse.

Gresham, Charles R. Preach the Word. LC 83-71917. 200p. (Orig.). 1983. pap. 3.95 (ISBN 0-89900-198-X). College Pr Pub.

Gulledge, Jack. Ideas & Illustrations for Inspirational Talks. LC 85-24268. (Orig.). 1985. pap. 4.95 (ISBN 0-8054-5017-3). Broadman.

Gunther, Peter F., ed. Great Sermons of the Twentieth Century. LC 86-70286. 224p. (Orig.). 1986. pap. 7.95 (ISBN 0-89107-397-3, Crossway Bks). Good News.

--Sermon Classics by Great Preachers. LC 81-16899. 1982. pap. 4.95 (ISBN 0-8024-3328-6). Moody.

Gutierrez, Rolando C. Mensaje de los Salmos, Tomo III. 160p. 1983. pap. 5.95 (ISBN 0-311-04028-4). Casa Bautista.

Hall, Jim. Pressings from the Vine. (Orig.). 1987. pap. 7.00 (ISBN 0-915541-18-1). Star Bks Inc.

Hallam, Arthur F. Christian Capitalist Sermons One Thru Twenty-Six. 232p. 1983. pap. 30.00 (ISBN 0-938770-02-0). Capitalist Pr OH.

Hamilton, Ronald R. Reluctant Followers: A Chosen People? Sherer, Michael L., ed. (Orig.). 1986. pap. 6.25 (ISBN 0-89536-824-2, 6833). CSS of Ohio.

Hanson, Fred. The Old Time Religion. 1986. pap. 1.00 (ISBN 0-89265-099-0). Randall Hse.

Harbour, Brian L. From Cover to Cover. LC 81-67197. 1982. pap. 7.50 (ISBN 0-8054-2241-2). Broadman.

Harms, Paul. Seek Good, Not Evil (That You May Live) 1985. 6.25 (ISBN 0-89536-754-8, 5860). CSS of Ohio.

Hayden, Eric W. All-Occasion Sermon Outlines. (Sermon Outline Ser.). pap. 2.50 (ISBN 0-8010-4206-2). Baker Bk.

Hermann, Dolores E. Preparing Your Own Chapel Talks for Children. 1987. pap. 3.95 (ISBN 0-570-04466-9). Concordia.

Heslop, William G. Sermon Seeds from Psalms. LC 76-12080. (W. G. Heslop Bible Study Aids Ser.). 144p. 1976. pap. 4.50 (ISBN 0-8254-2831-9). Kregel.

Higdon, Barbara M. Good News for Today. 1981. pap. 7.00 (ISBN 0-8309-0298-8). Herald Hse.

Hodge, Charles. Princeton Sermons. 1979. 13.95 (ISBN 0-85151-285-2). Banner of Truth.

Holmes, Robert M. Why Jesus Never Had Ulcers. 96p. (Orig.). 1986. pap. 6.95 (ISBN 0-687-45359-3). Abingdon.

Hooker, Thomas. Redemption: Three Sermons, 1637-1656. LC 56-9145. 1977. Repr. 30.00x (ISBN 0-8201-1234-8). Schol Facsimiles.

Horne, Chevis F. Preaching the Great Themes of the Bible. (Orig.). 1986. pap. 7.95 (ISBN 0-8054-2262-5). Broadman.

Horton, Wade H. Sound Scriptural Sermon Outlines, No. 4. 1979. 7.95 (ISBN 0-87148-783-7); pap. 6.95 (ISBN 0-87148-784-5). Pathway Pr.

--Sound Scriptural Sermon Outlines, No. 5. (YA) 1982. text ed. 7.95 (ISBN 0-87148-799-3); pap. 6.95 (ISBN 0-87148-800-0). Pathway Pr.

Hudson, Van D., ed. Choice Messages from Free Will Baptist Pulpits. 1976. pap. 2.50 (ISBN 0-89265-030-3). Randall Hse.

Hughes, John J. Homilies for the C Cycle: Proclaiming the Good News. LC 85-60893. 160p. 1985. text ed. 14.95 (ISBN 0-87973-724-7, 724). Our Sunday Visitor.

--Proclaiming the Good News: Homilies for the "B" Cycle. LC 84-60750. 156p. 1984. 14.95 (ISBN 0-87973-723-9, 723). Our Sunday Visitor.
Hunt, Ernest E., III. Sermon Struggles: Four Methods of Sermon Preparation. 160p. (Orig.). 1982. pap. 8.95 (ISBN 0-8164-2375-X, HarpR). Har-Row.
Johanson, Gregory J., ed. Feed My Sheep: Sermons on Contemporary Issues in Pastoral Care. 6.95. Paulist Pr.
John Wesley's Fifty-Three Sermons. 800p. 1983. stamped, flexible bdg. 17.95 (ISBN 0-687-20493-3). Abingdon.
John of Ford. John of Ford: Sermons on the Final Verses of the Song of Songs, Vol. 6. Beckett, Wendy M., tr. from Latin. (Cistercian Fathers Ser.: No. 46). 26.95 (ISBN 0-87907-646-1). Cistercian Pubns.
--John of Ford: Sermons on the Final Verses of the Song of Songs, Vol. 7. Beckett, Wendy M., tr. from Latin. (Cistercian Fathers Ser.: No. 47). 1985. 26.95 (ISBN 0-87907-647-X). Cistercian Pubns.
--Sermons on the Final Verses of the Song of Songs, Vol. 1. (Cistercian Fathers Ser.: No. 29). 14.95 (ISBN 0-87907-629-1). Cistercian Pubns.
--Sermons on the Final Verses of the Song of Songs, Vol. 4. (Cistercian Fathers Ser.: No. 44). 24.95 (ISBN 0-87907-644-5). Cistercian Pubns.
--Sermons on the Final Verses of the Song of Songs, Vol. 5. (Cistercian Fathers Ser.: No. 45). 24.95 (ISBN 0-87907-645-3). Cistercian Pubns.
--Sermons on the Final Verses of the Song of Songs, Vol. 6. 24.95 (ISBN 0-87907-646-1). Cistercian Pubns.
--Sermons on the Final Verses of the Song of Songs, Vol. 7. 24.95. Cistercian Pubns.
Johnson, Merle A. Sermons for Christians Seasons. LC 75-44210. Repr. of 1976 ed. 21.10 (ISBN 0-8357-9026-6, 2016406). Bks Demand UMI.
Johnson, S. Lawrence. The Cross-Eyed Bear & Other Children's Sermons. LC 79-24765. (Orig.). 1980. pap. 6.50 (ISBN 0-687-09980-3). Abingdon.
Johnson, Samuel. Sermons: The Yale Edition of the Works of Samuel Johnson, Vol. 14. Hagstrum, Jean H. & Gray, James, eds. LC 57-918. (Illus.). 1978. 42.00x (ISBN 0-300-02104-6). Yale U Pr.
Jones, Bob. All Fulness Dwells. 152p. 1971. 4.95 (ISBN 0-89084-002-4). Bob Jones Univ Pr.
Jones, Bob, III. A Sermon a Day Keeps the Devil Away. 208p. (Orig.). 1980. pap. 2.95 (ISBN 0-89084-114-4). Bob Jones Univ Pr.
Jones, Bob, Sr. Bob Jones' Sermons. (Illus.). 148p. 1983. pap. 3.95 (ISBN 0-89084-232-9). Bob Jones Univ Pr.
--Things I Have Learned: Chapel Talks. 224p. 1944. pap. 3.95 (ISBN 0-89084-022-9). Bob Jones Univ Pr.
Jones, Bob, Sr., et al. Heritage of Faith. 183p. (Orig.). 1973. pap. 3.95 (ISBN 0-89084-009-1). Bob Jones Univ Pr.
Jordan, Jerry M. The Brown Bag: A Bag Full of Sermons for Children. LC 77-16813. (Illus.). 117p. 1981. pap. 6.95 (ISBN 0-8298-0411-0). Pilgrim NY.
Joyce, Jon L. Who Are You? (Orig.). 1985. pap. 2.95 (ISBN 0-937172-61-8). JLJ Pubs.
Jung, Leo. The Rhythm of Life. 742p. 32.50 (ISBN 0-87559-145-0). Shalom.
Kameeta, Zephania. Why, O Lord? Psalms & Sermons from Namibia. LC 86-45211. 80p. 1987. pap. 3.95 (ISBN 0-8006-1923-4, 1-1923). Fortress.
Keiningham, C. W. Year 'Round Sermon Outlines. (Pulpit Library). 96p. 1987. pap. price not set (ISBN 0-8010-5483-4). Baker Bk.
Kelderman, Duane. The Gentle Whisper. 1985. 6.25 (ISBN 0-89536-752-1, 5858). CSS of Ohio.
Kemper, Frederick & Bass, George M. You Are My Beloved Sermon Book. 1980. pap. 6.95 (ISBN 0-570-03821-9, 12-2761). Concordia.
King, Martin Luther, Jr. Strength to Love. LC 80-2374. 160p. 1981. pap. 4.95 (ISBN 0-8006-1441-0, 1-1441). Fortress.
Kirby, Wallace. If Only... 1985. 6.25 (ISBN 0-89536-753-X, 5859). CSS of Ohio.
Klinger, Harry E. One Day in the Life of Christ. 96p. 1987. 6.95 (ISBN 0-8059-3042-6). Dorrance.
Knox, Ronald. The Pastoral Sermons. 1960. 12.50 (ISBN 0-8199-0823-1). Franciscan Herald.
Kolatch, Alfred J. Sermons for the Seventies. LC 75-164518. 1971. 7.95x (ISBN 0-8246-0122-X). Jonathan David.
Koller, Charles W. Sermon Starters for Fifty-Two Sundays. 160p. (Orig.). 1982. pap. 6.95 (ISBN 0-8010-5440-0). Baker Bk.
Korth, Bob, compiled by. Object Talks on the Teachings of Jesus. (Illus.). 48p. (Orig.). 1984. pap. 2.95 (ISBN 0-87239-722-X, 2858). Standard Pub.
Krahn, John H. Seasonings for Sermons, Vol. 3. 1983. 4.50 (ISBN 0-89536-585-5, 1922). CSS of Ohio.
Krempa, S. Joseph. Daily Homilies, 3 Vols. Incl. Vol. 1. Ordinary Time (Year One) 242p. 1985 (ISBN 0-8189-0480-1); Vol. 2. Ordinary Time (Year Two) 253p. 1985 (ISBN 0-8189-0481-X); Vol. 3. Seasonal & Sanctoral Cycle: Advent, Christmas, Lent & Easter & all Obligatory Memorials. 217p. 1985 (ISBN 0-8189-0479-8). 1985. pap. 7.50 ea.; Set. pap. 19.95 (ISBN 0-8189-0483-6). Alba.
Kyker, Rex P. Sermons for Today, No. 1. LC 80-50106. 196p. 1980. 11.95 (ISBN 0-89112-401-2, Bibl Res Pr). Abilene Christ U.
Lacy, Donald C. Healing Echoes: Values for Christian Unity. Sherer, Michael L., ed. (Orig.). 1986. pap. 6.25 (ISBN 0-89536-826-9, 6835). CSS of Ohio.
Lampkin, Bill. Palm Leaves, Peanuts, & Sixty-One Other Children's Sermons. LC 81-3497. 112p. 1981. pap. 6.50 (ISBN 0-687-30000-2). Abingdon.
Larson, Betsy. Kidstories: Seasonal & Topical Sermons for Children. (Paperback Program Ser.). 128p. 1980. pap. 2.95 (ISBN 0-8010-5598-9). Baker Bk.
Lauer, Eugene F. Sunday Morning Insights. 252p. 1984. pap. 8.95 (ISBN 0-8146-1361-6). Liturgical Pr.
LaVon Kincaid, J., Sr., ed. Thanks Giving: Stewardship Sermons out of the Ethnic Minority Experience. LC 83-73266. 88p. 1984. pap. text ed. 6.95 (ISBN 0-88177-007-8, DR007B). Discipleship Res.
Leavell, Landrum P. Sermons for Celebrating. LC 77-90220. 1978. pap. 3.75 (ISBN 0-8054-2231-5). Broadman.
Leffler, John C. Go into the City: Sermons for a Strenuous Age. LC 85-23366. 288p. 1986. 15.95 (ISBN 0-88089-014-2). Madrona Pubs.
Lehman, Gaylord L. Sunday Words for a Monday World. 75p. (Orig.). 1985. pap. price not set (ISBN 0-938828-03-7). Falls Tar.
Lever, Thomas. Sermons. 143p. pap. 15.00 (ISBN 0-87556-200-0). Saifer.
Liguori, Alphonsus de. Sermons of St. Alphonsus Liguori for All the Sundays of the Year. LC 82-50894. 408p. 1982. pap. 10.00 (ISBN 0-89555-193-4). TAN Bks Pubs.
Limb, Akio. Because of Jesus. Thomas, J. D., ed. (Twentieth Century Sermons Ser). 1972. 11.95 (ISBN 0-89112-307-5, Bibl Res Pr). Abilene Christ U.
Lindsay, Gordon. John G. Lake: Sermons on Dominion over Demons, Disease, & Death. (Divine Healing & Health Ser.). 3.50 (ISBN 0-89985-028-6). Christ Nations.
--Maria Woodworth Etter: Her Life & Ministry. 2.50 (ISBN 0-89985-022-7). Christ Nations.
--The New John G. Lake Sermons. 1982. 1.75 (ISBN 0-686-79435-4). Christ Nations.
--The Sermons of John Alexander Dowie. (Champion of the Faith Ser.). 2.50 (ISBN 0-89985-193-2). Christ Nations.
Liptak, David Q. Sacramental & Occasional Homilies. LC 80-29287. 96p. (Orig.). 1981. pap. 5.95 (ISBN 0-8189-0408-9). Alba.
Litchfield, Hugh. Preaching the Easter Story. (Orig.). 1987. pap. 5.95 (ISBN 0-8054-2117-3). Broadman.
Lloyd-Jones, D. Martyn. Evangelistic Sermons. 294p. (Orig.). 1983. pap. 9.45 (ISBN 0-85151-362-X). Banner of Truth.
Lockaby, George W. Sermon Outlines on Christian Living. LC 81-68536. 1981. pap. 2.95 (ISBN 0-8054-2244-7). Broadman.
Lorber, Jakob. The Lord's Sermons. Ozols, Violet & Von Koerber, Hildegard, trs. from Ger. LC 80-50280. (Jakob Lorber Ser.). 278p. 1981. 15.95 (ISBN 0-934616-06-X). Valkyrie Pub Hse.
Lowry, Eugene L. Doing Time in the Pulpit. 112p. (Orig.). pap. 6.95 (ISBN 0-687-11034-3). Abingdon.
Luoma, William. God So Loved the World. 1986. pap. 3.95 (6806). CSS of Ohio.
McChesney, Stewart R. Let the Children Come. LC 81-67995. 1982. pap. 4.25 (ISBN 0-8054-4925-6). Broadman.
M'Cheyne, R. M. Sermons of R. M. M'Cheyne. 1985. pap. 4.95 (ISBN 0-85151-165-1). Banner of Truth.
MacDonald, George. Creation in Christ: Unspoken Sermons. Hein, Rolland, ed. LC 76-11282. (Wheaton Literary Ser.). 342p. 1976. pap. 8.95 (ISBN 0-87788-860-4). Shaw Pubs.
--Getting to Know Jesus. LC 79-93430. (Shepherd Illustrated Classics Ser.). 208p. (Orig.). 1980. pap. 5.95 (ISBN 0-87983-219-3). Keats.
Machen, J. Gresham. The Christian View of Man. pap. 6.95 (ISBN 0-85151-112-0). Banner of Truth.
Macleod, Donald. Know the Way, Keep the Truth, Win the Life. (Orig.). 1987. pap. price not set (ISBN 0-89536-872-2, 7858). CSS of Ohio.
Maestri, William F. A Word in Season. LC 84-11026. 153p. (Orig.). 1983. pap. 6.95 (ISBN 0-8189-0459-3). Alba.
Makrakis, Apostolos. Kyriakodromion (Sunday Sermonary) Orthodox Christian Educational Society, ed. Cummings, D., tr. from Hellenic. 637p. 1951. 12.00x (ISBN 0-938366-20-3). Orthodox Chr.
--Three Great Friday Sermons & Other Theological Discourses. Orthodox Christian Educational Society, ed. Cummings, Denver, tr. from Hellenic. 107p. (Orig.). 1952. pap. 3.00x (ISBN 0-938366-48-3). Orthodox Chr.
Mann, Leonard. Life-Size Living. Sherer, Michael L., ed. (Orig.). 1986. pap. 6.25 (ISBN 0-89536-820-X, 6829). CSS of Ohio.
Marlette, Doug. Preacher: The Wit & Wisdom of Reverend Will B. Dunn. 128p. 1984. pap. 4.95 (ISBN 0-8407-5895-2). Nelson.
Marston, Leslie R. He Lived on Our Street. 1979. pap. 4.95 (ISBN 0-89367-042-1). Light & Life.
Martin, Ralph. Mark. Hayes, John, ed. LC 81-82350. (Knox Preaching Guides). 96p. 1981. pap. 4.95 (ISBN 0-8042-3234-2). John Knox.
Martinez De Toledo, Alfonso. Little Sermons on Sin: The Archpriest of Talavera. Byrd, Leslie, tr. 1977. pap. 2.85 (ISBN 0-520-03281-0, CAL 346). U of Cal Pr.
Massey, James E. Designing the Sermon: Order & Movement in Preaching. LC 80-17920. (Abingdon Preacher's Library). 128p. (Orig.). 1980. pap. 6.95 (ISBN 0-687-10490-4). Abingdon.
Meador, Prentice A., Jr. Sermons for Today. LC 80-70788. 1981. 11.95 (ISBN 0-89112-402-0, Bibl Res Pr). Abilene Christ U.
Meyer, F. B. The Best of F. B. Meyer. 176p. 1984. pap. 5.95 (ISBN 0-8010-6179-2). Baker Bk.
Mocko, George. Good God, Where in the World Are You? (Orig.). 1987. pap. price not set (ISBN 0-89536-878-1, 7864). CSS of Ohio.
Moore, Harvey D. & Moore, Patsie S. The Mysterious Marvelous Snowflake. LC 80-20996. 128p. (Orig.). 1981. pap. 5.50 (ISBN 0-687-27640-3). Abingdon.
Morentz, Jim & Morentz, Doris. Minister's Annual: Preaching in 1987. 432p. 1986. 9.95 (ISBN 0-687-26990-3). Abingdon.
--Our Time Together: Children's Sermons Based on Lectionary Series A. 112p. (Orig.). 1983. pap. 8.75 (ISBN 0-687-29775-3). Abingdon.
Morgan, G. Campbell. Voices of Twelve Hebrew Prophets. (Morgan Library). 128p. 1975. pap. 3.95 (ISBN 0-8010-5977-1). Baker Bk.
Morris, Elias C. Sermons, Addresses & Reminiscences & Important Correspondence, with a Picture Gallery of Eminent Ministers & Scholars. Gaustad, Edwin S., ed. LC 79-52598. (The Baptist Tradition Ser.). (Illus.). 1980. Repr. of 1901 ed. lib. bdg. 27.50x (ISBN 0-405-12465-1). Ayer Co Pubs.
Motte, G. Homilies for Sundays of the Year: Cycles B. 1976. 7.50 ea. (ISBN 0-8199-0575-5). Franciscan Herald.
Motte, Gonzague. Homilies for Sundays of the Year Cycle 'C', 1974. Drury, John, tr. from Fr. Tr. of Homilies pour une annees. 312p. 1973. 10.00 (ISBN 0-8199-0461-9). Franciscan Herald.
Mueller, Daniel. Just Follow the Signs. 1984. 5.00 (ISBN 0-89536-676-2, 4851). CSS of Ohio.
Muller, George. George Muller Treasury. Steer, Roger, ed. LC 86-72058. 192p. (Orig.). 1987. pap. 7.95 (ISBN 0-89107-416-3, Crossway Bks). Good News.
Murray, Frank S., ed. Standard, Vols. 11-26. Incl. Vol. 11, o.s.i; Vol. 12; Vol. 13. 1961; Vol. 14. 1962 (ISBN 0-910840-62-8); Vol. 15. 1963 (ISBN 0-910840-63-6); Vol. 16. 1964 (ISBN 0-910840-64-4); Vol. 17. 1965 (ISBN 0-910840-65-2); Vol. 18. 1966 (ISBN 0-910840-66-0); Vol. 19. 1967 (ISBN 0-910840-67-9); Vol. 20. 1968 (ISBN 0-910840-68-7); Vol. 21. 1969 (ISBN 0-910840-69-5); Vol. 22. 1970 (ISBN 0-910840-70-9); Vol. 23. 1971 (ISBN 0-910840-71-7); Vol. 24. 1972 (ISBN 0-910840-72-5); Vol.25. 1973 (ISBN 0-910840-73-3); Vol. 26. 1974 (ISBN 0-910840-74-1). 2.00x ea. Kingdom.
--Standard, Vol. 30. 1978. 3.00x (ISBN 0-910840-78-4). Kingdom.
--The Standard Nineteen Seventy-Nine. 192p. 1979. 3.00x (ISBN 0-910840-79-2). Kingdom.
--The Standard 1982. (Sermons Ser.). 192p. 1982. 3.00x (ISBN 0-910840-82-2). Kingdom.
--The Standard 1983 Termination. (Sermons Ser.). 192p. 1983. 3.00x (ISBN 0-910840-83-0). Kingdom.
Murray, John. Collected Writings of John Murray: Studies in Theology, Vol. 4. 390p. 1983. 24.95 (ISBN 0-85151-340-9). Banner of Truth.
Nadal, J. C. Dictionnaire d'Eloquence Sacree, Vol. 6. Migne, J. P., ed. (Nouvelle Encyclopedie Theologique Ser.). (Fr.). 650p. Repr. of 1851 ed. lib. bdg. 83.00x (ISBN 0-89241-256-9). Caratzas.
Nelson, Welsley W. Don't Park Behind a Truck & Other Chapel Talks. 40p. 1982. pap. 2.95 (ISBN 0-910452-51-2). Covenant.
Niguidula, Lydia N. Celebration: a Sourcebook for Christian Worship. 1975. wrps. 6.50x (ISBN 0-686-18680-X). Cellar.
Odom, Stephen A., ed. Steady in an Unsteady World. 144p. 1986. pap. 7.95 (ISBN 0-8170-1097-1). Judson.
O'Neal, Glenn. Make the Bible Live. pap. 3.50 (ISBN 0-88469-020-2). BMH Bks.
Owens, Milton E., Jr., ed. Outstanding Black Sermons, Vol. 3. 80p. 1982. pap. 4.95 (ISBN 0-8170-0973-6). Judson.
Parr, Catharine. Prayers or Medytacions, Wherin the Mynde Is Styrred Patiently to Suffre All Afflictions Here. LC 76-57370. (English Experience Ser.: No. 788). 1977. Repr. of 1545 ed. PLB 6.00 (ISBN 90-221-0788-4). Walter J Johnson.
Patt, Richard W. Partners in the Impossible. 1984. 4.95 (ISBN 0-89536-678-9, 4854). CSS of Ohio.
Paulsell, William O., ed. Sermons in a Monastery: Chapter Talks by Matthew Kelty Ocso, No. 59. (Cistercian Studies Series). 1983. 14.95 (ISBN 0-87907-858-8); pap. 6.00 (ISBN 0-87907-958-4). Cistercian Pubns.
Pearce, J. Winston. Planning Your Preaching. LC 78-73135. 1979. pap. 6.25 (ISBN 0-8054-2108-4). Broadman.
Pentz, Croft M. Sermon Outlines from Acts. (Sermon Outline Ser.). 1978. pap. 2.50 (ISBN 0-8010-7039-2). Baker Bk.
Peterson, Thomas. Doing Something by Doing Nothing. 1985. 6.25 (ISBN 0-89536-747-5, 5853). CSS of Ohio.
Phillips, E. Lee. Breaking Silence Before the Lord. (Pulpit Library). 160p. 1986. pap. 5.95 (ISBN 0-8010-7093-7). Baker Bk.
Phillips, John. One Hundred Sermon Outlines from the Old Testament. 2nd ed. pap. 4.95 (ISBN 0-8024-7816-6). Moody.
Preacher's Homiletic Commentary, 31 vols. 1978. 450.00 (ISBN 0-8010-6962-9). Baker Bk.
Preacher's Homiletic Library, 14 vols. Set. 189.50 (ISBN 0-8010-6916-5). Baker Bk.
Prescott, Roger. The Promise of Life. 1984. 4.75 (ISBN 0-89536-683-5, 4859). CSS of Ohio.
Radecke, Mark. In Christ: A New Creation. Sherer, Michael L., ed. (Orig.). 1986. pap. 6.25 (ISBN 0-89536-821-8, 6830). CSS of Ohio.
Radecke, Mark W. In Many & Various Ways. 1985. 5.75 (ISBN 0-89536-721-1, 5806). CSS of Ohio.
Radius, Marianne. New Testament Story Sermons for Children's Church. 120p. 1984. pap. 5.95 (ISBN 0-8010-7723-0). Baker Bk.
Robertson, Frederick W. Sermons on Religion & Life. 332p. 1981. Repr. of 1906 ed. lib. bdg. 15.00 (ISBN 0-89984-437-5). Century Bookbindery.
--Sermons on Religion & Life. 332p. 1983. Repr. of 1982 ed. lib. bdg. 20.00 (ISBN 0-89987-731-1). Darby Bks.
Robinson, Generalee. Have You Heard from Heaven Lately: Sermons for All Occasions. 1984. 8.95 (ISBN 0-533-05804-X). Vantage.
Robinson, James. A Cup Running Over. (Orig.). 1987. pap. price not set (ISBN 0-89536-873-0, 7859). CSS of Ohio.
Robleto, Adolfo. Sermones para Dias Especiales, Tomo II. 96p. 1985. Repr. of 1984 ed. 2.75 (ISBN 0-311-07011-6). Casa Bautista.
--Sermones para Dias Especiales, Tomo I. (Span.). 112p. 1986. Repr. of 1983 ed. 2.50 (ISBN 0-311-07009-4). Casa Bautista.
Rueter, Alvin. The Freedom to Be Wrong. 1985. 6.25 (ISBN 0-89536-749-1, 5855). CSS of Ohio.
Runk, Wesley T. Shiny New Lives. 108p. (Orig.). 1975. pap. 4.50 (ISBN 0-89536-224-4, 1938). CSS of Ohio.
St. John Chrysostom. Homilies on Genesis 1-17. Hill, Robert C., tr. from Gr. (The Fathers of the Church Ser.: Vol. 74). 1986. 29.95 (ISBN 0-8132-0074-1). Cath U Pr.
Samuels, Daniel G. Old Testament Truth Sermons by Jesus. pap. 12.50 (ISBN 0-686-34378-6). New Age Min Spiritualist.
--Old Testament Truth Sermons on Jeremiah by Jesus. pap. 5.00 (ISBN 0-686-12713-7). New Age Min Spiritualist.
Sattler, Gary. God's Glory, Neighbor's Good: Francke's Biography & Sermons. 272p. 1982. pap. 8.95 (ISBN 0-910452-50-4). Covenant.
Schleiner, Winfried. The Imagery of John Donne's Sermons. LC 70-91655. Repr. of 1970 ed. 66.00 (2027523). Bks Demand UMI.
Schmalenberger & Crotts. From Sunday to Sunday. (Orig.). 1986. pap. 4.25 (ISBN 0-937172-63-4). JLJ Pubs.
Schmalenberger, Jerry. Saints Who Shaped the Church. Sherer, Michael L., ed. (Orig.). 1987. pap. 6.50 (ISBN 0-89536-856-0, 7815). CSS of Ohio.
Sermons for Eighteen Special Occasions. LC 12-2963. 1982. pap. 5.75 (ISBN 0-570-03870-7). Concordia.

Sermons for Special Occasions. 1981. pap. 5.95 (ISBN 0-570-03825-1, 12-2790). Concordia.
Shedd, W. G. Sermons to the Natural Man. 1977. 13.95 (ISBN 0-85151-260-7). Banner of Truth.
Sibbes, Richard. Works of Richard Sibbes, Vol. VI. 560p. 1983. Repr. 16.95 (ISBN 0-85151-372-7). Banner of Truth.
--Works of Richard Sibbes, Vol. IV. 527p. 1983. Repr. 16.95 (ISBN 0-85151-371-9). Banner of Truth.
Smith, Chuck. The Answer for Today, Vol. 1. 72p. (Orig.). 1980. pap. 1.95 (ISBN 0-936728-09-4). Word for Today.
Smith, Gerald B., compiled by. Jesus, Our Man in Glory. Date not set. pap. price not set (ISBN 0-87509-390-6). Chr Pubns.
Smith, W. Alan. Children Belong in Worship: A Guide to the Children's Sermon. Lambert, Herbert, ed. LC 84-5840. 128p. 1984. pap. 7.95 (ISBN 0-8272-0445-0). CBP.
Smith, Warren T. Journey in Faith. 1984. 5.50 (ISBN 0-89536-679-7, 4855). CSS of Ohio.
Sosland, Henry Adler. Guide for Preachers on Composing & Delivering Sermons. (Illus.). 1987. text ed. 20.00 (ISBN 0-87334-026-4, Pub. by Jewish Theol Seminary). Ktav.
Spray, Russell E. Blessed Assurance Sermon Outlines. (Pulpit Library). 80p. 1985. pap. 3.95 (ISBN 0-8010-8255-2). Baker Bk.
--Easy-to-Use Sermon Outlines. (Sermon Outline Ser.). 1978. pap. 2.45 (ISBN 0-8010-8143-2). Baker Bk.
--Instant Sermons for Busy Pastors. (Sermon Outline Ser.). (Orig.). 1981. pap. 1.95 (ISBN 0-8010-8192-0). Baker Bk.
Spurgeon, C. H. Farm Sermons. 328p. Date not set. pap. write for info. Pilgrim Pubns.
--Sermons on Unusual Occasions. 1978. pap. 6.25 (ISBN 0-686-00494-9). Pilgrim Pubns.
--Soul Winner. 1978. pap. 2.50 (ISBN 0-686-02430-3). Pilgrim Pubns.
--Twelve Sermons on Holiness. pap. 3.75 (ISBN 0-685-88395-7). Reiner.
Spurgeon, Charles H. Sermons for Special Days & Occasions. 160p. 1984. pap. 4.95 (ISBN 0-8010-8247-1). Baker Bk.
--Spurgeon's Expository Encyclopedia, 15 vols. 1977. 195.00 (ISBN 0-8010-8104-1). Baker Bk.
--Spurgeon's Sermons, 10 vols. (Charles H. Spurgeon Library). 1983. pap. 99.95 (ISBN 0-8010-8231-5). Baker Bk.
--Spurgeon's Sermons on Christ's Names & Titles. Cook, Charles T., ed. 1965. Repr. of 1961 ed. 7.95 (ISBN 0-87921-033-8). Attic Pr.
Stacy, John. Sermons That Should Be in Print. (Illus.). 104p. (Orig.). 1986. pap. 9.95. Brentwood Comm.
--Soul Touching Sermons. (Illus.). 114p. (Orig.). 1986. pap. 9.95 (ISBN 1-55630-015-8). Brentwood Comm.
Stagg, Frank. Galatians & Romans. LC 79-92066. (Knox Preaching Guides Ser.). 128p. (Orig., John Hayes series editor). 1980. pap. 4.95 (ISBN 0-8042-3238-5); pap. 4.95. John Knox.
Steindam, Harold. As the Twig Is Bent: Sermons for Children. (Illus.). 128p. (Orig.). 1983. pap. 6.95 (ISBN 0-8298-0679-2). Pilgrim NY.
Stevenson, Dwight E. & Diehl, Charles F. Reaching People from the Pulpit: A Guide to Effective Sermon Delivery. (Notable Books on Preaching). 1978. pap. 4.50 (ISBN 0-8010-8133-5). Baker Bk.
Suarez, Oscar S. Liberating the Pulpit: Selected Sermons. 164p. (Orig.). 1984. pap. 8.25 (ISBN 0-318-20555-6, Pub. by New Day Philippines). Cellar.
Summers, Georgianna. The Light Shines in the Darkness. (Orig.). 1987. pap. price not set (ISBN 0-89536-888-9, 7874). CSS of Ohio.
Swanson, Reuben J. Roots out of Dry Ground. 1979. 8.50 (ISBN 0-915948-06-0); pap. 6.50 (ISBN 0-686-57420-6). Bks Distinction.
Sweeting, George. Special Sermons by George Sweeting. 1985. pap. 11.95 (ISBN 0-8024-8211-2). Moody.
Swords, Liam, ed. Funeral Homilies. 2.95 (ISBN 0-8091-2784-9). Paulist Pr.
--Marriage Homilles. 2.95. Paulist Pr.
Taylor, Robert R. Sermons That Save. 1984. 10.95 (ISBN 0-317-16702-2). Firm Foun Pub.
Teaching of the Twelve Apostles. Die Lateinische Ubersetzung der Didache. 142p. Repr. of 1913 ed. 12.00 (ISBN 0-384-59780-7). Johnson Repr.
Thomas, Leslie G. Thomas' Valedictory Sermons. 1973. 6.95 (ISBN 0-88428-021-7). Parchment Pr.
Thomas, W. H. Expository Sermon Outlines. 136p. 1987. pap. 5.95 (ISBN 0-8254-3830-6). Kregel.
Thulin, Richard L. The Caller & the Called. Sherer, Michael L, ed. (Orig.). 1986. pap. 6.25 (ISBN 0-89536-819-6, 6828). CSS of Ohio.
Tozer, A. W. Echoes from Eden. Smith, Gerald B., ed. LC 1-67321. (Tozer Pulpit: Vol. 8). 121p. (Orig.). 1981. 2.95 (ISBN 0-87509-227-6). Chr Pubns.
--I Talk Back to the Devil. Smith, Gerald B., ed. Orig. Title: Tozer Pulpit, Vol. 4. Twelve Sermons on Spiritual Perfection. (Illus.). 144p. (Orig.). 1972. pap. 3.45 (ISBN 0-87509-206-3). Chr Pubns.
--The Tozer Pulpit, 8 vols. Smith, Gerald B., ed. Incl. Vol. 1. Selected Quotations from the Sermons of A. W. Tozer. 158p. 1967. pap. 3.95 (ISBN 0-87509-199-7); Vol. 2. Ten Sermons on the Ministry of the Holy Spirit. 146p. 1968. pap. 3.95 (ISBN 0-87509-178-4); cloth 5.95 (ISBN 0-87509-177-6); Vol. 3. Ten Sermons from the Gospel of John. 167p. 1970. cloth 5.95 (ISBN 0-87509-201-2); Vol. 4. Twelve Sermons on Spiritual Perfection. 144p. 1972. 5.95 (ISBN 0-87509-204-7); Vol. 5. Twelve Sermons in Peter's First Epistle. 159p. 1974. 5.95 (ISBN 0-87509-207-1); Vol. 6. Twelve Messages on Well-Known & Favorite Bible Texts. 174p. 1975. 5.95 (ISBN 0-87509-210-1); Vol. 7. Twelve Sermons Relating to the Life & Ministry of the Christian Church. 1978. 5.95 (ISBN 0-87509-213-6); Vol. 8. Ten Sermons on the Voices of God Calling Man. 5.95 (ISBN 0-87509-225-X). pap. Chr Pubns.
Trull, Joe E. Seven Last Words of the Risen Christ. (Pulpit Library). 96p. 1985. pap. 4.95 (ISBN 0-8010-8879-8). Baker Bk.
Turner, J. J. Practical Sermons That Motivate. pap. 2.95 (ISBN 0-89315-211-0). Lambert Bk.
--Sermons You Should Preach. 1984. pap. 3.95 (ISBN 0-89137-547-3). Quality Pubns.
Ulmer, Louise. Charity & the Great Adventure. (Orig.). 1987. pap. price not set (ISBN 0-89536-882-X, 7868). CSS of Ohio.
Vaughan, Curtis & Corley, Bruce. Romans: A Study Guide Commentary. 1976. pap. 4.95 (ISBN 0-310-33573-6, 10960P). Zondervan.
Vines, Jerry. A Guide to Effective Sermon Delivery. 1986. text ed. 9.95 (ISBN 0-8024-4896-8). Moody.
--A Practical Guide to Sermon Preparation. 1985. 9.95 (ISBN 0-8024-6744-X). Moody.
Wagner, Clarence M. The Bethlehem Mystery. (Orig.). 1981. 3.50 (ISBN 0-937498-03-3). Tru-Faith.
--The Salt of the Earth. Tru-Faith Pub, ed. 80p. (Orig.). 1981. pap. 3.50x (ISBN 0-937498-01-7). Tru-Faith.
--The Same Jesus. Tru-Faith Publishers, ed. 72p. (Orig.). 1981. pap. 3.50x (ISBN 0-937498-00-9). Tru-Faith.
Wall, Ronald E. Sermons on Prayer. (Pulpit Library). 144p. 1986. pap. 6.95 (ISBN 0-8010-9672-3). Baker Bk.
Wallace, Mary H., ed. Harvestime Guest Pulpit Library, Vol. 1. 432p. (Orig.). 1982. pap. 6.95 (ISBN 0-912315-14-8). Word Aflame.
--Harvestime Pulpit Library: Let Them Know, Vol. 2. (Illus.). 379p. (Orig.). 1984. pap. 8.95 (ISBN 0-912315-67-9). Word Aflame.
Wallis, Charles L., compiled by. Treasury of Story Sermons for Children. (Charles L. Wallis Library Pulpit Helps). 290p. 1974. pap. 6.95 (ISBN 0-8010-9556-5). Baker Bk.
Walsh, Kilian & Edmonds, Irene, trs. Bernard of Clairvaux: Sermons on the Song of Songs, Vol. III. (Cistercian Fathers Ser.: No. 31). 1979. 15.95 (ISBN 0-87907-131-1); pap. 5.00 (ISBN 0-87907-931-2). Cistercian Pubns.
Ward, C. M. Sermons from Luke. 96p. (Orig.). 1983. pap. 2.25 (ISBN 0-89274-260-7). Harrison Hse.
Watley, William D. Sermons on Special Days: Preaching Through the Year in the Black Church. 128p. 1987. pap. 6.95 (ISBN 0-8170-1089-0). Judson.
Wedel, Alton. The Word Today. 1984. 5.25 (ISBN 0-89536-684-3, 4860). CSS of Ohio.
Weekley, James. Tilted Haloes. (Orig.). 1987. pap. price not set (ISBN 0-89536-871-4, 7857). CSS of Ohio.
Wendland, E. H., ed. Sermon Texts. 1984. 9.95 (ISBN 0-8100-0186-1, 15N0409). Northwest Pub.
Wesley's Fifty-Two Standard Sermons. 9.95 (ISBN 0-686-12929-6). Schmul Pub Co.
Wesley's Veterans, 7 vols. pap. 5.95 ea. Schmul Pub Co.
Westphal, Arnold C. Fold 'n Snip Story Sermonettes, No. 6. 1973. pap. 4.95 (ISBN 0-915398-05-2). Visual Evangels.
--Visual Evangels, 6 vols. (Orig.). 1979. pap. text ed. 4.95 ea. No. 1 (ISBN 0-915398-12-5). No. 2 (ISBN 0-915398-13-3). No. 3 (ISBN 0-915398-14-1). No. 4 (ISBN 0-915398-15-X). No. 5 (ISBN 0-915398-16-8). No. 6 (ISBN 0-915398-17-6). Visual Evangels.
Wheelwright, John. John Wheelwright's Writings, Including His Fast-Day Sermon, 1637, & His Mercurius Americanus, 1645. facs. ed. LC 70-128897. (Select Bibliographies Reprint Ser). 1876. 18.00 (ISBN 0-8369-5517-X). Ayer Co Pubs.
When You Need a Special Sermon Series. 1981. pap. 5.95 (ISBN 0-570-03836-7, 12-2801). Concordia.
White, Willie. Fifty-Two Winning Sermons. 117p. (Orig.). 1973. cancelled (ISBN 0-89900-129-7). College Pr Pub.
Wiersbe, Warren W., compiled by. Classic Sermons on Faith & Doubt. LC 85-9767. (Classic Sermon Ser.). 160p. 1985. pap. 8.95 (ISBN 0-8254-4028-9). Kregel.
Wiersbe, Warren W., ed. Classic Sermons on Prayer. (Classic Sermons Ser.). (Orig.). 1987. pap. 9.95 (ISBN 0-8254-4029-7). Kregel.
Wiersbe, Warren W., compiled by. Classic Sermons on Suffering. LC 84-11260. (Classic Sermon Ser.). 204p. (Orig.). 1984. pap. text ed. 9.95 (ISBN 0-8254-4027-0). Kregel.
--Treasury of the World's Great Sermons. LC 77-72366. 1977. 24.95 (ISBN 0-8254-4011-4). Kregel.
Williams, H. A. The True Wilderness. (The Crossroad Paperback Ser.). 160p. 1982. pap. 5.95 (ISBN 0-8245-0470-4). Crossroad NY.
Work of Richard Sibbes, 7 Vols. Set. 108.95 (ISBN 0-85151-398-0). Banner of Truth.
The Works of John Wesley: Sermons 1-33, Vol. 1. 1008p. 1984. 49.95 (ISBN 0-687-46210-X). Abingdon.
Wurmbrand, Richard. With God in Solitary Confinement. 1979. pap. 4.95 (ISBN 0-88264-002-X). Diane Bks.
Zelle, Donald. Wind Through the Valleys. (Orig.). 1987. pap. price not set (ISBN 0-89536-876-5, 7862). CSS of Ohio.

SERMONS–ILLUSTRATIONS

see also Homiletical Illustrations

Andersen, Richard & Deffner, Donald. For Example... 1978. pap. 7.95 (ISBN 0-570-03766-2, 12-2701). Concordia.
Chinn, Edward. The Wonder of Words, Bk. II. Sherer, Michael L., ed. (Orig.). 1987. pap. 7.50 (ISBN 0-89536-867-6, 7826, Co. Pub. by Forward Movement). CSS of Ohio.
Sangster, W. E. The Craft of Sermon Illustration. (Notable Books on Preaching). 1973. pap. 7.95 (ISBN 0-8010-8214-5). Baker Bk.
Tan, Paul L. Encyclopedia of Seven Thousand-Seven Hundred Illustrations: Signs of the Times. 7th ed. LC 78-72973. (Illus.). 2032p. 1979. 34.95 (ISBN 0-932940-02-1). Assurance Pubs.
Westphal, Arnold C. Junior Surprise Sermons with Handmade Objects, 2 bks. Set. pap. 9.90 (ISBN 0-686-70924-1); No. 1. pap. 4.50 (ISBN 0-915398-18-4); No. 2. pap. 4.95 (ISBN 0-915398-19-2). Visual Evangels.

SERMONS–OUTLINES

Apostolon, Billy. Special Days & Occasions. (Sermon Outline Ser). 1978. pap. 2.50 (ISBN 0-8010-0007-6). Baker Bk.
Bess, C. W. Sparkling Object Sermons for Children. (Object Lesson Ser.). 120p. (Orig.). 1982. pap. 4.95 (ISBN 0-8010-0824-7). Baker Bk.
Blackwood, A. W. La Preparacion de Sermones Biblicos. Crane, Santiago D., tr. (Span.). 255p. 1985. pap. 3.95 (ISBN 0-311-42030-3). Casa Bautista.
Bolick, James H. Sermon Outlines for Revival Preaching. (Pulpit Library). 106p. 1986. pap. 2.95 (ISBN 0-8010-0922-7). Baker Bk.
--Sermon Outlines from the Word. (Sermon Outline Ser.). (Orig.). 1980. pap. 2.50 (ISBN 0-8010-0528-0). Baker Bk.
Burns, Jabez. Ninety-One Sermon Outlines on Types & Metaphors. LC 86-27347. 128p. (Orig.). 1987. pap. 5.95 (ISBN 0-8254-2270-1). Kregel.
--One Hundred Fifty-One Sermon Outlines. LC 86-27520. 208p. (Orig.). 1987. pap. 7.95 (ISBN 0-8254-2266-3). Kregel.
--One Hundred Forty-Nine Sermon Outlines. LC 86-27436. 208p. (Orig.). 1987. pap. 7.95 (ISBN 0-8254-2265-5). Kregel.
--One Hundred Ninety-Nine Sermon Outlines. LC 86-27540. 256p. (Orig.). 1987. pap. 8.95 (ISBN 0-8254-2267-1). Kregel.
--Two Hundred One Sermon Outlines. LC 86-27758. 256p. 1987. pap. 8.95 (ISBN 0-8254-2269-8). Kregel.
--Two Hundred Sermon Outlines. LC 75-92502. 128p. 1987. pap. 6.95 (ISBN 0-8254-2264-7). Kregel.
Chapman, Morris H., compiled by. Jesus: Author & Finisher. 1987. pap. 6.95 (ISBN 0-8054-5047-5). Broadman.
Cooper, W. Norman. Dance with God. LC 81-69932. 128p. (Orig.). 1982. 7.50 (ISBN 0-87516-491-9); pap. 4.50 (ISBN 0-87516-468-4). De Vorss.
Cox, Frank L. One Hundred One Sermon Outlines. 1971. 3.00 (ISBN 0-88027-028-4). Firm Foun Pub.
--Seventy-Seven Sermon Outlines. 1958. pap. 1.75 (ISBN 0-88027-052-7). Firm Foun Pub.
Crabtree, T. T. The Zondervan Pastor's Annual, 1986. 384p. 1985. pap. 11.95 (ISBN 0-310-22691-0, 11383P). Zondervan.
Dalton, A. E. Brief & to the Point: Suggestions for Preachers. 272p. 1973. Repr. of 1961 ed. 17.95 (ISBN 0-227-67419-7). Attic Pr.
Detrick, R. Blaine. Favorite Men of the Bible. Sherer, Michael L., ed. (Orig.). 1987. pap. 7.25 (ISBN 0-89536-855-2, 7814). CSS of Ohio.
Fowler, J. B., Jr. Illustrated Sermon Outlines. LC 86-2674. 1987. 4.95 (ISBN 0-8054-2261-7). Broadman.
Havner, Vance. Messages on Revival. (Pulpit Library). 128p. 1983. pap. 4.50 (ISBN 0-8010-4275-5). Baker Bk.
--Pepper & Salt. (Pulpit Library). 128p. 1983. pap. 4.95 (ISBN 0-8010-4276-3). Baker Bk.
Holbrook, Becky T. Revised Handful of Ideas. 5.95 (ISBN 0-89137-611-9). Quality Pubns.
Horton, Wade H. Sound Scriptural Sermon Outlines, No. 2. 1974. 7.25 (ISBN 0-87148-769-1); pap. 6.25 (ISBN 0-87148-770-5). Pathway Pr.
--Sound Scriptural Sermon Outlines, No. 6. 1984. text ed. 7.95 (ISBN 0-87148-806-X); pap. text ed. 6.95 (ISBN 0-87148-807-8). Pathway Pr.
Johnson, Carl G. Special Occasion Sermon Outlines. (Pocket Pulpit Library). 112p. 1980. pap. 3.50 (ISBN 0-8010-5126-6). Baker Bk.
Keiningham, C. W. Sermon Outlines for Funerals. (Sermon Outline Ser.). (Orig.). 1981. pap. 2.50 (ISBN 0-8010-5427-3). Baker Bk.
Koopman, LeRoy. Seasonal Sermon Outlines. (Sermon Outlines Ser.). 1979. pap. 2.50 (ISBN 0-8010-5405-2). Baker Bk.
Lockaby, George W. Sermon Outlines on the Person & Work of Christ. LC 80-67916. 1981. pap. 2.95 (ISBN 0-8054-2238-2). Broadman.
Lyon, Roy B. Bosquejos Utiles para Laicos. (Span., Illus.). 96p. 1985. pap. 1.95 (ISBN 0-311-42401-5). Casa Bautista.
MacPherson, Ian. Sermon Outlines from Pulpit Masters. (Pulpit Library). 224p. 1984. pap. 4.95 (ISBN 0-8010-6180-6). Baker Bk.
Mason, H. Lee. Sermon Outlines for Evangelism. (Sermon Outline Ser.). (Orig.). 1981. pap. 2.50 (ISBN 0-8010-6120-2). Baker Bk.
Mayshack, John L. One Hundred & Seventy-Five Sermon Outlines. (Sermon Outline Ser.). 1979. pap. 2.50 (ISBN 0-8010-6085-0). Baker Bk.
Meyer, John S. Outlines for Christmas Sermons. (Sermon Outline Ser.). 48p. 1980. pap. 2.95 (ISBN 0-8010-6107-5). Baker Bk.
Naismith, A. Twelve Hundred Scripture Outlines. (Source Book for Ministers). 1978. pap. 5.95 (ISBN 0-8010-6692-1). Baker Bk.
O'Guin, C. M. Special Occasion Helps. (Pulpit Library). 88p. 1983. pap. 2.95 (ISBN 0-8010-6650-6). Baker bk.
Pentz, Croft M. Outlines on Revelation. (Sermon Outline Ser.). 1978. pap. 2.50 (ISBN 0-8010-7030-9). Baker Bk.
--Outlines on the Holy Spirit. (Sermon Outline Ser.). 1978. pap. 2.50 (ISBN 0-8010-7029-5). Baker Bk.
--Sermon Outlines for Special Days. (Sermon Outline Ser.). 1979. pap. 2.50 (ISBN 0-8010-7046-5). Baker Bk.
Perry, Lloyd M. Biblical Preaching for Today's World. LC 73-7471. 256p. 1973. 18.95 (ISBN 0-8024-0707-2). Moody.
Phillips, John. One Hundred Sermon Outlines from the New Testament. 1979. pap. 4.95 (ISBN 0-8024-7817-4). Moody.
Quincer, Sheldon B., ed. Matthew Henry's Sermon Outlines. 1955. pap. 5.95 (ISBN 0-8028-1155-8). Eerdmans.
Ridenhour, Lynn. Seasonings for Sermons, Vol. 2. 1982. 4.75 (ISBN 0-89536-577-4, 1916). CSS of Ohio.
Schultz, W. A. Sermon Outlines. 3.95 (ISBN 0-88027-092-6). Firm Foun Pub.
Sermon Illustrations for the Gospel Lessons. LC 12-2968. 1983. pap. 5.75 (ISBN 0-570-03875-8). Concordia.
Spray, Russell E. Concise Sermon Outlines. (Paperback Library). 72p. 1985. pap. 3.95 (ISBN 0-8010-8258-7). Baker Bk.
--How To-Sermon Outlines. (Pulpit Library). 96p. 1984. pap. 4.50 (ISBN 0-8010-8252-8). Baker Bk.
--Practical Sermon Outlines. 80p. 1984. pap. 3.95 (ISBN 0-8010-8240-4). Baker Bk.
--Ready to Use Sermon Outlines. 80p. 1987. pap. 3.95 (ISBN 0-8010-8268-4). Baker Bk.
--Soul Building Sermon Outlines. (Dollar Sermon Library). 1977. pap. 1.95 (ISBN 0-8010-8118-1). Baker Bk.
--Special Day Sermon Outlines. 80p. 1984. pap. 3.95 (ISBN 0-8010-8241-2). Baker Bk.
--Time-Saving Sermon Outlines. (Sermon Outline Ser.). (Orig.). 1981. pap. 2.50 (ISBN 0-8010-8193-9). Baker Bk.
--Why Sermon Outlines. (Sermon Outline Ser.). 48p. (Orig.). 1980. pap. 2.50 (ISBN 0-8010-8188-2). Baker Bk.
Spurgeon, Charles H. Apuntes de Sermones. Orig. Title: Spurgeon's Sermon Notes. (Span.). 432p. 1975. pap. 8.95 (ISBN 0-8254-1675-2). Kregel.
Suggs, Roy A. Expository Sermon Outlines to Saints & Sinners. 1981. pap. 2.75 (ISBN 0-934942-24-2). White Wing Pub.
Taylor, John B. Preaching Through the Prophets. LC 84-23773. 110p. 1985. pap. 7.95 (ISBN 0-8272-2929-1). CBP.

Wood, Charles R. Sermon Outlines from the Sermon on the Mount. LC 85-23734. 64p. (Orig.). 1986. pap. 2.95 (ISBN 0-8254-4032-7). Kregel.

--Sermon Outlines on the Psalms. LC 85-23735. 64p. (Orig.). 1986. pap. 2.95 (ISBN 0-8254-4033-5). Kregel.

SERMONS–TRANSLATIONS FROM FOREIGN LANGUAGES

Bechett, Wendy M., tr. John of Ford: Sermons on the Song of Songs I. LC 77-3697. (Cistercian Fathers Ser.: No. 29). 1977. 14.95 (ISBN 0-87907-629-1). Cistercian Pubns.

Bullinger, Henry. The Decades of Henry Bullinger, Minister of the Church of Zurich, 4 vols. 1849-1851. Set. 144.00 (ISBN 0-384-06315-2). Johnson Repr.

Calvin, Jean. Certain Homilies Containing Profitable Admonition for This Time. LC 73-6108. (English Experience Ser.: No. 576). 120p. 1973. Repr. of 1553 ed. 8.00 (ISBN 90-221-0576-8). Walter J Johnson.

Eckhart, Meister. Breakthrough: Meister Eckhart's Creation Spirituality. LC 80-909. 600p. 1980. pap. 10.95 (ISBN 0-385-17034-3, Im). Doubleday.

Kierkegaard, Soren. For Self-Examination & Judge for Yourself. (American-Scandinavian Foundation Ser.). 1944. pap. 8.50x (ISBN 0-691-01952-5). Princeton U Pr.

Lehmann, Helmut T. & Doberstein, John W., eds. Luther's Works: Sermons I, Vol. 51. Doberstein, John W., tr. LC 55-9893. 1959. 19.95 (ISBN 0-8006-0351-6, 1-353). Fortress.

Lejeune, R. Christoph Blumhardt & His Message. LC 63-15816. 1963. 7.00 (ISBN 0-87486-200-0). Plough.

Lynch, Kilian F., ed. John de la Rochelle: Eleven Marian Sermons. (Text Ser). 1961. 7.00 (ISBN 0-686-11557-0). Franciscan Inst.

Turner, Charles W. Pulpit Words Translated for Pew People. pap. 4.95 (ISBN 0-88469-046-6). BMH Bks.

SERMONS, AMERICAN

Abilene Christian University Lectureship Staff. Crowning Fifty Years. Thomas, J. D., ed. LC 68-21004. 1968. 9.95 (ISBN 0-89112-030-0, Bibl Res Pr). Abilene Christ U.

Adler, Morris. Voice Still Speaks. Chinitz, Jacob, ed. LC 68-57433. 1969. pap. text ed. 20.00x (ISBN 0-8197-0052-5). Bloch.

Allen, Charles L. Touch of the Master's Hand: Christ's Miracles for Today. 160p. 1956. pap. 2.75 (ISBN 0-8007-8093-0, Spire Bks). Revell.

Anderson, Lynn. Steps to Life. (Twentieth Century Sermons Ser.). 1977. 11.95 (ISBN 0-89112-310-5, Bibl Res Pr). Abilene Christ U.

Angell, C. Roy. God's Gold Mines. LC 62-9194. 1962. 7.95 (ISBN 0-8054-5113-7). Broadman.

--Price Tags of Life. LC 59-9692. 1959. 6.95 (ISBN 0-8054-5108-0). Broadman.

Ash, Anthony L. The Word of Faith. Thomas, J. D., ed. LC 73-89757. (Twentieth Century Sermons Ser.). 1973. 11.95 (ISBN 0-89112-308-3, Bibl Res Pr). Abilene Christ U.

Bacon, Margaret Hope. Lucretia Mott Speaking: Excerpts from the Sermons & Speeches of a Famous 19th Century Quaker Minister & Reformers. LC 80-84890. 31p. (Orig.). 1980. pap. 2.50x (ISBN 0-87574-234-3). Pendle Hill.

Beecher, Lyman. Lyman Beecher & the Reform of Society: Four Sermons, 1804-1828. LC 71-38437. (Religion in America Series Two). 214p. 1972. Repr. of 1972 ed. 19.00 (ISBN 0-405-04058-X). Ayer Co Pubs.

Bosco, Ronald A., ed. Puritan Sermon in America, 1630-1750, 4 vols. LC 78-114749. (Sermon in America Ser.). 1978. Repr. 200.00x set (ISBN 0-8201-1320-4). Schol Facsimiles.

Bracken, et al. Women of the Word: Contemporary Sermons by Women Clergy. Hackett, Charles, ed. LC 84-52656. (Illus.). 144p. (Orig.). 1985. pap. 7.95 (ISBN 0-932419-00-3). Susan Hunter.

Brawley, Edward M., ed. Negro Baptist Pulpit. facs. ed. LC 74-154072. (Black Heritage Library Collection Ser). 1890. 19.25 (ISBN 0-8369-8783-7). Ayer Co Pubs.

Brooks, Phillips. Selected Sermons. facs. ed. Scarlett, William, ed. LC 79-142610. (Essay Index Reprint Ser). 1949. 19.50 (ISBN 0-8369-2146-1). Ayer Co Pubs.

Bushnell, Horace. God in Christ. LC 76-39568. Repr. of 1849 ed. 25.00 (ISBN 0-404-01245-0). AMS Pr.

Chalk, John A. Jesus' Church. Thomas, J. D., ed. (Twentieth Century Sermons Ser). 1969. 11.95 (ISBN 0-89112-303-2, Bibl Res Pr). Abilene Christ U.

Chapin, Edwin H. Humanity in the City. LC 73-11901. (Metropolitan America Ser.). 254p. 1974. Repr. 19.00 (ISBN 0-405-05389-4). Ayer Co Pubs.

Chase, Harry E. Eden in Winter. LC 78-71941. 1978. write for info. (ISBN 0-9601662-2-X). C Schneider.

Cherry, Conrad, ed. Horace Bushnell: Sermons. LC 85-60410. (Sources of American Spirituality Ser.). 256p. (Orig.). 1985. 12.95 (ISBN 0-8091-0362-1). Paulist Pr.

Church of St. Paul the Apostle, New York Staff. Sermons Preached at the Church of St. Paul the Apostle, New York, During the Year, 1863. 32.00 (ISBN 0-405-10851-6, 11854). Ayer Co Pubs.

Clark, Vynomma. So You're a Woman. LC 70-180790. 4.95 (ISBN 0-89112-050-5, Bibl Res Pr). Abilene Christ U.

Cotton, John. God's Mercie Mixed with His Justice. LC 58-5651. 1977. Repr. of 1641 ed. 30.00x (ISBN 0-8201-1242-9). Schol Facsimiles.

--Two Sermons. LC 79-141108. (Research Library of Colonial Americana). 1971. Repr. of 1642 ed. 22.00 (ISBN 0-405-03322-2). Ayer Co Pubs.

Criswell, W. A. Expository Sermons on Revelation, 5 Vols. in 1. 1961-66. 24.95 (ISBN 0-310-22840-9, 9442). Zondervan.

Davis, Gerald L. I Got the Word in Me & I Can Sing It, You Know: A Study of the Performed African American Sermon. LC 85-2544. (Illus.). 272p. 1986. text ed. 24.95 (ISBN 0-8122-7987-5). U of Pa Pr.

Davis, Ron L. Gold in the Making. LC 83-21931. 160p. 1984. pap. 5.95 (ISBN 0-8407-5869-3). Nelson.

Davis, Thomas M. & Davis, Virginia L., eds. Edward Taylor's "Church Records" & Related Sermons. (American Literary Manuscripts Ser.). 1981. lib. bdg. 36.50 (ISBN 0-8057-9650-9, Twayne). G K Hall.

Douglas, Robert C. Freedom in Christ. Thomas, J. D., ed. LC 72-140290. (Twentieth Century Sermons Ser). 1970. 11.95 (ISBN 0-89112-305-9, Bibl Res Pr). Abilene Christ U.

Douglass, William. Sermons Preached in the African Protestant Episcopal Church of St. Thomas' Philadelphia. facs. ed. LC 79-157366. (Black Heritage Library Collection Ser). 1854. 20.00 (ISBN 0-8369-8804-3). Ayer Co Pubs.

Edwards, Jonathan. The Works of Jonathan Edwards, 2 vols. 1979. Set. 66.95 (ISBN 0-85151-397-2); Vol. 1. 36.95 (ISBN 0-85151-216-X); Vol. 2. 36.95 (ISBN 0-85151-217-8). Banner of Truth.

Ferguson, Charles W., compiled by. Great Themes of the Christian Faith, As Presented by G. C. Morgan. facs. ed. LC 68-58788. (Essay Index Reprint Ser). 1930. 17.50 (ISBN 0-8369-1034-6). Ayer Co Pubs.

Finney, Charles G. Charles G. Finney Memorial Library, 8 vols. 1975. Set. pap. 31.50 (ISBN 0-8254-2623-5). Kregel.

--Guilt of Sin. LC 65-25845. (Charles G. Finney Memorial Library). 124p. 1975. pap. 4.50 (ISBN 0-8254-2616-2). Kregel.

--Prevailing Prayer. LC 65-25846. (Charles G. Finney Memorial Library). 1975. pap. 3.50 (ISBN 0-8254-2603-0). Kregel.

--So Great Salvation. LC 65-25844. (Charles G. Finney Memorial Library). 128p. 1975. pap. 4.50 (ISBN 0-8254-2621-9). Kregel.

--True & False Repentance. LC 66-10576. (Charles G. Finney Memorial Library). 122p. 1975. pap. 4.50 (ISBN 0-8254-2617-0). Kregel.

--True Saints. LC 66-24880. (Charles G. Finney Memorial Library). 120p. 1975. pap. 4.50 (ISBN 0-8254-2622-7). Kregel.

--True Submission. LC 66-24881. (Charles G. Finney Memorial Library). 128p. 1975. pap. 4.50 (ISBN 0-8254-2618-9). Kregel.

--Victory Over the World. LC 66-24879. (Charles G. Finney Memorial Library). 124p. 1975. pap. 4.50 (ISBN 0-8254-2619-7). Kregel.

Finney, Charles G. & Parkhurst, L. B. Principles of Liberty. rev. ed. LC 82-20705. (Finney's Sermons on Romans Ser.). 194p. (Orig.). 1983. pap. 5.95 (ISBN 0-87123-475-0, 210475). Bethany Hse.

Fosdick, Harry E. Great Time to Be Alive: Sermons on Christianity in Wartime. LC 78-167341. (Essay Index Reprint Ser.). Repr. of 1944 ed. 18.00 (ISBN 0-8369-2688-9). Ayer Co Pubs.

Freehof, Solomon B. Preaching the Bible. 1974. 12.50x (ISBN 0-87068-244-X). Ktav.

Gillingham, E. Leonard. Dealing with Conflict. LC 81-20662. 144p. 1982. 8.75 (ISBN 0-687-10329-0). Abingdon.

Glennie, Alexander. Sermons Preached on Plantations to Congregations of Negroes. facsimile ed. LC 75-161260. (Black Heritage Library Collection). Repr. of 1844 ed. 16.25 (ISBN 0-8369-8819-1). Ayer Co Pubs.

Hamilton, Charles G. You Can't Steal First Base. LC 74-164909. 1972. 6.95 (ISBN 0-8022-2057-6). Philos Lib.

Hare, Eric B. Fullness of Joy. 1985. pap. 5.95 (ISBN 0-8163-0586-2). Pacific Pr Pub Assn.

Herron, George D. Social Meanings of Religious Experiences. (American Studies Ser.). 1969. Repr. of 1896 ed. 18.00 (ISBN 0-384-22660-4). Johnson Repr.

Hinson, William H. Solid Living in a Shattered World. 160p. 1985. 8.95 (ISBN 0-687-39048-6). Abingdon.

Hoard, Walter B., ed. Outstanding Black Sermons, Vol. 2. 1978. pap. 5.95 (ISBN 0-8170-0832-2). Judson.

Hodge, Charles B. Will God Run. LC 70-187827. (Illus.). 1965. 6.95 (ISBN 0-89112-053-X, Bibl Res Pr). Abilene Christ U.

Hodge, Charles B., Jr. Hodge Podge. LC 71-92047. 1969. 6.95 (ISBN 0-89112-051-3, Bibl Res Pr). Abilene Christ U.

Jones, Rufus M. Thou Dost Open up My Life. LC 63-11819. (Orig.). 1963. pap. 2.50x (ISBN 0-87574-127-4). Pendle Hill.

Keck, Leander E. The Bible in the Pulpit: The Renewal of Biblical Preaching. LC 77-12015. 1978. pap. 8.95 (ISBN 0-687-03160-5). Abingdon.

Killinger, John, ed. Experimental Preaching. LC 72-8419. Repr. of 1973 ed. 33.30 (ISBN 0-8357-9006-1, 2009067). Bks Demand UMI.

King, Martin Luther, Jr. Strength to Love. 208p. 1985. pap. 11.95 (ISBN 0-8027-2472-8). Walker & Co.

Lemmons, Reuel. The King & His Kingdom. Thomas, J. D., ed. LC 68-59307. (Twentieth Century Sermons Ser). 1968. 11.95 (ISBN 0-89112-301-6, Bibl Res Pr). Abilene Christ U.

McGaughey, C. E. The Hope of the World. Thomas, J. D., ed. LC 74-180791. (Twentieth Century Sermons Ser). 1971. 11.95 (ISBN 0-89112-306-7, Bibl Res Pr). Abilene Christ U.

Manton, Joseph. Straws from the Crib. (Orig.). 1964. 5.95 (ISBN 0-8198-0150-X); pap. 4.95 (ISBN 0-8198-0151-8). Dghtrs St Paul.

Manton, Joseph E. Pennies from a Poor Box. 1962. 6.50 (ISBN 0-8198-0119-4). Dghtrs St Paul.

March, Daniel. Night Scenes in the Bible. LC 77-189204. 348p. 1977. 12.95 (ISBN 0-8254-3211-1). Kregel.

Mather, Cotton. Day of Humiliation: Times of Affliction & Disaster. LC 68-24211. 1970. 55.00x (ISBN 0-8201-1067-1). Schol Facsimiles.

Mather, Increase. Departing Glory: Eight Jeremiads of Increase Mather. LC 86-31349. 1987. 50.00x (ISBN 0-8201-1415-4). Schol Facsimiles.

Mayhew, Jonathan. Sermons. LC 76-83429. (Religion in America, Ser. 1). 1969. Repr. of 1749 ed. 19.00 (ISBN 0-405-00254-8). Ayer Co Pubs.

Mitchell, Ella P., ed. Those Preachin' Women. 128p. 1985. pap. 7.95 (ISBN 0-8170-1073-4). Judson.

Moody, D. L. Way to God. pap. 3.95 (ISBN 0-8024-9231-2). Moody.

Mullens, Leonard. Unity in Christ. 1958. 3.00 (ISBN 0-88027-053-5). Firm Foun Pub.

Newbold, Robert T., Jr., ed. Black Preaching: Select Sermons in the Presbyterian Tradition. LC 77-4015. 180p. 1977. softcover 5.65 (ISBN 0-664-24323-1). Westminster.

Pack, Frank & Meador, Prentice A., Jr. Preaching to Modern Man. Thomas, J. D., ed. LC 73-75928. 1969. 10.95 (ISBN 0-89112-060-2, Bibl Res Pr). Abilene Christ U.

Palmer, Gordon. By Freedom's Holy Light. 1964. 9.95 (ISBN 0-8159-5110-8). Devin.

Paregien, Stanley. The Day Jesus Died. 1970. 3.00 (ISBN 0-88027-004-7). Firm Foun Pub.

Payne, Daniel A. Sermons & Addresses, 1853-1891. LC 70-38458. (Religion in America, Ser. 2). 1972. 19.00 (ISBN 0-405-04079-2). Ayer Co Pubs.

Proctor, Samuel D. & Watley, William D. Sermons from the Black Pulpit. 128p. 1984. pap. 7.95 (ISBN 0-8170-1034-3). Judson.

Pullias, Athens C. Sermons of Athens Clay Pullias. Thomas, J. D., ed. (Great Preachers Ser). 1962. 11.95 (ISBN 0-89112-203-6, Bibl Res Pr). Abilene Christ U.

Sanders, James A. God Has a Story Too: Biblical Sermons in Context. LC 77-15244. 160p. 1979. pap. 6.95 (ISBN 0-8006-1353-8, 1-1353). Fortress.

Sandford, Frank W. Majesty of Snowy Whiteness. 1963. pap. 1.50 (ISBN 0-910840-10-5). Kingdom.

Scott, W. A. Wedge of Gold. 1974. pap. 3.95 (ISBN 0-685-52824-3). Reiner.

Seixas, Gershom M. A Religious Discourse: Thanksgiving Day Sermon, November 26, 1789. LC 77-7298. (Illus.). 1977. pap. 2.00 (ISBN 0-916790-00-2). Jewish Hist.

Sermons from Early America. 2nd ed. 1974. 6.00 (ISBN 0-9606952-0-6). PBBC Pr.

Skinner, Clarence R., ed. Free Pulpit in Action. facsimile ed. LC 71-156718. (Essay Index Reprint Ser.). Repr. of 1931 ed. 22.00 (ISBN 0-8369-2333-2). Ayer Co Pubs.

Smith, Gerrit. Sermons & Speeches of Gerrit Smith. LC 73-82222. (Anti-Slavery Crusade in America Ser). 1969. Repr. of 1861 ed. 11.50 (ISBN 0-405-00660-8). Ayer Co Pubs.

Smith, J. Alfred, ed. Outstanding Black Sermons. LC 76-2084. 96p. 1976. pap. 4.95 (ISBN 0-8170-0664-8). Judson.

Souldiery Spiritualized: Seven Sermons Preached Before the Artillery Companies of New England, 1674-1774. LC 79-9727. 1979. 60.00x (ISBN 0-8201-1325-5). Schol Facsimiles.

Spurgeon, Charles H. Gleanings among the Sheaves. 1974. pap. 1.95 (ISBN 0-87509-085-0). Chr Pubns.

Steimle, Edmund A. God the Stranger: Reflections About Resurrection. LC 78-14674. 80p. 1979. pap. 4.95 (ISBN 0-8006-1354-6, 1-1354). Fortress.

Taylor, Nathaniel W. Practical Sermons: New York, 1858. Kuklick, Bruce, ed. (American Religious Thought of the 18th & 19th Centuries Ser.). 455p. 1987. lib. bdg. 60.00 (ISBN 0-8240-6959-5). Garland Pub.

Thomas, J. D. Facts & Faith: Reason, Science & Faith, Vol. 1. 1966. 13.95 (ISBN 0-89112-011-4, Bibl Res Pr). Abilene Christ U.

Thomas, J. D., ed. Sermons of Batsell Barrett Baxter. (Great Preachers Ser). 1960. 11.95 (ISBN 0-89112-201-X, Bibl Res Pr). Abilene Christ U.

--Sermons of Frank Pack. (Great Preachers Ser). 1963. 11.95 (ISBN 0-89112-205-2, Bibl Res Pr). Abilene Christ U.

--Sermons of George W. Bailey. (Great Preachers Ser). 1961. 11.95 (ISBN 0-89112-202-8, Bibl Res Pr). Abilene Christ U.

--Sermons of Gus Nichols. (Great Preachers Ser). 1966. 11.95 (ISBN 0-89112-209-5, Bibl Res Pr). Abilene Christ U.

--Sermons of John H. Banister. (Great Preachers Ser). 1965. 11.95 (ISBN 0-89112-208-7, Bibl Res Pr). Abilene Christ U.

--Sermons of M. Norvel Young. (Great Preachers Ser). 1963. 11.95 (ISBN 0-89112-204-4, Bibl Res Pr). Abilene Christ U.

--Sermons of William S. Banowsky. (Great Preachers Ser). 1967. 11.95 (ISBN 0-89112-211-7, Bibl Res Pr). Abilene Christ U.

Thomas, J. D., et al. Sorrow & Joy. 1963. 11.95 (ISBN 0-89112-025-4, Bibl Res Pr). Abilene Christ U.

--Spiritual Power: Great Single Sermons. LC 74-170920. 1972. 13.95 (ISBN 0-89112-026-2, Bibl Res Pr). Abilene Christ U.

Thornton, John W., ed. Pulpit of the American Revolution: Political Sermons of the Period of 1776. LC 71-109611. (Era of the American Revolution Ser). 1970. Repr. of 1860 ed. lib. bdg. 49.50 (ISBN 0-306-71907-X). Da Capo.

Thurman, Howard. The Growing Edge. LC 74-14866. 192p. 1974. pap. 6.95 (ISBN 0-913408-14-X). Friends United.

Tillich, Paul. The Eternal Now. LC 63-17938. 1963. pap. 6.95 (ISBN 0-684-71907-X, ScribT). Scribner.

--The New Being. 1955. pap. 6.95 (ISBN 0-684-71908-8, ScribT). Scribner.

--Shaking of the Foundations. 1948. pap. 8.95 (ISBN 0-684-71910-X, ScribT). Scribner.

Toulouse, Teresa. The Art of Prophesying: New England Sermons & the Shaping of Belief. LC 86-7121. 224p. 1987. 23.00x (ISBN 0-8203-0892-7). U of Ga Pr.

Turner, J. J. Christ's Stamp of Approval & Other Sermonettes. 1977. pap. 2.50 (ISBN 0-89315-014-2). Lambert Bk.

Willard, Samuel. Compleat Body of Divinity. (American Studies). Repr. of 1726 ed. 62.00 (ISBN 0-384-68533-1). Johnson Repr.

Woodmason, Charles. Carolina Backcountry on the Eve of the Revolution: The Journal & Other Writings of Charles Woodmason, Anglican Itinerant. Hooker, Richard J., ed. (Institute of Early American History & Culture Ser.). xxxix, 305p. 1953. 25.00x (ISBN 0-8078-0643-9). U of NC Pr.

Young, Robert T. A Sprig of Hope. LC 79-20946. 1980. pap. 6.50 (ISBN 0-687-39260-8). Abingdon.

SERMONS, AMERICAN (SELECTIONS: EXTRACTS, ETC.)

Augsburg Sermons. LC 80-65552. (Old Testament Lessons, Ser. A). 264p. 15.95 (ISBN 0-8066-1797-7, 10-0530). Augsburg.

Horton, Wade H. Evangel Sermons. LC 76-57860. 1977. pap. 3.95 (ISBN 0-87148-287-8). Pathway Pr.

Mead, Sidney E. Love & Learning. Doyle, Mary L., ed. 1978. lib. bdg. 12.95x (ISBN 0-914914-13-8); pap. 5.00 (ISBN 0-914914-12-X). New Horizons.

Philpot, William M. Best Black Sermons. LC 72-75358. 96p. 1972. pap. 4.95 (ISBN 0-8170-0533-1). Judson.

Simeon, Charles. Evangelical Preaching: An Anthology of Sermons. Houston, James M., ed. LC 85-28389. (Classics of Faith & Devotion Ser.). 1986. 12.95 (ISBN 0-88070-120-X); pap. 9.95. Multnomah.

SERMONS, ANGLO-SAXON

Aelfric. Aelfric's Catholic Homilies: The Second Series. Godden, Malcolm, ed. (Early English Text Ser.: No. 5). (Illus.). 486p. 1979. text ed. 54.00x (ISBN 0-19-722405-9). Oxford U Pr.

--The Homilies of the Anglo-Saxon Church, 2 Vols. Thorpe, Benjamin, tr. Repr. of 1846 ed. 60.00 ea. (ISBN 0-384-00340-0). Johnson Repr.

SERMONS, CATECHETICAL

see Catechetical Sermons

SERMONS, ENGLISH

Baxter, Richard. The Reformed Pastor. 1979. pap. 4.95 (ISBN 0-85151-191-0). Banner of Truth.

Bazire, Joyce & Cross, James E., eds. Eleven Old English Rogationtide Homilies. LC 83-107819. (Toronto Old English Ser.: No. 7). pap. 35.80 (2056127). Bks Demand UMI.

Bell, David N., tr. & intro. by. Baldwin of Ford: Spirtual Tractates, 2 vols. 1987. Set. 50.00; Set. pap. 20.00. Vol. 1 (ISBN 0-87907-438-8, CF38). Vol. 2 (ISBN 0-87907-441-8, CF41). Cistercian Pubns.

Blench, J. W. Preaching in England in the Late Fifteenth & Sixteenth Centuries. 378p. 1981. Repr. of 1964 ed. lib. bdg. 50.00 (ISBN 0-8495-0604-2). Arden Lib.

Burrell, Percival. Suttons Synagogue: Or the English Centurion (A Sermon) LC 74-28822. (English Experience Ser.: No. 647). 1974. Repr. of 1629 ed. 3.50 (ISBN 90-221-0647-0). Walter J Johnson.

Calvin, Jean. Certain Homilies Containing Profitable Admonition for This Time. LC 73-6108. (English Experience Ser.: No. 576). 120p. 1973. Repr. of 1553 ed. 8.00 (ISBN 90-221-0576-8). Walter J Johnson.

Church of England Staff. Certaine Sermons or Homilies Appointed to Be Read in the Churches in the Time of Elizabeth 1st, 1547-1571, 2 vols. in 1. LC 68-17016. 1968. Repr. of 1623 ed. 50.00x (ISBN 0-8201-1008-6). Schol Facsimiles.

Clarke, Samuel. The Works, 4 vols. LC 75-11207. (British Philosophers & Theologians of the 17th & 18th Century Ser.: Vol. 12). 3274p. 1976. Repr. of 1742 ed. Set. lib. bdg. 204.00 (ISBN 0-8240-1762-5). Garland Pub.

Cleverly, D. W. Preaching Through the Life of Christ. Lambert, Herbert, ed. LC 85-19002. 112p. 1986. pap. 7.95 (ISBN 0-8272-2930-5). CBP.

Dering, Edward. M. Derings Workes: More at Large Than Ever Hath Heer-to-Fore Been Printed, 3 pts. LC 74-38171. (English Experience Ser.: No. 448). 692p. 1972. Repr. of 1597 ed. 95.00 (ISBN 90-221-0448-6). Walter J Johnson.

Donders, Joseph G. Jesus, the Stranger. LC 77-21783. 298p. (Orig.). 1978. pap. 8.95x (ISBN 0-88344-235-3). Orbis Bks.

Donne, John. John Donne's Sermons on the Psalms & Gospels: With a Selection of Prayers & Meditations. Simpson, Evelyn M., ed. & intro. by. LC 63-16249. 1963. pap. 7.95 (ISBN 0-520-00340-3, CAL84). U of Cal Pr.

Early English Homilies, from the Twelfth Century Ms. Part I. (EETS, OS Ser.: No. 152). Repr. of 1917 ed. 16.00 (ISBN 0-527-00148-1). Kraus Repr.

Fisher, John. This Treatise Concernynge the Fruytfull Saynges of Davyd..Was Made & Compyled by..John Fyssher..Bysshop of Rochester. LC 79-84106. (English Experience Ser.: No. 925). 296p. 1979. Repr. of 1509 ed. lib. bdg. 28.00 (ISBN 90-221-0925-9). Walter J Johnson.

Gilbert Of Hoyland. Gilbert of Hoyland: Sermons on the Song of Songs, III. Braceland, Lawrence C., tr. (Fathers Ser.: No. 26). 1979. 8.95 (ISBN 0-87907-426-4). Cistercian Pubns.

Hammond, Henry. Practical Catechism, 3 Vols. LC 79-168238. (Library of Anglo-Catholic Theology: No. 8). Repr. of 1850 ed. Set. 87.50 (ISBN 0-404-52090-1). AMS Pr.

Herr, Alan F. Elizabethan Sermon. LC 77-75996. 1969. Repr. of 1940 ed. lib. bdg. 16.50x (ISBN 0-374-93838-5, Octagon). Hippocrene Bks.

Hooker, Richard. Two Sermons Upon S. Judes Epistle. LC 70-26033. (English Experience Ser.: No. 195). 56p. 1969. Repr. of 1614 ed. 8.00 (ISBN 90-221-0195-9). Walter J Johnson.

--Works of That Learned & Judicious Divine Mr. Richard Hooker with an Account of His Life & Death by Isaac Walton, 3 vols. 7th ed. LC 76-125020. (Research & Source Works Ser.: No. 546). 1970. Repr. of 1888 ed. 103.00 (ISBN 0-8337-1731-6). B Franklin.

Hutchinson, Roger. Works. 1842. 31.00 (ISBN 0-384-25120-X). Johnson Repr.

The Incomparable Jewell: Shewed in a Sermon. LC 76-57393. (English Experience Ser.: No. 810). 1977. Repr. of 1632 ed. lib. bdg. 7.00 (ISBN 90-221-0810-4). Walter J Johnson.

Jarrett, Bede. No Abiding City. 1.95 (ISBN 0-87243-012-X). Templegate.

King, Henry. A Sermon Preached at Pauls Crosse Touching the Supposed Apostasie of J. King, Late Bishop of London. LC 76-57392. (English Experience Ser.: No. 809). 1977. Repr. of 1621 ed. lib. bdg. 9.50 (ISBN 90-221-0809-0). Walter J Johnson.

Latimer, Hugh. Sermons. LC 76-172301. Repr. of 1906 ed. 23.50 (ISBN 0-404-03886-7). AMS Pr.

--Sermons. 379p. 1985. Repr. of 1984 ed. lib. bdg. 35.00 (ISBN 0-8482-4878-3). Norwood Edns.

--Seven Sermons Before Edward VI, Fifteen Forty-Nine. Arber, Edward, ed. 1985. pap. 17.50. Saifer.

--Works of Hugh Latimer, Sometime Bishop of Worcester, Martyr, 1555, 2 Vols. Repr. of 1845 ed. Set. 80.00 (ISBN 0-384-31480-5). Johnson Repr.

Lloyd-Jones, D. Martyn. God's Way of Reconciliation: Studies in Ephesians II. 1972. 12.95 (ISBN 0-8010-5519-9). Baker Bk.

--Romans: The Law-Chapter 7: 1 to 8: 4. 368p. 1974. 14.95 (ISBN 0-310-27910-0, 10574); Six-volume Set. text ed. 87.70 (ISBN 0-310-27948-8, 10575). Zondervan.

--Spiritual Depression: Its Causes & Cure. 1965. pap. 5.95 (ISBN 0-8028-1387-9). Eerdmans.

Maclaren, Alexander. Best of Alexander Maclaren. Atkins, Gaius G., ed. LC 74-179733. (Biography Index Reprint Ser). Repr. of 1949 ed. 14.00 (ISBN 0-8369-8101-4). Ayer Co Pubs.

Morris, Richard, ed. Old English Homilies & Homiletic Treatises, Pts. I & II. (EETS. OS Ser. I: No. 29, 31). Repr. of 1868 ed. 25.00 (ISBN 0-527-00029-9). Kraus Repr.

Murray, Andrew. Absolute Surrender. 1962. pap. 2.95 (ISBN 0-87508-398-6). Chr Lit.

--Spirit of Christ. 1970. pap. 4.50 (ISBN 0-87508-395-1). Chr Lit.

Newman, John H. The Kingdom Within: Discourses to Mixed Congregations. 1984. pap. 14.95 (ISBN 0-87193-216-4). Dimension Bks.

--A Reason for the Hope Within: Sermons on the Theory of Religious Belief. 368p. 1985. pap. 14.95 (ISBN 0-87193-219-9). Dimension Bks.

Pocklington, John. Sunday No Sabbath: A Sermon. LC 74-28881. (English Experience Ser.: No. 759). 1975. Repr. of 1636 ed. 6.00 (ISBN 90-221-0759-0). Walter J Johnson.

Poling, David, ed. This Great Company: A Treasury of Sermons by Outstanding Preachers of the Christian Tradition. LC 74-75977. (Illus.). 1976. 8.95 (ISBN 0-87983-123-5); pap. 4.95 (ISBN 0-87983-124-3). Keats.

Rabinowitz, Louis I. Torah & Flora. (Illus.). 1977. 11.95 (ISBN 0-88482-917-0, Sanhedrin Pr). Hebrew Pub.

Redpath, Alan. Blessings Out of Buffetings: Studies in Second Corinthians. 256p. 1965. 11.95 (ISBN 0-8007-0026-0). Revell.

Reeves, Troy D. An Annotated Index to the Sermons of John Donne: Index to Proper Names, Vol. II. Hogg, James, ed. (Elizabethan & Renaissance Studies). 148p. (Orig.). 1980. pap. 15.00 (ISBN 0-317-40117-3, Pub by Salzburg Studies). Longwood Pub Group.

--An Annotated Index to the Sermons of John Donne: Index to the Scriptures, Vol. I. Hogg, James, ed. (Elizabethan & Renaissance Studies). 229p. (Orig.). 1979. pap. 15.00 (ISBN 0-317-40114-9, Pub by Salzburgh Studies). Longwood Pub Group.

--An Annotated Index to the Sermons of John Donne: Index to Topics, Vol. III. Hogg, James, ed. (Elizabethan & Renaissance Studies). 226p. (Orig.). 1981. pap. 15.00 (ISBN 0-317-40118-1, Pub by Salzburg Studies). Longwood Pub Group.

Ross, Bob L. Acts Two: Thirty-Eight. 1976. 2.25 (ISBN 0-686-09114-0). Pilgrim Pubns.

--Campbellism: Its History & Heresies. 1981. 2.90 (ISBN 0-686-09113-2). Pilgrim Pubns.

Russell, B., et al. If I Could Preach Just Once. facsimile ed. LC 73-167364. (Essay Index Reprint Ser). Repr. of 1929 ed. 17.00 (ISBN 0-8369-2457-6). Ayer Co Pubs.

Sandys, Edwin. Sermons of Edwin Sandys D. D. Repr. of 1841 ed. 41.00 (ISBN 0-384-53200-4). Johnson Repr.

Scott, Thomas. Christs Politician & Solomon's Puritan: Two Sermons. LC 73-6159. (English Experience Ser.: No. 622). 1973. Repr. of 1616 ed. 6.00 (ISBN 90-221-0622-5). Walter J Johnson.

Small, John, ed. English Metrical Homilies from Manuscripts of the Fourteenth Century. LC 79-178504. Repr. of 1862 ed. 22.50 (ISBN 0-404-56674-X). AMS Pr.

Smart, Peter. The Vanitie & Downe-Fall of Superstitious Popish Ceremonies. LC 77-7428. (English Experience Ser.: No. 894). 1977. Repr. of 1628 ed. lib. bdg. 6.00 (ISBN 90-221-0894-5). Walter J Johnson.

Smith, Henry. A Preparative to Mariage: Whereunto Is Annexed a Treatise of the Lords Supper, & Another of Usurie. LC 74-28885. (English Experience Ser.: No. 762). 1975. Repr. of 1591 ed. 16.00 (ISBN 90-221-0762-0). Walter J Johnson.

--Three Sermons: The Benefit of Contentation, the Affinitie of the Faithful, the Lost Sheep Is Found. LC 76-57418. (English Experience Ser.: No. 832). 1977. Repr. of 1599 ed. lib. bdg. 7.00 (ISBN 90-221-0832-5). Walter J Johnson.

South, Robert. Sermons Preached upon Various Occasions, 8 vols. LC 73-175991. Repr. of 1842 ed. Set. 155.00 (ISBN 0-404-06180-X). AMS Pr.

Spurgeon, C. H. Assurance. 1976. pap. 1.50 (ISBN 0-686-16842-9). Pilgrim Pubns.

--Cheque-Book of the Book of Faith. 1982. pap. 4.95 (ISBN 0-686-16836-4). Pilgrim Pubns.

--Complete Index to C. H. Spurgeon's Sermons. 1980. 5.95 (ISBN 0-686-27983-2). Pilgrim Pubns.

--Feathers for Arrows. 1973. pap. 3.25 (ISBN 0-686-09105-1). Pilgrim Pubns.

--John Ploughman's Talk. 1975. pap. 2.50 (ISBN 0-686-16833-X). Pilgrim Pubns.

--Memories of Stambourne. 1975. pap. 1.95 (ISBN 0-686-16838-0). Pilgrim Pubns.

--Metropolitan Tabernacle Pulpit, 1861-1917, Vols. 7-63. (C. H. Spurgeon's Sermon Ser.). Repr. black or gold bdgs. (vols. 7-61) 12.95 ea.; (vols. 62-63 combined) 15.95 (ISBN 0-686-31695-9). Pilgrim Pubns.

--Un Ministerio Ideal, 2 vols, Vols. 1 & 2. Vol. 1. 3.95 (ISBN 0-85151-410-3); Vol. 2. 3.95 (ISBN 0-85151-411-1). Banner of Truth.

--New Park Street Pulpit Index. 1976. pap. 1.50 (ISBN 0-686-16848-8). Pilgrim Pubns.

Spurgeon, C H. New Park Street Pulpit 1855-1860, 6 vols. 1981. Set. 60.00 (ISBN 0-686-16847-X). Pilgrim Pubns.

Spurgeon, C. H. The Salt-Cellars. 1976. pap. 7.75 (ISBN 0-686-16837-2). Pilgrim Pubns.

--Security. 1976. pap. 1.50 (ISBN 0-686-16846-1). Pilgrim Pubns.

--Speeches at Home & Abroad. 1974. 3.50 (ISBN 0-686-09111-6). Pilgrim Pubns.

--Sword & Trowel, 5 vols. 1985. pap. 7.50 ea. Pilgrim Pubns.

--Teachings of Nature in the Kingdom of Grace. 1976. pap. 3.95 (ISBN 0-686-18094-1). Pilgrim Pubns.

--Textual & Subject Indexes of C. H. Spurgeon's Sermons. (Key to the Metropolitan Tabernacle Pulpit set). 1971. 2.95 (ISBN 0-686-09095-0). Pilgrim Pubns.

--Till He Come. 1978. pap. 4.25 (ISBN 0-686-09089-6). Pilgrim Pubns.

--We Endeavor. 1975. pap. 2.25 (ISBN 0-686-16835-6). Pilgrim Pubns.

--What the Stones Say. 1975. pap. 2.50 (ISBN 0-686-18095-X). Pilgrim Pubns.

--Works. 1976. pap. 1.50 (ISBN 0-686-16845-3). Pilgrim Pubns.

Spurgeon, Charles H. Sermons for Special Occasions. Cook, Charles T, ed. 256p. 1977. Repr. of 1958 ed. limp bk. 5.95 (ISBN 0-551-05573-1). Attic Pr.

Thielicke, Helmut. How the World Began: Man in the First Chapters of the Bible. Doberstein, John W., tr. from Ger. LC 61-6756. 324p. 1961. pap. 6.95 (ISBN 0-8006-1894-7, 1-1894). Fortress.

Trevisa, J. Dialogus Inter Militem et Clericum: Richard FitzRalph's Sermon. (EETS, OS Ser.: No. 167). Repr. of 1925 ed. 20.00 (ISBN 0-527-00164-3). Kraus Repr.

Wallace, James D. Heirs of the Cross. 98p. (Orig.). 1984. pap. 3.25 (ISBN 0-934942-43-9, 2022). White Wing Pub.

Wenzel, Siegfried. Verses in Sermons: "Fasciculus morum" & Its Middle English Poems. LC 78-55887. 1978. 20.00x (ISBN 0-910956-66-9). Medieval Acad.

Wesley, John. The Works of Wesley: Wesley's Standard Sermons, 2 vols. Sugden, E. H. & Allison, Joseph, eds. 544p. 1986. Vol. 1. 24.95 (ISBN 0-310-51270-0, 17170); Vol. 2. 24.95 (ISBN 0-310-51280-8, 17171). Zondervan.

Whately, William. A Bride-Bush, or a Wedding Sermon. LC 74-28893. (English Experience Ser.: No. 769). 1975. Repr. of 1617 ed. 5.00 (ISBN 90-221-0769-8). Walter J Johnson.

Whichcote, Benjamin. Select Sermons of Benjamin Whichcote. LC 77-16025. 1977. Repr. of 1742 ed. 50.00x (ISBN 0-8201-1306-9). Schol Facsimiles.

Whitefield, George. Select Sermons of George Whitefield. 200p. 1985. pap. 3.95 (ISBN 0-85151-454-5). Banner of Truth.

SERMONS, ENGLISH–HISTORY AND CRITICISM

Morris, Richard, ed. Old English Homilies of the 13th Century. (EETS OS Ser. II: No. 53). Repr. of 1873 ed. 30.00 (ISBN 0-527-00048-5). Kraus Repr.

SERMONS, FRENCH

Dupont, Dom P. Sermons Capitulaires de la Chartreuse de Mayence du Debut du XV Siecle. Hogg, James, ed. (Analecta Cartusiana Ser.: No. 46). (Fr.). 193p. (Orig.). 1978. pap. 25.00 (ISBN 3-7052-0062-3, Pub by Salzburg Studies). Longwood Pub Group.

Roguet, A. M. Homilies for the Celebration of Marriage. Du Charme, Jerome, tr. from Fr. LC 76-53538. 1977. pap. 3.50 (ISBN 0-8199-0656-5). Franciscan Herald.

SERMONS, GERMAN

Schweitzer, Albert. Reverence for Life. Fuller, Reginald H., tr. LC 71-85052. 1980. Repr. of 1969 ed. 14.95 (ISBN 0-89197-920-4). Irvington.

Thielicke, Helmut. How the World Began: Man in the First Chapters of the Bible. Doberstein, John W., tr. from Ger. LC 61-6756. 324p. 1961. pap. 6.95 (ISBN 0-8006-1894-7, 1-1894). Fortress.

Von Staupitz, Johann. Tubinger Predigten. (Ger.). 34.00 (ISBN 0-384-57712-1); pap. 28.00 (ISBN 0-384-57711-3). Johnson Repr.

SERMONS, GREEK

Cowen, Gerald. Sermon Starters from the Greek New Testament. LC 84-27448. 1985. pap. 5.95 (ISBN 0-8054-1397-9). Broadman.

St. John Chrysostom. On Wealth & Poverty. Roth, Catharine P., tr. from Gr. LC 84-22920. 140p. 1984. pap. text ed. 5.95 (ISBN 0-88141-039-X). St Vladimirs.

SERMONS, JEWISH

see also Midrash

Adler, Morris. Voice Still Speaks. Chinitz, Jacob, ed. LC 68-57433. 1969. pap. text ed. 20.00x (ISBN 0-8197-0052-5). Bloch.

Bokser, Ben Z., tr. Minhah & Maariv Service. 45p. 1958. pap. 1.50 (ISBN 0-88482-125-0). Hebrew Pub.

Cronbach, Abraham. Stories Made of Bible Stories. 1961. 17.95x (ISBN 0-8084-0386-9). New Coll U Pr.

Freehof, Solomon B. Preaching the Bible. 1974. 12.50x (ISBN 0-87068-244-X). Ktav.

Hirsch, David E. Rabbi Emil G. Hirsch: The Reform Advocate. LC 68-24717. 1968. pap. 3.00x (ISBN 0-87655-502-4). Collage Inc.

Klein, Isaac. Spiritual Legacies: Holiday Sermons. 15.00x (ISBN 0-87068-276-8). Ktav.

Kohn, Zwi H. Ginzei Droshos V'rayons, Treasures of Ideas & Thoughts: Sermons in Yiddish Language for All Holidays, Memorials, Eulogies, Installations, & for All Other Occasions. 416p. 27.50 (ISBN 0-87559-149-3). Shalom.

Mantel, Herman & Mantel, Hugo. Mantel's Folks Redner: Mantel's Sermons & Address in Yiddish Language for All Jewish Holidays & Many Other Occasions. 320p. 27.50 (ISBN 0-87559-148-5). Shalom.

Narot, Joseph R. The Sermons of Joseph R. Narot. 6.00 (ISBN 0-686-15812-1). Rostrum Bks.

Pollak, P. S. Shaare Rahmin: Sermon Material for the High Holidays in Hebrew. 7.50 (ISBN 0-87559-104-3). Shalom.

--Tal Hermon: Sermon Material for Yom Kippur & Eulogy in Hebrew. (Heb). 9.50 (ISBN 0-87559-086-1); pap. 5.00 (ISBN 0-87559-085-3). Shalom.

Rabinowitz, Louis I. Torah & Flora. (Illus.). 1977. 11.95 (ISBN 0-88482-917-0, Sanhedrin Pr). Hebrew Pub.

Raffalovich, Isaiah. Our Inheritance: A Collection of Sermons & Addresses for All the Sabbaths & Festivals. 272p. 32.50 (ISBN 0-87559-146-9). Shalom.

Rosenblatt, Samuel. Hear, Oh Israel. 1958. 7.50 (ISBN 0-87306-106-3). Feldheim.

Rudin, Jacob P. Very Truly Yours. 1971. 6.50x (ISBN 0-8197-0279-X). Bloch.

Seixas, Gershom M. A Religious Discourse: Thanksgiving Day Sermon, November 26, 1789. LC 77-7298. (Illus.). 1977. pap. 2.00 (ISBN 0-916790-00-2). Jewish Hist.

Silverstein, Baruch. Unclaimed Treasures. 1983. 15.00x (ISBN 0-88125-029-5). Ktav.

Steinberg, Milton. Believing Jew: The Selected Writings. facsimile ed. LC 76-152215. (Essay Index Reprint Ser). Repr. of 1951 ed. 18.00 (ISBN 0-8369-2256-5). Ayer Co Pubs.

Werzberger, Shmuel. Not in Heaven or Beyond the Sea: Explorations in the World of Jewish Tradition. 17.95 (ISBN 0-88125-128-3). Ktav.

SERMONS, LATIN

Bechett, Wendy M., tr. John of Ford: Sermons on the Song of Songs I. LC 77-3697. (Cistercian Fathers Ser.: No. 29). 1977. 14.95 (ISBN 0-87907-629-1). Cistercian Pubns.

Reece, Benny R. Sermones Ratherii Episcopi Veronensis. 5.00 (ISBN 0-686-23377-8). Classical Folia.

SERMONS, REVIVAL

see Evangelistic Sermons

SERPENTS (IN RELIGION, FOLK-LORE, ETC.)

Forrest, Earle R. The Snake Dance of the Hopi Indians. LC 61-15835. (Illus.). 9.25 (ISBN 0-87026-018-9). Westernlore.

Pedrini, Lura & Pedrini, Duilio T. Serpent Imagery & Symbolism. 1966. 10.95 (ISBN 0-8084-0274-9); pap. 6.95x (ISBN 0-8084-0275-7). New Coll U Pr.

Squier, Ephraim G. The Serpent Symbol & the Worship of the Reciprocal Principles of Nature in America. LC 17-25223. 1975. Repr. of 1851 ed. 21.00 (ISBN 0-527-03228-X). Kraus Repr.

SERRA, JUNIPERO, FATHER, 1713-1784

Clough, Charles W. Madera: The Rich, Colorful & Exciting Historical Heritage of That Area Now Known As Madera County, California. (Illus.). 108p. 1983. casebound 14.95 (ISBN 0-317-44752-1); pap. 9.95 (ISBN 0-317-44753-X). Panorama West.

Lyngheim, Linda, et al. Father Junipero Serra, the Traveling Missionary. LC 85-82131. (Illus.). 64p. 1986. 12.95 (ISBN 0-915369-01-X). Langtry Pubns.

Morrill, Sibley S. The Texas Cannibals, or, Why Father Serra Came to California. 28p. 1964. octavo wrappers 5.00 (ISBN 0-910740-04-6). Holmes.

Piette, Charles J. Evocation de Junipero Serra, Foundateur de la Californie. (Fr., Illus.). 1946. 5.00 (ISBN 0-88382-251-2); pap. 5.00 (ISBN 0-88382-250-4). AAFH.

Scott, Bernice. Junipero Serra: Pioneer of the Cross. (Illus.). 248p. 1985. pap. 9.95 (ISBN 0-317-44750-5). Panorama West.

Tibesar, Antonine, ed. Writings of Junipero Serra, 4 vols. (Documentary Ser.). (Illus.). 1966. 60.00 (ISBN 0-88382-003-X). AAFH.

SERVANT OF JEHOVAH

Zimmerli, Walther. I Am Yahweh. Brueggemann, Walter, ed. Scott, Doug, tr. from German. LC 81-85326. 160p. 1982. 15.95 (ISBN 0-8042-0519-1). John Knox.

SERVERS

see Altar Boys

SERVETUS, MICHAEL, 1509-1553

Bainton, R. H. Hunted Heretic: The Life & Death of Michael Servetus. 11.25 (ISBN 0-8446-1580-3). Peter Smith.

Cuthbertson, David. A Tragedy of the Reformation: Being the Authentic Narrative of the History & Burning of the "Christianismi Restitution", 1953, with a Succinct Account of the Theological Controversy Between Michael Servetus, Its Author, & the Reformer, John Calvin. LC 83-45608. Date not set. Repr. of 1912 ed. 20.00 (ISBN 0-404-19826-0). AMS Pr.

Friedman, J. Michael Servetus: A Case Study in Total Heresy. 154p. (Orig.). 1978. pap. text ed. 34.00x (Pub. by Droz Switzerland). Coronet Bks.

Fulton, John F. & Stanton, Madeline E. Michael Servetus, Humanist & Martyr. (Illus.). 99p. 40.00 (ISBN 0-8139-1089-7). H Reichner.

Odhner, Carl T. Michael Servetus, His Life & Teachings. LC 83-45626. Date not set. Repr. of 1910 ed. 18.50 (ISBN 0-404-19844-9). AMS Pr.

Rilliet, Albert. Calvin & Servetus: The Reformer's Share in the Trial of Michael Servetus Historically Ascertained. Tweedie, W. K., tr. from Fr. LC 83-45631. Date not set. Repr. of 1846 ed. 31.50 (ISBN 0-404-19848-1). AMS Pr.

SERVICE (THEOLOGY)

Antonov, N. R. Khram Bozhij i Tserkovnija Sluzhbi. Tr. of The Temple of God & Church Services. 300p. 1983. pap. text ed. 10.00 (ISBN 0-317-30284-1). Holy Trinity.

Bokser, Ben Z., tr. Minhah & Maariv Service. 45p. 1958. pap. 1.50 (ISBN 0-88482-125-0). Hebrew Pub.

Cohen, Jeffrey M. Understanding the High Holyday Service. 218p. 1983. 12.50 (ISBN 0-317-26854-6). Hebrew Pub.

Constantelos, Demetrios J., intro. by. Orthodox Theology & Diakonia: Trends & Prospects. 398p. 1981. 24.95 (ISBN 0-916586-79-0); pap. 17.95 (ISBN 0-916586-80-4). Hellenic Coll Pr.

Mikhailovsky, V. Uchenije o Pravoslavnom Bogosluzhenii. Tr. of Teachings of the Orthodox Divine Services. 146p. pap. text ed. 6.00 (ISBN 0-317-30287-6). Holy Trinity.

Svirelin, Alexander. Tserkovnij Ustav. Tr. of Church Services. 143p. 1981. pap. text ed. 6.00 (ISBN 0-317-30282-5). Holy Trinity.

Swindoll, Chuck. Improving Your Serve. 1986. deluxe ed. 9.95 (ISBN 0-8499-3851-1). Word Bks.

Washburn, Henry B. Religious Motive in Philanthropy. LC 72-105047. (Essay Index Reprint Ser). 1931. 18.00 (ISBN 0-8369-1634-4). Ayer Co Pubs.

SERVICE BOOKS (MUSIC)

see also subdivision Liturgy and Ritual under denominations

Arango, Tony, tr. Armonias Corales, Vol. 1. (Span.). 144p. (Orig.). 1977. pap. 4.75 (ISBN 0-89922-082-7). Edit Caribe.

SERVICES, DEDICATION

see Dedication Services

SERVITUDE

see Slavery; Villeinage

SESSHU, 1420-1506

Chiba, Reiko. Sesshu's Long Scroll: A Zen Landscape Journey. LC 54-14085. (Illus.). 1959. 14.50 (ISBN 0-8048-0677-2). C E Tuttle.

SETON, ELIZABETH ANN, SAINT, 1774-1821

Celeste, Marie. Elizabeth Ann Seton - A Self-Portrait: A Study of Her Spirituality. LC 85-72765. (Illus.). 305p. 1986. 18.95 (ISBN 0-913382-33-7, 101-33). Prow Bks-Franciscan.

Daughters of St. Paul. Mother Seton. 1975. 3.95 (ISBN 0-8198-0487-8). Dghtrs St Paul.

Feeney, Leonard. Mother Seton: Saint Elizabeth of New York. LC 75-23224. 212p. 1975. 6.95 (ISBN 0-911218-05-X); pap. 3.95 (ISBN 0-911218-06-8). Ravengate Pr.

Kelly, Elin M., ed. Elizabeth Seton: Selected Writings, Vol. 5. (Sources of American Spirituality Ser.). 384p. 1986. 16.95 (ISBN 0-8091-0382-6). Paulist Pr.

Kelly, Ellin M., ed. Numerous Choirs: A Chronicle of Elizabeth Bayley Seton & Her Spiritual Daughters, Volume 1: the Seton Years 1774-1821. LC 81-80304. (Illus.). x, 296p. 1981. 15.00 (ISBN 0-9605784-0-4). Mater Dei Provincialate.

Melville, Annabelle M. Elizabeth Bayley Seton. 1976. pap. 2.25 (ISBN 0-515-09682-2). Jove Pubns.

--Elizabeth Bayley Seton. 1976. lib. bdg. 25.00x (ISBN 0-684-14735-1, ScribT). Scribner.

SEVEN DEADLY SINS

see Deadly Sins

SEVEN GODS OF FORTUNE

Chiba, Reiko. Seven Lucky Gods of Japan. LC 65-25467. (Illus.). 1966. 12.95 (ISBN 0-8048-0521-0). C E Tuttle.

SEVEN LAST WORDS

see Jesus Christ–Seven Last Words

SEVENTEENTH CENTURY

Trevor-Roper, Hugh R. European Witch Craze in the Sixteenth & Seventeenth Centuries & Other Essays. 1969. pap. 6.95x (ISBN 0-06-131416-1, TB1416, Torch). Har-Row.

Willey, Basil. Seventeenth Century Background: Studies in the Thought of the Age in Relation to Poetry & Religion. LC 34-21849. 1942. 31.00x (ISBN 0-231-01395-7). Columbia U Pr.

SEVENTH-DAY ADVENTISTS

Adams, Roy. The Sanctuary Doctrine: Three Approaches in the Seventh-Day Adventist Church. (Andrews University Seminary Doctoral Dissertation Ser.: Vol. 1). viii, 327p. (Orig.). 1981. pap. 9.95 (ISBN 0-943872-33-2). Andrews Univ Pr.

Bailey, Phyllis C. Fascinating Facts about the Spirit of Prophecy. 64p. pap. 2.95 (ISBN 0-317-01322-X). Review & Herald.

Ballis, Peter H., ed. In & Out of the World: Seventh-Day Adventists in New Zealand. 178p. 1986. pap. 12.95 (ISBN 0-86469-050-9, Pub. by Dunmore NZ). Intl Spec Bk.

Beach, Walter R. & Beach, Bert B. Pattern for Progress. Woolsey, Ray, ed. 142p. (Orig.). 1985. pap. text ed. 6.95 (ISBN 0-8280-0308-4). Review & Herald.

Bjorling, Joel. The Churches of God, Seventh Day: A Bibliography. Meton, J. Gordon, ed. LC 87-67. (Sects & Cults in America Bibliographical Guides Reference Library of Social Sciences Ser.: Vol. 362). 250p. 1987. lib. bdg. 48.00 (ISBN 0-8240-8537-X). Garland Pub.

Brians, Bert. My Wife the Prophetess. large print ed. (Illus.). 55p. 1982. pap. 9.50 (ISBN 0-9608650-7-1). VHI Library.

Brians, Bert, ed. My Wife the Prophetess. rev. ed. (Illus.). 24p. 1985. pap. 4.50 (ISBN 0-914009-73-7). VHI Library.

Brians, Charline. My Friends the Adventists. large print ed. (Illus.). 57p. 1982. pap. 9.50 (ISBN 0-9608650-6-3). VHI Library.

Canright, D. M. Seventh-Day Adventism in a Nutshell. 2.75 (ISBN 0-89225-162-X). Gospel Advocate.

--Seventh-Day Adventism Renounced. 1982. pap. 5.95. Gospel Advocate.

Carson, Gerald. Cornflake Crusade. LC 75-39240. (Getting & Spending: the Consumer's Dilemma). (Illus.). 1976. Repr. of 1957 ed. 25.50x (ISBN 0-405-08013-1). Ayer Co Pubs.

Chaij, Fernando. Preparation for the Final Crisis. LC 66-29118. 1966. pap. 6.95 (ISBN 0-8163-0137-9, 16510-0). Pacific Pr Pub Assn.

Coffen, Harold G. Origin by Design. Wheeler, Gerald, ed. LC 82-21445. (Illus.). 494p. 1983. text ed. 18.95 (ISBN 0-8280-0131-6). Review & Herald.

Crider, Charles C. & Kistler, Robert C. The Seventh-Day Adventist Family: An Empirical Study. 296p. 1979. pap. 3.95 (ISBN 0-943872-77-4). Andrews Univ Pr.

Damsteegt, P. Gerard. Foundations of the Seventh-Day Adventist Message & Mission. LC 76-56799. pap. 91.00 (ISBN 0-317-30135-7, 2025318). Bks Demand UMI.

Down, Goldie. Saga of an Ordinary Man. (Dest Two Ser.). 1984. pap. 4.95 (ISBN 0-8163-0554-4). Pacific Pr Pub Assn.

Dudley, Roger L. The World Love It or Leave It. (Anchor Ser.). 80p. (Orig.). 1987. pap. 5.95 (ISBN 0-8163-0665-6). Pacific Pr Pub Assn.

Dudley, Roger L. & Cummings, Des, Jr. Adventures in Church Growth. Wheeler, Gerald, ed. LC 83-16089. (Illus.). 160p. (Orig.). 1983. pap. 8.95 (ISBN 0-8280-0228-2). Review & Herald.

Durand, Eugene. The Biggest Little Church in the World. Wheeler, Gerald, ed. (Better Living Ser.). 32p. (Orig.). 1986. pap. 1.25 (ISBN 0-8280-0320-3). Review & Herald.

Emmerson, Walter L. Reformation & the Advent Movement. 224p. pap. 9.95 (ISBN 0-8280-0168-5). Review & Herald.

Gerstner, John H. Teachings of Seventh-Day Adventism. pap. 1.75 (ISBN 0-8010-3720-4). Baker Bk.

Gordon, Paul A. The Sanctuary, Eighteen Forty-Four & the Pioneers. Wheeler, Gerald, ed. LC 83-17611. 160p. (Orig.). 1984. pap. 9.95 (ISBN 0-8280-0217-7). Review & Herald.

Hare, Eric B. Fullness of Joy. 1985. pap. 5.95 (ISBN 0-8163-0586-2). Pacific Pr Pub Assn.

Herndon, Booton. The Seventh Day: The Story of the Seventh-Day Adventists. LC 78-11705. 1979. Repr. of 1960 ed. lib. bdg. 24.75x (ISBN 0-313-21054-3, HESD). Greenwood.

Hoekema, Anthony A. The Four Major Cults. 1963. 24.95 (ISBN 0-8028-3117-6). Eerdmans.

--Seventh-Day Adventism. 1974. pap. 3.95 (ISBN 0-8028-1490-5). Eerdmans.

Holmes, C. Raymond. Sing a New Song! Worship Renewal for Adventists Today. LC 84-70077. xii, 190p. 1984. pap. 9.95 (ISBN 0-943872-88-X). Andrews Univ Pr.

--Stranger in My Home. LC 73-9253. (Crown Ser.). 128p. 1974. pap. 5.95 (ISBN 0-8127-0075-9). Review & Herald.

Johnsson, William G. Why I'm a Seventh-Day Adventist. Coffen, Richard W., ed. (Better Living Ser.). 32p. (Orig.). 1986. pap. 1.25 (ISBN 0-8280-0352-1). Review & Herald.

Jordan, Jeanne. Marry Me, Marybeth. Woolsey, Raymond, ed. 96p. 1987. pap. price not set (ISBN 0-8280-0379-3). Review & Herald.

Keough, G. Arthur. Our Church Today: What It Is & Can Be. (Horizon Ser.). 160p. 1980. pap. 5.95 (ISBN 0-8127-0300-6). Review & Herald.

Knight, George R. Myths in Adventism Education. Wheeler, Gerald, ed. 1985. 16.95 (ISBN 0-8280-0277-0). Review & Herald.

Knoche, Keith. Side Trips. (FRD Ser.). 1985. pap. 4.95 (ISBN 0-8163-0596-X). Pacific Pr Pub Assn.

Land, Gary, ed. Adventism in America. 304p. (Orig.). 1986. pap. 14.95 (ISBN 0-8028-0237-0). Eerdmans.

Lantry, Eileen E. Dark Night, Brilliant Star. (Daybreak Ser.). 112p. 1981. pap. 2.89 (ISBN 0-8163-0397-5). Pacific Pr Pub Assn.

--He Chose to Listen. (Trailblazer Ser.). 85p. 1983. pap. 4.95 (ISBN 0-8163-0485-8). Pacific Pr Pub Assn.

Lewis, Gordon. Bible, Christian & Seventh Day Adventists. pap. 1.25 (ISBN 0-8010-5573-3). Baker Bk.

Lohne, Alf. Adventists in Russia. Woolsey, Raymond H., ed. 160p. (Orig.). 1987. pap. 9.95 (ISBN 0-8280-0373-4). Review & Herald.

Loughborough, J. N. The Great Second Advent Movement: Its Rise & Progress. LC 71-38453. (Religion in America, Ser. 2). 502p. 1972. Repr. of 1905 ed. 32.00 (ISBN 0-405-04073-3). Ayer Co Pubs.

McCall, Clark B. Taking Dreams Off Hold. (Out Ser.). 1984. pap. 1.25 (ISBN 0-8163-0551-X). Pacific Pr Pub Assn.

Nies, Richard C. The Security of Salvation. LC 78-17523. (Waymark Ser.). 1978. pap. 2.50 (ISBN 0-8127-0187-9). Review & Herald.

Noorbergen, Rene. Ellen G. White: Prophet of Destiny. LC 70-190456. 363p. 1970. text ed. 6.95 (ISBN 0-87983-014-X); pap. 2.50 (ISBN 0-87983-077-8); spanish version 1.95 (ISBN 0-87983-076-X). MMI Pr.

Numbers, Ronald L. & Butler, Jonathan M., eds. The Disappointed: Millerism & Millenarianism in the Nineteenth Century. (Religion in North America Ser.). 1987. 29.95 (ISBN 0-253-34299-6). Ind U Pr.

Olsen, Mahlon E. History of the Origin & Progress of Seventh-Day Adventists. LC 76-134375. Repr. of 1925 ed. 46.50 (ISBN 0-404-08423-0). AMS Pr.

Oosterwal, Gottfried & Staples, Russell L. Servants for Christ: The Adventist Church Facing the 80's. vi, 162p. 1980. pap. 3.95 (ISBN 0-943872-78-2). Andrews Univ Pr.

Paxton, Geoffrey J. El Zarandeo del Adventismo. Orig. Title: The Shaking of Adventism. (Span.). 172p. 1982. pap. 5.75 (ISBN 0-311-05604-0, Edit Mundo). Casa Bautista.

Price, E. B. Is It the Watchtower? LC 67-30889. 1967. pap. 1.25 (ISBN 0-8163-0106-9, 09665-1). Pacific Pr Pub Assn.

Reynolds, Louis B. We Have Tomorrow. Woolsey, Raymond H., ed. 480p. 1984. 19.95 (ISBN 0-8280-0232-0). Review & Herald.

Rice, Richard. The Reign of God: An Introduction to Christian Theology from a Seventh-Day Adventist Perspective. LC 85-70344. 400p. 1985. text ed. 23.95 (ISBN 0-943872-90-1). Andrews Univ Pr.

Robinson, Virgil. James White. LC 75-16921. (Illus.). 1976. 9.95 (ISBN 0-8280-0049-2). Review & Herald.

Schwartz, Gary. Sect Ideologies & Social Status. LC 72-120598. 1970. 18.00x (ISBN 0-226-74216-4). U of Chicago Pr.

Speck, Winsome. Too Late to Hide. (Lifline Ser.). 140p. 1984. pap. 7.95 (ISBN 0-8163-0541-2). Pacific Pr Pub Assn.

Vandeman, George E. Cry of a Lonely Planet. 352p. 1983. pap. 7.95 (ISBN 0-8163-0519-6). Pacific Pr Pub Assn.

--Day to Remember. LC 65-24345. (Stories That Win Ser.). 1965. pap. 1.25 (ISBN 0-8163-0096-8, 04140-0). Pacific Pr Pub Assn.

--Destination of Life. LC 66-21954. (Stories That Win Ser.). 1966. pap. 1.25 (ISBN 0-8163-0095-X, 04270-5). Pacific Pr Pub Assn.

--Hammers in the Fire. LC 79-154293. 1971. pap. 1.25 (ISBN 0-8163-0119-0, 08010-1). Pacific Pr Pub Assn.

Venden, Morris. Obedience of Faith. Wheeler, Gerald, ed. LC 83-13934. 96p. (Orig.). 1984. pap. 5.95 (ISBN 0-8280-0203-7). Review & Herald.

--Return of Elijah. (Harv Ser.). 1983. pap. 4.50 (ISBN 0-8163-0453-X). Pacific Pr Pub Assn.

--What Jesus Said About. 1984. pap. 6.95 (ISBN 0-8163-0555-2). Pacific Pr Pub Assn.

Venden, Morris L. Defeated Demons. (Uplook Ser.). 16p. 1982. pap. 0.99 (ISBN 0-8163-0487-4). Pacific Pr Pub Assn.

Wagner, Lilya. Heartquake. (Daybreak Ser.). 128p. 1983. pap. 4.95 (ISBN 0-8163-0510-2). Pacific Pr Pub Assn.

White, Ellen G. Colporteur Ministry. 1953. 3.25 (ISBN 0-8163-0110-7, 03431-4); pap. 5.95 (ISBN 0-8163-0111-5, 03430-6). Pacific Pr Pub Assn.

--Counsels on Education. 1968. deluxe ed. 8.95 (ISBN 0-8163-0112-3, 03555-0). Pacific Pr Pub Assn.

--Counsels on Health & Instruction to Medical Missionary Workers. 1951. deluxe ed. 10.95 (ISBN 0-8163-0114-X, 03561-8). Pacific Pr Pub Assn.

--Counsels to Parents, Teachers & Students Regarding Christian Education. 1943. Repr. of 1913 ed. deluxe ed. 10.95 (ISBN 0-8163-0115-8, 03591-5). Pacific Pr Pub Assn.

--Impending Conflict. (Stories That Win Ser.). 1960. pap. 0.95 (ISBN 0-8163-0141-7, 09366-6). Pacific Pr Pub Assn.

--Testimonies for the Church, 9 vols. 1948. 5.95 ea. (ISBN 0-8163-0152-2); Set. 79.95 (ISBN 0-8163-0153-0, 20140-0). Pacific Pr Pub Assn.

Wieland, Robert. Eighteen Eighty-Eight Message. LC 80-10807. (Horizon Ser.). 1980. pap. 5.95 (ISBN 0-8127-0283-2). Review & Herald.

Wilcox, Llewellyn A. Now Is the Time. rev. ed. 1966. 8.95 (ISBN 0-911080-06-6). Outdoor Pict.

Willis, Lloyd A. Archaeology in Adventist Literature, 1937-1980. (Andrews University Seminary Doctoral Dissertation Ser.: Vol. 7). x, 670p. 1984. pap. 14.95 (ISBN 0-943872-39-1). Andrews Univ Pr.

Willis, Mary. People of That Book. Van Dolson, Bobbie J., ed. 128p. 1981. pap. 4.95 (ISBN 0-8280-0033-6). Review & Herald.

SEVENTH-DAY ADVENTISTS–MISSIONS

Hare, Eric B. Fulton's Footprints in Fiji. 1985. pap. 5.95 (ISBN 0-8163-0583-8). Pacific Pr Pub Assn.

Leonard, Harry, ed. J. N. Andrews: The Man & the Mission. xii, 355p. (Orig.). 1985. pap. 11.95 (ISBN 0-943872-91-X). Andrews Univ Pr.

Pfeiffer, Baldur, ed. The European Seventh-Day Adventists Mission in the Middle East 1879-1939. (European University Studies: Ser. 23, Vol. 161). 124p. 1981. pap. 16.45 (ISBN 3-8204-5918-9). P Lang Pubs.

SEVENTH-DAY BAPTISTS

Lamech. Chronicon Ephratense: A History of the Community of Seventh Day Baptists at Ephrata, Lancaster County, Pennsylvania. Hark, J. Max, tr. LC 77-185946. (Research & Source Works Ser). 288p. 1972. Repr. of 1880 ed. lib. bdg. 22.50 (ISBN 0-8337-1993-9). B Franklin.

Seventh-Day Baptist General Conference. Seventh-Day Baptists in Europe & America: A Series of Historical Papers Written in Commemoration of the One Hundred Anniversary of the Organization, 2 vols. Gaustad, Edwin S., ed. LC 79-52605. (The Baptist Tradition Ser.). (Illus.). 1980. Repr. of 1910 ed. lib. bdg. 160.00x set (ISBN 0-405-12470-8). Ayer Co Pubs.

Seventh-Day Baptists General Conference. Seventh-Day Baptists in Europe & America, Vol. 1. 80.00 (ISBN 0-405-12478-3). Ayer Co Pubs.

--Seventh-Day Baptists in Europe & America, Vol. 2. 80.00 (ISBN 0-405-12479-1). Ayer Co Pubs.

SEVERINUS, SAINT, d. 482

Eugippius. Leben Des Heiligen Severin. 3rd ed. Rodenbery, C., tr. (Ger.). Repr. of 1912 ed. 12.00 (ISBN 0-384-14820-4). Johnson Repr.

McCann, A. M. The Portraits of Septimus Severus, A.D. 193-211. 222p. 1968. 48.00x (ISBN 0-271-00452-5). Pa St U Pr.

SEWALL, SAMUEL, 1652-1730

Sewall, Samuel. Letter-Book of Samuel Sewall, 1685-1729, 2 vols. LC 75-31101. Repr. of 1838 ed. 67.50 set (ISBN 0-404-13580-3). AMS Pr.

Strandness, T. B. Samuel Sewall: A Puritan Portrait. viii, 250p. 1967. 7.50 (ISBN 0-87013-119-2). Mich St U Pr.

Thomas, Halsey M., ed. The Diary of Samuel Sewall, 1674-1729, 2 vols. (Illus.). 1254p. 1973. 30.00 (ISBN 0-374-13952-0). FS&G.

SEX

see also Homosexuality

also headings beginning with the word Sexual

Daniel, R. P. Dating, Marriage, Sex & Divorce. 75p. pap. 3.95 (ISBN 0-88172-147-6). Believers Bkshelf.

Hettlinger, Richard. Sex Isn't That Simple: The New Sexuality on Campus. LC 73-17876. 256p. 1974. 6.95 (ISBN 0-8264-0155-4); pap. 3.95 (ISBN 0-8264-0156-2). Continuum.

Hildebrand, Dietrich von. Man & Woman. LC 65-25840. pap. 25.80 (ISBN 0-317-28166-6, 2022575). Bks Demand UMI.

Hodann, Max. History of Modern Morals. LC 72-9651. Repr. of 1937 ed. 47.50 (ISBN 0-404-57460-2). AMS Pr.

Howard, Alan. Sex in the Light of Reincarnation & Freedom. 1980. pap. 5.95 (ISBN 0-916786-48-X). St George Bk Serv.

Hunt, George W. John Updike & the Three Great Secret Things: Sex, Religion & Art. LC 80-23796. pap. 60.50 (ISBN 0-317-20577-3, 2023218). Bks Demand UMI.

John-Roger. Sex, Spirit & You. LC 77-81389. 1977. pap. 5.00 (ISBN 0-914829-18-1). Baraka Bk.

Masters, Roy. Sex, Sin & Salvation. LC 77-78040. 267p. 1977. pap. 6.50 (ISBN 0-933900-06-6). Foun Human Under.

Miles, Herbert J. Sexual Happiness in Marriage. 2nd rev. ed. 208p. 1982. pap. 3.95 (ISBN 0-310-29222-0). Zondervan.

Rousseau, Mary & Gallagner, Chuck. Sex Is Holy. (A Chrysalis Bk). 160p. (Orig.). 1986. pap. 9.95 (ISBN 0-916349-11-X). Amity Hous Inc.

Turner, Philip. Sex, Money & Power: An Essay on Christian Social Ethics. LC 84-72481. 135p. (Orig.). 1985. pap. 7.95 (ISBN 0-936384-22-0). Cowley Pubns.

Welwood, John. Challenge of the Heart: Love, Sex & Intimacy in Changing Times. LC 85-2461. 283p. (Orig.). 1985. pap. 9.95 (ISBN 0-87773-331-7, 74200-1). Shambhala Pubns.

SEX (THEOLOGY)

see also Homosexuality and Christianity

Babbage, Stuart B. Sex & Sanity: A Christian View of Sexual Morality. rev. ed. LC 67-11492. 1967. Westminster.

Baum, Gregory & Coleman, John, eds. Sexual Revolution, Vol 173. (Concilium Ser.). 128p. pap. 6.95 (ISBN 0-317-31462-9, Pub. by T & T Clark Ltd UK). Fortress.

Bruner, William T. The Sex Problem: Its Cause, Its Curse & Its Cure. 1977. 3.00 (ISBN 0-9606566-0-X). Bruner.

Christ Foundation Staff. A Spiritual Sex Manual. LC 82-72079. (Illus.). 176p. 1982. pap. 9.95 (ISBN 0-910315-01-9). Christ Found.

Colman, Barry, ed. Sex & the Single Christian. LC 85-30138. 120p. (Orig.). 1986. pap. 6.95 (ISBN 0-8307-1107-4, 5418696). Regal.

Constantelos, D. J. Marriage, Sexuality & Celibacy: A Greek Orthodox Perspective. 1975. pap. 4.95 (ISBN 0-937032-15-8). Light&Life Pub Co MN.

Crawford, Claud C. The End of the Rope. rev. ed. LC 85-90684. 96p. 1985. pap. 6.95 (ISBN 0-933697-00-7). Claud Crawford.

Drake, Terrance & Drake, Marvia. Teaching Your Child about Sex. LC 83-71726. 60p. 1983. 6.95 (ISBN 0-87747-951-8). Deseret Bk.

Dudley, Gwenyth, et al. Human Sexuality. (Illus.). 55p. (Orig.). 1984. pap. 5.95 (ISBN 0-85819-465-1, Pub. by JBCE). ANZ Religious Pubns.

Education in Human Sexuality for Christians, Guidelines for Discussion & Planning. 118p. 1981. pap. 8.50 (ISBN 1-55586-691-3). US Catholic.

Gollwitzer, Gerhard. Sex, Eros & Marital Love. pap. 0.75 (ISBN 0-87785-104-2). Swedenborg.

Grace, James H. God, Sex, & the Social Project: The Glassboro Papers on Religion & Human Sexuality. LC 78-65496. (Symposium Ser.: Vol. 2). x, 203p. 1978. 19.95x (ISBN 0-88946-900-8). E Mellen.

Gupta, Bina, ed. Sexual Archetypes: East & West. (God: The Contemporary Discussion Ser.). (Illus.). 344p. 1986. 22.95 (ISBN 0-913757-59-4, Pub. by New Era Bks); pap. 12.95 (ISBN 0-913757-68-3, Pub. by New Era Bks). Paragon Hse.

Hertzog, Ed. Sex & Violence under God. LC 81-84292. 212p. 1982. 12.00 (ISBN 0-937894-02-8); pap. 7.00 (ISBN 0-937894-03-6). Life Arts.

Huggett, Joyce. Dating, Sex & Friendship. LC 85-19734. 204p. 1985. pap. 5.95 (ISBN 0-87784-406-2). Inter-Varsity.

Kubo, Sakae. Theology & Ethics of Sex. (Horizon Ser.). 1980. pap. 5.95 (ISBN 0-8127-0288-3). Review & Herald.

Lantero, Erminie H. Feminine Aspects of Divinity. LC 73-84214. 36p. (Orig.). 1973. pap. 2.50x (ISBN 0-87574-191-6). Pendle Hill.

Lutzer. Living with Your Passion. 1983. 5.95 (ISBN 0-686-46315-3). Victor Bks.

Mace, David R. Christian Response to the Sexual Revolution. (Orig.). 1970. pap. 7.75 (ISBN 0-687-07570-X). Abingdon.

Mast, Coleen K., et al. Love & Life: A Christian Sexual Morality Guide for Teens. 118p. 1986. pap. 7.95 (ISBN 0-89870-106-6). Ignatius Pr.

May, William E. Sex, Love & Procreation: Synthesis Ser. 1976. pap. 0.75 (ISBN 0-8199-0711-1). Franciscan Herald.

Ochs, Carol. Behind the Sex of God: Toward a New Consciousness - Transcending Matriarchy & Patriarchy. LC 76-48519. 1977. pap. 8.95x (ISBN 0-8070-1113-4, Pub. by Ariadne Bks, BPA12). Beacon Pr.

Olson, Richard P. Changing Male Roles in Today's World: A Christian Perspective for Men - & the Women Who Care about Them. 160p. 1982. pap. 5.95 (ISBN 0-8170-0946-9). Judson.

Pittenger, Norman. Making Sexuality Human. LC 79-126862. 1979. pap. 4.95 (ISBN 0-8298-0368-8). Pilgrim NY.

Rabbi Nachman. Le Tikoun Haklali. Dimermanas, Alon, tr. from Hebrew. (Fr.). 125p. 1986. pap. text ed. 3.00 (ISBN 0-930213-24-6). Breslov Res Inst.

Rouner, Arthur A., Jr. Struggling With Sex: Serious Call to Marriage-Centered Sexual Life. LC 86-32028. 128p. (Orig.). (YA) 1986. pap. 6.50 (ISBN 0-8066-2243-1, 10-6096). Augsburg.

Russell, Letty M., ed. The Liberating Word: A Guide to Non-Sexist Interpretation of the Bible. LC 76-18689. 120p. 1976. pap. 7.95 (ISBN 0-664-24751-2). Westminster.

Sapp, Stephen. Sexuality, the Bible & Science. LC 76-62617. pap. 38.00 (2026976). Bks Demand UMI.

Schwartz, Mark F., et al, eds. Sex & Gender: A Theological & Scientific Inquiry. 385p. (Orig.). 1984. pap. 19.95 (ISBN 0-935372-13-X). Pope John Ctr.

Tomczak, Larry. Let's Talk about Sex: The Truth & God's Power to Live It. rev. ed. 123p. 1987. pap. 4.95 (ISBN 0-89283-353-X, Pub. by Vine Books). Servant.

Twenty-Four Magazine Editors & Burns, John. Sacred Sex. White, Thomas R., ed. LC 74-84538. (Illus.). 150p. (Orig.). 1975. pap. 1.95 (ISBN 0-914896-01-6, Strength). East Ridge Pr.

Wheat, Ed & Wheat, Gaye. Intended for Pleasure. rev. ed. (Illus.). 256p. 1981. 12.95 (ISBN 0-8007-1253-6). Revell.

Whitehead, K. D. Agenda for the "Sexual Revolution". Abortion, Contraception, Sex Education & Related Evils. 1981. 8.95 (ISBN 0-317-46866-9). Franciscan Herald.

Wilson, Earl D. Sexual Sanity. LC 83-22753. 156p. 1984. pap. 5.95 (ISBN 0-87784-919-6). Inter-Varsity.

Wojtyla, Karol. Fruitful & Responsible Love. (Orig.). 1979. pap. 2.95 (ISBN 0-8245-0310-4). Crossroad NY.

SEX AND LAW

see also Abortion; Birth Control; Prostitution

Buchanan, G. Sidney. Morality, Sex & the Constitution: A Christian Perspective on the Power of Government to Regulate Private Sexual Conduct Between Consenting Adults. LC 85-3249. 242p. (Orig.). 1985. lib. bdg. 26.25 (ISBN 0-8191-4602-1); pap. text ed. 11.75 (ISBN 0-8191-4603-X). U Pr of Amer.

SEX AND RELIGION

see also Homosexuality and Christianity; Mother-Goddesses; Sex (Theology); Sex in the Bible; Tantrism

Baisden, Major J., Jr. The World of Rosaphrenia: The Sexual Psychology of the Female. LC 72-178852. 224p. 1971. 6.95 (ISBN 0-912984-01-5). Allied Res Soc.

Bates, Carroll M. The Human Body - Good or Evil? 1986. 6.95 (ISBN 0-533-06780-4). Vantage.

Beslow, Audrey. Sex & the Single Christian. 1987. pap. 9.95 (ISBN 0-687-38197-5). Abingdon.

Bhagwan Shree Rajneesh. From Sex to Super Consciousness. Vora, V., tr. (Marathi.). 157p. 1975. pap. 2.95 (ISBN 0-89253-060-X). Ind-US Inc.

Boyle, Patrick J. Parvitas Materiae in Sexto in Contemporary Catholic Thought. 132p. (Orig.). 1987. lib. bdg. 21.50 (ISBN 0-8191-5790-2); pap. text ed. 9.25 (ISBN 0-8191-5791-0). U Pr of Amer.

Braun, J. R. The Consequences of Sexual Freedom. 150p. (Orig.). 1980. pap. text ed. 2.95 (ISBN 0-933656-04-1). Trinity Pub Hse.

--Male Sexual Fantasies: The Destruction of the Feminine Personality; The Christian Mandate Against Pornography. 48p. (Orig.). 1980. pap. 1.95 (ISBN 0-933656-05-X). Trinity Pub Hse.

--The Meaning of Sexual Pleasure: A Christian Understanding of Sexuality. 203p. (Orig.). 1976. pap. 4.95 (ISBN 0-933656-02-5). Trinity Pub Hse.

Brewer, Joan S., compiled by. Sex & the Modern Jewish Woman: Annotated Bibliography - Essays. 128p. 1986. pap. 9.25 (ISBN 0-930395-01-8). Biblio NY.

Brown, Sanger. Sex Worship & Symbolism: An Interpretation. LC 72-9624. Repr. of 1922 ed. 27.50 (ISBN 0-404-57419-X). AMS Pr.

Bullough, Vern & Brundage, James, eds. Sexual Practices & the Medieval Church. LC 80-85227. 289p. 1984. pap. 15.95 (ISBN 0-87975-268-8). Prometheus Bks.

Cahill, Lisa S. Between the Sexes. 160p. (Orig.). 1985. pap. 7.95 (ISBN 0-8091-2711-3). Paulist Pr.

Chang, Stephen T. The Tao of Sexology. (Illus.). 224p. 1985. 17.00 (ISBN 0-942196-03-1). Tao Pub.

Clark, Keith. Being Sexual...& Celibate. LC 85-73158. 184p. (Orig.). 1986. pap. 4.95 (ISBN 0-87793-329-4). Ave Maria.

Cohen, Chapman. Religion & Sex. LC 72-9631. Repr. of 1919 ed. 40.00 (ISBN 0-404-57430-0). AMS Pr.

Constable, Benjamin. God & the "New" Psychology of Sex. (Illus.). 265p. 1976. 53.75 (ISBN 0-89266-043-0). Am Classical Coll Pr.

Contemporary Theology Series 2. Incl. A Christian View of Abortion. 3.95 (ISBN 0-570-06721-9, 12-2560); Form Criticism Reexamined. 3.95 (ISBN 0-570-06722-7, 12-2561); The Lord's Supper Today. 4.25 (ISBN 0-570-06723-5, 12-2562); Marxism & Christianity (ISBN 0-570-06724-3, 12-2563); Unity & Fellowship & Ecumenicity (ISBN 0-570-06725-1, 12-2564). 1973. pap. 3.50 ea. Concordia.

Crowley, Aleister & Motta, Marcelo. Equinox: Sex & Religion, Vol. 5. (No. 4). 1981. 44.00 (ISBN 0-933454-04-X, Pub. by Thelema Pub). O T O.

DeMaria, Richard. Communal Love at Oneida: A Perfectionist Vision of Authority, Property & Sexual Order. 2nd. ed. LC 78-60958. (Texts & Studies in Religion: Vol. 2). 248p. 1983. 49.95x (ISBN 0-88946-988-1). E Mellen.

The Determinations of the Most Famous Universities of Italy & France. LC 72-189. (English Experience Ser.: No. 329). 308p. Repr. of 1531 ed. 22.00 (ISBN 90-221-0329-3). Walter J Johnson.

Dickman, R. Thomas. Of Sex & Sin. LC 85-91068. 1986. 10.00 (ISBN 0-87212-195-X). Libra.

Drakeford, John W. Hechos el Uno Para el Otro. De Plou, Dafne C., tr. (Sexo en la Vida Cristiana Ser.). 1983. pap. 3.50 (ISBN 0-311-46256-1). Casa Bautista.

Dulaure, Jacques-Antoine. The Gods of Generation. LC 72-9635. Tr. of De Divinites Generatrices. Repr. of 1934 ed. 42.00 (ISBN 0-404-57433-5). AMS Pr.

Edens, David. Estoy Creciendo Estoy Cambiando. Du Plou, Dafne C., tr. (Sexo en la Vida Cristiana Ser). (Illus.). 1985. pap. 1.75 (ISBN 0-311-46252-9). Casa Bautista.

Evola, Julius. Metaphysics of Sex. Ormrod, J. A., tr. from Ital. LC 82-11909. (Illus.). 384p. 1983. pap. 9.95 (ISBN 0-89281-025-4). Inner Tradit.

Farah, Madelain. Marriage & Sexuality in Islam: A Translation of al-Ghazali's Book on the Etiquette of Marriage from the Ihya' 192p. 1984. 20.00 (ISBN 0-87480-231-8). U of Utah Pr.

Foster, Lawrence. Religion & Sexuality: Three American Communal Experiments of the Nineteenth Century. 1981. 24.95x (ISBN 0-19-502794-9). Oxford U Pr.

Gallagher, Charles A. & Maloney, George A. Embodied in Love: The Sacramental Spirituality of Sexual Intimacy. 176p. (Orig.). 1983. pap. 9.95 (ISBN 0-686-46141-X). Crossroad NY.

Gamble, Eliza B. The God-Idea of the Ancients: Or Sex in Religion. LC 79-66997. 339p. 1981. Repr. of 1897 ed. 30.00 (ISBN 0-8305-0110-X). Hyperion Conn.

Goldberg, B. Z. The Sacred Fire. 285p. 1974. pap. 3.95 (ISBN 0-8065-0456-0). Citadel Pr.

--Sacred Fire. (Illus.). 1958. 7.50 (ISBN 0-8216-0146-6). Univ Bks.

Goodland, Roger. A Bibliography of Sex Rites & Customs. LC 72-9839. Repr. of 1931 ed. 42.50 (ISBN 0-404-57445-9). AMS Pr.

--A Bibliography of Sex Rites & Customs. LC 77-11605. 1977. Repr. of 1931 ed. lib. bdg. 60.00 (ISBN 0-89341-193-0). Longwood Pub Group.

Gordis, Robert. Love & Sex: A Modern Jewish Perspective. 290p. 1978. 8.95 (ISBN 0-374-19252-9). FS&G.

Grace, James H. God, Sex, & the Social Project: The Glassboro Papers on Religion & Human Sexuality. LC 78-65496. (Symposium Ser.: Vol. 2). x, 203p. 1978. 19.95x (ISBN 0-88946-900-8). E Mellen.

--Sex & Marriage in the Unification Movement: A Sociological Study. LC 85-2961. (Studies in Religion & Society: Vol. 13). 304p. 1985. 49.95x (ISBN 0-88946-861-3). E Mellen.

Grant, Wilson W. De Padres a Hijos Acerca del Sexo. La Valle, Maria T., et al, trs. from Eng. (Sexo en la Vida Cristiana Ser.). (Span., Illus.). 192p. 1982. pap. 3.95 (ISBN 0-311-46255-3). Casa Bautista.

Groeschel, Benedict J. The Courage to Be Chaste. 128p. (Orig.). 1985. pap. 4.95 (ISBN 0-8091-2705-9). Paulist Pr.

Guindon, Andre. The Sexual Creators: An Ethical Proposal for Concerned Christians. 256p. (Orig.). 1986. lib. bdg. 28.00 (ISBN 0-8191-5239-0); pap. text ed. 13.00 (ISBN 0-8191-5240-4). U Pr of Amer.

Harty, Robert & Harty, Annelle. Creados Para Crecer. De Plou, Dafne C., tr. (Sexo en la Vida Cristiana Ser.). (Illus.). 1985. pap. 1.50 (ISBN 0-311-46251-0). Casa Bautista.

Hogan, Richard M. & Levoir, John M. Covenant of Love: Pope John Paul II on Sexuality, Marriage & Family in the Modern World. LC 84-18666. 264p. 1985. 15.95 (ISBN 0-385-19540-0). Doubleday.

Holland, John M., et al. Religion & Sexuality: Judaic-Christian Viewpoints in the U. S. A. LC 81-66867. (The Association of Sexologists Monographs: No. 1). 80p. 1981. pap. 5.95 (ISBN 0-939902-00-1). Assn Sexologists.

Horner, Tom. Sex in the Bible. LC 73-87676. 1974. 8.50 (ISBN 0-8048-1124-5). C E Tuttle.

Hosmer, Rachel. Gender & God: Love & Desire in Christian Spirituality. LC 86-8980. 142p. (Orig.). 1986. pap. 7.95 (ISBN 0-936384-39-5). Cowley Pubns.

Howard, Clifford. Sex & Religion. LC 72-9654. Repr. of 1925 ed. 34.50 (ISBN 0-404-57463-7). AMS Pr.

Human Sexuality: A Preliminary Study - the United Church of Christ. LC 77-25398. 1977. pap. 5.95 (ISBN 0-8298-0341-6). Pilgrim NY.

Human Sexuality & Personhood. LC 80-85411. ix, 254p. (Orig.). 1981. pap. 9.95 (ISBN 0-935372-09-1). Pope John Ctr.

Johnson, Edwin C. In Search of God in the Sexual Underworld: A Mystical Journey. LC 83-943. 224p. 1983. 13.95 (ISBN 0-688-01478-X). Morrow.

Kaiser, Robert B. The Politics of Sex & Religion: A Case History in the Development of Doctrine, 1962-1984. LC 84-82552. 200p. (Orig.). 1985. pap. 10.95 (ISBN 0-934134-16-2, Leaven Pr). Sheed & Ward MO.

Keane, Philip. Sexual Morality: A Catholic Perspective. LC 77-83536. 252p. 1978. pap. 8.95 (ISBN 0-8091-2070-4). Paulist Pr.

Kehle, Mary. You're Nearly There: Christian Sex Education for Ten-to-Teens. LC 73-85963. (Illus.). 80p. 1973. pap. 2.50 (ISBN 0-87788-969-4). Shaw Pubs.

Kelly, George, ed. Human Sexuality in Our Time. 1979. 5.95 (ISBN 0-8198-0610-2); pap. 4.95 (ISBN 0-8198-0611-0). Dghtrs St Paul.

Kern, Louis J. An Ordered Love: Sex Roles & Sexuality in Victorian Utopias--the Shakers, the Mormons, & the Oneida Community. LC 80-10763. xv, 430p. 1981. 27.00x (ISBN 0-8078-1443-1); pap. 9.95x (ISBN 0-8078-4074-2). U of NC Pr.

Knight, David. The Good News about Sex. 312p. (Orig.). 1980. pap. 4.95 (ISBN 0-912228-57-1). St Anthony Mess Pr.

Leites, Edmund. The Puritan Conscience & Modern Sexuality. LC 85-20198. 208p. 1986. 17.50 (ISBN 0-300-03490-3). Yale U Pr.

McCarthy, Donald G. & Bayer, Edward J., eds. A Handbook on Critical Sexual Issues. 240p. (Orig.). 1983. pap. 9.95 (ISBN 0-935372-11-3). Pope John Ctr.

May, William & Harvey, John. On Understanding Human Sexuality. (Synthesis Ser). 1978. pap. 1.50 (ISBN 0-8199-0720-0). Franciscan Herald.

Mayo, Mary A. A Christian Guide to Sexual Counseling: Recovering the Mystery & the Reality of "One Flesh". 288p. 1987. 16.95 (ISBN 0-310-35990-2). Zondervan.

Muse, Charles B. The Catholic Sex Manual for Teenagers. (Illus.). 1980. 31.85 (ISBN 0-89266-217-4). Am Classical Coll Pr.

Musser, Harlan C. Sex--Our Myth Theology? 196p. 1981. pap. 7.95 (ISBN 0-8059-2768-9). Dorrance.

Nelson, James B. Between Two Gardens: Reflections on Sexuality & Religious Experience. 160p. (Orig.). 1983. pap. 8.95 (ISBN 0-8298-0681-4). Pilgrim NY.
--Embodiment: An Approach to Sexuality & Christian Theology. LC 78-55589. 1979. pap. 11.95 (ISBN 0-8066-1701-2, 10-2071). Augsburg.
--Embodiment: An Approach to Sexuality & Christian Theology. 296p. 1978. 9.95 (ISBN 0-8298-0349-1). Pilgrim NY.
Ochshorn, Judith. The Female Experience & the Nature of the Divine. LC 81-47012. pap. 71.50 (2056237). Bks Demand UMI.
Ohanneson, Joan. And They Felt No Shame: Christians Reclaim Their Sexuality. 200p. (Orig.). 1982. pap. 11.95 (ISBN 0-86683-676-4, HarpR). Har-Row.
Parrinder, Geoffrey. Sex in the World's Religions. 1980. pap. 9.95x (ISBN 0-19-520202-3). Oxford U Pr.
Parsons, Elsie W. Religious Chastity: An Ethnological Study, by John Main (Pseud.) LC 72-9672. Repr. of 1913 ed. 52.00 (ISBN 0-404-57489-0). AMS Pr.
Penner, Clifford & Penner, Joyce. The Gift of Sex. 1981. pap. 11.95 (ISBN 0-8499-2893-1). Word Bks.
Phipps, William E. Was Jesus Married? The Distortion of Sexuality in the Christian Tradition. LC 85-32319. 250p. 1986. pap. text ed. 11.75 (ISBN 0-8191-5191-2). U Pr of Amer.
Pierson, Jack D. What a Teenager Ought to Know About Sex & God. (Teenager's Essential Education Library). (Illus.). 147p. 1981. 48.75 (ISBN 0-89266-288-3). Am Classical Coll Pr.
Pittinger, W. Norman. Love & Control in Sexuality. LC 73-19833. 128p. 1974. 4.25 (ISBN 0-8298-0268-1). Pilgrim NY.
Pope John Paul II. Love & Responsibility. Willetts, H. T., tr. 320p. 1981. 15.00 (ISBN 0-374-19247-2); pap. 7.95 (ISBN 0-374-51685-5). FS&G.
Puryear, Herbert B. Sex & the Spiritual Path. 256p. 1986. pap. 3.50 (ISBN 0-553-25635-1). Bantam.
Reichert, Richard. Sexuality & Dating. LC 81-51011. (Illus.). 160p. 1981. pap. 5.00x (ISBN 0-88489-133-X); tchrs' guide 9.00x (ISBN 0-88489-138-0); student workbook 2.00 (ISBN 0-88489-139-9). St Mary's.
Richards, Lawrence O. How Far I Can Go. (Answers for Youth Ser.). 1980. pap. 4.95 (ISBN 0-310-38951-8, 18025P). Zondervan.
Richardson, Herbert W. Nun, Witch, Playmate: The Americanization of Sex. 2nd ed. xii, 147p. 1977. Repr. of 1974 ed. 19.95x (ISBN 0-88946-950-4). E Mellen.
Ruether, Rosemary R. Religion & Sexism. 1974. pap. 10.95 (ISBN 0-671-21693-7, Touchstone Bks). S&S.
Sawicki, Marianne. Faith & Sexism: Guidelines for Religious Educators. 112p. 1979. pap. 4.95 (ISBN 0-8164-0105-5, HarpR). Har-Row.
Scanzoni, Letha D. Sexuality. LC 83-27375. (Choices: Guides for Today's Woman: Vol. 8). 114p. (Orig.). 1984. pap. 6.95 (ISBN 0-664-24548-X). Westminster.
Sha Rocco. The Masculine Cross & Ancient Sex Worship. (Illus.). 65p. 1873. pap. 7.95 (ISBN 0-88697-014-8). Life Science.
Sharp, Watson. The Catholic & the Jewish Approach to Sex & Their Relative Influence Upon the Cultural Character of Our Society. (Illus.). 1976. 47.75 (ISBN 0-89266-012-0). Am Classical Coll Pr.
Short, Ray E. Sex, Dating, & Love: Seventy-Seven Questions Most Often Asked. LC 83-72122. 144p. (Orig.). 1984. pap. 3.95 (ISBN 0-8066-2066-8, 10-5648). Augsburg.
Simmons, Paul D. & Crawford, Kenneth. Mi Desarrollo Sexual. Sabanes De Plou, Dafne, tr. from Eng. (El Sexo En la Vida Cristiana). (Span.). 96p. 1985. pap. 2.50 (ISBN 0-311-46257-X, Edit Mundo). Casa Bautista.
Smedes, Lewis. Sexologia para Cristianos. Sanchez, Jorge, tr. from Eng. Tr. of Sex for Christians. 288p. 1982. pap. 5.95 (ISBN 0-89922-175-0). Edit Caribe.
Stroup, Herbert W. & Wood, Norma S. Sexuality & the Counseling Pastor. LC 73-88344. pap. 33.50 (2027176). Bks Demand UMI.
Thielicke, Helmut. The Ethics of Sex. Doberstein, J. W., tr. from Ger. 340p. 1964. 13.95 (ISBN 0-227-67656-4). Attic Pr.
Thomas, Gordon. Desire & Denial: Celibacy & the Church. 1986. 19.95 (ISBN 0-316-84097-1). Little.
Timmerman, Joan. The Mardi Gras Syndrome: Rethinking Christian Sexuality. 144p. 1984. pap. 8.95 (ISBN 0-8245-0641-3). Crossroad NY.
Tomczak, Larry. Straightforward. LC 78-59856. 1978. pap. 4.95 (ISBN 0-88270-311-0). Bridge Pub.
Trible, Phyllis. God & the Rhetoric of Sexuality, No. 20. LC 77-78647. (Overtures to Biblical Theology Ser.). 228p. 1978. pap. 8.95 (ISBN 0-8006-0464-4, 1-464). Fortress.
Valentini, Norberto & Di Meglio, Clara. Sex & the Confessional. LC 73-91861. 1975. pap. 1.95 (ISBN 0-8128-1862-8). Stein & Day.
Vincent, M. O. God, Sex & You. 192p. 1985. pap. 3.95 (ISBN 0-916441-25-3). Barbour & Co.
Wall, O. A. Eroticism in Religions of the World. (Illus.). xv, 608p. 1986. Repr. text ed. 75.00 (ISBN 81-7047-015-3, Pub. by Mayur Pubns India). Apt Bks.
Zimbelman, Ernie, ed. Human Sexuality & Evangelical Christians. (Illus.). 394p. (Orig.). 1985. lib. bdg. 31.50 (ISBN 0-8191-4477-0); pap. text ed. 16.75 (ISBN 0-8191-4478-9). U Pr of Amer.

SEX IN MARRIAGE

Anzia, Joan & Durkin, Mary. Marital Intimacy: A Catholic Perspective. 81p. pap. 6.95. Loyola.
Guernsey, Dennis. Thoroughly Married. 145p. 1984. pap. text ed. 5.95 (ISBN 0-8499-3000-6, 3000-6). Word Bks.
Rice, F. Philip. Sexual Problems in Marriage: Help from a Christian Counselor. LC 77-27443. 252p. 1978. softcover 6.95 (ISBN 0-664-24194-8). Westminster.
Rouner, Arthur A., Jr. Struggling With Sex: Serious Call to Marriage-Centered Sexual Life. LC 86-32028. 128p. (Orig.). (YA) 1986. pap. 6.50 (ISBN 0-8066-2243-1, 10-6096). Augsburg.

SEX IN THE BIBLE

Akerley, Ben E. The X-Rated Bible: An Irreverent Survey of Sex in the Scriptures. (Illus.). 428p. (Orig.). 1985. pap. 8.00 (ISBN 0-910309-19-1). Am Atheist.
Cosby, Michael. Sex in the Bible: An Introduction to What the Scriptures Teach Us about Sexuality. LC 83-16090. 182p. 1984. 12.95 (ISBN 0-13-807280-9); pap. 5.95 (ISBN 0-13-807272-8). P-H.
Daniel, Eleanor. What the Bible Says about Sexuality Identity. LC 81-71836. (What the Bible Says Ser.). 350p. 1982. 13.95 (ISBN 0-89900-085-1). College Pr Pub.
Gerber, Aaron. Biblical Attitudes on Human Sexuality. 176p. 1982. 15.95 (ISBN 0-89962-301-8). Todd & Honeywell.
Larue, Gerald. Sex & the Bible. LC 83-60201. 212p. 1983. 19.95 (ISBN 0-87975-206-8); pap. 11.95 (ISBN 0-87975-229-7). Prometheus Bks.
Mayo, Mary A. Parents' Guide to Sex Education. 208p. pap. 6.95 (ISBN 0-310-44581-7, 11357P). Zondervan.
Morris, Leon. Testaments of Love: A Study of Love in the Bible. (Orig.). 1981. 12.95 (ISBN 0-8028-3502-3). Eerdmans.
Ochshorn, Judith. The Female Experience & the Nature of the Divine. LC 81-47012. pap. 71.50 (2056237). Bks Demand UMI.
Perry, Frank L., Jr. Sex & the Bible. LC 82-72143. (Orig.). 1982. pap. 7.95 (ISBN 0-943708-00-1). Chr Educ Res Inst.
Rocco, Sha. Sex Mythology. (Illus.). 55p. 1982. Repr. of 1874 ed. 3.00. Am Atheist.
Stuart, Friend. What the Bible Says about Sex. 40p. 1985. pap. 4.95 (ISBN 0-912132-17-5). Dominion Pr.
Terrien, Samuel. Till the Heart Sings: A Biblical Theology of Manhood & Womanhood. LC 85-47731. 272p. 1985. 24.95 (ISBN 0-8006-0752-X, 1-752). Fortress.

SEX INSTRUCTION

Amstutz, H. Clair. Growing up to Love: A Guide to Sex Education for Parents. rev. ed. LC 56-11527. (Illus.). 112p. (YA) 1966. pap. 1.95 (ISBN 0-8361-1535-X). Herald Pr.
Borowitz, Eugene B. Choosing a Sex Ethic: A Jewish Inquiry. LC 73-79123. 1970. pap. 5.95 (ISBN 0-8052-0276-5). Schocken.
Burn, Helen J. Better Than the Birds, Smarter Than the Bees. LC 69-12771. (YA) pap. 21.30 (ISBN 0-8357-9000-2, 2016348). Bks Demand UMI.
Christ Foundation Staff. A Spiritual Sex Manual. LC 82-72079. (Illus.). 176p. 1982. pap. 9.95 (ISBN 0-910315-01-9). Christ Found.
Education in Human Sexuality for Christians, Guidelines for Discussion & Planning. 118p. 1981. pap. 8.50 (ISBN 1-55586-691-3). US Catholic.
Gordon, Sol & Gordon, Judith. Raising a Child Conservatively in a Sexually Permissive World. 224p. 1986. pap. 7.95 (ISBN 0-671-62797-X, Fireside). S&S.
Hodann, Max. History of Modern Morals. LC 72-9651. Repr. of 1937 ed. 47.50 (ISBN 0-404-57460-2). AMS Pr.
Isberner, Fred, et al. Sex Education in a Church Setting: The OCTOPUS Training Manual. 128p. (Orig.). 1986. pap. text ed. 8.95x (ISBN 0-8093-1315-4). S Ill U Pr.
McDowell, Josh & Lewis, Paul. Givers, Takers & Other Kinds of Lovers. 1981. pap. 2.95 (ISBN 0-8423-1031-2). Tyndale.
Taylor, Kenneth N. Almost Twelve. 1968. pap. 2.50 (ISBN 0-8423-0060-0). Tyndale.
Wheat, Ed & Wheat, Gaye. Intended for Pleasure. rev. ed. (Illus.). 256p. 1981. 12.95 (ISBN 0-8007-1253-6). Revell.

SEX INSTRUCTION FOR CHILDREN AND YOUTH

Cooney, Nancy H. Sex, Sexuality, & You: A Handbook for Growing Christians. 100p. (Orig.). 1980. pap. text ed. 3.50 (ISBN 0-697-01741-9); tchrs.' resource guide 1.00 (ISBN 0-697-01742-7). Wm C Brown.
CSAA. When Children Ask about Sex. 42p. 1974. pap. 1.50 (ISBN 0-87183-243-7). Jewish Bd Family.
Drake, Terrance & Drake, Marvia. Teaching Your Child about Sex. LC 83-71726. 60p. 1983. 6.95 (ISBN 0-87747-951-8). Deseret Bk.
Jones, Shirley. Don't Give Me That Stuff about the Birds & the Bees. LC 82-24610. (Outreach Ser.). 32p. 1983. pap. 0.99 (ISBN 0-8163-0518-8). Pacific Pr Pub Assn.
Mayo, Mary A. Parents' Guide to Sex Education. 208p. pap. 6.95 (ISBN 0-310-44581-7, 11357P). Zondervan.
Pierson, Jack D. What a Teenager Ought to Know About Sex & God. (Teenager's Essential Education Library). (Illus.). 147p. 1981. 48.75 (ISBN 0-89266-288-3). Am Classical Coll Pr.
Sullivan, Susan & Kawiak, Matthew. Parents Talk Love: The Catholic Family Handbook on Sexuality. LC 84-80361. 164p. (Orig.). 1984. pap. 7.95 (ISBN 0-8091-2639-7). Paulist Pr.
Tengbom, Mildred. Talking Together about Love & Sexuality. 160p. 1985. pap. 4.95 (ISBN 0-87123-804-7, 210804). Bethany Hse.
Thomas, David M., ed. Sex Education Within the Family. LC 80-69136. (Marriage & Family Living in Depth Bk.). 80p. 1980. pap. 2.45 (ISBN 0-87029-171-8, 20248-1). Abbey.

SEX ROLE

Blitchington, W. Peter. Sex Roles & the Christian Family. 1983. pap. 5.95 (ISBN 0-8423-5896-X); leader's guide 2.95 (ISBN 0-8423-5897-8). Tyndale.
Dinnerstein, Dorothy. The Mermaid & the Minotaur: Sexual Arrangements & Human Malaise. LC 72-23879. 1977. pap. 7.95 (ISBN 0-06-090587-5, CN 587, PL). Har-Row.
Genne, Elizabeth S. & Genne, William H. First of All Persons: A New Look at Men-Women Relationships. (Orig.). 1973. pap. 1.95 (ISBN 0-377-03041-4). Friend Pr.
Ruether, Rosemary R. New Woman-New Earth: Sexist Ideologies & Human Liberation. 255p. 1978. pap. 9.95 (ISBN 0-8164-2185-4, HarpR). Har-Row.
Slater, Philip. Footholds: Understanding the Shifting Family & Sexual Tensions in Our Culture. LC 77-12124. 1978. 13.95x (ISBN 0-8070-4160-2). Beacon Pr.
Wolfman, Brunetta R. Roles. LC 83-12441. (Choices: Guides for Today's Woman: Vol. 3). 118p. (Orig.). 1983. pap. 6.95 (ISBN 0-664-24542-0). Westminster.

SEX WORSHIP

see Phallicism

SEXUAL BEHAVIOR

see Sex; Sexual Ethics

SEXUAL DEVIATION

Symonds, John A. Studies in Sexual Inversion. LC 72-9683. Repr. of 1928 ed. 32.50 (ISBN 0-404-57503-X). AMS Pr.
White, John. Eros Defiled: The Christian & Sexual Sin. LC 76-39711. 1977. pap. 6.95 (ISBN 0-87784-781-9). Inter-Varsity.

SEXUAL ETHICS

see also Birth Control; Chastity; Dating (Social Customs); Prostitution; Sex and Religion

Babbage, Stuart B. Sex & Sanity: A Christian View of Sexual Morality. rev. ed. LC 67-11492. 1967. Westminster.
Borowitz, Eugene B. Choosing a Sex Ethic: A Jewish Inquiry. LC 73-79123. 1970. pap. 5.95 (ISBN 0-8052-0276-5). Schocken.
Buchanan, G. Sidney. Morality, Sex & the Constitution: A Christian Perspective on the Power of Government to Regulate Private Sexual Conduct Between Consenting Adults. LC 85-3249. 242p. (Orig.). 1985. lib. bdg. 26.25 (ISBN 0-8191-4602-1); pap. text ed. 11.75 (ISBN 0-8191-4603-X). U Pr of Amer.
Burn, Helen J. Better Than the Birds, Smarter Than the Bees. LC 69-12771. (YA) pap. 21.30 (ISBN 0-8357-9000-2, 2016348). Bks Demand UMI.
Christie, Les. Dating & Waiting: A Chrisitan View of Love, Sex, & Dating. LC 83-1232. (Illus.). 80p. (Orig.). 1983. pap. 2.95 (ISBN 0-87239-643-6, 39972). Standard Pub.
Cohen, S. J., ed. The Holy Letter: A Study in Medieval Jewish Sexual Morality. pap. 7.95x (ISBN 0-87068-490-6). Ktav.
Constable, Benjamin. Art, the Metaphysics of Love & Its Universal Mystical Symbols. (Illus.). 1977. 47.25 (ISBN 0-89266-046-5). Am Classical Coll Pr.
Crawford, Claud C. The End of the Rope. rev. ed. LC 85-90684. 96p. 1985. pap. 6.95 (ISBN 0-933697-00-7). Claud Crawford.
The Determinations of the Most Famous Universities of Italy & France. LC 72-189. (English Experience Ser.: No. 329). 308p. Repr. of 1531 ed. 22.00 (ISBN 90-221-0329-3). Walter J Johnson.
Durkin, Mary. Sexuality. (Guidelines for Contemporary Catholics Ser.). (Orig.). 1987. pap. 7.95 (ISBN 0-88347-211-2). Thomas More.
Edwards, George R. Gay-Lesbian Liberation: A Biblical Perspective. 144p. (Orig.). 1984. pap. 9.95 (ISBN 0-8298-0725-X). Pilgrim NY.
Gordis, Robert. Love & Sex: A Modern Jewish Perspective. 290p. 1978. 8.95 (ISBN 0-374-19252-9). FS&G.
Guindon, Andre. The Sexual Creators: An Ethical Proposal for Concerned Christians. 256p. (Orig.). 1986. lib. bdg. 28.00 (ISBN 0-8191-5239-0); pap. text ed. 13.00 (ISBN 0-8191-5240-4). U Pr of Amer.
Hanigan, James. What Are They Saying about Sexual Morality? (WATSA Ser.). 128p. (Orig.). 1982. pap. 4.95 (ISBN 0-8091-2451-3). Paulist Pr.
Hodann, Max. History of Modern Morals. LC 72-9651. Repr. of 1937 ed. 47.50 (ISBN 0-404-57460-2). AMS Pr.
Mantle, Alexander. The Sex Tenets of the Catholic Church & the Ultimate Destinies of Man. 1979. 41.75 (ISBN 0-89266-146-1). Am Classical Coll Pr.
May, William E. The Nature & Meaning of Chastity. (Synthesis Ser.). 1977. pap. 1.75 (ISBN 0-8199-0710-3). Franciscan Herald.
Northcote, Hugh. Christianity & Sex Problems. 2nd ed. LC 72-9668. Repr. of 1916 ed. 49.50 (ISBN 0-404-57486-6). AMS Pr.
Smedes, Lewis B. Sex for Christians. 176p. 1976. pap. 5.95 (ISBN 0-8028-1618-5). Eerdmans.
Stewart, V. Mary. Sexual Freedom. pap. 0.75 (ISBN 0-87784-111-X). Inter-Varsity.
Swedenborg, Emanuel. Conjugal Love. Student ed. LC 79-93407. 12.00 (ISBN 0-87785-054-2). Swedenborg.
Thielicke, Helmut. The Ethics of Sex. Doberstein, J. W., tr. from Ger. 340p. 1964. 13.95 (ISBN 0-227-67656-4). Attic Pr.
Valentini, Norberto & Di Meglio, Clara. Sex & the Confessional. LC 73-91861. 1975. pap. 1.95 (ISBN 0-8128-1862-8). Stein & Day.
White, John. Eros Defiled: The Christian & Sexual Sin. LC 76-39711. 1977. pap. 6.95 (ISBN 0-87784-781-9). Inter-Varsity.
Yungblut, John. Sex & the Human Psyche. LC 75-19951. 32p. (Orig.). 1975. pap. 2.50x (ISBN 0-87574-203-3, 203). Pendle Hill.

SHABU'OTH

see Shavu'oth (Feast of Weeks)

SHAKERS

Andrews, Edward D. Gift to Be Simple. (Illus.). 1940. pap. 3.95 (ISBN 0-486-20022-1). Dover.
--Gift to Be Simple: Songs, Dances & Rituals of the American Shakers. (Illus.). 12.75 (ISBN 0-8446-1536-6). Peter Smith.
--People Called Shakers. new & enl. ed. 15.50 (ISBN 0-8446-1535-8). Peter Smith.
--People Called Shakers: A Search for the Perfect Society. (Illus.). 1953. pap. 6.95 (ISBN 0-486-21081-2). Dover.
Andrews, Edward D. & Andrews, Faith. Work & Workship among the Shakers. (Illus.). 224p. 1982. pap. 6.00 (ISBN 0-486-24382-6). Dover.
--Work & Worship among the Shakers. 1983. 14.00 (ISBN 0-8446-5942-8). Peter Smith.
Barker, Sr. R. Mildred. Holy Land: A History of the Alfred Shakers. 2nd ed. 53p. 1986. pap. 3.50 (ISBN 0-915836-03-3). Shaker Pr ME.
--The Sabbathday Lake Shakers: An Introduction to the Shaker Heritage. 2nd ed. (Illus.). 26p. 1985. pap. 3.00 (ISBN 0-915836-04-1). Shaker Pr ME.
Brown, Thomas. Account of the People Called Shakers. LC 77-17584. Repr. of 1812 ed. 27.00 (ISBN 0-404-08459-1). AMS Pr.
Catalogue of Fancy Goods...Alfred, ME. facsimile ed. (Hands to Work Ser.: No. 1). (Illus.). 10p. 1971. pap. 0.75 (ISBN 0-915836-05-X). Shaker Pr ME.
Catalogue of Herbs, Roots, Barks, Powdered Articles, &c., Prepared in the United Society, New Gloucester, Maine. facsimile ed. (Hands to Work Ser.: No. 2). 14p. 1981. pap. 0.75 (ISBN 0-915836-06-8). Shaker Pr ME.
Davies, J. G. & Van Zyl, P. A Shaker Dance Service Reconstucted. 1984. pap. 3.00 (ISBN 0-941500-34-9). Sharing Co.
Desroche, Henri. The American Shakers: From Neo-Christianity to Presocialism. Savacool, John K., ed. LC 78-123537. 368p. 1971. 20.00x (ISBN 0-87023-063-8). U of Mass Pr.
Dunlavy, John. Manifesto, or a Declaration of the Doctrines & Practice of the Church of Christ. LC 74-134416. Repr. of 1818 ed. 34.50 (ISBN 0-404-08460-5). AMS Pr.
Elkins, Hervey. Fifteen Years in the Senior Order of Shakers: A Narration of Facts, Concerning That Singular People. LC 72-2984. Repr. of 1853 ed. 16.00 (ISBN 0-404-10746-X). AMS Pr.
Ericson, Jack T., ed. Shaker Collection of the Western Reserve Historical Society. 77p. 1977. pap. 7.50 (ISBN 0-667-00522-6). Microfilming Corp.

Evans, Frederick W. Autobiography of a Shaker, & Revelation of the Apocalypse. enl. ed. LC 72-2986. Repr. of 1888 ed. 10.00 (ISBN 0-404-10748-6). AMS Pr.
--Shaker Communism: Or, Tests of Divine Inspiration. LC 72-2987. Repr. of 1871 ed. 14.50 (ISBN 0-404-10749-4). AMS Pr.
--Shaker Music: Inspirational Hymns & Melodies Illustrative of the Resurection, Life & Testimony of the Shakers. LC 72-2988. Repr. of 1875 ed. 27.50 (ISBN 0-404-10750-8). AMS Pr.
--Shakers: Compendium of the Origin, History, Principles, Rules & Regulations, Government & Doctrines of the United Society of Believers in Christ's Second Appearing. 4th ed. LC 72-2985. (Communal Societies in America). Repr. of 1867 ed. 14.00 (ISBN 0-404-10747-8). AMS Pr.
Faber, Doris. The Perfect Life: The Shakers in America. LC 73-90968. (Illus.). 224p. 1974. 10.95 (ISBN 0-374-35819-2). FS&G.
Filley, Dorothy M. Recapturing Wisdom's Valley: The Watervliet Shaker Heritage, 1775-1975. Richmond, Mary L., ed. LC 75-27133. (Illus.). 128p. 1975. 10.00 (ISBN 0-89062-010-5, Pub. by Town of Colonie); pap. 5.00 (ISBN 0-89062-029-6). Pub Ctr Cult Res.
Foster, Lawrence. Religion & Sexuality: Three American Communal Experiments of the Nineteenth Century. 1981. 24.95x (ISBN 0-19-502794-9). Oxford U Pr.
Gillon, Edmund. Shaker Village. (Illus.). 56p. 1986. pap. 5.95 (ISBN 0-88740-077-9). Schiffer.
Handberg, Ejner. Shop Drawings of Shaker Furniture & Woodenware, Vol. 2. LC 73-83797. 1975. pap. 5.95 (ISBN 0-912944-29-3). Berkshire Traveller.
Horgan, Edward R. The Shaker Holy Land: A Community Portrait. LC 81-20214. (Illus.). 272p. 1982. 15.95 (ISBN 0-916782-22-0). Harvard Common Pr.
Hulings, Martha. Shaker Days Remembered. pap. 5.00 (ISBN 0-317-17252-2). Shaker Her Soc.
Humez, Jean M., ed. Gifts of Power: The Writings of Rebecca Jackson, Black Visionary, Shaker Eldress. LC 81-4684. (Illus.). 376p. 1981. lib. bdg. 22.50x (ISBN 0-87023-299-1); pap. 11.95 (ISBN 0-87023-565-6). U of Mass Pr.
Johnson, Bro. Theodore E. Hands to Work & Hearts to God. 2nd ed. LC 72-78927. 64p. (Orig.). 1983. pap. 4.95 (ISBN 0-915836-08-4). Shaker Pr ME.
Johnson, Bro. Theodore E., frwd. by. A Concise Statement of the Principles of the Only True Church According to the Gospel of the Present Appearance of Christ...with a Letter from James Whittaker. facsimile ed. (Mother's Work Ser.: No. 2). 14p. 1963. pap. 1.75 (ISBN 0-915836-07-6). Shaker Pr ME.
Joy, A. F. We Are the Shakers. Orig. Title: The Queen of the Shakers. (Illus.). 130p. (Orig.). 1985. pap. 5.00 (ISBN 0-934703-00-0). Saturscent Pubns.
--We Are the Shakers. rev., & abr. ed. (Illus.). 130p. 1985. pap. 5.50 (ISBN 0-318-18279-3). A F Joy.
Judd, Kathy R. & Kalnitz, Joanne. World Shakers. 224p. 1986. pap. text ed. 13.95 (ISBN 0-03-006503-8, HoltC). HR&W.
King, Eldress E. A Shaker's Viewpoint. Facsimile ed. 4p. 1957. pap. 0.25 (ISBN 0-937942-15-4). Shaker Mus.
Lamson, David R. Two Years Experience Among the Shakers. LC 71-134418. Repr. of 1848 ed. 19.00 (ISBN 0-404-08477-X). AMS Pr.
Lossing, Benson T. Visiting the Shakers in 1857: Harper's New Monthly Magazine. Facsimile ed. (Illus.). 14p. 1975. pap. 2.50 (ISBN 0-937942-14-6). Shaker Mus.
Mace, Aurelia G. The Aletheia: Spirit of Truth. 2nd ed. LC 72-2989. Repr. of 1907 ed. 17.50 (ISBN 0-404-10751-6). AMS Pr.
MacLean, John P. Bibliography of Shaker Literature, with an Introductory Study of the Writings & Publications Pertaining to Ohio Believers. 1970. Repr. of 1905 ed. 18.50 (ISBN 0-8337-2173-9). B Franklin.
Marshall, Mary. Portraiture of Shakerism. LC 70-134420. Repr. of 1822 ed. 28.45 (ISBN 0-404-08461-3). AMS Pr.
Meader, Robert F., compiled by. Catalogue of the Emma B. King Library of the Shaker Museum. (Illus.). 63p. 1970. pap. write for info. (ISBN 0-937942-00-6). Shaker Mus.
Melcher, Marguerite F. Shaker Adventure. 319p. 1986. pap. 9.95 (ISBN 0-937942-08-1). Shaker Mus.
Morse, Flo. The Shakers & the World's People. LC 79-27271. 1981. 17.95 (ISBN 0-396-07809-5). Dodd.
--The Story of the Shakers. (Illus.). 96p. 1986. pap. 6.95 (ISBN 0-88150-062-3). Countryman.
Neal, Julia. The Kentucky Shakers. LC 82-1871. (Illus.). 120p. 1982. 10.00 (ISBN 0-8131-1458-6). U Pr of Ky.
Patterson, Daniel W. Nine Shaker Spirituals. (Illus.). 34p. 1981. pap. 2.00 (ISBN 0-937942-10-3). Shaker Mus.
--The Shaker Spiritual. LC 77-85557. (Illus.). 1979. text ed. 90.00x (ISBN 0-691-09124-2). Princeton U Pr.
Richmond, Mary L., compiled by. Shaker Literature: A Bibliography, 2 vols. LC 75-41908. 656p. 1976. Set. 60.00x (ISBN 0-87451-117-8). U Pr of New Eng.
Robinson, Charles E. A Concise History of the United Society of Believers Called Shakers. LC 75-342. (The Radical Tradition in America Ser.). 134p. 1975. Repr. of 1893 ed. 16.50 (ISBN 0-88355-245-0). Hyperion Conn.
Sears, Clara E. Gleanings from Old Shaker Journals. LC 75-345. (The Radical Tradition in America Ser). (Illus.). 311p. 1975. Repr. of 1916 ed. 30.25 (ISBN 0-88355-247-7). Hyperion Conn.
Shakers. A Collection of Millennial Hymns Adapted to the Present Order of the Church. LC 72-2991. (Communal Societies in America Ser). Repr. of 1847 ed. 21.50 (ISBN 0-404-10753-2). AMS Pr.
--The Constitution of the United Societies of Believers (Called Shakers) Containing Sundry Covenants & Articles of Agreement, Definitive of the Legal Grounds of the Institution. LC 72-2992. Repr. of 1833 ed. 16.00 (ISBN 0-404-10754-0). AMS Pr.
--A Summary View of the Millennial Church, or United Society of Believers, Commonly Called Shakers. LC 72-2993. Repr. of 1848 ed. 26.00 (ISBN 0-404-10755-9). AMS Pr.
--Testimonies in the Life, Character, Revelations, & Doctrines of Mother Ann Lee. 2nd ed. LC 72-2994. Repr. of 1888 ed. 20.00 (ISBN 0-404-10756-7). AMS Pr.
Shaver, Elizabeth. Watervliet Shaker Meeting House. 6p. 1986. pap. 2.50. Shaker Her Soc.
Shaver, Elizabeth D. Watervliet Shaker Cemetery, Albany, N. Y. 1986. pap. 2.50. Shaker Her Soc.
Sprigg, June. By Shaker Hands. (Illus.). 1975. pap. 15.95 (ISBN 0-394-73143-3). Knopf.
Van Kolken, Diana. Introducing the Shakers: An Explanation & Directory. (Illus.). 64p. (Orig.). 1985. pap. 3.95 (ISBN 0-911861-04-1). Gabriel's Horn.
Wertkin, Gerard C. The Four Seasons of Shaker Life. 1986. pap. 10.95 (ISBN 0-671-61815-6, Fireside). S&S.
White, Anna & Taylor, Lelia S. Shakerism, Its Meaning & Message. LC 73-134421. Repr. of 1904 ed. 31.50 (ISBN 0-404-08462-1). AMS Pr.
Whitson, Robley E., ed. The Shakers: Two Centuries of Spiritual Reflection. (Classics of Western Spirituality Ser.). 200p. 1983. 13.95 (ISBN 0-8091-0343-5); pap. 9.95 (ISBN 0-8091-2373-8). Paulist Pr.
Williams, John S. The Revolutionary War & Issachar Bates. 14p. 1960. 0.50 (ISBN 0-937942-02-2). Shaker Mus.
--Shaker Religious Concept. (Illus.). 32p. 1959. pap. 2.50 (ISBN 0-937942-04-9). Shaker Mus.
Williams, Richard E. Called & Chosen: The Story of Mother Rebecca Jackson & the Philadelphia Shakers. LC 80-25498. (ATLA Monograph Ser.: No. 17). 193p. 1981. 17.50 (ISBN 0-8108-1382-3). Scarecrow.

SHAKESPEARE, WILLIAM, 1564-1616

Masefield, John. Shakespeare & Spiritual Life. LC 77-1449. 1973. lib. bdg. 10.00 (ISBN 0-8414-2315-6). Folcroft.
Masson, David. Three Devils: Luther's, Milton's & Goethe's. LC 72-193946. 1874. lib. bdg. 20.00 (ISBN 0-8414-6495-2). Folcroft.
Rees, James. Shakespeare & the Bible. LC 72-14367. 1973. lib. bdg. 15.50 (ISBN 0-8414-1348-7). Folcroft.
Woodberry, George E. Great Writers. facs. ed. LC 67-30236. (Essay Index Reprint Ser). 1907. 14.50 (ISBN 0-8369-1008-7). Ayer Co Pubs.

SHAKESPEARE, WILLIAM, 1564-1616–CRITICISM, TEXTUAL

Evans, Malcolm. Signifying Nothing: Truth's True Contents in Shakespeare's Text. LC 85-28945. 256p. 1986. 25.00x (ISBN 0-8203-0837-4). U of GA Pr.
Noble, Richmond. Shakespeare's Biblical Knowledge & Use of the Book of Common Prayer. 1970. lib. bdg. 20.00x (ISBN 0-374-96115-8, Octagon). Hippocrene Bks.

SHAKESPEARE, WILLIAM, 1564-1616–KNOWLEDGE AND LEARNING

see also Shakespeare, William, 1564-1616–Philosophy; Shakespeare, William, 1564-1616–Religion and Ethics

Ackerman, Carl. Bible in Shakespeare. lib. bdg. 15.00 (ISBN 0-8414-2954-5). Folcroft.
Anders, Henry R. Shakespeare's Books. LC 76-158251. Repr. of 1904 ed. 12.50 (ISBN 0-404-00355-9). AMS Pr.
Eaton, Thomas R. Shakespeare & the Bible. LC 77-144601. Repr. of 1860 ed. 19.00 (ISBN 0-404-02237-5). AMS Pr.
Mutschmann, Heinrich & Wentersdorf, Karl. Shakespeare & Catholicism. LC 71-105107. 1970. Repr. of 1952 ed. 31.50 (ISBN 0-404-04547-2). AMS Pr.
Noble, Richmond. Shakespeare's Biblical Knowledge & Use of the Book of Common Prayer. 1970. lib. bdg. 20.00x (ISBN 0-374-96115-8, Octagon). Hippocrene Bks.
Sims, James H. Dramatic Uses of Biblical Allusions in Marlowe & Shakespeare. LC 66-64917. (University of Florida Humanities Monographs: No. 24). 1966. pap. 3.50 (ISBN 0-8130-0206-0). U Presses Fla.
Wilson, William. Shakespeare & Astrology, from a Student's Point of View. LC 77-178308. Repr. of 1903 ed. 16.00 (ISBN 0-404-06998-3). AMS Pr.

SHAKESPEARE, WILLIAM, 1564-1616–PHILOSOPHY

Birch, W. J. An Inquiry into the Philosophy & Religion of Shakespeare. LC 72-3660. (Studies in Shakespeare, No. 24). 1972. Repr. of 1848 ed. lib. bdg. 59.95x (ISBN 0-8383-1569-0). Haskell.
Birch, William. Inquiry into the Philosophy & Religion of Shakespeare. LC 76-39446. Repr. of 1848 ed. 15.00 (ISBN 0-404-00868-2). AMS Pr.

SHAKESPEARE, WILLIAM, 1564-1616–RELIGION AND ETHICS

Ackerman, Carl. The Bible in Shakespeare. 1978. lib. bdg. 18.00 (ISBN 0-8495-0134-2). Arden Lib.
Birch, William. Inquiry into the Philosophy & Religion of Shakespeare. LC 76-39446. Repr. of 1848 ed. 15.00 (ISBN 0-404-00868-2). AMS Pr.
Brown, James Buchan. Bible Truths with Shakespearian Parallels. 6th ed. LC 74-19106. Repr. of 1886 ed. 15.00 (ISBN 0-404-01136-5). AMS Pr.
Bryant, J. A., Jr. Hippolyta's View: Some Christian Aspects of Shakespeare's Plays. LC 61-6555. 256p. 1961. 24.00x (ISBN 0-8131-1057-2). U Pr of Ky.
Bullock, Charles. Shakespeare's Debt to the Bible. LC 72-187918. 1870. lib. bdg. 10.00 (ISBN 0-8414-2521-3). Folcroft.
Burgess, William. Bible in Shakespeare. 79.95 (ISBN 0-87968-728-2). Gordon Pr.
--Bible in Shakespeare. LC 68-24900. (Studies in Shakespeare, No. 24). 1969. Repr. of 1903 ed. lib. bdg. 75.00 (ISBN 0-8383-0921-6). Haskell.
Carter, Thomas. Shakespeare & Holy Scripture. LC 74-113574. Repr. of 1905 ed. 22.50 (ISBN 0-404-01398-8). AMS Pr.
--Shakespeare, Puritan & Recusant. LC 70-129386. Repr. of 1897 ed. 16.00 (ISBN 0-404-01397-X). AMS Pr.
Clark, C. Shakespeare & the Supernatural. LC 72-92957. (Studies in Shakespeare, No. 24). 1970. Repr. of 1931 ed. lib. bdg. 75.00x (ISBN 0-8383-0966-6). Haskell.
Clark, Cumberland. Shakespeare & the Supernatural. LC 72-186985. 1931. lib. bdg. 37.50 (ISBN 0-8414-0341-4). Folcroft.
Colton, G. Q. Shakespeare & the Bible. LC 74-8569. 1888. lib. bdg. 20.00 (ISBN 0-685-45608-0). Folcroft.
Coursen, Herbert R., Jr. Christian Ritual & the World of Shakespeare's Tragedies. 441p. 1976. 32.50 (ISBN 0-8387-1518-4). Bucknell U Pr.
De Groot, John H. Shakespeares-'The Old Faith.' facs. ed. LC 68-57315. (Essay Index Reprint Ser.). 1946. 18.00 (ISBN 0-8369-0368-4). Ayer Co Pubs.
Downing, Charles. The Messiahship of Shakespeare. LC 76-57998. (Studies in Shakespeare, No. 24). 1977. lib. bdg. 39.95x (ISBN 0-8383-2172-0). Haskell.
Ellis, C. The Christ in Shakespeare's Dramas & Sonnets. 59.95 (ISBN 0-87968-860-2). Gordon Pr.
Friedlander, G. Shakespeare & the Jew. 59.95 (ISBN 0-8490-1032-2). Gordon Pr.
Kelly, Henry A. Divine Providence in the England of Shakespeare's Histories. LC 75-111485. 1970. 22.50x (ISBN 0-674-21292-4). Harvard U Pr.
Kimpel, Ben. Moral Philosophies in Shakespeare's Plays. (Studies in Art & Religious Interpretation). 262p. 1987. text ed. 49.95 (ISBN 0-88946-558-4). E Mellen.
Milward, Peter. Biblical Influences in Shakespeare's Great Tragedies. 1987. 20.00 (ISBN 0-253-31198-5). Ind U Pr.
Milward, Peter, ed. Shakespeare's Religious Background. 312p. 1985. Repr. of 1973 ed. 8.95 (ISBN 0-8294-0508-9). Loyola.
Morris, Harry. Last Things in Shakespeare. LC 85-1453. (Illus.). 360p. 1986. 30.00 (ISBN 0-8130-0794-1). U Presses Fla.
Mutschmann, Heinrich & Wentersdorf, Karl. Shakespeare & Catholicism. LC 71-105107. 1970. Repr. of 1952 ed. 31.50 (ISBN 0-404-04547-2). AMS Pr.
Noble, R. Shakespeare's Biblical Knowledge. 59.95 (ISBN 0-8490-1039-X). Gordon Pr.
Noble, Richmond S. Shakespeare's Biblical Knowledge & Use of the Book of Common Prayer: As Exemplified in the Plays of the First Folio. 303p. 1980. Repr. of 1935 ed. lib. bdg. 37.50 (ISBN 0-8492-1971-X). R West.
Rees, James. Shakespeare & the Bible. LC 70-174307. Repr. of 1876 ed. 16.00 (ISBN 0-404-05235-5). AMS Pr.
Shalvi, Alice. The Relationship of Renaissance Concepts of Honour to Shakespeares Problem Plays. Hogg, James, ed. (Jacobean Drama Studies). 362p. (Orig.). 1972. pap. 15.00 (ISBN 3-7052-0306-1, Pub. by Salzburg Studies). Longwood Pub Group.
Simpson, Richard. Religion of Shakespeare. Bowden, Henry S., ed. LC 74-176025. Repr. of 1899 ed. 17.50 (ISBN 0-404-00961-1). AMS Pr.
--Religion of Shakespeare. 1973. Repr. of 1899 ed. 17.45 (ISBN 0-8274-1094-8). R West.
Spivack, Bernard. Shakespeare & the Allegory of Evil: The History of a Metaphor in Relation to His Major Villains. LC 57-12758. pap. 130.30 (ISBN 0-317-28960-8, 2017840). Bks Demand UMI.
Stevenson, Robert. Shakespeare's Religious Frontier. LC 73-16102. 1974. Repr. of 1958 ed. lib. bdg. 25.00 (ISBN 0-8414-7699-3). Folcroft.
Wordsworth, Charles. Shakespeare's Knowledge & Use of the Bible. 3rd ed. LC 73-144706. Repr. of 1880 ed. 27.50 (ISBN 0-404-07039-6). AMS Pr.

SHAKESPEARE, WILLIAM, 1564-1616–SUPERNATURAL ELEMENT

Clark, C. Shakespeare & the Supernatural. LC 72-92957. (Studies in Shakespeare, No. 24). 1970. Repr. of 1931 ed. lib. bdg. 75.00x (ISBN 0-8383-0966-6). Haskell.
Clark, Cumberland. Shakespeare & the Supernatural. LC 72-186985. 1931. lib. bdg. 37.50 (ISBN 0-8414-0341-4). Folcroft.
--Shakespeare & the Supernatural. 346p. Repr. of 1931 ed. 29.00 (ISBN 0-403-04266-6). Somerset Pub.
Fraser-Harris, D. Shakespeare & the Influence of the Stars. 69.95 (ISBN 0-8490-1031-4). Gordon Pr.
Gibson, J. Paul. Shakespeare's Use of the Supernatural. LC 79-144615. Repr. of 1908 ed. 15.00 (ISBN 0-404-02719-9). AMS Pr.
Knight, G. Wilson. Myth & Miracle: An Essay on the Mystic Symbolism of Shakespeare. 59.95 (ISBN 0-8490-0699-6). Gordon Pr.
--Myth & Miracle: Essay on the Mystic Symbolism of Shakespeare. 1978. Repr. of 1929 ed. lib. bdg. 17.50 (ISBN 0-8495-3014-8). Arden Lib.
Lucy, Margaret. Shakespeare & the Supernatural. LC 70-144653. Repr. of 1906 ed. 6.50 (ISBN 0-404-04065-9). AMS Pr.
--Shakespeare & the Supernatural. LC 73-16087. 1906. lib. bdg. 15.00 (ISBN 0-8414-5699-2). Folcroft.
Nutt, Alfred T. Fairy Mythology of Shakespeare. LC 71-139169. (Popular Studies in Mythology, Romance & Folklore: No. 6). Repr. of 1900 ed. 5.50 (ISBN 0-404-53506-2). AMS Pr.
Rogers, L. W. The Ghosts in Shakespeare. LC 72-3658. (Studies in Shakespeare, No. 24). 1972. Repr. of 1925 ed. lib. bdg. 75.00x (ISBN 0-8383-1567-4). Haskell.
Spalding, T. A. Elizabeth Demonology. 1880. lib. bdg. 27.50 (ISBN 0-8414-1620-6). Folcroft.
Stewart, Helen H. The Supernatural in Shakespeare. LC 72-13282. 1972. Repr. of 1908 ed. lib. bdg. 22.50 (ISBN 0-8414-1168-9). Folcroft.
Wiley, Edwin. Study of the Supernatural in Three Plays of Shakespeare. LC 74-32191. 1913. lib. bdg. 15.00 (ISBN 0-8414-9382-0). Folcroft.
Wilson, William. Shakespeare & Astrology, from a Student's Point of View. LC 77-178308. Repr. of 1903 ed. 16.00 (ISBN 0-404-06998-3). AMS Pr.

SHAKTISM

see also Tantras

Avalon, Arthur. The Serpent Power. LC 74-75259. (Illus.). 1974. pap. 8.95 (ISBN 0-486-23058-9). Dover.
--Shakti & Shakta. 1978. pap. 8.95 (ISBN 0-486-23645-5). Dover.
Gold, E. J. Shakti. (Illus.). 1973. pap. 4.95 (ISBN 0-89556-005-4). Gateways Bks & Tapes.
Wadley, Susan S. Shakti: Power in the Conceptual Structure of Karimpur Religion. LC 76-37612. (Univ. of Chicago Studies in Anthropology Ser. in Social, Cultural, & Linguistic Anthropology: No. 2). 222p. 1975. pap. 6.00 (ISBN 0-916256-01-4). U Chi Dept Anthro.
Woodroffe, John. Sakti & Sakta. 24.50 (ISBN 0-89744-116-8, Pub. by Ganesh & Co. India). Auromere.

SHAMANISM

see also Bon (Tibetan Religion); Medicine-Man

Achterberg, Jeanne. Imagery in Healing: Shamanism & Modern Medicine. LC 84-20748. (New Science Library Ser.). 256p. (Orig.). 1985. pap. 10.95 (ISBN 0-87773-307-4, 73031-3). Shambhala Pubns.

Andersen, Johannes C. The Maori Tohunga & His Spirit World. LC 75-35224. Repr. of 1948 ed. 20.00 (ISBN 0-404-14403-9). AMS Pr.

Blacker, Carmen. The Catalpa Bow: A Study of Shamanistic Practices in Japan. 2nd ed. (Illus.). 382p. 1986. pap. 14.95 (ISBN 0-04-398008-2). Allen Unwin.

Carroll, Peter. Liber Null & Psychonaut. (Illus.). 128p. (Orig.). 1987. pap. 12.50 (ISBN 0-87728-639-6). Weiser.

Covell, Alan C. Ecstasy: Shamanism in Korea. LC 83-81487. (Illus.). 107p. 1983. 19.50x (ISBN 0-930878-33-7). Hollym Intl.

Dow, James. The Shaman's Touch: Otomi Indian Symbolic Healing. (Illus.). 180p. (Orig.). 1986. 13.95 (ISBN 0-87480-257-1). U of Utah Pr.

Eckstorm, Fannie H. Old John Neptune & Other Maine Indian Shamans. 209p. 1980. pap. 5.95 (ISBN 0-89101-044-0). U Maine Orono.

Eliade, Mircea. Shamanism: Archaic Techniques of Ectasy. Trask, Willard R., tr. (Bollingen Ser.: Vol. 76). 1964. 50.00x (ISBN 0-691-09827-1); pap. 11.95x (ISBN 0-691-01779-4). Princeton U Pr.

Grim, John. Reflections on Shamanism: The Tribal Healer & the Technological Trance. (Teilhard Studies: No. 6). 20p. (Orig.). 1981. pap. 2.00 (ISBN 0-89012-029-3). Anima Pubns.

Halifax, Joan. Shaman: The Wounded Healer. Purce, Jill, ed. LC 81-67705. (The Illustrated Library of Sacred Imagination Ser.). (Illus.). 96p. 1982. pap. 9.95 (ISBN 0-8245-0066-0). Crossroad NY.

--Shamanic Voices: A Survey of Visionary Narratives. 1979. pap. 11.95 (ISBN 0-525-47525-7, 01160-350). Dutton.

Harner, Michael J., ed. Hallucinogens & Shamanism. (Illus.). 1973. pap. 9.95x (ISBN 0-19-501649-1). Oxford U Pr.

Huhm, Halla Pai. Kut: Korean Shamanist Rituals. 102p. 1980. 14.50x (ISBN 0-930878-18-3). Hollym Intl.

Krippner, Stanley & Villoldo, Alberto. The Realms of Healing. LC 75-7858. 320p. (Orig.). 1986. pap. 9.95 (ISBN 0-89087-474-3). Celestial Arts.

Lee, Jung Y. Korean Shamanistic Rituals. (Religion & Society Ser.: No. 12). 250p. 1980. 39.50 (ISBN 90-279-3378-2). Mouton.

Luna, Luis E. Vegetalismo: Shamanism among the Mestizo Population of the Peruvian Amazon. (Stockholm Studies in Comparative Religion). (Illus.). 202p. (Orig.). 1986. pap. text ed. 20.00x. Coronet Bks.

Maddox, J. L. The Medicine Man: A Sociological Study of the Character & Evolution of Shamanism. 1977. lib. bdg. 59.95 (ISBN 0-8490-2219-3). Gordon Pr.

Maddox, John L. The Medicine Man: A Sociological Study of the Character & Evolution of Shamanism. LC 75-23737. Repr. of 1923 ed. 45.00 (ISBN 0-404-13294-4). AMS Pr.

Nicholson, Shirley, compiled by. Shamanism. LC 86-40405. 402p. (Orig.). 1987. pap. 7.50 (ISBN 0-8356-0617-1). Theos Pub Hse.

Park, Willard Z. Shamanism in Western North America. LC 74-12553. 166p. 1975. Repr. of 1938 ed. lib. bdg. 22.50x (ISBN 0-8154-0497-2). Cooper Sq.

Rogers, Spencer. The Shamans Healing Way. 1976. pap. 4.95 (ISBN 0-916552-06-3). Acoma Bks.

Sharon, Douglas. Wizard of the Four Winds: A Shaman's Story. LC 78-3204. (Illus.). 1978. 19.95 (ISBN 0-02-928580-1). Free Pr.

Shirokogorov, Sergei M. Psychomental Complex of the Tungus. LC 76-44788. 488p. Repr. of 1935 ed. 120.00 (ISBN 0-404-15879-X). AMS Pr.

Speck, Frank G. Penobscot Shamanism. LC 20-13167. (AAA Memoirs Ser.: No. 25). 1919. pap. 15.00 (ISBN 0-527-00527-4). Kraus Repr.

Taussig, Michael. Shamanism, Colonialism, & the Wild Man: A Study in Terror & Healing. LC 86-11410. (Illus.). 544p. 1987. lib. bdg. 29.95 (ISBN 0-226-79012-6). U of Chicago Pr.

Yuan, Ch'u. The Nine Songs: A Study of Shamanism in Ancient China. 2nd ed. Waley, Arthur, tr. LC 73-84228. 1973. pap. 3.95 (ISBN 0-87286-075-2). City Lights.

SHAMASH

Schollmeyer, Anastasius, ed. Sumerisch-Babylonische Hymnen und Gebete an Samas. Repr. of 1912 ed. 12.00 (ISBN 0-384-54240-9). Johnson Repr.

SHAVU'OTH (FEAST OF WEEKS)

Goodman, Philip, ed. The Shavuot Anthology. LC 74-25802. (Illus.). 369p. 1975. 9.95 (ISBN 0-8276-0057-7, 366). Jewish Pubns.

Grimme, Hubert. Israelitische Pfingstfest und der Plejadenkult. 1907. pap. 12.00 (ISBN 0-384-20060-5). Johnson Repr.

Marcus, Audrey F. & Zwerin, Raymond A. Shabbat Can Be. Syme, Daniel B., ed. (Illus.). 1979. pap. text ed. 7.95 (ISBN 0-8074-0023-8, 102560); tchrs'. guide 3.00 (ISBN 0-8074-0024-6, 208025). UAHC.

Wengrov, Charles. The Story of Shavuot. (Holiday Ser.). (Illus.). 1965. pap. 1.50 (ISBN 0-914080-55-5). Shulsinger Sales.

SHAW, GEORGE BERNARD, 1856-1950

Berst, Charles A., ed. Shaw & Religion. LC 81-956. (Shaw: the Annual of Bernard Shaw Studies: Vol 1). 264p. 1981. 25.00x (ISBN 0-271-00280-8). Pa St U Pr.

Corrigan, Felicitas. The Nun, the Infidel, & the Superman: The Remarkable Friendships of Dame Laurentia McLachlan. LC 84-52822. (Illus.). viii, 152p. 1985. 14.95 (ISBN 0-226-11589-5). U of Chicago Pr.

Furlong, William B. Shaw & Chesterton: The Metaphysical Jesters. LC 77-114616. 1970. 21.95 (ISBN 0-271-00110-0). Pa St U Pr.

Schwartz, Grace H. Monarch Notes on Shaw's Saint Joan. (Orig.). pap. 2.95 (ISBN 0-671-00725-4). Monarch Pr.

Shaw, George B. St. Joan. (Modern Critical Interpretations--Modern British Literature Ser.). 1987. 19.95 (ISBN 1-55546-030-5). Chelsea Hse.

Slosson, Edwin E. Six Major Prophets. facsimile ed. LC 71-167421. (Essay Index Reprint Ser). Repr. of 1917 ed. 23.00 (ISBN 0-8369-2571-8). Ayer Co Pubs.

Smith, Warren S., ed. Religious Speeches of Bernard Shaw. LC 63-18890. 1963. 19.95x (ISBN 0-271-73095-1). Pa St U Pr.

SHEBA, QUEEN OF-LEGEND

Ullendorff, Edward. Ethiopia & the Bible. (British Academy Ser). 1968. 29.95x (ISBN 0-19-725904-9). Oxford U Pr.

SHE'ELOTH U-TESHUVOTH

see Responsa

SHEEN, FULTON J., 1895-1979

Sheen, Fulton J. Treasure in Clay: The Autobiography of Fulton J. Sheen. LC 81-43271. (Illus.). 384p. 1980. 15.95 (ISBN 0-385-15985-4). Doubleday.

--Treasure in Clay: The Autobiography of Fulton J. Sheen. LC 81-43271. (Illus.). 384p. 1982. pap. 8.95 (ISBN 0-385-17709-7, Im). Doubleday.

SHELDON, GILBERT, ARCHBISHOP OF CANTERBURY, 1598-1677

Sykes, Norman. From Sheldon to Secker: Aspects of English Church History, 1660-1768. LC 59-2371. (The Ford Lectures: 1958). pap. 62.50 (ISBN 0-317-20808-X, 2024534). Bks Demand UMI.

SHEOL

see Hell

SHERPAS

Paul, Robert A. The Tibetan Symbolic World: Psychoanalytic Explorations. LC 81-16505. (Chicago Originals Ser.). (Illus.). 360p. 1982. lib. bdg. 14.00x (ISBN 0-226-64987-3). U of Chicago Pr.

SHEVOUTH

see Shavu'oth (Feast of Weeks)

SHIITES

see also Babism; Bahaism; Druses; Motazilites

Al-Mufid, Shaykh. Kitab Al-Irshad: The Book of Guidance into the Lives of the Twelve Imams. Howard, I. K., tr. 616p. 1986. lib. bdg. 55.00 (ISBN 0-7103-0151-0). Methuen Inc.

Arjomand, Said A. The Shadow of God & the Hidden Iman: Religion, Political Order & Societal Change in Shi'ite Iran from the Beginning to 1890. LC 83-27196. (Publications of the Center for the Middle Eastern Studies: No. 17). (Illus.). xii, 356p. 1984. lib. bdg. 28.00x (ISBN 0-226-02782-1). U of Chicago Pr.

--The Shadow of God & the Hidden Inam: Religion, Political Order, & Societal Change in Shi'ite Iran from the Beginning to 1890. LC 83-27196. (Publications of the Center for Middle Eastern Studies: No. 117). (Illus.). 344p. 1987. lib. bdg. price not set; pap. text ed. price not set (ISBN 0-226-02784-8). U of Chicago Pr.

Chittick, W. C. & Tabataba'i, Allamah, eds. A Shi'ite Anthology. Chittick, W. C., tr. 152p. 1980. 40.00x (ISBN 0-317-39150-X, Pub. by Luzac & Co Ltd); pap. 29.00x (ISBN 0-317-39151-8). State Mutual Bk.

Cole, J. R. Roots of North Indian Shi'ism in Iran & Iraq: Religion & State in Awadh, 1722-1859. 340p. 1987. text ed. 38.00x (ISBN 0-520-05641-8). U of Cal Pr.

Cole, Juan R. & Keddie, Nikki R. Shi'ism & Social Protest. LC 85-22780. 352p. 1986. text ed. 40.00 (ISBN 0-300-03550-0); pap. 12.95 (ISBN 0-300-03553-5, Y-584). Yale U Pr.

Hussain, J. M. The Occultation of the Twelfth Imam: A Historical Background. 221p. 1982. 35.00x (ISBN 0-317-39132-1, Pub. by Luzac & Co Ltd). State Mutual Bk.

Hussain, Jassim M. The Occulation of Imam: A Historical Background. 221p. 1986. lib. bdg. 30.00 (ISBN 0-7103-0158-8). Methuen Inc.

Kramer, Milton, ed. Shi'ism, Resistance & Revolution. 350p. 1986. 39.85 (ISBN 0-8133-0453-9). Westview.

Momen, Moojan. An Introduction to Shi'i Islam. LC 85-40438. 480p. 1987. pap. 15.95x (ISBN 0-300-03531-4). Yale U Pr.

--An Introduction to Shi'i Islam: The History & Doctrines of Twelver Shi'ism. LC 85-40438. (Illus.). 397p. 1985. 25.00x (ISBN 0-300-03499-7). Yale U Pr.

Tabatabai, Hossein M. Introduction to Shii Law: A Bibliographical Study. 258p. 1985. text ed. 22.00 (ISBN 0-86372-015-3, Pub. by Ithaca England). Evergreen Dist.

Tabatabai, Muhammad. Shi'ite Islam. Nasr, Sayyed H., tr. from Persian. 253p. 1979. pap. 4.95 (ISBN 0-941722-19-8). Book-Dist-Ctr.

Tabataba'I, Allamah. A Shi'ite Anthology. Chittick, William C., ed. 152p. 1986. text ed. 25.00 (ISBN 0-7103-0159-6); pap. text ed. 12.95 (ISBN 0-317-40555-1). Methuen Inc.

Wright, Robin. Sacred Rage: The Wrath of Militant Islam. 336p. 1986. pap. 7.95 (ISBN 0-671-62811-9, Touchstone Bks). S&S.

SHINRAN, 1173-1263

Bloom, Alfred. Shinran's Gospel of Pure Grace. LC 64-8757. (Association for Asian Studies Monograph: No. 20). 97p. 1965. pap. 4.50x (ISBN 0-8165-0405-9). U of Ariz Pr.

Norihiko Kikumura. Shinran: His Life & Thought. LC 70-172538. 192p. 1972. 9.95 (ISBN 0-685-65548-2). Nembutsu Pr.

Takahatake, Takamichi. Young Man Shinran. (SR Supplements Ser.: Vol. 18). 180p. 1987. pap. 15.00 (ISBN 0-88920-169-2, Pub. by Wilfrid Laurier Canada). Humanities.

SHINTO

Ashton, W. G. Shinto: The Ancient Religion of Japan. 83p. 1921. 0.95 (ISBN 0-317-40426-1). Open Court.

Aston, W. G. Shinto, the Way of the Gods. lib. bdg. 75.00 (ISBN 0-87968-076-8). Krishna Pr.

Fujisawa, Chikao. Zen & Shinto: The Story of Japanese Philosophy. LC 78-139133. 92p. Repr. of 1959 ed. lib. bdg. 22.50x (ISBN 0-8371-5749-8, FUZS). Greenwood.

Holtom, Daniel C. The Political Philosophy of Modern Shinto: A Study of the State Religion of Japan. LC 84-3072. (BCC Ser.). 338p. 1984. Repr. of 1922 ed. 37.50 (ISBN 0-404-15937-0). AMS Pr.

Kanda, Christine G. Shinzo: Hachiman Imagery & Its Development. (Harvard East Asian Monographs: No. 119). 1985. text ed. 30.00x (ISBN 0-674-80650-6, Pub. by Coun East Asian Stud). Harvard U Pr.

Mason, J. W. Shinto, 2 vols. 200.00 (ISBN 0-8490-1050-0). Gordon Pr.

Matsunaga, Alicia. Buddhist Philosophy of Assimilation. LC 68-57058. (Illus.). 1969. 29.50 (ISBN 0-8048-0730-2). C E Tuttle.

Ono, Sokyo. Shinto: The Kami Way. LC 61-14033. 1962. 8.50 (ISBN 0-8048-0525-3). C E Tuttle.

Picken, Stuart D. Shinto: Japan's Spiritual Roots. LC 79-91520. (Illus.). 80p. 1980. 19.95 (ISBN 0-87011-410-7). Kodansha.

Ross, Floyd H. Shinto, the Way of Japan. LC 83-12970. (Illus.). xvii, 187p. 1983. Repr. of 1965 ed. lib. bdg. 35.00x (ISBN 0-313-24240-2, RSHI). Greenwood.

SHIRAZ-HISTORY

Loeb, L., ed. Outcaste: Jewish Life in Southern Iran. (Library of Anthroplogy). 354p. 1977. 42.95 (ISBN 0-677-04530-1). Gordon & Breach.

SHONA

see Mashona

SHRINES

see also Miracles; Pilgrims and Pilgrimages; Saints-Cultus; Tombs

Adair, John. The Pilgrim's Way: Shrines & Saints in Britain & Ireland. (Illus.). 1978. 12.98 (ISBN 0-500-25061-8). Thames Hudson.

Amatora, Sr. Mary. El Retrato de la Reina: La Historia de Nuestra Senora de Guadalupe. 1972. 7.50 (ISBN 0-682-47542-4, Lochinvar); pap. 5.00 (ISBN 0-682-47548-3, Lochinvar). Exposition Pr FL.

Ayyar, P. V. South Indian Shrines. 648p. 1986. Repr. 14.00X (ISBN 0-8364-1721-6, Pub. by Usha). South Asia Bks.

Higgins, Paul L. Pilgrimages: A Guide to the Holy Places of Europe for Today's Traveler. 146p. 1984. 12.95 (ISBN 0-13-676163-1); pap. 5.95 (ISBN 0-13-676155-0). P-H.

--Pilgrimages to Rome & Beyond: A Guide to the Holy Places of Southern Europe for Today's Traveler. (Illus.). 156p. 1985. 17.95 (ISBN 0-13-676073-2); pap. 7.95 (ISBN 0-13-676065-1). P-H.

Jarow, Rick. In Search of the Sacred. LC 86-40122. (Illus.). 242p. (Orig.). 1986. pap. 6.95 (ISBN 0-8356-0613-9). Theos Pub Hse.

Klein, Herbert A. Temple Beyond Time: Mount Moriah - From Solomon's Temple to Christian & Islamic Shrines. rev. ed. Simon, Joseph, ed. (Illus.). 192p. 1986. Repr. of 1970 ed. 27.50 (ISBN 0-934710-14-7). J Simon.

Natarajan, B. The City of the Cosmic Dance. 193p. 1974. text ed. 15.00x (ISBN 0-86125-035-4). Apt Bks.

Oliveira, Joseph De. Jacinta, Flower of Fatima. 192p. 1972. pap. 3.95 (ISBN 0-911988-45-9). AMI Pr.

Pepin, David. Discovering Shrines & Holy Places. (Discovering Ser.: No. 254). (Illus.). 80p. (Orig.). 1983. pap. 3.95 (ISBN 0-85263-514-1, Pub. by Shire Pubns England). Seven Hills Bks.

Pilgrimages to Rome & Beyond: A Guide to the Holy Places of Southern Europe for Today's Traveler. 1985. pap. 7.95. S&S.

Sherry, Gerard E. The Catholic Shrines of Europe. LC 86-62664. (Illus.). 119p. 1986. pap. 5.95 (ISBN 0-87973-548-1, 548). Our Sunday Visitor.

Thornton, Francis B. Catholic Shrines in the United States & Canada. LC 78-63480. Repr. of 1954 ed. 29.50 (ISBN 0-404-16546-X). AMS Pr.

Turner, Harold W. From Temple to Meeting House: The Phenomenology & Theology of Sacred Space. 1979. text ed. 39.20x (ISBN 90-279-7977-4). Mouton.

Walden, John. Bible Places: A Handbook to the Holy Land. 96p. 1984. pap. 4.95 (ISBN 0-8307-0933-9, 5018476). Regal.

SHROUD, HOLY

see Holy Shroud

SIBYLS

see also Oracles

Nikiprowetzky, Valentin. La Troisieme Sibylle. (Etudes Juives: No. 9). 1970. pap. 34.40x (ISBN 0-686-21819-1). Mouton.

SICARII

see Zealots (Jewish Party)

SICK-PRAYER-BOOKS AND DEVOTIONS

Becker, Arthur H. The Compassionate Visitor: Resources for Ministering to People Who Are Ill. LC 84-28370. 128p. (Orig.). 1985. pap. 5.95 (ISBN 0-8066-2094-3, 10-1620). Augsburg.

Berrigan, Daniel. We Die Before We Live: Talking with the Very Ill. 160p. 1980. 11.95 (ISBN 0-8164-0462-3, HarpR). Har-Row.

Brenneman, Helen G. My Comforters. LC 66-13156. 80p. (Orig.). 1966. deluxe ed. 3.95 o. p. (ISBN 0-8361-1751-4); pap. 2.50 (ISBN 0-8361-1529-5). Herald Pr.

Champlin, Joseph M. Together by Your Side: A Book for Comforting the Sick & Dying. LC 79-51016. 80p. 1979. pap. 1.95 (ISBN 0-87793-180-1). Ave Maria.

Communion of the Sick. 1984. pap. 1.95 (ISBN 0-8146-1368-3). Liturgical Pr.

DeMartini, Rodney J. Be with Me Lord: Prayers for the Sick. LC 82-71881. 96p. (Orig.). 1982. pap. 2.95 (ISBN 0-87793-256-5). Ave Maria.

Doerffler, Alfred. God at My Sickbed. 1966. 1.50 (ISBN 0-570-03062-5, 6-1114). Concordia.

Hall, Clement. Collection of Many Christian Experiences, Sentences, & Several Places of Scripture Improved. xxv, 51p. 1961. Repr. of 1753 ed. 5.00 (ISBN 0-86526-019-2). NC Archives.

Lauterbach, William A. When Shadows Fall. 1945. pap. 0.85 (ISBN 0-570-03537-6, 14-1573). Concordia.

Lynn, Holly. Disease: The Cause & Cure. 32p. pap. 3.00 (ISBN 0-942494-67-9). Coleman Pub.

McCall, Donald D. In God's Hand: Meditations for the Sick & Their Families. Lambert, Herbert, ed. LC 84-1744. 64p. 1984. pap. 4.95 (ISBN 0-8272-1606-8). CBP.

Oldenburg, Cornelius. My Grace Is Sufficient: Devotional Thoughts for Hospital Patients. (Solace Ser.). 1983. pap. 1.25 (ISBN 0-8010-6705-7). Baker Bk.

Pangrazzi, Arnaldo. Your Words in Prayer in Time of Illness. 72p. (Orig.). 1982. pap. 1.25 (ISBN 0-8189-0417-8). Alba.

Pinkston, Tom. A Spirit Soars. 34p. pap. 3.00 (ISBN 0-942494-47-4). Coleman Pub.

Power, P. B. A Book of Comfort. 1974. pap. 2.95 (ISBN 0-85151-203-8). Banner of Truth.

Rahner, Karl. Anointing of the Sick. 1979. 1.50 (ISBN 0-87193-108-7). Dimension Bks.

Rotman, Jayne. If Your Doctor's Busy, Call on God: A Spiritual Journey Through Ecological Illness. 190p. (Orig.). Date not set. pap. price not set (ISBN 0-931515-05-X). Triumph Pr.

Saleska, E. J. Strength from Above. 1946. 0.95 (ISBN 0-570-03677-1, 74-1002). Concordia.

Simundson, Daniel J. Where Is God in My Suffering? Biblical Responses to Seven Searching Questions. LC 83-72108. 80p. 1984. pap. 4.95 (ISBN 0-8066-2052-8, 10-7071). Augsburg.

Smith, Elwyn A. A Spiritual Exercise for the Sick. LC 83-48141. 64p. 1983. pap. 3.50 (ISBN 0-8006-1751-7, 1-1751). Fortress.

Taylor, Jeremy. Rule & Exercises of Holy Dying: Means & Instruments of Preparing Ourselves & Others Respectively for a Blessed Death. Kastenbaum, Robert & Thirlwall, Thomas, eds. LC 76-19590. (Death & Dying Ser.). 1977. Repr. of 1819 ed. lib. bdg. 25.50x (ISBN 0-405-09585-6). Ayer Co Pubs.

Turpin, Joanne. The Healing Mysteries: A Rosary for the Sick. 25p. (Orig.). 1983. pap. text ed. 1.35 (ISBN 0-86716-018-7). St Anthony Mess Pr.

Wisloff, Fredrik. On Our Father's Knee: Devotions for Times of Illness. LC 72-90264. 144p. 1973. pap. 5.95 (ISBN 0-8066-1309-2, 10-4765). Augsburg.
Zuck, Roy B. Barb, Please Wake Up! 128p. 1983. pap. 2.75 (ISBN 0-89323-042-1). Bible Memory.

SIGNS (OMENS)
see Omens

SIGNS AND SYMBOLS
see also Crosses; Emblems; Omens; Semantics (Philosophy); Symbolism
Ann Arbor Publishers Editorial Staff. Symbol Discrimination Series: Books 1, 2, 3, 4, 5, & 6. Reusable ed. (Symbol Discrimination Series). (Illus.). 16p. 1974. 3.00 ea.; Book 1. 3.00 (ISBN 0-89039-078-9); Book 2. 3.00 (ISBN 0-89039-079-7); Book 3. 3.00 (ISBN 0-89039-080-0); Book 4. 3.00 (ISBN 0-89039-081-9); Book 5. 3.00 (ISBN 0-89039-082-7); Book 6. 3.00 (ISBN 0-89039-083-5). Ann Arbor FL.
Berger, Arthur A. Signs in Contemporary Culture. (Annenberg Communication Ser.). (Illus.). 224p. 1984. text ed. 29.95 (ISBN 0-582-28487-2). Longman.
Cooper, J. C. An Illustrated Encyclopaedia of Traditional Symbols. LC 78-55429. (Illus.). 208p. 1987. pap. 12.95 (ISBN 0-500-27125-9). Thames Hudson.
Elder, Charles D. & Cobb, Roger W. The Political Uses of Symbols. Rockwood, Irving, ed. LC 82-12722. (Professional Studies in Political Communication). (Illus.). 192p. 1983. text ed. 22.50x (ISBN 0-582-28392-2); pap. text ed. 10.95 (ISBN 0-582-28393-0). Longman.
Fischer, Balthasar. Signs, Words & Gestures. O'Connell, Matthew J., tr. from Ger. 1981. pap. 5.95 (ISBN 0-916134-48-2). Pueblo Pub Co.
Lurker, Manfred. The Gods & Symbols of Ancient Egypt: An Illustrated Dictionary. Clayton, Peter A., rev. by. (Illus.). 144p. 1980. 19.95 (ISBN 0-500-11018-2, Quest). Thames Hudson.
Matthews, Boris, tr. from Ger. Herder Symbol Dictionary. LC 85-30872. Tr. of Herder Lexikon: Symbole. (Illus.). 222p. 1986. vinyl 14.95 (ISBN 0-933029-03-9). Chiron Pubns.
Obeyesekere, Gananath. Medusa's Hair: An Essay on Personal Symbols & Religious Experiences. LC 80-27372. (Illus.). 252p. 1981. lib. bdg. 22.50x (ISBN 0-226-61600-2). U of Chicago Pr.
Olson, Alan M., ed. Myth, Symbol & Reality. LC 80-11617. 189p. 1982. pap. text ed. 7.95 (ISBN 0-268-01349-7). U of Notre Dame Pr.
Rossi, Ino. From the Sociology of Symbols to the Sociology of Signs. LC 83-5261. 1983. 49.50 (ISBN 0-231-04844-0); pap. 17.50 (ISBN 0-231-04845-9). Columbia U Pr.
Schneider, D. Douglas. Symbolically Speaking. Michael, ed. (Illus.). 85p. 1987. pap. 5.95 (ISBN 0-939169-01-0). World Peace Univ.
Seward, Harold A. Freedom's Holy Light. (Illus.). 88p. 1986. 10.95 (ISBN 0-8059-3021-3). Dorrance.
Signs & Wonders Today. 1983. Repr. 4.95 (ISBN 0-88419-189-3). Creation Hse.
Stiebner, Erhardt D. & Urban, Dieter. Signs & Emblems. LC 83-14793. (Illus.). 352p. 1984. 17.95 (ISBN 0-442-28059-9). Van Nos Reinhold.
Tracy, George E. Charged World: A Theology of Symbol. 1980. lib. bdg. 8.00 (ISBN 0-87419-054-1, U Pr of Wash); 1981 students' ed. 5.00 (ISBN 0-686-77089-7). Larlin Corp.
Wengrov, Charles. Jewish Symbols. (Illus.). 1960. pap. 0.99 (ISBN 0-914080-24-5). Shulsinger Sales.

SIKH WARS
Butani, D. H. The Third Sikh War? Towards or Away from Khalistan? 137p. 1986. 25.00x (ISBN 81-85002-02-9, Pub. by Promilla). South Asia Bks.

SIKHISM
Anand, Balwant S. Guru Tegh Bahadur. 1979. text ed. 11.95 (ISBN 0-89684-076-X, Pub. by Sterling New Delhi). Orient Bk Dist.
Arora, Ranjit. Sikhism. (Religions of the World Ser.). (Illus.). 48p. 1987. lib. bdg. 11.40 (ISBN 0-531-18067-0, Pub. by Bookwright Pr). Watts.
Cole, W. Owen. The Guru in Sikhism. 1984. pap. 7.00x (ISBN 0-8364-1238-9, Pub. by D Longman & Todd). South Asia Bks.
Cole, W. Owen & Sambhi, Piara S. Sikhism. 1985. 13.00x (ISBN 0-7062-3147-3, Pub. by Ward Lock Educ Co Ltd). State Mutual Bk.
--The Sikhs. (Library of Religious Beliefs & Practices). 210p. 1986. pap. text ed. 14.95 (ISBN 0-7100-8843-4). Methuen Inc.
Danjhal, Beryl. Sikhism. (World Religions Ser.). (Illus.). 72p. 1987. 16.95 (ISBN 0-7134-5202-1, Pub. by Batsford England). David & Charles.
Gill, Pritam S. Concepts of Sikhism. 183p. 1979. 10.00x (ISBN 0-89684-379-3). Orient Bk Dist.
Gurbachan Singh Talib. Japuji: The Immortal Prayer-Chant. 1977. 7.00x (ISBN 0-88386-967-5). South Asia Bks.
Iqbal, Mohammad. Secrets of the Self. Nicholson, tr. (Orig.). 1979. pap. 3.95 (ISBN 0-89684-083-2, Pub. by Arnold Heinemann India). Orient Bk Dist.
Jain, Nirmal K. Sikh Religion & Philosophy. 1979. text ed. 12.50 (ISBN 0-89684-077-8, Pub. by Sterling New Delhi). Orient Bk Dist.
Juergensmeyer, Mark & Barrier, Gerald, eds. Sikh Studies: Comparative Perspectives of a Changing Tradition. 1980. 16.00 (ISBN 0-89581-100-6). Asian Human Pr.
Kaur, Madanjit. The Golden Temple, Past & Present. 1985. 17.50x (ISBN 0-8364-1325-3, Pub. by Nank Dev Univ India). South Asia Bks.
McLeod, H. W., ed. Sikhism. (Textual Sources for the Study of Religion). 224p. 1987. pap. 11.75 (ISBN 0-389-20718-7). B&N Imports.
McLeod, W. H. Way of the Sikh. (The Way Ser.). pap. 5.95 (ISBN 0-7175-0731-9). Dufour.
McLeod, W. H., ed. Sikhism. LC 84-410. (Textual Sources for the Study of Religion Ser.). 208p. 1984. 23.50x (ISBN 0-389-20479-X, 08041). B&N Imports.
Macuiliffe, Max A. Sikh Religion, 6 vols. 1270p. 200.00X set (ISBN 0-317-52153-5, Pub. by S Chand India). State Mutual Bk.
Malcolm. Sketch of the Sikhs. 202p. 1986. Repr. of 1812 ed. 20.00X (ISBN 0-8364-1755-0, PUb. by Abhinav India). South Asia Bks.
Nabha, Kahan S. Sikhs We Are Not Hindus. Singh, Jarnail, tr. 152p. 1986. pap. 12.00x (ISBN 0-8364-1839-5). South Asia Bks.
Nara, I. S. Safarnama & Zafarnama. 327p. 1986. 25.00x (ISBN 0-8364-1793-3, Pub. by Minerva India). South Asia Bks.
Rajneesh. Pointing the Way. 1979. text ed. 10.95 (ISBN 0-89684-070-0, Pub. by Motilal Banarsidass Delhi). Orient Bk Dist.
Sethi, A. S. Universal Sikhism. 1972. 5.95 (ISBN 0-88253-767-9). Ind-US Inc.
Shackle, C. An Introduction to the Sacred Language of the Sikhs. 1983. pap. 25.00x (ISBN 0-8364-1009-2, Pub. by London U Pr). South Asia Bks.
Singh, Daljeet. Sikhism. 1979. text ed. 17.95 (ISBN 0-89684-074-3, Pub. by Sterling New Delhi). Orient Bk Dist.
Singh, Daljit & Smith, Angela. The Sikh World. (Religions of the World Ser.). (Illus.). 48p. 1985. PLB 14.96 (ISBN 0-382-09158-2); pap. 9.25 (ISBN 0-382-09159-0). Silver.
Singh, Fauja. Guru Amar Das. 196p. 1979. text ed. 9.95 (ISBN 0-89684-080-8, Pub. by Sterling New Delhi). Orient Bk Dist.
Singh, Gopal. Guru Gobind Singh. (National Biography Ser.). (Orig.). 1979. pap. 2.50 (ISBN 0-89744-206-7). Auromere.
Singh, Harbans. Guru Gobind Singh. 1979. text ed. 6.95 (ISBN 0-89684-073-5, Pub. by Sterling New Delhi). Orient Bk Dist.
Singh, Jarnail. Sikh Symposium 1985. 121p. 1986. 8.00 (ISBN 0-8364-1840-9). South Asia Bks.
Singh, Khushwant & Rai, Raghu. Sikhs. LC 85-22359. 300p. 1985. Repr. lib. bdg. 44.95x (ISBN 0-89370-891-7). Borgo Pr.
Singh, Kirpal. The Way of the Saints: The Collected Short Writings of Kirpal Singh. Perkins, Russell, ed. LC 76-21987. 402p. 1978. 8.00 (ISBN 0-89142-026-6). Sant Bani Ash.
Singh, Pritam, ed. Sikh Concept of the Divine. 1986. 15.00x (ISBN 0-8364-1607-4, Pub. by Nanak Dev Univ India). South Asia Bks.
--Sikh Concept of the Divine. 223p. 1986. 15.00X (ISBN 0-8364-1670-8, Pub. by Abhinav India). South Asia Bks.
Singh, Puran. The Book of the Ten Masters. 1984. 6.00X (ISBN 0-8364-1159-5, Pub. by Punjabi). South Asia Bks.
--Spirit of the Sikhs, 3 vols. 1984. Repr. of 1920 ed. Pt.1. 7.50x (ISBN 0-8364-1115-3, Pub. by Punjabi); Pt.2, v.1. 7.50x (ISBN 0-8364-1116-1); Pt.2, Vol.2. 7.50x (ISBN 0-8364-1117-X). South Asia Bks.
Singh, Sohan, ed. The Ballad of God & Man: Asa Di Var. 1984. 9.00x (ISBN 0-8364-1220-6, Pub. by Nanak Dev Univ India). South Asia Bks.
Singh, Wazir. Philosophy of Sikh Religion. 127p. 1981. 13.95x (ISBN 0-940500-09-4, Pub. by Ess Ess Pubns India). Asia Bk Corp.
Singha, H. S. Junior Encyclopedia of Sikhism. 181p. 1985. text ed. 12.50x (ISBN 0-7069-2844-X, Pub. by Vikas India). Advent NY.

SIKHS
Aggarwal, Manju. I Am a Sikh. LC 85-5169. (My Heritage Ser.). (Illus.). 32p. 1985. PLB 9.90 (ISBN 0-531-10021-9). Watts.
Anand, Balwant S. Guru Tegh Bahadur. 1979. text ed. 11.95 (ISBN 0-89684-076-X, Pub. by Sterling New Delhi). Orient Bk Dist.
Brown, James. History of the Origin & Progress of the Sikhs, ISPP Vol. II, No. 4. 74p. 1975. Repr. 2.00 (ISBN 0-88065-068-0, Pub. by Messers Today & Tommorrows Printers & Publishers India). Scholarly Pubns.
Butani, D. H. The Third Sikh War? Towards or Away from Khalistan? 137p. 1986. 25.00x (ISBN 81-85002-02-9, Pub. by Promilla). South Asia Bks.
Feldhaus, Anne. The Religious Systems of the Mahanubhava Sect. 1983. 26.00x (ISBN 0-8364-1005-X). South Asia Bks.
Kapur, Rajiv A. Sikh Separatism: The Politics of Faith. 240p. 1986. text ed. 29.95x (ISBN 0-04-320179-2). Allen Unwin.
Kaur, Amarjit, et al. The Punjab Story. 1985. 12.50x (ISBN 0-8364-1319-9, Pub. by Roli Books). South Asia Bks.
Kaur, Jitender. The Politics of Sikhs. 280p. 1986. 24.00x (ISBN 0-8364-1795-X, Pub. by Manohar India). South Asia Bks.
Khosla, G. S. Bhai Vir Singh. 1984. 15.00x (ISBN 0-8364-1230-3, Pub. by Heritage India). South Asia Bks.
Khurana, G. British Histography on the Sikh Power in the Punjab. 159p. 1985. 35.00x (ISBN 0-7201-1767-4). Mansell.
--British Historiography on the Sikh Power in Punjab. 174p. 1985. 20.95x (ISBN 0-317-39858-X, Pub. by Allied Pubs India). Asia Bk Corp.
--British Historiography on the Sikh Power in Punjab. 1985. 14.50x (ISBN 0-8364-1504-3, Pub. by Allied India). South Asia Bks.
McLeod, W. H. The Evolution of the Sikh Community: Five Essays. 1976. 22.00x (ISBN 0-19-826529-8). Oxford U Pr.
Mansukhana, Gobind Sigh. Maharaja Ranjit Singh. (Illus.). 1982. 6.25 (ISBN 0-89744-247-4). Auromere.
Marenco, Ethne K. The Transformation of Sikh Society. 1974. pap. 16.95 (ISBN 0-913244-08-2). Hapi Pr.
Nabha, Kahan S. Sikhs We Are Not Hindus. Singh, Jarnail, tr. 152p. 1986. pap. 12.00x (ISBN 0-8364-1839-5). South Asia Bks.
Nanak, Guru. The Japji. Singh, Sangat, tr. from Punjabi. 128p. (Orig.). 1974. pap. 2.25 (ISBN 0-88253-317-7). Ind-US Inc.
Narang, A. S. Storm over the Sutlej: The Sikhs & Akali Politics. 1983. 24.00x (ISBN 0-8364-1079-3, Gitanjali). South Asia Bks.
Shackle, C. An Introduction to the Sacred Language of the Sikhs. 1983. pap. 25.00x (ISBN 0-8364-1009-2, Pub. by London U Pr). South Asia Bks.
Singh, Fauja. Guru Amar Das. 196p. 1979. text ed. 9.95 (ISBN 0-89684-080-8, Pub. by Sterling New Delhi). Orient Bk Dist.
Singh, Harbans. Guru Gobind Singh. 1979. text ed. 6.95 (ISBN 0-89684-073-5, Pub. by Sterling New Delhi). Orient Bk Dist.
--The Heritage of the Sikhs. 1983. 26.00x (ISBN 0-8364-1006-8); text ed. 16.00x (ISBN 0-8364-1007-6). South Asia Bks.
Singh, Khushwant. A History of the Sikhs, 2 vols. LC 63-7550. (Illus.). 1984. Vol. 1, 1469-1839, 430 pgs. pap. 13.50 (ISBN 0-691-00803-5); Vol. 2, 1839-1964, 408 pgs. pap. 13.50 (ISBN 0-691-00804-3); Set. pap. 25.00 (ISBN 0-691-00805-1). Princeton U Pr.
Singh, Khushwant & Rai, Raghu. Sikhs. LC 85-22359. 300p. 1985. Repr. lib. bdg. 44.95x (ISBN 0-89370-891-7). Borgo Pr.
Singh, Puran. The Book of the Ten Masters. 1984. 6.00X (ISBN 0-8364-1159-5, Pub. by Punjabi). South Asia Bks.
--Spirit of the Sikhs, 3 vols. 1984. Repr. of 1920 ed. Pt.1. 7.50x (ISBN 0-8364-1115-3, Pub. by Punjabi); Pt.2, v.1. 7.50x (ISBN 0-8364-1116-1); Pt.2, Vol.2. 7.50x (ISBN 0-8364-1117-X). South Asia Bks.

SIKHS–RELIGION
see Sikhism

SIKHS IN GREAT BRITAIN
Bhachu, Parminder. Twice Migrants: East African Sikh Settlers in Britain. 256p. 1986. text ed. 35.00 (ISBN 0-422-78910-0, 9773, Pub. by Tavistock England). Methuen Inc.
De Souza, Allan. Sikhs in Britain. (Communities in Britain Ser.). (Illus.). 72p. 1986. 16.95 (ISBN 0-7134-5100-9, Pub. by Batsford England). David & Charles.
Khurana, G. British Historiography on the Sikh Power in Punjab. 174p. 1985. 20.95x (ISBN 0-317-39858-X, Pub. by Allied Pubs India). Asia Bk Corp.

SILENCE
Hoyland, Geoffrey. The Use of Silence. 1983. pap. 2.50x (ISBN 0-87574-083-9, 083). Pendle Hill.
Paramananda, Swami. Silence as Yoga. 4th ed. 1974. pap. 3.50 (ISBN 0-911564-11-X). Vedanta Ctr.

SIMEON (BIBLICAL CHARACTER)
Tsirpanlis, Constance N. The Trinitarian & Mystical Theology of St. Symeon the New Theologian. 42p. 1981. pap. 2.00 (ISBN 0-686-36331-0). EO Pr.

SIMHAT TORAH
Simon, Norma. Simhat Torah. (Festival Series of Picture Story Books). (Illus.). 1960. bds. 4.50 lam. (ISBN 0-8381-0704-4). United Syn Bk.

SIMPLICITY
Corson-Finnerty, Adam. No More Plastic Jesus: Global Justice & Christian Lifestyle. LC 76-13174. 223p. (Orig.). 1977. pap. 6.95x (ISBN 0-88344-341-4). Orbis Bks.
Gish, Arthur G. Beyond the Rat Race. rev. ed. LC 73-9336. 208p. 1973. pap. 6.95 (ISBN 0-8361-1985-1). Herald Pr.
Gregg, Richard B. The Value of Voluntary Simplicity. 1983. pap. 2.50x (ISBN 0-87574-003-0, 003). Pendle Hill.
McEwen, June H. The Gift of Simplicity. LC 84-6327. 1984. pap. 3.75 (ISBN 0-8054-5914-6). Broadman.
Prevallet, Elaine. Reflections on Simplicity. LC 82-80439. 31p. 1982. pap. 2.50x (ISBN 0-87574-244-0). Pendle Hill.
Sider, Ronald J., ed. Lifestyle in the Eighties: An Evangelical Commitment to Simple Lifestyle. LC 82-7067. (Contemporary Issues in Social Ethics Ser.). 258p. 1982. pap. 10.95 (ISBN 0-664-24437-8). Westminster.
Storms, Kathleen. Simplicity of Life As Lived in the Everyday. LC 83-16812. 322p. (Orig.). 1984. lib. bdg. 27.75 (ISBN 0-8191-3601-8); pap. text ed. 13.75 (ISBN 0-8191-3602-6). U Pr of Amer.
Taylor, John V. Enough Is Enough: A Biblical Call for Moderation in a Consumer Oriented Societed. LC 77-72456. 1977. pap. 5.95 (ISBN 0-8066-1584-2, 10-2083). Augsburg.
Ziegler, Edward K. Simple Living. new ed. 128p. 1974. pap. 1.25 (ISBN 0-87178-791-1). Brethren.

SIMPSON, ALBERT BENJAMIN, 1844-1919
Dys, Pat. He Obeyed God: A Child's Life of A. B. Simpson. 55p. 1986. pap. 3.95 (ISBN 0-87509-382-5). Chr Pubns.
Thompson, A. W. A. B. Simpson: His Life & Work. rev. ed. (Illus.). 228p. 1960. pap. 4.95 (ISBN 0-87509-044-3). Chr Pubns.
Tozer, Aiden W. Wingspread. pap. 3.95 (ISBN 0-87509-218-7). Chr Pubns.

SIN
see also Atonement; Fall of Man; Forgiveness of Sin; Free Will and Determinism; God–Wrath; Guilt; Repentance; Sins; Temptation; Theodicy
Bruner, William T. The Truth about Sin: What Does the Bible Say? 1977. 2.00 (ISBN 0-9606566-1-8). Bruner.
Bunyan, John. The Jerusalem Sinner Saved. pap. 3.25 (ISBN 0-685-88378-7). Reiner.
Campolo, Anthony. Seven Deadly Sins. 156p. Date not set. 9.95 (ISBN 0-89693-533-7). Victor Bks.
Chambers, Oswald. Philosophy of Sin. 1961. pap. 2.25 (ISBN 0-87508-122-3). Chr Lit.
Cooke, Bernard. Reconciled Sinners: Healing Human Brokenness. 128p. (Orig.). 1986. pap. 4.95 (ISBN 0-89622-284-5). Twenty-Third.
De Soto, Domingo. De Natura et Gratia. 612p. Repr. of 1549 ed. text ed. 99.36 (ISBN 0-576-99423-5, Pub. by Gregg Intl Pubs England). Gregg Intl.
Fairlie, Henry. The Seven Deadly Sins Today. LC 79-893. (Illus.). 1979. pap. 5.95 (ISBN 0-268-01698-4, 85-16981). U of Notre Dame Pr.
Gaffney, James. Sin Reconsidered. LC 82-61424. 96p. (Orig.). 1983. pap. 3.95 (ISBN 0-8091-2516-1). Paulist Pr.
Hegre, T. A. How to Find Freedom from the Power of Sin. 96p. 1969. pap. 3.50 (ISBN 0-87123-217-0, 200217). Bethany Hse.
Kennedy, Eugene C. A Sense of Life, a Sense of Sin. 200p. 1976. pap. 3.50 (ISBN 0-385-12070-2, Im). Doubleday.
Kierkegaard, Soren. Fear & Trembling-Repetition, 2 vols. in 1. Hong, Howard V. & Hong, Edna H., eds. Hong, Howard V. & Hong, Edna H., trs. LC 82-9006. (Kierkegaard's Writings Ser.: No. VI). 420p. 1983. 37.00 (ISBN 0-691-07237-X); pap. 7.95 (ISBN 0-691-02026-4). Princeton U Pr.
Lash, Neil A. & Lash, Jamie S. Looking for Leaven. (Jewish Jewels: Vol. 1). (Illus.). 21p. (Orig.). 1985. pap. 1.50 (ISBN 0-915775-02-6). Love Song Mess Assn.
Lindsay, Gordon. The Scarlet Sin, Vol. 4. (Sorcery & Spirit World Ser.). 3.00 (ISBN 0-89985-087-1). Christ Nations.
Lovelace, Lawrence. The Theory of Sin & the Problem of the Damnation of Man. (Illus.). 137p. 1987. 97.75 (ISBN 0-89920-145-8). Am Inst Psych.
Lyonnet, Stanislas & Sabarin, Leopold. Sin Redemption & Sacrifice: A Biblical & Patristic Study. (Analecta Biblica: Vol. 48). (Eng.). 1971. pap. 22.00 (ISBN 88-7653-048-7, Biblical Inst. Press). Loyola.
MacArthur, John, Jr. Confession of Sin. (John MacArthur's Bible Studies). 1986. pap. 3.50 (ISBN 0-8024-5093-8). Moody.
--The Consequences of Sin. (John MacArthur's Bible Studies). 1985. pap. 3.50 (ISBN 0-8024-5109-8). Moody.
McClanahan, John H. Man As Sinner. LC 84-20036. (Layman's Library of Christian Doctrine Ser.). 1987. 5.95 (ISBN 0-8054-1637-4). Broadman.
Masters, Roy. Sex, Sin & Salvation. LC 77-78040. 267p. 1977. pap. 6.50 (ISBN 0-933900-06-6). Foun Human Under.
Menninger, Karl. Whatever Became of Sin? 1973. (Hawthorn); pap. 9.50 (ISBN 0-8015-8554-6, 0922-280, Hawthorn). Dutton.

Murphey, Cecil. Seven Daily Sins & What to Do about Them. 112p. (Orig.). 1981. pap. 2.95 (ISBN 0-89283-101-4). Servant.

Nystrom, Carolyn. Why Do I Do Things Wrong? (Children's Bible Basics Ser.). 32p. 1981. 4.95 (ISBN 0-8024-5996-X). Moody.

Palazzini, Pietro, ed. Sin: Its Reality & Nature. 238p. 1964. 9.95 (ISBN 0-933932-25-1). Scepter Pubs.

Pegram, Don R. Sinning Against the Holy Spirit. 1982. pap. 1.25 (ISBN 0-89265-085-0). Randall Hse.

Pepper, Clayton, ed. Keeping Converts & Restoring the Erring. pap. 2.25 (ISBN 0-89137-205-9). Quality Pubns.

Pollock, Algernon J. & Bennett, Gordon H. El Pecado Despues de la Conversion. 2nd ed. Bautista, Sara, tr. from Eng. (La Serie Diamante). Tr. of Sin After Conversion. (Span., Illus.). 36p. 1982. pap. 0.85 (ISBN 0-942504-04-6). Overcomer Pr.

Ramm, Bernard. Offense to Reason: The Theology of Sin. LC 84-48777. 288p. 1985. 15.45 (ISBN 0-06-066792-3, HarpR). Har-Row.

Rice, John R. When a Christian Sins. 1954. pap. 3.50 (ISBN 0-8024-9434-X). Moody.

Ricoeur, Paul. Symbolism of Evil. Buchanan, Emerson, tr. LC 67-11506. 1969. pap. 11.95x (ISBN 0-8070-1567-9, BPA18). Beacon Pr.

Schoonenberg, Piet. Man & Sin: A Theological View. 1965. 7.95 (ISBN 0-268-00167-7). U of Notre Dame Pr.

Shaw, Russell. Why We Need Confession. LC 85-63153. 125p. (Orig.). 1986. pap. 4.95 (ISBN 0-87973-537-6, 537). Our Sunday Visitor.

Stump, Donald V. & Arieti, James A., eds. Hamartia: The Concept of Error in the Western Tradition. LC 83-13087. (Texts & Studies in Religion: Vol. 16). 320p. 1984. 59.95x (ISBN 0-88946-805-2). E Mellen.

Tennant, F. R. The Origin & Propagation of Sin: Being the Hulsean Lectures Delivered Before the University of Cambridge, 1901-2. 235p. 1982. Repr. of 1908 ed. lib. bdg. 50.00 (ISBN 0-89987-822-9). Darby Bks.

Theisen, Jerome. Community & Disunity: Symbols of Grace & Sin. 144p. 1985. pap. 7.50 (ISBN 0-8146-1406-X). Liturgical Pr.

Thevenot, Xavier. Sin: A Christian View for Today. Marchand, Roger, ed. Inkel, Simone, tr. from Fr. 80p. 1984. pap. 2.95 (ISBN 0-89243-218-7). Liguori Pubns.

Unpardonable Sin Explained. 6th ed. 1976. pap. 0.50 (ISBN 0-686-15424-X). Crusade Pubs.

Van der Toorn, K. Sin & Sanction in Israel & Mesopotamia: A Comparative Study. (Studia Semitica Neerlandica: No. 22). 213p. 1985. pap. 20.00 (ISBN 90-232-2166-4, Pub. by Van Gorcum Holland). Longwood Pub Group.

Venerable Louis of Granada. The Sinner's Guide. LC 84-51820. 395p. 1985. pap. 8.00 (ISBN 0-89555-254-X). Tan Bks Pubs.

Villafranca, Anthony L. The Theory of Sin & the Equilibrium Between the Emotional & the Rational in Man. (Illus.). 104p. 1986. 88.50 (ISBN 0-89266-568-8). Am Classical Coll Pr.

Wilkerson, David. Victory over Sin & Self. 80p. 1982. pap. 2.95 (ISBN 0-8007-8434-0, Spire Bks). Revell.

Willimon, William H. Sighing for Eden: Sin, Evil & the Christian Faith. 208p. 1985. pap. 8.95 (ISBN 0-687-38447-8). Abingdon.

Yancey, Philip. True Confessions: Owning up to the Secret Everybody Knows. (Christian Essentials Ser.). 48p. (Orig.). 1987. pap. 1.95 (ISBN 0-89283-324-6). Servant.

SIN, FORGIVENESS OF

see Forgiveness of Sin

SIN, ORIGINAL

see also Fall of Man

Augustinus, Aurelius. De Perfectione Ivstitiae Hominis, De Gestis Pelagii, De Gratia Christi et De Peccato Originali Liber Duo. (Corpus Scriptorum Ecclesiasticorum Latinorum Ser: Vol. 42). Repr. of 1902 ed. 50.00 (ISBN 0-384-02495-5). Johnson Repr.

Edwards, Jonathan. Original Sin. Holbrook, Clyde A., ed. (Works of Jonathan Edwards Ser.: Vol. 3). 1970. 50.00x (ISBN 0-300-01198-9). Yale U Pr.

Mojzes, Paul & Foster, Durwood, eds. Society & Original Sin: Ecumenical Essays on the Impact of the Fall. LC 84-25406. (Interreligious Explorations Ser.). 216p. (Orig.). 1985. pap. 11.95 (ISBN 0-913757-15-2, Pub. by New Era Bks). Paragon Hse.

Murray, John. Imputation of Adam's Sin. 1977. pap. 2.95 (ISBN 0-87552-341-2). Presby & Reformed.

O'Connell, Patrick. Original Sin in the Light of Modern Science. 128p. 1973. pap. 3.00 (ISBN 0-912414-15-4). Lumen Christi.

Smith, Hilary S. Changing Conceptions of Original Sin: A Study in American Theology since 1750. Kuklick, Bruce, ed. (American Religious Thought of the 18th & 19th Centuries Ser.). 242p. 1987. lib. bdg. 35.00 (ISBN 0-8240-6954-4). Garland Pub.

Steiner, Rudolf. The Concepts of Original Sin & Grace. Osmond, D. S., tr. from Ger. 32p. 1973. pap. 1.95 (ISBN 0-85440-275-6, Pub. by Steinerbooks). Anthroposophic.

Storms, C. Samuel. Tragedy in Eden: Original Sin in the Theology of Jonathan Edwards. LC 85-17866. 328p. 1986. lib. bdg. 27.25 (ISBN 0-8191-4936-5); pap. text ed. 12.75 (ISBN 0-8191-4937-3). U Pr of Amer.

Vandervelde, G. Original Sin: Two Major Trends in Contemporary Roman Catholic Reinterpretation. LC 81-40000. 364p. 1982. lib. bdg. 32.50 (ISBN 0-8191-1849-4); pap. text ed. 15.75 o. p. (ISBN 0-8191-1850-8). U Pr of Amer.

Williams, Norman P. The Ideas of the Fall & of Original Sin: A Historical & Critical Study. LC 79-8125. Repr. of 1927 ed. 49.00 (ISBN 0-404-18439-1). AMS Pr.

SINAI, SAINT CATHARINE (BASILIAN MONASTERY)

Galey, John. Sinai & the Monastery of St. Catherine. 191p. 1986. 45.00 (ISBN 977-424-118-5, Pub. by Am Univ Cairo Pr); pap. 24.00x (ISBN 977-424-118-5). Columbia U Pr.

Weitzmann, Kurt. The Monastery of Saint Catherine at Mount Sinai, The Icons I: From the Sixth to the Tenth Century. LC 75-3482. 276p. 1976. 205.00x (ISBN 0-691-03543-1). Princeton U Pr.

SINGH, KIRPAL

Perkins, Russell, ed. Third World Tour of Kirpal Singh. (Illus.). 1974. pap. 2.50 (ISBN 0-89142-008-8). Sant Bani Ash.

Seader, Ruth, ed. The New Life: Kirpal Singh. (Teachings of Kirpal Ser.: Vol. 3). 1976. pap. 3.50 (ISBN 0-89142-030-4). Sant Bani Ash.

Singh, Kirpal. The Holy Path. Seader, Ruth, ed. (The Teachings of Kirpal Singh Ser., Vol. 1). (Illus.). viii, 94p. (Orig.). 1974. pap. 3.00 (ISBN 0-89142-013-4). Sant Bani Ash.

Singh, Kirpal, ed. & tr. Jap Ji: Message of Guru Nanak. 5th ed. 182p. 1976. pap. 3.50 (ISBN 0-89142-029-0). Sant Bani Ash.

SINGING, CHORAL

see Choral Singing

SINGLE-PARENT FAMILY

see also Divorcees; Unmarried Mothers; Widows

Barnes, Robert G., Jr. Single Parenting: A Wilderness Journey. 176p. 1984. pap. 5.95 (ISBN 0-8423-5892-7). Tyndale.

Brandt, Patricia & Jackson, Dave. Just Me & the Kids. (Family Ministry Ser.). (Illus.). 54p. 1985. pap. text ed. 19.95 (ISBN 0-89191-750-0). Cook.

Furrey, Donna M. God, Where's My Daddy? 32p. 1985. pap. 3.50 (ISBN 0-570-04130-9, 56-1542). Concordia.

Levine, Shlomo D. The Singular Problems of the Single Jewish Parent. 39p. (Orig.). 1981. pap. text ed. 1.25 (ISBN 0-8381-2115-2). United Synagogue.

Peppler, Alice S. Single Again--This Time with Children: A Christian Guide for the Single Parent. LC 81-52278. 128p. (Orig.). 1982. pap. 6.95 (ISBN 0-8066-1910-4, 10-5802). Augsburg.

Reisman, Bernard & Rosen, Gladys. Single-Parent Families at Camp: The Essence of an Experience. LC 84-70480. 54p. 1984. pap. 2.50 (ISBN 0-87495-061-9). Am Jewish Comm.

Smith, Virginia W. The Single Parent: Revised, Updated & Expanded. 192p. 1983. pap. 5.95 (ISBN 0-8007-5105-1, Power Bks). Revell.

SINGLE PEOPLE

see also Church Work with Single People; Divorcees; Single Women

Binford, Hugh & Binford, Helaina. Single? Single Again? A Handbook for Living. 120p. (Orig.). 1986. pap. 7.00 (ISBN 0-939313-22-7). Joshua-I-Minist.

Cavanaugh, Michael, ed. God's Call to the Single Adult. 130p. (Orig.). 1986. pap. text ed. 3.95 (ISBN 0-88368-187-0). Whitaker Hse.

Colman, Barry, ed. Sex & the Single Christian. LC 85-30138. 120p. (Orig.). 1986. pap. 6.95 (ISBN 0-8307-1107-4, 5418696). Regal.

Crawford, Dan R. Single Adults: Resource & Recipients for Revival. LC 85-7889. 1985. pap. 5.95 (ISBN 0-8054-3236-1). Broadman.

Fix, Janet & Levitt, Zola. For Singles Only. 128p. 1978. pap. 5.95 (ISBN 0-8007-5034-9, Power Bks). Revell.

Graver, Jane. Single But Not Alone. LC 12-2815. 1983. pap. 2.50 (ISBN 0-570-03880-4). Concordia.

Haystead, Wesley. Single Again. (Study & Grow Electives). 64p. 1985. pap. 3.95 (ISBN 0-8307-1042-6, 6102111). Regal.

Hensley, J. Clark. Coping with Being Single Again. LC 78-52623. 1978. 7.95 (ISBN 0-8054-5420-9). Broadman.

Israel, Martin. Living Alone. Kelsey, Morton T., intro. by. LC 82-77275. 144p. (Orig.). 1983. pap. 8.95 (ISBN 0-8245-0503-4). Crossroad NY.

Karssen, Gien. Getting the Most Out of Being Single. rev. ed. LC 82-62240. 192p. 1983. pap. 3.95 (ISBN 0-89109-505-5). NavPress.

Krebs, Richard. Alone Again. LC 77-84085. 1978. pap. 5.95 (ISBN 0-8066-1611-3, 10-0240). Augsburg.

Larson, Ray. A Season of Singleness. LC 83-81762. 128p. (Orig.). 1984. 2.50 (ISBN 0-88243-584-1, 02-0584). Gospel Pub.

Lyon, William. A Pew for One, Please. LC 76-41976. 1977. 6.95 (ISBN 0-8164-0374-0, HarpR). Har-Row.

Lyons, Bob E. Single Truth. 1982. text ed. 5.25 (ISBN 0-87148-801-9); pap. 4.25 (ISBN 0-87148-802-7); instr's. manual 6.95 (ISBN 0-87148-804-3). Pathway Pr.

Mitchell, Marcia. Spiritually Single. LC 83-15754. 112p. 1984. pap. 3.95 (ISBN 0-87123-591-9, 210591). Bethany Hse.

Muto, Susan A. & Kaam, Adrian Van. Celebrating the Single Life. LC 81-43770. 1985. pap. 6.95 (ISBN 0-385-19915-5, Im). Doubleday.

Niemann, Martha M. The Single Life: A Christian Challenge. 144p. 1986. pap. 4.25 (ISBN 0-89243-254-3). Liguori Pubns.

Parks, Joyce. Single, but Not Sorry. rev. ed. 235p. 1986. pap. 3.95 (ISBN 0-89084-307-4). Bob Jones Univ Pr.

Rinehart, Stacy & Rinehart, Paula. Choices: Finding God's Way in Dating, Sex, Singleness & Marriage. LC 82-62071. 170p. 1983. pap. 3.95 (ISBN 0-89109-494-6). NavPress.

Smoke, Jim. Suddenly Single. 120p. 1984. pap. 5.95 (ISBN 0-8007-5152-3, Power Bks). Revell.

SINGLE PEOPLE–RELIGIOUS LIFE

Binford, Hugh & Binford, Helaina. Single? Single Again? A Handbook for Living. 120p. (Orig.). 1986. pap. 7.00 (ISBN 0-939313-22-7). Joshua-I-Minist.

Cavanaugh, Michael, ed. God's Call to the Single Adult. 130p. (Orig.). 1986. pap. text ed. 3.95 (ISBN 0-88368-187-0). Whitaker Hse.

MacArthur, John, Jr. Guidelines for Singleness & Marriage. (John MacArthur's Bible Studies). (Orig.). 1986. pap. 3.95 (ISBN 0-8024-5343-0). Moody.

Niemann, Martha M. The Single Life: A Christian Challenge. 144p. 1986. pap. 4.25 (ISBN 0-89243-254-3). Liguori Pubns.

Parks, Joyce. Single, but Not Sorry. rev. ed. 235p. 1986. pap. 3.95 (ISBN 0-89084-307-4). Bob Jones Univ Pr.

Smith, Harold I. Single & Feeling Good. 160p. 1987. pap. 9.95 (ISBN 0-687-38552-0). Abingdon.

Thompson, Mervin E. Starting over Single: Life & Hope after the Death of a Marriage. 160p. 1985. 10.95 (ISBN 0-933173-00-8). Prince Peace Pub.

SINGLE WOMEN

see also Divorcees; Unmarried Mothers; Widows

Burton, Wilma. Without a Man in the House. LC 78-68403. pap. 5.95 (ISBN 0-89107-158-X). Good News.

McNamara, Jo Ann. A New Song: Celibate Women in the First Three Christian Centuries. LC 83-10852. (Women & History Ser.: Nos. 6 & 7). 154p. 1983. text ed. 29.95 (ISBN 0-86656-249-4, B249). Haworth Pr.

Payne, Dorothy. Singleness. LC 83-10174. (Choices: Guides for Today's Woman Ser.: Vol. 4). 112p. 1983. pap. 7.95 (ISBN 0-664-24541-2). Westminster.

Taylor, Rhena. Single & Whole. LC 85-8345. Orig. Title: Every Single Blessing. 96p. 1985. pap. 2.95 (ISBN 0-87784-510-7). Inter-Varsity.

Witte, Kaaren. Great Leaps in a Single Bound. LC 82-4163. 96p. (Orig.). 1982. pap. 3.95 (ISBN 0-87123-199-9, 210199). Bethany Hse.

SINKIANG

Chu, Wen-Djang. Moslem Rebellion in Northwest China, 1862-1878. (Central Asiatic Studies: No. 5). 1966. pap. text ed. 31.20x (ISBN 90-2790-017-5). Mouton.

SINS

see also Deadly Sins; Sin; Virtue and Virtues

Brians, Pearl. Carelessness & Indifference. large print ed. 25p. 1985. pap. 5.00 (ISBN 0-914009-39-7). VHI Library.

--Overeaters Feelings & Faith. large print ed. 40p. 1985. pap. 5.50 (ISBN 0-914009-31-1). VHI Library.

Brown, Bonaventure A. The Numerical Distinction of Sins According to the Franciscan School of the Seventeenth & Eighteenth Centuries. 1948. 3.50 (ISBN 0-686-11581-3). Franciscan Inst.

Lockyer, Herbert. Sins of Saints. LC 75-108378. 1970. pap. 5.95 (ISBN 0-87213-532-2). Loizeaux.

Webb, Lance. How Bad Are Your Sins? 224p. (Orig.). 1983. pap. 4.95 (ISBN 0-687-17520-8, Festival). Abingdon.

White, Ellen. Overeating: A Common Sin. large print ed. 52p. 1985. pap. 6.50 (ISBN 0-914009-45-1). VHI Library.

--Subdue Sins. large print ed. 41p. 1985. pap. 5.50 (ISBN 0-914009-44-3). VHI Library.

SISTERHOODS

see also Convents and Nunneries; Monasticism and Religious Orders; Monasticism and Religious Orders for Women

Ludlow, John M. Woman's Work in the Church. LC 75-33300. 1976. Repr. of 1866 ed. 14.95 (ISBN 0-89201-007-X). Zenger Pub.

SISTERS OF MERCY

Sheridan, Mary A. And Some Fell on Good Ground. 1981. 9.95 (ISBN 0-8062-1806-1). Carlton.

SISTERS OF ST. CLARE

see Poor Clares

SISTINE CHAPEL

Pietrangeli, Carlo, et al. The Sistine Chapel: The Art, the History, & the Restoration. (Illus.). 272p. 1986. 60.00 (ISBN 0-517-56274-X, Harmony). Crown.

SITUATION ETHICS

Fletcher, Joseph. Moral Responsibility: Situation Ethics at Work. LC 67-14515. 256p. (Orig.). 1967. pap. 4.95 (ISBN 0-664-24770-9). Westminster.

--Situation Ethics: The New Morality. LC 66-11917. 176p. 1966. pap. 6.95 (ISBN 0-664-24691-5). Westminster.

SIVA

Barrett, D. The Dancing Siva in Early South Indian Art. (Mortimer Wheeler Archaeological Lectures). 1976. pap. 2.50 (ISBN 0-85672-354-1, Pub. by British Acad). Longwood Pub Group.

Casey, Robert J. Four Faces of Siva. 1929. 25.00 (ISBN 0-8482-3565-7). Norwood Edns.

Clothey, Fred & Long, J. Bruce, eds. Experiencing Siva: Encounters with a Hindu Diety. 1983. 24.00x (ISBN 0-8364-1041-6). South Asia Bks.

Gaston, Anne-Marie. Siva in Dance, Myth & Iconography. (Illus.). 1982. 45.00x (ISBN 0-19-561354-6). Oxford U Pr.

Kramrisch, Stella. The Presence of Siva. LC 80-8558. (Illus.). 550p. 1981. 50.00x (ISBN 0-691-03964-X); pap. 18.95x (ISBN 0-691-10115-9). Princeton U Pr.

O'Flaherty, Wendy D. Siva: The Erotic Ascetic. (Illus.). 1981. pap. 9.95 (ISBN 0-19-520250-3). Oxford U Pr.

Pushpadanta. Siva-Mahimna Stotram (the Hymn on the Greatness of Siva) Pavitrananda, Swami, tr. pap. 1.50 (ISBN 0-87481-148-1). Vedanta Pr.

Ramanujan, A. K., tr. Speaking of Siva. (Classics Ser.). 200p. 1973. pap. 5.95 (ISBN 0-14-044270-7). Penguin.

Sharma, B. N. Iconography of Sadasiva. LC 76-902916. 1976. 12.50 (ISBN 0-88386-823-7). South Asia Bks.

Shetter, Janette. Rhythms of the Ecosystem. LC 76-26392. (Illus., Orig.). 1976. pap. 2.50x (ISBN 0-87574-208-4). Pendle Hill.

Singh, Jaideva. Siva Sutras: The Yoga of Supreme Identity. 1979. 16.95 (ISBN 0-89684-057-3, Pub. by Motilal Banarsidass India); pap. 12.50 (ISBN 0-89684-063-8, Pub. by Motilal Banarsidass India). Orient Bk Dist.

Yocum, Glenn E. Hymns to the Dancing Siva. 1982. 20.00x (ISBN 0-8364-0851-9). South Asia Bks.

SIVAISM

see also Shaktism

Bhandarkar, R. G. Vaisnavism Saivism & Minor Religious Systems. 238p. 1986. Repr. 14.00X (ISBN 0-8364-1704-6, Pub. by Minerva India). South Asia Bks.

Chatterji, J. C. Kashmir Shaivaism. (Cultural Perspectives Ser.). 176p. (Orig.). 1986. 29.50x (ISBN 0-88706-179-6); pap. 9.95x (ISBN 0-88706-180-X). State U NY Pr.

De Kleen, Tyra. Mudras: The Ritual Hand-Poses of the Buddha Priests & the Shiva Priests of Bali. 1970. 5.00 (ISBN 0-8216-0119-9). Univ Bks.

Dye, Joseph M. Ways to Shiva: Life & Ritual in Hindu India. LC 80-25113. (Illus.). 94p. (Orig.). 1980. pap. 4.95 (ISBN 0-87633-038-3). Phila Mus Art.

Gonda, J. Visnuism & Sivaism: A Comparison. LC 71-545904. 1976. 12.50x (ISBN 0-89684-465-X). Orient Bk Dist.

Nandimath, S. C. A Handbook of Virasaivism. 1979. 15.00 (ISBN 0-89684-053-0, Pub. by Motilal Banarsidass India). Orient Bk Dist.

Sivaraman, K. Saivism in Philosophical Perspective. 1973. 17.95 (ISBN 0-8426-0538-X). Orient Bk Dist.

Subramaniam, K. R. Origin of Saivism & Its Development in the Tamil Land. 88p. 1986. Repr. 15.00X (ISBN 0-8364-1715-1, Pub. by Usha). South Asia Bks.

Tamby, T. Isaac. Psalm of Saiva-being. 506p. 1986. Repr. of 1925 ed. 30.00X (ISBN 0-8364-1682-1, PUb. by Abhinav India). South Asia Bks.

SIXTEENTH CENTURY

see also Reformation

Chrisman, Miriam & Grundler, Otto, eds. Social Groups & Religious Ideas in the Sixteenth-Century. (Studies in Medieval Culture: No. XIII). 1978. pap. 4.95x (ISBN 0-918720-02-8). Medieval Inst.

D'Aubigne, Merle. History of the Reformation of the Sixteenth-Century, 1 vol. 1986. pap. 18.95 (ISBN 0-8010-2962-7). Baker Bk.

Hillerbrand, Hans J. Men & Ideas in the Sixteenth Century. 130p. 1984. pap. text ed. 7.95x (ISBN 0-88133-080-9). Waveland Pr.

SKEPTICISM

see also Belief and Doubt; Truth

Allen, Don C. Doubt's Boundless Sea. 1979. 25.50 (ISBN 0-405-10577-0). Ayer Co Pubs.

Annas, Julia & Barnes, Jonathan. The Modes of Scepticism: Ancient Texts & Modern Interpretations. 216p. 1985. 29.50 (ISBN 0-521-25682-8); pap. 9.95 (ISBN 0-521-27644-6). Cambridge U Pr.

Arnheim, Michael. Is Christianity True? LC 84-42861. (The Skeptic's Bookshelf Ser.). 198p. 1984. 20.95 (ISBN 0-87975-262-9). Prometheus Bks.

Carter, Curtis I. & Flew, Anthony, eds. Skepticism & Moral Principles: Modern Ethics in Review. 14.95 (ISBN 0-89044-017-4); pap. 8.95. Precedent Pub.

Carter, Curtis L., ed. Skepticism & Moral Principles: Modern Ethics in Review. LC 73-79477. (Studies in Ethics & Society Ser.: Vol. 1). 1973. 9.95 (ISBN 0-89044-017-4); pap. 4.95 (ISBN 0-89044-018-2). New Univ Pr.

Curley, E. M. Descartes Against the Skeptics. LC 77-14366. 1978. 17.50x (ISBN 0-674-19826-3). Harvard U Pr.

The Encyclopedia of Unbelief, 2 vols. LC 85-43327. 819p. 1985. Set. 99.95 (ISBN 0-87975-307-2). Prometheus Bks.

Grayling, Anthony C. Refutation of Scepticism. LC 85-5032. 150p. 1985. cloth 22.95 (ISBN 0-87548-314-3). Open Court.

Gutting, Gary. Religious Belief & Religious Skepticism. LC 82-50287. 192p. 1982. text ed. 15.95 (ISBN 0-268-01613-5). U of Notre Dame Pr.

Musser, Joe. A Skeptics Quest. 224p. (Orig.). 1984. pap. 6.95 (ISBN 0-86605-151-1). Campus Crusade.

Popkin, Richard H. The History of Scepticism from Erasmus to Spinoza. LC 78-65469. 1979. 37.00x (ISBN 0-520-03827-4); pap. 9.50x (ISBN 0-520-03876-2, CAMPUS NO. 226). U of Cal Pr.

Priestley, Joseph. An Examination of Dr. Reid's Inquiry into the Human Mind. Wellek, Rene, ed. LC 75-11249. (British Philosophers & Theologians of the 17th & 18th Centuries Ser.). 1978. Repr. of 1774 ed. lib. bdg. 51.00 (ISBN 0-8240-1800-1). Garland Pub.

Rescher, Nicholas. Scepticism: A Critical Reappraisal. LC 79-22990. 265p. 1980. 30.00x (ISBN 0-8476-6240-3). Rowman.

Richard, H. M. Skeptic & the Ten Commandmants. (Uplook Ser.). 1981. pap. 0.99 (ISBN 0-686-79998-4). Pacific Pr Pub Assn.

Santayana, George. Scepticism & Animal Faith. 14.75 (ISBN 0-8446-2863-8). Peter Smith.

--Scepticism & Animal Faith: Introduction to a System of Philosophy. 1955. pap. text ed. 6.00 (ISBN 0-486-20236-4). Dover.

Stein, Gordon, ed. An Anthology of Atheism & Rationalism. LC 80-81326. (The Skeptic's Bookshelf Ser.). 354p. 1984. pap. 15.95 (ISBN 0-87975-267-X). Prometheus Bks.

Tarrant, Harold. Scepticism or Platonism: The Philosophy of the Fourth Academy. (Cambridge Classical Studies). 192p. 1985. 39.50 (ISBN 0-521-30191-2). Cambridge U Pr.

Wiley, Margaret L. Subtle Knot: Creative Scepticism in Seventeenth-Century England. LC 68-54994. (Illus.). 1968. Repr. of 1952 ed. lib. bdg. 22.50x (ISBN 0-8371-0753-9, WISK). Greenwood.

SKEPTICISM–CONTROVERSIAL LITERATURE

Annas, Julia & Barnes, Jonathan. The Modes of Scepticism: Ancient Texts & Modern Interpretations. 216p. 1985. 29.50 (ISBN 0-521-25682-8); pap. 9.95 (ISBN 0-521-27644-6). Cambridge U Pr.

Saint Augustine. Against the Academicians. Garvey, Sr. M. Patricia, tr. (Mediaeval Philosophical Texts in Translation). 1957. pap. 7.95 (ISBN 0-87462-202-6). Marquette.

Sextus Empiricus Staff. Sextus Empiricus: Selections from the Major Writings on Scepticism, Man, & God. rev. ed. Hallie, Phillip P., ed. Etheridge, Sanford G., tr. from Gr. LC 85-27059. 256p. 1985. lib. bdg. 27.50 (ISBN 0-87220-007-8); pap. 6.95 (ISBN 0-87220-006-X). Hackett Pub.

SKITS, STUNTS, ETC.

see also Schools–Exercises and Recreations

Eisenberg, Larry & Eisenberg, Helen. Fun with Skits, Stunts, & Stories. (Game & Party Books). 64p. 1975. pap. 3.95 (ISBN 0-8010-3367-5). Baker Bk.

Ison, Colleen. Skits That Teach. (Illus.). 112p. 1985. pap. 4.95 (ISBN 0-87239-848-X, 3356). Standard Pub.

Skits, 2 vols. Set. 8.95 (ISBN 0-685-61260-0). Young Life.

Vaughn, Ruth. Skits That Win. (Orig.). (YA) 1968. pap. 2.95 (ISBN 0-310-33661-9, 10941P). Zondervan.

SLAVERY

see also Villeinage

Clarkson, Thomas. Essay on the Slavery & Commerce of the Human Species. facs. ed. LC 73-93417. (Black Heritage Library Collection Ser). 1786. 15.50 (ISBN 0-8369-8542-7). Ayer Co Pubs.

Elliott, Charles. The Bible & Slavery: In Which the Abrahamic & Mosaic Discipline is Considered. 17.25 (ISBN 0-8369-9167-2, 9042). Ayer Co Pubs.

Francklyn, G. Answer to the Rev. Mr. Clarkson's Essay on the Slavery & Commerce of the Human Species. facs. ed. LC 74-83963. (Black Heritage Library Collection Ser). 1789. 13.50 (ISBN 0-8369-8574-5). Ayer Co Pubs.

Sunderland, La Roy. Testimony of God Against Slavery, or a Collection of Passages from the Bible, Which Show the Sin Holding Property in Man. LC 73-92444. 1970. Repr. of 1835 ed. 17.00x (ISBN 0-403-03707-7, 403-00183-8). Scholarly.

Weld, Theodore D. Bible Against Slavery or an Inquiry into the Genius of the Mosaic System & the Teachings of the Old Testament on the Subject of Human Rights. LC 74-92447. 1970. Repr. of 1864 ed. 39.00x (ISBN 0-403-00185-4). Scholarly.

Williams, Sally. Aunt Sally: Or, the Cross, the Way of Freedom. facs. ed. LC 75-89438. (Black Heritage Library Collection Ser.). 1858. 14.25 (ISBN 0-8369-8692-X). Ayer Co Pubs.

SLAVERY–JUSTIFICATION

Armstrong, George D. Christian Doctrine of Slavery. LC 69-16595. Repr. of 1857 ed. 22.50x (ISBN 0-8371-0892-6, ARC&, Pub. by Negro U Pr). Greenwood.

Blanchard, Jonathan & Rice, N. L. Debate on Slavery: Is Slavery in Itself Sinful & the Relation Between Master & Slave a Sinful Relation. LC 72-82175. (Anti-Slavery Crusade in America Ser.). 1969. Repr. of 1846 ed. 21.00 (ISBN 0-405-00614-4). Ayer Co Pubs.

How, Samuel B. Slaveholding Not Sinful. facs. ed. LC 70-152922. (Black Heritage Library Collection Ser). 1855. 15.25 (ISBN 0-8369-8766-7). Ayer Co Pubs.

Lyman, Darius, Jr. Leaven for Doughfaces: Parables Touching Slavery. facs. ed. LC 78-146266. (Black Heritage Library Collection Ser). 1856. 18.00 (ISBN 0-8369-8741-1). Ayer Co Pubs.

Priest, Josiah & Brown, W. S. Bible Defence of Slavery. LC 74-92439. 1851. 79.00 (ISBN 0-403-00171-4). Scholarly.

Ross, Frederick. Slavery Ordained of God. LC 70-95445. (Studies in Black History & Culture, No. 54). 1970. Repr. of 1959 ed. lib. bdg. 48.95x (ISBN 0-8383-1202-0). Haskell.

Ross, Frederick A. Slavery Ordained by God. facs. ed. LC 74-83876. (Black Heritage Library Collection Ser). 1857. 14.25 (ISBN 0-8369-8647-4). Ayer Co Pubs.

Wheat, M. T. Progress & Intelligence of Americans: Collateral Proof of Slavery, from the First to the Eleventh Chapter of Genesis, As Founded on Organic Law. facs. ed. LC 77-83882. (Black Heritage Library Collection Ser.). 1862. 21.75 (ISBN 0-8369-8684-9). Ayer Co Pubs.

SLAVERY AND THE CHURCH

Barnes, Albert. Church & Slavery. LC 71-98714. Repr. of 1857 ed. 22.50 (ISBN 0-8371-2771-8, BAC&, Pub. by Negro U Pr). Greenwood.

--Church & Slavery. LC 79-82416. 15.00x (ISBN 0-403-00150-1). Scholarly.

--Inquiry into Scriptural Views of Slavery. LC 75-92415. 1855. 23.00x (ISBN 0-403-00151-X). Scholarly.

Birney, James G. American Churches: The Bulwarks of American Slavery. LC 79-82174. (Anti-Slavery Crusade in America Ser). 1969. Repr. of 1842 ed. 11.00 (ISBN 0-405-00611-X). Ayer Co Pubs.

Bolt, Christine & Dresher, Seymour, eds. Anti-Slavery, Religion & Reform. LC 79-41532. xi, 377p. 1980. 35.00 (ISBN 0-208-01783-6, Archon). Shoe String.

Cheever, George B. God Against Slavery. facs. ed. LC 76-78995. (Black Heritage Library Collection Ser). 1857. 13.00 (ISBN 0-8369-8537-0). Ayer Co Pubs.

Fawcett, Benjamin. A Compassionate Address to the Christian Negroes in Virginia. LC 72-168011. Repr. of 1756 ed. 11.50 (ISBN 0-404-00258-7). AMS Pr.

Foster, Stephen S. Brotherhood of Thieves: Or, A True Picture of the American Church & Clergy. LC 79-82190. (Anti-Slavery Crusade in America Ser). 1969. Repr. of 1886 ed. 9.00 (ISBN 0-405-00628-4). Ayer Co Pubs.

Harris, William L. Constitutional Powers of the General Conference: With a Special Application to the Subject of Slave Holding. facs. ed. LC 74-146265. (Black Heritage Library Collection Ser). 1860. 12.25 (ISBN 0-8369-8740-3). Ayer Co Pubs.

Hosmer, William. Slavery & the Church. LC 70-82465. Repr. of 1853 ed. 22.50 (ISBN 0-8371-1646-5, HOS&). Greenwood.

Lay, Benjamin. All Slave-Keepers That Keep the Innocent in Bondage, Apostates Pretending to Lay Claim to the Pure & Holy Christian Religion. LC 72-82203. (Anti-Slavery Crusade in America Ser). 1969. Repr. of 1737 ed. 12.00 (ISBN 0-405-00642-X). Ayer Co Pubs.

Lee, Luther. Slavery Examined in the Light of the Bible. LC 76-92434. 185p. 1855. Repr. 39.00x (ISBN 0-403-00166-8). Scholarly.

Lesick, Lawrence T. The Lane Rebels: Evangelicalism & Antislavery in Antebellum America. LC 80-24123. (Studies in Evangelicalism: No. 2). 287p. 1980. 21.00 (ISBN 0-8108-1372-6). Scarecrow.

Lotz, Adolf. Sklaverei, Staatskirche und Freikirche. pap. 10.00 (ISBN 0-384-33770-8). Johnson Repr.

Matlack, Lucius C. History of American Slavery & Methodism from 1780 to 1849. facs. ed. LC 77-138342. (Black Heritage Library Collection Ser.). 1849. 19.75 (ISBN 0-8369-8734-9). Ayer Co Pubs.

Mattison, H. Impending Crisis of Eighteen Sixty: The Present Connection of the Methodist Episcopal Church with Slavery. facs. ed. LC 75-149870. (Black Heritage Library Collection Ser). 1858. 14.25 (ISBN 0-8369-8750-0). Ayer Co Pubs.

Nuermberger, Ruth K. Free Produce Movement. LC 73-110135. (Duke University. Trinity College Historical Society. Historical Papers: No. 25). Repr. of 1942 ed. 24.50 (ISBN 0-404-51775-7). AMS Pr.

Scott, Orange. Grounds of Secession from the M. E. Church. LC 71-82219. (Anti-Slavery Crusade in America Ser). 1969. Repr. of 1848 ed. 14.00 (ISBN 0-405-00659-4). Ayer Co Pubs.

Soderlund, Jean R. Quakers & Slavery: A Divided Spirit. LC 85-42707. (Illus.). 240p. 1985. text ed. 27.50x (ISBN 0-691-04732-4). Princeton U Pr.

Stanton, Robert L. The Church & the Rebellion. facsimile ed. LC 70-168521. (Black Heritage Library Collection). Repr. of 1864 ed. 31.25 (ISBN 0-8369-8873-6). Ayer Co Pubs.

Turner, Mary. Slaves & Missionaries: The Disintegration of Jamaican Slave Society, 1787-1834. LC 82-6983. (Blacks in the New World Ser.). (Illus.). 240p. 1982. 25.95 (ISBN 0-252-00961-4). U of Ill Pr.

Vander-Velde, Lewis G. Presbyterian Churches & the Federal Union 1861-1869. LC 32-30007. (Historical Studies: No. 33). 1932. 35.00x (ISBN 0-674-70151-8). Harvard U Pr.

Weatherford, W. D. American Churches & the Negro. 310p. 1957. 8.95 (ISBN 0-8158-0207-2). Chris Mass.

Wheat, M. T. Progress & Intelligence of Americans: Collateral Proof of Slavery, from the First to the Eleventh Chapter of Genesis, As Founded on Organic Law. facs. ed. LC 77-83882. (Black Heritage Library Collection Ser.). 1862. 21.75 (ISBN 0-8369-8684-9). Ayer Co Pubs.

SLAVERY IN BRITISH GUIANA

London Missionary Society. London Missionary Society's Report of the Proceedings Against the Late Rev. J. Smith of Demerara, Who Was Tried Under Martial Law & Condemned to Death, on a Charge of Aiding & Assisting in a Rebellion of Negro Slaves. LC 78-79809. Repr. of 1824 ed. 22.50x (ISBN 0-8371-1506-X, LMS&, Pub. by Negro U Pr). Greenwood.

SLAVERY IN THE UNITED STATES–ANTI-SLAVERY MOVEMENTS

Lesick, Lawrence T. The Lane Rebels: Evangelicalism & Antislavery in Antebellum America. LC 80-24123. (Studies in Evangelicalism: No. 2). 287p. 1980. 21.00 (ISBN 0-8108-1372-6). Scarecrow.

Nuermberger, Ruth K. Free Produce Movement. LC 73-110135. (Duke University. Trinity College Historical Society. Historical Papers: No. 25). Repr. of 1942 ed. 24.50 (ISBN 0-404-51775-7). AMS Pr.

Perry, Lewis. Radical Abolitionism: Anarchy & the Government of God in Anti-Slavery Thought. 328p. 1973. 27.50x (ISBN 0-8014-0754-0). Cornell U Pr.

Soderlund, Jean R. Quakers & Slavery: A Divided Spirit. LC 85-42707. (Illus.). 240p. 1985. text ed. 27.50x (ISBN 0-691-04732-4). Princeton U Pr.

Stange, Charles D. British Unitarians Against American Slavery, 1833-1865. LC 82-48436. 256p. 1984. 29.50 (ISBN 0-8386-3168-1). Fairleigh Dickinson.

SLAVERY IN THE UNITED STATES–CONTROVERSIAL LITERATURE

Armstrong, George D. Christian Doctrine of Slavery. LC 69-16595. Repr. of 1857 ed. 22.50x (ISBN 0-8371-0892-6, ARC&, Pub. by Negro U Pr). Greenwood.

Barnes, Albert. Church & Slavery. LC 71-98714. Repr. of 1857 ed. 22.50 (ISBN 0-8371-2771-8, BAC&, Pub. by Negro U Pr). Greenwood.

--Inquiry into Scriptural Views of Slavery. LC 75-92415. 1855. 23.00x (ISBN 0-403-00151-X). Scholarly.

Blanchard, Jonathan & Rice, N. L. Debate on Slavery: Is Slavery in Itself Sinful & the Relation Between Master & Slave a Sinful Relation. LC 72-82175. (Anti-Slavery Crusade in America Ser.). 1969. Repr. of 1846 ed. 21.00 (ISBN 0-405-00614-4). Ayer Co Pubs.

Cheever, George B. God Against Slavery & the Freedom & Duty of the Pulpit to Rebuke It, As a Sin Against God. LC 79-82182. (Anti-Slavery Crusade in America Ser). 1969. Repr. of 1857 ed. 13.00 (ISBN 0-405-00621-7). Ayer Co Pubs.

--Guilt of Slavery & the Crime of Slaveholding. LC 69-16586. Repr. of 1860 ed. cancelled (ISBN 0-8371-1380-6, CHG&, Pub. by Negro U Pr). Greenwood.

Essays & Pamphlets on Antislavery. LC 68-55924. 1833-1898. Repr. 19.75x (ISBN 0-8371-1795-X, ESP&, Pub. by Negro U Pr). Greenwood.

Fee, John G. Anti-Slavery Manual, Being an Examination, in the Light of the Bible, & of Facts, into the Moral & Social Wrongs of American Slavery. LC 74-82189. (Anti-Slavery Crusade in America Ser). 1969. Repr. of 1848 ed. 14.00 (ISBN 0-405-00627-6). Ayer Co Pubs.

Foster, Stephen S. Brotherhood of Thieves: Or, A True Picture of the American Church & Clergy. LC 79-82190. (Anti-Slavery Crusade in America Ser). 1969. Repr. of 1886 ed. 9.00 (ISBN 0-405-00628-4). Ayer Co Pubs.

Grimke, Angelina E. Appeal to the Christian Women of the South. LC 77-82195. (Anti-Slavery Crusade in America Ser). 1969. Repr. of 1836 ed. 9.50 (ISBN 0-405-00635-7). Ayer Co Pubs.

Hosmer, William. Slavery & the Church. facs. ed. LC 78-133156. (Black Heritage Library Collection Ser). 1853. 14.25 (ISBN 0-8369-8711-X). Ayer Co Pubs.

--Slavery & the Church. LC 70-82465. Repr. of 1853 ed. 22.50 (ISBN 0-8371-1646-5, HOS&). Greenwood.

How, Samuel B. Slaveholding Not Sinful. facs. ed. LC 70-152922. (Black Heritage Library Collection Ser). 1855. 15.25 (ISBN 0-8369-8766-7). Ayer Co Pubs.

Lay, Benjamin. All Slave-Keepers That Keep the Innocent in Bondage, Apostates Pretending to Lay Claim to the Pure & Holy Christian Religion. LC 72-82203. (Anti-Slavery Crusade in America Ser). 1969. Repr. of 1737 ed. 12.00 (ISBN 0-405-00642-X). Ayer Co Pubs.

Lee, Luther. Slavery Examined in the Light of the Bible. LC 76-92434. 185p. 1855. Repr. 39.00x (ISBN 0-403-00166-8). Scholarly.

Priest, Josiah & Brown, W. S. Bible Defence of Slavery. LC 74-92439. 1851. 79.00 (ISBN 0-403-00171-4). Scholarly.

Ross, Frederick. Slavery Ordained of God. LC 70-95445. (Studies in Black History & Culture, No. 54). 1970. Repr. of 1959 ed. lib. bdg. 48.95x (ISBN 0-8383-1202-0). Haskell.

Smith, Gerrit. Sermons & Speeches of Gerrit Smith. LC 73-82222. (Anti-Slavery Crusade in America Ser). 1969. Repr. of 1861 ed. 11.50 (ISBN 0-405-00660-8). Ayer Co Pubs.

Sunderland, La Roy. Testimony of God Against Slavery, or a Collection of Passages from the Bible, Which Show the Sin Holding Property in Man. LC 73-92444. 1970. Repr. of 1835 ed. 17.00x (ISBN 0-403-03707-7, 403-00183-8). Scholarly.

Weld, Theodore D. Bible Against Slavery or an Inquiry into the Genius of the Mosaic System & the Teachings of the Old Testament on the Subject of Human Rights. LC 74-92447. 1970. Repr. of 1864 ed. 39.00x (ISBN 0-403-00185-4). Scholarly.

SLAVS–HISTORY

Drobena, Thomas J. & Kucharek, Wilma S. Heritage of the Slavs: The Christianization of the Great Moravian Empire. (Illus.). xviii, 174p. 1979. pap. 5.95 (ISBN 0-915887-01-0). Kosovo Pub Co.

Vlasto, A. P. The Entry of the Slavs into Christendom: An Introduction to the Medieval History of the Slavs. LC 70-98699. pap. 113.80 (ISBN 0-317-27094-X, 2024553). Bks Demand UMI.

SLESSOR, MARY MITCHELL, 1848-1945

Miller, Basil. Mary Slessor. 144p. 1985. pap. 3.50 (ISBN 0-87123-849-7, 200849). Bethany Hse.

SMET, PIERRE JEAN DE, 1801-1873

Pitrone, Jean. Great Black Robe. (Illus.). 1965. 4.00 (ISBN 0-8198-0050-3); pap. 3.00 (ISBN 0-8198-0051-1). Dghtrs St Paul.

SMITH, JOHN, 1790-1824

London Missionary Society. London Missionary Society's Report of the Proceedings Against the Late Rev. J. Smith of Demerara, Who Was Tried Under Martial Law & Condemned to Death, on a Charge of Aiding & Assisting in a Rebellion of Negro Slaves. LC 78-79809. Repr. of 1824 ed. 22.50x (ISBN 0-8371-1506-X, LMS&, Pub. by Negro U Pr). Greenwood.

Wallbridge, Edwin A. Demerara Martyr: Memoirs of the Reverend John Smith, Missionary to Demerara. LC 70-79812. (Illus.). Repr. of 1848 ed. 22.50x (ISBN 0-8371-1511-6, WAD&, Pub. by Negro U Pr). Greenwood.

SMITH, JOSEPH, 1805-1844

Andrus, Hyrum L. Joseph Smith & World Government. 144p. 1972. pap. 3.95 (ISBN 0-89036-032-4). Hawkes Pub Inc.

Barrett, Ivan J. Joseph Smith & the Restoration: A History of the LDS Church to 1846. rev. ed. LC 70-167990. (Illus.). 1973. pap. 9.95 (ISBN 0-8425-0672-1). Brigham.

Bluth, John V. Concordance to the Doctrine & Covenants. 10.95 (ISBN 0-87747-048-0). Deseret Bk.

Brodie, Fawn M. No Man Knows My History: The Life of Joseph Smith. (Illus.). 1971. 19.95 (ISBN 0-394-46967-4). Knopf.

Cook, Lyndon W. Joseph Smith & the Law of Consecration. 100p. 1985. 8.95 (ISBN 0-910523-24-X). E B Grandin.

Crowther, Duane S. The Prophecies of Joseph Smith. LC 83-80664. 413p. 1873. 10.95 (ISBN 0-88290-221-0). Horizon-Utah.

Etzenhouser, R. From Palmyra, New York, Eighteen Thirty to Independence, Missouri, Eighteen Ninety-Four. LC 73-134393. Repr. of 1894 ed. 29.50 (ISBN 0-404-08435-4). AMS Pr.

Hill, Donna. Joseph Smith: The First Mormon. 552p. 1983. pap. 5.95 (ISBN 0-941214-16-8). Signature Bks.

Jackson, Ron. The Seer: Joseph Smith. Orig. Title: Joseph Smith: the Seer. 1977. 5.95 (ISBN 0-89036-088-X). Hawkes Pub Inc.

Merrell, Karen D. Joseph Smith. 24p. 4.95 (ISBN 0-87747-561-X). Deseret Bk.

Reynolds, George & Sjodahl, Janne M. Commentary on the Pearl of Great Price. 9.95 (ISBN 0-87747-046-4). Deseret Bk.

Smith, Hyrum M. & Sjodahl, Janne M. Doctrine & Covenants Commentary. 14.95 (ISBN 0-87747-070-7). Deseret Bk.

Smith, Joseph F. Teachings of the Prophet Joseph Smith. 1976. 9.95 (ISBN 0-87747-626-8). Deseret Bk.

Smith, Lucy M. Biographical Sketches of Joseph Smith, the Prophet & His Progenitors for Many Generations. LC 73-83439. (Religion in America, Ser. 1). 1969. Repr. of 1853 ed. 15.00 (ISBN 0-405-00264-5). Ayer Co Pubs.

Taves, Ernest H. Trouble Enough: Joseph Smith & the Book of Mormon. LC 84-42790. (Illus.). 280p. 1984. 20.95 (ISBN 0-87975-261-0). Prometheus Bks.

SMITH, JOSEPH H.

Gibbons, Francis. Joseph F. Smith. LC 84-70071. (Illus.). 1984. 10.95 (ISBN 0-87747-988-7). Deseret Bk.

SMITH, SYDNEY, 1771-1845

Austin, Mrs., ed. A Memoir of the Reverend Sydney Smith by His Daughter, Lady Holland, 2 vols. 1973. Repr. of 1855 ed. 45.00 set (ISBN 0-8274-1210-X). R West.

Bullett, Gerald W. Sydney Smith: A Biography & a Selection. LC 77-138578. (Illus.). 1971. Repr. of 1951 ed. lib. bdg. 22.50x (ISBN 0-8371-5777-3, BUSS). Greenwood.

Pearson, Hesketh. The Smith of Smiths Being the Life, Wit & Humor of Sydney Smith. LC 73-145230. (Literature Ser.). (Illus.). 338p. 1972. Repr. of 1934 ed. 39.00x (ISBN 0-403-01146-9). Scholarly.

Reid, Stuart J. The Life & Times of Sydney Smith. Repr. of 1901 ed. lib. bdg. 30.00 (ISBN 0-8495-4533-1). Arden Lib.

--A Sketch of the Life & Times of Sydney Smith. 59.95 (ISBN 0-8490-1060-8). Gordon Pr.

--A Sketch of the Life & Times of the Rev. Sydney Smith. 1977. Repr. of 1885 ed. lib. bdg. 30.00 (ISBN 0-8495-4512-9). Arden Lib.

Russell, George W. E. Sydney Smith. 1973. lib. bdg. 20.00 (ISBN 0-8414-7488-5). Folcroft.

--Sydney Smith. LC 79-156929. 1971. Repr. of 1905 ed. 35.00x (ISBN 0-8103-3720-7). Gale.

Smith, Sydney. Wit & Wisdom of the Rev. Sydney Smith. 1880. Repr. 25.00 (ISBN 0-8274-3728-5). R West.

The Works of the Reverend Sydney Smith, 3 Vols. 1984. Repr. of 1845 ed. Set. lib. bdg. 200.00 (ISBN 0-8492-8121-0). Vol. 1, 474 pp. Vol. 2, 495 pp. Vol. 3, 479 pp. R West.

SMITH FAMILY

Smith, Lucy M. Biographical Sketches of Joseph Smith, the Prophet & His Progenitors for Many Generations. LC 73-83439. (Religion in America, Ser. 1). 1969. Repr. of 1853 ed. 15.00 (ISBN 0-405-00264-5). Ayer Co Pubs.

SMRTI LITERATURE

see Sanskrit Literature

SNAKES (IN RELIGION, FOLK-LORE, ETC.)

see Serpents (In Religion, Folk-Lore, etc.)

SOCIAL ACTION

Schumacher, E. F. & Gillingham, Peter N. Good Work. LC 76-5528. 1980. pap. 6.95x (ISBN 0-06-132053-6, TB 2053, Torch). Har-Row.

SOCIAL CHANGE

Here are entered works on the theory of social change.

see also Revolution (Theology)

American Marketing Association Staff. Changing Values & Social Trends: How Do Organizations React? Presented Jointly by the Market Research Society & the American Marketing Association, June 1974, Oxford, England. pap. 56.00 (ISBN 0-317-26627-6, 2011593). Bks Demand UMI.

Ben-Ami, Aharon. Social Change in a Hostile Environment: The Crusaders' Kingdom of Jerusalem. (Princeton Studies on the Near East Ser.). (Illus.). 1969. 25.50x (ISBN 0-691-09344-X). Princeton U Pr.

Bettelheim, Bruno & Janowitz, Morris B. Social Change & Prejudice. LC 64-11214. 1964. 18.95 (ISBN 0-02-903480-9). Free Pr.

Gerlach, Luther P. & Hine, Virginia H. People, Power, Change: Movements of Social Transformation. LC 70-109434. 1970. pap. 9.63 scp (ISBN 0-672-60613-5). Bobbs.

Haddad, Yvonne Y. & Findly, Ellison B., eds. Women, Religion, & Social Change. (Illus.). 564p. 1985. 49.00x (ISBN 0-88706-068-4); pap. 19.50x (ISBN 0-88706-069-2). State U NY Pr.

Leder, Arnold. Catalysts of Change: Marxist versus Muslim in a Turkish Community. LC 76-29323. (Middle East Monograph: No. 1). 70p. 1976. pap. text ed. 3.95x (ISBN 0-292-71042-9, Pub. by Ctr Mid East Stud). U of Tex Pr.

Mizruchi, Ephraim H. Regulating Society: Beguines, Bohemians, & Other Marginals. LC 82-48161. xvi, 208p. 1987. pap. 10.95 (ISBN 0-226-53284-4). U of Chicago Pr.

Mutahhari, Ayatullah M. Social & Historical Change: An Islamic Perspective. Algar, Hamid, ed. Campbell, R., tr. from Persian. (Contemporary Islamic Thought, Persian Ser.). 156p. 1986. 18.95 (ISBN 0-933782-18-7); pap. 7.95 (ISBN 0-933782-19-5). Mizan Pr.

Nicholson, Vincent D. Cooperation & Coercion as Methods of Social Change. 1983. pap. 2.50x (ISBN 0-87574-001-4, 001). Pendle Hill.

Schaller, Lyle E. The Change Agent: The Strategy of Innovative Leadership. LC 77-185544. 208p. (Orig.). 1972. pap. 7.95 (ISBN 0-687-06042-7). Abingdon.

Singer, Milton, ed. Traditional India: Structure & Change. (American Folklore Society Bibliographical & Special Ser.: No. 10). 356p. 1959. pap. 9.95x (ISBN 0-292-73504-9). U of Tex Pr.

Thompson, Michael. Rubbish Theory: The Creation & Destruction of Value. 1979. text ed. 24.00x (ISBN 0-19-217658-7). Oxford U Pr.

SOCIAL CONFLICT

Furman, D. Religion & Social Conflicts in the U. S. A. 254p. 1985. 7.95 (ISBN 0-8285-2975-2, Pub. by Progress Pubs USSR). Imported Pubns.

Mizruchi, Ephraim H. Regulating Society: Beguines, Bohemians, & Other Marginals. LC 82-48161. xvi, 208p. 1987. pap. 10.95 (ISBN 0-226-53284-4). U of Chicago Pr.

SOCIAL EQUALITY

see Equality

SOCIAL ETHICS

see also Altruism; Christian Ethics; Political Ethics; Sexual Ethics; Social Problems; Sociology, Christian; Sociology, Jewish; Wealth, Ethics Of

Beck, R. N. & Orr, J. B. Ethical Choice: A Case Study Approach. LC 70-122282. 1970. pap. text ed. 10.95 (ISBN 0-02-902060-3). Free Pr.

Bennett, John C. The Radical Imperative: From Theology to Social Ethics. LC 75-15538. 208p. 1975. 8.50 (ISBN 0-664-20824-X). Westminster.

Bockle, Franz, ed. Social Message of the Gospels. LC 68-31249. (Concilium Ser.: Vol. 35). 188p. 7.95 (ISBN 0-8091-0138-6). Paulist Pr.

Campbell, Keith. A Stoic Philosophy of Life. LC 86-13351. 216p. (Orig.). 1986. lib. bdg. 22.50 (ISBN 0-8191-5529-2); pap. text ed. 12.25 (ISBN 0-8191-5530-6). U Pr of Amer.

Curran, Charles E. American Catholic Social Ethics: Twentieth Century Approaches. LC 82-4829. 336p. 1982. 24.95 (ISBN 0-268-00603-2). U of Notre Dame Pr.

Fanfani, Amintore. Catholicism, Protestantism & Capitalism. LC 78-38251. (The Evolution of Capitalism Ser.). 234p. 1972. Repr. of 1935 ed. 23.50 (ISBN 0-405-04119-5). Ayer Co Pubs.

Forell, George W. Faith Active in Love. LC 15-5702. 1954. kivar 7.95 (ISBN 0-8066-0186-8, 10-2165). Augsburg.

Gladden, Washington. Ruling Ideas of the Present Age. 1971. Repr. of 1895 ed. 23.00 (ISBN 0-384-18865-6). Johnson Repr.

Harrison, Beverly W. Making the Connections: Essays in Feminist Social Ethics. Robb, Carol S., intro. by. LC 84-45718. (Illus.). 352p. 1985. 22.95 (ISBN 0-8070-1524-5). Beacon Pr.

Hauerwas, Stanley & Bondi, Richard. Truthfulness & Tragedy: Further Investigations in Christian Ethics. LC 76-30425. 1977. 18.95x (ISBN 0-268-01831-6); pap. text ed. 9.95 (ISBN 0-268-01832-4). U of Notre Dame Pr.

Howie, John, ed. Ethical Principles for Social Policy. LC 82-5801. 176p. 1982. 16.95x (ISBN 0-8093-1063-5). S Ill U Pr.

Hughey, Michael W. Civil Religion & Moral Order: Theoretical & Historical Dimensions. LC 82-15429. (Contributions in Sociology Ser.: No. 43). 256p. 1983. lib. bdg. 32.95 (ISBN 0-313-23522-8, HUR/). Greenwood.

Inwood, Brad. Ethics & Human Action in Early Stoicism. (Illus.). 1985. 32.00x (ISBN 0-19-824739-7). Oxford U Pr.

Lesnoff-Caravaglia, Gari, ed. Values, Ethics & Aging, Vol. 4. (Frontiers in Aging Ser.). 196p. 1985. 29.95 (ISBN 0-89885-162-9). Human Sci Pr.

Mappes, T. A. & Zembathy, J. S. Social Ethics: Morality & Social Policy. 3rd ed. 528p. 1987. 22.95 (ISBN 0-07-040125-X). McGraw.

Moltmann, Jurgen. On Human Dignity: Political Theology & Ethics. Meeks, M. Douglas, tr. from Ger. LC 83-48913. 240p. 1984. 15.95 (ISBN 0-8006-0715-5, 1-715). Fortress.

Niebuhr, Reinhold. Moral Man & Immoral Society. 16.75 (ISBN 0-8446-6221-6). Peter Smith.

--Moral Man & Immoral Society: A Study in Ethics & Politics. 1932. pap. 9.95 (ISBN 0-684-71857-X, ScribT). Scribner.

Obenhaus, Victor. Ethics for an Industrial Age: A Christian Inquiry. LC 73-15317. 338p. 1975. Repr. of 1965 ed. lib. bdg. 22.50x (ISBN 0-8371-7189-X, OBIA). Greenwood.

Pennock, Michael. Moral Problems: Student Text. LC 79-51015. (Illus.). 240p. 1979. pap. text ed. 5.50 (ISBN 0-87793-177-1); tchr's manual 2.95 (ISBN 0-87793-178-X). Ave Maria.

Purtill, Richard. Thinking about Ethics. 160p. 1976. pap. text ed. write for info. (ISBN 0-13-917716-7). P-H.

Ross, J. Elliott. Christian Ethics. 1951. 10.50 (ISBN 0-8159-5202-3). Devin.

Russell, Bertrand. Human Society in Ethics & Politics. 1954. text ed. 18.50x (ISBN 0-04-172004-0). Allen Unwin.

Ryrie, Charles C. What You Should Know about Social Responsibility. LC 81-16804. (Current Christian Issues Ser.). 1982. pap. 4.50 (ISBN 0-8024-9417-X). Moody.

Skurski, Roger. New Directions in Economic Justice. LC 83-1254. 304p. 1983. text ed. 20.95x (ISBN 0-268-01460-4, 85-14606); pap. text ed. 10.95x (ISBN 0-268-01461-2, 85-14614). U of Notre Dame Pr.

Ward, Alfred D. & Clark, John M. Goals of Economic Life. LC 72-167432. (Essay Index Reprint Ser.). Repr. of 1953 ed. 25.00 (ISBN 0-8369-2726-5). Ayer Co Pubs.

Weinreich-Haste, Helen & Locke, Don. Morality in the Making: Thought, Action & the Social Context. (Developmental Psychology & Its Application Ser.). 300p. 1983. 73.95 (ISBN 0-471-10423-X, Pub. by Wiley Interscience). Wiley.

Wilkes, Paul, ed. Merton: By Those Who Knew Him Best. LC 84-47824. (Illus.). 160p. 1984. 13.95 (ISBN 0-06-069416-5, HarpR). Har-Row.

Winter, Gibson. Liberating Creation: Foundations of Religious Social Ethics. LC 81-5364. 1981. 12.95 (ISBN 0-8245-0032-6). Crossroad NY.

Yoder, John H. The Politics of Jesus. 176p. 1972. pap. 7.95 (ISBN 0-8028-1485-9). Eerdmans.

--The Priestly Kingdom: Social Ethics As Gospel. LC 84-40358. 208p. 1986. text ed. 16.95 (ISBN 0-268-01627-5, 85-16270); pap. text ed. 8.95 (ISBN 0-268-01628-3, 85-16288). U of Notre Dame Pr.

SOCIAL GOSPEL

Carter, Paul A. The Decline & Revival of the Social Gospel: Social & Political Liberalism in American Protestant Churches, 1920-1940. 2nd ed. LC 70-122413. xxvi, 265p. 1971. Repr. of 1956 ed. 27.50 (ISBN 0-208-01083-1, Archon). Shoe String.

Chang, Lit-Sen. True Gospel vs. Social Activism. 1976. pap. 0.60 (ISBN 0-87552-134-7). Presby & Reformed.

Daniel, R. P. Gospel & the Path of Separation. pap. 3.25 (ISBN 0-88172-016-X). Believers Bkshelf.

Fishburn, Janet F. The Fatherhood of God & the Victorian Family: The Social Gospel in America. LC 81-43090. 220p. 1982. 4.95 (ISBN 0-8006-0671-X). Fortress.

Herron, George D. Social Meanings of Religious Experiences. (American Studies Ser.). 1969. Repr. of 1896 ed. 18.00 (ISBN 0-384-22660-4). Johnson Repr.

Hopkins, Charles H. The Rise of the Social Gospel in American Protestantism, 1865-1895. LC 75-41141. (BCL Ser.: Vol. II). 368p. Repr. of 1940 ed. 30.00 (ISBN 0-404-14771-2). AMS Pr.

McDowell, John P. The Social Gospel in the South: The Woman's Home Mission Movement in the Methodist Episcopal Church, South, 1886-1939. LC 82-15292. 167p. 1982. text ed. 20.00x (ISBN 0-8071-1022-1). La State U Pr.

SOCIAL PROBLEMS

see also Charities; Church and Social Problems; Divorce; Judaism and Social Problems; Poor; Progress; Prostitution; Race Relations; Social Action; Social Ethics; Sociology, Islamic; Sociology, Jewish; Suicide; Sunday Legislation

Baum, Gregory. The Priority of Labor: A Commentary on "Laborem Exercens", Encyclical Letter of Pope John Paul II. 112p. 1982. pap. 5.95 (ISBN 0-8091-2479-3). Paulist Pr.

Brickner, Balfour & Vorspan, Albert. Searching the Prophets for Values. 1981. 6.95 (ISBN 0-8074-0047-5). UAHC.

Camara, Dom H. Desert Is Fertile. 1976. pap. 1.50 (ISBN 0-89129-060-5). Jove Pubns.

Gilman, Nicholas P. Socialism & the American Spirit. facsimile ed. LC 70-150183. (Select Bibliographies Reprint Ser). Repr. of 1893 ed. 23.50 (ISBN 0-8369-5696-6). Ayer Co Pubs.

Inge, William R. Christian Ethics & Modern Problems. Repr. of 1930 ed. lib. bdg. 22.50x (ISBN 0-8371-3960-0, INCE). Greenwood.

Kavanaugh, John, ed. Quaker Approach to Contemporary Problems. Repr. of 1953 ed. lib. bdg. 22.50x (ISBN 0-8371-4432-9, KAGA). Greenwood.

Loomis, Samuel L. Modern Cities & Their Religious Problems. LC 73-112558. (Rise of Urban America). 1970. Repr. of 1887 ed. 23.50 (ISBN 0-405-02464-9). Ayer Co Pubs.

Reisman, W. Michael. Folded Lies: Bribery, Crusades, & Reforms. LC 78-3207. 1979. 12.95 (ISBN 0-02-926280-1). Free Pr.

Ryrie, Charles C. What You Should Know about Social Responsibility. LC 81-16804. (Current Christian Issues Ser.). 1982. pap. 4.50 (ISBN 0-8024-9417-X). Moody.

Steiner, Rudolf. The Social Future. new rev. ed. Monges, Henry B., tr. from Ger. LC 72-87742. 151p. 1972. pap. text ed. 7.95 (ISBN 0-910142-34-3). Anthroposophic.

SOCIAL PROBLEMS AND JUDAISM

see Judaism and Social Problems

SOCIAL PROBLEMS AND THE CHURCH

see Church and Social Problems

SOCIAL PROGRESS

see Progress

SOCIAL PSYCHOTECHNICS

see Psychology, Applied

SOCIAL REFORMERS–GREAT BRITAIN

Brown, Stewart J. Thomas Chalmers & Godly Commonwealth in Scotland. (Illus.). 1982. 55.00x (ISBN 0-19-213114-1). Oxford U Pr.

Martin, Hugh, ed. Christian Social Reformers of the Nineteenth Century. facsimile ed. LC 70-107725. (Essay Index Reprint Ser.). 1927. 18.00 (ISBN 0-8369-1526-7). Ayer Co Pubs.

SOCIAL STATUS AND RELIGION

see Religion and Social Status

SOCIALISM–GREAT BRITAIN

Wagner, Donald O. Church of England & Social Reform since 1854. LC 77-127438. (Columbia University. Studies in the Social Sciences: No. 325). 12.50 (ISBN 0-404-51325-5). AMS Pr.

SOCIALISM, CHRISTIAN

see also Christianity and Economics

Bakunin, Jack. Pierre Leroux & the Birth of Democratic Socialism. 1976. lib. bdg. 79.95 (ISBN 0-87700-221-5). Revisionist Pr.

Ballou, Adin. Practical Christian Socialism. LC 72-2936. (Communal Societies in America Ser.). Repr. of 1854 ed. 37.50 (ISBN 0-404-10702-8). AMS Pr.

Cofer, David B. Saint-Simonism in the Radicalism of Thomas Carlyle. (English Literature Ser., No. 33). 1970. pap. 39.95x (ISBN 0-8383-0017-0). Haskell.

Dombrowski, James. Early Days of Christian Socialism in America. 1966. lib. bdg. 19.50x (ISBN 0-374-92223-3, Octagon). Hippocrene Bks.

Gardner, E. Clinton. Christocentrism in Christian Social Ethics: A Depth Study of Eight Modern Protestants. LC 82-21843. 264p. (Orig.). 1983. lib. bdg. 28.50 (ISBN 0-8191-2954-2); pap. text ed. 13.50 (ISBN 0-8191-2955-0). U Pr of Amer.

Gilman, Nicholas P. Socialism & the American Spirit. facsimile ed. LC 70-150183. (Select Bibliographies Reprint Ser). Repr. of 1893 ed. 23.50 (ISBN 0-8369-5696-6). Ayer Co Pubs.

Gladden, Washington. Tools & the Man: Property & Industry under the Christian Law. LC 75-353. (The Radical Tradition in America Ser). 308p. 1975. Repr. of 1893 ed. 23.65 (ISBN 0-88355-222-1). Hyperion Conn.

Hendricks, Robert J. Bethel & Aurora. LC 75-134380. Repr. of 1933 ed. 26.50 (ISBN 0-404-08428-1). AMS Pr.

Lewis, John, et al, eds. Christianity & the Social Revolution. facsimile ed. LC 79-37892. (Select Bibliographies Reprint Ser). Repr. of 1935 ed. 25.00 (ISBN 0-8369-6729-1). Ayer Co Pubs.

Murchland, Bernard. The Dream of Christian Socialism: An Essay on its European Origins. 74p. 1982. pap. 4.25 (ISBN 0-8447-3470-5). Am Enterprise.
Norman, Edward. The Victorian Christian Socialists. 210p. Date not set. price not set (ISBN 0-521-32515-3). Cambridge U Pr.
Raven, Charles E. Christian Socialism, Eighteen Forty-Eight to Eighteen Fifty-Four. 396p. 1968. Repr. of 1920 ed. 35.00x (F Cass Co). Biblio Dist.
--Christian Socialism, Eighteen Forty-Eight to Eighteen Fifty-Four. LC 68-56058. 1968. Repr. of 1920 ed. 35.00x (ISBN 0-678-05148-8). Kelley.
Stern, Frederick C. F. O. Matthiessen: Christian Socialist As Critic. LC 80-29013. xv, 281p. 1981. 27.50x (ISBN 0-8078-1478-4). U of NC Pr.
Tillich, Paul. Political Expectation. Adams, James L., ed. LC 83-10294. 208p. 1983. pap. text ed. 11.25 (ISBN 0-8191-3320-5). U Pr of Amer.

SOCIALISM AND CATHOLIC CHURCH

see also Communism and Religion

Arce, Sergio. The Church & Socialism. 200p. pap. text ed. 6.95 (ISBN 0-936123-00-1). NY Circus Pubns.
De Leon, Daniel. Abolition of Poverty. 8th ed. 1969. pap. text ed. 0.50 (ISBN 0-935534-00-8). NY Labor News.

SOCIALISM AND RELIGION

see also Christianity and Economics

Ballou, Adin. Practical Christian Socialism, 2 vols. 655p. 1985. Repr. of 1854 ed. Set. lib. bdg. 69.00 (ISBN 0-932051-86-3, Pub. by Am Repr Serv). Am Biog Serv.
Brohi, A. K. Iqbal & the Concept of Islamic Socialism. pap. 1.00 (ISBN 0-686-18447-5). Kazi Pubns.
Castro, Fidel & Betto, Frei. Fidel & Religion: Castro Talks on Revolution & Religion with Frei Betto. 1987. 19.95 (ISBN 0-671-64114-X). S&S.
Ferrarotti, Franco. A Theology for Nonbelievers: Post-Christian & Post-Marxist Reflections. LC 86-10782. (Studies in Social Thought: Polity & Civil Society). Tr. of Una Teologia per Atei. 208p. 1987. text ed. 21.50x (ISBN 0-8046-9401-X, 9401). Assoc Faculty Pr.
Hussain, M. N. Islam vs. Socialism. pap. 6.50 (ISBN 0-686-18569-2). Kazi Pubns.
Levin, Nora. Jewish Socialist Movements, Eighteen Seventy-One to Nineteen Seventeen: While Messiah Tarried. (Littman Library of Jewish Civilization). (Illus.). 566p. 1978. 32.00x (ISBN 0-19-710029-5). Oxford U Pr.
Linden, Franz. Sozialismus und Religion. Repr. of 1932 ed. 16.00 (ISBN 0-384-32740-0). Johnson Repr.
Nitti, Francesco. Catholic Socialism. 1976. lib. bdg. 69.95 (ISBN 0-8490-1586-3). Gordon Pr.
Smith, Donald E. Religion, Politics & Social Change in the Third World. LC 73-143516. 1951. 14.95 (ISBN 0-02-929490-8); pap. text ed. 6.95 (ISBN 0-02-929460-6). Free Pr.
Stumme, Wayne. Christians & the Many Faces of Marxism. LC 84-10980. 176p. (Orig.). 1984. pap. 8.95 (ISBN 0-8066-2087-0, 10-1195). Augsburg.
Wistrich, Robert S. Socialism & the Jews: The Dilemmas of Assimilation in Germany & Austria-Hungary. (Littman Library of Jewish Civilization). 1982. 37.50x (ISBN 0-19-710053-8). Oxford U Pr.

SOCIETY AND THE CHURCH

see Church and the World

SOCIETY FOR PROMOTING CHRISTIAN KNOWLEDGE, LONDON

Allen, William O. Two Hundred Years: The History of the Society for Promoting Christian Knowledge, 1698-1898. LC 76-135171. (Research & Source Works Ser.: No. 622). 1971. Repr. of 1898 ed. 32.00 (ISBN 0-8337-0044-8). B Franklin.

SOCIETY FOR THE PROPAGATION OF THE FAITH

Hickey, Edward J. The Society for the Propagation of the Faith: Its Foundation, Organization & Success (1822-1922) LC 73-3557. (Catholic University of America. Studies in American Church History: No. 3). Repr. of 1922 ed. 25.00 (ISBN 0-404-57753-9). AMS Pr.

SOCIETY FOR THE PROPAGATION OF THE GOSPEL IN FOREIGN PARTS, LONDON

Humphreys, David. Historical Account of the Incorporated Society for the Propagation of the Gospel in Foreign Parts - to the Year 1728. LC 75-83426. (Religion in America, Ser. 1). 1969. Repr. of 1730 ed. 21.00 (ISBN 0-405-00251-3). Ayer Co Pubs.
Kemp, William W. Support of Schools in Colonial New York by the Society for the Propagation of the Gospel in Foreign Parts. LC 78-176933. (Columbia University. Teachers College. Contributions to Education: No. 56). Repr. of 1913 ed. 22.50 (ISBN 0-404-55056-8). AMS Pr.
--Support of Schools in Colonial New York by the Society for the Propagation of the Gospel in Foreign Parts. LC 72-89192. (American Education: Its Men, Institutions, & Ideas, Ser. 1). 1969. Repr. of 1913 ed. 12.00 (ISBN 0-405-01430-9). Ayer Co Pubs.
Lydekker, John W. Faithful Mohawks. LC 68-18362. (Empire State Historical Publications Ser.: No. 50). (Illus.). 1968. Repr. of 1938 ed. 27.50 (ISBN 0-87198-050-9). Friedman.
Mayhew, Jonathan. Observations on the Charter & Conduct of the Society for the Propagation of the Gospel in Foreign Parts; Designed to Show Their Non-Conformity to Each Other. LC 72-38456. (Religion in America, Ser. 2). 180p. 1972. Repr. of 1763 ed. 15.00 (ISBN 0-405-04077-6). Ayer Co Pubs.
Ritchie, Carson I. Frontier Parish: An Account of the Society for the Propagation of the Gospel & the Anglican Church in America, Drawn from the Records of the Bishop of London. LC 75-3564. 210p. 1976. 18.50 (ISBN 0-8386-1735-2). Fairleigh Dickinson.

SOCIETY OF JESUS

see Jesuits

SOCIETY OF THE SACRED HEART

Williams, Margaret. The Society of the Sacred Heart: History of a Spirit 1800-1975. 406p. 1978. pap. 12.50 (ISBN 0-232-51395-3). Attic Pr.

SOCIOLOGY

see also Charities; Equality; Family; Poor; Population; Race Relations; Secret Societies; Slavery; Social Change; Social Conflict; Social Ethics; Social Problems

Baum, Gregory, ed. Sociology & Human Destiny: Studies in Sociology, Religion & Society. 224p. 1980. 14.50 (ISBN 0-8164-0110-1, HarpR). Har-Row.
Dubos, Rene. A God Within. LC 76-37224. 320p. 1973. pap. 8.95 (ISBN 0-684-13506-X, SL 458, ScribT). Scribner.
James, Henry. Society, the Redeemed Form of Man, & the Earnest of God's Omnipotence in Human Nature: Affirmed in Letters to a Friend. 1971. Repr. of 1879 ed. 35.00 (ISBN 0-384-26735-1). Johnson Repr.
Lucas, J. R. Weeping in Ramah. LC 85-70477. 250p. (Orig.). 1985. pap. 7.95 (ISBN 0-89107-357-4, Crossway Bks). Good News.
Martin, David, et al, eds. Sociology & Theology. 170p. 1980. 26.00x (ISBN 0-312-74007-7). St Martin.
Miller, Gwendolyn. Let's Be Friends. 64p. 1971. pap. 1.50 (ISBN 0-87178-933-7). Brethren.
Noyes, John H. The Way of Holiness. LC 75-337. (The Radical Tradition in America Ser.). 230p. 1975. Repr. of 1838 ed. 21.50 (ISBN 0-88355-240-X). Hyperion Conn.
Restivo, Sal. The Social Relations of Physics, Mysticism & Mathematics. 1983. lib. bdg. 49.50 (ISBN 90-277-1536-X, Pub. by Reidel Holland). Kluwer Academic.
Strharsky, Harry, ed. Must We Choose Sides? (Christian Committment for the '80s: Vol. 1). (Illus.). 128p. (Orig.). 1980. pap. 5.95 (ISBN 0-936476-01-X). Inter-Religious Task.
Tillich, Paul. Theology of Culture. 1983. 14.50 (ISBN 0-8446-6021-3). Peter Smith.
Wach, Joachim. Sociology of Religion. 1944. 12.00x (ISBN 0-226-86707-2). U of Chicago Pr.
Ward, W. Reginald. Theology, Sociology & Politics: The German Protestant Social Conscience 1890-1933. 250p. 1979. 29.90 (ISBN 3-261-04617-1). P Lang Pubs.

SOCIOLOGY, BIBLICAL

Here are entered works on social ideas, institutions, and teachings of the Bible as distinct from the social ideas, institutions and teachings developed by post-Biblical Judaism and Christianity.

see also Bible–Ethics; Sociology, Christian; Sociology, Jewish

Dana, H. E. El Mundo Del Nuevo Testamento. Villarello, Ildefonso, tr. 288p. 1982. pap. 4.95 (ISBN 0-311-04342-9). Casa Bautista.
Elliott, John H., ed. Social-Scientific Criticism of the New Testament. (Semeia Ser.: No. 35). pap. 9.95 (06 20 35). Scholars Pr GA.
Gillum, Perry & Allen, Rob, eds. Issues: A Biblical Perspective on Current Social Themes. 128p. (Orig.). 1986. pap. 3.95 (ISBN 0-934942-57-9); discussion kit 2.95 (ISBN 0-934942-83-8). White Wing Pub.
Gottwald, Norman K. The Tribes of Yahweh: A Sociology of the Religion of Liberated Israel, 1250-1050 B.C. LC 78-24333. 944p. (Orig.). 1979. pap. 19.95 (ISBN 0-88344-499-2). Orbis Bks.
Mackie, George M. Bible Manners & Customs. LC 84-230883. (Illus.). 192p. 1984. 6.95 (ISBN 0-8007-5179-5, Power Bks.). Revell.
Mott, Stephen C. Biblical Ethics & Social Change. 1982. 21.95x (ISBN 0-19-502947-X); pap. 9.95x (ISBN 0-19-502948-8). Oxford U Pr.
Sandeen, Ernest, ed. The Bible & Social Reform. LC 81-9294. (SBL The Bible In American Culture Ser.). 1982. 12.95 (ISBN 0-89130-531-9, 061206, Co-pub. by Fortress Pr). Scholars Pr GA.
Schottroff, Willy & Stegemann, Wolfgang, eds. God of the Lowly: Socio-Historical Interpretation of the Bible. LC 84-5152. Tr. of Der Gott der Kleinen Leute. 192p. (Orig.). 1984. pap. 9.95 (ISBN 0-88344-153-5). Orbis Bks.
Walsh, J. P. The Mighty from Their Thrones: Power in the Biblical Tradition. LC 86-45198. (Overtures to Biblical Theology Ser.). 224p. 1987. pap. 12.95 (ISBN 0-8006-1546-8). Fortress.
Wight, Fred H. Usos y Costumbres de las Tierras Biblicas. Orig. Title: Manners & Customs of Bible Lands. (Span.). 336p. 1981. pap. 7.95 (ISBN 0-8254-1873-9). Kregel.
Wilson, Robert R. Sociological Approaches to the Old Testament. LC 83-16607. (Guides to Biblical Scholarship). 96p. 1984. pap. 4.50 (ISBN 0-8006-0469-5, 1-469). Fortress.
Wright, Fred. Manners & Customs of Bible Lands. (Affordables Ser.). 336p. pap. 5.50 (ISBN 0-8024-0416-2). Moody.

SOCIOLOGY, CHRISTIAN

Here are entered works on social theory from a Christian point of view. The relationship of this heading to Church and Social Problems is that of abstract to concrete.

see also Christian Democracy; Christianity and Economics; Christianity and Progress; Church and Social Problems; Social Ethics; Social Gospel; Sociology, Biblical; Wealth, Ethics of; Work (Theology)

Abbott, Lyman. Christianity & Social Problems. LC 4-3768. Repr. of 1896 ed. 30.00 (ISBN 0-384-00074-6). Johnson Repr.
Alberione, James. Designs for a Just Society. (Divine Master Ser.). 1976. 6.00 (ISBN 0-8198-0400-2); pap. 5.00 (ISBN 0-8198-0401-0); wkbk 0.60 (ISBN 0-8198-0402-9). Dghtrs St Paul.
Belloc, Hilaire. The Crisis of Civilization. LC 73-114465. 245p. 1973. Repr. of 1937 ed. lib. bdg. 22.50x (ISBN 0-8371-4761-1, BECC). Greenwood.
Benestad, Brian J. The Pursuit of a Just Social Order: Policy Statements of the U. S. Catholic Bishops, 1966-80. LC 82-18326. 220p. 1982. 12.00 (ISBN 0-89633-060-5); pap. 7.00 (ISBN 0-89633-061-3). Ethics & Public Policy.
Berger, Peter L. The Precarious Vision. LC 76-1981. 238p. 1976. Repr. of 1961 ed. lib. bdg. 22.50x (ISBN 0-8371-8657-9, BEPV). Greenwood.
Bland, Salem. New Christianity. LC 72-95815. (Social History of Canada Ser.). 1973. pap. 6.00 (ISBN 0-8020-6179-6). U of Toronto Pr.
Boase, Paul H. The Rhetoric of Christian Socialism. 9.00 (ISBN 0-8446-0501-8). Peter Smith.
Brandt, Walter I. & Lehmann, Helmut T., eds. Luther's Works: The Christian in Society II, Vol. 45. LC 55-9893. 1962. 19.95 (ISBN 0-8006-0345-1, 1-345). Fortress.
Bruehl, Charles P. The Pope's Plan for Social Reconstruction. 10.00 (ISBN 0-8159-6507-9). Devin.
Carmody, John. The Quiet Imperative: Meditations on Justice & Peace Based on Readings from the New Testament. 176p. (Orig.). 1986. pap. 6.95 (ISBN 0-8358-0518-2). Upper Room.
Carroll, Jackson W., et al, eds. Handbook for Congregational Studies. 192p. (Orig.). 1986. pap. 16.95 (ISBN 0-687-16562-8). Abingdon.
The Church in a Changing Society. 508p. (Orig.). 1979. pap. text ed. 35.00x (ISBN 91-8558-207-7). Coronet Bks.
Clarke, Thomas E., ed. Above Every Name: The Lordship of Christ & Social Systems. LC 80-82082. (Woodstock Studies). 312p. (Orig.). 1980. pap. 8.95 (ISBN 0-8091-2338-X). Paulist Pr.
Colwell, Stephen. New Themes for the Protestant Clergy. LC 71-83417. (Religion in America, Ser. 1). 1969. Repr. of 1851 ed. 32.00 (ISBN 0-405-00243-2). Ayer Co Pubs.
Cox, Jeffrey. The English Churches in a Secular Society: Lambeth, 1870-1930. (Illus.). 1982. 45.00x (ISBN 0-19-503019-2). Oxford U Pr.
Curran, Charles E. Directions in Catholic Social Ethics. LC 84-28079. 304p. (Orig.). 1985. pap. text ed. 8.95 (ISBN 0-268-00853-1, 85-08533). U of Notre Dame Pr.
Day, Thomas I. Dietrich Bonhoeffer on Christian Community & Common Sense. LC 83-25900. (Toronto Studies in Theology: Vol. 11). 248p. 1983. 49.95x (ISBN 0-88946-752-8). E Mellen.
Deane, Herbert A. The Political & Social Ideas of St. Augustine. LC 63-9809. 356p. 1963. pap. 14.00x (ISBN 0-231-08569-9). Columbia U Pr.
Dombrowski, James. Early Days of Christian Socialism in America. 1966. lib. bdg. 19.50x (ISBN 0-374-92223-3, Octagon). Hippocrene Bks.
Eliot, T. S. Christianity & Culture. Incl. The Idea of a Christian Society; Notes Towards the Definition of Culture. 202p. 1960. pap. 5.95 (ISBN 0-15-617735-8, HB32, Harv). HarBraceJ.
Enroth, Ronald M. & Melton, Gordon J. Why Cults Succeed Where the Church Fails. 128p. 1985. 6.95 (ISBN 0-87178-932-9). Brethren.
Ferre, Nels F. Christianity & Society. facs. ed. LC 78-117791. (Essay Index Reprint Ser). 1950. 19.00 (ISBN 0-8369-1924-6). Ayer Co Pubs.
Forell, George W. Faith Active in Love. LC 15-5702. 1954. kivar 7.95 (ISBN 0-8066-0186-8, 10-2165). Augsburg.
Furfey, Paul H. Fire on the Earth. 17.00 (ISBN 0-405-10830-3, 11837). Ayer Co Pubs.
Gaede, S. D. Where Gods May Dwell: Understanding the Human Condition. 168p. (Orig.). 1985. pap. 7.95 (ISBN 0-310-42971-4, 12756P). Zondervan.
Gingerich, Melvin. The Christian & Revolution. LC 68-12028. (Conrad Grebel Lecture, No. 12). 1968. 12.95 (ISBN 0-8361-1573-2). Herald Pr.
Gladden, Washington. Tools & the Man: Property & Industry under the Christian Law. LC 75-353. (The Radical Tradition in America Ser). 308p. 1975. Repr. of 1893 ed. 23.65 (ISBN 0-88355-222-1). Hyperion Conn.
Haines, J. Harry. I'm Only One Person, What Can I Do? (Orig.). 1985. pap. 5.95 (ISBN 0-8358-0521-2). Upper Room.
Hargrove, Barbara, ed. Religion & the Sociology of Knowledge: Modernization & Pluralism in Christian Thought & Structure. LC 83-22149. (Studies in Religion & Society: Vol. 8). 412p. 1984. 59.95x (ISBN 0-88946-872-9). E Mellen.
Hartman, Robert H., ed. Poverty & Economic Justice: A Philosophical Approach. 1984. pap. 10.95 (ISBN 0-8091-2597-8). Paulist Pr.
Hauerwas, Stanley. A Community of Character: Toward a Constructive Christian Social Ethic. LC 80-53072. 320p. 1981. text ed. 20.00 (ISBN 0-268-00733-0). U of Notre Dame Pr.
Hawkins, Peter S. Getting Nowhere: Christian Hope & Utopian Dream. LC 85-12758. 133p. (Orig.). 1985. pap. 8.95 (ISBN 0-936384-28-X). Cowley Pubns.
Henderson, George. A Religious Foundation of Human Relations: Beyond Games. LC 76-62510. 1977. 15.95x (ISBN 0-8061-1398-7). U of Okla Pr.
Herron, George D. Between Caesar & Jesus. LC 75-324. (The Radical Tradition in America Ser). 278p. 1975. Repr. of 1899 ed. 23.10 (ISBN 0-88355-227-2). Hyperion Conn.
--Christian Society. 1969. Repr. of 1894 ed. 19.00 (ISBN 0-384-22640-X). Johnson Repr.
--Christian State: A Political Vision of Christ. (American Studies). 1969. Repr. of 1894 ed. 22.00 (ISBN 0-384-22650-7). Johnson Repr.
Hsia, R. Po-chia. Society & Religion in Munster. LC 83-14819. (Yale Historical Publications Ser.: No. 131). 320p. 1984. text ed. 27.50x (ISBN 0-300-03005-3). Yale U Pr.
Hughley, Neal. Trends in Protestant Social Idealism. LC 74-167359. (Essay Index Reprint Ser.). Repr. of 1948 ed. 18.00 (ISBN 0-8369-2771-0). Ayer Co Pubs.
Johnson, Roger A., ed. Views from the Pews: Christian Beliefs & Attitudes. LC 82-18237. 272p. 1983. pap. 15.95 (ISBN 0-8006-1695-2, 1-1695). Fortress.
Kee, Howard C. Christian Origins in Sociological Perspective: Methods & Resources. LC 79-26668. 204p. 1980. soft cover 9.95 (ISBN 0-664-24307-X). Westminster.
Kelly, George. Sacrament of Penance & Reconciliation. (Synthesis Ser). 96p. 1976. 0.75 (ISBN 0-8199-0701-4). Franciscan Herald.
Kinast, Robert L. Caring for Society. 168p. 1985. pap. 9.95 (ISBN 0-88347-197-3). Thomas More.
King, Morton B. & Hunt, Richard A. Measuring Religious Dimensions: Studies of Congregational Involvement. (Studies in Social Science: No. 1). 1972. pap. 5.95x (ISBN 0-87074-174-8). SMU Press.
Knight, Frank H. & Merriam, Thornton W. The Economic Order & Religion. LC 78-31760. 1979. Repr. of 1945 ed. lib. bdg. 24.75x (ISBN 0-313-20970-7, KNEO). Greenwood.
Kreider, Alan. The Ethics of Social Holiness: A Way of Living for God's Global Nation. 1987. 14.95 (ISBN 0-310-38390-0). Zondervan.
Lamb, Matthew L. Solidarity with Victims: Toward a Theology of Social Transformation. LC 81-22145. 176p. 1982. 12.95 (ISBN 0-8245-0471-2). Crossroad NY.
Lane, Christel. Christian Religion in the Soviet Union: A Sociological Study. LC 77-801. 1978. 49.50 (ISBN 0-87395-327-4). State U NY Pr.
Lane, Dermot A. Foundations for Social Theology: Praxis, Process & Salvation. (Orig.). 1984. pap. 7.95 (ISBN 0-8091-2622-2). Paulist Pr.

Latourette, Kenneth, ed. Gospel, the Church & the World. LC 76-134107. (Essay Index Reprint Ser). 1946. 18.00 (ISBN 0-8369-1972-6). Ayer Co Pubs.

Laughlin, Sceva B., ed. Beyond Dilemmas. LC 79-86035. (Essay & General Literature Index Reprint Ser). 1969. Repr. of 1937 ed. 25.50x (ISBN 0-8046-0567-X, Pub. by Kennikat). Assoc Faculty Pr.

Lavender, Lucille. They Cry, Too. 176p. 1986. pap. 6.95 (ISBN 0-310-41651-5, 9970P). Zondervan.

Lay Commission on Catholic Social Teaching & the U. S. Economy. Toward the Future: Catholic Social Thought & the U. S. Economy, a Lay Letter. 120p. 1985. pap. text ed. 4.75 (ISBN 0-8191-4860-1). U Pr of Amer.

Lindsay, Alexander D. Religion, Science, & Society in the Modern World. facsimile ed. LC 70-37847. (Essay Index Reprint Ser). Repr. of 1943 ed. 12.00 (ISBN 0-8369-2604-8). Ayer Co Pubs.

Little, David. Religion, Order, & Law: A Study in Pre-Revolutionary England. LC 84-2611. 270p. 1984. pap. text ed. 11.00x (ISBN 0-226-48546-3). U of Chicago Pr.

Liu, Tai. Puritan London: A Study of Religion & Society in the City Parishes. LC 85-40534. 256p. 1986. 38.50x (ISBN 0-87413-283-5, Pub. by U Delaware Pr). Assoc Univ Prs.

Lutz, Charles P., ed. God, Goods & the Common Good: Eleven Perspectives on Economic Justice in Dialog with the Roman Catholic Bishops' Pastoral Letter. 160p. (Orig.). 1987. pap. 9.95 (ISBN 0-8066-2286-5, 10-2563). Augsburg.

Lyon, David. Sociology & the Human Image. LC 83-22644. 220p. 1983. pap. 9.95 (ISBN 0-87784-843-2). Inter-Varsity.

McGavran, Donald. Understanding Church Growth. rev. ed. 488p. (Orig.). 1980. pap. 12.95 (ISBN 0-8028-1849-8). Eerdmans.

Manhattan, Avro. Catholic Imperialism & World Freedom. LC 73-161336. (Atheist Viewpoint Ser). 528p. 1972. Repr. of 1952 ed. 29.00 (ISBN 0-405-03810-0). Ayer Co Pubs.

Maranell, Gary M. Responses to Religion: Studies in the Social Psychology of Religious Belief. LC 73-19860. (Illus.). xviii, 314p. 1974. 25.00x (ISBN 0-7006-0114-7). U Pr of KS.

Martin, Hugh, ed. Christian Social Reformers of the Nineteenth Century. facsimile ed. LC 70-107725. (Essay Index Reprint Ser.). 1927. 18.00 (ISBN 0-8369-1526-7). Ayer Co Pubs.

Mayers, Marvin. Christianity Confronts Culture. (Contemporary Evangelical Perspectives Ser.). 10.95 (ISBN 0-310-28891-6, 10230P). Zondervan.

Meeks, Wayne A. The First Urban Christians: The Social World of the Apostle Paul. LC 82-8447. (Illus.). 296p. 1982. 30.00x (ISBN 0-300-02876-8). Yale U Pr.

Milet, Jean. God or Christ: The Excesses of Christocentricity. LC 81-5566. 288p. 1981. 14.95 (ISBN 0-8245-0104-7). Crossroad NY.

National Conference of Catholic Bishops. Economic Justice for All: Pastoral Letter in Catholic Social Teaching & U. S. Economy. 192p. 1986. pap. 2.95 (ISBN 1-55586-101-6). US Catholic.

Nida, Eugene A. Customs & Cultures: Anthropology for Christian Missions. 2nd ed. LC 54-8976. (Applied Cultural Anthropology Ser.). 306p. 1975. Repr. of 1954 ed. 7.95x (ISBN 0-87808-723-0). William Carey Lib.

Norman, E. R. Christianity & the World Order. 1979. pap. 6.95x (ISBN 0-19-283019-8). Oxford U Pr.

Our Fathers World. (Social Studies Ser.). 3.55 (ISBN 0-686-37694-3). Rod & Staff.

Phillips, Charles S. New Commandment: An Inquiry into the Social Precept & Practice of the Ancient Church. LC 31-31370. (Church Historical Society Ser.: No. 4). 1930. 10.00x (ISBN 0-8401-5004-0). A R Allenson.

Rauschenbusch, Walter. The Social Principles of Jesus. LC 76-50566. 1976. Repr. of 1916 ed. lib. bdg. 22.00 (ISBN 0-8414-7308-0). Folcroft.

Read, Ralph H., ed. Younger Churchmen Look at the Church. facsimile ed. LC 74-156708. (Essay Index Reprint Ser). Repr. of 1935 ed. 21.50 (ISBN 0-8369-2330-8). Ayer Co Pubs.

Ruether, Rosemary. Liberation Theology: Human Hope Confronts Christian History & American Power. LC 72-92263. Repr. of 1972 ed. 50.50 (ISBN 0-8357-9487-3, 2015212). Bks Demand UMI.

Ryan, John A. Questions of the Day. facs. ed. LC 67-26779. (Essay Index Reprint Ser). 1931. 20.00 (ISBN 0-8369-0846-5). Ayer Co Pubs.

Sappington, Roger E. The Brethren in Industrial America. 512p. 1985. 24.95 (ISBN 0-87178-111-5). Brethren.

Schwartz, Gary. Sect Ideologies & Social Status. LC 72-120598. 1970. 18.00x (ISBN 0-226-74216-4). U of Chicago Pr.

Segundo, Juan L. The Liberation of Theology. Drury, John, tr. from Spanish. LC 76-7049. Orig. Title: Liberation de la Tealogia. 248p. (Orig.). 1976. pap. 10.95 (ISBN 0-88344-286-8). Orbis Bks.

Shriver, William P. Immigrant Forces: Factors in the New Democracy. LC 74-145493. (The American Immigration Library). 312p. 1971. Repr. of 1913 ed. lib. bdg. 20.95x (ISBN 0-89198-026-1). Ozer.

Stackhouse, Max. Ethics & the Urban Ethos: An Essay in Social Theory & Theological Reconstruction. LC 77-179155. 240p. 1974. pap. 4.95x (ISBN 0-8070-1137-1, BP479). Beacon Pr.

Stott, John. Involvement, Vol. I: Being a Responsible Christian in a Non-Christian Society. (Crucial Questions Ser.). 224p. 1985. 13.95 (ISBN 0-8007-1418-0). Revell.

Tidball, Derek. The Social Context of the New Testament: A Sociological Analysis. 160p. 1984. pap. 7.95 (ISBN 0-310-45391-7, 12602P). Zondervan.

Tillich, Paul. Political Expectation. Adams, James L., ed. LC 83-10294. 208p. 1983. pap. text ed. 11.25 (ISBN 0-8191-3320-5). U Pr of Amer.

Underwood, Kenneth W. Protestant & Catholic. LC 72-9051. (Illus.). 484p. 1973. Repr. of 1957 ed. lib. bdg. 22.50x (ISBN 0-8371-6567-9, UNPC). Greenwood.

Vance, Norman. The Sinews of the Spirit: The Ideal of Christian Manlines in Victorian Literature & Religious Thought. 256p. 1985. 34.50 (ISBN 0-521-30387-7). Cambridge U Pr.

Wilkins, Ronald J. Achieving Social Justice: A Christian Perspective. (To Live Is Christ Ser.). 1981. pap. text ed. 5.95 (ISBN 0-697-01775-3); tchr's manual, pap. 4.00 (ISBN 0-697-01776-1); spirit masters 10.95 (ISBN 0-697-01777-X). Wm C Brown.

Wilson, Grace H. The Religious & Educational Philosophy of the Young Women's Christian Association. LC 70-177632. (Columbia University. Teachers College. Contributions to Education: No. 554). Repr. of 1933 ed. 22.50 (ISBN 0-404-55554-3). AMS Pr.

SOCIOLOGY, CHRISTIAN–BIBLICAL TEACHING

see Sociology, Biblical

SOCIOLOGY, CHRISTIAN–HISTORY

Best, Ernest E. Religion & Society in Transition: The Church & Social Change in England, 1560-1850. LC 82-21699. (Texts & Studies in Religion: Vol. 15). 353p. 1983. 59.95x (ISBN 0-88946-804-4). E Mellen.

Case, Shirley J. The Social Triumph of the Ancient Church. facsimile ed. LC 76-164596. (Select Bibliographies Reprint Ser). Repr. of 1933 ed. 18.00 (ISBN 0-8369-5880-2). Ayer Co Pubs.

Curran, Charles E. American Catholic Social Ethics: Twentieth Century Approaches. LC 82-4829. 336p. 1982. 24.95 (ISBN 0-268-00603-2). U of Notre Dame Pr.

--American Catholic Social Ethics: Twentieth-Century Approaches. LC 82-4829. 353p. 1984. text ed. 9.95 (ISBN 0-268-00609-1, 85-06099). U of Notre Dame Pr.

Hollinger, Dennis P. Individualism & Social Ethics: An Evangelical Syncretism. 284p. 1984. lib. bdg. 28.50 (ISBN 0-8191-3580-1); pap. text ed. 13.50 (ISBN 0-8191-3581-X). U Pr of Amer.

Markus, R. A. Saeculum: History & Society in the Theology of St Augustine. LC 71-87136. 1970. 54.50 (ISBN 0-521-07621-8). Cambridge U Pr.

Moser, Mary T. The Evolution of the Option for the Poor in France, 1880-1965. (Illus.). 216p. (Orig.). 1985. lib. bdg. 24.00 (ISBN 0-8191-4814-8); pap. text ed. 11.75 (ISBN 0-8191-4815-6). U Pr of Amer.

Mullin, Robert B. Episcopal Vision-American Reality: High Church Theology & Social Thought in Evangelical America. 1986. 20.00 (ISBN 0-300-03487-3). Yale U Pr.

Storey, John W. Texas Baptist Leadership & Social Christianity, 1900-1980. LC 85-40747. (Texas A&M Southwestern Studies: No. 5). (Illus.). 237p. 1986. 22.50x (ISBN 0-89096-251-0). Tex A&M Univ Pr.

Wagner, Donald O. Church of England & Social Reform since 1854. LC 77-127438. (Columbia University. Studies in the Social Sciences: No. 325). 12.50 (ISBN 0-404-51325-5). AMS Pr.

SOCIOLOGY, CHRISTIAN–MODERN, 1500-

see Sociology, Christian

SOCIOLOGY, HINDU

Bhardwaj, Surinder M. Hindu Places of Pilgrimage in India: A Study in Cultural Geography. LC 73-174454. (Center for South & Southeast Asia Studies, U.C. Berkeley). (Illus.). 1973. 42.50x (ISBN 0-520-02135-5); pap. 8.95 (ISBN 0-520-04951-9, CAL 621). U of Cal Pr.

Dange, Sindhu S. Hindu Domestic Rituals. 1986. 12.00x (ISBN 81-202-0138-8, Pub. by Ajanta). South Asia Bks.

Heimsath, Charles H. Indian Nationalism & Hindu Social Reform. LC 63-20660. pap. 98.30 (ISBN 0-317-08688-X, 2000888). Bks Demand UMI.

Ross, Aileen D. The Hindu Family in Its Urban Setting. LC 62-2801. pap. 84.80 (ISBN 0-317-09747-4, 2014388). Bks Demand UMI.

Sarkar, Benoy K. The Positive Background of Hindu Sociology, 2 vols. LC 73-3807. (Sacred Books of the Hindus: Nos. 16 & 25). Repr. of 1926 ed. Set. 74.50 (ISBN 0-404-57839-X). AMS Pr.

--The Positive Background of Hindu Sociology: Introduction to Hindu Positivism. LC 74-17338. (Sacred Books of the Hindus: 32). Repr. of 1937 ed. 74.50 (ISBN 0-404-57850-0). AMS Pr.

SOCIOLOGY, ISLAMIC

see also Islam and Economics

Abdul-Rauf, Muhammad. The Islamic View of Women & the Family. 1977. text ed. 11.95 (ISBN 0-8315-0156-1). Speller.

Ahmad, Imtiaz, ed. Caste & Social Stratification Among Muslims. 2nd ed. 1978. 16.00x (ISBN 0-8364-0050-X). South Asia Bks.

Coulson, N. J. Succession in the Muslim Family. 1971. 54.50 (ISBN 0-521-07852-0). Cambridge U Pr.

Geller, Ernest. Muslim Society. LC 80-41103. (Cambridge Studies in Social Anthropology: No. 32). 267p. 1983. pap. 12.95 (ISBN 0-521-27407-9). Cambridge U Pr.

Kotb, Sayed. Social Justice in Islam. LC 75-96205. 1969. Repr. of 1953 ed. lib. bdg. 20.00x (ISBN 0-374-94617-5, Octagon). Hippocrene Bks.

Levy, Reuben. Social Structure of Islam. 1957. 70.00 (ISBN 0-521-05544-X). Cambridge U Pr.

Munson, Henry, Jr. The House of Si Abd Allah: The Oral History of a Moroccan Family. LC 83-19837. 280p. 1984. 22.50x (ISBN 0-300-03084-3). Yale U Pr.

Nasr, Seyyed H. Islamic Life & Thought. LC 81-4723. 232p. 1981. 44.50 (ISBN 0-87395-490-4); pap. 14.95x (ISBN 0-87395-491-2). State U NY Pr.

Salem, Elie A. Political Theory & Institutions of the Khawarij. LC 78-64226. (Johns Hopkins University. Studies in the Social Sciences. Seventy-Fourth Ser. 1956: 2). Repr. of 1956 ed. 15.50 (ISBN 0-404-61328-4). AMS Pr.

Sharif, M. Islamic Social Framework. 14.50 (ISBN 0-686-18446-7). Kazi Pubns.

Turner, Bryan S. Weber & Islam: A Critical Study. 1978. pap. 9.95x (ISBN 0-7100-8942-2). Methuen Inc.

SOCIOLOGY, JEWISH

see also Jewish Way of Life; Judaism and Social Problems; Sociology, Biblical

Elkins, Dov P. Clarifying Jewish Values: Clarification Strategies for Jewish Groups. LC 77-83774. 1977. softbound 10.00 (ISBN 0-918834-02-3). Growth Assoc.

--Jewish Consciousness Raising: A Handbook of 50 Experiential Exercises for Jewish Groups. LC 77-83775. 1977. softbound 10.00 (ISBN 0-918834-03-1). Growth Assoc.

Finkelstein, Louis. Social Responsibility in an Age of Revolution. 1971. 10.00x (ISBN 0-685-31421-9, Pub. by Jewish Theol Seminary). Ktav.

Gordis, Robert. Root & the Branch: Judaism & the Free Society. LC 62-17133. 1962. 20.00x (ISBN 0-226-30411-6). U of Chicago Pr.

Graff, Gil. Separation of Church & State: Dina de-Malkhuta Dina in Jewish Law, 1750-1848. LC 84-24061. (Judaic Studies Ser.). ix, 224p. 1985. 29.50 (ISBN 0-8173-0264-6). U of Ala Pr.

Jewish Idea of Community. 1982. 9.95 (ISBN 0-686-76521-4). Feldheim.

Mayer, Egon. From Suburb to Shtetl: The Jews of Boro Park. (Illus.). 196p. 1979. 29.95 (ISBN 0-87722-161-8). Temple U Pr.

National Council of Jewish Women. Our Heritage Speaks: Applying Jewish Values to Contemporary Issues. (Module I - Care of Aging Parents). (Illus.). 30p. (Orig.). 1985. pap. 3.50 (ISBN 0-941840-23-9). NCJW.

SOCIOLOGY, RELIGIOUS

see Religion and Sociology

SOCIOLOGY AND RELIGION

see Religion and Sociology

SOCRATES

Afnan, Ruhi. Zoroaster's Influence on Anaxagoras, the Greek Tragedians & Socrates. LC 68-18733. 161p. 1969. 6.95 (ISBN 0-8022-2250-1). Philos Lib.

Apuleius. Apuleius on the God of Socrates. Taylor, Thomas, tr. (Lat.). 1984. pap. 4.95 (ISBN 0-916411-25-7, Pub. by Alexandrian Pr). Holmes Pub.

Eckstein, Jerome. The Deathday of Socrates: Living, Dying & Immortality-The Theater of Ideas in Plato's "Phaedo". 1981. 17.95 (ISBN 0-914366-19-X); pap. 12.95 (ISBN 0-914366-20-3). Vanguard.

Kreeft, Peter. Best Things in Life. LC 84-6697. 160p. (Orig.). 1984. pap. 6.95 (ISBN 0-87784-922-6). Inter-Varsity.

Santas, Gerasimos X. Socrates. 1982. pap. 10.95 (ISBN 0-7100-9327-6). Methuen Inc.

Wenley, R. M. Socrates & Christ. 1977. 59.95 (ISBN 0-8490-2621-0). Gordon Pr.

SOFISM

see Sufism

SOLOMON, KING OF ISRAEL

Barnard, J. H., ed. The Odes of Solomon. (Texts & Studies Ser.: No. 1, Vol. 8, Pt. 3). pap. 13.00 (ISBN 0-8115-1710-1). Kraus Repr.

Bernard of Clairvaux. Song of Solomon. 560p. 1984. smythe sewn 21.00 (ISBN 0-86524-177-5, 2202). Klock & Klock.

Charlesworth, James H. The Odes of Solomon. LC 77-21285. (SBL Texts & Translations). 192p. 1983. pap. 8.95 (ISBN 0-89130-202-6, 06 02 13). Scholars Pr GA.

Conway, Moncure D. Solomon & Solomonic Literature. LC 72-2032. (Studies in Comparative Literature, No. 35). 1972. Repr. of 1899 ed. lib. bdg. 49.95x (ISBN 0-8383-1478-3). Haskell.

Gutmann, Joseph, ed. The Temple of Solomon: Archaeological Fact & Medieval Tradition in Christian, Islamic & Jewish Art. LC 75-19120. 1976. 9.00 (ISBN 0-89130-013-9, 090103). Scholars Pr GA.

Ironside, Harry. Notas Sobre el Cantar de los Cantares. Orig. Title: Song of Solomon. (Span.). 128p. Date not set. pap. 4.75 (ISBN 0-8254-1328-1). Kregel.

Jordan, Bernice C. Fighting Giants: Joshua-Solomon 14 Lessons, Vol. 3. (Footsteps of Faith Ser.). 1957. pap. text ed. 2.50 (ISBN 0-86508-031-3); figures text 11.45 (ISBN 0-86508-032-1). BCM Intl Inc.

King Solomon & His Followers, No. 13, Minnesota. 200p. (Printed cipher code). fabricord 13.50 (ISBN 0-88053-255-6). Macoy Pub.

King Solomon & His Followers: No. 5, Ohio. 200p. (Printed cipher code). fabricord bdg. 13.50 (ISBN 0-88053-250-5). Macoy Pub.

Lindsay, Gordon. Solomon & Rehoboam. (Old Testament Ser.). 1.25 (ISBN 0-89985-145-2). Christ Nations.

McCord, David. A Loser, a Winner, & a Wise-Guy: Saul, David & Solomon. LC 79-67438. 96p. 1980. pap. 2.25 (ISBN 0-87239-380-1, 40084). Standard Pub.

Petersen, Mark E. Three Kings of Israel. LC 80-36697. 179p. 1980. 6.95 (ISBN 0-87747-829-5). Deseret Bk.

Thieberger, Frederic. King Solomon. (Illus.). 313p. 1978. pap. 6.95 (ISBN 0-85222-200-9). Hebrew Pub.

SOLOVYEV, VLADIMIR SERGEEVICH, 1853-1900

Allen, Paul M. Vladimir Soloviev: Russian Mystic, Vol. 9. LC 72-81592. (Spiritual Science Library). (Illus.). 544p. 1978. lib. bdg. 22.00 (ISBN 0-89345-032-4, Spiritual Sci Lib); pap. 10.00 (ISBN 0-89345-213-0, Steinerbks). Garber Comm.

SOMA

Gundry, R. Soma, in Biblical Theology, with Emphasis on Pauline Anthropology. LC 75-22927. (Society for New Testament Studies: No. 29). 300p. 1976. o. p. 54.50 (ISBN 0-521-20788-6). Cambridge U Pr.

SON OF MAN

Borsch, Frederick H. Christian & Gnostic Son of Man. LC 77-131585. (Studies in Biblical Theology, 2nd Ser.: No. 14). (Orig.). 1970. pap. text ed. 10.00x (ISBN 0-8401-3064-3). A R Allenson.

Higgins, A. J. The Son of Man in the Teaching of Jesus. LC 79-42824. (Society for New Testament Studies Monographs: No. 39). 186p. 1981. 32.50 (ISBN 0-521-22363-6). Cambridge U Pr.

Hooker, Morna. The Son of Man in Mark: A Study of the Background of the Term "Son of Man" & Its Use in St. Mark's Gospel. LC 67-4912. pap. 60.00 (ISBN 0-317-26028-6, 2023832). Bks Demand UMI.

Kim, Seyoon. The Son of Man As the Son of God. 128p. (Orig.). 1985. pap. 12.95x (ISBN 0-8028-0056-4). Eerdmans.

SONG-BOOKS, SUNDAY-SCHOOL

see Sunday-Schools–Hymns

SONGS

see also Carols; Children's Songs; Part-Songs also subdivision Songs and Music under specific subjects, classes of persons, societies, institutions, etc., e.g. Cowboys–Songs and Music

Beierle, Herbert L. Song of the Spirit. 1978. 20.00 (ISBN 0-940480-01-8). U of Healing.

Johnson, Gary L. Come Songbook. 1980. pap. 2.50 (ISBN 0-87123-777-6, 280777). Bethany Hse.

--Reminded of His Goodness Songbook. 32p. 1981. pap. 2.50 (ISBN 0-87123-779-2, 280779). Bethany Hse.

--Thanks Songbook. 32p. 1980. pap. 2.50 (ISBN 0-87123-776-8, 280776). Bethany Hse.

Jones, Joseph. Poems & Hymn Tunes As Songs: Metrical Partners. 84p. 1983. with 2 audio cassettes 24.50, (ISBN 0-88432-119-3, S1560). J Norton Pubs.
Kaung, Stephen. Songs of Degrees. Fader, Herbert L., ed. 1970. 4.00 (ISBN 0-935008-32-2); pap. 2.75 (ISBN 0-935008-33-0). Christian Fellow Pubs.
Lalitananda, Swami. Yoga Mystic Songs for Meditation, 6 Vols. 1975. pap. 2.99 ea. (ISBN 0-934664-19-6). Yoga Res Foun.
Lash, Jamie S. Roots & Fruits. Date not set. pap. 3.00 (ISBN 0-915775-04-2). Love Song Mess Assn.
Lund, Lynn S. Songs of Inspiration: Artistic Piano Arrangements of New Latter-day Saint Hymns. 40p. 1986. pap. text ed. 7.95 (ISBN 0-88290-276-8). Horizon Utah.
Schlink, Basilea. Songs & Prayers of Victory. 1978. pap. 1.50 (ISBN 3-87209-652-4). Evang Sisterhood Mary.
Stevens, Carolyn S. Children's Favorites: Inspirational Songs Arranged for the Piano. 40p. 1986. pap. 7.95 (ISBN 0-88290-275-X). Horizon Utah.
Taraporewala, Irach J., ed. The Divine Songs of Zarathushtra. LC 74-21251. Repr. of 1951 ed. 125.00 (ISBN 0-404-12802-5). AMS Pr.
Wilson, Valerie & Hull, Shirley, eds. Preschoolers Sing & Say. 1976. wire spiral 2.50 (ISBN 0-87227-045-9). Reg Baptist.
Wofford, Nat, ed. Showers of Blessings: Hymns for the Shower. 16p. 1986. pap. 4.95 (ISBN 0-942820-18-5). Steam Pr MA.

SONGS, INDIC

Acyutananda, Swami, ed. Songs of the Vaisnava Acaryas. 1979. pap. 6.95 (ISBN 0-912776-56-0). Bhaktivedanta.
Alokeranjan, Dasgupta. Roots in the Void: Baul Songs of Bengal. 1983. 5.00x (ISBN 0-8364-0972-8, Pub. by KP Bagchi India). South Asia Bks.
Mojumder, Atindra, tr. from Bengali. The Caryapadas: Tantric Poems of the Eighty-Four Mahasiddhas (Siddhacaryas) 2nd rev. ed. 225p. 1980. text ed. 13.95x (ISBN 0-935548-03-3). Santarasa Pubns.
Sri Chinmoy. Supreme, I Sing Only for You. 105p. (Orig.). 1974. pap. 2.00 (ISBN 0-88497-079-5). Aum Pubns.

SONGS, JEWISH

Belgrado, Fernando D., ed. Songs of the Synagogue of Florence, 2 vols. Incl. Vol. 1. The Three Festivals (ISBN 0-87203-108-X); Vol. 2. The High Holy Days. 0p (ISBN 0-87203-109-8). (Illus.). 60p. 1982. 32.95 ea. Hermon.
Coopersmith, Harry. Companion Volume to the Songs We Sing. 1950. 3.50x (ISBN 0-8381-0210-7). United Syn Bk.
--New Jewish Songbook. LC 65-14593. pap. 9.95x (ISBN 0-87441-060-6). Behrman.
--Songs We Sing. (Illus.). 1950. 22.50x (ISBN 0-8381-0723-0). United Syn Bk.
Kalisch, Shoshana & Meister, Barbara. Yes, We Sang! Songs of the Ghettos & Concentration Camps. LC 84-48172. (Illus.). 160p. 1985. 22.45 (ISBN 0-06-015448-9, HarpT). Har-Row.
Mlotek, Chane & Gottlieb, Malke, eds. Yontefdike Teg. (Songbook for the Holidays Ser.). (Illus.). 105p. pap. 6.00 (ISBN 0-318-20363-4). Workmen's Circle.
Mlotek, Eleanor G. Mir Trogn Agezang Yiddish Songbook. 239p. 1977. pap. 8.50. Workmen's Circle.
Mlotek, Eleanor G. & Gottlieb, Malke. We Are Here: Songs of the Holocaust in Yiddish & Singable English Translation. 104p. 1983. 10.00 (ISBN 0-686-40805-5). Workmen's Circle.
Nix, Verolga & Cleveland, Jefferson, eds. Songs of Zion. LC 81-8039. 352p. (Orig.). 1981. pap. 7.95 accompanist ed. (ISBN 0-687-39121-0); pap. 7.95 (ISBN 0-687-39120-2). Abingdon.
Scherman, Nosson. Zemiroth - Sabbath Songs. Zlotowitz, Meir, ed. (Artscroll Mesorah Ser.). 1979. 13.95 (ISBN 0-89906-156-7); pap. 10.95 (ISBN 0-89906-157-5). Mesorah Pubns.
Segal, Robert. Responsive Singing: Sabbath Morning Service. 184p. 1972. 4.50x (ISBN 0-8381-0218-2). United Syn Bk.
Segal, Yocheved. Our Sages Showed the Way, Vol. 1. Falk, Esther, tr. (Hebrew.). pap. 9.95 (ISBN 0-87306-289-2). Feldheim.
Shakow, Zara, compiled by. Curtain Time: Plays, Readings, Sketches, Cantatas, & Poems for Jewish Programs. 1985. pap. 9.95 (ISBN 0-8246-0310-9). Jonathan David.

SORCERY

see Witchcraft

SORIANO, FRANCESCO

Kniseley, S. Philip. Masses of Francesco Soriano: A Style-Critical Study. LC 67-22198. (University of Florida Humanities Monographs: No. 26). (Illus.). 1967. pap. 3.50 (ISBN 0-8130-0131-5). U Presses Fla.

SORROW

see Grief; Joy and Sorrow

SORROWS OF THE BLESSED VIRGIN MARY, DEVOTION TO

Faber, Frederick W. The Foot of the Cross: The Sorrows of Mary. LC 78-66303. 1978. pap. 10.00 (ISBN 0-89555-078-4). TAN Bks Pubs.
Jongen, H. Look-the Madonna Is Weeping. pap. 3.00 (ISBN 0-910984-12-3). Montfort Pubns.

SOUL

see also Animism; Future Life; Immortality; Personality; Psychology; Spirit; Spiritual Life

Almaas, A. H. Essence. LC 85-51109. (Illus.). 208p. (Orig.). 1986. pap. 10.95 (ISBN 0-87728-627-2). Weiser.
Ansari, F. R. The Existence of the Soul. pap. 1.00 (ISBN 0-686-18460-2). Kazi Pubns.
Avens, Roberts. Imaginal Body: Para-Jungian Reflections on Soul, Imagination & Death. LC 81-43814. 264p. (Orig.). 1982. lib. bdg. 29.00 (ISBN 0-8191-2411-7); pap. text ed. 13.25 (ISBN 0-8191-2412-5). U Pr of Amer.
Avicenna. Avicenna'a Psychology. Rahman, F., ed. LC 79-2848. 127p. 1984. Repr. of 1952 ed. 15.25 (ISBN 0-8305-0024-3). Hyperion Conn.
Bettelheim, Bruno. Freud & Man's Soul. LC 82-47809. 112p. 1983. 11.95 (ISBN 0-394-52481-0). Knopf.
Bibago, Abraham. Derek Emunah: The Path of Faith. 204p. 1521. text ed. 49.68x (ISBN 0-576-80102-X, Pub. by Gregg Intl Pubs England). Gregg Intl.
Birdsong, Robert E. Way of the Immortal Threefold Self: The Straight Path. (Aquarian Academy Monograph: Ser. E, No. 4). 1980. pap. 1.45 (ISBN 0-917108-29-9). Sirius Bks.
--Way of the Soul: The "Heart Path" to Human Perfection. (Aquarian Academy Monograph: Ser. D, No. 2). 1980. pap. 1.45 (ISBN 0-917108-28-0). Sirius Bks.
--Way of the Spirit: The "Head Path" to Human Perfection, Ser. C, No. 2. (Aquarian Academy Monograph). 1980. pap. 1.45 (ISBN 0-917108-27-2). Sirius Bks.
Boehme, Jacob. A Discourse Between Two Souls. pap. 3.95 (ISBN 0-916411-89-3). Sure Fire.
Brengle, Samuel L. Helps to Holiness. 1978. pap. 3.95 (ISBN 0-86544-003-4). Salv Army Suppl South.
Bullinger, Ethelbert W. Word Studies on the Holy Spirit. LC 85-7631. 232p. 1985. pap. 7.95 (ISBN 0-8254-2246-9). Kregel.
Burns, Norman T. Christian Mortalism from Tyndale to Milton. LC 72-75406. 224p. 1972. 16.50x (ISBN 0-674-12875-3). Harvard U Pr.
Carr, Clare, ed. The Gathering of Souls. Freelander, Iris. LC 81-69576. 240p. 1981. pap. 11.00 (ISBN 0-910378-17-7). Christward.
Cavarnos, Constantine. Modern Greek Philosophers on the Human Soul. LC 86-83011. (Illus.). 144p. 1987. pap. 6.95. Inst Byzantine.
Charleton, Walter. The Immorality of the Human Soul, Demonstrated by the Light of Nature: In Two Dialogues. LC 83-46043. (Scientific AWakeningin the Restoration Ser.: No. 2). (Illus.). 224p. 1985. Repr. of 1657 ed. 87.50 (ISBN 0-404-63302-1). AMS Pr.
Clymer, R. Swinburne. Ciencia del Alma. Aparis, Fina, tr. (Span.). 272p. (Orig.). 1967. pap. 6.95 (ISBN 0-932785-51-4). Philos Pub.
--La Filosofia del Fuego. Morel, Hector V., tr. Tr. of The Philosophy of Fire. (Span.). 190p. (Orig.). 1980. pap. 5.95 (ISBN 0-932785-54-9). Philos Pub.
Clymer, R. Swinburne & Lippard, George. Cristification: And la Hermanidad de la Rosa Cruz. 2nd ed. Bucheli, J. E., tr. (Span.). 206p. 1980. pap. 6.95 (ISBN 0-932785-52-2). Philos Pub.
Colton, Ann R. The Soul & the Ethic. 262p. 1965. 7.95 (ISBN 0-917187-07-5). A R C Pub.
Critchlow, Keith. The Soul As Sphere & Androgyne. (Illus., Orig.). 1985. pap. 4.95 (ISBN 0-933999-28-3). Phanes Pr.
Culianu, Ioan P. Psychanodia I: A Survey of the Evidence Concerning the Ascension of the Soul & its Relevance. (Etudes Preliminaires aux Religions Orientales dans l'Empire Romain Ser.: No. 99). 81p. 1983. pap. text ed. 19.95x (ISBN 90-04-06903-8, Pub. by EJ Brill Holland). Humanities.
Drakeford, John W. Psychology in Search of a Soul. LC 64-15096. 1964. 11.95 (ISBN 0-8054-6701-7). Broadman.
Du Prel, Carl. The Philosophy of Mysticism, 2vols. in 1. Massey, C. C., tr. LC 75-36838. (Occult Ser.). 1976. Repr. of 1889 ed. 51.00x (ISBN 0-405-07951-6). Ayer Co Pubs.
Egan, Maurice F. The Life of St. Francis & the Soul of Modern Man. (Illus.). 131p. 1983. 88.85 (ISBN 0-89266-427-4). Am Classical Coll Pr.
Finamore, John. Iamblichus & the Theory of the Vehicle of the Soul. (APA-American Classical Studies). 1985. pap. 12.95 (ISBN 0-89130-883-0, 40-04-14). Scholars Pr GA.
Garfield, Samuel. The Immortality of the Soul & the Perfectibility of Man. (Illus.). 1977. 45.00 (ISBN 0-89266-026-0). Am Classical Coll Pr.
--The Life of the Spirit: The Immortality of the Soul & the Perfectibility of Man. (Illus.). 1978. deluxe bdg. 41.45 (ISBN 0-930582-04-7). Gloucester Art.
Hartman, Edwin. Substance, Body & Soul: Aristotelian Investigations. LC 77-71984. 1977. text ed. 34.50x (ISBN 0-691-07223-X). Princeton U Pr.
Hirsch, W. Rabbinic Psychology. LC 73-2208. (The Jewish People; History, Religion, Literature Ser.). Repr. of 1947 ed. 24.50 (ISBN 0-405-05272-3). Ayer Co Pubs.
John-Roger. The Consciousness of Soul. LC 77-81388. 1977. pap. 5.00 (ISBN 0-914829-05-X). Baraka Bk.
--Journey of the Soul. LC 77-81387. 1977. pap. 5.00 (ISBN 0-914829-12-2). Baraka Bk.
Kappeler, Max. Compendium for the Study of Christian Science: No. 6, Soul. 23p. 1952. pap. 3.50 (ISBN 0-85241-060-3). Kappeler Inst Pub.
Kenner, Dru A. My Friend Consider. LC 84-51459. 100p. (Orig.). 1985. pap. 4.95 (ISBN 0-930551-00-1). Vistara Pubns.
Kerenyi, Karl. Hermes-Guide of Souls: The Mythologem of the Masculine Source of Life. Stein, Murray, tr. LC 85-18263. (Dunquin Ser.: No. 7). 104p. 1986. pap. 8.50 (ISBN 0-88214-207-0). Spring Pubns.
Kugelmann, Robert. The Windows of Soul. LC 81-70032. 220p. 1983. 24.50 (ISBN 0-8387-5035-4). Bucknell U Pr.
Kurz, Ron. Step into Heaven, Here & Now: The Acrobatics of Soul. 48p. (Orig.). 1986. pap. 4.95 (ISBN 0-939829-00-2). R Kurz.
Laird, John. The Idea of the Soul. 1979. Repr. lib. bdg. 25.00 (ISBN 0-8495-3333-3). Arden Lib.
--Idea of the Soul. LC 76-107811. (Select Bibliographies Reprint Ser). 1924. 18.00 (ISBN 0-8369-5207-3). Ayer Co Pubs.
Leadbeater, C. W. The Soul & Its Vestures. 24p. 1983. pap. 1.50 (ISBN 0-918980-12-7). St Alban Pr.
Martell, Dwane K. The Nature of the Soul & Its Ultimate Goals. (Science of Man Library). (Illus.). 109p. 1983. 47.25 (ISBN 0-89920-048-6). Am Inst Psych.
Matrisian, Hugo. The Physiology of the Soul. (Illus.). 129p. 1980. deluxe ed. 49.75 (ISBN 0-89266-261-1). Am Classical Coll Pr.
Michaelsen, Robert S. The American Search for Soul. LC 74-82005. (Rockwell Lecture Ser.). 132p. 1975. 15.95x (ISBN 0-8071-0097-8). La State U Pr.
Mueller, Friedrich M. Anthropological Religion. LC 73-18822. (Gifford Lectures: 1891). 1975. Repr. of 1892 ed. 34.00 (ISBN 0-404-11428-8). AMS Pr.
Nee, Watchman. The Latent Power of the Soul. Kaung, Stephen, tr. 1972. pap. 2.50 (ISBN 0-935008-25-X). Christian Fellow Pubs.
--The Salvation of the Soul. Kaung, Stephen, tr. 1978. pap. 2.75 (ISBN 0-935008-31-4). Christian Fellow Pubs.
Phylos. The Growth of a Soul. LC 76-15521. 10.00 (ISBN 0-912216-07-7). Angel Pr.
Plato. Dialogue of the Immortality of the Soul. LC 73-161797. Repr. of 1713 ed. 20.00 (ISBN 0-404-54134-8). AMS Pr.
Preus, Mary. Eloquence & Ignorance in Augustine's "On the Nature & Origin of the Soul". (AAR Academy Ser.). 1986. 19.95 (ISBN 0-89130-927-6, 01-01-51); pap. 15.25 (ISBN 0-89130-928-4). Scholars Pr Ga.
Purce, Jill. The Mystic Spiral: Journey of the Soul. (Art & Imagination Ser.). (Illus.). 128p. 1980. pap. 10.95 (ISBN 0-500-81005-2). Thames Hudson.
--The Mystic Spiral: Journey of the Soul. 1983. 17.00 (ISBN 0-8446-5993-2). Peter Smith.
Quitoriano, James H. The Psychology of the Soul. (Illus.). 1979. 47.50 (ISBN 0-89266-204-2). Am Classical Coll Pr.
Randolph, Paschal B. Soul! The Soul World! Clymer, R. Swinburne, ed. 246p. 1932. 9.95 (ISBN 0-932785-45-X). Philos Pub.
Rank, Otto. The Psychology of the Soul, 2 vols. (Illus.). 201p. 1986. Set. 147.55 (ISBN 0-89920-127-X). Am Inst Psych.
Reyes, Benito F. Scientific Evidence of the Existence of the Soul. rev. ed. LC 70-122432. 1970. (Quest); pap. 7.50 (ISBN 0-8356-0404-7, Dist. by World Univ Amer). Theos Pub Hse.
Rusche, Franz. Blut, Leben und Seele, Ihr Verhaeltnis Nach Auffassung der Griechischen und Hellenistischen Antike, der Bibel und der Alten Alexandrinischen Theologen. Repr. of 1930 ed. 34.00 (ISBN 0-384-52515-6). Johnson Repr.
St. Augustine. Immortality of the Soul & Other Works. (Fathers of the Church Ser.: Vol. 4). 489p. 1947. 29.95x (ISBN 0-8132-0004-0). Cath U Pr.
Sanger, C. Bert. The Art of Travel by Soul: An Out of Body Experience. (Illus.). 150p. 1986. 15.00 (ISBN 0-9615362-0-9). Popular Pubns.
School of Philosophy Editorial Committee. The Physical & Transcendental Analysis of the Soul. 74p. 1986. 47.50 (ISBN 0-89266-565-3). Am Classical Coll Pr.
Stavely, Lilian. The Golden Fountain or the Soul's Love for God. LC 82-70082. (The Library of Traditional Wisdom). 95p. 1982. pap. 4.75 (ISBN 0-941532-02-X). Wrld Wisdom Bks.
Steiner, Rudolf. Christ & the Human Soul. 4th ed. 81p. 1984. pap. 6.50 (ISBN 0-85440-013-3, Pub. by Steinerbooks). Anthroposophic.
--The Human Soul & the Universe. (q). Orig. Title: Cosmic & Human Metamorphoses. 24p. 1982. pap. 2.95 (ISBN 0-919924-17-4, Pub. by Steiner Book Centre Canada). Anthroposophic.
--Metamorphoses of the Soul: Path of Experience, 2 vols. 2nd ed. Davy, Charles & Von Arnim, Christian, trs. from Ger. 1983. Set. pap. 12.00 ea. (ISBN 0-317-13485-X). Vol. 1: 171 pgs (ISBN 0-85440-414-7, Pub. by Steinerbooks). Vol. 2: 150 pgs (ISBN 0-85440-415-5, Pub. by Steinerbooks). Anthroposophic.
--The Waking of the Human Soul & the Forming of Destiny - The Need for Understanding Christ. Wannamaker, Olin D., tr. (Ger.). 25p. 1983. pap. 3.00 (ISBN 0-919924-19-0, Pub by Steiner Book Centre Canada). Anthroposophic.
Swedenborg, Emmanuel. The Theory of the Soul, 2 vols. (Illus.). 245p. 1986. Set. 187.45 (ISBN 0-89901-261-2). Found Class Reprints.
Swinburne, Richard. The Evolution of the Soul. 320p. 1986. 45.00x (ISBN 0-19-824915-2). Oxford U Pr.
Tebaldus, Massimiliano. Jews, Christians & the Theory of the Soul: New Discoveries in Classical Theology. (Illus.). 138p. 1984. 88.95 (ISBN 0-89266-480-0). Am Classical Coll Pr.
Thurston, Mark. Discovering Your Soul's Purpose. (Illus.). 161p. (Orig.). 1984. pap. 6.95 (ISBN 0-87604-157-8). ARE Pr.
--Discovering Your Soul's Purpose. 175p. 1984. with cassettes 24.95 (ISBN 0-87604-186-1). Allen Unwin.
--Discovering Your Soul's Purpose. 1984. 24.95 (ISBN 0-87604-186-1); incl 4 cassette tapes in vinyl binder. ARE Pr.
Tobin, Thomas H. Timaios of Locri, on the Nature of the World & the Soul. (Society of Biblical Literature, Texts & Translations Ser.: No. 26). 1985. 14.95 (ISBN 0-89130-767-2, 06 02 26); pap. 9.95 (ISBN 0-89130-742-7). Scholars Pr GA.
Tomval-Valtom. Soul Mates. 96p. (Orig.). 1985. pap. 5.95 (ISBN 0-9615048-0-3). St Thomas Pub.
Vann, Vicki. The Growth of the Soul from Impiety to Ecstasy. (Illus.). 1977. pap. 3.25 (ISBN 0-87516-235-5). De Vorss.
Wijsenbeek-Wijler, H. Aristotle's Concept of Soul, Sleep, & Dreams. 260p. 1978. pap. text ed. 53.50 (Pub. by A M Hakkert). Coronet Bks.
Winslow, Octavius. Personal Declension & Revival of Religion in the Soul. 1978. pap. 3.95 (ISBN 0-85151-261-5). Banner of Truth.

SOUTH AFRICA–BIOGRAPHY

Cassidy, Michael. Bursting the Wineskins: Spiritual Odyssey of a Peacemaker. 280p. 1983. pap. 6.95 (ISBN 0-87788-094-8). Shaw Pubs.
Davies, Horton. Great South African Christians. LC 70-104242. Repr. of 1951 ed. lib. bdg. 22.50x (ISBN 0-8371-3916-3, DAGC). Greenwood.
Helman, Ethel. An Autumn Life: How a Surgeon Faced His Fatal Illness. 120p. (Orig.). 1986. pap. 6.95 (ISBN 0-571-13704-0). Faber & Faber.

SOUTH AFRICA–CHURCH HISTORY

Hope, Marjorie & Young, James. South African Churches in a Revolutionary Situation. LC 81-9584. 288p. (Orig.). 1981. pap. 9.95 (ISBN 0-88344-466-6). Orbis Bks.
Moodie, T. Dunbar. The Rise of Afrikanerdom: Power, Apartheid, & the Afrikaner Civil Religion. LC 72-85512. (Perspectives on Southern Africa Ser). 1975. pap. 5.95 (ISBN 0-520-03943-2, CAL 433). U of Cal Pr.
Walshe, Peter. Church Versus State in South Africa: The Case of the Christian Institute. LC 82-14533. xvi, 256p. (Orig.). 1983. 19.95 (ISBN 0-88344-097-0). Orbis Bks.

SOUTH AFRICA–DESCRIPTION AND TRAVEL

Livingston, David. Missionary Travels & Researches in South Africa. LC 5-15250. 1971. Repr. of 1857 ed. 62.00 (ISBN 0-384-32983-7). Johnson Repr.
Moffat, Robert. Missionary Labours & Scenes in Southern Africa. (Landmarks in Anthropology Ser). (Illus.). 1969. Repr. of 1842 ed. 32.00 (ISBN 0-384-39470-1). Johnson Repr.
Shaw, Barnabas. Memorials of South Africa. LC 71-109358. Repr. of 1840 ed. cancelled (ISBN 0-8371-3737-3, SMS&, Pub. by Negro U Pr). Greenwood.

SOUTH AFRICA–RACE RELATIONS

Boesak, Allan A. & Villa-Vicencio, Charles, eds. When Prayer Makes News. 192p. (Orig.). 1986. pap. 10.95 (ISBN 0-664-24035-6). Westminster.

Brookes, Edgar H. Three Letters from Africa. LC 65-12948. (Orig.). 1965. pap. 2.50x (ISBN 0-87574-139-8, 139). Pendle Hill.
Brookes, Edgar H. & Vandenbosch, Amry. The City of God & the City of Man in Africa. LC 64-13998. (Illus.). 144p. 1964. 12.00x (ISBN 0-8131-1091-2). U Pr of Ky.
Cloete, G. D., ed. A Moment of Truth: The Confession of the Dutch Reformed Mission Church, 1982. 176p. (Orig.). 1984. pap. 10.95x (ISBN 0-8028-0011-4). Eerdmans.
De Gruchy, John W. & Villa-Vicencio, Charles, eds. Apartheid Is a Heresy. 208p. (Orig.). 1983. pap. 5.95 (ISBN 0-8028-1972-9). Eerdmans.
The Kairos Document: Challenge to the Churches. 80p. (Orig.). 1986. pap. 4.95 (ISBN 0-8028-0189-7). Eerdmans.
Stevens, Richard J. Community Beyond Division: Chrisitan Life under South Africa's Apartheid System. 1984. 8.95 (ISBN 0-533-05729-9). Vantage.

SOUTH AFRICA–RELIGION
Balsiger, David W., ed. & intro. by. Family Protection Scoreboard, Special Edition on South Africa, No. 1. 56p. 1987. 2.95 (ISBN 0-89921-021-X). Biblical News Serv.
De Gruchy, John W. The Church Struggle in South Africa. 2nd ed. 300p. 1986. pap. 10.95 (ISBN 0-8028-0243-5). Eerdmans.
DeGruchy, John W. Theology & Ministry in Context & Crisis: A South African Perspective. 182p. (Orig.). 1987. pap. 9.95 (ISBN 0-8028-0290-7). Eerdmans.
Kretzschmar, Louise. The Voice of Black Theology in South Africa. 136p. 1986. pap. 10.95 (ISBN 0-86975-269-3, Pub. by Ravan Pr). Ohio U Pr.
Mosala, Itumeleng & Tlhagale, Buti, eds. Hammering Swords Into Ploughshares: Essays in Honor of Archbishop Mpilo Desmond Tutu. 360p. (Orig.). 1987. pap. 12.95 (ISBN 0-8028-0269-9). Eerdmans.
Mosala, Itumeleng J. & Tlhagale, Buti, eds. The Unquestionable Right to Be Free: Black Theology from South Africa. 224p. (Orig.). 1986. pap. 11.95 (ISBN 0-88344-251-5). Orbis Bks.
Santmire, H. Paul. South African Testament: From Personal Encounter to Theological Challenge. 266p. (Orig.). 1987. pap. 7.95 (ISBN 0-8028-0266-4). Eerdmans.
South African Evangelicals. Evangelical Witness in South Africa: An Evangelical Critique of Evangelical Theology & Practice. 46p. (Orig.). 1987. pap. 3.95 (ISBN 0-8028-0291-5). Eerdmans.

SOUTH AFRICA–SOCIAL LIFE AND CUSTOMS
Dumont, Louis. Une Sous-Caste de L'Inde du Sud: Organisation Sociale et Religion des Pramalai Kallar. (Le Monde D'outre Mer Passe et Present Etudes: No. 1). (Fr.). 1957. pap. text ed. 21.60x (ISBN 0-686-22530-9). Mouton.
Mendelssohn, S. Judaic or Semitic Legends & Customs Amongst South African Natives. 1976. lib. bdg. 59.95 (ISBN 0-8490-2111-1). Gordon Pr.

SOUTH AMERICA–RELIGION
Browman, David L., ed. Spirits, Shamans, & Stars: Perspectives from South America. Scwartz, Ronald A. (World Anthropology Ser.). 1979. text ed. 28.50x (ISBN 90-279-7890-5). Mouton.

SOUTHERN BAPTIST CONVENTION
Baker, Robert A. The Southern Baptist Convention & Its People. 18.95 (ISBN 0-8054-6516-2). Broadman.
Barnhart, Joe E. The Southern Baptist Holy War. LC 86-5988. 256p. 1986. pap. 16.95 (ISBN 0-87719-037-2). Texas Month Pr.
Beale, David O. S. B. C.: House on the Sand? 246p. (Orig.). 1985. pap. 4.95 (ISBN 0-89084-281-7). Bob Jones Univ Pr.
Bennett, Harold G. Reflections of Faith. LC 81-67326. 1983. pap. 5.95 (ISBN 0-8054-6565-0). Broadman.
Brigham, Judith. A Historical Study of the Educational Agencies of the Southern Baptist Convention, 1845-1945. LC 77-177047. (Columbia University. Teachers College. Contributions to Education Ser.: No. 974). Repr. of 1951 ed. 17.50 (ISBN 0-404-55974-3). AMS Pr.
Cox, Norman W., ed. Encyclopedia of Southern Baptists, Vols. I & II. LC 58-5417. (Illus.). 1958. 39.95 (ISBN 0-8054-6501-4). Broadman.
Eighmy, John L. Churches in Cultural Captivity: A History of the Social Attitudes of Southern Baptists. LC 70-111047. 1972. 22.50x (ISBN 0-87049-115-6). U of Tenn Pr.
Elder, Lloyd. Blueprints. LC 84-7634. 1984. 7.50 (ISBN 0-8054-6581-2). Broadman.
Garrett, James L., Jr. & Hinson, E. Glenn. Are Southern Baptists "Evangelicals"? LC 82-18870. 247p. 1983. 14.95 (ISBN 0-86554-033-0, MUP-H44). Mercer Univ Pr.
Hefley, James C. The Truth in Crisis: The Controversy in the Southern Baptist Convention. LC 86-70962. 208p. 1986. pap. 7.95 (ISBN 0-937969-00-1). Criterion Pubns.
Lovette, Roger. Questions Jesus Raised. LC 85-15137. 1986. 4.95 (ISBN 0-8054-2259-5). Broadman.
McClellan, Albert, compiled by. Meet Southern Baptists. LC 78-52960. (Illus.). 1978. pap. 7.95 (ISBN 0-8054-6534-0). Broadman.
May, Lynn, ed. Encyclopedia of Southern Baptists, Vol. IV. LC 81-66989. 1982. 19.95 (ISBN 0-8054-6556-1). Broadman.
--Encyclopedia of Southern Baptists: Index to Vols. I-IV. 1982. pap. 1.75 (ISBN 0-8054-6562-6). Broadman.
Shurden, Walter B. Not a Silent People: Controversies That Have Shaped Southern Baptists. LC 79-178066. 128p. 1972. 6.50 (ISBN 0-8054-8801-4). Broadman.
Spain, Rufus B. At Ease in Zion: A Social History of Southern Baptists, 1865-1900. LC 66-10367. 1967. 12.95x (ISBN 0-8265-1096-5). Vanderbilt U Pr.
Tanner, William G. From Sea to Shining Sea. LC 86-9609. 1986. pap. 4.95 (ISBN 0-8054-5667-8). Broadman.
Thompson, James J. Jr. Tried As by Fire: Southern Baptists & the Religious Controversies of the 1920's. LC 82-8056. xvi, 224p. 1982. 13.95 (ISBN 0-86554-032-2, MUP-H62). Mercer Univ Pr.
Tull, James E. A History of Southern Baptist Landmarkism in the Light of Historical Baptist Ecclesiology: Doctoral Dissertation. Gaustad, Edwin S., ed. LC 79-52578. (Baptist Tradition Ser.). 1980. lib. bdg. 64.00x (ISBN 0-405-12446-5). Ayer Co Pubs.
Valentine, Foy D. & Gaustad, Edwin S., eds. A Historical Study of Southern Baptists & Race Relations 1917-1947: Doctoral Dissertation. LC 79-52579. (The Baptist Tradition Ser.). 1980. lib. bdg. 23.00x (ISBN 0-405-12447-3). Ayer Co Pubs.
Woolley, Davis C., ed. Encyclopedia of Southern Baptists, Vol. III. LC 58-5417. (Illus.). 1971. 19.95 (ISBN 0-8054-6511-1). Broadman.

SOUTHERN METHODIST UNIVERSITY
Thomas, Mary M. Southern Methodist University: Founding & Early Years. LC 74-80248. (Illus.). 1974. 15.00 (ISBN 0-87074-138-1). SMU Press.

SOUTHERN STATES–CHURCH HISTORY
Bailey, Kenneth K. Southern White Protestantism in the Twentieth Century. 15.50 (ISBN 0-8446-1035-6). Peter Smith.
Boney, F. N. Southerners All. LC 84-9127. x, 218p. 1984. 17.95 (ISBN 0-86554-114-0, MUP-P19); 12.95 (ISBN 0-86554-189-2). Mercer Univ Pr.
Caldwell, Erskine. Deep South: Memory & Observation. LC 80-16013. (Brown Thrasher Bks.). 270p. 1980. pap. 6.95 (ISBN 0-8203-0525-1). U of Ga Pr.
Harrell, David E., Jr., ed. Varieties of Southern Evangelicalism. LC 81-11312. xii, 114p. 1981. 9.95 (ISBN 0-86554-015-2, MUP-H18). Mercer Univ Pr.
Hill, Samuel S. The South & the North in American Religion. LC 80-234. (Mercer University Lamar Memorial Lecture Ser.: No. 23). 168p. 1980. 14.00x (ISBN 0-8203-0516-2). U of Ga Pr.
Mathews, Donald G. Religion in the Old South. LC 77-587. 1979. pap. 11.00x (ISBN 0-226-51002-6, P819, Phoen). U of Chicago Pr.
On Jordan's Stormy Banks: Religion in the South (A Southern Exposure Profile) Hill, Samuel S., Jr., ed. LC 82-14524. vi, 160p. 1982. pap. 11.95 (ISBN 0-86554-035-7, MUP-P10). Mercer Univ Pr.

SOUTHERN STATES–CIVILIZATION
Bruce, Dickson D., Jr. And They All Sang Hallelujah: Plain-Folk Camp-Meeting Religion, 1800-1845. LC 74-11344. (Illus.). 1974. 13.50x (ISBN 0-87049-157-1); pap. 5.95x (ISBN 0-87049-310-8). U of Tenn Pr.

SOUTHERN STATES–SOCIAL LIFE AND CUSTOMS
Connelly, Thomas L. & Bellows, Barbara. God & General Longstreet: The Lost Cause & the Southern Mind. 1982. 14.95 (ISBN 0-8071-1020-5). La State U Pr.

SOUTHWELL, ROBERT, 1561?-1595
Hood, Christobel M. The Book of Robert Southwell: Priest, Poet, Prisoner. LC 72-13696. 1972. Repr. of 1926 ed. lib. bdg. 30.00 (ISBN 0-8414-1290-1). Folcroft.
Janelle, Pierre. Robert Southwell the Writer. LC 72-162495. 347p. 1971. Repr. of 1935 ed. 12.00x (ISBN 0-911858-18-0). Appel.

SOUTHWELL FAMILY
Hood, Christobel M. The Book of Robert Southwell: Priest, Poet, Prisoner. LC 72-13696. 1972. Repr. of 1926 ed. lib. bdg. 30.00 (ISBN 0-8414-1290-1). Folcroft.

SOVEREIGNS
see Roman Emperors

SOVIET UNION–CHURCH HISTORY
Blane, Andrew, ed. The Ecumenical World of Orthodox Civilization: Russia & Orthodoxy, Vol. 3. (Slavistic Printings & Reprintings Ser: No. 260). 1974. text ed. 44.80x (ISBN 90-2792-610-7). Mouton.
Bolshakoff, Serge. Russian Nonconformity: The Story of Unofficial Religion in Russia. Repr. of 1950 ed. 10.00 (ISBN 0-404-00933-6). AMS Pr.
Cracraft, James. The Church Reform of Peter the Great. 1971. 27.50x (ISBN 0-8047-0747-2). Stanford U Pr.
Curtiss, John S. The Russian Church & the Soviet State, 1917-1950. 1953. 11.75 (ISBN 0-8446-1141-7). Peter Smith.
Floridi, Alexis. Moscow & the Vatican. 365p. 1986. 23.50 (ISBN 0-88233-647-9). Ardis Pubs.
Golubinskii, E. E. O Reforme v Byte Russkoi Tserkvi: Sbornik Statei. 142p. Repr. of 1913 ed. text ed. 33.12x (ISBN 0-576-99237-2, Pub. by Gregg Intl Pubs England). Gregg Intl.
Heard, Albert F. Russian Church & Russian Dissent. LC 70-127907. Repr. of 1887 ed. 24.50 (ISBN 0-404-03198-6). AMS Pr.
Regel, Vasilii E., ed. Analecta Byzantino-Russica. 1964. Repr. of 1891 ed. 23.50 (ISBN 0-8337-2919-5). B Franklin.
Smirnov, P. S. Istoriia Russkago Raskola Starobriadstva. 314p. Repr. of 1895 ed. text ed. 62.10x (ISBN 0-576-99245-3, Pub. by Gregg Intl Pubs England). Gregg Intl.
Syrtsov, V. L. The Insurrection of the Old-Ritualist Monks at the Solovetsk Monastery in the Seventeenth Century. 316p. Repr. of 1888 ed. text ed. 33.12 (ISBN 0-576-99180-5, Pub. by Gregg Intl Pubs England). Gregg Intl.
Zernov, Nicholas. Moscow, the Third Rome. 2nd ed. LC 76-149664. Repr. of 1938 ed. 12.50 (ISBN 0-404-07075-2). AMS Pr.

SOVIET UNION–RELIGION
Arseniev, Nicholas. Russian Piety. 143p. 1964. pap. 5.95 (ISBN 0-913836-21-4). St Vladimirs.
Babris, Peter J. Silent Churches: Persecution of Religions in Soviet Dominated Areas. LC 78-52811. (Illus.). 1978. 19.50 (ISBN 0-911252-02-9). Res Publs.
Belliustin, I. S. Description of the Clergy in Rural Russia: The Memoir of a Nineteenth Century Parish Priest. Freeze, Gregory L., ed. LC 85-47699. (Illus.). 224p. 1985. text ed. 29.95x (ISBN 0-8014-1796-1); pap. text ed. 9.95x (ISBN 0-8014-9335-8). Cornell U Pr.
Berdiaev, Nikolai A. The Russian Idea. French, R. M., tr. LC 78-32021. 1979. Repr. of 1948 ed. lib. bdg. 37.50x (ISBN 0-313-20968-5, BERN). Greenwood.
Berdyaev, Nicolas. Origin of Russian Communism. 1960. pap. 8.95 (ISBN 0-472-06034-1, 34, AA). U of Mich Pr.
Boiter, Albert. Religion in the Soviet Union. (The Washington Papers: Vol. VIII, No. 78). 88p. (Orig.). 1980. pap. text ed. 7.95 (ISBN 0-8191-6022-9, Pub. by CSIS). U Pr of Amer.
Cunningham, James. A Vanquished Hope: The Church in Russia on the Eve of the Revolution. 1981. pap. 40.00x (Pub. by Mowbrays Pub Div). State Mutual Bk.
Fletcher, William. Soviet Believers: The Religious Sector of the Population. LC 80-25495. 276p. 1981. 27.50x (ISBN 0-7006-0211-9). U Pr of KS.
Fletcher, William c. Soviet Charismatics: The Pentecostals in the U. S. S. R. (American University Studies VII (Theology & Religion): Vol. 9). 287p. 1985. text ed. 25.15 (ISBN 0-8204-0226-5). P Lang Pubs.
God in Our Hearts: Meditations from the Orthodox Church in Russia. 1987. pap. 9.95. Friend Pr.
Grabbe, George. Pravda o Russkoj Tserkvi na Rodinje i za Rubjezhom. Tr. of The Truth of the Russian Church at Home & Abroad. 216p. 1961. pap. 8.00 (ISBN 0-317-30359-7). Holy Trinity.
Hartfield, Hermann. Faith Despite the KGB. 248p. 1980. pap. 5.95 (ISBN 0-88264-156-5). Diane Bks.
Hecker, Julius F. Religion & Communism. LC 73-842. (Russian Studies: Perspectives on the Revolution Ser.). 302p. 1987. Repr. of 1934 ed. 26.75 (ISBN 0-88355-037-7). Hyperion Conn.
Johnstone, Parker L. Russia's New Religion. 208p. 1984. 7.95 (ISBN 0-917802-11-X). Theoscience Found.
Kincevicious, Joseph B. Russia's Attitude Towards Union with Rome: 9th-16th Centuries. 208p. 1983. Repr. of 1927 ed. 24.95x (ISBN 0-939738-10-4). Zubal Inc.
Kline, George L. Religious & Anti-Religious Thought in Russia. LC 68-54484. (The Weil Lectures). Repr. of 1968 ed. 47.30 (ISBN 0-317-09813-6, 2020097). Bks Demand UMI.
Kovalevsky, Pierre. St. Sergius & Russian Spirituality. LC 76-13018. (Illus.). 190p. 1976. 7.95 (ISBN 0-913836-24-9). St Vladimirs.
Marshall, Richard H., Jr., et al, eds. Aspects of Religion in the Soviet Union, 1917-1967. LC 70-115874. 1971. 35.00x (ISBN 0-226-50700-9). U of Chicago Pr.
Masters, Peter, ed. Remember the Prisoners: Current Accounts of Believers in Russia. pap. 6.95 (ISBN 0-8024-7388-1). Moody.
Medlin, William K. Moscow & East Rome: A Political Study of the Relation of Church & State in Muscovite Russia. LC 79-2913. 252p. 1980. Repr. of 1952 ed. 23.00 (ISBN 0-8305-0082-0). Hyperion Conn.
Nesdoly, Samuel J. Among the Soviet Evangelicals. (Orig.). 1986. pap. 6.45 (ISBN 0-85151-489-8). Banner of Truth.
Parsons, Howard L. Christianity Today in the U. S. S. R. LC 86-27320. 216p. (Orig.). 1987. pap. 6.95 (ISBN 0-7178-0651-0). Intl Pubs CO.
Powell, David E. Antireligious Propaganda in the Soviet Union: A Study of Mass Persuasion. LC 74-34127. 206p. 1975. pap. 8.95x (ISBN 0-262-66042-3). MIT Pr.
Ramet, Pedro, ed. Religion & Nationalism in Soviet & East European Politics. (Policy Studies). v, 282p. 1985. text ed. 35.00 (ISBN 0-8223-0608-5). Duke.
Romashkevitch, P. A., ed. Polnij Russkij Orthograficheskij Slovar' Tr. of Complete Russian Orthographic Dictionary. 264p. pap. 10.00 (ISBN 0-317-29290-0). Holy Trinity.
Rudin, A. James & Gillen, Ann, eds. The Struggle for Religious Survival in the Soviet Union. LC 86-72630. 76p. 1986. pap. 5.00 (ISBN 0-87495-085-6). Am Jewish Comm.
S. A. Rachinskij i jego Shkola. Tr. of S. A. Rachinsky & His School. 84p. 1956. pap. 2.00 (ISBN 0-317-30334-1). Holy Trinity.
Sawatsky, Walter. Soviet Evangelicals: Since World War II. LC 81-94121. 560p. 1981. 19.95x (ISBN 0-8361-1238-5); pap. 14.95x (ISBN 0-8361-1239-3). Herald Pr.
Shubin, Daniel H., ed. Spirit & Life, Book of the Sun. Volkov, John W., tr. from Russian. 768p. 1984. 40.00 (ISBN 0-318-20027-9). D H Shubin.
Smirnov, S. Drevne-Russkii Dukhovnik: Izsledovnatie Po Istorii Tserkovnago Byta. 870p. Repr. of 1914 ed. text ed. 74.52 (ISBN 0-576-99178-3, Pub. by Gregg Intl Pubs England). Gregg Intl.
Sokolov, P. Russkii Arkhierei iz Vizantii i Pravo Ego Naznacheniia do Nachala XV Veka. 582p. 1913. text ed. 74.52x (ISBN 0-576-99187-2, Pub. by Gregg Intl Pubs England). Gregg Intl.
Subbotin, N. The Acts of the Moscow Councils of the Years 1666 & 1667. 358p. 1893. text ed. 62.10x (ISBN 0-576-99199-6, Pub. by Gregg Intl Pubs England). Gregg Intl.
Swietochowski, T. Russian Azerbaijan, Nineteen Five to Nineteen Twenty. 255p. 1985. 125.00 (ISBN 0-317-40712-0, Pub. by Collets UK). State Mutual Bk.
Talberg, N. D. Russkaja Pravoslavnaja Tserkov' v Severnoj Ameriki. Tr. of The Russian Orthodox Church in North America. 224p. 1955. pap. 8.00 (ISBN 0-317-30366-X). Holy Trinity.
Thrower, James. Marxist-Leninist 'Scientific Atheism' & the Study of Religion & Atheism in the U. S. S. R. (Ger.). 500p. 1983. 78.00 (ISBN 90-279-3060-0). Mouton.
Timasheff, Nicholas S. Religion in Soviet Russia, Nineteen Seventeen to Nineteen Forty-Two. LC 78-23615. 1979. Repr. of 1942 ed. lib. bdg. 22.50x (ISBN 0-313-21040-3, TIRS). Greenwood.
Voieivkov, N. N. Tserkov', Rus' i Rim. Tr. of The Church, Russia & Rome. 512p. 1983. text ed. 25.00 (ISBN 0-88465-016-2); pap. text ed. 20.00 (ISBN 0-88465-015-4). Holy Trinity.
Zvegintzov, Catherine, compiled by. Our Mother Church, Her Worship & Offices. 1948 ed. LC 78-227697. pap. 6.50x (ISBN 0-281-00849-3). A R Allenson.

SPAIN–BIOGRAPHY
Peers, Edgar A. St. John of the Cross, & Other Lectures & Addresses, 1920-1945. facs. ed. LC 70-136650. (Biography Index Reprint Ser.). 1946. 16.00 (ISBN 0-8369-8045-X). Ayer Co Pubs.
Septimus, Bernard. Hispano-Jewish Culture in Transition: The Career & Controversies of Ramah. LC 81-13275. (Harvard Judiac Monographs: No. 4). 192p. 1982. text ed. 20.00x (ISBN 0-674-39230-2). Harvard U Pr.

SPAIN–CHURCH HISTORY
Brodman, James W. Ransoming Captives in Crusader Spain: The Order of Merced on the Christian-Islamic Frontier. LC 85-20362. (Middle Ages Ser.). (Illus.). 216p. 1986. text ed. 21.95 (ISBN 0-8122-8001-6). U of PA Pr.
Huff, Sr. M. Cyria. The Sonnet-No Me Mueve, Mi Dios-Its Theme in Spanish Tradition. LC 73-94177. (Catholic University of America Studies in Romance Languages & Literatures Ser: No. 33). Repr. of 1948 ed. 20.00 (ISBN 0-404-50333-0). AMS Pr.

Lea, Henry C. Chapters from the Religious History of Spain Connected with the Inquisition. LC 68-56760. (Research & Source Work Ser.: No. 245). 1967. Repr. of 1890 ed. 26.00 (ISBN 0-8337-2035-X). B Franklin.

Watts, H. E. The Christian Recovery of Spain. 69.95 (ISBN 0-87968-863-7). Gordon Pr.

Williams, Michael C. St. Alban's College, Valladolid: Four Centuries of English Catholic Presence in Spain. LC 86-17787. 278p. 1986. 35.00 (ISBN 0-312-69736-8). St Martin.

SPAIN–CIVILIZATION

Haines, Charles R. Christianity & Islam in Spain, A. D. 756-1031. LC 76-144625. Repr. of 1889 ed. 17.50 (ISBN 0-404-03024-6). AMS Pr.

SPAIN–FOREIGN RELATIONS

Jensen, DeLamar. Diplomacy & Dogmatism: Bernardino de Mendoza & the French Catholic League. LC 63-20769. (Illus.). 1964. 22.50x (ISBN 0-674-20800-5). Harvard U Pr.

SPAIN–HISTORY

Here are entered general works on Spanish history, and works on all periods of Spanish history.

Al-Maqqari, Ahmed, ed. History of the Mohammedan Dynasties in Spain, 2 Vols. De Gayangos, P., tr. 1969. Repr. of 1840 ed. Set. 175.00 (ISBN 0-384-35253-7). Johnson Repr.

Boxer, C. R. The Church Militant & Iberian Expansion: 1440-1770. LC 77-18386. (Johns Hopkins Symposia in Comparative History Ser.: No. 10). (Illus.). 1978. text ed. 17.50x (ISBN 0-8018-2042-1). Johns Hopkins.

Burns, Robert I. Muslims, Christians & Jews in the Crusader Kingdom of Valencia: Societies in Symbiosis. LC 83-2007. (Cambridge Iberian & Latin American Studies). 300p. 1984. 65.00 (ISBN 0-521-24374-2). Cambridge U Pr.

Chavez, Angelico, ed. The Oroz Codex, or Relation of the Description of the Holy Gospel Province in New Spain, & the Lives of the Founders & Other Note-Worthy Men of Said Province Composed by Fray Pedro Oroz: 1584-1586. (Documentary Ser.). 1972. 25.00 (ISBN 0-88382-011-0). AAFH.

Christian, William A., Jr. Local Religion in 16th Century Spain. LC 80-7513. 296p. 1981. 28.00 (ISBN 0-691-05306-5). Princeton U Pr.

De Aragon, Ray J. Padre Martinez & Bishop Lamy. 3rd ed. LC 78-70565. (History Ser.). (Illus.). 1978. pap. 7.95 (ISBN 0-932906-00-1). Pan-Am Publishing Co.

Glick, Thomas F. Islamic & Christian Spain in the Early Middle Ages: Comparative Perspectives on Social & Cultural Formation. LC 78-70296. 1978. 41.50 (ISBN 0-691-05274-3). Princeton U Pr.

Kamen, Henry. Inquisition & Society in Spain in the Sixteenth & Seventeenth Centuries. LC 85-10804. (Illus.). 320p. 1985. 27.50x (ISBN 0-253-33015-7); pap. 10.95x (ISBN 0-253-22775-5). Ind U Pr.

O'Duffy, E. Crusade in Spain. 69.95 (ISBN 0-87968-972-2). Gordon Pr.

Procter, Evelyn S. Curia & Cortes in Leon & Castille, Ten Seventy-Two to Twelve Ninety-Five. LC 79-51750. (Cambridge Iberian & Latin American Studies). (Illus.). 350p. 1980. 44.50 (ISBN 0-521-22639-2). Cambridge U Pr.

Smith, Hilary D. Preaching in the Spanish Golden Age: A Study of Some Preachers of the Reign of Philip III. (Modern Language & Literature Monographs). 1979. 29.95x (ISBN 0-19-815532-8). Oxford U Pr.

Tibi, Amin T. The Tibyan: Memoirs of Abd Allah b. Buluggin, Last Zirid Amir of Granada. Translated from the Emended Arabic Text & Provided with Introduction, Notes & Comments. (Medieval Iberian Peninsula Ser.: Vol. 5). xiii, 291p. 1986. 38.25 (ISBN 90-04-07669-7, Pub. by E J Brill). Heinman.

Ullman, Joan C. Tragic Week: A Study of Anticlericalism in Spain, 1875-1912. LC 67-27082. 1968. 27.50x (ISBN 0-674-90240-8). Harvard U Pr.

Wasserstein, David. The Rise & Fall the of Party-Kings: Politics & Society in Islamic Spain, 1002-1086. LC 94-16072. (Illus.). 344p. 1985. text ed. 35.00x (ISBN 0-691-05436-3). Princeton U Pr.

Yonge, Charlotte M. The Story of the Christians & Moors of Roman Spain. 1893. 30.00 (ISBN 0-89984-238-0). Century Bookbindery.

SPAIN–SOCIAL CONDITIONS

Hughey, John D. Religious Freedom in Spain: Its Ebb & Flow. facsimile ed. LC 77-119935. (Select Bibliographies Reprint Ser). Repr. of 1955 ed. 21.50 (ISBN 0-8369-5378-9). Ayer Co Pubs.

SPALDING, MARTIN JOHN, ABP., 1810-1872

Spalding, Thomas W. Martin John Spalding: American Churchman. LC 74-171040. pap. 96.80 (2029524). Bks Demand UMI.

SPANISH HYMNS

see Hymns, Spanish

SPANISH MISSIONS OF CALIFORNIA

Here is entered literature dealing chiefly with the old Spanish mission buildings. Material treating of organized missionary activities is entered under Missions–United States.

James, George W. The Old Franciscan Missions of California. LC 77-91532. 1977. Repr. of 1913 ed. lib. bdg. 25.00 (ISBN 0-89341-321-6). Longwood Pub Group.

Oak, Henry L. A Visit to the Missions of Southern California in February & March 1874. Axe, Ruth F., et al, eds. LC 81-52830. (Illus.). 87p. 1981. 20.00 (ISBN 0-916561-66-6). Southwest Mus.

Sitjar, Buenaventura. Vocabulary of the Language of San Antonio Mission, California. LC 10-26367. (Library of American Linguistics: No. 7). (Span.). Repr. of 1861 ed. 28.50 (ISBN 0-404-50987-8). AMS Pr.

Spizzirri Publishing, Inc. Staff & Spizzirri, Linda. California Missions: An Educational Coloring Book. (Illus.). 32p. 1985. pap. 1.49 (ISBN 0-86545-062-5). Spizzirri.

Sunset Editors. California Missions. 2nd ed. LC 79-88016. (Illus.). 320p. 1979. pap. 12.95 (ISBN 0-376-05172-8, Sunset Bks). Sunset-Lane.

SPANISH MISSIONS OF NEW MEXICO

Here is entered literature dealing chiefly with the old spanish mission buildings. Material treating of organized missionary activities is entered under Missions–United States.

Hill, Tomas. Rios De Tinta: Historia y Ministerio De la Casa Bautista De Publicaciones. Smith, Josie, tr. from Eng. Orig. Title: Rivers of Ink. 64p. 1980. pap. 2.50 (ISBN 0-311-29009-4). Casa Bautista.

SPANISH MISSIONS OF THE SOUTHWEST

Here is entered literature dealing chiefly with the old spanish mission buildings. Material treating of organized missionary activities is entered under Missions–United States.

Casteneda, Carlos E. Our Catholic Heritage in Texas, 1519-1936, 7 vols. LC 76-1471. (Chicano Heritage Ser.). (Illus.). 1976. Repr. Set. 248.00 (ISBN 0-405-09488-4). Ayer Co Pubs.

Van Well, Sr. Mary Stanislaus. Educational Aspects of the Missions of the Southwest. 1942. pap. 7.95 (ISBN 0-87462-438-X). Marquette.

SPEAKERS (RECITATION BOOKS)

see Recitations

SPEAKING

see Preaching

SPEAKING WITH TONGUES

see Glossolalia

SPECTERS

see Apparitions

SPELLMAN, FRANCIS JOSEPH, CARDINAL, 1889-1967

Cooney, John. The American Pope: The Life & Times of Francis Cardinal Spellman. (Illus.). 448p. 1986. pap. 4.50 (ISBN 0-440-10194-8). Dell.

--The American Pope: The Life & Times of Francis Cardinal Spellman 1889-1967. LC 84-40096. (Illus.). 416p. 1984. 19.95 (ISBN 0-8129-1120-2). Times Bks.

SPELLS

see Incantations

SPENSER, EDMUND, 1552?-1599

Albright, E. M. Spenser's Cosmic Philosophy of Religion. LC 72-100730. 1970. Repr. of 1929 ed. 39.95 (ISBN 0-8383-0001-4). Haskell.

Aptekar, Jane. Icons of Justice: Iconography & Thematic Imagery in Book Five of the Faerie Queen. LC 79-79189. (Illus.). 218p. 1969. 32.00x (ISBN 0-231-03246-3). Columbia U Pr.

Bennett, J. W. Theme of Spenser's "Foure Hymnes". LC 76-100731. 1970. pap. 39.95x (ISBN 0-8383-0003-0). Haskell.

Bloom, Harold, ed. Edmund Spenser. (Modern Critical Views-Medieval & Renaissance Ser.). 1986. 29.50 (ISBN 0-87754-672-X). Chelsea Hse.

Cornelius, Peter S. E. K.'s Commentary on the Shepheards Calender. Hogg, James, ed. (Elizabethan & Renaissance Studies). 111p. (Orig.). 1974. pap. 15.00 (ISBN 3-7052-0679-6, Pub. by Salzburg Studies). Longwood Pub Group.

Cullen, Patrick. Spenser, Marvell, & Renaissance Pastoral. LC 76-123566. pap. 42.60 (2014653). Bks Demand UMI.

Fletcher, Angus. The Prophetic Moment: An Essay on Spenser. LC 73-130587. 1971. 20.00x (ISBN 0-226-25332-5). U of Chicago Pr.

Gross, Kenneth. Spenserian Poetics: Idolatry, Iconoclasm & Magic. LC 85-47701. 256p. 1986. text ed. 24.95x (ISBN 0-8014-1805-4). Cornell U Pr.

Hieatt, A. Kent. Chaucer, Spenser, Milton: Mythopoeic Continuities & Transformations. (Illus.). 336p. 1975. 25.00x (ISBN 0-7735-0228-9). McGill-Queens U Pr.

Mayr, Roswitha. The Concept of Love in Sidney & Spenser. Hogg, James, ed. (Elizabethan & Renaissance Studies). 124p. (Orig.). 1978. pap. 15.00 (ISBN 0-317-40126-2, Pub. by Salzburg Studies). Longwood Pub Group.

Padelford, Frederick M. Political & Ecclesiastical Allegory of First Book of the Faerie Queen. 1911. lib. bdg. 10.00 (ISBN 0-8414-9237-9). Folcroft.

--Political & Ecclesiastical Allegory of the First Book of the Fairie Queen. LC 70-111785. Repr. of 1911 ed. 5.00 (ISBN 0-404-04856-0). AMS Pr.

SPINOZA, BENEDICTUS DE, 1632-1677

Akkerman, Fokke. Studies in the Posthumous Works of Spinoza: On Style, Earliest Translation & Reception, Earliest & Modern Edition of Some Texts. vi, 285p. (Orig.). 1980. pap. 17.00x (ISBN 0-317-19838-6, Pub. by Boumas Boekhuis Netherlands). Benjamins North AM.

Atkins, Dorothy. George Eliot & Spinoza. Hogg, James, ed. (Romantic Reassessment Ser.). 188p. (Orig.). 1978. pap. 15.00 (ISBN 3-7052-0535-8, Pub. by Salzburg Studies). Longwood Pub Group.

Balz, Albert G. Idea & Essence in the Philosophies of Hobbes & Spinoza. LC 70-161737. Repr. of 1918 ed. 17.00 (ISBN 0-404-00489-X). AMS Pr.

Bennett, Jonathan. A Study of Spinoza's Ethics. LC 83-18568. 416p. 1984. lib. bdg. 25.00 (ISBN 0-915145-82-0); pap. text ed. 13.75 (ISBN 0-915145-83-9). Hackett Pub.

Columbia University. Spinoza Bibliography. Oko, Adolph S., compiled by. 1964. lib. bdg. 79.00 (ISBN 0-8161-0699-1, Hall Library). G K Hall.

Dienstag, J. I., ed. Studies in Maimonides & Spinoza. (Texts, Studies & Translations in Maimonidean Thought & Scholarship: Vol. 3). 35.00x (ISBN 0-87068-330-6). Ktav.

Duff, Robert A. Spinoza's Political & Ethical Philosophy. LC 71-108858. 1920. Repr. of 1903 ed. lib. bdg. 37.50x (ISBN 0-678-00615-6). Kelley.

--Spinoza's Political & Ethical Philosophy. 1973. Repr. of 1903 ed. 14.00 (ISBN 0-8274-1391-2). R West.

Giancotti, Emilia, ed. Proceedings of the First Italian International Congress on Spinoza. (Illus.). 556p. 1985. 60.00x (ISBN 88-7088-121-0, Pub. by Bibliopolis Italy). Humanities.

Grene, Nails, ed. Spinoza & the Sciences. 1986. lib. bdg. 54.50 (ISBN 90-277-1976-4, Pub. by Reidel Holland). Kluwer-Academic.

Hampshire, Stuart. Spinoza. (Orig.). 1952. pap. 4.95 (ISBN 0-14-020253-6, Pelican). Penguin.

Jaspers, Karl. Spinoza. Arendt, Hannah, ed. Manheim, Ralph, tr. from Ger. LC 74-4336. (From the Great Philosophers Ser.). 120p. 1974. pap. 2.95 (ISBN 0-15-684730-2, Harv). HarBraceJ.

Kashap, S. Paul. Spinoza & Moral Freedom. (SUNY Series in Philosophy). 130p. 1987. text ed. 32.50x (ISBN 0-88706-529-5); pap. 10.95x. State U NY Pr.

Kashap, S. Paul, ed. Studies in Spinoza: Critical & Interpretative Essays. LC 71-174459. 360p. 1973. pap. 10.95x (ISBN 0-520-02590-3, CAMPUS 109). U of Cal Pr.

Kayser, Rudolf. The Saints of Qumran: Stories & Essays on Jewish Themes. Zohn, Harry, ed. LC 76-20273. 188p. 1977. 18.00 (ISBN 0-8386-2024-8). Fairleigh Dickinson.

Martineau, James. A Study of Spinoza. 3rd facsimile ed. LC 78-152994. (Select Bibliographies Reprint Ser). Repr. of 1895 ed. 23.50 (ISBN 0-8369-5746-6). Ayer Co Pubs.

Mellone, Sydney H. The Dawn of Modern Thought: Descartes, Spinoza, Leibniz, with Introductory Note by W. D. Ross. LC 72-85001. 124p. 1973. Repr. of 1930 ed. 10.00x (ISBN 0-8462-1686-8). Russell.

Misrahi, R. Le Desir et la Reflexion Dans la Philosophie De Spinoza. (Publications Gramma Ser.). 352p. 1972. pap. 30.25x (ISBN 0-677-50815-8). Gordon & Breach.

Pollock, Frederick. Spinoza: His Life & Philosophy. (Reprints in Philosophy Ser.). (Illus.). Repr. of 1880 ed. lib. bdg. 47.00x (ISBN 0-697-00055-9). Irvington.

Popkin, Richard H. & Signer, Michael, eds. Spinoza's Earliest Publication? 100p. 1987. 17.50 (ISBN 90-232-2223-7, Pub. by Van Gorcum Holland). Longwood Pub Group.

Roth, Leon. Spinoza. LC 78-14139. 1986. Repr. of 1954 ed. 23.75 (ISBN 0-88355-813-0). Hyperion Conn.

Schaub, Edward J. Spinoza: The Man & His Thought. 61p. 1933. pap. 0.95 (ISBN 0-317-40400-8). Open Court.

Shahan, Robert W. & Biro, J. I., eds. Spinoza: New Perspectives. LC 77-18541. 1980. 16.50x (ISBN 0-8061-1459-2); pap. text ed. 8.95x (ISBN 0-8061-1647-1). U of Okla Pr.

Spinoza, Baruch. The Collected Works of Spinoza, Vol. I. Curley, Edwin, ed. LC 84-11716. (Illus.). 720p. 1985. text ed. 45.00x (ISBN 0-691-07222-1). Princeton U Pr.

Strauss, Leo. Spinoza's Critique of Religion. Sinclair, E. M., tr. from Ger. LC 65-10948. 364p. 1982. pap. 8.50 (ISBN 0-8052-0704-X). Schocken.

Toland, John. Letters to Serena. Wellek, Rene, ed. LC 75-11259. (British Philosophers & Theologians of the 17th & 18th Centuries: Vol. 58). 295p. 1976. Repr. of 1704 ed. lib. bdg. 51.00 (ISBN 0-8240-1809-5). Garland Pub.

Wetlesen, Jon. The Sage & the Way: Spinoza's Ethics of Freedom. (Philosophia Spinozae Perennis Ser.: No. 4). 474p. 1979. text ed. 50.00 (ISBN 90-232-1596-6, Pub. by Van Gorcum Holland). Longwood Pub Group.

--The Sage & the Way: Studies in Spinoza's Ethics of Freedom. (Philosophia Spinozae Perennis Ser.: No. 4). 1979. text ed. 55.00x (ISBN 90-232-1596-6). Humanities.

Wienpahl, Paul. The Radical Spinoza. LC 78-65448. 1979. 32.50 (ISBN 0-8147-9186-7). NYU Pr.

Wilbur, James B. Spinoza's Metaphysics: Essays in Critical Appreciation. (Philosophia Spinozae Perennis Ser.: No. 1). 170p. 1976. pap. text ed. 19.00 (ISBN 90-232-1361-0, Pub. by Van Gorcum Holland). Longwood Pub Group.

SPIRIT

Here are entered works limited to the conception of spirit as differentiated from soul.

see also Consciousness; Holy Spirit; Mind and Body; Soul

Adams, George. Physical & Ethereal Spaces. (Illus.). 71p. 1978. pap. 5.00 (ISBN 0-85440-328-0, Pub. by Steinerbooks). Anthroposophic.

Berdyaev, Nicolas. Freedom & the Spirit. LC 72-2567. (Select Bibliographies Reprint Ser.). 1972. Repr. of 1935 ed. 24.50 (ISBN 0-8369-6848-4). Ayer Co Pubs.

Bethune, George. The Fruit of the Spirit. pap. 4.95 (ISBN 0-685-88375-2). Reiner.

Binyon, Pamela M. The Concepts of Spirit & Demon: A Study in the Use of Different Languages Describing the Same Phenomena. (IC-Studies in the International History of Christianity: Vol. 8). 132p. 1977. pap. 19.60 (ISBN 3-261-01787-2). P Lang Pubs.

Criswell, W. A. Great Doctrines of the Bible, Vol. 4: Pneumatology. 112p. 1984. 7.95 (ISBN 0-310-43910-8, 11662). Zondervan.

Flynn, Leslie B. Nineteen Gifts of the Spirit. LC 74-91027. 204p. 1974. pap. 6.95 (ISBN 0-88207-701-5). Victor Bks.

Geissler, Eugene S., compiled by. The Spirit Bible. LC 73-88004. 272p. 1973. pap. 2.25 (ISBN 0-87793-062-7). Ave Maria.

Hayford, Jack. Spirit-Filled. 112p. (Orig.). 1987. mass 2.95, (ISBN 0-8423-6407-2). Tyndale.

Hilgeman, George A. El Programa del Espiritu Santo. 174p. 1982. pap. 4.50 (ISBN 0-89922-216-1). Edit Caribe.

Hislop, John S. My Baba & I. LC 85-61733. 1985. pap. 6.30 (ISBN 0-9600958-8-8). Birth Day.

Hodges, Melvin L. When the Spirit Comes. (Charismatic Bks.). 46p. 1972. pap. 0.69 (ISBN 0-88243-919-7, 02-0919). Gospel Pub.

Inch, Morris A. Saga of the Spirit. 12.95 (ISBN 0-8010-5037-5). Baker Bk.

Lehrs, Ernst. Spiritual Science, Electricity & Michael Faraday. 30p. 1975. pap. 3.00 (ISBN 0-85440-296-9, Pub. by Steinerbooks). Anthroposophic.

Luke, Helen M. Life of the Spirit in Women: A Jungian Approach. 1983. pap. 2.50x (ISBN 0-87574-230-0, 230). Pendle Hill.

Lull, David J. The Spirit in Galatia: Paul's Interpretation of Pneuma As Divine Power. LC 79-26094. (Society of Biblical Literature Dissertation: No. 49). 15.95 (ISBN 0-89130-367-7, 06-01-49); pap. 10.95 (ISBN 0-89130-368-5). Scholars Pr GA.

Mahoney, John. Seeking the Spirit. 11.95 (ISBN 0-87193-187-7). Dimension Bks.

May, Gerald G. Will & Spirit: A Comtemplative Psychology. LC 82-47751. 384p. 1982. 24.45 (ISBN 0-686-98141-3, HarpR). Har-Row.

Montstuart, John W. The Theory of the Physical Spirit & the Nature of God. (Illus.). 129p. 1987. 98.85 (ISBN 0-89266-591-2). Am Classical Coll Pr.

Ross-Bryant, Lynn. Imagination & the Life of the Spirit: An Introduction to the Study of Religion & Literature. LC 79-28464. (Scholars Press General Ser.: Vol. 2). pap. 7.95x (ISBN 0-89130-378-2, 00 03 02). Scholars Pr GA.

Sandweiss, Samuel H. Spirit & the Mind. 1985. pap. 6.30 (ISBN 0-9600958-9-6). Birth Day.

Schwanktfeld, Kurt W. The Hegel-Kierkegaard Cosmology of the Spirit. (Illus.). 103p. 1984. 87.85 (ISBN 0-89266-497-5). Am Classical Coll Pr.

Sia, Santiago, ed. Word & Spirit VIII. (Studies in Process Theology). 1986. pap. 7.00 (ISBN 0-932506-46-1). St Bedes Pubns.

Solomon, Robert C. In the Spirit of Hegel: A Study of G. W. F. Hegel's "Phenomenology of Spirit". (Illus.). 1983. 32.50x (ISBN 0-19-503169-5); pap. 14.95x (ISBN 0-19-503650-6). Oxford U Pr.

Spirit Healing & Spirit Universe. 1985. 6.50 (ISBN 0-8062-2518-1). Carlton.

Spirit in Matter: A Scientist's Answer to the Bishop Quevies. 1948. 10.00 (ISBN 0-906492-16-5, Pub. by Kolisko Archives). St George Bk Serv.

Steiner, Rudolf. The World of the Senses & the World of the Spirit. (Ger.). 88p. 1979. pap. 4.95 (ISBN 0-919924-10-7, Pub. by Steiner Book Centre Canada). Anthroposophic.

SPIRIT, HOLY

see Holy Spirit

SPIRITS

see also Angels; Apparitions; Demonology; Witchcraft

Belhayes, Iris. Spirit Guides: You Are Not Alone. (Inner Visions Ser.). (Orig.). 1986. pap. 12.95 (ISBN 0-917086-80-5). A C S Pubns Inc.

Berkhof, Hendrik. Christ & the Powers. LC 62-13713. 80p. 1962. pap. 5.95 (ISBN 0-8361-1820-0). Herald Pr.

Crapanzano, Vincent & Garrison, Vivian, eds. Case Studies in Spirit Possession. LC 76-26653. (Contemporary Religious Movements Ser.). pap. 118.30 (ISBN 0-317-08510-7, 2055396). Bks Demand UMI.

The Enchanted World: Water Spirits. 1985. 16.95 (ISBN 0-8094-5245-6); lib. bdg. 22.60 (ISBN 0-8094-5246-4). Time-Life.

Lojnikov, Paul. Seven Years Conversing with Spirits. 1987. 6.95 (ISBN 0-533-07213-1). Vantage.

Mather, Cotton. The Wonders of the Invisible World. large type ed. pap. 6.95 (ISBN 0-910122-46-6). Amherst Pr.

Mulholland, John. Beware Familiar Spirits. LC 78-66328. 1938. pap. 5.95 (ISBN 0-684-16181-8). Brown Bk.

Napoleone, Mary A. & Johanson, E. Jane. Spirits & Seasons. (Illus.). 83p. 1982. pap. 3.95 (ISBN 0-9610038-0-4). Heatherdown Pr.

Schneider, Bernard N. The World of Unseen Spirits. pap. 5.95 (ISBN 0-88469-024-5). BMH Bks.

Teasley, D. O. The Holy Spirit & Other Spirits. 192p. pap. 1.75 (ISBN 0-686-29150-6). Faith Pub Hse.

Walker, Sheila S. Ceremonial Spirit Possession in Africa & Afro-America: Forms, Meanings & Functional Significance for Individuals & Social Groups. 179p. 1972. text ed. 37.50x (ISBN 90-040-3584-2). Humanities.

SPIRITUAL DIRECTION

Alexander, Archibald. Thoughts on Religious Experience. 1978. 11.95 (ISBN 0-85151-080-9). Banner of Truth.

Almaas, A. H. The Elixir of Enlightenment. LC 84-50159. 64p. (Orig.). 1984. pap. 3.95 (ISBN 0-87728-613-2). Weiser.

Belhayes, Iris. Spirit Guides: You Are Not Alone. (Inner Visions Ser.). (Orig.). 1986. pap. 12.95 (ISBN 0-917086-80-5). A C S Pubns Inc.

Bridge, William. A Lifting up for the Downcast. 1979. pap. 5.45 (ISBN 0-85151-298-4). Banner of Truth.

Carlson, G. Raymond. Spiritual Dynamics. LC 76-5633. (Radiant Life Ser.). 128p. 1976. pap. 2.50 (ISBN 0-88243-894-8, 02-0894); teacher's ed 3.95 (ISBN 0-88243-168-4, 32-0168). Gospel Pub.

Carroll, L. Patrick & Dyckman, Katharine M. Inviting the Mystic, Supporting the Prophet: An Introduction to Spiritual Direction. LC 81-80053. 112p. (Orig.). 1981. pap. 5.95 (ISBN 0-8091-2378-9). Paulist Pr.

Chakravarti, Sri S. Be Your Own Guru. 1971. pap. 2.50 (ISBN 0-685-58384-8). Ranney Pubns.

Chinmoy, Sri. The Jewel of Humility. (Illus.). 56p. (Orig.). 1980. pap. 2.00 (ISBN 0-88497-493-6). Aum Pubns.

--Perfection in the Head World. 55p. (Orig.). 1980. pap. 2.00 (ISBN 0-88497-492-8). Aum Pubns.

Cullingan, Kevin, intro. by. Spiritual Direction: Contemporary Readings. 237p. (Orig.). 1983. pap. 5.95 (ISBN 0-914544-43-8). Living Flame Pr.

Cully, Iris V. Education for Spiritual Growth. LC 83-48464. 192p. 1984. 14.45 (ISBN 0-06-061655-5, HarpR). Har-Row.

Devers, Dorothy. Faithful Friendship. 1980. 2.40 (ISBN 0-88028-011-5). Forward Movement.

Dobbins, Richard D. Votre Force Spirituelle et Emotionnelle. Cosson, Annie L., ed. Chardenal, Valerie, tr. from Eng. Tr. of Your Spiritual & Emotional Power. (Fr.). 188p. 1985. pap. text ed. 2.25 (ISBN 0-8297-0703-4). Life Pubs Intl.

Earl, Gloria. The Book. 1984. 6.75 (ISBN 0-8062-1572-0). Carlton.

Gratton, Carolyn. Guidelines for Spiritual Direction. 8.95 (ISBN 0-87193-130-3). Dimension Bks.

Hall, Ruth. Three Steps to Heaven. 1981. 4.95 (ISBN 0-8062-1560-7). Carlton.

Harrington, Michael. The Politics at God's Funeral: The Spiritual Crisis of Western Civilization. (Penguin Nonfiction Ser.). 320p. 1985. pap. 7.95 (ISBN 0-14-007689-1). Penguin.

Heller, Alfred L. Your Body, His Temple: Reaching a Balanced Christian View of Diet & Physical Fitness. LC 81-1897. 192p. 1981. pap. 4.95 (ISBN 0-8407-5769-7). Nelson.

Hembree, Ron. Fruits of the Spirit. (Direction Bks.). pap. 4.95 (ISBN 0-8010-4301-8). Baker Bk.

Ives, Kenneth H. Nurturing Spiritual Development: Stages, Structure, Style. (Studies in Quakerism: No. 8). 60p. (Orig.). 1982. pap. 4.00 (ISBN 0-89670-011-9). Progresiv Pub.

Johnson, Lin. The Growing Season. 96p. 1987. pap. 4.95 (ISBN 0-89693-009-2). Victor Bks.

Kelsey, Morton T. Companions on the Inner Way: The Art of Spiritual Guidance. LC 82-23541. 250p. 1983. 17.50 (ISBN 0-8245-0585-9); pap. 9.95 (ISBN 0-8245-0560-3). Crossroad NY.

Krishnamurti, J. Education & the Signficance of Life. LC 53-10971. 128p. 1981. pap. 6.95 (ISBN 0-06-064876-7, RD 356, HarpR). Har-Row.

Lewis, James C. The Key to Spiritual Growth. 128p. 1985. 5.95 (ISBN 0-87159-004-2). Unity School.

Lindsay, Gordon. Spiritual Hunger. 2.50 (ISBN 0-89985-020-0). Christ Nations.

Lowe, Cylvia Archer. Words of Wisdom from the Masters. 2nd ed. 120p. 1981. pap. 6.95 (ISBN 0-9606080-0-1). Book Dept.

MacArthur, John, Jr. The Legacy of Jesus. pap. 5.95 (ISBN 0-8024-8524-3). Moody.

Maloney, George. Inscape: God at the Heart of the Matter. 1978. pap. 4.95 (ISBN 0-87193-095-1). Dimension Bks.

--Jesus, Set Me Free! Inner Freedom Through Contemplation. 4.95 (ISBN 0-87193-096-X). Dimension Bks.

--Listen, Prophets! 5.95 (ISBN 0-87193-059-5). Dimension Bks.

--Nesting in the Rock. 6.95 (ISBN 0-87193-002-1). Dimension Bks.

Manning, Brennan. The Gentle Revolutionaries. 5.95 (ISBN 0-87193-012-9). Dimension Bks.

--The Wisdom of Accepted Tenderness. casebound 5.95 (ISBN 0-87193-110-9); pap. 4.95. Dimension Bks.

Molinos, Michael. The Spiritual Guide. Edwards, Gene, ed. 110p. pap. 5.95 (ISBN 0-940232-08-1). Christian Bks.

Muto, Susan. The Journey Homeward. 6.95 (ISBN 0-87193-001-3). Dimension Bks.

Newhouse, Flower A. Travel with Inner Perceptiveness. (Illus.). 112p. (Orig.). 1979. pap. text ed. 7.00 (ISBN 0-910378-16-9). Christward.

Olson, Nathanael. How to Win Your Family to Christ. LC 77-81561. pap. 3.95 (ISBN 0-89107-149-0). Good News.

Orsy, Ladislas. The Lord of Confusion. 5.00 (ISBN 0-87193-064-1). Dimension Bks.

Payne, Leanne. The Broken Image. LC 81-65468. 188p. 1981. pap. 6.95 (ISBN 0-89107-215-2, Crossway Bks). Good News.

Phillips, John. How to Live Forever. (Teach Yourself the Bible Ser.). 1964. pap. 2.75 (ISBN 0-8024-3700-1). Moody.

Rahner, Karl. Meditations on Freedom & the Spirit. 1978. pap. 3.95 (ISBN 0-8245-0325-2). Crossroad NY.

Religious Education Staff. The Spirit Alive in Service: Spirit Masters. 1979. 9.95 (ISBN 0-697-01712-5). Wm C Brown.

--The Spirit Alive in Vocations: Spirit Masters. 1980. 9.95 (ISBN 0-697-01755-9). Wm C Brown.

Roth, Charles. A New Way of Thinking. LC 78-64751. 1979. 5.95 (ISBN 0-87159-113-8). Unity School.

Sabbath, Linda. The Radiant Heart. 1986. Repr. of 1985 ed. 4.95 (ISBN 0-87193-003-X). Dimension Bks.

Sanders, J. Oswald & Gould, Dana. Spiritual Leadership: Leader's Guide. (Orig.). 1987. pap. 4.95 (ISBN 0-8024-8226-0). Moody.

Savary, Louis M., et al. Dreams & Spiritual Growth: A Christian Approach to Dreamwork. LC 84-60566. 241p. pap. 9.95 (ISBN 0-8091-2629-X). Paulist Pr.

Schachter, Zalman M. & Hoffman, Edward. Sparks of Light: Counseling in the Hasidic Tradition. LC 83-42804. 208p. (Orig.). 1983. pap. 9.95 (ISBN 0-87773-240-X). Shambhala Pubns.

Spiritual Direction: Letters of Starets Macarius of Optina Monastery. pap. 1.95 (ISBN 0-686-00254-7). Eastern Orthodox.

Spiritual Notes. pap. 2.95 (ISBN 0-317-11388-7). Eastern Orthodox.

Sudbrack, Josef. Spiritual Guidance. 1984. pap. 3.95 (ISBN 0-8091-2571-4). Paulist Pr.

Thompson, Helen. Journey Toward Wholeness: A Jungian Model of Adult Spiritual Growth. LC 81-83184. 96p. (Orig.). 1982. pap. 5.95 (ISBN 0-8091-2422-X). Paulist Pr.

Tozer, Aiden W. God Tells the Man Who Cares. Bailey, Anita, ed. 1970. 5.95 (ISBN 0-87509-184-9); pap. 4.45 (ISBN 0-87509-185-7); mass market ed. 2.95 (ISBN 0-87509-220-9). Chr Pubns.

Turner, Charles W. My Favorite Reflections. pap. 1.75 (ISBN 0-88469-029-6). BMH Bks.

Van Der Poel, Cornelius J. The Integration of Human Values. 5.95 (ISBN 0-87193-004-8). Dimension Bks.

Vanderwall, Francis W. Spiritual Direction: An Invitation to Abundant Life. LC 81-83185. 128p. (Orig.). 1982. pap. 4.95 (ISBN 0-8091-2399-1). Paulist Pr.

Van Kaam, Adrian. The Dynamics of Spiritual Self-Direction. 24.95 (ISBN 0-87193-122-2). Dimension Bks.

--In Search of Spiritual Identity. 14.95 (ISBN 0-87193-164-8). Dimension Bks.

--On Being Yourself. 6.95 (ISBN 0-87193-038-2). Dimension Bks.

--Spirituality & the Gentle Life. 6.95 (ISBN 0-87193-037-4). Dimension Bks.

Van Kaam, Adrian, et al. The Participant Self, 2 vols. pap. 4.95 (ISBN 0-87193-045-5). Dimension Bks.

Weil, Simone. A Gateway to God. LC 82-4688. 160p. 1982. pap. 6.95 (ISBN 0-8245-0534-4). Crossroad NY.

Willis, Elbert. Being Fully Persuaded. 1977. 1.25 (ISBN 0-89858-017-X). Fill the Gap.

--Faith's Explanation. 1977. 1.25 (ISBN 0-89858-007-2). Fill the Gap.

--God's Plan for Financial Prosperity. 1977. 3.00 (ISBN 0-89858-005-6). Fill the Gap.

--How Can I Be Healed. 1978. 1.25 (ISBN 0-89858-013-7). Fill the Gap.

--Keys to Prosperity. 1978. 1.25 (ISBN 0-89858-016-1). Fill the Gap.

--Overcoming Discouragement. 1976. 1.25 (ISBN 0-89858-000-5). Fill the Gap.

--Overcoming Worry. 1976. 1.25 (ISBN 0-89858-001-3). Fill the Gap.

Zimmer, Allen E. God, Make Me Brave for Life. LC 81-69110. (Illus.). 128p. (Orig.). 1981. pap. 4.95 (ISBN 0-89505-057-9, 21052). Argus Comm.

SPIRITUAL DIRECTORS

see also Spiritual Direction

Gatta, Julia. Three Spiritual Directors for Our Time: Julian of Norwich, the Cloud of Unknowing Walter Hilton. LC 86-29169. 137p. (Orig.). 1987. pap. 8.95 (ISBN 0-936384-44-1). Cowley Pubns.

Isabel, Damien. The Spiritual Director. (Synthesis Ser.). 1976. pap. 2.00 (ISBN 0-8199-0712-X). Franciscan Herald.

Neufelder, Jerome N. & Coelho, Mary C., eds. Writings on Spiritual Direction by Great Christian Masters. 224p. (Orig.). 1982. pap. 11.95 (ISBN 0-8164-2420-9, HarpR). Har-Row.

Phelps, Myron H. The Master in Akka: Including Recollections of the Greatest Holy Leaf. Orig. Title: Abbas Effendi: His Life & Teachings. (Illus.). 1985. Repr. of 1912 ed. 12.95 (ISBN 0-933770-49-9). Kalimat.

Sanders, J. Oswald. Spiritual Leadership. rev. ed. LC 67-14387. (J. Oswald Sanders Ser.). 160p. 1974. pap. 3.95 (ISBN 0-8024-8221-X). Moody.

Smith, Gregory M. The Fire in Their Eyes: Spiritual Mentors for the Christian Life. 1984. pap. 4.95 (ISBN 0-8091-2620-6). Paulist Pr.

Tarostar. Spiritual Worker's Handbook. (Illus.). 80p. (Orig.). 1985. pap. 3.95 (ISBN 0-943832-12-8). Intl Imports.

Van den Broek, Silvere, ed. The Spiritual Legacy of Sister Mary of the Holy Trinity. LC 81-82830. 364p. 1981. pap. 6.00 (ISBN 0-89555-165-9). TAN Bks Pubs.

SPIRITUAL EXERCISES

see also Retreats

DeMello, Anthony. Wellsprings: A Book of Spiritual Exercises. LC 86-4478. 240p. 1986. pap. 7.95 (ISBN 0-385-19617-2, Im). Doubleday.

Klug, Ronald. How to Keep a Spiritual Journal. LC 82-14383. 144p. 1982. pap. 4.95 (ISBN 0-8407-5815-4). Nelson.

McGuiness, Thomas. Pilgrimage of the Heart. LC 83-63477. 74p. (Orig.). 1984. pap. text ed. 2.95 (ISBN 0-911905-19-7). Past & Mat Rene Ctr.

Pousset, Edouard. Life in Faith & Freedom: An Essay Presenting Gaston Fessard's Analysis of the Dialectic of the Spiritual Exercises of St. Ignatius. Ganss, G. E., frwd. by. LC 79-84200. (Modern Scholarly Studies About Jesuits, in English Translation Ser.: No. 4). 286p. 1980. 9.00 (ISBN 0-912422-41-6); pap. 8.00 smythsewn (ISBN 0-912422-40-8); pap. 7.00 (ISBN 0-912422-39-4). Inst Jesuit.

Puhl, Louis J. The Spiritual Exercises of St. Ignatius Based on Studies in the Language of the Autograph. (Request Reprint). 1968. pap. 4.00 (ISBN 0-8294-0065-6). Loyola.

St. Ignatius. Spiritual Exercises of St. Ignatius. Mottola, Anthony, tr. pap. 3.95 (ISBN 0-385-02436-3, D170, Im). Doubleday.

Scientific Healing Affirmations. pap. 7.95 (ISBN 0-937134-15-5). Amrita Found.

Sheehan, John F. On Becoming Whole in Christ: An Interpretation of the Spiritual Exercises. 1978. pap. 3.95 (ISBN 0-8294-0278-0). Loyola.

SPIRITUAL GIFTS

see Gifts, Spiritual

SPIRITUAL HEALING

Here are entered works on the use of prayer, faith or sacramental means to treat illness. Works on the use of psychological or psychic means to treat illness are entered under Mental Healing.

Allan, John. The Healing Energy of Love: A Personal Journal. LC 85-40770. (Illus.). 175p. (Orig.). 1986. pap. 7.50 (ISBN 0-8356-0603-1, Quest). Theos Pub Hse.

Bailey, Keith M. The Children's Bread: Divine Healing. LC 77-83941. 1977. kivar cover 5.95 (ISBN 0-87509-233-0). Chr Pubns.

Bales, James D. Miracles or Mirages? 1956. 3.00 (ISBN 0-88027-010-1). Firm Foun Pub.

Bartow, Donald W. The Adventures of Healing: How to Use New Testament Practices & Receive New Testament Results. 3rd, rev. ed. 204p. 1981. pap. 11.95 (ISBN 0-938736-19-1). Life Enrich.

Beierle, Herbert L. How to Give a Healing Treatment. 1979. 1.00 (ISBN 0-940480-07-7). U of Healing.

--Proclaim Your God. 1.00 (ISBN 0-940480-09-3). U of Healing.

--Quiet Healing Zone. 1980. 10.00 (ISBN 0-940480-10-7). U of Healing.

--School for Masters. 1979. 1.00 (ISBN 0-940480-11-5). U of Healing.

--Why I Can Say I Am God. 1978. 1.00 (ISBN 0-940480-04-2). U of Healing.

Beierle, Herbert L., ed. Minister's Manual. 2nd ed. 1985. 10.00 (ISBN 0-940480-20-4). U of Healing.

Bertolucci, John. Healing: God's Work Among Us. 1987. pap. 3.95. Servant.

Bittner, Vernon J. Make Your Illness Count: A Hospital Chaplain Shows How God's Healing Power Can Be Released in Your Life. LC 76-3862. 128p. (Orig.). 1976. pap. 6.95 (ISBN 0-8066-1532-X, 10-4260). Augsburg.

--You Can Help with Your Healing: A Guide for Recovering Wholeness in Body, Mind, & Spirit. LC 78-66946. 1979. pap. 6.95 (ISBN 0-8066-1698-9, 10-7411). Augsburg.

Blades, Dudley. Spiritual Healing. 128p. (Orig.). 1980. pap. 4.95 (ISBN 0-85030-130-0). Newcastle Pub.

Bosworth, F. F. Christ the Healer. 241p. pap. 6.95 (ISBN 0-8007-5124-8, Power Bks). Revell.

Bricklin, Mark. The Practical Encyclopedia of Natural Healing. rev. ed. (Illus.). 592p. 1983. 21.95 (ISBN 0-87857-480-8). Rodale Pr Inc.

Bryson, Harold T. How Faith Works. LC 84-17601. 1985. pap. 5.95 (ISBN 0-8054-1394-4). Broadman.

Buhrmann, M. Vera. Living in Two Worlds: Communication Between a White Healer & Her Black Counterparts. 108p. 1986. pap. 9.95 (ISBN 0-933029-10-1). Chiron Pubns.

Carlozzi, Carl G. Promises & Prayers for Healing: Hope for the Future. (Pocketpac Books). 128p. (Orig.). 1985. pap. 2.50 (ISBN 0-87788-336-X). Shaw Pubs.

Carter, Craig. How to Use the Power of Mind in Everyday Life. 96p. 1976. pap. 4.50 (ISBN 0-911336-65-6). Sci of Mind.

Champlin, Joseph. Healing in the Catholic Church: Mending Wounded Hearts & Bodies. LC 84-62226. 160p. 1985. pap. 5.50 (ISBN 0-87973-719-0, 719). Our Sunday Visitor.

Cooper, Joyce. I Shall Fear No Evil. 1986. 8.95 (ISBN 0-317-43335-0). Vantage.

Cousins, Norman. Healing & Belief. LC 82-81098. 64p. 1982. 65.00 (ISBN 0-88014-041-0). Mosaic Pr OH.

Crabtree, Ronald. On Wings of Healing. 80p. 1986. 21.00X (ISBN 0-7223-2002-7, Pub. by A H Stockwell England). State Mutual Bk.

Daneel, M. L. Zionism & Faith-Healing in Rhodesia: Aspects of African Independent Churches. V. A. February Communications, tr. from Dutch. (Illus.). 1970. pap. 6.00x (ISBN 90-2796-278-2). Mouton.

DiOrio, Ralph A. Called to Heal: Releasing the Transforming Power of God. LC 82-45354. (Illus.). 264p. 1984. pap. 7.95 (ISBN 0-385-19704-7, Im). Doubleday.

--Miracle to Proclaim: First-Hand Experience of Healing. LC 83-18218. 224p. 1984. pap. 4.50 (ISBN 0-385-19241-X, Im). Doubleday.

Divine Physical Healing, Past & Present. 272p. pap. 2.50 (ISBN 0-686-29107-7). Faith Pub Hse.

Drury, Michael. The Adventure of Spiritual Healing. 304p. 1985. pap. 9.95 large print ed. (ISBN 0-8027-2493-0). Walker & Co.

Eddy, Mary B. Science & Health with Key to the Scriptures. Incl. Vol. 1. Danish Ed. 25.00 (ISBN 0-87952-103-1); Vol. 2. Dutch Ed. 25.00 (ISBN 0-87952-109-0); Vol. 3. French Ed. 25.00 (ISBN 0-87952-117-1); Vol. 4. German Ed. 25.00 (ISBN 0-87952-151-1); Vol. 5. Norwegian Ed. 25.00 (ISBN 0-87952-195-3); Vol. 6. Swedish Ed. 25.00 (ISBN 0-87952-250-X); Vol. 7. Russian Ed. 25.00 (ISBN 0-87952-220-8); Vol. 8. Greek Ed. 25.00 (ISBN 0-87952-170-8); Vol. 9. Italian Ed. 25.00 (ISBN 0-87952-180-5); Vol. 10. Spanish Ed. 25.00 (ISBN 0-87952-226-7). First Church.

Ellsworth, Paul. Direct Healing. LC 83-3920. 1983. lib. bdg. 15.95x (ISBN 0-89370-658-2). Borgo Pr.

Evans, W. Glyn. A Healing Mind. 160p. 1987. pap. 6.95 (ISBN 0-310-29381-2). Zondervan.

Fillmore, Charles. Curacion Cristiana. LC 84-52152. Tr. of Christian Healing. (Span.). 160p. 5.95 (ISBN 0-87159-020-4). Unity School.

--Jesus Christ Heals. 1939. 5.95 (ISBN 0-87159-070-0). Unity School.

Finker, Kaja. Spiritualist Healers in Mexico: Successes & Failures of Alternative Therapies. 256p. 1984. 29.95 (ISBN 0-03-063912-3, C1156). Praeger.

Finkler, Kaja. Spiritualist Healers in Mexico: Successes & Failures of Alternative Therapeutics. (Illus.). 272p. 1983. text ed. 29.95x (ISBN 0-03-063912-3); pap. text ed. 14.95 (ISBN 0-89789-092-2). Bergin & Garvey.

Fisk, Samuel. Divine Healing Under the Searchlight. LC 78-15083. 1978. pap. 2.25 (ISBN 0-87227-057-2). Reg Baptist.

Flammonde, Paris. Mystic Healers. LC 73-91856. (Illus.). 256p. 1974. 8.95 (ISBN 0-8128-1680-3). Stein & Day.

Gaitan, Elizabeth M. From Demon Deliverance to Divine Healing. 1985. 5.95 (ISBN 0-8062-2394-4). Carlton.

Gandolfo, Joseph B. Spiritual Psychic Healing: A Comparative Psychological & Biblical Study. 1986. 6.95 (ISBN 0-533-06839-8). Vantage.

Glas, Norbert. Fulfillment of Old Age. Easton, Stewart, tr. from Fr. Tr. of Lichtvolles Alter. 141p. 1987. pap. 9.95 (ISBN 0-88010-161-X). Anthroposophic.

Glennon, Canon J. Your Healing Is Within You. LC 80-82616. 1980. pap. 4.95 (ISBN 0-88270-457-5). Bridge Pub.

Glennon, Jim. How Can I Find Healing? LC 84-73039. 1985. pap. 3.50 (ISBN 0-88270-580-6). Bridge Pub.

Goldsmith, Joel S. Realization of Oneness: The Practice of Spiritual Healing. 200p. 1974. pap. 5.95 (ISBN 0-8065-0453-6). Citadel Pr.

Gunstone, John. Healing Power: What It Is & What to Do with It. 168p. (Orig.). 1987. pap. 4.95 (ISBN 0-89283-318-1, Pub. by Vine Books). Servant.

Hagin, Kenneth E. Seven Things You Should Know about Divine Healing. 1979. pap. 2.50 (ISBN 0-89276-400-7). Hagin Ministries.

Hagin, Kenneth, Jr. Seven Hindrances to Healing. 1980. pap. 0.50 mini bk. (ISBN 0-89276-705-7). Hagin Ministries.

Harrell, David E., Jr. All Things Are Possible: The Healing & Charismatic Revivals in Modern America. LC 75-1937. (Midland Bks.: No. 221). (Illus.). 320p. 1976. 20.00x (ISBN 0-253-10090-9); pap. 8.95x (ISBN 0-253-20221-3). Ind U Pr.

Hayes, Norvel. God's Power Through the Laying On of Hands. 45p. 1982. pap. 2.50 (ISBN 0-89274-280-1). Harrison Hse.

--Your Faith Can Heal You. 80p. 1983. pap. 2.50 (ISBN 0-89274-273-9). Harrison Hse.

Heijkoop, H. L. Faith Healing & Speaking in Tongues. 40p. pap. 2.95 (ISBN 0-88172-083-6). Believers Bkshelf.

Hofinger, Johannes. Pastoral Life in the Power of the Spirit. LC 81-1439. (Illus.). 215p. 1982. pap. 6.95 (ISBN 0-8189-0427-5). Alba.

Holmes, Fenwicke L. The Faith That Heals. 100p. 1986. pap. 6.00 (ISBN 0-89540-124-X, SB 124). Sun Pub.

Inayat Khan. The Development of Spiritual Healing. LC 85-22358. 112p. 1985. Repr. lib. bdg. 19.95x (ISBN 0-89370-582-9). Borgo Pr.

Jackson, Edgar N. The Role of Faith in the Process of Healing. 216p. 1982. pap. 9.95 (ISBN 0-86683-679-9, HarpR). Har-Row.

--Your Health & You: How Awareness, Attitudes, & Faith Contribute to a Healthy Life. LC 86-22226. (Augsburg Religion & Medicine). 112p. (Orig.). 1986. pap. 5.95 (ISBN 0-8066-2221-0, 10-7426). Augsburg.

Jeter, Hugh P. By His Stripes: The Doctrine of Divine Healing. LC 76-20893. 224p. 1977. pap. 4.95 (ISBN 0-88243-521-3, 02-0521). Gospel Pub.

Judd, Wayne. Healing: Faith or Fraud. (Uplook Ser.). 1978. pap. 0.99 (ISBN 0-8163-0199-9, 08303-0). Pacific Pr Pub Assn.

Justus, Adalu & Marlin, Ira J. My Son, My Mother: Indestructible Chain of Love. LC 86-3884. 200p. (Orig.). 1986. pap. 7.95 (ISBN 0-937109-00-2). Silo Pubs.

Kelsey, Morton. Healing & Christianity. LC 72-78065. 1976. pap. 10.95 (ISBN 0-06-064381-1, RD 161, HarpR). Har-Row.

Kinnear, Willis H., ed. Spiritual Healing. 110p. (Orig.). 1973. pap. 4.95 (ISBN 0-911336-50-8). Sci of Mind.

Kremers, Edward. Christ the Healer. 24p. 1911. pap. 0.95 (ISBN 0-317-40411-3). Open Court.

Kunz, Dora, compiled by. Spiritual Aspects of the Healing Art. LC 85-40410. 294p. (Orig.). 1985. pap. 6.50 (ISBN 0-8356-0601-5, Quest). Theos Pub Hse.

Landorf, Joyce. Irregular People. 1982. 9.95 (ISBN 0-8499-0291-6). Word Bks.

Lidiard, Victoria. Christianity: Faith, Love & Healing. LC 84-90145. 80p. 1985. 5.95 (ISBN 0-533-06204-7). Vantage.

Lightner, Robert P. Speaking in Tongues & Divine Healing. LC 65-5805. 1978. pap. 1.95 (ISBN 0-87227-059-9). Reg Baptist.

Lindsay, Gordon. The Real Reason Why Christians Are Sick. (Divine Healing & Health Ser.). 3.50 (ISBN 0-89985-029-4). Christ Nations.

--Twenty-Five Objections to Divine Healing & the Bible Answers. (Divine Healing & Health Ser.). 1.25 (ISBN 0-89985-030-8). Christ Nations.

Linn, Dennis M., et al. Praying with One Another for Healing. 1984. pap. 4.95 (ISBN 0-8091-2619-2). Paulist Pr.

Linn, Matthew L. & Linn, D. Healing of Memories: Prayers & Confession-Steps to Inner Healing. LC 74-17697. 112p. (Orig.). 1974. pap. 3.95 (ISBN 0-8091-1854-8). Paulist Pr.

Loomis, Evarts G. & Paulson, Sig. Healing for Everyone. 2nd, rev. ed. LC 74-345. (Illus., Orig.). 1979. pap. 5.95 (ISBN 0-87516-377-7). De Vorss.

Lynch, Richard. Health & Spiritual Healing. 140p. Date not set. pap. 8.00 (ISBN 0-89540-146-0, SB-146). Sun Pub.

MacDonald-Bayne, Murdo. Divine Healing of Mind & Body. 215p. 1983. pap. 8.75 (ISBN 0-85243-035-3). Ariel OH.

Mackes, Shy. Seven Steps to God's Healing Power. pap. 0.95 (ISBN 0-910924-28-7). Macalester.

Maclachlan, Lewis. How to Pray for Healing. 112p. 1977. pap. 2.95 (ISBN 0-227-67486-3). Attic Pr.

McManus, Jim. The Healing Power of the Sacraments. LC 83-83397. 112p. (Orig.). 1984. pap. 3.95 (ISBN 0-87793-313-8). Ave Maria.

MacNutt, Francis. Healing. LC 74-81446. (Illus.). 336p. 1974. pap. 4.95 (ISBN 0-87793-074-0). Ave Maria.

--Healing. 320p. 1986. pap. 4.50 (ISBN 0-553-25993-8). Bantam.

--The Prayer That Heals. LC 80-69770. 120p. (Orig.). 1981. pap. 2.95 (ISBN 0-87793-219-0). Ave Maria.

Mayhue, Richard. Divine Healing Today. 1983. pap. 6.95 (ISBN 0-8024-0453-7). Moody.

Milingo, Emmanuel. The World in Between: Christian Healing & the Struggle for Spiritual Survival. Macmillan, Mona, ed. 144p. (Orig.). 1985. pap. 5.95 (ISBN 0-88344-354-6). Orbis Bks.

Miner, Malcolm. Healing Is for Real. pap. 4.95 (ISBN 0-8192-1132-X). Morehouse.

Morgan, G. Campbell. The Great Physician. 416p. 1982. Repr. 16.95 (ISBN 0-8007-0485-1). Revell.

Morningland Publications, Inc., ed. Healing: As It Is, 2 vols. (Illus.). 320p. (Orig.). 1981. Set. pap. 10.00 (ISBN 0-935146-59-8). Morningland.

Murphy, Joseph. Amazing Laws of Cosmic Mind Power. 1965. pap. 4.95 (ISBN 0-13-023804-X, Reward). P-H.

--How to Use Your Healing Power. 158p. 1973. pap. 3.50 (ISBN 0-87516-186-3). De Vorss.

--Infinite Power for Richer Living. 1969. pap. 4.95 (ISBN 0-13-464396-8, Reward). P-H.

Murray, Andrew. Divine Healing. 1962. pap. 3.50 (ISBN 0-87508-375-7). Chr Lit.

--Divine Healing. 160p. 1982. pap. text ed. 3.50 (ISBN 0-88368-112-9). Whitaker Hse.

Osborn, T. L. Healing the Sick. 420p. 1981. pap. 7.95 (ISBN 0-89274-187-2, HH-187). Harrison Hse.

--Receive Miracle Healing. 1983. pap. 4.95 (ISBN 0-89274-221-6, HH221). Harrison Hse.

Parker, Faye W. Mental, Physical, Spiritual Health. LC 79-56170. 80p. 1980. pap. 2.95 (ISBN 0-87516-397-1). De Vorss.

Parkhurst, Genevieve. Healing & Wholeness. 6.95 (ISBN 0-910924-90-2). Macalester.

Peterman, Mary E. Healing: A Spiritual Adventure. LC 74-80416. 104p. 1974. pap. 3.95 (ISBN 0-8006-1086-5, 1-1086). Fortress.

Peterson, John H. Healing Touch. LC 81-80629. 112p. (Orig.). 1981. pap. 5.95 (ISBN 0-8192-1291-1). Morehouse.

Popejoy, Bill. The Case for Divine Healing. LC 75-43155. 64p. 1976. pap. 0.95 (ISBN 0-88243-478-0, 02-0478). Gospel Pub.

Powers, Darden. Blessings from Jehovah-Rophe: The Lord Doth Heal. LC 83-90951. 173p. 1984. 11.95 (ISBN 0-533-05957-7). Vantage.

Price, Frederick K. Is Healing for All? 127p. (Orig.). 1979. pap. 3.95 (ISBN 0-89274-005-1). Harrison Hse.

Prince, Derek. Laying on of Hands. (Foundation Ser.: Bk. V). 1965-66. pap. 1.95 (ISBN 0-934920-04-4, B-14). Derek Prince.

Puryear, Meredith. Healing Through Meditation & Prayer. 1978. pap. 5.95 (ISBN 0-87604-104-7). ARE Pr.

Reidt, Wilford H. & Lake, John G. Jesus God's Way of Healing & Power to Promote Health. 171p. 1981. pap. 5.95 (ISBN 0-89274-197-X). Harrison Hse.

Reinhart, J. R. The Power of Knowing Who I Am in Christ. LC 82-73254. 220p. 1983. pap. 7.95 (ISBN 0-918060-04-4). Burn-Hart.

Rowlands, Gerald. How to Minister God's Healing Power. (Cornerstone Ser.). 32p. pap. 2.00 (ISBN 0-930756-73-8, 533007). Aglow Pubns.

Samra, Cal. The Joyful Christ: The Healing Power of Humor. 1986. pap. 7.95 (ISBN 0-06-067032-0). Har-Row.

Sams, Earnell, Jr. Doctrine on Divine Healing. (Orig.). 1982. pap. write for info. (ISBN 0-940068-02-8). Doctrine Christ.

Sandford, John & Sandford, Paula. Healing the Wounded Spirit. LC 85-71640. 510p. 1986. pap. 8.95 (ISBN 0-932081-14-2). Victory Hse.

--The Transformation of the Inner Man. LC 82-72007. 432p. 1986. pap. 6.95 (ISBN 0-932081-13-4). Victory Hse.

Sanford, Agnes. Healing Gifts of the Spirit. 1983. pap. 2.75 (ISBN 0-515-07621-X). Jove Pubns.

--Healing Light. pap. 4.50 (ISBN 0-910924-37-6). pocketsize o.p. 2.50 (ISBN 0-910924-52-X). Macalester.

--Healing Power of the Bible. 224p. 1984. pap. 2.50 (ISBN 0-515-07104-8). Jove Pubns.

--The Healing Power of the Bible. LC 83-48999. 1984. pap. 6.95 (ISBN 0-06-067053-3, RD 520, HarpR). Har-Row.

Scanlan, Michael. Inner Healing. LC 74-81901. 96p. (Orig.). 1974. pap. 3.95 (ISBN 0-8091-1846-7). Paulist Pr.

Schuller, Robert H. & Schuller, Arvella. The Courage of Carol: Pearls from Tears. LC 78-65619. 1978. pap. 2.50 (ISBN 0-89081-182-2). Harvest Hse.

Shlemon, Barbara L. Healing Prayer. LC 75-36056. 88p. 1975. pap. 1.95 (ISBN 0-87793-108-9). Ave Maria.

Shlemon, Barbara L., et al. To Heal As Jesus Healed. LC 78-54126. 112p. 1978. pap. 2.95 (ISBN 0-87793-152-6). Ave Maria.

Sipley, Richard M. Understanding Divine Healing. 168p. 1986. pap. 5.95 (ISBN 0-89693-263-X). Victor Bks.

Smith, Harry D. The Secret of Instantaneous Healing. 1965. 8.95 (ISBN 0-13-797951-7, Reward); pap. 4.95 (ISBN 0-13-797936-3). P-H.

Steiner, Rudolf. Fundamentals of Therapy: An Extension of the Art of Healing Through Spiritual Knowledge. 4th ed. Frommer, Eva A. & Josephson, J. M., trs. from Ger. Tr. of Grundlegendes fur eine Erweiterung der Heilkunst nach geisteswissenschaftlichen Erkenntnissen. 128p. 1983. pap. 7.95 (ISBN 0-85440-423-6, Pub. by Steinerbooks). Anthroposophic.

Steinke, Frank F. Greater Works Shall Ye Do. 101p. (Orig.). 1980. pap. 2.25 (ISBN 0-686-73996-5). Impact Bks Mo.

Stone, Justin F. Meditation for Healing: Particular Meditations for Particular Results. rev. ed. LC 86-61661. (Illus.). 192p. 1986. pap. 11.95 (ISBN 0-937277-01-0). Satori Resources.

Talbot, Alice-Mary M. Faith Healing in Late Byzantium: The Posthumous Miracles of Patriarch Athanasios I of Constaninople by Theoktistos the Stoudite. Vaporis, N. M., ed. (The Archbishop Iakovos Library of Ecclesiastical & Historical Sources Ser.). 160p. (Orig.). 1983. 17.00 (ISBN 0-916586-92-8); pap. 12.00 (ISBN 0-916586-93-6). Hellenic College Pr.

Tapscott, Betty. Inner Healing Through Healing of Memories. 1975. pap. 4.95 (ISBN 0-917726-29-4). Hunter Bks.

Thompson, Jane H. Spiritual Considerations in the Preventive Treatment & Cure of Disease. 128p. 1984. cancelled (ISBN 0-85362-211-6, Oriel). Methuen Inc.

Tucker, Ronald D. Healing. 57p. (Orig.). 1985. pap. 2.50 (ISBN 0-933643-27-6). Grace World Outreach.

Weil, Andrew. Health & Healing: Understanding Conventional & Alternative Medicine. 304p. 1985. pap. 7.95 (ISBN 0-395-37764-1). HM.

White, Nelson & White, Anne. Spiritual Healing. LC 85-50745. (Illus.). 65p. (Orig.). 1985. pap. text ed. 10.00 (ISBN 0-939856-42-5). Tech Group.

Wolf, William. Healers, Gurus, Spiritual Guide. LC 76-2180. 1969. pap. 6.50 (ISBN 0-933900-07-4). Foun Human Under.

Woodward, Mary A., compiled by. That Ye May Heal: A Manual for Individual & Group Study of Meditation for Healing, from the Edgar Cayce Records. rev. ed. 53p. 1970. pap. 3.50 (ISBN 0-87604-075-X). ARE Pr.

Worrall, Ambrose & Worrall, Olga. The Gift of Healing. 240p. 1985. pap. 6.95 (ISBN 0-89804-142-2). Ariel OH.

Wright, Gordon. In Quest of Healing. LC 83-82030. 176p. (Orig.). 1984. pap. 4.95 (ISBN 0-88243-614-7, 02-0614). Gospel Pub.

Yeomans, Lilian B. The Great Physician. 80p. 1961. pap. 2.25 (ISBN 0-88243-729-1, 02-0729). Gospel Pub.

--Healing from Heaven. 145p. 1954. pap. 2.95 (ISBN 0-88243-730-5, 02-0730). Gospel Pub.

--Health & Healing. 64p. 1973. pap. 1.95 (ISBN 0-88243-732-1, 02-0732). Gospel Pub.

SPIRITUAL LIFE

see also Christian Life; Devotion; Faith; Monastic and Religious Life; Monastic and Religious Life of Women; Perfection (Catholic); Piety; Retreats; Sanctification; Spiritual Direction; Spiritual Exercises; Wilderness (Theology)

Adler, Felix. The Reconstruction of the Spiritual Ideal. LC 77-27148. (Hibbert Lectures: 1923). Repr. of 1924 ed. 25.00 (ISBN 0-404-60422-6). AMS Pr.

Aelred of Rievaulx. Spiritual Friendship. (Cistercian Fathers Ser.: No. 5). 144p. pap. 5.00 (ISBN 0-87907-705-0). Cistercian Pubns.

Aivanhov, Omraam M. Spiritual Alchemy. rev. ed. (Complete Works: Vol. 2). (Illus.). 205p. 1986. pap. 9.95 (ISBN 2-85566-371-7, Pub. by Prosveta France). Prosveta USA.

--What Is a Spiritual Master? (Izvor Collection Ser.: Vol. 207). 185p. pap. 4.95 (ISBN 2-85566-230-3, Pub. by Prosveta France). Prosveta USA.

Akhilananda, Swami. Spiritual Practices. LC 78-175140. 1972. 12.00 (ISBN 0-8283-1350-4). Branden Pub Co.

Albritton, Clarice & Newby, Grace. A Lamp Unto Our Faith. LC 76-24514. 1976. pap. 3.95 (ISBN 0-87516-218-5). De Vorss.

Ali, Yusuf H. Spirit, Soul, Consciousness, Realization. 1975. pap. 3.50 (ISBN 0-913358-10-X). El-Shabazz Pr.

Almaas, A. H. Diamond Heart, Bk. 1: Elements of the Real in Man. 280p. (Orig.). 1987. pap. 10.00 (ISBN 0-936713-01-1). Almaas Pubns.

Almirudas, Hiram, ed. El Fruto del Espiritu. (Span.). 112p. 1979. pap. 3.50 (ISBN 0-87148-303-3). Pathway Pr.

Al-Qunawi, Sadraddin. Reflection of the Awakened. Askari, Hasan, tr. 112p. 1987. pap. 12.95 (ISBN 0-7103-0217-7, Pub. by Routledge UK). Methuen Inc.

Andrews, Lynn V. Star Woman: We Are Made from Stars & to the Stars We Must Return. LC 86-40038. 256p. 1986. 16.95 (ISBN 0-446-51316-4). Warner Bks.

Angus, Fay. Running Around in Spiritual Circles. LC 85-42768. 192p. 1986. 13.45 (ISBN 0-06-060238-4, HarpR). Har-Row.

Anzar, Naosherwan, ed. The Best of the Glow: A Fifteen Year Retrospective, Vol. 1. LC 84-23518. 208p. (Orig.). 1984. pap. 8.95 (ISBN 0-913078-54-9). Sheriar Pr.

Archimandrite Amvrossy Pogodin. Svjatoj Mark Efesskij i Florentijskaja Unia. Tr. of St. Mark of Ephesus & the Unia of Florence. 436p. (Orig.). 1963. pap. 15.00x (ISBN 0-88465-026-X). Holy Trinity.

Aschwanden, Richard & Aschwanden, Maria. Escaping Collusion. 90p. (Orig.). 1983. pap. 4.20x (ISBN 0-913071-01-3). Rama Pub Co.

Aseshananda, Swami. Glimpses of a Great Soul: The Life of Swami Saradananda. 320p. (Orig.). 1982. pap. 7.95 (ISBN 0-87481-039-6). Vedanta Pr.

Augsburger, Myron S. Quench Not the Spirit. rev. ed. LC 62-7330. 1975. pap. 2.95 (ISBN 0-8361-1477-9). Herald Pr.

Aurobindo, Sri. The Life Divine: A Commentary on Isha Upanished. 108p. (Orig.). 1981. pap. 7.50 (ISBN 0-89744-230-X, Pub. by Sri Aurobindo Ashram Trust India). Auromere.

Ayatollah Morteza Motahhari. Spiritual Discourses. Tawhidi, M. Salman, ed. Pazargadi, Aluddin, tr. 139p. (Orig.). 1986. pap. 4.95 (ISBN 0-9616897-0-6). MSA Inc.

Baba, Meher. The Everything & the Nothing. 1976. 70p. 4.95, (ISBN 0-913078-49-2, Pub. by R J Mistry India); pap. 2.95, 115p. (ISBN 0-913078-48-4). Sheriar Pr.

Badra, Robert. Meditations for Spiritual Misfits. (Illus.). 93p. (Orig.). 1982. pap. 7.95 (ISBN 0-9610274-0-1). JCL Hse.

Bakken, Kenneth. Call to Wholeness. Kelsey, Morton, intro. by. LC 84-23837. 128p. (Orig.). 1985. pap. 7.95 (ISBN 0-8245-0683-9). Crossroad NY.

Baldwin, Skip. A Province into Being. Anderson, Douglas, ed. (Illus.). 80p. (Orig.). 1984. pap. 6.95 (ISBN 0-912549-04-1). Bread and Butter.

Balsekar, Ramesh s. Pointers from Nisargadatta Maharaj. LC 82-71505. xiv, 223p. 1983. Repr. of 1984 ed. 13.50 (ISBN 0-89386-004-2). Acorn NC.

Bamberg, Corona. Cost of Being Human. 7.95 (ISBN 0-87193-128-1). Dimension Bks.

Bangley, Bernard K. Spiritual Treasure: Paraphrases of Spiritual Classics. LC 84-61026. 144p. (Orig.). 1985. pap. 6.95 (ISBN 0-8091-2646-X). Paulist Pr.

Barniak, Carl K. The Food of Angels. 96p. (Orig.). 1984. pap. 4.95 (ISBN 0-9613803-0-6). Barniak Pubns.

Basham, Don. Spiritual Power. rev ed. 92p. 1976. pap. 2.25 (ISBN 0-88368-075-0). Whitaker Hse.

Batzler, L. Richard. Journeys on Your Spiritual Path. 1982. 7.95 (ISBN 0-935710-04-3). Hid Valley MD.

Bawa Muhaiyaddeen, M. R. God, His Prophets & His Children. LC 78-12891. (Illus.). 1978. pap. 5.95 (ISBN 0-914390-09-0). Fellowship Pr PA.

--Truth & Light: Brief Explanations. LC 74-76219. (Illus.). 144p. 1974. pap. 3.95 (ISBN 0-914390-04-X). Fellowship Pr PA.

Beagle, Bert. The Revelation. 160p. 1986. 11.95 (ISBN 0-89962-568-1). Todd & Honeywell.

Beausoleil, Beau. Witness. LC 76-39971. (Illus.). 60p. 1976. pap. 6.00 (ISBN 0-915572-23-0). Panjandrum.

Beihl, Bessie. Blessed Are Your Eyes. pap. 1.00 (ISBN 0-87516-131-6). De Vorss.

--Peace My Heart. pap. 1.00 (ISBN 0-87516-133-2). De Vorss.

Bell, Skip. These Are Gifts: A Study Guide for Understanding Spiritual Gifts. 72p. 1985. pap. write for info. (ISBN 0-910347-03-4). Chatham Comm Inc.

Bendit, Laurence & Bendit, Phoebe. The Transforming Mind. 2nd ed. LC 74-103415. 161p. 1983. pap. 5.75 (ISBN 0-8356-0012-2, Quest). Theos Pub Hse.

Benjamin. The Father Who Dwelleth Within. 1979. pap. 2.50 (ISBN 0-87516-293-2). De Vorss.

Bennett, Dennis. How to Pray for the Release of the Holy Spirit. 1985. pap. 3.95 (ISBN 0-88270-593-8). Bridge Pub.

Bennett, John G. Existence. 1977. 4.50 (ISBN 0-900306-40-8, Pub. by Coombe Springs Pr). Claymont Comm.

Benoit, Hubert. The Interior Realization. Mahoney, John F., tr. from Fr. (Illus.). 128p. (Orig.). 1987. pap. 6.95 (ISBN 0-87728-624-8). Weiser.

Benson, Bob & Benson, Michael. Disciplines of the Inner Life. 380p. 1985. 18.95 (ISBN 0-8499-0468-4, 0468-4). Word Bks.

Benson, Robert H. & More, Thomas. The Friendship of Christ. (Books to Live Ser.). 156p. 1984. 10.95 (ISBN 0-88347-171-X). Thomas More.

Berry, Thomas. Teilhard in the Ecological Age. (Teilhard Studies). 1982. 2.00 (ISBN 0-89012-032-3). Anima Pubns.

Besant, Annie. From the Outer Court to the Inner Sanctum. Nicholson, Shirley, ed. LC 82-42703. 130p. 1983. pap. 4.50 (ISBN 0-8356-0574-4, Quest). Theos Pub Hse.

Bhagavad Gita As It Is. (Illus.). 904p. 14.95 (ISBN 0-89213-123-3). Bhaktivedanta.

Bhagwan Shree Rajneesh. The Perfect Way. Mahasattva Swami Krishna Prem, ed. LC 84-42808. (Early Writings & Discourses Ser.). 208p. 1984. pap. 3.95 (ISBN 0-88050-707-1). Chidvilas Found.

--The Rainbow Bridge. Prabhu, Krishna, ed. LC 85-42535. (Initiation Talks Ser.). 368p. (Orig.). 1985. pap. 3.95 (ISBN 0-88050-618-0). Chidvilas Found.

Bhandarkar, T. A. Ramakrishna, Sri: Sahasra-Nama-Stotram. (Illus.). 200p. (Orig.). pap. 7.95x (ISBN 0-87481-509-6). Vedanta Pr.

Bharti, Ma Satya. Death Comes Dancing: Celebrating Life with Bhagwan Shree Rajneesh. 200p. 1981. pap. 9.95 (ISBN 0-7100-0705-1). Methuen Inc.

Biamonte, Edgar. Window of Eternity. LC 83-9944. 145p. 1984. 14.95 (ISBN 0-87949-230-9). Ashley Bks.

Bicket, Zenas J. Walking in the Spirit. LC 76-51000. 96p. 1977. pap. 1.25 (ISBN 0-88243-611-2, 02-0611, Radiant Bks). Gospel Pub.

Bittner, Vernon J. You Can Help with Your Healing: A Guide for Recovering Wholeness in Body, Mind, & Spirit. LC 78-66946. 1979. pap. 6.95 (ISBN 0-8066-1698-9, 10-7411). Augsburg.

Blanchard, Tim. A Practical Guide to Finding & Using Your Spiritual Gifts. 1983. pap. 6.95 (ISBN 0-8423-4898-0). Tyndale.

Boddy, A. A. To Kairwan the Holy. 320p. 1985. 49.00x (ISBN 0-317-39199-2, Pub. by Luzac & Co Ltd). State Mutual Bk.

Bodo, Murray. The Way of St. Francis: The Challenge of Franciscan Spirituality for Everyone. LC 83-14066. 1985. 6.95 (ISBN 0-385-19913-9, Im). Doubleday.

Boehme, Jacob. Of the Supersensual Life. pap. 4.95 (ISBN 0-916411-90-7). Sure Fire.

Boff, Leonardo & Boff, Clodovis. Liberation Theology: From Dialogue to Confrontation. 120p. (Orig.). 1986. pap. 8.95 (ISBN 0-86683-528-8, HarpR). Har-Row.

Bonhoeffer, Dietrich. Spiritual Care. Rochelle, Jay C., tr. LC 85-47711. 128p. 1985. pap. 4.95 (ISBN 0-8006-1874-2). Fortress.

Booth, Catherine. The Story. pap. 3.95 (ISBN 0-686-27773-2). Schmul Pub Co.

Booth, Leo. Walking on Water. 180p. (Orig.). 1985. pap. 8.95 (ISBN 0-932194-28-1). Health Comm.

Booth, William. The Seven Spirits. 128p. 1984. Repr. of 1890 ed. 3.95 (ISBN 0-86544-026-3). Salv Army Suppl South.

Bordow, Sita, compiled by. The Master's Touch: Disciples' Stories. LC 84-28857. 1984. pap. 4.95 (ISBN 0-932040-26-8). Integral Yoga Pubns.

Bowdle, Donald N., ed. La Redencion Lograda y Aplicada. (Span.). 126p. 1979. pap. 3.95 (ISBN 0-87148-521-4). Pathway Pr.

Boyer, Ernest, Jr. A Way in the World: Family Life as Spiritual Discipline. LC 83-48983. 192p. 1984. 13.45 (ISBN 0-06-061032-8, HarpR). Har-Row.

Bright, Laren. Laughter Is the Best Meditation: The Best of the Inner Jester. LC 78-4491. 1979. pap. 5.00 (ISBN 0-686-10176-6). Baraka Bk.

Brightman, Edgar S. The Spiritual Life. LC 75-3086. (Philosophy in America Ser.). Repr. of 1942 ed. 27.50 (ISBN 0-404-59085-3). AMS Pr.

Brinton, Anna. Wide Horizon. 1983. pap. 2.50x (ISBN 0-87574-038-3, 038). Pendle Hill.

Brisette, Claire M. Reflective Living: A Spiritual Approach to Everyday Life. LC 83-21369. (Illus.). 136p. (Orig.). 1983. pap. 8.00 (ISBN 0-89571-019-6). Affirmation.

Brunton, Paul. Discover Yourself. rev ed. LC 83-60832. 244p. 1983. pap. 7.95 (ISBN 0-87728-592-6). Weiser.

--The Notebooks of Paul Brunton, Vol. 3: Part 1, Practices for the Quest; Part 2, Relax & Retreat. Cash, Paul & Smith, Timothy, eds. LC 86-81030. 392p. 1986. smyth-sewn bdg, acid-free 22.50 (ISBN 0-943914-15-9, Dist. by Kampmann & Co); pap. 12.50 smyth-sewn bdg, acid free (ISBN 0-943914-16-7, Dist. by Kampmann & Co). Larson Pubns Inc.

--The Notebooks of Paul Brunton, Vol. 4: Pt. 1 - Meditation; Pt. 2 - The Body. Cash, Paul & Smith, Timothy, eds. LC 86-81949. 432p. 1986. smyth-sewn bdg, acid free 22.50 (ISBN 0-943914-18-3, Dist. by Kampmann & Co); Pt. 1: Meditation. pap. 10.95 smyth-sewn bdg (ISBN 0-943914-19-1, Dist. by Kampmann & Co); Pt. 2: The Body. pap. 9.95 smyth-sewn bdg (ISBN 0-943914-20-5, Dist. by Kampmann & Co). Larson Pubns Inc.

--The Notebooks of Paul Brunton, Vol. 7: Healing of the Self; the Negatives, 2 pts. Cash, Paul & Smith, Timothy, eds. (Illus.). 320p. 1987. 22.50 (ISBN 0-943914-26-4, Dist. by Kampmann & Co.); pap. 12.50 (ISBN 0-943914-27-2, Dist. by Kampmann & Co.). Larson Pubns Inc.

--The Notebooks of Paul Brunton, Vol. 8: Reflections on My Life & Writings. Smith, Timothy, ed. (Illus.). 224p. 1987. 22.50 (ISBN 0-943914-28-0); pap. 12.50 (ISBN 0-943914-29-9). Larson Pubns Inc.

--Spiritual Crisis of Man. rev. ed. LC 83-60829. 224p. 1984. pap. 7.95 (ISBN 0-87728-593-4). Weiser.

Bryant, Christopher. The River Within: The Search for God in Depth. 160p. 1983. pap. 5.50 (ISBN 0-8358-0468-2). Upper Room.

Buck, Harry M. Spiritual Discipline in Hinduism, Buddhism, & the West. LC 81-12812. (Focus on Hinduism & Buddhism Ser.). 64p. 1981. pap. 4.95x (ISBN 0-89012-022-6). Anima Pubns.

Budhananda. The Saving Challenge of Religion. 272p. (Orig.). 1982. pap. 9.50 (ISBN 0-87481-567-3). Vedanta Pr.

Burkan, Peggy D. Guiding Yourself into a Spiritual Reality: A Workbook. LC 83-91310. 96p. (Orig.). 1985. pap. 7.95 (ISBN 0-935616-06-3). Reunion Pr.

Burton, Earl H., ed. Your Spiritual Deposit. 68p. 1982. pap. 2.00 (ISBN 0-910068-66-6). Am Christian.

Call, David M. Within Our Reach. LC 83-26162. 68p. 1984. 5.95 (ISBN 0-87747-975-5). Deseret Bk.

Campbell, Peter A. & McMahon, Edwin M. Bio-Spirituality: Focusing As a Way to Grow. LC 84-21328. 1985. pap. 6.95 (ISBN 0-8294-0478-3). Loyola.

Candragomin. Difficult Beginnings: Three Works on the Bodhisattva Path. Tatz, Mark, tr. LC 83-2317. Tr. of Sanskrit. 121p. 1985. 22.50 (ISBN 0-87773-317-1, 54530-3). Shambhala Pubns.

Captain, Philip A. Eight Stages of Christian Growth: Human Development in Psycho-Spiritual Terms. (Illus.). 240p. 1984. pap. 6.95 (ISBN 0-13-246661-9). P-H.

Carmack, Derin. Seven Steps to Freedom. 31p. 1986. pap. 3.00 (ISBN 0-937093-25-4). Jewel Pr.

Carr, John & Carr, Adrienne. The Pilgrimage Project: Participant's Notebook. 48p. (Orig.). 1987. pap. 2.95 (ISBN 0-8358-0549-2). Upper Room.

Cecil, Robert & Rieu, Richard, eds. The King's Son: Readings in the Contemporary Psychologies & Contemporary Thoughts on Man. 181p. 1981. 14.95 (ISBN 0-900860-88-X, Pub. by Octagon Pr England). Ins Study Human.

Cerling, Chuck. Cleaning Out Your Mental Closet: Transforming Negative Emotions. 150p. 1987. pap. 9.95 (ISBN 0-87788-127-8). Shaw Pubs.

Chafer, Lewis S. He That Is Spiritual. 1918. 5.95 (ISBN 0-310-22341-5, 6307P, Pub. by Dunham). Zondervan.

Chinmoy, Sri. Everest-Aspiration. 1979. pap. 4.95 (ISBN 0-88497-460-X). Aum Pubns.

--The Master & the Disciple. LC 85-72172. 115p. (Orig.). 1985. pap. 3.95 (ISBN 0-317-46896-0). Aum Pubns.

--Sri Chinmoy Speaks, 10 pts. Incl. Pt. 1. 55p (ISBN 0-88497-282-8); Pt. 2. 58p (ISBN 0-88497-285-2); Pt. 3. 65p (ISBN 0-88497-286-0); Pt. 4. 62p (ISBN 0-88497-288-7); Pt. 5. 56p (ISBN 0-88497-289-5); Pt. 6. 57p (ISBN 0-88497-290-9); Pt. 7. 58p (ISBN 0-88497-294-1); Pt. 8. 56p (ISBN 0-88497-295-X); Pt. 9. 51p (ISBN 0-88497-296-8); Pt. 10. 62p (ISBN 0-88497-335-2). 1976-77. pap. 2.00 ea. Aum Pubns.

--Wisdom-Waves in New York, 2 pts. (Orig.). 1979. pap. 2.00 ea. Pt. 1, 53p (ISBN 0-88497-487-1). Pt. 2, 50p (ISBN 0-88497-488-X). Aum Pubns.

Chittick, William & Wilson, Peter, trs. Fakhruddin Iraqi: Divine Flashes. 1982. 12.95 (ISBN 0-8091-0329-X); pap. 7.95 (ISBN 0-8091-2372-X). Paulist Pr.

Chow Tun Yi. The Book of Universality: A Supplement to the Book of Changes. Hsu, F. G., tr. from Chinese. 70p. 1979. pap. 2.00 (ISBN 0-89071-242-5). Matagiri.

Christensen, Joe J. To Grow in Spirit. 81p. 1983. 6.95 (ISBN 0-87747-968-2). Deseret Bk.

Clare, Francis. Your Move, God. LC 82-81212. 144p. 1982. pap. 4.95 (ISBN 0-89221-102-4). New Leaf.

Claypool, John. The Light Within You: Looking at Life Through New Eyes. 1983. 9.95 (ISBN 0-8499-0273-8). Word Bks.

Clowers, Don. Spitural Growth. 164p. (Orig.). 1984. pap. text ed. 3.95 (ISBN 0-914307-31-2). Word Faith.

Clymer, R. Swinburne. Science of Spiritual Alchemy. 235p. 1959. 9.95 (ISBN 0-932785-44-1). Philos Pub.

Codd, Clara M. Technique of the Spiritual Life. 2nd ed. 1963. 6.95 (ISBN 0-8356-7090-2). Theos Pub Hse.

Cohen, Alan. The Peace That You Seek. (Illus.). 195p. (Orig.). 1985. pap. 5.95 (ISBN 0-910367-35-3, 157). A Cohen.

Cole-Whittaker, Terry. The Inner Path from Where You Are to Where You Want to Be: A Spiritual Odyssey. LC 84-42930. 239p. 1986. 14.95 (ISBN 0-89256-283-8). Rawson Assocs.

Collin, Rodney. The Mirror of Light. LC 84-22141. 89p. 1985. pap. 6.95 (ISBN 0-87773-314-7, 72996-X). Shambhala Pubns.

--The Theory of Conscious Harmony. LC 84-5494. 211p. 1984. pap. 8.95 (ISBN 0-87773-285-X, 72698-7). Shambhala Pubns.

Collins, Mabel. When the Sun Moves Northward. LC 86-40402. 195p. (Orig.). 1987. pap. 4.75 (ISBN 0-8356-0614-7). Theos Pub Hse.

Colton, Ann R. Draughts of Remembrance. 177p. 1959. 8.95 (ISBN 0-917187-09-1). A R C Pub.

--The Human Spirit. 289p. 1966. 8.95 (ISBN 0-917187-05-9). A R C Pub.

--Islands of Light. 203p. 1953. 6.95 (ISBN 0-917187-14-8). A R C Pub.

--The Lively Oracles. 151p. 1962. 5.95 (ISBN 0-917187-13-X). A R C Pub.

--Men in White Apparel. (Illus.). 202p. 1961. 6.95 (ISBN 0-917187-10-5). A R C Pub.

--The Third Music. LC 82-71249. (Illus.). 432p. 1982. 15.95 (ISBN 0-917187-00-8). A R C Pub.

--The Venerable One. 166p. 1963. 5.95 (ISBN 0-917187-11-3). A R C Pub.

--Vision for the Future. 139p. 1960. 5.95 (ISBN 0-917187-12-1). A R C Pub.

Combat Manual for Spiritual Warfare. (Aglow Prayer Diary: No. 2). 217p. 1983. pap. 10.95 3-ring notebook (ISBN 0-930756-81-9, 531015). Aglow Pubns.

Connelly, Douglas. Daniel: Spiritual Living in a Secular World. (LifeBuilder Bible Studies). 64p. (Orig.). 1986. pap. 2.95 (ISBN 0-8308-1031-5). Inter-Varsity.

Cook, Anna. The Isness of Your Life. (Illus.). 56p. 1986. pap. 3.95 (ISBN 0-936029-03-X). Western Bk Journ.

Cooke, Grace. The Jewel in the Lotus. 1973. pap. 5.95 (ISBN 0-85487-032-6). De Vorss.

Cousins, Kathryn, et al. How to Read a Spiritual Book. 1.25 (ISBN 0-8091-2415-7). Paulist Pr.

Cramer, Steven A. Great Shall Be Your Joy. 228p. 1984. 8.95 (ISBN 0-934126-48-8). Randall Bk Co.

Cribb, C. C. Digging Diamonds Daily. LC 77-70215. Set. (ISBN 0-932046-09-6); Vol. 1. 12.95 (ISBN 0-932046-07-X); Vol. 2. 12.95 (ISBN 0-932046-08-8). Manhattan Ltd NC.

Curtiss, Eleanor. For Young Souls. 1941. pap. 1.95 (ISBN 0-87516-303-3). De Vorss.

Curtiss, H. H. & Curtiss, F. H. Inner Radiance. 369p. Date not set. pap. 20.00 (ISBN 0-89540-149-5, SB-149). Sun Pub.

Da Free John. Enlightenment of the Whole Body. LC 77-94504. 600p. 1978. pap. 14.95 (ISBN 0-913922-35-8). Dawn Horse Pr.

--The Way That I Teach. LC 77-94503. 1978. 10.95 (ISBN 0-913922-38-2); pap. 6.95 (ISBN 0-913922-34-X). Dawn Horse Pr.

Danielou, Jea. God's Life in Us. 2.95 (ISBN 0-317-06464-9). Dimension Bks.

Das Goswami, Satsvarupa. Letters from Srila Prabhupada, Vol. 1. Mandalesvara dasa & Gaura Purnima dasa, eds. 274p. (Orig.). 1982. pap. text ed. 3.95 (ISBN 0-911233-03-2). Gita Nagari.

--Life with the Perfect Master. Dasa, Mathuresa, ed. 110p. 1983. pap. text ed. 3.50 (ISBN 0-911233-17-2). Gita Nagari.

--Lilamrta, Vol. 5. (Illus.). 297p. 12.95 (ISBN 0-89213-119-5). Bhaktivedanta.

--Lilmarta, Vol. 6. (Illus.). 12.95 (ISBN 0-89213-120-9). Bhaktivedanta.

--One Hundred & Eight Rosebushes: Preaching in Germany. Mandalesvara dasa & Bimala dasi, eds. (Prabupada-lila Ser.). 44p. (Orig.). 1982. pap. text ed. 2.00 (ISBN 0-911233-04-0). Gita-Nagari.

--Vaisnava Behavior: Twenty-Six Qualities of a Devotee. Dasa, Mandalesvara, ed. 201p. 1984. text ed. 5.50 (ISBN 0-911233-18-0). Gita Nagari.

Dass, B. Hari. Fire Without Fuel. Ma Renu & Tabachnick, A. Dass, eds. LC 86-60051. (Illus.). 200p. (Orig.). 1986. 35.00 (ISBN 0-918100-09-7); pap. 12.95 (ISBN 0-918100-08-9). Sri Rama.

Daughters of St. Paul. Seven Spiritual Works of Mercy. 1979. 1.75 (ISBN 0-8198-6805-1); pap. 1.00 (ISBN 0-8198-6806-X). Dghtrs St Paul.

Davis, Roy E. Light on the Spiritual Path. 138p. 1984. pap. 3.95 (ISBN 0-317-20861-6). CSA Pr.

Daya, Sr. The Guru & the Disciple. 1976. pap. 2.95 (ISBN 0-911564-26-8). Vedanta Ctr.

Deal, William S. Problems of the Spirit-Filled Life. 2.95 (ISBN 0-686-13724-8). Crusade Pubs.

DelBene, Ron & Montgomery, Herb. Hunger of the Heart. 96p. (Orig.). 1983. pap. 4.95 (ISBN 0-86683-801-5, HarpR). Har-Row.

De Lubicz, Isha S. The Opening of the Way. Gleadow, Rupert, tr. LC 81-782. 256p. 1981. pap. 9.95 (ISBN 0-89281-015-7). Inner Tradit.

De Purucker, G. The Path of Compassion: Time-honored Principles of Spiritual & Ethical Conduct. 84p. 1986. pap. 4.00 (ISBN 0-911500-69-3). Theos U Pr.

Desai, Yogi A. Journal of the Spirit. (Illus.). 160p. 1985. pap. 4.95 (ISBN 0-940258-18-8). Kripalu Pubns.

Deutschle, Phil. The Two-Year Mountain. LC 86-4026. 256p. 1986. 15.95 (ISBN 0-87663-471-4). Universe.

Devi, Indira & Roy, Dilip K. Pilgrims of the Stars. 2nd ed. (Illus.). 406p. 1985. pap. 14.95 (ISBN 0-931454-10-7). Timeless Bks.

The Dhammapada: Anonymous Translation with Explanatory Notes & a Short Essay on Buddha's Thought. ix, 139p. 3.00 (ISBN 0-938998-16-1). Theosophy.

Diachenko, Gregory. Dukhovnija Posjevi. Tr. of Spiritual Sowing. (Illus.). 475p. 1977. 20.00 (ISBN 0-317-30414-3); pap. 15.00 (ISBN 0-317-30415-1). Holy Trinity.

Diamond, Carlin J. Love It, Don't Label It: A Practical Guide for Using Spiritual Principles in Everyday Life. Peterson, Kim, ed. (Illus.). 200p. (Orig.). 1986. pap. 10.00 (ISBN 0-911761-03-9). Fifth Wave Pr.

DiLustre, Tawny. A Compilation of Thoughts, I Think?! 104p. 1985. 6.95 (ISBN 0-8059-2962-2). Dorrance.

Divine Perceptions. pap. 14.95 (ISBN 0-937134-09-0). Amrita Found.

Diwakar, R. R. Mahayogi: Life, Sadhana & Teachings of Sri Aurobindo. 292p. 1976. pap. 6.00 (ISBN 0-89744-240-7, Pub. by Bharatiya Vidya Bhavan India). Auromere.

Dobson, Theodore. How to Pray for Spiritual Growth: A Practical Handbook of Inner Healing. LC 81-83182. 176p. (Orig.). 1982. pap. 7.95 (ISBN 0-8091-2419-X). Paulist Pr.

Dobson, Theodoree. Inner Healing. 384p. 1985. 12.95 (ISBN 0-8027-2488-4). Walker & Co.

Donders, Josephs G. Empowering Hope. 112p. (Orig.). 1986. pap. 5.95 (ISBN 0-89622-281-0). Twenty-Third.

Donnelly, Morwenna. Founding the Life Divine. 176p. 1976. Repr. of 1976 ed. write for info. Auromere.

Doris. Listen...The Speaking Heart. LC 79-50254. 1979. pap. 3.75 (ISBN 0-87516-361-0). De Vorss.

Doshi, Nagin. Guidance from Sri Aurobindo: Letters to a Young Disciple, Vol. 2. 1976. pap. 4.50 (ISBN 0-89071-265-4). Matagiri.

Doulatram, J., et al, eds. The Collected Works of Mahatma Gandhi, 90 Vols. 48000p. 1983. 950.00 (ISBN 0-934676-35-6). Greenlf Bks.

Dowsett, Norman & Jayaswal, Sita R. Dimensions of Spiritual Education. (Integral Education Ser.: No.4). (Illus.). 91p. 1975. pap. 2.50 (ISBN 0-89071-216-6). Matagiri.

Dreikurs, Rudolf. Character Education & Spiritual Values in an Anxious Age. (AAI Monograph Ser.: No. 1). 1971. pap. 2.00x (ISBN 0-918560-16-0). A Adler Inst.

Drummond, Henry. Natural Law in the Spiritual World. 371p. 1981. pap. 20.00 (ISBN 0-89540-082-0, SB-082). Sun Pub.

Drummond, Lewis A. The Awakening That Must Come. LC 78-59239. 1979. pap. 4.50 (ISBN 0-8054-6535-9). Broadman.

Duerlinger, James P., ed. Ultimate Reality & Spiritual Discipline. (God Ser.). 240p. (Orig.). 1984. text ed. 21.95 (ISBN 0-913757-09-8, Pub. by New Era Bks); pap. text ed. 12.95 (ISBN 0-913757-08-X, Pub. by New Era Bks). Paragon Hse.

Dunnam, Maxie. The Workbook on Becoming Alive in Christ. 160p. (Orig.). 1986. pap. 5.50 (ISBN 0-8358-0542-5). Upper Room.

--Workbook on Spiritual Disciplines. LC 83-51402. 160p. 1984. wkbk. 4.50 (ISBN 0-8358-0479-8). Upper Room.

Dunnam, Maxie D. The Christian Way. 112p. 1987. pap. 4.95 (ISBN 0-310-20741-X). Zondervan.

Earth-Bound Journey & Heaven-Bound Journey. 2.00 (ISBN 0-685-61408-5). Aum Pubns.

Eastern Light for the Western Mind. 3.95 (ISBN 0-87847-014-X). Aum Pubns.

Easwaran, Eknath. Formulas for Transformation: A Mantram Handbook. 264p. 1977. 15.00 (ISBN 0-915132-41-9); pap. 8.00. Nilgiri Pr.

Eaves, Mary L. The Truth Will Make You Free. LC 83-90380. 59p. 1985. 7.95 (ISBN 0-533-05883-X). Vantage.

Edgerton, Dorothy. Walk on in Peace. LC 82-73133. 64p. (Orig.). 1982. pap. 1.45 (ISBN 0-87029-187-4, 20278-8). Abbey.

Edwards, Tilden. Spiritual Friend: Reclaiming the Gift of Spiritual Direction. LC 79-91408. 272p. 1980. pap. 9.95 (ISBN 0-8091-2288-X). Paulist Pr.

El Morya. The Sacred Adventure. LC 81-85464. 148p. 1981. 7.95 (ISBN 0-916766-53-5). Summit Univ.

Emert, Joyce R. Louis Martin: Father of a Saint. LC 83-2728. 208p. (Orig.). 1983. pap. 9.95 (ISBN 0-8189-0446-1). Alba.

Ernst, John. Sadhana in Our Daily Lives: A Handbook for the Awakening of the Spiritual Self. LC 81-51360. 320p. (Orig.). 1981. pap. 9.95 (ISBN 0-9606482-0-8). Valley Lights.

Escriva de Balaguer, Josemaria. The Way. Orig. Title: Camino. 1979. pap. 4.95 (ISBN 0-933932-01-4). Scepter Pubs.

Every, George, et al, eds. Time of the Spirit. LC 84-10696. 256p. (Orig.). 1984. pap. text ed. 9.95 (ISBN 0-88141-035-7). St Vladimirs.

Eyre, Margery. The Sacred Mirror: A Spiritual Diary. 94p. 9.95 (ISBN 0-86140-068-2). Dufour.

Fabel, Arthur. Cosmic Genesis. (Tielhard Studies). 1981. 2.00 (ISBN 0-89012-028-5). Anima Pubns.

Fardan, Dorothy B. Understanding Self & Society. LC 80-81696. 232p. 1981. 14.95 (ISBN 0-8022-2370-2). Philos Lib.

Farley, S. Brent. Spiritually Yours: Applying Gospel Principles for Personal Progression. LC 81-82054. 160p. 1982. 6.95 (ISBN 0-88290-192-3, 1068). Horizon Utah.

Farrell, Edward. Surprised by the Spirit. 4.95 (ISBN 0-87193-030-7). Dimension Bks.

Fenelon. Fenelon's Spiritual Letters. Edwards, Gene, ed. 139p. pap. 5.95 (ISBN 0-940232-09-X). Christian Bks.

Fenelon, Archbishop. The Royal Way of the Cross. Helms, Hal M., ed. LC 80-67874. (Living Library Ser.). 1982. 5.95 (ISBN 0-941478-00-9). Paraclete Pr.

Fenske, Elizabeth W., ed. Spiritual Insights for Daily Living: A Daybook of Reflections on Ancient Spiritual Truths of Relevance for Our Contemporary Lives. (Illus.). 416p. (Orig.). pap. 7.50 (ISBN 0-914071-09-2). Spirit Front Fellow.

Filmore, Charles. Descubre Tu Poder Interno. LC 81-69933. Orig. Title: Discover the Power Within You. (Eng.). 448p. 1983. 5.95 (ISBN 0-87159-026-3). Unity School.

Finley, James. The Awakening Call. LC 84-72094. 160p. (Orig.). 1985. pap. 4.95 (ISBN 0-87793-278-6). Ave Maria.

Fitch, George H. Great Spiritual Writers of America. 1977. lib. bdg. 59.95 (ISBN 0-8490-1904-4). Gordon Pr.

Fourteen American Mothers & Fourteen American Daughters with Sri Chimnoy. 1975. 2.00 (ISBN 0-88497-212-7). Aum Pubns.

Fox, Matthew. On Becoming a Musical Mystical Bear: Spirituality American Style. LC 75-34842. 192p. 1976. pap. 4.95 (ISBN 0-8091-1913-7). Paulist Pr.

--A Spirituality Named Compassion, & the Healing of the Global Village, Humpty Dumpty, & Us. 1979. pap. 7.95 (ISBN 0-86683-751-5, HarpR). Har-Row.

Franck, Frederick. Art As a Way: A Return to the Spiritual Roots. LC 81-7853. (Illus.). 160p. (Orig.). 1981. pap. 9.95 (ISBN 0-8245-0076-8). Crossroad NY.

Francuch, Peter D. Major Ideas of the New Revelation. LC 84-51914. 266p. 1985. pap. 8.95 (ISBN 0-939386-08-9). TMH Pub.

--Messages from Within. LC 82-60513. 220p. 1982. pap. 7.95 (ISBN 0-939386-03-8). TMH Pub.

--Reality, Myths & Illusions. LC 83-51193. 513p. 1984. 9.95 (ISBN 0-939386-06-2). TMH Pub.

--Who Are You & Why Are You Here? LC 83-51781. 256p. (Orig.). 1984. pap. 4.95 (ISBN 0-939386-07-0). TMH Pub.

Francuch, Peter D. & Jones, Arthur E. Intensive Spiritual Hypnotherapy. LC 82-62015. 543p. 1983. 9.95 (ISBN 0-939386-04-6). TMH Pub.

Free John, Da. The Paradox of Instruction: An Introduction to the Esoteric Spiritual Teaching of Da Free John. LC 77-81836. 9.95 (ISBN 0-913922-32-3). Dawn Horse Pr.

French, R. M., tr. The Way of the Pilgrim & the Pilgrim Continues His Way. 256p. pap. 7.95 (ISBN 0-86683-898-8, AY7444, HarpR). Har-Row.

Frey, Kessler. Satsang Notes of Swami Amar Jyoti. LC 77-89524. (Illus.). 1977. 4.95 (ISBN 0-933572-01-8); pap. 2.95 (ISBN 0-933572-02-6). Truth Consciousness.

Fry, D. B. The Nature of Religious Man. 1982. 15.95 (ISBN 0-900860-67-7, Pub. by Octagon Pr England). Ins Study Human.

Furcha, E. J., ed. Spirit within Structure: Essays in Honor of George Jonhston on the Occasion of His Seventieth Birthday. (Pittsburgh Theological Monographs: New Ser.: No. 3). xvi, 194p. 1983. pap. 12.50 (ISBN 0-915138-53-0). Pickwick.

Gage, Joy. Every Woman's Privilege: Taking Responsibility for Your Spiritual Growth. (Touch of Grace Ser.). 1986. pap. 6.95 (ISBN 0-88070-177-3). Multnomah.

Gamshirananda, Swami, tr. from Sanskrit. Chandogya Upanishad. 690p. 1987. 16.00 (ISBN 0-87481-416-2, Pub. by Advaita Ashram India). Vedanta Pr.

Gandhi, M. K. Ashram Observances in Action. 151p. 1983. pap. 1.00 (ISBN 0-934676-36-4). Greenlf Bks.

--An Autobiography: Or, the Story of My Experiments with Truth. 2nd ed. Desai, Mahadev, tr. from Gujarati. 432p. 1983. 8.00 (ISBN 0-934676-40-2). Greenlf Bks.

Garber, Bernard J. Shards from the Heart: A Spiritual Odyssey in Twentieth Century America. LC 64-13358. (Freedeeds Library). 160p. 1965. 8.00 (ISBN 0-89345-004-9, Freedeeds Bks). Garber Comm.

Gardner, Nancy & Gardner, Esmond, eds. Five Great Healers Speak Here. LC 82-50164. (Illus.). 138p. (Orig.). 1982. pap. 6.25 (ISBN 0-8356-0567-1, Quest). Theos Pub Hse.

Gaskin, Stephen. This Season's People: A Book of Spiritual Teachings. LC 86-159636. (Illus.). 1976. 3.00 (ISBN 0-913990-05-1). Book Pub Co.

Gause, R. Hollis. Living in the Spirit. 136p. 1980. pap. 5.25 (ISBN 0-87148-515-X). Pathway Pr.

Gawryn, Marvin. Reaching High: The Psychology of Spiritual Living. LC 80-24306. 200p. 1981. 11.95 (ISBN 0-938380-00-1); pap. 7.95 (ISBN 0-938380-01-X). Highreach Colorado.

Geiger, Lura J. Spiritual Renewal: Tapping Your Inner Resources. (Orig.). 1987. pap. 34.50 (ISBN 0-931055-37-7); cassette incl. LuraMedia.

Geshe, Rabten & Geshe, Dhargyey. Advice from a Spiritual Friend. rev. ed. Beresford, Brian, ed. (A Wisdom Basic Book, Orange Ser.). (Illus.). 160p. 1984. pap. 8.95 (ISBN 0-86171-017-7, Wisdom Pubns). Great Traditions.

Gill, Jean. Unless You Become Like a Little Child. 88p. (Orig.). 1985. pap. 4.95 (ISBN 0-8091-2717-2). Paulist Pr.

Ginn, Roman. Adventure in Spiritual Direction: A Prophetic Pattern. (Orig.). 1979. pap. 2.95 (ISBN 0-914544-27-6). Living Flame Pr.

A God-Lover's Earth-Heaven Life. 1974. 2.00 (ISBN 0-88497-187-2). Aum Pubns.

God the Supreme Humorist. 1974. 2.00 (ISBN 0-88497-184-8). Aum Pubns.

Godman, David, ed. Be As You Are: The Teachings of Sri Ramana Maharshi. 256p. 1985. pap. 8.95 (ISBN 1-85063-006-2, Ark Paperbks). Methuen Inc.

Gold, E. J. The Joy of Sacrifice: Secrets of the Sufi Way. LC 78-54140. (Illus.). 1978. pap. 5.95 (ISBN 0-89556-003-8, Pub. by IDHHB & HOHM Press). Gateways Bks & Tapes.

Goldsmith, Joel. The Master Speaks. 192p. 1984. pap. 5.95 (ISBN 0-8065-0912-0). Citadel Pr.

Goldsmith, Joel S. Living Between Two Worlds. LC 73-18679. 1974. 8.95 (ISBN 0-06-063191-0, HarpR). Har-Row.

--Our Spiritual Resources. LC 78-16010. 192p. 1983. pap. 3.50 (ISBN 0-06-063212-7, RD 478, HarpR). Har-Row.

Goswami, Satsvarupa D. Opening a Temple in Los Angelos: A Visit to Boston. Dasa, Mandalesvara, et al, eds. (Prabhupada-lila Ser.). 72p. 1981. pap. 2.25 (ISBN 0-911233-01-6). Gita Nagari.

Goswami, Satsvarupa das. Japa Reform Notebook. Dasi, Bimala & Dasa, Mandalesvara, eds. 144p. (Orig.). 1982. pap. text ed. 3.95 (ISBN 0-911233-07-5). Gita Nagari.

Goswami, Srila Hridayananda dasa, ed. The Glories of Sri Caitanya Mahaprabhu. Kusakratha dasa, tr. LC 83-7078. 64p. (Orig.). 1984. pap. 6.00 (ISBN 0-89647-018-0). Bala Bks.

Granberg-Michaelson, Wesley. A Wordly Spirituality: The Call to Take Care of the Earth. LC 83-48997. 224p. 1984. 13.45 (ISBN 0-06-063380-8, HarpR). Har-Row.

Grassi, Joseph A. Changing the World Within: The Dynamics of Personal & Spiritual Growth. 128p. (Orig.). 1986. pap. 5.95 (ISBN 0-8091-2755-5). Paulist Pr.

Gray, Alice & McAuley, Marilyn. Mirror, Mirror. 144p. (Orig.). 1985. pap. 5.95 (ISBN 0-310-42951-X, 11344). Zondervan.

Gray, William G. The Sangreal Sacrament. LC 82-62847. (The Sangreal Sodality Ser.: Vol. 2). 224p. 1983. pap. 8.95 (ISBN 0-87728-562-4). Weiser.

Griffin, John H. The Hermitage Journals. LC 82-45833. (Illus.). 240p. 1983. pap. 6.95 (ISBN 0-385-18470-0, Im). Doubleday.

Griffiths, Bede. River of Compassion. (Wellspring Bk.). 224p. (Orig.). pap. 11.95 (ISBN 0-916349-08-X). Amity Hous Inc.

Griffiths, John, ed. A Letter of Private Direction. LC 81-126. (The Spiritual Classics Ser.). 176p. 1981. 9.95 (ISBN 0-8245-0081-4). Crossroad NY.

--The Mirror of Simple Souls. LC 81-126. (The Spiritual Classics Ser.). 176p. 1981. 9.95 (ISBN 0-8245-0083-0). Crossroad NY.

Gross, Darwin. The Ancient Teachings of the Masters. (Illus.). 45p. (Orig.). 1987. pap. 10.00 (ISBN 0-931689-06-6). SOS Pub OR.

Guru, R. H. Talk Does Not Cook the Rice: The Teachings of Agni Yoga. LC 81-70390. (Vol. 2). 198p. (Orig.). 1985. pap. 8.95 (ISBN 0-87728-535-7). Weiser.

Gutierrez, Gustavo. We Drink from Our Own Wells: The Spiritual Journey of a People. O'Connell, Matthew J., tr. from Span. LC 83-22008. Orig. Title: Beber en Supropio Pozo: En el Itinerario Espiritual de un Pueblo. 208p. (Orig.). 1984. pap. 7.95 (ISBN 0-88344-707-X). Orbis Bks.

Haeri, Shaykh F. Beams of Illumination from the Divine Revelation. 340p. 1987. pap. 18.95 (ISBN 0-7103-0219-3, 02193, Kegan Paul). Methuen Inc.

Haffert, John M. Meet the Witnesses. (Illus.). 160p. 1981. pap. 3.25 (ISBN 0-911988-39-4). AMI Pr.

Hagin, Kenneth E. Growing up, Spiritually. 1976. pap. 3.50 (ISBN 0-89276-504-6). Hagin Ministries.

--The Name of Jesus. 1979. pap. 3.50 (ISBN 0-89276-502-X). Hagin Ministries.

--What to Do When Faith Seems Weak & Victory Lost. 1979. pap. 3.50 (ISBN 0-89276-501-1). Hagin Ministries.

Hampsch, John H. & Kelly, Clint. The Key to Inner Peace. LC 85-61758. (Keyhole Ser.: No. 2). 112p. (Orig.). 1985. pap. 6.95 (ISBN 0-9613575-2-5). Perf Pr.

Haney, Joy. The Carpenter. Wallace, Mary, ed. LC 85-26498. (Illus.). 96p. (Orig.). 1985. pap. 5.00 (ISBN 0-912315-97-0). Word Aflame.

Hanna, Ken. In Search of Spiritual Leadership. 144p. 1987. pap. 5.95 (ISBN 0-89693-246-X). Victor Bks.

Hansadutta. Fool's Paradise. LC 85-5839. (Illus.). 190p. (Orig.). 1985. pap. 5.95 (ISBN 0-933593-05-8). Hansa Pub.

Hardy, Alister. The Spiritual Nature of Man. 1979. 27.00x (ISBN 0-19-824618-8); pap. 12.95x (ISBN 0-19-824732-X). Oxford U Pr.

Harper, Michael. Spiritual Warfare. 120p. 1984. pap. 4.95 (ISBN 0-89283-175-8). Servant.

Harrison, Buddy. Maintaining a Spirit Filled Life. 1985. 0.75 (ISBN 0-89274-383-2). Harrison Hse.

Harvey. The King's Diamond. 3.95 (ISBN 0-686-27782-1). Schmul Pub Co.

Hatengdi, M. U. Nityananda: The Divine Presence. Navarro, Aurelia, ed. LC 84-60099. (Illus.). 192p. (Orig.). 1984. pap. 10.95 (ISBN 0-915801-00-0). Rudra Pr.

Hayes, Dan. Fireseeds of Spiritual Awakening. 144p. 1983. pap. 5.95 (ISBN 0-86605-130-9). Campus Crusade.

The Heart of a Holy Man. 1973. 3.00 (ISBN 0-685-61431-X). Aum Pubns.

Helminiak, Daniel A. Spiritual Development: An Interdisciplinary Study. 256p. 1987. 15.95 (ISBN 0-8294-0530-5). Loyola.

Heschel, Abraham J. I Asked for Wonder: A Spiritual Anthology. 128p. 1983. pap. 8.95 (ISBN 0-8245-0542-5). Crossroad NY.

Hession, Roy. When I Saw Him. 1975. pap. 2.95 (ISBN 0-87508-239-4). Chr Lit.

Higher Taste: Based on Teachings of A. C. Bhaktivedanta Swami. (Contemporary Vedic Library Ser.). (Illus.). 176p. 2.95 (ISBN 0-89213-128-4). Bhaktivedanta.

Hill, Harold & Harrell, Irene B. God's in Charge Here. 160p. (Orig.). 1982. pap. 6.95 (ISBN 0-8007-5078-0, Power Bks). Revell.

--How to Live the Bible Like a King's Kid. (Illus.). 128p. 1980. pap. 5.95 (ISBN 0-8007-5051-9, Power Bks). Revell.

Hill, John L. The Enlightened Society. LC 86-40403. 278p. (Orig.). 1987. pap. 7.95 (ISBN 0-8356-0615-5). Theos Pub Hse.

Hills, Christopher. To the One I Love. Ray, Ann & Hills, Norah, eds. LC 84-11814. (Illus.). 256p. 1984. 14.95; pap. text ed. pns (ISBN 0-916438-51-1). Univ of Trees.

Himalayan International Institute. Inner Paths. 110p. pap. 3.95 (ISBN 0-89389-049-9). Himalayan Pubs.

Hislop, John S. Conversations with Sathya Sai Baba. LC 79-51262. (Illus.). 1979. pap. 5.40 (ISBN 0-9600958-5-3). Birth Day.

Hitz, Donna. The Triangular Pattern of Life. LC 79-84851. 94p. 1980. 7.95 (ISBN 0-8022-2249-8). Philos Lib.

Hodgson, Joan. Hullo Sun. (Illus.). 1972. 5.95 (ISBN 0-85487-019-9). De Vorss.

Hodson. Pathway of Perfection. 2.50 (ISBN 0-8356-7018-X). Theos Pub Hse.

Hoffman, Dominic. Beginnings in the Spiritual Life. 1976. 5.25 (ISBN 0-8198-0387-1); pap. text ed. 4.25 (ISBN 0-8198-0388-X). Dghtrs St Paul.

Hofinger, Johannes. Pastoral Life in the Power of the Spirit. LC 81-1439. (Illus.). 215p. 1982. pap. 6.95 (ISBN 0-8189-0427-5). Alba.

Hogg, James, ed. Spiritualitat Heute und Gestern, Vol. 1. (Analceta Carusiana Ser.: No. 35). (Eng, Ger, & Fr.). 236p. (Orig.). 1982. pap. 25.00 (ISBN 3-7052-0037-2, Pub by Salzburg Studies). Longwood Pub Group.

--Spiritualitat Heute und Gestern, Vol. 3. (Analecta Carusiana Ser.: No. 35). (Ital, Ger, & Eng.). 174p. (Orig.). 1983. pap. 25.00 (ISBN 3-7052-0039-9, Pub by Salzburg Studies). Longwood Pub Group.

--Spiritualitat Heute und Gestern, Vol. 4. (Analecta Cartusiana Ser.: No. 35). (Fr, Ital, Ger, & Eng., Illus.). 131p. (Orig.). 1984. pap. 25.00 (ISBN 3-7052-0040-2, Pub by Salzburg Studies). Longwood Pub Group.

--Spiritualitat Heute und Gestern, Vol. 5. (Analecta Cartusiana Ser.: No. 35). (Orig.). 1984. pap. 25.00 (ISBN 3-7052-0041-0, Pub by Salzburg Studies). Longwood Pub Group.

--Spiritualitiat Heute und Gestern, Vol. 2. (Analecta Cartusiana Ser.: No. 35). (Ger. & Eng.). 200p. (Orig.). 1983. pap. 25.00 (ISBN 3-7052-0038-0, Pub by Salzburg Studies). Longwood Pub Group.

Holmes, Ernest. Spiritual Awareness. Kinnear, Willis H., ed. 96p. 1972. pap. 5.50 (ISBN 0-911336-41-9). Sci of Mind.

--Spiritual Universe & You. Kinnear, Willis, ed. 96p. 1971. pap. 4.50 (ISBN 0-911336-37-0). Sci of Mind.

Horn, Merritt C. The Call of the Spirit. 82p. (Orig.). 1984. pap. 5.95 (ISBN 0-932661-00-9). Archangel Pub.

Howard, Alan. The Study of Anthroposophy As an Aspect of the Free Spiritual Life. 1985. pap. 2.00 (ISBN 0-916786-80-3). St George Bk Serv.

Hua, Ellen K. Meditations of the Masters. LC 76-47649. (Illus., Orig.). 1977. pap. 3.00 (ISBN 0-87407-203-4, FP-3). Thor.

Hubbard, David A. Unwrapping Your Spiritual Gifts. 160p. 1985. 9.95 (ISBN 0-8499-0478-1, 0478-1). Word Bks.

Huegel, F. J. Enthroned Christian. 1967. pap. 2.95 (ISBN 0-87508-905-4). Chr Lit.

Hug, James E., ed. Tracing the Spirit: Communities, Social Action & Theological Reflection. LC 82-62419. (Woodstock Studies: No. 7). 288p. 1983. pap. 9.95 (ISBN 0-8091-2529-3). Paulist Pr.

Hull, Bill. Right Thinking: Insights for Spiritual Growth. LC 84-63115. 144p. 1985. pap. 4.95 (ISBN 0-89109-531-4). NavPress.

Hunter, Charles & Hunter, Frances. His Power Through You. 247p. (Orig.). 1986. pap. 4.95 (ISBN 0-917726-74-X). Hunter Bks.

Hunter, Frances. God Is Fabulous. 1978. pap. 3.25 (ISBN 0-87162-115-0). Hunter Bks.

--Hot Line to Heaven. 1978. pap. 3.25 (ISBN 0-87162-117-7). Hunter Bks.

Hunter, Robert L. Helping When It Hurts: A Practical Guide to Helping Relationships. LC 85-47738. 80p. 1985. pap. 3.95 (ISBN 0-8006-1879-3, 1-1879). Fortress.

Illustrations from the Life of R. G. Flexon. pap. 2.95 (ISBN 0-686-12882-6). Schmul Pub Co.

In The Lap of the Himalayas. Date not set. pap. 2.50 (ISBN 0-87481-540-1, Pub. by Ramakrishna Math Madras India). Vedanta Pr.

Ingram, Kristen. Quiet Time with God. 96p. 1984. pap. 3.95 (ISBN 0-8170-1026-2). Judson.

Israel, Martin. Smouldering Fire: The Work of the Holy Spirit. LC 81-9794. 192p. 1981. 10.95 (ISBN 0-8245-0072-5). Crossroad NY.

Jack, LaWant P. All Things in Their Time. pap. 5.95 (ISBN 0-89036-145-2). Hawkes Pub Inc.

Jackson, Paul, ed. Sharafuddin Maneri: The Hundred Letters. LC 79-56754. (Classics of Western Spirituality Ser.). 480p. 1980. 13.95 (ISBN 0-8091-0291-9); pap. 9.95 (ISBN 0-8091-2229-4). Paulist Pr.

Jackson, William J. Sai Krishna Lila. LC 80-67137. 1980. pap. 4.50 (ISBN 0-9600958-7-X). Birth Day.

Jae Jah Noh. Do You See What I See? LC 77-5255. (Orig.). 1977. pap. 3.95 (ISBN 0-8356-0499-3, Quest). Theos Pub Hse.

Jaideva Singh. Vijnana Bhairava or Divine Consciousness. 1979. text ed. 14.00 (ISBN 0-89684-100-6, Pub. by Motilal Banarsidas India); pap. 9.95 (ISBN 0-89684-099-9). Orient Bk Dist.

Jantzen, Grace. God's World, God's Body. LC 84-3697. 186p. (Orig.). 1984. pap. 10.95 (ISBN 0-664-24619-2). Westminster.

Jardine, Samuel. Anchor of the Soul. 1978. pap. 1.95 (ISBN 0-937396-05-2). Walterick Pubs.

Jeffrey, David L., ed. A Burning & a Shining Light: English Spirituality in the Age of Wesley. 512p. (Orig.). 1987. pap. 16.95 (ISBN 0-8028-0234-6). Eerdmans.

Jegen, Mary E. How You Can Be a Peacemaker. 128p. 1985. pap. 2.95 (ISBN 0-89243-231-4). Liguori Pubns.

John & Carr, Adrienne. The Pilgrimage Project: Leader's Guide. 64p. (Orig.). 1987. pap. 4.95 (ISBN 0-8358-0550-6). Upper Room.

John, Da Free. The Liberator, Eleutherios. (Illus.). 114p. 1982. 12.95 (ISBN 0-913922-66-8); pap. 6.95 (ISBN 0-913922-67-6). Dawn Horse Pr.

--Nirvanasara. 280p. (Orig.). 1982. pap. 9.95 (ISBN 0-913922-65-X). Dawn Horse Pr.

--The Yoga of Consideration & the Way That I Teach. (Orig.). 1982. pap. 3.95 (ISBN 0-913922-63-3). Dawn Horse Pr.

John-Roger. Possessions, Projections & Entities. 1976. pap. 5.00 (ISBN 0-914829-17-3). Baraka Bk.

--The Spiritual Family. 1976. pap. text ed. 5.00 (ISBN 0-914829-21-1, 978-5). Baraka Bk.

Johnston, Charles & Giles, Lionel, trs. Selections from the Upanishads & the Tao Te King. 142p. 1951. 3.00 (ISBN 0-938998-15-3). Theosophy.

Johnston, William. The Mirror Mind: Spirituality & Transformation. LC 80-8350. 192p. 1981. 10.45 (ISBN 0-06-064197-5, HarpR). Har-Row.

--The Mirror Mind: Spirituality & Transformation. LC 80-8350. 192p. 1984. pap. 6.95 (ISBN 0-06-064206-8, RD 516, HarpR). Har-Row.

Jones, Alan. Soul Making: The Desert Way of Spirituality. LC 84-48222. 192p. 1985. 14.45 (ISBN 0-06-064182-7, HarpR). Har-Row.

Jones, Alan W. Journey into Christ. 1977. pap. 6.95 (ISBN 0-8164-0338-4, HarpR). Har-Row.

Jones, E. Stanley. Growing Spiritually. (Festival Books). 1978. pap. 3.25 (ISBN 0-687-15968-7). Abingdon.

--A Song of Ascents: A Spiritual Autobiography. LC 68-17451. (Festival Bks). 1979. pap. 2.25 (ISBN 0-687-39100-8). Abingdon.

Jungerman, Joan. Spiritual Growth: I Am the Way, the Truth, & the Life. rev. ed. 1.17 (ISBN 0-8091-9314-0). Paulist Pr.

Jyoti, Swami Amar. Spirit of Himalaya: The Story of a Truth Seeker. LC 78-73995. (Illus.). 1979. 7.95 (ISBN 0-933572-00-X). Truth Consciousness.

Kaam, Adrian van & Muto, Susan. Am I Living A Spiritual Life? 4.95 (ISBN 0-87193-173-7). Dimension Bks.

Kabir. Ocean of Love: Anurag Sagar of Kabir. Perkins, Rusell, ed. Bagga, Raaj K. & Singh, Pratap, trs. LC 82-50369. (Illus.). 252p. (Orig.). 1982. pap. 15.00 (ISBN 0-89142-039-8). Sant Bani Ash.

Kane, Aletheia, tr. from Fr. Complete Works of Elizabeth of the Trinity: Major Spiritual Writings, Vol. 1. LC 84-3748. Tr. of J'ai Trouve Dieu, Oeuvres Completes. (Illus.). 208p. (Orig.). 1984. pap. 6.95x (ISBN 0-935216-01-4). ICS Pubns.

Kane, Thomas S. Journey of the Heart. LC 81-5278. 1981. pap. 4.95 (ISBN 0-932506-13-5). St Bedes Pubns.

Kao, Charles C. Psychological & Religious Development: Maturity & Maturation. LC 80-5852. 382p. (Orig.). 1981. lib. bdg. 30.00 (ISBN 0-8191-1759-5); pap. text ed. 15.25 (ISBN 0-8191-1760-9). U Pr of Amer.

Kappeler, Max. Compendium for the Study of Christian Science: No. 8, Life. 23p. 1952. pap. 3.50 (ISBN 0-85241-062-X). Kappeler Inst Pub.

--The Spiritual Breakthrough to the Next Millennium. LC 85-82058. 75p. 1986. pap. 7.00 (ISBN 0-942958-12-8). Kappeler Inst Pub.

Kaung, Stephen. The Splendor of His Way. Hsu, Lily, tr. from Eng. (Chinese.). 1984. pap. write for info. (ISBN 0-941598-14-4). Living Spring Pubns.

Kavanaugh, James. Search: A Guide for Those Who Dare Ask of Life Everything Good & Beautiful. LC 85-42781. 224p. 1985. 14.95 (ISBN 0-06-250448-7, HarpR). Har-Row.

Kaystal, Phyllis. Sai Baba the Ultimate Experience. (Illus.). 277p. (Orig.). 1985. pap. 7.95. Aura Bks.

Kearns, Thomas F. The Art of the Mystic: The Master Course in Spiritual & Psychic Development. Paterson, Kathy, ed. (Illus.). 160p. (Orig.). 1986. pap. 9.95 (ISBN 0-935251-00-6). Manchurch.

Kelly, Thomas. Reality of the Spiritual World. LC 76-9644. (Orig.). 1942. pap. 2.50x (ISBN 0-87574-021-9). Pendle Hill.

Kelsey, Morton T. Transcend: A Guide to the Spiritual Quest. 240p. (Orig.). 1981. pap. 9.95 (ISBN 0-8245-0015-6). Crossroad NY.

Kennedy, David G. The Incarnation & Hilton's Spirituality. LC 85-62297. x, 312p. (Orig.). 1986. pap. 12.95x (ISBN 0-934995-00-1). OLW Editions.

Khalsa, D. K., ed. The New Consciousness Sourcebook: Spiritual Community Guide, No. 6. 6th ed. 256p. 1985. pap. 8.95 (ISBN 0-89509-055-4). Arcline Pubns.

Khan, Hazrat I. Mastery Through Accomplishment: Developing Inner Strength for Life's Challenges. rev. ed. LC 79-101639. (Collected Works of Hazrat Inayat Khan Ser.). 336p. 1985. pap. 11.95 (ISBN 0-930872-07-X). Omega Pr NM.

Khan, M. K. The Science of Spirituality. 135p. 1983. text ed. 15.00x (ISBN 0-86590-164-3). Apt Bks.

Kieninger, Richard. Spiritual Seekers' Guidebook: And Hidden Threats to Mental & Spiritual Freedom. 1986. 12.95 (ISBN 0-9600308-6-7). Stelle.

Kierkegaard, Soren. Purity of Heart. Steere, Douglas, tr. pap. 7.95x (ISBN 0-06-130004-7, TB4, Torch). Har-Row.

--Works of Love: Some Christian Reflections in the Form of Discourse. pap. 7.95x (ISBN 0-06-130122-1, TB122, Torch). Har-Row.

--Works of Love: Some Christian Reflections in the Form of Discourses. Long, tr. LC 64-7445. 1962. 17.75 (ISBN 0-8446-2373-3). Peter Smith.

Kilpatrick, Gilbert. Our Hearts Are Restless. 1983. pap. 2.50x (ISBN 0-87574-032-4, 032). Pendle Hill.

Kinigsberg, David. Modern Man & An Old-Fashioned God. 1985. 7.95 (ISBN 0-533-06659-X). Vantage.

Klein, Jean. Ease of Being. 2nd ed. xiii, 110p. 1986. pap. 8.50 (ISBN 0-89386-015-8). Acorn NC.

Knight, Carol B. Passing the Torch. LC 81-82491. 130p. (Orig.). 1985. pap. 7.95 (ISBN 0-913299-16-2). Stillpoint.

Koberlein, Jean. A Spiritual Encounter with the Holy One. LC 84-8938. (Mellen Lives Ser.: Vol. 2). 200p. 1984. pap. 9.95x (ISBN 0-88946-012-4). E Mellen.

Kocache, R., tr. The Journey of the Soul: The Story of Hai bin Yaqzan. 1982. 11.95 (ISBN 0-900860-90-1, Pub. by Octagon Pr England). Ins Study Human.

Kornfield, Jack & Breiter, Paul. A Still Forest Pool. LC 85-40411. (Illus.). 225p. (Orig.). 1985. pap. 6.50 (ISBN 0-8356-0597-3, Quest). Theos Pub Hse.

Kripalvanandaji, Shri. A Pilgrimage of Love, Book I. LC 81-82015. 86p. (Orig.). 1981. pap. 4.50 (ISBN 0-940258-02-1). Kripalu Pubns.

Kripalvandji, Swami Shri. Pilgrimage of Love, Book II. LC 81-82015. 416p. (Orig.). 1982. pap. 7.50 (ISBN 0-940258-05-6). Kripalu Pubns.

Kung, Hans. Eternal Life: Life after Death As a Medical, Philosophical, & Theological Program. LC 82-45112. 288p. 1985. 9.95 (ISBN 0-385-19910-4, Im). Doubleday.

Kury, Zaher P. From a Gun to a Flower. (Illus.). 352p. (Orig.). 1985. pap. 13.50 (ISBN 0-9615041-0-2). Unity Pr.

LaHaye, Beverly. The Spirit-Controlled Woman. LC 76-5562. 1976. pap. 4.95 (ISBN 0-89081-020-6, 0206). Harvest Hse.

Lama Mipham. Clear Light: The Distinction Between Appearance & Reality. 1980. write for info. Dharma Pub.

Lambek, Ruth. A Passion for the Divine. 1979. pap. 4.95 (ISBN 0-87516-289-4). De Vorss.

Lamsa, George M. And the Scroll Opened. LC 67-23820. (Illus.). 1978. pap. 3.50 (ISBN 0-87516-274-6). De Vorss.

LaPlace, Jean. An Experience of Life in the Spirit. Mooney, John R., tr. 220p. 1977. 6.95 (ISBN 0-8199-0594-1). Franciscan Herald.

--Preparing for Spiritual Direction. 196p. 1975. 6.95 (ISBN 0-8199-0558-5). Franciscan Herald.

Law, Terry. Your Spiritual Weapons & How to Use Them. (Orig.). 1983. pap. write for info. (ISBN 0-88144-028-0, CPS028). Christian Pub.

Law, William. Spirit of Prayer & Spirit of Love. Spencer, Sydney, ed. 301p. 1969. 17.50 (ISBN 0-227-67720-X). Attic Pr.

--William Law: Selections on the Interior Life. Morrison, Mary, ed. LC 62-15272. (Orig.). 1962. pap. 2.50x (ISBN 0-87574-120-7). Pendle Hill.

Lawson, LeRoy. Where Do You Grow from Here? 128p. 1985. pap. 2.95 (ISBN 0-87239-967-2, 41034). Standard Pub.

Lee, Charles. Divine Wisdom & Awareness of a Spiritual & True Religious Life. 1986. 6.95 (ISBN 0-533-06748-0). Vantage.

Leichtman, Robert R. & Japikse, Carl. Books of Light. (Illus.). 160p. (Orig.). 1986. pap. 3.95 (ISBN 0-89804-049-3). Ariel OH.

--Life of Spirit, Vol. I. (Illus.). 216p. (Orig.). 1986. pap. 7.95 (ISBN 0-89804-132-5). Ariel OH.

--Life of Spirit Series. (Orig.). 1982. pap. 2.25 ea. Ariel OH.

Leon-Portilla, Miguel, ed. Native Mesoamerican Spirituality. Anderson, Arthur J. & Dibble, Charles E., trs. LC 80-80821. (Classics of Western Spirituality Ser.). 320p. 1980. 13.95 (ISBN 0-8091-0293-5); pap. 9.95 (ISBN 0-8091-2231-6). Paulist Pr.

Lewellen, Christine. I Am What I Am for God Whosoever Will. 1987. 8.95 (ISBN 0-533-07150-X). Vantage.

Lewis, Allan P. Living in Harmony: Through Kahuna Wisdom. LC 84-25244. (Illus.). 192p. (Orig.). 1985. pap. 10.95 (ISBN 0-915563-01-0). Homana Pubns.

Lewis, James C. The Key to Spiritual Growth. 128p. 1985. 5.95 (ISBN 0-87159-004-2). Unity School.

Lewis, Jim. Spiritual Gospel. LC 82-51231. 145p. (Orig.). 1982. pap. 8.95 (ISBN 0-942482-05-0). Unity Church Denver.

Lindsay, Gordon. Twenty-Two Questions Most Frequently Asked by the Unsaved. 1.50 (ISBN 0-89985-118-5). Christ Nations.

Linn, Dennis, et al. At Peace with the Unborn: A Book for Healing. 1.50 (ISBN 0-8091-5187-1). Paulist Pr.

Loomis, Evarts G. & Paulson, Sig. Healing for Everyone. 2nd, rev. ed. LC 74-345. (Illus., Orig.). 1979. pap. 5.95 (ISBN 0-87516-377-7). De Vorss.

Lord Gauranga: Love Incarnate. 2.00 (ISBN 0-685-61441-7). Aum Pubns.

Lovelace, Richard. Dynamics of Spiritual Life. LC 78-24757. 1979. pap. 11.95 (ISBN 0-87784-626-X). Inter-Varsity.

Lovelace, Richard F. Renewal As a Way of Life. LC 85-10029. 216p. 1985. pap. 7.95 (ISBN 0-87784-594-8). Inter-Varsity.

Lug Dukhovnij. Tr. of The Spiritual Meadow. 400p. 20.00 (ISBN 0-317-28903-9); pap. 15.00 (ISBN 0-317-28904-7). Holy Trinity.

Lugenbeel, Barbara. Your Spiritual Growth Handbook. LC 84-61016. 164p. (Orig.). 1984. pap. 5.95 (ISBN 0-8192-1352-7). Morehouse.

MacArthur, John, Jr. Spiritual Gifts. (John MacArthur's Bible Studies). 1985. pap. 5.95 (ISBN 0-8024-5121-7). Moody.

Macaulay, Ranald & Barrs, Jerram. Being Human: The Nature of Spiritual Experience. LC 77-11365. 1978. pap. 6.95 (ISBN 0-87784-796-7). Inter-Varsity.

MacDonald-Bayne, Murdo. Life Everlasting. 165p. 1981. pap. 9.50 (ISBN 0-85243-365-4). Ariel OH.

MacLaren, Alexander. Victory in Failure. LC 79-88309. (Shepherd Illustrated Classics Ser.). 208p. (Orig.). 1980. pap. 5.95 (ISBN 0-87983-212-6). Keats.

McMillan, E. W. The Minister's Spiritual Life. 1959. 4.50 (ISBN 0-88027-009-8). Firm Foun Pub.

Maezumi, Hakuyu T. & Loori, John D. The Way of Everyday Life. LC 78-8309. (Illus.). 1978. 17.50 (ISBN 0-916820-17-3); pap. 9.95 (ISBN 0-916820-06-8). Center Pubns.

Maimonides, Obadyah. The Treatise of the Pool. Fenton, Paul, tr. 1981. 19.95 (ISBN 0-900860-87-1, Pub. by Octagon Pr England). Ins Study Human.

Mains, David. Psalms That Touch Us Where We Live. (Chapel Talks Ser.). 64p. 0.95 (ISBN 0-89191-265-7, 52654). Cook.

Maloney, George. Nesting in the Rock. 6.95 (ISBN 0-87193-002-1). Dimension Bks.

Maloney, George A. Called to Intimacy. LC 83-3782. 164p. 1983. pap. 6.95 (ISBN 0-8189-0452-6). Alba.

Malyala, P. Vishnu Sahasranamam. (Illus.). 18p. (Orig.). 1986. pap. text ed. 5.00 (ISBN 0-938924-28-1). Sri Shirdi Sai.

Malyala, Panduranga. Sri Sarasvati Puja: Goddess of Knowledge & Education. (Illus.). 28p. 1982. 2.00 (ISBN 0-938924-10-9). Sri Shirdi Sai.

--Yagna (The Eternal Energy) (Illus.). 36p. (Orig.). 1984. pap. text ed. 4.00x (ISBN 0-938924-23-0). Sri Shirdi Sai.

Malyala, Panduranga R. New Clear Energy: Rudra Abhisekam. (Illus.). 120p. 1983. 5.00 (ISBN 0-938924-11-7). Sri Shirdi Sai.

Man & God. (Miniature Ser.). 0.50 (ISBN 0-685-61383-6). Aum Pubns.

Marcoux, Marcene. Cursillo: Anatomy of a Movement: The Experience of Spiritual Renewal. 299p. 1982. 16.95x (ISBN 0-931186-00-5). Lambeth Pr.

Margenau, Henry. The Miracle of Existence. 143p. 1987. pap. 9.95 (ISBN 0-87773-407-0). Shambhala Pubns.

Maritain, Jacques. The Things That Are Not Caesar's. Scanlan, J. F., tr. 227p. 1983. Repr. of 1930 ed. lib. bdg. 40.00 (ISBN 0-89760-589-6). Telegraph Bks.

Mark-Age. How to Do All Things: Your Use of Divine Power. LC 72-121118. 144p. 1970. pap. 5.00 (ISBN 0-912322-01-2). Mark-Age.

--One Thousand Keys to the Truth: Spiritual Guidelines for Latter Days & Second Coming. LC 75-40976. 156p. 1976. pap. 5.00 (ISBN 0-912322-51-9). Mark-Age.

Marsh, Michael. Philosophy of the Inner Light. LC 76-50674. (Orig.). 1976. pap. 2.50x (ISBN 0-87574-209-2). Pendle-Hill.

Marshall, Catherine. A Closer Walk: Spirtual Discoveries from Her Journal. LeSourd, Leonard, ed. 1985. 12.95 (ISBN 0-317-46132-X). Revell.

Massey, James E. Spiritual Disciplines: Growth Through the Practice of Prayer, Fasting, Dialogue, & Worship. rev. ed. Allison, Joseph D., ed. 112p. 1985. pap. 4.95 (ISBN 0-310-37151-1, 12410P). Zondervan.

Maurana, Humberto R. & Varela, Francisco. The Tree of Knowledge: The Biological Roots of Human Understanding. Crossen, Kendra, ed. LC 86-29698. (Illus.). 215p. 1987. 19.95 (ISBN 0-87773-373-2); pap. 12.95 (ISBN 0-87773-403-8). Shambhala Pubns.

Maxwell, Charles H. Adventures of the White Girl in Her Search for God. LC 74-20648. 1974. Repr. of 1933 ed. lib. bdg. 25.00 (ISBN 0-8414-5951-7). Folcroft.

Mayhall, Carole. Lord, Teach Me Wisdom. LC 78-78013. 180p. 1979. pap. 5.95 (ISBN 0-89109-432-6). NavPress.

Mazeroni, Robert S. Spiritual First Aid from A to Z. 176p. (Orig.). 1987. pap. 2.95 (ISBN 0-345-33824-3, Pub. by Ballantine Epiphany). Ballantine.

Mickaharic, Draja. Spiritual Cleansing. pap. 5.95 (ISBN 0-942272-09-9). Original Pubns.

Mills, Kenneth G. The New Land! Conscious Experience Beyond Horizons. (Illus.). 77p. 1978. pap. 4.95 (ISBN 0-919842-01-1). Sun-Scape Pubns.

Minichen, Sam. From God Through Me to You. 58p. 1984. 3.95 (ISBN 0-89697-188-0). Intl Univ Pr.

Mohr, Victor. A Spiritual View of Life. Ozols, Violet, tr. from Ger. 364p. 1985. pap. cancelled (ISBN 0-934616-15-9). Valkyrie Pub Hse.

Moline, Mary. The Eagle & the Butterfly. (Illus.). 57p. (Orig.). 1986. pap. 8.00 (ISBN 0-913444-10-3). Rumbleseat.

Moor, Mary-Margaret, ed. I Come As a Brother: Bartholomew. 192p. 1986. pap. 10.95 (ISBN 0-9614010-1-X). High Mesa Pr.

Morduch, Anna. Sovereign Adventure: The Grail of Mankind. 196p. 1970. 11.95 (ISBN 0-227-67754-4). Attic Pr.

Morgan, Elise N. Communion. (Meditation Ser.). 1928. 3.50 (ISBN 0-87516-328-9). De Vorss.

Mostrom, Donald G. Spiritual Privileges You Didn't Know Were Yours. LC 86-11383. 192p. (Orig.). 1986. pap. 5.95 (ISBN 0-87784-982-X). Inter-Varsity.

Mozumdar, A. K. Today & Tomorrow. 2nd ed. 1979. pap. 2.50 (ISBN 0-87516-369-6). De Vorss.

Muhaiyaddeen, Bawa. Maya Veeram or the Forces of Illusion. Marcus, Sharon, ed. Ganesan, K. & Ganesan, R., trs. from Tamil. (Illus.). 232p. 1982. pap. 10.95 (ISBN 0-87728-550-0). Weiser.

Mulholland, M. Robert. Shaped by the Word. (Orig.). 1985. pap. 7.95 (ISBN 0-8358-0519-0). Upper Room.

Mullan, Bob. Life as Laughter: Following Bhagwan Shree Rajneesh. (Illus.). 204p. 1984. 26.95x (ISBN 0-7102-0141-9); pap. 12.95 (ISBN 0-7102-0043-9). Methuen Inc.

Mullet, Rosa M. God's Marvelous Work, Bk. 2. 1981. write for info. (ISBN 0-686-25256-X); tchr's. ed. avail. (ISBN 0-686-25257-8). Rod & Staff.

Mullin, Glenn H. Selected Works of the Dalai Lama VII: Songs of Spiritual Change. Rev. ed. LC 85-8332. (Teachings of the Dalai Lamas Ser.). Orig. Title: Songs of Spiritual Change. (Tibetan., Illus.). 225p. 1985. pap. 10.95 (ISBN 0-937938-30-0). Snow Lion.

Murphy, Carol R. O Inward Traveller. LC 77-91637. 31p. (Orig.). 1977. pap. 2.50x (ISBN 0-87574-216-5). Pendle Hill.

Murray, Andrew. The Inner Life. 144p. 1984. pap. 5.95 (ISBN 0-310-29751-6, 10364P, Clarion Class). Zondervan.

--The Inner Life. 160p. 1984. pap. text ed. 3.50 (ISBN 0-88368-138-2). Whitaker Hse.

Murray, Ferne H. A Journey into His Presence. LC 78-73439. (Illus.). 1979. pap. 3.95 (ISBN 0-932994-00-8). Day Star.

Murro, Jonathan. God-Realization Journal. (Illus.). 337p. 1975. 10.00 (ISBN 0-917187-16-4). A R C Pub.

Muto, Susan. A Practical Guide to Spiritual Reading. 9.95 (ISBN 0-87193-046-3). Dimension Bks.

--Steps Along the Way: The Path of Spiritual Reading. 4.95 (ISBN 0-87193-048-X). Dimension Bks.

Muto, Susan A. Pathways of Spiritual Living. LC 84-1564. 192p. 1984. pap. 6.95 (ISBN 0-385-19473-0, Im). Doubleday.

Neagle, Larry. Underground Manual for Spiritual Survival. (Orig.). 1986. pap. 4.95 (ISBN 0-8024-9052-2). Moody.

Needleman, Carla. The Work of Craft. 160p. 1987. pap. 8.95 (ISBN 1-85063-061-5, 30615, Ark Paperbks). Methuen Inc.

Ni, Hua-Chung. Heavenly Way. LC 81-50158. (Illus.). 41p. (Orig.). 1981. pap. text ed. 2.50 (ISBN 0-937064-03-3). SEBT.

Nichols, Roy. The Greening of the Gospel. 1985. 6.25 (ISBN 0-89536-745-9, 5851). CSS of Ohio.

Ni Hua Ching. Workbook for Spiritual Development of All People. LC 83-51083. 240p. 1983. text ed. 12.50 (ISBN 0-937064-06-8). SEBT.

Nisargadatta Maharaj. The Blissful Life: As Realized Through the Teachings of Sri Nisargadatta Maharaj. Powell, Robert, compiled by. ix, 84p. pap. 6.95 (ISBN 0-89386-014-X). Acorn NC.

--I Am That; Talks with Sri Nisargadatta Maharaj. Frydman, Maurice, tr. from Marathi. Dikshit, Sudhakar S., ed. LC 81-66800. xx, 550p. 1986. Repr. of 1982 ed. 19.50 (ISBN 0-89386-002-6). Acorn NC.

Noel, Daniel. Approaching Earth. (Chrysalis Bk.). 192p. (Orig.). 1986. pap. 14.95 (ISBN 0-916349-12-8). Amity Hous Inc.

Norbu, Namkhai. The Cycle of Day & Night: Where One Proceeds Along the Path of the Primordial Yoga; A Basic Tibetan Text on the Practice of Dzogchen. Reynolds, John, ed. & tr. from Tibetan. (Illus.). 128p. 1987. pap. 9.95 (ISBN 0-88268-040-4). Station Hill Pr.

Norbu, Thinley. Magic Dance: The Display of the Self-Nature of the Five Wisdom Dakinis. rev. ed. LC 85-59. 166p. (Orig.). 1981. pap. 10.00 (ISBN 0-9607000-0-5). Jewel Pub Hse.

Nouwen, Henri J. Making All Things New: An Invitation to Life in the Spirit. LC 80-8897. 96p. 1981. 10.45 (ISBN 0-06-066326-X, HarpR). Har-Row.

Nouwen, Henri J. M. Reaching Out: The Three Movements of the Spiritual Life. LC 74-9460. 120p. 1975. 9.95 (ISBN 0-385-03212-9). Doubleday.

Oates, Wayne E. Managing Your Stress. LC 85-47715. 64p. 1985. pap. 3.95 (ISBN 0-8006-1880-7, 1-1880). Fortress.

--Your Right to Rest. LC 83-26045. (Potentials: Guides for Productive Living Ser.: Vol. 1). 104p. (Orig.). 1984. pap. 7.95 (ISBN 0-664-24517-X). Westminster.

O'Brien, Bonnie B. & Sample, Dorothy E. Life in the Fifth Dimension. 1984. pap. 6.50 (ISBN 0-8054-5214-1). Broadman.

Oldham, Dale. Dale Oldham Memorial Trilogy. 1984. Set. pap. 3.95 (ISBN 0-317-38180-6, D5042). Giants along My Path (ISBN 0-87162-162-2, D3784). How to Grow Spiritually (ISBN 0-87162-142-8, D5043). Living Close to God (ISBN 0-87162-013-8, D5304). Warner Pr.

O'Neil, Thomas. Towards the Life Divine: Sri Aurobindo's Vision. 1979. 10.50x (ISBN 0-8364-0546-3). South Asia Bks.

Open Path. Namgyal Rinpoche: Unfolding Through Art. Wongmo, Karma C., ed. (Illus.). 157p. (Orig.). 1982. text ed. 30.00x (ISBN 0-9602722-2-4). Open Path.

Orbeliani, Sulkhan-Saba. The Book of Wisdom & Lies. Vivian, Katherine, tr. 1982. 14.95 (Pub. by Octagon Pr England). Ins Study Human.

Osborn, R. R., ed. Grounds of Hope: Essays in Faith & Freedom. 184p. 1968. 3.95 (ISBN 0-87921-055-9). Attic Pr.

Osborne, Arthur, ed. The Collected Works of Ramana Maharshi. 192p. 1970. pap. 9.95 (ISBN 0-87728-070-3). Weiser.

Oster, Rose. Your Creative Workshop. 1977. pap. 0.75 (ISBN 0-87516-236-3). De Vorss.

Ouspensky, P. D. A Further Record. 352p. 1987. pap. 13.95 (ISBN 1-85063-056-9, 30569, Ark Paperbks). Methuen Inc.

Padilla, Gilbert. Refreshment in the Desert: Spiritual Connections in Daily Life. 144p. (Orig.). 1985. pap. 7.95 (ISBN 0-89622-228-4). Twenty-Third.

Panniker, Raimundo. The Vedic Experience. 937p. 1983. 28.50 (ISBN 0-89744-011-0). Auromere.

Panorelli, Dora. The Ultimate Relationship. 1985. 8.95 (ISBN 0-8062-2454-1). Carlton.

Para Research. World Ephemeris for the Twentieth Century. 1983. Midnight calculations. pap. 12.95 (ISBN 0-914918-60-5); Noon calculations. pap. 12.95 (ISBN 0-914918-61-3). Para Res.

Parker-Rhodes, Frederick. Wholesight. LC 77-95406. 30p. (Orig.). 1978. pap. 2.50x (ISBN 0-87574-217-3). Pendle Hill.

Parry, Danaan. The Essene Book of Days 1987. 400p. (Orig.). 1986. pap. 12.95 (ISBN 0-913319-02-3). Sunstone Pubns.

Parsley, Rod. Worshipping the Unknown God. 31p. 1986. pap. 2.75 (ISBN 0-88144-070-1). Christian Pub.

Paulsell, William O. Taste & See: A Personal Guide to the Spiritual Life. LC 76-5634. 1977. pap. 2.95 (ISBN 0-88489-093-7). St Mary's.

Pelton, Donald. Spiritual Quest: Variations on a Theme. (Illus., Orig.). 1986. pap. 7.95 (ISBN 0-933169-02-7). Heldon Pr.

Penington, Isaac. The Inward Journey of Isaac Penington. Leach, Robert J., ed. LC 44-280. (Orig.). 1944. pap. 2.50x (ISBN 0-87574-029-4). Pendle Hill.

Penn, Gregory E. Freedom, the Essence of Life. LC 78-75026. 1979. pap. 5.95 (ISBN 0-87516-288-6). De Vorss.

Perkins, Russell. The Impact of a Saint. LC 80-51959. 256p. 1980. pap. 7.50 (ISBN 0-89142-037-1). Sant Bani Ash.

Phylos the Thibetan. A Dweller on Two Planets, or the Dividing of the Way, Vol. 12. Oliver, Frederick S., as told to. LC 73-94420. (Spiritual Science Library). (Illus.). 432p. 1983. lib. bdg. 18.00 (ISBN 0-89345-039-1). Garber Comm.

Pilgrim, Peace. Steps Toward Inner Peace: Suggested Uses of Harmonious Principles for Human Living. (Illus.). 36p. 1987. pap. 2.50 leatherette (ISBN 0-943734-07-X). Ocean Tree Bks.

Pinnock, Clark. Three Keys to Spiritual Renewal. 112p. 1986. pap. 4.95 (ISBN 0-87123-656-7). Bethany Hse.

Plewe, Lucille J. Wayfinders: For Believers & Non-Believers. LC 77-78794. 1977. pap. 5.00 (ISBN 0-89555-028-8). TAN Bks Pubs.

Plummer, L. Gordon. By the Holy Tetrakyts: Symbol & Reality in Man & Universe. (Study Ser.: No. 9). (Illus.). 96p. (Orig.). 1982. pap. 5.75 (ISBN 0-913004-44-8). Point Loma Pub.

Pohier, Jaques. God in Fragments. 384p. 1986. 22.50 (ISBN 0-8245-0744-4). Crossroad NY.

Polen, O. W. Editorially Speaking, Vol. 2. 58p. 1980. pap. 2.25 (ISBN 0-87148-296-7). Pathway Pr.

Pollard, Nina T. Nothing but a Footprint. LC 85-29049. 1986. pap. 3.25 (ISBN 0-8054-5716-X). Broadman.

Postema, Donald H. Space for God, Study & Practice of Spirituality & Prayer. LC 83-15504. 180p. 1983. pap. 9.95 (ISBN 0-933140-46-0). CRC Pubns.

Prakash, Swami S. & Vidyalankar, Pandit S. Rigveda Samhita, 10 vols. (Eng.). vol. 17.00 ea. (Pub. by S Chand India). State Mutual Bk.

Prophet, Elizabeth C., intro. by. Prayer & Meditation. LC 76-28086. (Illus.). 306p. (Orig.). 1978. pap. 9.95 (ISBN 0-916766-19-5). Summit Univ.

Puls, Joan. Every Bush Is Burning: A Spirituality for Today. 2nd ed. 112p. 1986. pap. 5.95 (ISBN 0-89622-280-2). Twenty-Third.

Purdom, C. B. The Perfect Master. (Illus.). 330p. 1976. pap. 3.95 (ISBN 0-913078-24-7). Sheriar Pr.

Quinones de Dailey, Eva, ed. Vision Clara de Dios. (Span.). pap. 4.95 (ISBN 0-87148-884-1). Pathway Pr.

Radha, Swami S. The Divine Light Invocation. 54p. 1982. pap. 5.00 (ISBN 0-931454-08-5). Timeless Bks.

Rahner, Karl. Eternal Yes. 1.50 (ISBN 0-87193-119-2). Dimension Bks.

Raines, John C. & Day-Lower, Donna C. Modern Work & Human Meaning. LC 85-26370. (Illus.). 152p. (Orig.). 1986. pap. 12.95 (ISBN 0-664-24703-2). Westminster.

Rajneesh, Baghwan S. The Rajneesh Bible, Vol. 1. Rajneesh Academy Staff, ed. LC 85-42539. 800p. (Orig.). 1985. pap. 6.95 (ISBN 0-88050-200-2). Chidvilas Found.

Rajneesh, Bhagwan S. And Now, & Here, Vol. II. Vedant, Swami S., ed. LC 84-42798. (Early Writings & Discourses Ser.). 384p. (Orig.). 1985. pap. 4.95 (ISBN 0-88050-712-8). Chidvilas Found.

--The Book: An Introduction to the Teachings of Bhagwan Shree Rajneesh, Series III, R-Z. Rajneesh Academy Staff, ed. LC 84-42616. (Academy Ser.). 576p. (Orig.). 1984. pap. 5.95 (ISBN 0-88050-704-7). Chidvilas Found.

--The Book: An Introduction to the Teachings of Bhagwan Shree Rajneesh, Series I, A-H. Rajneesh Academy Staff, ed. LC 84-42616. (Academy Ser.). 620p. (Orig.). 1984. pap. 5.95 (ISBN 0-88050-702-0). Chidvilas Found.

--The Book: An Introduction to the Teachings of Bhagwan Shree Rajneesh, Series II, I-Q. Rajneesh Academy Staff, ed. (Academy Ser.). 576p. (Orig.). 1984. pap. 5.95 (ISBN 0-88050-703-9). Chidvilas Found.

--The Book of the Books, Vol. 3. Ma P. Karima, ed. LC 82-50462. (Buddha Ser.). 352p. (Orig.). 1984. pap. 4.95 (ISBN 0-88050-515-X). Chidvilas Found.

--Book of the Secrets, Vol. IV. 2nd ed ed. Rajneesh Foundation International, ed. LC 75-36733. (Tantra Ser.). 408p. 1982. pap. 7.95 (ISBN 0-88050-528-1). Chidvilas Found.

--The Book of the Secrets Two. LC 75-39733. 1979. pap. 8.95 (ISBN 0-06-090668-5, CN 668, PL). Har-Row.

--Book of Wisdom, Vol. I. Rajneesh Foundation International, ed. LC 82-23142. (Buddhist Masters Ser.). 420p. (Orig.). 1983. pap. 9.95 (ISBN 0-88050-530-3). Chidvilas Found.

--The Passion for the Impossible. Maneesha, Ma P., ed. LC 83-181944. (Initiation Talks Ser.). (Illus.). 464p. (Orig.). 1978. 18.95 (ISBN 0-88050-111-1). Chidvilas Found.

--The Secret. Chinmaya, Swami P., ed. LC 83-185068. (Sufi Ser.). (Illus.). 760p. (Orig.). 1980. 23.95 (ISBN 0-88050-127-8). Chidvilas Found.

--The Shadow of the Whip. Maneesha, Ma Prem, ed. LC 82-230735. (Initiation Talks Ser.). (Illus.). 554p. (Orig.). 1978. 18.95 (ISBN 0-88050-131-6). Chidvilas Found.

Rajneesh, Bhagwan Shree. Above All, Don't Wobble. Maneesha, Ma Prem, ed. LC 83-81247. (Initiation Talks Ser.). (Illus.). 488p. (Orig.). 1976. 21.95 (ISBN 0-88050-001-8). Chidvilas Found.

--Ah This! Rajneesh Foundation International, ed. LC 82-24026. (Zen Ser.). 268p. (Orig.). 1982. pap. 8.95 (ISBN 0-88050-502-8). Chidvilas Found.

--Ancient Music in the Pines. Veena, Ma Prem, ed. LC 78-901931. (Zen Ser.). (Illus.). 298p. (Orig.). 1977. 15.50 (ISBN 0-88050-003-4). Chidvilas Found.

--And the Flowers Showered. Somendra, Swami Anand, ed. LC 83-181344. (Zen Ser.). (Illus.). 288p. (Orig.). 1975. 16.95 (ISBN 0-88050-004-2); pap. 5.95 (ISBN 0-88050-504-4). Chidvilas Found.

--The Art of Dying. Veena, Ma Prema, ed. LC 78-905608. (Hasidism Ser.). (Illus.). 284p. (Orig.). 1978. 14.95 (ISBN 0-88050-005-0). Chidvilas Found.

--Be Realistic: Plan for a Miracle. Maneesha, Ma Prem, ed. LC 78-902296. (Initiation Talks Ser.). (Illus.). 418p. (Orig.). 1977. 19.95 (ISBN 0-88050-010-7). Chidvilas Found.

--Believing the Impossible Before Breakfast. Maneesha, Ma Prem, ed. LC 82-229302. (Initiation Talks Ser.). (Illus.). 266p. (Orig.). 1981. 22.95 (ISBN 0-88050-006-9). Chidvilas Found.

--The Beloved, 2 vols. Sudha, Ma Yoga, ed. LC 78-903022. (Baul Mystics Ser.). (Illus., Orig.). 1977. Vol. I, 324 pgs. 15.95 ea. (ISBN 0-88050-007-7). Vol. II, 288 pgs. 1978. Chidvilas Found.

--Beloved of My Heart. Maneesha, Ma Prem, ed. (Initiation Talks Ser.). (Illus.). 356p. (Orig.). 1978. 19.95 (ISBN 0-88050-009-3). Chidvilas Found.

--Blessed are the Ignorant. Maneesha, Ma Prem, ed. LC 83-181704. (Initiation Talks Ser.). (Illus.). 566p. (Orig.). 1979. 19.95 (ISBN 0-88050-012-3). Chidvilas Found.

--Books I Have Loved. Sambuddha, Swami Devaraj & Mahasattva, Swami Devageet, eds. LC 85-43070. (Biography Ser.). 288p. (Orig.). 1985. pap. 3.95 (ISBN 0-88050-716-0). Chidvilas Found.

--The Buddha Disease. Ma Prem Maneesha, ed. LC 83-181256. (Initiation Talks Ser.). (Illus.). 642p. (Orig.). 1979. 21.50 (ISBN 0-88050-032-8). Chidvilas Found.

--Come Follow Me, Vol. III. Swami Deva Paritosh, ed. LC 80-8343. (Jesus Ser.). (Illus.). 272p. (Orig.). 1976. 12.95 (ISBN 0-88050-036-0). Chidvilas Found.

--Come Follow Me, Vol. IV. Ma Yoga Sudha, ed. LC 80-8343. (Jesus Ser.). (Illus.). 286p. (Orig.). 1977. 12.95 (ISBN 0-88050-037-9). Chidvilas Found.

--Come Follow Me, Vol. II. Ma Satya Bharti, ed. LC 80-8343. (Jesus Ser.). (Illus.). 316p. (Orig.). 1977. 12.95 (ISBN 0-88050-035-2). Chidvilas Found.

--Come Follow Me, Vol. I. Ma Satya Bharti, ed. LC 80-8343. (Jesus Ser.). (Illus.). 292p. (Orig.). 1976. 12.95 (ISBN 0-88050-034-4). Chidvilas Found.

--The Cypress in the Courtyard. Maneesha, Ma Prem, ed. LC 83-181284. (Initiation Talks Ser.). (Illus.). 466p. (Orig.). 1978. 18.95 (ISBN 0-88050-039-5). Chidvilas Found.

--Dance Your Way to God. Maneesha, Ma Prem, ed. LC 78-907936. (Initiation Talks Ser.). (Illus.). 384p. (Orig.). 1978. 19.95 (ISBN 0-88050-041-7). Chidvilas Found.

--Dang Dang Doko Dang. Veena, Ma Prem, ed. LC 77-907636. (Zen Ser.). (Illus.). 290p. (Orig.). 1977. 14.50 (ISBN 0-88050-042-5). Chidvilas Found.

--The Diamond Sutra. Pratima, Ma Yoga, ed. LC 82-185071. (Buddha Ser.). (Illus.). 492p. (Orig.). 1979. 19.50 (ISBN 0-88050-043-3). Chidvilas Found.

--The Discipline of Transcendence, 4 vols. Vandana, Ma Ananda & Pratima, Ma Yoga, eds. LC 78-906087. (Buddha Ser.). (Illus., Orig.). 1978. Vol. I, 324 pgs. 16.50 ea. (ISBN 0-88050-045-X). Vol. II, 348 pgs (ISBN 0-88050-046-8). Vol. III, 320 pgs (ISBN 0-88050-047-6). Vol. IV, 376 pgs (ISBN 0-88050-048-4). Chidvilas Found.

--The Divine Melody. Bhasha, Ma Deva, ed. LC 83-174697. (Kabir Ser.). (Illus.). 284p. (Orig.). 1978. 16.50 (ISBN 0-88050-049-2). Chidvilas Found.

--Don't Bite My Finger, Look Where I Am Pointing. Maneesha, Ma Prem, ed. LC 82-21602. (Initiation Talks Ser.). 232p. (Orig.). 1982. pap. 14.95 (ISBN 0-88050-550-8). Chidvilas Found.

--Don't Just Do Something, Sit There. Maneesha, Ma Prem, ed. (Initiation Talks Ser.). (Illus.). 370p. (Orig.). 1980. 25.50 (ISBN 0-88050-052-2). Chidvilas Found.

--Ecstasy: The Forgotten Language. Chinmaya, Swami Prem, ed. LC 83-179587. (Kabir Ser.). (Illus.). 332p. (Orig.). 1978. 16.50 (ISBN 0-88050-055-7). Chidvilas Found.

--Far Beyond the Stars. Maneesha, Ma Prem, ed. LC 82-229145. (Initiation Talks Ser.). (Illus.). 306p. (Orig.). 1980. 20.95 (ISBN 0-88050-059-X). Chidvilas Found.

--The First Principle. Chinmaya, Swami Prem, ed. LC 83-179587. (Zen Ser.). (Illus.). 386p. (Orig.). 1979. 17.95 (ISBN 0-88050-061-1). Chidvilas Found.

--The Fish in the Sea is Not Thirsty. Anurag, Ma Yoga, ed. LC 82-244585. (Kabir Ser.). (Illus.). 524p. (Orig.). 1980. 22.95 (ISBN 0-88050-062-X). Chidvilas Found.

--For Madmen Only: Price of Admission: Your Mind. Maneesha, Ma Prem, ed. LC 83-186152. (Initiation Talks Ser.). (Illus.). 616p. (Orig.). 1979. 19.50 (ISBN 0-88050-063-8). Chidvilas Found.

--From Sex to Superconsciousness. Prem, Swami Krishna, ed. LC 77-20821. (Early Discourses & Writings Ser.). (Illus.). 256p. (Orig.). 1979. 15.50 (ISBN 0-88050-064-6). Chidvilas Found.

--The Further Shore. Maneesha, Ma Prem, ed. LC 83-181220. (Initiation Talks Ser.). (Illus.). 288p. (Orig.). 1980. 22.95 (ISBN 0-88050-065-4). Chidvilas Found.

--Get Out of Your Own Way. Pratima, Ma Yoga, ed. LC 83-181935. (Initation Talks Ser.). (Illus.). 374p. (Orig.). 1977. 18.95 (ISBN 0-88050-066-2). Chidvilas Found.

--Glimpses of a Golden Childhood. Sambuddha, Swami Devaraj & Mahasattva, Swami Devageet, eds. LC 85-43069. (Biography Ser.). 788p. (Orig.). 1985. pap. 6.95 (ISBN 0-88050-715-2). Chidvilas Found.

--God Is Not for Sale. Pratima, Ma Yoga, ed. LC 82-244555. (Initiation Talks Ser.). (Illus.). 450p. (Orig.). 1978. 18.95 (ISBN 0-88050-067-0). Chidvilas Found.

--God's Got a Thing about You. Maneesha, Ma Prem, ed. LC 83-11237. (Initiation Talks Ser.). 576p. (Orig.). 1983. pap. 4.95 (ISBN 0-88050-568-0). Chidvilas Found.

--The Goose Is Out. Rajneesh Foundation International, ed. LC 82-60497. (Question & Answer Ser.). 324p. (Orig.). 1982. pap. 10.95 (ISBN 0-88050-571-0). Chidvilas Found.

--The Grass Grows by Itself. Veena, Ma Prema, ed. LC 77-905411. (Zen Ser.). (Illus.). 254p. (Orig.). 1978. 15.50 (ISBN 0-88050-072-7); pap. 4.95 (ISBN 0-88050-572-9). Chidvilas Found.

--The Great Nothing. Maneesha, Ma Prem, ed. LC 83-173216. (Initation Talks Ser.). (Illus.). 488p. (Orig.). 1978. 18.95 (ISBN 0-88050-073-5). Chidvilas Found.

--Guida Spirituale. Rajneesh Foundation International, ed. LC 83-4435. (Western Mystics Ser.). 400p. (Orig.). 1983. pap. 4.95 (ISBN 0-88050-575-3). Chidvilas Found.

--Hallelujah! Maneesha, Ma Prem, ed. LC 83-180760. (Initiation Talks Ser.). (Illus.). 364p. (Orig.). 1981. 25.95 (ISBN 0-88050-076-X); pap. 18.95 (ISBN 0-88050-576-1). Chidvilas Found.
--Hammer on the Rock. Maneesha, Ma Prem, ed. LC 79-52012. (Initiation Talks Ser.). 464p. (Orig.). 1976. 22.50 (ISBN 0-88050-077-8). Chidvilas Found.
--The Heart Sutra. Sudha, ma Yoga, ed. LC 78-908490. (Buddha Ser.). (Illus.). 332p. (Orig.). 1978. 16.95 (ISBN 0-88050-078-6). Chidvilas Found.
--The Hidden Harmony. Anurag, Ma Yoga, ed. LC 83-184618. (Western Mystics Ser.). (Illus.). 364p. (Orig.). 1976. 16.95 (ISBN 0-88050-079-4). Chidvilas Found.
--I Say unto You, 2 vols. Asha, Ma Prem, ed. LC 82-245650. (Jesus Ser.). (Illus., Orig.). 1980. Vol. I, 384. 19.50 (ISBN 0-88050-085-9); Vol. II. pap. 15.95 (ISBN 0-88050-586-9); pap. 4.95 wkbk. (ISBN 0-88050-585-0). Chidvilas Found.
--In Search of the Miraculous, Vol. 1. Sambuddha, Swami Anand, ed. LC 84-42869. (Early Discourses & Writings Ser.). 368p. (Orig.). 1984. pap. 4.95 (ISBN 0-88050-710-1). Chidvilas Found.
--Just Like That. Somendra, Swami Anand, ed. (Sufi Ser.). (Illus.). 488p. (Orig.). 1975. 19.50 (ISBN 0-88050-089-1). Chidvilas Found.
--Let Go! Maneesha, Ma Prem, ed. LC 83-181279. (Initiation Talks Ser.). (Illus.). 654p. (Orig.). 1980. 22.95 (ISBN 0-88050-091-3). Chidvilas Found.
--The Long & the Short & the All. Prabhu, Swami Krishna, ed. LC 84-42806. (Early Writings & Discourses Ser.). 320p. 1984. pap. 4.95 (ISBN 0-88050-708-X). Chidvilas Found.
--My Way: The Way of the White Clouds. rev. ed. Teertha, Swami Ananda, ed. LC 79-2303. (Questions & Answers Ser.). (Illus.). 640p. 1975. 29.95 (ISBN 0-88050-096-4). Chidvilas Found.
--Neither This Nor That. Pratima, Ma Yoga, ed. LC 83-181238. (Zen Ser.). (Illus.). 280p. (Orig.). 1975. 14.95 (ISBN 0-88050-097-2). Chidvilas Found.
--The New Alchemy: To Turn You On. Bharti, Ma Satya, ed. LC 83-181814. (Western Mystics Ser.). (Illus.). 308p. (Orig.). 1978. 15.50 (ISBN 0-88050-098-0). Chidvilas Found.
--The Ninety-Nine Names of Nothingness. Maneesha, Ma Prem, ed. (Initiation Talks Ser.). (Illus.). 596p. (Orig.). 1980. pap. 18.95 (ISBN 0-88050-599-0). Chidvilas Found.
--Nirvana: The Last Nightmare. Pratima, Ma Yoga, ed. LC 77-902717. (Zen Ser.). (Illus.). 290p. (Orig.). 1976. 17.50 (ISBN 0-88050-101-4). Chidvilas Found.
--The No Book: No Buddha, No Teaching, No Discipline. Maneesha, Ma Prem, ed. (Initation Talks Ser.). (Illus.). 354p. (Orig.). 1981. 26.95 (ISBN 0-88050-102-2). Chidvilas Found.
--No Water, No Moon. 2nd ed. Anurag, Ma Yoga, ed. LC 75-907472. (Zen Ser.). (Illus.). 260p. 1978. 14.50 (ISBN 0-88050-105-7). Chidvilas Found.
--Notes of a Madman. Sambuddha, Swami Devaraj & Mahasattva, Swami Devageet, eds. LC 85-43071. (Biography Ser.). 140p. (Orig.). 1985. pap. 4.50 (ISBN 0-88050-714-4). Chidvilas Found.
--Nothing to Lose but Your Head. Maneesha, Ma Prem, ed. LC 78-901075. (Initiation Talks Ser.). (Illus.). 408p. (Orig.). 1977. 19.50 (ISBN 0-88050-104-9). Chidvilas Found.
--Only Losers Can Win In This Game. Maneesha, Ma Prem, ed. LC 82-229469. (Initation Talks Ser.). 610p. (Orig.). 1981. 23.50 (ISBN 0-88050-107-3). Chidvilas Found.
--The Open Door. Maneesha, Ma Prem, ed. LC 83-181263. (Initiation Talks Ser.). (Illus.). 336p. (Orig.). 1980. 18.95 (ISBN 0-88050-608-3). Chidvilas Found.
--The Open Secret. Maneesha, Ma Prem, ed. LC 83-180822. (Initiation Talks Ser.). 382p. (Orig.). 1980. 25.50 (ISBN 0-88050-109-X). Chidvilas Found.
--The Path of Love. Sudha, Ma Yoga, ed. LC 83-181255. (Kabir Ser.). (Illus.). 350p. (Orig.). 1978. 16.50 (ISBN 0-88050-112-X); pap. 12.95 358p (ISBN 0-88050-612-1). Chidvilas Found.
--The Perfect Master, 2 vols. Anurag, Ma Yoga, ed. LC 83-172954. (Sufi Ser.). (Illus.). 1980. Vol. I, 380 pgs. 19.95 ea. (ISBN 0-88050-113-8). Vol. II, 368 pgs. 1981 (ISBN 0-88050-114-6). Chidvilas Found.
--Returning to the Source. Sudha, Ma Yoga, ed. LC 83-182149. (Zen Ser.). (Illus.). 402p. (Orig.). 1976. 15.95 (ISBN 0-88050-120-0). Chidvilas Found.
--The Revolution. Vandana, Ma Ananda, ed. LC 83-181203. (Kabir Ser.). (Illus.). 424p. (Orig.). 1979. 16.95 (ISBN 0-88050-121-9). Chidvilas Found.
--A Rose Is a Rose Is a Rose. Pratima, Ma Yoga, ed. (Initiation Talks Ser.). (Illus.). 428p. (Orig.). 1978. 18.95 (ISBN 0-88050-123-5). Chidvilas Found.
--Snap Your Fingers, Slap Your Face & Wake Up! Sarito, Ma Deva, ed. LC 84-43011. (Initiation Talks Ser.). 256p. (Orig.). 1984. pap. 3.95 (ISBN 0-88050-632-6). Chidvilas Found.
--The Sound of One Hand Clapping. Pratima, Ma Yoga, ed. (Initiation Talks Ser.). (Illus.). 632p. (Orig.). 1981. pap. 22.50 (ISBN 0-88050-633-4). Chidvilas Found.
--A Sudden Clash of Thunder. Anurag, Ma Yoga, ed. LC 78-901998. (Zen Ser.). (Illus.). 284p. (Orig.). 1977. 16.50 (ISBN 0-88050-135-9). Chidvilas Found.
--The Sun Behind the Sun Behind the Sun. Maneesha, Ma Prem, ed. LC 83-181209. (Initiation Talks Ser.). (Illus.). 648p. (Orig.). 1980. 21.95 (ISBN 0-88050-138-3). Chidvilas Found.
--The Sun Rises in the Evening. Asha, Ma Prem, ed. LC 83-181196. (Zen Ser.). (Illus.). 372p. (Orig.). 1980. 17.95 (ISBN 0-88050-139-1). Chidvilas Found.
--Take It Easy, 2 vols. Anurag, Ma Yoga & Vandana, Ma Ananda, eds. LC 83-177521. (Zen Ser.). (Illus., Orig.). 1979. Vol. I, 584 pgs. 21.95 ea. (ISBN 0-88050-141-3). Vol. II, 584 pgs (ISBN 0-88050-142-1). Chidvilas Found.
--The Tantra Vision, 2 vols. Anurag, Ma Yoga, ed. (Tantra Ser.). (Illus., Orig.). 1978. Vol. I, 340 pgs. 16.50 ea. (ISBN 0-88050-144-8). Vol. II, 344 pgs (ISBN 0-88050-145-6). Chidvilas Found.
--Tao: The Pathless Path, 2 vols. Asha, Ma Prem & Veena, Ma Prema, eds. LC 82-232884. (Tao Ser.). (Illus.). 1979. Vol. I, 432 pgs. 17.95 ea. (ISBN 0-88050-148-0). Vol. II, 540 pgs (ISBN 0-88050-149-9). Vol. I, 440p. pap. 15.95 (ISBN 0-88050-648-2); Vol. II, 1978, 542p. pap. write for info. (ISBN 0-88050-649-0). Chidvilas Found.
--Tao: The Three Treasures, 4 vols. Veena, Ma Prema & Somendra, Swami Anand, eds. LC 76-905202. (Tao Ser.). (Illus., Orig.). 1977. Vol. II, 346 pgs., 1976. 15.95 ea. (ISBN 0-88050-151-0). Vol. III, 404 pgs. 1976 (ISBN 0-88050-152-9). Vol. IV, 422 pgs. 1977 (ISBN 0-88050-153-7). Chidvilas Found.
--Theologia Mystica. Asha, Ma Prem, ed. LC 83-11086. (Western Mystics Ser.). 400p. (Orig.). 1983. pap. 4.95 (ISBN 0-88050-655-5). Chidvilas Found.
--This Is It. Maneesha, ma Prem, ed. LC 82-230731. (Initiation Talks Ser.). (Illus.). 672p. (Orig.). 1979. 19.95 (ISBN 0-88050-156-1). Chidvilas Found.
--This Very Body the Buddha. Vandana, Ma Ananda, ed. LC 79-904227. (Zen Ser.). (Illus.). 360p. (Orig.). 1978. 16.95 (ISBN 0-88050-157-X). Chidvilas Found.
--This Very Place the Lotus Paradise. Madyapa, Swami Anand, ed. LC 84-42805. (Photobiography Ser.). 568p. (Orig.). 1984. 100.00x (ISBN 0-88050-705-5). Chidvilas Found.
--The Tongue-Tip Taste of Tao. Maneesha, Ma Prem, ed. (Initiation Talks Ser.). (Illus.). 350p. 1981. 26.95 (ISBN 0-88050-158-8). Chidvilas Found.
--The True Sage. Chaitanya, Swami Christ, ed. LC 83-183323. (Hasids Ser.). (Illus.). 410p. (Orig.). 1976. 16.50 (ISBN 0-88050-159-6). Chidvilas Found.
--Turn on, Tune in & Drop the Lot. Maneesha, Ma Prem, ed. (Initiation Talks Ser.). (Illus.). 312p. (Orig.). 1980. pap. 18.95 (ISBN 0-88050-660-1). Chidvilas Found.
--The Ultimate Alchemy, 2 vols. Prem, Ma Ananda, ed. LC 75-905370. (Upanishad Ser.). (Illus.). 1976. Vol. I, 442 pgs. 18.95 ea. (ISBN 0-88050-161-8). Vol. II, 424 pgs (ISBN 0-88050-162-6). Chidvilas Found.
--Unio Mystica, 2 vols. 2nd ed. Vandana, Ma Ananda, ed. LC 82-245842. (Sufi Ser.). (Illus.). 1980. Vol. I 384p. 17.95 ea. (ISBN 0-88050-163-4). Vol. II (ISBN 0-88050-164-2). Vol. I. pap. 13.95 ea. (ISBN 0-88050-663-6). Vol. II 368p 1981 (ISBN 0-88050-664-4). Chidvilas Found.
--Until You Die. Anurag, Ma Yoga, ed. LC 77-900984. (Sufi Ser.). (Illus.). 280p. (Orig.). 1976. 15.95 (ISBN 0-88050-165-0). Chidvilas Found.
--Vedanta: Seven Steps to Samadhi. Pratima, Ma Yoga, ed. LC 77-904425. (Upanishad Ser.). (Illus.). 518p. (Orig.). 1976. 16.50 (ISBN 0-88050-166-9). Chidvilas Found.
--Walk Without Feet, Fly Without Wings, & Think Without Mind. Anurag, Ma Yoga, ed. LC 83-181337. (Questions & Answers Ser.). (Illus.). 384p. (Orig.). 1979. 16.50 (ISBN 0-88050-167-7). Chidvilas Found.
--What Is Is, What Ain't, Ain't. Maneesha, Ma Prem, ed. LC 83-177697. (Initiation Talks Ser.). (Illus.). 624p. (Orig.). 1980. 18.95 (ISBN 0-88050-670-9). Chidvilas Found.
--When the Shoe Fits. Veena, Ma Prema, ed. LC 76-904914. (Zen Masters Ser.). (Illus.). 388p. (Orig.). 1976. 16.50 (ISBN 0-88050-171-5). Chidvilas Found.
--The White Lotus. Asha, Ma Prem, ed. LC 81-903266. (Zen Ser.). (Illus.). 430p. 1981. 17.95 (ISBN 0-88050-172-3); pap. 13.95 (ISBN 0-88050-672-5). Chidvilas Found.
--The Wisdom of the Sands, 2 vols. Sudha, Ma Yoga, ed. LC 80-903299. (Sufi Ser.). (Illus., Orig.). 1980. Vol. I, 380 pgs. 19.95 ea. (ISBN 0-88050-174-X). Vol. II, 404 pgs. 1980 (ISBN 0-88050-175-8). Vol.1 386p 1980. pap. 15.95 ea. (ISBN 0-88050-674-1). Chidvilas Found.
--The Zero Experience. Maneesha, Ma Prem, ed. (Initiation Talks Ser.). (Illus.). 632p. (Orig.). 1979. 21.50 (ISBN 0-88050-193-6). Chidvilas Found.
Ramakrishna Math Staff, ed. Sadhanas for Spiritual Life. 166p. pap. 2.75 (ISBN 0-87481-507-X). Vedanta Pr.
Rampa, T. Lobsang. Living with the Lama. pap. 2.95 (ISBN 0-552-08408-5). Weiser.
Ramtha. Ramtha. Weinberg, Steven L., ed. LC 85-61768. 224p. 1986. 19.95 (ISBN 0-932201-11-3). Sovereignty.
--Ramtha: A Treasure Chest of Wisdom. Fazio, Sue A. & Weischedel, Randall, eds. 250p. 1987. 16.95 (ISBN 0-932201-23-7). Sovereignty.
--Ramtha in Audience. 300p. 1987. 15.95 (ISBN 0-932201-90-3); pap. 9.95 (ISBN 0-932201-82-2). Sovereignty.
--Ramtha: Select Teachings. Weinberg, Steven L., ed. 150p. 1987. pap. 8.95 (ISBN 0-932201-19-9). Sovereignty.
Ravindra, Ravi. Whispers from the Other Shore. LC 84-40164. 170p. (Orig.). 1984. pap. 6.50 (ISBN 0-8356-0589-2, Quest). Theos Pub Hse.
Rawson, Raymond. The Way Home. LC 84-90242. 113p. 1985. 10.95 (ISBN 0-533-06294-2). Vantage.
Reddy, C. Narayana. Viswambhara. 66p. 1987. text ed. 12.50x (ISBN 81-207-0578-5, Pub. by Sterling Pubs India). Apt Bks.
Reftery, Larry, ed. Worship His Majesty. 32p. 1981. pap. 0.75 (ISBN 0-88144-056-6). Christian Pub.
Regamey, Pius R. Renewal in the Spirit. 1980. 5.95 (ISBN 0-8198-6402-1); pap. 4.95 (ISBN 0-8198-6403-X). Dghtrs St Paul.
Reichert, Richard. Community of the Spirit. 120p. 1982. pap. 3.60 (ISBN 0-697-01796-6); tchr's manual 4.00 (ISBN 0-697-01797-4); spirit masters 10.95 (ISBN 0-697-01798-2). Wm C Brown.
Reid, John C. God's Promises & My Needs. 80p. (Orig.). 1986. pap. 2.50 (ISBN 0-914733-06-0). Desert Min.
Reyes, Benito F. Dialogues with God: Sonnet Psalms on the Significance of Being Human. LC 78-244706. 139p. 1969. pap. 7.50 (ISBN 0-939375-37-0). World Univ Amer.
--Moments Without Self. 4th ed. LC 61-21760. 198p. Date not set. Repr. of 1970 ed. 10.00 (ISBN 0-939375-36-2). World Univ Amer.
Richard, Paul. Seven Steps to the New Age. 1979. pap. 3.95 (ISBN 0-89744-131-1, Pub. by Ganesh & Co India). Auromere.
Robb, James H. Man As Infinite Spirit. (Aquinas Lecture). 1974. 7.95 (ISBN 0-87462-139-9). Marquette.
Robert L. Humphrey, J. D., & Associates Staff. Paradigm Shift: Teach the Universal Values. LC 83-83386. (Illus.). 100p. 1984. pap. 7.95 (ISBN 0-915761-00-9). Life Values Pr.
Roberts, Bernadette. The Path to No-Self: Life at the Center. LC 84-19340. 224p. (Orig.). 1985. pap. 9.95 (ISBN 0-87773-306-6, 72999-4). Shambhala Pubns.
Roberts, Ursula. Reminiscences: A Lifetime of Spiritualism. 115p. 1985. 20.00x (ISBN 0-7212-0726-X, Pub. by Regency Pr). State Mutual Bk.
Robinson, Forbes & Kilpack, Gilbert. An Inward Legacy. 1983. pap. 5.00x (ISBN 0-87574-092-8, 092). Pendle Hill.
Robinson, Ras, ed. Spiritual Warfare. (Illus.). 72p. 1982. pap. 3.00 (ISBN 0-937778-05-2). Fulness Hse.
Roman, Sanaya. Living with Joy: Keys to Personal Power & Spiritual Transformation. Ratner, Elaine, ed. (Earth Life Ser.). 216p. (Orig.). 1986. pap. 9.95 (ISBN 0-915811-03-0). H J Kramer Inc.
Roman, Sanaya & Packer, Duane. Opening to Channel: How to Connect with Your Guide. Armstrong, Gregory, ed. (Birth into Light Ser.). 280p. (Orig.). 1987. pap. 12.95 (ISBN 0-915811-05-7). H J Kramer Inc.
Rosage, David. Climbing Higher: Reflections on Our Spiritual Journey. 112p. (Orig.). 1983. pap. 4.95 (ISBN 0-89283-147-2). Servant.
Roth, Charles. Mind: The Master Power. 1984. 5.95 (ISBN 0-87159-099-9). Unity School.
Ruhnau, Helena E. Journeys into the Fifth Dimension. LC 75-149286. (Illus.). 1975. 12.95 (ISBN 0-941036-02-2). Colleasius Pr.
--Light on a Mountain. (Illus.). 1976. 12.95 (ISBN 0-941036-00-6); pap. 6.50 (ISBN 0-941036-01-4). Colleasius Pr.
--Reappearance of the Dove. LC 75-27625. (Illus.). 1978. 12.95 (ISBN 0-941036-03-0). Colleasius Pr.
Russell, Robert A. You Try It. 1953. pap. 5.50 (ISBN 0-87516-326-2). De Vorss.
St. Cyril of Jerusalem. Oglasytel' Nija i Tajnovodstennija Pouchenija. Tr. of Prochatechisis & Mystagogical Catechesis. (Rus.). 376p. (Orig.). 1976. 18.00x (ISBN 0-88465-024-3); pap. 13.00x (ISBN 0-88465-025-1). Holy Trinity.
St. Dorotheos of Gaza. Dushepoljeznija Pouchjenija. Tr. of Spiritual Teachings. (Rus.). 300p. (Orig.). 1970. 15.00x (ISBN 0-88465-035-9); pap. 10.00x (ISBN 0-88465-036-7). Holy Trinity.
St. Ignatius of Antioch & St. Polycarp of Simirna. Poslanije Saviatago Ignatija Antiokhiskago i Sviatago Polykarpa Smirnskago. Tr. of Letters of St. Ignatius of Antioch & of St. Polycarp of Smirna. (Rus.). 80p. (Orig.). 1975. pap. 2.00x (ISBN 0-88465-023-5). Holy Trinity.
St. Nicodemos the Hagiorite, ed. Dobrotoljubije, Tom Pjatij: Philokalia, Vol. 5. Govoroff, Theophan, tr. from Greek. (Rus.). 350p. (Orig.). 1966. 20.00x (ISBN 0-88465-030-8); pap. 15.00x (ISBN 0-88465-029-4). Holy Trinity.
Saliers, Don E. Worship & Spirituality. LC 84-7211. (Spirituality & the Christian Life Ser.: Vol. 5). 114p. 1984. pap. 7.95 (ISBN 0-664-24634-6). Westminster.
Sampson, William. The Coming of Consolation. (Orig.). 1986. pap. 8.95 (ISBN 0-87061-132-1). Chr Classics.
Sanders, J. Oswald. Spiritual Maturity. Chao, Samuel & Chao, Lorna, trs. from Eng. (Chinese.). 1983. pap. write for info. (ISBN 0-941598-08-X). Living Spring Pubns.
Sanders, Stephen. To Him Who Conquers. LC 73-111183. 210p. 1970. 25.00 (ISBN 0-385-06306-7). Fellowship Crown.
Sandweiss, Samuel H. Sai Baba: The Holy Man & the Psychiatrist. LC 75-28784. 1975. 10.25 (ISBN 0-9600958-0-2); pap. 6.30 (ISBN 0-9600958-1-0). Birth Day.
Saraydarian, Torkom. Torchbearers. 1981. pap. 2.50 (ISBN 0-911794-49-2). Aqua Educ.
Satchidananda, Sri Swami. Kailash Journal: Pilgrimage into the Himalayas. LC 84-25296. 1984. pap. 6.95 (ISBN 0-932040-25-X). Integral Yoga Pubns.
Satchidandanda, Swami. To Know Yourself: The Essential Teachings of Swami Satchidananda. LC 77-80901. 1978. pap. 7.95 (ISBN 0-385-12613-1, Anch). Doubleday.
Sayers, Stanley E. Drink from the Deeper Wells. 7.50 (ISBN 0-89225-079-8). Gospel Advocate.
Saylor, Dennis. And You Visited Me. LC 79-88403. 1979. pap. 7.95 (ISBN 0-933350-21-X). Morse Pr.
Schneider, Bernard. Holy Spirit & You. pap. 4.95 (ISBN 0-88469-119-5). BMH Bks.
Schuon, Frithjof. Esoterism as Principle & as Way. 240p. 1981. pap. 7.50 (ISBN 0-900588-23-3). Wrld Wisdom Bks.
Schwaller de Lubicz, R. A. Nature Word: Verbe Nature. Lawlor, Deborah, tr. from Fr. & intro. by. LC 82-81069. (Illus.). 160p. (Orig.). 1982. pap. 6.95 (ISBN 0-940262-00-2, Lindisfarne Pr). Inner Tradit.
Schwarz, Jack. The Path of Action. LC 77-2247. 1977. pap. 8.95 (ISBN 0-525-48231-8, 0869-260). Dutton.
Schweitzer, Albert. The Light Within Us. (Philosophical Paperback Ser.). 58p. 1985. pap. 3.95 (ISBN 0-8022-2484-9). Philos Lib.
Secret Talks with Mr. G. LC 78-54137. (Illus.). 1978. pap. 5.95 (ISBN 0-89556-001-1). Gateways Bks & Tapes.
Sekowsky, Joanne. Spiritual Warfare...Strategy for Winning. (Workbook Ser.). 80p. pap. 4.95 (ISBN 0-930756-74-6, 581004). Aglow Pubns.
Self-Realization Fellowship. God Alone: The Life & Letters of a Saint - Sri Gyanamata. LC 84-52361. (Illus.). 324p. 1984. 8.50 (ISBN 0-87612-200-4, 1805). Self Realization.
Shah, Idries. Caravan of Dreams. 207p. 1968. 14.95 (ISBN 0-900860-14-6, Pub. by Octagon Pr England). Ins Study Human.
--The Dermis Probe. 191p. 1980. 15.95 (ISBN 0-900860-83-9, Pub. by Octagon Pr England). Ins Study Human.
--The Elephant in the Dark. 76p. 1982. 9.95 (ISBN 0-900860-36-7, Pub. by Octagon Pr England). Ins Study Human.
--Learning How to Learn. 302p. 1978. 14.95 (ISBN 0-900860-59-6, Pub. by Octagon Pr England). Ins Study Human.
--The Magic Monastery. 208p. 1972. 16.95 (ISBN 0-900860-89-8, Pub. by Octagon Pr England). Ins Study Human.
--A Perfumed Scorpion. 193p. 1982. 14.95 (ISBN 0-900860-62-6, Pub. by Octagon Pr England). Ins Study Human.
--Seeker after Truth. 1982. 16.95 (ISBN 0-900860-91-X, Pub. by Octagon Pr England). Ins Study Human.
--Special Illumination: The Sufi Use of Humour. 64p. 1977. 9.95 (ISBN 0-900860-57-X, Pub. by Octagon Pr England). Ins Study Human.

--A Veiled Gazelle: Seeing How to See. 103p. 1977. 9.95 (ISBN 0-900860-58-8, Pub. by Octagon Pr England). Ins Study Human.

Shah Waliullah. The Sacred Knowledge: The Altaf Al-Quds of Shah Waliullah. Jalbani, G. N. & Pendlebury, D. L., trs. 1982. 13.95 (ISBN 0-900860-93-6, Pub. by Octagon Pr England). Ins Study Human.

Shamblin, Steve. How To Grow Up Spiritually. (Orig.). 1986. pap. 5.95 (ISBN 0-910311-44-7). Huntington Hse Inc.

Sharma, I. C. Cayce, Karma & Reincarnation. LC 81-23214. 186p. 1982. pap. 5.50 (ISBN 0-8356-0563-9, Quest). Theos Pub Hse.

Shea, John. The Challenge of Jesus. (Encore Edition Ser.). 192p. 1984. pap. 8.95 (ISBN 0-88347-169-8). Thomas More.

Sheets, John. The Spirit Speaks in Us. 210p. 1986. 8.95 (ISBN 0-87193-250-4). Dimension Bks.

Shelby, Donald J. Forever Beginning: Exploration of the Faith for New Believers. 160p. (Orig.). 1987. pap. 5.95 (ISBN 0-8358-0557-3). Upper Room.

Shelly, Judith A. The Spiritual Needs of Children. LC 82-7223. (Orig.). 1982. pap. 5.95 (ISBN 0-87784-381-3). Inter-Varsity.

Sherrard, Philip. The Eclipse of Man & Nature: Spiritual Anthroposophy. 160p. (Orig.). Date not set. pap. 8.95 (Lindisfarne Pr). Inner Tradit.

Shideler, Mary M. In Search of the Spirit. 272p. (Orig.). 1985. 11.95 (ISBN 0-345-32107-3, Pub. by Ballantine Epiphany). Ballantine.

Silber, Edward S. God Is Otherwise Engaged. 317p. 1984. 10.95 (ISBN 0-89697-158-9). Intl Univ Pr.

Simons, George F. Journal for Life: Discovering Faith & Values Through Journal Keeping-Theology from Experience, Pt. 2, Pt. 2. LC 75-17161. (Illus.). 1977. pap. 1.95 (ISBN 0-914070-10-X). ACTA Found.

Singh, Ajaib. Streams in the Desert. Perkins, Russell & Perkins, Judith, eds. LC 81-85843. (Illus.). 468p. (Orig.). 1982. pap. 12.00 (ISBN 0-89142-038-X). Sant Bani Ash.

Singh, Darshan. Spiritual Awakening. LC 81-50726. (Illus.). 338p. (Orig.). 1982. pap. 6.50 (ISBN 0-918224-11-X). Sawan Kirpal Pubns.

Singh, Kirpal. The Light of Kirpal. LC 80-52537. xv, 446p. 1984. pap. 12.00 (ISBN 0-89142-033-9). Sant Bani Ash.

Singh, Tara. How to Learn from a Course in Miracles. rev. ed. LC 85-24790. (Orig.). 1985. 8.95 (ISBN 1-55531-000-1); pap. 4.50 (ISBN 1-55531-001-X). Life Action Pr.

Skariah, Matthew. Free, but Not Cheap. LC 85-91360. 144p. (Orig.). 1986. pap. 3.50 (ISBN 0-933495-01-3). World Prayer.

Slaughter, James N., Jr. & Jackson, David J. Where Grown Men Cry: An Endeavor to Free the Spirit. LC 86-32665. (Illus.). 176p. 1986. pap. 12.95 (ISBN 0-9617749-0-8). Cormac Inc.

Smith, Elwyn A. A Spiritual Exercise for New Parents. LC 85-47714. 64p. 1985. pap. 3.50 (ISBN 0-8006-1863-7, 1-1863). Fortress.

Sneck, William J. Charismatic Spiritual Gifts: A Phenomenological Analysis. LC 80-8291. 312p. (Orig.). 1981. lib. bdg. 29.25 (ISBN 0-8191-1765-X); pap. text ed. 14.50 (ISBN 0-8191-1766-8). U Pr of Amer.

Solomon, Charles R. Counseling with the Mind of Christ: The Dynamics of Spirituotherapy. 160p. 1977. pap. 5.95 (ISBN 0-8007-5049-7, Power Bks). Revell.

Solomon, Charmaine & Huxley, Dee. Love & a Wooden Spoon. LC 83-25446. 168p. 1985. pap. 10.00 (ISBN 0-385-19387-4). Doubleday.

Son-Ripened Fruit: Living Out the Fruit of the Spirit. (Orig.). 1986. pap. 1.95 (ISBN 0-8024-2551-8). Moody.

Spiker, Louise C. No Instant Grapes in God's Vineyard. 112p. 1982. pap. 5.95 (ISBN 0-8170-0955-8). Judson.

Spiritual Diary. 1962. 5.50 (ISBN 0-8198-6823-X); pap. 4.50 (ISBN 0-8198-6824-8). Dghtrs St Paul.

Spiritual Directory of St. Francis de Sales. 3.50 (ISBN 0-8198-6860-4); 2.25 (ISBN 0-8198-6861-2). Dghtrs St Paul.

Spurgeon, C. H. Spiritual Liberty. 1978. pap. 0.95 (ISBN 0-686-26197-6). Pilgrim Pubns.

Sri Aurobindo Ashram Publications Department Staff & Aurobindo, Sri. On Women. 126p. (Orig.). Date not set. pap. 6.00 (ISBN 0-89744-236-9, Pub. by Sri Aurobindo Ashram Trust India). Auromere.

Sri Aurobindo. Essays on the Gita. (Life Companion Library). 763p. 1983. 21.95 (ISBN 0-89744-006-4). Auromere.

--Thoughts & Aphorisms. 1979. pap. 6.00 (ISBN 0-89744-927-4). Auromere.

Sri Aurobindo & The Mother. Sri Aurobindo & the Mother on Education. 168p. 1973. pap. 3.50 (ISBN 0-89071-249-2). Matagiri.

--Sri Aurobindo & the Mother on Love. Saint-Hilaire, P. B., ed. & intro. by. 49p. 1973. pap. 2.00 (ISBN 0-89071-275-1). Matagiri.

Sri Chinmoy. Earth's Cry Meets Heaven's Smile, Bk. 2. 145p. (Orig.). 1975. Bk. 2. pap. 3.00 (ISBN 0-88497-143-0). Aum Pubns.

--Eternity's Silence-Heart. 200p. (Orig.). 1974. pap. 3.00 (ISBN 0-88497-106-6). Aum Pubns.

--Europe Blossoms. 1000p. (Orig.). 1974. pap. 15.00 (ISBN 0-88497-077-9). Aum Pubns.

--Father & Son. 100p. (Orig.). 1975. pap. 2.00 (ISBN 0-88497-119-8). Aum Pubns.

--Fifty Freedom-Boats to One Golden Shore, Pt. 5. 68p. (Orig.). 1975. pap. 2.00 (ISBN 0-88497-229-1). Aum Pubns.

--Flame-Waves, Pt. 1. 52p. (Orig.). 1975. pap. 2.00 (ISBN 0-88497-213-5). Aum Pubns.

--Flame-Waves, Pt. 2. 47p. (Orig.). 1975. pap. 2.00 (ISBN 0-88497-214-3). Aum Pubns.

--Flame-Waves, Pt. 3. 47p. (Orig.). 1975. pap. 2.00 (ISBN 0-88497-215-1). Aum Pubns.

--Flame-Waves, Pt. 4. 53p. (Orig.). 1975. pap. 2.00 (ISBN 0-88497-216-X). Aum Pubns.

--Flame-Waves, Pt. 5. 50p. (Orig.). 1975. pap. 2.00 (ISBN 0-88497-217-8). Aum Pubns.

--Fortune-Philosophy. 69p. (Orig.). 1974. pap. 2.00 (ISBN 0-88497-138-4). Aum Pubns.

--The Garden of Love-Light. 50p. (Orig.). 1974. pap. 2.00 (ISBN 0-88497-109-0). Aum Pubns.

--Matsyendranath & Gorakshanath: Two Spiritual Lions. 64p. (Orig.). 1974. pap. 2.00 (ISBN 0-88497-093-0). Aum Pubns.

--Sound Becomes, Silence Is. 200p. (Orig.). 1975. pap. 3.00 (ISBN 0-88497-118-X). Aum Pubns.

--The Vision of God's Dawn. 67p. 1974. pap. 2.00 (ISBN 0-685-53062-0). Aum Pubns.

Stanford, Miles J. The Green Letters: Principals of Spiritual Growth. 128p. 1975. pap. 3.95 (ISBN 0-310-33001-7, 9473P). Zondervan.

Stanger, Frank B. Gifts of the Spirit. 1974. pap. 0.95 (ISBN 0-87509-084-2). Chr Pubns.

Starr, Irina. The Sound of Light. LC 69-20335. 1977. pap. 3.50 (ISBN 0-87516-220-7). De Vorss.

Steere, Douglas V. Gleanings: A Random Harvest. 144p. (Orig.). 1986. pap. 6.95 (ISBN 0-8358-0543-3). Upper Room.

Steere, Douglas V., ed. Quaker Spirituality: Selected Writings. (Classics of Western Spirituality Ser.). 384p. 1984. 12.95 (ISBN 0-8091-0335-4); pap. 9.95 (ISBN 0-8091-2510-2). Paulist Pr.

Steinbrecher, Edwin. The Inner Guide Meditation: A Spiritual Technology for the 21st Century. 240p. (Orig.). 1987. pap. 7.95 (ISBN 0-87728-657-4). Weiser.

Steiner, Rudolf. At the Gates of Spiritual Science. Tr. of Vor dem Tore der Theosophie. 160p. 1986. 20.00 (ISBN 0-88010-224-1); pap. 8.95 (ISBN 0-88010-135-0). Anthroposophic.

--Earthly & Cosmic Man. Garber, Bernard J., ed. LC 85-80915. (Spiritual Science Library: Vol. 27). 176p. 1986. lib. bdg. 14.00 (ISBN 0-89345-055-3, Spiritual Sci Lib). Garber Comm.

--Life Between Death & New Birth. (Russian Language Ser.). 90p. 1985. pap. 6.00 (ISBN 0-89345-904-6, Steiner). Garber Comm.

--The Spiritual Guidance of Man. 1983. pap. 5.95 (ISBN 0-910142-35-1). Anthroposophic.

--Universe Earth & Man. (Russian Language Ser.). 136p. 1985. pap. 8.00 (ISBN 0-89345-903-8, Steiner). Garber Comm.

Steiner, Rudolf & Schure, Edward. The East in the Light of the West: The Children of Lucifer & the Brothers of Christ & Antique Drama in 5 Acts, Vol. 28. Garber, Bernard J., ed. LC 85-80914. (Spiritual Science Library Ser.: Vol. 28). 384p. 1986. lib. bdg. 21.00 (ISBN 0-89345-056-1, Spiritual Sci Lib). Garber Comm.

Steiner, Rudolf, et al. Education As an Art, Vol. 13. Allen, Paul M., ed. Tapp, Michael & Tapp, Elizabeth, trs. from Ger. LC 73-130816. (Spiritual Science Library). 128p. (Orig.). 1981. lib. bdg. 11.00 (ISBN 0-89345-024-3); pap. 6.00 (ISBN 0-89345-202-5, Steinerbks). Garber Comm.

Stewart, R. J. The Underworld Initiation: A Journey Towards Psychic Transformation. 272p. 1985. pap. 11.95 (ISBN 0-85030-399-0). Newcastle Pub.

Stoddard, Andrea. How to Bind & Loose in Spiritual Conflict. 56p. (Orig.). 1986. 3.95 (ISBN 0-936371-00-5). Spirit Faith.

Stringfellow, William. The Politics of Spirituality. LC 84-10434. (Spirituality & the Christian Life Ser.: Vol. 4). 90p. 1984. pap. 7.95 (ISBN 0-664-24633-8). Westminster.

Stuart, Vincent G. Changing Mind. LC 80-53447. 80p. 1981. 6.95 (ISBN 0-87773-206-X). Shambhala Pubns.

Studzinski, Raymond. Spiritual Direction & Mid-Life Development. 1985. 12.95 (ISBN 0-8294-0480-5). Loyola.

Subramuniya. The Clear White Light. (On the Path Ser.). (Illus.). 1979. pap. 2.00 (ISBN 0-87516-350-5). De Vorss.

--The Power of Affirmation. pap. 1.00 (ISBN 0-87516-357-2). De Vorss.

--Raja Yoga. (Illus.). 139p. 1973. 7.00 (ISBN 0-87516-348-3). De Vorss.

--The River of Life. pap. 1.00 (ISBN 0-87516-360-2). De Vorss.

--The Search Is Within. (On the Path Ser.). (Illus.). 1973. pap. 2.00 (ISBN 0-87516-349-1). De Vorss.

--The Self God. (On the Path Ser.). 72p. 1959. pap. 2.00 (ISBN 0-87516-353-X). De Vorss.

Suhrawardi, Shihabuddin Yahya. The Mystical & Visionary Treatises of Shihabuddin Yahya Suhrawardi. Thackston, W. H., Jr., tr. 1982. 16.95 (ISBN 0-900860-92-8, Pub. by Octagon Pr England). Ins Study Human.

Sullender, R. Scott. Grief & Growth: Pastoral Resources for Emotional & Spiritual Growth. LC 84-61024. 240p. (Orig.). 1985. pap. 9.95 (ISBN 0-8091-2652-4). Paulist Pr.

Swami, Bhakivedanta. Srimad Bhagavatam: Eleventh Canto, 4 Vols. (Illus.). 416p. 1983. 12.95 ea. (ISBN 0-89213-125-X). Bhaktivedanta.

Swami Abhedanenda. True Psychology. 1987. 6.50 (ISBN 0-87481-613-0, Pub. by Ramakrishna Math Madras India). Vedanta Pr.

Swami Amar Jyoti. Spirit of Himalaya: The Story of a Truth Seeker. 2nd rev. ed. LC 85-50206. (Illus.). 128p. 1985. pap. 5.95 (ISBN 0-933572-06-9). Truth Consciousness.

Swami Bhashyananda. From the Unreal to the Real. Date not set. price not set. Vivekananda.

Swami Durgananda. Where Are You Going? A Guide to the Spiritual Journey. LC 81-52192. 176p. (Orig.). 1981. pap. 6.95 (ISBN 0-914602-75-6). SYDA Found.

Swami Jyotir Maya Nanda. Yoga of Divine Love: A Commentary on Narada Bhakti Sutras. 1982. pap. 4.99 (ISBN 0-934664-42-0). Yoga Res Foun.

Swami Mukananda. I Have Become Alive: Secrets of the Inner Journey. Swami Durgananda, ed. Swami Chidvilasananda, tr. LC 85-50040. 240p. (Orig.). 1985. pap. 6.95 (ISBN 0-914602-89-6). SYDA Found.

Swami Muktananda. Does Death Really Exist? LC 81-50161. 64p. 1983. pap. 3.95 (ISBN 0-914602-56-X). SYDA Found.

--Getting Rid of What You Haven't Got. LC 74-19579. 64p. 1974. 3.25 (ISBN 0-914602-44-6). SYDA Found.

--Light on the Path. LC 81-51377. 112p. 1972. 4.95 (ISBN 0-914602-54-3). SYDA Found.

--Paramartha Katha Prasang: Spiritual Conversations with Swami Muktananda. 356p. 6.95 (ISBN 0-914602-90-X). SYDA Found.

--To Know the Knower. 40p. 1.75 (ISBN 0-317-03900-8). SYDA Found.

Swami Radha Sivananda. Seeds of Light. LC 76-67719. (Illus.). 116p. 1985. pap. 9.95 (ISBN 0-931454-11-5). Timeless Bks.

Swami Rudrananda. Spiritual Cannibalism. 208p. (Orig.). 1987. pap. 9.95 (ISBN 0-915801-07-8). Rudra Pr.

Swami Sivananda Radha. Gods Who Walk the Rainbow. LC 81-9410. (Illus.). 240p. (Orig.). 1981. pap. 7.95 (ISBN 0-931454-07-7). Timeless Bks.

--Radha: Diary of a Woman's Search. LC 80-26470. (Illus.). 230p. (Orig.). 1981. pap. 7.95 (ISBN 0-931454-06-9). Timeless Bks.

Swedenborg, Emanuel. Emanuel Swedenborg: Universal Human & Soul Body Interaction. (Classic of Western Spirituality Ser.). 258p. 1984. 12.95 (ISBN 0-8091-0344-3); pap. 9.95 (ISBN 0-8091-2554-4). Paulist Pr.

--Experientiae Spirituales, 6 Vols. 2nd ed. Odhner, John D., ed. (Lat.). 3600p. 1982. Set. 270.00 (ISBN 0-910557-00-4). Acad New Church.

Swindoll, Charles R. Baje la Guardia! Araujo, Juan S., tr. from Eng. Tr. of Dropping Your Guard. (Span.). 176p. 1987. pap. 4.95 (ISBN 0-88113-016-8). Edit Betania.

--Three Steps Forward, Two Steps Back: Persevering Through Pressure. LC 80-11892. 176p. 1980. 9.95 (ISBN 0-8407-5187-7); pap. 5.95 (ISBN 0-8407-5723-9). Nelson.

Taafaki, Irene. Thoughts: Education for Peace & One World. (Illus.). 336p. 1986. 19.95 (ISBN 0-85398-221-X); pap. text ed. 9.95 (ISBN 0-85398-222-8). G Ronald Pub.

Tarthang Tulku. Dimensions of Thought: Current Explorations in Time, Space & Knowledge, 2 vols. Moon, Ralph & Randall, Steve, eds. 1980. Vol. 1. 12.95 (ISBN 0-913546-77-1); Vol. 2. 12.95 (ISBN 0-913546-78-X). Dharma Pub.

--Hidden Mind of Freedom. Derman, Sylvia, ed. 1981. pap. 6.95 (ISBN 0-89800-120-X). Dharma Pub.

Taylor, Jack. Key to Triumphant Living. LC 76-166582. 1971. 8.95 (ISBN 0-8054-5514-0). Broadman.

Taylor, Jeremy. The Rule & Exercises of Holy Living. 295p. 1982. Repr. of 1982 ed. lib. bdg. 35.00 (ISBN 0-89984-468-5). Century Bookbindery.

Teaching of Sri Satya Sai Baba. 144p. 1974. pap. 2.95 (ISBN 0-317-20878-0). CSA Pr.

Teachings of Sri Saranda Devi. (The Holy Mother Ser.). 175p. 1983. 3.00 (ISBN 0-87481-520-7, Pub. by Ramakrishna Math Madras India). Vedanta Pr.

Temple of the People Publications Staff, ed. Temple Messages. (Illus.). 183p. 1983. 10.50 (ISBN 0-933797-07-9). Halcyon Bk.

--Theogenesis. (Illus.). 548p. 1981. 21.00 (ISBN 0-933797-06-0). Halcyon Bk.

Temple Talks: On Willingness to Be Wrong. 56p. 1978. pap. 2.95 (ISBN 0-933740-02-6). Mindbody Inc.

Tengbom, Mildred. Why Waste Your Illness: Let God Use It for Growth. LC 83-72113. 144p. (Orig.). 1984. pap. 6.95 (ISBN 0-8066-2057-9, 10-7182). Augsburg.

Theresa of Avila. The Conquest of the Perfect Love, 2 vols. (Illus.). 235p. 1986. 189.75 (ISBN 0-89266-552-1). Am Classical Coll Pr.

Thomas a Kempis & St. Therese of Lisieux. Just for Today: Selections from St. Therese of Lisieux & the Imitation of Christ. 250p. 1983. pap. 7.95 (ISBN 0-87243-121-5). Templegate.

Thornton, Edward E. Being Transformed: An Inner Way of Spiritual Growth. LC 83-27331. (Potentials: Guides for Productive Living Ser.: Vol. 4). 114p. (Orig.). 1984. pap. 7.95 (ISBN 0-664-24523-4). Westminster.

Thornton, Martin. English Spirituality. 330p. 1986. 24.95 (ISBN 0-936384-38-7); pap. 11.95 (ISBN 0-936384-31-X). Cowley Pubns.

Thurman, Howard. For the Inward Journey: The Writings of Howard Thurman. Harding, Vincent & Thurman, Anne S., eds. LC 83-26366. 352p. 1984. 17.95 (ISBN 0-15-132656-8). HarBraceJ.

Thurston, Mark. Discovering Your Soul's Purpose. 175p. 1984. with cassettes 24.95 (ISBN 0-87604-186-1). Allen Unwin.

Thurston, Mark A. Experiments in Practical Spirituality: Keyed to a Search for God, Book II. (Illus.). 147p. (Orig.). 1980. pap. 5.95 (ISBN 0-87604-122-5). ARE Pr.

Toth, Max & Nielson, Greg. Pyramid Power. (Illus.). 207p. 1985. pap. 4.95 (ISBN 0-89281-106-4). Inner Tradit.

Tozer, A. W. I Call It Heresy. pap. 3.45 (ISBN 0-87509-209-8). Chr Pubns.

--Keys to the Deeper Life. 56p. 1973. pap. 1.95 (ISBN 0-310-33362-8). Zondervan.

--The Knowledge of the Holy. LC 85-42794. 208p. 1985. pap. 12.95 large print (ISBN 0-06-068413-5, HarpR). Har-Row.

Transformation-Night, Immortality-Dawn. 1975. 2.00 (ISBN 0-88497-111-2). Aum Pubns.

Trobisch, Walter. Spiritual Dryness. pap. 0.75 (ISBN 0-87784-138-1). Inter-Varsity.

Trungpa, Chogyam. Shambhala: The Sacred Path of the Warrior. LC 83-20401. (Illus.). 199p. 1984. pap. 7.95 (ISBN 0-87773-264-7). Shambhala Pubns.

--Shambhala: The Sacred Path of the Warriors. 176p. 1986. pap. 3.95 (ISBN 0-553-26172-X). Bantam.

Tucker, Ronald D. The Word of God. 43p. (Orig.). 1985. pap. 2.50 (ISBN 0-933643-26-8). Grace World Outreach.

Tugwell, Simon. Ways of Imperfection. 252p. 1985. 12.95 (ISBN 0-87243-136-3). Templegate.

Tulku, T. Gesture of Balance: A Guide to Awareness, Self-Healing & Meditation. 170p. 1977. 25.00x (ISBN 0-317-39074-0, Pub. by Luzac & Co Ltd). State Mutual Bk.

Turner, Charles W. My Favorite Reflections. pap. 1.75 (ISBN 0-88469-029-6). BMH Bks.

Turner, Iris M., ed. The Road to Reality: The Spiritual Path for Everyone. 124p. 1986. 29.00x (ISBN 0-7212-0732-4, Pub. by Regency Pr). State Mutual Bk.

Twitchell, Paul. Le Carnet De Notes Spiritual. 1978. pap. 3.95 (ISBN 0-914766-40-6). IWP Pub.

--L' Etranger au Bord de La Riviere. 1979. pap. 5.95 (ISBN 0-914766-42-2). IWP Pub.

--Der Fremde Am Fluss. 1979. pap. 5.95 (ISBN 0-914766-43-0). Iwp Pub.

--Krauter: Die Magischen Heiler. 1978. pap. 3.95 (ISBN 0-914766-39-2). IWP Pub.

--The Spiritual Notebook. LC 74-178996. 218p. 1971. pap. 5.95 (ISBN 0-914766-94-5). IWP Pub.

--The Tiger's Fang. 1979. 5.95 (ISBN 0-914766-51-1). IWP Pub.

Underhill, Evelyn. The House of the Soul & Concerning the Inner Life. 150p. (Orig.). 1984. pap. 6.95 (ISBN 0-86683-882-1, 7459, HarpR). Har-Row.

--Mixed Pasture. facs. ed. LC 68-8501. (Essay Index Reprint Ser). 1933. 17.00 (ISBN 0-8369-0958-5). Ayer Co Pubs.

--The Spiritual Life. LC 84-60646. 128p. 1984. pap. 4.95 (ISBN 0-8192-1350-0). Morehouse.

Underwood, B. E. Spiritual Gifts: Ministries & Manifestations. pap. 3.95 student wkbk. (ISBN 0-911866-04-3); pap. 6.95 tchr's. guide (ISBN 0-911866-05-1). Advocate.

Upanayanam: (Twice Born) 1983. pap. 2.00 (ISBN 0-938924-15-X). Sri Shirdi Sai.

Van Eeden, Frederik. Paul's Awakening. Lake, H. S., tr. from Dutch. LC 83-81704. 96p. 1985. 6.95 (ISBN 0-86164-156-6, Pub. by Momenta Pub Ltd). Hunter Hse.

Van Kaam, Adrian. Personality Fulfillment in the Spiritual Life. 4.95 (ISBN 0-87193-043-9). Dimension Bks.
--Spirituality & the Gentle Life. 6.95 (ISBN 0-87193-037-4). Dimension Bks.
Van Kaam, Adrian & Muto, Susan. Tell Me Who I Am. 4.95 (ISBN 0-87193-145-1). Dimension Bks.
Van Rijckenborgh, Jan & De Petri, Catharose. Lightgarment of the New Man. Tr. of Het Lichtkleed van de Niewe Mens. 100p. (Orig.). Date not set. pap. 11.00. Rosycross Pr.
Van Rijn, J. C. Living. 49p. (Orig.). 1986. pap. 7.00 (ISBN 0-9617483-0-3). What Is Pr.
--Living. 2nd ed. 130p. Date not set. pap. 8.95 (ISBN 0-9617483-1-1). What Is Pr.
Van Waveren, Erlo. Pilgrimage to Rebirth. 125p. 1978. 7.95 (ISBN 0-87728-420-2); pap. 3.95. Weiser.
Vaughn, Ruth. To Be a Girl, to Be a Woman. 160p. 1982. 8.95 (ISBN 0-8007-1328-1). Revell.
Vedas: Immortality's First Call. 1972. pap. 2.00 (ISBN 0-87847-018-2). Aum Pubns.
Venden, Morris. To Know God: A Five-Day Plan. Woolsey, Raymond, ed. 125p. pap. 1.50 (ISBN 0-8280-0220-7). Review & Herald.
Villanueva, Emilio B., tr. from Span. Book of the True Life, Vol. I. abr. ed. Orig. Title: Libro de la Vida Verdadera. (Span., Illus.). 376p. (Orig.). 1983. text ed. 12.00 (ISBN 0-912753-00-5); pap. 6.00x (ISBN 0-912753-01-3). True Life Found.
Vining, Elizabeth G. A Quest There Is. 1983. pap. 2.50x (ISBN 0-87574-246-7, 246). Pendle Hill.
Vissell, Barry & Vissell, Joyce. The Shared Heart: Relationship Initiations & Celebrations. LC 85-10981. 192p. 1985. Repr. lib. bdg. 19.95x (ISBN 0-89370-883-6). Borgo Pr.
Vozdvizhensky, P. Moja pervaja Svjashchennaja Istorija, dlja detjej. Tr. of My First Sacred History, for Children. (Illus.). 101p. 1968. pap. 4.00 (ISBN 0-317-30407-0). Holy Trinity.
Walton, Lewis R. Advent! Woolsey, Raymond H., ed. 128p. (Orig.). 1986. pap. 6.95 (ISBN 0-8280-0349-1). Review & Herald.
Watson, David. The Hidden Battle: Strategies for Spiritual Victory. Rev. ed. 160p. 1985. pap. 2.95 (ISBN 0-87788-343-2). Shaw Pubs.
Wayman, Alex, tr. from Tibetan, Sanskrit. Chanting the Names of Manjusri: The Manjusri-Nama-Samgiti, Sanskrit & Tibetan Texts. LC 83-2309. 130p. 1985. 30.00 (ISBN 0-87773-316-3, 54531-1). Shambhala Pubns.
Webbe, Gale D. The Shape of Growth. 110p. (Orig.). 1985. pap. 9.95 (ISBN 0-8192-1356-X). Morehouse.
Wersell, Thomas W. Spiritual Thoughts & Prayers. LC 74-76920. pap. 20.00 (2026829). Bks Demand UMI.
Wesley, John & Weakley, Clare. The Nature of Spiritual Growth. rev. ed. 208p. 1986. pap. 5.95 (ISBN 0-87123-876-4). Bethany Hse.
Wesleys World Parish. 3.50 (ISBN 0-686-27780-5). Schmul Pub Co.
Wesner, Maralene & Wesner, Miles. Truth or Tradition: What Is the Gospel? LC 86-71139. 100p. 1986. pap. 4.95 (ISBN 0-936715-03-0). Diversity Okla.
--What's Your S. Q.? (Spiritual Quotient) LC 86-71133. 100p. 1986. pap. 4.95 (ISBN 0-936715-04-9). Diversity Okla.
Westerhoff, John H. & Eusden, John. The Spiritual Life: Learning East & West. 172p. 1982. 10.95 (ISBN 0-8164-0516-6, HarpR). Har-Row.
Westmeyer, Nancy. Parish Life: Manual for Spiritual Leadership Formation. 1983. pap. 8.95 (ISBN 0-8091-2489-0). Paulist Pr.
White, Mary. Growing Together: Building Your Family's Spiritual Life. 2nd ed. 144p. 1985. pap. 4.95 (ISBN 0-89109-484-9). NavPress.
White, Stewart E. & White, Harwood. Across the Unknown. 336p. 1987. pap. 7.95 (ISBN 0-89804-150-3). Ariel OH.
White Eagle. Golden Harvest. 1958. 3.95 (ISBN 0-85487-017-2). De Vorss.
--Morning Light. 1957. 3.95 (ISBN 0-85487-018-0). De Vorss.
--Spiritual Unfoldment One. 1942. 6.95 (ISBN 0-85487-012-1). De Vorss.
--Spiritual Unfoldment Two. 1969. 6.95 (ISBN 0-85487-001-6). De Vorss.
Widutis, Florence. The True Path. (Illus.). 1979. pap. 5.95 (ISBN 0-87516-266-5). De Vorss.
Williams, Merrill. His Spirit in You. 68p. 1982. 2.95 (ISBN 0-8341-0783-X). Beacon Hill.
Williamson, J. J. Cataclysm Has Begun, No. 1. 20.00x (ISBN 0-317-43559-0, Pub. by Soc of Metaphysicians). State Mutual Bk.
Willis, Elbert. An Interceding Faith. 1978. 1.25 (ISBN 0-89858-018-8). Fill the Gap.
Wilshire, Frances. Secrets. pap. 1.95 (ISBN 0-87516-318-1). De Vorss.
Wingate. Tilling the Soul. 1984. pap. 9.95 (ISBN 0-317-17441-X). Aurora Press.
Winter, David. Walking into Light. 160p. 1986. pap. 3.50 (ISBN 0-87788-916-3). Shaw Pubs.
Wojtyla, Karol. Sign of Contradiction. 1980. pap. 3.95 (ISBN 0-686-85827-1). Crossroad NY.
Wolsky, Alexander. Teilhard in Chardin's Biological Ideas. (Teilhard Studies). 1981. 2.00 (ISBN 0-89012-024-2). Anima Pubns.
Wood, Robert & Roy, Marie L. Day Four: A Pilgrim's Continued Journey. 64p. (Orig.). 1986. pap. 2.95 (ISBN 0-8358-0553-0). Upper Room.
Woodbridge, Barry A. A Guidebook for Spiritual Friends. LC 84-51827. 96p. (Orig.). 1985. pap. 4.95 (ISBN 0-8358-0498-4). Upper Room.
Worth, Grant A. Do Your Prayers Bounce off the Ceiling? LC 81-17411. 68p. 1982. 6.95 (ISBN 0-87747-895-3). Deseret Bk.
Yatiswarananda, Swami. Adventures in Religious Life. pap. 4.50 (ISBN 0-87481-498-7). Vedanta Pr.
Yocum. The Holy Way. pap. 8.95 (ISBN 0-686-12915-6). Schmul Pub Co.
Yogananda, Paramahansa. Whispers from Eternity, First Vision. 1977. 6.95 (ISBN 0-87612-102-4). Self Realization.
Yogananda, Paramhansa. Songs of the Soul. LC 80-69786. 1980. pap. 9.95 (ISBN 0-937134-02-3). Amrita Found.
--Whispers from Eternity. LC 85-71375. 1978. pap. 12.95 (ISBN 0-937134-03-1). Amrita Found.
Yungblut, John R. Discovering God Within. LC 78-21713. 198p. 1979. pap. 6.95 (ISBN 0-664-24231-6). Westminster.
Zitko, Howard J. New Age Tantra Yoga: The Sexual Gateway to Spiritual Fulfillment. 6th ed. LC 75-3657. 1985. pap. 7.50 (ISBN 0-941902-00-5). World Univ AZ.
Zweig, Paul. Muktananda: Selected Essays. LC 76-9994. 1977. pap. 7.95i (ISBN 0-06-069860-8, RD185, HarpR). Har-Row.

SPIRITUAL LIFE–BIBLICAL TEACHING

Atkinson, Franklin. A New Look at Spiritual Life. (Orig.). 1987. pap. 4.98 (ISBN 0-8054-1235-2). Broadman.
Bright, Bill. How to Be Filled with the Spirit. (Transferable Concepts Ser.). 58p. 1981. pap. 1.25 (ISBN 0-918956-90-0). Campus Crusade.
--How to Be Sure You Are a Christian. (Transferable Concepts Ser.). 63p. 1981. pap. 1.25 (ISBN 0-918956-88-9). Campus Crusade.
--How to Experience God's Love & Forgiveness. (Transferable Concepts Ser.). 63p. 1981. pap. 1.25 (ISBN 0-918956-89-7). Campus Crusade.
--How to Help Fulfill the Great Commission. (Transferable Concepts Ser.). 64p. 1981. pap. 1.25 (ISBN 0-918956-94-3). Campus Crusade.
--How to Pray. (Transferable Concepts Ser.). 63p. 1981. pap. 1.25 (ISBN 0-918956-96-X). Campus Crusade.
--How to Walk in the Spirit. (Transferable Concepts Ser.). 64p. 1981. pap. 1.25 (ISBN 0-918956-91-9). Campus Crusade.
--How to Witness in the Spirit. (Transferable Concepts Ser.). 64p. 1981. pap. 1.25 (ISBN 0-918956-92-7). Campus Crusade.
Coleman, Lyman. Spiritual Basics: New Life in Christ. (Free University - Lay Academy in Christian Discipleship Ser.). (Orig.). 1981. pap. 1.25 student's bk. (ISBN 0-687-37355-7); pap. 4.95 tchr's bk. (ISBN 0-687-37354-9). Abingdon.
Doyle, Stephen C. Covenant Renewal in Religious Life: Biblical Reflections. 140p. 1976. 6.95 (ISBN 0-8199-0585-2). Franciscan Herald.
Navone, John. Personal Witness. LC 67-13761. 1967. 4.95 (ISBN 0-685-42652-1, Pub-by Sheed). Guild Bks.
Sweeny, Z. T. Spirit & the Word. 1982. pap. 3.95 (ISBN 0-89225-264-2). Gospel Advocate.

SPIRITUAL LIFE–CATHOLIC AUTHORS

see also Perfection (Catholic)

Bandas, Rudolph G. Catholic Layman & Holiness. 1965. 8.95 (ISBN 0-8158-0046-0). Chris Mass.
Brown, Raphael. True Joy from Assisi. 276p. 1978. 8.95 (ISBN 0-8199-0688-3). Franciscan Herald.
Bush, Bernard J. Living in His Love: Essays on Prayer & Christian Living. LC 78-11809. 115p. 1978. pap. 3.95 (ISBN 0-89571-005-6). Affirmation.
De Catanzaro, C. J. Symeon, the New Theologian: The Discourses. LC 80-82414. (Classics of Western Spirituality Ser.). 416p. 1980. 13.95 (ISBN 0-8091-0292-7); pap. 9.95 (ISBN 0-8091-2230-8). Paulist Pr.
De Caussade, Jean-Pierre. Abandonment to Divine Providence. LC 74-2827. 120p. 1975. pap. 3.50 (ISBN 0-385-02544-0, Im). Doubleday.
Dobbin, Muriel. Going Live. Engelson, Joyce, ed. 432p. 1987. 17.95 (ISBN 0-525-24473-5). Dutton.
Doherty, Catherine D. Journey Inward: Interior Conversations 1960 to the Present. LC 84-443. 116p. (Orig.). 1984. pap. 6.95 (ISBN 0-8189-0468-2). Alba.
--Poustinia. LC 74-19961. 216p. 1975. pap. 3.95 (ISBN 0-87793-083-X). Ave Maria.
Falardeau, Ernest. One Bread & Cup: Source of Communion. 1987. pap. 7.95. M Glazier.
Fraile, Peter A. God Within Us: Movements, Powers, & Joys. 110p. 1986. 6.95 (ISBN 0-8294-0503-8). Loyola.
Gannon, Timothy J. Emotional Development & Spiritual Growth. pap. 0.75 (ISBN 0-8199-0386-8, L38135). Franciscan Herald.
Giles, Mary. Francisco de Osuna: The Third Spiritual Alphabet, Vol 1. (Classics of Western Spirtuality Ser.). 1982. 16.95 (ISBN 0-8091-0266-8); pap. 11.95 (ISBN 0-8091-2145-X). Paulist Pr.
Gregg, Robert C., ed. Athanasius: The Life of Antony & the Letter to Marcellinus. LC 79-56622. (Classics of Western Spirituality Ser.). 192p. 1980. 12.95 (ISBN 0-8091-0309-5); pap. 8.95 (ISBN 0-8091-2295-2). Paulist Pr.
Hakenewerth, Quentin. In His Likeness: A Manual of Direction for the Spiritual Life. 88p. (Orig.). 1977. pap. 1.75 (ISBN 0-9608124-1-5). Marianist Com Ctr.
Hardon, John. Spiritual Life in the Modern World. 1982. 3.50 (ISBN 0-8198-6839-6, SP0708); pap. 2.50 (ISBN 0-8198-6840-X). Dghtrs St Paul.
Hardon, John A. Holiness in the Church. 1976. 3.50 (ISBN 0-8198-0417-7); pap. 2.50 (ISBN 0-8198-0418-5). Dghtrs St Paul.
Hoffman, Dominic M. Maturing the Spirit. new ed. 1973. 5.00 (ISBN 0-8198-0257-3); pap. 4.00 (ISBN 0-8198-0258-1). Dghtrs St Paul.
Hudson, Winthrop S., ed. Walter Rauscenbusch: Selected Writings. (Sources of American Spirituality Ser.). 252p. 1985. text ed. 14.95 (ISBN 0-8091-0356-7). Paulist Pr.
Johnson, Edwin C. The Myth of the Great Secret: A Search for Spiritual Meaning in the Face of Emptiness. 1982. 10.50 (ISBN 0-688-00781-3). Morrow.
Keating, Charles J. The Gentle Touch. (Illus.). 112p. (Orig.). 1985. pap. 5.95 (ISBN 0-89622-217-9). Twenty-Third.
Lekeux, Martial. Short Cut to Divine Love. LC 61-11203. 332p. 1961. pap. 2.50 (ISBN 0-8199-0131-8, L38796). Franciscan Herald.
McNamara, William. Art of Being Human. pap. 3.50 (ISBN 0-385-08323-8, E45, Im). Doubleday.
Martin, Ralph. Hungry for God: Practical Help in Personal Prayer. LC 74-4830. 168p. 1974. pap. 6.50 (ISBN 0-385-09534-1). Doubleday.
Meehan, Francis X., ed. A Contemporary Social Spirituality. LC 82-2253. 133p. (Orig.). 1982. pap. 6.95 (ISBN 0-88344-022-9). Orbis Bks.
Merton, Thomas. The Asian Journal of Thomas Merton. Stone, Naomi B., et al, eds. LC 71-103370. (Illus.). 448p. 1973. pap. 8.95 (ISBN 0-8112-0570-3, NDP394). New Directions.
--Life & Holiness. 1964. pap. 2.95 (ISBN 0-385-06277-X, D183, Im). Doubleday.
--The Monastic Journey. Hart, Patrick, ed. LC 77-27714. 1978. pap. 4.50 (ISBN 0-385-14094-0, Im). Doubleday.
--The New Man. 256p. 1962. pap. 6.95 (ISBN 0-374-51444-5). FS&G.
--New Seeds of Contemplation. rev. ed. LC 61-17869. 1972. pap. 5.50 (ISBN 0-8112-0099-X, NDP337). New Directions.
--No Man Is an Island. LC 78-7108. 264p. 1978. pap. 5.95 (ISBN 0-15-665962-X, Harv). HarBraceJ.
--Seeds of Contemplation. LC 78-10255. 1979. Repr. of 1949 ed. lib. bdg. 27.50x (ISBN 0-313-20756-9, MESC). Greenwood.
Moore, Sebastian. Inner Loneliness. 1984. pap. 6.95 (ISBN 0-8245-0619-7). Crossroad NY.
Muto, Susan. Renewed at Each Awakening: The Formative Power of Sacred Words. 1985. pap. 4.95 (ISBN 0-87193-147-8). Dimension Bks.
Nouwen, Henri J. The Genesee Diary: Report from a Trappist Monastery. LC 85-7150. 352p. 1985. pap. 12.95 (ISBN 0-8027-2500-7). Walker & Co.
--Gracias! A Latin American Journal. LC 82-48935. 224p. 1983. 13.45 (ISBN 0-06-066318-9, HarpR). Har-Row.
On St. Basil the Great. LC 79-20045. (Word & Spirit Ser.: Vol. I). 1979. pap. 4.95 (ISBN 0-932506-07-0). St Bedes Pubns.
On St. Benedict. LC 80-25958. (Word & Spirit Ser.: Vol. II). 1980. pap. 6.00 (ISBN 0-932506-09-7). St Bedes Pubns.
Staton, Knofel. Spiritual Gifts for Christians Today. 118p. (Orig.). 1973. pap. 3.50 (ISBN 0-89900-134-3). College Pr Pub.
Sterner, John. How to Become Super-Spiritual: Or Kill Yourself Trying. LC 82-6636. 160p. (Orig.). 1982. pap. 7.50 (ISBN 0-687-17760-X). Abingdon.
Teilhard de Chardin, Pierre. The Heart of Matter. Hague, Rene, tr. LC 79-24527. 276p. 1980. pap. 7.95 (ISBN 0-15-640004-9, Harv). HarBraceJ.
Teresa. The Interior Castle or the Mansions, 2 vols. (Illus.). 325p. 1984. Set. 197.85 (ISBN 0-89266-488-6). Am Classical Coll Pr.
Torkington, Rayner. Peter Calvay -- Hermit: A Personal Rediscovery of Prayer. LC 80-13188. 107p. (Orig.). 1980. pap. 3.95 (ISBN 0-8189-0404-6). Alba.
Tugwell, Simon, ed. Early Dominicans, Selected Writings. (The Classics of Western Spirituality Ser.). 400p. 1982. 14.95 (ISBN 0-8091-0325-7); pap. 10.95 (ISBN 0-8091-2414-9). Paulist Pr.
Van Zeller, Hubert. Spirituality Recharted. 1985. pap. 4.95 (ISBN 0-932506-39-9). St Bedes Pubns.
Waywood, Robert F. Hanging in There with Christ. 1974. 4.95 (ISBN 0-8199-0498-8). Franciscan Herald.

SPIRITUAL LIFE–HISTORY OF DOCTRINES

Dunn, James D. Jesus & the Spirit: A Study of the Religious & Charismatic Experience of Jesus & the First Christians as Reflected in the New Testament. LC 75-9802. 528p. 1979. pap. 15.95 (ISBN 0-664-24290-1). Westminster.
Elder, Rozanne E., ed. The Spirituality of Western Christendom II: The Roots of Modern Christian Spirituality. (Cistercian Studies: Nbr. 55). pap. write for info. (ISBN 0-87907-855-3). Cistercian Pubns.
Gannon, Thomas M. & Traub, George W. The Desert & the City: An Interpretation of the History of Christian Spirituality. 338p. 1984. 8.95 (ISBN 0-8294-0452-X). Loyola.
Hambrick-Stowe, Charles E. The Practice of Piety: Puritan Devotional Disciplines in Seventeenth Century New England. LC 81-19806. (Published for the Institute of Early American History & Culture, Williamsburg, Virginia Ser.). xvi, 298p. 1986. pap. 10.95x (ISBN 0-8078-4145-5). U of Nc Pr.
Williams, Rowan. Christian Spirituality: A Theological History From the New Testament to Luther & St. John of the Cross. LC 80-82190. pap. 50.30 (2027154). Bks Demand UMI.

SPIRITUAL LIFE–ORTHODOX EASTERN AUTHORS

Archbishop Athanasius Martos. Religioznaya Tchuvstvo, Promisl Bozhil i Dukovnoje Prizvanije. Tr. of Religious Feeling, the Providence of God & Spiritual Calling. 30p. 1983. pap. 2.00 (ISBN 0-317-29069-X). Holy Trinity.
Dobrotoljubije tom Five, Vol. 5. Tr. of Philokalia. 343p. 20.00 (ISBN 0-317-28890-3); pap. 15.00 (ISBN 0-317-28891-1). Holy Trinity.
Dobrotoljubije Tom Four. Tr. of Philokalia. 451p. 25.00 (ISBN 0-317-28889-X); pap. 20.00 (ISBN 0-317-37275-0). Holy Trinity.
Grisbrooke, W. Jardine. The Spiritual Counsels of Father John of Kronstadt. 230p. (Orig.). 1982. pap. 8.95 (ISBN 0-913836-92-3). St Vladimirs.
Lavroff, S. Yako s Nami Bog. Tr. of For God is with Us. 73p. 1980. pap. 3.00 (ISBN 0-317-29142-4). Holy Trinity.
Moschus, Saint John. Spiritual Meadow: The Pratum Spirituale. pap. 1.25 (ISBN 0-686-16371-0). Eastern Orthodox.
Saint Nicodemos the Hagiorite. Njevidimaja Bran' Tr. of Unseen Warfare. 288p. 15.00 (ISBN 0-317-28905-5); pap. 10.00 (ISBN 0-317-28906-3). Holy Trinity.
Some Aspects of Orthodox Spirituality. pap. 0.25 (ISBN 0-686-02578-4). Eastern Orthodox.

SPIRITUAL-MINDEDNESS

see Spirituality

SPIRITUALITY

see also Soul; Spiritual Life

Aivanhov, Omraam M. Man's Subtle Bodies & Centers: The Aura, The Solar Plexus, The Chakras, Vol. 219. (IZVOR Collection). 154p. (Orig.). 1986. pap. 4.95 (ISBN 2-85566-383-0, 219). Prosveta USA.
Almaas, A. H. Essence. LC 85-51109. (Illus.). 208p. (Orig.). 1986. pap. 10.95 (ISBN 0-87728-627-2). Weiser.
--The Void: A Psychodynamic Investigation of the Relationship Between Mind & Space. LC 85-82559. 175p. (Orig.). 1986. pap. 8.00 (ISBN 0-936713-00-3). Almaas Pubns.
Anderson, Christopher A. Mind & Spirit. LC 86-72816. (Illus.). 90p. 1987. pap. 7.50 (ISBN 0-931353-09-2). Andersons Pubns.
Archimandrite Amvrossy Pogodin. Svjatoj Mark Efesskij i Florentijskaja Unia. Tr. of St. Mark of Ephesus & the Unia of Florence. 436p. (Orig.). 1963. pap. 15.00x (ISBN 0-88465-026-X). Holy Trinity.
Armstrong, A. H., ed. Classical Mediterranean Spirituality. (World Spirituality Ser.). 499p. 1986. 49.50x (ISBN 0-8245-0764-9). Crossroad NY.
Aubert, Roger. Sacralization & Secularization. LC 76-96949. (Concilium Ser.: Vol. 47). 190p. 7.95 (ISBN 0-8091-0128-9). Paulist Pr.
Augustine of Hippo. Augustine of Hippo: Selected Writings. Clark, Mary T., tr. (Classics of Western Spirituality Ser.). 544p. 1984. pap. 12.95 (ISBN 0-8091-2573-0). Paulist Pr.
Austin, R. W., ed. Ibn-Al-Arabi: The Bezels of Wisdom. LC 80-83892. (The Classics of Western Spirituality Ser.). 320p. 1980. 12.95 (ISBN 0-8091-0313-3); pap. 10.95 (ISBN 0-8091-2331-2). Paulist Pr.

Baker, Frank, ed. The Heart of True Spirituality: John Wesley's Own Choice, Vol. 2. 1986. pap. 4.95 (ISBN 0-310-45101-9, 17079P). Zondervan.

--Heart of True Spirituality: John Wesley's Own Choice, Vol. 2: Selections from Thomas a Kempis, et. al. 1985. pap. 4.95 (ISBN 0-317-46009-9). Zondervan.

Barry, William A. & Connolly, William J. The Practice of Spiritual Direction. 224p. (Orig.). 1982. pap. 11.95 (ISBN 0-8164-2357-1, AY7870, HarpR). Har-Row.

Bauman, David M. Spiritual Life for the Overbusy. 96p. (Orig.). 1987. pap. price not set (ISBN 0-88028-065-4). Forward Movement.

Bell, David N. The Image of Likeness: The Augustinian Spirituality of William of St. Thierry. 19.95 (ISBN 0-87907-878-2). Cistercian Pubns.

Bell, Richard H. Sensing the Spirit. LC 84-5158. (Spirituality & the Christian Life Ser.: Vol. 6). 120p. 1984. pap. 7.95 (ISBN 0-664-24632-X). Westminster.

Berdiaer, Nicolaii. The Realm of Spirit & the Realm of Caesar. Luurie, Donald A., tr. from Rus. LC 74-1554. 182p. 1975. Repr. of 1953 ed. lib. bdg. 55.00x (ISBN 0-8371-7395-7, BESC). Greenwood.

Bilheimer, Robert S. A Spirituality for the Long Haul: Biblical Risk & Moral Stand. LC 83-48918. 176p. 1984. pap. 8.95 (ISBN 0-8006-1760-6, 1-1760). Fortress.

Bosch, David J. A Spirituality of the Road. LC 79-10856. (Mennonite Missionary Fellowship: No. 6). 104p. 1979. pap. 4.95 (ISBN 0-8361-1889-8). Herald Pr.

Bouyer, Louis. Orthodox Spirituality & Protestant & Anglican Spirituality. (A History of Christian Spirituality Ser.: Vol. 3). 232p. 1982. pap. 9.95 (ISBN 0-8164-2374-1, HarpR). Har-Row.

Boylan, Eugene D. Difficulties in Mental Prayer. 128p. 1984. pap. 5.95 (ISBN 0-87061-105-4). Chr Classics.

Brennan, Patrick. Spirituality for an Anxious Age. 151p. 1985. pap. 7.95 (ISBN 0-88347-194-9). Thomas More.

Buck, Dorothy. The Dance of Life. (Patterns of World Spirituality Ser.). 160p. (Orig.). 1987. pap. 8.95 (ISBN 0-913757-52-7, Pub. by New Era Bks). Paragon Hse.

Carmody, John. Holistic Spirituality. 160p. 1984. pap. 7.95 (ISBN 0-8091-2564-1). Paulist Pr.

Carney, Mary L. Spiritual Harvest: Reflections on the Fruits of the Spirit. 112p. 1987. pap. 6.95 (ISBN 0-687-39231-4). Abingdon.

Carreiro, Mary E. The Psychology of Spiritual Growth. 160p. 1987. 24.95 (ISBN 0-89789-123-6); pap. 8.95 (ISBN 0-89789-124-4). Bergin & Garvey.

Carroll, L. Patrick & Dyckman, Katherine M. Chaos or Creation: Spirituality in Mid-Life. 176p. 1986. pap. 8.95 (ISBN 0-8091-2832-2). Paulist Pr.

Cassian, John. John Cassian: Conferences. Luibheid, Colm, tr. (Classics of Western Spirituality Ser.). 201p. 1985. 12.95 (ISBN 0-8091-0361-3); pap. 9.95 (ISBN 0-8091-2694-X). Paulist Pr.

Chadda, H. C., ed. Seeing Is Above All: Sant Darshan Singh's First Indian Tour. (Illus.). 1977. pap. 3.00 (ISBN 0-918224-04-7). Sawan Kirpal Pubns.

Cherry, Conrad, ed. Horace Bushnell: Sermons. LC 85-60410. (Sources of American Spirituality Ser.). 256p. (Orig.). 1985. 12.95 (ISBN 0-8091-0362-1). Paulist Pr.

Climacus, St. John. Ljestvitsa. Tr. of The Ladder. (Rus.). 266p. (Orig.). 1963. 18.00x (ISBN 0-88465-033-2); pap. 13.00x (ISBN 0-317-38080-X). Holy Trinity.

Conn, Joan W., ed. Women's Spirituality: Resources for Christian Development. 336p. (Orig.). 1986. pap. 11.95 (ISBN 0-8091-2752-0). Paulist Pr.

Connolly, Finbarr. God & Man in Modern Spirituality. 276p. 1984. pap. 9.95 (ISBN 0-87061-108-9). Chr Classics.

Cummings, Charles. Spirituality & the Desert Experience. 1976. cancelled (ISBN 0-87193-166-4). Dimension Bks.

Daughters of St. Paul. Spiritual Life in the Bible. 1980. 5.95 (ISBN 0-686-76825-6); pap. 4.00 (ISBN 0-8198-6813-2). Dghtrs St Paul.

Delacour, Jean. Dictionnaire des Mots d'Esprit. (Fr.). 352p. 1976. pap. 15.95 (ISBN 0-686-56849-4, M-6627). French & Eur.

Delaforge, Gaetan. The Templar Tradition in the Age of Aquarius. (Illus.). 175p. (Orig.). 1987. pap. 10.00 (ISBN 0-939660-20-2). Threshold VT.

Dicharry, Warren. To Live the Word Inspired & Incarnate: An Integral Biblical Spirituality. LC 85-7386. 464p. (Orig.). 1985. pap. 12.95 (ISBN 0-8189-0476-3). Alba.

Doherty, Barbara. I Am What I Do: Contemplation & Human Experience. 226p. 1982. pap. 9.95 (ISBN 0-88347-129-9). Thomas More.

Donders, Joseph G. Creation & Human Dynamism: A Spirituality for Life. 112p. (Orig.). 1985. pap. 5.95 (ISBN 0-89622-227-6). Twenty-Third.

Dorr, Donal. Spirituality & Justice. 264p. (Orig.). 1985. pap. 10.95 (ISBN 0-88344-449-6). Orbis Bks.

Doyle, Brendan. Meditations with TM Julian of Norwich. LC 82-73955. (Meditations with TM). (Illus.). 135p. (Orig.). 1983. pap. 6.95 (ISBN 0-939680-11-4). Bear & Co.

Duquoc, Christian. Secularization & Spirituality. LC 76-103390. (Concilium Ser.: Vol. 49). 187p. 7.95 (ISBN 0-8091-0136-X). Paulist Pr.

Duquoc, Christian, ed. Spirituality in the Secular City. LC 66-30386. (Concilium Ser.: Vol. 19). 192p. 7.95 (ISBN 0-8091-0140-8). Paulist Pr.

Elder, E. Rozanne, ed. The Spirituality of Western Christendom. LC 76-22615. (Cistercian Studies Ser.: No. 30). (Illus.). 1976. pap. 6.95 (ISBN 0-87907-987-8). Cistercian Pubns.

Faricy, Robert S. The Spirituality of Teilhard de Chardin. 128p. (Orig.). 1981. pap. 5.95 (ISBN 0-86683-608-X, HarpR). Har-Row.

Fiand, Barbara. Releasement: Spirituality for Ministry. 112p. 1987. 11.95 (ISBN 0-8245-0813-0). Crossroad NY.

Fleming, Austin H. Preparing for Liturgy: A Theology & Spirituality. (Orig.). 1985. pap. 6.95 (ISBN 0-912405-16-3). Pastoral Pr.

Foresi, Pascal. Reaching for More. Moran, Hugh J., tr. from Ital. Tr. of Conversazioni con i Focolarini. 128p. (Orig.). 1982. pap. 4.95 (ISBN 0-911782-40-0). New City.

Fox, Matthew. Meditations with TM Meister Eckhart. LC 82-71451. (Meditations with TM Ser.). (Illus.). 131p. (Orig.). 1982. pap. 6.95 (ISBN 0-939680-04-1). Bear & Co.

--Western Spirituality: Historical Roots, Ecumenical Routes. LC 81-67364. 440p. 1981. pap. 11.95 (ISBN 0-939680-01-7). Bear & Co.

--Whee! We, Wee All the Way Home: A Guide to a Sensual Prophetic Spirituality. LC 81-67365. 257p. 1981. pap. 8.95 (ISBN 0-939680-00-9). Bear & Co.

Francuch, Peter D. Fundamentals of Human Spirituality. LC 81-16660. 483p. 1982. 9.95x (ISBN 0-939386-01-1). TMH Pub.

Galilea, Segundo. The Future of Our Past: The Spanish Mystics Speak to Contemporary Spirituality. LC 85-71822. 96p. (Orig.). 1985. pap. 4.95 (ISBN 0-87793-296-4). Ave Maria.

Gandhi, Kishore. The Evolution of Consciousness: A Contemporary Mythic Journey into the Roots of Global Awareness. (Patterns of World Spirituality Ser.). 272p. 1986. pap. 11.95 (ISBN 0-913757-50-0, Pub. by New Era Bks). Paragon Hse.

Garvey, John, ed. Modern Spirituality: An Anthology. 156p. 1985. 12.95 (ISBN 0-87243-132-0). Templegate.

Gelberman, Joseph. To Be Fully Alive. 89p. pap. 5.95 (ISBN 0-942494-49-0). Coleman Pub.

Giles, Mary E. The Feminist Mystic & Other Essays on Women & Spirituality. 208p. 1982. pap. 8.95 (ISBN 0-8245-0432-1). Crossroad NY.

Goldsmith, Joel S. Our Spiritual Resources. LC 78-16010. 192p. 1983. pap. 3.50 (ISBN 0-06-063212-7, RD 478, HarpR). Har-Row.

Green, Arthur. Jewish Spirituality: Vol 1. Cousins, Ewert, ed. (World Spirituality Ser.). 496p. 1985. 49.50x (ISBN 0-8245-0762-2). Crossroad NY.

Greenberg, Martin. The Hamlet Vocation of Coleridge & Wordsworth. LC 85-18189. 232p. 1986. 22.50x (ISBN 0-87745-131-1). U of Iowa Pr.

Gregson, Vernon. Lonergan, Spirituality, & the Meeting of Religions. LC 85-3312. (College Theology Society-Studies in Religion: No. 2). 170p. (Orig.). 1985. lib. bdg. 24.50 (ISBN 0-8191-4619-6, Co-Pub by College Theo Soc); pap. text ed. 10.75 (ISBN 0-8191-4620-X). U Pr of Amer.

Grigsby, Daryl R. Reflections on Liberation. LC 84-72421. (Illus.). 176p. (Orig.). 1985. pap. 5.95 (ISBN 0-9614210-0-2). Asante Pubns.

Hakenewerth, Quentin. Mary in Modern Spirituality. 52p. (Orig.). 1966. pap. 1.25 (ISBN 0-9608124-2-3). Marianist Com Ctr.

Hardy, Alister. The Spiritual Nature of Man. 1979. 27.00x (ISBN 0-19-824618-8); pap. 12.95x (ISBN 0-19-824732-X). Oxford U Pr.

Haring, Bernard. In Pursuit of Wholeness: Healing in Today's Church. LC 85-80000. 128p. 1985. pap. 3.50 (ISBN 0-89243-236-5). Liguori Pubns.

Hatcher, John S. The Purpose of Physical Reality: The Kingdom of Names. Fisher, Betty J. & Hill, Richard A., eds. 250p. 1987. pap. 12.00 (ISBN 0-87743-208-2). Baha'i.

Hauser, Richard J. In His Spirit. LC 81-83187. 128p. (Orig.). 1982. pap. 5.95 (ISBN 0-8091-2421-1). Paulist Pr.

Hora, Thomas. Dialogues in Metapsychiatry. LC 77-8268. 238p. 16.00x (ISBN 0-913105-16-3). PAGL Pr.

--Forgiveness. (Discourses in Metapsychiatry Ser.). 48p. 1983. pap. 4.00 (ISBN 0-913105-05-8). PAGL Pr.

--Healing Through Spiritual Understanding. (Discourses in Metapsychiatry Ser.). 48p. (Orig.). 1983. pap. 4.00 (ISBN 0-913105-02-3). PAGL Pr.

--A Hierarchy of Values. (Discourses in Metapsychiatry Ser.). 48p. (Orig.). 1983. pap. 4.00 (ISBN 0-913105-03-1). PAGL Pr.

--The Soundless Music of Life. (Discourses in Metapsychiatry Ser.). 48p. 1983. pap. 3.95 (ISBN 0-913105-04-X). PAGL Pr.

Horn, Merritt C. The Call of the Spirit. 82p. (Orig.). 1984. pap. 5.95 (ISBN 0-932661-00-9). Archangel Pub.

Houston, James M. Motifs of Spirituality. Date not set. pap. cancelled (ISBN 0-88070-106-4). Multnomah.

Huck, Gabe & Klenicki, Leon, eds. Spirituality & Prayer, Jewish & Christian Understandings (Stimulus Bk.) LC 82-62966. 200p. (Orig.). 1983. pap. 7.95 (ISBN 0-8091-2538-2). Paulist Pr.

Irion, Clyde. Profit & Loss of Dying. 4.95 (ISBN 0-87516-030-1). De Vorss.

Irwin, Kevin W. Liturgy, Prayer & Spirituality. 1984. pap. 9.95 (ISBN 0-8091-2560-9). Paulist Pr.

Jocelyn, Beredene. Citizens of the Cosmos: Life's Unfolding from Conception Through Death to Rebirth. (Freedeeds Library). (Illus.). 198p. 1983. Repr. of 1981 ed. 14.00 (ISBN 0-89345-040-5, Freedeeds Bks). Garber Comm.

Johnson, Lawrence, ed. Called to Prayer: Liturgical Spirituality Today. 96p. 1986. pap. 4.95 (ISBN 0-8146-1488-4). Liturgical Pr.

Jones, Alan. Soul Making: The Desert Way of Spirituality. LC 84-48222. 192p. 1985. 14.45 (ISBN 0-06-064182-7, HarpR). Har-Row.

Kaam, Adrian V. Formative Spirituality: Fundamental Formation, Vol. I. LC 82-22079. (Formative Spirituality Ser.). 320p. 1983. 24.50x (ISBN 0-8245-0544-1). Crossroad NY.

Kannengiesser, Charles, ed. Early Christian Spirituality. Bright, Pamela, tr. from Lat. & Gr. LC 86-45226. (Sources of Early Christian Thought). 144p. 1986. pap. 7.95 (ISBN 0-8006-1416-X). Fortress.

Kaschmitter, William A. The Spirituality of the Catholic Church. 980p. 1982. 20.00 (ISBN 0-912414-33-2). Lumen Christi.

Keating, Dr. Charles J. Who We Are Is How We Pray: Matching Personality & Spirituality. 144p. (Orig.). 1987. 13.95 (ISBN 0-89622-292-6); pap. 7.95 (ISBN 0-89622-321-3). Twenty-Third.

Kerr, Howard. Mediums, & Spirit Rappers, & Roaring Radicals: Spiritualism in American Literature, 1850-1900. LC 78-170964. pap. 67.80 (ISBN 0-317-41918-8, 2025919). Bks Demand UMI.

Kieckhefer, Richard. Unquiet Souls: Fourteenth-Century Saints & Their Religious Milieu. LC 84-210. 248p. 1984. lib. bdg. 24.95x (ISBN 0-226-43509-1). U of Chicago Pr.

Kinlaw, Dennis F. We Have the Mind of Christ. 128p. Date not set. pap. text ed. 5.95 (ISBN 0-310-75231-0). Zondervan.

Klein, Jean. Ease of Being. 2nd ed. xiii, 110p. 1986. pap. 8.50 (ISBN 0-89386-015-8). Acorn NC.

Knoch, Adolph E. Spirit, Spirits & Spirituality. 157p. 1977. pap. text ed. 3.00 (ISBN 0-910424-69-1). Concordant.

Krishnananda & Bhagyalakshmi, S., eds. Facets of Spirituality: Dialogues & Discourses of Swami Krishnananda. 1986. 22.00X (ISBN 81-208-0087-7, Pub. by Motilal Banarsidass). South Asia Bks.

Kushner, Lawrence. The River of Light: Spirituality, Judaism, & the Evolution of Consciousness. LC 80-7738. 192p. (Orig.). 1981. pap. 7.95 (ISBN 0-06-064902-X, RD 370, HarpR). Har-Row.

--The River of Light: Spirituality, Judaism, & the Evolution of Consciousness. LC 80-7738. 192p. 1981. 12.95 (ISBN 0-940646-00-5). Rossel Bks.

Landregan, Steve. Reflections on Deacon Spirituality. (Orig.). Date not set. pap. price not set (ISBN 1-55586-150-4). US Catholic.

Lee, James M., ed. The Spirituality of the Religious Educator. 209p. (Orig.). 1985. pap. 12.95 (ISBN 0-89135-045-4). Religious Educ.

Leech, Kenneth. Soul Friend: The Practice of Christian Spirituality. LC 79-2994. 272p. 1980. 14.45 (ISBN 0-06-065225-X, HarpR). Har-Row.

Legere, Thomas E. Thoughts on the Run: Glimpses of Wholistic Spirituality. 144p. 1983. pap. 7.95 (ISBN 0-86683-698-5, HarpR). Har-Row.

L'Engle, Madeleine. Trailing Clouds of Glory: Spiritual Values in Children's Books. 144p. 1985. 12.95 (ISBN 0-664-32721-4). Westminster.

Linthorst, Ann T. Thus Saith the Lord: Giddyap: Metapsychiatric Commentaries on Human Experience & Spiritual Growth. 106p. (Orig.). 1986. pap. 11.00 (ISBN 0-913105-18-X). PAGL Pr.

Litvak, Stuart & Burba, Nora. In the World but Not of It: A Guide to More Spirituality in Your Life. 156p. 1984. pap. 5.95 (ISBN 0-13-453994-X). P-H.

Lorr, Regina E. & Crary, Robert W. The Path of Light. LC 83-71354. 180p. (Orig.). 1983. pap. 7.95 (ISBN 0-87516-520-6). De Vorss.

MacDonald, Gordon. Restoring Your Spiritual Passion. 192p. 1986. 12.95 (ISBN 0-8407-9069-4). Oliver-Nelson.

McGinn, Bernard & Meyendorf, John. Christian Spirituality. (World Spirituality Ser.). 1985. 49.50x (ISBN 0-8245-0681-2). Crossroad NY.

McGinn, Bernard, tr. Apocalyptic Spirituality. LC 79-90834. (Classics of Western Spirituality Ser.). 352p. 1979. 13.95 (ISBN 0-8091-0305-2); pap. 7.95 (ISBN 0-8091-2242-1). Paulist Pr.

May, Gerald G. Care of Mind-Care of Spirit: Psychiatric Dimensions of Spiritual Direction. LC 81-47840. 128p. 1982. 14.45 (ISBN 0-06-065533-X, HarpR). Har-Row.

May, William E. The Unity of the Moral & Spiritual Life. (Synthesis Ser). 1978. pap. 0.75 (ISBN 0-8199-0745-6). Franciscan Herald.

Mehta, Ved. Vedi. (Illus.). 1982. 18.95x (ISBN 0-19-503005-2). Oxford U Pr.

Mother Columba Hart, tr. Hadewijch: The Complete Works. LC 80-84500. (Classics of Western Spirituality Ser.). 440p. 1981. 13.95 (ISBN 0-8091-0311-7); pap. 10.95 (ISBN 0-8091-2297-9). Paulist Pr.

Muktananda. I Love You. (Illus.). 40p. (Orig.). 1975. 1.75 (ISBN 0-914602-58-6). SYDA Found.

Mullahy, Bernard. The Splendid Risk. LC 81-40445. 256p. 1982. text ed. 12.95 (ISBN 0-268-01705-0). U of Notre Dame Pr.

Nasr, Seyyed H., ed. Islamic Spirituality. (World Spirituality Ser.). (Illus.). 496p. 1987. 49.50x (ISBN 0-8245-0767-3). Crossroad NY.

Neame, Alan, tr. The Hermitage Within: Spirituality of the Desert. 160p. 1982. pap. 6.95 (ISBN 0-8091-2428-9). Paulist Pr.

Nee, Watchman. Spiritual Reality or Obsession. Kaung, Stephen, tr. 1970. pap. 2.25 (ISBN 0-935008-41-1). Christian Fellow Pubs.

Newcomb, Charles B. Psychic Philosophy & the Awakening of Spiritual Consciousness, 2 vols. (Illus.). 1985. Set. 187.65 (ISBN 0-89920-090-7). Am Inst Psych.

Newhouse, Flower A. Travel with Inner Perceptiveness. (Illus.). 112p. (Orig.). 1979. pap. text ed. 7.00 (ISBN 0-910378-16-9). Christward.

Niendorff, John S. Listen to the Light. 96p. 1983. pap. 4.50 (ISBN 0-911336-84-2). Sci of Mind.

Nisargadatta Maharaj. The Blissful Life: As Realized Through the Teachings of Sri Nisargadatta Maharaj. Powell, Robert, compiled by. ix, 84p. pap. 6.95 (ISBN 0-89386-014-X). Acorn NC.

--Prior to Consciousness: Talks with Sri Nisargadatta Maharaj. Dunn, Jean, ed. LC 85-71544. ix, 159p. (Orig.). pap. 9.95 (ISBN 0-317-19710-X). Acorn NC.

Ochs, Carol. Women & Spirituality. LC 83-3397. (New Feminist Perspectives Ser.). 166p. 1983. 18.95x (ISBN 0-8476-7232-8, Rowman & Allanheld); pap. 9.95x (ISBN 0-8476-7233-6). Rowman.

Packo, John E. Find & Use Your Spiritual Gifts. LC 80-69967. 117p. (Orig.). 1980. pap. 2.95 (ISBN 0-87509-293-4); Leader's Guide. 2.95 (ISBN 0-87509-294-2). Chr Pubns.

Pannenberg, Wolfhart. Christian Spirituality. LC 83-19662. 114p. (Orig.). 1983. pap. 8.95 (ISBN 0-664-24495-5). Westminster.

Paxson, Ruth. Como Vivir en el Plano Superior. Orig. Title: Life on the Highest Plane. (Span.). 254p. 1984. pap. 4.95 (ISBN 0-8254-1551-9). Kregel.

--Rivers of Living Water. (Moody Classics Ser.). 1984. pap. 3.50 (ISBN 0-8024-7367-9). Moody.

Perry, T. Anthony. Erotic Spirituality: The Integrative Tradition from Leone Ebreo to John Donne. 208p. 1980. 15.75 (ISBN 0-8173-0024-4). U of Ala Pr.

Pierrakos, Eva. Guide Lectures for Self-Transformation. LC 85-134343. 216p. (Orig.). 1985. 12.95 (ISBN 0-9614777-0-9); pap. 7.95 (ISBN 0-9614777-1-7). Pathwork Pr.

--Guide Lectures for Self Transformation. LC 85-134343. 195p. 1986. pap. 9.95 (ISBN 0-913299-32-4, Dist. by NAL). Stillpoint.

Pilch, John J. Wellness Spirituality. 112p. 1985. pap. 7.95 (ISBN 0-8245-0710-X). Crossroad NY.

--Wellness: Your Invitation to Full Life. Frost, Miriam, ed. Orig. Title: Wellness. 128p. (Orig.). 1981. pap. text ed. 5.95 (ISBN 0-86683-758-2, HarpR). Har-Row.

Pir Vilayat Inayat Khan. The Call of the Dervish. LC 81-52421. 224p. (Orig.). 1981. pap. 8.95 (ISBN 0-930872-26-6, 1013P). Omega Pr NM.

Price, John R. Practical Spirituality. 160p. (Orig.). 1985. pap. 6.95 (ISBN 0-942082-06-0). Quartus Bks.

Puls, Joan. Every Bush Is Burning: A Spirituality for Today. 2nd ed. 112p. 1986. pap. 5.95 (ISBN 0-89622-280-2). Twenty-Third.

Puri, Ishwar C. Beyond Logic & Reason. Ingram, Leonard, ed. 59p. 1983. pap. 3.00 (ISBN 0-937067-00-8). Inst Study Hum Aware.

--Go Within. Scott, Edward D., ed. 177p. (Orig.). 1986. pap. 6.00 (ISBN 0-937067-07-5). Inst Study Hum Aware.

--Journey to Totality. Scott, Edward D., ed. 121p. (Orig.). 1985. pap. 6.00 (ISBN 0-937067-05-9). Inst Study Hum Aware.

--Know Thyself. Ingram, Leonard, ed. 66p. 1983. pap. 3.00 (ISBN 0-937067-01-6). Inst Study Hum Aware.

--New Age-Old Path. Scott, Edward D., ed. 54p. (Orig.). 1985. pap. 3.00 (ISBN 0-937067-04-0). Inst Study Hum Aware.

--Spirituality & Total Health. Scott, Edward D., ed. 29p. (Orig.). 1986. pap. 2.00 (ISBN 0-937067-08-3). Inst Study Hum Aware.

Rahner, Karl. The Practice of Faith: A Handbook of Contemporary Spirituality. 354p. 1983. 19.50 (ISBN 0-8245-0603-0); pap. 14.95. Crossroad NY.

Rayez, Andre. Dictionnaire de Spiritualite, 12 vols. (Fr.). 1970. Set. 1195.00 (ISBN 0-686-57101-0, M-6125). French & Eur.

Rice, Joyce G. Love Never Ends. pap. 3.95 (ISBN 0-89036-147-9). Hawkes Pub Inc.

Roberts, Robert C. Spirituality & Human Emotion. 134p. 1983. pap. 5.95 (ISBN 0-8028-1939-7). Eerdmans.

Robinson, David, ed. William Ellery Channing: Selected Writings. LC 84-62567. (Source of American Spirituality Ser.: Vol. 2). 320p. 1985. 12.95 (ISBN 0-8091-0359-1). Paulist Pr.

Sadler, A. W. The Journey of Western Spirituality. 234p. 1986. lib. bdg. 23.00 (ISBN 0-8191-5722-8, Pub. by College Tehology Society); pap. text ed. 13.00 (ISBN 0-8191-5618-3). U Pr of Amer.

Sadler, A. W., ed. The Journey of Western Spirituality: CTS Annual Publication, 1980. LC 81-5831. 1981. text ed. 18.00 (ISBN 0-89130-505-X, 34 10 80). Scholars Pr GA.

Safed. Safed Spirituality: Rules of Mystical Piety, the Beginning of Wisdom. Fine, Lawrence, tr. (Classics of Western Spirituality Ser.). 1984. 12.95 (ISBN 0-8091-0349-4); pap. 9.95 (ISBN 0-8091-2612-5). Paulist Pr.

St. Ignatius of Antioch & St. Polycarp of Simirna. Poslanije Saviatago Ignatija Antiokhiskago i Sviatago Polykarpa Smirnskago. Tr. of Letters of St. Ignatius of Antioch & of St. Polycarp of Smirna. (Rus.). 80p. (Orig.). 1975. pap. 2.00x (ISBN 0-88465-023-5). Holy Trinity.

St. Nicodemos the Hagiorite, ed. Dobrotoljubije, Tom Pjatij: Philokalia, Vol. 5. Govoroff, Theophan, tr. from Greek. (Rus.). 350p. (Orig.). 1966. 20.00x (ISBN 0-88465-030-8); pap. 15.00x (ISBN 0-88465-029-4). Holy Trinity.

--Dobrotoljubije, Tom Tchetvjortij: Philokalia, Vol. 4. Govoroff, Theofan, tr. from Greek. (Rus.). 495p. (Orig.). 1965. 25.00x (ISBN 0-88465-027-8); pap. 20.00x (ISBN 0-88465-028-6). Holy Trinity.

Santa-Maria, Maria L. Growth Through Meditation & Journal Writing: A Jungian Perspective on Christian Spirituality. 1983. pap. 8.95 (ISBN 0-8091-2570-6). Paulist Pr.

Sethna, K. D. The Spirituality of the Future: A Search Apropos of R. C. Zaehner's Study in Sri-Aurobindo & Teilhard de Chardin. LC 76-14764. 320p. 1981. 32.50 (ISBN 0-8386-2028-0). Fairleigh Dickinson.

Singh, Kirpal. Godman: Finding a Spiritual Master. 2nd ed. LC 78-68503. (Illus.). 1979. pap. 5.95 (ISBN 0-918224-07-1). Sawan Kirpal Pubns.

--Spirituality: What It Is. 3rd ed. LC 81-52000. (Illus.). 112p. 1982. pap. 3.50 (ISBN 0-918224-16-0). Sawan Kirpal Pubns.

Smith, R. Pearsall. Walking in the Light. 128p. 1987. pap. 4.95 (ISBN 0-310-20921-8). Zondervan.

Spencer, Dean & Nelson, Dean. God Never Said We'd Be Leading at the Half. 116p. (Orig.). 1980. pap. 2.95 (ISBN 0-8341-0766-X). Beacon Hill.

Spidlik, Tomas. The Spirituality of the Christian East: A Systematic Handbook. Gythiel, Anthony P., tr. from Fr. (Cistercian Studies Ser.: No. 79). Tr. of La Spritiualite de l'Orient Chritienne. 1986. 48.95 (ISBN 0-87907-879-0); pap. 17.00 (ISBN 0-87907-979-7). Cistercian Pubns.

Spretnak, Charlene. Politics of Women's Spirituality: Essays on the Rise of Spiritualist Power Within the Feminist Movement. LC 80-2876. 624p. 1982. pap. 14.95 (ISBN 0-385-17241-9, Anch). Doubleday.

Steer, Roger, selected by. Spiritual Secrets of George Muller. 2nd ed. 126p. 1987. pap. 5.95 (ISBN 0-87788-782-9). Shaw Pubs.

Steiner, Rudolf. The Bridge Between Universal Spirituality & the Physical Constitution of Man. 2nd ed. Osmond, Dorothy S., tr. from Ger. 64p. (Orig.). 1979. pap. 3.95 (ISBN 0-910142-03-3). Anthroposophic.

--The Spiritual Being in the Heavenly Bodies & in the Kingdoms of Nature. (Ger.). 210p. 1981. pap. 9.95 (ISBN 0-919924-14-X, Pub. by Steiner Book Centre Canada). Anthroposophic.

--The Spiritual Foundation of Morality. Cotterell, Mabel, tr. 90p. 1979. pap. 4.75 (ISBN 0-919924-09-3, Pub. by Steiner Book Centre Canada). Anthroposophic.

Tablet Of London Editors. Spirituality Through the Ages. pap. 0.75 (ISBN 0-8199-0240-3, L38838). Franciscan Herald.

Tarneja, Sukh R. Nature, Spirituality & Science. 240p. 1980. text ed. 27.50x (ISBN 0-7069-1203-9, Pub by Vikas India). Advent NY.

Thayer, Nelson S. Spirituality & Pastoral Care. LC 84-48716. (Theology & Pastoral Care Ser.). 128p. 1985. pap. 7.95 (ISBN 0-8006-1734-7, 1-1734). Fortress.

Thurston, Mark. How to Change Attitudes & Emotions. Orig. Title: A Course in Practical Spirituality. 147p. 1986. wkbk., text, 4 cassettes 29.95 (ISBN 0-87604-181-0). ARE Pr.

Tooker, Elisabeth, ed. Native North American Spirituality of the Eastern Woodlands: Sacred Myths, Dreams, Vision Speeches, Healing Formulas, Rituals & Ceremonials. LC 79-66573. (Classics of Western Spirituality Ser.). 320p. 1979. pap. 9.95 (ISBN 0-8091-2256-1). Paulist Pr.

Tozer, Aiden W. Pursuit of God. LC 82-70768. 128p. 1982. 4.95 (ISBN 0-87509-191-1); pap. 3.95 (ISBN 0-87509-192-X); 3.25 (ISBN 0-87509-223-3); legacy ed. 5.95 (ISBN 0-87509-366-3). Chr Pubns.

Uhlein, Gabriele. Meditations with TM Hildegard of Bingen. LC 82-74151. (Meditations with TM). 129p. (Orig.). 1982. pap. 6.95 (ISBN 0-939680-12-2). Bear & Co.

Van Kaam, Adrian. Formative Spirituality: The Formation of the Human Heart, Vol. 3. 352p. 1985. 27.50 (ISBN 0-8245-0719-3). Crossroad NY.

--Human Formation. LC 84-29241. (Formative Spirituality Ser.: Vol. 2). 271p. 1985. 24.95x (ISBN 0-8245-0578-6). Crossroad NY.

Van Kamm, Adrian & Muto, Susan A. Creative Formation of Life & World. LC 82-16014. 462p. 1983. lib. bdg. 37.50 (ISBN 0-8191-2708-6); pap. text ed. 19.50 (ISBN 0-8191-2709-4). U Pr of Amer.

Van Rijckenborgh, Jan. Dei Gloria Intacta. 244p. 1987. 14.50 (ISBN 0-317-52802-5). Rosycross Pr.

Van Rijckenborgh, Jan & De Petri, Catharose. Brotherhood of Shamballah. Orig. Title: De Broederschap van Shamballa. 123p. 1987. pap. 11.00 (ISBN 90-6732-008-0). Rosycross Pr.

Van Zeller, Hubert. Current of Spirituality. pap. 3.95 (ISBN 0-87243-048-0). Templegate.

--Spirituality Recharted. 1985. pap. 4.95 (ISBN 0-932506-39-9). St Bedes Pubns.

Vaughan, Frances. The Inward Arc: Healing & Wholeness in Psychotherapy & Spirituality. LC 85-2504. (Illus.). 238p. (Orig.). 1986. pap. 10.95 (ISBN 0-87773-324-4, 74201-X, Pub. by New Sci Lib-Shambhala). Shambhala Pubns.

Veith, Gene E., Jr. Reformation Spirituality: The Religion of George Herbert. LC 83-46176. 288p. 1985. 34.50 (ISBN 0-8387-5071-0). Bucknell U Pr.

Von Duerckheim, Karlfried. Hara: The Vital Centre of Man. Van Kospoth, Sylvia-Monica & Healey, Estelle R., trs. from Ger. (Unwin Paperbacks). 1977. pap. 6.95 (ISBN 0-04-290011-5). Allen Unwin.

Wakefield, Gordon S., ed. The Westminster Dictionary of Christian Spirituality. LC 83-14527. 416p. 1983. 20.95 (ISBN 0-664-21396-0). Westminster.

Walton, Lewis R. Advent! Woolsey, Raymond H., ed. 128p. (Orig.). 1986. pap. 6.95 (ISBN 0-8280-0349-1). Review & Herald.

Waters, Frank. Mountain Dialogues. LC 81-732. x, 237p. 1981. 16.95 (ISBN 0-8040-0361-0, SB). Ohio U Pr.

Whalen, James. The Spiritual Teachings of Teresa of Avila & Adrian Van Kaam: Formative Spirituality. LC 83-3628. 334p. (Orig.). 1984. lib. bdg. 27.50 (ISBN 0-8191-3864-9); pap. text ed. 15.75 (ISBN 0-8191-3865-7). U Pr of Amer.

White, Nelson & White, Anne. Spiritual Intimidation. LC 84-51476. 65p. (Orig.). 1984. pap. 10.00 (ISBN 0-939856-39-5). Tech Group.

Wiedemann, Frederick. Between Two Worlds. LC 85-40773. 200p. (Orig.). 1986. pap. 6.95 (ISBN 0-8356-0602-3, Quest). Theos Pub Hse.

Wijngaards, John. Inheriting the Master's Cloak: Creative Biblical Spirituality. LC 85-71535. 192p. (Orig.). 1985. pap. 4.95 (ISBN 0-87793-288-3). Ave Maria.

Wild, Robert. The Post Charismatic Experience: The New Wave of the Spirit. 136p. (Orig.). 1984. pap. text ed. 4.50 (ISBN 0-914544-50-0). Living Flame Pr.

Winston, David, tr. Philo of Alexandria: The Contemplative Life, Giants & Selections. LC 80-84499. (Classics of Western Spirituality Ser.). 448p. 13.95 (ISBN 0-8091-0315-X); pap. 9.95 (ISBN 0-8091-2333-9). Paulist Pr.

Winterhalter, Robert. The Odes of Solomon: Original Christianity Revealed. Roche de Coppens, Peter, et al, eds. LC 85-45288. (Spiritual Perspectives Ser.). 240p. (Orig.). 1985. pap. 9.95 (ISBN 0-87542-875-4, L-875). Llewellyn Pubns.

Wolf, William. Healers, Gurus, Spiritual Guide. LC 76-2180. 1969. pap. 6.50 (ISBN 0-933900-07-4). Foun Human Under.

Woodruff, Sue. Meditations with TM Mechtild of Magdeburg. LC 82-73366. (Meditations with TM Ser.). (Illus.). 132p. (Orig.). 1982. pap. 6.95 (ISBN 0-939680-06-8). Bear & Co.

Wright, Machaelle S. Behaving As If the God in All Life Mattered: A New Age Ecology. (Illus.). 216p. 1986. pap. cancelled (ISBN 0-913299-33-2). Stillpoint.

Young, Meredith L. Agartha: A Journey to the Stars. LC 84-50109. (Illus.). 340p. (Orig.). 1984. pap. 9.95 (ISBN 0-913299-01-4). Stillpoint.

SPIRITUALS (SONGS)

see also Gospel Music

Bishop, Selma L. Isaac Watts's Hymns & Spiritual Songs (1707) A Publishing History & a Bibliography. LC 73-78316. 1974. 29.50 (ISBN 0-87650-033-5). Pierian.

Bryan, Ashley. Walk Together Children. (Illus.). 1981. pap. 2.95 (ISBN 0-689-70485-2, Aladdin). Macmillan.

Burleigh, Harry T. Negro Spirituals, 2 vols. in 1. LC 74-24262. Repr. of 1922 ed. 45.00 (ISBN 0-404-12874-2). AMS Pr.

Cohen, Lily Y. Lost Spirituals. facsimile ed. LC 74-39081. (Black Heritage Library Collection). (Illus.). Repr. of 1928 ed. 17.25 (ISBN 0-8369-9019-6). Ayer Co Pubs.

Coleridge-Taylor, S. Twenty-Four Negro Melodies. (Music Reprint Ser.: 1980). 1980. Repr. of 1905 ed. lib. bdg. 35.00 (ISBN 0-306-76023-1). Da Capo.

Fisher, William A. Seventy Negro Spirituals, for High Voice. LC 72-1637. Repr. of 1926 ed. 29.00 (ISBN 0-404-09921-1). AMS Pr.

Grissom, Mary A. Negro Sings a New Heaven. LC 70-168209. Repr. of 1930 ed. 11.50 (ISBN 0-404-08311-0). AMS Pr.

Jackson, George P., ed. Down-East Spirituals & Others: Three Hundred Songs Supplementary to the Author's "Spiritual Folk-Songs of Early America". LC 74-34317. (Music Reprint Ser.). (Illus.). 296p. 1975. Repr. of 1943 ed. lib. bdg. 35.00 (ISBN 0-306-70666-0). Da Capo.

Johnson, James Weldon & Johnson, J. R., eds. The Books of American Negro Spirituals, 2 vols. in one. LC 77-23414. 1977. Repr. of 1926 ed. text ed. 11.95 (ISBN 0-306-80074-8). Da Capo.

Paget, M. Spirituals Reborn: Melody. LC 74-76574. 96p. 1976. Pt. 1. pap. text ed. 5.95 (ISBN 0-521-08714-7); Pt. 2. pap. text ed. 5.95 (ISBN 0-521-21332-0); choral 13.95 (ISBN 0-521-08713-9). Cambridge U Pr.

Patterson, Daniel W. Nine Shaker Spirituals. (Illus.). 34p. 1981. pap. 2.00 (ISBN 0-937942-10-3). Shaker Mus.

Roberts, Frank, ed. Songs of Joyful Praise. 1975. pap. 2.00x (ISBN 0-88027-060-8). Firm Foun Pub.

Roes, Carol. Four Negro Spirituals. 1975. pap. 3.75 (ISBN 0-930932-24-2); record incl. M Loke.

SPIRITUALS (SONGS)–HISTORY AND CRITICISM

Bryan, Ashley. I'm Going to Sing: Black American Spirituals, Vol. II. (Illus.). 64p. 1982. 10.95 (ISBN 0-689-30915-5, Childrens Bk). Macmillan.

Cone, James H. The Spirituals & the Blues. pap. 5.95 (ISBN 0-8164-2073-4, SP74, HarpR). Har-Row.

Dixon, Christa K. Negro Spirituals: From Bible to Folk Song. LC 75-364444. pap. 31.80 (2026874). Bks Demand UMI.

Epstein, Dena J. Sinful Tunes & Spirituals: Black Folk Music to the Civil War. LC 77-6315. (Music in American Life Ser.). (Illus.). 1981. pap. 10.95 (ISBN 0-252-00875-8). U of Ill Pr.

Jackson, George P. White & Negro Spirituals, Their Life Span & Kinship. (Music Reprint Ser.). (Illus.). xii, 349p. 1975. Repr. of 1944 ed. lib. bdg. 42.50 (ISBN 0-306-70667-9). Da Capo.

Johnson, James Weldon & Johnson, J. R., eds. The Books of American Negro Spirituals, 2 vols. in one. LC 77-23414. 1977. Repr. of 1926 ed. text ed. 11.95 (ISBN 0-306-80074-8). Da Capo.

Saminsky, Lazare. Music of the Ghetto & the Bible. LC 74-24220. Repr. of 1934 ed. 16.00 (ISBN 0-404-12833-5). AMS Pr.

Thurman, Howard. Deep River. Bd. with The Negro Spiritual Speaks of Life & Death. LC 75-27041. 136p. 1975. pap. 5.95 (ISBN 0-913408-20-4). Friends United.

SPORTS AND RELIGION

see Religion and Sports

SPURGEON, CHARLES HADDON, 1834-1892

Bacon, Ernest W. Spurgeon. (Christian Biography Ser.). 184p. 1982. pap. 3.95 (ISBN 0-8010-0823-9). Baker Bk.

Fullerton, W. Y. Charles Spurgeon. (Golden Oldies Ser.). 288p. 1980. pap. 4.95 (ISBN 0-8024-1236-X). Moody.

Hayden, Eric W. Searchlight on Spurgeon: Spurgeon Speaks for Himself. 1973. pap. 3.50 (ISBN 0-686-09108-6). Pilgrim Pubns.

Murray, Iain. Spurgeon un Principe Olividado. 2nd ed. (Span.). 156p. 1984. pap. 3.95 (ISBN 0-85151-439-1). Banner of Truth.

Murray, Iain H. The Forgotton Surgeon. 1978. pap. 5.45 (ISBN 0-85151-156-2). Banner of Truth.

Ross, Bob L. Introduction to C. H. Spurgeon. 1985. pap. 0.95 (ISBN 0-686-18093-3). Pilgrim Pubns.

--Pictorial Biography of C. H. Spurgeon. 1981. 5.95 (ISBN 0-686-16830-5); pap. 3.95 (ISBN 0-686-16831-3). Pilgrim Pubns.

Spurgeon, C. H. Complete Index to C. H. Spurgeon's Sermons. 1980. 5.95 (ISBN 0-686-27983-2). Pilgrim Pubns.

Spurgeon, Charles H. Charles Haddon Spurgeon - Autobiography: The Early Years, 1834-1860, Vol. 1. 1976. 18.95 (ISBN 0-85151-076-0). Banner of Truth.

--Charles Haddon Spurgeon - Autobiography: The Full Harvest, 1861-1892, Vol. 2. 1975. 18.95 (ISBN 0-85151-182-1). Banner of Truth.

--Lectures to My Students. 1977. pap. 12.95 (ISBN 0-8010-8097-5). Baker Bk.

Thielicke, Helmut. Encounter with Spurgeon. Doberstein, J. W., tr. from Ger. 284p. 1978. Repr. 13.95 (ISBN 0-227-67655-6). Attic Pr.

Triggs, Kathy. Charles Spurgeon. 96p. (Orig.). 1986. pap. 3.50. Bethany Hse.

STAINED GLASS

see Glass Painting and Staining

STAPLETON, THOMAS, 1535-1598

Fulke, William. Stapleton's Fortress Overthrown: A Rejoinder to Martiall's Reply. Repr. of 1848 ed. 31.00 (ISBN 0-384-17240-7). Johnson Repr.

O'Connell, M. R. Thomas Stapleton & the Counter Reformation. 1964. 49.50x (ISBN 0-685-69850-5). Elliots Bks.

Whitaker, William. Disputation on Holy Scripture Against the Papists. 55.00 (ISBN 0-384-68010-0). Johnson Repr.

STAR OF BETHLEHEM

Boa, Kenneth & Proctor, William. The Return of the Star of Bethlehem. 224p. (Orig.). 1985. pap. 7.95 (ISBN 0-310-33631-7, 12770P). Zondervan.

Hughes, David. The Star of Bethlehem: An Astronomer's Confirmation. (Illus.). 1979. 14.95 (ISBN 0-8027-0644-4). Walker & Co.

STARS (IN RELIGION, FOLK-LORE, ETC.)

see also Star of Bethlehem

Haile, Berard. Starlore among the Navaho. LC 76-53085. 1977. lib. bdg. 15.00x (ISBN 0-88307-532-6). Gannon.

Schafer, Edward H. Pacing the Void: T'ang Approaches to the Stars. LC 76-48362. 1978. 49.50x (ISBN 0-520-03344-2). U of Cal Pr.

STATE, THE

Al Tunisi, Khayr. Surest Path: The Political Treatise of a Nineteenth-Century Muslim Statesman. Brown, Leon C., tr. LC 67-25399. (Middle Eastern Monographs Ser: No. 16). pap. 5.00x (ISBN 0-674-85695-3). Harvard U Pr.

Belloc, Hilaire. The Servile State. LC 77-2914. 1977. 8.00 (ISBN 0-913966-31-2, Liberty Clas); pap. 3.00 (ISBN 0-913966-32-0). Liberty Fund.

Cassirer, Ernst. Myth of the State. 1961. pap. 8.95x (ISBN 0-300-00036-7, y33). Yale U Pr.

Heering, Gerrit J. Fall of Christianity. LC 77-147670. (Library of War & Peace; Relig. & Ethical Positions on War). 1973. lib. bdg. 46.00 (ISBN 0-8240-0428-0). Garland Pub.

Laski, Harold J. Authority in the Modern State. LC 68-21685. 398p. 1968. Repr. of 1919 ed. 35.00 (ISBN 0-208-00460-2, Archon). Shoe String.

Maritain, Jacques. L' Homme et l'Etat. 2nd ed. 212p. 1965. 12.95 (ISBN 0-686-56353-0). French & Eur.

--Man & the State. LC 51-555. 1956. pap. 4.45x (ISBN 0-226-50552-9, P5, Phoen). U of Chicago Pr.

Maududi, A. A. Process of Islamic Revolution. pap. 1.50 (ISBN 0-686-18546-3). Kazi Pubns.
Pradera, Victor. The New State. Malley, B., tr. LC 79-180421. Repr. of 1939 ed. 29.50 (ISBN 0-404-56196-9). AMS Pr.
Rommen, Heinrich A. State in Catholic Thought: A Treatise in Political Philosophy. Repr. of 1945 ed. lib. bdg. 26.25x (ISBN 0-8371-2437-9, ROCT). Greenwood.
Waring, Luther H. Political Theories of Martin Luther. LC 68-15837. 1968. Repr. of 1910 ed. 21.50x (ISBN 0-8046-0488-6, Pub. by Kennikat). Assoc Faculty Pr.

STATE AND BUDDHISM
see Buddhism and State

STATE AND CHURCH
see Church and State

STATE AND RELIGION
see Religion and State

STATIONS OF THE CROSS
Harrington, Jeremy, ed. The Way of the Cross for Congregational Use. (Illus.). 28p. (Orig.). 1976. pap. text ed. 0.65 (ISBN 0-912228-24-5). St Anthony Mess Pr.
Hauber, Anajean. A Way of the Cross for the Separated & Divorced. (Illus.). 45p. (Orig.). 1985. pap. text ed. 2.95 (ISBN 0-86716-050-0). St Anthony Mess Pr.
McCarroll, Tolbert. A Way of the Cross. LC 84-61025. 128p. (Orig.). 1985. pap. 4.95 (ISBN 0-8091-2653-2). Paulist Pr.
Mother Teresa of Calcutta & Roger of Taize. Meditations on the Way of the Cross. (Illus.). 64p. (Orig.). 1987. pap. 5.95 (ISBN 0-8298-0585-0). Pilgrim NY.

STATUETTES
see Idols and Images; Jade

STAUPITZ, JOHANN VON, 1524
Steinmetz, David C. Luther & Staupitz: An Essay in the Intellectual Origins of the Protestant Reformation. LC 80-23007. (Duke Monographs in Medieval & Renaissance Studies: No. 4). xi, 149p. 1980. 18.50 (ISBN 0-8223-0447-3). Duke.
Wolf, Ernst. Staupitz Und Luther. (Ger). 34.00 (ISBN 0-384-69019-X); pap. 28.00 (ISBN 0-384-69018-1). Johnson Repr.

STEINER, RUDOLF, 1861-1925
Clark, Sonia T. Life of Rudolf Steiner. (Rudolf Steiner Publications Ser.). 40p. 1985. pap. 4.00 (ISBN 0-89345-905-4, Steiner). Garber Comm.
Easton, Stewart C. Rudolf Steiner: Herald of a New Epoch. LC 80-67026. (Illus.). 1980. pap. 10.95 (ISBN 0-910142-93-9). Anthroposophic.
Furness, C. J. Lotus Petals: The Life & Work of Rudolf Steiner. 59.95 (ISBN 0-8490-0557-4). Gordon Pr.
Katz, Ernst. About Your Relation to Rudolf Steiner. (Illus.). 64p. (Orig.). 1986. pap. 6.95 (ISBN 0-9613745-0-0, 86-1955). E Katz.
McDermott, Robert A., ed. The Essential Rudolf Steiner. LC 82-48934. 320p. 1983. pap. 10.95 (ISBN 0-06-065345-0, RD-399, HarpR). Har-Row.
Pusch, Hans. Working Together on Rudolf Steiner's Mystery Dramas. LC 80-67024. (Steiner's Mystery Dramas Ser.). (Illus.). 144p. (Orig.). 1980. 15.95 (ISBN 0-910142-90-4); pap. 9.95 (ISBN 0-910142-91-2). Anthroposophic.
Richards, Mary C. Toward Wholeness: Rudolf Steiner Education in America. LC 80-14905. 210p. 1980. 16.00 (ISBN 0-8195-5049-3); pap. 9.95 (ISBN 0-8195-6062-6). Wesleyan U Pr.
Spock, Marjorie. Eurythmy. (Illus.). 148p. (Orig.). 1980. 15.95 (ISBN 0-88010-023-0); pap. 9.95 (ISBN 0-910142-88-2). Anthroposophic.
Steiner, Rudolf. Course of My Life. Wannamaker, Olin D., tr. from Ger. Tr. of Mein Lebensgang. 400p. 1986. pap. 18.00 (ISBN 0-88010-159-8). Anthroposophic.
--Rudolf Steiner: An Autobiography, Vol. 1. 2nd ed. LC 72-95242. (Spiritual Science Library). (Illus.). 560p. 1980. lib. bdg. 25.00 (ISBN 0-89345-031-6); pap. 17.00 (ISBN 0-89345-210-6). Garber Comm.
--Soul Economy & Waldorf Education. Tr. of Die gesunde Entwicklung des Leiblich-Physischen als Grundlage der freien Enfaltung. 320p. (Orig.). pap. 20.00 (ISBN 0-88010-138-5); 30.00 (ISBN 0-88010-139-3). Anthroposophic.
Unger, Carl. Steiner's Theosophy: Notes on the Book "Theosophy". 1982. Repr. 5.95 (ISBN 0-916786-64-1). St George Bk Serv.
Van Goudoever, H. D. A Contemplation about Rudolf Steiner's "Calendar of the Soul". Weber, Giselher, tr. 1984. pap. 6.95 (ISBN 0-916786-76-5). St George Bk Serv.
Whicher, Olive. George Adams, Interpreter of Rudolf Steiner. 1978. pap. 8.95 (ISBN 0-904822-08-7). St George Bk Serv.

STEPHEN, SAINT, MARTYR
Lindsay, Gordon. Stephen's Defense & Martyrdom. (Acts in Action Ser.: Vol. 2). pap. 1.25 (ISBN 0-89985-963-1). Christ Nations.
Scharkemann, Martin N. Stephen: A Singular Saint. 207p. 1968. write for info. Concordia Schl Grad Studies.

STEPHEN, CAROLINE EMELIA, 1834-1909
Dalglish, Doris N. People Called Quakers. facsimile ed. LC 78-90628. (Essay Index Reprint Ser). 1938. 15.00 (ISBN 0-8369-1254-3). Ayer Co Pubs.

STEWARDSHIP, CHRISTIAN
see also Christianity and Economics
Alderfer, Helen, ed. Farthing in Her Hand: Stewardship for Women. LC 64-23376. 226p. 1964. pap. 4.95 (ISBN 0-8361-1515-5). Herald Pr.
Bayne, Raymond. Mini Messages on Stewardship. 130p. 1984. pap. 3.95 (ISBN 0-8010-0858-1). Baker Bk.
Clinard, Turner N. Responding to God: The Life of Stewardship. LC 79-24762. 118p. 1980. Westminster.
Cunningham, Richard B. Creative Stewardship. LC 79-973. (Creative Leadership Ser.). 1979. 6.95 (ISBN 0-687-09844-0). Abingdon.
Dowell, Spright. Columbus Roberts: Christian Steward Extraordinary. LC 83-887. xvi, 171p. 13.95 (ISBN 0-86554-071-3, H67). Mercer Univ Pr.
Fisher, Wallace E. All the Good Gifts: On Doing Bible Stewardship. LC 79-50077. 1979. pap. 5.95 (ISBN 0-8066-1702-0, 10-0227). Augsburg.
Foege, Richard H. Stewardship Preaching: Series C. 56p. (Orig.). 1985. pap. 4.95 (ISBN 0-8066-2152-4, 10-6003). Augsburg.
Hall, Douglas J. Imaging God: Dominion As Stewardship. 272p. (Orig.). 1986. pap. 8.95 (ISBN 0-8028-0244-3). Eerdmans.
Haugk, Kenneth C. Christian Caregiving: A Way of Life. LC 84-24341. (Orig.). 1984. pap. 7.95 (ISBN 0-8066-2123-0, 10-1103). Augsburg.
Heyd, Thomas. Planning for Stewardship: Developing a Giving Program for Congregations. (Administration for Churches Ser.). 40p. (Orig.). 1980. pap. 3.95 (ISBN 0-8066-1782-9, 10-4992). Augsburg.
Holck, Manfred, Jr. Cash Management: Stewardship of the Church's Cash Resources. (Administration for Churches Ser.). 1978. pap. 3.95 (ISBN 0-8066-1650-4, 10-0972). Augsburg.
Kauffman, Milo. Stewards of God. LC 74-13130. 264p. 1975. 9.95 (ISBN 0-8361-1747-6). Herald Pr.
Keene, Laurence C. Offering Meditations & Prayers. Lambert, Herbert, ed. LC 84-266. 64p. (Orig.). 1984. pap. 4.95 (ISBN 0-8272-2706-X). CBP.
Keese, Dayton. Re-Evaluation of the Eldership. pap. 2.50 (ISBN 0-89137-552-X). Quality Pubns.
Klay, Robin K. Counting the Cost: The Economics of Christian Stewardship. 176p. (Orig.). 1986. pap. 9.95 (ISBN 0-8028-0171-4). Eerdmans.
Knudsen, Raymond B. Developing Dynamic Stewardship: Fifteen Sermons on Commitment & Giving. LC 78-7846. 1978. pap. 5.50 (ISBN 0-687-10500-5). Abingdon.
--Stewardship Enlistment & Commitment. 130p. 1985. pap. 8.95 (ISBN 0-8192-1371-3). Morehouse.
Lindsay, Gordon. How to Be Enriched by Giving. 1.75 (ISBN 0-89985-012-X). Christ Nations.
McGinty, John. How to Raise the Level of Giving in Your Church. LC 78-12994. (P.A.C.E. Ser.). 1979. pap. 4.95 (ISBN 0-8272-1418-9). CBP.
Maseroni, Robert S. The Gift of Giving, No. 5. 1983. 0.80 (ISBN 0-89536-629-0, 0737). CSS of Ohio.
Oliver, Gerald. Stewardship: Lessons from the Bible. LC 84-62421. write for info. (ISBN 0-9614316-0-1). Natl Inst Phil.
Patterson, F. W. Manual de Finanzas Para Iglesias. (Illus.). 118p. 1986. pap. 2.50 (ISBN 0-311-17005-6). Casa Bautista.
Petry, Ronald D. Partners in Creation. 126p. (Orig.). 1979. pap. 4.95 (ISBN 0-87178-688-5). Brethren.
Powell, Timothy M. You've Gotta Hand It to God! LC 84-73557. 128p. 1985. 2.95 (ISBN 0-88243-859-X, 02-0859); tchr's. ed. 3.95 (ISBN 0-88243-199-4, 32-0199). Gospel Pub.
Price, Brena. Giving, Christian Stewardship: Teaching Bks. (Illus.). 14p. 1971. pap. text ed. 2.95 (ISBN 0-86508-154-9). BCM Intl Inc.
Scott, Latayne. Time, Talents, Things: A Woman's Workshop on Christian Stewardship. Sloan, J., ed. (Woman's Workshop Ser.). 96p. (Orig.). 1987. pap. 3.95 (ISBN 0-310-38771-X). Zondervan.
Shannon, Robert & Shannon, Michael. Stewardship Source Book. 160p. 1987. pap. price not set (ISBN 0-87403-250-4, 3180). Standard Pub.
Shedd, Charlie W. How to Develop a Tithing Church. (Orig.). 1961. pap. 5.95 (ISBN 0-687-17798-7). Abingdon.
Sherer, Michael L. Stewards of the Mysteries of God: Worship Resources. 1985. 2.75 (ISBN 0-89536-781-5, 5832). CSS of Ohio.
Speller, Jon P. Seed Money in Action. LC 65-26790. 1965. pap. 3.00 (ISBN 0-8315-0007-7). Speller.
Stackhouse, Max L. Public Theology & Political Economy: Christian Stewardship in Modern Society. 192p. (Orig.). 1987. pap. 8.95 (ISBN 0-8028-0267-2). Eerdmans.
Turner, J. J. Growth Through Biblical Stewardship. 1986. pap. 4.50 (ISBN 0-89137-561-9). Quality Pubns.
Van Benschoten, A. Q., Jr. What the Bible Says about Stewardship. 96p. 1983. pap. 4.95 (ISBN 0-8170-0993-0). Judson.
Webley, Simon. How to Give Away Your Money. 1979. pap. 1.95 (ISBN 0-87784-601-4). Inter-Varsity.
Werning, Waldo J. Christian Stewards: Confronted & Committed. LC 12-2814. 1983. pap. 8.95 (ISBN 0-570-03879-0). Concordia.
Wilkinson, Loren, ed. Earthkeeping: Christian Stewardship of Natural Resources. 2nd ed. (Orig.). 1980. pap. 10.95 (ISBN 0-8028-1834-X). Eerdmans.
Yoder, Robert A. Seeking First the Kingdom. LC 83-16618. 104p. (Orig.). 1983. pap. 4.50 (ISBN 0-8361-3349-8). Herald Pr.

STEWARDSHIP, CHRISTIAN–SERMONS
Bleick, Roy. Much More Than Giving. 112p. (Orig.). 1985. pap. 6.95 (ISBN 0-570-03951-7, 12-2886). Concordia.
Carter, James E. A Sourcebook for Stewardship Sermons. LC 78-74768. 1979. pap. 5.95 (ISBN 0-8054-6403-4). Broadman.
Gravrock, Mark. Stewardship Preaching. (Ser. B). 56p. (Orig.). 1984. pap. 4.95 (ISBN 0-8066-2076-5, 10-6002). Augsburg.
Schmalenberger, Jerry. Stewards of Creation. (Orig.). 1987. pap. price not set (ISBN 0-89536-894-3, 7880). CSS of Ohio.

STEWARDSHIP, CHRISTIAN–STUDY AND TEACHING
Sherer, Michael L. Stewards of the Mysteries of God: Group Leader's Guide. 1985. 2.50 (ISBN 0-89536-780-7, 5831). CSS of Ohio.
--Stewards of the Mysteries of God: Master Planning Guide. 1985. 1.75 (ISBN 0-89536-779-3, 5830). CSS of Ohio.

STILES, EZRA, 1727-1795
Morgan, Edmund S. The Gentle Puritan: A Life of Ezra Stiles, 1727-1795. LC 62-8257. (Institute of Early American History & Culture Ser.). 504p. 1962. 30.00x (ISBN 0-8078-1231-5). U of NC Pr.
--The Gentle Puritan: A Life of Ezra Stiles, 1727-1795. (Illus.). 512p. 1983. pap. 9.95 (ISBN 0-393-30126-5). Norton.
Parsons, Francis. Six Men of Yale. facsimile ed. LC 72-156702. (Essay Index Reprint Ser). Repr. of 1939 ed. 18.00 (ISBN 0-8369-2329-4). Ayer Co Pubs.

STOICS
Bevan, Edwyn. Stoics & Sceptics. Vlastos, Gregory, ed. LC 78-15852. (Morals & Law in Ancient Greece Ser.). 1979. Repr. of 1913 ed. lib. bdg. 14.00x (ISBN 0-405-11530-X). Ayer Co Pubs.
Davidson, William L. The Stoic Creed. Vlastos, Gregory, ed. LC 78-19341. (Morals & Law in Ancient Greece Ser.). 1979. Repr. of 1907 ed. lib. bdg. 23.00x (ISBN 0-405-11535-0). Ayer Co Pubs.
Goudard, Sr. M. Lucien. Etude Sur les Epistres Morales D'Honore D'Urfe. LC 70-94204. (Catholic University of America Studies in Romance Languages & Literatures Ser: No. 8). (Fr). Repr. of 1933 ed. 21.00 (ISBN 0-404-50308-X). AMS Pr.
Inwood, Brad. Ethics & Human Action in Early Stoicism. (Illus.). 1985. 32.00x (ISBN 0-19-824739-7). Oxford U Pr.
Seneca. Moral Letters, 3 vols. (Loeb Classical Library: No. 75-77). 12.50x (ISBN 0-686-76874-4). Vol. 1 (ISBN 0-674-99084-6). Vol. 2 (ISBN 0-674-99085-4). Vol. 3 (ISBN 0-674-99086-2). Harvard U Pr.

STONEHENGE
Branley, Franklyn M. Mystery of Stonehenge. LC 69-11823. (Illus.). 1969. PLB 12.89 (ISBN 0-690-57046-5, Crowell Jr Bks). HarpJ.
Chippindale, Christopher. Stonehenge Complete: Archaeology, History, Heritage. LC 83-70803. (Illus.). 300p. 1983. 32.50 (ISBN 0-8014-1639-6). Cornell U Pr.
Cohen, I. L. The Secret of Stonehenge. Murphy, G., ed. LC 82-19107. (Illus.). 310p. 1982. 16.95 (ISBN 0-910891-01-X). New Research.
Herner, Russell A. Stonehenge: An Ancient Masonic Temple. rev., enl. ed. LC 83-63526. (Illus.). 160p. 1984. text ed. 15.95 (ISBN 0-88053-077-4). Macoy Pub.
Lyon, Nancy. The Mystery of Stonehenge. LC 77-10044. (Great Unsolved Mysteries). (Illus.). 1977. PLB 14.65 (ISBN 0-8172-1049-0). Raintree Pubs.
--The Mystery of Stonehenge. LC 77-10044. (Great Unsolved Mysteries Ser.). (Illus.). 48p. 1983. pap. 9.27 (ISBN 0-8172-2164-6). Raintree Pubs.
Stukeley, William. Stonehenge, a Temple Restored to the British Druids; Abury, a Temple of the British Druids. Feldman, Burton & Richardson, Robert D., eds. LC 78-60898. (Myth & Romanticism Ser.). 1984. lib. bdg. 80.00 (ISBN 0-8240-3572-0). Garland Pub.
Wood, John E. Sun, Moon, & Standing Stones. (Illus.). 1978. 22.50x (ISBN 0-19-211443-3). Oxford U Pr.

STORY, THOMAS, 1662-1742
Dalglish, Doris N. People Called Quakers. facsimile ed. LC 78-90628. (Essay Index Reprint Ser). 1938. 15.00 (ISBN 0-8369-1254-3). Ayer Co Pubs.

STORY-TELLING
Bausch, William J. Storytelling, Imagination & Faith. 240p. (Orig.). 1984. pap. 7.95 (ISBN 0-89622-199-7). Twenty-Third.
Carlson, Bernice W. Listen & Help Tell the Story. (Illus.). 1965. 9.95 (ISBN 0-687-22096-3). Abingdon.
Driver, Tom F. Patterns of Grace: Human Experience As Word of God. 214p. 1985. pap. text ed. 9.75 (ISBN 0-8191-4637-4). U Pr of Amer.
Goldberg, Michael. Theology & Narrative: A Critical Introduction. 304p. (Orig.). 1982. pap. 11.95 (ISBN 0-687-41503-9). Abingdon.
Harrell, John. To Tell of Gideon: The Art of Storytelling in the Church. 1975. 8.00x (ISBN 0-9615389-4-5); cassette 6.95x (ISBN 0-9615389-5-3). York Hse.
Lane, Belden C. Storytelling: Study Guide, The Enchantment of Theology Cassette Tapes. LC 86-6079. 24p. (Orig.). 1982. pap. 2.50 (ISBN 0-8272-3419-8, 10S2113). CBP.
McCarthy, Flor. And the Master Answered. LC 84-72678. (Illus.). 96p. (Orig.). 1985. pap. 4.95 (ISBN 0-87793-279-4). Ave Maria.
Morgan, Peter. Story Weaving. Lambert, Herbert, ed. LC 86-6079. 128p. (Orig.). 1986. pap. 8.95 (ISBN 0-8272-3423-6). CBP.
Wangerin, Walter, Jr. Ragman & Other Cries of Faith. LC 83-48980. 176p. 1984. 12.45 (ISBN 0-06-069253-7, HarpT). Har-Row.

STOVE-PLATES
Mercer, Henry C. The Bible in Iron. 3rd ed. (Illus.). 356p. 1961. pap. 15.00 (ISBN 0-910302-01-4). Bucks Co Hist.

STOWE, HARRIET ELIZABETH (BEECHER), 1811-1896
Kimball, Gayle. The Religious Ideas of Harriet Beecher Stowe: Her Gospel of Womanhood. LC 82-80377. (Studies in Women & Religion: Vol. 8). 216p. 1982. 49.95x (ISBN 0-88946-544-4). E Mellen.

STRACHAN, JOHN, BP., 1778-1867
Henderson, John L. John Strachan, Seventeen Hundred Seventy-Eight to Eighteen Hundred Sixty-Seven. LC 70-408188. (Canadian Biographical Studies: No. 1). pap. 30.50 (ISBN 0-317-09154-9, 2019176). Bks Demand UMI.

STRATFORD-UPON-AVON
Arbuthnot, George, ed. Vestry Minute Book of the Parish of Stratford-on-Avon from 1617 to 1699. LC 72-142244. Repr. of 1899 ed. 11.50 (ISBN 0-404-00366-4). AMS Pr.
Bloom, James H. Shakespeare's Church. LC 73-116790. (Studies in Shakespeare, No. 24). 1971. Repr. of 1902 ed. lib. bdg. 49.95x (ISBN 0-8383-1032-X). Haskell.

STRAUSS, DAVID FRIEDRICH, 1808-1874
Lawler, Edwina. David Friedrich Strauss & His Critics: The Life of Jesus Debate in Early Nineteenth-Century German Journals. (American University Studies VII - Theology & Religion: Vol. 16). 170p. 1986. text ed. 21.95 (ISBN 0-8204-0290-7). P Lang Pubs.
Massey, Marilyn C. Christ Unmasked: The Meaning of "The Life of Jesus" in German Politics. LC 82-8547. (Studies in Religion Ser.). xi, 182p. 1983. 23.00x (ISBN 0-8078-1524-1). U of NC Pr.

STREET CHRISTIANS
see Jesus People

STUBBS, WILLIAM, BP. OF OXFORD, 1825-1901
Egenton, Judy, intro. by. Stubbs: Portraits in Detail. (Illus.). 48p. 1985. pap. 8.95 (ISBN 0-946590-17-6). Salem Hse Pubs.
Shaw, William A. Bibliography of the Historical Works of Dr. Creighton, Dr. Stubbs, Dr. S. R. Gardiner, & the Late Lord Acton. 1969. 17.50 (ISBN 0-8337-3242-0). B Franklin.

STUDD, CHARLES THOMAS, 1860-1931
Erskine, John T. Millionaire for God (C. T. Studd) 1968. pap. 2.95 (ISBN 0-87508-611-X). Chr Lit.
Grubb, Norman P. C. T. Studd. 1972. 7.95 (ISBN 0-87508-201-7); pap. 5.95 (ISBN 0-87508-202-5). Chr Lit.

STUDENTS
see also Church Work with Students
also headings beginning with College or School, e.g. college students
Benson, C. H. Conozcamos al Alumno. Villalobos, Fernando P., tr. from Eng. (Curso para Maestros Cristianos: No. 4). (Span.). 128p. 1972. pap. 3.50 (ISBN 0-89922-014-2). Edit Caribe.

Ristow, Kate S. & Comeaux, Maureen N. Harvest: A Faithful Approach to Life Issues for Junior High People. (Illus.). 167p. 1984. pap. 24.50 (ISBN 0-940634-20-1). Puissance Pubns.

STUDENTS–RELIGIOUS LIFE

Havens, Joseph. The Journal of a College Student. LC 65-19208. (Orig.). pap. 2.50x (ISBN 0-87574-141-X). Pendle Hill.
McShane, Philip. Music That is Soundless: An Introduction to God for the Graduate. 1977. pap. text ed. 9.25 (ISBN 0-8191-0236-9). U Pr of Amer.
Richards, Lawrence O. & LeFever, Marlene D. Nurturing My Students. (Complete Teacher Training Meeting Ser.). 48p. 1985. pap. text ed. 9.95 (ISBN 0-317-38010-9). Cook.
Wollenburg, David W. Campus Symbolism: Devotions for New Students. write for info. (ISBN 0-911770-52-6). Concordia Schl Grad Studies.

STURGES, A. A.

Crawford, David & Crawford, Leona. Missionary Adventures in the South Pacific. LC 67-15137. 1967. 5.50 (ISBN 0-8048-0403-6). C E Tuttle.

STURGES, SUSAN THOMPSON, 1820-1893

Crawford, David & Crawford, Leona. Missionary Adventures in the South Pacific. LC 67-15137. 1967. 5.50 (ISBN 0-8048-0403-6). C E Tuttle.

SUBLIME, THE

Arieti, James A. & Crossett, John M., trs. Longinus: On the Sublime. LC 84-25435. (Studies in Art & Religious Interpretation: Vol.21). 275p. 1985. 59.95x (ISBN 0-88946-554-1). E Mellen.

SUBSTANCE (PHILOSOPHY)

see also Ontology

Hartman, Edwin. Substance, Body & Soul: Aristotelian Investigations. LC 77-71984. 1977. text ed. 34.50x (ISBN 0-691-07223-X). Princeton U Pr.
Stead, G. C. Divine Substance. (Illus.). 1966. 49.50x (ISBN 0-19-826630-8). Oxford U Pr.

SUBUD

Bissing, Hurbert. Songs of Submission: On the Practice of Subud. 180p. (Orig.). 1982. pap. 9.50 (ISBN 0-227-67852-4, Pub. by J Clarke UK). Attic Pr.

SUBURBAN CHURCHES

see also City Churches; Rural Churches

LeFevre, Perry D., ed. Conflict in a Voluntary Association: A Case Study of a Classic Suburban Church Fight. LC 75-12388. (Studies in Ministry & Parish Life). 1975. 13.95x (ISBN 0-913552-03-8); pap. 6.95x (ISBN 0-913552-09-7). Exploration Pr.

SUBURBAN LIFE

see also Suburban Churches

Gordon, Albert I. Jews in Suburbia. LC 73-11749. 264p. 1973. Repr. of 1959 ed. lib. bdg. 15.00x (ISBN 0-8371-7088-5, COJS). Greenwood.

SUCCESS

see also Conduct of Life; Self-Realization

Addington, Jack & Addington, Cornelia. The Perfect Power Within You. new ed. LC 73-87712. 167p. 1973. pap. 4.95 (ISBN 0-87516-179-0). De Vorss.
Addington, Jack E. Psychogenesis: Everything Begins in the Mind. LC 79-145391. 1971. 10.95 (ISBN 0-396-06334-9). Dodd.
Belmar, John J. Success - It's Yours to Have. 1984. 5.75 (ISBN 0-8062-2305-7). Carlton.
Bland, Glenn. Success: The Glenn Bland Method. 1983. pap. 3.50 (ISBN 0-8423-6689-X). Tyndale.
Buess, Bob. Deliverance from the Bondage of Fear. 1972. pap. 2.50 (ISBN 0-934244-03-0). Sweeter Than Honey.
--Favor the Road to Success. 1982. pap. 2.50 (ISBN 0-934244-17-0). Sweeter Than Honey.
Bustanoby, Andre. Being a Success at Who You Are. 1986. pap. 4.95 (ISBN 0-310-45381-X, 9172P). Zondervan.
Caldwell, Louis O. Something Good for Those Who Feel Bad: Positive Solutions for Negative Emotions. 96p. 1985. pap. 6.95 (ISBN 0-8010-2505-2). Baker Bk.
Campolo, Anthony. The Success Fantasy. LC 79-67852. 144p. 1980. pap. 5.95 (ISBN 0-88207-796-1). Victor Bks.
Campus Crusade for Christ Staff. How to Make Your Mark. 540p. (Orig.). 1983. pap. 8.95 (ISBN 0-86605-142-2). Campus Crusade.
Collier, Robert. The Amazing Secrets of the Masters of the Far East. pap. 6.95 (ISBN 0-912576-16-2). R Collier.
--Prayer Works! 4.95 (ISBN 0-912576-01-4). R Collier.
Collins, Gary R. Getting Started. 224p. (Orig.). 1984. pap. 5.95 (ISBN 0-8007-5162-0, Power Bks). Revell.
Conwell, Russell H. Acres of Diamonds. 64p. 1975. pap. 2.50 (ISBN 0-8007-8091-4, Spire Bks). Revell.
Cottrell, Stan. To Run & Not Be Weary. (Illus.). 192p. 1985. 12.95 (ISBN 0-8007-1444-X). Revell.
Dean, Dave. Now Is Your Time to Win. Vries, Vickie De, ed. 1p. 1985. pap. 2.95 (ISBN 0-8423-4727-5). Tyndale.
Dean, Dave & Hefley, Marti. Now Is Your Time to Win. 1983. 8.95 (ISBN 0-8423-4724-0). Tyndale.
DeVos, Richard M. & Conn, Charles P. Believe! 128p. 1975. pap. 2.95 (ISBN 0-8007-8267-4, Spire). Revell.
Dobbins, Richard D. Votre Force Spirituelle et Emotionnelle. Cosson, Annie L., ed. Chardenal, Valerie, tr. from Eng. Tr. of Your Spiritual & Emotional Power. (Fr.). 188p. 1985. pap. text ed. 2.25 (ISBN 0-8297-0703-4). Life Pubs Intl.
Drakeford, John W. The Awesome Power of the Healing Thought. LC 80-70915. 1981. 8.95 (ISBN 0-8054-5294-X). Broadman.
Escandon, R. Como Llegar a Ser Vencedor. (Span.). 128p. 1982. pap. 3.95 (ISBN 0-311-46092-5, Edit Mundo). Casa Bautista.
Furman, Richard. Reaching Your Full Potential. 1984. pap. 6.95 (ISBN 0-89081-443-0). Harvest Hse.
Glass, Bill & McEachern, James E. Plan to Win. 160p. 1984. 8.95 (ISBN 0-8499-0431-5, 0431-5). Word Bks.
Greetings Etc. by Alfreda. Meeting Challenges: Scripture References. 1984. pap. text ed. 2.95 (ISBN 0-318-04372-6, Pub. by Greetings). Prosperity & Profits.
Hart, Archibald D. The Success Factor. 160p. 1984. pap. 5.95 (ISBN 0-8007-5138-8, Power Bks). Revell.
Havens, Teresina R. Standards of Success. 1983. pap. 2.50x (ISBN 0-87574-043-X, 043). Pendle Hill.
Hawkins, O. S. Clues to a Successful Life. LC 82-71561. (Orig.). 1982. pap. 6.95 (ISBN 0-8054-5515-9). Broadman.
Jackson, Neil E., Jr. Beyond All Expectations. (Orig.). 1987. pap. 6.95 (ISBN 0-8054-5044-0). Broadman.
Kaeser, Clifford. Beyond Authority: How to Play to Win by the New Ethics. LC 82-4020. 143p. 1984. pap. 9.95 (ISBN 0-87949-222-8). Ashley Bks.
Kennedy, Nell. Dream Your Way to Success. LC 79-93290. 1980. pap. 4.95 (ISBN 0-88270-407-9). Bridge Pub.
Klein, Sydney T. The Way of Attainment. 220p. 1981. pap. 13.00 (ISBN 0-89540-106-1, SB-106). Sun Pub.
Lewis, H. Spencer. Self Mastery & Fate with the Cycles of Life. 33rd ed. LC 55-16785. 253p. 1982. 11.95 (ISBN 0-912057-05-X, G-507). AMORC.
Lewis, Jim. Finding the Treasure Within You. LC 81-70339. 128p. 1982. pap. 4.75 (ISBN 0-87516-469-2). De Vorss.
Lorenzo. The Relaxation Sensation: The Number One Success Factor in Life. (Illus.). 128p. (Orig.). 1981. pap. 9.95 (ISBN 0-941122-00-X). Prema Bks.
Lovett, C. S. C. S. Lovett: Maranatha Man. (Illus.). 1978. pap. 5.95 (ISBN 0-938148-02-8). Personal Christianity.
McBirnie, William S. How to Motivate Your Child Toward Success. 1979. pap. 3.95 (ISBN 0-8423-1528-4). Tyndale.
McLemore, Clinton W. Good Guys Finish First: Success Strategies from the Book of Proverbs for Business Men & Women. LC 83-14708. 142p. 1983. pap. 7.95 (ISBN 0-664-26004-7, A Bridgebooks Publication). Westminster.
Mandino, Og. The Greatest Gift in the World. LC 76-43508. (Illus.). 128p. 1976. 8.95 (ISBN 0-8119-0274-9). Fell.
Manning, A. J. Helping Yourself with White Witchcraft. 1972. 9.95 (ISBN 0-13-386565-7, Reward); pap. 4.95 (ISBN 0-13-386573-8). P-H.
Montapert, Alfred A. Pray to Win: A Blueprint for Success. pap. 4.95 (ISBN 0-9603174-4-9, Pub. by Bks of Value). Borden.
Murphy, Joseph. Amazing Laws of Cosmic Mind Power. 1965. pap. 4.95 (ISBN 0-13-023804-X, Reward). P-H.
--Great Bible Truths for Human Problems. 1976. pap. text ed. 7.00 (ISBN 0-87516-214-2). De Vorss.
--Infinite Power for Richer Living. 1969. pap. 4.95 (ISBN 0-13-464396-8, Reward). P-H.
Nieman, Charles. God's Plan for Your Financial Success. 230p. (Orig.). 1985. pap. text ed. 6.95 (ISBN 0-914307-34-7). Word Faith.
Otterholt, Howard V. How to Be Your Own Good Samaritan. LC 81-3465. 1982. 15.95 (ISBN 0-87949-195-7). Ashley Bks.
Pandurangarao Malyaya. Model Building of Solar Systems. (Worship Technology Around the World Ser.: No. 1). Orig. Title: Sri Satyanarayana Katha. (Illus.). 100p. (Orig.). 1981. 9.99 (ISBN 0-938924-00-1). Sri Shirdi Sai.
Peale, Norman V. Enthusiasm Makes the Difference. 1978. pap. 2.50 (ISBN 0-449-23698-6, Crest). Fawcett.
--A Guide to Confident Living. 1977. pap. 2.25 (ISBN 0-449-24173-4, Crest). Fawcett.
--Positive Imaging: The Powerful Way to Change Your Life. 192p. 1981. pap. 2.95 (ISBN 0-8007-8484-7). Revell.
--The Power of Positive Thinking. 552p. 1985. pap. 15.95 large print ed. (ISBN 0-8027-2465-5). Walker & Co.
Ponder, Catherine. The Millionaires of Genesis. (The Millionaires of the Bible Ser.). 1976. pap. 4.95 (ISBN 0-87516-215-0). De Vorss.
Reeves, R. Daniel & Jenson, Ronald. Always Advancing. LC 83-73182. 196p. (Orig.). 1984. pap. 8.95 (ISBN 0-86605-120-1, 403188). Campus Crusade.
Schaefer, Christopher & Voors, Tijno. Vision in Action: The Art of Taking & Shaping Initiatives. 199p. (Orig.). 1986. pap. text ed. 12.95 (ISBN 0-88010-150-4). Anthroposophic.
Schuller, Robert. God's Way to the Good Life. (Religion Ser.). 144p. 1987. pap. 2.95 (ISBN 0-553-26803-1). Bantam.
--Tough Times Never Last but Tough People Do! 256p. 1984. pap. 3.95 (ISBN 0-553-24245-8). Bantam.
Schuller, Robert H. Discover Your Possibilities. (Orig.). 1980. pap. 3.95 (ISBN 0-89081-214-4). Harvest Hse.
--Move Ahead with Possibility Thinking. 224p. 1973. pap. 2.95 (ISBN 0-8007-8105-8, Spire Bks). Revell.
--Tough Times Never Last, but Tough People Do! (General Ser.). 1984. lib. bdg. 13.95 (ISBN 0-8161-3677-7, Large Print Bks). G K Hall.
Shinn, Florence S. The Secret Door to Success. 1978. pap. 2.50 (ISBN 0-87516-258-4). De Vorss.
--Your Word Is Your Wand. 1978. pap. 2.50 (ISBN 0-87516-259-2). De Vorss.
Shinn, George. The American Dream Still Works. 1981. pap. 3.50 (ISBN 0-8423-0061-9). Tyndale.
Sinetar, Marsha. Do What You Love, the Money Will Follow. 1987. pap. 9.95. Paulist Pr.
Tilton, Robert. God's Laws of Success. 224p. (Orig.). 1983. pap. text ed. 7.95 (ISBN 0-914307-04-5, Dist. by Harrison Hse). Word Faith.
Towne, William E. Health & Wealth from Within. 157p. 1981. pap. 9.00 (ISBN 0-89540-081-2, SB-081). Sun Pub.
Turner, F. Bernadette. Prosperity & the Healing Power of Prayer. LC 83-21276. (Illus.). 166p. 1984. pap. 6.95 (ISBN 0-13-731324-1). P-H.
Turner, J. J. How to Turn Your Dreams into Realities. pap. 4.50 (ISBN 0-317-03774-9). Quality Pubns.
Waitley, Denis E. The Seeds of Greatness. 224p. 1983. 14.95 (ISBN 0-8007-1361-3); pap. 3.95 (ISBN 0-8007-8560-6). Revell.
Williams, Pat & Jenkins, Jerry. The Power Within You. LC 82-24825. 180p. 1983. 12.95 (ISBN 0-664-27008-5, A Bridgebooks Publication). Westminster.
Wood, George. The Successful Life. Sekowsky, Jo Anne, ed. 64p. 1984. pap. text ed. 3.25 (ISBN 0-930756-82-7, 531017). Aglow Pubns.

SUCCESSION, APOSTOLIC

see Apostolic Succession

SUCCOTH (FEAST OF TABERNACLES)

see Sukkoth

SUDAN, EGYPTIAN–HISTORY

Bennett, Ernest N. Downfall of the Dervishes. LC 71-79818. (Illus.). Repr. of 1899 ed. 22.50x (ISBN 0-8371-1545-0, BEB&). Greenwood.

SUDAN INTERIOR MISSION

Hunter, J. H. Flame of Fire. 5.00 (ISBN 0-685-20860-5). Univ Place.

SUFFERING

see also Consolation; Good and Evil; Joy and Sorrow; Loneliness; Martyrdom; Pain

Bakan, David. Disease, Pain & Sacrifice: Toward a Psychology of Suffering. 1971. pap. 3.95x (ISBN 0-8070-2971-8, BP394). Beacon Pr.
Bloem, Diane B. Into the Midst of Suffering: A Woman's Workshop on Job. (Woman's Workshop Ser.). (Orig.). 1985. Leader's ed., 64pp. pap. 3.95 (ISBN 0-310-42771-1, 11213P); Student's ed., 112pp. pap. 2.95 (ISBN 0-310-42781-9, 11213P). Zondervan.
Boros, Ladislaus. Pain & Providence. 132p. 1975. pap. 2.95 (ISBN 0-686-85825-5). Crossroad NY.
Bowker, John. Problems of Suffering in the Religions of the World. LC 77-93706. 1975. 47.50 (ISBN 0-521-07412-6); pap. 12.95x (ISBN 0-521-09903-X). Cambridge U Pr.
Bunyan, John. Advice to Sufferers. pap. 3.25 (ISBN 0-685-19821-9). Reiner.
Burkle, Howard R. God, Suffering, & Belief. LC 76-26496. Repr. of 1977 ed. 24.40 (ISBN 0-8357-9010-X, 2016364). Bks Demand UMI.
Carretto, Carlo. Why O Lord? The Inner Meaning of Suffering. Barr, Robert R., tr. from Ital. LC 85-29874. Tr. of Perche Signore? Il Dolore: Segreto Nascosto Nei Secoli. 128p. (Orig.). 1986. 10.95 (ISBN 0-88344-224-8); pap. 6.95 (ISBN 0-88344-222-1). Orbis Bks.
Constable, Giles. Attitudes Toward Self-Inflicted Suffering in the Middle Ages. (Stephen J. Brademas Lectures Ser.). 28p. (Orig.). pap. text ed. 2.50 (ISBN 0-916586-87-1). Hellenic Coll Pr.
Day, Dan. Hurting. (Uplook Ser.). 1978. pap. 0.99 (ISBN 0-8163-0088-7, 08889-8). Pacific Pr Pub Assn.
Deal, William S. The Furnace of Affliction. 6th ed. 1978. 1.50 (ISBN 0-686-05833-X). Crusade Pubs.
Dougherty, Flavian, ed. The Meaning of Human Suffering. LC 81-6267. 349p. 1982. 39.95 (ISBN 0-89885-011-8). Human Sci Pr.
Emerson, James G. Suffering: Its Meaning & Ministry. 176p. (Orig.). 1986. pap. 8.95 (ISBN 0-687-40573-4). Abingdon.
Falwell, Jerry. When It Hurts Too Much to Cry. 160p. 1984. 9.95 (ISBN 0-8423-7993-2). Tyndale.
Fichter, Joseph H. Religion & Pain: The Spiritual Dimensions of Health Care. 128p. 1981. 9.95 (ISBN 0-8245-0102-0). Crossroad NY.
Fretheim, Terence E. The Suffering of God: An Old Testament Perspective. Brueggemann, Walter, ed. LC 84-47921. (Overtures to Biblical Theology Ser.). 224p. 1984. pap. 10.95 (ISBN 0-8006-1538-7). Fortress.
Frost, Gerhard E. Color of the Night: Reflections on the Book of Job. LC 77-72458. 1977. pap. 5.95 (ISBN 0-8066-1583-4, 10-1520). Augsburg.
Gerber, Isreal J. Job on Trial: A Book for Our Time. 217p. 1982. 14.95 (ISBN 0-318-01102-6). E P Press.
Hayden, Edwin. Beloved Sufferer. 144p. 1987. pap. 5.95 (ISBN 0-87403-236-9, 3178). Standard Pub.
Heagle, John. Suffering & Evil. (Guidelines for Contemporary Catholics Ser.). (Orig.). 1987. pap. 7.95 (ISBN 0-88347-212-0). Thomas More.
Israel, Martin. The Pain That Heals: The Place of Suffering in the Growth of the Person. (Crossroad Paperback Ser.). 192p. 1982. pap. 8.95 (ISBN 0-8245-0437-2). Crossroad NY.
Kite, Roger. Evil & Suffering. 1985. 19.00x (ISBN 0-7062-3911-3, Pub. by Ward Lock Educ Co Ltd). State Mutual Bk.
Kollar, Nathan R. Songs of Suffering. 160p. (Orig.). 1982. pap. 7.95 (ISBN 0-86683-672-1, HarpR). Har-Row.
Kosicki, George W. The Good News of Suffering. LC 81-13644. 87p. (Orig.). 1981. pap. 1.95 (ISBN 0-8146-1240-7). Liturgical Pr.
Kreeft, Peter. Making Sense Out of Suffering. 160p. (Orig.). 1986. pap. 6.95 (ISBN 0-89283-219-3). Servant.
Lacomara, Aelred, ed. The Language of the Cross. 1977. 5.95 (ISBN 0-8199-0617-4). Franciscan Herald.
Landorf, Joyce. Silent September. 1984. pap. 10.00 (ISBN 0-317-14051-5). Word Bks.
Lee, Laurel. To Comfort You. Phillips, Cheryl M. & Harvey, Bonnie C., eds. (Illus.). 32p. (Orig.). 1984. pap. 0.98 (ISBN 0-937420-11-5). Stirrup Assoc.
McKenna, David. The Whisper of His Grace: A Fresh Look at Suffering Through the Eyes of Job & Jesus. 192p. 1987. 12.95 (ISBN 0-8499-0560-5). Word Bks.
McWhorter, Jane. Let This Cup Pass. (Illus.). 1979. pap. 4.95 (ISBN 0-89137-414-0). Quality Pubns.
Meyer, F. B. The Gift of Suffering. LC 79-93432. (Shepherd Illustrated Classics Ser.). (Illus.). 208p. (Orig.). 1980. pap. 5.95 (ISBN 0-87983-211-8). Keats.
On the Christian Meaning of Human Suffering. 48p. 1984. pap. 3.95 (ISBN 1-55586-919-X). US Catholic.
Powell, Paul. When the Hurt Won't Go Away. 144p. 1986. pap. 4.95 (ISBN 0-89693-365-2). Victor Bks.
Pursell, Cleo. Triumph Over Suffering. 1982. pap. 1.50 (ISBN 0-89265-079-6). Randall Hse.
Rogers, Dale E. God in the Hard Times. LC 85-10479. 160p. 1985. pap. 8.95 (ISBN 0-8027-2516-3). Walker & Co.
Saher, Parwez J. The Conquest of Suffering. 1977. 12.50 (ISBN 0-89684-189-8, Pub. by Motilal Banarsidass India). Orient Bk Dist.
Schaeffer, Edith. Affliction. 256p. 1978. 10.95 (ISBN 0-8007-0926-8); 7.95 (ISBN 0-8007-5150-7). Revell.
Schlink, Basilea. Blessings of Illness. 1973. pap. 2.50 (ISBN 0-551-00446-0, Pub. by Marshall Morgan & Scott UK). Evang Sisterhood Mary.
Simons, C. P. Valuing Suffering As a Christian: Some Psychological Perspectives. (Synthesis Ser.). 1976. pap. 0.75 (ISBN 0-8199-0708-1). Franciscan Herald.
Simundson, Danile J. Faith under Fire: Biblical Interpretations of Suffering. LC 79-54119. 158p. 1980. pap. 7.95 (ISBN 0-8066-1756-X, 10-2195). Augsburg.
Slatoff, Walter J. The Look of Distance: Reflections on Suffering & Sympathy in Modern Literature - Auden to Agee, Whitman to Woolf. LC 85-10447. 309p. 1985. 25.00x (ISBN 0-8142-0385-X). Ohio St U Pr.
Soelle, Dorothee. Suffering. Kalin, Everett R., tr. from Ger. LC 75-13036. 192p. 1975. 10.95 (ISBN 0-8006-1813-0, 1-813); pap. 5.95. Fortress.

Springsted, Eric O. Simone Weil & the Suffering of Love. 131p. (Orig.). 1986. pap. 8.95 (ISBN 0-936384-33-6). Cowley Pubns.

Steiner, Rudolf. The Origin of Suffering, The Origin of Evil, Illness & Death. Cotterell, Mabel & Watkin, V. E., trs. (Ger.). 31p. 1980. pap. 2.95 (ISBN 0-919924-12-3, Pub. by Steiner Book Centre Canada). Anthroposophic.

Stowell, Joseph M. Through the Fire. 156p. 1985. pap. 5.95 (ISBN 0-89693-601-5). Victor Bks.

Struzzo, John A., et al. Suffering: Issues of Emotional Living in an Age of Stress for Clergy & Religious. Gilmartin, Richard J., ed. LC 84-9334. 144p. 1984. pap. 8.00 (ISBN 0-89571-020-X). Affirmation.

Taylor, Michael J., ed. The Mystery of Suffering & Death. LC 72-13294. 203p. 1973. pap. 5.95 (ISBN 0-8189-0263-9). Alba.

Van Impe, Jack. God I'm Suffering, Are You Listening. 36p. 1985. pap. 1.95 (ISBN 0-934803-00-5). J Van Impe.

Watson, Jeffrey A. Looking Beyond. 132p. 1986. pap. 4.95 (ISBN 0-89693-155-2). Victor Bks.

White, Willie W. What the Bible Says about Suffering. (What the Bible Says Ser.). 350p. 1984. 13.95 (ISBN 0-317-05126-1). College Pr Pub.

Wiersbe, Warren W., compiled by. Classic Sermons on Suffering. LC 84-11260. (Classic Sermon Ser.). 204p. (Orig.). 1984. pap. text ed. 9.95 (ISBN 0-8254-4027-0). Kregel.

Yancey, Philip. Where Is God When It Hurts? 1977. pap. 5.95 (ISBN 0-310-35411-0, 9992P); 2.95 (ISBN 0-310-35431-5, 9992G). Zondervan.

Yonggi Cho, Paul. Suffering.... Why Me? LC 86-70741. 1986. pap. 3.50 (ISBN 0-88270-601-2). Bridge Pub.

SUFISM

Abbas, H. & Khan, Emir A. Sufi Principles Action, Learning Methods, Imitators, Meeting-Places. (Sufi Research Ser.). 64p. 1982. pap. 4.95 (ISBN 0-86304-001-2, Pub. by Octagon Pr England). Ins Study Human.

Al-Muqaddasi: Revelation of the Secrets of the Birds & Flowers. 1980. 18.95 (ISBN 0-900860-75-8). Ins Study Human.

Al-Husayn al-Sulami, Ibn. The Book of Sufi Chivalry: Lessons to a Son of the Moment (Futuwwah) Bayrak, Tosun, tr. from Arabic. 1983. 8.95 (ISBN 0-89281-031-9). Inner Tradit.

Allens, Alexi. Images of Sai Baba. (Illus.). 104p. (Orig.). 1985. pap. 12.95 (ISBN 0-318-18477-X). Masterpiece Pub.

Amina Shah. Assemblies of Al-Hariri. 267p. 1980. 16.95 (ISBN 0-900860-86-3, Pub. by Octagon Pr England). Ins Study Human.

Arabi, Ibn. Journey to the Lord of Power: A Sufi Manual on Retreat. Harris, Rabia, tr. from Arab. (Illus.). 144p. 1981. pap. 8.95 (ISBN 0-89281-018-1). Inner Tradit.

Arberry, A. J. Doctrine of the Sufis. 12.95 (ISBN 0-686-18608-7). Kazi Pubns.

--The Doctrine of the Sufis. 1966. 12.95x (ISBN 0-87902-195-0). Orientalia.

Arberry, Arthur J. The Doctrine of the Sufis. LC 76-58075. 1977. pap. 13.95 (ISBN 0-521-29218-2). Cambridge U Pr.

Ardalan, Nader & Bakhtiar, laleh. The Sense of Unity: The Sufi Tradition in Persian Architecture. LC 72-92278. (Illus.). xx, 152p. 1986. pap. 29.95 (ISBN 0-226-02560-8). U of Chicago Pr.

Arif of Herat. The Book of Ecstacy. Greenshields, R. S., tr. 1980. 9.95 (ISBN 0-900860-74-X, Pub. by Octagon Pr England). Ins Study Human.

Austin, R. W. Sufis of Andalusia: The Ruh Al-Quds & Al-Durrat Al-Fakhirah of Ibn 'Arabi. Austin, R. W., tr. LC 77-165230. (California Library Reprint: Vol. 91). 1978. Repr. of 1971 ed. 33.00x (ISBN 0-520-03553-4). U of Cal Pr.

Bawa Muhaiyaddeen, M. R. Four Steps to Pure Iman. LC 81-1429. (Illus.). 70p. 1979. pap. 3.95 (ISBN 0-914390-17-1). Fellowship Pr PA.

--Zikr, the Remembrance of God. LC 75-27816. 52p. 1975. pap. 2.95 (ISBN 0-914390-05-8). Fellowship Pr PA.

Beek, Wil van. Hazrat Inayat Khan: Master of Life-Modern Sufi Mystic. 1983. 12.95 (ISBN 0-533-05453-2). Vantage.

Bell, Gertrude. Teachings of Hafiz. 1979. 10.95 (ISBN 0-900860-63-4, Pub. by Octagon Pr England). Ins Study Human.

Bennett, John G. Gurdjieff Today. (Transformation of Man Ser.). 1978. 4.50 (ISBN 0-900306-13-0, Pub. by Coombe Springs Pr). Claymont Comm.

Brenner, Louis. West African Sufi: The Religious Heritage & Spiritual Quest of Cerno Bokar Saalif Taal. LC 83-4803. 215p. 1984. lib. bdg. 24.95x (ISBN 0-520-05008-8). U of Cal Pr.

Burke, O. M. Among the Dervishes. 1973. 11.95 (ISBN 0-900860-17-0, Pub. by Octagon Pr England); pap. 5.95 (ISBN 0-525-47386-6). Ins Study Human.

Chittick, William C. The Sufi Path of Love: The Spiritual Teachings of Rumi. LC 82-19511. (SUNY Series in Islam). 400p. 1983. 44.50x (ISBN 0-87395-723-7); pap. 12.95x (ISBN 0-87395-724-5). State U NY Pr.

Corbin, Henry. Creative Imagination in the Sufism of Ibn Arabi. Manheim, R., tr. (Bollingen Ser.: Vol. 91). 1969. 40.00 (ISBN 0-691-09852-2); pap. 12.95 (ISBN 0-691-01828-6). Princeton U Pr.

--Spiritual Body & Celestial Earth: From Mazdean Iran to Shi Ite Iran. Pearson, Nancy, tr. (Bollingen Ser: No. 91). 1977. text ed. 40.00x (ISBN 0-691-09937-5). Princeton U Pr.

Cragg, Kenneth. The Wisdom of the Sufis. LC 76-7032. (The Wisdom Books). 1976. pap. 2.75 (ISBN 0-8112-0627-0, NDP424). New Directions.

Danner, Victor & Thackston, Wheeler. Ibn 'Ata Illah-Kwaja Abdullah Ansari: The Book of Wisdom-Intimate Conversations. LC 78-1022. (Classics of Western Spirituality-Sufi Ser.). 256p. 1978. 12.95 (ISBN 0-8091-0279-X); pap. 8.95 (ISBN 0-8091-2182-4). Paulist Pr.

Eastwick, Edward. Sadi: The Rose Garden. 1979. 16.95 (ISBN 0-900860-65-0). Ins Study Human.

Eaton, Richard M. Sufis of Bijapur, 1300-1700 Social Roles of Sufis in Medieval India. LC 77-71978. (Illus.). 1978. 42.00x (ISBN 0-691-03110-X). Princeton U Pr.

Ernst, Carl W. Words of Ecstasy in Sufism. (SUNY Series in Islam). 230p. 1985. 44.50x (ISBN 0-87395-917-5); pap. 16.95x (ISBN 0-87395-918-3). State U NY Pr.

Fatemi, Nasrollah S. & Fatemi, Faramarz S. Love, Beauty, & Harmony in Sufism. 12.95 (ISBN 0-8453-2248-6, Cornwall Bks). Assoc Univ Prs.

Feild, Reshad. The Invisible Way: A Sufi Love Story. LC 78-19501. 176p. 1983. pap. 7.95 (ISBN 0-06-062588-0, RD/457, HarpR). Har-Row.

--The Last Barrier. LC 75-9345. 1977. pap. 8.95 (ISBN 0-06-062586-4, RD 202, HarpR). Har-Row.

Friedlander, Shems. When You Hear Hoofbeats, Think of a Zebra Talks on Sufism. LC 86-45657. 128p. (Orig.). 1987. pap. 5.95 (ISBN 0-06-096128-7, PL 6128, PL). Har-Row.

Gairdner, Canon W. H. T. Theories, Practices & Training Systems of a Sufi School. (Sufi Research Ser.). 1980. pap. 5.95 (ISBN 0-86304-003-9, Pub. by Octagon Pr England). Ins Study Human.

Grisell, R. Sufism. 120p. 1983. pap. 4.95 (ISBN 0-89496-038-5). Ross Bks.

Hazrat Inayat Khan. The Awakening of the Human Spirit. LC 82-80091. (The Collected Works of Hazyat Inayat Khan Ser.). 224p. (Orig.). 1982. pap. 8.95 (ISBN 0-930872-27-4, 1014P). Omega Pr NM.

Heron-Allen, E., tr. A Fool of God: The Mystical Verse of Baba Tahir. 1979. 12.95 (ISBN 0-900860-70-7, Pub. by Octagon England). Ins Study Human.

Hossain, Seyyed F. The Sufis of Today. (Sufi Research Ser.). 1981. pap. 4.95 (ISBN 0-86304-007-1, Pub. by Octagon Pr England). Ins Study Human.

Izutsu, Toshihiko. Sufism & Taoism: A Comparative Study of Key Philosophical Concepts. LC 84-78. 493p. 1984. text ed. 40.00x (ISBN 0-520-05264-1). U of Cal Pr.

Jamal, Hafiz, ed. Key Concepts in Sufi Understanding. (Sufi Research Ser.). 47p. 1980. pap. 4.95 (ISBN 0-86304-006-3, Pub. by Octagon Pr England). Ins Study Human.

Javad, Nurbakhsh. Spiritual Poverty in Sufism. Lewishon, Leonard, tr. 1984. pap. 6.00x (ISBN 0-933546-11-4). KhaniQahi-Nimatullahi-Sufi.

Kalabadhi, Muhammed. The Doctrine of the Sufis. Arberry, Arthur J., tr. from Arabic. LC 75-41003. Repr. of 1935 ed. 18.00 (ISBN 0-404-14637-6). AMS Pr.

Khan, Hazrat I. The Inner Life: An Introduction to Sufism. (Orient Paperbacks Ser.). 1980. pap. 3.25 (ISBN 0-86578-082-X). Ind-US Inc.

--The Soul Whence & Whither. LC 77-15697. (The Collected Works of Hazrat Inayat Khan Ser.). 190p. 1977. 7.95 (ISBN 0-930872-00-2). Omega Pr NM.

--The Unity of Religious Ideals. (The Collected Works of Hazrat Inayat Khan Ser.). 264p. 1979. 9.95 (ISBN 0-930872-09-6); pap. 6.95 (ISBN 0-930872-10-X). Omega Pr NM.

Khan, Inayat. The Art of Personality. (Sufi Message of Hazrat Inayat Khan Ser.: Vol. 3). 256p. 1979. 14.95 (ISBN 90-6077-570-8, Pub. by Servire BV Netherlands). Hunter Hse.

--The Bowl of Saki. rev., 4th ed. LC 78-65653. 128p. (Orig.). 1979. pap. 4.95 (ISBN 0-900217-12-X, Pub. by Sufi Pub Co England). Hunter Hse.

--In an Eastern Rose Garden. (Sufi Message of Hazrat Inayat Khan Ser.: Vol. 7). 256p. 1979. 14.95 (ISBN 90-6325-096-7, Pub. by Servire BV Netherlands). Hunter Hse.

--The Inner Life. (Sufi Message of Hazrat Inayat Khan Ser.: Vol. 1). 256p. 1979. 14.95 (ISBN 90-6325-094-0, Pub. by Servire BV Netherlands). Hunter Hse.

--The Mysticism of Sound. (Sufi Message of Hazrat Inayat Khan Ser.: Vol. 2). 262p. 1979. 14.95 (ISBN 90-6077-569-4, Pub. by Servire BV Netherlands). Hunter Hse.

--The Path of Initiation. (Sufi Message of Hazrat Inayat Khan Ser.: Vol. 10). 270p. 1979. 14.95 (ISBN 90-6325-098-3, Pub. by Servire BV Netherlands). Hunter Hse.

--Philosophy, Psychology & Mysticism. (Sufi Message of Hazrat Inayat Khan Ser.: Vol. 11). 256p. 1979. 14.95 (ISBN 90-6325-099-1, Pub. by Servire BV Netherlands). Hunter Hse.

--Sacred Readings: The Gathas. (Sufi Message of Hazrat Inayat Khan Ser.: Vol. 13). 304p. 1982. 14.95 (ISBN 90-6325-021-5, Pub. by Servire BV Netherlands). Hunter Hse.

--Spiritual Liberty. (Sufi Message of Hazrat Inayat Khan Ser.: Vol. 5). 256p. 1979. 14.95 (ISBN 90-6325-095-9, Pub. by Servire BV Netherlands). Hunter Hse.

--The Unity of Religious Ideals. (Sufi Message of Hazrat Inayat Khan Ser.: Vol. 9). 280p. 1979. 14.95 (ISBN 90-6325-097-5, Pub. by Servire BV Netherlands). Hunter Hse.

Khan, M. M. Pages in the Life of a Sufi. 1979. 14.95 (ISBN 11-1910-334-7, Pub. by Sufi Pub Co England). Hunter Hse.

Khan, Pir V. The Message in Our Time: The Life & Teachings of the Sufi Master, Hazrat Inayat Khan. LC 78-4751. (Illus.). 1979. 15.45 (ISBN 0-06-064237-8, HarpR). Har-Row.

Lefort, Rafael. The Teachers of Gurdjieff. LC 66-68145. 157p. (Orig.). 1975. pap. 6.95 (ISBN 0-87728-283-8). Weiser.

Lewis, Samuel L. & Khan, Hazrat I. The Bowl of Saki Commentary. Jablonski, Moineddin & Klotz, Saadi, eds. 180p. (Orig.). 1981. pap. 18.00 (ISBN 0-915424-08-8). Sufi Islamia-Prophecy.

Lings, Martin. A Sufi Saint of the Twentieth Century: Shaikh Ahmad al-'Alawi, His Spiritual Heritage & Legacy. (Near Eastern Center, UCLA Ser.). (Illus.). 242p. 1972. 30.00x (ISBN 0-520-02174-6); pap. 4.95 (ISBN 0-520-02486-9). U of Cal Pr.

Litvak, Stuart. Seeking Wisdom: The Sufi Path. LC 82-60163. 128p. (Orig.). 1984. pap. 6.95 (ISBN 0-87728-543-8). Weiser.

Mahmud Shabistari. The Secret Garden. 1969. 10.95 (ISBN 0-900860-38-3). Ins Study Human.

Mah Talat Etemad Moghadam. From the Prophet to the Great Sufi Mir Ghotbeddin Mohammad. Peyravan, Abdosalam & Shahrivar, Mitra, trs. from Farsi. 231p. (Orig.). 1982. pap. 12.50 (ISBN 0-317-01145-6). M T O Shahmag.

Massignon, Louis. The Passion of Al-Hallaj: Mystic & Martyr of Islam, 4 vols. Mason, Herbert, tr. from Fr. LC 80-11085. (Bollingen Ser.: No. XCVIII). 2010p. 1983. Set. 145.00x (ISBN 0-691-09910-3); 24.50x (ISBN 0-691-10203-1). Princeton U Pr.

Matheson, D. M. & Burckhardt, T. An Introduction to Sufi Doctrine. 1971. pap. 4.75x (ISBN 0-87902-175-6). Orientalia.

Milson, Menahem, tr. from Arabic. A Sufi Rule for Novices. LC 74-27750. (Middle Eastern Studies: No. 17). 112p. 1975. text ed. 8.95x (ISBN 0-674-85400-4); pap. 3.50 (ISBN 0-674-85403-9). Harvard U Pr.

Moinuddin, Shaykh. The Book of Sufi Healing. (Illus.). 256p. (Orig.). 1985. pap. 12.95 (ISBN 0-89281-043-2). Inner Tradit.

Molana-al-Moazam Hazrat Shah & Maghsoud Sadegh-ibn-Mohammad Angha. The Mystery of Humanity: Tranquilty & Survival. 74p. (Orig.). 1986. lib. bdg. 19.75 (ISBN 0-8191-5329-X); pap. text ed. 8.75 (ISBN 0-8191-5330-3). U Pr of Amer.

Muhaiyaddeen, M. R. Golden Words of a Sufi Sheikh. LC 82-11854. 472p. 1983. 15.95 (ISBN 0-914390-24-4). Fellowship Pr PA.

Musa, Adam, ed. Letters & Lectures of Idries Shah. 40p. 1981. pap. 4.95 (ISBN 0-86304-010-1, Pub. by Octagon Pr England). Ins Study Human.

Nasr, Sayyed H. Sufi Essays. 1973. 34.50x (ISBN 0-87395-233-2); pap. 10.95 (ISBN 0-87395-389-4). State U NY Pr.

Nicholson, R. A. The Essence of Sufism. 1984. pap. 3.95 (ISBN 0-916411-49-4, Near Eastern). Holmes Pub.

--Idea of Personality in Sufism. 12.50 (ISBN 0-686-18606-0). Kazi Pubns.

--Ideas of Personality in Sufism. 1970. 12.50 (ISBN 0-87902-180-2). Orientalia.

--The Kashf al-Mahjub: The Oldest Persian Treatise on Sufism by Ali B. Uthman al-Hullabi al-Hujwiri. 441p. 1976. Repr. 30.00x (ISBN 0-317-39100-3, Pub. by Luzac & Co Ltd). State Mutual Bk.

--The Sufi Doctrine of the Perfect Man. 1984. pap. 3.95 (ISBN 0-916411-48-6, Near Eastern). Holmes Pub.

Nicholson, Reynold A. The Mystics of Islam: An Introduction to Sufism. LC 75-10713. 192p. 1975. pap. 5.95 (ISBN 0-8052-0492-X). Schocken.

Nurbakhsh, Javad. In the Paradise of the Sufis. LC 79-83588. 1979. pap. 6.00x (ISBN 0-933546-01-7). KhaniQahi-Nimatullahi-Sufi.

--In the Tavern of Ruin: Seven Essays on Sufism. LC 78-102838. (Orig.). 1978. pap. 6.00x (ISBN 0-933546-00-9). KhaniQahi-Nimatullahi-Sufi.

--Masters of the Path: A History of the Masters of the Nimatullahi Sufi Order. LC 80-80902. (Illus.). 144p. 1980. pap. 6.00x (ISBN 0-933546-03-3). KhaniQahi-Nimatullahi-Sufi.

--Sufism: Fear & Hope, Contraction & Expansion, Gathering & Dispersion, Intoxication, & Sobriety, Annihilation & Subsistence. Chittick, William, tr. from Persian. (Orig.). 1982. pap. 6.00x (ISBN 0-933546-07-6). KhaniQahi-Nimatullahi-Sufi.

--Sufism-III: Submission, Contentment, Absence, Presence, Intimacy. Graham, Terry & Lewisohn, Leonard, trs. 133p. 1985. pap. 6.00x (ISBN 0-933546-19-X). KhaniQahi-Nimatullahi-Sufi.

--Sufism: Meaning, Knowledge, & Unity. Wilson, Peter, tr. from Persian. 128p. (Orig.). 1981. pap. 6.00x (ISBN 0-933546-05-X). Khaniqahi-Nimatullahi-Sufi.

--The Truths of Love. Lewisohn, Leonard, tr. 1982. pap. 6.00x (ISBN 0-933546-08-4). KhaniQahi Nimatullahi-Sufi.

Nurbakhsh, Dr. Javad. Sufi Symbolism, Vol. 1. Lewisohn, Leonard & Graham, Terry, trs. 260p. 1986. 20.00 (ISBN 0-933546-12-2). Khaniqahi-Nimatullahi-Sufi.

Osborne, Arthur. The Incredible Sai Baba: The Life & Miracles of a Modern-Day Saint. 102p. 1985. pap. text ed. 5.00x (ISBN 0-86125-105-9, Pub. by Orient Longman Ltd India). Apt Bks.

Pendlebury, David. Jami: Yusuf & Zulaika. 1980. 16.95 (ISBN 0-900860-77-4). Ins Study Human.

Qureshi, Regula B. Sufi Music of India & Pakistan: Sound, Context & Meaning in Qawwali. (Cambridge Studies in Ethnomusicology). (Illus.). 300p. 1987. 69.50 (ISBN 0-521-26767-6); cassette 18.96 (ISBN 0-521-32598-6). Cambridge U Pr.

Rajneesh, Bhagwan S. The Secret. Chinmaya, Swami P., ed. LC 83-185068. (Sufi Ser.). (Illus.). 760p. (Orig.). 1980. 23.95 (ISBN 0-88050-127-8). Chidvilas Found.

Rajneesh, Bhagwan Shree. The Perfect Master, 2 vols. Anurag, Ma Yoga, ed. LC 83-172954. (Sufi Ser.). (Illus.). 1980. Vol. I, 380 pgs. 19.95 ea. (ISBN 0-88050-113-8). Vol. II, 368 pgs. 1981 (ISBN 0-88050-114-6). Chidvilas Found.

--Sufis: The People of the Path, 2 vols. Veena, Ma Prema, ed. (Sufi Ser.). (Illus., Orig.). 1979. Vol. I, 552 pgs. 18.50 (ISBN 0-88050-136-7); Vol. II, 552 pgs. 1980. 19.50 (ISBN 0-88050-137-5). Chidvilas Found.

--Unio Mystica, 2 vols. 2nd ed. Vandana, Ma Ananda, ed. LC 82-245842. (Sufi Ser.). (Illus.). 1980. Vol. I 384p. 17.95 ea. (ISBN 0-88050-163-4). Vol. II (ISBN 0-88050-164-2). Vol. I. pap. 13.95 ea. (ISBN 0-88050-663-6). Vol. II 368p 1981 (ISBN 0-88050-664-4). Chidvilas Found.

--Until You Die. Anurag, Ma Yoga, ed. LC 77-900984. (Sufi Ser.). (Illus.). 280p. (Orig.). 1976. 15.95 (ISBN 0-88050-165-0). Chidvilas Found.

--The Wisdom of the Sands, 2 vols. Sudha, Ma Yoga, ed. LC 80-903299. (Sufi Ser.). (Illus., Orig.). 1980. Vol. I, 380 pgs. 19.95 ea. (ISBN 0-88050-174-X). Vol. II, 404 pgs. 1980 (ISBN 0-88050-175-8). Vol.1 386p 1980. pap. 15.95 ea. (ISBN 0-88050-674-1). Chidvilas Found.

Rajneesh, Bhagwan Shree & Sudha, Ma Yoga. The Wisdom of the Sands. LC 80-903299. (Sufi Ser.: Vol. II). 412p. (Orig.). 1980. pap. 15.95 (ISBN 0-88050-675-X). Chidvilas Found.

Renard, John, tr. IBN Abbad of Ronda, Letters on the Sufi Path. (Classics of Western Spirituality Ser.: No. 49). 256p. 1986. 12.95 (ISBN 0-8091-0365-6); pap. 9.95 (ISBN 0-8091-2730-X). Paulist PR.

Sahukar, Mani. Sai Baba, the Saint of Shirdi. LC 75-29273. 1977. 3.95 (ISBN 0-913922-11-0). Dawn Horse Pr.

Schimmel, Annemarie. Mystical Dimensions of Islam. LC 73-16112. (Illus.). xxi, 506p. 1975. 30.00x (ISBN 0-8078-1223-4); pap. 8.95x (ISBN 0-8078-1271-4). U of NC Pr.

Schuon, Frithjof. Sufism: Veil & Quintessence. LC 81-69573. (The Library of Traditional Wisdom). 163p. pap. 7.00 (ISBN 0-941532-00-3). Wrld Wisdom Bks.

Scott, Ernest. The People of the Secret. 1983. 16.95 (ISBN 0-86304-027-6, Pub. by Octagon Pr England); pap. 8.95 (ISBN 0-86304-038-1). Ins Study Human.

Shah, Adries. Seeker after Truth: A Handbook of Sufi Tales & Teachings. LC 82-48401. 232p. (Orig.). 1982. pap. 7.64 (ISBN 0-06-067257-9, CN-4049, HarpR). Har-Row.

Shah, Idries. The Book of the Book. 146p. 1976. 9.95 (ISBN 0-900860-12-X, Pub. by Octagon Pr England). Ins Study Human.
--Caravan of Dreams. 207p. 1968. 14.95 (ISBN 0-900860-14-6, Pub. by Octagon Pr England). Ins Study Human.
--The Dermis Probe. 191p. 1980. 15.95 (ISBN 0-900860-83-9, Pub. by Octagon Pr England). Ins Study Human.
--The Elephant in the Dark. 76p. 1982. 9.95 (ISBN 0-900860-36-7, Pub. by Octagon Pr England). Ins Study Human.
--Learning How to Learn. 302p. 1978. 14.95 (ISBN 0-900860-59-6, Pub. by Octagon Pr England). Ins Study Human.
--Learning How to Learn: Psychology & Spirituality in the Sufi Way. LC 80-8892. 304p. 1981. pap. 9.95 (ISBN 0-06-067255-2, CN4015, HarpR). Har-Row.
--The Magic Monastery. 208p. 1972. 16.95 (ISBN 0-900860-89-8, Pub. by Octagon Pr England). Ins Study Human.
--Neglected Aspects of Sufi Study. 83p. 1977. 9.95 (ISBN 0-900860-56-1, Pub. by Octagon Pr England). Ins Study Human.
--A Perfumed Scorpion. 193p. 1982. 14.95 (ISBN 0-900860-62-6, Pub. by Octagon Pr England). Ins Study Human.
--Seeker after Truth. 1982. 16.95 (ISBN 0-900860-91-X, Pub. by Octagon Pr England). Ins Study Human.
--Special Illumination: The Sufi Use of Humour. 64p. 1977. 9.95 (ISBN 0-900860-57-X, Pub. by Octagon Pr England). Ins Study Human.
--Special Problems in the Study of Sufi Ideas. 45p. 1978. pap. 5.95 (ISBN 0-900860-21-9, Pub by Octagon Pr England). Ins Study Human.
--Sufis. LC 64-11299. 1971. pap. 6.95 (ISBN 0-385-07966-4, Anch). Doubleday.
--The Sufis. 1983. 19.95 (ISBN 0-86304-020-9, Pub. by Octagon Pr England). Ins Study Human.
--Way of the Sufi. 1970. pap. 8.95 (ISBN 0-525-47261-4, 0869-260). Dutton.
--The Way of the Sufi. 1983. 16.95 (ISBN 0-900860-80-4, Pub. by Octagon Pr England). Ins Study Human.
--The World of the Sufi. 1979. 18.95 (ISBN 0-900860-66-9). Ins Study Human.
Shea, David & Troyer, Anthony. The Religion of the Sufis. 1979. 11.95 (ISBN 0-900860-65-0). Ins Study Human.
Siddiqui, Najib. Twelve Years with the Sufi Herb Doctors. 1983. 4.95 (ISBN 0-86304-014-4, Pub. by Octagon Pr England). Ins Study Human.
Smith, Margaret. Rabi'a the Mystic & Her Fellow-Saints in Islam. 2nd ed. 256p. 1984. 37.50 (ISBN 0-521-26779-X); pap. 13.95 (ISBN 0-521-31863-7). Cambridge U Pr.
--The Way of the Mystics: The Early Christian Mystics & the Rise of the Sufis. 1978. pap. 6.95 (ISBN 0-19-519967-7). Oxford U Pr.
The Sufi Message of Hazrat Inayat Khan. (Sufi Message Ser.). 14.95 (ISBN 90-6325-101-7, Pub. by Servire BV Netherlands). Hunter Hse.
Thurlnas, Chawan. Current Sufi Activity Work, Literature, Groups & Techniques. (Sufi Research Ser.). 40p. 1982. pap. 4.95 (ISBN 0-86304-004-7, Pub. by Octagon Pr England). Ins Study Human.
Tweedie, Irina. Daughter of Fire: A Diary of a Spiritual Training with a Sufi Master. Clemens, Paul M., ed. LC 86-72368. 832p. 1986. 29.95 (ISBN 0-931892-05-8); pap. 19.95 (ISBN 0-931892-04-X). B Dolphin Pub.
Valiuddin, Mir. Love of God. (Orig.). 1979. pap. 9.95 (ISBN 0-900217-02-2, Pub. by Sufi Pub Co England). Hunter Hse.
--The Quranic Sufism. 2nd rev. ed. 1977. 16.95 (ISBN 0-89684-300-9, Pub. by Motilal Banarsidass India). Orient Bk Dist.
--The Quranic Sufism. 221p. 1981. pap. 13.25 (ISBN 0-88004-007-6). Sunwise Turn.
Whinfield, E. H., tr. Teachings of Rumi: The Masnavi. 1979. 15.95 (ISBN 0-900860-64-2, Pub. by Octagon Pr England). Ins Study Human.
Widad El Sakkakini. First among Sufis: The Life & Thought of Rabia al-Adawiyya. Safwat, Nabil, tr. from Arabic. 1982. 15.95 (ISBN 0-900860-45-6, Pub. by Octagon Pr England). Ins Study Human.
Wood, Ramsey. Kalila & Dimna. 1980. 10.95 (Pub. by Octagon Pr England). Ins Study Human.

SUICIDE

Athill, Diana. After a Funeral. 176p. 1986. 15.95 (ISBN 0-89919-454-0). Ticknor & Fields.
Battin, Margaret & Rudick, Michael, eds. John Donne's Biathanatos: A Modern-Spelling Critical Edition. (Garland English Texts Ser.). 1982. lib. bdg. 55.00 (ISBN 0-8240-9481-6). Garland Pub.
Battin, Margaret P. Ethical Issues in Suicide. 250p. 1982. write for info. (ISBN 0-13-290155-2). P-H.
Battin, Margaret P. & Maris, Ronald, eds. Suicide & Ethics. (Special Issue S Ser.: Vol. 13, No. 3). 112p. 1984. pap. 9.95. Guilford Pr.
Beauchamp, Thom & Perlin, Seymour. Ethical Issues in Death & Dying. 1978. pap. write for info. (ISBN 0-13-290114-5). P-H.
Brisco, Jill. Caleb's Colt. 1986. pap. 5.95. Ideals.
Danto, Bruce L., et al. Suicide & Bereavement. 17.50 (ISBN 0-405-12505-4). Ayer Co Pubs.
Davis, Patricia A. Suicidal Adolescents. 108p. 1983. 20.50x (ISBN 0-398-04866-5). C C Thomas.
Donne, John. Suicide. Clebsch, William A., ed. LC 83-4466. (SP Studies in the Humanities). 134p. 1983. pap. 8.95 (ISBN 0-89130-624-2). Scholars Pr GA.
Getz, William L. & Allen, David B. Brief Counseling with Suicidal Persons. LC 80-8375. 288p. 1982. 29.00x (ISBN 0-669-04090-8). Lexington Bks.
Gordon, Sol. When Living Hurts. 1985. pap. 8.95 (ISBN 0-8074-0310-5). UAHC.
Hadar, Eric. No Reason to Die. 32p. 1983. pap. 5.00 (ISBN 0-942494-76-8). Coleman Pub.
Heillig, Roma J. Adolescent Suicidal Behavior: A Family Systems Model. Nathan, Peter E., ed. LC 83-3594. (Research in Clinical Psychology Ser.: No. 7). 170p. 1983. 37.95 (ISBN 0-8357-1390-3). Univ Microfilms.
Hewett, John H. After Suicide. LC 79-24373. (Christian Care Bks.: Vol. 4). 118p. 1980. pap. 7.95 (ISBN 0-664-24296-0). Westminster.
Hillman, James. Suicide & the Soul. LC 85-11901. (Dunquin Ser.: No. 8). 191p. 1964. pap. 12.00 (ISBN 0-88214-208-9). Spring Pubns.
Hipple, John & Cimbolic, Peter. The Counselor & Suicidal Crisis: Diagnosis & Intervention. 136p. 1979. 16.25x (ISBN 0-398-03872-4). C C Thomas.
Jacobs, Jerry. The Moral Justification of Suicide. (Illus.). 148p. 1982. pap. 16.25x spiral bdg. (ISBN 0-398-04725-1). C C Thomas.
Landsberg, Paul-Louis. The Experience of Death: The Moral Problem of Suicide. Kastenaum, Robert, ed. LC 76-19579. (Death & Dying Ser.). 1977. Repr. of 1953 ed. lib. bdg. 19.00x (ISBN 0-405-09576-7). Ayer Co Pubs.
Maestri, William. Choose Life & Not Death: A Primer on Abortion, Euthanasia, & Suicide. LC 85-28687. 9.95 (ISBN 0-8189-0490-9). Alba.
Morselli, Henry. Suicide: An Essay on Comparative Moral Statistics. LC 74-25770. (European Sociology Ser.). 402p. 1975. Repr. 27.00x (ISBN 0-405-06524-8). Ayer Co Pubs.
Novak, David. Suicide & Morality: The Theories of Plato, Aquinas & Kant & Their Relevance for Suicidology. LC 75-37543. x, 136p. 1976. lib. bdg. 7.50 (ISBN 0-685-69079-2). Scholars Studies.
Portwood, Doris. Commonsense Suicide: The Final Right. 142p. 1983. pap. 8.00 (ISBN 0-394-62013-5). Hemlock Soc.
Rosenfeld, Linda & Prupas, Marilynne. Left Alive: After a Suicide Death in the Family. 120p. 1984. 20.75 (ISBN 0-398-04953-X). C C Thomas.
Savalan, Karen O. Suicide. 248p. 1982. 10.00 (ISBN 0-86690-210-4, 2363-01). Am Fed Astrologers.
Seward, Jack. Hara-Kiri: Japanese Ritual Suicide. LC 68-11973. 1968. pap. 7.95 (ISBN 0-8048-0231-9). C E Tuttle.
Shneidman, Edwin S., ed. On the Nature of Suicide. LC 78-92890. (Jossey-Bass Behavioral Science Ser.). pap. 40.00 (ISBN 0-317-08618-9, 2013857). Bks Demand UMI.
Wallace, Samuel E. After Suicide. LC 73-9793. Repr. of 1973 ed. 71.30 (ISBN 0-8357-9833-X, 2012586). Bks Demand UMI.
Weightman, Judith M. Making Sense of the Jonestown Suicides: A Sociological History of Peoples Temple. LC 83-21999. (Studies in Religion & Society: Vol. 7). 240p. 1984. 49.95x (ISBN 0-88946-871-0). E Mellen.

SUKKOTH

Chaikin, Miriam. Shake a Palm Branch: The Story & Meaning of Sukkot. LC 84-5022. (Illus.). 80p. 1984. PLB 12.95 (ISBN 0-89919-254-8, Clarion). HM.
--Shake a Palm Branch: The Story & Meaning of Sukkot. LC 84-5022. (Illus.). 88p. 1986. pap. 4.95 (ISBN 0-89919-428-1, Pub. by Clarion). Ticknor & Fields.
Donin, Hayyim H., ed. Sukkot. 128p. pap. 4.50 (ISBN 0-686-95148-4). ADL.
Edelman, Lily. Sukkah & the Big Wind. (Holiday Series of Picture Story Books). (Illus.). 1956. 5.95 (ISBN 0-8381-0716-8). United Syn Bk.
Simon, Norma. Our First Sukkah. (Festival Series of Picture Story Books). (Illus.). 1959. plastic cover 4.50 (ISBN 0-8381-0703-6). United Syn Bk.

SUMERIAN HYMNS

see Hymns, Sumerian

SUMERIANS–RELIGION

Kutscher, Raphael. Oh Angry Sea (a-ab-ba hu-luh-ha) The History of a Sumerian Congregational Lament. LC 74-77343. (Near Eastern Researches Ser.: No. 6). (Illus.). 208p. 1975. 24.50x (ISBN 0-300-01579-8). Yale U Pr.
Weir, Cecil J. A Lexicon of Accadian Prayers in the Rituals of Expiation. LC 78-72774. (Ancient Mesopotamian Texts & Studies). Repr. of 1934 ed. 35.00 (ISBN 0-404-18236-4). AMS Pr.

SUN (IN RELIGION, FOLK-LORE, ETC.)

see also Sun-Worship

Kingsford, Anna & Maitland, Edward. Clothed with the Sun. 248p. Date not set. pap. 14.00 (ISBN 0-89540-132-0, SB 132). Sun Pub.
Olcott, William T. Sun Lore of All Ages. 1976. lib. bdg. 59.95 (ISBN 0-8490-2718-7). Gordon Pr.
Palmer, Abram S. Samson-Saga & Its Place in Comparative Religion. Dorson, Richard, ed. LC 77-70613. (International Folklore Ser.). 1977. Repr. of 1913 ed. lib. bdg. 23.50x (ISBN 0-405-10112-0). Ayer Co Pubs.

SUN-WORSHIP

Aivanhov, Omraam M. Toward a Solar Civilization. (Izvor Collection Ser.: Vol. 201). (Illus.). 148p. 1982. pap. 4.95 (ISBN 0-911857-00-1). Prosveta USA.
Cook, Arthur B. Zeus: A Study of Ancient Religion, 2 vols. Incl. Vol. 1. Zeus, God of the Bright Sky. LC 64-25839. (Illus.). 885p. Repr. of 1914 ed. 50.00x (ISBN 0-8196-0148-9); Vol. 2. Zeus, God of the Dark Sky: Thunder & Lightning, 2 pts. LC 64-25839. Repr. of 1925 ed. 100.00xset (ISBN 0-8196-0156-X); Vol. 2, Pt. 1. Text & Notes. xliii, 858p; Vol. 2, Pt. 2. Appendixes & Index. (Illus.). 539p. Biblo.
Olcott, William Tyler. Sun Lore of All Ages. 346p. 1984. Repr. of 1914 ed. lib. bdg. 25.00 (ISBN 0-89341-148-5). Longwood Pub Group.

SUNDAY, WILLIAM ASHLEY, 1862-1935

Ellis, William T. Billy Sunday. (Golden Oldies Ser.). 1959. pap. 3.95 (ISBN 0-8024-0042-6). Moody.
Stocker, Fern N. Billy Sunday: Baseball Preacher. (Preteen Biography Ser.). (Orig.). 1985. pap. text ed. 3.95 (ISBN 0-8024-0442-1). Moody.

SUNDAY

see also Sabbath; Sunday Legislation

Beckwith, Roger T. & Scott, Wilfrid. This Is the Day: The Biblical Doctrine of the Christian Sunday in it's Jewish & Early Church Setting. 192p. 1978. 9.50 (ISBN 0-551-05568-5). Attic Pr.
Carson, D. A., ed. From Sabbath to Lord's Day. 432p. (Orig.). 1982. pap. 10.95 (ISBN 0-310-44531-0, 12035P). Zondervan.
Heylyn, Peter. The History of the Sabbath, 2 pts. LC 75-26002. (English Expericne Ser.: No. 150). 272p. 1969. Repr. of 1636 ed. 49.00 (ISBN 90-221-0150-9). Walter J Johnson.
Solberg, Winton U. Redeem the Time: The Puritan Sabbath in Early America. (Illus.). 1977. 25.00x (ISBN 0-674-75130-2). Harvard U Pr.
Wansbrough, Dom H. The Sunday Word: A Commentary on the Sunday Readings. 400p. 1984. pap. 14.95 (ISBN 0-225-66254-X, HarpR). Har-Row.
Why a Gift on Sunday. 1979. 2.95 (ISBN 0-8198-0603-X); pap. 1.95 (ISBN 0-8198-0604-8). Dghtrs St Paul.

SUNDAY LEGISLATION

Blakely, W. A., ed. American State Papers Bearing on Sunday Legislation. LC 79-122165. (Civil Liberties in American History Ser.). 1970. Repr. of 1911 ed. lib. bdg. 95.00 (ISBN 0-306-71973-8). Da Capo.
Friedenberg, Albert M. The Sunday Laws of the United States & Leading Judicial Decisions Having Special Reference to the Jews. LC 12-23685. 42p. 1986. pap. 12.50 (ISBN 0-89941-475-3). W S Hein.
Harris, George E. A Treatise on Sunday Laws: The Sabbath-the Lord's Day, Its History & Observance, Civil & Criminal. xxiii, 338p. 1980. Repr. of 1892 ed. lib. bdg. 32.50x (ISBN 0-8377-2232-2). Rothman.
Myers, Gustavus. Ye Olden Blue Laws. 274p. 1980. Repr. of 1921 ed. lib. bdg. 25.00 (ISBN 0-8495-3795-9). Arden Lib.
Sunday Work, 1794-1856. LC 72-2547. (British Labour Struggles Before 1850 Ser). (7 pamphlets). 1972. 12.00 (ISBN 0-405-04438-0). Ayer Co Pubs.

SUNDAY-SCHOOL SUPERINTENDENTS

see also Directors of Religious Education

Gangel, Kenneth. You Can Be an Effective Sunday School Superintendent. 64p. 1981. pap. 3.50 (ISBN 0-88207-141-6). Victor Bks.
Jones, Idris W. The Superintendent Plans His Work. 1956. pap. 4.95 (ISBN 0-8170-0172-7). Judson.
Leavitt, Guy P. Superintend with Success. rev. ed. Langston, A. Leon, ed. LC 79-66658. (Illus.). 144p. 1980. pap. 7.95 (ISBN 0-87239-377-1, 3203). Standard Pub.
Westing, Harold J. Super Superintendent: A Layman's Guide to Sunday School Management. LC 80-66721. (Accent Teacher Training Ser.). 160p. (Orig.). 1980. pap. 4.95 (ISBN 0-89636-057-1). Accent Bks.

SUNDAY-SCHOOLS

see also Bible–Study; Religious Education

Allen, Charles L. & Parker, Mildred. How to Increase Your Sunday School Attendance. 128p. 1980. 8.95 (ISBN 0-8007-1088-6). Revell.
Andersen, Richard. A Little Library of Inspiration for Sunday School Teachers. 1982. pap. 2.25 (ISBN 0-570-03846-4, 12-2949). Concordia.
Benson, C. H. Escuela Dominical en Accion. Villalobos, Fernando P., tr. from Eng. (Curso Para Maestros Cristianos: No. 6). (Span.). 122p. 1972. pap. 3.50 (ISBN 0-89922-018-5); instructor's manual 1.50 (ISBN 0-89922-019-3). Edit Caribe.
--Poesia y Profecia del Antiquo Testamento. Villalobos, Fernando P., tr. from Eng. (Curso Para Maestros Cristianos: No. 2). (Span.). 122p. 1972. pap. 3.50 (ISBN 0-89922-010-X). Edit Caribe.
Bower, Robert K. Administering Christian Education. LC 64-22018. 1964. pap. 8.95 (ISBN 0-8028-1559-6). Eerdmans.
Carey, Floyd D., ed. Sunday School Basics. 1976. 5.25 (ISBN 0-87148-778-0); pap. 4.25 (ISBN 0-87148-777-2). Pathway Pr.
Conaway, John. Teaching the Bible. (Complete Teacher Training Meeting ser.). 48p. 1986. tchr's ed 9.95 (ISBN 0-89191-319-X). Cook.
Coursen, Virgene. Bulletin Board Ideas for Sunday School & Church. 32p. 1977. pap. 3.50 (ISBN 0-687-04374-3). Abingdon.
Davis, Billie C. Dynamic Classroom. LC 86-83084. (Sunday School Staff Training Text for 1988). 144p. (Orig.). 1987. pap. 2.95 (ISBN 0-88243-798-4). Gospel Pub.
Deal, William S. The Sunday School Teacher's Guide, 1984. 1984. pap. 3.95 (ISBN 0-318-18717-5). Crusade Pubs.
Dresselhaus, Richard. Your Sunday School at Work. 78p. 1980. pap. 2.95 (ISBN 0-88243-793-3, 02-0793). Gospel Pub.
Duckert, Mary. Help: I'm a Sunday School Teacher. LC 77-83133. (Illus.). 126p. 1969. pap. 3.95 (ISBN 0-664-24862-4). Westminster.
Dunnett, W. M. Sintesis del Nuevo Testamento. Blanch, Jose M., tr. from Eng. (Curso Para Maestros Cristianos: No. 3). (Span.). 128p. 1972. pap. 3.50 (ISBN 0-89922-012-6). Edit Caribe.
Dyet, James T. Getting Through to Adults. LC 79-53294. (Accent Teacher Training Ser.). (Orig.). 1980. pap. 4.95 (ISBN 0-89636-037-7). Accent Bks.
Edge, Findley B. Helping the Teacher. 1959. 10.95 (ISBN 0-8054-3403-8). Broadman.
Edgerly, George A. & Crosby, Harold E. Strategies for Sunday School Growth. LC 83-80404. (Worker's Training Ser.). 128p. (Orig.). 1983. pap. 2.50 (ISBN 0-88243-591-4, 02-0591). Gospel Pub.
Fry, Malcolm C. Discipling & Developing. (Sunday School Workers Training Course Ser.: No. 4). 1971. pap. 3.95 (ISBN 0-89265-006-0, Free Will Baptist Dept). Randall Hse.
General Conference Sabbath School Department. Sabbath School Manual. rev. ed. 1982. pap. 5.50 (ISBN 0-8127-0228-X). Review & Herald.
Goodwin, Wayne & Cook, Gregory D. The Serving Sunday School. (Complete Teacher Training Meeting Ser.). 48p. 1986. tchr's ed 9.95 (ISBN 0-89191-315-7). Cook.
Hall, Terry. How to Be the Best Sunday School Teacher You Can Be. (Orig.). 1986. pap. 6.95 (ISBN 0-8024-3631-5). Moody.
Hanson, Richard S. The Sunday Church School Teacher. 1986. 5.95 (ISBN 0-89536-796-3, 6814); leader's guide 1.75 (ISBN 0-89536-806-4, 6824). CSS of Ohio.
Harner, Nevin C. Factors Related to Sunday School Growth & Decline in the Eastern Synod of the Reformed Church in the U. S. LC 71-176839. (Columbia University. Teachers College. Contributions to Education Ser.: No. 479). Repr. of 1931 ed. 22.50 (ISBN 0-404-55479-2). AMS Pr.
Harrison, Harrold D. Commissioned to Communicate. (Sunday School Workers Training Course Ser.: No. 2). 1969. pap. 3.95 (ISBN 0-89265-003-6, Free Will Baptist Dept). Randall Hse.
Hawley. The True Confessions of a Sunday School Teacher. 1983. 3.95 (ISBN 0-88207-285-4). Victor Bks.
Hill, William. Organizing & Developing a Free Will Baptist Sunday School. (Sunday School Workers Training Course Ser.: No. 1). 1969. pap. 3.95 (ISBN 0-89265-002-8, Free Will Baptist Dept). Randall Hse.
Humbertson, Jame E., ed. Evangelical Sunday School Lesson Commentary, 1982-1983. (YA) 1982. 3.65 (ISBN 0-87148-298-3). Pathway Pr.
Humbertson, James E., ed. Evangelical Sunday School Lesson Commentary 1980-1981. 448p. 3.50 (ISBN 0-87148-294-0). Pathway Pr.

Jahsmann, Allan H. Church Teaching Her Young. 1967. text ed. 3.75 (ISBN 0-570-06330-2, 22-1287); teacher's guide 4.50 (ISBN 0-570-06331-0, 22-1289). Concordia.
Jansen, Harris. The Making of a Sunday School. 128p. 1972. pap. 1.95 (ISBN 0-88243-737-2, 02-0737). Gospel Pub.
Joy, Donald M. Meaningful Learning in the Church. 1969. 3.25 (ISBN 0-89367-019-7). Light & Life.
Klausmeier, Robert. Elementary Teacher Survival Kit. 80p. 1986. tchr's ed 9.95 (ISBN 0-89191-363-7). Cook.
--Teen Teacher Survival Kit. 80p. 1986. tchr's ed 9.95 (ISBN 0-89191-364-5). Cook.
Latham, Joy. Living & Learning with Nursery Children. (Teaching Helps Ser.). 128p. 1976. pap. 2.95 (ISBN 0-8010-5562-8). Baker Bk.
Lebar, Lois & Berg, Miguel. Llamados a Ensenar. Blanch, Jose M., tr. from Eng. LC 77-5183. (Span., Illus.). 160p. 1970. pap. 3.95 (ISBN 0-89922-006-1). Edit Caribe.
McBride, Neal F. Teacher! A Christlike Model in Students. (Complete Teacher Training Meeting Ser.). 48p. 1986. 9.95 (ISBN 0-89191-313-0). Cook.
Martin, William J. The Church in Mission: Sunday School Staff Training Text for 1987. LC 86-80022. 128p. (Orig.). 1986. pap. 2.50 (ISBN 0-88243-803-4, 02-0803). Gospel Pub.
Merril, Dean. Teaching for Life-Response. (Complete Teacher Training Meeting Ser.). 48p. 1986. 9.95 (ISBN 0-89191-316-5). Cook.
Murray, Dick. Strengthening the Adult Sunday School Class. LC 81-3667. (Creative Leadership Ser.). 128p. (Orig.). 1981. pap. 6.95 (ISBN 0-687-39989-0). Abingdon.
O'Donnell, J. D. Faith for Today. LC 65-29130. (Sunday School Workers Training Course Ser.: No. 5). 1974. pap. 3.95 (ISBN 0-89265-000-1). Randall Hse.
Owens, Joanne. The Unofficial Sunday School Teacher's Handbook. (Illus.). 240p. (Orig.). 1987. pap. 7.95 (ISBN 0-916260-42-9). Meriwether Pub.
Poganski, Donald J. Fifty Object Lessons. 1967. 4.50 (ISBN 0-570-03172-9, 12-2282). Concordia.
Pole, Thomas. A History of the Origin & Progress of Adult Schools: With an Account of Some Beneficial Effects. (First Ser. in the Social History of Education: No. 8). 108p. 1968. Repr. of 1814 ed. 25.00x (ISBN 0-7130-0009-0, Pub. by Woburn Pr England). Biblio Dist.
Reeds, Roger C. Pupil Profiles. (Sunday School Workers Training Course Ser.: No. 3). 1973. pap. 3.95 (ISBN 0-89265-010-9). Randall Hse.
Rexroat, Stephen V. The Sunday School Spirit. LC 79-51833. (Workers Training Book of the Year Ser.). 128p. (Orig.). 1979. pap. 1.50 (ISBN 0-88243-594-9, 02-0594). Gospel Pub.
Ryan, Roy. Strong Sunday Schools-Strong Churches: The Pastor's Role. LC 86-71810. 72p. (Orig.). 1987. pap. 4.95 (ISBN 0-88177-035-3, DR035B). Discipleship Res.
Schaal, John H. Feed My Sheep. 1972. pap. 1.95 (ISBN 0-8010-7958-6). Baker Bk.
Sisemore, John T. Rejoice, You're a Sunday School Teacher. LC 76-20053. 1977. 9.50 (ISBN 0-8054-5147-1). Broadman.
Taulman, James E. Encouragers: The Sunday School Worker's Counseling Ministry. LC 85-19523. 1986. pap. 4.95 (ISBN 0-8054-3712-6). Broadman.
Thomas, W. W. Sunday School Outreach. 112p. 1979. 5.25 (ISBN 0-87148-787-X); pap. 4.25 (ISBN 0-87148-788-8). Pathway Pr.
Towns, Elmer. The Successful Sunday School & Teachers Guidebook. revised ed. LC 75-23009. (Illus.). 430p. 1986. pap. 10.95 (ISBN 0-88419-118-4). Creation Hse.
Understanding Sunday School. 96p. 1980. pap. text ed. 4.95 (ISBN 0-910566-31-3); Perfect bdg. instr's guide by Robert E. Clark 5.95 (ISBN 0-910566-32-1). Evang Tchr.
Varner, Jeanne. How to Make Children's Church Come Alive. 1979. 4.95 (ISBN 0-87148-407-2). Pathway Pr.
Wayne, Jones R. Overcoming Barriers to Sunday School Growth. LC 86-23290. (Orig.). 1987. pap. 5.95 (ISBN 0-8054-3238-8). Broadman.
Wyckoff, D. Campbell, ed. Renewing the Sunday School & the CCD. LC 85-19419. 254p. (Orig.). 1986. pap. 14.95 (ISBN 0-89135-053-5). Religious Educ.

SUNDAY-SCHOOLS–EXERCISES, RECITATIONS, ETC.

Abbott, Grace, ed. Ideas for Use with Two's & Three's. 176p. (Orig.). 1985. pap. 7.95 (ISBN 0-8341-1056-3). Beacon Hill.
Dorsett, Judy. Handbook of Creativity. (Illus.). 128p. 1985. pap. 7.95 (ISBN 0-87239-729-7, 3226). Standard Pub.
Earle, Ralph. Peloubet's Sunday School Notes, 1987-1988. 1987. pap. 7.95 (ISBN 0-8010-3439-6). Baker Bk.
Humbertson, James E., ed. Evangelical Sunday School Lesson Commentary, 1981-1982. 448p. text ed. 3.65 (ISBN 0-87148-297-5). Pathway Pr.
Ison, Colleen. Skits That Teach. (Illus.). 112p. 1985. pap. 4.95 (ISBN 0-87239-848-X, 3356). Standard Pub.
Smith, Sidney. Ten Super Sunday Schools in the Black Community. LC 86-926. 1986. pap. 5.95 (ISBN 0-8054-6252-X). Broadman.
Talbot, Gordon, et al. Higley Sunday School Commentary. Triplett, Loren, ed. (Illus.). 528p. (Orig.). 1985. text ed. 8.95 (ISBN 0-9614116-1-9); pap. text ed. 6.95 (ISBN 0-9614116-0-0). Higley.
Taylor, Robert. Studies in James & Jude. 2.50 (ISBN 0-89315-293-5). Lambert Bk.
Weisheit, Eldon. To the Kid in the Pew-Series A. LC 74-4548. 128p. 1974. 6.75 (ISBN 0-570-03238-5, 15-2132). Concordia.
Witter, Evelyn. How to Make Sunday School Fun for Everyone. Ronaldson, Dolores, ed. LC 82-62793. (Illus.). 80p. 1983. pap. text ed. 6.95 (ISBN 0-916260-22-4). Meriwether Pub.

SUNDAY-SCHOOLS–HISTORY

Anderson, Andy. Effective Methods of Church Growth. LC 85-6620. 1985. pap. 5.95 (ISBN 0-8054-3237-X). Broadman.
Laqueur, Thomas W. Religion & Respectability: Sunday Schools & English Working Class Culture, 1780-1850. LC 74-29728. 1976. 38.50x (ISBN 0-300-01859-2). Yale U Pr.
Lynn, Robert W. & Wright, Elliott. The Big Little School: Two Hundred Years of Sunday School. 178p. 1980. pap. 7.75 (ISBN 0-687-03523-6). Abingdon.
Rice, Edwin W. Sunday-School Movement, 1780-1917, & the American Sunday-School Union, 1817-1917. LC 70-165728. (American Education Ser, No. 2). (Illus.). 1971. Repr. of 1917 ed. 36.00 (ISBN 0-405-03717-1). Ayer Co Pubs.
Sisemore, John T. Church Growth Through the Sunday School. LC 82-70870. (Orig.). 1983. pap. 6.50 (ISBN 0-8054-6237-6). Broadman.
Sokolosky, Barbara A., ed. American Sunday School Union Papers, 1817-1915: A Guide to the Microfilm Edition. 154p. (Orig.). 1980. pap. text ed. 50.00 (ISBN 0-667-00582-X). Microfilming Corp.

SUNDAY-SCHOOLS–HYMNS

see also Children's Hymns

Burow, Daniel R. & Greene, Carol, eds. The Little Christian's Songbook. 64p. 1975. pap. 5.50 (56-1266). Concordia.
Gross, Arthur W. & Jahsmann, Allan H. Little Children Sing to God! 1960. 8.95 (ISBN 0-570-03471-X, 56-1036). Concordia.
Hartzler, Arlene & Gaeddert, John, eds. Children's Hymnary. LC 67-24327. 1967. 5.95 (ISBN 0-87303-095-8). Faith & Life.
Hymnal for Juniors in Worship & Study. 2.25 (ISBN 0-664-10082-1). Westminster.
Lunde, Alfred E. Christian Education Thru Music. LC 78-51509. (Evangelical Leadership Preparation Ser.). 80p. 1978. pap. 3.95 (ISBN 0-910566-83-6). Evang Tchr.
Miller, Max B. & Drew, Louise C., eds. Sing of Life & Faith. LC 68-22233. (Illus.). 1969. 5.95 (ISBN 0-8298-0123-5). Pilgrim NY.
Olson, Ruth L., ed. Hymns & Songs for Church Schools. LC 62-13898. (Illus.). 1962. 7.95 ea. (12-1500). 25 or more 7.65 ea. Augsburg.
Royer, Katherine, ed. Nursery Songbook. (Illus.). 48p. 1957. pap. 2.95x (ISBN 0-8361-1278-4). Herald Pr.
Songs for Young Children. LC 75-40910. (Illus.). 1976. spiral bdg. 3.50 (ISBN 0-916406-31-8). Accent Bks.
Stauffer, J. Mark, ed. Our Hymns of Praise. (Illus.). 168p. 1958. 4.95x (ISBN 0-8361-1126-5). Herald Pr.
Stelzer, Theodore G. Child's Garden of Song. (Concordia Primary Religion Ser). 1949. 9.95 (ISBN 0-570-03479-5, 56-1003). Concordia.

SUPERIORS, RELIGIOUS

see also Abbots

Alberione, James. Superior Follows the Master. (Orig.). 1965. pap. 2.00 (ISBN 0-8198-0153-4). Dghtrs St Paul.

SUPERMAN

see also Demonology; Messiah

Berg, Leo. The Superman in Modern Literature: Flaubert, Carlyle, Emerson, Nietzsche. Repr. 20.00 (ISBN 0-8274-3555-X). R West.
Guedalla, Philip. Super & Superman. 1924. Repr. 20.00 (ISBN 0-8274-3554-1). R West.
Magnus, Bernd. Nietzsche's Existential Imperative. LC 77-9864. (Studies in Phenomenology & Existential Philosophy Ser.). 256p. 1978. 20.00x (ISBN 0-253-34062-4). Ind U Pr.

SUPERNATURAL

see also Inspiration; Miracles; Psychical Research; Revelation; Spirits; Superstition

Bennett, Charles A. Dilemma of Religious Knowledge. LC 71-85986. (Essay & General Literature Index Reprint Ser). 1969. pap. text ed. 15.95x (ISBN 0-8046-0538-6, Pub. by Kennikat). Assoc Faculty Pr.
Blashford-Snell, John. Mysteries: Encounters with the Unexplained. 256p. 1984. 16.95 (ISBN 0-370-30479-9, Pub. by Bodley Head). Salem Hse Pubs.
Bright, Bill. Promises: A Daily Guide to Supernatural Living. LC 82-72302. 365p. 1983. 9.95 (ISBN 0-317-00638-X). Campus Crusade.
Bushnell, Horace. Nature & the Supernatural As Together Constituting the One System of God. LC 70-39569. Repr. of 1858 ed. 29.50 (ISBN 0-404-01246-9). AMS Pr.
Casaubon, Meric. A Letter of Meric Casaubon to Peter du Moulin Concerning Natural Experimental Philosophie. LC 76-47045. 1976. Repr. of 1669 ed. 90.00x (ISBN 0-8201-1284-4). Schol Facsimiles.
Case, Shirley J. Experience with the Supernatural in Early Christian Times. LC 75-174851. Repr. of 1929 ed. 26.50 (ISBN 0-405-08345-9, Blom Pubns). Ayer Co Pubs.
Eberhart, George M. Monsters: A Guide to Information on Unaccounted for Creatures, Including Bigfoot, Many Water Monsters, & Other Irregular Animals. LC 82-49029. (Supernatural Studies). 358p. 1983. lib. bdg. 28.00 (ISBN 0-8240-9213-4). Garland Pub.
Hufford, David J. The Terror That Comes in the Night: An Experience Centered Study of Supernatural Assault Traditions. LC 82-40350. 352p. 1982. 27.50x (ISBN 0-8122-7851-8). U of Pa Pr.
Kelsey, Morton. The Christian & the Supernatural. LC 76-3865. 160p. (Orig.). 1976. pap. 8.95 (ISBN 0-8066-1525-7, 10-1100). Augsburg.
Kenny, John P. The Supernatural. new ed. LC 72-3575. 165p. 1972. 4.95 (ISBN 0-8189-0251-5). Alba.
Knox, Ian P. Above or Within? The Supernatural in Religious Education. LC 76-55589. 164p. (Orig.). 1977. pap. 10.95 (ISBN 0-89135-006-3). Religious Educ.
McCosh, James. The Supernatural in Relation to the Natural. LC 75-3267. Repr. of 1862 ed. 38.00 (ISBN 0-404-59255-4). AMS Pr.
Oman, John W. The Natural & the Supernatural. LC 79-39696. (Select Bibliographies Reprint Ser.). 1972. Repr. of 1931 ed. 20.75 (ISBN 0-8369-9941-X). Ayer Co Pubs.
Phillips, McCandlish. The Bible, the Supernatural & the Jews. LC 77-92532. 1970. pap. 8.95 (ISBN 0-87123-036-4, 210036). Bethany Hse.
Prince, Derek. Philosophy, the Bible & the Supernatural. 1969. pap. 0.10 (ISBN 0-934920-22-2, B71). Derek Prince.
Reader's Digest Editors. Mysteries of the Unexplained. LC 82-60791. (Illus.). 320p. 1983. 21.95 (ISBN 0-89577-146-2, Pub. by RD Assn). Random.
Spiro, Melford E. Burmese Supernaturalism. enlarged ed. LC 77-17280. pap. 84.00 (ISBN 0-317-42082-8, 2025708). Bks Demand UMI.
Stead, W. T. Borderland: A Casebook of True Supernatural Stories. LC 69-16361. 358p. 1970. 5.95 (ISBN 0-8216-0058-3). Univ Bks.
Summers, Montague. Supernatural Omnibus. 624p. 1982. 22.50 (ISBN 0-575-03120-4, Pub. by Gollancz England). David & Charles.

SUPERNATURAL (THEOLOGY)

see also Beatific Vision

Ashcroft, J. Robert. The Sequence of the Supernatural. 80p. 1972. pap. 1.00 (ISBN 0-88243-748-8, 02-0748). Gospel Pub.
Korem, Danny & Meier, Paul. The Fakers: Exploding the Myths of the Supernatural. LC 80-23180. (Illus.). 1981. pap. 4.95 (ISBN 0-8010-5435-4). Baker Bk.

SUPERSTITION

see also Apparitions; Demonology; Evil Eye; Exorcism; Fetishism; Folk-Lore; Incantations; Omens; Voodooism; Witchcraft

Ashley, Leonard R. The Wonderful World of Superstition, Prophecy & Luck. LC 83-23182. (Illus.). 192p. (Orig.). 1984. pap. 8.95 (ISBN 0-934878-33-1). Dembner Bks.
Blinkenberg, C. The Thunderweapon in Religion & Folklore. xii, 122p. 1985. Repr. of 1911 ed. lib. bdg. 25.00x (ISBN 0-89241-205-4). Caratzas.
Bonnerjea, Biren. Dictionary of Superstitions & Mythology. LC 69-17755. 1969. Repr. of 1927 ed. 43.00x (ISBN 0-8103-3572-7). Gale.
Bormann, Eugenie. Glauben und Aberglauben. LC 84-70173. 120p. 23.00x (ISBN 0-938100-32-7). Camden Hse.
Canavaggio, Pierre. Dictionnaire Raisonne Des Superstitions et Des Croyances Populaires. (Fr.). 247p. 1977. pap. 19.95 (ISBN 0-686-56937-7, M-6059). French & Eur.
Cannon, Anthon S., et al, eds. Popular Beliefs & Superstitions from Utah. 526p. 1984. 45.00x (ISBN 0-87480-236-9). U of Utah Pr.
Chaundler, Christine. The Book of Superstitions. pap. 2.45 (ISBN 0-8065-0302-5). Citadel Pr.
Crosby, Nina E. & Marten, Elizabeth H. Don't Teach! Let Me Learn about World War II, Adventure, Dreams & Superstition. (The Dont't Teach! Let Me Learn Ser.). (Illus.). 72p. (Orig.). 1984. 5.95 (ISBN 0-88047-044-5, 8411). DOK Pubs.
Deerforth, Daniel. Knock Wood! Superstition Through the Ages. LC 79-164220. 200p. 1974. Repr. of 1928 ed. 43.00x (ISBN 0-8103-3964-1). Gale.
DeLys, Claudia. Giant Book of Superstitions. 1979. pap. 5.95 (ISBN 0-8065-0721-7). Citadel Pr.
D'Holbach, Paul H. & Meslier, Jean. Superstition in All Ages. 69.95 (ISBN 0-87968-108-X). Gordon Pr.
Dobie, J. Frank, ed. Spur-Of-The-Cock. LC 34-1434. (Texas Folklore Society Publications: No. 11). 1965. Repr. of 1933 ed. 11.95 (ISBN 0-87074-043-1). SMU Press.
Dore, Henri. Researches into Chinese Superstitions, 5 vols. (vols. I-X & XIII) Repr. of 1914 ed. Set. text ed. 97.00x (ISBN 0-89644-108-3, Pub. by Chinese Matl Ctr). Coronet Bks.
Elworthy, Frederick T. The Evil Eye: An Account of This Ancient & Widespread Superstition. (Illus.). 1986. pap. 7.95 (ISBN 0-517-55971-4, Julian). Crown.
Frazer, J. G. Psyche's Task: A Discourse Concerning the Influence of Superstition on the Growth of Institutions. 2nd ed. 1979. Repr. of 1913 ed. lib. bdg. 27.50 (ISBN 0-8495-1636-6). Arden Lib.
Hedley, George P. The Superstitions of the Irreligious. LC 78-10274. 1979. Repr. of 1951 ed. lib. bdg. 22.50x (ISBN 0-313-20755-0, HESU). Greenwood.
Higgens, Elford. Hebrew Idolatry & Superstition. 1971. Repr. of 1893 ed. 19.50x (ISBN 0-8046-1150-5, Pub. by Kennikat). Assoc Faculty Pr.
Igglesden, Charles. Those Superstitions. LC 73-12798. 1974. Repr. of 1932 ed. 40.00x (ISBN 0-8103-3621-9). Gale.
Jahoda, Gustav. The Psychology of Superstition. LC 74-9667. 158p. 1974. Repr. 20.00x (ISBN 0-87668-185-2). Aronson.
Knowlson, Thomas S. Origins of Popular Superstitions & Customs. LC 68-30946. 1968. Repr. of 1910 ed. 36.00x (ISBN 0-8103-3357-0). Gale.
Lasne, Sophie & Gaultier, Andre P. A Dictionary of Superstitions. LC 84-11717. 304p. 1984. 20.95 (ISBN 0-13-210881-X); pap. 10.95 (ISBN 0-13-210873-9). P-H.
Mallock, W. H. Studies in Contemporary Superstition. 1973. Repr. of 1895 ed. 25.00 (ISBN 0-8274-1566-4). R West.
Mallock, William H. Studies of Contemporary Superstition. LC 72-333. (Essay Index Reprint Ser.). Repr. of 1895 ed. 20.00 (ISBN 0-8369-2804-0). Ayer Co Pubs.
Maple. Superstition, Are You Superstitious? pap. 2.00 (ISBN 0-87980-245-6). Wilshire.
Meslier, Jean. Superstition in All Ages. Knoop, Anna, tr. from Fr. LC 77-161337. (Atheist Viewpoint Ser). (Illus.). 346p. 1972. Repr. of 1890 ed. 23.50 (ISBN 0-405-03795-3). Ayer Co Pubs.
Nevins, Ann. Super Stitches: A Book of Superstitions. LC 82-15875. (Illus.). 64p. 1983. reinforced bdg. 9.95 (ISBN 0-8234-0476-5). Holiday.
O'Farrell, Padraic. Superstitions of the Irish Country People. rev. ed. 92p. 1982. pap. 5.95 (ISBN 0-85342-530-2, Pub. by Mercier Pr Ireland). Irish Bks Media.
Oman, John C. Cults, Customs, & Superstitions of India: Being a Revised & Enlarged Edition of Indian Life, Religious & Social. LC 70-179232. (Illus.). Repr. of 1908 ed. 36.00 (ISBN 0-404-54859-8). AMS Pr.
Platt, Charles. Popular Superstitions. LC 70-167114. 244p. 1973. Repr. of 1925 ed. 46.00x (ISBN 0-8103-3170-5). Gale.
Radford, Edwin & Radford, Mona A. Encyclopedia of Superstitions. Repr. of 1949 ed. lib. bdg. 45.00x (ISBN 0-8371-2115-9, RASU). Greenwood.
Rappoport, Angelo S. Superstitions of Sailors. LC 71-158207. 1971. Repr. of 1928 ed. 43.00x (ISBN 0-8103-3739-8). Gale.
Rosenbaum, Brenda. How to Avoid the Evil Eye: Five Thousand Years of Jewish Superstition. (Illus.). 96p. 1985. pap. 5.95 (ISBN 0-312-39584-1). St Martin.
Shorr, Philip. Science & Superstition in the Eighteenth Century: A Study of the Treatment of Science in Two Encyclopedias of 1725-1750. LC 33-3916. (Columbia University. Studies in the Social Sciences: No. 364). Repr. of 1932 ed. 10.00 (ISBN 0-404-51364-6). AMS Pr.
Shortland, Edward. Traditions & Superstitions of the New Zealanders. 2nd ed. LC 75-35270. Repr. of 1856 ed. 32.50 (ISBN 0-404-14439-X). AMS Pr.
Siebers, Tobin. The Mirror of Medusa. LC 82-20071. (Illus.). 180p. 1983. text ed. 26.95x (ISBN 0-520-04856-3). U of Cal Pr.
Sinclair, George. Satan's Invisible World Discovered. LC 68-17017. 1969. Repr. of 1685 ed. 45.00x (ISBN 0-8201-1068-X). Schol Facsimiles.

Steele, Phillip W. Ozark Tales & Superstitions. LC 82-22425. (Illus.). 96p. 1983. pap. 4.95 (ISBN 0-88289-404-8). Pelican.

Thompson, C. J. Hand of Destiny: The Folk-Lore & Superstition of Everyday Life. LC 70-125600. 1970. Repr. of 1932 ed. 46.00x (ISBN 0-8103-3419-4). Gale.

Trachtenberg, Joshua. Jewish Magic & Superstition. LC 39-14212. (Temple Bks). 1970. pap. text ed. 6.95x (ISBN 0-689-70234-5, T15). Atheneum.

Two Thousand One Southern Superstitions. 2.00 (ISBN 0-936672-34-X). Aerial Photo.

Waterman, Philip F. Story of Superstition. LC 78-107770. Repr. of 1929 ed. 15.00 (ISBN 0-404-06849-9). AMS Pr.

SUPERSTITION IN LITERATURE

Siebers, Tobin. The Mirror of Medusa. LC 82-20071. (Illus.). 180p. 1983. text ed. 26.95x (ISBN 0-520-04856-3). U of Cal Pr.

SUPREMACY OF THE POPE

see Popes–Primacy

SUSS, HEINRICH, 1300-1366

Clark, James M. Great German Mystics: Eckhart, Tauler & Suso. LC 73-81493. 1970. Repr. of 1949 ed. 15.00x (ISBN 0-8462-1351-6). Russell.

SUSSEX, ENGLAND

Curtis, Lewis P. Chichester Towers. LC 66-21514. (Illus.). Repr. of 1966 ed. 32.50 (ISBN 0-8357-1319-9, 2013199). Bks Demand UMI.

SUTRAS

Anand, Mulk R., ed. Kama Sutra of Vatsyayana. 276p. 1981. text ed. 125.00x (ISBN 0-391-02224-5). Humanities.

Aranya, Hariharananda. Samkhya-Sutras of Pancasikha & the Samkhyatattvalcka. 1977. 11.25 (ISBN 0-89684-313-0, Pub. by Motilal Banarsidass India); pap. 6.95 (ISBN 0-89684-346-7). Orient Bk Dist.

Conze, Edward. The Large Sutra on Perfect Wisdom: With the Divisions of the Abhisamayalankara. LC 71-189224. (Center for South & Southeastern Asia Studies, UC Berkeley). 697p. 1985. pap. 12.95 (ISBN 0-520-05321-4, CAL 668). U of Cal Pr.

Conze, Edward, tr. from Sanskrit. & pref. by. The Perfection of Wisdom in Eight Thousand Lines & Its Verse Summary. LC 72-76540. (Wheel Ser.: No. 1). 348p. 1973. 15.00 (ISBN 0-87704-048-6); pap. 8.95 (ISBN 0-87704-049-4). Four Seasons Foun.

Emmerick, R. E. The Sutra of Golden Light: A Mahayana Text. 1980. write for info. Dharma Pub.

Gangopadhyaya, M., tr. Nyaya: Gautama's Nyaya Sutra with Vatsyayana's Commentary. 1983. 28.50x (ISBN 0-8364-1000-9, Pub. by Indian Stud). South Asia Bks.

Gautama Buddha. The Diamond Sutra. (Sacred Texts Ser.). viii, 72p. 1983. pap. 8.75 (ISBN 0-88695-004-X). Concord Grove.

Heng Sure & Heng Chau. With One Heart Bowing to the City of Ten Thousand Buddhas, Vol. VI. (Illus.). 200p. (Orig.). 1981. pap. 6.00 (ISBN 0-917512-92-8). Buddhist Text.

Hua, Tripitaka Master. Heart Sutra & Verses Without a Stand, With Prose Commentary. Buddhist Text Translation Society, tr. from Chinese. (Illus.). 160p. (Orig.). 1980. pap. 7.50 (ISBN 0-917512-27-8). Buddhist Text.

Hua, Tripitaka Master, commentary by. Flower Adornment Sutra, Chapter 39: Entering the Dharma Realm Part VIII. Buddhist Text Translation Society, tr. from Chinese. 228p. (Orig.). 1984. pap. 8.50 (ISBN 0-88139-055-0). Buddhist Text.

Hui Seng, commentary by. Brahma Net Sutra, Vol. 1. Buddhist Text Translation Society, tr. from Chinese. (Illus.). 312p. (Orig., Bilingual Text). 1981. pap. 10.00 (ISBN 0-917512-79-0). Buddhist Text.

Jacobi, H. Gaina Sutras, 2 vols. lib. bdg. 200.00 (ISBN 0-87968-526-3). Krishna Pr.

Jaimini. The Mimamsa Sutras of Jaimini. Sandal, Mohan L., tr. LC 73-3820. (Sacred Books of the Hindus: No. 27). (Eng. & Sanskrit.). Repr. of 1925 ed. 79.50 (ISBN 0-404-57827-6). AMS Pr.

--The Purva-Mimamsa-Sutras of Jaimini. Jha, Ganganath, tr. & commentary by. LC 73-3797. (Sacred Books of the Hindus: No. 10). Repr. of 1916 ed. 55.00 (ISBN 0-404-57810-1). AMS Pr.

Kanada. The Vaisesika Sutras of Kanada, with the Commentary of Sankara & Extracts from the Gloss of Jayanarayana. Sinha, Nandalal, tr. & intro. by. Incl. Notes from the Commentary of Chandrakanta. LC 73-3791. (Sacred Books of the Hindus: No. 6). Repr. of 1911 ed. 42.50 (ISBN 0-404-57806-3). AMS Pr.

Kato, Bunno, et al, trs. The Threefold Lotus Sutra. LC 74-23158. Orig. Title: Hokke Sambu-Kyo. 404p. 1975. 19.75 (ISBN 0-8348-0105-1); pap. 10.95 (ISBN 0-8348-0106-X). Weatherhill.

Leggett, Trevor. Shankara on the Yoga Sutras. (Vol. 1). 140p. 1981. 30.00 (ISBN 0-7100-0826-0). Methuen Inc.

Master Hua, Tripitaka, commentary by. Dharma Flower Sutra, Vol. IV. Buddhist Text Translation Society, tr. from Chinese. (Illus.). 371p. (Orig.). 1980. pap. 9.00 (ISBN 0-917512-62-6). Buddhist Text.

--Dharma Flower Sutra, Vol. VII. Buddhist Text Translation Society, tr. from Chinese. (Illus.). 250p. (Orig.). 1980. pap. 8.50 (ISBN 0-917512-93-6). Buddhist Text.

--Dharma Flower Sutra, Vol. VIII. Buddhist Text Translation Society, tr. from Chinese. (Illus.). 160p. (Orig.). 1980. pap. 8.00 (ISBN 0-917512-71-5). Buddhist Text.

--Flower Adornment Sutra, Chapter 39: Entering the Dharma Realm., Part I. Buddhist Text Translation Society, tr. from Chinese. (Illus.). 284p. (Orig.). 1980. pap. 8.50 (ISBN 0-917512-68-5). Buddhist Text.

--Flower Adornment Sutra, Chapter 39: Entering the Dharma Realm, Part II. Buddhist Text Translation Society, tr. from Chinese. (Illus.). 312p. (Orig.). 1980. pap. 8.50 (ISBN 0-917512-70-7). Buddhist Text.

--Shurangama Sutra, Vol. 3. Buddhist Text Translation Society, tr. from Chinese. (Illus.). 240p. (Orig.). 1980. pap. 8.50 (ISBN 0-917512-94-4). Buddhist Text.

--Shurangama Sutra, Vol. 4. Buddhist Text Translation Society, tr. from Chinese. (Illus.). 285p. (Orig.). 1980. pap. 8.50 (ISBN 0-917512-90-1). Buddhist Text.

--Shurangama Sutra, Vol. 5. Buddhist Text Translation Society, tr. from Chinese. (Illus.). 250p. (Orig.). 1980. pap. 8.50 (ISBN 0-917512-91-X). Buddhist Text.

Mullin, Glenn, et al. Selected Works of the Dalai Lama I: Bridging the Sutras & Tantras. Rev. ed. LC 85-8333. (Teachings of the Dalai Lamas Ser.). Orig. Title: Bridging the Sutras & Tantras. (Tibetan., Illus.). 288p. (Orig.). 1985. pap. 12.95 (ISBN 0-937938-27-0). Snow Lion.

National Master Ch'ing Liang. Flower Adornment Sutra Preface. Bilingual ed. Tripitaka Master Hua, commentary by. Buddhist Text Translation Society, tr. from Chinese. (Illus.). 244p. (Orig.). 1980. pap. 7.00 (ISBN 0-917512-28-6). Buddhist Text.

--Flower Adornment Sutra Prologue: Vol. II, The Second Door, Part I. Tripitaka Master Hua, commentary by. Buddhist Text Translation Society, tr. from Chinese. (Illus.). 280p. (Orig.). 1981. pap. 10.00 (ISBN 0-917512-73-1). Buddhist Text.

--Flower Adornment Sutra Prologue, Vol. IV: The Second Door, Part III. Buddhist Text Translation Society, tr. from Chinese. 170p. (Orig.). 1983. pap. 8.00 (ISBN 0-88139-009-7). Buddhist Text.

O'Neil, Kevin. The Diamond Sutra. 1978. pap. 5.00 (ISBN 0-86627-004-3). Crises Res Pr.

Parasurama. Bases of Tantra Sadhana. Pandit, M. P., tr. (Sanskrit.). 52p. 1980. 2.00 (ISBN 0-941524-02-7). Lotus Light.

Patanjali. Yoga Sutras of Patanjali. 7th ed. Johnston, Charles, tr. from Sanskrit. 1984. pap. 6.00 (ISBN 0-914732-08-0). Bro Life Inc.

Rajneesh, Bhagwan Shree. The Heart Sutra. Sudha, ma Yoga, ed. LC 78-908490. (Buddha Ser.). (Illus.). 332p. (Orig.). 1978. 16.95 (ISBN 0-88050-078-6). Chidvilas Found.

Sivanada, Swami. Brahma Sutras. 2nd ed. 1977. pap. 28.00 (ISBN 0-89684-181-2, Pub. by Motilal Banarsidass India). Orient Bk Dist.

Tola, Fernanda & Carmen, D. The Yoga Sutra of Patanjali on Concentration of Mind. 1986. 21.00 (ISBN 81-208-0258-6, Pub. by Motilal Banarsidass). South Asia Bks.

Tripitaka Master Hua. The Dharma Flower Sutra; Vol. I: Introduction. Buddhist Text Translation Society, tr. from Chinese. (Illus.). 85p. (Orig.). 1977. pap. 5.00 (ISBN 0-917512-16-2). Buddhist Text.

--The Shurangama Mantra: A Commentary, Vol. I. Buddhist Text Translation Society, tr. from Chinese. (Illus.). 296p. (Orig.). 1981. pap. 8.50 (ISBN 0-917512-69-3). Buddhist Text.

Tripitaka Master Hua, commentary by. The Dharani Sutra. Buddhist Text Translation Society, tr. from Chinese. (Illus.). 352p. (Orig.). 1976. pap. 12.00 (ISBN 0-917512-13-8). Buddhist Text.

--Dharma Flower Sutra, Vol. IX. Buddhist Text Translation Society, tr. from Chinese. (Illus.). 270p. (Orig.). 1982. pap. 8.50 (ISBN 0-917512-85-5). Buddhist Text.

--Dharma Flower Sutra, Vol. III. Buddhist Text Translation Society, tr. from Chinese. (Illus.). 183p. (Orig.). 1979. pap. 8.00 (ISBN 0-917512-26-X). Buddhist Text.

--Flower Adornment Sutra, Chapter 16: Brahma Conduct. Buddhist Text Translation Society, tr. from Chinese. (Illus.). 86p. (Orig.). 1981. pap. 5.00 (ISBN 0-917512-80-4). Buddhist Text.

--Flower Adornment Sutra, Chapter 26: The Ten Grounds, Part Two. Buddhist Text Translation Society, tr. from Chinese. (Illus.). 200p. (Orig.). 1981. pap. 8.00 (ISBN 0-917512-74-X). Buddhist Text.

--Flower Adornment Sutra, Chapter 39: Entering the Dharma Realm, Part IV. Buddhist Text Translation Society, tr. from Chinese. (Illus.). 280p. (Orig.). 1981. pap. 8.00 (ISBN 0-917512-76-6). Buddhist Text.

--The Shurangama Sutra, Vol. 1. Buddhist Text Translation Society, tr. from Chinese. (Illus.). 289p. (Orig.). 1977. pap. 9.00 (ISBN 0-917512-17-0). Buddhist Text.

--Shurangama Sutra, Vol. 6. Buddhist Text Translation Society, tr. from Chinese. (Illus.). 220p. (Orig.). 1981. pap. 8.50 (ISBN 0-917512-37-5). Buddhist Text.

--The Sutra in Forty-Two Sections. Buddhist Text Translation Society, tr. from Chinese. (Illus.). 114p. (Orig.). 1977. pap. 5.00 (ISBN 0-917512-15-4). Buddhist Text.

--Sutra of the Past Vows of Earth Store Bodhisattva. Buddhist Text Translation Society Staff, tr. from Chinese. (Illus.). 235p. (Orig.). 1976. 16.00 (ISBN 0-915078-00-7). Buddhist Text.

Upadhyaya, S. C., tr. from Sanskrit. Kama Sutra of Vatsyayana. (Illus.). xvi, 270p. 1981. Repr. of 1961 ed. text ed. 45.00x (ISBN 0-86590-027-2, Pub. by Taraporevala India). Apt Bks.

SWEDEN–CHURCH HISTORY

Anjou, Lars A. The History of the Reformation in Sweden. Mason, Henry M., tr. from Swedish. LC 83-45598. Date not set. Repr. of 1859 ed. 62.50 (ISBN 0-404-19866-X). AMS Pr.

Bergendoff, Conrad J. Olavus Petri & the Ecclesiastical Transformation in Sweden (1521-1552) A Study in the Swedish Reformation. LC 83-45600. Date not set. Repr. of 1928 ed. 32.50 (ISBN 0-404-19868-6). AMS Pr.

Ferre, Nels F. Swedish Contributions to Modern Theology: With Special Reference to Lundensian Thought. 1967. lib. bdg. 17.50x (ISBN 0-88307-092-8). Gannon.

Stendahl, Brita. The Force of Tradition: A Case Study of Women Priests in Sweden. LC 84-48713. (Illus.). 208p. 1985. pap. 14.95 (ISBN 0-8006-1808-4, 1-1808). Fortress.

Stromberg, Peter G. Symbols of Community: The Cultural System of a Swedish Church. LC 85-30229. (Anthropology of Form & Meaning Ser.). 127p. 1986. 17.95x (ISBN 0-8165-0967-0). U of Ariz Pr.

Waddams, Herbert M. The Swedish Church. LC 81-7021. (Illus.). viii, 70p. 1981. Repr. of 1946 ed. lib. bdg. 22.50x (ISBN 0-313-22184-7, WASW). Greenwood.

Wordsworth, John. National Church of Sweden. LC 11-35349. 1911. 20.00x (ISBN 0-8401-2821-5). A R Allenson.

SWEDENBORG, EMANUEL, 1688-1772

Acton, Alfred, ed. & tr. The Letters & Memorials of Emanuel Swedenborg, Vols. I & II. 1948. Set. 17.00 (ISBN 0-915221-04-7); Vol. I, 1709-1748, 508p. 9.00 (ISBN 0-915221-29-2); Vol. II, 1748-1772, 803p. 8.00 (ISBN 0-915221-30-6). Swedenborg Sci Assn.

Beaman, Edmund A. Swedenborg & the New Age. LC 77-134422. (Communal Societies in America Ser.). Repr. of 1881 ed. 18.00 (ISBN 0-404-08458-3). AMS Pr.

De Charms, George. Lectures on the Philosophy of Swedenborg's Principia. 68p. 1970. pap. 3.00 (ISBN 0-915221-39-X). Swedenborg Sci Assn.

Hitchcock, Ethan A. Swedenborg: A Hermetic Philosopher. 59.95 (ISBN 0-8490-1164-7). Gordon Pr.

James, Henry, Sr. The Secret of Swedenborg: Being an Elucidation of His Doctrine of the Divine Humanity. LC 72-914. (The Selected Works of Henry James, Sr.: Vol. 7). 264p. 1983. Repr. of 1869 ed. 30.00 (ISBN 0-404-10087-2). AMS Pr.

Morris, H. N. Flaxman, Blake, Coleridge, & Other Men of Genius Influenced by Swedenborg. 1973. Repr. of 1915 ed. lib. bdg. 20.00 (ISBN 0-8414-1515-3). Folcroft.

Odhner, Hugo L. Swedenborg's System of Degrees. 25p. 1970. pap. 1.00 (ISBN 0-915221-16-0). Swedenborg Sci Assn.

Pitcairn, Harold F., ed. A Concordance of Selected Subjects Treated of in the Rational Psychology of Emmanuel Swedenborg. 337p. 1960. 7.00 (ISBN 0-915221-11-X). Swedenborg Sci Assn.

Sigstedt, Cyriel O. Swedenborg Epic. LC 78-137269. (Illus.). Repr. of 1952 ed. 34.50 (ISBN 0-404-05999-6). AMS Pr.

Spalding, J. Howard. Introduction to Swedenborg's Religious Thought. LC 77-78682. 1973. pap. 2.95 (ISBN 0-87785-121-2). Swedenborg.

Spalding, John H. The Kingdom of Heaven As Seen by Swedenborg. LC 72-8245. Repr. of 1916 ed. 18.00 (ISBN 0-404-11006-1). AMS Pr.

Sutton, Eric A. The Living Thoughts of Swedenborg. 122p. 1981. Repr. of 1944 ed. lib. bdg. 20.00 (ISBN 0-8495-5041-6). Arden Lib.

Swedenborg, Emanuel. Emanuel Swedenborg's Journal of Dreams. LC 86-70341. 1986. pap. 8.95 (ISBN 0-87785-133-6). Swedenborg.

Synnestvedt, Sig. Essential Swedenborg. LC 76-57901. 3.95 (ISBN 0-87785-116-6); pap. 2.95 (ISBN 0-87785-152-2). Swedenborg.

Toksvig, Signe. Emanuel Swedenborg, Scientist & Mystic. LC 72-5447. (Biography Index Reprint Ser.). 1972. Repr. of 1948 ed. 25.00 (ISBN 0-8369-8140-5). Ayer Co Pubs.

Wunsch, William F. An Outline of Swedenborg's Teaching. LC 74-23796. 275p. 1975. pap. 3.95 (ISBN 0-87785-151-4). Swedenborg.

SWEDENBORGIANISM

see New Jerusalem Church

SWEDES IN FOREIGN COUNTRIES

Norelius, Eric. The Pioneer Swedish Settlements & Swedish Lutheran Churches in America 1845-1860. Bergendoff, Conrad, tr. from Swedish. LC 84-71391. (Publication Ser.: No. 31). Orig. Title: De Svenska Luterska Forsamlingarnas och Svenska Historia i Amerika. 419p. 1984. 15.00 (ISBN 0-910184-31-3). Augustana.

Nothstein, Ira O., ed. & tr. The Planting of the Swedish Church in America: Graduation Dissertation of Tobias Eric Biorck. LC 43-18182. (Augustana College Library Publication Ser.: No. 19). 39p. 1943. pap. 3.00x (ISBN 0-910182-14-0). Augustana Coll.

Stephenson, George M. Religious Aspects of Swedish Immigration: A Study of Immigrant Churches. LC 69-18790. (American Immigration Collection Ser., No. 1). (Illus.). 1969. Repr. of 1932 ed. 22.50 (ISBN 0-405-00539-3). Ayer Co Pubs.

--Religious Aspects of Swedish Immigration. LC 71-137294. Repr. of 1932 ed. 14.00 (ISBN 0-404-06257-1). AMS Pr.

SWEDISH MYTHOLOGY

see Mythology, Norse

SWIFT, JONATHAN, 1667-1745

Backscheider, Paula R. A Being More Intense: A Study of the Prose Works of Bunyan, Swift, & Defoe. LC 83-45274. (Studies in the Eighteenth Century: No. 7). 222p. 1984. 32.50 (ISBN 0-404-61473-6). AMS Pr.

Dark, Sidney. Five Deans. facsimile ed. LC 71-93332. (Essay Index Reprint Ser.). 1928. 18.00 (ISBN 0-8369-1285-3). Ayer Co Pubs.

--Five Deans: John Colet, John Donne, Jonathan Swift, Arthur Penrhyn Stanley & William Ralph Inge. LC 70-86011. (Essay & General Literature Index Reprint Ser.). 1969. Repr. of 1928 ed. 22.50x (ISBN 0-8046-0555-6, Pub. by Kennikat). Assoc Faculty Pr.

Rawson, Claude, ed. The Character of Swift's Satire: A Revised Focus. LC 81-72062. 344p. 1983. 34.50 (ISBN 0-87413-209-6). U Delaware Pr.

SWINFIELD, RICHARD DE BP. OF HEREFORD, d. 1317

De Kemeseye, Johannes. Roll of the Household Expenses of Richard De Swinfield, Bishop of Hereford, 1289-1290, 2 Vols. 1854-1855. 65.00 (ISBN 0-384-29130-9). Johnson Repr.

SWITHUN, SAINT, BP. OF WINCHESTER, d. 862

Aelfric. Lives of Three English Saints. Needham, G. I., ed. (Old English Ser.). 1966. pap. text ed. 9.95x (ISBN 0-89197-564-0). Irvington.

SYMBOLICS

see Creeds

SYMBOLISM

see also Anthropomorphism; Christian Art and Symbolism; Crosses; Emblems; Idols and Images; Jewish Art and Symbolism; Mandala; Ritual; Semantics (Philosophy); Signs and Symbols; Typology (Theology)

also references under Religion, Primitive

Biezais, Haralds, ed. Religious Symbols & Their Functions. 178p. (Orig.). 1979. pap. text ed. 22.50 (ISBN 91-22-00199-9, Pub. by Almqvist & Wiksell). Coronet Bks.

Bucknell, R. S. & Stuart-Fox, Martin. The Twilight Language: Explanations in Buddhist Meditation & Symbolism. 227p. 1986. 27.50 (ISBN 0-312-82540-4). St Martin.

Bynum, Caroline W., et al, eds. Gender & Religion: On the Complexity of Symbols. LC 86-47552. 296p. 1986. 25.00 (ISBN 0-8070-1008-1). Beacon Pr.

Caris, John. Foundation for a New Consciousness. LC 86-20201. (Illus.). 136p. (Orig.). 1987. pap. 8.95 (ISBN 0-9607320-1-2). Westgate Hse.

Cassirer, Ernst. Philosophy of Symbolic Forms, Vol. 2, Mythical Thought. Manheim, Ralph, tr. 1955. pap. 11.95x (ISBN 0-300-00038-3, Y147). Yale U Pr.

Cooper, J. C. Symbolism: The Universal Language. LC 86-18838. 176p. 1986. lib. bdg. 19.95x (ISBN 0-8095-7001-7). Borgo Pr.

Dillistone, F. W. The Power of Symbols in Religion & Culture. 176p. 1986. 14.95 (ISBN 0-8245-0784-3). Crossroad NY.

Edelman, Murray. The Symbolic Uses of Politics: With a New Afterword. LC 84-16195. 232p. 1985. pap. 6.95 (ISBN 0-252-01202-X). U of Ill Pr.

Fisher, Leonard E. Symbol Art: Thirteen Squares, Circles & Triangles from Around the World. LC 85-42805. (Illus.). 64p. 1986. 12.95 (ISBN 0-02-735270-6, Four Winds). Macmillan.

Howell, Alice O. Jungian Symbolism in Astrology. LC 86-40406. 238p. (Orig.). 1987. pap. 6.95 (ISBN 0-8356-0618-X). Theos Pub Hse.

Mackenzie, Donald A. Migration of Symbols & Their Relations to Beliefs & Customs. LC 68-18029. 1968. Repr. of 1926 ed. 34.00x (ISBN 0-8103-3074-1). Gale.

Masson, Robert, ed. The Pedagogy of God's Image: Essays on Symbol & the Religious Imagination. 214p. 1986. lib. bdg. 23.00 (ISBN 0-8191-5721-X, Pub. by College Theology Society); pap. text ed. 13.00 (ISBN 0-8191-5619-1, Pub. by College Theology Society). U Pr of Amer.

Mathews, Patricia. Aurier's Symbolist Art Criticism & Theory. Kuspit, Donald, ed. LC 85-20944. (Studies in the Fine Arts: Criticism: No. 18). 130p. 1986. 49.95 (ISBN 0-8357-1686-4). UMI Res Pr.

Morris, Charles W. Symbolism & Reality: A Study in the Nature of Mind. LC 86-17602. (Foundations of Semiotics Ser.: No. 15). v, 150p. 1987. 34.00x (ISBN 90-272-3287-3). Benjamins North Am.

Olderr, Steven. Symbolism: A Comprehensive Dictionary. LC 85-42833. 159p. 1986. lib. bdg. 25.95 (ISBN 0-89950-187-7). McFarland & Co.

Sinha, B. C. Hinduism & Symbol Worship. 1985. 17.50x (ISBN 0-8364-1297-4, Pub. by Agam Kala Prakashan). South Asia Bks.

Todorov, Tzvetan. Symbolism & Interpretation. Porter, Catherine, tr. from Fr. LC 82-5078. 192p. 1982. text ed. 24.95x (ISBN 0-8014-1269-2). Cornell U Pr.

Wagner, Roy. Symbols That Stand for Themselves. LC 85-16448. (Illus.). 1986. lib. bdg. 27.00x (ISBN 0-226-86928-8); pap. text ed. 9.95x (ISBN 0-226-86929-6). U of Chicago Pr.

SYMBOLISM (PSYCHOLOGY)

Huggins, William H. & Entwisle, Doris R. Iconic Communication: An Annotated Bibliography. LC 73-8130. (Illus.). 184p. 1974. 18.50x (ISBN 0-8018-1528-2). Johns Hopkins.

Jung, Carl G. Psychology & Religion. (Terry Lecture Ser.). 1938. pap. 5.95 (ISBN 0-300-00137-1, Y14). Yale U Pr.

SYMBOLISM IN ART

see also Christian Art and Symbolism; Jewish Art and Symbolism

Anderson, Johan G. Symbolism in the Prehistoric Painted Ceramics of China. 1929. 13.00 (ISBN 0-317-43918-9, Pub. by Han-Shan Tang Ltd). State Mutual Bk.

Goldsmith, E. E. The Psychological Meaning of the Sacred Symbols in Art, 2 vols. (Illus.). 311p. 1987. Set. 167.50 (ISBN 0-89920-149-0). Am Inst Psych.

Gombrich, E. H. Symbolic Images: Studies in the Art of the Renaissance, No. II. LC 84-28111. (Illus.). xii, 356p. 1985. pap. 14.95 (ISBN 0-226-30217-2). U of Chicago Pr.

Howe, Jeffery W. The Symbolist Art of Fernand Khnoff. Foster, Stephen, ed. LC 82-4734. (Studies in the Fine Arts: The Avant Garde: No. 28). 274p. 1982. 44.95 (ISBN 0-8357-1317-2). UMI Res Pr.

Landow, George. William Holman Hunt & Typological Symbolism. LC 77-91017. 1979. 42.00x (ISBN 0-300-02196-8). Yale U Pr.

Pincus-Witten, Robert. Occult Symbolism in France: Josephin Peladan & the Salons De la Rose-Croix. LC 75-23809. (Outstanding Dissertations in the Fine Arts-20th Century). (Illus.). 300p. 1976. lib. bdg. 50.00 (ISBN 0-8240-2003-0). Garland Pub.

Saunders, E. Dale. Mudra: A Study of Symbolic Gestures in Japanese Buddhist Sculpture. (Bollingen Ser.: Vol. 58). (Illus.). 1960. 37.00x (ISBN 0-691-09796-8). Princeton U Pr.

Wittkower, Rudolf. Allegory & the Migration of Symbols. LC 86-50689. (Illus.). 224p. 1987. pap. 14.95 (ISBN 0-500-85004-6). Thames Hudson.

SYMBOLISM IN LITERATURE

Bell, Robert E. Dictionary of Classical Mythology: Symbols, Attributes, & Associations. LC 81-19141. 390p. 1982. 30.00 (ISBN 0-87436-305-5). ABC Clio.

Bloomfield, Morton W., ed. Allegory, Myth, & Symbol. (Harvard English Studies: 9). 440p. 1982. text ed. 32.50x (ISBN 0-674-01640-8); pap. text ed. 10.95x (ISBN 0-674-01641-6). Harvard U Pr.

Bogdanos, Theodore. Pearl, Image of the Ineffable: A Study in Medieval Poetic Symbolism. LC 82-42783. 184p. 1983. 22.50x (ISBN 0-271-00339-1). Pa St U Pr.

Frey, John A. Motif Symbolism in the Disciples of Mallarme. LC 73-94193. (Catholic University of America Studies in Romance Languages & Literatures Ser: No. 55). Repr. of 1957 ed. 23.00 (ISBN 0-404-50355-1). AMS Pr.

Luke, Helen. The Inner Story: Myth & Symbol in the Bible & Literature. 112p. 1982. 8.95 (ISBN 0-8245-0443-7). Crossroad NY.

Miner, Earl, ed. Literary Uses of Typology from the Late Middle Ages to the Present. LC 76-45904. 1977. 47.50 (ISBN 0-691-06327-3). Princeton U Pr.

Musurillo, Herbert A. Symbol & Myth in Ancient Poetry. LC 77-2395. 1977. Repr. of 1961 ed. lib. bdg. 24.75x (ISBN 0-8371-9554-3, MUSM). Greenwood.

Powell, James N. Mandalas: The Dynamics of Vedic Symbolism. Ghai, S. K., ed. 127p. 1980. 9.95 (ISBN 0-914794-36-1). Wisdom Garden.

Ross, Malcolm M. Poetry & Dogma. LC 78-86284. 1969. Repr. of 1954 ed. lib. bdg. 18.50x (ISBN 0-374-96973-6, Octagon). Hippocrene Bks.

Senior, John. Way Down & Out: The Occult in Symbolist Literature. LC 68-23326. (Illus.). 1968. Repr. of 1959 ed. lib. bdg. 22.50x (ISBN 0-8371-0218-9, SESL). Greenwood.

Temple, Ruth Z. The Critic's Alchemy. (Orig.). 1953. pap. 10.95x (ISBN 0-8084-0097-5). New Coll U Pr.

SYMBOLISM IN THE BIBLE

see also Typology (Theology)

Diel, Paul. The God-Symbol. 240p. 1985. 17.95 (ISBN 0-86683-475-3, HarpR). Har-Row.

Edwards, Charles L. Understanding Biblical Symbols. 96p. 1981. 6.00 (ISBN 0-682-49704-5). Exposition Pr FL.

Fairbridge, Maurice H. Studies in Biblical & Semitic Symbolism. 1977. lib. bdg. 59.95 (ISBN 0-8490-2700-4). Gordon Pr.

Jech, Carl. Shadows & Symbols. 1985. 6.25 (ISBN 0-89536-751-3, 5857). CSS of Ohio.

Lurker, Manfred. Woerterbuch Biblischer Bilder und Symbole. (Ger.). 1973. 25.00 (ISBN 3-466-20158-6, M-7046). French & Eur.

Norden, Rudolph F. Symbols & Their Meaning. 1985. pap. 3.50 (ISBN 0-570-03949-5, 12-2883). Concordia.

Webber, Frederick R. Church Symbolism: An Explanation of the More Important Symbols of the Old & New Testament, the Primitive, the Mediaeval & the Modern Church. rev. 2nd ed. LC 79-107627. (Illus.). 1971. Repr. of 1938 ed. 56.00x (ISBN 0-8103-3349-X). Gale.

Wilson, Walter L. Wilson's Dictionary of Bible Types. 1957. pap. 10.95 (ISBN 0-8028-1453-0). Eerdmans.

SYNAGOGUE ARCHITECTURE

Chiat, Marilyn. Handbook of Synagogue Architecture. LC 81-9419. (Brown Judiac Studies). 1982. pap. 20.00 (ISBN 0-89130-524-6, 14-00-29). Scholars Pr GA.

Halperin, Don A. Ancient Synagogues of the Iberian Peninsula. LC 78-62577. (University of Florida Social Sciences Monographs: No. 38). (Illus.). 1969. pap. 3.50 (ISBN 0-8130-0272-9). U Presses Fla.

Krinsky, Carol H. Synagogues of Europe: Architecture, History, Meaning. (Architectural History Foundation Ser.). 470p. 1987. pap. 25.00 (ISBN 0-262-61048-5). MIT Pr.

Pearson, H. F., et al. Preliminary Report on the Synagogue at Dura-Europos. (Illus.). 1936. pap. 49.50x (ISBN 0-686-51290-1). Elliots Bks.

SYNAGOGUE MUSIC

see also Chants (Jewish); Jews–Liturgy and Ritual

Posner, Raphael, et al, eds. Jewish Liturgy: Prayer & Synagogue Service Through the Ages. (Illus.). 1976. 25.00 (ISBN 0-8148-0596-5). L Amiel Pub.

SYNAGOGUE MUSIC–HISTORY AND CRITICISM

see also Bible–Music

Werner, Eric. A Voice Still Heard: The Sacred Songs of the Ashkenazic Jews. LC 75-26522. 1976. 32.50 (ISBN 0-271-01167-X). Pa St U Pr.

SYNAGOGUES

see also Genizah; Synagogue Architecture

Davis, Patricia T. Together They Built a Mountain. LC 74-14727. (Illus.). 196p. 1974. 6.95 (ISBN 0-915010-00-3). Sutter House.

Eisenberg, Azriel. The Synagogue Through the Ages: An Illustrated History of Judaism's Houses of Worship. LC 73-77284. (Illus.). 1973. 15.00 (ISBN 0-8197-0290-0). Bloch.

Fine, Jo Renee & Wolfe, Gerard R. The Synagogues of New York's Lower East Side. LC 75-15126. (Illus.). 1978. 27.50 (ISBN 0-8147-2559-7). NYU Pr.

Freeman, Grace & Sugarman, Joan. Inside the Synagogue. rev. ed. (Illus.). 64p. 1984. pap. 6.00 (ISBN 0-8074-0268-0, 301785). UAHC.

Gilbert, Arthur. Your Neighbor Worships. 31p. 1.50 (ISBN 0-686-74968-5). ADL.

Goble, Phillip E. Everything You Need to Grow a Messianic Synagogue. LC 74-28017. (Illus., Orig.). 1974. pap. 3.95 (ISBN 0-87808-421-5). William Carey Lib.

Gutmann, Joseph. The Synagogue: Studies in Origins, Archeology, & Architecture. 1974. 35.00x (ISBN 0-87068-265-2). Ktav.

Gutmann, Joseph, ed. Ancient Synagogues: The State of Research. LC 81-5252. (Brown Univ. BJS Ser.). 1981. pap. 14.00 (ISBN 0-89130-467-3, 140022). Scholars Pr GA.

Halperin, Don A. The Old Synagogues of Turkey: A Pictorial Narrative. LC 86-50586. (Illus.). 73p. (Orig.). 1987. pap. text ed. 9.95x (ISBN 0-932269-89-3). Wyndham Hall.

Hannaford, Claudia. The ABC's of Financing Church & Synagogue Libraries, No. 13. LC 85-13286. (CSLA Guide Ser.). (Illus.). 36p. (Orig.). 1985. pap. 5.95X (ISBN 0-915324-23-7). CSLA.

Harvey, John F., ed. Church & Synagogue Libraries. LC 80-11736. 299p. 1980. 20.00 (ISBN 0-8108-1304-1). Scarecrow.

Israel Exploration Society, Jerusalem & Levine, Lee I., eds. Ancient Synagogues Revealed. LC 81-53031. (Illus.). 199p. 1982. 27.50x (ISBN 0-8143-1706-5). Wayne St U Pr.

Israelowitz, Oscar. Synagogues of New York City. 1983. 14.00 (ISBN 0-8446-5954-1). Peter Smith.

--Synagogues of New York City: A Pictorial Survey in 150 Photographs. (Illus.). 155p. (Orig.). pap. 6.00 (ISBN 0-486-24231-5). Dover.

Kampf, Avram. Contemporary Synagogue Art: Developments in the United States, 1945-1965. LC 65-25292. (Illus.). 1976. 15.00 (ISBN 0-8074-0085-8, 382630). UAHC.

Kraeling, C. H. The Synagogue. rev ed. 1979. 100.00x (ISBN 0-87068-331-4). Ktav.

Lane, George A. Chicago Churches & Synagogues. iv, 236p. 1981. 25.00 (ISBN 0-8294-0373-6). Loyola.

Levin, Meyer & Kurzband, Toby. Story of the Synagogue. LC 57-13093. (Jewish Heritage Ser: Vol. 2). 1957. pap. 5.95x (ISBN 0-87441-006-1). Behrman.

Litvin, Baruch & Litvin, Jeanne. The Sanctity of the Synagogue. 1987. 19.95 (ISBN 0-88125-113-5). KTAV.

Paris, Janelle A. Planning Bulletin Boards for Church & Synagogue Libraries. LC 83-7331. (CSLA Guide Two Ser. No. 11). (Orig.). 1983. pap. 6.95 (ISBN 0-915324-20-2); pap. 5.50 members. CSLA.

Roberts, Anne F. & Cockrell, Marcia W., eds. Historic Albany: Its Churches & Synagogues. (Illus.). 415p. (Orig.). 1986. pap. 15.00 (ISBN 0-941237-00-1). Libr Commns Servs.

Salzburgs Weideraofgebaute Synagogue. cancelled (ISBN 0-686-76252-5). Feldheim.

Smith, Ruth S. Getting the Books Off the Shelves: Making the Most of Your Congregation's Library, No. 12. rev. ed. LC 85-11650. (CSLA Guide Ser.). (Illus.). 40p. 1985. pap. 6.95X (ISBN 0-915324-22-9). CSLA.

Sukenik, E. L. Ancient Synagogues in Palestine & Greece. (British Academy, London, Schweich Lectures on Biblical Archaeology Series, 1930). pap. 19.00 (ISBN 0-8115-1272-X). Kraus Repr.

Tebeau, Charlton W. Synagogue in the Central City: Temple Israel of Greater Miami 1922-1972. LC 72-85107. 5.00 (ISBN 0-87024-239-3). Rostrum Bks.

Weisser, M. My Synagogue. (Illus.). 25p. 1984. pap. text ed. 2.95x (ISBN 0-87441-386-9). Behrman.

Wigoder, Geoffrey. Synagogues Through the Ages. LC 86-45032. (Illus.). 208p. 1986. 35.00 (ISBN 0-06-069401-7, HarpR). Har-Row.

Zwerin, Raymond A. & Friedman, Audrey. Our Synagogue, 3 vols. (Illus.). 1974. pap. text ed. 3.50x (ISBN 0-03-012671-1). Behrman.

SYNANON FOUNDATION

Mitchell, David & Mitchell, Cathy. Light on Synanon. 1982. pap. 7.50 (ISBN 0-87223-761-3, Wideview Bks). Putnam Pub Group.

SYNCRETISM (CHRISTIANITY)

see Christianity and Other Religions

SYNCRETISM (RELIGION)

Berling, Judith A. The Syncretic Religion of Lin Chao-En. LC 79-25606. (Institute for Advanced Studies of World Religions; Neo-Confucian Studies). 1980. 31.00x (ISBN 0-231-04870-X). Columbia U Pr.

SYNODS

see Councils and Synods

SYRIA

Bliss, Frederick J. Religions of Modern Syria & Palestine. LC 76-39454. Repr. of 1912 ed. 20.00 (ISBN 0-404-00897-6). AMS Pr.

SYRIAC LITERATURE

Goshen-Gottstein, Moshe H. Syriac Manuscripts in the Harvard College Library: A Catalogue. LC 77-13132. (Harvard Semitic Studies: No. 23). 1979. 15.00 (ISBN 0-89130-189-5, 040423). Scholars Pr GA.

Wright, William. A Short History of Syriac Literature. LC 78-14330. 1978. Repr. of 1894 ed. lib. bdg. 42.50 (ISBN 0-8414-9709-5). Folcroft.

SYRIAN CHURCH

see also Nestorian Church

Garsoian, Nina & Mathews, Thomas, eds. East of Byzantium: Syria & Armenia in the Formative Period. LC 82-9665. (Dumbarton Oaks Symposium). (Illus.). 266p. 1982. 35.00x (ISBN 0-88402-104-1). Dumbarton Oaks.

Haddad, Robert M. Syrian Christians in Muslim Society: An Interpretation. LC 81-6202. (Princeton Studies on the Near East). viii, 118p. 1981. Repr. of 1970 ed. lib. bdg. 22.50x (ISBN 0-313-23054-4, HASYC). Greenwood.

McCullough, W. Stewart. A Short History of Syriac Christianity to the Rise of Islam. LC 80-29297. (Scholars Press Polebridge Bks.). 1981. 21.95 (ISBN 0-89130-454-1, 00-03-04). Scholars Pr GA.

SYSTEMATIC THEOLOGY

see Theology, Doctrinal

T

TABERNACLE

see also Ark of the Covenant

Corbett, James A. & Moore, Philip S., eds. Petri Pictaviensis Allegoriae Super Tabernaculum Moysi. (Mediaeval Studies Ser.: No. 3). 1938. 17.95 (ISBN 0-268-00207-X). U of Notre Dame Pr.

Daniel, R. P. The Tabernacle Talks Today. pap. 5.25 (ISBN 0-88172-020-8). Believers Bkshelf.

Dolman, Dirk H. The Tabernacle. 525p. 1982. Repr. lib. bdg. 19.75 smythe sewn (ISBN 0-86524-152-X, 0203). Klock & Klock.

Gooding, D. W. The Account of the Tabernacle. (Texts & Studies, New Ser.: Vol. 6). Repr. of 1959 ed. 28.00 (ISBN 0-8115-1719-5). Kraus Repr.

Guest, Dean. Tabernacle, God's Dwelling Place. 64p. (Orig.). 1979. pap. 1.95 (ISBN 0-89841-012-6). Zoe Pubns.

Hayden, Eric. A History of Spurgeons Tabernacle. 1971. 5.95 (ISBN 0-686-09091-8). Pilgrim Pubns.

Kiene, Paul F. The Tabernacle of God in the Wilderness of Sinai. 1977. 19.95 (ISBN 0-310-36200-8, 11066). Zondervan.

Laity, Edward. Tabernacle Types & Teaching. 1980. pap. 2.95 (ISBN 0-86544-011-5). Salv Army Suppl South.

Little, David. Tabernacle in the Wilderness. pap. 1.50 (ISBN 0-87213-520-9). Loizeaux.

Menken, John, ed. The Tent of Meeting Texts. (Illus.). 134p. (Orig.). 1985. pap. 8.00 (ISBN 0-9615531-0-3). Tent Meeting.

Olford, Stephen F. The Tabernacle: Camping with God. LC 78-173686. 1971. 8.95 (ISBN 0-87213-675-2). Loizeaux.

Ritchie, John. The Tabernacle. LC 82-178. 122p. 1982. pap. 4.50 (ISBN 0-8254-3616-8). Kregel.

--El Tabernaculo en el Desierto. Orig. Title: The Tabernacle in the Desert. (Span.). 144p. Date not set. pap. 3.95 (ISBN 0-8254-1616-7). Kregel.

Soltau, Henry W. Holy Vessels & Furniture of the Tabernacle. LC 74-85428. (Illus.). 148p. 1986. pap. 12.95 (ISBN 0-8254-3751-2). Kregel.

--Tabernacle, Priesthood & the Offerings. LC 72-88590. 486p. 1974. 14.95 (ISBN 0-8254-3703-2); Published 1986. pap. 12.95 (ISBN 0-8254-3750-4). Kregel.

Walton, Anna, ed. The Tent of Meeting Catalogue & Guide. 40p. (Orig.). 1985. 5.00 (ISBN 0-9615531-1-1). Tent Meeting.

TABERNACLES, FEAST OF

see Sukkoth

TABLE BLESSINGS

see Grace at Meals

TABLETS, MEMORIAL

see Sepulchral Monuments

TABOO

see also Totemism

Browne, Ray B. Forbidden Fruits: Taboos & Tabooism in Culture. LC 84-71938. 192p. 1984. 21.95 (ISBN 0-317-14769-2); pap. 9.95 (ISBN 0-87972-256-8). Bowling Green Univ.

Burriss, Eli E. Taboo, Magic, Spirits: A Study of Primitive Elements in Roman Religion. LC 72-114489. x, 250p. Repr. of 1931 ed. lib. bdg. 22.50x (ISBN 0-8371-4724-7, BUTA). Greenwood.

Freud, Sigmund. Totem & Taboo. Strachey, James, tr. 1962. pap. 3.95 (ISBN 0-393-00143-1, Norton Lib.). Norton.

--Totem & Taboo. Brill, Abraham A., tr. 1960. pap. 2.95 (ISBN 0-394-70124-0, Vin, V124). Random.

Webster, Hutton. Taboo: A Sociological Study. LC 73-4250. xii, 393p. 1973. Repr. of 1942 ed. lib. bdg. 26.00x (ISBN 0-374-98324-0, Octagon). Hippocrene Bks.

T'AI CHI CH'UAN

Chen, Y. K. T'ai Chi Ch'uan: Its Effects & Practical Applications. 1979. pap. 6.95 (ISBN 0-87877-043-7). Newcastle Pub.

Cheng, Man-Ch'ing & Smith, Robert W. T'ai-Chi the Supreme Ultimate Exercise for Health, Sport, & Self-Defense. LC 67-23009. (Illus.). 1967. 22.50 (ISBN 0-8048-0560-1). C E Tuttle.

Chen Wei-Ming. Questions & Answers on T'ai Chi Ch'uan. Pang Jeng Lo, Benjamin & Smith, Robert, trs. from Chinese. Tr. of T'ai Chi Ch'uan Ta Wen. 64p. (Orig.). 1985. 20.00 (ISBN 0-938190-77-6). North Atlantic.

Huang, Al C. Embrace Tiger, Return to Mountain: The Essence of T'ai Chi. LC 73-80134. (Illus.). 185p. 1973. 10.00 (ISBN 0-911226-12-5); pap. 6.50 (ISBN 0-911226-13-3). Real People.

Kauz, Herman. T'ai Chi Handbook: Exercise, Meditation, Self-Defense. LC 73-10552. (Illus.). 192p. 1974. pap. 9.95 (ISBN 0-385-09370-5, Dolp). Doubleday.

Kimmelman, Susan & Horwitz, Tem, eds. T'ai Chi Ch'uan: The Technique of Power. LC 76-41613. (Illus.). 1980. pap. 9.95 (ISBN 0-914090-24-0). Chicago Review.

Lee, Douglas. T'ai Chi Ch'uan the Philosophy of Yin & Yang & Its Applications. Lucas, Charles, ed. LC 76-6249. (Ser. 317). (Illus.). 1976. pap. text ed. 6.95 (ISBN 0-89750-044-X). Ohara Pubns.

Liang, T. T. T'ai Chi Ch'uan for Health & Self-Defense: Philosophy & Practice. 1977. pap. 5.95 (ISBN 0-394-72461-5, Vin). Random.

Liu Da. T'ai Chi Ch'uan & I Ching: A Choreography of Body & Mind. LC 79-183640. 1987. pap. 5.95 (ISBN 0-06-091309-6, PL-1309, PL). Har-Row.

Lum, A. Advanced Tai Chi. 11.95x (ISBN 0-685-63740-9). Wehman.

Lum, A. C. Combat Tai Chi. 11.95x (ISBN 0-685-63750-6). Wehman.

Ming-Shih, Y. T'ai Chi Ch'uan. 6.95x (ISBN 0-685-63782-4). Wehman.

Murphy, Carol R. The Sound of Silence: Moving with T'ai Chi. LC 75-41548. (Orig.). 1976. pap. 2.50x (ISBN 0-87574-205-X, 205). Pendle Hill.

Olson, Stuart A. Imagination Becomes Reality Vol. 1: One Hundred Fifty Posture Solo Dance. Kuehl, Gerald, ed. (T'ai Chi Ch'uan-the Teaching of Master T. T. Liang Ser.). (Illus., Orig.). 1986. pap. 19.94 (ISBN 0-938045-01-6). Bubbling Well.

--The Wind Sweeps Away the Plum Blossoms: The Principles & Techniques of Yang Style T'ai Chi Spear & Staff. Olson, Stuart A., tr. from Chinese. (Illus.). 150p. (Orig.). 1986. pap. 14.95 (ISBN 0-938045-00-8). Bubbling Well.

Olson, Stuart A., compiled by. & tr. from Chinese. Cultivating the Ch'i: Translated from Original Writings in the Pang Family's Secret Journal, Describing T'ai Chi Chi-Kung Exercises. (Illus.). 98p. 1986. pap. 10.95 (ISBN 0-938045-02-4). Bubbling-Well.

Pang, Chia S. & Hock, Goh E. T'ai Chi: Ten Minutes to Health. LC 85-22388. (Illus.). 131p. (Orig.). 1986. pap. 12.95 (ISBN 0-916360-30-X). CRCS Pubns NV.

Smith, R. W. Pakua. pap. 8.25x (ISBN 0-685-22068-0). Wehman.

Smith, Robert W. Secrets of Shaolin Temple Boxing. LC 64-22002. (Illus.). 1964. 7.95 (ISBN 0-8048-0518-0). C E Tuttle.

--Shaolin Temple Boxing Secrets. 7.95x (ISBN 0-685-22107-5). Wehman.

Stone, Justin F. T'ai Chi Chih! Joy Thru Movement. rev. ed. (Illus.). 136p. 1986. pap. 9.95 (ISBN 0-937277-02-9). Satori Resources.

Yang Ming-shih. T'ai Chi Ch'uan. (Quick & Easy Ser.). (Illus.). 60p. (Orig.). 1974. pap. 3.95 (ISBN 4-07-973783-1, Pub. by Shufunmato Co Ltd Japan). C E Tuttle.

Ying-Arng, Lee. Lee's Modified Tai Chi for Health. 10.95x (ISBN 0-685-70688-5). Wehman.

TAIPING REBELLION, 1850-1864

Clarke, Prescott & Gregory, J. S., eds. Western Reports on the Taiping: A Selection of Documents. LC 81-68942. 484p. 1982. text ed. 25.00x (ISBN 0-8248-0807-X); pap. text ed. 15.95x (ISBN 0-8248-0809-6). UH Pr.

Curwen, C. A. Taiping Rebel: The Deposition of Li Hsiu-Ch' eng. LC 76-8292. (Cambridge Studies in Chinese History, Literature & Institutions). (Illus.). 1977. 57.50 (ISBN 0-521-21082-8). Cambridge U Pr.

Lin, Robert H. The Taiping Revolution: A Failure of Two Missions. 1979. pap. text ed. 10.75 (ISBN 0-8191-0734-4). U Pr of Amer.

Michael, Franz & Chang, Chung-Li. The Taiping Rebellion: Documents & Comments. Incl. Vol. 2. 756p (ISBN 0-295-73959-2); Vol. 3. 1107p (ISBN 0-295-73958-4). LC 66-13538. (Publications on Asia of the Institute for Foreign & Area Studies: No. 14, Pt. 2). 1971. 35.00x ea. U of Wash Pr.

--The Taiping Rebellion: History, Vol. 1. (Publications on Asia of the Institute for Foreign & Area Studies: No. 14, Pt. 1). 256p. 1966. pap. 8.95x (ISBN 0-295-95244-X). U of Wash Pr.

Teng Ssu-Ya. Historiography of the Taiping Rebellion. LC 63-1158. (East Asian Monographs: No. 14). 1962. pap. 11.00x (ISBN 0-674-39451-8). Harvard U Pr.

TAIWAN–RELIGION

Swanson, Allen J. Mending the Nets: Taiwan Church Growth & Loss in the 1980's. LC 86-47704. 320p. 1986. pap. 7.95 (ISBN 0-87808-207-7, WCL 207-7). William Carey Lib.

TAIZE (RELIGIOUS COMMUNITY)

Balado, J. L. The Story of Taize. (Illus.). 144p. (Orig.). 1981. pap. 4.95 (ISBN 0-8164-2321-0, HarpR). Har-Row.

TALANSI (AFRICAN TRIBE)

Fortes, Meyer. Oedipus & Job in West African Religion. 1980. Repr. of 1959 ed. lib. bdg. 15.50x (ISBN 0-374-92820-7, Octagon). Hippocrene Bks.

Fortes, Meyer & Horton, Robin. Oedipus & Job in West African Religion. LC 83-7587. (Cambridge Studies in Social Anthropology: No. 48). 128p. 1984. 32.50 (ISBN 0-521-26208-9); pap. 9.95 (ISBN 0-521-27719-1). Cambridge U Pr.

TALENSE

see Talansi (African Tribe)

TALES, AFRICAN

Tollerson, Marie S. Mythology & Cosmology in the Narratives of Bernard Dadie & Birago Diop: A Structural Approach. LC 81-51668. 152p. 1985. 20.00 (ISBN 0-89410-156-0); pap. 10.00 (ISBN 0-89410-157-9). Three Continents.

TALES, BUDDHIST

Dharma Realm Buddhist University Faculty. Human Roots: Buddhist Stories for Young Readers, Vol. 2. (Illus.). 140p. (Orig.). 1984. pap. 6.00 (ISBN 0-88139-017-8). Buddhist Text.

Fausboll, V., ed. Buddhist Birth Stories; or Jataka Tales, Vol. 1. Davids, Rhys T., tr. LC 78-72443. Repr. of 1880 ed. 42.50 (ISBN 0-404-17309-8). AMS Pr.

Morrell, Robert E. Sand & Pebbles: The Tales of Muju Ichien, a Voice for Pluralism in Kamakura Buddhism. (Series in Buddhist Studies). 337p. 1985. 44.50 (ISBN 0-88706-059-5); pap. 16.95x (ISBN 0-88706-060-9). State U NY Pr.

TALES, HASSIDIC

Berger, Alan A. Witness to the Sacred: Mystical Tales of Primitive Hasidism. (Illus.). 1977. pap. text ed. 4.00x (ISBN 0-914914-10-3). New Horizons.

Buber, Martin. The Legend of the Baal-Shem. LC 76-86849. 1969. pap. 7.95 (ISBN 0-8052-0233-1). Schocken.

Eliach, Yaffa. Hasidic Tales of the Holocaust. 336p. 1983. pap. 4.95 (ISBN 0-380-64725-7, Discus). Avon.

Martinet, Jan. Hasidic Legends: A Suite by H. N. Werkman. (Eng. & Dutch., Illus.). 80p. (Orig.). 1985. 175.00x (ISBN 90-6243-048-1, Pub. by Boumas Boekhuis Netherlands). Benjamins North Am.

Meyer, Levin. Classic Hassidic Tales. 300p. 1985. 16.95 (ISBN 0-88029-035-8, Pub. by Dorset Pr). Hippocrene Bks.

Newman, Louis I., ed. Maggidim & Hasidim: Their Wisdom. 1962. 14.95x (ISBN 0-8197-0161-0). Bloch.

Rajneesh, Bhagwan Shree. The Art of Dying. Veena, Ma Prema, ed. LC 78-905608. (Hasidism Ser.). (Illus.). 284p. (Orig.). 1978. 14.95 (ISBN 0-88050-005-0). Chidvilas Found.

Wiesel, Elie. Somewhere a Master: Further Tales of the Hasidic Masters. 336p. 1982. 13.95 (ISBN 0-671-44170-1). Summit Bks.

Zevin, Schlomo Y. A Treasury of Chassidic Tales: On the Torah, Vol. 2. Kaploun, Uri, tr. (Art Scroll Judaica Classics Ser.). 352p. 1980. 13.95 (ISBN 0-89906-902-9); pap. 10.95 (ISBN 0-89906-903-7); gift box ed. 29.95 (ISBN 0-89906-904-5). Mesorah Pubns.

Zevin, Shlomo Y. A Treasury of Chassidic Tales, Vol. 1. Kaploun, Uri, tr. from Heb. (Art Scroll Judaica Classics Ser.). 320p. 1981. 13.95 (ISBN 0-89906-912-6); pap. 10.95 (ISBN 0-89906-913-4). Mesorah Pubns.

TALES, HAWAIIAN

Barrere, Dorothy B. The Kumuhonua Legends: A Study of Late 19th Century Hawaiian Stories of Creation & Origins. (Pacific Anthropological Records: No. 3). 47p. 1969. pap. 5.00 (ISBN 0-910240-59-0). Bishop Mus.

TALES, HEBREW

see also Tales, Jewish

Anderson, Joseph & Lipshitz, Devora. Tall Tales Told & Retold in Biblical Hebrew. (Hebrew., Illus.). 96p. (Orig.). 1983. pap. text ed. 8.95 (ISBN 0-939144-07-7). EKS Pub Co.

TALES, JEWISH

Ausubel, Nathan, ed. Treasury of Jewish Folklore. 1948. 14.95 (ISBN 0-517-50293-3). Crown.

The Best of Olomeinu: Pesach & Other Stories, Bk. 5. (Illus.). 160p. 9.85 (ISBN 0-317-53889-6); pap. 7.15. Torah Umesorah.

Beth Jacob Hebrew Teachers College Staff. Deeds of the Righteous. (Illus.). 160p. 6.95 (ISBN 0-934390-00-2). B J Hebrew Tchrs.

--The Rebbe's Treasure. write for info. (ISBN 0-934390-01-0); pap. write for info. (ISBN 0-934390-02-9). B J Hebrew Tchrs.

Bialik, Hayyim N. Knight of Onions & Knight of Garlic. 55p. 1934. 4.95 (ISBN 0-88482-734-8). Hebrew Pub.

Birnbaum, Philip, tr. Selihot. 61p. 1952. pap. 1.95 (ISBN 0-88482-344-X). Hebrew Pub.

Boruch, Behn. The Patriarchs. 28p. 1959. 3.95 (ISBN 0-88482-729-1). Hebrew Pub.

Brinner, William M., tr. An Elegant Composition Concerning Relief Adversity. LC 49-9495. (Judaica Ser.: No. 20). 1977. 26.50x (ISBN 0-300-01952-1). Yale U Pr.

Drachman, Bernard. From the Heart of Israel. LC 72-110183. (Short Story Index Reprint Ser.). 1905. 23.50 (ISBN 0-8369-3334-6). Ayer Co Pubs.

Einhorn, David. Seventh Candle & Other Folk Tales of Eastern Europe. Pashin, Gertrude, tr. LC 68-10968. (Illus.). 1968. 7.95x (ISBN 0-87068-369-1). Ktav.

Gaster, Moses. Exempla of the Rabbis. rev. ed. 1968. 25.00x (ISBN 0-87068-055-2). Ktav.

Gaster, Moses, tr. from Judeo-German. Ma'aseh Book: Book of Jewish Tales & Legends. LC 81-80356. 694p. 1981. pap. 10.95 (ISBN 0-8276-0189-1, 471). Jewish Pubns.

Glenn, Menachem. Jewish Tales & Legends. 441p. 1929. 6.95 (ISBN 0-88482-857-3). Hebrew Pub.

Golinkin, Noah. Shalom Aleichem. 77p. 1978. pap. 4.95x (ISBN 0-88482-696-1). Hebrew Pub.

Isaacs, Abram S. Stories from the Rabbis. LC 79-175868. Repr. of 1911 ed. 20.00 (ISBN 0-405-08661-X, Blom Pubns). Ayer Co Pubs.

Kleinbard, Gitel. Oh, Zalmy! Or, the Tale of the Porcelain Pony, Bk. 1. (Oh, Zalmy Ser.). (Illus.). 1976. 4.95 (ISBN 0-917274-04-0); pap. 2.95 (ISBN 0-917274-01-6). Mah Tov Pubns.

Kruckman, Herbert L. Joey Meets His People. 44p. 1940. 2.95 (ISBN 0-88482-732-1). Hebrew Pub.

Montague, E. R. Takes from the Talmud, 1906. 1977. 22.50 (ISBN 0-686-19672-4). Mill Bks.

Newman, Louis I., ed. Maggidim & Hasidim: Their Wisdom. 1962. 14.95x (ISBN 0-8197-0161-0). Bloch.

Noy, Dov, ed. Folktales of Israel. Baharav, Gene, tr. LC 63-16721. (Folktales of the World Ser). 1963. 14.00x (ISBN 0-226-59719-9); pap. 7.95x (ISBN 0-226-59720-2, FW8). U of Chicago Pr.

Omer, Devorah. Path Beneath the Sea. 192p. 1969. 3.50 (ISBN 0-88482-744-5). Hebrew Pub.

Prose, Francine. Stories from Our Living Past. new ed. Harlow, Jules, ed. LC 74-8514. (Illus.). 128p. 1974. 6.95x (ISBN 0-87441-081-9). Behrman.

Sacher-Masoch, L. Jewish Tales. 59.95 (ISBN 0-8490-0445-4). Gordon Pr.

Wiesel, Elie, ed. The Golem: The Story of a Legend. Borchardt, Anne, tr. LC 83-9304. (Illus.). 105p. 1983. 12.95 (ISBN 0-671-45483-8); Special ed., signed, limited. 50.00 (ISBN 0-671-49624-7). Summit Bks.

TALES, POLYNESIAN

Gifford, E. W. Tongan Myths & Tales. (BMB). Repr. of 1924 ed. 25.00 (ISBN 0-527-02111-3, BMB, NO. 8). Kraus Repr.

TALES, SANSKRIT

Narasimha, N. S. & Babaji, Ramananda. The Way of Vaisnava Sages: A Medieval Story of South Indian Sadhus. LC 86-28251. (Sanskrit Notes of Visnu-vijay Swami). 422p. (Orig.). 1987. lib. bdg. 33.50 (ISBN 0-8191-6060-1); pap. text ed. 18.75 (ISBN 0-8191-6061-X). U Pr of Amer.

TALES, SUFI

Ahmed, Shemsu-D-Din, ed. Legends of the Sufis. 1977. pap. 7.95 (ISBN 0-7229-5050-0). Theos Pub Hse.

TALES, THAI

Wray, Elizabeth, et al. Ten Lives of the Buddha: Siamese Temple Paintings & Jataka Tales. LC 73-179982. (Illus.). 156p. 1972. 20.00 (ISBN 0-8348-0067-5). Weatherhill.

TALLENSI

see Talansi (African Tribe)

TALLEYRAND-PERIGORD, CHARLES MAURICE DE, PRINCE DE BENEVENT, 1754-1838

Cooper, Duff. Talleyrand. 1932. 25.00x (ISBN 0-8047-0616-6). Stanford U Pr.

TALMUD

see also Rabbinical Literature; Tannaim

Abodah Zarah, 2 vols. 30.00 (ISBN 0-910218-77-3). Bennet Pub.

Adler, Morris. The World of the Talmud. 2nd ed. LC 63-18390. 1963. pap. 4.95 (ISBN 0-8052-0058-4). Schocken.

Arakin, 1 vol. 15.00 (ISBN 0-910218-83-8). Bennet Pub.

Avery-Peck, Alan J., tr. from Hebrew-Aramaic. The Talmud of Babylonia: An American Translation, VII Tractate Besah. (Brown Judaic Studies). 358p. 1986. pap. 39.95 (ISBN 1-55540-054-X, 14-01-17). Scholars Pr GA.

Baba Bathra, 3 vols. 45.00 (ISBN 0-910218-73-0). Bennet Pub.

Baba Mezia, 2 vols. 30.00 (ISBN 0-910218-72-2). Bennet Pub.

Bekoroth, 1 vol. 18.00 (ISBN 0-910218-82-X). Bennet Pub.

Berakoth. 18.00 (ISBN 0-910218-51-X). Bennet Pub.

Bezah, 1 vol. 15.00 (ISBN 0-910218-60-9). Bennet Pub.

Breuer, Salomon. Chochmo U'Mussar, 3 vols. 1972. Set. 24.00 (ISBN 0-87306-205-1). Feldheim.

Bulka, Reuven P. Sex in the Talmud. (Illus.). 64p. 1979. 5.95 (ISBN 0-88088-488-6). Peter Pauper.

--Wit & Wisdom of the Talmud. 2nd ed. (PPP Gift Editions). (Illus.). 1983. 5.95 (ISBN 0-88088-507-6). Peter Pauper.

Carmell, Aryeh. Aiding Talmud Study. 5th ed. (Illus.). 88p. 1987. 6.95 (ISBN 0-87306-413-5); pap. 4.95 (ISBN 0-87306-428-3). Feldheim.

Chajes. Student's Guide Through the Talmud. 13.95 (ISBN 0-87306-089-X). Feldheim.

Chapter of Talmud. 1982. 4.50 (ISBN 0-686-76490-0). Feldheim.

Cohen, Abraham. Everyman's Talmud. LC 75-10750. 446p. 1975. pap. 11.25 (ISBN 0-8052-0497-0). Schocken.

The Complete Talmud, 64 vols. Set. 995.00 (ISBN 0-910218-50-1). Bennet Pub.

Corre, Allan. Understanding the Talmud. 1971. pap. 8.95x (ISBN 0-685-22510-0). Ktav.

Dilling, E. The Plot Against Christianity: A Study of the Talmud. 1982. lib. bdg. 69.95 (ISBN 0-87700-359-9). Revisionist Pr.

Epstein, I. Minor Tractates. 480p. 1965. write for info. (ISBN 0-900689-86-2). Soncino Pr.

--Tractate Nedarim. 1985. 22.95 (ISBN 0-900689-90-0). Soncino Pr.

--Tractate Yevamoth. 1984. 22.95 (ISBN 0-900689-92-7). Soncino Pr.

Epstein, I., ed. Tractate Baba Kamma. 1977. 22.95 (ISBN 0-900689-59-5). Soncino Pr.

--Tractate Baba Kamma. 1964. student's ed. 15.00 (ISBN 0-900689-67-6). Soncino Pr.

--Tractate Berakoth. 1960. 22.95 (ISBN 0-900689-56-0). Soncino Pr.

--Tractate Erubin. 1983. 22.95 (ISBN 0-900689-80-3). Soncino Pr.

--Tractate Gitten. 1973. 22.95 (ISBN 0-900689-58-7). Soncino Pr.

--Tractate Hullin. 1980. 22.95 (ISBN 0-900689-17-X). Soncino Pr.

--Tractate Kethuboth. 1971. 22.95 (ISBN 0-900689-06-4). Soncino Pr.

--Tractate Pesachim. 1983. 22.95 (ISBN 0-900689-81-1). Soncino Pr.

--Tractate Sanhadrin. 1969. 22.95 (ISBN 0-900689-04-8). Soncino Pr.

--Tractate Shabbath, 2 vols. 1972. Set. 45.95 (ISBN 0-900689-62-5). Soncino Pr.

--Tractate Yoma. 1974. 22.95 (ISBN 0-900689-63-3). Soncino Pr.

--Tractates Baba Bathra, 2 Vols. 1976. Set. write for info. (ISBN 0-900689-64-1). Soncino Pr.

Erubin, 3 vols. 45.00 (ISBN 0-910218-54-4). Bennet Pub.

Feinsilver, Alexander, ed. The Talmud Today. 320p. 1980. 14.95 (ISBN 0-312-78479-1). St Martin.

Freeman, Gordon M. The Heavenly Kingdom: Aspects of Political Thought in the Talmud & Midrash. 196p. (Orig.). 1986. lib. bdg. 24.75 (ISBN 0-8191-5139-4, Co-pub. by Ctr Jewish Comm Studies); pap. text ed. 11.75 (ISBN 0-8191-5140-8). U Pr of Amer.

Gittin, 2 vols. 30.00 (ISBN 0-910218-66-8). Bennet Pub.

Goldenberg, Robert. The Sabbath-Law of R. Meir. LC 78-14370. (Brown University. Brown Judaic Studies: No. 6). 1978. pap. 9.00 (ISBN 0-89130-249-2, 140006). Scholars Pr GA.

Goldin, Judah. The Living Talmud. 1957. pap. 3.95 (ISBN 0-451-62344-4, Ment). NAL.

Haas, Peter J., tr. from Hebrew-Aramaic. The Talmud of Babylonia: An American Translation XXXV: Meilah & Tamid. (Brown Judaic Studies). 180p. 1986. 29.95 (ISBN 1-55540-086-8, 14-01-09). Scholars Pr GA.

Hagigah, 1 vol. 15.00 (ISBN 0-910218-61-7). Bennet Pub.

Haskelevich, B., ed. Introduction to Talmud Study. (Rus.). 400p. 1982. pap. 6.00x (ISBN 0-938666-01-0). CHAMAH Pubs.

Haut, Irwin H. The Talmud As Law Or Literature: An Analysis of David W. Halivni's Mekorot Umasorot. x, 83p. pap. 6.95 (ISBN 0-87203-107-1). Hermon.

Herford, R. Travers, ed. The Ethics of the Talmud: Sayings of the Fathers. LC 62-13138. 1962. pap. 6.25 (ISBN 0-8052-0023-1). Schocken.

Horayoth 'Eduyyoth & Aboth, 1 vol. 15.00 (ISBN 0-910218-78-1). Bennet Pub.

Hullin, 2 vols. 36.00 (ISBN 0-910218-81-1). Bennet Pub.

Jacobs, Louis. The Talmudic Argument: A Study in Talmudic Reasoning & Methodology. LC 84-4351. 240p. 1984. 44.50 (ISBN 0-521-26370-0). Cambridge U Pr.

--Teyku: The Unsolved Problem in the Babylonian Talmus. LC 80-70887. 312p. 1981. 20.00 (ISBN 0-8453-4501-X, Cornwall Bks). Assoc Univ Prs.

Kaplan, Aryeh. Ethics of the Talmud. 2nd ed. 336p. 1981. pap. 2.95 (ISBN 0-940118-31-9). Maznaim.

Katz, Mordecai. Protection of the Weak in the Talmud. LC 26-5707. (Columbia University. Oriental Studies: No. 24). Repr. of 1925 ed. 12.50 (ISBN 0-404-50514-7). AMS Pr.

Kerithoth, 1 vol. 15.00 (ISBN 0-910218-85-4). Bennet Pub.

Kethuboth, 3 vols. 45.00 (ISBN 0-910218-65-X). Bennet Pub.

Kiddushin, 2 vols. 30.00 (ISBN 0-910218-67-6). Bennet Pub.

Kolatch, Alfred J. Who's Who in the Talmud. rev. ed. LC 64-24891. 228p. 1981. Repr. 9.95 (ISBN 0-8246-0263-3). Jonathan David.

Lessons in Talmud. 1982. 3.00 (ISBN 0-686-76537-0). Feldheim.

Low, Leopold. Beitrage zur Judischen Alterthumskunde, 2 vols. 922p. Date not set. Repr. text ed. 149.04x (ISBN 0-576-80127-5, Pub. by Gregg Intl Pubs England). Gregg Intl.

Makkoth, 1 vol. 15.00 (ISBN 0-910218-76-5). Bennet Pub.

Malter, Henry, tr. & The Treatise Ta'anit of the Babylonian Talmud. LC 78-1171. (JPS Library of Jewish Classics). 528p. 1978. 6.50 (ISBN 0-8276-0108-5, 422). Jewish Pubns.

Marmorstein, Arthur. Studies in Jewish Theology: The Arthur Marmorstein Memorial Volume. Rabbinowitz, Joseph & Lew, Meyer S., eds. LC 76-39174. (Essay Index Reprint Ser.). Repr. of 1950 ed. 21.00 (ISBN 0-8369-2702-8). Ayer Co Pubs.

Megillah & Shekalim, 1 vol. 15.00 (ISBN 0-910218-59-5). Bennet Pub.

Me'ilah, Kimmin, Tamid & Middoth, 1 vol. 15.00 (ISBN 0-910218-86-2). Bennet Pub.

Menahoth, 2 vols. 30.00 (ISBN 0-910218-80-3). Bennet Pub.

Mielziner, Moses. Introduction to the Talmud. 4th ed. LC 68-29908. 1969. 17.95 (ISBN 0-8197-0156-4); pap. 12.95 (ISBN 0-8197-0015-0). Bloch.

Mishnayoth Zera im, 2 vols. 30.00 (ISBN 0-910218-52-8). Bennet Pub.

Mo'ed Katan, 1 vol. 15.00 (ISBN 0-910218-63-3). Bennet Pub.

Morag, Shelomo. Vocalised Talmudic Manuscripts in the Cambridge Genizah Collections: Taylor-Schnechter Old Series, Vol. 1. (Cambridge University Library Genizan Ser.: No. 4). 60p. Date not set. Vol. I: Taylor-Schechter Old Series. price not set (ISBN 0-521-26863-X). Cambridge U Pr.

Nazir, 1 vol. 15.00 (ISBN 0-910218-69-2). Bennet Pub.

Nedarim, 1 vol. 18.00 (ISBN 0-910218-68-4). Bennet Pub.

Neusner, Jacob. In the Margins of the Yerushalmi: Glosses on the English Translation. LC 83-20113. (Brown Judaic Studies). 160p. 1983. pap. 14.00 (ISBN 0-89130-663-3, 14 00 55). Scholars Pr GA.

--Invitation to the Talmud. Rev. ed. LC 83-48422. 320p. 1984. 19.45 (ISBN 0-06-066099-6, HarpR). Har-Row.

--Judaism: The Classical Statement, the Evidence of the Bavli. LC 85-28875. (CSHJ Ser.). 288p. 1986. 37.00 (ISBN 0-226-57620-5). U of Chicago Pr.

--Learn Talmud. (Illus.). 1979. pap. 4.95x (ISBN 0-87441-292-7). Behrman.

--The Peripatetic Saying: The Problem of the Thrice-Told Tale in the Canon of Talmudic Literature. (Brown Judaic Studies: No. 89). 208p. 1985. 18.95 (ISBN 0-89130-830-X, 14 00 89); pap. 15.95 (ISBN 0-89130-831-8). Scholars Pr GA.

--There We Sat Down: Talmudic Judaism in the Making. pap. 9.95x (ISBN 0-87068-676-3). Ktav.

Neusner, Jacob, ed. The Talmud of the Land of Israel: A Preliminary Translation & Explanation- Vol. 25, Gittin. (Chicago Studies in the History of Judaism). 270p. 1985. 33.00 (ISBN 0-226-57684-1). U of Chicago Pr.

--The Talmud of the Land of Israel: A Preliminary Translation & Explanation- Vol. 24, Nazir. (Chicago Studies in the History of Judaism). 268p. 1985. 33.00 (ISBN 0-226-57683-3). U of Chicago Pr.

Neusner, Jacob, ed. & tr. The Talmud of the Land of Israel: A Preliminary Translation & Explanation- Vol. 23, Nedarim. (Chicago Studies in the History of Judaism). 248p. 1985. 31.00 (ISBN 0-226-57682-5). U of Chicago Pr.

--The Talmud of the Land of Israel: A Preliminary Translation & Explanation: Hagigah & Moed Qatan, Vol. 20. LC 85-29037. (Chicago Studies in the History of Judaism). 242p. 1986. 35.00x (ISBN 0-226-57679-5). U of Chicago Pr.

Neusner, Jacob, ed. The Talmud of the Land of Israel: A Preliminary Translation & Explanation, Vol. 22: Ketubot. (Chicago Studies in the History of Judaism). 384p. 1985. lib. bdg. 49.00x (ISBN 0-226-57681-7). U of Chicago Pr.

Neusner, Jacob, ed. & tr. The Talmud of the Land of Israel: A Preliminmary Translation & Explanation-Vol. 26, Qiddushin. 1984. 25.00 (ISBN 0-226-57686-8). U of Chicago Pr.

--The Talmud of the Land of Israel: A Preliminary Translation & Explanation-Vol. 27, Sotah. 1984. 25.00 (ISBN 0-226-57687-6). U of Chicago Pr.

--The Talmud of the Land of Israel: A Preliminary Translation & Explanation-Vol. 28, Baba Qamma. 1984. 25.00 (ISBN 0-226-57688-4). U of Chicago Pr.

--The Talmud of the Land of Israel: A Preliminary Translation & Explanation-Vol. 29, Baba Mesia. 1984. 25.00 (ISBN 0-226-57689-2). U of Chicago Pr.

--The Talmud of the Land of Israel: A Preliminary Translation & Explanation-Vol. 30, Baba Batra. 1984. 25.00 (ISBN 0-226-57690-6). U of Chicago Pr.

--The Talmud of the Land of Israel: A Preliminary Translation & Explanation-Vol. 31, Sanhedrin & Makkot. 1984. 45.00 (ISBN 0-226-57691-4). U of Chicago Pr.

--The Talmud of the Land of Israel: A Preliminary Translation & Explanation-Vol. 33, Abodah Zarah. 1982. 27.00 (ISBN 0-226-57693-0). U of Chicago Pr.

--The Talmud of the Land of Israel: A Preliminary Translation & Explanation-Vol. 34, Horayot & Niddah. 1982. 29.00 (ISBN 0-226-57694-9). U of Chicago Pr.

--The Talmud of the Land of Israel: A Preliminary Translation & Explanation-Vol. 35, Introduction & Taxonomy. 1984. 19.00 (ISBN 0-226-57695-7). U of Chicago Pr.

Neusner, Jacob, ed. The Talmud of the Land of Israel: A Preliminary Translation & Explanation: Vol. 19, Megillah. LC 86-25284. (Chicago Studies in the History of Judaism). 200p. 1987. text ed. 27.50 (ISBN 0-226-57678-7). U of Chicago Pr.

Neusner, Jacob, ed. & tr. The Talmud of the Land of Israel: A Preliminary Translation & Explanation-Yebamot, Vol. 21. LC 86-11406. (Chicago Studies in the History of Judaism). 514p. 1987. text ed. 58.00x (ISBN 0-226-57680-9). U of Chicago Pr.

Neusner, Jacob, tr. The Talmud of Babylonia: An American Translation XXIII: Tractate Sanhedrin-Chap. 9-11. (Brown Judiac Studies). 1985. 29.95 (ISBN 0-89130-803-2, 14-0087); pap. 23.00 (ISBN 0-89130-804-0). Scholars Pr GA.

Newman, Louis I., ed. The Talmudic Anthology. LC 45-9682. 1978. pap. text ed. 12.95x (ISBN 0-87441-303-6). Behrman.

Niddah, 2 vols. 30.00 (ISBN 0-910218-87-0). Bennet Pub.

Peters, Madison C. Wit & Wisdom of the Talmud. 169p. 1980. Repr. of 1900 ed. lib. bdg. 20.00 (ISBN 0-8414-6852-4). Folcroft.

Prainatis. The Talmud Unmasked. 1979. lib. bdg. 59.95 (ISBN 0-8490-3010-2). Gordon Pr.

Preuss, Julius. Biblisch-Talmudische Medizin. rev. ed. (Ger). 1970. 150.00 (ISBN 0-87068-121-4). Ktav.

Rohling, A. The Jew According to the Talmud. 1982. lib. bdg. 69.95 (ISBN 0-87700-361-0). Revisionist Pr.

Rosh Hashanah, 1 vol. 15.00 (ISBN 0-910218-56-0). Bennet Pub.

Rosner, F. Medicine in the Bible & the Talmud: Selections from Classical Jewish Sources. (Library of Jewish Law & Ethics: Vol. 5). 9.95x (ISBN 0-87068-326-8). Ktav.

Saldarini, Anthony J. Scholastic Rabbinism: A Literary Study of the Fathers According to Rabbi Nathan. LC 81-13564. (Brown Judaic Studies). 1982. pap. text ed. 12.00 (ISBN 0-89130-523-8, 14-00-14). Scholars Pr GA.

Sanhedrin, 2 vols. 30.00 (ISBN 0-910218-74-9). Bennet Pub.

Shebu'oth, 1 vol. 18.00 (ISBN 0-910218-75-7). Bennet Pub.

Silberg, Moshe. Talmudic Law & the Modern State. 1973. 9.00x (ISBN 0-8381-3112-3). United Syn Bk.

The Soncino Hebrew-English Talmud. Incl. Tractate Berakoth. 22.95x (ISBN 0-685-23064-3); Tractate Baba Mezia. 22.95x (ISBN 0-685-23065-1); Tractate Gittin. 22.95x (ISBN 0-685-23066-X); Tractate Baba Kamma. 22.95x (ISBN 0-685-23067-8); Tractate Kiddushin. 22.95x (ISBN 0-685-23068-6); Tractate Pesahim. 22.95x (ISBN 0-685-23069-4); Tractate Sanhedrin. 22.95x (ISBN 0-685-23070-8); Tractate Kethuboth. 22.95x (ISBN 0-685-23071-6); Tractate Shabbath, 2 vols. Set. 45.95x (ISBN 0-685-23072-4); Tractate Yoma. 22.95x (ISBN 0-685-23073-2); Baba Bathra, 2 vols. 45.95x (ISBN 0-686-85719-4); Hullin. 22.95x (ISBN 0-686-85720-8). Bloch.

Sotah, 1 vol. 15.00 (ISBN 0-910218-70-6). Bennet Pub.

Steinsaltz, Adin. Essential Talmud. LC 75-36384. 1982. pap. 8.95 (ISBN 0-465-02063-1, CN-5112). Basic.

Strack, Hermann L. Introduction to the Talmud & Midrash. LC 59-7191. (Temple Books). 1969. pap. text ed. 8.95x (ISBN 0-689-70189-6, T10). Atheneum.

Sukkah, 1 vol. 15.00 (ISBN 0-910218-58-7). Bennet Pub.

Temurah, 1 vol. 15.00 (ISBN 0-910218-84-6). Bennet Pub.

Tractate Rosh Hashana, Bezah, Shekalim. 1983. 22.95 (ISBN 0-900689-82-X). Soncino Pr.

Tractate Taanit, Megilla, Chagiga. 1984. write for info. (ISBN 0-900689-84-6). Soncino Pr.

Trattner, Ernest R. Understanding the Talmud. LC 77-27887. 1978. Repr. of 1955 ed. lib. bdg. 22.50x (ISBN 0-313-20253-2, TRUT). Greenwood.

Unterman, Isaac. The Talmud: An Analytical Guide. LC 73-148291. 351p. 1985. text ed. 17.95 (ISBN 0-8197-0189-0); pap. text ed. 10.95 (ISBN 0-8197-0005-3). Bloch.

Yebamoth, 3 vols. 45.00 (ISBN 0-910218-64-1). Bennet Pub.

Yoma: Or, Yom Kippur, 2 vols. 30.00 (ISBN 0-910218-57-9). Bennet Pub.

Zahavy, Tzvee. The Traditions of Eleazar Ben Azariah. LC 76-46373. (Brown University. Brown Judaic Studies: No. 2). 1977. pap. 13.50 (ISBN 0-89130-095-3, 140002). Scholars Pr GA.

Zebahim, 2 vols. 36.00 (ISBN 0-910218-79-X). Bennet Pub.

TANNAIM

Green, William S., ed. Persons & Institutions in Early Rabbinic Judaism. LC 79-20712. (Brown University, Brown Judaic Studies: No. 3). 1977. pap. 13.50 (ISBN 0-89130-131-3, 14 00 03). Scholars Pr GA.

Tractate Taanit, Megilla, Chagiga. 1984. write for info. (ISBN 0-900689-84-6). Soncino Pr.

TANTRAS

Aiyar, K. N. Thirty Minor Upanishads: Including the Yoga Upanishads. 300p. 1980. Repr. of 1914 ed. 16.95 (ISBN 0-935548-00-9). Santarasa Pubns.

Allen, Marcus. Tantra for the West: A Guide to Personal Freedom. LC 80-316. 235p. 1981. pap. 7.95 (ISBN 0-931432-06-5). Whatever Pub.

Avalon, Arthur, pseud. Mahanirvana Tantra. (Sanskrit.). 473p. 1982. text ed. 28.00 (ISBN 0-89744-237-7). Auromere.

Avalon, Arthur. Tantra of the Great Liberation. (Illus.). 512p. 1913. pap. 8.50 (ISBN 0-486-20150-3). Dover.

Avalon, Arthur & Shastri, Lakshmana. Tantraraja Tantra. (Sanskrit.). 740p. 1982. text ed. 52.00 (ISBN 0-89744-238-5). Auromere.

Avalon, Arthur, ed., pseud. Prapanchasara Tantra. (Sanskrit.). 617p. 1982. text ed. 48.00 (ISBN 0-89744-239-3). Auromere.

Bhatt, S. R. Philosophy of Pancharatra: An Advaitic Approach. 137p. pap. 4.25 (ISBN 0-89744-122-2, Pub. by Ganesh & Co. India). Auromere.

Bose, D. N. Tantras: Their Philosophy & Occult Secrets. rev. 3rd ed. 1981. Repr. of 1956 ed. 12.00x (ISBN 0-8364-0737-7, Pub. by Mukhopadhyay). South Asia Bks.

Cozort, Dan. Highest Yoga Tantra. 220p. (Orig.). 1986. pap. 10.95 (ISBN 0-937938-32-7). Snow Lion.

Dyczkowski, Mark S. The Canon of the Saivagama & the Kubjika: Tantras of the Western Kaula Tradition. (Kashmir Shaivism Ser.). 256p. 1987. text ed. 34.50x (ISBN 0-88706-494-9). State U NY Pr.

Gibson, Morgan & Murakami, Hiroshi, trs. Tantric Poetry of Kukai. 1985. 7.00 (ISBN 0-934834-67-9). White Pine.

Johari, Harish. Tools for Tantra. (Illus.). 192p. 1986. pap. 14.95 (ISBN 0-89281-055-6, Inner Traditions). Inner Tradit.

Jyotir Maya Nanda, Swami. Mantra, Kirtana, Yantra & Tantra. (Illus.). 1974. pap. 3.99 (ISBN 0-934664-06-4). Yoga Res Foun.

Pandit, M. P. Lights on the Tantra. 3.95 (ISBN 0-89744-107-9, Pub. by Ganesh & Co. India). Auromere.

--More on Tantras. 152p. 1986. text ed. 22.50x (ISBN 81-207-0122-4, Pub. by Sterling Pubs India). Apt Bks.

--Studies in the Tantras & the Veda. 1973. 3.95 (ISBN 0-89744-110-9, Pub. by Ganesh & Co India). Auromere.

Parasurama. Bases of Tantra Sadhana. Pandit, M. P., tr. (Sanskrit.). 52p. 1980. 2.00 (ISBN 0-941524-02-7). Lotus Light.

Rajneesh, Bhagwan S. The Book of the Secrets. pap. 8.95 (ISBN 0-06-090564-6, CN 564, PL). Har-Row.

Rajneesh, Bhagwan Shree. The Tantra Vision, 2 vols. Anurag, Ma Yoga, ed. (Tantra Ser.). (Illus., Orig.). 1978. Vol. I, 340 pgs. 16.50 ea. (ISBN 0-88050-144-8). Vol. II, 344 pgs (ISBN 0-88050-145-6). Chidvilas Found.

Rao, S. K. Tantra Mantra Yantra: The Tantra Psychology. (Illus.). 1977. text ed. 12.50x (ISBN 0-391-01286-X). Humanities.

Rawson, Philip. Tantra: The Indian Cult of Ecstasy. (Art & Imagination Ser.). (Illus.). 1984. pap. 10.95f (ISBN 0-500-81001-X). Thames Hudson.

Reigle, David. The Books of Kiu-Te in the Tibetan Buddhist Tantras. LC 83-60416. (Secret Doctrine Reference Ser.). (Illus.). 80p. (Orig.). 1983. pap. 5.00 (ISBN 0-913510-49-1). Wizards.

Schoterman, J. A., ed. The Yonitantra. 1985. 11.00x (ISBN 0-8364-1326-1, Pub. by Manohar India). South Asia Bks.

Snellgrove, David L. Hevajra Tantra, 2 Vols. 1959. 59.00x (ISBN 0-19-713516-1). Oxford U Pr.

Vidyaratna, T. & Avalon, A. Kularnava Tantra. (Sanskrit.). 1975. Repr. 25.00 (ISBN 0-8426-0966-0). Orient Bk Dist.

Woodroffe, John. The Garland of Letters. 18.00 (ISBN 0-89744-112-5, Pub. by Ganesh & Co. India). Auromere.

TANTRIC BUDDHISM

see also Lamaism

Agehananda Bharati. The Tantric Tradition. LC 77-7204. 1977. Repr. of 1965 ed. lib. bdg. 22.50x (ISBN 0-8371-9660-4, AGTT). Greenwood.

Cozort, Dan. Highest Yoga Tantra. 220p. (Orig.). 1986. pap. 10.95 (ISBN 0-937938-32-7). Snow Lion.

Dawa-Samdup, Kazi, tr. from Tibetan. Shrichakrasambhara Tantra: A Buddhist Tantra. 255p. 1984. Repr. of 1919 ed. lib. bdg. 22.50x (ISBN 0-88181-000-2). Canon Pubns.

George, Christopher S., ed. Candramaharosana Tantra. (American Oriental Ser.: Vol. 56). 1974. pap. 15.00x (ISBN 0-940490-56-0). Am Orient Soc.

Guenther, Herbert V. & Trungpa, Chogyam. The Dawn of Tantra. LC 74-10250. (Illus.). 92p. pap. 6.95 (ISBN 0-87773-059-8). Shambhala Pubns.

Lessing, F. D. & Wayman, Alex. Introduction to the Buddhist Tantric System. 1978. 21.00 (ISBN 0-89684-037-9, Pub. by Motilal Banarsidass India). Orient Bk Dist.

Mullin, Glenn, et al. Selected Works of the Dalai Lama I: Bridging the Sutras & Tantras. Rev. ed. LC 85-8333. (Teachings of the Dalai Lamas Ser.). Orig. Title: Bridging the Sutras & Tantras. (Tibetan., Illus.). 288p. (Orig.). 1985. pap. 12.95 (ISBN 0-937938-27-0). Snow Lion.

Mullin, Glenn H., et al. Selected Works of the Dalai Lama II: The Tantric Yogas of the Sister Niguma. LC 85-40081. (Teachings of the Dalai Lamas Ser.). (Tibetan., Illus.). 240p. (Orig.). 1985. pap. 10.95 (ISBN 0-937938-28-9). Snow Lion.

Rajneesh, Bhagwan Shree. Tantra: The Supreme Understanding. 2nd ed. Apa, Ma Prem & Vadan, Ma Anand, eds. LC 84-42797. (Tantra Ser.). 336p. 1984. pap. 4.95 (ISBN 0-88050-643-1). Chidvilas Found.

Rinbochay, Khetsun S. Tantric Practice in Nying-ma. Hopkins, Jeffery & Klein, Anne, eds. LC 86-3762. 238p. (Orig.). 1983. lib. bdg. 16.00 cancelled (ISBN 0-937938-13-0); pap. text ed. 12.50 (ISBN 0-937938-14-9). Snow Lion.

Trungpa, Chogyam. Journey Without Goal: The Tantric Wisdom of the Buddha. LC 85-8175. 150p. 1985. pap. 8.95 (ISBN 0-87773-334-1, 74194-3). Shambhala Pubns.

Wayman, Alex. The Buddhist Tantras: Light on Indo-Tibetan Esotericism. LC 73-79801. (Illus.). 247p. 1973. 12.50 (ISBN 0-87728-223-4). Weiser.

Wayman, Alex & Lessing, F. D. Introduction to the Buddhist Tantric System. 382p. 1980. pap. 7.95 (ISBN 0-87728-450-4). Weiser.

TANTRISM

Agehananda Bharati. The Tantric Tradition. LC 77-7204. 1977. Repr. of 1965 ed. lib. bdg. 22.50x (ISBN 0-8371-9660-4, AGTT). Greenwood.

Bhattacharyya, N. N. History of the Tantric Religion. 1983. 34.00x (ISBN 0-8364-0942-6, Pub. by Manohar India); pap. 17.50x (ISBN 0-8364-0943-4). South Asia Bks.

Hopkins, Jeffrey. The Tantric Distinction. Klein, Anne C., ed. (A Wisdom Intermediate Book, White Ser.). 184p. (Orig.). 1984. pap. 8.95 (ISBN 0-86171-023-1, Wisdom Pubns). Great Traditions.

Pal, Pratapaditya. Hindu Religion & Iconology According to the Tantrasara. LC 81-52893. (Tantric Tradition Ser.). Orig. Title: Tantrasara. (Illus.). 172p. 1982. pap. 10.95 (ISBN 0-941582-00-0). Vichitra Pr.

Rastogi, Navjivan. Introduction to the Tantraloka. 400p. 1986. 22.00 (ISBN 81-208-0180-6, Pub. by Motilal Banarsidass). South Asia Bks.

Woodroffe, John. Introduction to Tantra Shastra. 9.00 (ISBN 0-89744-114-1, Pub. by Ganesh & Co. India). Auromere.

--Principles of Tantra, 2 vols. 1979. Set. 42.00 (ISBN 0-89744-129-X, Pub. by Ganesh & Co India). Auromere.

Woodroffe, John, tr. Great Liberation (Mahanirvana Tantra) (Sanskrit.). 28.00 (ISBN 0-89744-237-7, Pub. by Ganesh & Co. India). Auromere.

TAO TE CHING

Heider, John. The Tao of Leadership: Lao Tzu's Tao te Ching Adapted for a New Age. LC 84-19750. 184p. (Orig.). 1984. pap. 9.95 (ISBN 0-89334-079-0). Humanics Ltd.

Huang, Al C. Embrace Tiger, Return to Mountain: The Essence of T'ai Chi. LC 73-80134. (Illus.). 185p. 1973. 10.00 (ISBN 0-911226-12-5); pap. 6.50 (ISBN 0-911226-13-3). Real People.

Lao Tsu. Tao Te Ching. Gia-Fu Feng, ed. English, Jane, tr. 1972. pap. 10.95 (ISBN 0-394-71833-X, V-833, Vin). Random.

Lin, Paul J. A Translation of Lao Tzu's "Tao Te Ching" & Wang Pi's "Commentary.". (Michigan Monographs in Chinese Studies: No. 30). 232p. (Orig.). 1977. pap. 8.50 (ISBN 0-89264-030-8). U of Mich Ctr Chinese.

Mears, tr. Tao Teh King. 5.25 (ISBN 0-8356-5123-1). Theos Pub Hse.

Tsu, Lao. Tao Te Ching. Wilhelm, Richard, tr. 224p. 1985. pap. 5.95 (ISBN 1-85063-011-9). Methuen Inc.

TAOISM

Balfour, Frederic H. Taoist Texts. lib. bdg. 79.95 (ISBN 0-87968-191-8). Krishna Pr.

Bhagwan Shree Rajneesh. Tao: The Golden Gate, Vol. 2. Prabhu, Swami Krishna, ed. LC 84-42615. (Tao Ser.). 304p. (Orig.). 1985. pap. 4.95 (ISBN 0-88050-647-4). Chidvilas Found.

Blofeld, John. Taoism: The Road to Immortality. LC 77-90882. 195p. 1978. pap. 9.95 (ISBN 0-87773-116-0, 73582-X). Shambhala Pubns.

Bock, Felicia G. Classical Learning & Taoist Practices in Early Japan, with Translation of Books XVI & XX of the Engi-Shiki. Bock, Felicia G., tr. from Japanese. & intro. by. LC 82-84464. (Occasional Paper Arizona State Univ., Center for Asian Studies: No. 17). 102p. 1985. pap. 8.00 (ISBN 0-939252-13-9). ASU Ctr Asian.

Capra, Fritjof. The Tao of Physics. 2nd ed. LC 82-42679. (New Science Library Ser.). (Illus.). 308p. 1975. pap. 10.95 (ISBN 0-87773-246-9, 71612-4). Shambhala Pubns.

Chan, Wing-Tsit. The Way of Lao Tzu. 1963. pap. text ed. write for info. (ISBN 0-02-320700-0). Macmillan.

Chang, Jolan. The Tao of the Loving Couple: True Liberation Through the Tao. (Illus.). 129p. 1983. pap. 8.95 (ISBN 0-525-48042-0, 0869-260). Dutton.

Chang, Stephen T. Complete System of Self-Healing. LC 86-1859. (Illus.). 224p. 1986. 17.00 (ISBN 0-942196-06-6). Tao Pub.

--The Great Tao. (Illus.). 464p. 1985. 26.00 (ISBN 0-942196-01-5). Tao Pub.

--The Tao of Sexology. (Illus.). 224p. 1985. 17.00 (ISBN 0-942196-03-1). Tao Pub.

Chang Chung-Yuan. Creativity & Taoism. (Illus.). 1970. pap. 6.95x (ISBN 0-06-131968-6, TB1968, Torch). Har-Row.

Chang Po-tuan & Liu I-ming. The Inner Teachings of Taoism. Cleary, Thomas, tr. from Chinese. & intro. by. LC 86-11841. 100p. (Orig.). 1986. pap. 9.95 (ISBN 0-87773-363-5). Shambhala Pubns.

Chappell, David W., ed. Buddhist & Taoist Practice in Medieval Chinese Society: Buddhist & Taoist Studies II. (Asian Studies at Hawaii: No. 34). 256p. 1987. pap. text ed. 18.00x (ISBN 0-8248-0957-2). UH Pr.

Chee Soo. The Tao of Long Life: The Chinese Art of Ch'ang Ming. 176p. 1983. pap. 7.95 (ISBN 0-85030-320-6). Newcastle Pub.

--Taoist Yoga: The Chinese Art of K'ai Men. 160p. 1983. pap. 7.95 (ISBN 0-85030-332-X). Newcastle Pub.

Chia, Mantak. Taoist Secrets of Love: Cultivating Male Sexual Energy. 1984. pap. 14.00 (ISBN 0-943358-19-1). Aurora Press.

--Taoist Ways to Transform Stress into Vitality: The Inner Smile - Six Healing Sounds. LC 85-81656. (Illus.). 160p. (Orig.). 1986. pap. 9.95 (ISBN 0-935621-00-8). Heal Tao Bks.

Chia, Mantak & Chia, Maneewan. Healing Love Through the Tao: Cultivating Female Sexual Energy. LC 86-81049. (Illus.). 320p. (Orig.). 1986. 22.50 (ISBN 0-935621-04-0); pap. 12.95 (ISBN 0-935621-05-9). Heal Tao Bks.

Chiu, Milton M. The Tao of Chinese Religion. (Illus.). 432p. (Orig.). 1985. lib. bdg. 29.50 (ISBN 0-8191-4263-8); pap. text ed. 17.50 (ISBN 0-8191-4264-6). U Pr of Amer.

Cooper, J. C. Taoism: The Way of the Mystic. 1973. pap. 7.95 (ISBN 0-85030-096-7). Weiser.

Creel, Herrlee G. What Is Taoism? And Other Studies in Chinese Cultural History. LC 77-102905. (Midway Reprint Ser.). viii, 192p. 1982. pap. text ed. 11.00x (ISBN 0-226-12047-3). U of Chicago Pr.

Da Liu. The Tao & Chinese Culture. LC 78-26767. 192p. (Orig.). 1982. pap. 7.95 (ISBN 0-8052-0702-3). Schocken.

DeMile, James W. Tao of E Wing Chun Do, 2 pts, Vol. 1, pt. 1. 4th ed. (Illus.). 1983. 6.95 ea. (ISBN 0-918642-01-9); Pt. 1. Pt. 2. Tao of Wing.

Deng Ming-Dao. The Wandering Taoist. LC 82-48925. (Illus.). 272p. 1986. pap. 6.95 (ISBN 0-06-250226-3, HarpR). Har-Row.

Douglas, R. Confucianism & Taoism. 59.95 (ISBN 0-87968-930-7). Gordon Pr.

Ellwood, Rober S., ed. Eastern Spirituality in America: Selected Writings. (Sources of American Spirituality Ser.). 256p. 1987. pap. 16.95 (ISBN 0-8091-0388-5). Paulist Pr.

Finazzo, Giancarlo. The Notion of Tao in Lao Tzu & Chuang Tsu. 240p. 1980. 11.95 (ISBN 0-89955-146-7, Pub. by Mei Ya China). Intl Spec Bk.

Fulder, Stephen. Tao of Medicine: Ginseng, Oriental Remedies & the Pharmacology of Harmony. LC 82-1066. (Illus.). 328p. 1982. text ed. 9.95 (ISBN 0-89281-027-0, Destiny Bks). Inner Tradit.

Galt, Tom. The World Has a Familiar Face. 85p. 1981. pap. 5.00 (ISBN 0-938050-03-6). Shearwater.

Girardot, N. J. Myth & Meaning in Early Taoism: The Themes of Chaos (hun-tun) LC 81-21964. (Hermeneutics Studies in the History of Religions). (Illus.). 430p. 1983. 39.50x (ISBN 0-520-04330-8). U of Cal Pr.

Hoff, Benjamin. The Tao of Pooh. (Illus.). 162p. 1982. 8.95 (ISBN 0-525-24124-8, 0869-260). Dutton.

Izutsu, Toshihiko. Sufism & Taoism: A Comparative Study of Key Philosophical Concepts. LC 84-78. 493p. 1984. text ed. 40.00x (ISBN 0-520-05264-1). U of Cal Pr.

Johnston, Charles & Giles, Lionel, trs. Selections from the Upanishads & The Tao Te King. 142p. 1951. Repr. of 1897 ed. 3.00 (ISBN 0-938998-15-3). Cunningham Pr.

Jou, Tsung H. The Tao of Meditation: Way to Enlightenment. (Illus.). 186p. 1983. 15.00 (ISBN 0-8048-1465-1, Pub. by Tai Chi Foun). C E Tuttle.

Kaltenmark, Max. Lao-Tzu & Taoism. Greaves, Roger, tr. LC 69-13179. 1969. 15.00x (ISBN 0-8047-0688-3); pap. 5.95 (ISBN 0-8047-0689-1, SP96). Stanford U Pr.

Lao Tse. Tao. Mackintosh, Charles H., tr. 1971. pap. 3.25 (ISBN 0-8356-0426-8, Quest). Theos Pub Hse.

Lao Tze. Treatise on Response & Retribution. Carus, Paul & Suzuki, D. T., trs. from Chin. LC 6-28775. (Illus.). 139p. 1973. pap. 2.95 (ISBN 0-87548-244-9). Open Court.

Lee, Bruce. Tao of Jeet Kune Do. LC 75-13803. (Series 401). (Illus.). 1975. pap. 12.50 (ISBN 0-89750-048-2). Ohara Pubns.

Legeza, Laszlo. Tao Magic: The Secret Language of Diagrams & Calligraphy. LC 86-51463. (Illus.). 167p. 1987. pap. 10.95 (ISBN 0-500-27062-7). Thames Hudson.

Legge, J., tr. Texts of Taoism: The Sacred Books of China, 2 Vols. (Sacred Books of the East Ser). 28.50 set (ISBN 0-8446-3059-4). Peter Smith.

Legge, James. The Religions of China. LC 78-2685. 1979. Repr. of 1880 ed. lib. bdg. 45.00 (ISBN 0-8495-3313-9). Arden Lib.

Legge, James, tr. The Texts of Taoism, 2 vols. Muller, F. Max, ed. 396p. 1891. Vol. 1. pap. 6.95 (ISBN 0-486-20990-3); Vol. 2. pap. 6.95 (ISBN 0-486-20991-1). Dover.

Lewanski, Robert T. & Zuraw, Robert A. Health Force. 2nd, rev. ed. (Illus.). 252p. 1982. 14.95 (ISBN 0-9608030-0-9). Taoist Pubs.

Liu, Da. Taoist Health Exercise Book. 3rd ed. (Illus.). 172p. 1983. pap. 5.95 (ISBN 0-399-50745-0, Perigee). Putnam Pub Group.

McNaughton, William, ed. Taoist Vision. LC 70-143183. (Illus.). 1971. 7.95 (ISBN 0-472-09174-3). U of Mich Pr.

Maspero, Henri. Taoism & Chinese Religion. Kierman, Frank A., Jr., tr. from Fr. LC 80-13444. Orig. Title: Le Taoisme et les religions Chinoises. 656p. 1981. lib. bdg. 40.00x (ISBN 0-87023-308-4). U of Mass Pr.

Master Ni. The Footsteps of the Mystical Child. 180p. 1986. pap. text ed. 9.50 (ISBN 0-937064-11-4). SEBT.

Merton, Thomas. Way of Chuang Tzu. LC 65-27556. (Illus.). 1969. pap. 4.95 (ISBN 0-8112-0103-1, NDP276). New Directions.

Meyrink, Gustav. Some Taoist Alchemical Legends. 1986. pap. 3.95 (ISBN 0-916411-52-4, Pub. by Alchemical Pr). Holmes Pub.

Neville, Robert C. The Tao & the Daimon: Segments of a Religious Inquiry. 304p. 1982. 44.50x (ISBN 0-87395-661-3); pap. 14.95x (ISBN 0-87395-662-1). State U NY Pr.

Ni, Hua-Ching. The Complete Works of Lao Tzu: Tao Teh Ching & Hua Hu Ching. LC 79-88745. (Illus.). 219p. (Orig.). 1979. pap. 9.50 (ISBN 0-937064-00-9). SEBT.

--Tao: The Subtle Universal Law & the Integral Way of Life. LC 79-91720. (Illus.). 166p. (Orig.). 1979. pap. text ed. 7.50 (ISBN 0-937064-01-7). SEBT.

--The Taoist Inner View of the Universe & the Immortal Realm. LC 79-92389. (Illus.). 218p. (Orig.). 1979. pap. text ed. 12.50 (ISBN 0-937064-02-5). SEBT.

Ni Hua Ching. Eight Thousand Years of Wisdom: Conversations with Taoist Master Ni, Hua Ching, Bk. 1. LC 83-51082. 248p. (Orig.). 1983. pap. text ed. 12.50 (ISBN 0-937064-07-6). SEBT.

--Eight Thousand Years of Wisdom: Conversations with Taoist Master Ni, Hua Ching, Bk. 2. LC 83-51082. 248p. (Orig.). 1983. pap. text ed. 12.50 (ISBN 0-937064-08-4). SEBT.

--Workbook for Spiritual Development of All People. LC 83-51083. 240p. 1983. text ed. 12.50 (ISBN 0-937064-06-8). SEBT.

Ni Hua-Ching, Master & Hua-Ching. The Complete Works of Lao Tzu: Tao Teh Ching & Hua Hu Ching. LC 79-88745. 219p. 1979. pap. text ed. 7.50x (ISBN 0-937064-00-9). Wisdom Garden.

--Tao-The Subtle Universal Law & the Integral Way of Life. LC 79-91720. 166p. 1980. pap. text ed. 7.50 (ISBN 0-937064-01-7). Wisdom Garden.

--The Taoist Inner View of the Universe & the Immortal Realm. LC 79-91720. 218p. 1980. pap. text ed. 12.50x (ISBN 0-937064-02-5). Wisdom Garden.

Powell, James N. The Tao of Symbols. 1982. 11.50 (ISBN 0-688-01351-1). Morrow.

Rajneesh, Bhagwan S. The Secret of Secrets, Vol. 2. Sudha, Ma Y., ed. LC 82-50464. (Tao Ser.). 528p. (Orig.). 1983. pap. 4.95 (ISBN 0-88050-629-6). Chidvilas Found.

--The Way of Tao: Part II. Didi, Dolli, tr. 1979. 24.00 (ISBN 0-89684-056-5, Pub. by Motilal Banarsidass India). Orient Bk Dist.

Rajneesh, Bhagwan Shree. Tao: The Pathless Path, 2 vols. Asha, Ma Prem & Veena, Ma Prema, eds. LC 82-232884. (Tao Ser.). (Illus.). 1979. Vol. I, 432 pgs. 17.95 ea. (ISBN 0-88050-148-0). Vol. II, 540 pgs (ISBN 0-88050-149-9). Vol. I, 440p. pap. 15.95 (ISBN 0-88050-648-2); Vol. II, 1978, 542p. pap. write for info. (ISBN 0-88050-649-0). Chidvilas Found.

--Tao: The Three Treasures, 4 vols. Veena, Ma Prema & Somendra, Swami Anand, eds. LC 76-905202. (Tao Ser.). (Illus., Orig.). 1977. Vol. II, 346 pgs., 1976. 15.95 ea. (ISBN 0-88050-151-0). Vol. III, 404 pgs. 1976 (ISBN 0-88050-152-9). Vol. IV, 422 pgs. 1977 (ISBN 0-88050-153-7). Chidvilas Found.

--When the Shoe Fits. Veena, Ma Prema, ed. LC 76-904914. (Zen Masters Ser.). (Illus.). 388p. (Orig.). 1976. 16.50 (ISBN 0-88050-171-5). Chidvilas Found.

Rawson, Philip & Legeza, Laszlo. Tao: The Chinese Philosophy of Time & Change. (Art & Imagination Ser.). (Illus.). 1984. pap. 10.95f (ISBN 0-500-81002-8). Thames Hudson.

Saso, Michael & Chappell, David W., eds. Buddhist & Taoist Studies Number One. (Asian Studies at Hawaii: No. 18). (Illus.). 174p. 1977. pap. text ed. 10.50x (ISBN 0-8248-0420-1). UH Pr.

Saso, Michael R. Taoism & the Rite of Cosmic Renewal. (Illus.). 1972. pap. 4.00x (ISBN 0-87422-011-4). Wash St U Pr.

Schafer, Edward H. Mirages in the Sea of Time: The Taoist Poetry of Ts'ao T'ang. 1985. 18.00x (ISBN 0-520-05429-6). U of Cal Pr.

Schneeberger, Pierre-F. Japanese Lacquer: Selected Pieces. Watson, K., tr. (The Baur Collection Ser.). (Illus.). 193p. 1985. 195.00 (ISBN 0-7102-0320-9). Methuen Inc.

Seaton, Jerome, tr. The Wine of Endless Life: Taoists Drinking Songs. 1985. 6.00 (ISBN 0-934834-59-8). White Pine.

Smullyan, Raymond M. The Tao Is Silent. LC 76-62939. (Orig.). 1977. 8.95 (ISBN 0-685-75421-9, HarpR); pap. 4.95i (ISBN 0-06-067469-5, RD 206, HarpR). Har-Row.

Tao & T'ai Chi Kung. (Illus.). 55p. 1978. pap. 7.95x (ISBN 0-933740-00-X). Mindbody Inc.

Tao: Mastery of Life. 1962. 4.95 (ISBN 0-88088-508-4). Peter Pauper.

Teeguarden, Iona M. The Joy of Feeling Body-Mind: Acupressure--Jin Shin Do. LC 85-80534. (Illus.). 176p. (Orig.). 1986. pap. 13.95 (ISBN 0-87040-634-5). Japan Pubns USA.

Tzu, Huai-nan. Tao, the Great Luminant: Essays from Huai-Nan-Tzu. Morgan, Evan, tr. from Chinese. 301p. Repr. of 1935 ed. text ed. 24.00x (ISBN 0-89644-062-1, Pub. by Chinese Matl Ctr). Coronet Bks.

Tzu, Lao. The Way of the Ways Tao. Maurer, Herrymon, tr. from Chinese. 108p. 1985. 10.95 (ISBN 0-8052-3985-5). Schocken.

Wallacker, Benjamin E. The Huai-nan-tzu, Book Eleven: Behavior, Culture, & the Cosmos. (American Oriental Ser.: Vol. 48). 1962. pap. 5.00x (ISBN 0-940490-48-X). Am Orient Soc.

Watts, Alan & Chung-Liang Huang, Al. Tao: The Watercourse Way. LC 76-4762. 1977. pap. 5.95 (ISBN 0-394-73311-8). Pantheon.

Weber, Max. Religion of China. 1968. 14.95 (ISBN 0-02-934440-9); text ed. 14.95 (ISBN 0-02-934450-6). Free Pr.

Welch, Holmes. Taoism: The Parting of the Way. Orig. Title: Parting of the Way. 1966. pap. 6.95 (ISBN 0-8070-5973-0, BP224). Beacon Pr.

Welch, Holmes & Seidel, Anna, eds. Facets of Taoism: Essays in Chinese Religion. LC 77-28034. 1979. 38.00x (ISBN 0-300-01695-6); pap. 8.95x (ISBN 0-300-02673-0). Yale U Pr.

Wing, R. L. Tao of Power. LC 85-10210. (Illus.). 192p. 1986. pap. 12.50 (ISBN 0-385-19637-7, Dolp). Doubleday.

TAPPAN, LEWIS, 1788-1873

Winter, Rebecca J. The Night Cometh: Two Wealthy Evangelicals Face the Nation. LC 77-87594. 1977. pap. 2.95 (ISBN 0-87808-429-0). William Carey Lib.

TAULER, JOHANN, 1300-1361

Clark, James M. Great German Mystics: Eckhart, Tauler & Suso. LC 73-81493. 1970. Repr. of 1949 ed. 15.00x (ISBN 0-8462-1351-6). Russell.

TAVISTOCK ABBEY

Finberg, H. P. Tavistock Abbey. LC 69-10850. (Illus.). 1969. Repr. of 1951 ed. 35.00x (ISBN 0-678-05597-1). Kelley.

TAXATION

Clotfelter, Charles T. & Salamon, Lester M. The Federal Government & the Nonprofit Sector: The Impact of the 1981 Tax Act on Individual Charitable Giving. LC 82-113321. cancelled. Urban Inst.

Eddleman, H. Leo. Hail Mary, Are You Heeding the Blessed Virgin? In Defense of Public Schools. (Orig.). 1982. pap. 4.00 (ISBN 0-682-49899-8). Exposition Pr FL.

Kaufman, Donald D. What Belongs to Caeser? LC 70-109939. 128p. 1969. pap. 5.95 (ISBN 0-8361-1621-6). Herald Pr.

TAXATION, EXEMPTION FROM

see also Church Property–Taxation

Treusch, Paul E. & Sugarman, Norman A. Tax Exempt Charitable Organizations. 2nd ed. LC 83-70067. 726p. 1983. text ed. 95.00 (ISBN 0-8318-0429-7, B429). Am Law Inst.

TAYLOR, JAMES HUDSON, 1832-1905

Davey, Cyril. On del Clouds to China (J. Hudson Taylor) 1964. pap. 2.95 (ISBN 0-87508-617-9). Chr Lit.

Stocker, Fern N. Hudson Taylor: Trusting God No Matter What. (Guessing Bks.). (Orig.). 1986. pap. 3.95 (ISBN 0-8024-8575-8). Moody.

Taylor, Howard & Taylor, Mary G. Hudson Taylor's Spiritual Secret. pap. 3.95 (ISBN 0-8024-0029-9). Moody.

TAYLOR, JEREMY, BP. OF DOWN AND CONNOR, 1613-1667

Armstrong, Martin. Jeremy Taylor: A Selection from His Works. 1973. lib. bdg. 15.00 (ISBN 0-8414-1165-4). Folcroft.

Gosse, Edmund. Jeremy Taylor. 1904. Repr. 9.50 (ISBN 0-8274-2609-7). R West.

Gosse, Edmund W. Jeremy Taylor. LC 4-1683. 1969. Repr. of 1904 ed. 11.00x (ISBN 0-403-00088-2). Scholarly.

Selections from the Works of Jeremy Taylor: With Some Account of the Author & His Writings. 306p. 1983. Repr. of 1865 ed. lib. bdg. 40.00 (ISBN 0-89760-853-4). Telegraph Bks.

Stranks, C. J. The Life & Writings of Jeremy Taylor. LC 73-11259. 1973. lib. bdg. 35.00 (ISBN 0-8414-7595-4). Folcroft.

Williamson, Hugh Ross. Jeremy Taylor. LC 73-15705. 1902. lib. bdg. 20.00 (ISBN 0-8414-9472-X). Folcroft.

TAYLOR, JEREMY, BP. OF DOWN AND CONNOR, 1613-1667–BIBLIOGRAPHY

Gathorne-Hardy, Robert & Williams, William P., eds. Bibliography of the Writings of Jeremy Taylor to 1700: With a Section of Tayloriana. LC 71-149932. 159p. 1971. 20.00 (ISBN 0-87580-023-8). N Ill U Pr.

TEACHERS–DEVOTIONAL LITERATURE

Foner, Philip S. & Pacheco, Josephine F. Three Who Dared: Prudence Crandall, Margaret Douglass, Myrtilla Miner-Champions of Antebellum Black Education. LC 83-12830. (Contributions in Women's Studies: No. 47). xviii, 234p. 1984. lib. bdg. 32.95 (ISBN 0-313-23584-8, FTH/). Greenwood.

MacHaffie, Ingeborg S. To Teachers with Love. Nielsen, Margaret, ed. (Illus.). 90p. (Orig.). 1986. pap. 5.95 perfect bdg. (ISBN 0-9609374-2-0). Skribent.

Monsma, Hester, compiled by. One Step at a Time. 86p. 1984. 5.95 (ISBN 0-8010-6177-6). Baker Bk.

Vandermey, Mary A. Love Is Like the Sunlight. 1985. pap. 5.95 (ISBN 0-8010-9294-9). Baker Bk.

TEACHING

see also Object-Teaching

Davis, Ron, et al. You Can Teach Adults Successfully. (Training Successful Teachers Ser.). 48p. (Orig.). 1984. pap. 2.95 (ISBN 0-87239-808-0, 3208). Standard Pub.

Ford, LeRoy. Using Problem Solving in Teaching & Training. LC 77-178060. (Multi-Media Teaching & Training Ser.). (Orig.). 1972. pap. 5.50 (ISBN 0-8054-3415-1). Broadman.

Gregory, John M. Seven Laws of Teaching. 1954. 7.95 (ISBN 0-8010-3652-6). Baker Bk.

--The Seven Laws of Teaching. (Orig.). 1886. 1.95x (ISBN 0-9606952-1-4). PBBC Pr.

Noddings, Nel & Shore, Paul J. Awakening the Inner Eye: Intuition in Education. LC 83-1805. 236p. 1984. 26.95x (ISBN 0-8077-2751-2). Tchrs Coll.

Rinehart, Alice D. Mortals in the Immortal Profession: An Oral History of Teaching. LC 82-17200. 410p. 1983. pap. text ed. 19.95x (ISBN 0-8290-1049-1). Irvington.

Schrank, Jeffrey. Teaching Human Beings: One Hundred One Subversive Activities for the Classroom. LC 73-179154. 288p. (Orig.). 1972. 9.95x (ISBN 0-8070-3176-3); pap. 5.95x (ISBN 0-8070-3177-1, BP425). Beacon Pr.

Sias, Twila. You Can Teach Children Successfully. (Training Successful Teachers Ser.). 48p. (Orig.). 1984. pap. 2.95 (ISBN 0-87239-806-4, 3206). Standard Pub.

Tom, Alan R. Teaching As a Moral Craft. LC 83-17520. 256p. 1984. pap. text ed. 12.95 (ISBN 0-582-28307-8). Longman.

Welch, Mary L. Methods of Teaching in the Catholic School. 1986. 6.60 (ISBN 0-318-20570-X). Natl Cath Educ.

TEACHING AUTHORITY OF THE CHURCH
see Catechetics–Catholic Church

TEACHING OFFICE OF THE CHURCH
see Church–Teaching Office

TEACHINGS OF JESUS
see Jesus Christ–Teachings

TECHNOLOGY–MORAL AND RELIGIOUS ASPECTS
see Technology and Ethics

TECHNOLOGY AND ETHICS

Allen, Anne S., ed. New Options, New Dilemmas: An Interprofessional Approach to Life or Death Decisions. LC 85-45436. 144p. 1985. 22.00 (ISBN 0-669-11730-7). Lexington Bks.

Jonas, Hans. The Imperative of Responsibility: In Search of an Ethics for the Technological Age. LC 83-18249. xii, 256p. 1985. lib. bdg. 25.00x (ISBN 0-226-40596-6); pap. 10.95 (ISBN 0-226-40597-4). U of Chicago Pr.

Mitcham, Carl & Grote, Jim, eds. Theology & Technology: Essays in Christian Analysis & Exegesis. LC 84-2183. 534p. (Orig.). 1984. lib. bdg. 36.00 (ISBN 0-8191-3808-8); pap. text ed. 20.50 (ISBN 0-8191-3809-6). U Pr of Amer.

Monsma, Stephen, et al. Responsible Technology: A Christian Perspective. 248p. (Orig.). 1986. pap. 12.95 (ISBN 0-8028-0175-7). Eerdmans.

Los Poderes Tecnologicos y la Persona. 370p. 1984. pap. cancelled (ISBN 0-935372-16-4). Pope John Ctr.

Winter, Gibson. Liberating Creation: Foundations of Religious Social Ethics. LC 81-5364. 1981. 12.95 (ISBN 0-8245-0032-6). Crossroad NY.

TEEN-AGE
see Adolescence

TEEN-AGERS
see Youth

TEILHARD DE CHARDIN, PIERRE, 1881-1955

Barthelemy-Madaule. Bergson et Teilhard de Chardin. 23.50 (ISBN 0-685-36604-9). French & Eur.

Birx, H. James. Pierre Teilhard De Chardin's Philosophy of Evolution. 192p. 1972. 21.50x (ISBN 0-398-02466-9). C C Thomas.

Culliton, Joseph T. A Processive World View for Pragmatic Christians. LC 75-3781. 302p. 1975. 13.95 (ISBN 0-8022-2170-X). Philos Lib.

Dodson, E. O. The Phenomenon of Man Revisited: A Biological Viewpoint on Teilhard de Chardin. LC 83-20959. (Illus.). 288p. 1984. 26.50x (ISBN 0-231-05850-0). Columbia U Pr.

Faricy, Robert S. The Spirituality of Teilhard de Chardin. 128p. (Orig.). 1981. pap. 5.95 (ISBN 0-86683-608-X, HarpR). Har-Row.

Grau, Joseph A. Morality & the Human Future in the Thought of Teilhard De Chardin: A Critical Study. LC 74-4976. 389p. 1976. 28.50 (ISBN 0-8386-1579-1). Fairleigh Dickinson.

Gray, Donald P. A New Creation Story: The Creative Sprituality of Teilhard de Chardin. (Teilhard Studies). 1979. pap. 2.00 (ISBN 0-89012-014-5). Anima Pubns.

Hale, Robert. Christ & the Universe. Meilach, Michael, ed. (Theilhard de Chardin & the Universe Ser.). 5.50 (ISBN 0-8199-0449-X). Franciscan Herald.

King, Thomas M. Teilhard's Mysticism of Knowing. 192p. 1981. 14.95 (ISBN 0-8164-0491-7, HarpR). Har-Row.

King, Thomas M. & Salmon, James F., eds. Teilhard & the Unity of Knowledge. LC 82-60590. 1983. pap. 6.95 (ISBN 0-8091-2491-2). Paulist Pr.

King, Ursula. Towards a New Mysticism: Teilhard de Chardin & Eastern Religions. 320p. 1980. (HarpR); pap. 8.95 (ISBN 0-8164-2327-X). Har-Row.

Kraft, R. Wayne. Reason to Hope: A Synthesis of Teilhard de Chardin's Vision & Systems Thinking. (Systems Inquiry Ser.). 292p. 1983. pap. 12.95x (ISBN 0-914105-14-0). Intersystems Pubns.

Kropf, Richard W. Teilhard, Scripture, & Revelation: Teilhard de Chardin's Reinterpretation of Pauline Themes. LC 73-20907. 352p. 1980. 29.50 (ISBN 0-8386-1481-7). Fairleigh Dickinson.

Lyons, J. A. The Cosmic Christ in Origen & Teilhard de Chardin. Wiles, Maurice, ed. (Theological Monographs). 1982. 34.95x (ISBN 0-19-826721-5). Oxford U Pr.

Neilson, Francis. Teilhard de Chardin's Vision of the Future. 1979. lib. bdg. 39.50 (ISBN 0-685-96640-2). Revisionist Pr.

Sethna, K. D. The Spirituality of the Future: A Search Apropos of R. C. Zaehner's Study in Sri-Aurobindo & Teilhard de Chardin. LC 76-14764. 320p. 1981. 32.50 (ISBN 0-8386-2028-0). Fairleigh Dickinson.

Tucker, Mary E. The Ecological Spirituality of Teilhard. (Teilhard Studies). 1985. pap. 2.00 (ISBN 0-89012-040-4). Anima Pubns.

UNESCO Colloqium, 10th Anniversary of the Death of Albert Einstein & Teilhard De Charden. Science & Synthesis: An International Colloquium Organized by UNESCO on the Tenth Anniversary of the Death of Albert Einstein & Teilhard De Chardin. Crook, B. M., tr. LC 77-143044. 1971. 29.00 (ISBN 0-387-05344-1). Springer-Verlag.

TELEPHONE IN CHURCH WORK

Grindal, Harald. Telecare Ministry: Using the Telephone in a Care Ministry. 40p. 1984. pap. 3.95 (ISBN 0-8066-2099-4, 23-1899). Augsburg.

TELEVISION–MORAL AND RELIGIOUS ASPECTS

Ball-Rokeach, Sandra & Grube, Joel W. The Great American Values Test: Influencing Behavior & Belief Through Television. LC 83-48468. 208p. 1983. 25.00x (ISBN 0-02-926850-8). Free Pr.

Brown, Les. Keeping Your Eye on Television. LC 79-15828. (Orig.). 1979. pap. 4.95 (ISBN 0-8298-0376-9). Pilgrim NY.

Coleman, William L. Making TV Work for Your Family. LC 83-11881. 112p. (Orig.). 1983. pap. 4.95 (ISBN 0-87123-322-3, 210322). Bethany Hse.

Fore, William F. Television & Religion: The Shaping of Faith & Value. 208p. (Orig.). 1987. pap. 11.95 (ISBN 0-8066-2268-7, 10-6229). Augsburg.

Media Mirror: A Study Guide on Christian Values & Television. 3.60 (ISBN 0-318-03691-6); tchrs. guide 4.00 (ISBN 0-318-03692-4). Natl Cath Educ.

Perrotta, Kevin. Taming the TV Habit. 162p. (Orig.). 1982. pap. 6.95 (ISBN 0-89283-155-3). Servant.

TELEVISION IN RELIGION

Brown, Edna M. & Hill, George H. Coloring the Electric Church-Black Religious Broadcaster: A Selected Annotated Bibliography. 60p. 1987. text ed. 15.00X (ISBN 0-933650-31-0); pap. text ed. 7.00 (ISBN 0-933650-30-2). Daystar Co Carson.

Durfey, Thomas C. & Ferrier, James A. Religious Broadcast Management Handbook. 1986. pap. 14.95 (ISBN 0-310-39741-3). Zondervan.

Elvy, Peter. Buying Time: The Foundation of the Electronic Church. (Illus.). 1987. pap. 5.95 (ISBN 0-89622-325-6). Twenty-Third.

Frankl, Razelle. Televangelism: The Marketing of Popular Religion. (Illus.). 224p. 1987. 19.95 (ISBN 0-8093-1299-9). S Ill U Pr.

Gates, Larry W. Dwelling in Scullerland. LC 85-40200. 105p. (Orig.). 1985. pap. text ed. 8.95 (ISBN 0-938232-68-1). Winston-Derek.

Horsfield, Peter. Religious Television: The Experience in America. LC 83-11313. (Communication & Human Values Ser.). (Illus.). 192p. 1984. text ed. 15.00 (ISBN 0-582-28432-5). Longman.

Turner, Chip R. The Church Video Answerbook. LC 85-242884. 1986. pap. 5.95 (ISBN 0-8054-3713-4). Broadman.

TELLOH (MOUND)

Lau, Robert J. Old Babylonian Temple Records. (Columbia University. Oriental Studies: No. 3). Repr. of 1906 ed. 15.50 (ISBN 0-404-50493-0). AMS Pr.

TEMPERAMENT
see also Emotions

LaHaye, Tim. Your Temperament: Discover Its Potential. 400p. 1984. 12.95 (ISBN 0-8423-8752-8). Tyndale.

--Your Temperament: Discover Its Potential. (Living Bk). 400p. 1987. pap. cancelled (ISBN 0-8423-8757-9). Tyndale.

TEMPERANCE
see also Alcohol and Youth; Alcoholics; Alcoholism; Temperance and Religion

Blocker, Jack S., Jr. Give to the Winds Thy Fears: The Women Temperance Crusade, 1873-1874. LC 84-15718. (Contributions in Women Studies: No. 55). (Illus.). xix, 280p. 1985. lib. bdg. 35.00 (ISBN 0-313-24556-8, BGW/). Greenwood.

Constable, Giles. Attitudes Toward Self-Inflicted Suffering in the Middle Ages. (Stephen J. Brademas Lectures Ser.). 28p. (Orig.). pap. text ed. 2.50 (ISBN 0-916586-87-1). Hellenic Coll Pr.

Porterfield, Kay M. Keeping Promises: The Challenge of the Sober Parent. 172p. (Orig.). 1984. pap. 4.95 (ISBN 0-89486-245-6). Hazelden.

Raymond, Irving W. Teaching of the Early Church on the Use of Wine & Strong Drink. LC 79-120207. (Columbia University. Studies in the Social Sciences: No. 286). Repr. of 1927 ed. 14.50 (ISBN 0-404-51286-0). AMS Pr.

Teetotalism, Eighteen Forty-Two. 25p. 1984. pap. text ed. 12.50 (ISBN 0-87556-380-5). Saifer.

Twerski, Abraham J. Self-Discovery in Recovery. 128p. (Orig.). 1984. pap. 3.95 (ISBN 0-89486-238-3). Hazelden.

W, Carolyn. Detaching with Love. 24p. (Orig.). 1984. pap. 0.95 (ISBN 0-89486-232-4). Hazelden.

Willard, Frances E. Woman & Temperance; or, the Work & Workers of the Woman's Christian Temperance Union. LC 74-38443. (Religion in America, Ser. 2). 654p. 1972. Repr. of 1883 ed. 38.00 (ISBN 0-405-04093-8). Ayer Co Pubs.

TEMPERANCE AND RELIGION

De Swarte, Carolyn G. & Dayton, Donald, eds. The Ideal of "The New Woman" According to the Woman's Christian Temperance Union. (Women in American Protestant Religion 1800-1930). 394p. 1987. lib. bdg. 55.00 (ISBN 0-8240-0655-0). Garland Pub.

Wilkerson, David. Sipping Saints. 128p. 1979. pap. 2.95 (ISBN 0-8007-8339-5, Spire Bks). Revell.

TEMPLARS
see also Freemasons–Knights Templars

Addison, Charles G. The Knights Templar History. rev. ed. LC 76-29832. Repr. of 1912 ed. 59.50 (ISBN 0-404-15407-7). AMS Pr.

Barber, M. C. The Trial of the Templars. LC 77-85716. 320p. 1978. 54.50 (ISBN 0-521-21896-9); pap. 15.95 (ISBN 0-521-28018-4). Cambridge U Pr.

Burman, Edward. The Templars: Knights of God. (Crucible Ser.). 208p. 1987. pap. 9.95 (ISBN 0-85030-396-6). Thorsons Pubs.

Campbell, George A. The Knights Templars, Their Rise & Fall. LC 78-63330. (The Crusades & Military Orders: Second Ser.). Repr. of 1937 ed. 35.00 (ISBN 0-404-17005-6). AMS Pr.

Froude, James A. Spanish Story of the Armada & Other Essays. LC 71-144613. Repr. of 1892 ed. 24.50 (ISBN 0-404-02628-1). AMS Pr.

Martin, Edward J. The Trial of the Templars. LC 76-29845. Repr. of 1928 ed. 24.50 (ISBN 0-404-15424-7). AMS Pr.

Parker, Thomas W. The Knights Templars in England. LC 63-11983. pap. 48.80 (ISBN 0-317-08903-X, 2055370). Bks Demand UMI.

Records of the Templars in England in the Twelfth Century: The Inquest of 1185 with Illustrative Charters & Documents. (British Academy, London, Records of the Social & Economic History Of England & Wales Ser.: Vol. 9). pap. 70.00 (ISBN 0-8115-1249-5). Kraus Repr.

Rees, William. A History of the Order of St. John of Jerusalem in Wales & on the Welsh Border: Including an Account of the Templars. LC 76-29839. (Illus.). Repr. of 1947 ed. 26.50 (ISBN 0-404-15427-1). AMS Pr.

Simon, Edith. The Piebald Standard. LC 76-29836. Repr. of 1959 ed. 40.00 (ISBN 0-404-15419-0). AMS Pr.

TEMPLE, WILLIAM, ABP. OF CANTERBURY, 1881-1944

Fletcher, Joseph F. William Temple, Twentieth-Century Christian. LC 63-12587. 1963. text ed. 15.00x (ISBN 0-8401-0741-2). A R Allenson.

Iremonger, Frederick A. William Temple, Archbishop of Canterbury: His Life & Letters. LC 83-45439. Repr. of 1948 ed. 62.50 (ISBN 0-404-20128-8). AMS Pr.

Lowry, Charles W. William Temple: An Archbishop for All Seasons. LC 81-43869. 170p. (Orig.). 1982. lib. bdg. 22.25 (ISBN 0-8191-2355-2); pap. text ed. 7.75 (ISBN 0-8191-2356-0). U Pr of Amer.

Thomas, Owen C. William Temple's Philosophy of Religion. LC 61-4400. 1961. 10.00x (ISBN 0-8401-2330-2). A R Allenson.

TEMPLE OF GOD
see also Cave Temples; Mosques

Barrois, Georges A. Jesus Christ & the Temple. LC 80-19700. 163p. (Orig.). 1980. pap. 5.95 (ISBN 0-913836-73-7, BS680 T4837). St Martin.

TEMPLES
see also Cave Temples; Mosques

Arnold, Dieter. The Temple of Mentuhotep at Dier El Bahari. (Publications of the Metropolitan Museum of Art Egyptian Expedition: Vol. XXI). (Illus.). 1979. 60.00 (ISBN 0-87099-163-9). Metro Mus Art.

Ben-Dov, Meir. In the Shadow of the Temple. LC 84-48639. (Illus.). 384p. 1985. 24.45i (ISBN 0-06-015362-8, HarpT). Har-Row.

Berner, Ronald M. Temple Arts of Kerala: A South Indian Tradition. 272p. 100.00 (ISBN 0-317-52158-6, Pub. by S Chand India). State Mutual Bk.

Bernier, Ronald M. The Temples of Napal: An Introductory Survey. (Illus.). 247p. 1970. text ed. 27.50x. Coronet Bks.

--The Temples of Nepal. 204p. 25.00X (ISBN 0-317-52159-4, Pub. by S Chand India). State Mutual Bk.

Cousens, H. The Architectural Antiquities of Western India. (Illus.). 1983. text ed. 34.00x. Coronet Bks.

Dehejia, Vidya. Early Stone Temples of Orissa. LC 78-54434. (Illus.). 217p. 1979. 37.75 (ISBN 0-89089-092-7). Carolina Acad Pr.

Epigraphic Survey. The Temple of Khonsu: Vol. 2, Scenes & Inscriptions in the Court & the First Hypostyle Hall. LC 80-82999. (Oriental Institute Publications Ser.: Vol. 103). 1981. pap. 95.00x incl. 96 plates in portfolio (ISBN 0-918986-29-X). Oriental Inst.

Fujioka, Michio. Angkor Wat. LC 71-158641. (This Beautiful World Ser.: Vol. 29). (Illus.). 138p. (Orig.). 1972. pap. 4.95 (ISBN 0-87011-156-6). Kodansha.

Hamilton, Charles M. & Cutrubus, C. Nina, eds. The Salt Lake Temple: A Monument to a People. (Illus.). 208p. 1983. write for info. (ISBN 0-913535-01-X); pap. write for info. (ISBN 0-913535-02-8); Ltd. Ed. 250.00 (ISBN 0-913535-00-1). Univ Servs Inc.

Hanson, John A. Roman Theater-Temples. LC 78-5510. (Illus.). 1978. Repr. of 1959 ed. lib. bdg. 27.50x (ISBN 0-313-20477-2, HATT). Greenwood.

Haran, Menahem. Temples & Temple-Service in Ancient Israel. 416p. 1985. Repr. of 1978 ed. text ed. 20.00x (ISBN 0-931464-18-8). Eisenbrauns.

Jones, Julie. Houses for the Hereafter: Funerary Temples from Guerrero, Mexico. (Illus.). 32p. 1987. pap. 10.00 (ISBN 0-9617356-1-9). Metro Mus Art.

Kaur, Madanjit. The Golden Temple, Past & Present. 1985. 17.50x (ISBN 0-8364-1325-3, Pub. by Nank Dev Univ India). South Asia Bks.

Kramrisch, Stella. Hindu Temple, 2 vols. 1986. Repr. 60.00 (ISBN 81-208-0222-5, Pub. by Motilal Banarsidass). South Asia Bks.

Lau, Robert J. Old Babylonian Temple Records. (Columbia University. Oriental Studies: No. 3). Repr. of 1906 ed. 15.50 (ISBN 0-404-50493-0). AMS Pr.

Malyala, Panduranga R. Temples & Idol Worship. Date not set. 4.99 (ISBN 0-938924-02-8). Sri Shirdi Sai.

Mehta, Rustam J. Masterpieces of Indian Temples. LC 75-901641. (Illus.). 110p. 1974. 22.00x (ISBN 0-89684-433-1). Orient Bk Dist.

Meister, Michael W., ed. Encyclopedia of Indian Temple Architecture: South India, Lower Dravidadesa, 300 B.C.-A.D. 1326, 2 pts, Vol. 1. LC 82-50173. (Illus.). 736p. 1982. Set. 84.00x (ISBN 0-8122-7840-2). U of Pa Pr.

Meister, Michael W. & Dhaky, M. A., eds. Encyclopedia of Indian Temple Architecture, Vol. 1, Part II: South India: Upper Dravidadesa. (Illus.). 736p. 1982. Set. text ed. 84.00x. U of Pa Pr.

Metropulous, Lyman. The Illustrated Book of the Great Ancient Temples. (The Masterpieces of World Architecture Library). (Illus.). 141p. 1983. 112.50 (ISBN 0-86650-042-1). Gloucester Art.

Michell, George, ed. Brick Temples of Bengal: From the Archives of David McCutchion. LC 82-3872. (Illus.). 450p. 1983. 90.00x (ISBN 0-691-04010-9). Princeton U Pr.

Murray, Margaret A. Egyptian Temples. LC 75-41203. Repr. of 1931 ed. 27.50 (ISBN 0-404-14719-4). AMS Pr.

Nataraja Temple: History, Art & Architecture. (Illus.). 1977. 12.00x (ISBN 0-686-22668-2). Intl Bk Dist.

Natarajan, B. The City of the Cosmic Dance. 193p. 1974. text ed. 15.00x (ISBN 0-86125-035-4). Apt Bks.

Nelson, Harold H. Key Plans Showing Locations of Theban Temple Decorations. LC 42-21551. (Oriental Institute Pubns. Ser: No. 56). (Illus.). 1941. 30.00x (ISBN 0-226-62154-5, OIP56). U of Chicago Pr.

Nikopol, Georg R. The Artistic & Mystical Significance of Indian & Egyptian Temples. (Illus.). 187p. 1984. 137.45 (ISBN 0-86650-131-2). Gloucester Art.
Porter, Bertha & Moss, Rosalind. Theban Temples, Vol. 2. rev ed. (Topographical Bibliography of Ancient Egyptian Hieroglyphic Texts, Reliefs & Paintings Ser.). 586p. 1972. text ed. 60.00 (ISBN 0-900416-18-1, Pub. by Aris & Phillips UK). Humanities.
--Upper Egypt Chief Temples, Six. (Topographical Bibliography of Ancient Egyptian Hieroglyphic Texts, Reliefs & Paintings Ser.: Vol. 6). 264p. 1939. text ed. 38.50 (ISBN 0-900416-30-0, Pub. by Aris & Phillips UK). Humanities.
Ramanayyan, Venkata. An Essay on the Origin of the South Indian Temples. (Illus.). 92p. 1986. Repr. 15.00X (ISBN 0-8364-1725-9, Pub. by Manohar India). South Asia Bks.
Reddy, C. Mookka. The Tirumalavadi Temple: History & Culture Through the Ages. xii, 236p. 1986. text ed. 30.00x (ISBN 81-7018-329-4, Pub. by B. R. Pub Corp Delhi). Apt Bks.
Rupprecht, Konrad. Der Tempel Von Jerusalem. (Beihefte 144 Zur Zeitschrift Fuer die Alttestamentliche Wissenschaft). 1976. text ed. 22.80x (ISBN 3-11-006619-X). De Gruyter.
Sampson, Gloria. Historic Churches & Temples of Georgia. (Illus.). 144p. 1987. 24.95 (ISBN 0-86554-242-2, MUP-H212). Mercer Univ Pr.
Save-Soderbergh, Torgny, ed. Temples & Tombs of Ancient Nubia. LC 86-50517. (Illus.). 1987. 29.95 (ISBN 0-500-01392-6). Thames Hudson.
Scully. The Earth, the Temple, & the Gods. LC 79-12717. 1979. pap. 16.95x (ISBN 0-300-02397-9, Y-346). Yale U Pr.
Shryock, John K. The Temples of Anking & Their Cults, a Study of Modern Chinese Religion. LC 70-38083. Repr. of 1931 ed. 26.00 (ISBN 0-404-56947-1). AMS Pr.
Sitwell, Sacheverell. Great Temples of the East. 1962. 12.95 (ISBN 0-8392-1041-8). Astor-Honor.
Usui, Shiro. A Pilgrim's Guide to Forty-Six Temples. (Illus.). 336p. (Orig.). 1986. pap. 12.50 (ISBN 0-8348-0211-2). Weatherhill.
Van Siclen, Charles C., III. The Chapel of Sesostris III at Uronarti. 58p. 1982. pap. text ed. 10.00x (ISBN 0-933175-02-7). Van Siclen Bks.
Von Winning, Hasso. Two Maya Monuments in Yucatan: The Palace of the Stuccoes at Acanceh & the Temple of the Owls at Chicken Itza. (Frederick Webb Hodge Publications: No. XII). (Illus.). 104p. (Orig.). 1985. pap. write for info. (ISBN 0-916561-68-2). Southwest Mus.
Wang, Robert. The Secret Temple. 1980. 15.00 (ISBN 0-87728-490-3); pap. 7.95 (ISBN 0-87728-518-7). Weiser.
Woodford, Susan. The Parthenon. (Cambridge Introduction to the History of Mankind Ser.). 1981. pap. 4.95 (ISBN 0-521-22629-5). Cambridge U Pr.
Zannas, Eliky. Khajuraho. (Illus.). 1960. 132.00x (ISBN 0-686-21868-X). Mouton.

TEMPTATION

see also Fall of Man; Good and Evil; Sin

Arrowood, Larry M. Overcoming Temptation. Bernard, David, ed. LC 86-24735. (Illus.). 120p. (Orig.). 1986. pap. text ed. 5.50 (ISBN 0-932581-04-8). Word Aflame.
Bonhoeffer, Dietrich. Creation & Fall. Bd. with Temptation. 1965. pap. 4.95 (ISBN 0-02-083890-5). Macmillan.
Bussell, Harold. Lord, I Can Resist Anything but Temptation. (Orig.). 1985. pap. 5.95 (ISBN 0-310-37271-2, 12389P). Zondervan.
Carroll, Frances L. Temptation: How Christians Can Deal with It. 192p. 1984. 13.95 (ISBN 0-13-903229-0); pap. 5.95 (ISBN 0-13-903211-8). P-H.
Downame, John. The Christian Warfare. LC 74-80174. (English Experience Ser.: No. 653). 674p. 1974. Repr. of 1604 ed. 67.00 (ISBN 90-221-0653-5). Walter J Johnson.
Durham, Charles. Temptation: Help for Struggling Christians. LC 82-153. 164p. (Orig.). 1982. pap. 4.95 (ISBN 0-87784-382-1). Inter-Varsity.
Gilpin, R. Biblical Demonology: A Treatise on Satan's Temptations. 1982. lib. bdg. 20.00 (ISBN 0-86524-093-0, 9805). Klock & Klock.
King, Pat & Botz, Myrna. Triumph Through Temptation. (Basic Bible Study). 64p. 1978. 2.95 (ISBN 0-932305-35-0, 521012). Aglow Pubns.
Patterson, Ward. Triumph over Temptation. (Illus.). 96p. (Orig.). 1984. pap. 2.95 (ISBN 0-87239-730-0, 39976). Standard Pub.
Perryman, F. J. How to Resist the Devil. 48p. pap. 0.50 (ISBN 0-686-29122-0). Faith Pub Hse.
Scroggie, W. Graham. Tested by Temptation. LC 79-2559. (W. Graham Scroggie Library). 76p. 1980. pap. 4.50 (ISBN 0-8254-3732-6). Kregel.
Souter, John C. Temptation (Magazine Format, No. 3. 64p. 1984. 4.95 (ISBN 0-8423-6957-0). Tyndale.
Stedman, Ray C. Spiritual Warfare: Winning the Daily Battle with Satan. LC 85-2893. (Authentic Christianity Ser.). 145p. 1985. pap. 6.95 (ISBN 0-88070-094-7). Multnomah.
Underwood, Jon. Triumph over Temptation: Leader's Guide. 48p. (Orig.). 1984. pap. 2.95 (ISBN 0-87239-790-4, 39977). Standard Pub.

TEN COMMANDMENTS

see Commandments, Ten

TENT OF MEETING

see Tabernacle

TERESA, MOTHER, 1910-

Balado, Jose L. Stories of Mother Teresa: Her Smile & Her Words. Diaz, Olimpia, tr. from Span. 96p. 1983. pap. 2.95 (ISBN 0-89243-181-4). Liguori Pubns.
Craig, Mary. Mother Teresa. (Profiles Ser.). (Illus.). 64p. 1983. 8.95 (ISBN 0-241-10933-7, Pub. by Hamish Hamilton England). David & Charles.
Easwaran, Eknath. Love Never Faileth: The Inspiration of St. Francis, St. Augustine, St. Paul & Mother Teresa. (Illus.). 208p. (Orig.). 1985. 15.00 (ISBN 0-915132-31-1); pap. 8.00 (ISBN 0-915132-32-X). Nilgiri Pr.
Egan, Eileen. Such a Vision of the Street: Mother Teresa; The Spirit & The Work. LC 81-43570. (Illus.). 456p. 1985. 16.95 (ISBN 0-385-17490-X). Doubleday.
--Such a Vision of the Street: Mother Teresa-The Spirit & the Work. LC 81-43570. (Illus.). 528p. 1986. pap. 9.95 (ISBN 0-385-17491-8, Im). Doubleday.
Gasnick, Roy. Mother Teresa of Calcutta. 1.25. Paulist Pr.
Giff, Patricia R. Mother Teresa: A Sister to the Poor. LC 85-40885. (Illus.). 64p. 1986. 9.95 (ISBN 0-670-81096-7, Viking Kestrel). Viking.
Gonzalez, Jose L. & Playfoot, Jane, eds. My Life for the Poor: Mother Teresa of Calcutta. 1987. pap. 2.95 (ISBN 0-345-33780-8, Pub. by Ballantine Epiphany). Ballantine.
Gonzalez-Balado, Jose L. & Playfoot, Janet, eds. My Life for the Poor: The Story of Mother Teresa in Her Own Words. LC 85-42787. 128p. 1985. 10.95 (ISBN 0-06-068237-X, HarpR). Har-Row.
Greene, Carol. Mother Teresa: Friend of the Friendless. LC 83-7386. (Picture-Story Biographies Ser.). (Illus.). 32p. 1983. PLB 10.60 (ISBN 0-516-03559-2). Childrens.
Joly, Edward Le. Mother Teresa: A Biography. LC 84-48238. (Illus.). 352p. 1985. 16.30 (ISBN 0-06-065217-9, HarpR). Har-Row.
Lee, Betsy. Mother Teresa: Caring for All God's Children. LC 80-20286. (Taking Part Ser.). (Illus.). 48p. 1981. PLB 8.95 (ISBN 0-87518-205-4). Dillon.
Leigh, Vanora. Mother Teresa. LC 85-72245. (Great Lives Ser.). 32p. 1986. lib. bdg. 10.40 (ISBN 0-531-18033-6, Pub. by Bookwright Pr). Watts.
Mother Teresa. Mother Teresa: Contemplative in the Heart of the World. 154p. 1985. pap. 8.95 (ISBN 0-89283-279-7). Servant.
Mother Teresa of Calcutta. Life in the Spirit: Reflections, Meditations, & Prayers. LC 82-48938. 128p. 1983. 10.45i (ISBN 0-06-066021-X, HarpR). Har-Row.
--A Mother Teresa Treasury: Mother Teresa of Calcutta, 3 vols. Incl. Vol. 1. A Gift for God. 96p; Vol. 2. The Love of Christ. 128p; Vol. 3. Life in the Spirit. 96p. LC 85-42786. 1985. 19.95 (ISBN 0-06-068228-0, HarpR). Har-Row.
Muggeridge, Malcolm. Something Beautiful for God. 312p. 1985. pap. 8.95 (ISBN 0-8027-2474-4). Walker & Co.
Murthy, B. Srinivasa. Mother Teresa & India. LC 82-80522. (Illus.). 144p. (Orig.). 1983. pap. 6.95x (ISBN 0-941910-00-8). Long Beach Pubns.
Porter, David. Mother Teresa: The Early Years. 120p. (Orig.). 1986. pap. 5.95 (ISBN 0-8028-0185-4). Eerdmans.
Rae, Daphne. Love Until It Hurts: The Work of Mother Teresa & Her Missionaries of Charity. LC 81-47424. (Illus., Orig.). 1981. pap. 9.95 (ISBN 0-06-066729-X, RD 368, HarpR). Har-Row.
Shrady, Maria. The Mother Teresa Story. 1987. pap. 2.50. Paulist Pr.
Spink, Kathryn. The Miracle of Love: Mother Teresa of Calcutta, Her Missionaries of Charity, & Her Co-Workers. LC 81-47717. (Illus.). 256p. 1982. 15.00 (ISBN 0-06-067497-0, HarpR). Har-Row.

TERESA, SAINT, 1515-1582

Campbell, Camille. Meditations With Teresa of Avila. LC 85-71856. (Meditations With Ser.). 142p. (Orig.). 1985. pap. 6.95 (ISBN 0-939680-23-8). Bear & Co.
Clissold, Stephen. St. Teresa of Avila. 288p. (Orig.). 1982. pap. 8.95 (ISBN 0-8164-2621-X, HarpR). Har-Row.
Froude, James A. Spanish Story of the Armada & Other Essays. LC 71-144613. Repr. of 1892 ed. 24.50 (ISBN 0-404-02628-1). AMS Pr.
Griffin, Michael D., tr. from Span. Lingering with my Lord: Post-Communion Experiences of St. Teresa of Avila. LC 84-18590. Orig. Title: Obras Completas de Teresa de Jesus Doctora de la Iglesia. 79p. 1985. pap. 3.95 (ISBN 0-317-19366-X). Alba.
Kavanaugh, Kieran & Rodrigues, Otilio, trs. from Span. Teresa of Avila: The Interior Castle. LC 79-66484. (Classics of Western Spirituality Ser.). 256p. 1979. 12.95 (ISBN 0-8091-0303-6); pap. 9.95 (ISBN 0-8091-2254-5). Paulist Pr.
Kavanaugh, Kieran & Rodriguez, Otilio, trs. from Span. The Collected Works of St. Teresa of Avila, Vol. 3. LC 75-31305. (Illus.). 504p. (Orig.). 1985. pap. 7.95x (ISBN 0-935216-06-5). ICS Pubns.
Kavanaugh, Kieran & Rodriquez, Otillo, trs. from Span. The Collected Works of St. Teresa of Avila, Vol. 1. Incl. The Book of Her Life, Spiritual Testimonies, Soliloguies. LC 75-31305. 416p. (Orig.). 1976. 6.95x (ISBN 0-9600876-2-1). ICS Pubns.
Lincoln, Victoria. Teresa: A Woman; A Biography of Teresa of Avila. Rivers, Elias & De Nicolas, Antonio T., eds. LC 84-8561. (Series in Cultural Perspectives). 440p. 1984. 44.50x (ISBN 0-87395-936-1); pap. 16.95 (ISBN 0-87395-937-X). State U NY Pr.
O'Connor, Patricia. Therese of Lisieux: A Biography. LC 83-63169. 168p. 1984. pap. 5.95 (ISBN 0-87973-607-0, 607). Our Sunday Visitor.
Peers, E. Alison. The Life of Teresa of Jesus. 1960. pap. 5.50 (ISBN 0-385-01109-1, Im). Doubleday.
Sullivan, John, intro. by. Carmelite Studies III: Centenary of Saint Theresa. LC 84-4498. 240p. (Orig.). 1984. pap. 6.95x (ISBN 0-935216-03-0). ICS Pubns.
Teresa, Saint The Letters of St. Teresa, 4 vols. Gasquet, Cardinal, ed. 1977. Set. lib. bdg. 400.00 (ISBN 0-8490-2154-5). Gordon Pr.
Whalen, James. The Spiritual Teachings of Teresa of Avila & Adrian Van Kaam: Formative Spirituality. LC 83-3628. 334p. (Orig.). 1984. lib. bdg. 27.50 (ISBN 0-8191-3864-9); pap. text ed. 15.75 (ISBN 0-8191-3865-7). U Pr of Amer.

TERMINAL CARE

see also Death

Advances in Thanatology, Vol. 5, No. 2. 17.00 (ISBN 0-405-14221-8, 745). Ayer Co Pubs.
Ajemian, Ina & Mount, Balfour M., eds. The R. V. H. Manual on Palliative-Hospice Care: A Resource Book. pap. 34.00 (ISBN 0-405-13934-9). Ayer Co Pubs.
Amenta, Madalon & Rohnet, Nancy. Nursing Care of the Terminally Ill. 1986. pap. text ed. 22.00 (ISBN 0-316-03693-5). Little.
Archives of the Foundation of Thanatology: Social Work & Terminal Care, Vol. 9, No. 3. pap. 15.00 (ISBN 0-405-14207-2). Ayer Co Pubs.
Beauchamp, Thom & Perlin, Seymour. Ethical Issues in Death & Dying. 1978. pap. write for info. (ISBN 0-13-290114-5). P-H.
Callari, Elizabeth S. A Gentle Death: Personal Caregiving to the Terminally Ill. 123p. 1986. 11.95 (ISBN 0-936389-00-1); pap. 7.95 (ISBN 0-936389-01-X). Tudor Pubs.
Chirban, John T., ed. Coping with Death & Dying: An Interdisciplinary Approach. 108p. 1986. lib. bdg. 22.00 (ISBN 0-8191-4984-5); pap. text ed. 8.75 (ISBN 0-8191-4985-3). U Pr of Amer.
Davidson, Glen W. Living with Dying. LC 74-14186. 112p. (Orig.). 1975. pap. 5.95 (ISBN 0-8066-1468-4, 10-3980); study guide 00.30 (10-3981). Augsburg.
DeBellis, Robert, et al, eds. Medical Care of the Dying Patient. 30.00 (ISBN 0-405-13947-0). Ayer Co Pubs.
--Continuing Care: For the Dying Patient, Family & Staff. LC 85-19165. (The Foundation of Thanatology Ser.: Vol. 5). 190p. 1985. 37.95 (ISBN 0-03-000357-1, C1334). Praeger.
--The House Staff & Thanatology. 15.00 (ISBN 0-405-14211-0). Ayer Co Pubs.
Doyle, Derek. Coping With a Dying Relative. 1983. 30.00x (ISBN 0-86334-028-8, Pub. by Macdonald Pub UK); pap. 20.00x (ISBN 0-86334-026-1). State Mutual Bk.
Facing a Catastrophic Illness with Hope. 20p. (Orig.). 1986. pap. 0.85 (ISBN 0-89486-344-4). Hazelden.
Feifel, Herman. New Meanings of Death. (Illus.). 1977. 25.00 (ISBN 0-07-020350-4); pap. 18.95 (ISBN 0-07-020349-0). McGraw.
Gerchick, Elias. The Role of the Community Hospital in the Care of the Dying Patient, & the Bereaved. 16.50 (ISBN 0-405-12506-2). Ayer Co Pubs.
Goldberg, Ivan K., et al, eds. Pain, Anxiety & Grief: Pharmacotherapeutic Care of the Dying Patient & the Bereaved. 224p. 1985. 24.00x (ISBN 0-231-04742-8). Columbia U Pr.
Herter, Frederic P., et al, eds. Human & Ethical Issues in the Surgical Care of Patients with Life-Threatening Disease. 264p. 1986. 31.50x (ISBN 0-398-05194-1). C C Thomas.
Leone, Bruno, et al, eds. Death-Dying, 1985 Annual. (Opposing Viewpoints SOURCES Ser.). 115p. 1985. pap. text ed. 9.95 (ISBN 0-89908-511-3). Greenhaven.
Margolis, Otto S. & Cherico, Daniel J. Thanatology Abstracts 1979. 15.00 (ISBN 0-405-14222-6, 19702). Ayer Co Pubs.
Naylor, Harriet H. The Role of the Volunteer Director in the Care of the Terminal Patient & the Family. 17.00 (ISBN 0-405-13092-9). Ayer Co Pubs.
O'Connor, Brian, et al. The Role of the Minister in Caring for the Dying Patient & the Bereaved. 16.50 (ISBN 0-405-12504-6). Ayer Co Pubs.
Ogg, Elizabeth. Facing Death & Loss. LC 85-51126. 106p. 1985. pap. 19.00 (ISBN 0-87762-423-2). Technomic.
Shannon, Thomas A. & Faso, Charles N. Let Them Go Free: A Family Prayer Service & Guidelines for the Withdrawal of Life Support Systems. 1987. pap. 2.95. Paulist Pr.
Simpson, M. A. Dying, Death, & Grief: A Critically Annotated Bibliography & Source Book of Thanatology & Terminal Care. LC 78-27273. 300p. 1979. 35.00x (ISBN 0-306-40147-9, Plenum Pr). Plenum Pub.
Tengbom, M. Help for Families of the Terminally Ill. LC 12-2819. (Trauma Bks.: Ser. 2). 1983. pap. 2.75 ea. (ISBN 0-570-08256-0). Concordia.
Upson, Norma S. When Someone You Love Is Dying. 192p. 1986. pap. 6.95 (ISBN 0-671-61079-1, Fireside). S&S.

TERRA-COTTA SCULPTURE

Pritchard, James B. Palestinian Figurines in Relation to Certain Goddesses Known Through Literature. (American Oriental Ser.: Vol. 24). 1943. 11.00 (ISBN 0-527-02698-0). Kraus Repr.
Young, J. H. & Young, S. H. Terracotta Figurines from Kourion in Cyprus. (University Museum Monographs: No. 11). (Illus.). x, 260p. 1955. 16.50x (ISBN 0-934718-03-2). Univ Mus of U PA.

TEUTONIC MYTHOLOGY

see Mythology, Germanic

TEXAS CHRISTIAN UNIVERSITY

Clark, Randolph. Reminiscences, Biographical & Historical. LC 86-1286. 96p. 1986. Repr. of 1919 ed. 25.00x (ISBN 0-87565-064-3). Tex Christian.

THAILAND–HISTORY

Cadet, J. M. Ramakien: The Thai Epic. LC 70-128685. (Illus.). 256p. 1970. 35.00 (ISBN 0-87011-134-5). Kodansha.
Smith, Bardwell L., ed. Religion & Legitimation of Power in Thailand, Laos & Burma. LC 77-7444. 1978. pap. 7.95 (ISBN 0-89012-009-9). Anima Pubns.
Wales, Q. Divination in Thailand. 145p. 1983. text ed. 10.50x (ISBN 0-7007-0147-8, Pub. by Curzon Pr UK). Humanities.

THAILAND–RELIGION

Desai, Santosh N. Hinduism in Thai Life. 163p. 1980. 23.95x (ISBN 0-940500-66-3, Pub by Popular Prakashan India). Asia Bk Corp.
Suksamran, Somboon. Buddhism & Politics in Thailand. 180p. (Orig.). 1982. pap. text ed. 25.00 (ISBN 9971-902-43-5, Pub. by Inst Southeast Asian Stud). Gower Pub Co.

THANKSGIVING DAY

Anderson, J. I. I Can Read About the First Thanksgiving. LC 76-54400. (Illus.). 1977. pap. 1.50 (ISBN 0-89375-034-4). Troll Assocs.
Barth, Edna. Turkeys, Pilgrims, & Indian Corn: The Story of the Thanksgiving Symbols. LC 75-4703. (Illus.). 96p. 1975. 12.95 (ISBN 0-395-28846-0, Clarion). HM.
Kellogg, Alice M., ed. How to Celebrate Thanksgiving & Christmas. facs. ed. LC 76-139765. (Granger Index Reprint Ser). 1897. 15.00 (ISBN 0-8369-6219-2). Ayer Co Pubs.
Things to Make & Do for Thanksgiving. (Things to Make & Do Ser.). 1977. lib. bdg. 8.90 (ISBN 0-531-01324-3). Watts.
Wyndham, Lee. Thanksgiving. LC 63-13890. (Holiday Bks.). (Illus.). 1963. PLB 7.56 (ISBN 0-8116-6551-8). Garrard.

THEATER–MORAL AND RELIGIOUS ASPECTS

Balmforth, R. The Problem-Play. LC 76-52915. (Studies in Drama, No. 39). 1977. lib. bdg. 41.95x (ISBN 0-8383-2129-1). Haskell.
Clark, Barrett H. Blush of Shame: A Few Considerations on Verbal Obscenity in the Theatre. 1932. pap. 1.50 (ISBN 0-910664-01-3). Gotham.
Collier, Jeremy. Short View of the Immorality, & Profaneness of the English Stage. 3rd ed. LC 74-3401. Repr. of 1698 ed. 21.50 (ISBN 0-404-01619-7). AMS Pr.
--Short View of the Profaneness & Immorality of the English Stage. 1969. Repr. of 1730 ed. cancelled (ISBN 3-4870-2589-2). Adlers Foreign Bks.

Crashaw, William. The Sermon Preached at the Cross, February 14, 1607. Repr. of 1608 ed. 27.00 (ISBN 0-384-10125-9). Johnson Repr.
Davison, Peter, ed. Theatrum Redivivum, 17 vols. Repr. 535.00 (ISBN 0-384-59985-0). Johnson Repr.
Eaton, Thomas R. Shakespeare & the Bible. LC 77-144601. Repr. of 1860 ed. 19.00 (ISBN 0-404-02237-5). AMS Pr.
Evans, Colin. The Mirror & the Skylight. 1986. 40.00x (ISBN 0-317-54255-9, Pub. by Elmcrest Uk). State Mutual Bk.
Nash, Thomas. Pierce Penilesse, His Supplication to the Divell. Repr. of 1924 ed. lib. bdg. 22.50x (ISBN 0-8371-2919-2, NAPP). Greenwood.
Northbrooke, John. Treatise Against Dicing, Dancing, Plays & Interludes. LC 77-149667. Repr. of 1843 ed. 19.00 (ISBN 0-404-04793-9). AMS Pr.
Rousseau, Jean-Jacques. Lettre a M. d'Alembert sur les Spectacles. 208p. 1948. 7.95 (ISBN 0-686-55352-7). French & Eur.
Thompson, Elbert N. Controversy Between the Puritans & the Stage. LC 76-176150. Repr. of 1903 ed. 21.50 (ISBN 0-404-06396-9). AMS Pr.

THEATER–GREAT BRITAIN–HISTORY

Anstruther, Sir William. Essays, Moral & Divine. LC 74-170474. (The English Stage Ser.: Vol. 40). 1973. lib. bdg. 61.00 (ISBN 0-8240-0623-2). Garland Pub.
Bedford, Arthur. The Evil & Danger of Stage Plays. LC 72-170479. (The English Stage Ser.: Vol. 43). lib. bdg. 61.00 (ISBN 0-8240-0626-7). Garland Pub.
--Serious Reflections on the Scandalous Abuse & Effects of the Stage. Bd. with A Second Advertisement Concerning the Profaneness of the Play-House; A Sermon Preached in the Parish-Church of St. Butolph's Algate, in the City of London: Occasioned by the Erecting of a Play-House in the Neighborhood. (The English Stage Ser.: Vol. 41). 1974. lib. bdg. 61.00 (ISBN 0-8240-0624-0). Garland Pub.
Bedfrod, Arthur. A Serious Remonstrance in Behalf of the Christian Religion Against English Play-Houses. LC 79-170478. (The English Stage Ser.: Vol. 42). lib. bdg. 61.00 (ISBN 0-8240-0625-9). Garland Pub.
Collier, Jeremy. A Defence of the Short View off the Profaneness & Immorality of the English Stage. LC 72-170444. (The English Stage Ser.: Vol. 30). 1973. lib. bdg. 61.00 (ISBN 0-8240-0613-5). Garland Pub.
Collier Tracts 1698: Immorality of the English Pulpit. Bd. with A Letter to A. H. Esq. Concerning the Stage. Hopkins, Charles; A Letter to Mr. Congreve on His Pretended Amendments; The Occasional Paper. Willis, Richard; Some Remarks Upon Mr. Collier's Defence of His Short View of the English Stage; A Vindication of the Stage. LC 76-170453. (The English Stage Ser.: Vol. 27). 1973. lib. bdg. 61.00 (ISBN 0-8240-0610-0). Garland Pub.
Heinemann, Margot. Puritanism & Theatre: Thomas Middleton & Opposition Drama Under the Early Stuarts. LC 79-14991. (Past & Present Publications Ser.). 309p. 1982. 34.50 (ISBN 0-521-22602-3); pap. 13.95 (ISBN 0-521-27052-9). Cambridge U Pr.
Neuss, Paula, ed. Aspects of Early English Drama. LC 83-21331. (Illus.). 176p. 1985. Repr. of 1983 ed. 42.50x (ISBN 0-389-20428-5, 07314). B&N Imports.
Ridpath, George. The Stage Condemn'd. LC 79-170443. (The English Stage Ser.: Vol. 29). 1973. lib. bdg. 61.00 (ISBN 0-8240-0612-7). Garland Pub.
Thompson, Elbert N. Controversy Between the Puritans & the Stage. LC 76-176150. Repr. of 1903 ed. 21.50 (ISBN 0-404-06396-9). AMS Pr.

THEBES, EGYPT

Davies, Norman. The Tomb of Rekh-Mi-Re at Thebes: Metropolitan Museum of Art Egyptian Expedition Publications, 2 vols. in 1, Vol. 11. LC 75-168403. (Metropolitan Museum of Art Publications in Reprint). (Illus.). 374p. 1972. Repr. of 1943 ed. 47.50 (ISBN 0-405-02267-0). Ayer Co Pubs.
Davies, Norman De Garis. The Tomb of Ken-Amun at Thebes: Metropolitan Museum of Art Egyptian Expedition Publications, 2 vols. in 1, Vol. 5. LC 78-168401. (Metropolitan Museum of Art Publications in Reprint). (Illus.). 208p. 1972. Repr. of 1930 ed. 39.00 (ISBN 0-405-02267-0). Ayer Co Pubs.
--The Tomb of Nefer-Hotep at Thebes: Metropolitan Museum of Art Egyptian Expedition Publications, 2 vols in 1, Vol. 9. LC 71-168402. (Metropolitan Museum of Art Publications in Reprint). (Illus.). 192p. 1972. Repr. of 1933 ed. 39.00 (ISBN 0-405-02236-0). Ayer Co Pubs.
Hayes, William C. Ostraka & Name Stones from the Tomb of Sen-Mut (No. 71) at Thebes: Metropolitan Museum of Art Publications in Reprint. LC 76-168406. (Illus.). 136p. 1972. Repr. of 1942 ed. 22.00 (ISBN 0-405-02239-5). Ayer Co Pubs.
Heyder, Wolfgang & Mallwitz, Alfred. Das Kabirenheiligtum Bei Theben: Die Bauten Im Kabirenheiligtum Bei Theben, Vol. 2. (Illus.). 1978. 52.00 (ISBN 3-11-005754-9). De Gruyter.
Seele, Keith C. Tomb of Tjanefer at Thebes. LC 59-14285. (Oriental Institute Pubns. Ser: No. 86). (Illus.). 1959. 22.00x (ISBN 0-226-62187-1, OIP86). U of Chicago Pr.
Winlock, Herbert E. The Tomb of Queen Meryet-Amun at Thebes: Metropolitan Museum of Art Egyptian Expedition Publication, Vol. 6. LC 70-168415. (Metropolitan Museum of Art Publication in Reprint). (Illus.). 204p. 1972. Repr. of 1932 ed. 32.00 (ISBN 0-405-02253-0). Ayer Co Pubs.

THEISM

see also Atheism; Christianity; Deism; God; Monotheism; Pantheism

Armstrong, Richard A. Agnosticism & Theism in the Nineteenth Century. 1977. lib. bdg. 59.95 (ISBN 0-8490-1406-9). Gordon Pr.
Balfour, A. J. Theism & Humanism. Repr. of 1915 ed. 32.00 (ISBN 0-527-04810-0). Kraus Repr.
Balfour, Arthur J. Theism & Thought: A Study in Familiar Beliefs. LC 77-27208. (Gifford Lectures: 1922-23). Repr. of 1923 ed. 22.50 (ISBN 0-404-60469-2). AMS Pr.
Bowne, Borden P. Studies in Theism. LC 7-25071. 1968. Repr. of 1907 ed. 28.00 (ISBN 0-527-10450-7). Kraus Repr.
--Theism... Comprising the Deems Lectures for 1902. LC 75-3075. (Philosophy in America Ser.). Repr. of 1902 ed. 37.50 (ISBN 0-404-59076-4). AMS Pr.
Caldecott, Alfred & MacKintosh, H. R. Selections from the Literature of Theism. 1979. Repr. of 1909 ed. lib. bdg. 65.00 (ISBN 0-8495-0932-7). Arden Lib.
Carpenter, J. Estlin. Theism in Medieval India. 564p. Repr. of 1921 ed. text ed. 37.50x. Coronet Bks.
Carpenter, Joseph E. Theism in Medieval India. LC 77-27152. (Hibbert Lectures: 1919). Repr. of 1921 ed. 48.00 (ISBN 0-404-60419-6). AMS Pr.
Clark, Stephen R. From Athens to Jerusalem: The Love of Wisdom & the Love God. 1984. 29.95x (ISBN 0-19-824698-6); pap. 11.95x (ISBN 0-19-824697-8). Oxford U Pr.
Cole, Lawrence T. The Basis of Early Christian Theism. lib. bdg. 59.95 (ISBN 0-8490-1478-6). Gordon Pr.
Eddy, George S. Man Discovers God. facs. ed. LC 68-24849. (Essay Index Reprint Ser). 1968. Repr. of 1942 ed. 18.00 (ISBN 0-8369-0401-X). Ayer Co Pubs.
Fenn, William W. Theism: The Implication of Experience. 1969. 10.00 (ISBN 0-87233-005-2). Bauhan.
Ford, Lewis S. The Lure of God: A Biblical Background for Process Theism. 158p. 1985. Repr. of 1978 ed. lib. bdg. 8.75 (ISBN 0-8191-4902-0). U Pr of Amer.
Fraser, Alexander C. Philosophy of Theism. LC 77-27228. (Gifford Lectures: 1894-95). Repr. of 1895 ed. 24.50 (ISBN 0-404-60453-6). AMS Pr.
--Philosophy of Theism: Second Series. LC 77-27227. (Gifford Lectures: 1895-96). Repr. of 1896 ed. 30.00 (ISBN 0-404-60454-4). AMS Pr.
Hackett, Stuart C. The Resurrection of Theism: Prolegomena to Christian Apology. (Twin Brooks Ser.). 381p. 1982. pap. 11.95 (ISBN 0-8010-4263-1). Baker Bk.
Hawkins, Denis J. The Essentials of Theism. LC 72-9373. 151p. 1973. Repr. of 1949 ed. lib. bdg. 22.50x (ISBN 0-8371-6579-2, HAET). Greenwood.
Henderson, Charles P., Jr. God & Science: The Death & Rebirth of Theism. LC 85-23091. 216p. 1986. pap. 10.95 (ISBN 0-8042-0668-6). John Knox.
Hicks, George D. The Philosophical Bases of Theism. LC 77-27142. (Hibbert Lectures: 1931). Repr. of 1937 ed. 31.00 (ISBN 0-404-60427-7). AMS Pr.
Jennings, Theodore W., Jr. Beyond Theism: A Grammar of God-Language. 1985. 29.95x (ISBN 0-19-503613-1). Oxford U Pr.
Klemke, E. D., intro. by. Humanism vs Theism. 154p. 1982. pap. 8.50x (ISBN 0-8138-0916-9). Iowa St U Pr.
Laird, John. Theism & Cosmology. facs. ed. LC 74-84317. (Essay Index Reprint Ser). 1942. 21.50 (ISBN 0-8369-1147-4). Ayer Co Pubs.
McCarthy, Gerald. The Ethics of Belief Debate. (AAR Studies in Religion). 1986. 20.95 (ISBN 0-89130-892-X, 01-00-41); pap. 15.95 (ISBN 0-89130-893-8). Scholars Pr GA.
Mackie, J. L. The Miracle of Theism. 1982. text ed. 32.50x (ISBN 0-19-824665-X); pap. text ed. 10.95x (ISBN 0-19-824682-X). Oxford U Pr.
McLarney, James J. The Theism of Edgar Sheffied Brightman. LC 75-3089. Repr. of 1936 ed. 11.50 (ISBN 0-404-59087-X). AMS Pr.
Mill, John S. Three Essays on Religion. LC 76-130995. Repr. of 1874 ed. 23.45 (ISBN 0-404-04325-9). AMS Pr.
--Three Essays on Religion. Repr. of 1874 ed. lib. bdg. 37.50x (ISBN 0-8371-1986-3, MIER). Greenwood.
Molnar, Thomas. Theist & Atheist: A Typology of Non-Belief. 1979. text ed. 30.00x (ISBN 90-279-7788-7). Mouton.
Prospo, R. C. de. Theism in the Discourse of Jonathan Edwards. LC 84-40406. 296p. 1985. 37.50 (ISBN 0-87413-281-9). U Delaware Pr.
Schlesinger, G. Religion & Scientific Method. 1977. lib. bdg. 29.00 (ISBN 90-277-0815-0, Pub. by Reidel Holland); pap. 10.50 (ISBN 90-277-0816-9, Pub. by Reidel Holland). Kluwer Academic.
Sutherland, Stewart R. God, Jesus & Belief: The Legacy of Theism. 160p. 1984. 29.95x (ISBN 0-631-13548-0); pap. 12.95 (ISBN 0-631-13591-X). Basil Blackwell.
Thompson, Bert. Theistic Evolution. pap. 5.50 (ISBN 0-89315-300-1). Lambert Bk.
Ward, James. The Realm of Ends: Or, Pluralism & Theism. LC 77-27173. (Gifford Lectures: 1907-10). Repr. of 1911 ed. 34.50 (ISBN 0-404-60464-1). AMS Pr.

THEODICY

Here are entered works that attempt to vindicate the wisdom and goodness of God in the creation and government of the world, and to rebut the charge that these are brought into question by the existence of evil and sin.

see also Good and Evil; Sin

Blair, Joe. When Bad Things Happen, God Still Loves. LC 85-13240. 1986. pap. 4.95 (ISBN 0-8054-5010-6). Broadman.
Blood, Benjamin P. Optimism, the Lesson of Ages. LC 75-3055. Repr. of 1860 ed. 18.00 (ISBN 0-404-59053-5). AMS Pr.
Center for Learning Staff. World Literature I. 1985. pap. text ed. 34.95 (ISBN 0-697-02073-8). Wm C Brown.
--World Literature II. 1985. pap. text ed. 34.95 (ISBN 0-697-02074-6). Wm C Brown.
Crenshaw, James L., ed. Theodicy in the Old Testament. LC 83-8885. (Issues in Religion & Theology Ser.). 176p. 1983. pap. 7.95 (ISBN 0-8006-1764-9). Fortress.
Forrer, Richard. Theodicies in Conflict: A Dilemma in Puritan Ethics & Nineteenth-Century American Literature. LC 85-27220. (Contributions to the Study of Religion: No. 17). 302p. 1986. lib. bdg. 37.95 (ISBN 0-313-25191-6, FTS/). Greenwood.
Geach, P. T. Providence & Evil. LC 76-28005. 1977. 24.95 (ISBN 0-521-21477-7). Cambridge U Pr.
Geisler, Norman L. The Roots of Evil. (Christian Free University Curriculum Ser.). 1978. pap. 4.95 (ISBN 0-310-35751-9, 12655P). Zondervan.
Hatcher, John S. The Purpose of Physical Reality: The Kingdom of Names. Fisher, Betty J. & Hill, Richard A., eds. 250p. 1987. pap. 12.00 (ISBN 0-87743-208-2). Baha'i.
Kushner, Harold S. When Bad Things Happen to Good People. (General Ser.). 1982. lib. bdg. 13.95 (ISBN 0-8161-3465-0, Large Print Bks). G K Hall.
Maritain, Jacques. Dieu et la Permission du Mal. 3rd ed. 116p. 1963. 8.95 (ISBN 0-686-56349-2). French & Eur.
Ormsby, Eric. Theodicy in Islamic Thought. LC 84-3396. 320p. 1984. text ed. 30.00x (ISBN 0-691-07278-7). Princeton U pr.
Plantinga, Alvin. God, Freedom, & Evil. 1978. pap. 7.95 (ISBN 0-8028-1731-9). Eerdmans.
Schilling, S. Paul. God & Human Anguish. LC 77-5857. Repr. of 1977 ed. 76.00 (ISBN 0-8357-9009-6, 2016362). Bks Demand UMI.
Surin, Kenneth. Theology & the Problem of Evil. (Signposts in Theology Ser.). 192p. 1986. text ed. 39.95 (ISBN 0-631-14664-4); pap. text ed. 14.95 (ISBN 0-631-14663-6). Basil Blackwell.
Taylor, Michael J., ed. The Mystery of Suffering & Death. LC 72-13294. 203p. 1973. pap. 5.95 (ISBN 0-8189-0263-9). Alba.
Towner, W. Sibley. How God Deals with Evil. LC 76-24916. (Biblical Perspectives on Current Issues). 186p. 1976. softcover 4.95 (ISBN 0-664-24127-1). Westminster.
Wall, George B. Is God Really Good? Conversations with a Theodicist. LC 82-24854. 130p. (Orig.). 1983. pap. text ed. 9.50 (ISBN 0-8191-3032-X). U Pr of Amer.

THEODORUS STUDITA, SAINT, 759-826

Gardner, Alice. Theodore of Studium, His Life & Times 759-826. 1905. 19.50 (ISBN 0-8337-1280-2). B Franklin.

THEOLOGIANS

see also Christian Biography; also subdivisions Biography or Clergy under names of Christian denominations

Almond, Philip C. Rudolf Otto: An Introduction to His Philosophical Theology. LC 83-19865. (Studies in Religion). x, 172p. 1984. 23.00x (ISBN 0-8078-1589-6). U of NC Pr.
Armstrong, Christopher. Evelyn Underhill: Eighteen Seventy-Five to Nineteen Forty-One: An Introduction to Her Life & Writing. LC 75-33401. Repr. of 1976 ed. 81.80 (ISBN 0-8357-9127-0, 2012859). Bks Demand UMI.
Bird, Thomas E., ed. Modern Theologians, Christians & Jews. 2nd ed. 1967. 15.95 (ISBN 0-268-00183-9). U of Notre Dame Pr.
Bretall. Empirical Theology of Henry Nelson Weiman. 1981. pap. 6.95 (ISBN 0-8298-0485-4). Pilgrim NY.
Brown, Robert M. Gustavo Gutierrez. LC 80-82185. (Makers of Contemporary Theology Ser.). 89p. 1981. pap. 3.95 (ISBN 0-8042-0651-1). John Knox.
Burg, B. Richard. Richard Mather. (United States Authors Ser.). 1982. lib. bdg. 16.50 (ISBN 0-8057-7364-9, Twayne). G K Hall.
Cecil, Anthony C., Jr. The Theological Development of Edwards Amasa Park: Last of the "Consistent Calvinists". LC 74-83338. (American Academy of Religion. Dissertation Ser.). 1974. pap. 9.95 (ISBN 0-88420-118-X, 010101). Scholars Pr GA.
Cone, James H. My Soul Looks Back. 144p. 1986. pap. 8.95 (ISBN 0-88344-355-4). Orbis Bks.
Crenshaw, James. Gerhard von Rad. (Makers of the Modern Theological Mind Ser.). 1978. 8.95 (ISBN 0-8499-0112-X). Word Bks.
Edward, Herbert. First Baron Herbert of Cherbury. Wellek, Rene, ed. (British Philosophers & Theologians of the 17th & 18th Centuries Ser.). 1979. 51.00 (ISBN 0-8240-1779-X). Garland Pub.
Ellul, Jacques. Perspectives on Our Age: Jacques Ellul Speaks on His Life & Work. Vanderburg, William H., ed. Neugroschel, Joachim, tr. 1981. 10.95 (ISBN 0-8164-0485-2, HarpR). Har-Row.
Ericksen, Robert P. Theologians under Hitler: Gerhard Kittel, Paul Althaus, & Emanuel Hirsch. LC 84-40731. (Illus.). 256p. 1985. 20.00x (ISBN 0-300-02926-8). Yale U Pr.
Erickson, Millard J., ed. New Life: Readings in Christian Theology. LC 79-53903. 1979. pap. 11.95 (ISBN 0-8010-3340-3). Baker Bk.
Erickson, Robert P. Theologians under Hitler. LC 84-40731. 256p. 1987. pap. 8.95 (ISBN 0-300-03889-5, Y-618). Yale U Pr.
Gaspar, Karl. How Long? Prison Reflections from the Philippines. Graham, Helen & Noonan, Breda, eds. LC 85-25851. 176p. (Orig.). 1986. pap. 9.95 (ISBN 0-88344-226-4). Orbis Bks.
Grossman, Walter. Johann Christian Edelmann: From Orthodoxy to Enlightenment. (Religion & Society Ser: No. 3). 209p. 1976. text ed. 22.25x (ISBN 90-2797-691-0). Mouton.
Hastings, A. W. & Hastings, E., eds. Theologians of Our Time. LC 66-73626. 224p. pap. 7.95 (ISBN 0-567-22301-9, Pub. by T & T Clark Ltd UK). Fortress.
Hoffecker, W. Andrew. Piety & the Princeton Theologians: Archibald Alexander, Charles Hodge, & Benjamin Warfield. 1981. pap. 5.95 (ISBN 0-87552-280-7). Presby & Reformed.
Jennings, Theodore W., Jr., ed. Vocation of the Theologian. LC 84-48722. 160p. 1985. pap. 7.95 (ISBN 0-8006-1838-6, 1-1838). Fortress.
Jones, W. Paul. The Province Beyond the River: The Diary of a Protestant at a Trappist Monastery. 160p. (Orig.). 1986. pap. 6.95 (ISBN 0-8358-0546-8). Upper Room.
Kershner, Frederick D. Pioneers of Christian Thought. facs. ed. LC 68-57327. (Essay Index Reprint Ser). 1930. 20.00 (ISBN 0-8369-0594-6). Ayer Co Pubs.
Loetscher, Lefferts A. Facing the Enlightenment & Pietism: Archibald Alexander & the Founding of Princeton Theological Seminary. LC 82-11995. (Contributions to the Study of Religion Ser.: No. 8). x, 303p. 1983. lib. bdg. 35.00 (ISBN 0-313-23677-1, LOE/). Greenwood.
Macdonald, Allan J. Berengar & the Reform of the Sacramental System. 444p. 1977. Repr. of 1930 ed. lib. bdg. 30.00 (ISBN 0-915172-25-9). Richwood Pub.
Marty, Martin E. & Peerman, Dean G., eds. A Handbook of Christian Theologians. 736p. (Orig.). 1984. pap. 13.50 (ISBN 0-687-16563-6). Abingdon.
Merrill, Thomas F. Willian Perkins 1558-1602, English Puritanist--His Pioneer Works on Casuistry: Discourse on Conscience & the Whole Treatise of Cases of Conscience. xx, 242p. 1966. text ed. 28.50x (Pub. by B De Graaf Netherlands). Coronet Bks.
Mills, Liston M. Pastoral Theologian of the Year: Seward Hiltner; Special Issue PP 29, No. 1. LC 80-82467. 112p. 1980. pap. 12.95 (ISBN 0-89885-068-1). Human Sci Pr.

Mulligan, James J. Theologians & Authority Within the Living Church. 131p. (Orig.). 1986. pap. 13.95 (ISBN 0-935372-18-0). Pope John Ctr.

Patterson, Bob. Carl F. Henry, Makers of the Modern Theological Mind. 1983. pap. 8.95 (ISBN 0-8499-2951-2). Word Bks.

Peguy, Charles. Un Nouveau Theologien, M. Laudet. pap. 3.95 (ISBN 0-685-37044-5). French & Eur.

Rademaker, C. S. Life & Work of Gerardus Joannes Vossius 1577-1649. (Respublica Literaria Neerlandica: No. 5). 472p. 1981. text ed. 39.50 (ISBN 90-232-1785-3, Pub. by Van Gorcum Holland). Longwood Pub Group.

Reinisch, Leonhard, ed. Theologians of Our Time. 1964. 17.95x (ISBN 0-268-00271-1); pap. 7.95x (ISBN 0-268-00378-5). U of Notre Dame Pr.

Rexine, John E. An Explorer of Realms of Art, Life, & Thought: A Survey of the Works of Philosopher & Theologian Constantine Cavarnos. LC 85-81278. (Illus.). 184p. 1985. 9.00 (ISBN 0-914744-69-0, 85-81278); pap. 6.00 (ISBN 0-914744-70-4). Inst Byzantine.

Robbins, John W. Cornelius VanTil: The Man & the Myth. (Trinity Papers: No. 15). 40p. (Orig.). 1986. pap. 2.45 (ISBN 0-940931-15-X). Trinity Found.

Rusch, William G. The Later Latin Fathers. (Studies in Theology). 214p. 1977. pap. 13.50 (ISBN 0-7156-1674-9, Pub. by Duckworth London). Longwood Pub Group.

Scharlemann, Martin H. The Making of a Theologian. 182p. 1984. pap. 6.50 (ISBN 0-911770-54-2). Concordia Schl Grad Studies.

Soper, David W. Men Who Shape Belief. LC 76-86061. (Essay & General Literature Index Reprint Ser). 1969. Repr. of 1955 ed. 24.00x (ISBN 0-8046-0588-2, Pub. by Kennikat). Assoc Faculty Pr.

Sykes, S. W. Karl Barth: Studies of His Theological Method. 1979. text ed. 34.95x (ISBN 0-19-826649-9). Oxford U Pr.

Tsirpanlis, Constance N. The Liturgical & Mystical Theology of Nicolas Cabasilas. 2nd ed. 103p. 1979. pap. 6.99 (ISBN 0-686-36328-0). EO Pr.

Visser, Derk. Zacharias Ursinus: The Reluctant Reformer-His Life & Times. 192p. 1983. pap. 7.95 (ISBN 0-8298-0691-1). Pilgrim NY.

Weigle, Richard. The Glory Days: From the Life of Luther Allan Weigle. (Illus., Orig.). 1976. pap. 5.95 (ISBN 0-377-00058-2). Friend Pr.

THEOLOGICAL ANTHROPOLOGY
see Man (Theology)

THEOLOGICAL BELIEF
see Faith

THEOLOGICAL EDUCATION
see Religious Education; Theology–Study and Teaching

THEOLOGICAL LIBRARIES

Adams, Herbert B. Seminary Libraries & University Extension. LC 78-63777. (Johns Hopkins University. Studies in the Social Sciences. Fifth Ser. 1887: 11). Repr. of 1887 ed. 11.50 (ISBN 0-404-61043-9). AMS Pr.

Freudenberger, Elsie. Reference Works in the Field of Religion 1977-1985. (Orig.). 1986. pap. 15.00 (ISBN 0-87507-037-X). Cath Lib Assn.

Slavens, Thomas P. Theological Libraries at Oxford. 160p. 1984. pap. text ed. 32.50 (ISBN 3-598-10563-0). K G Saur.

Union Theological Seminary Library. Shelf List of the Union Theological Seminary Library (New York), 10 vols. 1960. Set. lib. bdg. 990.00 (ISBN 0-8161-0499-9, Hall Library). G K Hall.

THEOLOGICAL SEMINARIES
see also Seminarians

Adams, Herbert B., et al. Seminary Notes & Historical Literature. LC 78-63798. (Johns Hopkins University. Studies in the Social Sciences. Eighth Ser. 1890: 11-12). Repr. of 1890 ed. 11.50 (ISBN 0-404-61063-3). AMS Pr.

Copeland, Robert M. Spare No Exertions: One Hundred Seventy-Five Years of the Reformed Presbyterian Theological Seminary. LC 86-60501. (Illus.). 144p. 1986. 7.95x (ISBN 0-9616417-0-3). Ref Presby Theo.

Daniel, William A. Education of Negro Ministers. LC 77-78581. Repr. of 1925 ed. cancelled (ISBN 0-8371-1410-1, DNM&, Pub. by Negro U Pr). Greenwood.

Day, Heather F. Protestant Theological Education in America: A Bibliography. LC 85-18300. (ATLA Biobliography Ser.: No. 15). 523p. 1985. 42.50 (ISBN 0-8108-1842-6). Scarecrow.

Ellis, William E. A "Man of Books & a Man of the People". E. Y. Mullins & the Crisis Moderate Southern Baptist Leadership. xi, 275p. 1985. text ed. 18.95 (ISBN 0-86554-175-2, MUP-H165). Mercer Univ Pr.

Gambrell, Mary L. Ministerial Training in Eighteenth-Century New England. (Columbia University. Studies in the Social Sciences: No. 428). Repr. of 1937 ed. 16.50 (ISBN 0-404-51428-6). AMS Pr.

Handy, Robert T. A History of Union Theological Seminary in New York, 1836-1986. (Illus.). 388p. 1987. 30.00 (ISBN 0-231-06454-3). Columbia U Pr.

Howard, Diana. London Theatres & Music Halls, 1850-1950. 291p. 1986. text ed. 40.00x (ISBN 0-85365-471-9, L471-9). ALA.

Modoc Press, Inc., Staff. Guide to Schools & Departments of Religion & Seminaries in the U. S. & Canada. 736p. 1986. reference 90.00x (ISBN 0-02-921650-8). Macmillan.

Pegues, Albert W. Our Baptist Ministers & Schools. Repr. of 1892 ed. 44.00 (ISBN 0-384-45660-X). Johnson Repr.

THEOLOGICAL SEMINARIES, CATHOLIC

Fisher, Eugene J. Seminary Education & Christian-Jewish Relationss. 100p. 1983. 4.80 (ISBN 0-318-20615-3). Natl Cath Educ.

Hemrick, Eugene F., et al. Seminarians in Theology: A National Profile. 128p. 1986. pap. 8.95 (ISBN 1-55586-978-5). US Catholic.

Liturgical Formation in Seminaries: A Commentary. 120p. 1984. pap. 4.95 (ISBN 1-55586-917-3). US Catholic.

NCEA Roman Catholic Theological Seminaries Fact Book: National Summary of Key Issues 1980-1984. 72p. 1985. 6.00 (ISBN 0-318-20614-5). Natl Cath Educ.

Norms for Priestly Formation: A Compendium of Official Documents on Training of Candidates for the Priesthood. 344p. 1982. pap. 17.50 (ISBN 1-55586-838-X). US Catholic.

Pastoral Formation & Pastoral Field Edcation in the Catholic Seminary. 84p. 1985. pap. 4.95 (ISBN 1-55586-936-X). US Catholic.

Potvin, Raymond H. Seminarians of the Eighties: A National Survey. 64p. 1986. 5.65 (ISBN 0-318-20579-3). Natl Cath Educ.

The Program of Priestly Formation, NCCB. 3rd ed. 174p. 1982. pap. 14.95 (ISBN 1-55586-837-1). US Catholic.

Seminaries in Dialogue, No. 1. 1980. 2.40 (ISBN 0-318-20625-0). Natl Cath Educ.

Seminaries in Dialogue, No. 2. 24p. 1981. 2.40 (ISBN 0-318-20624-2). Natl Cath Educ.

Seminaries in Dialogue, No. 3. 20p. 1982. 2.40 (ISBN 0-318-20623-4). Natl Cath Educ.

Seminaries in Dialogue, No. 4. 1982. 2.40 (ISBN 0-318-20622-6). Natl Cath Educ.

Seminaries in Dialogue, No. 5. 20p. 1983. 2.40 (ISBN 0-318-20621-8). Natl Cath Educ.

Seminaries in Dialogue, No. 6. 24p. 1984. 2.40 (ISBN 0-318-20620-X). Natl Cath Educ.

Seminaries in Dialogue, No. 7. 24p. 1984. 2.40 (ISBN 0-318-20619-6). Natl Cath Educ.

Seminaries in Dialogue, No. 8. 24p. 1984. 2.40 (ISBN 0-318-20618-8). Natl Cath Educ.

Seminaries in Dialogue, No. 9. 24p. 1985. 2.40 (ISBN 0-318-20617-X). Natl Cath Educ.

Seminaries in Dialogue, No. 10. 24p. 1985. 2.40 (ISBN 0-318-20616-1). Natl Cath Educ.

Spiritual Formation in the Catholic Seminary. 64p. 1984. pap. 4.95 (ISBN 1-55586-920-3). US Catholic.

THEOLOGICAL STUDENTS
see Seminarians

THEOLOGY
see also Atheism; Calvinism; Christianity; Church; Church History; Deism; Ethics; Free Thought; Monotheism; Natural Theology; Pantheism; Rationalism; Religion; Religion and Science; Secularism; Theism

Abbott, Lyman, et al. The New Puritanism: During the Semi-Centennial Celebration of Plymouth Church, N.Y., 1847-1897. LC 70-39672. (Essay Index Reprint Ser.). 19.00 (ISBN 0-8369-2732-X). Ayer Co Pubs.

Ahlers, Rolf. The Barmen Theological Declaration of 1934: Archeology of a Confessional Text, Vol. 24. (Toronto Studies in Theology: No. 23). 1986. 59.95 (ISBN 0-88946-768-4). E Mellen.

Alexander, Jon & Dimock, Giles, eds. Religion in Western Civilization Since the Reformation: Select Readings. 184p. 1983. pap. text ed. 6.75 (ISBN 0-8191-3391-4). U Pr of Amer.

Allen, Joseph J., ed. Orthodox Synthesis: The Unity of Theological Thought. 231p. (Orig.). 1981. pap. 8.95 (ISBN 0-913836-84-2). St Vladimirs.

Allen, Ronald B. A Shelter in the Fury: A Prophet's Stunning Picture of God. (Living Theology Ser.). (Orig.). 1986. pap. 6.95 (ISBN 0-88070-158-7). Multnomah.

Alluntis, Felix & Wolter, Allan B., trs. from Lat. John Duns Scotus: God & Creatures; the Quodlibetal Questions. LC 80-28098. Orig. Title: Quaestiones Quodlibetales. (Illus.). 548p. pap. 16.95x (ISBN 0-8132-0557-3). Cath U Pr.

Almagno, Romano S. & Harkins, Conrad L., eds. Studies Honoring Ignatius Charles Brady O. F. M. (Theology Ser.). 1976. 25.00 (ISBN 0-686-17960-9). Franciscan Inst.

Ambrose, St. Theological & Dogmatic Works. (Fathers of the Church Ser.: Vol. 44). 343p. 1963. 21.95x (ISBN 0-8132-0044-X). Cath U Pr.

Ames, William. The Marrow of Theology. Eusden, John D., ed. & tr. from Latin. Orig. Title: Medulla Theologiae. xiv, 354p. 1983. pap. 14.95 (ISBN 0-939464-14-4). Labyrinth Pr.

Andersen, Loren. Theo-History: The Parallel Covenants Theory. 120p. 1983. pap. 4.25 (ISBN 0-9611310-0-4). Day Bk Co.

Anderson, Gerald H. & Stansky, Thomas F., eds. Mission Trends: Third World Theologies, No. 3. LC 76-24451. (Mission Trend Ser.). 264p. 1976. pap. 4.95 (ISBN 0-8091-1984-6). Paulist Pr.

Anderson, Gerald H. & Stransky, Thomas F., eds. Christ's Lordship & Religious Pluralism. LC 80-25406. 256p. (Orig.). 1981. pap. 8.95 (ISBN 0-88344-088-1). Orbis Bks.

Apczynski, John V., ed. Foundations of Religious Literacy. 186p. 1986. pap. text ed. 12.00 (ISBN 0-8191-5617-5, Pub. by College Theology Society). U Pr of Amer.

Aristotelian Society for the Systematic Study of Philosophy Staff. Science History & Theology: Proceedings, Suppl. 14. 13.00 (ISBN 0-384-54410-X); pap. 8.00 (ISBN 0-384-54411-8). Johnson Repr.

Aulen, Gustav. Christus Victor. (Orig.). 1969. pap. 6.95 (ISBN 0-02-083400-4, Collier). Macmillan.

Aycock, Don M. The E. Y. Mullins Lectures on Preaching with Reference to the Aristotelian Triad. LC 79-6080. 113p. 1980. text ed. 20.50 (ISBN 0-8191-0981-9); pap. text ed. 9.25 (ISBN 0-8191-0982-7). U Pr of Amer.

Bancroft, Emery. Christian Theology. Mayers, Ronald B., pref. by. 1976. 15.95 (ISBN 0-310-20440-2, 9141). Zondervan.

Bancroft, Emery & Mayers, Ronald B. Elemental Theology. 1977. 15.95 (ISBN 0-310-20460-7, 9146). Zondervan.

Barber, Cyril J. Introduction to Theological Research. 1982. pap. 9.95 (ISBN 0-8024-4134-3). Moody.

Berenbaum, Michael. The Vision of the Void: Theological Reflections on the Works of Elie Wiesel. LC 78-27321. 1978. 17.50x (ISBN 0-8195-5030-2). Wesleyan U Pr.

Bernard, David. Essentials of Oneness Theology. (Illus.). 32p. (Orig.). 1985. pap. 2.25 (ISBN 0-912315-89-X). Word Aflame.

Boethius. Theological Tractates. Bd. with Consolation of Philosophy. (Loeb Classical Library: No. 74). 13.95x (ISBN 0-674-99083-8). Harvard U Pr.

Boff, Clodovis & Boff, Leonardo. Salvation & Liberation: In Search of a Balance Between Faith & Politics. Barr, Robert R., tr. from Port. LC 84-7220. Tr. of Da Liberatacas. 128p. (Orig.). 1984. pap. 6.95 (ISBN 0-88344-451-8). Orbis Bks.

Bogorodskii, N. The Doctrine of St. John Damascene on the Procession of the Holy Spirit. LC 80-2351. Tr. of Uchenie Sv. Ioann Damaskina Ob' Iskhozhdenii Sv. Dukha. Repr. of 1879 ed. 28.50 (ISBN 0-404-18903-2). AMS Pr.

Bouman, Herbert J., tr. Luther's Works, Vol. 16. 1968. 14.95 (ISBN 0-570-06416-3, 15-1758). Concordia.

Bowden, John. Edward Schillebeeckx: In Search of the Kingdom of God. 160p. 1983. pap. 8.95 (ISBN 0-8245-0610-3). Crossroad NY.

Bracken, Joseph A. The Triune Symbol: Persons, Process & Community. (Studies in Religion: No. 1). 216p. (Orig.). 1985. lib. bdg. 25.00 (ISBN 0-8191-4440-1, College Theo Soc); pap. text ed. 11.75 (ISBN 0-8191-4441-X). U Pr of Amer.

Bradford, Charles E. The God Between. Coffen, Richard W., ed. 96p. 1984. pap. 4.95 (ISBN 0-8280-0243-6). Review & Herald.

Bradford, John. Writings of Bradford. 1979. Set. 34.95 (ISBN 0-85151-359-X). Vol. 1 (ISBN 0-85151-283-6). Vol. 2 (ISBN 0-85151-284-4). Banner of Truth.

Brightman, Edgare S. The Problem of God. 1979. Repr. of 1930 ed. lib. bdg. 30.00 (ISBN 0-8482-7365-6). Norwood Edns.

Brooks, Thomas. Works of Brooks, 6 vols. 1980. Set. 108.95 (ISBN 0-85151-302-6). Banner of Truth.

Brown, Raymond E., et al. Peter in the New Testament. LC 73-84424. (Orig.). 1973. pap. 5.95 (ISBN 0-8091-1790-8). Paulist Pr.

Brown, Robert M. Theology in a New Key: Responding to Liberation Themes. LC 78-6494. 212p. 1978. pap. 8.95 (ISBN 0-664-24204-9). Westminster.

Browning, Don S., ed. Practical Theology: The Emerging Field in Theology, Church & World. LC 82-47739. 128p. (Orig.). 1982. pap. 7.95 (ISBN 0-06-061153-7, RD-410, HarpR). Harrow.

Brummer, Vincent. Theology & Philosophical Inquiry: An Introduction. LC 81-11557. 320p. (Orig.). 1982. pap. 16.95 (ISBN 0-664-24398-3). Westminster.

Burtner, Robert W. & Chiles, Robert E., eds. John Wesley's Theology: A Collection from His Works. 304p. 1982. pap. 7.95 (ISBN 0-687-20529-8). Abingdon.

Burton, Asa. Essays on Some of the First Principles of Metaphysicks, Ethicks, & Theology. LC 73-4839. (History of Psychology Ser.). 432p. 1973. Repr. of 1824 ed. lib. bdg. 60.00x (ISBN 0-8201-1114-7). Schol Facsimiles.

Buswell, James O., Jr. Systematic Theology of the Christian Religion. 27.95 (ISBN 0-310-22190-0, 9364P). Zondervan.

Cahill, P. Joseph. Mended Speech: The Crisis of Religious Study & Theology. 272p. 1982. 14.95 (ISBN 0-8245-0421-6). Crossroad NY.

Caird, George B. The Apostolic Age. (Studies in Theology). 222p. 1982. pap. 13.50 (ISBN 0-7156-1680-3, Pub. by Duckworth London). Longwood Pub Group.

Cargas, Harry J., ed. Responses to Elie Wiesel. LC 77-94055. 1978. o. p. 15.00 (ISBN 0-89255-031-7); pap. 5.95 (ISBN 0-89255-032-5). Persea Bks.

Carmody, John. Ecology & Religion: Toward a New Christian Theology of Nature. LC 82-62412. 1983. pap. 6.95 (ISBN 0-8091-2526-9). Paulist Pr.

Casalis, George. Correct Ideas Don't Fall from the Skies: Elements for an Inductive Theology. Lyons, Jeanne M. & John, Michael, trs. from Fr. LC 83-19374. Tr. of Les Idees Justes Ne Tombent Pas du Ciel. 240p. (Orig.). 1984. pap. 8.95 (ISBN 0-88344-023-7). Orbis Bks.

Chadwick, Henry, ed. Boethius: The Consolations of Music, Logic, Theology, & Philosophy. 1981. text ed. 47.00x (ISBN 0-19-826447-X). Oxford U Pr.

Chopp, Rebecca S. The Praxis of Suffering: An Interpretation of Liberation & Political Theologies. LC 86-824. 192p. (Orig.). 1986. pap. 12.95 (ISBN 0-88344-256-6). Orbis Bks.

Clasper, Paul. Theological Ferment: Personal Reflections. 226p. (Orig.). 1982. pap. 6.75 (ISBN 0-686-37687-0, Pub. by New Day Philippines). Cellar.

Clements, K. W. The Theology of Ronald Gregor Smith. (Zeitschrift fur Religions- und Geistesgeschichte Ser.: No. 27). xii, 328p. 1986. pap. 49.00 (ISBN 90-04-07298-5, Pub. by E J Brill). Heinman.

Cleobury, F. H. Return to Natural Theology. 246p. 1967. 17.95 (ISBN 0-227-67722-6). Attic Pr.

Clutton-Brock, Arthur. Essays on Religion. facs. ed. LC 79-84302. (Essay Index Reprint Ser). 1926. 14.50 (ISBN 0-8369-1078-8). Ayer Co Pubs.

--More Essays on Religion. facsimile ed. LC 76-156632. (Essay Index Reprint Ser). Repr. of 1928 ed. 18.00 (ISBN 0-8369-2349-9). Ayer Co Pubs.

Coll, Alberto R. The Western Heritage & American Values: Law, Theology & History. Thompson, Kenneth W., ed. LC 81-43761. (American Values Projected Abroad Ser.: Vol. I). 126p. 1982. lib. bdg. 24.00 (ISBN 0-8191-2526-1); pap. text ed. 8.25 (ISBN 0-8191-2527-X). U Pr of Amer.

Collins, Raymond F. Models of Theological Reflections. LC 83-21733. (Illus.). 240p. (Orig.). 1984. lib. bdg. 25.75 (ISBN 0-8191-3661-1); pap. text ed. 12.25 (ISBN 0-8191-3662-X). U Pr of Amer.

Conn, Harvie M. Contemporary World Theology. 1974. pap. 4.95 (ISBN 0-87552-149-5). Presby & Reformed.

Conway, Anne. The Principles of the Most Ancient & Modern Philosophy. 1982. 35.00 (ISBN 90-247-2671-9, Pub. by Martinus Nijhoff Netherlands). Kluwer Academic.

Cooper, John W. The Theology of Freedom: The Legacy of Jacque Maritain & Reinhold Niebuhr. ix, 186p. 1985. text ed. 16.95 (ISBN 0-86554-172-8, MUP-H162). Mercer Univ Pr.

Corduan, Winfried. Handmaid to Theology. 176p. (Orig.). 1981. pap. 7.95 (ISBN 0-8010-2468-4). Baker Bk.

Cranor, Phoebe. Why Did God Let Grandpa Die? LC 76-17737. 128p. 1976. pap. 3.50 (ISBN 0-87123-603-6, 200603). Bethany Hse.

Cross, James A. A Study of the Holy Ghost. 1973. pap. 4.25 (ISBN 0-87148-006-9). Pathway Pr.

Cupitt, Don. Taking Leave of God. 192p. 1981. 9.95 (ISBN 0-8245-0045-8). Crossroad NY.

Curtis, Charles, et al. Perspectives on God: Sociological, Theological & Philosophical. LC 78-62943. 1978. pap. text ed. 11.50 (ISBN 0-8191-0605-4). U Pr of Amer.

Dagg, John L. Manual of Theology... Christian Doctrine... Church Order, 2 vols. in one. Gausted, Edwins., ed. LC 79-52592. (The Baptist Tradition Ser.). 1980. Repr. of 1858 ed. lib. bdg. 57.50x (ISBN 0-405-12459-7). Ayer Co Pubs.

Davis, John J. Foundations of Evangelical Theology: A Contextualized Approach. 232p. 1984. pap. 9.95 (ISBN 0-8010-2937-6). Baker Bk.

--Theology Primer. LC 81-67093. 128p. (Orig.). 1981. pap. 5.95 (ISBN 0-8010-2912-0). Baker Bk.

Davis, William H. Philosophy of Religion. LC 75-92048. (Way of Life Ser: No. 114). (Orig.). 1969. pap. 3.95 (ISBN 0-89112-114-5, Bibl Res Pr). Abilene Christ U.

DeBurgh, David. The Maturing Salesian. 1977. pap. 3.95 (ISBN 0-89944-028-2). Don Bosco Multimedia.

DeGruchy, John W. Bonhoeffer & South Africa: Theology in Dialogue. 128p. (Orig.). 1984. pap. 9.95 (ISBN 0-8028-0042-4). Eerdmans.

De Margerie, Bertrand. Christ for the World. Carroll, Malachy, tr. from Fr. Tr. of Christ Pour le Monde. write for info (ISBN 0-8199-0460-0); pap. 3.95 (ISBN 0-8199-0485-6). Franciscan Herald.

Devin-Adair Staff. Dogmatic Canons & Decrees of the Council of Trent, Vatican Council I, Plus the Decree on the Immaculate Conception & the Syllabus of Errors. LC 79-112469. (Eng.). 1977. pap. 5.00 (ISBN 0-89555-018-0). TAN Bks Pubs.

Dewart, Joanne. The Theology of Grace of Theodore of Mopsuestia. LC 65-18319. (Studies in Christian Antiquity: Vol. 16). 160p. 1971. 12.95x (ISBN 0-8132-0523-9). Cath U Pr.

D'hert, Ignace. Wittgenstein's Relevance for Theology. (European University Studies: Ser. 23, Vol. 44). 237p. 1978. pap. 27.15 (ISBN 3-261-03092-5). P Lang Pubs.

Eggenstein, Kurt. The Unknown Prophet Jakob Lorber. LC 79-89530. 78p. (Orig.). 1979. pap. 3.50 (ISBN 0-912760-99-0). Valkyrie Pub Hse.

Ellul, Jacques. In Season Out of Season. 1983. 16.00 (ISBN 0-8446-6029-9). Peter Smith.

--To Will & to Do. Hopkin, C. Edward, tr. LC 70-91166. 1969. 12.50 (ISBN 0-8298-0137-5). Pilgrim NY.

Erickson, Millard J. Christian Theology, Vol. 3. 1985. 19.95 (ISBN 0-8010-3425-6). Baker Bk.

Erickson, Millard J., ed. Christian Theology, 1 vol. 1986. 39.95 (ISBN 0-8010-3433-7). Baker Bk.

--New Life: Readings in Christian Theology. LC 79-53903. 1979. pap. 11.95 (ISBN 0-8010-3340-3). Baker Bk.

Evans, G. Rosemary. Old Arts & New Theology: The Beginnings of Theology As an Academic Discipline. 1980. text ed. 34.95x (ISBN 0-19-826653-7). Oxford U Pr.

Evans-Wentz, W. Y., ed. Tibet's Great Yogi, Milarepa. 2nd ed. (Illus.). 1969. pap. 9.95 (ISBN 0-19-500301-2). Oxford U Pr.

Exeler, Adolf & Mette, Norbert, eds. A People's Theology. 192p. pap. 9.95 cancelled (ISBN 0-8245-0477-1). Crossroad NY.

Fabella, Virginia & Torres, Sergio, eds. Doing Theology in a Divided World. LC 84-14712. 224p. (Orig.). 1985. pap. 11.95 (ISBN 0-88344-197-7). Orbis Bks.

Farmer, William R., ed. New Synoptic Studies: The Cambridge Gospel Conference & Beyond. LC 83-13396. xii, 533p. 1983. 32.95 (ISBN 0-86554-087-X, MUP/H76). Mercer Univ Pr.

Faure, Sebastian. Does God Exist? lib. bdg. 59.95 (ISBN 0-8490-0054-8). Gordon Pr.

Ferm, Vergilius. Toward an Expansive Christian Theology. LC 64-16359. 201p. 1964. 5.95 (ISBN 0-8022-0496-1). Philos Lib.

Festugiere, A. J. Freedom & Civilization among the Greeks. Brannan, P. T., tr. from Fr. & intro. by. (Princeton Theological Monograph: No. 10). Tr. of Liberte et Civilisation chez les Grecs. (Orig.). 1987. pap. price not set (ISBN 0-915138-98-0). Pickwick.

Finney, Charles G. Finney's Systematic Theology. LC 76-3500. Orig. Title: Finney's Lectures on Systematic Theology. 448p. 1976. pap. 9.95 (ISBN 0-87123-153-0, 210153). Bethany Hse.

Fiorenza, Francis S. Foundational Theology: Jesus & the Church. rev. ed. 352p. 1985. pap. 14.95 (ISBN 0-8245-0706-1). Crossroad NY.

Fleming, Austin H. Preparing for Liturgy: A Theology & Sprituality. (Orig.). 1985. pap. 6.95 (ISBN 0-912405-16-3). Pastoral Pr.

Flew, Antony. God: A Critical Enquiry. 210p. 1984. pap. 8.95 (ISBN 0-87548-371-2). Open Court.

Forell, George W. & Lehmann, Helmut T., eds. Luther's Works: Career of the Reformer II, Vol. 32. LC 55-9893. 1958. 19.95 (ISBN 0-8006-0332-X, 1-332). Fortress.

Fortenbaugh, William. Quellen zur Ethik Theophrasts. 380p. 1983. 48.00x (ISBN 90-6032-218-5, Pub by B R Gruener Amsterdam). Benjamins North Am.

Foster, K. Neill. The Discerning Christian. 104p. (Orig.). 1982. 6.95 (ISBN 0-87509-312-4); pap. 3.95 (ISBN 0-87509-316-7). Chr Pubns.

Fransen, P. Intelligent Theology, Vol. 3: A Universal Theology. 183p. pap. 2.50 (ISBN 0-8199-0402-3). Franciscan Herald.

Fruchtenbaum, Arnold G. Hebrew Christianity: Its Theology, History & Philosophy. Rev. ed. 142p. 1983. pap. 3.50 (ISBN 0-8010-3497-3). Ariel Pr CA.

Fullerton, Kemper. Essays & Sketches: Oberlin, 1904-1934. facsimile ed. LC 70-156644. (Essay Index Reprint Ser). Repr. of 1938 ed. 17.00 (ISBN 0-8369-2361-8). Ayer Co Pubs.

Geissler, Suzanne B. Jonathan Edwards to Aaron Burr, Jr. From Great Awakening to Democratic Politics. LC 81-38353. (Studies in American Religion: Vol. 1). xii, 298p. 1981. 49.95x (ISBN 0-88946-906-7). E Mellen.

Godwin, William. Essays. LC 77-23245. 1977. Repr. of 1873 ed. lib. bdg. 35.00 (ISBN 0-8414-4502-8). Folcroft.

Gorman, G. E. & Gorman, Lyn. Theological & Religious Reference Materials: Systematic Theology & Church History. LC 83-22759. (Bibliographies & Indexes in Religious Studies: No. 2). xiv, 401p. 1985. lib. bdg. 47.50 (ISBN 0-313-24779-X, GOS/). Greenwood.

Greer, Rowan A. Broken Lights & Mended Lives: Theology & Common Life in the Early Church. LC 85-21823. 251p. 1986. 19.50x (ISBN 0-271-00422-3). Pa St U Pr.

Grimm, Harold J. & Lehmann, Helmut T., eds. Luther's Works: Career of the Reformer I, Vol. 31. LC 55-9893. 1957. 19.95 (ISBN 0-8006-0331-1, 1-331). Fortress.

Gritsch, Eric W. & Jenson, Robert W. Lutheranism: The Theological Movement & Its Confessional Writings. LC 76-7869. 228p. 1976. pap. 8.95 (ISBN 0-8006-1246-9, 1-1246). Fortress.

Guerrero, Andres G. A Chicano Theology. LC 86-23561. 192p. (Orig.). 1987. pap. 11.95 (ISBN 0-88344-407-0). Orbis Bks.

Gundry, Stanley N. & Johnson, Alan F., eds. Tensions in Contemporary Theology. 2nd ed. 478p. 1983. pap. 15.95 (ISBN 0-8010-3796-4). Baker Bk.

Gustafson, James M. Ethics from a Theocentric Perspective: Theology & Ethics, Vol. 1. LC 81-11603. 284p. 1981. 27.50x (ISBN 0-226-31110-4). U of Chicago Pr.

Guthrie, Harvey H., Jr. Theology As Thanksgiving: From Israel's Psalms to the Church's Eucharist. 1981. 15.95 (ISBN 0-8164-0486-0, HarpR). Har-Row.

Hall, Douglas J. Lighten Our Darkness: Toward an Indigenous Theology of the Cross. LC 75-38963. 252p. 1980. pap. 9.95 (ISBN 0-664-24359-2). Westminster.

Hart, Ray L., ed. Trajectories in the Study of Religion: Addresses at the Seventy-Fifth Anniversary of the American Academy of Religion. (Studies in Religion & Theological Scholarship (American Academy of Religion)). 333p. 25.95 (ISBN 1-55540-064-7, 00-08-03). Scholars Pr GA.

Harvey, Van A. The Historian & the Believer: The Morality of Historical Knowledge & Christian Belief. LC 80-27941. 320p. 1981. Westminster.

Hebblethwaite, Brian L. The Problems of Theology. LC 79-41812. 176p. 1980. o. p. 29.95 (ISBN 0-521-23104-3); pap. 9.95 (ISBN 0-521-29811-3). Cambridge U Pr.

Hefling, Charles C., Jr. Jacob's Ladder: Theology & Spirituality in the Thought of Austin Farrer. LC 80-117760. xiii, 132p. (Orig.). 1979. pap. 5.00 (ISBN 0-936384-01-8). Cowley Pubns.

Hegel, G. W. Early Theological Writings. Knox, T. M. & Kroner, R., trs. from Ger. (Works in Continental Philosophy Ser). 1971. pap. 12.95x (ISBN 0-8122-1022-0, Pa. Paperbacks). U of Pa Pr.

Heyward, Isabel C. The Redemption of God: A Theology of Mutual Relation. LC 81-43706. 266p. (Orig.). 1982. lib. bdg. 29.25 (ISBN 0-8191-2389-7); pap. text ed. 12.25 (ISBN 0-8191-2390-0). U Pr of Amer.

Hodge, A. A. Outlines of Theology. 1983. 16.95 (ISBN 0-85151-160-0). Banner of Truth.

Hodge, Charles. Way of Life. 1978. pap. 4.95 (ISBN 0-85151-273-9). Banner of Truth.

Hodgson, Peter C. & King, Robert H., eds. Christian Theology: An Introduction to Its Traditions & Tasks. rev. & enl. 2nd ed. LC 84-48720. 432p. 1985. pap. 16.95 (ISBN 0-8006-1848-3, 1-1848). Fortress.

--Readings in Christian Theology. LC 84-48721. 432p. 1985. pap. 19.95 Kivar (ISBN 0-8006-1849-1, 1-1849). Fortress.

Hoffecker, W. Andrew. Piety & the Princeton Theologians. (Orig.). 1981. pap. 5.95 (ISBN 0-8010-4253-4). Baker Bk.

Holmgren, Frederick & Knight, George A., eds. International Theological Commentary, 6 vols. Incl. Vol. 1. Joshua. Hamlin, E. J. 8.95. 1983. pap. write for info. Eerdmans.

Horne, James. The Moral Mystic. 144p. 1983. pap. text ed. 9.25x (ISBN 0-88920-149-8, Pub. by Wilfrid Lauries Canada). Humanities.

Howe, Claude L., Jr. The Theology of William Newton Clarke: Doctoral Dissertation. Gaustad, Edwin S., ed. LC 79-52571. (The Baptist Tradition Ser.). 1980. lib. bdg. 14.00x (ISBN 0-405-12440-6). Ayer Co Pubs.

Hunter, Victor L. & Johnson, Phillip. The Human Church in the Presence of Christ: The Congregation Rediscovered. xii, 180p. 1985. 15.50 (ISBN 0-86554-171-X, MUP-H161). Mercer Univ Pr.

Hynes, William J. Shirley Jackson Case & the Chicago School: The Socio-Historical Method. Richards, Kent, ed. LC 81-8973. (The Society of Biblical Literature Biblical Scholarship in North America Ser.). 1981. pap. text ed. 15.00 (ISBN 0-89130-510-6, 06-11-05). Scholars Pr GA.

Idziak, Janine M. Divine Command Morality: Historical & Contemporary Readings. LC 79-91621. (Texts & Studies in Religion: Vol. 5). 348p. 1980. 49.95x (ISBN 0-88946-969-5). E Mellen.

Inge, W. R. Science & Ultimate Truth. LC 73-7513. 1926. Repr. lib. bdg. 8.50 (ISBN 0-8414-2109-9). Folcroft.

Inge, William R. The Post Victorians. 1933. Repr. lib. bdg. 21.45 (ISBN 0-8414-5059-5). Folcroft.

Irish, Charles M. The Gospel Conspiracy Workbook. 40p. 1986. wkbk. 2.95 (ISBN 0-8192-1387-X). Morehouse.

Ivanoff, N. K Tchemu Privodit Bezbozhije. Tr. of What are the Consequeces of Godlessness. 24p. 1983. pap. 1.50 (ISBN 0-317-29144-0). Holy Trinity.

Jaki, Stanley L. The Road of Science & the Ways to God. LC 77-21667. 1978. lib. bdg. 14.95x (ISBN 0-226-39144-2). U of Chicago Pr.

Jennings, Theodore W. Introduction to Theology: An Invitation to Reflection upon the Christian Mythos. LC 76-7867. pap. 48.00 (2027873). Bks Demand UMI.

Jepson, J. W. Don't Blame It All on Adam. 144p. 1984. pap. 4.95 (ISBN 0-87123-437-8, 210437). Bethany Hse.

Joranson, Philip N. & Butigan, Ken, eds. Cry of the Environment: Rebuilding the Christian Creation Tradition. LC 84-72254. (Illus.). 476p. (Orig.). 1984. pap. 14.95 (ISBN 0-939680-17-3). Bear & Co.

Jordan, Robert L. Black Theology Exposed. LC 81-90503. (Illus.). 92p. 1983. 8.95 (ISBN 0-533-05215-7). Vantage.

Joseph, Howard, et al, eds. Truth & Compassion: Essays on Judaism & Religion in Memory of Rabbi Dr. Solomon Frank, Vol. 12. 217p. 1983. pap. text ed. 13.95x (ISBN 0-919812-17-1, Pub. by Wilfrid Laurier Canada). Humanities.

Jungel, Eberhard. God As the Mystery of the World: On the Foundation of the Theology of the Crucified One in the Dispute Between Theism & Atheism. Guder, Darrell L., tr. (Ger.). 428p. 1983. 20.95 (ISBN 0-8028-3586-4). Eerdmans.

Kaiser, Walter C., Jr. Toward an Exegetical Theology. LC 80-68986. 224p. 1981. 11.95 (ISBN 0-8010-5425-7). Baker Bk.

Kane, G. Stanley. Anselm's Doctrine of Freedom & The Will. LC 81-16939. (Texts & Studies in Religion, Vol. 10). 240p. 1982. 49.95x (ISBN 0-88946-914-8). E Mellen.

Kaufman, Gordon D. An Essay on Theological Method. LC 75-31656. (American Academy of Religion. Studies in Religion: No. 11). 1975. pap. 10.25 (010011). Scholars Pr GA.

Kavanagh, Aidan. On Liturgical Theology. 216p. (Orig.). 1984. pap. 9.95 (ISBN 0-916134-67-9). Pueblo Pub Co.

Kay, Jeffrey A. Theological Aesthetics: Theology. (European University Studies: Ser. 23, Vol. 60). 115p. 1976. pap. 12.90 (ISBN 3-261-01893-3). P Lang Pubs.

Kelsey, Morton. Encounter with God: A Theology of Christian Experience. 48p. 1972. pap. 8.95 (ISBN 0-87123-123-9, 210123); study guide 1.25 (ISBN 0-87123-506-4, 210506). Bethany Hse.

--Myth, History & Faith: The Re-Mythologizing of Christianity. LC 73-94216. 192p. 1974. pap. 5.95 (ISBN 0-8091-1827-0). Paulist Pr.

Kim, Young O. The Types of Modern Theology. LC 83-80105. 296p. 1983. pap. 11.95 (ISBN 0-910621-32-2). Rose Sharon Pr.

Kim, Young Oon. An Introduction to Theology. LC 82-94722. 190p. (Orig.). 1983. pap. 7.50 (ISBN 0-910621-25-X). HSA Pubns.

King, Paul G. & Woodyard, David O. The Journey Toward Freedom. (Illus.). 248p. 1982. 28.50 (ISBN 0-8386-3115-0). Fairleigh Dickinson.

Kirk, J. Andrew. Liberation Theology: An Evangelical View from the Third World. LC 79-5212. (New Foundations Theological Library). 246p. (Peter Toon & Ralph Martin series editor). 1980. 12.95 (ISBN 0-8042-3704-2). John Knox.

Kliever, Lonnie D. The Shattered Spectrum: A Survey of Contemporary Theology. LC 80-82184. 276p. (Orig.). 1981. pap. 10.95 (ISBN 0-8042-0707-0). John Knox.

Kopas, Jane, ed. Interpreting Tradition: The Art of Theological Reflection. (College Theology Society - Annual Publications Ser.). 1984. pap. 11.95 (ISBN 0-89130-621-8, 34 10 83). Scholars Pr GA.

Koyama, Kosuke. Waterbuffalo Theology. LC 74-80980. (Illus.). 250p. (Orig.). 1974. pap. 7.95 (ISBN 0-88344-702-9). Orbis Bks.

Kress, Robert. The Church: Communion, Sacrament, Communication. 288p. (Orig.). 1985. pap. 9.95 (ISBN 0-8091-2663-X). Paulist Pr.

Krumbine, Miles H., ed. The Process of Religion: Essays in Honor of Dean Shailer Mathews. facsimile ed. LC 71-38776. (Essay Index Reprint Ser). Repr. of 1933 ed. 18.00 (ISBN 0-8369-2667-6). Ayer Co Pubs.

Kuyper, Abraham. Principles of Sacred Theology. DeVries, J. Hendrick, tr. from Dutch. (Twin Brooks Ser.). 712p. 1980. pap. 12.95 (ISBN 0-8010-5420-6). Baker Bk.

Lacy, G. H. Introduccion a la Teologia Sistematica. (Span.). 417p. 1983. pap. 6.95 (ISBN 0-311-09032-X). Casa Bautista.

Lampert, E. The Apocalypse of History: Problems of Providence & Human Destiny. 1948. 34.50x (ISBN 0-317-07646-9). Elliots Bks.

Land, Philip, ed. Theology Meets Progress: Human Implications of Development. 1971. pap. 6.50 (ISBN 0-8294-0326-4, Pub. by Gregorian U Pr). Loyola.

Langford, Thomas A. Wesleyan Theology: A Sourcebook. 326p. 1984. lib. bdg. 24.95 (ISBN 0-939464-40-3); pap. 14.95 (ISBN 0-939464-41-1). Labyrinth Pr.

Laycock, Steven W. & Hart, James G., eds. Essays in Phenomenological Theology. 204p. (Orig.). 1986. 44.50x (ISBN 0-88706-164-8); pap. 14.95x (ISBN 0-88706-165-6). State U NY Pr.

Lehman, Martin E. & Lehman, Helmut T., eds. Luther's Works: Word & Sacrament IV, Vol. 38. LC 55-9893. 1971. 19.95 (ISBN 0-8006-0338-9, 1-338). Fortress.

Leibrecht, Walter. Religion & Culture: Essays in Honor of Paul Tillich. facsimile ed. LC 78-167376. (Essay Index Reprint Ser). Repr. of 1959 ed. 24.50 (ISBN 0-8369-2558-0). Ayer Co Pubs.

Lewis, C. S. God in the Dock. Hooper, Walter, ed. 1970. pap. 8.95 (ISBN 0-8028-1456-5). Eerdmans.

Lewis, Gordon R. & Demarest, Bruce A. Integrative Theology: Knowing Ultimate Reality; The Living God, Vol. 1. 352p. 1986. 16.95 (ISBN 0-310-39230-6). Zondervan.

Littlejohn, Ronnie. Exploring Christian Theology. 542p. (Orig.). 1985. lib. bdg. 37.25 (ISBN 0-8191-4459-2); pap. text ed. 19.75 (ISBN 0-8191-4460-6). U Pr of Amer.

Locke, Hubert G., ed. The Barmen Confession: Papers from the Seattle Assembly. LC 86-23874. (Toronto Studies in Theology: Vol. 26). 370p. 1987. 59.95x (ISBN 0-88946-770-6). E Mellen.

Lokhande, Ajit. Tukarama, His Person & His Religion: A Relio-Historical, Phenomenological & Typological Enquiry. (European University Studies: Series 20, Philosophy: Vol. 22). 210p. 1976. 23.50 (ISBN 3-261-02009-1). P Lang Pubs.

Lonning, Per. The Dilemma of Contemporary Theology Prefigured in Luther, Pascal, Kierkegaard, Nietzsche. LC 78-16470. 1978. Repr. of 1962 ed. lib. bdg. cancelled (ISBN 0-313-20596-5, LODC). Greenwood.

Lossky, Vladimir. Mystical Theology of the Eastern Church. 252p. 1973. Repr. of 1957 ed. 17.95 (ISBN 0-227-67536-3). Attic Pr.

Louth, Andrew. Discerning the Mystery: An Essay on the Nature of Theology. 1983. text ed. 32.00x (ISBN 0-19-826657-X). Oxford U Pr.

Lubich, Chiara. Servants of All. Moran, Hugh, tr. from It. LC 78-59470. 176p. 1978. pap. 3.50 (ISBN 0-911782-05-2). New City.

Lutheran Church in America Task Group for Long-Range Planning. Theology: An Assessment of Current Trends Report. LC 68-557557. pap. 43.50 (2026880). Bks Demand UMI.

Luther's Works, Vol. 29. 1968. 13.95 (ISBN 0-570-06429-5, 15-1771). Concordia.

Luther's Works: Genesis Chapters 26-30, Vol. 5. LC 55-9893. 1967. 15.95 (ISBN 0-570-06405-8, 15-1747). Concordia.

Lynch, Stanley G. A Bird's Eye View of the Dispensation of Time. 1986. 7.00 (ISBN 0-8062-2433-9). Carlton.

McCutcheon, W. J. Essays in American Theology: The Life & Thought of Harris Franklin Rall. LC 72-190198. 350p. 1972. 15.00 (ISBN 0-8022-2085-1). Philos Lib.

McGill, Arthur C. Suffering: A Test of Theological Method. LC 82-6934. 130p. 1982. pap. 7.95 (ISBN 0-664-24448-3). Westminster.

Macha, Karel. Glaube und Vernunft: Eight Hundred Sixty-Three to Eighteen Hundred. 350p. 1987. lib. bdg. 50.00 (ISBN 3-598-20130-3). K G Saur.

Macintosh, Douglas C. Theology As an Empirical Science. Gaustad, Edwin S., ed. LC 79-52601. (The Baptist Tradition Ser.). 1980. Repr. of 1919 ed. lib. bdg. 23.00x (ISBN 0-405-12466-X). Ayer Co Pubs.

Macquarrie, John. God-Talk: An Examination of the Language & Logic of Theology. 1979. pap. 7.95 (ISBN 0-8164-2205-2, HarpR). Har-Row.

--Mystery & Truth. (Pere Marquette Theology Lectures). 1970. 6.95 (ISBN 0-87462-518-1). Marquette.

McShane, Philip. The Shaping of the Foundations: Being at Home in the Transcendental Method. 12.25 (ISBN 0-8191-0209-1). U Pr of Amer.

Maguire, Daniel. The New Subversives: Anti-Americanism of the Religious Right. 160p. 1982. 9.95 (ISBN 0-8264-0189-9). Continuum.

Mahoney, John. The Making of Moral Theology: A Study of the Roman Catholic Tradition. 1987. 55.00. Oxford U Pr.

Makrakis, Apostolos. A Revelation of Treasure Hid--Concerning Freedom, Concerning the Motherland, Concerning Justice, Apostolical Canons Respecting Baptism. Orthodox Christian Educational Society, ed. Cummings, Denver, tr. from Hellenic. 80p. (Orig.). 1952. pap. 2.00x (ISBN 0-938366-23-8). Orthodox Chr.

--Theology: An Orthodox Standpoint. Orthodox Christian Educational Society, ed. Cummings, Denver, tr. from Hellenic. (The Logos & Holy Spirit in the Unity of Christian Thought Ser.: Vol. 4). 216p. 1977. pap. 5.00x (ISBN 0-938366-03-3). Orthodox Chr.

Maquarrie, John. Twentieth Century Religion Thought: The Frontiers of Philosophy & Theology, 1900-1980. rev. ed. 429p. 1981. pap. text ed. write for info. (ISBN 0-02-374500-2, Pub. by Scribner). Macmillan.

Maritain, Jacques. On the Church of Christ: The Person of the Church & Her Personnel. Evans, Joseph W., tr. from Fr. LC 73-11559. Orig. Title: De l'Eglise Du Christ. (Eng. & Fr.). 352p. 1973. text ed. 24.95 (ISBN 0-268-00519-2); pap. text ed. 8.95x (ISBN 0-268-00525-7). U of Notre Dame Pr.

Marshall, Michael E. The Gospel Conspiracy in the Episcopal Church. (Orig.). 1986. pap. 6.95 (ISBN 0-8192-1386-1). Morehouse.

Martin, David, et al, eds. Sociology & Theology. 170p. 1980. 26.00x (ISBN 0-312-74007-7). St Martin.

Meyendorff, John. Vvedenie v Sviatootecheskoe Bogoslovia. rev. ed. Volokhonsky, Larisa, tr. from Eng. LC 85-61006. (Rus.). 359p. 1985. pap. 16.00 (ISBN 0-934927-00-6). RBR.

Micks, Marianne H. Introduction to Theology. rev. ed. 160p. 1983. pap. 9.95 (ISBN 0-8164-2465-9, HarpR). Har-Row.

Miles, Margaret R. Augustine on the Body. LC 79-14226. (American Academy of Religion, Dissertation Ser.: No. 31). 1979. 14.00 (ISBN 0-89130-288-3, 010131); pap. 9.95 (ISBN 0-89130-289-1). Scholars Pr GA.

Milet, Jean. God or Christ: The Excesses of Christocentricity. LC 81-5566. 288p. 1981. 14.95 (ISBN 0-8245-0104-7). Crossroad NY.

Mi-pham, Lama. Calm & Clear. LC 73-79058. (Tibetan Translation Ser., Vol. 1). (Illus.). 128p. 1973. pap. 6.95 (ISBN 0-913546-02-X). Dharma Pub.

Moltmann, Juergen. The Church in the Power of the Spirit. LC 76-62932. 1977. 21.45 (ISBN 0-06-065905-X, HarpR). Har-Row.

Moltmann, Jurgen. The Theology of Hope. LC 67-21550. 1976. pap. 10.00x (ISBN 0-06-065900-9, RD127, HarpR). Har-Row.

Moon, Cyris H. A Korean Minjung Theology: An Old Testament Perspective. 96p. (Orig.). 1986. pap. 7.95 (ISBN 0-88344-250-7). Orbis Bks.

Morgan, Everett J., ed. Christian Witness in the Secular City. LC 75-133951. (Orig.). 1970. pap. 4.00 (ISBN 0-8294-0198-9). Loyola.

Most, William G. The Heart Has Its Reasons: The Sacred Heart of Jesus & the Immaculate Heart of Mary. 35p. (Orig.). 1985. pap. 1.50 (ISBN 0-913382-50-7, 105-40). Prow Bks-Franciscan.

Mozley, E. N. The Theology of Albert Schweitzer. LC 73-16630. 108p. 1974. Repr. of 1950 ed. lib. bdg. 22.50x (ISBN 0-8371-7204-7, SCTH). Greenwood.

Muelder, Walter G. The Ethical Edge of Christian Theology: Forty Years of Communitarian Personalism. LC 83-21935. (Toronto Studies in Theology: Vol. 13). 435p. 1984. 69.95x (ISBN 0-88946-754-4). E Mellen.

Murphy, Emmy L. Who Made God. 1978. pap. 2.25 (ISBN 0-915374-07-2, 07-2). Rapids Christian.

Nash, Ron, ed. Liberation Theology. 1984. 15.95 (ISBN 0-88062-121-4). Mott Media.

Nash, Ronald H. The Word of God & the Mind of Man: The Crisis of Revealed Truth in Contemporary Theology. 176p. (Orig.). 1982. pap. 6.95 (ISBN 0-310-45131-0, 12380P). Zondervan.

Navone, John. Gospel Love: A Narrative Theology. (Good News Studies Ser.: Vol. 12). 1984. pap. 8.95 (ISBN 0-89453-437-8). M Glazier.

Newlands, George M. Hilary of Poitiers: A Study in Theological Method. (European University Studies: Series 23, Vol. 108). xiii, 216p. 1978. pap. 25.25 (ISBN 3-261-03133-6). P Lang Pubs.

Newman, John H. An Essay in Aid of a Grammar of Assent. LC 78-51523. 1979. text ed. 18.95 (ISBN 0-268-00999-6, NDP-214); pap. text ed. 9.95 (ISBN 0-268-01000-5). U of Notre Dame Pr.

Newman, Cardinal John H. A Newman Anthology. Lilly, W. S., ed. 1977. lib. bdg. 59.95 (ISBN 0-8490-2341-6). Gordon Pr.

Nielsen, Kai E. Scepticism. LC 72-77776. (New Studies in the Philosophy of Religion Ser.). 96p. 1973. 18.95 (ISBN 0-312-70070-9). St Martin.

Noll, Mark A., compiled by. The Princeton Theology: An Anthology. 432p. (Orig.). 1983. pap. 14.95 (ISBN 0-8010-6737-5). Baker Bk.

Norris, Elwood G. Be Not Deceived: A Scriptural Refutation of the Adam-God Theory. LC 78-70362. 141p. 1978. 8.95 (ISBN 0-88290-101-X). Horizon Utah.

Norris, John. Treatises Upon Several Subjects. Wellek, Rene, ed. LC 75-11244. (British Philosophers & Theologians of the 17th & 18th Centuries Ser.). 1978. Repr. of 1698 ed. lib. bdg. 51.00 (ISBN 0-8240-1796-X). Garland Pub.

Noyes, John H. Berean. LC 74-83431. (Religion in America, Ser. 1). 1969. Repr. of 1847 ed. 32.00 (ISBN 0-405-00256-4). Ayer Co Pubs.

Oberman, Heiko A. The Harvest of Medieval Theology: Gabriel Biel & Late Medieval Nominalism. xvi, 495p. 1983. pap. 17.50 (ISBN 0-939464-05-5). Labyrinth Pr.

O'Collins, Gerald. Foundations of Theology. LC 70-153756. 1971. pap. 3.95 (ISBN 0-8294-0201-2). Loyola.

--Fundamental Theology. LC 80-82809. 288p. (Orig.). 1981. pap. 8.95 (ISBN 0-8091-2347-9). Paulist Pr.

Ong, Walter J. American Catholic Crossroads: Religious-Secular Encounters in the Modern World. LC 80-29660. xi, 160p. 1981. Repr. of 1959 ed. lib. bdg. 22.50x (ISBN 0-313-22467-6, ONAM). Greenwood.

Osthathios, Geervarghese M. Theology of a Classless Society. LC 79-27013. 160p. (Orig.). 1980. pap. 2.24 (ISBN 0-88344-500-X). Orbis Bks.

Otto, A. S. The Theologia Twenty-One Encyclopedia, 2 vols. 1985. Set. vinyl 39.95 (ISBN 0-912132-16-7). Dominion Pr.

Padmasambhava, Guru. The Legend of the Great Stupa. LC 73-79059. (Tibetan Translation Ser., Vol. 2). (Illus.). 144p. 1973. pap. 6.95 (ISBN 0-913546-03-8). Dharma Pub.

Pahl, Paul D., tr. Luther's Works, Vol. 6. LC 55-9893. 1969. 16.95 (ISBN 0-570-06406-6, 15-1748). Concordia.

Pannenberg, Wolfhart. Basic Questions in Theology: Collected Essays, Vol. II. LC 82-15984. 258p. 1983. pap. 12.95 (ISBN 0-664-24467-X). Westminster.

--Faith & Reality. LC 77-682. 148p. 1977. softcover 6.50 (ISBN 0-664-24755-5). Westminster.

--Theology & the Philosophy of Science. McDonagh, Francis, tr. LC 76-20763. 464p. 1976. 17.50 (ISBN 0-664-21337-5). Westminster.

Pascal. The Christian Mind. Houston, James, ed. (Classics of Faith & Devotion Ser.). cancelled (ISBN 0-88070-159-5). Multnomah.

Pasquariello, Ronald D., et al, eds. Redeeming the City: Theology, Politics & Urban Policy. 224p. 1982. pap. 11.00 (ISBN 0-317-02300-4). Schalkenbach.

Pawlikowski, John & Senior, Donald, eds. Biblical & Theological Reflections on the Challenge of Peace. (Theology & Life Ser.: Vol. 10). 1984. pap. 9.95 (ISBN 0-89453-433-5). M Glazier.

Pelikan, Jaroslav, ed. Luther's Works, Vol. 21. LC 55-9893. 16.95 (ISBN 0-570-06421-X, 15-1763). Concordia.

Peukert, Helmut. Science, Action, & Fundamental Theology: Toward a Theology of Communicative Action. Bohman, James, tr. (Studies in Contemporary German Social Thought Ser.). 360p. 1986. pap. text ed. 12.50x (ISBN 0-262-66060-1). MIT Pr.

Pike, Nelson. God & Evil: Reading on the Theological Problem of Evil. 1964. pap. 14.95 ref.ed. (ISBN 0-13-357665-5). P-H.

Premm, Mattias. Dogmatic Theology for the Laity. 1977. pap. 12.00 (ISBN 0-89555-022-9). TAN Bks Pubs.

Preus, Robert D. Theology of Post-Reformation Lutheranism, Vol. 2. 350p. 1972. 16.95 (ISBN 0-570-03226-1, 15-2123). Concordia.

Primeaux, Patrick. Richard R. Niebuhr on Christ & Religion: The Four-Stage Development of His Thought. (Toronto Studies in Theology: Vol. 4). (Illus.). xiv, 288p. 1981. 49.95x (ISBN 0-88946-973-3). E Mellen.

Quenstedt, J. A. The Nature & Character of Theology. Poellet, Luther, tr. 208p. 1986. 12.95 (ISBN 0-570-03984-3, 12-3011). Concordia.

Rahner, Karl. Concern for the Church: Theological Investigations Vol. 20. (Theological Investigations Ser.). (Ger.). 272p. 1981. 16.95 (ISBN 0-8245-0027-X). Crossroad NY.

--Faith & Ministry. (Theological Investigations Ser.: Vol. 19). 352p. 1983. 24.50x (ISBN 0-8245-0572-7). Crossroad NY.

--God & Revelation, Vol. 18. (Theological Investigations Ser.). 352p. 1983. 24.50x (ISBN 0-8245-0571-9). Crossroad NY.

Ramanathan, P. The Western Approach to the Law & the Prophets of the Ancient World. (Illus.). 188p. 1984. 88.95 (ISBN 0-89920-113-X). Am Inst Psych.

Raschke, Carl A., ed. New Dimensions in Philosophical Theology. (AAR Thematic Studies). 19.50 (ISBN 0-89130-682-X, 01-24-91). Scholars Pr GA.

Reardon, Bernard M. Religious Thought in the Nineteenth Century. (Orig.). 1966. 49.50 (ISBN 0-521-06049-4); pap. 16.95x (ISBN 0-521-09386-4). Cambridge U Pr.

Regazzi, John J. & Hines, Theodore C. A Guide to Indexed Periodicals in Religion. LC 75-22277. 328p. 1975. 20.00 (ISBN 0-8108-0868-4). Scarecrow.

Riches, John, ed. The Analog of Beauty: Essays for Hans Urs von Balthasar at Eighty. 256p. 1986. 19.95 (ISBN 0-567-09351-4, Pub. by T & T Clark Ltd UK). Fortress.

Ricoeur, Paul. The Reality of the Historical Past. LC 84-60012. (Aquinas Lecture Ser.). 51p. 1984. 7.95 (ISBN 0-87462-152-6). Marquette.

Rikhof, Herwi. The Concept of Church: A Methodological Inquiry into the Use of Metaphors in Ecclesiology. LC 80-84751. xvi, 304p. 1981. 35.00x (ISBN 0-915762-11-0). Patmos Pr.

Riley, Patrick. The General Will Before Fousseau: The Transformation of the Divine into the Civic. (Studies in Moral, Political, & Legal Philosophy). 272p. 1986. text ed. 27.50 (ISBN 0-691-07720-7). Princeton U Pr.

Ritschl, Dietrich. The Logic of Theology. Bowden, John, tr. LC 86-45920. 336p. 1987. pap. 24.95 (ISBN 0-8006-1975-7). Fortress.

Roark, Dallas M. Christian Faith: Introduction to Christian Thought. 1977. pap. 4.95 (ISBN 0-8010-7652-8). Baker Bk.

Roberts, James D. Black Theology Today: Liberation & Contextualization. LC 83-17246. (Toronto Studies in Theology: Vol. 12). 218p. 1984. 49.95x (ISBN 0-88946-755-2). E Mellen.

Ross, James F. Philosophical Theology. 366p. 1982. 15.50 (ISBN 0-8290-0335-5). Irvington.

Russell, Letty M., ed. Changing Contexts of Our Faith. LC 85-4418. 112p. 1985. pap. 4.95 (ISBN 0-8006-1862-9). Fortress.

Sakenfeld, Katharine D. Faithfulness in Action: Loyalty in Biblical Perspective. LC 84-18738. (Overtures to Biblical Theology Ser.). 176p. 1985. pap. 8.95 (ISBN 0-8006-1540-9, 1-1540). Fortress.

Saward, John. Perfect Fools. 1980. text ed. 29.95x (ISBN 0-19-213230-X). Oxford U Pr.

Schick, G. V., tr. Luther's Works: Genesis Chapters 21-25, Vol. 4. LC 55-9893. 1964. 16.95 (ISBN 0-570-06404-X, 15-1746). Concordia.

Schilpp, Paul A., ed. Theology & Modern Life: Essays in Honor of Harris Franklin Rall. (Essay Index Reprint Ser.). 307p. 1982. Repr. of 1940 ed. lib. bdg. 18.00 (ISBN 0-686-79705-1). Irvington.

Schmidt, Paul F. Religious Knowledge. LC 79-8726. ix, 147p. 1981. Repr. of 1961 ed. lib. bdg. 22.50x (ISBN 0-313-22188-X, SCRK). Greenwood.

Schneider, Hans. Der Konziliarismus als Problem der Neueren Katholischen Theologie. (Arbeiten Zur Kirchengeschichte Ser.). 1976. 50.80x (ISBN 3-11-005744-1). De Gruyter.

Schopenhauer, Arthur. The Essence of Religion. (Illus.). 109p. 1985. 98.85 (ISBN 0-89266-505-X). Am Classical Coll Pr.

Schreiter, Robert J. Constructing Local Theologies. LC 84-14797. 240p. (Orig.). 1985. pap. 8.95 (ISBN 0-88344-108-X). Orbis Bks.

Schrodt, Paul. The Problem of the Beginning of Dogma in Recent Theology: Theology. (European University Studies: Ser. 23, Vol. 103). xxvi, 339p. 1978. pap. 40.40 (ISBN 3-261-02464-X). P Lang Pubs.

Schweitzer, Albert. The Theology of Albert Schweitzer for Christian Inquirers. Mozley, E. N., ed. 1977. lib. bdg. 59.95 (ISBN 0-8490-2740-3). Gordon Pr.

Schwertner, Siegfried. Internationales Abkuerzungsverzeichnis fuer Theologie und Grenzgebiete. LC 72-77418. 1974. pap. 35.20x (ISBN 3-11-004027-1). De Gruyter.

Scott, Walter. Exposition of the Revelation of Jesus Christ. LC 79-88736. 1979. Repr. 16.95 (ISBN 0-8254-3731-8). Kregel.

Seeliger, Wes. Western Theology. LC 72-96685. 103p. 1985. pap. 6.95 (ISBN 0-915321-00-9). Pioneer Vent.

Sell, Alan P. Robert Mackintosh: Theologian of Integrity. (European University Studies: Ser. 23, Vol. 95). 107p. 1977. pap. 16.95 (ISBN 3-261-03008-9). P Lang Pubs.

--Theology in Turmoil: The Roots, Course & Significance of the Conservative-Liberal. 144p. 1984. pap. 9.95 (ISBN 0-8010-8246-3). Baker Bk.

Selwyn, Edward G., ed. Essays, Catholic & Critical. facs. ed. LC 75-142695. (Essay Index Reprint Ser). 1926. 24.50 (ISBN 0-8369-2075-9). Ayer Co Pubs.

Sheed, F. J. Theology & Sanity. rev. ed. LC 78-62340. 1978. pap. 6.95 (ISBN 0-87973-854-5). Our Sunday Visitor.

--Theology for Beginners. Rev. ed. 200p. 1982. pap. 6.95 (ISBN 0-89283-124-3). Servant.

Shelp, Earl E. Theology & Bioethics: Exploring the Foundation & Frontiers. 1985. lib. bdg. 39.50 (ISBN 90-277-1857-1, Pub. by Reidel Holland). Kluwer Academic.

Sibbes, Richard. Works of Richard Sibbes, Vol. 1. 1979. 16.95 (ISBN 0-85151-169-4). Banner of Truth.

Singer, C. Gregg. From Rationalism to Irrationality. 1979. pap. 14.50 (ISBN 0-87552-428-1). Presby & Reformed.

Smart, Ninian. Concept & Empathy. Wiebe, Donald, ed. LC 85-18957. 240p. 1986. 35.00. NYU Pr.

Smith, John. Select Discourses. Wellek, Rene, ed. LC 75-11252. (British Philosophers & Theologians of the 17th & 18th Centuries Ser.). 1978. Repr. of 1660 ed. lib. bdg. 51.00 (ISBN 0-8240-1803-6). Garland Pub.

Song, C. S. Theology from the Womb of Asia. 256p. (Orig.). 1986. pap. 12.95 (ISBN 0-88344-518-2, 85-31008). Orbis Bks.

Song, Choan-Seng. The Tears of Lady Meng: A Parable of People's Political Theology. LC 82-2295. (Illus.). 80p. (Orig.). 1982. pap. 4.95 (ISBN 0-88344-505-0). Orbis Bks.

Southard, Samuel. Religious Inquiry: An Introduction to the Why & How. LC 76-20449. Repr. of 1976 ed. 24.20 (ISBN 0-8357-9024-X, 2016398). Bks Demand UMI.

Spencer, Geoffrey F. Strangers & Pilgrims. 221p. (Orig.). 1984. pap. text ed. 12.50 (ISBN 0-8309-0399-2). Herald Hse.

Spitz, Lewis W. & Lehmann, Helmut T., eds. Luther's Works: Career of the Reformer IV, Vol. 34. LC 55-9893. 1960. 19.95 (ISBN 0-8006-0334-6, 1-334). Fortress.

Sproule, John A. In Defense of Pretribulationism. 56p. (Orig.). 1980. pap. 2.95 (ISBN 0-88469-133-0). BMH Bks.

Stein, Robert H. Synoptic Problem. 280p. 1987. pap. 17.95 (ISBN 0-8010-8272-2). Baker Bk.

Stephan, Horst & Schmidt, Martin. Geschichte der Evangelischen Theologie in Deutschland seit dem Idealismus. 3rd ed. (De Gruyter Lehrbuch). 1973. 24.80x (ISBN 3-11-003752-1). De Gruyter.

Stone, James. Introduction to Basic Theology. 123p. (Orig.). 1983. pap. text ed. 5.95 (ISBN 0-934942-39-0). White Wing Pub.

Strharsky, Harry, ed. Must We Choose Sides? (Christian Committment for the '80s: Vol. 1). (Illus.). 128p. (Orig.). 1980. pap. 5.95 (ISBN 0-936476-01-X). Inter-Religious Task.

Stroup, George W. The Promise of Narrative Theology: Recovering the Gospel in the Church. LC 80-84654. 216p. (Orig.). 1982. pap. 9.95 (ISBN 0-8042-0683-X). John Knox.

Stuhlmacher, Peter. Reconciliation, Law & Righteousness: Essays in Biblical Theology. Kalin, Everett R., tr. LC 85-45482. 240p. 1986. 24.95 (ISBN 0-8006-0770-8, 1-770). Fortress.

Swedenborg, Emanuel. Divine Providence. LC 74-30441. 1974. trade ed. o.p. 10.00 (ISBN 0-87785-060-7); student ed. 12.00 (ISBN 0-87785-059-3); pap. 3.95 (ISBN 0-87785-061-5). Swedenborg.

Swimme, Brian. The Universe Is a Green Dragon: A Cosmic Creation Story. LC 84-72255. (Illus.). 173p. (Orig.). 1984. pap. 8.95 (ISBN 0-939680-14-9). Bear & Co.

Tavard, George. Theology for Ministry. (Theology & Life Ser.: Vol. 6). pap. 7.95 (ISBN 0-89453-337-1). M Glazier.

Taylor, Mark C. Deconstructing Theology. (American Academy of Religion Studies). 176p. 1983. 12.95 (ISBN 0-8245-0533-6). Crossroad NY.

--Deconstructing Theology. LC 82-5970. (AAR Studies in Religion). 152p. 1982. 12.95 (ISBN 0-89130-582-3, 01-00-28). Scholars Pr GA.

--Erring: A Post Modern A-Theology. LC 84-88. xiv, 220p. 1987. pap. 9.95 (ISBN 0-226-79142-4). U of Chicago Pr.

--Erring: A Postmodern, A-Theology. LC 84-88. (Illus.). 232p. 1984. lib. bdg. 20.00x (ISBN 0-226-79141-6). U of Chicago Pr.

Taylor, Michael J., ed. The Sacraments: Readings in Contemporary Theology. LC 80-9534. 274p. (Orig.). 1981. pap. 8.95 (ISBN 0-8189-0406-2). Alba.

Teilhard de Chardin, Pierre. Christianity & Evolution. LC 73-12926. 255p. 1974. pap. 6.95 (ISBN 0-15-617740-4, Harv). HarBraceJ.
Thielicke, Helmut. Between Heaven & Earth. Doberstein, J. W., tr. from Ger. 192p. 1978. Repr. 13.95 (ISBN 0-227-67726-9). Attic Pr.
Thiessen, Henry C. Lectures in Systematic Theology. rev. ed. Doerksen, Vernon C., rev. by. 1981. 16.95 (ISBN 0-8028-3529-5). Eerdmans.
Thomas, Owen C. Introduction to Theology. 2nd ed. LC 82-61890. 304p. 1983. pap. 13.95 (ISBN 0-8192-1319-5). Morehouse.
--Theological Questions: Analysis & Argument. LC 83-60658. 134p. (Orig.). 1983. pap. 8.95 (ISBN 0-8192-1328-4). Morehouse.
Thompson, John, ed. Theology Beyond Christendom. Essays on the Centenary of the Birth of Karl Barth, May 10, 1886. (Princeton Theological Monograph Ser.: No. 6). (Orig.). 1986. pap. 36.00 (ISBN 0-915138-85-9). Pickwick.
Thompson, Norma H., ed. Religious Education & Theology. LC 81-17852. 254p. 1982. pap. 12.95 (ISBN 0-89135-029-2). Religious Educ.
Thompson, Robert. What Comes After Pentecost. 1982. pap. 6.95 (ISBN 0-686-95485-8). Omega Pubns Or.
Tillich, Paul. The Construction of the History of Religion in Schelling's Positive Philosophy: Its Presuppositions & Principles. Nuovo, Victor, tr. 184p. 1975. 18.00 (ISBN 0-8387-1422-6). Bucknell U Pr.
--Theology of Culture. 1983. 14.50 (ISBN 0-8446-6021-3). Peter Smith.
Tinsley, John. Tragedy: Irony & Faith. 75p. (Orig.). 1985. pap. 5.95x (ISBN 0-317-26992-5). Wyndham Hall.
Toinet, Paul. Theological Cautions. Wrenn, Michael J., tr. 1982. 12.00 (ISBN 0-8199-0835-5). Franciscan Herald.
Topel, John. The Way to Peace: Liberation Through the Bible. LC 78-9148. 208p. (Orig.). 1979. pap. 7.95 (ISBN 0-88344-704-5). Orbis Bks.
Torrance, Thomas F. Theological Science. 1969. pap. 7.95 (ISBN 0-19-520083-7). Oxford U Pr.
Torres, Sergio & Eagleson, John, eds. The Challenge of Basic Christian Communities. Drury, John, tr. LC 81-38361. 283p. (Orig.). 1981. pap. 9.95 (ISBN 0-88344-503-4). Orbis Bks.
Torres, Sergio & Fabella, Virginia, eds. The Emergent Gospel: Theologies from the Underside of History. LC 77-22134. 303p. (Orig.). 1978. pap. 5.95 (ISBN 0-88344-113-6). Orbis Bks.
Tracy, David. Blessed Rage for Order: The New Pluralism in Theology. 1979. pap. 9.95 (ISBN 0-8164-2202-8, HarpR). Har-Row.
Tripolitis, Antonia. Origen: A Critical Reading. (American University Studies VII (Theology & Religion): Vol. 8). 208p. 1985. text ed. 21.55 (ISBN 0-8204-0213-3). P Lang Pubs.
Tuck, William P. Knowing God: Religious Knowledge in the Theology of John Baillie. LC 78-52865. 1978. pap. text ed. 9.50 (ISBN 0-8191-0484-1). U Pr of Amer.
Turner, William B. Theology - The Quintessence of Science. LC 80-82649. 306p. 1981. 17.50 (ISBN 0-8022-2375-3). Philos Lib.
Van Kaam, Adrian. In Search of Spiritual Identity. 14.95 (ISBN 0-87193-164-8). Dimension Bks.
Von Balthasar, Hans U. The Glory of the Lord: A Theological Aesthetics. Riches, John, ed. Louth, Andrew, et al, trs. from Ger. LC 82-23553. (Studies in Theological Style: Clerial Styles: Vol. 2). Orig. Title: Herrlichkeit: Eine Theologische Asthetik II Facher der Stile 1: Klerikale Style. 366p. 29.95 (ISBN 0-89870-048-5). Ignatius Pr.
--The Glory of the Lord; A Theological Aesthetics: Vol. I-Seeing the Form. Fessio, Joseph & Riches, John, eds. Leiva-Merikakis, Erasmo, tr. from Ger. LC 82-23553. Tr. of Herrlickeit: Eine Theologische Asthetik, I-Schau der Gestalt. 691p. 1982. 35.00 (ISBN 0-89870-031-0). Ignatius Pr.
--The Von Balthasar Reader. Kehl, Medard & Loser, Werner, eds. Lawrence, Fred & Daly, Robert J., trs. 400p. 1982. 27.50 (ISBN 0-8245-0468-2). Crossroad NY.
Wallace, Dewey D., Jr. Puritans & Predestination: Grace in English Protestant Theology, 1525 to 1695. LC 81-11563. (Studies in Religion). xiii, 289p. 1982. 29.95x (ISBN 0-8078-1499-7). U of NC Pr.
Walvoord, John F. Rapture Question. rev. enlarged ed. 1970. pap. 8.95 (ISBN 0-310-34151-5, 10978P). Zondervan.
Ward, Keith. Rational Theology & the Creativity of God. LC 82-81888. 256p. 1982. 17.95 (ISBN 0-8298-0618-0). Pilgrim NY.
Ward, W. Reginald. Theology, Sociology & Politics: The German Protestant Social Conscience 1890-1933. 250p. 1979. 29.90 (ISBN 3-261-04617-1). P Lang Pubs.
Warfield, B. B. The Works of Benjamin B. Warfield, 10 vols. 1981. Repr. of 1932 ed. 149.50 (ISBN 0-8010-9645-6). Baker Bk.
Weber, J. G. In Quest of the Absolute. LC 77-3596. (Cistercian Studies: No. 51). 1977. 10.95 (ISBN 0-87907-851-0); pap. 4.95 (ISBN 0-87907-951-7). Cistercian Pub.
Weischedel, Wilhelm, et al. Philosophische Theologie im Schatten des Nihilismus. Salaquarda, Joerg, ed. (Ger). 1971. pap. 9.60x (ISBN 3-11-001604-4). De Gruyter.
Wenger, J. C. Introduction to Theology. LC 53-9049. 418p. 1954. pap. 12.95 (ISBN 0-8361-1791-3). Herald Pr.
White, Victor. God & the Unconscious. rev. ed. LC 82-19153. (Jungian Classics Ser.: No. 4). xxxiii, 245p. 1982. pap. 15.00 (ISBN 0-88214-503-7). Spring Pubns.
Whittemore, Robert C. The Transformation of the New England Theology. (American University Studies VII-Theology & Religion: Vol. 23). 441p. 1987. text ed. 42.00 (ISBN 0-8204-0374-1). P Lang Pubs.
Wildiers, N. Max. The Theologian & His Universe: Theology & Cosmology from the Middle Ages to the Present. 320p. (Orig.). 1982. 21.95 (ISBN 0-8164-0533-6, HarpR). Har-Row.
William Of Ockham. Predestination, God's Foreknowledge & Future Contingents. 2nd ed. Kretzmann, Norman & Adams, Marilyn M., trs. LC 82-23317. 146p. 1983. 19.50 (ISBN 0-915144-14-X); pap. text ed. 4.95x (ISBN 0-915144-13-1). Hackett Pub.
Williams, Colin W. John Wesley's Theology Today. LC 60-5238. 256p. 1983. pap. 9.95 (ISBN 0-687-20531-X). Abingdon.
Wilm, Emil C., ed. Studies in Philosophy & Theology. LC 75-3078. Repr. of 1922 ed. 17.00 (ISBN 0-404-59079-9). AMS Pr.
Wingren, Gustaf. Creation & Gospel: The New Situation of European Theology. LC 78-78183. (Toronto Studies in Theology: Vol. 2). lii, 189p. 1979. pap. 39.95x (ISBN 0-88946-994-6). E Mellen.
Work of Richard Sibbes, 7 Vols. Set. 108.95 (ISBN 0-85151-398-0). Banner of Truth.
Wynne, Edward J., Jr. The Implications of Carl Michalson's Theological Method for Christian Education. Thompson, Henry O., ed. LC 82-24760. (Illus.). 400p. (Orig.). 1983. lib. bdg. 31.25 (ISBN 0-8191-3021-4); pap. text ed. 15.75 (ISBN 0-8191-3022-2). U Pr of Amer.
Young, Josiah U. Black & African Theologies: Siblings or Distant Cousins? LC 85-32090. 240p. (Orig.). 1986. pap. 12.95 (ISBN 0-88344-252-3). Orbis Bks.
Yourgrau, Wolfgang & Breck, Allen D., eds. Cosmology, History, & Theology. LC 76-54269. (Illus.). 416p. 1977. 69.50x (ISBN 0-306-30940-8, Plenum Pr). Plenum Pub.

THEOLOGY–BIBLIOGRAPHY

see also Religious Literature–Bibliography; Theological Libraries

Bollier, John A. The Literature of Theology: A Guide for Students & Pastors. LC 78-10962. 208p. 1979. pap. 5.95 (ISBN 0-664-24225-1). Westminster.
Botfield, Beriah. Notes on the Cathedral Libraries of England. LC 68-23138. 1969. Repr. of 1849 ed. 65.00x (ISBN 0-8103-3174-8). Gale.
Earnest, James D. & Tracey, Gerard. John Henry Newman: An Annotated Bibliography of His Tract & Pamphlet Collection. LC 84-48069. (Reference Library of Social Science). 600p. 1984. lib. bdg. 78.00 (ISBN 0-8240-8958-8). Garland pub.
Hadidian, Dikran Y., ed. Bibliography of British Theological Literature 1850-1940. (Bibliographia Tripotampolitana Ser.: No. 12). (Illus.). 500p. 1985. pap. 35.00 (ISBN 0-931222-11-7). Pitts Theolog.
Hurst, John F. Literature of Theology. LC 77-85625. 1977. Repr. of 1896 ed. lib. bdg. 50.00 (ISBN 0-89341-196-5). Longwood Pub Group.
Hurter, Hugo. Nomenclator Litterarius Theologiae Catholicae Theologo Sexhibens Aetate, Natione, Disciplins Distinctos, 5 Vols. in 6. 1903. Set. 294.00 (ISBN 0-8337-1772-3). B Franklin.
Kepple, Robert J. Reference Works for Theological Research: An Annotated Selective Bibliographical Guide. 2nd ed. LC 81-40350. 298p. 1981. lib. bdg. 29.00 (ISBN 0-8191-1679-3); pap. text ed. 13.75 (ISBN 0-8191-1680-7). U Pr of Amer.
Sayre, John L. & Hamburger, Roberta, eds. Tools for Theological Research. rev. 7th ed. LC 85-11979. 120p. (Orig.). 1985. pap. 5.00x (ISBN 0-912832-22-3). Seminary Pr.
Union Theological Seminary. Library. Alphabetical Arrangement of Main Entries from the Shelf List of the Union Theological Seminary Library, 10 Vols. 1960. Set. 1415.00 (ISBN 0-8161-0595-2, Hall Library). G K Hall.
Union Theological Seminary Library. Shelf List of the Union Theological Seminary Library (New York), 10 vols. 1960. Set. lib. bdg. 990.00 (ISBN 0-8161-0499-9, Hall Library). G K Hall.
Wainwright, William J. Philosophy of Religion: An Annotated Bibliography of Twentieth-Century Writings in English. LC 77-83374. (Library of Humanities Reference Bks.: No. 111). lib. bdg. 83.00 (ISBN 0-8240-9849-8). Garland Pub.

THEOLOGY–BIOGRAPHY

see Theologians

THEOLOGY–COLLECTED WORKS

Bancroft, Emery H. Fundamentos de Teologia Biblica. Tr. of Elemental Theology. (Span.). 496p. 1987. pap. 10.95 (ISBN 0-8254-1050-9). Kregel.
Church, R. W. Occasional Papers, 2 vols. 1973. Repr. of 1897 ed. 20.00 set (ISBN 0-8274-1533-8). R West.
Dominican Fathers of the Province of St. Joseph, ed. The Maritain Volume of "The Thomist", Dedicated to Jacques Maritain on the Occasion of His 60th Anniversary. LC 77-92509. (Essay Index in Reprint Ser.). 1978. Repr. 24.50x (ISBN 0-8486-3003-3). Roth Pub Inc.
Erickson, Millard J., ed. Readings In Christian Theology. 1973. pap. 12.95 (ISBN 0-8010-3305-5). Baker Bk.
Fletcher's Complete Works, 4 vols. 59.95 (ISBN 0-686-12868-0). Schmul Pub Co.
Gerstner, John H. A Primer on the Deity of Christ. 40p. 1984. pap. 1.75 (ISBN 0-87552-277-7). Presby & Reformed.
Luther, Martin. Luthers Werke, 4 vols. (Ger.). 1920p. 1982. Set. pap. 67.50 (ISBN 3-11-008942-4). De Gruyter.
Marquart, Kurt E., et al, eds. A Lively Legacy: Essays in Honor of Robert Preus. 224p. (Orig.). 1985. 13.95 (ISBN 0-9615927-0-2); pap. 11.95 (ISBN 0-9615927-1-0). Concordia Theo Sem.
Murray, John. The Collected Writings of John Murray: The Claims of Truth, 4 vols. 1976. Set. 88.95 (ISBN 0-85151-396-4). Banner of Truth.
Pannenberg, Wolfhart. Basic Questions in Theology: Collected Essays, Vol. I. LC 82-15984. 256p. 1983. pap. 12.95 (ISBN 0-664-24466-1). Westminster.
Scotus, Joannes D. Opera Omnia, 26 vols. 18302p. 1895. text ed. 4843.80x (ISBN 0-576-99127-9, Pub. by Gregg Intl Pubs England). Gregg Intl.
Trobisch, Walter. The Complete Works of Walter Trobisch. 700p. 1987. 19.95 (ISBN 0-87784-524-7). Inter-Varsity.
Wesley, John. The Appeals to Men of Reason & Religion. Gragg, Gerald R., ed. (The Works of John Wesley: Vol. XI). (Illus.). 1975. 49.95x (ISBN 0-19-812498-8). Oxford U Pr.
--Works of John Wesley, 14 vols. Set. 249.50 (ISBN 0-8010-9616-2). Baker Bk.

THEOLOGY–COLLECTED WORKS–EARLY CHURCH, ca. 30-600

Ambrosius, Saint Opera, 3 Vols. Set. 210.00 (ISBN 0-384-01038-5). Johnson Repr.
Burleigh, John S., ed. Augustine: Earlier Writings. LC 53-13043. (Library of Christian Classics). 410p. 1979. softcover 8.95 (ISBN 0-664-24162-X). Westminster.
Cassianus, Johannes. Opera, Pt. 2. Petschenig, M., ed. (Corpus Scriptorum Ecclesiasticorum Latinorum Ser: Vol. 13). 1886. 50.00 (ISBN 0-384-07860-5). Johnson Repr.
Cyprianus, Saint Opera Omnia. (Corpus Scriptorum Ecclesiasticorum Latinorum Ser: Vol. 3). 1868-1871. pap. 131.00 (ISBN 0-384-10518-1). Johnson Repr.
Ennodius, Magnus F. Opera Omnia. (Corpus Scriptorum Ecclesiasticorum Latinorum Ser.: Vol. 6). 1882. pap. 60.00 (ISBN 0-384-14370-9). Johnson Repr.
Faustus, Saint Praeter Sermones Pseudo-Eusebianos Opera. Engelbrecht, A., ed. (Corpus Scriptorum Ecclesiasticorum Latinorum Ser: Vol. 21). 1891. unbound 50.00 (ISBN 0-384-15200-7). Johnson Repr.
Hilarius, Saint Opera. Feder, A., ed. (Corpus Scriptorum Ecclesiasticorum Latinorum Ser: Vol. 65). 1916. 50.00 (ISBN 0-384-23110-1). Johnson Repr.
Lactantius, Lucius C. Opera Omnia: 1890-97, 4 pts. (Corpus Scriptorum Ecclesiasticorum Latinorum Ser: Vols. 19, 2 Pts.). 1890-97. Set Pts. 1 & 2. Vol 19. pap. 50.00 (ISBN 0-384-30865-1); Pts. 1 & 2 Vol 27. pap. 44.00 ea. Johnson Repr.
Lucifer of Cagliari. Opvuscula. (Corpus Scriptorum Ecclesiasticorum Latinorum Ser: Vol. 14). (Lat). pap. 40.00 (ISBN 0-384-34090-3). Johnson Repr.
Mamertus, Claudianus. Opera. Engelbrecht, A., ed. (Corpus Scriptorum Ecclesiasticorum Latinorum Ser: Vol. 11). 1885. 50.00 (ISBN 0-384-09245-4). Johnson Repr.
Palmer, G. E., et al, eds. The Philokalia, Vol. 2: The Complete Text. 408p. 1981. 30.00 (ISBN 0-571-11725-2). Faber & Faber.
Sedulius. Opera Omnia. Huemer, Iohnnes, ed. (Corpus Scriptorum Ecclesiasticorum Latinorum Ser: Vol. 10). Repr. of 1885 ed. 50.00 (ISBN 0-384-54730-3). Johnson Repr.
Tertullianus, Quintus S. Opera, 2 Vols. (Lat). Repr. of 1890 ed. Set. 100.00 (ISBN 0-384-59850-1). Johnson Repr.
Victorinus, Saint Opera. Haussleiter, I., ed. (Corpus Scriptorum Ecclesiasticorum Latinorum Ser: Vol. 49). Repr. of 1916 ed. 40.00 (ISBN 0-384-64555-0). Johnson Repr.

THEOLOGY–COLLECTED WORKS–MIDDLE AGES, 600-1500

Brown, Sr. Mary A., ed. Paul of Pergula: Logica & Tractatus De Sensu Composito et Diviso. (Text Ser). 1961. 11.00 (ISBN 0-686-11558-9). Franciscan Inst.
Miller, W. M. & Dinda, R. J., trs. Luther's Works, Vol. 20. LC 55-9893. 300p. 1973. 14.95 (ISBN 0-570-06420-1, 15-1762). Concordia.
Oberman, Heiko A. Forerunners of the Reformation: The Shape of Late Medieval Thought, Illustrated by Key Documents: Nyhus, Paul L., tr. LC 81-66518. pap. 86.80 (2027871). Bks Demand UMI.
Palmer, G. E., et al, eds. The Philokalia, Vol. 2: The Complete Text. 408p. 1981. 30.00 (ISBN 0-571-11725-2). Faber & Faber.
St. Thomas Aquinas. Introduction to Saint Thomas Aquinas. Pegis, Anton C., ed. (Modern Library College Editions Ser.). 1965. pap. 3.75x (ISBN 0-394-30974-X, T74, RanC). Random.
--Summa Theologica, 5 vols. 3057p. 1982. 225.00 (ISBN 0-87061-063-5); pap. 150.00 (ISBN 0-87061-069-4). Chr Classics.
Wycliffe, John D. Wycliffe, Select English Writings. Winn, Herbert E., ed. LC 75-41303. Repr. of 1929 ed. 18.50 (ISBN 0-404-14635-X). AMS Pr.

THEOLOGY–COLLECTED WORKS–16TH CENTURY

Bale, John. Select Works of John Bale, Bishop of Ossory. 51.00 (ISBN 0-384-03135-8). Johnson Repr.
Becon, Thomas. The Catechism of Thomas Becon. Repr. of 1884 ed. 55.00 (ISBN 0-384-03715-1). Johnson Repr.
--The Early Works of Thomas Becon, Chaplain to Archbishop Cranmer. Repr. of 1843 ed. 41.00 (ISBN 0-384-03725-9). Johnson Repr.
--Prayers & Others Pieces of Thomas Becon, Chaplain to Archbishop Cranmer. Repr. of 1844 ed. 55.00 (ISBN 0-384-03730-5). Johnson Repr.
Bradford, John. Writings of John Bradford...Martyr, 1555, 2 Vols. Repr. of 1853 ed. Set. 92.00 (ISBN 0-384-05440-4). Johnson Repr.
Calvin, Jean. Opera Quae Supersunt Omnia, 59 Vols. in 58. Baum, G., et al, eds. 1863-1900. Set. 2600.00 (ISBN 0-384-07195-3); 50.00 ea. Johnson Repr.
Coverdale, Myles. Remains of Myles Coverdale, Bishop of Exeter. 1846. 51.00 (ISBN 0-384-09950-5). Johnson Repr.
Dillenberger, John, ed. John Calvin: Selections from His Writings. LC 75-26875. (American Academy of Religion. Aids for the Study of Religion). 590p. 1975. pap. 10.95 (ISBN 0-89130-025-2, 010302). Scholars Pr GA.
Furcha, E. J., ed. & tr. Selected Writings of Hans Denck. LC 76-7057. (Pittsburgh Original Texts & Translations Ser.: No. 1). 1976. 5.50 (ISBN 0-915138-15-8). Pickwick.
Greenham, Richard. The Works, Examined, Corrected & Published: By H. Holland. LC 72-5999. (English Experience Ser.: No. 524). 496p. 1973. Repr. of 1599 ed. 70.00 (ISBN 90-221-0524-5). Walter J Johnson.
Hooper, John. The Early Writings of John Hooper. 1843. 51.00 (ISBN 0-384-24210-3). Johnson Repr.
--The Later Writings of Bishop Hooper. 1852. 55.00 (ISBN 0-384-24211-1). Johnson Repr.
Jewel, John. Works, 4 Vols. 1845-1850. Set. 204.00 (ISBN 0-384-27217-7). Johnson Repr.
Knox, John. Works of John Knox, 6 Vols. Laing, David, ed. LC 67-35016. Repr. of 1864 ed. Set. 345.00 (ISBN 0-404-52880-5). AMS Pr.
Luther, Martin. Martin Luther: Selections from His Writings. Dillenberger, John, ed. LC 61-9503. pap. 7.95 (ISBN 0-385-09876-6, Anch). Doubleday.
Melanchthon, Philipp. Opera Quae Supersunt Omnia, 28 Vols. (Corpus Reformatorum). Repr. of 1860 ed. Set. 1650.00 (ISBN 0-384-38050-6); 60.00 ea. Johnson Repr.
--Selected Writings. Flack, Elmer E. & Satre, Lowell J., eds. Hill, Charles L., tr. LC 78-5175. 1978. Repr. of 1962 ed. lib. bdg. cancelled (ISBN 0-313-20384-9, MESW). Greenwood.
Pilkington, James. Works of James Pilkington, Lord Bishop of Durham. 1842. Repr. of 1842 ed. 55.00 (ISBN 0-384-46530-7). Johnson Repr.

Ridley, Nicholas. Works of Nicholas Ridley, D.D., Sometime Lord Bishop of London, Martyr, 1555. Repr. of 1841 ed. 41.00 (ISBN 0-384-50840-5). Johnson Repr.
Schultz, Robert C. & Lehmann, Helmut T., eds. Luther's Works: The Christian in Society III, Vol. 46. LC 55-9893. 1967. 19.95 (ISBN 0-8006-0346-X, 1-346). Fortress.
Tyndale, William. Doctrinal Treatises, an Introduction to Different Portions of the Holy Scriptures. Repr. of 1848 ed. 51.00 (ISBN 0-384-62250-X). Johnson Repr.
Wenger, John C., ed. Complete Writings of Menno Simons: Circa 1496-1561. Verduin, Leonard, tr. LC 55-9815. 1104p. 1956. 35.00 (ISBN 0-8361-1353-5). Herald Pr.
Yoder, John H., ed. The Legacy of Michael Sattler. LC 72-6333. (Classics of the Radical Reformation Ser., No. 1). 208p. 1973. 12.95 (ISBN 0-8361-1187-7). Herald Pr.

THEOLOGY–COLLECTED WORKS–17TH CENTURY

Barrow, Isaac. Theological Works of Isaac Barrow, 9 Vols. Napier, Alexander, ed. LC 72-161751. Repr. of 1859 ed. Set. lib. bdg. 215.00 (ISBN 0-404-00670-1); lib. bdg. 25.00 ea. AMS Pr.
Beveridge, William. Complete Works, 12 vols. LC 72-39437. (Library of Anglo-Catholic Theology: No. 2). Repr. of 1848 ed. Set. 360.00 (ISBN 0-404-52040-5). AMS Pr.
Chillingworth, William. Works of William Chillingworth, 3 Vols. Repr. of 1838 ed. Set. lib. bdg. 95.00 (ISBN 0-404-01570-0). Vol. 1 (ISBN 0-404-01571-9). Vol. 3 (ISBN 0-404-01572-7). Vol. 4 (ISBN 0-404-01573-5). AMS Pr.
Digby, Sir Kenelme. Two Treatises: In the One of Which the Nature of Bodies; In the Other the Nature of Man's Soule is Look'd into the Way of Discovery of the Immortality of Reasonable Souls. Wellek, Rene, ed. LC 75-11217. (British Philosophers & Theologians of the 17th & 18th Centuries Ser.). 514p. 1978. lib. bdg. 51.00 (ISBN 0-8240-1771-4). Garland Pub.
Hales, John. The Works of the Ever Memorable Mr. John Hales of Eaton, 3 vols. in 2. Dalrymple, D., ed. LC 77-131037. Repr. of 1765 ed. 82.50 (ISBN 0-404-03050-5). AMS Pr.
Hall, Joseph. Works of Bishop Joseph Hall, 10 Vols. Wynter, P., ed. LC 76-86830. Repr. of 1863 ed. Set. 375.00 (ISBN 0-404-03070-X); 37.50 ea. AMS Pr.
Howe, John. Whole Works of John Howe, 6 Vols. Rogers, H., ed. LC 71-169450. Repr. of 1863 ed. Set. lib. bdg. 115.00 (ISBN 0-404-03360-1); lib. bdg. 20.00 ea. AMS Pr.
Laud, William. The Works of the Most Reverend Father in God, William Laud, D. D, 3 vols. LC 74-5373. (Library of Anglo-Catholic Theology: No. 11). Repr. of 1860 ed. Set. 350.00 (ISBN 0-404-52120-7). AMS Pr.
Shepard, Thomas. Works, 3 vols. Albro, John A., ed. LC 49-1393. Repr. of 1853 ed. Set. 85.00 (ISBN 0-404-05990-2). Vol. 1 (ISBN 0-404-05991-0). Vol. 2 (ISBN 0-404-05992-9). Vol. 3 (ISBN 0-404-05993-7). AMS Pr.
Sherlock, Thomas. The Tryal of the Witnesses of the Resurrection of Jesus. 2nd ed. Wellek, Rene, ed. Bd. with The Use & Extent of Prophecy. LC 75-25131. (British Philosophers & Theologians of the 17th & 18th Centuries Ser.). 348p. 1979. lib. bdg. 51.00 (ISBN 0-8240-1761-7). Garland Pub.
Thorndike, Herbert. Complete Theological Works of Herbert Thorndike, 6 Vols. in 10. LC 76-177454. (Library of Anglo-Catholic Theology: No. 17). Repr. of 1856 ed. Set. 295.00 (ISBN 0-404-52150-9). AMS Pr.

THEOLOGY–COLLECTED WORKS–18TH CENTURY

Edwards, Jonathan. Selected Writings of Jonathan Edwards. Simonson, Harold P., ed. LC 78-115064. (Milestones of Thought Ser.). 1970. pap. 7.95 (ISBN 0-8044-6132-5). Ungar.
--Works of President Edwards, 10 Vols. Williams, Edward & Parsons, Edward, eds. LC 68-56782. (Research & Source Works Ser.: No. 271). 1968. Repr. of 1847 ed. 245.00 (ISBN 0-8337-1019-2). B Franklin.
Law, William. The Power of the Spirit. Murray, Andrew, ed. LC 76-57110. (Classics of Devotions Ser). 224p. 1977. pap. 4.95 (ISBN 0-87123-463-7, 200463). Bethany Hse.
Lessing, Gotthold. Lessing's Theological Writings: Selections in Translation. Chadwick, Henry, tr. 1957. pap. 3.25x (ISBN 0-8047-0335-3). Stanford U Pr.
Swedenborg, Emanuel. Miscellaneous Theological Works. LC 76-46143. 1970. cancelled (ISBN 0-87785-071-2); student ed. 12.00 (ISBN 0-87785-070-4). Swedenborg.

THEOLOGY–COLLECTED WORKS–19TH CENTURY

Channing, William E. Works of William Ellery Channing, 2 vols. in 1. LC 70-114815. (Research & Source Works Ser.: No. 626). 1971. Repr. of 1882 ed. lib. bdg. 46.50 (ISBN 0-8337-0530-X). B Franklin.
Dwight, Timothy. Theology, 5 vols. LC 75-3132. Repr. of 1819 ed. 200.00 set (ISBN 0-404-59136-1). AMS Pr.
Mackintosh, C. H. The Mackintosh Treasury: Miscellaneous Writings of C. H. Mackintosh. rev. ed. LC 75-44323. 1976. 6 vols. in 1 19.95 (ISBN 0-87213-609-4). Loizeaux.
Newman, John H. Essays & Sketches. Harrold, Charles F., ed. Repr. of 1948 ed. lib. bdg. 41.00x (ISBN 0-8371-2842-0, NEER). Greenwood.
Parker, Theodore. Works - Centenary Edition, 15 vols. LC 75-3307. Repr. of 1911 ed. 595.00 set (ISBN 0-404-59300-3). AMS Pr.

THEOLOGY–COLLECTED WORKS–20TH CENTURY

Adams, James L. The Prophethood of All Believers. Beach, George K., ed. LC 85-73368. 324p. 1986. 25.00 (ISBN 0-8070-1602-0). Beacon Pr.
Billington, James, et al. Virtue: Public & Private. Neuhaus, Richard J., ed. (The Encounter Ser.). 96p. (Orig.). 1986. pap. 5.95 (ISBN 0-8028-0201-X). Eerdmans.
Cook, James I., ed. Saved by Hope: Essays in Honor of Richard C. Oudersluys. LC 78-5416. Repr. of 1978 ed. 49.50 (ISBN 0-8357-9132-7, 2016060). Bks Demand UMI.
Finney, Charles G. The Heart of Truth: Finney's Outlines of Theology. LC 75-46128. Orig. Title: Skeletons of a Course of Theological Lectures. 256p. 1976. pap. 6.95 (ISBN 0-87123-226-X, 210226). Bethany Hse.
Hopper, Jeffery. Understanding Modern Theology I: Cultural Revolutions & New World. LC 86-45210. 192p. 1986. 14.95 (ISBN 0-8006-1929-3). Fortress.
Kilby, Clyde S., ed. A Mind Awake: An Anthology of C. S. Lewis. LC 80-14133. 256p. 1980. pap. 3.95 (ISBN 0-15-659772-1, Harv). HarBraceJ.
Lawrence, Fred, ed. The Beginning & the Beyond: Papers from the Gadamer & Voegelin Conferences. LC 84-13940. (Boston College-Supplements to Lonergan Workshop Ser.). 1984. pap. 13.50 (ISBN 0-89130-772-9, 19 20 04). Scholars Pr GA.
Lewis, C. S. The Joyful Christian: One Hundred Readings from the Works of C. S. Lewis. LC 77-21685. 1977. 11.95 (ISBN 0-02-570900-3). Macmillan.
Lonergan, Bernard J. A Second Collection. LC 74-14798. 314p. 1975. 12.00 (ISBN 0-664-20721-9). Westminster.
McCool, Gerald, ed. Rahner Reader. (Orig.). 1975. pap. 10.95 (ISBN 0-8245-0370-8). Crossroad NY.
Ruoff, Norman D., ed. Writings of President Frederick M. Smith, Vol. 1. LC 78-6428. 1978. pap. 10.00 (ISBN 0-8309-0215-5). Herald Hse.
Schmitt, Keith R. Death & After-Life in the Theologies of Karl Barth & John Hick: A Comparative Study. (Amsterdam Studies in Theology Ser.: Vol. 5). 230p. 1985. pap. 32.50x (ISBN 90-6203-528-0, Pub. by Rodopi Holland). Humanities.
Wells, David F., ed. Reformed Theology: Essays in Its Modern Expression in America. 296p. (Orig.). 1985. pap. 19.95 (ISBN 0-8028-0096-3). Eerdmans.

THEOLOGY–COLLECTIONS

Erickson, Millard J., ed. Man's Need & God's Gift: Readings in Christian Theology. LC 76-17965. 512p. 1976. pap. 12.95 (ISBN 0-8010-3324-1). Baker Bk.
Hick, John. Classical & Contemporary Readings in the Philosophy of Religion. 2nd ed. LC 75-98092. (Philosophy Ser). 1969. text ed. write for info. (ISBN 0-13-135269-5). P-H.
Kerr, Hugh T., ed. Readings in Christian Thought. LC 66-14992. 1966. 25.95 (ISBN 0-687-35549-4). Abingdon.
Parker Society-London. Parker Society Publications, 55 Vols. Repr. of 1841 ed. Set. 2200.00 (ISBN 0-384-44880-1). Johnson Repr.
Rousseau, Richard W., ed. Interreligious Dialogue: Facing the Next Frontier. LC 81-52035. (Modern Theological Themes Ser.: Selection from the Literature: Vol. I). 234p. (Orig.). 1981. pap. 13.50 (ISBN 0-940866-00-5). Ridge Row.
Runyon, Randolph. Fowles, Irving, Barthes: Canonical Variations on an Apocryphal Theme. LC 81-11125. (Illus.). 134p. 1982. 17.50x (ISBN 0-8142-0335-3). Ohio St U Pr.

THEOLOGY–DICTIONARIES

Alvarez, J. Mateos. Vocabulario Teologico del Evangelio de Saint Juan. (Span.). 310p. 1980. pap. 13.95 (ISBN 84-7057-270-9, S-33107). French & Eur.
Amanne, E. Dictionnaire de Theologie Catholigue. (Fr.). Set. pap. 1995.00 (ISBN 0-686-56893-1, M-6003). French & Eur.
Bauer. Diccionario De Teologia Biblica. 2nd ed. (Span.). 582p. 1976. 38.95 (ISBN 84-254-0360-X, S-50203). French & Eur.
Bauer, J. B. Encyclopedia of Biblical Theology: The Concise Sacramentum Verbi. 1172p. 1981. 39.50x (ISBN 0-8245-0042-3). Crossroad NY.
Benton, Angelo Ames. The Church Cyclopaedia: A Dictionary of Church Doctrine, History, Organization & Ritual, & Containing Original Articles on Special Topics, Written Expressly for This Work by Bishops, Presbyters, & Laymen. LC 74-31499. 810p. 1975. Repr. of 1883 ed. 65.00x (ISBN 0-8103-4204-9). Gale.
Bouyer, Louis. Diccionario De Teologia. 4th ed. (Span.). 672p. 1977. 25.50 (ISBN 84-254-0377-4, S-14671). French & Eur.
Cox, Norman W., ed. Encyclopedia of Southern Baptists, Vols. I & II. LC 58-5417. (Illus.). 1958. 39.95 (ISBN 0-8054-6501-4). Broadman.
De Grandmaison, C. Dictionnaires Heraldique. Migne, J. P., ed. (Nouvelle Encyclopedie Theologique Ser.: Vol. 13). (Fr.). 688p. Repr. of 1852 ed. lib. bdg. 90.00x (ISBN 0-89241-262-3). Caratzas.
Dufour, Leon. Vocabulario de Teologila Biblica. 9th ed. (Span.). 976p. 1977. 35.95 (ISBN 84-254-0809-1, S-50205); pap. 29.95 (ISBN 84-254-0808-3, S-50204). French & Eur.
Elwell, Walter A. Evangelical Dictionary of Theology. LC 84-71575. 1984. 29.95 (ISBN 0-8010-3413-2). Baker Bk.
Erickson, Millard J. Concise Dictionary of Christian Theology. 1986. 9.95 (ISBN 0-8010-3436-1). Baker Bk.
Hardon, John A. Pocket Catholic Dictionary. LC 85-5790. 528p. 1985. pap. 6.95 (ISBN 0-385-23238-1, Im). Doubleday.
Harrison, Everett F., ed. Baker's Dictionary of Theology. pap. 12.95 (ISBN 0-8010-4289-5). Baker Bk.
Hobbs, Herschel H. A Layman's Handbook of Christian Doctrine. LC 74-78615. 1975. 5.75 (ISBN 0-8054-1927-6). Broadman.
Loth, Bernard & Michel, Albert. Dictionnaire de Theologie Catholique, Tables Generales: De Raison a Stolz, 3 vols. (Fr.). 256p. 1970. Set. 295.00 (ISBN 0-686-57021-9, M-6379). French & Eur.
McClintock, John & Strong, James. Cyclopaedia of Biblical, Theological, & Ecclesiastical Literature: Cyclopaedia of Biblical Literature, Vol. 1-10. 250.00 (ISBN 0-405-00020-0, 11917). Ayer Co Pubs.
--Cyclopedia of Biblical, Theological, & Ecclesiastical Literature, 12 vols. 12400p. 1981. text ed. 395.00 (ISBN 0-8010-6123-7). Baker Bk.
Migne, J. P., ed. Encyclopedie Theologique, 168 vols. in 171. (Fr., Illus.). 119060p. Repr. of 1873 ed. Set. lib. bdg. 14,177.48 (ISBN 0-89241-230-5). Caratzas.
--Nouvelle Encyclopedie Theologique (Second Series, 52 vols. in 53. 37237p. Repr. of 1862 ed. lib. bdg. 4695.75x (ISBN 0-89241-202-X). Caratzas.
--Troisieme et Derniere Encyclopedie Theologique (Third Series, 66 vols. (Fr.). 47232p. Repr. of 1873 ed. lib. bdg. 5716.75x (ISBN 0-89241-203-8). Caratzas.
Rahner & Vorgrimmler. Kleines Theologisches Woerterbuch. (Ger.). 460p. 1976. 11.95 (ISBN 0-686-56624-6, M-7508, Pub. by Herder). French & Eur.
Rahner, K. Herders Theologisches Taschenlexikon. (Ger.). 3180p. 1976. pap. 99.50 (ISBN 0-686-56481-2, M-7463, Pub. by Herder). French & Eur.
Rahner, Karl. Dictionary of Theology. 548p. 1985. pap. 17.50 (ISBN 0-8245-0691-X). Crossroad NY.
Rahner, Karl, ed. Encyclopedia of Theology: The Concise Sacramentum Mundi. rev., abr. ed. LC 82-7285. 1536p. 1975. 49.50x (ISBN 0-8245-0303-1). Crossroad NY.
Ramm, Bernard. Diccionario de Teologia Contemporanea. Valle, Roger V., tr. 143p. 1984. pap. 3.75 (ISBN 0-311-09064-8). Casa Bautista.
Richardson, Alan & Bowden, John, eds. The Westminster Dictionary of Christian Theology. LC 83-14521. 632p. 1983. 24.95 (ISBN 0-664-21398-7). Westminster.
Rossi, Leandro & Valsecchi, Ambrogio. Diccionario Enciclopedico De Teologia Moral. 3rd ed. (Span.). 1488p. 1978. 38.95 (ISBN 84-285-0468-7, S-50077); pap. 32.95 (ISBN 84-285-0467-9, S-50078). French & Eur.
--Diccionario Enciclopedico De Teologia Moral: Suplemento. (Span.). 256p. 1978. 13.95 (ISBN 84-285-0709-0, S-50079). French & Eur.
Taylor, Richard S., ed. Beacon Dictionary of Theology. 560p. 1984. 29.95 (ISBN 0-8341-0811-9). Beacon Hill.
Wolter, Michael, ed. Theologische Realenzyklopaedie: Agende-Anselm Von Cantebury, Vol. 2. (Illus.). 1978. 128.00x (ISBN 3-11-007379-X). De Gruyter.
Wright, Charles & Neil, Charles, eds. The Protestant Dictionary: Containing Articles on the History, Doctrines, & Practices of the Christian Church. LC 73-155436. 1971. Repr. of 1933 ed. 65.00x (ISBN 0-8103-3388-0). Gale.

THEOLOGY–METHODOLOGY

Boff, Clodovis. Theology & Praxis: Epistemological Foundations. Barr, Robert R., tr. LC 86-21671. Tr. of Teologia e Pratica: Teologia do Politico e Suas Mediacoes. (Port.). 416p. (Orig.). 1987. pap. 19.95 (ISBN 0-88344-416-X). Orbis Bks.
Crowe, Frederick E. Method in Theology: An Organon for Our Time. LC 80-81015. (Pere Marquette Ser.). 68p. 1980. 7.95 (ISBN 0-87462-519-X). Marquette.
Downey, John K. Beginning at the Beginning: Wittgenstein & Theological Conversation. 166p. (Orig.). 1986. lib. bdg. 23.50 (ISBN 0-8191-5650-7); pap. text ed. 12.50 (ISBN 0-8191-5651-5). U Pr of Amer.
Evans, Robert A. & Parker, Thomas D., eds. Christian Theology: A Case Method Approach. LC 76-9963. 1976. pap. 9.95xi (ISBN 0-06-062252-0, HarpR, RD 176, HarpR). Har-Row.
Everett, William W. & Bachmeyer, T. J. Disciplines in Transformation: A Guide to Theology & the Behavioral Sciences. LC 78-68570. 1979. pap. text ed. 11.75 (ISBN 0-8191-0692-5). U Pr of Amer.
Farley, Edward. Ecclesial Reflection: An Anatomy of Theological Method. LC 81-43088. 1982. 29.95 (ISBN 0-8006-0670-1). Fortress.
Kerr, Fergus. Theology after Wittgenstein. 224p. 1986. text ed. 45.00 (ISBN 0-631-14688-1). Basil Blackwell.
Lonergan, Bernard. Method in Theology. LC 78-181008. 1979. pap. 11.50 (ISBN 0-8164-2204-4, HarpR). Har-Row.
McClendon, James W., Jr. Biography as Theology: How Life Stories Can Remake Today's Theology. LC 74-9715. 224p. 1974. pap. 7.75 (ISBN 0-687-03539-2). Abingdon.
Meland, Bernard E. Fallible Forms & Symbols: Discourses on Method in a Theology of Culture. LC 76-7868. pap. 56.50 (2026957). Bks Demand UMI.
Moody, Dale. The Word of Truth. 624p. 1981. 24.95 (ISBN 0-8028-3533-3). Eerdmans.
Mueller, J. J. What Are They Saying about Theological Method? LC 84-61031. (WATSA Ser.). 88p. (Orig.). 1985. pap. 4.95 (ISBN 0-8091-2657-5). Paulist Pr.
Ommen, Thomas B. The Hermeneutic of Dogma. LC 75-29493. (American Academy of Religion. Dissertation Ser.). 1975. pap. 9.95 (ISBN 0-89130-039-2, 010111). Scholars Pr GA.
Wiles, M. F. What Is Theology? 1977. pap. 5.95x (ISBN 0-19-289066-2). Oxford U Pr.
Wood, Charles M. Vision & Discernment: An Orientation in Theological Study. (Studies in Religious & Theological Scholarship). 1985. 15.95 (ISBN 0-89130-922-5, 00-08-02); pap. 11.95 (ISBN 0-89130-923-3). Scholars Pr GA.

THEOLOGY–MISCELLANEA

Cumming, James T. & Moll, Hans G. Hey God, What about...? (Illus.). 1977. pap. 4.50 (ISBN 0-570-03758-1, 12-2666). Concordia.
Kirban, Salem. Questions Frequently Asked Me on Prophecy. (Illus.). 1981. pap. 4.95 (ISBN 0-912582-01-4). Kirban.
Lind, Millard C. Yahweh Is a Warrior. LC 80-16038. (Christian Peace Shelf Ser.). 240p. 1980. pap. 11.95x (ISBN 0-8361-1233-4). Herald Pr.
Montgomery, John W. How Do We Know There Is a God? LC 73-16882. 96p. 1973. pap. 3.50 (ISBN 0-87123-221-9, 200221). Bethany Hse.
Morris, Henry M. Bible Has the Answer. pap. 8.95 (ISBN 0-8010-5905-4). Baker Bk.
Regan, Cronan. Signpost: Questions About the Church & Religion You Always Wanted Answered. LC 70-169056. (Illus.). 340p. 1972. 7.50 (ISBN 0-8199-0432-5). Franciscan Herald.
Robertson, Pat. Answers to Two Hundred of Life's Most Probing Questions. 1987. pap. 3.95. Bantam.
Vander Meer, Charles. Quickie Quizzes No. 2. (Quiz & Puzzle Bks.). pap. 1.95 (ISBN 0-8010-9266-3). Baker Bk.
Wagner, Doris M., ed. Missiological Abstracts. LC 84-82346. 180p. (Orig.). 1984. pap. text ed. write for info. (ISBN 0-9602638-3-7). Fuller Theol Soc.

THEOLOGY–PHILOSOPHY

see Christianity–Philosophy

THEOLOGY–STUDY AND TEACHING

see also Catechisms; Christian Education; Church and Education; Religious Education; Seminarians; Theological Seminaries

Bolich, Gregory G. The Christian Scholar: An Introduction to Theological Research. 352p. (Orig.). 1986. lib. bdg. 30.00 (ISBN 0-8191-5135-1, Pub. by Inst Christ Stud); pap. text ed. 15.75 (ISBN 0-8191-5136-X). U Pr of Amer.
Clark, Henry. The Irony of American Morality. 1972. 13.95x (ISBN 0-8084-0036-3); pap. 9.95x (ISBN 0-8084-0037-1). New Coll U Pr.

Daniel, William A. Education of Negro Ministers. LC 77-78581. Repr. of 1925 ed. cancelled (ISBN 0-8371-1410-1, DNM&, Pub. by Negro U Pr). Greenwood.

Ebeling, Gerhard. The Study of Theology. Duane, Priebe A., tr. LC 78-5393. pap. 76.50 (2026983). Bks Demand UMI.

Farley, Edward. Theologia: The Fragmentation & Unity of Theological Education. LC 82-48621. 224p. 1983. pap. 14.95 (ISBN 0-8006-1705-3). Fortress.

Gambrell, Mary L. Ministerial Training in Eighteenth-Century New England. (Columbia University. Studies in the Social Sciences: No. 428). Repr. of 1937 ed. 16.50 (ISBN 0-404-51428-6). AMS Pr.

Gorman, G. E., et al, eds. Theological & Religious Reference Materials: Practical Theology. LC 86-380. (Bibliographies & Indexes in Religious Studies: No. 7). 402p. 1986. lib. bdg. 49.95 (ISBN 0-313-25397-8, GPA/). Greenwood.

Greathouse, William & Dunning, H. Ray. An Introduction to Wesleyan Theology. 128p. 1982. 4.95 (ISBN 0-8341-0762-7). Beacon Hill.

Ham, Wayne. More Than Burnt Offerings. LC 78-17646. 1978. pap. 7.00 (ISBN 0-8309-0217-1). Herald Hse.

Hough, Joseph C., Jr. & Cobb, John B., Jr. Christian Identity & Theological Education. (Studies in Religious & Theological Scholarship). 1985. pap. 11.95 (ISBN 0-89130-855-5, 00-08-01). Scholars Pr GA.

Kirwen, Michael C., ed. A Model Four Semester Syllabus for Transcultural Theology Overseas. LC 86-8618. 224p. 1986. 49.95 (ISBN 0-88946-047-7). E Mellen.

McKinney, Lois. Writing for Theological Education by Extension. 64p. (Prog. Bk.). 1975. 1.95x (ISBN 0-87808-905-5). William Carey Lib.

Moxcey, Mary E. Some Qualities Associated with Success in the Christian Ministry. LC 76-177095. (Columbia University. Teachers College. Contributions to Education: No. 122). Repr. of 1922 ed. 22.50 (ISBN 0-404-55122-X). AMS Pr.

Patterson, George. Church Planting Through Obedience Oriented Teaching. LC 81-285. (Illus.). 64p. (Orig.). 1981. pap. 3.95x (ISBN 0-87808-910-1). William Carey Lib.

Sprunger, W. Frederic. TEE in Japan: A Realistic Vision: the Feasibility of Theological Education by Extension for Churches in Japan. LC 81-7739. (Illus., Orig.). 1981. pap. 15.95x (ISBN 0-87808-434-7). William Carey Lib.

Thielicke, Helmut. Little Exercise for Young Theologians. (Orig.). 1962. pap. 2.95 (ISBN 0-8028-1198-1). Eerdmans.

Warfield, B. B. Biblical & Theological Studies. 12.95 (ISBN 0-8010-9584-0). Baker Bk.

Warfield, Benjamin B. The Religious Life of Theological Students. 1983. pap. 0.95 (ISBN 0-87552-524-5). Presby & Reformed.

Whitehead, James D. & Whitehead, Evelyn E. Method in Ministry: Theological Reflection & Christian Ministry. 224p. 1980. (HarpR); pap. 9.95 (ISBN 0-86683-459-1). Har-Row.

Wood, Charles M. Vision & Discernment: An Orientation in Theological Study. (Studies in Religious & Theological Scholarship). 1985. 15.95 (ISBN 0-89130-922-5, 00-08-02); pap. 11.95 (ISBN 0-89130-923-3). Scholars Pr GA.

THEOLOGY–TERMINOLOGY

Harvey, Van A. Handbook of Theological Terms. 1964. pap. 4.95 (ISBN 0-02-085430-7, Collier). Macmillan.

Manton, J. D. Introduction to Theological German. 1973. pap. 4.95 (ISBN 0-8028-1514-6). Eerdmans.

Morris, Leon. Apostolic Preaching of the Cross. 1956. pap. 5.95 (ISBN 0-8028-1512-X). Eerdmans.

Stroup, George W. The Promise of Narrative Theology: Recovering the Gospel in the Church. LC 80-84654. 216p. (Orig.). 1982. pap. 9.95 (ISBN 0-8042-0683-X). John Knox.

THEOLOGY–EARLY CHURCH, ca. 30-600

Beggiani, Seely J. Early Syriac Theology: With Special Reference to the Maronite Tradition. LC 83-3658. 172p. (Orig.). 1983. lib. bdg. 26.00 (ISBN 0-8191-3152-0); pap. text ed. 10.75 (ISBN 0-8191-3153-9). U Pr of Amer.

Berthold, George C., ed. Maximus the Confessor. (Classics of Western Spirituality Ser.: Vol. 45). 1985. 12.95 (ISBN 0-8091-0353-2); pap. 9.95 (ISBN 0-8091-2659-1). Paulist Pr.

Cassianus, Joannes. De Institutis Coenobiorum et De Octo Principalium Remediis Liber Xii: De Incarnatione Domini Contra Nestorium Liber Vii, Bk. 12. (Corpus Scriptorum Ecclesiasticorum Latinorum Ser: Vol. 17). (Cat). 1888. 50.00 (ISBN 0-384-07850-8). Johnson Repr.

Clarke, Graehme W., tr. The Letters of St. Cyprian, Vol. 1. (Ancient Christian Writers Ser.: No. 43). 416p. 1983. 24.95 (ISBN 0-8091-0341-9). Paulist Pr.

Clarke, Graeme W., tr. The Letters of St. Cyprian, Vol. 2. (Ancient Christian Writers Ser.: No. 44). 352p. 1983. 22.95 (ISBN 0-8091-0342-7). Paulist Pr.

Greenslade, S. L. Early Latin Theology. LC 56-5229. (The Library of Christian Classics). 412p. 1978. pap. 8.95 (ISBN 0-664-24154-9). Westminster.

Kelly, J. N. Early Christian Creeds. 3rd ed. 446p. 1981. text ed. 16.95 (ISBN 0-582-49219-X). Longman.

Lowry, Charles W. The First Theologians. 200p. (Orig.). 1986. pap. 7.95 (ISBN 0-89526-804-3). Regnery Bks.

McDonald, J. H. Kerygma & Didache: The Articulation & Structure of the Earliest Christian Message. LC 77-95446. (Society for New Testament Studies Monograph: No. 37). 1980. 29.95 (ISBN 0-521-22055-6). Cambridge U Pr.

Optatus, Saint Optati Milevitani Libri Septum. (Corpus Scriptorum Ecclesiasticorum Latinorum Ser: Vol. 26). (Lat). pap. 50.00 (ISBN 0-384-43390-1). Johnson Repr.

Paulinus of Nola, Saint Sancti Pontii Meropii Paulini Nolani Epistulae. (Corpus Scriptorum Ecclesiasticorum Latinorum Ser: Vol. 29). (Lat). Repr. of 1894 ed. 50.00 (ISBN 0-384-45195-0). Johnson Repr.

Rufinius, Tyrannius. Opera Pars 1. Orationum Gregorii Nazianzeni Novem Interpretation. Engelbrecht, A., ed. Repr. of 1910 ed. 40.00 (ISBN 0-384-52540-7). Johnson Repr.

Saint Augustine. Enchiridion on Faith, Hope & Love. Paolucci, Henry, ed. 177p. 1961. pap. 4.95 (ISBN 0-89526-938-4). Regnery Bks.

Severus, Sulpicius. Sulpicii Severi Libri Qui Supersunt. Halm, Carolus, ed. (Corpus Scriptorum Ecclesiasticorum Latinorum Ser: Vol. 1). (Lat). unbound 50.00 (ISBN 0-384-54955-1). Johnson Repr.

Whiteley, D. E. The Theology of St. Paul. 2nd ed. 312p. 1975. pap. 14.95x (ISBN 0-631-16430-8). Basil Blackwell.

--The Theology of St. Paul. 312p. 1967. 45.00x (ISBN 0-631-15710-7). Basil Blackwell.

THEOLOGY–MIDDLE AGES, 600-1500

Buytaert, Eligius M., ed. Saint John Damascene: De Fide Orthodoxa, Versions of Burgundio & Cerbanus. (Text Ser). 1955. 23.00 (ISBN 0-686-11554-6). Franciscan Inst.

Colligan, Owen A., ed. Saint John Damascene: Dialectica, Version of Robert Grosseteste. (Text Ser.). 1953. 3.50 (ISBN 0-686-11552-X). Franciscan Inst.

Companion to the Summa, 4 vols. 1985. Set. pap. 50.00 (ISBN 0-87061-117-8). Chr Classics.

Heath, Robert G. Crux Imperatorum Philosophia: Imperial Horizons of the Cluniac Confraternitas, 964-1109. LC 76-56099. (Pittsburgh Theological Monographs: No. 13). 1977. pap. 10.00 (ISBN 0-915138-17-4). Pickwick.

Hopkins, Jasper. Nicholas of Cusa on God as Not-other: A Translation & an Appraisal of De li non aliud. LC 78-22006. pap. 46.30 (ISBN 0-317-39689-7, 2055880). Bks Demand UMI.

Luther, Martin. Bondage of the Will. Cole, Henry, tr. (Summit Books). 1976. pap. 6.95 (ISBN 0-8010-5570-9). Baker Bk.

Pelikan, Jaroslav. The Christian Tradition: A History of the Development of Doctrine Vol. III: the Growth of Medieval Theology (600-1300) LC 78-1501. 1978. 27.50x (ISBN 0-226-65374-9). U of Chicago Pr.

Petuchowski, Jacob J., ed. & tr. Theology & Poetry Studies in the Medieval Piyyut. (Littman Library of Jewish Civilization). 1978. 18.50x (ISBN 0-19-710014-7). Oxford U Pr.

Preller, Victor. Divine Science & the Science of God: A Reformulation of Thomas Aquinas. LC 66-21838. pap. 72.80 (ISBN 0-317-08468-2, 2010543). Bks Demand UMI.

Preus, James S. From Shadow to Promise: Old Testament Interpretation from Augustine to the Young Luther. LC 69-12732. (Illus.). xii, 301p. 1969. 20.00x (ISBN 0-674-32610-5, Belkap Pr). Harvard U Pr.

Rolle, Richard. The Fire of Love. Wolters, Clifton, tr. (Classics Ser.). 192p. 1972. pap. 4.95 (ISBN 0-14-044256-1). Penguin.

St. Thomas Aquinas. Middle High German Translation of the "Summa Theologica". Morgan, Bayard Q. & Strothmann, Friedrich W., eds. LC 50-8471. (Stanford University. Stanford Studies in Language & Literature: No. 8). (Lat. & Ger., Glossary). Repr. of 1950 ed. 42.50 (ISBN 0-404-51816-8). AMS Pr.

--St. Thomas Aquinas: Theological Texts. Gilby, Thomas, ed. 444p. 1982. pap. 12.50x (ISBN 0-939464-01-2). Labyrinth Pr.

THEOLOGY–16TH CENTURY

Atkinson, James, ed. Luther: Early Theological Works. LC 62-12358. (Library of Christian Classics). 376p. 1980. pap. 9.95 (ISBN 0-664-24166-2). Westminster.

Collins, Anthony. A Disclosure on Free-Thinking. LC 75-11209. (British Philosophers & Theologians of the 17th & 18th Centuries Ser.). 395p. 1976. lib. bdg. 51.00 (ISBN 0-8240-1764-1). Garland Pub.

Gleason, Elisabeth G. Reform Thought in Sixteenth Century Italy. Massey, James A., ed. LC 81-5648. (American Academy of Religion Texts & Translations Ser.). 1981. pap. text ed. 10.95 (ISBN 0-89130-498-3, 01-02-04). Scholars Pr GA.

Krodel, Gottfried G. & Lehman, Helmut T., eds. Luther's Works: Letters I, Vol. 48. LC 55-9893. 1963. 19.95 (ISBN 0-8006-0348-6). Fortress.

Krodel, Gottfried G. & Lehmann, Helmut T., eds. Luther's Works: Letters III, Vol. 50. LC 74-76934. 416p. 1975. 19.95 (ISBN 0-8006-0350-8, 1-350). Fortress.

Lehmann, Helmut T. & Atkinson, James, eds. Luther's Works: The Christian in Society I, Vol. 44. LC 55-9893. 1966. 19.95 (ISBN 0-8006-0344-3, 1-344). Fortress.

Loeschen, John R. The Divine Community: Trinity, Church, & Ethics in Reformation Theologies. (Sixteenth Century Essays & Studies Ser.: Vol. I). 238p. 1981. 25.00x (ISBN 0-940474-01-8). Sixteenth Cent.

Lowde, James. Disclosure Concerning the Nature of Man, 1694. LC 75-11233. (British Philosophers & Theologians in the 17th & 18th Century Ser.). 271p. 1979. lib. bdg. 51.00 (ISBN 0-8240-1786-2). Garland Pub.

McDonnell, Kilian. John Calvin, the Church, & the Eucharist. LC 65-17149. pap. 105.00 (ISBN 0-317-08461-5, 2010572). Bks Demand UMI.

Pauck, Wilhelm, ed. Melanchthon & Bucer. LC 69-12309. (Library of Christian Classics). 422p. 1980. pap. 9.95 (ISBN 0-664-24164-6). Westminster.

Ray, John. The Wisdom of God Manifested in the Works of the Creation. LC 75-11250. (British Philosophers & Theologians in the 17th & 18th Century Ser.). 247p. 1979. lib. bdg. 51.00 (ISBN 0-8240-1801-X). Garland Pub.

THEOLOGY–17TH CENTURY

Collins, Anthony. A Disclosure on Free-Thinking. LC 75-11209. (British Philosophers & Theologians of the 17th & 18th Centuries Ser.). 395p. 1976. lib. bdg. 51.00 (ISBN 0-8240-1764-1). Garland Pub.

Lowde, James. Disclosure Concerning the Nature of Man, 1694. LC 75-11233. (British Philosophers & Theologians in the 17th & 18th Century Ser.). 271p. 1979. lib. bdg. 51.00 (ISBN 0-8240-1786-2). Garland Pub.

Ray, John. The Wisdom of God Manifested in the Works of the Creation. LC 75-11250. (British Philosophers & Theologians in the 17th & 18th Century Ser.). 247p. 1979. lib. bdg. 51.00 (ISBN 0-8240-1801-X). Garland Pub.

Rescher, Nicholas. Pascal's Wager: A Study of Practical Reasoning in Philosophical Theology. LC 84-40820. 176p. 1985. text ed. 19.95 (ISBN 0-268-01556-2, 85-15561). U of Notre Dame Pr.

THEOLOGY–18TH CENTURY

Holifield, E. Brooks. The Gentlemen Theologians: American Theology in Southern Culture, 1795-1860. LC 78-59580. x, 262p. 1978. 23.00 (ISBN 0-8223-0414-7). Duke.

Wellek, Rene, ed. A View of the Prinicpal Deistical Writers That Have Appeared in England in the Last & Present Century, 3 vols. LC 75-11232. (British Philosophers & Theologians of the 17th & 18th Centuries Ser.). 1348p. 1978. lib. bdg. 153.00 (ISBN 0-8240-1785-4). Garland Pub.

THEOLOGY–19TH CENTURY

Elliott-Binns, L. The Development of English Theology in the Later Nineteenth Century. LC 72-122411. ix, 137p. 1971. Repr. of 1952 ed. 17.50 (ISBN 0-208-01045-9, Archon). Shoe String.

Holifield, E. Brooks. The Gentlemen Theologians: American Theology in Southern Culture, 1795-1860. LC 78-59580. x, 262p. 1978. 23.00 (ISBN 0-8223-0414-7). Duke.

Jukes, Andrew. The Restitution of All Things. 194p. 1976. pap. text ed. 4.00 (ISBN 0-910424-65-9). Concordant.

Lilly, W. S., ed. A Newman Anthology. 356p. 1981. 25.00x (ISBN 0-234-77060-0, Pub. by Dobson Bks England). State Mutual Bk.

Peake, A. S., et al. Germany in the Nineteenth Century. facs. ed. LC 67-30189. (Manchester University Publications Historical Ser.: No. 24). 1915. 15.00 (ISBN 0-8369-0472-9). Ayer Co Pubs.

Swanston, Hamish. Ideas of Order: Anglicans & the Renewal of Theological Method in the Middle Years of the 19th Century. 256p. 1974. pap. text ed. 22.00 (ISBN 90-232-1124-3, Pub. by Van Gorcum Holland). Longwood Pub Group.

Wolf, William J. An Abridgement of Maurice's Kingdom of Christ: The Original Two Volumes Abridged into One Based on the 1842 Edition Amended with an Introduction. LC 83-3516. 276p. (Orig.). 1983. lib. bdg. 28.25 (ISBN 0-8191-3150-4); pap. text ed. 13.50 (ISBN 0-8191-3151-2). U Pr of Amer.

THEOLOGY–20TH CENTURY

see also Death of God Theology

Adler, Mortimer J. How to Think About God: A Guide for the Twentieth-Century Pagan. 1980. 10.95 (ISBN 0-02-500540-5). Macmillan.

Alszeghy, Zoltan & Flick, Maurizio. Introductory Theology. 1983. 8.95 (ISBN 0-87193-198-2). Dimension Bks.

Altizer, Thomas, et al. Deconstruction & Theology. 176p. 1982. 14.95 (ISBN 0-8245-0475-5); pap. 8.95 (ISBN 0-8245-0412-7). Crossroad NY.

Andersen, Verlan. Many Are Called but Few Are Chosen. 96p. 1967. pap. 2.95 (ISBN 0-89036-002-2). Hawkes Pub Inc.

Barth, Karl. The Christian Life. Bromiley, Geoffrey W., ed. LC 80-39942. 328p. 1981. 17.95 (ISBN 0-8028-3523-6). Eerdmans.

Berkhof, Louis. Systematic Theology. 1978. 24.95 (ISBN 0-8028-3020-X). Eerdmans.

Brown, Robert M., ed. The Essential Reinhold Niebuhr: Selected Essays & Addresses. LC 85-22798. 272p. 1986. 19.95 (ISBN 0-300-03464-4). Yale U Pr.

Brunner, Emil. The Divine-Human Encounter. Loos, Amandus W., tr. from Ger. 207p. 1980. Repr. of 1943 ed. lib. bdg. 24.75x (ISBN 0-313-22398-X, BRDH). Greenwood.

Cauthen, Kenneth. Systematic Theology: A Modern Protestant Approach. LC 86-23807. (Toronto Studies in Theology: Vol. 25). 480p. 1986. lib. bdg. 69.95x (ISBN 0-88946-769-2). E Mellen.

Clarke's Christian Theology. 8.95 (ISBN 0-686-12856-7). Schmul Pub Co.

Conn, Harvie M. Eternal Word & Changing Worlds: Theology, Anthropology & Mission in Trialogue. 336p. 1984. pap. 10.95 (ISBN 0-310-45321-6, 11647P). Zondervan.

Cooper, Barry. The Political Theory of Eric Voegelin. LC 86-23517. (Toronto Studies in Theology: Vol. 21). 256p. 1986. text ed. 49.95 (ISBN 0-88946-771-4). E Mellen.

Cox, Harvey. Feast of Fools: A Theological Essay on Festivity & Fantasy. LC 75-75914. (William Belden Noble Lectures Ser). 1969. 15.00x (ISBN 0-674-29525-0). Harvard U Pr.

--Religion in the Secular City: Toward a Postmodern Theology. 304p. 1985. pap. 7.95 (ISBN 0-671-52805-X, Touchstone Bks). S&S.

Daly, Robert J., ed. Rising from History: U. S. Catholic Theology Looks to the future. LC 87-2011. (The Annual Publication of the College Theology Society, 1984: Vol. 30). 234p. (Orig.). 1987. lib. bdg. 24.50 (ISBN 0-8191-6155-1, Pub. by College Theology Society); pap. text ed. 12.75 (ISBN 0-8191-6156-X, Pub. by College Theology Society). U Pr of Amer.

Deloria, Vine, Jr. The Metaphysics of Modern Existence. LC 76-8708. (Native American Publishing Program Ser.). 1978. 8.45 (ISBN 0-06-450250-3, HarpR). Har-Row.

Devine, George, ed. That They May Live: Theological Reflections on the Quality of Life. 314p. 1984. pap. text ed. 10.50 (ISBN 0-8191-3852-5, College Theo Soc). U Pr of Amer.

Downey, John K. Beginning at the Beginning: Wittgenstein & Theological Conversation. 166p. (Orig.). 1986. lib. bdg. 23.50 (ISBN 0-8191-5650-7); pap. text ed. 12.50 (ISBN 0-8191-5651-5). U Pr of Amer.

Drummond, Richard H. Toward a New Age in Christian Theology. LC 85-5155. 272p. 1985. pap. 12.95 (ISBN 0-88344-514-X). Orbis Bks.

Ericksen, Robert P. Theologians under Hitler: Gerhard Kittel, Paul Althaus, & Emanuel Hirsch. LC 84-40731. (Illus.). 256p. 1985. 20.00x (ISBN 0-300-02926-8). Yale U Pr.

Esler, Philip S. Community & Gospel in Luke-Acts: The Social & Political Motivations of Lucan Theory. (Society for New Testament Studies Monographs: No. 57). 224p. Date not set. price not set (ISBN 0-521-32965-5). Cambridge U Pr.

Fabella, Virginia, ed. Asia's Struggle for Full Humanity: Towards a Relevant Theology. LC 80-14923. 229p. (Orig.). 1980. pap. 8.95 (ISBN 0-88344-015-6). Orbis Bks.

Ferm, Deane W. Contemporary American Theologies II: A Book of Readings. 214p. (Orig.). 1982. pap. 15.95 (ISBN 0-8164-2407-1, HarpR). Har-Row.

Ferm, Vergilius T., ed. Contemporary American Theology. LC 78-86749. (Essay Index Reprint Ser). 1933. 21.50 (ISBN 0-8369-1181-4). Ayer Co Pubs.

Ferre, Frederick. Language, Logic, & God. LC 81-27305. viii, 184p. 1987. pap. text ed. 10.00 (ISBN 0-226-24457-1, Midway Reprint). U of Chicago Pr.

Fey, Harold E., ed. How My Mind Has Changed. 7.00 (ISBN 0-8446-2056-4). Peter Smith.

Fierro, Alfredo. The Militant Gospel: A Critical Introduction to Political Theologies. Drury, John, tr. from Span. LC 77-1652. Orig. Title: El Evangelio Beligerente. 459p. (Orig.). 1977. pap. 3.48 (ISBN 0-88344-311-2). Orbis Bks.
Flynn, Robert. And Holy Is His Name. 1983. 5.95 (ISBN 0-87193-197-4). Dimension Bks.
Gabriel. Divine Intimacy, Vol. III. 1983. 12.95 (ISBN 0-87193-203-2). Dimension Bks.
Garrison, James. The Darkness of God: Theology after Hiroshima. LC 83-1415. pap. 62.00 (ISBN 0-317-30139-X, 2025322). Bks Demand UMI.
Germino, Dante. Beyond Ideology: The Revival of Political Theory. (Midway Reprint Ser.). 1976. pap. 14.00x (ISBN 0-226-28849-8). U of Chicago Pr.
Gleeson, John R., III. Sportscape. LC 84-52105. (Illus.). 176p. (Orig.). 1984. pap. 12.95 (ISBN 0-912661-04-6). Woodsong Graph.
Hamann, Henry P. Justification by Faith in Modern Theology. 114p. 1957. write for info. Concordia Schl Grad Studies.
Happold, F. C. Religious Faith & Twentieth Century Man. 192p. 1981. 6.95 (ISBN 0-8245-0046-6). Crossroad NY.
Hartt, Julian N., ed. The Critique of Modernity: Theological Reflections on Contemporary Culture. (Virginia Lectures on Individual & Society). 160p. 1987. text ed. 16.95x (ISBN 0-8139-1118-4). U Pr of VA.
Hazelton, Roger. New Accounts in Contemporary Theology. LC 78-12237. 1979. Repr. of 1960 ed. lib. bdg. cancelled (ISBN 0-313-21181-7, HANA). Greenwood.
Hellwig, Monika. What Are the Theologians Saying. (Orig.). 1970. pap. 2.95 (ISBN 0-8278-9051-6, Pub. by Pflaum Pr). Peter Li.
Hoffman, Wayne. Letters to the Modern Church. LC 79-88401. 1979. pap. 3.75 (ISBN 0-933350-23-6). Morse Pr.
Hunt, Garth. God Is Not Hiding. 1974. pap. 0.95 (ISBN 0-87509-087-7). Chr Pubns.
Johns, Roger D. Man in the World: The Political Theology of Johannes Baptist Metz. LC 76-26491. (American Academy of Religion. Dissertation Ser.). 1976. pap. 9.95 (ISBN 0-89130-079-1, 010116). Scholars Pr GA.
Jowett, Benjamin. Theological Essays of the Later Benjamin Jowett. 1906. 20.00 (ISBN 0-932062-91-1). Sharon Hill.
Katoppo, Marianne. Compassionate & Free: An Asian Woman's Theology. (Illus.). 96p. (Orig.). 1980. pap. 4.95 (ISBN 0-88344-085-7). Orbis Bks.
Kirk, J. Andrew. Theology & the Third World Church. LC 83-8560. (Outreach & Identity: Evangelical Theological Monographs). 64p. (Orig.). 1983. pap. 2.95 (ISBN 0-87784-892-0). Inter-Varsity.
Kliever, Lonnie D. The Shattered Spectrum: A Survey of Contemporary Theology. LC 80-82184. 276p. (Orig.). 1981. pap. 10.95 (ISBN 0-8042-0707-0). John Knox.
Knight, David M. Saving Presence: The Ministry & Mystery of the Church. 1983. 6.95 (ISBN 0-87193-205-9). Dimension Bks.
Le Saux, Henri. The Eyes of Light. 1983. 12.95 (ISBN 0-87193-202-4). Dimension Bks.
Macquarrie, John. Twentieth Century Religious Thought. 1983. 19.95 (ISBN 0-684-17333-6). Scribner.
Maddox, Randy L. Toward an Ecumenical Fundamental Theology. LC 84-13838. (American Academy of Religion Studies in Religion). 1984. 13.50 (ISBN 0-89130-771-0, 01 01 47). Scholars Pr GA.
Magliola, Robert R. Derrida on the Mend. LC 82-62779. 256p. 1984. 18.00 (ISBN 0-911198-69-5). Purdue U Pr.
Mallow, Vernon. The Demonic: A Selected Theological Study: An Examination into the Theology of Edwin Lewis, Karl Barth, & Paul Tillich. LC 83-1143. 192p. (Orig.). 1983. lib. bdg. 26.00 (ISBN 0-8191-3069-9); pap. text ed. 11.50 (ISBN 0-8191-3070-2). U Pr of Amer.
Migliore, Daniel L. Called to Freedom: Liberation Theology & the Future of Christian Doctrine. LC 79-21879. 128p. 1980. pap. 5.95 (ISBN 0-664-24289-8). Westminster.
Nacpil, Emerito & Elwood, Douglas J., eds. The Human & the Holy: Asian Perspectives in Christian Theology. LC 80-14134. 384p. (Orig.). 1980. pap. 3.74 (ISBN 0-88344-195-0). Orbis Bks.
Oden, Thomas C. Agenda for Theology. LC 78-19506. 1979. pap. text ed. 11.00 (ISBN 0-06-066347-2, HarpR). Har-Row.
Ogden, Schubert M. On Theology. 180p. 1986. 19.50 (ISBN 0-86683-529-6, HarpR). Har-Row.
Peacocke, Arthur R., ed. The Sciences & Theology in the Twentieth Century. LC 81-14771. 327p. 1986. pap. 12.95 (ISBN 0-268-01725-5). U of Notre Dame Pr.
Pennsylvania University Bicentennial Conference. Religion & the Modern World. Maritain, Jacques & Hromadka, Joseph, eds. LC 68-26204. Repr. of 1941 ed. 22.50x (ISBN 0-8046-0360-X, Pub. by Kennikat). Assoc Faculty Pr.
Richardson, Herbert W. Toward an American Theology. (Richard Ser.: No. 2). 1967. 29.95 (ISBN 0-88946-028-0). E Mellen.
Runzo, Joseph. Reason, Relativism & God. LC 85-27893. 308p. 1986. 29.95x (ISBN 0-312-66538-5). St Martin.
Sanford, John A., intro. by. Fritz Kunkel: Selected Writings. 400p. 1984. pap. 12.95 (ISBN 0-8091-2558-7). Paulist Pr.
Schillebeeckx, Edward. God Is New Each Moment: Conversations with Huub Oosterhuis & Piet Hoogeveen. LC 83-614. 160p. (Orig.). 1983. pap. 7.95 (ISBN 0-8164-2475-6, HarpR). Har-Row.
Schilpp, Paul, ed. Theology & Modern Life. LC 70-117852. (Essay Index Reprint Ser). 1940. 19.00 (ISBN 0-8369-1727-8). Ayer Co Pubs.
Segundo, Juan L. The Liberation of Theology. Drury, John, tr. from Spanish. LC 76-7049. Orig. Title: Liberation de la Tealogia. 248p. (Orig.). 1976. pap. 10.95 (ISBN 0-88344-286-8). Orbis Bks.
Six, Jean-Francois. Is God Endangered by Believers? A Critical Study of the Gap Between Religion & Real Faith. 1983. 11.95 (ISBN 0-87193-207-5). Dimension Bks.
Smith, Wilfred C. Towards a World Theology: Faith & the Comparative History of Religion. LC 80-50826. 212p. 1981. 20.00 (ISBN 0-664-21380-4). Westminster.
Sohl, Robert & Carr, Audrey, eds. Gospel According to Zen: Beyond the Death of God. (Orig.). 1970. pap. 2.95 (ISBN 0-451-62184-0, ME2184, Ment). NAL.
Story, Ronald. Guardian of the Universe? 1980. 8.95 (ISBN 0-312-35216-6). St Martin.
Stout, Jeffrey. Flight from Authority: Religion, Morality & the Quest for Autonomy. LC 81-2340. (Revisions Ser.: Vol. 1). 307p. 1987. pap. text ed. 12.95x (ISBN 0-268-00971-6, Dist. by Har-Row). U of Notre Dame Pr.
Sutphin, Stanley T. Options in Contemporary Theology. 1978. pap. text ed. 10.75 (ISBN 0-8191-0277-6). U Pr of Amer.
Thompson, Francis. The Hound of Heaven. (Illus.). 1983. 3.95 (ISBN 0-87193-157-5). Dimension Bks.
Tillich, Paul. Systematic Theology, Vol. 1. LC 51-2235. 1973. pap. 11.00x (ISBN 0-226-80337-6, P556, Phoen). U of Chicago Pr.
--Systematic Theology, Vol. 2. LC 51-2235. xii, 188p. 1975. pap. 7.50X (ISBN 0-226-80338-4, P633, Phoen). U of Chicago Pr.
Van Til, Cornelius. Christian Theory of Knowledge. 1969. pap. 10.95 (ISBN 0-87552-480-X). Presby & Reformed.
Vasileios of Stavronikita. Hymn of Entry. Briere, Elizabeth, tr. from Gr. LC 84-5512. 138p. 1984. pap. text ed. 6.95 (ISBN 0-88141-026-8). St Vladimirs.
Wolfe, S. Key to Dooyeweerd. 1978. pap. 2.95 (ISBN 0-87552-542-3). Presby & Reformed.

THEOLOGY, ASCETICAL
see Asceticism

THEOLOGY, COVENANT
see Covenants (Theology)

THEOLOGY, CRISIS
see Dialectical Theology

THEOLOGY, DEVOTIONAL
see Devotional Exercises; Devotional Literature; Meditations; Prayers

THEOLOGY, DISPENSATIONAL
see Dispensationalism

THEOLOGY, DOCTRINAL
see also Angels; Antinomianism; Apologetics; Asceticism; Assurance (Theology); Atonement; Authority (Religion); Baptism; Bible–Theology; Catechisms; Catholicity; Christian Ethics; Christianity–Philosophy; Communion of Saints; Conversion; Covenants (Theology); Creeds; Devil; Dialectical Theology; Dispensationalism; Dogma; Election (Theology); Empirical Theology; Eschatology; Faith; Fall of Man; Forgiveness of Sin; Free Will and Determinism; Freedom (Theology); Gifts, Spiritual; God; Good and Evil; Grace (Theology); Heresies and Heretics; Heresy; Holiness; Holy Spirit; Incarnation; Inspiration; Islamic Theology; Jesus Christ; Justification; Knowledge, Theory of (Religion); Law (Theology); Law and Gospel; Lord's Supper; Love (Theology); Man (Theology); Mary, Virgin–Theology; Miracles; Mystical Union; Mysticism; New England Theology; Paschal Mystery; Peace (Theology); Perfection; Perseverance (Theology); Philosophical Theology; Power (Theology); Predestination; Process Theology; Providence and Government of God
also subdivision Doctrinal and Controversial Works under names of Christian denominations, e.g. baptists–Doctrinal and Controversial Works

Aguilar, Enrique. El Crepusculo. Tr. of The Twilight. 1971. 3.50 (ISBN 0-686-27937-9). Franciscan Inst.
--Pensamientos Sobre la Cultura Intelectual y Moral. Tr. of Thoughts on Intellectual & Moral Culture. 1967. 7.00 (ISBN 0-686-27936-0). Franciscan Inst.
Allgaier, Karl. Der Einfluss Bernhards von Clairvaux auf Gottfried von Strassburg. (European University Studies Ser.: No. 1, Vol. 641). (Ger.). 185p. 1983. 24.20 (ISBN 3-8204-7541-9). P Lang Pubs.
Almond, Philip C. Mystical Experience & Religious Doctrine: An Investigation of the Study of Mysticism in World Religions. (Religion & Reason: No. 26). 197p. 1982. text ed. 40.00 (ISBN 90-279-3160-7). Mouton.
Anderson, Robert. Redemption Truths. LC 80-16161. (Sir Robert Anderson Library). Orig. Title: For Us Men. 192p. 1980. pap. 4.95 (ISBN 0-8254-2131-4). Kregel.
Angeles, Peter. Dictionary of Christian Theology. LC 79-2988. 336p. 1985. 17.45 (ISBN 0-06-060237-6, HarpR). Har-Row.
Anselm of Canterbury. Trinity, Incarnation, & Redemption: Theological Treatises. (Anselm Ser.: No. 6). 1974. 9.95 (ISBN 0-88946-008-6). E Mellen.
Arndt, William. Fundamental Christian Beliefs. pap. text ed. 3.25 (ISBN 0-570-06324-8, 22-1144); pap. 3.75 guide (ISBN 0-570-06325-6, 22-1146); pap. tests 1.50 (ISBN 0-570-06362-0, 22-1145). Concordia.
Arseniev, Nicholas. Revelation of Life Eternal: An Introduction to the Christian Message. 144p. 1964. pap. 5.95 (ISBN 0-913836-00-1). St Vladimirs.
Ashcraft, Morris. Christian Faith & Beliefs. LC 83-71872. 1984. 9.75 (ISBN 0-8054-1603-X). Broadman.
Aulen, Gustaf. The Faith of the Christian Church. rev. ed. Wahlstrom, Eric H., tr. from Swedish. LC 61-5302. 416p. 1973. pap. 8.95 (ISBN 0-8006-1655-3, 1-1655). Fortress.
Barnes, Robert. A Supplicatyon... Unto Henry the Eighth. LC 73-6098. (English Experience Ser.: No. 567). 1973. Repr. of 1534 ed. 18.50 (ISBN 90-221-0567-9). Walter J Johnson.
Barnhouse, Donald C. Expositions of Bible Doctrines, 10 vols. in four. (Bible Study). 1952-64. Set. 49.95 (ISBN 0-8028-3014-5). Eerdmans.
Barth, Karl. The Church of Reconciliation: The Subject Matter & Problems of the Doctrine of Reconciliation. Bromiley, G. W. & Torrance, T. F., eds. Bromiley, G. W. & Torrance, T. F., trs. from Ger. (Church Dogmatics: Vol. 4, Pt. 1). 814p. 1956. 29.95 (ISBN 0-567-09041-8, Pub. by T & T Clark Ltd UK). Fortress.
--The Doctrine of Creation: The Creator & His Creature. Bromiley, G. W. & Torrance, T. F., eds. Bromiley, G. W. & Torrance, T. F., trs. from Ger. (Church Dogmatics: Vol. 3, Pt. 3). 560p. 29.95 (ISBN 0-567-09033-7, Pub. by T & T Clark Ltd UK). Fortress.
--The Doctrine of Creation: The Work of Creation. Bromiley, G. W. & Torrance, T. F., eds. Bromiley, G. W. & Torrance, T. F., trs. from Ger. (Church Dogmatics Ser.: Vol. 3, Pt. 1). 440p. 1958. 29.95 (ISBN 0-567-09031-0, Pub. by T & T Clark Ltd UK). Fortress.
--The Doctrine of God: The Election of God, The Command of God. Torrance, T. F. & Bromiley, G. W., eds. Bromiley, G. W. & Torrance, T. F., trs. from Ger. (Church Dogmatics Ser.: Vol. 2, Pt. 2). 820p. 1957. 29.95 (ISBN 0-567-09022-1, Pub. by T & T Clark Ltd UK). Fortress.
--The Doctrine of God: The Knowledge of God. Bromiley, G. W. & Torrance, T. F., eds. Bromiley, G. W. & Torrance, T. F., trs. from Ger. (Church Dogmatics Ser.: Vol. 2, Pt. 1). 710p. 1957. text ed. 29.95 (ISBN 0-567-09021-3, Pub. by T & T Clark Ltd UK). Fortress.
--The Doctrine of Reconciliation: Jesus Christ the Servant as Lord. Bromiley, G. W. & Torrance, T. F., eds. Bromiley, G. W. & Torrance, T. F., trs. from Ger. 882p. 1958. 26.95x (ISBN 0-567-09042-6, Pub. by T & T Clark Ltd UK). Fortress.
--The Doctrine of Reconciliation: Jesus Christ the True Witness. Bromiley, G. W. & Torrance, T. F., eds. Bromiley, G. W. & Torrance, T. F., trs. from Ger. 496p. 1961. 29.95 (ISBN 0-567-09043-4, Pub. by T & T Clark Ltd UK). Fortress.
--The Doctrine of Reconciliation: The Christian Life. Bromiley, G. W. & Torrance, T. F., eds. Bromiley, G. W., tr. from Ger. (Church Dogmatics Ser.: Vol. 4, Pt. 4). 240p. 1969. 19.95 (ISBN 0-567-09045-0, Pub. by T & T Clark Ltd UK). Fortress.
--The Doctrine of the Word of God: Prolegomena to Church Dogmatics. Bromiley, G. W. & Torrance, T. F., eds. Bromiley, G. W. & Torrance, T. F., trs. from Ger. (Church Dogmatics Ser.: Vol. 1, Pt. 1). 528p. 29.95 (ISBN 0-567-09013-2, Pub. by T & T Clark Ltd UK). Fortress.
--The Doctrine of the Word of God: The Revelation of God, Holy Scripture, the Proclamation of the Church. Bromiley, G. W. & Torrance, T. F., eds. (Church Dogmatics Ser.: Vol. 1. Pt. 2). 924p. 1956. 29.95 (ISBN 0-567-09012-4, Pub. by T & T Clark Ltd UK). Fortress.
--Dogmatics in Outline. pap. 5.95x (ISBN 0-06-130056-X, TB56, Torch). Har-Row.
Bavinck, Herman. The Doctrine of God. Hendricksen, W., tr. (Student's Reformed Theological Library Ser.). 1977. 16.95 (ISBN 0-85151-255-0). Banner of Truth.
Bergier, N. S. Dictionnaire de Theologique Dogmatique, Liturgique, Canonique et Disciplinaire, 3 vols. in 4. Migne, J. P., ed. (Encyclopedie Theologique Ser.: Vols. 33-35). (Fr.). 2681p. Repr. of 1851 ed. lib. bdg. 341.00x (ISBN 0-89241-243-7). Caratzas.
Berkhof, Hendrikus. Introduction to the Study of Dogmatics. Vriend, John, tr. from Dutch. 120p. (Orig.). 1985. pap. 7.95 (ISBN 0-8028-0045-9). Eerdmans.
Berkhof, Louis. History of Christian Doctrines. (Twin Brooks Ser). 288p. 1975. pap. 8.95 (ISBN 0-8010-0636-8). Baker Bk.
--Introduction to Systematic Theology. (Twin Brooks Ser.). 1979. pap. 7.95 (ISBN 0-8010-0768-2). Baker Bk.
--Manual of Christian Doctrine. 1933. pap. 7.95 (ISBN 0-8028-1647-9). Eerdmans.
--Sumario de Doctrina Cristiana. 5th ed. Vila, David, tr. from Eng. Tr. of Summary of Christian Doctrine. (Span.). 240p. 1986. pap. 3.00 (ISBN 0-939125-31-5). Evangelical Lit.
--Summary of Christian Doctrine. 1939. pap. 5.95 (ISBN 0-8028-1513-8). Eerdmans.
Berkouwer, Gerrit C. Studies in Dogmatics: Theology. Incl. Vol. 1. Faith & Sanctification; Vol. 2. The Providence of God. 10.95 (ISBN 0-8028-3029-3); Vol. 3. Faith & Justification. 8.95 (ISBN 0-8028-3030-7); Vol. 4. The Person of Christ. 9.95 (ISBN 0-8028-3031-5); Vol. 5. General Revelation. 10.95 (ISBN 0-8028-3032-3); Vol. 6. Faith & Perseverance. 8.95 (ISBN 0-8028-3033-1); Vol. 7. Divine Election. 9.95 (ISBN 0-8028-3034-X); Vol. 8. Man-The Image of God. 12.95 (ISBN 0-8028-3035-8); Vol. 9. The Work of Christ. 9.95 (ISBN 0-8028-3036-6); Vol. 10. The Sacraments. 12.95 (ISBN 0-8028-3037-4); Vol. 11. Sin. 17.95 (ISBN 0-8028-3027-7); Vol. 12. The Return of Christ. 13.95 (ISBN 0-8028-3393-4); The Church. 9.95 (ISBN 0-8028-3433-7); Holy Scripture. 11.95 (ISBN 0-8028-3394-2). 1952. Eerdmans.
Berton, C. Dictionnaire du Parallele entre Diverses Doctrines Philosophiques et Religieuses. Migne, J. P., ed. (Troisieme et Derniere Encycolpedie Theologique Ser.: Vol. 38). (Fr.). 698p. Repr. of 1858 ed. lib. bdg. 90.00x (ISBN 0-89241-317-4). Caratzas.
Boehner, Philotheus & Brown, Stephen, eds. Guillelmi de Ockham: Opera Philosophica, Vol. 2. 1978. 40.00 (ISBN 0-686-27930-1). Franciscan Inst.
Boesak, Allan A. Comfort & Protest. LC 86-28076. 120p. (Orig.). 1987. pap. 7.95 (ISBN 0-664-24602-8). Westminster.
Boettner, Loraine. Studies in Theology. 1947. 7.95 (ISBN 0-87552-131-2). Presby & Reformed.
Borchert, Gerald L. Assurance & Warning. (Orig.). 1987. pap. 5.95 (ISBN 0-8054-1011-2). Broadman.
Brown, William A. Christian Theology in Outline. LC 75-41044. (BCL Ser. II). Repr. of 1906 ed. 28.00 (ISBN 0-404-14648-1). AMS Pr.
Brunner, Emil. The Christian Doctrine of God. Wyon, Olive, tr. LC 50-6821. (Dogmatics Ser.: Vol. 1). 376p. 1980. pap. 11.95 (ISBN 0-664-24304-5). Westminster.
--Scandal of Christianity: The Gospel as Stumbling Block to Modern Man. LC 65-12729. 1965. pap. 5.95 (ISBN 0-8042-0708-9). John Knox.
Buri, Fritz. Theology of Existence. Oliver, Harold H, tr. 128p. 1965. 3.95 (ISBN 0-87921-001-X). Attic Pr.
Bussmann, Claus. Who Do You Say? Jesus Christ in Latin American Theology. Barr, Robert, tr. from Ger. LC 84-16476. Tr. of Befreiung durch Jesus? 192p. (Orig.). 1985. pap. 9.95 (ISBN 0-88344-711-8). Orbis Bks.
Caird, Edward. Evolution of Theology in the Greek Philosophers, 2 Vols in 1. LC 4-16272. (Gifford Lectures 1900-1902). 1968. Repr. of 1904 ed. 46.00 (ISBN 0-527-14130-5). Kraus Repr.
--Evolution of Theology in the Greek Philosophers, the Gifford Lectures, 1900-1902, 2 Vols. 1968. 39.00x (ISBN 0-403-00116-1). Scholarly.
Calvin, Jean. Aphorismes of Christian Religion or a Verie Compendious Abridgement of M. I. Calvins Institutions Set Forth by M I Piscator. Holland, H., tr. LC 73-6107. (English Experience Ser.: No. 575). 1973. Repr. of 1596 ed. 26.00 (ISBN 90-221-0575-X). Walter J Johnson.

Calvin, John. Institutes of the Christian Religion: Beveridge Translation, 2 Vols. 1953. Set. pap. 16.95 (ISBN 0-8028-8026-6). Eerdmans.

Capon, Robert F. Hunting the Divine Fox: Images & Mystery in the Christian Faith. 176p. 1977. pap. 6.95 (ISBN 0-8164-2137-4, AY7359, HarpR). Har-Row.

Carnes, John. Axiomatics & Dogmatics. (Theology & Scientific Culture Ser.). 1982. 16.95x (ISBN 0-19-520377-1). Oxford U Pr.

Carson, D. A. Divine Sovereignty & Human Responsibility: Biblical Perspectives in Tension. Toon, Peter & Martin, Ralph, eds. LC 79-27589. (New Foundations Theological Library). 228p. 1981. 12.95 (ISBN 0-8042-3707-7); pap. 11.95 (ISBN 0-8042-3727-1). John Knox.

Carson, D. A. & Woodbridge, John D., eds. Scripture & Truth. 1986. pap. 11.95 (ISBN 0-310-43791-1, 12643P). Zondervan.

Carver, C. C. Church of God Doctrines. 180p. 1948. pap. 2.00 (ISBN 0-686-29106-9). Faith Pub Hse.

Chrysostomos & Auxentios, Hieromonk. Contemporary Traditionalist Orthodox Thought. 80p. (Orig.). 1986. pap. 5.00 (ISBN 0-911165-07-X). Ctr Trad Orthodox.

Clark, Gordon H. In Defense of Theology. 1986. text ed. 12.95 (ISBN 0-8010-2520-6). Baker Bk.

Clowney, Edmund P. Living in Christ's Church. 1986. pap. text ed. 4.95 (ISBN 0-934688-22-2); leader's guide 3.95 (ISBN 0-934688-24-9). Great Comm Pubns.

Cobb, John B., Jr. Living Options in Protestant Theology: A Survey of Methods. 336p. 1986. pap. text ed. 14.75 (ISBN 0-8191-5488-1). U Pr of Amer.

Cohn-Sherbok, Dan. On Earth As It Is in Heaven: Jews, Christians, & Liberation Theology. LC 86-23509. 128p. (Orig.). 1987. pap. 7.95 (ISBN 0-88344-410-0). Orbis Bks.

Comentario de las Epistoles Generales. (Span.). 194p. 1986. pap. 3.50 (ISBN 0-939125-31-5). Evangelical Lit.

Compton, Robert. La Teologia de la Liberaccion: Una Introduccion. (Span.). 112p. (Orig.). 1985. pap. 3.75 (ISBN 0-311-09106-7). Casa Bautista.

Conner, Kevin. The Name of God. (Illus.). 90p. 1975. 8.95 (ISBN 0-914936-15-8). Bible Temple.

Conner, Kevin J. Foundations of Christian Doctrine. 313p. 1979. pap. 14.95 (ISBN 0-914936-38-7). Bible Temple.

Conner, Walter T. Christian Doctrine. 1940. 15.95 (ISBN 0-8054-1701-X). Broadman.

Cook, Keningale. The Fathers of Jesus: A Study of the Lineage of the Christian Doctrine & Tradition, 2 vols. 1977. lib. bdg. 250.00 (ISBN 0-8490-1807-2). Gordon Pr.

Cox, Harvey. Just As I Am. LC 82-11631. 160p. 1983. 10.95 (ISBN 0-687-20687-1). Abingdon.

Craig, William L. The Only Wise God. 1987. pap. 7.95 (ISBN 0-8010-2519-2). Baker Bk.

Crawford, C. C. Survey Course in Christian Doctrine, Vols. III & IV. LC 71-1388. (The Bible Study Textbook Ser.). 1964. 13.80 (ISBN 0-89900-054-1). College Pr Pub.

Criswell, W. A. Great Doctrines of the Bible, Vol. 1. 144p. 1982. 9.95 (ISBN 0-310-43850-0, 9427). Zondervan.

--Great Doctrines of the Bible, Vols. 1, 2, 3, & 4. 192p. 1982. Repr. 44.75 (ISBN 0-310-43868-3, 11663). Zondervan.

Cunliffe-Jones, Hubert & Drewery, Benjamin, eds. A History of Christian Doctrine. LC 79-21689. 616p. 1980. 29.95 (ISBN 0-8006-0626-4, 1-626). Fortress.

Daly, Robert J. Origins of the Christian Doctrine of Sacrifices. LC 77-78628. pap. 40.00 (2026875). Bks Demand UMI.

Dampier, Joseph H. Workbook on Christian Doctrine- NIV. rev. ed. 64p. 1986. wkbk. 2.50 (ISBN 0-87403-177-X, 3344). Standard Pub.

Davenport, John. A Just Complaint Against an Unjust Doer, Mr. J. Paget. LC 76-57376. (English Experience Ser.: No. 793). 1977. Repr. of 1634 ed. lib. bdg. 5.00 (ISBN 90-221-0793-0). Walter J Johnson.

Del Punta, Francesco, ed. Guillelmi de Ockham: Opera Philosophica, Vol. 3. 1979. 29.00 (ISBN 0-686-27931-X). Franciscan Inst.

DeWitt, David. Beyond the Basics. 1983. pap. 5.95 (ISBN 0-8024-0178-3). Moody.

Diaz, Jorge E. Guia De Estudios Sobre Doctrina Cristiana. (Guias De Estudio). 88p. pap. 3.25 (ISBN 0-311-43500-9). Casa Bautista.

Di Brandi, Herman A. Introduction to Christian Doctrine. 128p. (Orig.). 1976. pap. 4.95 (ISBN 0-8192-1194-X). Morehouse.

Doctrinal Distinctives of Asbury. pap. 2.95 (ISBN 0-686-12867-2). Schmul Pub Co.

Dubitsky, Cora M. Building the Faith Community. LC 74-12632. 192p. 1975. pap. 2.95 (ISBN 0-8091-1848-3). Paulist Pr.

Ellingsen, Mark. Doctrine & Word: Theology in the Pulpit. LC 82-21311. pap. 51.00 (2027152). Bks Demand UMI.

English, E. Schuyler. Things Surely to Be Believed. 1970. Repr. of 1946 ed. 4.95 (ISBN 0-87213-146-7). Loizeaux.

Erickson, Millard J. Christian Theology, Vol. 1. 432p. 1983. 19.95 (ISBN 0-8010-3391-8). Baker Bk.

--Christian Theology, Vol. 2. 432p. 1984. 19.95 (ISBN 0-8010-3419-1). Baker Bk.

Etzkorn, Girard J., ed. Guillelmi de Ockham: Scriptum in Librum Primum Sententiarum, Ordinatio, Opera Theologica, Vol. 3, Distinctiones 4-18. 1977. 46.00 (ISBN 0-686-27929-8). Franciscan Inst.

Etzkorn, Girard J. & Kelley, Francis E., eds. Guillelmi de Ockham: Scriptum in Librum Primum Sententiarum, Ordinatio, Opera Theologica, Vol. 4, Distinctiones 19-48. 1979. 48.00 (ISBN 0-686-27932-8). Franciscan Inst.

Finger, Thomas. Christian Theology: An Eschatological Approach, Vol. 1. 320p. 1985. text ed. 18.95 (ISBN 0-8407-7505-9). Nelson.

Ford, W. Herschel. Simple Sermons of Great Christian Doctrines. 138p. 1985. pap. 4.50 (ISBN 0-8010-3519-8). Baker Bk.

Forell, George W. The Protestant Faith. LC 74-26341. 320p. 1975. pap. 9.95 (ISBN 0-8006-1095-4, 1-1095). Fortress.

Fox, Douglas A. What Do You Think about God. 96p. 1985. pap. 4.95 (ISBN 0-8170-1077-7). Judson.

Fransen, P. Intelligent Theology, Vol. 1: The Trinity Lives in Us As We Celebrate Life. LC 77-85505. 148p. pap. 2.50 (ISBN 0-8199-0400-7). Franciscan Herald.

Gaston, Hugh. A Complete Common-Place Book to the Holy Bible; or, a Scriptural Account of the Faith & Practices of Christians: Comprehending a Thorough Arrangement of the Various Texts of Scripture Bearing upon the Doctrines, Duties, & C., of Revealed Religion. 1979. Repr. of 1847 ed. lib. bdg. 15.00 (ISBN 0-8482-4186-X). Norwood Edns.

Gilkey, Langdon. Message & Existence: An Introduction to Christian Theology. 272p. 1980. 12.95 (ISBN 0-8164-0450-X, HarpR); pap. 7.95 (ISBN 0-8164-2023-8). Har-Row.

Gill, Jerry H. Toward Theology. LC 82-45009. 130p. (Orig.). 1982. PLB 24.00 (ISBN 0-8191-2429-X); pap. text ed. 9.25 (ISBN 0-8191-2430-3). U Pr of Amer.

Gollwitzer, Helmut. An Introduction to Protestant Theology. Cairns, David, tr. LC 82-4798. 236p. 1982. pap. 12.95 (ISBN 0-664-24415-7). Westminster.

Guthrie, Shirley C., Jr. Christian Doctrine: Teachings of the Christian Church. (Illus., Orig.). 1969. pap. 7.95 (ISBN 0-8042-9051-2). John Knox.

Halverson, Marvin & Cohen, Arthur. Handbook of Christian Theology. (Fount Paperback Ser.). pap. 7.95 (ISBN 0-687-16567-9). Abingdon.

Hanson, Paul D. The Diversity of Scripture: Trajectories in the Confessional Heritage. LC 81-43079. (Overtures to Biblical Theology Ser.: No. 11). 1982. pap. 8.95 (ISBN 0-8006-1535-2, 1-1535). Fortress.

--Dynamic Transcendence: The Correlation of Confessional Heritage & Contemporary Experience in Biblical Model of Divine Activity. LC 78-54552. pap. 27.30 (2026940). Bks Demand UMI.

Hardy, Edward R., ed. Christology of the Later Fathers. LC 54-9949. (Library of Christian Classics). 396p. 1977. pap. 10.95 (ISBN 0-664-24152-2). Westminster.

Harries, Richard. What Christians Believe. 176p. 1982. pap. 4.95 (ISBN 0-86683-677-2, HarpR). Har-Row.

Harris, Charles. The Proofs of Christianity. LC 77-77215. (Radiant Life Ser.). 128p. 1977. pap. 2.50 (ISBN 0-88243-911-1, 02-0911); teacher's ed 3.95 (ISBN 0-88243-181-1, 32-0181). Gospel Pub.

Hendricks, William L. A Theology for Aging. 1986. 10.95 (ISBN 0-8054-1712-5). Broadman.

Henry, Carl F., ed. Basic Christian Doctrines. (Twin Brooks Ser). pap. 8.95 (ISBN 0-8010-4033-7). Baker Bk.

Heppe, Heinrich. Reformed Dogmatics. Bizer, Ernst, ed. Thomson, G. T., tr. (Twin Brooks Ser.). 1978. pap. 19.95 (ISBN 0-8010-4207-0). Baker Bk.

Herbert, R. T. Paradox & Identity in Theology. LC 78-20784. 221p. 1979. 24.50x (ISBN 0-8014-1222-6). Cornell U Pr.

Hodge, Charles. Systematic Theology, 3 Vols. 1960. Set. 49.95 (ISBN 0-8028-8135-1). Eerdmans.

Hole, F. B. Assembly Principles. Daniel, R. P., ed. 40p. pap. 3.50 (ISBN 0-88172-141-7). Believers Bkshelf.

Horton, Walter M. Realistic Theology. 207p. 1982. Repr. of 1934 ed. lib. bdg. 30.00 (ISBN 0-89760-362-1). Telegraph Bks.

Humphreys, Fisher. La Naturaleza de Dios. Canclini, Arnoldo, tr. from Eng. (Biblioteca de Doctrina Cristiana). Tr. of The Nature of God. (Span.). 144p. (Orig.). 1987. pap. 5.95 (ISBN 0-311-09114-8). Casa Bautista.

Humphreys, Fisher & Wise, Philip. A Dictionary of Doctrinal Terms. LC 81-86635. (Orig.). 1983. pap. 4.95 (ISBN 0-8054-1141-0). Broadman.

Index, with Aids to the Preacher. (Church Dogmatics Ser.: Vol. 5). 562p. 1977. 29.95 (ISBN 0-567-09046-9, Pub. by T & T Clark Ltd UK). Fortress.

The Institution of a Christen Man. LC 76-57371. (English Experience Ser.: No. 789). 1977. Repr. of 1537 ed. lib. bdg. 20.00 (ISBN 90-221-0789-2). Walter J Johnson.

Introduction to Doctrina Christiana. 1.00 (ISBN 0-317-46857-X). Dghtrs St Paul.

James, Henry, Sr. The Church of Christ Not An Ecclesiasticism: A Letter to a Sectarian. LC 72-922. (The Selected Works of Henry James Sr.: Vol. 2). 80p. Repr. of 1854 ed. 17.00 (ISBN 0-404-10082-1). AMS Pr.

--Lectures & Miscellanies. LC 72-923. (The Selected Works of Henry James, Sr.: Vol. 3). 456p. 1983. Repr. of 1852 ed. 42.50 (ISBN 0-404-10083-X). AMS Pr.

Kane, John F. Pluralism & Truth in Religion. Dietrich, Wendell, ed. LC 80-20659. (American Academy of Religion Dissertation Ser.). 1981. 13.95 (ISBN 0-89130-413-4, 01-01-33); pap. 9.95 (ISBN 0-89130-414-2). Scholars Pr GA.

Kim, Young O. An Introduction to Theology. LC 82-84722. 190p. 1983. pap. 8.95 (ISBN 0-318-11687-1). Rose Sharon Pr.

Krause, G. & Mueller, G., eds. Theologische Realeuzyklopaedic, 25 vols. (Ger.). write for info. De Gruyter.

Kung, Hans. The Incarnation of God. 660p. 1987. 34.50 (ISBN 0-8245-0793-2). Crossroad NY.

--Justification: The Doctrine of Karl Barth & a Catholic Reflection. LC 80-26001. 378p. 1981. pap. 14.95 (ISBN 0-664-24364-9). Westminster.

Ladd, George T. Knowledge, Life & Reality: An Essay in Systemic Philosophy. LC 75-3221. Repr. of 1909 ed. 37.50 (ISBN 0-404-59217-1). AMS Pr.

Lake, Frank. Clinical Theology. 256p. 1987. 18.95 (ISBN 0-8245-0821-1). Crossroad NY.

Lawson, John. Introduction to Christian Doctrine. Burgess, Harold, ed. 1980. pap. 9.95 (ISBN 0-310-75021-0). Zondervan.

--Introduction to Christian Doctrine. 1986. 14.95 (ISBN 0-310-75020-2). Zondervan.

Lewis, John M. & Deiros, Pablo A. La Revelacion e Inspiracion de las Escrituras. (Biblioteca de Doctrina Cristiana). (Span.). 162p. 1986. pap. 5.95 (ISBN 0-311-09113-X). Casa Bautista.

Ludlow, Daniel H. A Companion to Your Study of the Doctrine & Covenants, 2 vols. LC 78-64752. 1978. Set. 17.95 (ISBN 0-87747-722-1). Deseret Bk.

Luther, Martin. The Bondage of the Will. Packer, J. I. & Johnston, O. R., trs. from Ger. 323p. 1973. Repr. of 1957 ed. cancelled 15.95 (ISBN 0-227-67417-0). Attic Pr.

McClendon, James W., Jr. Ethics: Systematic Theology. 400p. 1986. 22.95 (ISBN 0-687-12015-2). Abingdon.

MacDonald, George. On Tangled Paths. Hamilton, Dan, ed. 288p. 1987. pap. 5.95 (ISBN 0-89693-791-7). Victor Bks.

McDonald, H. D. The God Who Responds. 200p. (Orig.). 1986. pap. 5.95 (ISBN 0-87123-840-3, 210840). Bethany Hse.

Macquarrie, John. Principles of Christian Theology. 2nd ed. LC 76-23182. 544p. 1977. pap. text ed. write for info. (ISBN 0-02-374510-X, Pub. by Scribner). Macmillan.

--Theology, Church & Ministry. 224p. 1986. 16.95 (ISBN 0-8245-0787-8). Crossroad NY.

Makdisi, G. Censure of Speculative Theology. 156p. 1962. 40.00x (ISBN 0-317-39046-5, Pub. by Luzac & Co Ltd). State Mutual Bk.

Martens, Elmer A. God's Design: A Focus on Old Testament Theology. pap. 10.95 (ISBN 0-8010-6209-8). Baker Bk.

Matic, Marko. Juergen Moltmanns Theologie in Auseinandersetzung mit Ernst Bloch. (European University Studies Ser.: No. 23, Vol. 209). (Ger.). 428p. 1983. 41.05 (ISBN 3-8204-7741-1). P Lang Pubs.

Metropolitan Stefan Yavorsky. Dogmat o Svjatejshej Evkharistii. Tr. of The Dogma of the Holy Eucharist. 32p. pap. 1.00 (ISBN 0-317-28973-X). Holy Trinity.

Meyer, F. B. The Blessed Life. 1979. pap. 0.95 (ISBN 0-87509-052-4). Chr Pubns.

Moltmann, Jurgen, et al. Communities of Faith & Radical Discipleship. Mitchell, Carlton T. & Bryan, McLeod G., eds. (Luce Program on Religion & the Social Crisis Ser.). x, 130p. 1986. 16.95 (ISBN 0-86554-216-3). Mercer Univ Pr.

Morse, Christopher. The Logic of Promise in Moltmann's Theology. LC 78-54556. 192p. 1979. 12.95 (ISBN 0-8006-0523-3, 1-523). Fortress.

Mueller, John T. Christian Dogmatics. 1934. 18.95 (ISBN 0-570-03221-0, 15-1071). Concordia.

Mullins, Edgar Y. La Religion Cristiana En Su Expresion Doctrinal. Hale, Sara A., tr. Orig. Title: The Christian Religion in Its Doctrinal Expression. 522p. 1980. pap. 10.95 (ISBN 0-311-09042-7). Casa Bautista.

Murray, John. The Collected Writings of John Murray: Lectures in Systematic Theology, Vol. 2. 1978. 24.95 (ISBN 0-85151-242-9). Banner of Truth.

Napier, B. D. On New Creation. LC 70-134553. (Rockwell Lectures). 1971. 14.95x (ISBN 0-8071-0524-4). La State U Pr.

Newport, John P. What Is Christian Doctrine? LC 83-71266. (Layman's Library of Christian Doctrine Ser.). 1984. 5.95 (ISBN 0-8054-1631-5). Broadman.

Oglasytel'nija I Tajnovdstvennija Pouchenija Svjatago Kirilma Jerusalimskago. Tr. of Prochatechisis & Mystagogical Catechesis of St. Cyril of Jerusalem. 366p. 18.00 (ISBN 0-317-28884-9); pap. 13.00 (ISBN 0-317-28885-7). Holy Trinity.

Palmer, Edwin H. Doctrinas Claves. 2.95 (ISBN 0-85151-407-3). Banner of Truth.

Pardington, G. P. Studies in Christian Doctrine, 4 Vols. Freligh, H. M. & Schroeder, E. H., eds. 312p. 1964. pap. 1.95 ea. Vol. 1 (ISBN 0-87509-135-0). Vol. 2 (ISBN 0-87509-136-9). Vol. 3 (ISBN 0-87509-137-7). Vol. 4 (ISBN 0-87509-138-5). Chr Pubns.

Pelikan, Jaroslav. The Christian Tradition: A History of the Development of Doctrine, Vol. 4: Reformation of Church & Dogma (1300-1700) LC 79-142042. lii, 426p. 1985. 27.50x (ISBN 0-226-65376-5); pap. 14.95 (ISBN 0-226-65377-3). U of Chicago Pr.

Pendleton, J. M. Compendio de Teologia Cristiana. Trevino, Alejandro, tr. Orig. Title: Christian Doctrines: Compendium of Theology. (Span.). 413p. 1983. pap. 5.95 (ISBN 0-311-09008-7). Casa Bautista.

Pendleton, James H. Christian Doctrines: A Compendium of Theology. 16.95 (ISBN 0-8170-0037-2). Judson.

Pennington, M. Basil, et al. The Living Testament: The Essential Writings of Christianity since the Bible. LC 85-42790. 400p. 1985. 22.45 (ISBN 0-06-066499-1, HarpR); pap. 14.95 (ISBN 0-06-066498-3). Har-Row.

Picirilli, Robert E. Doctrine of Last Things. 29p. 1973. pap. 0.95 (ISBN 0-89265-103-2). Randall Hse.

Pieper, Francis. Christian Dogmatics, 4 Vols. Engelder, Theodore, et al, trs. 1950-1957. Vol. 1. 18.95 (ISBN 0-570-06712-X, 15-1001); Vol. 2. 18.95 (ISBN 0-570-06713-8, 15-1002); Vol. 3. 18.95 (ISBN 0-570-06714-6, 15-1003); Vol. 4. 25.95 (ISBN 0-570-06711-1, 15-1000); Set. 69.95 (ISBN 0-570-06715-4, 15-1852). Concordia.

Power, David N. The Sacrifice We Offer: Tridentine Dogma & Its Reinterpretation. 240p. 1987. 16.95 (ISBN 0-8245-0743-6). Crossroad NY.

Protopresbyter Michael Pomazansky. Pravosavnoje Dogmaticheskoje Bogoslovije. Tr. of Orthodox Dogmatic Theology. 280p. 1963. pap. text ed. 20.00 (ISBN 0-317-29309-5). Holy Trinity.

Rahner, Karl. Theological Investigations, Vols. 1-17, 20. Incl. Vol. 1. 22.50x (ISBN 0-8245-0377-5); Vol. 2. Man & the Church. 22.50x (ISBN 0-8245-0378-3); Vol. 3. Theology of the Spiritual Life. 24.50x (ISBN 0-8245-0379-1); Vol. 4. More Recent Writings. 24.50x (ISBN 0-8245-0380-5); Vol. 5. Later Writings. 27.50x (ISBN 0-8245-0381-3); Vol. 6. Concerning Vatican Council II. 24.50x (ISBN 0-8245-0382-1); Vol. 7. Further Theology of the Spiritual Life I. 19.50x (ISBN 0-8245-0383-X); Vol. 8. Further Theology of the Spiritual Life II. 19.50x (ISBN 0-8245-0384-8); Vol. 9. Writings of 1965-1967, I. 19.50x (ISBN 0-8245-0385-6); Vol. 10. Writings of 1965-1967, II. 22.50x (ISBN 0-8245-0386-4); Vol. 11. Confrontation I. 22.50 (ISBN 0-8245-0387-2); Vol. 12. Confrontations II. 22.50x (ISBN 0-8245-0388-0); Vol. 13. Theology Anthropology, Christology. 22.50x (ISBN 0-8245-0389-9); Vol. 14. In Dialogue with the Future. 22.50 (ISBN 0-8245-0390-2); Penance in the Early Church. 500p. 29.50x (ISBN 0-8245-0025-3); Vol. 16. Experience of the Spirit: Source of Theology. 1979. 19.50x (ISBN 0-8245-0392-9); Vol. 17. Jesus, Man & the Church. 19.50x (ISBN 0-8245-0026-1); Vol. 20. Concern for the Church. 14.50x (ISBN 0-8245-0027-X). Crossroad NY.

Ratzinger, Joseph. Introduction to Christianity. 1970. 8.95 (ISBN 0-8245-0319-8). Crossroad NY.

Rice, Richard. The Reign of God: An Introduction to Christian Theology from a Seventh-Day Adventist Perspective. LC 85-70344. 400p. 1985. text ed. 23.95 (ISBN 0-943872-90-1). Andrews Univ Pr.

Richard, Pablo, et al. The Idols of Death & the God of Life: A Theology. Campbell, Barbara E. & Shepard, Bonnie, trs. from Span. LC 83-6788. Tr. of La Lucha de los Dioses: la Idolos de la Opresion y la Busqueda del Dios Liberador. 240p. (Orig.). 1983. pap. 12.95 (ISBN 0-88344-048-2). Orbis Bks.

Robinson, H. Wheeler. The Christian Doctrine of Man. 368p. 1958. 19.95 (ISBN 0-567-22219-5, Pub. by T & T Clark Ltd UK). Fortress.

Roth, Robert P. The Theater of God: Story in Christian Doctrine. LC 84-48725. 208p. 1985. pap. 10.95 (ISBN 0-8006-1841-6, 1-1841). Fortress.

Schleiermacher, Friedrich. On the Glaubenslehre: Two Letters to Dr. Lucke. Massey, James A., ed. Duke, James & Fiorenza, Francis S., trs. from Ger. LC 80-20717. (American Academy of Religion, Texts & Translations Ser.: No. 3). Orig. Title: Sendschreiben Uber Seine Glaubenslehre an Lucke. 1981. pap. 9.95 (ISBN 0-89130-420-7, 01-02-03). Scholars Pr GA.

Schlieben, Richard. Christliche Theologie und Philologie in der Spaetantike: Die schulwissenschaftlichen Methoden der Psalmenexegese Cassiodors. LC 74-77213. (Arbeiten zur Kirchengeschichte, Vol. 46). (Ger.). 132p. 1974. 19.00x (ISBN 3-11-004634-2). De Gruyter.

Schmid, Heinrich. Doctrinal Theology of the Evangelical Lutheran Church. LC 66-13052. 1961. 25.95 (ISBN 0-8066-0107-8, 10-1930). Augsburg.

Schopenhauer, Arthur. Pantheism & the Christian System. (Illus.). 119p. 1987. 117.50 (ISBN 0-89266-588-2). Am Classical Coll Pr.

Sears, William. The Wine of Astonishment. 192p. 1963. pap. 3.95 (ISBN 0-85398-009-8). G Ronald Pub.

Segundo, Juan L. Evolution & Guilt. Drury, John, tr. from Span. LC 73-89054. (A Theology for Artisans of a New Humanity Ser: Vol. 5). Orig. Title: Evolucion y Culpa. 154p. (Orig.). 1974. 7.95 (ISBN 0-88344-485-2). Orbis Bks.

--Jesus of Nazareth Yesterday & Today. Drury, John, tr. from Span. LC 83-19386. (Faith & Ideologies Ser.: Vol. 1). Tr. of El Hombre de Hoy Ante Jesus de Nazaret: Fe e Ideologia Ser. 368p. (Orig.). 1984. pap. 14.95 (ISBN 0-88344-127-6). Orbis Bks.

--Our Idea of God. Drury, John, tr. from Span. LC 73-77358. (Theology for Artisans of a New Humanity Ser.: Vol. 3). Orig. Title: Nuestra idea de Dios. 212p. (Orig.). 1974. 7.95x (ISBN 0-88344-483-6); pap. 4.95 o. p. (ISBN 0-88344-489-5). Orbis Bks.

--The Sacraments Today. Drury, John, tr. from Span. LC 73-77359. (Theology for Artisans of a New Humanity Ser: Vol. 4). Orig. Title: Los Sacramentos Hay y. 192p. (Orig.). 1974. pap. 4.95x (ISBN 0-88344-490-9). Orbis Bks.

Sell, Jesse. The Knowledge of the Truth - Two Doctrines: The Book of Thomas the Contender(CGII, 7) & the False Teachers in the Pastoral Epistles. (European University Studies Ser.: No. 23, Vol. 194). 114p. 1982. pap. 14.20 (ISBN 3-8204-7224-X). P Lang Pubs.

Sibbes, Richard. Works of Richard Sibbes, Vol. 3. 543p. 1981. 16.95 (ISBN 0-85151-329-8). Banner of Truth.

Sizemore, Denver. Thirteen Lessons in Christian Doctrine. 11th ed. 1968. pap. 2.95 (ISBN 0-89900-136-X). College Pr Pub.

--Trece Lecciones de Doctrina Biblica. Martinez, Raul, tr. from Eng. Tr. of Thirteen Lessons in Christian Doctrine. (Span.). 114p. pap. 1.95 (ISBN 0-89900-300-1). College Pr Pub.

Sokolowski, Robert. The God of Faith & Reason: Foundations of Christian Theology. LC 81-19813. 192p. 1982. 15.95 (ISBN 0-268-01006-4); pap. text ed. 6.95 (ISBN 0-268-01007-2). U of Notre Dame Pr.

Song, C. S. Tell Us Our Names: Story Theology from an Asian Perspective. LC 84-5139. (Illus.). 224p. (Orig.). 1984. pap. 10.95 (ISBN 0-88344-512-3). Orbis Bks.

Song, Choan-Seng. Third-Eye Theology: Theology in Formation in Asian Settings. LC 79-4208. pap. 72.00 (ISBN 0-317-26666-7, 2025121). Bks Demand UMI.

Staniloae, Dumitru. Theology & the Church. Barringer, Robert, tr. from Romanian. LC 80-19313. 240p. 1980. pap. 7.95 (ISBN 0-913836-69-9). St Vladimirs.

Stein, Jock & Taylor, Howard. In Christ All Things Hold Together: An Introduction to Christian Doctrine. 176p. (Orig.). 1985. pap. 5.95 (ISBN 0-8028-0083-1). Eerdmans.

Stephens, Lynn. As God Intended. 1973. pap. 1.25 (ISBN 0-89114-045-X). Baptist Pub Hse.

Stevens, William W. Doctrines of the Christian Religion. LC 77-83282. 1977. pap. 10.95 (ISBN 0-8054-1706-0). Broadman.

Strong, Augustus H. Systematic Theology, 3 Vols in 1. 21.95 (ISBN 0-8170-0177-8). Judson.

--Systematic Theology. Incl. The Doctrine of God; The Doctrine of Man; The Doctrine of Salvation. 1168p. 24.95 (ISBN 0-8007-0302-2). Revell.

Summa Theologiae, 61 vols. 1981. Set. 2000.00x (ISBN 0-686-75401-8, Pub. by Eyre & Spottiswoode England). State Mutual Bk.

Sutphin, Stanley T. Options in Contemporary Theology. rev. ed. LC 86-28199. 176p. 1987. lib. bdg. 22.50 (ISBN 0-8191-6058-X); pap. text ed. 10.75 (ISBN 0-8191-6059-8). U Pr of Amer.

Sweetman, James W. Islam & Christian Theology: A Study of the Interpretations of Theological Ideas in the Two Religions, 3 vols. 1980. Set. lib. bdg. 229.95 (ISBN 0-8490-3136-2). Gordon Pr.

Tano, Rodrigo D. Theology in the Philippine Setting: A Case Study in the Contextualization of Theology. 184p. 1981. pap. 7.50x (ISBN 0-686-32582-6, Pub. by New Day Phillipines). Cellar.

Tan Tai Wei. The Worth of Religious Truth-Claims: A Case for Religious Education. LC 81-43864. 128p. (Orig.). 1982. pap. text ed. 9.50 (ISBN 0-8191-2369-2). U Pr of Amer.

Teilhard De Chardin, Pierre. La Messe sur le Monde. pap. 6.25 (ISBN 0-685-36598-0). French & Eur.

--Mon Univers. pap. 6.95 (ISBN 0-685-36599-9). French & Eur.

--Le Pretre. pap. 4.95 (ISBN 0-685-36600-6). French & Eur.

Theological Concerns of the Christian Conference of Asia Commission, ed. Minjung Theology: People As the Subjects of History. LC 83-7279. 224p. (Orig.). 1983. pap. 9.95 (ISBN 0-88344-336-8). Orbis Bks.

Thomas, Thomas A. Doctrine of the Word of God. 1972. pap. 3.50 (ISBN 0-87552-450-8). Presby & Reformed.

Tillich, Paul. Systematic Theology, 3 vols. in 1. LC 51-2235. 950p. 1967. 49.95x (ISBN 0-226-80336-8). U of Chicago Pr.

--Systematic Theology: Life & the Spirit History & the Kingdom of God, Vol. 3. LC 51-2235. 1976. pap. 11.00x (ISBN 0-226-80339-2, P706, Phoen). U of Chicago Pr.

Trillhaas, Wolfgang. Dogmatik. 4th ed. 543p. 1972. 24.80x (ISBN 3-11-008423-6). De Gruyter.

Understanding Bible Doctrine: Leader's Guide. (Electives Ser.). 1983. pap. 2.50 (ISBN 0-8024-0308-5). Moody.

Van Til, Cornelius. An Introduction to Systematic Theology. 1974. pap. 8.95 syllabus (ISBN 0-87552-488-5). Presby & Reformed.

Vengco, Sabino A. Juan de Cartagena, O.F.M. (1563-1618) The Mariology of His Homiliae Catholicae & Its Baroque Scripturism. (Theology Ser.). 1978. 13.00 (ISBN 0-686-27934-4). Franciscan Inst.

Walters, Dorothy, ed. The Synergists. (Illus.). 269p. 1984. 16.95 (ISBN 0-934344-14-0, Pub. by Royal CBS). Fell.

Ward, Wayne E. The Holy Spirit. (Layman's Library of Christian Doctrine). 1987. 5.95 (ISBN 0-8054-1640-4). Broadman.

Warfield, Benjamin B. Biblical & Theological Studies. 1952. 12.95 (ISBN 0-87552-525-3). Presby & Reformed.

Warren, Samuel. A Compendium of Swedenborg's Theological Writings. LC 73-94196. 816p. 1974. 5.00 (ISBN 0-87785-123-9). Swedenborg.

Weber, Otto. Foundations of Dogmatics, Vol. 2. Guder, Darrell L., tr. from Ger. 736p. 1983. 27.00 (ISBN 0-8028-3564-3). Eerdmans.

Werner, Karl. Geschichte Der Katholischen Theologie. 2nd ed. 50.00 (ISBN 0-384-66815-1). Johnson Repr.

Whale, John S. Christian Doctrine. 1941. pap. 10.95 (ISBN 0-521-09642-1). Cambridge U Pr.

Whitehead, James D. & Whitehead, Evelyn E. Method in Ministry: Theological Reflection & Christian Ministry. 224p. 1980. (HarpR); pap. 9.95 (ISBN 0-86683-459-1). Har-Row.

Will, Paul J., et al. Public Education Religion Studies: An Overview. LC 80-12237. (Aids for the Study of Religion Ser.). 1981. write for info. (ISBN 0-89130-401-0); pap. 12.00 (ISBN 0-89130-402-9, 01-03-07). Scholars Pr GA.

Williams, Ernest S. Systematic Theology, 3 vols. Incl. Vol. 1. pap. 6.95 (ISBN 0-88243-643-0, 02-0643); Vol. 2. pap. 6.95 (ISBN 0-88243-644-9, 02-0644); Vol. 3. pap. 6.95 (ISBN 0-88243-645-7, 02-0645). 1953. pap. 18.00 Set 3 vol (ISBN 0-88243-650-3, 02-0650). Gospel Pub.

Work of Richard Sibbes, 7 Vols. Set. 108.95 (ISBN 0-85151-398-0). Banner of Truth.

Zatko, James J., ed. Valley of Silence: Catholic Thought in Contemporary Poland. 1967. 21.95x (ISBN 0-268-00290-8). U of Notre Dame Pr.

THEOLOGY, DOCTRINAL–ADDRESSES, ESSAYS, LECTURES

Altizer, Thomas, et al. Deconstruction & Theology. 176p. 1982. 14.95 (ISBN 0-8245-0475-5); pap. 8.95 (ISBN 0-8245-0412-7). Crossroad NY.

Basinger, David & Basinger, Randall. Predestination & Free Will. LC 85-23887. 180p. 1986. pap. 6.95 (ISBN 0-87784-567-0). Inter-Varsity.

Bunyan, John. The Miscellaneous Works of John Bunyan, Vols. 8 & 9. Greaves, Richard L., ed. (Oxford English Texts). 1979. 79.00x (ISBN 0-19-812736-7); Vol. 9, 1981 95.00x, (ISBN 0-19-812737-5). Oxford U Pr.

Cobb, John B., Jr. God & the World. LC 69-11374. 138p. 1969. pap. 5.95 (ISBN 0-664-24860-8). Westminster.

Curran, Charles E. Transition & Tradition in Moral Theology. LC 78-20877. 1979. text ed. 18.95x (ISBN 0-268-01837-5, Dist. by Har Row). U of Notre Dame Pr.

Cushman, Robert E. Faith Seeking Understanding: Essays Theological & Critical. LC 80-69402. xvi, 373p. 1981. 30.25 (ISBN 0-8223-0444-9). Duke.

Dabney, R. L. Lectures in Systematic Theology. 1985. pap. 24.95 (ISBN 0-8010-2956-2). Baker Bk.

--Systematic Theology. 903p. 1985. 19.95 (ISBN 0-85151-453-7). Banner of Truth.

Dabney, Robert L. Discussions, 3 vols. 1982. 51.95 (ISBN 0-85151-395-6). Banner of Truth.

Gibellini, Rosino, ed. Frontiers of Theology in Latin America. Drury, John, tr. from Ital. LC 78-9147. Orig. Title: La nuova frontiera della Teologia in Latina America. 333p. (Orig.). 1979. pap. 10.95 (ISBN 0-88344-144-6). Orbis Bks.

Hadidian, Dikran Y., ed. From Faith to Faith, Essays in Honor of Donald G. Miller, on His Seventieth Birthday. LC 79-23408. (Pittsburgh Theological Monographs: No. 31). 1979. 18.00 (ISBN 0-915138-38-7). Pickwick.

Jackson, Jared J. & Kessler, Martin, eds. Rhetorical Criticism: Essays in Honor of James Muilenburg. LC 74-22493. (Pittsburgh Theological Monographs: No. 1). 1974. pap. 9.50 (ISBN 0-915138-00-X). Pickwick.

Knudsen, Johannes, ed. N. F. S. Grundtvig: Selected Writings. LC 76-7873. 192p. 1976. pap. 1.50 (ISBN 0-8006-1238-8, 1-1238). Fortress.

Lee, Jung Y. The Theology of Change: A Christian Concept of God in an Eastern Perspective. LC 78-16745. 155p. (Orig.). 1979. pap. 5.95 (ISBN 0-88344-492-5). Orbis Bks.

Lilly, W. S., ed. A Newman Anthology. 356p. 1981. 25.00x (ISBN 0-234-77060-0, Pub. by Dobson Bks England). State Mutual Bk.

Lindberg, David C., ed. John Pecham: Tractatus De Perspectiva. (Text Ser). 1972. 13.00 (ISBN 0-686-11561-9). Franciscan Inst.

Long, Eugene Thomas, ed. God, Secularization, and History: Essays in Memory of Ronald Gregor Smith. LC 73-15712. (Illus.). xiv, 164p. 1974. 21.95x (ISBN 0-87249-293-1). U of SC Pr.

Melanchthon, Philip. Melanchthon on Christian Doctrine: Loci Communes 1555. Manschreck, Clyde L., ed. & tr. (Twin Brooks Ser.). 414p. 1982. pap. 11.95 (ISBN 0-8010-6143-1). Baker Bk.

Miller, J. Allen. Christian Doctrine: Lectures & Sermons. 1946. 2.50x (ISBN 0-934970-01-7). Brethren Ohio.

Pannenberg, Wolfhart. The Idea of God & Human Freedom. LC 73-3165. 224p. 1973. 6.95 (ISBN 0-664-20971-8). Westminster.

Raven, Charles E. Natural Religion & Christian Theology: First & Second Series, 2 vols. LC 77-27176. (Gifford Lectures: 1951-52). Repr. of 1953 ed. Set. 37.50 (ISBN 0-404-60540-0). AMS Pr.

St. Symeon. St. Symeon, the New Theologian: Theological & Practical Discourses & Three Theological Discourses. Bell, David N., ed. McGuckin, Paul, tr. from Greek. (Cistercian Studies: No. 41). 1982. write for info. (ISBN 0-87907-841-3); pap. 8.00 (ISBN 0-87907-941-X). Cistercian Pubns.

Schillebeeckx, Edward & Willems, Boniface, eds. Man As Man & Believer. LC 67-17789. (Concilium Ser.: Vol. 21). 188p. 7.95 (ISBN 0-8091-0093-2). Paulist Pr.

Shairp, J. C. John Keble: An Essay on the Author of the 'Christian Year' 1866. Repr. 15.00 (ISBN 0-8274-3919-9). R West.

Shedd, W. G. Sermons to the Natural Man. 1977. 13.95 (ISBN 0-85151-260-7). Banner of Truth.

--Theological Essays. 1981. lib. bdg. 26.00 (ISBN 0-86524-079-5, 8602). Klock & Klock.

Stob, Henry. Theological Reflections: Essays on Related Themes. LC 81-1472. pap. 69.30 (ISBN 0-317-20015-1, 2023223). Bks Demand UMI.

Streeter, Burnett H. Foundations: A Statement of Christian Belief in Terms of Modern Thought by 70 Oxford Men. facs. ed. (Essay Index Reprint Ser). 1912. 20.50 (ISBN 0-8369-2189-5). Ayer Co Pubs.

Tillich, Paul. Protestant Era. abr ed. Adams, James L., tr. 1957. pap. 7.00x (ISBN 0-226-80342-2, P19, Phoen). U of Chicago Pr.

Verhovskoy, Serge S. The Light of the World. LC 82-16963. 163p. 1982. pap. 6.95 (ISBN 0-88141-004-7). St Vladimirs.

Winquist, Charles E. Epiphanies of Darkness: Deconstruction in Theology. LC 85-45479. 144p. 1986. pap. 12.95 (ISBN 0-8006-1903-X, 1-1903). Fortress.

THEOLOGY, DOCTRINAL–COLLECTED WORKS

see Theology–Collected Works

THEOLOGY, DOCTRINAL–HISTORY

see also Dogma, Development of; Religious Thought

also specific subjects with or without the subdivision History of Doctrines, e.g. Jesus Christ–History of Doctrines

Aaseng, Rolf E. Basic Christian Teachings. LC 81-52276. 112p. (Orig.). 1982. pap. 5.50 (ISBN 0-8066-1908-2, 10-0547). Augsburg.

Belloc, Hilaire. Great Heresies. facs. ed. LC 68-16908. (Essay Index Reprint Ser). 1938. 18.00 (ISBN 0-8369-0189-4). Ayer Co Pubs.

Berkhof, Louis. The History of Christian Doctrine. 1978. 14.95 (ISBN 0-85151-005-1). Banner of Truth.

Biasiotto, Peter R. History of the Development of the Devotion to the Holy Name. 1943. 3.50 (ISBN 0-686-11579-1). Franciscan Inst.

Bonansea, B. M. Man & His Approach to God in John Duns Scotus. 258p. (Orig.). 1983. lib. bdg. 29.75 (ISBN 0-8191-3299-3); pap. text ed. 13.50 o. p. (ISBN 0-8191-3300-0). U Pr of Amer.

Borresen, Kari E. Subordination & Equivalence: The Nature & Role of Women in Augustine & Thomas Aquinas. Talbot, Charles H., tr. from Fr. & Ital. LC 80-67199. 390p. 1981. lib. bdg. 29.25 (ISBN 0-8191-1681-5). U Pr of Amer.

Bromiley, Geoffrey W. Historical Theology: An Introduction. LC 77-17030. 1978. 14.95 (ISBN 0-8028-3509-0). Eerdmans.

Burkill, T. A. Evolution of Christian Thought. LC 76-127775. 518p. 1971. 29.50x (ISBN 0-8014-0581-5). Cornell U Pr.

Caird, Edward. Evolution of Theology in the Greek Philosophers, 2 Vols in 1. LC 4-16272. (Gifford Lectures 1900-1902). 1968. Repr. of 1904 ed. 46.00 (ISBN 0-527-14130-5). Kraus Repr.

--Evolution of Theology in the Greek Philosophers, the Gifford Lectures, 1900-1902, 2 Vols. 1968. 39.00x (ISBN 0-403-00116-1). Scholarly.

Carol, Juniper. A History of the Controversy over the "Debitum Peccati". (Theology Ser.). 1978. 7.00 (ISBN 0-686-27935-2). Franciscan Inst.

Clayton, John P. The Concept of Correlation: Paul Tillich & the Possibility of a Mediating Theology. (Theologische Bibliothek Topelmann Ser.: No. 37). 427p. 1979. text ed. 44.25x (ISBN 3-11007-914-3). De Gruyter.

Cunningham, William. Historical Theology, 2 vols. 1979. Set. 38.95 (ISBN 0-85151-058-2); Vol. 1. (ISBN 0-85151-286-0); Vol. 2. (ISBN 0-85151-287-9). Banner of Truth.

Cushman, Robert E. Faith Seeking Understanding: Essays Theological & Critical. LC 80-69402. xvi, 373p. 1981. 30.25 (ISBN 0-8223-0444-9). Duke.

Dorner, Isaak A. Geschichte Der Protestantischen Theologie. 1867. 55.00 (ISBN 0-384-12385-6). Johnson Repr.

--History of Protestant Theology, 2 Vols. LC 72-133823. Repr. of 1871 ed. Set. 87.50 (ISBN 0-404-02147-6). AMS Pr.

Evans, G. R. Alan of Lille: The Frontiers of Theology in the Twelfth Century. LC 83-1834. 240p. 1983. 54.50 (ISBN 0-521-24618-0). Cambridge U Pr.

Fisher, George P. History of Christian Doctrine. LC 75-41095. Repr. of 1901 ed. 41.50 (ISBN 0-404-14663-5). AMS Pr.

Gonzalez, Justo L. The History of Christian Thought: From the Beginnings to the Council of Chalcedon in A. D. 451. rev. ed. LC 74-109679. Set. text ed. 56.00 (ISBN 0-687-17181-4); Vol. II. text ed. 18.75; Vol. I. text ed. 20.00 (ISBN 0-687-17150-4); Vol. III. text ed. 20.00. Abingdon.

Gratsch, Edward J. Aquinas' Summa: An Introduction & Interpretation. LC 85-15842. 305p. (Orig.). 1985. pap. 12.95 (ISBN 0-8189-0485-2). Alba.

Harnack, Adolph. History of Dogma, 2 vols. in 1, Vols. 2 & 3. Buchanan, Neil, tr. from Ger. Set. 18.00 (ISBN 0-8446-2207-9). Peter Smith.

Henderson, E. Harold. Roman Dogma vs. Bible Doctrine. 152p. 1964. pap. 1.00 (ISBN 0-89114-060-3). Baptist Pub Hse.

Hordern, William E. Layman's Guide to Protestant Theology. rev. ed. 1968. pap. 5.95 (ISBN 0-02-085470-6, Collier). Macmillan.

Howard, George. Paul: Crisis in Galatia: A Study in Early Christian Theology. LC 77-84002. (Society for New Testament Studies Monographs: No. 35). pap. 31.50 (ISBN 0-317-29375-3, 2024478). Bks Demand UMI.

Huxley, Julian S., ed. The New Systematics. LC 40-35139. 583p. 1940. Repr. 49.00 (ISBN 0-403-01786-6). Scholarly.

Kershner, Frederick D. Pioneers of Christian Thought. facs. ed. LC 68-57327. (Essay Index Reprint Ser). 1930. 20.00 (ISBN 0-8369-0594-6). Ayer Co Pubs.

Langford, Thomas A. Practical Divinity: Theology in the Wesleyan Tradition. 304p. (Orig.). 1983. pap. 9.95 (ISBN 0-687-33326-1). Abingdon.

Leith, John H., ed. Creeds of the Churches: A Reader in Christian Doctrine from the Bible to the Present. 3rd ed. LC 82-48029. 1982. pap. 10.95 (ISBN 0-8042-0526-4). John Knox.

Pelikan, Jaroslav. The Christian Tradition, a History of the Development of Doctrine: The Spirit of Eastern Christendom, 600-1700, Vol. 2. LC 79-142042. 1977. pap. 10.95 (ISBN 0-226-65373-0, P738, Phoen). U of Chicago Pr.

Pennington, M. Basil, et al. The Living Testament: The Essential Writings of Christianity since the Bible. LC 85-42790. 400p. 1985. 22.45 (ISBN 0-06-066499-1, HarpR); pap. 14.95 (ISBN 0-06-066498-3). Har-Row.

Perreiah, Alan, ed. Paul of Venice: Logica Magna, Tractatus De Suppositione. (Text Ser). 1971. 16.00 (ISBN 0-686-11560-0). Franciscan Inst.

Placher, William C. A History of Christian Theology: An Introduction. LC 83-16778. 324p. 1983. pap. 16.95 (ISBN 0-664-24496-3). Westminster.

Preus, Robert D. Theology of Post-Reformation Lutheranism: A Study of Theological Prolegomena. LC 70-121877. 1970. 16.95 (ISBN 0-570-03211-3, 15-2110). Concordia.

Que es la Doctrina Cristiana? Su Valor, Necesidad y Base. (Biblioteca de Doctrina Cristiana Ser.). Tr. of What is Christian Doctrine? (Span.). 1985. pap. 5.95 (ISBN 0-311-09111-3). Casa Bautista.

Richardson, Alan. Science, History & Faith. LC 86-22863. 216p. 1986. Repr. of 1950 ed. lib. bdg. 39.75x (ISBN 0-313-25325-0, RISHF). Greenwood.

Robinson, Donald. Faith's Framework: The Structure of New Testament Theology. 152p. 1986. pap. 9.95 (ISBN 0-85364-317-2, Pub. by Paternoster UK). Attic Pr.

Romanides, John S. Franks, Romans, Feudalism, & Doctrine: An Interplay Between Theology & Society. (Patriarch Athenagoras Memorial Lectures Ser.). 98p. (Orig.). 1982. pap. text ed. 4.95 (ISBN 0-916586-54-5). Holy Cross Orthodox.

St. Augustine. Eighty-Three Different Questions. LC 81-2546. (Fathers of the Church Ser.: Vol. 70). 257p. 1982. 29.95x (ISBN 0-8132-0070-9). Cath U Pr.

Schillebeeckx, Edward, ed. The Movement of Theology since the Council. (Concilium 1983: Vol. 170). 128p. (Orig.). 1983. pap. 6.95 (ISBN 0-8164-2450-0, HarpR). Har-Row.

Shorter, Aylward. African Christian Theology: Adaptation or Incarnation? LC 77-23325. 180p. (Orig.). 1977. 7.95 (ISBN 0-88344-002-4); pap. 4.95 (ISBN 0-88344-003-2). Orbis Bks.

Slater, Peter. The Dynamics of Religion: Meaning & Change in Religious Traditions. LC 78-4426. 1978. pap. 6.95x (ISBN 0-685-53934-2, RD 280, HarpR). Har-Row.

Soper, David W. Men Who Shape Belief. LC 76-86061. (Essay & General Literature Index Reprint Ser). 1969. Repr. of 1955 ed. 24.00x (ISBN 0-8046-0588-2, Pub. by Kennikat). Assoc Faculty Pr.

Templin, J. Alton. Ideology on a Frontier: The Theological Foundation of Afrikaner Nationalism, 1652-1910. LC 83-10884. (Contributions in Intercultural & Comparative Studies: No. 11). (Illus.). xiii, 360p. 1984. lib. bdg. 35.00 (ISBN 0-313-24104-X, TIF/). Greenwood.

Urban, Linwood. A Short History of Christian Thought. LC 85-10654. 1986. text ed. 29.95x (ISBN 0-19-503716-2); pap. text ed. 10.95x (ISBN 0-19-503717-0). Oxford U Pr.

Weber, Otto. Foundations of Dogmatics, Vol. 1. Guder, Darrel L., tr. 656p. 1982. 27.00 (ISBN 0-8028-3554-6). Eerdmans.

Williams, Daniel D. Andover Liberals: A Study in American Theology. LC 79-111636. 1970. Repr. of 1941 ed. lib. bdg. 17.50x (ISBN 0-374-98584-7, Octagon). Hippocrene Bks.

THEOLOGY, DOCTRINAL–HISTORY–EARLY CHURCH, ca. 30-600

see also Alexandrian School, Christian; Church Orders, Ancient; Gnosticism; Manichaeism

Bowers, G. M. The Faith & Doctrines of the Early Church. LC 78-60521. 1978. pap. 4.95 (ISBN 0-917182-09-X). Triumph Pub.

Bray, Gerald. Creeds, Councils & Christ. LC 83-26443. 220p. 1984. pap. 6.95 (ISBN 0-87784-969-2). Inter-Varsity.

Danielou, Jean. A History of Early Christian Doctrine Before the Council of Nicaea. Baker, John A., tr. Incl. Vol. 1. The Theology of Jewish Christianity. 1977; Vol. 2. Gospel Message & Hellenistic Culture. LC 72-7090. 1973; Vol. 3. The Origins of Latin Christianity. LC 76-44380. 528p. 1977. 27.50 (ISBN 0-664-21064-3). Westminster.

Richardson, Alan. Creeds in the Making: A Short Introduction to the History of Christian Doctrine. LC 81-43073. 128p. 1981. pap. 5.95 (ISBN 0-8006-1609-X, 1-1609). Fortress.

St. Cyprian of Carthage. The Lord's Prayer. Bonin, Edmond, ed. 112p. (Orig.). 1983. pap. 6.95 (ISBN 0-87061-076-7). Chr Classics.

Turner, Henry E. The Pattern of Christian Truth: A Study in the Relations Between Orthodoxy & Heresy in the Early Church. LC 77-84707. (Bampton Lectures: 1954). 1977. Repr. of 1954 ed. 47.50 (ISBN 0-404-16114-6). AMS Pr.

Wiles, Maurice F. Making of Christian Doctrine. 1967. 32.50 (ISBN 0-521-06803-7). Cambridge U Pr.

Willis, John R. A History of Christian Thought: From Apostolic Times to Saint Augustine. LC 76-16237. 1976. 16.00 (ISBN 0-682-48583-7, University). Exposition Pr FL.

Wolfson, Harry A. Philosophy of the Church Fathers: Faith, Trinity, Incarnation. 3rd rev. ed. LC 70-119077. 1970. 32.50x (ISBN 0-674-66551-1). Harvard U Pr.

THEOLOGY, DOCTRINAL–HISTORY–MIDDLE AGES, 600-1500

Burr, David. Eucharistic Presence & Conversion in Late Thirteenth Century Franciscan Thought. LC 83-73283. (Transactions Ser.: Vol. 74 Pt. 3). 113p. 1984. 12.00 (ISBN 0-87169-743-2). Am Philos.

Del Punta, Francesco, ed. Paul of Venice, Logica Magna, Part II, Fasc. 6. Adams, Marilyn M., tr. from Latin. 288p. 1978. 27.00 (ISBN 0-85672-695-8, Pub. by British Acad). Longwood Pub Group.

Heimmel, Jennifer P. God Is Our Mother: Julian of Norwich & the Medieval Image of Christian Feminine Divinity. Hogg, James, ed. (Elizabethan & Renaissance Studies). 111p. (Orig.). 1982. pap. 15.00 (ISBN 0-317-40145-9, Pub by Salzburg Studies). Longwood Pub Group.

Kretzmann, Norman, ed. Paul of Venice, Logica Magna, Pt. I, Fasc. I. 344p. 1979. 52.50 (ISBN 0-85672-690-7, Pub. by British Acad). Longwood Pub Group.

Little, A. G. Some Recently Discovered Franciscan Documents & Their Relation to the Second Life by Celano & the "Speculum Perfections". 1926. pap. 2.25 (ISBN 0-85672-691-5, Pub. by British Acad). Longwood Pub Group.

Martinez, Jose L. Cuando el Dinero Causa Problemas. (Serie de la Familia). (Span.). 96p. 1986. pap. 3.50 (ISBN 0-311-46265-0). Casa Bautista.

Moehs, Teta E., tr. The Gospel of Jesus Christ According to Mistress Ava. (Senda de Estudios & Ensayos Ser.). (Ger. & Eng., Illus.). 176p. (Orig.). 1986. pap. 12.95 (ISBN 0-918454-53-0). Senda Nueva.

Oberman, Heiko A. Forerunners of the Reformation: The Shape of Late Medieval Thought, Illustrated by Key Documents: Nyhus, Paul L., tr. LC 81-66518. pap. 86.80 (2027871). Bks Demand UMI.

Robleto, Adolfo. Conozca Quienes Son. (Span.). 112p. 1986. pap. 3.25 (ISBN 0-311-05764-0). Casa Bautista.

Szittya, Penn R. The Antifraternal Tradition in Medieval Literature. LC 85-43316. (Illus.). 320p. 1986. text ed. 40.00x (ISBN 0-691-06680-9). Princeton U Pr.

Walsingham, Thomas. De Archana Deorum. Van Kluyme, Robert, ed. LC 67-31120. xxii, 227p. 1968. 24.75 (ISBN 0-8223-0183-0). Duke.

THEOLOGY, DOCTRINAL–HISTORY–MODERN PERIOD, 1500-

Grabbe, George. Dogmat Tserkvi v Sovrjemjennom Mire. Tr. of The Dogma of the Church in the Modern World. 1975. pap. 1.50 (ISBN 0-317-30381-3). Holy Trinity.

Gurnall, William. The Christian in Complete Armour. 1979. 26.95 (ISBN 0-85151-196-1). Banner of Truth.

McGiffert, A. C. Protestant Thought Before Kant. 11.25 (ISBN 0-8446-0204-3). Peter Smith.

Muller, Richard A. Christ & the Decree: Christology & Predestination in Reformed Theology from Calvin to Perkins. (Studies in Historical Theology: Vol. 2). 250p. 1986. lib. bdg. 30.00x (ISBN 0-939464-39-X). Labyrinth Pr.

THEOLOGY, DOCTRINAL–HISTORY–16TH CENTURY

Aulen, Gustaf E. Reformation & Catholicity. Wahlstrom, Eric H., tr. from Swedish. LC 78-25981. 1979. Repr. of 1961 ed. lib. bdg. 22.50x (ISBN 0-313-20809-3, AURC). Greenwood.

Beard, Charles. The Reformation of the Sixteenth Century in Its Relation to Modern Thought & Knowledge. LC 80-12915. xxviii, 450p. 1980. Repr. of 1962 ed. lib. bdg. 37.50x (ISBN 0-313-22410-2, BERF). Greenwood.

Cunningham, William. Reformers & the Theology of Reformation. 1979. 19.95 (ISBN 0-85151-013-2). Banner of Truth.

Reardon, Bernard. Religious Thoughts in the Reformation. 1981. pap. text ed. 14.95 (ISBN 0-582-49031-6). Longman.

THEOLOGY, DOCTRINAL–HISTORY–17TH CENTURY

Burg, B. Richard. Richard Mather. (United States Authors Ser.). 1982. lib. bdg. 16.50 (ISBN 0-8057-7364-9, Twayne). G K Hall.

Cunningham, William. Reformers & the Theology of Reformation. 1979. 19.95 (ISBN 0-85151-013-2). Banner of Truth.

Dennison, James T., Jr. The Market Day of the Soul: The Puritan Doctrine of the Sabbath in England, 1532-1700. LC 83-6990. (Illus.). 188p. (Orig.). 1983. lib. bdg. 25.00 (ISBN 0-8191-3204-7); pap. text ed. 11.25 (ISBN 0-8191-3205-5). U Pr of Amer.

Owen, John. Works of John Owen, Vol. I. 1980. 16.95 (ISBN 0-85151-123-6). Banner of Truth.

--Works of John Owen, Vol. II. 1980. 16.95 (ISBN 0-85151-124-4). Banner of Truth.

--Works of John Owen, Vol. III. 1980. 16.95 (ISBN 0-85151-125-2). Banner of Truth.

--Works of John Owen, Vol. IV. 1980. 16.95 (ISBN 0-85151-068-X). Banner of Truth.

--Works of John Owen, Vol. V. 1980. 16.95 (ISBN 0-85151-067-1). Banner of Truth.

--Works of John Owen, Vol. VI. 1980. 16.95 (ISBN 0-85151-126-0). Banner of Truth.

--Works of John Owen, Vol. VII. 1980. 16.95 (ISBN 0-85151-127-9). Banner of Truth.

--Works of John Owen, Vol. VIII. 1980. 16.95 (ISBN 0-85151-066-3). Banner of Truth.

--Works of John Owen, Vol. IX. 1980. 16.95 (ISBN 0-85151-065-5). Banner of Truth.

--Works of John Owen, Vol. X. 1980. 16.95 (ISBN 0-85151-064-7). Banner of Truth.

--Works of John Owen, Vol. XI. 1980. 16.95 (ISBN 0-85151-128-7). Banner of Truth.

--Works of John Owen, Vol. XII. 1980. 16.95 (ISBN 0-85151-129-5). Banner of Truth.

--Works of John Owen, Vol. XIII. 1980. 16.95 (ISBN 0-85151-063-9). Banner of Truth.

--Works of John Owen, Vol. XIV. 1980. 16.95 (ISBN 0-85151-062-0). Banner of Truth.

--Works of John Owen, Vol. XV. 1980. 16.95 (ISBN 0-85151-130-9). Banner of Truth.

--Works of John Owen, Vol. XVI. 1980. 16.95 (ISBN 0-85151-061-2). Banner of Truth.

--Works of John Owen, 16 vols. 1980. Set. 244.95 (ISBN 0-85151-392-1). Banner of Truth.

Rosenberg, A. Nicolas Gueudeville & His Work Sixteen Fifty-Two to Seventeen Twenty-Five. 1982. 49.50 (ISBN 90-247-2533-X, Pub. by Martinus Nijhoff Netherlands). Kluwer Academic.

Watson, Thomas. A Body of Divinity. 1978. pap. 9.95 (ISBN 0-85151-383-2). Banner of Truth.

THEOLOGY, DOCTRINAL–HISTORY–18TH CENTURY

Barth, Karl. Protestant Thought. facs. ed. LC 73-142606. (Essay Index Reprint Ser). 1959. 23.50 (ISBN 0-8369-2102-X). Ayer Co Pubs.

Rosenberg, A. Nicolas Gueudeville & His Work Sixteen Fifty-Two to Seventeen Twenty-Five. 1982. 49.50 (ISBN 90-247-2533-X, Pub. by Martinus Nijhoff Netherlands). Kluwer Academic.

THEOLOGY, DOCTRINAL–HISTORY–19TH CENTURY

Barth, Karl. Humanity of God. Weiser, Thomas & Thomas, John N., trs. LC 60-3479. 1960. pap. 5.95 (ISBN 0-8042-0612-0). John Knox.

--Protestant Thought. facs. ed. LC 73-142606. (Essay Index Reprint Ser). 1959. 23.50 (ISBN 0-8369-2102-X). Ayer Co Pubs.

DuBose, William P. A DuBose Reader. Armentrout, Donald S., ed. LC 84-51878. 256p. 1984. pap. 10.95 (ISBN 0-918769-06-X). Univ South.

Fraser, James W. Pedagogue for God's Kingdom: Lyman Beecher & the Second Great Awakening. LC 85-17794. 248p. 1985. lib. bdg. 27.50 (ISBN 0-8191-4905-5); pap. text ed. 12.75 (ISBN 0-8191-4906-3). U Pr of Amer.

Gerrish, B. A. Tradition & the Modern World: Reformed Theology in the Nineteenth Century. LC 78-4982. 1978. lib. bdg. 20.00x (ISBN 0-226-28866-8). U of Chicago Pr.

Griffin, Paul R. Black Theology As the Foundation of Three Methodist Colleges: The Educational Views & Labors of Daniel Payne, Joseph Price, Isaac Lane. LC 84-13070. 148p. (Orig.). 1984. lib. bdg. 20.75 (ISBN 0-8191-4160-7); pap. text ed. 9.50 (ISBN 0-8191-4161-5). U Pr of Amer.

Moore, J. R. The Post Darwinian Controversies. LC 77-94372. 1979. 57.50 (ISBN 0-521-21989-2); pap. 24.95 (ISBN 0-521-28517-8). Cambridge U Pr.

Reardon, Bernard M. Religion in the Age of Romanticism: Studies in Early Nineteenth Century Thought. 320p. 1985. 39.50 (ISBN 0-521-30088-6); pap. 14.95 (ISBN 0-521-31745-2). Cambridge U Pr.

THEOLOGY, DOCTRINAL–HISTORY–20TH CENTURY

see also Transcendence of God

Barth, Karl. Humanity of God. Weiser, Thomas & Thomas, John N., trs. LC 60-3479. 1960. pap. 5.95 (ISBN 0-8042-0612-0). John Knox.

Bird, Thomas E., ed. Modern Theologians, Christians & Jews. 2nd ed. 1967. 15.95 (ISBN 0-268-00183-9). U of Notre Dame Pr.

Ferm, Deane W. Third World Liberation Theologies: An Introductory Survey. LC 85-15534. pap. 10.95 (ISBN 0-88344-515-8). Orbis Bks.

Hamilton, Kenneth. What's New in Religion? A Critical Study of New Theology, New Morality & Secular Christianity. 176p. 1969. pap. 3.95 (ISBN 0-85364-092-0). Attic Pr.

Hordern, William. Introduction. (New Directions in Theology Today: Vol. 1). 168p. 1966. pap. 4.95 (ISBN 0-664-24706-7). Westminster.

MacDonald, Timothy I. The Ecclesiology of Yves Congar: Foundational Themes. LC 83-19882. 346p. (Orig.). 1984. lib. bdg. 28.75 (ISBN 0-8191-3644-1); pap. text ed. 14.75 (ISBN 0-8191-3645-X). U Pr of Amer.

MacNamara, Vincent. Faith & Ethics. 216p. (Orig.). 1985. 17.95 (ISBN 0-87840-426-0); pap. 10.95 (ISBN 0-87840-414-7). Georgetown U Pr.

Montgomery, John W. Crisis in Lutheran Theology, 2 vols. in one. 1973. pap. 8.95 (ISBN 0-87123-050-X, 210050). Bethany Hse.

Reinisch, Leonhard, ed. Theologians of Our Time. 1964. 17.95x (ISBN 0-268-00271-1); pap. 7.95x (ISBN 0-268-00378-5). U of Notre Dame Pr.

Robinson, James M. & Cobb, John B., Jr., eds. The Later Heidegger & Theology. LC 78-23619. 1979. Repr. of 1963 ed. lib. bdg. 22.50x (ISBN 0-313-20783-6, ROLH). Greenwood.

Vahanian, Gabriel. No Other God. LC 66-28591. (Orig.). 1966. pap. 2.50 (ISBN 0-8076-0389-9). Braziller.

Williams, Daniel D. What Present-Day Theologians Are Thinking. rev. ed. LC 78-16410. 1978. Repr. of 1959 ed. lib. bdg. 22.50x (ISBN 0-313-20587-6, WIWP). Greenwood.

Wing-hung Lam. Chinese Theology in Construction. LC 81-15483. 320p. 1983. pap. 11.95x (ISBN 0-87808-180-1). William Carey Lib.

Wolterstorff, Nicholas. Until Justice & Peace Embrace. 232p. (Orig.). 1983. 13.95 (ISBN 0-8028-3344-6). Eerdmans.

THEOLOGY, DOCTRINAL–HISTORY–GERMANY

Barth, Karl. Protestant Thought. facs. ed. LC 73-142606. (Essay Index Reprint Ser). 1959. 23.50 (ISBN 0-8369-2102-X). Ayer Co Pubs.

Gindele, Egon, ed. Bibliographie zur Geschichte und Theologie des Augustiner Eremiten Ordens bis zum Beginn der Reformation. (Spaetmittelalter und Reformation: Texte und Untersuchungen, Vol. 1). 1977. text ed. 74.00x (ISBN 3-11-004949-X). De Gruyter.

Ziefle, Helmut W. Theological German. 256p. 1986. pap. 14.95 (ISBN 0-8010-9931-5). Baker Bk.

THEOLOGY, DOCTRINAL–HISTORY–GREAT BRITAIN

Davies, Horton. The Ecumenical Century: 1900-1965. (Worship & Theology in England Ser.: Vol. 5). 1965. 39.50x (ISBN 0-691-07145-4). Princeton U Pr.

Dennison, James T., Jr. The Market Day of the Soul: The Puritan Doctrine of the Sabbath in England, 1532-1700. LC 83-6990. (Illus.). 188p. (Orig.). 1983. lib. bdg. 25.00 (ISBN 0-8191-3204-7); pap. text ed. 11.25 (ISBN 0-8191-3205-5). U Pr of Amer.

Elliott-Binns, L. The Development of English Theology in the Later Nineteenth Century. LC 72-122411. ix, 137p. 1971. Repr. of 1952 ed. 17.50 (ISBN 0-208-01045-9, Archon). Shoe String.

Horton, Walter M. Contemporary Continental Theology: An Interpretation for Anglo-Saxons. 1979. Repr. of 1938 ed. lib. bdg. 30.00 (ISBN 0-8482-4497-4). Norwood Edns.

Jerrold, Blanchard. The Chronicles of the Crutch. 1979. Repr. of 1860 ed. lib. bdg. 40.00 (ISBN 0-8482-1394-7). Norwood Edns.

Moore, J. R. The Post Darwinian Controversies. LC 77-94372. 1979. 57.50 (ISBN 0-521-21989-2); pap. 24.95 (ISBN 0-521-28517-8). Cambridge U Pr.

New, John F. Anglican & Puritan: The Basis of Their Opposition, 1558-1640. 1964. 18.00x (ISBN 0-8047-0066-4). Stanford U Pr.

Willey, Basil. Seventeenth Century Background: Studies in the Thought of the Age in Relation to Poetry & Religion. LC 34-21849. 1942. 31.00x (ISBN 0-231-01395-7). Columbia U Pr.

THEOLOGY, DOCTRINAL–HISTORY–UNITED STATES

Abell, Aaron I. The Urban Impact on American Protestantism, 1865-1900. x, 275p. 1962. Repr. of 1943 ed. 22.50 (ISBN 0-208-00587-0, Archon). Shoe String.

Burg, B. Richard. Richard Mather. (United States Authors Ser.). 1982. lib. bdg. 16.50 (ISBN 0-8057-7364-9, Twayne). G K Hall.

Dean, William. American Religious Empiricism. (Religious Studies). 126p. (Orig.). 1986. 34.50x (ISBN 0-88706-280-6); pap. 10.95 (ISBN 0-88706-281-4). State U NY Pr.

Dunn, Charles W. American Political Theology: Historical Perspective & Theoretical Analysis. LC 84-13308. 208p. 1984. 31.95 (ISBN 0-03-071843-0); pap. 13.95 (ISBN 0-03-071844-9, B1603). Praeger.

Ferm, Deane W. Contemporary American Theologies: A Critical Survey. 192p. (Orig.). 1981. pap. 8.95 (ISBN 0-8164-2341-5, HarpR). Har-Row.

Foster, Frank H. Modern Movement in American Theology. facs. ed. LC 76-86751. (Essay Index Reprint Ser). 1939. 14.50 (ISBN 0-8369-1131-8). Ayer Co Pubs.

Fraser, James W. Pedagogue for God's Kingdom: Lyman Beecher & the Second Great Awakening. LC 85-17794. 248p. 1985. lib. bdg. 27.50 (ISBN 0-8191-4905-5); pap. text ed. 12.75 (ISBN 0-8191-4906-3). U Pr of Amer.

Jordan, Theodus J. The Contributions of Black Theology to Contemporary Thought. 1987. 7.95 (ISBN 0-533-06711-1). Vantage.

Moore, J. R. The Post Darwinian Controversies. LC 77-94372. 1979. 57.50 (ISBN 0-521-21989-2); pap. 24.95 (ISBN 0-521-28517-8). Cambridge U Pr.

Oppenheim, Frank M., ed. The Reasoning Heart: Toward a North American Theology. 160p. (Orig.). 1986. pap. 9.95 (ISBN 0-87840-433-3); 17.95 (ISBN 0-87840-439-2). Georgetown U Pr.

Post, Stephen G. Christian Love & Self-Denial: A Historical & Normative Study of Jonathan Edwards, Samuel Hopkins & American Theological Ethics. 138p. (Orig.). 1987. lib. bdg. 22.50 (ISBN 0-8191-5261-7); pap. text ed. 8.75 (ISBN 0-8191-5262-5). U Pr of Amer.

Richardson, Herbert W. Toward an American Theology. (Richard Ser.: No. 2). 1967. 29.95 (ISBN 0-88946-028-0). E Melien.

Torres, Sergio. Theology in the Americas. Eagleson, John, ed. LC 76-22545. 466p. (Orig.). 1976. 12.95 (ISBN 0-88344-479-8); pap. 12.95 (ISBN 0-88344-476-3). Orbis Bks.

THEOLOGY, DOCTRINAL–OUTLINES, SYLLABI, ETC.

Christman, Ronald & Schibilla, Linda. Lessons on Doctrine: For Youth (Teacher) 48p. (Orig.). 1982. pap. 1.95 (ISBN 0-87239-604-5, 3376). Standard Pub.

--Lessons on Doctrine: For Youth (Workbook) (Illus.). 64p. (Orig.). 1982. pap. 3.50 (ISBN 0-87239-603-7, 3377). Standard Pub.

Pardington, George P. Outline Studies in Christian Doctrine. pap. 5.95 (ISBN 0-87509-116-4). Chr Pubns.

THEOLOGY, DOCTRINAL–POPULAR WORKS

Boice, James M. The Sovereign God. LC 77-14879. (Foundations of the Christian Faith: Vol. 1). 1978. pap. 7.95 (ISBN 0-87784-743-6). Inter-Varsity.

Brunner, Emil. Our Faith. 1936. pap. text ed. 7.95 (ISBN 0-684-16856-1, SL87, ScribT). Scribner.

Coffin, Henry S. Some Christian Convictions: A Practical Restatement in Terms of Present-Day Thinking. LC 79-167328. (Essay Index Reprint Ser.). Repr. of 1915 ed. 17.00 (ISBN 0-8369-2763-X). Ayer Co Pubs.

Demaray, Donald E. Basic Beliefs. 1958. pap. 4.50 (ISBN 0-8010-2827-2). Baker Bk.

Ebner, James H. God Present As Mystery: A Search for Personal Meaning in Contemporary Theology. LC 76-13750. 1976. pap. 5.95 (ISBN 0-88489-084-8). St Marys.

Evans, William. The Great Doctrines of the Bible. rev. ed. 350p. 1974. enlarged edition 11.95 (ISBN 0-8024-3301-4). Moody.

Haliel. The Book of the New Age, Bk. 1. 50p. (Orig.). 1985. pap. 3.00. Westgate Pr.

Harner, Nevin C. I Believe. (Orig.). 1950. 3.95 (ISBN 0-8298-0066-2); pap. 2.95 (ISBN 0-8298-0067-0). Pilgrim NY.

Henderlite, Rachel. Call to Faith. LC 55-5552. 224p. 1955. pap. 2.49 (ISBN 0-8042-3136-2). John Knox.

Herzog, Frederick. Justice Church: The New Function of the Church in North American Christianity. LC 80-15091. 176p. (Orig.). 1980. pap. 6.95 (ISBN 0-88344-249-3). Orbis Bks.

Hobbs, Herschel H. Fundamentals of Our Faith. LC 60-5200. (Orig.). 1960. pap. 6.95 (ISBN 0-8054-1702-8). Broadman.

--What Baptists Believe. LC 64-12411. 1963. bds. 4.25 (ISBN 0-8054-8101-X). Broadman.

Huggenvik, Theodore. We Believe. 1950. pap. 3.95 (ISBN 0-8066-0151-5, 15-7102). Augsburg.

Humphreys, Fisher. Thinking about God. LC 74-81556. 228p. (Orig.). 1974. pap. 9.00 (ISBN 0-914520-00-8). Insight Pr.

Hylkema, G. W. & Tuuk, E. J. A First Book of Christian Doctrine. rev. ed. (YA) pap. 2.95 (ISBN 0-8028-8012-6). Eerdmans.

Ironside, H. A. Sailing with Paul. pap. 1.35 (ISBN 0-87213-387-7). Loizeaux.

Koehler, Alfred W. Light from Above. 1960. 3.95 (ISBN 0-570-03506-6, 14-1260). Concordia.

Lewis, Gordon R. Decide for Yourself: A Theological Workbook. LC 71-116046. (Orig.). 1970. pap. 7.95 (ISBN 0-87784-633-2). Inter-Varsity.

McClanahan, John H. Man As Sinner. LC 84-20036. (Layman's Library of Christian Doctrine Ser.). 1987. 5.95 (ISBN 0-8054-1637-4). Broadman.

Macquarrie, John. The Faith of the People of God: A Lay Theology. LC 72-1224. 188p. 1973. pap. 7.95 (ISBN 0-684-13060-2, ScribT). Scribner.

Matthews, W. R., ed. Christian Faith: Essays in Explanation & Defence. facsimile ed. LC 73-152162. (Essay Index Reprint Ser). Repr. of 1936 ed. 21.50 (ISBN 0-8369-2348-0). Ayer Co Pubs.

Merton, Thomas. Disputed Questions. 297p. 1960. 12.50 (ISBN 0-374-14061-8). FS&G.

Pentecost, J. Dwight. Things Which Become Sound Doctrine. 1970. Repr. 5.95 (ISBN 0-310-30901-8, 6504P). Zondervan.

Read, David H. The Christian Faith. LC 85-10473. 256p. 1985. pap. 9.95 (ISBN 0-8027-2515-5). Walker & Co.

Robinson, A. E. Layman & the Book. pap. 1.95 (ISBN 0-911866-58-2). Advocate.

Ryrie, Charles C. Basic Theology. 544p. 1986. 16.95 (ISBN 0-89693-814-X). Victor Bks.

Sisson, Richard. Answering Christianity's Most Puzzling Questions, Vol. 2. 240p. (Orig.). 1983. pap. 8.95 (ISBN 0-8024-5148-9). Moody.

Smith, F. G. The Last Reformation. 256p. 5.00 (ISBN 0-686-29154-9); pap. 3.50 (ISBN 0-686-29155-7). Faith Pub Hse.

Stott, John R. Basic Christianity. 1957. pap. 2.95 (ISBN 0-8028-1189-2). Eerdmans.

Streng, William D. Faith for Today: A Brief Outline of Christian Thought. LC 75-2843. 48p. (Orig.). 1975. pap. 2.95 (ISBN 0-8066-1488-9, 10-2180). Augsburg.

Truemper, David G. & Niedner, Frederick A., Jr. Keeping the Faith: A Guide to the Christian Message. LC 81-43072. 144p. 1981. pap. 6.95 (ISBN 0-8006-1608-1, 1-1608). Fortress.

Wilson, Frank E. Faith & Practice. rev. ed. (Orig.). 1961. pap. 7.95 (ISBN 0-8192-1082-X). Morehouse.

THEOLOGY, DOGMATIC

see Theology, Doctrinal

THEOLOGY, ECCLESIASTICAL

see Church

THEOLOGY, EMPIRICAL

see Empirical Theology

THEOLOGY, ETHICAL

see Christian Ethics

THEOLOGY, FEDERAL

see Covenants (Theology)

THEOLOGY, FUNDAMENTAL

see Apologetics

THEOLOGY, ISLAMIC

see Islamic Theology

THEOLOGY, JEWISH

see Jewish Theology

THEOLOGY, MORAL

see Christian Ethics

THEOLOGY, MUSLIM

see Islamic Theology

THEOLOGY, MYSTICAL

see Mysticism; Mysticism–Catholic Church; Mysticism–Orthodox Eastern Church

THEOLOGY, NATURAL

see Natural Theology

THEOLOGY, NEW ENGLAND

see New England Theology

THEOLOGY, PASTORAL

see Pastoral Theology

THEOLOGY, PHILOSOPHICAL

see Philosophical Theology

THEOLOGY, PRACTICAL

see also Baptism; Canon Law; Catechetics; Christian Art and Symbolism; Christian Education; Christian Life; Church Polity; Church Renewal; Church Work; Church Year; Clergy; Devotional Exercises; Devotional Literature; Ecclesiastical Law; Evangelistic Work; Fasts and Feasts; Gifts, Spiritual; Hymns; Liturgics; Liturgies; Lord's Supper; Missions; Pastoral Theology; Prayer; Preaching; Religious Education; Revivals; Sacraments; Sermons; Spiritual Life; Sunday-Schools; Worship

Bower, William C., ed. Church at Work in the Modern World. facs. ed. LC 67-26717. (Essay Index Reprint Ser). 1935. 18.00 (ISBN 0-8369-0231-9). Ayer Co Pubs.

Lane, Dermot A. Foundations for Social Theology: Praxis, Process & Salvation. (Orig.). 1984. pap. 7.95 (ISBN 0-8091-2622-2). Paulist Pr.

Leech, Kenneth. Experiencing God: Theology as Spirituality. LC 84-48237. 352p. 1985. 20.45 (ISBN 0-06-065226-8, HarpR). Har-Row.

McCann, Dennis P. & Strain, Charles R. Polity & Praxis: A Program for American Practical Theology. 176p. 1985. 15.95 (ISBN 0-86683-986-0, AY8571, HarpR). Har-Row.

Milavec, Aaron. To Empower as Jesus Did: Acquiring Spiritual Power through Apprenticeship. LC 82-6466. (Toronto Studies in Theology: Vol. 9). 358p. 1982. 59.95x (ISBN 0-88946-966-0). E Mellen.

Moltmann-Wendel, Elisabeth. A Land Flowing with Milk & Honey: Perspectives on Feminist Theology. 224p. 1986. 14.95 (ISBN 0-8245-0791-6). Crossroad NY.

Morneau, Robert F. Spiritual Aids for Those in Renew: Ponderings, Poems & Promises. LC 84-12299. 111p. (Orig.). 1984. pap. 4.50 (ISBN 0-8189-0473-9). Alba.

Oppenheim, Frank M., ed. The Reasoning Heart: Toward a North American Theology. 160p. (Orig.). 1986. pap. 9.95 (ISBN 0-87840-433-3); 17.95 (ISBN 0-87840-439-2). Georgetown U Pr.

Priestley, Joseph. The Theological & Miscellaneous Works, 25 vols. in 26. Repr. Set. 1352.00 (ISBN 0-527-72751-2). Kraus Repr.

Ransom, John C. God Without Thunder: An Unorthodox Defense of Orthodoxy. LC 65-17410. x, 334p. 1965. Repr. of 1930 ed. 29.50 (ISBN 0-208-00085-2, Archon). Shoe String.

Schaller, Lyle E. The Pastor & the People: Building a New Partnership for Effective Ministry. LC 72-8567. 176p. (Orig.). 1973. pap. 7.95 (ISBN 0-687-30136-X). Abingdon.

Schillebeeckx, Edward & Baptist-Metz, Johannes. Martyrdom Today. (Concilium 1983: Vol. 163). 128p. 1983. pap. 6.95 (ISBN 0-8164-2443-8, HarpR). Har-Row.

Schleiermacher, Friedrich. Die Praktische Theologie nach den Grundsatzen. (Ger.). 845p. 1983. 96.00 (ISBN 3-11-009699-4). De Gruyter.

Seldon, Eric. The God of the Present Age. LC 80-26149. 1981. pap. 9.00 (ISBN 0-8309-0305-4). Herald Hse.

Turnbull, Ralph G., ed. Baker's Handbook of Practical Theology. 469p. 1967. 14.95 (ISBN 0-8010-8880-1). Baker Bk.

THEOLOGY, PROCESS

see Process Theology

THEOLOGY, PURITAN

Rowse, A. L. Milton the Puritan: Portrait of a Mind. 298p. 1985. pap. text ed. 12.50 (ISBN 0-8191-4778-8). U Pr of Amer.

THEOLOGY, SCHOLASTIC

see Scholasticism

THEOLOGY, SYSTEMATIC

see Theology, Doctrinal

THEOPHANIES

see also Apparitions; Incarnation; Revelation; Visions

Moscow Synod. Staff, ed. Bogojavlenije Gospodnje. Tr. of Theophany. 194p. pap. 8.00 (ISBN 0-317-29167-X). Holy Trinity.

Stahl, John. Theophany. 24p. deluxe ed. 100.00 (ISBN 0-318-21735-X). Evanescent Pr.

--Theophany. (Illus.). 24p. 100.00 (ISBN 0-318-21736-8); Proofs of main edition, 1979. 20.00; Early manuscript edition, 1978. 20.00. Evanescent Pr.

--The World Union Company. 60p. 1980. pap. 5.00 (ISBN 0-318-21734-1). Evanescent Pr.

Yoseph. The Gilgal Theophany. 1985. 6.95 (ISBN 0-533-06448-1). Vantage.

THEOSOPHICAL SOCIETY

Brown, Loren R. Point Loma Theosophical Society: A List of Publications, 1898 - 1942. LC 81-187499. (Illus.). 136p. 1977. pap. 10.00 (ISBN 0-913510-46-7). Wizards.

Ryan, Charles J. H. P. Blavatsky & the Theosophical Movement. 2nd,rev. ed. Knoche, Grace F., ed. LC 75-4433. (Illus.). 1975. 9.00 (ISBN 0-911500-79-0); pap. 6.00 (ISBN 0-911500-80-4). Theos U Pr.

Society for Psychical Report. Report on Theosophical Society. LC 75-36920. (Occult Ser.). (Illus.). 1976. 26.50x (ISBN 0-405-07975-3). Ayer Co Pubs.

THEOSOPHY

see also Anthroposophy; Avatars; Chakras (Theosophy); Gnosticism; Jesus Christ–Theosophical Interpretations; Karma; Neoplatonism; Reincarnation; Rosicrucians; Vedanta; Yoga

Alcyone, pseud. At the Feet of the Master. 1967. 4.50 (ISBN 0-8356-0098-X). Theos Pub Hse.

Alcyone. At the Feet of the Master. 1970. pap. 1.95 (ISBN 0-8356-0196-X, Quest). Theos Pub Hse.

--At the Feet of the Master. leatherette 3.00 (ISBN 0-911662-17-0). Yoga.

--At the Feet of the Master. 1.75 (ISBN 0-8356-7323-5). Theos Pub Hse.

Amneus, Nils. Life's Riddle. 1975. pap. 5.25 (ISBN 0-913004-26-X). Point Loma Pub.

Annie Beseant - An Autobiography. 17.50 (ISBN 0-8356-7568-8). Theos Pub Hse.

Anrias, David. Through the Eyes of the Masters. 1972. pap. 7.95 (ISBN 0-87728-116-5). Weiser.

Ashish, Sri Madhava. Man, Son of Man. LC 79-98267. 1970. 8.50 (ISBN 0-8356-0011-4). Theos Pub Hse.

Bailey, Alice A. The Soul & Its Mechanism. 1971. 15.00 (ISBN 0-85330-015-1); pap. 7.00 (ISBN 0-85330-115-8). Lucis.

--A Treatise on the Seven Rays, 5 vols. Incl. Vol. 1. Esoteric Psychology. 1984. 20.00 (ISBN 0-85330-018-6); pap. 9.00 (ISBN 0-85330-118-2); Vol. 2. Esoteric Psychology. 1982. 28.00 (ISBN 0-85330-019-4); pap. 17.00 (ISBN 0-85330-119-0); Vol. 3. Esoteric Astrology. 1983. 28.00 (ISBN 0-85330-020-8); pap. 17.00 (ISBN 0-85330-120-4); Vol. 4. Esoteric Healing. 1984. 28.00 (ISBN 0-85330-021-6); pap. 17.00 (ISBN 0-85330-121-2); Vol. 5. The Rays & the Initiations. 1982. 28.00 (ISBN 0-85330-022-4); pap. 17.00 (ISBN 0-85330-122-0). pap. Lucis.

Barborka. Story of Human Evolution. 8.95 (ISBN 0-8356-7550-5). Theos Pub Hse.

Barborka, Geoffrey. Divine Plan: Commentary on the Secret Doctrine. 3rd ed. 1972. 19.95 (ISBN 0-8356-7167-4). Theos Pub Hse.

Barborka, Geoffrey A. H. P. Blavatsky: Tibet & Tulku. (Illus.). 1974. 12.95 (ISBN 0-8356-7159-3). Theos Pub Hse.

Barker, A. Trevor, ed. Mahatma Letters to A. P. Sinnett. 3rd ed. 1972. 11.50 (ISBN 0-8356-7013-9). Theos Pub Hse.

Beasant. Path of Discipleship. 4.25 (ISBN 0-8356-7044-9). Theos Pub Hse.

--The Riddle of Life. 4.50 (ISBN 0-8356-0231-1). Theos Pub Hse.

Beasant & Leadbeater. Talks on the Path of Occultism, Vol. 2: Voice of the Silence. 9.50 (ISBN 0-8356-7021-X). Theos Pub Hse.

Behem, Jacob. Three Principles of the Divine Essence. 1978. Repr. of 1909 ed. 12.00 (ISBN 0-911662-65-0). Yoga.

Bendit, Laurence J. Mirror of Life & Death. 7.25 (ISBN 0-8356-7394-4). Theos Pub Hse.

--Self Knowledge: A Yoga for the West. LC 67-7871. (Orig.). 1967. pap. 1.25 (ISBN 0-8356-0032-7, Quest). Theos Pub Hse.

Benjamin, Elsie. Search & Find: Theosophical Reference Index. Small, W. Emmett & Todd, Helen, eds. (Study: No. 1). 1978. pap. 3.95 (ISBN 0-913004-32-4). Point Loma Pub.

Besant. Dharma. 3.25 (ISBN 0-8356-7116-X). Theos Pub Hse.

--Doctrine of the Heart. 1.95 (ISBN 0-8356-7189-5). Theos Pub Hse.

--Mahabarata. 5.25 (ISBN 0-8356-7539-4). Theos Pub Hse.

--Seven Principles of Man. 3.25 (ISBN 0-8356-7321-9). Theos Pub Hse.

--Study in Karma. 2.25 (ISBN 0-8356-7292-1). Theos Pub Hse.

--Thought Power. 4.50 (ISBN 0-8356-7460-6). Theos Pub Hse.

Besant & Leadbeater. Thought Forms. 8.75 (ISBN 0-8356-7187-9). Theos Pub Hse.

Besant, Annie. Ancient Wisdom. 9th ed. 1972. 7.95 (ISBN 0-8356-7038-4). Theos Pub Hse.

--Death & After. 1972. 2.95 (ISBN 0-8356-7039-2). Theos Pub Hse.

--Esoteric Christianity. 8th ed. 1966. 7.00 (ISBN 0-8356-7052-X). Theos Pub Hse.

--Man & His Bodies. 12th ed. 1967. 4.50 (ISBN 0-8356-7083-X). Theos Pub Hse.

--Study in Consciousness. 6th ed. 1972. 7.50 (ISBN 0-8356-7287-5). Theos Pub Hse.

--Thought Power: Its Control & Culture. LC 73-7644. 1967. pap. 3.50 (ISBN 0-8356-0312-1, Quest). Theos Pub Hse.

Besant, Annie & Leadbeater, Charles W. Thought Forms. abr. ed. (Illus.). 1969. pap. 5.50 (ISBN 0-8356-0008-4, Quest). Theos Pub Hse.

Blavatsky. Two Books on Stanzas of Dzyan. 4.95 (ISBN 0-8356-7223-9). Theos Pub Hse.

Blavatsky, H. P. Key to Theosophy. 7.50 (ISBN 0-8356-5131-2). Theos Pub Hse.

--A Modern Panarion. 504p. 1981. Repr. of 1895 ed. 15.00 (ISBN 0-938998-22-6). Theosophy.

--Theosophical Articles: Reprinted from the Theosophist, Lucifer & other Nineteenth-Century Journals, 3 vols. 1692p. 1982. Set. 37.50 (ISBN 0-938998-26-9). Theosophy.

Blavatsky, H. P., et al. Theosophical Articles & Notes. 300p. 1985. Repr. 10.50 (ISBN 0-938998-29-3). Theosophy.

Blavatsky, Helena P. Abridgement of the Secret Doctrine. Preston, Elizabeth & Humphreys, Christmas, eds. 1968. pap. 5.50 (ISBN 0-8356-0009-2, Quest). Theos Pub Hse.

--The Circle of Wisdom. rev ed. Parley, Winifred A., ed. LC 78-8790. 1978. pap. 3.25 (ISBN 0-8356-0516-7, Quest). Theos Pub Hse.

--Collected Writings of H. P. Blavatsky, Vols. 1-11. Incl. Vol. 1. 1874-1878. rev. ed. 16.50 (ISBN 0-8356-0082-3); Vol. 2. 1879-1880 (ISBN 0-8356-0091-2); Vol. 3. 1881-1882 (ISBN 0-8356-0099-8); Vol. 4. 1882-1883 (ISBN 0-8356-0106-4); Vol. 5. 1883 (ISBN 0-8356-0117-X); Vol. 6. 1883-1884-1885 (ISBN 0-8356-0125-0); Vol. 7. 1886-1887 (ISBN 0-8356-0222-2); Vol. 8. 1887 (ISBN 0-8356-7166-6); Vol. 9. 1888 (ISBN 0-8356-0217-6); Vol. 10. 1888-1889 (ISBN 0-8356-0218-4); Vol. 11. 1889. 16.50 (ISBN 0-686-86789-0). (Illus.). 16.50 ea. Theos Pub Hse.

--Dynamics of the Psychic World: Comments by H. P. Blavatsky on Magic, Mediumship, Psychism, & the Powers of the Spirit. LC 72-78193. 150p. (Orig.). 1972. pap. 1.95 (ISBN 0-8356-0429-2, Quest). Theos Pub Hse.

--H. P. Blavatsky to the American Conventions: 1888-1891, with a Historical Perspective. LC 78-74256. 1979. pap. 4.00 (ISBN 0-911500-88-X). Theos U Pr.

--Isis Unveiled, 2 Vols. De Zirkoff, Boris, ed. 1971. Set. 30.00 (ISBN 0-8356-0193-5). Theos Pub Hse.

--Isis Unveiled, 2 vols. LC 72-186521. 1976. Set. 20.00 (ISBN 0-911500-02-2); Set. pap. 14.00 (ISBN 0-911500-03-0). Theos U Pr.

--Isis Unveiled: A Master-Key to the Mysteries of Ancient & Modern Science & Theology, 2 vols. in 1. (Illus.). xlix, 1260p. 1931. Repr. of 1877 ed. 17.00 (ISBN 0-938998-01-3). Theosophy.

--The Key to Theosophy. xii, 310p. 1930. Repr. of 1889 ed. 6.00 (ISBN 0-938998-03-X). Theosophy.

--The Key to Theosophy: Verbatim with 1889 Edition. LC 72-95701. 1972. 9.00 (ISBN 0-911500-06-5); pap. 6.00 (ISBN 0-911500-07-3). Theos U Pr.

--The Secret Doctrine, 3 vols. 7th ed. De Zirkoff, Boris, ed. (Illus.). 1980. 45.00 ea. (ISBN 0-8356-7525-4). Theos Pub Hse.

--The Secret Doctrine: The Synthesis of Science, Religion, & Philosophy, 2 vols. in 1. xci, 1474p. 1925. Repr. of 1888 ed. 18.50 (ISBN 0-938998-00-5). Theosophy.

--The Theosophical Glossary: A Photographic Reproduction of the Original Edition, As First Issued at London, England, 1892. Mead, G. R., ed. & intro. by. vi, 389p. 1930. Repr. of 1892 ed. 8.50 (ISBN 0-938998-04-8). Theosophy.

--The Theosophist: Oct. Eighteen Seventy-Nine to Sept. Eighteen Eighty. 2nd ed. (Secret Doctrine Reference Ser.). (Illus.). 320p. 1979. pap. 12.00 (ISBN 0-913510-31-9). Wizards.

--Voice of the Silence. LC 73-7619. 1970. pap. 2.50 (ISBN 0-8356-0380-6, Quest). Theos Pub Hse.

--The Voice of the Silence: Verbatim with 1889 ed. LC 76-25345. 1976. 5.00 (ISBN 0-911500-04-9); pap. 2.75 (ISBN 0-911500-05-7). Theos U Pr.

Blavatsky, Helena P., tr. & intro. by. The Voice of the Silence: Chosen Fragments from the Book of the Golden Precepts. iv, 110p. 1928. Repr. of 1889 ed. 3.00 (ISBN 0-938998-06-4). Theosophy.

Blavatsky, Helene P. Theosophical Glossary. LC 74-142546. 1971. Repr. of 1892 ed. 46.00x (ISBN 0-8103-3679-0). Gale.

Boehme, Jakob. The Confessions. 69.95 (ISBN 0-87968-258-2). Gordon Pr.

Campbell, Bruce F. Ancient Wisdom Revived: A History of the Theosophical Movement. LC 79-64664. 224p. 1980. 18.95x (ISBN 0-520-03968-8). U of Cal Pr.

Carter. Astrology of Accidents. 3.95 (ISBN 0-7229-5059-4). Theos Pub Hse.

--Symbolic Directions: Modern Astrology. 7.95 (ISBN 0-7229-5145-0). Theos Pub Hse.

Carter, C. E. Essays On Foundation of Astrology. 9.95 (ISBN 0-8356-5506-7). Theos Pub Hse.

--Essays on Foundation of Astrology. pap. 5.95 (ISBN 0-8356-5503-2). Theos Pub Hse.

Challoner. Out of Chaos. 6.95 (ISBN 0-8356-5051-0). Theos Pub Hse.

--Regents of Seven Spheres. 8.75 (ISBN 0-8356-5009-X). Theos Pub Hse.

--What of Tomorrow. 5.95 (ISBN 0-8356-5300-5). Theos Pub Hse.

Challoner, H. K. The Path of Healing. LC 76-3660. 175p. 1976. pap. 5.25 (ISBN 0-8356-0480-2, Quest). Theos Pub Hse.

--Path of Healing. 10.50 (ISBN 0-8356-5227-0). Theos Pub Hse.

Chatterji, Mohini M. Viveka-Chudamani or the Crest Jewel of Wisdom. 5.75 (ISBN 0-8356-7091-0). Theos Pub Hse.

Codd. Way of the Disciple. 5.00 (ISBN 0-8356-7049-X). Theos Pub Hse.

Codd, Clara & Blavatsky, eds. Key to Theosophy Simplified. 5.25 (ISBN 0-8356-7060-0). Theos Pub Hse.

Codd, Clara M. Ageless Wisdom of Life. LC 67-8630. 1967. pap. 1.75 (ISBN 0-8356-0145-5, Quest). Theos Pub Hse.

--Ageless Wisdom of Life. 4.95 (ISBN 0-8356-7329-4). Theos Pub Hse.

--Meditation, Its Practice & Results. 4th ed. 1968. 2.25 (ISBN 0-8356-7212-3). Theos Pub Hse.

--Technique of the Spiritual Life. 2nd ed. 1963. 6.95 (ISBN 0-8356-7090-2). Theos Pub Hse.

--Trust Yourself to Life. LC 75-4245. 116p. 1975. pap. 1.75 (ISBN 0-8356-0464-0, Quest). Theos Pub Hse.

Collins. Light on the Path. 1.50 (ISBN 0-8356-7192-5). Theos Pub Hse.

Collins, Mabel. Light on the Path. 1970. pap. 1.75 (ISBN 0-8356-0299-0, Quest). Theos Pub Hse.

Collins, Mabel C. Light on the Path. leatherette 3.00 (ISBN 0-911662-13-8). Yoga.

Conger, Margaret. Combined Chronology for Use with the Mahatma Letters to A. P. Sinnett & the Letters of H. P. Blavatsky to A. P. Sinnett. LC 73-92461. 1973. pap. 3.00 (ISBN 0-911500-17-0). Theos U Pr.

Cooper, Irving S. Secret of Happiness. LC 75-26815. 75p. 1976. pap. 1.75 (ISBN 0-8356-0469-1, Quest). Theos Pub Hse.

--Theosophy Simplified. 59.95 (ISBN 0-8490-1191-4). Gordon Pr.

--Theosophy Simplified. new ed. LC 78-64905. 1979. pap. 3.25 (ISBN 0-8356-0519-1, Quest). Theos Pub Hse.

Crookall. Next World-& the Next. 7.95 (ISBN 0-8356-5008-1). Theos Pub Hse.

Crosbie, Robert. Answers to Questions on the Ocean of Theosophy. 249p. 1933. 5.00 (ISBN 0-938998-12-9). Theosophy.

--The Friendly Philosopher. (Illus.). vii, 415p. 1934. Repr. 6.00 (ISBN 0-938998-13-7). Theosophy.

De Purucker, G. Dialogues of G. de Purucker, 3 vols. Conger, Arthur L., ed. LC 79-65630. 1948. Set. 25.00 (ISBN 0-911500-59-6). Theos U Pr.

--The Four Sacred Seasons. LC 79-63565. 1979. 5.00 (ISBN 0-911500-83-9); pap. 2.75 (ISBN 0-911500-84-7). Theos U Pr.

--Fundamentals of the Esoteric Philosophy. 2nd, rev. ed. Knoche, Grace F., ed. LC 78-74258. 1979. 14.00 (ISBN 0-911500-63-4); pap. 8.00 (ISBN 0-911500-64-2). Theos U Pr.

--Golden Precepts of Esotericism. 3rd, rev. ed. LC 78-74257. 1979. 5.00 (ISBN 0-911500-85-5); pap. 3.00 (ISBN 0-911500-86-3). Theos U Pr.

--Man in Evolution. 2nd rev. ed. Knoche, Grace F., ed. LC 76-45503. 1977. pap. 6.00 (ISBN 0-911500-55-3). Theos U Pr.

--Occult Glossary. LC 53-37086. (A Compendium of Oriental & Theosophical Terms). 1972. 7.50 (ISBN 0-911500-50-2); pap. 4.00 (ISBN 0-911500-51-0). Theos U Pr.

De Purucker, G. & Tingley, Katherine. H. P. Blavatsky: The Mystery. rev. ed. Small, W. Emmett & Todd, Helen, eds. (Illus.). 256p. 1974. pap. 5.25 (ISBN 0-913004-14-6). Point Loma Pub.

De Zirkoff, Boris. The Dream That Never Dies: Boris de Zirkoff Speaks Out on Theosophy. Small, W. Emmett, ed. (Illus.). 242p. 1983. pap. 11.50 lexitone (ISBN 0-913004-45-6). Point Loma Pub.

De Zirkoff, Boris, ed. H. P. Blavatsky: Collected Writings, Vol. XIV. LC 84-50694. (Illus.). 750p. 1985. text ed. 16.50 (ISBN 0-8356-0234-6). Theos Pub Hse.

Elliott, Scott. Story of Atlantis & the Lost Lemuria. 8.95 (ISBN 0-8356-5509-1). Theos Pub Hse.

Ellwood, Rober S., ed. Eastern Spirituality in America: Selected Writings. (Sources of American Spirituality Ser.). 256p. 1987. pap. 16.95 (ISBN 0-8091-0388-5). Paulist Pr.

Ellwood, Robert. Theosophy. LC 85-40843. (Illus.). 236p. (Orig.). 1986. pap. 6.50 (ISBN 0-8356-0607-4, Quest). Theos Pub Hse.

Emmons, Viva. Roots of Peace. LC 73-78911. (Orig.). 1969. pap. 1.75 (ISBN 0-8356-0505-1, Quest). Theos Pub Hse.

Farthing. When We Die. 3.25 (ISBN 0-8356-5118-5). Theos Pub Hse.

Farthing, Geoffrey. Theosophy: What's It All About. 1967. 5.25 (ISBN 0-8356-5075-8). Theos Pub Hse.

Five Years of Theosophy. 575p. 1981. Repr. of 1885 ed. 14.00 (ISBN 0-938998-21-8). Theosophy.

Greenwalt, Emmett A. The Point Loma Community in California, 1897-1942: A Theosophical Experiment. LC 76-42802. Repr. of 1955 ed. 22.00 (ISBN 0-404-60068-9). AMS Pr.

Hanlon. Into the Fourth Dimension. 3.95 (ISBN 0-8356-7529-7). Theos Pub Hse.

Harris, Iverson L. Theosophy under Fire: A Miniature Key to Theosophy As Recorded in a Legal Deposition. 2nd ed. 120p. (Orig.). 1970. pap. 3.00 (ISBN 0-913004-03-0). Point Loma Pub.

Hitchcock, John. Atoms, Snowflakes & God. LC 85-40842. (Illus.). 222p. 1986. pap. 6.75 (ISBN 0-8356-0604-X, Quest). Theos Pub Hse.

Hodson. Basic Theosophy. 18.95 (ISBN 0-8356-7560-2). Theos Pub Hse.

--Occult Powers in Nature & in Man. 5.50 (ISBN 0-8356-7085-6). Theos Pub Hse.

--Through the Gateway of Death. 2.95 (ISBN 0-8356-7202-6). Theos Pub Hse.

Hodson, Geoffrey. Kingdom of the Gods. 7th ed. (Illus.). 1972. 15.95 (ISBN 0-8356-7081-3). Theos Pub Hse.

--Reincarnation, Fact or Fallacy. rev. ed. LC 67-4405. 1967. pap. 2.95 (ISBN 0-8356-0046-7, Quest). Theos Pub Hse.

--Seven Human Temperaments. 6th ed. 1977. 3.25 (ISBN 0-8356-7222-0). Theos Pub Hse.

Humphreys. Search Within. pap. 8.95 (ISBN 0-8356-5143-6). Theos Pub Hse.

Jinarajadasa. K. H. Letters to C. W. Leadbeater. 5.95 (ISBN 0-8356-7552-1). Theos Pub Hse.

--Letters From the Masters of the Wisdom. (Series 1). 3.50 (ISBN 0-8356-7135-6). Theos Pub Hse.

--Letters From the Masters of Wisdom. (Series 2). 3.50 (ISBN 0-8356-7311-1). Theos Pub Hse.

Jinarajadasa, C. Seven Veils over Consciousness. 2.50 (ISBN 0-8356-7231-X). Theos Pub Hse.

Judge, W. Q. The Ocean of Theosophy. 69.95 (ISBN 0-8490-0752-6). Gordon Pr.

Judge, William Q. Letters That Have Helped Me. Niemand, Jasper, ed. & intro. by. (Illus.). x, 300p. 1946. 6.00 (ISBN 0-938998-08-0). Theosophy.

--The Ocean of Theosophy. LC 73-78147. 1973. 6.00 (ISBN 0-911500-25-1); pap. 3.50 (ISBN 0-911500-26-X). Theos U Pr.

--The Ocean of Theosophy. (Illus.). 153p. 1915. Repr. of 1893 ed. 5.00 (ISBN 0-938998-07-2). Theosophy.

--El Oceano de la Teosofia. Polanco, Bermudez Y., tr. from Eng. Tr. of The Ocean of Theosophy. (Span.). 128p. 1983. pap. 3.75 (ISBN 0-938998-28-5). Theosophy.

--Theosophical Articles: Articles by Wm. Q. Judge Reprinted from Nineteenth-Century Theosophical Periodicals, 2 vols. 1276p. 1980. Set. 25.00 (ISBN 0-938998-20-X). Theosophy.

Judge, William Q. & Crosbie, Robert. Notes on the Bhagavad-Gita. 237p. 1918. Repr. 4.00 (ISBN 0-938998-10-2). Theosophy.

Krishnamurti, J. Talks & Dialogues of J. Krishnamurti. 1976. pap. 4.95 (ISBN 0-380-01573-0, Discus). Avon.

Kuhn, Alvin B. Rebirth for Christianity. LC 76-104032. 1970. 6.50 (ISBN 0-8356-0015-7). Theos Pub Hse.

Leadbeater. Devachanic Plane. 5.50 (ISBN 0-8356-7075-9). Theos Pub Hse.

--Invisible Helpers. 6.95 (ISBN 0-8356-7160-7). Theos Pub Hse.

--Life after Death. 4.50 (ISBN 0-8356-7148-8). Theos Pub Hse.

--Monad. 3.00 (ISBN 0-8356-7646-3). Theos Pub Hse.

--Outline of Theosophy. 2.95 (ISBN 0-8356-7185-2). Theos Pub Hse.

--Science of the Sacraments. 18.95 (ISBN 0-8356-7126-7). Theos Pub Hse.

--Textbook of Theosophy. 6.95 (ISBN 0-8356-7110-0). Theos Pub Hse.

Leadbeater & Besant. Talks on the Path of Occultism, Vol. 1: At the Feet of the Master. 9.50 (ISBN 0-8356-7047-3). Theos Pub Hse.

--Talks on the Path of Occultism, Vol. 3: Light on the Path. 7.95 (ISBN 0-8356-7068-6). Theos Pub Hse.

Leadbeater, Charles W. Astral Plane. 1973. 5.95 (ISBN 0-8356-7093-7). Theos Pub Hse.

--Man, Visible & Invisible. 9.95 (ISBN 0-8356-7388-X). Theos Pub Hse.

Long, James A. Expanding Horizons. LC 65-24093. 1965. pap. 3.50 (ISBN 0-911500-75-8). Theos U Pr.

Mead, G. R. Five Years of Theosophy: Mystical, Philosophical, Theosophical, Historical & Scientific Essay. LC 75-36850. (Occult Ser.). 1976. Repr. of 1894 ed. 30.00x (ISBN 0-405-07966-4). Ayer Co Pubs.

--World-Mystery: Four Comparative Studies in General Theosophy. 201p. 1987. pap. text ed. 15.95 (ISBN 0-915032-73-2). Natl Poet Foun.

Mehta, Rohit. Eternal Light. 1961. 8.95 (ISBN 0-8356-7004-X). Theos Pub Hse.

Mills, Joy. One Hundred Years of Theosophy. 245p. (Orig.). 1987. pap. 9.95 (ISBN 0-8356-0235-4). Theos Pub Hse.

Mills, Joy, ed. H. P. Blavatsky: The Key to Theosophy, an Abridgement. LC 75-18176. pap. 4.50 (ISBN 0-8356-0427-6, Quest). Theos Pub Hse.

Mooney, Lucindi F. Storming Eastern Temples. LC 76-4903. 1976. 9.75x (ISBN 0-8356-0482-9). Theos Pub Hse.

Mueller, Friedrich M. Theosophy: Or, Psychological Religion. LC 73-18830. (Gifford Lectures: 1892). Repr. of 1903 ed. 47.00 (ISBN 0-404-14460-8). AMS Pr.

Occult Glossary: A Compendium of Oriental & Theosophical Terms. 69.95 (ISBN 0-8490-0749-6). Gordon Pr.

Olcott, Henry S. Old Diary Leaves. 1973. 7.50 ea. Vol. I (ISBN 0-8356-7106-2). Vol. II (ISBN 0-8356-7123-2). Vol. III (ISBN 0-8356-7480-0). Vol. IV (ISBN 0-8356-7484-3). Vol. V (ISBN 0-8356-7487-8). Vol. VI (ISBN 0-8356-7491-6). Theos Pub Hse.

Osborn, Arthur W. Cosmic Womb: An Interpretation of Man's Relationship to the Infinite. LC 69-17714. (Orig.). 1969. pap. 2.25 (ISBN 0-8356-0001-7, Quest). Theos Pub Hse.

Pearson, E. Norman. Space Time & Self. rev. ed. LC 71-1546. (Illus.). pap. 5.95 (ISBN 0-8356-0409-8, Quest). Theos Pub Hse.

Percival, Harold W. Man & Woman, & Child. LC 52-6126. 1979. pap. 6.95 (ISBN 0-911650-08-3). Word Foun.

Perkins, J. S. Geometry of Space & Consciousness. 2nd ed. 1973. 3.50 (ISBN 0-8356-7006-6). Theos Pub Hse.

Plummer, L. Gordon. Mathematics of the Cosmic Mind. rev. ed. LC 77-114206. (Illus.). 1970. 18.95 (ISBN 0-8356-0030-0). Theos Pub Hse.

Powell. Etheric Double. 12.50 (ISBN 0-8356-5068-5). Theos Pub Hse.

Powell, A. E. Causal Body. 1972. 18.95 (ISBN 0-8356-5034-0); pap. 11.75 (ISBN 0-8356-5302-1). Theos Pub Hse.

--Mental Body. 1975. 11.95 (ISBN 0-8356-5504-0). Theos Pub Hse.

Powell, Arthur E. Etheric Double. (Illus.). 1969. pap. 3.95 (ISBN 0-8356-0075-0, Quest). Theos Pub Hse.

Ram, Sri. Thoughts for Aspirants. Series II. 3.95 (ISBN 0-8356-7449-5). Theos Pub Hse.

Robson. Eternal Truths of Life. 4.75 (ISBN 0-8356-7030-9). Theos Pub Hse.

Ross, Lydia & Ryan, Charles J. Theosophia: An Introduction. 1974. pap. 1.75 (ISBN 0-913004-13-8). Point Loma Pub.

Row, Subba T. Esoteric Writings. 17.95 (ISBN 0-8356-7544-0). Theos Pub Hse.

Rudhyar, Dane. Culture, Crisis & Creativity. LC 76-43008. (Orig.). 1977. pap. 4.25 (ISBN 0-8356-0487-X, Quest). Theos Pub Hse.

--The Fullness of Human Experience. LC 85-40771. 272p. (Orig.). 1986. pap. 7.75 (ISBN 0-8356-0606-6, Quest). Theos Pub Hse.

Ryan, Charles J. H. P. Blavatsky & the Theosophical Movement: With 7 Appendixes. Small, W. Emmett & Todd, Helen, eds. (Illus.). 484p. 1975. pap. 7.00 (ISBN 0-913004-25-1). Point Loma Pub.

--What Is Theosophy? A General View of Occult Doctrine. rev. ed. Small, W. Emmett & Todd, Helen, eds. (Theosophical Manual: No. 1). 92p. 1975. pap. 2.25 (913004-18-9). Point Loma Pub.

Shearman, Hugh. Desire & Fulfillment. 1.75 (ISBN 0-8356-7054-6). Theos Pub Hse.

--Passionate Necessity. 3.50 (ISBN 0-8356-0200-1). Theos Pub Hse.

Sinnett. Esoteric Buddhism. 11.25 (ISBN 0-8356-5230-0). Theos Pub Hse.

Sinnett, A. P. Occult World. 9th ed. 1969. 12.95 (ISBN 0-8356-5019-7). Theos Pub Hse.

Society for Psychical Report. Report on Theosophical Society. LC 75-36920. (Occult Ser.). (Illus.). 1976. 26.50x (ISBN 0-405-07975-3). Ayer Co Pubs.

South Ctr. of Theos. Devas & Men. 8.95 (ISBN 0-8356-7518-1). Theos Pub Hse.

Sri Ram, N. Approach To Reality. 5.75 (ISBN 0-8356-7339-1). Theos Pub Hse.

--Human Interest. 2nd ed. 1968. 2.50 (ISBN 0-8356-7170-4). Theos Pub Hse.

--Life's Deeper Aspects. 1968. 3.50 (ISBN 0-8356-7172-0). Theos Pub Hse.

--Thoughts for Aspirants. 7th ed. (Series 2). 1969. 4.25 (ISBN 0-8356-7195-X). Theos Pub Hse.

Steiner, Rudolf. At the Gates of Spiritual Science. Tr. of Vor dem Tore der Theosophie. 160p. 1986. 20.00 (ISBN 0-88010-224-1); pap. 8.95 (ISBN 0-88010-135-0). Anthroposophic.

--Theosophy: An Introduction to Supersensible Knowledge. rev. ed. LC 78-135997. 195p. (Orig.). 1971. 14.00 (ISBN 0-910142-65-3); pap. 6.95 (ISBN 0-910142-39-4). Anthroposophic.

--Theosophy: An Introduction to the Supersensible Knowledge of the World & the Destination of Man. Monges, Henry B., tr. from Ger. Tr. of Theosophie: Einfuehrung in uebersinnliche Welterkenntnis und Menschenbestimmung. 200p. 1987. pap. 6.95 (ISBN 0-88010-179-2). Anthroposophic.

--Theosophy: Introduction to the Supersensible Knowledge of the World & the Destination of Man. Church, Gilbert, ed. Monges, Henry B., tr. Tr. of Theosophie: Einfuehrung in uebersinnliche Welterkenntnis und Mmenschenbestimmung. (Ger.). 195p. 1986. pap. cancelled (ISBN 0-910142-39-4). Anthroposophic.

--Theosophy of the Rosicrucian. Cotterell, Mabel & Osmond, D. S., trs. (Ger.). 168p. 1981. 15.95 (ISBN 0-85440-113-X, Pub. by Steinerbooks); pap. 11.95 (ISBN 0-85440-401-5). Anthroposophic.

--True & False Paths in Spiritual Investigation. Parker, A. H., tr. from Ger. Tr. of Das Initiaten-Bewusstsein. Die wahren und die falschen Wege der geistigen Forschung. 222p. 1986. pap. 10.95 (ISBN 0-88010-135-0). Anthroposophic.

Sven Eek. Damodar & the Pioneers of the Theosophical Movement. 19.95 (ISBN 0-8356-7003-1). Theos Pub Hse.

Taimni, I. K. Gayatri. 5.95 (ISBN 0-8356-7069-4). Theos Pub Hse.

Taylor, Alfred. A Human Heritage. LC 74-18360. 150p. (Orig.). 1975. pap. 2.50 (ISBN 0-8356-0455-1, Quest). Theos Pub Hse.

Temple of the People Publications Staff, ed. From the Mountain Top, 1 of 3 vols, Vol. I. 278p. 1974. Repr. of 1914 ed. 11.25 (ISBN 0-933797-00-1). Halcyon Bk.

The Theosophical Movement, 1875-1950. rev. ed. xiii, 351p. 1951. 6.00 (ISBN 0-938998-14-5). Cunningham Pr.

The Theosophical Movement 1875-1950: Theosophy Company. xiii, 351p. 1951. 6.00 (ISBN 0-938998-14-5). Theosophy.

Theosophical Research Centre, London. Mystery of Healing. 1968. pap. 3.50 (ISBN 0-8356-0114-5, Quest). Theos Pub Hse.

Theosophy Company. Index to the Secret Doctrine. x, 172p. 1939. 6.00 (ISBN 0-938998-02-1). Theosophy.

Tingley, Katherine. Theosophy: The Path of the Mystic. 3rd rev ed. LC 77-82604. 1977. 8.50 (ISBN 0-911500-33-2); pap. 5.00 (ISBN 0-911500-34-0). Theos U Pr.

Trismegistos, Hermes. The Hymns of Hermes. Mead, G. R. S., tr. from Gr. 84p. (Orig.). 1985. pap. 4.00 (ISBN 0-933999-57-7). Phanes Pr.

Unger, Carl. Cosmic Understanding. 1982. pap. 1.95 (ISBN 0-916786-62-5). St George Bk Serv.

--Steiner's Theosophy: Notes on the Book "Theosophy". 1982. Repr. 5.95 (ISBN 0-916786-64-1). St George Bk Serv.

Van der Leeuw. Gods in Exile. 2.75 (ISBN 0-8356-7056-2). Theos Pub Hse.

Van Der Leeuw, J. J. Conquest of Illusion. 1967. pap. 1.95 (ISBN 0-8356-0400-4, Quest). Theos Pub Hse.

Wachtmeister, Constance. Reminiscences of H. P. Blavatsky. rev. new ed. LC 76-44810. 1977. pap. 3.75 (ISBN 0-8356-0488-8, Quest). Theos Pub Hse.

Westcott. Numbers. 9.50 (ISBN 0-7229-5027-6). Theos Pub Hse.

Winner, Anna K. Basic Ideas of Occult Wisdom. LC 75-116528. (Orig.). 1970. pap. 4.50 (ISBN 0-8356-0391-1, Quest). Theos Pub Hse.

Wood. Mind & Memory Training. 10.50 (ISBN 0-8356-5115-0). Theos Pub Hse.

--Mind & Memory Training. pap. 7.95 (ISBN 0-8356-5126-6). Theos Pub Hse.

Wood, Ernest. The Seven Rays. LC 76-4909. 191p. 1976. pap. 4.95 (ISBN 0-8356-0481-0, Quest). Theos Pub Hse.

THEOTHANATOLOGY

see Death of God Theology

THERESE DE LISIEUX, SAINT, 1873-1897

Beevers, John. Saint Therese, the Little Flower: The Making of a Saint. LC 73-80147. (Orig.). 1976. pap. 3.50 (ISBN 0-89555-035-0). TAN Bks Pubs.

Clarke, John, tr. from Fr. St. Therese of Lisieux: Her Last Conversations. LC 76-27207. (Illus.). 1977. pap. 6.95x (ISBN 0-9600876-3-X). ICS Pubns.

--Story of a Soul: The Autobiography of St. Therese of Lisieux. LC 76-43620. 1976. pap. 6.95x (ISBN 0-9600876-4-8). ICS Pubns.

Day, Dorothy. Therese. 1979. pap. 7.95 (ISBN 0-87243-090-1). Templegate.

Ducrocq, Marie-Pascale. Therese of Lisieux: A Vocation of Love. LC 81-20512. 77p. (Orig.). 1982. pap. 3.95 (ISBN 0-8189-0431-3). Alba.

Eustace, Cecil J. Infinity of Questions. facs. ed. LC 70-84356. (Essay Index Reprint Ser.). 1946. 16.50 (ISBN 0-8369-1080-X). Ayer Co Pubs.

Fox, Robert J. St. Therese of Lisieux: Her Life As She Might Tell It. 20p. 1982. pap. 1.00 (ISBN 0-911988-54-8). AMI Pr.

Gesualda Of The Holy Spirit, Sr. Saint Theresa, the Little Flower. (Illus.). 1960. 4.95 (ISBN 0-8198-0142-9); pap. 3.95. Dghtrs St Paul.

Jamart, Francois. Complete Spiritual Doctrine of St. Therese of Lisieux. Van De Putte, Walter, tr. LC 61-8203. 1977. pap. 6.95 (ISBN 0-8189-0347-3). Alba.

Kaye-Smith, Sheila. Quartet in Heaven. facs. ed. LC 75-136649. (Biography Index Reprint Ser.). 1952. 18.00 (ISBN 0-8369-8044-1). Ayer Co Pubs.

Reddish, Robert O., Jr. Satan, God & Saint Teresa. (Illus.). 1967. soft cover 5.00 (ISBN 0-686-08728-3). Rorge Pub Co.

St. Teresa of Lisieux. Autobiography of Saint Therese of Lisieux: The Story of a Soul. 1957. pap. 3.95 (ISBN 0-385-02903-9, D56, Im). Doubleday.

THOMAS, SAINT, APOSTLE

McInerny, Ralph. Rhyme & Reason: St. Thomas & Modes of Discourse. LC 81-80234. (Aquinas Lecture Ser.). 84p. 1981. 7.95 (ISBN 0-87462-148-8). Marquette.

THOMAS A BECKET, SAINT, ABP. OF CANTERBURY, 1118?-1170

Abbott, Edwin A. St. Thomas of Canterbury: His Death & Miracles, 2 vols. in 1. LC 80-18216. (The Crusades & Military Orders: Second Ser.). Repr. of 1898 ed. 55.00 (ISBN 0-404-16366-1). AMS Pr.

Alan of Tewkesbury. Alani Priors Cantuariensis Postea Abbatis Tewkesberiensis Scripta Quae Extant. Giles, J. A., ed. 1966. Repr. of 1848 ed. 24.00 (ISBN 0-8337-1340-X). B Franklin.

Barlow, Frank. Thomas Becket. (Illus.). 360p. 1986. 25.00 (ISBN 0-520-05920-4). U of Cal Pr.

Corfe, Tom. The Murder of Archbishop Thomas. LC 76-22419. (Cambridge Topic Bks). (Illus.). 1977. PLB 8.95 (ISBN 0-8225-1202-5). Lerner Pubns.

Duggan, Anne. Thomas Becket: A Textual History of His Letters. 1980. 56.00x (ISBN 0-19-822486-9). Oxford U Pr.

Hutton, W. H. S. Thomas of Canterbury. 59.95 (ISBN 0-8490-0983-9). Gordon Pr.

Ide, Arthur F. Calendar of Death: The Socio-Psychological Factors Influencing the Martyrdom of Thomas of Canterbury. LC 86-15455. (Medieval People: Vol. 2). (Illus.). viii, 157p. (Orig.). 1986. pap. 9.95 (ISBN 0-934667-02-0). Tangelwuld.

Knowles, M. D. Archbishop Thomas Beckett: A Character Study. (Raleigh Lectures on History). 1970. pap. 2.25 (ISBN 0-85672-313-4, Pub. by British Acad). Longwood Pub Group.

Magnusson, M. eirikr. Thomas Saga Erkibyskups: A Life of Archbishop Thomas Becket, in Icelandic, with English Translation, Notes & Glossary, 2 vols. (Rolls Ser.: No. 65). Repr. of 1883 ed. Set. 120.00 (ISBN 0-8115-1133-2). Kraus Repr.

Robertson, James C. & Sheppard, J. B., eds. Materials for the History of Thomas Becket, 7 vols. (Rolls Ser.: No. 67). Repr. of 1885 ed. Set. 308.00 (ISBN 0-8115-1135-9). Kraus Repr.

THOMAS A BECKET, SAINT, ABP. OF CANTERBURY, 1118?-1170–DRAMA

Anouilh, Jean. Becket. 1960. pap. 5.95 (ISBN 0-698-10031-X, Coward). Putnam Pub Group.

--Becket ou, l'Honneur de Dieu. 1973. pap. 5.50 (ISBN 0-685-11038-9, 1716). French & Eur.

THOMAS A KEMPIS, 1380-1471

De Montmorency, J. E. Thomas A'Kempis: His Age & Book. LC 73-103183. 1970. Repr. of 1906 ed. 30.00x (ISBN 0-8046-0820-2, Pub by Kennikat). Assoc Faculty Pr.

Kettlewell, S. Thomas A'Kempis, 2 vols. 1882. 85.00 set (ISBN 0-8274-3599-1). R West.

THOMAS AQUINAS, SAINT, 1225?-1274

Adler, Mortimer J. Saint Thomas & the Gentiles. (Aquinas Lecture). 1938. 7.95 (ISBN 0-87462-102-X). Marquette.

Banes, F. Dominico. Scholastica Commentaria in Primam Partem Summae Theologicae S. Thomae Aquinatis, De Deo Uno. Urbano, Luis, ed. (Medieval Studies Reprint Ser.). (Lat. & Span.). Repr. of 1934 ed. lib. bdg. 45.00x (ISBN 0-697-00028-1). Irvington.

Bobik, Joseph. Aquinas on Being & Essence: A Translation & Interpretation. LC 65-23516. pap. 75.50 (ISBN 0-317-26719-1, 2024364). Bks Demand UMI.

Bourke, Vernon J. Saint Thomas & the Greek Moralists. (Aquinas Lecture). 1947. 7.95 (ISBN 0-87462-111-9). Marquette.

Brennan, Sr. M. Rose. Intellectual Virtues According to the Philosophy of St. Thomas. (Orig.). 1957. pap. text ed. 4.95x (ISBN 0-87015-075-8). Pacific Bks.

Brennan, Robert E., ed. Essays in Thomism. LC 72-1149. (Essay Index Reprint Ser.). Repr. of 1942 ed. 27.50 (ISBN 0-8369-2834-2). Ayer Co Pubs.

Brown, Barry F. Accidental Being: A Study in the Metaphysics of St. Thomas Aquinas. LC 85-15653. 440p. (Orig.). 1985. lib. bdg. 32.75 (ISBN 0-8191-4886-5); pap. text ed. 19.50 (ISBN 0-8191-4887-3). U Pr of Amer.

Burrell, David B. Aquinas: God & Action. LC 78-51519. 1979. text ed. 14.95x (ISBN 0-268-00588-5). U of Notre Dame Pr.

--Knowing the Unknowable God: Ibn-Sina, Maimonides, Aquinas. LC 85-40600. 160p. 1986. text ed. 15.95x (ISBN 0-268-01225-3, 85-12253). U of Notre Dame Pr.

--Knowing the Unknowable God: Ibn-Sina, Maimonides, Aquinas. 130p. 1986. pap. text ed. 8.95x (ISBN 0-268-01226-1, Dist. by Har-Row). U of Notre Dame Pr.

Cessario, Romanus. Christian Satisfaction in Aquinas: Towards a Personalist Understanding. LC 81-43836. 390p. (Orig.). 1982. lib. bdg. 32.00 (ISBN 0-8191-2557-1); pap. text ed. 15.75 (ISBN 0-8191-2558-X). U Pr of Amer.

Chesterton, G. K. Saint Thomas Aquinas. 200p. 1974. pap. 3.95 (ISBN 0-385-09002-1, Im). Doubleday.

Clark, Mary T., ed. An Aquinas Reader. LC 72-76709. pap. 6.95 (ISBN 0-385-02505-X, Im). Doubleday.

Companion to the Summa, 4 vols. 1985. Set. pap. 50.00 (ISBN 0-87061-117-8). Chr Classics.

Copleston, F. C. Aquinas. 272p. 1956. pap. 5.95 (ISBN 0-14-020349-4, Pelican). Penguin.

D'Entreves, A. P., ed. Thomas Aquinas: Selected Political Writings. Dawson, J. G., tr. 136p. 1981. 26.50x; pap. 9.95x (ISBN 0-389-20244-4). B&N Imports.

D'Entreves, Alexander P. Medieval Contribution to Political Thought: Thomas Aquinas, Marsilius of Padua, Richard Hooker. 1959. Repr. of 1939 ed. text ed. 12.50x (ISBN 0-391-00513-8). Humanities.

Dienstag, Jacob I. Maimonides & St. Thomas Aquinas. 1974. 39.50x (ISBN 0-87068-249-0). Ktav.

Diggs, Bernard J. Love & Being: An Investigation into the Metaphysics of St. Thomas Aquinas. 180p. 1947. 6.75 (ISBN 0-913298-45-X). S F Vanni.

Durantel, J. Saint Thomas et le Pseudo-Denis. (Medieval Studies Ser.). (Fr.). Repr. of 1919 ed. lib. bdg. 45.00x (ISBN 0-697-00036-2). Irvington.

Edwards, Steven A. Interior Acts: Teleology, Justice, & Friendship in the Religious Ethics of Thomas Aquinas. LC 85-29530. 184p. (Orig.). 1986. lib. bdg. 24.75 (ISBN 0-8191-5212-9); pap. text ed. 11.75 (ISBN 0-8191-5213-7). U Pr of Amer.

Fairweather, A. M., ed. Aquinas on Nature & Grace. LC 54-10259. (Library of Christian Classics). 382p. 1978. pap. 10.95 softcover (ISBN 0-664-24155-7). Westminster.

Fairweather, Alan M. The Word As Truth: A Critical Examination of the Christian Doctrine of Revelation in the Writings of Thomas Aquinas & Karl Barth. LC 78-26040. 1979. Repr. of 1944 ed. lib. bdg. cancelled (ISBN 0-313-20808-5, FAWT). Greenwood.

Figurski, Leszek. Finality & Intelligence. LC 78-62252. 1978. pap. text ed. 11.25 (ISBN 0-8191-0565-1). U Pr of Amer.

Gilbert, Allan H. Dante's Conception of Justice. LC 76-166199. (BCL Ser.: I). Repr. of 1925 ed. 15.00 (ISBN 0-404-02757-1). AMS Pr.

Gilson, Etienne. The Christian Philosophy of St. Thomas Aquinas. x, 502p. 1983. Repr. of 1956 ed. lib. bdg. 45.00 (ISBN 0-88254-874-3, Octagon). Hippocrene Bks.

--History of Philosophy & Philosophical Education. (Aquinas Lecture). 1947. 7.95 (ISBN 0-87462-112-7). Marquette.

--Thomist Realism. Wauck, Mark A., tr. LC 86-80104. 215p. 1986. pap. 12.95 (ISBN 0-89870-094-9). Ignatius Pr.

--Wisdom & Love in Saint Thomas Aquinas. (Aquinas Lecture). 1951. 7.95 (ISBN 0-87462-116-X). Marquette.

Glenn, Paul J. Tour of the Summa. LC 78-66307. 1978. pap. 12.50 (ISBN 0-89555-081-4). TAN Bks Pubs.

Gratsch, Edward J. Aquinas' Summa: An Introduction & Interpretation. LC 85-15842. 305p. (Orig.). 1985. pap. 12.95 (ISBN 0-8189-0485-2). Alba.

Haberman, Jacob. Maimonides & Aquinas: A Contemporary Appraisal. 25.00x (ISBN 0-87068-685-2). Ktav.

Healy, Mary E. Society & Social Change in the Writings of St. Thomas, Ward, Sumner, & Cooley. LC 75-156191. 159p. 1972. Repr. of 1948 ed. lib. bdg. 22.50x (ISBN 0-8371-6140-1, HESC). Greenwood.

Jaffa, Harry V. Thomism & Aristotelianism: A Study of the Commentary by Thomas Aquinas on the Nicomachean Ethics. LC 78-21520. 1979. Repr. of 1952 ed. lib. bdg. 29.75x (ISBN 0-313-21149-3, JATA). Greenwood.

Jordon, Mark D. Ordering Wisdom: The Hierarchy of Philosophical Discourses in Aquinas. LC 86-40335. (Publications in Medieval Studies: No. 24). 448p. 1986. text ed. 35.00 (ISBN 0-268-01500-7). U of Notre Dame Pr.

Kenny, Anthony. Aquinas. (Past Masters Ser.). 1980. pap. 4.95 (ISBN 0-19-287500-0). Oxford U Pr.

--The Five Ways: St. Thomas Aquinas' Proofs of God's Existence. LC 80-10416. 140p. 1980. pap. text ed. 4.95 (ISBN 0-268-00952-X). U of Notre Dame Pr.

Klauder, Francis J. The Wonder of the Real: A Sketch in Basic Philosophy. rev., enlarged ed. LC 72-94706. (Illus.). 116p. 1973. 9.95 (ISBN 0-8158-0300-1). Chris Mass.

Klocker, Harry R., ed. Thomism & Modern Thought. LC 62-9414. 1962. 32.50x (ISBN 0-89197-451-2). Irvington.

Klubertanz, George P. St. Thomas Aquinas on Analogy: A Textual Analysis & Systematic Synthesis. LC 60-9602. (Jesuit Studies). pap. 81.80 (ISBN 0-317-09004-6, 2000813). Bks Demand UMI.

Kuhn, Wilfried. Das Prinzipieproblem in der Philosophie des Thomas von Aquin. (Bochum Studies in Philosophy Ser.: No. 1). 531p. 1982. 40.00x (ISBN 90-6032-227-4, Pub by B R Gruener Amsterdam). Benjamins North Am.

McCormick, John F. Saint Thomas & the Life of Learning. (Aquinas Lecture). 1937. 7.95 (ISBN 0-87462-101-1). Marquette.

McInerny, Ralph. Being & Predication: Thomistic Interpretations. (Studies in Philosophy & the History of Philosophy: Vol. 16). 1986. 36.95 (ISBN 0-8132-0612-X). Cath U Pr.

--Ethica Thomistica: The Moral Philosophy of Thomas Aquinas. LC 78-62029. 129p. 1982. pap. 7.95 (ISBN 0-8132-0561-1). Cath U Pr.

--St. Thomas Aquinas. LC 81-16293. 197p. 1982. pap. text ed. 5.95 (ISBN 0-268-01707-7). U of Notre Dame Pr.

McInerny, Ralph M., ed. Thomism in an Age of Renewal. 1968. pap. 5.95x (ISBN 0-268-00276-2). U of Notre Dame Pr.

McLean, George F., ed. Thomas & Bonaventure: A Septicentenary Commemoration. LC 75-319639. (Proceedings of the American Catholic Philosophical Association: Vol. 48). 1974. pap. 15.00 (ISBN 0-918090-08-3). Am Cath Philo.

Manthey, F. Die Sprachphilosophie Des Hl, Thomas Von Aquin. (Philosophy Reprints Ser.). (Ger.). Repr. of 1937 ed. lib. bdg. 45.00x (ISBN 0-697-00042-7). Irvington.

Margenau, Henry. Thomas & the Physics of Nineteen Fifty-Eight: A Confrontation. (Aquinas Lecture). 1958. 7.95 (ISBN 0-87462-123-2). Marquette.

Maritain, Jacques. Saint Thomas & the Problem of Evil. (Aquinas Lecture). 1942. 7.95 (ISBN 0-87462-106-2). Marquette.

--True Humanism. Adamson, M. R., tr. LC 71-114888. (Select Bibliographies Reprint Ser). 1938. 22.00 (ISBN 0-8369-5292-8). Ayer Co Pubs.

--True Humanism. 3rd ed. Adamson, Margot, tr. Repr. of 1941 ed. lib. bdg. 35.00x (ISBN 0-8371-2902-8, MAHU). Greenwood.

Maurer, Armand A. St. Thomas & Historicity. LC 79-84278. (Aquinas Lecture Ser.). 1979. 7.95 (ISBN 0-87462-144-5). Marquette.

Miethe, Terry L. & Bourke, Vernon J., eds. Thomistic Bibliography, 1940-1978. LC 80-1195. xxii, 318p. 1980. lib. bdg. 45.00 (ISBN 0-313-21991-5, MTH/). Greenwood.

Mitchell, Thomas A. Hedonism & Eudonism in Aquinas. 1983. 2.00 (ISBN 0-686-45793-5). Franciscan Herald.

Moskop, John C. Divine Omniscience & Human Freedom: Thomas Aquinas & Charles Hartshorne. LC 84-1172. xviii, 105p. 1984. 14.95 (ISBN 0-86554-123-X, MUP/H102). Mercer Univ Pr.

Novak, David. Suicide & Morality: The Theories of Plato, Aquinas & Kant & Their Relevance for Suicidology. LC 75-37543. x, 136p. 1976. lib. bdg. 7.50 (ISBN 0-685-69079-2). Scholars Studies.

O'Connor, William R. Natural Desire for God: Aquinas Lectures. 1948. 7.95 (ISBN 0-87462-113-5). Marquette.

O'Neil, Charles J. Imprudence in Saint Thomas Aquinas. (Aquinas Lecture Ser.). 1955. 7.95 (ISBN 0-87462-120-8). Marquette.

Owens, Joseph. St. Thomas Aquinas on the Existence of God: Collected Papers of Joseph Owens. Catan, John R., ed. LC 79-13885. 1980. 44.50x (ISBN 0-87395-401-7); pap. 16.95x (ISBN 0-87395-446-7). State U NY Pr.

Owens, Joseph C. Saint Thomas & the Future of Metaphysics. (Aquinas Lecture). 1957. 7.95 (ISBN 0-87462-122-4). Marquette.

Patterson, Robert L. The Conception of God in the Philosophy of Thomas Aquinas. 508p. 1977. Repr. of 1935 ed. lib. bdg. 30.00 (ISBN 0-915172-27-5). Richwood Pub.

Pegis, Anton C. Saint Thomas & Philosophy. (Aquinas Lecture). 1964. 7.95 (ISBN 0-87462-129-1). Marquette.

--Saint Thomas & the Greeks. (Aquinas Lecture). 1939. 7.95 (ISBN 0-87462-103-8). Marquette.

Pepler, C. The Basis of the Mysticism of St. Thomas Aquinas. 1977. lib. bdg. 59.95 (ISBN 0-8490-1479-4). Gordon Pr.

Phelan, Gerald B. Saint Thomas & Analogy. (Aquinas Lecture). 1941. 7.95 (ISBN 0-87462-105-4). Marquette.

Pieper, Josef. Guide to Thomas Aquinas. LC 86-40588. 192p. 1987. pap. text ed. 8.95x (ISBN 0-268-01013-7, Dist. by Har-Row). U of Notre Dame Pr.

Pieper, Josef, et al. Guide to Thomas Aquinas. Winston, Richard & Winston, Clara, trs. from Ger. 182p. 1982. Repr. of 1962 ed. lib. bdg. 20.50 (ISBN 0-374-96448-3, Octagon). Hippocrene Bks.

Preller, Victor. Divine Science & the Science of God: A Reformulation of Thomas Aquinas. LC 66-21838. pap. 72.80 (ISBN 0-317-08468-2, 2010543). Bks Demand UMI.

Rand, Edward K. Cicero in the Courtroom of Saint Thomas Aquinas. (Aquinas Lecture Ser.). 1945. 7.95 (ISBN 0-87462-109-7). Marquette.

Redpath, Peter A. The Moral Wisdom of St. Thomas: An Introduction. LC 83-3590. 216p. (Orig.). 1983. lib. bdg. 26.00 (ISBN 0-8191-3144-X); pap. text ed. 11.00 (ISBN 0-8191-3145-8). U Pr of Amer.
--A Simplified Introduction to the Wisdom of St. Thomas. LC 80-5230. 180p. 1980. lib. bdg. 24.00 (ISBN 0-8191-1058-2); pap. text ed. 10.50 (ISBN 0-8191-1059-0). U Pr of Amer.
Regis, Louis-Marie. Saint Thomas & Epistemology. (Aquinas Lecture Ser.). 1946. 7.95 (ISBN 0-87462-110-0). Marquette.
Robb, James H. Saint Thomas Aquinas: Questions on the Soul. (Medieval Philosophical Texts in Translation: NO. 27). 1984. 24.95 (ISBN 0-87462-226-3). Marquette.
St. Thomas Aquinas. Political Ideas of St. Thomas Aquinas: A Selection from His Writings. 1973. pap. 9.95x (ISBN 0-317-30522-0). Free Pr.
Shahan, Robert W. & Kovach, Francis J. Bonaventure & Aquinas: Enduring Philosophers. LC 75-40963. (Illus.). 200p. 1976. pap. 8.95x (ISBN 0-8061-1349-9). U of Okla Pr.
Steiner, Rudolf. The Redemption of Thinking: A Study in the Philosophy of Thomas Aquinas. Sheperd, A. P. & Nicoll, Mildred R., trs. from Ger. Orig. Title: Die Philosophie des Thomas von Aquino. 191p. 1983. pap. text ed. 8.95 (ISBN 0-88010-044-3). Anthroposophic.
Van Steenberghen, Fernand. Thomas Aquinas & Radical Aristotelianism. O'Meara, Dominic J., et al, trs. from Fr. 114p. 1980. pap. 6.95 (ISBN 0-8132-0552-2). Cath U Pr.
Werner, Karl. Heilige Thomas Von Aquino, 3 vols. rev. ed. 1963. Set. 107.00 (ISBN 0-8337-3738-4). B Franklin.
Wicksteed, Philip H. Dante & Aquinas. LC 79-153489. (Studies in Dante, No. 9). 1971. Repr. of 1913 ed. lib. bdg. 49.95x (ISBN 0-8383-1240-3). Haskell.
Wippel, John F. Metaphysical Themes in Thomas Aquinas. LC 82-7296. (Studies in Philosophy & the History of Philosophy: Vol. 10). 294p. 1984. 31.95x (ISBN 0-8132-0578-6). Cath U Pr.

THOMISM
see Thomists

THOMISM (MODERN PHILOSOPHY)
see Neo-Scholasticism

THOMISTS
Brezik, Victor B., ed. One Hundred Years of Thomism: Aeterni Patris & Afterwards - A Symposium. LC 85-14986. 210p. pap. text ed. 9.95 (ISBN 0-9605456-0-3). U of Notre Dame Pr.

THONRAKETZI
see Paulicians

THOREAU, HENRY DAVID, 1817-1862
Christy, Arthur. Orient in American Transcendentalism: A Study of Emerson, Thoreau & Alcott. 1963. lib. bdg. 26.00x (ISBN 0-374-91539-3, Octagon). Hippocrene Bks.
Pillai, A. K. Transcendental Self: A Comparative Study of Thoreau & the Psycho-Philosophy of Hinduism & Buddhism. LC 85-686. 130p. (Orig.). 1985. lib. bdg. 21.75 (ISBN 0-8191-4572-6). U Pr of Amer.
Stoehr, Taylor. Nay-Saying in Concord: Emerson, Alcott & Thoreau. LC 78-25580. 179p. 1979. 21.50 (ISBN 0-208-01767-4, Archon). Shoe String.
Thoreau, Henry David. Henry David Thoreau: A Week on the Concord & Merrimack Rivers; Walden; The Maine Woods; Cape Cod. 1114p. 27.50. Library of America.
Wolf, William J. Thoreau: Mystic, Prophet, Ecologist. LC 73-22368. 224p. 1974. 6.95 (ISBN 0-8298-0269-X). Pilgrim NY.

THORPE, WILLIAM d. 1407
Bale, John. Select Works of John Bale, Bishop of Ossory. 51.00 (ISBN 0-384-03135-8). Johnson Repr.

THOUGHT, FREE
see Free Thought

THOUGHT, NEW
see New Thought

TIBET
Gyatso, Tenzin. My Land & My People. 3rd ed. (Illus.). 271p. 1983. Repr. of 1962 ed. 6.95. Potala.
Illion, Theodore. Darkness over Tibet. 192p. 1983. pap. 6.95 (ISBN 0-912181-03-6). East School Pr.
--In Secret Tibet: In Disguise Amongst Lamas, Robbers & Wise Men. A Key to the Mysteries of Tibet. 190p. 1983. pap. 6.95 (ISBN 0-912181-01-X). East School Pr.

TIBET-CIVILIZATION
Aziz, Barbara N. & Kapstein, M. Soundings in Tibetan Civilization. 1986. 32.00x (ISBN 0-8364-1587-6, Pub. by Manohar India). South Asia Bks.
Chophel, Norbu. Folk Culture of Tibet. 105p. 1986. Repr. 7.50X (ISBN 0-8364-1676-7, Pub. by Manohar India). South Asia Bks.
Nebesky-Wojkowitz, Rene De. Oracles & Demons of Tibet. 100.00 (ISBN 0-87968-463-1). Gordon Pr.
Paul, Robert A. The Tibetan Symbolic World: Psychoanalytic Explorations. LC 81-16505. (Chicago Originals Ser.). (Illus.). 360p. 1982. lib. bdg. 14.00x (ISBN 0-226-64987-3). U of Chicago Pr.
Snellgrove, David & Richardson, Hugh. A Cultural History of Tibet. LC 85-27861. (Illus.). 307p. 1986. pap. 12.95 (ISBN 0-87773-353-8, 74380-6, Dist. by Random). Shambhala Pubns.

TIBET-DESCRIPTION AND TRAVEL
Blavatsky, Helena P. The Caves & Jungles of Hindustan. De Zirkoff, Boris, ed. LC 74-26605. (Illus.). 750p. 1975. 18.50 (ISBN 0-8356-0219-2). Theos Pub Hse.
Chapman, F. Spencer. Lhasa the Holy City. facsimile ed. LC 75-37875. (Select Bibliographies Reprint Ser). Repr. of 1940 ed. 32.00 (ISBN 0-8369-6712-7). Ayer Co Pubs.
David-Neel, Alexandra. My Journey to Lhasa. LC 85-47947. (Illus.). 320p. 1986. lib. bdg. 22.00x (ISBN 0-8070-5900-5); pap. 10.95 (ISBN 0-8070-5901-3, BP713). Beacon Pr.
Hedin, Sven A. Central Asia & Tibet Towards the Holy City of Lassa, 2 Vols. Bealby, J. T., tr. LC 68-55192. (Illus.). 1968. Repr. of 1903 ed. lib. bdg. 97.50x (ISBN 0-8371-3893-0, HECA). Greenwood.

TIBET-HISTORY
Fleming, Peter. Bayonets to Lhasa. LC 73-16737. (Illus.). 1974. Repr. of 1961 ed. lib. bdg. 22.50x (ISBN 0-8371-7216-0, FLBL). Greenwood.
Heruka, Tsang N. The Life of Marpa the Translator. Nalanda Translation Committee & Trungpa, Chogyam, trs. from Tibetan. LC 86-11837. 320p. 1986. pap. 12.95 (ISBN 0-87773-377-5). Shambhala Pubns.

TIBET-RELIGION
Barborka, Geoffrey A. H. P. Blavatsky: Tibet & Tulku. (Illus.). 1974. 12.95 (ISBN 0-8356-7159-3). Theos Pub Hse.
Bell, Charles A. The Religion of Tibet. lib. bdg. 79.95 (ISBN 0-87968-482-8). Krishna Pr.
Beyer, Stephan. The Cult of Tara: Magic & Ritual in Tibet. LC 74-186109. (Hermeneutics: Studies in the History of Religions). (Illus.). 1974. pap. 12.95 (ISBN 0-520-03635-2, CAL 383). U of Cal Pr.
Blavatsky, Helena P. The Caves & Jungles of Hindustan. De Zirkoff, Boris, ed. LC 74-26605. (Illus.). 750p. 1975. 18.50 (ISBN 0-8356-0219-2). Theos Pub Hse.
Burman, Bina R. Religion & Politics in Tibet. 1979. text ed. 17.50x (ISBN 0-7069-0801-5, Pub. by Vikas India). Advent NY.
Dargyay, Eva M. The Rise of Esoteric Buddhism in Tibet. 1977. 14.00 (ISBN 0-8426-0915-6, Pub by Molilal Banarsidass India). Orient Bk Dist.
Douglas, N. & White, M. Karmapa the Black Hat Lama of Tibet. 248p. 1976. 40.00x (ISBN 0-317-39097-X, Pub. by Luzac & Co Ltd). State Mutual Bk.
Gold, Peter. Tibetan Reflections. (Illus.). 112p. (Orig.). 1984. pap. 11.95 (ISBN 0-86171-022-3, Wisdom Pubns). Great Traditions.
Guenther, Herbert V. Tibetan Buddhism in Western Perspective. LC 76-47758. (Illus.). 1977. pap. 8.95 (ISBN 0-913546-50-X). Dharma Pub.
Gyalsten, Khenpo K. The Garland of Mahamudra Practices. 140p. 1986. pap. 9.95 (ISBN 0-937938-35-1). Snow Lion.
--Prayer Flags: The Spiritual Life & Songs of Jigten Sumgon. 96p. (Orig.). 1986. pap. 6.95 (ISBN 0-937938-37-8). Snow Lion.
Hopkins, Jeffrey & Klein, Ann. Compassion in Tibetan Buddhism. 2nd ed. Napper, Elizabeth, ed. LC 80-85453. 263p. 1980. pap. 10.95 (ISBN 0-937938-04-1). Snow Lion.
Lopez, Donald S, Jr. A Study of Svatantrika. 490p. (Orig.). 1987. lib. bdg. 35.00 (ISBN 0-937938-20-3); pap. 19.95 (ISBN 0-937938-19-X). Snow Lion.
Muses, C. A. Esoteric Teachings of the Tibetan Tantra. 319p. 1982. pap. 8.95 (ISBN 0-87728-307-9). Weiser.
Pallis, Marco. Peaks & Lamas. lib. bdg. 100.00 (ISBN 0-87968-327-9). Gordon Pr.
Rao, S. K. Tibetan Tantrik Tradition. (Illus.). 1977. text ed. 10.50x (ISBN 0-391-01105-7). Humanities.
Rinbochay, Lati. Mind in Tibetan Buddhism. Napper, Elizabeth, ed. LC 86-3799. 172p. (Orig.). 1980. lib. bdg. 12.95 cancelled (ISBN 0-937938-03-3); pap. 10.95 (ISBN 0-937938-02-5). Snow Lion.
Trungpa, Chogyam. The Rain of Wisdom. Nalanda Translation Committee, tr. from Tibetan. LC 80-51130. Tr. of Bka'-Rgyud Mgur-Mtsho. 384p. 1985. pap. 18.95 (ISBN 0-87773-345-7, 73972-8). Shambhala Pubns.
Waddell, Austine. Buddhism & Lamaism of Tibet. 1985. text ed. 40.00x (ISBN 0-86590-615-7, Pub. by Sterling Pubs India). Apt Bks.
Wijers, L. His Holiness the Fourteenth Dalai Lama of Tibet Talks to Louwrier Wijers. 192p. 1982. 29.00x (ISBN 0-317-39082-1, Pub. by Luzac & Co Ltd). State Mutual Bk.

TIECK, JOHANN LUDWIG, 1773-1853
Danton, George H. Nature Sense in the Writings of Ludwig Tieck. LC 78-163673. (Columbia University. Germanic Studies, Old Ser.: No. 9). Repr. of 1907 ed. 15.00 (ISBN 0-404-50409-4). AMS Pr.
Lang, Edgar A. Ludwig Tieck's Early Concept of Catholic Clergy & Church. LC 74-140044. (Catholic University Studies in German Ser.: No. 8). Repr. of 1936 ed. 28.00 (ISBN 0-404-50228-8). AMS Pr.
Matenko, Percy. Ludwig Tieck & America. LC 54-62860. (North Carolina University. Studies in the Germanic Languages & Literatures: No. 12). Repr. of 1954 ed. 27.00 (ISBN 0-404-50912-6). AMS Pr.
Scheiber, Sr. Mary M. Ludwig Tieck & the Medieval Church. LC 74-140028. (Catholic University Studies in German: No. 12). Repr. of 1939 ed. 22.00 (ISBN 0-404-50232-6). AMS Pr.
Tieck, Johann L. Letters of Ludwig Tieck, Hitherto Unpublished, 1792-1853. Zeydel, Edwin H., et al, eds. LC 73-9682. (MLA Gen. Ser.: No. 7). 636p. 1973. Repr. of 1937 ed. 41.00 (ISBN 0-527-90100-8). Kraus Repr.
Tieck, Ludwig. The Land of Upside Down. Mandel, Oscar, tr. LC 76-50288. 123p. 1978. 17.50 (ISBN 0-8386-2061-2). Fairleigh Dickinson.

TILLICH, PAUL, 1886-1965
Adams, James L., et al, eds. The Thought of Paul Tillich. 1985. 24.45 (ISBN 0-06-060072-1). Har-Row.
Carey, John J., ed. Theonomy & Autonomy: Studies in Paul Tillich's Engagement with Modern Culture. LC 83-25847. xxii, 287p. 1984. Repr. of 1978 ed. 21.95 (ISBN 0-86554-105-1, MUP/H99). Mercer Univ Pr.
Clayton, John P. The Concept of Correlation: Paul Tillich & the Possibility of a Mediating Theology. (Theologische Bibliothek Topelmann Ser.: No. 37). 427p. 1979. text ed. 44.25x (ISBN 3-11007-914-3). De Gruyter.
Crossman, Richard C. Paul Tillich: A Comprehensive Bibliography & Keyword Index of Primary & Secondary Writings in English. LC 83-15026. (ATLA Bibliography Ser.: No. 9). 193p. 1983. 17.50 (ISBN 0-8108-1650-4). Scarecrow.
Eisenbeis, Walter. The Key Ideas of Paul Tillich's Systematic Theology. LC 82-21834. (Ger. & Eng.). 268p. (Orig.). 1983. lib. bdg. 27.50 (ISBN 0-8191-2948-8); pap. text ed. 13.25 (ISBN 0-8191-2949-6). U Pr of Amer.
Freeman, David H. Tillich. (Modern Thinkers Ser.). 1960. pap. 2.00 (ISBN 0-87552-589-X). Presby & Reformed.
Grigg, Richard. Symbol & Empowerment: Paul Tillich's Post-Theistic System. xvi, 148p. 1985. text ed. 14.50 (ISBN 0-86554-163-9, MUP H153). Mercer Univ Pr.
Johnson, Wayne G. Theological Method in Luther & Tillich: Law-Gospel & Correlation. LC 80-5691. 204p. 1982. lib. bdg. 27.50 (ISBN 0-8191-1895-8); pap. text ed. 12.50 (ISBN 0-8191-1896-6). U Pr of Amer.
Kegley, Charles W., ed. The Theology of Paul Tillich. rev. ed. LC 82-301. 432p. 1982. pap. 10.95 (ISBN 0-8298-0499-4). Pilgrim NY.
Lyons, James R., ed. The Intellectual Legacy of Paul Tillich. LC 68-63714. (Slaughter Foundation Lectures: 1966). pap. 29.80 (2027636). Bks Demand UMI.
Mahan, Wayne W. Tillich's System. LC 73-91170. 1974. 10.00 (ISBN 0-911536-52-3). Trinity U Pr.
Mallow, Vernon. The Demonic: A Selected Theological Study: An Examination into the Theology of Edwin Lewis, Karl Barth, & Paul Tillich. LC 83-1143. 192p. (Orig.). 1983. lib. bdg. 26.00 (ISBN 0-8191-3069-9); pap. text ed. 11.50 (ISBN 0-8191-3070-2). U Pr of Amer.
Martin, Bernard. The Existentialist Theology of Paul Tillich. 1963. 14.95x (ISBN 0-8084-0399-0); pap. 10.95x (ISBN 0-8084-0400-8). New Coll U Pr.
Modras, Ronald E. Paul Tillich's Theology of the Church: A Catholic Appraisal. LC 76-6082. 326p. 1976. 25.95x (ISBN 0-8143-1552-6). Wayne St U Pr.
Murphy, Carol. A Deeper Faith. 1983. pap. 2.50x (ISBN 0-87574-099-5, 099). Pendle Hill.
Newport, John P. Paul Tillich. 320p. 1984. 12.95 (ISBN 0-8499-2952-0). Word Bks.
Palmer, Michael. Paul Tillich's Philosophy of Art. LC 83-15056. (Theologische Bibliothek Toepelmann Ser.: Vol. 41). xxii, 217p. 1983. 49.50x (ISBN 3-11-009681-1). De Gruyter.
Pauck, Wilhelm & Pauck, Marion. Paul Tillich: His Life & Thought, Vol. 1: Life. LC 74-25709. (Illus.). 352p. 1976. 15.00 (ISBN 0-06-066474-6, HarpR). Har-Row.
Plaskow, Judith. Sex, Sin & Grace: Women's Experience & the Theologies of Reinhold Niebuhr & Paul Tillich. LC 79-5434. 1980. pap. text ed. 11.25 (ISBN 0-8191-0882-0). U Pr of Amer.
Ross, Robert R. N. The Non-Existence of God: Linguistic Paradox in Tillich's Thought. LC 78-65486. (Toronto Studies in Theology: Vol. 1). xiv, 216p. 1978. 39.95x (ISBN 0-88946-905-9). E Mellen.
Scharlemann, Robert P. Reflection & Doubt in the Thought of Paul Tillich. LC 79-81430. Repr. of 1969 ed. 45.60 (ISBN 0-8357-9481-4, 2013185). Bks Demand UMI.
Smith, Kent D. Faith: Reflections on Experience, Theology & Fiction. 114p. (Orig.). 1984. lib. bdg. 22.00 (ISBN 0-8191-3634-4); pap. text ed. 9.25 (ISBN 0-8191-3635-2). U Pr of Amer.
Stone, Ronald H. Paul Tillich's Radical Social Thought. 180p. 1986. pap. text ed. 10.75 (ISBN 0-8191-5152-1). U Pr of Amer.
Stumme, John R. Socialism in Theological Perspective: A Study of Paul Tillich, Nineteen Eighteen to Nineteen Thirty-Three. LC 78-3675. (American Academy of Religion. Dissertation Ser.: No. 21). 1978. pap. 9.95 (ISBN 0-89130-232-8, 010121). Scholars Pr GA.
Thatcher, Adrian. The Ontology of Paul Tillich. (Oxford Theological Monographs). 1978. text ed. 29.95x (ISBN 0-19-826715-0). Oxford U Pr.
Tillich, Hannah. From Place to Place: Travels with Paul Tillich, Travels Without Paul Tillich. LC 75-34490. (Illus.). 224p. 1976. 10.00 (ISBN 0-8128-1902-0). Stein & Day.
Wheat, Leonard F. Paul Tillich's Dialectical Humanism: Unmasking the God above God. LC 74-105365. (Illus.). 287p. 1970. 26.50x (ISBN 0-8018-1161-9). Johns Hopkins.
Williamson, Rene De Visme. Politics & Protestant Theology: An Interpretation of Tillich, Barth, Bonhoeffer, & Brunner. LC 76-20817. 1976. 20.00x (ISBN 0-8071-0193-1). La State U Pr.

TIME
Beckmann, Beverly. Time in God's World. (In God's World Ser.). (Illus.). 24p. 1985. 5.95 (ISBN 0-570-04128-7, 56-1539). Concordia.
Jaspers, Karl. Die Geistige Situation der Zeit. (Sammlung Goeschen: No. 1000). 1979. 7.80x (ISBN 3-11007-878-3). De Gruyter.
Macey, Samuel L. Clocks & the Cosmos: Time in Western Life & Thought. LC 79-18891. (Illus.). 256p. 1980. 25.00 (ISBN 0-208-01773-9, Archon). Shoe String.

TIME (THEOLOGY)
Blake, A. G. A Seminar on Time. LC 79-52756. 1980. 5.95 (ISBN 0-934254-00-1). Claymont Comm.
Boodin, John E. Time & Reality. LC 75-3064. (Philosophy in America Ser.). Repr. of 1904 ed. 20.00 (ISBN 0-404-59063-2). AMS Pr.
Herrmann, Siegfried. Time & History. Belvins, James L., tr. LC 80-25323. (Biblical Encounter Ser.). 208p. (Orig.). 1981. pap. 9.95 (ISBN 0-687-42100-4). Abingdon.
Slaatte, Howard A. Time & Its End: A Comparative Existential Interpretation of Time & Eschatology. LC 80-7814. 298p. 1980. pap. text ed. 13.25 (ISBN 0-8191-1070-1). U Pr of Amer.

TISSUE TRANSPLANTATION
see Transplantation of Organs, Tissues, etc.

TISSUES-TRANSPLANTATION
see Transplantation of Organs, Tissues, etc.

TITHES
Badillo, Tony. Tithing: God's Command Or Man's Demand - Which? (Illus.). 102p. (Orig.). 1984. pap. 9.50 (ISBN 0-912977-00-0). Xavier Pr.
Baldwin, James E., Sr. Old Testament Tithing versus New Testament Giving. 1984. 6.95 (ISBN 0-317-03291-7). Vantage.
Champlin, Joseph M. Sharing Treasure, Time, & Talent: A Parish Manual for Sacrificial Giving or Tithing. LC 82-16178. 88p. (Orig.). 1982. pap. 4.95 (ISBN 0-8146-1277-6). Liturgical Pr.
Goy, Joseph. Les Fluctuations Du Produit De la Dime: Conjoncture Decimale et Domaniale De la Fin Dumoyen Age Au XV11e Siecle. (Cahiers Des Etudes Rurales: No. 3). 1972. pap. 34.40x (ISBN 90-2797-000-9). Mouton.
Jaffee, Martin. Mishnah's Theology of Tithing: A Study of Tractate Maaserot. Neusner, Jacob, ed. LC 80-29333. (Brown Judaic Studies). 1981. pap. text ed. 15.00 (ISBN 0-89130-459-2, 14-00-19). Scholars Pr GA.
Johnson, Douglas W. The Tithe: Challenge or Legalism. 128p. 1984. pap. 5.95 (ISBN 0-687-42127-6). Abingdon.
Kendall, R. T. Tithing: A Call to Serious, Biblical Giving. 128p. 1983. pap. 4.95 (ISBN 0-310-38331-5, 9279P). Zondervan.
Merrell, Karen D. Tithing. 22p. pap. 4.95 (ISBN 0-87747-560-1). Deseret Bk.
Moss, Roy L. The Lord's Portion: A Scriptural Study of Tithing. (Illus.). 80p. (Orig.). 1980. pap. 2.95 (ISBN 0-912315-48-2). Word Aflame.
Pink, A. W. Tithing. pap. 0.50 (ISBN 0-686-48166-6). Reiner.
Selden, John. The History of Tithes. LC 75-25833. (English Experience Ser.: No. 147). 1968. Repr. of 1618 ed. 49.00 (ISBN 90-221-0147-9). Walter J Johnson.

Tillesley, Richard. Animadversions Upon M. Seldens History of Tithes & His Review Thereof. LC 77-7435. (English Experience Ser.: No. 896). 1977. Repr. of 1619 ed. lib. bdg. 26.50 (ISBN 90-221-0896-1). Walter J Johnson.

TITIAN (TIZIANO, VECELLI), 1477-1576

Goffen, Rona. Piety & Patronage in Renaissance Venice: Bellini, Titian, & Franciscans. LC 85-91280. 320p. 1986. 40.00 (ISBN 0-300-03455-5). Yale U Pr.

TOCQUEVILLE, ALEXIS CHARLES HENRI MAURICE CLEREL DE, 1805-1859

Goldstein, Doris. Trial of Faith: Religion & Politics in Tocqueville's Thought. 144p. 1975. 21.00 (ISBN 0-444-99001-1). Elsevier.

Goldstein, Doris S. Trial of Faith: Religion & Politics in Tocqueville's. LC 75-4753. pap. 39.00 (2026263). Bks Demand UMI.

TOLERATION

see also Liberty of Conscience; Minorities

Basnage De Beauval, Henry. Tolerance Des Religions. Repr. 20.00 (ISBN 0-384-03522-1). Johnson Repr.

Bellah, Robert & Greenspahn, Frederick. Uncivil Religion: Interreligious Hostility in America. 256p. 1986. 16.95. Crossroad NY.

Bigelow, John. Toleration, & Other Essays & Studies. facs. ed. LC 78-84298. (Essay Index Reprint Ser). 1927. 14.25 (ISBN 0-8369-1075-3). Ayer Co Pubs.

Jordan, W. K. The Development of Religious Toleration in England, 4 vols. Incl. Vol. 1. From the Beginning of the English Reformation to the Death of Queen Elizabeth (ISBN 0-8446-1251-0); Vol. 2. From the Accession of James One to the Convention of the Long Parliament; Vol. 3. From the Convention of the Long Parliament to the Restoration (ISBN 0-8446-1253-7); Vol. 4. Attainment of the Theory & Accommodations in Thought & Institutions (ISBN 0-8446-1254-5). 1932. 16.50 ea. Peter Smith.

Katz, Jacob. Exclusiveness & Tolerance. 208p. 1983. pap. 7.95x (ISBN 0-87441-365-6). Behrman.

Newman, Jay. Foundations of Religious Tolerance. 192p. 1982. 27.50x (ISBN 0-8020-5591-5); pap. 9.95 (ISBN 0-8020-6507-4). U of Toronto Pr.

Seaton, Alexander A. The Theory of Toleration under the Later Stuarts. 1972. lib. bdg. 23.00x (ISBN 0-374-97233-8, Octagon). Hippocrene Bks.

Slafter, Edmund F. & Slafter, Edmund F., eds. John Checkley, or, Evolution of Religious Tolerance in Massachusetts, 2 vols. (Prince Soc. Pubns: Nos. 22 & 23). 1966. 39.00 (ISBN 0-8337-0553-9). B Franklin.

Wismar, Adolph L. Study in Tolerance As Practiced by Muhammed & His Immediate Successors. LC 27-24455. (Columbia University. Contributions to Oriental History & Philology: No. 13). Repr. of 1927 ed. 14.00 (ISBN 0-404-50543-0). AMS Pr.

Wolff, Robert P., et al. Critique of Pure Tolerance. LC 65-20788. 1969. pap. 7.95x (ISBN 0-8070-1559-8, BP328). Beacon Pr.

TOMBS

see also Catacombs; Epitaphs; Sepulchral Monuments

Badawy, Alexander. The Tomb of Nyhetep-Ptah at Giza & the Tomb of 'Ankhm' Ahor at Saqqara. (U. C. Publications: Occasional Papers Ser.: Vol. 11). 1978. pap. 29.00x (ISBN 0-520-09575-8). U of Cal Pr.

--Tombs of Iteti, Sekhem ankh-Ptah, & Kaemnofert at Giza. (University of California Publications, Occasional Papers, Archaeology: No. 9). pap. 26.30 (ISBN 0-317-29106-8, 2021386). Bks Demand UMI.

Cleveland, Ray L. An Ancient South Arabian Necropolis: Objects from the Second Campaign 1951 in the Timna Cemetery. (American Foundation for the Study of Man: Vol. 4). (Illus.). 202p. 1965. 40.00x (ISBN 0-8018-0129-X). Johns Hopkins.

Davisson, Emmett D. Art & Mysteries in Tombs, Mummies & Catacombs. (Illus.). 1980. deluxe ed. 97.45 deluxe binding (ISBN 0-930582-63-2). Gloucester Art.

Eogan, George. Knowth: And the Passage Tombs of Ireland. LC 86-50218. (New Aspects of Antiquity Ser.). (Illus.). 248p. 1987. 29.95 (ISBN 0-500-39023-1). Thames Hudson.

Fujian Sheng Museum Staff. Thirteenth-Century Tomb Near Fuzhou. 145p. 1982. 100.00x (ISBN 0-317-43751-8, Pub. by Han-Shan Tang Ltd). State Mutual Bk.

Guangzhou Municipal Museum. Guangzhou Hanmu Excavation of the Han Tombs at Guangzhou. 526p. 1981. 150.00x (ISBN 0-317-44071-3, Pub. by Han-Shan Tang Ltd). State Mutual Bk.

Hunt, John. Irish Medieval Figure Sculpture 1200-1600: A Study of Irish Tombs with Notes on Costume & Armour, 2 vols. (Illus.). 550p. 1974. 75.00 (ISBN 0-85667-012-X). Sotheby Pubns.

Institute of Oriental Studies. Chinese Tomb Pottery Figures: Catalogue of Exhibition Arranged by the Institute of Oriental Studies. 1953. pap. 22.50x (ISBN 0-317-44053-5, Pub. by Han-Shan Tang Ltd). State Mutual Bk.

Porter, Kingsley A. Construction of Lombard & Gothic Vaults. 1911. 75.00x (ISBN 0-685-69851-3). Elliots Bks.

Reisner, G. A. Excavations at Kerma, Pts. I-V. Hooton, E. A. & Bates, Natica I., eds. (Harvard African Studies: Vol. 5). Pts. I-III. lib. bdg. 118.00set (ISBN 0-527-01028-6); Pts. IV-V. lib. bdg. 69.00 set (ISBN 0-527-01029-4). Kraus Repr.

Reisner, George A. A Provincial Cemetery of the Pyramid Age, Naga-Ed-Der, Pt. 3. (Publications in Egyptian Archaeology: Vol. 6). 1932. 110.00x (ISBN 0-520-01060-4). U of Cal Pr.

Roos, Paavo. Survey of Rook-Cut Chamber-Tombs in Caria, Pt. I: Southeastern Caria & the Lyco-Carian Borderland. (Studies in Mediterranean Archaeology). (Illus.). 132p. (Orig.). 1985. pap. text ed. 82.50X (Pub. by Almqvist & Wiksell). Coronet Bks.

Save-Soderbergh, Torgny, ed. Temples & Tombs of Ancient Nubia. LC 86-50517. (Illus.). 1987. 29.95 (ISBN 0-500-01392-6). Thames Hudson.

Simpson, William K. Heka-Nefer & the Dynastic Material from Toshka & Arminna. (Pubns of the Penn-Yale Expedition to Egypt: No. 1). (Illus.). xiv, 53p. 1963. 16.50x (ISBN 0-686-17767-3). Univ Mus of U PA.

Weigall, Arthur. Tutankhamen & Other Essays. LC 73-115210. 1971. Repr. of 1924 ed. 24.50x (ISBN 0-8046-1103-3, Pub by Kennikat). Assoc Faculty Pr.

Zhenyu, Luo. Gu Mingqi Tulu. 1916. 300.00x (ISBN 0-317-44070-5, Pub. by Han-Shan Tang Ltd). State Mutual Bk.

TOMBSTONES

see Sepulchral Monuments

TONGUES, GIFT OF

see Glossolalia

TORAH SCROLLS

Adahan, Miriam. E. M. E. T. T. A Step-by-Step Guide to Emotional Maturity Established Through Torah. 1987. 14.95 (ISBN 0-87306-410-0). Feldheim.

Beiner, Stan J. Sedra Scenes: Skits for Every Torah Portion. LC 82-71282. 225p. (Orig.). 1982. pap. text ed. 8.75 (ISBN 0-86705-007-1). AIRE.

Birnbaum, Philip. The Torah & the Haftarot. 933p. 1983. 19.50 (ISBN 0-88482-456-X). Hebrew Pub.

Call of the Torah, 2 vols. 1981. 24.50 (ISBN 0-87306-146-2); pap. 18.50 (ISBN 0-87306-232-9). Feldheim.

Chavel, Charles B. Encyclopedia of Torah Thoughts. Orig. Title: Rabeinu Bachya Ben Asher "Kad Hakemach". 734p. 1980. 19.50 (ISBN 0-88328-016-7); pap. 14.50 (ISBN 0-88328-017-5). Shilo Pub Hse.

--Ramban (Nachmanides) Commentary on the Torah, 5 vols. 2575p. 1971. 84.75 set (ISBN 0-686-86743-2); Vol. I, Book Of Genesis. 16.95 ea. (ISBN 0-88328-006-X). Vol. II, Book Of Exodus (ISBN 0-88328-007-8). Vol. III, Book Of Leviticus (ISBN 0-88328-008-6). Vol. IV, Book Of Numbers (ISBN 0-88328-009-4). Vol. V, Book Of Deuteronomy (ISBN 0-88328-010-8). Shilo Pub Hse.

--Ramban (Nachmanides) Writings & Discourses, 2 vols. 768p. 1978. Set. slipcase 33.00 (ISBN 0-88328-013-2). Shilo Pub Hse.

Cowan, Paul & Cowan, Rachel. A Torah Is Written. (Illus.). 32p. 1986. 12.95 (ISBN 0-8276-0270-7). Jewish Pubns.

Gaer, Joseph, ed. The Torah for Family Reading. LC 86-70620. 559p. 1986. Repr. 30.00 (ISBN 0-87668-915-2). Aronson.

Grishaver, Joel L. Being Torah Student Commentary, 2 Vols. (Illus.). 72p. (Orig.). 1986. pap. text ed. 3.25 ea. Vol. 1 (ISBN 0-933873-09-3). Vol. 2 (ISBN 0-933873-10-7). Torah Aura.

Liberman, David. The Eternal Torah: A Commentary upon the Books of Joshua-Judges-Smauel One, Samuel Two, Pt. 2. 360p. 1983. 20.00 (ISBN 0-9609840-1-1). Twin Pines Pr.

Lieberman, David. The Eternal Torah: A Commentary upon Torah Pentateuch Consolidating the Scholarship Throughout Hebrew Literature, Pt. 1. 570p. 1986. Repr. of 1979 ed. 25.00 (ISBN 0-9609840-0-3). Twin Pines Pr.

Loeb, Sorel G. & Kadden, Barbara B. Teaching Torah: A Treasury of Activities & Insights. LC 84-70318. 300p. 1984. pap. text ed. 15.00 (ISBN 0-86705-013-6). AIRE.

Luzzatto, Mosche Chaim. Daat Tevnoth: The Knowing Heart. Silverstein, Shraga, tr. from Hebrew. (Torah Classics Library). 357p. 1982. 12.95 (ISBN 0-87306-194-2); pap. 9.95 (ISBN 0-87306-345-7). Feldheim.

Maimondies & Hyamson, Moses. Book of Adoration. (Mishneh Torah Ser.). 330p. 1981. 11.95 (ISBN 0-87306-086-5). Feldheim.

Maimonides. Book of Knowledge. Hyamson, Moses, tr. from Herbrew. (Mishneh Torah Ser.). 1981. 13.95 (ISBN 0-87306-085-7). Feldheim.

Maimonides, Moses. Mishneh Torah. Abr. ed. Birnbaum, Philip, tr. (Eng. & Hebrew.). 755p. 1944. 19.50 (ISBN 0-88482-437-3). Hebrew Pub.

--Mishneh Torah. Abr. ed. Birnbaum, Philip, tr. 344p. 1944. pap. 9.95 (ISBN 0-317-26820-1). Hebrew Pub.

Matt, Daniel. The Book of Mirrors: Sefer Mar'ot ha-Zove'ot. LC 81-9308. (Brown Judiac Studies Ser.). 1982. pap. 22.50 (ISBN 0-89130-525-4, 14-00-30). Scholars Pr GA.

Neusner, Jacob. The Oral Torah: The Sacred Books of Judaism. LC 85-42788. 256p. 1986. 19.45 (ISBN 0-06-066103-8, HarpR). Har-Row.

--Torah from Our Sages: Pirke Avot. 214p. 1986. 18.95 (ISBN 0-940646-39-0); pap. 9.95. Rossel Bks.

--Torah: From Scroll to Symbol in Formative Judaism. LC 84-45190. (Foundations of Judaism Trilogy Ser.). 208p. 1985. 24.95 (1-734). Fortress.

Petuchowski, Jakob J. Ever since Sinai. 3rd ed. LC 79-64324. 1979. pap. text ed. 5.95 (ISBN 0-930038-11-8). Arbit.

Plaut, W. Gunther. Deuteronomy: The Torah. (A Modern Commentary Ser.). 528p. 1983. 20.00 (ISBN 0-8074-0045-9). UAHC.

--Exodus: A Modern Commentary. (The Torah Commentary Ser.). 571p. 1983. 20.00 (ISBN 0-8074-0040-8, 381606). UAHC.

--The Torah: A Modern Commentary: Numbers. (The Torah Commentary Ser.). 476p. 1980. 20.00 (ISBN 0-8074-0039-4, 381602). UAHC.

Plaut, W. Gunther & Bamberger, Bernard J. The Torah: A Modern Commentary. (Illus.). 1824p. 1981. 30.00 (ISBN 0-8074-0055-6). UAHC.

Ray, Eric. Sofer: The Story of a Torah Scroll. LC 85-52420. (Illus.). 32p. (Orig.). 1986. pap. text ed. 4.95 (ISBN 0-933873-04-2). Torah Aura.

Saypol, Judyth & Wikler, Madeline, illus. My Very Own Simchat Torah. (Illus.). 24p. 1981. pap. 2.95 (ISBN 0-930494-11-3). Kar Ben.

Torah Readings for Festivals. 5.95 (ISBN 0-87677-069-3). Prayer Bk.

Tractate Sukkah-Moedkattan. 1984. 22.95 (ISBN 0-900689-83-8). Soncino Pr.

With Fury Poured Out: A Torah Perspective on the Holocaust. 300p. 1987. 16.95 (ISBN 0-88125-107-0). KTAV.

TOTAL ABSTINENCE

see Temperance

TOTEMISM

see also Sacred Meals; Totems

Durkheim, Emile. Elementary Forms of the Religious Life. Swain, Joseph W., tr. 1965. pap. text ed. 14.95 (ISBN 0-02-908010-X). Free Pr.

Elkin, Adolphus P. Studies in Australian Totemism. LC 76-44712. Repr. of 1933 ed. 31.50 (ISBN 0-404-15857-9). AMS Pr.

Feld, Lipman G. Harassment & Other Collection Taboos. 156p. 1976. pap. 8.95 (ISBN 0-934914-08-7). NACM.

Freud, Sigmund. Totem & Taboo. Strachey, James, tr. 1962. pap. 3.95 (ISBN 0-393-00143-1, Norton Lib.). Norton.

--Totem & Taboo. Brill, Abraham A., tr. 1960. pap. 2.95 (ISBN 0-394-70124-0, Vin, V124). Random.

Goldenweiser, Alexander. Totemism. 59.95 (ISBN 0-8490-1223-6). Gordon Pr.

Hadfield, Percival. The Savage & His Totem. LC 75-32825. Repr. of 1938 ed. 20.00 (ISBN 0-404-14129-3). AMS Pr.

Lang, Andrew. Secret of the Totem. LC 70-115094. 1970. Repr. of 1905 ed. 16.75 (ISBN 0-404-03866-2). AMS Pr.

Leach, Edmund, ed. Structural Study of Myth & Totenism. (Orig.). 1968. pap. 12.95 (ISBN 0-422-72530-7, NO.2287, Pub by Tavistock England). Methuen Inc.

Levi-Strauss, Claude. Totemism. (Orig.). 1963. pap. 7.95x (ISBN 0-8070-4671-X, BP157). Beacon Pr.

Moret, A. & Davy, G. From Tribe to Empire: Social Organization among the Primitives & in the Ancient East. Childe, V. Gordon, tr. from Fr. LC 71-139997. (Illus.). 339p. 1971. Repr. of 1926 ed. lib. bdg. 24.50x (ISBN 0-8154-0368-2). Cooper Sq.

Roheim, Geza. Eternal Ones of the Dream: Myth & Ritual, Dreams & Fantasies-Their Role in the Lives of Primitive Man. 1970. pap. text ed. 19.95 (ISBN 0-8236-8044-4, 021760). Intl Univs Pr.

TOTEMS

Barbeau, Marius. Modern Growth of the Totem Pole on the Northwest Coast. facs. ed. (Shorey Indian Ser.). 16p. pap. 0.95 (ISBN 0-8466-0098-6, S98). Shorey.

Garfield, Viola E. & Forrest, Linn A. Wolf & the Raven: Totem Poles of Southeastern Alaska. 2nd ed. LC 49-8492. (Illus.). 161p. 1961. pap. 8.95 (ISBN 0-295-73998-3). U of Wash Pr.

Harris, Lorie K. Tlingit Tales: Potlach & Totem Pole. (Illus.). 64p. 11.95 (ISBN 0-87961-152-9); pap. 5.95 (ISBN 0-87961-153-7). Naturegraph.

Lloyd, J. P. Message of an Indian Relic: Seattle's Own Totem Pole. facs. ed. (Shorey Indian Ser.). (Illus.). 29p. pap. 1.95 (ISBN 0-8466-4006-6, I6). Shorey.

TOWN CHURCHES

see City Churches

TOZER, AIDEN WILSON, 1897-

Fant, David J., Jr. A. W. Tozer: A Twentieth Century Prophet. LC 64-21945. (Illus.). 180p. 1964. pap. 3.95 (ISBN 0-87509-048-6). Chr Pubns.

Tozer, A. W. The Best of A. W. Tozer. (Best Ser). 1978. pap. 3.95 (ISBN 0-8010-8845-3). Baker Bk.

Wiersbe, W. Best of A. W. Tozer. 249p. 1979. pap. 3.95. Chr Pubns.

TRACTARIANISM

see Oxford Movement

TRACY, WILLIAM, fl. 1530

Tyndale, William. An Answer to Sir Thomas More's Dialogue, the Supper of the Lord After the True Meaning of John 6 & or. 11. Repr. of 1850 ed. 31.00 (ISBN 0-384-62240-2). Johnson Repr.

TRADITION (JUDAISM)

Faur, Jose. Golden Doves with Silver Dots: Semiotics & Textuality in Rabbinic Tradition. LC 84-47967. (Jewish Literature & Culture Ser.). 256p. 1986. 27.50x (ISBN 0-253-32600-1). Ind U Pr.

Fisher, Eugene J. & Polish, Daniel F., eds. The Formation of Social Policy in the Catholic & Jewish Tradition. new ed. LC 80-50268. 208p. text ed. 17.95 (ISBN 0-268-00953-8); pap. text ed. 8.95 (ISBN 0-268-00951-1). U of Notre Dame Pr.

Gersh, Harry & Platzner, Robert S. Mishnah, the Oral Law. 64p. 1984. pap. 2.95 (ISBN 0-87441-390-7); tchr's 6.95 (ISBN 0-317-15397-8). Behrman.

Oring, Elliott. Israeli Humor: The Content & Structure of the Chizbat of the Palmah. LC 80-25483. (Modern Jewish Literature & Culture Ser.). 210p. 1981. 44.50 (ISBN 0-87395-512-9); pap. 14.95x (ISBN 0-87395-513-7). State U NY Pr.

Petuchowski, Jacob J. Heirs of the Pharisees. LC 86-1496. (Brown Classics in Judaica Ser.). 214p. 1986. pap. text ed. 12.00 (ISBN 0-8191-5256-0). U Pr of Amer.

Schimmel. The Oral Law. cancelled (ISBN 0-87306-088-1). Feldheim.

Weingreen, Jacob. From Bible to Mishna: The Continuity of Tradition. LC 75-37728. 250p. 1976. text ed. 27.00x (ISBN 0-8419-0249-6). Holmes & Meier.

TRADITION (THEOLOGY)

see also Kerygma

Allchin, A. M. The Living Presence of the Past: The Dynamic of Christian Tradition. 192p. (Orig.). 1981. pap. 7.95 (ISBN 0-8164-2334-2, HarpR). Har-Row.

Allen, Ronald & Allen, Beverly. Liberated Traditionalism: Men & Women in Balance. LC 85-8969. (Critical Concern Bks.). 1985. 11.95 (ISBN 0-88070-112-9). Multnomah.

Aulen, Gustaf E. Reformation & Catholicity. Wahlstrom, Eric H., tr. from Swedish. LC 78-25981. 1979. Repr. of 1961 ed. lib. bdg. 22.50x (ISBN 0-313-20809-3, AURC). Greenwood.

Benoit, Pierre, et al, eds. Dynamism of Biblical Tradition. LC 67-15983. (Concilium Ser.: Vol. 20). 226p. 1967. 7.95 (ISBN 0-8091-0035-5). Paulist Pr.

Francis, Fred O. & Wallace, Raymond P., eds. Tradition As Openness to the Future: Essays in Honor of Willis W. Fisher. (Illus.). 236p. (Orig.). 1984. lib. bdg. 25.00 (ISBN 0-8191-3722-7); pap. text ed. 12.25 (ISBN 0-8191-3723-5). U Pr of Amer.

Kelley, Gail. Traditionally Yours. LC 86-43230. 100p. (Orig.). 1987. pap. text ed. 7.95 (ISBN 0-89390-103-2). Resource Pubns.

Lutz, Jesse G. & El-Shakhs, Salah S. Tradition & Modernity: The Role of Traditionalism in the Modernization Process. LC 81-43464. 234p. 1982. lib. bdg. 29.00 (ISBN 0-8191-2326-9). U Pr of Amer.

TRADITIONS

see Folk-Lore; Legends; Superstition

TRAHERNE, THOMAS, d. 1674

Ames, Kenneth J. The Religious Language of Thomas Traherne's Centuries. (Religion & Literature Ser.). 1979. lib. bdg. 59.95 (ISBN 0-87700-260-6). Revisionist Pr.

Grant, Patrick. The Transformation of Sin: Studies in Donne, Herbert, Vaughan & Traherne. LC 73-93174. 308p. 1974. 20.00x (ISBN 0-87023-158-8). U of Mass Pr.

--The Transformation of Sin: Studies in Donne, Herbert, Vaughan & Traherne. LC 73-93174. pap. 63.50 (ISBN 0-317-26444-3, 2023850). Bks Demand UMI.

Wade, Gladys I. Thomas Traherne. LC 73-96171. 1969. Repr. of 1944 ed. lib. bdg. 20.00x (ISBN 0-374-98113-2, Octagon). Hippocrene Bks.

White, Helen C. The Metaphysical Poets: A Study in Religious Experience. LC 83-45866. 1936. 39.50 (ISBN 0-404-20285-3, PR549). AMS Pr.

Wohrer, Franz K. Thomas Traherne's 'The Growth of a Mystic's Mind: A Study of the Evolution & the Phenomenology of Traherne's Mystical Consciousness. Hogg, James, ed. (Elizabethan & Renaissance Studies). 207p. (Orig.). 1982. pap. 15.00 (ISBN 3-7052-0747-4, Pub. by Salzburg Studies). Longwood Pub Group.

TRANCE

see also Ecstasy

Belo, Jane. Trance in Bali. LC 77-6361. 1977. Repr. of 1960 ed. lib. bdg. 35.75x (ISBN 0-8371-9652-3, BETR). Greenwood.

Bourguignon, Erika, ed. Religion, Altered States of Consciousness, & Social Change. LC 72-8448. (Illus.). 399p. 1973. 12.50 (ISBN 0-8142-0167-9). Ohio St U Pr.

Lambek, Michael. Human Spirits: A Cultural Account of Trance in Mayotte. LC 81-1842. (Cambridge Studies in Cultural Systems). (Illus.). 272p. 1981. 39.50 (ISBN 0-521-23844-7); pap. 17.95 (ISBN 0-521-28255-1). Cambridge U Pr.

TRANSACTIONAL ANALYSIS

Murphree, Jon T. When God Says You're OK: A Christian Approach to Transactional Analysis. new ed. LC 75-21452. 132p. 1975. pap. 2.95 (ISBN 0-87784-716-9). Inter-Varsity.

TRANSCENDENCE OF GOD

Daly, Gabriel. Transcendence & Immanence: A Study in Catholic Modernism & Integralism. 1980. 37.50x (ISBN 0-19-826652-9). Oxford U Pr.

TRANSCENDENTAL MEDITATION

Chang, Lit-Sen. Transcendental Meditation. 1978. pap. 2.95 (ISBN 0-87552-133-9). Presby & Reformed.

Gerberding, Kieth A. How to Respond to Transcendental Meditation. (The Response Ser.). 1977. 1.95 (ISBN 0-570-07676-5, 12-2659). Concordia.

Goldhaber, Nat & Denniston, Denise. TM: An Alphabetical Guide to the Transcendental Meditation Program. (Illus.). 1976. pap. 3.95 (ISBN 0-345-24096-0). Ballantine.

Haddon, David. Transcendental Meditation. new ed. 32p. (Orig.). 1975. pap. 0.75 (ISBN 0-87784-155-1). Inter-Varsity.

Haddon, David & Hamilton, Vail. TM Wants You. (Direction Bks). 160p. 1976. pap. 1.95 (ISBN 0-8010-4151-1). Baker Bk.

Marharishi Mahesh Yogi. Transcendental Meditation. 320p. 1973. pap. 4.95 (ISBN 0-451-14081-8, Sig). NAL.

Persinger, Michael A., et al. TM & Cult Mania. 208p. 1980. 10.95 (ISBN 0-8158-0392-3). Chris Mass.

Russell, Peter. The TM Technique: A Skeptic's Guide to the TM Program. 1977. pap. 7.95 (ISBN 0-7100-0337-4). Methuen Inc.

Truch, Stephen. TM Technique & the Art of Learning. (Quality Paperback Ser: No. 329). 250p. 1977. pap. 4.95 (ISBN 0-8226-0329-2). Littlefield.

TRANSCENDENTALISM

see also Idealism; Immanence of God

Albanese, Catherine L. Corresponding Motion: Transcendental Religion & the New America. LC 77-70329. 234p. 1977. 29.95 (ISBN 0-87722-098-0). Temple U Pr.

Cooke, George W. The Poets of Transcendentalism: An Anthology. 59.95 (ISBN 0-8490-0868-9). Gordon Pr.

Frothingham, Octavius B. Transcendentalism in New England: A History. LC 59-10346. 1972. pap. 14.95x (ISBN 0-8122-1038-7, Pa. Paperbacks). U of Pa Pr.

Goddard, H. C. Studies in New England Transcendentalism. 1978. Repr. of 1960 ed. lib. bdg. 30.00 (ISBN 0-8492-4906-6). R West.

Greene, William B. Transcendentalism; bd. with Equality. LC 81-8972. (Repr. of 1849 eds.). 1981. 35.00x (ISBN 0-8201-1366-2). Schol Facsimiles.

Hoehler, Richard S. Three Transcendentalists: Kant, Thoreau, & Contemporary. LC 71-185781. (Illus.). 432p. 1972. 10.00 (ISBN 0-930590-00-7). R S Hoehler.

Horstmann, Rolf-Peter, et al, eds. Transcendental Arguments & Science. (Synthese Library: No. 133). 1979. lib. bdg. 34.00 (ISBN 90-277-0963-7, Pub. by Reidel Holland); pap. 16.00 (ISBN 90-277-0964-5). Kluwer Academic.

Hunt, John. Pantheism & Christianity. LC 78-102573. 1970. Repr. of 1884 ed. 25.50 (ISBN 0-8046-0733-8, Pub. by Kennikat). Assoc Faculty Pr.

Husserl, Edmund. Crisis of European Sciences & Transcendental Phenomenology: An Introduction to Phenomenological Philosophy. Carr, David, tr. LC 77-82511. (Studies in Phenomenology & Existential Philosophy Ser). 1970. 28.95 (ISBN 0-8101-0255-2); pap. 11.95 (ISBN 0-8101-0458-X). Northwestern U Pr.

Kant, Immanuel. Metaphysical Knowledge & Transcendental Problems. (Illus.). 167p. 1985. Repr. 89.55 (ISBN 0-89901-200-0). Found Class Reprints.

Lauer, Quentin. The Triumph of Subjectivity: An Introduction to Transcendental Phenomenology. 2nd ed. LC 58-12363. xxiv, 182p. 1978. 20.00 (ISBN 0-8232-0336-0); pap. 9.00 (ISBN 0-8232-0337-9). Fordham.

Mayers, Ronald B. Religious Ministry in a Transcendentless Culture. LC 79-3424. 1980. pap. text ed. 10.75 (ISBN 0-8191-0889-8). U Pr of Amer.

Metheny, Burton R. How to Develop the Power of Transcendental Experience. (Illus.). 139p. 1980. 59.45 (ISBN 0-89920-014-1). Am Inst Psych.

Myerson, Joel, ed. The Transcendentalists: A Review of Research & Criticism. (Reviews of Research Ser.). 450p. 1984. 30.00x (ISBN 0-87352-260-5); pap. 20.00x (ISBN 0-87352-261-3). Modern Lang.

Olson, Alan M. Transcendence & Hermeneutics. (Studies in Philosophy & Religion: No. 2). 1979. lib. bdg. 35.00 (ISBN 90-247-2092-3, Pub. by Martinus Nijhoff Netherlands). Kluwer Academic.

Orr, Robert P. The Meaning of Transcendence. Dietrich, Wendell, ed. LC 80-12872. (American Academy of Religion Dissertation Ser.). 172p. 1981. pap. 9.95 (ISBN 0-89130-408-8, 01 01 35). Scholars Pr GA.

Stoehr, Taylor. Nay-Saying in Concord: Emerson, Alcott & Thoreau. LC 78-25580. 179p. 1979. 21.50 (ISBN 0-208-01767-4, Archon). Shoe String.

Stutsman, Gerald. Transcendency. LC 81-69736. 96p. 1982. pap. 4.75 (ISBN 0-87516-466-8). De Vorss.

Villamette, Gaston. How to Gain the Psychological Power of Transcendental Thinking. (Illus.). 118p. 1987. 117.55 (ISBN 0-89920-147-4). Am Classical Coll Pr.

Zaleski, Carol. Otherworld Journeys: Accounts of Near-Death Experience in Medieval & Modern Times. 288p. 1987. 18.95 (ISBN 0-19-503915-7). Oxford U Pr.

TRANSCENDENTALISM (NEW ENGLAND)

see also Brook Farm

Barbour, Brian M., ed. American Transcendentalism: An Anthology of Criticism. LC 72-12640. 384p. 1973. pap. 8.95x (ISBN 0-268-00494-3). U of Notre Dame Pr.

Buell, Lawrence. Literary Transcendentalism: Style & Vision in the American Rennaisance. LC 73-8409. 336p. (Orig.). 1975. pap. 9.95x (ISBN 0-8014-9152-5). Cornell U Pr.

Cooke, George W., ed. Poets of Transcendentalism: An Anthology. LC 72-126410. (Literature & Criticism Ser). 1971. Repr. of 1903 ed. lib. bdg. 21.00 (ISBN 0-8337-0652-7). B Franklin.

Delano, Sterling F. The Harbinger & New England Transcendentalism: A Portrait of Associationism in America. 224p. 27.50 (ISBN 0-8386-3138-X). Fairleigh Dickinson.

Ellis, Charles M. Essay on Transcendentalism. LC 70-91761. Repr. of 1954 ed. lib. bdg. 22.50x (ISBN 0-8371-3092-1, ELTR). Greenwood.

Frothingham, O. C. Transcendentalism in New England: A History. 11.25 (ISBN 0-8446-1191-3). Peter Smith.

Geller, L. D. Between Concord & Plymouth: The Transcendentalists & the Watsons. (Illus.). 1973. 6.00 (ISBN 0-685-42210-0). Thoreau Found.

Gohdes, Clarence. Periodicals of American Transcendentalism. LC 77-136380. Repr. of 1931 ed. 16.00 (ISBN 0-404-02854-3). AMS Pr.

Gohdes, Clarence L. Periodicals of American Transcendentalism. LC 76-107803. (Select Bibliographies Reprint Ser). 1931. 19.00 (ISBN 0-8369-5206-5). Ayer Co Pubs.

Kaplan, N. & Katsanos, T. Origins of American Transcendentalism. 1975. pap. 11.95x (ISBN 0-8084-0415-6). New Coll U Pr.

Leighton, Walter L. French Philosophers-New England Transcendentalism. LC 68-19289. 1968. Repr. of 1908 ed. lib. bdg. 22.50x (ISBN 0-8371-0143-3, LEPT). Greenwood.

McBee, Alice F. From Utopia to Florence: The Story of a Transcendentalist Community in Northampton, Massachusetts, 1830-1852. LC 74-31281. (American Utopian Adventure Ser). (Illus.). ix, 93p. 1975. Repr. of 1947 ed. lib. bdg. 17.50x (ISBN 0-87991-027-5). Porcupine Pr.

Miller, Perry, ed. American Transcendentalists: Their Prose & Poetry. 17.25 (ISBN 0-8446-2595-7). Peter Smith.

Miller, Perry G., ed. Transcendentalists: An Anthology. LC 50-7360. 1950. pap. 9.95x (ISBN 0-674-90333-1). Harvard U Pr.

Myerson, Joel. New England Transcendentalists & the DIAL: A History of the Magazine & Its Contributors. LC 78-66814. 400p. 1980. 35.00 (ISBN 0-8386-2294-1). Fairleigh Dickinson.

Pochmann, Henry A. New England Transcendentalism & St. Louis Hegelianism. LC 68-55163. (Studies in Comparative Literature, No. 35). 1969. Repr. of 1948 ed. lib. bdg. 39.95x (ISBN 0-8383-0610-1). Haskell.

Rose, Anne C. Transcendentalism As a Social Movement, 1830-1850. LC 81-3340. 288p. 1986. pap. 11.95x (ISBN 0-300-03757-0). Yale U Pr.

Wells, Ronald V. Three Christian Transcendentalists: James Marsh, Caleb Sprague Henry, Frederic Henry Hedge. LC 75-159256. xxxii, 290p. 1971. Repr. of 1943 ed. lib. bdg. 20.00x (ISBN 0-374-98345-3, Octagon). Hippocrene Bks.

TRANSPLANTATION OF ORGANS, TISSUES, ETC.

Cowan, Dale H. Human Organ Transplantation: Societal, Medical-Legal, Regulatory, & Reimbursement Issues. LC 86-29478. 1987. price not set (ISBN 0-910701-20-2). Health Admin Pr.

TRANSUBSTANTIATION

see also Mass

Fisher, Lizette A. Mystic Vision in the Grail Legend & in the Divine Comedy. LC 79-168029. Repr. of 1917 ed. 16.50 (ISBN 0-404-02389-4). AMS Pr.

TRAPPISTS

see also Cistercians

Krailsheimer, A. J. Rance & the Trappist Legacy. 16.95 (ISBN 0-87907-886-3); pap. 6.95. Cistercian Pubns.

Merton, Thomas. The Seven Storey Mountain. LC 85-6375. 784p. 1985. pap. 19.95 (ISBN 0-8027-2497-3). Walker & Co.

--The Waters of Siloe. LC 79-10372. 377p. 1979. pap. 6.95 (ISBN 0-15-694954-7, Harv). HarBraceJ.

Mott, Michael. The Seven Mountains of Thomas Merton. LC 84-10944. 1984. 24.95 (ISBN 0-395-31324-4). HM.

Nouwen, Henri J. The Genesee Diary: Report from a Trappist Monastery. LC 80-23632. 192p. 1981. pap. 4.50 (ISBN 0-385-17446-2, Im). Doubleday.

TREES, FOLK-LORE OF

see Folk-Lore of Trees

TRENT, COUNCIL OF 1545-1563

see also Counter-Reformation

Chemnitz, Martin. Examination of the Council of Trent. Kramer, Fred, tr. from Lat. LC 79-143693. 1971. 29.95 (ISBN 0-570-03213-X, 15-2113). Concordia.

--Examination of the Council of Trent: Part II. 1979. 29.95 (ISBN 0-570-03272-5, 15-2717). Concordia.

Council of Trent Staff. The Catechism of the Council of Trent. LC 82-50588. 603p. 1983. pap. 15.00 (ISBN 0-89555-185-3). TAN Bks Pubs.

Evennett, Henry O. The Cardinal of Lorraine & the Council of Trent: A Study in the Counter-Reformation. LC 83-45592. Date not set. Repr. of 1940 ed. 57.50 (ISBN 0-404-19885-6). AMS Pr.

Froude, James A. Lectures on the Council of Trent, Delivered at Oxford 1892-3. LC 68-8244. 1969. Repr. of 1901 ed. 27.00x (ISBN 0-8046-0159-3, Pub. by Kennikat). Assoc Faculty Pr.

Pascal, Blaise & Lafuma, Louis. Deux Pieces Imparfaites sur la Grace et le Concile de Trente, Extraites du M. S. de l'Abbe Perier. 76p. 1947. 5.95 (ISBN 0-686-54845-0). French & Eur.

Schroeder, H. J., tr. Canons & Decrees of the Council of Trent. LC 78-66132. 293p. 1978. pap. 8.00 (ISBN 0-89555-074-1). TAN Bks Pubs.

TRIADS (RELIGION)

see Trinities

TRIALS (WITCHCRAFT)

Boyer, Paul & Nissenbaum, Stephen, eds. The Salem Witchcraft Papers: Verbatim Transcripts, 3 vols. (Civil Liberties in American History Ser.). 1977. Set. lib. bdg. 145.00 (ISBN 0-306-70655-5). Da Capo.

Fox, Sanford J. Science & Justice: The Massachusetts Witchcraft Trials. LC 68-18771. (Illus.). Repr. of 1968 ed. 27.40 (ISBN 0-8357-9285-4, 2016570). Bks Demand UMI.

Kieckhefer, Richard. European Witch Trials: Their Foundations in Popular & Learned Culture, 1300-1500. 1976. 34.00x (ISBN 0-520-02967-4). U of Cal Pr.

Midelfort, H. Erik. Witch Hunting in Southwestern Germany, 1562-1684: The Social & Intellectual Foundations. LC 75-183891. 320p. 1972. 26.50x (ISBN 0-8047-0805-3). Stanford U Pr.

TRIBUNALS, ECCLESIASTICAL

see Ecclesiastical Courts

TRINITARIANS

Baily, Michael. Small Net in a Big Sea: The Redemptorists in the Philippines, 1905-1929. (Illus.). 8.00x (ISBN 0-686-24529-6, San Carlos Pubns); pap. 5.00x (ISBN 0-686-24530-X). Cellar.

Tsirpanlis, Constance N. The Trinitarian & Mystical Theology of St. Symeon the New Theologian. 42p. 1981. pap. 2.00 (ISBN 0-686-36331-0). EO Pr.

TRINITIES

Schaberg, Jane. The Father, the Son & the Holy Spirit: An Investigation of the Origin & Meaning of the Triadic Phrase in Matt 28: 19b. LC 81-14466. (SBL Dissertation Ser.). 1982. pap. 18.00 (ISBN 0-89130-543-2, 060161). Scholars Pr GA.

TRINITY

see also God; Holy Spirit; Jesus Christ; Monotheism; Trinities; Unitarianism

Abailard, Pierre. Abailard's Christian Theology. McCullum, James R., tr. from Fr. LC 76-1128. 117p. 1976. Repr. of 1948 ed. lib. bdg. 14.50x (ISBN 0-915172-07-0). Richwood Pub.

Anselm of Canterbury. Trinity, Incarnation, & Redemption: Theological Treatises. (Anselm Ser.: No. 6). 1974. 9.95 (ISBN 0-88946-008-6). E Mellen.

Augsburger, David. Diferencias Personales? Enfrentelas con Amor. Olmedo, Alfonso, tr. from Eng. Tr. of Caring Enough to Confront. 176p. 1985. pap. 5.95 (ISBN 0-311-46098-4, Edit Mundo). Casa Bautista.

Augustine, St. The Trinity. LC 63-72482. (Fathers of the Church Ser.: Vol. 45). 539p. 1963. 27.95x (ISBN 0-8132-0045-8). Cath U Pr.

Beisner, E. Calvin. God in Three Persons. 180p. 1984. pap. 5.95 (ISBN 0-8423-1073-8); 2.95 (ISBN 0-8423-1074-6). Tyndale.

Bennett, Dennis & Bennett, Rita. Trinidad Del Hombre. Carrodeguas, Andy, ed. Lievano, Franscisco, tr. from Span. Orig. Title: Trinity of Man. 224p. 1982. pap. 3.50 (ISBN 0-8297-1298-4). Life Pubs Intl.

Benson, Clarence H. The Triune God. rev. ed. 96p. 1970. pap. text ed. 4.95 (ISBN 0-910566-09-7); Perfect bdg. instr's. guide 5.95 (ISBN 0-910566-24-0). Evang Tchr.

Bickersteth, Edward H. The Trinity. LC 59-13770. 182p. 1976. pap. 5.95 (ISBN 0-8254-2226-4). Kregel.

Bloesch, Donald G. Battle for the Trinity: The Debate over Inclusive God-Language. 1985. 8.95 (ISBN 0-89283-230-4, Pub. by Vine Books). Servant.

Clark, Gordon H. The Trinity. (Trinity Papers: No. 8). 139p. (Orig.). 1985. pap. 8.95 (ISBN 0-940931-08-7). Trinity Found.

Clarke, Samuel. The Works, 4 vols. LC 75-11207. (British Philosophers & Theologians of the 17th & 18th Century Ser.: Vol. 12). 3274p. 1976. Repr. of 1742 ed. Set. lib. bdg. 204.00 (ISBN 0-8240-1762-5). Garland Pub.

Cooke, Bernard J. Beyond Trinity. (Acquinas Lecutre). 1969. 7.95 (ISBN 0-87462-134-8). Marquette.

Crossley, Robert. The Trinity. rev. ed. 32p. 1987. pap. 0.75 (ISBN 0-87784-077-6). Inter-Varsity.

D'Arcy, Martin C. Revelation & Love's Architecture. 90p. 1976. 8.00 (ISBN 0-89182-010-8). Charles River Bks.

De Margerie, Bertrand. The Christian Trinity in History. Fortman, E. J., tr. from Fr. LC 81-8735. Tr. of La Trinite Christienne dans l'histoire. 1982. cloth 29.95 (ISBN 0-932506-14-3). St Bedes Pubns.

Fortman, Edmund J. The Triune God: A Historical Study of the Doctrine of the Trinity. (Twin Brooks Ser.). 408p. 1982. pap. 10.95 (ISBN 0-8010-3505-8). Baker Bk.

Gordon, Alexander, ed. Milton on the Son of God & the Holy Spirit (From the Treatise on Christian Doctrine) LC 73-4827. 1973. lib. bdg. 15.00 (ISBN 0-8414-2028-9). Folcroft.

Gruenler, Royce G. The Trinity in the Gospel of John. 1986. pap. 9.95 (ISBN 0-8010-3806-5). Baker Bk.

Hagerty, Cornelius J. The Holy Trinity. 362p. 1976. 8.95 (ISBN 0-8158-0316-8). Chris Mass.

Hanson, Calvin B. The Trinity Story. LC 83-81575. 1983. 8.95 (ISBN 0-911802-58-4). Free Church Pubns.

Herrmann, Robert A. Oneness, the Trinity & Logic. Wallace, Mary, ed. 112p. 1984. pap. 4.95 (ISBN 0-912315-80-6). Word Aflame.

Hilary Of Poitiers, St. The Trinity. LC 67-28585. (Fathers of the Church Ser: Vol. 25). 555p. 1954. 34.95 (ISBN 0-8132-0025-3). Cath U Pr.

Hill, Edmund. The Mystery of God: St. Augustine on the Trinity. (Catholic Theology Ser.). 200p. pap. 14.95 (ISBN 0-225-66470-4, HarpR). Har-Row.

Hill, William J. The Three-Personed God: The Trinity As a Mystery of Salvation. LC 81-18012. 354p. 1982. 37.95x (ISBN 0-8132-0560-3). Cath U Pr.

Hillriegel, Caroleen, et al, eds. Alpha & Omega: Essays on the Trinity in Honor of James A. Nichols, Jr. 140p. (Orig.). 1980. pap. 4.50 (ISBN 0-913439-01-0). Henceforth.

Holy Trinity Monastry: A History. (Illus.). 47p. 1983. pap. 1.00 (ISBN 0-317-30446-1). Holy Trinity.

Ironside, H. A. Holy Trinity. pap. 1.50 (ISBN 0-87213-348-6). Loizeaux.

Jordanville: A Portrait of Holy Trinity Monastery. 1985. pap. 5.00 (ISBN 0-317-30449-6). Holy Trinity.

Jungel, Eberhard. La Doctrina de la Trinidad. Canclini, Arnoldo, tr. from Eng. Tr. of The Doctrine of the Trinity. (Span.). 152p. 1980. pap. 4.50 (ISBN 0-89922-153-X). Edit Caribe.

Lanier, Roy, Sr. The Timeless Trinity. pap. 9.95 (ISBN 0-89137-551-1). Quality Pubns.

Maloney, George. Invaded by God: Mysticism & the Indwelling Trinity. 1979. 5.95 (ISBN 0-87193-107-9). Dimension Bks.

Miller, David L. Three Faces of God: Traces of the Trinity in Literature & Life. LC 85-45493. 176p. 1986. pap. 11.95 (ISBN 0-8006-1895-5, 1-1895). Fortress.

Minz, Karl-Heinz. Pleroma Trinitatis: Die Trinitaetstheologie bei Matthias Joseph Scheeben. (Disputationes Theologicae Ser.: Vol. 10). 404p. 1982. 40.55 (ISBN 3-8204-6182-5). P Lang Pubs.

Moltmann, Jurgen. The Trinity & the Kingdom. LC 80-8352. 320p. 1981. 19.45 (ISBN 0-06-065906-8, HarpR). Har-Row.

Moyer, Katy. The Father the Son the Holy Spirit. 1983. pap. 1.25 (ISBN 0-910709-18-1). PTL Repro.

O'Donnell, John J. Trinity & Temporality. (Oxford Theological Monographs). 1983. 32.50x (ISBN 0-19-826722-3). Oxford U Pr.

One God or Three. LC 78-15674. 1978. pap. 2.50 (ISBN 0-915540-19-3). Friends Israel-Spearhead Pr.

Panikkar, Raimundo. The Trinity & the Religious Experience of Man: Icon, Person, Mystery. LC 73-77329. pap. 24.50 (ISBN 0-317-26668-3, 2025122). Bks Demand UMI.

Pittenger, Norman. The Divine Trinity. LC 76-55002. 1977. 5.95 (ISBN 0-8298-0330-0). Pilgrim NY.

Ratzinger, Joseph Cardinal. The God of Jesus Christ. Cunningham, Robert, tr. from Fr. Tr. of Le Dieu de Jesus Christ. 1978. 6.95 (ISBN 0-8199-0697-2). Franciscan Herald.

Servetus, Michael. Two Treatises of Servetus on the Trinity. Wilbur, Earl M., tr. (Harvard Theological Studies). 1932. 24.00 (ISBN 0-527-01016-2). Kraus Repr.

Stephens, Bruce M. God's Last Metaphor: The Doctrine of the Trinity in New England Theology. LC 80-11421. (American Academy of Religion Studies in Religion). pap. 11.95 (ISBN 0-89130-386-3, 01-00-24). Scholars Pr GA.

Tavard, George H. The Vision of the Trinity. LC 80-5845. 166p. (Orig.). 1981. lib. bdg. 25.25 (ISBN 0-8191-1412-X); pap. text ed. 10.75 (ISBN 0-8191-1413-8). U Pr of Amer.

Thurmer, John. A Detection of the Trinity. 93p. 1986. pap. 8.75 (ISBN 0-85364-395-4, Pub. by Paternoster UK). Attic Pr.

Victorinus, Marius. Theological Treatises on the Trinity. (Fathers of the Church Ser.: Vol. 69). 357p. 1981. 29.95x (ISBN 0-8132-0069-5). Cath U Pr.

Warfield, Benjamin B. Studies in Tertullian & Augustine. Repr. of 1930 ed. lib. bdg. 29.00x (ISBN 0-8371-4490-6, WATT). Greenwood.

Weisser, Thomas H. Three Persons from the Bible: Or Babylon. (Illus.). 44p. pap. 2.00 (ISBN 0-317-17477-0). Tom Weisser.

Wolfson, Harry A. Philosophy of the Church Fathers: Faith, Trinity, Incarnation. 3rd rev. ed. LC 70-119077. 1970. 32.50x (ISBN 0-674-66551-1). Harvard U Pr.

Wood, Nathan R. & Morgan, G. Campbell. The Trinity in the Universe. 2nd ed. LC 78-5483. 220p. 1984. pap. 6.95 (ISBN 0-8254-4018-1). Kregel.

TRINITY COLLEGE, WASHINGTON, D.C.

Mullaly, Columba. Trinity College, Washington, DC: The First Eighty Years, 1897-1977. 500p. 1987. 40.00 (ISBN 0-87061-140-2); pap. 35.00 (ISBN 0-87061-139-9). Chr Classics.

TRINITY UNIVERSITY, SAN ANTONIO, TEXAS–HISTORY

Everett, Donald E. Trinity University: A Record of One Hundred Years. LC 68-24632. (Illus.). 1968. 5.00 (ISBN 0-911536-21-3). Trinity U Pr.

TROELTSCH, ERNST, 1865-1923

Hugel, Friedrich Von. Essays & Addresses on the Philosophy of Religion. LC 72-9828. 308p. 1974. Repr. of 1921 ed. lib. bdg. 29.50x (ISBN 0-8371-6219-X, HUPR). Greenwood.

Morgan, Robert & Pye, Michael, eds. Ernst Troeltsch: Writings on Theology & Religion. LC 77-79596. 1977. 9.95 (ISBN 0-8042-0554-X). John Knox.

Wyman, Walter E., Jr. The Concept of Glaubenslehre: Ernst Troeltsch & the Theological Heritage of Schleiermacher. LC 83-4432. (American Academy of Religion, Academy Ser.). 276p. 1983. 14.95 (ISBN 0-89130-620-X, 01 01 44). Scholars Pr GA.

TRUEBLOOD, DAVID ELTON, 1900-

Trueblood, Elton. While It Is Day. 163p. 1983. pap. write for info. (ISBN 0-932970-36-2). Yokefellow Pr.

TRUST IN GOD

see also Faith

Allen, R. Earl. Just When You Need Him. (Contempo Ser). pap. 0.95 (ISBN 0-8010-0074-2). Baker Bk.

Bernard, Mary. Who Can We Trust? LC 80-80531. 128p. 1980. 2.50 (ISBN 0-89221-075-3). New Leaf.

Droege, Thomas A. Faith Passages & Patterns. LC 82-48544. (Lead Bks.). 128p. 1983. pap. 4.95 (ISBN 0-8006-1602-2, 1-1602). Fortress.

Goldsmith, Elizabeth. God Can Be Trusted. 1974. pap. 3.95 (ISBN 0-903843-85-4). OMF Bks.

Gripper, Clinton. Words of Inspiration. 32p. 1987. 5.95 (ISBN 0-89962-569-X). Todd & Honeywell.

Hunt, Sonjia L. Shaping Faith Through Involvement. 72p. (Orig.). 1981. pap. text ed. 2.50 (ISBN 0-87148-796-9). Pathway Pr.

Merchant, Robert. Trust. (Literacy Volunteers of America Readers Ser.). 32p. (Orig.). 1983. pap. 1.95 (ISBN 0-8428-9618-X). Cambridge Bk.

St. John Vianney. Thoughts of the Cure d'Ars. LC 84-50404. 79p. 1984. pap. 1.50 (ISBN 0-89555-240-X). TAN Bks Pubs.

Saint-Jure, Jean B. & De La Colombiere, Claude. Trustful Surrender to Divine Providence: The Secret of Peace & Happiness. LC 83-50252. 139p. 1983. pap. 3.00 (ISBN 0-89555-216-7). TAN Bks Pubs.

Smith, Hannah W. The God of All Comfort. (One Evening Christian Classic Ser.). pap. 2.50 (ISBN 0-89107-008-7). Good News.

Sumners, Roxanne. Trust Is the Key. (Illus.). 52p. (Orig.). 1983. pap. 4.95 (ISBN 0-913627-00-3). Agadir Pr.

TRUTH, SOJOURNER, d. 1883

Ortiz, Victoria. Sojourner Truth. LC 73-22290. (Illus.). 160p. (YA) 1974. PLB 10.89 (ISBN 0-397-31504-X, Lipp Jr Bks). HarpJ.

Pauli, Hertha. Her Name Was Sojourner Truth. (YA) 1976. pap. 1.50 (ISBN 0-380-00719-3, 29074). Avon.

Truth, Sojourner. Narrative of Sojourner Truth. LC 68-29021. (American Negro: His History & Literature Ser., No. 1). 1968. Repr. of 1878 ed. 15.00 (ISBN 0-405-01841-X). Ayer Co Pubs.

TRUTH

see also Agnosticism; Reality; Skepticism

Achad, Frater. Melchizedek Truth Principles. pap. 6.95 (ISBN 0-87516-166-9). De Vorss.

Alain, pseud. The Gods. Pevear, Richard, tr. from Fr. LC 74-8291. 192p. 1974. 8.95 (ISBN 0-8112-0547-9); pap. 3.95 (ISBN 0-8112-0548-7, NDP382). New Directions.

Bambrough, Renford. Reason, Truth & God. (Library Reprints Ser.). 174p. 1979. 45.00x (ISBN 0-416-72530-9, NO. 2823). Methuen Inc.

Brown, Thomas S. The Personal Relevance of Truth. 1983. pap. 2.50x (ISBN 0-87574-081-2, 081). Pendle Hill.

Conybeare, Fred C. The Key of Truth. cancelled 93.00 (ISBN 0-686-12403-0). Church History.

Cooper, Thomas J. Guidebook to Biblical Truth. Cooper, Willia S., ed. (Make the Path Clear Ser.: Vol. 1). 99p. (Orig.). 1984. pap. 4.95 (ISBN 0-931429-01-3). Cooper & Cooper Pub.

De Saint-Martin, Louis-Claude. Of Errors & Truth. Vadenais, Philip & Vadenais, Antoinette, trs. from Fr. LC 86-63353. 435p. (Orig.). 1987. pap. write for info. (ISBN 0-912057-47-5, G-651). AMORC.

Dessler, Eliyahu. Strive for Truth, Vol. 2. 1985. 12.95 (ISBN 0-87306-395-3); pap. 9.95 (ISBN 0-87306-396-1). Feldheim.

Deutsch, Eliot. On Truth: An Ontological Theory. LC 79-12754. 1979. text ed. 14.00x (ISBN 0-8248-0615-8). UH Pr.

DeWelt, Don. Ten Timely Truths. 1949. pap. 2.00 (ISBN 0-89900-135-1). College Pr Pub.

Dugan, LeRoy. Help Yourself to a Healthier Mind. 112p. (Orig.). 1980. 5.95 (ISBN 0-87123-205-7, 210205). Bethany Hse.

Ebner, Louise. Exploring Truths Through. pap. 3.95 (ISBN 0-89957-602-8). AMG Pubs.

Foster, K. The Idea of Truth in Manzoni & Leopardi. (Italian Lectures). 1967. pap. 2.25 (ISBN 0-85672-283-9, Pub. by British Acad). Longwood Pub Group.

Glanvill, Joseph. Two Choice & Useful Treatises: The One, One Lux Orientalis,...the Other, A Discourse of Truth by the Late Reverend Dr. Rust. Wellek, Rene, ed. LC 75-11223. (British Philosophers & Theologians of the 17th & 18th Centuries Ser.). 532p. 1978. lib. bdg. 51.00 (ISBN 0-8240-1777-3). Garland Pub.

Hole, F. B. Outlines of Truth. Daniel, R. P., ed. 73p. pap. 3.75 (ISBN 0-88172-143-3). Believers Bkshelf.

Inge, W. R. Science & Ultimate Truth. 1978. lib. bdg. 12.50 (ISBN 0-8495-2603-5). Arden Lib.

Jardine, N. The Fortunes of Inquiry. (Clarendon Library of Logic & Philosophy). 204p. 36.00 (ISBN 0-19-824929-2). Oxford U Pr.

Jyoti, Swami Amar. Retreat into Eternity: An Upanishad-Book of Aphorisms. LC 80-54236. (Illus.). 128p. (Orig.). 1981. pap. 12.95 (ISBN 0-933572-03-4). Truth Consciousness.

Kappeler, Max. Compendium for the Study of Christian Science: No. 9, Truth. 20p. 1953. pap. 3.50 (ISBN 0-85241-063-8). Kappeler Inst Pub.

Khalid, Anas. The Search for Truth. Abdal-aziz, Aliyah F., ed. LC 86-51061. 56p. 1986. pap. 5.00 (ISBN 0-9617422-0-8). A Khalid.

Levin, Samuel R. The Semantics of Metaphor. LC 77-4550. pap. 44.00 (ISBN 0-317-41827-0, 2025626). Bks Demand UMI.

McLean, George F., ed. Truth & the Historicity of Man. (Proceedings of the American Catholic Philosophical Association: Vol. 43). 1969. pap. 15.00 (ISBN 0-918090-03-2). Am Cath Philo.

Maurer, Herrymon. The Power of Truth. 1983. pap. 2.50x (ISBN 0-87574-053-7, 053). Pendle Hill.

Milne, Bruce. Know the Truth. LC 82-4711. 288p. 1982. pap. 9.95 (ISBN 0-87784-392-9). Inter-Varsity.

Murphy, Joseph. These Truths Can Change Your Life. 280p. 1982. pap. 7.50 (ISBN 0-87516-476-5). De Vorss.

Murray, John. Collected Writings of John Murray: Claims of Truth, Vol. 1. 374p. 1976. 22.95 (ISBN 0-85151-241-0). Banner of Truth.

Pak, Bo Hi. Truth Is My Sword. LC 78-74661. 110p. (Orig.). 1978. pap. 2.00 (ISBN 0-318-03063-2). HSA Pubns.

Palma, Anthony D. Truth-Antidote for Error. LC 76-52177. (Radiant Life Ser.). 128p. 1977. pap. 2.50 (ISBN 0-88243-904-9, 02-0904); teacher's ed 3.95 (ISBN 0-88243-174-9, 32-0174). Gospel Pub.

Priestley, Joseph. An Examination of Dr. Reid's Inquiry into the Human Mind. Wellek, Rene, ed. LC 75-11249. (British Philosophers & Theologians of the 17th & 18th Centuries Ser.). 1978. Repr. of 1774 ed. lib. bdg. 51.00 (ISBN 0-8240-1800-1). Garland Pub.

Rawson, Natasha. Search for Truth. LC 80-85047. 150p. 1981. 14.95 (ISBN 0-89896-149-1, Pub. by the Linolean Press). Larksdale.

Saint Thomas Aquinas. Truth & the Disputed Questions on Truth. (Illus.). 107p. 1987. 117.50 (ISBN 0-89266-582-3). Am Classical Coll Pr.

Scharlemann, Robert P. The Being of God: Theology & the Experience of Truth. 224p. 1981. 14.95 (ISBN 0-8164-0494-1, HarpR). Har-Row.

Scofield, C. I. Traza Bien la Palabra de Verdad. Orig. Title: Rightly Dividing the Word of Truth. (Span.). 92p. 1971. pap. 3.25 (ISBN 0-8254-1660-4). Kregel.

Scott, Thomas. Force of Truth. 1984. pap. 3.45 (ISBN 0-85151-425-1). Banner of Truth.

Shestov, Lev. In Job's Balances: On the Sources of the Eternal Truths. Coventry, Camilla & Macartney, C. A., trs. from Ger. LC 73-92902. (Eng.). l, 379p. 1975. 20.00x (ISBN 0-8214-0143-2, 82-81461). Ohio U Pr.

Solomon, Robert C. In the Spirit of Hegel: A Study of G. W. F. Hegel's "Phenomenology of Spirit". (Illus.). 1983. 32.50x (ISBN 0-19-503169-5); pap. 14.95x (ISBN 0-19-503650-6). Oxford U Pr.

Spencer, Richard A. The Fire of Truth. LC 82-71218. (Orig.). 1982. pap. 6.95 (ISBN 0-8054-2248-X). Broadman.

Steiner, Rudolf. Truth & Knowledge: Introduction to "Philosophy of Spiritual Activity", Vol. 14. 2nd ed. Allen, Paul M., ed. Stebbing, Rita, tr. from Ger. LC 81-51762. (The Major Writings of Rudolf Steiner in English Translation Ser.). 112p. 1981. Repr. of 1963 ed. lib. bdg. 10.00 (ISBN 0-89345-008-1, Spiritual Sci Lib). Garber Comm.

--Truth, Beauty & Goodness. 1986. pap. 1.50 (ISBN 0-916786-86-2). St George Bk Serv.

Syme, George S. & Syme, Charlotte U. The Scripture of Truth. 121p. 1983. pap. 5.95 (ISBN 0-88062-019-6). Mott Media.

--Scripture of Truth. 1986. pap. 5.95 (ISBN 0-8010-8274-9). Baker Bk.

Thomas, Nancy, ed. & intro. by. On the Edge of a Truth. 112p. (Orig.). pap. 4.50 (ISBN 0-913342-25-4). Barclay Pr.

Tucker, Bruce. Twisting the Truth. 192p. (Orig.). 1987. pap. 5.95 (ISBN 0-87123-931-0). Bethany Hse.

Von Wright, G. H. Truth, Knowledge & Modality: Philosophical Papers, Vol. III. 248p. 1985. 24.95x (ISBN 0-631-13367-4). Basil Blackwell.

Whittaker, John H. Matters of Faith & Matter of Principle: Religious Truth Claims & Their Logic. LC 80-51940. (Trinity University Monograph Series in Religion: Vol. 6). 173p. 1981. 12.00 (ISBN 0-911536-87-6). Trinity U Pr.

Zimmerman, Dean R. Evolution: A Golden Calf. 232p. (Orig.). 1976. pap. 3.95 (ISBN 0-89036-059-6). Hawkes Pub Inc.

TUAMOTU ISLANDS

Emory, K. P. Tuamotuan Religious Structures & Ceremonies. (BMB Ser.). Repr. of 1947 ed. 14.00 (ISBN 0-527-02299-3). Kraus Repr.

Stimson, J. F. Tuamotuan Religion. (BMB Ser.). Repr. of 1933 ed. 21.00 (ISBN 0-527-02209-8). Kraus Repr.

TUATHA DE DANANN

Gregory, Isabella A. Gods & Fighting Men. LC 76-115243. 1971. Repr. of 1904 ed. 23.00x (ISBN 0-403-00400-4). Scholarly.

TUDOR, HOUSE OF

Heal, Felicity. Of Prelates & Princes: A Study of the Economic & Social Position of the Tudor Episcopate. LC 79-41791. (Illus.). 368p. 1980. 59.50 (ISBN 0-521-22950-2). Cambridge U Pr.

TUNSTALL, ENGLAND (PARISH)

Chippindall, W. H. History of the Parish of Tunstall. 1940. 16.00 (ISBN 0-384-08875-9). Johnson Repr.

TURIYANADA, SWAMI, 1863-1922

Ritajananda, Swami. Swami Turiyananda. (Illus.). pap. 1.95 (ISBN 0-87481-473-1). Vedanta Pr.

TURKEY

Allen, Henry E. Turkish Transformation: A Study in Social & Religious Development. LC 68-57588. (Illus.). 1968. Repr. of 1935 ed. lib. bdg. 22.50x (ISBN 0-8371-0284-7, ALTT). Greenwood.

TURKEY–RELIGION

Allen, Henry E. Turkish Transformation: A Study in Social & Religious Development. LC 68-57588. (Illus.). 1968. Repr. of 1935 ed. lib. bdg. 22.50x (ISBN 0-8371-0284-7, ALTT). Greenwood.

Braude, Benjamin & Lewis, Bernard, eds. Christians & Jews in the Ottoman Empire: The Functioning of a Plural Society, 2 vols. LC 80-11337. 1982. Set. text ed. 94.50x. Vol. 1, The Central Lands, 450p (ISBN 0-8419-0519-3). Vol. 2, The Arabic-speaking Lands, 248p (ISBN 0-8419-0520-7). Holmes & Meier.

Garnett, Lucy M. Mysticism & Magic in Turkey: An Account of the Religious Doctrines, Monastic Organisation & Ecstatic Powers of the Dervish Orders. LC 77-87628. (Illus.). Repr. of 1912 ed. 22.00 (ISBN 0-404-16453-6). AMS Pr.

Landau, Jacob M. The Hejaz Railway & the Muslim Pilgrimage: A Case of Ottoman Political Progaganda. LC 78-12918. pap. 73.80 (2027676). Bks Demand UMI.

Pantazopoulos, N. J. Church & Law in the Balkan Peninsula during the Ottoman Rule. (Illus.). 125p. 1983. pap. text ed. 24.00 (Pub. by A M Hakkert). Coronet Bks.

TURKEY–SOCIAL CONDITIONS

Allen, Henry E. Turkish Transformation: A Study in Social & Religious Development. LC 68-57588. (Illus.). 1968. Repr. of 1935 ed. lib. bdg. 22.50x (ISBN 0-8371-0284-7, ALTT). Greenwood.

Leder, Arnold. Catalysts of Change: Marxist versus Muslim in a Turkish Community. LC 76-29323. (Middle East Monograph: No. 1). 70p. 1976. pap. text ed. 3.95x (ISBN 0-292-71042-9, Pub. by Ctr Mid East Stud). U of Tex Pr.

TUTANKHAMEN, KING OF EGYPT

Aldred, Cyril. Tut-Ankh-Amun-& His Friends. pap. 2.95 (ISBN 0-88388-043-1). Bellerophon Bk.

Budge, E. Wallis. Tutankhamen: Amenism, Atenism & Egyptain Monotheism. LC 79-160615. (Illus.). Repr. of 1923 ed. 12.75 (ISBN 0-405-08323-8, Blom Pubns). Ayer Co Pubs.

Carter, Howard & Mace, A. C. The Discovery of the Tomb of Tutankhamen. LC 77-71042. (Illus.). 382p. 1977. pap. 6.50 (ISBN 0-486-23500-9). Dover.

--Tomb of Tut-Ankh-Amen, 3 Vols. LC 63-17462. (Illus.). Repr. of 1954 ed. Set. 85.00x (ISBN 0-8154-0048-9). Cooper Sq.

Desroches-Noblecourt, Christiane. Tutankhamen. LC 63-15145. 312p. 1976. pap. 8.95 (ISBN 0-8212-0695-8, 857017). NYGS.

Reiff, Stephanie A. Secrets of Tut's Tomb & the Pyramids. LC 77-22770. (Great Unsolved Mysteries). (Illus.). 1977. PLB 14.65 (ISBN 0-8172-1051-2). Raintree Pubs.

Ventura, Piero & Ceserani, Gian P. In Search of Tutankhamun. LC 85-40416. (In Search of... Ser.). (Illus.). 48p. 1985. text ed. 12.96 (ISBN 0-382-09119-1); pap. 7.75 (ISBN 0-382-09122-1). Silver.

Weigall, Arthur. Tutankhamen & Other Essays. LC 73-115210. 1971. Repr. of 1924 ed. 24.50x (ISBN 0-8046-1103-3, Pub by Kennikat). Assoc Faculty Pr.

TWELFTH NIGHT
see Epiphany

TYNDALE, WILLIAM, d. 1536

Mozley, James F. William Tyndale. LC 70-109801. (Illus.). 1971. Repr. of 1937 ed. lib. bdg. 22.50x (ISBN 0-8371-4292-X, MOWT). Greenwood.

Smeeton, Donald. Lollard Themes in Reformation Theology of William Tyndale. (Sixteenth Century Essays & Studies: Vol. VI). (Illus.). 240p. 1986. smyth sewn 30.00x (ISBN 0-940474-06-9). Sixteenth Cent.

Smith, G. Barnett. William Tyndale & the Translation of the English Bible. 20.00 (ISBN 0-8274-3719-6). R West.

Vernon, Louise A. Bible Smuggler. LC 67-15994. (Illus.). 138p. 1967. pap. 4.50 (ISBN 0-8361-1557-0). Herald Pr.

TYPES, BIBLICAL
see Typology (Theology)

TYPOLOGY (THEOLOGY)
see also Covenants (Theology); Wilderness (Theology)

Baron, David. Types, Psalms & Prophecies. 1981. lib. bdg. 14.00 (ISBN 0-86524-077-9, 9511). Klock & Klock.

Bercovitch, Sacvan, ed. Typology & Early American Literature. LC 74-181362. (New England Writers Ser.). 352p. 1971. 20.00x (ISBN 0-87023-096-4). U of Mass Pr.

Charity, Alan. Events & Their Afterlife: The Dialectics of Christian Typology in the Bible & Dante. 300p. Date not set. pap. price not set (ISBN 0-521-34923-0). Cambridge U Pr.

Glasson, T. Francis. Moses in the Fourth Gospel. LC 63-5666. (Studies in Biblical Theology: No. 40). 1963. pap. 10.00x (ISBN 0-8401-3040-6). A R Allenson.

Habershon, Ada R. Study of the Types. LC 67-24340. 240p. 1975. pap. 7.95 (ISBN 0-8254-2850-5). Kregel.

Haines, Victor Y. The Fortunate Fall of Sir Gawain: The Typology of Sir Gawain & the Green Knight. LC 80-5847. (Illus.). 240p. (Orig.). 1982. PLB 29.00 (ISBN 0-8191-2437-0); pap. text ed. 12.75 (ISBN 0-8191-2438-9). U Pr of Amer.

Jukes, Andrew. The Law of the Offerings. LC 68-19198. 220p. 1976. pap. 6.95 (ISBN 0-8254-2957-9). Kregel.

Landow, George. William Holman Hunt & Typological Symbolism. LC 77-91017. 1979. 42.00x (ISBN 0-300-02196-8). Yale U Pr.

Mather, Samuel. The Figures or Types of the Old Testament. 1969. Repr. of 1705 ed. 34.00 (ISBN 0-384-35880-2). Johnson Repr.

Miner, Earl, ed. Literary Uses of Typology from the Late Middle Ages to the Present. LC 76-45904. 1977. 47.50 (ISBN 0-691-06327-3). Princeton U Pr.

Olford, Stephen F. The Tabernacle: Camping with God. LC 78-173686. 1971. 8.95 (ISBN 0-87213-675-2). Loizeaux.

Shepherd, Coulson. Jewish Holy Days: Their Prophetic & Christian Significance. LC 61-16660. 1961. pap. 3.25 (ISBN 0-87213-780-5). Loizeaux.

Wilson, Walter L. Wilson's Dictionary of Bible Types. 1957. pap. 10.95 (ISBN 0-8028-1453-0). Eerdmans.

TYSSOT DE PATOT, SIMON, b. 1655

McKee, David R. Simon Tyssot de Patot & the Seventeenth-Century Background of Critical Deism. (Johns Hopkins University Studies in Romance Literatures & Languages: Vol. 40). 105p. pap. 14.00 (ISBN 0-384-34885-8). Johnson Repr.

U

UGANDA–RELIGION

Byabazaire, Deogratias M. The Contribution of the Christian Churches to the Development of Western Uganda 1894-1974: Theology. (European University Studies: Ser. 23, Vol. 112). 198p. 1979. pap. 21.95 (ISBN 3-261-02553-0). P Lang Pubs.

Hansen, H. B. Mission, Church & State in a Colonial Setting: Uganda 1890-1925. LC 84-16052. 608p. 1985. 39.95 (ISBN 0-312-53474-4). St Martin.

UKRAINE–CHURCH HISTORY

Zinkewych, Osyp & Lonchyna, Taras. Martyrology of Ukrainian Churches: Vol. 1, Ukrainian Catholic Church. (Ukrainian Ser.). 839p. 1985. 29.75 (ISBN 0-914834-36-3). Smoloskyp.

ULMECAS
see Olmecs

UNCTION

Ellard, G. Ordination Anointings in the Western Church Before 1000 A. D. (Med Acad of Amer Pubns). 1932. 18.00 (ISBN 0-527-01688-8). Kraus Repr.

Empereur, James L. Prophetic Anointing: God's Call to the Sick, the Elderly, & the Dying. (Message of the Sacraments Ser.: Vol. 7). 1982. text ed. 15.95 (ISBN 0-89453-397-5); pap. 10.95 (ISBN 0-89453-233-2). M Glazier.

Enright, Michael J. Iona, Tara, & Soissons: The Origin of the Royal Anointing Ritual in Francia. (Arbeiten zur Fruehmittelalterforschung: Vol. 17). x, 198p. 1985. 67.25x (ISBN 3-11-010628-0). De Gruyter.

Rite of Anointing & Pastoral Care of the Sick. pocket ed. 6.95 (ISBN 0-89942-156-3, 156/04). Catholic Bk Pub.

Shlemon, Barbara L., et al. To Heal As Jesus Healed. LC 78-54126. 112p. 1978. pap. 2.95 (ISBN 0-87793-152-6). Ave Maria.

UNDSET, SIGRID, 1882-

Slochower, Harry. Three Ways of Modern Man. LC 37-17328. 1968. Repr. of 1937 ed. 20.00 (ISBN 0-527-83656-7). Kraus Repr.

Winsnes, Andreas H. Sigrid Undset: A Study in Christian Realism. Foote, P. G., tr. LC 74-110276. (Illus.). ix, 258p. Repr. of 1953 ed. lib. bdg. 22.50x (ISBN 0-8371-4502-3, WISU). Greenwood.

UNION, HYPOSTATIC
see Hypostatic Union

UNION, MYSTICAL
see Mystical Union

UNION WITH CHRIST
see Mystical Union

UNITARIAN CHURCHES

Ahlstrom, Sydney E. & Carey, Jonathan S., eds. An American Reformation: A Documentary History of Unitarian Christianity. vi, 506p. 1984. 39.50x (ISBN 0-8195-5080-9). Wesleyan U Pr.

Alger, Horatio, Sr. & Sheaf, J. P., Jr. Addresses Delivered at the Semi-Centennial Celebration of the Dedication of the First Unitarian Church, South Natick (Massachusetts) November 20, 1878. (Illus.). 41p. 1977. pap. 6.00 (ISBN 0-686-35760-4). G K Westgard.

Barth, Joseph. Art of Staying Sane. facs. ed. LC 70-117757. (Essay Index Reprint Ser). 1948. 18.00 (ISBN 0-8369-1783-9). Ayer Co Pubs.

Channing, William E. Works of William Ellery Channing, 2 vols. in 1. LC 70-114815. (Research & Source Works Ser.: No. 626). 1971. Repr. of 1882 ed. lib. bdg. 46.50 (ISBN 0-8337-0530-X). B Franklin.

Gannett, William C. Ezra Stiles Gannett: Unitarian Minister in Boston, 1824-1871. 1979. Repr. of 1875 ed. lib. bdg. 30.00 (ISBN 0-8492-4932-5). R West.

Howe, Daniel W. The Unitarian Conscience. LC 75-116737. 15.00 (ISBN 0-674-92121-6). Harvard U Pr.

Kuklick, Bruce, ed. The Unitarian Controversy, 1819-1823, 2 vols. (American Religious Thought of the 18th & 19th Centuries Ser.). 857p. 1987. Set. lib. bdg. 120.00 (ISBN 0-8240-6958-7). Garland Pub.

Lavan, Spencer. Unitarians & India. 1984. pap. 5.95 (ISBN 0-933840-23-3). Unitarian Univ.

UNITARIAN CHURCHES–SERMONS

Mayhew, Jonathan. Sermons. LC 76-83429. (Religion in America, Ser. 1). 1969. Repr. of 1749 ed. 19.00 (ISBN 0-405-00254-8). Ayer Co Pubs.

UNITARIAN UNIVERSALIST ASSOCIATION

Miller, Russell. Larger Hope, Vol. 2. 1986. 25.00 (ISBN 0-933840-25-X). Unitarian Univ.

UNITARIANISM
see also Humanism, Religious; Jesus Christ–Divinity; Trinity

Allen, Joseph H. Our Liberal Movement in Theology: Chiefly As Shown in Recollections of the History of Unitarianism in New England. 3rd ed. LC 73-38432. (Religion in America, Ser. 2). 230p. 1972. Repr. of 1892 ed. 20.00 (ISBN 0-405-04053-9). Ayer Co Pubs.

Arnason, Wayne. Follow the Gleam. 1980. pap. 3.50 (ISBN 0-933840-07-1). Unitarian Univ.

Bartol, Cyrus A. Discourses on the Christian Spirit & Life: With an Introduction. 2nd ed. LC 72-4951. (The Romantic Tradition in American Literature Ser.). 418p. 1972. Repr. of 1850 ed. 30.00 (ISBN 0-405-04622-7). Ayer Co Pubs.

Clark, John R. The Great Living System. 1984. pap. 7.95 (ISBN 0-933840-24-1). Unitarian Univ.

Cooke, George W. Unitarianism in America. LC 72-155153. Repr. of 1902 ed. 12.50 (ISBN 0-404-01699-5). AMS Pr.

Drummond, Audrey. Honor Thy Womanself. 1982. pap. 7.50 (ISBN 0-933840-12-8). Unitarian Univ.

Gilbert, Richard. The Prophetic Imperative. 1980. pap. 6.75 (ISBN 0-933840-16-0). Unitarian Univ.

Johnstone, Parker L. A Book for Unitarians. LC 76-21519. 1977. cloth 7.95 (ISBN 0-917802-02-0). Theoscience Found.

Kring, Walter D. Henry Whitney Bellows. 1979. pap. 7.95 (ISBN 0-933840-03-9). Unitarian Univ.

--Liberals Among the Orthodox: Unitarian Beginnings in New York City, 1819-1839. LC 73-21275. (Illus.). 1974. 14.95x (ISBN 0-8070-1662-4). Beacon Pr.

McKinsey, Elizabeth R. The Western Experiment: New England Transcendentalists in the Ohio Valley. LC 72-83467. (Essays in History & Literature Ser.). 80p. 1973. pap. 4.95x (ISBN 0-674-95040-2). Harvard U Pr.

MacLean, Angus. The Wind in Both Ears. 2nd ed. 1987. pap. write for info. (ISBN 0-933840-30-6, Skinner Hse Bks). Unitarian Univ.

Miller, Russell. The Larger Hope, Vol. 1. 25.00 (ISBN 0-933840-00-4). Unitarian Univ.

Parke, David. The Epic of Unitarianism. 1957. pap. 3.50 (ISBN 0-933840-05-5). Unitarian Univ.

Parke, David, ed. The Right Time: The Best of Kairos. 1982. pap. 7.95 (ISBN 0-933840-13-6). Unitarian Univ.

Parker, Theodore. A Discourse of Matters Pertaining to Religion. LC 72-4968. (Romantic Tradition in American Literature Ser.). 510p. 1972. Repr. of 1842 ed. 35.00 (ISBN 0-405-04639-1). Ayer Co Pubs.

Robinson, David. Apostle of Culture: Emerson As Preacher & Lecturer. LC 81-16228. 200p. 1982. 21.00x (ISBN 0-8122-7824-0). U of Pa Pr.

--The Unitarians & the Universalists. LC 84-9031. (Denominations in America Ser.: No. 1). xiii, 368p. 1985. lib. bdg. 37.50 (ISBN 0-313-20946-4, RUN/). Greenwood.

Scott, Clinton L. These Live Tomorrow. 1964. pap. write for info. (ISBN 0-933840-06-3). Unitarian Univ.

Seaburg, Carl. Great Occasions. 1968. pap. 9.95 (ISBN 0-933840-09-8). Unitarian Univ.

UUA. Hymns of the Spirit. 7.50 (ISBN 0-933840-11-X). Unitarian Univ.

Wigmore-Beddoes, Dennis G. Yesterday's Radicals: A Study of the Affinity Between Unitarianism & Broad Church Anglicanism in the Nineteenth Century. 182p. 1971. 19.95 (ISBN 0-227-67751-X). Attic Pr.

Wilbur, Earl M. Our Unitarian Heritage: An Introduction to the History of the Unitarian Movement. LC 83-45635. Date not set. Repr. of 1925 ed. 49.50 (ISBN 0-404-19877-5). AMS Pr.

The Works of William E. Channing, D.D. 1060p. 1982. Repr. of 1889 ed. lib. bdg. 100.00 (ISBN 0-8495-0959-9). Arden Lib.

Wright, Conrad. A Stream of Light. 1975. pap. 5.75 (ISBN 0-933840-14-4). Unitarian Univ.

Wright, Conrad, ed. Three Prophets of Religious Liberalism. 1961. pap. 4.00 (ISBN 0-933840-20-9). Unitarian Univ.

UNITAS FRATRUM
see Moravians

UNITED BRETHREN
see Moravians

UNITED CHURCH OF CHRIST

Bass, Dorothy C. & Smith, Kenneth B., eds. The United Church of Christ: Studies in Identity & Polity. LC 86-83022. (Studies in Ministry & Parish Life). 112p. 1987. text ed. 16.95x (ISBN 0-913552-37-2); pap. text ed. 6.95x (ISBN 0-913552-36-4). Exploration Pr.

Bricker, Florence M. Church & Pastoral Records in the Archives of the United Church of Christ. 1982. pap. 6.00 (ISBN 0-910564-01-9). Evang & Ref.

Goddard. On the Trail of the UCC. 1981. pap. 8.95 (ISBN 0-8298-0353-X). Pilgrim NY.

Gunnemann, Louis H. The Shaping of the United Church of Christ: An Essay in the History of American Christianity. LC 77-4900. 1977. 6.95 (ISBN 0-8298-0335-1). Pilgrim NY.

Keiling, Hanns P., compiled by. The Formation of the United Church of Christ (U. S. A.) Battles, Ford L., ed. LC 79-25049. (Bibliographia Tripotamopolitana: No.2). 1970. 7.00x (ISBN 0-931222-01-X). Pitts Theolog.

Thompson, Harry. Guide to the Archives of the South Dakota Conference of the United Church of Christ. 128p. 1986. pap. 4.00 (ISBN 0-931170-31-1). Ctr Western Studies.

Townsend, Charles D., ed. The History of the Third Congregational Church of Middleborough, Known Today As North Congregational Church, United Church of Christ, North Middleboro, Massachusetts: Includes S. Hopkins Emery's Church History Reprinted from 1876 Edition. (Illus.). 300p. 1982. 22.50 (ISBN 0-9607906-0-8). ACETO Bookmen.

Zikmund, Barbara B., ed. Hidden Histories in the United Church of Christ. 192p. (Orig.). 1984. pap. 9.95 (ISBN 0-8298-0704-7). Pilgrim NY.

--Hidden Histories in the United Church of Christ, Pt. 2. 228p. (Orig.). 1987. pap. 10.95 (ISBN 0-8298-0753-5). Pilgrim NY.

Zuck, Lowell H. Socially Responsible Believers: Puritans, Pietists, & Unionists in the History of the United Church of Christ. 164p. (Orig.). 1987. pap. 8.95 (ISBN 0-8298-0744-6). Pilgrim NY.

UNITED CHURCH OF CHRIST–CATECHISMS AND CREEDS

Paul, Robert S. Freedom with Order: The Doctrine of the Church in the United Church of Christ. 160p. (Orig.). 1987. pap. 8.95 (ISBN 0-8298-0749-7). Pilgrim NY.

UNITED CHURCH OF CHRIST–HYMNS–HISTORY AND CRITICISM

Ferguson, John & Nelson, William, eds. The United Church of Christ Hymnal. LC 74-12571. 1974. Pew Edition. spiral bound 12.50x (ISBN 0-8298-0300-9); 9.95x. Pilgrim NY.

UNITED LUTHERAN CHURCH IN AMERICA

Cottrell, Donald P. Instruction & Instructional Facilities in the Colleges of the United Lutheran Church in America. LC 79-176672. (Columbia University. Teachers College. Contributions to Education: No. 376). Repr. of 1929 ed. 22.50 (ISBN 0-404-55376-1). AMS Pr.

Le Sourd, Howard M. The University Work of the United Lutheran Church in America: A Study of the Work Among Lutheran Students at Non-Lutheran Institutions. LC 70-176990. (Columbia University. Teachers College. Contributions to Education: No. 377). Repr. of 1929 ed. 17.50 (ISBN 0-404-55377-X). AMS Pr.

Schott, Carl P. Physical Education in the Colleges of the United Lutheran Church of America: A Survey & Program. (Columbia University. Teachers College. Contributions to Education: No. 379). Repr. of 1929 ed. 22.50 (ISBN 0-404-55379-6). AMS Pr.

UNITED PRESBYTERIAN CHURCH IN THE U. S. A.
see also Presbyterian Church in the U. S. A.

Black, Donald. Merging Mission & Unity. LC 86-14847. 180p. (Orig.). 1986. pap. 9.95 (ISBN 0-664-24047-X, A Geneva Press Publication). Westminster.

Parker, Inez M. The Rise & Decline of the Program for Black Education in the United Presbyterian Church, U. S. A. 1865-1970. LC 76-49248. (Presbyterian Historical Ser.). 320p. 1977. 10.00 (ISBN 0-911536-66-3). Trinity U Pr.

Paschal, George H., Jr. & Benner, Judith A. One Hundred Years of Challenge & Change: A History of the Synod of Texas of the United Presbyterian Church in the U. S. A. LC 68-20488. 259p. 1968. 4.00 (ISBN 0-911536-32-9). Trinity U Pr.

UNITED STATES–CHURCH HISTORY
see also names of various religious denominations, with or without the subdivision history

Baird, Robert. Religion in the United States of America. LC 70-83411. (Religion in America, Ser. 1). 1969. Repr. of 1844 ed. 38.50 (ISBN 0-405-00232-7). Ayer Co Pubs.

Bilhartz, Terry D. Urban Religion & the Second Great Awakening. LC 83-49455. 240p. 1986. 27.50x (ISBN 0-8386-3227-0). Fairleigh Dickinson.

Brauer, Jerald C. Protestantism in America: A Narrative History. rev. ed. LC 66-12686. 320p. 1972. Westminster.

Catholic University of America Staff. Studies in American Church History, 25 vols. Repr. of 1942 ed. 662.50 (ISBN 0-404-57750-4). AMS Pr.

Cleveland, Catherine C. The Great Revival in the West, 1797-1805. 11.25 (ISBN 0-8446-1117-4). Peter Smith.

Cole, Charles C., Jr. Social Ideas of the Northern Evangelists, Eighteen Twenty-Six to Eighteen Sixty. 1966. lib. bdg. 20.50x (ISBN 0-374-91843-0, Octagon). Hippocrene Bks.

Garrison, Winfred E. March of Faith: The Story of Religion in America Since 1865. LC 79-138112. 1971. Repr. of 1933 ed. lib. bdg. 22.50x (ISBN 0-8371-5688-2, GAMF). Greenwood.

Handy, Robert T. A Christian America: Protestant Hopes & Historical Realities. 2nd & enl. ed. 1983. 27.00x (ISBN 0-19-503386-8); pap. 10.95x (ISBN 0-19-503387-6). Oxford U Pr.

Hudson, Winthrop S. American Protestantism. LC 61-15936. (Chicago History of American Civilization Ser). 1961. pap. 4.95x (ISBN 0-226-35803-8, CHAC10). U of Chicago Pr.

Marty, Martin E. Christian Churches in the United States, 1800-1983. (Illus.). 126p. 1984. 12.95 (ISBN 0-86683-172-X, 1412, HarpR). Har-Row.

Mead, Sidney E. Lively Experiment: The Shaping of Christianity in America. 1963. pap. 6.95xi (ISBN 0-06-065545-3, RD-194, HarpR). Har-Row.

Mode, Peter G. Source Book & Bibliographical Guide to American Church History. 1964. Repr. of 1921 ed. 17.50x (ISBN 0-910324-06-9). Canner.

Mullin, Robert B. Episcopal Vision-American Reality: High Church Theology & Social Thought in Evangelical America. 1986. 20.00 (ISBN 0-300-03487-3). Yale U Pr.

Salpointe, J. B. Soldiers of the Cross: Notes on the Ecclesiastical History of New Mexico, Arizona, & Colorado. LC 67-29317. 299p. 1982. lib. bdg. 44.95x (ISBN 0-89370-733-3). Borgo Pr.

Slater, Rosalie J. Teaching & Learning America's Christian History. LC 65-26334. 1965. lib. bdg. 10.00 (ISBN 0-912498-02-1). Found Am Christ.

Smith, Timothy L. Revivalism & Social Reform: American Protestantism on the Eve of the Civil War. 11.25 (ISBN 0-8446-2960-X). Peter Smith.

Sprunger, Keith L. The Learned Doctor William Ames: Dutch Backgrounds of English & American Puritanism. LC 77-175172. pap. 76.30 (ISBN 0-317-08400-3, 2020215). Bks Demand UMI.

Stanton, Robert L. The Church & the Rebellion. facsimile ed. LC 70-168521. (Black Heritage Library Collection). Repr. of 1864 ed. 31.25 (ISBN 0-8369-8873-6). Ayer Co Pubs.

Stoeckli, Walter A. Church-State & School in Switzerland & the U. S. A Study in Comparative Constitutional Law. (European University Studies: Series 2, Law: Vol. 23). 50p. 1969. 5.85 (ISBN 3-261-00081-3). P Lang Pubs.

Tracy, Joseph. Great Awakening: A History of the Revival of Religion in the Time of Edwards & Whitefield. LC 72-83444. (Religion in America Ser). 1969. Repr. of 1945 ed. 21.00 (ISBN 0-405-00280-7). Ayer Co Pubs.

Weber, Timothy P. Living in the Shadow of the Second Coming: American Premillennialism, 1875-1982. rev. & enl. ed. xiv, 306p. 1987. pap. 12.95 (ISBN 0-226-87732-9). U of Chicago Pr.

Wimberly, Edward P. & Streaty, Anne. Liberation & Human Wholeness: The Conversion Experiences of Black People in Slavery & Freedom. 144p. (Orig.). 1986. pap. 10.95 (ISBN 0-687-21698-2). Abingdon.

UNITED STATES–CHURCH HISTORY–SOURCES

Allison, W. H. Inventory of Unpublished Material for American Religion History in Protestant Church Archives & Other Repositories. (CI.G Ser.). 1910. 21.00 (ISBN 0-527-00683-1). Kraus Repr.

Heimert, Alan E. & Miller, Perry, eds. Great Awakening: Documents Illustrating the Crisis & Its Consequences. LC 66-23537. (Orig.). 1967. pap. 14.47 scp (ISBN 0-672-60044-7, AHS34). Bobbs.

Mathisen, Robert R., ed. The Role of Religion in American Life: An Interpretive Historical Anthology. LC 80-6246. 420p. (Orig.). 1982. pap. text ed. 14.75 (ISBN 0-8191-2514-8). U Pr of Amer.

Mode, Peter G. Source Book & Bibliographical Guide to American Church History. 1964. Repr. of 1921 ed. 17.50x (ISBN 0-910324-06-9). Canner.

UNITED STATES–CHURCH HISTORY–20TH CENTURY

Marty, Martin E. Modern American Religion, Vol. 1: The Irony of It All, 1893-1919. LC 86-16524. (Illus.). 398p. 1986. 24.95 (ISBN 0-226-50893-5). U of Chicago Pr.

Miller, Robert M. American Protestantism & Social Issues, 1919-1939. LC 77-22031. 1977. Repr. of 1958 ed. lib. bdg. 26.75x (ISBN 0-8371-9777-5, MIAM). Greenwood.

Russell, Letty M., ed. Changing Contexts of Our Faith. LC 85-4418. 112p. 1985. pap. 4.95 (ISBN 0-8006-1862-9). Fortress.

Schneider, Herbert W. Religion in Twentieth Century America. LC 52-8219. (The Library of Congress Ser. in American Civilization). (Illus.). 1952. 16.50x (ISBN 0-674-75700-9). Harvard U Pr.

Trigg, Joseph W. & Sachs, William L. Of One Body: Renewal Movements in the Church. LC 86-2788. 168p. (Orig.). 1986. pap. 9.95 (ISBN 0-8042-0677-5). John Knox.

UNITED STATES–CIVILIZATION

Flood, Robert. Faith for All Generations. LC 86-70628. Orig. Title: Up with America. 96p. 1986. pap. 4.95 (ISBN 0-89636-214-0). Accent Bks.

King, James M. Facing the Twentieth Century. Grob, Gerald, ed. LC 76-46085. (Anti-Movements in America Ser.). (Illus.). 1977. Repr. of 1899 ed. lib. bdg. 54.00x (ISBN 0-405-09958-4). Ayer Co Pubs.

Merrill, Abbey R. Day Dawns in Fire: America's Quest for Meaning. LC 75-36439. pap. 32.00. Bks Demand UMI.

Miller, Perry G. Errand into the Wilderness. LC 56-11285. 1956. 15.00x (ISBN 0-674-26151-8, Belknap Pr); pap. 6.95x (ISBN 0-674-26155-0). Harvard U Pr.

Moore, R. Laurence. In Search of White Crows: Spiritualism, Parapsychology, & American Culture. LC 76-50720. 1977. 22.50x (ISBN 0-19-502259-9). Oxford U Pr.

Morey-Gaines, Ann-Janine. Apples & Ashes: Culture, Metaphor & Morality in the American Dream. LC 81-14346. (AAR Academy Ser.). 1982. 12.95 (ISBN 0-89130-535-1, 01-01-38). Scholars Pr GA.

Paterson, Isabel B. God of the Machine. LC 77-172225. (Right Wing Individualist Tradition in America Ser). 1972. Repr. of 1943 ed. 25.50 (ISBN 0-405-00434-6). Ayer Co Pubs.

Perry, Ralph B. Puritanism & Democracy. 688p. 1944. 19.50 (ISBN 0-8149-0180-8). Vanguard.

Seward, Harold A. Freedom's Holy Light. (Illus.). 88p. 1986. 10.95 (ISBN 0-8059-3021-3). Dorrance.

Sweet, William W. American Culture & Religion. LC 72-78372. ix, 114p. 1972. Repr. of 1951 ed. lib. bdg. 19.50x (ISBN 0-8154-0421-2). Cooper Sq.

UNITED STATES–HISTORY–SOURCES

Adams, Herbert B. Norman Constables in America. pap. 9.00 (ISBN 0-384-00333-8). Johnson Repr.

UNITED STATES–HISTORY–REVOLUTION, 1775-1783

Brauer, Jerald. Religion & the American Revolution. LC 76-9718. pap. 22.30 (2026888). Bks Demand UMI.

David, Ebenezer. Rhode Island Chaplain in the Revolution. Black, Jeannette D. & Roelker, W. Greene, eds. LC 73-159068. 1971. Repr. of 1949 ed. 21.50x (ISBN 0-8046-1662-0, Pub. by Kennikat). Assoc Faculty Pr.

Noll, Mark A. Christians & the American Revolution. LC 77-23354. pap. 48.80 (ISBN 0-8357-9125-4, 2016042). Bks Demand UMI.

Williams, John S. The Revolutionary War & Issachar Bates. 14p. 1960. 0.50 (ISBN 0-937942-02-2). Shaker Mus.

Wolf, Simon. The American Jew As Patriot, Soldier, & Citizen. LC 72-8739. (American Revolutionary Ser.). 1979. Repr. of 1895 ed. lib. bdg. 47.00x (ISBN 0-8398-2179-4). Irvington.

UNITED STATES–HISTORY–WAR OF 1812

Smith, Page. Religious Origins of the American Revolution. LC 76-13157. (American Academy of Religion, Aids for the Study of Religion). 1976. pap. 8.95 (ISBN 0-89130-121-6, 010303). Scholars Pr GA.

UNITED STATES–HISTORY–WAR WITH MEXICO, 1845-1848

Berry, Philip A. A Review of the Mexican War on Christian Principles: And an Essay on the Means of Preventing War. LC 76-143427. (Peace Movement in America Ser). ix, 87p. 1972. Repr. of 1849 ed. lib. bdg. 11.95x (ISBN 0-89198-057-1). Ozer.

Cook, Blanche, et al. Sermons on War by Theodore Parker. LC 70-149546. (Library of War & Peace; Relig. & Ethical Positions on War). 1973. lib. bdg. 46.00 (ISBN 0-8240-0499-X). Garland Pub.

UNITED STATES–HISTORY–CIVIL WAR, 1861-1865–ADDRESSES, SERMONS, ETC.

Haven, Gilbert. Sermons, Speeches, Letters on Slavery & Its War 1850-1868. LC 74-82197. (Anti-Slavery Crusade in America Ser.). 1969. Repr. of 1869 ed. 26.00 (ISBN 0-405-00637-3). Ayer Co Pubs.

UNITED STATES–HISTORY–CIVIL WAR, 1861-1865–RELIGIOUS ASPECTS

Goen, C. C. Broken Churches, Broken Nation: Denominational Schism & the Coming of the American Civil War. 208p. 1985. 17.95 (ISBN 0-86554-166-3, MUP-H156). Mercer Univ Pr.

Horst, Samuel L. Mennonites in the Confederacy: A Study in Civil War Pacifism. LC 67-15991. (Illus.). 148p. 1967. 8.95x (ISBN 0-8361-1180-X). Herald Pr.

Moorhead, James H. American Apocalypse: Yankee Protestants & the Civil War, 1860-1869. LC 77-14360. 1978. 32.00x (ISBN 0-300-02152-6). Yale U Pr.

Silver, James W. Confederate Morale & Church Propaganda. 1967. pap. 1.35x (ISBN 0-393-00422-8, Norton Lib). Norton.

UNITED STATES–INTELLECTUAL LIFE

Ellis, John T. American Catholicism. 2nd ed. Boorstin, Daniel J., ed. LC 69-19274. (Chicago History of American Civilization Ser.). 1969. pap. 10.00x (ISBN 0-226-20556-8, CHAC5). U of Chicago Pr.

Liderbach, Daniel. The Theology of Grace & the American Mind: A Representation of Catholic Doctrine. LC 83-22154. (Toronto Studies in Theology: Vol. 15). 170p. 1983. lib. bdg. 39.95x (ISBN 0-88946-761-7). E Mellen.

May, Henry F. Ideas, Faiths, & Feelings: Essays on American Intellectual & Religious History, 1952-1982. 1983. 25.00x (ISBN 0-19-503235-7); pap. 9.95 (ISBN 0-19-503236-5). Oxford U Pr.

Miller, Perry G. Nature's Nation. LC 67-17316. 1967. 20.00x (ISBN 0-674-60550-0, Belknap Pr). Harvard U Pr.

Shaw, James. Twelve Years in America Being Observations on the Country, the People, Institutions, & Religion. text ed. 25.50 (ISBN 0-8369-9234-2, 9088). Ayer Co Pubs.

Williams, David R. Wilderness Lost: The Religious Origins of the American Mind. LC 85-43475. 296p. 1987. 38.50x (ISBN 0-941664-21-X). Susquehanna U Pr.

UNITED STATES–MORAL CONDITIONS

America's Attack on Itself: Truth, Faith, Ideas, Morality, & God. (Analysis Ser.: No. 16.). Date not set. 12.50 (ISBN 0-686-45487-1). Inst Analysis.

Horwitz, Robert H., ed. The Moral Foundations of the American Republic. 3rd ed. LC 85-17772. (Kenyon Public Affairs Conference Center Ser.). xii, 347p. 1986. 25.00x (ISBN 0-8139-1081-1); pap. 5.95x (ISBN 0-8139-1082-X). U Pr of Va.

Hyde, Henry J. For Every Idle Silence: A Congressman Speaks Out. 140p. (Orig.). 1985. pap. 6.95 (ISBN 0-89283-282-7). Servant.

Markun, Leo. Mrs. Grundy: A History of Four Centuries of Morals Intended to Illuminate Present Problems in Great Britain & the United States. 1930. 69.00 (ISBN 0-403-00130-7). Scholarly.

Mayo, Allen. Contract at Mount Horeb. LC 75-13402. (Illus.). 1977. 10.95 (ISBN 0-918268-01-X). Tex-Mex.

Meyer, Donald H. The Instructed Conscience: The Shaping of the American National Ethic. LC 76-175512. (Illus.). 1972. 18.95x (ISBN 0-8122-7651-5); pap. 9.95x (ISBN 0-8122-1066-2). U of Pa Pr.

Niebuhr, Reinhold. Pious & Secular America. LC 79-128063. 1977. Repr. of 1958 ed. 17.50x (ISBN 0-678-02756-0). Kelley.

Phillips, McCandlish. The Bible, the Supernatural & the Jews. LC 77-92532. 1970. pap. 8.95 (ISBN 0-87123-036-4, 210036). Bethany Hse.

Pivar, David J. Purity Crusade: Sexual Morality & Social Control, 1868-1900. LC 70-179650. (Contributions in American History Ser.: No. 23). 308p. 1973. lib. bdg. 29.95 (ISBN 0-8371-6319-6, PPC/). Greenwood.

Pyron, Bernard, ed. National Sin & the Decline of American Advantages: Loss of the American Edge in War. 230p. (Orig.). 1986. pap. text ed. 7.00 (ISBN 0-9615024-1-X). Rebound Pubns.

Thaman, Mary P. Manners & Morals of the Nineteen Twenties: A Survey of the Religious Press. LC 77-8129. 1977. Repr. of 1954 ed. lib. bdg. 22.50x (ISBN 0-8371-9679-5, THMM). Greenwood.

Tranter, John W., Jr. Images. 180p. (Orig.). 1986. pap. text ed. 3.95 (ISBN 0-88368-183-8). Whitaker Hse.

UNITED STATES–POPULATION

Day, Donald D. This I Believe. 224p. 1972. pap. 1.95 (ISBN 0-9600500-1-9). Three D Pubs.

Mumford, Stephen D. American Democracy & the Vatican: Population Growth & National Security. LC 84-72500. 268p. (Orig.). 1984. 11.95 (ISBN 0-931779-00-6); pap. 7.95 (ISBN 0-931779-01-4). Humanist Pr.

UNITED STATES–RELIGION

Adams, Doug. Meeting House to Camp Meeting: Toward a History of American Free Church Worship from 1620-1835. 160p. (Orig.). 1981. pap. text ed. 6.95 (ISBN 0-941500-26-8). Sharing Co.

Ahlstrom, S. E. A Religious History of the American People. LC 72-151564. (Illus.). 1120p. 1972. 50.00x (ISBN 0-300-01475-9); pap. 18.95x (ISBN 0-300-01762-6). Yale U Pr.

Albanese, Catherine L. America: Religions & Religion. LC 80-21031. (The Wadsworth Series in Religion Studies). 389p. 1981. pap. write for info (ISBN 0-534-00928-X). Wadsworth Pub.

Alexander, Jon. American Personal Religious Accounts, 1600-1980: Toward an Inner History of America's Faiths. LC 83-21950. (Studies in American Religion: Vol. 8). 518p. 1984. 69.95x (ISBN 0-88946-654-8). E Mellen.

Backman, Milton V., Jr. Christian Churches of America. rev. ed. 288p. 1984. 17.95 (ISBN 0-684-17992-X, P656, ScribT); pap. 12.95 (ISBN 0-684-17995-4). Scribner.

Baird, Robert. Religion in America: A Critical Abridgment. 11.25 (ISBN 0-8446-0471-2). Peter Smith.

--Religion in the U. S. A, 2 vols. (Works of Rev. Robert Baird Ser.). 1985. Repr. Set. lib. bdg. 79.00 (ISBN 0-932051-57-X, Pub. by Am Repr Serv). Am Biog Serv.

Baldwin, Leland D. The American Quest for the City of God. ix, 368p. 1981. 18.95x (ISBN 0-86554-016-0). Mercer Univ Pr.

Barkun, Michael. Crucible of the Millennium: The Burned-Over District of New York in the 1840s. LC 86-5777. (New York State Studies). (Illus.). 240p. (Orig.). 1986. text ed. 27.50x (ISBN 0-8156-2371-2); pap. text ed. 14.95x (ISBN 0-8156-2378-X). Syracuse U Pr.

Bedell, George C., et al. Religion in America. 2nd ed. LC 81-8239. 1982. text ed. write for info. (ISBN 0-02-307810-3). Macmillan.

Benne, Robert & Hefener, Philip. Defining America: Christian Critique of the American Dream. LC 73-89062. pap. 40.00 (2026941). Bks Demand UMI.

Bilhartz, Terry D. Urban Religion & the Second Great Awakening. LC 83-49455. 240p. 1986. 27.50x (ISBN 0-8386-3227-0). Fairleigh Dickinson.

Bishop, Isabella L. The Aspects of Religion in the United States of America. LC 75-38438. (Religion in America, Ser. 2). 200p. 1972. Repr. of 1859 ed. 20.00 (ISBN 0-405-04059-8). Ayer Co Pubs.

Bonomi, Patricia U. Under the Cope of Heaven: Religion, Society & Politics in Colonial America. 292p. 1986. 24.95x (ISBN 0-19-504118-6). Oxford U Pr.

Bradley, Joshua. Accounts of Religious Revivals in Many Parts of the United States from 1815 to 1818: Collected from Numerous Publications & Letters from Persons of Piety & Correct Information. (Reival Library). 300p. lib. bdg. 11.95 (ISBN 0-940033-13-5). R O Roberts.

Burr, Nelson R., compiled by. Religion in American Life. LC 70-136219. (Goldentree Bibliographies in American History Ser.). (Orig.). 1971. 15.95x (ISBN 0-88295-507-1). Harlan Davidson.

Carlson, George A. George Carlson: The Spirit of the Tarahumara. Maxon, Gayle & Hopkins, Quincie, eds. LC 85-62063. (Illus.). 27p. (Orig.). 1985. pap. 18.00 (ISBN 0-935037-00-4). Peters Corp NM.

Carter, Paul A. Spiritual Crisis of the Gilded Age. LC 72-156938. (Illus.). 295p. 1971. 10.00 (ISBN 0-87580-026-2). N Ill U Pr.

Cauthen, Kenneth. The Impact of American Religious Liberalism. 2nd ed. LC 82-23902. 308p. 1983. pap. text ed. 14.25 (ISBN 0-8191-2762-0). U Pr of Amer.

Cherry, Conrad. Nature & Religious Imagination: From Edwards to Bushnell. LC 79-7374. 256p. 1980. 3.00 (ISBN 0-8006-0550-0, 1-550). Fortress.

Clark, Erskine. Wrestlin Jacob: A Portrait of Religion in the Old South. LC 78-52453. 1979. pap. 3.95 (ISBN 0-8042-1089-6). John Knox.

Clark, Henry. The Irony of American Morality. 1972. 13.95x (ISBN 0-8084-0036-3); pap. 9.95x (ISBN 0-8084-0037-1). New Coll U Pr.

Clark, Michael D. Worldly Theologians: The Persistence of Religion in Nineteenth Century American Thought. LC 80-5840. 328p. (Orig.). 1982. lib. bdg. 29.25 (ISBN 0-8191-1778-1); pap. text ed. 14.50 (ISBN 0-8191-1779-X). U Pr of Amer.

Clebsch, William A. From Sacred to Profane America: The Role of Religion in American History. LC 81-9142. (Classics & Reprints Series of the American Academy of Religion & Scholars Press). 1981. 9.95 (ISBN 0-89130-517-3, 01 05 02). Scholars Pr GA.

Coalter, Milton J., Jr. Gilbert Tennent, Son of Thunder: A Case Study of Continental Pietism's Impact on the First Great Awakening in the Middle Colonies. LC 86-9967. (Contributions to the Study of Religion: No. 18). 247p. 1986. 35.00 (ISBN 0-313-25514-8, CGI/). Greenwood.

Cross, Robert D., ed. The Church & the City: 1865-1910. LC 66-17273. 1967. 49.50x (ISBN 0-672-50994-6). Irvington.

Cross, Whitney R. The Burned-over District: The Social & Intellectual History of Enthusiastic Religion in Western New York, 1800-1850. LC 81-2636. xii, 383p. 1981. Repr. of 1950 ed. lib. bdg. 31.50x (ISBN 0-374-91932-1, Octagon). Hippocrene Bks.

Doan, Ruth A. The Miller Heresy, Millenialism, & American Culture. 270p. 1987. price not set (ISBN 0-87722-481-1). Temple U Pr.

Ediger, Peter J. The Prophets' Report on Religion in North America. rev. ed. LC 78-150650. 1978. pap. 2.00 (ISBN 0-87303-686-7). Faith & Life.

Ellwood, Rober S., ed. Eastern Spirituality in America: Selected Writings. (Sources of American Spirituality Ser.). 256p. 1987. pap. 16.95 (ISBN 0-8091-0388-5). Paulist Pr.

Finkelstein, et al. Religions of Democracy. 1941. 9.50 (ISBN 0-8159-6708-X). Devin.

Finkelstein, Louis, ed. Thirteen Americans. LC 68-26190. (Essay & General Literature Index Reprint Ser.). 1969. Repr. of 1953 ed. 23.50x (ISBN 0-8046-0219-0, Pub by Kennikat). Assoc Faculty Pr.

Frederick, John T. The Darkened Sky: Nineteenth-Century American Novelists & Religion. LC 69-14811. pap. 72.50 (ISBN 0-317-29688-4, 2022068). Bks Demand UMI.

Garrison, Winfred E. March of Faith: The Story of Religion in America Since 1865. LC 79-138112. 1971. Repr. of 1933 ed. lib. bdg. 22.50x (ISBN 0-8371-5688-2, GAMF). Greenwood.

Gaustad, Edwin, ed. A Documentary History of Religion in America, Vol. 1. 1982. pap. 19.95 (ISBN 0-8028-1871-4). Eerdmans.

Gaustad, Edwin S. Religion in America: History & Historiography. LC 73-91240. (AHA Pamphlets: No. 260). 60p. 1974. pap. text ed. 1.50 (ISBN 0-87229-016-6). Am Hist Assn.

Gaustad, Edwin S., ed. Religion in America, 38 vols. 1969. Repr. Set. 2510.50 (ISBN 0-405-00229-7). Ayer Co Pubs.

--Religion in America: Ser. 2, 40 vols. 1972. Repr. 830.00 set (ISBN 0-405-04050-4). Ayer Co Pubs.

Gehrig, Gail. American Civil Religion: An Assessment. LC 81-82801. (Society for the Scientific Study of Religion Monograph: No. 3). (Orig.). 1981. pap. 5.50 (ISBN 0-932566-02-2). Soc Sci Stud Rel.

Geisendorfer, James. Religion in America. 175p. 1983. pap. text ed. 19.95x (ISBN 90-04-06910-0, Pub. by Magnes Pr Israel). Humanities.

Gura, Philip F. The Wisdom of Words: Language, Theology & Literature in the New England Renaissance. x, 203p. 1985. pap. 12.95 (ISBN 0-8195-6120-7). Wesleyan U Pr.

Halvorson, Peter L. & Newman, William M. Atlas of Religious Change in America: 1952-1971. LC 78-67653. (Illus.). 1978. pap. 6.50 (ISBN 0-914422-09-X). Glenmary Res Ctr.

Harrington, Norman W. Shaping of Religion in America. (Illus.). 168p. 1980. 29.95 (ISBN 0-937692-01-8). Queen Anne Pr.

Hart, Roderick P. The Political Pulpit. LC 76-12290. 160p. 1977. 7.95 (ISBN 0-911198-44-X). Purdue U Pr.

Herberg, Will. Protestant, Catholic, Jew: An Essay in American Religious Sociology. LC 83-9120. xvi, 310p. 1983. pap. 11.00x (ISBN 0-226-32734-5). U of Chicago Pr.

Jones, Jenkin L. The Agricultural Social Gospel in America: The Gospel of the Farm. Graham, Thomas E., ed. & intro. by. (Studies in American Religion: Vol. 19). 349p. 1986. lib. bdg. 59.95x (ISBN 0-88946-663-7). E Mellen.

Lindt, Gillian, ed. Religion in America. LC 75-54571. (Great Contemporary Issues Ser.). 1977. lib. bdg. 35.00x (ISBN 0-405-09865-0). Ayer Co Pubs.

Lucas, Paul R. Valley of Discord: Church & Society along the Connecticut River, 1636-1725. LC 75-22520. (Illus.). 288p. 1976. 25.00x (ISBN 0-87451-121-6). U Pr of New Eng.

Mabee, Charles. Reimagining America: A Theological Critique of the American Mythos & Biblical Hermeneutics. LC 84-27335. xvi, 156p. 1985. 13.95 (ISBN 0-86554-148-5, MUP/H139). Mercer Univ Pr.

McDannell, Colleen. The Christian Home in Victorian America, 1840-1900. LC 85-42947. (Religion in North America Ser.). (Illus.). 224p. 1986. 25.00x (ISBN 0-253-31376-7). Ind U Pr.

Mandelker, Ira L. Religion, Society, & Utopia in Nineteenth-Century America. LC 84-47. 200p. 1984. lib. bdg. 22.00x (ISBN 0-87023-436-6). U of Mass Pr.

Manschreck, Clyde L. & Zikmund, Barbara B., eds. The American Religious Experiment: Piety & Practicality. LC 76-7199. (Studies in Ministry & Parish Life). 128p. 1976. 13.95x (ISBN 0-913552-06-2); pap. 6.95x (ISBN 0-913552-07-0). Exploration Pr.

Manuel, Frank E. The Changing of the Gods. LC 82-40475. 216p. 1983. 20.00x (ISBN 0-87451-254-9). U Pr of New Eng.

Maranell, Gary M. Responses to Religion: Studies in the Social Psychology of Religious Belief. LC 73-19860. (Illus.). xviii, 314p. 1974. 25.00x (ISBN 0-7006-0114-7). U Pr of KS.

Marty, Martin E. The New Shape of American Religion. LC 78-1576. 1978. Repr. of 1959 ed. lib. bdg. 22.50x (ISBN 0-313-20353-9, MANE). Greenwood.

--Pilgrims in Their Own Land. 512p. 1985. pap. 7.95 (ISBN 0-14-008268-9). Penguin.

--Pilgrims in Their Own Land: Five Hundred Years of Religion in America. (Illus.). 416p. 1984. 25.00 (ISBN 0-316-54867-7). Little.

--Religion & Republic: The American Circumstance. LC 86-47755. 320p. 1987. 25.00 (ISBN 0-8070-1206-8). Beacon Pr.

Marx, Herbert L., ed. Religions in America. (Reference Shelf Ser.). 1977. 8.00 (ISBN 0-8242-0608-8). Wilson.

Mathews, Donald G. Religion in the Old South. LC 77-587. 1979. pap. 11.00x (ISBN 0-226-51002-6, P819, Phoen). U of Chicago Pr.

May, Henry F. Ideas, Faiths, & Feelings: Essays on American Intellectual & Religious History, 1952-1982. 1983. 25.00x (ISBN 0-19-503235-7); pap. 9.95 (ISBN 0-19-503236-5). Oxford U Pr.

Mead, Frank S. & Hill, Samuel S. Handbook of Denominations in the United States. 8th ed. 400p. 1985. text ed. 10.95 (ISBN 0-687-16571-7). Abingdon.

Merrill, Abbey R. Day Dawns in Fire: America's Quest for Meaning. LC 75-36439. pap. 32.00. Bks Demand UMI.

The Millennium in America: From the Puritan Migration to the Civil War, 41 vols. Incl. Vol. 1. The Puritan Interpretation of Scripture. LC 78-67510 (ISBN 0-404-60901-5); Vol. 2. The Puritan Doctrine of the Last Judgment. LC 78-67512 (ISBN 0-404-60902-3); Vol. 3. The Puritan Vision of New Jerusalem. LC 78-67513 (ISBN 0-404-60903-1); Vol. 4. Increase Mather: Selected Works. LC 78-67514 (ISBN 0-404-60904-X); Vol. 5. Samuel Willard: Selected Works. LC 78-67515 (ISBN 0-404-60905-8); Vol. 6. Cotton Mather: Selected Works. LC 78-67516 (ISBN 0-404-60906-6); Vol. 7. Representative Writings of the Eighteenth Century: Scriptural Interpretations. LC 78-67517 (ISBN 0-404-60907-4); Representative Writings of the Eighteenth Century: Applications of Prophecy. LC 78-67518 (ISBN 0-404-60908-2); Vol. 9. The Earthquakes of the Apocalypse. LC 78-67519 (ISBN 0-404-60909-0); Vol. 10. Edwardsian Revivalism from the Great Awakening to the Revolution. LC 78-67520 (ISBN 0-404-60910-4); Vol. 11. Charles Chauncy. LC 78-67586 (ISBN 0-404-60911-2); Vol. 12. The French & Indian Wars. LC 78-67587 (ISBN 0-404-60912-0); Vol. 13. Sermons of the American Revolution. LC 78-67588 (ISBN 0-404-60913-9); Vol. 14. The Celebration of Nationhood. LC 78-67590 (ISBN 0-404-60914-7); Vol. 15. Loyalist Millenarians. LC 78-67591 (ISBN 0-404-60915-5); Vol. 16. Poems on the Rising Glory of America. LC 78-67592 (ISBN 0-404-60916-3); Vol. 17. Interpretations of the French Revolution. LC 78-67599 (ISBN 0-404-60917-1); Vols. 18 & 19, Pts. 1 & 2. Signs of the Times: The Late Eighteenth Century. LC 78-67595. Set. 115.00 (ISBN 0-404-60942-2). Vol. 18 (ISBN 0-404-60918-X). Vol. 19 (ISBN 0-404-60919-8); Vols. 20 & 21. Elhanan Winchester. LC 78-67596. Set. 115.00 (ISBN 0-404-60943-0). Vol. 20 (ISBN 0-404-60920-1). Vol. 21 (ISBN 0-404-60921-X); Vol. 22. Timothy Dwight: Selected Writings. LC 78-67598 (ISBN 0-404-60922-8). Vols. 1-17, & 22-41. write for info. ea.; Set. write for info. (ISBN 0-404-60900-7). AMS Pr.

The Millennium in America: From the Puritan Migration to the Civil War, 41 vols. Incl. Vol. 23. Representative Writings of the Early Nineteenth Century (1800-1839) LC 78-67600 (ISBN 0-404-60923-6); Vol. 24. The Garden of the West. LC 78-67601 (ISBN 0-404-60924-4); Vol. 25. Three Women Prophets: Harriet Livermore. LC 78-67603 (ISBN 0-404-60925-2); Vol. 26. Three Women Prophets: Phoebe Palmer. LC 78-67604 (ISBN 0-404-60926-0); Vol. 27. Three Women Prophets: Ellen Gould White. LC 78-67605 (ISBN 0-404-60927-9); Vol. 28. Allegorical Narratives. LC 78-67606 (ISBN 0-404-60928-7); Vol. 29, Pt. 1. Slavery & Abolition. LC 78-67607 (ISBN 0-404-60929-5); Vol. 30, Pt. 2. Slavery & Abolition. LC 78-67608 (ISBN 0-404-60930-9); Vol. 31. Millennial Optimism & Despair. LC 78-67610 (ISBN 0-404-60931-7); Vol. 32. Hymns to the Millennium. LC 78-67611 (ISBN 0-404-60932-5); Vol. 33. Millenarian Anthologies. LC 78-67612 (ISBN 0-404-60933-3); Vol. 34. Elias Smith: Selected Writings. LC 78-67613 (ISBN 0-404-60934-1); Vol. 35. Elias Boudinot. LC 78-67614 (ISBN 0-404-60935-X); Vol. 36. Ethan Smith: Selected Writings. LC 78-67615 (ISBN 0-404-60936-8); Vol. 37. Lyman Beecher: Selected Works. LC 78-67616 (ISBN 0-404-60937-6); Vol. 38. Millennial Debate: Owen vs. Campbell. LC 78-67618 (ISBN 0-404-60938-4); Vol. 39. George Duffield: Selected Works. LC 78-67619 (ISBN 0-404-60939-2); Vol. 40. William Miller: Selected Works. LC 78-67620 (ISBN 0-404-60940-6); Vol. 41. Representative Writings, 1840-1860. LC 78-67621 (ISBN 0-404-60941-4). Vols. 1-17 & 22-41. write for info.; Set. write for info. (ISBN 0-404-60900-7). AMS Pr.

Miller, Perry G. Nature's Nation. LC 67-17316. 1967. 20.00x (ISBN 0-674-60550-0, Belknap Pr). Harvard U Pr.

Miller, Randall M. & Marzik, Thomas D., eds. Immigrants & Religion in Urban America. LC 76-62866. 208p. 1977. 32.95 (ISBN 0-87722-093-X); pap. 9.95 (ISBN 0-87722-146-4). Temple U Pr.

Mode, P. G. The Frontier Spirit in American Christianity. 1977. lib. bdg. 59.95 (ISBN 0-8490-1870-6). Gordon Pr.

Moore, Martin. Boston Revival, Eighteen Forty-Two: A Brief History of the Evangelical Churches of Boston, Together with a More Particular Account of the Revival of 1842. (Revival Library). (Illus.). 148p. 1980. Repr. of 1842 ed. lib. bdg. 9.95. R O Roberts.

Moore, R. Laurence. Religious Outsiders & the Making of Americans. 288p. 1986. text ed. 24.95x (ISBN 0-19-503663-8). Oxford U Pr.

Morey-Gaines, Ann-Janine. Apples & Ashes: Culture, Metaphor & Morality in the American Dream. LC 81-14346. (AAR Academy Ser.). 1982. 12.95 (ISBN 0-89130-535-1, 01-01-38). Scholars Pr GA.

Neitz, Mary J. Charisma & Community: A Study of Religion in American Culture. 275p. 1987. 34.95 (ISBN 0-88738-130-8). Transaction Bks.

Nelson, John W. Your God Is Alive & Well & Appearing in Popular Culture. LC 76-26092. 216p. 1976. softcover 5.95 (ISBN 0-664-24866-7). Westminster.

Pestana, Carla G. Liberty of Conscience & the Growth of Religious Diversity in Early America, 1636-1786. (Illus.). 104p. 1986. pap. 30.00 (ISBN 0-916617-02-5); bibliographical suppl. 10.00 (ISBN 0-916617-03-3). J C Brown.

Photiadis, John D., ed. Religion in Appalachia. 1979. 10.75 (ISBN 0-686-26337-5). W Va U Ctr Exten.

Piepkorn, Arthur C. Profiles in Belief: The Religious Bodies of the United States & Canada, Vols. 3 & 4. Incl. Vol. 3. Holiness & Pentecostal Bodies; Vol. 4. Evangelical, Fundamental, & Other Christian Bodies. 1979. Set. 25.45i (ISBN 0-06-066581-5, HarpR). Har-Row.

Quimby, Ian M., ed. Winterthur Portfolio No. 8: Thematic Issue on Religion in America. (A Winterthur Bk.). (Illus.). 1973. 15.00X (ISBN 0-226-92134-4). U of Chicago Pr.

Reichley, A. James. Religion in American Public Life. LC 85-21312. 402p. 1985. 31.95 (ISBN 0-8157-7378-1); pap. 11.95 (ISBN 0-8157-7377-3). Brookings.

Ricard, Robert. The Spiritual Conquest of Mexico: An Essay on the Apostolate & the Evangelizing Methods of the Mendicant Orders in New Spain, 1523-1572. Simpson, Lesley B., tr. from Sp. (California Library Reprint Ser.: No. 57). (Illus.). 435p. 1974. pap. 9.95 (ISBN 0-520-04784-2, CAL 593). U of Cal Pr.

Robbins, Thomas & Anthony, Dick, eds. In Gods We Trust: New Patterns of Religious Pluralism in America. LC 79-66441. 224p. 1980. pap. text ed. 12.95 (ISBN 0-87855-746-6). Transaction Bks.

Robertson, Archibald T. That Old-Time Religion. LC 78-24159. 1979. Repr. of 1950 ed. lib. bdg. 24.75x (ISBN 0-313-20823-9, ROOT). Greenwood.

Roof, Wade C. & McKinney, William. America Mainline Religion: Its Changing Shape of the Religious Establishment. 272p. 1987. text ed. 27.00 (ISBN 0-8135-1215-8); pap. text ed. 10.00 (ISBN 0-8135-1216-6). Rutgers U Pr.

Roozen, David A. Churched & Unchurched in America: A Comparative Profile. LC 77-94682. 1978. pap. 2.00 (ISBN 0-914422-07-3). Glenmary Res Ctr.

Rosten, Leo, ed. Religions of America. LC 74-11705. 1975. pap. 11.95 (ISBN 0-671-21971-5, Touchstone Bks). S&S.

Rowe, David. Thunder & Trumpets: The Millerite Movement & Dissenting Religion in Upstate New York, 1800-1850. (American Academy of Religion Studies in Religion: No. 38). 1985. 24.95 (ISBN 0-89130-770-2, 01 00 38); pap. 16.95 (ISBN 0-89130-769-9). Scholars Pr GA.

Rupp, Israel D. He Pasa Ekklesia: An Original History of the Religious Denominations at Present Existing in the United States Containing Authentic Accounts of Their Rise, Progress, Statistics. 30.00 (ISBN 0-8369-7149-3, 7981). Ayer Co Pubs.

Sandeen, Ernest R. & Hale, Frederick, eds. American Religion & Philosophy: A Guide to Information Sources. LC 73-17562. (American Studies Information Guide: Vol. 5). 1978. 62.00x (ISBN 0-8103-1262-X). Gale.

Scherer, Lester B. A Short History of Religion in America. (Illus.). 145p. (Orig.). 1980. pap. 8.95x (ISBN 0-89894-011-7). Advocate Pub Group.

Scherer, Ross P., ed. American Denominational Organization: A Sociological View. LC 80-13859. 378p. 1980. pap. 14.95x (ISBN 0-87808-173-9, Ecclesia). William Carey Lib.

Schneider, Louis & Dornbusch, Sanford M. Popular Religion: Inspirational Books in America. LC 58-11958. (Midway Reprint Ser.). pap. 46.50 (2026741). Bks Demand UMI.

Semple, Robert. History of the Rise & Progress of the Baptists in Virginia. 1976. Repr. of 1894 ed. 15.00 (ISBN 0-686-12331-X). Church History.

Shaw, James. Twelve Years in America Being Observations on the Country, the People, Institutions, & Religion. text ed. 25.50 (ISBN 0-8369-9234-2, 9088). Ayer Co Pubs.

Shulman, Albert M. The Religious Heritage of America. LC 81-3594. (Illus.). 480p. 1982. 25.00 (ISBN 0-498-02162-9). A S Barnes.

Singer, C Gregg. A Theological Interpretation of American History. rev. ed. 1981. pap. 7.95 (ISBN 0-87552-426-5). Presby & Reformed.

Smith, Elwyn A. The Religion of the Republic. LC 70-130326. pap. 76.00 (2026890). Bks Demand UMI.

Smith, Gary S. The Seeds of Secularization: Calvinism, Culture, & Pluralism in America, 1870-1915. 248p. (Orig.). 1985. pap. 14.95x (ISBN 0-8028-0058-0). Eerdmans.

Smith, Page. Religious Origins of the American Revolution. LC 76-13157. (American Academy of Religion, Aids for the Study of Religion). 1976. pap. 8.95 (ISBN 0-89130-121-6, 010303). Scholars Pr GA.

Spencer, J. H. The History of the Kentucky Baptists from 1769 to 1885, 2 vols. 1984. Repr. of 1886 ed. 54.00 (ISBN 0-686-12335-2). Church History.

Stark, Rodney & Glock, Charles Y. American Piety: The Nature of Religious Commitment. 1968. 35.95x (ISBN 0-520-01210-0); pap. 2.65 (ISBN 0-520-01756-0, CAL197). U of Cal Pr.

Sweet, William W. American Culture & Religion. LC 72-78372. ix, 114p. 1972. Repr. of 1951 ed. lib. bdg. 19.50x (ISBN 0-8154-0421-2). Cooper Sq.

--Religion on the American Frontier. Incl. Vol. 1. The Baptists, 1783-1830. 652p. Repr. of 1931 ed; Vol. 2. The Presbyterians, 1783-1840. (Illus.). 939p. 1964. Repr. of 1936 ed. 37.50x (ISBN 0-8154-0223-6); Vol. 3. The Congregationalists, 1783-1850. (Illus.). 435p. 1964. Repr. of 1934 ed. 37.50x (ISBN 0-8154-0224-4); Vol. 4. The Methodists, 1783-1840. (Illus.). 800p. 1964. Repr. of 1946 ed. 37.50x (ISBN 0-8154-0225-2). LC 63-21092. 1964. Repr. of 1946 ed. Cooper Sq.

Waldrum, Harold J. Harold Joe Waldrum: Las Sombras de los Edificios Religiosos de Nuevo Mexico Norte. Maxon, Gayle & Hopkins, Quincie, eds. (Illus., Orig.). 1985. pap. 12.50 (ISBN 0-318-18712-4). Peters Corp NM.

--Harold Joe Waldrum: The Churches of Northern New Mexico. Maxon, Gayle & Hopkins, Quincie, eds. (Illus.). 34p. (Orig.). 1985. pap. 12.50 (ISBN 0-935037-01-2). Peters Corp NM.

Weeks, Stephen B. The Religious Development in the Province of North Carolina. LC 78-63811. (Johns Hopkins University. Studies in the Social Sciences. Tenth Ser. 1892: 5-6). Repr. of 1892 ed. 11.50 (ISBN 0-404-61074-9). AMS Pr.

Whalen, William J. Minority Religions in America. rev. ed. LC 81-3664. 222p. (Orig.). 1981. pap. 7.95 (ISBN 0-8189-0413-5). Alba.

Wilkins, Ronald J. Religion in North America. (To Live Is Christ Ser.). 208p. 1984. pap. 5.75 (ISBN 0-697-01930-6); tchr's manual 4.95 (ISBN 0-697-01931-4); spirit masters 10.95 (ISBN 0-697-01735-4). Wm C Brown.

Williams, David R. Wilderness Lost: The Religious Origins of the American Mind. LC 85-43475. 296p. 1987. 38.50x (ISBN 0-941664-21-X). Susquehanna U Pr.

Wilson, Charles R., ed. Religion in the South. LC 85-5361. (Chancellor's Symposium Ser.). (Orig.). 1985. 15.00x (ISBN 0-87805-256-9); pap. 8.95 (ISBN 0-87805-257-7). U Pr of Miss.

Wilson, John F. & Mulder, John M. Religion in American History: Interpretive Essays. 448p. 1978. pap. text ed. write for info. (ISBN 0-13-771980-9). P-H.

Wilson, Robert J., III. The Benevolent Deity: Ebenezer Gay & the Rise of Rational Religion in New England, 1669-1787. LC 83-3657. (Illus.). 320p. 1984. 26.00x (ISBN 0-8122-7891-7). U of Pa Pr.

UNITED STATES–RELIGION–20TH CENTURY

Albanese, Catherine L. Corresponding Motion: Transcendental Religion & the New America. LC 77-70329. 234p. 1977. 29.95 (ISBN 0-87722-098-0). Temple U Pr.

Allworthy, A. W. The Petition Against God: The Full Story Behind RM-2493. LC 75-43375. (Illus.). 150p. 1976. pap. 3.95 (ISBN 0-686-16824-0, Pub. by Christ the Light). Mho & Mho.

Bayne, Stephen F. The Optional God. LC 80-80876. 134p. 1980. pap. 6.95 (ISBN 0-8192-1268-7). Morehouse.

Beckwith, Burnham P. The Decline of U. S. Religious Faith: 1912 - 1984 & the Effect of Education & Intelligence on Such Faith. 1985. 9.00x (ISBN 0-9603262-4-3). Beckwith.

Bell, Bernard I. Crowd Culture. facs. ed. LC 74-117758. (Essay Index Reprint Ser). 1952. 17.00 (ISBN 0-8369-1742-1). Ayer Co Pubs.

Bellah, Robert N. The Broken Covenenant: American Civil Religion in Time of Trail. 1976. pap. 5.95 (ISBN 0-8164-2123-4, HarpR). Har-Row.

Braden, Charles S., ed. Varieties of American Religion. facsimile ed. LC 76-156616. (Essay Index Reprint Ser). Repr. of 1936 ed. 15.50 (ISBN 0-8369-2307-3). Ayer Co Pubs.

Carey, Ken. Terra Christa: The Global Spiritual Awakening. Gross, Jim, ed. 256p. (Orig.). 1985. pap. 7.95t (ISBN 0-912949-02-3). Uni-Sun.

Carnes, Ralph & Carnes, Valerie. The Road to Damascus. 336p. 1986. 16.95 (ISBN 0-312-68517-3, Thomas Dunne Bks). St Martin.
Douglas, Mary & Tipton, Steven M., eds. Religion & America: Spirituality in a Secular Age. LC 82-72500. 256p. 1983. 25.00x (ISBN 0-8070-1106-1); pap. 13.95x (ISBN 0-8070-1107-X, BP648). Beacon Pr.
Glazier, Michael, ed. Where We Are: American Catholics in the 1980's. 1985. pap. 7.95 (ISBN 0-89453-471-8). M Glazier.
Hale, J. Russell. The Unchurched: Who They Are & Why They Stay Away. LC 79-2993. 192p. 1980. 12.00 (ISBN 0-06-063560-6, HarpR). Har-Row.
Holland, Clifton L. The Religious Dimension in Hispanic Los Angeles: A Protestant Case Study. LC 74-5123. 542p. (Orig.). 1974. pap. 10.95 (ISBN 0-87808-309-X). William Carey Lib.
Jacquet, Constant H., Jr., ed. Yearbook of American & Canadian Church 1986. 304p. (Orig.). 1986. pap. 17.95 (ISBN 0-687-46641-5). Abingdon.
Jacquet, H. Constant, ed. Yearbook of American & Canadian Churches, 1987. 304p. 1987. pap. 18.95 (ISBN 0-687-46642-3). Abingdon.
Johnson, Paul, et al. Unsecular America. Neuhaus, Richard J., ed. (The Encounter Ser.). 176p. (Orig.). 1986. pap. 8.95 (ISBN 0-8028-0202-8). Eerdmans.
Jorstad, Erling. Being Religious in America: The Deepening Crises over Public Faith. LC 86-3360. 128p. (Orig.). 1986. pap. 6.95 (ISBN 0-8066-2222-9, 10-0585). Augsburg.
Land, Gary, ed. Adventism in America. 304p. (Orig.). 1986. pap. 14.95 (ISBN 0-8028-0237-0). Eerdmans.
Lincoln, C. Eric. Race, Religion, & the Continuing American Dilemma. 304p. 1984. 17.95 (ISBN 0-8090-8016-8). Hill & Wang.
Luccock, Halford E. Contemporary American Literature & Religion. LC 73-111471. 1970. Repr. of 1934 ed. 20.50 (ISBN 0-404-00607-8). AMS Pr.
Lynd, Robert S. & Lynd, Helen M. Middletown. 550p. 1959. pap. 8.95 (ISBN 0-15-659550-8, Harv). HarBraceJ.
--Middletown in Transition: A Study in Cultural Conflicts. LC 37-27243. 604p. 1982. pap. 9.95 (ISBN 0-15-659551-6, Harv). HarBraceJ.
Marty, Martin E. Modern American Religion, Vol. 1: The Irony of It All, 1893-1919. LC 86-16524. (Illus.). 398p. 1986. 24.95 (ISBN 0-226-50893-5). U of Chicago Pr.
--Religious Crises in Modern America. LC 81-80740. (Charles Edmondson Historical Lectures Ser.). 40p. (Orig.). 1981. pap. 4.50 (ISBN 0-918954-26-6). Baylor Univ Pr.
Melton, J. Gordon, ed. Encyclopedia of American Religions. 2nd ed. 1200p. 1986. 165.00x (ISBN 0-8103-2133-5). Gale.
Melton, James G. & Geisendorfer, James V. A Directory of Religious Bodies in the United States. (Reference Library of the Humanities: Vol. 91). (LC 76-052700). 1977. lib. bdg. 40.00 (ISBN 0-8240-9882-X). Garland Pub.
Miller, Perry G. Errand into the Wilderness. LC 56-11285. 1956. 15.00x (ISBN 0-674-26151-8, Belknap Pr); pap. 6.95x (ISBN 0-674-26155-0). Harvard U Pr.
Religion & the Public Schools. Incl. The Legal Issue. Freund, Paul A. (The Burton Lectures Ser: 1965); The Educational Issue. Ulich, Robert. (Inglis Lectures Ser: 1965). LC 65-26011. vi, 56p. 1965. 2.00x (ISBN 0-674-75600-2). Harvard U Pr.
Rouse, John E., Jr., et al, eds. The Political Role of Religion on the U. S. (Special Study Ser.). 300p. 1985. pap. text ed. 24.50x (ISBN 0-8133-7030-2). Westview.
Schneider, Herbert W. Religion in Twentieth Century America. LC 52-8219. (The Library of Congress Ser. in American Civilization). (Illus.). 1952. 16.50x (ISBN 0-674-75700-9). Harvard U Pr.
Sperry, Willard L., ed. Religion & Our Divided Denominations. facs. ed. LC 74-128315. (Essay Index Reprint Ser). 1945. 14.00 (ISBN 0-8369-2201-8). Ayer Co Pubs.
Stark, Rodney & Glock, Charles Y. American Piety: The Nature of Religious Commitment. 1968. 35.95x (ISBN 0-520-01210-0); pap. 2.65 (ISBN 0-520-01756-0, CAL197). U of Cal Pr.
Steltenkamp, Michael. The Sacred Vision: Native American Religion & Its Practice Today. LC 82-60594. 1983. pap. 5.95 (ISBN 0-8091-2481-5). Paulist Pr.
Stevens, Edward. The Religion Game, American Style. LC 76-9367. 168p. 1976. pap. 5.95 (ISBN 0-8091-1951-X). Paulist Pr.
Van Baalen, Jan K. Chaos of Cults. 4th ed. rev. ed. 1962. 11.95 (ISBN 0-8028-3278-4). Eerdmans.
Vidich, Arthur J. & Lyman, Stanford M. American Sociology: Worldly Rejections of Religion & Their Directions. LC 84-2268. 400p. 1985. pap. 30.00x (ISBN 0-300-03037-1). Yale U Pr.
White, Ronald C., Jr. & Hopkins, C. Howard. The Social Gospel: Religion & Reform in Changing America. LC 75-34745. (Illus.). 326p. 1975. 29.95 (ISBN 0-87722-083-2); pap. 9.95x (ISBN 0-87722-084-0). Temple U Pr.
White, Ronald C., Jr., et al, eds. American Christianity: A Case Approach. 208p. (Orig.). 1986. pap. text ed. 11.95 (ISBN 0-8028-0241-9). Eerdmans.
Zaretsky, Irving I. & Leone, Mark P., eds. Religious Movements in Contemporary America. LC 73-39054. 900p. 1974. 71.00 (ISBN 0-691-07186-1); pap. 18.50x (ISBN 0-691-01993-2). Princeton U Pr.

UNITY SCHOOL OF CHRISTIANITY

Butterworth, Eric. Unity: A Quest for Truth. (Orig.). 1965. pap. 3.00 (ISBN 0-8315-0020-4). Speller.
--Unity: A Quest for Truth. 160p. 1985. 5.95 (ISBN 0-87159-165-0, X1965, ROBERT SPELLER & SONS PUB.). Unity School.
Fillmore, Charles. Revealing Word. 1959. 5.95 (ISBN 0-87159-137-5). Unity School.
Freeman, James D. The Story of Unity. rev. ed. (Illus.). 1978. 5.95 (ISBN 0-87159-145-6). Unity School.
Kemp, Russell A. Live Youthfully Now. LC 69-93890. 1969. 5.95 (ISBN 0-87159-232-0). Unity School.
Linn, Elbridge B. That They May All Be One. 1969. 4.50 (ISBN 0-88027-020-9). Firm Foun Pub.
Turner, Elizabeth S. Let There Be Light. 1954. 5.95 (ISBN 0-87159-085-9). Unity School.
Wilson, Ernest C. Like a Miracle. 202p. 1971. 5.95 (ISBN 0-87159-088-3). Unity School.

UNIVERSAL PRIESTHOOD

see Priesthood, Universal

UNIVERSAL RELIGION

see Religions (Proposed, Universal, Etc.)

UNIVERSAL SALVATION

see Universalism

UNIVERSALISM

see also Future Punishment; Salvation; Salvation outside the Catholic Church

Cassara, Ernest, ed. Universalism in America. 1984. pap. 5.95 (ISBN 0-933840-21-7). Unitarian Univ.
Chauncy, Charles. Mystery Hid from All Ages & Generations. LC 70-83414. (Religion in American, Ser. 1). 1969. Repr. of 1784 ed. 23.50 (ISBN 0-405-00235-1). Ayer Co Pubs.
DeCelles, Charles. The Unbound Spirit: God's Universal, Sanctifying Work. LC 85-20047. 367p. (Orig.). 1985. pap. 9.95 (ISBN 0-8189-0486-0). Alba.
Jenkins, Joe. The Theologic Principle of Universalism: A Way of Life. (Orig.). 1984. pap. 4.00 (ISBN 0-916801-00-4). Inst Univ.
Punt, Neal. Unconditional Good News: Toward an Understanding of Biblical Universalism. LC 80-10458. pap. 44.80 (ISBN 0-317-39671-4, 2023222). Bks Demand UMI.
Sadler, Williams S., Jr. A Study of the Master Universe. LC 68-58958. (Illus.). 150p. 1968. 13.00 (ISBN 0-686-05760-0); pap. write for info. (ISBN 0-686-05761-9). Second Soc Foun.
Williams, George H. American Universalism. pap. 3.50 (ISBN 0-933840-18-7). Unitarian Univ.

UNIVERSALIST CHURCH

Chapin, Edwin H. Humanity in the City. LC 73-11901. (Metropolitan America Ser.). 254p. 1974. Repr. 19.00 (ISBN 0-405-05389-4). Ayer Co Pubs.
Robinson, David. The Unitarians & the Universalists. LC 84-9031. (Denominations in America Ser.: No. 1). xiii, 368p. 1985. lib. bdg. 37.50 (ISBN 0-313-20946-4, RUN/). Greenwood.

UNIVERSE

see Cosmogony; Cosmology

UNIVERSITIES AND COLLEGES–RELIGION

Ash, James L., Jr. Protestantism & the American University: An Intellectual Biography of William Warren Sweet. LC 82-10629. (Illus.). 180p. 1982. 15.95x (ISBN 0-87074-183-7). SMU Press.
Elbin, Paul N. Improvement of College Worship. LC 72-176744. (Columbia University. Teachers College. Contributions to Education: No. 530). Repr. of 1932 ed. 22.50 (ISBN 0-404-55530-6). AMS Pr.
Fredman, Ruth G., ed. Jewish Life on Campus: A Directory of B'nai B'rith Hillel Foundations & Other Campus Agencies. 1986. pap. 8.95 (ISBN 0-9603058-5-8). B'nai B'rith Hillel.
Helmreich, Ernst C. Religion at Bowdoin College: A History. LC 81-71331. (Illus.). 1981. pap. 7.50 (ISBN 0-916606-03-1). Bowdoin Coll.
Holmes, Arthur F. The Idea of A Christian College. rev. ed. 104p. 1987. pap. 6.95 (ISBN 0-8028-0258-3). Eerdmans.
McKinney, Richard I. Religion in Higher Education among Negroes. LC 75-38785. (Religion in America, Ser. 2). 186p. 1972. Repr. of 1945 ed. 15.00 (ISBN 0-405-04075-X). Ayer Co Pubs.
Payne, Alfred C. A University at Prayer. LC 86-14613. (Illus.). 1987. 13.95x (ISBN 0-9617635-0-7). VA Tech Educ Found.
Sandin, Robert T. The Search for Excellence: The Christian College in an Age of Educational Competition. LC 82-12482. vi, 242p. 1982. text ed. 13.50x (ISBN 0-86554-037-3, MUP-H39). Mercer Univ Pr.
Solberg, Richard W. & Strommen, Merton P. How Church-Related Are Church-Related Colleges? Answers Based on a Comprehensive Survey of Supporting Constituencies of 18 LCA Colleges. LC 80-13833. 96p. (Orig.). 1980. pap. 3.95 (ISBN 0-8006-1388-0, 1-1388). Fortress.

UNMARRIED MOTHERS

Pierce, Ruth I. Single & Pregnant. LC 72-119678. 1970. pap. 3.95 (ISBN 0-8070-2779-0, BP407). Beacon Pr.

UPANISHADS

Aurobindo, Sri. The Upanishads. (Sanskrit & Eng.). 466p. 1981. 40.00 (ISBN 0-89744-026-9, Pub. by Sri Aurobindo Ashram Trust India); pap. 30.00 (ISBN 0-89744-025-0). Auromere.
--The Upanishads: Texts, Translations & Commentaries, Pt. 1. 466p. 1986. 14.95 (ISBN 0-89071-295-6, Pub. by Sri Aurobindo Ashram India); pap. 11.95 (ISBN 0-89071-294-8). Matagiri.
Besant. Wisdom of the Upanishads. 3.50 (ISBN 0-8356-7092-9). Theos Pub Hse.
Boner, Alice. Vastusutra Upanisad: The Essence of Form in Sacred Art. xii, 192p. 1986. 32.00 (Pub. by Motilal Banarsidass). South Asia Bks.
Deussen, Paul. Philosophy of the Upanishads. Geden, A. S., tr. (Orig.). 1966. pap. 8.50 (ISBN 0-486-21616-0). Dover.
Gough, Edward. The Philosophy of the Upanishads. 268p. 1979. Repr. of 1882 ed. 19.95 (ISBN 0-89684-158-8). Orient Bk Dist.
Hume, R. E., tr. from Sanskrit. Upanishas: The Thirteen Principal Upanishads. 2nd ed. 1931. pap. 16.95x (ISBN 0-19-561641-3). Oxford U Pr.
Johnston, Charles & Giles, Lionel, trs. Selections from the Upanishads & The Tao Te King. 142p. 1951. Repr. of 1897 ed. 3.00 (ISBN 0-938998-15-3). Cunningham Pr.
Keith, A. B. The Religion & Philosophy of the Veda & Upanishads, 2 vols. 1976. Repr. Set. 42.00 (ISBN 0-89684-304-1). Orient Bk Dist.
Keith, Arthur B. The Religion & Philosophy of the Veda & Upanishads, 2 vols. LC 71-109969. Repr. of 1925 ed. lib. bdg. 34.00x (ISBN 0-8371-4475-2, KEVU). Greenwood.
Lal, P., tr. from Sanskrit. The Avyakta Upanisad. 25p. 1973. 8.00 (ISBN 0-88253-272-3). Ind-US Inc.
--The Brhadaranyaka Upanisad. (Saffronbird Bk.). (Eng.). 117p. 1975. pap. text ed. 6.75 (ISBN 0-88253-828-4). Ind-US Inc.
Madhavananda, tr. The Brihadaranyaka Upanishad: With the Commentary of Shankaracharya. LC 83-45479. 1935. 78.50 (ISBN 0-404-20271-3, PK3521). AMS Pr.
Madhavananda, Swami, tr. Minor Upanishads. pap. 2.00 (ISBN 0-87481-061-2). Vedanta Pr.
Mahadevan, T. M. Upanisads: The Selections from 108 Upanisads. Mahadevan, T. M., tr. from Sanskrit. 240p. (Orig.). 1975. pap. 3.20 (ISBN 0-88253-985-X). Ind-US Inc.
Mahanarayanopanisad. Vimalananda, Swami, tr. from Sanskrit. 1979. pap. 6.50 (ISBN 0-87481-492-8). Vedanta Pr.
Muller, F. Max. The Upanishads, 2 vols. 1974. lib. bdg. 250.00 (ISBN 0-8490-1252-X). Gordon Pr.
Nanda, Jyotir M. Yoga Wisdom of the Upanishads: Kena..Mundaka..Prashna..Ishavasya. (Illus.). 1974. pap. 4.99 (ISBN 0-934664-36-6). Yoga Res Foun.
Pandit, M. P. Mystic Approach to the Veda & the Upanishad. 4.25 (ISBN 0-89744-108-7, Pub. by Ganesh & Co. India). Auromere.
--The Upanisads: Gateways of Knowledge. 2nd ed. 1968. 4.00 (ISBN 0-89744-111-7, Pub. by Ganesh & Co. India). Auromere.
Parrinder, Geoffrey, tr. from Sanskrit. & intro. by. The Wisdom of the Forest: Selections from the Hindu Upanishads. LC 75-42114. (The Wisdom Bks). 96p. 1976. pap. 1.95 (ISBN 0-8112-0607-6, NDP414). New Directions.
Patanjali, Swami S. The Ten Principal Upanishads. Yeats, W. B., tr. (Orig.). 1970. pap. 5.95 (ISBN 0-571-09363-9). Faber & Faber.
Prabhavananda, Swami & Manchester, Frederick, trs. Upanishads: Breath of the Eternal. LC 48-5935. pap. 6.95 (ISBN 0-87481-040-X). Vedanta Pr.
Rajneesh, Bhagwan Shree. The Ultimate Alchemy, 2 vols. Prem, Ma Ananda, ed. LC 75-905370. (Upanishad Ser.). (Illus.). 1976. Vol. I, 442 pgs. 18.95 ea. (ISBN 0-88050-161-8). Vol. II, 424 pgs (ISBN 0-88050-162-6). Chidvilas Found.
--Vedanta: Seven Steps to Samadhi. Pratima, Ma Yoga, ed. LC 77-904425. (Upanishad Ser.). (Illus.). 518p. (Orig.). 1976. 16.50 (ISBN 0-88050-166-9). Chidvilas Found.
Sandal, Mohan L. Philosophical Teachings in the Upanisats. LC 73-3831. (Sacred Books of the Hindus: Extra Vol. 5). Repr. of 1926 ed. 17.00 (ISBN 0-404-57849-7). AMS Pr.
Sarvananda, Swami, tr. Aitareyopanisad. (Sanskrit & English). pap. 1.00 (ISBN 0-87481-463-4). Vedanta Pr.
--Isavasyopanisad. (Sanskrit & English). pap. 1.00 (ISBN 0-87481-456-1). Vedanta Pr.
--Kathopanisad. (Sanskrit & English). pap. 1.00 (ISBN 0-87481-458-8). Vedanta Pr.
--Kenopanisad. (Sanskrit & Eng.). pap. 1.00 (ISBN 0-87481-457-X). Vedanta Pr.
--Mundakopanisad. (Sanskrit & English). pap. 1.00 (ISBN 0-87481-460-X). Vedanta Pr.
--Prasnopanisad. (Sanskrit & English). pap. 1.00 (ISBN 0-87481-459-6). Vedanta Pr.
Sastry, Alladi M., tr. Taitiriya Upanishad. 93p. 1980. 36.00 (ISBN 0-89744-145-1, Pub. by Samata Bks India). Auromere.
Sharma, Shubhra. Life in the Upanishads. 1985. 15.00x (ISBN 81-7017-202-0, Pub. by Abhinav India). South Asia Bks.
Singh, B. The Philosophy of Upanishads. 160p. 1983. text ed. 10.50x (ISBN 0-391-02935-5). Humanities.
Sircar, M. Hindu Mysticism According to the Upanisads. 1974. text ed. 19.00x. Coronet Bks.
Sri Aurobindo. Isha Upanishad. Aurobindo, Sri, tr. 1979. pap. 6.00 (ISBN 0-89744-922-3). Auromere.
--Kena Upanishad. Sri Aurobindo, tr. (Life Companion Library). 1979. pap. 5.95 (ISBN 0-89744-923-1). Auromere.
Subrahmanian, N. S. Encyclopedia of the Upanishads. 564p. 1986. text ed. 50.00x (ISBN 0-86590-771-4, Pub. by Sterling Pubs India). Apt Bks.
Swami Bhaktivedanta. Sri Isopanisad: Discovering the Original Person. 1985. 7.95; pap. 2.95 (ISBN 0-89213-138-1). Bhaktivedanta.
The Upanishads: A Selection for the Modern Reader. 1987. 10.95 (ISBN 0-915132-40-0); pap. 5.95 (ISBN 0-915132-39-7). Nilgiri Pr.
Van Buitenen, J. A. The Maitrayaniya Upanisad: A Critical Essay with Text, Translation & Commentary. (Disputationes Rheno-Trajectinae: No. 6). 1962. pap. 17.60x (ISBN 90-2790-032-9). Mouton.
Vasu, Srisa Chandra. Studies in the First Six Upanisads, & the Isa & Kena Upanisads with the Commentary of Sankara. Vidyarnava, Srisa Chandra, tr. LC 73-3814. (Sacred Books of the Hindus: No. 22, Pt. 1). Repr. of 1919 ed. 14.50 (ISBN 0-404-57822-5). AMS Pr.
Vasu, Srisa Chandra, tr. The Brihadaranyaka Upanisad. LC 73-3802. (Sacred Books of the Hindus: No. 14). Repr. of 1916 ed. 47.50 (ISBN 0-404-57814-4). AMS Pr.
--Chhandogya Upanisad. LC 73-3788. (Sacred Books of the Hindus: No. 3). Repr. of 1910 ed. 44.50 (ISBN 0-404-57803-9). AMS Pr.
--The Upanisads. 2nd ed. LC 73-4980. (Sacred Books of the Hindus: No. 1). Repr. of 1911 ed. 27.50 (ISBN 0-404-57801-2). AMS Pr.
Vidyarnava, Srisa Chandra & Sandal, Mohan L., trs. Aitareya Upanisat, 2 pts. in 1. LC 73-3823. (Sacred Books of the Hindus: No. 30, Pts. 1-2). Repr. of 1925 ed. 14.50 (ISBN 0-404-57830-6). AMS Pr.
--The Kausitaki Upanisat. LC 73-3825. (Sacred Books of the Hindus: No. 31, Pt. 1). Repr. of 1925 ed. 14.50 (ISBN 0-404-57831-4). AMS Pr.
--The Maitri Upanisat. LC 73-3827. (Sacred Books of the Hindus: No. 31, Pt. 2). Repr. of 1926 ed. 14.50 (ISBN 0-404-57832-2). AMS Pr.
Warrier, A. Krishna. Sakta Upanisads. 3.50 (ISBN 0-8356-7318-9). Theos Pub Hse.
Yeats, William B. & Shree, Swami. The Ten Principal Upanishads. 1975. pap. 6.95 (ISBN 0-02-071550-1, Collier). Macmillan.

UPJOHN, RICHARD, 1802-1878

Upjohn, Everard M. Richard Upjohn, Architect & Churchman. LC 68-26119. (Architecture & Decorative Art Ser). (Illus.). 1968. Repr. of 1939 ed. lib. bdg. 45.00 (ISBN 0-306-71043-9). Da Capo.

URBAN CHURCHES

see City Churches

URBAN CLERGY

see City Clergy

URBAN MINISTRY

see City Clergy

URDU LITERATURE

Rai, Amrit. A House Divided: The Origin & Development of Hindi-Hindavi. 1985. 29.95x (ISBN 0-19-561643-X). Oxford U Pr.

URSULINES

McDowell, Catherine, ed. Letters from the Ursuline 1852-1853. LC 77-85460. 1978. boxed 20.00 (ISBN 0-911536-69-8); 18.00. Trinity U Pr.

UTAH–DESCRIPTION AND TRAVEL

Clayton, William. William Clayton's Journal: A Daily Record of the Journey of the Original Company of Mormon Pioneers from Nauveo, Illinois, to the Valley of the Great Salt Lake. LC 72-9435. (The Far Western Frontier Ser.). 380p. 1973. Repr. of 1921 ed. 26.50 (ISBN 0-405-04965-X). Ayer Co Pubs.

Ferris, B. G. Mormons at Home. LC 70-134395. Repr. of 1856 ed. 24.00 (ISBN 0-404-08437-0). AMS Pr.

Hemingway, Donald W., ed. Utah & the Mormons. (Travel Ser.). (Illus.). 32p. 1983. pap. write for info. (ISBN 0-938440-47-0). Colourpicture.

Robinson, Philip S. Sinners & Saints. LC 75-134400. Repr. of 1883 ed. 25.00 (ISBN 0-404-08444-3). AMS Pr.

UTAH–HISTORY

Arrington, Leonard J. Great Basin Kingdom: An Economic History of the Latter-Day Saints, 1830-1900. LC 58-12961. (Illus.). xx, 550p. 1966. pap. 13.95 (ISBN 0-8032-5006-1, BB 342, Bison). U of Nebr Pr.

Bailey, Paul. Holy Smoke: A Dissertation on the Utah War. (Great West & Indian Ser.: Vol. 44). (Illus.). 1977. 10.50 (ISBN 0-87026-037-5). Westernlore.

Carr, Stephen L. The Historical Guide to Utah Ghost Towns. 166p. 1972. Western Epics.

Goldberg, Robert A. Back to the Soil: The Jewish Farmers of Clarion, Utah, & Their World. (Utah Centennial Ser.: Vol. 2). (Illus.). 208p. 1986. 19.95 (ISBN 0-87480-263-6). U of Utah Pr.

Hickman, Bill. Brigham's Destroying Angel. facsimile ed. LC 74-165642. (Select Bibliographies Reprint Ser). Repr. of 1904 ed. 18.00 (ISBN 0-8369-5951-5). Ayer Co Pubs.

Larson, Gustave O. Prelude to the Kingdom: Mormon Desert Conquest, a Chapter in American Cooperative Experience. LC 78-5694. 1978. Repr. of 1947 ed. lib. bdg. 25.75x (ISBN 0-313-20452-7, LAPK). Greenwood.

Long, E. B. The Saints & the Union: Utah Territory During the Civil War. LC 80-16775. (Illus.). 292p. 1981. 22.50 (ISBN 0-252-00821-9). U of Ill Pr.

Stegner, Wallace. Mormon Country. LC 81-3410. x, 362p. 1981. 25.50x (ISBN 0-8032-4129-1); pap. 8.50 (ISBN 0-8032-9125-6, BB 778, Bison). U of Nebr Pr.

Stott, Clifford L. Search for Sanctuary: Brigham Young & the White Mountain Expedition. (American West Ser.: Vol. 19). (Illus.). 272p. 1984. 19.95 (ISBN 0-87480-237-7). U of Utah Pr.

Warren, Steve. Drat! Mythed Again: Second Thoughts on Utah. (Illus.). 183p. 1986. pap. 10.95 (ISBN 0-938117-02-5). Altair Pub UT.

UTAH EXPEDITION, 1857-1858

Furniss, Norman F. The Mormon Conflict, 1850-1859. LC 77-5424. (Illus.). 1977. Repr. of 1960 ed. lib. bdg. 23.75x (ISBN 0-8371-9636-1, FUMC). Greenwood.

V

VACATION BIBLE SCHOOLS

see Vacation Schools, Religious

VACATION SCHOOLS, RELIGIOUS

see also Church Camps

Freese, Doris. Vacation Bible School. LC 77-76179. 96p. 1977. pap. text ed. 4.95 (ISBN 0-910566-11-9); Perfect bdg. instr's. guide by Werner Graendorf 5.95 (ISBN 0-910566-27-5). Evang Tchr.

VACATION SCHOOLS, RELIGIOUS–TEXT-BOOKS

Huggenvik, Theodore. We Believe. 1950. pap. 3.95 (ISBN 0-8066-0151-5, 15-7102). Augsburg.

VAIKHANASAS

Goudriaan, T., tr. Kasyapa's Book of Wisdom: A Ritual Handbook of the Vaikhanasas. (Disputationes Rheno-Trajectinae Ser.: No. 10). 1965. pap. text ed. 37.60 (ISBN 90-2790-036-1). Mouton.

VAISHNAVISM

Acyutananda, Swami, ed. Songs of the Vaisnava Acaryas. 1979. pap. 6.95 (ISBN 0-912776-56-0). Bhaktivedanta.

Bhandarkar, R. G. Vaisnavism Saivism & Minor Religious Systems. 238p. 1986. Repr. 14.00X (ISBN 0-8364-1704-6, Pub. by Minerva India). South Asia Bks.

Chatterjee, A. N. Sri Krsna Caitanya: A Historical Study of Gaudiya Vaisnavism. 1985. 22.00x (ISBN 0-8364-1321-0, Pub. by Assoc Bks India). South Asia Bks.

De, Sushil K. Early History of the Vaisnava Faith & Movement in Bengal from Sanskrit & Bengal Sources. 700p. 1986. 54.00X (ISBN 0-8364-1642-2, Pub. by Mukhopadhyay). South Asia Bks.

Judah, J. Stillson. Hare Krishna & the Counterculture. LC 74-8209. (Contemporary Religious Movements Ser.). pap. 80.00 (ISBN 0-317-07867-4, 2007717). Bks Demand UMI.

Mallik, G. N. Philosophy of Vaisnava Religion. 59.95 (ISBN 0-8490-0829-8). Gordon Pr.

Mukherjee, Prabhat. The History of Medieval Vaishnavism in Orissa. 200p. 1986. Repr. 14.00X (ISBN 0-8364-1754-2, Pub. by Manohar India). South Asia Bks.

VALDENSES

see Waldenses

VALENCIA–HISTORY

Burns, Robert I. Diplomatarium of the Crusader Kingdom of Valencia: The Registered Charters of Its Conqueror, Jaume I, 1257-1276. Volume I: Society & Documentation in Crusader Valencia. LC 84-17828. (Illus.). 288p. 1985. text ed. 40.00x (ISBN 0-691-05435-5). Princeton U Pr.

--Medieval Colonialism: Post-Crusade Exploitation of Islamic Valencia. (Illus.). 432p. 1975. 44.50 (ISBN 0-691-05227-1). Princeton U Pr.

--Muslims, Christians & Jews in the Crusader Kingdom of Valencia: Societies in Symbiosis. LC 83-2007. (Cambridge Iberian & Latin American Studies). 300p. 1984. 65.00 (ISBN 0-521-24374-2). Cambridge U Pr.

VALUES

Here are entered works on moral and esthetic values, etc.

see also Spirituality

Allan, George. The Importances of the Past: A Meditation on the Authority of Tradition. 308p. 1985. 44.50x (ISBN 0-88706-116-8); pap. 14.95x (ISBN 0-88706-117-6). State U NY Pr.

Almond, Brenda & Wilson, Bryan, eds. Values: A Symposium. 300p. 1987. text ed. 45.00 (ISBN 0-391-03368-9). Humanities.

Altgeld, John P. The Cost of Something for Nothing. (Illus.). 135p. Repr. of 1904 ed. 12.95 (ISBN 0-88286-152-2). C H Kerr.

American Marketing Association Staff. Changing Values & Social Trends: How Do Organizations React? Presented Jointly by the Market Research Society & the American Marketing Association, June 1974, Oxford, England. pap. 56.00 (ISBN 0-317-26627-6, 2011593). Bks Demand UMI.

Andrews, Lewis M. To Thine Own Self Be True: The Re-Birth of Values in the New Ethical Therapy. 288p. 1987. 16.95 (ISBN 0-385-23736-7, Anch). Doubleday.

Bahm, Archie J. Axiology: The Science of Values. abbreviated ed. LC 84-51726. 84p. 1984. pap. 3.00 (ISBN 0-911714-14-6, World Bks). Bahm.

Bellance, James A. Values & the Search for Self. LC 75-12724. pap. 27.80 (ISBN 0-317-42175-1, 2025922). Bks Demand UMI.

Bellegarde, Ida R. Understanding Cultural Values. LC 79-51620. 1979. 4.45x (ISBN 0-918340-09-8). Bell Ent.

Bond, E. J. Reason & Value. LC 82-4564. (Cambridge Studies in Philosophy). 220p. 1983. 32.50 (ISBN 0-521-24571-0); pap. 11.95 (ISBN 0-521-27079-0). Cambridge U Pr.

Canning, Jeremiah W., ed. Values in an Age of Confrontation: A Symposium Sponsored by the Religion in Education Foundation. LC 72-109054. (Studies of the Person). pap. 41.10 (ISBN 0-317-09226-X, 2055239). Bks Demand UMI.

Chase, Lewis. A Sense of Values. LC 79-92431. 67p. 1980. 8.95 (ISBN 0-8022-2362-1). Philos Lib.

Cleveland, Harlan & Wilson, Thomas W., Jr. Humangrowth: An Essay on Growth, Values & the Quality of Life. 54p. (Orig.). 1978. pap. text ed. 7.00 (ISBN 0-8191-5904-2, Pub. by Aspen Inst for Humanistic Studies). U Pr of Amer.

Coll, Alberto R. The Western Heritage & American Values: Law, Theology & History. Thompson, Kenneth W., ed. LC 81-43761. (American Values Projected Abroad Ser.: Vol. I). 126p. 1982. lib. bdg. 24.00 (ISBN 0-8191-2526-1); pap. text ed. 8.25 (ISBN 0-8191-2527-X). U Pr of Amer.

Dumont, L. On Value. (Radcliffe-Brown Lectures on Social Anthropology). 1980. pap. 4.00 (ISBN 0-85672-239-1, Pub. by British Acad). Longwood Pub Group.

Fried, Charles. An Anatomy of Values: Problems of Personal & Social Choice. LC 78-111483. 1970. 18.50x (ISBN 0-674-03151-2). Harvard U Pr.

Grunfeld, Joseph. Science & Values. 210p. (Orig.). 1973. pap. 22.00x (ISBN 90-6032-016-6, Pub. by B R Gruener). Benjamins North AM.

Handy, Rollo. The Measurement of Values. LC 79-110107. 232p. 1970. 12.50 (ISBN 0-87527-040-9). Fireside Bks.

Hester, Joseph P. & Killian, Don R. Cartoons for Thinking: Issues in Ethics & Values. (Illus.). 1984. 9.95 (ISBN 0-89824-007-7). Trillium Pr.

Ikeda, Diasaku & Wilson, Bryan. Human Values in a Changing World. 384p. (Orig.). 1987. 20.00 (ISBN 0-8184-0427-2). Lyle Stuart.

Jonassen, Christen T. Value Systems & Personality in a Western Civilization: Norwegians in Europe & America. LC 83-11391. 400p. 1984. 25.00x (ISBN 0-8142-0347-7). Ohio St U Pr.

Kane, R. Free Will & Values. (Series in Philosophy). 328p. 1985. 44.50 (ISBN 0-88706-101-X); pap. 18.95 (ISBN 0-88706-102-8). State U NY Pr.

Larsen, Sandy. Things. 144p. 1984. pap. 3.95 (ISBN 0-88207-109-2). Victor Bks.

Laszlo, Ervin & Wilbur, James B., eds. Human Values & Natural Science. (Current Topics of Contemporary Thought Ser.: Vol. 4). 310p. 1970. 63.95 (ISBN 0-677-13960-8). Gordon & Breach.

Lee, Dorothy. Valuing the Self: What We Can Learn from Other Cultures. (Illus.). 1986. pap. text ed. 6.95x (ISBN 0-88133-229-1). Waveland Pr.

Lewis, Paul. Forty Ways to Teach Your Child Values. 224p. 1985. pap. 6.95 (ISBN 0-8423-0920-9). Tyndale.

McClelland, David C., ed. Education for Values. 220p. 1982. 29.50x (ISBN 0-8290-0090-9). Irvington.

McMurrin, Sterling M., ed. The Tanner Lectures on Human Values, Vol. IV: 1983. 300p. 1983. 20.00x (ISBN 0-87480-216-4). U of Utah Pr.

--The Tanner Lectures on Human Values, Vol. VII: Nineteen Eighty-Six. 288p. 1986. 20.00x (ISBN 0-87480-259-8). U of Utah Pr.

Meyners, Robert & Wooster, Claire. Solomon's Sword: Clarifying Values in the Church. LC 77-9391. Repr. of 1977 ed. 27.40 (ISBN 0-8357-9028-2, 2016408). Bks Demand UMI.

Oxenham, John, ed. Appropriate Values & Education in Developing Nations. (Illus.). 304p. 1987. 22.95 (ISBN 0-89226-050-5, Pub. by ICUS). Paragon Hse.

Ragland, Margaret. What's It Worth? Probing Our Values with Questions Jesus Asked. 1977. pap. 4.95 (ISBN 0-89137-409-4). Quality Pubns.

Ramsey, Paul. The Truth of Value. 139p. 1985. text ed. 15.00x (ISBN 0-391-03058-2). Humanities.

Renshaw, Betty, et al. Values & Voices. 3rd ed. 334p. 1986. pap. text ed. 16.95 (ISBN 0-03-071039-1, HoltC). HR&W.

Rokeach, Milton. Beliefs, Attitudes & Values: A Theory of Organization & Change. LC 68-21322. (Social & Behavioral Science Ser.). 1968. 25.95x (ISBN 0-87589-013-X). Jossey-Bass.

--Understanding Human Values: Individual & Societal. LC 78-24753. (Illus.). 1979. 14.95 (ISBN 0-02-926760-9). Free Pr.

Sondhi, Krishan. Communication & Values. 1986. 22.50X (Pub. by Somaiya). South Asia Bks.

Thompson, Michael. Rubbish Theory: The Creation & Destruction of Value. 1979. text ed. 24.00x (ISBN 0-19-217658-7). Oxford U Pr.

Thurstone, Louis L. The Measurement of Values. LC 58-11960. (Midway Reprint Ser.). pap. 82.50 (2026748). Bks Demand UMI.

Tool, Marc R. Essays in Social Value Theory. 1986. 35.00 (ISBN 0-87332-382-3). M E Sharpe.

Wang-Mong, Cheng. Eight Virtues: Culture. 1987. 6.95 (ISBN 0-533-07189-5). Vantage.

Westerhoff, John H., III. Building God's People in a Materialistic Society. 144p. 1983. pap. 8.95 (ISBN 0-8164-2466-7, HarpR). Har-Row.

VANITY

see Pride and Vanity

VATICAN

Baldassarre, John E. The New, Fully Illustrated Book of the Most Dramatic Paintings in the Vatican. (Illus.). 127p. 1982. 121.45 (ISBN 0-89266-323-5). Am Classical Coll Pr.

Barth, Lewis M. Analysis of Vatican Thirty. 1973. 20.00x (ISBN 0-87820-400-8, Pub. by Hebrew Union). Ktav.

Bull, George. Inside the Vatican. 294p. 1983. 13.95 (ISBN 0-312-41884-1). St Martin.

Calvesi, M. Treasures of the Vatican. 39.95 (ISBN 0-517-62643-8). Outlet Bk Co.

Carrieri, Mario, photos by. The Vatican & Christian Rome. (Illus.). 522p. 1979. 100.00 (ISBN 0-89860-025-1). Eastview.

Chadwick, Owen. Britain & the Vatican During the Second World War. 350p. 1987. 39.50 (ISBN 0-521-32242-1). Cambridge U Pr.

Charles, Rodger. Social Teaching of Vatican II: Its Origin & Development. Catholic Social Ethics-an Historical & Comparative Study. LC 81-83567. (Illus.). 597p. 1982. 30.00 (ISBN 0-89870-013-2). Ignatius Pr.

Chastel, Andre, intro. by. The Vatican Frescoes of Michelangelo, 2 vols. Rosenthal, Raymond, tr. from Fr. LC 80-66646. (Illus.). 528p. 1980. ltd. ed. 7500.00 (ISBN 0-89659-158-1). Abbeville Pr.

De Poncins, Leon. Freemasonry & the Vatican. 1982. lib. bdg. 69.95 (ISBN 0-87700-351-3). Revisionist Pr.

--Judaism & the Vatican. 1982. lib. bdg. 65.00 (ISBN 0-87700-381-5). Revisionist Pr.

DH - TE Research Studies. The Vatican & the Third World: Diplomacy & the Future. LC 75-14400. 1975. pap. 3.50 (ISBN 0-686-11971-1). Bks Intl DH-TE.

DiFederico, Frank. The Mosaics of Saint Peter's: Decorating the New Basilica. LC 82-42777. (Illus.). 176p. 1983. 42.50x (ISBN 0-271-00344-8). Pa St U Pr.

Ezcurra, Ana M. The Vatican & the Reagan Administration. New York CIRCUS Publications, Inc. Staff, ed. Tr. of El Vaticano y la Administracion Reagan. 220p. (Orig.). 1986. pap. text ed. 6.95 (ISBN 0-318-20240-9). NY Circus Pubns.

Fagin, Gerald M., ed. Vatican II: Open Questions & New Horizons. (Theology & Life Ser.: Vol. 8). pap. 6.95 (ISBN 0-89453-366-5). M Glazier.

Fellucci, Mario. The Masterpieces of the Vatican. (A Science of Man Library Bk). (Illus.). 40p. 1975. 97.45 (ISBN 0-913314-54-4). Am Classical Coll Pr.

Fogarty, Gerald P. The Vatican & the American Hierarchy from 1870 to 1965. 1985. pap. 16.95 (ISBN 0-317-42752-0). M Glazier.

Graham, Robert A. Vatican Diplomacy: A Study of Church & State on the International Plane. LC 59-13870. pap. 113.00 (ISBN 0-317-08423-2, 2015012). Bks Demand UMI.

Hebblethwaite, Peter. In the Vatican. LC 86-7927. 214p. 1986. 16.95 (ISBN 0-917561-24-4). Adler & Adler.

Hebblethwaite, Peter, et al. The Vatican. LC 80-50854. (Illus.). 226p. 1980. 50.00 (ISBN 0-86565-002-0). Vendome.

Heuzinger, Lutz & Mancinelli, Fabrizio. The Sistine Chapel. LC 84-50553. (Illus.). 96p. (Orig.). 1984. pap. 13.95 (ISBN 0-935748-58-X). Scala Books.

Hoagland, Donald. Rome & the Political Theory of History with Cogent Applications to the Rivalries Between the United States & Soviet Russia. (Illus.). 166p. 1985. 167.95 (ISBN 0-86722-103-8). Inst Econ Pol.

John Paul II, Pope Sources of Renewal: The Fulfillment of Vatican II. LC 79-1780. 448p. 1980. 15.00 (ISBN 0-06-064188-6, HarpR). Har-Row.

Keogh, Dermot F. The Vatican, the Bishops & Irish Politics: Church & State in Ireland, 1919-1939. (Illus.). 318p. 1986. 39.50 (ISBN 0-521-30129-7). Cambridge U Pr.

Manhattan, Avro. The Vacation Moscow Washington Alliance. 352p. (Orig.). pap. 7.95 (ISBN 0-937958-12-3). Chick Pubns.

--The Vatican Billions. 304p. (Orig.). 1983. pap. 7.50 (ISBN 0-937958-16-6). Chick Pubns.

Martin, Malachi. Vatican. LC 85-42645. 672p. 1986. 18.45 (ISBN 0-06-015478-0, HarpT). Har-Row.

Matini, Aldo, ed. The Gold Seals of the Vatican: Secret Archives. (Illus.). 288p. 150.00 (ISBN 0-8478-5404-3). Rizzoli Intl.

Packard, Jerrold M. Peter's Kingdom: Inside the Papal City. (Illus.). 352p. 1985. 17.95 (ISBN 0-684-18430-3, ScribT). Scribner.

Pollard, John F. The Vatican & Italian Fascism, Nineteen Twenty-Nine to Nineteen Thirty-Two: A Study in Conflict. 240p. 1985. 34.50 (ISBN 0-521-26870-2). Cambridge U Pr.

Rappoport, Angelo S. The Love Affairs of the Vatican. 35.00 (ISBN 0-8490-0561-2). Gordon Pr.

Rome & the Vatican in Color. (Sterling Travel Guide in Color Ser.). (Illus.). 140p. (Orig.). 1983. pap. 4.95 (ISBN 0-8069-1372-X). Sterling.

Seymour, Charles, Jr., ed. & intro. by. Michelangelo: The Sistine Chapel Ceiling. (Critical Studies in Art History). (Illus.). 243p. 1972. pap. 7.95x (ISBN 0-393-09889-3). Norton.

Shearman, J. The Vatican Stanze: Functions & Decoration. (Italian Lectures). 1971. pap. 2.50 (ISBN 0-85672-062-3, Pub. by British Acad). Longwood Pub Group.

Toynbee, Jocelyn M. The Shrine of St. Peter & the Vatican Excavations. LC 78-63482. Repr. of 1956 ed. 32.00 (ISBN 0-404-16548-6). AMS Pr.

Walsh, Michael J. Vatican City-State. (World Bibliographical Ser.: No. 41). 105p. 1983. lib. bdg. 22.00 (ISBN 0-903450-72-0). ABC-Clio.

Zivojinovic, Dragan. The United States & Vatican Policies, 1914-1918. LC 78-52438. 1978. 22.50x (ISBN 0-87081-112-6). Colo Assoc.

VATICAN–JUVENILE LITERATURE

Wuerl, Donald & Wilson, Michael. A Visit to the Vatican for Young People. (Illus.). 1980. 3.50 (ISBN 0-8198-8002-7). Dghtrs St Paul.

VATICAN COUNCIL, 1869-1870

see also Popes–Infallibility

Ryan, Alvan, ed. Newman & Gladstone: The Vatican Decrees. 1962. 13.95 (ISBN 0-268-00190-1). U of Notre Dame Pr.

Sivric, Ivo. Bishop J. G. Strossmayer: New Light on Vatican I. 1975. 7.95 (ISBN 0-8199-0491-0). Franciscan Herald.

VATICAN COUNCIL, 2ND, 1962-1965

Abbott, Walter M., ed. The Documents of Vatican II. pap. cancelled (ISBN 0-686-19062-9, EC-101). US Catholic.
--The Documents of Vatican II with Notes & Comments by Catholic, Protestant & Orthodox Authorities. LC 82-80350. 794p. 1974. pap. 8.95 (ISBN 0-8329-1115-1, Assn Pr). New Century.
Baney, Margaret M. Witness: One Response to Vatican II. 1987. 12.50 (ISBN 0-533-07210-7). Vantage.
Bea, Augustin. Church & Mankind. 6.50 (ISBN 0-8199-0012-5, L38112). Franciscan Herald.
--Word of God & Mankind. 1968. 6.50 (ISBN 0-8199-0149-0, L39003). Franciscan Herald.
Burghardt, Walter J., ed. Religious Freedom, Nineteen Sixty-Five to Nineteen Seventy-Five: A Symposium on a Historic Document. LC 76-45938. 1977. pap. 2.95 (ISBN 0-8091-1993-5). Paulist Pr.
Caird, G. B. Our Dialogue with Rome: The Second Vatican Council & After. 7.25 (ISBN 0-8446-1797-0). Peter Smith.
Daughters Of St. Paul. Christ of Vatican Two. (St. Paul Editions). (Illus.). 1968. 2.00 (ISBN 0-8198-0024-4); pap. 1.00 (ISBN 0-8198-0025-2). Dghtrs St Paul.
--Religious Life in the Light of Vatican 2. (Orig.). 4.00 (ISBN 0-8198-0132-1). Dghtrs St Paul.
Fesquet, Henri. Has Rome Converted. Salemson, Harold J., tr. 1968. 9.50 (ISBN 0-685-11959-9). Heineman.
Flannery, Austin. Vatican Council II: The Conciliar & Post Conciliar Documents, Vol. 2. 994p. 1983. pap. 9.95 (ISBN 0-8146-1299-7). Liturgical Pr.
Flannery, Austin, ed. Vatican Council II. 1976. pap. 7.95 (ISBN 0-685-77498-8). Franciscan Herald.
Flannery, Austin P. Document of Vatican 11. 1975. pap. 7.95 (ISBN 0-8028-1623-1). Eerdmans.
Flannery, Austin P., ed. Vatican II: More Postconciliar Documents. 944p. (Orig.). 1983. pap. 9.95 (ISBN 0-8028-1638-X). Eerdmans.
Gremillion, Joseph. Church & Culture since Vatican II: The Experience of North & Latin America. LC 84-40364. 350p. 1985. pap. text ed. 12.95 (ISBN 0-268-00753-5, 85-07535). U of Notre Dame Pr.
Hebblethwaite, Peter. Synod Extraordinary: An Evaluation of the Catholic Church on the 20th Anniversary of Vatican Council II. LC 85-27160. 144p. 1986. 15.95 (ISBN 0-385-23466-X). Doubleday.
Kloppenburg, Bonaventure. Ecclesiology of Vatican II. 1974. 6.95 (ISBN 0-8199-0484-8). Franciscan Herald.
Latourelle, Rene. Theology of Revelation. LC 65-15734. 1966. pap. 12.95 (ISBN 0-8189-0143-8). Alba.
McDonald, William J. The General Council: Special Studies in Doctrinal & Historical Background. LC 62-20329. pap. 48.00 (ISBN 0-317-07854-2, 2005223). Bks Demand UMI.
McDonald, William J., ed. The General Council: Special Studies in Doctrinal & Historical Background. LC 78-10099. 1979. Repr. of 1962 ed. lib. bdg. cancelled (ISBN 0-313-20753-4, MCGC). Greenwood.
Neuner, J. & Dupuis, J., eds. The Christian Faith. rev. ed. LC 82-22700. 740p. 1983. pap. 13.95 (ISBN 0-8189-0453-4). Alba.
Paulist Editorial Committee, ed. Liturgy Constitution. 192p. 1964. pap. 1.95 (ISBN 0-8091-1620-0, 192, Deus). Paulist Pr.
Pawley, B. The Second Vatican Council: Studies by Eight Anglican Observers. 12.00 (ISBN 0-8446-2713-5). Peter Smith.
Ruffolo, Marina E., ed. The Dynamic Voice of Vatican II. 1977. 4.50 (ISBN 0-8198-0405-3); pap. 2.95 (ISBN 0-8198-0406-1). Dghtrs St Paul.
Schner, George P. The Church Renewed: The Documents of Vatican II Reconsidered. 164p. (Orig.). 1986. lib. bdg. 24.50 (ISBN 0-8191-5505-5, Pub. by Regis College Toronto CN); pap. text ed. 10.75 (ISBN 0-8191-5506-3). U Pr of Amer.
Stacpoole, Dom A., ed. Vatican Two Revisited: By Those Who Were There. 448p. 1986. 24.50 (ISBN 0-86683-531-8, HarpR). Har-Row.
Wathen, James F. The Great Sacrilege. LC 76-183571. 1971. pap. 5.00 (ISBN 0-89555-014-8). TAN Bks Pubs.
Weakland, Rembert G. All God's People: Catholic Identity after the Second Vatican Council. LC 84-61493. 216p. (Orig.). 1985. pap. 7.95 (ISBN 0-8091-2665-6). Paulist Pr.
Wigginton, Peter. Popes of Vatican Council II. 329p. 1983. 15.00 (ISBN 0-8199-0828-2). Franciscan Herald.
Wiltgen, Ralph M. The Rhine Flows into the Tiber: A History of Vatican II. LC 82-50583. 304p. pap. 8.00 (ISBN 0-89555-186-1). Tan Bks Pubs.

VAUDOIS

see Waldenses

VAUGHAN, HENRY, 1622-1695

Bennett, Joan. Five Metaphysical Poets: Donne, Herbert, Vaughan, Crashaw, Marvell. 1964. 32.50 (ISBN 0-521-04156-2); pap. 9.95 (ISBN 0-521-09238-8). Cambridge U Pr.
Grant, Patrick. The Transformation of Sin: Studies in Donne, Herbert, Vaughan & Traherne. LC 73-93174. 308p. 1974. 20.00x (ISBN 0-87023-158-8). U of Mass Pr.
Holmes, Elizabeth. Henry Vaughan & the Hermetic Philosophy. (English Literature Ser., No. 33). 1970. pap. 22.95x (ISBN 0-8383-0094-4). Haskell.
Post, Jonathan F. Henry Vaughan: The Unfolding Vision. LC 82-47609. 264p. 1983. 26.50 (ISBN 0-691-06527-6). Princeton U Pr.
Simmonds, James D. Masques of God: Form & Theme in the Poetry of Henry Vaughan. LC 78-170144. 1972. 24.95x (ISBN 0-8229-3236-9). U of Pittsburgh Pr.

VAULTS

Ward, Clarence. Mediaeval Church Vaulting. LC 72-177847. Repr. of 1915 ed. 19.50 (ISBN 0-404-06836-7). AMS Pr.

VAULTS (SEPULCHRAL)

see Tombs

VEDANTA

see also Advaita; Maya (Hinduism)

Abhedananda. Human Affection & Divine Love. 64p. 3.95 (ISBN 0-87481-610-6, Pub. by Ramakrishna Math Madras India). Vedanta Pr.
Abhedananda, Swami. The Complete Works of Swami Abhedananda, 11 vols. (Illus.). Set. 125.00x (ISBN 0-87481-621-1). Vedanta Pr.
--A Study of Heliocentric Science. 5.95 (ISBN 0-87481-619-X). Vedanta Pr.
Abhendananda. Songs Divine. Aiyer, P. S., tr. from Sanskrit. 69p. 1985. 6.50 (ISBN 0-87481-653-X, Pub. by Ramakrishna Math Madras India). Vedanta Pr.
Ananda. Spiritual Practice. pap. 3.00 (ISBN 0-87481-155-4). Vedanta Pr.
Anantendra-Yati. Vedanta-Sara-Sangraha. Mahadevan, T. M., tr. 1974. pap. 3.50 (ISBN 0-89744-124-9, Pub. by Ganesh & Co. India). Auromere.
Arapura, J. G. Hermeneutical Essays on Vedantic Topics. 326p. 1986. 18.00 (ISBN 81-208-0183-0, Pub. by Motilal Banarsidass). South Asia Bks.
Arapura, John G. Gnosis & the Question of Thought in Vedanta. 1986. lib. bdg. 65.25 (ISBN 90-247-3061-9, Pub. by Martinus Nijhoff Netherlands). Kluwer Academic.
Astavakra. Astavakra Samhita. Nityaswarupananda, Swami, tr. (Sanskrit & Eng.). pap. 4.50 (ISBN 0-87481-165-1). Vedanta Pr.
Athar-Veda (Summary) Date not set. 5.00 (ISBN 0-938924-32-X). Sri Shirdi Sai.
Badarayana. Brahma Sutra: The Philosophy of Spiritual Life. Radhakrishnan, S., tr. LC 68-21330. 1968. Repr. of 1960 ed. lib. bdg. 37.25x (ISBN 0-8371-0291-X, BABS). Greenwood.
Beidler, W. Vision of Self in Early Vedanta. 1975. 12.50 (ISBN 0-8426-0990-3). Orient Bk Dist.
Bhattacharrya, K. C. Search for the Absolute in Neo-Vedanta. Burch, George B., ed. LC 75-17740. 202p. 1976. text ed. 14.00x (ISBN 0-8248-0296-9). UH Pr.
Chakravarty, Sharat C. Talks with Swami Vivekananda. 6.95 (ISBN 0-87481-156-2). Vedanta Pr.
Chari, S. M. Fundamentals of Visistadvaita Vedanta. 1987. 36.00 (Pub. by Motilal Banarsidass). South Asia Bks.
Damrell, Joseph D. Seeking Spiritual Meaning: The World of Vedanta. LC 77-9145. (Sociological Observations Ser.: No. 2). pap. 63.00 (ISBN 0-317-08760-6, 2021885). Bks Demand UMI.
Dattatreya. Avadhuta Gita of Dattatreya. Ashokananda, Swami, tr. from Sanskrit. 1978. pap. 3.95 (ISBN 0-87481-482-0). Vedanta Pr.
Dayton, Brandt, ed. Practical Vedanta: Of Swami Rama Tirtha. LC 78-10567. 350p. 8.95 (ISBN 0-89389-038-3). Himalayan Pubs.
Deutsch, Eliot. Advaita Vedanta: A Philosophical Reconstruction. LC 69-19282. 1969. pap. text ed. 5.95x (ISBN 0-8248-0271-3, Eastwest Ctr). UH Pr.
Dhar, Niranjan. Vedanta & the Bengal Renaissance: Progress or Reaction. LC 76-52210. 1977. 11.00x (ISBN 0-88386-837-7). South Asia Bks.
Duraiswami, Pandit M. Sri Pancaratra-Raksha of Vedanta Desika. 2nd ed. 1967. 6.00 (ISBN 0-8356-7482-7, ALS 36). Theos Pub Hse.
Fausset, Hugh A. Flame & the Light: Meanings in Vedanta & Buddhism. LC 69-10089. Repr. of 1969 ed. lib. bdg. 22.50x (ISBN 0-8371-0996-5, FAVB). Greenwood.
Gambhirananda, Swami, ed. Apostles of Ramakrishna. (Illus.). 6.95x (ISBN 0-87481-098-1). Vedanta Pr.
Gospel of the Holy Mother. Tr. of Bengali. 410p. (Orig.). 1985. pap. 8.95 (ISBN 0-87481-531-2, Pub. by Ramakrishna Math Madras India). Vedanta Pr.
In the Company of the Holy Mother. Orig. Title: At Holy Mother's Feet. 382p. 1980. pap. 5.95 (ISBN 0-87481-208-9). Vedanta Pr.
Indich, William M. Consciousness in Advaita Vedanta. 1980. 14.00x (ISBN 0-8364-0607-9). South Asia Bks.
Isherwood, Christopher. Approach to Vedanta. 1970. pap. 3.95 (ISBN 0-87481-003-5). Vedanta Pr.
--My Guru & His Disciple. 352p. 1981. pap. 4.95 (ISBN 0-14-005837-0). Penguin.
Isherwood, Christopher, ed. Vedanta for the Western World: A Symposium on Vedanta. LC 46-25052. 1945. pap. 7.95 (ISBN 0-87481-000-0). Vedanta Pr.
Iyer, B. R. Rambles in Vedanta. 1974. Repr. 22.50 (ISBN 0-8426-0601-7). Orient Bk Dist.
Jones, Richard H. Science & Mysticism: A Comparative Study of Western Natural Science, Theravada Buddhism, & Advaita Vedanta. LC 84-46098. 272p. 1986. 35.00x (ISBN 0-8387-5093-1, Pub. by Bucknell U Pr). Assoc Univ Prs.
Jyotir Maya Nanda. Vedanta in Brief. (Orig.). 1978. pap. 3.99 (ISBN 0-934664-37-4). Yoga Res Foun.
Jyotirmayananda, Swami. Yoga Vasistha, Vol. III. 304p. (Orig.). 1986. pap. 4.99 (ISBN 0-934664-33-1). Yoga Res Foun.
Kashinath. The Scientific Vedanta. LC 73-900893. 129p. 1974. 7.50x (ISBN 0-89684-451-X). Orient Bk Dist.
Kriyananda, Goswami. The Spiritual Science of Kriya Yoga. 2nd ed. (Illus.). pap. text ed. 16.95 (ISBN 0-9613099-1-1). Temple Kriya Yoga.
Lipner, Julius J. The Face of Truth: A Study of Meaning & Metaphysics in the Vedantic Theology of Ramanuja. 224p. 1986. 44.50x (ISBN 0-88706-038-2); pap. 18.95x (ISBN 0-88706-039-0). State U NY Pr.
Lord Sri Venkateswara. Date not set. 5.00 (ISBN 0-938924-33-8). Sri Shirdi Sai.
Lott, Eric. Vedantic Approaches to God. LC 78-17886. (Library of Philosophy & Religion Ser.). 214p. 1980. text ed. 28.50x (ISBN 0-06-494365-8). B&N Imports.
Madhava-Vidyaranya. Sankara-Dig-Vijaya: The Traditional Life of Sri Sankaracharya. Tapasyananda, Swami, tr. 1979. pap. 6.95 (ISBN 0-87481-484-7). Vedanta Pr.
Mainkar, T. G. The Making of the Vedanta. 1980. 14.00x (ISBN 0-8364-0623-0, Pub. by Ajanta). South Asia Bks.
Malkani, Ghanshamdas R. Philosophy of the Self. 15.00 (ISBN 0-384-35112-3); pap. 10.00 (ISBN 0-685-13549-7). Johnson Repr.
Monks of the Ramakrishna Order. Meditation. Bhavyananda, Swami, ed. 1977. pap. 8.50 (ISBN 0-7025-0019-4). Vedanta Pr.
Muller, F. M. Vedanta Philosophy. 182p. 1984. text ed. 27.00x. Coronet Bks.
Nikhilananda, Swami, tr. Drg-Drsya-Viveka. (Sanskrit & Eng.). pap. 1.50 (ISBN 0-87481-402-2). Vedanta Pr.
--Self-Knowledge: Sankara's "Atmabodha". LC 50-36440. 248p. with notes 7.00 (ISBN 0-911206-11-6). Ramakrishna.
Paramananda, Swami. Book of Daily Thoughts & Prayers. 1977. 9.50 (ISBN 0-911564-01-2); soft lexotone bdg. 7.50 (ISBN 0-911564-32-2). Vedanta Ctr.
--Emerson & Vedanta. 2nd ed. 1985. pap. 3.50 (ISBN 0-911564-13-6). Vedanta Ctr.
--Faith is Power. 2nd ed. Orig. Title: Faith as Constructive Force. 1961. 4.50 (ISBN 0-911564-09-8). Vedanta Ctr.
--Principles & Purposes of Vedanta. 8th ed. 1937. pap. 1.00 (ISBN 0-911564-30-6). Vedanta Ctr.
--Right Resolutions. 2nd ed. 1981. pap. 1.00 (ISBN 0-911564-29-2). Vedanta Ctr.
--Vedanta in Practice. 3rd ed. 1985. pap. 3.50 (ISBN 0-911564-04-7). Vedanta Ctr.
--Way of Peace & Blessedness. 3rd ed. 1961. 4.50 (ISBN 0-911564-06-3). Vedanta Ctr.
Prabhavananda, Swami. Yoga & Mysticism: An Introduction to Vedanta. 53p. 1984. pap. 3.95 (ISBN 0-87481-020-5). Vedanta Pr.
Prabhavananda, Swami & Isherwood, Christopher, trs. from Sanskrit. How to Know God: The Yoga Aphorisms of Patanjali. 224p. 1983. pap. 6.95 (ISBN 0-87481-041-8). Vedanta Pr.
Prajnanananda. Christ the Savior & Christ Myth. rev. ed. 7.95 (ISBN 0-87481-652-1, Pub. by Ramakrishna Math Madras India). Vedanta Pr.
Prajnananda, Swami. The Philosophical Ideas of Swami Abhenananda: A Critical Study (A Guide to the Complete Works of Swami Abhedananda) (Illus.). 7.95 (ISBN 0-87481-623-8). Vedanta Pr.
Raja, C. Kunhan. Poet Philosophers of the Rig Veda. (Sanskrit & eng.). 10.00 (ISBN 0-89744-121-4, Pub. by Ganesh & Co. India). Auromere.
Rajagopalachari, C. Ramakrishna Upanishad. pap. 1.95 (ISBN 0-87481-430-8). Vedanta Pr.
Rajneesh, Bhagwan Shree. Vedanta: Seven Steps to Samadhi. Pratima, Ma Yoga, ed. LC 77-904425. (Upanishad Ser.). (Illus.). 518p. (Orig.). 1976. 16.50 (ISBN 0-88050-166-9). Chidvilas Found.
Ramakrishna, Sri. Tales & Parables of Sri Ramakrishna. pap. 5.00 (ISBN 0-87481-493-6). Vedanta Pr.
--Teachings of Sri Ramakrishna. pap. 4.95 (ISBN 0-87481-133-3). Vedanta Pr.
Ramakrishna's Disciples. Spiritual Talks. 5.95 (ISBN 0-87481-103-1). Vedanta Pr.
Ranganathananda, Swami. Science & Religion. 1979. pap. 3.75 (ISBN 0-87481-190-2). Vedanta Pr.
Rao, P. Nagaraja. Epistemology of Dvaita Vedanta. 6.50 (ISBN 0-8356-7442-8). Theos Pub Hse.
Rig-Veda (Summary) Date not set. 5.00 (ISBN 0-938924-29-X). Sri Shirdi Sai.
Saama-Veda (Summary) Date not set. 5.00 (ISBN 0-938924-31-1). Sri Shirdi Sai.
Sadananda. Vedantasara of Sadananda. pap. 3.00 (ISBN 0-87481-073-6). Vedanta Pr.
Sankaracarya. Saudaryalahari or, Flood of Beauty. Brown, William N., ed. LC 57-9072. (Oriental Ser: No. 43). (Illus.). 1958. 16.50x (ISBN 0-674-78990-3). Harvard U Pr.
Sankaracharya, Sri. Dakshinamurti Stotra. Sastri, Alladi M., tr. 1979. 12.00 (ISBN 0-89744-189-3). Auromere.
Sarada Devi, Sri: The Great Wonder. 508p. 1985. pap. 8.95 (ISBN 0-87481-569-X, Pub. by Ramakrishna Mission India). Vedanta Pr.
Sarada Devi, Sri the Holy Mother, 2 bks. rev. ed. Incl. Bk. 1. Life. Tapasyananda, Swami. pap. 4.95 (ISBN 0-87481-485-5); Bk. 2. Conversations. Nikhilananda, Swami, tr. from Bengali. pap. 3.95 (ISBN 0-87481-486-3). 1978. pap. Vedanta Pr.
Sastri, A. Mahadeva. The Vedanta Doctrine of Sri Sankaracharya. 245p. 1986. Repr. of 1899 ed. lib. bdg. 16.95 (ISBN 81-7030-029-0, Pub. by Sri Satguru Pubns India). Orient Bk Dist.
Satprakashananda, Swami. The Goal & the Way: The Vedantic Approach to Life's Problems. LC 77-75279. 302p. 1977. 12.50 (ISBN 0-916356-56-6). Vedanta Soc St Louis.
--Swami Vivekananda's Contribution to the Present Age. (Illus.). 249p. 1978. 9.50 (ISBN 0-916356-58-2, 77-91628). Vedanta Soc St Louis.
Sekkizhaar. Periya Puranam. Mahalingam, N., ed. Vanmikanathan, G., tr. from Tamil. 612p. 1985. text ed. 11.95x (ISBN 0-87481-534-7, Pub. by RamaKrishna Math). Vedanta Pr.
Shankara. Aparokshanubhuti (Self-Realization) Vimuktananda, Swami, tr. (Sanskrit & Eng). pap. 2.50 (ISBN 0-87481-065-5). Vedanta Pr.
--Brahma-Sutra Bhasya of Sankaracarya. Gambhirananda, Swami, tr. (Sanskrit & Eng.). 20.00 (ISBN 0-87481-066-3). Vedanta Pr.
--Upadesa Sahasri: A Thousand Teachings. Jagadananda, Swami, tr. (Sanskrit & Eng). pap. 4.95 (ISBN 0-87481-423-5). Vedanta Pr.
--Vakyavritti & Atmajnanopadeshavidhi. (Sanskrit & Eng). pap. 1.95 (ISBN 0-87481-424-3). Vedanta Pr.
--Vivekachudamani of Shri Shankaracharya. Madhavananda, Swami, tr. (Sanskrit & Eng.). pap. 3.50 (ISBN 0-87481-147-3). Vedanta Pr.
Sharma, B. N. History of the Dvaita School of Vedant & Its Literature. 2nd ed. 1981. 48.00x (ISBN 0-8364-0754-7, Pub. by Motilal Banarsidass). South Asia Bks.
Siddheswarananda, Swami. Some Aspects of Vedanta Philosophy. Bhakti, Krishna & Marar, K. Narayana, trs. 318p. (Orig.). 1976. pap. 4.50 (ISBN 0-87481-471-5). Vedanta Pr.
Sprung, G. M., ed. The Problems of Two Truths in Buddhism & Vedanta. LC 73-83570. 1973. lib. bdg. 26.00 (ISBN 90-277-0335-3, Pub. by Reidel Holland). Kluwer Academic.
Sri Shirdi Sai Baba. Date not set. 5.00 (ISBN 0-938924-34-6). Sri Shirdi Sai.
Srinivasachari, P. N. Synthetic View of Vedanta. 2.75 (ISBN 0-8356-7512-2). Theos Pub Hse.
Srinivasadasa. Yatindramatadipika. Adidevananda, Swami, tr. (Sanskrit & Eng.). 2.75 (ISBN 0-87481-428-6). Vedanta Pr.
Swahananda, Swami. Service & Spirituality. 211p. (Orig.). 1980. pap. 4.95 (ISBN 0-87481-500-2). Vedanta Pr.
Swami Vireshwarananda. Brahma Sutra Sri Bhasya. 1979. 10.00 (ISBN 0-87481-189-9). Vedanta Pr.
Swami Vishwashrayananda. Swami Vijnanananda: His Life & Sayings. Devavrata Basu Ray, tr. from Bengoli. 72p. 1981. pap. 1.95 (ISBN 0-87481-502-9). Vedanta Pr.
Swami Vivekananda. Complete Works of Swami Vivekananda, 8 Vols. 75.00x (ISBN 0-87481-092-2); Vol. 1. 10.95x (ISBN 0-87481-137-6); Vol. 2. 10.00x (ISBN 0-87481-138-4); Vol. 3. 10.95x (ISBN 0-87481-139-2); Vol. 4. 10.95x (ISBN 0-87481-140-6); Vol. 5. 10.95x (ISBN 0-87481-141-4); Vol. 6. 10.95x (ISBN 0-87481-142-2); Vol. 7. 10.95x (ISBN 0-87481-143-0); Vol. 8. 10.95x (ISBN 0-87481-144-9). Vedanta Pr.

--Complete Works of Swami Vivekananda, 8 vols. pap. 55.00x (ISBN 0-87481-176-7). Vedanta Pr.

--Practical Vedanta. pap. 2.00 (ISBN 0-87481-124-4). Vedanta Pr.

--Selections from Swami Vivekananda. 10.00x (ISBN 0-87481-094-9); pap. 6.95 (ISBN 0-87481-174-0). Vedanta Pr.

Teachings of Sri Saranda Devi. (The Holy Mother Ser.). 175p. 1983. 3.00 (ISBN 0-87481-520-7, Pub. by Ramakrishna Math Madras India). Vedanta Pr.

Thibaut, G., ed. The Vedanta Sutras. 1974. lib. bdg. 75.00 (ISBN 0-8490-1256-2). Gordon Pr.

Thibaut, G., tr. The Vendanta Sutras, 3 vols. lib. bdg. 300.00 (ISBN 0-87968-562-X). Krishna Pr.

Tiwari, Kapil N. Dimensions of Renunciation in Advaita Vedanta. 1977. 11.00x (ISBN 0-8364-0109-3). South Asia Bks.

Tyagisananda, Swami, tr. Svetasvataropanisad. (Sanskrit & Eng.). pap. 2.00 (ISBN 0-87481-418-9). Vedanta Pr.

Usha, Brahmacharini, ed. Ramakrishna-Vedanta Wordbook: A Brief Dictionary of Hinduism. (Orig.). pap. 3.25 (ISBN 0-87481-017-5). Vedanta Pr.

Woodroffe, John, tr. from Sanskrit. The Serpent Power (Sat-Chakra-Nirupana & Paduka-Panchaka) (Illus.). 512p. (Eng. only). 1973. 24.00 (ISBN 0-89744-117-6, Pub. by Ganesh & Co. India). Auromere.

Yajurveda (Summary) Date not set. 5.00 (ISBN 0-938924-30-3). Sri Shirdi Sai.

VEDAS

see also Upanishads

Arnold, E. V. Vedic Metre in Its Historical Development. 1967. Repr. 25.00 (ISBN 0-89684-338-6). Orient Bk Dist.

Aurobindo, Sri. The Secret of the Veda. (Sanskrit & Eng.). 1979. oversize ed. 40.00 (ISBN 0-89744-975-4, Pub. by Sri Aurobindo Ashram Trust India); pap. 30.00. Auromere.

--The Secret of the Veda. 581p. 1982. 15.00 (ISBN 0-89071-303-0, Pub. by Sri Aurobindo Ashram India); pap. 10.00 (ISBN 0-89071-302-2, Pub. by Sri Aurobindo Ashram India). Matagiri.

Bharata Krsna Tirthaji Maharaj. Vedic Metaphysics. 1978. Repr. 16.95 (ISBN 0-89684-337-8). Orient Bk Dist.

Blair, Chauncey J. Heat in the Rig Veda & Atharva Veda. (American Oriental Ser.: Vol. 45). 1961. 8.00x (ISBN 0-940490-45-5). Am Orient Soc.

Bloomfield, M., tr. Hymns of the Atharva-Veda: Together with Extracts from the Ritual Books & the Commentaries. LC 69-14131. 716p. 1897. Repr. lib. bdg. 32.50x (ISBN 0-8371-1879-4, VEHA). Greenwood.

Bloomfield, Maurice. Religion of the Veda. LC 70-94310. (BCL Ser. II). Repr. of 1908 ed. 18.00 (ISBN 0-404-00912-3). AMS Pr.

Chatterji, J. C. Wisdom of the Vedas. LC 80-51550. 100p. 1980. pap. 3.95 (ISBN 0-8356-0538-8, Quest). Theos Pub Hse.

Gonda, J. Vision of the Vedic Poets. (Disputationes Rheno-Trajectinae Ser.: No. 8). (Orig.). 1963. pap. text ed. 28.80x (ISBN 90-2790-034-5). Mouton.

Gonda, Jan. Epithets in the Rgveda. (D. R. T. Ser: No. 3). 1959. pap. text ed. 29.60x (ISBN 90-2790-030-2). Mouton.

--Some Observations on the Relations Between Gods & Powers in the Veda, a Propos of the Phrase, Sunah Sahasah. (Disputationes Rheno-Trajectinae Ser.: No. 1). (Orig.). 1957. pap. text ed. 12.80x (ISBN 90-2790-027-2). Mouton.

Hale, Edward W. Asura in Early Vedic Religion. 275p. 1986. 16.00 (ISBN 81-208-0061-3, Pub. by Motilal Banarsidass). South Asia Bks.

Hall, Manly P. Light of the Vedas. (Adepts Ser.). pap. 3.95 (ISBN 0-89314-530-0). Philos Res.

Heesterman, J. C. Ancient Indian Royal Consecration: The Rajasuya Described According to the Yajus Texts & Annotated. (Disputationes Rheno-Trajectinae Ser: No. 2). (Orig.). 1957. pap. text ed. 25.60x (ISBN 90-2790-028-0). Mouton.

Howard, Wayne. Veda Recitation in Varanasi. 1986. 42.00x (ISBN 0-8364-0872-1). South Asia Bks.

Keith, A. B. The Religion & Philosophy of the Veda & Upanishads, 2 vols. 1976. Repr. Set. 42.00 (ISBN 0-89684-304-1). Orient Bk Dist.

--The Veda of the Black Yajus School: Taittiriya Sanhita, 2 vols. 1967. Repr. Set. 42.00 (ISBN 0-89684-334-3). Orient Bk Dist.

Keith, Arthur B. The Religion & Philosophy of the Veda & Upanishads, 2 vols. LC 71-109969. Repr. of 1925 ed. lib. bdg. 34.00x (ISBN 0-8371-4475-2, KEVU). Greenwood.

Miller, Jeanine. The Vision of Cosmic Order in the Vedas. 320p. 1985. 39.95x (ISBN 0-7102-0369-1). Methuen Inc.

Mueller, Friedrich M. Physical Religion. LC 73-18811. (Gifford Lectures: 1890). Repr. of 1891 ed. 34.00 (ISBN 0-404-11451-2). AMS Pr.

Muller, Max, ed. Sacred Book of the East: Vedic Hymns, 2 vols. 250.00 (ISBN 0-87968-438-0). Krishna Pr.

Murty, K. S. Revelation & Reason in Advaita Vedanta. 1974. Repr. 11.25 (ISBN 0-8426-0662-9). Orient Bk Dist.

Nanda-Nandana, Sri. The Secret Teachings of the Vedas: The Ancient Knowledge of the East. LC 86-51209. 320p. (Orig.). 1987. pap. 14.95 (ISBN 0-9617410-0-7). World Relief.

Neve, Felix. An Essay on the Myth of the Rbhus. Davanc, G. V., tr. from Fr. 370p. 1985. 42.50 (ISBN 81-202-0150-7, Pub. by Ajanta). South Asia Bks.

Pandit, M. P. Aditi & Other Deities in the Veda. 1979. 3.95 (ISBN 0-941524-01-9). Lotus Light.

--Mystic Approach to the Veda & the Upanishad. 4.25 (ISBN 0-89744-108-7, Pub. by Ganesh & Co. India). Auromere.

Paramananda, Swami. Plato & Vedic Idealism. (Orig.). 1924. 4.50 (ISBN 0-911564-15-2). Vedanta Ctr.

Patel, Ishwarbhai, ed. Sciences & the Vedas. 1986. 12.50X (ISBN 0-8364-1663-5, Pub. by Somaiya). South Asia Bks.

Pateria, A. K. Modern Commentators of Veda. 120p. 1986. text ed. 22.50x (ISBN 81-7018-252-2, Pub. by B R Pub Corp Delhi). Apt Bks.

Popley, H. A., ed. & tr. The Sacred Kural. 2nd. ed. Orig. Title: The Tamil Veda of Tiruvalluvar. 159p. pap. 2.80 (ISBN 0-88253-386-X). Ind-US Inc.

Prabhavananda, Swami. Vedic Religion & Philosophy. 3.95 (ISBN 0-87481-411-1). Vedanta Pr.

Satyavrata, Siddhantalankar. Glimpses of the Vedas. 140p. 1980. 9.95 (ISBN 0-940500-12-4, Pub. by Milind Pubns India). Asia Bk Corp.

Shastri, J. L. The Vedas of Raja Rammohan Rai. rev. ed. 1977. 7.95 (ISBN 0-89684-335-1). Orient Bk Dist.

Staal, J. F. Nambudiri Veda Recitation. (Disputationes Rheno-Trajectinae: No. 5). (Illus.). pap. 13.60 (ISBN 90-2790-031-0). Mouton.

Zysk, Kenneth G. Religious Healing in the Veda. LC 84-45899. (Transaction Ser.: Vol. 75 Pt. 7). 300p. 1986. 30.00 (ISBN 0-87169-757-2). Am Philos.

VEDAS RIGVEDA

Aurobindo, Sri. Hymns to the Mystic Fire. Aurobindo, Sri, tr. Date not set. 18.00 (ISBN 0-89744-918-5). Auromere.

Blair, Chauncey J. Heat in the Rig Veda & Atharva Veda. (American Oriental Ser.: Vol. 45). 1961. 8.00x (ISBN 0-940490-45-5). Am Orient Soc.

De Nicolas, Antonio T. Meditations Through the Rg Veda: Four-Dimensional Man. LC 76-39692. 1976. 12.95 (ISBN 0-89254-004-4). Nicolas-Hays.

Griffith, R. T. The Hymns of the Rigveda. rev. ed. 1976. 39.95 (ISBN 0-8426-0592-4). Orient Bk Dist.

Griswold, H. D. Religion of the Rigveda. 1971. 8.50 (ISBN 0-89684-305-X). Orient Bk Dist.

Horowitz, Franklin E. Sievers' Law & the Evidence of the Rigveda. LC 73-81807. (Janua Linguarum, Ser. Practica: No. 216). 74p. (Orig.). 1974. pap. text ed. 18.00x (ISBN 90-2792-706-5). Mouton.

Johnson, Willard, Jr. Poetry & Speculation of the Rg Veda. LC 80-14040. (Hermaneutics: Studies in the History of Religions). 175p. 1980. 25.95x (ISBN 0-520-02560-1). U of Cal Pr.

Keith, Arthur, ed. Rigveda Brahmanas. lib. bdg. 100.00 (ISBN 0-87968-440-2). Krishna Pr.

Mueller, Friedrich M. Rig-Veda-Samhita: The Sacred Hymns of the Brahmans, 4 vols. 2nd ed. LC 73-18831. 1892. Set. 176.00 (ISBN 0-404-11461-X); Vol. 1. (ISBN 0-404-11462-8); Vol. 2. (ISBN 0-404-11463-6); Vol. 3. (ISBN 0-404-11464-4); Vol. 4. (ISBN 0-404-11465-2). AMS Pr.

O'Flaherty, Wendy. Rig Veda. (Pengiun Classic Ser.). 1982. pap. 5.95 (ISBN 0-14-044402-5). Penguin.

Ogibenin, B. L. Structure d'un Mythe Vedique: Le Mythe Cosmogonique dans le Rgveda. (Approaches to Semiotics: No. 30). 1973. 27.20x (ISBN 0-686-21821-3). Mouton.

Pandit, M. P., ed. Gems from the Veda. Aurobindo, Sri, tr. 102p. 1974. 3.95 (ISBN 0-89744-104-4, Pub. by Ganesh & Co. India). Auromere.

Srinivasan, Doris. Concept of Cow in the Rig Veda. 1979. 9.95 (ISBN 0-89684-060-3, Pub. by Motilal Banarsidass India). Orient Bk Dist.

Wilson, H. H. The Rig-Veda Sanhita, 7 vols. Incl. Vol. I. 348p. Repr. of 1850 ed (ISBN 0-89684-125-1); Vol. II. 346p. Repr. of 1854 ed (ISBN 0-89684-126-X); Vol. III. 249p. Repr. of 1857 ed (ISBN 0-89684-127-8); Vol. IV. 179p. Repr. of 1857 ed (ISBN 0-89684-128-6); Vol. V. 314p. Repr. of 1866 ed (ISBN 0-89684-129-4); Vol VI. 443p. Repr. of 1888 ed (ISBN 0-89684-130-8); Vol. VII. 436p. Repr. of 1888 ed (ISBN 0-89684-131-6). 1977. 120.00 set (ISBN 0-686-77518-X, Pub. by Cosmo Pubns India). Orient Bk Dist.

VEDIC CIVILIZATION

see Civilization, Hindu

VEDIC LITERATURE

Alphonso-Karkala, John B., ed. Vedic Vision. 80p. 1980. pap. 4.50 (ISBN 0-86578-004-8). Ind-US Inc.

Atma: Contemporary Vedic Library Series Based on the Teachings of A. C. Bhaktivedanta Swami Prabhupada. 1.50 (ISBN 0-89213-122-5). Bhaktivedanta.

Bhaktivedanta, Swami Prabhupada A. C. Srimad-Bhagavatam: Tenth Canto, Vol. 3. (Illus.). 112p. 1980. 12.95 (ISBN 0-89213-107-1). Bhaktivedanta.

Das Gosvami, Satsvarupa. Readings in Vedic Literature. 1985. 7.95 (ISBN 0-912776-88-9). Bhaktivedanta.

Devasthali, G., ed. Glimpses of Veda & Vyakarana. 1985. 26.00x (ISBN 0-8364-1408-X, Pub. by Popular Prakashan). South Asia Bks.

Origins: Contemporary Vedic Library Series Based on the Teachings of A. C. Bhaktivedanta Swami Prabhupada. 1.50 (ISBN 0-89213-137-3). Bhaktivedanta.

Powell, James N. Mandalas: The Dynamics of Vedic Symbolism. Ghai, S. K., ed. 127p. 1980. 9.95 (ISBN 0-914794-36-1). Wisdom Garden.

Rocher, Ludo, ed. Ezourvedam: A French Veda of the Eighteenth Century. LC 84-6308. (University of Pennsylvania Studies on Southeast Asia: No. 1). 250p. 1984. 34.00x (ISBN 0-915027-05-4); pap. 16.00 (ISBN 0-915027-06-2). Benjamins North Am.

Saini, Uma A. Valdika Mantras with Transliteration & Translation. LC 85-52267. (Sanskrit.). 288p. 1986. text ed. 19.00 (ISBN 0-9616357-0-3). U & K Pub.

VEDIC MYTHOLOGY

see Mythology, Hindu

VEGETARIANISM

Berman, Louis A. Vegetarianism & the Jewish Tradition. LC 81-11729. 120p. 1982. 10.00x (ISBN 0-87068-756-5); pap. 7.95. Ktav.

Carson, Gerald. Cornflake Crusade. LC 75-39240. (Getting & Spending: the Consumer's Dilemma). (Illus.). 1976. Repr. of 1957 ed. 25.50x (ISBN 0-405-08013-1). Ayer Co Pubs.

VEGETARIANISM–RELIGIOUS ASPECTS

Berman, Louis A. Vegetarianism & the Jewish Tradition. LC 81-11729. 120p. 1982. 10.00x (ISBN 0-87068-756-5); pap. 7.95. Ktav.

Kapleau, Roshi P. To Cherish All Life: A Buddhist View of Animal Slaughter & Meat Eating. LC 81-51149. (Illus., Orig.). 1981. pap. text ed. 4.25 (ISBN 0-940306-00-X). Zen Ctr.

Micah Publications Editors, et al. Haggadah for the Liberated Lamb. LC 84-43165. (Illus.). 96p. (Orig.). 1985. pap. 8.95 (ISBN 0-916288-19-6). Micah Pubns.

Muccie, Frank J., Jr. Jesus Was a Vegetarian. 62p. pap. 1.95 (ISBN 0-938520-03-2). Edenite.

Rosen, Steven. Food for the Spirit: Vegetarianism & the World Religions. Greene, Joshua M., ed. (Illus.). 144p. (Orig.). 1987. 9.95 (ISBN 0-89647-022-9); pap. 6.95 (ISBN 0-89647-021-0). Bala Bks.

VENERATION OF SAINTS

see Saints–Cultus

VENEZUELA–CHURCH HISTORY

Walters, M. History of the Church in Venezuela. 1976. lib. bdg. 59.95 (ISBN 0-8490-1991-5). Gordon Pr.

Watters, Mary. History of the Church in Venezuela, 1810-1930. LC 70-137303. Repr. of 1933 ed. 22.00 (ISBN 0-404-06877-4). AMS Pr.

VERMIGLI, PIETRO MARTIRE, 1500-1562

McLelland, Joseph C. The Visible Words of God: An Exposition of the Sacramental Theology of Peter Martry Vermigli A.D. 1500-1562. LC 58-9551. 1957. text ed. 17.50x (ISBN 0-8401-1515-6). A R Allenson.

McLelland, Joseph C., ed. Peter Martyr Vermigli & Italian Reform. 155p. 1980. text ed. 17.95x (ISBN 0-88920-092-0, Pub. by Wilfrid Laurier Canada). Humanities.

VESTMENTS

see Church Vestments

VIANNEY, JEAN BAPTISTE MARIE, SAINT, 1786-1859

Trochu, Francis. The Cure D'Ars. LC 79-112487. (Eng.). 1977. pap. 15.00 (ISBN 0-89555-020-2). TAN Bks Pubs.

VICELINUS, SAINT, BP. OF OLDENBURG, d. 1154

Helmold Priest Of Bosau. Chronicle of the Slavs. Tschan, Francis J., tr. 1967. lib. bdg. 29.00x (ISBN 0-374-98018-7, Octagon). Hippocrene Bks.

VILLAGE CHURCHES

see Rural Churches

VILLAINAGE

see Villeinage

VILLEINAGE

Vinogradoff, Paul. Villainage in England: Essays in English Medieval History. 1968. Repr. of 1892 ed. 9.00x (ISBN 0-403-00048-3). Scholarly.

VIMALAKIRTINIRDESA-SUTRA

O'Neil, Kevin, ed. The Sutra Spoken by Vimilakirti. pap. 6.00 (ISBN 0-86627-009-4). Crises Res Pr.

VINCENT, JOHN HEYL, BP., 1832-1920

Vincent, Leon H. John Heyl Vincent: A Biographical Sketch. facs. ed. LC 71-124263. (Select Bibliographies Reprint Ser). 1925. 18.00 (ISBN 0-8369-5451-3). Ayer Co Pubs.

VIOLENCE–MORAL AND RELIGIOUS ASPECTS

see also War and Religion

A Christian Response to Domestic Violence: A Reconciliation Model for Social Workers. (Practice Monograph Ser.). 50p. 6.00 (ISBN 0-318-17617-3). N American Assn.

Cotta, Sergio. Why Violence? A Philosophical Interpretation. Gullace, Giovanni, tr. from Ital. LC 84-25779. Orig. Title: Perche la violenza? Una Interpretazione Filosofica. xiv, 150p. 1985. pap. 12.00 (ISBN 0-8130-0824-7). U Presses Fla.

Durland, William R. No King But Caesar? LC 74-30093. (Christian Peace Shelf Ser.). 184p. 1975. o. p. 6.95 (ISBN 0-8361-1757-3); pap. 4.95 (ISBN 0-8361-1927-4). Herald Pr.

Fields, Rona M. Northern Ireland: Society under Siege. LC 80-80316. 267p. 1980. pap. 5.95 (ISBN 0-87855-806-3). Transaction Bks.

Harris, John. Violence & Responsibility. 1980. 20.00x (ISBN 0-7100-0448-6). Methuen Inc.

Hertzog, Ed. Sex & Violence under God. LC 81-84292. 212p. 1982. 12.00 (ISBN 0-937894-02-8); pap. 7.00 (ISBN 0-937894-03-6). Life Arts.

Jewett, Robert. The Captain America Complex. LC 82-73362. 220p. (Orig.). 1984. pap. 4.95 (ISBN 0-939680-15-7). Bear & Co.

McFadden, Thomas M., ed. Liberation, Revolution & Freedom-Theological Perspectives: Proceedings of the College Theology Society. 222p. 1984. pap. text ed. 13.00 (ISBN 0-8191-4021-X). U Pr of Amer.

Merton, Thomas. Faith & Violence: Christian Teaching & Christian Practice. 1968. pap. 6.95 (ISBN 0-268-00094-8). U of Notre Dame Pr.

Newman, Graeme R. Understanding Violence. 1979. pap. text ed. 15.50 scp (ISBN 0-397-47396-6, HarpC). Har-Row.

Sider, Ronald J. Christ & Violence. LC 79-9239. (Christian Peace Shelf Ser.). 104p. 1979. pap. 4.95 (ISBN 0-8361-1895-2). Herald Pr.

Tournier, Paul. The Violence Within. 2nd ed. LC 78-3139. 208p. 1982. pap. 6.95 (ISBN 0-06-068295-7, RD376, HarpR). Har-Row.

VIRGIN BIRTH

see also Immaculate Conception; Mary, Virgin

Campenhausen, Hans Von. Virgin Birth in the Theology of the Ancient Church. LC 64-55217. (Studies in Historical Theology: No. 2). 1964. pap. 10.00x (ISBN 0-8401-0322-0). A R Allenson.

Carus, Paul, ed. Virgil's Prophecy on the Saviour's Birth. 97p. 1918. 2.95 (ISBN 0-317-40414-8). Open Court.

Custance, Arthur C. The Virgin Birth & the Incarnation, Vol. 5. 1976. 12.95 (ISBN 0-310-22990-1). Zondervan.

Gromacki, Robert G. The Virgin Birth of Christ. 200p. 1981. pap. 5.95 (ISBN 0-8010-3765-4). Baker Bk.

Lawlor, George. Almah: Virgin or Young Woman? LC 73-76072. 1973. pap. 1.50 (ISBN 0-87227-036-X). Reg Baptist.

Machen, J. Gresham. Virgin Birth of Christ. 427p. 1958. Repr. of 1930 ed. 13.95 (ISBN 0-227-67630-0). Attic Pr.

--Virgin Birth of Christ. (Twin Brooks Ser). 1967. pap. 10.95 (ISBN 0-8010-5885-6). Baker Bk.

Stevens, Clifford. The Blessed Virgin. LC 84-60745. 160p. 1985. pap. 6.95 (ISBN 0-87973-704-2, 704). Our Sunday Visitor.

Stewart, Frances T. & Stewart, Charles P. The Birth of Jesus. (Stick & Learn Book Ser.). (Orig.). 1985. pap. 6.95 (ISBN 0-8054-4171-9). Broadman.

Stott, John R. The Authentic Jesus. LC 85-23831. 96p. 1986. pap. 2.95 (ISBN 0-87784-619-7). Inter-Varsity.

Zodhiates, Spiros. The Perfect Gift. (Illus.). 1973. pap. 1.75 (ISBN 0-89957-511-0). AMG Pubs.

VIRGIN MARY

see Mary, Virgin

VIRGINIA–GENEALOGY

Bell, James P. Our Quaker Friends of Ye Olden Time. LC 76-22486. (Illus.). 287p. 1976. Repr. of 1905 ed. 17.50 (ISBN 0-8063-0732-3). Genealog Pub.

Meade, William. Old Churches, Ministers & Families of Virginia, 2 vols. Bd. with Digested Index & Genealogical Guide. Wise, Jennings C. Repr. of 1910 ed. LC 65-28854. 1100p. 1978. Repr. of 1857 ed. Set. 50.00 (ISBN 0-8063-0238-0). Genealog Pub.

Moore, J. Staunton. The Annals & History of Henrico Parish, Diocese of Virginia, & St. John's P. E. Church. LC 78-72949. (Illus.). 578p. 1979. Repr. of 1904 ed. 25.00 (ISBN 0-8063-0829-X). Genealog Pub.

Smith, George M. Hebron Church Register 1750-1825, Madison, Virginia, 2 vols. 1981. pap. 13.00 set (ISBN 0-917968-08-5). Shenandoah Hist.

Stewart, John & Wust, Klaus. Davidsburg Church Baptisms 1785-1845 New Market, Virginia. Stewart, John, tr. from Virginia German. 44p. 1983. pap. 6.75 (ISBN 0-917968-10-7). Shenandoah Hist.

Wust, Klaus. Record of Hawksbill Church 1788-1850, Page County, Virginia. 1979. pap. 5.50 (ISBN 0-917968-06-9). Shenandoah Hist.

Wust, Klaus, ed. Lutheran Zion-Pine Church Record, 1786-1827-Stony Creek, Virginia, Vol. I & II. Martin, Ilse & Smith, George M., trs. from Ger. (Shenandoah Genealogical Source Bks.: Nos. 8 & 9). (Illus.). 1985. pap. 15.00 set (ISBN 0-917968-13-1). Vol. I, 49p. Vol. II, 44p. Shenandoah Hist.

VIRGINIA–HISTORY–COLONIAL PERIOD, ca. 1600-1775

Crowson, Elmer T. Life As Revealed Through Early American Court Records, Including the Story of Col. John Custis of Arlington, Queen's Creek & Williamsburg. (Illus.). 1981. 20.00 (ISBN 0-89308-146-9). Southern Hist Pr.

Davis, Vernon P. & Rawlings, James S. The Colonial Churches of Virginia, Maryland, & North Carolina. 1985. pap. 25.00 (ISBN 0-87517-057-9). Dietz.

Duvall, Lindsay O. James City County, Virginia 1634-1659, Vol. 4. (Virginia Colonial Abstracts, Series II). 1979. Repr. of 1957 ed. 20.00 (ISBN 0-89308-065-9). Southern Hist Pr.

--Northumberland County, Virginia 1678-1713, Vol. 1. (Virginia Colonial Abstracts, Series II). 160p. 1979. pap. 20.00 (ISBN 0-89308-062-4). Southern Hist Pr.

--Prince George County, Virginia, Vol. 6. (Virginia Colonial Abstracts, Series II). 80p. 1978. pap. 20.00 (ISBN 0-89308-067-5). Southern Hist Pr.

Meade, William. Old Churches, Ministers & Families of Virginia, 2 vols. Bd. with Digested Index & Genealogical Guide. Wise, Jennings C. Repr. of 1910 ed. LC 65-28854. 1100p. 1978. Repr. of 1857 ed. Set. 50.00 (ISBN 0-8063-0238-0). Genealog Pub.

VIRGINIA–RELIGION

Bell, Landon C. Charles Parish, York County, Virginia: History & Registers -- Births, 1648-1789; Deaths 1665-1787. LC 33-27865. vi, 285p. 1984. Repr. of 1932 ed. 12.50 (ISBN 0-88490-114-9). VA State Lib.

Berman, Myron. Richmond's Jewry, Seventeen Sixty-Nine to Nineteen Seventy-Six. LC 78-6377. 438p. 1979. 20.00x (ISBN 0-8139-0743-8). U Pr of Va.

Chamberlane, C. G., ed. The Vestry Book of Petsworth Parish, Glouster County, Virginia, 1670-1793. LC 79-13640. xv, 429p. 1979. Repr. of 1933 ed. 10.00 (ISBN 0-88490-032-0). VA State Lib.

Chamberlayne, C. G. The Vestry Book & Register of St. Peter's Parish, New Kent & James City Counties, Virginia, 1684-1786. xxvi, 840p. 1973. Repr. of 1937 ed. 12.50 (ISBN 0-88490-037-1). VA State Lib.

Chamberlayne, C. G., ed. The Vestry Book of Blisland (Blissland) Parish, New Kent & James City Counties, Virginia, 1721-1786. LC 79-16401. ixii, 277p. 1979. Repr. of 1935 ed. 10.00 (ISBN 0-88490-030-4). VA State Lib.

--The Vestry Book of St. Paul's Parish, Hanover County, Virginia, 1706-1786. xx, 672p. 1973. Repr. of 1940 ed. 12.50 (ISBN 0-88490-038-X). VA State Lib.

Chamberlyne, C. G., ed. The Vestry Book of Stratton Major Parish, King & Queen County, Virginia, 1729-1783. LC 80-14672. xxi, 257p. 1980. Repr. of 1933 ed. 10.00 (ISBN 0-88490-087-8). VA State Lib.

Cocke, Charles F. Parish Lines, Diocese of Southern Virginia. (Virginia State Library Publications: No. 22). 287p. 1979. Repr. of 1964 ed. 5.00 (ISBN 0-88490-049-5). VA State Lib.

--Parish Lines, Diocese of Southwestern Virginia. (Virginia State Library Publications: No. 14). 196p. 1980. Repr. of 1960 ed. 5.00 (ISBN 0-686-74611-2). VA State Lib.

--Parish Lines, Diocese of Virginia. LC 78-19035. (Virginia State Library Publications: No. 28). xv, 321p. 1978. Repr. of 1967 ed. 5.00 (ISBN 0-88490-062-2). VA State Lib.

Eckenrode, Hamilton J. Separation of Church & State in Virginia. LC 75-122164. (Civil Liberties in American History Ser). 1971. Repr. of 1910 ed. lib. bdg. 22.50 (ISBN 0-306-71969-X). Da Capo.

Givens, Lula P. Christiansburg Montgomery County, Virginia in the Heart of the Alleghenies. LC 80-68026. (Illus.). 256p. 1981. 12.00 (ISBN 0-9614765-1-6). Pat G Johnson.

Graham, James R. The Planting of the Presbyterian Church in Northern Virginia Prior to the Organization of Winchester Presbytery, December Fourth, Seventeen Ninenty Four. LC 26-22114. 168p. 1904. 15.00x (ISBN 0-685-65067-7). Va Bk.

Hall, Wilmer L., ed. The Vestry Book of the Upper Parish, Nansemond County, Virginia, 1793-1943. LC 50-9492. ixxiv, 328p. 1949. 10.00 (ISBN 0-88490-039-8). VA State Lib.

James, Charles F. Documentary History of the Struggle for Religious Liberty in Virginia. LC 70-121101. (Civil Liberties in American History Ser). 1971. Repr. of 1900 ed. lib. bdg. 37.50 (ISBN 0-306-71977-0). Da Capo.

McIlwaine, H. R. The Struggle of Protestant Dissenters for Religious Toleration in Virginia. pap. 9.00 (ISBN 0-384-34893-9). Johnson Repr.

McIlwaine, Henry R. The Struggle of Protestant Dissenters for Religious Toleration in Virginia. LC 78-63830. (Johns Hopkins University. Studies in the Social Sciences. Twelfth Ser. 1894: 4). Repr. of 1894 ed. 11.50 (ISBN 0-404-61090-0). AMS Pr.

Moore, J. Staunton. The Annals & History of Henrico Parish, Diocese of Virginia, & St. John's P. E. Church. LC 78-72949. (Illus.). 578p. 1979. Repr. of 1904 ed. 25.00 (ISBN 0-8063-0829-X). Genealog Pub.

VIRGINITY

see also Celibacy

Ford, J. Massingberd. Trilogy on Wisdom & Celibacy. 1967. 16.95x (ISBN 0-268-00285-1). U of Notre Dame Pr.

VIRTUE AND VIRTUES

see also Ethics; Sins

also specific virtues, e.g. Charity, Kindness

Alberione, James. Living Our Commitment. 1968. 4.00 (ISBN 0-8198-4411-X); pap. 3.00 (ISBN 0-8198-4412-8). Dghtrs St Paul.

Alberione, Rev. James. Growing in Perfect Union. 1964. 3.00 (ISBN 0-8198-3019-4); pap. 2.00 (ISBN 0-8198-3020-8). Dghtrs St Paul.

Barnes, Barnabe. Foure Bookes of Offices: Enabling Privat Persons for the Service of All Good Princes & Policies. LC 74-28830. (English Experience Ser.: No. 712). 1975. Repr. of 1606 ed. 24.00 (ISBN 9-0221-0712-4). Walter J Johnson.

Brennan, Sr. M. Rose. Intellectual Virtues According to the Philosophy of St. Thomas. (Orig.). 1957. pap. text ed. 4.95x (ISBN 0-87015-075-8). Pacific Bks.

Campbell, Keith. A Stoic Philosophy of Life. LC 86-13351. 216p. (Orig.). 1986. lib. bdg. 22.50 (ISBN 0-8191-5529-2); pap. text ed. 12.25 (ISBN 0-8191-5530-6). U Pr of Amer.

Capps, Donald. Deadly Sins & Saving Virtues. LC 85-45912. 176p. 1987. pap. text ed. 10.95 (ISBN 0-8006-1948-X, 1-1948). Fortress.

Cooper, A. A. An Inquiry Concerning Virtue, or Merit. Walford, D. E., ed. 152p. 1977. 23.00 (ISBN 0-7190-0657-0, Pub. by Manchester Univ Pr). Longwood Pub Group.

Crossin, John W. What Are They Saying about Virtue. (WATSA Ser.). pap. 4.95 (ISBN 0-8091-2674-5). Paulist Pr.

Dent, N. J. The Moral Psychology of the Virtues. LC 83-26208. (Cambridge Studies in Philosophy). 240p. 1984. 37.50 (ISBN 0-521-25726-3). Cambridge U Pr.

Edwards, Jonathan. Nature of True Virtue. 1960. pap. 5.95 (ISBN 0-472-06037-6, 37, AA). U of Mich Pr.

Hutcheson, Francis. Inquiry into the Original of Our Ideas of Beauty & Virture. 4th ed. 1986. lib. bdg. 20.00X (ISBN 0-935005-22-6); pap. text ed. 12.50X (ISBN 0-935005-33-1). Ibis Pub VA.

Kant, Immanuel. The Doctrine of Virtue: Metaphysic of Morals, Pt. II. (Works in Contin. Philos. Ser.). 1971. 10.95x (ISBN 0-8122-1025-5). U of Pa Pr.

King, William. An Essay on the Origin of Evil. Bd. with Dissertations Concerning the Fundamental Principle & Immediate Criterion of Virtue. LC 75-11228. (British Philosophers & Theologians of the 17th & 18th Centuries Ser.). 391p. 1978. lib. bdg. 51.00 (ISBN 0-8240-1782-X). Garland Pub.

Kruschwitz & Roberts. Virtues: Contemporary Essay of Moral Character. King, Ken, ed. (Orig.). 1986. write for info. (ISBN 0-534-06720-4). Wadsworth Pub.

Lowery, Daniel L. Growth Through Virtue. 64p. 1984. pap. 1.50 (ISBN 0-89243-222-5). Liguori Pubns.

Meilaender, Gilbert C. The Theory & Practice of Virtue. LC 83-40598. 202p. 1985. pap. text ed. 8.95 (ISBN 0-268-01858-8, 85-18581). U of Notre Dame Pr.

Palmour, Jody. On Moral Character: A Practical Guide to Aristotle's Virtues & Vices. 350p. (Orig.). 1986. 29.00 (ISBN 0-9616203-1-5); pap. 18.00 (ISBN 0-9616203-0-7). Archon Inst Leader Dev.

Pieper, Josef. Four Cardinal Virtues. 1966. pap. 5.95 (ISBN 0-268-00103-0). U of Notre Dame Pr.

St. Thomas Aquinas. Treatise on the Virtues. Oesterle, John A., tr. LC 84-10691. 171p. 1984. pap. text ed. 7.95 (ISBN 0-268-01855-3, 85-18557). U of Notre Dame Pr.

Shoemaker, Stephen H. The Jekyll & Hyde Syndrome. (Orig.). 1987. text ed. 9.95 (ISBN 0-8054-1538-6). Broadman.

Wallace, James D. Virtues & Vices. LC 77-90912. (Contemporary Philosophy Ser.). 208p. 1986. pap. 7.95x (ISBN 0-8014-9372-2). Cornell U Pr.

Webb, Lance. How Good are your Virtues? 176p. (Orig.). 1983. pap. 3.95 (ISBN 0-687-17528-3, Festival). Abingdon.

Weinstein, Michael A. Finite Perfection: Reflections on Virtue. LC 84-16215. 176p. 1985. lib. bdg. 22.50x (ISBN 0-87023-474-9); pap. 9.95 (ISBN 0-87023-475-7). U of Mass Pr.

Winward, Stephen F. Fruit of the Spirit. 208p. (Orig.). 1984. pap. 4.95 (ISBN 0-8028-0003-3). Eerdmans.

VISHNU

Jolly, J. The Institutes of Vishnu. lib. bdg. 79.95 (ISBN 0-87968-528-X). Krishna Pr.

Krishna, Nanditha. The Art & Iconography of Vishnu-Narayana. (Illus.). xiv, 122p. 1981. text ed. 45.00x (ISBN 0-86590-025-6, Pub. by Taraporevala India). Apt Bks.

Prabhavananda, Swami. Bhagavatam, Srimad: The Wisdom of God. 1978. Repr. of 1943 ed. 5.95 (ISBN 0-87481-483-9). Vedanta Pr.

VISION, BEATIFIC

see Beatific Vision

VISIONS

see also Apparitions; Fantasy; Theophanies

AE, pseud. Candle of Vision. LC 73-17195. 1974. pap. 2.25 (ISBN 0-8356-0445-4, Quest). Theos Pub Hse.

Brown, Vinson. Voices of Earth & Sky. LC 76-41761. (Illus.). 177p. 1976. pap. 6.95 (ISBN 0-87961-060-3). Naturegraph.

DeArteaga, William. Past Life Visions: A Christian Exploration. 256p. 1983. pap. 9.95 (ISBN 0-8164-2414-4, HarpR). Har-Row.

Eshleman, Clayton. Visions of the Fathers of Lascaux. 44p. (Orig.). 1983. pap. 5.00 (ISBN 0-915572-70-2). Panjandrum.

Hall, Manly P. Visions & Metaphysical Experiences. pap. 2.50 (ISBN 0-89314-378-2). Philos Res.

Huxley, Aldous. Doors of Perception. Bd. with Heaven & Hell. pap. 5.95 (ISBN 0-06-090007-5, CN7, PL). Har-Row.

--Doors of Perception. 1970. pap. 3.95 (ISBN 0-06-080171-9, P171, PL). Har-Row.

Rawlings, Maurice. Beyond Death's Door. 1979. pap. 3.50 (ISBN 0-553-25204-6). Bantam.

Wedgeworth, Ann. Magnificent Strangers. LC 78-67446. 128p. 1979. pap. 1.95 (ISBN 0-88243-568-X, 02-0568, Radiant Bks). Gospel Pub.

Wilkerson, David. Vision. (Orig.). 1984. pap. 2.95. Jove Pubns.

VISITATIONS (CHURCH WORK)

Churches Alive, Inc. Staff. Visitation Evangelism Leader's Guide. rev. ed. LC 84-73068. (Illus.). 112p. 1985. pap. text ed. 11.95 (ISBN 0-934396-40-X). Churches Alive.

--Visitation Evangelism Member's Notebook. rev. ed. (Illus.). 80p. 1985. pap. text ed. 9.95 (ISBN 0-934396-39-6). Churches Alive.

Erickson, K. Please, Lord, Untie My Tongue. LC 12-2816. 1983. pap. 2.50 (ISBN 0-570-03881-2). Concordia.

Flynn, Johanna & Canfield, Anita. Visiting Teaching: A Call to Serve. 80p. (Orig.). 1984. pap. 3.95 (ISBN 0-934126-42-9). Randall Bk Co.

Koehler, George E. Visiting Two-by-Two: Visitor's Guide. LC 86-70579. 72p. (Orig.). 1986. 2.95 (ISBN 0-88177-034-5, DR034B). Discipleship Res.

Lindsay, Gordon. Visitation: Key to Church Growth. 1.25 (ISBN 0-89985-119-3). Christ Nations.

Shockey, Richard W. Training for Hospital Visitation: A Three-Week Course for Laypersons. LC 86-42930. 40p. (Orig.). 1986. pap. 4.00 (ISBN 0-937021-01-6). Sagamore Bks MI.

Southard, Samuel. Training Church Members for Pastoral Care. 96p. 1982. pap. 4.95 (ISBN 0-8170-0944-2). Judson.

VISITATIONS, ECCLESIASTICAL

London - St. Paul'S Cathedral. Visitations of Churches Belonging to St. Paul's Cathedral in 1297 & 1458. Repr. of 1895 ed. 27.00 (ISBN 0-384-33490-3). Johnson Repr.

Norwich England Diocese. Visitations of the Diocese of Norwich, A. D. 1492-1532. Jessopp, A., ed. Repr. of 1888 ed. 30.00 (ISBN 0-384-41985-2). Johnson Repr.

Sisemore, J. T. Practiquemos la Visitacion. Gonzalez, Ananias, ed. Grijalva, Josue, tr. Orig. Title: The Ministry of Visitation. 1981. Repr. of 1979 ed. 2.50 (ISBN 0-311-11034-7). Casa Bautista.

Southwell Cathedral. Visitations & Memorials of Southwell Minister. Leach, Arthur F., ed. Repr. of 1891 ed. 27.00 (ISBN 0-384-56770-3). Johnson Repr.

VITAL RECORDS

see Registers of Births, Deaths, Marriages, Etc.

VIVEKANANDA, SWAMI, 1863-1902

Burke, Marie L. Swami Vivekananda: His Second Visit to the West (New Discoveries) 20.00 (ISBN 0-87481-151-1). Vedanta Pr.

--Swami Vivekananda in the West: New Discoveries, Vol. II. (Illus.). 457p. 1985. 12.95x (ISBN 0-87481-219-4, Pub. by Advaita Ashrama India). Vedanta Pr.

Eastern & Western Disciples of Vivekananda. The Life of Swami Vivekananda, 2 Vols. rev. ed. Vol. 1, 1980, 629p. 12.95x (ISBN 0-87481-196-1); Vol. 2. 16.00x (ISBN 0-87481-197-X). Vedanta Pr.

Nikhilananda, Swami. Vivekananda: A Biography. LC 53-7851. 364p. 5.95 (ISBN 0-911206-08-6). Ramakrishna.

Nivedita, Sr. Master As I Saw Him. 6.95 (ISBN 0-87481-088-4). Vedanta Pr.

Ray, Irene R. & Gupta, Mallika C. Story of Vivekananda. (Illus.). 1971. pap. 3.00 (ISBN 0-87481-125-2). Vedanta Pr.

Rolland, Romain. Life of Vivekananda. 1987. 7.95 (ISBN 0-87481-090-6, Pub. by Advaita Ashrama). Vedanta Pr.

--La Vie de Ramakrishna. 1978. 16.95 (ISBN 0-686-55279-2). French & Eur.

--La Vie de Vivekananda. 352p. 1978. 16.95 (ISBN 0-686-55280-6). French & Eur.

Sarma, D. S. The Master & the Disciple. pap. 1.00 (ISBN 0-87481-466-9). Vedanta Pr.

Swami Nikhilananda, compiled by. Vivekananda: The Yogas & Other Works. LC 53-7534. (Illus.). 1018p. includes biography 19.95 (ISBN 0-911206-04-3). Ramakrishna.

Swami Vivekananda. Vivekananda: A Biography in Pictures. 2nd ed. Advaita Ashrama Staff, ed. (Illus.). 1974. 30.00x (ISBN 0-87481-136-8). Vedanta Pr.

Vivekananda, Swami. Inspired Talks. pap. 5.50 (ISBN 0-87481-455-3). Vedanta Pr.

VOCAL MUSIC, SACRED

see Sacred Vocal Music

VOCATION

see also Work (Theology)

Beardslee, William A. Human Achievement & Divine Vocation in the Message of Paul. LC 61-4760. (Studies in Biblical Theology: No. 31). 1961. pap. 10.00x (ISBN 0-8401-3031-7). A R Allenson.

Lockhart, Earl G., compiled by. My Vocation, by Eminent Americans; or, What Eminent Americans Think of Their Callings. LC 72-5602. (Essay Index Reprint Ser.). 1972. Repr. of 1938 ed. 32.00 (ISBN 0-8369-2997-7). Ayer Co Pubs.

Rossman, Peter & Noyce, Gaylord. Helping People Care on the Job. 144p. 1985. pap. 5.95. Judson.

VOCATION (IN RELIGIOUS ORDERS, CONGREGATIONS, ETC.)

see also Clergy–Appointment, Call and Election

Butler, Richard O. Religious Vocation: An Unnecessary Mystery. LC 78-14365. 1979. Repr. of 1961 ed. lib. bdg. cancelled (ISBN 0-313-21018-7, BURV). Greenwood.

Byers, David, ed. Vocations & Church Leadership. 96p. (Orig.). 1986. pap. 5.95 (ISBN 1-55586-108-3). US Catholic.

Canals, Salvatore. Jesus As Friend. 117p. (Orig.). 1979. pap. 6.95 (ISBN 0-906127-11-4, Pub. by Four Courts Pr Ireland). Scepter Pubs.

Challenge of Vocation & Ministry. 5.95 (ISBN 0-8215-9874-0). Sadlier.

Doig, Desmond. Mother Teresa: Her Work & Her People. LC 75-39857. (Illus.). 176p. 1980. pap. 11.95 (ISBN 0-06-061941-4, RD336, HarpR). Har-Row.

Fichter, Joseph H. Religion As an Occupation. (Orig.). 1966. pap. 3.95x (ISBN 0-268-00229-0). U of Notre Dame Pr.

Godin, Andre. The Psychology of Religious Vocations: Problems of the Religious Life. Wauck, LeRoy A., ed. LC 82-24708. 136p. (Orig.). 1983. lib. bdg. 24.00 (ISBN 0-8191-3007-9); pap. text ed. 9.50 (ISBN 0-8191-3008-7). U Pr of Amer.

Herr, Vincent V., et al. Screening Candidates for the Priesthood & Religious Life. (Illus.). 1964. 2.80 (ISBN 0-8294-0038-9). Loyola.

National Conference of Religious Vocation Directors. Ministries for the Lord: A Resource Guide & Directory of Catholic Church Vocations for Men, 1985. 128p. (Orig.). 1985. pap. 4.95 (ISBN 0-8091-2724-5). Paulist Pr.
Rulla, Luigi M. Entering & Leaving Vocation: Intrapsychic Dynamics. 1976. 20.00 (ISBN 88-7652-407-X). Loyola.

VOCATION, ECCLESIASTICAL
see also Missionaries–Appointment, Call, and Election; Vocation (In Religious Orders, Congregations, etc.)
The Gift of the Redemption. 55p. 1984. pap. 3.95 (ISBN 1-55586-925-4). US Catholic.
Guidelines for Diocesan Vocation Offices: May 1983. 2nd ed. 48p. 1983. pap. 5.50 (ISBN 1-55586-868-1). US Catholic.
Hoge, Dean R., et al. Research on Men's Vocations to the Priesthood & the Religious Life. 104p. 1984. pap. 6.50 (ISBN 1-55586-904-1). US Catholic.
Laborers for the Vineyard: Proceedings of a Conference on Church Vocations. 180p. 1984. pap. 7.50 (ISBN 1-55586-908-4). US Catholic.
Rossman, Peter & Noyce, Gaylord. Helping People Care on the Job. 144p. 1985. pap. 5.95. Judson.

VOCATION, RELIGIOUS
see Vocation (In Religious Orders, Congregations, etc.)

VOCATIONAL GUIDANCE–RELIGIOUS ASPECTS
see Vocation

VOLITION
see Will

VOLTAIRE, FRANCOIS MARIE AROUET DE, 1694-1778
Schwartzbach, B. E. Voltaire's Old Testament Criticism. 275p. (Orig.). 1970. pap. text ed. 24.00x (Pub. by Droz Switzerland). Coronet Bks.
Trapnell, William H. Christ & His Associates in Voltairian Polemic: An Assault on the Trinity and the Two Natures. (Stanford French & Italian Studies: Vol. 26). vi, 268p. 1982. pap. 25.00 (ISBN 0-915838-13-3). Anma Libri.
Waterman, Mina. Voltaire, Pascal & Human Destiny. LC 70-120676. 1970. Repr. lib. bdg. 14.50x (ISBN 0-374-98279-1, Octagon). Hippocrene Bks.

VOLUNTARISM
Prelinger, Catherine M. Charity, Challenge, & Change: Religious Dimensions of the Mid-Nineteenth Century Women's Movement in Germany. LC 86-19432. (Contributions in Women's Studies Ser.: No. 75). 225p. 1987. lib. bdg. 29.95 (ISBN 0-313-25401-X, PCY). Greenwood.
Senter, Mark, III. The Art of Recruiting Volunteers. 96p. 1983. pap. 9.95 (ISBN 0-88207-297-8). Victor Bks.
Wilson, Marlene. How to Mobilize Church Volunteers. LC 83-70506. 160p. (Orig.). 1983. pap. 8.95 (ISBN 0-8066-2012-9, 10-3175). Augsburg.
Yeager, Robert J. Volunteers. (How to Ser.). 28p. 1986. 5.65 (ISBN 0-318-20573-4). Natl Cath Educ.

VOODOOISM
Blagrove, Luanna C. Voodoo Lost Arts & Sciences. abr. ed. 250p. 1987. 25.95 (ISBN 0-939776-22-7); text ed. 24.95. Blagrove Pubns.
Campbell, Allan. Ten Sails in the Sunrise. 200p. 1986. 14.95 (ISBN 0-317-39595-5). C I L Inc.
Christesen, Barbara. The Magic & Meaning of Voodoo. LC 77-12781. (Myth, Magic & Superstition Ser.). 1977. PLB 14.65 (ISBN 0-8172-1030-X). Raintree Pubs.
Courlander, Harold & Bastien, Remy. Religion & Politics in Haiti. LC 66-26633. (Illus.). 1970. 3.95 (ISBN 0-911976-00-0). ICR.
Davis, Wade. The Serpent & the Rainbow: A Harvard Scientist Uncovers the Startling Truth about the Secret World of Haitian Voodoo & Zombis. 384p. (Orig.). 1987. pap. 4.95 (ISBN 0-446-34387-0). Warner Bks.
Denning, Melita & Phillips, Osborne. Voudoun Fire: The Living Reality of the Mystical Religions. LC 79-3375. (Mystery Religions Series: No. 1). (Illus.). 172p. (Orig.). 1979. pap. 9.95 (ISBN 0-87542-699-9). Llewellyn Pubns.
Gover, Robert. Voodoo Contra. LC 84-52293. 128p. (Orig.). 1985. pap. 6.95 (ISBN 0-87728-619-1). Weiser.
Mars, Louis B. Crisis of Possession in Voodoo. Collins, Kathleen, tr. LC 76-51943. 1977. 10.00 (ISBN 0-918408-07-5); pap. 4.95 (ISBN 0-918408-00-8). Reed & Cannon.
Metraux, Alfred. Voodoo in Haiti. LC 77-185327. (Illus.). 1972. pap. 8.95 (ISBN 0-8052-0341-9). Schocken.
Owen, Mary A. Voodoo Tales As Told among the Negroes of the Southwest. facs. ed. LC 70-149874. (Black Heritage Library Collection). (Illus.). 1893. 17.00 (ISBN 0-8369-8754-3). Ayer Co Pubs.
--Voodoo Tales, As Told among the Negroes of the Southwest. LC 78-78773. (Illus.). Repr. of 1893 ed. cancelled (ISBN 0-8371-1395-4). Greenwood.
Puckett, Newbell N. Folk Beliefs of the Southern Negro. LC 68-55780. (Criminology, Law Enforcement, & Social Problems Ser.: No. 22). (Illus.). 1968. Repr. of 1926 ed. 18.00x (ISBN 0-87585-022-7). Patterson Smith.
Rigaud, Milo. Secrets of Voodoo. Cross, Robert B., tr. from Fr. (Illus.). 256p. 1985. pap. 7.95 (ISBN 0-87286-171-6). City Lights.
Smith, Austine. Haiti Is Waiting. 78p. 1985. pap. 3.50 (ISBN 0-88144-035-3). Christian Pub.
Tallant, Robert. Voodoo in New Orleans. 248p. 1983. pap. 3.50 (ISBN 0-88289-336-X). Pelican.
--The Voodoo Queen. 314p. 1983. pap. 3.50 (ISBN 0-88289-332-7). Pelican.
Williams, Joseph J. Voodoos & Obeahs. LC 74-11170. 1970. Repr. of 1932 ed. 23.00 (ISBN 0-404-06986-X). AMS Pr.

VOTIVE OFFERINGS
see also Vows
Eash, John E. Bring an Offering. 1985. pap. 1.95 (ISBN 0-317-38498-8). Brethren.
Rouse, William H. Greek Votive Offerings: An Essay in the History of Greek Religion. facsimile ed. LC 75-10654. (Ancient Religion & Mythology Ser.). (Illus.). 1976. Repr. of 1902 ed. 36.50x (ISBN 0-405-07262-7). Ayer Co Pubs.

VOWS
see also Oaths
Ridick, Joyce. Treasures in Earthen Vessels: The Vows, a Wholistic Approach. LC 84-2817. 166p. 1984. pap. 9.95 (ISBN 0-8189-0467-4). Alba.

W

WACH, JOACHIM, 1898-1955
Flasche, Rainer. Die Religionswissenschaft Joachim Wachs. (Theologische Bibliothek Toeelmann: Vol. 35). 1978. 35.20x (ISBN 3-11-007238-6). De Gruyter.
Wach, Joachim. Understanding & Believing: Essays. Kitagawa, Joseph M., ed. LC 75-31987. 204p. 1976. Repr. of 1968 ed. lib. bdg. 25.00x (ISBN 0-8371-8488-6, WAUB). Greenwood.
Wood, Charles M. Theory & Religious Understanding: A Critique of the Hermeneutics of Joachim Wach. LC 75-26839. (American Academy of Religion. Dissertation Ser.). 1975. pap. 9.95 (ISBN 0-89130-026-0, 010112). Scholars Pr GA.

WALA, SAINT, ABBOT OF CORBIE, d. 836
Cabaniss, Allen, ed. Charlemagne's Cousins: Contemporary Lives of Adalard & Wala. LC 67-26919. 1967. 14.95x (ISBN 0-8156-2115-9). Syracuse U Pr.

WALDENSES
Cameron, Euan. The Reformation of the Heretics: The Waldenses of the Alps, 1480-1580. (Oxford Historical Monographs). (Illus.). 291p. 1984. 48.00x (ISBN 0-19-822930-5). Oxford U Pr.
Comba, Emilio. History of the Waldenses of Italy: From Their Origin to the Reformation. LC 77-84713. Repr. of 1889 ed. 41.00 (ISBN 0-404-16119-7). AMS Pr.
Doellinger, Johann J. Beitraege Zur Sektengenchichte des Mittelalter, 2 vols in 1. LC 91-26634. (Social Science Ser). (Ger). 1970. Repr. of 1890 ed. Set. lib. bdg. 57.50 (ISBN 0-8337-0880-5). B Franklin.
Jones, William. The History of the Waldenses, 2 vols. 2nd enl. ed. LC 78-63186. (Heresies of the Early Christian & Medieval Era: Second Ser.). Repr. of 1816 ed. 125.00 set (ISBN 0-404-16080-8). AMS Pr.
Lacoste, Auguste. Henri Arnaud und die Waldenser. (Basler und Berner Studien zur historischen und systematischen: Vol. 47). 213p. 1982. 20.00 (ISBN 3-261-04890-5). P Lang Pubs.
Melia, Pius. The Origin, Persecutions, & Doctrines of the Waldenses from Documents: Many Now for the First Time Collected & Edited. LC 77-84716. Repr. of 1870 ed. 27.50 (ISBN 0-404-16122-7). AMS Pr.
Monastier, Antoine. A History of the Vaudois Church from Its Origin & of the Vaudois of Piedmont to the Present Day. LC 80-24096. (Heresies of the Early Christian & Medieval Era: Second Ser.). Repr. of 1849 ed. 45.00 (ISBN 0-404-16554-0). AMS Pr.
Muston, Alexis. The Israel of the Alps: A Complete History of the Waldenses & Their Colonies, 2 vols. Montgomery, John, tr. LC 77-84718. Repr. of 1875 ed. 84.50 set (ISBN 0-404-16140-5). AMS Pr.

WALES–CHURCH HISTORY
Bell, Philip. Disestablishment in Ireland & Wales. LC 73-488607. (Church Historical Society Ser.: No. 90). 1969. pap. 21.50x (ISBN 0-8401-5090-3). A R Allenson.
Bowen, E. G. Dewi Sant. Saint David-Patron Saint of Wales. (St. David's Day Bilingual). 90p. 1983. pap. text ed. 6.95x (ISBN 0-7083-0839-2, Pub. by U of Wales). Humanities.
Brooke, Christopher. The Church & the Welsh Border in the Central Middle Ages. Dunville, D. N. & Brooke, C. N., eds. (Studies in Celtic History). 1986. 40.00 (ISBN 0-85115-175-2, Pub. by Boydell & Bower). Longwood Pub Group.
Clarke, M. L. Bangor Cathedral. 125p. 1969. text ed. 6.95x (ISBN 0-900768-23-1, Pub. by U of Wales Pr). Humanities.
Cowley, F. G. The Monastic Order in South Wales: 1066-1349. (Studies in Welsh History: No. 1). 325p. 1977. text ed. 32.50x (ISBN 0-7083-0648-9, Pub. by U of Wales Pr). Humanities.
Doble, G. H. Lives of the Welsh Saints. Evans, D. Simon, ed. 258p. 1984. text ed. 15.00x (ISBN 0-7083-0870-8, Pub. by U of Wales). Humanities.
Evans, G. Nesta. Religion & Politics in Mid-Eighteenth Century Anglesey. 251p. 1953. text ed. 17.50x (ISBN 0-7083-0071-5, Pub. by U of Wales). Humanities.
Hughes, Glyn T. Williams Pantycelyn. (Writer of Wales Ser.). 180p. 1983. pap. text ed. 8.50x (ISBN 0-7083-0840-6, Pub. by U of Wales). Humanities.
Hutton, Ronald. The Restoration: A Political & Religious History of England & Wales 1658-1667. (Illus.). 379p. 1985. 29.95x (ISBN 0-19-822698-5). Oxford U Pr.
Jenkins, G. H. Literature, Religion & Society in Wales: 1660-1730. (Studies in Welsh History: Vol. 2). 357p. 1980. text ed. 32.50x (ISBN 0-7083-0669-1, Pub. by U of Wales). Humanities.
Thomas, D. Aneurin. The Welsh Elizabethan Catholic Martyrs. 351p. 1971. text ed. 28.50 (ISBN 0-900768-97-5, Pub. by U of Wales). Humanities.
Williams, Glanmor. The Welsh Church from Conquest to Reformation. 612p. 1976. text ed. 28.50x (ISBN 0-7083-0651-9, Pub. by U of Wales). Humanities.

WALES–RELIGION
Williams, Glanmor. Religion & Welsh Literature in the Age of the Reformation. (Sir John Rhys Memorial Lectures in Celtic Studies). 1985. pap. 4.25 (ISBN 0-85672-497-1, Pub. by British Acad). Longwood Pub Group.

WALL DECORATION
see Mural Painting and Decoration

WALL PAINTING
see Mural Painting and Decoration

WALLOONS
Moens, William J. The Walloons & Their Church at Norwich: Their History & Registers, 1565-1832, 2 pts. in 1 vol. (Hugenot Society of London Publications Ser.: Vol. 1). Repr. of 1887 ed. 30.00 (ISBN 0-8115-1642-3). Kraus Repr.

WALTHER, CARL FERDINAND WILHELM, 1811-1887
Spitz, Lewis W., Sr. Life of Doctor C. F. W. Walther. (Illus.). 1961. 3.95 (ISBN 0-570-03247-4, 15-1246). Concordia.
Walther, C. F. Convention Essays. Seuflow, August R., tr. (Selected Writings of C. F. W. Walther Ser.). 1981. 12.95 (ISBN 0-570-08277-3, 15-2735). Concordia.
--Editorials from Lehre und Wehre. Bouman, Herbert J., tr. (Selected Writings of C. F. W. Walther Ser.). 1981. 12.95 (ISBN 0-570-08280-3, 15-2738). Concordia.
--Selected Sermons. Bouman, Herbert J., tr. (Selected Writings of C. F. W. Walther Ser.). 1981. 12.95 (ISBN 0-570-08276-5, 15-2734). Concordia.
--Walther on the Church. Dreckamer, John M., tr. (Selected Writings of C. F. W. Walther Ser.). 1981. 12.95 (ISBN 0-570-08278-1, 15-2736). Concordia.

WANDERING JEW
Hasan-Rokem, Galit & Dundes, Alan, eds. The Wandering Jew: Essays in the Interpretation of a Christian Legend. LC 84-48248. (Illus.). 288p. 1986. 27.50x (ISBN 0-253-36340-3). Ind U Pr.
Viereck, George S. & Eldridge, Paul. My First Two Thousand Years. 1984. Repr. 25.00 (ISBN 0-911378-16-2). Sheridan.

WAR–MORAL ASPECTS
see War and Morals; War and Religion

WAR AND CHRISTIANITY
see War and Religion

WAR AND MORALS
see also War and Religion
Childress, James F. Moral Responsibility in Conflicts: Essays on Nonviolence, War, & Conscience. LC 82-15197. 224p. 1982. text ed. 25.00x (ISBN 0-8071-1019-1). La State U Pr.
Eller, Vernard. War & Peace from Genesis to Revelation. LC 80-26280. (Christian Peace Shelf Ser.). 232p. 1981. pap. 9.95 (ISBN 0-8361-1947-9). Herald Pr.
Gara, Larry. War Resistance in Historical Perspective. 1983. pap. 2.50x (ISBN 0-87574-171-1, 171). Pendle Hill.
Hartigan, Richard S. The Forgotten Victim: A History of the Civilian. 173p. 1982. 16.95x (ISBN 0-913750-19-0). Transaction Bks.
Hauerwas, Stanley. Should War Be Eliminated? Philosophical & Theological Investigations. LC 84-60236. (Pere Marquette Lecture Ser.). 75p. 1984. 7.95 (ISBN 0-87462-539-4). Marquette.
Lansbury, George. My Pilgrimage for Peace. Bd. with Peace Through Economic Cooperation. Lansbury, George. LC 70-147723. (Library of War & Peace; Peace Leaders: Biographies & Memoirs). 1972. lib. bdg. 46.00 (ISBN 0-8240-0251-2). Garland Pub.
McFadden, Thomas M., ed. Liberation, Revolution & Freedom-Theological Perspectives: Proceedings of the College Theology Society. 222p. 1984. pap. text ed. 13.00 (ISBN 0-8191-4021-X). U Pr of Amer.
Mandeville, Bernard. Enquiry into the Origin of Honour & the Usefullness of Christianity in War. 240p. 1971. Repr. of 1732 ed. 32.50x (ISBN 0-7146-2314-8, F Cass Co). Biblio Dist.
Matty, Thomas. Peace & Conscience Formation. (Faith & Justice Issues Ser.). (Illus.). 68p. (Orig.). 1983. tchr's ed. 14.95 (ISBN 0-88489-147-X). St Mary's.
Van Praagh, Richard. Survival: A New Approach from the Life Sciences to the Major Problem of Our Time. LC 85-80038. 208p. (Orig.). 1985. pap. 7.95 (ISBN 0-941404-35-8). Falcon Pr Az.

WAR AND RELIGION
see also Jihad; Nonviolence; Pacifism; War and Morals
also subdivision Religious Aspects under specific wars, e.g. World War, 1939-1945–Religious Aspects
Aho, James A. Religious Mythology & the Art of War: Comparative Religious Symbolisms of Military Violence. LC 80-23465. (Contributions to the Study of Religion Ser.: No. 3). 264p. 1981. lib. bdg. 29.95 (ISBN 0-313-22564-8, ARM/). Greenwood.
Bainton, Roland H. Christian Attitudes Toward War & Peace. LC 60-12064. 1979. pap. 7.95 (ISBN 0-687-07027-9). Abingdon.
Ballou, Adin. Christian Non-Resistance. LC 70-121104. (Civil Liberties in American History Ser). 1970. Repr. of 1910 ed. lib. bdg. 35.00 (ISBN 0-306-71980-0). Da Capo.
Boettner, Loraine. The Christian Attitude Toward War. 104p. 1986. pap. 3.95 (ISBN 0-87552-118-5). Presby & Reformed.
Bowman, Rufus D. Church of the Brethren & the War, 1788-1914. LC 75-147667. (Library of War & Peace; Relig. & Ethical Positions on War). 1972. 46.00 (ISBN 0-8240-0425-6). Garland Pub.
Cadoux, C. John. The Early Christian Attitude Toward War. 69.95 (ISBN 0-87968-198-5). Gordon Pr.
Cesaretti, Charles A. & Vitale, Joseph T., eds. Rumors of War: A Moral & Theological Perspective on the Arms Race. 128p. (Orig.). 1982. pap. 6.95 (ISBN 0-8164-2365-2, HarpR). Har-Row.
Coues, Elliott. War & Christianity. 250.00 (ISBN 0-8490-1276-7). Gordon Pr.
Croke, B. F. & Harris, J. D. Religious Conflict in Fourth Century Rome. (Sources in Ancient History Ser.). 139p. (Orig.). 1982. pap. 21.00x (ISBN 0-424-00091-1, Pub. by Sydney U Pr Australia). Intl Spec Bk.
Dodge, David L. War Inconsistent with the Religion of Jesus Christ. LC 75-137540. (Peace Movement in America Ser). xxiv, 168p. 1972. Repr. of 1905 ed. lib. bdg. 15.95x (ISBN 0-89198-067-9). Ozer.
Dumezil, Georges. The Destiny of the Warrior. Hiltebeitel, Alf, tr. LC 75-113254. 184p. 1971. pap. write for info. (ISBN 0-226-16971-5). U of Chicago Pr.
Dymond, Jonathan. Inquiry into the Accordancy of War with the Principles of Christianity. LC 79-147432. (Library of War & Peace; Proposals for Peace: a History). 1973. lib. bdg. 46.00 (ISBN 0-8240-0222-9). Garland Pub.
Ferguson, John. War & Peace in the World's Religions. 1978. pap. 5.95 (ISBN 0-19-520074-8). Oxford U Pr.
Grant, Christian P. The Syrian Desert. LC 78-63341. (The Crusades & Military Orders: Second Ser.). (Illus.). Repr. of 1937 ed. 41.00 (ISBN 0-404-17017-X). AMS Pr.
Grimke, Thomas S. Address on the Truth, Dignity, Power & Beauty of the Principles of Peace, & on the Unchristian Character & Influence of War & the Warrior. LC 72-137542. (Peace Movement in America Ser). 56p. 1972. Repr. of 1832 ed. lib. bdg. 11.95x (ISBN 0-89198-070-9). Ozer.

Hatchell, L. F. Apocalypse: World War III, Vol. I. (Illus.). 160p. 1980. pap. 3.95x (ISBN 0-940532-02-6). AOG.
Hauerwas, Stanley. Should War Be Eliminated? Philosophical & Theological Investigations. LC 84-60236. (Pere Marquette Lecture Ser.). 75p. 1984. 7.95 (ISBN 0-87462-539-4). Marquette.
Heering, Gerrit J. Fall of Christianity. LC 77-147670. (Library of War & Peace; Relig. & Ethical Positions on War). 1973. lib. bdg. 46.00 (ISBN 0-8240-0428-0). Garland Pub.
Hirst, Margaret E. Quakers in Peace & War. LC 70-147671. (Library of War & Peace; Relig. & Ethical Positions on War Ser.). lib. bdg. 46.00 (ISBN 0-8240-0429-9). Garland Pub.
Holmes, Arthur F. War & Christian Ethics. LC 75-14602. pap. 13.95 (ISBN 0-8010-4170-8). Baker Bk.
Horsch, John. Principle of Non-Resistance As Held by the Mennonite Church. Bd. with Hutterian Brethren, Fifteen Twenty-Eight to Nineteen Thirty-One. Horsch, John. LC 74-147672. (Library of War & Peace; Relig. & Ethical Positions on War). lib. bdg. 46.00 (ISBN 0-8240-0430-2). Garland Pub.
Hoyt, Herman A., et al. War: Four Christian Views. Clouse, Robert G., ed. 216p. (Orig.). 1981. pap. 5.95 (ISBN 0-88469-097-0). BMH Bks.
Lasserre, Jean. War & the Gospel. (Christian Peace Shelf Ser.). 243p. 1962. 12.95 (ISBN 0-8361-1475-2). Herald Pr.
McFadden, Thomas M., ed. Liberation, Revolution & Freedom-Theological Perspectives: Proceedings of the College Theology Society. 222p. 1984. pap. text ed. 13.00 (ISBN 0-8191-4021-X). U Pr of Amer.
Mandeville, Bernard. Enquiry into the Origin of Honour & the Usefullness of Christianity in War. 240p. 1971. Repr. of 1732 ed. 32.50x (ISBN 0-7146-2314-8, F Cass Co). Biblio Dist.
Muste, A. J. Non-Violence in an Aggressive World. LC 76-137551. (Peace Movement in America Ser). 220p. 1972. Repr. of 1940 ed. lib. bdg. 15.95x (ISBN 0-89198-081-4). Ozer.
Nelson, John O. The Christian Conscience & War. 47p. 1950. pap. 1.00 (ISBN 0-8361-1547-3). Herald Pr.
Oliverus. The Capture of Damietta. Gavigan, John J., tr. LC 78-63353. (The Crusades & Military Orders: Second Ser.). Repr. of 1948 ed. 17.50 (ISBN 0-404-17026-9). AMS Pr.
On War, Abortion & the Homeless. (Sermon Ser.: No. 1). 18p. 1982. pap. 2.00 (ISBN 0-936384-10-7). Cowley Pubns.
Potter, Ralph B. War & Moral Discourse. LC 69-18111. (Orig.). 1969. pap. 3.95 (ISBN 0-8042-0863-8). John Knox.
Quigley, Thomas E., ed. American Catholics & Vietnam. LC 68-54102. pap. 49.30 (ISBN 0-317-07878-X, 2012814). Bks Demand UMI.
Ramsey, Paul. War & the Christian Conscience: How Shall Modern War Be Conducted Justly? LC 61-10666. xxiv, 331p. 1985. pap. 9.95 (ISBN 0-8223-0361-2). Duke.
--War & the Christian Conscience: How Shall Modern War be Conducted Justly? LC 61-10666. pap. 88.30 (ISBN 0-317-26099-5, 2023766). Bks Demand UMI.
Raven, Charles E. War & the Christian. LC 75-147675. (Library of War & Peace; Relig. & Ethical Positions on War). 1972. lib. bdg. 46.00 (ISBN 0-8240-0432-9). Garland Pub.
Scully, Michael. The Best of This World. 416p. (Orig.). 1987. lib. bdg. 32.50 (ISBN 0-8191-5605-1, Pub. by IEA); pap. text ed. 19.75 (ISBN 0-8191-5606-X). U Pr of Amer.
Shattuck, Gardiner H., Jr. A Shield & Hiding Place: The Religious Life of the Civil War Armies. (Illus.). 192p. 1987. 24.95 (ISBN 0-86554-273-2, H236). Mercer Univ Pr.
Swaim, J. Carter. War, Peace & the Bible. LC 81-16889. 144p. (Orig.). 1982. pap. 3.48 (ISBN 0-88344-752-5). Orbis Bks.
Thielicke, Helmut. Man in God's World. Doberstein, J. W., tr. from Ger. 224p. 1978. Repr. 13.95 (ISBN 0-227-67709-9). Attic Pr.
--The Prayer That Spans the World. Doberstein, J. W., tr. from Ger. 160p. 1978. Repr. 13.95 (ISBN 0-227-67671-8). Attic Pr.
Topping, Peter W., tr. Feudal Institutions As Revealed in the Assizes of Romania. LC 80-13052. (The Crusades & Military Orders: Second Ser.). Repr. of 1949 ed. 23.50 (ISBN 0-404-17023-4). AMS Pr.
Weigel, George. The Peace Bishops & the Arms Race: Can Religious Leadership Help in Preventing War? 54p. 1982. 2.00 (ISBN 0-318-18653-5). World Without War.
Wells, Ronald A. Wars of America: Christian Views. 280p. (Orig.). 1981. pap. 9.95 (ISBN 0-8028-1899-4). Eerdmans.
Willmott, A. A Christian Approach to National Defense. rev. ed. 122p. 1986. pap. 20.00X (ISBN 0-7223-1968-1, Pub. by A H Stockwell England). State Mutual Bk.
Yinger, Milton J. Religion in the Struggle for Power: A Study in the Sociological Study of Religion. Zuckerman, Harriet & Merton, Robert K., eds. LC 79-9040. (Dissertations in Sociology Ser.). 1980. Repr. of 1946 ed. lib. bdg. 26.50x (ISBN 0-405-13007-4). Ayer Co Pubs.
Yoder, John H. The Original Revolution. LC 76-181577. (Christian Peace Shelf Ser.). 208p. 1972. pap. 6.95 (ISBN 0-8361-1812-X). Herald Pr.
--When War Is Unjust: Being Honest in Just-War Thinking. LC 84-2859. 96p. (Orig.). 1984. pap. 5.95 (ISBN 0-8066-2077-3, 10-7084). Augsburg.

WAR AND RELIGION–BIBLIOGRAPHY
Harnack, Adolf. Militia Christi: The Christian Religion & the Military in the First Three Centuries. Gracie, David M., tr. from Ger. LC 81-43089. Tr. of Militia Christi: Die christliche Religion und der Soldatenstand in den ersten drei Jahrhunderten. 112p. 1981. 3.00 (ISBN 0-8006-0673-6, 1-673). Fortress.
Potter, Ralph B. War & Moral Discourse. LC 69-18111. (Orig.). 1969. pap. 3.95 (ISBN 0-8042-0863-8). John Knox.

WARD, WILLIAM GEORGE, 1812-1882
Ward, Wilfrid P. William George Ward & the Catholic Revival. LC 75-29626. Repr. of 1893 ed. 41.75 (ISBN 0-404-14042-4). AMS Pr.
--William George Ward & the Oxford Movement. LC 75-29625. Repr. of 1889 ed. 41.75 (ISBN 0-404-14043-2). AMS Pr.

WARSAW–HISTORY–UPRISING OF 1943
Ainsztein, Reuben. Warsaw Ghetto Revolt. LC 78-71295. (Illus.). 1979. pap. 10.95 (ISBN 0-8052-5007-7, Pub. by Holocaust Library). Schocken.
Goldstein, Charles. Bunker. Malkin, Esther, tr. from Fr. LC 74-116978. (Temple Bks). 1973. pap. 3.95 (ISBN 0-689-70347-3, T27). Atheneum.
Gutman, Yisrael. The Jews of Warsaw, 1939-1943: Ghetto, Underground, Revolt. Friedman, Ina, tr. LC 81-47570. (Illus.). 512p. 1982. 24.95x (ISBN 0-253-33174-9). Ind U Pr.
Hanson, Joanna K. The Civilian Population & the Warsaw Uprising of 1944. LC 81-15545. (Illus.). 375p. 1982. 39.50 (ISBN 0-521-23421-2). Cambridge U Pr.
Hilberg, Raul & Staron, Stanislaw, eds. The Warsaw Diary of Adam Czerniakow: Prelude to Doom. 480p. Repr. 14.00 (ISBN 0-686-95101-8). ADL.
Zawodny, J. K. Nothing but Honour: The Story of the Warsaw Uprising, 1944. LC 76-51880. (Publication Ser: No. 183). (Illus.). 1978. 16.95x (ISBN 0-8179-6831-8). Hoover Inst Pr.

WASHINGTON, GEORGE, PRES. U. S., 1732-1799
Boller, Paul F., Jr. George Washington & Religion. LC 63-9755. 1963. 12.95 (ISBN 0-87074-021-0). SMU Press.

WASHINGTON, D. C.–CHURCH OF THE SAVIOR
O'Connor, Elizabeth. Call to Commitment. LC 63-10963. 224p. 1976. pap. 5.95 (ISBN 0-06-066330-8, RD131, HarpR). Har-Row.
--Journey Inward, Journey Outward. LC 75-9313. 192p. 1975. pap. 5.95 (ISBN 0-06-066332-4, RD100, HarpR). Har-Row.

WATCH TOWER BIBLE AND TRACT SOCIETY
Schnell, William J. Thirty Years a Watchtower Slave. (Direction Bks). pap. 3.95 (ISBN 0-8010-7933-0). Baker Bk.

WATER–JUVENILE LITERATURE
Mock, Dorothy. Thank You, God, for Water. (Happy Day Bks.). (Illus.). 24p. 1985. 1.59 (ISBN 0-87239-880-3, 3680). Standard Pub.

WATER (IN RELIGION, FOLK-LORE, ETC.
see also Holy Wells
Love, Bessie & Newey, Paul. Water, 4 bks. Incl. Bk. 1. Source of Life; Bk. 2. Destroyer; Bk. 3. Sustainer; Bk. 4. Transformer. (Illus., Orig.). 1974. Set. pap. 3.50x (ISBN 0-8192-4041-9); leaders guide 2.50x (ISBN 0-8192-4042-7). Morehouse.
Masani, Rustom P. Folklore of Wells. LC 77-11936. 1977. Repr. lib. bdg. 32.00 (ISBN 0-8414-6216-X). Folcroft.

WAY OF LIFE, JEWISH
see Jewish Way of Life

WAY OF THE CROSS
see Stations of the Cross

WAYNFLETE, WILLIAM OF, 1395-1486
Heylyn, Peter. Memorials of Bishop Waynflete, Founder of St. Mary Magdalen College, Oxford. Bloxam, John R., ed. 1851. 24.00 (ISBN 0-8337-0311-0). B Franklin.

WEALTH, ETHICS OF
see also Business Ethics; Christianity and Economics
Birch, Bruce C. & Rasmussen, Larry L. The Predicament of the Prosperous. LC 78-18412. (Biblical Perspectives on Current Issues). 212p. 1978. pap. 7.95 (ISBN 0-664-24211-1). Westminster.

WEBSTER, JOHN, 1580?-1625?
Courtade, Anthony E. The Structure of John Webster's Play. Hogg, James, ed. (Jacobean Drama Studies). 172p. (Orig.). 1980. pap. 15.00 (ISBN 0-317-40036-3, Salzburg Studies). Longwood Pub Group.
Goreau, Eloise K. Integrity of Life: Allegorical Imagery in the Plays of John Webster. Hogg, James, ed. (Jacobean Drama Studies). 194p. (Orig.). 1974. pap. 15.00 (ISBN 0-317-40056-8, Pub. by Salzburg Studies). Longwood Pub Group.
Griffin, Robert P. John Webster: Politics & Tragedy. Hogg, James, ed. (Jacobean Drama Studies). 179p. (Orig.). 1972. pap. 15.00 (ISBN 3-7052-0311-8, Pub. by Salzburg Studies). Longwood Pub Group.
Haworth, Peter. English Hymns & Ballads. 1927. lib. bdg. 16.50 (ISBN 0-8414-4975-9). Folcroft.
Hogg, James. Webster 'Reformed' A Study of Post-Restoration Versions of John Webster's Plays, 2 vols. (Jacobean Drama Studies). (Orig.). 1986. pap. 30.00 (ISBN 3-7052-0323-1, Pub. by Salzburg Studies). Longwood Pub Group.
Stodder, Joseph H. Moral Perspective in Webster's Major Tragedies. Hogg, James, ed. (Jacobean Drama Studies). 164p. (Orig.). 1974. pap. 15.00 (ISBN 3-7052-0343-6, Salzburg Studies). Longwood Pub Group.

WEDDING ETIQUETTE
Lewis, Kay O. The Christian Wedding Handbook. 192p. 1981. 10.95 (ISBN 0-8007-1259-5). Revell.
Our Christian Wedding Guest Book. (Illus.). 48p. 1983. padded cover 8.50 (ISBN 0-8007-1345-1). Revell.
Post, Elizabeth L. Emily Post on Weddings. LC 86-12094. (Illus.). 192p. (Orig.). 1987. pap. 2.95 (ISBN 0-06-080812-8, P 812, PL). Har-Row.
Swadley, Elizabeth. Your Christian Wedding. LC 66-15149. 1966. 8.95 (ISBN 0-8054-7902-3). Broadman.

WEDDING SERMONS
Braaten, John. Together... Till Death Us Do Part. Sherer, Michael L., ed. (Orig.). 1987. pap. 5.95 (ISBN 0-89536-852-8, 7811). CSS of Ohio.
Brill, Mordecai, et al. Write Your Own Wedding: A Personal Guide for Couples of All Faiths. rev. ed. LC 85-7156. 120p. 1985. pap. 5.95 (ISBN 0-8329-0398-1). New Century.
Roguet, A. M. Homilies for the Celebration of Marriage. Du Charme, Jerome, tr. from Fr. LC 76-53538. 1977. pap. 3.50 (ISBN 0-8199-0656-5). Franciscan Herald.

WEDDINGS
see also Marriage Customs and Rites; Marriage Service; Wedding Etiquette
Bowen, Francis A. A Bride's Guide to a Christian Wedding. LC 78-73642. (Illus.). 1979. text ed. 2.95 (ISBN 0-9602830-0-5). F A Bowen.
Diamant, Anita. The New Jewish Wedding. LC 84-24102. (Illus.). 1985. 16.95 (ISBN 0-671-49527-5). Summit Bks.
--New Jewish Wedding. 272p. 1986. 8.95 (ISBN 0-671-62882-8). Summit Bks.
Follett, Barbara L. Checklist for a Perfect Wedding. rev. & expanded ed. LC 85-29206. (Illus.). 160p. 1986. pap. 3.95 (ISBN 0-385-23588-7). Doubleday.
Homburg, Arthur. A New Wedding Service For You. 1985. 5.95 (ISBN 0-89536-731-9, 5815). CSS of Ohio.
Knight, George W. Wedding Ceremony Idea Book. 96p. 1982. pap. 7.95 (ISBN 0-939298-01-5). J M Prods.
Krause, Paul M. Planning a Christian Wedding. 1963. pap. 0.95 (ISBN 0-570-03504-X, 14-2010). Concordia.
Latner, Helen. Your Jewish Wedding. LC 83-45567. (Illus.). 224p. 1985. pap. 4.95 (ISBN 0-385-18873-0). Doubleday.
Muzzy, Ruth & Hughes, R. Kent. The Christian Wedding Planner. 320p. 1984. pap. 9.95 (ISBN 0-8423-0253-0). Tyndale.
Nehmer, Nancy L. Celebrating Our Wedding. 96p. 1987. text ed. 14.95 (ISBN 0-8423-0273-5). Tyndale.
Our Christian Wedding. (Illus.). 48p. 1982. padded cover boxed 12.95 (ISBN 0-8007-1309-5). Revell.
Peters, William J. What Your Wedding Can Be. LC 80-65402. 136p. (Orig.). 1980. pap. 2.95 (ISBN 0-87029-163-7, 20350-5). Abbey.
Szews, George R. We Will Celebrate a Church Wedding. 88p. 1983. pap. 1.50 (ISBN 0-8146-1288-1). Liturgical Pr.

WEEK-DAY CHURCH SCHOOLS
Martin, Florence. Observing National Holidays & Church Festivals: A Weekday Church School Unit in Christian Citizenship Series for Grades Three & Four. LC 76-174077. 1971. Repr. of 1940 ed. 44.00x (ISBN 0-8103-3804-1). Gale.
Peshkin, Alan. God's Choice: The Total World of a Fundamentalist Christian School. LC 85-24524. x, 350p. 1986. lib. bdg. 24.95 (ISBN 0-226-66198-9). U of Chicago Pr.

WEEK-DAY CHURCH SCHOOLS–TEXT-BOOKS
Baden, Marian. Being in God's Family. (Concordia Weekday Ser. - Gr. 3-4. Bk. 4, 2-V). 1967. pap. text ed. 2.75 (ISBN 0-570-06658-1, 22-2028); manual 5.85 (ISBN 0-686-82886-0, 22-2029). Concordia.
Noonan, Eileen. Books for Catholic Elementary Schools. pap. 2.50 (ISBN 0-87507-024-8). Cath Lib Assn.

WEEMS, MASON LOCKE, 1759-1825
Kellock, Harold. Parson Weems of the Cherry-Tree. LC 75-107137. 1971. Repr. of 1928 ed. 35.00x (ISBN 0-8103-3785-1). Gale.
Leary, Lewis. The Book-Peddling Parson: An Account of the Life & Works of Mason Locke Weems. (Illus.). 1984. 15.95 (ISBN 0-912697-09-1). Algonquin Bks.
Weems, Mason L. Mason Locke Weems, His Works & Ways, 3 vols. Skeel, Emily E., ed. LC 75-31140. Repr. of 1929 ed. 120.00 set (ISBN 0-404-13670-2). AMS Pr.
Wroth, Lawrence C. Parson Weems: A Biographical & Critical Study. LC 75-31143. Repr. of 1911 ed. 10.00 (ISBN 0-404-13615-X). AMS Pr.

WELLS, HOLY
see Holy Wells

WELSH MYTHOLOGY
see Mythology, Welsh

WERBURGA, SAINT
Bradshaw, H. Bradshaw's Life of St. Werburge of Chester. Horstmann, C., ed. (EETS, OS Ser.: No. 88). Repr. of 1887 ed. 20.00 (ISBN 0-527-00085-X). Kraus Repr.
Bradshaw, Henry. Holy Life & History of Saynt Werburg. Repr. of 1848 ed. 28.00 (ISBN 0-384-05450-1). Johnson Repr.

WESLEY, CHARLES, 1707-1788
Green, Richard. The Works of John & Charles Wesley. 2nd rev. ed. LC 74-26049. Repr. of 1906 ed. 23.00 (ISBN 0-404-12924-2). AMS Pr.
Kimbrough, S., Jr. Lost in Wonder: Charles Wesley - The Meaning of His Hymns Today. 176p. (Orig.). 1987. pap. 6.95 (ISBN 0-8358-0558-1). Upper Room.
Rogal, Samuel J. John & Charles Wesley. (English Authors Ser.: No. 368). 197p. 1983. lib. bdg. 16.95 (ISBN 0-8057-6854-8, Twayne). G K Hall.
Tyson, John R. Charles Wesley on Sanctification: A Biographical & Theological Study. 240p. 1986. pap. 10.95 (ISBN 0-310-75131-4, 17054P). Zondervan.
Whaling, Frank, ed. John & Charles Wesley: Selected Writings & Hymns. LC 81-82207. 432p. 1981. 13.95 (ISBN 0-8091-0318-4); pap. 10.95. Paulist Pr.
Wilder, Franklin. The Methodist Riots: The Testing of Charles Wesley. (Illus.). 160p. 1982. 8.95 (ISBN 0-89962-236-4). Todd & Honeywell.

WESLEY, JOHN, 1703-1791
Ayling, Stanley. John Wesley. 1983. 16.95 (ISBN 0-687-20376-7). Abingdon.
Bewes, Richard, ed. John Wesley's England: A Nineteenth Century Pictorial History Based on an 18th Century Journal. (Illus.). 128p. (Orig.). 1981. pap. 9.95 (ISBN 0-8164-2319-9, HarpR). Har-Row.
Borgen, Ole E. John Wesley on the Sacraments. 312p. 1986. pap. 12.95 (ISBN 0-310-75191-8, 17085P). Zondervan.
Brantley, Richard E. Locke, Wesley & the Method of English Romanticism. LC 83-26026. 311p. 1984. 30.00 (ISBN 0-8130-0783-6). U Presses Fla.
Cannon, William R. The Theology of John Wesley: With Special Reference to the Doctrine of Justification. 284p. 1984. pap. text ed. 12.75 (ISBN 0-8191-4001-5). U Pr of Amer.
Cell, George C. The Rediscovery of John Wesley. LC 83-6505. 438p. 1983. pap. text ed. 15.50 (ISBN 0-8191-3222-5). U Pr of Amer.
Davey, Cyril. Horseman of the King (John Wesley) 1964. pap. 2.95 (ISBN 0-87508-605-5). Chr Lit.
--John Wesley & the Methodists. 49p. (Orig.). 1986. 6.95 (ISBN 0-687-20434-8). Abingdon.
Dobree, Bonamy. John Wesley. LC 74-7428. 1973. lib. bdg. 17.50 (ISBN 0-8414-3739-4). Folcroft.
--Three Eighteenth Century Figures: Sarah Churchill, John Wesley, Giacomo Casanova. LC 80-19398. xi, 248p. 1981. Repr. of 1962 ed. lib. bdg. 25.00x (ISBN 0-313-22682-2, DOTF). Greenwood.
Green, Richard. The Works of John & Charles Wesley. 2nd rev. ed. LC 74-26049. Repr. of 1906 ed. 23.00 (ISBN 0-404-12924-2). AMS Pr.
Harper, Steve. John Wesley's Message for Today. Chapman, Ben, ed. 1983. pap. 4.95 (ISBN 0-310-45711-4, 12382P). Zondervan.
Harrison, G. E. Haworth Parsonage: Study of Wesley & the Brontes. 1937. lib. bdg. 16.50 (ISBN 0-8414-5008-0). Folcroft.

Harrison, G. Elsie. Son to Susanna: The Private Life of John Wesley. 1937. Repr. 35.00 (ISBN 0-8274-3468-5). R West.

Hartley, John E. & Shelton, R. L., eds. Salvation. (Wesleyan Theological Perspectives Ser.: Vol. I). 1981. 14.95 (ISBN 0-87162-240-8, D4850). Warner Pr.

Heitzenrater, Richard P. The Elusive Mr. Wesley: John Wesley His Own Biographer. LC 83-25882. 220p. 1984. pap. 9.75 (ISBN 0-687-11554-X); Set. pap. 19.50 (ISBN 0-687-11556-6). Abingdon.

Hillis, Newell D. Great Men As Prophets of a New Era. facs. ed. LC 68-16939. (Essay Index Reprint Ser). 1968. Repr. of 1922 ed. 15.00 (ISBN 0-8369-0541-5). Ayer Co Pubs.

John Wesley the Soul Winner. pap. 4.95 (ISBN 0-686-27010-X). Schmul Pub Co.

Knox, Robert B. James Ussher, Archbishop of Armagh: 1581-1656. 205p. 1968. text ed. 17.50x (ISBN 0-7083-0061-8, Pub. by U of Wales). Humanities.

Lee, Umphrey. Historical Backgrounds of Early Methodist Enthusiasm. LC 31-18047. (Columbia University. Studies in the Social Sciences: No. 339). Repr. of 1931 ed. 17.50 (ISBN 0-404-51339-5). AMS Pr.

Lindstrom, Harold. Wesley & Sanctification. LC 83-17025. 256p. (Orig.). 1984. 8.95 (ISBN 0-310-75011-3, 17025P). Zondervan.

Lipsky, Abram. John Wesley: A Portrait. LC 76-155619. Repr. of 1928 ed. 20.50 (ISBN 0-404-03994-4). AMS Pr.

McCown, Wayne & Massey, James, eds. God's Word for Today. (Wesleyan Theological Perspectives Ser.: Vol. II). 1982. 14.95 (ISBN 0-87162-257-2, D4851). Warner Pr.

McNeer, May & Ward, Lynd. John Wesley. 1957. pap. 3.95 (ISBN 0-687-20430-5). Abingdon.

Macphail, Andrew. Essays in Puritanism: Jonathan Edwards, John Winthrop, Margaret Fuller, Walt Whitman, John Wesley. LC 68-26205. 1969. Repr. of 1905 ed. 22.50x (ISBN 0-8046-0286-7, Pub. by Kennikat). Assoc Faculty Pr.

Miller, Basil. John Wesley. 144p. 1969. pap. 3.50 (ISBN 0-87123-272-3, 200272). Bethany Hse.

Moore, Robert L. John Wesley & Authority: A Psychological Perspective. LC 79-13709. (American Academy of Religion. Dissertation Ser.: No. 29). 1979. 14.00 (ISBN 0-89130-290-5, 010129); pap. 9.95 (ISBN 0-89130-291-3). Scholars Pr GA.

Outler, Albert, ed. John Wesley. 1964. pap. 13.95 (ISBN 0-19-502810-4). Oxford U Pr.

Outler, Albert C. The Works of John Wesley, Volume 2: Sermons II, 34-70. 600p. 1985. 49.95 (ISBN 0-687-46211-8). Abingdon.

Reddish, Robert O., Jr. John Wesley, His Way of Knowing God. 1972. soft cover 4.00 (ISBN 0-686-08730-5). Rorge Pub Co.

Rogal, Samuel J. John & Charles Wesley. (English Authors Ser.: No. 368). 197p. 1983. lib. bdg. 16.95 (ISBN 0-8057-6854-8, Twayne). G K Hall.

Rowe, Kenneth E., ed. The Place of Wesley in the Christian Tradition: Essays Delevered at Drew University in Celebration of the Commencement of the Publication of the Oxford Edition of the Works of John Wesley. LC 76-27659. 168p. 1976. 16.50 (ISBN 0-8108-0981-8). Scarecrow.

Shepherd, T. B. Methodism & the Literature of the 18th Century. LC 68-4718. (Studies in Comparative Literature, No. 35). 1969. Repr. of 1940 ed. lib. bdg. 75.00x (ISBN 0-8383-0680-2). Haskell.

Slaatte, Howard A. Fire in the Brand: An Introduction to the Creative Work & Theology of John Wesley. LC 83-16721. 158p. 1983. pap. text ed. 11.25 (ISBN 0-8191-3552-6). U Pr of Amer.

Smith, Timothy L. Whitefield & Wesley on the New Birth. 544p. 1986. pap. 7.95 (ISBN 0-310-75151-9). Zondervan.

Snell, F. J. Wesley & Methodism. 243p. 1983. Repr. of 1900 ed. lib. bdg. 43.50 (ISBN 0-8495-4977-9). Arden Lib.

Snyder, Howard. The Radical Wesley. LC 80-18197. 180p. (Orig.). 1980. pap. 5.95 (ISBN 0-87784-625-1). Inter-Varsity.

Spurgeon, C. H. The Two Wesleys. 1975. pap. 1.95 (ISBN 0-686-16834-8). Pilgrim Pubns.

Taylor, Blaine. John Wesley: A Blueprint for Church Renewal. 221p. (Orig.). 1984. pap. 10.00 (ISBN 0-914527-19-3). C-Four Res.

Thompson, D. D. John Wesley As a Social Reformer. facsimile ed. LC 70-164396. (Black Heritage Library Collection). Repr. of 1898 ed. 12.25 (ISBN 0-8369-8855-8). Ayer Co Pubs.

Tuttle, Robert G., Jr. John Wesley: His Life & Theology. 368p. 1982. pap. 9.95 (ISBN 0-310-36661-5, 11260P). Zondervan.

Tyerman, Luke. The Life & Times of the Rev. John Wesley, 3 vols. LC 72-82522. 1973. Repr. of 1872 ed. Set. lib. bdg. 89.00 (ISBN 0-8337-4710-X). B Franklin.

Vickers, John. John Wesley. (Ladybird Ser.). 1977. 2.50 (ISBN 0-87508-841-4). Chr Lit.

Vulliamy, C. E. John Wesley. (Heroes of the Faith Ser.). 359p. 1985. Repr. 6.95 (ISBN 0-916441-14-8). Barbour & Co.

Warner, Wellman J. Wesleyan Movement in the Industrial Revolution. LC 66-24768. 1967. Repr. of 1930 ed. 8.00x (ISBN 0-8462-0960-8). Russell.

Wesley, John. The Works of John Wesley: Letters I, 1721-1739, Vol. 25. Baker, Frank, ed. (Oxford Edition of the Works of John Wesley Ser.). 1980. 45.00x (ISBN 0-19-812545-3). Oxford U Pr.

--The Works of Wesley, Vol. 3 & 4: The Journal of John Wesley. 1986. Vol. 3, 496p. 24.95 (ISBN 0-310-51290-5); Vol. 4, 544p. 24.95 (ISBN 0-310-51300-6). Zondervan.

Wesley's Works, 14 vols. 125.00 set (ISBN 0-686-23581-9). Schmul Pub Co.

Wesleys World Parish. 3.50 (ISBN 0-686-27780-5). Schmul Pub Co.

Whaling, Frank, ed. John & Charles Wesley: Selected Writings & Hymns. LC 81-82207. 432p. 1981. 13.95 (ISBN 0-8091-0318-4); pap. 10.95. Paulist Pr.

Wilder, Franklin. The Remarkable World of John Wesley: Pioneer in Mental Health. (Illus.). 1978. 7.00 (ISBN 0-682-49129-2). Exposition Pr FL.

Wood, A. Skevington. The Burning Heart: John Wesley, Evangelist. LC 78-52837. 1978. pap. 7.95 (ISBN 0-87123-043-7, 210043). Bethany Hse.

The Works of John Wesley: Sermons 1-33, Vol. 1. 1008p. 1984. 49.95 (ISBN 0-687-46210-X). Abingdon.

WESLEY, SUSANNA (ANNESLEY) 1670-1742

Doughty, W. L., ed. The Prayers of Susanna Wesley. 80p. 1984. pap. 3.95 (ISBN 0-310-36351-9, 12368P, Clarion Class). Zondervan.

Harmon, Rebecca L. Susanna: Mother of the Wesleys. rev. ed. 1968. 7.50 (ISBN 0-687-40766-4). Abingdon.

Ponzani, Joe & Ponzan, Mrs. Joe. Susanna Wesley, a Study Guide. 1983. 1.75 (ISBN 0-89536-607-X, 1930). CSS of Ohio.

WESLEY FAMILY

Routley, Erik. The Musical Wesleys. LC 75-36511. (Illus.). 1976. Repr. of 1968 ed. text ed. 22.50x (ISBN 0-8371-8644-7, ROMW). Greenwood.

Spurgeon, C. H. The Two Wesleys. 1975. pap. 1.95 (ISBN 0-686-16834-8). Pilgrim Pubns.

Wright, David & Wright, Jill. Thirty Hymns of the Wesleys. 65p. 1986. pap. 4.95 (ISBN 0-85364-414-4, Pub. by Paternoster UK). Attic Pr.

WESLEYAN METHODIST CHURCH–MISSIONS

Marsden, Joshua. The Narrative of a Mission to Nova Scotia, New Brunswick & the Somers Islands. Repr. of 1816 ed. 25.00 (ISBN 0-384-35430-0). Johnson Repr.

WESLEYAN METHODIST CHURCH OF AMERICA

Gentry, Peter W. Heritage in the Warmed Heart. 63p. 1986. pap. 2.50 (ISBN 0-8341-0955-7). Beacon Hill.

Matlack, Lucius C. History of American Slavery & Methodism from 1780 to 1849. facs. ed. LC 77-138342. (Black Heritage Library Collection Ser.). 1849. 19.75 (ISBN 0-8369-8734-9). Ayer Co Pubs.

Mickey, Paul. Essentials of Wesleyan Theology: A Contemporary Affirmation. 160p. 1980. pap. 5.95 (ISBN 0-310-39151-2, 9312P). Zondervan.

Runyon, Theodore H., ed. Santification & Liberation: Liberation Theologies in Light of the Wesleyan Tradition. LC 80-20287. 1981. pap. 6.95 (ISBN 0-687-36810-3). Abingdon.

Stokes, Mack B. The Bible in the Wesleyan Heritage. LC 80-23636. 96p. (Orig.). 1981. pap. 4.95 (ISBN 0-687-03100-1). Abingdon.

WEST AND EAST

see East and West

WEST INDIES–DESCRIPTION AND TRAVEL

Bell, Henry H. Obeah: Witchcraft in the West Indies. LC 78-106879. Repr. of 1889 ed. 22.50x (ISBN 0-8371-3275-4, BEO&, Pub. by Negro U Pr). Greenwood.

Truman, George, et al. Narrative of a Visit to the West Indies: In 1840 & 1841. facsimile ed. LC 71-38027. (Black Heritage Library Collection). Repr. of 1844 ed. 15.25 (ISBN 0-8369-8993-7). Ayer Co Pubs.

Underhill, Edward B. West Indies: Their Social & Religious Condition. LC 73-107525. Repr. of 1862 ed. 24.75x (ISBN 0-8371-3772-1, UWI&). Greenwood.

WEST TOWN, CHINA

Hsu, Francis L. Religion, Science & Human Crises. LC 73-7308. (Illus.). 142p. 1973. Repr. of 1952 ed. lib. bdg. 22.50x (ISBN 0-8371-6921-6, HSRS). Greenwood.

WESTERN SCHISM

see Schism, the Great Western, 1378-1417

WESTMINSTER, ENGLAND

Cox, Montagu H. & Forrest, G. Topham. Parish of St. Margaret, Westminster: Neighbourhood of Whitehall, Vol. 1. LC 70-138272. (London County Council. Survey of London: No. 13). Repr. of 1930 ed. 74.50 (ISBN 0-404-51663-7). AMS Pr.

Cox, Montagu H., ed. The Parish of St. Margaret, Westminster. LC 70-138272. (London County Council. Survey of London: No. 10). (Illus.). Repr. of 1926 ed. 74.50 (ISBN 0-404-51660-2). AMS Pr.

WESTMINSTER ASSEMBLY OF DIVINES. CONFESSION OF FAITH

Clark, Gordon H. What Do Presbyterians Believe? 1965. pap. 6.95 (ISBN 0-87552-140-1). Presby & Reformed.

Davis, L. Edward, pref. by. The Westminster Confession of Faith: An Authentic Modern Version. rev., 2nd ed. x, 89p. (Orig.). 1985. pap. text ed. write for info. (ISBN 0-9614303-1-1). Summertown.

Rolston, Holmes, III. John Calvin Vs. the Westminster Confession. LC 75-37422. (Orig.). 1972. pap. 4.95 (ISBN 0-8042-0488-8). John Knox.

WESTMINSTER ASSEMBLY OF DIVINES. SHORTER CATECHISM

Willard, Samuel. Compleat Body of Divinity. (American Studies). Repr. of 1726 ed. 62.00 (ISBN 0-384-68533-1). Johnson Repr.

WHEELOCK, ELEAZAR, 1711-1779

M'Clure, David & Parish, Elijah. Memoirs of the Rev. Eleazar Wheelock, D. D. LC 75-38454. (Religion in America, Ser. 2). 338p. 1972. Repr. of 1811 ed. 22.00 (ISBN 0-405-04074-1). Ayer Co Pubs.

WHEWELL, WILLIAM, 1794-1866

Todhunter, Isaac. William Whewell, D.D., Master of Trinity College, Cambridge, 2 Vols. (Sources of Science Ser.: No. 92). Repr. of 1876 ed. 68.00 (ISBN 0-384-60880-9). Johnson Repr.

WHITE, ELLEN GOULD (HARMON), 1827-1915

Doukhan, Jacques. Ellen G. White & the Jews: An Interpretative Analysis of Her Writings & Their Significance for Our Time. Adar Publications, ed. LC 85-70340. 35p. (Orig.). 1985. pap. 1.75x (ISBN 0-916169-01-4). Adar Pubns.

Graham, Roy E. Ellen G. White: Co-Founder of the Seventh-Day Adventist Church. (American University Studies VII: Theology & Religion: Vol 12). 506p. 1985. text ed. 41.00 (ISBN 0-8204-0255-9). P Lang Pubs.

Noorbergen, Rene. Ellen G. White: Prophet of Destiny. LC 70-190456. 363p. 1970. text ed. 6.95 (ISBN 0-87983-014-X); pap. 2.50 (ISBN 0-87983-077-8); spanish version 1.95 (ISBN 0-87983-076-X). MMI Pr.

White, Ellen G. Christian Experience & Teaching of Ellen G. White. 1940. deluxe ed. 10.95 (ISBN 0-8163-0126-3, 03310-0). Pacific Pr Pub Assn.

WHITE, WILLIAM HALE, 1831-1913

Stone, Wilfred. Religion & Art of William Hale White (Mark Rutherford) 1979. Repr. of 1954 ed. lib. bdg. 30.00 (ISBN 0-8492-8233-0). R West.

Stone, Wilfred H. Religion & Art of William Hale White. LC 79-176447. Repr. of 1954 ed. 28.00 (ISBN 0-404-51822-2). AMS Pr.

WHITE FATHERS

Linden, Ian & Linden, Jane. Church & Revolution in Rwanda. LC 76-58329. 295p. 1977. text ed. 39.50x (ISBN 0-8419-0305-0, Africana). Holmes & Meier.

WHITE FRIARS

see Carmelites

WHITE-SLAVE TRAFFIC

see Prostitution

WHITEFIELD, GEORGE, 1714-1770

Smith, Timothy L. Whitefield & Wesley on the New Birth. 544p. 1986. pap. 7.95 (ISBN 0-310-75151-9). Zondervan.

Tracy, Joseph. Great Awakening: A History of the Revival of Religion in the Time of Edwards & Whitefield. LC 72-83444. (Religion in America Ser). 1969. Repr. of 1945 ed. 21.00 (ISBN 0-405-00280-7). Ayer Co Pubs.

Tyerman, Luke. The Life of the Rev. George Whitefield, 2 vols. LC 75-31102. Repr. of 1877 ed. 97.50 (ISBN 0-404-13540-4). AMS Pr.

Whitefield, George. George Whitefield's Journals. 1978. 18.95 (ISBN 0-85151-147-3). Banner of Truth.

--The Works of Reverend G. W, 6 vols. LC 75-31107. Repr. of 1772 ed. 230.00 set (ISBN 0-404-13530-7). AMS Pr.

Whitefield, Goerge. George Whitefield's Letters: Seventeen Thirty-Four to Seventeen Forty-Two. 1976. 16.95 (ISBN 0-85151-239-9). Banner of Truth.

WHITEHEAD, ALFRED NORTH, 1861-1947

Belaief, Lynne. Toward a Whiteheadian Ethics. LC 84-15248. 208p. (Orig.). 1985. lib. bdg. 26.00 (ISBN 0-8191-4229-8); pap. text ed. 12.75 (ISBN 0-8191-4230-1). U Pr of Amer.

Christensen, Darrel E. The Search for Concreteness-Reflections on Hegel & Whitehead: A Treatise on Self-Evidence & Critical Method in Philosophy. LC 85-63421. 516p. 1986. 45.00x (ISBN 0-941664-22-8, Pub. by Susquehanna U Pr). Assoc Univ Prs.

Christian, William A. An Interpretation of Whitehead's Metaphysics. LC 77-5619. 1977. Repr. of 1959 ed. lib. bdg. 35.00x (ISBN 0-8371-9638-8, CHIW). Greenwood.

Lambert, Jean C. The Human Action of Forgiving: A Critical Application of the Metaphysics of Alfred North Whitehead. (Illus.). 300p. (Orig.). 1985. lib. bdg. 26.00 (ISBN 0-8191-4596-3); pap. text ed. 14.50 (ISBN 0-8191-4597-1). U Pr of Amer.

Lango, John. Whitehead's Ontology. LC 78-171184. 1972. 34.50x (ISBN 0-87395-093-3). State U NY Pr.

Leclerc, Ivor. Whitehead's Metaphysics: An Introductory Exposition. LC 86-4027. 248p. 1986. pap. text ed. 11.00 (ISBN 0-8191-4852-0). U Pr of Amer.

Lowe, Victor. Alfred North Whitehead: The Man & His Work, Vol. 1: 1861-1910. LC 84-15467. 392p. 1985. 27.50 (ISBN 0-8018-2488-5). Johns Hopkins.

Lucas, George R. Two Views of Freedom in Process & Thought. LC 79-12287. (American Academy of Religion, Dissertation Ser.: No. 28). 1979. 14.00 (ISBN 0-89130-285-9, 010128); pap. 9.95 (ISBN 0-89130-304-9). Scholars Pr GA.

Nobo, Jorge L. Whitehead's Metaphysics of Extension & Solidarity. (Philosophy Ser.). 544p. (Orig.). 1986. 49.50x (ISBN 0-88706-261-X); pap. 24.50x (ISBN 0-88706-262-8). State U NY Pr.

Pols, Edward. Whitehead's Metaphysics: A Critical Examination of Process & Reality. LC 67-10721. 217p. 1967. 8.95x (ISBN 0-8093-0280-2). S Ill U Pr.

Reese, William L. & Freeman, Eugene, eds. Process & Divinity: The Hartshorne Festschrift. LC 64-13547. 644p. 1964. 32.95 (ISBN 0-87548-054-3). Open Court.

Sherburne, Donald W., ed. A Key to Whitehead's "Process & Reality". LC 81-11661. 264p. 1981. pap. 10.00x (ISBN 0-226-75293-3). U of Chicago Pr.

Wallack, F. Bradford. The Epochal Nature of Process in Whitehead's Metaphysics. LC 79-22898. 1980. 44.50x (ISBN 0-87395-404-1); pap. 16.95 (ISBN 0-87395-454-8). State U NY Pr.

Wilmot, Laurence. Whitehead & God: Prolegomena to Theological Reconstruction. 200p. 1979. text ed. 17.25x (ISBN 0-88920-070-X, Pub. by Wilfrid Laurier Canada). Humanities.

Wood, Forrest, Jr. Whiteheadian Thought as a Basis for a Philosophy of Religion. LC 86-9282. 110p. (Orig.). 1986. lib. bdg. 19.50 (ISBN 0-8191-5422-9); pap. text ed. 8.75 (ISBN 0-8191-5423-7). U Pr of Amer.

WHITTIER, JOHN GREENLEAF, 1807-1892

Hawkins, C. The Mind of Whittier: A Study of Whittier's Fundamental Religious Ideas. LC 73-6984. (American Literature Ser., No. 49). 1973. Repr. of 1904 ed. lib. bdg. 39.95x (ISBN 0-8383-1700-6). Haskell.

Rowntree, Arthur. Whittier: Crusader & Prophet. LC 73-13660. 1946. Repr. 15.00 (ISBN 0-8414-7230-0). Folcroft.

Sloane, Kennedy W. John Greenleaf Whittier: His Life, Genius & Writings. 373p. 1982. Repr. of 1903 ed. lib. bdg. 25.00 (ISBN 0-89760-432-6). Telegraph Bks.

Stevens, James S. Whittier's Use of the Bible. LC 74-13173. 1974. Repr. of 1930 ed. lib. bdg. 15.00 (ISBN 0-8414-7798-1). Folcroft.

WHOLE AND PARTS (PHILOSOPHY)

see also Holism

Arber, Agnes. Manifold & the One. 1967. pap. 1.45 (ISBN 0-8356-0018-1, Quest). Theos Pub Hse.

Vaught, Carl G. The Quest for Wholeness. LC 81-18365. 224p. 1982. 44.50 (ISBN 0-87395-593-5); pap. 14.95 (ISBN 0-87395-594-3). State U NY Pr.

WICLIFITES

see Lollards

WIDOWS

see also Remarriage; Single-Parent Family; Women

DeStefano, Patricia. Interlude of Widowhood. (Greeting Book Line Ser.). 48p. (Orig.). 1983. pap. 1.50 (ISBN 0-89622-200-4). Twenty-Third.

Durland, Frances C. Coping with Widowhood. 1979. pap. 1.50 (ISBN 0-89243-098-2). Liguori Pubns.

Jebb, Philip. Widowed. LC 83-11160. 1984. pap. 3.95 (ISBN 0-932506-30-5). St Bedes Pubns.

Nye, Miriam B. But I Never Thought He'd Die: Practical Help for Widows. LC 78-9644. 150p. 1978. pap. 7.95 (ISBN 0-664-24208-1). Westminster.

Silverman, Phyllis R. Widow-to-Widow. 240p. 1986. text ed. 19.95 (ISBN 0-8261-5030-6). Springer Pub.

WIEMAN, HENRY NELSON, 1884-1913

Rosen, Harold. Religious Education & Our Ultimate Committment: An Application of Henry Nelson Wieman's Philosophy of Creative Interchange. LC 84-19651. 196p. (Orig.). 1985. lib. bdg. 24.25 (ISBN 0-8191-4341-3, Unitarian Univ Assn); pap. text ed. 10.75 (ISBN 0-8191-4342-1, Unitarian Univ. Assn.). U Pr of Amer.

WIESEL, ELIE, 1928-

Berenbaum, Michael. The Vision of the Void: Theological Reflections on the Works of Elie Wiesel. xii, 240p. 1987. pap. 12.95 (ISBN 0-8195-6189-4). Wesleyan U Pr.

Frost, Christopher J. Religious Melancholy or Psychological Depression: Some Issues Involved in Relating Psychology & Religion As Illustrated in a Study of Elie Wiesel. 274p. (Orig.). 1985. lib. bdg. 27.75 (ISBN 0-8191-4496-7); pap. text ed. 13.50 (ISBN 0-8191-4497-5). U Pr of Amer.

Rosenfeld, Alvin H. & Greenberg, Irving, eds. Confronting the Holocaust: The Impact of Elie Wiesel. LC 78-15821. pap. 61.80 (ISBN 0-317-27853-3, 2056054). Bks Demand UMI.

WILBERFORCE, SAMUEL, BP. OF WINCHESTER, 1805-1873

Daniell, G. W. Bishop Wilberforce. 1978. Repr. of 1891 ed. lib. bdg. 20.00 (ISBN 0-8482-0607-X). Norwood Edns.

Meacham, Standish. Lord Bishop: The Life of Samuel Wilberforce, 1805-1873. LC 70-102669. 1970. 20.00x (ISBN 0-674-53913-3). Harvard U Pr.

WILBERFORCE, WILLIAM, 1759-1833

Ludwig, Charles. He Freed Britains Slaves. LC 77-9521. 208p. 1977. 7.95 (ISBN 0-8361-1822-7). Herald Pr.

Pollock, John. Wilberforce. LC 77-86525. (Illus.). 1978. 26.00x (ISBN 0-312-87942-3). St Martin.

Wilberforce, Robert I. & Wilberforce, Samuel. The Life of William Wilberforce: By His Sons, 5 vols. LC 72-5506. (Black Heritage Library Collections Ser.). 1972. Repr. of 1838 ed. Set. 121.00 (ISBN 0-8369-9151-6). Ayer Co Pubs.

WILDERNESS (THEOLOGY)

see also Asceticism

Cummings, Charles. Spirituality & the Desert Experience. 1976. cancelled (ISBN 0-87193-166-4). Dimension Bks.

Glasson, T. Francis. Moses in the Fourth Gospel. LC 63-5666. (Studies in Biblical Theology: No. 40). 1963. pap. 10.00x (ISBN 0-8401-3040-6). A R Allenson.

Nouwen, Henri J. The Way of the Heart: Desert Spirituality & Contemporary Ministry. 96p. 1981. 8.95 (ISBN 0-86683-913-5, AY7443, HarpR). Har-Row.

WILFRED, SAINT, BP. OF YORK, 634-709

Duckett, Eleanor S. Anglo-Saxon Saints & Scholars. x, 484p. 1967. Repr. of 1947 ed. 35.00 (ISBN 0-208-00200-6, Archon). Shoe String.

Stephanus, Eddius. The Life of Bishop Wilfrid. Colgrave, Bertram, ed. 207p. 1985. 37.50 (ISBN 0-521-30927-1); pap. 12.95 (ISBN 0-521-31387-2). Cambridge U Pr.

WILKINS, JOHN, BP. OF CHESTER, 1614-1672

Shapiro, Barbara J. John Wilkins, Sixteen Fourteen to Sixteen Seventy-Two: An Intellectual Biography. LC 73-84042. 1969. 40.00x (ISBN 0-520-01396-4). U of Cal Pr.

WILKINSON, JEMIMA, 1752-1819

Hudson, David. Memoir of Jemima Wilkinson, a Preacheress of the 18th Century. LC 78-134417. Repr. of 1844 ed. 23.00 (ISBN 0-404-08475-3). AMS Pr.

WILKINSON, THOMAS, 1751-1836

Dalglish, Doris N. People Called Quakers. facsimile ed. LC 78-90628. (Essay Index Reprint Ser). 1938. 15.00 (ISBN 0-8369-1254-3). Ayer Co Pubs.

WILL

see also Belief and Doubt; Free Will and Determinism; Self

Burbidge, John. Being & Will: An Essay in Philosophical Theology. LC 76-45934. pap. 40.70 (ISBN 0-8357-9484-9, 2013527). Bks Demand UMI.

Dunn, Robert. The Possibility of Weakness of Will. LC 85-24784. 192p. 1986. lib. bdg. 25.00 (ISBN 0-915145-99-5); pap. 14.50 (ISBN 0-915145-98-7). Hackett Pub.

Eilberg-Schwartz, Howard. The Human Will in Judaism: The Mishnah's Philosophy of Intention. (Brown Judaic Studies). 164p. 1986. 31.95 (ISBN 0-89130-938-1, 14-01-03). Scholars Pr GA.

Lehrer, Keith, ed. Freedom & Determinism. 204p. 1976. pap. text ed. 7.95x (ISBN 0-391-00537-5). Humanities.

WILLIAM, SAINT, 1133-1144

Dechanet, Jean M. William of St. Thierry: The Man & His Work. Strachen, Richard, tr. from Fr. LC 73-152485. (Cistercian Studies: No. 10). Tr. of Guillaume de Saint-Thierry. 192p. 1972. 10.95 (ISBN 0-87907-810-3). Cistercian Pubns.

WILLIAMS, ROGER, 1604?-1683

Easton, Emily. Roger Williams, Prophet & Pioneer. LC 76-101266. Repr. of 1930 ed. 40.00 (ISBN 0-404-02236-7). AMS Pr.

--Roger Williams, Prophet & Pioneer. LC 71-102235. (Select Bibliographies Reprint Ser). 1930. 32.00 (ISBN 0-8369-5120-4). Ayer Co Pubs.

--Roger Williams: Prophet & Pioneer. LC 78-144994. 399p. 1972. Repr. of 1930 ed. 17.00x (ISBN 0-403-00793-3). Scholarly.

Ernst, James E. Roger Williams: New England Firebrand. LC 76-90097. (BCL Ser.: I). Repr. of 1932 ed. 24.50 (ISBN 0-404-02355-X). AMS Pr.

Gilpin, W. Clark. The Millenarian Piety of Roger Williams. LC 78-20786. 1979. lib. bdg. 19.00x (ISBN 0-226-29397-1). U of Chicago Pr.

Morgan, Edmund S. Roger Williams: The Church & the State. 176p. 1987. pap. 5.95 (ISBN 0-393-30403-5). Norton.

Straus, Oscar S. Roger Williams, the Pioneer of Religious Liberty. facs. ed. LC 76-137385. (Select Bibliographies Reprint Ser). 1936. 20.00 (ISBN 0-8369-5586-2). Ayer Co Pubs.

WINDOWS, STAINED GLASS

see Glass Painting and Staining

WINTHROP, JOHN, 1588-1649

Macphail, Andrew. Essays in Puritanism: Jonathan Edwards, John Winthrop, Margaret Fuller, Walt Whitman, John Wesley. LC 68-26205. 1969. Repr. of 1905 ed. 22.50x (ISBN 0-8046-0286-7, Pub. by Kennikat). Assoc Faculty Pr.

Morgan, Edmund S. The Puritan Dilemma: The Story of John Winthrop. (Library of American Biography). 224p. 1962. pap. 8.75 (ISBN 0-316-58286-7). Little.

Wheelwright, John. John Wheelwright's Writings, Including His Fast-Day Sermon, 1637, & His Mercurius Americanus, 1645. facs. ed. LC 70-128897. (Select Bibliographies Reprint Ser). 1876. 18.00 (ISBN 0-8369-5517-X). Ayer Co Pubs.

WISDOM

Bergant, Dianne. What Are They Saying about Wisdom Literature? LC 83-82027. (WATSA Ser.). (Orig.). 1984. pap. 4.95 (ISBN 0-8091-2605-2). Paulist Pr.

Besant. Wisdom of the Upanishads. 3.50 (ISBN 0-8356-7092-9). Theos Pub Hse.

Bowen, Patrick G. The Sayings of the Ancient One. lib. bdg. 79.95 (ISBN 0-87968-490-9). Krishna Pr.

Conze, Edward. The Large Sutra on Perfect Wisdom: With the Divisions of the Abhisamayalankara. LC 71-189224. (Center for South & Southeastern Asia Studies, UC Berkeley). 697p. 1985. pap. 12.95 (ISBN 0-520-05321-4, CAL 668). U of Cal Pr.

Conze, Edward, tr. from Sanskrit. & pref. by. The Perfection of Wisdom in Eight Thousand Lines & Its Verse Summary. LC 72-76540. (Wheel Ser.: No. 1). 348p. 1973. 15.00 (ISBN 0-87704-048-6); pap. 8.95 (ISBN 0-87704-049-4). Four Seasons Foun.

De Montfort, St. Louis. Love of Eternal Wisdom. 4.95 (ISBN 0-910984-51-4); pap. 2.95 (ISBN 0-910984-05-0). Montfort Pubns.

De Purucker, G. Wind of the Spirit. 2nd, rev. ed. LC 84-50118. 328p. 1984. 10.00 (ISBN 0-911500-67-7); pap. 5.00 (ISBN 0-911500-68-5). Theos U Pr.

Eternal Wisdom. 10.00 (ISBN 0-8198-2310-4); 8.00 (ISBN 0-8198-2311-2). Dghtrs St Paul.

Hartley, Elda. Perennial Wisdom. (Chrysalis Bk). (Illus.). 80p. (Orig.). 1986. pap. 4.95 (ISBN 0-916349-09-8). Amity Hous Inc.

Hayes, Norvel. The Gift of the Word of Wisdom. 1979. pap. 0.75 (ISBN 0-89274-367-0). Harrison Hse.

Jyoti, Swami A. In Light of Wisdom. 2nd ed. LC 84-50889. 74p. 1984. handbound 13.00 (ISBN 0-933572-05-0). Truth Consciousness.

Keshavadas, Satguru S. This Is Wisdom. (Illus.). 96p. (Orig.). 1975. pap. 3.50 (ISBN 0-942508-07-6). Vishwa.

Lloyd, Helen Y. The Awakening Soul. 1984. 10.95 (ISBN 0-8062-2346-4). Carlton.

McCormick, John F. Saint Thomas & the Life of Learning. (Aquinas Lecture). 1937. 7.95 (ISBN 0-87462-101-1). Marquette.

McDonald, Kathleen. How to Meditate: A Practical Guide. Courtin, Robina, ed. (A Wisdom Basic Book, Orange Ser.). 200p. (Orig.). 1984. pap. 9.95 (ISBN 0-86171-009-6, Wisdom Pubns). Great Traditions.

Maly, Eugene H. Wisdom. (Bible Ser.). pap. 1.00 (ISBN 0-8091-5156-1). Paulist Pr.

Maritain, Jacques, et al. Wisdom: A Manifesto. 1965. pap. 1.00x (ISBN 0-87343-015-8). Magi Bks.

Nast, Seyyed H., ed. The Essential Writings of Frithjof Schuon. (A Roots of Wisdom Bk). 512p. 1986. 34.95 (ISBN 0-916349-05-5). Amity Hous Inc.

Nieman, Charles. Wisdom & Guidance. 206p. (Orig.). 1984. pap. text ed. 5.00 (ISBN 0-914307-19-3, Dist. by Harrison Hse). Word Faith.

Orbeliani, Sulkhan-Saba. The Book of Wisdom & Lies. Vivian, Katherine, tr. 1982. 14.95 (Pub. by Octagon Pr England). Ins Study Human.

Pearls of Wisdom, Nineteen Eighty-Two: Kuan Yin Opens the Door to the Golden Age, Vol. 25, Bks. I & II. LC 83-50756. (Illus.). Bk. 1, 322 pgs. 25.00 (ISBN 0-916766-58-6); Bk. 2, 476 pgs. 25.00 (ISBN 0-916766-59-4). Summit Univ.

Perry, Whitall N. A Treasury of Traditional Wisdom. 1986. pap. 19.95 (ISBN 0-317-52385-6, PL 4136, HarpR). Har-Row.

The Psychological Wisdom from the Sanskrit, 2 Vols. (Illus.). 301p. 1985. 167.85 (ISBN 0-89920-080-X). Am Inst Psych.

Rabten, Geshe. The Essential Nectar. Wilson, Martin, ed. (A Wisdom Basic Book, Orange Ser.). 304p. (Orig.). 1984. pap. 11.95 (ISBN 0-86171-013-4, Wisdom Pubns). Great Traditions.

Randall, John. Wisdom Instructs Her Children: The Power of the Spirit & the Word. 128p. (Orig.). 1981. pap. 3.95 (ISBN 0-914544-36-5). Living Flame Pr.

Schwartz, Amy. Yossel Zissel & the Wisdom of Chelm. (Illus.). 32p. 9.95 (ISBN 0-8276-0258-8). Jewish Pubns.

Sternberg, Robert J. & Wagner, Richard K., eds. Practical Intelligence: Origins of Competence in the Everyday World. (Illus.). 240p. 1986. 49.50 (ISBN 0-521-30253-6); pap. 15.95 (ISBN 0-521-31797-5). Cambridge U Pr.

Suggs, M. Jack. Wisdom, Christology, & Law in Matthew's Gospel. LC 75-95930. Repr. of 1970 ed. 36.00 (ISBN 0-8357-9185-8, 2017749). Bks Demand UMI.

Wilken, Robert L., ed. Aspects of Wisdom in Judaism & Early Christianity. LC 74-27888. (University of Notre Dame, Center for the Study of Judaism & Christianity in Antiquity: No. 1). pap. 60.00 (ISBN 0-317-26715-9, 2024365). Bks Demand UMI.

Wood, James D. Wisdom Literature: An Introduction. LC 67-108276. (Studies in Theology: No. 64). 1967. text ed. 8.50x (ISBN 0-8401-6064-X). A R Allenson.

WISDOM LITERATURE

Charlesworth, James H. The Odes of Solomon. LC 77-21285. (SBL Texts & Translations). 192p. 1983. pap. 8.95 (ISBN 0-89130-202-6, 06 02 13). Scholars Pr GA.

Feuerstein, Georg. Crazy Wisdom. 140p. 1987. pap. 7.95 (ISBN 0-941255-37-9). Integral Pub.

Gittner, Louis. Listen Listen Listen. Farish, Starr, ed. 320p. (Orig.). 1980. pap. 8.95 (ISBN 0-9605492-0-X). Touch Heart.

Hardon, John A. Treasury of Catholic Wisdom. LC 86-19648. 768p. 1987. 27.50 (ISBN 0-385-23079-6). Doubleday.

Hermetic Wisdom. (Sacred Texts Ser.). 130p. 1986. pap. 8.75 (ISBN 0-88695-042-2). Concord Grove.

The Interpreter's Concise Commentary, Vol. III: Wisdom Literature & Poetry. 4.95 (ISBN 0-687-19234-X). Abingdon.

Kloppenborg, John S. The Formation of Q: Trajectories in Ancient Wisdom Collections. LC 86-45225. 416p. 1987. 39.95 (ISBN 0-8006-3101-3). Fortress.

Murphy, Roland E. Wisdom Literature: Ruth, Esther, Job, Proverbs, Ecclesiastes, Canticles. (The Forms of the Old Testament Literature Ser.). (Orig.). 1981. pap. 12.95 (ISBN 0-8028-1877-3). Eerdmans.

Murphy, Roland E., ed. & intro. by. Medieval Exegesis of Wisdom Literature: Essays by Beryl Smalley. (Scholars Press Reprints & Translations Ser.). 1986. 13.95 (ISBN 1-55540-026-4, 00 07 16). Scholars Pr GA.

Sanders, Jack T. Ben Sira & Demotic Wisdom. LC 82-21464. (SBL Monograph). 134p. 1983. pap. 19.50 (ISBN 0-89130-586-6). Scholars Pr GA.

Smith, Steve, ed. Ways of Wisdom: Readings on the Good Life. (Illus.). 312p. (Orig.). 1983. lib. bdg. 29.75 (ISBN 0-8191-3387-6); pap. text ed. 14.25 (ISBN 0-8191-3388-4). U Pr of Amer.

Von Rad, Gerhard. Wisdom in Israel. rev. ed. Martin, James D., tr. from Ger. Orig. Title: Weisheit in Israel. 336p. 1973. 15.95 (ISBN 0-687-45757-2). Abingdon.

Wood, James D. Wisdom Literature: An Introduction. LC 67-108276. (Studies in Theology: No. 64). 1967. text ed. 8.50x (ISBN 0-8401-6064-X). A R Allenson.

WISE, ISAAC MAYER, 1819-1900

Wise, Isaac. Reminiscences. Philipson, David, ed. LC 73-2233. (The Jewish People; History, Religion, Literature Ser.). Repr. of 1901 ed. 30.00 (ISBN 0-405-05294-4). Ayer Co Pubs.

WITCHCRAFT

see also Demonology; Evil Eye; Exorcism; Medicine-Man; Trials (Witchcraft); Voodooism

Ashley, Leonard R. The Wonderful World of Magic & Witchcraft. LC 85-25310. (Illus.). 1986. 17.50 (ISBN 0-934878-71-4); pap. 10.95 (ISBN 0-934878-72-2). Dembner Bks.

Ashton, John. The Devil in Britain & America. LC 80-19692. 363p. 1980. Repr. of 1972 ed. lib. bdg. 19.95x (ISBN 0-89370-608-6). Borgo Pr.

Baroja, Julio C. The World of Witches. Glendinning, O. N., tr. LC 64-15829. (Nature of Human Society Ser.). xiv, 314p. 1973. pap. 12.00x (ISBN 0-226-03763-0, P497, Phoen). U of Chicago Pr.

Baskin, Wade. The Sorcerer's Handbook. (Illus.). 640p. 1974. pap. 4.95 (ISBN 0-8065-0399-8). Citadel Pr.

Basso, Keith H. Western Apache Witchcraft. LC 69-16329. (University of Arizona, Anthroplological Papers: No. 15). pap. 20.30 (ISBN 0-317-28645-5, 2055359). Bks Demand UMI.

Ben-Yehuda, Nachman. Deviance & Moral Boundaries: Witchcraft, the Occult, Science Fiction, Deviant Sciences & Scientists. LC 85-1167. x, 260p. 1985. 25.00x (ISBN 0-226-04335-5). U of Chicago Pr.

Bird, Malcolm. The Witch's Handbook. (Illus.). 96p. 1985. 10.95 (ISBN 0-312-88458-3). St Martin.

Black, George F., ed. Calendar of Cases of Witchcraft in Scotland, 1510-1727. LC 78-137707. (New York Public Library Publications in Reprint Ser.). (Illus.). 1971. Repr. of 1938 ed. 8.00 (ISBN 0-405-01751-0). Ayer Co Pubs.

Bourne, Lois. Witch Amongst Us. 208p. 1986. 13.95 (ISBN 0-312-88425-7). St Martin.

Buckland, Raymond. Ray Buckland's Complete Book of Witchcraft. Weschcke, Carl L., ed. LC 85-45280. (Sourcebook Ser.). (Illus.). 320p. (Orig.). 1986. wkbk. 12.95 (ISBN 0-87542-050-8). Llewellyn Pubns.

--The Tree: The Complete Book of Saxon Witchcraft. LC 74-79397. (Illus.). 158p. 1974. pap. 5.95 (ISBN 0-87728-258-7). Weiser.

--Witchcraft from the Inside. 2nd ed. (Illus.). 145p. 1975. pap. 3.95 (ISBN 0-87542-085-0). Llewellyn Pubns.

Budapest, Zsuzsanna. The Holy Book of Women's Mysteries, 2 vols. rev. ed. 1986. pap. write for info. (ISBN 0-937081-03-5). SBA Coven.

--The Holy Book of Women's Mysteries, Pt. 1. rev. ed. 1986. pap. text ed. write for info. (ISBN 0-937081-01-9). SBA Coven.

--The Holy Book of Women's Mysteries, Pt. 2. rev. ed. 1986. pap. write for info. (ISBN 0-937081-02-7). SBA Coven.

Campbell, John G. Witchcraft & Second Sight in the Highlands & Islands of Scotland. 1976. Repr. 20.00x (ISBN 0-85409-978-6). Charles River Bks.

Casaubon, Meric. A Letter of Meric Casaubon to Peter du Moulin Concerning Natural Experimental Philosophie. LC 76-47045. 1976. Repr. of 1669 ed. 90.00x (ISBN 0-8201-1284-4). Schol Facsimiles.

Cornell University, Libraries Staff. Catalogue of the Witchcraft Collection in Cornell University Library. LC 76-41552. 1977. lib. bdg. 120.00 (ISBN 0-527-19705-X). Kraus Intl.

Cotta, John. The Triall of Witch-Craft Shewing the True Methode of the Discovery. LC 68-54629. (English Experience Ser.: No. 39). 128p. 1968. Repr. of 1616 ed. 21.00 (ISBN 90-221-0039-1). Walter J Johnson.

Crowley, Aleister. Diary of a Drug Fiend. 1973. lib. bdg. 79.95 (ISBN 0-87968-110-1). Krishna Pr.

Dauraul. Witches & Sorcerers. pap. 2.95 (ISBN 0-8065-0286-X). Citadel Pr.

Devine, Mary. Brujeria: A Study of Mexican American Folk-Magic. Weschcke, Carl L., ed. LC 82-83427. (Illus.). 266p. (Orig.). 1982. pap. 7.95 (ISBN 0-87542-775-8). Llewellyn Pubns.

Drake, Samuel G. Annals of Witchcraft in New England & Elsewhere in the United States. 69.95 (ISBN 0-87968-641-3). Gordon Pr.

Elwood, Roger. Historias Extranas de Brujeria. Lockward, George, tr. from Eng. (Span.). 112p. 1974. pap. 1.95 (ISBN 0-89922-028-2). Edit Caribe.

Evans, Arthur. Witchcraft: The Gay Counterculture. 1977. pap. 5.95 (ISBN 0-915480-01-8). Fag Rag.

Farrar, Janet & Farrar, Stuart. A Witches Bible, 2 vols. (Illus., Orig.). 1984. Vol. I - The Sabbats. pap. 10.95 (ISBN 0-939708-06-X); Vol. II - The Rituals. pap. 10.95 (ISBN 0-939708-07-8); pap. 21.90 boxed set (ISBN 0-939708-08-6). Magickal Childe.

Flower, Margaret. The Wonderful Discoveries of the Witchcrafts of M. & P. Flower. LC 72-5992. (English Experience Ser.: No. 517). 50p. 1972. Repr. of 1619 ed. 6.00 (ISBN 90-221-0517-2). Walter J Johnson.

Fritscher, John. Popular Witchcraft. 224p. 1973. 6.95 (ISBN 0-8065-0380-7). Citadel Pr.
Frost & Frost. Magic Power of Witchcraft. 1977. 14.95 (ISBN 0-13-545376-3, Reward); pap. 5.95 (ISBN 0-13-545368-2). P-H.
Gainer, Patrick W. Witches, Ghosts & Signs, Folklore of the Southern Appalachians. LC 75-29893. 192p. 1975. 7.95 (ISBN 0-89092-006-0). Seneca Bks.
Gardner, Gerald B. Witchcraft Today. 1970. pap. 2.45 (ISBN 0-8065-0002-6). Citadel Pr.
Gardner, Gerard B. Witchcraft Today. (Illus.). 184p. pap. 9.95 (ISBN 0-939708-03-5). Magickal Childe.
Gifford, George. A Discourse of the Subtill Practises of Devilles by Witches & Sorcerers. LC 77-6745. (English Experience Ser.: No. 871). 1977. Repr. of 1587 ed. lib. bdg. 8.00 (ISBN 90-221-0871-6). Walter J Johnson.
Glanvill, Joseph. Saducismus Triumphatus: Or, Full & Plain Evidence Concerning Witches & Apparitions. LC 66-60009. 1966. Repr. of 1689 ed. 75.00x (ISBN 0-8201-1021-3). Schol Facsimiles.
Glass, Justine. Witchcraft-the Sixth Sense. pap. 7.00 (ISBN 0-87980-174-3). Wilshire.
Haining, Peter. The Witchcraft Papers. 1974. 7.95 (ISBN 0-8216-0223-3). Univ Bks.
Harris, Marvin. Cows, Pigs, Wars, & Witches: The Riddles of Culture. 1974. pap. 2.36 (ISBN 0-394-71372-9, Vin) (ISBN 0-394-48338-3). Random.
Harrison, Michael. The Roots of Witchcraft. 280p. 1974. 7.95 (ISBN 0-8065-0444-7). Citadel Pr.
Holmes, Ronald. Witchcraft in History. 1977. pap. 5.95 (ISBN 0-8065-0575-3). Citadel Pr.
Hoyt, Charles A. Witchcraft. LC 80-24731. 160p. 1981. pap. 12.95 (ISBN 0-8093-1015-5). S Ill U Pr.
Hoyt, Olga. Witches. LC 68-13233. (Illus.). 1969. 11.70i (ISBN 0-200-71593-3, B91350, AbS-J). HarpJ.
Johnson, F. Roy. Witches & Demons in History & Folklore. (Illus.). 1978. Repr. 9.50 (ISBN 0-930230-31-0). Johnson NC.
Jong, Erica. Witches. (Illus.). 1982. pap. 12.50 (ISBN 0-452-25357-8, Z5357, Plume). NAL.
King, Francis. Sexuality, Magic & Perversion. (Illus.). 1972. 6.95 (ISBN 0-8065-0289-4). Citadel Pr.
Klaits, Joseph. Servants of Satan: The Age of the Witch Hunts. LC 84-48252. (Illus.). 224p. 1987. 24.95X (ISBN 0-253-35182-0); pap. 7.95 (ISBN 0-253-20422-4). Ind U Pr.
Knauft, Bruce M. Good Company & Violence: Sorcery & Social Action in a Lowland New Guinea Society. LC 85-967. (Studies in Melanasian Anthropology). 1985. 40.00x (ISBN 0-520-05530-6). U of Cal Pr.
Kors, Alan C. & Peters, Edward, eds. Witchcraft in Europe, 1100-1700: A Documentary History. LC 71-170267. (Illus.). 1972. pap. 13.95x (ISBN 0-8122-1063-8, Pa Paperbks). U of Pa pr.
Kramer, Heinrich & Sprenger, James. The Malleus Maleficarum: The Witches Hammer of Heinrich Kramer & James Sprenger. Summers, Montague, tr. 15.50 (ISBN 0-8446-0169-1). Peter Smith.
Larner, Christina. Witchcraft & Religion: The Politics of Popular Belief. 256p. 1984. 29.95x (ISBN 0-631-13447-6). Basil Blackwell.
--Witchcraft & Religion: The Politics of Popular Belief. Macfarlane, Alan, ed. 184p. 1986. pap. text ed. 12.95x (ISBN 0-631-14779-9). Basil Blackwell.
Leek, Sybil. The Complete Art of Witchcraft. (Illus.). 208p. 1973. pap. 2.95 (ISBN 0-451-12714-5, AE2714, Sig). NAL.
Lehmann, Arthur C. & Myers, James E. Magic, Witchcraft, & Religion. (Illus.). 416p. 1985. pap. text ed. 22.95 (ISBN 0-87484-685-4). Mayfield Pub.
Lehner, Ernst & Lehner, Johanna. Picture Book of Devils, Demons & Witchcraft. (Illus.). 15.50 (ISBN 0-8446-5830-8). Peter Smith.
Llewellyn Publications Staff. The Truth about Witchcraft. Galde, Phyllis, ed. (Educational Guide Ser.). 32p. 1987. pap. 2.00 (ISBN 0-87542-357-4). Llewellyn Pubns.
Lowell, James R. Among My Books. LC 75-126666. 1970. 11.50 (ISBN 0-404-04039-X). AMS Pr.
Manning, A. J. Helping Yourself with White Witchcraft. 1972. 9.95 (ISBN 0-13-386565-7, Reward); pap. 4.95 (ISBN 0-13-386573-8). P-H.
Mappen, Marc. Witches & Historians: Interpretations of Salem. LC 78-2579. (American Problem Studies). 126p. 1980. pap. 6.50 (ISBN 0-88275-653-2). Krieger.
Martello, Leo L. Witchcraft: The Old Religion. 1987. pap. 6.95 (ISBN 0-8065-1028-5). Citadel Pr.
Marwick, Max, ed. Witchcraft & Sorcery. 494p. 1987. pap. 6.95 (ISBN 0-14-022678-8, Pelican). Penguin.
Masters, R. E. Eros & Evil: The Sexual Psychopathology of Witchcraft. LC 79-8114. Repr. of 1962 ed. 36.50 (ISBN 0-404-18427-8). AMS Pr.
Michelet, Jules. Satanism & Witchcraft. 352p. 1983. pap. 5.95 (ISBN 0-8065-0059-X, 89). Citadel Pr.
Midelfort, H. Erik. Witch Hunting in Southwestern Germany, 1562-1684: The Social & Intellectual Foundations. LC 75-183891. 320p. 1972. 26.50x (ISBN 0-8047-0805-3). Stanford U Pr.
Morrison, Sarah L. The Modern Witch's Spellbook. LC 71-135588. 256p. 1973. pap. 5.95 (ISBN 0-8065-0372-6). Citadel Pr.
--The Modern Witch's Spellbook, Vol. 2. 224p. 1986. pap. 6.95 (ISBN 0-8065-1015-3). Citadel Pr.
O'Connell, Margaret. The Magic Cauldron: Witchcraft for Good & Evil. LC 75-26757. (Illus.). 256p. 1975. 15.95 (ISBN 0-87599-187-4). S G Phillips.
Olliver, C. W. An Analysis of Magic & Witchcraft: A Retrospective Introduction to the Study of Modern Metaphysics. 244p. 1985. Repr. of 1928 ed. Set. lib. bdg. 100.00 (ISBN 0-89984-775-7). Century Bookbindery.
Pearson, D'Orsay W., ed. Pedro Ciruelo's A Treatise Reproving All Superstitions & Forms of Witchcraft: Very Necessary & Useful for All Good Christians Zealous for Their Salvation. Maio, Eugene & Pearson, D'Orsay W., trs. LC 74-4979. 366p. 1976. 27.50 (ISBN 0-8386-1580-5). Fairleigh Dickinson.
Peters, Edward. The Magician, the Witch & the Law. LC 78-51341. (Middle Ages Ser.). 1982. 23.50x (ISBN 0-8122-7746-5); pap. 9.95x (ISBN 0-8122-1101-4). U of Pa Pr.
Pratt, Sr. Antoinette M. The Attitude of the Catholic Church Toward Witchcraft & the Allied Practices of Sorcery & Magic. LC 79-8116. 144p. Repr. of 1945 ed. 22.50 (ISBN 0-404-18429-4). AMS Pr.
Records of Salem Witchcraft, 2 vols. in 1. (Woodward's Historical Ser.: Nos. 1 & 2). 1968. Repr. of 1864 ed. 40.50 (ISBN 0-8337-2916-0). B Franklin.
Riva, Anna. Spellcraft, Hexcraft & Witchcraft. (Illus.). 64p. 1977. pap. 3.50 (ISBN 0-943832-00-4). Intl Imports.
Roberts. Witches & Witch-Hunters. 1978. Repr. of 1973 ed. lib. bdg. 27.50 (ISBN 0-8414-2928-6). Folcroft.
Runeberg, Anne. Witches, Demons & Fertility Magic. 273p. 1980. Repr. of 1947 ed. lib. bdg. 30.00 (ISBN 0-8414-7399-4). Folcroft.
Runeberg, Arne. Witches, Demons & Fertility Magic. LC 74-3091. (Folklore Ser). 39.50 (ISBN 0-88305-560-0). Norwood Edns.
Russel, Jeffrey B. Witchcraft in the Middle Ages. (Illus.). 1976. pap. 5.95 (ISBN 0-8065-0504-4). Citadel Pr.
Russell, Jeffrey B. A History of Witchcraft: Sorcerers, Heretics & Pagans. (Illus.). 1982. pap. 10.95f (ISBN 0-500-27242-5). Thames Hudson.
Saletore, R. N. Indian Witchcraft. 216p. 1981. text ed. 17.50x (ISBN 0-391-02480-9). Humanities.
Sargeant, Phillip W. Witches & Warlocks. 1976. 20.00x (ISBN 0-7158-1028-6). Charles River Bks.
Scott, Gini G. Cult & Countercult: A Study of a Spiritual Growth Group & a Witchcraft Order. LC 79-54057. (Contributions in Sociology: No. 38). (Illus.). 1980. lib. bdg. 29.95x (ISBN 0-313-22074-3, SCC/). Greenwood.
Scott, Walter. Demonology & Witchcraft. 1970. 7.95 (ISBN 0-8065-0213-4). Citadel Pr.
Sergeant, Philip W. Witches & Warlocks. LC 72-82208. (Illus.). Repr. of 1936 ed. 24.50 (ISBN 0-405-08898-1). Ayer Co Pubs.
--Witches & Warlocks. LC 72-164055. (Illus.). 290p. 1975. Repr. of 1936 ed. 34.00x (ISBN 0-8103-3979-X). Gale.
--Witches & Warlocks. 1972. 24.50 (ISBN 0-405-08950-3, 1457). Ayer Co Pubs.
Shepard, Leslie. How to Protect Yourself Against Black Magic & Witchcraft. 1978. 7.95 (ISBN 0-8065-0646-6). Citadel Pr.
Simmons, Marc. Witchcraft in the Southwest: Spanish & Indian Supernaturalism on the Rio Grande. LC 79-18928. (Illus.). xiv, 184p. 1980. pap. 5.50 (ISBN 0-8032-9116-7, BB 729, Bison). U of Nebr Pr.
Sinclair, George. Satan's Invisible World Discovered. LC 68-17017. 1969. Repr. of 1685 ed. 45.00x (ISBN 0-8201-1068-X). Schol Facsimiles.
Sleigh, Bernard. Witchcraft. 69.95 (ISBN 0-8490-1311-9). Gordon Pr.
Stewart, W. Grant. The Popular Superstitions & Festive Amusements of the Highlanders of Scotland. 1978. Repr. of 1851 ed. lib. bdg. 37.50 (ISBN 0-8492-8007-9). R West.
Summers, Montague. The Geography of Witchcraft. 624p. 1973. pap. 4.95 (ISBN 0-8065-0391-2). Citadel Pr.
--History of Witchcraft. 1970. pap. 5.95 (ISBN 0-8065-0209-6, 0209-6). Citadel Pr.
--History of Witchcraft & Demonology. (Illus.). 370p. 1973. pap. 8.95 (ISBN 0-7100-7613-4). Methuen Inc.
--Malleus Maleficarum. 288p. 1971. pap. 7.50 (ISBN 0-486-22802-9). Dover.
Summers, Montague, ed. & tr. Malleus Maleficarum. LC 68-57193. 1969. Repr. of 1928 ed. 27.50 (ISBN 0-405-09016-1, Pub. by Blom). Ayer Co Pubs.
Taylor, John M. Witchcraft Delusion in Colonial Connecticut, 1647-97. LC 73-165414. (American Classics in History & Social Science Ser.: No. 196). 1971. Repr. of 1908 ed. lib. bdg. 21.00 (ISBN 0-8337-4445-3). B Franklin.
Thompson, C. J. Hand of Destiny: The Folk-Lore & Superstition of Everyday Life. LC 70-125600. 1970. Repr. of 1932 ed. 46.00x (ISBN 0-8103-3419-4). Gale.
Verner, Gerald, et al. Prince of Darkness: A Witchcraft Anthology. 1978. Repr. of 1946 ed. lib. bdg. 25.00 (ISBN 0-8492-2816-6). R West.
Wickwar, J. W. Witchcraft & the Black Art: A Book Dealing with the Psychology & Folklore of the Witches. LC 71-151817. 1971. Repr. of 1925 ed. 48.00x (ISBN 0-8103-3692-8). Gale.
Wood, John M. Witchcraft & Superstitious Record in the Southwestern District of Scotland. LC 76-25108. 1976. 40.00 (ISBN 0-8414-9530-0). Folcroft.

WITCHCRAFT–JUVENILE LITERATURE

Cartwright & Rawson. Wizards. (Story Books). 1980. 6.95 (ISBN 0-86020-381-6, Usborne-Hayes); PLB 11.96 (ISBN 0-88110-052-8); pap. 2.95 (ISBN 0-86020-380-8). EDC.
Cohen, Daniel. Famous Curses. LC 79-52039. (High Interest-Low Vocabulary Ser.). (Illus.). 1979. 8.95 (ISBN 0-396-07712-9). Dodd.
DeLage, Ida. What Does a Witch Need? LC 76-143305. (Old Witch Bks.). (Illus.). 48p. 1971. PLB 6.69 (ISBN 0-8116-4058-2). Garrard.
Foxglove, Lady. We've got the Power: Witches among Us. LC 81-11098. (A Jem Book Ser.). (Illus.). 64p. (Teens reading on a 2-3rd grade level). 1981. lib. bdg. 9.29 (ISBN 0-671-43604-X). Messner.
Hawkins, Colin. Witches. LC 85-40425. (Illus.). 32p. 1985. 7.45 (ISBN 0-382-09132-9). Silver.
Rawson & Carlwright. Witches. (Story Book). 1979. 6.95 (ISBN 0-86020-341-7, Usborne-Hayes); PLB 11.96 (ISBN 0-88110-057-9); pap. 2.95 (ISBN 0-86020-340-9). EDC.
Revesz, Therese R. Witches. LC 77-10626. (Myth, Magic, & Superstition Ser.). (Illus.). 1977. PLB 14.65 (ISBN 0-8172-1034-2). Raintree Pubs.
Sattler, Helen R. The Smallest Witch. LC 81-2202. (Illus.). 32p. 1982. 6.75 (ISBN 0-525-66747-4). Dandelion Pr.

WITCHCRAFT–AFRICA

Beattie, John & Middleton, John. Spirit Mediumship & Society in Africa. LC 70-80849. 310p. 1969. 35.00x (ISBN 0-8419-0009-4, Africana). Holmes & Meier.
Boroffka, Alexander. Benedict Nta Tanka's Commentary & Dramatized Ideas on Disease & Witchcraft in Our Society: A Schreber Case from Cameroon African on His Mental Illness. (Medical Care in Developing Countries Ser.: Vol. 7). 150p. 1980. 19.45 (ISBN 3-8204-6901-X). P Lang Pubs.
Hallen, Barry & Sodipo, J. O. Knowledge, Belief & Witchcraft. 144p. 1986. text ed. 24.95x (ISBN 0-936508-19-1, Ethnographica). Barber Pr.
Shorter, Aylward. Jesus & the Witchdoctor: An Approach to Healing & Wholeness. 268p. (Orig.). 1985. pap. 10.95 (ISBN 0-88344-225-6). Orbis Bks.

WITCHCRAFT–EUROPE

Cohn, Norman. Europe's Inner Demons: An Enquiry Inspired by the Great Witch-Hunt. 1977. pap. 8.95 (ISBN 0-452-00761-5, Mer). NAL.
Favret-Saada, Jeanne. Deadly Words. Cullen, Catherine, tr. from Fr. LC 79-41607. (Illus.). 1981. o. p. 57.50 (ISBN 0-521-22317-2); pap. text ed. 15.95 o. p. (ISBN 0-521-29787-7). Cambridge U Pr.
Garber, Marjorie, ed. Cannibals, Witches, & Divorce: Estranging the Renaissance. LC 86-45472. (Selected Papers from the English Institute, 1985 New Ser.: No. 11). 256p. 1987. text ed. 19.50x (ISBN 0-8018-3405-8). Johns Hopkins.
Henningsen, Gustav. The Witches' Advocate: Basque Witchcraft & the Spanish Inquisition, 1609-1614. LC 79-20340. (Basque Book Ser.). (Illus.). xxxii, 607p. 1980. 24.00 (ISBN 0-87417-056-7). U of Nev Pr.
Kieckhefer, Richard. European Witch Trials: Their Foundations in Popular & Learned Culture, 1300-1500. 1976. 34.00x (ISBN 0-520-02967-4). U of Cal Pr.
Kors, Alan C. & Peters, Edward, eds. Witchcraft in Europe, 1100-1700: A Documentary History. LC 71-170267. (Illus.). 1972. pap. 13.95x (ISBN 0-8122-1063-8, Pa Paperbks). U of Pa pr.
Kunze, Michael. Highroad to the Stake: A Tale of Witchcraft. Yuill, William, tr. LC 86-11230. (Illus.). 440p. 1987. 24.95 (ISBN 0-226-46211-0). U of Chicago Pr.
Sebald, H. Witchcraft: The Heritage of a Heresy. 262p. 1978. pap. 15.50 (ISBN 0-444-99059-3). Elsevier.
Sharpe, Charles K. Historical Account of the Belief in Witchcraft in Scotland. LC 74-8196. 1974. Repr. of 1884 ed. 48.00x (ISBN 0-8103-3590-5). Gale.
Trevor-Roper, Hugh R. European Witch Craze in the Sixteenth & Seventeenth Centuries & Other Essays. 1969. pap. 6.95x (ISBN 0-06-131416-1, TB1416, Torch). Har-Row.

WITCHCRAFT–GREAT BRITAIN

Ashton, John. The Devil in Britain & America. LC 80-19692. 363p. 1980. Repr. of 1972 ed. lib. bdg. 19.95x (ISBN 0-89370-608-6). Borgo Pr.
Briggs, Katherine M. Pale Hecates Team: Examination of the Beliefs on Witchcraft & Magic Among Shakespeare's Contemporaries & His Immediate Succesors. Dorson, Richard M., ed. LC 77-70582. (International Folklore Ser.). (Illus.). 1977. lib. bdg. 24.50x (ISBN 0-405-10083-3). Ayer Co Pubs.
Davies, R. Trevor. Four Centuries of Witch-Belief. LC 74-180026. Repr. of 1947 ed. 27.50 (ISBN 0-405-08437-4). Ayer Co Pubs.
Larner, Christina. Enemies of God: The Witch-Hunt in Scotland. LC 81-47605. 256p. 1981. text ed. 25.00x (ISBN 0-8018-2699-3). Johns Hopkins.
McPherson, Joseph M. Primitive Beliefs in the North-East of Scotland. Dorson, Richard M., ed. LC 77-70605. (International Folklore Ser.). 1977. Repr. of 1929 ed. lib. bdg. 24.50x (ISBN 0-405-10109-0). Ayer Co Pubs.
Notestein, Wallace. History of Witchcraft in England from 1558 to 1718. LC 65-18824. 1965. Repr. of 1911 ed. 16.00x (ISBN 0-8462-0649-8). Russell.
Potts, Thomas. Potts' Discovery of Witches in the County of Lancaster. Repr. of 1745 ed. 31.00 (ISBN 0-384-47430-6). Johnson Repr.
Sergeant, Philip W. Witches & Warlocks. LC 72-82208. (Illus.). Repr. of 1936 ed. 24.50 (ISBN 0-405-08898-1). Ayer Co Pubs.
--Witches & Warlocks. 1972. 24.50 (ISBN 0-405-08950-3, 1457). Ayer Co Pubs.
Wood, J. Maxwell. Witchcraft & Superstitious Record in the Southwestern District of Scotland. (Illus.). 1976. 25.00x (ISBN 0-7158-1139-8). Charles River Bks.

WITCHCRAFT–IRELAND

Byrne, Patrick. Witchcraft in Ireland. 80p. 1967. pap. 6.95 (ISBN 0-85342-038-6, Pub. by Mercier Pr Ireland). Irish Bk Ctr.

WITCHCRAFT–MEXICO

Madsen, William & Madsen, Claudia. A Guide to Mexican Witchcraft. (Illus.). 96p. 1977. pap. 4.50 (ISBN 0-912434-10-4). Ocelot Pr.

WITCHCRAFT–NEW ENGLAND

Boyer, Paul & Nissenbaum, Stephen. Salem Possessed: The Social Origins of Witchcraft. LC 73-84399. 320p. 1974. pap. 6.95x (ISBN 0-674-78526-6). Harvard U Pr.
Brunelle, Jim, ed. Over to Home & From Away. (Illus.). 340p. (Orig.). 1980. pap. 9.95 (ISBN 0-930096-11-8). G Gannett.
Burr, George L. New England's Place in the History of Witchcraft. facsimile ed. LC 71-164592. (Select Bibliographies Reprint Ser). Repr. of 1911 ed. 15.00 (ISBN 0-8369-5876-4). Ayer Co Pubs.
Demos, John P. Entertaining Satan: Witchcraft & the Culture of Early New England. LC 81-22463. 558p. 1982. 29.95x (ISBN 0-19-503131-8); pap. 12.95 (ISBN 0-19-503378-7). Oxford U Pr.
Drake, Samuel G. Annals of Witchcraft in New England & Elsewhere in the United States from Their First Settlement. LC 67-13327. 1967. Repr. of 1869 ed. 20.00 (ISBN 0-405-08466-8, Blom Pubns). Ayer Co Pubs.
--Annals of Witchcraft in New England, & Elsewhere in the United States. LC 73-161683. (Woodward's Historical Ser.: No. 8). 306p. 1972. Repr. of 1869 ed. lib. bdg. 23.50 (ISBN 0-8337-0898-8). B Franklin.
--Witchcraft Delusion in New England, 3 vols. LC 79-120720. (Research & Source Works Ser.: No. 471). 1970. Repr. of 1866 ed. lib. bdg. 62.00 (ISBN 0-8337-0908-9). B Franklin.
Ferguson, Henry. Essays in American History. LC 68-26266. 1969. Repr. of 1894 ed. 21.50x (ISBN 0-8046-0144-5, Pub. by Kennikat). Assoc Faculty Pr.
Hansen, Chadwick. Witchcraft at Salem. LC 69-15825. (Illus.). 1969. 11.95 (ISBN 0-8076-0492-5). Braziller.
--Witchcraft at Salem. LC 99-943950. 252p. (YA) pap. 3.95 (ISBN 0-451-62214-6, ME2214, Ment). NAL.
--Witchcraft at Salem. (Illus.). 252p. 1985. pap. 7.95 (ISBN 0-8076-1137-9). Braziller.
Jackson, Shirley. Witchcraft of Salem Village. (Landmark Ser.: No. 69). (Illus.). 1956. PLB 6.99 (ISBN 0-394-90369-2, BYR). Random.

Levin, David. Did the Mathers Disagree about the Salem Witchcraft Trials? Proceedings of the American Antiquarian Society. 19p. 1985. pap. 3.95 (ISBN 0-912296-77-1, Dist. by U Pr of Va). Am Antiquarian.

Petry, Ann. Tituba of Salem Village. LC 64-20691. (YA) 1964. 14.70i (ISBN 0-690-82677-X, Crowell Jr Bks). HarpJ.

Records of Salem Witchcraft, Copied from the Original Documents, 2 Vols. LC 78-75274. (Law, Politics & History Ser.). 1969. Repr. of 1864 ed. lib. bdg. 45.00 (ISBN 0-306-71309-8). Da Capo.

Starkey, Marion. The Visionary Girls: Witchcraft in Salem Village. 1973. 15.45i (ISBN 0-316-81087-8). Little.

Starkey, Marion L. Devil in Massachusetts: A Modern Enquiry into the Salem Witch Trials. LC 49-10395. 1969. pap. 5.95 (ISBN 0-385-03509-8, Anch). Doubleday.

--Devil in Massachusetts: A Modern Inquiry into the Salem Witch Trials. 15.00 (ISBN 0-8446-2996-0). Peter Smith.

Taylor, John. The Witchcraft Delusion in Colonial Connecticut, 1647-1747. 172p. 1974. 16.95 (ISBN 0-87928-053-0). Corner Hse.

Taylor, John M. Witchcraft Delusion in Colonial Connecticut, 1647-97. LC 73-165414. (American Classics in History & Social Science Ser.: No. 196). 1971. Repr. of 1908 ed. lib. bdg. 21.00 (ISBN 0-8337-4445-3). B Franklin.

Upham, C. Salem Witchcraft, 2 vols. 1022p. 1971. Repr. of 1867 ed. Set. 48.00 (ISBN 0-87928-024-7). Corner Hse.

Upham, Charles W. Salem Witchcraft, 2 Vols. LC 59-10887. (American Classics Ser.). (Illus.). 1959. 40.00 (ISBN 0-8044-1947-7). Ungar.

W. W. True & Just Recorde of the Information, Examination & Confession of All the Witches, Taken at S. Oses in the Countie of Essex. LC 81-4330. 1981. Repr. of 1582 ed. 35.00x (ISBN 0-8201-1363-8). Schol Facsimiles.

Weisman, Richard. Witchcraft, Magic & Religion in Seventeenth Century Massachusetts. LC 83-15542. 288p. 1985. pap. text ed. 9.95x (ISBN 0-87023-494-3). U of MAss Pr.

WITHERS, GEORGE, 1588-1667

Wither, George. The Psalmes of David, 2 vols. in 1. 1967. Repr. of 1632 ed. 89.00 (ISBN 0-8337-3838-0). B Franklin.

WITHERSPOON, JOHN, 1723-1794

Collins, Varnum L. President Witherspoon. LC 78-83416. (Religion in America, Ser. 1). 1969. Repr. of 1925 ed. 30.00 (ISBN 0-405-00242-4). Ayer Co Pubs.

WITNESS BEARING (CHRISTIANITY)

see also Evangelistic Work; Martyrdom; Prophecy (Christianity)

Bonnici, Roberta L. I'm Scared to Witness! (Discovery Bks.). (Illus.). 48p. (Orig.). (YA) 1979. pap. 1.50 (ISBN 0-88243-931-6, 02-0931); tchr's ed 3.95 (ISBN 0-88243-330-X, 02-0330). Gospel Pub.

Brainerd, David. David Brainerd's Personal Testimony. (Summit Bks.). pap. 3.95 (ISBN 0-8010-8159-9). Baker Bk.

Burkhart, Rob. I Hate Witnessing Leader's Guide. LC 84-18165. 64p. 1985. pap. 3.95 (ISBN 0-8307-1011-6, 6101987). Regal.

Cassizzi, Vic. Overlook: A Castle in the Kingdom. (Illus.). 1981. 3.95 (ISBN 0-686-30374-1). Cassizzi.

Chaffin, Kenneth L. The Reluctant Witness. LC 74-84548. 1975. 6.95 (ISBN 0-8054-5550-7). Broadman.

Christian Witness to Nominal Christians Among Roman Catholics. 38p. pap. 1.00 (ISBN 0-935120-04-1). Christs Mission.

Foglio, Frank. Hey God! A Large Italian Family's Amazing Experience with God. LC 72-87328. 1972. pap. 4.95 (ISBN 0-88270-007-3). Bridge Pub.

George, Denise, compiled by. When Night Becomes as Day. LC 86-6887. (Orig.). 1986. pap. 5.95 (ISBN 0-8054-5434-9). Broadman.

Hunter, Frances. Let's Go Witnessing. 1978. pap. 3.25 (ISBN 0-685-90803-8). Hunter Bks.

Innes, Dick. I Hate Witnessing. LC 84-27531. 1985. pap. 2.95 (ISBN 0-8307-1003-5, 5418403). Regal.

--I Hate Witnessing: A Handbook for Effective Christian Communication. LC 84-27531. 1985. pap. text ed. 2.95 (ISBN 0-8307-1003-5, 5418403). Vision Hse.

Jaki, Stanley L. The Keys of the Kingdom: A Tool's Witness to Truth. (Illus.). 1986. 9.95 (ISBN 0-8199-0898-3). Franciscan Herald.

Jones, G. Curtis. We Knew His Power: Nine Whose Lives Were Touched by Jesus. LC 75-44181. pap. 24.40 (ISBN 0-8357-9031-2, 2016419). Bks Demand UMI.

Kolb, Erwin J. Witness Primer. 128p. (Orig.). 1986. pap. 4.95 (ISBN 0-570-04441-3). Concordia.

Larson, Muriel. Ways Women Can Witness. LC 84-5006. 1984. pap. 5.95 (ISBN 0-8054-5250-8). Broadman.

Little, Paul E. Como Compartir Su Fe. 144p. 1985. pap. 3.95 (ISBN 0-311-13025-9). Casa Bautista.

--How to Give Away Your Faith. LC 66-20710. 1966. pap. 5.95 (ISBN 0-87784-553-0). Inter-Varsity.

Lohfink, Gerhard. The Work of God Goes On. LC 86-45202. (The Bible for Christian Life Ser.). 80p. 1987. pap. 4.95 (ISBN 0-8006-2026-7). Fortress.

Lovett, C. S. Teach Witnessing. 1966. pap. 5.95 tchr's. guide (ISBN 0-938148-09-5). Personal Christianity.

--Witnessing Made Easy. 1964. pap. 5.95 (ISBN 0-938148-01-X). Personal Christianity.

McLeish, James. Faithful Witness. LC 85-4300. 276p. (Orig.). 1985. pap. 6.95 (ISBN 0-87784-531-X). Inter-Varsity.

McPhee, Arthur G. Friendship Evangelism: The Caring Way to Share Your Faith. 1979. pap. 4.95 (ISBN 0-310-37311-5, 11262P). Zondervan.

Miles, Delos. Overcoming Barriers to Witnessing. LC 83-70641. (Orig.). 1984. pap. 5.50 (ISBN 0-8054-6245-7). Broadman.

Petersen, Jim. Evangelism As a Lifestyle. LC 80-83874. 144p. 1980. pap. 5.95 (ISBN 0-89109-475-X). NavPress.

Pope John Paul II. Witnesses of Christ. 398p. 1983. 5.50 (ISBN 0-8198-8206-2); pap. 4.25 (ISBN 0-8198-8207-0). Dghtrs St Paul.

Purves, Jock. The Unlisted Legion. 1978. pap. 4.45 (ISBN 0-85151-245-3). Banner of Truth.

Rinker, Rosalind. You Can Witness with Confidence. pap. 2.95 (ISBN 0-310-32152-2). Zondervan.

--You Can Witness with Confidence. 112p. 1984. pap. 5.95 (ISBN 0-310-32151-4, 10714P). Zondervan.

Rumpf, Oscar J. & Rumpf, David A. Fourteen Witnesses. 1985. 5.95 (ISBN 0-89536-722-X, 5805). CSS of Ohio.

Stewart, John J. How to Gain a Testimony of the Gospel of Jesus Christ. LC 78-52122. 74p. 1978. 5.50 (ISBN 0-88290-097-8). Horizon Utah.

Stratman, Chrysostomos H. & Makrakis, Apostolos. The Roman Rite in Orthodoxy, Part I: Additional Testimonies, Pt. II. 62p. 1957. pap. 1.00x (ISBN 0-938366-38-6). Orthodox Chr.

Sweeting, George. How to Witness Successfully. LC 78-1959. 1978. pap. 3.95 (ISBN 0-8024-3791-5). Moody.

Torrey, R. A. The NIV Vest Pocket Companion for Christian Workers. rev. ed. 96p. 1980. pap. 1.95 saddle-stitch (ISBN 0-310-33331-8, 12152P). Zondervan.

Trites, A. A. The New Testament Concept of Witness. LC 76-11067. (Society for New Testament Studies Monograph: No. 31). 1977. 59.50 (ISBN 0-521-21015-1). Cambridge U Pr.

Witmore, Nyla. How to Reach the Ones You Love: Help for the Family. LC 81-81849. 180p. (Orig.). 1981. pap. 5.95 (ISBN 0-89840-016-3). Campus Crusade.

Witnessing, Telling Others about Jesus. (Teaching Bks.). (Illus.). 15p. 1972. pap. text ed. 2.95 (ISBN 0-86508-155-7). BCM Intl Inc.

Worrell, George E. How to Take the Worry Out of Witnessing. LC 76-13342. 96p. 1976. pap. 4.95 (ISBN 0-8054-5568-X, 4255-68). Broadman.

Worship & Witness. (Faith & Life Ser.). 2.10 (ISBN 0-02-805110-6, 80511). Benziger Pub Co.

WITTGENSTEIN, LUDWIG, 1889-1951

Cavell, Stanley. The Claim of Reason: Wittgenstein, Skepticism, Morality, & Tragedy. 1979. pap. 11.95 (ISBN 0-19-503195-4). Oxford U Pr.

Downey, John K. Beginning at the Beginning: Wittgenstein & Theological Conversation. 166p. (Orig.). 1986. lib. bdg. 23.50 (ISBN 0-8191-5650-7); pap. text ed. 12.50 (ISBN 0-8191-5651-5). U Pr of Amer.

Eller, Vernard. The Language of Canaan & the Grammar of Feminism: An Exercise in Wittgensteinian Analysis. 64p. 1982. pap. 2.95 (ISBN 0-8028-1902-8). Eerdmans.

Kerr, Fergus. Theology after Wittgenstein. 224p. 1986. text ed. 45.00 (ISBN 0-631-14688-1). Basil Blackwell.

Nieli, Russell. Wittgenstein: From Mysticism to Ordinary Language: A Study of Viennese Positivism & the Thought of Ludwig Wittgenstein. (SUNY Series in Philosophy). 224p. 1987. 39.50x (ISBN 0-88706-397-7); pap. 12.95x (ISBN 0-88706-398-5). State U NY Pr.

Poulain, Jacques. Logique & Religion: L'Atomisme Logique de L. Wittgenstein & la Possibilite des Propositions Religieuses. (Religion & Reason: No. 7). 1974. 18.40x (ISBN 90-2797-284-2). Mouton.

WIVES

see also Clergymen's Wives

Bristow, Benny. Ten Commandments for Wives. pap. 4.95 (ISBN 0-89137-430-2). Quality Pubns.

Morgan, Marabel. The Total Woman. 192p. 1973. spire bks. 3.50 (ISBN 0-8007-8218-6). Revell.

Nelson, Martha. On Being a Deacon's Wife. LC 72-96150. 96p. 1973. 7.95 (ISBN 0-8054-3505-0). Broadman.

WOLSEY, THOMAS, CARDINAL 1475?-1530

Belloc, Hilaire. Wolsey. 1978. Repr. of 1933 ed. lib. bdg. 20.00 (ISBN 0-8495-0382-5). Arden Lib.

Cavendish, George. The Life of Cardinal Wolsey. 1887. Repr. 15.00 (ISBN 0-8274-2879-0). R West.

Creighton, Mandell. Cardinal Wolsey. 226p. 1982. Repr. of 1888 ed. lib. bdg. 35.00 (ISBN 0-8495-0878-9). Arden Lib.

Roy, William. Rede Me & Be Nott Wrothe for I Say No Thynge but Trothe. LC 76-38221. (English Experience Ser.: No. 485). 144p. 1972. Repr. of 1528 ed. 13.00 (ISBN 90-221-0485-0). Walter J Johnson.

Sylvester, Richard S. & Harding, Davis P., eds. Two Early Tudor Lives. Incl. The Life & Death of Cardinal Wolsey. Cavendish, George; The Life of Sir Thomas More. Roper, William. xxi, 260p. 1962. pap. 8.95x (ISBN 0-300-00239-4, Y81). Yale U Pr.

Taunton, Ethelred L. Thomas Wolsey: Legate & Reformer. LC 72-112819. 1970. Repr. of 1902 ed. 23.50x (ISBN 0-8046-1086-X, Pub by Kennikat). Assoc Faculty Pr.

WOMAN (THEOLOGY)

Arthur, Rose H. The Wisdom Goddess: Feminine Motifs in Eight Nag Hammadi Documents. Arthur, Richard L., tr. (Illus.). 256p. (Orig.). 1984. lib. bdg. 26.25 (ISBN 0-8191-4171-2); pap. text ed. 13.50 (ISBN 0-8191-4172-0). U Pr of Amer.

Fiorenza, Elisabeth S., ed. In Memory of Her: A Feminist Theological Reconstruction of Christian Origins. 384p. 1984. pap. 12.95 (ISBN 0-8245-0667-7). Crossroad NY.

Jung, Leo. Woman. 239p. 1970. 9.50 (ISBN 0-900689-07-2). Soncino Pr.

Otwell, John H. And Sarah Laughed: The Status of Woman in the Old Testament. LC 76-54671. 222p. 1977. pap. 8.95 (ISBN 0-664-24126-3). Westminster.

Russell, Letty M., ed. The Liberating Word: A Guide to Non-Sexist Interpretation of the Bible. LC 76-18689. 120p. 1976. pap. 7.95 (ISBN 0-664-24751-2). Westminster.

Sekowsky, JoAnne. Restored Value: A Woman's Status in Christ. (Encourager Ser.). 32p. 1985. pap. 2.25 (ISBN 0-932305-01-6, 523001). Aglow Pubns.

WOMEN

see also Mothers; Single Women; Widows; Wives also headings beginning with the word Women

Burghardt, Walter J., ed. Woman: New Dimensions. LC 76-50965. 1977. pap. 5.95 (ISBN 0-8091-2011-9). Paulist Pr.

Coble, Betty J. Woman: Aware & Choosing. new ed. LC 75-7943. 156p. 1975. 8.95 (ISBN 0-8054-5613-9). Broadman.

Elliott, Elisabeth. Let Me Be a Woman. 1977. pap. 5.95 (ISBN 0-8423-2161-6); pap. 3.95 (ISBN 0-8423-2162-4). Tyndale.

Harding, M. Esther. Woman's Mysteries. 1976. pap. 6.95 (ISBN 0-06-090525-5, CN525, PL). Har-Row.

Klaven, Janet & Buckley, Mary I., eds. Women's Spirit Bonding. 320p. (Orig.). 1984. pap. 12.95 (ISBN 0-8298-0707-1). Pilgrim NY.

WOMEN–BIOGRAPHY

Acornley, John H. The Colored Lady Evangelist, Being the Life, Labors, & Experiences of Mrs. Harriet A. Baker. De Swarte, Carolyn G. & Dayton, Donald, eds. (Women in American Protestant Religion Series 1800-1930). 78p. 1987. lib. bdg. 20.00 (ISBN 0-8240-0652-6). Garland Pub.

Andrews, C. W. Memoire of Mrs. Ann R. Page. De Swarte, Carolyn G. & Dayton, Donald, eds. (Women in American Protestant Religion Series 1800-1930). 95p. 1987. lib. bdg. 25.00 (ISBN 0-8240-0657-7). Garland Pub.

Andrews, Lynn V. Medicine Woman. LC 81-47546. 224p. 1983. pap. 7.95 (ISBN 0-06-250026-0, CN 4062, HarpR). Har-Row.

Armstrong, Martin. Lady Hester Stanhope. (Women Ser.). 1928. 17.50 (ISBN 0-8482-7275-7). Norwood Edns.

Arnold, Eberhard, et al. Else Von Hollander. LC 72-96191. 1973. 4.50 (ISBN 0-87486-111-X). Plough.

Beach, Seth C. Daughters of the Puritans: A Group of Brief Biographies. facs. ed. LC 67-22054. (Essay Index Reprint Ser). 1905. 19.00 (ISBN 0-8369-0180-0). Ayer Co Pubs.

Blunt, Hugh F. Great Magdelens. facs. ed. LC 71-86731. (Essay Index Reprint Ser). 1928. 18.50 (ISBN 0-8369-1122-9). Ayer Co Pubs.

Boyd, Nancy. Three Victorian Women Who Changed Their World: Josephine Butler, Octavia Hill, Florence Nightingale. 1982. 22.95x (ISBN 0-19-520271-6). Oxford U Pr.

Brown, George. The Lady Preacher: Or, the Life & Labors of Mrs. Hannah Reeves, the Late Wife of the Rev. William Reeves of the Methodist Church. De Swarte, Carolyn G. & Dayton, Donald, eds. (Women in American Protestant Religion Series 1800-1930). 341p. 1987. lib. bdg. 50.00 (ISBN 0-8240-0660-7). Garland Pub.

Brown, Oswald E. & Brown, Anna M. Life & Letters of Laura Askew Haygood. De Swarte, Carolyn G., ed. (Women in American Protestant Religion Series 1800-1930). 522p. 1987. lib. bdg. 75.00 (ISBN 0-8240-0661-5). Garland Pub.

Cazden, Elizabeth. Antoinette Brown Blackwell: A Biography. LC 82-4986. (Illus.). 328p. 1983. 24.95 (ISBN 0-935312-00-5); pap. 9.95 (ISBN 0-935312-04-8). Feminist Pr.

Clark, Elizabeth A. The Life of Melania the Younger: Introduction, Translation & Commentary. LC 84-20635. (Studies in Women & Religion: Vol. 14). 305p. 1985. 49.95x (ISBN 0-88946-535-5). E Mellen.

Crovitz, Elaine & Buford, Elizabeth. Courage Knows No Sex. 1978. 8.95 (ISBN 0-8158-0363-X). Chris Mass.

De Swarte, Carolyn G., ed. The Nineteenth-Century American Methodist Itinerant Preacher's Wife. Dayton, Doanald, tr. (Women in American Protestant Religion Series 1800-1930). 276p. 1987. lib. bdg. 40.00 (ISBN 0-8240-0656-9). Garland Pub.

De Swarte, Carolyn G. & Dayton, Donald, eds. The Defense of Women's Rights to Ordination in the Methodist Episcopal Church. (Women in American Protestant Religion Series 1800-1930). 230p. 1987. lib. bdg. 35.00 (ISBN 0-8240-0654-2). Garland Pub.

Etheridge, Myrna L. Fearing No Evil. (Illus.). 119p. (Orig.). 1984. pap. 5.00x (ISBN 0-937417-00-9). Etheridge Minist.

Foster, John O. Life & Labors of Mrs. Maggie Newton Van Cott, the First Lady Licensed to Preach in the Methodist Episcopal Church in the United States. Gifford, Carolyn & Dayton, Donald, eds. (Women in American Protestant Religion 1800-1930 Ser.). 339p. 1987. lib. bdg. 50.00 (ISBN 0-8240-0663-1). Garland Pub.

Goehri Ethridge, Myrna L. Fearing No Evil: One Woman's Life of Tragedy & Victory. (Illus.). 108p. (Orig.). 1984. pap. 5.95 (ISBN 0-941018-12-1). Martin Pr CA.

Griffith, Elisabeth. In Her Own Right: The Life of Elizabeth Cady Stanton. LC 83-25120. (Illus.). 1984. 19.95 (ISBN 0-19-503440-6). Oxford U Pr.

Hawley, Gloria H. Frankly Feminine: God's Idea of Womanhood. LC 81-50348. 128p. (Orig.). 1981. pap. 3.50 (ISBN 0-87239-455-7, 2969). Standard Pub.

Horton, Isabelle. High Adventure: Life of Lucy Rider Meyer. Gifford, Carolyn & Dayton, Donald, eds. (Women in American Protestant Religion 1800-1930 Ser.). 359p. 1987. lib. bdg. 50.00 (ISBN 0-8240-0665-8). Garland Pub.

Kershaw, Beulah S. Scared Woman: True Expose, Vol. I. (Illus.). 44p. (Orig.). 1981. pap. 3.00x (ISBN 0-911870-03-2). Beulah.

Ladies Home Journal & Christian Science Monitor. America's Twelve Great Women Leaders During the Past Hundred Years As Chosen by the Women of America. facs. ed. LC 74-90600. (Essay Index Reprint Ser). 1933. 14.00 (ISBN 0-8369-1202-0). Ayer Co Pubs.

MacDonell, Robert W. Belle Harris Bennett, Her Life Work. Gifford, Carolyn D. & Dayton, Donald, eds. (Women in American Protestant Religion 1800-1930 Ser.). 297p. 1987. lib. bdg. 40.00 (ISBN 0-8240-0669-0). Garland Pub.

Montgomery, Carrie J. The Life & the Teaching of Carrie Judd Montgomery. Dayton, Donald W., ed. (The Higher Christian Life Ser.). 420p. 1985. 50.00 (ISBN 0-8240-6430-5). Garland Pub.

Montgomery, Ruth. Ruth Montgomery: Herald of the New Age. LC 85-25424. 288p. 1986. 16.95 (ISBN 0-385-23311-6, Dolp). Doubleday.

Mueller, Friedrich M. Life & Religion. LC 73-18821. Repr. of 1905 ed. 19.75 (ISBN 0-404-11448-2). AMS Pr.

Murphy, Carol. Four Women: Four Windows on Light. Mather, Eleanore P., ed. LC 81-80220. 26p. 1981. pap. 2.50x (ISBN 0-87574-236-X, 236). Pendle Hill.

Palmer, Phoebe & Wheatley, Richard. The Life & Letters of Mrs. Phoebe Palmer. Dayton, Donald W., ed. (The Higher Christian Life Ser.). 636p. 1985. 80.00 (ISBN 0-8240-6432-1). Garland Pub.

Prentiss, George L. The Life & Letters of Elizabeth Prentiss. Gifford, Carolyn D. & Dayton, Donald, eds. (Women in American Protestant Religion 1800-1930 Ser.). 573p. 1987. lib. bdg. 80.00 (ISBN 0-8240-0672-0). Garland Pub.

Raser, Harold E. Phoebe Palmer: Her Life & Thought. LC 86-31251. (Studies in Women & Religion: Vol. 22). 392p. 1987. 59.95 (ISBN 0-88946-527-4). E Mellen.

Schmidt, Margaret F. Passion's Child: The Extraordinary Life of Jane Digby. 5.95 (ISBN 0-7043-3202-7, Pub. by Quartet England). Charles River Bks.

Sleeper, Sarah. Memoir of the Late Martha Hazeltine Smith. Gifford, Carolyn D. & Dayton, Donald, eds. (Women in American Protestant Religion 1800-1930 Ser.). 294p. 1987. lib. bdg. 40.00 (ISBN 0-8240-0686-0). Garland Pub.

Smith, Amanda B. An Autobiography: The Story of the Lord's Dealings with Mrs. Amanda Smith, The Colored Evangelist, Containing an Account of Her Life Work of Faith, & Her Travels in America, England, Ireland, Scotland, India & Africa, as an Independent Missionary. Gifford, Carolyn D. & Dayton, Donald, eds. (Women in American Protestant Religion 1800-1930 Ser.). 506p. 1987. lib. bdg. 70.00 (ISBN 0-8240-0674-7). Garland Pub.

Swain, Clara A. A Glimpse of India, Being a Collection of Extracts from the Letters of Dr. Clara A. Swain. Gifford, Carolyn D. & Dayton, Donald, eds. (Women in American Protestant Religion 1800-1930 Ser.). 366p. 1987. lib. bdg. 50.00 (ISBN 0-8240-0677-1). Garland Pub.

Tsatsos, Ioanna. Hours on Sinai. Vaporis, N. M., ed. Demos, Jean, tr. from Gr. Orig. Title: Apo to Tetradio Mou: Hores Tou Sina. 76p. 1984. pap. text ed. 8.00 (ISBN 0-917653-00-9). Hellenic Coll Pr.

Wagenknecht, Edward. Daughters of the Covenant: Portraits of Six Jewish Women. LC 83-3562. (Illus.). 200p. 1983. lib. bdg. 17.50x (ISBN 0-87023-396-3). U of Mass Pr.

Walsh, James J., compiled by. These Splendid Sisters. LC 75-128326. (Essay Index Reprint Ser). 1927. 18.00 (ISBN 0-8369-1856-8). Ayer Co Pubs.

Way, Nancy L. A Second Chance. 1985. 5.95 (ISBN 0-8062-2444-4). Carlton.

Winslow, Miron. Memoir of Mrs. Harriet L. Winslow, Thirteen Years a Member of the American Mission in Ceylon. Gifford, Carolyn D. & Dayton, Donald, eds. (Women in American Protestant Religion 1800-1930 Ser.). 480p. 1987. lib. bdg. 70.00 (ISBN 0-8240-0684-4). Garland Pub.

WOMEN–PRAYER-BOOKS AND DEVOTIONS

see also Women–Religious Life

Aglow Editors. Come Celebrate: A Daily Devotional. 266p. 1984. pap. 6.95 (ISBN 0-930756-78-9, 531018). Aglow Pubns.

Andersen, Linda. Love Adds the Chocolate. 1984. 4.95 (ISBN 0-8010-0198-6). Baker Bk.

Anderson, Evelyn M. Good Morning, Lord: Devotions for Women. (Good Morning Lord Ser.). 1971. 4.95 (ISBN 0-8010-0023-8). Baker Bk.

Bacher, June M. Quiet Moments for Women: A Daily Devotional. LC 79-84722. 1979. pap. 7.95 (ISBN 0-89081-187-3). Harvest Hse.

Baker, Pat A. A Minute in the Morning: One Hundred & Fifty Devotionals for Women. 1984. pap. 4.95 (ISBN 0-8010-0864-6). Baker Bk.

Barkman, Alma. Sunny-Side Up. (Quiet Time Bks.). 1984. pap. 3.50 (ISBN 0-8024-8431-X). Moody.

Blaquiere, Georgette. The Grace to Be a Woman. Wild, Robert, tr. from Fr. LC 83-15858. 127p. 1983. pap. 6.95 (ISBN 0-8189-0449-6). Alba.

Bolding, Amy. Please Give a Devotion: For Women's Groups. (Paperback Program Ser.). 108p. 1976. pap. 3.95 (ISBN 0-8010-0583-3). Baker Bk.

Carroll, Frances. A Book of Devotions for Today's Woman. 192p. 1983. pap. 5.95 (ISBN 0-13-080028-7). P-H.

Davis, Melodie M. You Know You're a Mother When... 112p. 1987. pap. 4.95 (ISBN 0-310-44811-5). Zondervan.

Esway, Judy. Prayers of a Working Mother. (Getting Book Line Ser.). 32p. (Orig.). 1985. pap. 1.50 (ISBN 0-89622-269-1). Twenty-Third.

Fenelon, Francois. Spiritual Letters to Women. 224p. 1984. pap. 5.95 (ISBN 0-310-36371-3, 12366P, Clarion Class). Zondervan.

Harrell, Irene B. A Prayerable a Day. (Orig.). 1987. pap. 7.00 (ISBN 0-915541-15-7). Star Bks Inc.

Hillen, Kathryn. Cooking up Dreams. 160p. 1987. pap. 9.95 (ISBN 0-310-34551-0). Zondervan.

Holmes, Marjorie. Hold Me up a Little Longer, Lord. LC 76-42338. (Illus.). 1977. 9.95 (ISBN 0-385-12403-1). Doubleday.

--I've Got to Talk to Somebody, God. 160p. 1985. pap. 3.50 (ISBN 0-553-26428-1). Bantam.

--I've Got to Talk to Somebody, God. LC 69-10938. 1969. 8.95 (ISBN 0-385-05209-X). Doubleday.

Isler, Betty. A Time for Every Purpose. 80p. (Orig.). 1986. pap. 4.95 (ISBN 0-570-03986-X, 12-3013). Concordia.

Johnson, Lois. Just a Minute, Lord: Prayers for Girls. LC 73-78265. (Illus.). 96p. (Orig.). 1973. pap. 3.95 (ISBN 0-8066-1329-7, 10-3605). Augsburg.

Larson, Mobby. Prayers of a New Mother. (Greeting Book Line Ser.). 48p. (Orig.). 1985. pap. 1.50 (ISBN 0-89622-230-6). Twenty Third.

Lee, Helen. This Is My Home, Lord. 128p. 1983. pap. 4.95 (ISBN 0-86683-683-7, HarpR). Har-Row.

Lenzkes, Susan. When the Handwriting on the Wall Is in Brown Crayon. 1986. pap. 4.95 (ISBN 0-310-43631-1, 6891P). Zondervan.

Nelson, Ruth Y. God's Song in My Heart: Daily Devotions. LC 56-11912. 432p. 1957. 8.95 (ISBN 0-8006-0254-4, 1-254). Fortress.

Richards, Lawrence O. The Christian Man's Promise Book. 1986. pap. 2.50 (ISBN 0-310-43582-X, 18211P). Zondervan.

--The Christian Woman's Promise Book. 1986. pap. 2.50 (ISBN 0-310-43592-7, 18212P). Zondervan.

Roller, Karen L., ed. Women Pray. 96p. (Orig.). 1986. pap. 3.95 (ISBN 0-8298-0737-3). Pilgrim NY.

Shaw, Jean. Greater Love: A Woman's Workshop on Friendship. 96p. 1984. pap. 2.95 (ISBN 0-310-43531-5, 9596P). Zondervan.

Summers, Georgianna. The Ladies, God Bless 'Em. 1983. 3.75 (ISBN 0-89536-581-2, 1264). CSS of Ohio.

Voigt, Tracy. Prayers of a Woman. rev. 3rd ed. 55p. 1982. Repr. of 1976 ed. spiral bdg. 4.00 (ISBN 0-686-37419-3). T Voigt.

Webb, Barbara O. Waiting for My Baby. 80p. 1985. 6.95 (ISBN 0-570-04219-4, 15-2180). Concordia.

Witmore, Nyla. Homemaking Programs, Talks & Activities. LC 82-5626. (Illus.). 160p. (Orig.). 1982. pap. 4.95 (ISBN 0-87239-565-0, 2973). Standard Pub.

Woman to Woman: Selected Talks from the BYU Women's Conferences. LC 86-2048. 223p. 1986. 9.95 (ISBN 0-87579-035-6). Deseret Bk.

WOMEN–RELIGIOUS LIFE

see also Monastic and Religious Life of Women

Alberione, James. Woman: Her Influence & Zeal. (Orig.). 1964. 3.50 (ISBN 0-8198-0176-3); pap. 1.25 (ISBN 0-8198-0177-1). Dghtrs St Paul.

Alderfer, Helen, ed. Farthing in Her Hand: Stewardship for Women. LC 64-23376. 226p. 1964. pap. 4.95 (ISBN 0-8361-1515-5). Herald Pr.

Alexander, Myrna. Behold Your God: A Woman's Workshop on the Attributes of God. pap. 3.95 (ISBN 0-310-37131-7, 10916P). Zondervan.

Ammerman, Leila T. Inspiring Devotional Programs for Women's Groups. (Paperback Program Ser). 1971. pap. 3.50 (ISBN 0-8010-0015-7). Baker Bk.

Andersen, Linda. Slices of Life. 112p. 1986. pap. 6.95 (ISBN 0-8010-0205-2). Baker Bk.

Andrews, C. W. Memoire of Mrs. Ann R. Page. De Swarte, Carolyn G. & Dayton, Donald, eds. (Women in American Protestant Religion Series 1800-1930). 95p. 1987. lib. bdg. 25.00 (ISBN 0-8240-0657-7). Garland Pub.

Armstrong, Karen. Gospel According to Woman. LC 86-26610. 384p. 1987. 17.95 (ISBN 0-385-24078-3, Anchor Pr). Doubleday.

Avallone, Paul P. The Consecrated Woman: A Guide to the Don Bosco Volunteers. (Salesian Family Ser.). 27p. 1983. pap. 3.00 (ISBN 0-89944-075-4). Don Bosco Multimedia.

Baker, Derek, ed. Medieval Women. (Studies in Church History: Subsidia 1). 412p. 1981. pap. 9.95x (ISBN 0-631-12539-6). Basil Blackwell.

Bankson, Marjory Z. Braided Streams: Esther & a Woman's Way of Growing. LC 85-50203. (Illus.). 184p. (Orig.). 1985. pap. 8.95 (ISBN 0-931055-05-9). LuraMedia.

Birkey, Verna. You Are Very Special: A Biblical Guide to Self-Worth. 160p. 1977. pap. 5.95 (ISBN 0-8007-5032-2, Power Bks). Revell.

Bloem, Diane. A Womans Workshop on Proverbs. 1978. leader's manual 5.95 (ISBN 0-310-21371-1, 10684); student manual 2.95 (ISBN 0-310-21361-4, 10683). Zondervan.

--A Woman's Workshop on the Beautitudes. (Orig.). 1981. Leader's Manual, 160 Pages. pap. 3.95 (ISBN 0-310-42641-3, 112160); Student's Manual, 96 Pages. pap. 2.95 (ISBN 0-310-42651-0, 11217). Zondervan.

Bloem, Diane B. Leader's Manual: A Woman's Workshop on Bible Women. 128p. 1983. pap. 3.95 student Manual (ISBN 0-310-23151-5); tchr's. manual avail. (ISBN 0-310-23141-8, 10747). Zondervan.

Bohn, Carol & Getz, Lorine, eds. A Registry of Women in Religious Studies, 1981-1982. (Bohn Ser.). 1981. 9.95 (ISBN 0-88946-277-1). E Mellen.

Bonds of Sisterhood: A History of the RLDS Women's Organization, 1842-1983. 170p. 1985. pap. 9.75 (ISBN 0-8309-0401-8). Herald Hse.

Brand, Irene. Meet Mary & Martha. 144p. 1985. pap. 4.95 (ISBN 0-87239-899-4, 2978). Standard Pub.

Broome, Connie. Vessels Unto Honor. LC 76-22242. 1977. pap. 3.50 (ISBN 0-87148-879-5). Pathway Pr.

Brown, George. The Lady Preacher: Or, the Life & Labors of Mrs. Hannah Reeves, the Late Wife of the Rev. William Reeves of the Methodist Church. De Swarte, Carolyn G. & Dayton, Donald, eds. (Women in American Protestant Religion Series 1800-1930). 341p. 1987. lib. bdg. 50.00 (ISBN 0-8240-0660-7). Garland Pub.

Brown, Oswald E. & Brown, Anna M. Life & Letters of Laura Askew Haygood. De Swarte, Carolyn G., ed. (Women in American Protestant Religion Series 1800-1930). 522p. 1987. lib. bdg. 75.00 (ISBN 0-8240-0661-5). Garland Pub.

Budapest, Zsuzsanna. The Holy Book of Women's Mysteries, 2 vols. rev. ed. 1986. pap. write for info. (ISBN 0-937081-03-5). SBA Coven.

--The Holy Book of Women's Mysteries, Pt. 1. rev. ed. 1986. pap. text ed. write for info. (ISBN 0-937081-01-9). SBA Coven.

--The Holy Book of Women's Mysteries, Pt. 2. rev. ed. 1986. pap. write for info. (ISBN 0-937081-02-7). SBA Coven.

Burroughs. The Christian Woman's Resource Book. LC 83-26063. 1987. 9.95 (A Bridgebooks Publication). Westminster.

Burroughs, Melba G. The Christian Woman's Resource Book. LC 83-26063. 202p. (Orig.). 1984. pap. 9.95 (ISBN 0-664-26008-X, A Bridgebooks Publication). Westminster.

Burrus, Virginia. Chastity As Autonomy: Women in the Stories of Apocryphal Acts. (Studies in Women & Religion). 184p. 1987. text ed. 39.95 (ISBN 0-88946-526-6). E Mellen.

Bush, Barbara. Heart Trouble: A Woman's Workshop on Christian Character. Kobobel, Janet, ed. (Woman's Workshop Ser.). (Orig.). 1985. pap. 2.95 (ISBN 0-310-29431-2, 12016P). Zondervan.

Byrd & Horton. Keeping Your Balance. 1986. 6.95 (ISBN 0-8499-3056-1). Word Bks.

Campbell, R. K. Woman's Place. 32p. pap. 0.60 (ISBN 0-88172-014-3). Believers Bkshelf.

Canadian Christian Movement for Peace Staff. Women & Human Wholeness. Huntly, Alyson, et al, eds. (People Living for Justice Ser.). 160p. 1983. pap. text ed. 29.95 (ISBN 0-697-01920-9). Wm C Brown.

Caprio, Betsy. The Woman Sealed in the Tower: A Psychological Approach to Feminine Spirituality. 1983. pap. 5.95 (ISBN 0-8091-2486-6). Paulist Pr.

Carmody, Denise L. Seizing the Apple: A Feminist Spirituality of Personal Growth. 176p. (Orig.). 1984. pap. 10.95 (ISBN 0-8245-0652-9). Crossroad NY.

Carroll, Alexander. Women of Early Christianity. 75.00 (ISBN 0-87968-268-X). Gordon Pr.

Chervin, Ronda. Feminine Free & Faithful. LC 86-80785. 143p. 1986. pap. 7.95 (ISBN 0-89870-103-1). Ignatius Pr.

Christ, Carol. Diving Deep & Surfacing: Women Writers on Spiritual Quest. 2nd, rev. ed. LC 86-70552. 157p. 1986. pap. 8.95 (ISBN 0-8070-6351-7, BP 722). Beacon Pr.

Christ, Carol P. & Plaskow, Judith. Womanspirit Rising: A Feminist Reader in Religion. LC 78-3363. (Orig.). 1979. pap. 8.95 (ISBN 0-06-061385-8, RD 275, HarpR). Har-Row.

Christenson, Evelyn & Blake, Viola. What Happens When Women Pray. 144p. 1975. pap. 5.95 (ISBN 0-88207-715-5). Victor Bks.

Clark, Elizabeth A. Ascetic Piety & Women's Faith: Essays in Late Ancient Christianity. (Studies in Women & Religion: Vol. 20). 1986. 69.95 (ISBN 0-88946-529-0). E Mellen.

--Ascetic Piety & Women's Faith: Essays on Late Ancient Christianity. LC 86-21828. (Studies in Women & Religion: Volume 20). 448p. 1986. lib. bdg. 69.95 (ISBN 0-88946-529-0). E Mellen.

--Jerome, Chrysostom & Friends: Essays & Translations. LC 82-20829. (Studies in Women & Religion: Vol. 2). xi, 270p. 1983. Repr. of 1979 ed. 49.95x (ISBN 0-88946-541-X). E Mellen.

--The Life of Melania the Younger: Introduction, Translation & Commentary. LC 84-20635. (Studies in Women & Religion: Vol. 14). 305p. 1985. 49.95x (ISBN 0-88946-535-5). E Mellen.

Clark, Mary F. Hiding, Hurting, Healing. 176p. (Orig.). 1985. pap. 6.95 (ISBN 0-310-30551-9, 11612). Zondervan.

Cooper, Darien B. The Christian Woman's Planner. 160p. (Orig.). 1986. pap. 8.95 spiral bdg. (ISBN 0-310-44621-X, 11742P). Zondervan.

Coppin, Fanny J. Reminiscences of School Life & Hints On Teaching. De Swarte, Carolyn G. & Dayton, Donald, eds. (Women in American Protestant Religion Series 1800-1930). 191p. 1987. lib. bdg. 30.00 (ISBN 0-8240-0662-3). Garland Pub.

Cosby, Clair. Reflecting the Lord's Radiance. (Orig.). 1987. pap. 5.95 (ISBN 0-8054-5916-2). Broadman.

D'Addio, Janie. Every Woman Can. Cox, Terri, ed. (Illus.). 112p. 1983. pap. 9.95 (ISBN 0-914759-00-0). Preferred Pr.

Darst, H. W. Far above Rubies. 128p. (Orig.). 1982. pap. 2.50 (ISBN 0-89114-110-3). Baptist Pub Hse.

Daughters of St. Paul. Thoughts of the Servant of God, Mother Thecla Merlo. LC 68-59045. 1974. flexible plastic 2.25 (ISBN 0-8198-0509-2). Dghtrs St Paul.

Davis, Joy M. A Woman's Song. LC 83-70376. (Orig.). 1984. pap. 5.95 (ISBN 0-8054-5243-5). Broadman.

Dayton, Donald W., ed. Holiness Tracts Defending the Ministry of Women. (The Higher Christian Life Ser.). 304p. 1985. 40.00 (ISBN 0-8240-6411-9). Garland Pub.

Deshon, George. Guide for Catholic Young Women. 24.50 (ISBN 0-405-10816-8). Ayer Co Pubs.

De Swarte, Carolyn G., ed. The Nineteenth-Century American Methodist Itinerant Preacher's Wife. Dayton, Doanald, tr. (Women in American Protestant Religion Series 1800-1930). 276p. 1987. lib. bdg. 40.00 (ISBN 0-8240-0656-9). Garland Pub.

Douglass, Jane D. Women, Freedom, & Calvin. LC 85-8778. 156p. 1985. pap. 11.95 (ISBN 0-664-24663-X). Westminster.

Drake, Marsha. The Submissive Wife & other Legends. 176p. (Orig.). 1987. pap. 5.95 (ISBN 0-87123-926-4). Bethany Hse.

Emswiler, Sharon & Neufer, Thomas. Women & Worship. rev., expanded ed. LC 83-48459. 144p. 1984. pap. 5.95 (ISBN 0-06-066101-1, RD 507, HarpR). Har-Row.

Evans, Debra. The Mystery of Womanhood. LC 86-72262. 256p. (Orig.). 1987. pap. 8.95 (ISBN 0-89107-426-0, Crossway Bks). Good News.

Falk, Nancy A. & Gross, Rita M., eds. Unspoken Worlds. LC 79-2989. (Women's Religious Lives Ser.). 304p. (Orig.). 1980. pap. text ed. 5.95x (ISBN 0-06-063492-8, RD 308, HarpR). Har-Row.

Fiorenza, Elisabeth S. & Collins, Mary, eds. Women: Invisible In Church & Theology. (Concilium Ser.: Vol. 182). 128p. 1985. pap. 6.95 (Pub. by T & T Clark Ltd UK). Fortress.

Foster, John O. Life & Labors of Mrs. Maggie Newton Van Cott, the First Lady Licensed to Preach in the Methodist Episcopal Church in the United States. Gifford, Carolyn & Dayton, Donald, eds. (Women in American Protestant Religion 1800-1930 Ser.). 339p. 1987. lib. bdg. 50.00 (ISBN 0-8240-0663-1). Garland Pub.

Foster, Warren D., ed. Heroines of Modern Religion. LC 77-107700. (Essay Index Reprint Ser.). 1913. 20.00 (ISBN 0-8369-1572-0). Ayer Co Pubs.

Franklin, Margaret A., ed. The Force of the Feminine: Women, Men & the Church. 232p. 1986. text ed. 29.95x (ISBN 0-86861-930-2); pap. text ed. 12.95x (ISBN 0-86861-914-0). Allen Unwin.

Frost, Marie H. Frankly Feminine: Leader's Guide. 48p. (Orig.). 1984. pap. 2.95 (ISBN 0-87239-746-7, 2970). Standard Pub.

Gage, Joy. Every Woman's Privilege: Taking Responsibility for Your Spiritual Growth. (Touch of Grace Ser.). 1986. pap. 6.95 (ISBN 0-88070-177-3). Multnomah.

Gage, Matilda J. Woman, Church, & State: A Historical Account of the Status of Woman Through the Christian Ages, with Reminiscenses of the Matriarchate. 2nd ed. LC 72-2602. (American Women Ser.: Images & Realities). 558p. 1972. Repr. of 1900 ed. 32.00 (ISBN 0-405-04458-5). Ayer Co Pubs.

Garcia, Jo, ed. Walking on the Water: Women Talk about Spirituality. Maitland, Sara. (Illus.). 224p. 1984. pap. 5.95 (ISBN 0-86068-381-8, Pub by Virago Pr). Salem Hse Pubs.

Glaphre. Talking with God: A Woman's Workshop on Prayer. (Woman's Workshop Ser.). 160p. (Orig.). 1985. pap. 3.95 (ISBN 0-310-45301-1, 12240P). Zondervan.

Goldberg, Louis. Deuteronomy. (Bible Study Commentary Ser.). 208p. 1986. pap. 7.95 (ISBN 0-310-20201-9, 11412P). Zondervan.

Grams, Betty J. Women of Grace. LC 77-93409. 128p. 1978. pap. 3.95 (ISBN 0-88243-751-8, 02-0751, Radiant Books); tchr's. ed 3.95 (ISBN 0-88243-336-9, 02-0336). Gospel Pub.

Graver, Jane. Please, Lord, Don't Put Me on Hold! 1979. pap. 2.25 (ISBN 0-570-03790-5, 12-2753). Concordia.

Hagin, Kenneth E. The Woman Question. 2nd ed. 1983. pap. 2.50 (ISBN 0-89276-405-8). Hagin Ministries.

Hammett, Jenny. Woman's Transformation: A Psychological Theology. LC 82-14287. (Symposium Ser.: Vol. 8). 112p. 1982. pap. 19.95x (ISBN 0-88946-918-0). E Mellen.

Handford, Elizabeth R. & Martin, Joy R. Fatigue: Satan's Secret Weapon against Women. 23p. (Orig.). 1986. pap. 1.00 (ISBN 0-912623-03-9). Joyful Woman.

Hardesty. Great Women of Faith. 2.95 (ISBN 0-318-18173-8). WCTU.

Hassey, Janette. No Time for Silence: Evangelical Women in Public Ministry Around the Turn of the Century. 176p. 1986. pap. 7.95 (ISBN 0-310-29451-7, 12786P). Zondervan.

Haughton, Rosemary. The Re-Creation of Eve. 1985. pap. 8.95 (ISBN 0-87243-135-5). Templegate.

Hellwig, Monika K. Christian Women in a Troubled World: Madeleva Lecture 1984. 60p. (Orig.). 1985. 2.95 (ISBN 0-8091-2713-X). Paulist Pr.

Hepburn, Daisy. Look, You're a Leader. LC 85-19637. 284p. 1985. pap. write for info. (ISBN 0-8307-1098-1, 5418647); resource manual avail. (ISBN 0-8307-1074-4, 5203023). Regal.

Hepburn, Daisy & Klope, Joan B. How to Grow a Women's Minis-Tree. (Illus., Orig.). 1986. resource manual 7.95 (ISBN 0-8307-1055-8, 5203018). Regal.

Herr, Ethel. Bible Study for Busy Women. 160p. 1983. pap. 6.95 (ISBN 0-8024-0147-3). Moody.

Herrscher, Michele W. Forever Fit: Aerobic Dance & Exercise for the Latter-day Saint Woman. LC 85-13637. (Illus.). 120p. 1985. pap. 12.95 (ISBN 0-87747-768-X). Deseret Bk.

Hicks, Margaret. Christian Woman's Answer to Aging. 29p. (Orig.). 1986. pap. 0.75 (ISBN 0-89274-394-8). Harrison Hse.

Hobbs, Carolyn. And He Loved Her. 185p. (Orig.). 1979. pap. 1.95 (ISBN 0-89084-113-6). Bob Jones Univ Pr.

Horton, Isabelle. High Adventure: Life of Lucy Rider Meyer. Gifford, Carolyn & Dayton, Donald, eds. (Women in American Protestant Religion 1800-1930 Ser.). 359p. 1987. lib. bdg. 50.00 (ISBN 0-8240-0665-8). Garland Pub.

Hurd, Jerrie W. Our Sisters in the Latter-Day Scriptures. 1987. 10.95 (ISBN 0-87579-091-7). Deseret Bk.

Hyde, Kathy. Teaching the Bible to Change Lives. LC 84-47801. 143p. (Orig.). 1984. pap. 6.95 (ISBN 0-89840-064-3). Heres Life.

Ingraham, Sarah R. Walks of Usefulness: Or Reminiscenes of Mrs. Margaret Prior. Gifford, Carolyn & Dayton, Donald, eds. (Women in American Protestant Religion 1800-1930 Ser.). 324p. 1987. lib. bdg. 45.00 (ISBN 0-8240-0666-6). Garland Pub.

Jennings, Sr. Vivian. Valiant Woman: At the Heart of Reconciliation. LC 74-6037. 128p. 1974. 3.95 (ISBN 0-8189-0291-4). Alba.

Jepsen, Dee. Women, the Challenge & the Call: An Agenda for Christian Women in Today's World. (Christian Essentials Ser.). 48p. (Orig.). 1987. pap. 1.95 (ISBN 0-89283-323-8). Servant.

Jicks, John M. & Morton, Bruce L. Woman's Role in the Church. pap. 2.95 (ISBN 0-89315-362-1). Lambert Bk.

Karssen, Gien. Her Name Is Woman, 2 bks. LC 77-81187. Bk. 1, 1975. pap. 5.95 (ISBN 0-89109-420-2); Bk. 2, 1977. pap. 5.95 (ISBN 0-89109-424-5). NavPress.

Kimball, Gayle. The Religious Ideas of Harriet Beecher Stowe: Her Gospel of Womanhood. LC 82-80377. (Studies in Women & Religion: Vol. 8). 216p. 1982. 49.95x (ISBN 0-88946-544-4). E Mellen.

Knorr, Dandi D. A Spiritual Handbook for Women. 192p. 1984. 13.95 (ISBN 0-13-834796-4, Spec); pap. 6.95 (ISBN 0-13-834788-3). P-H.

La Haye, Beverly. I Am a Woman by God's Design. 160p. 1980. pap. 5.95 (ISBN 0-8007-5100-0, Power Bks); study guide o.p. 3.95 (ISBN 0-8007-1294-3). Revell.

Lake, Alice. Our Own Years. 244p. 1982. pap. 8.95 (ISBN 0-86683-667-5, HarpR). Har-Row.

Lehman, Edward C., Jr. Women Clergy: Breaking Through Gender Barriers. 300p. 1985. 24.95 (ISBN 0-88738-071-9). Transaction Bks.

Levi, Shonie B. & Kaplan, Sylvia R. Guide for the Jewish Homemaker. 2nd ed. LC 59-12039. (Illus.). 1965. pap. 6.95 (ISBN 0-8052-0087-8). Schocken.

Livingston, Mrs. J. B. Today's Victorious Woman, Vol. 2. pap. 4.00 (ISBN 0-89137-427-2). Quality Pubns.

Loeks, Mary F. The Glorious Names of God. 1986. pap. 3.95 (ISBN 0-8010-5629-2). Baker Bk.

Luke, Helen M. Life of the Spirit in Women: A Jungian Approach. 1983. pap. 2.50x (ISBN 0-87574-230-0, 230). Pendle Hill.

McBeth, Leon. Women in Baptist Life. LC 78-54245. 1979. 7.95 (ISBN 0-8054-6925-7). Broadman.

McCarthy, Caritas. The Spirituality of Cornelia Connelly: In God, For God, With God. LC 86-21718. (Studies in Women & Religion Ser.). 280p. 1986. text ed. 49.95 (ISBN 0-88946-530-4). E Mellen.

MacDonald, Gail. High Call, High Privilege. 1981. pap. 6.95 (ISBN 0-8423-1424-5). Tyndale.

MacHaffie, Barbara J. Her Story: Women in Christian Tradition. LC 85-45494. 192p. 1986. pap. 9.95 (ISBN 0-8006-1893-9). Fortress.

McIntyre, Marie. Female & Catholic: A Journal of Mind & Heart. 80p. (Orig.). 1986. pap. 3.95 (ISBN 0-89622-307-8). Twenty-Third.

McKay, Bobbie. The Unabridged Woman. LC 79-14297. (Orig.). 1979. pap. 5.95 (ISBN 0-8298-0369-6). Pilgrim NY.

Malmgreen, Gail, ed. Religion in the Lives of English Women, 1760-1930. LC 86-45172. 224p. 1986. 29.95x (ISBN 0-253-34973-7). Ind U Pr.

Malone, Mary T. Women Christian: New Vision. 176p. 1985. pap. 6.95 (ISBN 0-697-02064-9). Wm C Brown.

Marshall, Helen L. Inspirational Resources for Women's Groups. 64p. 1985. pap. 3.95 (ISBN 0-8010-6196-2). Baker Bk.

Mather, Cotton. Ornaments for the Daughters of Zion. LC 78-8588. 1978. 35.00x (ISBN 0-8201-1311-5). Schol Facsimiles.

Mattox, Beverly. Help! I'm a Woman! LC 77-21631. 1977. pap. 1.95 (ISBN 0-87227-053-X). Reg Baptist.

Mollencott, Virginia R. Women of Faith in Dialogue. 144p. (Orig.). 1987. pap. 9.95 (ISBN 0-8245-0823-8). Crossroad NY.

Moloney, Francis J. Woman: First among the Faithful. LC 85-73197. 128p. 1986. pap. 4.95 (ISBN 0-87793-333-2). Ave Maria.

Monks Of Solesmes, ed. Woman in the Modern World: Six Hundred & Thirty-Seven Pronouncements from Leo Thirteenth to Pius Twelfth. 4.00 (ISBN 0-8198-0178-X). Dghtrs St Paul.

Montgomery, Carrie J. The Life & the Teaching of Carrie Judd Montgomery. Dayton, Donald W., ed. (The Higher Christian Life Ser.). 420p. 1985. 50.00 (ISBN 0-8240-6430-5). Garland Pub.

Moravec, Marilyn, et al. Push Me Gently, Lord. LC 85-80100. 186p. (Orig.). 1985. pap. 4.95 (ISBN 0-935797-21-1). Harvest IL.

Morley, Raoul. Womanhood: The Feminine in Ancient Hellenism Gnosticism, Christianity & Islam. 119p. 1985. 16.95 (ISBN 0-9594165-0-1, Pub. by Delacroix Pr); pap. 8.95 (ISBN 0-317-41343-0). Intl Spec Bk.

Morrissey, Kirkie. Designed by God: A Woman's Workshop on Wholeness. (Woman's Workshop Ser.). 160p. (Orig.). 1985. pap. 3.95 (ISBN 0-310-45011-X, 16246P). Zondervan.

Morton, Nelle. The Journey Is Home: The Distinguished Feminist Theologian Traces the Development of Her Personal & Theoretical Vision. LC 85-42342. 285p. 1986. pap. 8.95 (ISBN 0-8070-1133-9, BP 718). Beacon Pr.

Mulliken, Frances H. First Ladies of the Restoration. 1985. pap. 6.50 (ISBN 0-8309-0419-0). Herald Hse.

Murphey, Cecil B., compiled by. The Encyclopedia for Today's Christian Woman. (Encyclopedias Ser.). 512p. 1984. 16.95 (ISBN 0-8007-1393-1). Revell.

Murphy, Sheila M. Midlife Wanderer: The Woman Religious in Midlife Transition. LC 83-25806. 176p. (Orig.). 1983. pap. 8.00 (ISBN 0-89571-018-8). Affirmation.

Nelson, Martha. The Christian Woman in the Working World. LC 76-127198. 141p. 1975. pap. 1.50 (ISBN 0-8054-6915-X). Broadman.

--On Being a Deacon's Wife: Study Guide. LC 72-96150. 1977. saddlewire 2.25 (ISBN 0-8054-3507-7). Broadman.

Nichols, John A. & Shank, M. Thomas, eds. Medieval Religious Women I: Distant Echoes. (Cistercian Studies: No. 71). 1984. 29.95 (ISBN 0-87907-871-5); pap. 11.95 (ISBN 0-87907-971-1). Cistercian Pubns.

Nystrom, Carolyn. Basic Beliefs: A Woman's Workshop on the Christian Faith. (Woman's Workshop Ser.). 124p. 1986. pap. 3.95 (ISBN 0-310-41971-9). Zondervan.

--Characters & Kings: A Woman's Workshop on the History of Israel, 2 pts. (Woman's Workshop Ser.). 240p. (Orig.). 1985. Part 1. pap. 2.95 (ISBN 0-310-41881-X, 11279P); Part 2. pap. 3.95 (ISBN 0-310-41871-2, 11283). Zondervan.

Nystrom, Carolyn & Fromer, Margaret. People in Turmoil: A Woman's Workshop on First Corinthians. (Woman's Workshop Ser.). 128p. (Orig.). 1985. pap. 3.95 (ISBN 0-310-41891-7, 11278P). Zondervan.

Ochs, Carol. Women & Spirituality. LC 83-3397. (New Feminist Perspectives Ser.). 166p. 1983. 18.95x (ISBN 0-8476-7232-8, Rowman & Allanheld); pap. 9.95x (ISBN 0-8476-7233-6). Rowman.

Ohanneson, Joan. Woman: Survivor in the Church. (Orig.). 1980. pap. 6.95 (ISBN 0-86683-607-1, HarpR). Har-Row.

O'Hara, Magdalen, ed. The Directory of Women Religious in the United States. 1985. 65.00 (ISBN 0-89453-528-5). M Glazier.

Ortland, Anne. Disciplines of the Heart. 1987. 12.95. Word Bks.

Ortlund, Anne. Disciplines of the Beautiful Woman. (QP Proven-Word Ser.). 132p. 1984. pap. 5.95 (ISBN 0-8499-2983-0). Word Bks.

Ortlund, Anne, et al. Yes, God...I Am a Creative Woman. LC 83-80610. 225p. (Orig.). 1983. pap. 4.50 (ISBN 0-935797-02-5). Harvest IL.

Palmer, Phoebe & Wheatley, Richard. The Life & Letters of Mrs. Phoebe Palmer. Dayton, Donald W., ed. (The Higher Christian Life Ser.). 636p. 1985. 80.00 (ISBN 0-8240-6432-1). Garland Pub.

Patterson, Bessie. The Wise Woman Knows. 4.95 (ISBN 0-89137-422-1). Quality Pubns.

Penn-Lewis, Jessie. The Magna Charta of Woman. LC 75-28655. 112p. 1975. pap. 3.50 (ISBN 0-87123-377-0, 200377). Bethany Hse.

Plaskow, Judith. Women & Religion. Arnold, Joan & Romero, Joan A., eds. LC 74-83126. (American Academy of Religion. Aids for the Study of Religion). Repr. of 1974 ed. 54.00 (ISBN 0-8357-9581-0, 2017557). Bks Demand UMI.

Pollard, Nina T. Nothing but a Footprint. LC 85-29049. 1986. pap. 3.25 (ISBN 0-8054-5716-X). Broadman.

Pratt, Yvonne K. Especially for the Single Woman. 1980. pap. 2.25 (ISBN 0-87148-295-9). Pathway Pr.

Prentiss, George L. The Life & Letters of Elizabeth Prentiss. Gifford, Carolyn D. & Dayton, Donald, eds. (Women in American Protestant Religion 1800-1930 Ser.). 573p. 1987. lib. bdg. 80.00 (ISBN 0-8240-0672-0). Garland Pub.

Price, Eugenia. God Speaks to Women Today. 192p. 1984. pap. 6.95 (ISBN 0-310-31301-5, 10530P). Zondervan.

--Woman to Woman. pap. 3.95 (ISBN 0-310-31392-9, 10589P). Zondervan.

--A Woman's Choice: Living Through Your Problems. 192p. 1983. pap. 5.95 (ISBN 0-310-31381-3, 16217P). Zondervan.

Putnam, Joanne. A Time to Grow. Wallace, Mary, ed. LC 85-20190. (Illus.). 112p. (Orig.). 1985. pap. 4.95 (ISBN 0-912315-92-X). Word Aflame.

Rabuzzi, Kathryn A. The Sacred & the Feminine: Toward a Theology of Housework. 224p. 1982. 15.95 (ISBN 0-8164-0509-3, HarpR). Har-Row.

Radl, Shirley R. The Invisible Woman: Target of the Religious New Right. LC 83-5345. 264p. 1983. 17.95 (ISBN 0-385-29232-5, Sey Lawr). Delacorte.

--The Invisible Woman: Target of the Religious New Right. LC 83-5345. 264p. 1983. pap. 9.95 (ISBN 0-385-29210-4, Delta). Dell.

Raser, Harold E. Phoebe Palmer: Her Life & Thought. LC 86-31251. (Studies in Women & Religion: Vol. 22). 392p. 1987. 59.95 (ISBN 0-88946-527-4). E Mellen.

Reamer, Judy. Feelings Women Rarely Share. Arthur, Donna, ed. 150p. (Orig.). 1987. pap. text ed. 3.50 (ISBN 0-88368-186-2). Whitaker Hse.

Reapsome, Martha. A Woman's Path to Godliness. 176p. 1986. 10.95 (ISBN 0-8407-9067-8). Oliver-Nelson.

Religious Woman Minister of Faith: A Compilation of Addresses Given at First International Assembly, Consotium Perfecte Caritatis. LC 74-16745. 1974. pap. 2.50 (ISBN 0-8198-0508-4). Dghtrs St Paul.

Rich, Elaine S. Mennonite Women: A Story of God's Faithfulness. LC 82-15452. 256p. 1983. pap. 9.95 (ISBN 0-8361-3311-0). Herald Pr.

Ross, Bette M. Hannah's Daughters. Date not set. pap. 5.95 (ISBN 0-8007-5232-5, Power Bks). Revell.

--Journey of No Return. Date not set. pap. 5.95 (ISBN 0-8007-5231-7, Power Bks). Revell.

Ruether, Rosemary R. Women-Church. 1986. 16.45 (ISBN 0-06-066834-2). Har-Row.

Ruether, Rosemary R. & Keller, Rosemary S., eds. Women & Religion in America: Nineteen Hundred to Nineteen Sixty-Eight, Vol. 3. (Illus.). 452p. 1986. 26.45 (ISBN 0-06-066833-4, HarpT). Har-Row.

Sanford, Ruth. More Than Survivors: God's Way of Restoration for Women. 200p. (Orig.). 1981. pap. 4.95 (ISBN 0-89283-102-2). Servant.

Saraydarian, Torkom. Woman - Torch of the Future. LC 80-67680. 1980. pap. 8.00 (ISBN 0-911794-00-X). Aqua Educ.

Seashore, Gladys. Women of Faith. 1983. pap. 2.25 (ISBN 0-911802-55-X). Free Church Pubns.

Shaffer, Wilma. Fourteen Women's Programs: Making Your House a Home. 96p. (Orig.). 1984. pap. 3.95 (ISBN 0-87239-743-2, 2974). Standard Pub.

Shenk, Sara W. And Then There Were Three. LC 85-13936. 208p. (Orig.). 1985. pap. 8.95 (ISBN 0-8361-3398-6). Herald Pr.

Shropshire, Marie. In Touch with God: How God Speaks to a Prayerful Heart. (Orig.). 1985. pap. 4.95 (ISBN 0-89081-447-3). Harvest Hse.

Shull, Barbara. How to Become a Skilled Intercessor. 32p. 1978. pap. 2.00 (ISBN 0-930756-35-5, 533001). Aglow Pubns.

Sleeper, Sarah. Memoir of the Late Martha Hazeltine Smith. Gifford, Carolyn D. & Dayton, Donald, eds. (Women in American Protestant Religion 1800-1930 Ser.). 294p. 1987. lib. bdg. 40.00 (ISBN 0-8240-0686-0). Garland Pub.

Smith, Joyce M. Becoming God's Woman. 1979. pap. 2.50 (ISBN 0-8423-0130-5). Tyndale.

--Celebration of Womanhood. (New Life Bible Studies). 64p. 1985. pap. 2.95 (ISBN 0-8423-0254-9). Tyndale.

Smith, Kenneth G. & Smith, Floy. Learning to Be a Woman. LC 76-127932. (Orig.). 1970. pap. 3.95 (ISBN 0-87784-693-6). Inter-Varsity.

Souter, Susan J. How to Be a Confident Woman: A Bible Study Guide for Women. LC 78-51904. 80p. 1978. pap. 2.95 (ISBN 0-89081-124-5). Harvest Hse.

Spaeth, Barbara J. Laurie Miracle by Miracle. 48p. 1986. 6.95 (ISBN 0-317-43316-4). Todd & Honeywell.

Spencer, Anita. Seasons: Women's Search for Self Through Life's Stages. LC 81-85379. 128p. (Orig.). 1982. pap. 4.95 (ISBN 0-8091-2437-8). Paulist Pr.

Sr. Clare. Journey Out of Chaos. LC 81-22885. 248p. (Orig.). 1981. pap. 8.00 (ISBN 0-89571-012-9). Affirmation.

Sri Aurobindo Ashram Publications Department Staff & Aurobindo, Sri. On Women. 126p. (Orig.). Date not set. pap. 6.00 (ISBN 0-89744-236-9, Pub. by Sri Aurobindo Ashram Trust India). Auromere.

Stamm, Millie. Meditation Moments for Women. 1967. pap. 7.95 (ISBN 0-310-32981-7). Zondervan.

Stanton, Sybil. The Twenty-Five Hour Woman. 256p. 1986. 9.95 (ISBN 0-8007-1487-3). Revell.

Steele, Sharon A. Keys to Contentment. (Aglow Bible Study Basic Ser.). 80p. 1981. pap. 2.95 (ISBN 0-930756-65-7, 521013). Aglow Pubns.

Stewart, Marjorie. Women in Neighborhood Evangelism. LC 77-93410. 128p. 1978. pap. 1.50 (ISBN 0-88243-723-2, 02-0723, Radiant Books). Gospel Pub.

Swain, Clara A. A Glimpse of India, Being a Collection of Extracts from the Letters of Dr. Clara A. Swain. Gifford, Carolyn D. & Dayton, Donald, eds. (Women in American Protestant Religion 1800-1930 Ser.). 366p. 1987. lib. bdg. 50.00 (ISBN 0-8240-0677-1). Garland Pub.

Swidler, Arlene & Conn, Walter E., eds. Mainstreaming: Feminist Research for Teaching Religious Studies. 96p. (Orig.). 1985. lib. bdg. 20.25 (ISBN 0-8191-4724-9, Co-Pub by College Theo Soc); pap. text ed. 7.75 (ISBN 0-8191-4725-7). U Pr of Amer.

Taege, Marlys. Women Through the Bible: Devotions for Women's Groups. 160p. 1987. pap. 5.95 (ISBN 0-570-04460-X, 12-3064). Concordia.

Taylor, Rhena. Single & Whole. LC 85-8345. Orig. Title: Every Single Blessing. 96p. 1985. pap. 2.95 (ISBN 0-87784-510-7). Inter-Varsity.

Thomas, Sr. Evangeline, ed. Women's Religious History Sources. 264p. 1983. 65.00 (ISBN 0-8352-1681-0). Bowker.

Thompsett, Fredrica H. Christian Feminist Perspectives on History, Theology & the Bible. 56p. (Orig.). 1986. pap. 2.50 (ISBN 0-88028-051-4). Forward Movement.

Tobin, Mary L. Hope is an Open Door. LC 80-21414. (Journeys in Faith Ser). 1981. 7.95 (ISBN 0-687-17410-4). Abingdon.

Tsatsos, Ioanna. Hours on Sinai. Vaporis, N. M., ed. Demos, Jean, tr. from Gr. Orig. Title: Apo to Tetradio Mou: Hores Tou Sina. 76p. 1984. pap. text ed. 8.00 (ISBN 0-917653-00-9). Hellenic Coll Pr.

Unrau, Ruth. Encircled: Stories of Mennonite Women. LC 86-80403. (Illus.). 352p. 1986. pap. 12.95 (ISBN 0-87303-114-8). Faith & Life.

Urfer, Pamela & Jones, Judie. Self-Destructive Tendencies of Christian Women. 109p. (Orig.). 1983. pap. text ed. 7.95 (ISBN 0-912801-04-2). Creat Arts Dev.

Valentine, Mary H. Saints for Today's Women. 1987. 11.95 (ISBN 0-88347-210-4). Thomas More.

Van Wyke, Millie. You're Hired! Insights for Christian Women Who Work Outside the Home. 120p. 1983. pap. 5.95 (ISBN 0-8010-9292-2). Baker Bk.

Wallace, Mary H. My Name Is Christian Woman. LC 85-31575. (Illus., Orig.). 1982. pap. 6.95 (ISBN 0-912315-20-2). Word Aflame.

Warr, Irma. The Godly Woman. 1978. pap. 5.95 (ISBN 2-01064-201-5, 40123). Word Bks.

Washbourn, Penelope. Becoming Woman: The Quest for Spiritual Wholeness in Female Experience. LC 76-9948. 1979. pap. 7.95 (ISBN 0-06-069261-8, RD 256, HarpR). Har-Row.

Washbourn, Penelope, ed. Seasons of Woman: Song, Poetry, Ritual, Prayer, Myth, Story. LC 78-3359. (Illus.). 128p. (Orig.). 1982. pap. 7.95 (ISBN 0-06-250930-6, CN4042, HarpR). Har-Row.

Watkins, George. Women in Today's Church. 56p. 1984. pap. 2.25 (ISBN 0-88144-025-6). Christian Pub.

Webber, Robert E. I Believe: A Woman's Workshop on Relational Doctrine. (Woman's Workshop Ser.). 160p. 1986. pap. 3.95 (ISBN 0-310-36701-8). Zondervan.

--In Heart & Home: A Woman's Workshop on Worship. (Woman's Workshop Ser.). 112p. (Orig.). 1985. pap. 2.95 (ISBN 0-310-36681-X, 12209P). Zondervan.

Weidman, Judith L., ed. Christian Feminism: Visions of a New Humanity. LC 83-48462. 224p. 1984. 7.95i (ISBN 0-06-069292-8, HarpR). Har-Row.

Wellman, Pat. Mirror, Mirror... Please Lie. 86p. (Orig.). 1984. pap. 3.50 (ISBN 0-8341-0931-X). Beacon Hill.

Why Not I, 2 vols. write for info. Dghtrs St Paul.

Wilcox, Anne. Your God, My God: A Woman's Workshop on Ruth. (Woman's Workshop Ser.). 1985. tchr's. manual 2.95 (ISBN 0-310-44691-0, 12026P); student's manual 2.95 (ISBN 0-310-44711-9, 12027P). Zondervan.

Winslow, Miron. Memoir of Mrs. Harriet L. Winslow, Thirteen Years a Member of the American Mission in Ceylon. Gifford, Carolyn D. & Dayton, Donald, eds. (Women in American Protestant Religion 1800-1930 Ser.). 480p. 1987. lib. bdg. 70.00 (ISBN 0-8240-0684-4). Garland Pub.

Wogaman, J. P. Economics & Ethics: A Christian Inquiry. LC 85-45478. 160p. 1986. pap. 9.95 (ISBN 0-8006-1904-8). Fortress.

Wold, Margaret. The Shalom Woman. LC 75-2828. 128p. 1975. pap. 6.95 (ISBN 0-8066-1475-7, 10-5740). Augsburg.

--Women of Faith & Spirit: Profiles of Fifteen Biblical Witnesses. LC 86-28770. 128p. (Orig.). 1987. pap. 6.95 (ISBN 0-8066-2251-2, 10-7236). Augsburg.

Woodrow, Ralph. Women's Adornment: What Does the Bible Really Say? LC 76-17711. (Illus.). 1976. pap. 3.00 (ISBN 0-916938-01-8). R Woodrow.

Zanotti, Barbara, ed. A Faith of One's Own: Explorations by Catholic Lesbians. (Feminist Ser.). 224p. (Orig.). 1986. 20.95 (ISBN 0-89594-210-0); pap. 8.95 (ISBN 0-89594-209-7). Crossing Pr.

WOMEN, ISLAMIC

see Women, Muslim

WOMEN, JEWISH

Adelman, Penina V. Miriam's Well: Rituals for Jewish Women Around the Year. LC 84-71828. (Illus.). 143p. (Orig.). 1986. pap. 9.95 (ISBN 0-930395-00-X); music cassette 6.00. Biblio NY.

Adler, Ruth. Women of the Shtetl: Through the Eye of Y. L. Peretz. LC 78-69895. (Illus.). 152p. 1979. 17.50 (ISBN 0-8386-2336-0). Fairleigh Dickinson.

Arendt, Hannah. Rahel Varnhagen: The Life of a Jewish Woman. Winston, Richard & Winston, Clara, trs. from Ger. LC 74-6478. (Illus.). 236p. 1974. pap. 7.95 (ISBN 0-15-676100-9, Harv). HarBraceJ.

Bernstein, Fred. The Jewish Mothers' Hall of Fame. LC 85-24541. (Illus.). 192p. 1986. pap. 6.95 (ISBN 0-385-23377-9, Dolp). Doubleday.

Biale, Rachel. Women & Jewish Law: An Exploration of Women's Issues in Halakhic Sources. LC 83-40457. 256p. 1984. 18.95 (ISBN 0-8052-3887-5). Schocken.

--Women & Jewish Law: An Exploration of Women's Issues in Halakhic Sources. 304p. 1986. pap. 8.95 (ISBN 0-8052-0810-0). Schocken.

Bitton-Jackson, Livia. Madonna or Courtesan: The Jewish Woman in Christian Literature. 160p. 1983. pap. 7.95 (ISBN 0-8164-2440-3, HarpR). Har-Row.

Brayer, Menachem M. The Jewish Woman in Rabbinic Literature: A Psychohistorical Perspective. 400p. 1986. text ed. 20.00x (ISBN 0-88125-073-2); pap. text ed. 11.95x (ISBN 0-88125-072-4). Ktav.

--Jewish Woman in Rabbinic Literature: A Psychosocial Perspective. 300p. 1986. text ed. 20.00x (ISBN 0-88125-071-6); pap. text ed. 11.95x (ISBN 0-88125-070-8). Ktav.

Brewer, Joan S., compiled by. Sex & the Modern Jewish Woman: Annotated Bibliography - Essays. 128p. 1986. pap. 9.25 (ISBN 0-930395-01-8). Biblio NY.

Brooten, Bernadette J. Women Leaders in the Ancient Synagogue: Inscriptional Evidence & Background Issues. LC 82-10658. (Brown Judaic Studies). 292p. 1982. pap. 20.00 (ISBN 0-89130-587-4, 14 00 36). Scholars Pr GA.

Brown, Charlotte & Hyman, Paula. The Jewish Woman in America. 1977. pap. 7.95 (ISBN 0-452-25786-7, Z5282, Plume). NAL.

Cantor, Aviva & Hamelsdorf, Ora, eds. The Jewish Woman: 1900-1985 Bibliography. 2nd ed. 200p. 1987. pap. 8.95 (ISBN 0-930395-04-2). Biblio NY.

Elwell, Sue L., compiled by. The Jewish Women's Studies Guide. 2nd ed. 1987. pap. 19.75 (Co-Pub by U Press of America); pap. 9.75 (Co-Pub. by U Press of America). Biblio NY.

Epstein, Louis M. The Jewish Marriage Contract: A Study in the Status of the Woman in Jewish Law. LC 73-2195. (The Jewish People; History, Religion, Literature Ser.). Repr. of 1927 ed. 33.00 (ISBN 0-405-05261-8). Ayer Co Pubs.

Fine, Irene. Educating the New Jewish Woman: A Dynamic Approach. LC 85-51215. 80p. (Orig.). 1985. pap. 8.95 (ISBN 0-9608054-4-3). Womans Inst-Cont Jewish Ed.

Ghatan, H. Yedidiah. Our Invaluable Pearl: The Unique Status of Women in Judaism. LC 85-73454. 200p. (Orig.). 1986. pap. 9.95x (ISBN 0-8197-0502-0). Bloch.

Glanz, Rudolf. The German Jewish Women, Vol. 2. 25.00x (ISBN 0-87068-462-0). Ktav.

--The Jewish Female in America: Two Female Generations, 1820-1929, Vol. 1. The Eastern European Jewish Woman 25.00x (ISBN 0-87068-461-2). Ktav.

Hamelsdorf, Ora, et al, eds. Jewish Women & Jewish Law: Bibliography. 60p. 1981. pap. 3.00 (ISBN 0-9602036-2-1). Biblio NY.

Kaplan, Marion. The Jewish Feminist Movement in Germany: The Campaigns of the Judischer Frauenbund, 1904-1938. LC 78-67567. (Contributions in Women's Studies: No. 8). (Illus.). lib. bdg. 29.95 (ISBN 0-313-20736-4, KGJ/). Greenwood.

Kaye, Evelyn. The Hole in the Sheet. 224p. 1987. 14.95 (ISBN 0-8184-0437-X). Lyle Stuart.

Key, Ellen S. Rahel Varnagen. LC 75-7680. (Pioneers of the Woman's Movement: an International Perspective Ser.). (Illus.). xix, 312p. 1976. Repr. of 1913 ed. 23.10 (ISBN 0-88355-351-1). Hyperion Conn.

Koltun, Elizabeth, ed. The Jewish Woman: New Perspectives. LC 75-35445. 320p. 1976. pap. 7.95 (ISBN 0-8052-0532-2). Schocken.

Kruger, Mollee. Daughters of Chutzpah: Humorous Verse on the Jewish Woman. LC 82-71394. (Illus.). 112p. (Orig.). 1983. pap. 5.00 (ISBN 0-9602036-7-2). Biblio NY.

Lavender, Abraham D., ed. A Coat of Many Colors: Jewish Subcommunities in the United States. LC 77-71865. (Contributions in Family Studies: No. 1). 1977. lib. bdg. 29.95 (ISBN 0-8371-9539-X, LCM/). Greenwood.

Marcus, Jacob R. The American Jewish Woman: A Documentary History. 1981. 35.00x (ISBN 0-87068-752-2). Ktav.

Marcus, Jacob R., ed. The American Jewish Woman: 1654-1980. 1981. 15.00x (ISBN 0-87068-579-1). Ktav.

Meiselman, M. Jewish Woman in Jewish Law. (Library of Jewish Law & Ethics: Vol. 6). 9.95x (ISBN 0-87068-329-2). Ktav.

Miller, Yisroel. In Search of the Jewish Woman. 149p. 1984. 8.95 (ISBN 0-87306-358-9); pap. 6.95 (ISBN 0-87306-359-7). Feldheim.

Morton, Leah, pseud. I Am a Woman & a Jew. (Masterworks of Modern Jewish Writing Ser.). (Illus.). 380p. 1986. pap. 9.95 (ISBN 0-910129-56-8, Distr. by Schocken Books). Wiener Pub Inc.

Omaha Section National Council of Jewish Women. The Kitchen Connection. Kutler, Sandy & Polikov, Sheila, eds. (Illus., Orig.). 1983. pap. 11.95 (ISBN 0-9612406-0-1). Omaha Sec Nat.

Peters, Barbarba & Samuels, Victoria, eds. Dialogue on Diversity: A New Agenda for Women. 88p. 1978. pap. 1.95 (ISBN 0-87495-003-1). Am Jewish Comm.

Priesand, Sally. Judaism & the New Woman. LC 75-21951. (Jewish Concepts & Issues Ser.). 162p. (Orig.). 1975. pap. 2.50x (ISBN 0-87441-230-7). Behrman.

Roth, Cecil. Dona Gracia of the House of Nasi. LC 77-92984. 208p. 1978. pap. 4.95 (ISBN 0-8276-0099-2, 415). Jewish Pubns.

Shapolsky, Ian. The Second Jewish Trivia & Information Book. (Illus.). 400p. 1986. pap. 6.95 (ISBN 0-933503-45-8). Shapolsky Pubs.

Spiegel, Marcia C. & Kremsdorf, Deborah L., eds. Women Speak To God: The Prayers & Poems of Jewish Women. LC 86-51498. 100p. (Orig.). 1987. pap. 9.98 (ISBN 0-9608054-6-X). Womans Inst-Cont Jewish Ed.

Umansky, Ellen J. Lily Montagu: Sermons, Addresses, Letters & Prayers. LC 85-3053. (Studies in Women & Religion: Vol. 15). (Illus.). 415p. 1985. 69.95x (ISBN 0-88946-534-7). E Mellen.

Wagenknecht, Edward. Daughters of the Covenant: Portraits of Six Jewish Women. LC 83-3562. (Illus.). 200p. 1983. lib. bdg. 17.50x (ISBN 0-87023-396-3). U of Mass Pr.

Weinstein, Frida S. A Hidden Childhood: A Jewish Girl's Sanctuary in a French Convent, 1942-1945. Kennedy, Barbara L., tr. 160p. 1986. pap. 6.95 (ISBN 0-8090-1529-3). Hill & Wang.

Weiss, Avraham. Women's Prayer Groups: A Halakhic Analysis. 1987. pap. 8.95 (ISBN 0-88125-126-7). Ktav.

Zones, Jane S., ed. San Diego Women's Haggadah. rev. ed. LC 85-51376. (Illus.). 80p. 1986. pap. 7.50 (ISBN 0-9608054-5-1). Womans Inst-Cont Jewish Ed.

WOMEN, MUSLIM

Abdul-Rauf, Muhammad. The Islamic View of Women & the Family. 1977. text ed. 11.95 (ISBN 0-8315-0156-1). Speller.

Badawi, Gamal. The Status of Woman in Islam. Al-Jarrahi, Abdussamad, ed. Bekkari, Muhammad, tr. from English. (Illus.). 20p. (Orig.). 1982. pap. 2.00 (ISBN 0-89259-036-X). Am Trust Pubns.

Badawi, Gamal A. The Status of Woman in Islam: (French Edition) Quinlan, Hamid, ed. LC 82-74127. (Illus.). 28p. 1983. pap. 0.75 (ISBN 0-89259-039-4). Am Trust Pubns.

Beck, Lois & Keddie, Nikki, eds. Women in the Muslim World. LC 78-3633. 712p. 1978. 40.00x (ISBN 0-674-95480-7); pap. 12.50 (ISBN 0-674-95481-5). Harvard U Pr.

Boutas, V., ed. Women in Islam: Social Attitudes & Historical Perspectives. 224p. 1983. 30.00x (ISBN 0-7007-0154-0, Pub. by Curzon England). State Mutual Bk.

Clark, Peter. Marmaduke Pickthall: British Muslim. (Illus.). 156p. 1987. 19.95 (ISBN 0-7043-2514-4, Pub. by Quartet Bks). Salem Hse Pubs.

Cloudsley, Anne. Women of Omdurman: Life, Love & the Cult of Virginity. LC 83-40625. 181p. 1985. 22.50 (ISBN 0-312-88755-8). St Martin.

Cooper, Elizabeth. Harim & the Purdah: Studies of Oriental Women. LC 68-23147. 312p. 1975. Repr. of 1915 ed. 43.00x (ISBN 0-8103-3167-5). Gale.

El Saadawi, Nawal. The Hidden Face of Eve: Women in the Arab World. Hetata, Sherif, tr. from Egyptian. LC 81-68358. 212p. 1982. pap. 9.95 (ISBN 0-8070-6701-6, BP 627). Beacon Pr.

Fernea, Elizabeth W. & Bezirgan, Basima Q., eds. Middle Eastern Muslim Women Speak. (Illus.). 452p. 1977. 23.50x (ISBN 0-292-75033-1); pap. 12.50x (ISBN 0-292-75041-2). U of Tex Pr.

Ginat, Joseph. Women in Muslim Rural Society. LC 79-66432. 259p. 1981. 29.95 (ISBN 0-87855-342-8). Transaction Bk.

Hussain, Freeda, ed. Muslim Women: The Ideal & Contextual Realities. LC 83-11189. 240p. 1984. 22.50 (ISBN 0-312-55586-5). St Martin.

Jones, Violet R. Woman in Islam: A Manual with Special Reference to Conditions in India. LC 79-2942. (Illus.). 455p. 1980. Repr. of 1941 ed. 31.50 (ISBN 0-8305-0107-X). Hyperion Conn.

Layish, Ahron. Women & Islamic Law in a Non-Muslim State. 369p. 1975. 19.95. Transaction Bks.

Lemu, Aisha & Heeren, Fatima. Women in Islam. 51p. (Orig.). 1978. pap. 3.50 (ISBN 0-86037-004-6, Pub. by Islamic Found UK). New Era Pubns MI.

Maududi, A. A. Purdah & the Status of Women in Islam. pap. 9.50 (ISBN 0-686-18464-5). Kazi Pubns.

Mikhail, Mona N. Images of Arab Women: Fact & Fiction. LC 78-19969. 137p. (Orig.). 1978. 20.00 (ISBN 0-89410-023-8); pap. 10.00 (ISBN 0-89410-024-6). Three Continents.

Nutanhhery, Murtaza. Women & Her Rights. Ansari, M. A., tr. from Arabic. 286p. 1984. pap. 9.00 (ISBN 0-941724-30-1). Islamic Seminary.

Raccagni, Michelle. The Modern Arab Woman: A Bibliography. LC 78-15528. 272p. 1978. lib. bdg. 19.00 (ISBN 0-8108-1165-0). Scarecrow.

Sabbah, Fatna A. Woman in the Muslim Unconscious. LC 84-11343. (Athene Ser.). 188p. 1984. 27.00 (ISBN 0-08-031626-3); pap. 11.00 (ISBN 0-08-031625-5). Pergamon.

Shariati, Ali. Fatima Is Fatima. Bakhtiar, Laleh, tr. from Arabic. LC 81-52831. 226p. 1982. pap. 4.95 (ISBN 0-940368-09-9). Tahrike Tarsile Quran.

Shibany, Roy. Status of Muslim Women in North India. 1979. 21.00x (ISBN 0-8364-0353-3). South Asia Bks.

Siddique, Kaukab. The Struggle of Muslim Women. LC 86-70641. 152p. (Orig.). 1986. pap. 9.95 (ISBN 0-942978-10-2). Am Soc Ed & Rel.

Siddiqui, M. M. Women in Islam. 10.50 (ISBN 0-686-18462-9). Kazi Pubns.

Siddiqui, M. S. Blessed Women of Islam. 16.95 (ISBN 0-686-83898-X). Kazi Pubns.

Smith, Margaret. Rabi'a the Mystic & Her Fellow-Saints in Islam. 2nd ed. 256p. 1984. 37.50 (ISBN 0-521-26779-X); pap. 13.95 (ISBN 0-521-31863-7). Cambridge U Pr.

Tabari, Azar & Yeganeh, Nahid, eds. In the Shadow of Islam: The Women's Movement in Iran. 256p. 1983. 24.75x (ISBN 0-86232-022-4, Pub. by Zed Pr England); pap. 10.25 (ISBN 0-86232-039-9). Humanities.

Waddy, Charis. Women in Muslim History. LC 80-40161. (Illus.). 224p. 1980. text ed. 27.95x (ISBN 0-582-78084-5). Longman.

Walther, Wiebke. Woman in Islam. (Image of Women Ser.). (Illus.). 192p. 1982. 35.00 (ISBN 0-8390-0256-4, Allanheld & Schram). Abner Schram Ltd.

Woodsmall, Ruth F. Moslem Women Enter a New World. LC 75-180309. Repr. of 1936 ed. 31.50 (ISBN 0-404-56334-1). AMS Pr.

--Women in the Changing Islamic System. (Illus.). 432p. 1983. text ed. 60.00x (ISBN 0-86590-154-6). Apt Bks.

WOMEN, ORDINATION OF

see Ordination of Women

WOMEN, QUAKER

Bacon, Margaret H. Mothers of Feminism: The Story of Quaker Women in America. 1986. 16.95 (ISBN 0-06-250043-0, HarpR). Har-Row.

Stoneburner, John & Stoneburner, Carol, eds. The Influence of Quaker Women on American Society: Biographical Studies. (Studies in Women & Religion: Vol. 21). 496p. 1986. text ed. 69.95x (ISBN 0-88946-528-2). E Mellen.

WOMEN (IN RELIGION, FOLKLORE, ETC.)

Atkinson, Clarissa W., et al, eds. Immaculate & Powerful: The Female in Sacred Image & Social Reality. LC 85-70448. 338p. 1987. pap. 12.95 (ISBN 0-8070-1005-7, BP-732). Beacon Pr.

Carmichael, C. Women, Law, & the Genesis Tradition. 112p. 1979. 16.50x (ISBN 0-85224-364-2, Pub. by Edinburgh U Pr Scotland). Columbia U Pr.

De Caro, Francis A., compiled by. Women & Folklore: A Bibliographic Survey. LC 83-12837. xiv, 170p. 1983. lib. bdg. 35.00 (ISBN 0-313-23821-9, DWF/). Greenwood.

Farrer, Claire R., ed. Women & Folklore: Images & Genres. (Illus.). 100p. 1986. pap. text ed. 6.95x (ISBN 0-88133-227-5). Waveland Pr.

Harding, M. Esther. Woman's Mysteries. 1976. pap. 6.95 (ISBN 0-06-090525-5, CN525, PL). Har-Row.

Heiler, Friedrich. Die Frau in den Religionen der Menschheit. Heiler, Anne M., ed. (Theologische Bibliothek Toepelmann: Vol. 33). 1977. 15.20x (ISBN 3-11-006583-5). De Gruyter.

Luke, Helen. Woman, Earth & Spirit: The Feminine in Symbol & Myth. 144p. 1981. 9.95 (ISBN 0-8245-0018-0). Crossroad NY.

Mollenkott, Virginia R. The Divine Feminine: The Biblical Imagery of God As Female. 128p. 1984. pap. 8.95 (ISBN 0-8245-0669-3). Crossroad NY.

Moloney, Francis J. Woman: First among the Faithful. LC 85-73197. 128p. 1986. pap. 4.95 (ISBN 0-87793-333-2). Ave Maria.

Preston, James J., ed. Mother Worship: Theme & Variations. LC 81-3336. (Studies in Religion). xxiv, 360p. 1982. text ed. 29.00x (ISBN 0-8078-1471-7). U of NC Pr.

Roberts, Richard. From Eden to Eros: Origins of the Put down of Women. (Illus.). 167p. (Orig.). 1985. pap. 8.95x (ISBN 0-942380-05-3). Vernal Equinox.

WOMEN AND RELIGION

see also Women–Religious Life; Women Clergy

Baker, Derek, ed. Medieval Women. (Studies in Church History: Subsidia 1). 412p. 1981. pap. 9.95x (ISBN 0-631-12539-6). Basil Blackwell.

Behnke, Donna A. Religious Issues in Nineteenth Century Feminism. LC 80-52544. 300p. 1982. 22.50x (ISBN 0-87875-203-X). Whitston Pub.

Blanton, Alma E. God & Mrs. Adam. (Illus.). 152p. (Orig.). 1978. lib. bdg. 4.95 (ISBN 0-938134-00-0, G-1); pap. 4.95 (ISBN 0-686-73968-X). Loving Pubs.

Bradford, Mary L., ed. Mormon Women Speak. LC 82-62366. 1982. 9.95 (ISBN 0-913420-94-8). Olympus Pub Co.

Buckley, Jorunn J. Female Fault & Fulfilment in Gnosticism. LC 85-29020. (Studies in Religion). xvi, 180p. 1986. 32.50x (ISBN 0-8078-1696-5). U of NC Pr.

Bulletin Committee Staff. Fiftieth Anniversary Issue: Kingston Lake Woman's Baptist Educational & Missionary Convention of Horry County, South Carolina. rev. ed. Dozier, Etrulia P., ed. (Illus.). 80p. (Orig.). 1985. pap. text ed. 5.00 (ISBN 0-9615271-2-9). Positive Images.

Carmody, Denise L. Feminism & Christianity: A Two-Way Reflection. LC 82-1709. 192p. (Orig.). 1982. pap. 9.95 (ISBN 0-687-12914-1). Abingdon.

Christ, Carol. Diving Deep & Surfacing: Women Writers on Spiritual Quest. 2nd, rev. ed. LC 86-70552. 157p. 1986. pap. 8.95 (ISBN 0-8070-6351-7, BP 722). Beacon Pr.

Christovale, Cindy. Your Real Beauty. 80p. (Orig.). 1983. pap. 2.95 (ISBN 0-88144-018-3, CPS-018). Christian Pub.

Clark, Elizabeth & Richardson, Herbert W., eds. Women & Religion: Readings in the Western Tradition from Aeschylus to Mary Daly. LC 76-9975. 1976. pap. 9.95 (ISBN 0-06-061398-X, RD-178, HarpR). Har-Row.

Clark, Elizabeth A. The Life of Melania the Younger: Introduction, Translation & Commentary. LC 84-20635. (Studies in Women & Religion: Vol. 14). 305p. 1985. 49.95x (ISBN 0-88946-535-5). E Mellen.

Cooper, Mildred & Fanning, Martha. What Every Woman Still Knows: A Celebration of the Christian Liberated Woman. LC 78-17182. 182p. 1978. 7.95 (ISBN 0-87131-271-9). M Evans.

Douglass, Jane D. Women, Freedom, & Calvin. LC 85-8778. 156p. 1985. pap. 11.95 (ISBN 0-664-24663-X). Westminster.

Edwards, Deborah. Opening Devotions for Womens Groups. 96p. 1985. pap. 4.95 (ISBN 0-8010-3428-0). Baker Bk.

Elizondo, Virgil & Greinacher, Norbert, eds. Women in a Man's Church, Concilium 134. (New Concilium 1980: Vol. 134). 128p. 1980. pap. 5.95 (ISBN 0-8164-2276-1, HarpR). Har-Row.

Fitzwater, Perry B. La Mujer: Su Mision, Posicion y Ministerio. Orig. Title: Woman: Mission, Position, Ministry. (Span.). 76p. 1972. pap. 2.25 (ISBN 0-8254-1233-1). Kregel.

Foh, Susan. Women & the Word of God. pap. 6.95 (ISBN 0-87552-268-8). Presby & Reformed.

Fowler, Richard A. & House, H. Wayne. The Christian Confronts His Culture. 228p. (Orig.). 1983. pap. 7.95 (ISBN 0-8024-0232-1). Moody.

Gross, Rita M., ed. Beyond Androcentrism: New Essays on Women & Religion. LC 77-13312. (AAR Aids for the Study of Religion: No. 6). 1981. pap. 9.95 (ISBN 0-89130-196-8, 010306). Scholars Pr GA.

Hepburn, Daisy & Klope, Joan B. How to Grow a Women's Minis-Tree. (Illus., Orig.). 1986. resource manual 7.95 (ISBN 0-8307-1055-8, 5203018). Regal.

Hill, Elsie Isensce & Dudley, Cliff. Abused But Chosen. LC 83-61439. 144p. 1983. 4.95 (ISBN 0-89221-106-7). New Leaf.

Ide, Arthur F. Sex, Woman & Religion. (Illus.). xi, 212p. (Orig.). 1984. 14.95 (ISBN 0-930383-00-1). Monument Pr.

James, Janet W., ed. Women in American Religion. LC 79-5261. 288p. 1980. 32.00x (ISBN 0-8122-7780-5); pap. 13.50x (ISBN 0-8122-1104-9). U of Pa Pr.

Lantero, Erminie H. Feminine Aspects of Divinity. LC 73-84214. 36p. (Orig.). 1973. pap. 2.50x (ISBN 0-87574-191-6). Pendle Hill.

Luder, Hope E. Women & Quakerism. LC 74-82914. 36p. (Orig.). 1974. pap. 2.50x (ISBN 0-87574-196-7). Pendle Hill.

Moloney, Francis J. Woman: First among the Faithful. LC 85-73197. 128p. 1986. pap. 4.95 (ISBN 0-87793-333-2). Ave Maria.

O'Hair, Madalyn M. Women & Atheism: The Ultimate Liberation. 23p. 1979. 2.50 (ISBN 0-911826-17-3). Am Atheist.

Ohanneson, Joan. Woman: Survivor in the Church. (Orig.). 1980. pap. 6.95 (ISBN 0-86683-607-1, HarpR). Har-Row.

Phipps, William E. Influential Theologians on Wo-Man. LC 79-5431. 1980. lib. bdg. 23.00 (ISBN 0-8191-1383-2); pap. text ed. 9.50 (ISBN 0-8191-0880-4). U Pr of Amer.

Porterfield, Amanda. Feminine Spirituality in America: From Sarah Edwards to Martha Graham. 248p. 1980. 29.95 (ISBN 0-87722-175-8). Temple U Pr.

Prokes, M. Timothy. Women's Challenge: Ministry in the Flesh. 2.95 (ISBN 0-87193-006-4). Dimension Bks.

Ruether, Rosemary & McLaughlin, Eleanor. Women of Spirit. 1979. pap. 10.95 (ISBN 0-671-24805-7, Touchstone Bks). S&S.

Ruether, Rosemary R. & Keller, Rosemary S., eds. Women & Religion in America: The Colonial & Revolutionary Period, Vol. II. LC 80-8346. (Illus.). 448p. 1983. 24.45 (ISBN 0-06-066832-6, HarpR). Har-Row.

Shore, Sally R., tr. John Chrysostom: On Virginity; Against Remarriage. Clark, Elizabeth A. LC 83-8193. (Studies in Women & Religion: Vol. 9). 200p. 1984. 49.95x (ISBN 0-88946-543-6). E Mellen.

Sit, Amy. The Rib. LC 76-22278. 1977. pap. 3.95 (ISBN 0-89221-026-5). New Leaf.

Skold, Betty W. I'm Glad You're Open Weekdays: Everyday Prayers to the God Who Works Between Sundays. LC 85-3923. 112p. (Orig.). 1985. pap. 5.95 (ISBN 0-8066-2129-X, 10-3201). Augsburg.

Stone, Merlin. When God Was a Woman. LC 77-16262. (Illus.). 265p. 1978. pap. 6.95 (ISBN 0-15-696158-X, Harv). HarBraceJ.

Swidler, Arlene & Conn, Walter E., eds. Mainstreaming: Feminist Research for Teaching Religious Studies. 96p. (Orig.). 1985. lib. bdg. 20.25 (ISBN 0-8191-4724-9, Co-Pub by College Theo Soc); pap. text ed. 7.75 (ISBN 0-8191-4725-7). U Pr of Amer.

Tournier, Paul. The Gift of Feeling. pap. 9.95 (ISBN 0-8042-2071-9). John Knox.

Vandermey, Mary A. Sparkling Devotions for Women's Groups. 144p. 1985. pap. 4.95 (ISBN 0-8010-9300-7). Baker Bk.

Van Scoyoc, Nancy. Women, Change, & the Church. LC 80-15739. (Into Our Third Century Ser.). 96p. (Orig.). 1980. pap. 3.95 (ISBN 0-687-45958-3). Abingdon.

Warenski, Marilyn. Patriarchs & Politics. (McGraw-Hill Paperbacks Ser.). 352p. 1980. pap. 6.95 (ISBN 0-07-068271-2). McGraw.

--Patriarchs & Politics. (Illus.). 1978. 10.95 (ISBN 0-07-068270-4). McGraw.

Watkins, George. Women in Today's Church. 56p. 1984. pap. 2.25 (ISBN 0-88144-025-6). Christian Pub.

Williams, James G. Women Recounted: Narrative Thinking & the God of Israel. (Bible & Literature Ser.: No. 6). 128p. 1982. text ed. 21.95x (ISBN 0-907459-18-8, Pub. by Almond Pr England); pap. 10.95x (ISBN 0-907459-19-6). Eisenbrauns.

WOMEN CLERGY

see also Ordination of Women

Bozarth-Campbell, Alla. Womanpriest: A Personal Odyssey. 229p. 1978. 9.95 (ISBN 0-8091-0243-9). Wisdom House.

Canham, Elizabeth. Pilgrimage to Priesthood. 128p. (Orig.). 1985. pap. 9.95 (ISBN 0-8164-2492-6, 8603, HarpR). Har-Row.

Carroll, Jackson W. & Hargrove, Barbara J. Women of the Cloth: New Opportunity for the Churches. LC 82-47740. 288p. 1983. 14.45 (ISBN 0-06-061321-1, HarpR). Har-Row.

Cazden, Elizabeth. Antoinette Brown Blackwell: A Biography. LC 82-4986. (Illus.). 328p. 1983. 24.95 (ISBN 0-935312-00-5); pap. 9.95 (ISBN 0-935312-04-8). Feminist Pr.

Chittister, Joan. Women, Ministry, & the Church. LC 82-62418. 1983. pap. 5.95 (ISBN 0-8091-2528-5). Paulist Pr.

Davis, Almond H. The Female Preacher: Memoir of Salome Lincoln, Afterwards the Wife of Elder Junia S. Mowry. LC 72-2599. (American Women Ser.: Images & Realities). (Illus.). 168p. 1972. Repr. of 1843 ed. 13.50 (ISBN 0-405-04489-5). Ayer Co Pubs.

Demarest, Victoria B. God, Woman & Ministry. rev. ed. LC 76-42915. (Illus.). 1978. 6.95 (ISBN 0-912760-61-3). Valkyrie Pub Hse.

--Sex & Spirit: God, Woman, & the Ministry. LC 76-42915. (Illus.). 1977. 6.95 (ISBN 0-912760-38-9); pap. 4.95 (ISBN 0-912760-29-X). Valkyrie Pub Hse.

Donovan, Mary S. A Different Call: Women's Ministries in the Episcopal Church. 216p. (Orig.). 1986. text ed. 19.95 (ISBN 0-8192-1396-9). Morehouse.

Dunham, Craig R. Women Ministers?! Women in Paul & Adventchristendom. 98p. (Orig.). 1986. pap. 4.95 (ISBN 0-913439-04-5). Henceforth.

Fitzwater, Perry B. La Mujer: Su Mision, Posicion y Ministerio. Orig. Title: Woman: Mission, Position, Ministry. (Span.). 76p. 1972. pap. 2.25 (ISBN 0-8254-1233-1). Kregel.

Jones, Jeffrey D. Youth Ministry: Making & Shaping Disciples. 96p. 1986. pap. 5.95 (ISBN 0-8170-1091-2). Judson.

Leach, Robert J. Women Ministers: A Quaker Contribution. Blattenberger, Ruth, ed. LC 79-84922. 1979. pap. 2.50x (ISBN 0-87574-227-0). Pendle Hill.

Lehman, Edward C., Jr. English Church Members' Responses to Women Clergy: A Sociological Analysis. LC 86-28547. (Studies in Religion & Society). 224p. 1987. text ed. 49.95 (ISBN 0-88946-858-3). E Mellen.

Maxwell, L. E. Women in Ministry. 156p. 1987. pap. 6.95 (ISBN 0-89693-337-7). Victor Bks.

Morton, Nelle. The Journey Is Home: The Distinguished Feminist Theologian Traces the Development of Her Personal & Theoretical Vision. LC 85-42342. 285p. 1986. pap. 8.95 (ISBN 0-8070-1133-9, BP 718). Beacon Pr.

Prokes, M. Timothy. Women's Challenge: Ministry in the Flesh. 2.95 (ISBN 0-87193-006-4). Dimension Bks.

Resources for Women's Ministries. (Women's Ministries Commission Ser.). 1975. 4.00 (ISBN 0-8309-0258-9). Herald Hse.

Schaller, Lyle E., ed. Women As Pastors. LC 81-20667. (Creative Leadership Ser.). (Orig.). 1982. pap. 5.95 (ISBN 0-687-45957-5). Abingdon.

Schmidt, Elisabeth. When God Calls a Woman: The Struggle of a Woman Pastor in France & Algeria. Hackett, Allen, tr. from Fr. LC 81-12009. 224p. (Orig.). 1981. pap. 7.95 (ISBN 0-8298-0430-7). Pilgrim NY.

Smith, Betsy. Breakthrough: Women in Religion. LC 78-3016. (Breakthrough Ser.). 1978. 7.95 (ISBN 0-8027-6286-7). Walker & Co.

Spencer, Aida B. Beyond the Curse: Women Called to Ministry. 224p. 1985. 10.95 (ISBN 0-8407-5482-5). Nelson.

Stendahl, Brita. The Force of Tradition: A Case Study of Women Priests in Sweden. LC 84-48713. (Illus.). 208p. 1985. pap. 14.95 (ISBN 0-8006-1808-4, 1-1808). Fortress.

Tetlow, Elisabeth M. Women & Ministry in the New Testament: Called to Serve. 170p. 1985. pap. text ed. 10.75 (ISBN 0-8191-4461-4, College Theo Soc). U Pr of Amer.

Tucker, Cynthia G. A Woman's Ministry: Mary Collson's Search for Reform as a Unitarian Minister, Hull House Social Worker, & a Christian Science Practioner. (American Civilization Ser.). 222p. 1984. 27.95 (ISBN 0-87722-338-6). Temple U Pr.

Van Der Meer, Haye S. Women Priests in the Catholic Church? A Theological-Historical Investigation. Swidler, Leonard & Swidler, Arlene, trs. from Ger. LC 73-79480. Orig. Title: Priestertum der Frau? 230p. 1973. 12.95 (ISBN 0-87722-059-X). Temple U Pr.

Ware, Kallistos & Barrois, Georges. Women & the Priesthood: Essays from the Orthodox Tradition. Hopko, Thomas, ed. 190p. 1982. pap. 8.95 (ISBN 0-88141-005-5). St Vladimirs.

Weidman, Judith L., ed. Women Ministers: How Women Are Re-defining Traditional Roles. LC 80-8345. 192p. (Orig.). 1981. pap. 7.95 (ISBN 0-06-069291-X, RD 528, HarpR). Har-Row.

Wemple, Suzanne F. Women in Frankish Society: Marriage & the Cloister, 500-900. LC 80-54051. (Illus.). 352p. 1985. pap. text ed. 18.95 (ISBN 0-8122-1209-6). U of Pa Pr.

Wijngaards, J. N. Did Christ Rule Out Women Priests? 96p. 1977. pap. 1.95 (ISBN 0-85597-204-1). Attic Pr.

Willard, Frances E. Woman in the Pulpit. LC 75-34240. 1976. Repr. of 1889 ed. 15.95 (ISBN 0-89201-014-2). Zenger Pub.

WOMEN IN CHRISTIANITY

see also Monasticism and Religious Orders for Women; Women Clergy; Women in the Bible; Women Missionaries

Alford, Nancy I. Who, Me, Give a Speech? Handbook for the Reluctant Christian Woman. 160p. (Orig.). 1987. pap. price not set (ISBN 0-8010-0211-7). Baker Bk.

Ashe, Kaye. Today's Woman, Tomorrow's Church. 200p. 1984. pap. 8.95 (ISBN 0-88347-168-X). Thomas More.

Atkinson, Clarissa W. Mystic & Pilgrim: The "Book" & the World of Margery Kempe. LC 82-22219. 248p. (Orig.). 1983. 27.50x (ISBN 0-8014-1521-7); pap. text ed. 8.95x (ISBN 0-8014-9895-3). Cornell U Pr.

Blitchington, W. Peter. The Christian Woman's Search for Self-Esteem. LC 81-18963. 168p. 1983. pap. 4.95 (ISBN 0-8407-5830-8). Nelson.

Borresen, Kari E. Subordination & Equivalence: The Nature & Role of Women in Augustine & Thomas Aquinas. Talbot, Charles H., tr. from Fr. & Ital. LC 80-67199. 390p. 1981. lib. bdg. 29.25 (ISBN 0-8191-1681-5). U Pr of Amer.

Burghardt, Walter J., ed. Woman: New Dimensions. LC 76-50965. 1977. pap. 5.95 (ISBN 0-8091-2011-9). Paulist Pr.

Cirner, Therese. The Facts About Your Feelings: What Every Christian Woman Should Know. 142p. 1982. pap. 4.95 (ISBN 0-89283-103-0). Servant.

Clark, Elizabeth A. Women in the Early Church. (Message of the Fathers of the Church Ser.: Vol. 13). 17.95 (ISBN 0-89453-353-3); pap. 12.95 (ISBN 0-89453-332-0). M Glazier.

Cooper, Thomas J. Guidebook to Biblical Truth. Cooper, Willia S., ed. (The Ministry of Women in God's Plan Ser.: Vol. 6). 50p. (Orig.). 1985. pap. 4.00 (ISBN 0-931429-06-4). Cooper & Cooper Pub.

Deen, Edith. Great Women of the Christian Faith. (The Christian Library). 410p. 1986. Repr. of 1959 ed. 6.95 (ISBN 0-916441-46-6). Barbour & Co.

Fiorenza, Elisabeth S. In Memory of Her: A Feminist Theological Reconstruction of Christian Origins. LC 82-19896. 275p. 1983. 22.50 (ISBN 0-8245-0493-3). Crossroad NY.

Fryman, Sarah. The Measure of a Woman. LC 77-74533. (The Measure of... Ser.). 64p. 1985. pap. 3.95 (ISBN 0-8307-0988-6, 6101888). Regal.

Grana, Janice, ed. Images: Women in Transition. LC 75-46441. 1977. pap. 4.95 (ISBN 0-88489-092-9). St Mary's.

Greeley, Andrew & Durkin, Mary. Angry Catholic Women. 1984. pap. 15.95 (ISBN 0-88347-165-5). Thomas More.

Hardesty, Nancy A. Women Called to Witness: Evangelical Feminism in the Nineteenth Century. LC 83-45959. 176p. (Orig.). 1984. pap. 8.95 (ISBN 0-687-45959-1). Abingdon.

Hestenes, Roberta & Curley, Lois, eds. Women & the Ministries of Christ. pap. 6.95x (ISBN 0-9602638-2-9). Fuller Theol Soc.

Huber, Elaine C. Women & the Authority of Inspiration: A Reexamination of Two Prophetic Movements from a Contemporary Feminist Perspective. LC 85-15823. 262p. (Orig.). 1985. lib. bdg. 27.75 (ISBN 0-8191-4903-9); pap. text ed. 13.75 (ISBN 0-8191-4904-7). U Pr of Amer.

Ide, Arthur F. Woman as Priest, Bishop & Laity in the Early Catholic Church to 440 A.D. 2nd ed. LC 81-13464. (Woman in History Ser.: Vol. 9B). (Illus.). viii, 125p. 1983. 20.95 (ISBN 0-86663-037-6); pap. 5.95 (ISBN 0-86663-038-4). Ide Hse.

Jackson, Anne A. & Spears, Cleola I. Women in Ministry. (Illus.). 350p. (Orig.). pap. write for info. (ISBN 0-9605892-3-6). Dawn Ministries.

Kellogg, Mrs. Dennis. He Lifted Me. 1966. pap. 3.95 (ISBN 0-88027-046-2). Firm Foun Pub.

LaPorte, Jean. The Role of Women in Early Christianity. LC 82-8281. (Studies in Women & Religion: Vol. 7). 196p. 1982. 39.95x (ISBN 0-88946-545-2). E Mellen.

Livingstone, W. P. Mary Slessor of Calabar. (Heroes of the Faith Ser.). 1986. Repr. 6.95 (ISBN 0-916441-49-0). Barbour & Co.

MacDonald, Dennis R. The Legend & the Apostle: The Battle for Paul in Story & Canon. LC 82-21953. 144p. (Orig.). 1983. pap. 9.95 (ISBN 0-664-24464-5). Westminster.

Maitland, Sara. A Map of the New Country: Women & Christianity. LC 82-13142. 218p. 1983. pap. 8.95 (ISBN 0-7100-9301-2). Methuen Inc.

Moltmann-Wendel, Elisabeth. The Women Around Jesus. LC 82-72478. 160p. 1982. pap. 7.95 (ISBN 0-8245-0535-2). Crossroad NY.

Morton, Nelle. The Journey Is Home: The Distinguished Feminist Theologian Traces the Development of Her Personal & Theoretical Vision. LC 85-42342. 285p. 1986. pap. 8.95 (ISBN 0-8070-1133-9, BP 718). Beacon Pr.

Overrein, Judy. The King's Daughters. 116p. (Orig.). 1982. pap. text ed. 3.00 (ISBN 0-941630-00-5). Freedom Pr.

Popson, Martha. That We Might Have Life. LC 80-2080. 128p. 1981. pap. 2.95 (ISBN 0-385-17438-1, Im). Doubleday.

Ruether, Rosemary R. New Woman-New Earth: Sexist Ideologies & Human Liberation. 255p. 1978. pap. 9.95 (ISBN 0-8164-2185-4, HarpR). Har-Row.

Ryrie, Charles C. The Role of Women in the Church. LC 58-8329. 1979. pap. 5.95 (ISBN 0-8024-7371-7). Moody.

Schreiber, Clara S. Katherine: Life of Luther. 1981. 6.95 (ISBN 0-8100-0144-6, 15N0385). Northwest Pub.

Scott, Latayne C. Open up Your Life: A Woman's Workshop on Christian Hospitality. 144p. 1983. pap. 2.95 (ISBN 0-310-38901-1, 10451P). Zondervan.

Sewell, Daisy M. Ideal Womanhood. 1947. pap. 1.50 (ISBN 0-88027-048-9). Firm Foun Pub.

Stendahl, Brita. The Force of Tradition: A Case Study of Women Priests in Sweden. LC 84-48713. (Illus.). 208p. 1985. pap. 14.95 (ISBN 0-8006-1808-4, 1-1808). Fortress.

Stowe, Faye C. The Whole Woman: Fashioned in His Image. 135p. 1984. pap. 4.95 (ISBN 0-8341-0913-1). Beacon Hill.

Swidler, Arlene & Conn, Walter E., eds. Mainstreaming: Feminist Research for Teaching Religious Studies. 96p. (Orig.). 1985. lib. bdg. 20.25 (ISBN 0-8191-4724-9, Co-Pub by College Theo Soc); pap. text ed. 7.75 (ISBN 0-8191-4725-7). U Pr of Amer.

Tapp, Mrs. Vernon. For Such a Time. (Illus.). 160p. 1979. pap. 3.00 (ISBN 0-89114-083-2); pap. 0.75 tchr's. guide, 15 pg. (ISBN 0-89114-084-0). Baptist Pub Hse.

Tavard, George H. Woman in Christian Tradition. LC 72-12637. pap. 67.30 (ISBN 0-317-26144-4, 2024373). Bks Demand UMI.

Willetts, Phoebe. Sharing a Vision. 116p. 1978. pap. 4.95 (ISBN 0-227-67842-7). Attic Pr.

Witherington, Ben. Women in the Ministry of Jesus: A Study of Jesus' Attitude to Women & Their Roles As Reflected in His Earthly Life. LC 83-18957. (Society for the New Testament Studies Monograph: No. 51). 210p. 1984. 29.95 (ISBN 0-521-25658-5). Cambridge U Pr.

WOMEN IN CHURCH WORK

see also Clergymen's Wives; Women–Religious Life

Benjamin, Dick. Women's Ministries in the New Testament Church. 1983. pap. 1.75 (ISBN 0-911739-16-5). Abbott Loop.

Berry, Jo. Growing, Sharing, Serving. LC 78-73461. 1979. pap. 3.95 (ISBN 0-89191-073-5). Cook.

Bouyer, Louis. Woman in the Church. Teichert, Marilyn, tr. from Fr. LC 79-84878. Orig. Title: Mystere et Ministeres de la femme dans l'Eglise. 132p. (Orig.). 1979. pap. 7.95 (ISBN 0-89870-002-7). Ignatius Pr.

Capetti, Giselda, ed. Cronistoria, 5 vols. LC 80-68484. 400p. (Orig.). 1980. Set. pap. 40.00 (ISBN 0-89944-043-6); Vol. 1. pap. (ISBN 0-89944-044-4); Vol. 2. pap. (ISBN 0-89944-045-2); Vol. 3. pap. (ISBN 0-89944-046-0); Vol. 4. pap. (ISBN 0-89944-047-9); Vol. 5. pap. (ISBN 0-89944-048-7). Don Bosco Multimedia.

Clare, Frances. Wow God. 189p. pap. 4.95 (ISBN 0-89221-131-8). New Leaf.

Feucht, Oscar E. Guidelines for Women's Groups in the Congregation. 1981. pap. 3.95 (ISBN 0-570-03828-6, 12-2793). Concordia.

Franklin, Margaret A., ed. The Force of the Feminine: Women, Men & the Church. 232p. 1986. text ed. 29.95x (ISBN 0-86861-930-2); pap. text ed. 12.95x (ISBN 0-86861-914-0). Allen Unwin.

Haughton, Rosemary. The Re-Creation of Eve. 1985. pap. 8.95 (ISBN 0-87243-135-5). Templegate.

Jicks, John M. & Morton, Bruce L. Woman's Role in the Church. pap. 2.95 (ISBN 0-89315-362-1). Lambert Bk.

Kuhns, Dennis R. Women in the Church. LC 78-53968. 80p. (Orig.). 1978. pap. 2.95 (ISBN 0-8361-1852-9). Herald Pr.

Lambert, Regina. Every Woman Has a Ministry. LC 79-84321. (Illus.). 1979. pap. 2.95 (ISBN 0-89221-062-1). New Leaf.

Nicholas, David R. What's a Woman to Do in Church? 148p. 1979. 7.95 (ISBN 0-88469-123-3). BMH Bks.

Ryrie, Charles C. The Role of Women in the Church. LC 58-8329. 1979. pap. 5.95 (ISBN 0-8024-7371-7). Moody.

Tozer, Tom. Amazing Grace & Her Incredible Place. 1984. 4.75 (ISBN 0-89536-706-8, 4802). CSS of Ohio.

Verdesi, Elizabeth H. In But Still Out: Women in the Church. LC 75-34365. 218p. 1976. pap. 3.95 (ISBN 0-664-24788-1). Westminster.

WOMEN IN HINDUISM

Kinsley, David. Hindu Goddesses: Visions of the Divine Feminine in the Hindu Religious Tradition. LC 84-28000. (Hermeneutics: Studies in the History of Religions). 1985. 35.00x (ISBN 0-520-05393-1). U of Cal Pr.

Marglin, Frederique A. Wives of the God-King: The Rituals of the Devadasis of Puri. (Illus.). 1985. 29.95x (ISBN 0-19-561731-2). Oxford U Pr.

Nebeker, Helen. Jean Rhys: Woman in Passage. 250p. (Orig.). 1981. pap. 8.95 (ISBN 0-920792-04-9). Eden Pr.

Nivedita, Sr. Notes of Some Wanderings. 3.00 (ISBN 0-87481-185-6). Vedanta Pr.

Pinkham, Mildred W. Woman in the Sacred Scriptures of Hinduism. LC 41-7015. Repr. of 1941 ed. 16.50 (ISBN 0-404-05055-7). AMS Pr.

The Mother. Glimpses of the Mother's Life, Vol. 2. Das, Nilima, ed. 335p. 1980. 11.00 (ISBN 0-89071-291-3). Matagiri.

WOMEN IN MISSIONARY WORK

Beaver, R. Pierce. American Protestant Women in World Mission. LC 80-14366. Orig. Title: All Loves Excelling. Repr. of 1960 ed. 45.10 (ISBN 0-8357-9122-X, 2019317). Bks Demand UMI.

Bulletin Committee Staff. Fiftieth Anniversary Issue: Kingston Lake Woman's Baptist Educational & Missionary Convention of Horry County, South Carolina. rev. ed. Dozier, Etrulia P., ed. (Illus.). 80p. (Orig.). 1985. pap. text ed. 5.00 (ISBN 0-9615271-2-9). Positive Images.

Chesham, Sallie. Preaching Ladies. (Illus.). 179p. (Orig.). 1983. pap. 3.50 (ISBN 0-89216-045-4). Salvation Army.

Elliot, Elisabeth. These Strange Ashes. LC 74-25684. 132p. 1979. pap. 6.95 (ISBN 0-06-062234-2, RD 488, HarpR). Har-Row.

Goering, Gladys V. Women in Search of Mission. LC 80-66787. (Illus.). 136p. 1980. pap. 3.95 (ISBN 0-87303-062-1). Faith & Life.

Goodman, Mark N. The Ninth Amendment: History, Interpretation & Meaning. 74p. 1981. 5.00 (ISBN 0-682-49630-8, University). Exposition Pr FL.

Hill, Patricia R. The World Their Household: The American Women's Foreign Mission Movement & Cultural Transformation, 1870-1920. (Women & Culture Ser.). 300p. 1985. text ed. 19.50x (ISBN 0-472-10055-6). U of Mich Pr.

Hunter, Jane. The Gospel of Gentility: American Women Missionaries in Turn-of-the Century-China. LC 83-15668. 352p. 1984. 27.50x (ISBN 0-300-02878-4). Yale U Pr.

WOMEN IN RELIGION

see also Women in Christianity; Women in Church Work; Women in Hinduism

Acornley, John H. The Colored Lady Evangelist, Being the Life, Labors, & Experiences of Mrs. Harriet A. Baker. De Swarte, Carolyn G. & Dayton, Donald, eds. (Women in American Protestant Religion Series 1800-1930). 78p. 1987. lib. bdg. 20.00 (ISBN 0-8240-0652-6). Garland Pub.

Appleman, Solomon. The Jewish Woman in Judaism: The Significance of Women's Status in Religious Culture. 1979. 10.00 (ISBN 0-682-49431-3). Exposition Pr FL.

Bass, Dorothy C. & Boyd, Sandra H. Women in American Religious History: An Annotated Bibliography. (Reference Bks). 205p. 1986. lib. bdg. 30.00x (ISBN 0-8161-8151-9). G K Hall.

Boyd, Lois A. & Brackenridge, R. Douglas. Presbyterian Women in America: Two Centuries of a Quest for Status. LC 82-15845. (Contributions to the Study of Religion: No. 9). 416p. 1983. lib. bdg. 35.00 (ISBN 0-313-23678-X, BOY/). Greenwood.

Brown, Earl K. Women of Mr. Wesley's Methodism. LC 83-22010. (Studies in Women & Religion: Vol. 11). 273p. 1984. 49.95x (ISBN 0-88946-538-X). E Mellen.

Clark, Elizabeth A. Jerome, Chrysostom, & Friends: Essays & Translations. LC 79-66374. (Studies in Women & Religion: Vol. 2). xi, 270p. 1979. soft cover 34.95x (ISBN 0-88946-548-7). E Mellen.

Coll, Regina. Women & Religion: A Reader for the Clergy. 128p. 1982. pap. 5.95 (ISBN 0-8091-2461-0). Paulist Pr.

Dail, Shirley M. Jesus Said "Leave Her Alone". (Illus.). 1979. pap. 2.95x (ISBN 0-9602440-0-X). Jesus-First.

De Swarte, Carolyn G. & Dayton, Donald, eds. The Defense of Women's Rights to Ordination in the Methodist Episcopal Church. (Women in American Protestant Religion Series 1800-1930). 230p. 1987. lib. bdg. 35.00 (ISBN 0-8240-0654-2). Garland Pub.

Fiorenza, Elizabeth S. Bread Not Stone: The Challenge of Feminist Biblical Interpretation. LC 84-14669. 207p. 1985. 17.95 (ISBN 0-8070-1100-2). Beacon Pr.

Foster, Theodora C. Women, Religion, & Development in the Third World. LC 83-13670. 288p. 1984. 30.95 (ISBN 0-03-064108-X). Praeger.

Franklin, Margaret A., ed. The Force of the Feminine: Women, Men & the Church. 232p. 1986. text ed. 29.95x (ISBN 0-86861-930-2); pap. text ed. 12.95x (ISBN 0-86861-914-0). Allen Unwin.

Gifford, Carolyn D. & Dayton, Donald, eds. The American Deaconess Movement in the Early Twentieth Century. (Women in American Protestant Religion 1800-1930 Ser.). 288p. 1987. lib. bdg. 40.00 (ISBN 0-8240-0650-X). Garland Pub.

--The American Ideal of the "True Woman" As Reflected in Advice Books to Young Women. Gifford, Carolyn, tr. (Women in American Protestant Religion 1800-1930 Ser.). 431p. 1987. lib. bdg. 60.00 (ISBN 0-8240-0651-8). Garland Pub.

Giles, Mary E. When Each Leaf Shines: Voices of Women's Ministry. 1986. pap. 4.95 (ISBN 0-87193-246-6). Dimension Bks.

Goodman, Mark N. The Ninth Amendment: History, Interpretation & Meaning. 74p. 1981. 5.00 (ISBN 0-682-49630-8, University). Exposition Pr FL.

Greaves, Richard L., ed. Triumph over Silence: Women in Protestant History. LC 85-961. (Contributions to the Study of Religion Ser.: No. 15). xii, 295p. 1985. lib. bdg. 35.00 (ISBN 0-313-24799-4, GTS/). Greenwood.

Greenberg, Blu. On Women & Judaism: A View from Tradition. LC 81-11779. 192p. 1983. pap. 5.95 (ISBN 0-8276-0195-6, 482). Jewish Pubns.

Hammack, Mary L. A Dictionary of Women in Church History. LC 84-14710. 1984. 11.95 (ISBN 0-8024-0332-8). Moody.

Hepburn, Daisy & Klope, Joan B. How to Grow a Women's Minis-Tree. LC 86-11812. (Illus.). 140p. (Orig.). 1986. pap. 5.95 (ISBN 0-8307-1159-7, 5418863). Regal.

Holden, Pat, ed. Women's Religious Experience. LC 82-24314. 218p. 1983. text ed. 28.50x (ISBN 0-389-20363-7, 07226). B&N Imports.

Holley, Marietta. Samantha among the Brethren, By Josiah Allen's Wife. Gifford, Carolyn & Dayton, Donald, eds. (Women in American Protestan Religion 1800-1930 Ser.). 437p. 1987. lib. bdg. 60.00 (ISBN 0-8240-0664-X). Garland Pub.

Irwin, Joyce L. Womanhood in Radical Protestantism: 1525-1675. LC 79-66370. (Studies in Women & Religion: Vol. 1). xxx, 296p. 1979. 49.95x (ISBN 0-88946-547-9). E Mellen.

Jewett, Paul K. The Ordination of Women. LC 80-15644. 160p. (Orig.). 1980. pap. 5.95 (ISBN 0-8028-1850-1). Eerdmans.

Johnson, Dale A., ed. Women in English Religion, Seventeen Hundred thru Nineteen Twenty-Five. LC 83-12124. (Studies in Women & Religion: Vol. 10). 368p. 1984. 49.95x (ISBN 0-88946-539-8). E Mellen.

Kellogg, Hallie A. Woman of God. 1962. pap. 3.95 (ISBN 0-88027-051-9). Firm Foun Pub.

Kimball, Spencer W., et al. Woman. LC 79-64908. 1979. 8.95 (ISBN 0-87747-758-2). Deseret Bk.

King, Ursula, ed. Women in the World Religions, Past & Present. (God Ser.). 256p. (Orig.). 1987. 22.95 (ISBN 0-913757-32-2, Pub. by New Era Bks.); pap. 12.95 (ISBN 0-913757-33-0, Pub. by New Era Bks). Paragon Hse.

Lambert, Regina. Every Woman Has a Ministry. LC 79-84321. (Illus.). 1979. pap. 2.95 (ISBN 0-89221-062-1). New Leaf.

MacDonell, Robert W. Belle Harris Bennett, Her Life Work. Gifford, Carolyn D. & Dayton, Donald, eds. (Women in American Protestant Religion 1800-1930 Ser.). 297p. 1987. lib. bdg. 40.00 (ISBN 0-8240-0669-0). Garland Pub.

Mann, Denese B. The Woman in Judaism. 1979. pap. 5.50 (ISBN 0-9603348-0-7). Jonathan Pubns.

Moltmann-Wendel, Elizabeth. Liberty, Equality, Sisterhood: On the Emancipation of Women in Church & Society. Gritsch, Ruth, tr. LC 77-15240. pap. 23.80 (2026919). Bks Demand UMI.

Nichol, Christopher, ed. Women & the Church. 102p. (Orig.). 1984. pap. 8.95 (ISBN 0-318-20037-6, Pub. by Tertiary Christian Studies). ANZ Religious Pubns.

Ochshorn, Judith. The Female Experience & the Nature of the Divine. LC 81-47012. pap. 71.50 (2056237). Bks Demand UMI.

Patterson, Mrs. Elmer. Wisely Train the Younger Women. 1973. pap. 4.95 (ISBN 0-89137-406-X). Quality Pubns.

Paul, Diana. Women in Buddhism: Images of the Feminine in the Mahayana Tradition. 1985. 35.00x (ISBN 0-520-05445-8); pap. 10.95 (ISBN 0-520-05428-6, CAL 740). U of Cal Pr.

Rice, Helen S. Mothers are a Gift of Love. (Illus.). 128p. 1980. 12.95 (ISBN 0-8007-1135-1). Revell.

Ruether, Rosemary R. Womanguides: Readings Toward a Feminist Theology. LC 84-14508. 286p. 1986. 21.95 (ISBN 0-8070-1202-5); pap. 10.95 (ISBN 0-8070-1203-3, BP 726). Beacon Pr.

Sexton, Lydia. Autobiography of Lydia Sexton, the Story of Her Life Through a Period of over Seventy-Five Years from 1799 to 1872: Her Early Privations, Adventures, & Reminiscences. Gifford, Carolyn D. & Dayton, Donald, eds. (Women in American Protestant Religion 1800-1930 Ser.). 655p. 1987. lib. bdg. 95.00 (ISBN 0-8240-0673-9). Garland Pub.

Sharma, Arvind, ed. Women in World Religions. (McGill Studies in the History of Religions). 256p. (Orig.). 1986. 34.50x (ISBN 0-88706-374-8); pap. 10.95x (ISBN 0-88706-375-6). State U NY Pr.

Smith, Amanda B. An Autobiography: The Story of the Lord's Dealings with Mrs. Amanda Smith, The Colored Evangelist, Containing an Account of Her Life Work of Faith, & Her Travels in America, England, Ireland, Scotland, India & Africa, as an Independent Missionary. Gifford, Carolyn D. & Dayton, Donald, eds. (Women in American Protestant Religion 1800-1930 Ser.). 506p. 1987. lib. bdg. 70.00 (ISBN 0-8240-0674-7). Garland Pub.

Spinning a Sacred Yarn: Women Speak from the Pulpit. LC 82-569. 230p. (Orig.). 1982. pap. 8.95 (ISBN 0-8298-0604-0). Pilgrim NY.

Starr, Lee A. The Bible Status of Women. Gifford, Carolyn D. & Dayton, Donald, eds. (Women in American Protestant Religion 1800-1930 Ser.). 416p. 1987. lib. bdg. 60.00 (ISBN 0-8240-0675-5). Garland Pub.

Stevens, Abel. The Women of Methodism: Its Three Foundresses, Susanna Wesley, the Countess of Huntingdon, & Barbara Heck. Gifford, Carolyn D. & Dayton, Donald, eds. (Women in American Protestant Religion 1800-1930 Ser.). 304p. 1987. lib. bdg. 45.00 (ISBN 0-8240-0676-3). Garland Pub.

Thomas, Hilah F. & Keller, Rosemary S., eds. Women in New Worlds: Vol. 1. LC 81-7984. (Historical Perspectives on the Wesleyan Tradition Ser.). 448p. (Orig.). 1981. pap. 13.95 (ISBN 0-687-45968-0). Abingdon.

Ulanov, Ann B. Receiving Woman: Studies in the Psychology & Theology of the Feminine. LC 80-26813. 186p. 1981. pap. 9.95 (ISBN 0-664-24360-6). Westminster.

Vonk, Idalee. Thirty-Six Devotionals for Women's Groups. LC 81-52993. 112p. (Orig.). 1982. pap. 3.95 (ISBN 0-87239-493-X, 3216). Standard Pub.

Wahlberg, Rachel C. Jesus & the Freed Woman. LC 78-61718. 176p. (Orig.). 1978. pap. 3.95 (ISBN 0-8091-2139-5). Paulist Pr.

Wilson-Kastner, Patricia, et al. A Lost Tradition: Women Writers of the Early Church. LC 80-6290. 210p. (Orig.). 1981. lib. bdg. 25.00 (ISBN 0-8191-1642-4); pap. text ed. 11.50 (ISBN 0-8191-1643-2). U Pr of Amer.

Wittenmyer, Annie T. Woman's Work for Jesus. Gifford, Carolyn D. & Dayton, Donald, eds. (Women in American Protestant Religion 1800-1930 Ser.). 240p. 1987. lib. bdg. 35.00 (ISBN 0-8240-0685-2). Garland Pub.

Woman's Institute for Continuing Jewish Education. Taking the Fruit: Modern Women's Tales of the Bible. Sprague, Jane, ed. (Illus.). 61p. 1982. pap. 5.95 (ISBN 0-9608054-1-9). Womans Inst-Cont Jewish Ed.

WOMEN IN THE BIBLE

Alex, Marlee. Esther. (Outstanding Women of the Bible Ser.). (Illus.). 32p. 1987. 8.95 (ISBN 0-8028-5016-2). Eerdmans.

--Mary. (Women of the Bible Ser.). 32p. 1987. 8.95 (ISBN 0-8028-5018-9). Eerdmans.

--Ruth. (Women of the Bible Ser.). (Illus.). 32p. 1987. 8.95 (ISBN 0-8028-5017-0). Eerdmans.

--Sarah. (Outstanding Women of the Bible Ser.). 32p. 1987. 8.95 (ISBN 0-8028-5015-4). Eerdmans.

Benton, Josephine M. Martha & Mary: A Woman's Relationship to Her Home. 1983. pap. 2.50x (ISBN 0-87574-036-7, 036). Pendle Hill.

Blanton, Alma E. God & Mrs. Adam. (Illus.). 152p. (Orig.). 1978. lib. bdg. 4.95 (ISBN 0-938134-00-0, G-1); pap. 4.95 (ISBN 0-686-73968-X). Loving Pubs.

--Our Gospel's Women. (Illus.). 114p. (Orig.). 1979. pap. 3.00 (ISBN 0-938134-01-9). Loving Pubs.

Bloem, Diane B. Leader's Manual: A Woman's Workshop on Bible Women. 128p. 1983. pap. 3.95 student Manual (ISBN 0-310-23151-5); tchr's. manual avail. (ISBN 0-310-23141-8, 10747). Zondervan.

Brawner, Mina R. Woman in the Word. 1.25 (ISBN 0-89985-105-3). Christ Nations.

Brenner, Athalya. The Israelite Woman: Social Role & Literary Type in Biblical Narrative. (The Biblical Seminar Ser.: No. 2). 144p. 1985. pap. text ed. 7.95x (ISBN 0-905774-83-3, Pub. by JSOT Pr England). Eisenbrauns.

Briscoe, Jill. Prime Rib & Apple. 1976. 5.95 (ISBN 0-310-21810-1, 9257P); pap. 4.95 (ISBN 0-310-21811-X). Zondervan.

--Women in the Life of Jesus. 96p. 1986. pap. 4.95 (ISBN 0-89693-254-0). Victor Bks.

Brown, Marguerite D. Women of Calvary. 1982. pap. 5.25 ea. (ISBN 0-89536-526-X, 2331). CSS of Ohio.

Buckingham, Betty Jo, ed. Women at the Well: Expressions of Faith, Life & Worship Drawn from Our Own Wisdom. Carachei, Maria E., tr. LC 87-6224. (Orig.). (YA) 1987. pap. 7.95 (ISBN 0-9618243-0-1). Womens Caucus Church.

Burns, Rita J. Has the Lord Indeed Spoken Only Through Moses? A Study of the Biblical Portrait of Miriam. (Society of Biblical Literature Dissertation Ser.). 148p. 1987. 16.95 (ISBN 0-89130-964-0, 06-01-84); pap. 12.95 (ISBN 0-89130-965-9). Scholars Pr GA.

Buswell, Sara. Challenge of Old Testament Women Two. 176p. (Orig.). 1987. pap. 5.95 (ISBN 0-8010-0932-4). Baker Bk.

Cady, Susan A., et al. Sophia: The Future of Feminist Spirituality. 120p. 1986. 14.95 (ISBN 0-06-254200-1, HarpR). Har-Row.

Carlisle, Thomas J. Beginning with Mary: Women of the Gospels in Portrait. 120p. (Orig.). 1986. pap. 5.95 (ISBN 0-8028-0194-3). Eerdmans.

Carney, Mary Lou. Heart Cries: Prayers of Biblical Women. 128p. (Orig.). 1986. pap. 5.95 (ISBN 0-687-16762-0). Abingdon.

Christensen, Winnie. Women Who Achieved for God. (Fisherman Bible Studyguide). 80p. 1984. pap. 2.95 (ISBN 0-87788-937-6). Shaw Pubs.

--Women Who Believed God. (Fisherman Bible Studyguide Ser.). 77p. 1983. saddle-stiched 2.95 (ISBN 0-87788-936-8). Shaw Pubs.

Coalition on Women & Religion Staff. The Women's Bible: Study Guide. 1975. 5.95 (ISBN 0-9603042-2-3). Coalition Women-Relig.

Daughters of St. Paul. Women of the Bible. LC 71-145574. (Illus.). 5.95 (ISBN 0-8198-0322-7); pap. 4.95 (ISBN 0-8198-0323-5). Dghtrs St Paul.

--Women of the Gospel. LC 74-32122. 1975. 5.95 (ISBN 0-8198-0495-9); pap. 4.95 (ISBN 0-8198-0496-7). Dghtrs St Paul.

Deen, Edith. All of the Women of the Bible. LC 55-8621. 1955. 18.45 (ISBN 0-06-061810-8, HarpR). Har-Row.

Elder, Dorothy. Women of the Bible Speak to Women of Today. LC 86-70873. (Illus.). 288p. (Orig.). 1986. pap. 12.00 (ISBN 0-87516-574-5). De Vorss.

Evans, Mary J. Woman in the Bible. LC 84-4641. 160p. 1984. pap. 6.95 (ISBN 0-87784-978-1). Inter-Varsity.

Eve's Version: One Hundred Fifty Women of the Bible Speak Through Modern Poets. (Illus.). 1983. 13.95. Paramount TX.

Faxon, Alicia C. Women & Jesus. LC 72-11868. 1973. 4.95 (ISBN 0-8298-0244-4). Pilgrim NY.

Field, Faye. Women Who Encountered Jesus. LC 81-65798. 1982. 4.50 (ISBN 0-8054-5182-X). Broadman.

Fiorenza, Elizabeth S. Bread Not Stone: The Challenge of Feminist Biblical Interpretation. LC 84-14669. 207p. 1985. 17.95 (ISBN 0-8070-1100-2). Beacon Pr.
Gilliland, Dolores S. Selected Women of the Scriptures of Stamina & Courage. (Illus.). 1978. pap. 3.95 (ISBN 0-931446-02-3). Honor Bks.
Hardesty, Nancy A. Great Women of Faith. (Festival Ser.). 144p. 1982. pap. 3.25 (ISBN 0-687-15728-5). Abingdon.
Harris, Dixie L. Twenty Stories of Bible Women. 1980. 12.50 (ISBN 0-682-49526-3). Exposition Pr FL.
Harris, Kevin. Sex, Ideology & Religion: The Representation of Women in the Bible. LC 84-12413. 144p. 1984. 22.50x (ISBN 0-389-20509-5, BNB08067). B&N Imports.
Hartsoe, Colleen I. Dear Daughter: Letters from Eve & Other Women of the Bible. LC 81-80627. 1981. pap. 4.95 (ISBN 0-8192-1288-1). Morehouse.
Haughton, Rosemary. The Re-Creation of Eve. 1985. pap. 8.95 (ISBN 0-87243-135-5). Templegate.
Herr, Ethel. Chosen Women of the Bible. LC 75-36503. 96p. (Orig.). 1976. pap. 4.95 (ISBN 0-8024-1297-1). Moody.
Hess, Margaret. Unconventional Women. 1981. pap. 5.95 (ISBN 0-88207-340-0). Victor Bks.
Hurd, Jerrie W. Our Sisters in the Bible. LC 83-50986. 168p. 1983. 8.95 (ISBN 0-87747-981-X). Deseret Bk.
Jacobs, Joy. They Were Women Like Me: Women of the New Testament in Devotions for Today. 216p. 1985. 14.95 (ISBN 0-13-917048-0); pap. 7.95 (ISBN 0-13-917030-8). P-H.
--They Were Women, Too. LC 1-67319. 375p. 1981. pap. 8.95 (ISBN 0-87509-304-3). Chr Pubns.
Jensen, Mary E. Bible Women Speak to Us Today. LC 83-70507. 128p. (Orig.). 1983. pap. 5.95 (ISBN 0-8066-2013-7, 10-0708). Augsburg.
--Women of the Bible Tell Their Stories. LC 78-52193. 1978. pap. 6.95 (ISBN 0-8066-1663-6, 10-7235). Augsburg.
Kuyper, Abraham. Women of the New Testament. pap. 4.95 (ISBN 0-310-36751-4, 9996P). Zondervan.
--Women of the Old Testament. pap. 5.95 (ISBN 0-310-36761-1, 9997P). Zondervan.
Latham, Judy. Women in the Bible: Helpful Friends. (BibLearn Ser.). (Illus.). 1979. 5.95 (ISBN 0-8054-4248-0, 4242-48). Broadman.
Lightfoot, Neil R. The Role of Women: New Testament Perspectives. (Orig.). 1978. pap. 2.95 (ISBN 0-931118-00-X). Student Assn.
Macartney, Clarence E. Great Women of the Bible. (Macartney Bible Characters Library). (Orig.). 1974. pap. 5.95 (ISBN 0-8010-5961-5). Baker Bk.
Matheson, George. Portraits of Bible Women. LC 86-7429. Orig. Title: Representative Women of the Bible (Eve to Mary Magdalene) 304p. 1986. pap. 7.95 (ISBN 0-8254-3250-2). Kregel.
Mickelsen, Alvera. Women, Authority & the Bible. LC 86-7158. 252p. (Orig.). 1986. pap. 9.95 (ISBN 0-87784-608-1). Inter-Varsity.
Milburn, B. A. Curious Cases: A Collection of American & English Decisions Selected for Their Readability. (Illus.). xvi, 441p. 1985. Repr. of 1902 ed. lib. bdg. 37.50x (ISBN 0-8377-0819-2). Rothman.
Mollenkott, Virginia R. The Divine Feminine: The Biblical Imagery of God As Female. 128p. 1984. pap. 8.95 (ISBN 0-8245-0669-3). Crossroad NY.
Moore, Carey A. Judith. LC 83-11694. (Anchor Bible Ser.: Vol. 40). (Illus.). 312p. 1985. 14.00 (ISBN 0-385-14424-5). Doubleday.
Munn, Elijah H. The Progress(?) of Woman. 84p. 6.95 (ISBN 0-9609828-0-9). EHM Pub.
Musgrove, Peggy. Who's Who Among Bible Women. LC 81-81126. 128p. (Orig.). 1981. 2.50 (ISBN 0-88243-883-2, 02-0883); teacher's ed. 3.95 (ISBN 0-88243-193-5, 32-0193). Gospel Pub.
Nunnally-Cox, Janice. Foremothers: Women of the Bible. 192p. (Orig.). 1981. pap. 6.95 (ISBN 0-8164-2329-6, HarpR). Har-Row.
Overby, Coleman. Bible Women. 1936. pap. 2.95 (ISBN 0-88027-082-9). Firm Foun Pub.
Price, Eugenia. The Unique World of Women. 248p. 1982. pap. 7.95 (ISBN 0-310-31351-1, 16216P). Zondervan.
Pride, Mary. The Way Home Beyond Feminism, Back to Reality. LC 84-73078. 240p. (Orig.). 1985. pap. 7.95 (ISBN 0-89107-345-0, Crossway Bks). Good News.
Ruether, Rosemary R. Womanguides: Readings Toward a Feminist Theology. LC 84-14508. 286p. 1986. 21.95 (ISBN 0-8070-1202-5); pap. 10.95 (ISBN 0-8070-1203-3, BP 726). Beacon Pr.
Sandys, Edwina & Morton, James P. Women of the Bible: Sculpture. Piche, Thomas, Jr., ed. LC 86-83188. (Illus.). 24p. (Orig.). 1986. pap. text ed. write for info. (ISBN 0-914407-07-4). Everson Mus.
Schelkle, Karl H. The Spirit & the Bride: Woman in the Bible. Schneider, John, ed. O'Connell, Matthew J., tr. from Ger. LC 79-16976. 191p. (Orig.). 1979. pap. 3.50 (ISBN 0-8146-1008-0). Liturgical Pr.
Sekowsky, JoAnne. Restored Value: A Woman's Status in Christ. (Encourager Ser.). 32p. 1985. pap. 2.25 (ISBN 0-932305-01-6, 523001). Aglow Pubns.
Seltman, Charles T. Women in Antiquity. LC 78-20490. 1981. Repr. of 1956 ed. 25.85 (ISBN 0-88355-867-X). Hyperion Conn.
Shenk, Barbara K. The God of Sarah, Rebekah, & Rachel. LC 85-5503. 132p. 1985. 19.95 (ISBN 0-8361-3392-7). Herald Pr.
Smith, Joyce M. Esther, a Woman of Courage. 1981. pap. 2.95 (ISBN 0-8423-0729-X). Tyndale.
--A Woman's Priorities. 1976. pap. 2.95 (ISBN 0-8423-8380-8). Tyndale.
Stagg, Evelyn & Stagg, Frank. Woman in the World of Jesus. LC 77-28974. 292p. 1978. pap. 9.95 (ISBN 0-664-24195-6). Westminster.
Stanton, Elizabeth C. The Original Feminist Attack on the Bible. LC 74-9343. 258p. 1974. 6.95 (ISBN 0-405-05997-3). Ayer Co Pubs.
--The Woman's Bible, 2 vols. in 1. LC 72-2626. (American Women Ser: Images & Realities). 380p. 1972. Repr. of 1895 ed. 25.50 (ISBN 0-405-04481-X). Ayer Co Pubs.
Staton, Julia. What the Bible Says about Women. LC 80-66128. (What the Bible Says Ser.). 400p. 1980. 13.95 (ISBN 0-89900-079-7). College Pr Pub.
Steinsaltz, Adin. Biblical Images: Men & Women of the Book. LC 83-46081. 256p. 1985. pap. 6.95 (ISBN 0-465-00671-X, PL-5158). Basic.
Swidler, Leonard. Biblical Affirmations of Woman. LC 79-18886. 382p. 1979. 19.50 (ISBN 0-664-21377-4); softcover 10.95 (ISBN 0-664-24285-5). Westminster.
Tetlow, Elisabeth M. Women & Ministry in the New Testament: Called to Serve. 170p. 1985. pap. text ed. 10.75 (ISBN 0-8191-4461-4, College Theo Soc). U Pr of Amer.
VanderVelde, Frances. Women of the Bible. rev. ed. LC 83-19894. (Illus.). 260p. 1973. pap. 6.95 (ISBN 0-8254-3951-5). Kregel.
Watson, Elizabeth. Daughters of Zion. LC 82-70600. 100p. (Orig.). 1982. pap. 8.95 (ISBN 0-913408-79-4). Friends United.
Willing, Ora M. & Davidson, C. T. Hidden Treasures for Women. 144p. (Orig.). 1983. pap. 3.95 (ISBN 0-934942-37-4). White Wing Pub.
Wogaman, J. P. Economics & Ethics: A Christian Inquiry. LC 85-45478. 160p. 1986. pap. 9.95 (ISBN 0-8006-1904-8). Fortress.

WOMEN MISSIONARIES

see also Women in Missionary Work

Baker, Frances J. The Story of the Woman's Foreign Missionary Society of the Methodist Episcopal Church, 1869-1895. De Swarte, Carolyn G. & Dayton, Donald, eds. (Women in American Protestant Religion Series 1800-1930). 438p. 1987. lib. bdg. 65.00 (ISBN 0-8240-0658-5). Garland Pub.
Hill, Patricia R. The World Their Household: The American Women's Foreign Mission Movement & Cultural Transformation, 1870-1920. (Women & Culture Ser.). 300p. 1985. text ed. 19.50x (ISBN 0-472-10055-6). U of Mich Pr.
Hunter, Jane. The Gospel of Gentility: American Women Missionaries in Turn-of-the Century-China. LC 83-16668. 352p. 1984. 27.50x (ISBN 0-300-02878-4). Yale U Pr.
Montgomery, Helen B. Western Women in Eastern Lands: An Outline Study of Fifty Years of Woman's Work in Foreign Missions. Gifford, Carolyn & Dayton, Donald, eds. (Women's American Protestant Religion 1800-1930 Ser.). 286p. 1987. lib. bdg. 40.00 (ISBN 0-8240-0670-4). Garland Pub.

WOOLMAN, JOHN, 1720-1772

Moulton, Phillips P. The Living Witness of John Woolman. LC 72-94969. 36p. (Orig.). 1973. 2.50x (ISBN 0-87574-187-8, 187). Pendle Hill.
Moulton, Phillips P., ed. The Journal & Major Essays of John Woolman. (A Library of Protestant Thought). (Illus.). 336p. 1971. pap. text ed. 7.95 (ISBN 0-19-501419-7). Religious Soc Friends.
Reynolds, Reginald. John Woolman & the Twentieth Century. 1983. pap. 2.50x (ISBN 0-87574-096-0, 096). Pendle Hill.
Rosenblatt, Paul. John Woolman. (Great American Thinkers Ser.). 1969. lib. bdg. 17.95 (ISBN 0-89197-813-5). Irvington.
Young, Mildred B. Woolman & Blake: Prophets of Today. LC 72-170018. (Orig.). 1971. pap. 2.50x (ISBN 0-87574-177-0). Pendle Hill.

WORCESTER, NOAH, 1758-1837

Ware, Henry. Memoirs of the Reverend Noah Worcester, D. D. LC 78-137557. (Peace Movement in America Ser). xii, 155p. 1972. Repr. of 1844 ed. lib. bdg. 14.95x (ISBN 0-89198-088-1). Ozer.

WORD (THEOLOGY)

see Communication (Theology); Logos

WORK

see also Job Satisfaction; Vocation

Barry, Colman J. Worship & Work. LC 80-10753. (Illus.). 526p. 1980. pap. text ed. 12.50 (ISBN 0-8146-1123-0). Liturgical Pr.
Buback, Kenneth A. & Grant, Mary K., eds. Quality of Work Life: Health Care Applications. LC 82-12766. 300p. 1985. pap. 24.00 (ISBN 0-87125-074-8). Cath Health.
Cabot, Richard C. What Men Live By. 341p. 1985. Repr. of 1941 ed. lib. bdg. 35.00 (ISBN 0-89760-187-4). Telegraph Bks.
Lehman, Harold D. In Praise of Leisure. LC 74-16399. 200p. 1974. 6.95 (ISBN 0-8361-1752-2); leader's guide o.p. 1.75 (ISBN 0-8361-1750-6). Herald Pr.

WORK (THEOLOGY)

Illanes, Jose L. On the Theology of Work: Aspects of the Teaching of the Founder of Opus Dei. Adams, Michael, tr. from Span. Tr. of La Santification del Trabajo. 107p. (Orig.). 1983. pap. 3.95 (ISBN 0-906127-56-4). Scepter Pubs.
Moran, Pam. Christian Job Hunter. 224p. (Orig.). 1984. pap. 7.95 (ISBN 0-89283-178-2). Servant.
Omi, Maurice M., ed. Work & Faith in Society. 96p. (Orig.). 1986. pap. 6.95 (ISBN 1-55586-988-2). US Catholic.
Pope John Paul II. On Human Work. 62p. 1981. pap. 3.95 (ISBN 1-55586-825-8). US Catholic.
Purkiser, W. T. Called unto Holiness, Vol. 2. 368p. 1983. 14.95 (ISBN 0-8341-0868-2). Beacon Hill.
Raines, John C. & Day-Lower, Donna C. Modern Work & Human Meaning. LC 85-26370. (Illus.). 152p. (Orig.). 1986. pap. 12.95 (ISBN 0-664-24703-2). Westminster.
Wyszynski, Cardinal Work. 184p. 1960. 5.95 (ISBN 0-933932-18-9). Scepter Pubs.

WORLD AND THE CHURCH

see Church and the World

WORLD CONFERENCE ON CHURCH, COMMUNITY AND STATE, OXFORD, 1937

Raven, Charles E. War & the Christian. LC 75-147675. (Library of War & Peace; Relig. & Ethical Positions on War). 1972. lib. bdg. 46.00 (ISBN 0-8240-0432-9). Garland Pub.

WORLD COUNCIL OF CHURCHES

Bell, George K. The Kingship of Christ: The Story of the World Council of Churches. LC 78-10482. 1979. Repr. of 1954 ed. lib. bdg. 22.50x (ISBN 0-313-21121-3, BEKC). Greenwood.
Gaines, David P. The World Council of Churches. 1966. 18.50 (ISBN 0-87233-816-9). Bauhan.
Lefever, Ernest W. Amsterdam to Nairobi: The World Council of Churches & the Third World. LC 79-2607. 126p. 1979. 10.00 (ISBN 0-89633-025-7); pap. 6.00 (ISBN 0-89633-024-9). Ethics & Public Policy.
--Amsterdam to Nairobi: The World Council of Churches & the Third World. 128p. 1985. pap. text ed. 7.50 (ISBN 0-8191-4484-3). U Pr of Amer.
Long, Charles H. Vancouver Voices. 144p. (Orig.). 1983. pap. 1.40 (ISBN 0-88028-026-3). Forward Movement.
McDonnell, John J. The World Council of Churches & the Catholic Church. (Toronto Studies in Theology: Vol. 21). 479p. 1985. lib. bdg. 49.95x (ISBN 0-88946-765-X). E Mellen.

WORLD HISTORY

see also History, Ancient; Middle Ages–History

Baldwin, Marshall W. The Mediaeval Church. (Development of Western Civilization Ser). 124p. (Orig.). 1953. pap. 4.95x (ISBN 0-8014-9842-2). Cornell U Pr.
DeKosky, Robert K. Knowledge & Cosmos: Development & Decline of the Medieval Perspective. LC 79-66226. 1979. text ed. 26.00 (ISBN 0-8191-0814-6); pap. text ed. 15.25 (ISBN 0-8191-0815-4). U Pr of Amer.
Ellis, Mark H., ed. In an Age of Holocaust. (A Chrysalis Bk). 128p. (Orig.). 1986. pap. 14.95 (ISBN 0-916349-13-6). Amity Hous Inc.
Painter, Sidney. Mediaeval Society. (Development of Western Civilization Ser). (Illus.). 109p. 1951. pap. 5.95x (ISBN 0-8014-9850-3). Cornell U Pr.

WORLD WAR, 1914-1918–RELIGIOUS ASPECTS

Eisenhower, David & Murray, John. Warwords: U. S. Militarism the Catholic Right & the Bulgarian Connection. Smith, Betty, ed. 138p. 1987. pap. 3.95 (ISBN 0-7178-0650-2). Intl Pubs Co.
Hartzler, Jonas S. Mennonites in the World War: Or, Nonresistance under Test. LC 76-137543. (Peace Movement in America Ser). 246p. 1972. Repr. of 1922 ed. lib. bdg. 18.95x (ISBN 0-89198-071-7). Ozer.
Lynch, Frederick H. Christian in Wartime. LC 71-147674. (Library of War & Peace; Relig. & Ethical Positions on War). 1972. lib. bdg. 46.00 (ISBN 0-8240-0431-0). Garland Pub.
Marrin, Albert. The Last Crusade: The Church of England in the First World War. LC 72-97471. xv, 303p. 1973. 19.75 (ISBN 0-8223-0298-5). Duke.
Moynihan, Michael. God on Our Side: The British Padre in World War I. (Illus.). 196p. 1983. 19.95 (ISBN 0-436-29402-8, Pub. by Secker & Warburg UK). David & Charles.
Williams, Michael. American Catholics in the War: National Catholic War Council, 1917-1921. LC 74-75244. (The United States in World War 1 Ser.). x, 467p. 1974. Repr. of 1921 ed. lib. bdg. 26.95x (ISBN 0-89198-110-1). Ozer.

WORLD WAR, 1939-1945–ADDRESSES, SERMONS, ETC.

Fosdick, Harry E. Great Time to Be Alive: Sermons on Christianity in Wartime. LC 78-167341. (Essay Index Reprint Ser.). Repr. of 1944 ed. 18.00 (ISBN 0-8369-2688-9). Ayer Co Pubs.

WORLD WAR, 1939-1945–CHURCHES

see World War, 1939-1945–Religious Aspects

WORLD WAR, 1939-1945–JEWS

Campion, Joan. To Save the Rest of Them: Gisi Fleischmann & the Rescue of Central European Jews. 2nd, rev. ed. (Illus.). 196p. 1985. lib. bdg. 18.95 (ISBN 0-9614649-0-9); pap. text ed. 10.95 (ISBN 0-9614649-1-7). G Hein.
Dobroszycki, Lucjan, ed. The Chronicle of the Lodz Ghetto, 1941-1944. LC 84-3614. (Illus.). 603p. 1984. 37.50x (ISBN 0-300-03208-0). Yale U Pr.
Ferencz, Benjamin B. Less Than Slaves: Jewish Forced Labor & the Quest for Compensation. LC 79-10690. 1979. 17.50x (ISBN 0-674-52525-6). Harvard U Pr.
Frank, Anne. Anne Frank: The Diary of a Young Girl. rev. ed. Mooyaart, B. M., tr. 312p. (YA) 1967. 16.95 (ISBN 0-385-04019-9). Doubleday.
--Diary of a Young Girl. LC 58-11474. 1958. o.s. 5.95 (ISBN 0-394-60451-2). Modern Lib.
Friedman, Philip. Their Brothers' Keepers: The Christian Heroes & Heroines Who Helped the Oppressed Escape the Nazi Terror. LC 57-8773. 1978. pap. 8.95 (ISBN 0-8052-5002-6, Pub. by Holocaust Library). Schocken.
Gar, Josef & Friedman, Philip. Biblyografye Fun Yidishe Bikher Vegn Khurbn un Gvure. (Yad Vashem-Yivo Joint Documentary Projects Bibliographical Ser.: No. 3). (Yiddish.). 330p. 1962. 10.00 (ISBN 0-914512-12-9, HE-65-1134). Yivo Inst.
Kowalski, Isaac. Anthology on Armed Jewish Resistance 1939-1945, Vol. 2. 648p. 1985. Repr. 30.00x (ISBN 0-317-46999-1). Jewish Com Pub.
--Anthology on Armed Jewish Resistance 1939-1945, Vol. 3. 648p. 1986. Repr. 30.00x (ISBN 0-317-47002-7). Jewish Com Pub.
Latour, Anny. The Jewish Resistance in France, Nineteen Forty to Nineteen Forty-Four. (Illus.). 1981. 14.95 (ISBN 0-8052-5025-5, Pub. by Holocaust Library); pap. 8.95 (ISBN 0-8052-5024-7). Schocken.
Ramati, Alexander & Niccacci, Rufino. The Assisi Underground. 1978. 3.50 (ISBN 0-8128-8135-4). Stein & Day.
Robinson, Jacob. Guide to Jewish History Under Nazi Impact. 1974. 45.00x (ISBN 0-87068-231-8). Ktav.
Shepherd, Naomi. A Refuge from Darkness: Wilfrid Israel & the Rescue of the Jews. LC 83-22000. 18.45 (ISBN 0-394-52503-5). Pantheon.
Stein, R. Conrad. Warsaw Ghetto. LC 84-23202. (World at War Ser.). (Illus.). 48p. 1985. lib. bdg. 10.60 (ISBN 0-516-04779-5). Childrens.
Szajkowski, Soza. Analytical Franco-Jewish Gazetteer, 1939-1945. 1966. 50.00 (ISBN 0-87068-112-5). Ktav.
Tec, Nechama. When Light Pierced the Darkness: Christian Rescue of Jews in Nazi-Occupied Poland. (Illus.). 320p. 1986. 19.95 (ISBN 0-19-503643-3). Oxford U Pr.
Wyman, David S. The Abandonment of the Jews: America & the Holocaust, 1941-1945. LC 84-42711. 450p. 1984. 6.00 (ISBN 0-394-42813-7). Pantheon.
Zuker, Simon. The Unconquerable Spirit. Hirschler, Gertrude, ed. (Illus.). 160p. 1980. pap. 8.95 (ISBN 0-89906-203-2). Mesorah Pubns.

WORLD WAR, 1939-1945–RELIGIOUS ASPECTS

Arad, Yitzhak. The Partisan: From the Valley of Death to Mount Zion. LC 78-71299. 1979. 16.95 (ISBN 0-8052-5011-5, Pub. by Holocaust Library); pap. 10.95 (ISBN 0-8052-5010-7, Pub. by Holocaust Library). Schocken.

Midlam, Don S. Flight of the Lucky Lady. (Illus.). 1954. 8.95 (ISBN 0-8323-0091-8). Binford-Metropolitan.

Niebuhr, Reinhold. Christianity & Power Politics. LC 69-12421. xi, 226p. 1969. Repr. of 1940 ed. 24.50 (ISBN 0-208-00740-7, Archon). Shoe String.

Temple, William. Hope of a New World. LC 74-121507. (Essay Index Reprint Ser). 1940. 13.00 (ISBN 0-8369-1778-2). Ayer Co Pubs.

WORLDLINESS (THEOLOGY)

see Church and the World

WORRY

see also Anxiety

Adams, J. What to Do about Worry. 1972. pap. 0.75 (ISBN 0-87552-065-0). Presby & Reformed.

Adams, Jay E. What to Do about Worry. 1976. pap. 1.50 (ISBN 0-8010-0048-3). Baker Bk.

Campion, M. G. Worry: A Maieutic Analysis. 350p. 1986. text ed. 47.50x (ISBN 0-566-05118-4). Gower Pub Co.

Kirkpatrick, Jean. Fear & Worry: Our Common Enemies. 14p. 1982. pap. 1.50 (ISBN 0-686-19760-7). WFS.

Living Beyond Worry & Anger. LC 79-83659. 1979. 7.95 (ISBN 0-89081-194-6). Harvest Hse.

WORSHIP

see also Ancestor Worship; Church Attendance; Cultus; Devotional Exercises; God–Worship and Love; Idols and Images; Liturgics; Meditation; Phallicism; Prayer; Public Worship; Ritual; Sacrifice; Saints–Cultus; Sun-Worship

Allison, C. FitzSimons. Fear, Love, & Worship. pap. 4.95 (ISBN 0-8164-2020-3, SP17, HarpR). Har-Row.

Alternative Futures for Worship, 7 vols. Incl. Vol. 1. General Introduction. Cowan, Michael A., et al. Duffy, Regis A., ed. 176p (ISBN 0-8146-1493-0); Vol. 2. Baptism & Confirmation. Thompson, Andrew D., et al. 152p (ISBN 0-8146-1494-9); Vol. 3. The Eucharist. Westerhoff, John H., III, et al. 176p (ISBN 0-8146-1495-7); Vol. 4. Reconciliation. Woods, Denis J., et al. Fink, Peter E., ed. 160p (ISBN 0-8146-1496-5); Vol. 5. Marriage. Roberts, William, et al. Cooke, Bernard, ed. 80p (ISBN 0-8146-1497-3); Vol. 6. Leadership Ministry in Community. Power, David N., et al. Cowan, Michael A., ed. 176p (ISBN 0-8146-1498-1); Vol. 7. Anointing of the Sick. Duffy, Mary F., et al. 152p (ISBN 0-8146-1499-X). 1987. Set. pap. 49.00 (ISBN 0-8146-1491-4); pap. 8.95 ea. Liturgical Pr.

Avila, Rafael. Worship & Politics. Neely, Alan, tr. LC 81-38356. 144p. (Orig.). 1981. pap. 6.95 (ISBN 0-88344-714-2). Orbis Bks.

Barry, Colman J. Worship & Work. LC 80-10753. (Illus.). 526p. 1980. pap. text ed. 12.50 (ISBN 0-8146-1123-0). Liturgical Pr.

Buckley, Frank. Come Worship with Us: Explaining the Mass. 32p. 1987. pap. 1.95 (ISBN 0-89243-263-2). Liguori Pubns.

Burkhardt, John E. Worship. LC 81-23116. 162p. 1982. pap. 8.95 (ISBN 0-664-24409-2). Westminster.

Cabot, Richard C. What Men Live By. 341p. 1985. Repr. of 1941 ed. lib. bdg. 35.00 (ISBN 0-89760-187-4). Telegraph Bks.

Carroll, James. Wonder & Worship. LC 70-133469. 168p. 1970. pap. 2.95 (ISBN 0-8091-1871-8). Paulist Pr.

Christensen, James L. Contemporary Worship Services. LC 75-137445. Repr. of 1971 ed. 64.00 (ISBN 0-8357-9517-9, 2011444). Bks Demand UMI.

Christian Worship. rev. ed. (Time of Life Learning Ser.). (Illus.). 32p. pap. 2.95 (ISBN 0-89622-245-4). Twenty-Third.

Cok, Jerry O. Worship Resources for Youth. 133p. (Orig.). 1983. pap. 12.00 (ISBN 0-914527-25-8). C-Four Res.

Cornwall, Judson. Elements of Worship. LC 85-61459. 1985. pap. 5.95 (ISBN 0-88270-594-6). Bridge Pub.

Craddock, Fred B., et al, eds. Preaching the New Common Lectionary: Year C, Lent, Holy Week, Easter. 240p. (Orig.). 1986. pap. 9.95 (ISBN 0-687-33849-2). Abingdon.

Crawford, Dan R. Where One Is Gathered in His Name. LC 85-19519. 1986. 6.95 (ISBN 0-8054-5025-4). Broadman.

Daniels, Harold M. What to Do with Sunday Morning. LC 78-21040. 132p. 1979. softcover 4.95 (ISBN 0-664-24237-5). Westminster.

Davies, J. G., ed. The Westminster Dictionary of Worship. LC 78-25582. (Illus.). 400p. 1979. 18.95 (ISBN 0-664-21373-1). Westminster.

Dickinson, Helena. A Treasury of Worship. 59.95 (ISBN 0-8490-1230-9). Gordon Pr.

Dittmer, Terry. Creating Contemporary Worship. 80p. (Orig.). 1985. pap. 6.95 (ISBN 0-570-03954-1, 12-2889). Concordia.

Duffy, Regis. Real Presence: Worship, Sacraments, & Commitment. LC 81-47877. 192p. 1982. pap. 8.95 (ISBN 0-06-062105-2, RD 383, HarpR). Har-Row.

Dunstan, Alan. Interpreting Worship. 102p. 1985. pap. 5.95 (ISBN 0-8192-1357-8). Morehouse.

Edgar, William. In Spirit & in Truth: Ten Bible Studies on Worship. 72p. (Orig.). 1976. pap. 2.25 (ISBN 0-87784-458-5). Inter-Varsity.

Ellard, Gerald. Christian Life & Worship. 35.50 (ISBN 0-405-10819-2). Ayer Co Pubs.

Empereur, James. Worship: Exploring the Sacred. 1987. pap. 11.95. Pastoral Pr.

Engle, Paul E. Discovering the Fullness of Worship. (Illus.). 129p. (Orig.). 1978. pap. 4.95 (ISBN 0-934688-01-X). Great Comm Pubns.

Fisher, Constance L. Dancing the Old Testament: Christian Celebrations of Israelite Heritage for Worship & Education. Adams, Doug, ed. (Illus.). 1980. pap. 5.95 (ISBN 0-941500-07-1). Sharing Co.

Friedman, Edwin H. Generation to Generation: Family Process in Church & Synagogue. (Family Therapy Ser.). 319p. 1986. Repr. of 1985 ed. lib. bdg. 25.00 (ISBN 0-89862-059-7). Guilford Pr.

Gibbs, A. P. Scriptural Principles of Gathering. pap. 1.95 (ISBN 0-937396-37-0). Walterick Pubs.

--Worship: The Christian's Highest Occupation. pap. 5.95 (ISBN 0-937396-57-5). Walterick Pubs.

Hamill, Paul, ed. Introits & Responses for Contemporary Worship. (Orig.). 1983. pap. 2.95 (ISBN 0-8298-0649-0). Pilgrim NY.

Hardin, H. Grady. The Leadership of Worship. LC 79-26863. 1980. 6.95 (ISBN 0-687-21160-3). Abingdon.

Hislop, D. H. Our Heritage in Public Worship. 354p. 1935. 12.95 (ISBN 0-567-02138-6, Pub. by T & T Clark Ltd UK). Fortress.

Holmes, C. Raymond. Sing a New Song! Worship Renewal for Adventists Today. LC 84-70077. xii, 190p. 1984. pap. 9.95 (ISBN 0-943872-88-X). Andrews Univ Pr.

Huck, Gabe & Sloyan, Virginia, eds. Parishes & Families: A Model for Christian Formation Through Liturgy. 1973. pap. 5.00 (ISBN 0-918208-11-4). Liturgical Conf.

Hybels, Lynne. Joy of Personal Worship. 156p. 1984. pap. 5.95 (ISBN 0-89693-373-3). Victor Bks.

Irwin, Kevin W. Sunday Worship. 1983. pap. 14.95 (ISBN 0-916134-52-0). Pueblo Pub Co.

Laughlin, Paul A. Lectionary Worship Aids B: Series II. (Orig.). 1987. pap. price not set (ISBN 0-89536-886-2, 7872). CSS of Ohio.

MacArthur, John, Jr. True Worship. (John MacArthur's Bible Studies). 1985. pap. 3.50 (ISBN 0-8024-5108-X). Moody.

Marshall, Michael E. Renewal in Worship. rev. ed. 120p. 1985. pap. 6.95 (ISBN 0-8192-1374-8). Morehouse.

Martimort, A. G., et al. The Church at Prayer: The Eucharist, Vol. 2. Martimort, A. G., ed. O'Connell, Matthew, tr. from Fr. Orig. Title: L'Eglise en Priere: L'eucharistie. 286p. 1986. pap. 14.95 (ISBN 0-8146-1364-0). Liturgical Pr.

Mick, Lawrence E. To Live As We Worship. 100p. (Orig.). 1984. pap. 4.95 (ISBN 0-8146-1327-6). Liturgical Pr.

Micks, Marianne H. Future Present: The Phenomenon of Christian Worship. LC 75-103844. 1970. pap. 6.95 (ISBN 0-8164-2109-9, HarpR). Har-Row.

Morey, Robert A. Worship Is All of Life. LC 83-73375. (Illus.). 115p. (Orig.). 1984. pap. 5.45 (ISBN 0-87509-336-1). Chr Pubns.

Neufer, Sharon & Emswiler, Tom N. Wholeness in Worship. LC 79-2982. 192p. (Orig.). 1980. pap. 6.95 (ISBN 0-06-062247-4, RD 314, HarpR). Har-Row.

O'Day, Rey & Powers, Edward. Theatre of the Spirit: A Worship Handbook. LC 80-14165. 190p. (Orig.). 1980. pap. 7.95 (ISBN 0-8298-0363-7). Pilgrim NY.

Panikkar, Raimundo. Worship & Secular Man: An Essay on the Liturgical Nature of Man. LC 72-93339. pap. 29.80 (ISBN 0-317-26670-5, 2025123). Bks Demand UMI.

Parrinder, Geoffrey. Worship in the World's Religions. 2nd ed. (Quality Paperback: No. 316). 239p. 1976. pap. 4.95 (ISBN 0-8226-0316-0). Littlefield.

Pearson, Keith, ed. Worship in the Round: Patterns of Informative & Participative Worship. (Illus.). 88p. (Orig.). 1983. pap. 5.95 (ISBN 0-85819-343-4, Pub. by JBCE). ANZ Religious Pubns.

Price, Charles P. & Weil, Louis. Liturgy for Living. (Church's Teaching Ser.: Vol. 5). 1979. 5.95 (ISBN 0-8164-0422-4, HarpR); pap. 4.95 (ISBN 0-8164-2218-4); user guide 1.50 (ISBN 0-8164-2225-7). Har-Row.

Rayburn, Robert G. O Come, Let Us Worship: Corporate Worship in the Evangelical Church. LC 79-55192. 1980. 11.95 (ISBN 0-8010-7690-0); pap. 8.95 (ISBN 0-8010-7728-1). Baker Bk.

Rowell, Cy. Thankful Praise: A Studyguide. 24p. (Orig.). 1987. pap. 2.50 (ISBN 0-8272-3651-4). CBP.

Saraydarian, Torkom. A Daily Discipline of Worship. 1986. pap. 1.00 (ISBN 0-911794-52-2). Aqua Educ.

Schackel, James. O Come, O Come, Emmanuel. (Candlelight Ser.). 1984. 2.25 (ISBN 0-89536-691-6, 4867). CSS of Ohio.

Schaper, Robert. In His Presence: Appreciating Your Worship Tradition. LC 84-1305. 204p. 1984. pap. 5.95 (ISBN 0-8407-5887-1). Nelson.

Schwartz, Faye & Mohr, David. Creative Worship. 1982. 4.50 (ISBN 0-89536-567-7, 0376). CSS of Ohio.

Seaton, Linda K. Scriptural Choreography: Biblical Dance Forms in Shaping Contemporary Worship. 1979. 2.50 (ISBN 0-941500-15-2). Sharing Co.

Sherer, Michael L., ed. The Lectionary Series from the Common Lectionary: Series B (RSV) (Orig.). 1987. pap. price not set (ISBN 0-89536-884-6, 7870). CSS of Ohio.

Snell, Beatrice S. Joint & Visible Fellowship. LC 65-19207. (Orig.). 1965. pap. 2.50x (ISBN 0-87574-140-1). Pendle Hill.

Sorge, Bob. Exploring Worship: Practical Guide to Praise & Worship. 304p. (Orig.). 1987. pap. 5.95 (ISBN 0-936369-04-3). Son-Rise Pubns.

Tozer, A. W. Whatever Happened to Worship? Smith, Gerald B., ed. LC 85-71185. 128p. (Orig.). 1985. pap. 5.95 (ISBN 0-87509-367-1). Chr Pubns.

Trotter, W. Five Letters on Worship & Ministry. 39p. pap. 0.60 (ISBN 0-88172-128-X). Believers Bkshelf.

Trzeciak, Cathi. Worship: Our Gift to God. (Concept Ser.). (Illus.). 24p. 1986. pap. 3.95 saddlestitched (ISBN 0-570-08531-4, 56-1558). Concordia.

Underhill, Evelyn. Worship. LC 78-20499. 1983. Repr. of 1937 ed. 31.35 (ISBN 0-88355-874-2). Hyperion Conn.

--Worship. (Crossroad Paperback Ser.). (Illus.). 1982. pap. 12.95 (ISBN 0-8245-0466-6). Crossroad NY.

Wade, David L. Prayers of Confession: Series B. (Orig.). 1987. pap. price not set (ISBN 0-89536-885-4, 7871). CSS of Ohio.

Wainwright, Geoffrey. Doxology: The Praise of God in Worship, Doctrine & Life: A Systematic Theology. 1980. 35.00x (ISBN 0-19-520192-2); pap. 12.95 (ISBN 0-19-520433-6). Oxford U Pr.

Watkins, Keith. Thankful Praise. LC 86-24514. 192p. (Orig.). 1987. pap. 9.95 (ISBN 0-8272-3650-6). CBP.

Webber, Robert E. Worship Is a Verb. 224p. 1985. 12.95 (ISBN 0-8499-0371-8, 0371-8). Word Bks.

Welch, Marni & Linley, Eliza, eds. Forms for Faith: Art & Architecture for Worship. LC 86-82529. (Illus.). 24p. (Orig.). 1986. pap. 5.95 (ISBN 0-943376-36-X). Magnes Mus.

Wesberry, James P. The Lord's Day. pap. 8.95 (ISBN 0-8054-2264-1). Broadman.

Wiersbe, Warren W. Real Worship. 192p. 1986. 12.95 (ISBN 0-8407-9045-7). Oliver-Nelson.

Wilkins, Ronald J. Understanding Christian Worship: Short Edition. (To Live Is Christ Ser.). 80p. 1977. pap. 3.95 (ISBN 0-697-01663-3); tchr's. ed. 6.00 (ISBN 0-697-01669-2). Wm C Brown.

Willimon, William H. With Glad & Generous Hearts. 176p. 1986. pap. 7.95 (ISBN 0-8358-0536-0, ICN 613183, Dist. by Abingdon Press). Upper Room.

--Word, Water, Wine, & Bread. 1980. pap. 5.95 (ISBN 0-8170-0858-6). Judson.

Woolman, John. Worship. 1983. pap. 2.50x (ISBN 0-87574-051-0, 051). Pendle Hill.

WORSHIP–EARLY CHURCH

Caemmerer, Richard R., Jr. Visual Art in the Life of the Church: Encouraging Creative Worship & Witness in the Congregation. LC 83-70504. 96p. (Orig.). 1983. pap. 10.95 (ISBN 0-8066-2010-2, 10-6855). Augsburg.

Hahn, Ferdinand. The Worship of the Early Church. Reumann, John, ed. Green, David E., tr. from Ger. LC 72-87063. 144p. 1973. pap. 4.95 (ISBN 0-8006-0127-0, 1-127). Fortress.

Jungmann, Josef A. Early Liturgy, to the Time of Gregory the Great. Brunner, Francis A., tr. (Liturgical Studies: No. 7). 1959. 10.95 (ISBN 0-268-00083-2). U of Notre Dame Pr.

Martin, Ralph P. Worship in the Early Church. rev. ed. 144p. 1975. pap. 7.95 (ISBN 0-8028-1613-4). Eerdmans.

WORSHIP–HISTORY

Martimort, A. G., et al. Principles of the Liturgy. Martimort, A. G., ed. O'Connell, Matthew J., tr. (The Church at Prayer: Vol. 1). 300p. 1987. pap. 14.95 (ISBN 0-8146-1363-2). Liturgical Pr.

WORSHIP (RELIGIOUS EDUCATION)

Ban, Arline J. Children's Time in Worship. 128p. 1981. pap. 6.95 (ISBN 0-8170-0902-7). Judson.

Campbell, Stan. Any Old Time, Bk. 4. 80p. 1985. pap. 6.95 (ISBN 0-89693-640-6). Victor Bks.

Church of Scotland, Committee on Public Worship & Aids to Devotion. New Ways to Worship. 1980. pap. 4.95x (ISBN 0-7152-0454-8). Outlook.

Church of Scotland - Committee on Public Worship & Aids to Devotion. Prayers for Contemporary Worship. 1977. pap. 4.95x (ISBN 0-7152-0351-7). Outlook.

--Prayers for Sunday Services. 1980. pap. 6.95x (ISBN 0-7152-0456-4). Outlook.

Church of Scotland, the Woman's Guild Staff. Let's Choose Our Worship: Prayers for Women's Meetings. 1980. pap. 1.65 (ISBN 0-7152-0461-0). Outlook.

Haas, James & Haas, Lynne. Make a Joyful Noise! (Illus.). 40p. (Orig.). 1973. pap. 1.95 (ISBN 0-8192-1146-X). Morehouse.

Hays, Edward. Prayers for the Domestic Church: A Handbook for Worship in the Home. rev. ed. LC 82-72077. (Illus.). 216p. 1979. pap. 8.95 (ISBN 0-939516-02-0); pap. 10.95 spiral bound (ISBN 0-939516-08-X); leather 17.95 (ISBN 0-939516-09-8). Forest Peace.

Hoard, Laurie, ed. Christmas Programs for Children. 48p. 1986. pap. 1.95 (ISBN 0-87239-940-0, 8601). Standard Pub.

Johnson, Philip E. Celebrating the Seasons with Children. 112p. (Orig.). 1984. pap. 6.95 (ISBN 0-8298-0723-3). Pilgrim NY.

Larose, Paul. Working with Children & the Liturgy. LC 81-14984. (Illus.). 95p. 1982. pap. 2.95 (ISBN 0-8189-0428-3). Alba.

Merrill, Dean & Shelley, Marshall, eds. Fresh Ideas for Preaching, Worship & Evangelism. (Fresh Ideas Ser.). 155p. 1984. pap. 6.95 (ISBN 0-917463-00-5). Chr Today.

Pachomius, Saint Instructions of St. Pachomius. Budge, E. Wallis, tr. pap. text ed. 1.95 (ISBN 0-686-25553-4). Eastern Orthodox.

Price, Charles P. & Weil, Louis. Liturgy for Living. (Church's Teaching Ser.: Vol. 5). 1979. 5.95 (ISBN 0-8164-0422-4, HarpR); pap. 4.95 (ISBN 0-8164-2218-4); user guide 1.50 (ISBN 0-8164-2225-7). Har-Row.

Quinley, Ernest & Quinley, Rachel. Lets Have Church, Children, No. 1. 1981. pap. 7.95 (ISBN 0-87148-512-5). Pathway Pr.

Rathert, Donna & Prahlow, Lois. Time for Church. 24p. 1985. pap. 2.95 (ISBN 0-570-04129-5, 56-1540). Concordia.

Stauffer, S. Anita. Altar Guild Handbook. LC 85-47713. 128p. 1985. pap. 5.95 (ISBN 0-8006-1868-8, 1-1868). Fortress.

Worship & Witness. (Faith & Life Ser.). 2.10 (ISBN 0-02-805110-6, 80511). Benziger Pub Co.

WORSHIP OF SAINTS

see Saints–Cultus

WORSHIP PROGRAMS

see also Dedication Services; Installation Service (Church Officers)

Alessi, Vincie, ed. Programs for Advent & Christmas. 1978. pap. 4.95 (ISBN 0-8170-0808-X). Judson.

Ammerman, Leila T. Inspiring Devotional Programs for Women's Groups. (Paperback Program Ser). 1971. pap. 3.50 (ISBN 0-8010-0015-7). Baker Bk.

Beck, Norman A. Scripture Notes: Series B (Common Consensus Lectionary) 1984. 7.25 (ISBN 0-89536-687-8, 4863). CSS of Ohio.

Bloom, James M. & Sherer, Michael L. A Festival of Lights. (Orig.). 1986. pap. 2.25 (ISBN 0-89536-833-1, 6847). CSS of Ohio.

Bolding, Amy. Fingertip Devotions. 1970. 3.95 (ISBN 0-8010-0798-4). Baker Bk.

Brand, Irene. A Year of Programs for Today's Women. 96p. (Orig.). 1984. pap. 3.95 (ISBN 0-87239-744-0, 2975). Standard Pub.

Christensen, James L. Contemporary Worship Services. LC 75-137445. Repr. of 1971 ed. 64.00 (ISBN 0-8357-9517-9, 2011444). Bks Demand UMI.

Crisci, Elizabeth. Fifteen Fun-Filled Programs for Adults. (Illus.). 112p. 1986. pap. 4.95 (ISBN 0-87403-078-1, 3198). Standard Pub.

Engle, Paul E. Worship Planbook. (Orig.). 1981. pap. 3.95 (ISBN 0-934688-03-6). Great Comm Pubns.

Eslinger, Elise S., compiled by. The Upper Room Worshipbook. 208p. (Orig.). 1985. pap. 7.50 (ISBN 0-8358-0515-8). Upper Room.

Fittro, Pat, compiled by. Easter Programs for the Church, No. 11. (Illus.). 64p. 1987. pap. 3.50 (ISBN 0-87403-283-0, 8723). Standard Pub.

--Standard Easter Program Book, No. 37. 48p. 1986. pap. 1.95 (ISBN 0-87403-083-8, 8707). Standard Pub.

Gray, G. Franklin & Woods, Charles A. Welcome, Blessed Morning! Sherer, Michael L., ed. (Orig.). 1987. pap. 3.50 (ISBN 0-89536-849-8, 7808). CSS of Ohio.

Grimbol, William. The Darkest Day. 1986. 1.75 (ISBN 0-89536-789-0, 6807). CSS of Ohio.

--Passion Paths. Sherer, Michael L., ed. (Orig.). 1987. pap. 3.95 (ISBN 0-89536-842-0, 7801). CSS of Ohio.
Herring, Reuben. Your Family Worship Guidebook. LC 78-19976. 1978. 4.50 (ISBN 0-8054-5627-9). Broadman.
Hickman, Hoyt. Word & Table. 1983. pap. 3.95 (ISBN 0-687-46127-8). Abingdon.
Hoard, Laurie. Standard Christmas Program Book, No. 46. 48p. 1985. pap. 1.95 (ISBN 0-87239-850-1, 8646). Standard Pub.
Hoard, Laurie, ed. Christmas Programs for Children. 48p. 1986. pap. 1.95 (ISBN 0-87239-940-0, 8601). Standard Pub.
--Christmas Programs for the Church, No. 19. 64p. 1986. pap. 2.95 (ISBN 0-87239-914-1, 8619). Standard Pub.
Hoard, Laurie, compiled by. Easter Programs for the Church, No. 8. 64p. (Orig.). 1984. pap. 2.95 (ISBN 0-87239-767-X, 8720). Standard Pub.
--Easter Programs for the Church, No. 9. 64p. 1985. pap. 2.95 (ISBN 0-87239-845-5, 8721). Standard Pub.
--Easter Programs for the Church, No. 10. 64p. 1986. pap. 2.95 (ISBN 0-87403-082-X, 8722). Standard Pub.
Hoard, Laurie, ed. Mother-Daughter-Father-Son Banquets & Programs, No. 7. 64p. (Orig.). 1984. pap. 2.95 (ISBN 0-87239-769-6, 8737). Standard Pub.
--Standard Easter Program Book, No. 35. 48p. (Orig.). 1984. pap. 1.95 (ISBN 0-87239-768-8, 8705). Standard Pub.
Hoard, Laurie, compiled by. Standard Easter Program Book, No. 36. 48p. 1985. pap. 1.95 (ISBN 0-87239-870-6, 8706). Standard Pub.
Holy Communion & Worship of the Eucharist Outside Mass. gold cloth 8.50 (ISBN 0-89942-648-4, 648/22). Catholic Bk Pub.
Iverson, Shari. Worship Leader's Guide. (Illus.). 40p. 1986. pap. 4.50 (ISBN 0-914936-97-2). Bible Temple.
Johnson, John R. Liturgy for the Free Church. LC 86-18782. 176p. 1986. lib. bdg. 19.95x (ISBN 0-89370-527-6). Borgo Pr.
Joseph, Curt M. Crossroads. (Orig.). 1987. pap. 4.75 (ISBN 0-89536-843-9, 7802). CSS of Ohio.
Kemper, Frederick W. Variety for Worship: Resources for Festival Worship Liturgies. 1984. pap. 7.95 (ISBN 0-570-03936-3, 12-2871). Concordia.
Koopman, LeRoy. Scriptural Worship Aids. (Illus.). 1978. pap. 2.95 (ISBN 0-8010-5392-7). Baker Bk.
Langford, Thomas A., III & Jones, Bonnie S. The Worship Handbook: A Practical Guide to Reform & Renewal. LC 84-70648. 88p. (Orig.). 1984. pap. 5.95 (ISBN 0-88177-011-6, DR011B). Discipleship Res.
Mann, Leonard. Where Two or Three Are Gathered. 1986. 6.25 (ISBN 0-89536-791-2, 6809). CSS of Ohio.
Mocko, George P. Lord, Empower Us! Sherer, Michael L., ed. (Orig.). 1987. pap. 2.75 (ISBN 0-89536-851-X, 7810). CSS of Ohio.
Mueller, Robert. For People Just Like Us. Sherer, Michael L., ed. (Orig.). 1986. pap. 3.75 (ISBN 0-89536-834-X, 6848). CSS of Ohio.
Orbaker, Douglas & Blake, Robert A. Day of Redemption. Sherer, Michael L., ed. (Orig.). 1987. pap. 2.25 (ISBN 0-89536-848-X, 7807). CSS of Ohio.
Ortmayer, Roger. Sing & Pray & Shout Hurray. 1974. pap. 2.75 (ISBN 0-377-00004-3). Friend Pr.
Parr, Micheal. Given & Shed for You. Sherer, Micheal L., ed. (Orig.). 1987. pap. 2.50 (ISBN 0-89536-847-1, 7806). CSS of Ohio.
Pratt, Louis. Sing Praises to His Name. Sherer, Michael L., ed. (Orig.). 1986. pap. 6.75 (ISBN 0-89536-831-5, 6845). CSS of Ohio.
Rest, Friedrich. Our Christian Worship: Advent-Christmas. 1985. 4.75 (ISBN 0-89536-761-0, 5868). CSS of Ohio.
The Service for the Lord's Day: The Worship of God. LC 84-5220. (Supplemental Liturgical Resource Ser.: No. 1). 192p. 1984. text ed. 7.95 kivar (ISBN 0-664-24643-5); pap. 14.75 pack of five, pew edition (ISBN 0-664-24641-9). Westminster.
Shaffer, Wilma. Fourteen Women's Programs: Making Your House a Home. 96p. (Orig.). 1984. pap. 3.95 (ISBN 0-87239-743-2, 2974). Standard Pub.
Shannon, Robert & Shannon, Michael. Celebrating the Birth of Christ. 112p. 1985. pap. 4.95 (ISBN 0-87239-916-8, 3022). Standard Pub.
Sherer, Mike & Aaseng, Nathan. Night of Wonder: Service-Story for Christmas Eve. 1985. 2.75 (ISBN 0-89536-762-9, 5869). CSS of Ohio.
Sparkman, G. Temp. Writing Your Own Worship Materials. 1980. pap. 2.95 (ISBN 0-8170-0857-8). Judson.
Sparks, Judith, ed. Standard Christmas Program Book, No. 45. 48p. 1984. pap. 1.95 (ISBN 0-87239-749-1, 8645). Standard Pub.
Standard Christmas Program Book, No. 47. Hoard, Laurie, compiled by. 48p. 1986. pap. 1.95 (ISBN 0-87239-935-4, 8647). Standard Pub.
Summers, Georgianna. The Light Shines in the Darkness. (Orig.). 1987. pap. price not set (ISBN 0-89536-888-9, 7874). CSS of Ohio.
Tozer, Tom & Dessem, Ralph E. Deck the Halls. Sherer, Michael L., ed. (Orig.). 1986. pap. 2.25 (ISBN 0-89536-827-7, 6844). CSS of Ohio.
Vogel, Cora. Easy to Use Christmas Programs. 144p. 1986. 7.95 (ISBN 0-8010-9302-3). Baker Bk.
Weekley, James. Praise & Thanksgiving. 1986. 6.95 (ISBN 0-89536-792-0, 6810). CSS of Ohio.
Weekley, James & Reeves, James. Beginnings. Sherer, Michael L., ed. (Orig.). 1987. pap. 3.95 (ISBN 0-89536-859-5, 7818). CSS of Ohio.
Weems, Ann. Reaching for Rainbows: Resources for Creative Worship. LC 80-19330. 156p. 1980. pap. 8.95 (ISBN 0-664-24355-X). Westminster.
Werman, Linda J. Draw Us Nearer to You, Lord. Sherer, Michael L., ed. (Orig.). 1987. pap. 7.25 (ISBN 0-89536-858-7, 7817). CSS of Ohio.
Willimon, William H. Preaching & Leading Worship. LC 83-26021. (The Pastor's Handbooks Ser.: Vol. 1). 116p. (Orig.). 1984. pap. 7.95 (ISBN 0-664-24616-8). Westminster.
Willimon, William H. & Wilson, Robert L. Preaching & Worship in the Small Church. LC 79-24529. (Creative Leadership Ser.). (Orig.). 1980. pap. 6.95 (ISBN 0-687-33820-4). Abingdon.
Winburn, Wanda. Learning to Love like Jesus. Large Type ed. (Twenty-Six Children's Church Programs Ser.). (Illus.). 112p. 1984. 7.95 (ISBN 0-87239-708-4, 3319). Standard Pub.
Worshipbook: Services & Hymns. Pew ed. 688p. 1972. 7.95 (ISBN 0-664-10108-9). Westminster.

WORSHIP PROGRAMS FOR YOUTH
see Worship (Religious Education); Worship Programs

WRATH OF GOD
see God–Wrath

WREN, CHRISTOPHER, SIR, 1632-1723
Gray, Ronald. Christopher Wren & St. Paul's Cathedral. LC 81-13696. (Cambridge Topic Bks.). (Illus.). 52p. 1982. PLB 8.95 (ISBN 0-8225-1222-X). Lerner Pubns.

WRONG AND RIGHT
see Right and Wrong

WULFSTAN 2ND, ABP., OF YORK d. 1203
Lamb, John W. Saint Wulstan, Prelate & Patriot: A Study of His Life & Times. (Church Historical Society, London, New Ser.: No. 16). Repr. of 1933 ed. 40.00 (ISBN 0-8115-3139-2). Kraus Repr.

WYCLIFFE, JOHN, d. 1384
Buddensieg, Rudolf. John Wycliffe: Patriot & Reformer. Life & Writings. 1979. Repr. of 1884 ed. lib. bdg. 40.00 (ISBN 0-8495-0535-6). Arden Lib.
Carrick, J. C. Wycliffe & the Lollards. 1977. lib. bdg. 59.95 (ISBN 0-8490-2824-8). Gordon Pr.
Dahmus, Joseph H. The Prosecution of John Wyclyf. xi, 167p. 1970. Repr. of 1952 ed. 22.50 (ISBN 0-208-00953-1, Archon). Shoe String.
Daly, Lowrie J. The Political Theory of John Wyclif. LC 62-20515. (Jesuit Studies). 1962. 4.95 (ISBN 0-8294-0020-6). Loyola.
Hall, Louis B. The Perilous Vision of John Wyclif. LC 82-18890. 288p. 1983. lib. bdg. 23.95X (ISBN 0-8304-1006-6). Nelson-Hall.
Kenny, Anthony. Wyclif. (Past Masters Ser.). 1985. 13.95x (ISBN 0-19-287647-3); pap. 4.95 (ISBN 0-19-287646-5). Oxford U Pr.
Knapp, P. The Style of John Wyclif's English Sermons. 1977. 16.00x (ISBN 90-279-3156-9). Mouton.
Lechler, Gotthard V. John Wycliffe & His English Precursors. LC 78-63197. (Heresies of the Early Christian & Medieval Era: Second Ser.). Repr. of 1884 ed. 49.50 (ISBN 0-404-16235-5). AMS Pr.
Lewis, John. The History of the Life & Sufferings of the Revered & Learned John Wiclif, D. D. LC 74-178543. Repr. of 1820 ed. 39.50 (ISBN 0-404-56625-1). AMS Pr.
Lewis, Sergeant. John Wycliffe: Last of the Schoolmen & First of the Reformers. 1978. Repr. of 1892 ed. lib. bdg. 25.00 (ISBN 0-8492-8060-5). R West.
Loserth, Johann. Wiclif & Hus. Evans, M. J., tr. LC 78-63198. (Heresies of the Early Christian & Medieval Era: Second Ser.). 1979. Repr. of 1884 ed. 48.00 (ISBN 0-404-16236-3). AMS Pr.
Mudroch, Vaclav. The Wyclyf Tradition. Reeves, A. Compton, ed. LC 77-92253. xvii, 91p. 1979. 15.00x (ISBN 0-8214-0403-2). Ohio U Pr.
Netter, Thomas. Fasciculi Zizaniorium Magistri Johannis Wyclif Cum Tritico. Shirley, Walter W., ed. (Rolls Ser.: No. 5). Repr. of 1858 ed. 60.00 (ISBN 0-8115-1006-9). Kraus Repr.
Poole, Reginald L. Wycliffe & Movements for Reform. LC 77-84729. Repr. of 1889 ed. 28.00 (ISBN 0-404-16129-4). AMS Pr.
Seargent, Lewis. John Wycliffe: Last of the Schoolmen & First of the English Reformers. 1908. 30.00 (ISBN 0-8274-2629-1). R West.
Sergeant, Lewis. John Wycliffe. LC 73-14468. (Heroes of the Nations Ser.). Repr. of 1893 ed. 30.00 (ISBN 0-404-58286-9). AMS Pr.
Stacey, John. John Wycliffe & Reform. LC 78-63199. (Heresies of the Early Christian & Medieval Era: Second Ser.). 1979. Repr. of 1964 ed. 24.50 (ISBN 0-404-16239-8). AMS Pr.
Trevelyan, George M. England in the Age of Wycliffe. 3rd ed. LC 78-178560. Repr. of 1900 ed. 34.50 (ISBN 0-404-56677-4). AMS Pr.
Vaughan, Robert. The Life & Opinions of John de Wycliffe, D. D, 2 vols. 2nd ed. LC 71-178561. Repr. of 1831 ed. Set. 75.00 (ISBN 0-404-56678-2). Vol. 1 o.p (ISBN 0-404-56679-0). Vol. 2 o.p (ISBN 0-404-56680-4). AMS Pr.

WYCLIFITES
see Lollards

X

Y

YABHALAHA 3RD, PATRIARCH OF THE NESTORIANS, 1244-1317
Budge, Ernest A. The Monks of Kublai Khan, Emperor of China. LC 71-38051. Repr. of 1928 ed. 32.50 (ISBN 0-404-56905-6). AMS Pr.
Montgomery, James A., ed. History of Yaballaha III. 1967. lib. bdg. 14.00x (ISBN 0-374-95814-9, Octagon). Hippocrene Bks.

YAHVEH, SERVANT OF
see Servant of Jehovah

YALE UNIVERSITY
Gabriel, Ralph H. Religion & Learning at Yale: Church of Christ in the College & University, 1757-1957. 1958. 39.50x (ISBN 0-685-69820-3). Elliots Bks.

YALE UNIVERSITY–DIVINITY SCHOOL
Wayland, John T. The Theological Department in Yale College, 1822-1858. Kuklick, Bruce, ed. (American Religious Thought of the 18th & 19th Centuries Ser.). 500p. 1987. lib. bdg. 70.00 (ISBN 0-8240-6962-5). Garland Pub.
Weigle, Richard. The Glory Days: From the Life of Luther Allan Weigle. (Illus., Orig.). 1976. pap. 5.95 (ISBN 0-377-00058-2). Friend Pr.

YEAR, CHURCH
see Church Year

YESHIVA
Helmreich, William B. The World of the Yeshiva: An Intimate Portrait of Orthodox Jewry. 405p. 1982. 19.95 (ISBN 0-02-914640-2). Free Pr.
--The Yeshiva in America. 384p. 1981. text ed. 19.95 (ISBN 0-02-914640-2, 914640). Free Pr.

YEZIDIS
see also Religions
Drower, Ethel S. Peacock Angel: Being Some Account of Votaries of a Secret Cult & Their Sanctuaries. LC 77-87643. Repr. of 1941 ed. 20.00 (ISBN 0-404-16425-0). AMS Pr.
Empson, Ralph H. The Cult of the Peacock Angel: A Short Account of the Yezidi Tribes of Kurdistan. LC 77-87646. Repr. of 1928 ed. 21.00 (ISBN 0-404-16416-1). AMS Pr.

YIDDISH LITERATURE
Berlin, Charles. Catalog of the Yiddish Collection: Harvard University College Library, 3 vols. 2100p. 1987. lib. bdg. 490.00 (ISBN 3-598-41242-8). K G Saur.
Bovarsky, Abraham & Sarna, Lazar, eds. Canadian Yiddish Writings. LC 77-362060. pap. 37.50 (ISBN 0-317-10945-6, 2022287). Bks Demand UMI.
Emiot, Israel. The Birobidzhan Affair: A Yiddish Writer in Siberia. Rosenfeld, Max, tr. from Yiddish. LC 81-2511. 220p. 1981. 13.95 (ISBN 0-8276-0191-3, 477). Jewish Pubns.
Gar, Josef & Friedman, Philip. Biblyografye Fun Yidishe Bikher Vegn Khurbn un Gvure. (Yad Vashem-Yivo Joint Documentary Projects Bibliographical Ser.: No. 3). (Yiddish.). 330p. 1962. 10.00 (ISBN 0-914512-12-9, HE-65-1134). Yivo Inst.
Gordon, R., ed. Yiddish Literature, 10 Vols, No. IV. 1986. lib. bdg. 975.00 (ISBN 0-8490-3859-6). Gordon Pr.
--Yiddish Literature, 10 Vols, No. III. 1986. lib. bdg. 950.95 (ISBN 0-8490-3858-8). Gordon Pr.
--Yiddish Literature, 10 Vols, No. II. 1986. lib. bdg. 975.00 (ISBN 0-8490-3857-X). Gordon Pr.
Grodon, R., ed. Yiddish Literature, 10 Vols, Series I. 1986. lib. bdg. 975.95 (ISBN 0-8490-3856-1). Gordon Pr.
Howe, Irving & Greenberg, Eliezer, eds. Ashes out of Hope: Fiction by Soviet-Yiddish Writers. LC 76-49731. 1978. pap. 4.95 (ISBN 0-8052-0605-1). Schocken.
Kogos, Fred. One Thousand One Yiddish Proverbs. 160p. 1974. pap. 3.95 (ISBN 0-8065-0455-2). Citadel Pr.
Leftwich, Joseph, ed. An Anthology of Modern Yiddish Literature. LC 74-82386. (Anthology Ser: No. 1). 346p. 1974. pap. text ed. 13.60x (ISBN 90-2793-496-7). Mouton.
Rubin, Ruth. Voices of a People: The Story of Yiddish Folksong. LC 79-84679. 558p. 1979. pap. 8.95 (ISBN 0-8276-0121-2, 445). Jewish Pubns.
Weinreich, Uriel, ed. The Field of Yiddish: Studies in Yiddish Language, Folklore, & Literature. LC 54-12380. 317p. 1954. Repr. 12.50 (ISBN 0-936368-02-0). Lexik Hse.

YIDDISH LITERATURE–HISTORY AND CRITICISM
Gittleman, Sol. From Shtetl to Suburbia: The Family in Jewish Literary Imagination. LC 78-53646. 1978. 12.95x (ISBN 0-8070-6364-9); pap. 5.95 o. p. (ISBN 0-8070-6365-7). Beacon Pr.
Howe, Irving & Greenberg, Eliezer, eds. A Treasury of Yiddish Stories. LC 54-9599. (Illus.). 630p. 1973. pap. 11.95 (ISBN 0-8052-0400-8). Schocken.
Pinsker, Sanford. Schlemiel As Metaphor: Studies in the Yiddish & American Jewish Novel. LC 77-132487. (Crosscurrents-Modern Critiques Ser.). 185p. 1971. 6.95x (ISBN 0-8093-0480-5). S Ill U Pr.
Roback, A. A. The Story of Yiddish Literature. 75.00 (ISBN 0-87968-084-9). Gordon Pr.
Siegel, Ben. The Controversial Sholem Asch: An Introduction to His Fiction. LC 76-43446. 1976. 12.95 (ISBN 0-87972-076-X); pap. 7.95 (ISBN 0-87972-170-7). Bowling Green Univ.
Steinberg, Theodore L. Mendele Mocher Seforim. (World Authors Ser.). 1977. lib. bdg. 16.95 (ISBN 0-8057-6308-2, Twayne). G K Hall.

YODER, ROSANNA (MCGONEGAL)
Yoder, Joseph W. Rosanna of the Amish. rev. ed. 256p. 1973. pap. 3.95 (ISBN 0-8361-1714-X). Herald Pr.

YOGA
see also Samadhi
Abhedananda, Swami. How to Be a Yogi. 59.95 (ISBN 0-8490-0375-X). Gordon Pr.
--How to Be a Yogi. 5.95 (ISBN 0-87481-609-2). Vedanta Pr.
--How to Be a Yogi. 6th ed. 64p. pap. 7.95 (ISBN 0-88697-040-7). Life Science.
--Yoga Psychology. 10.95 (ISBN 0-87481-614-9). Vedanta Pr.
Acharya, Pundit. Breath, Sleep, the Heart, & Life: The Revolutionary Health Yoga of Pundit Acharya. LC 74-24306. 190p. 1975. pap. 7.95 (ISBN 0-913922-09-9). Dawn Horse Pr.
Ackerman, Dorothy. A Quaker Looks at Yoga. LC 76-23909. (Orig.). 1976. pap. 2.50x (ISBN 0-87574-207-6, 207). Pendle Hill.
Agarwal, R. S. Yoga of Perfect Sight: With Letters of Sri Aurobindo. (Illus.). 1974. pap. 5.45 (ISBN 0-89071-261-1). Matagiri.
Aivanhov, Omraam M. The Yoga of Nutrition. (Izvor Collection Ser.: Vol. 204). 130p. pap. 4.95 (ISBN 0-911857-03-6). Prosveta USA.
Aiyar, K. N. Thirty Minor Upanishads: Including the Yoga Upanishads. 300p. 1980. Repr. of 1914 ed. 16.95 (ISBN 0-935548-00-9). Santarasa Pubns.
Aiyer, K. Narayanaswami, tr. Laghu-Yoga-Vasistha. 1971. 19.95 (ISBN 0-8356-7497-5). Theos Pub Hse.
Ajaya, Swami. Yoga Psychology: A Practical Guide to Meditation. rev. ed. LC 76-374539. 115p. 1976. pap. 5.95 (ISBN 0-89389-052-9). Himalayan Pubs.
Alexander, Mithrapuram K. Yoga System. rev. ed. LC 77-140373. (Illus.). 1971. 8.95 (ISBN 0-8158-0257-9); pap. 6.95 (ISBN 0-686-66311-X). Chris Mass.
Aranya, S. Hariharananda. Yoga Philosophy of Patanjali: Containing His Yoga Aphorisms with Vyasa's Commentary in Sanskrit & a Translation with Annotations Containing Many Suggestions for the Practice of Yoga. Mukerji, P. N., tr. from Sanskrit. 510p. 1983. 39.50x (ISBN 0-87395-728-8); pap. 10.95x (ISBN 0-87395-729-6). State U NY Pr.
Arundale, George S. Kundalini. 1972. 4.95 (ISBN 0-8356-7102-X). Theos Pub Hse.
Arya, Pandit U. Yoga-Sutras of Patanjali with the Exposition of Vyasa: A Translation & Commentary Volume I. xxi, 493p. 1986. pap. 16.95 (ISBN 0-89389-092-8). Himalayan Pubs.
Aurobindo. Life Companion Paperback Supplement Series. (Life Companion Ser.). 1339p. (Orig.). 1984. pap. 39.25 (ISBN 0-89744-013-7, Pub. by Madanlal Himatsinghlea). Auromere.

--Sri Aurobindo Life Companion Library. (Life Companion Ser.). 4522p. 1984. Repr. of 1979 ed. 111.85 (ISBN 0-317-19956-0, Pub. by Mandanlal Himatsinghlea). Auromere.

Aurobindo, Sri. Bases of Yoga. 108p. 1983. pap. 3.50 (ISBN 0-89744-012-9). Auromere.

--Bases of Yoga. 168p. 1981. pap. 2.00 (ISBN 0-89071-309-X, Pub. by Sri Aurobindo Ashram India). Matagiri.

--Dictionary of Sri Aurobindo's Yoga. Pandit, Sri M., ed. 1979. Repr. of 1966 ed. 7.95 (ISBN 0-941524-04-3). Lotus Light.

--Letters on Yoga, Vol. I. 502p. 1979. 16.00 (ISBN 0-89744-984-3, Pub. by Sri Aurogindo Ashram Trust); pap. 12.00 (ISBN 0-89744-985-1). Auromere.

--Letters on Yoga, Vol. III. 720p. 1979. 22.00 (ISBN 0-89744-988-6, Pub. by Sri Aurobindo Ashram Trust); pap. 19.00 (ISBN 0-89744-989-4). Auromere.

--Letters on Yoga, Vol. II. 587p. 1979. 19.00 (ISBN 0-89744-986-X, Pub. by Sri Arobindo Ashram Trust); pap. 16.00 (ISBN 0-89744-987-8). Auromere.

--More Lights on Yoga. 1979. pap. 3.50 (ISBN 0-89744-950-9). Auromere.

--Practical Guide to Integral Yoga. 7th ed. Manibhai, ed. 1979. pap. 9.00 (ISBN 0-89744-942-8). Auromere.

--The Synthesis of Yoga. 1976. pap. 8.00 (ISBN 0-89071-268-9). Matagiri.

--The Synthesis of Yoga. 899p. 1984. 16.75 (ISBN 0-89071-313-8, Pub. by Sri Aurobindo Ashram India); pap. 12.50 (ISBN 0-89071-312-X, Pub. by Sri Aurobindo Ashram India). Matagiri.

--The Yoga & Its Objects. 33p. 1984. pap. 0.75 (ISBN 0-89071-314-6, Pub. by Sri Aurobindo Ashram India). Matagiri.

Avalon, Arthur. The Serpent Power. LC 74-75259. (Illus.). 1974. pap. 8.95 (ISBN 0-486-23058-9). Dover.

Bahadur, K. P. The Wisdom of Yoga. LC 77-985594. (The Wisdom of India Ser.: Vol. 1). 116p. 1977. 9.25 (ISBN 0-89684-471-4). Orient Bk Dist.

Bailey, Alice A. The Light of the Soul. 1972. 20.00 (ISBN 0-85330-012-7); pap. 9.00 (ISBN 0-85330-112-3). Lucis.

Ball, John. Ananda: Where Yoga Lives. LC 82-82100. 240p. 1982. 15.95 (ISBN 0-87972-207-X); pap. 8.95 (ISBN 0-87972-208-8). Bowling Green Univ.

--Ananda: Where Yoga Lives. (Illus.). 232p. 1982. pap. 8.95 (ISBN 0-87972-208-8). Dawn Pubns CA.

Ballantyne & Shastri. Yoga-Sutras of Patanjali. Tailang, S. B., ed. Repr. of 1983 ed. 8.50 (ISBN 0-89684-474-9). Orient Bk Dist.

Beesley, Ronald P. Yoga of the Inward Path. 1978. pap. 4.95 (ISBN 0-87516-269-X). De Vorss.

Berg, Vibeke. Yoga During Pregnancy. 1983. 6.95 (ISBN 0-686-44925-8, Fireside). S&S.

--Yoga in Pregnancy. 135p. 1977. 11.95 (ISBN 0-940500-24-8, Pub. by D B Taraporwala India). Asia Bk Corp.

Besant, Annie. Introduction to Yoga. 1972. 3.50 (ISBN 0-8356-7120-8). Theos Pub Hse.

--Yoga: The Hatha Yoga & Raja Yoga of India. 73p. 1974. pap. 7.95 (ISBN 0-88697-035-0). Life Science.

Bhaktivedanta, Swami A. C. Perfection of Yoga. LC 72-76302. (Illus.). 1972. pap. 1.95 (ISBN 0-912776-36-6). Bhaktivedanta.

Bhamre, Suresh T. Hatha Yoga for Kids: A Guidebook for Parents & Children. (Illus.). 1985. 8.00 (ISBN 0-682-40164-1). Exposition Pr FL.

Bhikshu, Yogi. Bhakti Yoga. 6.00 (ISBN 0-911662-21-9). Yoga.

--Karma Yoga. 1928. 6.00 (ISBN 0-911662-20-0). Yoga.

Bordow, Sita, et al. Sri Swami Satchidananda: Apostle of Peace. LC 86-10533. (Illus.). 454p. (Orig.). 1986. pap. 14.95 (ISBN 0-932040-31-4). Integral Yoga Pubns.

Brahmachari, Dhirenda. Yoga: Yogic Suksma Vyayama. (Illus.). 232p. 1975. 8.95 (ISBN 0-88253-802-0). Ind-US Inc.

Brunton, Paul. Hidden Teaching Beyond Yoga. rev. ed. LC 83-60830. 366p. (Orig.). 1984. pap. 8.95 (ISBN 0-87728-590-X). Weiser.

Chakravarti, Sri S. Scientific Yoga for the Man of Today. 1971. pap. 3.50 (ISBN 0-685-58385-6). Ranney Pubns.

Chang, Garma C. The Six Yogas of Naropa & Mahamudra. 2nd ed. LC 86-10020. 128p. 1986. pap. 9.95 (ISBN 0-937938-33-5). Snow Lion.

--Teachings of Tibetan Yoga. 128p. 1974. pap. 3.45 (ISBN 0-8065-0460-9). Citadel Pr.

Chapple, Christopher, ed. Samkyha-Yoga: Proceedings of the IASWR Conference, 1981. 181p. 1983. pap. text ed. 10.00 (ISBN 0-915078-04-X). Inst Adv Stud Wld.

Chaudhuri, Haridas. Integral Yoga. LC 73-17170. 1981. pap. 4.95 (ISBN 0-8356-0444-6, Quest). Theos Pub Hse.

Chee Soo. Taoist Yoga: The Chinese Art of K'ai Men. 160p. 1983. pap. 7.95 (ISBN 0-85030-332-X). Newcastle Pub.

Chinmoy, Sri. Fifty Freedom-Boats to One Golden Shore, Pt. 1. 93p. (Orig.). 1974. pap. 3.00 (ISBN 0-88497-087-6). Aum Pubns.

--Fifty Freedom-Boats to One Golden Shore, Pt. 2. 108p. 1974. pap. 3.00 (ISBN 0-88497-101-5). Aum Pubns.

--Fifty Freedom-Boats to One Golden Shore, Pt. 3. 94p. 1974. pap. 3.00 (ISBN 0-88497-071-X). Aum Pubns.

--Fifty Freedom-Boats to One Golden Shore, Pt. 4. 112p. (Orig.). 1974. pap. text ed. 3.00 (ISBN 0-88497-073-6). Aum Pubns.

--Yoga & Spiritual Life. rev. ed. LC 74-81309. 160p. 1974. pap. 4.95 (ISBN 0-88497-040-X). Aum Pubns.

Choudhury, Bikram & Reynolds, Bonnie J. Bikram's Beginning Yoga Class. new ed. LC 76-29218. (Illus.). 224p. 1977. 13.50 (ISBN 0-87477-081-5); pap. 9.95 (ISBN 0-87477-082-3). J P Tarcher.

Christensen, Alice & Rankin, David. Easy Does It: Yoga for Older People. LC 78-4755. (Illus.). 1979. spiral bdg. 11.95 (ISBN 0-06-250145-3, RD 289, HarpR). Har-Row.

Cohen, Kenneth K. Imagine That! A Child's Guide to Yoga. (Illus.). 48p. 1983. pap. 8.95 (ISBN 0-915520-55-9). Santa Barb Pr.

Cornold, W. The Yoga of Yama. 64p. 1970. pap. 4.95 (ISBN 0-88697-041-5). Life Science.

Crowley, Aleister. Eight Lectures on Yoga. 1972. pap. 5.95 (ISBN 0-87728-122-X). Weiser.

--Eight Lectures on Yoga. 80p. 1985. pap. 5.95 (ISBN 0-941404-36-6). Falcon Pr AZ.

Crowley, Aleister & Motta, Marcelo. Oriflamme, Vol. VI, No. 1: Yoga & Magick. 1984. 8.00 (ISBN 0-913735-02-7). O T O.

Da Free John. Conscious Exercise & the Transcendental Sun. 3rd rev. ed. LC 77-83388. (Illus.). 272p. 1977. o. p. (ISBN 0-913922-33-1); pap. 8.95 (ISBN 0-913922-30-7). Dawn Horse Pr.

Dasgupta, S. Yoga As Philosophy & Religion. lib. bdg. 79.95 (ISBN 0-87968-104-7). Krishna Pr.

--Yoga As Philosophy & Religion. 1978. Repr. 13.95 (ISBN 0-8426-0488-X). Orient Bk Dist.

Dass, Baba Hari, et al. Silence Speaks--from the Chalkboard of Baba Hari Dass. LC 76-53902. (Illus.). 224p. (Orig.). 1977. pap. 5.95 (ISBN 0-918100-01-1). SRI Rama.

Davis, Roy E. Philosophy & Practice of Yoga. 192p. 1983. pap. 4.95 (ISBN 0-317-20862-4). CSA Pr.

--Science of Kriya Yoga. 192p. 1984. 7.95 (ISBN 0-317-20860-8). CSA Pr.

Day, Harvey. Pratical Yoga. pap. cancelled (ISBN 0-7225-0351-2). Thorsons Pubs.

--Yoga Illustrated Dictionary. (Illus.). 1970. 10.95 (ISBN 0-87523-177-2). Emerson.

Dayspring of Youth. (Illus.). 357p. 1985. 12.00 (ISBN 0-911662-67-7). Yoga.

Dayton, Brandt. The Swami & Sam: A Yoga Book. (Illus.). 95p. (Orig.). pap. 0.95 (ISBN 0-89389-014-6). Himalayan Pubs.

Desai, Amrit. Kripalu Yoga: Meditation-in-Motion, - Focusing Inward, Bk. II. Tennen, Laura, ed. (Illus.). 120p. 1987. wkbk. 9.95 (ISBN 0-940258-16-1). Kripalu Pubns.

Desikachar, T. K. Religiousness in Yoga: Lectures on Theory & Practice. Skelton, Mary L. & Carter, J. R., eds. LC 79-9643. (Illus.). 314p. 1980. text ed. 27.00 (ISBN 0-8191-0966-5); pap. text ed. 11.75 (ISBN 0-8191-0967-3). U Pr of Amer.

Donnelly, Morwenna. Founding the Life Divine: An Introduction to the Integral Yoga of Sri Aurobindo. LC 74-2430. 250p. 1976. pap. 7.95 (ISBN 0-913922-13-7). Dawn Horse Pr.

Dunn, Sharon, ed. The Agni Review. 1985. 4.00. Agni Review.

Eliade, Mircea. Patanjali & Yoga. LC 75-10785. (Illus.). 224p. 1975. pap. 5.95 (ISBN 0-8052-0491-1). Schocken.

--Yoga: Immortality & Freedom. 2nd ed. Trask, Willard R., tr. LC 58-8986. (Bollingen Ser.: Vol. 56). 1970. 45.00x (ISBN 0-691-09848-4); pap. 11.50x (ISBN 0-691-01764-6). Princeton U Pr.

Ellsworth, Paul. Direct Healing. 1982. pap. 5.95 (ISBN 0-87877-058-5). Newcastle Pub.

Evans-Wentz, W. Y., ed. Tibetan Yoga & Secret Doctrines. 2nd ed. 1958. 24.95x (ISBN 0-19-501438-3). Oxford U Pr.

--Tibetan Yoga & Secret Doctrines. (Illus.). 1967. pap. 11.95 (ISBN 0-19-500278-4). Oxford U Pr.

Feuerstein, Georg. The Essence of Yoga. LC 75-42897. 1976. pap. 3.95 (ISBN 0-394-17902-1, E671, Ever). Grove.

Finger, Alan & Guber, Lynda. Yoga Moves with Alan Finger. (Illus.). 160p. (Orig.). 1984. pap. 9.95 (ISBN 0-671-50064-3, Wallaby). S&S.

Fuller, J. F. C. Yoga. 180p. 1975. 7.00 (ISBN 0-911662-55-3). Yoga.

Funderburk, James. Science Studies Yoga. 270p. (Orig.). pap. 8.95 (ISBN 0-89389-026-X). Himalayan Pubs.

Ghosh, Jajneshwar. A Study of Yoga. 2nd rev. ed. 1977. 16.95 (ISBN 0-89684-014-X, Pub. by Motilal Banarsidass India); pap. 12.50 (ISBN 0-89684-015-8). Orient Bk Dist.

Gnaneswarananda, Swami. Yoga for Beginners. Gupta, Mallika C., ed. LC 74-29557. 200p. 1975. pap. 4.95 (ISBN 0-9600826-1-1). Vivekananda.

Gupta, Yogi. Yoga & Yogic Powers. LC 63-14948. (Illus.). 1963. 20.00 (ISBN 0-911664-02-5). Yogi Gupta.

Hafen, Brent & Frandsen, Katherine. From Acupuncture to Yoga: Alternative Methods of Healing. (Illus.). 136p. 1983. 12.95 (ISBN 0-13-330845-6). P-H.

Haich, Elisabeth. The Day with Yoga. pap. 3.95 (ISBN 0-943358-12-4). Aurora Press.

--Sexual Energy & Yoga. 160p. 1983. 7.95 (ISBN 0-943358-03-5). Aurora Press.

Hamblin, Henry T. Dynamic Thought. limited ed. 8.00 (ISBN 0-911662-22-7). Yoga.

Hans-Ulrich, Rieker. The Yoga of Light: The Classic Esoteric Handbook of Kundalini Yoga. Becherer, Elsy, tr. LC 79-167868. (Illus.). 1974. pap. 7.95 (ISBN 0-913922-07-2). Dawn Horse Pr.

Hara, O. Hashnu. Practical Yoga: Thoroughly Practical Lessons upon the Philosophy & Practice of Yoga. 6th ed. 79p. 1970. pap. 4.95 (ISBN 0-88697-032-6). Life Science.

Harbhajan, Khalsa S. The Teachings of Yogi Bhajan: The Power of the Spoken Word. LC 85-22347. 196p. 1985. Repr. of 1977 ed. lib. bdg. 19.95x (ISBN 0-89370-878-X). Borgo Pr.

Hari Dass, Baba. Ashtanga Yoga Primer. Ault, Karuna K., ed. LC 81-51052. (Illus.). 72p. (Orig.). 1981. pap. 4.95 (ISBN 0-918100-04-6). Sri Rama.

--A Child's Garden of Yoga. Ault, Karuna, ed. LC 80-80299. (Illus.). 108p. 1980. pap. 6.95 (ISBN 0-918100-02-X). Sri Rama.

Health, Food & Healing in Yoga. (Life Companion Library). 300p. 1983. pap. 6.95 (ISBN 0-89744-007-2). Auromere.

Herrick, Joy F. & Schraffenberger, Nancy. Something's Got to Help-& Yoga Can. LC 73-80177. (Illus.). 128p. 1974. 5.95 (ISBN 0-87131-126-7). M Evans.

Hewitt, James. The Complete Yoga Book: Yoga of Breathing, Yoga of Postures, & Yoga of Meditation. LC 77-15934. (Illus., Orig.). 1978. pap. 11.95 (ISBN 0-8052-0592-6). Schocken.

Hills, Christopher. The Rise of the Phoenix: Universal Government by Nature's Laws. new ed. Ray, Ann & Rozman, Deborah, eds. LC 76-53176. (Illus.). 1024p. (Orig.). 1979. 24.95 (ISBN 0-916438-04-X). Univ of Trees.

Hughes, Eric, ed. Sri Aurobindo & the Mother on Collective Yoga. 75p. 1974. pap. 1.25 (ISBN 0-89071-000-7). Matagiri.

Iijima, Kanjitsu. Buddhist Yoga. (Illus.). 184p. 1975. pap. 8.95 (ISBN 0-87040-349-4). Japan Pubns USA.

Isaacson, Cheryl. Yoga for All Ages. (Illus., Orig.). 1986. pap. 10.95 (ISBN 0-7225-1210-4). Thorsons Pubs.

Iyengar, B. K. The Concise Light on Yoga. LC 82-5473. (Illus.). 256p. 1982. pap. 7.95 spiral (ISBN 0-8052-0723-6). Schocken.

Iyengar, K. R. On the Mother: The Chronicle of a Manifestation & Ministry, 2 vols. 1979. pap. 45.00 (ISBN 0-89744-947-9). Auromere.

Japananda, K. Yoga, You, Your New Life. (Illus.). 208p. pap. 5.95 spiral bdg. (ISBN 0-9613099-0-3). Temple Kriya Yoga.

Jarrell, Howard R. International Yoga Bibliography, 1950 to 1980. LC 81-13518. 231p. 1981. 17.50 (ISBN 0-8108-1472-2). Scarecrow.

Joshi, K. S. Yogic Pranayama: Breathing for Long, Long Life. 180p. 1983. pap. 9.00 (ISBN 0-86578-222-9). Ind-US Inc.

Judge, W. Q. Yoga Aphorisms. 59.95 (ISBN 0-8490-1343-7). Gordon Pr.

Jyotir Maya Nanda, Swami. Applied Yoga. (Illus.). 1971. 6.99 (ISBN 0-934664-01-3). Yoga Res Foun.

--Jnana Yoga (Yoga Secrets of Wisdom) (Illus.). 1974. pap. 1.99 (ISBN 0-934664-05-6). Yoga Res Foun.

--Yoga Can Change Your Life. (Illus.). 1975. pap. 4.99 (ISBN 0-934664-14-5). Yoga Res Foun.

--Yoga Guide. (Illus.). 1972. pap. 2.99 (ISBN 0-934664-16-1). Yoga Res Foun.

--Yoga in Practice. (Illus.). 1974. pap. 0.99 (ISBN 0-934664-18-8). Yoga Res Foun.

--Yoga Mystic Stories & Parables. (Illus.). 1974. pap. 3.99 (ISBN 0-934664-24-2). Yoga Res Foun.

--Yoga of Perfection (Srimad Bhagavad Gita) (Illus.). 1973. pap. 3.99 (ISBN 0-934664-25-0). Yoga Res Foun.

--Yoga of Sex-Sublimation, Truth & Non-Violence. (Illus.). 1974. pap. 3.99 (ISBN 0-934664-26-9). Yoga Res Foun.

--Yoga Secrets of Psychic Powers. (Illus.). 1974. pap. 4.99 (ISBN 0-934664-28-5). Yoga Res Foun.

Jyotirmayananda, Swami. Yoga Vasistha, Vol. III. 304p. (Orig.). 1986. pap. 4.99 (ISBN 0-934664-33-1). Yoga Res Foun.

Keeping up with Kundalini Yoga. LC 85-13215. 1985. Repr. of 1980 ed. lib. bdg. 19.95x (ISBN 0-89370-884-4). Borgo Pr.

Kent, Howard. Yoga for the Disabled: A Practical Self-Help Guide to a Happier Healthier Life. (Illus.). 160p. 1985. pap. 7.95 (ISBN 0-7225-0902-2). Thorsons Pubs.

Khalsa, Harbhajan S. Yoga for the Eighties: Kundalini Yoga. LC 85-11680. 1985. Repr. lib. bdg. 19.95x (ISBN 0-89370-879-8). Borgo Pr.

Kieffer, Gene. Kundalini for the New Age. 288p. (Orig.). 1987. pap. 7.95 (ISBN 0-553-34433-1). Bantam.

Kramer, Joel. The Passionate Mind. 122p. 1983. pap. 7.95 (ISBN 0-938190-12-1). North Atlantic.

Kripalu Center for Holistic Health Staff. The Best of Kripalu Yoga Quest: Handbook for Total Living. LC 82-84671. 101p. (Orig.). 1983. pap. 4.95 (ISBN 0-940258-08-0). Kripalu Pubns.

Kripalvanandji, Shri. Pilgrimage of Love: Premyatra, Bk. III. LC 81-82015. (Illus.). 136p. (Orig.). 1984. pap. 5.50 (ISBN 0-940258-12-9). Kripalu Pubns.

Krishna Prem, Sri. The Yoga of the Kathopanishad. 1983. Repr. 15.00x (ISBN 0-318-20321-9, Pub. by New Order Bk Co India). Humanities.

Kriyananda, Swami. The Shortened Path: Autobiography of a Western Yogi. abr. ed. 240p. 1980. pap. 6.95 (ISBN 0-916124-19-3). Dawn Pubns CA.

--Yoga Postures for Higher Awareness. 2nd, enl. ed. (Illus.). 140p. 1971. pap. 8.95 (ISBN 0-916124-25-8). Dawn Pubns CA.

Kundalini Yoga-Sadhana Guidelines. LC 85-9918. 107p. 1985. Repr. of 1978 ed. lib. bdg. 19.95x (ISBN 0-89370-886-0). Borgo Pr.

Lalitananda, Swami. Yoga in Life. (Illus.). 1972. pap. 2.99 - (ISBN 0-934664-17-X). Yoga Res Foun.

--Yoga Mystic Songs for Meditation, 6 Vols. 1975. pap. 2.99 ea. (ISBN 0-934664-19-6). Yoga Res Foun.

Lalitananda, Swami, ed. Yoga Quotations from the Wisdom of Swami Jyotir Maya Nanda. (Illus.). 1974. pap. 3.99 (ISBN 0-934664-27-7). Yoga Res Foun.

Leaves of Morya's Garden, Vol. I: The Call. 3rd ed. Incl. Leaves of Morya's Garden, Vol. II: Illumination. (Agni Yoga Ser.). 1979. pap. 12.00, Repr. of 1952 ed. (ISBN 0-933574-01-0). (Agni Yoga Ser.). 1978. Repr. of 1953 ed. softbound 12.00 (ISBN 0-933574-00-2). Agni Yoga Soc.

Leggett, Trevor. The Chapter of the Self. (Illus.). 1978. 12.95 (ISBN 0-7100-8702-0). Methuen Inc.

--Encounters in Yoga & Zen. 1982. pap. 9.95 (ISBN 0-7100-9241-5). Methuen Inc.

--Shankara on the Yoga Sutras. (Vol. 1). 140p. 1981. 30.00 (ISBN 0-7100-0826-0). Methuen Inc.

Letters of Helena Roerich, Vol. II. 1982. Repr. of 1967 ed. index 16.00 (ISBN 0-933574-15-0). Agni Yoga Soc.

Luk, Charles. Taoist Yoga. 1970. pap. 6.95 (ISBN 0-87728-067-3). Weiser.

McArthur, Tom. Yoga & the Bhagavad-Gita. 128p. 1986. pap. 11.95 (ISBN 0-85030-479-2). Newcastle Pub.

--Yoga & the Bhagavad-Gita. 1986. Repr. lib. bdg. 19.95x (ISBN 0-8095-7037-8). Borgo Pr.

Majundar, Sachindra Kumar. Introduction to Yoga. 1977. pap. 4.95 (ISBN 0-8065-0542-7). Citadel Pr.

Manda, Swami Jyotir. Yoga Stories & Parables. (Illus.). 1976. pap. 3.99 (ISBN 0-934664-41-2). Yoga Res Foun.

Mann, Richard D. The Light of Consciousness: Explorations in Transpersonal Psychology. 208p. 1984. 39.50 (ISBN 0-87395-905-1); pap. 10.95 trade disc. (ISBN 0-87395-906-X). State U NY Pr.

Matus, Thomas. Yoga & the Jesus Prayer Tradition: An Experiment in Faith. 200p. (Orig.). 1984. pap. 8.95 (ISBN 0-8091-2638-9). Paulist Pr.

Mayo, DeBarra. Runners' World Yoga, Bk. II. 180p. (Orig.). 1983. pap. 9.95 (ISBN 0-89037-274-8). Anderson World.

Mehta. Yoga: The Art of Integration. 15.95 (ISBN 0-8356-7513-0). Theos Pub Hse.

Michaelle. Yoga & Prayer. Cumming, Diane, tr. pap. 6.50 (ISBN 0-87061-059-7). Chr Classics.

Moore, Marcia & Douglas, Mark. Yoga, Science of the Self. rev. ed. LC 67-19602. (Illus.). 1979. 10.00 (ISBN 0-912240-01-6). Arcane Pubns.

Mother of Agni Yoga. 1977. pap. 3.00 (ISBN 0-933574-18-5). Agni Yoga Soc.

Mother of the World. 1977. pap. 3.00 (ISBN 0-933574-17-7). Agni Yoga Soc.

Mukerji, A. P. Doctrine & Practice of Yoga. 6.00 (ISBN 0-911662-23-5). Yoga.

--Yoga Lessons for Developing Spiritual Consciousness. 7.00 (ISBN 0-911662-24-3). Yoga.

Mumford, J. Psychosomatic Yoga. (Paths to Inner Power Ser.). 96p. 1974. 1.25 (ISBN 0-85030-208-0). Weiser.

Nanda, Jyotir M. Yoga Wisdom of the Upanishads: Kena..Mundaka..Prashna..Ishavasya. (Illus.). 1974. pap. 4.99 (ISBN 0-934664-36-6). Yoga Res Foun.

Narayananda, Swami. The Primal Power in Man: The Kundalini Shakti Yoga. 155p. 1971. pap. 11.95 (ISBN 0-88697-027-X). Life Science.

New Era Community. (Agni Yoga Ser.). 1978. Repr. of 1951 ed. flexible cover 12.00 (ISBN 0-933574-03-7). Agni Yoga Soc.

Norbu, Namkhai. The Cycle of Day & Night, Where One Proceeds along the Path of the Primordial Yoga: A Basic Text on the Practice of Dzog Chen. 80p. Date not set. 8.50 (ISBN 0-931892-09-0). B Dolphin Pub.

Oki, Masahiro. Zen Yoga Therapy. LC 79-1060. (Illus.). 1979. pap. 12.50 (ISBN 0-87040-459-8). Japan Pubns USA.

Orr, Leonard. The New Yoga. write for info. L Orr.

Pandit, M. P. Dhyana. 1979. pap. 1.95 (ISBN 0-941524-03-5). Lotus Light.

--Dynamics of Yoga, Vol. I. 182p. 1979. 9.95 (ISBN 0-941524-05-1). Lotus Light.

--Dynamics of Yoga, Vol. II. 1979. 9.95 (ISBN 0-941524-06-X). Lotus Light.

--Dynamics of Yoga, Vol. III. 164p. 1980. 10.95 (ISBN 0-941524-07-8). Lotus Light.

--Kundalini Yoga. LC 79-88734. 1979. 4.95 (ISBN 0-89744-004-8); pap. 3.00 (ISBN 0-89744-005-6). Auromere.

--Kundalini Yoga. pap. 3.00 (ISBN 0-89744-106-0). Auromere.

--Sadhana in Sri Aurobindo's Yoga. LC 78-59851. 1978. pap. 3.95 (ISBN 0-89744-000-5, Pub. by Atmaniketan Ashram). Auromere.

--Satsang. Golikhere, Vasanti R., ed. (Vol. I). 298p. (Orig.). 1979. pap. 11.00 (ISBN 0-941524-10-8). Lotus Light.

--Yoga for the Modern Man. 115p. 1979. 4.00 (ISBN 0-941524-13-2). Lotus Light.

--The Yoga of Knowledge. LC 79-88735. (Talks at Centre Ser.: Vol. II). 1979. pap. 5.95 (ISBN 0-89744-003-X). Auromere.

--The Yoga of Knowledge: Talks at Centre, Vol. II. LC 86-80692. 282p. (Orig.). 1986. pap. 7.95 (ISBN 0-941524-23-X). Lotus Light.

--The Yoga of Works: Talks at Centre I. LC 85-50695. 192p. 1985. pap. 7.95 (ISBN 0-941524-21-3). Lotus Light.

Pandit, Madhav P. The Yoga of Love. LC 81-86373. (Talks at Center Ser.: Vol. III). 112p. (Orig.). 1982. pap. 3.95 (ISBN 0-941524-16-7). Lotus Light.

--Yoga of Self-Perfection. LC 83-81299. (Talks at Centre Ser.: Vol. IV). 312p. (Orig.). 1983. pap. 7.95 (ISBN 0-941524-20-5). Lotus Light.

Pandit, Sri M. Japa. 41p. 1979. Repr. of 1959 ed. 1.95 (ISBN 0-941524-09-4). Lotus Light.

--Yoga in Sri Aurobindo's Epic Savitri. 236p. 1979. 7.95 (ISBN 0-941524-15-9). Lotus Light.

Paramananda, Swami. Science & Practice of Yoga. 1918. pap. 0.50 (ISBN 0-911564-31-4). Vedanta Ctr.

Parvati, Jeannine. Prenatal Yoga & Natural Birth. rev. ed. (Illus.). 64p. 1986. pap. 7.95 (ISBN 0-938190-89-X). North Atlantic.

Patanjali. Patanjali's Yoga Sutras. 2nd ed. Prasada, Rama, tr. from Sanskrit. 318p. 1981. Repr. of 1912 ed. 28.50 (ISBN 0-89744-220-2, Pub. by Orient Reprint India). Auromere.

--Patanjali's Yoga Sutras. (the Aphorisms of Yoga, by Patanjali.) with the Commentary of Vyasa & the Gloss of Vachaspati Misra. Rama Prasada, tr. LC 73-3789. Repr. of 1912 ed. 29.00 (ISBN 0-404-57804-7). AMS Pr.

--Yoga Sutras of Patanjali. 7th ed. Johnston, Charles, tr. from Sanskrit. 1984. pap. 6.00 (ISBN 0-914732-08-0). Bro Life Inc.

Patanjali, Bhagwan S. Aphorisms of Yoga. (Illus.). 96p. (Orig.). 1973. pap. 5.50 (ISBN 0-571-10320-0). Faber & Faber.

Patrick, Priscilla. To Life! Yoga with Priscilla Patrick. LC 82-71187. (Illus.). 76p. (Orig.). 1982. pap. 9.95 (ISBN 0-943274-00-1). SC Ed Comm Inc.

Pavitrananda, Swami. Common Sense about Yoga. pap. 1.25 (ISBN 0-87481-105-8). Vedanta Pr.

Peck, Robert L. American Meditation & Beginning Yoga. 1976. 6.00 (ISBN 0-685-71846-8). Personal Dev Ctr.

Penn, Bennett. The Path of Transcendence. 144p. 1987. pap. text ed. 10.00 (ISBN 0-682-40332-6). Exposition Pr FL.

Podgorski, Frank R. Ego: Revealer-Concealer, a Key to Yoga. (Illus.). 306p. 1985. lib. bdg. 27.50 (ISBN 0-8191-4345-6); pap. text ed. 14.50 (ISBN 0-8191-4346-4). U Pr of Amer.

Prabhavananda, Swami & Isherwood, Christopher. How to Know God: The Yoga Aphorisms of Patanjali. 1969. pap. 2.95 (ISBN 0-451-62330-4, ME2330, Ment). NAL.

Prasad, R. C. Lifting the Veil (Kundalini Yoga) A Compendium of Rajneesh's Essential Teachings. 1975. pap. 6.50 (ISBN 0-89684-244-4). Orient Bk Dist.

Prem, Krishna. Initiation into Yoga. LC 76-10790. (Orig.). 1976. pap. 3.25 (ISBN 0-8356-0484-5, Quest). Theos Pub Hse.

Pullen-Burry, Henry B. Qabalism. 167p. 1972. Repr. of 1925 ed. 10.00 (ISBN 0-911662-45-6). Yoga.

Radha, Sivananda. Kundalini Yoga for the West. LC 81-40488. (Illus.). 379p. 1981. pap. 14.95 (ISBN 0-87773-211-6). Shambhala Pubns.

Raghavan, K. Yoga, Facts & Fancies. 1983. 7.50x (ISBN 0-8364-0950-7, Pub. by Mukhopadhyay India). South Asia Bks.

Rajneesh, Bhagwan Shree. Yoga: The Alpha & the Omega, 10 vols, Vols. 1-5. Prem, Ma Ananda & Sudha, Ma Yoga, eds. LC 76-902396. (Yoga Ser.). (Illus., Orig.). 1976. Vol I, 272 pgs. 16.95 ea. (ISBN 0-88050-177-4). Vol II, 266 pgs. 1976 (ISBN 0-88050-178-2). Vol. III, 298 pgs. 1976 (ISBN 0-88050-179-0). Vol. IV, 280 pgs. 1976 (ISBN 0-88050-180-4). Vol. V, 266 pgs. 1976 (ISBN 0-88050-181-2). Chidvilas Found.

--Yoga: The Alpha & the Omega, 10 vols, Vols. 6-10. Chinmaya, Swami Prem & Sudha, Ma Yoga, eds. LC 76-902396. (Yoga Ser.). (Illus., Orig.). 1977. Vol. VI, 270 pgs. 16.95 ea. (ISBN 0-88050-182-0). Vol. VII250p 1977 (ISBN 0-88050-183-9). Vol. VIII, 298 pgs. 1977 (ISBN 0-88050-184-7). Vol. IX, 346 pgs. 1978 (ISBN 0-88050-185-5). Vol. X, 270 pgs. 1978 (ISBN 0-88050-186-3). Chidvilas Found.

--Yoga: The Science of the Soul, Vol. 1. 2nd ed. Mahasattva, Swami Krishna, ed. LC 84-42812. (Yoga Ser.). 304p. 1984. pap. 4.95 (ISBN 0-88050-677-6). Chidvilas Found.

Rama, Swami. Lectures on Yoga. LC 79-114571. (Illus.). 208p. pap. 7.95 (ISBN 0-89389-050-2); 6.95 (ISBN 0-89389-051-0). Himalayan Pubs.

Ramacharaka, Yogi. Fourteen Lessons in Yoga Philosophy. 8.00 (ISBN 0-911662-01-4). Yoga.

--Gnani Yoga. 8.00 (ISBN 0-911662-04-9). Yoga.

--Hindu-Yogi Practical Water Cure. leatherette 3.00 (ISBN 0-911662-12-X). Yoga.

--Mystic Christianity. 8.00 (ISBN 0-911662-08-1). Yoga.

--Raja Yoga. 8.00 (ISBN 0-911662-03-0). Yoga.

Ravindra. The White Lotus: At the Feet of the Mother. (Illus.). 1978. 8.50x (ISBN 0-89684-466-8). Orient Bk Dist.

Reality of Living Yoga. 212p. 1978. pap. 6.95x (ISBN 0-933740-01-8). Mindbody Inc.

Richabhchand. Integral Yoga of Sri Aurobindo. 2nd ed. 1979. 20.00 (ISBN 0-89744-939-8); pap. 16.00 (ISBN 0-89744-940-1). Auromere.

Rishabhchand. The Integral Yoga of Sri Aurobindo. 473p. 1974. pap. 5.30 (ISBN 0-89071-281-6). Matagiri.

Rudrananda, Swami, pseud. Behind the Cosmic Curtain: The Further Writings of Swami Rudrananda. Mann, John, ed. (Illus.). 176p. (Orig.). pap. 9.95x (ISBN 0-9613477-0-8). Neolog.

Rutledge, Dom D. In Search of a Yogi: Himalayan Pilgrimage. lib. bdg. 69.95 (ISBN 0-8490-0392-X). Gordon Pr.

Sachdeva, I. P. Yoga & Depth Psychology. 269p. 1978. 16.95x (ISBN 0-317-12334-3, Pub. by Motilal Banarsi). Asia Bk Corp.

Sadhu, M. Concentration: A Guide to Mental Mastery. pap. 5.00 (ISBN 0-87980-023-2). Wilshire.

Saher, P. J. Zen Yoga. 1976. 15.00 (ISBN 0-8426-0822-2). Orient Bk Dist.

Satchidanada, Sri Swam i. Beyond Words. Alexander, Lester, ed. LC 76-29896. (Illus.). 190p. 1977. pap. 5.95 (ISBN 0-03-016911-9). Integral Yoga Pubns.

Satchidananda, S., ed. Living Yoga. (Psychic Studies). 336p. 1977. 30.95 (ISBN 0-677-05230-8). Gordon & Breach.

Satprakashananda, Swami. Meditation: Its Process, Practice, & Culmination. LC 76-15722. 264p. 1976. 10.00 (ISBN 0-916356-55-8). Vedanta Soc St Louis.

Schreiber, Suzanne L. Yoga for the Fun of It! Hatha Yoga for Preschool Children. 2nd ed. (Illus.). 54p. (Orig.). 1981. pap. 6.00 (ISBN 0-9608320-0-9). Sugar Marbel Pr.

Self Healing Yoga & Destiny. 1983. 4.95 (ISBN 0-943358-06-X). Aurora Press.

Shankaranarayanan, S. Sri Chakra. 1979. 14.95 (ISBN 0-941524-11-6). Lotus Light.

Sharma, H. L. The Psychodynamics of Yoga. 160p. 1981. 16.95x (ISBN 0-317-12326-2, Pub. by G D K Pubns India). Asia Bk Corp.

Shekhawat, Virenda. Yoga: The Technique of Liberation. 90p. 1979. text ed. 7.50 (ISBN 0-89684-264-9, Pub. by Sterling India). Orient Bk Dist.

Shiv Brat Lal. Light on Ananda Yoga. Morrow, Steve, tr. LC 82-61990. 134p. 1982. pap. 10.00 (ISBN 0-89142-041-X). Sant Bani Ash.

Singh, Jaideva. Siva Sutras: The Yoga of Supreme Identity. 1979. 16.95 (ISBN 0-89684-057-3, Pub. by Motilal Banarsidass India); pap. 12.50 (ISBN 0-89684-063-8, Pub. by Motilal Banarsidass India). Orient Bk Dist.

Singh, Kirpal. The Crown of Life: A Study of Yoga. (Illus.). xv, 255p. 1980. pap. 7.00 (ISBN 0-89142-000-2). Sant Bani Ash.

--The Crown of Life: A Study of Yoga. 4th ed. LC 79-67543. (Illus.). 256p. pap. 6.95 (ISBN 0-918224-09-8). Sawan Kirpal Pubns.

Sinha, Phulgenda. Yoga: Meaning, Values & Practice. 1973. pap. 2.50 (ISBN 0-88253-259-6). Ind-US Inc.

Sivananda, Swami. Practice of Karma Yoga. 1974. 7.95 (ISBN 0-8426-0675-0); pap. 3.50 (ISBN 0-686-67764-1). Orient Bk Dist.

Sivananda Yoga Center. The Sivananda Companion to Yoga. 1983. pap. 9.95 (ISBN 0-671-47088-4). S&S.

Spiritual Diary. 380p. 1982. 2.95 (ISBN 0-87612-021-4). Self Realization.

Sri Aurobindo. The Mother. 62p. 1980. 19.00 (ISBN 0-89744-914-2, Pub. by Sri Aurobindo Ashram Trust India); pap. 2.00 (ISBN 0-89744-915-0, Pub. by Sru Aurobindo Ashram Trust India); pap. 1.00 miniature size 1980 (ISBN 0-89744-148-6). Auromere.

SriAnanda. The Complete Book of Yoga: Harmony of Body & Mind. 175p. 1980. 11.95x (ISBN 0-317-12476-5, Pub. by Vision Bks India). Asia Bk Corp.

Sri Aurobindo. Letters on Yoga, 3 vols. 1979. Vol. 1. 11.25 (ISBN 0-89071-236-0); Vol. 2. 12.50 (ISBN 0-89071-238-7); Vol. 3. 14.50 (ISBN 0-89071-240-9); Vol. 1. pap. 10.00 (ISBN 0-89071-237-9); Vol. 2. pap. 11.25 (ISBN 0-89071-239-5); Vol. 3. pap. 12.50 (ISBN 0-89071-241-7). Matagiri.

--Lights on Yoga. 1979. pap. 3.00 (ISBN 0-89744-916-9). Auromere.

--On Yoga II: Letters on Yoga Tome I. 1979. 15.00 (ISBN 0-89744-911-8). Auromere.

--A Practical Guide to Integral Yoga. (Illus.). 1985. 9.00 (ISBN 0-89071-217-4); pap. 6.95. Matagiri.

--Yoga of Divine Works. 2nd ed. (Life Companion Library). (Illus.). 270p. Date not set. pap. 8.95 (ISBN 0-89744-015-3). Auromere.

Sri Swami Satchidananda. The Golden Present. 448p. (Orig.). Date not set. pap. write for info. (ISBN 0-932040-30-6). Integral Yoga Pubns.

--Guru & Disciple. 1977. pap. 1.95 (ISBN 0-932040-18-7). Integral Yoga Pubns.

--Integral Yoga: The Yoga Sutras of Patanjali. Pocket ed. LC 85-125. 124p. (Orig.). 1985. pap. 3.95 (ISBN 0-932040-28-4). Integral Yoga Pubns.

--The Mother Is the Baby's First Guru: Pregnancy, Infant Care & Yoga. 1976. pap. 3.95 (ISBN 0-932040-15-2). Integral Yoga Pubns.

Stearn, Jess. Yoga, Youth & Reincarnation. (Illus.). 352p. 1986. pap. 3.95 (ISBN 0-553-26057-X). Bantam.

Strutt, Malcolm. Wholistic Health & Living Yoga. LC 77-85790. (Illus.). 320p. (Orig.). 1978. pap. 9.95 (ISBN 0-916438-08-2). Univ of Trees.

Swami Kripalvananda. The Sadhak's Companion. Darshana Shakti Ma, ed. Gauri Modi, tr. from Gujarati. Orig. Title: Guru Vachanamrit. (Illus., Orig.). 1977. pap. text ed. 2.95 (ISBN 0-933116-04-7). Sanatana.

Swami, Jyotir & Nanda, Maya. Yoga Essays for Self-Improvement. LC 81-65248. 248p. 1981. pap. 4.99 (ISBN 0-934664-39-0, 030). Yoga Res Foun.

Swami Kuvalayananda. Popular Yoga Asanas. LC 76-130420. (Illus.). (YA) 1972. Repr. of 1931 ed. 12.50 (ISBN 0-8048-0673-X). C E Tuttle.

Swami Chetanananda. Dynamic Stillness: A Practice Guide to Kundalini Yoga. 208p. 1987. pap. 9.95 (ISBN 0-915801-06-X). Rudra Pr.

Swami Jyotir, Maya N. Integral Yoga Today. 96p. (Orig.). 1983. pap. 2.50 (ISBN 0-934664-43-9). Yoga Res Foun.

Swami Jyotir Maya Nanda. Yoga Integral. (Span., Illus.). 112p. 1984. pap. 2.85 (ISBN 0-934664-51-X). Yoga Res Foun.

Swami Karunananda Ma, ed. Lotus Prayer Book. LC 86-10384. 224p. (Orig.). 1986. pap. 9.95 (ISBN 0-932040-33-0). Integral Yoga Pubns.

Swami Kriyanada. Lessons in Yoga: Fourteen Steps to Higher Awareness. 2nd, rev. ed. 1979. pap. write for info. (ISBN 0-916124-16-9). Dawn Pubns CA.

Swami Rama. Choosing a Path. 200p. (Orig.). pap. 8.95 (ISBN 0-89389-077-4). Himalayan Pubs.

--Inspired Thoughts of Swami Rama. 260p. (Orig.). pap. 8.95 (ISBN 0-89389-086-3). Himalayan Pubs.

--Path of Fire & Light: Advanced Practices of Yoga. 180p. (Orig.). 1986. pap. 8.95 (ISBN 0-89389-097-9). Himalayan Pubs.

--A Practical Guide to Holistic Health. 152p. 8.95 (ISBN 0-89389-066-9); pap. 6.95 (ISBN 0-89389-065-0). Himalayan Pubs.

Swami Rama, et al. Yoga & Psychotherapy: The Evolution of Consciousness. 332p. 13.95 (ISBN 0-89389-000-6); pap. 9.95 (ISBN 0-89389-036-7). Himalayan Pubs.

Swami Satprakashananda. The Universe, God, & God-Realization: From the Viewpoint of Vedanta. LC 77-79829. 310p. 1977. 12.50 (ISBN 0-916356-57-4). Vedanta Soc St Louis.

Swami Sivananda. Karma Yoga. Swami Venkatesananda, ed. (Life & Works of Swami Sivananda). 192p. (Orig.). 1985. pap. 6.95 (ISBN 0-949027-05-7). Integral Yoga Pubns.

Swami Sivananda & Swami Venkatesananda. Health & Hatha Yoga. (Life & Works of Swami Sivananda). (Illus.). 350p. (Orig.). 1985. pap. 9.95 (ISBN 0-949027-03-0). Integral Yoga Pubns.

Swami Sivananda Radha. Mantras: Words of Power. LC 80-10293. (Illus.). 150p. 1980. pap. 7.95 (ISBN 0-931454-05-0). Timeless Bks.

Swami Venkatesananda, ed. Sivananda: Biography of a Modern Sage. (Life & Works of Swami Sivananda). (Illus.). 448p. (Orig.). 1985. pap. 9.95 (ISBN 0-949027-01-4). Integral Yoga Pubns.

Swami Vivekananda. Bhakti-Yoga: The Yoga of Love & Devotion. pap. 1.50 (ISBN 0-87481-157-0). Vedanta Pr.

--Jnana-Yoga. pap. 4.95 (ISBN 0-87481-158-9). Vedanta Pr.

--Karma-Yoga. pap. 1.50 (ISBN 0-87481-159-7). Vedanta Pr.

--Karma-Yoga & Bhakti-Yoga. LC 55-8657. 336p. pocket ed. 6.95 (ISBN 0-911206-07-8); pap. 6.95 large size (ISBN 0-911206-22-1). Ramakrishna.

--Raja-Yoga. LC 55-12231. 320p. pocket ed. 6.95 (ISBN 0-911206-06-X); pap. 6.95 large size (ISBN 0-911206-23-X). Ramakrishna.

--Teachings of Swami Vivekananda. 1971. pap. 3.95 (ISBN 0-87481-134-1). Vedanta Pr.

Szekely, Edmond B. Creative Work: Karma Yoga. (Illus.). 32p. 1973. pap. 2.95 (ISBN 0-89564-066-X). IBS Intl.

--The Living Buddha. (Illus.). 70p. 1977. pap. 4.50 (ISBN 0-89564-059-7). IBS Intl.

Taimni. Science of Yoga. 10.95 (ISBN 0-8356-7140-2). Theos Pub Hse.

Taimni, I. K. Glimpses into the Psychology of Yoga. 1973. 10.95 (ISBN 0-8356-7290-5). Theos Pub Hse.

--The Science of Yoga. LC 67-4112. pap. 6.95 (ISBN 0-8356-0023-8, Quest). Theos Pub Hse.

Taylor, Renee. Yoga... The Art of Living: The Hunza-Yoga Way to Better Living. LC 78-75329. (Illus.). 224p. 1975. pap. 4.50 (ISBN 0-87983-112-X). Keats.

Thakar, Vimala. Life As Yoga: Discourses at Chorwad, 2 bks. Singh, Devendra, tr. 286p. 1977. 14.00 (ISBN 0-89684-242-8, Pub. by Motilal Banarsidass India); pap. 10.95 (ISBN 0-89684-241-X). Orient Bk Dist.

The Mother. Glimpses of the Mother's Life, Vol. 2. Das, Nilima, ed. 335p. 1980. 11.00 (ISBN 0-89071-291-3). Matagiri.

Thomas, Edward. Grail Yoga. 2nd ed. LC 74-84399. (A Grail Bk). (Illus.). 128p. 1975. pap. 2.95 (ISBN 0-914896-28-8). East Ridge Pr.

Tola, Fernanda & Carmen, D. The Yoga Sutra of Patanjali on Concentration of Mind. 1986. 21.00 (ISBN 81-208-0258-6, Pub. by Motilal Banarsidass). South Asia Bks.

Udupa, K. N. Stress & Its Management by Yoga. 400p. 1986. 25.00X (ISBN 81-208-0000-1, Pub. by Motilal Banarsidass). South Asia Bks.

Van Lysebeth, Andre. Yoga Self-Taught. Congreve, Carola, tr. from Fr. Orig. Title: J'Apprends le Yoga. (Illus.). 264p. 1973. pap. 5.95 (ISBN 0-06-463360-8, EH 360, B&N Bks). Har-Row.

Varenne, Jean. Yoga & the Hindu Tradition. Coltman, Derek, tr. from Fr. LC 75-19506. 1976. pap. 5.45X (ISBN 0-226-85116-8, P744, Phoen). U of Chicago Pr.

Vasu, Srisa Chandra. An Introduction to the Yoga Philosophy. LC 73-3806. (Scared Books of the Hindus: No. 15, Pt. 4). Repr. of 1915 ed. 14.50 (ISBN 0-404-57838-1). AMS Pr.

Venkatesananda, Swami, tr. from Sanskrit. The Concise Yoga Vasistha. 445p. 1984. lib. bdg. 34.50x (ISBN 0-87395-955-8); pap. 10.95 (ISBN 0-87395-954-X). State U NY Pr.

Vithaldes. The Yoga System of Health & Relief from Tension. 1961. pap. 4.95 (ISBN 0-346-12500-6). Cornerstone.

Vyas, R. N. The Bhagavadgita & Jivana Yoga. 1986. 14.00x (ISBN 81-7017-203-9, Pub. by Abhinav India). South Asia Bks.

Wayman, Alex. Yoga of the Guhyasamjatantra. 386p. 1980. pap. 7.95 (ISBN 0-87728-451-2). Weiser.

Weiman, Mark. Yoga: A Bibliography. 135p. 1979. lib. bdg. 22.50 (ISBN 0-8482-7051-7). Norwood Edns.

Wentz, Walter Y., ed. Tibetan Yoga & Secret Doctrines: Or Seven Books of Wisdom of the Great Path. LC 78-70140. Repr. of 1935 ed. 49.50 (ISBN 0-404-17413-2). AMS Pr.

Werner, Karel. Yoga & Indian Philosophy. 1977. 11.00 (ISBN 0-8426-0900-8, Pub. by Motilal Banarsidass India). Orient Bk Dist.
--Yoga & Indian Philosophy. 1979. 12.50x (ISBN 0-8364-0479-3). South Asia Bks.
Winding, Eleanor. Yoga for Musicians & Other Special People. (Illus.). 68p. (Orig.). 1982. pap. 7.95 (ISBN 0-88284-193-9). Alfred Pub.
Woman. 1977. pap. 3.00 (ISBN 0-933574-19-3). Agni Yoga Soc.
Wood, Ernest. Seven Schools of Yoga: An Introduction. LC 72-13120. Orig. Title: The Occult Training of the Hindus. 120p. 1973. pap. 2.25 (ISBN 0-8356-0435-7, Quest). Theos Pub Hse.
Woods, James. The Yoga-Systems of Patanjali: The Doctrine of the Concentration of the Mind. lib. bdg. 90.00 (ISBN 0-87968-083-0). Krishna Pr.
Worthington, Vivian. A History of Yoga. 176p. 1982. pap. 8.95 (ISBN 0-7100-9258-X). Methuen Inc.
Yesudian, Selvarajan. Self-Reliance Through Yoga. 3rd ed. (Unwin Paperbacks). 1979. pap. 7.50 (ISBN 0-04-149054-1). Allen Unwin.
Yesudian, Selvarajan & Haich, Elisabeth. Yoga & Health. (Unwin Paperbacks). (Illus.). 1978. pap. 5.95 (ISBN 0-04-149033-9). Allen Unwin.
Yoga for the Eighties. (Illus.). 36p. 6.95 (ISBN 0-89509-055-4). Arcline Pubns.
Yogananda, Paramahansa. Autobiography of a Yogi. LC 78-151319. (Illus.). 605p. 1974. Bengali ed. 4.00x (ISBN 0-87612-071-0); Dutch ed. 17.00x (ISBN 90-202-4016-1); German ed. 12.50x (ISBN 3-87041-015-9); Gujarati ed. 4.00x (ISBN 0-87612-072-9); Japanese ed. 11.00x (ISBN 0-87612-073-7); pap. 3.50 (ISBN 0-87612-079-6). Self Realization.
--Autobiography of a Yogi. (Illus.). 1971. pap. 9.50x British ed. (ISBN 0-09-021051-4); pap. 14.50x Danish ed. (ISBN 87-418-7082-4); pap. 11.75x French ed. (ISBN 0-87612-066-4); pap. 14.00x Greek ed. (ISBN 0-87612-069-9); pap. 6.95x Italian ed. (ISBN 0-87612-067-2); pap. 10.50x Spanish ed. (ISBN 0-87612-068-0); pap. 4.00x Hindi ed. (ISBN 0-87612-077-X); pap. 13.50x Portuguese ed. (ISBN 0-87612-081-8). Self Realization.
--How You Can Talk with God. 2nd ed. (Illus.). 1985. pap. 0.95 (ISBN 0-87612-160-1); pap. 2.00 French ed. (ISBN 0-87612-163-6). Self Realization.
--Law of Success. 1980. pap. 0.95 (ISBN 0-87612-150-4); pap. 1.00x Span. ed. (ISBN 0-87612-151-2); pap. 2.00 French ed. (ISBN 0-87612-152-0). Self Realization.
--Metaphysical Meditations. 11th ed. LC 40-16548. 124p. 1964. pap. 1.95 (ISBN 0-87612-041-9). pap. 5.00x German ed. (ISBN 3-87041-111-2); pap. 1.25x Span. ed. (ISBN 0-87612-043-5); pap. 3.00x Italian ed. (ISBN 0-87612-046-X). Self Realization.
--Whispers from Eternity. 9th ed. LC 86-60584. (Illus.). 239p. 1986. 7.95 (ISBN 0-87612-103-2); pap. 3.50x Span. ed. (ISBN 0-87612-101-6); German ed. 10.00x (ISBN 3-85399-034-7). Self Realization.
Yogeswar. Textbook of Yoga. (Illus.). 574p. 1980. 24.95x (ISBN 0-940500-37-X). Asia Bk Corp.
Yogi Ramacharaka. Practical Water Cure. leatherette 3.00 (ISBN 0-911662-12-X). Yoga.
Yogi Vithaldas. Yoga System of Health. 1981. pap. 3.95 (ISBN 0-686-82888-7). Cornerstone.
Zitko, Howard J. New Age Tantra Yoga: The Sexual Gateway to Spiritual Fulfillment. 6th ed. LC 75-3657. 1985. pap. 7.50 (ISBN 0-941902-00-5). World Univ AZ.
Zom. True Yoga. 4.95 (ISBN 0-8065-0336-X). Citadel Pr.

YOGA, HATHA

Acharya, Pundit. Breath, Sleep, the Heart, & Life: The Revolutionary Health Yoga of Pundit Acharya. LC 74-24306. 190p. 1975. pap. 7.95 (ISBN 0-913922-09-9). Dawn Horse Pr.
Agarwal, R. S. Yoga of Perfect Sight. 3rd ed. 1979. pap. 14.00 (ISBN 0-89744-948-7). Auromere.
Arya, Pandit U. Philosophy of Hatha Yoga. 2nd ed. 95p. pap. 5.95 (ISBN 0-89389-088-X). Himalayan Pubs.
Atreya, B. L. Deification of Man: Its Methods & Stages According to the Yoga Vasistha Including a Translation of the Essence of Vasistha's Teachings. 116p. 1980. pap. 4.50 (ISBN 0-935548-02-5). Santarasa Pubns.
Bates, Charles. Ransoming the Mind: An Integration of Yoga & Modern Therapy. LC 86-50084. (Illus.). 352p. (Orig.). 1986. pap. 11.95 (ISBN 0-936663-00-6). Yes Intl.
Brosnan, Barbara. Yoga for Handicapped People. (Human Horizon Ser.). (Illus.). 208p. 1982. pap. 15.95 (ISBN 0-285-64952-3, Pub. by Souvenir Pr England). Brookline Bks.
Carrol, Frieda, compiled by. Meditation & Yoga Retreats: An International Directory. 200p. 1983. text ed. 4.75 (ISBN 0-913597-06-6, Pub. by Alpha Pyramis). Prosperity & Profits.
Caughlan, Lar. Yoga: The Spirit of Union. 96p. 1981. pap. text ed. 13.00 (ISBN 0-8403-2487-1). Kendall-Hunt.
Chaney, Earlyne & Messick, William L. Kundalini & the Third Eye. Chaney, Sita, ed. LC 80-67635. (Illus.). 127p. 1982. pap. 12.95 (ISBN 0-918936-08-X). Astara.
Colton, Ann R. Kundalini West. (Illus.). 403p. 1978. 12.95 (ISBN 0-917187-01-6). A R C Pub.
Dalal, Nergis. Yoga for Rejuvenation. 128p. (Orig.). 1984. pap. 6.95 (ISBN 0-7225-0948-0). Thorsons Pubs.
Desai, Yogi A. Working Miracles of Love: A Collection of Teachings. LC 85-50126. (Illus.). 184p. 1985. pap. text ed. 5.95 (ISBN 0-940258-15-3). Kripalu Pubns.
Devi, Indra. Yoga for Americans. 1971. pap. 2.25 (ISBN 0-451-09869-2, E9869, Sig). NAL.
Hatha Yoga. rev. ed. LC 81-51182. (Illus.). 128p. 1983. pap. 6.95 (ISBN 0-914602-72-1). SYDA Found.
Himalayan International Institute. Therapeutic Value of Yoga. 108p. (Orig.). pap. 3.95 (ISBN 0-89389-054-5). Himalayan Pubs.
Hittleman, Richard. Yoga for Health. LC 82-90825. 256p. (Orig.). 1983. pap. 7.95 (ISBN 0-345-30852-2). Ballantine.
Hopkins, Jeffrey. Emptiness Yoga. LC 86-6484. 504p. 1987. 35.00 (ISBN 0-937938-36-X); pap. 19.95 (ISBN 0-937938-31-9). Snow Lion.
Integral Yoga Institutes. Integral Yoga Hatha Booklet & Tape. 1979. 6.95 (ISBN 0-932040-23-3). Integral Yoga Pubns.
Joshi, K. S. Yoga in Daily Life. 163p. 1971. pap. 2.00 (ISBN 0-88253-044-5). Ind-US Inc.
Keeping up with Kundalini Yoga. LC 85-13215. 1985. Repr. of 1980 ed. lib. bdg. 19.95x (ISBN 0-89370-884-4). Borgo Pr.
Khalsa, Harbhajan S. Yoga for the Eighties: Kundalini Yoga. LC 85-11680. 1985. Repr. lib. bdg. 19.95x (ISBN 0-89370-879-8). Borgo Pr.
Krishna, Gopi. Kundalini: The Evolutionary Energy in Man. LC 73-75656. 252p. 1971. pap. 8.95 (ISBN 0-87773-043-1). Shambhala Pubns.
Majumdar, Sachindra K. Yoga for Physical & Mental Fitness. LC 68-31613. (Illus.). 1968. 7.95 (ISBN 0-87396-013-0); pap. 3.95 (ISBN 0-87396-014-9). Stravon.
Marshall, Lyn. Everyday Yoga. LC 83-24177. (Illus.). 96p. (Orig.). 1984. pap. 6.95 (ISBN 0-8069-7864-3). Sterling.
Muktananda, Swami. I Am That. rev. ed. 104p. 1983. pap. 3.95 (ISBN 0-914602-27-6). SYDA Found.
--Perfect Relationship. LC 80-54457. 240p. 1980. pap. 6.95 (ISBN 0-914602-53-5). SYDA Found.
--Play of Consciousness. LC 78-62769. 322p. 1978. 9.95 (ISBN 0-914602-36-5); pap. 6.95 (ISBN 0-914602-37-3). SYDA Found.
--Secret of the Siddhas. LC 80-53590. 256p. 1980. pap. 6.95 (ISBN 0-914602-52-7). SYDA Found.
Rama, Swami. Exercise Without Movement. (Illus.). 88p. (Orig.). pap. 5.95 (ISBN 0-89389-089-8). Himalayan Pubs.
Ramacharaka, Yogi. Hatha Yoga. 8.00 (ISBN 0-911662-06-5). Yoga.
Rawlinson, Ian. Yoga for the West: A Manual for Designing Your Own Practice. McNeilage, Alastair, ed. (Illus.). 200p. (Orig.). 1987. lib. bdg. 12.95 (ISBN 0-916360-26-1). CRCS Pubns NV.
Sadhana Guidelines. (Illus.). 122p. 9.95 (ISBN 0-89509-004-X). Arcline Pubns.
Samskriti & Franks, Judith. Hatha Yoga Manual II. 176p. plastic comb bdg. 9.95 (ISBN 0-89389-043-X). Himalayan Pubs.
Samskrti & Veda. Hatha Yoga Manual I. 2nd ed. (Illus.). 187p. plastic comb. 9.95 (ISBN 0-89389-053-7). Himalayan Pubs.
Sannella, Lee. The Kundalini Experience: Psychosis or Transcendence. rev. ed. (Illus.). 160p. 1987. pap. 9.95 (ISBN 0-941255-29-8). Integral Pub.
Schutz, Albert & Schaps, Hilda W. Kosher Yoga: Cabalistic Roots of Western Mysticism. LC 83-60144. 128p. (Orig.). 1983. 12.95 (ISBN 0-936596-09-0); pap. 8.95 (ISBN 0-936596-08-2). Quantal.
Scott, Mary. Kundalini in the Physical World. (Illus.). 240p. (Orig.). 1983. pap. 11.95 (ISBN 0-7100-9417-5). Methuen Inc.
Sivananda Radha, Swami. Kundalini Yoga for the West. LC 78-1857. (Illus.). 1978. 24.95 (ISBN 0-931454-01-8). Timeless Bks.
Slater, Wallace. Simplified Course in Hatha Yoga. 1967. pap. 2.75 (ISBN 0-8356-0138-2, Quest). Theos Pub Hse.
Swami Muktananda. Kundalini Stavaha. 45p. 1980. pap. 2.50 (ISBN 0-914602-55-1). SYDA Found.
--Kundalini: The Secret of Life. (Illus.). 64p. (Orig.). 1983. pap. 3.95 (ISBN 0-914602-47-0). SYDA Found.
--Reflections of the Self: Poems of Spiritual Life. LC 80-50391. (Illus.). 205p. (Orig.). 1980. pap. 5.95 (ISBN 0-914602-50-0). SYDA Found.
Swami Sivananda Radha. Mantras: Words of Power. LC 80-10293. (Illus.). 150p. 1980. pap. 7.95 (ISBN 0-931454-05-0). Timeless Bks.
Swami Vishnudevananda. Complete Illustrated Book of Yoga. 1981. pap. 3.50 (ISBN 0-671-44787-4). PB.
The Mother. Health & Healing in Yoga. 305p. 1982. 6.00 (ISBN 0-89071-284-0, Pub. by Sri Aurobindo Ashram India); pap. 6.00 (ISBN 0-89071-283-2). Matagiri.
Van Lysebeth, Andre. Pranayama: The Yoga of Breathing. (Unwin Paperbacks). (Illus.). 1979. pap. 6.95 (ISBN 0-04-149050-9). Allen Unwin.
Yogi Vithaldas. Yoga System of Health. 1981. pap. 3.95 (ISBN 0-686-82888-7). Cornerstone.

YOGA, RAJA

see also Samadhi

Aurobindo, Sri. Ideal of the Karmayogin. 170p. Date not set. 7.00 (ISBN 0-317-17429-0). Auromere.
--Letters on Yoga, 2 vols. (Life Companion Library Bible Paper Ser.). 1984p. 40.00 (ISBN 0-89744-014-5). Auromere.
--Synthesis of Yoga. 6th ed. 1979p. 36.00 (ISBN 0-89744-931-2). Auromere.
--Synthesis of Yoga. 1979p. 30.00 (ISBN 0-89744-932-0). Auromere.
--Synthesis of Yoga. (Life Companion Bible Bks.). 1984p. 24.95 (ISBN 0-89744-017-X). Auromere.
Dash, Vaidya B. Handbook of Ayurveda. 221p. (Orig.). 1983. 28.00 (ISBN 0-317-17437-1, Pub. by Cultural Integration). Auromere.
Judge, William Q., tr. & pref. by. The Yoga Aphorisms of Patanjali. xxi, 74p. 1930. Repr. of 1889 ed. 3.00 (ISBN 0-938998-11-0). Theosophy.
Jyotir Maya Nanda, Swami. Raja Yoga (The Study of the Mind) (Illus.). 1970. 5.99 (ISBN 0-934664-09-9). Yoga Res Foun.
Patanjali. Raja Yoga Sutras. Swami Jyotir Maya Nanda, tr. from Sanskrit. (Illus.). 1978. pap. 2.99 (ISBN 0-934664-38-2). Yoga Res Foun.
Slater, Wallace. Raja Yoga: A Simplified & Practical Course. LC 71-3051. 1969. pap. 4.50 (ISBN 0-8356-0131-5, Quest). Theos Pub Hse.
Sri Aurobindo Album. 55p. Date not set. 15.00 (ISBN 0-317-17482-7). Auromere.
Swami Vivekananda, tr. Raja-Yoga: The Yoga Aphorisms of Patanjali. pap. 3.25 (ISBN 0-87481-160-0). Vedanta Pr.
Yesudian, Selvarajan & Haich, Elisabeth. Raja Yoga. (Unwin Paperbacks). (Illus.). 1980. pap. 5.95 (ISBN 0-04-149056-8). Allen Unwin.
Yogananda, Paramahansa & Self-Realization Fellowship Editorial Staff. Sayings of Paramahansa Yogananda. LC 79-66287. (Illus.). 136p. 1980. 4.95 (ISBN 0-87612-115-6); Italian ed. 4.00x (ISBN 0-87612-113-X); German ed. 7.50x (ISBN 0-87612-114-8); Spanish ed. 2.25x (ISBN 0-87612-111-3); Icelandic ed. 9.00x (ISBN 0-87612-112-1). Self Realization.

YOGA COOKERY

see Cookery, Yoga

YOGA EXERCISES

see Yoga, Hatha

YOGANANDA, PARAMAHANSA, 1893-1952

Kriyananda, Swami. The Path: Autobiography of a Western Yogi. LC 77-72787. (Illus.). 640p. 1977. 15.00 (ISBN 0-916124-11-8); pap. 4.95 (ISBN 0-916124-12-6). Dawn Pubns CA.
Self-Realization Fellowship. Paramahansa Yogananda: In Memoriam. (Illus.). 127p. 1986. pap. 2.50 (ISBN 0-87612-170-9). Self Realization.

YOGIS

Bhajan, Yogi. The Teachings of Yogi Bhajan. 1985. pap. 8.95 (ISBN 0-317-38485-6). Arcline Pubns.
Billion, Anna. Kundalini: Secret of the Ancient Yogis. 1982. pap. 4.95 (ISBN 0-686-97516-2, Reward). P-H.
Das Goswami, Satsvarupa. Prabhupada: He Built a House in Which the Whole World Could Live. 7.95 (ISBN 0-89213-133-0). Bhaktivedanta.
Davis, Roy E., ed. The Teachings of Sri Satya Sai Baba. 2.95 (ISBN 0-317-46972-X). CSA Pr.
Ghosh, Sananda L. Mejda: The Family & the Early Life of Paramahansa Yogananda. LC 80-54206. (Illus.). 330p. 1980. 8.50 (ISBN 0-87612-265-9). Self Realization.
Kriyananda, Swami. The Path: Autobiography of a Western Yogi. LC 77-72787. (Illus.). 640p. 1977. 15.00 (ISBN 0-916124-11-8); pap. 4.95 (ISBN 0-916124-12-6). Dawn Pubns CA.
Satsvarupa dasa Goswami. The Life Story of His Divine Grace A. C. Bhaktivedanta Swami Prabhupada. 32p. 1984. saddlestitch 3.50 (ISBN 0-89647-019-9). Bala Bks.
Warren, Sukanya & Mellen, Francis. Gurudev: The Life of Yogi Amrit Desai. LC 82-83357. 117p. (Orig.). 1982. pap. 6.95 (ISBN 0-940258-07-2). Kripalu Pubns.

YOM KIPPUR

see also Ark of the Covenant

Chaikin, Miriam. Sound the Shofar: The Story & Meaning of Rosh HaShanah & Yom Kippur. LC 86-2651. (Illus.). 96p. 1986. 13.95 (ISBN 0-89919-373-0, Pub. by Clarion); pap. 4.95 (ISBN 0-89919-427-3, Pub. by Clarion). Ticknor & Fields.
Friedman, Audrey M. & Zwerin, Raymond. High Holy Day Do It Yourself Dictionary. (Illus.). 32p. 1983. pap. 5.00 (ISBN 0-8074-0162-5, 101100). UAHC.
Saypol, Judyth R. & Wikler, Madeline. My Very Own Yom Kippur Book. (Illus.). 32p. 1978. pap. 2.95 (ISBN 0-930494-05-9). Kar Ben.
Silverman, Morris. Evening Service for Yom Kippur. large type ed. 17.50 (ISBN 0-87677-073-1). Prayer Bk.
Simon, Norma. Yom Kippur. (Festival Series of Picture Story Books). (Illus.). 1959. plastic cover 4.50 (ISBN 0-8381-0702-8). United Syn Bk.

YORK, ENGLAND (DIOCESE)

Raine, James, ed. The Historians of the Church of York & Its Archbishops, 3 vols. (Rolls Ser.: No. 71). Repr. of 1894 ed. Set. 180.00 (ISBN 0-8115-1139-1). Kraus Repr.

YORKSHIRE, ENGLAND–HISTORY

Clark, David. Between Pulpit & Pew: Folk Religion in a North Yorkshire Fishing Village. LC 81-18166. (Illus.). 216p. 1982. 32.50 (ISBN 0-521-24071-9). Cambridge U Pr.

YORUBAS

Bascom, W. R. The Sociological Role of the Yoruba Cult-Group. LC 44-47266. (American Anthro. Association Memoirs). Repr. of 1944 ed. 15.00 (ISBN 0-527-00562-2). Kraus Repr.
Bascom, William. The Yoruba of Southwestern Nigeria. (Illus.). 118p. 1984. pap. text ed. 7.95x (ISBN 0-88133-038-8). Waveland Pr.
Durodola, James I. Scientific Insights into Yoruba Traditional Medicine. (Traditional Healing Ser.). 1985. 27.50 (ISBN 0-686-85813-1). Conch Mag.
Farrow, Stephen S. Faith, Fancies & Fetish or Yoruba Paganism. LC 76-98718. (Illus.). Repr. of 1926 ed. 22.50x (ISBN 0-8371-2759-9, FFF&, Pub. by Negro U Pr). Greenwood.
Laitin, David D. Hegemony & Culture: Politics & Religious Change among the Yoruba. (Illus.). xiv, 252p. 1986. 30.00 (ISBN 0-226-46789-9); pap. 13.95 (ISBN 0-226-46790-2). U of Chicago Pr.

YOUNG, BRIGHAM, 1801-1877

Cooley, Everett L., ed. Diary of Brigham Young, 1857. 105p. 1980. 17.50 (ISBN 0-941214-37-0). Signature Bks.
Crockwell, J. H. Pictures & Biographies of Brigham Young & His Wives. 1980. lib. bdg. 59.95 (ISBN 0-8490-3158-3). Gordon Pr.
Palmer, Richard F. & Butler, Karl D. Brigham Young: The New York Years. Alexander, Thomas G. & Christy, Howard A., eds. (Charles Redd Monographs in Western History: No. 14). (Illus.). 106p. 1982. 9.95 (ISBN 0-941214-07-9, Dist. by Signature Bks). C Redd Ctr.
Stott, Clifford L. Search for Sanctuary: Brigham Young & the White Mountain Expedition. (American West Ser.: Vol. 19). (Illus.). 272p. 1984. 19.95 (ISBN 0-87480-237-7). U of Utah Pr.
Werner, Morris R. Brigham Young. LC 75-351. (The Radical Tradition in America Ser.). xvi, 478p. 1975. Repr. of 1925 ed. 32.50 (ISBN 0-88355-254-X). Hyperion Conn.
--Brigham Young. 1977. Repr. of 1925 ed. lib. bdg. 30.00 (ISBN 0-8492-2907-3). R West.

YOUNG ADULTS

see also Church Work with Young Adults

Drane, James F. A New American Reformation: A Study of Youth Culture & Religion. (Quality Paperback Ser.: No. 293). 166p. 1974. pap. 2.95 (ISBN 0-8226-0293-8). Littlefield.
Pittman, Thomas B., 3rd. Reaching for the Sky. 1976. pap. 3.95 (ISBN 0-87148-731-4). Pathway Pr.

YOUNG GERMANY

Butler, E. M. The Saint-Simonian Religion in Germany. 1968. Repr. of 1926 ed. 45.00x (ISBN 0-86527-177-1). Fertig.

YOUNG MEN'S CHRISTIAN ASSOCIATIONS

Garrett, Shirley. Social Reformers in Urban China: The Chinese Y. M. C. A., Eighteen Ninety-Five to Nineteen Twenty-Six. LC 74-133218. (East Asian Ser.: No. 56). 1970. 16.50x (ISBN 0-674-81220-4). Harvard U Pr.
Macleod, David I. Building Character in the American Boy: The Boy Scouts, YMCA, & Their Forerunners, 1870-1920. LC 83-47763. 464p. 1983. text ed. 27.50x (ISBN 0-299-09400-6). U of Wis Pr.
Westcott, Wayne L. Building Strength at the YMCA. LC 86-20838. (Illus.). 104p. (Orig.). 1987. pap. text ed. 8.00x (ISBN 0-87322-082-X, LWES4885). Human Kinetics.
YMCA of the U. S. A. Staff. Examining Our Faith. 32p. 1980. pap. 4.95x (ISBN 0-88035-030-X). Human Kinetics.

--Y Basics: Yesterday, Today, & Tomorrow in the YMCA. LC 84-23443. 93p. 1984. pap. text ed. 5.00x (ISBN 0-931250-77-3). Human Kinetics.

YMCA of the USA. More Than a Job. 139p. 1984. 3-ring notebook 25.00x (ISBN 0-931250-76-5). Human Kinetics.

--Vital Signs of Family Life & the YMCA: Resource Notebook. (Illus.). 26p. (Orig.). 1983. pap. 19.95 3 ring Notebook (ISBN 0-88035-014-8, YMCA USA). Human Kinetics.

YOUNG PEOPLE'S MEETINGS (CHURCH WORK)

see also Church Group Work; Church Work with Youth; Worship Programs

Fortunato, Connie. Children's Music Ministry. 222p. 1981. pap. 6.95 (ISBN 0-89191-341-6). Cook.

Gladman, Donna. It's Sunday Night Again? Zapel, Arthur L., ed. LC 79-84726. (Illus.). 1979. pap. text ed. 4.95 (ISBN 0-916260-04-6). Meriwether Pub.

Madsen, Erik C. Youth Ministry & Wilderness Camping. 160p. 1982. pap. 7.95 (ISBN 0-8170-0962-0). Judson.

Miller, Kevin. Our Heroes: Four Complete Meetings for Junior High Youth Groups. (The Best of Young Teen Action Ser.). 32p. 1985. pap. 4.95 (ISBN 0-89191-380-7). Cook.

Rice, Wayne & Yaconelli, Mike. Super Ideas for Youth Groups. (Orig.). 1979. pap. 6.95 (ISBN 0-310-34981-8, 10773P). Zondervan.

Robinson, James H. & Darline, R. One Hundred Bible Quiz Activities for Church School Classes. 1981. pap. 3.95 (ISBN 0-570-03829-4, 12-2794). Concordia.

Sparks, Lee, ed. The Youth Group How-To Book. LC 81-81966. (Illus.). 224p. (Orig.). 1981. pap. 14.95 (ISBN 0-936664-03-7). Group Bks.

YOUNG WOMEN–RELIGIOUS LIFE

Harper, Vessa. Suddenly It's Springtime. 1967. pap. 3.50 (ISBN 0-88027-050-0). Firm Foun Pub.

Zamboni, Camillo. He Speaks to You. 1966. pap. 1.25 (ISBN 0-8198-0055-4). Dghtrs St Paul.

YOUNG WOMEN'S CHRISTIAN ASSOCIATIONS

Boyd, Nancy. Emissaries: The Overseas Work of the American YWCA, 1895-1970. (Illus.). 412p. 16.95 (ISBN 0-9614878-0-1). Woman's Pr.

Radcliffe, Florence J. A Simple Matter of Justice: The Phyllis Wheatly YWCA Story. 304p. 1985. 13.00 (ISBN 0-682-40199-4). Exposition Pr FL.

Rothman, David J. & Rothman, Sheila M., eds. First Ten Annual Reports 1871-1880, Young Women's Christian Association, New York, 1871-1880. (Women & Children First Ser.). 375p. 1986. lib. bdg. 45.00 (ISBN 0-8240-7682-6). Garland Pub.

Wilson, Grace H. The Religious & Educational Philosophy of the Young Women's Christian Association. LC 70-177632. (Columbia University. Teachers College. Contributions to Education: No. 554). Repr. of 1933 ed. 22.50 (ISBN 0-404-55554-3). AMS Pr.

YOUTH

see also Adolescence; Church Work with Youth; Conduct of Life; Marriage Counseling

Campbell. How to Really Love Your Teenager. LC 81-51515. 1982. 4.95 (ISBN 0-88207-274-9). Victor Bks.

Daniel, R. P. Outlines for Christian Youth. pap. 5.95 (ISBN 0-88172-019-4). Believers Bkshelf.

Friedman, Maurice. Modern Promethean: A Dialogue with Today's Youth. LC 73-104050. (Orig.). 1969. pap. 2.50x (ISBN 0-87574-168-1). Pendle Hill.

Hargrove, Barbara & Jones, Stephen D. Reaching Youth Today: Heirs to the Whirlwind. 1983. pap. 5.95 (ISBN 0-8170-0977-9). Judson.

Kimbrough, M. The Joy & Adventure of Growing Younger. LC 12-2969. 1983. pap. 4.95 (ISBN 0-570-03876-6). Concordia.

Oraker, James & Meredith, Char. Almost Grown: A Christian Guide for Parents of Teenagers. LC 78-20585. 192p. 1982. pap. 6.95 (ISBN 0-06-066398-7, RD 380, HarpR). Har-Row.

Richards, Lawrence O. Youth Ministry: Its Renewal In the Local Church. rev. ed. 1972. 15.95 (ISBN 0-310-32010-0). Zondervan.

YOUTH–CONDUCT OF LIFE

Aaseng, Rolf E. Sense & Nonsense: A Word for Teens. 64p. 1976. pap. 2.50 (ISBN 0-8010-0090-4). Baker Bk.

Aranza, Jacob & Lamson, Theresa. A Reasonable Reason to Wait. 101p. (Orig.). 1984. pap. 4.95 (ISBN 0-910311-21-8). Huntington Hse Inc.

Armstrong, Sue. Who Do you Think You Are. 1983. 24.00x (ISBN 0-86334-046-6, Pub. by Macdonald Pub UK). State Mutual Bk.

Augsburger, David. From Here to Maturity. 1982. pap. 2.50 (ISBN 0-8423-0938-1). Tyndale.

Bergin, Feryl J. You...& Being a Teenager. (Illus.). 112p. 4.95 (ISBN 0-936955-00-7). Eminent Pubns.

Betz, Margaret. Faith & Justice. LC 80-50259. 176p. 1980. pap. text ed. 5.00x (ISBN 0-88489-114-3); tchr's guide 9.00x (ISBN 0-88489-121-6). St Mary's.

Bly, Stephen & Bly, Janet. Questions I'd Like to Ask. LC 82-2252. 1982. 3.50 (ISBN 0-8024-7058-0). Moody.

Cee Cee, pseud. Inside My Head. 1985. 6.50 (ISBN 0-8062-2521-1). Carlton.

Cisek, James & George, Anthea. Deciding for Yourself Youth Manual. (Illus.). 60p. (Orig.). 1985. pap. 5.95 (ISBN 0-9604510-1-3). Life Skills.

Coombs, H. Samm. Teenage Survival Manual: How to Enjoy the Trip to Twenty. (Illus.). 1978. pap. 5.95 (ISBN 0-87516-277-0). De Vorss.

Cooper, Darien. How to Be Happy Though Young. (Illus.). 224p. 1979. 5.95 (ISBN 0-8007-5048-9, Power Bks). Revell.

Denim, B. C. Different Is Not the Same As Wrong. 1982. pap. 1.95 (ISBN 0-570-08408-3, 39-1083). Concordia.

Donahue, Bob & Donahue, Marilyn. How to Make People Like You When You Know They Don't. 1982. pap. 4.95 (ISBN 0-8423-1531-4). Tyndale.

Fox, Robert. Teenagers & Purity, Teenagers & Going Steady, Teenagers & Looking Ahead to Marriage. 1978. pap. 0.75 (ISBN 0-8198-0370-7). Dghtrs St Paul.

Hulme, William E. I Hate to Bother You, But: Clues for Youth on Personal Problems. rev. ed. Orig. Title: Face Your Life with Confidence. 1970. pap. 4.95 (ISBN 0-570-06617-4, 12-2327). Concordia.

Kishpaugh, Charles R. & Finnell, Kathy B. A Fork in the Road: Young Adult Decisions. 72p. (Orig.). 1986. pap. 3.75 (ISBN 0-88177-042-6, DR042B). Discipleship Res.

Kohler, Mary C. Young People Learning to Care: Making a Difference through Youth Participation. 160p. 1983. pap. 7.95 (ISBN 0-8164-2429-2, HarpR). Har-Row.

Krutza, William J. & Dicicco, Philip P. Youth Face Today's Issues 2. (Contemporary Discussion Ser.). pap. 3.50 (ISBN 0-8010-5311-0). Baker Bk.

Larsen, Sandy. For Real People Only. 96p. 1986. pap. 1.95 student bk. (ISBN 0-89693-516-7); tchr's. ed. 11.95 (ISBN 0-89693-513-2). Victor Bks.

--Things. 144p. 1984. pap. 3.95 (ISBN 0-88207-109-2). Victor Bks.

Larson, Nora E. As a Little Child. LC 81-66072. (Illus.). 56p. (Orig.). 1981. pap. 4.00 (ISBN 0-87516-451-X). De Vorss.

Leman, Kevin. Smart Girls Don't & Guys Don't Either. LC 82-7686. 1982. 8.95 (ISBN 0-8307-0824-3, 5419026). Regal.

McLean, Gordon. Danger at Your Door. LC 83-70954. 183p. 1984. pap. 5.95 (ISBN 0-89107-296-9). Good News.

Martin, Robert J. Wise Words to the Graduate. (Contempo Ser.). 1978. pap. 1.50 (ISBN 0-8010-6043-5). Baker Bk.

Mueller, Charles S. Thank God I Have a Teenager. LC 84-24363. 128p. (Orig.). 1985. pap. 5.95 (ISBN 0-8066-2126-5, 10-6239). Augsburg.

Polen, O. W. Living by the Word. LC 77-79942. 1977. pap. 1.95 (ISBN 0-87148-509-5). Pathway Pr.

Pratney, Winkie. Devil Take the Youngest. Keith, Bill, ed. 300p. (Orig.). 1985. pap. 6.95 (ISBN 0-910311-29-3). Huntington Hse Inc.

Rice, Wayne. Junior High Ministry: A Guidebook for the Leading & Teaching of Early Adolescents. 1978. pap. 6.95 (ISBN 0-310-34971-0, 10825P). Zondervan.

Scwab, Penny V. Thirteen Going on Twenty. LC 83-12292. 144p. (Orig.). 1983. pap. 4.95 (ISBN 0-87123-587-0, 210587). Bethany Hse.

Sorenson, Stephen & Sorenson, Amanda. When Easy Answers Play Hard to Get: Decision Making for Young Teens. LC 84-11123. (Young Teens Ser.). 128p. (Orig.). 1984. pap. 3.95 (ISBN 0-8066-2084-6, 10-7080). Augsburg.

Souter, John. Moods. 96p. (Orig.). 1986. 4.95 (ISBN 0-8423-4498-5). Tyndale.

Strommen, Merton P. Five Cries of Youth. LC 73-18690. 192p. 1974. pap. 8.95 (ISBN 0-06-067748-1, RD224, HarpR). Har-Row.

Wright, Norman & Inmon, Marvin. Preparing Youth for Dating, Courtship & Marriage-Teacher's Guide. LC 78-56879. (Orig.). 1978. pap. 9.95 (ISBN 0-89081-147-4); transparencies & repro masters incl. Harvest Hse.

Zanzig, Thomas. Understanding Your Faith: An Introduction to Catholic Christianity for Freshmen. LC 80-50258. (Illus.). 192p. 1980. pap. text ed. 7.00x (ISBN 0-88489-115-1); tchr's guide 9.00x (ISBN 0-88489-122-4); spiritmasters 9.95 (ISBN 0-88489-131-3). St Mary's.

YOUTH–PRAYER-BOOKS AND DEVOTIONS

Ahrens, Herman C., Jr., ed. Tune In. LC 68-54031. (Illus.). 1968. pap. 3.95 (ISBN 0-8298-0138-3). Pilgrim NY.

Bly, Stephen & Bly, Janet. Devotions with a Difference. LC 82-8304. 128p. 1982. pap. 5.95 (ISBN 0-8024-1789-2). Moody.

Bolding, Amy. Please Give a Devotion for Active Teens. (Direction Bks). 1974. pap. 3.95 (ISBN 0-8010-0827-1). Baker Bk.

Brokering, Herbert F. Surprise Me, Jesus. LC 73-83785. 96p. (YA) 1973. pap. 6.95 (ISBN 0-8066-1338-6, 10-6150). Augsburg.

Bryant, Al. Time Out. pap. 2.95 (ISBN 0-310-22122-6). Zondervan.

Burgess, Allan K. Helping Your Child Stay Morally Clean. LC 84-71705. 100p. 1984. 6.95 (ISBN 0-87747-671-3). Deseret Bk.

Case, Charles C. Talking Trees & Singing Whales. Woolsey, Raymond H., ed. (Devotional Ser.). 365p. 1985. 7.95 (ISBN 0-8280-0285-1). Review & Herald.

Clapp, Steve, et al. Youth Experiential Annual Resource 1. 122p. (Orig.). 1981. pap. 10.00 (ISBN 0-914527-42-8). C-Four Res.

Dieleman, Dale, compiled by. The Go Book. (Good Things for Youth Leaders). 64p. 1982. pap. 4.50 (ISBN 0-8010-2929-5). Baker Bk.

Earles, Brent D. Proverbs for Graduates. 1984. 5.95 (ISBN 0-8010-3415-9). Baker Bk.

Hare, Eric B. Fullness of Joy. 1985. pap. 5.95 (ISBN 0-8163-0586-2). Pacific Pr Pub Assn.

Hesch, John B. Prayer & Meditation for Middle School Kids. 144p. (Orig.). 1985. pap. 7.95 (ISBN 0-8091-2723-7). Paulist Pr.

Johnson, Ruth I. Devotions for Early Teens, 4 vols. 1960-74. Vol. 1. pap. 2.95 (ISBN 0-8024-2181-4); Vol. 3. pap. 2.95 (ISBN 0-8024-2183-0). Moody.

Kamstra, Doug. The Get-Away Book. (Good Things for Youth Leaders Ser.). 1984. pap. 5.95 (ISBN 0-8010-5459-1). Baker Bk.

Kramer, William A. Teenagers Pray. LC 55-12193. 1956. 4.50 (ISBN 0-570-03018-8, 6-1054). Concordia.

Pennock, Michael. Prayer & You. LC 85-70162. (Illus., Orig.). 1985. pap. text ed. 5.50 student ed., 160 pg. (ISBN 0-87793-284-0); tchr's. ed., 144 pg. 7.95 (ISBN 0-87793-285-9). Ave Maria.

Schmidt, J. David. More Graffiti: Devotions for Guys. (Illus.). 128p. 1984. pap. 4.95 (ISBN 0-8007-5142-6, Power Bks). Revell.

YOUTH–RECREATION

Bimler, Richard W. The Youth Group Meeting Guide. LC 83-82574. 256p. (Orig.). 1984. pap. 11.95 (ISBN 0-936664-17-7). Group Bks.

Pratney, Winkie. Devil Take the Youngest. Keith, Bill, ed. 300p. (Orig.). 1985. pap. 6.95 (ISBN 0-910311-29-3). Huntington Hse Inc.

Rice, Wayne & Yaconelli, Mike. Right-on Ideas for Youth Groups. (Illus.). 96p. 1973. pap. 6.95 (ISBN 0-310-34951-6, 10796P). Zondervan.

--Way Out Ideas for Youth Groups. pap. 6.95 (ISBN 0-310-34961-3, 10795P). Zondervan.

YOUTH–RELIGIOUS LIFE

see also Jesus People

Anderson, Geraldine, ed. Forty Devotions That Work with Youth. (Youth Work Guide Ser.). (Illus.). 60p. (Orig.). 1983. pap. 7.45 (ISBN 0-85819-414-7, Pub. by JBCE). ANZ Religious Pubns.

Angell, James. Roots & Wings. 80p. 1983. text ed. 7.95 (ISBN 0-687-36585-6). Abingdon.

Auer, Jim. What's Right? A Teenager's Guide to Christian Living. 96p. 1987. pap. 3.25 (ISBN 0-89243-265-9). Liguori Pubns.

Aultman, Donald S. Guiding Youth. 1977. pap. 3.95 (ISBN 0-87148-358-0). Pathway Pr.

Baker, Pat & Marshall, Mary R. Using Simulation Games. (Youth Work Guide Ser.). (Illus.). 96p. (Orig.). 1973. pap. 7.95 (ISBN 0-85819-090-7, Pub. by JBCE). ANZ Religious Pubns.

Bertolucci, John. Straight from the Heart: A Call to the New Generation. 126p. 1986. pap. 4.95 (ISBN 0-89283-290-8). Servant.

Burke, John. Bible Sharing Youth Retreat: Manual for Retreat Team. 1986. pap. 4.50 (ISBN 0-697-02209-9). Wm C Brown.

Burns, Jim. Getting in Touch with God. 1986. pap. 4.95 (ISBN 0-89081-520-8). Harvest Hse.

Burns, Jim & Fields, Doug. Congratulations! You are Gifted! (Jim Burns Youth Ser.: No. 2). 64p. (Orig.). (YA) 1986. pap. 3.95 (ISBN 0-89081-478-3, 4783). Harvest Hse.

Carney, Russell & Moss, Jim. Building Your Youth Ministry. 1986. 4.95 (ISBN 0-931097-09-6). Sentinel Pub.

Christian Movement for Peace Staff. Rich World, Poor World: A Curriculum Resource on Youth & Development. (YA) 1986. pap. text ed. 29.95 (ISBN 0-697-02203-X). Wm C Brown.

Cirino, Andre & Rogers, Francine. Teens Encounter Christ. LC 77-88321. (Illus., Orig.). 1978. pap. 2.25 (ISBN 0-8189-1156-5, 156, Pub. by Alba Bks). Alba.

Coleman, John & Baum, Gregory, eds. Youth Without a Future, Vol. 181. (Conciliun Ser.). 128p. 1985. pap. 6.95 (ISBN 0-567-30061-7, Pub. by T&T Clark Ltd UK). Fortress.

Cronbach, Abraham. Stories Made of Bible Stories. 1961. 17.95x (ISBN 0-8084-0386-9). New Coll U Pr.

Crossan, Bettie. Beware! Be Wise. 130p. (Orig.). 1984. pap. 2.95 (ISBN 0-87508-148-7). Chr Lit.

Davitz, Lois L. & Davitz, Joel R. How to Live (Almost) Happily with a Teenager. 230p. (Orig.). 1982. pap. 8.95 (ISBN 0-86683-624-1, AY8208, HarpR). Har-Row.

Deal, William S. What Every Young Christian Should Know. 1982. 1.95. Crusade Pubs.

Di Giacomo, James. When Your Teenager Stops Going to Church. LC 80-65401. (When Books). (Illus.). 96p. (Orig.). 1980. pap. 2.45 (ISBN 0-87029-165-3, 20260-6). Abbey.

Donnell, Nils. It's Not the Same Old Me. 1975. pap. 2.00 (ISBN 0-88027-007-1). Firm Foun Pub.

Drane, James F. A New American Reformation: A Study of Youth Culture & Religion. (Quality Paperback Ser.: No. 293). 166p. 1974. pap. 2.95 (ISBN 0-8226-0293-8). Littlefield.

Earles, Brent D. The Gospels for Graduates. 160p. 1987. text ed. 5.95 (ISBN 0-8010-3438-8). Baker Bk.

Edwards, Steve L. Connections. 112p. 1986. pap. 7.95x (ISBN 0-8170-1110-2). Judson.

Elder, Carl A. Youth & Values: Getting Self Together. LC 76-58063. 1978. 6.75 (ISBN 0-8054-5326-1, 4253-26). Broadman.

Eyre, Linda & Eyre, Richard. Teaching Children Charity: A Program to Help Teens & Preteens Forget Themselves. LC 85-27468. (Illus.). 280p. 1986. 9.95 (ISBN 0-87579-024-0). Deseret Bk.

Flumiani, Carlo M. What a Teenager Ought to Know About God. (Illus.). 1978. 42.50 (ISBN 0-89266-140-2). Am Classical Coll Pr.

Foote, Evelyn C. Time with God: Devotional Readings for Youth. LC 72-97604. 1978. pap. 2.75 (ISBN 0-8054-5164-1, 4251-64). Broadman.

Fox, Robert J. Catholic Truth for Youth. LC 78-104309. (Illus.). 448p. 1978. pap. 5.95 (ISBN 0-911988-05-X). AMI Pr.

Gesch, Roy C. Confirmed in Christ. 1983. pap. 2.25 (ISBN 0-570-03911-8, 12-2852). Concordia.

Gibson, Eva. Intimate Moments: Teaching Your Child to Walk with God. 1987. pap. 5.95. Heres Life.

Grierson, Denham, et al. Discovering the Needs & Interests of Young People. (Youth Work Guides Ser.). (Illus.). 88p. (Orig.). 1977. pap. 8.95 (ISBN 0-85819-177-6, Pub. by JBCE). ANZ Religious Pubns.

Harris, Maria. Portrait of Youth Ministry. LC 80-84512. 232p. (Orig.). 1981. pap. 8.95 (ISBN 0-8091-2354-1). Paulist Pr.

Hensley, Dennis E. & Groen, Jim. One Young Billion: The Youth For Christ Story-the People, the Promise, & the Hope for Reaching... 224p. Date not set. 10.95 (ISBN 0-8407-5455-8). Nelson.

Holderness, Ginny W. The Exuberant Years: A Guide for Junior High Leaders. LC 75-13458. 128p. 1976. pap. 7.95 (ISBN 0-8042-1225-2). John Knox.

--Youth Ministry: The New Team Approach. LC 80-82186. (Illus.). 160p. (Orig.). 1981. pap. 11.95 (ISBN 0-8042-1410-7). John Knox.

Howard, David M. Moving Out: The Story of Student Initiative in World Missions. 80p. 1984. pap. 2.95 (ISBN 0-87784-565-4). Inter-Varsity.

Huggett, Joyce. Dating, Sex & Friendship. LC 85-19734. 204p. 1985. pap. 5.95 (ISBN 0-87784-406-2). Inter-Varsity.

Judah, J. Stillson. Hare Krishna & the Counterculture. LC 74-8209. (Contemporary Religious Movements Ser.). pap. 80.00 (ISBN 0-317-07867-4, 2007717). Bks Demand UMI.

Kageler, Len & Dale, Daryl. Discipleship for High School Teens. 76p. 1984. wkbk. 5.25 (ISBN 0-87509-351-5). Chr Pubns.

Kauffman, Richard A. Big Questions. (Illus.). 128p. 1984. pap. 2.95 (ISBN 0-8361-3353-6). Herald Pr.

Kettinger, Leroy. Youth as Learners. (C. E. Ministries Ser.). 96p. 1983. pap. 3.50 (ISBN 0-89367-086-3). Light & Life.

Kishpaugh, Charles R. & Finnell, Kathy B. A Fork in the Road: Young Adult Decisions. 72p. (Orig.). 1986. pap. 3.75 (ISBN 0-88177-042-6, DR042B). Discipleship Res.

Klug, Ron. Lord I've Been Thinking: Prayer Thoughts for High School Boys. LC 78-52183. 1978. pap. 3.95 (ISBN 0-8066-1657-1, 10-4105). Augsburg.

Kramer, William A. Living for Christ. rev. ed. LC 72-96585. 1973. 3.25 (ISBN 0-570-03157-5, 12-2542). Concordia.

Krutza, William J. Graduate's Guide to Success. 96p. 1976. 4.95 (ISBN 0-8010-5374-9). Baker Bk.

Larsen, Sandy. Choosing: Which Way Do I Go? (Bible Discovery Guide for Campers Ser.). 32p. 1985. pap. 1.50 camper (ISBN 0-87788-115-4); pap. 3.50 counselor (ISBN 0-87788-116-2). Shaw Pubs.
--For Real People Only. 96p. 1986. pap. 1.95 student bk. (ISBN 0-89693-516-7); tchr's. ed. 11.95 (ISBN 0-89693-513-2). Victor Bks.
--Standing Strong: Notes from Joseph's Journal. (Bible Discovery Guides for Teen Campers Ser.). (Illus.). 32p. (Orig.). (YA) 1986. pap. 1.50 camper (ISBN 0-87788-784-5); pap. 1.50 counselor (ISBN 0-87788-785-3). Shaw Pubs.
Ligon, Ernest M. Christian Social Potential: Junior High Unit. (A Research Curriculum for Character Education Ser.). 1978. lesson bk. 2.00 (ISBN 0-915744-12-0); junior high unit plan 0.75 (ISBN 0-915744-14-7); junior high home assignment sheets 0.75 (ISBN 0-915744-13-9). Character Res.
Litherland, Janet. Youth Ministry from Start to Finish. Zapel, Arthur L., ed. LC 85-62467. (Illus.). 115p. (Orig.). 1985. pap. 7.95 (ISBN 0-916260-35-6, B-193). Meriwether Pub.
Lovett, C. S. What's a Parent to Do? 1971. pap. 6.45 (ISBN 0-938148-27-3). Personal Christianity.
McCant, Jerry. Teens & Self Esteem: Helping Christian Youth Discover Their Worth. 152p. (Orig.). 1985. pap. 5.95 (ISBN 0-8341-1055-5). Beacon Hill.
McLean, Gordon. Danger at Your Door. LC 83-70954. 183p. 1984. pap. 5.95 (ISBN 0-89107-296-9). Good News.
Maddox, Robert L. & Maddox, Linda C. Get off My Back. (Orig.). 1987. pap. 5.95 (ISBN 0-8054-5344-X). Broadman.
Mallison, John, ed. Youth Outreach & Evangelism: Youth Work Guides Ser. (Illus.). 104p. (Orig.). 1975. pap. 5.95 (ISBN 0-85819-108-3, Pub. by JBCE). ANZ Religious Pubns.
Marshall, Mary R. It's Tuesday Night Again: Planning This Week's Program for Youth Group & Clubs. (Australian Youth Leadership Ser.). (Illus.). 56p. (Orig.). 1983. pap. 6.95 (ISBN 0-85819-416-3, Pub. by JBCE). ANZ Religious Pubns.
--Looking Ahead: Planning the Year's Program for Youth Groups & Clubs. (Australian Youth Leadership Ser.). 32p. (Orig.). 1983. pap. 4.95 (ISBN 0-85819-417-1, Pub. by JBCE). ANZ Religious Pubns.
Mast, Coleen K. Love & Life: A Christian Sexual Morality Guide for Teens Teacher's Guide. 150p. 1986. pap. 10.95 (ISBN 0-89870-108-2). Ignatius Pr.
Mast, Coleen K., et al. Love & Life: A Christian Sexual Morality Guide for Teens Parents' Guide. LC 86-80604. 48p. 1986. pap. 5.95 (ISBN 0-89870-107-4). Ignatius Pr.
Moskos, C. C., Jr. & Papajohn, J. C. Greek Orthodox Youth Today. Vaporis, N. M., intro. by. (Saints Peter & Paul Youth Ministry Lectures Ser.). 56p. (Orig.). 1983. pap. 3.00 (ISBN 0-916586-56-1). Holy Cross Orthodox.
Mueller, Charles S. & Bardill, Donald R. Thank God I'm a Teenager. LC 76-3854. 1976. pap. 5.95 (ISBN 0-8066-1536-2, 10-6242). Augsburg.
Narramore, Clyde M. Counseling Youth. new ed. 128p. (Orig.). 1974. pap. 5.95 (ISBN 0-310-29891-1, 12229P). Zondervan.
Naylor, Phyllis R. A Triangle Has Four Sides: True-to-Life Stories Show How Teens Deal with Feelings & Problems. LC 83-72123. 128p. (Orig.). (YA) 1984. pap. 3.95 (ISBN 0-8066-2067-6, 10-6700). Augsburg.
Ng, David. Youth in the Community of Disciples. 80p. 1984. pap. 3.95 (ISBN 0-8170-1015-7). Judson.
Nystrom, Carolyn & Floding, Mathew. Who Am I? A Look in the Mirror. (Young Fisherman Bible Studyguides). 64p. (Orig.). (YA) 1987. pap. 4.95 tchr's. ed. (ISBN 0-87788-933-3); pap. 2.95 student ed. (ISBN 0-87788-932-5). Shaw Pubs.
Nystrom, Carolyn & Floding, Matthew. Relationships: Face to Face. (Young Fisherman Bible Studyguide Ser.). 64p. (Orig.). (YA) 1986. pap. 2.95 student ed. (ISBN 0-87788-722-5); tchr's ed. 4.95 (ISBN 0-87788-723-3). Shaw Pubs.
Olson, G. Keith. Why Teenagers Act the Way They Do. (Orig.). 1987. pap. 15.95 (ISBN 0-931529-17-4). Group Bks.
Parsons, Richard D. Adolescents in Turmoil, Parents under Stress: A Pastoral Ministry Primer. 160p. (Orig.). 1987. pap. 7.95 (ISBN 0-8091-2855-1). Paulist Pr.
Pastva, M. Loretta. Growing up to God: A Guide for Teenagers on the Sacrement of Reconciliation. LC 83-15538. 82p. (Orig.). 1983. pap. 4.95 (ISBN 0-8189-0455-0). Alba.
Patrick, Ted & Dulack, Tom. Let Our Children Go! 1977. pap. 2.25 (ISBN 0-345-28343-0). Ballantine.
Pittman, Thomas B., 3rd. Reaching for the Sky. 1976. pap. 3.95 (ISBN 0-87148-731-4). Pathway Pr.
Polen, O. W. Living by the Word. LC 77-79942. 1977. pap. 1.95 (ISBN 0-87148-509-5). Pathway Pr.
Pope John Paul II. I Believe in Youth, Christ Believes in Youth. 1981. 4.95 (ISBN 0-8198-3602-8); pap. 3.95 (ISBN 0-8198-3603-6). Dghtrs St Paul.
Poyner, Alice. From the Campus to the World. LC 86-3024. 150p. (Orig.). 1986. pap. 6.95 (ISBN 0-87784-947-1). Inter-Varsity.
Pratney, Winkey. Youth Aflame. 448p. (Orig.). 1983. pap. 7.95 (ISBN 0-87123-659-1, 210659). Bethany Hse.
Qubein, Nido. What Works & What Doesn't in Youth Ministry. Zapel, Arthur L. & Pijanowski, Kathy, eds. (Illus.). 211p. 1986. pap. 7.95 (ISBN 0-916260-40-2). Meriwether Pub.
Reynolds, Thomas L., Jr. Youth's Search for Self. LC 82-70866. (Orig.). 1983. pap. 4.50 (ISBN 0-8054-5338-5, 4253-38). Broadman.
Rice, Wayne & Yaconelli, Mike. Way Out Ideas for Youth Groups. pap. 6.95 (ISBN 0-310-34961-3, 10795P). Zondervan.
Richards, Larry. Teaching Youth. 156p. 1982. pap. 4.95 (ISBN 0-8341-0776-7). Beacon Hill.
Say, Lauren E., et al. Youth Ministries Ideas Two. (Orig.). 1985. pap. 6.00 (ISBN 0-8309-0427-1). Herald Hse.
Schroeder, Theodore W. & Nadasdy, Dean. Questions Teens Are Asking Today. 1987. pap. 5.95 (ISBN 0-570-04454-5). Concordia.
Schultz, Thom & Schultz, Joani. Involving Youth in Youth Ministry. 200p. (Orig.). 1987. pap. 9.95 (ISBN 0-931529-20-4). Group Bks.
Scwab, Penny V. Thirteen Going on Twenty. LC 83-12292. 144p. (Orig.). 1983. pap. 4.95 (ISBN 0-87123-587-0, 210587). Bethany Hse.
Shaheen, David. Growing a Junior High Ministry. LC 86-19410. 300p. (Orig.). 1986. pap. 12.95 (ISBN 0-931529-15-8). Group Bks.
Shellenberger, Susie. There's Sheep in My Mirror. 108p. 1985. pap. 4.50 (ISBN 0-8341-1054-7). Beacon Hill.
Shelton, Charles M. Adolescent Spirituality: Pastoral Ministry for High School & College Youth. rev. ed. 1983. 15.00 (ISBN 0-8294-0422-8). Loyola.
Sherer, Michael L. It's My Life: True-to-Life Stories for Young Teens. (Illus.). 112p. (Orig.). 1986. pap. 3.95 (ISBN 0-8066-2216-4, 10-3454). Augsburg.
Short, Ray E. Sex, Love, or Infatuation: How Can I Really Know? LC 78-52180. 1978. pap. 3.95 (ISBN 0-8066-1653-9, 10-5650). Augsburg.
Simmons, Arthur G. & Simmons, Beborah T. Create in Me: Young Adult Bible Study. 1985. 5.75 (ISBN 0-89536-765-3, 5872). CSS of Ohio.
Sims, Tim & Pegoda, Dan. One Hundred & One Things to Do During a Dull Sermon. 85p. (Orig.). pap. 6.95 (ISBN 0-910125-05-8). Youth Special.
Smith, Barrie & Smith, Ruth. Youth Ministries Handbook. 120p. 1984. pap. text ed. 12.50 (ISBN 0-8309-0402-6). Herald Hse.
Sparkman, G. Temp, ed. Knowing & Helping Youth. LC 77-75621. 1978. 8.50 (ISBN 0-8054-3219-1, 4232-19). Broadman.
Sparks, Lee, ed. The Youth Worker's Personal Management Handbook. LC 84-73152. 264p. 1985. 16.95 (ISBN 0-931529-03-4). Group Bks.
Spotts, Dwight & Veerman, David. Reaching Out to Troubled Youth. 204p. 1987. pap. 11.95 (ISBN 0-89693-296-6). Victor Bks.
Strommen, Merton P. Five Cries of Youth. LC 73-18690. 192p. 1974. pap. 8.95 (ISBN 0-06-067748-1, RD224, HarpR). Har-Row.
Taylor, Robert. Remembering God in Youth. 2.50 (ISBN 0-89315-238-2). Lambert Bk.
Tickfer, Mildred. Healing the Hurt: For Teenagers Whose Parents Are Divorced. 1985. pap. 4.50 (ISBN 0-8010-8876-3). Baker Bk.
To the Youth of the World. 64p. 1985. pap. 3.95 (ISBN 1-55586-962-9). US Catholic.
Trobisch, Walter. Longing for Love. LC 86-72059. Orig. Title: Living with Unfulfilled Desires. 128p. 1987. pap. 5.95 (ISBN 0-89107-417-1, Crossway Bks). Good News.
Tucker, Beverly. Confessions for Teens. 1985. 0.75 (ISBN 0-89274-353-0). Harrison Hse.
Ulmer, Louise. Help, I'm in Trouble: True-to-Life Stories for Young Teens. LC 86-8034. (Illus.). 112p. (Orig.). 1986. pap. 3.95 (ISBN 0-8066-2215-6, 10-3008). Augsburg.
Vest, Lamar. The Church & Its Youth. (CTC Ser.). 1980. 5.25 (ISBN 0-87148-170-7); pap. 4.25 (ISBN 0-87148-171-5); instr's guide 7.95 (ISBN 0-87148-172-3). Pathway Pr.
A Vision of Youth Ministry: Bilingual Edition. (Eng. & Span.). 48p. 1986. pap. text ed. 2.95 (ISBN 1-55586-107-5). US Catholic.
Walker, Paul L. Faith in Action. LC 75-3504. (Illus.). 1975. pap. 1.99 (ISBN 0-87148-331-9). Pathway Pr.
Ward, Elaine M. Movers of Mountains. 88p. (Orig.). (YA) 1984. pap. 12.95 (ISBN 0-940754-24-X). Ed Ministries.
Wiersbe, Warren. Be Challenged! rev. ed. LC 82-12404. 1982. pap. 3.50 (ISBN 0-8024-1080-4). Moody.
Wilkerson, Don & Manuel, David. Ruta de Escape. Araujo, Juan S., tr. from Eng. Tr. of Hellbound. (Span.). 224p. 1986. pap. 4.75 (ISBN 0-88113-266-7). Edit Betania.
Wood, Charles R. Outline Talks for Teens. LC 83-25543. 64p. (Orig.). 1984. pap. 2.95 (ISBN 0-8254-4024-6). Kregel.

YOUTH–SEXUAL BEHAVIOR

Aranza, Jacob & Lamson, Theresa. A Reasonable Reason to Wait. 101p. (Orig.). 1984. pap. 4.95 (ISBN 0-910311-21-8). Huntington Hse Inc.
Burns, Jim & Bostrom, Carol. Handling Your Hormones. (Illus.). 64p. (Orig.). 1984. involvement guide 4.95 (ISBN 0-915929-10-4); leader's guide 1.95 (ISBN 0-915929-14-7). Merit Bks.
Collins, Mary J., ed. A Church Divided: Catholics' Attitudes about Family Planning, Abortion, & Teenage Sexuality. (The Bishops Watch Ser.). (Orig.). 1986. pap. 5.00 (ISBN 0-915365-12-X). Cath Free Choice.
Mast, Coleen K. Love & Life: A Christian Sexual Morality Guide for Teens Teacher's Guide. 150p. 1986. pap. 10.95 (ISBN 0-89870-108-2). Ignatius Pr.
Mast, Coleen K., et al. Love & Life: A Christian Sexual Morality Guide for Teens Parents' Guide. LC 86-80604. 48p. 1986. pap. 5.95 (ISBN 0-89870-107-4). Ignatius Pr.
Short, Ray E. Sex, Love, or Infatuation: How Can I Really Know? LC 78-52180. 1978. pap. 3.95 (ISBN 0-8066-1653-9, 10-5650). Augsburg.

YOUTH, JEWISH

Bentwich, Norman D. Jewish Youth Comes Home. LC 75-6422. (The Rise of Jewish Nationalism & the Middle East Ser). 159p. 1976. Repr. of 1944 ed. 19.25 (ISBN 0-88355-309-0). Hyperion Conn.
Cronbach, Abraham. Stories Made of Bible Stories. 1961. 17.95x (ISBN 0-8084-0386-9). New Coll U Pr.
Franzblau, Abraham N. Religious Belief & Character among Jewish Adolescents. LC 78-176783. (Columbia University. Teachers College. Contributions to Education: No. 634). Repr. of 1934 ed. 22.50 (ISBN 0-404-55634-5). AMS Pr.
Gottesman, Meir U. Shpeter: Book One. (Judaica Youth Ser.). (Illus.). 1981. 5.95 (ISBN 0-910818-35-5); pap. 4.95 (ISBN 0-910818-36-3). Judaica Pr.
--Shpeter: Book Two. (Judaica Youth Ser.). (Illus.). 1981. 5.95 (ISBN 0-910818-39-8); pap. 4.95 (ISBN 0-910818-40-1). Judaica Pr.

YOUTH AND ALCOHOL

see Alcohol and Youth

Z

ZACCHAEUS (BIBLICAL CHARACTER)–JUVENILE LITERATURE

Higby, Roy C. A Man from the Past. 2nd ed. (Illus.). pap. 4.25 (ISBN 0-914692-02-X). Big Moose.

ZEALOTS (JEWISH PARTY)

Roth, Cecil. Dead Sea Scrolls: A New Historical Approach. 1966. pap. 3.95x (ISBN 0-393-00303-5, Norton Lib). Norton.

ZEN BUDDHISM

see also Koan

Abe, Masao, ed. A Zen Life: D. T. Suzuki Remembered. (Illus.). 288p. (Orig.). 1986. pap. 19.95 (ISBN 0-8348-0213-9). Weatherhill.
Aitken, Robert. Taking the Path of Zen. LC 82-81475. (Illus.). 176p. (Orig.). 1982. pap. 9.50 (ISBN 0-86547-080-4). N Point Pr.
Ames, Van Meter. Zen & American Thought. 1978. Repr. of 1962 ed. lib. bdg. 26.50 (ISBN 0-313-20066-1, AMZA). Greenwood.
Bancroft, Anne. Zen: Direct Pointing to Reality. (Art & Imagination Ser.). (Illus.). 1987. pap. 10.95. Thames Hudson.
Barnet, Sylvan & Burto, William. Zen Ink Paintings. LC 82-80648. (Great Japanese Art Ser.). (Illus.). 96p. 1982. 22.95 (ISBN 0-87011-521-9). Kodansha.
Benares, Camden. Zen Without Zen Masters. 2nd ed. (Illus.). 128p. 1985. pap. 6.95 (ISBN 0-941404-34-X). Falcon Pr AZ.
Benoit, Hubert. The Supreme Doctrine: Psychological Studies in Zen Thought. 248p. 1984. pap. 8.95 (ISBN 0-89281-058-0). Inner Tradit.
Blackstone, Judith & Josipovic, Zoran. Zen for Beginners. (Writers & Readers Documentary Comic Bks.). (Illus.). 176p. (Orig.). 1986. pap. 6.95 (ISBN 0-86316-116-2). Writers & Readers.
Callaway, Tucker N. Zen Way - Jesus Way. LC 76-6032. 1976. 11.00 (ISBN 0-8048-1190-3). C E Tuttle.
Chang Cheng-Chi. The Practice of Zen. LC 78-618. 1978. Repr. of 1959 ed. lib. bdg. 29.75x (ISBN 0-313-20264-8, CHPZ). Greenwood.
Chiba, Reiko. Sesshu's Long Scroll: A Zen Landscape Journey. LC 54-14085. (Illus.). 1959. 14.50 (ISBN 0-8048-0677-2). C E Tuttle.
Chinul. The Korean Approach to Zen: The Collected Works of Chinul. Buswell, Robert E., Jr., tr. LC 82-23873. 484p. 1983. text ed. 29.95x (ISBN 0-8248-0785-5). UH Pr.
Cleary, Thomas, ed. The Original Face: An Anthology of Rinzai Zen. LC 77-91354. 1978. pap. 4.95 (ISBN 0-394-17038-5, E707, Ever). Grove.
Cleary, Thomas, tr. Sayings & Doings of Pai-Chang. LC 78-21228. (Zen Writings Ser.: Vol. 6). 1979. pap. 5.95 (ISBN 0-916820-10-6). Center Pubns.
Collcutt, Martin. Five Mountains: The Rinzai Zen Monastic Institution in Medieval Japan. (Harvard East Asian Monograph: Vol. 85). (Illus.). 450p. 1980. 27.50x (ISBN 0-674-30497-7). Harvard U Pr.
Covell, Jon Carter & Yamada, Abbot S. Unraveling Zen's Red Thread: Ikkyu's Controversial Way. LC 80-81040. (Illus.). 341p. 1980. 21.50x (ISBN 0-930878-19-1). Hollym Intl.
Davidson, A. K. The Art of Zen Gardens: A Guide to Their Creation & Enjoyment. (Illus.). 160p. 1983. 15.95 (ISBN 0-87477-253-2); pap. 9.95 (ISBN 0-87477-254-0). J P Tarcher.
Deshimaru, Taisen. Questions to a Zen Master. Amphoux, Nancy, tr. 160p. 1985. pap. 8.95 (ISBN 0-525-48141-9, 0869-260). Dutton.
Dogen. A Primer of Soto Zen: A Translation of Dogen's Shobogenzo Zuimonki. Masunaga, Reiho, tr. from Japanese. LC 76-126044. 128p. 1975. pap. text ed. 5.95x (ISBN 0-8248-0357-4, Eastwest Ctr). UH Pr.
--Shobogenzo: Zen Essays by Dogen. Cleary, Thomas, tr. LC 85-20979. 136p. 1986. 14.00x (ISBN 0-8248-1014-7). UH Pr.
Dollarhide, Kenneth. Nichiren's Senji-sho: An Essay on the Selection of Proper Time. LC 82-21687. (Studies in Asian Thought & Religion: Vol. 1). 184p. 1983. 39.95x (ISBN 0-88946-051-5). E Mellen.
Dumoulin, Heinrich. Zen Enlightenment: Origins & Meaning. LC 78-27310. 188p. 1979. pap. 7.95 (ISBN 0-8348-0141-8). Weatherhill.
Eliot, Alexander. Zen Edge. 1979. 3.95 (ISBN 0-8264-0177-5). Continuum.
Fox, Frank, et al. Beginner's Guide to Zen & the Art of Windsurfing. 3rd ed. (Illus.). 160p. 1985. pap. 6.95 (ISBN 0-934965-02-1). Amber Co Pr.
Franck, Frederick. Zen of Seeing. 1973. pap. 8.95 (ISBN 0-394-71968-9, V968, Vin). Random.
Franck, Frederick, ed. Zen & Zen Classics: Selections from R. H. Blyth. (Illus.). 1978. pap. 7.95 (ISBN 0-394-72489-5, Vin). Random.
Fromm, Erich, et al. Zen Buddhism & Psychoanalysis. LC 60-5293. 1970. pap. 6.95 (ISBN 0-06-090175-6, CN175, PL). Har-Row.
Fujisawa, Chikao. Zen & Shinto: The Story of Japanese Philosophy. LC 78-139133. 92p. Repr. of 1959 ed. lib. bdg. 22.50x (ISBN 0-8371-5749-8, FUZS). Greenwood.
Furlong, Monica. Zen Effects: The Life of Alan Watts. 1986. 17.95 (ISBN 0-395-35344-0). HM.
Gilbert, Donald. Jellyfish Bones the Humor of Zen. Angilly, Richard, ed. (Illus.). 168p. (Orig.). 1980. pap. 7.95x (ISBN 0-931290-25-2). Blue Dragon.
Hall, Manly P. Zen of the Bright Virtue. pap. 4.00 (ISBN 0-89314-374-X). Philos Res.
Harding, D. E. On Having No Head: Zen & the Rediscovery of the Obvious. rev. ed. (Illus.). 96p. 1986. pap. 4.95 (ISBN 0-317-40544-6). Methuen Inc.
Heifetz, Harold, ed. Zen & Hasidism. LC 78-9073. 1978. 10.95 (ISBN 0-8356-0514-0). Theos Pub Hse.
Herrigel, Eugen. Zen in the Art of Archery. 1971. pap. 3.95 (ISBN 0-394-71663-9, V663, Vin). Random.
Herrigel, Eugene. Method of Zen. Hull, R. F. & Watts, Alan, eds. LC 74-5120. 1974. pap. 2.95 (ISBN 0-394-71244-7, Vin). Random.
Herrigel, Gustie L. Zen in the Art of Flower Arrangement: An Introduction to the Spirit of the Japanese Art of Flower Arrangement. 1974. pap. 6.95 (ISBN 0-7100-7942-7). Methuen Inc.
Hirai, Tomio. Zen & the Mind: A Scientific Approach to Zen Practice. (Illus., Orig.). 1978. 10.50 (ISBN 0-87040-391-5). Japan Pubns USA.
--Zen Meditation & Psychotherapy. LC 85-81591. (Illus.). 160p. (Orig.). 1986. pap. 11.95 (ISBN 0-87040-666-3). Japan Pubns USA.
Hisamatsu, Shinichi. Zen & the Fine Arts. Tokiwa, Gishin, tr. LC 76-136562. (Illus.). 400p. 1982. pap. 24.95 (ISBN 0-87011-519-7). Kodansha.
Holmes, Stewart W. & Horioka, Chimyo. Zen Art for Meditation. LC 73-78279. (Illus.). 1978. pap. 4.75 (ISBN 0-8048-1255-1). C E Tuttle.

Hoover, Thomas. The Zen Experience. (Illus., Orig.). 1980. pap. 5.95 (ISBN 0-452-25315-2, Z5315, Plume). NAL.
Huang Po. The Zen Teaching of Huang Po: On the Transmission of the Mind. Blofeld, John, tr. 1959. pap. 9.95 (ISBN 0-394-17217-5, E171, Ever). Grove.
Hui-neng. The Sutra of Wei Lang. Wong Mou-lam, tr. from Chinese. LC 73-879. (China Studies: from Confucius to Mao Ser.). 128p. 1973. Repr. of 1944 ed. 15.75 (ISBN 0-88355-073-3). Hyperion Conn.
Humphreys, Christmas. Western Approach to Zen. LC 72-76428. 212p. 1981. pap. 5.50 (ISBN 0-8356-0550-7, Quest). Theos Pub Hse.
--Zen: A Way of Life. LC 65-17332. 1971. pap. 7.70i (ISBN 0-316-38160-8). Little.
Hyams, Joe. Zen in the Martial Arts. 144p. 1982. pap. 3.50 (ISBN 0-553-26078-2). Bantam.
Izutsu, Toshihiko. The Interior & Exterior in Zen Buddhism. LC 84-5580. (Eranos Lectures Ser.: No. 1). 36p. (Orig.). 1984. pap. 7.00 (ISBN 0-88214-401-4). Spring Pubns.
Jiyu-Kennett, Roshi & MacPhillamy, Daizui. The Book of Life. (Illus.). 1979. pap. 9.95 (ISBN 0-930066-04-9). Shasta Abbey.
Johnston, William. Christian Zen: A Way of Meditation. 2nd ed. LC 80-8430. (Illus.). 144p. 1981. pap. 6.95 (ISBN 0-06-064198-3, RD 343, HarpR). Har-Row.
--Still Point: Reflections on Zen & Christian Mysticism. LC 75-95713. 1986. pap. 9.00 (ISBN 0-8232-0861-3). Fordham.
Kadowaki, J. K. Zen & the Bible: A Priest's Experience. (Orig.). 1980. pap. 8.95 (ISBN 0-7100-0402-8). Methuen Inc.
Kapleau, Philip. The Three Pillars of Zen: Teaching, Practice, Enlightenment. LC 78-22794. (Illus.). 1980. pap. 9.95 (ISBN 0-385-14786-4, Anch). Doubleday.
--Zen: Dawn in the West. LC 78-22794. (Illus.). 1980. pap. 5.95 (ISBN 0-385-14274-9, Anch). Doubleday.
Kasulis, T. P. Zen Action-Zen Person. LC 80-27858. 192p. 1985. pap. text ed. 7.95x (ISBN 0-8248-1023-6). UH Pr.
Kim, Chang S. & Kim, Maria. The Art of Zen Sword: The History of Shim Gum Do, Pt. I. LC 85-5973. (Illus.). 144p. 1985. 19.95 (ISBN 0-9614427-0-0). Am Buddhist Shim Do.
King, Winston. Death Was His Koan: The Samurai Zen of Suzuki Shosan. 1986. 40.00 (ISBN 0-89581-998-8). Asian Human Pr.
LaFleur, William R., ed. Dogen Studies. LC 85-16427. (Studies in East Asian Buddhism Ser.: No. 2). 288p. 1985. pap. text ed. 19.00x (ISBN 0-8248-1011-2). UH Pr.
Lassalle, H. M. Enomiya: Zen Meditation for Christians. Maraldo, John C., tr. 187p. 1974. 16.95 (ISBN 0-87548-151-5). Open Court.
Leggett, Trevor. Encounters in Yoga & Zen. 1982. pap. 9.95 (ISBN 0-7100-9241-5). Methuen Inc.
--The Warrior Koans: Early Zen in Japan. 256p. 1985. pap. 8.95 (Ark Paperbks). Methuen Inc.
--Zen & the Ways. Sakade, Florence, ed. (Illus.). 258p. (Orig.). 1987. pap. 9.95 (ISBN 0-8048-1524-0). C E Tuttle.
Leggett, Trevor P. First Zen Reader. LC 60-12739. (Illus.). 1960. pap. 6.95 (ISBN 0-8048-0180-0). C E Tuttle.
Leigh, Dub. A Zen Approach to Bodytherapy: From Rolf to Feldenfrais to Tanouye Roshi. 1987. pap. 10.95x (ISBN 0-8248-1099-6, Pub. by Inst Zen Studies). UH Pr.
Linssen, Robert. Living Zen. Abrahams-Curiel, Diana, tr. 1960. pap. 3.95 (ISBN 0-394-17391-0, E578, Ever). Grove.
Low, Albert. The Iron Cow of Zen. LC 85-40413. 226p. (Orig.). 1985. pap. 6.50 (ISBN 0-8356-0598-1, Quest). Theos Pub Hse.
--Zen & Creative Management. 272p. 1982. pap. 3.50 (ISBN 0-86721-083-4). Jove Pubns.
McFarland, H. Neill. Daruma: The Founder of Zen in Japanese Art & Popular Culture. LC 87-45214. (Illus.). 120p. 1987. 22.50 (ISBN 0-87011-817-X). Kodansha.
Maezumi, Hakuyu T. & Glassman, Bernard T. The Hazy Moon of Enlightenment: On Zen Practice III. LC 77-81974. (Zen Writings Ser.: Vol. Four). (Illus.). 1978. pap. 5.95 (ISBN 0-916820-05-X). Center Pubns.
Maezumi, Hakuyu T. & Loori, John D. The Way of Everyday Life. LC 78-8309. (Illus.). 1978. 17.50 (ISBN 0-916820-17-3); pap. 9.95 (ISBN 0-916820-06-8). Center Pubns.
Maezumi, Hakuyu T. & Glassman, Bernard T., eds. On Zen Practice: Foundations of Practice. LC 76-9463. (Zen Writings Ser.: Vol. 1). (Illus.). 1976. pap. 5.00 (ISBN 0-916820-02-5). Center Pubns.
Masunaga, Shizuto & Brown, Stephen. Zen Imagery Exercises: Meridian Exercises for Wholesome Living. LC 86-80220. (Illus.). 192p. (Orig.). 1986. pap. 13.95 (ISBN 0-87040-669-8). Japan Pubns USA.
Matthiessen, Peter. Nine-Headed Dragon River. 1987. pap. 9.95 (ISBN 0-87773-401-1). Shambhala Pubns.
--Nine-Headed Dragon River: Zen Journals 1969-1982. LC 85-27918. (Dragons Ser.). 288p. 1987. pap. 9.95 (ISBN 0-87773-401-1). Shambhala Pubns.
Norbu, Namkhai. Dzog Chen & Zen. Lipman, Kennard, ed. Norbu, Namkhai, tr. from Ital. (Illus.). 52p. (Orig.). 1987. pap. 5.00 (ISBN 0-931892-08-2). B Dolphin Pub.
Nukariva, K. The Religion of the Samurai: A Study of Zen Philosophy & Discipline in China & Japan. 253p. 1973. 30.00x (ISBN 0-317-39142-9, Pub. by Luzac & Co Ltd); pap. 20.00x (ISBN 0-317-39143-7). State Mutual Bk.
Park, O'Hyun, tr. Essentials of Zen Buddhism. 143p. 1985. pap. 4.95 (ISBN 0-317-20880-2). CSA Pr.
Park, Sung-Bae. Buddhist Faith & Sudden Enlightenment. LC 82-10459. 222p. 1983. 44.50x (ISBN 0-87395-673-7); pap. 12.95x (ISBN 0-87395-674-5). State U NY Pr.
Powell, Robert. The Great Awakening. Nicholson, Shirley, ed. LC 83-70688. Orig. Title: Zen & Reality. 179p. 1983. pap. 6.50 (ISBN 0-8356-0577-9, Quest). Theos Pub Hse.
Pye, Michael. Zen & Modern Japanese Religions. 1985. 13.00 (ISBN 0-7062-3148-1, Pub. by Ward Lock Educ Co Ltd). State Mutual Bk.
Rajneesh, Bhagwan S. The Grass Grows by Itself. (Illus.). 1978. pap. 4.95 (ISBN 0-87516-251-7). De Vorss.
--Roots & Wings: Talks on Zen. (Orig.). 1979. pap. 9.95 (ISBN 0-7100-0420-6). Methuen Inc.
Rajneesh, Bhagwan Shree. The Grass Grows by Itself. Veena, Ma Prema, ed. LC 77-905411. (Zen Ser.). (Illus.). 254p. (Orig.). 1978. 15.50 (ISBN 0-88050-072-7); pap. 4.95 (ISBN 0-88050-572-9). Chidvilas Found.
--Nirvana: The Last Nightmare. Pratima, Ma Yoga, ed. LC 77-902717. (Zen Ser.). (Illus.). 290p. (Orig.). 1976. 17.50 (ISBN 0-88050-101-4). Chidvilas Found.
--No Water, No Moon. 2nd ed. Anurag, Ma Yoga, ed. LC 75-907472. (Zen Ser.). (Illus.). 260p. 1978. 14.50 (ISBN 0-88050-105-7). Chidvilas Found.
--Returning to the Source. Sudha, Ma Yoga, ed. LC 83-182149. (Zen Ser.). (Illus.). 402p. (Orig.). 1976. 15.95 (ISBN 0-88050-120-0). Chidvilas Found.
--The Shadow of the Bamboo. Maneesha, Ma Prem, ed. LC 84-42807. (Initiation Talks Ser.). 240p. (Orig.). 1984. pap. 3.95 (ISBN 0-88050-630-X). Chidvilas found.
--A Sudden Clash of Thunder. Anurag, Ma Yoga, ed. LC 78-901998. (Zen Ser.). (Illus.). 284p. (Orig.). 1977. 16.50 (ISBN 0-88050-135-9). Chidvilas Found.
--The Sun Rises in the Evening. Asha, Ma Prem, ed. LC 83-181196. (Zen Ser.). (Illus.). 372p. (Orig.). 1980. 17.95 (ISBN 0-88050-139-1). Chidvilas Found.
--Take It Easy, 2 vols. Anurag, Ma Yoga & Vandana, Ma Ananda, eds. LC 83-177521. (Zen Ser.). (Illus., Orig.). 1979. Vol. I, 584 pgs. 21.95 ea. (ISBN 0-88050-141-3). Vol. II, 584 pgs (ISBN 0-88050-142-1). Chidvilas Found.
--Walking in Zen, Sitting in Zen. Rajneesh Foundation International, ed. LC 82-24025. (Questions & Answers Ser.). 444p. (Orig.). 1982. pap. 10.95 (ISBN 0-88050-668-7). Chidvilas Found.
--The Wild Geese & the Water. Prabhu, Swami Krishna, ed. LC 85-43053. (Responses to Questions Ser.). 416p. (Orig.). 1985. pap. 4.95 (ISBN 0-88050-673-3). Chidvilas Found.
--Zen: The Path of Paradox, 3 vols. Veena, Ma Prema & Vandana, Ma Ananda, eds. LC 82-246214. (Zen Ser.). (Illus.). 1978. Vol. I, 376 pgs. 16.95 ea. (ISBN 0-88050-188-X). Vol. II, 372pgs 1979 (ISBN 0-88050-189-8). Vol. III, 392 pgs. 1979 (ISBN 0-88050-190-1). Chidvilas Found.
--Zen: The Special Transmission. Ma Prem Rajo & Ma Deva Sarito, eds. LC 84-43010. (Zen Ser.). 368p. (Orig.). 1984. pap. 4.95 (ISBN 0-88050-691-1). Chidvilas Found.
--Zen: Zest, Zip Zap & Zing. Asha, Ma Prem, ed. LC 83-183222. (Question & Answer Ser.). (Illus.). 472p. (Orig.). 1981. pap. 19.95 468p 1981 (ISBN 0-88050-692-X). Chidvilas Found.
Reps, Paul. Square Sun Square Moon: A Collection of Prose Essays. LC 67-14277. (Illus., Orig.). 1967. pap. 6.50 (ISBN 0-8048-0544-X). C E Tuttle.
--Unwrinkling Plays. LC 65-12270. (Illus., Orig.). 1965. pap. 4.75 (ISBN 0-8048-0607-1). C E Tuttle.
--Zen Flesh, Zen Bones. LC 57-10199. (Illus.). 1957. 11.50 (ISBN 0-8048-0644-6). C E Tuttle.
--Zen Telegrams: Seventy-Nine Picture Poems. LC 59-8189. (Illus.). 1959. pap. 7.95 (ISBN 0-8048-0645-4). C E Tuttle.
Reps, Paul, ed. Zen Flesh, Zen Bones: A Collection of Zen & Pre-Zen Writings. pap. 3.95 (ISBN 0-385-08130-8, A233, Anch). Doubleday.
Ross, Nancy W. Three Ways of Asian Wisdom: Hinduism, Buddhism, Zen. (Illus.). 1978. pap. 12.95 (ISBN 0-671-24230-X, Touchstone Bks). S&S.
Ross, Nancy W., ed. World of Zen. (Illus.). 1960. pap. 8.95 (ISBN 0-394-70301-4, Vin). Random.
Roth, Martin & Stevens, John. Zen Guide: Where to Meditate in Japan. (Illus.). 152p. pap. 7.50 (ISBN 0-8348-0202-3). Weatherhill.
Rupp, George. Beyond Existentialism & Zen: Religion in a Pluralistic World. 1979. 14.95x (ISBN 0-19-502462-1). Oxford U Pr.
Sahn, Seung. Only Don't Know: The Teaching Letters of Zen Master Seung Sahn. LC 82-17380. (Wheel Ser.: No. 3). 205p. (Orig.). 1982. pap. 7.95 (ISBN 0-87704-054-0). Four Seasons Foun.
Sasaki, Ruth F., et al, trs. A Man of Zen: The Recorded Sayings of Layman P'ang. LC 77-157273. (Illus.). 124p. 1976. 6.95 (ISBN 0-8348-0057-8); pap. 4.95 (ISBN 0-8348-0121-3). Weatherhill.
Sekida, Katsuki. Zen Training: Methods & Philosophy. Grimstone, A. V., ed. LC 75-17573. (Illus.). 264p. 1975. 12.50 (ISBN 0-8348-0111-6); pap. 9.95 (ISBN 0-8348-0114-0). Weatherhill.
Shigematsu, Soiku. A Zen Forest: Sayings of the Masters. LC 81-31. (Illus.). 200p. 1981. 19.95 (ISBN 0-8348-0159-0). Weatherhill.
Sogen, Omori & Katsujo, Terayama. Zen & the Art of Calligraphy. Stevens, John, tr. from Japanese. (Illus.). 128p. (Orig.). 1983. pap. 13.95 (ISBN 0-7100-9284-9). Methuen Inc.
Sohl, Robert & Carr, Audrey. Games Zen Masters Play: The Writings of R. H. Blyth. 1976. pap. 3.50 (ISBN 0-451-62416-5, Ment). NAL.
Stryk, Lucien. Encounter with Zen: Writings on Poetry & Zen. LC 81-9611. x, 259p. 1982. 26.95x (ISBN 0-8040-0405-6, Pub. by Swallow); pap. 10.95 (ISBN 0-8040-0406-4, Pub. by Swallow). Ohio U Pr.
Stryk, Lucien & Ikemoto, Takashi, trs. from Japanese. Zen: Poems, Prayers, Sermons, Anecdotes, Interviews. LC 81-50909. 210p. 1982. 18.95x (ISBN 0-8040-0377-7, 82-75232, Pub by Swallow); pap. 8.95 (ISBN 0-8040-0378-5, 82-75240, Pub by Swallow). Ohio U Pr.
Sunim, Kusan. The Way of Korean Zen. Fages, Martine, tr. (Illus.). 182p. pap. 12.50 (ISBN 0-8348-0201-5). Weatherhill.
Suzuki, D. T. Essays in Zen Buddhism. 1961. pap. 5.95 (ISBN 0-394-17230-2, E309, Ever). Grove.
--Introduction to Zen Buddhism. 1964. pap. 3.95 (ISBN 0-394-17474-7, B341, BC). Grove.
--Living by Zen. pap. 5.95 (ISBN 0-87728-194-7). Weiser.
--Manual of Zen Buddhism. (Orig.). 1960. pap. 5.95 (ISBN 0-394-17224-8, E231, Ever). Grove.
--Zen & Japanese Culture. (Bollingen Ser.: Vol. 64). (Illus.). 1959. 52.00x (ISBN 0-691-09849-2); pap. 10.95x (ISBN 0-691-01770-0). Princeton U Pr.
--Zen Buddhism: Selected Writings of D. T. Suzuki. 1956. pap. 5.50 (ISBN 0-385-09300-4, A90, Anch). Doubleday.
--Zen Doctrine of No Mind. 1981. pap. 8.50 (ISBN 0-87728-182-3). Weiser.
Suzuki, Daisetz T. The Essentials of Zen Buddhism. Phillips, Bernard, ed. & intro. by. LC 61-5041. 544p. 1973. Repr. of 1962 ed. lib. bdg. 45.00x (ISBN 0-8371-6649-7, SUEZ). Greenwood.
Tanahashi, Kazuaki. Penetrating Laughter: Hakuin's Zen & Art. LC 83-43155. (Illus.). 144p. 1984. 16.95 (ISBN 0-87951-952-5); pap. 8.95 (ISBN 0-87951-280-6). Overlook Pr.
Thien-An, Thich. Zen Philosophy, Zen Practice. LC 75-20003. (Illus.). 192p. 1975. pap. 7.95 (ISBN 0-913546-33-X). Dharma Pub.
Thien-An, Thieh. Buddhism & Zen in Vietnam: In Relation to the Development in Asia. LC 74-83391. (Illus.). 300p. 1975. 12.50 (ISBN 0-8048-1144-X). C E Tuttle.
Tripitaka Master Hua, commentary by. The Sixth Patriarch's Sutra: Great Master Hui Neng. Buddhist Text Translation Society Staff, tr. from Chinese. (Illus.). 235p. (Orig.). 1977. 15.00 (ISBN 0-917512-19-7); pap. 10.00 (ISBN 0-917512-33-2). Buddhist Text.
Vitale, Manjushri J. Zen & the Art of Writing. 90p. (Orig.). 1984. pap. 10.95 (ISBN 0-932896-07-3). Westcliff Pubns.
Watts, Alan W. The Spirit of Zen: A Way of Life, Work & Art in the Far East. 1958. pap. 2.95 (ISBN 0-394-17418-6, E219, Ever). Grove.
--This Is It. 1972. pap. 3.95 (ISBN 0-394-71904-2, Vin). Random.
--Way of Zen. 1974. pap. 4.95 (ISBN 0-394-70298-0, Vin). Random.
Watts, Dale. Zen Sensualism: The Union of Spirituality & Sexuality. LC 86-82338. 56p. (Orig.). 1986. pap. 9.25 (ISBN 0-937497-39-8). Hart Eden Pr.
Wood, Ernest. Zen Dictionary. LC 72-77518. 1972. pap. 5.25 (ISBN 0-8048-1060-5). C E Tuttle.
Yampolsky, Philip B., tr. Platform Sutra of the Sixth Patriarch. LC 67-11847. (Records of Civilization, Studies & Sources: No. 76). 1967. pap. 15.00x (ISBN 0-231-08361-0). Columbia U Pr.
Yokoi, Yuho & Victoria, Daizen. Zen Master Dogen: An Introduction with Selected Writings. LC 75-33200. (Illus.). 220p. 1976. 12.50 (ISBN 0-8348-0112-4); pap. 9.75 (ISBN 0-8348-0116-7). Weatherhill.

ZEN BUDDHIST LITERATURE

see Zen Literature

ZEN LITERATURE

Aitken, Robert. A Zen Wave: Basho's Haiku & Zen. LC 78-13243. (Illus.). 192p. 1979. pap. 9.95 (ISBN 0-8348-0137-X). Weatherhill.
Arntzen, Sonja. Ikkyu Sojun: A Zen Monk & His Poetry. LC 73-620051. (Occasional Papers: Vol. 4). (Illus.). 171p. 1973. microfiche 1.00 (ISBN 0-914584-99-5). WWUCEAS.
Bancroft, Anne. Zen: Direct Pointing to Reality. Purce, Jill, ed. LC 81-67702. (The Illustrated Library of Sacred Imagination). (Illus.). 96p. 1982. pap. 9.95 (ISBN 0-8245-0068-7). Crossroad NY.
Cleary, Thomas, tr. Timeless Spring: A Soto Zen Anthology. LC 79-26677. 176p. 1980. pap. 7.95 (ISBN 0-8348-0148-5). Weatherhill.
Eusden, John. Zen & Christian: The Journey Between. 224p. 1981. 10.95 (ISBN 0-8245-0099-7). Crossroad NY.
Hakeda, Yoshito S., ed. Bankei Zen. Haskel, Peter, tr. LC 83-81372. (Eastern Bks.). 240p. 1985. 27.50 (ISBN 0-394-53524-3, GP 886). Grove.
--Bankei Zen. Haskel, Peter, tr. LC 83-81372. (Eastern Bks.). 1985. pap. 8.95 (ISBN 0-394-62493-9, E-272, Ever). Grove.
Hakuin. The Zen Master Hakuin: Selected Writings. Yampolsky, Philip B., tr. from Japanese. 253p. 1985. 29.00 (ISBN 0-231-03463-6); pap. 14.00x (ISBN 0-231-06041-6). Columbia U Pr.
Hunttmiller, Patrique. A Zen Song: Twenty Meditations for the Black Martial Artist. 52p. 1986. pap. 5.95 (ISBN 0-9615560-3-X). Scojtia Renee.
Leggett, Trevor. Second Zen Reader. Sakade, Florence, ed. (Illus.). 192p. (Orig.). 1987. pap. 7.95 (ISBN 0-8048-1525-9). C E Tuttle.
Lovelace, Glen. Zenzen: A Book of Illustrated Koans. (Illus.). 1978. pap. 4.00 (ISBN 0-87516-279-7). De Vorss.
Luk, Charles. The Transmission of the Mind Outside the Teaching. LC 75-15055. 1976. pap. 2.95 (ISBN 0-394-17888-2, E666, Ever). Grove.
Melville, James. The Wages of Zen. 224p. 1985. pap. 2.95 (ISBN 0-449-20838-9, Crest). Fawcett.
Merton, Thomas. Zen & the Birds of Appetite. LC 68-25546. 1968. 6.50 (ISBN 0-8112-0314-X); pap. 4.95 (ISBN 0-8112-0104-X, NDP261). New Directions.
Pollack, David. Zen Poems of the Five Mountains. LC 84-13910. (American Academy of Religion Studies in Religion). 1984. 22.50 (ISBN 0-89130-776-1, 01 00 37); pap. 14.95 (ISBN 0-89130-775-3). Scholars Pr GA.
Rajneesh, Bhagwan S. The Supreme Doctrine: Discourses on the Kenopanishad. 356p. (Orig.). 1980. pap. 12.95 (ISBN 0-7100-0572-5). Methuen Inc.
Rajneesh, Bhagwan Shree. Ancient Music in the Pines. Veena, Ma Prem, ed. LC 78-901931. (Zen Ser.). (Illus.). 298p. (Orig.). 1977. 15.50 (ISBN 0-88050-003-4). Chidvilas Found.
--And the Flowers Showered. Somendra, Swami Anand, ed. LC 83-181344. (Zen Ser.). (Illus.). 288p. (Orig.). 1975. 16.95 (ISBN 0-88050-004-2); pap. 5.95 (ISBN 0-88050-504-4). Chidvilas Found.
--No Water, No Moon. Prabhu, Swami Krishna, ed. LC 84-42871. (Zen Ser.). 320p. 1984. pap. 4.95 (ISBN 0-88050-605-9). Chidvilas Found.
Richie, Donald. Zen Inklings: Some Stories, Fables, Parables, Sermons & Prints with Notes & Commentaries. LC 82-2561. (Illus.). 162p. 1982. 17.95 (ISBN 0-8348-0170-1). Weatherhill.
Rosen, Gerald. Zen in the Art of J. D. Salinger. LC 77-72494. (Modern Authors Monograph Ser.: No. 3). 40p. 1977. pap. 3.50 (ISBN 0-916870-06-5). Creative Arts Bk.
Sasaki, Sokei-an. Zen Eye. Farkas, Mary, ed. LC 84-48129. 136p. (Orig.). Date not set. pap. 10.95 (ISBN 0-87011-696-7). Kodansha.
Sato, Koji. The Zen Life: Daily Life in a Zen Monastery. Victoria, Ryojun, tr. LC 79-185602. (Illus.). 194p. 1983. pap. 7.50 (ISBN 0-8348-1517-6). Weatherhill.
Schloegl, Irmgard, ed. The Wisdom of the Zen Masters. LC 75-42115. (The Wisdom Bks.). 96p. 1976. pap. 5.95 (ISBN 0-8112-0610-6, NDP415). New Directions.

Shibayama, Zenkei. Zen Comments on the Mumonkan. LC 73-18692. (Illus.). 384p. 1984. pap. 10.95 (ISBN 0-06-067278-1, CN 4091, HarpR). Har-Row.

Soho, Takuan. The Unfettered Mind: Writings of the Zen Master to the Sword Master. LC 86-45072. 92p. 1986. 12.95 (ISBN 0-87011-776-9). Kodansha.

Suzuki, Shunryu. Zen Mind, Beginner's Mind. Dixon, Trudy, ed. LC 70-123326. 132p. 1970. 9.95 (ISBN 0-8348-0052-7); pap. 5.95 (ISBN 0-8348-0079-9). Weatherhill.

Uchiyama, Kosho & Uchiyama, Kosho. Refining Your Life: From the Zen Kitchen to Enlightenment. Wright, Tom, tr. LC 82-20295. 136p. 1983. pap. 9.95 (ISBN 0-8348-0179-5). Weatherhill.

Watts, Alan. The Way of Liberation: Essays & Lectures on the Transformation of the Self. Watts, Mark & Shropshire, Rebecca, eds. LC 82-21917. 120p. 1983. pap. 8.95 (ISBN 0-8348-0181-7). Weatherhill.

Wood, E., ed. Diccionario Zen. (Span.). 190p. 1980. pap. 13.95 (ISBN 84-7509-010-9, S-32724). French & Eur.

Yuasa, Nobuyuki, tr. from Jap. The Zen Poems of Ryokan. LC 80-8585. (Princeton Library of Asian Translations). (Illus.). 196p. 1981. 25.00x (ISBN 0-691-06466-0). Princeton U Pr.

ZEND-AVESTA

see Avesta

ZENO, SAINT, BP., 4TH CENTURY

Lofstedt, Bengt M. & Packard, David W. A Concordance to the Sermons of Bishop Zeno of Verona. (APA Philological Monographs). 1974. 37.00 (ISBN 0-89130-715-X, 40-00-32). Scholars Pr GA.

ZEUS

Cook, Arthur B. Zeus: A Study of Ancient Religion, 2 vols. Incl. Vol. 1. Zeus, God of the Bright Sky. LC 64-25839. (Illus.). 885p. Repr. of 1914 ed. 50.00x (ISBN 0-8196-0148-9); Vol. 2. Zeus, God of the Dark Sky: Thunder & Lightning, 2 pts. LC 64-25839. Repr. of 1925 ed. 100.00xset (ISBN 0-8196-0156-X); Vol. 2, Pt. 1. Text & Notes. xliii, 858p; Vol. 2, Pt. 2. Appendixes & Index. (Illus.). 539p. Biblo.

ZIONISM

Here are entered works dealing with the movement looking toward the creation and maintenance of a Jewish state or a national home in Palestine.

see also Jews–Political and Social Conditions; Jews–Restoration; Nationalism–Jews

Alexander, Yona & Chertoff, Mordecai, eds. Bibliography on Israel & Zionism. 1980. write for info. Herzl Pr.

Al-Fatih, Zudhi. The Jews in Review: The World's Greatest Minds on Zionism. 1984. lib. bdg. 79.95 (ISBN 0-87700-581-8). Revisionist Pr.

Almog, Shmuel. Zionism & History: Zionist Attitudes to the Jewish Historical Past, 1896-1906. Friedman, Ina, tr. from Hebrew. 350p. 1986. 29.95 (ISBN 0-312-89885-1). St Martin.

Al-Raheb, Hani. The Zionist Character in the English Novel. 220p. 1985. pap. 9.95 (ISBN 0-86232-364-9, Pub. by Zed Pr England). Humanities.

Avineri, Shlomo. The Making of Modern Zionism: Intellectual Origins of the Jewish State. LC 81-66102. 272p. 1981. 15.50 (ISBN 0-465-04328-3). Basic.

--The Making of Modern Zionism: The Intellectual Origins of the Jewish State. LC 81-66102. 244p. 1984. pap. 7.95 (ISBN 0-465-04330-5, CN 5113). Basic.

Avishai, Bernard. The Tragedy of Zionism. LC 85-10235. 389p. 1985. 19.95 (ISBN 0-374-27863-6). FS&G.

--The Tragedy of Zionism. 389p. 1986. pap. 8.95 (ISBN 0-374-52044-5). FS&G.

Bardin, Shlomo, ed. Self-Fulfillment Through Zionism: A Study in Jewish Adjustment. LC 70-142605. (Biography Index Reprint Ser). Repr. of 1943 ed. 17.00 (ISBN 0-8369-8076-X). Ayer Co Pubs.

Berger, Rabbi E., et al. Judaism, Zionism, & Anti-Semitism. 72p. (Orig.). 1985. pap. 2.50 (ISBN 0-935177-01-9). Palestine Focus.

Black, Ian. Zionism & the Arabs, Nineteen Thirty-Six to Nineteen Thirty-Nine. (Outstanding Theses from the London School of Economics & Political Science Ser.). 500p. 1987. lib. bdg. 75.00 (ISBN 0-8240-1911-3). Garland Pub.

Borochov, Ber. Class Struggle & the Jewish Nation: Selected Essays in Marxist Zionism. Cohen, Mitchell, ed. LC 83-4695. 358p. 1983. 29.95 (ISBN 0-87855-479-3). Transaction Bks.

Brandeis, Louis D. Brandeis on Zionism. LC 75-6425. (The Rise of Jewish Nationalism & the Middle East Ser.). 156p. 1975. Repr. of 1942 ed. 17.60 (ISBN 0-88355-312-0). Hyperion Conn.

Brenner, Lenni. The Iron Wall: Zionist Revisionism from Jabotinsky to Shamir. 230p. 1984. 26.25x (ISBN 0-86232-216-2, Pub. by Zed Pr England); pap. text ed. 9.25 (ISBN 0-86232-217-0, Pub. by Zed Pr England). Humanities.

--Zionism in the Age of the Dictators. LC 82-23369. 300p. 1983. pap. 8.95 osi (ISBN 0-88208-164-0). Lawrence Hill.

Caplan, Neil. Futile Diplomacy: Early Arab-Zionist Negotiation Attempts, 1913-1931, Vol. 1. (Illus.). 296p. 1983. text ed. 32.00x (ISBN 0-7146-3214-7, F Cass Co). Biblio Dist.

Chaim, B., ed. Neturei Karta; Voice of Anti-Zionist Judaism: A Study. 1980. 75.00 (ISBN 0-87700-273-8). Revisionist Pr.

Chaim, Bezalel. Against the Tide: Jewish Nonconformist Views of Israel & Zionism. 1979. lib. bdg. 42.95 (ISBN 0-686-24783-3). M Buber Pr.

Chertoff, Mordechai, ed. Zionism: A Basic Reader. 1976. 1.00 (ISBN 0-685-82601-5). Herzl Pr.

Chissin, Chaim. A Palestine Diary. 1976. 10.00 (ISBN 0-685-82598-1). Herzl Pr.

Cohen, Israel, ed. The Rebirth of Israel. LC 75-6427. (The Rise of Jewish Nationalism & the Middle East Ser.). 338p. 1975. Repr. of 1952 ed. 25.85 (ISBN 0-88355-314-7). Hyperion Conn.

--Zionist Work in Palestine. LC 75-6428. (The Rise of Jewish Nationalism & the Middle East Ser.). (Illus.). 208p. 1975. Repr. of 1911 ed. 24.75 (ISBN 0-88355-315-5). Hyperion Conn.

Cohen, Mitchell. Zion & State: Nation, Class & the Shaping of Modern Israel. 288p. 1987. 24.95 (ISBN 0-631-15243-1). Basil Blackwell.

Cohen, Naomi. American Jews & the Zionist Idea. pap. 9.95x (ISBN 0-87068-272-5). Ktav.

Cohen, Saul B. Jerusalem Undivided. 1980. pap. 3.00 (ISBN 0-930832-58-2). Herzl Pr.

Cruetz, W. New Light on the Protocols of Zion. 1982. lib. bdg. 69.95 (ISBN 0-87700-366-1). Revisionist Pr.

Davis, Moshe, ed. Call to America to Build Zion: An Original Anthology. LC 77-70723. (America & the Holy Land Ser.). 1977. lib. bdg. 20.00x (ISBN 0-405-10306-9). Ayer Co Pubs.

--Christian Protagonists for Jewish Restoration: An Original Anthology. LC 77-70678. (America & the Holy Land Ser.). 1977. lib. bdg. 20.00x (ISBN 0-405-10221-6). Ayer Co Pubs.

--Zionism in Transition. LC 80-67905. 1980. lib. bdg. 24.00x (ISBN 0-405-13825-3). Ayer Co Pubs.

--Zionism in Transition. 1980. pap. 8.00 (ISBN 0-930832-61-2). Herzl Pr.

Duvernoy, Claude. Controversy of Zion. LC 86-6386. 232p. 1987. pap. 6.96 (ISBN 0-89221-144-X). New Leaf.

Eaford & Ajaz. Judaism or Zionism? What Difference for the Middle East? 320p. 1986. 32.50 (ISBN 0-86232-475-0, Pub. by Zed Pr England); pap. 12.50 (ISBN 0-86232-476-9, Pub. by Zed Pr England). Humanities.

Elmessiri, Abdelwahab M. The Land of Promise: A Critique of Political Zionism. LC 77-83664. 1977. text ed. 11.95x (ISBN 0-930244-02-8); pap. text ed. 7.95x (ISBN 0-930244-01-X). North American Inc.

Field, Frederick V. From Right to Left: An Autobiography. LC 82-23407. 336p. 1983. 16.95 (ISBN 0-88208-162-4); pap. 8.95 (ISBN 0-88208-161-6). Lawrence Hill.

Fink, Reuben & Moshe, Davis, eds. America & Palestine: The Attitude of Official America & of the American People Toward the Rebuilding of Palestine As a Free & Democratic Jewish Commonwealth. LC 77-70680. (America & the Holy Land Ser.). 1977. Repr. of 1944 ed. lib. bdg. 40.00x (ISBN 0-405-10245-3). Ayer Co Pubs.

Fisch, H. Zionist Revolution. LC 78-424. 1978. 19.95x (ISBN 0-312-89886-X). St Martin.

Friedman, Isaiah. Germany, Turkey, & Zionism, 1897-1918. 1977. 59.00x (ISBN 0-19-822528-8). Oxford U Pr.

Fry, L. An Analysis of Zionism. 1982. lib. bdg. 59.00 (ISBN 0-87700-416-1). Revisionist Pr.

Gal, Allon. Socialist Zionism: Theory & Issues in Contemporary Jewish Nationalism. 225p. 1973. pap. 5.50 (ISBN 0-87073-669-8). Transaction Bks.

Ganin, Zvi. Truman, American Jewry, & Israel, 1945-1948. 238p. 1979. text ed. 34.50x (ISBN 0-8419-0401-4); pap. 22.50 (ISBN 0-8419-0497-9). Holmes & Meier.

Glubb, Faris. Zionist Relations with Nazi Germany. LC 79-90569. 6.00 (ISBN 0-911026-11-8). New World Press NY.

Goldstein, Israel. Toward a Solution. facs. ed. LC 79-128248. (Essay Index Reprint Ser). 1940. 21.00 (ISBN 0-8369-1877-0). Ayer Co Pubs.

Gordon, Benjamin L. New Judea: Jewish Life in Modern Palestine & Egypt. Davis, Moshe, ed. LC 77-70697. (America & the Holy Land Ser.). (Illus.). 1977. Repr. of 1919 ed. lib. bdg. 30.00x (ISBN 0-405-10251-8). Ayer Co Pubs.

Goren, Arthur A., ed. Dissenter in Zion: From the Writings of Judah L. Magnes. (Illus.). 576p. 1982. text ed. 32.50X (ISBN 0-674-21283-5). Harvard U Pr.

Gorny, Joseph. The British Labour Movement & Zionism 1917-1948. 270p. 1983. text ed. 30.00x (ISBN 0-7146-3162-0, F Cass Co). Biblio Dist.

Greenstein, Howard. Turning Point: Zionism & Reform Judaism. LC 81-8996. (Brown BJS Ser.). 1981. pap. 12.00 (ISBN 0-89130-512-2, 140012). Scholars Pr GA.

Grimstad, William. Antizion: The Jewish & Zionist Question Through the Ages. 1982. lib. bdg. 69.95 (ISBN 0-686-97529-4). Revisionist Pr.

Grimstad, William, compiled by. Antizion. 2nd rev. ed. 1980. pap. 6.00 (ISBN 0-911038-20-5). Noontide.

Grose, Peter. Israel & the Mind of America. 1983. 17.95 (ISBN 0-394-51658-3). Random.

Gwynne, H. A., intro. by. The Cause of World Unrest. 1978. pap. 5.00x (ISBN 0-911038-40-X). Noontide.

Ha-am, Achad, pseud. Ten Essays on Zionism & Judaism. LC 73-2202. (The Jewish People; History, Religion, Literature Ser.). Repr. of 1922 ed. 26.50 (ISBN 0-405-05267-7). Ayer Co Pubs.

Hadawi, S. The Jews, Zionism & the Bible. 1984. lib. bdg. 79.95 (ISBN 0-87700-572-9). Revisionist Pr.

Haim, Yehoyada. Abandonment of Illusions: Zionist Political Attitudes Toward Palestinian Arab Nationalism, 1936-1939. (Relica Edition Ser.). 170p. 1983. softcover 22.50x (ISBN 0-86531-971-5). Westview.

Halpern, Ben. The American Jew: A Zionistic Analysis. LC 82-16875. 192p. 1983. pap. 6.95 (ISBN 0-8052-0742-2). Schocken.

--Idea of the Jewish State. rev. ed. LC 71-89969. (Middle Eastern Studies: No. 3). (Illus.). 1969. 30.00x (ISBN 0-674-44201-6). Harvard U Pr.

Hardie, Frank & Herrman, Irwin. Britain & Zion: The Fateful Entanglement. 192p. 1980. 11.95 (ISBN 0-85640-229-X, Pub. by Blackstaff Pr). Longwood Pub Group.

Hein, Virginia H. The British Followers of Theodor Herzl: English Zionist Leaders, 1896-1904. McNeill, William H. & Stansky, Peter, eds. (Modern European History Ser.). 325p. 1987. lib. bdg. 50.00 (ISBN 0-8240-7815-2). Garland Pub.

Hertzberg, Arthur, ed. Zionist Idea: A Historical Analysis & Reader. LC 77-90073. (Temple Books). 1969. pap. text ed. 7.95x (ISBN 0-689-70093-8, T4). Atheneum.

--Zionist Idea: A Historical Analysis & Reader. Repr. of 1959 ed. 23.50x (ISBN 0-8371-2565-0, HEZI). Greenwood.

Herzl, Theodor. Diaries of Theodor Herzl. Lowenthal, ed. 16.50 (ISBN 0-8446-2247-8). Peter Smith.

Hess, Moses. Judische Schriften. Katz, Steven, ed. LC 79-7135. (Jewish Philosophy, Mysticism & History of Ideas Ser.). 1980. Repr. of 1905 ed. lib. bdg. 14.00x (ISBN 0-405-12261-6). Ayer Co Pubs.

Heymann, Michael, intro. by. The Uganda Controversy: Minutes of the Zionist General Council, Vol. 1. 136p. 1970. casebound 12.95x (ISBN 0-87855-185-9). Transaction Bks.

Hong, Christopher C. To Whom the Land of Palestine Belongs. 1979. 6.50 (ISBN 0-682-49161-6). Exposition Pr FL.

Hyamson, Albert M. Palestine: A Policy. LC 75-6438. (The Rise of Jewish Nationalism & the Middle East Ser). 214p. 1975. Repr. of 1942 ed. 20.35 (ISBN 0-88355-325-2). Hyperion Conn.

Institute for Palestine, Beirut, Lebanon Staff. Palestine & the Zionist Threat. Date not set. cancelled (ISBN 0-88728-190-7). Inst Palestine.

Intercollegiate Zionist Association of America. Kadimah. Davis, Moshe, ed. LC 77-70704. (America & the Holy Land Ser.). (Illus.). 1977. Repr. of 1918 ed. lib. bdg. 20.00x (ISBN 0-405-10255-0). Ayer Co Pubs.

Jansen, G. H. Zionism, Israel & Asian Nationalism. 347p. 1971. 6.00 (ISBN 0-88728-112-5); pap. 3.00 (ISBN 0-88728-113-3). Inst Palestine.

Jastrow, Morris. Zionism & the Future of Palestine. (The Rise of Jewish Nationalism & the Middle East Ser.). 159p. 1975. Repr. of 1919 ed. 18.15 (ISBN 0-88355-326-0). Hyperion Conn.

Jerusalem Ideological Conference Hebrew University. Proceedings, World Zionist Organization. Repr. of 1959 ed. lib. bdg. 23.00x (ISBN 0-8371-4120-6, WOZO). Greenwood.

Jewish Frontier (Periodical) Anthology, Nineteen Thirty-Four to Nineteen Forty-Four. facsimile ed. LC 76-167370. (Essay Index Reprint Ser). Repr. of 1945 ed. 31.00 (ISBN 0-8369-2459-2). Ayer Co Pubs.

Jones, Barry, tr. from Rus. Zionism: Enemy of Peace & Social Progress Issue, No. 3. 220p. 1984. 13.75x (ISBN 0-317-53829-2, Pub. by Collets (UK)). State Mutual Bk.

Kaganoff, Nathan M., ed. Solidarity & Kinship: Essays on American Zionism. (Illus.). 1980. 5.00 (ISBN 0-911934-14-6). Am Jewish Hist Soc.

Kahana, S. Z. Legends of Zion. 256p. 1986. pap. 9.95 (ISBN 0-943688-63-9). Res Ctr Kabbalah.

Kallen, Horace M. Frontiers of Hope. Davis, Moshe, ed. LC 77-70711. (America & the Holy Land Ser.). 1977. Repr. of 1929 ed. lib. bdg. 37.50x (ISBN 0-405-10260-7). Ayer Co Pubs.

Karta, Neturei. Judaism & Zionism: Principles & Definitions. 1980. lib. bdg. 59.95 (ISBN 0-87700-305-X). Revisionist Pr.

Kedourie, Elie & Haim, Sylvia G., eds. Zionism & Arabism in Palestine & Israel. 266p. 1982. text ed. 37.50x (ISBN 0-7146-3169-8, F Cass Co). Biblio Dist.

Khalidi, Walid, ed. From Haven to Conquest: Readings in Zionism & the Palestine Problem until 1948. 2nd ed. LC 85-237727. (Antholgy Ser. (Mu'assasat Al Dirasatal-Filastiniyah): No. 2). 914p. 1987. text ed. 29.95 (ISBN 0-88728-155-9); pap. 17.50 (ISBN 0-88728-156-7). Inst Palestine.

--Zionist Congress Resolutions, 1897-1972. Date not set. text ed. price not set (ISBN 0-88728-164-8). Inst Palestine.

Kimmering, Barach. Zionism & the Economy. 170p. 1983. 18.95 (ISBN 0-87073-775-9); pap. 11.25 (ISBN 0-87073-784-8). Schenkman Bks Inc.

Kimmerling, Baruch. Zionism & Territory: The Socio-Territorial Dimensions of Zionist Politics. LC 83-102. (Illus.). xii, 288p. 1983. pap. 12.50x (ISBN 0-87725-151-7). U of Cal Intl St.

Kisch, Frederick H. Palestine Diary. LC 73-180354. Repr. of 1938 ed. 31.45 (ISBN 0-404-56286-8). AMS Pr.

Klieman, Aaron. Zionist Evidence Before the Peel Commission, 1933-1937. Sachar, Howard M., ed. (The Rise of Israel Ser.). 320p. 1987. lib. bdg. 65.00 (ISBN 0-8240-4921-7). Garland Pub.

Knee, Stuart E. The Concept of Zionist Dissent in the American Mind 1917-1941. 1979. 14.95 (ISBN 0-8315-0177-4). Speller.

Korn, Yitshak. Jews at the Crossroads. LC 81-86479. 208p. 1983. 12.95 (ISBN 0-8453-4754-3, Cornwall Bks). Assoc Univ Prs.

Laqueur, Walter. A History of Zionism. LC 75-36491. (Illus.). 1976. pap. 12.95 (ISBN 0-8052-0523-3). Schocken.

Lesser, Allen. Israel's Impact, Nineteen Hundred Fifty to Fifty-One: A Personal Record. LC 84-12013. (Orig.). 1984. lib. bdg. 28.00 (ISBN 0-8191-4125-9); pap. text ed. 15.50 (ISBN 0-8191-4126-7). U Pr of Amer.

Liebman, Charles S. & Don-Yehiya, Eliezer. Civil Religion in Israel: Traditional Judaism & Political Culture in the Jewish State. LC 82-17427. 270p. 1983. 27.50x (ISBN 0-520-04817-2). U of Cal Pr.

Lilienthal, Alfred M. The Zionist Connection II. 1983. pap. 10.95 (ISBN 0-949667-33-1). Concord Bks.

--The Zionist Connection II: What Price Peace? Rev. ed. LC 82-61135. 904p. 1982. 11.95 (ISBN 0-686-43256-8); pap. 9.95. North American Inc.

Lipsky, Louis. Thirty Years of American Zionism, Vol.1. Davis, Moshe, ed. LC 77-70718. (America & the Holy Land Ser.). 1977. Repr. of 1927 ed. lib. bdg. 26.50x (ISBN 0-405-10263-1). Ayer Co Pubs.

Lipstadt, Deborah E. The Zionist Career of Louis Lipsky, 1900-1921. 35.00 (ISBN 0-405-14086-X). Ayer Co Pubs.

McIntosh, Carol P. & Cole, Carole O. What Price Zion? LC 82-23567. 126p. 1983. 6.95 (ISBN 0-87747-927-5). Deseret Bk.

Magnes, Judah L. & Buber, Martin. Arab-Jewish Unity: Testimony Before the Anglo-American Inquiry for the Ihud (Union) LC 75-7678. (The Rise of Jewish Nationalism & the Middle East Ser). 96p. 1975. Repr. of 1947 ed. 15.00 (ISBN 0-88355-348-1). Hyperion Conn.

Malachy, Yona. American Fundamentalism & Israel: The Relation of Fundamentalist Churches to Zionism & the State of Israel. 178p. 1978. pap. text ed. 10.50x (Pub. by Magnes Pr Israel). Humanities.

Marmorstein, Emil. The Murder of Jacob De Haan by the Zionists: A Martyr's Message. 1980. lib. bdg. 59.95 (ISBN 0-686-68747-7). Revisionist Pr.

Marsden, Victor E., tr. from Russian. The Protocols of the Meetings of the Learned Elders of Zion. 1978. pap. 4.00x (ISBN 0-911038-42-6). Noontide.

Marxist-Leninist Party, USA. Zionism Is Racism in the Service of Imperialism. National Executive Committee of the MLP, USA, ed. (Illus.). 112p. (Orig.). 1983. pap. 1.00 (ISBN 0-86714-025-9). Marxist-Leninist.

Meah Shaerim Centennial: A Study of the Neturei Karta. 1980. lib. bdg. 59.95 (ISBN 0-686-68746-9). Revisionist Pr.

Mendelsohn, Ezra. Zionism in Poland: The Formative Years, 1915-1926. LC 81-10301. 416p. 1982. text ed. 42.00x (ISBN 0-300-02448-7). Yale U Pr.
Mtshali, Oswald. Fireflames. (Illus.). 72p. (Orig.). 1983. pap. 6.95 (ISBN 0-88208-501-8). Lawrence Hill.
Navon, Yitzhak. The Six Days & the Seven Gates. 1980. 6.00 (ISBN 0-930832-57-4); pap. 4.00 (ISBN 0-686-70336-7). Herzl Pr.
Neusner, Jacob. Stranger at Home: "The Holocaust," Zionism, & American Judaism. LC 80-19455. x, 214p. 1985. pap. 8.95 (ISBN 0-226-57629-9). U of Chicago Pr.
Nicosia, Francis R. The Third Reich & the Palestine Question. 335p. 1986. text ed. 35.00x (ISBN 0-292-72731-3). U of Tex Pr.
Nilus. Protocols of the Learned Elders of Zion. Marsden, Victor E., ed. & tr. 1977. lib. bdg. 59.95 (ISBN 0-8490-1388-7). Gordon Pr.
O'Brien, Conor C. The Siege: The Saga of Israel & Zionism. 800p. 1986. 24.95 (ISBN 0-671-60044-3). S&S.
Paolucci, Henry. Zionism, the Superpowers, & the P.L.O. LC 82-15728. 80p. 1982. pap. 7.95 (ISBN 0-918680-18-2, GHGP 708). Griffon Hse.
Papers Presented at the Conference, Convened by the American Jewish Historical Society & the Theodor Herzl Foundation in New York City, December 26-27,1955. Early History of Zionism in America: Proceedings. LC 77-70725. (America & the Holy Land Ser.). 1977. Repr. of 1958 ed. lib. bdg. 26.50x (ISBN 0-405-10268-2). Ayer Co Pubs.
Patai, Raphael, ed. Herzl Year Book: Vol. 5, Studies in the History of Zionism in America. LC 72-117807. (Essay Index Reprint Ser). 1963. 22.00 (ISBN 0-8369-1951-3). Ayer Co Pubs.
Pinsker, Lev S. Road to Freedom. LC 70-162734. 142p. 1975. Repr. of 1944 ed. lib. bdg. 22.50x (ISBN 0-8371-6195-9, PIRF). Greenwood.
The Political World of American Zionism. LC 61-10126. pap. 112.30 (ISBN 0-317-08433-X, 2001332). Bks Demand UMI.
Poppel, Stephen M. Zionism in Germany 1897-1933: The Shaping of a Jewish Identity. LC 76-14284. 229p. 1977. 7.95 (ISBN 0-8276-0085-2, 395). Jewish Pubns.
Rabinowitz, Oskar K. Arnold Toynbee on Judaism & Zionism: A Critique. 372p. 1975. 17.95x (ISBN 0-8464-0149-5). Beekman Pubs.
Rausch, David A. Zionism Within Early American Fundamentalism, 1878-1918: A Convergence of Two Traditions. LC 79-66371. (Texts & Studies in Religion: Vol. 4). viii, 386p. 1980. 59.95x (ISBN 0-88946-875-3). E Mellen.
Reed, Douglas. Behind the Scene. (Pt. 2 of Far & Wide). 1976. pap. 3.50x (ISBN 0-911038-41-8). Noontide.
Rifkind, Simon H., et al. The Basic Equities of the Palestine Problem. Davis, Moshe, ed. LC 77-70736. (America & the Holy Land Ser.). 1977. Repr. of 1947 ed. lib. bdg. 17.00x (ISBN 0-405-10279-8). Ayer Co Pubs.
Rose, N. A. Gentile Zionists: Study in Anglo-Zionist Diplomacy 1929-1939. 246p. 1973. 29.50x (ISBN 0-7146-2940-5, F Cass Co). Biblio Dist.
Rosenblatt, Bernard A. Two Generations of Zionism. LC 67-18134. 1967. 7.95 (ISBN 0-88400-017-6). Shengold.
Rotenstreich, Nathan, ed. Essays on Zionism & the Contemporary Jewish Condition. 1981. write for info. Herzl Pr.
Rowland, Robert C. The Rhetoric of Menachem Begin: The Myth of Redemption Through Return. 330p. (Orig.). 1985. lib. bdg. 29.50 (ISBN 0-8191-4735-4); pap. text ed. 14.75 (ISBN 0-8191-4736-2). U Pr of Amer.
Rubinstein, Amnon. The Zionist Dream Revisited: From Herzl to Gush Emunim & Back. LC 83-40471. 224p. 1984. 14.95 (ISBN 0-8052-3886-7). Schocken.
--The Zionist Dream Revisited: From Herzl to Gush Emunim & Back. LC 83-40470. 224p. 1987. pap. 8.95 (ISBN 0-8052-0835-6). Schocken.
Rubinstein, Leon. The First Swallows. LC 83-45138. (Illus.). 216p. 1986. 14.50 (ISBN 0-8453-4758-6, Cornwall Bks). Assoc Univ Prs.
Ruoff, Norman D., ed. The Writings of President Frederick M. Smith, Vol. III: The Zionic Enterprise. 1981. pap. 10.00 (ISBN 0-8309-0300-3). Herald Hse.
Ruppin, Arthur. The Agricultural Colonization of the Zionist Organization in Palestine. Feiwel, R. J., tr. from Ger. LC 75-6451. (The Rise of Jewish Nationalism & the Middle East Ser). vii, 209p. 1975. Repr. of 1926 ed. 20.35 (ISBN 0-88355-337-6). Hyperion Conn.
Sacher, Harry, ed. Zionism & the Jewish Future. LC 75-6452. (The Rise of Jewish Nationalism & the Middle East Ser.). viii, 252p. 1975. Repr. of 1916 ed. 25.85 (ISBN 0-88355-338-4). Hyperion Conn.
Samuel, Maurice. Harvest in the Desert. LC 82-985. 316p. 1982. Repr. lib. bdg. 27.50x (ISBN 0-313-23354-3, SAHA). Greenwood.
Sandmel, Samuel. The Several Israels. 1971. 12.50x. Ktav.
Sanua, Victor D., ed. Fields of Offerings: Studies in Honor of Raphael Patai. LC 82-21072. (Illus.). 352p. 1983. 28.50 (ISBN 0-8386-3171-1). Fairleigh Dickinson.
Schiff, Gary S. Tradition & Politics: The Religious Parties of Israel. LC 77-5723. 267p. 1977. 25.00x (ISBN 0-8143-1580-1). Wayne St U Pr.
Seliktar, Ofira. New Zionism & the Foreign Policy System of Israel. 256p. cancelled (ISBN 0-7099-3341-X, Pub. by Croom Helm Ltd). Methuen Inc.
--New Zionism & the Foreign Policy System of Israel. (Middle East Research Institute Special Studies). 272p. 1986. text ed. 32.50x (ISBN 0-8093-1287-5). S Ill U Pr.
Sharif, Regina S. Non-Jewish Zionism: Its Roots in Western History. 160p. 1983. 18.75x (ISBN 0-86232-151-4, Pub. by Zed Pr England); pap. 8.75 (ISBN 0-86232-152-2). Humanities.
Sharot, Stephen. Messianism, Mysticism, & Magic: A Sociological Analysis of Jewish Religious Movements. LC 81-11688. (Studies in Religion). ix, 306p. 1987. pap. 12.95x (ISBN 0-8078-4170-6). U of NC Pr.
Sokolow, Nahum. History of Zionism, 2 Vols. in 1. rev. ed. LC 68-19730. (Illus.). 1969. 45.00x (ISBN 0-87068-107-9). Ktav.
Stevens, Richard P. American Zionism & U. S. Foreign Policy, 1942-1947. 236p. 1970. Repr. of 1962 ed. 6.00 (ISBN 0-88728-095-1). Inst Palestine.
Sykes, Christopher. Crossroads to Israel 1917-1948. LC 72-93912. (Midland Bks.: No. 165). 416p. 1973. pap. 8.95x (ISBN 0-253-20165-9). Ind U Pr.
Taylor, Alan. Prelude to Israel: An Analysis of Zionist Diplomacy, 1897-1947. rev. ed. 126p. 1970. Repr. of 1961 ed. 3.50 (ISBN 0-88728-093-5). Inst Palestine.
Taylor, Alan R. The Zionist Mind, No. 39. 1974. 6.00 (ISBN 0-88728-118-4); pap. 4.00 (ISBN 0-88728-119-2). Inst Palestine.
Tsur, Jacob. Zionism: The Saga of a National Liberation Movement. LC 76-24801. Tr. of L'epopee Du Siosnisme. 112p. 1977. pap. text ed. 9.95x (ISBN 0-87855-631-1). Transaction Bks.
Urofsky, Melvin, ed. Essays in American Zionism Nineteen-Seventeen to Nineteen Forty-Eight. 1979. 12.50 (ISBN 0-930832-56-6). Herzl Pr.
Vital, David. The Origins of Zionism. (Illus.). 1975. pap. 14.95x (ISBN 0-19-827439-4). Oxford U Pr.
--Zionism: The Formative Years. 1982. 34.50x (ISBN 0-19-827443-2). Oxford U Pr.
Ware, William. Julian: Scenes in Judea, 2 vols. in one. Davis, Moshe, ed. LC 77-70754. (America & the Holy Land Ser.). 1977. Repr. of 1841 ed. lib. bdg. 40.00x (ISBN 0-405-10299-2). Ayer Co Pubs.
Yaroslavtsev, I. Zionism Stands Accused. 157p. 1985. pap. 3.95 (ISBN 0-8285-3095-5, Pub. by Progress Pubs USSR). Imported Pubns.
Yinon, Oded & Shahak, Israel, trs. Zionist Plan for the Middle East. (Special Document: No. 1). 26p. (Orig.). 1983. pap. text ed. 2.50 (ISBN 0-937694-56-8). Assn Arab-Amer U Grads.
Zayed, Ismail. Zionism: The Myth & the Reality. Date not set. pap. 2.75 (ISBN 0-89259-013-0). Am Trust Pubns.
Ziff, William B. The Rape of Palestine. LC 73-97310. (Illus.). 612p. 1975. Repr. of 1938 ed. lib. bdg. 29.25x (ISBN 0-8371-2639-8, ZIRP). Greenwood.
Zionism-Conceptual Bases in the Prayerbook-Kit. pap. 2.00 (ISBN 0-686-96092-0). United Syn Bk.
Zionism: Enemy of Peace & Social Progress. (A Miscellany of Papers under the General Editorship of Lionel Dadiani). 160p. 1981. 7.50x (ISBN 0-317-53802-0, Pub. by Collets (UK)). State Mutual Bk.
Zionism Today: A Symposium. LC 86-70642. 72p. (Orig.). 1986. pap. 5.00 (ISBN 0-87495-079-1). Am Jewish Comm.

ZIONISTS

Almog, Shmuel. Zionism & History: Zionist Attitudes to the Jewish Historical Past, 1896-1906. Friedman, Ina, tr. from Hebrew. 350p. 1986. 29.95 (ISBN 0-312-89885-1). St Martin.
Armstrong, George. The Zionists. 1982. lib. bdg. 69.95 (ISBN 0-87700-341-6). Revisionist Pr.
Elon, Amos. Herzl. (Illus.). 496p. 1986. pap. 12.95 (ISBN 0-8052-0790-2). Schocken.
Hacohen, David. Time to Tell. Dagut, Menachem, tr. LC 84-45243. 256p. 1985. 18.50 (ISBN 0-8453-4789-6, Cornwall Bks). Assoc Univ Prs.
Hammer, Gottlieb. Good Faith & Credit. LC 85-13962. (Illus.). 280p. 1986. 17.95 (ISBN 0-8453-4798-5, Cornwall Bks). Assoc Univ Prs.
Lipstadt, Deborah E. The Zionist Career of Louis Lipsky, 1900-1921. 35.00 (ISBN 0-405-14086-X). Ayer Co Pubs.
Shapiro, Yonathan. Leadership of the American Zionist Organization, 1897-1930. LC 71-126521. pap. 77.50 (ISBN 0-317-11047-0, 2022265). Bks Demand UMI.
Simon, Julius. Certain Days: Zionist Memoirs & Selected Papers. Friesel, Evyatar, ed. 388p. 1971. casebound 12.95x (ISBN 0-87855-183-2). Transaction Bks.
They Looked for a City. LC 58-17705. 1955. pap. 3.95 (ISBN 0-915540-15-0). Friends Israel-Spearhead Pr.
Weizmann, Chaim. Trial & Error: The Autobiography of Chaim Weizmann. LC 70-156215. 498p. 1972. Repr. of 1949 ed. lib. bdg. 35.00x (ISBN 0-8371-6166-5, WETE). Greenwood.

ZIZKA, JAN, 1360-1424

Heymann, Frederick G. John Zizka & the Hussite Revolution. LC 71-77671. (Illus.). 1969. Repr. of 1955 ed. 17.50x (ISBN 0-8462-1344-3). Russell.

ZOHAR

Ashlag, Yehuda. An Entrance to the Zohar. Berg, Philip S., ed. 1974. 12.95 (ISBN 0-943688-04-3); 10.95 (ISBN 0-943688-34-5). Res Ctr Kabbalah.
Bar Yohai, Shimon. Hashmotot Zohar: Hebrew Text. 1969. 20.00 (ISBN 0-943688-20-5). Res Ctr Kabbalah.
--Zohar: Hebrew Text, 21 vols. 378.00 set (ISBN 0-943688-67-1); 18.00 ea. Res Ctr Kabbalah.
--Zohar: Hebrew Text, 10 vols. condensed ed. 1981. 15.00 ea. (ISBN 0-943688-68-X); 150.00 set. Res Ctr Kabbalah.
Berg, Phillip S. The Zohar: Parashat Pinhas, Vol. II. 288p. 1987. 14.95 (ISBN 0-943688-52-3); pap. 9.95 (ISBN 0-943688-53-1). Res Ctr Kabbalah.
--The Zohar: Parashat Pinhas, Vol. III. 288p. 1987. 14.95 (ISBN 0-943688-54-X); pap. 9.95 (ISBN 0-943688-55-8). Res Ctr Kabbalah.
Brandwein, Yehuda. Tikune Zohar: Hebrew Text, 2 vols. 1973. Vol. 1. 25.00 (ISBN 0-943688-27-2); Vol. 2. 25.00 (ISBN 0-943688-28-0). Res Ctr Kabbalah.
De Manhar, Nurho. The Zohar: Bereshith. rev.,3rd ed. (Secret Doctrine Reference Ser.). 432p. 1985. 21.00 (ISBN 0-913510-53-X). Wizards.
Joel, David H. Religionsphilosophie des Sohar und Ihr Verhaltnis zur Allgemeinen Judischen Theologie. Katz, Steven, ed. LC 79-7139. (Jewish Philosophy, Mysticism & History of Ideas Ser.). 1980. Repr. of 1923 ed. lib. bdg. 34.50x (ISBN 0-405-12265-9). Ayer Co Pubs.
Mathers, S. L., tr. The Kabbala Unveiled: Books of the Zohar. lib. bdg. 100.00 (ISBN 0-87968-124-1). Krishna Pr.
Matt, Daniel C. Zohar, The Book of Enlightment. (The Classics of Western Spirituality). 320p. 1982. 12.95 (ISBN 0-8091-0320-6); pap. 9.95 (ISBN 0-8091-2387-8). Paulist pr.
Simon, Maurice & Levertoff, Paul, trs. Zohar. 1934. 75.00 (ISBN 0-900689-39-0); pap. 55.00. Soncino Pr.
Tishby, Isaiah, ed. The Wisdom of the Zohar, 3 vols. Goldstein, David, tr. (The Litman Library of Jewish Civilization). 2000p. 1986. Set. 198.00x (ISBN 0-19-710043-0). Oxford U Pr.

ZOROASTRIANISM

see also Avesta; Mithraism

Afnan, Ruhi. Zoroaster's Influence on Anaxagoras, the Greek Tragedians & Socrates. LC 68-18733. 161p. 1969. 6.95 (ISBN 0-8022-2250-1). Philos Lib.
--Zoroaster's Influence on Greek Thought. LC 64-20423. 1965. 8.95 (ISBN 0-8022-0011-7). Philos Lib.
Avesta. The Hymns of Zarathustra. Henning, M., tr. LC 78-20446. 1985. Repr. of 1952 ed. 21.00 (ISBN 0-88355-826-2). Hyperion Conn.
Boyce, Mary. Zoroastrianism. Boyce, Mary, tr. (Textual Sources for the Study of Religion). 224p. 1987. pap. 11.75 (ISBN 0-389-20717-9). B&N Imports.
--Zoroastrians. Hinnells, John, ed. (Library of Religious Beliefs & Practices). 260p. 1986. pap. text ed. 9.95 (ISBN 0-7102-0156-7). Methuen Inc.
Boyce, Mary, ed. Zoroastrianism. LC 84-383. (Textual Sources for the Study of Religion Ser.). 176p. 1984. 23.50x (ISBN 0-389-20478-1, 08040); pap. 11.75x (ISBN 0-389-20717-9). B&N Imports.
Carter, George W. Zoroastrianism & Judaism. LC 70-112489. 1970. Repr. of 1918 ed. 14.00 (ISBN 0-404-01396-1). AMS Pr.
Dawson, Miles M. Ethical Religion of Zoroaster. LC 73-90100. (BCL Ser. I). Repr. of 1931 ed. 22.50 (ISBN 0-404-01999-4). AMS Pr.
Dhalla, M. N. Zoroastrian Civilization from the Earlist Times to the Downfall of the Last Zoroastrian Empire, 651 A. D. 1976. lib. bdg. 59.95 (ISBN 0-8490-2857-4). Gordon Pr.
--Zoroastrian Theology. lib. bdg. 79.95 (ISBN 0-87968-516-6). Krishna Pr.
Dhalla, Maneckji N. History of Zoroastrianism. LC 74-21256. Repr. of 1938 ed. 40.00 (ISBN 0-404-12806-8). AMS Pr.
--Our Perfecting World: Zarathushtra's Way of Life. LC 74-21257. Repr. of 1930 ed. 27.50 (ISBN 0-404-12807-6). AMS Pr.
--Zoroastrian Civilization: From the Earliest Times to the Downfall of the Last Zoroastrian Empire, 651 A.D. LC 74-21258. Repr. of 1922 ed. 30.00 (ISBN 0-404-12808-4). AMS Pr.
--Zoroastrian Theology from the Earliest Times to the Present Day. LC 70-131038. Repr. of 1914 ed. 30.00 (ISBN 0-404-02123-9). AMS Pr.
Duchesne-Guillemin, J. The Western Response to Zoroaster. LC 72-9593. 112p. 1973. Repr. of 1958 ed. lib. bdg. 27.50x (ISBN 0-8371-6590-3, DUWR). Greenwood.
Geiger, Wilhelm & Windischmann, Friedrich, eds. Zarathushtra in the Gathas & in the Greek & Roman Classics. 2nd ed. LC 74-21260. Repr. of 1899 ed. 24.50 (ISBN 0-404-12810-6). AMS Pr.
Greenlees. Gospelof Zarathustra. 7.95 (ISBN 0-8356-7239-5). Theos Pub Hse.
Guthrie, Kenneth S., tr. The Life of Zoroaster: In the Words of His Own Hymns the "Gathas". LC 73-131036. Repr. of 1914 ed. 14.50 (ISBN 0-404-02964-7). AMS Pr.
Hinnells, John. Zoroastrianism & the Parsis. 1985. 13.00x (ISBN 0-7062-3973-3, Pub. by Ward Lock Educ Co Ltd). State Mutual Bk.
Hinnells, John R. Persian Mythology. LC 85-70554. (The Library of the World's Myths & Legends). (Illus.). 144p. 1985. 18.95 (ISBN 0-87226-017-8). P Bedrick Bks.
Jackson, Abraham V. Zoroaster: Prophet of Ancient Iran. LC 98-2277. (Columbia University. Indo-Iranian Ser.: No. 14). Repr. of 1928 ed. 26.00 (ISBN 0-404-50484-1). AMS Pr.
--Zorostrian Studies: Iranian Religion & Various Monographs. LC 28-29344. (Columbia University. Indo-Iranian Ser.: No. 12). Repr. of 1928 ed. 27.50 (ISBN 0-404-50482-5). AMS Pr.
Karaka, Dosabhai F. History of the Parsis, 2 vols. LC 74-21259. Repr. of 1884 ed. Set. 70.00 (ISBN 0-404-12812-2). AMS Pr.
Klima, Otakar. Mazdak: Geschichte einer sozialen Bewegung im sassanidischen Persien. Finley, Moses, ed. LC 79-4986. (Ancient Economic History Ser.). (Ger.). 1980. Repr. of 1957 ed. lib. bdg. 27.50x (ISBN 0-405-12371-X). Ayer Co Pubs.
Kotwal, Firoze M. & Boyd, James W. A Guide to the Zoroastrian Religion: A Nineteenth-Century Catechism with Modern Commentary. LC 82-3236. (Harvard University - Center for the Study of World Religions Ser.). 1982. 18.75 (ISBN 0-89130-573-4, 03-00-03); pap. 12.50 (ISBN 0-89130-574-2). Scholars Pr GA.
Kotwal, Firoze M. & Boyd, James W., eds. Erbadistan ud Nirangistan: Facsimile Edition of the Manuscript TD. (Harvard Iranian Ser.: No. 3). 152p. 1981. text ed. 16.00x (ISBN 0-674-26040-6). Harvard U Pr.
Mills, Lawrence H. Avesta Eschatology: Compared with the Books of Daniel & Revelations. LC 74-24644. Repr. of 1908 ed. 14.00 (ISBN 0-404-12816-5). AMS Pr.
--Dictionary of the Gathic Language. LC 74-21253. (Gaelic.). Repr. of 1913 ed. 57.50 (ISBN 0-404-12804-1). AMS Pr.
--Zarathushtra, Philo, the Achaemenids & Israel. LC 74-21261. Repr. of 1906 ed. 34.50 (ISBN 0-404-12815-7). AMS Pr.
Mills, Lawrence H., ed. A Study of the Five Zarathustrian (Zorastrian) Gathas, 4 pts. in 1 vol, Pts. I-IV. LC 74-21252. Repr. of 1894 ed. 74.50 (ISBN 0-404-12803-3). AMS Pr.
Monna, M. C. The Gathas of Zarathustra: A Reconstruction of the Text. 1978. pap. text ed. 35.00x (ISBN 90-6203-582-5). Humanities.
Moulton, J. H. Treasure of the Magi: A Study of Modern Zoroastrianism. lib. bdg. 59.95 (ISBN 0-8490-2759-4). Gordon Pr.
Moulton, James H. Early Zoroastrianism. 1976. lib. bdg. 59.95 (ISBN 0-8490-1743-2). Gordon Pr.
--Early Zoroastrianism: Lectures Delivered at Oxford & in London, February to May, 1912. LC 77-27517. (Hibbert Lectures Ser.). Repr. of 1913 ed. 37.00 (ISBN 0-404-60414-5). AMS Pr.
--Treasure of the Magi: A Story of Modern Zoroastrianism. LC 73-173004. Repr. of 1917 ed. 21.75 (ISBN 0-404-04508-1). AMS Pr.
Neusner, Jacob. Judaism, Christianity & Zoroastrianism in Talmudic Babylonia. (Studies in Judaism). 240p. (Orig.). 1987. lib. bdg. 26.50 (ISBN 0-8191-5727-9, Pub. by Studies in Judaism); pap. text ed. 13.50 (ISBN 0-8191-5728-7). U Pr of Amer.
Pangborn, Cyrus R. Zoroastrianism. 178p. 1982. text ed. 15.95x (ISBN 0-89891-006-4). Advent NY.
Pavry, Jal D. Zoroastrian Doctrine of a Future Life from Death to the Individual Judgment. 2nd. ed. LC 79-10518. Repr. of 1929 ed. 16.50 (ISBN 0-404-50481-7). AMS Pr.

Safa-Isfahani, Nezhat. The Rivayat-i Hemit-i Asawahistan: A Study in Zoroastrian Law. (Harvard Iranian Ser.: No. 2). 304p. 1981. text ed. 25.00x (ISBN 0-674-77305-5). Harvard U Pr.

Westcott, William W. The Chaldean Oracles Attributed to Zoroaster. pap. 5.95 (ISBN 0-916411-16-8). Sure fire.

Zaehner, Robert C. The Teachings of the Magi. 1976. pap. 7.95 (ISBN 0-19-519857-3). Oxford U Pr.

ZULUS

Hexham, Irving, ed. Texts on Zulu Religion: Traditional Zulu Ideas about God. (African Studies). 496p. 1987. text ed. 69.95 (ISBN 0-88946-181-3). E Mellen.

Koch, Kurt E. God among the Zulus. 336p. 1981. pap. 4.95 (ISBN 0-8254-3046-1). Kregel.

ZUMMARRAGA, JUAN DE, ABP., 1468-1548

Garcia Icazbalceta, Joaquin. Obras de Joaquin Garcia Icazbalceta, 10 vols. LC 68-58758. (Span). 1969. Repr. of 1898 ed. Set. 225.00 (ISBN 0-8337-1798-7). B Franklin.

Greenleaf, Richard E. Zumarraga & the Mexican Inquisition: 1536-1543. (Monograph Ser.). (Illus.). 1962. 20.00 (ISBN 0-88382-053-6). AAFH.

ZWINGLI, ULRICH, 1484-1531

Christoffel, R. Zwingli or the Rise of the Reformation in Switzerland. 1977. lib. bdg. 59.95 (ISBN 0-8490-2859-0). Gordon Pr.

Furchs, E. J. & Pipkin, H. Wayne, eds. Prophet, Pastor, Protestant: The Work of Huldrych Zwingli after Five Hundred Years. LC 84-14723. (Pittsburgh Theological Monographs (New Series): No. 11). (Orig.). 1984. pap. 15.00 (ISBN 0-915138-64-6). Pickwick.

Gabler, Ulrich. Huldrych Zwingli: His Life & Work. Gritsch, Ruth C., tr. LC 85-16199. 208p. 1986. 24.95 (ISBN 0-8006-0761-9, 1-761). Fortress.

Jackson, Samuel M. Huldrych Zwingli: The Reformer of German Switzerland. 2nd rev. ed. LC 75-170836. Repr. of 1901 ed. 24.50 (ISBN 0-404-03543-4). AMS Pr.

Kohler, Walther. Zwingli und Luther, Ihr Streit uber das Abendmahl nach Seinen Politischen und Religiosen Beziehung En. (Ger). 61.00 (ISBN 0-384-30019-7); pap. 55.00 (ISBN 0-384-30018-9). Johnson Repr.

Milton, John & Potter, G. R. Zwingli. LC 75-46136. (Illus.). 1977. 59.50 (ISBN 0-521-20939-0). Cambridge U Pr.

Pipkin, H. Wayne, compiled by. A Zwingli Bibliography. LC 73-153549. (Bibliographia Tripotamopolitana: No.7). 1972. 7.00x (ISBN 0-931222-06-0). Pitts Theolog.

Schenker, Walter. Die Sprache Huldrych Zwinglis im Kontrast zur Sprache Luthers. (Studia Linguistica Germanica: Vol. 14). (Illus.). 1977. 66.00x (ISBN 3-11-006605-X). De Gruyter.

Stephens, W. P. The Theology of Huldrych Zwingli. 360p. 1985. 52.00x (ISBN 0-19-826677-4). Oxford U Pr.

Zwingli, Ulrich. Early Writings, Fifteen Ten to Fifteen Twenty-Two, Vol. 1. Jackson, Samuel M., ed. Orig. Title: Latin Writings of Huldreich Zwingli. 308p. 1987. pap. 15.95 (ISBN 0-939464-42-X). Labyrinth Pr.

Books
Author Index

A

A. J., jt. auth. see Schweitzer, Albert.

A. Abd Al-Magid Haridi, jt. ed. see Butterworth, C. E.

Aaberg, J. C. Hymns & Hymnwriter of Denmark. 170p. Repr. of 1945 ed. 29.00 (ISBN 0-932051-28-6, Pub. by Am Repr Serv). Am Biog Serv.

Aaen, Bernhard. No Appointment Needed. Van Dolson, Bobbie J., ed. 128p. 1981. pap. 5.95 (ISBN 0-8280-0025-5). Review & Herald.

Aalders, C. C. Student's Commentary - Genesis, 2 vols. Set. 29.95 (ISBN 0-310-43968-X, 11755). Zondervan.

Aarons, Victoria. Author As Character in the Works of Sholom Aleichem. LC 84-22703. (Studies in Art & Religious Interpretation: Vol. 3). 192p. 1985. 39.95x (ISBN 0-88946-553-3). E Mellen.

Aaseng, Nathan. I'm Learning, Lord, but I Still Need Help: Story Devotions for Boys. LC 81-65652. 112p. (Orig.). 1981. pap. 3.95 (ISBN 0-8066-1888-4, 10-3202). Augsburg.

--I'm Searching, Lord, but I Need Your Light. LC 82-72644. (Young Readers Ser.). 112p. 1983. pap. 3.95 (ISBN 0-8066-1950-3, 10-3203). Augsburg.

--Which Way Are You Leading Me, Lord? Bible Devotions for Boys. LC 84-21562. (Young Readers Ser.). 112p. (Orig.). 1984. pap. 3.95 (ISBN 0-8066-2113-3, 10-7099). Augsburg.

Aaseng, Nathan, jt. auth. see Sherer, Mike.

Aaseng, Rolf E. Basic Christian Teachings. LC 81-52276. 112p. (Orig.). 1982. pap. 5.50 (ISBN 0-8066-1908-2, 10-0547). Augsburg.

--Sense & Nonsense: A Word for Teens. 64p. 1976. pap. 2.50 (ISBN 0-8010-0090-4). Baker Bk.

Abadie, M. J., jt. auth. see Campbell, Joseph.

Abadir, Akef, tr. see Mahfuz, Nagib.

Abailard, P. Sic et Non: A Critical Edition, 7 fascicles. Boyer, Blanche & McKeon, Richard, eds. Incl. Fascicle 1. (ISBN 0-226-00058-3);;; Fascicle 4. (ISBN 0-226-00061-3); Fascicle 5. (ISBN 0-226-00062-1); (ISBN 0-226-00064-8);. LC 74-7567. 1978. pap. text ed. 16.00x ea. O. P.; fascicles 1-7 complete in one clothbound vol. 130.00x (ISBN 0-226-00066-4). U of Chicago Pr.

Abailard, Pierre. Abailard's Christian Theology. McCullum, James R., tr. from Fr. LC 76-1128. 117p. 1976. Repr. of 1948 ed. lib. bdg. 14.50x (ISBN 0-915172-07-0). Richwood Pub.

Abajian, Diane. Praying & Doing the Stations of the Cross with Children. (Illus.). 24p. 1980. pap. 1.50 (ISBN 0-89622-118-0). Twenty-Third.

Abarbenel, Don I. Abarbenel Al Hatorah, 3 Vols. (Hebrew.). Set. 45.00 (ISBN 0-87559-078-0). Shalom.

Abata, Russell M. How to Develop a Better Self-Image. LC 79-91440. (Orig.). 1980. pap. 2.95 (ISBN 0-89243-119-9, 41150). Liguori Pubns.

--Is Love in & Sin Out? LC 85-81325. 80p. 1985. pap. 2.95 (ISBN 0-89243-246-2). Liguori Pubns.

Abata, Russell M., jt. auth. see Weir, William.

Abba, R. Nature & Authority of the Bible. 349p. 1958. 8.95 (ISBN 0-227-67539-8). Attic Pr.

Abbas, H. & Khan, Emir A. Sufi Principles Action, Learning Methods, Imitators, Meeting-Places. (Sufi Research Ser.). 64p. 1982. pap. 4.95 (ISBN 0-86304-001-2, Pub. by Octagon Pr England). Ins Study Human.

Abbas, Kathleen, jt. auth. see Johnston, Dorothy G.

Abbay, Ellen. Noah Takes Two. LC 85-80406. 1985. 9.95 (ISBN 0-9615015-0-2). Kudzu.

Abbey, Charles J. The English Church & Its Bishops, 1700-1800, 2 Vols. LC 77-130230. Repr. of 1887 ed. Set. 74.50 (ISBN 0-404-00290-0). AMS Pr.

Abbey, Hermione, ed. Three Psalm Tunes by Thomas Tallis. 16p. (Orig.). 1982. pap. 2.50 (ISBN 0-939400-02-2). RWS Bks.

Abbey, Merrill R. Communication in Pulpit & Parish. LC 72-14329. 238p. 1980. pap. 8.50 (ISBN 0-664-24312-6). Westminster.

--The Epic of United Methodist Preaching: A Profile in American Social History. 216p. (Orig.). 1983. lib. bdg. 26.75 (ISBN 0-8191-3691-3); pap. text ed. 12.25 (ISBN 0-8191-3692-1). U Pr of Amer.

Abbot, Francis E. Scientific Theism. LC 75-3012. (Philosophy in America Ser.). Repr. of 1885 ed. 27.50 (ISBN 0-404-59004-7). AMS Pr.

--The Way Out of Agnosticism: Or the Philosophy of Free Religion. LC 75-3014. (Philosophy in America Ser.). Repr. of 1890 ed. 20.00 (ISBN 0-404-59008-X). AMS Pr.

Abbot, John & Bamberger, Eudes. The Abbey Psalter: The Book of Psalms Used by the Trappist Monks of Genesee Abbey. LC 81-80871. 368p. 1981. 24.95 (ISBN 0-8091-0316-8). Paulist Pr.

Abbot, Wilbur C. Bibliography of Oliver Cromwell. 1929. Repr. 65.00 (ISBN 0-8482-7261-7). Norwood Edns.

Abbott, Edwin A. St. Thomas of Canterbury: His Death & Miracles, 2 vols. in 1. LC 80-18216. (The Crusades & Military Orders: Second Ser.). Repr. of 1898 ed. 55.00 (ISBN 0-404-16366-1). AMS Pr.

Abbott, Grace, jt. auth. see Hockett, Betty.

Abbott, Grace, ed. Ideas for Use with Two's & Three's. 176p. (Orig.). 1985. pap. 7.95 (ISBN 0-8341-1056-3). Beacon Hill.

Abbott, J. Indian Ritual & Belief. Orig. Title: Keys of Power: A Study of Indian Religion & Ritual. 1985. Repr. of 1932 ed. 40.00x (ISBN 0-8364-1294-X, Pub. by Usha). South Asia Bks.

Abbott, Justin E. Life of Eknath. cancelled (ISBN 0-8364-0746-6, Pub. by Motilal Banarsidass). South Asia Bks.

Abbott, Lyman. Christianity & Social Problems. LC 4-3768. Repr. of 1896 ed. 30.00 (ISBN 0-384-00074-6). Johnson Repr.

--The Evolution of Christianity. (American Studies Ser.). Repr. of 1892 ed. 24.00 (ISBN 0-384-00075-4). Johnson Repr.

--The Evolution of Christianity. vi, 258p. 1985. Repr. of 1919 ed. 34.00 (ISBN 0-318-04538-9, Pub. by Am Repr Serv). Am Biog Serv.

Abbott, Lyman, et al. The New Puritanism: During the Semi-Centennial Celebration of Plymouth Church, N.Y., 1847-1897. LC 70-39672. (Essay Index Reprint Ser.). 19.00 (ISBN 0-8369-2732-X). Ayer Co Pubs.

Abbott, Nabia. Aishah: The Beloved of Mohammed. LC 73-6264. (The Middle East Ser.). Repr. of 1942 ed. 18.00 (ISBN 0-405-05318-5). Ayer Co Pubs.

Abbott, Stan. Holy Spirit: The Anointing of God. (Illus.). 86p. (Orig.). 1984. pap. 2.95 (ISBN 0-915545-00-4). S R Abbott Mini.

Abbott, T. K. A Critical & Exegetical Commentary on the Epistles to the Ephesians & Colossians. Driver, Samuel R., et al, eds. LC 40-15742. (International Critical Commentary Ser.). 392p. 1897. 24.95 (ISBN 0-567-05030-0, Pub. by T & T Clark Ltd UK). Fortress.

Abbott, Thomas K., tr. see Kant, Immanuel.

Abbott, Walter M., ed. The Documents of Vatican II. pap. cancelled (ISBN 0-686-19062-9, EC-101). US Catholic.

--The Documents of Vatican II with Notes & Comments by Catholic, Protestant & Orthodox Authorities. LC 82-80350. 794p. 1974. pap. 8.95 (ISBN 0-8329-1115-1, Assn Pr). New Century.

Abbott-Smith, G. A Manual Greek Lexicon of the New Testament. 3rd ed. 528p. 1937. 21.95 (ISBN 0-567-01001-5, Pub. by T & T Clark Ltd UK). Fortress.

Abdalati, Hammudah. The Family Structure in Islam. LC 77-79635. 1976. 10.95 (ISBN 0-89259-004-1); pap. 8.50. Am Trust Pubns.

--Islam in Focus. 2nd ed. LC 75-4382. (Illus.). 211p. 1975. pap. 5.00 (ISBN 0-89259-000-9). Am Trust Pubns.

Abdal-aziz, Aliyah F., ed. see Khalid, Anas.

Abd-Al-Kahir Ibn-Tahir Ibn Muhammad, Abu M. Moslem Schisms & Sects: Being the History of the Various Philosophic Systems Developed in Islam. Seelye, Kate C., tr. LC 75-158216. (Columbia University Oriental Studies: No. 15). 1920. 20.00 (ISBN 0-404-50505-8). AMS Pr.

Abdallah, Umar F. The Islamic Struggle in Syria. 24.95 (ISBN 0-933782-10-1). Mizan Pr.

Abd Allah Ansarti, Khwajih. Munajat: The Intimate Prayers. Morris, Lawrence & Sarfeh, Rustam, trs. from Fari. LC 75-30173. (Eng. & Persian.). 1975. 7.50 (ISBN 0-917220-00-5). Khaneghah & Maktab.

Abd al-Rahman al Jami. The Precious Pearl: Al-Durrah Al-Fakhirah. Heer, Nicholas L., tr. from Arabic. LC 78-126071. 1979. 29.50 (ISBN 0-87395-379-7). State U NY Pr.

Abdel-Massih, Ernest. The Life & Miracles of Pope Kirillos VI. 139p. (Orig.). 1982. pap. text ed. 3.00 (ISBN 0-932098-20-7). St Mark Coptic Orthodox.

Abdel-Massih, Ernest T., et al, trs. from Coptic. The Divine Liturgy of St. Basil the Great. 257p. 1982. pap. 7.00 (ISBN 0-932098-19-3). St Mark Coptic Orthodox.

Abdu, Hani R. Christian Psychology. 288p. 1981. 11.00 (ISBN 0-682-49643-X). Exposition Pr FL.

--The True Christian Science. 64p. 1981. 5.00 (ISBN 0-682-49632-4). Exposition Pr FL.

Abdul, M. A. The Quran, Sh. Tabarsi's Commentary. 15.95 (ISBN 0-317-01596-6). Kazi Pubns.

Abdu'l-Baha. Memorials of the Faithful. Gail, Marzieh, tr. LC 77-157797. 1971. 10.95 (ISBN 0-87743-041-1, 106-012). Baha'i.

--Secret of Divine Civilization. 2nd ed. Gail, Marzieh, tr. LC 56-12427. 1970. 15.95 (ISBN 0-87743-008-X, 106-006). Baha'i.

--Selections from the Writings of Abdu'l-Baha. Effendi, Shoghi & Gail, Marzieh, trs. 1978. 14.95 (ISBN 0-85398-081-0, 106-025); pap. 7.95 (ISBN 0-85398-084-5, 106-026); Lightweight. pap. 6.00 (ISBN 0-85398-136-1). Baha'i.

--Some Answered Questions. Barney, Laura C., tr. from Persian. LC 81-2467. xviii, 324p. 1981. 17.95 (ISBN 0-87743-162-0). Baha'i.

--Some Answered Questions. Barney, Laura C., tr. from Persian. LC 83-21353. xviii, 324p. 1984. Pocket sized. pap. 5.95 (ISBN 0-87743-190-6). Baha'i.

--Tablets of the Divine Plan. rev. ed. LC 76-10624. 1977. o.s.i 10.95 (ISBN 0-87743-107-8, 106-010); pap. 5.95 (ISBN 0-87743-116-7, 106-011). Baha'i.

--A Traveler's Narrative: Written to Illustrate the Episode of the Bab. rev. ed. Browne, Edward G., tr. from Persian. LC 79-19025. 1980. 10.95 (ISBN 0-87743-134-5, 106-027); pap. 5.95 (ISBN 0-686-96668-6, 106-028). Baha'i.

Abdu'l-Baha, jt. auth. see Baha'u'llah, Bab.

Abdu'l-Baha, jt. auth. see Baha'u'llah, the Bab.

Abdul Fattah Rashid Hamid. Self Knowledge & Spiritual Yearning. Quinlan, Hamid, ed. LC 82-70348. (Illus.). 116p. 1982. pap. 4.00 (ISBN 0-89259-027-0). Am Trust Pubns.

Abdul-Haqq, Adiyah Akbar. Sharing Your Faith with a Muslim. 192p. (Orig.). 1980. pap. 5.95 (ISBN 0-87123-553-6, 210553). Bethany Hse.

Abdullah. The Prophet's Speech at Tabuk. abr. ed. 16p. (Orig.). 1984. pap. 1.00 (ISBN 0-916157-02-4). African Islam Miss Pubns.

--The Why & How of Burial & Death of a Muslim. (Illus.). 22p. (Orig.). 1985. pap. 1.50 (ISBN 0-916157-04-0). African Islam Miss Pubns.

Abdul-Rauf, Muhammad. The Islamic View of Women & the Family. 1977. text ed. 11.95 (ISBN 0-8315-0156-1). Speller.

--A Muslim's Reflections on Democratic Capitalism. 1984. pap. 4.95 (ISBN 0-8447-3537-X). Am Enterprise.

Abdul-Rauf, Muhammed. Marriage in Islam: A Manual. LC 75-186483. 1972. 8.50 (ISBN 0-682-47431-2, Banner). Exposition Pr FL.

Abe, Masao, ed. A Zen Life: D. T. Suzuki Remembered. (Illus.). 288p. (Orig.). 1986. pap. 19.95 (ISBN 0-8348-0213-9). Weatherhill.

Abehsera, Michael, compiled by see Muramoto, Naboru.

Abel, Armand, et al. Unity & Variety in Muslim Civilization. Von Grunebaum, Gustave E., ed. LC 55-11191. (Comparative Studies of Cultures & Civilizations: No. 7). pap. 99.30 (ISBN 0-317-11328-3, 2013614). Bks Demand UMI.

Abel, Ernest L. The Roots of Anti-Semitism. LC 73-8286. 264p. 1975. 25.00 (ISBN 0-8386-1406-X). Fairleigh Dickinson.

Abel, Evelyn, tr. see Givet, Jacques.

Abel, Otto, tr. see Wattenbach, W.

Abel, Reuben E., ed. Humanistic Pragmatism: The Philosophy of F. C. S. Schiller. (Orig.). 1966. pap. text ed. 6.95 (ISBN 0-02-900120-X). Free Pr.

Abelard, Peter. The Cruel Tragedy of My Life: The Autobiography of Peter Abelard. (Illus.). 131p. 1985. 97.45 (ISBN 0-89901-198-5). Found Class Reprints.

--Ethics. Luscombe, D. E., ed. (Oxford Medieval Texts Ser). 1971. 54.00X (ISBN 0-19-822217-3). Oxford U Pr.

--Historia Calamitatum: Story of My Misfortunes. 59.95 (ISBN 0-8490-0305-9). Gordon Pr.

Abell, Aaron I. American Catholicism & Social Action: A Search for Social Justice, 1865-1950. LC 80-16876. 306p. 1980. Repr. of 1963 ed. lib. bdg. 27.50x (ISBN 0-313-22513-3, ABAC). Greenwood.

--The Urban Impact on American Protestantism, 1865-1900. x, 275p. 1962. Repr. of 1943 ed. 22.50 (ISBN 0-208-00587-0, Archon). Shoe String.

Abella, Irving & Troper, Harold. None is Too Many: Canada & the Jews of Europe, 1933-1948. LC 83-42864. 368p. 1983. 17.95 (ISBN 0-394-53328-3). Random.

Abells, Chana B. The Children We Remember. LC 85-24876. (Illus.). 48p. 1986. 9.95 (ISBN 0-688-06371-3); PLB 10.88 (ISBN 0-688-06372-1). Greenwillow.

Abelson, Joshua. Jewish Mysticism: An Introduction to Kabbalah. LC 80-54593. (The Judaic Studies Library: SHP 7). 192p. 1981. pap. 6.95 (ISBN 0-87203-096-2). Hermon.

Aberbach, M. & Grossfeld, B. Targum Onkelos to Genesis. 45.00x (ISBN 0-87068-339-X). Ktav.

Abercrombie, A. Vaughn. His Everlasting Words. 80p. 7.95 (ISBN 0-89962-326-3). Todd & Honeywell.

Abercrombie, V. T. & Williams, Helen, eds. Christmas in Texas. LC 79-66212. (Illus., Orig.). 1979. pap. 7.95 (ISBN 0-933988-00-1). Brown Rabbit.

Aberg, Gilbert S. Esther: A Play. LC 69-17410. (Illus.). 163p. 1969. 4.50 (ISBN 0-87601-001-X). Carnation.

Aberle, David F. The Peyote Religion among the Navaho. 2nd ed. LC 82-2562. (Illus.). 454p. 1982. lib. bdg. 35.00x (ISBN 0-226-00082-6); pap. text ed. 15.00x (ISBN 0-226-00083-4). U of Chicago Pr.

Abernathy, David & Perrin, Norman. Understanding the Teaching of Jesus. 288p. (Orig.). 1983. pap. 13.95 (ISBN 0-8164-2438-1, HarpR). Har-Row.

Abernethy, George L. & Langford, Thomas A., eds. Philosophy of Religion: A Book of Readings. 2nd ed. 1968. write for info. (ISBN 0-02-300150-X, 30015). Macmillan.

Abhayadatta. Buddha's Lions. Robinson, James, tr. from Tibean. (Tibetan Translation Ser.). (Illus.). 1979. 19.95 (ISBN 0-913546-60-7). Dharma Pub.

Abhedananda. Human Affection & Divine Love. 64p. 3.95 (ISBN 0-87481-610-6, Pub. by Ramakrishna Math Madras India). Vedanta Pr.

Abhedananda, Swami. Bhagavad Gita: The Divine Message, 2 vols. 25.00 set (ISBN 0-87481-625-4). Vedanta Pr.

--The Complete Works of Swami Abhedananda, 11 vols. (Illus.). Set. 125.00x (ISBN 0-87481-621-1). Vedanta Pr.

--Doctrine of Karma. 5.95 (ISBN 0-87481-608-4). Vedanta Pr.

--How to Be a Yogi. 59.95 (ISBN 0-8490-0375-X). Gordon Pr.

--How to Be a Yogi. 5.95 (ISBN 0-87481-609-2). Vedanta Pr.

--How to Be a Yogi. 6th ed. 64p. pap. 7.95 (ISBN 0-88697-040-7). Life Science.

--Life Beyond Death: A Critical Study of Spiritualism. 6.95 (ISBN 0-87481-616-5). Vedanta Pr.

--Reincarnation. 2.95 (ISBN 0-87481-604-1). Vedanta Pr.

--A Study of Heliocentric Science. 5.95 (ISBN 0-87481-619-X). Vedanta Pr.

--Yoga Psychology. 10.95 (ISBN 0-87481-614-9). Vedanta Pr.

Abhendananda. Songs Divine. Aiyer, P. S., tr. from Sanskrit. 69p. 1985. 6.50 (ISBN 0-87481-653-X, Pub. by Ramakrishna Math Madras India). Vedanta Pr.

Abhishiktananda. Prayer. LC 73-600. 88p. 1973. pap. 3.95 (ISBN 0-664-24973-6). Westminster.

Abilene Christian University Lectureship Staff. Crowning Fifty Years. Thomas, J. D., ed. LC 68-21004. 1968. 9.95 (ISBN 0-89112-030-0, Bibl Res Pr). Abilene Christ U.

Abraham, Antoine J. Khoumani, Islamic Fundamentalists & the Contributions of Islamic Sciences to Modern Civilization. 60p. (Orig.). 1985. pap. 5.95x (ISBN 0-932269-51-6). Wyndham Hall.

Abraham, B. Hayya. The Meditation of the Sad Soul. Wigoder, Geoffrey, tr. (The Littman Library of Jewish Civilization Ser.). 1969. 14.50x (ISBN 0-19-710018-X). Oxford U Pr.

Abraham Ben Moses Ben Maimon. High Ways to Perfection of Abraham Maimonides. Rosenblatt, Samuel, tr. LC 74-158221. (Columbia University Oriental Studies: No. 27). 1927. 19.00 (ISBN 0-404-50517-1); Suppl., 1982. 35.00; Supp., 1983. 43.50. AMS Pr.

Abraham, Kurt. Introduction to the Seven Rays. LC 86-80170. 108p. (Orig.). 1986. pap. 6.95 (ISBN 0-9609002-2-5). Lampus Pr.

Abraham, William J. The Coming Great Revival: Recovering the Full Evangelical Tradition. LC 84-47710. 160p. 1984. 12.45 (ISBN 0-06-060035-7, HarpR). Har-Row.

--Divine Inspiration of Holy Scripture. 1981. 32.00x (ISBN 0-19-826659-6). Oxford U Pr.

--Divine Revelation & the Limits of Historical Criticism. 1982. 29.95x (ISBN 0-19-826665-0). Oxford U Pr.

Abrahams, Doug. Doug: Man & Missionary. 1983. pap. 3.95 (ISBN 0-85363-151-4). OMF Bks.

Abrahams, Israel. The Book of Delight & Other Papers. Katz, Steven, ed. LC 79-7124. (Jewish Philosophy, Mysticism & History of Ideas Ser.). 1980. Repr. of 1912 ed. lib. bdg. 26.50x (ISBN 0-405-12238-1). Ayer Co Pubs.

--By-Paths in Hebraic Bookland. LC 77-174368. Repr. of 1920 ed. 17.00 (ISBN 0-405-08177-4, Pub. by Blom Publications). Ayer Co Pubs.

--Jewish Life in the Middle Ages. LC 58-11933. (Temple Books). 1969. pap. text ed. 7.95x (ISBN 0-689-70001-6, T1). Atheneum.

--A Short History of Jewish Literature. 1906. Repr. 20.00 (ISBN 0-8274-3400-6). R West.

Abrahams, Israel & Buchler, Adolf. The Foundations of Jewish Life: Three Studies. LC 73-2197. (The Jewish People; History, Religion, Literature Ser.). 38.50 (ISBN 0-405-05263-4). Ayer Co Pubs.

Abrahams, Israel, jt. auth. see Yellin, David.

Abrahams, Israel, tr. see Alon, Gedalyahu.

Abrahams, Israel, tr. see Cassuto, U.

Abrahams-Curiel, Diana, tr. see Linssen, Robert.

Abrahamse, Dorothy, ed. see Alexander, Paul J.

Abrahamsen, Samuel. The Holocaust in Norway: An Historical Perspective. 1987. 20.95 (ISBN 0-89604-116-6); pap. 13.95 (ISBN 0-89604-117-4). Holocaust Pubns.

Abrahamsson, Hans. The Origin of Death: Studies in African Mythology. Kastenbaum, Robert, ed. LC 76-19555. (Death and Dying Ser.). 1977. Repr. of 1951 ed. lib. bdg. 23.50x (ISBN 0-405-09551-1). Ayer Co Pubs.

Abram, Victor P. Restoration of All Things. LC 62-18059. 1962. 4.00 (ISBN 0-910840-07-5). Kingdom.

Abramov, S. Zalman. Perpetual Dilemma: Jewish Religion in the Jewish State. 1979. pap. 7.50 (ISBN 0-8074-0088-2, 382500, WUPJ). UAHC.

Abramowitz, Bernard. Marriage & Family Life Code of the Jewish Faith. (Hebrew., Heb, & Eng). 12.50 (ISBN 0-87559-098-5). Shalom.

Abramowski, Luise & Goodman, Allan E., eds. Nestorian Collection of Christological Texts, 2 vols. Incl. Vol. 1. Syriac Text. 59.50 (ISBN 0-521-07578-5); Vol. 2. Introduction, Translation & Indexes. 49.50 (ISBN 0-521-08126-2). LC 77-130904. (Oriental Publications Ser.: No. 18, 19). 1972. Cambridge U Pr.

Abrams, Alan. Special Treatment: The Untold Story of the Survival of Thousands of Jews in Hitler's Third Reich. (Illus.). 261p. 1985. 14.95 (ISBN 0-8184-0364-0). Lyle-Stuart.

Abrams, Barbara C. Estates of Grace: The Architectural Heritage of Religious Structures in Rye, N. Y. Morison, Susan A., intro. by. (Illus.). 20p. (Orig.). 1986. pap. text ed. 4.00 (ISBN 0-9615327-1-8). Rye Hist Soc.

Abrams, Connie. God Is in the Night. (Happy Day Bks.). (Illus.). 24p. 1984. 1.59 (ISBN 0-87239-733-5, 3703). Standard Pub.

Abrams, M. H. Natural Supernaturalism: Tradition & Revolution in Romantic Literature. 550p. 1973. pap. 11.95 (ISBN 0-393-00609-3). Norton.

Abramson, Glenda & Parfitt, Tudor, eds. The Great Transition: The Recovery of the Lost Centres of Modern Hebrew Literature. (Oxford Centre for Postgraduate Hebrew Studies). 184p. 1985. 35.00x (ISBN 0-8476-7437-1, Rowman & Allanheld). Rowman.

Abramson, Ruth. Benjamin: Journey of a Jew. (The Life-Cycle Bookshelf Ser.). (Orig.). 1987. pap. 10.00 (ISBN 0-933771-02-9). Alpha Pub Co.

Abravanal, Isaac. Principles of Faith (Rosh Amanah) (Littman Library of Jewish Civilization). 272p. 1982. 26.00x (ISBN 0-19-710045-7). Oxford U Pr.

Abray, Lorna J. The People's Reformation: Magistrates, Clergy & Commons in Strasbourg, 1500-1598. LC 84-45805. 288p. 1985. text ed. 27.50x (ISBN 0-8014-1776-7). Cornell U Pr.

Abrecht, Paul. Faith, Science, & the Future. LC 79-7035. pap. 60.00 (2026942). Bks Demand UMI.

Abreu Gomez, Emilio. Canek, History & Legend of a Maya Hero. Davila, Mario L. & Wilson, Carter, trs. from Span. LC 75-32674. 1979. 19.50x (ISBN 0-520-03148-2); pap. 2.95 (ISBN 0-520-03982-3, CAL 441). U of Cal Pr.

Abri, Amir F., tr. see Mutahhari, Morteza.

Abu-Ghazaleh, Adnan. American Missions in Syria. 120p. (Orig.). 1985. 16.95 (ISBN 0-915597-26-8); pap. 8.95 (ISBN 0-915597-25-X). Amana Bks.

Abul-Fadl, Mirza. The Baha'i Proofs & A Short Sketch of the History & Lives of the Leaders of This Religion. Khan, Ali-Kuli, tr. from Arabic. LC 83-22486. (Illus.). xi, 305p. 1983. 17.95 (ISBN 0-87743-191-4). Baha'i.

Abun-Nasr, Jamil M. A History of the Maghrib in the Islamic Period. (Illus.). 512p. Date not set. price not set (ISBN 0-521-33184-6); pap. price not set (ISBN 0-521-33767-4). Cambridge U Pr.

Abu-Saud, Mahmoud. Concept of Islam. Quinlan, Hamid, ed. LC 83-70184. 147p. 1983. pap. 6.50 (ISBN 0-89259-043-2). Am Trust Pubns.

Academy of Religion & Mental Health Staff. Psychological Testing for Ministerial Selection: Proceedings of the Seventh Academy Symposium. Bier, W. C., ed. LC 73-79568. 1970. 25.00 (ISBN 0-8232-0850-8). Fordham.

A. C. Bhaktivedanta Prabhupada. Sri Namamrta: The Holy Nectar of the Holy Name. (Illus.). 586p. 1982. pap. 12.95 (ISBN 0-89213-113-6). Bhaktivedanta.

Achad, Frater. Melchizedek Truth Principles. pap. 6.95 (ISBN 0-87516-166-9). De Vorss.

Acharya, P. K. Dictionary of Hindu Architecture. 1981. text ed. 58.50x. Coronet Bks.

--Encyclopedia of Hindu Architecture. (Illus.). 1979. text ed. 38.50x. Coronet Bks.

Acharya, Pundit. Breath, Sleep, the Heart, & Life: The Revolutionary Health Yoga of Pundit Acharya. LC 74-24306. 190p. 1975. pap. 7.95 (ISBN 0-913922-09-9). Dawn Horse Pr.

Acheson, Edna L. The Construction of Junior Church School Curricula. LC 73-176503. Repr. of 1929 ed. 22.50 (ISBN 0-404-55331-1). AMS Pr.

Achtemeier, Elizabeth. The Committed Marriage. LC 76-7611. (Biblical Perspectives on Current Issues Ser.). 224p. 1976. pap. 8.95 (ISBN 0-664-24754-7). Westminster.

--The Community & Message of Isaiah Fifty Six-Sixty Six: A Theological Commentary. LC 81-52284. 160p. (Orig.). 1982. pap. 8.95 (ISBN 0-8066-1916-3, 10-1610). Augsburg.

--Creative Preaching: Finding the Words. LC 80-16890. (Abingdon Preacher's Library). 128p. (Orig.). 1980. pap. 6.95 (ISBN 0-687-09831-9). Abingdon.

--Jeremiah. Hayes, John H., ed. LC 86-45402. (Preaching Guides). 120p. (Orig.). 1987. pap. 7.95 (ISBN 0-8042-3222-9). John Knox.

--Nahum-Malachi. LC 85-45458. (Interpretation Ser.). 216p. 1986. 17.95 (ISBN 0-8042-3129-X). John Knox.

--Preaching As Theology & Art. 144p. 1984. pap. 8.75 (ISBN 0-687-33828-X). Abingdon.

Achtemeier, Elizabeth, jt. auth. see Achtemeier, Paul J.

Achtemeier, Elizabeth, ed. see Carlston, Charles.

Achtemeier, Elizabeth, ed. see Clifford, Richard J. & Rockwell, Hays H.

Achtemeier, Elizabeth, ed. see Fiorenza, Elisabeth S. & Holmes, Urban T.

Achtemeier, Elizabeth, ed. see Fuller, Reginald H.

Achtemeier, Elizabeth, ed. see Perkins, Pheme.

Achtemeier, Elizabeth, et al, eds. see Achtemeier, Paul J. & Mebust, J. Leland.

Achtemeier, Elizabeth, et al, eds. see Borsch, Frederick H. & Napier, Davie.

Achtemeier, Elizabeth, et al, eds. see Burgess, Joseph A. & Winn, Albert C.

Achtemeier, Elizabeth, et al, eds. see Edwards, O. C., Jr. & Taylor, Gardner C.

Achtemeier, Elizabeth, et al, eds. see Fuller, Reginald H.

Achtemeier, Elizabeth, et al, eds. see Furnish, Victor P. & Thulin, Richard L.

Achtemeier, Elizabeth, et al, eds. see Harrisville, Roy A. & Hackett, Charles D.

Achtemeier, Elizabeth, et al, eds. see Jeske, Richard L. & Barr, Browne.

Achtemeier, Elizabeth, et al, eds. see Juel, Donald H. & Buttrick, David.

Achtemeier, Elizabeth, et al, eds. see Kee, Howard C. & Gomes, Peter J.

Achtemeier, Elizabeth, et al, eds. see Kingsbury, Jack D. & Pennington, Chester.

Achtemeier, Elizabeth, et al, eds. see Krentz, Edgar & Vogel, Arthur A.

Achtemeier, Elizabeth, et al, eds. see Micks, Marianne H. & Ridenhour, Thomas E.

Achtemeier, Elizabeth, et al, eds. see Minear, Paul S. & Adams, Harry B.

Achtemeier, Elizabeth, et al, eds. see Nieting, Lorenz.

Achtemeier, Elizabeth, et al, eds. see Pervo, Richard I. & Carl, William J., III.

Achtemeier, Elizabeth, et al, eds. see Reid, Richard & Crum, Milton, Jr.

Achtemeier, Elizabeth, et al, eds. see Saunders, Ernest W. & Craddock, Fred B.

Achtemeier, Elizabeth, et al, eds. see Thulin, Richard L.

Achtemeier, Elizabeth, et al, eds. see Tiede, David L. & Kavanagh, Aidan.

Achtemeier, Elizabeth, et al, eds. see Trotti, John B.

Achtemeier, Paul J. The Inspiration of Scripture: Problems & Proposals. LC 80-10286. (Biblical Perspectives on Current Issues). 188p. 1980. pap. 8.95 (ISBN 0-664-24313-4). Westminster.

--Mark. rev., enl., 2nd ed. Krodel, Gerhard, ed. LC 85-46020. (Proclamation Commentaries: The New Testament Witnesses for Preaching Ser.). 144p. 1986. pap. 4.50 (ISBN 0-8006-1916-1, 1-1916). Fortress.

--Pentecost Three. LC 84-18756. (Proclamation Three C Ser.). 64p. 1986. pap. 3.75 (1-4132). Fortress.

--The Quest for Unity in the New Teatament Church: A Study in Paul & Acts. LC 86-45911. 128p. 1987. pap. 7.95 (ISBN 0-8006-1972-2, 1-1972). Fortress.

--The Quest for Unity in the New Testament Church: A Study in Paul & Acts. 1987. pap. 7.95. Fortress.

--Romans: Interpretation: A Bible Commentary for Teaching & Preaching. Mays, James L., ed. LC 84-47796. 240p. 1985. 17.95 (ISBN 0-8042-3137-0). John Knox.

--Society of Biblical Literature: Seminar Papers Nineteen Eighty. (SBL Seminar Papers & Abstracts). pap. 9.00 (ISBN 0-89130-357-X, 06-09-19). Scholars Pr GA.

Achtemeier, Paul J. & Achtemeier, Elizabeth. The Old Testament Roots of Our Faith. LC 78-14659. 160p. 1979. pap. 5.95 (ISBN 0-8006-1348-1, 1-1348). Fortress.

Achtemeier, Paul J. & Mebust, J. Leland. Advent-Christmas. Achtemeier, Elizabeth, et al, eds. LC 79-7377. (Proclamation 2: Aids for Interpreting the Lessons of the Church Year, Ser. B). 64p. (Orig.). 1981. pap. 3.75 (ISBN 0-8006-4060-8, 1-4060). Fortress.

Achtemeier, Paul J., ed. see Best, Ernest.

Achtemeier, Paul J., jt. ed. see Mays, James L.

Achtemeier, Paul J., jt. ed. see Society of Biblical Literature.

Achtemeier, Paul J., ed. see Williamson, Lamar, Jr.

Achterberg, Jeanne. Imagery in Healing: Shamanism & Modern Medicine. LC 84-20748. (New Science Library Ser.). 256p. (Orig.). 1985. pap. 10.95 (ISBN 0-87773-307-4, 73031-3). Shambhala Pubns.

Acker, Louis S., jt. auth. see Sakoian, Frances.

Ackerman, Carl. The Bible in Shakespeare. 1978. lib. bdg. 18.00 (ISBN 0-8495-0134-2). Arden Lib.

--Bible in Shakespeare. lib. bdg. 15.00 (ISBN 0-8414-2954-5). Folcroft.

Ackerman, Dorothy. A Quaker Looks at Yoga. LC 76-23909. (Orig.). 1976. pap. 2.50x (ISBN 0-87574-207-6, 207). Pendle Hill.

Ackerman, Paul D. It's a Young World after All. 128p. 1986. pap. 6.95 (ISBN 0-8010-0204-4). Baker Bk.

Ackerman, Walter. Out of Our People's Past: Sources for the Study of Jewish History. 1978. 7.50x (ISBN 0-8381-0221-2). United Syn Bk.

Ackermann, Robert J. Religion as Critique. LC 84-16471. 184p. 1985. lib. bdg. 20.00x (ISBN 0-87023-462-5); pap. 8.95x (ISBN 0-87023-463-3). U of Mass Pr.

Ackland, Donald F. Broadman Comments, January-March, 1987. (Orig.). 1986. pap. 2.50 (ISBN 0-8054-1554-8). Broadman.

--Broadman Comments: October-December, 1986. 1986. pap. 2.50 (ISBN 0-8054-1499-1). Broadman.

--Broadman Comments, 1987-88. (Orig.). 1987. pap. 5.95 (ISBN 0-8054-1558-0). Broadman.

--Day by Day with John. LC 81-67374. 1982. pap. 4.95 (ISBN 0-8054-5187-0). Broadman.
--Day by Day with the Prophets. LC 82-82950. 1983. pap. 4.95 (ISBN 0-8054-5193-5). Broadman.
Ackland, Donald F., et al. Broadman Comments: April-June 1987. (Orig.). 1987. pap. 2.50 (ISBN 0-8054-1555-6). Broadman.
--Broadman Comments, October-December 1987. (Orig.). 1987. pap. 2.50 (ISBN 0-8054-1557-2). Broadman.
--Broadman Comments, 1986-87. (Orig.). 1986. pap. 5.95 (ISBN 0-8054-1553-X). Broadman.
Ackland, Donald P. Day by Day with the Master. LC 83-70209. 1985. pap. 5.95 (ISBN 0-8054-5196-X). Broadman.
Ackley, Phil. Get Wise: Studies in Proverbs. (Young Fisherman Bible Studyguides). (Illus.). 80p. 1985. tchr's. ed. 4.95 (ISBN 0-87788-696-2); student ed. 2.95 (ISBN 0-87788-695-4). Shaw Pubs.
Ackroyd, Peter R. Exile & Restoration: A Study of Hebrew Thought of the Sixth Century B. C. LC 68-27689. (Old Testament Library). 302p. 1968. 14.95 (ISBN 0-664-20843-6). Westminster.
--First Book of Samuel: Cambridge Bible Commentary on the New English Bible. LC 77-128636. (Old Testament Ser.). (Illus.). 1971. 27.95 (ISBN 0-521-07965-9); pap. 9.95x (ISBN 0-521-09635-9). Cambridge U Pr.
--Israel under Babylon & Persia. (New Clarendon Bible Ser.). 1970. 15.95x (ISBN 0-19-836917-4). Oxford U Pr.
--The Second Book of Samuel: Cambridge Bible Commentary on the New English Bible. LC 76-58074. (Old Testament Ser.). (Illus.). 1977. 32.50 (ISBN 0-521-08633-7); pap. 11.95 (ISBN 0-521-09754-1). Cambridge U Pr.
Acomb, Evelyn M. French Laic Laws: 1879-1889. LC 67-18747. 1968. Repr. lib. bdg. 21.50 (ISBN 0-374-90038-8, Octagon). Hippocrene Bks.
Aconcio, Giacomo. Darkness Discovered (Satans Stratagems) LC 78-9490. 1978. Repr. of 1651 ed. 45.00x (ISBN 0-8201-1313-1). Schol Facsimiles.
Acornley, John H. The Colored Lady Evangelist, Being the Life, Labors, & Experiences of Mrs. Harriet A. Baker. De Swarte, Carolyn G. & Dayton, Donald, eds. (Women in American Protestant Religion Series 1800-1930). 78p. 1987. lib. bdg. 20.00 (ISBN 0-8240-0652-6). Garland Pub.
Actemeier, Elizabeth, et al, eds. see Brown, Schuyler & Saliers, Don E.
Acton. Essays on Freedom & Power. 13.25 (ISBN 0-8446-0000-8). Peter Smith.
Acton, Alfred, ed. & tr. The Letters & Memorials of Emanuel Swedenborg, Vols. I & II. 1948. Set. 17.00 (ISBN 0-915221-04-7); Vol. I, 1709-1748, 508p. 9.00 (ISBN 0-915221-29-2); Vol. II, 1748-1772, 803p. 8.00 (ISBN 0-915221-30-6). Swedenborg Sci Assn.
Acton, Henry. Religious Opinions & Example of Milton, Locke, & Newton. LC 71-158223. Repr. of 1833 ed. 11.50 (ISBN 0-404-00283-8). AMS Pr.
Acton, Lord. Essays on Church & State. 12.00 (ISBN 0-8446-1505-6). Peter Smith.
Acuff, jt. auth. see Dean.
Acyutananda, Swami, ed. Songs of the Vaisnava Acaryas. 1979. pap. 6.95 (ISBN 0-912776-56-0). Bhaktivedanta.
Adahan, Miriam. E. M. E. T. T. A Step-by-Step Guide to Emotional Maturity Established Through Torah. 1987. 14.95 (ISBN 0-87306-410-0). Feldheim.
Adair, James, ed. see Wiersbe, Warren W.
Adair. James R. Saints Alive. facsimile ed. LC 76-117319. (Biography Index Reprint Ser). 1951. 18.00 (ISBN 0-8369-8011-5). Ayer Co Pubs.
Adair, James R., jt. auth. see Jorden, Paul J.
Adair, John. Founding Fathers: The Puritans in England & America. 314p. 1982. 24.95x (ISBN 0-460-04421-4, Pub. by J M Dent England). Biblio Dist.
--The Pilgrim's Way: Shrines & Saints in Britain & Ireland. (Illus.). 1978. 12.98 (ISBN 0-500-25061-8). Thames Hudson.
Adam, ed. see Descartes, Rene.
Adam, Adolf. The Liturgical Year: Its History & Its Meaning after the Reform of the Liturgy. O'Connell, Matthew J., tr. from Ger. 1981. pap. 16.60 (ISBN 0-916134-47-4). Pueblo Pub Co.
Adam, Antoine, jt. auth. see Pascal, Blaise.
Adam, James. Religious Teachers of Greece. LC 72-2565. (Select Bibliographies Reprint Ser). 1972. Repr. of 1908 ed. 26.00 (ISBN 0-8369-6843-3). Ayer Co Pubs.
--The Religious Teachers of Greece. LC 65-22806. (Library of Religious & Philosophical Thought). 1966. Repr. of 1908 ed. lib. bdg. 35.00x (ISBN 0-678-09950-2, Reference Bk Pubs). Kelley.
Adam, Karl. The Spirit of Catholicism. McCann, Dom J., tr. from German. 237p. 1981. Repr. of 1929 ed. lib. bdg. 30.00 (ISBN 0-89987-028-7). Darby Bks.
Adamiak, Richard. Justice & History in the Old Testament: The Evolution of Divine Retribution in the Historiographies of the Wilderness Generation. 1982. 14.95x (ISBN 0-939738-08-2). Zubal Inc.
Adamnan, Saint. Vita Sancti Columbae. Reeves, William, ed. LC 79-174801. (Bannatyne Club, Edinburgh. Publications: No. 103). Repr. of 1857 ed. 45.00 (ISBN 0-404-52858-9). AMS Pr.
Adams, Anne. Brittany: Child of Joy. LC 86-24477. (Orig.). 1987. pap. 7.95 (ISBN 0-8054-5038-6). Broadman.
Adams, Anthony, ed. New Directions in English Teaching. 245p. 1982. text ed. 29.00x (ISBN 0-905273-37-0, Falmer Pr); pap. 16.00x (ISBN 0-905273-36-2, Falmer Pr). Taylor & Francis.
Adams, Arthur M. Effective Leadership for Today's Church. LC 77-27547. 202p. 1978. pap. 6.95 (ISBN 0-664-24196-4). Westminster.
Adams, Bob, tr. see Maston, T. B.
Adams, Carl & McElhaney, Dolly. Born with a Mission. Wallace, Mary H., ed. (Illus.). 240p. 1981. pap. 5.95 (ISBN 0-912315-15-6). Word Aflame.
Adams, Charles F The Antinomian Controversy. LC 74-164507. 1976. Repr. of 1892 ed. lib. bdg. 25.00 (ISBN 0-306-70290-8). Da Capo.
Adams, Charles F., ed. Antinomianism in the Colony of Massachusetts Bay, 1636-38, Including the Short Story & Documents. 1966. 26.00 (ISBN 0-8337-0010-3). B Franklin.
Adams, Charles J., ed. A Reader's Guide to the Great Religions. 2nd ed. LC 76-10496. 1977. 24.95 (ISBN 0-02-900240-0). Free Pr.
Adams, Charles L., ed. see Evans-Wentz, W. Y.
Adams, Charles R. & Seno, William J., eds. Success in God's Word: Bible Scriptures for a Fulfilling Life. 112p. 1986. pap. 2.95 (ISBN 0-933437-01-3). Round River Pub.
Adams, Daniel J. Thomas Merton's Shared Contemplation: A Protestant Perspective. Doyle, Teresa A., ed. (Cistercian Studies: No. 62). 1979. 8.00 (ISBN 0-87907-862-6). Cistercian Pubns.
Adams, Dickinson W., ed. Jefferson's Extracts from the Gospels: "The Philosophy of Jesus" & "The Life & Morals of Jesus". LC 82-61371. (The Papers of Thomas Jefferson, Second Ser.). 456p. 1986. text ed. 31.50 (ISBN 0-691-04699-9); pap. text ed. 14.50 (ISBN 0-691-10210-4). Princeton U Pr.
Adams, Doug. Appropriating Australian Folk Dances into Sacred Dance. 1987. pap. 3.00 (ISBN 0-941500-45-4). Sharing Co.
--Changing Biblical Imagery & Artistic Identity in 20th Century Liturgical Dance. 1984. pap. 3.00 (ISBN 0-941500-31-4). Sharing Co.
--Congregational Dancing in Christian Worship. rev. ed. 1984. 4.95 (ISBN 0-941500-02-0). Sharing Co.
--Humor in the American Pulpit from George Whitefield Through Henry Ward Beecher. rev. ed. 1981. 6.95 (ISBN 0-941500-10-1). Sharing Co.
--Involving the People in Dancing Worship: Historic & Contemporary Patterns. 1975. 2.00 (ISBN 0-941500-11-X). Sharing Co.
--Meeting House to Camp Meeting: Toward a History of American Free Church Worship from 1620-1835. 160p. (Orig.). 1981. pap. text ed. 6.95 (ISBN 0-941500-26-8). Sharing Co.
--Sacred Dance with Senior Citizens in Churches, Convalescent Homes, & Retirement Homes. 1982. pap. 3.00 (ISBN 0-941500-27-6). Sharing Co.
Adams, Doug & Rock, Judith. Biblical Criteria in Modern Dance: Modern Dance As a Prophetic Form. 1979. 2.50 (ISBN 0-941500-01-2). Sharing Co.
Adams, Doug, jt. auth. see Fisher, Constance.
Adams, Doug, jt. auth. see Taylor, Margaret.
Adams, Doug, ed. Dancing Christmas Carols. LC 78-63292. 1978. pap. 7.95 (ISBN 0-89390-006-0). Resource Pubns.
Adams, Doug, ed. see Blessin, Ann M.
Adams, Doug, ed. & intro. by see De Sola, Carla.
Adams, Doug, ed. see Fisher, Constance.
Adams, Doug, ed. see Fisher, Constance L.
Adams, Doug, ed. see Hoeckmann, Olaf.
Adams, Doug, ed. see Huff, Joan.
Adams, Doug, ed. see Kirk, Martha A.
Adams, Doug, ed. see MacLeod, Marian B.
Adams, Doug, ed. & intro. by see Neilan, Ruth E.
Adams, Doug, ed. see Packard, Dane.
Adams, Doug, ed. see Reed, Carlynn.
Adams, Doug, ed. see Sautter, Cynthia D.
Adams, Doug, ed. see Skidmore, Janet.
Adams, Doug, ed. see Taylor, Margaret F.
Adams, Doug, ed. see Winton-Henry, Cynthia.
Adams, Doug, ed. & intro. by see Winton-Henry, Cynthia.
Adams, Dour & Apostolos-Cappadona, Diane. Art as Religious Studies. (Illus.). 272p. (Orig.). 1987. pap. 17.95 (ISBN 0-8245-0809-2). Crossroad NY.
Adams, Eleanor B. Bio-Bibliography of Franciscan Authors in Colonial Central America. (Bibliographical Ser.). 1953. 10.00 (ISBN 0-88382-101-X). AAFH.
Adams, Elie M. Ethical Naturalism & the Modern World-View. LC 73-3019. 229p. 1973. Repr. of 1960 ed. lib. bdg. 45.00 (ISBN 0-8371-6820-1, ADEN). Greenwood.
Adams, Evangeline. Astrology for Everyone. LC 81-3107. 1981. pap. 5.95 (ISBN 0-396-07985-7). Dodd.
Adams, Frank O. Sindon: A Layman's Guide to the Shroud of Turin. DeSalvo, John A., ed. LC 82-90138. (Illus.). 1982. 12.50 (ISBN 0-86700-008-2, Synergy Bks). P Walsh Pr.
Adams, G. B. Civilization During the Middle Ages. 75.00 (ISBN 0-87968-873-4). Gordon Pr.
--History of England from the Norman Conquest to the Death of John, 1066-1216. (Political History of England Monograph). Repr. of 1905 ed. 35.00 (ISBN 0-527-00847-8). Kraus Repr.
Adams, George. The Lemniscatory Ruled Surface in Space & Counterspace. Eberhart, Stephen, tr. from Ger. & Eng. (Illus.). 83p. 1979. pap. 9.95x (ISBN 0-686-43395-5, Pub. by Steinerbooks). Anthroposophic.
--Physical & Ethereal Spaces. (Illus.). 71p. 1978. pap. 5.00 (ISBN 0-85440-328-0, Pub. by Steinerbooks). Anthroposophic.
Adams, George, tr. see Steiner, Rudolf.
Adams, George, et al, trs. see Steiner, Rudolf.
Adams, George J. A Lecture on the Doctrine of Baptism for the Dead. new ed. (Orig.). 1983. pap. 1.00 (ISBN 0-942284-04-6). Restoration Re.
Adams, H. Mont-Saint-Michel & Chartres: A Study of 13th Century Unity. LC 81-47279. (Illus.). 448p. 1981. 40.00x (ISBN 0-691-03971-2); pap. 9.95x (ISBN 0-691-00335-1). Princeton U Pr.
Adams, Harry B. What Jesus Asks: Meditations on Questions in the Gospels. Lambert, Herbert, ed. LC 85-18991. 160p. (Orig.). 1986. pap. 10.95 (ISBN 0-8272-4217-4). CBP.
Adams, Harry B., jt. auth. see Minear, Paul S.
Adams, Henry. Mont Saint Michel & Chartres. LC 36-27246. 397p. 1978. 18.95 (ISBN 0-910220-94-8). Berg.
Adams, Henry B. Mont-Saint-Michel & Chartres. LC 82-14018. 408p. 1982. 25.00 (ISBN 0-89783-019-9). Larlin Corp.
Adams, Henry H. English Domestic or Homiletic Tragedy: 1575-1642. LC 65-16225. Repr. of 1943 ed. 17.00 (ISBN 0-405-08178-2, Pub. by Blom). Ayer Co Pubs.
Adams, Herbert B. The Church & Popular Education. LC 78-63876. (Johns Hopkins University. Studies in the Social Sciences. Eighteenth Ser. 1900: 8-9). Repr. of 1900 ed. 11.50 (ISBN 0-404-61132-X). AMS Pr.
--The Church & Popular Education. Repr. of 1900 ed. 10.00 (ISBN 0-384-00323-0). Johnson Repr.
--The Church & Popular Education. (The Works of Herbert B. Adams Ser.). 84p. 1985. Repr. of 1900 ed. lib. bdg. 29.00 (ISBN 0-318-03787-4, Pub. by Am Repr Serv). Am Biog Serv.
--Norman Constables in America. pap. 9.00 (ISBN 0-384-00333-8). Johnson Repr.
--Seminary Libraries & University Extension. LC 78-63777. (Johns Hopkins University. Studies in the Social Sciences. Fifth Ser. 1887: 11). Repr. of 1887 ed. 11.50 (ISBN 0-404-61043-9). AMS Pr.
--Village Communities of Cape Anne & Salem, from the Historical Collections of the Essex Institute. pap. 9.00 (ISBN 0-384-00334-6). Johnson Repr.
Adams, Herbert B., et al. Seminary Notes & Historical Literature. LC 78-63798. (Johns Hopkins University. Studies in the Social Sciences. Eighth Ser. 1890: 11-12). Repr. of 1890 ed. 11.50 (ISBN 0-404-61063-3). AMS Pr.
Adams, J. Journal of Pastoral Practice, Vol. I, No. 2. 1978. 3.50 (ISBN 0-87552-024-3). Presby & Reformed.
--What about Nouthetic Counseling? 1976. pap. 2.50 (ISBN 0-87552-064-2). Presby & Reformed.
--What to Do about Worry. 1972. pap. 0.75 (ISBN 0-87552-065-0). Presby & Reformed.
Adams, J. McKee, jt. ed. see Callaway, Joseph A.
Adams, James E. Liberacion: El Evangelo de Dios. 1980. pap. 2.95 (ISBN 0-85151-417-0). Banner of Truth.
--Three to Win. LC 77-72255. (Radiant Life Ser.). 125p. pap. 2.50 (ISBN 0-88243-906-5, 02-0906); tchr's ed 3.95 (ISBN 0-88243-176-5, 32-0176). Gospel Pub.
Adams, James L. On Being Human Religiously. 2nd ed. Stackhouse, Max L., ed. 1986. pap. 10.95 (ISBN 0-933840-29-2, Skinner Hse Bks). Unitarian Univ.
--The Prophethood of All Believers. Beach, George K., ed. LC 85-73368. 324p. 1986. 25.00 (ISBN 0-8070-1602-0). Beacon Pr.
Adams, James L., ed. see Tillich, Paul.
Adams, James L., tr. see Tillich, Paul.
Adams, James L., et al, eds. The Thought of Paul Tillich. 1985. 24.45 (ISBN 0-06-060072-1). Har-Row.
Adams, Janiece, jt. auth. see Speelman, Marlene.
Adams, Jay. The Biblical View of Self-Esteem, Self-Love & Self-Image. 1986. pap. 5.95 (ISBN 0-89081-553-4). Harvest Hse.
--Sermon Analysis. LC 85-73072. (Pastor's Library). 224p. 1986. 17.95 (ISBN 0-89636-193-4). Accent Bks.
Adams, Jay E. Capacitado para Orientar. Orig. Title: Competent to Counsel. (Span.). 328p. 1981. pap. 7.95 (ISBN 0-8254-1000-2). Kregel.
--Christ & Your Problems. 1976. pap. 1.25 (ISBN 0-8010-0035-1). Baker Bk.
--Christ & Your Problems. 33p. 1973. pap. 1.25 (ISBN 0-87552-011-1). Presby & Reformed.
--Christian Counselor's Casebook. (Companion Vol. to Christian Counselor's Manual). 1976. pap. 5.95 (ISBN 0-8010-0075-0). Baker Bk.
--Christian Counselor's Casebook. 223p. 1974. pap. 7.95 (ISBN 0-87552-012-X). Presby & Reformed.
--The Christian Counselor's Casebook. (A Jay Adams Library). 224p. 1986. pap. 7.95 (ISBN 0-310-51161-5, 12128). Zondervan.
--Christian Counselor's Manual. 490p. 1973. 19.95 (ISBN 0-87552-013-8). Presby & Reformed.
--The Christian Counselor's Manual: The Practice of Nouthetic Counseling. (Jay Adams Library). 496p. 1986. 16.95 (ISBN 0-310-51150-X, 12127). Zondervan.
--The Christian Counselor's New Testament. 1977. 24.95 (ISBN 0-8010-0119-6). Baker Bk.
--Christian Counselor's Wordbook. 1981. pap. 1.95 (ISBN 0-8010-0172-2). Baker Bk.
--Christian Counselor's Wordbook: A Primer of Nouthetic Counseling. 90p. 1981. pap. 1.95 (ISBN 0-87552-069-3). Presby & Reformed.
--Christian Living in the Home. 1974. pap. 3.95 (ISBN 0-8010-0052-1). Baker Bk.
--Christian Living in the Home. 1972. pap. 3.95 (ISBN 0-87552-016-2). Presby & Reformed.
--Communicating with Twentieth Century Man. 41p. 1979. pap. 1.95 (ISBN 0-87552-008-1). Presby & Reformed.
--Competent to Counsel. 1977. pap. 6.95 (ISBN 0-8010-0047-5). Baker Bk.
--Competent to Counsel. 309p. 1970. pap. 6.95 (ISBN 0-87552-017-0). Presby & Reformed.
--Competent to Counsel: Introduction to Nouthetic Counseling. Smith, Michael, ed. (A Jay Adams Library). 320p. 1986. 15.95 (ISBN 0-310-51140-2, 12126). Zondervan.
--Coping with Counseling Crises. 98p. 1976. pap. 2.95 (ISBN 0-87552-018-9). Presby & Reformed.
--Counseling & the Five Points of Calvinism. 1981. pap. 0.75 (ISBN 0-87552-072-3). Presby & Reformed.
--Essays on Biblical Preaching. (Jay Adams Library). 160p. 1986. pap. 7.95 (ISBN 0-310-51041-4, 12116P). Zondervan.
--Essays on Counseling. (A Jay Adams Library). 288p. 1986. pap. 9.95 (ISBN 0-310-51171-2, 1219P). Zondervan.
--Four Weeks with God & Your Neighbor. pap. 2.50 (ISBN 0-8010-0140-4). Baker Bk.
--Four Weeks with God & Your Neighbor. 75p. 1978. pap. 2.50 (ISBN 0-87552-020-0). Presby & Reformed.
--Godliness Through Discipline. 1977. pap. 1.25 (ISBN 0-8010-0057-2). Baker Bk.
--Godliness Through Discipline. 1972. pap. 0.95 (ISBN 0-87552-021-9). Presby & Reformed.
--Grist from Adams' Mill. 96p. 1983. pap. 2.50 (ISBN 0-87552-079-0). Presby & Reformed.
--Handbook of Church Discipline. (Jay Adams Library). 144p. 1986. pap. 6.95 (ISBN 0-310-51191-7). Zondervan.
--Helps for Counselors. (Orig.). 1980. pap. 2.95 (ISBN 0-8010-0156-0). Baker Bk.
--How to Help People Change. (Jay Adams Library). 208p. 1986. pap. 7.95 (ISBN 0-310-51181-X). Zondervan.
--How to Overcome Evil. (Direction Bks). 1978. pap. 1.95 (ISBN 0-8010-0126-9). Baker Bk.
--How to Overcome Evil. 116p. 1978. pap. 2.50 (ISBN 0-87552-022-7). Presby & Reformed.
--Insight & Creativity in Christian Counseling: An Antidote to Rigid & Mechanical Approaches. (A Jay Adams Library). 144p. 1986. pap. 6.95 (ISBN 0-310-51131-3, 12125P). Zondervan.
--Journal of Pastoral Practice, Vol. IV, No. II. pap. 5.00 (ISBN 0-8010-0169-2). Baker Bk.
--Journal of Pastoral Practice, Vol. 1, No. 1 - Winter, 1977. 1977. pap. 3.50 (ISBN 0-8010-0116-1). Baker Bk.
--Journal of Pastoral Practice, Vol. V, No. 1. 1981. pap. 5.00 (ISBN 0-87552-035-9). Presby & Reformed.
--Journal of Pastoral Practice, Vol. IV, No. 1. 1979. 5.00 (ISBN 0-87552-031-6). Presby & Reformed.
--Journal of Pastoral Practice, Vol. V, No.1. 1981. pap. 5.00 (ISBN 0-8010-0178-1). Baker Bk.

--Journal of Pastoral Practice, Vol. I, No. 2. 1977. pap. 3.50 (ISBN 0-8010-0125-0). Baker Bk.
--Journal of Pastoral Practice, Vol. V, No. 2. 1981. pap. 5.00 (ISBN 0-87552-036-7). Presby & Reformed.
--Journal of Pastoral Practice, Vol. V, No. 2. 1981. pap. 5.00 (ISBN 0-8010-0183-8). Baker Bk.
--Journal of Pastoral Practice, Vol. IV, No. 3. pap. 5.00 (ISBN 0-8010-0170-6). Baker Bk.
--Journal of Pastoral Practice, Vol. IV, No. 3. 1981. pap. 5.00 (ISBN 0-87552-033-2). Presby & Reformed.
--Journal of Pastoral Practice, Vol. V, No 3. 1982. pap. 5.00 (ISBN 0-8010-0186-2). Baker Bk.
--Journal of Pastoral Practice, Vol. IV, No. 4. pap. 5.00 (ISBN 0-8010-0177-3). Baker Bk.
--Journal of Pastoral Practice, Vol. IV, No. 4. 1981. pap. 5.00 (ISBN 0-87552-034-0). Presby & Reformed.
--Language of Counseling. 90p. 1981. pap. 2.45 (ISBN 0-87552-009-X). Presby & Reformed.
--The Language of Counseling & the Christian Counselor's WordBook. (A Jay Adams Library). 160p. 1986. pap. 7.95 (ISBN 0-310-51061-9, 12118P). Zondervan.
--Lectures on Counseling. 281p. 1977. kivar 4.50 (ISBN 0-87552-041-3). Presby & Reformed.
--Lectures on Counseling. (A Jay Adams Library). 288p. 1986. pap. 9.95 (ISBN 0-310-51121-6, 12124P). Zondervan.
--Marriage, Divorce, & Remarriage in the Bible. (A Jay Adams Library). 128p. 1986. pap. 6.95 (ISBN 0-310-51111-9, 12123P). Zondervan.
--The Meaning & Mode of Baptism. 63p. 1975. pap. 3.75 (ISBN 0-87552-043-X). Presby & Reformed.
--More Than Redemption. 350p. 1979. pap. 10.95 (ISBN 0-87552-039-1). Presby & Reformed.
--Prayers for Troubled Times. 1979. pap. 1.50 (ISBN 0-87552-067-7). Presby & Reformed.
--Preaching to the Heart. 40p. 1983. pap. 1.75 (ISBN 0-87552-080-4). Presby & Reformed.
--Preaching with Purpose. 1983. pap. 6.95 (ISBN 0-87552-078-2). Presby & Reformed.
--Preaching with Purpose: The Urgent Task of Homiletics. (A Jay Adams Library). 160p. 1986. pap. 7.95 (ISBN 0-310-51091-0, 12121P). Zondervan.
--Ready to Restore. (Orig.). 1981. pap. 3.50 (ISBN 0-8010-0171-4). Baker Bk.
--Ready to Restore. 1981. pap. 3.50 (ISBN 0-87552-070-7). Presby & Reformed.
--Shepherding God's Flock. 1979. pap. 10.95 (ISBN 0-87552-058-8). Presby & Reformed.
--Shepherding God's Flock: A Handbook on Pastoral Ministry, Counseling, & Leadership. (A Jay Adams Library). 544p. 1986. pap. 14.95 (ISBN 0-310-51071-6, 12119P). Zondervan.
--Shepherding God's Flock: Pastoral Leadership, Vol. III. 1975. pap. 4.75 (ISBN 0-87552-057-X). Presby & Reformed.
--Solving Marriage Problems. 1983. pap. 4.50 (ISBN 0-8010-0197-8). Baker Bk.
--Solving Marriage Problems. 132p. 1983. pap. 5.95 (ISBN 0-87552-081-2). Presby & Reformed.
--Solving Marriage Problems: Biblical Solutions for Christian Counselors. (A Jay Adams Library). 144p. 1986. pap. 6.95 (ISBN 0-310-51081-3, 12120P). Zondervan.
--Time Is at Hand. 1970. pap. 3.50 (ISBN 0-87552-060-X). Presby & Reformed.
--Update on Christian Counseling, Vol. II. 1981. pap. 2.75 (ISBN 0-87552-071-5). Presby & Reformed.
--Update on Christian Counseling, 2 vols. (A Jay Adams Library). 288p. 1986. pap. 9.95 (ISBN 0-310-51051-1, 12117P). Zondervan.
--Update on Christian Counseling, Vol. 1. pap. 3.50 (ISBN 0-8010-0153-6). Baker Bk.
--Update on Christian Counseling, Vol. 1. 1979. pap. 3.50 (ISBN 0-87552-062-6). Presby & Reformed.
--Update on Christian Counseling, Vol. 2. 1981. pap. 2.75 (ISBN 0-8010-0180-3). Baker Bk.
--Use of Scripture in Counseling. 1975. pap. 2.95 (ISBN 0-87552-063-4). Presby & Reformed.
--What about Nouthetic Counseling? The Question & Answer Book. 1977. pap. 2.50 (ISBN 0-8010-0114-5). Baker Bk.
--What to Do about Worry. 1976. pap. 1.50 (ISBN 0-8010-0048-3). Baker Bk.
--What to do on Thursday: A Layman's Guide to the Practical Use of the Scriptures. 144p. 1982. pap. 3.95 (ISBN 0-8010-0188-9). Baker Bk.

Adams, Jay E. & Thompson, Lyle A. Predicar Al Corazon-Bosquejos Selectos. Carrodeguas, Angel A., tr. from English. (Span.). 175p. 1986. pap. 2.95 (ISBN 0-8297-0699-2). Life Pubs Intl.

Adams, Jay E., ed. Journal of Practical Practice, Vol. IV, No. 2. 1980. pap. 5.00 (ISBN 0-87552-032-4). Presby & Reformed.

Adams, Jennifer A. The Solar Church. Hoffman, Douglas R., ed. LC 82-11281. 288p. (Orig.). 1982. pap. 9.95 (ISBN 0-8298-0482-X). Pilgrim NY.

Adams, Jennifer K. With All My Heart. Wallace, Mary, ed. (Illus.). 104p. 1984. pap. 4.95 (ISBN 0-912315-78-4). Word Aflame.

Adams, Judith. Against the Gates of Hell. 152p. pap. 2.50 (ISBN 0-87509-232-2). Chr Pubns.

Adams, Kenneth. Foolishness of God. 1981. pap. 5.95 (ISBN 0-87508-036-7). Chr Lit.

Adams, Lane. How Come Its Taking Me So Long? (Living Studies). 156p. 1985. pap. 5.95 (ISBN 0-8423-1491-1); leader's guide 2.95 (ISBN 0-8423-1492-X). Tyndale.

Adams, Marilyn M., tr. see Del Punta, Francesco.

Adams, Marilyn M., tr. see William Of Ockham.

Adams, Mary, tr. see Steiner, Rudolf.

Adams, Michael, tr. see Huber, Georges.

Adams, Michael, tr. see Illanes, Jose L.

Adams, Michael, tr. see Orlandis, Jose.

Adams, Q. A. Neither Male nor Female. 4.95 (ISBN 0-89985-104-5). Christ Nations.

Adams, Robert E. Encuentro con Jesus. (Illus.). 80p. 1977. pap. 1.50 (ISBN 0-311-04657-6). Casa Bautista.

Adams, Robert M. The Virtue of Faith & Other Essays in Philosophical Theology. 256p. 1987. 29.95 (ISBN 0-19-504145-3); pap. 12.95 (ISBN 0-19-504146-1). Oxford U Pr.

Adams, Roger J. The Eastern Portal of the North Transept at Chartres: Christological Rather Than Mariological. (Kultstatten der Gallisch-frankischen Kirche Vol.2). 190p. 1982. pap. 27.90 (ISBN 3-8204-6902-8). P Lang Pubs.

Adams, Roy. The Sanctuary Doctrine: Three Approaches in the Seventh-Day Adventist Church. (Andrews University Seminary Doctoral Dissertation Ser.: Vol. 1). viii, 327p. (Orig.). 1981. pap. 9.95 (ISBN 0-943872-33-2). Andrews Univ Pr.

Adams, Ruth. One Little Candle. 4th ed. 206p. 1981. Repr. of 1966 ed. text ed. 6.50 (ISBN 0-88053-314-5, S-251). Macoy Pub.

Adams, Ruth, et al. Gathered Memories. 152p. 1985. pap. 5.00 (ISBN 0-88053-308-0, S-76). Macoy Pub.

Adams, Sebastian C. A Chronological Chart of Ancient, Modern & Biblical History. 1982. Repr. of 1877 ed. educational chart 14.95 (ISBN 0-943388-04-X). South Oregon.

Adams, Thomas. A Crucifix: A Message on Christ's Sufferings. pap. 0.75 (ISBN 0-685-88372-8). Reiner.
--Lore Power is "Man" Power. 64p. 1981. pap. write for info. (ISBN 0-9609242-0-5). T Adams.

Adams, Walter E. Abortion: A Spiritual Holocast. 60p. (Orig.). 1986. pap. 3.95 (ISBN 0-937408-38-7). GMI Pubns Inc.
--You Can Be Absolutely Irrefutably Supernaturally Healed by God Today. 100p. (Orig.). 1987. pap. 4.95 (ISBN 0-937408-39-5). GMI Pubns Inc.

Adams, Walter H. Church Administration: A Handbook for Church Leaders. 1979. pap. 2.95 (ISBN 0-88027-001-2). Firm Foun Pub.

Adams, William H. Famous Caves & Catacombs. facsimile ed. LC 70-37773. (Essay Index Reprint Ser). Repr. of 1886 ed. 23.00 (ISBN 0-8369-2577-7). Ayer Co Pubs.

Adamson, James. Commentary on the Epistle of James. (New International Commentary on the New Testament). 480p. 1976. 13.95 (ISBN 0-8028-2377-7). Eerdmans.

Adamson, James B. James: The Man & His Message. 432p. (Orig.). 1987. pap. 16.95 (ISBN 0-8028-0167-6). Eerdmans.

Adamson, M. R., tr. see Maritain, Jacques.

Adamson, Margot, tr. see Maritain, Jacques.

Adar Publications, ed. see Doukhan, Jacques.

Adar, Zvi. Humanistic Values in the Bible. Tcherikover, Victor, tr. from Hebrew. LC 67-24730. 429p. 1967. 11.00 (ISBN 0-935457-02-X). Reconstructionist Pr.

Adare, Viscount. Experiences in Spiritualism with Mr. D. D. Home. LC 75-36824. (Occult Ser.). 1976. Repr. of 1870 ed. 16.00x (ISBN 0-405-07937-0). Ayer Co Pubs.

Adb al-Wahhab ibn Ali, Taj. Kitab Mu'id an-Ni'am Wa-Mubid an-Niqam: The Restorer of Favours & the Restrainer of Chastisements. LC 78-53829. (Luzac's Semitic Text & Translation Ser.: Vol. 18). 1978. Repr. of 1908 ed. 32.50 (ISBN 0-404-11291-9). AMS Pr.

Adcock, Joy. Building Your Christian Day School, Bk. 1: Policies & Procedures. 60p. 1985. pap. text ed. 3.95 (ISBN 0-931097-07-X). Sentinel Pub.
--Building Your Christian Day School, Bk. 2: Handwork & Curriculum. 410p. 1985. pap. text ed. 14.95 (ISBN 0-931097-08-8). Sentinel Pub.

Adcock, Mabel & Blackwell, Elsie. Creative Activities. (Illus.). 1984. 4.95 (ISBN 0-87162-011-1, D3195). Warner Pr.

Addams, Jane. Peace & Bread in Time of War. LC 75-137524. (Peace Movement in America Ser). 269p. 1972. Repr. of 1922 ed. lib. bdg. 18.95x (ISBN 0-89198-051-2). Ozer.

Addington, Cornelia & Addington, Jack. All about Prosperity & How You Can Prosper. LC 83-73342. (Orig.). 1984. pap. 4.95 (ISBN 0-87516-533-8). De Vorss.

Addington, Cornelia, jt. auth. see Addington, Jack.

Addington, Gordon. Discipline. 0.75 (ISBN 0-911802-51-7). Free Church Pubns.

Addington, Gordon L. The Christian & Social Drinking. 1984. 1.75 (ISBN 0-911802-63-0). Free Church Pubns.

Addington, Jack & Addington, Cornelia. The Joy of Meditation. LC 78-75078. 1979. pap. 4.95 (ISBN 0-87516-292-4). De Vorss.
--The Perfect Power Within You. new ed. LC 73-87712. 167p. 1973. pap. 4.95 (ISBN 0-87516-179-0). De Vorss.
--Your Needs Met. 156p. 1982. pap. 3.95 (ISBN 0-87516-490-0). De Vorss.

Addington, Jack, jt. auth. see Addington, Cornelia.

Addington, Jack E. Psychogenesis: Everything Begins in the Mind. LC 79-145391. 1971. 10.95 (ISBN 0-396-06334-9). Dodd.
--Psychogenesis: Everything Begins in the Mind. 1987. pap. 8.95 (ISBN 0-396-09021-4). Dodd.
--Secret of Healing. 204p. 1979. pap. 7.95 (ISBN 0-911336-80-X). Sci of Mind.

Addison, Agnes. Romanticism & the Gothic Revival. 204p. 1967. Repr. of 1938 ed. 17.50x (ISBN 0-87752-000-3). Gordian.

Addison, Charles G. The Knights Templar History. rev. ed. LC 76-29832. Repr. of 1912 ed. 59.50 (ISBN 0-404-15407-7). AMS Pr.

Addison, Charles M. The Theory & Practice of Mysticism. 1977. lib. bdg. 59.95 (ISBN 0-8490-2742-X). Gordon Pr.

Addison, James T. The Christian Approach to the Moslem. LC 76-158227. (BCL Ser.: No. II). Repr. of 1942 ed. 24.50 (ISBN 0-404-00294-3). AMS Pr.

Addison, Joseph. Criticisms on Paradise Lost. (Works of Joseph Addison Ser.). 200p. 1985. Repr. of 1892 ed. lib. bdg. 29.00 (ISBN 0-932051-91-X, Pub. by Am Repr Serv). Am Biog Serv.

Addison, Wendy, ed. see Bennett, J. G. & Montessori, Mario.

Addison, William. Local Styles of the English Parish Church. (Illus.). 192p. 1982. text ed. 35.00x (ISBN 0-8419-6401-7). Holmes & Meier.

Addison, William G. The Renewed Church of the United Brethren, 1722-1930. (Church Historical Society London Ser.: No. 9). Repr. of 1932 ed. 40.00 (ISBN 0-8115-3133-3). Kraus Repr.

Addy, Sidney O. Church & Manor: A Study in English Economic History. LC 70-107902. (Illus.). 1970. Repr. of 1913 ed. 37.50x (ISBN 0-678-00632-6). Kelley.

Addyman, Peter & Morris, Richard, eds. The Archaeological Study of Churches. LC 77-365546. (Council for British Archaeology Research Report Ser.: No. 13). (Illus.). pap. 24.00 (ISBN 0-317-09531-5, 2014021). Bks Demand UMI.

Adeboye, E. A., ed. The Crucified Life. 48p. (Orig.). 1985. pap. 0.95 (ISBN 0-88144-053-1, CPS022). Christian Pub.

Adede, Rose. Joel Litu: African Quaker. LC 82-81325. 32p. 1982. pap. 2.50x (ISBN 0-87574-243-2). Pendle Hill.

Adelman, Penina V. Miriam's Well: Rituals for Jewish Women Around the Year. LC 84-71828. (Illus.). 143p. (Orig.). 1986. pap. 9.95 (ISBN 0-930395-00-X); music cassette 6.00. Biblio NY.

Adels, Jill H. Wisdom of the Saints: An Anthology of Voices. 288p. 1987. 16.95 (ISBN 0-19-504152-6). Oxford U Pr.

Adelsperger, Charlotte. Effective Encouragement. (Illus.). 64p. 1986. pap. 2.95 (ISBN 0-87403-077-3, 3197). Standard Pub.
--When Your Child Hurts. LC 81-68639. 1985. pap. 5.95 (ISBN 0-8066-2161-3, 10-7088). Augsburg.

Adeney, Carol, ed. This Morning with God. LC 68-28080. 1978. pap. 9.95 (ISBN 0-87784-870-X). Inter-Varsity.

Adeney, David H. China: The Church's Long March. LC 85-25666. (Worldview Ser.). 238p. 1985. pap. 7.95 (ISBN 0-8307-1096-5, 5418621). Regal.

Adeney, Miriam. God's Foreign Policy. LC 83-25343. 152p. (Orig.). 1984. pap. 6.95 (ISBN 0-8028-1968-0). Eerdmans.

Adeney, Walter D. The Books of Ezra & Nehemiah. 1980. 13.00 (ISBN 0-86524-050-7, 7004). Klock & Klock.

Adeney, Walter F. The Greek & Eastern Churches. LC 65-22087. (Library of Religious & Philosophical Thought). 1966. Repr. of 1908 ed. lib. bdg. 45.00x (ISBN 0-678-09951-0, Reference Bk Pubs). Kelley.

Aderman, James. Challeging Christianity: Leader's Guide. Fischer, William E., ed. (Bible Class Course Ser.). 48p. 1986. pap. 2.95 (ISBN 0-938272-25-X). WELS Board.
--I'm Listening, Lord: Leader's Guide. Fischer, William E., ed. (Bible Class Course for Young Adults Ser.). 64p. 1984. pap. text ed. 2.95 (ISBN 0-938272-19-5). Wels Board.
--I'm Listening, Lord: Student's Guide. Fischer, William E., ed. (Bible Class Course for Young Adults Ser.). (Illus.). 48p. 1984. pap. text ed. 2.95 (ISBN 0-938272-18-7). Wels Board.
--Is He the One? Fischer, William E., ed. (Bible Class Course for Young Adults Ser.). (Illus.). 64p. 1985. pap. 2.95 leaders guide (ISBN 0-938272-21-7); pap. 2.95 students guide (ISBN 0-938272-20-9). WELS Board.

Aderman, James & Fischer, William E. Challenging Christianity: Student's Guide. (Bible Class Course Ser.). 40p. 1986. pap. 2.95 (ISBN 0-938272-24-1). WELS Board.

Aderman, James A. A Survival Guide to the Last Times. Fischer, William E., ed. (Bible Class Course for Young Adults Ser.). (Illus.). 64p. (Orig.). 1987. pap. text ed. 2.95 (ISBN 0-938272-30-6); tchr's ed. 2.95 (ISBN 0-938272-29-2). Wels Board.
--You Can't Lose. Fischer, William E., ed. (Bible Class for Young Adults Ser.). (Illus.). 64p. (Orig.). 1987. pap. 2.95 (ISBN 0-938272-28-4). Wels Board.

Adhvarindra, Dharmaraja. Vedanta-Paribhasa. Madhavananda, Swami, tr. (English & Sanskrit). pap. 8.95 (ISBN 0-87481-072-8). Vedanta Pr.

Adidevananda, Swami, tr. see Srinivasadasa.

Adjali, Mia. Of Life & Hope: Toward Effective Witness in Human Rights. (Orig.). 1979. pap. 2.95 (ISBN 0-377-00084-1). Friend Pr.

Adkins, Rose A., jt. auth. see Hensley, Dennis E.

Adlam, Diana, et al, eds. Ideology & Consciousness, No. 5. 1979. pap. text ed. 6.95x (ISBN 0-391-01189-8). Humanities.

Adler. The Itinerary of Benjamin of Tudela. Adler, Marcus N., tr. LC 68-9344. 1964. 25.00 (ISBN 0-87306-033-4). Feldheim.

Adler, Chaim, jt. auth. see Inbar, Michael.

Adler, Cyrus & Margalith, Aaron M. With Firmness in the Right: American Diplomatic Action Affecting Jews, 1840-1945. Davis, Moshe, ed. LC 77-70651. (America & the Holy Land Ser.). 1977. Repr. of 1946 ed. lib. bdg. 40.00x (ISBN 0-405-10222-4). Ayer Co Pubs.

Adler, David A. Bible Fun Book: Puzzles, Riddles, Magic, & More. (A Bonim Fun-to-Do Bk.). (Illus., Orig.). 1979. pap. 3.95 (ISBN 0-88482-769-0). Hebrew Pub.
--Hanukkah Fun Book: Puzzles, Riddles, Magic & More. LC 76-47459. (Illus.). 1976. pap. 3.95 (ISBN 0-88482-754-2, Bonim Bks). Hebrew Pub.
--Hanukkah Game Book: Games, Riddles, Puzzles & More. (Fun-to-Do Bk). (Illus.). 1978. pap. 3.95 (ISBN 0-88482-764-X, Bonim Bks). Hebrew Pub.
--Passover Fun Book: Puzzles, Riddles, Magic & More. (Bonim Fun-to-Do Bk.). (Illus.). 1978. saddlewire bdg. 3.95 (ISBN 0-88482-759-3, Bonim Bks). Hebrew Pub.
--A Picture Book of Hanukkah. LC 82-2942. (Illus.). 32p. 1982. reinforced bdg. 12.95 (ISBN 0-8234-0458-7). Holiday.
--A Picture Book of Hanukkah. LC 82-2942. (Illus.). 1985. pap. 5.95 (ISBN 0-8234-0574-5). Holiday.
--A Picture Book of Jewish Holidays. LC 81-2765. (Illus.). 32p. 1981. reinforced bdg. 12.95 (ISBN 0-8234-0396-3). Holiday.
--A Picture Book of Passover. LC 81-6983. (Illus.). 32p. 1982. reinforced bdg. 10.95 (ISBN 0-8234-0439-0); pap. 5.95 (ISBN 0-8234-0609-1). Holiday.

Adler, Denise R. Jesus, the Man Who Changes Lives. 1982. pap. 2.50 (ISBN 0-8423-1872-0). Tyndale.

Adler, Elkan N., ed. Jewish Travellers in the Middle Ages: Nineteen Firsthand Accounts. 416p. 1987. pap. 8.95 (ISBN 0-486-25397-X). Dover.

Adler, Felix. The Reconstruction of the Spiritual Ideal. LC 77-27148. (Hibbert Lectures: 1923). Repr. of 1924 ed. 25.00 (ISBN 0-404-60422-6). AMS Pr.

Adler, Gerard, et al, eds. The Collected Works of C. G. Jung: Psychology & Religion - West & East, No. 11. 2nd ed. Hull, R. F., tr. (Bollingen Ser.: No. 20). 1969. 45.50 (ISBN 0-691-09772-0). Princeton U Pr.

Adler, L. W. & Castberg, C. Reading Hebrew. 1972. pap. 3.95x (ISBN 0-87441-042-8). Behrman.

Adler, Marcus N., tr. see Adler.

Adler, Margot. Drawing down the Moon: Witches, Druids, Goddess-Worshippers, & Other Pagans in America Today. rev. & enl. ed. LC 86-70551. 608p. 1987. pap. 14.95 (ISBN 0-8070-3253-0, BP 723). Beacon Pr.

Adler, Morris. Voice Still Speaks. Chinitz, Jacob, ed. LC 68-57433. 1969. pap. text ed. 20.00x (ISBN 0-8197-0052-5). Bloch.
--The World of the Talmud. 2nd ed. LC 63-18390. 1963. pap. 4.95 (ISBN 0-8052-0058-4). Schocken.

Adler, Mortimer J. The Angels & Us. 205p. 1982. 11.95 (ISBN 0-02-500550-2). Macmillan.
--Art & Prudence. Jowett, Garth S., ed. LC 77-11371. (Aspects of Film Ser.). 1978. Repr. of 1937 ed. lib. bdg. 59.50x (ISBN 0-405-11126-6). Ayer Co Pubs.
--How to Think About God: A Guide for the Twentieth-Century Pagan. 1980. 10.95 (ISBN 0-02-500540-5). Macmillan.
--Saint Thomas & the Gentiles. (Aquinas Lecture). 1938. 7.95 (ISBN 0-87462-102-X). Marquette.

Adler, Nancy, tr. see Magnuson, Torgil.

Adler, Rudolph J. Biblical Beginnings: Archaeology & the Roots of Scripture. LC 85-16970. (Illus.). 320p. 1985. 17.95 (ISBN 0-13-076233-4). P-H.

Adler, Ruth. Women of the Shtetl: Through the Eye of Y. L. Peretz. LC 78-69895. (Illus.). 152p. 1979. 17.50 (ISBN 0-8386-2336-0). Fairleigh Dickinson.

Adler, Wolfgang. Rubens: Landscapes. (A Harvey Miller Publication Ser.). (Illus.). 320p. 1982. 74.00x (ISBN 0-19-921027-6). Oxford U Pr.

Adolf, Erman. Die Religion der Aegypter. (Illus.). 1978. Repr. of 1934 ed. 19.20x (ISBN 3-11-005187-7). De Gruyter.

Adolph, Harold & Bourne, David L. Stop Making Yourself Sick. 132p. 1986. pap. 4.95 (ISBN 0-89693-325-3). Victor Bks.

Adomeit, Ruth. Three Centuries of Thumb Bibles. LC 78-68238. (Garland Reference Library of Humanities). (Illus.). 435p. 1980. 73.00 (ISBN 0-8240-9818-8). Garland Pub.

Adorno, Theodor W., jt. auth. see Horkheimer, Max.

Adouse, J., jt. auth. see Balian, R.

Adriel, Jean. Avatar. 285p. 1972. 8.95 (ISBN 0-940700-02-6); pap. 4.95 (ISBN 0-940700-01-8). Meher Baba Info.

Advaita Ashrama Staff, ed. Altar Flowers: A Bouquet of Choicest Sanskrit Hymns. (Eng. & Sanskrit). 1974. pap. 5.95 (ISBN 0-87481-146-5). Vedanta Pr.

Advaita Ashrama Staff, compiled by. Life of Sri Ramakrishna. 12.00 (ISBN 0-87481-077-9). Vedanta Pr.

Advaita Ashrama Staff, ed. Ramakrishna: A Biography in Pictures. (Illus.). 1976. 30.00x (ISBN 0-87481-167-8). Vedanta Pr.

Advaita Ashrama Staff, ed. see Swami Vivekananda.

Advisory Committee. The Community of Women & Men in the Church: A Study Program. (Orig.). 1978. pap. 1.95 (ISBN 0-377-00092-2). Friend Pr.

AE, pseud. Candle of Vision. LC 73-17195. 1974. pap. 2.25 (ISBN 0-8356-0445-4, Quest). Theos Pub Hse.

Aelfric. Aelfric's Catholic Homilies: The Second Series. Godden, Malcolm, ed. (Early English Text Ser.: No. 5). (Illus.). 486p. 1979. text ed. 54.00x (ISBN 0-19-722405-9). Oxford U Pr.
--The Homilies of the Anglo-Saxon Church, 2 Vols. Thorpe, Benjamin, tr. Repr. of 1846 ed. 60.00 ea. (ISBN 0-384-00340-0). Johnson Repr.
--Lives of Three English Saints. Needham, G. I., ed. (Old English Ser.). 1966. pap. text ed. 9.95x (ISBN 0-89197-564-0). Irvington.

Aelfric, Abbot. A Testimonie of Antique. LC 73-36208. (English Experience Ser.: No. 214). Repr. of 1567 ed. 13.00 (ISBN 90-221-0214-9). Walter J Johnson.

Aelred Of Rievaulx. Dialogue on the Soul. (Cistercian Fathers Ser.: No. 22). Orig. Title: De Anima. 1981. 10.95 (ISBN 0-87907-222-9). Cistercian Pubns.
--The Mirror of Charity. Connor, Elizabeth, tr. from Latin. (Cistercian Fathers Ser.: No. 17). Orig. Title: Speculum Caritatis. Date not set. pns (ISBN 0-87907-217-2); pap. pns (ISBN 0-87907-717-4). Cistercian Pubns.
--Spiritual Friendship. (Cistercian Fathers Ser.: No. 5). 144p. pap. 5.00 (ISBN 0-87907-705-0). Cistercian Pubns.
--Treatises & the Pastoral Prayer. pap. 5.00 (ISBN 0-87907-902-9). Cistercian Pubns.

Aengus, Saint Martyrology of St. Aengus. pap. 12.50 (ISBN 0-686-25554-2). Eastern Orthodox.

Aers, D., ed. see Milton, John.

Aeschliman, Gordon, jt. auth. see Wilson, Samuel.

Afaque, Khan M. Gandhian Approach to Communal Harmony: A Critical Study. 140p. 1986. 11.00 (ISBN 81-202-0163-9, Pub. by Ajanta). South Asia Bks.

Affifi, A. E. Mystical Philosophy of Muhyid Din Ibn-Ul-Arabi. 1964. 12.00x (ISBN 0-87902-035-0). Orientalia.

Affifi, Abul E. The Mystical Philosophy of Muhyid Din-Ibnul 'Arabi. LC 77-180312. (Mid-East Studies). Repr. of 1939 ed. 12.00 (ISBN 0-404-56205-1). AMS Pr.

Affleck, Bert, ed. see Monk, Robert C., et al.

Aflaki. The Whirling Ecstasy. Huart, C., tr. (Illus.). 30p. (Orig.). 1973. pap. 1.95 (ISBN 0-915424-02-9, Prophecy Pressworks). Sufi Islamia-Prophecy.

Afnan, Ruhi. Great Prophets. 1960. 7.95 (ISBN 0-8022-0010-9). Philos Lib.
--Zoroaster's Influence on Anaxagoras, the Greek Tragedians & Socrates. LC 68-18733. 161p. 1969. 6.95 (ISBN 0-8022-2250-1). Philos Lib.
--Zoroaster's Influence on Greek Thought. LC 64-20423. 1965. 8.95 (ISBN 0-8022-0011-7). Philos Lib.

Afnan, Ruhi M. Baha'u'llah & the Bab Confront Modern Thinkers: Spinoza: Concerning God, Bk. 2. LC 75-109166. 188p. 1977. 10.00 (ISBN 0-8022-2197-1). Philos Lib.

Afrukhtih, Yunis Khan. Khatirat-i Nuh Salih. (Persian., Illus.). 1983. 15.95 (ISBN 0-933770-20-0, P-31). Kalimat.

Agape Ministries Staff. Prayer Life. (Orig.). 1984. pap. 3.50 (ISBN 0-89274-346-8). Harrison Hse.

Agar, Frederick A. The Deacon at Work. 1923. 4.95 (ISBN 0-8170-0783-0). Judson.

Agarwal, R. S. Yoga of Perfect Sight. 3rd ed. 1979. pap. 14.00 (ISBN 0-89744-948-7). Auromere.
--Yoga of Perfect Sight: With Letters of Sri Aurobindo. (Illus.). 1974. pap. 5.45 (ISBN 0-89071-261-1). Matagiri.

Agassi, Joseph. The Gentle Art of Philosophical Polemics. 304p. 1986. 28.95 (ISBN 0-912050-63-2); pap. 13.95 (ISBN 0-8126-9036-2). Open Court.

Agathias. Agathiae Myrinaei Historiarum Libri quinque. Keydell, Rudolfus, ed. (Corpus Fontium Historiae Byzantinae Ser. Berolinensis Vol. 2). 232p. (Lat). 1967. 40.40x (ISBN 3-11-001348-7). De Gruyter.

Agehananda Bharati. The Tantric Tradition. LC 77-7204. 1977. Repr. of 1965 ed. lib. bdg. 22.50x (ISBN 0-8371-9660-4, AGTT). Greenwood.

Aggarwal, Manju. I Am a Hindu. LC 85-50166. (My Heritage Ser.). (Illus.). 32p. 1985. PLB 9.90 (ISBN 0-531-10018-9). Watts.
--I Am a Muslim. (My Heritage Ser.). 32p. 1985. PLB 9.90 (ISBN 0-531-10020-0). Watts.
--I Am a Sikh. LC 85-5169. (My Heritage Ser.). (Illus.). 32p. 1985. PLB 9.90 (ISBN 0-531-10021-9). Watts.

Agle, Nan H. A Promise Is to Keep. 160p. (Orig.). 1985. pap. 6.95 (ISBN 0-310-41591-8, 9290P). Zondervan.

Aglow Editors. Aglow Prayer Diary I. 226p. 1982. 10.95 (ISBN 0-930756-70-3). Aglow Pubns.
--Come Celebrate: A Daily Devotional. 266p. 1984. pap. 6.95 (ISBN 0-930756-78-9, 531018). Aglow Pubns.

Aglow Staff. Aglow in the Kitchen. 160p. 1976. 4.95 (ISBN 0-930756-21-5, 532001). Aglow Pubns.

Agnew, Daniel. History of the Region of Pennsylvania North of the Ohio & West of the Allegheny River. LC 75-146371. (First American Frontier Ser). 1971. Repr. of 1887 ed. 16.00 (ISBN 0-405-02821-0). Ayer Co Pubs.

Agnon, S. Y. In the Heart of the Seas: A Story of a Journey to the Land of Israel. Lask, I. M., tr. from Hebrew. LC 66-30349. (Illus.). 128p. 1980. pap. 6.95 (ISBN 0-8052-0647-7). Schocken.
--A Simple Story. Halkin, Hillel, tr. from Hebrew. & afterword by. LC 85-2481. 256p. 1985. 14.95 (ISBN 0-8052-3999-5). Schocken.

Agnon, Y. Days of Awe: A Treasury of Tradition, Legends & Learned Commentaries Concerning Rosh Hashanah, Yom Kippur & the Days Between. LC 48-8316. 1965. pap. 8.95 (ISBN 0-8052-0100-9). Schocken.

Agostini, Beatrice, tr. see McConkey, James H.

Agrawala, P. K. Goddesses in Ancient India. 180p. 1983. text ed. 50.00x (ISBN 0-391-02960-6). Humanities.

Agreda, Mary. The Mystical City of God: A Popular Abridgement. abr. ed. Marison, Fiscar & Blatter, George J., trs. from Sp. LC 78-62255. 1978. pap. 15.00 (ISBN 0-89555-070-9). TAN Bks Pubs.

Agudo, Philomena. Affirming the Human & the Holy. LC 79-1499. (Illus.). 101p. 1979. pap. 4.95 (ISBN 0-89571-006-4). Affirmation.

Agudo, Philomena, et al. Guilt: Issues of Emotional Living in an Age of Stress for Clergy & Religious. Kelley, Kathleen E., ed. LC 80-10747. 144p. 1980. pap. 5.00 (ISBN 0-89571-008-0). Affirmation.

Aguilar, Enrique. El Crepusculo. Tr. of The Twilight. 1971. 3.50 (ISBN 0-686-27937-9). Franciscan Inst.
--Pensamientos Sobre la Cultura Intelectual y Moral. Tr. of Thoughts on Intellectual & Moral Culture. 1967. 7.00 (ISBN 0-686-27936-0). Franciscan Inst.

Agus, Irving A. Heroic Age of Franco-German Jewry. LC 75-94444. 1969. 20.00x (ISBN 0-8197-0053-3). Bloch.

Agus, Jacob B. The Evolution of Jewish Thought. LC 73-2185. (The Jewish People; History, Religion, Literature Ser.). Repr. of 1959 ed. 30.00 (ISBN 0-405-05251-0). Ayer Co Pubs.
--Jewish Identity in an Age of Ideologies. LC 76-14230. 1978. 25.00 (ISBN 0-8044-5018-8). Ungar.
--The Jewish Quest: Essays on Basic Concepts of Jewish Theology. LC 83-258. 264p. 1983. 25.00x (ISBN 0-88125-012-0). Ktav.

Agus, Jacob B., et al, eds. The Jewish People: History, Religion, Literature, 41 bks. 1973. Set. 1106.50 (ISBN 0-405-05250-2). Ayer Co Pubs.

Aharon, Shmuel Ben see Ben Aharon, Shmuel.

Aharoni, Yohanan. The Land of the Bible: A Historical Geography. rev. & enlarged ed. Rainey, Anson F., tr. LC 80-14168. 496p. 1980. pap. 19.95 (ISBN 0-664-24266-9). Westminster.

Aharoni, Yohanon & Avi-Yonah, Michael. The Macmillan Bible Atlas. rev. ed. LC 77-4313. (Illus.). 183p. 1977. 25.95 (ISBN 0-02-500590-1). Macmillan.

Ahemd, Akbar S. & Hart, David M., eds. Islam in Tribal Societies: From the Atlas to the Indus. 320p. (Orig.). 1984. pap. 21.95x (ISBN 0-7100-9320-9). Methuen Inc.

Ahern, Barnabas M. The Epistle to the Romans. 1979. 1.75 (ISBN 0-8199-0629-8). Franciscan Herald.

Ahern, Denise. Bread & the Wine, No. Sixteen. (Arch Bk.). (Illus.). 1979. 0.99 (ISBN 0-570-06127-X, 59-1245). Concordia.

Ahern, Emily M. Cult of the Dead in a Chinese Village. LC 72-97202. (Illus.). 296p. 1973. 22.50x (ISBN 0-8047-0835-5). Stanford U Pr.

Ahimaaz Ben Paltiel. Chronicle of Ahimaaz. Salzman, Marcus, tr. LC 79-158233. (Columbia University Oriental Studies: No. 18). Repr. of 1924 ed. 15.75 (ISBN 0-404-50508-2). AMS Pr.

Ahir, D. C. Buddhist Shrines in India. (Illus.). xii, 132p. 1986. text ed. 25.00x (ISBN 81-7018-326-X, Pub. by D K Pub Corp Delhi). Apt Bks.

Ahlberg, Sture. Messianic Movements: A Comparative Analysis of the Sabbatians, the People's Temple & the Unification Church. 128p. (Orig.). pap. text ed. 19.00x (ISBN 91-22-00787-3, Pub. by Almqvist & Wiksell). Coronet Bks.

Ahlborn, Richard. The Sculpted Saints of a Borderland Mission. LC 74-18171. (Illus.). 124p. 1974. pap. 7.50 (ISBN 0-915076-03-9). SW Mission.

Ahlborn, Richard E. The Penitente Moradas of Abiquiu. LC 85-43242. (Illus.). 52p. 1986. pap. 3.95x (ISBN 0-87474-253-6). Smithsonian.
--The San Antonio Missions: Edward Everett & the American Occupation, 1847. LC 85-71971. (Illus.). 62p. 1985. pap. 6.95 (ISBN 0-88360-076-5). Amon Carter.

Ahlem, Lloyd. Help for Families of the Mentally Ill. LC 12-2820. (Trauma Bks.: Ser. 2). 1983. pap. 2.75 (ISBN 0-570-08257-9). Concordia.

Ahlers, Rolf. The Barmen Theological Declaration of 1934: Archeology of a Confessional Text, Vol. 24. (Toronto Studies in Theology: No. 23). 1986. 59.95 (ISBN 0-88946-768-4). E Mellen.

Ahlstrom, Gosta W. Who Were the Israelites? x, 134p. 1986. text ed. 12.50x (ISBN 0-931464-24-2). Eisenbrauns.

Ahlstrom, S. E. A Religious History of the American People. LC 72-151564. (Illus.). 1120p. 1972. 50.00x (ISBN 0-300-01475-9); pap. 18.95x (ISBN 0-300-01762-6). Yale U Pr.

Ahlstrom, Sydney E. & Mullin, Robert B. The Scientific Theist: A Life of Francis Ellingwood Abbot. 208p. 1987. 29.95 (ISBN 0-86554-236-8). Mercer Univ Pr.

Ahlstrom, Sydney E. & Carey, Jonathan S., eds. An American Reformation: A Documentary History of Unitarian Christianity. vi, 506p. 1984. 39.50x (ISBN 0-8195-5080-9). Wesleyan U Pr.

Ahluwalia, B. K., ed. Muslims & India's Freedom Movement. 1985. 26.50x (ISBN 0-8364-1349-0, Pub. by Heritage India). South Asia Bks.

Ahmad, Aftab, tr. see Iqbal, Sufi M.

Ahmad, Akbar S. Towards Islamic Anthropology. 80p. (Orig.). 1986. pap. 7.50 (ISBN 0-317-52455-0). New Era Pubns MI.

Ahmad, Aziz. An Intellectual History of Islamic India. 1970. 13.00x (ISBN 0-85224-057-0, Pub. by Edinburgh U Pr Scotland). Columbia U Pr.

Ahmad, G. Sayings of Muhammad. 8.25 (ISBN 0-87902-036-9). Orientalia.

Ahmad, Ghazi. Sayings of Muhammad. pap. 2.00 (ISBN 0-686-18342-8). Kazi Pubns.

Ahmad, Imtiaz, ed. Caste & Social Stratification Among Muslims. 2nd ed. 1978. 16.00x (ISBN 0-8364-0050-X). South Asia Bks.
--Family, Kinship, & Marriage among the Muslims. LC 77-74484. 1977. 18.50x (ISBN 0-88386-757-5). South Asia Bks.
--Modernization & Social Change among Muslims in India. 1983. 28.00x (ISBN 0-88386-892-X). South Asia Bks.
--Ritual & Religion among Muslims in India. 1982. 20.00x (ISBN 0-8364-0852-7, Pub. by Manohar India). South Asia Bks.

Ahmad, K. Islam & the West. pap. 2.00 (ISBN 0-686-18572-2). Kazi Pubns.

Ahmad, Khurshid. Family Life in Islam. 38p. (Orig.). 1974. pap. 2.25x (ISBN 0-86037-016-X, Pub by Islamic Found UK). New Era Pubns MI.

Ahmad, Khurshid, ed. Islam: Its Meaning & Message. 279p. (Orig.). 1976. pap. 8.95 (ISBN 0-86037-000-3, Pub. by Islamic Found UK). New Era Pubns MI.
--Studies in Islamic Economics. 390p. (Orig.). 1980. 31.50x (ISBN 0-86037-066-6, Pub. by Islamic Found UK); pap. 15.95 (ISBN 0-86037-067-4). New Era Pubns MI.

Ahmad, Khurshid, tr. see Maududi, Abul A.

Ahmad, Khurshid, tr. see Mawdudi, Sayyid A.

Ahmad, Mohammad A. Traditional Education among Muslims: A Study of Some Aspects in Modern India. viii, 216p. 1986. text ed. 30.00x (ISBN 81-7018-259-X, Pub. by B R Pub Corp Delhi). Apt Bks.

Ahmad, Mufassir M. The Koran. LC 81-52147. (Illus.). 600p. 1981. pap. 30.00 (ISBN 0-940368-04-8). Tahrike Tarsile Quran.

Ahmad, Nafis. Muslim Contributions to Geography. (Illus.). 178p. (Orig.). 1981. pap. 10.25 (ISBN 0-88004-014-9). Sunwise Turn.

Ahmad Ibn Yahya, Al-Baladuri. Origins of the Islamic State, 2 vols. Incl. Vol. 1. Hitti, Philip K., tr. Repr. of 1916 ed (ISBN 0-404-51694-7); Vol. 2. Murgotten, Francis C., tr. Repr. of 1924 ed (ISBN 0-404-51695-5). LC 76-82247. (Columbia University Studies in the Social Sciences: No. 163 & No. 163a). Set. 82.50 (ISBN 0-404-51163-5). AMS Pr.

Ahmann, Mathew, ed. see National Conference on Religion & Race.

Ahmanson, John. Secret History: An Eyewitness Expose of the Rise of Mormonism. Archer, Gleason L., tr. from Danish. 1984. 9.95 (ISBN 0-8024-0277-1). Moody.

Ahmed, Abkar S. Religion & Politics in Muslim Society: Order & Conflict in Pakistan. LC 82-14774. (Illus.). 225p. 1983. 44.50 (ISBN 0-521-24635-0). Cambridge U Pr.

Ahmed, Ishtiaq. The Concept of an Islamic State: An Analysis of the Ideological Controversy in Pakistan. 266p. (Orig.). 1985. pap. text ed. 37.50x (ISBN 91-7146-458-1, Pub. by Almqvist & Wiksell). Coronet Bks.

Ahmed, K. Fanaticism, Intolerance & Islam. pap. 1.00 (ISBN 0-686-18491-2). Kazi Pubns.

Ahmed, Rafiuddin. The Bengal Muslims, Eighteen Seventy-One to Nineteen Six: A Quest for Identity. (Illus.). 1981. 34.00x (ISBN 0-19-561260-4). Oxford U Pr.

Ahmed, Shemsu-D-Din, ed. Legends of the Sufis. 1977. pap. 7.95 (ISBN 0-7229-5050-0). Theos Pub Hse.

Aho, Gerhard, jt. auth. see Rossow, Francis.

Aho, Gerhard, et al. Glory in the Cross-Fruit of the Spirit from the Passion of Christ. 1984. pap. 7.95 (ISBN 0-570-03940-1, 12-2876). Concordia.

Aho, James A. Religious Mythology & the Art of War: Comparative Religious Symbolisms of Military Violence. LC 80-23465. (Contributions to the Study of Religion Ser.: No. 3). 264p. 1981. lib. bdg. 29.95 (ISBN 0-313-22564-8, ARM/). Greenwood.

Ahonen, Lauri. Missions Growth: A Case Study on Finnish Free Foreign Missions. LC 84-12636. 96p. (Orig.). 1984. pap. 5.95 (ISBN 0-87808-335-9). William Carey Lib.

Ahrendts, Juergen, ed. Bibliographie zur alteuropaeischen Religionsgeschichte II, 1965-1969: Eine interdisziplinaere Auswahl von Literatur zu den Rand-und Nachfolgekulturen der Antike in Europa unter besonderer Beruecksichtigung der nichtchristlichen Religionen. LC 68-86477. (Arbeiten Zur Fruehmittelalterforschung: Vol. 5). xxvi, 591p. 1974. 59.20x (ISBN 3-11-003398-4). De Gruyter.

Ahrens, Herman C., Jr. Feeling Good about Yourself. (Orig.). 1983. pap. 1.25 (ISBN 0-8298-0644-X). Pilgrim NY.
--Life with Your Parents. (Looking Up Ser.). 24p. 1983. pap. 1.25 booklet (ISBN 0-8298-0667-9). Pilgrim NY.

Ahrens, Herman C., Jr., ed. Tune In. LC 68-54031. (Illus.). 1968. pap. 3.95 (ISBN 0-8298-0138-3). Pilgrim NY.

Ahrens, L., jt. auth. see Schlesselman, R.

Ahroni, Reuben. Yemenite Jewry: Origins, Culture, & Literature. LC 84-48649. (Jewish Literature and Culture Ser.). (Illus.). 288p. 1986. 27.50x (ISBN 0-253-36807-3). Ind U Pr.

Ahsan, Manazir. Islam: Faith & Practice. (Illus.). 48p. (Orig.). 1980. pap. 3.00 (ISBN 0-86037-001-1, Pub. by Islamic Found UK). New Era Pubns MI.
Aikat, Amulyachandra. On the Poetry of Matthew Arnold, Robert Browning & Rabindranath Tagore. 1978. lib. bdg. 37.00 (ISBN 0-8495-0053-2). Arden Lib.
--On the Poetry of Matthew Arnold, Robert Browning & Rabindranath Tagore. LC 72-13660. 1972. Repr. of 1921 ed. lib. bdg. 20.00 (ISBN 0-8414-1237-5). Folcroft.
Aiken, Henry D. Reason & Conduct: New Bearings in Moral Philosophy. LC 77-26079. 1978. Repr. of 1962 ed. lib. bdg. 28.50 (ISBN 0-313-20083-1, AIRD). Greenwood.
Aiken, Henry D., ed. see Hume, David.
Aikins, Carrol, tr. see Grimm, George.
Ainslie, Douglas, tr. see Croce, Benedetto.
Ainstein, Reuben. The Warsaw Ghetto Revolt. (Illus.). 238p. 1979. pap. 10.95 (ISBN 0-89604-007-0). Holocaust Pubns.
Ainsworth, Henry. A True Confession of the Faith, Which Wee Falsley Called Brownists, Doo Hold. LC 78-26338. (English Experience Ser.: No. 158). 24p. 1969. Repr. of 1956 ed. 7.00 (ISBN 90-221-0158-4). Walter J Johnson.
Ainsworth, Henry & Johnson, Francis. An Apologie or Defence of Such True Christians as Are Commonly Called Brownists. LC 70-25742. (English Experience Ser.: No. 217). Repr. of 1604 ed. 16.00 (ISBN 90-221-0424-9). Walter J Johnson.
Ainsztein, Reuben. Warsaw Ghetto Revolt. LC 78-71295. (Illus.). 1979. pap. 10.95 (ISBN 0-8052-5007-7, Pub. by Holocaust Library). Schocken.
Airhart, Arnold E. Beacon Bible Expositions: Vol. 5, Acts. Greathouse, William M. & Taylor, Willard H., eds. (Beacon Bible Exposition Ser.). 1977. 8.95 (ISBN 0-8341-0316-8). Beacon Hill.
Aish Hatorah Women's Organization Staff, compiled by. The Taste of Shabbos, The Complete Cookbook. 1987. 16.95. Feldheim.
Aitken, John. Compilations of Litanies & Vesper Hymns. 25.00x (ISBN 0-87556-004-0). Saifer.
Aitken, Kenneth T. Proverbs. LC 86-15660. (The Daily Study Bible-Old Testament). 276p. 1986. 15.95 (ISBN 0-664-21837-7); pap. 8.95 (ISBN 0-664-24586-2). Westminster.
Aitken, Robert. The Mind of Clover: Essays in Zen Buddhist Ethics. 224p. (Orig.). 1984. pap. 11.50 (ISBN 0-86547-158-4). N Point Pr.
--Taking the Path of Zen. LC 82-81475. (Illus.). 176p. (Orig.). 1982. pap. 9.50 (ISBN 0-86547-080-4). N Point Pr.
--A Zen Wave: Basho's Haiku & Zen. LC 78-13243. (Illus.). 192p. 1979. pap. 9.95 (ISBN 0-8348-0137-X). Weatherhill.
Aivanhov, Omraam M. Christmas & Easter in the Initiatic Tradition. (Izvor Collection: Vol. 209). (Illus.). 139p. (Orig.). pap. 4.95 (ISBN 2-85566-226-5, Pub. by Prosveta France). Prosveta USA.
--Cosmic Moral Laws. 2nd ed. (Complete Works: Vol. 12). 294p. (Orig.). 1984. pap. 9.95 (ISBN 2-85566-112-9). Prosveta USA.
--The Key to the Problems of Existence. rev. ed. (Complete Works: Vol. 11). (Illus.). 263p. (Orig.). 1985. pap. 9.95 (ISBN 2-85566-111-0). Prosveta USA.
--Know Thyself: Jnani Yoga. (Complete Works: Vol. 17). (Illus.). 271p. 1981. pap. 9.95 (ISBN 2-85566-162-5). Prosveta USA.
--Life. (Complete Works: Vol. 5). (Illus.). 266p. 1978. pap. 9.95 (ISBN 2-85566-108-0). Prosveta USA.
--Love & Sexuality, Pt. I. (Complete Works: Vol. 14). (Illus.). 250p. 1976. pap. 9.95 (ISBN 2-85566-114-5). Prosveta USA.
--Man Master of His Destiny. (Izvor Collection Ser.: Vol. 202). 194p. 1982. pap. 4.95 (ISBN 0-911857-01-X). Prosveta USA.
--Man's Subtle Bodies & Centers: The Aura, The Solar Plexus, The Chakras, Vol. 219. (IZVOR Collection). 154p. (Orig.). 1986. pap. 4.95 (ISBN 2-85566-383-0, 219). Prosveta USA.
--The Mysteries of Yesod. (Complete Works: Vol. 7). (Illus.). 217p. (Orig.). 1982. pap. 9.95 (ISBN 2-85566-109-9). Prosveta USA.
--A New Earth: Methods, Exercises, Formulas, Prayers. (Complete Works: Vol. 13). (Illus.). 232p. (Orig.). 1982. pap. 9.95 (ISBN 2-85566-113-7). Prosveta USA.
--New Light on the Gospels. (Izvor Collection: Vol. 217). (Orig.). 1985. pap. 4.95 (ISBN 2-85566-339-3, Pub. by Prosveta France). Prosveta USA.
--On the Art of Teaching from the Initiatic Point of View. (Complete Works: Vol. 29). (Illus.). 245p. 1981. pap. 9.95 (ISBN 2-85566-142-0). Prosveta USA.
--The Second Birth. (Complete Works of O. M. Aivanhov: Vol. 1). 210p. 1981. pap. 9.50 (ISBN 0-87516-418-8). De Vorss.
--Spiritual Alchemy. rev. ed. (Complete Works: Vol. 2). (Illus.). 205p. 1986. pap. 9.95 (ISBN 2-85566-371-7, Pub. by Prosveta France). Prosveta USA.
--Toward a Solar Civilization. (Izvor Collection Ser.: Vol. 201). (Illus.). 148p. 1982. pap. 4.95 (ISBN 0-911857-00-1). Prosveta USA.
--The True Meaning of Christ's Teaching, Vol. 215. (Izvor Collection Ser.). (Illus.). 186p. (Orig.). 1984. pap. 4.95 (ISBN 2-85566-322-9). Prosveta USA.
--What Is a Spiritual Master? (Izvor Collection Ser.: Vol. 207). 185p. pap. 4.95 (ISBN 2-85566-230-3, Pub. by Prosveta France). Prosveta USA.
--The Yoga of Nutrition. (Izvor Collection Ser.: Vol. 204). 130p. pap. 4.95 (ISBN 0-911857-03-6). Prosveta USA.
Aixala, Jerome, ed. see Arrupe, Pedro.
Aixala, Jerome, tr. see Dalmases, Candido de.
Aiyangar, Narayan. Essays on Indo-Aryan Mythology. 656p. 1986. Repr. 34.00X (ISBN 0-8364-1712-7, Pub. by Manohar India). South Asia Bks.
Aiyar, K. N. Thirty Minor Upanishads: Including the Yoga Upanishads. 300p. 1980. Repr. of 1914 ed. 16.95 (ISBN 0-935548-00-9). Santarasa Pubns.
Aiyar, M. S. Thiagaraja: A Great Musician Saint. 238p. 1986. Repr. 20.00X (ISBN 0-8364-1766-6, Pub. by Usha). South Asia Bks.
Aiyer, K. Narayanaswami, tr. Laghu-Yoga-Vasistha. 1971. 19.95 (ISBN 0-8356-7497-5). Theos Pub Hse.
Aiyer, P. S., tr. see Abhendananda.
Ajaya, Swami. Yoga Psychology: A Practical Guide to Meditation. rev. ed. LC 76-374539. 115p. 1976. pap. 5.95 (ISBN 0-89389-052-9). Himalayan Pubs.
Ajaya, Swami, ed. Living with the Himalayan Masters: Spiritual Experiences of Swami Rama. LC 80-82974. 490p. 1980. pap. 12.95 (ISBN 0-89389-070-7). Himalayan Pubs.
--Meditational Therapy. 100p. (Orig.). pap. 3.95 (ISBN 0-89389-032-4). Himalayan Pubs.
Ajayi, J. F. Christian Missions in Nigeria, Eighteen Forty-One to Eighteen Ninety-One: The Making of a New Elite. 1965. 19.95 (ISBN 0-8101-0038-X). Northwestern U Pr.
Ajaz, jt. auth. see Eaford.
Ajemian, Ina & Mount, Balfour M., eds. The R. V. H. Manual on Palliative-Hospice Care: A Resource Book. pap. 34.00 (ISBN 0-405-13934-9). Ayer Co Pubs.
Ajijola, A. D. Essence of Faith in Islam. pap. 12.50 (ISBN 0-686-63898-0). Kazi Pubns.
--Myth of the Cross. pap. 9.50 (ISBN 0-686-63907-3). Kazi Pubns.
Akbar, Na'im. Chains & Images of Psychological Slavery. 76p. (Orig.). pap. 3.50 (ISBN 0-933821-00-X). New Mind Prod.
Akehurst, John. The Faith Within You: The Essence & Meaning of the Christian Faith. 141p. (Orig.). 1984. pap. 10.95 (ISBN 0-85819-469-4, Pub. by JBCE). ANZ Religious Pubns.
Akenson, Donald H. The Church of Ireland: Ecclesiastical Reform & Revolution, 1880-1885. LC 76-151565. pap. 81.40 (ISBN 0-317-08435-6, 2013197). Bks Demand UMI.
--A Protestant in Purgatory: Richard Whately, Archbishop of Dublin. LC 81-3522. (Conference on British Studies (CBS) Biography: Vol. II). xiii, 276p. 1981. 25.00 (ISBN 0-208-01917-0, Archon). Shoe String.
Akerley, Ben E. The X-Rated Bible. pap. 8.00. Am Atheist.
--The X-Rated Bible: An Irreverent Survey of Sex in the Scriptures. (Illus.). 428p. (Orig.). 1985. pap. 8.00 (ISBN 0-910309-19-1). Am Atheist.
Akeroyd, Richard H. He Made Us a Kingdom: The Principles to be Applied in Establishing Christ's Kingdon Now. 1985. 5.00 (ISBN 0-916620-79-4). Portals Pr.
--The Spiritual Quest of Albert Camus. LC 76-3324. 1976. 7.50 (ISBN 0-916620-03-4). Portals Pr.
Akhavi, Shahrough. Religion & Politics in Contemporary Iran. LC 79-22084. 1980. 44.50 (ISBN 0-87395-408-4); pap. 16.95 (ISBN 0-87395-456-4). State U NY Pr.
Akhilananda, Swami. Hindu View of Christ. pap. 12.00 (ISBN 0-8283-1355-5). Branden Pub Co.
--Modern Problems & Religion. pap. 9.00 (ISBN 0-8283-1146-3). Branden Pub Co.
--Spiritual Practices. LC 78-175140. 1972. 12.00 (ISBN 0-8283-1350-4). Branden Pub Co.
Akin, Herbert L. Clergy Compensation & Financial Planning Workbook. (Illus.). 100p. 1982. wkbk. 6.95 (ISBN 0-938736-05-1). Life Enrich.
Akiyama, Aisaburo. Buddhist Hand-Symbol. LC 78-72367. Repr. of 1939 ed. 22.50 (ISBN 0-404-17214-8). AMS Pr.
Akkerman, Fokke. Studies in the Posthumous Works of Spinoza: On Style, Earliest Translation & Reception, Earliest & Modern Edition of Some Texts. vi, 285p. (Orig.). 1980. pap. 17.00x (ISBN 0-317-19838-6, Pub. by Boumas Boekhuis Netherlands). Benjamins North AM.
Alabaster, Henry. The Wheel of the Law: Buddhism Illustrated from Siamese Sources. 384p. Repr. of 1871 ed. text ed. 49.68x (ISBN 0-576-03126-7, Pub. by Gregg Intl Pubs England). Gregg Intl.
Al-Abidin, Zayn. Supplication: Makarim al-Akhlaq. Chittick, William C., tr. 30p. 1984. pap. 3.95 (ISBN 0-940368-45-5). Tahrike Tarsile Quran.
Alain, pseud. The Gods. Pevear, Richard, tr. from Fr. LC 74-8291. 192p. 1974. 8.95 (ISBN 0-8112-0547-9); pap. 3.95 (ISBN 0-8112-0548-7, NDP382). New Directions.
Ala Maudoodi, Abul. Come Let Us Change This World. 4th ed. Siddique, Kaukab, intro. by. & tr. from Urdu. 151p. 1983. pap. 2.00 (ISBN 0-942978-05-6). Am Soc Ed & Rel.
Alamuddin, Nura S. & Starr, Paul D. Crucial Bonds: Marriage Among the Lebanese Druze. LC 78-10465. 1980. 25.00x (ISBN 0-88206-024-4). Caravan Bks.
Alanahally, Shrikrishna. The Woods. Taranath, Rajeeve, tr. from Kannada. Orig. Title: Kaadu. 112p. 1979. pap. 2.95 (ISBN 0-86578-091-9). Ind-US Inc.
Aland, Barbara, jt. auth. see Aland, Kurt.
Aland, K., ed. Synopsis of the Four Gospels (English Only) 1983. 5.95x (ISBN 0-8267-0500-6, 08564). Am Bible.
Aland, Kurt. A History of Christianity, Vol. 1: From the Beginnings to the Threshold of the Reformation. Schaaf, James L., tr. LC 84-47913. 464p. 24.95 (ISBN 0-8006-0725-2, 1-725). Fortress.
--A History of Christianity, Vol. 2: From the Reformation to the Present. Schaaf, James L., tr. from Ger. LC 85-47913. 608p. 1986. 29.95 (ISBN 0-8006-0759-7, 1-759). Fortress.
Aland, Kurt & Aland, Barbara. The Text of the New Testament. Rhodes, Erroll F., tr. from Ger. (Illus.). 344p. 1987. 29.95x (ISBN 0-8028-3620-8). Eerdmans.
Aland, Kurt, ed. Die Alten Uebersetzungen des Neuen Testaments, die Kirchenvaeterzitate und Lektionare: Der Gegenwaertige Stand Ihrer Erforschung und Ihre Bedeutung fuer die Griechische Textgeschichte. (Arbeiten zur neutestamentlichen Textforschung 5). xxiv, 590p. 1972. 62.40x (ISBN 3-11-004121-9). De Gruyter.
--Repertorium der Griechischen Christlichen Papyri, Pt.1: Biblische Papyri, Altes Testament, Neues Testament, Varia, Apokryphen. (Patristische Texte und Studien, Vol. 18). 473p. 1976. 63.20x (ISBN 3-11-004674-1). De Gruyter.
Aland, Kurt, jt. ed. see Institut fuer Neutestamentliche Textforschung, Muenster-Westf.
Alan Of Lille. The Art of Preaching. Evans, Gillian R., tr. (Cistercian Fathers Ser.: No. 23). (Lat., Orig.). 1981. pap. 13.95 (ISBN 0-87907-923-1). Cistercian Pubns.
Alan of Tewkesbury. Alani Priors Cantuariensis Postea Abbatis Tewkesberiensis Scripta Quae Extant. Giles, J. A., ed. 1966. Repr. of 1848 ed. 24.00 (ISBN 0-8337-1340-X). B Franklin.
Al-Arabi, Muhyiddin. The Seals of Wisdom. (Sacred Texts Ser.). (Illus., Orig.). 1983. pap. 8.75 (ISBN 0-88695-010-4). Concord Grove.
Alarcon, Hernando R. de see Ruiz de Alarcon, Hernando.
Al-Askari, Allama M. Hadith: A Probe into the History of. Haq, M. Fazal, tr. 120p. 1983. pap. 4.00 (ISBN 0-941724-16-6). Islamic Seminary.
Al-Attas, Syed Muhammad Al-Naquib see Al-Naquib Al-Attas, Syed Muhammad.
Al-Azmeh, Aziz, ed. Islamic Law: Social & Historical Contents. 1986. 39.00 (ISBN 0-7099-0588-2, Pub. by Croom Helm Ltd). Longwood Pub Group.
Albanese, Catherine L. America: Religions & Religion. LC 80-21031. (The Wadsworth Series in Religion Studies). 389p. 1981. pap. write for info (ISBN 0-534-00928-X). Wadsworth Pub.
--Corresponding Motion: Transcendental Religion & the New America. LC 77-70329. 234p. 1977. 29.95 (ISBN 0-87722-098-0). Temple U Pr.
Albanese, Gayle, jt. auth. see Garrison, Eileen.
Albeck, Chanoch. Einfuehrung in die Mischna. (Studia Judaica, 6). 493p. 1971. 33.60x (ISBN 3-11-006429-4). De Gruyter.
Alberding, Faye V. Morrow & Miracles. (Illus.). 1983. 5.95 (ISBN 0-8062-2203-4). Carlton.
Albergio, Giuseppe & Provost, James, eds. The Extraordinary Synod Nineteen Eighty-Five: An Evaluation. (Concilium Nineteen Eighty-Six Ser.). 120p. 1986. pap. 6.95 (ISBN 0-567-30068-4, Pub. by T & T Clark Ltd UK). Fortress.
Alberigo, Giuseppe, ed. Where Does the Church Stand, Vol. 146. (Concilium 1981). 128p. (Orig.). 1981. pap. 6.95 (ISBN 0-8164-2313-X, HarpR). Har-Row.
Alberione, James. Call to Total Consecration. 1974. 3.00 (ISBN 0-8198-0312-X); pap. 2.00 (ISBN 0-8198-0313-8). Dghtrs St Paul.
--Christ, Model & Reward of Religious. 1964. 5.00 (ISBN 0-8198-0023-6); pap. 4.00. Dghtrs St Paul.
--Designs for a Just Society. (Divine Master Ser.). 1976. 6.00 (ISBN 0-8198-0400-2); pap. 5.00 (ISBN 0-8198-0401-0); wkbk 0.60 (ISBN 0-8198-0402-9). Dghtrs St Paul.
--Insights into Religious Life. 1977. 3.00 (ISBN 0-8198-0424-X); pap. 2.00 (ISBN 0-8198-0425-8). Dghtrs St Paul.
--Last Things. (Orig.). 1965. 4.50 (ISBN 0-8198-0072-4). Dghtrs St Paul.
--Living Our Commitment. 1968. 4.00 (ISBN 0-8198-4411-X); pap. 3.00 (ISBN 0-8198-4412-8). Dghtrs St Paul.
--Lord, Teach Us to Pray. Daughters of St. Paul, tr. from Ital. 295p. 1982. 4.00 (ISBN 0-8198-4422-5, SP0408); pap. 3.00 (ISBN 0-8198-4423-3). Dghtrs St Paul.
--Mary, Queen of Apostles. rev. ed. 1976. 4.00 (ISBN 0-8198-0438-X); pap. 3.00 (ISBN 0-8198-0439-8). Dghtrs St Paul.
--Month with Saint Paul. 1952. pap. 2.25 (ISBN 0-8198-0104-6). Dghtrs St Paul.
--Paschal Mystery in Christian Living. Daughters Of St. Paul, tr. LC 68-28102. (St. Paul Editions). (Illus.). 1968. 3.95 (ISBN 0-8198-0114-3); pap. 2.95 (ISBN 0-8198-0115-1). Dghtrs St Paul.
--Pray Always. 1966. 4.00 (ISBN 0-8198-0126-7); pap. 3.00 (ISBN 0-8198-0127-5). Dghtrs St Paul.
--Queen of Apostles Prayerbook. 7.50 (ISBN 0-8198-0266-2); plastic bdg. 6.00 (ISBN 0-8198-0267-0). Dghtrs St Paul.
--Saint & Thought for Every Day. 1976. 4.50 (ISBN 0-8198-0471-1); pap. 3.50 (ISBN 0-8198-6800-0). Dghtrs St Paul.
--The Spirit in My Life. 1977. pap. 0.95 (ISBN 0-8198-0460-6). Dghtrs St Paul.
--Superior Follows the Master. (Orig.). 1965. pap. 2.00 (ISBN 0-8198-0153-4). Dghtrs St Paul.
--That Christ May Live in Me. 1980. 3.50 (ISBN 0-8198-7300-4); pap. 2.25 (ISBN 0-8198-7301-2). Dghtrs St Paul.
--Thoughts. 1973. 3.00 (ISBN 0-8198-0332-4). Dghtrs St Paul.
--A Time for Faith. 1978. 4.00 (ISBN 0-8198-0371-5); pap. 3.00 (ISBN 0-8198-0372-3). Dghtrs St Paul.
--Woman: Her Influence & Zeal. (Orig.). 1964. 3.50 (ISBN 0-8198-0176-3); pap. 1.25 (ISBN 0-8198-0177-1). Dghtrs St Paul.
Alberione, James J. Personality & Configuration with Christ. (Orig.). 3.50 (ISBN 0-8198-0120-8); pap. 2.50 (ISBN 0-8198-0121-6). Dghtrs St Paul.
Alberione, Rev. James. Glories & Virtues of Mary. 1970. 5.00 (ISBN 0-8198-3017-8); pap. 4.00 (ISBN 0-8198-3018-6). Dghtrs St Paul.
--Growing in Perfect Union. 1964. 3.00 (ISBN 0-8198-3019-4); pap. 2.00 (ISBN 0-8198-3020-8). Dghtrs St Paul.
Albert, Harold & Morentz, James. The Compleat Sermon Program for Lent. 1982. 4.35 (ISBN 0-89536-533-2, 0347). CSS of Ohio.
Albert, Phyllis C. The Modernization of French Jewry: Consistory & Community in the Nineteenth Century. LC 76-50680. (Illus.). 472p. 1977. 40.00x (ISBN 0-87451-139-9). U Pr of New Eng.
Albert, Phyllis C., jt. ed. see Malino, Frances.
Albin, Rochelle S. Emotions. LC 83-10187. (Choices: Guides for Today's Woman: Vol. 1). 120p. 1983. pap. 6.95 (ISBN 0-664-24540-4). Westminster.
Al-Biruni. Alberni's India: An Account of the Religion, Philosophy, Literature, Geography, Chronology, Astronomy, Customs, Laws & Astrology of India about AD 1030, 2 vols. Sachau, Edward C., tr. Repr. of 1888 ed. Set. text ed. 54.00x. Coronet Bks.
Albran, Kehlog. The Profit. 108p. (Orig.). 1973. pap. 2.95 (ISBN 0-8431-0260-8). Price Stern.
Albrecht, Earl. Altar Prayer Workbook A. rev. ed. Sherer, Michael L., ed. 1986. 7.75 (ISBN 0-89536-812-9, 6841). CSS of Ohio.
--Altar Prayer Workbook B: (Common-Luth) 1984. 7.75 (ISBN 0-89536-688-6, 4865). CSS of Ohio.
Albright, E. M. Spenser's Cosmic Philosophy of Religion. LC 72-100730. 1970. Repr. of 1929 ed. 39.95 (ISBN 0-8383-0001-4). Haskell.
Albright, William F. Archaeology of Palestine. rev. ed. 11.25 (ISBN 0-8446-0003-2). Peter Smith.
--Biblical Period from Abraham to Ezra: A Historical Survey. pap. 4.95x (ISBN 0-06-130102-7, TB102, Torch). Har-Row.
--Yahweh & the Gods of Canaan: An Historical Analysis of Two Contrasting Faiths. 1978. Repr. of 1968 ed. 12.00x (ISBN 0-931464-01-3). Eisenbrauns.
Albright, William F. & Mann, C. S., eds. Matthew. LC 77-150875. (Anchor Bible Ser.: Vol. 26). 1971. 18.00 (ISBN 0-385-08658-X, Anchor Pr). Doubleday.

Albritton, Clarice. The Untold Story: Jesus Son of God. LC 83-73188. 1983. pap. 5.95 (ISBN 0-318-00817-3). W P Brownell.

Albritton, Clarice & Newby, Grace. A Lamp Unto Our Faith. LC 76-24514. 1976. pap. 3.95 (ISBN 0-87516-218-5). De Vorss.

Albritton, Claude C., Jr., ed. see Ray, John.

Albritton, Claude C., Jr., ed. see Whiston, William.

Albro, John A., ed. see Shepard, Thomas.

Alcala, Angel, ed. The Spanish Inquisition & the Inquisitional Mind. (Atlantic Studies: No. 49). write for info (ISBN 0-88033-952-7). Brooklyn Coll Pr.

Alcalay. Basic Encyclopedia of Jewish Proverbs, Quotations, Folk Wisdom. 19.95 (ISBN 0-87677-153-3). Hartmore.

Alcalay, Reuben. Complete English-Hebrew, Hebrew-English Dictionary, 3 vols. (Eng. & Hebrew.). 7180p. 1980. Repr. of 1965 ed. 69.00 set (ISBN 0-89961-017-X). Vol. 1 (ISBN 0-89961-003-X). Vol. 2 (ISBN 0-89961-007-2). Vol. 3 (ISBN 0-89961-008-0). SBS Pub.

--The Massada English-Hebrew Student Dictionary. (Eng. & Hebrew.). 734p. 1980. Repr. 18.95 (ISBN 0-89961-006-4). SBS Pub.

Alcantara, S. Peter. A Golden Treatise of Mental Prayer. Hollings, G. S., ed. LC 77-18960. Repr. of 1978 ed. 35.20 (ISBN 0-8357-9135-1, 2019096). Bks Demand UMI.

Alcock, John. Mons Perfectionis. LC 74-28823. (English Experience Ser.: No. 706). 1974. Repr. of 1497 ed. 6.00 (ISBN 90-221-0706-X). Walter J Johnson.

--Spousage of a Virgin to Christ. LC 74-80158. (English Experience Ser.: No. 638). (Illus.). 19p. 1974. Repr. of 1496 ed. 3.50 (ISBN 90-221-0638-1). Walter J Johnson.

Alcock, T. The Life of Samuel of Kalamon. 144p. 1983. pap. text ed. 35.00x (ISBN 0-85668-219-5, Pub. by Aris & Phillips UK). Humanities.

Alcorn, Randy C. Christians in the Wake of the Sexual Revolution: Recovering Our Sexual Sanity. LC 85-4959. (Critical Concern Ser.). 1985. 13.95 (ISBN 0-88070-095-5). Multnomah.

Alcorn, Wallace. Momentum. (Living Studies Ser.). 128p. (Orig.). 1986. pap. 5.95 (ISBN 0-8423-4538-8); guide 2.95study (ISBN 0-8423-4539-6). Tyndale.

Alcott, A. Bronson, ed. Conversations with Children on the Gospels (Record of Conversations on the Gospels, Held in Mr. Alcott's School; Unfolding the Doctrine & Discipline of Human Culture, 2 vols. in 1. LC 72-4948. (The Romantic Tradition in American Literature Ser.). 616p. 1972. Repr. of 1836 ed. 40.00 (ISBN 0-405-04621-9). Ayer Co Pubs.

Alcott, Amos B. Ralph Waldo Emerson. LC 68-24930. (American Biography Ser., No. 32). 1969. Repr. of 1881 ed. lib. bdg. 49.95x (ISBN 0-8383-0908-9). Haskell.

Alcyone, pseud. At the Feet of the Master. 1967. 4.50 (ISBN 0-8356-0098-X). Theos Pub Hse.

Alcyone. At the Feet of the Master. 1970. pap. 1.95 (ISBN 0-8356-0196-X, Quest). Theos Pub Hse.

--At the Feet of the Master. leatherette 3.00 (ISBN 0-911662-17-0). Yoga.

--At the Feet of the Master. 1.75 (ISBN 0-8356-7323-5). Theos Pub Hse.

Aldan, Daisy. Foundation Stone Meditation by Rudolf Steiner. 1981. pap. 2.00 (ISBN 0-916786-53-6). St George Bk Serv.

Alden, Henry M. A Study of Death: Works of Henry Mills Alden. (Works of Henry Mills Alden Ser.). vii, 335p. 1985. Repr. of 1895 ed. 39.00 (Pub. by Am Repr Serv). Am Biog Serv.

Alden, Laura. I Read about God's Care: Grade 2. rev. ed. (Basic Bible Readers Ser.). (Illus.). 128p. 1983. text ed. 7.95 (ISBN 0-87239-662-2, 2952). Standard Pub.

Alden, Robert L. Proverbs: A Commentary on an Ancient Book of Timeless Advice. 222p. 1984. 12.95 (ISBN 0-8010-0194-3). Baker Bk.

--Psalms: Songs of Discipleship, 3 vols. (Everyman's Bible Commentary Ser.). 1975. pap. 5.95 ea. Vol. 1 (ISBN 0-8024-2018-4). Vol. 2 (ISBN 0-8024-2019-2). Vol. 3 (ISBN 0-8024-2020-6). Moody.

Alder, Felix. Creed & Deed: A Series of Discourses. LC 76-38430. (Religion in America Ser: 2). 254p. 1972. Repr. of 1877 ed. 17.00 (ISBN 0-405-04051-2). Ayer Co Pubs.

Alderfer, Gordon E., jt. ed. see Tolles, Frederick.

Alderfer, Helen, ed. Farthing in Her Hand: Stewardship for Women. LC 64-23376. 226p. 1964. pap. 4.95 (ISBN 0-8361-1515-5). Herald Pr.

Alderink, Larry J. Creation & Salvation in Ancient Orphism. LC 81-5772. (APA American Classical Studies Ser.). 1981. pap. 10.00 (ISBN 0-89130-502-5, 400408). Scholars Pr GA.

Alderman, Paul R., Jr. God's Spotlight on Tomorrow: Seven Sevens Concerning the Return of Christ. 1960. pap. 1.25 (ISBN 0-87213-010-X). Loizeaux.

Al-din, Minhaj. General History of Muhammadan Dynasties of Asia from 810 to 1260 AD, 2 vols. Raverty, H. C., tr. from Persian. Repr. of 1881 ed. Set. text ed. 77.50x. Coronet Bks.

Al-Din, Shaykh M. The Rising of al-Husayn: Its Impact on the Consciousness of Muslim Society. Howard, I. K., tr. Date not set. pap. 15.95 (ISBN 0-7103-0191-X, Kegan Paul). Methuen Inc.

Aldington, William, tr. see Henley, W. E.

Aldous, Joan, jt. ed. see D'Antonio, William V.

Aldred, Cyril. Tut-Ankh-Amun-& His Friends. pap. 2.95 (ISBN 0-88388-043-1). Bellerophon Bk.

Aldrich, Joseph C. Life-style Evangelism: Crossing Traditional Boundaries to Reach the Unbelieving World. LC 80-27615. (Critical Concern Bks.). 1981. 10.95 (ISBN 0-930014-46-4). Multnomah.

--Life-Style Evangelism: Crossing Traditional Boundaries to Reach the Unbelieving World. LC 80-27615. (Critical Concern Ser.). 246p. 1983. pap. 6.95 (ISBN 0-88070-023-8). Multnomah.

--Life-Style Evangelism: Study Guide. 1983. pap. 2.95 (ISBN 0-88070-020-3). Multnomah.

--Love for All Your Worth! A Quest for Personal Value & Lovability. LC 85-11420. 1985. pap. 6.95 (ISBN 0-88070-119-6). Multnomah.

--Secrets to Inner Beauty. LC 84-9970. 142p. 1984. pap. 5.95 (ISBN 0-88070-069-6). Multnomah.

Aldrich, Keith, tr. Apollodorus: The Library of Greek Mythology. 298p. 1975. 15.00x (ISBN 0-87291-072-5). Coronado Pr.

Aldridge, Betty. You Can Teach Preschoolers Successfully. (Training Successful Teachers Ser.). 48p. (Orig.). 1984. pap. 2.95 (ISBN 0-87239-805-6, 3205). Standard Pub.

Aldridge, John W. In Search of Heresy: American Literature in an Age of Conformity. LC 74-3618. 208p. 1974. Repr. of 1956 ed. lib. bdg. 82.50x (ISBN 0-8371-7452-X, ALSH). Greenwood.

Aldridge, Marion D. The Pastor's Guidebook: A Manual for Worship. LC 83-70213. 1984. 9.95 (ISBN 0-8054-2312-5). Broadman.

Aldwinckle, Russell. Jesus: A Savior or the Savior? Religious Pluralism in Christian Perspective. LC 81-19033. viii, 232p. 1982. 15.95 (ISBN 0-86554-023-3, MUP-H24). Mercer Univ Pr.

Aldworth, Thomas. Shaping a Healthy Religion. 132p. 1985. pap. 8.95 (ISBN 0-88347-200-7). Thomas More.

Ales, Anatole, ed. see Charles Louis De Bourbon.

Al-Esman, Mashef, ed. Quran. (Arabic.). 25.00x (ISBN 0-86685-135-6). Intl Bk Ctr.

Alessi, Vincie. Programs for Lent & Easter, Vol. 2. 64p. 1983. pap. 5.95 (ISBN 0-8170-1016-5). Judson.

Alessi, Vincie, ed. Programs for Advent & Christmas. 1978. pap. 4.95 (ISBN 0-8170-0808-X). Judson.

--Programs for Advent & Christmas, Vol. 2. 64p. 1981. pap. 4.95 (ISBN 0-8170-0930-2). Judson.

--Programs for Lent & Easter. 1979. pap. 3.95 (ISBN 0-8170-0861-6). Judson.

Alessio, Luis & Munoz, Hector. Marriage & the Family: The Domestic Church. Owen, Aloysius, tr. from Span. LC 82-6853. 121p. 1982. pap. 3.95 (ISBN 0-8189-0433-X). Alba.

Alex, Marlee. Esther. (Outstanding Women of the Bible Ser.). (Illus.). 32p. 1987. 8.95 (ISBN 0-8028-5016-2). Eerdmans.

--Mary. (Women of the Bible Ser.). 32p. 1987. 8.95 (ISBN 0-8028-5018-9). Eerdmans.

--Ruth. (Women of the Bible Ser.). (Illus.). 32p. 1987. 8.95 (ISBN 0-8028-5017-0). Eerdmans.

--Sarah. (Outstanding Women of the Bible Ser.). 32p. 1987. 8.95 (ISBN 0-8028-5015-4). Eerdmans.

Alexamder, P., ed. see Frank, Penny.

Alexander, A. G., tr. see Makrakis, Apostolos.

Alexander, Albert G., tr. see Makrakis, Apostolos.

Alexander, Archibald. Evidence of the Authenticity, Inspiration & Canonical Authority of the Holy Scriptures. (Works of Reverend Archibald Alexander). 308p. Repr. of 1842 ed. lib. bdg. 39.00 (ISBN 0-932051-73-1, Pub. by Am Repr Serv). Am Biog Serv.

--Evidences of the Authenticity, Inspiration, & Canonical Authority of the Holy Scriptures. LC 70-38431. (Religion in America, Ser. 2). 314p. 1972. Repr. of 1836 ed. 23.50 (ISBN 0-405-04052-0). Ayer Co Pubs.

--Feathers on the Moor. facs. ed. LC 67-22050. (Essay Index Reprint Ser). 1928. 17.00 (ISBN 0-8369-0145-2). Ayer Co Pubs.

--Thoughts on Religious Experience. 1978. 11.95 (ISBN 0-85151-080-9). Banner of Truth.

Alexander, Calvert. Catholic Literary Revival. LC 68-16288. 1968. Repr. of 1935 ed. 31.50x (ISBN 0-8046-0005-8, Pub. by Kennikat). Assoc Faculty Pr.

Alexander, Charles. Church's Year. (Illus.). 1950. 3.00x (ISBN 0-19-273007-X). Oxford U Pr.

Alexander, David & Alexander, Pat, eds. Eerdmans' Concise Bible Handbook. LC 80-20131. (Illus.). 384p. (Orig.). 1981. pap. 9.95 (ISBN 0-8028-1875-7). Eerdmans.

--Eerdmans' Handbook to the Bible. rev. ed. (Illus.). 680p. 1983. 24.95 (ISBN 0-8028-3486-8). Eerdmans.

Alexander, Dorsey & Alexander, Joyce. A Flurry of Angels: Angels in Literature. (Illus.). 1986. pap. 5.00. Turtles Quill.

--Psalm One Hundred Four. 32p. (Calligraphy & Illus.). 1978. pap. 5.00 (ISBN 0-912020-19-9). Turtles Quill.

Alexander, E. Curtis. African Foundations of Judaism & Christianity. LC 84-48679. (Alkebu-Ian Historical Research Society Monograph: No. 3). 84p. (Orig.). 1985. pap. 5.95 (ISBN 0-938818-08-2). ECA Assoc.

--African Historical Religions: A Conceptual & Ethical Foundation for Western Religions. LC 83-83096. (Alkelbulan Historical Research Society Monograph Ser.: No. 2). (Illus.). 70p. 1984. pap. 4.95 (ISBN 0-938818-05-8). ECA Assoc.

Alexander, Edward. The Resonance of Dust: Essays on Holocaust Literature & Jewish Fate. LC 79-15515. 276p. 1979. 20.00 (ISBN 0-8142-0303-5). Ohio St U Pr.

Alexander, Frank J. In the Hours of Meditation. pap. 1.75 (ISBN 0-87481-162-7). Vedanta Pr.

Alexander, George M. The Handbook of Biblical Personalities. 320p. 1981. pap. 6.95 (ISBN 0-8164-2316-4, HarpR). Har-Row.

Alexander, Hartley B. God & Man's Destiny: Inquiries into the Metaphysical Foundations of Faith. LC 75-3017. 1976. Repr. of 1936 ed. 16.50 (ISBN 0-404-59010-1). AMS Pr.

--Latin American Mythology. LC 63-19096. (Mythology of All Races Ser.: Vol. 11). (Illus.). 1964. Repr. of 1932 ed. 30.00x (ISBN 0-8154-0006-3). Cooper Sq.

--North American Mythology. LC 63-19095. (Mythology of All Races Ser.: Vol. 10). (Illus.). 1964. Repr. of 1932 ed. 30.00x (ISBN 0-8154-0007-1). Cooper Sq.

--The World's Rim: Great Mysteries of the North American Indians. LC 53-7703. (Illus.). xx, 259p. 1967. pap. 7.95 (ISBN 0-8032-5003-7, BB 160, Bison). U of Nebr Pr.

Alexander, Horace. Everyman's Struggle for Peace. 1983. pap. 2.50x (ISBN 0-87574-074-X, 074). Pendle Hill.

--Gandhi Remembered. LC 71-84674. (Orig.). 1969. pap. 2.50x (ISBN 0-87574-165-7). Pendle Hill.

--Quakerism in India. 1983. pap. 2.50x (ISBN 0-87574-031-6, 031). Pendle Hill.

Alexander, J. A. Acts of the Apostles, 2 vols. in 1. (Banner of Truth Geneva Series Commentaries). 1980. 23.95 (ISBN 0-85151-309-3). Banner of Truth.

--Mark. (Geneva Series Commentaries). 1984. 15.95 (ISBN 0-85151-422-7). Banner of Truth.

Alexander, J. J., ed. The Decorated Letter. LC 78-6487. (Magnificent Paperback Ser.). 1978. 22.95 (ISBN 0-8076-0894-7); pap. 12.95 (ISBN 0-8076-0895-5). Braziller.

--Italian Renaissance Illuminations. LC 77-2841. (Magnificent Paperback Ser.). (Illus.). 1977. 19.95 (ISBN 0-8076-0863-7); pap. 11.95 (ISBN 0-8076-0864-5). Braziller.

Alexander, J. L. Memorable Ceremonies & Poems: Including Material from "Along the Story Trail". 192p. 1986. Repr. of 1928 ed. 5.50 (ISBN 0-88053-302-1, S-109). Macoy Pub.

Alexander, J. W. God is Love: Communion Addresses. 368p. 1985. pap. 5.95 (ISBN 0-85151-459-6). Banner of Truth.

--Plan Para Memorizar las Escrituras. Orig. Title: Fire in My Bones. 48p. 1981. Repr. of 1979 ed. 1.75 (ISBN 0-311-03660-0). Casa Bautista.

Alexander, John. Your Money or Your Life: A New Look at Jesus' View of Wealth & Power. LC 86-45010. 256p. 1986. 13.95 (ISBN 0-06-060151-5, HarpR). Har-Row.

Alexander, John W. Hope for a Troubled World. 32p. 1978. pap. 0.75 (ISBN 0-87784-165-9). Inter-Varsity.

--Scripture Memory One Hundred One. 1975. pap. 0.75 (ISBN 0-87784-153-5). Inter-Varsity.

--What Is Christianity. pap. 0.75 (ISBN 0-87784-133-0). Inter-Varsity.

Alexander, Jon. American Personal Religious Accounts, 1600-1980: Toward an Inner History of America's Faiths. LC 83-21950. (Studies in American Religion: Vol. 8). 518p. 1984. 69.95x (ISBN 0-88946-654-8). E Mellen.

Alexander, Jon & Dimock, Giles, eds. Religion in Western Civilization Since the Reformation: Select Readings. 184p. 1983. pap. text ed. 6.75 (ISBN 0-8191-3391-4). U Pr of Amer.

Alexander, Joseph. Commentary on the Acts of the Apostles. 1979. 27.50 (ISBN 0-86524-025-6, 4401). Klock & Klock.

--Commentary on the Gospel of Mark. 1980. 16.75 (ISBN 0-86524-018-3, 4101). Klock & Klock.

Alexander, Joseph A. Isaiah, 2 Vols. 1981. Set. lib. bdg. 29.95 (ISBN 0-86524-072-8, 2302). Klock & Klock.

--Mark. (Thornapple Commentaries Ser.). 1980. pap. 8.95 (ISBN 0-8010-0150-1). Baker Bk.

Alexander, Joyce, jt. auth. see Alexander, Dorsey.

Alexander, Joyce & Alexander, Dorsey, illus. David: Psalm Twenty-Four. (Illus., Calligraphy & Illus.). 1970. pap. 5.00 (ISBN 0-912020-17-2). Turtles Quill.

Alexander, Kay, jt. auth. see Herberholz, Don.

Alexander Kohut Memorial Foundation Staff. Jewish Studies in Memory of Israel Abrahams. Katz, Steven, ed. LC 79-7164. (Jewish Philosophy, Mysticism & History of Ideas Ser.). (Illus.). 1980. Repr. of 1927 ed. lib. bdg. 45.00x (ISBN 0-405-12274-8). Ayer Co Pubs.

Alexander, Lester, ed. see Satchidanada, Sri Swam i.

Alexander, Mithrapuram K. Yoga System. rev. ed. LC 77-140373. (Illus.). 1971. 8.95 (ISBN 0-8158-0257-9); pap. 6.95 (ISBN 0-686-66311-X). Chris Mass.

Alexander, Morris. Israel & Me. (Illus.). 278p. 1977. 14.50x (ISBN 0-87073-204-8). Schenkman Bks Inc.

Alexander, Myrna. After God's Heart. (Woman's Workshop Ser.). 160p. (Orig.). 1982. pap. 3.95p (ISBN 0-310-37141-4, 10921). Zondervan.

--Behold Your God: A Woman's Workshop on the Attributes of God. pap. 3.95 (ISBN 0-310-37131-7, 10916P). Zondervan.

--With Him in the Struggle: A Woman's Workshop on II Samuel. (Woman's Workshop Ser.). 128p. 1986. pap. 3.95 (ISBN 0-310-37211-9, 10918P). Zondervan.

Alexander, P., ed. see Frank, Penny.

Alexander, P., ed. see Langley, Myrtle, et al.

Alexander, P., ed. see Vesey, Susan.

Alexander, P. C. Buddhism in Kerala. LC 78-72369. Repr. of 1949 ed. 37.50 (ISBN 0-404-17216-4). AMS Pr.

Alexander, Pat, ed. Eerdmans Book of Christian Poetry. 128p. 1981. 12.95 (ISBN 0-8028-3555-4). Eerdmans.

--Eerdmans' Concise Bible Encyclopedia. LC 80-19885. (Illus.). 256p. (Orig.). 1981. pap. 8.95 (ISBN 0-8028-1876-5). Eerdmans.

--The Lion Encyclopedia of the Bible. 352p. 1986. 24.95 (ISBN 0-7459-1113-7). Lion USA.

Alexander, Pat, retold by. Nelson Children's Bible. 6.95 (ISBN 0-8407-5238-5). Nelson.

Alexander, Pat, jt. ed. see Alexander, David.

Alexander, Patricia, ed. Eerdmans' Family Encyclopedia of the Bible. (Illus.). 1978. 18.95 (ISBN 0-8028-3517-1). Eerdmans.

--The Life & Words of Jesus. LC 83-47715. (Illus.). 96p. 1983. 10.95 (ISBN 0-06-065255-1, HarpR). Har-Row.

Alexander, Paul J. The Byzantine Apocalyptic Tradition. Abrahamse, Dorothy, ed. LC 82-23816. 248p. 1985. 32.50x (ISBN 0-520-04998-5). U of Cal pr.

--The Oracle of Baalbek: The Tiburtine Sibyl in Greek Dress. LC 75-27113. (Dumbarton Oaks Studies: Vol. 10). (Illus.). 151p. 1967. 12.00x (ISBN 0-88402-020-7). Dumbarton Oaks.

--The Patriarch Nicephorus of Constantinople: Ecclesiastical Policy & Image Worship in the Byzantine Empire. LC 78-63177. (Heresies Ser.: No. II). Repr. of 1958 ed. 42.50 (ISBN 0-404-16195-2). AMS Pr.

Alexander, Philip, ed. & tr. Judaism. (Textual Sources for the Study of Religion). 240p. 1987. pap. 11.75 (ISBN 0-389-20719-5). B&N Imports.

Alexander, Philip S., ed. Judaism. LC 84-6199. (Textual Sources for the Study of Religion Ser.). 208p. 1984. 23.50x (ISBN 0-389-20477-3, BNB 08039); pap. 11.75x (ISBN 0-389-20719-5). B&N Imports.

Alexander, Ralph. Ezekiel. (Everyman's Bible Commentary Ser). 160p. (Orig.). 1976. pap. 5.95 (ISBN 0-8024-2026-5). Moody.

--Ezequiel (Comentario Biblico Portavoz) Orig. Title: Ezekiel (Everyman's Bible Commentary) (Span.). 128p. 1979. pap. 4.50 (ISBN 0-8254-1002-9). Kregel.

Alexander, S. Space, Time & Deity: The Gifford Lectures at Glasgow 1916-1918, 2 Vols. Set. 32.00 (ISBN 0-8446-1521-8). Peter Smith.

Alexander, Sidney. Marc Chagall: A Biography. (Illus.). 525p. 1979. 26.95x (ISBN 0-8464-1196-2). Beekman Pubs.

Alexander, Stella. Church & State in Yugoslavia since Nineteen Forty-Five. LC 77-88668. (Soviet & East European Studies). 1979. 52.50 (ISBN 0-521-21942-6). Cambridge U Pr.

Alexander, Thomas G. Mormonism in Transition: The Latter-day Saints & Their Church, 1890-1930. LC 84-22164. (Illus.). 396p. 1986. 19.95 (ISBN 0-252-01185-6). U of Ill Pr.

Alexander, Thomas G., ed. see Cornwall, Rebecca & Arrington, Leonard J.

Alexander, Thomas G., ed. see Palmer, Richard F. & Butler, Karl D.

Alexander, Thomas G., ed. see Shipps, Jan, et al.

Alexander, Yona & Chertoff, Mordecai, eds. Bibliography on Israel & Zionism. 1980. write for info. Herzl Pr.

Alexander, Yonah & Kittrie, Nicholas N. F., eds. Crescent & Star: Arab & Israeli Perspectives on the Middle East Conflict. LC 72-5797. (AMS Studies in Modern Society: Political & Social Issues). 37.50 (ISBN 0-404-10522-X); pap. 14.00 (ISBN 0-404-10523-8). AMS Pr.

Alexander of Lycopolis. Alexander of Lycopolis Against Manichaeism. Koenen, Ludwig, ed. (Reprints & Translations). 1988. pap. write for info. (ISBN 0-89130-895-4, 00-07-12). Scholars Pr GA.

Alexeyeva, Ludmilla. Soviet Dissent: Contemporary Movements for National, Religious & Human Rights. Glad, John & Pearce, Carol, trs. from Rus. LC 84-11811. 1985. 35.00 (ISBN 0-8195-5124-4, Dist. by Harper). Wesleyan U Pr.

Alfaric, Prosper. Les Ecritures Manicheennes. (Reprints & Translations). Date not set. Vol. 1, Vue Generale. pap. price not set (ISBN 0-89130-896-2, 00-07-13). Vol. 2, Etude Analythique. Scholars Pr GA.

Alfaro, Juan. Preguntas y Respuestas sobre la Biblia. (Span.). 64p. 1982. pap. 1.50 (ISBN 0-89243-162-8). Liguori Pubns.

Al Farugi, I. R. Towards Islamic Arabic. 64p. (Orig.). 1986. pap. 5.00 (ISBN 0-317-52453-4). New Era Pubns MI.

--Trialogue of Abrahamic Faiths. 88p. (Orig.). 1986. pap. 7.50 (ISBN 0-317-52454-2). New Era Pubns MI.

Alfaruqi, Ismael R., jt. auth. see Chan, Wing T.

Al-Fatih, Zudhi. The Jews in Review: The World's Greatest Minds on Zionism. 1984. lib. bdg. 79.95 (ISBN 0-87700-581-8). Revisionist Pr.

Alfen, Nicholas Van see Van Alfen, Nicholas.

Alferirff, E. E., ed. Pisoma Tsarskoj Semji iz Zatotchenija. LC 73-91829. Tr. of Letters of the Tsar's Family from Captivity. (Illus.). 544p. 1974. 25.00 (ISBN 0-317-29225-0). Holy Trinity.

Alfonso, Regina M. How Jesus Taught: The Methods & Techniques of the Master. (Illus.). 129p. (Orig.). 1986. pap. 6.95 (ISBN 0-8189-0506-9). Alba.

Alford, Dean H. The Book of Genesis & Part of the Book of Exodus. 1979. 12.50 (ISBN 0-86524-001-9, 7002). Klock & Klock.

Alford, Delton L. Music in the Pentecostal Church. 113p. 1969. 5.25 (ISBN 0-87148-561-3); pap. 4.25 (ISBN 0-87148-562-1). Pathway Pr.

Alford, Henry. The New Testament for English Readers, 4 vols. 1983. Repr. of 1976 ed. 54.95 (ISBN 0-8010-0195-1). Baker Bk.

Alford, Nancy I. Who, Me, Give a Speech? Handbook for the Reluctant Christian Woman. 160p. (Orig.). 1987. pap. price not set (ISBN 0-8010-0211-7). Baker Bk.

Algar, Hamid. Religion & State in Iran, 1785-1906: The Role of the 'Ulama in the Qajar Period. LC 72-79959. (Near Eastern Center, UCLA; Ca. Library Reprint Ser.: No. 106). 1980. 34.50x (ISBN 0-520-04100-3). U of Cal Pr.

Algar, Hamid, ed. see Mutahhari, Ayatullah M.

Algar, Hamid, tr. from Persian. Constitution of the Islamic Republic of Iran. 94p. 1980. 9.95 (ISBN 0-933782-07-1); pap. 4.95 (ISBN 0-933782-02-0). Mizan Pr.

Algar, Hamid, tr. see Khomeini, Imam.

Algar, Hamid, tr. see Khumayni, Ruh A.

Algar, Hamid, tr. see Shari'ati, Ali.

Alger, Horatio, Sr. & Sheaf, J. P., Jr. Addresses Delivered at the Semi-Centennial Celebration of the Dedication of the First Unitarian Church, South Natick (Massachusetts) November 20, 1878. (Illus.). 41p. 1977. pap. 6.00 (ISBN 0-686-35760-4). G K Westgard.

Alger, William R. Destiny of the Soul: Critical History of the Doctrine of a Future Life, 2 Vols. 10th ed. LC 68-19263. 1968. Repr. of 1880 ed. Set. lib. bdg. 43.25x (ISBN 0-8371-0003-8, ALDS). Greenwood.

Al-Ghazali. Inner Dimensions of Islamic Worship. Holland, Muhtar, tr. from Arabic. 142p. (Orig.). 1983. pap. 6.95 (ISBN 0-86037-125-5, Pub. by Islamic Found UK). New Era Pubns MI.

--On the Duties of Brotherhood. 7.95 (ISBN 0-686-83895-5). Kazi Pubns.

--On the Duties of Brotherhood in Islam. Holland, Muhtar, tr. from Arabic. 95p. (Orig.). 1980. pap. 4.95 (ISBN 0-86037-068-2, Pub. by Islamic Found UK). New Era Pubns MI.

Al-Ghazzal, see Ghazzali, Al.

Al-Ghazzali. Alchemy of Happiness. 1964. 3.75x (ISBN 0-87902-055-5). Orientalia.

--The Book of Knowledge. 1970. 15.00x (ISBN 0-87902-106-3). Orientalia.

--Confessions of Al-Ghazzali. Watt, W. M., tr. 3.25x (ISBN 0-87902-059-8). Orientalia.

--Foundations of the Articles of Faith. 1969. 7.50x (ISBN 0-87902-058-X). Orientalia.

--Just Balance. 6.50 (ISBN 0-317-01603-2). Kazi Pubns.

--Mishkat Al-Anwar: A Niche for Lights. 1952. 4.25x (ISBN 0-87902-051-2). Orientalia.

--The Mysteries of Almsgiving. Faris, Nabik A., tr. 1966. 12.95x (ISBN 0-8156-6002-2, Am U Beirut). Syracuse U Pr.

--Mysteries of Fasting. 1970. 3.50x (ISBN 0-87902-052-0). Orientalia.

--Mysteries of Purity. 1966. 4.50x (ISBN 0-87902-053-9). Orientalia.

--On Divine Predicates & Their Attributes. 1970. 6.50x (ISBN 0-87902-057-1). Orientalia.

--Some Moral & Religious Teachings. 4.50x (ISBN 0-87902-056-3). Orientalia.

--Tahafut Al-Falasifah. 8.25x (ISBN 0-87902-054-7). Orientalia.

--Worship in Islam. Calverley, Edwin E., ed. LC 79-2860. 242p. 1981. Repr. of 1925 ed. 23.00 (ISBN 0-8305-0032-4). Hyperion Conn.

Al-Gita, Kashif, ed. The Shia Origin & Faith. Haq, M. Fazal, tr. from Arabic. 284p. 1984. pap. 7.50 (ISBN 0-941724-23-9). Islamic Seminary.

Alhaji Obaba Abdullahi Muhammad. Three Little Africans. (Illus.). 36p. (Orig.). 1978. pap. 2.50 (ISBN 0-916157-00-8). African Islam Miss Pubns.

Al-Hassan, Ahmed & Hill, Donald. Islamic Technology: An Illustrated History. (Illus.). 300p. 1987. 39.50 (ISBN 0-521-26333-6). Cambridge U Pr.

Al-Husaini, Ishak M. The Moslem Brethren: The Greatest of the Modern Islamic Movements. LC 79-2866. 186p. 1987. Repr. of 1956 ed. 21.00 (ISBN 0-8305-0039-1). Hyperion Conn.

Al-Husayn al-Sulami, Ibn. The Book of Sufi Chivalry: Lessons to a Son of the Moment (Futuwwah) Bayrak, Tosun, tr. from Arabic. 1983. 8.95 (ISBN 0-89281-031-9). Inner Tradit.

Ali, A. A. Holy Qur'an, 2 Vols. 29.50x (ISBN 0-87902-038-5). Orientalia.

Ali, A. Yusuf, tr. from Arabic. Holy Qur'an. lib. bdg. 14.00. Am Trust Pubns.

Ali, A. Yusuf, tr. Qur'an: The Holy. (Eng. & Arabic.). 1862p. 1983. text ed. 20.00 (ISBN 0-940368-32-3); pap. 10.00 (ISBN 0-940368-31-5). Tahrike Tarsile Quran.

Ali, A. Yusuf, tr. see Razwy, Sayed A.

Ali, Abdullah. The Spirit & the Future of Islam, 2 vols. 155p. 1983. Set. 187.50x (ISBN 0-86722-051-1). Inst Econ Pol.

Ali, Abdullah Y. & Ali, Abdullah Y. The Meaning of the Glorious Qur'an, 2 Vols. Set. 24.00 (ISBN 0-686-37146-1). New World Press NY.

Ali, Abdullah Yusuf. A Cultural History of India During the British Period. LC 75-41006. Repr. of 1940 ed. 25.50 (ISBN 0-404-14723-2). AMS Pr.

Ali, B. Hajjat-ul-Wada: Last Sermon. 1981. 1.25 (ISBN 0-686-97858-7). Kazi Pubns.

Ali, M. M. Introduction to the Study of the Holy Qur'an. 5.25x (ISBN 0-87902-040-7). Orientalia.

Ali, Muhammad K., ed. Islamic Unity & Happiness. Pazargali, Alaedin, tr. from Persian. 1985. pap. 3.95 (ISBN 0-940368-47-1). Tahrike Tarsile Quran.

Ali, Muhammed K., ed. see Mutahhari, Murtaza.

Ali, S. V. Husain the Savior of Islam. LC 81-51900. 252p. 1981. 5.95 (ISBN 0-940368-05-6); pap. 3.95 (ISBN 0-940368-03-X). Tahrike Tarsile Quran.

Ali, S. V., tr. from Arabic. The Holy Qur'an. 550p. 1981. text ed. 9.00 (ISBN 0-940368-08-0); pap. 4.95 (ISBN 0-940368-07-2). Tahrike Tarsile Quran.

Ali, Shahrazad. How Not to Eat Pork: Or Life Without the Pig. LC 85-70171. (Illus.). 120p. (Orig.). 1985. pap. 5.95 (ISBN 0-933405-00-6). Civilized Pubns.

Ali, Yousuf. The Holy Quran with Arabic Text Commentary & Translation. 25.75 (ISBN 0-686-18528-5). Kazi Pubns.

Ali, Yusef. The Holy Quran. (Arabic & Eng.). 20.00x (ISBN 0-86685-167-4). Intl Bk Ctr.

Ali, Yusuf. The Holy Quran. LC 77-78098. 1915p. 14.00 (ISBN 0-89259-006-8). Am Trust Pubns.

Ali, Yusuf H. Spirit, Soul, Consciousness, Realization. 1975. pap. 3.50 (ISBN 0-913358-10-X). El-Shabazz Pr.

Ali, Zaki. Islam in the World. LC 74-180314. (Mid-East Studies). Repr. of 1947 ed. 31.00 (ISBN 0-404-56209-4). AMS Pr.

Ali ibn Isma'il, A. H., et al. Al ibanah 'an usul addiyanah. Klein, W. C., tr. (American Oriental Ser.: Vol. 19). 1940. 18.00 (ISBN 0-527-02693-X). Kraus Repr.

Alimenti, Dante. Padre Pio. (Illus.). 179p. 1987. 49.95 (ISBN 0-87973-491-4). Our Sunday Visitor.

Ali-Nadawi, Abul H. Prophet's Stories. Quinlan, Hamid, ed. El-Helbawy, Kamal, tr. from Arabic. LC 82-70453. Tr. of Qasas An Nabiyin. (Illus.). 200p. (Orig.). Date not set. pap. 5.00 (ISBN 0-89259-038-6). Am Trust Pubns.

Aling, Charles F. Egypt & Bible History: From Earliest Times to 1000 B.C. (Baker Studies in Biblical Archaeology). 144p. (Orig.). 1981. pap. 5.95 (ISBN 0-8010-0174-9). Baker Bk.

Alioto, Joseph L., et al, eds. Teilhard de Chardin: In Quest of the Perfection of Man. LC 72-9596. 290p. 1973. 24.50 (ISBN 0-8386-1258-X). Fairleigh Dickinson.

Al-Islam, Da'i. The Companions of the Cave. 23p. 1985. pap. 3.95 (ISBN 0-940368-55-2). Tahrike Tarsile Quran.

--Prophet Sulaiman. 32p. 1985. pap. 3.95 (ISBN 0-940368-53-6). Tahrike Tarsile Quran.

Alison, Richard. A Confutation of Brownisme. LC 68-54608. (English Experience Ser.: No. 9). 130p. 1968. Repr. of 1590 ed. 16.00 (ISBN 90-221-0009-X). Walter J Johnson.

Al-Jarrahi, Abdussamad, ed. see Badawi, Gamal.

Al-Jarrahi, Abdussamad, tr. see Boisard, Marcel.

Al-Johani, Maneh, tr. see Yakan, Fathi.

Al-Khui, Ayatullah A. Articles of Islamic Acts. Haq, M. Fazal, tr. from Arabic. 236p. 1983. pap. 6.00 (ISBN 0-941724-21-2). Islamic Seminary.

Alkow, Jacob. In Many Worlds. LC 84-52110. (Illus.). 260p. 1985. pap. 13.95 (ISBN 0-88400-111-3). Shengold.

Al-Kulayni Ar-Razi. Al-Kafi: The Book of Divine Proof, II. Hasan-Rizvi, S. Muhammad, tr. from Arabic. LC 85-52242. 80p. (Orig.). 1985. pap. 6.00 (ISBN 0-940368-65-X). Tahrike Tarsile Quran.

--Al-Kafi: The Book of Divine Proof, IV. Hasan-Rizvi, S. Muhammad, tr. from Arabic. LC 85-52242. 90p. (Orig.). 1986. pap. 12.00 (ISBN 0-940368-66-8). Tahrike Tarsile Quran.

Alladin, Bilzik. Story of Mohammad the Prophet. (Illus.). 1979. 7.25 (ISBN 0-89744-139-7). Auromere.

Allan, George. The Importances of the Past: A Meditation on the Authority of Tradition. 308p. 1985. 44.50x (ISBN 0-88706-116-8); pap. 14.95x (ISBN 0-88706-117-6). State U NY Pr.

Allan, John. The Healing Energy of Love: A Personal Journal. LC 85-40770. (Illus.). 175p. (Orig.). 1986. pap. 7.50 (ISBN 0-8356-0603-1, Quest). Theos Pub Hse.

--The Kingdom of God. pap. 2.50 (ISBN 0-87516-286-X). De Vorss.

--Mysteries. (Book of Beliefs). 1981. 9.95 (ISBN 0-89191-477-3, 54775). Cook.

--Shopping for a God. 218p. 1987. pap. price not set (ISBN 0-8010-0212-5). Baker Bk.

Allan, Leslie. Chronicles First & Second, Vol. 10. 400p. 1987. 24.95 (ISBN 0-8499-0415-3). Word Bks.

Allard, Jean-Louis. Education for Freedom: The Philosophy of Education of Jacques Maritain. Nelson, Ralph C., tr. 130p. 1982. pap. text ed. 8.95 (ISBN 0-268-00909-0). U of Notre Dame Pr.

Allbritton, Cliff. How to Get Married: And Stay That Way. LC 82-71219. (Orig.). 1983. pap. 5.95 (ISBN 0-8054-5653-8). Broadman.

Allbutt, Mary E., jt. ed. see Fraser, J. O.

Allchin, A. L., rev. by see Thunberg, Lars.

Allchin, A. M. The Joy of All Creation: An Anglican Meditation on the Place of Mary. LC 84-72479. 162p. 1985. pap. 7.50 (ISBN 0-936384-24-7). Cowley Pubns.

--The Kingdom of Love & Knowledge: The Encounter Between Orthodoxy & the West. 224p. (Orig.). 1982. 14.95 (ISBN 0-8164-0532-8, HarpR). Har-Row.

--The Living Presence of the Past: The Dynamic of Christian Tradition. 192p. (Orig.). 1981. pap. 7.95 (ISBN 0-8164-2334-2, HarpR). Har-Row.

--The World Is a Wedding: Explorations in Christian Spirituality. (Crossroad Paperback Ser.). 512p. 1982. pap. 6.95 (ISBN 0-8245-0411-9). Crossroad NY.

Allchin, A. M. & Waal, Esther de, eds. Daily Readings from Prayers & Praises in the Celtic Tradition. 1987. pap. 4.95 (ISBN 0-87243-151-7). Templegate.

Allchin, Arthur M., jt. ed. see Coulson, John.

Allegra, Gabriel. Mary's Immaculate Heart: A Way of God. 156p. 1985. 9.50 (ISBN 0-8199-0875-4). Franciscan Herald.

Allegro, J. M. Dead Sea Scrolls. 1956. pap. 4.95 (ISBN 0-14-020376-1, Pelican). Penguin.

Allegro, John. The Dead Sea Scrolls & the Christian Myth. LC 83-63566. (Illus.). 248p. 1984. 19.95 (ISBN 0-87975-241-6). Prometheus Bks.

Allegro, John M. All Manner of Men. (Illus.). 186p. 1982. spiral bdg. 18.50x (ISBN 0-398-04575-5). C C Thomas.

Alleman, Herman & Scovil, Elizabeth R. Prayers for Boys & Prayers for Girls. 3.95x. Nelson.

Alleman, Herman C. Prayers for Boys. LC 81-142145. pap. 3.95 (ISBN 0-8407-5241-5). Nelson.

--Prayers for Girls. 3.95 (ISBN 0-8407-5242-3). Nelson.

Allen. Faith, Hope & Love. 5.95 (ISBN 0-318-18178-9). WCTU.

Allen & Asselineau. Biography of Crevecoeur. 1987. write for info (ISBN 0-670-81345-1). Viking.

Allen, Alexander. Jonathan Edwards: Seventeen Three to Seventeen Fifty-Eight. lib. bdg. 23.50 (ISBN 0-8337-3926-3). B Franklin.

Allen, Anne S., ed. New Options, New Dilemmas: An Interprofessional Approach to Life or Death Decisions. LC 85-45436. 144p. 1985. 22.00 (ISBN 0-669-11730-7). Lexington Bks.

Allen, Beverly, jt. auth. see Allen, Ronald.

Allen, Blair H. Atlantis Trilogy. 1982. pap. 1.25 (ISBN 0-917458-09-5). Kent Pubns.

Allen, Cady H., jt. auth. see Rasooli, Jay M.

Allen, Carlos & Estudios, Guias de. Guia De Estudios Sobre Estudios En el Nuevo Testamento. (Illus.). 96p. 1981. pap. 3.25 (ISBN 0-311-43502-5). Casa Bautista.

Allen, Catherine. The New Lottie Moon Story. LC 79-52336. 1980. 9.95 (ISBN 0-8054-6319-4). Broadman.

Allen, Charles. My Lord & My God. 48p. 1985. 6.95 (ISBN 0-8378-5083-5). Gibson.

Allen, Charles L. All Things Are Possible Through Prayer. 1984. pap. 2.95 (ISBN 0-515-08808-0, PV072). Jove Pubns.

--All Things Are Possible Through Prayer. o. p. 7.95 (ISBN 0-8007-0007-4); pap. 2.95 (ISBN 0-8007-8000-0, Spire Bks). Revell.

--Faith, Hope, & Love. 192p. 1982. pap. 5.95 (ISBN 0-8007-5096-9, Power Bks). Revell.

--God's Psychiatry. 1984. pap. 2.95 (ISBN 0-515-08234-1). Jove Pubns.

--God's Psychiatry. 160p. 9.95 (ISBN 0-8007-0113-5); pap. 2.95 (ISBN 0-8007-8015-9, Spire Bks); pap. 5.95 (ISBN 0-8007-5010-1, Power Bks). Revell.

--Inspiring Thoughts for Your Marriage. 1985. 7.95 (ISBN 0-8007-1401-6). Revell.

--Life More Abundant. pap. 2.25 (ISBN 0-515-06412-2). Jove Pubns.

--Meet the Methodists: An Introduction to the United Methodist Church. 96p. 1986. pap. 3.50 (ISBN 0-687-24650-4). Abingdon.

--The Secret of Abundant Living. 160p. 1980. 8.95 (ISBN 0-8007-1123-8); Spire Bks. pap. 3.50 (ISBN 0-8007-8479-0). Revell.

--La Siquiatria de Dios. 176p. 1975. 2.95 (ISBN 0-88113-280-2). Edit Betania.

--Touch of the Master's Hand: Christ's Miracles for Today. 160p. 1956. pap. 2.75 (ISBN 0-8007-8093-0, Spire Bks). Revell.

--Twenty-Third Psalm. (Illus.). 64p. 1961. 7.95 (ISBN 0-8007-0330-8). Revell.

--Victory in the Valleys of Life. 128p. 1984. pap. 2.95 (ISBN 0-8007-8488-X, Spire Bks). Revell.

--When You Lose a Loved One. 64p. 1959. 7.95 (ISBN 0-8007-0347-2). Revell.

--You Are Never Alone. 160p. 1984. pap. 5.95 (ISBN 0-8007-5145-0, Power Bks). Revell.

Allen, Charles L. & Parker, Mildred. How to Increase Your Sunday School Attendance. 128p. 1980. 8.95 (ISBN 0-8007-1088-6). Revell.

Allen, Charles L. & Rice, Helen S. The Prayerful Heart. 160p. (Orig.). 1981. pap. 5.95 (ISBN 0-8007-5073-X, Power Bks). Revell.

--When You Lose a Loved One-Life Is Forever. 128p. 1979. pap. 5.95 (ISBN 0-8007-5031-4, Power Bks). Revell.

Allen, Clifton J., et al, eds. Broadman Bible Commentary, 12 vols. Incl. Vol. 1, General Articles, Genesis-Exodus. rev. ed (ISBN 0-8054-1125-9); Vol. 2 (ISBN 0-8054-1102-X); Vol. 3 (ISBN 0-8054-1103-8); Vol. 4 (ISBN 0-8054-1104-6); Vol. 5 (ISBN 0-8054-1105-4); Vol. 6 (ISBN 0-8054-1106-2); Vol. 7 (ISBN 0-8054-1107-0); Vol. 8, General Articles, Matthew-Mark. rev. ed (ISBN 0-8054-1108-9); Vol. 9 (ISBN 0-8054-1109-7); Vol. 10 (ISBN 0-8054-1110-0); Vol. 11 (ISBN 0-8054-1111-9); Vol. 12 (ISBN 0-8054-1112-7). LC 78-93918. 1969. lib. bdg. 16.95 ea.; 195.00 set (ISBN 0-8054-1100-3). Broadman.

Allen, Darrel J., jt. auth. see Mead, Daniel L.

Allen, David B., jt. auth. see Getz, William L.

Allen, Devere. Fight for Peace, 2 vols. LC 74-147439. (Library of War & Peace; Histories of the Organized Peace Movement). 1972. Set. lib. bdg. 92.00 (ISBN 0-8240-0228-8); lib. bdg. 38.00 ea. Garland Pub.

Allen, Diogenes. Love: Christian Romance, Marriage, Friendship. 149p. (Orig.). 1987. pap. 8.95 (ISBN 0-936384-47-6). Cowley Pubns.

--Philosophy for Understanding Theology. LC 84-48510. 252p. 1985. pap. 14.95 (ISBN 0-8042-0688-0). John Knox.

--The Traces of God in a Frequently Hostile World. LC 80-51570. 108p. (Orig.). 1981. pap. 6.00 (ISBN 0-936384-03-4). Cowley Pubns.

Allen, Don C. Doubt's Boundless Sea. 1979. 25.50 (ISBN 0-405-10577-0). Ayer Co Pubs.

--The Legend of Noah: Renaissance Rationalism in Art, Science, & Letters. LC 49-49065. (Reprint of Studies in Language & Literature Ser.: Vol. 33, No. 3-4, 1949). (Illus.). 1963. pap. 8.95 (ISBN 0-252-72516-6). U of Ill Pr.

Allen, Douglas. Structure & Creativity in Religion. (Religion & Reason Ser.: No. 14). 1978. 20.40x (ISBN 90-279-7594-9). Mouton.

Allen, E. L. Freedom in God: A Guide to the Thought of Nicholas Berdyaev. LC 73-5751. lib. bdg. 12.50 (ISBN 0-8414-1740-7). Folcroft.

Allen, Edith B. One Hundred Bible Games. (Paperback Program Ser). (YA) 1968. pap. 3.95 (ISBN 0-8010-0033-5). Baker Bk.

Allen, Edward J. The Second United Order among the Mormons. LC 73-38483. (Columbia University Studies in the Social Sciences: No. 419). Repr. of 1936 ed. 15.00 (ISBN 0-404-51419-7). AMS Pr.

Allen, Eula. Creation Trilogy, 3 vols. rev. ed. Incl. Vol. 1. Before the Beginning. 1966 (ISBN 0-87604-054-7); Vol. 2. The River of Time. 1965 (ISBN 0-87604-055-5); Vol. 3. You Are Forever. 1966 (ISBN 0-87604-056-3). (Illus.). pap. 10.95 set (ISBN 0-87604-125-X); pap. 3.95 ea. ARE Pr.

Allen, Fay W. Waldo Emerson. (Illus.). 782p. 1982. pap. 10.95 (ISBN 0-14-006278-5). Penguin.

Allen, Gary. Jimmy Carter-Jimmy Carter. 96p. pap. 1.00 (ISBN 0-686-31145-0). Concord Pr.

Allen, Gay W. Waldo Emerson: A Biography. LC 81-65275. (Illus.). 696p. 1981. 25.00 (ISBN 0-670-74866-8). Viking.

Allen, George, tr. Book of the Dead; or, Going Forth by Day: Ideas of the Ancient Egyptians Concerning the Hereafter As Expressed in Their Own Terms. LC 74-10338. (Studies in Ancient Oriental Civilization Ser: No. 37). 1974. pap. text ed. 20.00x (ISBN 0-226-62410-2). U of Chicago Pr.

Allen, Grant. The Evolution of the Idea of God. 1977. lib. bdg. 59.95 (ISBN 0-8490-1796-3). Gordon Pr.

Allen, Henry E. Turkish Transformation: A Study in Social & Religious Development. LC 68-57588. (Illus.). 1968. Repr. of 1935 ed. lib. bdg. 22.50x (ISBN 0-8371-0284-7, ALTT). Greenwood.

Allen, Hope E. Writings Ascribed to Richard Rolle Hermit of Hampole & Materials for His Biography. 568p. 1981. Repr. of 1927 ed. lib. bdg. 125.00 (ISBN 0-89987-023-6). Darby Bks.

--Writings Ascribed to Richard Rolle, Hermit of Hampole & Materials for His Biography. (MLA. MS Ser.). 1927. 44.00 (ISBN 0-527-01280-7). Kraus Repr.

Allen, Horace T., Jr. A Handbook for the Lectionary. LC 80-19735. 254p. 1980. softcover 8.95 (ISBN 0-664-24347-9, A Geneva Press Pub.). Westminster.

Allen, J. Catling. Pictorial Bible Atlas. 14.95 (ISBN 0-7175-0991-5); pap. 9.95 (ISBN 0-7175-0857-9). Dufour.

--Way of the Christian. (The Way Ser.). pap. 5.95 (ISBN 0-7175-0782-3). Dufour.

Allen, J. F., et al. Illustrated Bible for Children. (Illus.). 9.95 (ISBN 0-8407-5264-4). Nelson.

Allen, James. As a Man Thinketh. pap. 1.00 (ISBN 0-87516-000-X). De Vorss.

--As a Man Thinketh. 1959. 3.95 (ISBN 0-399-12829-8, G&D). Putnam Pub Group.

--As a Man Thinketh. 4.95 (ISBN 0-529-05908-8, F12); pap. 2.95 (ISBN 0-529-05906-1, D6). World Bible.

--As a Man Thinketh. 1985. 4.95 (ISBN 0-915720-20-5). Brownlow Pub Co.

--As You Thinketh: Update & Revision of James Allen's Classic "As a Man Thinketh". rev. ed. 88p. 1984. pap. 5.95 (ISBN 0-914295-03-9). Top Mtn Pub.

--From Passion to Peace. 64p. 1981. pap. 4.50 (ISBN 0-89540-077-4, SB-077). Sun Pub.

--The Life Triumphant. 112p. 1983. pap. 6.50 (ISBN 0-89540-125-8, SB-125). Sun Pub.

Allen, James B. Trials of Discipleship: The Story of William Clayton, a Mormon. 416p. 1987. 22.95 (ISBN 0-252-01369-7). U of Ill Pr.

Allen, James B., ed. see Clayton, William.

Allen, John, ed. Three Medieval Plays: The Coventry Nativity Play, Everyman, Master Pierre Pathelin. 1968. pap. 3.50x (ISBN 0-87830-529-7). Theatre Arts.

Allen, John H. Judah's Sceptre & Joseph's Birthright. 1946. 8.00 (ISBN 0-685-08809-X). Destiny.

Allen, John W. English Political Thought, Sixteen Hundred Three to Sixteen Forty-Four. x, 525p. 1967. Repr. of 1938 ed. 37.50 (ISBN 0-208-00144-1, Archon). Shoe String.

Allen, Joseph H. Our Liberal Movement in Theology: Chiefly As Shown in Recollections of the History of Unitarianism in New England. 3rd ed. LC 73-38432. (Religion in America, Ser. 2). 230p. 1972. Repr. of 1892 ed. 20.00 (ISBN 0-405-04053-9). Ayer Co Pubs.

Allen, Joseph J., jt. auth. see Metropolitan Philip Saliba.

Allen, Joseph J., ed. Orthodox Synthesis: The Unity of Theological Thought. 231p. (Orig.). 1981. pap. 8.95 (ISBN 0-913836-84-2). St Vladimirs.

Allen, Joseph L. Love & Conflict: A Covenantal Model of Christian Ethics. 336p. 1984. pap. 12.95 (ISBN 0-687-22806-9). Abingdon.

Allen, Judson B. Friar as Critic: Literary Attitudes in the Later Middle Ages. LC 77-123037. 1971. 11.50x (ISBN 0-8265-1158-9). Vanderbilt U Pr.

Allen, June, tr. see Garin, Eugenio.

Allen, Kring. The Paradox of Preaching. (Illus.). 104p. (Orig.). 1986. pap. 9.95 (ISBN 1-55630-018-2). Brentwood Comm.

Allen, Leslie. Joel, Obadiah, Jonah, Micah. (New International Commentary on Old Testament Ser.). 16.95 (ISBN 0-8028-2373-4). Eerdmans.

Allen, Marcus. Tantra for the West: A Guide to Personal Freedom. LC 80-316. 235p. 1981. pap. 7.95 (ISBN 0-931432-06-5). Whatever Pub.

Allen, Milton H. Why Do Good People Suffer? LC 82-82949. 1983. pap. 4.95 (ISBN 0-8054-5208-7). Broadman.

Allen, P. S. Erasmus' Services to Learning. 1974. lib. bdg. 59.95 (ISBN 0-8490-0123-4). Gordon Pr.

--Erasmus' Services to Learning. (Studies in Philosophy: No. 40). 1972. pap. 39.95x (ISBN 0-8383-0111-8). Haskell.

Allen, Paul M. Vladimir Soloviev: Russian Mystic, Vol. 9. LC 72-81592. (Spiritual Science Library). (Illus.). 544p. 1978. lib. bdg. 22.00 (ISBN 0-89345-032-4, Spiritual Sci Lib); pap. 10.00 (ISBN 0-89345-213-0, Steinerbks). Garber Comm.

Allen, Paul M., ed. A Christian Rosenkreutz Anthology, Vol. 10. 2nd, rev. ed. LC 68-13130. (Spiritual Science Library). (Illus.). 640p. 1981. Repr. of 1968 ed. lib. bdg. 65.00 (ISBN 0-89345-009-X, Steinerbks). Garber Comm.

Allen, Paul M., ed. see Steiner, Rudolf, et al.

Allen, Paul M., ed. see Steiner, Rudolf.

Allen, Pauline, tr. see Grillmeier, Aloys.

Allen, R. Praise: A Matter of Life & Breath. Chan, Silas, tr. (Chinese.). 204p. 1982. pap. write for info. (ISBN 0-941598-04-7). Living Spring Pubns.

Allen, R. C. Immortal Words of Jesus Christ. 1981. pap. 4.95 (ISBN 0-910228-11-6). Best Bks.

Allen, R. Earl. Funeral Source Book. (Preaching Helps Ser.). (Orig.). 1984. pap. 3.50 (ISBN 0-8010-0076-9). Baker Bk.

--Good Morning, Lord: Devotions for Hospital Patients. 96p. 1975. 4.95 (ISBN 0-8010-0079-3). Baker Bk.

--Just When You Need Him. (Contempo Ser). pap. 0.95 (ISBN 0-8010-0074-2). Baker Bk.

--Let It Begin in Me. LC 84-19934. 1985. pap. 3.75 (ISBN 0-8054-5005-X). Broadman.

Allen, R. Earl & Gregory, Joel. Southern Baptist Preaching Today. 1987. pap. 11.95 (ISBN 0-8054-5714-3). Broadman.

Allen, Richard. Imperialism & Nationalism in the Fertile Crescent: Sources & Prospects of the Arab-Israeli Conflict. (Illus.). 1974. 29.95x (ISBN 0-19-501782-X). Oxford U Pr.

--The Life Experience & Gospel Labors of the Rt. Rev. Richard Allen. 96p. (Orig.). 1983. pap. 3.95 (ISBN 0-687-21844-6). Abingdon.

Allen, Rob, jt. ed. see Gillum, Perry.

Allen, Robert. Hot & Cold & in Between. 1985. 4.25 (ISBN 0-89536-717-3, 5801). CSS of Ohio.

Allen, Roger & Rose, Ron. Common Sense Discipline. LC 86-61522. 1986. 12.95 (ISBN 0-8344-0135-5, BA110H). Sweet.

Allen, Roger, tr. see Mahfuz, Nagib.

Allen, Roland. The Compulsion of the Spirit: A Roland Allen Reader. Long, Charles H. & Paton, David, eds. 160p. 1983. pap. 3.70 (ISBN 0-88028-025-5). Forward Movement.

--Missionary Methods: St. Paul's or Our's? 1962. pap. 5.95x (ISBN 0-8028-1001-2). Eerdmans.

--The Spontaneous Expansion of the Church. 1962. pap. 4.95 (ISBN 0-8028-1002-0). Eerdmans.

Allen, Ronald & Allen, Beverly. Liberated Traditionalism: Men & Women in Balance. LC 85-8969. (Critical Concern Bks.). 1985. 11.95 (ISBN 0-88070-112-9). Multnomah.

Allen, Ronald B. Lord of Song: The Messiah Revealed in the Psalms. LC 85-21693. (Living Theology Bks.). 1985. pap. 7.95 (ISBN 0-88070-129-3). Multnomah.

--The Majesty of Man: The Dignity of Being Human. LC 84-984. (Critical Concern Ser.). 1984. 11.95 (ISBN 0-88070-065-3). Multnomah.

--Praise! A Matter of Life & Breath. LC 80-23894. 248p. 1980. pap. 5.95 (ISBN 0-8407-5733-6). Nelson.

--Rediscovering Prophecy: A New Song for a New Kingdom. 1987. pap. 7.95. Multnomah.

--A Shelter in the Fury: A Prophet's Stunning Picture of God. (Living Theology Ser.). (Orig.). 1986. pap. 6.95 (ISBN 0-88070-158-7). Multnomah.

Allen, Ronald B. & Borror, Gordon. Worship: Rediscovering the Missing Jewel. (Critical Concern Bks.). 1987. pap. 7.95 (ISBN 0-88070-140-4). Multnomah.

Allen, Ronald J. Contemporary Biblical Interpretation for Preaching. 160p. 1984. pap. 5.95 (ISBN 0-8170-1002-5). Judson.

--Our Eyes Can Be Opened: Preaching the Miracle Stories of the Synoptic Gospels Today. LC 81-43679. 146p. 1983. pap. text ed. 9.50 (ISBN 0-8191-2671-3). U Pr of Amer.

Allen, Ruth. What's the Matter with Christy? LC 82-8036. 110p. (Orig.). 1982. pap. 3.95 (ISBN 0-87123-629-X, 210629). Bethany Hse.

Allen, W. E., ed. see Finney, Charles G.

Allen, William. Libri Tres, Id Est: De Sacramentis in Genere, De Sacramento Eucharistiae, De Sacrificio Eucharistiae. 699p. Repr. of 1576 ed. text ed. 124.20x (ISBN 0-576-99475-8, Pub. by Gregg Intl Pubs England). Gregg Intl.

Allen, William O. Two Hundred Years: The History of the Society for Promoting Christian Knowledge, 1698-1898. LC 76-135171. (Research & Source Works Ser.: No. 622). 1971. Repr. of 1898 ed. 32.00 (ISBN 0-8337-0044-8). B Franklin.

Allender, Dan B., jt. auth. see Crabb, Lawrence J., Jr.

Allens, Alexi. Images of Sai Baba. (Illus.). 104p. (Orig.). 1985. pap. 12.95 (ISBN 0-318-18477-X). Masterpiece Pub.

Allenson, Robert D., compiled by. John Henry Newman, 1801-1890: A Preliminary Register of Editions from 1818 to 1890. 1976. pap. text ed. 5.00x (ISBN 0-8401-0050-7, Aleph Pr). A R Allenson.

Alley, Robert, ed. James Madison on Religious Liberty. LC 85-42957. 343p. 1985. 19.95 (ISBN 0-87975-298-X). Prometheus Bks.

Allgaier, Karl. Der Einfluss Bernhards von Clairvaux auf Gottfried von Strassburg. (European University Studies Ser.: No. 1, Vol. 641). (Ger.). 185p. 1983. 24.20 (ISBN 3-8204-7541-9). P Lang Pubs.

Allgeier, Arthur. Die Chester Beatty-Papyri Zum Pentateuch. 12.00 (ISBN 0-384-00860-7). Johnson Repr.

--Die Psalmen der Vulgata: Ihre Eigenart. 22.00 (ISBN 0-384-00870-4). Johnson Repr.

Allies, Mary H. Three Catholic Reformers of the Fifteenth Century. facsimile ed. LC 73-38755. (Essay Index Reprint Ser). Repr. of 1878 ed. 13.00 (ISBN 0-8369-2633-1). Ayer Co Pubs.

Allies, Mary H., tr. see Joannes, Damascenus.

Allione, Tsultrim. Women of Wisdom. (Illus.). 224p. (Orig.). 1985. pap. 12.95 (ISBN 0-7102-0240-7). Methuen Inc.

Allis, Oswald T. Bible Numerics. 1949. pap. 0.95 (ISBN 0-87552-100-2). Presby & Reformed.

--The Five Books of Moses. 1977. pap. 5.95 (ISBN 0-8010-0108-0). Baker Bk.

--Five Books of Moses. 1949. pap. 7.95 (ISBN 0-87552-102-9). Presby & Reformed.

--God Spake by Moses. 1951. pap. 5.95 (ISBN 0-87552-103-7). Presby & Reformed.

--God Spake by Moses: An Exposition of the Pentateuch. 1951. pap. 5.95 (ISBN 0-8010-0109-9). Baker Bk.

--Prophecy & the Church. 1977. pap. 5.95 (ISBN 0-8010-0110-2). Baker Bk.

--Prophecy & the Church. 1945. pap. 5.95 (ISBN 0-87552-104-5). Presby & Reformed.

--Unity of Isaiah. 1952. pap. 4.50 (ISBN 0-87552-105-3). Presby & Reformed.

--The Unity of Isaiah: A Study in Prophecy. 1974. pap. 4.50 (ISBN 0-8010-0111-0). Baker Bk.

Allison, C. FitzSimons. Fear, Love, & Worship. pap. 4.95 (ISBN 0-8164-2020-3, SP17, HarpR). Har-Row.

Allison, Dale C., Jr. The End of the Ages Has Come: An Early Interpretation of the Passion & Resurrection of Jesus. LC 85-47732. 208p. 1985. 19.95 (ISBN 0-8006-0753-8, 1-753). Fortress.

Allison, Henry E. Kant's Transcendental Idealism. LC 85-5756. 400p. 1986. 12.95x (ISBN 0-300-03629-9, Y-567). Yale U Pr.

Allison, Joseph, ed. see Wesley, John.

Allison, Joseph D. The Devotional Resource Guide: Selecting the Best in Classic & Contemporary Christian Literature. 176p. 1986. pap. 8.95 (ISBN 0-8407-5950-9). Nelson.

Allison, Joseph D., ed. see Bangs, Carl.

Allison, Joseph D., ed. see Massey, James E.

Allison, Joseph D., ed. see Meyer, F. B.

Allison, Joseph D., ed. see Welch, Reuben R.

Allison, Thomas. English Religious Life in the Eighth Century. LC 75-106708. Repr. of 1929 ed. lib. bdg. 22.50x (ISBN 0-8371-3438-2, ALRL). Greenwood.

--English Religious Life in the Eighth Century As Illustrated by Contemporary Letters. LC 70-136409. Repr. of 1929 ed. 9.00 (ISBN 0-404-00348-6). AMS Pr.

Allison, W. H. Inventory of Unpublished Material for American Religion History in Protestant Church Archives & Other Repositories. (CI.G Ser.). 1910. 21.00 (ISBN 0-527-00683-1). Kraus Repr.

Allison, William H. & Barnes, W. W. Baptist Ecclesiology: An Original Anthology. Gaustad, Edwin S., ed. LC 79-52582. (The Baptist Tradition Ser.). 1980. lib. bdg. 21.00x (ISBN 0-405-12449-X). Ayer Co Pubs.

Allison, Winn O. Jeremiah, Lamentations: God's Unfailing Love. Wolf, Earl C., ed. (Small-Group Bible Studies). 96p. (Orig.). 1986. pap. text ed. 2.50 (ISBN 0-8341-1106-3). Beacon Hill.

Allmen, Jean-Jacques Von, ed. Vocabulaire Biblique. (Fr.). 320p. 1964. pap. 24.95 (ISBN 0-686-57248-3, M-6759). French & Eur.

Allon, Dafna, et al, trs. see Ringelblum, Emmanuel.

Allott, Kenneth, ed. Writers & Their Background: Matthew Arnold. LC 75-15339. (Writers & Their Background Ser.). xxvi, 353p. 1976. 20.00x (ISBN 0-8214-0197-1); pap. 10.00x (ISBN 0-8214-0198-X). Ohio U Pr.

Allphin, McKay. Eternal Grit: Up-to-Heaven Insights & Down-to-Earth Wisdom. LC 78-70363. 138p. 1978. 7.95 (ISBN 0-88290-102-8). Horizon Utah.

Allport, Gordon W. Individual & His Religion. 1967. pap. 4.95 (ISBN 0-02-083130-7). Macmillan.

Allred, Gordon T. God the Father. 1979. 8.95 (ISBN 0-87747-746-9). Deseret Bk.

Alluntis, Felix & Wolter, Allan B., trs. from Lat. John Duns Scotus: God & Creatures; the Quodlibetal Questions. LC 80-28098. Orig. Title: Quaestiones Quodlibetales. (Illus.). 548p. pap. 16.95x (ISBN 0-8132-0557-3). Cath U Pr.

Allworthy, A. W. The Petition Against God: The Full Story Behind RM-2493. LC 75-43375. (Illus.). 150p. 1976. pap. 3.95 (ISBN 0-686-16824-0, Pub. by Christ the Light). Mho & Mho.

Almaas, A. H. Diamond Heart, Bk. 1: Elements of the Real in Man. 280p. (Orig.). 1987. pap. 10.00 (ISBN 0-936713-01-1). Almaas Pubns.

--The Elixir of Enlightenment. LC 84-50159. 64p. (Orig.). 1984. pap. 3.95 (ISBN 0-87728-613-2). Weiser.

--Essence. LC 85-51109. (Illus.). 208p. (Orig.). 1986. pap. 10.95 (ISBN 0-87728-627-2). Weiser.

--The Void: A Psychodynamic Investigation of the Relationship Between Mind & Space. LC 85-82559. 175p. (Orig.). 1986. pap. 8.00 (ISBN 0-936713-00-3). Almaas Pubns.

Almagno, Romano S. & Harkins, Conrad L., eds. Studies Honoring Ignatius Charles Brady O. F. M. (Theology Ser). 1976. 25.00 (ISBN 0-686-17960-9). Franciscan Inst.

Almagno, Stephen, pref. by see Wright, John.

Al-Majilisi, Muhammad B. The Life & Religion of Muhammad. Merrick, James, tr. 463p. 1987. pap. 19.95 (ISBN 0-7103-0216-9, 02169, Kegan Paul). Methuen Inc.

Almand, Joan & Wooderson, Joy. Establishing Values. LC 76-17147. 1976. pap. 1.99 (ISBN 0-87148-283-5). Pathway Pr.

Almanza, Francisco, tr. see Dobson, James.

Almanza, Francisco G., tr. see Baker, R. A.

Al-Maqqari, Ahmed, ed. History of the Mohammedan Dynasties in Spain, 2 Vols. De Gayangos, P., tr. 1969. Repr. of 1840 ed. Set. 175.00 (ISBN 0-384-35253-7). Johnson Repr.

Almaraz, Felix D., Jr. Tragic Cavalier: Governor Manuel Salcedo of Texas, 1808-1813. 218p. 1971. pap. text ed. 6.95 (ISBN 0-292-78039-7). U of Tex Pr.

Almeder, Robert. Beyond Death: Evidence for Life after Death. 176p. 1987. 24.50x (ISBN 0-398-05327-8). C C Thomas.

Almeida, Abraao de see De Almeida, Abraao.

Almirudas, Hiram, ed. El Fruto del Espiritu. (Span.). 112p. 1979. pap. 3.50 (ISBN 0-87148-303-3). Pathway Pr.

Almirudus, Hiram, ed. Antologia de Homilias Biblicas, Vol. IV. (Span.). 162p. 1981. 6.95 (ISBN 0-87148-025-5). Pathway Pr.

--Antologia de Homilias Biblicas, Vol. V. (Span.). 158p. 1982. 6.95 (ISBN 0-87148-026-3). Pathway Pr.

--Antologia de Homilias Biblicas, Vol. VI. (Span.). 158p. 1982. 6.95 (ISBN 0-87148-027-1). Pathway Pr.

--Antologia de Homilias Biblicas, Vol. III. (Span.). 148p. 1980. 6.95 (ISBN 0-87148-024-7). Pathway Pr.

--Antologia de Homilias Biblicas, Vol. I. (Span.). 159p. 1977. 6.95 (ISBN 0-87148-022-0). Pathway Pr.

--Antologia de Homilias Biblicas, Vol. II. (Span.). 159p. 1979. 6.95 (ISBN 0-87148-023-9). Pathway Pr.

--Los Dones del Espiritu. (Span.). 88p. 1978. pap. 2.75 (ISBN 0-87148-520-6). Pathway Pr.

Almog, Shmuel. Zionism & History: Zionist Attitudes to the Jewish Historical Past, 1896-1906. Friedman, Ina, tr. from Hebrew. 350p. 1986. 29.95 (ISBN 0-312-89885-1). St Martin.

Almond, Brenda & Wilson, Bryan, eds. Values: A Symposium. 300p. 1987. text ed. 45.00 (ISBN 0-391-03368-9). Humanities.

Almond, Philip C. Mystical Experience & Religious Doctrine: An Investigation of the Study of Mysticism in World Religions. (Religion & Reason: No. 26). 197p. 1982. text ed. 40.00 (ISBN 90-279-3160-7). Mouton.

--Rudolf Otto: An Introduction to His Philosophical Theology. LC 83-19865. (Studies in Religion). x, 172p. 1984. 23.00x (ISBN 0-8078-1589-6). U of NC Pr.

Al-Mufid, Shaykh. Kitab Al-Irshad: The Book of Guidance into the Lives of the Twelve Imams. Howard, I. K., tr. 616p. 1986. lib. bdg. 55.00 (ISBN 0-7103-0151-0). Methuen Inc.

Al-Muminin, Amir. Supplications (Du'a) Chittick, William C., tr. from Arabic & Eng. 63p. 1986. text ed. 24.95 (ISBN 0-7103-0156-1). Methuen Inc.

Al-Muzaffar, Muhammad. The Faith of Shi'a Islam. LC 83-50153. 80p. pap. 4.00 (ISBN 0-940368-26-9). Tahrike Tarsile Quran.

Al-Muzaffar, Muhammad Rida. The Faith of Shi'ia Islam. 89p. 1982. 20.00x (ISBN 0-317-39062-7, Pub. by Luzac & Co Ltd). State Mutual Bk.

Al-Muzaffar, Muhammed R. The Faith of Shi'a Islam. 89p. (Orig.). 1986. pap. text ed. 8.95 (ISBN 0-7103-0157-X). Methuen Inc.

Al-Naquib Al-Attas, Syed Muhammad. Islam, Secularism & the Philosophy of the Future. LC 84-26108. 239p. 1985. 31.00x (ISBN 0-7201-1740-2). Mansell.

Alokeranjan, Dasgupta. Roots in the Void: Baul Songs of Bengal. 1983. 5.00x (ISBN 0-8364-0972-8, Pub. by KP Bagchi India). South Asia Bks.

Alon, Gedaliah. The Jews in Their Land in the Talmudic Age, Vol. 1. Gershon, Levi, tr. from Hebrew. 324p. 1980. text ed. 32.50x (ISBN 965-223-352-8, Pub. by Magnes Pr Israel). Humanities.

Alon, Gedalyahu. Jews, Judaism & the Classical World. Abrahams, Israel, tr. from Hebrew. 499p. 1977. text ed. 38.50x (Pub. by Magnes Pr Israel). Humanities.

Alonso, Joaquin M. The Secret of Fatima Fact & Legend. Dominican Nuns of the Perpetual Rosary, tr. from Span. LC 79-13182. (Illus.). 1979. 8.95 (ISBN 0-911218-14-9); pap. 3.95 (ISBN 0-911218-15-7). Ravengate Pr.

Alpers, Antony. The World of the Polynesians Seen Through Their Myths & Legends, Poetry, & Art. (New Zealand Classics Ser.). (Illus.). 432p. 1986. 10.95 (ISBN 0-19-558142-3). Oxford U Pr.

Alpert, Nancy L. Religion & Psychology: A Medical Subject Analysis & Research Index with Bibliography. LC 83-71657. 150p. 1985. 34.50 (ISBN 0-88164-034-4); pap. 26.50 (ISBN 0-88164-035-2). ABBE Pubs Assn.

Alpert, Rebecca T. & Staub, Jacob J. Exploring Judaism: A Reconstructionist Approach. 108p. 1985. 11.95 (ISBN 0-935457-01-1); pap. 5.95 (ISBN 0-935457-00-3). Reconstructionist Pr.

Alphandery, Paul. Les Idees Morales Chez les Heterodoxes Latins Au Debut Du Xiiie Siecle. LC 78-63184. (Heresies of the Early Christian & Medieval Era: Second Ser.). Repr. of 1903 ed. 27.50 (ISBN 0-404-16198-7). AMS Pr.

Alpher, Joseph, ed. Encyclopedia of Jewish History. (Illus.). 288p. 1986. 35.00x (ISBN 0-8160-1220-2). Facts on File.

--Encyclopedia of Jewish History: Events & Eras of the Jewish People. Amir, Haya, tr. LC 85-23941. (Illus.). 285p. 1985. 35.00. Facts on File.

Alphonso-Karkala, John B., ed. Vedic Vision. 80p. 1980. pap. 4.50 (ISBN 0-86578-004-8). Ind-US Inc.

Alphonsus, Mary. St. Rose of Lima. LC 81-86444. 304p. 1982. pap. 8.00 (ISBN 0-89555-172-1). TAN Bks Pubs.

Al-Qaradawi, Yusuf. The Lawful & the Prohibited in Islam. Siddiqui, Mohammed M., et al, trs. from Arabic. LC 80-81562. Orig. Title: Al-Halal Wal-Haram Fil Islam. (Eng.). 355p. (Orig.). 1981. pap. 10.00 (ISBN 0-89259-016-5). Am Trust Pubns.

Al-Qaradawl, Yusuf. Non Muslims in the Islamic Society. Hamad, Khalil M. & Shah, Sayed M., trs. LC 83-72763. 68p. (Orig.). 1985. pap. 3.75 (ISBN 0-89259-049-1). Am Trust Pubns.

Al-Qibrisi, Shaykh N. Mercy Oceans: Teachings of Maulana Abdullah al-Faiza ad-Daghestani. 190p. (Orig.). 1980. pap. 4.75x (ISBN 0-939830-11-6, Pub. by Leon). New Era Pubns MI.

Al-Qirqisani, Ya'Qub. Kitab Al-Anwar Wal-Maraoib: Code of Karaite Law, 3 vols. Incl. Vol. 1. First Discourse - Historical Introduction; Second Discourse - Philosophical & Theological Principles of JurisPrudence; Vol. 2. Third Discourse - Criticism of Sectarian Doctrines; Fourth Discourse - Methods of Construction & Interpretation of Law; Vol. 3. Fifth Discourse - Circumcion - Sabbath; Sixth Discourse - Civil & Criminal Law Liturgy. pap. 49.50 ea. in arabic; Set. pap. 125.00x (ISBN 0-686-52167-6). Elliots Bks.

Al-Qunawi, Sadraddin. Reflection of the Awakened. Askari, Hasan, tr. 112p. 1987. pap. 12.95 (ISBN 0-7103-0217-7, Pub. by Routledge UK). Methuen Inc.

Al-Raheb, Hani. The Zionist Character in the English Novel. 220p. 1985. pap. 9.95 (ISBN 0-86232-364-9, Pub. by Zed Pr England). Humanities.

Al-Sadr, Ayatullah B. He His Messenger & His Message. x ed. Ansari, M. A., tr. from Arabic. 116p. pap. 6.00 (ISBN 0-941724-12-3). Islamic Seminary.

Al Sadr, Muhammad B. Awaited Saviour. 110p. 1983. pap. text ed. 4.00 (ISBN 0-686-90398-6). Islamic Seminary.

--Islam & Schools of Economics. Ansari, M. A., tr. 160p. 1983. pap. text ed. 6.00 (ISBN 0-686-90405-2). Islamic Seminary.

Al-Sayed, Abdul M. Social Ethics of Islam: Classical Islamic Political Theory & Practice. 1982. 14.95 (ISBN 0-533-04671-8). Vantage.

Al-Sayyid-Marsot, A. L., ed. Society & the Sexes in Medieval Islam. LC 79-63268. (Giorgio Levi Della Vida Biennial Conference Ser.: Vol. 6). 149p. 1979. pap. 18.50x (ISBN 0-89003-033-2). Undena Pubns.

Al-Shahi, Ahmed, jt. ed. see MacEoin, Denis.

Alsop, John R. An Index to the Revised Bauer Arndt, Gingrich Greek Lexicon. 2nd ed. (Gr.). 1981. 14.95 (ISBN 0-310-44031-9, 6773P). Zondervan.

Alsup, John E., tr. see Goppelt, Leonard.

Alszeghy, Zoltan & Flick, Maurizio. Introductory Theology. 1983. 8.95 (ISBN 0-87193-198-2). Dimension Bks.

Alt, Franz. Peace Is Possible: The Politics of the Sermon on the Mount. Neugroschel, Joachim, tr. from Ger. LC 84-23499. 136p. 1985. 12.95 (ISBN 0-8052-3969-3). Schocken.

Al-Tabari. The History of al-Tabari, Vol. 4: The Ancient Kingdoms. Yarshater, Ehsan, et al, eds. Perlmann, Moshe, tr. (The History of al-Tabari Ser.). 160p. 1986. 39.50x (ISBN 0-88706-181-8); pap. 14.95x (ISBN 0-88706-182-6). State U NY Pr.

--History of al-Tabari, Vol. 7: Foundation of the Community - Muhammad at al-Madina, A. D. 622-626, Hijra-4 A.H. McDonald, V. M. & Watt, Montgomery, eds. McDonald, V. M., tr. from Ancient Parsi. (Series in Near Eastern Studies). 154p. (Orig.). 1987. 44.50x (ISBN 0-88706-344-6); pap. 16.95x (ISBN 0-88706-345-4). State U NY Pr.

Al-Tahafut, Tahafut. Averroes's, 2 vols. in 1. Van Den Bergh, S., tr. 593p. 1985. Repr. of 1978 ed. 60.00x (ISBN 0-317-39039-2, Pub. by Luzac & Co Ltd). State Mutual Bk.

Altasen, J., et al. Immortality. 733p. 1978. 7.45 (ISBN 0-8285-0939-5, Pub. by Progress Pubs USSR). Imported Pubns.

Altbauer, Mosha & Lunt, Horace G., eds. An Early Slavonic Psalter from Rus' Vol. 1: Phoreproduction. LC 78-59967. (Harvard Ukrainian Research Institute, Sources & Documents Ser.). 1979. text ed. 15.00x (ISBN 0-674-22310-1). Harvard U Pr.

Alter, Judy & Roach, Joyce G., eds. Texas & Christmas: A Collection of Traditions, Memories & Folklore. LC 83-4717. (Illus.). 86p. 1983. pap. 6.50 (ISBN 0-912646-81-0). Tex Christian.

Alter, Robert. The Art of Biblical Narrative. LC 80-68958. 208p. 1981. 14.95 (ISBN 0-465-00424-5). Basic.

--The Art of Biblical Narrative. LC 80-68958. 195p. 1983. pap. 7.95 (ISBN 0-465-00427-X, CN-5099). Basic.

--The Art of Biblical Poetry. LC 85-47550. 272p. 1985. 17.95 (ISBN 0-465-00430-X). Basic.

--The Art of Biblical Poetry. LC 85-47550. 228p. 1987. pap. 8.95 (ISBN 0-465-00431-8, PL 5180). Basic.

Alter, Robert, ed. Modern Hebrew Literature. LC 75-9928. (Library of Jewish Studies). 384p. 1975. pap. text ed. 9.95x (ISBN 0-87441-235-8); cloth 15.95x. Behrman.

Alternative Museun Staff. Disinformation: The Manufacture of Consent. LC 85-70365. (Illus.). 64p. (Orig.). 1985. pap. text ed. 8.00 (ISBN 0-932075-01-0). Alternative Mus.

Altfeld, E. Milton. The Jews' Struggle for Religious & Civil Liberty in Maryland. LC 78-99859. (Civil Liberties in American History Ser). 1970. Repr. of 1924 ed. lib. bdg. 29.50 (ISBN 0-306-71859-6). Da Capo.

Altgeld, John P. The Cost of Something for Nothing. 59.95 (ISBN 0-87968-948-X). Gordon Pr.

--The Cost of Something for Nothing. (Illus.). 135p. Repr. of 1904 ed. 12.95 (ISBN 0-88286-152-2). C H Kerr.

Althaus, Paul. The Ethics of Martin Luther. Schultz, Robert C., tr. from Ger. LC 72-164552. 192p. 1972. pap. 8.95 (ISBN 0-8006-1709-6, 1-1709). Fortress.

--Fact & Faith in the Kerygma of Today. Cairas, David, tr. 89p. 1978. Repr. of 1959 ed. lib. bdg. cancelled (ISBN 0-313-20446-2, ALFA). Greenwood.

--Theology of Martin Luther. Schultz, Robert C., tr. from Ger. LC 66-17345. 480p. 1966. pap. 12.95 (ISBN 0-8006-1855-6, 1-855). Fortress.

Altheim, Franz & Stiehl, Ruth. Christentum am Roten Meer. Vol. 1, 1971. 153.00x (ISBN 3-11-003790-4); Vol. 2, 1973. 153.00x (ISBN 3-11-003791-2). De Gruyter.

Althoff, Karl F. The Magna Charta of the Christian Church. Grimm, Werner, tr. from Ger. 19p. 1982. pap. 3.00 (ISBN 0-919924-15-8, Pub. by Steiner Book Centre Canada). Anthroposophic.

Althouse, LaVonne. When Jew & Christian Meet. (Illus.). 1966. pap. 1.50 (ISBN 0-377-36221-2). Friend Pr.

Althouse, Lawrence. Rediscovering the Gift of Healing. 2nd ed. 144p. 1983. pap. 5.95 (ISBN 0-87728-604-3). Weiser.

Altizer, Thomas, et al. Deconstruction & Theology. 176p. 1982. 14.95 (ISBN 0-8245-0475-5); pap. 8.95 (ISBN 0-8245-0412-7). Crossroad NY.

Altizer, Thomas J. The Descent into Hell: A Study of the Radical Reversal of the Christain Consciousness. 222p. 1979. pap. 6.95 (ISBN 0-8164-1194-8, HarpR). Har-Row.

--History As Apocalypse. LC 84-16289. (SUNY Series in Religion). 250p. 1985. 44.50 (ISBN 0-88706-013-7); pap. 16.95 (ISBN 0-88706-014-5). State U NY Pr.

--New Apocalypse: The Radical Christian Vision of William Blake. 1967. 8.50 (ISBN 0-87013-108-7). Mich St U Pr.

--Total Presence: The Language of Jesus & the Language of Today. 128p. 1980. 9.95 (ISBN 0-8164-0461-5, HarpR). Har-Row.

Altman, Nat. Ahimsa: Dynamic Compassion. LC 80-51548. 150p. (Orig.). 1981. pap. 4.95 (ISBN 0-8356-0537-X, Quest). Theos Pub Hse.

Altmann, Alexander. Essays in Jewish Intellectual History. LC 80-54471. 336p. 1981. 30.00x (ISBN 0-87451-192-5). U Pr of New Eng.

--Studies in Religious Philosophy & Mysticism. (New Reprints in Essay & General Literature Index Ser.). 1975. Repr. of 1969 ed. 24.25 (ISBN 0-518-10194-0). Ayer Co Pubs.

Altmann, Alexander, intro. by see Mendelssohn, Moses.

Altmann, Walter. Die Romischen Grabaltare der Kaiserzeit. facsimile ed. LC 75-10626. (Ancient Religion & Mythology Ser.). (Ger., Illus.). 1975. Repr. of 1905 ed. 26.50x (ISBN 0-405-07002-0). Ayer Co Pubs.

Alton, Wright. The Third Eye, Book I. (The Third Eye Bks.). (Illus.). 160p. (Orig.). Date not set. pap. 10.95. Creat Gospel Prod A Wright.

Altschuler, David, ed. The Precious Legacy: Judaic Treasures from the Czechoslavak State Collection. (Illus.). 256p. (Orig.). 1983. 40.00 (ISBN 0-671-49448-1); pap. 17.50 (ISBN 0-671-49498-8). Summit Bks.

Altschuler, Glenn C. & Saltzgaber, Jan M. Revivalism, Social Conscience, & Community in the Burned-Over District: The Trial of Rhoda Bement. (Illus.). 184p. 1983. 27.95x (ISBN 0-8014-1541-1); pap. 8.95x (ISBN 0-8014-9246-7). Cornell U Pr.

Altshuler, David, ed. see Neusner, Jacob.

Altshuler, David A. Hitler's War Against the Jews - the Holocaust: A Young Reader's Version of the War Against the Jews: 1933-1945 by Lucy Dawidowicz. LC 78-5418. (Illus.). 1978. 8.95x (ISBN 0-87441-293-5); pap. 6.50x (ISBN 0-87441-222-6). Behrman.

Altshuler, Mordechai. Soviet Jewry since the Second World War: Population & Social Structure. LC 86-12139. (Studies in Population & Urban Demography: No. 5). (Illus.). 296p. 1987. lib. bdg. 37.95 (ISBN 0-313-24494-4, ASO). Greenwood.

Al Tunisi, Khayr. Surest Path: The Political Treatise of a Nineteenth-Century Muslim Statesman. Brown, Leon C., tr. LC 67-25399. (Middle Eastern Monographs Ser: No. 16). pap. 5.00x (ISBN 0-674-85695-3). Harvard U Pr.

Alvarez, J. Mateos. Vocabulario Teologico del Evangelio de Saint Juan. (Span.). 310p. 1980. pap. 13.95 (ISBN 84-7057-270-9, S-33107). French & Eur.

Alvarez, Octavio. The Celestial Brides: A Study in Mythology & Archaeology. LC 77-91208. (Illus.). 1978. 30.00 (ISBN 0-9601520-0-8). H Reichner.

Alves, Rubem. I Believe in the Resurrection of the Body. McCoy, L. M., tr. from Ger. & Port. LC 85-16246. 80p. 1986. pap. 4.95 (ISBN 0-8006-1885-8, 1-1885). Fortress.

--Protestantism & Repression: A Brazilian Case Study. Drury, John, tr. from Portuguese. LC 82-3594. Tr. of Protestantismo e repressao. 256p. (Orig.). 1985. pap. 11.95 (ISBN 0-88344-098-9). Orbis Bks.

--What Is Religion? Vinzant, Don, tr. from Portugese. LC 83-19398. Orig. Title: O Que E Religiao. 96p. (Orig.). 1984. pap. 4.95 (ISBN 0-88344-705-3). Orbis Bks.

Al-Wahhab, Muhammad I. Kitab Al Tawhid. (Arabic.). 120p. (Orig.). 1978. pap. 4.95 (ISBN 0-939830-20-5, Pub. by IIFSO Kuwait). New Era Pubns MI.

Al-Yassini, Ayman. Religion & State in the Kingdom of Saudi Arabia. (WVSS on the Middle East Ser.). 190p. 1985. 30.00x (ISBN 0-8133-0058-4). Westview.

Amadeus Of Lausanne, jt. auth. see Bernard Of Clairvaux.

Amaldas, Swami. Christian Yogic Meditation. (Ways of Prayer Ser.: Vol. 8). pap. 5.95 (ISBN 0-89453-368-1). M Glazier.

Aman, Kenneth, ed. Border Regions of Faith: An Anthology of Religion & Social Change. LC 86-23551. 520p. (Orig.). 1987. pap. 23.95 (ISBN 0-88344-415-1). Orbis Bks.

Aman, Reinhold, ed. Maledicta 1980. LC 77-649633. (Maledicta: International Journal of Verbal Aggression Ser.: Vol. 4, No. 1 & 2). (Illus.). 320p. 1980. pap. 20.00 (ISBN 0-916500-55-1). Maledicta.

Amandry, Pierre. La Mantique Apollinienne a Delphes: Essai Sur le Fonctionnement De L'Oracle. facsimile ed. LC 75-10627. (Ancient Religion & Mythology Ser.). (Fr., Illus.). 1976. Repr. of 1950 ed. 23.50x (ISBN 0-405-07003-9). Ayer Co Pubs.

Amanne, E. Dictionnaire de Theologie Catholigue. (Fr.). Set. pap. 1995.00 (ISBN 0-686-56893-1, M-6003). French & Eur.

Amano, J. Yutaka, jt. auth. see Geisler, Norman L.

Amato, Joseph. Ethics, Living or Dead? xii, 132p. 1982. 10.50 (ISBN 0-9614119-0-2, Co-Pub Portals Press). V Amati.

Amato, Joseph A. Death Book: Terrors, Consolations, Contradictions & Paradoxes. 1985. 13.95 (ISBN 0-9614119-1-0, Co-Pub Ellis Press). V Amati.

Amato, Joseph A., II. Guilt & Gratitude: A Study of the Origins of Contemporary Conscience. LC 81-6991. (Contributions in Philosophy Ser.: No. 20). xxv, 218p. 1982. lib. bdg. 29.95 (ISBN 0-313-22946-5, AGG/). Greenwood.

Amatora, Sr. Mary. The Queen's Heart of Gold: The Complete Story of Our Lady of Beauraing. LC 78-188443. 1972. 7.50 (ISBN 0-682-47467-3, Banner); pap. 5.00 (ISBN 0-682-47480-0, Banner). Exposition Pr FL.

--The Queen's Portrait: The Story of Guadalupe. LC 74-188442. 1972. 7.50 (ISBN 0-682-47468-1, Lochinvar); (Lochinvar). Exposition Pr FL.

--El Retrato de la Reina: La Historia de Nuestra Senora de Guadalupe. 1972. 7.50 (ISBN 0-682-47542-4, Lochinvar); pap. 5.00 (ISBN 0-682-47548-3, Lochinvar). Exposition Pr FL.

Amber, Lee. Chosen. rev ed. LC 81-51985. 176p. 1981. pap. 3.95 (ISBN 0-88449-079-3, A424025). Vision Hse.

Amberley, John R. An Analysis of Religious Belief. LC 76-161318. (Atheist Viewpoint Ser.). 745p. 1972. Repr. of 1877 ed. 41.00 (ISBN 0-405-03621-3). Ayer Co Pubs.

--An Analysis of Religious Belief. 59.95 (ISBN 0-87968-619-7). Gordon Pr.

Amberson, Talmadge R. Reaching Out to People. LC 79-55435. 1979. pap. 5.95 (ISBN 0-8054-6321-6). Broadman.

Ambrose, St. Complete Letters. LC 67-28583. (Fathers of the Church Ser.: Vol. 26). 515p. 1954. 26.95x (ISBN 0-8132-0026-1). Cath U Pr.

--Hexameron Paradise, Cain & Abel. LC 77-81354. (Fathers of the Church Ser.: Vol. 42). 449p. 1961. 34.95x (ISBN 0-8132-0042-3). Cath U Pr.

--Seven Exegetical Works: Isaac, or the Soul, Death As a Good, Jacob & the Happy Life, Joseph, the Patriarchs, Flight from the World, the Prayer of Job & David. (Fathers of the Church Ser.: Vol. 65). 447p. 1972. 34.95x (ISBN 0-8132-0065-2). Cath U Pr.

--Theological & Dogmatic Works. (Fathers of the Church Ser.: Vol. 44). 343p. 1963. 21.95x (ISBN 0-8132-0044-X). Cath U Pr.

Ambrose, St., jt. auth. see Gregory Nazianzen, St.

Ambrosios, Hieromonk, jt. auth. see Chrysostomos, Archimandrite.

Ambrosius, Saint Concerning the Mysteries. 1977. pap. 1.25 (ISBN 0-686-19348-2). Eastern Orthodox.

--Opera, 3 Vols. Set. 210.00 (ISBN 0-384-01038-5). Johnson Repr.

Amedroz, H. F., tr. see Miskawayh, et al.

Amen, Carol. Hyacinths to Feed the Soul. LC 74-33850. (Better Living Ser.). 64p. 1975. pap. text ed. 0.99 (ISBN 0-8127-0094-5). Review & Herald.
--Teetering on the Tightrope. LC 79-18718. (Orion Ser.). 1979. pap. 2.95 (ISBN 0-8127-0250-6). Review & Herald.
Amen, Carol V. Love Goes 'Round the Circle. (Better Living Ser.). pap. 0.99 (ISBN 0-8280-1268-7). Review & Herald.
Ament, Susan, jt. auth. see Sherwin, Byron.
Amenta, Madalon & Rohnet, Nancy. Nursing Care of the Terminally Ill. 1986. pap. text ed. 22.00 (ISBN 0-316-03693-5). Little.
American Academy for Jewish Research Staff. Facets of Medieval Judaism: Proceedings. (Jewish People; History, Religion, Literature Ser.). 19.00 (ISBN 0-405-05262-6). Ayer Co Pubs.
American & British Committee for the International Greek New Testament Project. The New Testament in Greek: The Gospel According to St. Luke, Vol. 3, Pt. 1. (The New Testament in Greek Ser.). 1983. 98.00x (ISBN 0-19-826167-5). Oxford U Pr.
American Catholic Historic Association Staff. Catholic Philosophy of History, Vol. 3. facs. ed. LC 67-23190. (Essay Index Reprint Ser). 1936. 16.00 (ISBN 0-8369-0285-8). Ayer Co Pubs.
American Catholic Missionary Staff. The First American Catholic Missionary Congress: Proceedings of the American Catholic Missionary, 1st, Chicago, 1908. 51.00 (ISBN 0-405-10837-0, 11844). Ayer Co Pubs.
American Catholic Philosophical Association Staff. Ethics & Other Knowledge: Proceedings, Vol. 31. 1957. 18.00 (ISBN 0-384-14760-7). Johnson Repr.
--Philosophy & the Experimental Sciences: Proceedings, Vol. 26. 1952. 18.00 (ISBN 0-384-46400-9). Johnson Repr.
--Role of the Christian Philosopher: Proceedings. 1958. 18.00. Johnson Repr.
American Historical Association, ed. see American Jewish Historical Society Staff, et al.
American Jewish Archives, Cincinnati Staff, ed. Manuscript Catalog of the American Jewish Archives, 4 vols. 1971. Set. lib. bdg. 400.00 (ISBN 0-8161-0899-4, Hall Library). G K Hall.
--Manuscript Catalog of the American Jewish Archives, Cincinnati: First Supplement. 1978. lib. bdg. 105.00 (ISBN 0-8161-0934-6, Hall Library). G K Hall.
American Jewish Committee. The Jewish Communities of Nazi-Occupied Europe. 400p. 1982. Repr. of 1944 ed. 42.50x (ISBN 0-86527-337-5). Fertig.
--The Jews in Nazi Germany. x, 177p. 1982. Repr. of 1935 ed. 22.50x (ISBN 0-86527-110-0). Fertig.
American Jewish Historical Society Staff, et al. The Palestine Question in American History. American Historical Association, ed. 14.00 (ISBN 0-405-11521-0). Ayer Co Pubs.
American Map Corp. Staff. Student Atlas of the Bible. (Series 9500: No. 9559). (Illus.). 1978. 2.95 (ISBN 0-8416-9559-8); Span. lang. ed. write for info. Am Map.
American Marketing Association Staff. Changing Values & Social Trends: How Do Organizations React? Presented Jointly by the Market Research Society & the American Marketing Association, June 1974, Oxford, England. pap. 56.00 (ISBN 0-317-26627-6, 2011593). Bks Demand UMI.
American School of Needlework Staff. The Great Christmas Craft Book. (Illus.). 144p. 1983. 19.95 (ISBN 0-8069-5498-1). Sterling.
American Tract Society Staff. The American Tract Society Documents, Eighteen Twenty-Four to Nineteen Twenty-Five. LC 74-38434. (Religion in America, Ser. 2). 484p. 1972. Repr. of 1874 ed. 29.00 (ISBN 0-405-04055-5). Ayer Co Pubs.
Amery & Haron. First Thousand Words in Hebrew. (First Thousand Words Ser.). (Illus.). 62p. 1985. PLB 10.95 (ISBN 0-86020-863-X, Pub. by Usborne). EDC.
Amery, Jean. At the Mind's Limits: Contemplations by a Survivor on Auschwitz & Its Realities. Rosenfeld, Sidney & Rosenfeld, Stella P., trs. 128p. 1986. pap. 5.95 (ISBN 0-8052-0761-9). Schocken.
--Radical Humanism: Selected Essays. Rosenfeld, Sidney & Rosenfeld, Stella P., eds. Rosenfeld, Stella & Rosenfeld, Sidney, trs. from Fr. LC 83-49525. 160p. 1984. 22.50x (ISBN 0-253-34770-X). Ind U Pr.
Ames, David A. & Gracey, Colin B. Good Genes? Emerging Values for Science, Religion & Society. (Illus.). 136p. 1984. pap. 3.60 (ISBN 0-88028-034-4). Forward Movement.
Ames, Kenneth J. The Religious Language of Thomas Traherne's Centuries. (Religion & Literature Ser.). 1979. lib. bdg. 59.95 (ISBN 0-87700-260-6). Revisionist Pr.
Ames, Percy. Milton Memorial Lectures 1909. LC 65-15895. (Studies in Milton, No. 22). 1969. Repr. of 1909 ed. lib. bdg. 49.95x (ISBN 0-8383-0501-6). Haskell.
Ames, Percy W. Milton Memorial Lectures. 1974. Repr. 32.50 (ISBN 0-8274-2738-7). R West.
Ames, Roger T., jt. auth. see Hall, David L.
Ames, Ruth M. God's Plenty. 288p. 1984. 12.95 (ISBN 0-8294-0426-0). Loyola.
Ames, Van Meter. Zen & American Thought. 1978. Repr. of 1962 ed. lib. bdg. 26.50 (ISBN 0-313-20066-1, AMZA). Greenwood.
Ames, William. Conscience with the Power & Cases Thereof. LC 74-28826. (English Experience Ser.: No. 708). 1975. Repr. of 1639 ed. 35.00 (ISBN 9-0221-0708-6). Walter J Johnson.
--A Fresh Suit Against Human Ceremonies in God's Worship. 886p. Repr. of 1633 ed. text ed. 82.80x (ISBN 0-576-99734-X, Pub. by Gregg Intl Pubs England). Gregg Intl.
--The Marrow of Theology. Eusden, John D., ed. & tr. from Latin. Orig. Title: Medulla Theologiae. xiv, 354p. 1983. pap. 14.95 (ISBN 0-939464-14-4). Labyrinth Pr.
--Technometry. Gibbs, Lee W., tr. from Lat. LC 78-65117. (Haney Foundation Ser.). (Illus.). 1979. 31.50x (ISBN 0-8122-7756-2). U of Pa Pr.
Amey, Peter, et al. Luther, Erasmus & Loyola. Yapp, Malcolm, et al, eds. (World History Ser.). (Illus.). 1980. lib. bdg. 6.95 (ISBN 0-89908-043-X); pap. text ed. 2.45 (ISBN 0-89908-018-9). Greenhaven.
Ami Press Staff. The Message of Marienfried: According to Our Lady's Apparitions in 1946. 20p. 1983. 1.00 (ISBN 0-911988-50-5). AMI Pr.
Amichai, Yehuda, ed. see Yeshurun, Avoth.
Amina Shah. Assemblies of Al-Hariri. 267p. 1980. 16.95 (ISBN 0-900860-86-3, Pub. by Octagon Pr England). Ins Study Human.
Amir, Haya, tr. see Alpher, Joseph.
Amir, Jehoshua, tr. see Schalit, Abraham.
Amjad-Ali, Charles & Pitcher, W. Alvin, eds. Liberation & Ethics: Essays in Religious Social Ethics in Honor of Gibson Winter. LC 83-73425. (Studies in Religion & Society). 233p. 1985. text ed. 24.95x (ISBN 0-913348-22-8). Ctr Sci Study.
Amlaw, Mary. From Praying Never to Praying Always. 100p. (Orig.). 1985. pap. 5.95 (ISBN 0-916134-69-5). Pueblo Pub Co.
Ammerman, Leila T. Inspiring Devotional Programs for Women's Groups. (Paperback Program Ser). 1971. pap. 3.50 (ISBN 0-8010-0015-7). Baker Bk.
--Installation Services That Inspire. LC 81-67371. 1982. pap. 5.50 (ISBN 0-8054-3616-2). Broadman.
Amneus, Nils. Life's Riddle. 1975. pap. 5.25 (ISBN 0-913004-26-X). Point Loma Pub.
AMORC Staff, tr. see Cerve, Wishar S.
AMORC Staff, tr. see Cihlar, Many.
AMORC Staff, tr. see Lewis, H. Spencer.
AMORC Staff, tr. see Lewis, Ralph M.
Amore, Roy C., ed. Developments in Buddhist Thought: Canadian Contributions to Buddhist Studies. 196p. 1979. pap. text ed. 9.95x (ISBN 0-919812-11-2, Pub. by Wilfred Laurier Canada). Humanities.
Amort, Eusebio. Vetus Disciplina Canocorum Regularium & Saecularium ex Documentis Magna Parte Hucusque Ineditis a Temporibus Apostolicis ad Saeculum XVII. 1112p. 1747. text ed. 248.40x (ISBN 0-576-99833-8, Pub. by Gregg Intl Pubs England). Gregg Intl.
Amos, C. M. Israel Becomes a Nation. (Discovering the Bible Ser.). pap. 8.95 (ISBN 0-7175-1160-X). Dufour.
Amphoux, Nancy, tr. see Deshimaru, Taisen.
Amram, David. Makers of Hebrew Books in Italy. 350p. 1983. 55.00 (ISBN 0-87556-013-X). Saifer.
Amram, David W. Leading Cases in the Bible. ix, 220p. 1985. Repr. of 1905 ed. lib. bdg. 22.50x (ISBN 0-8377-0218-6). Rothman.
Amrine, Frederick, tr. see Steiner, Rudolf.
Amritachandra. Purushartha-Siddhyupaya (Jaina-Pravachana-Rahasya-Kosha) Prasada, Ajit, ed. & tr. LC 73-3838. (The Sacred Books of the Jainas: No. 4). Repr. of 1933 ed. 22.50 (ISBN 0-404-57704-0). AMS Pr.
Amsel. Judaism & Psychology. pap. 5.95 (ISBN 0-87306-064-4). Feldheim.
Amsel, Avrohom. Rational Irrational Man: Torah Psychology. 1976. pap. 7.95 (ISBN 0-87306-129-2). Feldheim.
Amstutz, Beverly. Benjamin & the Bible Donkeys. (Illus.). 36p. 1981. pap. 2.50x (ISBN 0-937836-03-6). Precious Res.
Amstutz, H. Clair. Growing up to Love: A Guide to Sex Education for Parents. rev. ed. LC 56-11527. (Illus.). 112p. (YA) 1966. pap. 1.95 (ISBN 0-8361-1535-X). Herald Pr.
--Marriage in Today's World. LC 78-955. 160p. 1978. pap. 6.95 (ISBN 0-8361-1849-9). Herald Pr.
Amundsen, Darrel W., jt. ed. see Numbers, Ronald L.
Amundson, Kris. Religion in the Public Schools. 80p. (Orig.). 1986. pap. write for info. Am Assn Sch Admin.
Amy, William O. & Recob, James B. Human Nature in the Christian Tradition. LC 82-45049. 118p. (Orig.). 1982. lib. bdg. 24.75 (ISBN 0-8191-2512-1); pap. text ed. 8.75 (ISBN 0-8191-2513-X). U Pr of Amer.
Amyx, D. A. & Lawrence, Patricia. Archaic Corinthian Pottery & the Anaploga Well. LC 75-4551. (Corinth Ser.: Vol. 7, Pt. 2). (Illus.). 1976. 35.00x (ISBN 0-87661-072-6, NK4647). Am Sch Athens.
Anacker, Christopher A. Exhaustive Outline of the Entire Bible. LC 81-90358. (Orig.). 1981. 10.95 (ISBN 0-9607942-5-5); lib. bdg. 12.95 (ISBN 0-9607942-7-1); pap. 8.95 (ISBN 0-9607942-0-4). Ref Guide Bks.
Anand, Balwant S. Guru Nanak: His Life Was His Message - A Biography. 1985. 9.00x (ISBN 0-8364-1456-X, Pub. by Nanak Dev Univ India). South Asia Bks.
--Guru Tegh Bahadur. 1979. text ed. 11.95 (ISBN 0-89684-076-X, Pub. by Sterling New Delhi). Orient Bk Dist.
Anand, Kewal K. Indian Philosophy: The Concept of Karma. 396p. 1982. 34.95 (ISBN 0-940500-91-4, Pub by Bharatiya Vidya Prakashan India). Asia Bk Corp.
Anand, Mulk R., ed. Kama Sutra of Vatsyayana. 276p. 1981. text ed. 125.00x (ISBN 0-391-02224-5). Humanities.
Ananda. Spiritual Practice. pap. 3.00 (ISBN 0-87481-155-4). Vedanta Pr.
Ananda-Maitreya. The Religion of Burma & Other Papers. LC 77-87482. Repr. of 1929 ed. 31.50 (ISBN 0-404-16790-X). AMS Pr.
Anandamurti, Shrii S. A Guide to Human Conduct. LC 80-70792. 55p. 1981. pap. 3.00 (ISBN 0-88476-010-3). Ananda Marga.
Anandamurti, Shrii Shrii. Namami Krsnasundaram - Salutations to Lord Krsna. 252p. 1981. pap. 4.00 (ISBN 0-686-95432-7). Ananda Marga.
Anandanagar. Caryacarya, Vol. I & II. Vol. I - 37 p. pap. 2.00 (ISBN 0-686-95445-9); Vol. II - 49 p. pap. 1.00 (ISBN 0-686-99507-4). Ananda Marga.
Ananikian, Mardiros H. Armenian Mythology & African Mythology. (Mythology of All Races Ser.: Vol. VII). Repr. of 1932 ed. 30.00x (ISBN 0-8154-0011-X). Cooper Sq.
Anan Isho, compiled by. The Wit & Wisdom of the Christian Fathers of Egypt: The Syrian Version of the Apophthegmata Patrum. Wallis Budge, Ernest A., tr. LC 80-2354. Repr. of 1934 ed. 53.50 (ISBN 0-404-18900-8). AMS Pr.
Anantendra-Yati. Vedanta-Sara-Sangraha. Mahadevan, T. M., tr. 1974. pap. 3.50 (ISBN 0-89744-124-9, Pub. by Ganesh & Co. India). Auromere.
Anastasas, Florence H. And They Called Him Amos: The Story of John Amos Comenius-a Woodcut in Words. LC 73-86540. 1973. 10.00 (ISBN 0-682-47814-8, University). Exposition Pr FL.
Anatolius of Mohilew & Mstislaw. Greek Orthodox Faith: Scriptural Presentation. Bjerring, Nicholas, tr. from Rus. 1974. pap. 1.00 (ISBN 0-686-10205-3). Eastern Orthodox.
Ancona, Antoinette. St. Jude & "His People". LC 85-90095. 124p. 1985. 10.95 (ISBN 0-533-06604-2). Vantage.
Anderhub, Rita, jt. auth. see Polek, David.
Anders, Henry R. Shakespeare's Books. LC 76-158251. Repr. of 1904 ed. 12.50 (ISBN 0-404-00355-9). AMS Pr.
Anders, Isabel, jt. auth. see Williamsen, Glen.
Anders, Max, jt. auth. see Boa, Kenneth.
Andersen, David W. & Brooker, Wendell. Expanding Your Church School Program: Planning Elective Classes for Adults. 88p. 1983. pap. 3.95 (ISBN 0-8170-1009-2). Judson.
Andersen, Dines & Smith, Helmer, eds. The Sutta-Nipata. LC 78-70124. Repr. of 1913 ed. 27.00 (ISBN 0-404-17383-7). AMS Pr.
Andersen, Francis I. The Hebrew Verbless Clause in the Pentateuch. (SBL Monograph). 8.95 (ISBN 0-89130-321-9, 06-00-14). Scholars Pr GA.
--Job. Wiseman, D. J., ed. LC 76-12298. (Tyndale Old Testament Commentary Ser.). 1976. 12.95 (ISBN 0-87784-869-6); pap. 6.95 (ISBN 0-87784-263-9). Inter-Varsity.
--The Sentence in Biblical Hebrew. (Janua Linguarum, Ser. Practica: No. 231). 209p. 1974. pap. text ed. 23.20x (ISBN 90-2792-673-5). Mouton.
Andersen, Francis I. & Forbes, A. Dean. Eight Minor Prophets: A Linguistic Concordance. (Computer Bible Ser.: Vol. X). 1976. pap. 25.00 (ISBN 0-935106-11-1). Biblical Res Assocs.
--A Linguistic Concordance of Ruth & Jonah: Hebrew Vocabulary & Idiom. (Computer Bible Ser.: Vol. IX). 1976. pap. 15.00 (ISBN 0-935106-12-X). Biblical Res Assocs.
Andersen, Georg & Dean, Edith. Interior Decorating: A Reflection of the Creator's Design. 192p. 1983. 16.95 (ISBN 0-87123-288-X, 230288). Bethany Hse.
Andersen, Johannes C. The Maori Tohunga & His Spirit World. LC 75-35224. Repr. of 1948 ed. 20.00 (ISBN 0-404-14403-9). AMS Pr.
--Myths & Legends of the Polynesians. LC 75-35170. (Illus.). Repr. of 1931 ed. 43.50 (ISBN 0-404-14200-1). AMS Pr.
Andersen, Linda. Love Adds the Chocolate. 1984. 4.95 (ISBN 0-8010-0198-6). Baker Bk.
--Slices of Life. 112p. 1986. pap. 6.95 (ISBN 0-8010-0205-2). Baker Bk.
Andersen, Loren. Theo-History: The Parallel Covenants Theory. 120p. 1983. pap. 4.25 (ISBN 0-9611310-0-4). Day Bk Co.
Andersen, R. & Barlag, R. They Were There. 1977. pap. 4.50 (ISBN 0-570-03769-7, 12-2704). Concordia.
Andersen, Richard. Devotions for Church School Teachers. LC 76-2158. 64p. 1976. pap. 2.25 (ISBN 0-570-03722-0, 12-2624). Concordia.
--Inspirational Meditations for Sunday Church School Teachers. 1980. pap. 2.25 (ISBN 0-570-03810-3, 12-2919). Concordia.
--A Little Library of Inspiration for Sunday School Teachers. 1982. pap. 2.25 (ISBN 0-570-03846-4, 12-2949). Concordia.
--Positive Power of Christian Partnership. 1982. pap. 1.95 (ISBN 0-570-03844-8, 12-2947). Concordia.
Andersen, Richard & Deffner, Donald. For Example... 1978. pap. 7.95 (ISBN 0-570-03766-2, 12-2701). Concordia.
Andersen, Svend. Ideal und Singularitat: Uber die Funktion des Gottesbegriffes in Kants theoretischer Philosophie. 278p. 1983. 28.80 (ISBN 3-11-009649-8). De Gruyter.
Andersen, U. S. Secret Power of the Pyramids. 1977. pap. 7.00 (ISBN 0-87980-343-6). Wilshire.
Andersen, Uell S. Magic in Your Mind. pap. 7.00 (ISBN 0-87980-089-5). Wilshire.
--Secret of Secrets. pap. 7.00 (ISBN 0-87980-134-4). Wilshire.
Andersen, Verlan. Many Are Called but Few Are Chosen. 96p. 1967. pap. 2.95 (ISBN 0-89036-002-2). Hawkes Pub Inc.
Andersen, Walter K. & Damle, Shridhar D. The Brotherhood in Saffron: The Rashtriya Swayamsevak Sangh & Hindu Revivalism. (Special Studies on South & Southeast Asia). 246p. 1987. pap. 27.50 (ISBN 0-8133-7358-1). Westview.
Anderson. The Lakeside Story. LC 86-70041. (Illus.). 242p. 1986. 12.50 (ISBN 0-87483-010-9). August Hse.
--Teach What You Preach. 1982. pap. 8.95 (ISBN 0-8298-0481-1). Pilgrim NY.
Anderson, A. L. The Way. 1978. pap. 2.50 (ISBN 0-8100-0006-7, 12N1715). Northwest Pub.
Anderson, Andrew R. Alexander's Gate, Gog & Magog & the Inclosed Nations. 1932. 7.50x (ISBN 0-910956-07-3). Medieval Acad.
Anderson, Andy. Effective Methods of Church Growth. LC 85-6620. 1985. pap. 5.95 (ISBN 0-8054-3237-X). Broadman.
--Fasting Changed My Life. LC 77-82404. 1977. pap. 3.95 (ISBN 0-8054-5259-1). Broadman.
Anderson, Ann K. I Gave God Time. 1982. 7.95 (ISBN 0-8423-1560-8); pap. 5.95 1984 (ISBN 0-8423-1559-4). Tyndale.
--My Favorite Verse: Favorite Ser. LC 85-70000. 24p. 1986. pap. 4.95 (ISBN 0-89636-209-4). Accent Bks.
Anderson, Arthur J., tr. see Leon-Portilla, Miguel.
Anderson, Arthur J., tr. see Sahagun, Bernardino de.
Anderson, Arthur L. Divided We Stand: Institutional Religion As a Reflection of Pluralism & Integration in America. LC 78-61582. 1978. pap. text ed. 9.95 (ISBN 0-8403-1935-5). Kendall-Hunt.
Anderson, Arthur W. Wild Beasts & Angels. 1979. pap. 4.50 (ISBN 0-910452-43-1). Covenant.
Anderson, Berhard W., jt. auth. see Noth, Martin.
Anderson, Bernhard W. The Eighth Century Prophets: Amos, Hosea, Isaiah, Micah. McCurley, Foster R., ed. LC 78-54545. (Proclamation Commentatries: the Old Testament Witnesses for Preaching). 128p. 1978. pap. 5.95 (ISBN 0-8006-0595-0, 1-595). Fortress.
--The Living Word of the Bible. LC 78-27108. 118p. 1979. pap. 4.95 (ISBN 0-664-24247-2). Westminster.
--Out of the Depths: The Psalms Speak for Us Today. Revised & Expanded ed. LC 83-19801. 254p. 1983. pap. 11.95 (ISBN 0-664-24504-8). Westminster.
--Understanding the Old Testament. 4th ed. (Illus.). 672p. 1986. text ed. write for info (ISBN 0-13-935925-7). P-H.
--The Unfolding Drama of the Bible. rev. ed. LC 78-14057. 1971. pap. 3.95 (ISBN 0-8329-1068-6, Assn Pr). New Century.

Anderson, Bernhard W., ed. Creation in the Old Testament. LC 83-48910. (Issues in Religion & Theology Ser.). 192p. 1984. pap. 7.95 (ISBN 0-8006-1768-1, 1-768). Fortress.

Anderson, C. Alan. God in a Nutshell. (Illus.). 28p. (Orig.). 1981. pap. 3.00 (ISBN 0-9607532-0-6). Squantum Pr.

--The Problem Is God: The Selection & Care of Your Personal God. LC 84-50108. (Illus.). 304p. (Orig.). 1985. pap. 9.95 (ISBN 0-913299-02-2). Stillpoint.

Anderson, Charles S. Augsburg Historical Atlas of Christianity in the Middle Ages & Reformation. LC 67-11723. 1973. pap. 9.95 (ISBN 0-8066-1317-3, 10-0521). Augsburg.

Anderson, Charles S., ed. see Prenter, Regin.

Anderson, Christopher A. Mind & Spirit. LC 86-72816. (Illus.). 90p. 1987. pap. 7.50 (ISBN 0-931353-09-2). Andersons Pubns.

Anderson, D. Carl. Trial by Death & Fire. LC 80-14446. (Orion Ser.). 160p. 1980. pap. 3.95 (ISBN 0-8127-0292-1). Review & Herald.

Anderson, Dave. More Funny Things on the Way to Church. Wilcox, Tim, ed. (Continued Applied Christianity Ser.). 1983. pap. 4.50 (ISBN 0-570-03893-6, 12-2975). Concordia.

Anderson, Dave & Wilcox, Tim. A Funny Thing Happened on the Way to Church. 1981. pap. 4.50 (ISBN 0-570-03834-0, 12YY2799). Concordia.

Anderson, David, tr. from Greek. On the Divine Images: St. John of Damascus. LC 80-13409. 106p. 1980. pap. 4.95 (ISBN 0-913836-62-1). St Vladimirs.

Anderson, David, tr. see St. Basil The Great.

Anderson, Debby. All Year Long. (Sparklers Ser.). 1986. comb binding 2.95 (ISBN 1-55513-043-7, Chariot Bks). Cook.

--Being a Friend Means... (Sparkler Bks.). (Illus.). 32p. 1986. plastic comb bndg. 2.95 (ISBN 0-89191-932-5, 59329, Chariot Bks). Cook.

--God Gives Me a Smile. LC 85-71985. (Illus.). 24p. 1985. comb bdg. 3.95 (ISBN 0-89191-669-5, 56697). Cook.

--God Is the Greatest. LC 85-71986. (Illus.). 24p. 1985. comb bdg. 3.95 (ISBN 0-89191-673-3, 56739). Cook.

--God Is with Me. (Happy Day Bks.). (Illus.). 24p. 1984. 1.39 (ISBN 0-87239-734-3, 3704). Standard Pub.

--God Is with Me. (Sparklers Ser.). 1986. comb binding 2.95 (ISBN 0-89191-269-X, Chariot Bks). Cook.

--God Loves Even Me. (Happy Day Bks.). (Illus.). 24p. 1985. 1.59 (ISBN 0-87239-873-0, 3673). Standard Pub.

--Thank You, God. (Sparkler Bks.). (Illus.). 1986. plastic comb bdg. 2.95 (ISBN 0-89191-931-7, 59311, Chariot Bks). Cook.

Anderson, Don. Abraham: Delay Is Not Denial. (Kingfisher Ser.). 200p. 1987. pap. 6.95 (ISBN 0-87213-000-2). Loizeaux.

--Ecclesiastes: The Mid-Life Crisis. (Kingfisher Ser.). 268p. (Orig.). 1987. pap. 7.95 (ISBN 0-87213-001-0). Loizeaux.

Anderson, Dorothy P. Leader's Guide for Jay E. Adams's Christian Living in the Home: A Teaching Manual for Use in Adult Study Groups. (Orig.). 1977. pap. 2.95 (ISBN 0-934688-05-2). Great Comm Pubns.

Anderson, Douglas, ed. see Baldwin, Skip.

Anderson, Douglas A. New Approaches to Family Pastoral Care. LC 79-8898. (Creative Pastoral Care & Counseling Ser.). pap. 24.00 (2029614). Bks Demand UMI.

Anderson, Earl R. Cynewulf: Structure, Style, & Theme in His Poetry. LC 81-65464. 248p. 1983. 32.50 (ISBN 0-8386-3091-X). Fairleigh Dickinson.

Anderson, Edward F. Peyote: The Divine Cactus. LC 79-20173. 248p. 1980. pap. 9.95 (ISBN 0-8165-0613-2). U of Ariz Pr.

Anderson, Einar. History & Beliefs of Mormonism. LC 81-13671. Orig. Title: Inside Story of Mormonism. 176p. 1981. pap. 6.95 (ISBN 0-8254-2122-5). Kregel.

Anderson, Elaine. With God's Help Flowers Bloom. 1978. pap. 4.95 (ISBN 0-89137-411-6); study guide 2.85 (ISBN 0-89137-412-4). Quality Pubns.

Anderson, Elizabeth Y. Faith in the Furnace. LC 84-72818. (Illus.). 1985. 10.00 (ISBN 0-9614002-0-X). E Y Anderson.

Anderson, Emma D. & Campbell, Mary J. In the Shadow of the Himalayas: A Historical Narrative of the Missions of the United Presbyterian Church of North America as Conducted in the Punjab, India 1855-1940. 373p. 1983. Repr. of 1942 ed. lib. bdg. 45.00 (ISBN 0-89987-042-2). Darby Bks.

Anderson, Eric, jt. auth. see Ingraham, F.

Anderson, Erica, ed. see Schweitzer, Albert.

Anderson, Esther & Kvindlog, Norma. Beyond Me: A Christ Centered Approach to Self-Esteem. 160p. 1987. pap. 5.95 (ISBN 0-8423-1310-9). Tyndale.

Anderson, Evelyn M. Good Morning, Lord: Devotions for Women. (Good Morning Lord Ser.). 1971. 4.95 (ISBN 0-8010-0023-8). Baker Bk.

Anderson, Florence M. Religious Cults Associated with the Amazons. LC 73-158253. Repr. of 1912 ed. 16.00 (ISBN 0-404-00749-X). AMS Pr.

Anderson, Fred R. Singing Psalms of Joy & Praise. LC 86-1550. 78p. (Orig.). 1986. pap. 5.95 ea. (ISBN 0-664-24696-6). Westminster.

Anderson, Fulton H., ed. The New Organon: Bacon. 1960. pap. text ed. write for info. (ISBN 0-02-303380-0). Macmillan.

Anderson, G. W. A Critical Introduction to the Old Testament. (Studies in Theology). 262p. 1979. pap. 13.50 (ISBN 0-7156-0077-X, Pub. by Duckworth London). Longwood Pub Group.

--The History & Religion of Israel. (New Clarendon Bible-OT Ser.). (Illus.). 1966. pap. 11.95x (ISBN 0-19-836915-8). Oxford U Pr.

--Tradition & Interpretation. 1979. 34.50x (ISBN 0-19-826315-5). Oxford U Pr.

Anderson, George K. The Legend of the Wandering Jew. LC 65-14290. (Brown University Bicentennial Publication Ser.). pap. 125.80 (ISBN 0-317-52056-3, 2027498). Bks Demand UMI.

Anderson, Gerald & Stransky, Thomas, eds. Mission Trends: Faith Meets Faith, No. 5. LC 81-80983. 320p. (Orig.). 1981. pap. 4.95 (ISBN 0-8091-2356-8). Paulist Pr.

--Mission Trends: Liberation Theologies in North America & Europe, No. 4. LC 78-70827. 1978. pap. 3.95 (ISBN 0-8028-1709-2). Eerdmans.

Anderson, Gerald H. & Stansky, Thomas. Missions Trends, No. 2. LC 75-29836. 1975. pap. 3.95 (ISBN 0-8028-1624-X). Eerdmans.

Anderson, Gerald H. & Stranskey, Thomas F. Mission Trends: "Evangelization", No. 2. LC 75-29836. (Mission Trend Ser.). 288p. 1976. pap. 4.95 (ISBN 0-8091-1900-5). Paulist Pr.

Anderson, Gerald H., ed. Witnessing to the Kingdom: Melbourne & Beyond. LC 82-3530. 176p. (Orig.). 1982. pap. 7.95 (ISBN 0-88344-708-8). Orbis Bks.

Anderson, Gerald H. & Stansky, Thomas F., eds. Mission Trends: Third World Theologies, No. 3. LC 76-24451. (Mission Trend Ser.). 264p. 1976. pap. 4.95 (ISBN 0-8091-1984-6). Paulist Pr.

Anderson, Gerald H. & Stransky, Thomas F., eds. Christ's Lordship & Religious Pluralism. LC 80-25406. 256p. (Orig.). 1981. pap. 8.95 (ISBN 0-88344-088-1). Orbis Bks.

--Mission Trends: Crucial Issues in Mission Today, No. 1. LC 74-81222. (Mission Trend Ser.). (Orig.). 1974. pap. 4.95 (ISBN 0-8091-1843-2). Paulist Pr.

--Mission Trends: Faith Meets Faith, No. 5. (Mission Trends Ser.). 320p. (Orig.). 1981. pap. 3.95 (ISBN 0-8028-1821-8). Eerdmans.

Anderson, Gerald H., jt. ed. see Stransky, Thomas.

Anderson, Geraldine, ed. Forty Devotions That Work with Youth. (Youth Work Guide Ser.). (Illus.). 60p. (Orig.). 1983. pap. 7.45 (ISBN 0-85819-414-7, Pub. by JBCE). ANZ Religious Pubns.

Anderson, Glenn P., ed. Covenant Roots: Sources & Affirmations. Jansson, Fred O., et al, trs. from Swedish. 238p. (Orig.). 1980. pap. 6.95 (ISBN 0-910452-46-6). Covenant.

Anderson, Godfrey T. Spicer: Leader with the Common Touch. Wheeler, Gerald, ed. LC 83-3279. (Illus.). 128p. (Orig.). 1983. pap. 5.95 (ISBN 0-8280-0150-2). Review & Herald.

Anderson, Gordon A. Latin Compositions in the Sixth Fascile of the Notre-Dame Manuscript Wolfenbuttel 1099. (Wissenschaftliche Abhandlungen-Musicological Studies Ser.: Vol. 24). Pt. 1. lib. bdg. 50.00 (ISBN 0-931902-02-9); Pt. 2. lib. bdg. 50.00 (ISBN 0-931902-03-7). Inst Mediaeval Mus.

Anderson, H., ed. Gospel of Mark. (New Century Bible Ser.). 384p. 1976. 9.50 (ISBN 0-551-00579-3). Attic Pr.

Anderson, H. George, tr. see Maurer, Wilhelm.

Anderson, Herbert. The Family & Pastoral Care. Browining, Don S., ed. LC 83-48914. (Theology & Pastoral Care Ser.). 128p. pap. 7.95 (ISBN 0-8006-1728-2, 1-1728). Fortress.

Anderson, Herbert, jt. auth. see Mitchell, Kenneth R.

Anderson, Hugh. The Gospel of Mark. rev. ed. (New Century Bible Commentary Ser.). 384p. 1981. pap. 8.95 (ISBN 0-8028-1887-0). Eerdmans.

Anderson, J. I. I Can Read About the First Thanksgiving. LC 76-54400. (Illus.). 1977. pap. 1.50 (ISBN 0-89375-034-4). Troll Assocs.

Anderson, J. K. Genetic Engineering: The Ethical Issues. 128p. (Orig.). 1982. pap. 6.95 (ISBN 0-310-45051-9, 12707). Zondervan.

Anderson, J. Kerby, jt. auth. see Geisler, Norman L.

Anderson, J. N. Evidence for the Resurrection. pap. 0.75 (ISBN 0-87784-124-1). Inter-Varsity.

--The World's Religions. rev. ed. LC 75-26654. 1976. pap. 5.95 (ISBN 0-8028-1636-3). Eerdmans.

Anderson, Jacqulyn, compiled by. How to Administer & Promote a Church Media Library. LC 84-21452. 1985. pap. 5.95 (ISBN 0-8054-3711-8). Broadman.

Anderson, James D. & Jones, Ezra E. The Management of Ministry. LC 76-62942. 1978. 13.45 (ISBN 0-06-060235-X, HarpR). Har-Row.

--Ministry of the Laity. LC 84-48211. 224p. 1985. 14.45 (ISBN 0-06-060194-9, HarpR). Har-Row.

Anderson, James E. Two Literary Riddles in the Exeter Book: Riddle 1 & the Easter Riddle. LC 85-40471. (Illus.). 288p. 1986. 27.50x (ISBN 0-8061-1947-0). U of Okla Pr.

Anderson, James F. Introduction to the Metaphysics of St. Thomas Aquinas. LC 53-6515. 1969. pap. 6.50 (ISBN 0-89526-970-8). Regnery Bks.

Anderson, James F. see St. Thomas Aquinas.

Anderson, James N. Islamic Law in the Modern World. LC 75-31816. 106p. 1976. Repr. of 1959 ed. lib. bdg. 22.50x (ISBN 0-8371-8451-7, ANIL). Greenwood.

Anderson, James V., jt. auth. see Schenk, Fredrick J.

Anderson, Jean, jt. auth. see Kasten, Lloyd.

Anderson, Joan. Christmas on the Prairie. LC 85-4095. (Illus.). 48p. 1985. 13.95 (ISBN 0-89919-307-2, Clarion). Ticknor & Fields.

Anderson, Joan W. Dear World: Don't Spin So Fast, I'm Having Trouble Hanging On. LC 82-73131. 160p. 1982. pap. 4.95 (ISBN 0-87029-188-2, 20280-4). Abbey.

Anderson, Johan G. Symbolism in the Prehistoric Painted Ceramics of China. 1929. 13.00 (ISBN 0-317-43918-9, Pub. by Han-Shan Tang Ltd). State Mutual Bk.

Anderson, Johannes E. Myths & Legends of the Polynesians. LC 69-13509. (Illus.). 1969. Repr. of 1928 ed. 37.50 (ISBN 0-8048-0414-1). C E Tuttle.

Anderson, John, jt. auth. see De Blassie, Richard R.

Anderson, John D., ed. see William of St. Thierry.

Anderson, John D. & Kennan, Elizabeth T., trs. Bernard of Clairvaux: Consideration: Advice to a Pope. LC 75-27953. (Cistercian Fathers Ser.: No. 37). 1976. 5.00 (ISBN 0-87907-137-0). Cistercian Pubns.

Anderson, Joseph. Prayerbook Hebrew Teacher's Guide. Simon, Ethelyn & Kelman, Victoria, eds. (Orig.). 1985. pap. text ed. 4.95 (ISBN 0-939144-10-7). EKS Pub Co.

Anderson, Joseph & Lipshitz, Devora. Tall Tales Told & Retold in Biblical Hebrew. (Hebrew., Illus.). 96p. (Orig.). 1983. pap. text ed. 8.95 (ISBN 0-939144-07-7). EKS Pub Co.

Anderson, Joseph, et al. Prayerbook Hebrew the Easy Way. 2nd ed. Simon, Ethelyn, ed. 1985. pap. text ed. 14.95 (ISBN 0-939144-12-3). EKS Pub Co.

Anderson, Julian G. The New Testament in Everyday American English (EAE) LC 84-194786. (Illus.). 896p. 1984. pap. 4.95 (ISBN 0-9602128-4-1). Anderson Publ.

--The Story of Jesus the Messiah: Acts & Letters. (New Testament Wkbk.). (Illus.). 1979. pap. text ed. 3.95 (ISBN 0-9602128-3-3). Anderson Publ.

--The Story of Jesus the Messiah, Four Gospels. LC 76-52054. (A Life of Christ Wkbk). (Illus.). 1977. pap. 3.95 (ISBN 0-9602128-1-7). Anderson Publ.

--The Story of Jesus the Messiah, Old Testament. (An Old Testament Wkbk). (Illus.). 1977. pap. 3.95 (ISBN 0-9602128-2-5). Anderson Publ.

Anderson, Justo C. Historia de los Bautistas Tomo I: Sus Bases y Principios. 1978. pap. 5.75 (ISBN 0-311-15036-5). Casa Bautista.

Anderson, Lavina F., jt. ed. see Beecher, Maureen U.

Anderson, Leith. Making Happiness Happen. 132p. 1987. pap. 5.95 (ISBN 0-89693-776-3). Victor Bks.

Anderson, Lynn. Steps to Life. (Twentieth Century Sermons Ser.). 1977. 11.95 (ISBN 0-89112-310-5, Bibl Res Pr). Abilene Christ U.

Anderson, Margaret. Momentos Felices Con Dios. 192p. 1977. 3.95 (ISBN 0-88113-312-4). Edit Betania.

--The Unknowable Gurdjieff. 1st 1973 ed. (Illus.). 212p. (Orig.). 1969. pap. 7.50 (ISBN 0-87728-219-6). Weiser.

Anderson, Margaret, ed. see Pelletier, Robert.

Anderson, Margaret J. The Christian Writer's Handbook. rev. ed. LC 82-48917. 288p. 1983. 9.95 (ISBN 0-06-060195-7, RD/246, HarpR). Har-Row.

--I Want the Truth. 96p. 1969. pap. 1.25 (ISBN 0-88243-531-0, 02-0531). Gospel Pub.

Anderson, Margaret L. Windthorst: A Political Biography. 1981. 75.00x (ISBN 0-19-822578-4). Oxford U Pr.

Anderson, Marian. My Lord, What a Morning: An Autobiography. 312p. Repr. of 1956 ed. lib. bdg. 39.00 (Pub. by Am Repr Serv). Am Biog Serv.

Anderson, Mary. Numerology: The Secret Power of Numbers. (Paths to Inner Power Ser.). 1972. pap. 3.50 (ISBN 0-85030-183-1). Weiser.

--Palmistry. (Paths to Inner Power Ser.). 1973. pap. 3.50 (ISBN 0-85030-164-5). Weiser.

--PATHS Numerology-Secret Power. pap. 4.95x (ISBN 0-317-07306-0, Regent House). B of A.

Anderson, Norman. Christianity & World Religions. rev. ed. LC 84-115291. 192p. 1984. pap. 9.95 (ISBN 0-87784-981-1). Inter-Varsity.

--Jesus Christ: The Witness of History. LC 84-15703. 210p. 1985. pap. 6.95 (ISBN 0-87784-336-8). Inter-Varsity.

--The Mystery of the Incarnation. LC 79-13879. 1979. pap. 3.95 (ISBN 0-87784-530-1). Inter-Varsity.

--The Teachings of Jesus. LC 83-4312. (The Jesus Library). 216p. 1983. pap. 6.95 (ISBN 0-87784-926-9). Inter-Varsity.

Anderson, Paul. Building Christian Character. (Trinity Teen Curriculum Ser.). 48p. 1984. Repr. student wkbk. 3.95 (ISBN 0-87123-436-X, 210436); tchr's. guide 4.95 (ISBN 0-87123-430-0). Bethany Hse.

Anderson, Paul B. People, Church & State in Modern Russia. LC 79-5204. 240p. 1980. Repr. of 1944 ed. 23.00 (ISBN 0-8305-0058-8). Hyperion Conn.

Anderson, Per M., ed. see McGill, Arthur.

Anderson, Philip A. Church Meetings That Matter. enl. ed. 128p. 1987. pap. 5.95 (ISBN 0-8298-0752-7). Pilgrim NY.

Anderson, R. A. The International Theological Commentary on Daniel. Knight, George A., ed. (The International Theological Commentary Ser.). 192p. (Orig.). 1984. pap. 7.95 (ISBN 0-8028-1038-1). Eerdmans.

--Unfolding Daniel. LC 75-16526. (Dimension Ser.). 192p. 1975. pap. 6.95 (ISBN 0-8163-0180-8, 21390-0). Pacific Pr Pub Assn.

Anderson, R. B. Norse Mythology or the Religion of Our Forefathers. LC 77-6879. 1977. Repr. of 1891 ed. lib. bdg. 25.00 (ISBN 0-89341-147-7). Longwood Pub Group.

Anderson, Ray S. Minding God's Business. 176p. (Orig.). 1986. pap. 9.95 (ISBN 0-8028-0168-4). Eerdmans.

--On Being Human: Essays in Theological Anthropology. 234p. (Orig.). 1982. pap. 9.95 (ISBN 0-8028-1926-5). Eerdmans.

--Theological Foundations for Ministry. LC 78-13613. 1978. pap. 8.95 (ISBN 0-8028-1776-9). Eerdmans.

--Theology, Death & Dying. LC 85-30806. 192p. 1986. 34.95 (ISBN 0-631-14846-9); pap. 8.95 (ISBN 0-631-14847-7). Basil Blackwell.

Anderson, Ray S. & Guernsey, Dennis B. On Being Family: Essays on a Social Theology of the Family. 192p. (Orig.). 1986. pap. 9.95 (ISBN 0-8028-1990-7). Eerdmans.

Anderson, Richard L. Understanding Paul. LC 83-72103. 448p. 1983. 10.95 (ISBN 0-87747-984-4). Deseret Bk.

Anderson, Robert. Forgotten Truths. LC 80-17526. (Sir Robert Anderson Library). 166p. 1980. pap. 4.50 (ISBN 0-8254-2130-6). Kregel.

--The Gospel & Its Ministry. LC 78-9539. (Sir Robert Anderson Library). 224p. 1978. pap. 4.95 (ISBN 0-8254-2126-8). Kregel.

--The Lord from Heaven. LC 78-9533. (Sir Robert Anderson Library). 120p. 1978. pap. 3.50 (ISBN 0-8254-2127-6). Kregel.

--Redemption Truths. LC 80-16161. (Sir Robert Anderson Library). Orig. Title: For Us Men. 192p. 1980. pap. 4.95 (ISBN 0-8254-2131-4). Kregel.

--The Silence of God. LC 78-9528. (Sir Robert Anderson Library). 232p. 1978. pap. 5.95 (ISBN 0-8254-2128-4). Kregel.

--El Silencio de Dios. Orig. Title: The Silence of God. (Span.). 192p. 1981. pap. 3.95 (ISBN 0-8254-1022-3). Kregel.

--Types in Hebrews. LC 78-9545. (Sir Robert Anderson Library). 192p. 1978. pap. 4.95 (ISBN 0-8254-2129-2). Kregel.

Anderson, Robert C. The Effective Pastor: A Practical Guide to the Ministry. 1985. 15.95 (ISBN 0-8024-6359-2). Moody.

Anderson, Robert M. Vision of the Disinherited: The Making of American Pentecostalism. 1979. 24.95x (ISBN 0-19-502502-4). Oxford U Pr.

Anderson, Robin. Between Two Wars: The Story of Pope Pius XI. 1978. 7.95 (ISBN 0-8199-0687-5). Franciscan Herald.

--St. Pius V - A Brief Account of His Life, Times, Virtues & Miracles. LC 78-55637. 1978. pap. 2.50 (ISBN 0-89555-068-7). TAN Bks Pubs.

Anderson, Roy A. Unfolding the Revelation. LC 61-10884. (Dimension Ser.). 223p. 1961. pap. 6.95 (ISBN 0-8163-0027-5, 21400-7). Pacific Pr Pub Assn.

Anderson, Thomas C. The Foundation & Structure of Sartrean Ethics. LC 79-11762. x, 186p. 1979. 22.50x (ISBN 0-7006-0191-0). U Pr of KS.

Anderson, Vincent P. Robert Browning As a Religious Poet: An Annotated Bibliography of the Crticism. LC 82-50407. 350p. 1984. 25.00X (ISBN 0-87875-221-8). Whitston Pub.

Anderson, William. Journeying in His Light. 160p. 1982. wire coil 4.95 (ISBN 0-697-01858-X). Wm C Brown.

--Journeying Toward Marriage. (Journeying with Christ Ser.). 176p. 1985. pap. 6.75 (ISBN 0-697-02059-2). Wm C Brown.

Anderson, William A. In His Light. 1985. pap. 5.75 (ISBN 0-697-02111-4). Wm C Brown.

--RCIA: A Total Parish Process. 1986. pap. 12.95 (ISBN 0-697-02200-5). Wm C Brown.

Anderson, William J. & Spiers, Richard P. The Architecture of Ancient Rome: An Account of Its Historic Development. LC 27-24681. 202p. 1927. Repr. 49.00x (ISBN 0-403-08618-3). Somerset Pub.

Anderson, William K., ed. Protestantism. facs. ed. LC 69-18918. (Essay Index Reprint Ser). 1944. 17.50 (ISBN 0-8369-1018-4). Ayer Co Pubs.

Andrae, Tor. Mohammed: The Man & His Faith. facsimile ed. Menzel, Theophil, tr. LC 79-160954. (Select Bibliographies Reprint Ser). Repr. of 1936 ed. 19.00 (ISBN 0-8369-5821-7). Ayer Co Pubs.

Andre. Dictionnaire Alphabetique, Theorique et Pratique de Droit Civil Ecclesiastique, 2 vols. Migne, J. P., ed. (Troisieme et Derniere Encyclopedie Theologique Ser.: Vols. 64-65). (Fr.). 1332p. Repr. of 1873 ed. lib. bdg. 170.00x (ISBN 0-89241-328-X). Caratzas.

Andre, Evelyn, compiled by. Rejoice & Sing Praise: A Collection of Songs & Materials to Be Used with Elementary Boys & Girls. LC 77-1604. 1977. pap. 9.95 (ISBN 0-687-35930-9). Abingdon.

--Sing & Be Joyful: Enjoying Music with Young Children. LC 79-14787. 1979. pap. 8.95 (ISBN 0-687-38550-4). Abingdon.

Andre, Evelyn M. Places I Like to Be. LC 79-23964. (Illus.). 1980. 7.75g (ISBN 0-687-31540-9). Abingdon.

Andre, G. David, the Man after God's Own Heart. (Let's Discuss It Ser.). pap. 2.50 (ISBN 0-88172-134-4). Believers Bkshelf.

--Gideon, Samson & Other Judges of Israel. (Let's Discuss It Ser.). pap. 1.95 (ISBN 0-88172-132-8). Believers Bkshelf.

--Jeremiah, the Prophet. (Let's Discuss It Ser.). pap. 1.95 (ISBN 0-88172-135-2). Believers Bkshelf.

--Moses, the Man of God. 47p. pap. 1.95 (ISBN 0-88172-131-X). Believers Bkshelf.

Andrea, Raymond. Technique of the Disciple. 4th ed. 168p. 1981. pap. 7.95 (ISBN 0-912057-12-2, G-643). AMORC.

--The Technique of the Master. 12th ed. 174p. 1981. 7.95 (ISBN 0-912057-10-6, G-513). AMORC.

Andreason, Neils-Erik. Rest & Redemption: A Study of the Biblical Sabbath. (Andrews University Monographs, Studies in Religion: Vol. XI). vii, 137p. 1978. pap. 3.95 (ISBN 0-943872-11-1). Andrews Univ Pr.

Andrew, John A., III. Rebuilding the Christian Commonwealth: New England Congregationalists & Foreign Missions, 1800-1830. LC 75-38214. 240p. 1976. 22.00x (ISBN 0-8131-1333-4). U Pr of Ky.

Andrew, Laurel B. The Early Temples of the Mormons: The Architecture of the Millennial Kingdom in the American West. LC 77-23971. (Illus.). 1978. 29.50 (ISBN 0-87395-358-4). State U NY Pr.

Andrewes, Lancelot. Private Devotions of Lancelot Andrewes. Brightman, F. E., tr. & intro. by. 15.25 (ISBN 0-8446-1534-X). Peter Smith.

Andrews, C. W. Memoire of Mrs. Ann R. Page. De Swarte, Carolyn G. & Dayton, Donald, eds. (Women in American Protestant Religion Series 1800-1930). 95p. 1987. lib. bdg. 25.00 (ISBN 0-8240-0657-7). Garland Pub.

Andrews, Carol. The Ancient Egyptian Book of the Dead. Faulkner, R. O., tr. (Illus.). 268p. 1985. text ed. 40.00x (ISBN 0-02-901470-0). Macmillan.

Andrews, Edward D. Gift to Be Simple. (Illus.). 1940. pap. 3.95 (ISBN 0-486-20022-1). Dover.

--Gift to Be Simple: Songs, Dances & Rituals of the American Shakers. (Illus.). 12.75 (ISBN 0-8446-1536-6). Peter Smith.

--People Called Shakers. new & enl. ed. 15.50 (ISBN 0-8446-1535-8). Peter Smith.

--People Called Shakers: A Search for the Perfect Society. (Illus.). 1953. pap. 6.95 (ISBN 0-486-21081-2). Dover.

Andrews, Edward D. & Andrews, Faith. Religion in Wood: A Book of Shaker Furniture. LC 66-12722. (Midland Bks Ser.: No. 286). (Illus.). 128p. 1966. 20.00 (ISBN 0-253-17360-4); pap. 7.95x (ISBN 0-253-20286-8). Ind U Pr.

--Work & Workship among the Shakers. (Illus.). 224p. 1982. pap. 6.00 (ISBN 0-486-24382-6). Dover.

--Work & Worship among the Shakers. 1983. 14.00 (ISBN 0-8446-5942-8). Peter Smith.

Andrews, Elsie M. Facing & Fulfilling the Later Years. LC 68-16318. (Orig.). 1968. pap. 2.50x (ISBN 0-87574-157-6). Pendle Hill.

Andrews, Faith, jt. auth. see Andrews, Edward D.

Andrews, Gini. Esther: The Star & the Sceptre. 288p. 1981. pap. 7.95 (ISBN 0-310-20181-0, 10859). Zondervan.

--A Violent Grace. 112p. 1987. pap. 4.95 (ISBN 0-310-20131-4). Zondervan.

Andrews, J. Richard, ed. see Ruiz de Alarcon, Hernando.

Andrews, J. S. A Study of German Hymns in Current English Hymnals. (German Language & Literature-European University Studies: No. 1, Vol. 614). 398p. 1982. pap. 36.30 (ISBN 3-261-05068-3). P Lang Pubs.

Andrews, James E. & Burgess, Joseph A. An Invitation to Action: The Lutheran-Reformed Dialogue, Ser. III, 1981-1983; A Study of Ministry, Sacraments & Recognition. LC 84-47885. 144p. 1984. pap. 2.00 (ISBN 0-8006-1818-1, 1-1818). Fortress.

Andrews, Judy, jt. auth. see Gilchrist, John.

Andrews, Judy, jt. auth. see Sullivan, Daniel.

Andrews, Lewis M. To Thine Own Self Be True: The Re-Birth of Values in the New Ethical Therapy. 288p. 1987. 16.95 (ISBN 0-385-23736-7, Anch). Doubleday.

Andrews, Lynn V. Flight of the Seventh Moon: The Teaching of the Shields. LC 83-48414. (Illus.). 208p. 1984. 13.45 (ISBN 0-06-250027-9, HarpR). Har-Row.

--Medicine Woman. LC 81-47546. 224p. 1983. pap. 7.95 (ISBN 0-06-250026-0, CN 4062, HarpR). Har-Row.

--Star Woman: We Are Made from Stars & to the Stars We Must Return. LC 86-40038. 256p. 1986. 16.95 (ISBN 0-446-51316-4). Warner Bks.

Andrews, Mildred & Riddle, Pauline. Church Organ Method. 123p. 1973. pap. 15.00 (ISBN 0-8258-0050-1, 04904). Fischer Inc NY.

Andrews, Samuel J. Christianity & Anti-Christianity in Their Final Conflict. 1982. lib. bdg. 15.00 (ISBN 0-86524-084-1, 9804). Klock & Klock.

Andrews, Samuel J. & Gifford, E. H. Man & the Incarnation: The Study of Philippians 2 & Psalm 110. 1981. lib. bdg. 15.00 (ISBN 0-86524-078-7, 9510). Klock & Klock.

Andrews, William, ed. Antiquities & Curiosities of the Church: Folklore & Historical Traditions About English Churches. LC 77-87673. Repr. of 1897 ed. 20.00 (ISBN 0-404-16465-X). AMS Pr.

Andrews, William L., ed. Sisters of the Spirit: Three Black Women's Autobiographies of the Nineteenth Century. LC 85-42544. (Religion in North America Ser.). 256p. 1986. 29.50x (ISBN 0-253-35260-6); pap. 8.95x (ISBN 0-253-28704-9). Ind U Pr.

Andreyev, I. M. Pravoslavno-Khristijanskaja Apologetika. Tr. of Orthodox-Christian Apologetics. 92p. 1965. pap. text ed. 5.00 (ISBN 0-317-30249-3). Holy Trinity.

--Pravoslavno-Khristijanskoe Nravstvennoje Bogoslovije. Tr. of Orthodox-Christian Moral Theology. 148p. 1966. pap. text ed. 5.00 (ISBN 0-317-30264-7). Holy Trinity.

Androgeus, John C., ed. The Lost Gospel of the Ages: Key to Immortality & Companion to the Holy Bible. (Illus.). 979p. 1978. pap. text ed. 95.00 (ISBN 0-9609802-3-7). Life Science.

Andronis, Constantine. Apostolos Makrakis--An Evaluation of Half a Century. 369p. (Orig.). 1966. pap. 4.00x (ISBN 0-938366-33-5). Orthodox Chr.

Andrus, Hyrum L. Joseph Smith & World Government. 144p. 1972. pap. 3.95 (ISBN 0-89036-032-4). Hawkes Pub Inc.

Andrzejewski, Jerzy. The Inquisitors. Syrop, Konrad, tr. from Polish. LC 76-6896. 1976. Repr. of 1960 ed. lib. bdg. 22.50x (ISBN 0-8371-8868-7, ANIN). Greenwood.

Anesaki, Masaharu. History of Japanese Religion. LC 63-19395. 1963. Repr. of 1930 ed. 23.50 (ISBN 0-8048-0248-3). C E Tuttle.

Anesaki, Masaharu see Ferguson, John C.

Anesaki, Masharu. Nichiren: The Buddhist Prophet. 1916. 11.25 (ISBN 0-8446-1029-1). Peter Smith.

Anfuso, Joseph & Sczepanski, David. Efrain Rios Montt - Servant or Dictator? The Real Story of Guatemala's Controversial "Born Again" President. LC 84-7553. pap. 5.95 (ISBN 0-88449-110-2, A424705). Vision Hse.

Angel, Marc D. The Rhythms of Jewish Living: The Sephardic Approach. LC 86-25993. 208p. 1987. 14.95 (ISBN 0-87203-125-X). Hermon.

Angel, Marc D., ed. Studies in Sephardic Culture: The David N. Barocas Memorial Volume. LC 79-92737. (Illus.). 190p. 1980. 15.00 (ISBN 0-87203-090-3). Hermon.

Angeles, Peter. Dictionary of Christian Theology. LC 79-2988. 336p. 1985. 17.45 (ISBN 0-06-060237-6, HarpR). Har-Row.

Angeles, Peter, ed. Critiques of God. pap. 7.00 (ISBN 0-87980-349-5). Wilshire.

Angeles, Peter A. The Problem of God: A Short Introduction. rev. ed. LC 73-85469. 156p. 1981. pap. text ed. 11.95 (ISBN 0-87975-216-5). Prometheus Bks.

Angell, C. Roy. God's Gold Mines. LC 62-9194. 1962. 7.95 (ISBN 0-8054-5113-7). Broadman.

--Price Tags of Life. LC 59-9692. 1959. 6.95 (ISBN 0-8054-5108-0). Broadman.

Angell, James. Roots & Wings. 80p. 1983. text ed. 7.95 (ISBN 0-687-36585-6). Abingdon.

Angell, James W. Accept No Imitations: Finding a Genuine Faith in a Counterfeit World. 144p. 1984. pap. 8.75 (ISBN 0-687-00692-9). Abingdon.

--Learning to Manage Our Fears. LC 81-1878. 128p. 1981. 7.75 (ISBN 0-687-21329-0). Abingdon.

--Seek It Lovingly. (Illus.). 1974. pap. 3.95 (ISBN 0-87516-184-7). De Vorss.

Angeloglou, George, tr. see Tsakonas, Demetrios.

Angers, Joann. Meeting the Forgiving Jesus: A Child's First Penance Book. 32p. 1984. pap. 1.75 (ISBN 0-89243-201-2). Liguori Pubns.

Angers, JoAnn M. My Beginning Mass Book. (Illus.). 32p. (Orig.). 1978. pap. 1.95 (ISBN 0-89622-082-6). Twenty-Third.

Angilly, Richard, ed. see Gilbert, Donald.

Anglican Consultative Council Staff. For the Sake of the Kingdom. 72p. (Orig.). 1986. pap. 2.25 (ISBN 0-88028-054-9). Forward Movement.

Anglin, E. Warren. Seven Thunderers Utter Their Voices: History & Verse by Verse Study in the Book of Revelation of the Bible. 2nd ed. 176p. (Orig.). pap. 7.95 (ISBN 0-318-04199-5). Total Comm Ministries.

Anglund, Joan W. Christmas Is a Time of Giving. LC 61-10106. (Illus.). 1961. 7.95 (ISBN 0-15-217863-5, HJ). HarBraceJ.

Angoff, Charles, ed. see Cherry, Conrad, et al.

Angus, Fay. Running Around in Spiritual Circles. LC 85-42768. 192p. 1986. 13.45 (ISBN 0-06-060238-4, HarpR). Har-Row.

Angus, S. The Environment of Early Christianity. 1977. lib. bdg. 59.95 (ISBN 0-8490-1778-5). Gordon Pr.

--The Religious Quests of the Graeco-Roman World. 1929. 30.00 (ISBN 0-686-20108-6). Quality Lib.

Angus, Samuel. The Environment of Early Christianity. facsimile ed. LC 75-157322. (Select Bibliographies Reprint Ser). Repr. of 1915 ed. 17.00 (ISBN 0-8369-5781-4). Ayer Co Pubs.

--The Mystery Religions. LC 74-12637. 360p. 1975. pap. 6.95 (ISBN 0-486-23124-0). Dover.

--The Mystery Religions & Christianity. 1977. lib. bdg. 59.95 (ISBN 0-8490-2314-9). Gordon Pr.

--The Religious Quests of the Graeco-Roman World: A Study in the Historical Background of Early Christianity. LC 66-30791. 1929. 18.00 (ISBN 0-8196-0196-9). Biblo.

Anirvan. Buddhiyoga of the Gita & Other Essays. LC 84-900102. 1984. 16.00x (ISBN 0-8364-1120-X, Pub. by Biblia Impex). South Asia Bks.

Anjou, Lars A. The History of the Reformation in Sweden. Mason, Henry M., tr. from Swedish. LC 83-45598. Date not set. Repr. of 1859 ed. 62.50 (ISBN 0-404-19866-X). AMS Pr.

Ankori, Zvi. Karaites in Byzantium: The Formative Years, 970-1100. LC 71-158258. (Columbia University Studies in the Social Sciences: No. 597). Repr. of 1959 ed. 28.50 (ISBN 0-404-51597-5). AMS Pr.

Ann Arbor Publishers Editorial Staff. Symbol Discrimination Series: Books 1, 2, 3, 4, 5, & 6. Reusable ed. (Symbol Discrimination Series). (Illus.). 16p. 1974. 3.00 ea.; Book 1. 3.00 (ISBN 0-89039-078-9); Book 2. 3.00 (ISBN 0-89039-079-7); Book 3. 3.00 (ISBN 0-89039-080-0); Book 4. 3.00 (ISBN 0-89039-081-9); Book 5. 3.00 (ISBN 0-89039-082-7); Book 6. 3.00 (ISBN 0-89039-083-5). Ann Arbor FL.

Annas, Julia & Barnes, Jonathan. The Modes of Scepticism: Ancient Texts & Modern Interpretations. 216p. 1985. 29.50 (ISBN 0-521-25682-8); pap. 9.95 (ISBN 0-521-27644-6). Cambridge U Pr.

Annas, Julia, ed. Oxford Studies in Ancient Philosophy, Vol. 2. 1984. text ed. 39.95x (ISBN 0-19-824769-9); pap. text ed. 16.95x (ISBN 0-19-824768-0). Oxford U Pr.

Annese, Lucius. Pope John Paul II in America. LC 79-56497. 1980. 50.00 (ISBN 0-933402-10-4). Charisma Pr.

--The Purpose of Authority? LC 78-72295. (Orig.). 1978. 50.00 (ISBN 0-933402-12-0). Charisma Pr.

Annesley, Samuel. Puritan Sermons, Sixteen Fifty-Nine To Sixteen Eighty-Nine Being the Morning Exercises at Cripplegate, St. Giles in the Fields & in Southwark: By 75 Ministers of the Gospel in or Near London, with Notes & Translations by James Nichols, 6 vols. Nichols, James, ed. 4200p. 1981. Set. lib. bdg. 120.00 (ISBN 0-940033-19-4). R O Roberts.

Annesley, Samuel, et al. Puritan Sermons, 1659-1689, 6 vols. Nichols, James, ed. 4220p. 1981. Repr. of 1845 ed. lib. bdg. 120.00 set (ISBN 0-939464-07-1). Labyrinth Pr.

Annette, Miserendino, ed. Catholic Telephone Guide. 296p. 1986. 22.00 (ISBN 0-910635-54-4). Cath News Pub Co.

Anouilh, Jean. Alouette. 1963. pap. 3.95 (ISBN 0-685-10991-7, 1153). French & Eur.

--Becket. 1960. pap. 5.95 (ISBN 0-698-10031-X, Coward). Putnam Pub Group.

--Becket ou, l'Honneur de Dieu. 1973. pap. 5.50 (ISBN 0-685-11038-9, 1716). French & Eur.

--Lark. Fry, Christopher, tr. 1956. 10.95x (ISBN 0-19-500393-4). Oxford U Pr.

Anquetil-Duperron, A. H. Zend-Avesta, Ouvrage de Zoroastre. Feldman, Burton & Richardson, Robert, eds. LC 78-60878. (Myth & Romanticism Ser.). 1984. lib. bdg. 240.00 (ISBN 0-8240-3550-X). Garland Pub.

Anrias, David. Through the Eyes of the Masters. 1972. pap. 7.95 (ISBN 0-87728-116-5). Weiser.

Ansari, F. R. The Existence of the Soul. pap. 1.00 (ISBN 0-686-18460-2). Kazi Pubns.

--Foundations of Faith. pap. 1.50 (ISBN 0-686-18472-6). Kazi Pubns.

--Islam & Christianity in the Modern World. pap. 14.95 (ISBN 0-686-18577-3). Kazi Pubns.

--Islam & the Western Civilization. pap. 1.50 (ISBN 0-686-18533-1). Kazi Pubns.

--Philosophy of Worship in Islam. pap. 1.00 (ISBN 0-686-18603-6). Kazi Pubns.

--Through Science & Philosophy to Religion. pap. 1.25 (ISBN 0-686-18536-6). Kazi Pubns.

Ansari, Khwajih Abd Ansari see Abd Allah Ansarti, Khwajih.

Ansari, M. A., tr. from Persian. Man & His Destiny. Tr. of Insan wa Sarnawisht. 124p. 1985. pap. 5.00 (ISBN 0-941724-39-5). Islamic Seminary.

Ansari, M. A., tr. see Al-Sadr, Ayatullah B.

Ansari, M. A., tr. see Al Sadr, Muhammad B.

Ansari, M. A., tr. see Mutahhery, Murtaza.

Ansari, M. A., tr. see Nutanhhery, Murtaza.

Ansari, M. A., tr. see Sadr, Muhammad B.

Ansari, M. A., tr. see Sadr, Muhhammad B.

Anscombe, Elizabeth, ed. see Descartes, Rene.

Anscombe, Elizabeth, tr. see Descartes, Rene.

Anscombe, G. E. Collected Philosophical Papers: Ethics, Religion & Politics, Vol. 3. LC 81-4315. 192p. 1981. 27.50x (ISBN 0-8166-1082-7); pap. 10.95x (ISBN 0-8166-1083-5). U of Minn Pr.

Anselm, St. Saint Anselm: Basic Writings. 2nd ed. Deane, Sidney M., tr. Incl. Proslogium; Monologium; Gaunilo's "In Behalf of the Fool"; Cur Deus Homo. LC 74-3309. 371p. 1974. 19.95 (ISBN 0-87548-108-6); pap. 8.95 (ISBN 0-87548-109-4). Open Court.

Anselm Of Canterbury. Anselm of Canterbury: Vol. I, Monologion, Proslogion, Debate with Gaunilo, & a Meditation on Human Redemption. Hopkins, Jasper & Richardson, Herbert, trs. LC 74-19840. 161p. 1974. 39.95x (ISBN 0-88946-000-0). E Mellen.

--Anselm of Canterbury: Vol. II, Philosophical Fragments; De Grammatico; on Truth; Freedom of Choice; the Fall of the Devil; the Harmony of the Foreknowledge, the Predestination, & the Grace of God with Free Choice. Hopkins, Jasper & Richardson, Herbert, trs. LC 74-19840. 237p. 1976. 49.95x (ISBN 0-88946-250-X). E Mellen.

--Anselm of Canterbury: Vol. III, Two Letters Concerning Roscelin; the Incarnation of the Word; Why God Became a Man; the Virgin Conception & Original Sin; the Procession of the Holy Spirit; Three Letters on the Sacraments. Hopkins, Jasper & Richardson, Herbert, trs. LC 74-19840. 265p. 1976. 39.95x (ISBN 0-88946-350-6). E Mellen.

--Anselm of Canterbury: Why God Became Man. Hopkins, Jasper & Richardson, Herbert, eds. 105p. 1980. soft cover 7.95x (ISBN 0-88946-009-4). E Mellen.

--Trinity, Incarnation, & Redemption: Theological Treatises. (Anselm Ser.: No. 6). 1974. 9.95 (ISBN 0-88946-008-6). E Mellen.

--Why God Became Man & the Virgin Conception & Original Sin. Colleran, Joseph M., tr. from Latin. & intro. by. LC 71-77166. 256p. (Orig.). 1982. pap. text ed. 4.95x (ISBN 0-87343-025-5). Magi Bks.

Anshen, Ruth N. Anatomy of Evil. Orig. Title: The Reality of the Devil. (Illus.). 224p. 1985. pap. 8.95 (ISBN 0-918825-15-6, Dist. by Kampmann & Co.). Moyer Bell Limited.

Anshen, Ruth N., ed. see Tillich, Paul.

Anson, Doris C., tr. see Maritain, Jacques.

Anstice, R. H. Satan of Milton. LC 72-191957. 1910. lib. bdg. 10.00 (ISBN 0-8414-0289-2). Folcroft.

Anstruther, Godfrey. The Seminary Priests: A Dictionary of the Secular Clergy of England & Wales, 1558-1850, 4 vols. Incl. Vol. 1. Elizabethan, 1558-1603. 1968 (ISBN 0-87921-059-1); Vol. 2. Early Stuarts, 1603-1659. 1975 (ISBN 0-85597-082-0); Vol. 3 Paperback. 660-1715. 1976 (ISBN 0-85597-116-9); Vol. 4 Paperback. 1716-1800. 1977 (ISBN 0-85597-118-5). text ed. 18.50x ea. Attic Pr.

--The Seminary Priests: A Dictionary of the Secular Clery of England & Wales, 1558 to 1800, Vols. 1-4. Incl. Vol. 1. Elizabethan 1558-1603. 1969. text ed. 21.50x (ISBN 0-8401-0071-X); Vol. 2. Early Stuarts 1603-1659. 1975. text ed. 21.50x (ISBN 0-8401-0072-8); Vol. 3. 1660-1715. 1976. text ed. 27.50x (ISBN 0-8401-0073-6); Vol. 4. 1716-1800. 1977. text ed. 27.50x (ISBN 0-8401-0074-4). LC 76-441910. A R Allenson.

Anstruther, Sir William. Essays, Moral & Divine. LC 74-170474. (The English Stage Ser.: Vol. 40). 1973. lib. bdg. 61.00 (ISBN 0-8240-0623-2). Garland Pub.

Ante-Nicene Fathers. Writings of the Ante-Nicene Fathers, 10 vols. Roberts, A. & Donaldson, J., eds. 1951. Set. 179.50 (ISBN 0-8028-8097-5); 17.95 ea. Eerdmans.

Anthimos. Reply of the Orthodox Church to Roman Catholic Overtures on Reunion. rev., enl. ed. 64p. 1986. pap. 2.00 (ISBN 0-913026-62-X). St Nectarios.

Anthony, Carol K. Guide to I Ching. 3rd ed. 400p. Date not set. pap. write for info. Anthony Pub Co.

--The Philosophy of the I Ching. LC 81-69537. 160p. 1981. pap. 6.50 (ISBN 0-9603832-1-2). Anthony Pub Co.

Anthony, Dick, jt. ed. see Robbins, Thomas.

Anthony, Dick, et al, eds. Spiritual Choices, the Problem of Recognizing Authentic Paths to Inner Transformation: The Problem of Recognizing Authentic Paths to Inner Transformation. 448p. 1986. 24.95 (ISBN 0-913729-14-0); pap. 12.95 (ISBN 0-913729-19-1). Paragon Hse.

Anthony, Susan B. Sidewalk Contemplatives: A Spirituality for Concerned Christians. 160p. (Orig.). 1987. pap. 8.95 (ISBN 0-8245-0795-9). Crossroad NY.

Anthony, William. Bible Stories. LC 77-71655. (Illus., Orig.). pap. 5.00 (ISBN 0-912330-25-2, Dist. by Inland Bk). Jargon Soc.

Anthony of Sourozh. God & Man. 2nd ed. 125p. 1983. pap. text ed. 4.95 (ISBN 0-88141-024-1). St Vladimirs.

Anti-Defamation League of B'nai Brith Staff. The Holocaust & Genocide: A Search for Conscience, An Anthology for Students. 217p. 9.95 (ISBN 0-317-03375-1). ADL.

--The Holocaust & Genocide: A Search for Conscience, A Curriculum Guide. 184p. 12.00 (ISBN 0-317-03374-3). ADL.

Anti-Defamation League Staff. Perspectives on Soviet Jewry. 150p. pap. 2.50 (ISBN 0-686-95144-1). ADL.

Anti-Sabbath Convention Staff. Proceedings of the Anti-Sabbath Convention, Melodeon, Boston. Parkhurst, Henry M., ed. LC 79-122662. 1971. Repr. of 1848 ed. 16.50x (ISBN 0-8046-1311-7, Pub. by Kennikat). Assoc Faculty Pr.

Antin, Mary. From Plotzk to Boston. Sarna, Jonathan D., ed. (Masterworks of Modern Jewish Writing Ser.). 140p. 1986. pap. 6.95 (ISBN 0-910129-45-2, Dist. by Schocken). Wiener Pub Inc.

Antoine, Robert. Rama & the Bards: Epic Memory in the Ramayana. (Greybird Book). 114p. 1975. 12.00 (ISBN 0-88253-821-7); pap. 6.75 (ISBN 0-88253-822-5). Ind-US Inc.

Antonellis, Costanzo J. The Story of Peter Donders. 115p. 3.50 (ISBN 0-8198-6834-5, BI0217); pap. 2.50 (ISBN 0-8198-6835-3). Dghtrs St Paul.

Antonio, Joannes A. Bibliotheca Universa Franciscana, 3 vols. 1640p. Date not set. Repr. of 1733 ed. text ed. 496.80x (ISBN 0-576-72343-6, Pub. by Gregg Intl Pubs England). Gregg Intl.

Antonio, T. De Nicolas see Lincoln, Victoria.

Antonov, N. R. Khram Bozhij i Tserkovnija Sluzhbi. Tr. of The Temple of God & Church Services. 300p. 1983. pap. text ed. 10.00 (ISBN 0-317-30284-1). Holy Trinity.

Antony, Judith. Where Time Becomes Space. 1978. 8.95 (ISBN 0-8199-0699-9). Franciscan Herald.

Antosik, Stanley J. The Question of Elites: An Essay on the Cultural Elitism of Nietzche, George & Hesse. (New York University Ottendorfer Series, Neue Folge: Vol. 11). 204p. 1978. 22.75 (ISBN 3-261-03102-6). P Lang Pubs.

Anuman, Rajadhon Phraya. Life & Ritual in Old Siam: Three Studies of Thai Life & Customs. Gedney, William J., ed. LC 78-23833. (Illus.). 1979. Repr. of 1961 ed. lib. bdg. 24.75x (ISBN 0-313-21193-0, ARLF). Greenwood.

Anurag, Ma Yoga, ed. see Rajneesh, Bhagwan Shree.

Anwarali, Maulana, ed. see Rizvi, Allama S.

Anway, Carol. Family Enrichment Book. 1979. pap. 8.00 (ISBN 0-8309-0247-3). Herald Hse.

Anwyl, Edward. Celtic Religion: In Prechristian Times. 1977. lib. bdg. 59.95 (ISBN 0-8490-1590-1). Gordon Pr.

Anzar, Naosherwan, ed. The Best of the Glow: A Fifteen Year Retrospective, Vol. 1. LC 84-23518. 208p. (Orig.). 1984. pap. 8.95 (ISBN 0-913078-54-9). Sheriar Pr.

Anzia, Joan & Durkin, Mary. Marital Intimacy: A Catholic Perspective. 81p. pap. 6.95. Loyola.

Anzul, Dario. The Paintings of Mysticism & Violence in Full Colours of Dario Anzul. (Illus.). 97p. 1983. 225.75x (ISBN 0-86650-073-1). Gloucester Art.

Apa, Ma Prem, ed. see Rajneesh, Bhagwan Shree.

Aparis, Fina, tr. see Clymer, R. Swinburne.

Apczynski, John. Foundations of Religious Literacy. LC 83-4453. (College Theology Society Annual Publications Ser.). 188p. 1983. pap. 10.50 (ISBN 0-89130-621-8, 34 10 82). Scholars Pr GA.

Apczynski, John V. Doers of the Word. LC 76-51640. (American Academy of Religion. Dissertation Ser.). 1977. pap. 10.50 (ISBN 0-89130-128-3, 010118). Scholars Pr GA.

Apczynski, John V., ed. Foundations of Religious Literacy. 186p. 1986. pap. text ed. 12.00 (ISBN 0-8191-5617-5, Pub. by College Theology Society). U Pr of Amer.

Apel, Willi. Gregorian Chant. LC 57-10729. (Illus.). 544p. 1958. 35.00x (ISBN 0-253-32650-8). Ind U Pr.

Apel, William D. Witnesses Before Dawn. 1984. pap. 6.95 (ISBN 0-8170-1031-9). Judson.

Apenszlak, Jacob, ed. The Black Book of Polish Jewry: An Account of the Martyrdom of Polish Jewry Under Nazi Occupation. xvi, 343p. 1982. Repr. of 1943 ed. 27.50x (ISBN 0-86527-340-5). Fertig.

Apollodorus. Library, 2 Vols. (Loeb Classical Library: No. 121, 122). 13.95x ea. Vol. 1, Bks. 1-3 (ISBN 0-674-99135-4). Vol. 2 (ISBN 0-674-99136-2). Harvard U Pr.

Apostle, Hippocrates G., tr. see Aristotle.

Apostola, Nicholas K., tr. see Lungu, N., et al.

Apostolic Fathers. Early Christian Writings. Staniforth, Maxwell, tr. (Gr.). 320p. 1986. 16.95 (ISBN 0-88029-074-9, Pub. by Dorset). Hippocrene Bks.

--Works of Apostolic Fathers, 2 vols. Incl. Vol. 1. Clement, Ignatius, Polycarp, Didache, Barnabas (ISBN 0-674-99027-7); Vol. 2. Shepherd of Hermas, Martyrdom of Polycarp, Epistle to Diognetus (ISBN 0-674-99028-5). (Loeb Classical Library: No. 24-25). 13.95x ea. Harvard U Pr.

Apostolon, Billy. Evangelistic Sermon Outlines. (Sermon Outline Ser.). pap. 2.50 (ISBN 0-8010-0144-7). Baker Bk.

--Preach the Word. (Sermon Outline Ser.). 1978. pap. 2.50 (ISBN 0-8010-0039-4). Baker Bk.

--Special Days & Occasions. (Sermon Outline Ser). 1978. pap. 2.50 (ISBN 0-8010-0007-6). Baker Bk.

Apostolos-Cappadona, Diane, jt. auth. see Adams, Dour.

Apostolos-Cappadona, Diane, ed. Art, Creativity & the Sacred: An Anthology in Religion & Art. (Illus.). 352p. 1983. pap. 16.95 (ISBN 0-8245-0609-X). Crossroad NY.

--The Sacred Play of Children. 160p. 1983. pap. 9.95 (ISBN 0-8164-2427-6, HarpR). Har-Row.

Apostolos-Cappadona, Diane, tr. see Eliade, Mircea.

App, Austin J. Hitler-Himmler Order on the Jews. 1984. lib. bdg. 79.95 (ISBN 0-87700-516-8). Revisionist Pr.

--Holocaust: Sneak Attack on Christianity. 1984. lib. bdg. 79.95 (ISBN 0-87700-517-6). Revisionist Pr.

Appel, David L. Marketing. (How to Ser.). 43p. 1986. 5.65 (ISBN 0-318-20575-0). Natl Cath Educ.

Appel, G. The Concise Code of Jewish Law: Daily Prayers & Religious Observances in the Life-Cycle of the Jew, Vol. 1. 11.95 (ISBN 0-87068-298-9). Ktav.

Appel, Georgius. De Romanorum Precationibus. facsimile ed. LC 75-10628. (Ancient Religion & Mythology Ser.). 1976. Repr. of 1909 ed. 18.00x (ISBN 0-405-07004-7). Ayer Co Pubs.

Appel, Gersion. A Philosophy of Mizvot. pap. 11.95x (ISBN 0-87068-250-4). Ktav.

--Samuel K. Mirsky Memorial Volume. 1970. 25.00x (ISBN 0-87068-084-6). Ktav.

Appel, Jeanette, jt. auth. see Keller, Clifton.

Appel, Richard G. The Music of the Bay Psalm Book: Ninth Edition (1698) LC 75-34880. (I.S.A.M. Monographs: No. 5). 44p. (Orig.). 1975. pap. 4.00 (ISBN 0-914678-04-3). Inst Am Music.

Appelman, Hyman. Seeds for Sermons. (Sermon Outline Ser.). 1980. pap. 2.50 (ISBN 0-8010-0026-2). Baker Bk.

--Sermon Outlines on Key Bible Themes. (Sermon Outline Ser.). pap. 1.95 (ISBN 0-8010-0003-3). Baker Bk.

Appiah-Kubi, Kofi. Man Cures, God Heals: Religion & Medical Practice Among the Akans of Ghana. LC 81-65019. (Illus.). 188p. 1981. text ed. 18.95x (ISBN 0-86598-011-X). Allanheld.

--Man Cures, God Heals: Religion & Medical Practice Among the Akans of Ghana. (Orig.). 1981. pap. 10.95 (ISBN 0-377-00114-7). Friend Pr.

Appiah-Kubi, Kofi & Torres, Sergio, eds. African Theology En Route: Papers from the Pan-African Conference of Third World Theologians, December 17-23, 1977, Accra, Ghana. LC 78-10604. 224p. (Orig.). 1978. pap. 10.95 (ISBN 0-88344-010-5). Orbis Bks.

Apple, Jody L. Hermeneutical Agnosticism: A Critique of Subjectivism in Biblical Interpretation. LC 84-62067. 195p. (Orig.). 1985. pap. 7.95 (ISBN 0-931247-00-4). New Testament Christ Pr.

Applebaum, S., tr. see Tcherikover, Victor.

Applebury, T. R. Moments with the Master. 1974. pap. 1.50 (ISBN 0-89900-115-7). College Pr Pub.

Appleby, Jerry. Missions Have Come Home to America. 120p. 1986. pap. 3.95 (ISBN 0-8341-1132-2). Beacon Hill.

Applegarth, Albert C. Quakers in Pennsylvania. LC 78-63813. (Johns Hopkins University. Studies in the Social Sciences. Tenth Ser. 1892: 8-9). Repr. of 1892 ed. 11.50 (ISBN 0-404-61076-5). AMS Pr.

--Quakers in Pennsylvania. pap. 9.00 (ISBN 0-384-01765-7). Johnson Repr.

Appleman, Solomon. The Jewish Woman in Judaism: The Significance of Women's Status in Religious Culture. 1979. 10.00 (ISBN 0-682-49431-3). Exposition Pr FL.

Appleton, George. Prayers from a Troubled Heart. LC 83-48010. 64p. 1983. pap. 3.50 (ISBN 0-8006-1711-8, 1-1711). Fortress.

--The Quiet Heart: Prayers & Meditations for Each Day of the Year. LC 84-6019. 480p. 1984. pap. 7.95 (ISBN 0-8006-1789-4). Fortress.

Appleton, George, ed. The Oxford Book of Prayer. 416p. 1985. 22.95 (ISBN 0-19-213222-9). Oxford U Pr.

Appold, Mark L. The Oneness Motif in the Fourth Gospel: Motif Analysis & Exegetical Probe into the Theology of John. 322p. 1976. pap. text ed. 38.50x (ISBN 0-89563-577-1, Pub. by J. C. B. Mohr BRD). Coronet Bks.

ApRoberts, Ruth. Arnold & God. LC 82-10847. 304p. 1983. text ed. 29.00x (ISBN 0-520-04747-8). U of Cal Pr.

Aptecker, George. Beyond Despair. (Illus.). 72p. 1980. 25.00 (ISBN 0-9604286-0-7). Kahn & Kahan.

Aptekar, Jane. Icons of Justice: Iconography & Thematic Imagery in Book Five of the Faerie Queen. LC 79-79189. (Illus.). 218p. 1969. 32.00x (ISBN 0-231-03246-3). Columbia U Pr.

Aptheker, Herbert. The Urgency of Marxist - Christian Dialogue. LC 73-109081. 1976. Repr. of 1970 ed. 24.00 (ISBN 0-527-03002-3). Kraus Repr.

Aptheker, Herbert, ed. see Dubois, W. E. B.

Aptowitzer, V. & Schwarz, A. Z. Abhandlungen zur Erinnerung an Hirsch Perez Chajes. LC 7-7163. (Jewish Philosophy, Mysticism & History of Ideas Ser.). 1980. Repr. of 1933 ed. lib. bdg. 60.00x (ISBN 0-405-12237-3). Ayer Co Pubs.

Aptowitzer, Victor. Das Schriftwort in der Rabbinischen Literatur. rev. ed. (Library of Biblical Studies Ser). 1970. 45.00x (ISBN 0-87068-005-6). Ktav.

Apuleius. Apuleius on the God of Socrates. Taylor, Thomas, tr. (Lat.). 1984. pap. 4.95 (ISBN 0-916411-25-7, Pub. by Alexandrian Pr). Holmes Pub.

--Cupid & Psyche. Balme, M. G. & Morwood, J. H., eds. (Illus.). 1976. pap. 6.95x (ISBN 0-19-912047-1). Oxford U Pr.

Apurvananda, compiled by. Swami Vijanananda: A Short Life. 173p. 1987. pap. 4.50 (ISBN 0-87481-547-9, Pub. by Ramakrishna Math Madras India). Vedanta Pr.

Apurvananda, Swami. Acharya Shankara. 362p. 1985. pap. 7.95 (ISBN 0-87481-529-0, Pub. by Ramakrishna Math Madras India). Vedanta Pr.

Arab Office, London Staff. The Future of Palestine. LC 75-12167. (The Rise of Jewish Nationalism & the Middle East Ser). 166p. 1976. Repr. of 1947 ed. 16.50 (ISBN 0-88355-229-9). Hyperion Conn.

Arabi, Ibn. Journey to the Lord of Power: A Sufi Manual on Retreat. Harris, Rabia, tr. from Arab. (Illus.). 144p. 1981. pap. 8.95 (ISBN 0-89281-018-1). Inner Tradit.

--Tarjuma'n Al-Ashwa'q. 14.25 (ISBN 0-8356-5505-9). Theos Pub Hse.

Arad, Yitzhak. Belzec, Sobibor, Treblinka: The Operation Reinhard Death Camps. 1987. 29.95 (ISBN 0-253-34293-7). Ind U Pr.

--Ghetto in Flames. LC 80-50198. (Illus.). 500p. 1982. pap. 14.95 (ISBN 0-89604-043-7). Holocaust Pubns.

--The Partisan. LC 78-71299. (Illus.). 288p. 1979. 16.95 (ISBN 0-317-06371-5); pap. 10.95 (ISBN 0-89604-011-9). Holocaust Pubns.

--The Partisan: From the Valley of Death to Mount Zion. LC 78-71299. 1979. 16.95 (ISBN 0-8052-5011-5, Pub. by Holocaust Library); pap. 10.95 (ISBN 0-8052-5010-7, Pub. by Holocaust Library). Schocken.

Arad, Yitzhak, compiled by. The Einsatzgruppen Reports: Selections from the Official Dispatches of the Nazi Death Squads' Campaign Against the Jews. 1986. 15.95 (ISBN 0-89604-057-7); pap. 10.95 (ISBN 0-89604-058-5). Holocaust Pubns.

Aragon, Ray J. De see De Aragon, Ray J.

Aragon, Ray J. De see Sanchez, Pedro.

Arai, Toshikazu, tr. see Sakakibara, Tokuso, et al.

Arand, Louis A., tr. see Kuasten, J. & Plumpe, J.

Arango, Tony, tr. Armonias Corales, Vol. 1. (Span.). 144p. (Orig.). 1977. pap. 4.75 (ISBN 0-89922-082-7). Edit Caribe.

Aranya, Hariharananda. Samkhya-Sutras of Pancasikha & the Samkhyatattvalcka. 1977. 11.25 (ISBN 0-89684-313-0, Pub. by Motilal Banarsidass India); pap. 6.95 (ISBN 0-89684-346-7). Orient Bk Dist.

Aranya, S. Hariharananda. Yoga Philosophy of Patanjali: Containing His Yoga Aphorisms with Vyasa's Commentary in Sanskrit & a Translation with Annotations Containing Many Suggestions for the Practice of Yoga. Mukerji, P. N., tr. from Sanskrit. 510p. 1983. 39.50x (ISBN 0-87395-728-8); pap. 10.95x (ISBN 0-87395-729-6). State U NY Pr.

Aranza, Jacob. Backward Masking Unmasked: Backward Satanic Messages of Rock & Roll Exposed. LC 83-80043. 118p. (Orig.). 1983. pap. 5.95 (ISBN 0-910311-04-8). Huntington Hse Inc.

--More Rock, Country & Backward Masking. 1985. pap. 5.95 (ISBN 0-910311-30-7). Huntington Hse Inc.

Aranza, Jacob & Lamson, Theresa. A Reasonable Reason to Wait. 101p. (Orig.). 1984. pap. 4.95 (ISBN 0-910311-21-8). Huntington Hse Inc.

Arapura, J. G. Hermeneutical Essays on Vedantic Topics. 326p. 1986. 18.00 (ISBN 81-208-0183-0, Pub. by Motilal Banarsidass). South Asia Bks.

--Religion As Anxiety & Tranquillity: An Essay in Comparative Phenomenology of the Spirit. (Religion & Reason Ser.: No. 5). 1973. 19.00x (ISBN 90-2797-180-3). Mouton.

Arapura, John G. Gnosis & the Question of Thought in Vedanta. 1986. lib. bdg. 65.25 (ISBN 90-247-3061-9, Pub. by Martinus Nijhoff Netherlands). Kluwer Academic.

Arasteh, A. R. Rumi the Persian: Rebirth in Creativity & Love. 1970. 6.50x (ISBN 0-87902-043-1). Orientalia.

Araten, Rachel S. Michalina, Daughter of Israel: True Story of A Jewish Girl Abducted by the Catholic Church. 1986. 12.95 (ISBN 0-87306-412-7). Feldheim.

Araujo, Juan, tr. see Swindoll, Charles.

Araujo, Juan S., tr. see Blair, Maury & Brendel, Doug.

Araujo, Juan S., tr. see Campbell, Ross.

Araujo, Juan S., tr. see Cho, Paul Y. & Manzano, R. Whitney.

Araujo, Juan S., tr. see Cunningham, Loren & Rogers, Janice.

Araujo, Juan S., tr. see Fleming, Jean.

Araujo, Juan S., tr. see Ortiz, Juan Carlos.

Araujo, Juan S., tr. see Swindoll, Charles R.

Araujo, Juan S., tr. see Wilkerson, Don & Manuel, David.

Araya, Victorio. God of the Poor. Barr, Robert R., tr. from Span. 224p. (Orig.). 1987. 19.95 (ISBN 0-88344-566-2); pap. 9.95 (ISBN 0-88344-565-4). Orbis Bks.

Arber, Agnes. Manifold & the One. 1967. pap. 1.45 (ISBN 0-8356-0018-1, Quest). Theos Pub Hse.

Arber, Edward, ed. see Latimer, Hugh.

Arberry, A. J. Doctrine of the Sufis. 12.95 (ISBN 0-686-18608-7). Kazi Pubns.

--The Doctrine of the Sufis. 1966. 12.95x (ISBN 0-87902-195-0). Orientalia.

Arberry, A. J., ed. & tr. Al-Niffari, Muhammad ibn'Abdi 'L-Jabbar. 276p. 1985. Repr. of 1978 ed. 50.00x (ISBN 0-317-39030-9, Pub. by Luzac & Co Ltd). State Mutual Bk.

Arberry, Arthur J. Aspects of Islamic Civilization As Depicted in the Original Texts. LC 77-673. 1977. Repr. of 1964 ed. lib. bdg. 29.25x (ISBN 0-8371-9494-6, ARAI). Greenwood.

--Aspects of Islamic Civilization as Depicted in the Original Text. 1967. pap. 9.95 (ISBN 0-472-06130-5, 130, AA). U of Mich Pr.
--The Doctrine of the Sufis. LC 76-58075. 1977. pap. 13.95 (ISBN 0-521-29218-2). Cambridge U Pr.
--Religion in the Middle East, 2 Vols. LC 68-21187. (Illus.). 1969. Set. 105.00 (ISBN 0-521-07400-2). Vol. 1. 62.50 (ISBN 0-521-20543-3); Vol. 2. 59.50 (ISBN 0-521-20544-1). Cambridge U Pr.
--Revelation & Reason in Islam. LC 80-1936. (BCL: Series I & II). Repr. of 1957 ed. 20.00 (ISBN 0-404-18952-0). AMS Pr.
Arberry, Arthur J., tr. see Avicenna.
Arberry, Arthur J., tr. see Kalabadhi, Muhammed.
Arbit, Bruce, jt. ed. see Berliant, Howard M.
Arbour, Basil. The Final Gift: A New Way of the Cross. (Illus.). 64p. 1981. pap. 2.95 (ISBN 0-86683-647-0, HarpR). Har-Row.
--Time Out: Prayers for Busy People. 96p. 1984. pap. 3.95 (ISBN 0-86683-828-7, HarpR). Har-Row.
Arbuckle, Gerald A. Strategies for Growth in Religious Life. LC 86-17359. 240p. (Orig.). 1986. pap. 11.95 (ISBN 0-8189-0505-0). Alba.
Arbuckle, Gwendolyne & Wolcott, Carolyn. Paul: Adventurer for Christ. (Illus.). 96p. (Orig.). 1984. pap. 5.50 (ISBN 0-687-30487-3). Abingdon.
Arbuthnot, George, ed. Vestry Minute Book of the Parish of Stratford-on-Avon from 1617 to 1699. LC 72-142244. Repr. of 1899 ed. 11.50 (ISBN 0-404-00366-4). AMS Pr.
Arce, Sergio. The Church & Socialism. 200p. pap. text ed. 6.95 (ISBN 0-936123-00-1). NY Circus Pubns.
Archbishop Athanasius Martos. Religioznaya Tchuvstvo, Promisl Bozhil i Dukovnoje Prizvanije. Tr. of Religious Feeling, the Providence of God & Spiritual Calling. 30p. 1983. pap. 2.00 (ISBN 0-317-29069-X). Holy Trinity.
Archbishop Averky Taushev. O Monashistvje. Tr. of On Monasticism. 46p. pap. 2.00 (ISBN 0-317-29064-9). Holy Trinity.
--Provozvjestnik Karl Bozhijej Russkomy Narodu. Tr. of The Prophet of the Wrath of God upon the Russian People. 30p. 1968. pap. 1.00 (ISBN 0-317-29066-5). Holy Trinity.
--Rukovodstvo k Izuchjeniju Svjashchennago Pisanija Novago Zavjeta-Tchetvjerojevangelija. Tr. of A Guide for Study of the Holy Scriptures of the New Testament-The Four Gospels. 345p. 1974. pap. text ed. 12.00 (ISBN 0-317-29299-4). Holy Trinity.
--Rukovodstvo po Gomiletikje. Tr. of Handbook for Homiletics. 110p. 1961. pap. text ed. 5.00 (ISBN 0-317-30276-0). Holy Trinity.
--Visokopreosvjashennij Theofan, Arkhiepiskop Poltavsky i Perejaslavsky. Tr. of His Eminance Theophan, Archbishop of Poltava & Perejaslavl. 88p. 1974. pap. 5.00 (ISBN 0-317-29284-6). Holy Trinity.
Archbishop Konstantine Zaitsev. Pamjati Igumena Fillimona. Tr. of In Memory of Igumen Philimon. 58p. 1954. pap. 2.00 (ISBN 0-317-29287-0). Holy Trinity.
Archbishop Metodies. O Znamjenii Obnovlenija Svatykh Ikon. Tr. of On the Signs of the Renewing of Holy Icons. 82p. 1963. pap. 3.00 (ISBN 0-317-29041-X). Holy Trinity.
Archbishop Nikon Rklitsky, ed. Zhizneopisanie i Tvorenije Blazhennejshago Antonia, Mitropolita Kievskago i Galitzkago, v 17 tomakh, 17 vols. Tr. of The Life & Works of His Beatitude Anthony, Metropolitan of Kiev & Galitch. 6000p. 1971. pap. 200.00 (ISBN 0-317-29015-0). Holy Trinity.
Archbishop of York. Palmer's Bible Atlas (Facsimile Edition) 84p. 1982. 14.95 (ISBN 0-686-43010-7, Carta Pub Isreal). Hippocrene Bks.
Archbishop Vitaly Maximenko. Motivi Moijej Zhizni. Tr. of Motives of My Life. 205p. 1955. pap. 7.00 (ISBN 0-317-29054-1). Holy Trinity.
Archdiocese of Baltimore Staff. Partners in Catechesis. 96p. 1984. pap. 9.95 (ISBN 0-697-02016-9). Wm C Brown.
Archdiocese of Dubuque Staff. R. C. I. A. Foundations of Christian Initiation. 96p. 1982. wire coil 7.95 (ISBN 0-697-01781-8). Wm C Brown.
Archdiocese of Newark, Office of Pastoral Renewal Staff. Renew, Leadership Book. 1980. write for info. (ISBN 0-8091-9195-4). Paulist Pr.
--Renew, Parish Book. 1980. write for info. (ISBN 0-8091-9191-1). Paulist Pr.
--Renew, Participant Book: Empowerment by the Spirit. 1980. write for info. (ISBN 0-8091-9194-6). Paulist Pr.
--Renew, Participant Book: Our Response. 1980. write for info. (ISBN 0-8091-9193-8). Paulist Pr.
--Renew, Participant Book: The Lord's Call. 1980. write for info. (ISBN 0-8091-9192-X). Paulist Pr.
--Renew, Pastoral Staff Book. 1980. write for info. (ISBN 0-8091-9196-2). Paulist Pr.
Archdiocese of Newark Staff. Growing in Faith with Your Child. Ivory, Thomas P., ed. Tr. of Cresciendo en Fe con su Nino. 48p. (Orig.). pap. 2.95 (ISBN 0-697-01693-5). Wm C Brown.
Archenti, Augustine & Petrini, Arnold. Every Day with Saint Francis de Sales. Klauder, Francis, ed. Cornell, W. L., tr. from Italian. LC 85-72838. Tr. of Buon Giorno. (Illus.). 390p. (Orig.). 1985. pap. 11.95 (ISBN 0-89944-082-7). Don Bosco Multimedia.
Archer, Gleason L. The Encyclopedia of Bible Difficulties. 352p. 1982. 19.95 (ISBN 0-310-43570-6, 112252). Zondervan.
--Resena Critica De Una Introduccion al Antiguo Testament (Survey of Old Testament Introduction) (Span.). 507p. 1982. pap. 14.95 (ISBN 0-8254-1033-9). Kregel.
--A Survey of Old Testament Introduction. LC 64-20988. 582p. 1973. 16.95 (ISBN 0-8024-8447-6). Moody.
Archer, Gleason L. & Chirichigno, G. C. Old Testament Quotations in the New Testament: A Complete Survey. 1983. 21.95 (ISBN 0-8024-0236-4). Moody.
Archer, Gleason L., tr. see Ahmanson, John.
Archer, Gleason L., Jr. The Book of Job: God's Answer to the Problem of Undeserved Suffering. 128p. (Orig.). 1983. pap. 5.95 (ISBN 0-8010-0190-0). Baker Bk.
Archer, Gleason L., Jr., ed. & frwd. by see Jones, Alfred.
Archer, John C. Faiths Men Live by. facsimile ed. LC 79-156606. (Essay Index Reprint Ser). Repr. of 1934 ed. 25.50 (ISBN 0-8369-2266-2). Ayer Co Pubs.
--Mystical Elements in Mohammed. LC 80-26396. (Yale Oriental Ser. Researches: No. 11 Pt. 1; All Published). Repr. of 1924 ed. 22.50 (ISBN 0-404-60281-9). AMS Pr.
Archer, Jr., et al. The Expositor's Bible Commentary, Vol. 7. 1986. 24.95 (ISBN 0-88469-194-2). BMH Bks.
Archer, Mildred, ed. see Archer, William G.
Archer, Raymond L. Muhammadan Mysticism in Sumatra. LC 77-87487. (Royal Asiatic Society, Malayan Branch. Journal: Vol. 15). Repr. of 1937 ed. 16.50 (ISBN 0-404-16695-4). AMS Pr.
Archer, T. A. The Crusades. 1894. 15.00 (ISBN 0-8482-7265-X). Norwood Edns.
Archer, Thomas A. The Crusade of Richard I, 1189-92. LC 76-29828. Repr. of 1889 ed. 65.00 (ISBN 0-404-15408-5). AMS Pr.
Archer, Thomas A. & Kingsford, Charles L. The Crusades: The Story of the Latin Kingdom of Jerusalem. LC 76-29833. Repr. of 1900 ed. 39.50 (ISBN 0-404-15409-3). AMS Pr.
Archer, William G. Songs for the Bride: Wedding Rites of Rural India. Miller, Barbara S. & Archer, Mildred, eds. (Studies in Oriental Culture). 224p. 1985. 22.50x (ISBN 0-317-18769-4). Brooklyn Coll Pr.
Archibald, Robert R. An Economic History of the California Missions. (Monograph). 1977. 25.00 (ISBN 0-88382-063-3). AAFH.
Archilla, Rogelio. Meditaciones Sobre el Padrenuestro. (Span.). 96p. 1984. pap. 3.95 (ISBN 0-311-40046-9, Edit Mundo). Casa Bautista.
Archimandrite Amvrossy Pogodin. Svjatoj Mark Efesskij i Florentijskaja Unia. Tr. of St. Mark of Ephesus & the Unia of Florence. 436p. (Orig.). 1963. pap. 15.00x (ISBN 0-88465-026-X). Holy Trinity.
Archimandrite Anthony Yamshcikov, ed. Sovremennost' v svjetje Slova Bozhija - Slove i Rechi Arkiepiskopa Averkija, 4 vols. Tr. of Comtemporaneity in Light of the Word of God - the Works & Writings of Archbishop Averky. 2100p. 1976. 89.00 (ISBN 0-317-29057-6); pap. 69.00 (ISBN 0-317-29058-4). Holy Trinity.
Archimandrite Kallistos Ware, jt. tr. see Mother Mary.
Archimandrite Lazarus Moore, tr. see Brianchianinov, Ignatius.
Archimandrite Simeon. Ijevangel'skije Poichjenija. Tr. of Lessons from the Gospel. 40p. 1970. pap. 2.00 (ISBN 0-317-29123-8). Holy Trinity.
Architectural Record Magazine Staff. Religious Buildings. 1980. 43.50 (ISBN 0-07-002342-5). McGraw.
Archpriest Boris Molchanov. Antikhrist. Tr. of The Antichrist. 24p. 1976. pap. 1.00 (ISBN 0-317-29128-9). Holy Trinity.
--Epokha Apostasii. Tr. of The Epoch of Apostasy. 24p. 1976. pap. 1.00 (ISBN 0-317-29125-4). Holy Trinity.
Archpriest John Vostorgov. O Monashestvje. Tr. of On Monasticism. 48p. 1969. pap. 2.00 (ISBN 0-317-29004-5). Holy Trinity.
Archpriest Kyrill Zaits. Tserkov' Boga Ahivago, Stolp i Utverzhdjenije Istini. Tr. of The Church of the Living God, Piller & Affirmation of Truth. 92p. 1956. pap. 2.00 (ISBN 0-317-29113-0). Holy Trinity.
Archpriest Michael Bogoslovsky. Prigotovlenije k Ispovjedi i Blagogvejnomy Prithashcheniju Svijatikh Khristvikh Tajin. Tr. of Preporation for Confession & the Receiving of the Holy Mysteries. 169p. pap. 8.00 (ISBN 0-317-29105-X). Holy Trinity.
Archpriest Michael Kheraskov & Athanasiev, D. Rukovodstvo k Izucheniju Svijashchennago Pisanija Vjetkhago Zavjeta, 3 vols. Tr. of A Guide for Study of the Holy Scriptures of the Old Testament. 942p. pap. text ed. 32.00 (ISBN 0-317-29295-1). Holy Trinity.
Archpriest Mitrophan Znosko-Borovsky. Iz Missionersko-pastirskoj dejatel'nosti na Nivje Khristovoj v Emigratsii. Tr. of From My Missionary-Pastoral Activities in Christ's Field in the Immigration. 320p. 1985. pap. 12.00 (ISBN 0-317-29117-3). Holy Trinity.
Ardalan, Nader & Bakhtiar, laleh. The Sense of Unity: The Sufi Tradition in Persian Architecture. LC 72-92278. (Illus.). xx, 152p. 1986. pap. 29.95 (ISBN 0-226-02560-8). U of Chicago Pr.
Are, Thomas L. Faithsong: A New Look at the Ministry of Music. LC 81-4789. 96p. 1981. pap. 6.95 (ISBN 0-664-24375-4). Westminster.
--The Gospel for the Clockaholic. 128p. 1985. pap. 5.95 (ISBN 0-8170-1075-0). Judson.
Arendt, Hannah. Antisemitism. LC 66-22273. Orig. Title: Origins of Totalitarianism, Pt. 1. 136p. 1968. pap. 3.95 (ISBN 0-15-607810-4, HB131, Harv). HarBraceJ.
--Eichmann in Jerusalem: A Report of the Banality of Evil. rev ed. 1977. pap. 6.95 (ISBN 0-14-004450-7). Penguin.
--Lectures on Kant's Political Philosophy. Beiner, Ronald, ed. LC 82-4817. 192p. 1982. 17.50 (ISBN 0-226-02594-2). U of Chicago Pr.
--Rahel Varnhagen: The Life of a Jewish Woman. Winston, Richard & Winston, Clara, trs. from Ger. LC 74-6478. (Illus.). 236p. 1974. pap. 7.95 (ISBN 0-15-676100-9, Harv). HarBraceJ.
Arendt, Hannah, ed. see Jaspers, Karl.
Arendzen, J. P. Purgatory & Heaven. (Canterbury Ser.). 1972. pap. 2.00 (ISBN 0-89555-045-8). TAN Bks Pubs.
Ares, Jacques d' Encyclopedie de l'Esoterisme, 1: Mythologies. (Fr.). 232p. 1975. pap. 19.95 (ISBN 0-686-56898-2, M-6008). French & Eur.
--Encyclopedie De l'Esoterisme1risme, 2: Religions Non Chretiennes. Jacques D'ares. (Fr.). 244p. 1975. pap. 19.95 (ISBN 0-686-56899-0, M-6009). French & Eur.
Argenti, Philip P. The Occupation of Chios by the Genoese & Their Administration of the Island, 1346-1566, 3 vols. LC 78-63339. (The Crusades & Military Orders: Second Ser.). Repr. of 1958 ed. Set. 120.00 (ISBN 0-404-17000-5); 40.00 ea. AMS Pr.
Arguelles, Jose. The Mayan Factor: Path Beyond Technology. (Illus.). 160p. (Orig.). 1987. pap. 10.95 (ISBN 0-939680-38-6). Bear & Co.
Arguelles, Jose & Arguelles, Miriam. Mandala. LC 70-189856. (Illus.). 144p. 1972. pap. 14.95 (ISBN 0-87773-033-4, 73000-3). Shambhala Pubns.
Arguelles, Miriam, jt. auth. see Arguelles, Jose.
Argyle, Aubrey W., ed. Gospel According to Matthew. (Cambridge Bible Commentary on the New Testament Ser.). (Orig.). 1963. o. p. 19.95 (ISBN 0-521-04197-X); pap. 10.95 (ISBN 0-521-09198-5). Cambridge U Pr.
Argyle, Michael & Beit-Hallahmi, Benjamin. Social Psychology of Religion. 1975. 25.00x (ISBN 0-7100-7997-4); pap. 10.95X (ISBN 0-7100-8043-3). Methuen Inc.
Arian, Philip, jt. auth. see Eisenberg, Azriel.
Ariarajah, Wesley & Thomas, T. K. The Way of Dialogue: Christians & People of Other Faiths. 40p. (Orig.). 1986. pap. 4.50 (ISBN 0-377-00164-3). Friend Pr.
Arias, Mortimer. Announcing the Reign of God: Evangelization & the Subversive Memory of Jesus. LC 83-5696. 176p. 1984. pap. 8.95 (ISBN 0-8006-1712-6, 1-1712). Fortress.
Arichea, D. C., Jr. & Nida, E. A. Translator's Handbook on Paul's Letter to the Galatians. LC 79-115359. (Helps for Translators Ser.). 176p. Repr. of 1976 ed. soft cover 3.65x (ISBN 0-8267-0142-6, 08527, Pub. by United Bible). Am Bible.
Aridas, Chris. Discernment: Seeking God in Every Situation. 120p. (Orig.). 1981. pap. 3.50 (ISBN 0-914544-37-3). Living Flame Pr.
--Reconciliation: Celebrating God's Healing Forgiveness. LC 87-5344. 160p. 1987. pap. 3.95 (ISBN 0-385-24022-8, Im). Doubleday.
Aridas, Christopher. Soundings: A Thematic Guide for Daily Scripture Prayer. LC 83-16509. 224p. 1984. pap. 4.50 (ISBN 0-385-19157-X, Im). Doubleday.
--Your Catholic Wedding: A Complete Plan-Book. LC 81-43250. (Illus.). 192p. 1982. pap. 2.95 (ISBN 0-385-17731-3, Im). Doubleday.
Arienda, Roger & Roque, Marichelle. Libre Dentro de la Carcel. (Span.). 176p. 1986. pap. 2.95 (ISBN 0-311-46102-6). Casa Bautista.
Aries, Philippe. Images of Man & Death. Lloyd, Janet, tr. from Fr. LC 85-768. (Illus.). 271p. 1985. 35.00 (ISBN 0-674-44410-8). Harvard U Pr.
--Western Attitudes Toward Death: From the Middle Ages to the Present. Ranum, Patricia, tr. from Fr. LC 73-19340. (Symposia in Comparative History Ser). (Illus.). 122p. 1974. pap. 4.95x (ISBN 0-8018-1762-5). Johns Hopkins.
Arieti, James A., jt. ed. see Stump, Donald V.
Arieti, James A. & Crossett, John M., trs. Longinus: On the Sublime. LC 84-25435. (Studies in Art & Religious Interpretation: Vol.21). 275p. 1985. 59.95x (ISBN 0-88946-554-1). E Mellen.
Arieti, Silvano. Abraham & the Contemporary Mind. LC 80-68187. 187p. 1981. 14.95 (ISBN 0-465-00005-3). Basic.
Ariew, Roger, ed. see Duhem, Pierre.
Arif of Herat. The Book of Ecstacy. Greenshields, R. S., tr. 1980. 9.95 (ISBN 0-900860-74-X, Pub. by Octagon Pr England). Ins Study Human.
Aringhi, Paolo. The Catacombs of Rome, 2 vols. (Printed Sources of Western Ser.). (Lat., Illus.). 1981. pap. 120.00 slipcase (ISBN 0-915346-61-3). A Wofsy Fine Arts.
Arintero, John G. Mystical Evolution, 2 vols. Aumann, Jordan, tr. from Sp. LC 78-62254. Orig. Title: La Evolucion Mistica. 1979. Set. pap. 24.00 (ISBN 0-89555-071-7); Vol. I. pap. (ISBN 0-89555-072-5); Vol. II. pap. (ISBN 0-89555-073-3). TAN Bks Pubs.
Aristotelian Society for the Systematic Study of Philosophy Staff. Relativity, Logic & Mysticism: Proceedings, Supplementary Vol. 3. 14.00 (ISBN 0-384-50269-5); pap. 9.00. Johnson Repr.
--Science History & Theology: Proceedings, Suppl. 14. 13.00 (ISBN 0-384-54410-X); pap. 8.00 (ISBN 0-384-54411-8). Johnson Repr.
Aristotle. Athenian Constitution. Bd. with Eudemian Ethics, Bks 1-3, 7 & 8; Virtues & Vices. (Loeb Classical Library: No. 285). 13.95x (ISBN 0-674-99315-2). Harvard U Pr.
--Ethics. Warrington, John, tr. 1975. Repr. of 1963 ed. 12.95x (ISBN 0-460-00547-2, Evman). Biblio Dist.
--Nicomachean Ethics. Ostwald, Martin, tr. LC 62-15690. (Orig.). 1962. pap. 6.65 scp (ISBN 0-672-60256-3, LLA75). Bobbs.
--Nicomachean Ethics. (Loeb Classical Library: No. 73). 13.95x (ISBN 0-674-99081-1). Harvard U Pr.
--The Nicomachean Ethics. Apostle, Hippocrates G., tr. LC 75-5871. (Synthese Historical Library: No. 13). 372p. 1975. lib. bdg. 71.00 (ISBN 90-277-0569-0, Pub. by Reidel Holland). Kluwer Academic.
Arjmand, Mihdi. Gulshan-i Haqayiq. (Persian.). 320p. 1982. Repr. 12.95 (ISBN 0-933770-15-4). Kalimat.
Arjomand, Said A. The Shadow of God & the Hidden Iman: Religion, Political Order & Societal Change in Shi'ite Iran from the Beginning to 1890. LC 83-27196. (Publications of the Center for the Middle Eastern Studies: No. 17). (Illus.). xii, 356p. 1984. lib. bdg. 28.00x (ISBN 0-226-02782-1). U of Chicago Pr.
--The Shadow of God & the Hidden Inam: Religion, Political Order, & Societal Change in Shl'ite Iran from the Beginning to 1890. LC 83-27196. (Publications of the Center for Middle Eastern Studies: No. 117). (Illus.). 344p. 1987. lib. bdg. price not set; pap. text ed. price not set (ISBN 0-226-02784-8). U of Chicago Pr.
Arkes, Hadley. First Things: An Inquiry into the First Principles of Morals & Justice. LC 85-43267. 480p. 1986. text ed. 45.00 (ISBN 0-691-07702-9); pap. 9.95 (ISBN 0-691-02247-X). Princeton U Pr.
Arkin, Alan. Halfway Through the Door: First Steps on a Path of Enlightenment. LC 83-48415. 112p. 1984. pap. 5.95 (ISBN 0-06-060307-0, CN 4094, HarpR). Har-Row.
Arkush, Allan, tr. see Mendelssohn, Moses.
Arkush, Allan, tr. see Scholem, Gershom.
Arledge, Byron W. Laugh with Your Teenager. 128p. 1985. pap. 4.95 (ISBN 0-8423-2102-0). Tyndale.
Arlington, R. Rene, jt. auth. see Murphy, Paul I.
Armajani, Yahya, tr. see Elder, John.
Armas, Frederick A. de see De Armas, Frederick A.
Armbrister, David, jt. auth. see Brown, Jack.
Armbruster, Wally. A Bag of Noodles. (Illus.). (YA) 1973. pap. 3.95 (ISBN 0-570-03158-3, 12-2543). Concordia.
--Let Me Out: I'm a Prisoner in a Stained Glass Jail. LC 85-11561. 1985. pap. 6.95 (ISBN 0-88070-111-0). Multnomah.
Armeding, Carl E. The Old Testament & Criticism. 144p. 1983. pap. 6.95 (ISBN 0-8028-1951-6). Eerdmans.
Armentrout, Donald S., ed. see DuBose, William P.

Armerding, Hudson T. A Word to the Wise. 1980. pap. 3.95 (ISBN 0-8423-0099-6). Tyndale.
Armistead, Samuel G. & Silverman, Joseph H. Folk-Literature of the Sephardic Jews, Vol. 1. The Judeo-Spanish Ballad Chapbooks of Yacob Abraham Yona. LC 71-78565. 1971. 60.00x (ISBN 0-520-01648-3). U of Cal Pr.
Armour, Robert. God & Myths of Ancient Egypt. 1986. pap. 15.00 (ISBN 977-424-113-4, Pub. by Am Univ Cairo Pr). Columbia U Pr.
Armour, Rollin S. Anabaptist Baptism. LC 66-19026. (Study in Anabaptist & Mennonite History No. 11). 1966. 16.95x (ISBN 0-8361-1178-8). Herald Pr.
Armstrog, William H. Minister Heal Thyself. 64p. (Orig.). 1985. pap. 4.95 (ISBN 0-8298-0551-6). Pilgrim NY.
Armstrong, A. H. An Introduction to Ancient Philosophy. 3rd ed. LC 81-3731. (Quality Paperback Ser.: No. 418). 260p. 1981. pap. 7.45 (ISBN 0-8226-0418-3). Littlefield.
Armstrong, A. H., ed. Classical Mediterranean Spirituality. (World Spirituality Ser.). 499p. 1986. 49.50x (ISBN 0-8245-0764-9). Crossroad NY.
Armstrong, Allen. Belief, Truth & Knowledge. LC 72-83586. 240p. 1973. 42.50 (ISBN 0-521-08706-6); pap. 13.95 (ISBN 0-521-09737-1). Cambridge U Pr.
Armstrong, Anne see Armstrong, Terry R.
Armstrong, Brian G. Calvinism & the Amyraut Heresy: Protestant Scholasticism & Humanism in Seventeenth-Century France. LC 72-84949. (Illus.). 350p. 1969. 30.00 (ISBN 0-299-05490-X). U of Wis Pr.
Armstrong, C. F. Hymns for Little Children. 1977. lib. bdg. 59.95 (ISBN 0-8490-2030-1). Gordon Pr.
Armstrong, Christopher. Evelyn Underhill: Eighteen Seventy-Five to Nineteen Forty-One: An Introduction to Her Life & Writing. LC 75-33401. Repr. of 1976 ed. 81.80 (ISBN 0-8357-9127-0, 2012859). Bks Demand UMI.
Armstrong, D., et al. The Old Church Slavonic Translation of the Andron Hagion Biblos in the Edition of Nikolas Van Wijk. Van Schooneveld, C. H., ed. (Slavistic Printings & Reprintings Ser: No. 1). 310p. 1975. text ed. 67.20x (ISBN 90-2793-196-8). Mouton.
Armstrong, D. Wade. Evangelistic Growth in Acts One & Two. LC 83-70375. (Orig.). 1983. pap. 4.95 (ISBN 0-8054-6242-2). Broadman.
Armstrong, David M., ed. see Berkeley, George.
Armstrong, Edward A. St. Francis, Nature Mystic: The Derivation & Significance of the Nature Stories in the Franciscan Legend. LC 74-149949. (Hermeneutics: Studies in the History of Religions). 1973. pap. 5.95 (ISBN 0-520-03040-0, CAL 314). U of Cal Pr.
Armstrong, Garner T. The Real Jesus. 1983. pap. 2.25 (ISBN 0-380-40055-3, 40055-3). Avon.
Armstrong, George. The Zionists. 1982. lib. bdg. 69.95 (ISBN 0-87700-341-6). Revisionist Pr.
Armstrong, George D. Christian Doctrine of Slavery. LC 69-16595. Repr. of 1857 ed. 22.50x (ISBN 0-8371-0892-6, ARC&, Pub. by Negro U Pr). Greenwood.
Armstrong, Gregory, ed. see Roman, Sanaya & Packer, Duane.
Armstrong, Helen, jt. ed. see Armstrong, O. V.
Armstrong, Hylma, jt. auth. see Armstrong, Max.
Armstrong, James A. From the Underside: Evangelism from a Third World Vantage Point. LC 81-9509. 112p. (Orig.). 1981. pap. 4.95 (ISBN 0-88344-146-2). Orbis Bks.
Armstrong, Janice G., jt. auth. see Pike, Martha V.
Armstrong, John. The Idea of Holiness & the Humane Response: A Study of the Concept of Holiness & Its Social Consequences. 177p. 1982. 16.95 (ISBN 0-04-200042-4). Allen Unwin.
Armstrong, Karen. Gospel According to Woman. LC 86-26610. 384p. 1987. 17.95 (ISBN 0-385-24078-3, Anchor Pr). Doubleday.
--Through the Narrow Gate. 288p. 1981. 12.95 (ISBN 0-312-80383-4). St Martin.
Armstrong, Karen, ed. Tongues of Fire: An Anthology of Religious & Poetic Experience. 444p. 1986. 19.95 (ISBN 0-670-80878-4). Viking.
Armstrong, Larry. Disaster & Deliverance. LC 79-88400. 1979. pap. 3.75 (ISBN 0-933350-22-8). Morse Pr.
Armstrong, Mark, jt. auth. see Gebhardt, Richard F.
Armstrong, Martin. Jeremy Taylor: A Selection from His Works. 1973. lib. bdg. 15.00 (ISBN 0-8414-1165-4). Folcroft.
--Lady Hester Stanhope. (Women Ser.). 1928. 17.50 (ISBN 0-8482-7275-7). Norwood Edns.
Armstrong, Max & Armstrong, Hylma. A Conscience Is... (I'm Growing Up Ser.). (Illus.). 32p. 1986. casebound 3.95 (ISBN 0-87403-122-2, 3602). Standard Pub.
Armstrong, O. V., compiled by. Comfort for Those Who Mourn. LC 77-17182. pap. 20.00 (ISBN 0-8357-9003-7, 2016353). Bks Demand UMI.
Armstrong, O. V. & Armstrong, Helen, eds. Prayer Poems. facsimile ed. LC 72-86793. (Granger Index Reprint Ser). 1942. 16.00 (ISBN 0-8369-6094-7). Ayer Co Pubs.
Armstrong, Regis J. & Brady, Ignatius C., eds. Francis & Clare: The Complete Works. (Classics of Western Spirituality Ser.). 1983. pap. 8.95 (ISBN 0-8091-2446-7). Paulist Pr.
Armstrong, Richard A. Agnosticism & Theism in the Nineteenth Century. 1977. lib. bdg. 59.95 (ISBN 0-8490-1406-9). Gordon Pr.
Armstrong, Richard S. The Pastor As Evangelist. LC 84-10359. 202p. 1984. pap. 9.95 (ISBN 0-664-24556-0). Westminster.
--The Pastor-Evangelist in Worship. LC 85-26380. 216p. (Orig.). 1986. pap. 9.95 (ISBN 0-664-24693-1). Westminster.
--Service Evangelism. LC 78-26701. 198p. 1979. pap. 8.95 (ISBN 0-664-24252-9). Westminster.
Armstrong, Robert C. Light from the East: Studies in Japanese Confucianism. lib. bdg. 79.95 (ISBN 0-87968-134-9). Krishna Pr.
Armstrong, Sue. Who Do you Think You Are. 1983. 24.00x (ISBN 0-86334-046-6, Pub. by Macdonald Pub UK). State Mutual Bk.
Armstrong, Terry, et al, eds. A Reader's Hebrew-English Lexicon of the Old Testament: Genesis-II Kings. (Hebrew & Eng.). 1982. 16.95 (ISBN 0-310-37040-X, 6291). Zondervan.
Armstrong, Terry A., et al. Reader's Hebrew-English Lexicon of the Old Testament: Isaiah-Malachi, Vol. 3. 208p. 1985. 14.95 (ISBN 0-310-37010-8, 6293). Zondervan.
Armstrong, Terry R., ed. Planning to Stay Together. Armstrong, Anne. 1980. pap. 1.99 (ISBN 0-8309-0308-9). Herald Hse.
Armstrong, William. Health, Happiness, Humor & Holiness: As Seen Through Children's Eyes. Graves, Helen, ed. (Illus.). 150p. 1987. pap. text ed. 6.95 (ISBN 1-55523-065-2). Winston-Derek.
Armstrong, William H. Through Troubled Waters: A Young Father's Struggles with Grief. 96p. (Orig.). 1983. pap. 3.35 (ISBN 0-687-41895-X, Festival). Abingdon.
Armstrong, William H., ed. see Smith, Edward P.
Armstrong, William P., ed. Calvin & the Reformation: Four Studies. (Twin Brooks Ser.). 1980. pap. 6.95 (ISBN 0-8010-2901-5). Baker Bk.
Armstrong, Wm. Benedictine Cartoons. (Armstrong Cartoon Ser.). (Illus., Orig.). 1973. pap. 1.00 (ISBN 0-913452-25-4). Jesuit Bks.
--Clerical Cartoons. 2nd ed. (Armstrong Cartoon Ser.). (Illus.). 48p. (Orig.). 1971. pap. 1.00 (ISBN 0-913452-02-5). Jesuit Bks.
--Ecclesiastical Cartoons. 2nd ed. (Armstrong Cartoon Ser.). (Illus.). 48p. (Orig.). 1972. pap. 1.00 (ISBN 0-913452-08-4). Jesuit Bks.
--Franciscan Cartoons. (Armstrong Cartoon Ser.). (Illus., Orig.). 1974. pap. 1.00 (ISBN 0-913452-24-6). Jesuit Bks.
Arn, Winfield, jt. auth. see McGavran, Donald.
Arn, Winfield C., jt. auth. see McGavran, Donald A.
Arnal, Oscar L. Priests in Working Class Blue: The History of the Worker-Priests, (1943-1954) 248p. (Orig.). 1986. pap. 11.95 (ISBN 0-8091-2831-4). Paulist Pr.
Arnander, Primose & Skipwith, Ashkain. The Son of a Duck is a Floater: An Illustrated Book of Arab Proverbs. (Illus.). 90p. 1985. 7.95 (ISBN 0-905743-41-5, Pub. by Stacey Intl UK). Humanities.
Arnandez, Richard, tr. see De Lubac, Henri.
Arnandez, Richard, tr. see Manteau-Bonamy, H. M.
Arnason, Wayne. Follow the Gleam. 1980. pap. 3.50 (ISBN 0-933840-07-1). Unitarian Univ.
Arnauld, Antoine. The Arrainment of the Whole Societie of Jesuites in Fraunce: Holden-the Twelfth & Thirteenth of July, 1594. LC 79-84084. (English Experience Ser.: No. 904). 68p. 1979. Repr. of 1594 ed. lib. bdg. 8.00 (ISBN 0-686-71069-X). Walter J Johnson.
Arndt, Andreas, ed. see Schleiermacher, Friedrich D.
Arndt, Elise. A Mother's Touch. 156p. 1983. pap. 5.95 (ISBN 0-88207-101-7). Victor Bks.
Arndt, Herman. Why Did Jesus Fast? 87p. 1962. pap. 7.95 (ISBN 0-88697-039-3). Life Science.
Arndt, Karl J. George Rapp's Successors & Material Heirs: 1847-1916. LC 76-147268. (Illus.). 445p. 1972. 45.00 (ISBN 0-8386-7889-0). Fairleigh Dickinson.
Arndt, Karl J. R. George Rapp's Harmony Society: 1785-1847. rev. ed. LC 72-147267. (Illus.). 713p. 1972. 45.00 (ISBN 0-8386-7888-2). Fairleigh Dickinson.
Arndt, Rick. Athletes Afire. LC 85-71182. 1985. pap. 3.50 (ISBN 0-88270-590-3). Bridge Pub.
--Winning with Christ. 1982. pap. 4.95 (ISBN 0-570-03627-5, 39-1073). Concordia.
Arndt, William. Fundamental Christian Beliefs. pap. text ed. 3.25 (ISBN 0-570-06324-8, 22-1144); pap. 3.75 guide (ISBN 0-570-06325-6, 22-1146); pap. tests 1.50 (ISBN 0-570-06362-0, 22-1145). Concordia.
Arndt, William F. Bible Difficulties & Seeming Contradictions. 1987. pap. 8.95 (ISBN 0-570-04470-7). Concordia.
Arndt, William F., tr. see Bauer, Walter, et al.
Arnett, Ronald C. Dwell in Peace. 156p. (Orig.). 1980. pap. 7.95 (ISBN 0-87178-199-9). Brethren.
Arnett, Willard E. Religion & Judgment: An Essay on the Method & Meaning of Religion. LC 66-11680. (Century Philosophy Ser.). 1966. 39.50x (ISBN 0-89197-377-X). Irvington.
Arnett, Willard E., ed. Modern Reader in the Philosophy of Religion. LC 66-20470. (Century Philosophy Ser.). 1966. 39.50x (ISBN 0-89197-482-2); pap. text ed. 24.50x (ISBN 0-89197-483-0). Irvington.
Arnez, John A., intro. by. Slovenian Letters by Missionaries in America, 1851-1874. (Studia Slovenica Special Ser.: No.4). 230p. 1984. pap. 11.00 (ISBN 0-318-01454-8). Studia Slovenica.
Arnheim, Michael. Is Christianity True? LC 84-42861. (The Skeptic's Bookshelf Ser.). 198p. 1984. 20.95 (ISBN 0-87975-262-9). Prometheus Bks.
Arnim, Christian von see Steiner, Rudolf.
Arno Press Staff. Judaism & Christianity: Selected Accounts, 1892-1962. LC 73-2212. (The Jewish People; History, Religion, Literature Ser.). 22.00 (ISBN 0-405-05276-6). Ayer Co Pubs.
Arnobius, Afer. Adversvs Nationes Libri Seven, Bk. 7. (Corpus Scriptorum Ecclesiasticorum Latinorum, Vol. 4). 31.00. Johnson Repr.
Arnold, Caroline. How People Get Married. (Ceremonies & Celebrations Ser.). (Illus.). 32p. 1987. PLB 9.90 (ISBN 0-531-10096-0). Watts.
Arnold, Caroline & Silverstein, Herma. Anti-Semitism: A Modern Perspective. LC 84-16351. (Illus.). 224p. 1985. 10.79 (ISBN 0-671-49850-9). Messner.
Arnold, Charlotte. Group Readings for the Church. (Paperback Program Ser.). (Orig.). 1975. pap. 1.95 (ISBN 0-8010-0065-3). Baker Bk.
Arnold, Denis. Monteverdi Church Music. LC 81-71298. (BBC Music Guides Ser.). 64p. (Orig.). 1983. pap. 4.95 (ISBN 0-295-95923-1). U of Wash Pr.
Arnold, Dieter. The Temple of Mentuhotep at Dier El Bahari. (Publications of the Metropolitan Museum of Art Egyptian Expedition: Vol. XXI). (Illus.). 1979. 60.00 (ISBN 0-87099-163-9). Metro Mus Art.
Arnold, Duane W. & Fry, C. George. The Way, the Truth, & the Life: An Introduction to Lutheran Christianity. (Illus.). 204p. (Orig.). 1982. pap. 9.95 (ISBN 0-8010-0189-7). Baker Bk.
Arnold, E. Pearls of Faith. 319p. 1984. 60.00x (ISBN 0-317-39177-1, Pub. by Luzac & Co Ltd). State Mutual Bk.
--Pearls of the Faith: Islam's Rosary. pap. 3.50x (ISBN 0-87902-044-X). Orientalia.
Arnold, E. V. Vedic Metre in Its Historical Development. 1967. Repr. 25.00 (ISBN 0-89684-338-6). Orient Bk Dist.
Arnold, Ebehard. God's Revolution: The Witness of Eberhard Arnold. Hutterian Society of Brothers & Yoder, John H., eds. pap. 8.95 (ISBN 0-8091-2609-5). Paulist Pr.
Arnold, Eberhard. Children's Education in Community: The Basis of Bruderhof Education. Mow, Merrill, ed. LC 76-27728. 1976. pap. 3.25 (ISBN 0-87486-164-0). Plough.
--The Early Anabaptists. 2nd, rev. ed. Brethren, Hutterian, ed. LC 84-14259. Tr. of History of the Baptizers Movement. (Ger.). 64p. 1984. pap. 4.00 (ISBN 0-87486-192-6). Plough.
--Early Christians: After the Death of the Apostles. LC 70-115839. (Illus.). 1970. 13.00 (ISBN 0-87486-110-1). Plough.
--Foundation & Orders of Sannerz & the Rhon Bruderhof: Introductory History: The Basis for Our Orders, Vol. 1. LC 76-5856. 1976. pap. 2.50 (ISBN 0-87486-162-4). Plough.
--God's Revolution: The Witness of Eberhard Arnold. Hutterian Society of Brothers & Yoder, John H., eds. LC 83-62952. 230p. 1984. pap. 8.95 (Pub. by Paulist Pr). Plough.
--Innenland: Ein Wegweiser In Die Seele Der Bibel und In Den Kampf Um Die Wirklichkeit. (Ger.). 492p. 1936. 9.00 (ISBN 0-87486-150-0). Plough.
--Inner Land: A Guide into the Heart & Soul of the Bible. LC 74-30356. 608p. 1976. 12.00 (ISBN 0-87486-152-7). Plough.
--The Inner Land, Vol. 1: The Inner Life. LC 74-18434. 1975. postpaid 3.50 (ISBN 0-87486-153-5). Plough.
--The Inner Land, Vol. 2: The Struggle of the Conscience. LC 75-1335. 1975. 3.50 (ISBN 0-87486-154-3). Plough.
--The Inner Land, Vol. 3: The Experience of God. LC 75-9720. 1975. 3.50 (ISBN 0-87486-155-1). Plough.
--The Inner Land, Vol. 4: Light & Fire & the Holy Spirit. LC 75-16303. 1975. 3.50 (ISBN 0-87486-156-X). Plough.
--The Inner Land, Vol. 5: The Living Word. LC 75-33241. 1975. 3.50 (ISBN 0-87486-157-8). Plough.
--Living Churches: The Essence of Their Life - Love to Christ & Love to the Brothers, Vol. 1. LC 73-21273. 1974. pap. 2.50 (ISBN 0-87486-116-0). Plough.
--Living Churches: The Essence of Their Life - the Meaning & Power of Prayer Life, Vol. 2. LC 75-42829. 1976. pap. 2.50 (ISBN 0-87486-159-4). Plough.
--Love & Marriage in the Spirit. LC 64-24321. 1965. 7.00 (ISBN 0-87486-103-9). Plough.
--Revolution Gottes. 110p. 1984. pap. 7.00 (ISBN 3-87173-689-9). Plough.
--Salt & Light: Talks & Writings of the Sermon on the Mount. LC 77-1204. 1977. pap. 6.00 (ISBN 0-87486-170-5). Plough.
--Salt & Light: Talks & Writings on the Sermon on the Mount. LC 67-18009. 1967. 8.00 (ISBN 0-87486-105-5). Plough.
--Salt & Light: Talks & Writings on the Sermon on the Mount. rev. ed. Hutterian Brethren, ed. & tr. from Ger. 338p. 1986. pap. 6.00 (ISBN 0-87486-174-8). Plough.
--Sendbrief from the Alm Bruderhof to the Rhoen Bruderhof. LC 74-23145. 1974. pap. 2.50 (ISBN 0-87486-148-9). Plough.
--Why We Live in Community. 1976. pap. 1.50 (ISBN 0-87486-168-3). Plough.
Arnold, Eberhard & Arnold, Emmy. Seeking for the Kingdom of God: Origins of the Bruderhof Communities. LC 74-6317. 200p. 1974. 6.50 (ISBN 0-87486-133-0). Plough.
Arnold, Eberhard, et al. Else Von Hollander. LC 72-96191. 1973. 4.50 (ISBN 0-87486-111-X). Plough.
--When the Time Was Fulfilled: Talks & Writings on Advent & Christmas. LC 65-17599. 1965. 7.00 (ISBN 0-87486-104-7). Plough.
--The Heavens Are Opened. LC 73-20715. (Illus.). 190p. 1974. 8.00 (ISBN 0-87486-113-6). Plough.
Arnold, Edward V. Rigveda. LC 73-139172. (Popular Studies in Mythology, Romance & Folklore: No. 9). Repr. of 1900 ed. 5.50 (ISBN 0-404-53509-7). AMS Pr.
Arnold, Edwin. Light of Asia. LC 79-4436. 1969. pap. 4.50 (ISBN 0-8356-0405-5, Quest). Theos Pub Hse.
--The Light of Asia or, the Great Renunciation (Mahabhinishkramana) Being the Life & Teaching of Gautama, Prince of India, Founder of Buddhism. x, 176p. 1972. pap. 5.00 (ISBN 0-7100-7006-3). Methuen Inc.
--The Light of Asia: The Life & Teaching of Gautama Buddha. xi, 238p. 1977. 5.00 (ISBN 0-938998-17-X). Theosophy.
--Song Celestial. 1971. pap. 1.50 (ISBN 0-8356-0418-7, Quest). Theos Pub Hse.
Arnold, Edwin, tr. from Sanskrit. Song Celestial: Bhagavad-Gita. 176p. 1985. pap. 3.50 (ISBN 0-87612-210-1). Self Realization.
Arnold, Edwin, tr. The Song Celestial or Bhaggvad-Gita: From the Mahabharata, Being a Discourse Between Arjuna, Prince of India, & the Supreme Being under the Form of Krishna. 1967. pap. 5.00 (ISBN 0-7100-6268-0). Methuen Inc.
Arnold, Emmy. Gegen Den Strom. (Ger.). 200p. 1983. pap. 5.50 (ISBN 3-87067-206-4, Pub. by Brendow-Verlag, West Germany). Plough.
--Torches Together: The Beginning & Early Years of the Bruderhof Communities. LC 63-23426. 1971. 8.95 (ISBN 0-87486-109-8). Plough.
--Torches Together: The Beginning & Early Years of the Bruderhof Communities. Society of Brothers, tr. from Ger. LC 77-166341. (Illus.). 1976. pap. 6.00 (ISBN 0-87486-171-3). Plough.
Arnold, Emmy, jt. auth. see Arnold, Eberhard.
Arnold, Emmy, ed. Inner Words for Every Day of the Year. LC 77-164915. 1963. 3.50 (ISBN 0-87486-101-2). Plough.
Arnold, Emmy. Ein Inneres Wort Fur Jeden Tag Des Jahres. LC 76-10987. 192p. 1976. 4.50 (ISBN 0-87486-166-7). Plough.
Arnold, Heini. Freedom from Sinful Thoughts: Christ Alone Breaks the Curse. LC 73-20199. 130p. 1973. 3.50 (ISBN 0-87486-115-2). Plough.
--Freiheit Von Gedankensunden Nur Christus Bricht Den Fluch. LC 73-20198. (Ger.). 118p. 1973. text ed. 3.50. Plough.
--Give Us Burning Hearts. 36p. 1985. pap. 1.50 (ISBN 0-87486-196-9). Plough.
--In the Image of God: Marriage & Chastity in Christian Life. LC 76-53542. 1977. pap. 3.50 (ISBN 0-87486-169-1). Plough.
--Lead Us on the Way. 36p. 1985. pap. 1.50 (ISBN 0-87486-194-2). Plough.
--Make Us Ready. 36p. 1985. pap. 1.50 (ISBN 0-87486-198-5). Plough.
--Man, the Image of God & Modern Psychology. 14p. 1973. pap. 1.25 (ISBN 0-87486-176-4). Plough.
--May the Light Shine. 36p. 1985. pap. 1.50 (ISBN 0-87486-197-7). Plough.

--May Thy Light Shine: Prayers. Hutterian Brethren, ed. LC 86-9387. (Illus.). 240p. 1986. 6.00 (ISBN 0-87486-199-3, BV245.A748 1986 242.80973). Plough.
--Thine Is the Kingdom. 36p. 1985. pap. 1.50 (ISBN 0-87486-182-9). Plough.
--Thou Art the Vine. 36p. 1985. pap. 1.50 (ISBN 0-87486-178-0). Plough.
--We Are Thy Children. 36p. 1985. pap. 1.50 (ISBN 0-87486-193-4). Plough.
Arnold, Heini & Blough, Dwight. Christmas Night, O Night of Nights. 1976. pap. 1.25 (ISBN 0-87486-120-9). Plough.
Arnold, Joan, ed. see Plaskow, Judith.
Arnold, John D. & Tompkins, Bert. How to Make the Right Decisions. 1986. pap. 5.95 (ISBN 0-8010-0209-5). Baker Bk.
Arnold, L. Eugene & Estreicher, Donna G. Parent-Child Group Therapy: Building Self-Esteem in a Cognitive-Behavioral Group. LC 84-40723. 288p. 1985. 29.00 (ISBN 0-669-09934-1). Lexington Bks.
Arnold, Matthew. The Complete Prose Works of Matthew Arnold, 11 vols. Super, R. H., ed. Incl. Vol. 1. On the Classical Tradition. 282p. 1960. 19.95x (ISBN 0-472-11651-7); Vol. 2. Democratic Education. 430p. 1962. 19.95x (ISBN 0-472-11652-5); Vol. 3. Lectures & Essays in Criticism. 586p. 1962. 19.95x (ISBN 0-472-11653-3); Vol. 4. Schools & Universities on the Continent. 446p. 1964. 19.95x (ISBN 0-472-11654-1); Vol. 5. Culture & Anarchy. 580p. 1965. 19.95x (ISBN 0-472-11655-X); Vol. 6. Dissent & Dogma. 624p. 1967. 19.95x (ISBN 0-472-11656-8); Vol. 7. God & the Bible. 604p. 1970. 19.95x (ISBN 0-472-11657-6); Vol. 8. Essays Religious & Mixed. 576p. 1972. 19.95x (ISBN 0-472-11658-4); Vol. 9. English Literature & Irish Politics. 1973. 19.95x (ISBN 0-472-11659-2); Vol. 10. Philistinism in England & America. 1974. 19.95x (ISBN 0-472-11660-6); Vol. 11. The Last Word. 1976. 19.95x (ISBN 0-472-11661-4). LC 60-5018. U of Mich Pr.
--God & the Bible: A Review of Objections to "Literature & Dogma". LC 75-129382. Repr. of 1875 ed. 15.00 (ISBN 0-404-00386-9). AMS Pr.
--God & the Bible: A Review of Objections to Literature & Dogma. 1973. Repr. of 1875 ed. 14.75 (ISBN 0-8274-1704-7). R West.
--Literature & Dogma. Repr. of 1873 ed. lib. bdg. 20.00 (ISBN 0-8414-3076-4). Folcroft.
--Literature & Dogma. Livingston, James C., ed. LC 79-107032. (Milestones of Thought Ser). 1970. pap. 3.95x (ISBN 0-8044-6011-6). Ungar.
--Literature & Dogma: An Essay Towards a Better Apprehension of the Bible. LC 78-126650. 1970. Repr. of 1883 ed. 15.00 (ISBN 0-404-00387-7). AMS Pr.
--Works of Matthew Arnold, 15 Vols. LC 70-107157. 1970. Repr. of 1903 ed. Set. 395.00x (ISBN 0-403-00201-X); 40.00 ea. Scholarly.
Arnold, Oren. Junior Saints: The Rich Rare Humor of Kids in Church. LC 75-12108. (Illus.). 128p. 1976. pap. 4.95 (ISBN 0-8254-2117-9). Kregel.
--Snappy Steeple Stories. LC 79-128150. (Church Humor Series). 80p. 1970. pap. 1.95 (ISBN 0-8254-2107-1). Kregel.
Arnold, Oren, ed. More Steeple Stories. LC 77-76437. (Church Humor Series). 1969. pap. 1.95 (ISBN 0-8254-2105-5). Kregel.
Arnold, T. Preaching of Islam. 1968. 27.50x (ISBN 0-87902-045-8). Orientalia.
Arnold, T. K., tr. see Hengstenberg, E. W.
Arnold, T. W. The Old & New Testaments in Muslim Religious Art. (British Academy, London, Schweidr Lectures in Biblical Archaeology Series, 1928). pap. 19.00 (ISBN 0-8115-1270-3). Kraus Repr.
--Preaching of Islam. 32.50 (ISBN 0-686-18455-6). Kazi Pubns.
--The Preachings of Islam. 467p. 1984. Repr. of 1913 ed. text ed. 50.00x (ISBN 0-86590-250-X, Pub. by Renaissance New Delhi). Apt Bks.
Arnold, T. W. & Guillaume, A. The Legacy of Islam. 1976. lib. bdg. 75.00 (ISBN 0-8490-2141-3). Gordon Pr.
Arnold, Thomas W. Painting in Islam. (Illus.). 16.25 (ISBN 0-8446-1553-6). Peter Smith.
--The Preaching of Islam: A History of Propagation of the Muslim Faith. LC 72-180319. (Mid-East Studies). Repr. of 1913 ed. 27.50 (ISBN 0-404-56214-0). AMS Pr.
Arnold, William V. Introduction to Pastoral Care. LC 81-16092. 222p. 1982. pap. 10.95 (ISBN 0-664-24400-9). Westminster.
--The Power of Your Perceptions. LC 83-26089. (Potentials: Guides for Productive Living Ser.,: Vol. 6). 118p. (Orig.). 1984. pap. 7.95 (ISBN 0-664-24524-2). Westminster.
--When Your Parents Divorce, Vol. 1. LC 79-20055. (Christian Care Bks.). 118p. 1980. pap. 7.95 (ISBN 0-664-24294-4). Westminster.
Arnold, William V., et al. Divorce: Prevention or Survival. LC 77-22066. 128p. 1977. pap. 5.95 (ISBN 0-664-24142-5). Westminster.
Arnot, Frederick S. Garenganze or Seven Years' Pioneer Mission Work in Central Africa. 2nd, rev. ed. (Illus.). 276p. 1969. 29.50x (ISBN 0-7146-1860-8, BHA 01860, F Cass Co). Biblio Dist.
Arnot, William. The Lesser Parables of Our Lord. LC 80-8066. 464p. 1981. 12.95 (ISBN 0-8254-2121-7). Kregel.
--The Parables of Our Lord. LC 80-8065. 532p. 1981. 14.95 (ISBN 0-8254-2119-5). Kregel.
--Studies in Acts: The Church in the House. LC 78-59141. 464p. 1978. 12.95 (ISBN 0-8254-2120-9). Kregel.
--Studies in Proverbs. LC 78-6014. (Reprint Library). Orig. Title: Laws From Heaven for Life on Earth. 584p. 1986. pap. 14.95 (ISBN 0-8254-2123-3). Kregel.
Arnott, Anne. Valiant for Truth: The Story of John Bunyan. 160p. (Orig.). 1986. pap. 5.95 (ISBN 0-8028-0192-7). Eerdmans.
Arnoudt, Peter J. The Imitation of the Sacred Heart of Jesus. LC 79-112463. 1974. pap. 10.00 (ISBN 0-89555-012-1). TAN Bks Pubs.
Arnould, E. J., ed. see Henry Duke Of Lancaster.
Arnstein, Walter L. The Bradlaugh Case: Atheism, Sex, & Politics among the Late Victorians. LC 83-6814. (Illus.). 384p. 1984. text ed. 30.00x; pap. text ed. 13.50x (ISBN 0-8262-0417-1). U of Mo Pr.
--Protestant vs. Catholic in Mid-Victorian England: Mr. Newdegate & the Nuns. LC 81-11451. 272p. text ed. 20.00x (ISBN 0-8262-0354-X). U of Mo Pr.
Arntz, Mary Luke. Richard Rolle & de Holy Boke Gratia Dei: An Edition with Commentary. Hogg, James, ed. (Elizabethan & Renaissance Studies). 207p. (Orig.). 1981. pap. 15.00 (ISBN 3-7052-0743-1, Pub. by Salzburg Studies). Longwood Pub Group.
Arntzen, Sonja. Ikkyu Sojun: A Zen Monk & His Poetry. LC 73-620051. (Occasional Papers: Vol. 4). (Illus.). 171p. 1973. microfiche 1.00 (ISBN 0-914584-99-5). WWUCEAS.
Aron, Arthur, jt. auth. see Aron, Elaine.
Aron, Elaine & Aron, Arthur. The Maharishi Effect: A Revolution Through Meditation. 235p. (Orig.). 1986. pap. 9.95 (ISBN 0-913299-26-X, Dist. by NAL). Stillpoint.
Aron, Milton. Ideas & Ideals of the Hassidim. 1969. 7.95 (ISBN 0-8065-0319-X). Citadel Pr.
--Ideas & Ideals of the Hassidim. 1980. pap. 5.95 (ISBN 0-8065-0722-5). Citadel Pr.
Aronica, Paul, tr. see Bosco, St. John.
Aronin, Ben. The Secret of the Sabbath Fish. LC 78-63437. (Illus.). 1979. 5.95 (ISBN 0-8276-0110-7, 433). Jewish Pubns.
Aronoff, Carol A., ed. see Nydahl, Ole.
Aronoff, Myron J., ed. Religion & Politics. (Political Anthropology Ser.: Vol. III). 145p. 1983. 24.95 (ISBN 0-87855-459-9); pap. 12.95 (ISBN 0-87855-977-9). Transaction Bks.
Aronow, Sara. Seven Days of Creation. (Bible Stories in Rhymes Ser.: Vol. 1). (Illus.). 32p. 1985. 4.95 (ISBN 0-87203-119-5). Hermon.
Aronowicz, Annette, et al, trs. see Dumezil, Georges.
Aronsfeld, C. C. The Text of the Holocaust: A Documentation of the Nazis' Extermination Propaganda from 1919-45. 1985. 16.00 (ISBN 0-916288-17-X); pap. 10.00 (ISBN 0-916288-18-8). Micah Pubns.
Aronsfeld, Caesar C. The Ghosts of Fourteen Ninety-Two. (Conference on Jewish Social Studies). 1979. 10.00x (ISBN 0-910430-00-4, Pub by Conf Jewish Soc Studies). Columbia U Pr.
Aronson, David. Jewish Way of Life. 1957. 5.00x (ISBN 0-8381-1107-6). United Syn Bk.
Aronson, Harvey B. Love & Sympathy in Theravada Buddhism. cancelled (ISBN 0-8364-0627-3, Pub. by Motilal Banarsidass). South Asia Bks.
Arora, Ranjit. Sikhism. (Religions of the World Ser.). (Illus.). 48p. 1987. lib. bdg. 11.40 (ISBN 0-531-18067-0, Pub. by Bookwright Pr). Watts.
Arp, Claudia, jt. auth. see Arp, Dave.
Arp, Dave & Arp, Claudia. Ten Dates for Mates. LC 83-3954. 176p. 1983. pap. 7.95 (ISBN 0-8407-5845-6). Nelson.
Arpee, Leon. The Armenian Awakening. (Works of Leon Arpee Ser.). xi, 234p. 1985. Repr. of 1909 ed. 34.00 (ISBN 0-932051-67-7, Pub. by Am Repr Serv). Am Biog Serv.
Arraj, James. St. John of the Cross & Dr. C. G. Jung: Christian Mysticism in the Light of Jungian Psychology. LC 86-11315. 200p. (Orig.). 1986. pap. 11.95 (ISBN 0-914073-02-8). Tools for Inner.
Arrastia, Cecilio. Itinerario De la Pasion: Meditaciones De la Semana Santa. 1985. pap. 2.95 (ISBN 0-311-43036-8). Casa Bautista.
Ar-Razi, Al-Kulayni. Al-Kafi: The Book of Divine Proof, No. I. Rizvi, S. Muhammad, tr. from Arabic. LC 85-52242. 90p. (Orig.). 1985. pap. 12.00 (ISBN 0-940368-64-1). Tahrike Tarsile Quran.
--Al-Kafi: The Book of Divine Proof, No. V. Rizvi, S. Muhammad, tr. from Arabic. LC 85-52242. 80p. (Orig.). 1985. pap. 12.00 (ISBN 0-940368-67-6). Tahrike Tarsile Quran.
--Al-Kafi: The Book of Divine Unity. Rizvi, S. Muhammad, tr. from Arabic. LC 85-52265. 70p. (Orig.). 1985. pap. 12.00 (ISBN 0-940368-62-5). Tahrike Tarsile Quran.
--Al-Kafi: The Book of Excellence of Knowledge. Rizvi, S. Muhammad, tr. from Arabic. LC 85-52264. 72p. (Orig.). 1985. pap. 12.00 (ISBN 0-940368-61-7). Tahrike Tarsile Quran.
--Al-Kafi: The Book of Reason & Ignorance. Rizvi, S. Muhammad, tr. from Arabic. LC 85-52263. 72p. (Orig.). 1985. pap. 12.00 (ISBN 0-940368-63-3). Tahrike Tarsile Quran.
Arrington, French. Maintaining the Foundations. 1983. pap. 4.95 (ISBN 0-8010-0192-7). Baker Bk.
Arrington, Leonard J. Great Basin Kingdom: An Economic History of the Latter-Day Saints, 1830-1900. LC 58-12961. (Illus.). xx, 550p. 1966. pap. 13.95 (ISBN 0-8032-5006-1, BB 342, Bison). U of Nebr Pr.
Arrington, Leonard J. & Bitton, Davis. The Mormon Experience: A History of the Latter-Day Saints. LC 78-20561. (Illus.). 1979. 17.50 (ISBN 0-394-46566-0). Knopf.
--The Mormon Experience: A History of the Latter-Day Saints. LC 80-11843. (Illus.). 404p. 1980. pap. 5.95 (ISBN 0-394-74102-1, Vin). Random.
--Saints Without Halos: The Human Side of Mormon History. 168p. 1981. 10.95 (ISBN 0-941214-01-X). Signature Bks.
Arrington, Leonard J., jt. auth. see Cornwall, Rebecca.
Arrington, Leonard J., ed. The Presidents of the Church. LC 85-31117. 468p. 1986. 15.95 (ISBN 0-87579-026-7). Deseret Bk.
Arrington, Renee, et al. Voices of Inspiration. 34p. 1982. pap. 3.50 (ISBN 0-939296-04-7). Bond Pub Co.
Arrowood, Larry M. Overcoming Temptation. Bernard, David, ed. LC 86-24735. (Illus.). 120p. (Orig.). 1986. pap. text ed. 5.50 (ISBN 0-932581-04-8). Word Aflame.
Arrowsmith, Richard S. The Prelude to the Reformation: A Study of English Church Life from the Age of Wycliffe to the Breach with Rome. LC 83-45573. Date not set. Repr. of 1923 ed. 30.00 (ISBN 0-404-19891-0). AMS Pr.
Arroyo, Stephen & Greene, Liz. The Jupiter-Saturn Conference Lectures: New Insights in Modern Astrology. LC 82-45632. (Lectures on Modern Astrology). 1983. pap. 8.95 (ISBN 0-916360-16-4). CRCS Pubns NV.
Arrupe, Pedro. Challenge to Religious Life Today: Selected Letters & Addresses--I. Aixala, Jerome, ed. LC 79-87603. 310p. 1979. 7.00 (ISBN 0-912422-45-9); pap. 6.00 smyth sewn (ISBN 0-912422-44-0). Inst Jesuit.
--In Him Alone Is Our Hope: Texts on the Heart of Christ (1966-1983) Aixala, Jerome, ed. Ganss, G. E., et al, trs. from Span. LC 83-80037. (Selected Letters & Addresses of: IV). xvi, 180p. 1984. pap. 7.00 Smyth sewn (ISBN 0-912422-85-8); pap. 6.00 (ISBN 0-912422-87-4). Inst Jesuit.
--Justice with Faith Today: Selected Letters & Addresses--II. Aixala, Jerome, ed. LC 80-81055. 336p. 1980. 8.00 (ISBN 0-912422-51-3); pap. 7.00 smyth sewn (ISBN 0-912422-50-5). Inst Jesuit.
--One Jesuit's Spiritual Journey: Autobiographical Conversations with Jean-Claude Dietsch, S. J. Ganss, George E., frwd. by. Bradley, Ruth, tr. LC 84-81990. Orig. Title: Itineraire d'un Jesuite. Entretiens avec Jean-Claude Dietsch, S. J. 174p. 1986. 10.00 (ISBN 0-912422-69-6); smyth sewn 8.00 (ISBN 0-912422-68-8). Inst Jesuit.
--Other Apostolates Today: Selected Letters & Addresses - III. Aixala, Jerome, ed. LC 81-80741. 380p. 1981. 9.00 (ISBN 0-912422-81-5); pap. 8.00 smyth sewn (ISBN 0-912422-80-7). Inst Jesuit.
Arsapada, see Gotama.
Arsen'ev, Nicolai S. We Beheld His Glory. Ewer, Mary A., tr. LC 76-113545. Repr. of 1936 ed. 18.00 (ISBN 0-404-00407-5). AMS Pr.
Arseniev, Nicholas. Mysticism & the Eastern Church. 173p. 1979. pap. 7.95 (ISBN 0-913836-55-9). St Vladimirs.
--Revelation of Life Eternal: An Introduction to the Christian Message. 144p. 1964. pap. 5.95 (ISBN 0-913836-00-1). St Vladimirs.
--Russian Piety. 143p. 1964. pap. 5.95 (ISBN 0-913836-21-4). St Vladimirs.
Arseniew, Nicholas. Mysticism & the Eastern Church. 1977. lib. bdg. 59.95. Gordon Pr.
Art Institute of Chicago. The Great Eastern Temple: Treasures of Japanese Buddhist Art from Todai-ji. Mino, Yutaka, ed. LC 86-45044. (Midland Bks.: No. 390). (Illus.). 180p. 1986. 45.00x (ISBN 0-253-32634-6); pap. 20.00x (ISBN 0-253-20390-2). Ind U Pr.
Arthur, Donna, ed. see Reamer, Judy.
Arthur, Kay. How Can I Be Blessed? 256p. (Orig.). 1984. pap. 6.95 (ISBN 0-317-06624-2, Power Bks). Revell.
--How Can I Live. 528p. (Orig.). 1981. pap. 7.95 (ISBN 0-8007-5077-2, Power Bks). Revell.
--Lord, I Want to Know You. 192p. (Orig.). 1984. pap. 6.95 (ISBN 0-8007-5159-0, Power Bks). Revell.
--Teach Me How to Live. 384p. (Orig.). 1983. pap. 6.95 (ISBN 0-8007-5125-6, Power Bks). Revell.
Arthur, Richard L., tr. see Arthur, Rose H.
Arthur, Rose H. The Wisdom Goddess: Feminine Motifs in Eight Nag Hammadi Documents. Arthur, Richard L., tr. (Illus.). 256p. (Orig.). 1984. lib. bdg. 26.25 (ISBN 0-8191-4171-2); pap. text ed. 13.50 (ISBN 0-8191-4172-0). U Pr of Amer.
Artos, Allen. Jonah. 52p. (Orig.). 1984. cancelled 10.00 (ISBN 0-934852-00-6); pap. 3.50 (ISBN 0-934852-24-3). Lorien Hse.
Artz, Thomas, jt. auth. see Farrell, Christopher.
Artz, Thomas R. God's People: The Now & Future Church. 64p. 1986. pap. 1.95 (ISBN 0-89243-248-9). Liguori Pubns.
Arundale. Nirvana. 7.50 (ISBN 0-8356-7537-8). Theos Pub Hse.
Arundale, George S. Kundalini. 1972. 4.95 (ISBN 0-8356-7102-X). Theos Pub Hse.
Arx, Jeffery P. von see Von Arx, Jeffrey P.
Arya, Pandit U. Philosophy of Hatha Yoga. 2nd ed. 95p. pap. 5.95 (ISBN 0-89389-088-X). Himalayan Pubs.
--Superconcious Meditation. 150p. 1978. pap. 6.95 (ISBN 0-89389-035-9). Himalayan Pubs.
--Yoga-Sutras of Patanjali with the Exposition of Vyasa: A Translation & Commentary Volume I. xxi, 493p. 1986. pap. 16.95 (ISBN 0-89389-092-8). Himalayan Pubs.
Arya, Usharbudh. God. 162p. (Orig.). pap. 7.95 (ISBN 0-89389-060-X). Himalayan Pubs.
--Meditation & the Art of Dying. 196p. pap. 7.95 (ISBN 0-89389-056-1). Himalayan Pubs.
Arya, Usharbudh & Litt, D. Mantra & Meditation. LC 81-84076. 237p. (Orig.). 1981. pap. 8.95 (ISBN 0-89389-074-X). Himalayan Pubs.
Arya-Sura. The Gatnkamala: Or, Garland of Birth-Stories. Muller, F. Max, ed. Speyer, J. C., tr. from Sanskrit. LC 78-72371. Repr. of 1895 ed. 37.50 (ISBN 0-404-17218-0). AMS Pr.
Aryasura. The Marvelous Companion: Life Stories of the Buddha. (Illus.). 250p. 1983. 25.00 (ISBN 0-913546-88-7). Dharma Pub.
Arzt, Max. Joy & Remembrance. 1979. 12.50 (ISBN 0-87677-147-9). Hartmore.
Arzt, Max, jt. auth. see Silverman, Morris.
Asad, Muhammad. Islam at the Crossroads. 104p. (Orig.). 1982. 8.95 (ISBN 0-317-52459-3, Pub. by Dar Al Andalus). New Era Pubns MI.
--Message of the Quran. 998p. (Orig.). 1980. 49.95 (ISBN 0-317-52456-9, Pub. by Dar Al Andalus). New Era Pubns MI.
--Road to Mecca. 380p. (Orig.). 1981. 14.95 (ISBN 0-317-52460-7, Pub. by Dar Al Andalus). New Era Pubns MI.
--Sahih Al-Bukhari: The Early Years. 306p. (Orig.). 1981. 24.95 (ISBN 0-317-52458-5, Pub. by Dar Al Andalus). New Era Pubns MI.
Asbury, Francis. Heart & Church. pap. 4.95 (ISBN 0-686-23583-5). Schmul Pub Co.
Asch, Sholem. In the Beginning: Stories from the Bible. Cunningham, Caroline, tr. from Yiddish. LC 66-24907. (Illus.). 1979. pap. 3.95 (ISBN 0-8052-0626-4). Schocken.
Aschenbrenner, George. A God for a Dark Journey. 1984. pap. 5.95 (ISBN 0-87193-211-3). Dimension Bks.
Ascher, A., et al, eds. The Mutual Effects of the Islamic & Judeo-Christian Worlds: The East European Pattern. LC 77-90629. (Studies on Society in Change: No. 3). 1979. write for info (ISBN 0-930888-00-6). Brooklyn Coll Pr.
Aschkenasy, Nehama. Eve's Journey: Feminine Images In Hebraic Literary Tradition. LC 85-29427. 176p. 1986. text ed. 29.95 (ISBN 0-8122-8033-4); pap. 15.95. U of Pa Pr.
Aschkenasy, Nehama, jt. ed. see Hirsch, David H.
Aschwanden, Charles R., ed. see Aschwanden, Richard J. & Aschwanden, Maria.
Aschwanden, Maria, jt. auth. see Aschwanden, Richard.
Aschwanden, Maria, jt. auth. see Aschwanden, Richard J.
Aschwanden, Richard & Aschwanden, Maria. Escaping Collusion. 90p. (Orig.). 1983. pap. 4.20x (ISBN 0-913071-01-3). Rama Pub Co.
Aschwanden, Richard J. & Aschwanden, Maria. A Time of Personal Regeneration. Aschwanden, Charles R., ed. 60p. 1984. pap. 3.40x (ISBN 0-913071-00-5, TX1-202-40). Rama Pub Co.
Ascroft, Winifred. The Quickening Flame: A Scriptural Study of Revival. (Basic Bible Study). 64p. 1985. pap. 2.95 (ISBN 0-932305-20-2, 521020). Aglow Pubns.

Aseshananda, Swami. Glimpses of a Great Soul: The Life of Swami Saradananda. 320p. (Orig.). 1982. pap. 7.95 (ISBN 0-87481-039-6). Vedanta Pr.

Asghar Khan, Mohammad, ed. Islam, Politics & the State - The Pakistan Experience. 320p. 1985. 32.95x (ISBN 0-86232-471-8, Pub. by Zed Pr England); pap. 12.95 (ISBN 0-86232-472-6, Pub. by Zed Pr England). Humanities.

Ash, Anthony. Commentary on Jeremiah & Lamentations. 500p. 1987. 16.95 (ISBN 0-915547-94-5). Abilene Christ U.

Ash, Anthony L. Decide to Love. LC 80-80294. (Journey Bks.). 140p. (Orig.). 1980. pap. 3.50 (ISBN 0-8344-0116-9). Sweet.

--The Word of Faith. Thomas, J. D., ed. LC 73-89757. (Twentieth Century Sermons Ser.). 1973. 11.95 (ISBN 0-89112-308-3, Bibl Res Pr). Abilene Christ U.

Ash, James L., Jr. Protestantism & the American University: An Intellectual Biography of William Warren Sweet. LC 82-10629. (Illus.). 180p. 1982. 15.95x (ISBN 0-87074-183-7). SMU Press.

Asha, Ma P., ed. see Rajneesh, Bhagwan S.

Asha, Ma Prem, ed. see Rajneesh, Bhagwan Shree.

Ashbee, Charles R., ed. Parish of Bromley-By-Bow. LC 73-138270. (London County Council. Survey of London: No. 1). Repr. of 1900 ed. 74.50 (ISBN 0-404-51651-3). AMS Pr.

Ashbrook, James B. The Human Mind & the Mind of God: Theological Promise in Brain Research. (Illus.). 408p. (Orig.). 1985. lib. bdg. 30.75 (ISBN 0-8191-4225-5); pap. text ed. 17.75 (ISBN 0-8191-4226-3). U Pr of Amer.

Ashby, Philip H. Modern Trends in Hinduism. LC 73-20262. (Lectures in the History of Religions Ser.: No. 10). 143p. 1974. 22.50x (ISBN 0-231-03768-6). Columbia U Pr.

Ashcraft, Morris. Christian Faith & Beliefs. LC 83-71872. 1984. 9.75 (ISBN 0-8054-1603-X). Broadman.

--The Will of God. LC 80-65714. 1980. pap. 4.95 (ISBN 0-8054-1620-X). Broadman.

Ashcraft, Nancy. At the Scent of Water. 1986. pap. 4.95 (ISBN 0-87508-049-9). Chr Lit.

Ashcroft, J. Robert. The Sequence of the Supernatural. 80p. 1972. pap. 1.00 (ISBN 0-88243-748-8, 02-0748). Gospel Pub.

Ashcroft-Nowicki, Dolores. First Steps in Ritual: Safe, Effective Techniques for Experiencing the Inner Worlds. 96p. 1983. pap. 6.95 (ISBN 0-85030-314-1). Newcastle Pub.

--First Steps in Ritual: Safe, Effective Techniques for Experiencing the Inner Worlds. LC 86-18829. 176p. 1986. lib. bdg. 19.95x (ISBN 0-8095-7010-6). Borgo Pr.

Ashe, Kaye. Today's Woman, Tomorrow's Church. 200p. 1984. pap. 8.95 (ISBN 0-88347-168-X). Thomas More.

Ashenhurst, Harry J. Divorce & Beyond. 1984. pap. 7.75 (ISBN 0-8309-0385-2). Herald Hse.

Asher, Jeremiah. Incidents in the Life of the Rev. J. Asher. facsimile ed. LC 74-168506. (Black Heritage Library Collection). Repr. of 1850 ed. 12.00 (ISBN 0-8369-8860-4). Ayer Co Pubs.

Asher, Joseph. Moral Choices: A Religious Perspective. 50p. (Orig.). 1984. pap. write for info. (ISBN 0-936434-14-7, Pub. by Zellerbach Fam Fund). SF Study Ctr.

Asheri, Michael. Living Jewish: The Lore & the Law of the Practicing Jew. 446p. 1983. pap. 9.95 (ISBN 0-396-08263-7). Dodd.

Ashery, R. E., jt. ed. see Sereni, Ezo H.

Ashford, Ray. The Surrender & the Singing: Happiness Through Letting Go. 168p. (Orig.). 1985. pap. 7.95 (ISBN 0-86683-964-X, AY8546, HarpR). Har-Row.

Ashish, Sri Madhava. Man, Son of Man. LC 79-98267. 1970. 8.50 (ISBN 0-8356-0011-4). Theos Pub Hse.

Ashish, Sri Madhava, jt. auth. see Prem, Sri K.

Ashkenazi, Michael & Weingrod, Alex. Ethiopian Jews & Israel. 188p. 1987. 24.95 (ISBN 0-88738-133-2). Transaction Bks.

Ashlag, R. Yehuda. A Gift of the Bible. 160p. 1984. pap. 9.95 (ISBN 0-943688-22-1). Res Ctr Kabbalah.

Ashlag, Yehuda. An Entrance to the Tree of Life of Rabbi Isaac Luria. Berg, Philip S., ed. 1977. 13.95 (ISBN 0-943688-05-1); pap. 10.95 (ISBN 0-943688-35-3). Res Ctr Kabbalah.

--An Entrance to the Zohar. Berg, Philip S., ed. 1974. 12.95 (ISBN 0-943688-04-3); 10.95 (ISBN 0-943688-34-5). Res Ctr Kabbalah.

--Etz Chaim: Hebrew Text, 2 vols. condensed ed. 40.00 (ISBN 0-943688-18-3). Res Ctr Kabbalah.

--Ten Luminous Emanations, Vol. 1. 1970. 11.95 (ISBN 0-943688-08-6); pap. 9.95 (ISBN 0-943688-29-9). Res Ctr Kabbalah.

--Ten Luminous Emanations, Vol. 2. Berg, Philip S., ed. 1972. 11.95 (ISBN 0-943688-09-4); pap. 9.95 (ISBN 0-943688-25-6). Res Ctr Kabbalah.

Ashley, April, jt. auth. see Fallowell, Duncan.

Ashley, Benedict M. Theologies of the Body: Humanist & Christian. (Illus.). 770p. (Orig.). 1985. pap. 20.95 (ISBN 0-935372-15-6). Pope John Ctr.

Ashley, Benedict M. & O'Rourke, Kevin D. Health Care Ethics: A Theological Analysis. 2nd ed. LC 81-17973. 1982. 25.00 (ISBN 0-87125-075-6); pap. 16.00 (ISBN 0-87125-070-5). Cath Health.

Ashley, Clara, jt. auth. see Gambill, Sandra.

Ashley, Leonard R. The Wonderful World of Magic & Witchcraft. LC 85-25310. (Illus.). 1986. 17.50 (ISBN 0-934878-71-4); pap. 10.95 (ISBN 0-934878-72-2). Dembner Bks.

--The Wonderful World of Superstition, Prophecy & Luck. LC 83-23182. (Illus.). 192p. (Orig.). 1984. pap. 8.95 (ISBN 0-934878-33-1). Dembner Bks.

Ashley, Maurice. Financial & Commercial Policy under Cromwellian Protectorate. 2nd ed. 190p. 1962. Repr. of 1934 ed. 28.50x (ISBN 0-7146-1265-0, BHA 01265, F Cass Co). Biblio Dist.

Ashley, Meg. Meg. LC 83-1332. 128p. 1983. pap. text ed. 2.95 (ISBN 0-88449-101-3, A324581). Vision Hse.

Ashman, Chuck. The Gospel According to Billy. 1977. 8.95 (ISBN 0-8184-0251-2). Lyle Stuart.

Ashmole, Elias. Institution, Laws & Ceremonies of the Most Noble Order of the Garter. LC 78-147882. (Illus.). 720p. 1971. Repr. of 1672 ed. 50.00 (ISBN 0-8063-0467-7). Genealog Pub.

Ashmun, Jehudi, ed. see Bacon, Samuel.

Ashokananda, Swami, tr. see Dattatreya.

Ashraf. Lessons in Islam, 5. 8.50 (ISBN 0-686-18391-6). Kazi Pubns.

Ashraf, Mujeeb. Muslim Attitudes Toward British Rule & Western Culture in India. 1983. 19.00x (ISBN 0-8364-1076-9, Pub. by Idarah). South Asia Bks.

Ashton, J. The Devil in Britain & America. 75.00 (ISBN 0-87968-450-X). Gordon Pr.

Ashton, John. The Devil in Britain & America. LC 80-19692. 363p. 1980. Repr. of 1972 ed. lib. bdg. 19.95x (ISBN 0-89370-608-6). Borgo Pr.

--Righte Merrie Christmasse. LC 68-56543. (Illus.). 1968. Repr. of 1894 ed. 15.00 (ISBN 0-405-08225-8, Pub. by Blom). Ayer Co Pubs.

Ashton, John, ed. The Interpretation of John. LC 85-45536. (Issues in Religion & Theology Ser.). 176p. 1986. pap. 7.95 (ISBN 0-8006-1774-6, 1-1774). Fortress.

Ashton, Leila. Checks from God. (My Church Teaches Ser.). 32p. 1981. pap. 1.95 (ISBN 0-8127-0314-6). Review & Herald.

Ashton, Leila M. It's Sabbath. (My Church Teaches Ser.). (Illus.). 1978. pap. 1.95 (ISBN 0-8127-0177-1). Review & Herald.

--My "Feel Good" Secrets. (My Church Teaches Ser.). (Illus.). 1978. pap. 1.50 (ISBN 0-8127-0178-X). Review & Herald.

--Today Is Friday. (My Church Teaches Ser.). (Illus.). 1978. pap. 1.954 (ISBN 0-8127-0176-3). Review & Herald.

Ashton, Marvin J. What Is Your Destination? LC 78-14982. 1978. 8.95 (ISBN 0-87747-719-1). Deseret Bk.

--Ye Are My Friends. 151p. 1982. 7.95 (ISBN 0-87747-934-8). Deseret Bk.

Ashton, Sylvia, ed. see Gestwicki, Ronald.

Ashton, Sylvia, ed. see Goodman, Marguerite.

Ashton, Sylvia, ed. see Jacobson, James R.

Ashton, W. G. Shinto: The Ancient Religion of Japan. 83p. 1921. 0.95 (ISBN 0-317-40426-1). Open Court.

Ashtor, Eliyahu. The Jews of Moslem Spain, Vol. III. Klein, Aaron & Klein, Jenny M., trs. from Hebrew. 380p. 1985. 19.95 (ISBN 0-8276-0237-5). Jewish Pubns.

--The Jews of Moslem Spain, Vol. 1. Machlowitz Klein, Aaron, tr. from Heb. LC 73-14081. (Illus.). 469p. 1974. 12.00 (ISBN 0-8276-0017-8, 352). Jewish Pubns.

--The Jews of Moslem Spain, Vol. 2. 381p. 1978. 12.00 (ISBN 0-8276-0100-X, 411). Jewish Pubns.

Ashworth, Mae H. Candles in the Dark. LC 83-70253. 1983. 6.95 (ISBN 0-8054-5256-7). Broadman.

Asifi, Allama M. Al-Salat. 1983. pap. 4.00 (ISBN 0-941724-10-7). Islamic Seminary.

--Children's Guide to Islam. 112p. 1983. pap. 5.00 (ISBN 0-941724-11-5). Islamic Seminary.

Asimov, Isaac. Asimov's Guide to the Bible: The New Testament. 640p. 1971. pap. 8.95 (ISBN 0-380-01031-3, 60255-5). Avon.

--Asimov's Guide to the Bible: The Old Testament. 720p. 1971. pap. 10.95 (ISBN 0-380-01032-1). Avon.

--Words from the Myths. (Illus.). 224p. 1961. 12.95 (ISBN 0-395-06568-2). HM.

--Words from the Myths. (Illus.). 144p. 1969. pap. 2.50 (ISBN 0-451-14097-4, Sig). NAL.

Askari, Hasan, jt. auth. see Hick, John.

Askari, Hasan, tr. see Al-Qunawi, Sadraddin.

Askew, Thomas A., Jr. & Spellman, Peter W. The Churches & the American Experience. 205p. 1984. pap. 9.95 (ISBN 0-8010-0199-4). Baker Bk.

Asmussen, Jes P., compiled by. Manichaean Literature: Representative Texts, Chiefly from Middle Persian & Parthian Writings. LC 74-22063. (Unesco Collection of Representative Works, Oriental Ser.). 160p. 1975. lib. bdg. 30.00x (ISBN 0-8201-1141-4). Schol Facsimiles.

Aspell, A. L. Catholics: A Celebration. Date not set. pap. price not set (ISBN 0-940518-05-8). Guildhall Pubs.

Asplund, John. The Annual Register of the Baptist Denomination in North America to 1970. 1979. Repr. 10.00 (ISBN 0-317-01254-1). Church History.

--The Universal Register of the Baptist Denomiation in North America for the Years 1790, 1791, 1792, 1793, & Part of 1794. Gaustad, Edwin S., ed. LC 79-52581. (The Baptist Tradition Ser.). 1980. Repr. of 1794 ed. lib. bdg. 14.00x (ISBN 0-405-12448-1). Ayer Co Pubs.

Aspurz-Iriarte, Lazaro De see De Aspurz-Iriarte, Lazaro.

Asquith, Glenn H. Church Officers at Work. pap. 4.95 (ISBN 0-8170-0048-8). Judson.

--Mature Faith: A Spiritual Pilgrimage. LC 84-12890. 120p. (Orig.). 1984. pap. 6.95 (ISBN 0-8361-3366-8). Herald Pr.

--Renewed Power for Preaching. 128p. 1983. pap. 3.95 (ISBN 0-8170-1003-3). Judson.

As-Said, Labib. Recited Koran: A History of the First Recorded Version. Weiss, Bernard, ed. LC 73-20717. (Illus.). 156p. 1975. 10.00 (ISBN 0-87850-024-3). Darwin Pr.

Assamani, Joseph A. De Catholicis Seu Patriarchis Chaldaeorum et Nestorianorum Commentarius: De Unione et Communione Ecclesiastica. 410p. Repr. of 1775 ed. text ed. 82.80x (ISBN 0-576-99702-1, Pub. by Gregg Intl Pubs England). Gregg Intl.

Asselineau, jt. auth. see Allen.

Assendelft, Marion M. van see Van Assendelft, Marion M.

Assfalg, Julius & Krueger, P. Kleines Woerterbuch Des Christlichen Orients. 1st ed. (Ger.). 1975. 52.00 (ISBN 3-447-01707-4, M-7514, Pub. by Harrassowitz). French & Eur.

Associated Women's Organization, Mars Hill Bible School. Something Special. Simpson, Peggy & Stanley, Linda, eds. 1977. pap. 4.95 (ISBN 0-89137-408-6). Quality Pubns.

--What Are We Doing Here? 1972. pap. 4.95 (ISBN 0-89137-404-3). Quality Pubns.

Association for Research & Enlightenment, Readings Research Dept., compiled by. Christ Consciousness. (Library: Vol. 11). 277p. 1980. 10.95 (ISBN 0-87604-124-1). ARE Pr.

--Daily Living. (Library: Vol. 12). 241p. 1981. 10.95 (ISBN 0-87604-133-0). ARE Pr.

Association for Research & Enlightement, Readings Research Dept., compiled by. The Early Christian Epoch. (Library: Vol. 6). (Illus.). 593p. 1976. 10.95 (ISBN 0-87604-089-X). ARE Pr.

--The Expanded Search for God: Pts. 1 & 2. (Library: Vol.16 & 17). Pt. 1 499pgs. 11/1983. 12.95 (ISBN 0-87604-153-5); Pt. 2 662pgs. 12/1983. 14.95 (ISBN 0-87604-154-3). ARE Pr.

Association for Research & Enlightenment, Readings Research Dept., compiled by. Jesus the Pattern: Library. (Vol. 10). 336p. 1980. 10.95 (ISBN 0-87604-123-3). ARE Pr.

--Meditation, 1: Healing, Prayer, & the Revelation. (Library: Vol. 2). 306p. 1974. 10.95 (ISBN 0-87604-072-5). ARE Pr.

Association for Research & Enlightenment, Readings Research Dept., ed. Meditation, 2: Meditation, Endocrine Glands, Prayer, & Affirmations. (Library: Vol. 3). 274p. 1975. 10.95 (ISBN 0-87604-082-2). ARE Pr.

Association for Research & Enlightenment, Inc. Virginia Beach, Va. Study Groups, et al, eds. Search for God: Nineteen Forty-Two to Nineteen Fifty, 2 Bks. 1942-1950. 4.95 ea. Bk. 1 (ISBN 0-87604-000-8). Bk. 2 (ISBN 0-87604-001-6). ARE Pr.

Association of Christian Publishers & Booksellers. Libros Cristianos En Existencia. (Span.). 384p. (Orig.). 1984. write for info. (ISBN 0-943258-01-4). Assn Christian Pub.

Association of Orthodox Jewish Scientists. Proceedings. Set. cancelled (ISBN 0-87306-072-5); Vol. 1. 5.95 (ISBN 0-686-67018-3); Vol. 2. 6.95 (ISBN 0-87306-073-3). Feldheim.

--Proceedings, Vol. 5. Rosner, Fred, ed. 1978. pap. 8.95 (ISBN 0-87306-150-0). Feldheim.

Associations of Orthodox Jewish Scientists Staff. Proceedings, Vol. 3 & 4. Rosner, Fred, ed. 248p. 1976. pap. 9.95 (ISBN 0-87306-074-1). Feldheim.

Astavakra. Astavakra Samhita. Nityaswarupananda, Swami, tr. (Sanskrit & Eng.). pap. 4.50 (ISBN 0-87481-165-1). Vedanta Pr.

Asten, Dietrich V. Sacramental & Spiritual Communion. Glas, Werner, ed. (Orig.). 1984. pap. 2.50 (ISBN 0-88010-121-0). Anthroposophic.

Aster, Sidney. British Foreign Policy, Nineteen Eighteen to Nineteen Forty-Five: A Guide to Research & Research Materials. LC 84-5339. 324p. 1984. 25.00 (ISBN 0-8420-2176-0). Scholarly Res Inc.

Astley, H. J. Biblical Anthropology. 1977. Repr. of 1929 ed. 32.50 (ISBN 0-685-82796-8). Sharon Hill.

Aston, Hugh see Buck, P. C. & Fellowes, E. H.

Aston, Margaret. Lollards & Reformers: Images & Literacy in Late Medieval Religion. 405p. 1984. 35.00 (ISBN 0-907628-03-6). Hambledon Press.

Aston, W. G. Shinto, the Way of the Gods. lib. bdg. 75.00 (ISBN 0-87968-076-8). Krishna Pr.

Asvaghosa. The Buddhacharita or Acts of the Buddha, 2 vols. in 1. Johnson, E. H., ed. & tr. Repr. of 1936 ed. text ed. 25.00x. Coronet Bks.

--The Principle & Practice of Mahayana Buddhism: An Interpretation of Professor Suzuki's Translation of Ashvaghosa's Awakening of Faith. Goodard, Dwight, ed. LC 78-72373. Repr. of 1933 ed. 18.00 (ISBN 0-404-17223-7). AMS Pr.

Asvaghosha. Acvaghosa's Discourse on the Awakening of Faith in the Mahayana. Suzuki, D. T., tr. from Chinese. 178p. 1900. Repr. text ed. 17.50x (ISBN 0-89644-475-9, Pub. by Chinese Matl Ctr). Coronet Bks.

Asvaghosha, B. Asvaghosha's Discourse on the Awakening of Faith in the Mahayana. lib. bdg. 79.95 (ISBN 0-87968-472-0). Krishna Pr.

--A Life of Buddha. lib. bdg. 79.95 (ISBN 0-87968-473-9). Krishna Pr.

A. S. Van, Der Woude see Van Hartingsveld, L.

A. S. Van, Der Woude see Van Selms, A.

Atcheson, Jean, ed. see Sass, Lorna J.

Atemed, M. G. The Teachings of Islam: A Solution of Five Fundamental Religious Problems from the Muslim Point of View. 208p. 1984. text ed. 23.00. Coronet Bks.

Athanasiev, D., jt. auth. see Archpriest Michael Kheraskov.

Athanasius. Contra Gentes & De Incarnatione. Thomas, Robert W., ed. (Oxford Early Christian Texts Ser.). 1971. 45.00x (ISBN 0-19-826801-7). Oxford U Pr.

Athanasius, Saint The Life of St. Anthony the Great. pap. 2.95 (ISBN 0-686-16367-2). Eastern Orthodox.

--On the Incarnation of the Word. pap. 2.95 (ISBN 0-686-25556-9). Eastern Orthodox.

Athanasius, St. Select Treatises of St. Athanasius in Controversy with the Arians, 2 vols. 5th ed. Newman, John H., tr. LC 77-84694. (Heresies of the Early Christian & Medieval Era Ser.). Repr. of 1890 ed. 72.00 set (ISBN 0-404-16100-6). AMS Pr.

Athanassakis, Apostolos N. The Life of Pachomius. LC 84-4046. (Society of Biblical Literature. Texts & Translation-Early Christian Literature Ser.). 216p. 1975. pap. 14.25 (ISBN 0-89130-065-1, 06 02 07). Scholars Pr GA.

Athanassakis, Apostolos N., tr. see Hesiod.

Athenagoras. Legatio & De Resurrectione. Schoedel, William R., ed. (Oxford Early Christian Texts Ser.). 1972. 34.95x (ISBN 0-19-826808-4). Oxford U Pr.

Athill, Diana. After a Funeral. 176p. 1986. 15.95 (ISBN 0-89919-454-0). Ticknor & Fields.

Athos Monasteries Staff. Catalogue of the Greek Manuscripts in the Library of the Monastery of Vatopedi on Mt. Athos. (Harvard Theological Studies Ser.). 1924. 24.00 (ISBN 0-527-01011-1). Kraus Repr.

Ati, H. A. Islam in Focus. pap. 9.50 (ISBN 0-686-18504-8). Kazi Pubns.

Atiya, Aziz S. The Crusade: Historiography & Bibliography. LC 75-22640. 1976. lib. bdg. 22.50x (ISBN 0-8371-8364-2, ATTC). Greenwood.

--The Crusade of Nicopolis. LC 76-29829. (Illus.). Repr. of 1934 ed. 29.50 (ISBN 0-404-15410-7). AMS Pr.

--History of Eastern Christianity. LC 80-232. 1980. Repr. lib. bdg. 52.00 (ISBN 0-527-03703-6). Kraus Repr.

--History of Eastern Christianity. LC 67-31393. pap. 125.00 (ISBN 0-317-42117-4, 2025944). Bks Demand UMI.

Atiyeh, Wadeeha. Fourth Wise Man. 1959. pap. 3.00 (ISBN 0-8315-0038-7). Speller.

Atkin, Abraham. Chelkeinu. 200p. text ed. 5.50 (ISBN 0-914131-09-5, A16). Torah Umesorah.

--Darkeinu Aleph & Bais: In One Volume. pap. text ed. 3.50 (ISBN 0-686-33046-3, A13). Torah Umesorah.

--Darkeinu Daled. text ed. 3.75 (ISBN 0-914131-13-3, A15). Torah Umesorah.

Atkins, Abraham. Darkeinu Gimel. text ed. 3.50 (ISBN 0-686-33046-3, A14). Torah Umesorah.

Atkins, Dorothy. George Eliot & Spinoza. Hogg, James, ed. (Romantic Reassessment Ser.). 188p. (Orig.). 1978. pap. 15.00 (ISBN 3-7052-0535-8, Pub. by Salzburg Studies). Longwood Pub Group.

Atkins, G. Douglas. The Faith of John Dryden: Change & Continuity. LC 80-12890. 208p. 1980. 19.00x (ISBN 0-8131-1401-2). U Pr of Ky.

Atkins, Gaius. Modern Religious Cults & Movements. LC 74-126684. Repr. of 1923 ed. 26.50 (ISBN 0-404-00415-6). AMS Pr.

Atkins, Gaius G. Pilgrims of the Lonely Road. facs. ed. LC 67-28741. (Essay Index Reprint Ser). 1913. 18.00 (ISBN 0-8369-0162-2). Ayer Co Pubs.

Atkins, Gaius G., ed. see Maclaren, Alexander.

Atkins, Ivor A. The Early Occupants of the Office of Organist & Master of the Choristers of the Cathedral Church of Christ & the Blessed Virgin Mary, Worcester. LC 74-27329. Repr. of 1913 ed. 24.50 (ISBN 0-404-12855-6). AMS Pr.

Atkins, Stanley & McConnell, Theodore, eds. Churches on the Wrong Road. 270p. (Orig.). 1986. pap. 7.95 (ISBN 0-89526-803-5). Regnery Bks.

Atkins, Susan & Slosser, Bob. Child of Satan, Child of God. LC 77-81947. 1977. (Pub. by Logos); pap. 2.95 (ISBN 0-88270-276-9). Bridge Pub.

Atkinson, Clarissa W. Mystic & Pilgrim: The "Book" & the World of Margery Kempe. LC 82-22219. 248p. (Orig.). 1983. 27.50x (ISBN 0-8014-1521-7); pap. text ed. 8.95x (ISBN 0-8014-9895-3). Cornell U Pr.

Atkinson, Clarissa W., et al, eds. Immaculate & Powerful: The Female in Sacred Image & Social Reality. LC 85-70448. 338p. 1987. pap. 12.95 (ISBN 0-8070-1005-7, BP-732). Beacon Pr.

Atkinson, Clifford W. A Lay Reader's Guide to the Book of Common Prayer. 1981. pap. 3.95 (ISBN 0-8192-1222-9). Morehouse.

Atkinson, David. The Message of Ruth. LC 84-27785. (Bible Speaks Today Ser.). 128p. 1983. pap. 5.95 (ISBN 0-87784-294-9). Inter-Varsity.

Atkinson, Donald A. A Barnabas Life-Style. (Orig.). 1987. pap. 3.25 (ISBN 0-8054-5728-3). Broadman.

Atkinson, Franklin. A New Look at Spiritual Life. (Orig.). 1987. pap. 4.98 (ISBN 0-8054-1235-2). Broadman.

Atkinson, Gary M. & Moraczewski, Albert S. Genetic Counseling, the Church & the Law. LC 79-92084. xvii, 259p. (Orig.). 1980. pap. 9.95 (ISBN 0-935372-06-7). Pope John Ctr.

--A Moral Evaluation of Contraception & Sterilization: A Dialogical Study. LC 79-90971. viii, 115p. (Orig.). 1979. pap. 4.95 (ISBN 0-935372-05-9). Pope John Ctr.

Atkinson, James. Martin Luther & the Birth of Protestantism. LC 81-82356. 348p. 1981. pap. 5.25 (ISBN 0-8042-0941-3). John Knox.

--Martin Luther: Prophet to the Church Catholic. LC 83-16462. Repr. of 1983 ed. 58.00 (2027535). Bks Demand UMI.

Atkinson, James, ed. Daily Readings with Martin Luther. 1987. pap. 4.95 (ISBN 0-87243-157-6). Templegate.

--Luther: Early Theological Works. LC 62-12358. (Library of Christian Classics). 376p. 1980. pap. 9.95 (ISBN 0-664-24166-2). Westminster.

Atkinson, James, jt. ed. see Lehmann, Helmut T.

Atkinson, Linda. Have We Lived Before? (High Interest, Low Vocabulary Ser.). (Illus.). 112p. 1982. PLB 8.95 (ISBN 0-396-07999-7). Dodd.

--In Kindling Flame: The Story of Hannah Senesh 1921-1944. LC 83-24392. 256p. 1985. 13.50 (ISBN 0-688-02714-8). Lothrop.

Atkinson, M. J., ed. A Commentary on Plotinus: Ennead. (Classical & Philosophical Monographs: Vol. 1). 1983. 47.50x (ISBN 0-19-814719-8). Oxford U Pr.

Atkinson, William W. Mind Power: The Secret of Mental Magic. limited ed. limited ed. 9.00 (ISBN 0-911662-27-8). Yoga.

--Reincarnation & Law of Karma. 8.00 (ISBN 0-911662-26-X). Yoga.

Atreya, B. L. Deification of Man: Its Methods & Stages According to the Yoga Vasistha Including a Translation of the Essence of Vasistha's Teachings. 116p. 1980. pap. 4.50 (ISBN 0-935548-02-5). Santarasa Pubns.

At-Tabatabai, S. Muhammad. Al-Mizan: En Exegesis of the Quran, Vol. 3. Rizvi, S. Saeed, tr. from Arabic. LC 85-52243. 334p. (Orig.). 1985. pap. 30.00 (ISBN 0-940368-58-7). Tahrike Tarsile Quran.

At Tabatabai, S. Muhammad Husayn see Husayn at-Tabatabai, S. Muhammad & S. Saeed, Akhtar-Rizvi.

Attanasio, Salvator, tr. see Danielou, Jean.

Attanasio, Salvator, tr. see Lohfink, Gerhard.

Attanasio, Salvator, tr. see Ratzinger, Joseph & Messori, Vittorio.

Attanasio, Salvatore, tr. see Pedraz, Juan L.

Attar, Chaim B. Light of Life: A Compendium of the Writings of Rabbi Chaim Ben Attar. 236p. 1986. pap. 9.95 (ISBN 0-87877-090-9). Newcastle Pub.

Attar, Chaim ben Moshe. Light of Life: A Compendium of the Writings of Rabbi Chaim ben Moshe Attar. 160p. 1986. Repr. lib. bdg. 19.95x (ISBN 0-89370-690-6). Borgo Pr.

Attar, Farid Ud-Din. The Conference of the Birds: A Sufi Fable. Nott, C. S., tr. (Clear Light Ser). (Illus.). 147p. (Orig.). 1971. pap. 6.95 (ISBN 0-87773-031-8, 73001-1). Shambhala Pubns.

Atterbury, Anson P. Islam in Africa. LC 73-91254. Repr. of 1899 ed. 22.50x (ISBN 0-8371-2064-0, ATI&, Pub. by Negro U Pr). Greenwood.

Atthill, William L., ed. Documents Relating to the Foundation & Antiquities of the Collegiate Church of Middleham in the County of York. LC 70-161702. (Camden Society, London. Publications, First Ser.: No. 38). Repr. of 1847 ed. 19.00 (ISBN 0-404-50138-9). AMS Pr.

--Documents Relating to the Foundation & Antiquities of the Collegiate Church of Middleham, County of York. (Camden Society Ser.: Vol. 38). 19.00 (ISBN 0-384-02270-7). Johnson Repr.

Attoe, Wayne, jt. auth. see Young, Mary E.

Attwater, Donald. Golden Book of Eastern Saints. facsimile ed. LC 72-156607. (Essay Index Reprint Ser). Repr. of 1938 ed. 18.00 (ISBN 0-8369-2267-0). Ayer Co Pubs.

--Names & Name-Days: A Dictionary of Catholic Christian Names in Alphabetical Order with Origins & Meanings. LC 68-30595. 1968. Repr. of 1939 ed. 40.00x (ISBN 0-8103-3108-X). Gale.

--The Penguin Dictionary of Saints. rev. ed. John, Catherine R., rev. by. 352p. 1984. pap. 7.95 (ISBN 0-14-051123-7). Penguin.

Attwater, Donald, ed. Modern Christian Revolutionaries. facsimile ed. LC 76-156608. (Essay Index Reprint Ser). Repr. of 1947 ed. 23.00 (ISBN 0-8369-2304-9). Ayer Co Pubs.

Attwater, Donald, tr. see Solovyev, Vladimir.

Attwater, Thurston, ed. see Butler, Alban.

Atwater, George P. The Episcopal Church: Its Message for Today. rev ed. 1978. pap. 4.95 (ISBN 0-8192-1244-X). Morehouse.

Au, William A. The Cross, the Flag, & the Bomb: American Catholics Debate War & Peace, 1960-1983. LC 84-25290. (Contributions to the Study of Religion Ser.: No. 12). xviii, 278p. 1985. lib. bdg. 35.00 (ISBN 0-313-24754-4, AUC/). Greenwood.

Aubert & Goubet. Cathedrales Abbatiales, Collegiales et Prieures Romans en France. 153.25 (ISBN 0-685-34010-4). French & Eur.

--Cathedrales et Tresors Gothiques en France. 153.25 (ISBN 0-685-34011-2). French & Eur.

Aubert, Henri. Diccionario de Mitologia. (Span.). 238p. 1961. 14.95 (ISBN 0-686-56710-2, S-33055). French & Eur.

Aubert, Roger. Christian Centuries: Church in a Secularized Society, Vol. 5. LC 78-53496. 820p. 1978. 22.95 (ISBN 0-8091-0244-7). Paulist Pr.

--Le Problem de L'acte de Foi: Donnees Traditionnelles et Resultants des Controverses Recentes. 1978. Repr. of 1958 ed. lib. bdg. 85.00 (ISBN 0-8492-0092-X). R West.

--Prophets in the Church. LC 68-57877. (Concilium Ser.: Vol. 37). 160p. 1964. 7.95 (ISBN 0-8091-0120-3). Paulist Pr.

--Sacralization & Secularization. LC 76-96949. (Concilium Ser.: Vol. 47). 190p. 7.95 (ISBN 0-8091-0128-9). Paulist Pr.

Aubert, Roger & Van Cauwenberg. Dictionnaire d'Histoire et de Geographie Ecclesiastiques, 16 vols. (Fr.). Set. pap. 1795.00 (ISBN 0-686-56903-2, M-6014). French & Eur.

Aubert, Roger, ed. Historical Investigations. LC 66-29260. (Concilium Ser.: Vol. 17). 196p. 1966. 7.95 (ISBN 0-8091-0063-0). Paulist Pr.

--Historical Problems of Church Renewal. LC 65-26792. (Concilium Ser.: Vol. 7). 196p. 1965. 7.95 (ISBN 0-8091-0064-9). Paulist Pr.

--Progress & Decline in the History of Church Renewal. LC 67-30136. (Concilium Ser.: Vol. 27). 191p. 1967. 7.95 (ISBN 0-8091-0119-X). Paulist Pr.

Aubin, tr. see De Liguori, Alphonse.

Aubin, Pierre & Cotter, George. Agencies for Project Assistance: Sources of Support for Small Church & or Lay Sponsored Projects in Africa, Asia, Latin America & the Pacific. 2nd ed. (Illus.). 330p. 1984. pap. 50.00 (ISBN 0-319671-03-7). Mission Proj Serv.

Auboyer, J. Buddha: A Pictorial History of His Life & Legacy. (Illus.). 272p. 1987. 40.00 (ISBN 0-8334-1000-8, Freedeeds Bks). Garber Comm.

Auboyer, Jeannine. Buddha: A Pictorial History of His Life & Legacy. Marans, Nelly, tr. from Fr. LC 83-10140. (Illus.). 272p. 1983. 100.00 (ISBN 0-8245-0588-3). Crossroad NY.

Aubrey, Bryan. Watchmen of Eternity: Blake's Debt to Jacob Boehme. (Illus.). 208p. (Orig.). 1986. PLB 27.00 (ISBN 0-8191-5220-X); pap. text ed. 13.25 (ISBN 0-8191-5221-8). U Pr of Amer.

Aubrey, John. Remaines of Gentilisme & Judaisme, Sixteen Hundred Eighty-Six to Eighty-Seven. Britten, James, ed. (Folk-Lore Society, London, Monograph Ser.: Vol. 4). pap. 29.00 (ISBN 0-8115-0501-4). Kraus Repr.

Aubry, Joseph. The Renewal of Our Salesian Life, 2 vols. Bedard, Paul & Whitehead, Kenneth, trs. from Ital. LC 84-70210. Orig. Title: Rinnovare la Nostra Vita Salesiana. 426p. 1984. pap. text ed. write for info. (ISBN 0-89944-071-1); Vol. I:The Active Apostolate. pap. 5.00; Vol. II:The Salesian Community & Family. pap. 5.50 (ISBN 0-89944-077-0). Don Bosco Multimedia.

--Savio: A Study Guide. Boenzi, Joe, tr. from Ital. LC 79-50460. (Orig.). 1979. pap. 2.75 (ISBN 0-89944-038-X). Don Bosco Multimedia.

Aubry, Joseph, ed. The Spiritual Writings of St. John Bosco. Caselli, Joseph, tr. from Italian. LC 83-71820. Tr. of Giovanni Bosco, Scritti Spirituali. 412p. 1984. pap. 12.95 (ISBN 0-89944-049-5). Don Bosco Multimedia.

Auchmuty, James A., Jr. Brothers of the Bible. LC 84-17510. 1985. pap. 4.50 (ISBN 0-8054-2254-4). Broadman.

Audah, A. Q. Islam Between Ignorant Followers & Incapable Scholars. pap. 4.50 (ISBN 0-686-18505-6). Kazi Pubns.

Audah, Abdul Q. Al-Islam bain Jahl 'Abna'ihi wa Ajz Ulama'ihi. (Arabic.). 79p. (Orig.). 1980. pap. 1.55x (ISBN 0-939830-12-4, Pub. by IIFSO Kuwait). New Era Pubns MI.

Audah, Adbul Q. Islam Between Ignorant Followers & Incapable Scholars. Tr. of Al-Islam bain Jahl 'Abna'ihi wa Ajz Ulama'ihi. 115p. (Orig.). pap. 3.50 (ISBN 0-939830-01-9, Pub. by IIFSO Kuwait). New Era Pubns MI.

Aude, Sapere, ed. The Chaldean Oracles. LC 78-58111. 1978. 10.00 (ISBN 0-935214-02-X). Heptangle.

Auden, W. H., jt. ed. see Greenberg, Noah.

Auden, W. H., et al. What I Believe. Booth, Mark, ed. 182p. 1984. 16.95 (ISBN 0-8245-0676-6); pap. 8.95 (ISBN 0-8245-0677-4). Crossroad NY.

Audi, Robert & Wainwright, William J., eds. Rationality, Religious Belief, & Moral Commitment: New Essays in the Philosophy of Religion. LC 85-48200. 352p. 1986. text ed. 42.50x (ISBN 0-8014-1856-9); pap. text ed. 12.95x (ISBN 0-8014-9381-1). Cornell U Pr.

Audra, R. Ashley, tr. see Bergson, Henri.

Auer, Jim. For Teens Only: Straight Talk about Parents - Life - Love. 64p. 1985. pap. 1.95 (ISBN 0-89243-228-4). Liguori Pubns.

--Sorting It Out with God. 64p. 1982. pap. 1.95 (ISBN 0-89243-163-6). Liguori Pubns.

--A Teenager's (Absolutely Basic) Introduction to the New Testament. 96p. 1986. pap. 2.95 (ISBN 0-89243-257-8). Liguori Pubns.

--What's Right? A Teenager's Guide to Christian Living. 96p. 1987. pap. 3.25 (ISBN 0-89243-265-9). Liguori Pubns.

Auerbach, Elias. Moses. Lehman, Israel O. & Barclay, R. A., trs. from Ger. LC 72-6589. 255p. 1975. text ed. 25.00x (ISBN 0-8143-1491-0). Wayne St U Pr.

Auffray, A. Saint John Bosco. 393p. (Orig.). 1983. pap. 12.95 (ISBN 0-89944-060-6). Don Bosco Multimedia.

Aufrecht, Walter, ed. Studies in the Book of Job. (SR Supplements Ser.: No. 16). 104p. 1985. pap. text ed. 8.95x (ISBN 0-88920-179-X, Pub. by Wilfrid Laurier Canada). Humanities.

Augenstein, John J. A Collaborative Approach to Personnel Relations: A Model Process for Justice in the Catholic School Community of Faith. 191p. 1980. 2.35 (ISBN 0-686-39900-5). Natl Cath Educ.

Augsburger & Curry. Nuclear Arms: Two Views on World Peace. 1987. 14.95 (ISBN 0-8499-0576-1). Word Bks.

Augsburger, David. Caring Enough to Forgive Caring Enough Not to Forgive. LC 81-80913. 160p. (Orig.). 1981. pap. 5.95 (ISBN 0-8361-1965-7). Herald Pr.

--Caring Enough to Confront. rev. ed. LC 73-83400. 144p. 1980. pap. 5.95 (ISBN 0-8307-0733-6, 5411602). Regal.

--Caring Enough to Forgive: Caring Enough to Not Forgive. LC 80-50545. 176p. 1981. pap. 5.95 (ISBN 0-8307-0749-2, 5413702). Regal.

--Caring Enough to Hear & Be Heard. LC 82-81000. (Caring Enough Bks.). 176p. (Orig.). 1982. pap. 4.95 (ISBN 0-8361-3307-2). Herald Pr.

--Diferencias Personales? Enfrentelas con Amor. Olmedo, Alfonso, tr. from Eng. Tr. of Caring Enough to Confront. 176p. 1985. pap. 5.95 (ISBN 0-311-46098-4, Edit Mundo). Casa Bautista.

--The Freedom of Forgiveness. 128p. 1973. pap. 3.50 (ISBN 0-8024-2875-4). Moody.

--The Freedom of Forgiveness. (Moody Press Electives Ser.). 1984. pap. 3.95 (ISBN 0-8024-0695-5); leader's guide 2.50 (ISBN 0-8024-0692-0). Moody.

--From Here to Maturity. 1982. pap. 2.50 (ISBN 0-8423-0938-1). Tyndale.

--Perdonar para Ser Libre. Orig. Title: Freedom of Forgiveness. (Span.). 160p. 1977. pap. 3.50 (ISBN 0-8254-1046-0). Kregel.

--When Enough Is Enough. LC 84-11644. 1984. pap. 5.95 (ISBN 0-8307-0979-7, 5418273). Regal.

Augsburger, David W. Anger & Assertiveness in Pastoral Care. Clinebell, Howard J. & Stone, Howard W., eds. LC 78-14660. (Creative Pastoral Care & Counseling Ser.). 96p. 1979. pap. 0.50 (ISBN 0-8006-0562-4, 1-562). Fortress.

--The Book that Reads You. (New Life Ser.). pap. 3.00 (ISBN 0-8361-1685-2). Herald Pr.

--Like Falling in Love. (New Life Ser.). pap. 3.00 (ISBN 0-8361-1686-0). Herald Pr.

--Pastoral Counseling Across Cultures. LC 86-13343. 408p. 1986. 21.95 (ISBN 0-664-21272-7). Westminster.

--What Do You Fear? (New Life Ser.). pap. 3.00 (ISBN 0-8361-1687-9). Herald Pr.

--What Do You Want? (New Life Ser.). pap. 3.00 (ISBN 0-8361-1688-7). Herald Pr.

--When Caring Is Not Enough: Resolving Conflicts Through Fair Fighting. LC 83-80999. (Caring Enough Ser.: No. 4). 196p. (Orig.). 1983. pap. 5.95 (ISBN 0-8361-3343-9). Herald Pr.

Augsburger, Don A., ed. Marriages That Work. LC 84-15637. 112p. (Orig.). 1984. pap. 6.95 (ISBN 0-8361-3374-9). Herald Pr.

Augsburger, Myon S. Evangelism As Discipling. LC 82-83387. (Mennonite Faith Ser.: Vol. 12). 80p. 1983. pap. 1.50 (ISBN 0-8361-3322-6). Herald Pr.

Augsburger, Myron S. Broken Chalice. LC 70-160721. (Illus.). 1971. 7.95 (ISBN 0-8361-1651-8). Herald Pr.

--Evangelizacion y Discipulado. Rindzinski, Milka, tr. from Eng. LC 84-80159. (Mennonite Faith Ser.: No. 12). 72p. (Orig.). 1984. pap. 1.50x (ISBN 0-8361-1267-9). Herald Pr.

--The Peacemaker. 208p. 1987. pap. 9.95 (ISBN 0-687-30353-2). Abingdon.

--Pilgrim Aflame. LC 67-15993. (Illus.). 288p. 1967. pap. 2.25 (ISBN 0-8361-1840-5). Herald Pr.

--Practicing the Presence of the Spirit. LC 81-20170. 200p. (Orig.). 1982. pap. 7.95 (ISBN 0-8361-1990-8). Herald Pr.

--Quench Not the Spirit. rev. ed. LC 62-7330. 1975. pap. 2.95 (ISBN 0-8361-1477-9). Herald Pr.

--When Reason Fails. 112p. 1985. pap. 4.95 (ISBN 0-8423-7999-1). Tyndale.

Augur, Dorothy. Love's Old Song. 1984. pap. 6.95 (ISBN 0-89221-129-6, Pub. by Sonlife Intl). New Leaf.

Augustine. Confessions of St. Augustine. abr. ed. (Summit Books). 1977. pap. 4.95 (ISBN 0-8010-0118-8). Baker Bk.

Augustine, Aurelius. What Augustine Says. Geisler, Norman L., ed. 204p. (Orig.). 1982. pap. 8.95 (ISBN 0-8010-0185-4). Baker Bk.

Augustine, St. Aurelius. Select Letters. Baxter, James H., tr. LC 75-41012. Repr. of 1930 ed. 37.50 (ISBN 0-404-14503-5). AMS Pr.

Augustine, St. The Catholic & Manichaean Ways of Life. LC 66-11337. (Fathers of the Church Ser.: Vol. 56). 128p. 1966. 14.95x (ISBN 0-8132-0056-3). Cath U Pr.

--Christian Instruction, Admonition & Grace, The Christian Combat, Faith, Hope & Charity. LC 66-20314. (Fathers of the Church Ser.: Vol. 2). 494p. 1950. 34.95x (ISBN 0-8132-0002-4). Cath U Pr.

Augustine, Saint City of God, 2 Vols. Tasker, R. V., ed. Healey, John, tr. 1973. Repr. of 1945 ed. 12.95x ea. (ISBN 0-686-66408-6, Evman). Vol. 1 (ISBN 0-460-00982-6). Vol. 2 (ISBN 0-460-00983-4). Biblio Dist.

Augustine, St. City of God, Bks. 8-16. LC 63-19613. (Fathers of the Church Ser.: Vol. 14). 567p. 1952. 27.95x (ISBN 0-8132-0014-8). Cath U Pr.

--City of God, Bks. 17-22. LC 63-19613. (Fathers of the Church Ser.: Vol. 24). 461p. 1954. 27.95x (ISBN 0-8132-0024-5). Cath U Pr.

Augustine, Saint City of God Against the Pagans, 7 vols. (Loeb Classical Library: No. 411-417). 13.95x ea. Harvard U Pr.

Augustine, St. Commentary on the Lord's Sermon on the Mount with Seventeen Related Sermons. Bd. with Related Sermons. LC 63-18827. (Fathers of the Church Ser.: Vol. 11). 382p. 1951. 21.95x (ISBN 0-8132-0011-3). Cath U Pr.

--The Happy Life & Other Works. (Fathers of the Church Ser.: Vol. 5). 450p. 1948. 22.95x (ISBN 0-8132-0005-9). Cath U Pr.

--Letters, Nos. 1-82. LC 64-19948. (Fathers of the Church Ser.: Vol. 12). 420p. 1951. 22.95x (ISBN 0-8132-0012-1). Cath U Pr.

--Letters, Nos. 131-164. (Fathers of the Church Ser.: Vol. 20). 398p. 1953. 34.95x (ISBN 0-8132-0020-2). Cath U Pr.

--Letters, Nos. 83-130. LC 64-19948. (Fathers of the Church Ser.: Vol. 18). 401p. 1953. 34.95x (ISBN 0-8132-0018-0). Cath U Pr.

Augustine, Saint Presdestinacion of Saintes. Bd. with Perserveraunce Unto Thende. LC 68-54611. (English Experience Ser.: No. 32). Repr. of 1556 ed. 20.00 (ISBN 90-221-0032-4). Walter J Johnson.

Augustine, St. Retractations. (Fathers of the Church Ser.: Vol. 60). 451p. 1968. 17.95x (ISBN 0-8132-0060-1). Cath U Pr.

--St. Augustine on the Psalms, Vol. 1. Quasten, J. & Burghardt, W. J., eds. Hebgin, Scholastica & Corrigan, Felicitas, trs. LC 60-10722. (Ancient Christian Writers Ser.: No. 29). 360p. 1960. 12.95 (ISBN 0-8091-0104-1). Paulist Pr.

--St. Augustine, Sermons for Christmas & Epiphany. Quasten, J. & Plumpe, J., eds. Lawler, Thomas, tr. LC 78-62464. (Ancient Christian Writers Ser.: No. 15). 250p. 1952. 10.95 (ISBN 0-8091-0137-8). Paulist Pr.

--St. Augustine, the First Catechetical Instruction. Quasten, J. & Plumpe, J., eds. Christopher, Joseph P., tr. LC 78-62449. (Ancient Christian Writers Ser.: No. 2). 170p. 1946. 10.95 (ISBN 0-8091-0047-9). Paulist Pr.

--St. Augustine: The Greatness of the Soul, Vol. 9. Quasten, J. & Plumpe, J., eds. Colleran, Joseph M., tr. LC 78-62455. (Ancient Christian Writers Ser.). 255p. 1950. 14.95 (ISBN 0-8091-0060-6). Paulist Pr.

--The Teacher, The Free Choice of the Will, Grace & Free Will. Bd. with Two Works on Free Will. LC 67-30350. (Fathers of the Church Ser.: Vol. 59). 232p. 1968. 17.95x (ISBN 0-8132-0059-8). Cath U Pr.

--Treatises on Marriage & Other Subjects. LC 73-75002. (Fathers of the Church Ser.: Vol. 27). 456p. 1955. 34.95x (ISBN 0-8132-0027-X). Cath U Pr.

--Treatises on Various Moral Subjects. LC 65-18319. (Fathers of the Church Ser.: Vol. 16). 479p. 1952. 24.95x (ISBN 0-8132-0016-4). Cath U Pr.

--The Trinity. LC 63-72482. (Fathers of the Church Ser.: Vol. 45). 539p. 1963. 27.95x (ISBN 0-8132-0045-8). Cath U Pr.

Augustine, St. see St. Augustine.

Augustine of Hippo. Augustine of Hippo: Selected Writings. Clark, Mary T., tr. (Classics of Western Spirituality Ser.). 544p. 1984. pap. 12.95 (ISBN 0-8091-2573-0). Paulist Pr.

Augustinian Educational Conferences Staff. Augustinian Studies: Papers Read at Recent Augustinian Educational Conferences. facs. ed. LC 67-22052. (Essay Index Reprint Ser.). 1937. 16.00 (ISBN 0-8369-0163-0). Ayer Co Pubs.

Augustinus, Aurelius. Contra Felicem De Natura Boni Epistula Secundini, Contra Secundinum, Pt. 2. Bd. with De Natura Boni Epistula Secundini; Contra Secundinum. (Corpus Scriptorum Ecclesiasticorum Latinorum Ser: Vol. 25). (Lat.). Repr. of 1892 ed. unbound 50.00 (ISBN 0-384-02365-7). Johnson Repr.

--De Peccatorum Meritis et Remissione et de Baptismo Parvulorum, Ad Marcellinum Liber Tres, Bk. 3. Urba, C. F. & Zycha, I., eds. (Corpus Scriptorum Ecclesiasticorum Latinorum Ser: Vol. 60). 50.00 (ISBN 0-384-02490-4). Johnson Repr.

--De Perfectione Ivstitiae Hominis, De Gestis Pelagii, De Gratia Christi et De Peccato Originali Liber Duo. (Corpus Scriptorum Ecclesiasticorum Latinorum Ser: Vol. 42). Repr. of 1902 ed. 50.00 (ISBN 0-384-02495-5). Johnson Repr.

--De Utilitate Credendi, Pt. 1. Bd. with De Duabus Animabus; Contra Fortunatem; Contra Adimantum. (Corpus Scriptorum Ecclesiasticorum Latinorum Ser: Vol. 25). Repr. of 1891 ed. 50.00 (ISBN 0-384-02364-9). Johnson Repr.

Augustinus, Saint Aurelius. De Civitate Dei Liber 22: Sec. 5, 2 pts, Pts. 1 & 2. (Corpus Scriptorum Ecclesiasticorum Latinorum Ser: Vol. 40). Repr. of 1899 ed. 50.00 ea. (ISBN 0-384-02370-3). Johnson Repr.

--De Consensu Evangelistarum Librer4, Bk. 4. Weihrich, F., ed. (Corpus Scriptorum Ecclesiasticorum Latinorum Ser: Vol. 43). 40.00 (ISBN 0-384-02480-7). Johnson Repr.

--De Fide et Symbolo, De Fide et Operibus, De Agone Christiano, Pt. 3. (Corpus Scriptorum Ecclesiasticorum Latinorum Ser: Vol. 41). 65.00 (ISBN 0-384-02385-1). Johnson Repr.

--De Genesi ad Litteram Libri Duodecim Eiusdem Libri Capitula, Pt. 1. (Corpus Scriptorum Ecclesiasticorum Latinorum Ser: Vol. 28). 50.00 (ISBN 0-384-02485-8). Johnson Repr.

--Liber Qvi Appellatvr Specvlvm et Liber De Divinis Scriptvris. (Corpus Scriptorum Ecclesiasticorum Latinorum Ser: Vol. 12). 50.00 (ISBN 0-384-02505-6). Johnson Repr.

--Quaestionum in Heptateuchum Libri 7, Adnotationum in Iob Liber Unus. (Corpus Scriptorum Ecclesiasticorum Latinorum Ser: Vol. 38, Pt. 2). 50.00 (ISBN 0-384-02515-3). Johnson Repr.

--Spurious & Doubtful Works, Pseudo-Augustini Quaestiones Veterils et Novi Testamenti CXXVII. Souter, A., ed. (Corpus Scriptorum Ecclesiasticorum Latinorum Ser: Vol. 50). 40.00 (ISBN 0-384-02575-7). Johnson Repr.

Augustinus, Saint Scripta Contra Donatistas, 3 Vols, Pts. 3. (Corpus Scriptorum Ecclesiasticorum Latinorum Ser: Vols. 51, 52, 53). Set. 130.00 (ISBN 0-384-02553-6). Johnson Repr.

Auken, John Van see Van Auken, John.

Aukerman, Dale. Darkening Valley. 1981. pap. 8.95 (ISBN 0-8164-2295-8, HarpR). Har-Row.

Aulard, Alphonse. Christianity & the French Revolution. 1966. 27.50x (ISBN 0-86527-025-2). Fertig.

Auld, A. Graeme. Amos. (Old Testament Guides Ser.). 96p. 1986. pap. 3.95x (ISBN 1-85075-005-X, Pub. by JSOT Pr England). Eisenbrauns.

--First & Second Kings. LC 86-15658. (The Daily Study Bible - Old Testament Ser.). 266p. 1986. 15.95 (ISBN 0-664-21836-9); pap. 8.95 (ISBN 0-664-24585-4). Westminster.

--Joshua, Judges, & Ruth. LC 84-22076. (The Daily Study Bible-Old Testament). 290p. 1985. 15.95 (ISBN 0-664-21809-1); pap. 8.95 (ISBN 0-664-24576-5). Westminster.

--Joshua, Moses & the Land. 158p. 1981. 19.95 (ISBN 0-567-09306-9, Pub. by T & T Clark Ltd UK). Fortress.

Auld, William M. Christmas Traditions. LC 68-58167. 1968. Repr. of 1931 ed. 42.00x (ISBN 0-8103-3353-8). Gale.

--Christmas Traditions. 1977. lib. bdg. 59.95 (ISBN 0-8490-1619-3). Gordon Pr.

Auldtomes, Niles. Deathly Trivia from the Bible. (Odd Books for Odd Moments Ser.: No. 6). (Illus.). 120p. (Orig.). 1986. pap. 5.95 (ISBN 0-930937-34-1). Winds World Pr.

Aulen, Gustaf. Dag Hammarskjold's Fortress White Book: An Analysis of Markings. LC 75-84608. pap. 40.50 (2026974). Bks Demand UMI.

--The Faith of the Christian Church. rev. ed. Wahlstrom, Eric H., tr. from Swedish. LC 61-5302. 416p. 1973. pap. 8.95 (ISBN 0-8006-1655-3, 1-1655). Fortress.

Aulen, Gustaf E. Reformation & Catholicity. Wahlstrom, Eric H., tr. from Swedish. LC 78-25981. 1979. Repr. of 1961 ed. lib. bdg. 22.50x (ISBN 0-313-20809-3, AURC). Greenwood.

Aulen, Gustav. Christus Victor. (Orig.). 1969. pap. 6.95 (ISBN 0-02-083400-4, Collier). Macmillan.

Aulson, Nan & Aulson, Pam. Fun 'n Festive Holiday Trimmers. (Illus.). 1983. pap. 3.00 (ISBN 0-9601896-6-1). Patch as Patch.

Aulson, Pam, jt. auth. see Aulson, Nan.

Ault, Karuna, ed. see Hari Dass, Baba.

Ault, Karuna K., ed. see Hari Dass, Baba.

Ault, Norman. The Poets' Life of Christ. 30.00 (ISBN 0-686-17669-3). Quaker City.

--Poets's Life of Christ. LC 72-2513. (Select Bibliographies Reprint Ser). 1972. Repr. of 1922 ed. 22.00 (ISBN 0-8369-6847-6). Ayer Co Pubs.

Aultman, Donald S. Contemporary Christian Education. 122p. 1968. 4.95 (ISBN 0-87148-159-6); pap. 3.95 (ISBN 0-87148-160-X). Pathway Pr.

--Guiding Youth. 1977. pap. 3.95 (ISBN 0-87148-358-0). Pathway Pr.

--Learning Christian Leadership. 1960. 4.95 (ISBN 0-87148-501-X). Pathway Pr.

--The Ministry of Christian Teaching. 111p. 1966. 4.95 (ISBN 0-87148-554-0); pap. 3.95 (ISBN 0-87148-555-9). Pathway Pr.

Aultman, Donald S., jt. auth. see Conn, Charles P.

Aumann, Jordan. Christian Spirituality in the Catholic Tradition. 336p. 1985. pap. 11.95 (ISBN 0-89870-068-X). Ignatius Pr.

Aumann, Jordan, tr. see Arintero, John G.

Aumann, Jordan, tr. see John Paul II, Pope.

Aumann, Jordan, tr. see Louis Of Granada.

Aune, Bruce. Kant's Theory of Morals. LC 79-17938. 1980. 26.50 (ISBN 0-691-07238-8). Princeton U Pr.

--Metaphysics: The Elements. LC 85-2540. xiv, 235p. 1985. 25.00 (ISBN 0-8166-1412-1); pap. 12.95 (ISBN 0-8166-1414-8). U of Minn Pr.

Aune, David E. Jesus & the Synoptic Gospels: A Bibliographic Study Guide. Branson, Mark L., ed. (TSF - IBR Bibliographic Study Guides Ser.). 99p. (Orig.). 1981. pap. 2.95 (ISBN 0-8308-5498-3). Inter-Varsity.

--The New Testament in Its Literary Environment. Meeks, Wayne A., ed. (Library of Early Christianity: Vol. 8). 262p. 1987. 22.95 (ISBN 0-664-21912-8). Westminster.

--Prophecy in Early Christianity & the Ancient Mediterranean World. 400p. 1983. 29.95 (ISBN 0-8028-3584-8). Eerdmans.

Aunt Naomi, pseud. Jewish Fairy Tales & Legends. 16.95 (ISBN 0-89190-314-3, Pub. by Am Repr). Amereon ltd.

Auraham, Samuel & Kushner, Arlene. Treacherous Journey: My Escape from Ethiopia. 1986. 14.95 (ISBN 0-933503-46-6). Shapolsky Pubs.

Aurelio, John. Gather Round: Christian Fairy Tales for All Ages. LC 81-84389. (Illus.). 128p. (Orig.). 1982. pap. 5.95 (ISBN 0-8091-2444-0). Paulist Pr.

--Mosquitoes in Paradise. 144p. 1985. pap. 7.95 (ISBN 0-8245-0698-7). Crossroad NY.

Aurelio, John R. Once upon a Christmas Time: Stories for a Family Christmas. (Illus.). 224p. 1986. pap. 8.95 (ISBN 0-8091-2819-5). Paulist Pr.

--Story Sunday: Christian Fairy Tales for Children, Parents & Educators. LC 78-51587. 104p. 1978. pap. 3.95 (ISBN 0-8091-2115-8). Paulist Pr.

Aurelius, Marcus. Meditations. Grube, G. M. A., ed. & tr. LC 83-22722. (HPC Philosophical Classics Ser.). 170p. 1984. lib. bdg. 16.50 (ISBN 0-915145-78-2); pap. text ed. 4.95 (ISBN 0-915145-79-0). Hackett Pub.

Aurobindo. Life Companion Paperback Supplement Series. (Life Companion Ser.). 1339p. (Orig.). 1984. pap. 39.25 (ISBN 0-89744-013-7, Pub. by Madanlal Himatsinghlea). Auromere.

--Sri Aurobindo Life Companion Library. (Life Companion Ser.). 4522p. 1984. Repr. of 1979 ed. 111.85 (ISBN 0-317-19956-0, Pub. by Mandanlal Himatsinghlea). Auromere.

Aurobindo, tr. from Fr. Prayers & Meditations. rev. ed. 380p. (Orig.). 1979. pap. 16.00 (ISBN 0-89744-998-3, Sri Aurobindo Ashram Trust India); text ed. 21.00 (ISBN 0-89744-219-9). Auromere.

Aurobindo, Sri. Bases of Yoga. 108p. 1983. pap. 3.50 (ISBN 0-89744-012-9). Auromere.

--Bases of Yoga. 168p. 1981. pap. 2.00 (ISBN 0-89071-309-X, Pub. by Sri Aurobindo Ashram India). Matagiri.

--Bhagavad Gita in Light of Sri Aurobindo. Maheshwar, ed. 1979. 20.00 (ISBN 0-89744-902-9); pap. 15.00 (ISBN 0-89744-903-7). Auromere.

--Dictionary of Sri Aurobindo's Yoga. Pandit, Sri M., ed. 1979. Repr. of 1966 ed. 7.95 (ISBN 0-941524-04-3). Lotus Light.

--The Durga Stotra. 31p. (Orig.). 1982. pap. 5.00 (ISBN 0-89744-235-0). Auromere.

--Essays on the Gita. 1979. 20.00 (ISBN 0-89744-907-X); lib. bdg. 30.00 (ISBN 0-89744-906-1); pap. 16.00 (ISBN 0-89744-908-8). Auromere.

--Essays on the Gita. 588p. 1983. 12.50 (ISBN 0-89071-297-2, Pub. by Sri Aurobindo Ashram India); pap. 8.75 (ISBN 0-89071-296-4, Pub. by Sri Aurobindo Ashram India). Matagiri.

--The Future Evolution of Man. Saint-Hilaire, P. B., ed. 157p. 1982. pap. 2.95 (ISBN 0-89071-323-5, Pub. by Sri Aurobindo Ashram India). Matagiri.

--The Gita with Text, Translation & Sri Aurobindo's Comments. rev. ed. Jhunjhunwala, Shyam S., ed. 270p. 1974. 9.45 (ISBN 0-89071-207-7); pap. 4.50 (ISBN 0-89071-200-X). Matagiri.

--Hymns to the Mystic Fire. Aurobindo, Sri, tr. Date not set. 18.00 (ISBN 0-89744-918-5). Auromere.

--Hymns to the Mystic Fire. 506p. 1985. pap. 14.00 (ISBN 0-89071-298-0, Pub. by Sri Aurobindo Ashram India). Matagiri.

--Ideal of the Karmayogin. 170p. Date not set. 7.00 (ISBN 0-317-17429-0). Auromere.

--Letters on Yoga, Vol. I. 502p. 1979. 16.00 (ISBN 0-89744-984-3, Pub. by Sri Aurogindo Ashram Trust); pap. 12.00 (ISBN 0-89744-985-1). Auromere.

--Letters on Yoga, Vol. III. 720p. 1979. 22.00 (ISBN 0-89744-988-6, Pub. by Sri Aurobindo Ashram Trust); pap. 19.00 (ISBN 0-89744-989-4). Auromere.

--Letters on Yoga, Vol. II. 587p. 1979. 19.00 (ISBN 0-89744-986-X, Pub. by Sri Arobindo Ashram Trust); pap. 16.00 (ISBN 0-89744-987-8). Auromere.

--Letters on Yoga, 2 vols. (Life Companion Library Bible Paper Ser.). 1984p. 40.00 (ISBN 0-89744-014-5). Auromere.

--Life Divine. (Life Companion Library Bible Paper Ser.). 1112p. 1983. Repr. of 1949 ed. deluxe ed. 24.95 (ISBN 0-89744-008-0); write for info. Auromere.

--The Life Divine. 1112p. 1982. 19.50 (ISBN 0-89071-301-4, Pub. by Sri Aurobindo Ashram India); pap. 15.00 (ISBN 0-89071-300-6, Pub. by Sri Aurobindo Ashram India). Matagiri.

--The Life Divine: A Commentary on Isha Upanished. 108p. (Orig.). 1981. pap. 7.50 (ISBN 0-89744-230-X, Pub. by Sri Aurobindo Ashram Trust India). Auromere.

--Love Treasures: "The Mother", Book One. (Illus.). 98p. 1985. 36.00x (ISBN 0-89071-333-2, Pub. by Sri Aurobindo Ashram India). Matagiri.

--The Message of the Gita: With Text, Translation & Notes. Roy, Anilbaran, ed. (Sanskrit & Eng.). 1979. (Pub. by Sri Aurobindo Ashram Trust India); pap. 9.00 (ISBN 0-89744-977-0, Pub. by Sri Aurobindo Ashramtrust India). Auromere.

--More Lights on Yoga. 1979. pap. 3.50 (ISBN 0-89744-950-9). Auromere.

--The Mother, with Letters on the Mother & Translations of Prayers & Meditations. 500p. 1982. 11.95 (ISBN 0-89071-311-1, Pub. by Sri Aurobindo Ashram India); pap. 8.95 (ISBN 0-89071-310-3, Pub. by Sri Aurobindo Ashram India). Matagiri.

--Practical Guide to Integral Yoga. 7th ed. Manibhai, ed. 1979. pap. 9.00 (ISBN 0-89744-942-8). Auromere.

--The Problem of Rebirth. 186p. 1983. 7.50 (ISBN 0-89071-305-7, Pub. by Sri Aurobindo Ashram India); pap. 5.50 (ISBN 0-89071-304-9, Pub. by Sri Aurobindo Ashram India). Matagiri.

--The Riddle of This World. 98p. 1984. pap. 1.25 (ISBN 0-89071-306-5, Pub. by Sri Aurobindo Ashram India). Matagiri.

--Santan Dharma Ka Mahatva: (Uttarpara Speech) 14p. 3.00 (ISBN 0-317-17480-0). Auromere.

--The Secret of the Veda. (Sanskrit & Eng.). 1979. oversize ed. 40.00 (ISBN 0-89744-975-4, Pub. by Sri Aurobindo Ashram Trust India); pap. 30.00. Auromere.

--The Secret of the Veda. 581p. 1982. 15.00 (ISBN 0-89071-303-0, Pub. by Sri Aurobindo Ashram India); pap. 10.00 (ISBN 0-89071-302-2, Pub. by Sri Aurobindo Ashram India). Matagiri.

--Sri Aurobindo Birth Centenary Library: Complete Writings of Sri Aurobindo, 30 vols. 1979. Set. 300.00x (ISBN 0-89744-964-9); lib. bdg. 400.00x (ISBN 0-89744-965-7). Auromere.

--Sri Aurobindo on Himself. 513p. 1985. 14.95 (ISBN 0-89071-317-0, Pub. by Sri Aurobindo Ashram India); pap. 11.75 (ISBN 0-89071-316-2, Pub. by Sri Aurobindo Ashram India). Matagiri.

--The Supramental Manifestation on Earth. 108p. 1980. pap. 2.25 (ISBN 0-89071-307-3, Pub. by Sri Aurobindo Ashram India). Matagiri.

--The Synthesis of Yoga. 1976. pap. 8.00 (ISBN 0-89071-268-9). Matagiri.

--Synthesis of Yoga. 6th ed. 1979p. 36.00 (ISBN 0-89744-931-2). Auromere.

--Synthesis of Yoga. 1979p. 30.00 (ISBN 0-89744-932-0). Auromere.

--Synthesis of Yoga. (Life Companion Bible Bks.). 1984p. 24.95 (ISBN 0-89744-017-X). Auromere.

--The Synthesis of Yoga. 899p. 1984. 16.75 (ISBN 0-89071-313-8, Pub. by Sri Aurobindo Ashram India); pap. 12.50 (ISBN 0-89071-312-X, Pub. by Sri Aurobindo Ashram India). Matagiri.

--Thoughts & Glimpses. 30p. 1973. pap. 0.60 (ISBN 0-89071-308-1, Pub. by Sri Aurobindo Ashram India). Matagiri.

--The Upanishads. (Sanskrit & Eng.). 466p. 1981. 40.00 (ISBN 0-89744-026-9, Pub. by Sri Aurobindo Ashram Trust India); pap. 30.00 (ISBN 0-89744-025-0). Auromere.

--The Upanishads: Texts, Translations & Commentaries, Pt. 1. 466p. 1986. 14.95 (ISBN 0-89071-295-6, Pub. by Sri Aurobindo Ashram India); pap. 11.95 (ISBN 0-89071-294-8). Matagiri.

--The Yoga & Its Objects. 33p. 1984. pap. 0.75 (ISBN 0-89071-314-6, Pub. by Sri Aurobindo Ashram India). Matagiri.

Aurobindo, Sri & Mother. The Hierachy of Minds. Sobel, Prem & Sobel, Jyoti, eds. 174p. 1984. pap. 5.50 (ISBN 0-89071-324-3, Pub. by Sri Aurobindo Ashram India). Matagiri.

Aurobindo, Sri, jt. auth. see Sri Aurobindo Ashram Publications Department Staff.

Aurobindo, Sri, tr. see Pandit, M. P.

Aurobindo, Sri, tr. see Sri Aurobindo.

Aus, Roger, jt. auth. see Hultgren, Arland J.

Ausmus, Harry J. The Polite Escape: On the Myth of Secularization. xii, 189p. 1982. lib. bdg. 22.95x (ISBN 0-8214-0650-7, 82-84192). Ohio U Pr.

--Will Herberg: From Right to Right. LC 86-19357. (Studies in Religion). xx, 276p. 1987. 29.95x (ISBN 0-8078-1724-4). U of NC Pr.

Austgen, Robert J. Natural Motivation in the Pauline Epistles. rev. ed. 1969. 10.95 (ISBN 0-268-00374-2). U of Notre Dame Pr.

Austin, Althea. First Impressions: From the Diary of Althea Austin. 1984. 6.95 (ISBN 0-533-05806-6). Vantage.

Austin, Bill. How to Get What You Pray For. LC 83-50970. 160p. 1984. pap. 4.95 (ISBN 0-8423-1473-3); leader's guide 2.95 (ISBN 0-8423-1474-1). Tyndale.

--When God Has Put You on Hold. 112p. 1986. pap. 4.95 (ISBN 0-8423-7989-4). Tyndale.

Austin, Bill R. Austin's Topical History of Christianity. 527p. 1983. 14.95 (ISBN 0-8423-0096-1). Tyndale.

Austin, E. L. Earth's Greatest Day. 96p. (Orig.). 1980. pap. 3.95 (ISBN 0-8010-0163-3). Baker Bk.

--Gift of Christmas. pap. 3.95 (ISBN 0-8010-0149-8). Baker Bk.

Austin, Gerard. Anointing with the Spirit. (Reformed Rites of the Catholic Church Ser.: Vol. 2). 192p. (Orig.). 1985. pap. 10.95 (ISBN 0-916134-70-9). Pueblo Pub Co.

Austin, Lou. You Are Greater Than You Know. 7.50 (ISBN 0-934538-16-6); pap. 4.50 (ISBN 0-934538-11-5). Partnership Foundation.

Austin, Mary. Experiences Facing Death. Kastenbaum, Robert, ed. LC 76-19557. (Death and Dying Ser.). 1977. Repr. of 1931 ed. lib. bdg. 23.50x (ISBN 0-405-09553-8). Ayer Co Pubs.

Austin, Mrs., ed. A Memoir of the Reverend Sydney Smith by His Daughter, Lady Holland, 2 vols. 1973. Repr. of 1855 ed. 45.00 set (ISBN 0-8274-1210-X). R West.

Austin, R. W. Sufis of Andalusia: The Ruh Al-Quds & Al-Durrat Al-Fakhirah of Ibn 'Arabi. Austin, R. W., tr. LC 77-165230. (California Library Reprint: Vol. 91). 1978. Repr. of 1971 ed. 33.00x (ISBN 0-520-03553-4). U of Cal Pr.

Austin, R. W., ed. Ibn-Al-Arabi: The Bezels of Wisdom. LC 80-83892. (The Classics of Western Spirituality Ser.). 320p. 1980. 12.95 (ISBN 0-8091-0313-3); pap. 10.95 (ISBN 0-8091-2331-2). Paulist Pr.

Austin, William H. The Relevance of Natural Science to Theology. LC 75-43222. (Library of Philosophy & Religion). 132p. 1976. text ed. 28.50x (ISBN 0-06-490240-4, 06321). B&N Imports.

Aust-Schminke, Janith. From Mary's Side: Summons for Change. 160p. (Orig.). Date not set. price not set (ISBN 0-916865-00-2); pap. price not set (ISBN 0-916865-01-0). Sansper.

Ausubel, Nathan. Book of Jewish Knowledge. (Illus.). 1962. 23.95 (ISBN 0-517-09746-X). Crown.

--Pictorial History of the Jewish People: From Biblical Times to Our Own Day Throughout the World. rev ed. (Illus.). 1984. 19.95 (ISBN 0-517-55283-3). Crown.

--Pictorial History of the Jewish People. (Illus.). 1953. 19.95 (ISBN 0-517-09757-5). Crown.

Ausubel, Nathan, ed. Treasury of Jewish Folklore. 1948. 14.95 (ISBN 0-517-50293-3). Crown.

--Treasury of Jewish Humor. LC 51-10639. 1951. 17.95 (ISBN 0-385-04499-2). Doubleday.

Autery & Holl. Help I Need a Bulletin Board. pap. 5.50 (ISBN 0-89137-621-6). Quality Pubns.

Autry, Jarry, jt. auth. see Lindsay, Gordon.

Auxentios, Hieromonk, jt. auth. see Chrysostomos.

Auxentios, Hieromonk, jt. auth. see Chrysostomos, Archimandrite.

Auxentios, Hieromonk, tr. see Cavarnos, Constantine.

Auxter, Thomas. Kant's Moral Teleology. LC 82-7838. xvi, 194p. 1982. 16.95 (ISBN 0-86554-022-5, MUP-H23). Mercer Univ Pr.

Avadhuta. Avadhuta Gita: The Song of the Ever-Free. Chetanananda, tr. from Sanskrit. 138p. 1985. text ed. 3.50 (ISBN 0-87481-224-0, Pub. by Advaita Ashram India). Vedanta Pr.

Avallone, Paul. Reason, Religion, & Kindness. 3rd, rev. ed. LC 77-83952. 1977. pap. 4.75 (ISBN 0-89944-030-4). Don Bosco Multimedia.

Avallone, Paul P. The Consecrated Woman: A Guide to the Don Bosco Volunteers. (Salesian Family Ser.). 27p. 1983. pap. 3.00 (ISBN 0-89944-075-4). Don Bosco Multimedia.

Avalon, A., jt. auth. see Vidyaratna, T.

Avalon, Arthur, pseud. Mahanirvana Tantra. (Sanskrit.). 473p. 1982. text ed. 28.00 (ISBN 0-89744-237-7). Auromere.

Avalon, Arthur. The Serpent Power. LC 74-75259. (Illus.). 1974. pap. 8.95 (ISBN 0-486-23058-9). Dover.

--Shakti & Shakta. 1978. pap. 8.95 (ISBN 0-486-23645-5). Dover.

--Tantra of the Great Liberation. (Illus.). 512p. 1913. pap. 8.50 (ISBN 0-486-20150-3). Dover.

Avalon, Arthur & Shastri, Lakshmana. Tantraraja Tantra. (Sanskrit.). 740p. 1982. text ed. 52.00 (ISBN 0-89744-238-5). Auromere.

Avalon, Arthur, ed., pseud. Prapanchasara Tantra. (Sanskrit.). 617p. 1982. text ed. 48.00 (ISBN 0-89744-239-3). Auromere.

Avato, Rose, jt. ed. see Foy, Felician A.

Avato, Rose M., jt. ed. see Foy, Felician A.

Avedichian, Gabriel, tr. see Migne, J. P.

Avedon, John F. An Interview with the Dalai Lama. LC 80-83015. (Illus.). 83p. (Orig.). 1980. pap. 6.95 (ISBN 0-937896-00-4). Littlebird.

Aveling, Harry, tr. Arjuna in Meditation. 1976. flexible cloth 8.00 (ISBN 0-89253-800-7). Ind-US Inc.

Aveling, J. C. The Jesuits. LC 81-40482. 396p. 1982. 19.95 (ISBN 0-8128-2838-0). Stein & Day.

Aveling, J. C., et al. Rome & The Anglicans: Historical & Doctrinal Aspects of Anglican-Roman Catholic Relations. Haase, Wolfgang, ed. 301p. 1982. 81.50 (ISBN 3-11-008267-5). De Gruyter.

Aven, Russell E. Devotions for Laymen...by a Layman. LC 81-67751. 1982. pap. 6.50 (ISBN 0-8054-5185-4). Broadman.

Aveni, Anthony F. Skywatchers of Ancient Mexico. (Texas Pan American Ser.). (Illus.). 369p. 1980. text ed. 30.00x (ISBN 0-292-77557-1). U of Tex Pr.

Aveni, Anthony F., ed. Native American Astronomy. LC 76-53569. (Illus.). 304p. 1977. text ed. 18.95x (ISBN 0-292-75511-2). U of Tex Pr.

Avens, Roberts. Imaginal Body: Para-Jungian Reflections on Soul, Imagination & Death. LC 81-43814. 264p. (Orig.). 1982. lib. bdg. 29.00 (ISBN 0-8191-2411-7); pap. text ed. 13.25 (ISBN 0-8191-2412-5). U Pr of Amer.

--The New Gnosis: Heidegger, Hillman, & Angels. LC 84-5297. 155p. (Orig.). 1984. 18.50 (ISBN 0-88214-328-X); pap. 12.50 (ISBN 0-88214-327-1). Spring Pubns.

Avento, Genarro P. The Church's Moral Teaching, Bk. III. pap. 3.95 (ISBN 0-941850-08-0). Sunday Pubns.

Averett, Joy & Smith, Donna. Bible Handwork Ideas for Twos & Threes. 1983. pap. 3.25 (ISBN 0-89137-613-5). Quality Pubns.

Averintsev, Sergei. Religya i Literatura: Religion & Literature. LC 81-4115. (Rus.). 140p. 1981. pap. 7.00 (ISBN 0-938920-02-2). Hermitage.

Avery, Benedict R., tr. see Gregorius I.

Avery, Kevin Quinn. The Numbers of Life. LC 76-45969. 354p. 1977. pap. 8.95 (ISBN 0-385-12629-8, Dolp). Doubleday.

Avery, Valeen T., jt. auth. see Newell, Linda K.

Avery-Peck, Alan J. Mishnah's Division of Agriculture: A History & Theology of Seder Zeriam. (Brown Judaic Studies). 1985. 39.25 (ISBN 0-89130-888-1, 14-00-79); pap. 32.25 (ISBN 0-89130-889-X). Scholars Pr GA.

Avery-Peck, Alan J., tr. from Hebrew-Aramaic. The Talmud of Babylonia: An American Translation, VII Tractate Besah. (Brown Judaic Studies). 358p. 1986. pap. 39.95 (ISBN 1-55540-054-X, 14-01-17). Scholars Pr GA.

Avesta. The Hymns of Zarathustra. Henning, M., tr. LC 78-20446. 1985. Repr. of 1952 ed. 21.00 (ISBN 0-88355-826-2). Hyperion Conn.

Aviad, Janet. Return to Judaism: Religious Renewal in Israel. LC 82-17663. xiv, 194p. 1985. pap. 8.95 (ISBN 0-226-03235-3). U of Chicago Pr.

Aviad, Janet, jt. auth. see Elazar, Daniel J.

Avicenna. Avicenna on Theology. Arberry, Arthur J., tr. LC 78-59000. 1983. Repr. of 1951 ed. 15.00 (ISBN 0-88355-676-6). Hyperion Conn.

--Avicenna'a Psychology. Rahman, F., ed. LC 79-2848. 127p. 1984. Repr. of 1952 ed. 15.25 (ISBN 0-8305-0024-3). Hyperion Conn.

Avila, Charles. Ownership: Early Christian Teaching. LC 83-8330. 256p. (Orig.). 1981. pap. 9.95 (ISBN 0-88344-384-8). Orbis Bks.

Avila, Rafael. Worship & Politics. Neely, Alan, tr. LC 81-38356. 144p. (Orig.). 1981. pap. 6.95 (ISBN 0-88344-714-2). Orbis Bks.

Avineri, Shlomo. The Making of Modern Zionism: Intellectual Origins of the Jewish State. LC 81-66102. 272p. 1981. 15.50 (ISBN 0-465-04328-3). Basic.

--The Making of Modern Zionism: The Intellectual Origins of the Jewish State. LC 81-66102. 244p. 1984. pap. 7.95 (ISBN 0-465-04330-5, CN 5113). Basic.

Avis, Paul. Truth Beyond Words: Problems & Prospects for Anglican-Roman Catholic Unity. 142p. (Orig.). 1985. pap. 7.95 (ISBN 0-936384-26-3). Cowley Pubns.

Avis, Paul, ed. A History of Christian Theology, Vol. 1: The Science of Theology. 336p. (Orig.). 1986. pap. 14.95 (ISBN 0-8028-0195-1). Eerdmans.

Avis, Paul D. The Church in the Theology of the Reformers. Toon, Peter & Martin, Ralph, eds. LC 80-16186. (New Foundations Theological Library). 256p. 1981. 6.49 (ISBN 0-8042-3708-5); pap. 2.99 (ISBN 0-8042-3728-X). John Knox.

Avishai, Bernard. The Tragedy of Zionism. LC 85-10235. 389p. 1985. 19.95 (ISBN 0-374-27863-6). FS&G.

--The Tragedy of Zionism. 389p. 1986. pap. 8.95 (ISBN 0-374-52044-5). FS&G.

Avi-Yonah, Michael. The Art of Mosaics. LC 72-10793. (The Lerner Archaeology Ser.: Digging up the Past). (Illus.). 96p. 1975. PLB 8.95 (ISBN 0-8225-0828-1). Lerner Pubns.

--The Jews under Roman & Byzantine Rule: A Political History of Palestine from the Bar-Kokhba War to the Arab Conquest. LC 84-5612. Orig. Title: The Jews of Palestine. (Illus.). 304p. 1984. Repr. 23.00x (ISBN 0-8052-3580-9). Schocken.

Avi-Yonah, Michael, jt. auth. see Aharoni, Yohanon.

Avi-Yonah, Michael, jt. auth. see Mazar, Benjamin.

Avi-Yonah, Michael see Mazar, Benjamin & Avi-Yonah, Michael.

Avni, Baruch, tr. see Nachman of Breslov.

Avni, Haim. Spain, the Jews & Franco. Shimoni, Emanuel, tr. from Hebrew. LC 80-39777. 320p. 1981. 19.95 (ISBN 0-8276-0188-3, 469). Jewish Pubns.

Avramis, Tom. Preparing to Receive Holy Communion. 1986. pap. 1.95 (ISBN 0-937032-43-3). Light&Life Pub Co MN.

Aw, S. E. Chemical Evolution. LC 81-70575. 1982. pap. 9.95 (ISBN 0-89051-082-2). Master Bks.

Axe, Ruth F., et al, eds. see Oak, Henry L.

Axel, Larry E., jt. ed. see Dean, William.

Axel, Larry E., ed. see Wieman, Henry N.

Axelrad, Albert S. Call to Conscience: Jews, Judaism, & Conscientious Objection. LC 85-24010. 207p. 1986. text ed. 25.00x (ISBN 0-88125-092-9); pap. 14.95x (ISBN 0-88125-081-3). Ktav.

--Meditations of a Maverick Rabbi. Whitfield, Stephen, ed. 256p. (Orig.). 1985. pap. 8.95 (ISBN 0-940646-12-9). Rossel Bks.

--Refusenik: Voices of Struggle & Hope. 75p. (Orig.). 1986. pap. text ed. 9.95x (ISBN 0-932269-56-7). Wyndham Hall.

Axton, Richard. European Drama of the Early Middle Ages. LC 74-24680. 1975. 19.95x (ISBN 0-8229-3301-2). U of Pittsburgh Pr.

Ayala, Francisco. El Problema de Liberalismo. 2nd ed. pap. 4.35 (ISBN 0-8477-2402-6). U of PR Pr.

Ayalon, O., et al. The Holocaust & Its Perseverance. (SANAI Ser.: No. 2). 64p. 1983. pap. text ed. 9.95x (Pub. by Van Gorcum Holland). Humanities.

Ayalon, Ofra, et al. The Holocaust & Its Perserverance: Stress, Coping, & Disorder. (Sinai-Papers, Studies in Integral Psychology). 80p. 1983. pap. text ed. 8.00 (Pub. by Van Gorcum Holland). Longwood Pub Group.

Ayalti, Hanan J., ed. Yiddish Proverbs. LC 49-11135. (Illus., Bilingual). 1963. pap. 4.75 (ISBN 0-8052-0050-9). Schocken.

Ayandele, Emmanuel A. Missionary Impact on Modern Nigeria, 1842-1914. (Ibadan History Ser.). 1967. pap. text ed. 17.50x (ISBN 0-582-64512-3). Humanities.

Ayati, Ibrahim. A Probe into the History of Ashura. Tr. of Barasi Tarkh-i-Ashura. 234p. 1985. pap. 9.00 (ISBN 0-941724-41-7). Islamic Seminary.

Ayatollah Morteza Motahhari. Spiritual Discourses. Tawhidi, M. Salman, ed. Pazargadi, Aluddin, tr. 139p. (Orig.). 1986. pap. 4.95 (ISBN 0-9616897-0-6). MSA Inc.

Ayatullah Al-Khu'i. Islamic Practical Law, Pts. I & II. Shaikh Muhammad Sarwar, tr. from Arabic. 1981. 15.00 (ISBN 0-941724-08-5); pap. 10.00 (ISBN 0-941724-01-8). Islamic Seminary.

--Rules of HAJJ. Shaikh Muhammad Sarwar, tr. from Arabic. 50p. 1981. pap. 3.00 (ISBN 0-941724-02-6). Islamic Seminary.

Aycock, Alan, jt. auth. see Leach, Edmund.

Aycock, Don, ed. Preaching with Purpose & Power: Selected E. Y. Mullins Lectures on Preaching. LC 81-22388. vi, 314p. 1982. 15.95 (ISBN 0-86554-027-6, MUP-H27). Mercer Univ Pr.

Aycock, Don M. The E. Y. Mullins Lectures on Preaching with Reference to the Aristotelian Triad. LC 79-6080. 113p. 1980. text ed. 20.50 (ISBN 0-8191-0981-9); pap. text ed. 9.25 (ISBN 0-8191-0982-7). U Pr of Amer.

--Heralds to a New Age: Preaching for the Twenty-First Century. 228p. 1985. 11.95 (ISBN 0-87178-352-5). Brethren.

--Walking Straight in a Crooked World. (Orig.). 1987. pap. 3.25 (ISBN 0-8054-5034-3). Broadman.

Aycock, Don M. & Goss, Leonard G. Writing Religiously. 1986. 13.95 (ISBN 0-8010-0210-9). Baker Bk.

Aycock, Wendell M. & Klein, Theodore M., eds. Classical Mythology in Twentieth-Century Thought & Literature. (Proceedings of the Comparative Literature Symposium, Vol. XI). (Illus.). 221p. (Orig.). 1980. pap. 12.00 (ISBN 0-89672-079-9). Tex Tech Univ Pr.

Ayer, Joseph C. Sourcebook of Ancient Church History. LC 70-113536. Repr. of 1913 ed. lib. bdg. 64.50 (ISBN 0-404-00436-9). AMS Pr.

Ayers, Robert H. Judaism & Christianity: Origins, Developments & Recent Trends. LC 83-3548. (Illus.). 478p. (Orig.). 1983. lib. bdg. 35.75 (ISBN 0-8191-3156-3); pap. text ed. 16.50 (ISBN 0-8191-3157-1). U Pr of Amer.

Ayling, Stanley. John Wesley. 1983. 16.95 (ISBN 0-687-20376-7). Abingdon.

Aylmer, G. E. & Cant, R. C., eds. A History of York Minster. (Illus.). 1977. 32.50x (ISBN 0-19-817199-4). Oxford U Pr.

Aylward, Gladys. La Pequena Gran Mujer en la China. Orig. Title: Little Woman in China. (Span.). 160p. 1974. pap. 3.50 (ISBN 0-8254-1048-7). Kregel.

Aylward, Gladys & Hunter, Christine. Gladys Aylward. 1970. pap. 3.50 (ISBN 0-8024-2986-6). Moody.

Aymes, Maria de la Cruz see De la Cruz Aymes, Maria, et al.

Aymes, Maria de la Maria see De La Cruz Aymes, Maria, et al.

Ayoub, M. Great Tiding: Thirtieth Part of Holy Quran. pap. 4.50 (ISBN 0-317-01597-4). Kazi Pubns.

Ayoub, Mahmoud. Redemptive Suffering in Islam. (Religion & Society Ser.: No. 10). 1978. 35.25 (ISBN 90-279-7948-0). Mouton.

Ayoub, Mahmoud M. The Qur'an & Its Interpreters, Vol. 1. LC 82-21713. 290p. 1984. 29.50x (ISBN 0-87395-727-X). State U NY Pr.

Ayres, C. E. Science - The False Messiah. Bd. with Holier Than Thou; The Way of the Righteous. LC 71-130660. 1973. Repr. of 1927 ed. 37.50x (ISBN 0-678-00774-8). Kelley.

Ayyar, P. V. South Indian Shrines. 648p. 1986. Repr. 14.00X (ISBN 0-8364-1721-6, Pub. by Usha). South Asia Bks.

Azami, M. M. Early Hadith Literature. LC 77-90341. 1978. 10.50 (ISBN 0-89259-012-2). Am Trust Pubns.

Azami, Mustafa. Studies in Hadith Methodology & Literature. Beg, Anwer, ed. LC 77-90335. 1978. pap. 5.50 (ISBN 0-89259-011-4); pap. text ed. 5.50. Am Trust Pubns.

Azcar. How to Talk Directly with God. 51p. 1977. pap. 1.95 (ISBN 0-931865-05-0). Psychegenics.

Azevedo, Carlos de see De Azevedo, Carlos.

Azevedo, Marcello C. de see De Azevedo, Marcello C.

Azhar, A. Christianity in History. 12.50 (ISBN 0-686-18580-3). Kazi Pubns.

Aziz, Barbara N. & Kapstein, M. Soundings in Tibetan Civilization. 1986. 32.00x (ISBN 0-8364-1587-6, Pub. by Manohar India). South Asia Bks.

Azizullah. Glimpses of Hadith, 3. pap. 6.50 (ISBN 0-686-18380-0). Kazi Pubns.

--Glimpses of the Holy Quran. pap. 6.50 (ISBN 0-686-18517-X). Kazi Pubns.

Aziz-us-Samad, U. Islam & Christianity. 150p. 1985. write for info. (Pub. by IIFSO Kuwait). New Era Pubns MI.

Azrael. Wisdom for the New Age. LC 81-85815. 208p. (Orig.). 1982. pap. 6.95 (ISBN 0-87516-477-3). De Vorss.

Azzam, Abd-Al-Rahman. Eternal Message of Muhammad. 1964. 9.50 (ISBN 0-8159-5401-8). Devin.

Azzam, Salem. Islam & Contemporary Society. LC 82-253. 256p. 1982. 16.95x (ISBN 0-582-78323-2); pap. 7.95x (ISBN 0-582-78322-4). Longman.

B

Baal, J. van see Van Baal, T. & Van Beek, W. E.

Baalen, Jan K. Van see Van Baalen, Jan K.

Baali, F. Ibn Khaldun's Science of Human Culture. 16.50 (ISBN 0-317-01604-0). Kazi Pubns.

Baal-Teshuva, Jacob. Mission of Israel. 1963. 10.95 (ISBN 0-8315-0046-8). Speller.

Baars, Conrad. The Homosexual's Search for Happiness. (Synthesis Ser.). 1977. pap. 1.25 (ISBN 0-8199-0709-X). Franciscan Herald.

Baars, Conrad W. Born Only Once: The Miracle of Affirmation. 1977. pap. 4.00 (ISBN 0-8199-0700-6). Franciscan Herald.

--Feeling & Healing Your Emotions. LC 79-53629. 1979. pap. 5.95 (ISBN 0-88270-384-6, Pub. by Logos). Bridge Pub.

--How to Treat & Prevent the Crisis in the Priesthood. 1972. pap. 0.75 (ISBN 0-8199-0399-X). Franciscan Herald.

--A Priest for Now: Masculine & Celibate. LC 72-87091. (Synthesis Ser). 1972. pap. 1.25 (ISBN 0-8199-0375-2). Franciscan Herald.

Baars, Conrad W. & Terruwe, Anna A. Psychic Wholeness & Healing: Using All the Powers of the Human Psyche. LC 81-4964. 245p. (Orig.). 1981. pap. 8.95 (ISBN 0-8189-0410-0). Alba.

Baasten, Matthew. Pride According to Gregory the Great: A Study of the Moralia. LC 86-18057. (Studies in the Bible & Early Christianity: Vol. 7). 216p. 1986. lib. bdg. 49.95 (ISBN 0-88946-606-8). E Mellen.

Bab. Selections from the Writings of the Bab. LC 79-670141. 1976. 14.95 (ISBN 0-85398-066-7, 105-050); pap. 7.95 (ISBN 0-85398-135-3). Baha'i.

Bab, jt. auth. see Bahaullah.

Baba, Bangali. The Yogasutra of Patanjali: With Commentary of Vyasa. 115p. 1982. 12.95 (ISBN 81-208-0154-7, Pub. by Motilal Banarsidass India); pap. 9.95 (ISBN 81-208-0155-5, Pub. by Motilal Banarsidass India). Orient Bk Dist.

Baba, Meher. The Everything & the Nothing. 1976. 70p. 4.95, (ISBN 0-913078-49-2, Pub. by R J Mistry India); pap. 2.95, 115p. (ISBN 0-913078-48-4). Sheriar Pr.

--The Face of God. (Illus.). 28p. pap. 1.75 (ISBN 0-913078-00-X). Sheriar Pr.

--The Narrow Lane. Le Page, William, ed. 148p. 1979. pap. 3.95 (ISBN 0-913078-39-5). Sheriar Pr.

--Sparks of the Truth: From the Dissertations of Meher Baba. Deshmukh, C. D., ed. (Illus.). 96p. (Orig.). 1971. pap. 2.95 (ISBN 0-913078-02-6). Sheriar Pr.

Baba, Meher, ed. God to Man & Man to God. 287p. 1984. 8.95 (ISBN 0-913078-27-1); pap. 6.95 (ISBN 0-913078-21-2). Sheriar Pr.

Baba, Meher, et al. Meher Baba Journal, Vol. 1, No. 11. Patterson, Elizabeth, ed. (No. 11). (Illus.). 66p. 1974. pap. 2.50x (ISBN 0-913078-18-2). Sheriar Pr.

--Meher Baba Journal, Vol. 1, No. 6. Patterson, Elizabeth C., ed. (Illus.). 68p. 1972. pap. 2.50x (ISBN 0-913078-10-7). Sheriar Pr.

--Meher Baba Journal, Vol. 1, No. 7. Patterson, Elizabeth C., ed. (Illus.). 68p. 1972. pap. 2.50x (ISBN 0-913078-11-5). Sheriar Pr.

--Meher Baba Journal, Vol. 1, No. 9. Patterson, Elizabeth C., ed. (Illus.). 1973. pap. 2.50x (ISBN 0-913078-13-1). Sheriar Pr.

--Meher Baba Journal, Vol. 1, No. 10. Patterson, Elizabeth C., ed. (Illus.). 1973. pap. 2.50x (ISBN 0-913078-14-X). Sheriar Pr.

--Treasures from the Meher Baba Journals. Haynes, Jane B., ed. LC 79-92169. (Illus.). 246p. 1980. pap. 6.95 (ISBN 0-913078-37-9). Sheriar Pr.

Babaja, Thomas. Take Jesus for Example. (Illus.). 66p. (Orig.). 1985. pap. text ed. 3.50 (ISBN 0-318-18797-3). Dovehaven Pr Ltd.

Babaji, Ramananda, jt. auth. see Narasimha, N. S.

Babb, Lawrence. Moral Cosmos of Paradise Lost. 1970. 7.50 (ISBN 0-87013-154-0). Mich St U Pr.

Babb, Lawrence A. The Divine Hierarchy: Popular Hinduism in Central India. LC 75-61693. (Illus.). 266p. 1975. 27.50x (ISBN 0-231-03882-8). Columbia U Pr.

Babbage, Stuart B. Puritanism & Richard Bancroft. LC 63-2799. (Church Historical Society Ser.: No. 84). 1962. 20.00x (ISBN 0-8401-5084-9). A R Allenson.

--Sex & Sanity: A Christian View of Sexual Morality. rev. ed. LC 67-11492. 1967. Westminster.

Babbitt, Irving, tr. see Buddha, Gautama.

Babcock, Maltbie D. Letters from Egypt & Palestine. Davis, Moshe, ed. LC 77-70662. (America & the Holy Land Ser.). (Illus.). 1977. Repr. of 1902 ed. lib. bdg. 19.00x (ISBN 0-405-10223-2). Ayer Co Pubs.

Babcox, Neil. A Search for Charismatic Reality: One Man's Pilgrimage. LC 84-25506. 160p. 1985. pap. 5.95 (ISBN 0-88070-085-8). Multnomah.

Babin, Lawrence J. Agony in the Garden. LC 75-158476. 1971. deluxe ed. 3.00x (ISBN 0-912492-25-2); pap. 1.00 (ISBN 0-912492-00-7). Pyquag.

Babineau, Edmour J. Love of God & Social Duty in the Ramcaritmanas. 1979. 13.95 (ISBN 0-89684-050-6, Pub. by Motilal Banarsidass India). Orient Bk Dist.

Babington, J. A. Reformation. LC 71-118513. 1971. Repr. of 1901 ed. 28.75x (ISBN 0-8046-1135-1, Pub. by Kennikat). Assoc Faculty Pr.

Babris, Janina. The Covenant of Love. (Illus.). 228p. (Orig.). pap. 6.95 (ISBN 0-913382-19-1, 101-25). Prow Bks-Franciscan.

--In Human Touch. 17p. 1976. 5.95 (ISBN 0-912414-20-0). Lumen Christi.

Babris, Peter J. Silent Churches: Persecution of Religions in Soviet Dominated Areas. LC 78-52811. (Illus.). 1978. 19.50 (ISBN 0-911252-02-9). Res Publs.

Babuscio, Jack. We Speak for Ourselves: Experiences in Homosexual Counseling. LC 77-78623. pap. 40.00 (2026837). Bks Demand UMI.

Baca, Joyce. Divorce: Making It a Growth Experience. LC 85-13067. 136p. 1985. 8.95 (ISBN 0-87747-835-X). Deseret Bk.

Bacci, Judy L. The Second Coming: Why Jesus Christ Became a Carpenter Instead of an Electrician. 110p. (Orig.). 1981. pap. 5.95 (ISBN 0-940002-00-0). Studio J Pub.

Bach, H. I. The German Jew: A Synthesis of Judaism & Western Civilization, 1730-1930. (Litman Library of Jewish Civilization). 1985. 29.95x (ISBN 0-19-710033-3). Oxford U Pr.

Bach, Johann C. Music for Vespers II. (Johann Christian Bach: The Collected Works). 400p. 1985. lib. bdg. 85.00 (ISBN 0-8240-6072-5). Garland Pub.

Bach, Johann Sebastian. Eleven Great Cantatas in Full Vocal & Instrumental Score. Date not set. 16.50 (ISBN 0-8446-5459-0). Peter Smith.

Bach, Marcus. Major Religions of the World. 128p. 1984. pap. 4.95 (ISBN 0-87516-543-5). De Vorss.

--Make It an Adventure. LC 75-32232. 206p. 1975. pap. 6.95 (ISBN 0-918936-01-2). Astara.

--The Power of Total Living. 1978. pap. 2.50 (ISBN 0-449-23747-8, Crest). Fawcett.

--The Unity Way. LC 82-50085. 387p. 1982. 5.95 (ISBN 0-87159-164-2). Unity School.

--The Will to Believe. 186p. 1973. pap. 7.50 (ISBN 0-911336-46-X). Sci of Mind.

Bach, Marcus L. They Have Found a Faith. facsimile ed. LC 74-134049. (Essay Index Reprint Ser). Repr. of 1946 ed. 18.00 (ISBN 0-8369-2481-9). Ayer Co Pubs.

Bach, Morcus. Because of Christmas. (Illus.). 192p. 1986. pap. 8.00 (ISBN 0-940581-00-0). Fellowship Spirit.

Bach, Othello, jt. auth. see D'Addio, Janie.

Bachelard, Gaston. Poetics of Reverie: Childhood, Language & the Cosmos. 1971. pap. 8.95x (ISBN 0-8070-6413-0, BP375). Beacon Pr.

Bachelder, Louise. Christmas Tidings. 2nd ed. LC 84-60961. (Illus.). 64p. 1984. Repr. of 1969 ed. 5.95 (ISBN 0-88088-088-0, 880880). Peter Pauper.

Bachelder, Robert S. Between Dying & Birth. 1983. 5.95 (ISBN 0-89536-623-1, 0236). CSS of Ohio.

--Mystery & Miracle. 1983. 3.00 (ISBN 0-89536-606-1, 1340). CSS of Ohio.

Bacher, June M. Great Gifts of Christmas Joy. LC 83-70005. 96p. 1983. pap. 4.95 (ISBN 0-8054-5707-0). Broadman.

--A Mother's Joy. 1984. pap. 6.95 (ISBN 0-8010-0852-2). Baker Bk.

--Quiet Moments for Women: A Daily Devotional. LC 79-84722. 1979. pap. 7.95 (ISBN 0-89081-187-3). Harvest Hse.

Bacher, June Masters. A Mother's Joy. 128p. 1984. pap. 6.95 6x (ISBN 0-89081-415-5). Harvest Hse.

Bacher, Wilhelm. Abraham Ibn Esra Als Grammatiker: Ein Beitrag zur Geschichte der Hebraischen Sprachwissenschaft. Katz, Steven, ed. LC 79-7125. (Jewish Philosophy, Mysticism & History of Ideas Ser.). 1980. Repr. of 1882 ed. lib. bdg. 16.00x (ISBN 0-405-12239-X). Ayer Co Pubs.

Bachman, John W. Faith That Makes a Difference. LC 83-70508. 128p. (Orig.). 1983. pap. 6.95 (ISBN 0-8066-2014-5, 10-2193). Augsburg.

--Media-Wasteland Or Wonderland: Opportunities & Dangers for Christians in the Electronic Age. LC 84-24319. 176p. (Orig.). 1984. pap. 7.95 (ISBN 0-8066-2116-8, 10-4307). Augsburg.

Bachmann, E. Theodore, tr. see Bornkamm, Heinrich.

Bachmann, Theodore & Lehmann, Helmut T., eds. Luther's Works: Word & Sacrament I, Vol. 35. LC 55-9893. 426p. 1960. 19.95 (ISBN 0-8006-0335-4, 1-335). Fortress.

Bachmeyer, T. J., jt. auth. see Everett, William W.

Bachrach, Bernard S. Jews in Barbarian Europe. 1977. 7.50x (ISBN 0-87291-088-1). Coronado Pr.

Bachrach, Yehoshua. Mother of Royalty. Oschry, Leonard, tr. 1973. pap. 6.95 (ISBN 0-87306-018-0). Feldheim.

Bacigalupo, Leonard F. The American Franciscan Missions in Central America. LC 80-68205. 483p. (Orig.). 1980. 19.50 (ISBN 0-933402-20-1); pap. 9.95 (ISBN 0-933402-21-X). Charisma Pr.

Bacik, James J. Apologetics & the Eclipse of Mystery: Mystagogy According to Karl Rahner. LC 80-123. 192p. 1980. 15.00 (ISBN 0-268-00592-3); pap. 6.95 (ISBN 0-268-00593-1). U of Notre Dame Pr.

Backhouse, Janet. The Lindisfarne Gospels. LC 81-65990. (Cornell Phaidon Bks.). (Illus.). 96p. 1981. 29.95 (ISBN 0-8014-1354-0). Cornell U Pr.

Backman, Eugene L. Religious Dances in the Christian & in Popular Medicine. Classen, E., ed. LC 77-8069. 1977. Repr. of 1952 ed. 32.00x (ISBN 0-8371-9678-7, BARD). Greenwood.

Backman, Milton V., Jr. Christian Churches of America. rev. ed. 288p. 1984. 17.95 (ISBN 0-684-17992-X, P656, ScribT); pap. 12.95 (ISBN 0-684-17995-4). Scribner.

--Christian Churches of American Origins & Beliefs. rev. ed. 278p. 1983. pap. text ed. write for info. (ISBN 0-02-305090-X, Pub. by Scribner). Macmillan.

--Eyewitness Accounts of the Restoration. 1986. Repr. of 1983 ed. 10.95 (ISBN 0-87579-027-5). Deseret Bk.

--The Heavens Resound: A History of the Latter-Day Saints in Ohio 1830-1838. LC 83-12882. (Illus.). 480p. 1983. 14.95 (ISBN 0-87747-973-9). Deseret Bk.

Backman, Pat. Journey with Matthew. (Orig.). 1984. tchr's. ed. 4.95 (ISBN 0-931055-03-2). LuraMedia.

Backman, Pat & Geiger, Lura J. Braided Streams: Leader's Guide. 128p. (Orig.). 1986. pap. 12.95 spiral bound (ISBN 0-931055-09-1). LuraMedia.

Backman, Robert L. Be Master of Yourself. LC 86-2047. 227p. 1986. 9.95 (ISBN 0-87579-033-X). Deseret Bk.

--Take Charge of Your Life. LC 83-70332. 168p. 1983. 7.95 (ISBN 0-87747-970-4). Deseret Bk.

Backmen, Richard J. & Nerheim, Steven J. Toward a Healing Ministry: Exploring & Implementing a Congregational Ministry. 72p. (Orig.). 1985. pap. 5.95 (ISBN 0-8066-2176-1, 12-2022). Augsburg.

Backscheider, Paula R. A Being More Intense: A Study of the Prose Works of Bunyan, Swift, & Defoe. LC 83-45274. (Studies in the Eighteenth Century: No. 7). 222p. 1984. 32.50 (ISBN 0-404-61473-6). AMS Pr.

Backus, Irena. The Reformed Roots of the English New Testament: The Influence of Theodore Beza on the English New Testament. (Pittsburgh Theological Monographs: No. 28). 1980. pap. 10.00 (ISBN 0-915138-36-0). Pickwick.

Backus, Isaac. The Diary of Isaac Backus, 3 vols. McLoughlin, William G., ed. LC 76-12018. (Illus.). 1834p. 1979. Set. 120.00x (ISBN 0-87057-148-6). U Pr of New Eng.

--History of New England. LC 76-83410. (Religion in America, Ser. 1). 1969. Repr. of 1871 ed. 54.00 (ISBN 0-405-00231-9). Ayer Co Pubs.

Backus, William. Finding the Freedom of Self-Control. 176p. (Orig.). 1987. pap. 5.95 (ISBN 0-87123-676-1). Bethany Hse.

--Telling the Truth to Troubled People. 256p. (Orig.). 1985. pap. 6.95 (ISBN 0-87123-811-X, 210811). Bethany Hse.

Backus, William & Chapian, Marie. Telling Yourself the Truth. LC 80-10136. 41p. (Orig.). 1980. pap. 5.95 (ISBN 0-87123-562-5, 210562); study guide 2.50 (ISBN 0-87123-567-6, 210567). Bethany Hse.

--Why Do I Do What I Don't Want to Do? LC 84-6336. 144p. 1984. pap. 4.95 (ISBN 0-87123-625-7, 210625). Bethany Hse.

Backus, William & Chaplan, Marie. Digase la Verdad. 1983. 3.75 (ISBN 0-88113-049-4). Edit Betania.

Bacon, Ann, tr. see Jewel, John.

Bacon, Banjamin W. Non-Resistance: Christian or Pagan. 1918. pap. 19.50x (ISBN 0-686-83649-9). Elliots Bks.

Bacon, Benjamin W. Christianity, Old & New. 1914. 29.50x (ISBN 0-686-83503-4). Elliots Bks.

--Is Mark a Roman Gospel? (Harvard Theological Studies: Vol. 7). 1919. 11.00 (ISBN 0-527-01007-3). Kraus Repr.

Bacon, Daniel W. From Faith to Faith. 1984. pap. 5.95 (ISBN 9971-972-03-4). OMF Bks.

--Who Me? A Missionary? 1985. pap. 1.25 (ISBN 9971-972-32-8). OMF Bks.

Bacon, Ernest W. Bunyan Pilgrim & Dreamer: John Bunyan - His Life & Work. 186p. 1984. pap. 5.95 (ISBN 0-8010-0869-7). Baker Bk.

--Pilgrim & Dreamer: John Bunyan: His Life & Work. 176p. pap. text ed. 8.95 cancelled (ISBN 0-85364-309-1). Attic Pr.

--Spurgeon. (Christian Biography Ser.). 184p. 1982. pap. 3.95 (ISBN 0-8010-0823-9). Baker Bk.

Bacon, Francis. De Sapientia Veterum, Repr. Of 1609 Ed. Bd. with The Wisedome of the Ancients. Gorges, Arthur, tr. Repr. of 1619 ed. LC 75-27863. (Renaissance & the Gods Ser.: Vol. 20). (Illus.). 1976. lib. bdg. 88.00 (ISBN 0-8240-2068-5). Garland Pub.

--Essays & Colours of Good & Evil. LC 72-56. (Select Bibliographies Reprint Ser.). 1972. Repr. of 1862 ed. 20.25 (ISBN 0-8369-9951-7). Ayer Co Pubs.

--Wisedome of the Ancients. Gorges, A., tr. LC 68-54614. (English Experince Ser.: No. 1). 176p. 1968. Repr. of 1619 ed. 13.00 (ISBN 90-221-0001-4). Walter J Johnson.

Bacon, Gershon C., jt. auth. see Hundert, Gershon D.

Bacon, Josephine, tr. see De Pomiane, Edouard.

Bacon, Leonard. A Discourse Preached in the Center Church. facsimile ed. LC 78-168507. (Black Heritage Library Collection). Repr. of 1828 ed. 11.50 (ISBN 0-8369-8861-2). Ayer Co Pubs.

--The Genesis of the New England Churches. LC 74-38435. (Religion in America, Ser. 2). 510p. 1972. Repr. of 1874 ed. 32.00 (ISBN 0-405-04056-3). Ayer Co Pubs.

Bacon, Margaret H. Mothers of Feminism: The Story of Quaker Women in America. 1986. 16.95 (ISBN 0-06-250043-0, HarpR). Har-Row.

--The Quiet Rebels: The Story of the Quakers in America. 250p. 1985. lib. bdg. 24.95 (ISBN 0-86571-058-9); pap. 8.95 (ISBN 0-86571-057-0). New Soc Pubs.

Bacon, Margaret Hope. Lucretia Mott Speaking: Excerpts from the Sermons & Speeches of a Famous 19th Century Quaker Minister & Reformers. LC 80-84890. 31p. (Orig.). 1980. pap. 2.50x (ISBN 0-87574-234-3). Pendle Hill.

Bacon, Samuel. Memoir of the Life & Character of the Rev. Samuel Bacon. facs. ed. Ashmun, Jehudi, ed. (Black Heritage Library Collection). 1822. 20.25 (ISBN 0-8369-8781-0). Ayer Co Pubs.

Bacote, Samuel W. Who's Who among the Colored Baptists of the United States. Gaustad, Edwin S., ed. LC 79-52588. (The Baptist Tradition Ser.). (Illus.). 1980. Repr. of 1913 ed. lib. bdg. 28.50x (ISBN 0-405-12455-4). Ayer Co Pubs.

Badarayana. Brahma Sutra: The Philosophy of Spiritual Life. Radhakrishnan, S., tr. LC 68-21330. 1968. Repr. of 1960 ed. lib. bdg. 37.25x (ISBN 0-8371-0291-X, BABS). Greenwood.

--Brahma-Sutras (Vedanta-Sutras) Vireswarananda, Swami, tr. (Sanskrit & Eng.). 11.95 (ISBN 0-87481-076-0). Vedanta Pr.

Badawi, G. A. Polygamy in Islamic Law. pap. 1.00 (ISBN 0-686-18440-8). Kazi Pubns.

Badawi, Gamal. The Status of Woman in Islam. Al-Jarrahi, Abdussamad, ed. Bekkari, Muhammad, tr. from English. (Illus.). 20p. (Orig.). 1982. pap. 2.00 (ISBN 0-89259-036-X). Am Trust Pubns.

Badawi, Gamal A. The Status of Woman in Islam: (French Edition) Quinlan, Hamid, ed. LC 82-74127. (Illus.). 28p. 1983. pap. 0.75 (ISBN 0-89259-039-4). Am Trust Pubns.

Badawy, Alexander. The Tomb of Nyhetep-Ptah at Giza & the Tomb of 'Ankhm' Ahor at Saqqara. (U. C. Publications: Occasional Papers Ser.: Vol. 11). 1978. pap. 29.00x (ISBN 0-520-09575-8). U of Cal Pr.

--Tombs of Iteti, Sekhem ankh-Ptah, & Kaemnofert at Giza. (University of California Publications, Occasional Papers, Archaeology: No. 9). pap. 26.30 (ISBN 0-317-29106-8, 2021386). Bks Demand UMI.

Baden. The Greatest Gift Is Love. LC 59-1314. (Arch Bks.). 24p. 1985. pap. 0.99 (ISBN 0-570-06196-2). Concordia.

Baden, Marian. Being in God's Family. (Concordia Weekday Ser. - Gr. 3-4. Bk. 4, 2-V). 1967. pap. text ed. 2.75 (ISBN 0-570-06658-1, 22-2028); manual 5.85 (ISBN 0-686-82886-0, 22-2029). Concordia.

Baden, Robert. Adam & His Family. (Arch Bks.). (Illus.). 24p. 1986. pap. 0.99 saddlestitched (ISBN 0-570-06198-9, 59-1421). Concordia.

--How to Understand Your Parents & Maybe Like the Ones You Love. 1987. pap. 4.95 (ISBN 0-570-04467-7). Concordia.

Badenas, Robert. Christ the End of the Law: Romans 10-4 in Pauline Perspective. (JSoT Supplement Ser.: No. 10). 312p. 1985. text ed. 36.50x (ISBN 0-905774-93-0, Pub. by JSOT Pr England); pap. text ed. 15.95x (ISBN 0-905774-94-9). Eisenbrauns.

Badham, Linda, jt. auth. see Badham, Paul.

Badham, Paul & Badham, Linda. Death & Immortality in the Religions of the World. 256p. 1987. 22.95 (ISBN 0-913757-54-3, Pub. by New Era Bks); pap. 12.95 (ISBN 0-913757-67-5, Pub. by New Era Bks). Paragon Hse.

--Immortality or Extinction? LC 81-17595. (Library of Philosophy & Religion). 156p. 1982. text ed. 28.50x (ISBN 0-389-20251-7, 07055). B&N Imports.

Badia, Leonard F. Basic Catholic Beliefs for Today: The Creed Explained. LC 84-14632. 170p. (Orig.). 1984. pap. 8.95 (ISBN 0-8189-0469-0). Alba.

--Jesus: Introducing His Life & Teaching. 208p. (Orig.). 1985. pap. 7.95 (ISBN 0-8091-2689-3). Paulist Pr.

Badia, Leonard F. & Sarno, Ronald. Morality: How to Live It Today. LC 79-20498. 1980. pap. 9.95 (ISBN 0-8189-0391-0). Alba.

Badillo, Tony. Tithing: God's Command Or Man's Demand - Which? (Illus.). 102p. (Orig.). 1984. pap. 9.50 (ISBN 0-912977-00-0). Xavier Pr.

Badley, John H. Form & Spirit. LC 77-113347. (Essay & General Literature Index Reprint Ser). 1971. Repr. of 1951 ed. 19.50x (ISBN 0-8046-1398-2, Pub. by Kennikat). Assoc Faculty Pr.

Badra, Robert. Meditations for Spiritual Misfits. (Illus.). 93p. (Orig.). 1982. pap. 7.95 (ISBN 0-9610274-0-1). JCL Hse.

Badri, M. C. Islam & Alcoholism. LC 76-42173. 1976. pap. 2.75 (ISBN 0-89259-005-X). Am Trust Pubns.

Baeck, Leo. Essence of Judaism. rev. ed. LC 61-8992. 1961. pap. 8.50 (ISBN 0-8052-0006-1). Schocken.

Baedeker, Karl. Baedeker's Historical Palestine. (Baedeker's Handbooks for Traveler's Ser.). (Illus.). 240p. 1985. Repr. of 1930 ed. 19.95 (ISBN 0-88254-699-6). Hippocrene Bks.

Baelz, Peter. Does God Answer Prayer? (Illus.). 122p. (Orig.). 1983. pap. 6.95 (ISBN 0-87243-117-7). Templegate.

Baender, Paul, ed. & intro. by see Twain, Mark.

Baer, Gabriel, jt. ed. see Cohen, Amnon.

Baer, Hans A. The Black Spiritual Movement: A Religious Response to Racism. LC 83-14559. 232p. 1984. text ed. 22.95x (ISBN 0-87049-413-9); pap. 8.95x (ISBN 0-87049-515-1). U of Tenn Pr.

Baer, Mervin. The Christian Home. 1976. 1.95 (ISBN 0-686-11147-8). Rod & Staff.

Baer, Mervin J. El Hogar Cristiano. (Span.). pap. 1.75 (ISBN 0-686-32324-6). Rod & Staff.

Baer, S. Tikkun. 332p. 1900. Repr. text ed. 41.40x (ISBN 0-576-80143-7, Pub. by Gregg Intl Pubs England). Gregg Intl.

Baer, Yitzhak. History of the Jews in Christian Spain, 2 Vols. LC 61-16852. 1966. pap. 6.95 ea. (ISBN 0-8276-0115-8, 425). Jewish Pubns.

Baez-Camargo, Gonzalo. Archaeological Commentary on the Bible. LC 82-45473. (Illus.). 336p. 1986. pap. 9.95 (ISBN 0-385-17969-3, Galilee). Doubleday.

--Comentario Arqueologico de la Biblia. (Span.). 339p. (Orig.). 1979. pap. 7.95 (ISBN 0-89922-148-3). Edit Caribe.

Bagga, Raaj K., tr. see Kabir.

Bagga, Raaj K., tr. see Singh, Ajaib.

Baggett, Lee. Utilice Su Casa para Evangelizar. 32p. 1984. Repr. of 1983 ed. 1.50 (ISBN 0-311-13832-2). Casa Bautista.

Bagiackas, Joseph. The Future Glory. LC 83-70962. 130p. (Orig.). 1983. pap. 3.95 (ISBN 0-943780-02-0, 8020). Charismatic Ren Servs.

Bagley, Clarence B. Indian Myths of the Northwest. (Shorey Indian Ser.). (Illus.). 145p. pap. 8.95 (ISBN 0-8466-4041-4, I41). Shorey.

Bagley, F. R., tr. see Dashti, Ali.

Bagley, Pat. Treasures of Half-Truths. 100p. 1986. pap. 4.95 (ISBN 0-941214-47-8). Signature Bks.

Bagley, Val C. Mission Mania: A Cartoonist's View of the Best Two Years of Life. (Illus.). 98p. (Orig.). 1980. pap. 3.95 (ISBN 0-88290-140-0). Horizon Utah.

Bagot, Jean-Pierre. How to Understand Marriage. 144p. (Orig.). 1987. pap. 9.95 (ISBN 0-8245-0810-6). Crossroad NY.

Bagster, Samuel. Bagster's Bible Handbook. Elwell, Walter, intro. by. 264p. 1983. Repr. 9.95 (ISBN 0-8007-1334-6). Revell.

--Bagster's Keyword Concordance. 96p. 1983. Repr. 5.95 (ISBN 0-8007-1335-4). Revell.

--Daily Light. 1985. Repr. of 1975 ed. 6.95 (ISBN 0-916441-09-1). Barbour & Co.

Bahadur, K. P. The Wisdom of Saankhya. LC 78-901698. (The Wisdom of India Ser.: Vol. 2). 222p. 1977. 9.25 (ISBN 0-89684-469-2). Orient Bk Dist.

--The Wisdom of Vaisheshika. (The Wisdom of India Ser.: Vol. 4). 207p. 1979. 10.50 (ISBN 0-89684-470-6). Orient Bk Dist.

--The Wisdom of Yoga. LC 77-985594. (The Wisdom of India Ser.: Vol. 1). 116p. 1977. 9.25 (ISBN 0-89684-471-4). Orient Bk Dist.

Ba Han, Maung. William Blake: His Mysticism. 1978. Repr. of 1924 ed. lib. bdg. 35.00 (ISBN 0-8495-0377-9). Arden Lib.

--William Blake: His Mysticism. LC 72-13650. 1974. Repr. of 1924 ed. lib. bdg. 30.00 (ISBN 0-8414-1234-0). Folcroft.

Baharav, Gene, tr. see Noy, Dov.

Bahat, S., tr. see Weinreich, Uriel.

Baha'u'llah. Epistle to the Son of the Wolf. rev. ed. Effendi, Shoghi, tr. LC 53-18798. 1976. 12.95 (ISBN 0-87743-048-9, 103-001). Baha'i.

--Gleanings from the Writings of Baha'u'llah. 2nd rev. ed. Shoghi Effendi, tr. from Persian. LC 76-45364. (Illus.). 346p. 1976. 16.95 (ISBN 0-87743-111-6, 103-003). Baha'i.

--Gleanings from the Writings of Baha'u'llah. Effendi, Shoghi, tr. from Persian. 346p. 1983. pap. 5.95 pocket size (ISBN 0-87743-187-6). Baha'i.

--The Hidden Words of Baha'u'llah. rev. ed. Effendi, Shoghi, tr. LC 54-7328. 1985. 7.95 (ISBN 0-87743-007-1, 103-005); pap. 3.50 (ISBN 0-87743-002-0, 103-006). Baha'i.

Bahaullah. Prayers & Meditations. Effendi, Shoghi, tr. 1978. 14.95 (ISBN 0-900125-39-X). Baha'i.

Baha'u'llah. The Proclamation of Baha'u'llah. LC 72-237435. 1967. 8.95 (ISBN 0-87743-064-0, 103-012); pap. 4.95 (ISBN 0-87743-065-9, 103-013). Baha'i.

--Selected Writings of Baha'u'llah. LC 79-15136. 1979. 10.95 (ISBN 0-87743-133-7, 303-024); pap. 1.00 (ISBN 0-87743-077-2, 303-023). Baha'i.

--Tablets of Baha'u'llah Revealed after the Kitab-i-Aqdas. Effendi, Shoghi & Taherzadeh, Habib, trs. LC 79-670079. 1978. 14.95 (ISBN 0-85398-077-2, 103-021, Pub. by Universal Hse. of Justice); pap. 7.95 (ISBN 0-85398-137-X). Baha'i.

Bahaullah & Bab. O God, Guide Me: A Selection of Prayers Revealed. (Illus.). 1986. pap. 4.75 (ISBN 0-87743-202-3). Baha'i.

Baha'u'llah, et al. The Pattern of Baha'i Life. 3rd ed. 1963. pap. 2.95 (ISBN 0-900125-15-2, 315-030-10). Baha'i.

Baha'u'llah, Bab & Abdu'l-Baha. Baha'i Prayers: A Selection of Prayers Revealed by Baha'u'llah, the Bab & Abdu'l-Baha. LC 82-11502. 1985. 11.95 (ISBN 0-87743-175-2, 115-070); pap. 4.95 (ISBN 0-87743-176-0, 115-071). Baha'i.

Baha'u'llah, the Bab & Abdu'l-Baha. Communion with God. large-type ed. 1976. pap. 1.50 (ISBN 0-87743-110-8, 315-011). Baha'i.

--Baha'i Prayers. LC 54-10901. 6.95 (ISBN 0-87743-012-8, 315-005). Baha'i.

Bahm, Archie J. Axiology: The Science of Values. abbreviated ed. LC 84-51726. 84p. 1984. pap. 3.00 (ISBN 0-911714-14-6, World Bks). Bahm.

--Ethics: The Science of Oughtness. LC 80-66406. 260p. 1980. 15.00 (ISBN 0-911714-12-X). Bahm.

--World's Living Religions. (Arcturus Books Paperbacks). 384p. 1971. pap. 12.95x (ISBN 0-8093-0529-1). S Ill U Pr.

Bahm, Linda, et al. Fiestas of San Juan Nuevo: Ceremonial Art from Michoacan, Mexico. LC 83-42809. (Illus.). 70p. 1983. pap. 12.50 (ISBN 0-912535-00-8). Max Mus.

Bahnsen, Greg. Theonomy in Christian Ethics. 1977. kivar 12.50 (ISBN 0-934532-00-1). Presby & Reformed.

Bahnsen, Greg L. By This Standard. 432p. 1985. pap. 4.95 (ISBN 0-930464-06-0). Dominion Pr.

Bahr, Donald M., et al. Piman Shamanism & Staying Sickness: Ka: cim Mumkidag. LC 72-92103. 332p. 1974. pap. 9.95 (ISBN 0-8165-0303-6). U of Ariz Pr.

Bahr, Howard M., et al. Life in Large Families: Views of Mormon Women. LC 82-45005. 264p. (Orig.). 1982. lib. bdg. 29.25 (ISBN 0-8191-2551-2); pap. text ed. 13.25 o. p. (ISBN 0-8191-2552-0). U Pr of Amer.

Bahree, Pat. Hinduism. (World Religions Ser.). (Illus.). 72p. 1984. 16.95 (ISBN 0-7134-3654-9, Pub. by Batsford England). David & Charles.

Bahree, Patricia. The Hindu World. LC 83-50691. (Religions of the World Ser.). 48p. 1983. lib. bdg. 14.96 (ISBN 0-382-06718-5); 9.25 (ISBN 0-382-06931-5). Silver.

Baier, Walter. Untersuchungen zu den Passionbetrachtungen in der "Vita Christi" des Ludolfvon Sachsen: Ein Quellen-Kritischer Beitrag zu Leben und Werk Ludolfs und Zur Geschichte des Passionsthelogie, 3 Vols. Hogg, James, ed. (Analecta Cartsiana Ser.: No. 44-1, 2, 3). (Ger.). 614p. (Orig.). 1977. pap. 32.00 (ISBN 3-7052-0060-7, Pub. by Salzburg Studies). Longwood Pub Group.

Baig, M. A. Wisdom of Islamic Civilization. 9.95 (ISBN 0-317-01595-8). Kazi Pubns.

Baig, M. R. Muslim Dilemma in India. 1974. 7.50 (ISBN 0-7069-0311-0). Intl Bk Dist.

Baikie, James. A History of Egypt: From the Earliest Times to the End of the Eighteenth Dynasty, 2 vols. facsimile ed. LC 79-157323. (Select Bibliographies Reprint Ser.). Repr. of 1929 ed. Set. 66.00 (ISBN 0-8369-5782-2). Ayer Co Pubs.

Baildon, Henry B. Ralph Waldo Emerson: Man & Teacher. LC 72-14362. Repr. of 1884 ed. lib. bdg. 10.00 (ISBN 0-8414-1340-1). Folcroft.

Bailey, Albert E. Gospel in Hymns. (Illus.). 1950. lib. rep. ed. 45.00x (ISBN 0-684-15554-0, PG104HHRE, ScribT). Scribner.

Bailey, Alice A. From Bethlehem to Calvary. 1975. 19.00 (ISBN 0-85330-007-0); pap. 7.00 (ISBN 0-85330-107-7). Lucis.

--From Intellect to Intuition. 1973. 18.00 (ISBN 0-85330-008-9); pap. 7.00 (ISBN 0-85330-108-5). Lucis.

--The Light of the Soul. 1972. 20.00 (ISBN 0-85330-012-7); pap. 9.00 (ISBN 0-85330-112-3). Lucis.

--The Reappearance of the Christ. 1978. 18.00 (ISBN 0-85330-014-3); pap. 7.00 (ISBN 0-85330-114-X). Lucis.

--The Soul & Its Mechanism. 1971. 15.00 (ISBN 0-85330-015-1); pap. 7.00 (ISBN 0-85330-115-8). Lucis.

--A Treatise on the Seven Rays, 5 vols. Incl. Vol. 1. Esoteric Psychology. 1984. 20.00 (ISBN 0-85330-018-6); pap. 9.00 (ISBN 0-85330-118-2); Vol. 2. Esoteric Psychology. 1982. 28.00 (ISBN 0-85330-019-4); pap. 17.00 (ISBN 0-85330-119-0); Vol. 3. Esoteric Astrology. 1983. 28.00 (ISBN 0-85330-020-8); pap. 17.00 (ISBN 0-85330-120-4); Vol. 4. Esoteric Healing. 1984. 28.00 (ISBN 0-85330-021-6); pap. 17.00 (ISBN 0-85330-121-2); Vol. 5. The Rays & the Initiations. 1982. 28.00 (ISBN 0-85330-022-4); pap. 17.00 (ISBN 0-85330-122-0). pap. Lucis.

Bailey, Anita, ed. see Tozer, Aiden W.

Bailey, Barry. Living with the Unexpected. 128p. 1984. 8.95 (ISBN 0-687-22366-0). Abingdon.

Bailey, Betty, jt. auth. see Bailey, Ron.

Bailey, Betty J., intro. by. Eyes to See, Ears to Heart: A Study Guide to the Theme "Peoples & Churches of the U. S. S. R.". 1987. pap. 5.95. Friend Pr.

Bailey, Cyril. Phases in the Religion of Ancient Rome. LC 75-114460. 340p. 1972. Repr. of 1932 ed. lib. bdg. 22.50x (ISBN 0-8371-4759-X, BARA). Greenwood.

Bailey, D. Sherwin. Homosexuality & the Western Christian Tradition. LC 75-34384. xii, 181p. 1975. Repr. of 1955 ed. 22.50 (ISBN 0-208-01492-6, Archon). Shoe String.

Bailey, D. Waylon & Strange, John O. Biblical Hebrew Grammar. LC 85-60960. 246p. 1985. 17.00 (ISBN 0-914520-23-7). Insight Pr.

Bailey, David C. Viva Cristo Rey: The Cristero Rebellion & the Church-State Conflict in Mexico. (Illus.). 360p. 1974. 22.50x (ISBN 0-292-78700-6). U of Tex Pr.

Bailey, David T. Shadow on the Church: Southwestern Evangelical Religion & the Issue of Slavery, 1783-1860. LC 84-45795. 264p. 1985. text ed. 26.95x (ISBN 0-8014-1763-5). Cornell U Pr.

Bailey, Deloros S. God's Country U. S. A. 1982. 17.95 (ISBN 0-913730-04-1). Robinson Pr.

Bailey, Elmer J. Religious Thought in the Greater American Poets. facs. ed. LC 68-8436. (Essay Index Reprint Ser). 1968. Repr. of 1922 ed. 16.00 (ISBN 0-8369-0167-3). Ayer Co Pubs.

Bailey, F. My Summer in a Mormon Village. 59.95 (ISBN 0-8490-0692-9). Gordon Pr.

Bailey, Faith C. Adoniram Judson. (Golden Oldies Ser.). 128p. 1980. pap. 3.50 (ISBN 0-8024-0287-9). Moody.

--D. L. Moody. (Golden Oldies Ser.). 1959. pap. 3.50 (ISBN 0-8024-0039-6). Moody.

--George Mueller. 160p. 1980. pap. 3.50 (ISBN 0-8024-0031-0). Moody.

Bailey, Foster. Running God's Plan. 190p. (Orig.). 1972. pap. 5.00 (ISBN 0-85330-128-X). Lucis.

--The Spirit of Masonry. rev. ed. 143p. 1979. pap. 6.00 (ISBN 0-85330-135-2). Lucis.

Bailey, G. M. The Mythology of Brahma. 1983. 27.00x (ISBN 0-19-561411-9). Oxford U Pr.

Bailey, Harold W. Khotanese Buddhist Texts. rev. ed. LC 80-41425. (University of Cambridge Oriental Publications Ser.: No. 31). 168p. 1981. 57.50 (ISBN 0-521-23717-3). Cambridge U Pr.

Bailey, Jack S. Inside a Mormon Mission. 190p. pap. 3.95 (ISBN 0-89036-076-6). Hawkes Pub Inc.

Bailey, James. The Happy Hour. 1985. 6.95 (ISBN 0-89536-750-5, 5856). CSS of Ohio.

--Sermons from the Parables. 128p. (Orig.). 1981. pap. 2.95 (ISBN 0-8341-0730-9). Beacon Hill.

Bailey, John C. Milton. LC 73-12210. 1973. lib. bdg. 17.50 (ISBN 0-8414-3218-X). Folcroft.

Bailey, K. M. Christ's Coming & His Kingdom. LC 80-70733. 175p. 1981. pap. 4.95 (ISBN 0-87509-296-9); Leader's Guide. 2.95 (ISBN 0-87509-309-4). Chr Pubns.

Bailey, Keith M. Aprender a Vivir: Learning to Live. Bucher, Dorothy, tr. (Span.). 125p. 1980. 1.50 (ISBN 0-87509-299-3). Chr Pubns.

--The Children's Bread: Divine Healing. LC 77-83941. 1977. kivar cover 5.95 (ISBN 0-87509-233-0). Chr Pubns.

--Learning to Live. 64p. (Orig.). 1978. pap. 0.95 (ISBN 0-87509-158-X). Chr Pubns.

--Servants in Charge. 123p. 1979. pap. 3.95 (ISBN 0-87509-160-1); Leader's Guide. 0.95 (ISBN 0-87509-261-6). Chr Pubns.

Bailey, Keith M., compiled by see Simpson, A. B.

Bailey, Kenneth. The Cross & the Prodigal. LC 72-90957. 176p. 1973. pap. 5.25 (ISBN 0-570-03139-7, 12-2523). Concordia.

Bailey, Kenneth K. Southern White Protestantism in the Twentieth Century. 15.50 (ISBN 0-8446-1035-6). Peter Smith.

Bailey, Liberty H. The Holy Earth. 59.95 (ISBN 0-8490-0369-5). Gordon Pr.

Bailey, Lloyd R. Leviticus. Hayes, John H., ed. LC 86-46035. (Knox Preaching Guide Series). 108p. (Orig.). 1987. pap. 5.95 (ISBN 0-8042-3203-2). John Knox.

--The Pentateuch. LC 81-4495. (Interpreting Biblical Texts Ser.). 160p. (Orig.). 1981. pap. 8.95 (ISBN 0-687-30610-8). Abingdon.

Bailey, Lloyd R., ed. see Fretheim, Terence E.

Bailey, Lloyd R., ed. see Murphy, Roland E.

Bailey, Lloyd R., Sr. Biblical Perspectives on Death, No. 5. Brueggemann, Walter & Donahue, John R., eds. LC 78-145661. (Overtures to Biblical Theology Ser.). 180p. 1978. pap. 8.95 (ISBN 0-8006-1530-1, 1-1530). Fortress.

Bailey, Margaret L. Milton & Jakob Boehme. LC 65-15885. (Studies in Comparative Literature, No. 35). 1969. Repr. of 1914 ed. lib. bdg. 39.95x (ISBN 0-8383-0505-9). Haskell.

Bailey, Martin. One Thousand Years: Stories from the History of Christianity in the U. S. S. R., 988-1988. 1987. pap. 4.95. Friend Pr.

Bailey, Mary Frances, jt. auth. see Bailey, Robert.

Bailey, Ney. Faith Is Not a Feeling. LC 78-60077. 1979. pap. 4.95 (ISBN 0-918956-45-5). Campus Crusade.

Bailey, Paul. Ghost Dance Messiah: The Jack Wilson Story. LC 75-135152. 12.95 (ISBN 0-87026-025-1). Westernlore.

--Holy Smoke: A Dissertation on the Utah War. (Great West & Indian Ser.: Vol. 44). (Illus.). 1977. 10.50 (ISBN 0-87026-037-5). Westernlore.

Bailey, Paul C., tr. see Rudin, Josef.

Bailey, Phyllis C. Fascinating Facts about the Spirit of Prophecy. 64p. pap. 2.95 (ISBN 0-317-01322-X). Review & Herald.

Bailey, Richard D. Estate Planning: A Workbook for Christians. LC 81-14907. 96p. (Orig.). 1982. pap. 7.75 (ISBN 0-687-12004-7). Abingdon.

Bailey, Robert & Bailey, Mary Frances. Coping with Stress in the Minister's Home. LC 79-51135. 1979. 6.95 (ISBN 0-8054-5266-4). Broadman.

Bailey, Robert W. The Joy of Discipleship. LC 81-69402. 1982. pap. 5.95 (ISBN 0-8054-5188-9). Broadman.

--New Ways in Christian Worship. LC 81-65390. 1981. pap. 6.95 (ISBN 0-8054-2311-7). Broadman.

Bailey, Ron & Bailey, Betty. Team Teaching Children in Bible Class. 1972. 4.95 (ISBN 0-931097-05-3). Sentinel Pub.

Bailey, Waylon. As You Go. LC 81-47888. 118p. (Orig.). 1981. pap. 4.00 (ISBN 0-914520-15-6). Insight Pr.

Baillet, Maurice, ed. Qumran Grotte Four, No. III. (Discoveries in the Judean Desert Ser.: Vol. 7). (Illus.). 1982. 140.00x (ISBN 0-19-826321-X). Oxford U Pr.

Baillie, Donald M. God Was in Christ. 232p. 1977. pap. 6.50 (ISBN 0-571-05685-7). Faber & Faber.

--God Was in Christ. 1948. pap. 8.95x (ISBN 0-684-17474-X, PG56, ScribT); lib. bdg. 20.00 lib. rep. ed. (ISBN 0-684-16470-1, PG104HRE). Scribner.

--God Was in Christ. 230p. 1980. pap. text ed. write for info. (ISBN 0-02-305440-9, Pub. by Scribner). Macmillan.

Baillie, John. Diario de Oracions Privada. pap. 2.75 (ISBN 0-8358-0412-7). Upper Room.

--A Diary of Private Prayer. 136p. 1978. 8.95 (ISBN 0-684-30997-1, ScribT). Scribner.

--A Diary of Private Prayer. 1979. pap. 3.95 (ISBN 0-684-16323-3, ScribT). Scribner.

--A Diary of Readings. 400p. 1986. pap. 4.95 (ISBN 0-02-048360-0, Collier). Macmillan.

--The Idea of Revelation in Recent Thought. LC 56-8158. (Bantam Lectures in America Ser.). 151p. 1956. 23.00x (ISBN 0-231-02142-9); pap. 11.00x (ISBN 0-231-08554-0). Columbia U Pr.

Baillie, N. B. Digest of Moohammudan Law, 2 Vols. 1965. 65.50x (ISBN 0-87902-048-2). Orientalia.

Bailly, Constantina R. Shaira Devotional Songs of Kashmir: A Translation & Study of Utpaladeva's Shivastotravali. (Kashmir Shaivism Ser.). 224p. 1987. 39.50x (ISBN 0-88706-492-2); pap. 12.95x (ISBN 0-88706-493-0). State U NY Pr.

Baily, Keith M. Care of Converts. 95p. (Orig.). 1979. pap. 1.50 (ISBN 0-87509-156-3); leader's guide 0.75 (ISBN 0-87509-157-1). Chr Pubns.

Baily, Michael. Small Net in a Big Sea: The Redemptorists in the Philippines, 1905-1929. (Illus.). 8.00x (ISBN 0-686-24529-6, San Carlos Pubns); pap. 5.00x (ISBN 0-686-24530-X). Cellar.

Bailyn, Bernard. The Apologia of Robert Keayne: The Self-Portrait of a Puritan Merchant. 11.25 (ISBN 0-8446-0470-4). Peter Smith.

Bain, Kenneth R. The March to Zion: United States Policy & the Founding of Israel. LC 79-7413. 256p. 1980. 18.50 (ISBN 0-89096-076-3). Tex A&M Univ Pr.

Bainbridge, William S. Satan's Power: A Deviant Psychotherapy Cult. LC 77-80466. 1978. 33.00x (ISBN 0-520-03546-1). U of Cal Pr.

Bainbridge, William S., jt. auth. see Stark, Rodney.

Baines, J. Fecundity Figures: Egyptian Personification & the Iconology of a Genre. (Illus.). 200p. 1983. 60.00 (ISBN 0-85668-087-7, Pub. by Aris & Phillips UK). Humanities.

Baines, John. Fecundity Figures: Egyptian Personification & the Iconology of a Genre. (Egyptology Ser.). (Illus.). 400p. (Orig.). 1985. pap. 59.00 (ISBN 0-86516-122-4). Bolchazy-Carducci.

Baines, John, jt. tr. see Hornung, Erik.

Bains, Rae. Pilgrims & Thanksgiving. LC 84-2686. (Illus.). 32p. 1985. PLB 7.59 (ISBN 0-8167-0222-5); pap. text ed. 1.95 (ISBN 0-8167-0223-3). Troll Assocs.

Bainton, R. H. Hunted Heretic: The Life & Death of Michael Servetus. 11.25 (ISBN 0-8446-1580-3). Peter Smith.

Bainton, Roland. Erasmus of Christendom. (Crossroad Paperback Ser.). 320p. 1982. pap. 12.95 (ISBN 0-8245-0415-1). Crossroad NY.

--The Martin Luther Easter Book. LC 82-15996. 88p. 1983. pap. 3.95 (ISBN 0-8006-1685-5). Fortress.

--Reformation of the Sixteenth Century. 18.50 (ISBN 0-8446-1581-1). Peter Smith.

Bainton, Roland, jt. auth. see Brokering, Herb.

Bainton, Roland H. The Age of the Reformation. LC 83-25145. 192p. pap. 7.50 (ISBN 0-89874-736-8). Krieger.

--Christian Attitudes Toward War & Peace. LC 60-12064. 1979. pap. 7.95 (ISBN 0-687-07027-9). Abingdon.

--The Church of Our Fathers. (Illus.). 222p. 1978. pap. text ed. write for info. (ISBN 0-02-305450-6, Pub. by Scribner). Macmillan.

--Concerning Heretics. 1965. Repr. lib. bdg. 27.50x (ISBN 0-374-90323-9, Octagon). Hippocrene Bks.

--Early Christianity. LC 83-25150. 188p. 1984. pap. text ed. 7.50 (ISBN 0-89874-735-X). Krieger.

--Erasmus of Christendom. LC 68-27788. (Illus.). 1969. 20.00 (ISBN 0-684-15380-7, ScribT). Scribner.

--Here I Stand: A Life of Martin Luther. (Festival Books). 1978. pap. 4.95 (ISBN 0-687-16894-5, Co-Pub. with NAL). Abingdon.

--Here I Stand: A Life of Martin Luther. pap. 3.95 (ISBN 0-451-62404-1, ME2103, Ment). NAL.

--Here I Stand: A Life of Martin Luther. 13.25 (ISBN 0-8446-6225-9). Peter Smith.

--The Medieval Church. LC 78-11433. (Anvil Ser.). 192p. 1979. pap. 7.50 (ISBN 0-88275-786-5). Krieger.

--Reformation of the Sixteenth Century. enl. ed. LC 85-47516. (Illus.). 290p. 1985. pap. 9.95 (ISBN 0-8070-1301-3, BP697). Beacon Pr.

Bainton, Roland H. & Gritsch, Eric W. Bibliography of the Continental Reformation: Materials Available in English. 2nd ed. LC 72-8216. ix, 220p. 1974. 24.50 (ISBN 0-208-01219-2, Archon). Shoe String.

Bainton, Roland H., tr. Martin Luther Christmas Book with Celebrated Woodcuts by His Contemporaries. LC 59-2930. 80p. 1948. pap. 3.95 (ISBN 0-8006-1843-2, 1-1843). Fortress.

Bainton, Roland H., tr. see Holborn, Hajo.

Bainton, Ronald H. The Church of Our Fathers. 1984. 16.75 (ISBN 0-8446-6120-1). Peter Smith.

Bainvel, S. J. Is There Salvation Outside the Catholic Church? LC 79-55461. 1979. pap. 1.50 (ISBN 0-89555-132-2). TAN Bks Pubs.

Bair, Lillian, jt. auth. see Bair, Ray.

Bair, Ray & Bair, Lillian. God's Managers. 48p. 1981. pap. 4.00 (ISBN 0-8361-3406-0). Herald Pr.

Bair, Robert, tr. see Munoz, Hector.

Baird, Arthur J., ed. see Parunak, Van Dyke H.

Baird, Arthur J., ed. see Radday, Yehuda & Levi, Yaakov.

Baird, Coleen. Seven Days & Prayer. (Illus.). 1980. pap. 2.95 (ISBN 0-87747-802-3). Deseret Bk.

Baird, Henry M. History of the Rise of the Huguenots of France, 2 Vols. LC 79-130236. Repr. of 1879 ed. Set. 90.00 (ISBN 0-404-00520-9); 45.00 ea. Vol. 1 (ISBN 0-404-00521-7). Vol. 2 (ISBN 0-404-00522-5). AMS Pr.

--Huguenots & Henry of Navarre, 2 Vols. LC 76-130987. Repr. of 1903 ed. Set. 74.50 (ISBN 0-404-00540-3). AMS Pr.

--The Huguenots & the Revocation of the Edict of Nantes, 2 vols. LC 76-161752. Repr. of 1895 ed. Set. 74.50 (ISBN 0-404-08003-0). AMS Pr.

--The Huguenots & the Revocation of the Edict of Nantes, 2 vols. 1977. lib. bdg. 250.00 (ISBN 0-8490-2025-5). Gordon Pr.

--Theodore Beza, The Counsellor of the French Reformation, 1519-1605. LC 76-121596. 1970. Repr. of 1899 ed. 25.50 (ISBN 0-8337-0151-7). B Franklin.

Baird, J. Arthur. Audience Criticism & the Historical Jesus. 1969. 6.50 (ISBN 0-664-20846-0). Biblical Res Assocs.

--Rediscovering the Power of the Gospel: Jesus' Theology of the Kingdom. LC 82-83623. 1982. pap. 9.95 (ISBN 0-910789-00-2). Iona Pr.

Baird, J. Arthur, ed. see Morton, A. Q., et al.

Baird, J. Arthur, ed. see Morton, A. Q. & Michaelson, S.

Baird, J. Arthur, ed. see Morton, A. Q. & Michaelson, Sidney.

Baird, J. Arthur, ed. see Tyson, Joseph B. & Longstaff, Thomas R. W.

Baird, John, jt. auth. see DeWelt, Don.

Baird, Robert. Religion in America: A Critical Abridgment. 11.25 (ISBN 0-8446-0471-2). Peter Smith.

--Religion in the U. S. A, 2 vols. (Works of Rev. Robert Baird Ser.). 1985. Repr. Set. lib. bdg. 79.00 (ISBN 0-932051-57-X, Pub. by Am Repr Serv). Am Biog Serv.

--Religion in the United States of America. LC 70-83411. (Religion in America, Ser. 1). 1969. Repr. of 1844 ed. 38.50 (ISBN 0-405-00232-7). Ayer Co Pubs.

Baird, Robert D. Category Formation & the History of Religions. (Religion & Reason Ser: No. 1). 178p. 1971. text ed. 20.50x (ISBN 90-2796-889-6). Mouton.

Baird, Robert D. & Bloom, Alfred. Religion & Man: Indian & Far Eastern Religious Traditions. (Religion & Man: An Introduction, Pts. 2 & 3). 1972. pap. text ed. 14.95 scp (ISBN 0-06-040448-5, HarpC). Har-Row.

Baird, Robert D., ed. Methodological Issues in Religious Studies. LC 75-44170. (Orig.). 1976. lib. bdg. 14.95x (ISBN 0-914914-08-1); pap. text ed. 5.95x (ISBN 0-914914-07-3). New Horizons.

Baird, William see Hayes, John.

Baird, William, ed. see Bassler, Jouette M.

Baird, William, ed. see Fowler, Robert M.

Baisden, Major J., Jr. The World of Rosaphrenia: The Sexual Psychology of the Female. LC 72-178852. 224p. 1971. 6.95 (ISBN 0-912984-01-5). Allied Res Soc.

Bajaj, Harbhajan S. Meaning of Things in Life. 1986. 6.95 (ISBN 0-533-06697-2). Vantage.

--What Is Karma & All about God. 1987. 6.95 (ISBN 0-533-06697-2). Vantage.

Bajema, Clifford E. Abortion & the Meaning of Personhood. (Direction Bks). 1974. pap. 1.25 (ISBN 0-8010-0672-4). Baker Bk.

Bakan, David. Disease, Pain & Sacrifice: Toward a Psychology of Suffering. 1971. pap. 3.95x (ISBN 0-8070-2971-8, BP394). Beacon Pr.

--Duality of Human Existence: Isolation & Communion in Western Man. (Illus.). 1971. pap. 4.95x (ISBN 0-8070-2969-6, BP395). Beacon Pr.

Baker, A. Baptist Source Book. LC 66-22076. 1974. pap. 7.50 (ISBN 0-8054-6519-7). Broadman.

Baker, A. E., ed. see Temple, William.

Baker, Albert E. Prophets for a Day of Judgment. facsimile ed. LC 72-90605. (Essay Index Reprint Ser). 1944. 17.00 (ISBN 0-8369-1390-6). Ayer Co Pubs.

Baker, Alonzo. My Sister Alma & I. (Daybreak Ser.). 1981. pap. 4.50 (ISBN 0-8163-0373-8). Pacific Pr Pub Assn.

Baker, Alvin L. Berkouwer's Doctrine of Election: Balance or Imbalance? 1981. pap. 5.95 (ISBN 0-87552-119-3). Presby & Reformed.

Baker, Andrew & Goodman, Lori. Working with the Intermarried: A Practical Guide for Workshop Leaders. LC 85-71160. 36p. (Orig.). 1985. pap. 4.00 (ISBN 0-87495-071-6). Am Jewish Comm.

Baker, Archibald G., ed. Short History of Christianity. LC 40-34185. (Midway Reprints Ser.). 1983. Repr. of 1940 ed. 11.00x (ISBN 0-226-03527-1). U of Chicago Pr.

Baker, Benjamin S. Feeding the Sheep. LC 85-15139. 1985. pap. 5.95 (ISBN 0-8054-2544-6). Broadman.

--Shepherding the Sheep. LC 82-73531. 1983. 8.95 (ISBN 0-8054-2543-8). Broadman.

Baker, Bo. The Lift of Love. 1986. 7.95 (ISBN 0-8054-5039-4). Broadman.

Baker, C. J. Beyond Death. 1977. 2.50 (ISBN 0-87813-953-2). Christian Light.

Baker, Charles. The Book of Bible History. 1980. lib. bdg. 59.95 (ISBN 0-8490-3159-1). Gordon Pr.

--Manual of Bible History: Reading Lessons, Explanations, Questions & Geographical Notes, 2 vols. 1980. lib. bdg. 195.95 (ISBN 0-8490-3117-6). Gordon Pr.

Baker, Clara B. Sing & Be Happy: Songs for the Young Child. LC 80-13421. (Illus.). 96p. 1980. pap. 7.95 spiral (ISBN 0-687-38547-4). Abingdon.

Baker, Derek. Religious Motivation: Biographical & Sociological Problems for the Church Historian. (Studies in Church History: Vol. 15). 516p. 1978. 45.00x (ISBN 0-631-19250-6). Basil Blackwell.

--Renaissance & Renewal in Christian History. (Studies in Church History: Vol. 14). 428p. 1977. 45.00x (ISBN 0-631-17780-9). Basil Blackwell.

Baker, Derek, ed. The Church in Town & Countryside: Papers Read at the Seventeenth Summer Meeting & the Eighteenth Winter Meeting of the Ecclesiastical History Society. (Studies in Church History: Vol. 16). 502p. 1979. 45.00 (ISBN 0-631-11421-1). Basil Blackwell.

--Church Society & Politics. (Studies in Church History Ser.: Vol. 12). 440p. 1976. 45.00x (ISBN 0-631-16970-9). Basil Blackwell.

--Medieval Women. (Studies in Church History: Subsidia 1). (Illus.). 412p. 1979. 45.00x (ISBN 0-631-19260-3). Basil Blackwell.

--Medieval Women. (Studies in Church History: Subsidia 1). 412p. 1981. pap. 9.95x (ISBN 0-631-12539-6). Basil Blackwell.

--The Orthodox Churches & the West. (Studies in Church History Ser.: Vol. 13). 350p. 1976. 45.00x (ISBN 0-631-17180-0). Basil Blackwell.

--Reform & Reformation: England & the Continent c.1500-c.1750. (Studies in Church History: Subsidia 2). (Illus.). 336p. 1980. 45.00x (ISBN 0-631-19270-0). Basil Blackwell.

Baker, Derek, jt. ed. see Sheils, W. J.

Baker, Don. Acceptance: Loosing the Webs of Personal Insecurity. LC 84-27246. 1985. pap. 6.95 (ISBN 0-88070-079-3). Multnomah.

--Beyond Choice: The Abortion Story No One Is Telling. LC 85-15295. 1985. 8.95 (ISBN 0-88070-127-7). Multnomah.

--Beyond Forgiveness: The Healing Touch of Church Discipline. LC 84-3417. 1984. 8.95 (ISBN 0-88070-054-8). Multnomah.

--Beyond Rejection: The Church, Homosexuality, & Hope. LC 85-8789. 1985. 8.95 (ISBN 0-88070-108-0). Multnomah.

--A Fresh New Look at God. LC 85-29659. 1986. 8.95 (ISBN 0-88070-104-8). Multnomah.

--Heaven: A Glimpse of Your Future Home. expanded ed. (Orig.). 1986. pap. 3.95 (ISBN 0-88070-168-4). Multnomah.

--Pain's Hidden Purpose: Finding Perspective in the Midst of Suffering. LC 83-22135. 1984. pap. 5.95 (ISBN 0-88070-035-1). Multnomah.

--Philippians. (Lifebuilder Bible Studies). 60p. (Orig.). 1985. pap. text ed. 2.95 (ISBN 0-8308-1013-7). Inter-Varsity.

Baker, Don & Nester, Emery. Depression: Finding Hope & Meaning in Life's Darkest Shadow. LC 82-24609. (Critical Concern Ser.). 1983. 10.95 (ISBN 0-88070-011-4). Multnomah.

Baker, Donald C. & Murphy, J. L., eds. The Late Medieval Religious Plays of Bodleian Manuscripts Digby 133 & E Museo 160. (Early English Text Society Ser.). (Illus.). 1982. 37.50x (ISBN 0-19-722285-4). Oxford U Pr.

Baker, Dorothy Z. Mythic Masks in Self-Reflexive Poetry: A Study of Pan & Orpheus. LC 85-16468. (Studies in Comparative Literature Ser.: No. 62). x, 186p. 1986. 20.00x (ISBN 0-8078-7062-5). U of NC Pr.

Baker, Douglas. In the Steps of the Master. 1982. 40.00x (ISBN 0-9505502-4-8, Pub. by Baker Pubns England). State Mutual Bk.

Baker, Dwight C. T'ai Shan: An Account of the Sacred Eastern Peak of China. lib. bdg. 79.95 (ISBN 0-87968-474-7). Krishna Pr.

Baker, Elizabeth V. Chronicles of a Faith Life. (The Higher Christian Life Ser.). 270p. 1984. 35.00 (ISBN 0-8240-6403-8). Garland Pub.

Baker, Eugene. What's Right? Buerger, Jane, ed. LC 80-17552. (Illus.). 112p. 1980. 5.95 (ISBN 0-89565-175-0, 4932). Standard Pub.

--Your Manners Are Showing. Buerger, Jane, ed. (Illus.). 112p. 1980. 5.95 (ISBN 0-89565-178-5, 4935). Standard Pub.

Baker, Frances J. The Story of the Woman's Foreign Missionary Society of the Methodist Episcopal Church, 1869-1895. De Swarte, Carolyn G. & Dayton, Donald, eds. (Women in American Protestant Religion Series 1800-1930). 438p. 1987. lib. bdg. 65.00 (ISBN 0-8240-0658-5). Garland Pub.

Baker, Frank. From Wesley to Asbury: Studies in Early American Methodism. LC 75-39454. xiv, 223p. 1976. 22.50 (ISBN 0-8223-0359-0). Duke.

Baker, Frank, ed. The Heart of True Spirituality: John Wesley's Own Choice, Vol. 2. 1986. pap. 4.95 (ISBN 0-310-45101-9, 17079P). Zondervan.

--Heart of True Spirituality: John Wesley's Own Choice, Vol. 2: Selections from Thomas a Kempis, et. al. 1985. pap. 4.95 (ISBN 0-317-46009-9). Zondervan.

--Heart of True Spirituality: Selections from William Law, Vol. 1. 2nd ed. 128p. 1985. pap. 5.95 (ISBN 0-310-39621-2, 17064P). Zondervan.

Baker, Frank, ed. see Wesley, John.

Baker, George, jt. ed. see Needleman, Jacob.

Baker, George C., Jr. Introduction to the History of Early New England Methodism. LC 70-95393. 1969. Repr. of 1941 ed. 16.00 (ISBN 0-404-00466-0). AMS Pr.

Baker, H. A. Visions Beyond the Veil. 1973. pap. 3.95 (ISBN 0-88368-019-X). Whitaker Hse.

Baker, Herschel. The Wars of Truth: Studies in the Decay of Christian Humanism in the Earlier 17th Century. 11.75 (ISBN 0-8446-0472-0). Peter Smith.

Baker, Imogene, jt. ed. see Fry, Timothy.

Baker, J. & Nicholson, E. W., eds. The Commentary of Rabbi David Kimhi on Psalms 120-150. (Cambridge Oriental Publications Ser.: No. 22). 44.50 (ISBN 0-521-08670-1). Cambridge U Pr.

Baker, J., tr. see Eichrodt, Walther.

Baker, J. A., tr. see Von Campenhausen, Hans.

Baker, J. C. Baptist History of the North Pacific Coast. Gaustad, Edwin S., ed. LC 79-52589. (The Baptist Tradition Ser.). (Illus.). 1980. Repr. of 1912 ed. lib. bdg. 48.50x (ISBN 0-405-12456-2). Ayer Co Pubs.

Baker, J. Wayne. Heinrich Bullinger & the Covenant: The Other Reformed Tradition. LC 80-14667. xxvi, 300p. 1980. 24.95x (ISBN 0-8214-0554-3). Ohio U Pr.

Baker, James T. Thomas Merton: Social Critic. LC 76-132827. 184p. 1971. 17.00x (ISBN 0-8131-1238-9). U Pr of Ky.

Baker, Jan. The Church of England. 1978. pap. 3.35 (ISBN 0-08-021408-8). Pergamon.

Baker, John A., tr. see Danielou, Jean.

Baker, Kenneth. Fundamentals of Catholicism: Church, Grace, Sacraments & Eschatology or the Last Things, Vol. III. 1983. pap. 10.95 (ISBN 0-317-02736-0, Co-Pub. by Ignatius Pr-Catholic Polls). Guild Bks.

--Fundamentals of Catholicism: God, Trinity, Creation, Christ, Mary, Vol. II. LC 82-80297. 1983. pap. 10.95 (ISBN 0-89870-019-1, Co-Pub. by Ignatius Pr-Catholic Polls). Guild Bks.

--Fundamentals of Catholicism: Grace, the Church, the Sacraments, Eschatology, Vol. 3. LC 82-80297. 388p. (Orig.). 1983. pap. 11.95 (ISBN 0-89870-027-2). Ignatius Pr.

--Fundamentals of Catholicism: The Creed, the Commandments, Vol. I. LC 82-80297. 1982. pap. 9.95 (ISBN 0-89870-017-5, Co-Pub. by Ignatius Pr-Catholic Polls). Guild Bks.

Baker, Kenneth S. Fundamentals of Catholicism: God, Trinity, Creation, Christ, Mary, Vol. 2. LC 82-80297. 387p. (Orig.). 1983. pap. 11.95 (ISBN 0-89870-019-1). Ignatius Pr.

Baker, Margaret. Discovering Christmas Customs & Folklore: A Guide to Seasonal Rites. 3.25 (ISBN 0-913714-56-9). Legacy Bks.

--Discovering Christmas Customs & Folklore. (Discovering Ser.: No. 32). (Illus.). 56p. (Orig.). 1985. pap. 3.50 (ISBN 0-85263-173-1, Pub. by Shire Pubns England). Seven Hills Bks.

Baker, Marguerite. And Then the Angels Came to the First Grade Children. 1964. pap. 1.50 (ISBN 0-685-79136-X). Summit Univ.

Baker, Martha. How to Survive & Live in Heaven on Earth. rev. ed. LC 81-4234. 165p. 1981. pap. 1.95 (ISBN 0-86663-763-X). Ide Hse.

Baker, Nina B. Peter the Great. (Illus.). 310p. 1943. 10.95 (ISBN 0-8149-0263-4). Vanguard.

Baker, Pat & Marshall, Mary R. More Simulation Games. (Youth Work Guide Ser.). (Illus.). 88p. (Orig.). 1977. pap. 7.95 (ISBN 0-85819-194-6, Pub. by JBCE). ANZ Religious Pubns.

--Using Simulation Games. (Youth Work Guide Ser.). (Illus.). 96p. (Orig.). 1973. pap. 7.95 (ISBN 0-85819-090-7, Pub. by JBCE). ANZ Religious Pubns.

Baker, Pat A. In This Moment. LC 76-28802. Repr. of 1977 ed. 23.50 (ISBN 0-8357-9012-6, 2016370). Bks Demand UMI.

--A Minute in the Morning: One Hundred & Fifty Devotionals for Women. 1984. pap. 4.95 (ISBN 0-8010-0864-6). Baker Bk.

--Mom, Take Time. 128p. 1976. pap. 3.95 (ISBN 0-8010-0857-3). Baker Bk.

Baker, Paul. Contemporary Christian Music: Where It Came from, Where It Is, Where It Is Going. rev. ed. 1985. pap. 8.95 (ISBN 0-89107-343-4, Crossway Bks). Good News.

Baker, R. A. Compendio de la Historia Cristiana. Almanza, Francisco G., tr. Orig. Title: A Summary of Christian History. (Span.). 372p. 1985. pap. 9.50 (ISBN 0-311-15032-2). Casa Bautista.

Baker, Robert A. Relations Between Northern & Southern Baptists. rev. ed. Gaustad, Edwin S., ed. LC 79-52590. (The Baptist Tradition Ser.). 1980. Repr. of 1954 ed. lib. bdg. 23.00x (ISBN 0-405-12457-0). Ayer Co Pubs.

--The Southern Baptist Convention & Its People. 18.95 (ISBN 0-8054-6516-2). Broadman.

--Summary of Christian History. (Illus.). 1959. 16.95 (ISBN 0-8054-6502-2). Broadman.

Baker, Ruth. Rainbow Book of Poems. 1984. 3.95 (ISBN 0-89536-993-1, 7544). CSS of Ohio.

Baker, S. Hidden Manna. pap. 5.00 (ISBN 0-686-12875-3). Schmul Pub Co.

Baker, Sanna A. Who's a Friend of the Water-Spurting Whale? (Illus.). 1987. 7.95 (ISBN 0-89191-587-7). Cook.

Baker, Thomas & Ferrone, Frank. Liturgy Committee Basics: A No-nonsense Guide. (Orig.). 1985. pap. 6.95 (ISBN 0-912405-11-2). Pastoral Pr.

Baker, Tod A. & Steed, Robert P., eds. Religion & Politics in the South: Mass & Elite Perspectives. LC 83-21155. 208p. 1983. 29.95 (ISBN 0-03-069558-9, C0940). Praeger.

Baker, William. Sanctification. 160p. 1986. pap. 6.95 (ISBN 0-310-35301-7, 11140P). Zondervan.

Baker, William J. Beyond Port & Prejudice. 1981. 20.00 (ISBN 0-89101-032-7). U Maine Orono.

Bakhtiar, laleh, jt. auth. see Ardalan, Nader.

Bakhtiar, Laleh, tr. see Shariati, Ali.

Bakke, Johnny. Evangelical Ministry in Ethiopia: The Ethiopian Evangelical Church Mekana Yesus. (Studia Missionalia Upsaliensia). 96p. 1987. text ed. price not set (ISBN 0-391-03544-4, Pub. by Solum Verlag). Humanities.

Bakke, Raymond. The Urban Christian. 160p. 1987. pap. 6.95 (ISBN 0-87784-523-9). Inter-Varsity.

Bakke, Raymond J. & Roberts, Samuel K. The Expanded Mission of "Old First" Churches. 128p. 1986. pap. 8.95 (ISBN 0-8170-1100-5). Judson.

Bakken, Kenneth. Call to Wholeness. Kelsey, Morton, intro. by. LC 84-23837. 128p. (Orig.). 1985. pap. 7.95 (ISBN 0-8245-0683-9). Crossroad NY.

Bakker, Dorothy, jt. auth. see Rigsbee, Ron.

Bakker, Dorothy F., jt. auth. see Hornbrook, John.

Bakker, Jim. Eight Keys to Success. LC 79-92249. 128p. 1980. pap. 2.50 (ISBN 0-89221-071-0). New Leaf.

--Survival-Unite to Live. LC 80-84504. 1980. 7.95 (ISBN 0-89221-081-8). New Leaf.

Bakker, Tammy & Dudley, Cliff. Run to the Roar. LC 80-80656. 142p. 1980. 7.95 (ISBN 0-89221-073-7). New Leaf.

Bakole Wa Ilunga. Paths of Liberation: A Third World Spirituality. O'Connell, Matthew J., tr. from Fr. LC 84-5177. Tr. of Chemins de Liberation. 240p. (Orig.). 1984. pap. 12.95 (ISBN 0-88344-401-1). Orbis Bks.

Bakshi, S. R. Gandhi & Khilafat. 1985. 18.00x (ISBN 0-8364-1491-8, Pub. by Gitanjali Prakashan). South Asia Bks.

Bakunin, Jack. Pierre Leroux & the Birth of Democratic Socialism. 1976. lib. bdg. 79.95 (ISBN 0-87700-221-5). Revisionist Pr.

Bakunin, Michael. God & the State. facsimile ed. LC 78-148871. (Select Bibliographies Reprint Ser.). Repr. of 1916 ed. 12.00 (ISBN 0-8369-5643-5). Ayer Co Pubs.

--God & the State. LC 75-105664. 1970. pap. 3.50 (ISBN 0-486-22483-X). Dover.

Bakvis, Herman. Catholic Power in the Netherlands. (Illus.). 254p. 1981. 26.50x (ISBN 0-7735-0361-7). McGill-Queens U Pr.

Bal, Mieke. Murder & Difference: Gender, Genre & Scholarship Sisera's Death. (Indiana Studies in Biblical Literature). (Illus.). Date not set. price not set. Ind U Pr.

Balabanov, Kosta. Freske i Ikone u Makedoniji, iv-xv vek (Frescos & Icons in Macedonia, iv-xv Centory) 158p. 1983. 20.00 (ISBN 0-918660-26-2). Ragusan Pr.

Balabkins, Nicholas. West German Reparations to Israel. LC 70-152724. 1971. 32.00 (ISBN 0-8135-0691-3). Rutgers U Pr.

Balado, J. L. The Story of Taize. (Illus.). 144p. (Orig.). 1981. pap. 4.95 (ISBN 0-8164-2321-0, HarpR). Har-Row.

Balado, Jose L. Stories of Mother Teresa: Her Smile & Her Words. Diaz, Olimpia, tr. from Span. 96p. 1983. pap. 2.95 (ISBN 0-89243-181-4). Liguori Pubns.

Balaguer, Josemaria Escriva de see Escriva de Balaguer, Josemaria.

Balaquer, Josemaria Escriva de see Escriva de Balaguer, Josemaria.

Balaramiah, V. The Art of Deathlessness. (Illus.). 128p. 1980. pap. 4.95 (ISBN 0-937698-01-6). Golden Mean.

Balasuriya, Tissa. The Eucharist & Human Liberation. LC 78-9160. 184p. (Orig.). 1979. pap. 6.95 (ISBN 0-88344-118-7). Orbis Bks.

--Planetary Theology. LC 83-19339. 352p. (Orig.). 1984. pap. 10.95 (ISBN 0-88344-400-3). Orbis Bks.

Balbani, Niccolo. Newes from Italy of a Second Moses or, the Life of Galeacius Caracciolus the Noble Marquese of Vico. Crashaw, W., tr. LC 79-84085. (English Experience Ser.: No. 905). 92p. 1979. Repr. of 1608 ed. lib. bdg. 10.00 (ISBN 90-221-0905-4). Walter J Johnson.

Balbus, Joannes. Catholicon. 746p. 1460. text ed. 186.30x (ISBN 0-576-72240-5, Pub. by Greggg Intl Pubs England). Gregg Intl.

Balch, David. Let Wives Be Submissive: The Domestic Code in 1 Peter. LC 80-21203. (Society of Biblical Literature Monograph). 196p. 1981. pap. 21.00 (ISBN 0-89130-429-0). Scholars Pr GA.

Balch, David L., jt. auth. see Stambaugh, John E.

Balch, Dianne. All Joy. LC 82-72303. 169p. 1982. pap. 5.95 (ISBN 0-86605-098-1). Here's Life.

Balch, Glenn M., Jr., jt. auth. see Mead, James J.

Balchin, John. Citizens of Another Kingdom. 141p. 1986. pap. 4.95 (ISBN 0-89109-535-7). NavPress.

Balchin, John F. Understanding Scripture: What Is the Bible & How Does It Speak? LC 81-8271. 98p. (Orig.). 1981. pap. 2.95 (ISBN 0-87784-875-0). Inter-Varsity.

--What the Bible Teaches about the Church. 1979. pap. 3.95 (ISBN 0-8423-7883-9). Tyndale.

Balcom, Mary G. The Catholic Church in Alaska. LC 78-97897. (Illus.). 1970. 2.50 (ISBN 0-685-47728-2). Balcom.

Balda, Wesley. Heirs of the Same Promise: Using Acts As a Study Guide for Evangelizing Ethnic America. 1984. 3.95 (ISBN 0-912552-44-1). Missions Adv Res Com Ctr.

Baldassarre, John E. The New, Fully Illustrated Book of the Most Dramatic Paintings in the Vatican. (Illus.). 127p. 1982. 121.45 (ISBN 0-89266-323-5). Am Classical Coll Pr.

Balderas, Eduardo, tr. see Dean, Bessie.

Baldini, Baccio. Discorso Sopra la Mascherata Della Genealogia Delg'Iddei, Repr. Of 1565 Ed. Bd. with Discorso Sopra Li Dei De'Gentili. Zucchi, Jacopo. Repr. of 1602 ed. LC 75-27852. (Renaissance & the Gods Ser.: Vol. 10). (Illus.). 1976. lib. bdg. 88.00 (ISBN 0-8240-2059-6). Garland Pub.

Baldree, J. Martin. Sunday School Growth. 1971. 5.25 (ISBN 0-87148-761-6); pap. 4.25 (ISBN 0-87148-762-4). Pathway Pr.

Baldwin, David M. Friendless American Male: Leader's Guide. LC 82-21518. 48p. 1984. pap. 3.95 (ISBN 0-8307-0991-6, 6101914). Regal.

Baldwin, Ed & Baldwin, Stevie. Celebrations of Christmas. LC 85-47331. (A Family Workshop Bk.). 248p. 1985. pap. 12.95 (ISBN 0-8019-7448-8). Chilton.

Baldwin, H. A. Holiness & the Human Element. pap. 3.95 (ISBN 0-686-12876-1). Schmul Pub Co.

Baldwin, Helene L. Samuel Beckett's Real Silence. LC 80-21465. 184p. 1981. 19.95x (ISBN 0-271-00301-4). Pa St U Pr.

Baldwin, James. Fire Next Time. 1985. pap. 3.95 (ISBN 0-440-32542-0, LE). Dell.

Baldwin, James E., Sr. Old Testament Tithing versus New Testament Giving. 1984. 6.95 (ISBN 0-317-03291-7). Vantage.

Baldwin, John W. The Scholastic Culture of the Middle Ages: 1000-1300. LC 70-120060. (Civilization & Society Ser.). 192p. 1971. pap. 8.95x (ISBN 0-669-62059-9). Heath.

Baldwin, Joyce. Haggai, Zechariah, Malachi. LC 72-75980. (Tyndale Old Testament Commentary Ser.). 256p. 1972. 12.95 (ISBN 0-87784-908-0); pap. 6.95 (ISBN 0-87784-276-0). Inter-Varsity.

--Lamentations-Daniel. (Bible Study Commentaries Ser.). 128p. 1984. pap. 4.95 (ISBN 0-317-43378-4). Chr Lit.

Baldwin, Joyce G. Daniel. Wiseman, D. J., ed. LC 78-18547. (Tyndale Old Testament Commentary Ser.). 1978. 12.95 (ISBN 0-87784-961-7); pap. 6.95 (ISBN 0-87784-273-6). Inter-Varsity.

--Esther. Wiseman, D. J., ed. LC 84-15670. (Tyndale Old Testament Commentaries Ser.). 122p. 1984. 12.95 (ISBN 0-87784-964-1); pap. 6.95 (ISBN 0-87784-262-0). Inter-Varsity.

--The Message of Genesis 12-50: From Abraham to Joseph. Motyer, J. A. & Stott, John R., eds. LC 86-10615. (The Bible Speaks Today). 224p. (Orig.). 1986. pap. 7.95 (ISBN 0-87784-298-1). Inter Varsity.

Baldwin, Leland D. The American Quest for the City of God. ix, 368p. 1981. 18.95x (ISBN 0-86554-016-0). Mercer Univ Pr.

Baldwin, Lewis V. Invisible Strands in African Methodism: A History of the African Union Methodist Protestant & Union American Methodist Episcopal Churches, 1805-1980. LC 83-15039. (ATLA Monographs: No. 19). (Illus.). 306p. 1983. 27.50 (ISBN 0-8108-1647-4). Scarecrow.

Baldwin, Lindley. The March of Faith: Samuel Morris. 96p. 1969. pap. 2.95 (ISBN 0-87123-360-6, 200360). Bethany Hse.

--Samuel Morris. 74p. 1980. 1.50 (ISBN 0-88113-319-1). Edit Betania.

--Samuel Morris. 96p. 1987. pap. 3.50 (ISBN 0-87123-950-7). Bethany Hse.

Baldwin, Louis. Portraits of God: Word Pictures of the Deity from the Earliest Times Through Today. LC 85-43571. 192p. 1986. lib. bdg. 18.95x (ISBN 0-89950-198-2). McFarland & Co.

Baldwin, Marshall W. The Mediaeval Church. (Development of Western Civilization Ser.). 124p. (Orig.). 1953. pap. 4.95x (ISBN 0-8014-9842-2). Cornell U Pr.

--The Mediaeval Church. LC 82-2992. (The Development of Western Civilization Ser.). xii, 124p. 1982. Repr. of 1953 ed. lib. bdg. 22.50x (ISBN 0-313-23554-6, BAME). Greenwood.

--Raymond III of Tripolis & the the Fall of Jerusalem: 1140-1187. LC 76-29830. Repr. of 1936 ed. 28.50 (ISBN 0-404-15411-5). AMS Pr.

Baldwin, Marshall W. see Setton, Kenneth M.

Baldwin, Marshall W., tr. see Erdmann, Carl.

Baldwin, Robert F. The End of the World: A Catholic View. LC 83-63166. 192p. 1984. pap. 5.95 (ISBN 0-87973-608-9, 608). Our Sunday Visitor.

--The Healers. LC 85-62815. 175p. (Orig.). 1986. pap. 4.95 (ISBN 0-87973-836-7, 836). Our Sunday Visitor.

Baldwin, Skip. A Province into Being. Anderson, Douglas, ed. (Illus.). 80p. (Orig.). 1984. pap. 6.95 (ISBN 0-912549-04-1). Bread and Butter.

Baldwin, Stanley C. How to Build Your Own Christian Character. 1982. pap. 4.95 (ISBN 0-88207-271-4). Victor Bks.

--What Did Jesus Say about That? 224p. 1984. pap. 2.95 missal size (ISBN 0-89693-312-1). Victor Bks.

--When Death Means Life: Choosing the Way of the Cross. (Living Theology Ser.). 1986. pap. 6.95 (ISBN 0-88070-161-7). Multnomah.

Baldwin, Stanley C., jt. auth. see MacGregor, Malcolm.

Baldwin, Stanley C., jt. auth. see Mallory, James D.

Baldwin, Stevie, jt. auth. see Baldwin, Ed.

Baldwin, Summerfield. Organization of Medieval Christianity. 1986. 11.25 (ISBN 0-8446-1051-8). Peter Smith.

Baldwin, William. Treatise of Morall Philosophie. rev. ed. LC 67-10126. 1967. Repr. of 1620 ed. 50.00x (ISBN 0-8201-1003-5). Schol Facsimiles.

Bale, John. Chief Promises of God. LC 70-133635. (Tudor Facsimile Texts. Old English Plays: No. 21). Repr. of 1908 ed. 49.50 (ISBN 0-404-53321-3). AMS Pr.

--The First Two Partes of the Acts or Unchaste Examples of the Englyshe Votaryes. LC 79-84086. (English Experience Ser.: No. 906). 540p. 1979. Repr. of 1560 ed. lib. bdg. 40.00 (ISBN 90-221-0906-2). Walter J Johnson.

--The Image of Bothe Curches, After the Moste Wonderfull & Heavenly Revelation of Sainct John the Evangelist. LC 72-5965. (English Experience Ser.: No. 498). 872p. 1973. Repr. of 1548 ed. 51.00 (ISBN 90-221-0498-2). Walter J Johnson.

--Select Works of John Bale, Bishop of Ossory. 51.00 (ISBN 0-384-03135-8). Johnson Repr.

--Temptation of Christ. LC 74-133636. (Tudor Facsimile Texts. Old English Plays: No. 22). Repr. of 1909 ed. 49.50 (ISBN 0-404-53322-1). AMS Pr.

Balentine, Samuel E. The Hidden God: The Hiding of the Face of God in the Old Testament. (Oxford Theological Monographs). 1983. 34.00x (ISBN 0-19-826719-3). Oxford U Pr.

Bales, J. D. Communism & the Reality of Moral Law. 1969. pap. 3.75 (ISBN 0-934532-01-X). Presby & Reformed.

Bales, James. Biblical Doctrine of God. pap. 2.50 (ISBN 0-89315-021-5). Lambert Bk.

--Evangelism: Every Member, Every Day. pap. 2.50 (ISBN 0-89315-038-X). Lambert Bk.

--Jesus the Master Respondent. 2.50 (ISBN 0-89315-130-0). Lambert Bk.

--Romans. 2.50 (ISBN 0-89315-241-2). Lambert Bk.

--Two Worlds: Christianity & Communism. pap. 2.25 (ISBN 0-686-80419-8). Lambert Bk.

--You Believe. pap. 2.95 (ISBN 0-89315-425-3). Lambert Bk.

Bales, James & Teller, Woosey. Bales Teller Debate. pap. 4.95 (ISBN 0-89315-018-5). Lambert Bk.

Bales, James D. Miracles or Mirages? 1956. 3.00 (ISBN 0-88027-010-1). Firm Foun Pub.

--Pentecostalism in the Church. pap. 2.95 (ISBN 0-89315-204-8). Lambert Bk.

--The Psalm for the Frightened & Frustrated Sheep. 1977. pap. 1.50 (ISBN 0-89315-216-1). Lambert Bk.

--Soils & Seeds of Sectarianism. 1977. pap. 4.50 (ISBN 0-89315-264-1). Lambert Bk.

Balfour, A. J. Theism & Humanism. Repr. of 1915 ed. 32.00 (ISBN 0-527-04810-0). Kraus Repr.

Balfour, Arthur J. Theism & Thought: A Study in Familiar Beliefs. LC 77-27208. (Gifford Lectures: 1922-23). Repr. of 1923 ed. 22.50 (ISBN 0-404-60469-2). AMS Pr.

Balfour, David, jt. auth. see St. Gregory.

Balfour, Frederic H. Taoist Texts. lib. bdg. 79.95 (ISBN 0-87968-191-8). Krishna Pr.

Balian, R. & Adouse, J. Physical Cosmology. (Les Houches Summer School Ser.: Vol. 32). 668p. 1980. 115.00 (ISBN 0-444-85433-9). Elsevier.

Balika, Susan S. Jesus Is My Special Friend. LC 81-86702. (Happy Day Bks.). (Illus.). 24p. (Orig.). 1982. pap. 1.59 (ISBN 0-87239-541-3, 3587). Standard Pub.

Balin, Peter. Xultun Tarot: A Maya Tarot Deck. 2nd ed. (Illus.). 78p. 1982. pap. 12.95 (ISBN 0-910261-00-8). Arcana Pub.

Balke, William. Calvin & the Anabaptist Radicals. Heynen, William, tr. LC 81-12438. pap. 87.50 (ISBN 0-317-30132-2, 2025315). Bks Demand UMI.

Ball, Ann. Modern Saints: Their Lives & Faces. LC 82-50357. (Illus.). 457p. 1983. pap. 10.00 (ISBN 0-89555-222-1). TAN Bks Pubs.

Ball, Barbara. Coffee Talk: Sharing Christ Through Friendly Gatherings. LC 79-53980. 80p. 1980. pap. 4.95 (ISBN 0-934396-08-6). Churches Alive.

Ball, Bryan W. The English Connection: The Puritan Roots of Seventh-Day Adventist Belief. 252p. 1981. text ed. 17.50 (ISBN 0-227-67844-3). Attic Pr.

Ball, Howard. There Is Help for Your Church. LC 81-65669. 40p. (Orig.). 1981. pap. text ed. 1.50 (ISBN 0-934396-14-0). Churches Alive.

Ball, John. Ananda: Where Yoga Lives. LC 82-82100. 240p. 1982. 15.95 (ISBN 0-87972-207-X); pap. 8.95 (ISBN 0-87972-208-8). Bowling Green Univ.

--Ananda: Where Yoga Lives. (Illus.). 232p. 1982. pap. 8.95 (ISBN 0-87972-208-8). Dawn Pubns CA.

Ball, John T. Barefoot in the Palace. 1985. 6.25 (ISBN 0-89536-748-3, 5854). CSS of Ohio.

Ball, Judy. Listenings. (Orig.). 1987. pap. 7.00 (ISBN 0-915541-12-2). Star Bks Inc.

Ball, Judy & Danich, John. The Brain, the Soul, God. 174p. 1986. pap. 6.95 (ISBN 0-88144-064-7). Christian Pub.

Ball, W. P., jt. ed. see Foote, G. W.

Ball, W. P., jt. auth. see Foote, G. W.

Balla, Mother Ignatius. Our Continuing Yes. 1973. pap. 2.00 (ISBN 0-8198-0243-3). Dghtrs St Paul.

Ballantyne & Shastri. Yoga-Sutras of Patanjali. Tailang, S. B., ed. Repr. of 1983 ed. 8.50 (ISBN 0-89684-474-9). Orient Bk Dist.

Ballard, JoeAnn, jt. auth. see Ballard, Monroe.

Ballard, L. S., jt. auth. see Warren, Thomas B.

Ballard, Monroe & Ballard, JoeAnn. Serving in the City: Nurturing the Poor to Independence. 88p. 1986. 3 ring binder 10.95 (ISBN 0-8341-1125-X, S-350). Beacon Hill.

Ballenger, A. F. A Believer's Guide to Christian Maturity. LC 82-72493. 256p. 1982. pap. 4.95 (ISBN 0-87123-278-2, 210278). Bethany Hse.

Ballis, Peter H., ed. In & Out of the World: Seventh-Day Adventists in New Zealand. 178p. 1986. pap. 12.95 (ISBN 0-86469-050-9, Pub. by Dunmore NZ). Intl Spec Bk.

Ballou, Adin. Christian Non-Resistance. LC 70-121104. (Civil Liberties in American History Ser). 1970. Repr. of 1910 ed. lib. bdg. 35.00 (ISBN 0-306-71980-0). Da Capo.

--Christian Non-Resistance in All Its Important Bearings, Illustrated & Defended. LC 76-137527. (Peace Movement in America Ser). 240p. 1972. Repr. of 1846 ed. lib. bdg. 18.95x (ISBN 0-89198-054-7). Ozer.

--History of the Hopedale Community, from Its Inception to Its Virtual Submergence in the Hopedale Parish. Heywood, William S., ed. LC 72-2935. (Communal Societies in America Ser.). Repr. of 1897 ed. 14.00 (ISBN 0-404-10701-X). AMS Pr.

--Practical Christian Socialism. LC 72-2936. (Communal Societies in America Ser.). Repr. of 1854 ed. 37.50 (ISBN 0-404-10702-8). AMS Pr.

--Practical Christian Socialism, 2 vols. 655p. 1985. Repr. of 1854 ed. Set. lib. bdg. 69.00 (ISBN 0-932051-86-3, Pub. by Am Repr Serv). Am Biog Serv.

Ballou, Hosea. Treatise on Atonement. Cassara, Ernest, ed. 1986. pap. 7.95 (ISBN 0-933840-26-8, 0495000). Unitarian Univ.

Ballou, R. O., et al, eds. The Bible of the World. 1415p. 1980. pap. 5.50 (ISBN 0-380-01057-7, 17350). Avon.

Ball-Rokeach, Sandra & Grube, Joel W. The Great American Values Test: Influencing Behavior & Belief Through Television. LC 83-48468. 208p. 1983. 25.00x (ISBN 0-02-926850-8). Free Pr.

Balme, M. G., ed. see Apuleius.

Balmforth, R. The Problem-Play. LC 76-52915. (Studies in Drama, No. 39). 1977. lib. bdg. 41.95x (ISBN 0-8383-2129-1). Haskell.

Balquir, Allama Muhammad Al-Majlisi. The Life & Religion of Muhammad, 3 vols, Vol. 2. Merrick, J. L., tr. from Persian. Tr. of Hiyat al-Qulub. 483p. 1982. 35.00x (ISBN 0-317-39115-1, Pub. by Luzac & Co Ltd). State Mutual Bk.

Balse, Mayah. Mystics & Men of Miracles in India. (Illus.). 1976. 5.95 (ISBN 0-913244-10-4). Hapi Pr.

Balsekar, Ramesh s. Pointers from Nisargadatta Maharaj. LC 82-71505. xiv, 223p. 1983. Repr. of 1984 ed. 13.50 (ISBN 0-89386-004-2). Acorn NC.

Balshone, Benjamin. Determined! 1984. 15.95 (ISBN 0-8197-0494-6). Bloch.

Balsiger, David W. Candidates Biblical Scoreboard. Balsiger, David W., intro. by. (Biblical News Ser., 1986: No. 1). 1986. 2.25 (ISBN 0-89921-015-5). Biblical News Serv.

Balsiger, David W., ed. & intro. by. Family Protection Scoreboard, Special Edition on South Africa, No. 1. 56p. 1987. 2.95 (ISBN 0-89921-021-X). Biblical News Serv.

Balskus, Pat. Mary's Pilgrim. LC 68-58160. (Encounter Ser.). 3.00 (ISBN 0-8198-0279-4). Dghtrs St Paul.

Balsley, Betsy, compiled by see Navarro, Dawn.

Balthasar. Le Chretien Bernanos. 27.90 (ISBN 0-685-37226-X). French & Eur.

Balthasar, Hans U. von see Von Balthasar, Hans U.

Balthasar, Hans U. Von see Von Balthasar, Hans U.

Balthasar, Hans Urs Von. A First Glance at Adrienne Von Speyr. Lawry, Antje & Englund, Sergia, trs. from Ger. LC 79-84879. Orig. Title: Erster Blick Auf Adrienne Von Speyr. 249p. (Orig.). 1981. pap. 9.95 (ISBN 0-89870-003-5). Ignatius Pr.

Balthasar, Hans Urs von see Urs von Balthasar, Hans.

Balthasar, Hans Urs von see Von Balthasar, Hans Urs.

Balthasar, Hans von see Von Balthasar, Hans, et al.

Balthasas, Hans von see Von Balthasar, Hans U.

Balthasur, Hans Urs Von see Von Balthasar, Hans Urs.

Balthazar, Vera & Batista, Joao, eds. Dictionario Biblico Buckland. Orig. Title: Buckland Bible Dictionary. (Illus.). 453p. text ed. 6.50 (ISBN 0-8297-0836-7); pap. 4.50 (ISBN 0-686-97837-4). Life Pubs Intl.

Baltimore Plenary Council Staff. Baltimore Catechism, No. 1. 1977. pap. 3.00 (ISBN 0-89555-010-5). TAN Bks Pubs.

--Baltimore Catechism, No. 2. 1977. pap. 1.75 (ISBN 0-89555-008-3). TAN Bks Pubs.

--Baltimore Catechism: Cathechism of Christian Doctrine. 1974. pap. 3.50 (ISBN 0-89555-007-5, 147). TAN Bks Pubs.

Baltz, Frederick. Bible Readings for Farm Living. LC 85-7421. 112p. (Orig.). 1985. pap. 3.95 (ISBN 0-8066-2164-8, 10-0688). Augsburg.

Baltzell, E. Digby. Puritan Boston & Quaker Philadelphia. LC 81-70494. 585p. 1982. pap. 12.95x (ISBN 0-8070-5415-1, BP 638). Beacon Pr.

Baltzer, Dieter. Ezechiel und Deuterojesaja: Beruehrungen in der Heilserwartung der beiden grossen Exilspropheten. (Beiheft 121 Zur Zeitschrift fuer die alttestamentliche Wissenschaft Ser.). 1971. 28.40x (ISBN 3-11-001756-3). De Gruyter.

Baltzer, Klaus, ed. see Zimmerli, Walther.

Baly, Denis. Basic Biblical Geography. LC 86-45206. 80p. 1987. pap. 4.95 (ISBN 0-8006-1922-6, 1-1922). Fortress.

Baly, Denis & Rhodes, Royal W. The Faith of Christians. LC 84-47914. 256p. 1984. pap. 14.95 (ISBN 0-8006-1790-8). Fortress.

Baly, Dennis. God: History & the Old Testament. LC 76-9984. 256p. 1976. pap. 10.95x (ISBN 0-06-060369-0, RD 186, HarpR). Har-Row.

Balyazi, H. M. Eminent Baha'is in the Time of Baha'u'llah. (Illus.). 400p. 1986. 28.50 (ISBN 0-85398-151-5); pap. 15.95 (ISBN 0-85398-152-3). G Ronald Pub.

Balyoz, Harold. Signs of Christ. LC 79-64608. 1979. 18.00 (ISBN 0-9609710-0-9). Altai Pub.

Balyuzi, H. M. The Bab: The Herald of the Day of Days. (Illus.). 272p. 1973. 14.95 (ISBN 0-85398-048-9). G Ronald Pub.

--Baha'u'llah: The King of Glory. (Illus.). 552p. 1980. 28.50 (ISBN 0-85398-090-X). G Ronald Pub.

--Baha'u'llah: The Word Made Flesh. 134p. 1963. 10.95 (ISBN 0-85398-014-4); pap. 5.95 (ISBN 0-85398-001-2). G Ronald Pub.

--Edward Granville Browne & the Baha'i Faith. (Illus.). 152p. 1970. 14.95 (ISBN 0-85398-023-3). G Ronald Pub.

--Khadijih Bagum: The Wife of the Bab. (Illus.). 52p. 7.95 (ISBN 0-85398-100-0); pap. 3.75 (ISBN 0-85398-101-9). G Ronald Pub.

Balz, Albert G. Descartes & the Modern Mind. xiv, 492p. 1967. Repr. of 1952 ed. 37.50 (ISBN 0-208-00023-2, Archon). Shoe String.

--Idea & Essence in the Philosophies of Hobbes & Spinoza. LC 70-161737. Repr. of 1918 ed. 17.00 (ISBN 0-404-00489-X). AMS Pr.

Balzano, Bill. Church of God & Roman Catholic Interfaith Marriage. (Truthway Ser.). 35p. (Orig.). 1981. pap. text ed. 1.25 (ISBN 0-87148-175-8). Pathway Pr.

Baman Das Basu, ed. The Sacred Books of the Hindus, 47 vols. Repr. of 1937 ed. 1251.50 (ISBN 0-404-19548-2). AMS Pr.

Bamberg, Corona. Cost of Being Human. 7.95 (ISBN 0-87193-128-1). Dimension Bks.

Bamberger, Bernard J. Commentary on Leviticus. Plaut, W. Gunther, ed. (The Torah: a Modern Commentary Ser.). 1979. 20.00 (ISBN 0-8074-0011-4, 3816). UAHC.

--The Search for Jewish Theology. new ed. LC 77-28457. 1978. pap. 4.95x (ISBN 0-87441-300-1). Behrman.

--Story of Judaism. rev. 3rd ed. LC 64-16463. 1964. pap. 12.95 (ISBN 0-8052-0077-0). Schocken.

--Story of Judaism. rev. ed. 1970. 9.95 (ISBN 0-8074-0193-5, 959291). UAHC.

Bamberger, Bernard J., jt. auth. see Plaut, W. Gunther.

Bamberger, David. My People: Abba Eban's History of the Jews, Vol. II. (Illus.). 1979. pap. 6.95x (ISBN 0-87441-280-3); tchr's guide by Geoffrey Horn 12.50 (ISBN 0-87441-341-9). Behrman.

--My People: Abba Eban's History of the Jews, Vol. I. LC 77-10667. (Illus.). 1978. pap. text ed. 6.95x (ISBN 0-87441-263-3). Behrman.

--A Young Person's History of Israel. Mandelkern, Nicholas, ed. (Illus.). 150p. (Orig.). 1985. pap. 6.95 (ISBN 0-87441-393-1). Behrman.

Bamberger, Eudes, jt. auth. see Abbot, John.

Bamberger, I. Nathan. The Viking Jews: The History of the Jews of Denmark. LC 83-50474. (Illus.). 160p. 1983. 10.95 (ISBN 0-88400-098-2). Shengold.

Bamberger, John E., tr. see Praktikos.

Bambrough, Renford. Reason, Truth & God. (Library Reprints Ser.). 174p. 1979. 45.00x (ISBN 0-416-72530-9, NO. 2823). Methuen Inc.

Bammate, Haidar. Muslim Contribution to Civilization. Date not set. 2.50 (ISBN 0-89259-029-7). Am Trust Pubns.

Bammel, E & Barrett, C. K., eds. Donum Gentilicium: New Testament Studies in Honor of David Daube. 1978. 59.00x (ISBN 0-19-826629-4). Oxford U Pr.

Bammel, E. & Moule, C. F., eds. Jesus & the Politics of His Day. 320p. 1985. pap. 17.95 (ISBN 0-521-31344-9). Cambridge U Pr.

Bammel, Ernst. Judaica. 330p. 1986. lib. bdg. 82.50x (ISBN 3-16-144971-1, Pub. by J C B Mohr BRD). Coronet Bks.

Bamonte, Louis J. Your Faith: Leader's Guide. 1978. tchr's ed 2.95 (ISBN 0-89243-085-0). Liguori Pubns.

Ban, Arline J. Children's Time in Worship. 128p. 1981. pap. 6.95 (ISBN 0-8170-0902-7). Judson.

Ban, Arline J. & Ban, Joseph D. The New Disciple: Church Membership Junior-Junior High. LC 75-35898. 96p. 1976. pap. 1.95 (ISBN 0-8170-0658-3). Judson.

--The New Disciple, Leader's Guide. 48p. 1976. pap. 1.50 (ISBN 0-8170-0706-7). Judson.

Ban, Joseph D., jt. auth. see Ban, Arline J.

Ban, Joseph D., jt. ed. see Dekar, Paul R.

Banabhatta. Harshacarita: Text of Uchchhvasas 1-VIII. Kane, P. V., ed. 645p. 1986. Repr. 22.00 (ISBN 81-208-0032-X, Pub. by Motilal Banarsidass). South Asia Bks.

Banas, Jackie. Hope & the Purple Onion. (Illus.). 39p. (Orig.). 1984. wkbk. 5.00 (ISBN 0-9614014-1-9). Know Him Pr.

--I Love Me, the Only Diet There Is: A Manual. (Orig.). 1986. spiral bdg. 7.00 (ISBN 0-9614014-3-5). Know Him Pr.

--Reflections in Righteousness. (Illus.). 56p. (Orig.). 1985. 5.00 (ISBN 0-9614014-2-7). Know Him Pr.

Banas, Josef. The Scapegoats: The Exodus of the Remnants of Polish Jewry. Szafar, Tadeusz, tr. 221p. 1979. text ed. 34.50 (ISBN 0-8419-6303-7). Holmes & Meier.

Bancroft, Anne. The Buddhist World. LC 84-51193. (Religions of the World Ser.). (Illus.). 48p. 1985. 9.25 (ISBN 0-382-06928-5); PLB 14.96 (ISBN 0-382-06747-9). Silver.

--The Luminous Vision: Six Medieval Mystics & Their Teachings. 194p. 1983. text ed. 18.50x (ISBN 0-04-189001-9). Allen Unwin.

--Origins of the Sacred. 240p. 1987. pap. 12.95 (ISBN 1-85063-028-3, 30283, Ark Paperbks). Methuen Inc.

--Zen: Direct Pointing to Reality. Purce, Jill, ed. LC 81-67702. (The Illustrated Library of Sacred Imagination). (Illus.). 96p. 1982. pap. 9.95 (ISBN 0-8245-0068-7). Crossroad NY.

--Zen: Direct Pointing to Reality. (Art & Imagination Ser.). (Illus.). 1987. pap. 10.95. Thames Hudson.

Bancroft, Emery. Christian Theology. Mayers, Ronald B., pref. by. 1976. 15.95 (ISBN 0-310-20440-2, 9141). Zondervan.

Bancroft, Emery & Mayers, Ronald B. Elemental Theology. 1977. 15.95 (ISBN 0-310-20460-7, 9146). Zondervan.

Bancroft, Emery H. Fundamentos de Teologia Biblica. Tr. of Elemental Theology. (Span.). 496p. 1987. pap. 10.95 (ISBN 0-8254-1050-9). Kregel.

Bancroft, Richard. Dangerous Positions & Proceedings. LC 74-38147. (English Experience Ser.: No. 427). 192p. 1972. Repr. of 1593 ed. 28.50 (ISBN 90-221-0427-3). Walter J Johnson.

--A Survey of the Pretended Holy Dicipline. LC 78-38148. (English Experience Ser.: No. 428). 472p. 1972. Repr. of 1593 ed. 67.00 (ISBN 90-221-0428-1). Walter J Johnson.

Band, Arnold. Nahman of Bratslav, the Tales. LC 78-53433. (Classics of Western Spirituality). 368p. 1978. pap. 9.95 (ISBN 0-8091-2103-4). Paulist Pr.

Band, Ora, ed. see Bergman, Bella.

Bandas, Rudolph G. Catholic Layman & Holiness. 1965. 8.95 (ISBN 0-8158-0046-0). Chris Mass.

Bandel, Betty. Sing the Lord's Song in a Strange Land: The Life of Justin Morgan. LC 78-73309. 264p. 1981. 24.50 (ISBN 0-8386-2411-1). Fairleigh Dickinson.

Bander, Peter. The Prophecies of St. Malachy. LC 74-125419. (Illus.). 1973. pap. 3.00 (ISBN 0-89555-038-5). TAN Bks Pubs.

--The Prophecies of St. Malachy & St. Columbkille. 3rd ed. 1979. pap. text ed. 6.95x (ISBN 0-901072-10-9). Humanities.

Bandini, Angelo M. Juntarum Typographiae Annales. 474p. Date not set. Repr. of 1791 ed. text ed. 82.80x (ISBN 0-576-72349-5, Pub. by Gregg Intl Pubs England). Gregg Intl.

Bandy, Melanie. Mind Forg'd Manacles: Evil in the Poetry of Blake & Shelley. LC 80-18779. (Illus.). 210p. 1981. text ed. 19.95 (ISBN 0-8173-0046-5). U of Ala Pr.

Bandyopadhyaya, Narayan C. Development of Hindu Polity & Political Theories. 1980. text ed. 28.50x. Coronet Bks.

Bane, Bernard M. On the Impact of Morality in Our Times. 113p. 1985. pap. 5.00 (ISBN 0-317-20545-5). BMB Pub Co.

Banek, Yvette. Christmas Search-a-Picture Puzzles. (Puzzleback Ser.). (Illus.). 64p. (Orig.). 1981. pap. 2.50 (ISBN 0-671-43365-2). Wanderer Bks.

Banerjee, J. N. Development of Hindu Iconography. 3rd ed. (Illus.). 1974. text ed. 36.00x. Coronet Bks.

Banerji, Barenya K. Towards Quiescence & Immortality. LC 80-81693. 149p. 1981. 10.95 (ISBN 0-8022-2366-4). Philos Lib.

Banerji, Ranan, jt. auth. see Wood, Raquel.

Banes, Daniel. Shakespeare, Shylock & Kabbalah. LC 78-58912. 1978. 9.99 (ISBN 0-686-10284-3); pap. 3.60 (ISBN 0-686-10285-1). Malcolm Hse.

Banes, F. Dominico. Scholastica Commentaria in Primam Partem Summae Theologicae S. Thomae Aquinatis, De Deo Uno. Urbano, Luis, ed. (Medieval Studies Reprint Ser.). (Lat. & Span.). Repr. of 1934 ed. lib. bdg. 45.00x (ISBN 0-697-00028-1). Irvington.

Baney, Margaret M. Witness: One Response to Vatican II. 1987. 12.50 (ISBN 0-533-07210-7). Vantage.

Bangert, William. Claude Jay & Alfonso Salmeron: Two Early Jesuits. 1985. 15.95 (ISBN 0-8294-0459-7). Loyola.

Bangert, William V. A Bibliographical Essay on the History of the Society of Jesus. Ganss, George E., ed. LC 76-12667. (Study Aids on Jesuit Topics Ser.: No. 6). 72p. 1976. pap. 1.50 (ISBN 0-912422-16-5); Smyth Sewn. pap. 2.50 (ISBN 0-912422-21-1). Inst Jesuit.

--A History of the Society of Jesus. 2nd, rev. ed. Ganss, George E., ed. LC 85-80693. 587p. 1986. pap. 21.00 (ISBN 0-912422-73-4); smyth sewn 17.50 (ISBN 0-912422-74-2). Inst Jesuit.

Bangham, Mary D. When Jesus Was Four-or Maybe Five. (Illus., Orig.). 1968. pap. 3.95 (ISBN 0-8066-0824-2, 10-7058). Augsburg.

Bangley, Bernard. Forgiving Yourself. 96p. (Orig.). 1986. pap. 4.95 (ISBN 0-87788-281-9). Shaw Pubs.

--Growing in His Image. LC 82-19579. (Illus.). 155p. 1983. pap. 3.50 (ISBN 0-87788-328-9). Shaw Pubs.

Bangley, Bernard K. Bible BASIC: Bible Games for Personal Computers. LC 83-48461. 128p. (Orig.). 1983. pap. 9.95 (ISBN 0-06-250042-2, CN 4092, HarpR). Har-Row.

--Spiritual Treasure: Paraphrases of Spiritual Classics. LC 84-61026. 144p. (Orig.). 1985. pap. 6.95 (ISBN 0-8091-2646-X). Paulist Pr.

Bangs, Carl. Arminius: A Study in the Dutch Reformation. rev. ed. Allison, Joseph D., ed. 384p. 1985. pap. 10.95 (ISBN 0-310-29481-9, 18368P). Zondervan.

Banisadr, Abolhassan. The Fundamental Principles & Precepts of Islamic Government. Ghanoonparvar, Mohammed R., tr. from Persian. LC 81-82634. (Iran-e NO Literary Collection Ser.). 120p. (Orig.). 1981. pap. 5.95 (ISBN 0-939214-01-6). Mazda Pubs.

Banks, Bill. Alive Again! 168p. (Orig.). 1977. pap. 3.95 (ISBN 0-89228-048-4). Impact Bks MO.

Banks, Bill & Banks, Sue. Ministering to Abortion's Aftermath. 144p. (Orig.). 1982. pap. 3.95 (ISBN 0-89228-057-3). Impact Bks MO.

Banks, Charles W. The Life & Times of John Calvin: With an Earnest Appeal for the Adoption of Open-Air Preaching. LC 83-45599. Date not set. Repr. of 1891 ed. 21.50 (ISBN 0-404-19867-8). Ams Pr.

Banks, J. A. Victorian Values: Secularism & the Smaller Family. 288p. 1981. 26.95x (ISBN 0-7100-0807-4). Methuen Inc.

Banks, Louis A. Immortal Hymns & Their Story. LC 77-75198. 1977. Repr. of 1899 ed. lib. bdg. 30.00 (ISBN 0-89341-088-8). Longwood Pub Group.

Banks, Martha. The Call of Jesus: Lessons in Becoming His Disciple. rev. ed. (Bible Study: Basic Ser.). 64p. (Orig.). pap. 2.95 (ISBN 0-932305-28-8, 521009). Aglow Pubns.

Banks, Natalie N. The Golden Thread. 1979. pap. 5.00 (ISBN 0-85330-127-1). Lucis.

Banks, Robert. Paul's Idea of Community: The Early House Churches in the Historical Setting. 1980. pap. 5.95 (ISBN 0-8028-1830-7). Eerdmans.

--The Tyranny of Time. LC 84-28855. 265p. 1985. pap. 6.95 (ISBN 0-87784-338-4). Inter-Varsity.

Banks, Sue, jt. auth. see Banks, Bill.

Banks, William. Questions You Have Always Wanted to Ask about Tongues, but... (Illus.). 1979. pap. 2.25 (ISBN 0-89957-526-9). AMG Pubs.

Banks, William, jt. auth. see Beall, Todd.

Banks, William D. The Heavens Declare... (Illus.). 288p. (Orig.). 1985. pap. 6.95 (ISBN 0-89228-101-4). Impact Bks MO.

Bankson, Marjory Z. Braided Streams: Esther & a Woman's Way of Growing. LC 85-50203. (Illus.). 184p. (Orig.). 1985. pap. 8.95 (ISBN 0-931055-05-9). LuraMedia.

--Seasons of Friendship: Naomi & Ruth As a Pattern. Broucek, Marcia, ed. 200p. (Orig.). 1987. pap. 9.95 (ISBN 0-931055-41-5). LuraMedia.

Bannerjee, Brojendra N. Religious Conversions in India. 384p. 1982. 29.95x (ISBN 0-940500-28-0, Pub. by Harnam Pub India). Asia Bk Corp.

Bannerman, Glenn & Fakkema, Robert. Guide for Recreation Leaders. LC 74-28523. 120p. (Orig.). 1975. pap. 7.95 (ISBN 0-8042-2154-5). John Knox.

Bannister, John, jt. auth. see Lemmons, Reuel.

Bannon, William J., jt. auth. see Donovan, Suzanne.

Bansemer, Richard. Day Full of Grace. Sherer, Michael, ed. (Orig.). 1987. pap. 5.95 (ISBN 0-89536-854-4, 7813). CSS of Ohio.

Banta, Martha. Henry James & the Occult: The Great Extension. LC 72-75386. Repr. of 1972 ed. 54.60 (ISBN 0-8357-9215-3, 2013010). Bks Demand UMI.

Banton, Michael, ed. Anthropological Approaches to the Study of Religion. 1968. pap. 13.95 (ISBN 0-422-72510-2, NO.2068, Pub. by Tavistock England). Methuen Inc.

Banuazizi, Ali & Weiner, Myron, eds. The State, Religion, & Ethnic Politics: Afghanistan, Iran, & Pakistan. (Contemporary Issues in the Middle East Ser.). (Illus.). 464p. 1986. text ed. 35.00x (ISBN 0-8156-2385-2). Syracuse U Pr.

Baptist-Metz, Johannes, jt. auth. see Schillebeeckx, Edward.

Barack, Nathan A. God Speaks Naturally: An Organic Perspective on the Prophets. LC 83-7836. 242p. 1983. 12.50 (ISBN 0-8246-0299-4). Jonathan David.

Barakat, Robert. Cistercian Sign Language. LC 70-152476. (Cistercian Studies: No. 11). 1976. 14.95 (ISBN 0-87907-811-1). Cistercian Pubns.

Baralt, Luce L. Huellas del Islam en la Literatura Espanola: De Juan Ruiz a Juan Goytisola. 262p. 1985. 18.00 (ISBN 84-7517-152-4). U of PR Pr.

Baramki, Dimitri, jt. auth. see Kelso, James L.

Barash, Meyer, tr. see Caillois, Roger.

Baravalle, Hermann Von see Von Baravalle, Hermann.

Barbeau, Clayton C. Delivering the Male: Out of the Tough-Guy Trap into a Better Marriage. 120p. (Orig.). 1982. pap. 6.95 (ISBN 0-86683-642-X, HarpR). Har-Row.

--Joy of Marriage. Orig. Title: Creative Marriage: the Middle Years. 132p. 1980. pap. 5.95 (ISBN 0-86683-759-0, HarpR). Har-Row.

Barbeau, Marius. Modern Growth of the Totem Pole on the Northwest Coast. facs. ed. (Shorey Indian Ser.). 16p. pap. 0.95 (ISBN 0-8466-0098-6, S98). Shorey.

Barbee, A. H. Behind the Iron Curtain: The Story of John Visser. 75p. 1985. pap. 2.95 (ISBN 0-89084-280-9). Bob Jones Univ Pr.

Barber, Aldyth A., jt. auth. see Barber, Cyril J.

Barber, Bill. A Second Hand Life: Discussions with Bill Barber. 144p. (Orig.). 1986. pap. 8.95 (ISBN 0-87418-025-2, 163). Coleman Pub.

Barber, Cyril J. Dynamic Personal Bible Study: Principles of Inductive Bible Study Based on the Life of Abraham. LC 81-8443. 1981. pap. 4.95 (ISBN 0-87213-023-1). Loizeaux.

--Habakkuk & Zephaniah. (Everyman's Bible Commentary Ser.). 1985. pap. 5.95 (ISBN 0-8024-2069-9). Moody.

--How to Gain Life: Changing Insights from the Book of Books. 1979. pap. 1.00 (ISBN 0-88469-100-4). BMH Bks.

--Introduction to Theological Research. 1982. pap. 9.95 (ISBN 0-8024-4134-3). Moody.

--The Minister's Library, Vol. I. 1985. 19.95 (ISBN 0-8024-5296-5). Moody.

--The Minister's Library, Vol. 2. 1987. text ed. 23.95 (ISBN 0-8024-5299-X). Moody.

--Nehemiah & the Dynamics of Effective Leadership: Study Guide. (Illus.). 56p. 1980. pap. text ed. 3.25 (ISBN 0-87213-022-3). Loizeaux.

--Nehemiah & the Dynamics of Effective Leadership. LC 76-22567. 1976. pap. 3.95 (ISBN 0-87213-021-5). Loizeaux.

Barber, Cyril J. & Barber, Aldyth A. Your Marriage Has Real Possibilities. LC 83-25537. 168p. (Orig.). 1984. pap. text ed. 6.95 (ISBN 0-8254-2249-3). Kregel.

Barber, James D. Erasmus: A Play on Words. LC 81-40002. 80p. (Orig.). 1982. lib. bdg. 23.50 (ISBN 0-8191-1868-0); pap. text ed. 5.75 (ISBN 0-8191-1869-9). U Pr of Amer.
Barber, Lucie W. The Religious Education of Preschool Children. LC 80-27623. 196p. (Orig.). 1981. pap. 12.95 (ISBN 0-89135-026-8). Religious Educ.
--Teaching Christian Values. LC 83-22981. 250p. (Orig.). 1984. pap. 12.95 (ISBN 0-89135-041-1). Religious Educ.
Barber, M. C. The Trial of the Templars. LC 77-85716. 320p. 1978. 54.50 (ISBN 0-521-21896-9); pap. 15.95 (ISBN 0-521-28018-4). Cambridge U Pr.
Barber, Marjorie, jt. auth. see Beall, James L.
Barber, Natalie. Dr. & Mrs. Fix-It: The Story of Frank & Bessie Beck. LC 79-130776. (Bold Believers Ser). (Orig.). 1969. pap. 0.95 (ISBN 0-377-84181-1). Friend Pr.
Barber, Virginia & Skaggs, Merrill M. The Mother Person. LC 76-48850. 1977. pap. 7.95 (ISBN 0-8052-0565-9). Schocken.
Barbernitz, Patricia. RCIA Team Manual: How to Implement the Rite of Christian Initiation of Adults in Your Parish. 88p. 1986. pap. 7.95 (ISBN 0-8091-2814-4). Paulist Pr.
--RCIA: The Rite of Christian Initiation of Adults. 48p. 1983. pap. 2.95 (ISBN 0-89243-190-3). Liguori Pubns.
Barbet, Jean. Architecture of Altars & Chimneys, 2 vols. (Printed Sources of Western Art Ser.). (Fr., Illus.). 1981. pap. 35.00 slipcase (ISBN 0-915346-59-1). A Wofsy Fine Arts.
Barbieri, Louis. First & Second Peter. (Everyman's Bible Commentary Ser.). 1977. pap. 5.95 (ISBN 0-8024-2061-3). Moody.
Barbieri, Louis A. Primera y Segunda Pedro, Comentario Biblico Portavoz. Orig. Title: First & Second Peter, Everyman's Bible Commentary. (Span.). 1981. pap. 3.95 (ISBN 0-8254-1051-7). Kregel.
Barborka. Story of Human Evolution. 8.95 (ISBN 0-8356-7550-5). Theos Pub Hse.
Barborka, Geoffrey. Divine Plan: Commentary on the Secret Doctrine. 3rd ed. 1972. 19.95 (ISBN 0-8356-7167-4). Theos Pub Hse.
--The Peopling of the Earth. LC 75-4243. (Illus.). 240p. 1975. 10.00 (ISBN 0-8356-0221-4). Theos Pub Hse.
Barborka, Geoffrey A. H. P. Blavatsky: Tibet & Tulku. (Illus.). 1974. 12.95 (ISBN 0-8356-7159-3). Theos Pub Hse.
Barbour, Brian M., ed. American Transcendentalism: An Anthology of Criticism. LC 72-12640. 384p. 1973. pap. 8.95x (ISBN 0-268-00494-3). U of Notre Dame Pr.
Barbour, Hugh. Margaret Fell Speaking. LC 76-4224. (Orig.). 1976. pap. 2.50x (ISBN 0-87574-206-8). Pendle Hill.
--The Quakers in Puritan England. LC 85-6963. 300p. 1985. pap. 14.95 (ISBN 0-913408-87-5). Friends United.
Barbour, Ian G. Issues in Science & Religion. 1971. pap. 8.95x (ISBN 0-06-131566-4, TB1566, Torch). Har-Row.
--Myths, Models, & Paradigms. LC 73-18690. 1976. pap. text ed. 6.95x (ISBN 0-06-060387-9, RD 183, HarpR). Har-Row.
Barbour, James, ed. see Howard, Leon.
Barbour, James M. The Church Music of William Billings. LC 72-39000. 167p. 1972. Repr. of 1960 ed. lib. bdg. 22.50 (ISBN 0-306-70434-X). Da Capo.
--The Church Music of William Billings. 167p. Repr. of 1960 ed. lib. bdg. 29.00 (Pub. by Am Repr Serv). Am Biog Serv.
Barbour, Mary, tr. see De Monfort, St. Louis.
Barbour, Mary E. You Can Teach Two's & Three's. 64p. 1981. pap. 3.50 (ISBN 0-88207-149-1). Victor Bks.
Barca, Pedro C. de la see De la Barca, Pedro C.
Barclay, Mark. Seven Bible Ways to Properly Relate to Your Pastor. 32p. 1982. pap. 2.25 (ISBN 0-88144-024-8). Christian Pub.
Barclay, Oliver R. The Intellect & Beyond: Developing a Christian Mind. 144p. (Orig.). 1985. pap. 6.95 (ISBN 0-310-33291-5, 12280P). Zondervan.
Barclay, R. A., tr. see Auerbach, Elias.
Barclay, William. All-Sufficient Christ: Studies in Paul's Letter to the Colossians. LC 63-18385. 142p. 1963. pap. 6.95 (ISBN 0-664-24480-7). Westminster.
--And He Had Compassion. LC 75-28099. 272p. 1976. pap. 5.95 (ISBN 0-8170-0686-9). Judson.
--And Jesus Said: A Handbook on the Parables of Jesus. LC 77-120410. 224p. 1970. pap. 7.95 (ISBN 0-664-24898-5). Westminster.
--The Beatitudes & the Lord's Prayer for Everyman. LC 75-9309. 256p. 1975. pap. 7.95 (ISBN 0-06-060393-3, RD112, HarpR). Har-Row.
--Christian Ethics for Today. LC 83-48994. 224p. 1984. pap. 7.95 (ISBN 0-06-060412-3, RD 512). Har-Row.
--Communicating the Gospel. 1978. pap. 3.25x (ISBN 0-7152-0401-7). Outlook.
--Everyday Prayers. LC 60-5326. 160p. 1981. pap. 6.95 (ISBN 0-06-060411-5, RD 361, HarpR). Har-Row.
--Great Themes of the New Testament. LC 79-18213. 122p. 1979. pap. 4.95 (ISBN 0-664-24286-3). Westminster.
--Guide to Daily Prayer. LC 62-11473. 1974. pap. 6.95 (ISBN 0-06-060401-8, RD75, HarpR). Har-Row.
--In the Hands of God. LC 80-25261. 154p. 1981. pap. 4.95 (ISBN 0-664-24362-2). Westminster.
--Introduction to John & the Acts of the Apostles. LC 75-38902. 352p. 1976. softcover 5.95 (ISBN 0-664-24771-7). Westminster.
--Introduction to the First Three Gospels: A Revised Edition of the First Three Gospels. LC 75-37545. 314p. 1976. pap. 9.95 (ISBN 0-664-24798-9). Westminster.
--Jesus As They Saw Him. LC 78-18224. 1978. pap. 7.95 (ISBN 0-8028-1775-0). Eerdmans.
--Jesus of Nazareth. 1977. pap. 1.95 (ISBN 0-345-27253-6). Ballantine.
--Jesus of Nazareth. 288p. 1985. pap. 12.95 (ISBN 0-8407-5759-X). Nelson.
--Letters to the Seven Churches. LC 82-2760. 128p. 1982. pap. 6.95 (ISBN 0-664-24433-5). Westminster.
--The Life of Jesus for Everyman. LC 75-12282. 96p. 1975. pap. 5.72 (ISBN 0-06-060404-2, RD 319, HarpR). Har-Row.
--The Lord Is My Shepherd: Expositions of Selected Psalms. LC 79-27096. 154p. 1980. pap. 5.95 (ISBN 0-664-24317-7). Westminster.
--The Lord's Supper. LC 82-2774. 128p. 1982. pap. 7.95 (ISBN 0-664-24432-7). Westminster.
--The Master's Men. (Festival Books). 1976. pap. 3.25 (ISBN 0-687-23732-7). Abingdon.
--The Master's Men. LC 85-6395. 224p. 1985. pap. 8.95 (ISBN 0-8027-2496-5). Walker & Co.
--The Men, the Meaning, the Message of the New Testament Books. LC 77-22184. 156p. 1978. pap. 4.95 (ISBN 0-664-24188-3). Westminster.
--The Mind of Jesus. LC 61-7332. 352p. 1976. pap. 8.95 (ISBN 0-06-060451-4, RD143, HarpR). Har-Row.
--The Mind of St. Paul. LC 75-9310. 256p. 1975. pap. 8.95 (ISBN 0-06-060471-9, RD110, HarpR). Har-Row.
--New Testament Words. LC 73-12737. 302p. 1976. softcover 5.95 (ISBN 0-664-24761-X). Westminster.
--Palabras Griegas Del Nuevo Testamento. Marin, Javier J., tr. 220p. 1985. pap. 4.50 (ISBN 0-311-42052-4). Casa Bautista.
--The Promise of the Spirit. LC 60-11200. 120p. 1978. pap. 6.95 (ISBN 0-664-24205-7). Westminster.
--The Ten Commandments for Today. LC 83-6103. 208p. (Orig.). 1983. pap. 7.95 (ISBN 0-06-060417-4, RD 476, HarpR). Har-Row.
--Turning to God. 1978. pap. 3.25x (ISBN 0-7152-0388-6). Outlook.
--William Barclay: A Spiritual Autobiography. LC 73-76528. 1977. pap. 1.50 (ISBN 0-8028-1667-3). Eerdmans.
Barcovitch, Sacvan, ed. Aspects of Puritan Religious Thought: Library, Vol. VI. LC 83-12782. (Library of American Puritan Writings). 728p. 1984. Repr. 57.50 (ISBN 0-404-60806-X). AMS Pr.
Barcus, Nancy B. The Family Takes a Child. 96p. 1983. pap. 5.95 (ISBN 0-8170-0998-1). Judson.
--Help Me, God, I'm a Working Mother! 64p. 1982. pap. 3.95 (ISBN 0-8170-0954-X). Judson.
Bard, Martin L. The Peril of Faith. 155p. (Orig.). 1982. pap. 5.00 (ISBN 0-910309-05-1). Am Atheist.
Bardi, Panos D. History of Thanatology: Philosophical, Religious, Psychological, & Sociological Ideas Concerning Death from Primitive Times to the Present. LC 81-43026. 102p. (Orig.). 1981. lib. bdg. 21.00 (ISBN 0-8191-1648-3); pap. text ed. 8.25 (ISBN 0-8191-1649-1). U Pr of Amer.
Bardill, Donald R., jt. auth. see Mueller, Charles S.
Bardin, Shlomo, ed. Self-Fulfillment Through Zionism: A Study in Jewish Adjustment. LC 70-142605. (Biography Index Reprint Ser). Repr. of 1943 ed. 17.00 (ISBN 0-8369-8076-X). Ayer Co Pubs.
Bardon, Franz. Initiation into Hermetics. 4th ed. Radspieler, A., tr. from Ger. (Illus.). 294p. 1981. 17.00 (ISBN 0-914732-10-2). Bro Life Inc.
Bardsley, C. W. Curiosities of Puritan Nomenclature. (The International Library of Names). 252p. Repr. of 1880 ed. text ed. cancelled (ISBN 0-8290-1239-7). Irvington.
Bardsley, Herbert J. Reconstructions of Early Christian Documents. 1977. lib. bdg. 59.95 (ISBN 0-8490-2504-4). Gordon Pr.
Barfield, Owen. History, Guilt, & Habit. LC 79-65333. 104p. 1981. pap. 9.95 (ISBN 0-8195-6064-2). Wesleyan U Pr.
--Saving the Appearances: A Study in Idolatry. LC 65-23538. 190p. 1965. pap. 4.95 (ISBN 0-15-679490-X, Harv). HarBraceJ.
Barfield, Owen, tr. see Steiner, Rudolf.
Bargad, Warren. Ideas in Fiction: The Works of Hayim Hazaz. LC 81-13621. (Brown Judiac Studies). 1982. pap. 13.50 (ISBN 0-89130-518-1, 14-00-31). Scholars Pr GA.
Barger, R. Curtis. Don't You Know? Haven't You Heard? Woolsey, Raymond H., ed. (Banner Ser.). 128p. (Orig.). 1985. pap. 5.95 (ISBN 0-8280-0278-9). Review & Herald.
Bargh, David J. De see De Bargh, David J.
Barghahn, Barbara von see Von Barghahn, Barbara.
Bargrave, John. Pope Alexander the Seventh & the College of Cardinals. Robertson, James C., ed. LC 78-160001. (Camden Society, London. Publications, First Ser.: No. 92). Repr. of 1867 ed. 19.00 (ISBN 0-404-50192-3). AMS Pr.
--Pope Alexander the Seventh & the College of Cardinals. 19.00 (ISBN 0-384-03435-7). Johnson Repr.
Barin. Jesus Came to Me. 2nd rev. ed. LC 86-60047. (Illus.). 150p. (Orig.). 1986. Repr. of 1973 ed. 17.95 (ISBN 0-935075-06-2). Sri Aurobindo.
Baring-Gould, S. Curious Myths of the Middle Ages. (Works of S. Baring-Gould Ser.). 254p. 1985. Repr. of 1867 ed. lib. bdg. 29.00 (ISBN 0-932051-19-7, Pub. by Am Repr Serv). Am Biog Serv.
--Freaks of Fanaticism, & Other Strange Events. 59.95 (ISBN 0-8490-0193-5). Gordon Pr.
--Legends of the Patriarchs & Prophets & Other Old Testament Characters. LC 74-9741. 1872. lib. bdg. 42.00 (ISBN 0-8414-3205-8). Folcroft.
--A Study of St. Paul: His Character & Opinions. 1977. lib. bdg. 59.95 (ISBN 0-8490-2712-8). Gordon Pr.
Baring-Gould, Sabine. Book of Werewolves: Being an Account of Terrible Superstition. Repr. of 1865 ed. 35.00x (ISBN 0-8103-4241-3). Gale.
--Curious Myths of the Middle Ages. 69.95 (ISBN 0-87968-261-2). Gordon Pr.
--Curious Myths of the Middle Ages. 1976. Repr. of 1867 ed. 69.00x (ISBN 0-403-06309-4, Regency). Scholarly.
--Eastern Orthodox Saints. pap. 0.95 (ISBN 0-686-01292-5). Eastern Orthodox.
--Freaks of Fanaticism & Other Strange Events. LC 68-21754. 1968. Repr. of 1891 ed. 40.00x (ISBN 0-8103-3503-4). Gale.
Barish, Louis & Barish, Rebecca. Varieties of Jewish Belief. 1979. Repr. 9.95 (ISBN 0-8246-0242-0). Jonathan David.
Barish, Rebecca, jt. auth. see Barish, Louis.
Bark, William C. Origins of the Medieval World. 1958. 15.00x (ISBN 0-8047-0513-5); pap. 5.95x (ISBN 0-8047-0514-3). Stanford U Pr.
Barker. Science & Religion: An Annotated Bibliography. 1986. lib. bdg. 40.00 (ISBN 0-8240-8762-3). Garland Pub.
Barker, A. Trevor, compiled by. The Letters of H. P. Blavatsky to A. P. Sinnett. facsimile of 1925 ed. LC 73-84138. 1973. 12.00 (ISBN 0-911500-23-5). Theos U Pr.
Barker, A. Trevor, ed. Mahatma Letters to A. P. Sinnett. 3rd ed. 1972. 11.50 (ISBN 0-8356-7013-9). Theos Pub Hse.
Barker, A. Trevor, compiled by. The Mahatma Letters to A. P. Sinnett. facsimile of 1926, 2nd ed. LC 75-10574. 1975. 12.00 (ISBN 0-911500-20-0); pap. 7.00 (ISBN 0-911500-21-9). Theos U Pr.
Barker, Arthur E. Milton & the Puritan Dilemma, 1641-1660. LC 58-3195. 1942. 30.00x (ISBN 0-8020-5025-5); pap. 8.50 o. p. (ISBN 0-8020-6306-3). U of Toronto Pr.
Barker, Dudley. G. K. Chesterton. LC 72-95988. 1975. 5.95 (ISBN 0-8128-1804-0). Stein & Day.
Barker, Eileen. The Making of a Moonie: Choice or Brainwashing? (Illus.). 299p. 1984. 19.95 (ISBN 0-631-13246-5). Basil Blackwell.
Barker, Eileen, ed. New Religious Movements: A Perspective for Understanding Society. LC 82-8263. (Studies in Religion & Society: Vol. 3). 440p. 1982. 69.95x (ISBN 0-88946-864-8). E Mellen.
--Of Gods & Men: New Religious Movements in the West. LC 83-23822. xiv, 347p. 1984. 26.50 (ISBN 0-86554-095-0, MUP/H87). Mercer Univ Pr.
Barker, Ernest. The Crusades. facsimile ed. LC 76-160956. (Select Bibliographies Reprint Ser). Repr. of 1923 ed. 12.00 (ISBN 0-8369-5823-3). Ayer Co Pubs.
--Oliver Cromwell & the English People. facsimile ed. LC 72-37329. (Select Bibliographies Reprint Ser). Repr. of 1937 ed. 12.00 (ISBN 0-8369-6674-0). Ayer Co Pubs.
Barker, Esther T. Unused Cradle. pap. 1.50x (ISBN 0-8358-0231-0). Upper Room.
Barker, George. Thurgarton Church. 1969. write for info. (ISBN 0-685-01054-6, Pub. by Trigram Pr); signed ed. 100 copies 12.00 ea.; pap. 2.00 (ISBN 0-685-01056-2). Small Pr Dist.
Barker, John C. Strange Contrarieties: Pascal in England During the Age of Reason. (Illus.). 352p. 1976. 20.00x (ISBN 0-7735-0188-6). McGill-Queens U Pr.
Barker, Kenneth. Religious Education, Catechesis & Freedom. LC 81-13962. 255p. (Orig.). 1981. pap. 12.95 (ISBN 0-89135-028-4). Religious Educ.
Barker, Kenneth, ed. The NIV: The Making of a Contemporary Translation. 240p. 1986. pap. 8.95 (ISBN 0-310-24181-2). Zondervan.
Barker, Nicolas, ed. see Morison, Stanley.
Barker, Peggy. What Happened When Grandma Died. 4.95 (ISBN 0-570-04090-6, 56-1458). Concordia.
Barker, Sr. R. Mildred. Holy Land: A History of the Alfred Shakers. 2nd ed. 53p. 1986. pap. 3.50 (ISBN 0-915836-03-3). Shaker Pr ME.
--The Sabbathday Lake Shakers: An Introduction to the Shaker Heritage. 2nd ed. (Illus.). 26p. 1985. pap. 3.00 (ISBN 0-915836-04-1). Shaker Pr ME.
Barker, Raymond C. The Science of Successful Living. LC 57-11392. 145p. 1984. pap. 5.50 (ISBN 0-87516-536-2). De Vorss.
Barker, Raymond C., jt. auth. see Holmes, Ernest.
Barker, William P. Everyone in the Bible. 384p. 1966. 15.95 (ISBN 0-8007-0084-8). Revell.
Barkman, Alma. Days Remembered. (Illus.). 96p. 1983. pap. 8.95 (ISBN 0-8024-0188-0). Moody.
--Sunny-Side Up. (Quiet Time Bks.). 1984. pap. 3.50 (ISBN 0-8024-8431-X). Moody.
Barkman, Betty. Anna. 171p. (Orig.). 1985. pap. 6.65 (ISBN 0-919797-10-5). Kindred Pr.
Barkun, Michael. Crucible of the Millennium: The Burned-Over District of New York in the 1840s. LC 86-5777. (New York State Studies). (Illus.). 240p. (Orig.). 1986. text ed. 27.50x (ISBN 0-8156-2371-2); pap. text ed. 14.95x (ISBN 0-8156-2378-X). Syracuse U Pr.
--Disaster & the Millennium. LC 86-5979. 256p. 1986. pap. text ed. 12.95x (ISBN 0-8156-2392-5). Syracuse U Pr.
Barkway, Lunsden & Menzies, Lucy, eds. An Anthology of the Love of God: From the Writings of Evelyn Underhill. 220p. 1981. Repr. of 1953 ed. lib. bdg. 30.00 (ISBN 0-8495-0067-2). Arden Lib.
Barlag, R., jt. auth. see Andersen, R.
Barley, L. M., et al. Religious Data: Recurrent Christian Sources, Non-Recurrent Christian Data, Judaism, Other Religions. (Reviews of U. K. Statistical Sources Ser.: No. 20). 635p. 1987. 86.50 (ISBN 0-08-034778-9). Pergamon.
Barlow, Christopher. Islam. (Today's World Ser.). (Illus.). 72p. 1983. 16.95 (ISBN 0-7134-3659-X, Pub. by Batsford England). David & Charles.
Barlow, Frank. The English Church, Ten Sixty-Six to Eleven Fifty-Four: A History of the Anglo-Norman Church. (Illus.). 1979. text ed. 40.00x (ISBN 0-582-50236-5). Longman.
--Thomas Becket. (Illus.). 360p. 1986. 25.00 (ISBN 0-520-05920-4). U of Cal Pr.
Barlow, Fred M. Heaven's Hall of Heroes. LC 78-16887. (Illus.). 1978. pap. 3.95 (ISBN 0-87227-062-9). Reg Baptist.
--Timeless Truth for Twentieth Century Times. 123p. 1970. 3.25 (ISBN 0-87398-838-8, Pub. by Bibl Evang Pr). Sword of Lord.
Barlow, Geoffrey, ed. Vintage Muggeridge: Religion & Society. 200p. (Orig.). 1986. pap. 7.95 (ISBN 0-8028-0181-1). Eerdmans.
Barlow, Philip L., ed. A Thoughtful Faith: Essays on Belief by Mormon Scholars. LC 86-71882. 275p. 1986. 14.95 (ISBN 0-939651-00-9). Canon Pr.
Barlow, T. Ed. Congregational House Churches. (Orig.). 1978. pap. 1.50 (ISBN 0-8309-0214-7). Herald Hse.
Barlow, T. Edward. Living Saints Witness at Work. 1976. 6.00 (ISBN 0-8309-0153-1). Herald Hse.
Barlow, William. A Dyaloge Descrybyng the Orygynall Ground of These Lutheran Saccyons, That Is, Faccyons. LC 74-80161. (English Experience Ser.: No. 641). 200p. 1974. Repr. of 1531 ed. 13.00 (ISBN 90-221-0641-1). Walter J Johnson.
Barna, George & McKay, William P. Vital Signs: Emerging Social Trends & the Future of American Christianity. LC 84-70658. 160p. (Orig.). 1984. 12.95 (ISBN 0-89107-324-8, Crossway Bks). Good News.
Barnabas. Gospel of Barnabas. 1981. pap. 9.95 (ISBN 0-686-77427-2). Kazi Pubns.
Barnabas, Bentley. Beatitudes for the Balmy: And Other Poems. 1985. 6.95 (ISBN 0-682-40211-7). Exposition Pr FL.
Barnard, E. K. The Windows of Portsmouth Cathedral. 1977. 42.00x (ISBN 0-317-43731-3, Pub. by City of Portsmouth). State Mutual Bk.
Barnard, Harry. Forging of an American Jew: The Life & Times of Judge Julian W. Mack. 1974. 7.95 (ISBN 0-685-52984-3). Herzl Pr.
Barnard, J. H., ed. The Odes of Solomon. (Texts & Studies Ser.: No. 1, Vol. 8, Pt. 3). pap. 13.00 (ISBN 0-8115-1710-1). Kraus Repr.

Barnard, Jerry. Something Worse Than Hell & Better Than Heaven. 1979. pap. 3.25 (ISBN 0-917726-31-6). Hunter Bks.

Barnard, Laura B. Biblical Basis of Missions. 32p. 1973. pap. 1.50 (ISBN 0-89265-100-8). Randall Hse.

Barnard, Laura B. & Hill, Georgia. Touching the Untouchables. 224p. 1985. pap. 6.95 (ISBN 0-8423-7296-2). Tyndale.

Barnard, Mary. Mythmakers. LC 66-20061. 213p. 1979. 16.95 (ISBN 0-8214-0024-X); pap. 6.50 (ISBN 0-8214-0562-4). Ohio U Pr.

--The Mythmakers. LC 66-20061. 213p. 1986. 12.95 (ISBN 0-932576-36-2); pap. 6.95 (ISBN 0-932576-37-0). Breitenbush Bks.

Barnard, Mary E. The Myth of Apollo & Daphne from Ovid to Quevedo. (Duke Monographs in Medieval & Renaissance Studies: No. 8). (Illus.). 190p. 1986. lib. bdg. 25.00 (ISBN 0-8223-0701-4). Duke.

Barnard, P. M., ed. The Biblical Text of Clement of Alexandria in the Four Gospels & the Acts of the Apostles. (Texts & Studies Ser.: No. 1, Vol. 5, Pt. 5). pap. 13.00 (ISBN 0-8115-1700-4). Kraus Repr.

Barnard, Tom. How to Grow an Adult Class. 88p. (Orig.). 1983. pap. 2.95 (ISBN 0-8341-0840-2). Beacon Hill.

Barndt, Joseph R., jt. auth. see Smith, Louis A.

Barnes, Albert. Acts & Romans. 18.95 (ISBN 0-8010-0844-1). Baker Bk.

--The Atonement. LC 80-65582. 1980. pap. 7.95 (ISBN 0-87123-016-X, 210016). Bethany Hse.

--Barnes' Notes on the New Testament. LC 62-8727. 1776p. 1966. 39.95 (ISBN 0-8254-2200-0). Kregel.

--Barnes' Notes on the Old & New Testaments, 14 vols. 249.50 (ISBN 0-8010-0834-4). Baker Bk.

--Church & Slavery. LC 71-98714. Repr. of 1857 ed. 22.50 (ISBN 0-8371-2771-8, BAC&, Pub. by Negro U Pr). Greenwood.

--Church & Slavery. LC 79-82416. 15.00x (ISBN 0-403-00150-1). Scholarly.

--Daniel. 16.95 (ISBN 0-8010-0841-7). Baker Bk.

--Ephesians-Philemon. 15.95 (ISBN 0-8010-0847-6). Baker Bk.

--Exodus-Esther. 24.95 (ISBN 0-8010-0836-0). Baker Bk.

--First Corinthians, Galatians. 18.95 (ISBN 0-8010-0846-8). Baker Bk.

--Genesis. 13.95 (ISBN 0-8010-0835-2). Baker Bk.

--The Gospels. 19.95 (ISBN 0-8010-0843-3). Baker Bk.

--Hebrews-Jude. 18.95 (ISBN 0-8010-0848-4). Baker Bk.

--Inquiry into Scriptural Views of Slavery. LC 75-92415. 1855. 23.00x (ISBN 0-403-00151-X). Scholarly.

--Isaiah. 23.95 (ISBN 0-8010-0840-9). Baker Bk.

--Job. 18.95 (ISBN 0-8010-0837-9). Baker Bk.

--Minor Prophets. 23.95 (ISBN 0-8010-0842-5). Baker Bk.

--Proverbs-Ezekiel. 10.95 (ISBN 0-8010-0839-5). Baker Bk.

--Psalms. 29.95 (ISBN 0-8010-0838-7). Baker Bk.

--Revelation. 12.95 (ISBN 0-8010-0849-2). Baker Bk.

Barnes, Arthur S. Christianity at Rome in the Apostolic Age. LC 72-114462. (Illus.). 1971. Repr. of 1938 ed. lib. bdg. 55.00x (ISBN 0-8371-4760-3, BACR). Greenwood.

Barnes, Barnabe. Foure Bookes of Offices: Enabling Privat Persons for the Service of All Good Princes & Policies. LC 74-28830. (English Experience Ser.: No. 712). 1975. Repr. of 1606 ed. 24.00 (ISBN 9-0221-0712-4). Walter J Johnson.

Barnes, Bruce. Introduction to Islam. (Illus.). 192p. (Orig.). 1984. pap. text ed. 7.00 (ISBN 0-913811-01-7). Northeast A S.

Barnes, C. L. Parallels in Dante & Milton. LC 74-3180. 1917. lib. bdg. 12.50 (ISBN 0-8414-9926-8). Folcroft.

Barnes, David H., jt. auth. see Morrison, Clinton D.

Barnes, Emilie. More Hours in My Day. (Orig.). 1982. pap. 5.95 (ISBN 0-89081-355-8). Harvest Hse.

Barnes, Ernest W. Scientific Theory & Religion. LC 77-27198. (Gifford Lectures: 1927-29). Repr. of 1933 ed. 42.50 (ISBN 0-404-60483-8). AMS Pr.

Barnes, Harry E. The Twilight of Christianity. 75.00 (ISBN 0-87700-037-9). Revisionist Pr.

Barnes, Hazel E. Sartre & Flaubert. LC 80-26872. x, 450p. 1982. pap. 10.95 (ISBN 0-226-03721-5, PHOEN). U of Chicago Pr.

Barnes, Irwin. Truth Is Immortal: The Story of Baptists in Europe. 127p. 1950. 2.95 (ISBN 0-87921-015-X); pap. 1.95 (ISBN 0-87921-019-2). Attic Pr.

Barnes, Jonathan, jt. auth. see Annas, Julia.

Barnes, Michael H. In the Presence of Mystery: An Introduction to the Study of Human Religiousness. 324p. (Orig.). 1984. pap. 9.95 (ISBN 0-89622-205-5). Twenty-Third.

Barnes, Peter. Milk of the World. 80p. (Orig.). 1985. pap. 2.95 (ISBN 0-85151-434-0). Banner of Truth.

Barnes, Robert. A Supplicatyon... Unto Henry the Eighth. LC 73-6098. (English Experience Ser.: No. 567). 1973. Repr. of 1534 ed. 18.50 (ISBN 90-221-0567-9). Walter J Johnson.

Barnes, Robert G., Jr. Single Parenting: A Wilderness Journey. 176p. 1984. pap. 5.95 (ISBN 0-8423-5892-7). Tyndale.

Barnes, Sandra T. Ogun: An Old God for a New Age. LC 79-26577. (ISHI Occasional Papers in Social Change: No. 3). 72p. 1980. pap. text ed. 5.95x (ISBN 0-89727-011-8). ISHI PA.

Barnes, Timothy. Constantine & Eusebius. LC 81-4248. (Illus.). 448p. 1981. text ed. 37.50x (ISBN 0-674-16530-6). Harvard U Pr.

Barnes, Vera F. Daybreak Below the Border. 1975. Repr. 2.50 (ISBN 0-87509-078-8). Chr Pubns.

--Miles Beyond in Brazil. 3.50 (ISBN 0-87509-104-0); pap. 2.00 (ISBN 0-87509-105-9). Chr Pubns.

Barnes, W. Emery. Gospel Criticism & Form Criticism. 84p. 1936. pap. text ed. 6.95 (ISBN 0-567-02020-7, Pub. by T & T Clark Ltd UK). Fortress.

Barnes, W. W., jt. auth. see Allison, William H.

Barnet, Sylvan & Burto, William. Zen Ink Paintings. LC 82-80648. (Great Japanese Art Ser.). (Illus.). 96p. 1982. 22.95 (ISBN 0-87011-521-9). Kodansha.

Barnett, Donald L. & McGregor, Jeffrey P. Speaking in Other Tongues: A Scholarly Defense. 840p. 1986. 25.00 (ISBN 0-934287-23-6). Comm Chapel Pubns.

Barnett, James H. The American Christmas: A Study in National Culture. LC 75-22799. (America in Two Centuries Ser.). 1976. Repr. of 1954 ed. 17.00x (ISBN 0-405-07671-1). Ayer Co Pubs.

Barnett, James M. The Diaconate: A Full & Equal Order. 256p. (Orig.). 1981. pap. 9.95 (ISBN 0-8164-2331-8, HarpR). Har-Row.

Barnett, Joe R. Live, with Peace, Power & Purpose. Thomas, J. D., ed. (Twentieth Century Sermons Ser.). 1978. 11.95 (ISBN 0-89112-311-3, Bibl Res Pr). Abilene Christ U.

Barnett, L. D. Brahma-Knowledge, Philosophy of Vedanta. 59.95 (ISBN 0-87968-780-0). Gordon Pr.

Barnett, Regina R. Create, Two. 31p. (Orig.). 1979. pap. text ed. 5.95 student work pad (ISBN 0-697-01705-2); tchrs.' manual 12.95 (ISBN 0-697-01706-0). Wm C Brown.

Barnett, Suzanne W. & Fairbank, John K., eds. Christianity in China: Early Protestant Missionary Writings. (Harvard Studies in American-East Asian Relations: 9). 280p. 1984. text ed. 20.00x (ISBN 0-674-12881-8). Harvard U Pr.

Barnett, Timothy L. & Flora, Steven R. Exploring God's Web of Life. 80p. 1982. pap. 5.25 (ISBN 0-942684-01-X). Camp Guidepts.

Barnett, Walter. Homosexuality & the Bible: An Interpretation. LC 79-84920. 1979. pap. 2.50x (ISBN 0-87574-226-2). Pendle Hill.

--Jesus: the Story of His Life: A Modern Retelling Based on the Gospels. LC 75-28260. 1976. 19.95x (ISBN 0-88229-308-7). Nelson Hall.

Barnette, Helen P. Your Child's Mind: Making the Most of Public Schools. LC 83-26109. (Potentials: Guides for Productive Living Ser.: Vol. 2). 112p. (Orig.). 1984. pap. 7.95 (ISBN 0-664-24519-6). Westminster.

Barnette, Henlee. Your Freedom to Be Whole. LC 84-2381. (Potentials: Guides to Productive Living Ser.: Vol. 7). 118p. 1984. pap. 7.95 (ISBN 0-664-24526-9). Westminster.

Barnette, Henlee H. Introducing Christian Ethics. LC 61-5629. 1961. 9.95 (ISBN 0-8054-6102-7). Broadman.

Barney, Garold D. Mormons, Indians & the Ghost Dance Religion of 1890. LC 85-29509. (Illus.). 258p. (Orig.). 1986. lib. bdg. 28.00 (ISBN 0-8191-5227-7); pap. text ed. 13.50 (ISBN 0-8191-5228-5). U Pr of Amer.

Barney, Kenneth D. Directions, Please. LC 82-82080. 128p. (Orig.). 1983. pap. 2.50 (ISBN 0-88243-856-5, 02-0856); tchr's. ed. 3.95 (ISBN 0-88243-197-8, 32-0197). Gospel Pub.

--A Faith to Live by. LC 76-27929. (Radiant Life Ser.). 128p. 1977. pap. 2.50 (ISBN 0-88243-899-9, 02-0899); teacher's ed. 3.95 (ISBN 0-88243-171-4, 32-0171). Gospel Pub.

--The Fellowship of the Holy Spirit. LC 77-70475. 96p. 1977. pap. 1.25 (ISBN 0-88243-515-9, 02-0515). Gospel Pub.

--Fourth Watch of the Night. 96p. 1973. 1.50 (ISBN 0-88243-724-0, 02-0724). Gospel Pub.

--Freedom: A Guarantee for Everybody. LC 75-34644. (Radiant Life Ser.). 128p. 1976. pap. 2.50 (ISBN 0-88243-891-3, 02-0891, Radiant Bks); teacher's ed 3.95 (ISBN 0-88243-165-X, 32-0165). Gospel Pub.

--If You Love Me... LC 75-22611. (Radiant Life Ser.). 128p. 1977. pap. 2.50 (ISBN 0-88243-889-1, 02-0889); teacher's ed 3.95 (ISBN 0-88243-163-3, 32-0163). Gospel Pub.

--It Began in an Upper Room. LC 78-67445. 128p. 1978. pap. 1.50 (ISBN 0-88243-528-0, 02-0528, Radiant Bks). Gospel Pub.

--The Longest War. LC 82-83915. 128p. (Orig.). 1984. pap. 2.50 (ISBN 0-88243-536-1, 02-0536). Gospel Pub.

--Preparing for the Storm. LC 74-21021. 96p. 1975. pap. 1.25 (ISBN 0-88243-576-0, 02-0576). Gospel Pub.

--We Interrupt This Crisis. 63p. 1970. pap. 1.25 (ISBN 0-88243-704-6, 02-0704). Gospel Pub.

Barney, Laura C., tr. see Abdu'l-Baha.

Barnhart, David R. The Church's Desperate Need for Revival. 163p. (Orig.). 1986. pap. 8.95 (ISBN 0-9617377-0-0). Abiding Word Pubns.

Barnhart, J. The Study of Religion & Its Meaning. 1977. 25.50x (ISBN 90-279-7762-3). Mouton.

Barnhart, J. E. Religion & the Challenge of Philosophy. (Quality Paperback Ser.: No. 291). 400p. (Orig.). 1975. pap. 5.95 (ISBN 0-8226-0291-1). Littlefield.

Barnhart, Joe, jt. auth. see Warren, Thomas B.

Barnhart, Joe E. The Southern Baptist Holy War. LC 86-5988. 256p. 1986. pap. 16.95 (ISBN 0-87719-037-2). Texas Month Pr.

Barnhart, Joe E. & Barnhart, Mary A. The New Birth: A Naturalist View of Religious Conversion. LC 81-9557. xiv, 174p. 1981. 15.50 (ISBN 0-86554-009-8, MUP-H11). Mercer Univ Pr.

Barnhart, Mary A., jt. auth. see Barnhart, Joe E.

Barnhart, Phil. More Seasonings for Sermons. 1985. 6.25 (ISBN 0-89536-723-8, 5807). CSS of Ohio.

--Still More Seasonings for Sermons, Vol. 3. 1986. 7.50 (ISBN 0-89536-787-4, 6805). CSS of Ohio.

Barnhart, Phillip H. Seasonings for Sermons. 88p. (Orig.). 1980. pap. text ed. 6.25 (ISBN 0-89536-451-4, 1967). CSS of Ohio.

Barnhouse, Donald. Is Anybody Up There. LC 76-51734. 1977. 6.95 (ISBN 0-9606562-0-0, BT1102-B26). L Victor Pr.

Barnhouse, Donald C. Expositions of Bible Doctrines, 10 vols. in four. (Bible Study). 1952-64. Set. 49.95 (ISBN 0-8028-3014-5). Eerdmans.

Barnhouse, Donald G. Revelation: An Expositional Commentary. 1971. 14.95 (ISBN 0-310-20490-9); pap. 11.95 (ISBN 0-310-20491-7, 9760P). Zondervan.

--Teaching the Word of Truth. 1958. Repr. 5.95 (ISBN 0-8028-1610-X). Eerdmans.

Barnhouse, Ruth T. Identity. LC 84-3664. (Choices: Guides for Today's Woman Ser.,: Vol. 7). 120p. (Orig.). 1984. pap. 6.95 (ISBN 0-664-24545-5). Westminster.

Barniak, Carl K. The Food of Angels. 96p. (Orig.). 1984. pap. 4.95 (ISBN 0-9613803-0-6). Barniak Pubns.

Barnidge, Thomas & Grow, Douglas. The Jim Hart Story. LC 77-12538. (Illus.). 1977. 6.95 (ISBN 0-8272-1705-6); pap. 4.95 (ISBN 0-8272-1704-8). CBP.

Barnouw, Adriaan J. Anglo-Saxon Christian Poetry. LC 74-20776. 1974. Repr. of 1914 ed. lib. bdg. 12.50 (ISBN 0-8414-3291-0). Folcroft.

Barnouw, Victor. Wisconsin Chippewa Myths & Tales & Their Relation to Chippewa Life. LC 76-53647. 304p. 1977. 25.00x (ISBN 0-299-07310-6). U of Wis Pr.

Barns, J. W. & Kilpatrick, G. D. A New Psalms Fragment. 1957. pap. 2.25 (ISBN 0-85672-621-4, Pub. by British Acad). Longwood Pub Group.

Barnstone, Willis, ed. The Other Bible. LC 83-48416. 768p. 1984. 24.45 (ISBN 0-06-250031-7, HarpR); pap. 14.95 (ISBN 0-06-250030-9, CN 4087). Har-Row.

Barnstone, Willis, tr. & intro. by see St. John Of The Cross.

Barnum, Priscilla H., ed. Dives & Pauper, Vol. I, Pt. 2. (Early English Text Society Original Ser.). (Illus.). 1980. 32.50x (ISBN 0-19-722282-X). Oxford U Pr.

Barnwell, William H. Our Story According to St. Mark. 288p. (Orig.). 1982. pap. 9.95 (ISBN 0-86683-634-9, HarpR). Har-Row.

Barocas, David N., tr. see Magriso, Yitzchak.

Barocio, Ernesto. Bosquejos de Sermones Selectos. 144p. 1986. pap. 5.95 (ISBN 0-311-43039-2). Casa Bautista.

Barocio, Ernesto, tr. see Broadus, J. A.

Barocio, Teofilo, tr. see Vedder, Enrique C.

Baroja, Julio C. The World of Witches. Glendinning, O. N., tr. LC 64-15829. (Nature of Human Society Ser.). xiv, 314p. 1973. pap. 12.00x (ISBN 0-226-03763-0, P497, Phoen). U of Chicago Pr.

Barolini, Helen, tr. see Zizola, Giancarlo.

Bar-On, A. Zvie, ed. On Shumuel Hugo Bergman's Philosophy. 134p. 1986. pap. 19.95x (ISBN 90-6203-947-2, Pub. by Rodopi Holland). Humanities.

Baron, David. Israel in the Plan of God. LC 82-18678. 320p. 1983. 14.95 (ISBN 0-8254-2241-8). Kregel.

--Types, Psalms & Prophecies. 1981. lib. bdg. 14.00 (ISBN 0-86524-077-9, 9511). Klock & Klock.

Baron, Henry. Touchstones, 4 vols. Incl. Vol. 1. Around Us (ISBN 0-8028-1532-4); Vol. 2. Within Us (ISBN 0-8028-1533-2); Vol. 3. Between Us (ISBN 0-8028-1534-0); Vol. 4. Above Us (ISBN 0-8028-1535-9). 1973. pap. 4.95 ea.; pap. 5.50 tchr's guide (ISBN 0-8028-1645-2). Eerdmans.

Baron, Salo W. The Jewish Community, 3 vols. LC 74-97269. 1972. Repr. of 1942 ed. Set. lib. bdg. 53.50x (ISBN 0-8371-3274-6, BAJC). Greenwood.

--Modern Nationalism & Religion. facs. ed. LC 79-134050. (Essay Index Reprint Ser). 1947. 19.50 (ISBN 0-8369-2142-9). Ayer Co Pubs.

--A Social & Religious History of the Jews, 18 vols. 2nd, rev. & enl. ed. Incl. Vol. 1. Ancient Times to the Beginning of the Christian Era. 1952 (ISBN 0-231-08838-8); Vol. 2. Ancient Times: Christian Era: the First Five Centuries. 1952 (ISBN 0-231-08839-6); Vol. 3. High Middle Ages: Heirs of Rome & Persia. 1957 (ISBN 0-231-08840-X); Vol. 4. High Middle Ages: Meeting of the East & West. 1957 (ISBN 0-231-08841-8); Vol. 5. High Middle Ages: Religious Controls & Dissensions. 1957 (ISBN 0-231-08842-6); Vol. 6. High Middle Ages: Laws, Homilies & the Bible. 1958 (ISBN 0-231-08843-4); Vol. 7. High Middle Ages: Hebrew Language & Letters. 1958 (ISBN 0-231-08844-2); Vol. 8. High Middle Ages: Philosophy & Science. 1958 (ISBN 0-231-08845-0); Vol. 9. Late Middle Ages & Era of European Expansion, 1200-1650: Under Church & Empire. 1965 (ISBN 0-231-08846-9); Vol. 10. Late Middle Ages & Era of European Expansion, 1200-1650: On the Empire's Periphery. 1965 (ISBN 0-231-08847-7); Vol. 11. Late Middle Ages & Era of European Expansion, 1200-1650: Citizen or Alien Conjurer. 1967 (ISBN 0-231-08848-5); Vol. 12. Late Middle Ages & Era of European Expansion, 1200-1650: Economic Catalyst. 1967 (ISBN 0-231-08849-3); Vol. 13. Late Middle Ages & Era of European Expansion, 1200-1650: Inquisition, Renaissance & Reformation. 1969 (ISBN 0-231-08850-7); Vol. 14. Late Middle Ages & Era of European Expansion, 1200-1650: Catholic Restoration & Wars of Religion. 1969 (ISBN 0-231-08851-5); Vol. 15. Late Middle Ages & Era of European Expansion, 1200-1650: Resettlement & Exploration. 1973 (ISBN 0-231-08852-3); Index. 32.00x (ISBN 0-231-08877-9). LC 52-404. 45.00x ea. Columbia U Pr.

--Steeled in Adversity. (Texts & Studies). (Hebrew.). 1977. 15.00 (ISBN 0-911934-15-4). Am Jewish Hist Soc.

Baron, Salo W., ed. Essays on Maimonides. LC 79-160004. Repr. of 1941 ed. 24.50 (ISBN 0-404-00658-2). AMS Pr.

Barr. Early Methodist under Persecution. pap. 4.95 (ISBN 0-686-23582-7). Schmul Pub Co.

Barr, Browne. High Flying Geese: Unexpected Reflections on the Church & Its Ministry. (Illus.). 96p. (Orig.). 1983. pap. 6.95 (ISBN 0-86683-900-3, HarpR). Har-Row.

Barr, Browne, jt. auth. see Jeske, Richard L.

Barr, David & Piediscalzi, Nicholas, eds. The Bible in American Education. LC 81-14436. (SBL The Bible in American Culture Ser.). 1982. 12.95 (ISBN 0-89130-538-6, 061205, Co-pub Fortress Pr). Scholars Pr GA.

Barr, Debbie. Caught in the Crossfire. 288p. (Orig.). 1985. pap. 8.95 (ISBN 0-310-28561-5, 12083P). Zondervan.

Barr, Helen W. Thy Word Is True. 1986. 5.75 (ISBN 0-8062-2355-3). Carlton.

Barr, James. Holy Scripture: Canon, Authority, Criticism. LC 82-20123. 190p. 1983. 18.95 (ISBN 0-664-21395-2); pap. 9.95 (ISBN 0-664-24477-7). Westminster.

--The Scope & Authority of the Bible. LC 80-21394. 164p. 1981. pap. 7.95 (ISBN 0-664-24361-4). Westminster.

Barr, Pat. To China With Love: The Lives & Times of Protestant Missionaries in China, 1860-1900. 1972. 16.95 (ISBN 0-436-03355-0, Pub. by Secker & Warburg UK). David & Charles.

Barr, Robert, tr. see Bussmann, Claus.

Barr, Robert R. What Is the Bible? A Nazareth Book. 128p. 1984. pap. 4.95 (ISBN 0-86683-727-2, HarpR). Har-Row.

Barr, Robert R., tr. see Araya, Victorio.

Barr, Robert R., tr. see Bermudez, Fernando.

Barr, Robert R., tr. see Boff, Clodovis.

Barr, Robert R., tr. see Boff, Clodovis & Boff, Leonardo.

Barr, Robert R., tr. see Boff, Leonardo.

Barr, Robert R., tr. see Cabestrero, Teofilo.

Barr, Robert R., tr. see Camara, Dom H.

Barr, Robert R., tr. see Carretto, Carlo.

Barr, Robert R., tr. see De Rosny, Eric.

Barr, Robert R., tr. see Eboussi Boulaga, F.

Barr, Robert R., tr. see Ela, Jean-Marc.

Barr, Robert R., tr. see Galdamez, Pablo.

Barr, Robert R., tr. see Galilea, Segundo.

Barr, Robert R., tr. see Lesbaupin, Ivo.

Barr, Robert R., tr. see Maduro, Otto.

Barr, Robert R., tr. see Miguez-Bonino, Jose.

Barr, Robert R., tr. see Miranda, Jose.

Barr, Robert R., tr. see Pallares, Jose C.

Barr, Robert R., tr. see Paoli, Arturo.

Barr, Robert R., tr. see Perez-Esquivel, Adolfo.

Barr, Robert R., tr. see Pixley, George V.

Barraclough, Geoffrey. The Crucible of Europe: The Ninth & Tenth Centuries in European History. LC 75-21934. (Illus.). 180p. 1976. 36.50x (ISBN 0-520-03105-9); pap. 6.95 (ISBN 0-520-03118-0, CAL 326). U of Cal Pr.

--The Medieval Papacy. (Library of World Civilization). (Illus.). 1979. pap. text ed. 7.95x (ISBN 0-393-95100-6). Norton.

Barragar, Pam. Spiritual Growth Through Creative Drama. 128p. 1981. pap. 5.95 (ISBN 0-8170-0923-X). Judson.

Barragar, Pamela. Creative Drama: A Complete Source Book for Church & School. 176p. 1987. pap. 9.95 (ISBN 0-87403-084-6, 3355). Standard Pub.

Barral, Mary R. The Body in Interpersonal Relations: Merleau-Ponty. 312p. 1984. pap. text ed. 14.50 (ISBN 0-8191-3755-3). U Pr of Amer.

Barratt, Robert S., jt. auth. see Wilson, Otto.

Barre, Michael. The God-List in the Treaty Between Hannibal & Philip V of Macedonia: A Study in Light of the Ancient Near Eastern Treaty Tradition. LC 82-13961. (Near Eastern Studies). 208p. 1983. text ed. 26.00x (ISBN 0-8018-2787-6). Johns Hopkins.

Barreiro, Alvaro. Basic Ecclesial Communities: The Evangelization of the Poor. Campbell, Barbara, tr. from Portuguese. LC 81-16898. Orig. Title: Comunidades Eclesiais De Base E Evangelizacao Dos Pobres. 96p. (Orig.). 1982. pap. 5.95 (ISBN 0-88344-026-1). Orbis Bks.

Barren, T. P. Van see Van Baaren, T. P. & Driljvers, H. J.

Barrere, Dorothy B. The Kumuhonua Legends: A Study of Late 19th Century Hawaiian Stories of Creation & Origins. (Pacific Anthropological Records: No. 3). 47p. 1969. pap. 5.00 (ISBN 0-910240-59-0). Bishop Mus.

Barrett, Arthur, jt. auth. see Magnani, Duane.

Barrett, C. K. Church, Ministry, & Sacraments in the New Testament. 112p. (Orig.). 1985. pap. 6.95 (ISBN 0-8028-1994-X). Eerdmans.

--Essays on John. LC 82-2759. 176p. 1982. 18.95 (ISBN 0-664-21389-8). Westminster.

--Essays on Paul. LC 82-2764. 180p. 1982. 18.95 (ISBN 0-664-21390-1). Westminster.

--The Gospel According to St. John. 2nd ed. LC 78-2587. 654p. 1978. 28.95 (ISBN 0-664-21364-2). Westminster.

--The Gospel of John & Judaism. Smith, D. M., tr. LC 75-15435. 112p. 1975. 3.95 (ISBN 0-8006-0431-8, 1-431). Fortress.

--Reading Through Romans. LC 76-55828. 96p. 1977. pap. 3.95 (ISBN 0-8006-1250-7, 1-1250). Fortress.

Barrett, C. K., jt. ed. see Bammel, E.

Barrett, Charles D. Understanding the Christian Faith. (Illus.). 1980. text ed. write for info. (ISBN 0-13-935882-X). P-H.

Barrett, Charles K. The Epistle to the Romans. LC 57-12722. 1958. 17.95 (ISBN 0-06-060550-2, HarpR). Har-Row.

--The First Epistle to the Corinthians. LC 68-17594. (New Testament Commentaries Ser., Vol. 9). 1968. 18.00 (ISBN 0-06-060551-0, HarpR). Har-Row.

--The Gospel of John & Judaiam. Smith, D. M., tr. LC 75-15435. pap. 27.80 (2026897). Bks Demand UMI.

--The Second Epistle to the Corinthians. LC 73-18682. 366p. 1974. 17.95 (ISBN 0-06-060552-9, HarpR). Har-Row.

Barrett, Charles K., ed. New Testament Background: Selected Documents. pap. 6.95x (ISBN 0-06-130086-1, TB86, Torch). Har-Row.

Barrett, Cyril, ed. see Wittgenstein, Ludwig.

Barrett, D. The Dancing Siva in Early South Indian Art. (Mortimer Wheeler Archaeological Lectures). 1976. pap. 2.50 (ISBN 0-85672-354-1, Pub. by British Acad). Longwood Pub Group.

Barrett, David, ed. World Christian Encyclopedia: A Comparative Survey of Churches & Religions in the Modern World, A. D. 1900 to 2000. (Illus.). 1982. text ed. 165.00x (ISBN 0-19-572435-6). Oxford U Pr.

Barrett, David, jt. ed. see Schreck, Harley.

Barrett, Eric C. & Fisher, David, eds. Scientists Who Believe: Twenty-One Tell Their Own Stories. 1984. pap. 4.50 (ISBN 0-8024-7634-1). Moody.

Barrett, Ethel. Abraham: God's Faithful Pilgrim. LC 82-12330. (Bible Biography Ser.). 128p. (Orig.). 1982. pap. 2.50 (ISBN 0-8307-0769-7, 5810906). Regal.

--Daniel. LC 79-65230. (Bible Biography Ser.). 128p. 1979. pap. 1.95 (ISBN 0-8307-0761-1, 5810306). Regal.

--David: The Giant-Slayer. LC 82-80009. (Bible Biography Ser.). 128p. 1982. pap. 2.50 (ISBN 0-8307-0770-0, 5811007). Regal.

--Ethel Barrett Tells Favorite Bible Stories, Vol.3. LC 77-93051. (Bible Biography Ser.). 128p. 1978. pap. 3.95 (ISBN 0-8307-0615-1, 5605806). Regal.

--Joseph. LC 79-65232. (Bible Biography Bible Ser.). 128p. 1979. pap. 1.95 (ISBN 0-8307-0715-8, 5607701). Regal.

--Joshua. LC 79-65233. (Bible Biography Ser.). 128p. 1979. pap. 2.50 (ISBN 0-8307-0707-7, 5607000). Regal.

--Moses. LC 82-16521. (Bible Biographies Ser.). 1982. pap. text ed. 2.50 (ISBN 0-8307-0772-7, 5811201). Regal.

--Paul. LC 81-51740. (Bible Biography Ser.). 128p. 1981. pap. text ed. 1.95 (ISBN 0-8307-0767-0, 5810701). Regal.

--The People Who Couldn't Be Stopped. LC 70-96703. (Illus., Orig.). 1970. pap. 1.95 (ISBN 0-8307-0007-2, S063107). Regal.

--Peter. LC 81-52942. (Bible Biography Ser.). 128p. (Orig.). 1982. pap. text ed. 1.95 (ISBN 0-8307-0768-9, 5810809). Regal.

--Ruth. LC 80-52961. (Bible Biography Ser.). 128p. 1980. pap. 1.95 (ISBN 0-8307-0764-6, 5810418). Regal.

--Steve Paxon: Can't Lose for Winning. LC 84-26238. 1985. pap. 4.95 (ISBN 0-8307-1022-1, 5418424). Regal.

--The Strangest Thing Happened. LC 76-84599. 144p. 1971. pap. 1.95 (ISBN 0-8307-0005-6, S061104). Regal.

Barrett, Ethel & Parker, Peggy. Will the Real Phony Please Stand up? rev. ed. LC 84-17777. 224p. 1984. pap. 4.95 (ISBN 0-8307-1001-9, 5418383); Leader's Guide 3.95 (ISBN 0-8307-1009-4, 6101966). Regal.

Barrett, Francis. The Magus: A Complete System of Occult Philosophy. 200p. 1975. pap. 12.00 (ISBN 0-8065-0462-5). Citadel Pr.

Barrett, Helen M. Boethius: Some Aspects of His Times & Works. LC 65-18789. 1965. Repr. of 1940 ed. 7.50x (ISBN 0-8462-0653-6). Russell.

Barrett, Ivan J. Joseph Smith & the Restoration: A History of the LDS Church to 1846. rev. ed. LC 70-167990. (Illus.). 1973. pap. 9.95 (ISBN 0-8425-0672-1). Brigham.

Barrett, J. Edward. Faith in Focus: A Compact Introduction to Christian Theology. LC 81-40167. 130p. (Orig.). 1982. lib. bdg. 24.25 (ISBN 0-8191-1878-8); pap. text ed. 9.50 (ISBN 0-8191-1879-6). U Pr of Amer.

Barrett, J. O. The Book of Revelation: Missionary Message of the New Testament. 123p. 1947. Repr. 2.95 (ISBN 0-87921-005-2). Attic Pr.

Barrett, James E. The Hymnary II: A Table For Service Planning. 2nd ed. Barrett, James E., ed. 96p. 1987. pap. text ed. 13.95 (ISBN 0-942466-11-X); 16.50 (ISBN 0-942466-12-8). Hymnary Pr.

--The Psalmnary: Gradual Psalms for Cantor & Congregation. 196p. 1982. incl. binder 24.00 (ISBN 0-942466-04-7); 21.00 (ISBN 0-942466-03-9). Hymnary Pr.

Barrett, James E., ed. The Daily Lectionary. 70p. 1982. 2.45 (ISBN 0-942466-02-0). Hymnary Pr.

--The Hymnary: A Table for Service Planning. 95p. 1979. incl. binder 16.00 (ISBN 0-942466-01-2); 13.50 (ISBN 0-942466-00-4). Hymnary Pr.

Barrett, James E., ed. see Hall, Linda B.

Barrett, James W., ed. End of 'The World' facs. ed. LC 72-117866. (Select Bibliographies Reprint Ser). 1931. 24.50 (ISBN 0-8369-5319-3). Ayer Co Pubs.

Barrett, John. That Better Country. 1966. 15.50x (ISBN 0-522-83525-2, Pub. by Melbourne U Pr). Intl Spec Bk.

Barrett, Kate W. Some Practical Suggestions on the Conduct of a Rescue Home: Including Life of Dr. Kate Waller Barrett. facsimile ed. LC 74-3928. (Women in America Ser). Orig. Title: Fifty Years Work with Girls. 186p. 1974. Repr. of 1903 ed. 20.00x (ISBN 0-405-06075-0). Ayer Co Pubs.

Barrett, Leonard E. The Rastafarians: Sounds of Cultural Dissonance. LC 76-48491. (Illus.). 1977. pap. 9.95 (ISBN 0-8070-1115-0, BP559). Beacon Pr.

Barrett, Lois. Building the House Church. LC 86-14324. 176p. (Orig.). 1986. pap. 8.95 (ISBN 0-8361-3415-X). Herald Pr.

--The Vision & the Reality: The Story of Home Missions in the General Conference Mennonite Church. LC 83-80402. 339p. (Orig.). 1983. pap. 16.95 (ISBN 0-87303-079-6). Faith & Life.

--The Way God Fights. (Peace & Justice Ser.: No. 1). 96p. (Orig.). 1987. pap. 4.95 (ISBN 0-8361-3445-1). Herald Pr.

Barrett, Marsha. Early Christians: Workers for Jesus. (BibLearn Ser.). (Illus.). 1979. 5.95 (ISBN 0-8054-4247-2, 4242-47). Broadman.

--Vena Aguillard: Woman of Faith. LC 82-73664. (Meet the Missionary Ser.). 1983. 5.50 (ISBN 0-8054-4281-2, 4242-81). Broadman.

Barrett, Paul, tr. see Dumery, Henry.

Barrett, Philip. The Organs & Organists of the Cathedral Church of St. Thomas of Canterbury at Portsmouth. 1975. Repr. of 1968 ed. 39.00x (ISBN 0-317-43672-4, Pub. by City of Portsmouth). State Mutual Bk.

Barrett, Thomas Van Braam. Great Morning of the World: The Unforgettable Story of Harry Barrett. LC 75-16416. Repr. of 1975 ed. 47.30 (ISBN 0-8357-9011-8, 2016366). Bks Demand UMI.

Barrett, William. Death of the Soul. LC 82-45317. 192p. 1986. 16.95 (ISBN 0-385-15965-X, Anchor Pr). Doubleday.

Barrett, William A. English Church Composers: The Great Musicians. facsimile ed. LC 70-102224. (Select Bibliographies Reprint Ser). 1882. 19.00 (ISBN 0-8369-5109-3). Ayer Co Pubs.

Barrier, Gerald, jt. ed. see Juergensmeyer, Mark.

Barringer, Robert, tr. see Staniloae, Dumitru.

Barrington, E. The Great Teachings of the Buddha, 2 vols. (Illus.). 211p. 1986. Set. 147.50 (ISBN 0-89901-273-6). Found Class Reprints.

Barrington, George. Use Even Me. 1983. pap. 10.00 (ISBN 0-8309-0375-5). Herald Hse.

Barrois, Georges, jt. auth. see Ware, Kallistos.

Barrois, Georges A. The Face of Christ in the Old Testament. 172p. 1974. pap. 6.95 (ISBN 0-913836-22-2). St Vladimirs.

--Jesus Christ & the Temple. LC 80-19700. 163p. (Orig.). 1980. pap. 5.95 (ISBN 0-913836-73-7, BS680 T4837). St Martin.

--Jesus Christ & the Temple. LC 80-19700. 163p. 1980. pap. 6.95 (ISBN 0-913836-73-7). St Vladimirs.

--Scripture Readings in Orthodox Worship. 197p. 1977. pap. 6.95 (ISBN 0-913836-41-9). St Vladimirs.

Barron, Bruce. The Health & Wealth Gospel: A Fresh Look at Healing, Prosperity & Positive Confession. LC 86-27503. 206p. (Orig.). 1987. pap. 6.95 (ISBN 0-87784-327-9). Inter Varsity.

Barron, Howard H. Orson Hyde: Missionary, Apostle, Colonizer. LC 77-74490. (Illus.). 336p. 1977. 10.95 (ISBN 0-88290-076-5). Horizon Utah.

Barron, Howard H., ed. Of Everlasting Value, Vol. 1. (Orig.). 1978. pap. 5.95 (ISBN 0-89036-129-0). Hawkes Pub Inc.

--Of Everlasting Value, Vol. 2. (Orig.). pap. 5.95 (ISBN 0-89036-130-4). Hawkes Pub Inc.

Barron, Sr. Mary C. Unveiled Faces: Men & Women of the Bible. LC 80-27728. 95p. 1981. softcover 4.50 (ISBN 0-8146-1212-1). Liturgical Pr.

Barrow, Alfred. Fifty Years in Western Africa. LC 79-92739. Repr. of 1900 ed. cancelled (ISBN 0-8371-2193-0, BAW&, Pub. by Negro U Pr). Greenwood.

Barrow, Isaac. Theological Works of Isaac Barrow, 9 Vols. Napier, Alexander, ed. LC 72-161751. Repr. of 1859 ed. Set. lib. bdg. 215.00 (ISBN 0-404-00670-1); lib. bdg. 25.00 ea. AMS Pr.

Barrow, Lu Ann, jt. auth. see Huffman, Carolyn.

Barrow, Robin. Moral Philosophy for Education. (Unwin Education Books). 1975. pap. text ed. 9.95x (ISBN 0-04-370060-8). Allen Unwin.

Barrs, Jerram. Who Are the Peacemakers? The Christian Case for Nuclear Deterrence. LC 83-62684. 60p. 1983. pap. 2.95 (ISBN 0-89107-307-8, Crossway Bks). Good News.

Barrs, Jerram, jt. auth. see Macaulay, Ranald.

Barrus, David F. The Way to the Sun: A Guide to Celestial Living. 104p. 1972. 5.95 (ISBN 0-88290-008-0). Horizon Utah.

Barry, Brian, jt. ed. see Sikora, R. I.

Barry, Colman J. Worship & Work. LC 80-10753. (Illus.). 526p. 1980. pap. text ed. 12.50 (ISBN 0-8146-1123-0). Liturgical Pr.

Barry, Colman J., ed. Readings in Church History, 3 vols. in 1. 1985. pap. 50.00 (ISBN 0-87061-104-6). Chr Classics.

Barry, David W. Ministry of Reconciliation: Modern Lessons from Scripture & Sacrament. LC 75-4630. 129p. (Orig.). 1975. pap. 2.95 (ISBN 0-8189-0317-1). Alba.

Barry, James C., ed. Preaching in Today's World. LC 83-24021. (Orig.). 1984. pap. 6.50 (ISBN 0-8054-2113-0). Broadman.

Barry, James D., ed. see McMahon, Thomas F., et al.

Barry, Lloyd E., intro. by. Geneva Bible: A Facsimile of the Fifteen-Sixty Edition. 1274p. 1969. 95.00x (ISBN 0-299-05251-6). U of Wis Pr.

Barry, William. Cardinal Newman. 1973. Repr. of 1904 ed. 20.00 (ISBN 0-8274-1797-7). R West.

--Ernest Renan. 1905. Repr. 25.00 (ISBN 0-8274-3825-7). R West.

Barry, William A. & Connolly, William J. The Practice of Spiritual Direction. 224p. (Orig.). 1982. pap. 11.95 (ISBN 0-8164-2357-1, AY7870, HarpR). Har-Row.

Barry, William F. Roma Sacra: Essays on Christian Rome. facs. ed. LC 68-14896. (Essay Index Reprint Ser). 1927. 18.00 (ISBN 0-8369-0174-6). Ayer Co Pubs.

Barstow, Anne L. Joan of Arc: Heretic, Mystic, Shaman. LC 86-12756. (Studies in Women & Religion: No. 17). (Illus.). 156p. 1986. lib. bdg. 49.95 (ISBN 0-88946-532-0). E Mellen.

--Married Priests & the Reforming Papacy: The 11th Century Debates. LC 82-7914. (Texts & Studies in Religion: Vol. 12). 288p. 1982. 49.95x (ISBN 0-88946-987-3). E Mellen.

Barsuhn, Rochelle. Sometimes I Feel. LC 85-10351. (Illus.). 32p. 1985. PLB 4.95 (ISBN 0-89693-228-1). Dandelion Hse.

Bartchy, S. Scott. First-Century Slavery & the Interpretation of I Corinthians 7: 21. LC 73-83723. (Society of Biblical Literature. Dissertation Ser.). 1973. pap. 12.00 (ISBN 0-89130-220-4, 060111). Scholars Pr GA.

Bartel, Bonnie. Night the Animals Talked. 1982. pap. 3.25 (ISBN 0-89536-551-0, 1410). CSS of Ohio.

Bartel, Floyd. A New Look at Church Growth. LC 79-53523. 1979. pap. 2.95 (ISBN 0-87303-027-3). Faith & Life.

Bartels, Francis L. The Roots of Ghana Methodism. LC 64-21525. pap. 95.50 (ISBN 0-317-08427-5, 2050799). Bks Demand UMI.

Barth. The Modern Jew Faces Eternal Problems. 7.50 (ISBN 0-685-48595-1). Feldheim.

Barth, A. Religions of India. 6th ed. Wood, J., tr. from Fr. 309p. 1980. Repr. of 1880 ed. 23.95x (ISBN 0-940500-64-7). Asia Bk Corp.

--The Religions of India. 1980. text ed. 22.00x (ISBN 0-89563-630-1). Coronet Bks.

--The Religions of India. 332p. 25.00X (ISBN 0-317-52150-0, Pub. by S Chand India). State Mutual Bk.

Barth, Edna. A Christmas Feast: Poems, Sayings, Greetings, & Wishes. (Illus.). 176p. 1979. 10.60 (ISBN 0-395-28965-3, Clarion). HM.

--Holly, Reindeer, & Colored Lights: The Story of the Christmas Symbols. LC 71-157731. (Illus.). 96p. 1981. pap. 4.95 (ISBN 0-89919-037-5, Clarion). HM.

--Holly, Reindeer, & Colored Lights: The Story of the Christmas Symbols. LC 71-157731. (Illus.). 96p. 1971. 8.95 (ISBN 0-395-28842-8, Clarion). HM.

--Lilies, Rabbits, & Painted Eggs: The Story of the Easter Symbols. LC 74-79033. (Illus.). 1970. 8.95 (ISBN 0-395-28844-4, Clarion). HM.

--Shamrocks, Harps, & Shillelaghs: The Story of the St. Patrick's Day Symbols. LC 77-369. (Illus.). 96p. 1977. 9.95 (ISBN 0-395-28845-2, Clarion). HM.

--Turkeys, Pilgrims, & Indian Corn: The Story of the Thanksgiving Symbols. LC 75-4703. (Illus.). 96p. 1975. 12.95 (ISBN 0-395-28846-0, Clarion). HM.

Barth, Fredrik. Ritual & Knowledge among the Baktaman of New Guinea. LC 74-19572. (Illus.). pap. 74.00 (ISBN 0-317-11336-4, 2021979). Bks Demand UMI.

Barth, Joseph. Art of Staying Sane. facs. ed. LC 70-117757. (Essay Index Reprint Ser). 1948. 18.00 (ISBN 0-8369-1783-9). Ayer Co Pubs.

Barth, Karl. Anselm: Fides Quaerens Intellectum. Robertson, Ian W., tr. from Ger. LC 76-10795. (Pittsburgh Reprint Ser.: No. 2). 1985. text ed. 15.00 (ISBN 0-915138-75-1). Pickwick.

--The Christian Life. Bromiley, Geoffrey W., ed. LC 80-39942. 328p. 1981. 17.95 (ISBN 0-8028-3523-6). Eerdmans.

--The Church of Reconciliation: The Subject Matter & Problems of the Doctrine of Reconciliation. Bromiley, G. W. & Torrance, T. F., eds. Bromiley, G. W. & Torrance, T. F., trs. from Ger. (Church Dogmatics: Vol. 4, Pt. 1). 814p. 1956. 29.95 (ISBN 0-567-09041-8, Pub. by T & T Clark Ltd UK). Fortress.

--Community, State & Church: Three Essays. 16.75 (ISBN 0-8446-1058-5). Peter Smith.

--The Doctrine of Creation: The Creator & His Creature. Bromiley, G. W. & Torrance, T. F., eds. Bromiley, G. W. & Torrance, T. F., trs. from Ger. (Church Dogmatics: Vol. 3, Pt. 3). 560p. 29.95 (ISBN 0-567-09033-7, Pub. by T & T Clark Ltd UK). Fortress.

--The Doctrine of Creation: The Work of Creation. Bromiley, G. W. & Torrance, T. F., eds. Bromiley, G. W. & Torrance, T. F., trs. from Ger. (Church Dogmatics Ser.: Vol. 3, Pt. 1). 440p. 1958. 29.95 (ISBN 0-567-09031-0, Pub. by T & T Clark Ltd UK). Fortress.

--The Doctrine of God: The Election of God, The Command of God. Torrance, T. F. & Bromiley, G. W., eds. Bromiley, G. W. & Torrance, T. F., trs. from Ger. (Church Dogmatics Ser.: Vol. 2, Pt. 2). 820p. 1957. 29.95 (ISBN 0-567-09022-1, Pub. by T & T Clark Ltd UK). Fortress.

--The Doctrine of God: The Knowledge of God. Bromiley, G. W. & Torrance, T. F., eds. Bromiley, G. W. & Torrance, T. F., trs. from Ger. (Church Dogmatics Ser.: Vol. 2, Pt. 1). 710p. 1957. text ed. 29.95 (ISBN 0-567-09021-3, Pub. by T & T Clark Ltd UK). Fortress.

--The Doctrine of Reconciliation: Jesus Christ the Servant as Lord. Bromiley, G. W. & Torrance, T. F., eds. Bromiley, G. W. & Torrance, T. F., trs. from Ger. 882p. 1958. 26.95x (ISBN 0-567-09042-6, Pub. by T & T Clark Ltd UK). Fortress.

--The Doctrine of Reconciliation: Jesus Christ the True Witness. Bromiley, G. W. & Torrance, T. F., eds. Bromiley, G. W. & Torrance, T. F., trs. from Ger. 496p. 1961. 29.95 (ISBN 0-567-09043-4, Pub. by T & T Clark Ltd UK). Fortress.

--The Doctrine of Reconciliation: Jesus Christ the True Witness. Bromiley, G. W. & Torrance, T. F., eds. Bromiley, G. W., tr. from Ger. (Church Dogmatics Ser.: Vol. 4, Pt. 3, 2nd Half). 492p. 1962. 29.95 (ISBN 0-567-09044-2, Pub. by T & T Clark Ltd UK). Fortress.

--The Doctrine of Reconciliation: The Christian Life. Bromiley, G. W. & Torrance, T. F., eds. Bromiley, G. W., tr. from Ger. (Church Dogmatics Ser.: Vol. 4, Pt. 4). 240p. 1969. 19.95 (ISBN 0-567-09045-0, Pub. by T & T Clark Ltd UK). Fortress.

--The Doctrine of the Word of God: Prolegomena to Church Dogmatics. Bromiley, G. W. & Torrance, T. F., eds. Bromiley, G. W. & Torrance, T. F., trs. from Ger. (Church Dogmatics Ser.: Vol. 1, Pt. 1). 528p. 29.95 (ISBN 0-567-09013-2, Pub. by T & T Clark Ltd UK). Fortress.

--The Doctrine of the Word of God: The Revelation of God, Holy Scripture, the Proclamation of the Church. Bromiley, G. W. & Torrance, T. F., eds. (Church Dogmatics Ser.: Vol. 1. Pt. 2). 924p. 1956. 29.95 (ISBN 0-567-09012-4, Pub. by T & T Clark Ltd UK). Fortress.

--Dogmatics in Outline. pap. 5.95x (ISBN 0-06-130056-X, TB56, Torch). Har-Row.

--Epistle to the Romans. 6th ed. Hoskyns, Edwyn C., tr. 1968. pap. 12.95 (ISBN 0-19-500294-6). Oxford U Pr.

--Ethics. 1981. 34.95 (ISBN 0-8164-0484-4, HarpR). Har-Row.

--Evangelical Theology: An Introduction. Foley, Grover, tr. LC 79-16735. Tr. of Einfuhrung in Die Evangelische Theologie. 1979. pap. 9.95 (ISBN 0-8028-1819-6). Eerdmans.

--Great Promise. LC 61-15239. 70p. 1963. 6.00 (ISBN 0-8022-0074-5). Philos Lib.

--Humanity of God. Weiser, Thomas & Thomas, John N., trs. LC 60-3479. 1960. pap. 5.95 (ISBN 0-8042-0612-0). John Knox.

--Karl Barth: Preaching Through the Christian Year. McTavish, John B. & Wells, Harold G., eds. 288p. 1978. 11.95 (ISBN 0-567-29052-2, Pub. by T&T Clark Ltd UK). Fortress.

--The Knowledge of God & the Service of God According to the Teaching of the Reformation: Recalling the Scottish Confession of 1560. LC 77-27187. (Gifford Lectures: 1937-38). Repr. of 1939 ed. 30.00 (ISBN 0-404-60495-1). AMS Pr.

--Learning Jesus Christ Through the Heidelberg Catechism. 144p. (Orig.). 1982. pap. 4.95 (ISBN 0-8028-1893-5). Eerdmans.

--Letters, Nineteen Sixty-One to Nineteen Sixty-Eight. Fangmeier, Jurgen & Stoevesand, Hinrich, eds. LC 80-29140. pap. 99.50 (ISBN 0-317-41616-2, 2023208). Bks Demand UMI.

--Prayer. 2nd ed. Saliers, Don E., ed. Terrien, Sara F., tr. from German. LC 84-25782. 96p. 1985. pap. 7.95 (ISBN 0-664-24626-5). Westminster.

--Protestant Thought. facs. ed. LC 73-142606. (Essay Index Reprint Ser). 1959. 23.50 (ISBN 0-8369-2102-X). Ayer Co Pubs.

--The Resurrection of the Dead. Kastenbaum, Robert, ed. LC 76-19559. (Death and Dying Ser.). 1977. Repr. of 1933 ed. lib. bdg. 23.50x (ISBN 0-405-09555-4). Ayer Co Pubs.

--The Theology of Schleiermacher. Bromiley, Geoffrey W., tr. 287p. 1982. 13.95 (ISBN 0-8028-3565-1). Eerdmans.

--Witness to the Word: A Commentary on John 1. Furst, Walther, ed. Bromiley, Geoffrey W., tr. from Ger. 160p. (Orig.). 1986. pap. 10.95 (ISBN 0-8028-0186-2). Eerdmans.

--The Word of God & the Word of Man. Horton, Douglas, tr. 1958. 13.50 (ISBN 0-8446-1599-4). Peter Smith.

Barth, Karl & Bultmann, Rudolf. Barth-Bultmann Letters, Nineteen Twenty-Two to Nineteen Sixty-Six. Bromiley, Geoffrey W., tr. 224p. 1981. 13.95 (ISBN 0-8028-3560-0). Eerdmans.

Barth, Karl & Zuckmayer, Carl. A Late Friendship: The Letters of Carl Zuckmayer & Karl Barth. Bromiley, Geoffrey W., tr. 80p. 1983. 8.95 (ISBN 0-8028-3574-0). Eerdmans.

Barth, Karl, et al. Christ & Adam: Man & Humanity in Romans Five. Small, T. A., tr. 96p. 1983. Repr. of 1957 ed. lib. bdg. 12.00 (ISBN 0-88254-864-6, Octagon). Hippocrene Bks.

Barth, Lewis M. Analysis of Vatican Thirty. 1973. 20.00x (ISBN 0-87820-400-8, Pub. by Hebrew Union). Ktav.

Barth, M. A. Bulletin of Religion, ISPP Vol. 1, No. 4. 60p. 1974. Repr. 2.00 (ISBN 0-88065-050-8, Pub. by Messers Today & Tomorrow Printers & Publishers India). Scholarly Pubns.

Barth, Markus. The People of God. (Journal for the Study of the New Testament, Supplement Ser.: No. 5). 100p. 1983. text ed. 15.95x (ISBN 0-905774-54-X, Pub. by JSOT Pr England); pap. text ed. 7.95x (ISBN 0-905774-55-8, Pub. by JSOT Pr England). Eisenbrauns.

Barthel, Manfred. The Jesuits: History & Legend of the Society of Jesus. Howson, Mark, tr. 324p. 1987. pap. 8.95 (ISBN 0-688-06970-3, Quill). Morrow.

--The Jesuits: Legend & Truth of the Society of Jesus - Yesterday, Today, Tomorrow. Howson, Mark, tr. LC 84-60446. (Illus.). 384p. 1984. 17.95 (ISBN 0-688-02861-6). Morrow.

--What the Bible Really Says: Casting New Light on the Book of Books. Howson, Mark, tr. LC 81-18679. Orig. Title: Was Wirklich in der Bibel Steht. (Illus.). 416p. 1982. 15.50 (ISBN 0-688-00821-6). Morrow.

--What the Bible Really Says: Casting New Light on the Book of Books. Howson, Mark, tr. from Ger. LC 83-3001. Tr. of Was Wirklich in der Bibel Steht. (Illus.). 416p. 1983. pap. 10.95 (ISBN 0-688-01979-X, Quill). Morrow.

Barthelemy-Madaule. Bergson et Teilhard de Chardin. 23.50 (ISBN 0-685-36604-9). French & Eur.

Barthell, Edward E., Jr. Gods & Goddesses of Ancient Greece. LC 72-129664. 1981. 49.50 (ISBN 0-87024-165-6). U of Miami Pr.

Barthes, R., et al. Structural Analysis & Biblical Exegesis. Johnson, Alfred M., Jr., tr. LC 74-31334. (Pittsburgh Theological Monographs: No. 3). 1974. pap. 9.95 (ISBN 0-915138-02-6). Pickwick.

Barthes, Roland. The Eiffel Tower & Other Mythologies. Howard, Richard, tr. from Fr. 152p. 1979. 9.95 (ISBN 0-8090-4115-4); pap. 5.25 (ISBN 0-8090-1391-6). Hill & Wang.

Barthes, Roland, et al. Analyse Structurale et Exegese Biblique. 128p. 1973. 17.50 (ISBN 0-686-53927-3). French & Eur.

Barthlet, John. The Pedegrewe of Heretiques. LC 79-76432. (English Experience Ser.: No. 76). 180p. 1969. Repr. of 1566 ed. 21.00 (ISBN 90-221-0076-6). Walter J Johnson.

Bartholomew. The Bible Tells Me. 1982. pap. 0.85 (ISBN 0-570-04074-4, 56-1377). Concordia.

--God Loves Me. 1982. pap. 0.85 (ISBN 0-570-04073-6, 56-1376). Concordia.

--I Go To Church. 1982. pap. 0.85 (ISBN 0-570-04072-8, 56-1375). Concordia.

--Jesus Teaches Me. 1982. pap. 0.85 (ISBN 0-570-04071-X, 56-1374). Concordia.

Bartleman, Frank. Another Wave of Revival. rev. ed. Meyers, John, ed. Orig. Title: Another Wave Rolls In. 176p. 1982. pap. text ed. 2.95 (ISBN 0-88368-111-0). Whitaker Hse.

--Azusa Street. LC 80-82806. 1980. pap. 5.95 (ISBN 0-88270-439-7). Bridge Pub.

Bartlet, James V. Church Life & Church Order During the First Four Centuries. Cadoux, Cecil J., ed. 1980. lib. bdg. 59.95 (ISBN 0-8490-3147-8). Gordon Pr.

Bartlett, Bede. Social Theories of the Middle Ages, Twelve Hundred to Twelve-Fifty. 1976. lib. bdg. 59.95 (ISBN 0-8490-2619-9). Gordon Pr.

Bartlett, Bob. Power Pack. LC 85-16841. 100p. 1985. pap. 4.95 (ISBN 0-89221-124-5). New Leaf.

Bartlett, David L. The Shape of Scriptural Authority. LC 83-48009. 176p. 1983. pap. 8.95 (ISBN 0-8006-1713-4, 1-1713). Fortress.

Bartlett, David L., jt. auth. see Orr, Dick.

Bartlett, Gene E. Postscript to Preaching: After Forty Years, How Will I Preach Today? 88p. 1981. pap. 3.95 (ISBN 0-8170-0909-4). Judson.

Bartlett, J. R., ed. The First & Second Books of the Maccabees: Cambridge Bible Commentary on the New English Bible. LC 72-87436. (Old Testament Ser.). (Orig.). 1973. 42.50 (ISBN 0-521-08658-2); pap. 15.95 (ISBN 0-521-09749-5). Cambridge U Pr.

Bartlett, John A. Jericho. Davies, Graham I., ed. (Cities of the Biblical World Ser.). 128p. (Orig.). 1983. pap. 6.95 (ISBN 0-8028-1033-0). Eerdmans.

Bartlett, Kenneth, ed. see Schultz, Albert L.

Bartlett, Oso, jt. auth. see Duryea, John S.

Bartlett, Robert M. The Pilgrim Way. LC 70-172790. 384p. 1971. 15.00 (ISBN 0-8298-0222-3). Pilgrim NY.

Bartlett, Samuel C. From Egypt to Palestine: Through Sinai, the Wilderness & the South Country: History of the Israelites. Davis, Moshe, ed. LC 77-70668. (America & the Holy Land Ser.). (Illus.). 1977. Repr. of 1879 ed. lib. bdg. 43.00x (ISBN 0-405-10227-5). Ayer Co Pubs.

--Historical Sketches of the Missions of the American Board. LC 78-38436. (Religion in America, Ser. 2). 210p. 1972. Repr. of 1972 ed. 21.00 (ISBN 0-405-04057-1). Ayer Co Pubs.

Bartok. Carols & Christmas Songs: Colinde, Vol. 4. (Rumanian Folk Music Ser). 1975. lib. bdg. 131.50 (ISBN 90-247-1737-X, Pub. by Martinus Nijhoff Netherlands). Kluwer Academic.

Bartol, Cyrus A. Discourses on the Christian Spirit & Life: With an Introduction. 2nd ed. LC 72-4951. (The Romantic Tradition in American Literature Ser.). 418p. 1972. Repr. of 1850 ed. 30.00 (ISBN 0-405-04622-7). Ayer Co Pubs.

Bartolocci, Giulio & Imbonati, Carlo. Bibliotheca Magna Rabbinica & Biblio Latino-Hebrauca. 4440p. Date not set. Repr. of 1694 ed. text ed. 1242.00x (ISBN 0-576-72820-9, Pub. by Gregg Intl Pubs England). Gregg Intl.

Barton, Bruce. Man Nobody Knows. 1925. pap. 6.95 (ISBN 0-672-50743-9). Bobbs.

--The Man Nobody Knows. 128p. 1987. pap. 5.95 (ISBN 0-02-083620-1, Collier). Macmillan.

Barton, Bruce W. The Tree at the Center of the World: The Story of the California Missions. LC 79-26434. (Illus., Orig.). 1980. lib. bdg. 19.95 (ISBN 0-915520-30-3); pap. 12.95 (ISBN 0-915520-29-X). Ross-Erikson.

Barton, Freeman, ed. Advent Christians & the Bible. 2nd, rev. ed. LC 84-80020. 96p. pap. 4.00 (ISBN 0-913439-03-7). Henceforth.

--Putting the Pieces Together: Advent Christians Interpret Prophecy. 80p. (Orig.). 1983. pap. 3.00 (ISBN 0-913439-02-9). Henceforth.

--Sovereignty & Freedom: A Struggle for Balance. 92p. (Orig.). 1978. pap. 2.50 (ISBN 0-913439-00-2). Henceforth.

Barton, George A. A Critical & Exegetical Commentary on Ecclesiastes. Driver, Samuel R. & Plummer, Alfred, eds. LC 8-15777. (International Critical Commentary Ser.). 236p. 1912. 22.95 (ISBN 0-567-05014-9, Pub. by T & T Clark Ltd UK). Fortress.

--Religions of the World. LC 74-90469. Repr. of 1929 ed. lib. bdg. 22.50x (ISBN 0-8371-2216-3, BARW). Greenwood.

Barton, J. Amos' Oracles Against the Nations. LC 78-67630. (Society for Old Testament Study Ser.). 1980. 22.95 (ISBN 0-521-22501-9). Cambridge U Pr.

Barton, John. Reading the Old Testament: Method in Biblical Study. LC 84-3640. 272p. 1984. pap. 12.95 (ISBN 0-664-24555-2). Westminster.

Barton, R. F. Religion of the Ifugaos. LC 48-3664. (American Anthropological Association Memoirs Ser). Repr. of 1946 ed. 21.00 (ISBN 0-527-00564-9). Kraus Repr.

Barton, Ralph. God's Country. 59.95 (ISBN 0-8490-0242-7). Gordon Pr.

Barton, Roy F. Philippine Pagans: The Autobiographies of Three Ifugaos. LC 76-44686. Repr. of 1938 ed. 30.00 (ISBN 0-404-15903-6). AMS Pr.

Barton, W. B., tr. see Heidegger, Martin.

Barton, Winifred W. John P. Williamson: A Brother to the Sioux. LC 80-53176. (Illus.). 308p. 1980. Repr. of 1919 ed. 16.00 (ISBN 0-9610012-0-8). Sunnycrest Pub.

Bartoo, Glenn. Decisions by Consensus: A Study of the Quaker Method. (Studies in Quakerism: No. 4). 48p. (Orig.). 1978. pap. 2.00 (ISBN 0-89670-003-8). Progresiv Pub.

Bartos, F. M. The Hussite Revolution: Fourteen Twenty-Four to Fourteen Thirty-Seven. 256p. 1986. 25.00 (ISBN 0-88033-097-X). East Eur Quarterly.

Bartow, Charles L. The Preaching Moment: A Guide to Sermon Delivery. LC 80-12370. (Abingdon Preacher's Library). (Orig.). 1980. pap. 5.95 (ISBN 0-687-33907-3). Abingdon.

Bartow, Donald W. The Adventures of Healing: How to Use New Testament Practices & Receive New Testament Results. 3rd, rev. ed. 204p. 1981. pap. 11.95 (ISBN 0-938736-19-1). Life Enrich.

--Ministry of Prayer. 3rd ed. 165p. 1983. pap. 7.95 (ISBN 0-938736-22-1). LIFE ENRICH.

Bart-Williams, P. J. Evolution & the Word of God. LC 83-91501. 87p. 1985. 8.95 (ISBN 0-533-06080-X). Vantage.

Barua, Benimadhab. A History of Pre-Buddhistic Indian Philosophy. 1981. Repr. of 1921 ed. 28.50x (ISBN 0-8364-0800-4, Pub. by Motilal Banarsidass). South Asia Bks.

Barwick, D., et al. Metaphors of Interpretation: Essays in Honour of W. E. H. Stanner. LC 84-71361. (Illus.). 318p. 1987. pap. 28.00 (ISBN 0-08-029875-3). Pergamon.

Barwick, Steven, tr. Two Mexico City Choirbooks of 1717: An Anthology of Sacred Polyphony from the Cathedral of Mexico. LC 82-3047. 213p. 1982. 16.95x (ISBN 0-8093-1065-1). S Ill U Pr.

Bary, William T. de see De Bary, William T.

Bary, William T. De see De Bary, W. Theodore & Bloom, Irene.

Bar Yohai, Shimon. Hashmotot Zohar: Hebrew Text. 1969. 20.00 (ISBN 0-943688-20-5). Res Ctr Kabbalah.

--Zohar: Hebrew Text, 21 vols. 378.00 set (ISBN 0-943688-67-1); 18.00 ea. Res Ctr Kabbalah.

--Zohar: Hebrew Text, 10 vols. condensed ed. 1981. 15.00 ea. (ISBN 0-943688-68-X); 150.00 set. Res Ctr Kabbalah.

Basabe, Fernando M. Religious Attitudes of Japanese Men. LC 68-57415. 1969. bds. 15.00 (ISBN 0-8048-0651-9). C E Tuttle.

Basaroff, F. The Sacrament of Matrimony According to the Doctrine & Ritual of the Eastern Orthodox Church. Bjerring, N., tr. from Russian. pap. 1.95 (ISBN 0-686-16370-2). Eastern Orthodox.

Bascio, Patrick. Building a Just Society. LC 80-27238. 176p. (Orig.). 1981. pap. 5.95 (ISBN 0-88344-205-1). Orbis Bks.

Bascom, Arlene, jt. auth. see Hanks, Darla.

Bascom, John. A Philosophy of Religion: Or, the Rational Grounds of Religious Belief. LC 75-3037. Repr. of 1876 ed. 57.50 (ISBN 0-404-59035-7). AMS Pr.

--Science, Philosophy & Religion. LC 75-3041. Repr. of 1871 ed. 36.00 (ISBN 0-404-59039-X). AMS Pr.

Bascom, W. R. The Sociological Role of the Yoruba Cult-Group. LC 44-47266. (American Anthro. Association Memoirs). Repr. of 1944 ed. 15.00 (ISBN 0-527-00562-2). Kraus Repr.

Bascom, William. The Yoruba of Southwestern Nigeria. (Illus.). 118p. 1984. pap. text ed. 7.95x (ISBN 0-88133-038-8). Waveland Pr.

Basetti-Sami, Giulio. Koran in the Light of Christ. 1977. 8.50 (ISBN 0-8199-0713-8). Franciscan Herald.

Basetti-Sani, Biuolio. Louis Massignon: Christian Ecumenist. 1974. 6.95 (ISBN 0-8199-0496-1). Franciscan Herald.

Bash, Ewald. Legends from the Future. (Illus., Orig.). 1972. pap. 1.75 (ISBN 0-377-02101-6). Friend Pr.

Basham, A. L., ed. A Cultural History of India. (Illus.). 1975. 29.95x (ISBN 0-19-561520-4). Oxford U Pr.

Basham, Don. Face up with a Miracle. 190p. 1971. pap. 2.95 (ISBN 0-88368-002-5). Whitaker Hse.

--A Handbook on Holy Spirit Baptism. (Handbk. Ser: No. 1). 118p. 1969. pap. 2.95 (ISBN 0-88368-003-3). Whitaker Hse.

--Handbook on Tongues, Interpretation & Prophecy. (Handbk. Ser.: No. 2). 1971. pap. 2.95 (ISBN 0-88368-004-1). Whitaker Hse.

--Lead Us Not into Temptation. (Quality Paper Ser.). 1986. pap. 6.95 (ISBN 0-8007-9082-0, Chosen Bks). Revell.

--Spiritual Power. rev ed. 92p. 1976. pap. 2.25 (ISBN 0-88368-075-0). Whitaker Hse.

Basil, St. Ascetical Works. LC 50-10735. (Fathers of the Church Ser.: Vol. 9). 525p. 1950. 26.95x (ISBN 0-8132-0009-1). Cath U Pr.

--Exegetic Homilies. LC 63-12483. (Father of the Church Ser.: Vol. 46). 378p. 1963. 19.95x (ISBN 0-8132-0046-6). Cath U Pr.

--Letters, Nos. 1-185. (Fathers of the Church Ser.: Vol. 13). 345p. 1951. 18.95x (ISBN 0-8132-0013-X). Cath U Pr.

--Letters, Nos. 186-368. LC 65-18318. (Fathers of the Church Ser.: Vol. 28). 369p. 1955. 19.95x (ISBN 0-8132-0028-8). Cath U Pr.

Basil, Saint St. Basil the Great on The Forty Martyrs of Sebaste, Paradise, & the Catholic Faith. 1979. pap. 3.95 (ISBN 0-686-25227-6). Eastern Orthodox.

Basilius. The Ascetic Works of Saint Basil. Clarke, W. K., tr. & intro. by. LC 80-2352. Repr. of 1925 ed. 47.50 (ISBN 0-404-18902-4). AMS Pr.

Basinger, David & Basinger, Randall. Philosophy & Miracle: The Contemporary Debate. LC 86-12766. (Problems in Contemporary Philosophy Ser.: No. 2). 130p. 1986. 39.95 (ISBN 0-88946-327-1). E Mellen.

--Predestination & Free Will. LC 85-23887. 180p. 1986. pap. 6.95 (ISBN 0-87784-567-0). Inter-Varsity.

Basinger, Randall, jt. auth. see Basinger, David.

Baskerville, B. C. The Polish Jew. 75.00 (ISBN 0-8490-0870-0). Gordon Pr.

Baskett, Mary. Footprints of the Buddha. LC 80-80133. (Illus.). 125p. (Orig.). 1980. pap. 8.95 (ISBN 0-87633-034-0). Phila Mus Art.

Baskin, Judith R. Pharaoh's Counsellors: Job, Jethro, & Balaam in Rabbinic & Patristic Tradition. LC 83-11535. (Brown Judaic Studies). 200p. 1983. pap. 18.00 (ISBN 0-89130-637-4, 14 00 47). Scholars Pr GA.

Baskin, Leonard, ed. & illus. see Central Conference of American Rabbis Staff.

Baskin, Wade. Dictionary of Satanism. 1972. pap. 3.95 (ISBN 0-8065-0292-4). Citadel Pr.
--The Sorcerer's Handbook. (Illus.). 640p. 1974. pap. 4.95 (ISBN 0-8065-0399-8). Citadel Pr.
Baskin, Wade, jt. auth. see Wedeck, Harry E.
Basler, Michael. Discipling One to One. (Pathfinder Pamphlets Ser.). 32p. (Orig.). 1986. pap. 1.95 (ISBN 0-87784-217-5). Inter-Varsity.
Basnage De Beauval, Henry. Tolerance Des Religions. Repr. 20.00 (ISBN 0-384-03522-1). Johnson Repr.
Basnayake, H. T. Sri Lankan Monastic Architecture. (Studies on Sri Lanka Ser.: No. 2). (Illus.). 186p. 1986. 85.00x (ISBN 81-7030-009-6, Pub. by SRI SATGURU Pubns India). Orient Bk Dist.
Bass, Charles D. Banishing Fear from Your Life. LC 85-23943. 168p. 1986. 14.95 (ISBN 0-385-23331-0). Doubleday.
Bass, Dorothy C. & Boyd, Sandra H. Women in American Religious History: An Annotated Bibliography. (Reference Bks). 205p. 1986. lib. bdg. 30.00x (ISBN 0-8161-8151-9). G K Hall.
Bass, Dorothy C. & Smith, Kenneth B., eds. The United Church of Christ: Studies in Identity & Polity. LC 86-83022. (Studies in Ministry & Parish Life). 112p. 1987. text ed. 16.95x (ISBN 0-913552-37-2); pap. text ed. 6.95x (ISBN 0-913552-36-4). Exploration Pr.
Bass, George. The Cradle, the Cross & the Crown. Sherer, Michael L., ed. (Orig.). 1986. pap. 7.25 (ISBN 0-89536-817-X, 6866). CSS of Ohio.
Bass, George M. The Man, the Message, & the Mission. 1982. 6.95 (ISBN 0-89536-565-0, 1336). CSS of Ohio.
--Plastic Flowers in the Holy Water. 1981. 4.35 (ISBN 0-89536-480-8, 1605). CSS of Ohio.
--The Song & the Story. 1984. 7.00 (ISBN 0-89536-652-5, 1970). CSS of Ohio.
--Telling the Whole Story. 1983. 6.95 (ISBN 0-89536-642-8, 2007). CSS of Ohio.
Bass, George M., jt. auth. see Kemper, Frederick.
Basser, Herbert W. Midrashic Interpretations of the Song of Moses. LC 83-49003. (American University Studies VII: Vol. 2). 312p. 1983. pap. text ed. 28.85 (ISBN 0-8204-0065-3). P Lang Pubs.
Bassett, Paul M. Keep the Wonder. 61p. 1979. pap. 1.95 (ISBN 0-8341-0608-6). Beacon Hill.
Bassett, Paul M. & Greathouse, William M. Exploring Christian Holiness: The Historical Development, Vol. 2. (Exploring Christian Holiness Ser.). 250p. 1984. 15.95 (ISBN 0-8341-0926-3). Beacon Hill.
Bassett, William T. Counseling the Childless Couple. LC 63-14722. (Successful Pastoral Counseling Ser.). pap. 34.80 (2026938). Bks Demand UMI.
Bassham, Rodger C. Mission Theology, Nineteen Forty Eight to Nineteen Seventy-Five: Years of Worldwide Creative Tension--Ecumenical, Evangelical & Roman Catholic. LC 79-17116. 1980. 10.95 (ISBN 0-87808-330-8). William Carey Lib.
Bassler, Jouette M. Divine Impartiality: Paul & a Theological Axiom. Baird, William, ed. LC 81-1367. (Society of Biblical Literature Dissertation Ser.). 1981. pap. text ed. 13.50 (ISBN 0-89130-475-4, 0-06-01-59). Scholars Pr GA.
Basso, Keith H. Western Apache Witchcraft. LC 69-16329. (University of Arizona, Anthroplological Papers: No. 15). pap. 20.30 (ISBN 0-317-28645-5, 2055359). Bks Demand UMI.
Basson, Marc D., jt. auth. see Ethics, Humanisms & Medicine Conference, University of Michigan, Ann Arbor, MI. 1981.
Bassuk, Daniel. Abraham Lincoln & the Quakers. (Orig.). 1987. pap. 2.50x (ISBN 0-87574-273-4). Pendle Hill.
Bassuk, Daniel, ed. see Zielinski, Stanislaw.
Bassuk, Daniel E. Incarnation in Hinduism & Christianity: The Myth of the God-Man. (Library of Philosophy & Religion Ser.). 256p. 1987. text ed. 35.00 (ISBN 0-391-03452-9). Humanities.
Bast, Henry. The Lord's Prayer. 2.50 (ISBN 0-686-23480-4). Rose Pub MI.
Bastian, Donald N. Along the Way. 128p. 1977. pap. 3.95 (ISBN 0-89367-008-1). Light & Life.
--Belonging! Adventures in Church Membership. 1978. pap. 4.95 (ISBN 0-89367-044-8). Light & Life.
Bastian, Ralph J., tr. see Portalie, Eugene.
Bastible, James C., ed. see Ott, Ludwig.
Bastide, Derek. Religious Education Five-Twelve. 27.00 (ISBN 1-85000-149-9, Falmer Press); pap. 14.00 (ISBN 1-85000-150-2). Taylor & Francis.
Bastide, Roger. The African Religions of Brazil: Toward a Sociology of the Interpenetration of Civilizations. Sebba, Helen, tr. (Johns Hopkins Studies in Atlantic History & Culture Ser.). 1978. text ed. 45.00x (ISBN 0-8018-2056-1); pap. text ed. 14.95x (ISBN 0-8018-2130-4). Johns Hopkins.
Bastien, Remy, jt. auth. see Courlander, Harold.
Bastin, Dom P. La Charterhouse Du Mont St. Jean Baptiste Pres de Fribourg en Brisgau, 1345-1782. Hogg, James, ed. (Analecta Cartusiana Ser.: No. 76). (Orig.). 1984. pap. 25.00 (ISBN 3-7052-0112-3, Pub. by Salzburg Studies). Longwood Pub Group.
Bastin, Marcel, et al. God Day by Day, Vol. 2: Ordinary Time: Matthew. 576p. (Orig.). 1984. pap. 14.95 (ISBN 0-8091-2643-5). Paulist Pr.
--God Day by Day, Vol. 1: Lent & the Easter Season. 320p. (Orig.). 1984. pap. 10.95 (ISBN 0-8091-2642-7). Paulist Pr.
--God Day by Day, Vol. 4: Advent & Christmas. 184p. (Orig.). 1985. pap. 8.95 (ISBN 0-8091-2699-0). Paulist Pr.
Batalden, Stephen K. Catherine II's Greek Prelate: Eugenios Voulgaris in Russia, 1771-1806. (East European Monographs: No. 115). 197p. 1983. 26.00x (ISBN 0-88033-006-6). East Eur Quarterly.
Batchelor, Edward, Jr., ed. Abortion: The Moral Issues. LC 82-7505. 256p. 1982. pap. 8.95 (ISBN 0-8298-0612-1). Pilgrim NY.
--Homosexuality & Ethics. rev. ed. LC 80-10533. 1982. 15.95 (ISBN 0-8298-0392-0); pap. 8.95 (ISBN 0-8298-0615-6). Pilgrim NY.
Batchelor, John. The Ainu of Japan: The Religion, Superstitions, & General History of the Hairy Aborigines of Japan. 26.00 (ISBN 0-8369-7153-1, 7985). Ayer Co Pubs.
Batchelor, Mary. Our Family Christmas Book. 96p. 1984. 9.95 (ISBN 0-687-29587-4). Abingdon.
Batchelor, Stephen. Alone with Others. Rosset, Hannelore, ed. LC 82-21054. (Grove Press Eastern Philosophy & Religion Ser.). 144p. 1983. pap. 5.95 (ISBN 0-394-62457-2, E843, Ever). Grove.
Batchelor, Stephen, ed. see Rabten, Geshe.
Batchelor, Walter D. Gateway to Survival Is Storage. 128p. 1974. pap. 3.95 (ISBN 0-89036-127-4). Hawkes Pub Inc.
Bateman, Helen R. Roots & Wings. LC 83-1868. (Illus.). 160p. 1983. 7.95 (ISBN 0-87747-950-X). Deseret Bk.
Bates, Carroll M. The Human Body - Good or Evil? 1986. 6.95 (ISBN 0-533-06780-4). Vantage.
Bates, Charles. Ransoming the Mind: An Integration of Yoga & Modern Therapy. LC 86-50084. (Illus.). 352p. (Orig.). 1986. pap. 11.95 (ISBN 0-936663-00-6). Yes Intl.
Bates, Katharine L. The English Religious Drama. 1975. Repr. of 1911 ed. 30.00 (ISBN 0-8274-4103-7). R West.
Bates, M. Searle. Religious Liberty: An Inquiry. LC 77-166096. (Civil Liberties in American History Ser.). 1972. Repr. of 1945 ed. lib. bdg. 59.50 (ISBN 0-306-70235-5). Da Capo.
Bates, Natica I., ed. see Reisner, G. A.
Bates, Raymond. Wilt Thou Be Made Whole? (Orig.). Date not set. pap. 5.00 (ISBN 0-915541-08-4). Star Bks Inc.
Bateson, Gregory. Naven: A Survey of the Problems Suggested by a Composite Picture of the Culture of a New Guinea Tribe Drawn from Three Points of View. 2nd ed. (Illus.). 1958. 25.00x (ISBN 0-8047-0519-4); pap. 10.95 (ISBN 0-8047-0520-8). Stanford U Pr.
Bateson, Gregory & Bateson, May C. Angels Fear: Towards an Epistemology of the Sacred. 224p. 1987. 18.95 (ISBN 0-02-507670-1). Macmillan.
Bateson, May C., jt. auth. see Bateson, Gregory.
Bathory, Peter D. Political Theory As Public Confession. LC 80-15667. 180p. 1981. 24.95 (ISBN 0-87855-405-X). Transaction Bks.
Batista, Jaoa, ed. see Getz, Gene.
Batista, Joao, jt. ed. see Balthazar, Vera.
Batman, Stephen. Doom & Warning All Men to the Judgement. LC 84-1441. 1984. Repr. of 1581 ed. 60.00x (ISBN 0-8201-1393-X). Schol Facsimiles.
--The Golden Booke of the Leaden Gods, Repr. Of 1577 Ed. Bd. with The Third Part of the Countess of Pembroke's Yvychurch. Fraunce, Abraham. Repr. of 1592 ed; The Fountaine of Ancient Fiction. Lynche, Richard. Repr. of 1599 ed. LC 75-27856. (Renaissance & the Gods Ser.: Vol. 13). (Illus.). 1976. lib. bdg. 88.00 (ISBN 0-8240-2062-6). Garland Pub.
Batra, Ravi. Muslim Civilization & the Crisis in Iran. 218p. 1980. pap. 2.00 (ISBN 0-686-95468-8). Ananda Marga.
Batson, C. Daniel, et al. Commitment Without Ideology. LC 72-13000. 1973. 6.95 (ISBN 0-8298-0245-2). Pilgrim NY.
Batson, Daniel C. & Ventis, W. Larry. The Religious Experience: A Social-Psychological Perspective. (Illus.). 1982. text ed. 29.95x (ISBN 0-19-503030-3); pap. text ed. 15.95x (ISBN 0-19-503031-1). Oxford U Pr.
Batson, E. Beatrice. John Bunyan: Allegory & Imagination. LC 83-21341. 168p. 1984. 27.50x (ISBN 0-389-20442-0, 08004). B&N Imports.
Batson, Gary, jt. ed. see Batson, Horace W.
Batson, Horace W. & Batson, Gary, eds. Overcoming Stress: Everything You Ever Need to Know! 100p. (Orig.). 1987. pap. 9.95 (ISBN 0-938503-00-6). Welstar Pubns.
Battaglia, Anthony. Toward a Reformulation of Natural Law. 1981. 14.95 (ISBN 0-8164-0490-9, HarpR). Har-Row.
Batten, Adrian. Four Anthems. Evans, David, ed. LC 68-65217. (Penn State Music Series, No. 17). 232p. pap. 3.25x (ISBN 0-271-09117-7). Pa St U Pr.
Batten, Loring W. A Critical & Exegetical Commentary on Ezra & Nehemiah. Driver, Samuel R., et al, eds. LC 13-12806. (International Critical Commentary Ser.). 400p. 1913. 22.95 (ISBN 0-567-05008-4, Pub. by T & T Clark Ltd UK). Fortress.
Battersby, W. J. De la Salle: A Pioneer of Modern Education. 236p. 1981. Repr. of 1949 ed. lib. bdg. 40.00 (ISBN 0-89987-065-1). Darby Bks.
Batterson, Herman G. Sketchbook of the American Episcopate, During One Hundred Years, 1783-1883. 1980. Repr. cancelled (ISBN 0-87921-047-8). Attic Pr.
Battey, Thomas C. The Life & Adventures of a Quaker among the Indians. 339p. 1972. Repr. of 1875 ed. 20.00 (ISBN 0-87928-025-5). Corner Hse.
Battin, Margaret & Rudick, Michael, eds. John Donne's Biathanatos: A Modern-Spelling Critical Edition. (Garland English Texts Ser.). 1982. lib. bdg. 55.00 (ISBN 0-8240-9481-6). Garland Pub.
Battin, Margaret P. Ethical Issues in Suicide. 250p. 1982. write for info. (ISBN 0-13-290155-2). P-H.
Battin, Margaret P. & Maris, Ronald, eds. Suicide & Ethics. (Special Issue S Ser.: Vol. 13, No. 3). 112p. 1984. pap. 9.95. Guilford Pr.
Battles, Ford L. & Walchenbach, John. An Analysis of "The Institute of the Christian Religion" of John Calvin. LC 79-57385. 1980. pap. 12.95 (ISBN 0-8010-0766-6). Baker Bk.
Battles, Ford L., jt. auth. see Rosenstock-Huessy, Eugen.
Battles, Ford L., tr. see Calvin, John.
Batzler, L. Richard. Journeys on Your Spiritual Path. 1982. 7.95 (ISBN 0-935710-04-3). Hid Valley MD.
Batzler, Louis R. Sunlight & Shadows: Portraits of Priorities for Living & Dying. (Illus.). 60p. (Orig.). 1986. pap. 4.95 (ISBN 0-935710-09-4). Hid Valley MD.
Bau, Iqnatius. This Ground Is Holy: Church Sanctuary & Central American Refugees. LC 84-60406. 304p. (Orig.). 1985. pap. 9.95 (ISBN 0-8091-2720-2). Paulist Pr.
Baudin. Etudes Historiques et Critiques sur la Philosophie de Pascal, 3 tomes. Incl. Tome I. Pascal et Descartes. 11.95 (ISBN 0-685-34021-X); Tome II. Pascal, les Libertins et les Jansenites. 22.50 (ISBN 0-685-34022-8); Tome III. Pascal et la Casuistique. 11.50 (ISBN 0-685-34023-6). (Coll. Etre et Penser). French & Eur.
Baudouin, Charles. Power Within Us. facs. ed. LC 68-16905. (Essay Index Reprint Ser). 1923. 15.00 (ISBN 0-8369-0176-2). Ayer Co Pubs.
--Suggestions & Autosuggestions. 1978. Repr. of 1920 ed. lib. bdg. 49.00 (ISBN 0-8495-0350-7). Arden Lib.
Bauer. Diccionario De Teologia Biblica. 2nd ed. (Span.). 582p. 1976. 38.95 (ISBN 84-254-0360-X, S-50203). French & Eur.
Bauer, Arthur O. Being in Mission: A Resource for the Local Church & Community. 1987. pap. 4.95. Friend Pr.
--Making Mission Happen. 1974. pap. 4.50 (ISBN 0-377-00019-1). Friend Pr.
Bauer, Caroline F. Celebrations: Read-Aloud Holiday & Theme Book Programs. LC 85-714. (Illus.). 301p. 1985. 35.00 (ISBN 0-8242-0708-4). Wilson.
Bauer, Erika. Heinrich Hallers Uberstzung Der'Imitatio Christi. Hogg, James, ed. (Analecta Cartusiana Ser.: No. 88). 224p. (Orig.). 1982. pap. 25.00 (ISBN 3-7052-0145-X, Pub by. Salzburg Studies). Longwood Pub Group.
Bauer, Fred. Just a Touch of Nearness. 48p. 1985. 6.95 (ISBN 0-8378-5082-7). Gibson.
Bauer, J. B. Encyclopedia of Biblical Theology: The Concise Sacramentum Verbi. 1172p. 1981. 39.50x (ISBN 0-8245-0042-3). Crossroad NY.
Bauer, Johannes B. Bibeltheologisches Woerterbuch, 2 vols. 3rd ed. (Ger.). 1967. Set. 150.00 (ISBN 3-222-10240-6, M-7308, Pub. by Styria). French & Eur.
Bauer, Walter. Orthodoxy & Heresy in Earliest Christianity. Kraft, Robert A. & Krodel, Gerhard, eds. LC 71-141252. 360p. 1979. pap. 2.50 (ISBN 0-8006-1363-5, 1-1363). Fortress.
--Orthodoxy & Heresy in Early Christianity. LC 71-141252. pap. 88.00 (2027876). Bks Demand UMI.
Bauer, Walter, et al, eds. A Greek-English Lexicon of the New Testament & Other Early Christian Literature. Arndt, William F., tr. from Ger. LC 78-14293. (2nd rev. & augmented edition). 1979. lib. bdg. 47.50x (ISBN 0-226-03932-3). U of Chicago Pr.
Bauer, Yehuda. American Jewry & the Holocaust: The American Jewish Joint Distribution Committee, 1939-1945. LC 80-26035. 522p. 1981. 35.00x (ISBN 0-8143-1672-7). Wayne St U Pr.
--The Jewish Emergence from Powerlessness. LC 78-25830. pap. 25.80 (ISBN 0-317-26941-0, 2023592). Bks Demand UMI.
--They Chose Life: Jewish Resistance in the Holocaust. LC 73-89085. (Illus.). 64p. (Orig.). 1973. pap. 2.00 (ISBN 0-87495-000-7). Am Jewish Comm.
Bauer, Yehuda & Keren, Nili. A History of the Holocaust. 453p. 1982. 17.95 (ISBN 0-531-09862-1); 12.95 (ISBN 0-531-05641-4). Watts.
Bauerle, Richard E. I, the Prophet. 1981. pap. 6.95 (ISBN 0-570-03835-9, 12YY2800). Concordia.
Baughen, Michael. The Moses Principle: Leadership & the Venture of Faith. LC 78-27498. 118p. 1978. pap. 2.95 (ISBN 0-87788-558-3). Shaw Pubs.
--Strengthened by Struggle: The Stress Factor in 2 Corinthians. 128p. 1984. pap. 5.95 (ISBN 0-87788-792-6). Shaw Pubs.
Baughman, Ray. La Vida Abundante. Orig. Title: The Abundant Life. (Span.). 192p. 1959. pap. 3.95 (ISBN 0-8254-1056-8). Kregel.
Baughman, Ray E. Abundant Life. 1959. pap. 3.50 (ISBN 0-8024-0047-7). Moody.
Baum, Mrs. C. L. Studies in Divine Science. 1964. 6.50 (ISBN 0-686-24362-5). Divine Sci Fed.
Baum, G., et al, eds. see Calvin, Jean.
Baum, Gregory. Constitution on the Church: De Ecclesia. LC 65-17864. 192p. 1965. pap. 2.95 (ISBN 0-8091-1528-X). Paulist Pr.
--Journeys: The Impact of Personal Experience on Religious Thought. LC 75-31401. pap. 52.90 (ISBN 0-8357-9486-5, 2013525). Bks Demand UMI.
--The Priority of Labor: A Commentary on "Laborem Exercens", Encyclical Letter of Pope John Paul II. 112p. 1982. pap. 5.95 (ISBN 0-8091-2479-3). Paulist Pr.
Baum, Gregory, ed. Religion & Alienation: A Theological Reading of Sociology. LC 75-28652. 304p. 1976. pap. 9.95 (ISBN 0-8091-1917-X). Paulist Pr.
--Sociology & Human Destiny: Studies in Sociology, Religion & Society. 224p. 1980. 14.50 (ISBN 0-8164-0110-1, HarpR). Har-Row.
Baum, Gregory & Coleman, John, eds. Neo-Conservatism: Social & Religious Phenomenon. (Concilium 1981 Ser.: Vol. 141). 128p. (Orig.). 1981. pap. 6.95 (ISBN 0-8164-2308-3, HarpR). Har-Row.
--New Religious Movements. (Concilium Ser. 1983: Vol. 161). 128p. (Orig.). 1983. pap. 6.95 (ISBN 0-8164-2441-1, HarpR); pap. 62.55 10 Volume Subscription (ISBN 0-8164-2453-5). Har-Row.
--Sexual Revolution, Vol 173. (Concilium Ser.). 128p. pap. 6.95 (ISBN 0-317-31462-9, Pub. by T & T Clark Ltd UK). Fortress.
Baum, Gregory, jt. ed. see Coleman, John.
Baum, Gregory B. & Coleman, John, eds. The Church & Racism. (Concilium Ser.: Vol. 151). 128p. (Orig.). 1982. pap. 6.95 (ISBN 0-8164-2382-2, HarpR). Har-Row.
Baum, Robert J. Ethical Arguments for Analysis. 2nd ed. LC 76-1952. 1976. pap. text ed. 19.95 (ISBN 0-03-089646-0, HoltC). HR&W.
--Ethical Arguments for Analysis: Brief Edition. 2nd ed. LC 78-10770. 1979. pap. text ed. 15.95 (ISBN 0-03-045011-X, HoltC). HR&W.
Bauman, Clarence. The Sermon on the Mount: The Modern Quest for Its Meaning. x, 440p. 1985. 41.95 (ISBN 0-86554-113-2, MUP/H107). Mercer Univ Pr.
Bauman, David M. Spiritual Life for the Overbusy. 96p. (Orig.). 1987. pap. price not set (ISBN 0-88028-065-4). Forward Movement.
Bauman, Edward W. An Introduction to the New Testament. LC 61-10616. 190p. 1979. pap. 5.95 (ISBN 0-664-24279-0). Westminster.
--Life & Teaching of Jesus. LC 60-7038. 240p. 1978. pap. 6.95 (ISBN 0-664-24221-9). Westminster.
Bauman, Elizabeth. Ascuas de Fuego. Patzan, Flora, tr. Tr. of Coals of Fire. (Span.). 128p. 1982. pap. 3.50 (ISBN 0-8361-3315-3). Herald Pr.
Bauman, Lewis. The Tongues Movement. 1979. pap. 1.00 (ISBN 0-88469-047-4). BMH Bks.
Bauman, Louis. The Faith: Once for All Delivered unto the Saints. pap. 2.95 (ISBN 0-88469-026-1). BMH Bks.
Bauman, Mark K. Warren Akin Candler: The Conservative As Idealist. LC 80-22230. 290p. 1981. 20.00 (ISBN 0-8108-1368-8). Scarecrow.

Bauman, Richard. Let Your Words Be Few: Symbolism of Speaking & Silence Among Seventeenth Century Quakers. LC 83-1982. (Cambridge Studies in Oral & Literate Culture Ser.: No. 8). 208p. 1984. 34.50 (ISBN 0-521-25506-6); pap. 10.95 (ISBN 0-521-27514-8). Cambridge U Pr.

Baumann, Dan. Confronted by Love. LC 85-2364. (Bible Commentary for Laymen Ser.). 144p. 1985. pap. 3.95 (ISBN 0-8307-1050-7, S391101). Regal.

--Which Way to Happiness? LC 81-50302. 144p. 1981. pap. 3.50 (ISBN 0-8307-0773-5, S351100). Regal.

Baumann, Fred, tr. see Strauss, Leo.

Baumann, J. Daniel. An Introduction to Contemporary Preaching. 1972. 14.95 (ISBN 0-8010-0572-8). Baker Bk.

Baumgartel, Elise J. The Cultures of Prehistoric Egypt, 2 vols. in 1. LC 80-24186. (Illus.). xxiii, 286p. 1981. Repr. of 1955 ed. lib. bdg. 60.00x (ISBN 0-313-22524-9, BACU). Greenwood.

Baumgarten, Murray. City Scriptures: Modern Jewish Writing. LC 81-6879. 240p. 1982. text ed. 17.50x (ISBN 0-674-13278-5). Harvard U Pr.

Baumgarth, William P., ed. see St. Thomas Acquinas.

Baumgartner, Aline & Fisher, Carl, eds. Jesus: Friend, Teacher, Leader. (Illus.). 1986. dupl. masterbook 9.95 (ISBN 0-89837-104-X, Pub. by Pflaum Pr). Peter Li.

Baumgartner, Anne S. Ye Gods! 192p. 1984. 14.95 (ISBN 0-8184-0349-7). Lyle Stuart.

Baumgartner, Apollinaris W. Catholic Journalism. LC 75-159997. (BCL Ser. I). Repr. of 1931 ed. 11.50 (ISBN 0-404-00693-0). AMS Pr.

Baumgartner, F. J. Radical Reactionaries: The Political Thought of the French Catholic League. 320p. (Orig.). 1976. pap. text ed. 37.50x (Pub. by Droz Switzerland). Coronet Bks.

Baumgartner, Keith A. & Schiff, Marty. The Armageddon: Color & Game Book. (Illus.). 28p. 1984. pap. 2.95 (ISBN 0-916343-02-2). J R Simon.

Baumgartner, Walter, jt. auth. see Koehler, Ludwig.

Baumstark, Anton. Festbrevier und Kirchenjahr der Syrischen Jakobiten. Repr. of 1910 ed. 22.00 (ISBN 0-384-03575-2). Johnson Repr.

--Die Modestianischen und Die Konstantinischen Bauten Am Heiligen Grabe Zu Jerusalem. Repr. of 1915 ed. 15.00 (ISBN 0-384-03585-X). Johnson Repr.

Baumstein, Paschal M. My Lord of Belmont: A Biography of Leo Haid. (Illus.). xxii, 396p. 1985. 20.00 (ISBN 0-9614976-0-2). Archives Belmont.

Baur, Benedict. Frequent Confession. 224p. 1980. 7.00 (ISBN 0-906127-20-3). Lumen Christi.

Baur, Ferdinand C. The Church History of the First Three Centuries, 2 vols. Menzies, A., ed. 1980. lib. bdg. 199.75 (ISBN 0-8490-3146-X). Gordon Pr.

Baur, Francis. Life in Abundance: A Contemporary Spirituality. 240p. 1983. pap. 7.95 (ISBN 0-8091-2507-2). Paulist Pr.

Baur, P. V., jt. auth. see Hopkins, C.

Bausch, Michael & Duck, Ruth. Everflowing Streams. LC 81-701. 96p. (Orig.). 1981. pap. 4.95 (ISBN 0-8298-0428-5). Pilgrim NY.

Bausch, Thomas. The Spiritual Exercises & Today's CLC: Making the Exercises Come to Life. 24p. 1973. pap. text ed. 1.50x (ISBN 0-913605-01-8). NFCLC.

Bausch, Thomas A. The Spiritual Exercises & CLC: The Role of the Exercises in Today's CLC's. 24p. 1973. pap. text ed. 1.50x (ISBN 0-913605-00-X). NFCLC.

Bausch, William J. The Christian Parish: Whispers of the Risen Christ. 232p. 1981. pap. 7.95 (ISBN 0-89622-146-6). Twenty-Third.

--Ministry: Traditions, Tensions, Transitions. LC 81-86345. 192p. 1982. pap. 7.95 (ISBN 0-89622-153-9). Twenty-Third.

--Pilgrim Church. LC 73-6608. 560p. 1980. pap. 9.95 (ISBN 0-89622-140-7). Twenty-Third.

--Storytelling, Imagination & Faith. 240p. (Orig.). 1984. pap. 7.95 (ISBN 0-89622-199-7). Twenty-Third.

--Take Heart, Father: A Hope-Filled Vision for Today's Priest. 216p. (Orig.). 1986. pap. 9.95 (ISBN 0-89622-309-4). Twenty-Third.

Bautista, Sara, tr. see Collingwood, Guillermo.

Bautista, Sara, tr. see Cutting, Jorge.

Bautista, Sara, tr. see Mackintosh, Carlos H.

Bautista, Sara, tr. see Marshall, Alejandro & Bennett, Gordon H.

Bautista, SAra, tr. see Pollock, Algernon J.

Bautista, Sara, tr. see Pollock, Algernon J. & Bennett, Gordon H.

Bautista, Sara, tr. see Rossier, H.

Bautista, Sara, tr. see Voorehoeve, H. C. & Bennett, Gordon H.

Bavarel, Michel. New Communities, New Ministries: The Church Resurgent in Africa, Asia, & Latin America. Martin, Francis, tr. from Fr. LC 82-22318. Orig. Title: Chretienes Du Bout Du Monde. 122p. (Orig.). 1983. pap. 5.95 (ISBN 0-88344-337-6). Orbis Bks.

Bavinck, Herman. Doctrine of God. (Twin Brooks Ser.). 1977. pap. 13.95 (ISBN 0-8010-0723-2). Baker Bk.

--The Doctrine of God. Hendricksen, W., tr. (Student's Reformed Theological Library Ser.). 1977. 16.95 (ISBN 0-85151-255-0). Banner of Truth.

--Our Reasonable Faith: A Survey of Christian Doctrine. Zylstra, Henry, tr. (Twin Brooks Ser). 1977. pap. 13.95 (ISBN 0-8010-0513-2). Baker Bk.

--Philosophy of Revelation. (Twin Brooks Ser.). 1980. pap. 7.95 (ISBN 0-8010-0767-4). Baker Bk.

Bavinck, J. H. Introduction to the Science of Missions. 1977. pap. 5.95 (ISBN 0-8010-0600-7). Baker Bk.

Bavinck, Johan H. The Church Between Temple & Mosque: A Study of the Relationship Between the Christian Faith & Other Religions. LC 66-22946. pap. 51.50 (ISBN 0-317-30133-0, 2025316). Bks Demand UMI.

Bavinck, John H. Introduction to Science of Missions. 1960. pap. 5.95 (ISBN 0-87552-124-X). Presby & Reformed.

Baw, Cindy & Brownlow, Paul C. Children of the Bible: Twenty-Six Exciting Stories about Children of the Bible. (Illus.). 1984. 10.95 (ISBN 0-915720-19-1). Brownlow Pub Co.

Bawa Muhaiyaddeen, M. R. The Asma'ul-Husna: The 99 Beautiful Names of Allah. LC 79-19619. (Illus.). 211p. 1979. pap. 4.95 (ISBN 0-914390-13-9). Fellowship Pr PA.

--A Book of God's Love. LC 81-4503. (Illus.). 126p. 1981. 7.95 (ISBN 0-914390-19-8). Fellowship Pr PA.

--The Divine Luminous Wisdom That Dispels the Darkness God-Man Man-God. rev. ed. (Illus.). 288p. 1977. pap. 6.95 (ISBN 0-914390-11-2). Fellowship Pr PA.

--Four Steps to Pure Iman. LC 81-1429. (Illus.). 70p. 1979. pap. 3.95 (ISBN 0-914390-17-1). Fellowship Pr PA.

--God, His Prophets & His Children. LC 78-12891. (Illus.). 1978. pap. 5.95 (ISBN 0-914390-09-0). Fellowship Pr PA.

--The Guidebook to the True Secret of the Heart, Vol. 2. LC 75-44557. (Illus.). 232p. 1976. pap. 5.95 (ISBN 0-914390-08-2). Fellowship Pr PA.

--Songs of God's Grace. LC 73-91016. (Illus.). 154p. 1974. pap. 4.95 (ISBN 0-914390-02-3). Fellowship Pr PA.

--Truth & Light: Brief Explanations. LC 74-76219. (Illus.). 144p. 1974. pap. 3.95 (ISBN 0-914390-04-X). Fellowship Pr PA.

--Wisdom of Man: Selected Discourses. LC 80-20541. (Illus.). 168p. 1980. 7.95 (ISBN 0-914390-16-3). Fellowship Pr PA.

--Zikr, the Remembrance of God. LC 75-27816. 52p. 1975. pap. 2.95 (ISBN 0-914390-05-8). Fellowship Pr PA.

Bawden, C. R. Shamans, Lamas & Evangelicals: The English Missionaries in Siberia. (Illus.). 400p. 1985. 50.00x (ISBN 0-7102-0064-1). Methuen Inc.

Bawden, Nina. St. Francis of Assisi. LC 82-13105. (Illus.). 32p. 1983. PLB 10.88 (ISBN 0-688-01653-7). Lothrop.

Bax, E. Belfort. Rise & Fall of the Anabaptists. 59.95 (ISBN 0-8490-0958-8). Gordon Pr.

Baxendale, Jean. First Bible Lessons: A Course for Two and Three-Year-Olds. rev. ed. LC 81-53021. (Illus.). 144p. 1982. pap. 7.95 (ISBN 0-87239-486-7, 3369). Standard Pub.

--Preschool Bible Activities, 4 vols. (Illus.). 24p. (Orig.). 1982. No. 1. pap. 1.50 (ISBN 0-87239-487-5, 2459); No. 2. pap. 1.50 (ISBN 0-87239-488-3, 2460); No. 3. pap. 1.25 (ISBN 0-87239-489-1, 2461); No. 4. pap. 1.50 (ISBN 0-87239-490-5, 2462). Standard Pub.

Baxter, Batsell B. I Believe Because. 1971. pap. 8.95 (ISBN 0-8010-0548-5). Baker Bk.

--Speaking for the Master. pap. 4.95 (ISBN 0-8010-0588-4). Baker Bk.

Baxter, Batsell B. & Hazelip, Harold. Anchors in Troubled Waters. Abr. ed. LC 82-50267. (Journey Adult Ser.). 126p. 1981. pap. text ed. 4.95 (ISBN 0-8344-0120-7). Sweet.

Baxter, Ern, et al. Secular Humanism. 1986. pap. 2.95 (ISBN 0-8010-0936-7). Baker Bk.

Baxter, J. Sidlow. Awake My Heart. 13.95 (ISBN 0-310-20590-5, 6729). Zondervan.

--Daily Wings. 384p. 1983. pap. 10.95 (ISBN 0-310-20751-7). Zondervan.

--Explore the Book. 36.95 (ISBN 0-310-20620-0, 6729). Zondervan.

--Majesty! The God You Should Know. LC 84-47805. 228p. 1984. 12.95 (ISBN 0-89840-070-8). Heres Life.

--The Master Theme of the Bible, Pt. I: The Doctrine of the Lamb. (Living Studies). 160p. 1985. pap. 5.95 (ISBN 0-8423-4187-0); study guide 2.95 (ISBN 0-8423-4191-9). Tyndale.

Baxter, James H. An Old St. Andrews Music Book. facsimile ed. LC 70-178515. (Medieval Studies Ser.). Repr. of 1931 ed. 34.50 (ISBN 0-404-56525-5). AMS Pr.

Baxter, James H., tr. see Augustine, St. Aurelius.

Baxter, Lucy E. The Cathedral Builders: The Story of a Great Masonic Guild. LC 78-58191. 1978. pap. 50.00 (ISBN 0-89341-354-2). Longwood Pub Group.

Baxter, Richard. The Practical Works of Richard Baxter. (Giant Summit Bks.). 1000p. 1981. pap. 14.95 (ISBN 0-8010-0804-2). Baker Bk.

--The Reformed Pastor. 1979. pap. 4.95 (ISBN 0-85151-191-0). Banner of Truth.

--The Reformed Pastor: A Pattern for Personal Growth & Ministry. rev. ed. Houston, James M., ed. LC 82-18825. (Classics of Faith & Devotion Ser.). 150p. 1983. 10.95 (ISBN 0-88070-003-3). Multnomah.

Baxter, Ronald E. The Charismatic Gift of Tongues. LC 81-17182. 162p. 1982. pap. 7.95 (ISBN 0-8254-2225-6). Kregel.

--Gifts of the Spirit. LC 83-14963. 280p. (Orig.). 1983. pap. 8.95 (ISBN 0-8254-2243-4). Kregel.

Bay, Bill. The Liturgical Guitarist. 360p. 1980. spiral bdg. 9.95 (ISBN 0-89228-055-7). Impact Bks MO.

--Mel Bay's Deluxe Guitar Praise Book. 64p. (Orig.). 1973. pap. 2.95 (ISBN 0-89228-007-7). Impact Bks MO.

--Mel Bay's Guitar Hymnal. 80p. (Orig.). 1972. pap. 2.95 (ISBN 0-89228-009-3). Impact Bks MO.

Bayard, Ralph. Lone-Star Vanguard: The Catholic Re-Occupation of Texas (1838-1848) LC 45-10779. 453p. 1982. lib. bdg. 59.95x (ISBN 0-89370-723-6). Borgo Pr.

Bayard, Tania. Bourges Cathedral: The West Portals. LC 75-23780. (Outstanding Dissertations in the Fine Arts Ser. - Medieval). (Illus.). 1976. lib. bdg. 55.00 (ISBN 0-8240-1977-6). Garland Pub.

Bayat, Mangol. Mysticism & Dissent: Socioreligious Thought in Qajar Iran. LC 82-5498. 320p. 1982. 25.00x (ISBN 0-8156-2260-0). Syracuse U Pr.

Baybak, Michael. Viewpoints. 32p. 1976. pap. 6.00 (ISBN 0-915598-09-4). Church of Scient Info.

Baydun, M., ed. Quran. (Arabic.). medium sized. 25.00x (ISBN 0-86685-134-8). Intl Bk Ctr.

Bayer, Charles H. A Guide to Liberation Theology for Middle-Class Congregations. Lambert, Herbert, ed. LC 86-6111. 176p. (Orig.). 1986. pap. 10.95 (ISBN 0-8272-1233-X). CBP.

Bayer, Edward J., jt. auth. see McCarthy, Donald G.

Bayer, Edward J., jt. ed. see McCarthy, Donald G.

Bayer, Edward J., ed. see Pope John Center Staff.

Bayer, Hans F. Jesus' Predictions of Vindication & Resurrection: The Provenance, Meaning, & Correlation of the Synoptic Predictions. 290p. 1986. pap. 50.00x (ISBN 3-16-145014-0, Pub. by J C B Mohr BRD). Coronet Bks.

Bayizian, Elise A. Mesrob Mashtotz: A Fifth Century Life. (Armenian Church Classics Ser.). (Illus.). 39p. (Orig.). 1984. pap. 4.00 (ISBN 0-934728-14-3). D O A C.

Bayles, Michael D. Morality & Population Policy. LC 79-23965. 208p. 1980. 15.75 (ISBN 0-8173-0032-5); pap. text ed. 7.50 (ISBN 0-8173-0033-3). U of Ala Pr.

--Professional Ethics. 176p. 1981. pap. text ed. write for info. (ISBN 0-534-00998-0). Wadsworth Pub.

Bayley, James R. A Brief Sketch of the Early History of the Catholic Church on the Island of New York. LC 77-359171. (Monograph Ser.: No. 29). 1973. Repr. of 1870 ed. 8.50x (ISBN 0-930060-09-1). US Cath Hist.

Bayley, P. French Pulpit Oratory: Fifteen Ninety-Eight to Sixteen Fifty. LC 79-50175. 1980. 57.50 (ISBN 0-521-22765-8). Cambridge U Pr.

Bayley, Robert G. Deliver Us from the Evil One. 36p. 1987. pap. 2.95 (ISBN 0-934421-09-9). Presby Renewal Pubns.

--The Healing Ministry of the Local Church. 32p. 1983. 1.95 (ISBN 0-934421-03-X). Presby Renewal Pubns.

Baylis, Robert. Ephesians: Living in God's Household. LC 76-43523. (Fisherman Bible Studyguide). 45p. 1976. saddle stitched 2.95 (ISBN 0-87788-223-1). Shaw Pubs.

Bayly, Joseph. The Gospel Blimp & Other Stories. LC 83-70533. 1983. pap. 4.95 (ISBN 0-89191-731-4). Cook.

--Heaven. LC 77-71035. (Illus.). 1977. pap. 2.95 (ISBN 0-89191-070-0). Cook.

--Psalms of My Life. 1969. pap. 0.95 pock. pap. (ISBN 0-8423-5002-0). Tyndale.

Bayly, Lewis. The Practice of Piety: Directing a Christian How to Walk, That He May Please God. LC 75-31081. Repr. of 1718 ed. 34.50 (ISBN 0-404-13500-5). AMS Pr.

Bayne, David C. Conscience, Obligation & the Law: The Moral Binding Power of the Civil Law. LC 66-12757. (Jesuit Studies). 1966. 3.45 (ISBN 0-8294-0001-X). Loyola.

Bayne, Raymond. Mini Messages on Stewardship. 130p. 1984. pap. 3.95 (ISBN 0-8010-0858-1). Baker Bk.

Bayne, Stephen F. The Optional God. LC 80-80876. 134p. 1980. pap. 6.95 (ISBN 0-8192-1268-7). Morehouse.

Baynes, N. H. Constantine the Great & the Christian Church. (Raleigh Lectures on History). 1977. Repr. of 1929 ed. 4.50 (ISBN 0-85672-000-3, Pub. by British Acad). Longwood Pub Group.

Baynes, Norman H. Constantine the Great & the Christian Church. 1974. lib. bdg. 59.95 (ISBN 0-87968-934-X). Gordon Pr.

--Constantine the Great & the Christian Church. LC 74-34500. (World History Ser., No. 48). 1972. Repr. of 1930 ed. lib. bdg. 75.00x (ISBN 0-8383-0131-2). Haskell.

Baynes, Norman H., jt. tr. see Dawes, Elizabeth.

Baynes, Paul. A Commentarie upon the First & Second Chapters of Saint Paul to the Colossians. 396p. Repr. of 1635 ed. text ed. 74.52X (ISBN 0-576-99737-4, Pub. by Gregg Intl Pubs England). Gregg Intl.

--The Diocesans Tryall. 102p. Repr. of 1621 ed. text ed. 33.12x (ISBN 0-576-99736-6, Pub. by Gregg Intl Pubs England). Gregg Intl.

Baynes, Pauline, illus. The Song of the Three Holy Children. LC 86-11952. (Illus.). 32p. 1986. 12.95 (ISBN 0-8050-0134-4). H Holt & Co.

Baynes, Richard W. God's OK-You're OK? Perspective on Christian Worship. LC 79-67440. 96p. (Orig.). 1981. pap. 2.25 (ISBN 0-87239-382-8, 40088). Standard Pub.

Bayrak, Tosun, tr. see Al-Husayn al-Sulami, Ibn.

Bays, Gwendolyn, tr. see Sutra, Buddhist.

Baz, Petros D. Dictionary of Proverbs. (Orig.). pap. 1.85 (ISBN 0-685-19399-3, 108, WL). Citadel Pr.

Bazak, Jacob. Jewish Law & Jewish Life, 8 bks. in 4 vols. Passamaneck, Stephen M., ed. Incl. Bk. 1. Selected Rabbinical Response (ISBN 0-8074-0034-3, 180210); Bks. 2-4. Contracts, Real Estate, Sales & Usury (180211); Bks. 5-6. Credit, Law Enforcement & Taxation (180212); Bks. 7-8. Criminal & Domestic Relations (ISBN 0-8074-0037-8, 180213). 1978. pap. 12.50 complete vol. (ISBN 0-8074-0038-6, 180218); pap. 5.00 ea. UAHC.

Bazargan, Mehdi. The Inevitable Victory. Yousefi, Mohammad, tr. from Persian. 35p. 1979. pap. 1.25x (ISBN 0-941722-03-1). Book-Dist-Ctr.

--Work & Islam. Yousefi, Mohammack, tr. from Persian. 62p. 1979. 4.00 (ISBN 0-941722-04-X). Book-Dist-Ctr.

Bazin, Germain. Mont-Saint-Michel. LC 75-24825. (Fr.). 1978. Repr. of 1933 ed. lib. bdg. 100.00 (ISBN 0-87817-190-8). Hacker.

Bazire, Joyce & Cross, James E., eds. Eleven Old English Rogationtide Homilies. LC 83-107819. (Toronto Old English Ser.: No. 7). pap. 35.80 (2056127). Bks Demand UMI.

Bea, Augustin. Church & Mankind. 6.50 (ISBN 0-8199-0012-5, L38112). Franciscan Herald.

--Word of God & Mankind. 1968. 6.50 (ISBN 0-8199-0149-0, L39003). Franciscan Herald.

Beach, Bert B., jt. auth. see Beach, Walter R.

Beach, Charles. The Not-So-Amazing Mormonism. (Truthway Ser.). 39p. 1981. pap. text ed. 1.25 (ISBN 0-87148-629-6). Pathway Pr.

Beach, Dan, jt. auth. see Moore, Ralph.

Beach, Edward. Dance of the Dialectic: A Dramatic Dialogue Presenting Hegel's Philosophy of Religion. LC 78-63255. pap. text ed. 6.75 (ISBN 0-8191-0615-1). U Pr of Amer.

Beach, George K., ed. see Adams, James L.

Beach, Milo C., jt. auth. see Welch, Stuart C.

Beach, Seth C. Daughters of the Puritans: A Group of Brief Biographies. facs. ed. LC 67-22054. (Essay Index Reprint Ser). 1905. 19.00 (ISBN 0-8369-0180-0). Ayer Co Pubs.

Beach, Waldo & Niebuhr, H. Richard, eds. Christian Ethics-Sources of the Living Tradition. 2nd ed. 550p. 1973. text ed. 25.00 (ISBN 0-394-34414-6). Random.

Beach, Walter R. & Beach, Bert B. Pattern for Progress. Woolsey, Ray, ed. 142p. (Orig.). 1985. pap. text ed. 6.95 (ISBN 0-8280-0308-4). Review & Herald.

Beachey, Duane. Faith in a Nuclear Age. LC 82-11785. (Christian Peace Shelf Ser.). 136p. (Orig.). 1983. pap. 6.95 (ISBN 0-8361-3308-0). Herald Pr.

Beachy, Alvin J. Worship As Celebration of Covenant & Incarnation. LC 68-57497. 1968. pap. 2.00 (ISBN 0-87303-940-8). Faith & Life.

Beacon Bible Commentary Staff. Acts, Vol. V. 6.95 (ISBN 0-8010-0679-1). Baker Bk.

--Corinthians, Vol. VII. 6.95 (ISBN 0-8010-0681-3). Baker Bk.

--Galatians-Philemon, Vol. IX. 13.95 (ISBN 0-8010-0696-1). Baker Bk.

--Genesis-Deuteronomy, Vol. I. 13.95 (ISBN 0-8010-0688-0). Baker Bk.
--Hebrews, James, I-II Peter, Vol. XI. 6.95 (ISBN 0-8010-0677-5). Baker Bk.
--Hebrews-Revelation, Vol. X. 13.95 (ISBN 0-8010-0698-8). Baker Bk.
--Hosea-Malachi, Vol. V. 13.95 (ISBN 0-8010-0692-9). Baker Bk.
--Isaiah-Daniel, Vol. IV. 13.95 (ISBN 0-8010-0691-0). Baker Bk.
--Job-Song of Solomon, Vol. III. 13.95 (ISBN 0-8010-0690-2). Baker Bk.
--John, Vol. IV. 6.95 (ISBN 0-8010-0777-1). Baker Bk.
--John: Acts, Vol. VII. 13.95 (ISBN 0-8010-0694-5). Baker Bk.
--Joshua-Esther, Vol. II. 13.95 (ISBN 0-8010-0689-9). Baker Bk.
--Luke, Vol. III. 6.95 (ISBN 0-8010-0678-3). Baker Bk.
--Mark, Vol. II. 6.95 (ISBN 0-8010-0755-0). Baker Bk.
--Matthew, Vol. I. 6.95 (ISBN 0-8010-0676-7). Baker Bk.
--Matthew-Luke, Vol. VI. 13.95 (ISBN 0-8010-0693-7). Baker Bk.
--Romans, Vol. VI. 8.95 (ISBN 0-8010-0680-5). Baker Bk.
--Romans, II-Corinthians, Vol. VIII. 13.95 (ISBN 0-8010-0695-3). Baker Bk.
--Thessalonians, Vol. X. 6.95 (ISBN 0-8010-0743-7). Baker Bk.

Beacon Hill Staff. Beacon Small-Group Bible Studies, I Corinthians, Living As a Responsible Christian. 60p. 1982. pap. 2.50 (ISBN 0-8341-0755-4). Beacon Hill.

Beagle, Bert. The Revelation. 160p. 1986. 11.95 (ISBN 0-89962-568-1). Todd & Honeywell.

Beal, Samuel. Buddhism in China. lib. bdg. 79.95 (ISBN 0-87968-479-8). Krishna Pr.
--Buddhism in China. 16.75 (ISBN 0-8369-7129-9, 7963). Ayer Co Pubs.
--A Catena of Buddhist Scriptures from the Chinese. 448p. Repr. of 1871 ed. text ed. 37.50x (ISBN 0-89644-188-1, Pub. by Chinese Matl Ctr). Coronet Bks.
--The Fo-sho-hing-tsan-king. (Sacred Books of the East: Vol. 19). 15.00 (ISBN 0-89581-523-0). Asian Human Pr.

Beal, Samuel, tr. see Dhammapada.

Beal, Samuel, tr. see Tsiang, Hiuen.

Bealby, J. T., tr. see Hedin, Sven A.

Beale, David. A Pictorial History of Our English Bible. (Illus.). 79p. (Orig.). 1982. pap. 2.95 (ISBN 0-89084-149-7). Bob Jones Univ Pr.

Beale, David O. In Pursuit of Purity: A History of American Fundamentalism since 1850. 1986. 15.95 (ISBN 0-89084-351-1); pap. 12.95 (ISBN 0-89084-350-3). Bob Jones Univ Pr.
--S. B. C.: House on the Sand? 246p. (Orig.). 1985. pap. 4.95 (ISBN 0-89084-281-7). Bob Jones Univ Pr.

Beale, G. K. The Use of Daniel in Jewish Apocalyptic Literature & in the Relevation of St. John. 364p. (Orig.). 1985. lib. bdg. 26.00 (ISBN 0-8191-4290-5); pap. text ed. 15.25 (ISBN 0-8191-4291-3). U Pr of Amer.

Beales, D. & Best, G., eds. History, Society & the Churches: Essays in Honour of Owen Chadwick. 335p. 1985. 49.50 (ISBN 0-521-25486-8). Cambridge U Pr.

Beall, James L. Laying the Foundation. LC 76-42084. 389p. 1976. pap. 5.95 (ISBN 0-88270-198-3). Bridge Pub.

Beall, James L. & Barber, Marjorie. Your Pastor, Your Shepherd. LC 77-77579. 1977. pap. 4.95 (ISBN 0-88270-216-5). Bridge Pub.

Beall, Otho T. & Shryock, Richard H. Cotton Mather. 1979. 21.00 (ISBN 0-405-10580-0). Ayer Co Pubs.

Beall, Pam & Nipp, Susan. Wee Sing for Christmas. (Illus.). 64p. (Orig.). 1984. pap. 2.25 (ISBN 0-8431-1197-6). Price Stern.

Beall, Pamela C. & Nipp, Susan H. Wee Color Wee Sing for Christmas. (Wee Sing Ser.). (Illus.). 48p. 1986. pap. 1.95 (ISBN 0-8431-1781-8); book & cassette 6.95 (ISBN 0-8431-1782-6). Price Stern.
--Wee Sing Bible Songs. (Illus.). 64p. 1986. pap. 2.25 (ISBN 0-8431-1566-1); book & cassette 8.95 (ISBN 0-8431-1780-X). Price Stern.

Beall, Todd & Banks, William. Old Testament Parsing Guide: Genesis - Esther. (Orig.). 1986. 25.95 (ISBN 0-8024-6315-0). Moody.

Beals, Ann. Christian Science Treatment. 26p. 1979. pap. 2.00 (ISBN 0-930227-06-9). Pasadena Pr.
--Crisis in the Christian Science Church. 145p. 1978. pap. 6.95 (ISBN 0-930227-08-5). Pasadena Pr.

Beals, Art. Beyond Hunger: A Biblical Mandate for Social Responsibility. LC 85-4912. (Critical Concern Ser.). 1985. 11.95 (ISBN 0-88070-098-X). Multnomah.

Beals, Ivan A. Beacon Small-Group Bible Studies: Psalms: Keeping the Heart Aglow. 96p. (Orig.). 1984. pap. 2.50 (ISBN 0-8341-0885-2). Beacon Hill.
--What It Means to Forgive. (Christian Living Ser.). 32p. (Orig.). 1987. pap. write for info. (ISBN 0-8341-1185-3). Beacon Hill.

Beals, Paul A. A People for His Name: A Church-Based Mission Strategy. LC 84-73488. (Illus.). 248p. (Orig.). 1985. pap. text ed. 9.95X (ISBN 0-87808-336-7). William Carey Lib.

Beaman, Edmund A. Swedenborg & the New Age. LC 77-134422. (Communal Societies in America Ser.). Repr. of 1881 ed. 18.00 (ISBN 0-404-08458-3). AMS Pr.

Beard, A. F. Crusade of Brotherhood, a History of the American Missionary Association. 1909. 24.00 (ISBN 0-527-06300-2). Kraus Repr.

Beard, Augustus F. Crusade of Brotherhood, a History of the American Missionary Association. LC 76-161728. Repr. of 1909 ed. 26.50 (ISBN 0-404-00004-5). AMS Pr.

Beard, Charles. Martin Luther & the Reformation in Germany until the Close of the Diet of Worms. LC 83-45638. Date not set. Repr. of 1889 ed. 49.50 (ISBN 0-404-19822-8). AMS Pr.
--The Reformation of the Sixteenth Century in Its Relations to Modern Thought & Knowledge. new ed. LC 77-27168. (Hibbert Lectures: 1883). Repr. of 1927 ed. 47.50 (ISBN 0-404-60404-8). AMS Pr.
--The Reformation of the Sixteenth Century in Its Relation to Modern Thought & Knowledge. LC 80-12915. xxviii, 450p. 1980. Repr. of 1962 ed. lib. bdg. 37.50x (ISBN 0-313-22410-2, BERF). Greenwood.

Beard, Charles, tr. see Renan, Ernest.

Beard, Charles A. Written History As an Act of Faith. 1960. pap. 3.00 (ISBN 0-87404-084-1). Tex Western.

Beard, Ray, jt. auth. see Matthews, Velda.

Beardslee, John W., III, ed. see Turrettin, Thomas.

Beardslee, William A. Human Achievement & Divine Vocation in the Message of Paul. LC 61-4760. (Studies in Biblical Theology: No. 31). 1961. pap. 10.00x (ISBN 0-8401-3031-7). A R Allenson.
--Literary Criticism of the New Testament. Via, Dan O., Jr., ed. LC 77-94817. (Guides to Biblical Scholarship: New Testament Ser.). 96p. (Orig.). 1970. pap. 4.50 (ISBN 0-8006-0185-8, 1-185). Fortress.

Beardslee, William A., ed. see Detweiler, Robert.

Beardslee, William A., ed. see Tannehill, Robert C.

Beardsley, Lou & Spry, Toni. The Fulfilled Woman. LC 74-29206. 1977. 3.25 (ISBN 0-89081-072-9). Harvest Hse.

Beare, F. W. The Gospel According to Matthew: Translation, Commentary, & Notes. LC 81-47837. 575p. 1982. 29.45 (ISBN 0-06-060731-9, HarpR). Har-Row.

Bearman, Jane. The Eight Nights: A Chanukah Counting Book. Syme, Daniel B., ed. LC 78-60781. (Illus.). 1979. pap. 4.50 (ISBN 0-8074-0025-4, 102562). UAHC.

Beasant. Path of Discipleship. 4.25 (ISBN 0-8356-7044-9). Theos Pub Hse.
--The Riddle of Life. 4.50 (ISBN 0-8356-0231-1). Theos Pub Hse.

Beasant & Leadbeater. Talks on the Path of Occultism, Vol. 2: Voice of the Silence. 9.50 (ISBN 0-8356-7021-X). Theos Pub Hse.

Beasley, Mrs. Jim. Missions Studies: Brazil. (Illus.). 32p. (Orig.). 1985. pap. 1.00 (ISBN 0-89114-155-3). Baptist Pub Hse.

Beasley-Murray, G. R. Baptism in the New Testament. 434p. 1973. pap. 8.95 (ISBN 0-8028-1493-X). Eerdmans.
--The Book of Revelation. (New Century Bible Commentay Ser.). 1981. pap. 7.95 (ISBN 0-8028-1885-4). Eerdmans.

Beasley-Murray, George. Matthew. (Bible Study Commentaries Ser.). 122p. 1984. pap. 4.95 (ISBN 0-317-43380-6). Chr Lit.

Beasley-Murray, George R. The Coming of God. 64p. 1983. pap. 3.95 (ISBN 0-85364-350-4, Pub. by Paternoster UK). Attic Pr.
--Jesus & the Kingdom of God. 512p. 1986. 29.95 (ISBN 0-8028-3609-7). Eerdmans.

Beasley-Murray, Stephen. Toward a Metaphysics of the Sacred: Development of the Concept of the Holy. LC 82-8288. viii, 110p. 1982. 7.95x (ISBN 0-86554-038-1, MUP-M08). Mercer Univ Pr.
--Towards a Metaphysics of the Sacred. LC 82-8288. (Special Studies: No. 8). viii, 110p. 1982. pap. 7.95 (ISBN 0-86554-038-1). NABPR.

Beaton, P., tr. see Frankl, Ludwig A.

Beattie, Frank. Jesus on the Cross. (Orig.). 1981. pap. 2.95 (ISBN 0-937172-17-0). JLJ Pubs.

Beattie, Frank A., Jr. Coming down from the Mountain. (Orig.). 1982. pap. 1.95 (ISBN 0-937172-38-3). JLJ Pubs.
--I Went to School with Jesus. (Orig.). 1982. pap. 1.95 (ISBN 0-937172-37-5). JLJ Pubs.

Beattie, James. Elements of Moral Science, 2 vols. Wellek, Rene, ed. LC 75-11195. (British Philosophers & Theologians of the 17th & 18th Centuries: Vol. 2). 1976. Repr. of 1793 ed. Set. lib. bdg. 101.00 (ISBN 0-8240-1751-X); lib. bdg. write for info. Garland Pub.

Beattie, John & Middleton, John. Spirit Mediumship & Society in Africa. LC 70-80849. 310p. 1969. 35.00x (ISBN 0-8419-0009-4, Africana). Holmes & Meier.

Beatty, Bill. Seven Steps Toward God. LC 85-82315. 102p. (Orig.). 1986. pap. 5.95 (ISBN 0-937779-01-6). Greenlawn Pr.

Beatty, Charles. Journal of a Two-Months Tour, with a View to Promoting Religion. LC 72-108459. 1768. 25.00x (ISBN 0-403-00456-X). Scholarly.

Beatty, David. He That Wins Souls Is Wise. 1982. pap. 0.75 (ISBN 0-88144-005-1, CPS-005). Christian Pub.

Beatty, Edward C. William Penn As Social Philosopher. 1972. lib. bdg. 24.50x (ISBN 0-374-90506-1, Octagon). Hippocrene Bks.

Beauchamp, Deanna, jt. auth. see Beauchamp, Gary.

Beauchamp, Gary & Beauchamp, Deanna. Religiously Mixed Marriage. 4.95 (ISBN 0-89137-528-7). Quality Pubns.

Beauchamp, Gary R. Sermons for Today. LC 80-70788. 1981. 11.95 (ISBN 0-89112-403-9, Bibl Res Pr). Abilene Christ U.

Beauchamp, Henry K., jt. auth. see Dubois, J. A.

Beauchamp, Thom & Perlin, Seymour. Ethical Issues in Death & Dying. 1978. pap. write for info. (ISBN 0-13-290114-5). P-H.

Beauchamp, Tom L. & Pinkard, Terry P., eds. Ethics & Public Policy: Introduction to Ethics. (Illus.). 416p. 1983. pap. write for info. (ISBN 0-13-290957-X). P-H.

Beauchamp, Virgil. The Life of Christ in the Paintings by Tissot. 1979. deluxe ed. 49.75 (ISBN 0-930582-29-2). Gloucester Art.

Beaumont, Timothy, ed. Modern Religious Verse. (Pocket Poet Ser.). 1966. pap. 2.95 (ISBN 0-8023-9039-0). Dufour.

Beausobre, Isaac de. Histoire Critique de Manichee et du Manicheisme. Feldman, Burton & Richardson, Robert D., eds. LC 78-60880. (Myth & Romanticism Ser.). 1984. lib. bdg. 160.00 (ISBN 0-8240-3552-6). Garland Pub.

Beausoleil, Beau. Witness. LC 76-39971. (Illus.). 60p. 1976. pap. 6.00 (ISBN 0-915572-23-0). Panjandrum.

Beauval, Henry Basnage De see Basnage De Beauval, Henry.

Beaver, R. Pierce. American Protestant Women in World Mission. LC 80-14366. Orig. Title: All Loves Excelling. Repr. of 1960 ed. 45.10 (ISBN 0-8357-9122-X, 2019317). Bks Demand UMI.

Beaver, R. Pierce, ed. American Missions in Bicentennial Perspective. LC 77-7569. 1977. pap. 10.95 (ISBN 0-87808-153-4). William Carey Lib.

Beaver, Robert P. Christianity & African Education: The Papers of a Conference at the University of Chicago. LC 65-25184. pap. 58.30 (ISBN 0-317-09800-4, 2012940). Bks Demand UMI.

Bebb, Philip N., ed. see Verkamp, Bernard J.

Bebb, Phillip, jt. auth. see Sessions, Kyle.

Bebbington, D. W. The Nonconformist Conscience: Chapel & Politics 1870-1914. 192p. 1982. text ed. 24.95x (ISBN 0-04-942173-5). Allen Unwin.

Bebis, George S., tr. see Trempelas, Panagiotes N.

Becherer, Elsy, tr. see Hans-Ulrich, Rieker.

Bechert, Heinz & Gombrich, Richard, eds. The World of Buddhism: Buddhist Monks & Nuns in Society & Culture. LC 84-8125. 1984. 49.95 (ISBN 0-87196-982-3). Facts on File.

Bechett, Wendy M., tr. John of Ford: Sermons on the Song of Songs I. LC 77-3697. (Cistercian Fathers Ser.: No. 29). 1977. 14.95 (ISBN 0-87907-629-1). Cistercian Pubns.

Bechler, Leroy. The Black Mennonite Church in North America 1886-1986. LC 86-25691. 192p. 1986. 17.95x (ISBN 0-8361-1287-3). Herald Pr.

Bechtel, Faythelma. The Creative Touch, No. 1. 1973. 5.50x (ISBN 0-87813-909-5). Christian Light.
--Creative Touch, No. 2. 1982. 5.50x (ISBN 0-87813-919-2). Christian Light.
--God's Marvelous Gifts. (Christian Day School Ser.). 1982. 13.75x (ISBN 0-87813-920-6). Christian Light.

Bechtel, Paul, ed. The Confessions of St. Augustine. LC 81-11163. 1981. 8.95 (ISBN 0-8024-1618-7). Moody.

Bechtel, Paul M., ed. see Thomas a Kempis.

Beck, L. A. The Story of Confucius & of the Other Great Chinese Mystics, 3 vols. (Illus.). 241p. 1986. Set. 187.75 (ISBN 0-89901-274-4). Found Class Reprints.

Beck, Lewis W., ed. see Seth, Andrew.

Beck, Lewis W., tr. see Kant, Immanuel.

Beck, Lois & Keddie, Nikki, eds. Women in the Muslim World. LC 78-3633. 712p. 1978. 40.00x (ISBN 0-674-95480-7); pap. 12.50 (ISBN 0-674-95481-5). Harvard U Pr.

Beck, Madeline H. & Williamson, Lamar, Jr. Mastering New Testament Facts, 4 bks. Incl. Bk. 1. Introduction & Synoptic Gospels (ISBN 0-8042-0326-1); Bk. 2. The Fourth Gospel & Acts (ISBN 0-8042-0327-X); Bk. 3. Pauline Letters (ISBN 0-8042-0328-8); Bk. 4. The General Letters & Revelation (ISBN 0-8042-0329-6). (Illus., Orig.). 1973. pap. 4.95 ea.; pap. 14.95 set. John Knox.
--Mastering Old Testament Facts, 4 bks. Incl. Bk. 1. Introduction on-Deut. 1979 (ISBN 0-8042-0134-X); Bk. 2. Joshua-Esther. 1979 (ISBN 0-8042-0135-8). (Illus., Orig.). pap. text ed. 4.95 ea.; pap. text ed. 14.95 set. John Knox.
--Mastering Old Testament Facts, Bk. 4: Isaiah-Malachi. (Mastering Old Testament Facts Ser.). (Illus.). 112p. (Orig.). 1981. pap. 4.95 (ISBN 0-8042-0137-4). John Knox.

Beck, Nestor. Doctrine of Faith. 1987. pap. 15.95 (ISBN 0-570-04469-3). Concordia.

Beck, Norman. Scripture Notes A. rev. ed. Sherer, Michael L., ed. 1986. pap. 9.95 (ISBN 0-89536-808-0, 6837). CSS of Ohio.

Beck, Norman A. Mature Christianity: The Recognition & Repudiation of the Anti-Jewish Polemic of the New Testament. LC 83-51047. (Illus.). 328p. 1985. 19.50 (ISBN 0-941664-03-1). Assoc Univ Prs.
--Scripture Notes: Series B (Common Consensus Lectionary) 1984. 7.25 (ISBN 0-89536-687-8, 4863). CSS of Ohio.
--Scripture Notes: Series C (Common Consensus Lectionary) 1985. 9.95 (ISBN 0-89536-755-6, 5861). CSS of Ohio.

Beck, Peggy V. & Walters, Anna L. The Sacred: Ways of Knowledge, Sources of Life. (Illus.). 384p. 1977. 16.00x (ISBN 0-912586-24-9). Navajo Coll Pr.

Beck, R. N. & Orr, J. B. Ethical Choice: A Case Study Approach. LC 70-122282. 1970. pap. text ed. 10.95 (ISBN 0-02-902060-3). Free Pr.

Beck, Robert, ed. see Brightman, Edgar S.

Beck, William F. The Holy Bible in the Language of Today: An American Translation. 1977. 16.95 (ISBN 0-87981-082-3). Holman Bible Pub.

Beck, William F., tr. Christ of the Gospels. rev. ed. LC 59-11068. 1959. pap. 6.95 (ISBN 0-570-03724-7, 12-2626). Concordia.

Becker, Arthur H. The Compassionate Visitor: Resources for Ministering to People Who Are Ill. LC 84-28370. 128p. (Orig.). 1985. pap. 5.95 (ISBN 0-8066-2094-3, 10-1620). Augsburg.
--Ministry with Older Persons: A Guide for Clergy & Congregations. LC 86-1101. 228p. (Orig.). 1986. pap. 12.95 (ISBN 0-8066-2196-6, 10-4444). Augsburg.

Becker, C. History of the Catholic Missions in Northeast India. 1980. 32.00x (ISBN 0-8364-0600-1, Pub. by Mukhopadhyay India). South Asia Bks.

Becker, C. H. Christianity & Islam. Chaytor, H. J., tr. LC 74-608. 120p. 1974. Repr. of 1909 ed. lib. bdg. 18.50 (ISBN 0-8337-4816-5). B Franklin.

Becker, Calvin W. First & Second Timothy & Titus: Letters to Two Young Men. (Teach Yourself the Bible Ser.). 1961. pap. 2.75 (ISBN 0-8024-2646-8). Moody.

Becker, Carl H. Beitrage zur Geschicte Agyptens unter Dem Islam, 2 vols. in 1. LC 77-10579. (Studies in Islamic History: No. 5). 1978. Repr. of 1903 ed. lib. bdg. 25.00x (ISBN 0-87991-454-8). Porcupine Pr.

Becker, Carl L. Heavenly City of the Eighteenth-Century Philosophers. (Storrs Lectures Ser.). 1932. pap. 6.95x (ISBN 0-300-00017-0, Y5). Yale U Pr.

Becker, Ernest. The Denial of Death. LC 73-1860. 1973. 19.95 (ISBN 0-02-902150-2); pap. 8.95 (ISBN 0-02-902380-7). Free Pr.
--Escape from Evil. LC 75-12059. 1976. pap. 8.95 (ISBN 0-02-902450-1). Free Pr.

Becker, J. Formation of the Old Testament. 1.25 (ISBN 0-8199-0513-5). Franciscan Herald.

Becker, Joachim. Messianic Expectation in the Old Testament. Green, David E., tr. LC 79-8891. pap. 24.00 (2027875). Bks Demand UMI.

Becker, Joyce. Bible Crafts. LC 82-80820. (Illus.). 128p. 1982. 12.95 (ISBN 0-8234-0467-6); pap. 6.95 (ISBN 0-8234-0469-2). Holiday.

Becker, Judy. The Missing Message of Revelation: Natural Catastrophes Ordained by God. Campbell, Evelyn, ed. (Illus.). 374p. (Orig.). 1986. pap. 9.95 (ISBN 0-9617493-0-X). Landmark Pr GA.

Becker, Lawrence C. On Justifying Moral Judgements. (International Library of Philosophy & Scientific Method). 199p. 1973. text ed. 19.95x (ISBN 0-7100-7524-3, Pub. by Routledge UK). Humanities.

Becker, Martin J. A History of Catholic Life in the Diocese of Albany, 1609-1864. LC 77-359170. (Monograph: No. 31). (Illus.). 1975. 15.00x (ISBN 0-930060-11-3). US Cath Hist.

Becker, Ralph. Lent, Good Friday & Easter. pap. 0.50 (ISBN 0-685-41825-1). Reiner.

--The Truth about Christmas. pap. 0.50 (ISBN 0-685-41826-X). Reiner.

Becker, Siegbert W. Foolishness of God. 1982. 8.95 (ISBN 0-8100-0155-1, 15N0383). Northwest Pub.

--Revelation. 1985. 16.95 (ISBN 0-8100-0190-X, 15N0410). Northwest Pub.

--The Scriptures: Inspired of God. 1971. pap. 2.25 (ISBN 0-8100-0027-X, 12-0340). Northwest Pub.

Becker, Verne, et al. Questions? Answers! (Campus Life Ser.). 158p. 1986. pap. 5.95 (ISBN 0-8423-5117-5). Tyndale.

Beckerlegge, Oliver A., ed. see Wesley, John.

Beckett, L. C. Movement & Emptiness. 1969. pap. 1.45 (ISBN 0-8356-0414-4, Quest). Theos Pub Hse.

Beckett, Wendy M., tr. from Latin. John of Ford: Sermons on the Final Verses of the Song of Songs, IV. (Cistercian Fathers Ser.: No. 44). 1983. 24.95 (ISBN 0-87907-644-5). Cistercian Pubns.

--John of Ford: Sermons on the Final Verses of the Song of Songs, V (Sermons 62-82) (Cistercian Fathers Ser.: No. 45). 1983. 24.95 (ISBN 0-87907-645-3). Cistercian Pubns.

Beckett, Wendy M., tr. see John Of Ford.

Beckett, Wendy M., tr. see John of Ford.

Beckford, James A. Cult Controversies: The Societal Response to the New Religious Movements. 336p. 1985. 39.95 (ISBN 0-422-79630-1, 9592, Pub. by Tavistock England); pap. 13.95 (ISBN 0-422-79640-9, 9593, Pub. by Tavistock England). Methuen Inc.

--Religious Organization: A Trend Report & Bibliography Prepared for the International Sociological Association Under the Auspices of the International Committee for Social Science Documentation. (Current Sociology La Sociologie Contemporaine: Vol. 21, No. 2). 1973. pap. 11.60x (ISBN 90-2797-851-4). Mouton.

Beckford, William. Recollections of an Excursion. 1983. 60.00x (ISBN 0-900000-78-3, Pub. by Centaur Bks). State Mutual Bk.

--Recollections of an Excursion to the Monasteries of Alcobaca & Batalha. 27.50 (ISBN 0-87556-541-7). Saifer.

Beckham, Stephen D., jt. ed. see Munnick, Harriet D.

Beckley, Robert E., jt. auth. see Chalfant, H. Paul.

Beckley, Robert E., jt. auth. see Chalfant, Paul H.

Beckley, Timothy G. & Carta, Maria. Kahuna: Authentic Chants, Prayers & Rituals of the Legendary Hawaiians. (Illus.). 200p. Date not set. 17.95x (ISBN 0-938294-52-0); pap. 9.95x (ISBN 0-938294-53-9). Global Comm.

Beckman, Beverly. Senses in God's World. 24p. 1986. 5.95 (ISBN 0-570-04150-3). Concordia.

--Shapes in God's World. LC 56-1462. 1984. 5.95 (ISBN 0-570-04094-9). Concordia.

--Sizes in God's World. 1984. 5.95 (ISBN 0-570-04095-7, 56-1463). Concordia.

Beckman, Stephan D., jt. ed. see Munnick, Harriet D.

Beckmann, Beverly. Emotions in God's World. 24p. 1986. 5.95 (ISBN 0-570-04149-X). Concordia.

--From. (Illus.). 1980. pap. 3.95 (ISBN 0-570-03489-2, 56-1343). Concordia.

--Numbers in God's World. 1983. 5.95 (ISBN 0-570-04083-3, 56-1438). Concordia.

--Seasons in God's World. (In God's World Ser.). (Illus.). 24p. 1985. 5.95 (ISBN 0-570-04127-9, 56-1538). Concordia.

--Time in God's World. (In God's World Ser.). (Illus.). 24p. 1985. 5.95 (ISBN 0-570-04128-7, 56-1539). Concordia.

Beckstrom, Kristen, jt. auth. see Wirt, Sherwood.

Beckwith, Burnham P. The Decline of U. S. Religious Faith: 1912 - 1984 & the Effect of Education & Intelligence on Such Faith. 1985. 9.00x (ISBN 0-9603262-4-3). Beckwith.

Beckwith, Francis. Bahai. 64p. 1985. saddle stitched 2.95 (ISBN 0-87123-848-9). Bethany Hse.

Beckwith, John. Early Christian & Byzantine Art. (Pelican History of Art Ser.). 1980. pap. 18.95 (ISBN 0-14-056133-1, Pelican). Penguin.

Beckwith, Martha W. Hawaiian Mythology. LC 70-97998. 1977. pap. 10.95 (ISBN 0-8248-0514-3). UH Pr.

--Mandan-Hidatsa Myths & Ceremonies. LC 38-19412. (American Folklore Society Memoirs). Repr. of 1938 ed. 29.00 (ISBN 0-527-01084-7). Kraus Repr.

--Myths & Hunting Stories of the Mandan & Hidatsa Sioux. LC 76-43665. (Vassar College Folklore Foundation: Publication No. 10). 1977. Repr. of 1930 ed. 16.00 (ISBN 0-404-15498-0). AMS Pr.

Beckwith, Martha W., ed. see Kepelino.

Beckwith, Mary, ed. see Greig, Doris W.

Beckwith, Mary, ed. see Maddux, Bob.

Beckwith, Merle R. A New List of Proverbs. LC 79-92430. cancelled (ISBN 0-8022-2361-3). Philos Lib.

Beckwith, Paul, et al, eds. Hymns II. LC 76-47503. 1976. text ed. 12.95 (ISBN 0-87784-898-X); pap. text ed. 7.95 (ISBN 0-87784-783-5); pap. text ed. 10.95 spiral text (ISBN 0-87784-750-9). Inter-Varsity.

Beckwith, Roger. The Old Testament Canon of the New Testament Church. 536p. 1986. 35.00 (ISBN 0-8028-3617-8). Eerdmans.

Beckwith, Roger T. & Scott, Wilfrid. This Is the Day: The Biblical Doctrine of the Christian Sunday in it's Jewish & Early Church Setting. 192p. 1978. 9.50 (ISBN 0-551-05568-5). Attic Pr.

Becon, Thomas. The Catechism of Thomas Becon. Repr. of 1884 ed. 55.00 (ISBN 0-384-03715-1). Johnson Repr.

--The Demaundes of Holy Scripture, with Answers to the Same. LC 79-84087. (English Experience Ser.: No.907). 116p. 1979. Repr. of 1577 ed. lib. bdg. 9.00 (ISBN 90-221-0907-0). Walter J Johnson.

--The Early Works of Thomas Becon, Chaplain to Archbishop Cranmer. Repr. of 1843 ed. 41.00 (ISBN 0-384-03725-9). Johnson Repr.

--The Physyke of the Soule. LC 74-28831. (English Experience Ser.: No. 713). 1975. Repr. of 1549 ed. 3.50 (ISBN 90-221-0713-2). Walter J Johnson.

--Prayers & Others Pieces of Thomas Becon, Chaplain to Archbishop Cranmer. Repr. of 1844 ed. 55.00 (ISBN 0-384-03730-5). Johnson Repr.

--The Principles of Christian Religion. LC 76-57355. (English Experience Ser.: No. 774). 1977. Repr. of 1552 ed. lib. bdg. 14.00 (ISBN 90-221-0774-4). Walter J Johnson.

Becton, Cleveland M., jt. auth. see Urshan, Nathaniel A.

Becton, Randy. The Beauty of God's Whisper. 1980. pap. 4.75 (ISBN 0-89137-310-1). Quality Pubns.

--The Gift of Life: A Message of Hope for the Seriously Ill. (Illus.). 1978. pap. 4.75 (ISBN 0-89137-309-8). Quality Pubns.

Beda. The History of the Church of Englande. (English Experience Ser.: No. 234). 382p. Repr. of 1565 ed. 55.00 (ISBN 90-221-0234-3). Walter J Johnson.

Bedard, Paul, tr. see Aubry, Joseph.

Bede. Historical Works, 2 Vols. (Loeb Classical Library: No. 246, 248). 13.95x ea. Vol. 1 (ISBN 0-674-99271-7). Vol. 2 (ISBN 0-674-99273-3). Harvard U Pr.

Bede, Elbert. The Landmarks of Freemasonry. 56p. 1980. pap. text ed. 3.00 (ISBN 0-88053-020-0). Macoy Pub.

Bedell, George C., et al. Religion in America. 2nd ed. LC 81-8239. 1982. text ed. write for info. (ISBN 0-02-307810-3). Macmillan.

Bedell, Kenneth. The Role of Computers in Religious Education. 144p. 1986. pap. 7.95 (ISBN 0-687-36540-6). Abingdon.

--Using Personal Computers in the Church. 112p. 1982. pap. 5.95 (ISBN 0-8170-0948-5). Judson.

Bedell, Kenneth & Rossman, Parker. Computers: New Opportunities for Personalized Ministry. 128p. 1984. pap. 4.95 (ISBN 0-8170-1039-4). Judson.

Bedell, William. True Relation of the Life & Death of the Right Reverend Father in God William Bedell, Lord Bishop of Kilmore in Ireland. Jones, Thomas W., ed. Repr. of 1872 ed. 27.00 (ISBN 0-384-03740-2). Johnson Repr.

Bede the Venerable. Ecclesiastical History of England. Giles, John A., ed. LC 78-136367. (Bohn's Antiquarian Lib.). (Illus.). Repr. of 1849 ed. 42.50 (ISBN 0-404-50001-3). AMS Pr.

--Ecclesiastical History of the English People. Colgrave, Bertram & Minors, R. A., eds. (Oxford Medieval Texts Ser). 1969. 87.00x (ISBN 0-19-822202-5). Oxford U Pr.

--The Ecclesiastical History of the English People. Hereford, Philip, ed. Stapleton, Thomas, tr. from Latin. 1983. Repr. of 1935 ed. lib. bdg. 45.00 (ISBN 0-89760-062-2). Telegraph Bks.

--Ecclesiastical History of the English Nation & Other Writings. Stevens, John, tr. 1978. Repr. of 1910 ed. 12.95x (ISBN 0-460-00479-4, Evman). Biblio Dist.

--History of the English Church & People. Sherley-Price, tr. (Classics Ser.). (Orig.). 1955. pap. 4.95 (ISBN 0-14-044042-9). Penguin.

--History of the English Church & People. Sherley-Price, Leo, tr. 400p. 1985. 16.95 (ISBN 0-88029-042-0, Pub. by Dorset Pr). Hippocrene Bks.

Bedford, Arthur. The Evil & Danger of Stage Plays. LC 72-170479. (The English Stage Ser.: Vol. 43). lib. bdg. 61.00 (ISBN 0-8240-0626-7). Garland Pub.

--Serious Reflections on the Scandalous Abuse & Effects of the Stage. Bd. with A Second Advertisement Concerning the Profaneness of the Play-House; A Sermon Preached in the Parish-Church of St. Butolph's Algate, in the City of London: Occasioned by the Erecting of a Play-House in the Neighborhood. (The English Stage Ser.: Vol. 41). 1974. lib. bdg. 61.00 (ISBN 0-8240-0624-0). Garland Pub.

Bedford, Stewart. Prayer Power & Stress Management. pap. 6.95 (ISBN 0-935930-05-1). A & S Pr.

Bedford, William K. The Order or the Hospital of St. John of Jerusalem. LC 76-29831. Repr. of 1902 ed. 31.25 (ISBN 0-404-15412-3). AMS Pr.

Bedfrod, Arthur. A Serious Remonstrance in Behalf of the Christian Religion Against English Play-Houses. LC 79-170478. (The English Stage Ser.: Vol. 42). lib. bdg. 61.00 (ISBN 0-8240-0625-9). Garland Pub.

Bedingfield, T., ed. see Cardano, Girolamo.

Bedini, Annabel, tr. see Sordi, Marta.

Bednarowski, Mary F. American Religion: A Cultural Perspective. LC 83-22895. (Illus.). 182p. 1984. pap. text ed. 17.00 (ISBN 0-13-029059-9). P-H.

Bedoian, Adriana P. de see Engstrom, Ted W.

Bedouelle, Guy. Saint Dominic: The Grace of the Word. (Illus.). 290p. (Orig.). 1987. pap. 11.95 (ISBN 0-89870-140-6). Ignatius Pr.

Bedwell, B. L. Sermons for Funeral Occasions. 1960. pap. 2.00 (ISBN 0-88027-029-2). Firm Foun Pub.

Beebe, Ralph K. A Garden of the Lord. LC 68-56609. (Illus.). 288p. 1968. 3.95 (ISBN 0-913342-13-0). Barclay Pr.

Beecher, Catherine E. Letters to the People on Health & Happiness. (The Works of Catherine E. Beecher Ser.). vi, 222p. Repr. of 1855 ed. lib. bdg. 29.00 (ISBN 0-932051-03-0, Pub by Am Repr Serv). Am Biog Serv.

Beecher, Edward. The Papal Conspiracy Exposed & Protestantism Defended. LC 76-46066. (Anti-Movements in America). (Illus.). 1977. Repr. of 1885 ed. lib. bdg. 32.00x (ISBN 0-405-09940-1). Ayer Co Pubs.

Beecher, Henry W. Yale Lectures on Preaching. 1976. Repr. of 1872 ed. 39.00x (ISBN 0-403-06546-1, Regency). Scholarly.

--Yale Lectures on Preaching. (The Works of Henry Ward Beecher Ser.). vii, 359p. Repr. of 1873 ed. lib. bdg. 29.00 (ISBN 0-932051-02-2, Pub. by Am Repr Serv). Am Biog Serv.

Beecher, Lyman. Autobiography of Lyman Beecher, 2 vols. Cross, Barbara M., ed. LC 61-6348. (The John Harvard Library). (Illus.). 896p. 1961. Set. 55.00x (ISBN 0-674-05400-8). Harvard U Pr.

--Lyman Beecher & the Reform of Society: Four Sermons, 1804-1828. LC 71-38437. (Religion in America Series Two). 214p. 1972. Repr. of 1972 ed. 19.00 (ISBN 0-405-04058-X). Ayer Co Pubs.

--A Pleas for the West. Grob, Gerald, ed. LC 76-46067. (Anti-Movements in America). 1977. lib. bdg. 17.00x (ISBN 0-405-09941-X). Ayer Co Pubs.

Beecher, Marguerite, jt. auth. see Beecher, Willard.

Beecher, Maureen U. & Anderson, Lavina F., eds. Sisters in Spirit: Mormon Women in Historical & Cultural Perspective. 350p. 1987. 21.95 (ISBN 0-252-01411-1). U of Ill Pr.

Beecher, Maureen U., jt. ed. see Bitton, Davis.

Beecher, Willard & Beecher, Marguerite. The Sin of Obedience. 88p. (Orig.). 1982. pap. 4.75 (ISBN 0-942350-00-6). Beecher Found.

Beechick, Allen. The Pre-Tribulation Rapture. LC 79-53291. 256p. (Orig.). 1980. pap. 4.95 (ISBN 0-89636-040-7). Accent Bks.

Beechick, Ruth. Teaching Kindergarteners. LC 79-53295. (Accent Teacher Training Ser.). 192p. 1980. pap. 4.95 (ISBN 0-89636-038-5). Accent Bks.

--Teaching Preschoolers: It's Not Exactly Easy but Here Is How to Do It. LC 78-73252. (Accent Teacher Training Ser.). 1979. pap. 4.95 (ISBN 0-89636-019-9). Accent Bks.

--Teaching Primaries. LC 80-66723. (Accent Teacher Training Ser.). 128p. (Orig.). 1980. pap. 4.95 (ISBN 0-89636-054-7). Accent Bks.

Beeching, Jack. Open Path: Christian Missionaries, 1515-1914. LC 80-21270. (Illus.). 350p. 1982. 19.95 (ISBN 0-915520-37-0); pap. 10.95 (ISBN 0-915520-53-2). Ross-Erikson.

Beeck, Frans J. van see Van Beeck, Frans J.

Beegle, Dewey M. God's Word into English. LC 79-84556. 1965. pap. 8.95 (ISBN 0-933462-02-6). Pryor Pettengill.

--Moses, the Servant of Yahweh. LC 79-84558. 368p. 1972. pap. text ed. 8.95 (ISBN 0-933462-03-4). Pryor Pettengill.

--Prophecy & Prediction. 274p. 1978. write for info. (ISBN 0-933462-00-X); pap. text ed. 8.95 (ISBN 0-933462-01-8). Pryor Pettengill.

--Scripture, Tradition & Infallibility. LC 79-84557. Orig. Title: The Inspiration of Scripture. 332p. pap. text ed. 8.95 (ISBN 0-933462-04-2). Pryor Pettengill.

Beegle, Shirley. Bible Quizzes. 1985. pap. 0.69 pocket size (ISBN 0-87239-823-4, 2813). Standard Pub.

--Easy Bible Quizzes for All Ages. rev. ed. 1983. pap. 1.95 (ISBN 0-87239-657-6, 3137). Standard Pub.

--Favorite Bible Verses. (Double Trouble Puzzles Ser.). (Illus.). 48p. 1987. pap. 2.50 (ISBN 0-87403-325-X, 2765). Standard Pub.

--Friends of God. (Double Trouble Puzzles Ser.). (Illus.). 48p. 1987. pap. 2.50 (ISBN 0-87403-328-4, 2768). Standard Pub.

--Friends of Jesus. (Double Trouble Puzzles Ser.). (Illus.). 48p. 1987. pap. 2.50 (ISBN 0-87403-327-6, 2767). Standard Pub.

--Jesus Quizzes. 1985. pap. 0.69 (ISBN 0-87239-824-2, 2814). Standard Pub.

--Life of Jesus. (Double Trouble Puzzles Ser.). (Illus.). 48p. 1987. pap. 2.50 (ISBN 0-87403-326-8, 2766). Standard Pub.

--Through the Bible Quizzes for Children. 64p. (Orig.). 1974. pap. 2.50 (ISBN 0-87239-324-0, 3249). Standard Pub.

Beegle, Shirley, ed. Creative Craft Ideas for All Ages. (Illus., Orig.). 1966. pap. 6.95 (ISBN 0-87239-321-6, 2795). Standard Pub.

Beek, W. E. van see Van Baal, T. & Van Beek, W. E.

Beek, Wil van. Hazrat Inayat Khan: Master of Life-Modern Sufi Mystic. 1983. 12.95 (ISBN 0-533-05453-2). Vantage.

Beemer, Theo., jt. auth. see Bockle, Franz.

Beer, Francis De see De Beer, Francis.

Beers. Choosing God's Way to See & Share. 1983. 12.95 (ISBN 0-88207-819-4). Victor Bks.

Beers, Gilbert. Victor Handbook of Bible Knowledge. Popular ed. LC 81-50695. 640p. 1981. 29.95 (ISBN 0-88207-811-9); pap. 21.95 (ISBN 0-88207-808-9). Victor Bks.

Beers, Henry A. Milton's Tercentenary. LC 73-39421. Repr. of 1910 ed. 7.50 (ISBN 0-404-00725-2). AMS Pr.

--Milton's Tercentenary. LC 73-9747. 1910. lib. bdg. 8.50 (ISBN 0-8414-3168-X). Folcroft.

Beers, Richard G. Walk the Distant Hills: The Story of Longri Ao. (Bold Believers Ser.). 1969. pap. 0.95 (ISBN 0-377-84171-4). Friend Pr.

Beers, Ronald, jt. auth. see Beers, V. Gilbert.

Beers, Ronald A., jt. auth. see Beers, V. Gilbert.

Beers, V. Gilbert. Along Thimblelane Trails. LC 81-14197. (Muffin Family Ser.). 96p. 1981. 11.95 (ISBN 0-8024-0298-4). Moody.

--Captain Maxi's Secret Island. (Muffin Family Ser.: No. 11). 96p. 1983. 11.95 (ISBN 0-8024-9573-7). Moody.

--Little Talks about God & You. 224p. (Orig.). 1986. pap. 7.95 (ISBN 0-89081-519-4). Harvest Hse.

--My Picture Bible to See & to Share. 1982. text ed. 11.95 (ISBN 0-88207-818-6, Sonflower Bks). SP Pubns.

--My Picture Bible to See & to Share. 1982. text ed. 12.95 (ISBN 0-88207-818-6). Victor Bks.

Beers, V. Gilbert & Beers, Ronald. The Victor Family Story Bible. 640p. 1985. 19.95 (ISBN 0-88207-822-4). Victor Bks.

Beers, V. Gilbert & Beers, Ronald A. Bible Stories to Live By. LC 82-84616. (Illus.). 192p. 1983. 12.95 (ISBN 0-89840-044-9). Heres Life.

--Walking with Jesus. (Illus.). 192p. 1984. 14.95 (ISBN 0-89840-069-4). Heres Life.

Beery, Angilee. So What Is Peace. 1971. pap. 1.50 (ISBN 0-87178-934-5). Brethren.

Beesley, Ronald P. The Creative Ethers. 1978. pap. 3.95 (ISBN 0-87516-268-1). De Vorss.

--Yoga of the Inward Path. 1978. pap. 4.95 (ISBN 0-87516-269-X). De Vorss.

Beeson, Trevor & Pearce, Jenny, eds. A Vision of Hope: The Churches & Change in Latin America. LC 83-48927. 288p. 1984. pap. 6.95 (ISBN 0-8006-1758-4, 1-1758). Fortress.

Beevers, John. St. Joan of Arc. 1974. pap. 5.00 (ISBN 0-89555-043-1). TAN Bks Pubs.

--Saint Therese, the Little Flower: The Making of a Saint. LC 73-80147. (Orig.). 1976. pap. 3.50 (ISBN 0-89555-035-0). TAN Bks Pubs.

Beg, Anwer, ed. see Azami, Mustafa.

Beg, Anwer, ed. see Bucaille, Maurice.

Beg, M. A. S. Fine Arts in Islamic Civilisation. 7.95 (ISBN 0-686-83581-6). Kazi Pubns.

Begay, Shirley M. & Clinton-Tullie, Verna. Kinaalada: A Navajo Puberty Ceremony. rev. ed. LC 83-61661. (Illus.). 171p. 1983. 15.00x (ISBN 0-936008-11-3); pap. 11.00x. Navajo Curr.

Begbie, Harold. Painted Windows. LC 77-108696. (Essay & General Literature Index Reprint Ser). 1970. Repr. of 1922 ed. 23.50x (ISBN 0-8046-0918-7, Pub. by Kennikat). Assoc Faculty Pr.

Begg, Ean. The Cult of the Black Virgin. (Illus.). 288p. (Orig.). 1985. pap. 11.95 (ISBN 1-85063-022-4, Ark Paperbks). Methuen Inc.

Beggiani, Seely J. Early Syriac Theology: With Special Reference to the Maronite Tradition. LC 83-3658. 172p. (Orig.). 1983. lib. bdg. 26.00 (ISBN 0-8191-3152-0); pap. text ed. 10.75 (ISBN 0-8191-3153-9). U Pr of Amer.

Beggs, David W. America's Schools & Churches. LC 65-12279. pap. 60.30 (ISBN 0-317-28577-7, 2055190). Bks Demand UMI.

Beguin, Albert. Leon Bloy: A Study in Impatience. Riley, Edith M., tr. from Fr. 247p. 1982. Repr. of 1947 ed. lib. bdg. 45.00 (ISBN 0-89984-081-7). Century Bookbindery.

Behem, Jacob. Three Principles of the Divine Essence. 1978. Repr. of 1909 ed. 12.00 (ISBN 0-911662-65-0). Yoga.

Behlim, S. A. Quran Made Easy (Yassar nal Quran) Date not set. pap. 7.50 (ISBN 0-317-43010-6). Kazi Pubns.

Behm, Douglas R. An Advent Covenant Wreath. 16p. 1981. pap. text ed. 2.65 (ISBN 0-89536-482-4, 0102). CSS of Ohio.

--The New Covenant's Power. 1983. 3.50 (ISBN 0-89536-600-2, 1412). CSS of Ohio.

Behm, Ronald, jt. auth. see Salley, Christopher.

Behn, Wolfgang, jt. ed. see Pearson, J. D.

Behnke, Daniel J. Fifty Worship Talks for Children. 1982. pap. 5.56 (ISBN 0-570-03850-2, 12-2805). Concordia.

Behnke, Donna A. Religious Issues in Nineteenth Century Feminism. LC 80-52544. 300p. 1982. 22.50x (ISBN 0-87875-203-X). Whitston Pub.

Behnke, John. Ten Plus One Bible Stories from Creation to Samson, Retold in Everyday Language for Today's Children. LC 83-82022. (Orig.). 1984. pap. 2.95 (ISBN 0-8091-6552-X). Paulist Pr.

Behrend, Genevieve. Your Invisible Power. 1921. pap. 2.75 (ISBN 0-87516-004-2). De Vorss.

Behrends, Rainer, et al. Biblia Pauperum: Apocalypsis. (Illus., LC 77-088869). 1978. boxed 500.00 (ISBN 0-87817-239-4). Hacker.

Behrendt, Leo. Ethical Teaching of Hugo of Trimberg. LC 77-140042. (Catholic University of America. Studies in German: No. 1). Repr. of 1926 ed. 18.00 (ISBN 0-404-50221-0). AMS Pr.

Behrens, June. Hanukkah. LC 82-17890. (Ethnic & Traditional Holidays Ser.). (Illus.). 32p. 1983. PLB 10.60 (ISBN 0-516-02386-1); pap. 2.95 (ISBN 0-516-42386-X). Childrens.

Behrman, Lucy. Muslim Brotherhoods & Politics in Senegal. LC 70-95918. 1970. 15.00x (ISBN 0-674-59490-8). Harvard U Pr.

Behzadnia, A., tr. see Shariati, Ali.

Beichner, Paul E. Petri Riage Biblia Versificato: Petri Rigue Biblia Versificato, a Verse Commentary on the Bible, 2 vols. (Mediaeval Studies Ser.: No. 19). 1965. 50.00 set (ISBN 0-268-00016-6). U of Notre Dame Pr.

Beidelman, T. O. Colonial Evangelism: A Socio-Historical Study of an East African Mission at the Grassroots. LC 81-47771. (Midland Bks. Ser.: No. 278). (Illus.). 296p. 1982. 29.95x (ISBN 0-253-31386-4); pap. 12.50x (ISBN 0-253-20278-7). Ind U Pr.

--W. Robertson Smith & the Sociological Study of Religion. LC 73-87311. 1974. pap. 1.95x (ISBN 0-226-04160-3, P618, Phoen). U of Chicago Pr.

Beiderwieden, George. Heaven. 1957. 1.50 (ISBN 0-570-03680-1, 74-1008). Concordia.

Beidler, W. Vision of Self in Early Vedanta. 1975. 12.50 (ISBN 0-8426-0990-3). Orient Bk Dist.

Beier, Lucinda. Mormans, Jehovah's Witnesses & Christian Scientists. 1985. 13.00x (ISBN 0-7062-3880-X, Pub. by Ward Lock Educ Co Ltd). State Mutual Bk.

Beier, Ulli. The Origin of Life & Death. (African Writers Ser.). 1966. pap. text ed. 4.50x (ISBN 0-435-90023-4). Heinemann Ed.

Beier, Ulli, jt. auth. see Gbadamosi, Bakare.

Beierle, Herbert L. Dualism. 1979. 10.00 (ISBN 0-940480-06-9). U of Healing.

--How Much of God I Express Is How Much I Profess. 1982. 1.00 (ISBN 0-686-35834-1). U of Healing.

--How to Give a Healing Treatment. 1979. 1.00 (ISBN 0-940480-07-7). U of Healing.

--Illumination: Handbook of Ascended Masters. 1978. 20.00 (ISBN 0-940480-02-6). U of Healing.

--Proclaim Your God. 1.00 (ISBN 0-940480-09-3). U of Healing.

--Quiet Healing Zone. 1980. 10.00 (ISBN 0-940480-10-7). U of Healing.

--School for Masters. 1979. 1.00 (ISBN 0-940480-11-5). U of Healing.

--Song of the Spirit. 1978. 20.00 (ISBN 0-940480-01-8). U of Healing.

--Why I Can Say I Am God. 1978. 1.00 (ISBN 0-940480-04-2). U of Healing.

Beierle, Herbert L., ed. Ministers Manual. 1978. 10.00 (ISBN 0-940480-03-4). U of Healing.

--Minister's Manual. 2nd ed. 1985. 10.00 (ISBN 0-940480-20-4). U of Healing.

Beihl, Bessie. Blessed Are Your Eyes. pap. 1.00 (ISBN 0-87516-131-6). De Vorss.

--Peace My Heart. pap. 1.00 (ISBN 0-87516-133-2). De Vorss.

Beilenson, John, ed. Prayers for Inner Strength. (Illus.). 64p. 1986. 5.95 (ISBN 0-88088-468-1, 884681). Peter Pauper.

Beilenson, Nick, ed. Gift of Friendship. LC 86-63857. (Illus.). 64p. 1987. 5.95 (ISBN 0-88088-216-6). Peter Pauper.

--Table Graces. LC 86-61119. (Illus.). 63p. 1986. 5.95 (ISBN 0-88088-509-2). Peter Pauper.

Beinart, Haim. Trujillo: A Jewish Community in Extremadura on the Eve of Expulsion from Spain. (Hispania Judaica Ser.: No. 2). 372p. 1980. text ed. 22.50x (ISBN 965-223-349-8, Pub. by Magnes Pr Israel). Humanities.

Beiner, Ronald, ed. see Arendt, Hannah.

Beiner, Stan J. Sedra Scenes: Skits for Every Torah Portion. LC 82-71282. 225p. (Orig.). 1982. pap. text ed. 8.75 (ISBN 0-86705-007-1). AIRE.

Beisner, E. Calvin. God in Three Persons. 180p. 1984. pap. 5.95 (ISBN 0-8423-1073-8); 2.95 (ISBN 0-8423-1074-6). Tyndale.

Beit-Hallahmi, Benjamin. Psychoanalysis & Religion. 1978. lib. bdg. 27.50 (ISBN 0-8482-7374-5). Norwood Edns.

Beit-Hallahmi, Benjamin, jt. auth. see Argyle, Michael.

Beitz, Charles R., et al, eds. International Ethics: A Philosophy & Public Affairs Reader. LC 84-42938. 352p. 1985. text ed. 24.50 (ISBN 0-691-07683-9); pap. 8.95 (ISBN 0-691-02234-8). Princeton U Pr.

Beitzel, Barry J. The Moody Atlas of Bible Lands. 1985. text ed. 31.95 (ISBN 0-8024-0438-3). Moody.

Bek, Lilla & Pullar, Philippa. The Seven Levels of Healing. 160p. 1987. pap. 11.95 (ISBN 0-7126-9473-0, Pub. by Century Hutchinson). David & Charles.

Beker, J. Christiaan. Paul's Apocalyptic Gospel: The Coming Triumph of God. LC 82-8670. 128p. (Orig.). 1982. pap. 7.95 (ISBN 0-8006-1649-9, 1-1649). Fortress.

Beker, J. Christian. Paul the Apostle: The Triumph of God in Life & Thought. LC 79-8904. 468p. 1980. pap. 14.95 (ISBN 0-8006-1811-4). Fortress.

Bekkari, Muhammad, tr. see Badawi, Gamal.

Belaief, Lynne. Toward a Whiteheadian Ethics. LC 84-15248. 208p. (Orig.). 1985. lib. bdg. 26.00 (ISBN 0-8191-4229-8); pap. text ed. 12.75 (ISBN 0-8191-4230-1). U Pr of Amer.

Belanger, Mel. Ah, Sweet Mystery. (Illus.). 150p. (Orig.). 1983. pap. text ed. 5.00 (ISBN 0-9608146-8-X). Western Sun Pubns.

Belanger, Merlyn. On Religious Maturity. LC 61-15238. 1962. 5.95 (ISBN 0-8022-0090-7). Philos Lib.

Belasic, David & Schmidt, Paul. The Penguin Principles. 1986. 5.95 (ISBN 0-89536-799-8, 6817). CSS of Ohio.

Belben, Howard. The Mission of Jesus. 96p. 1985. pap. 4.95 (ISBN 0-89109-529-2). NavPress.

Belcher, Carol, jt. auth. see Belcher, Lee.

Belcher, Jim, Jr. The Inspirations of God & the Emotions of Life. 64p. 1987. 6.95 (ISBN 0-89962-588-6). Todd & Honeywell.

Belcher, Lee & Belcher, Carol. Reaching Our Jewish Friends. (Truthway Ser.). 79p. (Orig.). 1981. pap. text ed. 1.50 (ISBN 0-87148-735-7). Pathway Pr.

Belford, William J. Special Ministers of the Eucharist. 1979. pap. 1.95 (ISBN 0-916134-39-3). Pueblo Pub Co.

Belgic Confession Translation Committee. Service Book, Part Six: Belgic Confession. 45p. (Orig.). 1984. pap. 1.25 (ISBN 0-933140-92-4). CRC Pubns.

Belgrado, Fernando D., ed. Songs of the Synagogue of Florence, 2 vols. Incl. Vol. 1. The Three Festivals (ISBN 0-87203-108-X); Vol. 2. The High Holy Days. 0p (ISBN 0-87203-109-8). (Illus.). 60p. 1982. 32.95 ea. Hermon.

Belgum, David. Religion & Personality in the Spiral of Life. LC 79-66478. 1979. pap. text ed. 14.25 (ISBN 0-8191-0832-4). U Pr of Amer.

Belhayes, Iris. Spirit Guides: You Are Not Alone. (Inner Visions Ser.). (Orig.). 1986. pap. 12.95 (ISBN 0-917086-80-5). A C S Pubns Inc.

Belin, David. Why Choose Judaism: New Dimensions of Jewish Outreach. 32p. 1985. pap. text ed. 4.00 (ISBN 0-8074-0302-4, 381900). UAHC.

Belisle, Bertrand. The Myths of Satan. 64p. 1982. 6.95 (ISBN 0-89962-284-4). Todd & Honeywell.

Belk, Fred R. The Great Trek of the Russian Mennonites to Central Asia. LC 75-28340. (Studies in Anabaptist & Mennonite History: No. 18). pap. 63.00 (ISBN 0-317-26601-2, 2025418). Bks Demand UMI.

Belkin, Samuel. In His Image: The Jewish Philosophy of Man As Expressed in Rabbinic Tradition. LC 78-10192. 1979. Repr. of 1960 ed. lib. bdg. 27.50x (ISBN 0-313-21234-1, BEIH). Greenwood.

--Philo & the Oral Law: The Philonic Interpretation of Biblical Law. (Harvard Semitic Ser.: Vol. 11). Repr. of 1940 ed. 25.00 (ISBN 0-384-03795-X). Johnson Repr.

Bell. Eastern Star. 8.95x (ISBN 0-685-21937-2). Wehman.

Bell, Bernard I. Crowd Culture. facs. ed. LC 74-117758. (Essay Index Reprint Ser). 1952. 17.00 (ISBN 0-8369-1742-1). Ayer Co Pubs.

Bell, Bernard I., ed. Affirmations, by a Group of American Anglo-Catholics, Clerical & Lay. facs. ed. LC 68-16906. (Essay Index Reprint Ser). 1938. 15.00 (ISBN 0-8369-0185-1). Ayer Co Pubs.

Bell, Buddy. Faithfulness: The Crowbar of God. 47p. 1986. pap. 2.95 (ISBN 0-89274-350-6). Christian Pub.

--Ministry of Helps Study Course. 40p. (Orig.). 1983. pap. 1.95 (ISBN 0-89274-292-5). Harrison Hse.

Bell, Charles A. The Religion of Tibet. lib. bdg. 79.95 (ISBN 0-87968-482-8). Krishna Pr.

Bell, Clara, tr. see Huysmans, Joris K.

Bell, D. Rayford. Apostolic Catechism. LC 84-90806. 60p. 1984. 1.50 (ISBN 0-317-39381-2). D R Bell.

--The Philosophy of Christ. LC 80-67408. 104p. 1980. 6.95 (ISBN 0-9604820-0-8); pap. 4.95 (ISBN 0-9604820-1-6). D R Bell.

Bell, Darlene, jt. auth. see Bell, Foster.

Bell, David N. The Image of Likeness: The Augustinian Spirituality of William of St. Thierry. 19.95 (ISBN 0-87907-878-2). Cistercian Pubns.

Bell, David N., ed. see St. Symeon.

Bell, David N., tr. & intro. by. Baldwin of Ford: Spirtual Tractates, 2 vols. 1987. Set. 50.00; Set. pap. 20.00. Vol. 1 (ISBN 0-87907-438-8, CF38). Vol. 2 (ISBN 0-87907-441-8, CF41). Cistercian Pubns.

--Besa: The Life of Shenoute. (Cistercian Studies: No. 73). 1983. pap. 11.95 (ISBN 0-87907-873-1). Cistercian Pubns.

Bell, Eric T. Numerology. LC 78-13855. (Illus.). 1985. Repr. of 1933 ed. 19.00 (ISBN 0-88355-774-6). Hyperion Conn.

Bell, F. A. Eastern Star Ritual. 5.50 (ISBN 0-685-19473-6). Powner.

Bell, Foster & Bell, Darlene. Queener: The Man Behind the Preaching. 1976. pap. 2.95 (ISBN 0-934942-13-7). White Wing Pub.

Bell, G. K. The English Church. 10.00 (ISBN 0-8414-1634-6). Folcroft.

Bell, George K. The Kingship of Christ: The Story of the World Council of Churches. LC 78-10482. 1979. Repr. of 1954 ed. lib. bdg. 22.50x (ISBN 0-313-21121-3, BEKC). Greenwood.

Bell, Gertrude. Teachings of Hafiz. 1979. 10.95 (ISBN 0-900860-63-4, Pub. by Octagon Pr England). Ins Study Human.

Bell, Gertrude L., jt. auth. see Ramsay, W. M.

Bell, H. I. Cults & Creeds in Graeco-Roman Egypt. 1975. pap. 7.50 (ISBN 0-89005-088-0). Ares.

Bell, H. Idris. Fragments of an Unknown Gospel & Other Early Christian Papyri. 59.95 (ISBN 0-8490-0188-9). Gordon Pr.

Bell, H. Idris & Skeat, T. C., eds. Fragments of an Unknown Gospel & Other Early Christian Papyri. (Illus.). 76p. 1935. Repr. of 1935 ed. 7.50 (ISBN 0-7141-0438-8, Pub. by British Lib). Longwood Pub Group.

Bell, Henry H. Obeah: Witchcraft in the West Indies. LC 78-106879. Repr. of 1889 ed. 22.50x (ISBN 0-8371-3275-4, BEO&, Pub. by Negro U Pr). Greenwood.

Bell, Irving. Christmas in Old New England. LC 80-69858. 54p. 1981. 8.95 (ISBN 0-917780-02-7). April Hill.

Bell, James P. Our Quaker Friends of Ye Olden Time. LC 76-22486. (Illus.). 287p. 1976. Repr. of 1905 ed. 17.50 (ISBN 0-8063-0732-3). Genealog Pub.

Bell, John. Bell's New Pantheon, 2 vols. Feldman, Burton & Richardson, Robert D., eds. LC 78-60919. (Myth & Romanticism Ser.: Vol. 4). 809p. 1979. Set. lib. bdg. 160.00 (ISBN 0-8240-3553-4). Garland Pub.

Bell, Joseph N. Love Theory in Later Hanbalite Islam. LC 78-5904. 1979. PLB 49.50x (ISBN 0-87395-244-8). State U NY Pr.

Bell, Landon C. Charles Parish, York County, Virginia: History & Registers -- Births, 1648-1789; Deaths 1665-1787. LC 33-27865. vi, 285p. 1984. Repr. of 1932 ed. 12.50 (ISBN 0-88490-114-9). VA State Lib.

Bell, Marion L. Crusade in the City: Revivalism in Nineteenth-Century Philadelphia. (Illus.). 1978. 22.50 (ISBN 0-8387-1929-5). Bucknell U Pr.

Bell, Martin. Nenshu & the Tiger: Parables of Life & Death. 112p. 1982. pap. 5.95 (ISBN 0-8164-2356-3, HarpR). Har-Row.

--Return of the Wolf. 128p. 1983. 12.50 (ISBN 0-8164-0545-X, HarpR); pap. 7.95 (ISBN 0-8164-2470-5). Har-Row.

--The Way of the Wolf. (Epiphany Ser.). 144p. 1983. pap. 2.95 (ISBN 0-345-30522-1). Ballantine.

--Way of the Wolf: The Gospel in New Images. LC 77-120366. (Illus.). 128p. 1970. pap. 8.95 (ISBN 0-8164-0202-7, AY6445, HarpR); 2 records 8.95 ea. Har-Row.

Bell, Michael D., ed. see Brackenridge, Hugh H. & Freneau, Philip.

Bell, P. G. Essentials of New Testament: Greek. 1983. pap. 9.95 Wkbk. (ISBN 0-89957-569-2); answer bk. for wkbk. 4.95 (ISBN 0-89957-570-6); answers for essentials 2.95. AMG Pubs.

Bell, Philip. Disestablishment in Ireland & Wales. LC 73-488607. (Church Historical Society Ser.: No. 90). 1969. pap. 21.50x (ISBN 0-8401-5090-3). A R Allenson.

Bell, R. C. Studies in Ephesians. 1971. pap. 2.75 (ISBN 0-88027-041-1). Firm Foun Pub.

--Studies in Galatians. 1954. pap. 2.75 (ISBN 0-88027-042-X). Firm Foun Pub.

--Studies in Philippians. 1956. pap. 2.75 (ISBN 0-88027-043-8). Firm Foun Pub.

--Studies in Romans. 1957. pap. 2.75 (ISBN 0-88027-025-X). Firm Foun Pub.

Bell, Richard, tr. see Muhammad.

Bell, Richard H. Sensing the Spirit. LC 84-5158. (Spirituality & the Christian Life Ser.: Vol. 6). 120p. 1984. pap. 7.95 (ISBN 0-664-24632-X). Westminster.

Bell, Robert E. Dictionary of Classical Mythology: Symbols, Attributes, & Associations. LC 81-19141. 390p. 1982. 30.00 (ISBN 0-87436-305-5). ABC Clio.

Bell, Robert S. Paul's Letter to the Romans. 1970. pap. 2.75 (ISBN 0-88027-036-5). Firm Foun Pub.

Bell, Rudolph M. Holy Anorexia. LC 85-8460. (Illus.). xii, 248p. 1985. 22.50 (ISBN 0-226-04204-9). U of Chicago Pr.

Bell, Rudolph M., jt. auth. see Weinstein, Donald.

Bell, Sadie. Church, the State, & Education in Virginia. LC 78-89148. (American Education: Its Men, Institutions & Ideas Ser). 1969. Repr. of 1930 ed. 43.00 (ISBN 0-405-01385-X). Ayer Co Pubs.

Bell, Skip. These Are Gifts: A Study Guide for Understanding Spiritual Gifts. 72p. 1985. pap. write for info. (ISBN 0-910347-03-4). Chatham Comm Inc.

Bell, Stephen. Rebel, Priest & Prophet: A Biography of Dr. Edward McGlynn. LC 75-301. (The Radical Tradition in America Ser). 303p. 1975. Repr. of 1937 ed. 24.75 (ISBN 0-88355-206-X). Hyperion Conn.

Bell, T. H., et al, eds. Excellence. LC 84-71872. 140p. 1984. 8.95 (ISBN 0-87747-776-0). Deseret Bk.

Bell, Thomas. The Anatomie of Popish Tyrannie. LC 74-28833. (English Experience Ser.: No. 714). 1975. Repr. of 1603 ed. 16.00 (ISBN 90-221-0714-0). Walter J Johnson.

Bellah, Robert & Greenspahn, Frederick. Uncivil Religion: Interreligious Hostility in America. 256p. 1986. 16.95. Crossroad NY.

Bellah, Robert N. Beyond Belief. LC 77-109058. 1976. pap. text ed. 7.95x (ISBN 0-06-060775-0, RD129, HarpR). Har-Row.

--Beyond Belief: Essays on Religion in a Post-Traditional World. LC 77-109058. 1970. 8.95x (ISBN 0-06-060774-2, RD-129, HarpR). Har-Row.

--The Broken Covenant: American Civil Religion in Time of Trail. 1976. pap. 5.95 (ISBN 0-8164-2123-4, HarpR). Har-Row.

--Tokugawa Religion. 272p. pap. 9.95 (ISBN 0-02-902460-9). Free Pr.

Bellah, Robert N. & Greenspahn, Frederick E., eds. Uncivil Religions: Interreligious Hostility. 1987. 16.95. Crossroad NY.

Bellah, Robert N., jt. ed. see Glock, Charles.

Bellah, Robert N., jt. ed. see Glock, Charles Y.

Bellamak, Lu. Non-Judgemental Sacred Dance: Simple Ways to Pray Through Dance. 1984. 3.00 (ISBN 0-941500-14-4). Sharing Co.

Bellamy, Edward. Selected Writings on Religion & Society. Schiffman, Joseph, ed. LC 74-40. (The American Heritage Ser.: No. 11). 139p. 1974. Repr. of 1955 ed. lib. bdg. 22.50 (ISBN 0-8371-7359-0, BEWR). Greenwood.

Bellamy, Lin, jt. auth. see Williamson, Tom.

Bellance, James A. Values & the Search for Self. LC 75-12724. pap. 27.80 (ISBN 0-317-42175-1, 2025922). Bks Demand UMI.

Bellefonds, Y. Linant De see Linant De Bellefonds, Y.

Bellegarde, Ida R. Understanding Cultural Values. LC 79-51620. 1979. 4.45x (ISBN 0-918340-09-8). Bell Ent.

Belleggia, Sr. Concetta. God & the Problem of Evil. 1980. 3.75 (ISBN 0-8198-3007-0); pap. 2.50 (ISBN 0-8198-3008-9). Dghtrs St Paul.

Beller, Dan. Progress Through Pioneer Evangelism. pap. 2.00 (ISBN 0-911866-80-9). Advocate.

Bellett, J. G. Short Meditations, 3 vols. pap. 13.95 set (ISBN 0-88172-003-8); pap. 4.95 ea. Believers Bkshelf.

Belli, Humberto. Breaking Faith: The Sandinista Revolution & Its Impact on Freedom & the Christian Faith in Nicaragua. LC 85-70475. 288p. 1985. pap. 8.95 (ISBN 0-89107-359-0, Crossway Bks). Good News.

Bellinger, W. H. Psalmody & Prophecy. (JSOT Supplement Ser.: No. 27). 146p. 1984. text ed. 28.50x (ISBN 0-905774-60-4, Pub. by JSOT Pr England); pap. text ed. 11.95x (ISBN 0-905774-61-2, Pub. by JSOT England). Eisenbrauns.

Bellini, Enzo. The Middle Ages, 900-1300. Drury, John, ed. & tr. from Ital. (An Illustrated History of the Church). 126p. 12.95 (ISBN 0-03-056828-5, HarpR). Har-Row.

Bellini, Enzo, et al. The Catholic Church Today, 1920-1981. Drury, John, ed. & tr. from Ital. (Illustrated History of the Church). (Illus.). 126p. 1982. 12.95 (ISBN 0-86683-160-6, HarpR). Har-Row.

--The Church & the Modern Nations, 1850-1920. Drury, John, ed. & tr. from Ital. (An Illustrated History of the Church). (Illus.). 126p. 1982. 12.95 (ISBN 0-86683-159-2, HarpR). Har-Row.

--The Church Established, 180-381. Drury, John, ed. & tr. from Ital. (An Illustrated History of the Church). (Illus.). 126p. 12.95 (ISBN 0-03-056824-2, HarpR). Har-Row.

--The Church in Revolutionary Times. Drury, John, ed. & tr. from Ital. (An Illustrated History of the Church). (Illus.). 126p. 1981. 12.95 (ISBN 0-86683-158-4, HarpR). Har-Row.

--The Church in the Age of Humanism, 1300-1500. Drury, John, ed. & tr. (An Illustrated History of the Church). 126p. 12.95 (ISBN 0-03-056829-3, HarpR). Har-Row.

--The End of the Ancient World, Three Hundred Eighty-One to Six Hundred. Drury, John, ed. & tr. from Ital. (Illustrated History of the Church). (Illus.). 126p. 1982. 12.95 (ISBN 0-03-056826-9, HarpR). Har-Row.

--The First Christians: An Illustrated History of the Church. Drury, John, ed. & tr. from Ital. (Illus.). 126p. 1980. 12.95 (ISBN 0-03-056823-4, HarpR). Har-Row.

--The Formation of Christian Europe: An Illustrated History of the Church. Drury, John, ed. & tr. (Illus.). 126p. 1980. text ed. 12.95 (ISBN 0-03-056827-7, HarpR). Har-Row.

--Protestant & Catholic Reform. Drury, John, ed. & tr. from Ital. (An Illustrated History of the Church). (Illus.). 124p. (Orig.). 1981. 12.95 (ISBN 0-03-056831-5, HarpR). Har-Row.

Bellinzoni, Arthur J., ed. The Two-Source Hypothesis: A Critical Appraisal. x, 486p. 1985. 39.95 (ISBN 0-86554-096-9, MUP/H88). Mercer Univ Pr.

Bellis, Dale, jt. auth. see McDowell, Josh.

Belliustin, I. S. Description of the Clergy in Rural Russia: The Memoir of a Nineteenth Century Parish Priest. Freeze, Gregory L., ed. LC 85-47699. (Illus.). 224p. 1985. text ed. 29.95x (ISBN 0-8014-1796-1); pap. text ed. 9.95x (ISBN 0-8014-9335-8). Cornell U Pr.

Belloc, Hilaire. Characters of the Reformation. facs. ed. LC 72-121449. (Essay Index Reprint Ser). 1936. 24.00 (ISBN 0-8369-1696-4). Ayer Co Pubs.

--Cranmer. LC 72-4495. (English Biography Ser., No. 31). 1972. Repr. of 1931 ed. lib. bdg. 55.95x (ISBN 0-8383-1610-7). Haskell.

--The Crisis of Civilization. LC 73-114465. 245p. 1973. Repr. of 1937 ed. lib. bdg. 22.50x (ISBN 0-8371-4761-1, BECC). Greenwood.

--Essays of a Catholic. facs. ed. LC 67-26713. (Essay Index Reprint Ser). 1931. 18.00 (ISBN 0-8369-0188-6). Ayer Co Pubs.

--Great Heresies. facs. ed. LC 68-16908. (Essay Index Reprint Ser). 1938. 18.00 (ISBN 0-8369-0189-4). Ayer Co Pubs.

--How the Reformation Happened. 12.00 (ISBN 0-8446-0483-6). Peter Smith.

--The Jews. 1981. lib. bdg. 75.00 (ISBN 0-8490-3220-2). Gordon Pr.

--The Jews. 1986. pap. 6.50 (ISBN 0-317-53001-1). Noontide.

--Milton. LC 78-100142. Repr. of 1935 ed. lib. bdg. 24.75x (ISBN 0-8371-3248-7, BEMI). Greenwood.

--Richelieu: A Study. 1978. Repr. of 1929 ed. lib. bdg. 20.00 (ISBN 0-8495-0383-3). Arden Lib.

--The Servile State. LC 77-2914. 1977. 8.00 (ISBN 0-913966-31-2, Liberty Clas); pap. 3.00 (ISBN 0-913966-32-0). Liberty Fund.

--Wolsey. 1978. Repr. of 1933 ed. lib. bdg. 20.00 (ISBN 0-8495-0382-5). Arden Lib.

Belloc, Hilarie. Richelieu. 1935. Repr. 17.50 (ISBN 0-8274-3281-X). R West.

Bellow, Saul. To Jerusalem & Back. 1977. pap. 1.95 (ISBN 0-380-01676-1, 33472-0). Avon.

Bellows, Barbara, jt. auth. see Connelly, Thomas L.

Bellville, Cheryl W. All Things Bright & Beautiful. 64p. (Orig.). 1983. pap. 7.95 (ISBN 0-86683-722-1, AY8363, HarpR). Har-Row.

Belmar, John J. Success - It's Yours to Have. 1984. 5.75 (ISBN 0-8062-2305-7). Carlton.

Belo, Fernando. A Materialist Reading of the Gospel of Mark. O'Connell, Matthew, tr. from Fr. LC 80-24756. Tr. of Lectero Materialiste de L'evangele de Marc. 384p. (Orig.). 1981. pap. 12.95 (ISBN 0-88344-323-6). Orbis Bks.

Belo, Jane. Trance in Bali. LC 77-6361. 1977. Repr. of 1960 ed. lib. bdg. 35.75x (ISBN 0-8371-9652-3, BETR). Greenwood.

Belouino, P. Dictionnaire General et Complet des Persecutions, 2 vols. Migne, J. P., ed. (Nouvelle Encyclopedie Theologique Ser.: Vols. 4-5). (Fr.). 1468p. Repr. of 1851 ed. lib. bdg. 186.50x (ISBN 0-89241-255-0). Caratzas.

Belth, Nathan C. A Promise to Keep: A Narrative of the American Encounter with Anti-Semitism. LC 81-40403. (Illus.). 1981. pap. 7.95 (ISBN 0-8052-0682-5). Schocken.

--A Promise to Keep: The American Encounter with Anti-Semitism. 305p. Repr. 6.95 (ISBN 0-686-95111-5). ADL.

Belting, Hans, et al. The Mosaics & Frescoes of St. Mary Pammakaristos (Fethiye Camii) at Istanbul. LC 77-99268. (Dumbarton Oaks Studies: Vol. 15). (Illus.). 118p. 1978. 30.00x (ISBN 0-88402-075-4). Dumbarton Oaks.

Beltroy, Manuel, tr. see Hume, Roberto E.

Beltrutti, Georgio. Le Certose D'Italia (Liguria) La Certosa di Toirano. Hogg, James, ed. (Analecta Cartusiana Ser.: No. 101). 95p. (Orig.). 1982. pap. 25.00 (ISBN 0-317-42563-3, Pub. by Salzburg Studies). Longwood Pub Group.

Beltrutti, Giorgio & Hogg, James. La Certosa Di Pesio. Hogg, James, ed. (Analecta Cartusiana Ser.: No. 73). 50p. (Orig.). 1979. pap. 25.00 (ISBN 3-7052-0108-5, Pub. by Salzburg Studies). Longwood Pub Group.

Beltz, Oliver S., ed. Te Decet Laus: To Thee Belongeth Praise. Revised ed. (Illus.). viii, 223p. 1982. 9.95 (ISBN 0-943872-84-7). Andrews Univ Pr.

Beltz, Walter. God & the Gods: Myths of the Bible. Heinegg, Peter, tr. 272p. 1983. pap. 6.95 (ISBN 0-14-022192-1, Pelican). Penguin.

Belvianes, Marcel. The Madonna in the Paintings of the Great Masters. (Illus.). 1980. Repr. 107.50 (ISBN 0-89901-010-5). Found Class Reprints.

Belvins, James L., tr. see Herrmann, Siegfried.

Belyi, Andre I. Anthroposophy & Russia. 1983. pap. 5.00 (ISBN 0-916786-69-2). St George Bk Serv.

Belzen, J. A. van see Van Belzen, J. A. & Van Der Lans, J. M.

Bembe, John P., jt. auth. see Darey-Bembe, Francoise.

Bemmel, Dolores van see Van Bemmel, John & Van Bemmel, Dolores.

Bemmel, John V. A Get Well Prayer Book. (Greeting Book Line Ser.). 48p. (Orig.). 1985. pap. 1.50 (ISBN 0-89622-231-4). Twenty Third.

Bemmel, John van see Van Bemmel, John & Van Bemmel, Dolores.

Bemporad, J., ed. A Rational Faith: Essays in Honor of Levi A. Olan. 15.00x (ISBN 0-87068-448-5). Ktav.

Ben, I., ed. Who's Who in Israel & Jewish Personalities from All over the World, 1985-86. 20th ed. (Who's Who in Israel Ser.). 1985. 100.00x (ISBN 0-318-18965-8). Heinman.

Benagh, Christine L. Meditations on the Book of Job. LC 64-25262. 1964. 3.95 (ISBN 0-686-05041-X). St Thomas.

Ben Aharon, Shmuel. Midrash Bet HaShem: The Alphabet. 3rd, rev. ed. (Illus.). 22p. 1986. pap. text ed. write for info. (ISBN 0-9616488-1-3). Alef Bet Comns.

Ben-Ami, Aharon. Social Change in a Hostile Environment: The Crusaders' Kingdom of Jerusalem. (Princeton Studies on the Near East Ser.). (Illus.). 1969. 25.50x (ISBN 0-691-09344-X). Princeton U Pr.

Ben-Ami, Yitshaq. Years of Wrath, Days of Glory. 2nd ed. LC 83-60834. (Illus.). 620p. 1983. Repr. of 1982 ed. 17.50 (ISBN 0-88400-096-6). Shengold.

Benard, Cheryl & Khalilzad, Zalmay. The Government of God: Iran's Islamic Republic. LC 83-20880. 232p. 1984. 28.00x (ISBN 0-231-05376-2); pap. 12.50 (ISBN 0-231-05377-0). Columbia U Pr.

Benard, Edmond, jt. ed. see Ryan, John K.

Benardete, Mair Jose. Hispanic Culture & Character of the Sephardic Jews. 2nd rev. ed. 226p. 1981. 15.00 (ISBN 0-87203-100-4). Hermon.

Benares, Camden. Zen Without Zen Masters. 2nd ed. (Illus.). 128p. 1985. pap. 6.95 (ISBN 0-941404-34-X). Falcon Pr AZ.

Ben-Asher, Naomi & Leaf, Hayim, eds. Junior Jewish Encyclopedia. 10th, rev. ed. LC 84-51583. (Illus.). 1984. 19.95 (ISBN 0-88400-110-5). Shengold.

Benbow, Doras R. Lantern in the Moonlight. (Illus.). 1974. lib. bdg. 3.00 (ISBN 0-931611-06-7); pap. 1.50. D R Benbow.

Bence, Evelyn. Following Jesus: A Woman's Workshop on Luke. (Woman's Workshop Ser.). 112p. 1986. pap. 3.95 (ISBN 0-310-44781-X, 11314P). Zondervan.

--Growing. 32p. 1985. 4.95 (ISBN 0-8378-2043-X). Gibson.

Bence, Evelyn, jt. auth. see Strasheim, Linda.

Benchley, Robert. A Good Old-Fashioned Christmas. (Illus.). 96p. (Orig.). 1981. pap. 7.95 (ISBN 0-938864-02-5). Ipswich Pr.

Bendall, Cecil & Rouse, W. H., eds. Siksa Samuccaya: A Compendium of Buddhist Doctrine. 1981. 18.50x (ISBN 0-8364-0793-8, Pub. by Motilal Banarsidass). South Asia Bks.

Bendall, Cecil, tr. see Santideva.

Bendann, Effie. Death Customs: An Analytical Study of Burial Rites. 1971. 37.00x (ISBN 0-8103-3733-9). Gale.

--Death Customs: An Analytical Study of Burial Rites. 59.95 (ISBN 0-8490-0010-6). Gordon Pr.

Bender, David L. & Leone, Bruno, eds. Religion & Human Experience: Opposing Viewpoints. LC 85-7660. 1981. 11.95 (ISBN 0-89908-333-1); pap. text ed. 6.95 (ISBN 0-89908-308-0). Greenhaven.

--Science & Religion: Opposing Viewpoints. LC 85-7641. 1981. 11.95 (ISBN 0-89908-334-X); pap. 6.95 (ISBN 0-89908-309-9). Greenhaven.

Bender, H. S. Biblical Revelation & Inspiration. pap. 1.45 (ISBN 0-8361-1322-5). Herald Pr.

Bender, Harold S. Anabaptist Vision. 1944. pap. 1.45 (ISBN 0-8361-1305-5). Herald Pr.

--Conrad Grebel, c. 1498-1526: The Founder of the Swiss Brethren Sometimes Called Anabaptists. (Studies in Anabaptist & Mennonite History Ser.: No. 6). pap. 85.80 (ISBN 0-317-28810-5, 2020335). Bks Demand UMI.

--These Are My People: The New Testament Church. LC 62-12947. (Conrad Grebel Lecture Ser.). 136p. 1962. pap. 6.95 (ISBN 0-8361-1479-5). Herald Pr.

Bender, Harold S. & Horsch, John. Menno Simons su Vida y Escritos. Palomeque, Carmen, tr. 160p. 1979. 4.95x (ISBN 0-8361-1218-0). Herald Pr.

Bender, Harold S. & Smith, C. Henry, eds. Mennonite Encyclopedia, 4vols. 1956-1969. Set. 160.00x (ISBN 0-8361-1018-8); 45.00x ea. Vol. 1 (ISBN 0-8361-1118-4). Vol. 2 (ISBN 0-8361-1119-2). Vol. 3 (ISBN 0-8361-1120-6). Vol. 4 (ISBN 0-8361-1121-4). Herald Pr.

Bender, Jan. Organ Improvisation for Beginners. LC 75-2934. (Illus.). 71p. 1975. bds. 8.25 (ISBN 0-570-01312-7, 99-1229). Concordia.

Bender, Philip. New Heaven on a New Earth. LC 85-81579. (Faith & Life Bible Studies). 106p. (Orig.). 1985. pap. 4.95 (ISBN 0-87303-106-7). Faith & Life.

Bender, Ross T. Christians in Families. LC 82-6058. (Conrad Grebel Lecture Ser.). 184p. (Orig.). pap. 8.95 (ISBN 0-8361-3301-3). Herald Pr.

Bender, Urie. Four Earthen Vessels. 320p. 1982. pap. 9.95x (ISBN 0-8361-1246-6). Herald Pr.

Bender, Urie A. To Walk in the Way. LC 79-83511. 208p. 1979. pap. 5.95 (ISBN 0-8361-1884-7). Herald Pr.

Bendit, Laurence & Bendit, Phoebe. The Transforming Mind. 2nd ed. LC 74-103415. 161p. 1983. pap. 5.75 (ISBN 0-8356-0012-2, Quest). Theos Pub Hse.

Bendit, Laurence J. Mirror of Life & Death. 1965. pap. 1.35 (ISBN 0-8356-0411-X, Quest). Theos Pub Hse.

--Mirror of Life & Death. 7.25 (ISBN 0-8356-7394-4). Theos Pub Hse.

--Self Knowledge: A Yoga for the West. LC 67-7871. (Orig.). 1967. pap. 1.25 (ISBN 0-8356-0032-7, Quest). Theos Pub Hse.

Bendit, Phoebe, jt. auth. see Bendit, Laurence.

Bendix, Regina. Progress & Nostalgia: Silvester-Klausen in Urnasch, Switzerland. LC 84-28128. (UC Publications in Folklore & Mythology: Vol. 33). 1985. 21.00 (ISBN 0-520-09959-1). U of Cal Pr.

Bendix, Reinhard. From Berlin to Berkeley: German-Jewish Identities. LC 85-8578. 320p. 1985. 29.95 (ISBN 0-88738-067-0). Transaction Bks.

Ben-Dov, Meir. In the Shadow of the Temple. LC 84-48639. (Illus.). 384p. 1985. 24.45i (ISBN 0-06-015362-8, HarpT). Har-Row.

Benedetto, Don, jt. auth. see Valdes, Juan de.

Benedict, Clare M. St. Sharbel, Mystic of the East. 1977. 6.95 (ISBN 0-911218-11-4); pap. 3.45 (ISBN 0-911218-12-2). Ravengate Pr.

Benedict, David. Fifty Years among the Baptists. Repr. of 1860 ed. 13.00 (ISBN 0-317-38297-7). Church History.

--A General History of the Baptist Denomination in America, 2 vols. 1985. Repr. of 1813 ed. 64.00 (ISBN 0-317-31642-7). Church History.

--General History of the Baptist Denomination in America & Other Parts of the World, 2 vols. facsimile ed. LC 73-152974. (Select Bibliographies Reprint Ser). Repr. of 1813 ed. Set. 60.00 (ISBN 0-8369-5726-1). Ayer Co Pubs.

--History of the Donatists. 1985. Repr. of 1875 ed. 15.00 (ISBN 0-317-31641-9). Church History.

Benedict, Don. Born Again Radical. LC 82-9100. 240p. (Orig.). 1982. pap. 7.95 (ISBN 0-8298-0371-8). Pilgrim NY.

Benedict, Ruth. Zuni Mythology, 2 Vols. LC 75-82366. (Columbia Univ. Contributions to Anthropology Ser.: No. 21). 1969. Repr. of 1935 ed. Set. 70.00 (ISBN 0-404-50571-6); 35.00 ea. AMS Pr.

Benedict, Ruth F. Concept of the Guardian Spirit in North America. LC 24-872. (American Anthropology Association Memoirs). 1923. 12.00 (ISBN 0-527-00528-2). Kraus Repr.

Benedict, Saint Rule of Saint Benedict. Gasquet, Cardinal, tr. LC 66-30730. (Medieval Library). (Illus.). 130p. 1966. Repr. of 1926 ed. 18.50x (ISBN 0-8154-0022-5). Cooper Sq.

Benedict, Samuel O. Catholicism & Americanism: The Vision of a Conflict? (Illus.). 147p. 1987. 98.85 (ISBN 0-89266-590-4). Am Classical Coll Pr.

Benedictine Sisters of Clyde, Missouri Staff. St. Gertrude the Great: Herald of Divine Love. 1977. pap. 0.75 (ISBN 0-89555-026-1). TAN Bks Pubs.

Benedictus, Saint Middle High German Translations of the Regula Sancti Benedicti. Selmer, Carl, ed. & intro. by. (Mediaeval Academy of America Publications). 1933. 28.00 (ISBN 0-527-01689-6). Kraus Repr.

Benedittis, Suzanne M. De see De Benedittis, Suzanne M.

Benesch, Otto. Rembrandt: Werk und Forschung. Repr. 17.00 (ISBN 0-384-03899-9). Johnson Repr.

Benestace, J. Brian & Butler, Frances J., eds. Quest for Justice. 487p. (Orig.). 1981. pap. 17.95 (ISBN 1-55586-649-2). US Catholic.

Benestad, Brian J. The Pursuit of a Just Social Order: Policy Statements of the U. S. Catholic Bishops, 1966-80. LC 82-18326. 220p. 1982. 12.00 (ISBN 0-89633-060-5); pap. 7.00 (ISBN 0-89633-061-3). Ethics & Public Policy.

Benet, Juan. A Meditation. Rabassa, Gregory, tr. from Span. Tr. of Una Meditacion. 366p. 1983. 15.95; pap. 8.95 (ISBN 0-89255-065-1). Persea Bks.

Benet, Stephen V. James Shore's Daughter. 277p. 1985. Repr. of 1934 ed. lib. bdg. 30.00 (ISBN 0-918377-67-6). Russell Pr.

Benevot, Maurice, ed. see Cyprian.

Benfey, Theodor. Friends & the World of Nature. LC 80-82941. 28p. (Orig.). 1980. pap. 2.50x (ISBN 0-87574-233-5). Pendle Hill.

Bengel, John A. New Testament Commentary, 2 Vols. LC 70-155250. 1910p. 1982. Set. 59.95 (ISBN 0-8254-2242-6). Kregel.

Bengtson, Athene, ed. see Newhouse, Flower A.

Bengtson, Melodie N., ed. see Newhouse, Flower A.

Ben-Gurion, David. Ben-Gurion Looks at the Bible. Kolatch, Jonathan, tr. LC 70-167600. 320p. 1972. 12.50 (ISBN 0-8246-0127-0). Jonathan David.

Benham, Hugh. Latin Church Music in England, Fourteen Sixty to Fifteen Seventy-Five. (Music Reprint Ser.: 1980). (Illus.). 1980. Repr. of 1977 ed. lib. bdg. 35.00 (ISBN 0-306-76025-8). Da Capo.

Ben-Horin, Meir. Common Faith-Uncommon People: Essays in Reconstructionist Judaism. LC 71-80691. 245p. 1970. 7.50 (ISBN 0-935457-03-8). Reconstructionist Pr.

Ben-Israel, Manasseh. The Conciliator: A Reconcilement of the Apparent Contradictions in Holy Scripture. Lindo, E. H., tr. from Span. LC 72-83942. (The Library of Judaic Studies: No. SHP 10). 688p. 1987. Repr. of 1904 ed. 23.50 (ISBN 0-87203-115-2). Hermon.

Benjamin. The Father Who Dwelleth Within. 1979. pap. 2.50 (ISBN 0-87516-293-2). De Vorss.

Benjamin, A. & Hackstaff, L. H. On Free Choice of the Will: Augustine. 1964. pap. text ed. write for info. (ISBN 0-02-308030-2). Macmillan.

Benjamin, A. S., tr. see Saint Augustine.

Benjamin, Carol. So You're Getting Married! 1982. pap. 3.95 (ISBN 0-911739-15-7). Abbott Loop.

Benjamin, Chaya, ed. The Copenhagen Haggadah. LC 86-63514. (Hebrew., Illus.). 68p. 1987. 40.00 (ISBN 0-8478-0820-3). Rizzoli Intl.

Benjamin, Dick. Abortion Is Murder. 1980. pap. 1.75 (ISBN 0-911739-04-1). Abbott Loop.

--Finding Your Place in the Body of Christ. 1980. pap. text ed. 3.95 (ISBN 0-911739-07-6). Abbott Loop.

--Pleading the Case of the Fatherless. 1982. pap. 0.95 (ISBN 0-911739-09-2). Abbott Loop.

--Should I Tithe? 1977. pap. 1.75 (ISBN 0-911739-11-4). Abbott Loop.

--Women's Ministries in the New Testament Church. 1983. pap. 1.75 (ISBN 0-911739-16-5). Abbott Loop.

Benjamin, Dick & Richardson, Jim. Remember the Poor. 1982. pap. 1.75 (ISBN 0-911739-26-2). Abbott Loop.

Benjamin, Don C. Deuteronomy & City Life: A Form Criticism of Texts with the Word City ('ir) in Deuteronomy 4: 41 -26: 19. LC 83-3609. (Illus.). 366p. (Orig.). 1983. lib. bdg. 31.25 (ISBN 0-8191-3138-5); pap. text ed. 15.75 (ISBN 0-8191-3139-3). U Pr of Amer.

Benjamin, Don-Paul & Miner, Ron. Come Sit with Me Again: Sermons for Children. (Illus.). 128p. (Orig.). 1987. pap. 6.95 (ISBN 0-8298-0748-9). Pilgrim NY.

Benjamin, Elsie. Search & Find: Theosophical Reference Index. Small, W. Emmett & Todd, Helen, eds. (Study: No. 1). 1978. pap. 3.95 (ISBN 0-913004-32-4). Point Loma Pub.

Benjamin, Harry. Everyone's Guide to Theosophy. 1969. 8.50 (ISBN 0-8356-5079-0). Theos Pub Hse.

Benjamin, Henri, jt. auth. see De Rebecque, Constant.

Benjamin, Israel B. Three Years in America: 1859-1862, 2 vols. in 1. facsimile ed. Reznikoff, Charles, tr. from Ger. LC 74-27962. (Modern Jewish Experience Ser.). (Eng.). 1975. Repr. of 1956 ed. 52.00x (ISBN 0-405-06693-7). Ayer Co Pubs.

Benjamin, Philip S. The Philadelphia Quakers in the Industrial Age, 1865-1920. LC 75-22967. 309p. 1976. 19.95 (ISBN 0-87722-086-7). Temple U Pr.

Benjamin, Rick & Richardson, Jim. God Is Greater. 1983. pap. 1.75 (ISBN 0-911739-00-9). Abbott Loop.

Benko, Stephen. Los Evangelicos, los Catolicos y la Virgen Maria, Los. Olmedo, Alfonso, tr. from Eng. Orig. Title: Protestants, Catholics & Mary. 1985. pap. 6.95 (ISBN 0-311-05041-7). Casa Bautista.

--Meaning of Sanctorum Communio. LC 64-55292. (Studies in Historical Theology: No. 3). 1964. pap. 10.00x (ISBN 0-8401-0178-3). A R Allenson.

--Pagan Rome & the Early Christians. LC 83-48898. 192p. 1985. 20.00x (ISBN 0-253-34286-4). Ind U Pr.

--Pagan Rome & the Early Christians. LC 83-48898. (Midland Books Ser.: no. 385). 192p. 1986. pap. 7.95x (ISBN 0-253-20385-6). Ind U Pr.

Benlliure, Felix, tr. see Hester, H. I.

Benlliure, Felix, tr. see Mehl, Roger.

Ben Menachem, Shmuel, ed. see Wahlie, Albert J.

Benn, Douglas R. Love-God's Greatest Gift. (Illus.). 1981. pap. 4.00 (ISBN 0-682-49736-3). Exposition Pr FL.

Benn, J. Solomon, III. Preaching from the Bible. (Resources for Black Ministries Ser.). 80p. (Orig.). 1981. pap. 2.45 (ISBN 0-8010-0801-8). Baker Bk.

Benne, Robert & Hefener, Philip. Defining America: Christian Critique of the American Dream. LC 73-89062. pap. 40.00 (2026941). Bks Demand UMI.

Benner, David G. Baker Encyclopedia of Psychology. 1376p. 1985. text ed. 39.95 (ISBN 0-8010-0865-4). Baker Bk.

Benner, David G., ed. Psychotherapy in Christian Perspective. 300p. 1987. pap. price not set (ISBN 0-8010-0942-1). Baker Bk.

Benner, Judith A., jt. auth. see Paschal, George H., Jr.

Bennet, Boyce M., Jr., ed. see Miller, Madeleine S. & Miller, J. Lane.

Bennett, et al. Twenty-Six Bible Programs for Preschools. (Illus.). 96p. 1987. 8.95 (ISBN 0-87403-147-8, 3417). Standard Pub.

Bennett, Adrian A. Missionary Journalist in China: Young J. Allen & His Magazines, 1860-1883. LC 81-19761. (Illus.). 336p. 1983. 28.00x (ISBN 0-8203-0615-0). U of Ga Pr.

Bennett, Allan. A Note on Genesis. (Equinox Reprints: Vol. 1, No. 2). 1976. pap. 1.50 (ISBN 0-87728-338-9). Weiser.

Bennett, Boyce M. Bennett's Guide to the Bible: Graphic Aids & Outlines. (Illus.). 128p. (Orig.). 1982. pap. 9.95 (ISBN 0-8164-2397-0, HarpR). Har-Row.

Bennett Brother's Printing, ed. see Wagner, Clarence M.

Bennett, Charles A. Dilemma of Religious Knowledge. LC 71-85986. (Essay & General Literature Index Reprint Ser.). 1969. pap. text ed. 15.95x (ISBN 0-8046-0538-6, Pub. by Kennikat). Assoc Faculty Pr.

Bennett, Cora N. One, Two, Three, Four, Five, Six, Seven, All Dead Children Go to Heaven. 32p. 1986. 5.95 (ISBN 0-89962-509-6). Todd & Honeywell.

Bennett, Curtis. God As Form: Essays in Greek Theology with Special Reference to Christianity & the Contemporary Theological Predicament. LC 75-43851. 1976. 39.50 (ISBN 0-87395-325-8). State U NY Pr.

Bennett, Dennis. How to Pray for the Release of the Holy Spirit. 1985. pap. 3.95 (ISBN 0-88270-593-8). Bridge Pub.

--Moving Right Along in the Spirit. 160p. 1982. 5.95 (ISBN 0-8007-5184-1, Power Bks). Revell.

Bennett, Dennis & Bennett, Rita. Holy Spirit & You Supplement. LC 73-75963. (To be used with The Holy Spirit & You). 1973. pap. 3.95 (ISBN 0-88270-031-6). Bridge Pub.

--The Holy Spirit & You: The Text Book of the Charismatic Renewal. LC 71-140673. 224p. 1971. pap. 5.95 (ISBN 0-912106-14-X). Bridge Pub.

--Trinidad Del Hombre. Carrodeguas, Andy, ed. Lievano, Franscisco, tr. from Span. Orig. Title: Trinity of Man. 224p. 1982. pap. 3.50 (ISBN 0-8297-1298-4). Life Pubs Intl.

--Trinity of Man. LC 79-67378. (Illus.). 1979. pap. text ed. 6.95 (ISBN 0-88270-287-4). Bridge Pub.

Bennett, Dennis J. Nine O'Clock in the Morning: An Episcopal Priest Discovers the Holy Spirit. LC 72-85205. 1970. pap. 5.95 (ISBN 0-912106-41-7). Bridge Pub.

Bennett, Ernest N. Downfall of the Dervishes. LC 71-79818. (Illus.). Repr. of 1899 ed. 22.50x (ISBN 0-8371-1545-0, BEB&). Greenwood.

Bennett, F. M. Religious Cults Associated with the Amazons. v, 79p. 1985. Repr. of 1912 ed. lib. bdg. 25.00x (ISBN 0-89241-204-6). Caratzas.

Bennett, G. F. When They Ask for Bread: Pastoral Care & Counseling. LC 77-15743. 1978. 8.95 (ISBN 0-8042-1159-0). John Knox.

Bennett, G. Willis. Effective Urban Church Ministry. LC 83-70370. 1983. pap. 5.95 (ISBN 0-8054-5526-4). Broadman.

Bennett, Georgaan. What the Bible Says About Goodness. LC 80-69626. (What the Bible Says Ser.). 405p. 1981. 13.50 (ISBN 0-89900-080-0). College Pr Pub.

Bennett, Georgann. Soulshine. 1978. pap. cancelled (ISBN 0-89900-133-5). College Pr Pub.

Bennett, George. When the Mental Patient Comes Home. LC 79-23809. (Christian Care Bks.). 118p. 1980. pap. 7.95 (ISBN 0-664-24295-2). Westminster.

Bennett, Gordon C. Acting Out Faith. Lambert, Herbert, ed. LC 86-6141. 160p. (Orig.). 1986. pap. 10.95 (ISBN 0-8272-0016-1). CBP.

--God Is My Fuehrer. (Orig.). 1970. pap. 1.50 (ISBN 0-377-80611-0). Friend Pr.

--Reader's Theatre Comes to Church. 2nd ed. LC 85-61999. 128p. 1985. pap. 7.95 (ISBN 0-916260-33-X, B-191). Meriwether Pub.

Bennett, Gordon H., jt. auth. see Marshall, Alejandro.

Bennett, Gordon H., jt. auth. see Pollock, Algernon J.

Bennett, Gordon H., jt. auth. see Voorehoeve, H. C.

Bennett, Gordon H., ed. see Collingwood, Guillermo.

Bennett, Gordon H., ed. see Cutting, Jorge.

Bennett, Gordon H., ed. see Mackintosh, Carlos H.

Bennett, Gordon H., ed. see Rossier, H.

Bennett, Harold G. Reflections of Faith. LC 81-67326. 1983. pap. 5.95 (ISBN 0-8054-6565-0). Broadman.

Bennett, J. A. Poetry of the Passion: Studies in Twelve Centuries of English Verse. 1982. 37.50x (ISBN 0-19-812804-5); pap. 16.95x (ISBN 0-19-812832-0). Oxford U Pr.

Bennett, J. G. Gurdjieff: A Very Great Enigma 1973. LC 72-91951. 100p. (Orig.). 1984. pap. 4.50 (ISBN 0-87728-581-0). Weiser.

--Works on Subud, 3 vols. 300.00 (ISBN 0-8490-1332-1). Gordon Pr.

Bennett, J. G. & Montessori, Mario. The Spiritual Hunger of the Modern Child. Addison, Wendy, ed. LC 87-71204. 220p. 1985. pap. 8.95 (ISBN 0-934254-06-0). Claymont Comm.

Bennett, J. W. Theme of Spenser's "Foure Hymnes". LC 76-100731. 1970. pap. 39.95x (ISBN 0-8383-0003-0). Haskell.

Bennett, Jane. Unthinking Faith & Enlightenment: Nature & Politics in a Post-Hegelian Era. 192p. 1987. 30.00 (ISBN 0-8147-1095-6). NYU Pr.

Bennett, Joan. Five Metaphysical Poets: Donne, Herbert, Vaughan, Crashaw, Marvell. 1964. 32.50 (ISBN 0-521-04156-2); pap. 9.95 (ISBN 0-521-09238-8). Cambridge U Pr.

Bennett, John C. The Radical Imperative: From Theology to Social Ethics. LC 75-15538. 208p. 1975. 8.50 (ISBN 0-664-20824-X). Westminster.

Bennett, John C., et al. Christian Values & Economic Life. facs. ed. LC 71-99624. (Essay Index Reprint Ser.). 1954. 21.50 (ISBN 0-8369-1559-3). Ayer Co Pubs.

Bennett, John G. Creation. 1978. 5.95 (ISBN 0-900306-41-6, Pub. by Coombe Springs Pr). Claymont Comm.

--Deeper Man. LC 84-73170. 254p. 1985. 8.95 (ISBN 0-934254-07-9). Claymont Comm.

--Existence. 1977. 4.50 (ISBN 0-900306-40-8, Pub. by Coombe Springs Pr). Claymont Comm.

--The Foundations of Moral Philosophy, Vol. 2. (Dramatic Universe Ser.). 12.95 (ISBN 0-900306-42-4, Pub. by Coombe Springs Pr). Claymont Comm.

--The Foundations of Natural Philosophy, Vol. 1. (The Dramatic Universe Ser.). 29.95 (ISBN 0-900306-39-4, Pub. by Coombe Springs Pr). Claymont Comm.

--Gurdjieff Today. (Transformation of Man Ser.). 1978. 4.50 (ISBN 0-900306-13-0, Pub. by Coombe Springs Pr). Claymont Comm.

--The Long Pilgrimage: The Life & Teaching of Shivapuri Baba. LC 81-66139. 191p. pap. 7.95 (ISBN 0-913922-54-4). Dawn Horse Pr.

--Talks on Beelzebub's Tales. 1977. 6.95 (ISBN 0-900306-36-X, Pub. by Coombe Springs Pr). Claymont Comm.

--What Are We Living for. 4.95 (ISBN 0-900306-07-6, Pub. by Coombe Springs Pr.). Claymont Comm.

--Witness. 1983. 8.95 (ISBN 0-934254-05-2). Claymont Comm.

Bennett, Jonathan. A Study of Spinoza's Ethics. LC 83-18568. 416p. 1984. lib. bdg. 25.00 (ISBN 0-915145-82-0); pap. text ed. 13.75 (ISBN 0-915145-83-9). Hackett Pub.

Bennett, Marian. Baby Jesus ABC's. (Little Happy Day Bks.). (Illus.). 24p. (Orig.). 1983. pap. 0.49 (ISBN 0-87239-651-7, 2121). Standard Pub.

--Bible Numbers. (Little Happy Day Bks.). (Illus.). 24p. (Orig.). 1983. pap. 0.49 (ISBN 0-87239-653-3, 2123). Standard Pub.

--David, the Shepherd. (Happy Day Bible Stories Bks.). (Illus.). 24p. 1984. 1.59 (ISBN 0-87239-763-7, 3723). Standard Pub.

--God Made Chickens. (Happy Day Bks.). (Illus.). 24p. 1985. 1.59 (ISBN 0-87239-874-9, 3674). Standard Pub.

--God's Animals. (My Shape Book Ser.). (Illus.). 10p. 1985. 2.95 (ISBN 0-87239-909-5, 2749). Standard Pub.

--God's Gifts. (My Shape Book Ser.). (Illus.). 10p. 1985. 2.95 (ISBN 0-87239-910-9, 2750). Standard Pub.

--House Full of Prayers. (Surprise Bks.). (Illus.). 14p. (Orig.). 1982. pap. 4.95 (ISBN 0-87239-563-4, 2709). Standard Pub.

--I Go to Church. (My Shape Book Ser.). (Illus.). 10p. 1985. 2.95 (ISBN 0-87239-911-7, 2751). Standard Pub.

--Jesus, God's Son. (Surprise Bks.). (Illus.). 14p. (Orig.). 1982. pap. 4.95 (ISBN 0-87239-564-2, 2705). Standard Pub.

--My Bible Book. (Wipe-Clean Bks.). (Illus.). 12p. 1985. pap. 1.39 (ISBN 0-87239-956-7, 3516). Standard Pub.

--Preschool Pattern Book. (Illus.). 48p. (Orig.). 1973. pap. 4.95 (ISBN 0-87239-339-9, 2145). Standard Pub.

--The Story of Baby Jesus. (Illus.). 24p. (Orig.). 1983. pap. 0.49 (ISBN 0-87239-654-1, 2124). Standard Pub.

--Thank You, God. (My Surprise Book Ser.). (Illus.). 10p. 1985. 4.95 (ISBN 0-87239-906-0, 2730). Standard Pub.

Bennett, Marian, ed. Baby Jesus. (My Shape Book Ser.). (Illus.). 10p. 1985. 2.95 (ISBN 0-87239-907-9, 2747). Standard Pub.

Bennett, Marian, compiled by. Bible Memory Verses. (Little Happy Day Bks.). (Illus.). 24p. (Orig.). 1983. pap. 0.49 (ISBN 0-87239-652-5, 2122). Standard Pub.

Bennett, Marian, ed. God Made Me. (My Shape Book Ser.). (Illus.). 10p. 1985. 2.95 (ISBN 0-87239-908-7, 2748). Standard Pub.

--Songs for Preschool Children. LC 80-25091. 96p. (Orig.). 1981. pap. 7.95 (ISBN 0-87239-429-8, 5754). Standard Pub.

Bennett, Michael D., ed. see McRae, Shirley W.

Bennett, Ralph F. Early Dominicans: Studies in 13th-Century Dominican History. LC 71-139903. 1971. Repr. of 1937 ed. 12.00x (ISBN 0-8462-1531-4). Russell.

Bennett, Rita. How to Pray for Inner Healing for Yourself & Others. 126p. (Orig.). 1983. pap. 5.95 (ISBN 0-8007-5126-4, Power Bks). Revell.

--I'm Glad You Asked That. rev. & updated ed. 160p. 1983. pap. 5.95 (ISBN 0-8007-5111-6, Power Bks). Revell.

Bennett, Rita, jt. auth. see Bennett, Dennis.

Bennett, Robert. God's Work of Liberation: A Journey Through the Old Testament with the Liberation Heroes of Israel. (Illus., Orig.). 1976. pap. text ed. 5.95 (ISBN 0-8192-4067-2); tchr's guide 2.25x (ISBN 0-8192-4068-0). Morehouse.

Bennett, Robert A. & Edwards, O. C. The Bible for Today's Church. (The Church's Teaching Ser.: Vol. 2). 320p. 1979. 5.95 (ISBN 0-8164-0419-4, HarpR); pap. 4.95 (ISBN 0-8164-2215-X); users guide 1.50 (ISBN 0-8164-2222-2). Har-Row.

Bennett, W. H., tr. see Skeireins.

Bennett, William H. Catholic Footsteps in Old New York: A Chronicle of Catholicity in the City of New York from 1524 to 1808. LC 77-359169. (Monograph Ser.: No. 28). 1973. Repr. of 1909 ed. 10.00x (ISBN 0-930060-08-3). US Cath Hist.

--An Exposition of the Books of Chronicles. 467p. 1983. lib. bdg. 17.50 (ISBN 0-86524-169-4, 1401). Klock & Klock.

Bennion, Lowell L. The Book of Mormon: A Guide to Christian Living. LC 85-16104. 138p. 1985. 8.95 (ISBN 0-87747-866-X). Deseret Bk.

--I Believe. LC 83-70024. 87p. 1983. 5.95 (ISBN 0-87747-954-2). Deseret Bk.

--Understanding the Scriptures. LC 81-66422. 88p. 1981. 6.95 (ISBN 0-87747-863-5). Deseret Bk.

Benoist De Matougues, L. Dictionnaire de Geographie Sacree et Ecclesiastique, 3 vols. Migne, J. P., ed. (Encyclopedie Theologique Ser.: Vols. 28-30). (Fr.). 1886p. Repr. of 1854 ed. lib. bdg. 240.50x (ISBN 0-89241-241-0). Caratzas.

Benoist Matougues, L. De see Benoist De Matougues, L.

Benoit, Hubert. The Interior Realization. Mahoney, John F., tr. from Fr. (Illus.). 128p. (Orig.). 1987. pap. 6.95 (ISBN 0-87728-624-8). Weiser.

--The Supreme Doctrine: Psychological Studies in Zen Thought. 248p. 1984. pap. 8.95 (ISBN 0-89281-058-0). Inner Tradit.

Benoit, Pierre, ed. How Does the Christian Confront the Old Testament. (Concilium Ser.: Vol. 30). 1967. 7.95 (ISBN 0-8091-0074-6). Paulist Pr.

Benoit, Pierre, et al, eds. Dynamism of Biblical Tradition. LC 67-15983. (Concilium Ser.: Vol. 20). 226p. 1967. 7.95 (ISBN 0-8091-0035-5). Paulist Pr.

--Human Reality of Sacred Scripture. LC 65-28869. (Concilium Ser.: Vol. 10). 220p. 7.95 (ISBN 0-8091-0075-4). Paulist Pr.

Ben-Sasson, Haim H., ed. A History of the Jewish People. (Illus.). 1108p. 1985. pap. 18.95 (ISBN 0-674-39731-2). Harvard U Pr.

Ben-Sasson, Haim H., et al. History of the Jewish People. (Illus.). 1040p. 1976. 60.00 (ISBN 0-674-39730-4). Harvard U Pr.

Benschoten, A. Q. Van see Van Benschoten, A. Q., Jr.

Bensen, D. R. Bibical Limericks. 1986. pap. 6.95 (Pub. by Ballantine-Epiphany). Ballantine.

Bensimon-Donath, Doris. L'Integration des Juifs Nord-Africains en France. (Publications de l'Institut d'Etudes et de Recherches Interethniques et Interculturelles: No. 1). 1971. pap. 14.00x (ISBN 90-2796-930-2). Mouton.

Benson, Alie H., jt. ed. see Harrell, Irene B.

Benson, Bob. He Speaks Softly. 160p. 1985. 8.95 (ISBN 0-8499-0449-8, 0449-8). Word Bks.

Benson, Bob & Benson, Michael. Disciplines of the Inner Life. 380p. 1985. 18.95 (ISBN 0-8499-0468-4, 0468-4). Word Bks.

Benson, C. H. Arte de Ensenar. Villalobos, Fernando P., tr. from Eng. (Curso Para Maestros Cristianos: No. 5). (Span.). 128p. 1971. pap. 3.50 (ISBN 0-89922-016-9). Edit Caribe.

--Conozcamos al Alumno. Villalobos, Fernando P., tr. from Eng. (Curso para Maestros Cristianos: No. 4). (Span.). 128p. 1972. pap. 3.50 (ISBN 0-89922-014-2). Edit Caribe.

--Escuela Dominical en Accion. Villalobos, Fernando P., tr. from Eng. (Curso Para Maestros Cristianos: No. 6). (Span.). 122p. 1972. pap. 3.50 (ISBN 0-89922-018-5); instructor's manual 1.50 (ISBN 0-89922-019-3). Edit Caribe.

--Poesia y Profecia del Antiquo Testamento. Villalobos, Fernando P., tr. from Eng. (Curso Para Maestros Cristianos: No. 2). (Span.). 122p. 1972. pap. 3.50 (ISBN 0-89922-010-X). Edit Caribe.

Benson, Clarence H. Old Testament Survey: Poetry & Prophecy. rev. ed. 96p. 1972. pap. text ed. 4.95 (ISBN 0-910566-02-X); Perfect bdg. instr's. guide 5.95 (ISBN 0-910566-21-6). Evang Tchr.

--Teaching Techniques. rev. ed. 96p. 1983. pap. text ed. 4.95 (ISBN 0-910566-05-4); Perfect bdg. instr's. guide 5.95 (ISBN 0-910566-23-2). Evang Tchr.

--The Triune God. rev. ed. 96p. 1970. pap. text ed. 4.95 (ISBN 0-910566-09-7); Perfect bdg. instr's. guide 5.95 (ISBN 0-910566-24-0). Evang Tchr.

Benson, Dan. The Total Man. 1977. pap. 3.95 (ISBN 0-8423-7289-X). Tyndale.

Benson, Dennis, jt. auth. see Benson, Marilyn.

Benson, Dennis C. Creative Bible Studies. LC 85-71044. (Illus.). 660p. (Orig.). 1985. pap. 19.95 (ISBN 0-931529-01-8). Group Bks.

--Creative Worship in Youth Ministry. LC 85-24735. (Illus.). 249p. (Orig.). 1985. pap. 11.95 (ISBN 0-931529-05-0). Group Bks.

Benson, Dennis C. & Benson, Marilyn J. Promises to Keep: A Workbook of Experiences for Covenant Living. (Orig.). 1978. pap. 3.95 (ISBN 0-377-00077-9). Friend Pr.

Benson, Dennis C. & Wolfe, Bill. The Basic Encyclopedia for Youth Ministry. LC 81-81967. (Illus.). 352p. 1981. 16.95 (ISBN 0-936664-04-5). Group Bks.

Benson, Donald. Biblical Limericks, Old Testament Stories Re-versed. 1986. 6.95 (ISBN 0-345-33033-1). Ballantine.

Benson, Elizabeth P., ed. Death & the Afterlife in Pre-Columbian America: A Conference at Dumbarton Oaks, October 27, 1973. LC 74-22694. (Illus.). 196p. 1975. 15.00x (ISBN 0-88402-062-2). Dumbarton Oaks.

Benson, Ezra T. Come unto Christ. 136p. 1984. 8.95 (ISBN 0-87747-997-6). Deseret Bk.

Benson, George W. The Cross: Its History & Symbolism. LC 73-88643. 1976. Repr. of 1934 ed. lib. bdg. 25.00 (ISBN 0-87817-149-5). Hacker.

Benson, John E., jt. auth. see Sargent, Richard B.

Benson, John L. Who Is the Antichrist? LC 78-2426. 1978. pap. 2.50 (ISBN 0-87227-058-0). Reg Baptist.

Benson, Kathleen. A Man Called Martin Luther. 1980. 7.50 (ISBN 0-570-03625-9, 39-1067). Concordia.

Benson, Lewis. Catholic Quakerism: A Vision for All Men. 108p. 1968. pap. text ed. 2.50 (ISBN 0-941308-03-0). Religious Soc Friends.

Benson, Louis. The English Hymn. (Music Reprint Ser.). 624p. 1985. Repr. of 1915 ed. 65.00 (ISBN 0-306-76261-7). Da Capo.

Benson, Marilyn & Benson, Dennis. The Hard Times Catalog for Youth Ministry. LC 82-81332. (Illus.). 288p. (Orig.). 1982. pap. 14.95 (ISBN 0-936664-06-1). Group Bks.

Benson, Marilyn J., jt. auth. see Benson, Dennis C.

Benson, Michael, jt. auth. see Benson, Bob.

Benson, Peter L. & Guerra, Michael J. Sharing the Faith: The Beliefs & Values of Catholic High School Teachers. 85p. 1985. 11.40 (ISBN 0-318-18578-4); member 8.55. Natl Cath Educ.

Benson, Peter L. & Hill, Dorothy. Religion on Capitol Hill: Myths & Realities. LC 86-16434. (Illus.). 223p. 1986. pap. 8.95x (ISBN 0-19-504168-2). Oxford U Pr.

Benson, Robert H. & More, Thomas. The Friendship of Christ. (Books to Live Ser.). 156p. 1984. 10.95 (ISBN 0-88347-171-X). Thomas More.

Benson, Robert L. The Bishop-Elect: A Study in Medieval Ecclesiastical Office. LC 65-17130. pap. 115.00 (ISBN 0-317-07842-9, 2010535). Bks Demand UMI.

Benson, Sally. Stories of the Gods & Heroes. (Illus.). 1940. 12.95 (ISBN 0-8037-8291-8, 01258-370). Dial Bks Young.

Benson, Warren S., jt. auth. see Gangel, Kenneth O.

Benson, Warren S., jt. ed. see Zuck, Roy B.

Bent, A. J. Van Der see Van Der Bent, A. J.

Bente, F. Historical Introduction to the Book of Concord. 1965. 12.95 (ISBN 0-570-03262-8, 15-1926). Concordia.

Bentham, Jeremy & Hart, H. L. Introduction to the Principles of Morals & Legislation. 385p. 1982. 14.95x (ISBN 0-416-31910-6, NO. 3710). Methuen Inc.

Bentley, Eric. The Cult of the Superman. Orig. Title: A Century of Hero Worship. 11.50 (ISBN 0-8446-0486-0). Peter Smith.

Bentley, James. A Calendar of Saints: The Lives of the Principal Saints of the Christian Year. (Illus.). 256p. 1987. 22.95 (ISBN 0-8160-1682-8). Facts on File.

--Ritualism & Politics in Victorian Britain. (Oxford Theological Monographs). (Illus.). 1978. 37.00x (ISBN 0-19-826714-2). Oxford U Pr.

Bentley, James, retold by. The Children's Bible. (Illus.). 237p. 1983. 7.95 (ISBN 0-531-03592-1). Watts.

Bentley, Jerry H. Humanists & Holy Writ. LC 83-42547. 264p. 1983. 25.50x (ISBN 0-691-05392-8). Princeton U Pr.

Bentley, Richard. Eight Boyle Lectures on Atheism. Wellek, Rene, ed. LC 75-11196. (British Philosophers & Theologians of the 17th & 18th Centuries Ser.: Vol. 3). 1976. Repr. of 1692 ed. lib. bdg. 51.00 (ISBN 0-8240-1752-8). Garland Pub.

Bentley, Richard, ed. see Milton, John.

Bentley, William. The Diary of Rev. William Bentley: 1784-1819, 4 vols. 72.00 (ISBN 0-8446-1071-2). Set. Peter Smith.

Bentley, William H., ed. see McCray, Walter A.

Bentley-Taylor, David. Java Saga. Orig. Title: Weathercocks Reward. 1975. pap. 2.25 (ISBN 0-85363-100-X). OMF Bks.

Bently, W. Holman. Pioneering on the Congo, 2 Vols. (Landmarks in Anthropology Ser). 1970. Repr. of 1900 ed. Set. lib. bdg. 85.00 (ISBN 0-384-03943-X). Johnson Repr.

Bently-Taylor, David. Augustine: Wayward Genius. 1981. pap. 5.95 (ISBN 0-8010-0807-7). Baker Bk.

Benton, Angelo Ames. The Church Cyclopaedia: A Dictionary of Church Doctrine, History, Organization & Ritual, & Containing Original Articles on Special Topics, Written Expressly for This Work by Bishops, Presbyters, & Laymen. LC 74-31499. 810p. 1975. Repr. of 1883 ed. 65.00x (ISBN 0-8103-4204-9). Gale.

Benton, John. Coming to Faith in Christ. 15p. 1977. pap. 0.80 (ISBN 0-85151-252-6). Banner of Truth.

--Do You Know Where Your Children Are? 160p. 1983. pap. 2.95 (ISBN 0-8007-8480-4). Revell.

--Kari. 192p. 1984. pap. 2.95 (ISBN 0-8007-8491-X, New Hope). Revell.

--Sheila. 192p. 1982. pap. 2.95 (ISBN 0-8007-8419-7, New Hope Bks.). Revell.

--Stephanie. 1983. pap. 2.95 (ISBN 0-8007-8472-3, Spire Bks). Revell.

--Tracy. 192p. (Orig.). 1984. pap. 2.95 (ISBN 0-8007-8495-2, New Hope). Revell.

--Valarie. 192p. (Orig.). 1982. pap. 2.95 (ISBN 0-8007-8430-8, New Hope Bks.). Revell.

Benton, Josephine M. A Door Ajar: Facing Death Without Fear. LC 65-16442. 1979. pap. 4.45 (ISBN 0-8298-0366-1). Pilgrim NY.

--Martha & Mary: A Woman's Relationship to Her Home. 1983. pap. 2.50x (ISBN 0-87574-036-7, 036). Pendle Hill.

Benton, Richard A. Spoken Pangasinan. LC 79-152457. (University of Hawaii, Honolulu. Pacific & Asian Linguistics Institute). pap. 160.00 (ISBN 0-317-10118-8, 2017214). Bks Demand UMI.

Bentwich, Norman D. Jewish Youth Comes Home. LC 75-6422. (The Rise of Jewish Nationalism & the Middle East Ser). 159p. 1976. Repr. of 1944 ed. 19.25 (ISBN 0-88355-309-0). Hyperion Conn.

Benware, Paul. Luke: Gospel of the Son of Man. (Everyman's Bible Commentary Ser.). 1985. pap. 5.95 (ISBN 0-8024-2074-5). Moody.

Benware, Paul N. Ambassadors of Armstrongism. 182p. (Orig.). 1984. pap. 5.95 (ISBN 0-87508-046-4). Chr Lit.

Ben-Yehuda, Eliezer, ed. Dictionary & Thesaurus of the Hebrew Language, 8 Vols. Set. 150.00 (ISBN 0-498-07038-7, Yoseloff); lea. bd. set o.p. 250.00 (ISBN 0-498-08915-0). A S Barnes.

Ben-Yehuda, Nachman. Deviance & Moral Boundaries: Witchcraft, the Occult, Science Fiction, Deviant Sciences & Scientists. LC 85-1167. x, 260p. 1985. 25.00x (ISBN 0-226-04335-5). U of Chicago Pr.

Benyus, Janine M. Christmas Tree Pests Manual. 107p. 1983. pap. 14.00 (ISBN 0-318-11762-2, S/N 001-001-00589-4). Gov Printing Office.

Benz, Larry L. Standards for Living. LC 77-70791. 1977. pap. 1.99 (ISBN 0-87148-779-9). Pathway Pr.

Benziger, James. Images of Eternity: Studies in the Poetry of Religious Vision, from Wordsworth to T. S. Eliot. LC 62-15007. (Arcturus Books Paperbacks). 333p. 1962. pap. 2.25 (ISBN 0-8093-0136-9). S Ill U Pr.

Ben Zion, Raphael, tr. from Hebrew. Anthology of Jewish Mysticism. 5.00 (ISBN 0-686-13334-X). Yesod Pubs.

Ben Zion, Raphael see Zion, Raphael Ben.

Beonio-Brocchieri Fumagalli, M. T. The Logic of Abelard. Pleasance, Simon, tr. from It. (Synthese Library: No. 1). 101p. 1969. lib. bdg. 18.50 (ISBN 90-277-0068-0, Pub. by Reidel Holland). Kluwer Academic.

Beougher, Lois. Now Lord, How Did You Manage That? 143p. 1984. 7.95 (ISBN 0-533-05912-7). Vantage.

Berachya. The Ethical Treatises of Berachya, Son of Rabbi Natronai Ha-Nakdan. LC 73-2187. (The Jewish People; History, Religion, Literature Ser.). Repr. of 1902 ed. 37.50 (ISBN 0-405-05253-7). Ayer Co Pubs.

Berardino, Angelo di see Quasten, Johannes & Di Berardino, Angelo.

Berchan, Richard. Inner Stage: An Essay on the Conflict of Vocations in the Early Works of Paul Claudel. 1966. 3.50 (ISBN 0-87013-097-8). Mich St U Pr.

Berchman, Robert M. From Philo to Origen: Middle Platonism in Transition. (Brown Judiac Studies: No. 69). 370p. 1985. 29.95 (ISBN 0-89130-750-8, 14 00 69); pap. 25.95 (ISBN 0-89130-815-6). Scholars Pr GA.

Bercovici, Konrad. The Crusades. 1979. Repr. of 1929 ed. lib. bdg. 25.00 (ISBN 0-8482-3439-1). Norwood Edns.

Bercovitch, S. The American Puritan Imagination. LC 73-94136. 256p. 1974. 39.50 (ISBN 0-521-20392-9); pap. 14.95 (ISBN 0-521-09841-6). Cambridge U Pr.

Bercovitch, Sacvan. The Puritan Origins of the American Self. LC 74-29713. 272p. 1975. pap. 9.95x (ISBN 0-300-02117-8). Yale U Pr.

Bercovitch, Sacvan, ed. The American Puritan Imagination: Essays in Revaluation. LC 73-94136. pap. 68.30 (2027269). Bks Demand UMI.

--Typology & Early American Literature. LC 74-181362. (New England Writers Ser.). 352p. 1971. 20.00x (ISBN 0-87023-096-4). U of Mass Pr.

Berdiaer, Nicolaii. The Realm of Spirit & the Realm of Caesar. Luurie, Donald A., tr. from Rus. LC 74-1554. 182p. 1975. Repr. of 1953 ed. lib. bdg. 55.00x (ISBN 0-8371-7395-7, BESC). Greenwood.

Berdiaev, Nikolai. The Destiny of Man. Duddington, Natalie, tr. LC 78-14100. 1987. Repr. of 1954 ed. 26.50 (ISBN 0-88355-775-4). Hyperion Conn.

Berdiaev, Nikolai A. The Beginning & the End. French, R. M., tr. from Russian. LC 76-6083. 1976. Repr. of 1952 ed. lib. bdg. 35.00x (ISBN 0-8371-8837-7, BEBE). Greenwood.

--The Russian Idea. French, R. M., tr. LC 78-32021. 1979. Repr. of 1948 ed. lib. bdg. 37.50x (ISBN 0-313-20968-5, BERN). Greenwood.

Berdoe, E. Browning & the Christian Faith. LC 79-130244. (Studies in Browning, No. 4). 1970. Repr. of 1896 ed. lib. bdg. 39.95x (ISBN 0-8383-1134-2). Haskell.

Berdyaev, Nicolas. Freedom & the Spirit. LC 72-2567. (Select Bibliographies Reprint Ser.). 1972. Repr. of 1935 ed. 24.50 (ISBN 0-8369-6848-4). Ayer Co Pubs.

--Origin of Russian Communism. 1960. pap. 8.95 (ISBN 0-472-06034-1, 34, AA). U of Mich Pr.

Beredene, Jocelyn. What Difference Did the Deed of Christ Make? 1979. pap. 1.50 (ISBN 0-88010-103-2). Anthroposophic.

Berenbaum, Michael. The Vision of the Void: Theological Reflections on the Works of Elie Wiesel. LC 78-27321. 1978. 17.50x (ISBN 0-8195-5030-2). Wesleyan U Pr.

--The Vision of the Void: Theological Reflections on the Works of Elie Wiesel. xii, 240p. 1987. pap. 12.95 (ISBN 0-8195-6189-4). Wesleyan U Pr.

Berens, E. M. The Myths & Legends of Ancient Greece & Rome. LC 77-91528. 1977. Repr. of 1880 ed. lib. bdg. 30.00 (ISBN 0-89341-029-2). Longwood Pub Group.

Berenson, Bernard. Contemporary Jewish Fiction. 1976. lib. bdg. 59.95 (ISBN 0-87968-939-0). Gordon Pr.

--Studies in Medieval Painting. LC 73-153884. (Graphic Art Ser.). (Illus.). 148p. 1971. Repr. of 1930 ed. lib. bdg. 39.50 (ISBN 0-306-70292-4). Da Capo.

Berenstain, Jan, jt. auth. see Berenstain, Stan.

Berenstain, Stan & Berenstain, Jan. How to Teach Your Children about God...Without Actually Scaring them out of their Wits. 1984. pap. 3.95 (ISBN 0-345-29457-2). Ballantine.

Beresford, Brian, ed. see Geshe, Rabten & Geshe, Dhargyey.

Berg, Carolyn. Bulletin Board Designs for the Christian Classroom. 1984. pap. 5.95 tchr's. material (ISBN 0-570-03930-4, 12-2866). Concordia.

Berg, Daniel N., jt. ed. see Dieter, Melvin E.

Berg, Kay K. & Rogers, Donald B. Teachable Moments. LC 85-71827. 52p. (Orig.). 1985. pap. 3.95 (ISBN 0-88177-019-1, DR019B). Discipleship Res.

Berg, Leo. The Superman in Modern Literature: Flaubert, Carlyle, Emerson, Nietzsche. Repr. 20.00 (ISBN 0-8274-3555-X). R West.

Berg, Miguel. El Placer De Estudiar la Biblia. (Span.). 127p. (Orig.). 1973. pap. 2.95 (ISBN 0-89922-026-6). Edit Caribe.

Berg, Miguel, jt. auth. see Lebar, Lois.

Berg, Philip S. The Kabbalah Connection. 224p. 1983. 12.95 (ISBN 0-943688-02-7); pap. 9.95 (ISBN 0-943688-03-5). Res Ctr Kabbalah.

--Kabbalah for the Layman. (Span.). 224p. 1986. 12.95 (ISBN 0-943688-43-4); pap. 9.95 (ISBN 0-943688-44-2). Res Ctr Kabbalah.

--Kabbalah for the Layman II. 224p. 1987. 14.95 (ISBN 0-943688-24-8); pap. 9.95 (ISBN 0-943688-26-4). Res Ctr Kabbalah.

--Kabbalah for the Layman III. 1987. 14.95 (ISBN 0-943688-69-8); pap. 9.95 (ISBN 0-943688-70-1). Res Ctr Kabbalah.

--Power of the Aleph Beth, Vol. 1. 288p. 1986. 14.95 (ISBN 0-943688-11-6); pap. 9.95 (ISBN 0-943688-10-8). Res Ctr Kabbalah.

--Wheels of a Soul. (Hebrew.). 160p. 1986. 12.95 (ISBN 0-943688-41-8); pap. 9.95 (ISBN 0-943688-42-6). Res Ctr Kabbalah.

--Wheels of a Soul. (Span.). 256p. 1986. 12.95 (ISBN 0-943688-45-0); pap. 9.95 (ISBN 0-943688-46-9). Res Ctr Kabbalah.

Berg, Philip S., ed. see Ashlag, Yehuda.

Berg, Phillip S. Power of the Aleph Beth, Vol. II. 1987. 14.95 (ISBN 0-943688-56-6); pap. 9.95 (ISBN 0-943688-57-4). Res Ctr Kabbalah.

--The Zohar: Parashat Pinhas, Vol. II. 288p. 1987. 14.95 (ISBN 0-943688-52-3); pap. 9.95 (ISBN 0-943688-53-1). Res Ctr Kabbalah.

--The Zohar: Parashat Pinhas, Vol. III. 288p. 1987. 14.95 (ISBN 0-943688-54-X); pap. 9.95 (ISBN 0-943688-55-8). Res Ctr Kabbalah.

Berg, Sandra B. The Book of Esther: Motifs, Themes & Structure. LC 78-32035. (SBL Dissertation Ser.). 1979. pap. 9.95 (ISBN 0-89130-279-4, 060144). Scholars Pr GA.

Berg, Vibeke. Yoga During Pregnancy. 1983. 6.95 (ISBN 0-686-44925-8, Fireside). S&S.

--Yoga in Pregnancy. 135p. 1977. 11.95 (ISBN 0-940500-24-8, Pub. by D B Taraporwala India). Asia Bk Corp.

Bergaigne, Abel. Vedic Religion. Paranjpe, V. G., tr. 1978. 25.00 (ISBN 0-89684-006-9, Pub. by Motilal Banarsidass India). Orient Bk Dist.

Bergan, Jacqueline & Schwan, S. Marie. Birth. (Take & Receive Ser.). (Illus.). 154p. (Orig.). 1985. pap. 6.95 (ISBN 0-88489-170-4). St Mary's.

--Forgiveness: A Guide for Prayer. (Take & Receive Ser.). 200p. (Orig.). 1985. pap. 6.95 (ISBN 0-88489-169-0). St Mary's.

--Love: A Guide for Prayer. (Take & Receive Ser.). 96p. (Orig.). 1984. pap. 5.95 (ISBN 0-88489-168-2). St Mary's.

Bergant, Dianne. Introduction to the Bible. (Bible Commentary Ser.). 72p. 1985. pap. 2.95 (ISBN 0-8146-1369-1). Liturgical Pr.

--Job, Ecclesiastes. (Old Testament Message Ser.: Vol. 18). 1982. 12.95 (ISBN 0-89453-418-1); pap. 9.95 (ISBN 0-89453-252-9). M Glazier.

--What Are They Saying about Wisdom Literature? LC 83-82027. (WATSA Ser.). (Orig.). 1984. pap. 4.95 (ISBN 0-8091-2605-2). Paulist Pr.

Bergendoff, Conrad. Augustana - A Profession of Faith: A History of Augustana College, 1860-1935. LC 76-92170. (Augustana College Library Ser.: No. 33). (Illus.). 220p. 1969. 5.95x (ISBN 0-910182-33-7). Augustana Coll.

--The Augustana Ministerium: A Study of the Careers of the 2504 Pastors of the Augustana Evangelical Lutheran Synod-Church 1850-1962. LC 80-66400. (Augustana Historical Society Ser.: No. 28). 246p. 1980. 15.00 (ISBN 0-910184-28-3). Augustana.

--One Hundred Years of Oratorio at Augustana: A History of the Handel Oratorio Society, 1881-1980. LC 81-52434. (Augustana Historical Society Publication Ser.: No. 29). 54p. 1981. 7.50 (ISBN 0-910184-00-3); pap. 5.00 (ISBN 0-910184-29-1). Augustana.

Bergendoff, Conrad & Lehman, Helmut H., eds. Luther's Works: Church & Ministry II, Vol. 40. LC 55-9893. 1958. 19.95 (ISBN 0-8006-0340-0, 1-340). Fortress.

Bergendoff, Conrad, tr. see Norelius, Eric.

Bergendoff, Conrad J. Olavus Petri & the Ecclesiastical Transformation in Sweden (1521-1552) A Study in the Swedish Reformation. LC 83-45600. Date not set. Repr. of 1928 ed. 32.50 (ISBN 0-404-19868-6). AMS Pr.

Bergendoff, Conrad L. Pastoral Care for Alcoholism: An Introduction. 36p. 1981. pap. 1.95 (ISBN 0-89486-123-9). Hazelden.

Berger & Hollerweger, eds. Celebrating the Easter Vigil. O'Connell, Matthew J., tr. (Ger.). 160p. 1983. pap. 9.95 (ISBN 0-916134-56-3). Pueblo Pub Co.

Berger, Alan A. Witness to the Sacred: Mystical Tales of Primitive Hasidism. (Illus.). 1977. pap. text ed. 4.00x (ISBN 0-914914-10-3). New Horizons.

Berger, Alan L. Crisis & Covenant: The Holocaust in American Jewish Fiction. (Series in Modern Jewish Literature & Culture). 234p. 1985. 39.50 (ISBN 0-88706-085-4); pap. 14.95 (ISBN 0-88706-086-2). State U NY Pr.

Berger, Arthur A. Signs in Contemporary Culture. (Annenberg Communication Ser.). (Illus.). 224p. 1984. text ed. 29.95 (ISBN 0-582-28487-2). Longman.

Berger, David. The Legacy of Jewish Migration: Eighteen Eighty-One & Its Impact. (Social Science Monographs, Brooklyn College Studies on Society in Change). 189p. 1983. 26.00x (ISBN 0-88033-026-0). East Eur Quarterly.

Berger, David & Wyschogrod, Michael. Jews & Jewish Christianity. 3.95x (ISBN 0-87068-675-5). Ktav.

Berger, David, ed. History & Hate: The Dimensions of Anti-Semitism. 160p. 1986. 14.95 (ISBN 0-8276-0267-7). Jewish Pubns.

Berger, Elmer. Memoirs of an Anti-Zionist Jew. 159p. 1978. 4.00 (ISBN 0-88728-127-3). Inst Palestine.

Berger, Gilda. Easter & Other Spring Holidays. (First Bks.). (Illus.). 72p. 1983. PLB 9.90 (ISBN 0-531-04547-1). Watts.

--Religion. (A Reference First Bk.). 96p. 1983. PLB 9.40 (ISBN 0-531-04538-2). Watts.

Berger, I. K. Everybody's Guide to Paradise. 204p. 1986. pap. 29.00x (ISBN 0-7212-0776-6, Pub. by Regency Pr). State Mutual Bk.

Berger, Jean, ed. see Perti, Giacomo Antonio.

Berger, Klaus. Die Amen-Worte Jesu: Eine Untersuchung zum Problem der Legitimation in Apokalyptischer Rede. (Beiheft 39 Zur Zeitschrift fuer Die neutestamentliche Wissenschaft Ser.). (Ger). 1970. 20.80x (ISBN 3-11-006445-6). De Gruyter.

Berger, Meyer, jt. auth. see Keller, James G.

Berger, Mike. Bittersweet: True Stories of Decisions That Shaped Eternal Paths. LC 80-81505. 124p. 1980. 6.95 (ISBN 0-88290-144-3). Horizon Utah.

Berger, Morroe. Islam in Egypt Today: Social & Political Aspects of Popular Religion. LC 70-113597. 1970. 34.50 (ISBN 0-521-07834-2). Cambridge U Pr.

Berger, P. William Blake: Poet & Mystic. LC 67-31287. (Studies in Blake, No. 3). 1969. Repr. of 1914 ed. lib. bdg. 75.00x (ISBN 0-8383-0778-7). Haskell.

Berger, Pamela. The Goddess Obscured: Transformation of the Grain Protectress from Goddess to Saint. LC 85-47524. (Illus.). 250p. 1986. 19.95 (ISBN 0-8070-6722-9). Beacon Pr.

Berger, Peter L. The Precarious Vision. LC 76-1981. 238p. 1976. Repr. of 1961 ed. lib. bdg. 22.50x (ISBN 0-8371-8657-9, BEPV). Greenwood.

--Religion in a Revolutionary Society. (Bicentennial Lecture Ser.). 16p. 1974. pap. 1.00 (ISBN 0-8447-1306-6). Am Enterprise.

--Sacred Canopy: Elements of a Sociological Theory of Religion. LC 67-19805. 1969. pap. 4.50 (ISBN 0-385-07305-4, Anch). Doubleday.

Berger, Rabbi E., et al. Judaism, Zionism, & Anti-Semitism. 72p. (Orig.). 1985. pap. 2.50 (ISBN 0-935177-01-9). Palestine Focus.

Berger, Rainer, jt. auth. see Nicholson, H. B.

Berger, Suzanne, ed. Religion in West European Politics. (Illus.). 200p. 1982. text ed. 29.50x (ISBN 0-7146-3218-X, F Cass Co). Biblio Dist.

Bergera, Gary J. & Priddis, Ronald. Brigham Young University: A House of Faith. 513p. (Orig.). 1985. pap. 19.95 (ISBN 0-941214-34-6). Signature Bks.

Bergessen, Albert. The Sacred & the Subversive: Political Witch-Hunts as National Rituals. LC 84-61370. (Society for Scientific Study of Religion Monograph: No. 4). 1984. pap. 5.50 (ISBN 0-932566-03-0). Soc Sci Stud Rel.

Bergey, Alyce. Beggar's Greatest Wish. (Arch Bks: No. 6). 1969. pap. 0.99 (ISBN 0-570-06040-0, 59-1155). Concordia.

--David & Jonathan. (Arch Bks.). (Illus.). 24p. 1987. pap. 00.99 (ISBN 0-570-09006-7, 59-01434). Concordia.

--Fishermen's Surprise. (Arch Bks: Set 4). 1967. laminated cover 0.99 (ISBN 0-570-06028-1, 59-1139). Concordia.

--Young Jesus in the Temple. (Arch Bks.). (Illus.). 24p. 1986. pap. 0.99 saddlestitched (ISBN 0-570-06203-9, 59-1426). Concordia.

Bergey, Alyce & Wind, Betty. Boy Who Saved His Family. (Arch Bks: Set 3). 1966. laminated cover 0.99 (ISBN 0-570-06017-6, 59-1126). Concordia.

Bergh, S. Van Den see Al-Tahafut, Tahafut.

Berghahn, Marion. German-Jewish Refugees in England: The Ambiguities of Assimilation. LC 83-9802. 270p. 1984. 30.00 (ISBN 0-312-32571-1). St Martin.

Berghoef, Gerard & DeKoster, Lester. The Believers Handbook. LC 82-72686. 295p. 1982. 15.95 (ISBN 0-934874-03-4); pap. 8.95 (ISBN 0-934874-05-0). Chr Lib Pr.

--The Deacon's Handbook. 269p. 15.95 (ISBN 0-934874-01-8). Chr Lib Pr.

--The Elders Handbook. LC 79-54143. 303p. 1979. 15.95 (ISBN 0-934874-00-X). Chr Lib Pr.

--Liberation Theology: The Church's Future Shock. 197p. 1984. 14.95 (ISBN 0-934874-07-7). Chr Lib Pr.

Bergier, N. S. Dictionnaire de Theologique Dogmatique, Liturgique, Canonique et Disciplinaire, 3 vols. in 4. Migne, J. P., ed. (Encyclopedie Theologique Ser.: Vols. 33-35). (Fr.). 2681p. Repr. of 1851 ed. lib. bdg. 341.00x (ISBN 0-89241-243-7). Caratzas.

Bergin, Feryl J. You...& Being a Teenager. (Illus.). 112p. 4.95 (ISBN 0-936955-00-7). Eminent Pubns.

Bergin, Joseph. Cardinal Richelieu: Power & the Pursuit of Wealth. 352p. 1985. 30.00x (ISBN 0-300-03495-4). Yale U Pr.

Berglund, Mary C. Gather the Children: Celebrating the Word with Ideas, Activities, Prayer & Projects. 1987. pap. 14.95. Pastoral Pr.

Berglund, Robert. A Philosophy of Church Music. (Orig.). 1985. pap. 9.95 (ISBN 0-8024-0279-8). Moody.

Bergman, Bella. Hebrew Level Two. Band, Ora, ed. (Illus.). 243p. 1983. pap. text ed. 7.95x (ISBN 0-87441-360-5). Behrman.

Bergman, Jerry. Jehovah's Witness & Kindred Groups: An Historical Compendium & Bibliography. LC 83-47603. (Social Science Ser.). 414p. 1985. lib. bdg. 58.00 (ISBN 0-8240-9109-4). Garland Pub.

Bergman, Simcha, tr. see Rabbi Nachman of Breslov.

Bergmann, Mark, jt. auth. see Otte, Elmer.

Bergren, Victor. The Prophets & the Law. 15.00x (ISBN 0-87820-403-2, Pub. by Hebrew Union College Press). Ktav.

Bergson, Henri. Creative Evolution. Mitxhell, Arthur, tr. LC 83-19859. 460p. 1984. pap. text ed. 13.50 (ISBN 0-8191-3553-4). U Pr of Amer.

--Study in Metaphysics. LC 61-10604. 1961. pap. 5.00 (ISBN 0-8022-0107-5). Philos Lib.

--The Two Sources of Morality & Religion. LC 74-10373. 308p. 1974. Repr. of 1935 ed. lib. bdg. 25.00x (ISBN 0-8371-7679-4, BETS). Greenwood.

--The Two Sources of Morality & Religion. Audra, R. Ashley, tr. from Fr. LC 77-89762. 1977. pap. text ed. 8.95 (ISBN 0-268-01835-9). U of Notre Dame Pr.

Bergsten, T., jt. ed. see Westin, G.

Beringause, Arthur see Lieberman, Leo.

Beringer, Robert. The Easter People. 1984. 4.75 (ISBN 0-89536-682-7, 4858). CSS of Ohio.

Berio, Paquita. Ahora Brillan las Estrellas. (Span.). 134p. (Orig.). 1981. pap. 3.75 (ISBN 0-89922-201-3). Edit Caribe.

Berk, Fred. Chasidic Dance. (YA) 1975. pap. 5.00 (ISBN 0-8074-0083-1, 582050). UAHC.

Berk, Stephen E. Calvinism vs. Democracy: Timothy Dwight & the Origins of American Evangelical Orthodoxy. LC 73-20053. xiv, 252p. 1974. 25.00 (ISBN 0-208-01419-5, Archon). Shoe String.

Berk, Stephen M. Year of Crisis, Year of Hope: Russian Jewry & the Pogroms of 1881-1882. LC 84-25216. (Contributions in Ethnic Studies Ser.: No. 11). xvi, 231p. 1985. lib. bdg. 39.95 (ISBN 0-313-24609-2, BPG/). Greenwood.

Berkeley, Dorothy S., ed. see Clayton, John.

Berkeley, Edmund, ed. see Clayton, John.

Berkeley, George. Berkeley's Philosophical Writings. Armstrong, David M., ed. (Orig.). 1965. pap. 5.95 (ISBN 0-02-064170-2, Collier). Macmillan.

--Philosophical Writings. Jessop, T. E., ed. LC 69-13823. Repr. of 1953 ed. lib. bdg. 22.50x (ISBN 0-8371-1056-4, BEPW). Greenwood.

Berkeley, James P. Knowing the Old Testament. (Illus.). (YA) 1954. pap. text ed. 5.95 (ISBN 0-8170-0088-7). Judson.

Berkey, Robert F. & Edwards, Sarah A., eds. Christological Perspectives. 320p. 18.95 (ISBN 0-8298-0491-9); pap. 10.95 (ISBN 0-8298-0606-7). Pilgrim NY.

Berkhof, Hendrik. Christ & the Powers. LC 62-13713. 80p. 1962. pap. 5.95 (ISBN 0-8361-1820-0). Herald Pr.

Berkhof, Hendrikus. Christian Faith: An Introduction to the Study of the Faith. rev. ed. Woudstra, Sierd, tr. from Dutch. 569p. 1986. 29.95 (ISBN 0-8028-3622-4). Eerdmans.

--Doctrine of the Holy Spirit. LC 64-16279. 1976. pap. 6.95 (ISBN 0-8042-0551-5). John Knox.

--Introduction to the Study of Dogmatics. Vriend, John, tr. from Dutch. 120p. (Orig.). 1985. pap. 7.95 (ISBN 0-8028-0045-9). Eerdmans.

Berkhof, Louis. The History of Christian Doctrine. 1978. 14.95 (ISBN 0-85151-005-1). Banner of Truth.

--History of Christian Doctrines. (Twin Brooks Ser). 288p. 1975. pap. 8.95 (ISBN 0-8010-0636-8). Baker Bk.

--Introduction to Systematic Theology. (Twin Brooks Ser.). 1979. pap. 7.95 (ISBN 0-8010-0768-2). Baker Bk.

--Manual of Christian Doctrine. 1933. pap. 7.95 (ISBN 0-8028-1647-9). Eerdmans.

--Principles of Biblical Interpretation. 1950. 9.95 (ISBN 0-8010-0549-3). Baker Bk.

--Sumario de Doctrina Cristiana. 5th ed. Vila, David, tr. from Eng. Tr. of Summary of Christian Doctrine. (Span.). 240p. 1986. pap. 3.00 (ISBN 0-939125-31-5). Evangelical Lit.

--Summary of Christian Doctrine. 1939. pap. 5.95 (ISBN 0-8028-1513-8). Eerdmans.

--Systematic Theology. 1978. 24.95 (ISBN 0-8028-3020-X). Eerdmans.

Berkhofer, Robert F. Salvation & the Savage: An Analysis of Protestant Missions & American Indian Response, 1787-1862. LC 77-22857. 1977. Repr. of 1965 ed. lib. bdg. 22.50x (ISBN 0-8371-9745-7, BESSA). Greenwood.

Berkhofer, Robert F., Jr. Salvation & the Savage: An Analysis of Protestant Missions & American Indian Response, 1787-1862. LC 65-11826. 1972. pap. text ed. 4.95x (ISBN 0-689-70290-6, 184). Atheneum.

Berkley, James D. Preaching to Convince. 192p. 1986. 9.95 (ISBN 0-8499-0577-X). Word Bks.

Berkley, Jim, ed. Preaching to Convince. (Leadership Library). 175p. 1986. 9.95 (ISBN 0-917463-11-0). Chr Today.

Berkouwer, Gerrit C. Studies in Dogmatics: Theology. Incl. Vol. 1. Faith & Sanctification; Vol. 2. The Providence of God. 10.95 (ISBN 0-8028-3029-3); Vol. 3. Faith & Justification. 8.95 (ISBN 0-8028-3030-7); Vol. 4. The Person of Christ. 9.95 (ISBN 0-8028-3031-5); Vol. 5. General Revelation. 10.95 (ISBN 0-8028-3032-3); Vol. 6. Faith & Perseverance. 8.95 (ISBN 0-8028-3033-1); Vol. 7. Divine Election. 9.95 (ISBN 0-8028-3034-X); Vol. 8. Man-The Image of God. 12.95 (ISBN 0-8028-3035-8); Vol. 9. The Work of Christ. 9.95 (ISBN 0-8028-3036-6); Vol. 10. The Sacraments. 12.95 (ISBN 0-8028-3037-4); Vol. 11. Sin. 17.95 (ISBN 0-8028-3027-7); Vol. 12. The Return of Christ. 13.95 (ISBN 0-8028-3393-4); The Church. 9.95 (ISBN 0-8028-3433-7); Holy Scripture. 11.95 (ISBN 0-8028-3394-2). 1952. Eerdmans.

Berkovits, Eliezer. Crisis & Faith. 224p. 1975. 8.95 (ISBN 0-88482-903-0, Sanhedrin Pr). Hebrew Pub.

--Faith After the Holocaust. 1973. pap. 7.95x (ISBN 0-87068-193-1). Ktav.

--Major Themes in Modern Philosophies of Judaism. 1974. 25.00x (ISBN 0-87068-264-4); pap. 11.95. Ktav.

--Not in Heaven: The Nature & Function of Halakha. LC 82-23255. 131p. 1983. 12.00x (ISBN 0-88125-003-1). Ktav.

--With God in Hell: Judaism in the Ghettos & Deathcamps. 1979. 9.95 (ISBN 0-88482-937-5, Sanhedrin Pr). Hebrew Pub.

Berkowitz, David S., ed. see Morison, Richard.

Berkowitz, Sarah B. In Search of Ashes. LC 83-50495. 128p. 1984. 7.95 (ISBN 0-88400-099-0). Shengold.

Berkowtiz, Marvin W. & Oser, Fritz, eds. Moral Education: International Perspectives. 472p. 1985. text ed. 45.00 (ISBN 0-89859-557-6). L Erlbaum Assocs.

Berkson, Isaac B. Theories of Americanization: A Critical Study. LC 77-87743. (American Education: Its Men, Institutions & Ideas, Ser. 1). 1969. Repr. of 1920 ed. 15.00 (ISBN 0-405-01387-6). Ayer Co Pubs.

--Theories of Americanization: A Critical Study, with Special Reference to the Jewish Group. LC 78-176558. (Columbia University. Teachers College. Contributions to Education: No. 109). Repr. of 1920 ed. 22.50 (ISBN 0-404-55109-2). AMS Pr.

Berkus, Rusty. To Heal Again: Toward Serenity & the Resolution of Grief. (Illus.). 32p. (Orig.). 1986. pap. 13.95 (ISBN 0-9609888-2-3). Red Rose Pr.

Berky, Andrew S., tr. see Sommer, Fedor.

Berler, Beatrice, tr. see Latorre Cabal, Hugo.

Berliant, Howard M. & Arbit, Bruce, eds. Jewish Literary Marketplace: A Directory of the Press, Periodicals, Publishers, & Booksellers. LC 79-18114. 1979. pap. 9.95 (ISBN 0-930038-16-9). Arbit.

Berlin, Adele. Poetics & Interpretation of Biblical Narrative. (Bible & Literature Ser.: No. 9). 180p. 1983. text ed. 22.95x (ISBN 0-907459-23-4, Pub. by Almond Pr England); pap. text ed. 10.95x (ISBN 0-907459-24-2). Eisenbrauns.

Berlin, Charles. Catalog of the Yiddish Collection: Harvard University College Library, 3 vols. 2100p. 1987. lib. bdg. 490.00 (ISBN 3-598-41242-8). K G Saur.

--Index to Festschriften in Jewish Studies. 1971. 50.00x (ISBN 0-87068-133-8). Ktav.

--Studies in Jewish Bibliography, History & Literature: In Honor of I. Edward Kiev. 1971. 50.00x (ISBN 0-87068-143-5). Ktav.

Berlin, William S. On the Edge of Politics: The Roots of Jewish Political Thought in America. (Contributions in Political Science Ser.: No. 14). 1978. lib. bdg. 29.95x (ISBN 0-313-20422-5, BEP/). Greenwood.

Berliner, Abraham. Aus dem Leben der Deuschen Juden im Mittelalter. Katz, Steven, ed. LC 79-7127. (Jewish Philosophy, Mysticism & History of Ideas Ser.). 1980. Repr. of 1900 ed. lib. bdg. 14.00x (ISBN 0-405-12241-1). Ayer Co Pubs.

Berliner, Paul F. The Soul of Mbira: Music & Traditions of the Shona People of Zimbabwe. LC 76-24578. (Perspectives on Southern Africa Ser.: No. 26). 1978. 36.50x (ISBN 0-520-03315-9); pap. 6.95 (ISBN 0-520-04268-9, CAL 466). U of Cal Pr.

Berling, Judith A. The Syncretic Religion of Lin Chao-En. LC 79-25606. (Institute for Advanced Studies of World Religions; Neo-Confucian Studies). 1980. 31.00x (ISBN 0-231-04870-X). Columbia U Pr.

Berlitz, Charles. The Lost Ship of Noah: In Search of the Ark at Ararat. (Illus.). 224p. 1986. 17.95 (ISBN 0-399-13182-5, Perigee). Putnam Pub Group.

Berlucchi, Jim. Person to Person: How to Be Effective in Evangelism. 144p. (Orig.). 1984. pap. 3.50 (ISBN 0-89283-164-2). Servant.

Berman, Constance H. Medieval Agriculture, the Southern French Countryside & the Early Cistercians: A Study of Forty-Three Monasteries. LC 84-71079. (Transaction Ser.: Vol. 76, Pt. 5). 179p. 1986. 18.00 (ISBN 0-87169-765-3). Am Philos.

Berman, Edgar. In Africa With Schweitzer. 300p. 1986. 16.95 (ISBN 0-88282-025-7). New Horizon NJ.

Berman, Harold, tr. see Sachs, Abraham S.

Berman, Lawrence V., et al, eds. The Study of Judaism: Vol. 2. 25.00x (ISBN 0-87068-486-8). Ktav.

Berman, Louis A. Vegetarianism & the Jewish Tradition. LC 81-11729. 120p. 1982. 10.00x (ISBN 0-87068-756-5); pap. 7.95. Ktav.

Berman, Myron. Richmond's Jewry, Seventeen Sixty-Nine to Nineteen Seventy-Six. LC 78-6377. 438p. 1979. 20.00x (ISBN 0-8139-0743-8). U Pr of Va.

Bermann, Richard A. The Mahdi of Allah: The Story of the Dervish, Mohammed Ahmed. John, Robin, tr. LC 80-1935. Repr. of 1932 ed. 36.00 (ISBN 0-404-18955-5). AMS Pr.

Bermejo, Luis M. Body Broken & Blood Shed. 368p. 1987. 8.95 (ISBN 0-8294-0554-2). Loyola.

Bermudes, Robert W. Conquering Cancer. 1983. 5.50 (ISBN 0-89536-619-3, 0388). CSS of Ohio.

Bermudez, Fernando. Death & Resurrection in Guatemala. Barr, Robert R., tr. from Span. LC 85-48305. Tr. of Cristo Muere y Resucita en Guatemala. 96p. (Orig.). 1986. pap. 7.95 (ISBN 0-88344-268-X). Orbis Bks.

Berna, Kurt. Christ Did Not Perish on the Cross: Christ's Body Buried Alive. (Illus.). 1975. 14.50 (ISBN 0-682-48139-4). Exposition Pr FL.

Bernadotte Af Wisborg, Folke G. To Jerusalem. LC 75-6424. (The Rise of Jewish Nationalism & the Middle East Ser.). 280p. 1975. Repr. of 1951 ed. 23.65 (ISBN 0-88355-311-2). Hyperion Conn.

Bernal, Luis, tr. see Wilson, William P. & Slattery, Kathryn.

Bernal, Luis L., ed. see Cho, Paul Y. & Manzano, R. Whitney.

Bernanos, Georges. Dialogue Des Carmelites. 1960. 13.50 (ISBN 0-685-11136-9). French & Eur.

--Dialogue Des Carmelites. (Coll. Le Livre de Vie). pap. 3.95 (ISBN 0-685-37216-2). French & Eur.

--The Diary of a Country Priest: Thomas More Books to Live Ser. Morris, Pamela, tr. (Fr.). 1983. 14.95 (ISBN 0-88347-155-8). Thomas More.

Bernard, Bruce. The Bible & Its Painters. LC 84-9740. (Illus.). 300p. 1984. 24.95 (ISBN 0-02-510130-7). Macmillan.

Bernard, David. Essentials of Oneness Theology. (Illus.). 32p. (Orig.). 1985. pap. 2.25 (ISBN 0-912315-89-X). Word Aflame.

Bernard, David, jt. auth. see Stegall, Neil.

Bernard, David, ed. see Arrowood, Larry M.

Bernard, David, ed. see Erickson, Gary D.

Bernard, David, ed. see Gray, David F.

Bernard, David K. The New Birth. Wallace, Mary H., ed. 346p. (Orig.). 1984. pap. 6.95 (ISBN 0-912315-77-6). Word Aflame.

--The Oneness of God. Wallace, Mary K., ed. LC 86-19051. 326p. (Orig.). 1983. pap. 6.95 (ISBN 0-912315-12-1). Word Aflame.

--Practical Holiness: A Second Look. 336p. (Orig.). 1985. pap. 6.95 (ISBN 0-912315-91-1). Word Aflame.

Bernard, David K., jt. auth. see Bernard, Loretta A.

Bernard, Helene. Great Women Initiates or the Feminine Mystic. Ziebel, Michelle, tr. from Fr. LC 84-50133. (Illus.). 151p. (Orig.). 1984. pap. 6.95 (ISBN 0-912057-36-X, G-650). AMORC.

Bernard, J. H. A Critical & Exegetical Commentary on the Gospel According to St. John, 2 vols. Driver, Samuel R. & Plummer, Alfred, eds. (International Critical Commentary Ser.). 24.95 ea. (Pub. by T & T ClarK Ltd UK). Vol. I, 480p (ISBN 0-567-05024-6). Vol. II, 456p (ISBN 0-567-05025-4). Fortress.

--The Pastoral Epistles: Timothy & Titus. (Thornapple Commentaries Ser.). 272p. 1980. pap. 6.95 (ISBN 0-8010-0797-6). Baker Bk.

Bernard, Jacqueline. The Children You Gave Us. LC 72-87122. (Illus.). 1972. 8.95x (ISBN 0-8197-0356-7). Bloch.

Bernard, Loretta A. & Bernard, David K. In Search of Holiness. 288p. (Orig.). 1981. pap. 6.95 (ISBN 0-912315-40-7). Word Aflame.

Bernard, Mary. Agony! Can the Church Survive Without Jesus? LC 79-84343. 1979. pap. 2.95 (ISBN 0-89221-059-1). New Leaf.

--Who Can We Trust? LC 80-80531. 128p. 1980. 2.50 (ISBN 0-89221-075-3). New Leaf.

Bernard, Otis. Put a Little Starch in Your Faith. 150p. 1980. pap. 4.95 (ISBN 0-89221-095-8). New Leaf.

Bernard, Paul P. Jesuits & Jacobins: Enlightenment & Enlightened Despotism in Austria. LC 78-151997. 207p. 1971. 19.95 (ISBN 0-252-00180-X). U of Ill Pr.

Bernard, Theos. Hindu Philosophy. LC 68-21323. 1968. Repr. of 1947 ed. lib. bdg. 22.50x (ISBN 0-8371-0311-8, BEHP). Greenwood.

--Hindu Philosophy. 1981. Repr. of 1947 ed. 14.00x (ISBN 0-8364-0765-2, Pub. by Motilal Banarsidass). South Asia Bks.

Bernard, Thomas D. The Central Teaching of Christ: A Study of John 13-17. 426p. 1985. Repr. lib. bdg. 16.25 (ISBN 0-86524-176-7, 9519). Klock & Klock.

Bernard de Clairvaux, Saint Letters. James, Bruno S., tr. LC 78-63344. (The Crusades & Military Orders: Second Ser.). Repr. of 1953 ed. 47.50 (ISBN 0-404-17004-8). AMS Pr.

Bernard de Clairvaux, St. On Loving God: Selections from Sermons by St. Bernard of Clairvaux. Martin, Hugh, ed. LC 79-8706. (A Treasury of Christian Bks.). 125p. 1981. Repr. of 1959 ed. lib. bdg. 22.50x (ISBN 0-313-20787-9, BEOL). Greenwood.

Bernardin, Joseph B. Burial Services: Revised & Updated. 1980. casebound 14.95 (ISBN 0-8192-1267-9). Morehouse.

--Introduction to the Episcopal Church. rev ed. (Orig.). 1978. pap. 4.95 (ISBN 0-8192-1231-8). Morehouse.

Bernardin, Joseph L. Christ Lives in Me: A Pastoral Reflection on Jesus & His Meaning for Christian Life. (Illus.). 69p. (Orig.). 1985. pap. 3.95 (ISBN 0-86716-044-6). St Anthony Mess Pr.

Bernard Of Clairvaux. Bernard of Clairvaux on the Song of Songs, Vol. II. Walsh, Kilian, tr. (Cistercian Fathers Ser.: No. 7). pap. 5.00 (ISBN 0-87907-707-7). Cistercian Pubns.

--Bernard of Clairvaux: Sermons I on Conversion; Lenten Sermons on the Psalm "He Who Dwells". Said, Marie-Bernard, tr. (Cistercian Fathers Ser.: No. 25). (Lat.). 1982. 25.95 (ISBN 0-87907-125-7); pap. 7.00 (ISBN 0-87907-925-8). Cistercian Pubns.

--Bernard of Clairvaux: Sermons on the Song of Songs, Vol. IV. Edmonds, Irene, tr. (Cistercian Fathers Ser.: N0. 40). 1980. 15.95 (ISBN 0-87907-140-0). Cistercian Pubns.

--The Life & Death of Saint Malachy the Irishman. (Cistercian Fathers Ser.: No. 10). 170p. 7.95. Cistercian Pubns.

--Sermons on the Song of Songs, Vol. 1. (Cistercian Fathers Ser.: No. 4). pap. 5.00 (ISBN 0-87907-704-2). Cistercian Pubns.

--Sermons on the Song of Songs, Vol. 4. (Cistercian Fathers Ser.: No. 40). 15.95. Cistercian Pubns.

--Song of Solomon. 560p. 1984. smythe sewn 21.00 (ISBN 0-86524-177-5, 2202). Klock & Klock.

--Treatises I: Apologia, Precept & Dispensation. (Cistercian Fathers Ser.: No. 1). 190p. 7.95 (ISBN 0-87907-101-X). Cistercian Pubns.

Bernard Of Clairvaux & Amadeus Of Lausanne. Magnificat: Homilies in Praise of the Blessed Virgin Mary. LC 78-6249. (Cistercian Fathers Ser.: No. 18). 1979. 15.95 (ISBN 0-87907-118-4). Cistercian Pubns.

Bernard of Clairvaux & William of St. Thierry. The Love of God. Houston, James M., ed. LC 83-10533. (Classics of Faith & Devotion). Orig. Title: Life & Works of St. Bernard. 1983. 11.95 (ISBN 0-88070-017-3). Multnomah.

Bernardoni, Gus. Golf God's Way. LC 77-80414. 1978. 9.95 (ISBN 0-88419-144-3). Creation Hse.

Bernards, Solomon S., jt. auth. see Greenberg, David.

Bernards, Solomon S., ed. The Living Heritage of the High Holy Days. 31p. 0.50 (ISBN 0-686-74964-2). ADL.

Bernardus Guidonis. Manuel de l'Inquisiteur, 2 vols. in 1. Mollat, G., ed. LC 78-63183. (Heresies of the Early Christian & Medieval Era: Second Ser.). Repr. of 1927 ed. 57.50 set (ISBN 0-404-16199-5). AMS Pr.

Berne, Patricia H., jt. auth. see Savary, Louis M.

Berne, Stanley, jt. auth. see Zekowski, Arlene.

Bernen, Robert, jt. auth. see Bernen, Satia.

Bernen, Satia & Bernen, Robert. A Guide to Myth & Religion in European Painting 1270-1700. LC 72-96070. 288p. 1973. 8.95 (ISBN 0-8076-0683-9). Braziller.

Berner, Carl W. Why Me, Lord? Meaning & Comfort in Times of Trouble. LC 73-78267. 112p. (Orig.). 1973. pap. 5.95 (ISBN 0-8066-1331-9, 10-7172). Augsburg.

Berner, Ronald M. Temple Arts of Kerala: A South Indian Tradition. 272p. 100.00 (ISBN 0-317-52158-6, Pub. by S Chand India). State Mutual Bk.

Bernheim, Gotthardt D. History of the German Settlements & of the Lutheran Church in North & South Carolina. LC 75-969. xvi, 557p. 1975. Repr. of 1872 ed. 20.00 (ISBN 0-8063-8001-2). Regional.

--History of the German Settlements & of the Lutheran Church in North & South Carolina. LC 76-187361. 573p. 1972. Repr. of 1872 ed. 25.00 (ISBN 0-87152-089-3). Reprint.

Bernier, Paul. Bread Broken & Shared. LC 81-67539. 144p. 1981. pap. 3.95 (ISBN 0-87793-232-8). Ave Maria.

Bernier, Ronald M. The Temples of Napal: An Introductory Survey. (Illus.). 247p. 1970. text ed. 27.50x. Coronet Bks.

--The Temples of Nepal. 204p. 25.00X (ISBN 0-317-52159-4, Pub. by S Chand India). State Mutual Bk.

Berniker, Bernard. Great Rabbis. Gorr, Samuel, ed. (Illus.). 1978. 10.00 (ISBN 0-87306-144-6); portfolio ed. 10.00 (ISBN 0-87306-195-0). Feldheim.

Bernstein, Fred. The Jewish Mothers' Hall of Fame. LC 85-24541. (Illus.). 192p. 1986. pap. 6.95 (ISBN 0-385-23377-9, Dolp). Doubleday.

Bernstein, George L. Liberalism & Liberal Politics in Edwardian England. 256p. 1986. text ed. 34.95x (ISBN 0-04-942198-0); pap. text ed. 14.95x (ISBN 0-04-942199-9). Allen Unwin.

Bernstein, Henrietta. Cabalah Primer: Introduction to English-Hebrew Cabalah. 192p. 1984. pap. 9.95 (ISBN 0-87516-526-5). De Vorss.

Bernstein, Joanne. Loss & How to Cope with It. LC 76-50027. 8.95 (ISBN 0-395-28891-6, Clarion). HM.

--Loss & How to Cope with It. 160p. 1981. pap. 4.95 (ISBN 0-395-30012-6, Clarion). HM.

Bernstein, John A. Nietzsche's Moral Philosophy. LC 85-46001. 1987. 32.50 (ISBN 0-8386-3283-1). Fairleigh Dickinson.

Bernstein, Louis. Challenge & Mission. LC 82-60203. 272p. 1982. 13.95 (ISBN 0-88400-081-8). Shengold.

Bernstein, Matt. This Messiah Fellow. 1985. 6.75 (ISBN 0-8062-2344-8). Carlton.

Bernstein, Mordecai W., ed. see Kruk, Herman.

Bernstein, Philip. To Dwell in Unity: The Jewish Federation Movement in America, 1960-1980. LC 83-9867. 394p. 1983. 19.95 (ISBN 0-8276-0228-6, 608). Jewish Pubns.

Bernstein, Philip S. What the Jews Believe. LC 77-28446. (Illus.). 1978. Repr. of 1951 ed. lib. bdg. 22.50x (ISBN 0-313-20228-1, BEWJ). Greenwood.

Bernstein, Richard. Beyond Objectivism & Relativism: Science, Hermeneutics, & Praxis. 320p. (Orig.). 1983. 28.95x (ISBN 0-8122-7906-9); pap. 10.95 (ISBN 0-8122-1165-0). U of Pa Pr.

Bernstein, Saul. The Renaissance of the Torah Jew. 1986. text ed. 20.00x (ISBN 0-88125-090-2). Ktav.

Ber Of Bolechow. The Memoirs of Ber of Bolechow (1723-1805) LC 73-2186. (The Jewish People; History, Religion, Literature Ser.). Repr. of 1922 ed. 19.00 (ISBN 0-405-05252-9). Ayer Co Pubs.

Berquist, Maurice. Miracle & Power of Blessing. 1984. pap. 2.95 (ISBN 0-87162-408-7, D8556). Warner Pr.

Berrie, W. W. A Theology of Generosity: Principles & Practice of Giving Based on Bible Teaching. 32p. 1982. pap. 2.50 (ISBN 0-8192-1293-8). Morehouse.

Berrigan, Daniel. Beside the Sea of Glass: The Song of the Lamb. (Classic Prayer Ser.). (Illus.). 112p. 1978. pap. 2.50 (ISBN 0-8164-2174-9, HarpR). Har-Row.

--A Book of Parables. 160p. 1977. 3.00 (ISBN 0-8164-0328-7, HarpR). Har-Row.

--The Mission: A Film Journal. LC 86-45012. 160p. 1986. 14.95 (ISBN 0-06-250056-2, HarpR). Har-Row.

--The Nightmare of God. LC 81-51877. (Sunburst Originals Ser.: No. 9). (Illus.). 144p. (Orig.). 1983. pap. 6.00 (ISBN 0-934648-08-5). Sunburst Pr.

--Portraits: O Those I Love. (Crossroad Paperback Ser.). 160p. 1982. pap. 6.95 (ISBN 0-8245-0416-X). Crossroad NY.

--Steadfastness of the Saints: A Journal of Peace & War in Central & North America. LC 85-5120. 160p. 1985. pap. 7.95 (ISBN 0-88344-447-X). Orbis Bks.

--We Die Before We Live: Talking with the Very Ill. 160p. 1980. 11.95 (ISBN 0-8164-0462-3, HarpR). Har-Row.

--The Words Our Saviour Gave Us. 1978. pap. 4.95 (ISBN 0-87243-081-2). Templegate.

Berry, Boyd M. Process of Speech: Puritan Religious Writing & Paradise Lost. LC 75-36933. pap. 80.00 (ISBN 0-317-41618-9, 2025830). Bks Demand UMI.

Berry, Diana L. The Psalms in Rhyme, Vol. I. LC 86-80658. 104p. (Orig.). 1986. pap. 6.95 (ISBN 0-931637-01-5). Ferndale Hse.

Berry, George R. Interlinear Greek-English New Testament. LC 78-54242. 1978. pap. 15.95 (ISBN 0-8054-1372-3). Broadman.

--Interlinear Greek-English New Testament. 24.95 (ISBN 0-310-21170-0, 9216). Zondervan.

Berry, George R. & Strong, James. Interlinear Greek-English New Testament. (Reference Set). 1187p. 24.95 (ISBN 0-915134-74-8). Mott Media.

Berry, Harold J. Treasures from the Original. 1985. pap. 4.95 (ISBN 0-8024-2956-4). Moody.

Berry, Jo. Beloved Unbeliever: A Woman's Workshop. (Woman's Workshop Ser.). 176p. (Orig.). 1985. leader's manual 2.95 (ISBN 0-310-42661-8, 11219P); student's manual 5.95 (ISBN 0-310-42691-X, 11220P). Zondervan.

--Beloved Unbeliever: Loving Your Husband into the Faith. 176p. (Orig.). 1981. pap. 5.95 (ISBN 0-310-42621-9, 11215). Zondervan.

--Can You Love Yourself? LC 77-89395. 160p. 1978. pap. 4.95 (ISBN 0-8307-0579-1, 5407206). Regal.

--Growing, Sharing, Serving. LC 78-73461. 1979. pap. 3.95 (ISBN 0-89191-073-5). Cook.

--Managing Your Life & Time. 192p. 1986. pap. 6.95 (ISBN 0-310-34181-7). Zondervan.

--The Priscilla Principle: Making Your Life a Ministry. 256p. 1984. pap. 6.95 (ISBN 0-310-42631-6, 11218P). Zondervan.

Berry, Joan P. Reflections in a Shop Window. 1983. 4.25 (ISBN 0-89536-605-3, 1817). CSS of Ohio.

--What If...? 1985. 3.50 (ISBN 0-89536-729-7, 5813). CSS of Ohio.

Berry, John R. Good Words for New Christians. (Orig.). 1987. pap. 2.95 (ISBN 0-9616900-0-3). J R Berry.

Berry, Karen. Beyond Broken Dreams: A Scriptural Pathway to New Life. 1984. pap. 3.50 (ISBN 0-86716-034-9). St Anthony Mess Pr.

--Signs Along Our Way: Biblical Reflections for Charting Life's Journey. 1987. pap. 4.95. St Anthony Mess Pr.

Berry, Leonidas H. I Wouldn't Take Nothin' for My Journey: Two Centuries of an American Minister's Family. 1981. 14.95 (ISBN 0-686-95206-5). Johnson Chi.

Berry, Linda. Christmas Plays for Older Children. 1981. saddle wire 2.50 (ISBN 0-8054-9733-1). Broadman.

Berry, Mary, ed. Cantors. LC 78-56178. (Resources of Music Ser.). 1979. pap. 5.95 (ISBN 0-521-22149-8). Cambridge U Pr.

Berry, MaryAnn. Answered Prayer. 28p. (Orig.). 1985. 4.95 (ISBN 0-9614947-0-0); pap. 2.50 (ISBN 0-9614947-1-9). First Love Min.

Berry, Nancee. At Home with Jesus. (Come Unto Me Library). 1979. pap. 1.65 (ISBN 0-8127-0236-0). Review & Herald.

--Jesus Cares for Me. (Come Unto Me Ser.). 16p. 1979. pap. 1.65 (ISBN 0-8127-0252-2). Review & Herald.

--When Jesus Comes. (Come Unto Me Library). 1979. pap. 1.65 (ISBN 0-8127-0210-7). Review & Herald.

Berry, Philip A. A Review of the Mexican War on Christian Principles: And an Essay on the Means of Preventing War. LC 76-143427. (Peace Movement in America Ser). ix, 87p. 1972. Repr. of 1849 ed. lib. bdg. 11.95x (ISBN 0-89198-057-1). Ozer.

Berry, R. J. Neo-Darwinism. (Studies in Biology: No. 144). 72p. 1982. pap. text ed. 9.95 (ISBN 0-7131-2849-6). E Arnold.

Berry, R. L. Adventures in the Land of Canaan. 128p. pap. 1.00 (ISBN 0-686-29096-8). Faith Pub Hse.

--Around Old Bethany. 83p. pap. 0.75 (ISBN 0-686-29097-6). Faith Pub Hse.

--Steps Heavenward. 123p. pap. 1.00 (ISBN 0-686-29142-5). Faith Pub Hse.

Berry, Roger L. God's World-His Story. (Christian Day School Ser.). 1976. 18.80x (ISBN 0-87813-911-7); tchr's guide 19.65x (ISBN 0-87813-914-1). Christian Light.

Berry, Steve, ed. see Irani, Adi K.

Berry, Thomas. Buddhism. LC 75-10518. 1967. pap. 5.95 (ISBN 0-89012-017-X). Anima Pubns.

--Teilhard in the Ecological Age. (Teilhard Studies). 1982. 2.00 (ISBN 0-89012-032-3). Anima Pubns.

Berry, Virginia G., ed. & tr. see Odo of Deuil.

Berry, W. Grinton. John Milton. LC 73-10007. 1909. lib. bdg. 17.50 (ISBN 0-8414-3150-7). Folcroft.

Berry, W. Grinton, ed. see Foxe, John.

Berryman, Charles. From Wilderness to Wasteland: The Trial of the Puritan God in the American Imagination. (National University Publications, Literary Criticism Ser.). 1979. 21.50x (ISBN 0-8046-9235-1, Pub. by Kennikat). Assoc Faculty Pr.

Berryman, Philip. The Religious Roots of Rebellion: Christians in Central American Revolutions. LC 83-19343. 480p. (Orig.). 1984. pap. 19.95 (ISBN 0-88344-105-5). Orbis Bks.

Berryman, Phillip. Liberation Theology: Essential Facts about the Revolutionary Movement in Latin America & Beyond. LC 86-42638. 224p. 1986. 16.95 (ISBN 0-394-55241-5); pap. 6.95 (ISBN 0-394-74652-X). Pantheon.

Berryman, Phillip, tr. see Boff, Clodovis.

Berryman, Phillip, tr. see Cabestrero, Teofilo.

Berryman, Phillip, tr. see Casaldaliga, Pedro.

Berryman, Phillip, tr. see Hinkelammert, Franz.

Berryman, Phillip, tr. see Sobrino, Jon & Pico, Juan H.

Berschin, Walter. Greek Letters & the Latin Middle Ages: From Jerome to Nicholas of Cusa. Frakes, Jerold C., tr. from Ger. Tr. of Griechisch-lateinisches mittelater von Hieronymus zu Nikolaus von Kues. 1987. price not set (ISBN 0-8132-0606-5). Cath U Pr.

Berselli, Costante & Gharib, Georges, eds. Sing the Joys of Mary. Jenkins, Phil, tr. from Italian. Tr. of Lodi alla Madonna. (Eng.). 136p. (Orig.). 1983. pap. 7.95 (ISBN 0-8192-1329-2). Morehouse.

Bershadsky, Luba & Millington, Ada. I Know His Touch. LC 83-72042. 192p. (Orig.). 1984. pap. 6.95 (ISBN 0-89107-299-3, Crossway Bks). Good News.

--I Know His Touch. 240p. 1985. pap. 2.95 (ISBN 0-345-32164-2). Ballantine.

Berst, Charles A., ed. Shaw & Religion. LC 81-956. (Shaw: the Annual of Bernard Shaw Studies: Vol 1). 264p. 1981. 25.00x (ISBN 0-271-00280-8). Pa St U Pr.

Bertaux, Daniel, ed. Biography & Society: The Life History Approach in the Social Sciences. (Sage Studies in International Sociology: Vol. 23). 308p. 1981. pap. 14.00 (ISBN 0-8039-9801-5). Sage.

Berthold, George C., ed. Maximus the Confessor. (Classics of Western Spirituality Ser.: Vol. 45). 1985. 12.95 (ISBN 0-8091-0353-2); pap. 9.95 (ISBN 0-8091-2659-1). Paulist Pr.

Bertholf, Robert J. & Levitt, Annette S., eds. William Blake & the Moderns. 352p. 1982. 44.50x (ISBN 0-87395-615-X); pap. 18.95x (ISBN 0-87395-616-8). State U NY Pr.

Bertocci, P. A. Empirical Argument for God in Late British Thought. Repr. of 1938 ed. 36.00 (ISBN 0-527-07300-8). Kraus Repr.

Bertocci, Peter A. Religion As Creative Insecurity. LC 73-1836. 128p. 1973. Repr. of 1958 ed. lib. bdg. 22.50x (ISBN 0-8371-6803-1, BECI). Greenwood.

Bertolucci, John. The Disciplines of a Disciple. 136p. (Orig.). 1985. pap. 4.95 (ISBN 0-89283-240-1). Servant.

--Healing: God's Work Among Us. 1987. pap. 3.95. Servant.

--Straight from the Heart: A Call to the New Generation. 126p. 1986. pap. 4.95 (ISBN 0-89283-290-8). Servant.

Bertolucci, John & Lilly, Fred. On Fire with the Spirit. 140p. (Orig.). 1984. pap. 4.95 (ISBN 0-89283-193-6). Servant.

Berton, C. Dictionnaire des Cardinaux. Migne, J. P., ed. (Troisieme et Derniere Encyclopedie Theologique Ser.: Vol. 31). (Fr.). 912p. Repr. of 1857 ed. lib. bdg. 115.00x (ISBN 0-89241-310-7). Caratzas.

--Dictionnaire des Cardinaux. 912p. Date not set. Repr. of 1866 ed. text ed. 186.30x (ISBN 0-576-78521-0, Pub. by Gregg Intl Pubs England). Gregg Intl.

--Dictionnaire du Parallele entre Diverses Doctrines Philosophiques et Religieuses. Migne, J. P., ed. (Troisieme et Derniere Encycolpedie Theologique Ser.: Vol. 38). (Fr.). 698p. Repr. of 1858 ed. lib. bdg. 90.00x (ISBN 0-89241-317-4). Caratzas.

Bertram, Martin, tr. see Pelikan, Jaroslav.

Bertram, Martin H., tr. Luther's Works, Vol. 23. LC 55-9893. 1958. 16.95 (ISBN 0-570-06423-6, 15-1765). Concordia.

Bertram, Martin H., tr. see Pelikan, Jaroslav.

Bertrand, F. M. Dictionnaire Universel, Historique et Comparatif des Toutes les Religions du Monde, 4 vols. Migne, J. P., ed. (Encyclopedie Theologique Ser.: Vols. 24-27). (Fr.). 2588p. Repr. of 1851 ed. lib. bdg. 329.50x (ISBN 0-89241-240-2). Caratzas.

Bertrin, G. Lourdes: A History of Its Apparitions & Cures. 59.95 (ISBN 0-8490-0560-4). Gordon Pr.

Berube, Francoise D. & Berube, John-Paul. Sacrament of Peace. Ages 7-8. childs bk. 2.95 (ISBN 0-8091-9166-0); Ages 9-12. childs bk. 2.95 (ISBN 0-8091-9167-9); director's guide 4.95 (ISBN 0-8091-9169-5). Paulist Pr.

Berube, John P., jt. auth. see Darcy-Berube, Francoise.

Berube, John-Paul, jt. auth. see Berube, Francoise D.

Berube, John-Paul, jt. auth. see Darcy-Berube, Francoise.

Berzin, Alexander, ed. see Yeshe, Lama & Rinpoche, Zopa.

Besanceney, Paul H. Interfaith Marriages: Who & Why. 1970. 12.95x (ISBN 0-8084-0164-5); pap. 8.95x (ISBN 0-8084-0165-3). New Coll U Pr.

Besancon, Its'hak, adapted by see Nachman of Breslov.

Besant. Dharma. 3.25 (ISBN 0-8356-7116-X). Theos Pub Hse.

--Doctrine of the Heart. 1.95 (ISBN 0-8356-7189-5). Theos Pub Hse.
--Hints on the Study of the Bhagavad Gita. 4.50 (ISBN 0-8356-7079-1). Theos Pub Hse.
--Mahabarata. 5.25 (ISBN 0-8356-7539-4). Theos Pub Hse.
--Seven Great Religions. 6.75 (ISBN 0-8356-7218-2). Theos Pub Hse.
--Seven Principles of Man. 3.25 (ISBN 0-8356-7321-9). Theos Pub Hse.
--Study in Karma. 2.25 (ISBN 0-8356-7292-1). Theos Pub Hse.
--Thought Power. 4.50 (ISBN 0-8356-7460-6). Theos Pub Hse.
--Wisdom of the Upanishads. 3.50 (ISBN 0-8356-7092-9). Theos Pub Hse.
Besant & Leadbeater. Thought Forms. 8.75 (ISBN 0-8356-7187-9). Theos Pub Hse.
Besant, jt. auth. see Leadbeater.
Besant, Annie. Ancient Wisdom. 9th ed. 1972. 7.95 (ISBN 0-8356-7038-4). Theos Pub Hse.
--Death & After. 1972. 2.95 (ISBN 0-8356-7039-2). Theos Pub Hse.
--Esoteric Christianity. 59.95 (ISBN 0-8490-0124-2). Gordon Pr.
--Esoteric Christianity. 8th ed. 1966. 7.00 (ISBN 0-8356-7052-X). Theos Pub Hse.
--The Freethinker's Textbook: Christianity, Its Evidences, Its Origin, Its Morality, Its History, Pt. 2. 3rd ed. LC 77-169205. (Atheist Viewpoint Ser). 288p. 1972. Repr. 21.00 (ISBN 0-405-03803-8). Ayer Co Pubs.
--From the Outer Court to the Inner Sanctum. Nicholson, Shirley, ed. LC 82-42703. 130p. 1983. pap. 4.50 (ISBN 0-8356-0574-4, Quest). Theos Pub Hse.
--Introduction to Yoga. 1972. 3.50 (ISBN 0-8356-7120-8). Theos Pub Hse.
--Karma. 10th ed. 1975. 3.50 (ISBN 0-8356-7035-X). Theos Pub Hse.
--Man & His Bodies. 12th ed. 1967. 4.50 (ISBN 0-8356-7083-X). Theos Pub Hse.
--Reincarnation. 11th ed. 1975. 5.25 (ISBN 0-8356-7019-8). Theos Pub Hse.
--Study in Consciousness. 6th ed. 1972. 7.50 (ISBN 0-8356-7287-5). Theos Pub Hse.
--Thought Power: Its Control & Culture. LC 73-7644. 1967. pap. 3.50 (ISBN 0-8356-0312-1, Quest). Theos Pub Hse.
--Yoga: The Hatha Yoga & Raja Yoga of India. 73p. 1974. pap. 7.95 (ISBN 0-88697-035-0). Life Science.
Besant, Annie & Leadbeater, Charles W. Thought Forms. abr. ed. (Illus.). 1969. pap. 5.50 (ISBN 0-8356-0008-4, Quest). Theos Pub Hse.
Besant, Walter, ed. see Conder, Claude R.
Beskow, Per. Strange Tales About Jesus: A Survey of Unfamiliar Gospels. LC 82-16001. 144p. 1983. pap. 9.95 (ISBN 0-8006-1686-3, 1-1686). Fortress.
Beslow, Audrey. Sex & the Single Christian. 1987. pap. 9.95 (ISBN 0-687-38197-5). Abingdon.
Besozzi, Cerbonio. Chronik Des Cerbonio Besozzi: 1548-1563. 185p. pap. 23.00 (ISBN 0-384-15678-9). Johnson Repr.
Bess, C. W. Nothing Can Separate Us. 1986. pap. 4.95 (ISBN 0-8054-2263-3). Broadman.
--Object-Centered Children's Sermons. (Object Lesson Ser.). 1978. pap. 3.95 (ISBN 0-8010-0734-8). Baker Bk.
--Sermons for the Seasons. LC 84-23226. 1985. pap. 4.95 (ISBN 0-8054-2256-0). Broadman.
--Sparkling Object Sermons for Children. (Object Lesson Ser.). 120p. (Orig.). 1982. pap. 4.95 (ISBN 0-8010-0824-7). Baker Bk.
Bess, C. W. & DeBand, Roy E. Bible-Centered Object Sermons for Children. (Object Lesson Ser.). 128p. 1985. pap. 4.95 (ISBN 0-8010-0886-7). Baker Bk.
Bess, Mary E. Tips for Ministers & Mates. 1987. pap. 5.95 (ISBN 0-8054-6943-5). Broadman.
Bessarion, Agioantonides. The House of Holy Wisdom: A Commentary on Proverbs 9. (Illus.). 60p. (Orig.). 1986. pap. 4.95 (ISBN 0-936649-12-7). St Anthony Orthodox.
Besserman, Lawrence L. The Legend of Job in the Middle Ages. LC 78-14936. (Illus.). 1979. 15.00x (ISBN 0-674-52385-7, Belknap Pr). Harvard U Pr.
Bessieres, Albert. Wife, Mother & Mystic: Blessed Anna Maria Taigi. Newton, Douglas, ed. Rigby, Stephen, tr. from Fr. (Eng.). 1977. pap. 5.50 (ISBN 0-89555-058-X). TAN Bks Pubs.
Besson, Clyde T. Growing Together. 1987. pap. 5.95 (ISBN 0-317-54043-2). Baker Bk.
Besson, Pablo, tr. from Greek. Nuevo Testamento de Nuestro Senor Jesucristo. (Span.). 576p. 1981. pap. 6.50 (ISBN 0-311-48710-6, Edit Mundo). Casa Bautista.
Best, E. A. Following Jesus: Discipleship in the Gospel of Mark. (Journal for the Study of the New Testament, Supplement Ser.: No. 4). 283p. 1981. text ed. 25.95 (ISBN 0-905774-28-0, Pub. by JSOT Pr England); pap. text ed. 12.50x (ISBN 0-905774-29-9, Pub. by JSOT Pr England). Eisenbrauns.
Best, Elsdon. Maori Religion & Mythology. LC 75-35236. Repr. of 1924 ed. 45.00 (ISBN 0-404-14412-8). AMS Pr.
Best, Ernest. Disciples & Discipleship: Studies in the Gospel According to Mark. 272p. 1986. 19.95 (ISBN 0-567-09369-7, Pub. by T & T Clark Ltd UK). Fortress.
--From Text to Sermon: Responsible Use of the New Testament in Preaching. LC 77-79584. 1978. 8.95 (ISBN 0-8042-0245-1). John Knox.
--I Peter. Black, Matthew, ed. (The New Century Bible Commentary Ser.). 188p. 1982. pap. 6.95 (ISBN 0-8028-1909-5). Eerdmans.
--Mark: The Gospel as Story. Riches, John, ed. 154p. 1983. 21.95 (ISBN 0-567-09342-5, Pub. by T&T Clark Ltd UK). Fortress.
--Second Corinthians. Mays, James L. & Achtemeier, Paul J., eds. LC 86-45404. (Interpretation: A Bible Commentary for Teaching & Preaching Ser.). 156p. 1987. 15.95 (ISBN 0-8042-3135-4). John Knox.
Best, Ernest, ed. Letter of Paul to the Romans: Cambridge Bible Commentary on the New English Bible. (New Testament Ser.). (Orig.). 1967. 21.95 (ISBN 0-521-04213-5); pap. 8.95x (ISBN 0-521-09401-1, 401). Cambridge U Pr.
Best, Ernest & Wilson, R. McL., eds. Text & Interpretation: Studies in the New Testament. LC 78-2962. pap. 71.50 (ISBN 0-317-26088-X, 2024416). Bks Demand UMI.
Best, Ernest E. Religion & Society in Transition: The Church & Social Change in England, 1560-1850. LC 82-21699. (Texts & Studies in Religion: Vol. 15). 353p. 1983. 59.95x (ISBN 0-88946-804-4). E Mellen.
Best, G., jt. ed. see Beales, D.
Best, Gary D. To Free a People: American Jewish Leaders & the Jewish Problem in Eastern Europe, 1890 to 1914. LC 81-4265. (Contributions in American History Ser.: No. 98). xi, 240p. 1982. lib. bdg. 32.95 (ISBN 0-313-22532-X, BTO/). Greenwood.
Best, James. Another Way to Live: Experiencing Intentional Community. LC 78-51384. 32p. (Orig.). 1978. pap. 2.50x (ISBN 0-87574-218-1). Pendle Hill.
Best, Mary A. Rebel Saints. facs. ed. LC 68-55839. (Essay Index Reprint Ser). 1925. 18.00 (ISBN 0-8369-0205-X). Ayer Co Pubs.
Best, Thomas F., ed. Hearing & Speaking the Word: An Anthology of the Works of James Muilenburg. (Scholars Press Homage Ser.: No. 7). 464p. 1985. 26.95 (ISBN 0-89130-665-X, 00 16 07). Scholars Pr GA.
Best, William. The Churches Plea for Her Right. LC 76-57357. (English Experience Ser.: No. 776). 1977. Repr. of 1635 ed. lib. bdg. 10.50 (ISBN 90-221-0776-0). Walter J Johnson.
Betancourt, Esdras, ed. Manual Comprensivo de Sicologia Pastoral. (Span.). 168p. 1980. pap. 4.95 (ISBN 0-87148-580-X). Pathway Pr.
Beth Jacob Hebrew Teachers College Staff. Deeds of the Righteous. (Illus.). 160p. 6.95 (ISBN 0-934390-00-2). B J Hebrew Tchrs.
--The Rebbe's Treasure. write for info. (ISBN 0-934390-01-0); pap. write for info. (ISBN 0-934390-02-9). B J Hebrew Tchrs.
Bethell, Ruth M., tr. see Zeeden, Ernest W.
Bethell, Samuel L. Literary Outlook. LC 73-9787. 1943. lib. bdg. 15.00 (ISBN 0-8414-3145-0). Folcroft.
Bethge, Eberhard. Costly Grace: An Illustrated Introduction to Dietrich Bonhoeffer in His Own Words. LC 78-19492. (Illus.). 1979. pap. 4.95i (ISBN 0-06-060773-4, RD294, HarpR). Har-Row.
Bethge, Ederhard. Dietrich Bonhoeffer. LC 70-10975. 1977. pap. 19.95 (ISBN 0-06-060771-8, RD 165, HarpR). Har-Row.
Bethlenfalvy, Geza. A Hand-List of the Ulan Bator Manuscript of the Kanjur-Rtse Them Spans-Ma. 112p. 1982. pap. text ed. 12.50 (ISBN 963-05-3260-3, Pub. by Akademiai Kiado Hungary). Humanities.
Bethune, George. The Fruit of the Spirit. pap. 4.95 (ISBN 0-685-88375-2). Reiner.
Bethune, Joanna. The Power of Faith Exemplified in the Life & Writings of the Late Mrs. Isabella Graham. De Swarte, Carolyn G. & Dayton, Donald, eds. (Women in American Protestant Religion Series 1800-1930). 440p. 1987. lib. bdg. 65.00 (ISBN 0-8240-0659-3). Garland Pub.
Bethune-Baker, J. F. Nestorius & His Teaching. 1908. 20.00 (ISBN 0-527-07500-0). Kraus Repr.
Betjeman, John. American's Guide to English Parish Churches. (Illus.). 1959. 20.00 (ISBN 0-8392-1004-3). Astor-Honor.
Betson, Martin. Here Begynneth a Treatyse to Dyspose Men to Be Vertously Occupyed in Theyr Myndes & Prayers. LC 77-6854. (English Experience Ser.: No. 848). 1977. Repr. of 1500 ed. lib. bdg. 5.00 (ISBN 90-221-0848-1). Walter J Johnson.
Bett, Henry. English Myths & Traditions. (Illus.). 144p. 1980. Repr. of 1952 ed. lib. bdg. 17.50 (ISBN 0-8414-2921-9). Folcroft.
--Nicholas of Cusa. LC 76-1131. (Great Medieval Churchmen Ser). x, 210p. 1976. Repr. of 1932 ed. lib. bdg. 17.50x (ISBN 0-915172-05-4). Richwood Pub.
Bettelheim, Bruno. Freud & Man's Soul. LC 82-47809. 112p. 1983. 11.95 (ISBN 0-394-52481-0). Knopf.
Bettelheim, Bruno & Janowitz, Morris B. Social Change & Prejudice. LC 64-11214. 1964. 18.95 (ISBN 0-02-903480-9). Free Pr.
Betten, Francis S. From Many Centuries: A Collection of Historical Papers. facs. ed. LC 68-16910. (Essay Index Reprint Ser). 1968. Repr. of 1938 ed. 18.00 (ISBN 0-8369-0206-8). Ayer Co Pubs.
Betten, Neil. Catholic Activism & the Industrial Worker. LC 76-17280. 1976. 10.00 (ISBN 0-8130-0503-5). U Presses Fla.
Bettenson, Henry, ed. Documents of the Christian Church. 2nd ed. 1970. pap. 8.95 (ISBN 0-19-501293-3). Oxford U Pr.
Bettenson, Henry, ed. & tr. The Later Christian Fathers: A Selection from the Writings of the Fathers from St. Cyril of Jerusalem to St. Leo the Great. 1972. pap. 8.95x (ISBN 0-19-283012-0). Oxford U Pr.
Bettenson, Henry, tr. Early Christian Fathers: A Selection from the Writings of the Fathers from St. Clement of Rome to St. Athanasius. 1969. pap. 9.95x (ISBN 0-19-283009-0). Oxford U Pr.
Better Homes & Gardens Editors. Better Homes & Gardens Christmas Joys to Craft & Stitch. (Illus.). 80p. 1985. pap. 6.95 (ISBN 0-696-01432-7). BH&G.
Bettey, J. H. Church & Community: The Parish Church in English Life. LC 79-14739. (Illus.). 142p. 1979. text ed. 26.50x (ISBN 0-06-490381-8, 06346). B&N Imports.
Bettis, Joseph & Johannesen, S. K., eds. The Return of the Millennium. LC 83-82671. 247p. 1984. pap. 11.95 (ISBN 0-913757-02-0). Rose Sharon Pr.
Bettis, Joseph & Johannesen, Stanley, eds. The Return of the Millenium. LC 83-82671. 232p. (Orig.). pap. 11.95 (ISBN 0-913757-02-0, Pub. by New Era Bks.). Paragon Hse.
Betto, Frei, jt. auth. see Castro, Fidel.
Bettoni, Efrem. Duns Scotus: The Basic Principles of His Philosophy. Bonansea, Berbardine, ed. LC 78-14031. 1979. Repr. of 1961 ed. lib. bdg. 35.00x (ISBN 0-313-21142-6, BEDS). Greenwood.
--Saint Bonaventure. Scuola, Editrice, Brescia, Italy, tr. from Ital. LC 81-13371. (The Notre Dame Pocket Library). Tr. of Santa Bonaventura. 127p. 1982. Repr. of 1964 ed. lib. bdg. 22.50x (ISBN 0-313-23271-7, BESB). Greenwood.
Betts, C. J. Early Deism in France. 1984. lib. bdg. 53.50 (ISBN 90-247-2923-8, Pub. by Martinus Nijhoff Netherlands). Kluwer Academic.
Betts, George H. The Curriculum of Religious Education. (Educational Ser.). 1924. Repr. 30.00 (ISBN 0-8482-7352-4). Norwood Edns.
Betts, Robert B. Christians in the Arab East. LC 78-8674. 1981. 12.50 (ISBN 0-8042-0796-8). John Knox.
Betty, L. Stafford. Vadiraja's Refutation of Sankara's Non-Dualism: Clearing the Way for Theism. 1978. 9.95 (ISBN 0-89684-001-8). Orient Bk Dist.
Betty, Stafford. Sing Like a Whippoorwill. (Illus., Orig.). 1987. pap. 6.95 (ISBN 0-89622-324-8). Twenty-Third.
Betz, H. D., ed. see Ebeling, Gerhard, et al.
Betz, Hans D. Essays on the Sermon on the Mount. LC 84-47910. 192p. 1984. 24.95 (ISBN 0-8006-0726-0). Fortress.
--Galatians. LC 77-78625. (Hermenia: A Critical & Historical Commentary on the Bible Ser.). 384p. 1979. 28.95 (ISBN 0-8006-6009-9, 20-6009). Fortress.
--Second Corinthians Eight & Nine: A Commentary on Two Administrative Letters of the Apostle Paul. LC 84-48904. (Hermeneia Ser.). 288p. 1985. 27.95 (ISBN 0-8006-6014-5, 20-6014). Fortress.
Betz, Hans D., ed. Christology & a Modern Pilgrimage: A Discussion with Norman Perrin. rev. ed. LC 79-31605. pap. 27.30 (ISBN 0-317-28877-6, 2020268). Bks Demand UMI.
Betz, Margaret. Faith & Justice. LC 80-50259. 176p. 1980. pap. text ed. 5.00x (ISBN 0-88489-114-3); tchr's guide 9.00x (ISBN 0-88489-121-6). St Mary's.
Betzer, Dan. Countdown. LC 79-53943. 112p. 1979. pap. 1.95 (ISBN 0-88243-481-0, 02-0481). Gospel Pub.
Beuchame, L., tr. see Melanchthon, Philip.
Beutner, Ed. Biblical Ballads. (Illus.). 1985. 4.95 (ISBN 0-911346-09-0). Christianica.
Bevan, Edwyn. Stoics & Sceptics. Vlastos, Gregory, ed. LC 78-15852. (Morals & Law in Ancient Greece Ser.). 1979. Repr. of 1913 ed. lib. bdg. 14.00x (ISBN 0-405-11530-X). Ayer Co Pubs.
Bevan, Edwyn R. Christianity. LC 80-24452. (The Home University Library of Modern Knowledge Ser.: No. 157). 255p. 1981. Repr. of 1948 ed. lib. bdg. 25.00x (ISBN 0-313-22681-4, BECY). Greenwood.
--Hellenism & Christianity. facs. ed. LC 67-26714. (Essay Index Reprint Ser). 1921. 18.00 (ISBN 0-8369-0207-6). Ayer Co Pubs.
--Holy Images: An Inquiry into Idolatry & Image-Worship in Ancient Paganism & in Christianity. LC 77-27191. (Gifford Lectures: 1933). Repr. of 1940 ed. 22.50 (ISBN 0-404-60489-7). AMS Pr.
--Sibyls & Seers. 1979. Repr. of 1928 ed. lib. bdg. 39.50 (ISBN 0-8495-0510-0). Arden Lib.
Bevan, Edwyn R., ed. Later Greek Religion. LC 76-179282. (Library of Greek Thought: No. 9). Repr. of 1927 ed. 12.50 (ISBN 0-404-07807-9). AMS Pr.
Beveridge, Henry, ed. see Calvin, John.
Beveridge, William. Complete Works, 12 vols. LC 72-39437. (Library of Anglo-Catholic Theology: No. 2). Repr. of 1848 ed. Set. 360.00 (ISBN 0-404-52040-5). AMS Pr.
Beversluis, John. C. S. Lewis & the Search for Rational Religion. 179p. (Orig.). 1985. pap. 9.95 (ISBN 0-8028-0046-7). Eerdmans.
Bevington, David. Medieval Drama. 1975. text ed. 34.95 (ISBN 0-395-13915-5). HM.
Bevington, David M., ed. The Macro Plays. LC 72-3905. 1972. 50.00 (ISBN 0-384-34920-X). Johnson Repr.
Bewer, Julius A. & Kraeling, Emil G. The Literature of the Old Testament. 3rd ed. LC 62-17061. (Records of Civilization: Sources & Studies: No. 5). pap. 128.00 (ISBN 0-317-26423-0, 2024975). Bks Demand UMI.
Bewes, Richard. Talking about Prayer. LC 80-7781. 128p. (Orig.). 1980. pap. 2.95 (ISBN 0-87784-465-8). Inter-Varsity.
Bewes, Richard, jt. auth. see Hicks, Robert.
Bewes, Richard, ed. John Wesley's England: A Nineteenth Century Pictorial History Based on an 18th Century Journal. (Illus.). 128p. (Orig.). 1981. pap. 9.95 (ISBN 0-8164-2319-9, HarpR). Har-Row.
Bey, E. Mohammed. 336p. 1985. 50.00x (ISBN 0-317-39181-X, Pub. by Luzac & Co Ltd). State Mutual Bk.
Bey, Serapis. Dossier on the Ascension. 212p. 1979. pap. 5.95 (ISBN 0-916766-21-7). Summit Univ.
Beyer, Douglas. Basic Beliefs of Christians. 64p. 1981. pap. 2.95 (ISBN 0-8170-0896-9). Judson.
--Commandments for Christian Living. 96p. 1983. pap. 5.95 (ISBN 0-8170-1008-4). Judson.
--Parables for Christian Living. 112p. 1985. pap. 5.95 (ISBN 0-8170-1074-2). Judson.
Beyer, Hermann W. Der Syrische Kirchenbau. (Studien Zur Spaetantiken Kunstgeschichte Ser.: Vol. 1). (Illus.). viii, 183p. 1978. Repr. of 1925 ed. 60.00x (ISBN 3-11-005705-0). De Gruyter.
Beyer, Jean. Religious Life or Secular Institute. 1970. pap. 2.75 (ISBN 0-8294-0319-1, Pub. by Gregorian U Pr). Loyola.
Beyer, Peter, tr. see Luhmann, Niklas.
Beyer, Stephan. The Cult of Tara: Magic & Ritual in Tibet. LC 74-186109. (Hermeneutics: Studies in the History of Religions). (Illus.). 1974. pap. 12.95 (ISBN 0-520-03635-2, CAL 383). U of Cal Pr.
Beyerle, Edith M., compiled by. Daily Meditations, 4 vols. 120p. Vol. 2. pap. 0.50 (ISBN 0-87509-075-3); Vol. 3. pap. 0.50 (ISBN 0-87509-076-1); Vol. 4. pap. 0.50 (ISBN 0-87509-077-X). Chr Pubns.
Beyerlin, Walter. We Are Like Dreamers. Livingstone, Dinah, tr. from Ger. Tr. of Wir Sind Wie Traumende. 76p. 1982. 13.95 (ISBN 0-567-09315-8, Pub. by T&T Clark Ltd). Fortress.
--Werden und Wesen Des 107 Psalms. (Beiheft 153 Zur Zeitschrift Fur Die Alttestamentliche Wissenschaft). 1979. 29.20 (ISBN 3-11-007755-8). De Gruyter.
Beyerlin, Walter, ed. Near Eastern Religious Texts Relating to the Old Testament. Bowden, John, tr. LC 77-28284. (Old Testament Library). (Illus.). 324p. 1978. 22.00 (ISBN 0-664-21363-4). Westminster.
Beza, Theodore. Bezae Codex Cantabrigiensis: Being an Exact Copy, in Ordinary Type of the Celebrated Uncial Graeco-Latin Manuscript of the Four Gospels & Acts of the Apostles. Scrivener, Frederick H., ed. LC 78-4144. (Pittsburgh Reprint Ser.: No. 5). 1978. pap. 19.95 (ISBN 0-915138-39-5). Pickwick.
Beze, Theodore de see De Beze, Theodore.
Bezirgan, Basima Q., jt. ed. see Fernea, Elizabeth W.
Bezold, Friedrich. Geschichte der Deutschen Reformation. LC 79-149654. (BCL Ser. I). (Ger.). Repr. of 1890 ed. 37.50 (ISBN 0-404-00797-X). AMS Pr.
Bhachu, Parminder. Twice Migrants: East African Sikh Settlers in Britain. 256p. 1986. text ed. 35.00 (ISBN 0-422-78910-0, 9773, Pub. by Tavistock England). Methuen Inc.
Bhagat, M. G. Ancient Indian Asceticism. LC 76-104001. 1976. 20.00 (ISBN 0-89684-476-5). Orient Bk Dist.

--Ancient Indian Asceticism. LC 76-904001. 1976. 18.50x (ISBN 0-88386-865-2). South Asia Bks.

Bhagat, Shantilal P. & Rieman, T. Wayne. What Does It Profit...? Christian Dialogue on the U. S. Economy. LC 83-3687. 144p. (Orig.). 1983. pap. 6.95 (ISBN 0-87178-927-2). Brethren.

Bhagavad-Gita. The Song of God. Prabhavananda, Swami & Isherwood, C., trs. pap. 2.95 (ISBN 0-451-62576-5, Ment). NAL.

Bhagowalia, Urmila. Vaisnavism & Society in Northern India. 1980. 22.00x (ISBN 0-8364-0664-8, Pub. by Intellectual India). South Asia Bks.

Bhagwan Shree Rajneesh. From Sex to Super Consciousness. Vora, V., tr. (Marathi.). 157p. 1975. pap. 2.95 (ISBN 0-89253-060-X). Ind-US Inc.

--The Perfect Way. Mahasattva Swami Krishna Prem, ed. LC 84-42808. (Early Writings & Discourses Ser.). 208p. 1984. pap. 3.95 (ISBN 0-88050-707-1). Chidvilas Found.

--The Rainbow Bridge. Prabhu, Krishna, ed. LC 85-42535. (Initiation Talks Ser.). 368p. (Orig.). 1985. pap. 3.95 (ISBN 0-88050-618-0). Chidvilas Found.

--Tao: The Golden Gate, Vol. 2. Prabhu, Swami Krishna, ed. LC 84-42615. (Tao Ser.). 304p. (Orig.). 1985. pap. 4.95 (ISBN 0-88050-647-4). Chidvilas Found.

Bhagwat, Ramachandra K., tr. see Jnanadev.

Bhagyalakshmi, S., jt. ed. see Krishnananda.

Bhajan, Yogi. The Teachings of Yogi Bhajan. 1985. pap. 8.95 (ISBN 0-317-38485-6). Arcline Pubns.

Bhakti, Krishna, tr. see Siddheswarananda, Swami.

Bhaktivedanta, A. C. Coming Back: The Science of Reincarnation. (Contemporary Vedic Library Ser.). (Illus.). 133p. 1982. 2.95 (ISBN 0-89213-114-4). Bhaktivedanta.

Bhaktivedanta, Swami. The Science of Self Realization. (Illus.). 1977. 3.95 (ISBN 0-89213-101-2). Bhaktivedanta.

Bhaktivedanta, Swami A. C. Beyond Birth & Death. LC 72-84844. (Illus.). 1972. pap. 1.95 (ISBN 0-912776-41-2). Bhaktivedanta.

--Easy Journey to Other Planets. LC 70-118080. (Illus.). 1970. pap. 1.95 (ISBN 0-912776-10-2). Bhaktivedanta.

--Krsna Consciousness: The Matchless Gift. LC 73-76634. (Illus.). 1974. pap. 1.95 (ISBN 0-912776-61-7). Bhaktivedanta.

--Krsna: The Supreme Personality of Godhead, 3 vols. LC 74-118081. (Illus.). 1970. Vol. 1. pap. 12.95 (ISBN 0-89213-136-5). Bhaktivedanta.

--Nectar of Devotion. LC 78-118082. (Illus.). 1970. 12.95 (ISBN 0-912776-05-6). Bhaktivedanta.

--Perfection of Yoga. LC 72-76302. (Illus.). 1972. pap. 1.95 (ISBN 0-912776-36-6). Bhaktivedanta.

--Prahlad, Picture & Story Book. LC 72-2032. (Illus.). 1973. pap. 2.95 (ISBN 0-685-47513-1). Bhaktivedanta.

--Raja-Vidya: The King of Knowledge. LC 72-84845. (Illus.). 1973. pap. 1.95 (ISBN 0-912776-40-4). Bhaktivedanta.

--Sri Caitanya Caritamrta: Antya-Lila, 5 vols. (Illus.). 1975. 12.95 ea. Vol. 1 (ISBN 0-912776-72-2). Vol. 2 (ISBN 0-912776-73-0). Vol. 3 (ISBN 0-912776-74-9). Vol. 4 (ISBN 0-912776-76-5). Vol. 5 (ISBN 0-912776-77-3). Bhaktivedanta.

--Sri Caitanya-Caritamrta: Madhya-Lila, 9 vols. (Illus.). 1975. 12.95 ea. Vol. 1 (ISBN 0-912776-63-3). Vol. 2 (ISBN 0-912776-64-1). Vol. 3 (ISBN 0-912776-65-X). Vol. 4 (ISBN 0-912776-66-8). Vol. 5 (ISBN 0-912776-67-6). Vol. 6 (ISBN 0-912776-68-4). Vol. 7 (ISBN 0-912776-69-2). Vol. 8, (ISBN 0-912776-70-6), Vol. 9 (ISBN 0-912776-71-4). Bhaktivedanta.

--Srimad Bhagavatam: First Canto, 3 vols. LC 73-169353. (Illus.). 1972. 12.95 ea. Vol. 1 (ISBN 0-912776-27-7). Vol. 2 (ISBN 0-912776-29-3). Vol. 3 (ISBN 0-912776-34-X). Bhaktivedanta.

--Srimad Bhagavatam: Fourth Canto, 4 vols. LC 73-169353. (Illus.). 1974. 12.95 ea. Vol. 1 (ISBN 0-912776-38-2). Vol. 2 (ISBN 0-912776-47-1). Vol. 3 (ISBN 0-912776-48-X). Vol. 4 (ISBN 0-912776-49-8). Bhaktivedanta.

--Srimad Bhagavatam: Second Canto, 2 vols. LC 73-169353. (Illus.). 1972. 12.95 ea. Vol. 1 (ISBN 0-912776-28-5). Vol. 2 (ISBN 0-912776-35-8). Bhaktivedanta.

--Srimad Bhagavatam: Third Canto, 4 vols. LC 73-169353. (Illus.). 1974. 12.95 ea. Vol. 1 (ISBN 0-912776-37-4). Vol. 2 (ISBN 0-912776-44-7). Vol. 3 (ISBN 0-912776-46-3). Vol. 4 (ISBN 0-912776-75-7). Bhaktivedanta.

Bhaktivedanta, Swami Prabhupada A. C. Srimad-Bhagavatam: Tenth Canto, Vol. 3. (Illus.). 112p. 1980. 12.95 (ISBN 0-89213-107-1). Bhaktivedanta.

Bhaktivedanta Swami. Light of the Bhagavat. 1985. 12.95 (ISBN 0-89213-135-7). Bhaktivedanta.

--Srimad Bhagavatam: 11th Canto, Vol. 5. 1985. 12.95 (ISBN 0-89213-126-8). Bhaktivedanta.

--Srimad Bhagavatam: 12th Canto, Vol. 1. 1985. 12.95 (ISBN 0-89213-129-2). Bhaktivedanta.

--Srimad Bhagavatam: 12th Canto, Vol. 2. 1985. 12.95 (ISBN 0-89213-130-6). Bhaktivedanta.

Bhaktivendanta, Swami A. C. Srimad Bhagavatam: Ninth Canto, 3 vols. LC 73-169353. (Sanskrit & Eng., Illus.). 1977. 12.95 ea. Vol. 1 (ISBN 0-912776-94-3). Vol. 2 (ISBN 0-912776-95-1). Vol. 3 (ISBN 0-912776-96-X). Bhaktivedanta.

Bhamre, Suresh T. Hatha Yoga for Kids: A Guidebook for Parents & Children. (Illus.). 1985. 8.00 (ISBN 0-682-40164-1). Exposition Pr FL.

Bhandarkar, R. G. Vaisnavism Saivism & Minor Religious Systems. 238p. 1986. Repr. 14.00X (ISBN 0-8364-1704-6, Pub. by Minerva India). South Asia Bks.

Bhandarkar, T. A. Ramakrishna, Sri: Sahasra-Nama-Stotram. (Illus.). 200p. (Orig.). pap. 7.95x (ISBN 0-87481-509-6). Vedanta Pr.

Bharata Krsna Tirthaji Maharaj. Vedic Metaphysics. 1978. Repr. 16.95 (ISBN 0-89684-337-8). Orient Bk Dist.

Bharati, Agahananda. The Ochre Robe: An Autobiography. 2nd ed. 300p. 1980. 14.95 (ISBN 0-915520-40-0); pap. 7.95 (ISBN 0-915520-28-1). Ross-Erikson.

Bharati, Agehananda. Hindu Views & Ways & the Hindu-Muslim Interface. 1981. 8.00x (ISBN 0-8364-0772-5, Pub. by Munshiram). South Asia Bks.

--Hindu Views & Ways & the Hindu-Muslim Interface: An Anthropological Assessment. 107p. 1982. Repr. of 1981 ed. 8.95 (ISBN 0-915520-54-0). Ross Erikson.

--The Light at the Center: Context & Pretext of Modern Mysticism. 1976. lib. bdg. 11.95 (ISBN 0-915520-03-6); pap. 6.95 (ISBN 0-915520-04-4). Ross-Erikson.

Bhardwaj, Surinder M. Hindu Places of Pilgrimage in India: A Study in Cultural Geography. LC 73-174454. (Center for South & Southeast Asia Studies, U.C. Berkeley). (Illus.). 1973. 42.50x (ISBN 0-520-02135-5); pap. 8.95 (ISBN 0-520-04951-9, CAL 621). U of Cal Pr.

Bharti, Ma S., ed. see Rajneesh, Bhagwan S.

Bharti, Ma Satya. Death Comes Dancing: Celebrating Life with Bhagwan Shree Rajneesh. 200p. 1981. pap. 9.95 (ISBN 0-7100-0705-1). Methuen Inc.

Bharti, Ma Satya, ed. see Rajneesh, Bhagwan Shree.

Bhartrihari. Vairagya-Satakam: The Hundred Verses on Renunciation. (Sanskrit & Eng.). pap. 1.75 (ISBN 0-87481-070-1). Vedanta Pr.

Bhasha, Ma Deva, ed. see Rajneesh, Bhagwan Shree.

Bhashycharaya, Pundit M. Catechism of the Visishtadwaita Philosophy. Robb, R. I., ed. (Secret Doctrine Reference Ser.). (Orig.). 1986. pap. 4.00 (ISBN 0-913510-56-4). Wizards.

Bhat, G. K. Theatric Aspects of Sanskrit Drama. 1985. 12.50x (ISBN 0-8364-1365-2, Pub. by Bhanarkar Oriental Inst). South Asia Bks.

Bhatt, S. R. Philosophy of Pancharatra: An Advaitic Approach. 137p. pap. 4.25 (ISBN 0-89744-122-2, Pub. by Ganesh & Co. India). Auromere.

Bhattacharji, Sukumari. The Indian Theogony: Comparative Study of Indian Mythology from the Vedas to the Puranas. rev. ed. 1978. Repr. of 1970 ed. 18.50x (ISBN 0-8364-0160-3). South Asia Bks.

Bhattacharrya, K. C. Search for the Absolute in Neo-Vedanta. Burch, George B., ed. LC 75-17740. 202p. 1976. text ed. 14.00x (ISBN 0-8248-0296-9). UH Pr.

Bhattacharya, Aparna. Religious Movements of Bengal, 1800-1850. 1984. pap. 9.00x (ISBN 0-8364-1118-8, Pub. by New Times). South Asia Bks.

Bhattacharya, Bhabani, ed. Contemporary Indian Short Stories, 2 vols. 1967. Vol. 1. 3.50 (ISBN 0-88253-409-2); Vol. 2. 3.50 (ISBN 0-88253-327-4). Ind-US Inc.

Bhattacharya, Dipak C. Studies in Buddhist Iconography. 1978. 22.50x (ISBN 0-8364-0016-X). South Asia Bks.

Bhattacharya, Gouriswar, ed. Deyadharma: Studies in Memory of Dr. D. C. Sircar. (Illus.). 276p. 1986. lib. bdg. 75.00x (ISBN 81-7030-021-5, Pub. by Sri Satguru Pubns India). Orient Bk Dist.

Bhattacharya, Ram Shankar, jt. ed. see Larson, Gerald J.

Bhattacharya, Vivek. The Spirit of Indian Culture: Saints of India. 622p. 1980. 29.95 (ISBN 0-940500-40-X). Asia Bk Corp.

Bhattacharyya, et al, eds. The Cultural Heritage of India, 5 vols. Incl. Vol. 1. Early Phases. Radhakrishnan, S., intro. by. (ISBN 0-87481-560-6); Vol. 2. Itihasas, Puranas, Dharma & Other Shastras (ISBN 0-87481-561-4); Vol. 3. The Philosophies (ISBN 0-87481-562-2); Vol. 4. The Religions (ISBN 0-87481-563-0); Vol. 5: Languages & Literatures (ISBN 0-87481-564-9). (Illus.). 40.00x ea.; Set. 175.00x (ISBN 0-87481-558-4). Vedanta Pr.

Bhattacharyya, Benoytosh. An Introduction to Buddhist Esoterism. 1980. Repr. of 1931 ed. 19.00x (ISBN 0-686-69019-2, Pub. by Motilal Banarsidas). South Asia Bks.

Bhattacharyya, N. N. History of the Tantric Religion. 1983. 34.00x (ISBN 0-8364-0942-6, Pub. by Manohar India); pap. 17.50x (ISBN 0-8364-0943-4). South Asia Bks.

--Indian Mother Goddess. 2nd ed. 1977. 16.50x (ISBN 0-88386-736-2). South Asia Bks.

Bhave, Vinoba. Talks on the Gita. 241p. 1983. 10.00 (ISBN 0-934676-37-2). Greenlf Bks.

Bhavyananda, Swami, ed. see Monks of the Ramakrishna Order.

Bhikshu, Yogi. Bhakti Yoga. 6.00 (ISBN 0-911662-21-9). Yoga.

--Karma Yoga. 1928. 6.00 (ISBN 0-911662-20-0). Yoga.

Bhikshu Hung Ju & Bhikshu Hung Yo. Three Steps, One Bow. (Illus.). 160p. (Orig.). 1976. pap. 5.00 (ISBN 0-917512-18-9). Buddhist Text.

Bhikshu Hung Yo, jt. auth. see Bhikshu Hung Ju.

Bhikshuni Heng Ch'ih, tr. see Buddhist Text Translation Society Staff.

Bhikshuni Heng Tao, tr. see Buddhist Text Translation Society Staff.

Bial, Morrison D. Liberal Judaism at Home: The Practices of Modern Reform Judaism. rev. ed. 1971. pap. 5.00 (ISBN 0-8074-0075-0, 383110); tchrs'. guide 1.50 (ISBN 0-8074-0225-7, 203110). UAHC.

--Your Jewish Child. Syme, Daniel B., ed. 1978. pap. 5.00 (ISBN 0-8074-0012-2, 101200). UAHC.

Bial, Morrison D., ed. see Stadtler, Bea.

Biale, David. Childhood, Marriage & the Family in the Eastern European Jewish Enlightement. 24p. 1983. pap. 1.50 (ISBN 0-87495-049-X). Am Jewish Comm.

--Gershom Scholem: Kabbalah & Counter-History. 2nd ed. 240p. 1982. pap. text ed. 7.95x (ISBN 0-674-36332-9). Harvard U Pr.

--Power & Powerlessness in Jewish History. 1986. 18.95 (ISBN 0-8052-4015-2). Schocken.

Biale, Rachel. Women & Jewish Law: An Exploration of Women's Issues in Halakhic Sources. LC 83-40457. 256p. 1984. 18.95 (ISBN 0-8052-3887-5). Schocken.

--Women & Jewish Law: An Exploration of Women's Issues in Halakhic Sources. 304p. 1986. pap. 8.95 (ISBN 0-8052-0810-0). Schocken.

Bialik, Hayyim N. And It Came to Pass. 281p. 1938. 6.95 (ISBN 0-88482-887-5). Hebrew Pub.

--Knight of Onions & Knight of Garlic. 55p. 1934. 4.95 (ISBN 0-88482-734-8). Hebrew Pub.

Biallas, Leonard J. Myths: Gods, Heroes & Saviors. 304p. (Orig.). 1986. pap. 9.95 (ISBN 0-89622-290-X). Twenty-Third.

Biamonte, Edgar. Window of Eternity. LC 83-9944. 145p. 1984. 14.95 (ISBN 0-87949-230-9). Ashley Bks.

Bianchi, Eugene C. On Growing Older. 176p. 1985. pap. 9.95 (ISBN 0-8245-0700-2). Crossroad NY.

Bianco, Enzo. Don Bosco's Lay Religious: Essays on the Salesian Brother, Pt. 1. Swain, Peter, tr. LC 84-72160. 75p. pap. 3.00 (ISBN 0-89944-078-9). Don Bosco Multimedia.

--Don Bosco's Lay Religious: Profiles in Courage, Pt. 2. Swain, Peter, tr. 101p. pap. 3.00 (ISBN 0-89944-079-7). Don Bosco Multimedia.

--Salesian Cooperators: A Practical Way of Life. Swain, Peter, tr. (Salesian Family Ser.). 40p. 1983. pap. 3.25 (ISBN 0-89944-073-8). Don Bosco Multimedia.

Biardeau, Madeleine. Theorie De la Connaissance et Philosophie De la Parole Dans le Brahmanisme Classique. (Le Monde D'outre-Mer Passe et Present, Etudes: No. 23). 1963. pap. 34.80x (ISBN 90-2796-178-6). Mouton.

Biasiotto, Peter R. History of the Development of the Devotion to the Holy Name. 1943. 3.50 (ISBN 0-686-11579-1). Franciscan Inst.

Bibago, Abraham. Derek Emunah: The Path of Faith. 204p. 1521. text ed. 49.68x (ISBN 0-576-80102-X, Pub. by Gregg Intl Pubs England). Gregg Intl.

Bibb, Benjamin O. & Weed, Joseph J. Amazing Secrets of Psychic Healing. 1976. pap. 5.95 (ISBN 0-13-023762-0). P-H.

Biber, Jacob. Survivors: A Personal Story of the Holocaust. LC 85-22415. (Studies in Judaica & the Holocaust: No. 2). 208p. 1986. lib. bdg. 18.95x (ISBN 0-89370-370-2); pap. text ed. 8.95x (ISBN 0-89370-470-9). Borgo Pr.

Biberfeld, Henry, tr. see Munk, Elie.

Biberfeld, Philip. Universal Jewish History, 4 vols. Vol. 1. 8.95 (ISBN 0-87306-052-0, Spero Foundation); Vol. 2. 8.95 (ISBN 0-87306-053-9); Vol. 3. 10.95 (ISBN 0-87306-054-7); Set. cancelled (ISBN 0-87306-051-2). Feldheim.

Bible, Ken. Beacon Small-Group Bible Studies, Genesis, Pt. II: God's Hand in History. Wolf, Earl C., ed. 96p. (Orig.). 1986. pap. 2.50 (ISBN 0-8341-0958-1). Beacon Hill.

--Genesis: Faithful to His Promises, Pt. 2. Wolf, Earl, ed. (Small Group Bible Studies). 72p. (Orig.). Date not set. pap. 2.50 (ISBN 0-8341-1108-X). Beacon Hill.

Bible Temple Staff. The Home Fellowship Meetings. rev. ed. 1975. 6.95 (ISBN 0-914936-14-X). Bible Temple.

Bibliotheca Press Research Division Staff, ed. On This Day We Will Pray: Prayers for Sunday Through Saturday. 7p. 1986. pap. 1.75 (ISBN 0-939476-19-3, Pub. by Biblio Pr GA). Prosperity & Profits.

Bickel, Margot & Steigert, Hermann. Harvest the Day. Frost, Gerhard E., ed. (Illus.). 64p. (Orig.). pap. 7.95 (ISBN 0-86683-730-2, HarpR). Har-Row.

Bickerman, Elias. Four Strange Books of the Bible: Jonah, Daniel, Koheleth, Esther. (Illus.). 252p. 1984. pap. 8.95 (ISBN 0-8052-0774-0). Schocken.

--From Ezra to the Last of the Maccabees: Foundations of Post-Biblical Judaism. 1962. pap. 5.95 (ISBN 0-8052-0036-3). Schocken.

--Studies in Jewish & Christian History, Pt. 3. (Arbeiten zur Geschichte des antiken Judentums und des Urchritentums Ser.: Band 9). xvi, 392p. 1986. 93.50 (ISBN 90-04-07480-5, Pub. by E J Brill). Heinman.

Bickers, Bernard W., jt. auth. see Holmes, Derek J.

Bickersteth, Edward H. Holy Spirit. LC 59-13640. 192p. 1976. pap. 5.95 (ISBN 0-8254-2227-2). Kregel.

--The Trinity. LC 59-13770. 182p. 1976. pap. 5.95 (ISBN 0-8254-2226-4). Kregel.

Bicket, Zenas J. The Effective Pastor. LC 74-80729. 185p. 1973. 3.95 (ISBN 0-88243-512-4, 02-0512). Gospel Pub.

--Walking in the Spirit. LC 76-51000. 96p. 1977. pap. 1.25 (ISBN 0-88243-611-2, 02-0611, Radiant Bks). Gospel Pub.

--We Hold These Truths. LC 78-56133. (Workers Training Book of the Year). (Illus.). 128p. 1978. pap. 1.50 (ISBN 0-88243-631-7, 02-0631). Gospel Pub.

Bickimer, David Arthur. Christ the Placenta. LC 82-24097. 239p. (Orig.). 1983. pap. 12.95 (ISBN 0-89135-034-9). Religious Educ.

Biddle, Perry. Abingdon Marriage Manual. 208p. pap. 12.95 (ISBN 0-687-00485-3). Abingdon.

Biddle, Perry H., Jr. The Goodness of Marriage: A Devotional Book for Newlyweds. LC 84-50840. 144p. 1984. 6.95 (ISBN 0-8358-0490-9). Upper Room.

Biddle, Perry, Jr. Lectionary Preaching Workbook B: Series II. (Orig.). 1987. pap. price not set (ISBN 0-89536-879-X, 7865). CSS of Ohio.

Biebel, David B. & Lawrence, Howard W., eds. Pastors Are People Too. LC 86-3835. 205p. (Orig.). 1986. pap. 5.95 (ISBN 0-8307-1102-3, 5418654). Regal.

Bieber, Richard. Rebirth of the Congregation. 1973. pap. 1.25 (ISBN 0-87508-012-X). Chr Lit.

Biechler, James E. The Religious Language of Nicholas of Cusa. LC 75-23096. (American Academy of Religion, Dissertation Ser.). 240p. 1975. pap. 10.25 (ISBN 0-89130-021-X, 01 01 08). Scholars Pr GA.

Biederwolf, William E. The Second Coming Bible Commentary. (Paperback Reference Library). 728p. 1985. pap. 17.95 (ISBN 0-8010-0887-5). Baker Bk.

--Study of the Holy Spirit. LC 84-25099. 128p. 1985. pap. 5.95 (ISBN 0-8254-2244-2). Kregel.

Biegert. Looking Up...While Lying Down. (Looking Up Ser.). 1979. pap. 1.25 booklet (ISBN 0-8298-0364-5). Pilgrim NY.

--So We're Growing Older. (Looking Up Ser.). 1982. pap. 1.25 booklet (ISBN 0-8298-0436-6). Pilgrim NY.

--When Death has Touched Your Life. 1981. pap. 1.25 (ISBN 0-8298-0455-2). Pilgrim NY.

Biegert, John E. Mirando Hacia Arriba en Medio de la Enfermedad: (Looking Up...While Lying Down) (Looking Up Ser.). (Span.). 24p. (Orig.). 1983. pap. 1.25 booklet (ISBN 0-8298-0663-6). Pilgrim NY.

--Staying in... (Looking Up Ser.). 1985. pap. 1.25 (ISBN 0-8298-0567-2). Pilgrim NY.

Biehl, Bobb & Hagelganz, James W. Praying: How to Start & Keep Going. LC 80-54003. 128p. 1981. pap. 2.50 (ISBN 0-8307-0781-6, 5016900). Regal.

Bien, David D. The Calas Affair: Persecution, Toleration, & Heresy in Eighteenth-Century Toulouse. LC 78-12393. 1979. Repr. of 1960 ed. lib. bdg. cancelled (ISBN 0-313-21206-6, BICA). Greenwood.
Bien, Peter. Tempted by Happiness: Razantzakis Post-Christian Christ. 1984. pap. 2.50x (ISBN 0-317-12307-6, 253). Pendle Hill.
Bienbar, Arthur, ed. see Silva, Owen F.
Bienert, Wolfgang. Dionysius Von Alexandrien Zur Frage Des Originismus. (Patristische Texte und Studien, 21). 1978. 35.20x (ISBN 3-11-007442-7). De Gruyter.
Bienert, Wolfgang A. Allegoria und Anagoge bei Didymos dem Blinden von Alexandria. (Patristische Texte und Studien Ser.: Vol. 13). xii, 188p. 1972. 23.20x (ISBN 3-11-003715-7). De Gruyter.
Bier, W. C., ed. Adolescent, His Search for Understanding. LC 62-17450. (Pastoral Psychology Ser.: No. 3). x, 246p. 1963. 17.50 (ISBN 0-8232-0480-4). Fordham.
--Human Life: Problems of Birth, of Living, & of Dying. LC 77-71939. (Pastoral Psychology Ser.: No. 9). 1977. 20.00 (ISBN 0-8232-1025-1). Fordham.
--Personality & Sexual Problems in Pastoral Psychology. LC 62-16224. (Pastoral Psychology Ser: No. 1). xvi, 256p. 1964. 20.00 (ISBN 0-8232-0585-1). Fordham.
--Privacy: A Vanishing Value? LC 79-56138. (Pastoral Psychology Ser.: No. 10). xiv, 398p. 1980. 25.00 (ISBN 0-8232-1044-8). Fordham.
Bier, W. C., ed. see Academy of Religion & Mental Health Staff.
Bier, William C., ed. Woman in Modern Life. LC 68-20626. (Pastoral Psychology Ser.: No. 5). x, 278p. 1968. 20.00 (ISBN 0-8232-0800-1). Fordham.
Bierbaum, Athanasius. Pusillum, 4 vols. 7.50 (ISBN 0-685-10971-2, L38675). Franciscan Herald.
Bierhorst, John. The Mythology of North America: Intro to Classic American Gods, Heroes & Tricksters. LC 86-12207. (Illus.). 256p. 1986. pap. 6.95 (ISBN 0-688-06666-6, Quill). Morrow.
Bierhorst, John, ed. The Red Swan: Myths and Tales of the American Indians. LC 76-196. 368p. 1976. pap. 7.95 (ISBN 0-374-51393-7). FS&G.
--The Sacred Path: Spells, Prayers & Power Songs of the American Indians. LC 82-14118. (Illus.). 191p. 1983. PLB 10.25 (ISBN 0-688-01699-5). Morrow.
--The Sacred Path: Spells, Prayers, & Power Songs of the American Indians. LC 83-19460. (Illus.). 192p. 1984. pap. 8.20 (ISBN 0-688-02647-8, Quill). Morrow.
Bierma, Lyle D., tr. see Von Harnack, Adolf.
Bierman, A. K. Life & Morals: An Introduction to Ethics. 596p. 1980. pap. text ed. 14.95 (ISBN 0-15-550725-7, HC). HarBraceJ.
Bierman, John. Odyssey. 288p. 1984. 16.95 (ISBN 0-671-50156-9). S&S.
Biermann, June & Toohey, Barbara. The Woman's Holistic Headache Relief Book. 212p. Repr. of 1979 ed. 8.95 (ISBN 0-686-35967-4). Sugarfree.
Biermans, John T. The Odyssey of New Religious Movements: Persecution, Struggle, Legitimation - a Case Study of the Unification Church. (Symposium Ser.). 232p. text ed. 49.95 (ISBN 0-88946-710-2). E Mellen.
Biersdorf, John E. Healing of Purpose: God's Call to Discipleship. 192p. (Orig.). 1985. pap. 11.95 (ISBN 0-687-16741-8). Abingdon.
Bietenholz, Peter G. & Deutscher, Thomas B., eds. Contemporaries of Erasmus: A Biographical Register of the Renaissance & Reformation, Vol. 1 (A-E) (Illus.). 480p. 1985. 72.50x (ISBN 0-8020-2507-2). U of Toronto Pr.
Biever, Bruce F. Religion, Culture & Values: A Cross-Cultural Analysis of Motivational Factors in Native Irish & American Irish Catholicism. LC 76-6322. (Irish Americans Ser). 1976. 62.00 (ISBN 0-405-09319-5). Ayer Co Pubs.
Biezais, Haralds, ed. New Religions. 233p. (Orig.). 1975. pap. text ed. 18.50x (Pub. by Almqvist & Wiksell). Coronet Bks.
--Religious Symbols & Their Functions. 178p. (Orig.). 1979. pap. text ed. 22.50 (ISBN 91-22-00199-9, Pub. by Almqvist & Wiksell). Coronet Bks.
Biffi, Inos. The Story of the Eucharist. Drury, John, tr. from Ital. LC 85-82173. (Illustrated History of Christian Culture Ser.). Orig. Title: Storia dell' eucaristia. (Illus.). 125p. 1986. 11.95 (ISBN 0-89870-089-2). Ignatius Pr.
Bigandet, Paul A. The Life, or Legend of Gaudama: The Buddha of the Burmese, 2 vols. 4th ed. LC 77-8749. Repr. of 1912 ed. Set. 52.50 (ISBN 0-404-16800-0). AMS Pr.
Bigart, Lois S. You Can Have Joy. 1984. 5.00 (ISBN 0-8062-2414-2). Carlton.
Bigelow, John. The Bible That Was Lost & Is Found. 4th ed. LC 78-65549. pap. 1.95 (ISBN 0-87785-159-X). Swedenborg.
--Toleration, & Other Essays & Studies. facs. ed. LC 78-84298. (Essay Index Reprint Ser). 1927. 14.25 (ISBN 0-8369-1075-3). Ayer Co Pubs.
Bigelow, William S. Buddhism & Immortality. LC 78-72379. Repr. of 1908 ed. 16.50 (ISBN 0-404-17228-8). AMS Pr.
Bigg, Charles. Christian Platonists of Alexandria: Eight Lectures. LC 75-123764. Repr. of 1886 ed. 27.50 (ISBN 0-404-00799-6). AMS Pr.
--The Church's Task Under the Roman Empire. 1977. lib. bdg. 59.95 (ISBN 0-8490-1629-0). Gordon Pr.
--A Critical & Exergetical Commentary on the Epistles of St. Peter & St. Jude. Driver, Samuel R., et al, eds. (International Critical Commentary Ser.). 376p. 1902. 24.95 (ISBN 0-567-05036-X, Pub. by T & T Clark Ltd UK). Fortress.
Biggar, Nigel, et al. Cities of Gods: Faith, Politics & Pluralism in Judaism, Christianity & Islam. LC 85-9879. (Contributions to the Study of Religion Ser.: No. 16). 253p. 1986. lib. bdg. 39.95 (ISBN 0-313-24944-X, BCG/). Greenwood.
Biggs, John, tr. see Firishtah, Muhammad.
Biggs, Mouzon, Jr. Moments to Hold Close. 144p. 1983. 9.95 (ISBN 0-687-27147-9). Abingdon.
Biggs-Davison, John & Chowdharay-Best, George. The Cross of Saint Patrick: The Catholic Unionist Tradition in Ireland. 1985. 50.80x (ISBN 0-946041-26-1, Pub. by Kensal Pr UK). State Mutual Bk.
Bigler, Robert M. The Politics of German Protestantism: The Rise of the Protestant Church Elite in Prussia, 1815-1848. LC 77-142055. 1972. 38.50x (ISBN 0-520-01881-8). U of Cal Pr.
Bigongiari, Dino, ed. see St. Thomas Aquinas.
Bilgray, A., jt. ed. see Marcus, J. R.
Bilhartz, Terry D. Urban Religion & the Second Great Awakening. LC 83-49455. 240p. 1986. 27.50x (ISBN 0-8386-3227-0). Fairleigh Dickinson.
Bilhartz, Terry O., ed. Francis Asbury's America: An Album of Early American Methodism. LC 83-18275. 128p. 1984. (Pub. by F. Asbury Pr); pap. 6.95 (ISBN 0-310-44791-7, 18275). Zondervan.
Bilheimer, Robert S. A Spirituality for the Long Haul: Biblical Risk & Moral Stand. LC 83-48918. 176p. 1984. pap. 8.95 (ISBN 0-8006-1760-6, 1-1760). Fortress.
--What Must the Church Do? facsimile ed. LC 70-134053. (Essay Index Reprints - Interseminary Ser.: Vol. 5). Repr. of 1947 ed. 17.00 (ISBN 0-8369-2384-7). Ayer Co Pubs.
Bilheimer, Robert S., ed. Faith & Ferment: An Interdisciplinary Study of Christian Beliefs & Practices. LC 83-70512. 352p. (Orig.). 1983. pap. 15.95 (ISBN 0-8066-2018-8, 10-2168). Augsburg.
Bilheimer, Robert S., ed. see Chittister, Joan D. & Marty, Martin E.
Bilich, Marion. Weight Loss from the Inside Out: Help for the Compulsive Eater. LC 83-633. 192p. (Orig.). 1983. pap. 9.95 (ISBN 0-8164-2485-3, HarpR). Har-Row.
Bilik, Dorothy S. Immigrant-Survivors: Post-Holocaust Consciousness in Recent Jewish-American Literature. LC 80-15326. 217p. 1981. 17.50x. Wesleyan U Pr.
Bill, E. G., compiled by. The Queen Anne Churches: A Catalogue of the Papers in Lambeth Palace Library of the Commission for Building Fifty New Churches in London & Westminster, 1711-1759. 280p. 1979. 53.00x (ISBN 0-7201-0919-1). Mansell.
Biller, Martie, jt. auth. see Biller, Tom A.
Biller, Tom A. & Biller, Martie. Simple Object Lessons for Children. (Object Lesson Ser.). 160p. 1980. pap. 4.95 (ISBN 0-8010-0793-3). Baker Bk.
Billheimer, Paul. Don't Waste Your Sorrows. 1977. pap. 4.95 (ISBN 0-87508-007-3). Chr Lit.
--Love Covers. 1981. pap. 4.95 (ISBN 0-87508-006-5). Chr Lit.
--The Mystery of God's Providence. 1983. pap. 3.95 (ISBN 0-8423-4664-3). Tyndale.
Billheimer, Paul E. Destined for the Cross. 1982. pap. 3.95 (ISBN 0-8423-0604-8). Tyndale.
--Destined for the Throne. LC 83-15151. 140p. (Orig.). 1983. pap. 4.95 (ISBN 0-87123-309-6, 210309). Bethany Hse.
--Destined for the Throne. 1983. pap. 4.95 (ISBN 0-87508-040-5). Chr Lit.
--Destined to Overcome. 123p. 1982. pap. 4.95 (ISBN 0-87123-287-1, 210287). Bethany Hse.
--Don't Waste Your Sorrows. LC 83-15821. 144p. (Orig.). 1983. pap. 4.95 (ISBN 0-87123-310-X, 210310). Bethany Hse.
--Love Covers. LC 83-15823. 174p. (Orig.). 1983. pap. 4.95 (ISBN 0-87123-400-9, 210400). Bethany Hse.
Billings, Jean, jt. auth. see Robson, Ralph.
Billings, Peggy. Paradox & Promise in Human Rights. (Orig.). 1979. pap. 2.95 (ISBN 0-377-00083-3). Friend Pr.
Billings, William. The Psalm Singer's Amusement. LC 73-5100. (Earlier American Music Ser.: Vol. 20). 104p. 1974. Repr. of 1781 ed. lib. bdg. 25.00 (ISBN 0-306-70587-7). Da Capo.
Billingsley, Lloyd. Religion's Rebel Son: Fanaticism in Our Time. LC 86-16311. 1986. 11.95 (ISBN 0-88070-139-0). Multnomah.
Billington, James, et al. Virtue: Public & Private. Neuhaus, Richard J., ed. (The Encounter Ser.). 96p. (Orig.). 1986. pap. 5.95 (ISBN 0-8028-0201-X). Eerdmans.
Billington, Ray A. The Origins of Nativism in the United States, 1800-1844. LC 73-19129. (Politics & People Ser.). (Illus.). 716p. 1974. Repr. 52.00x (ISBN 0-405-05854-3). Ayer Co Pubs.
Billion, Anna. Kundalini: Secret of the Ancient Yogis. 1982. pap. 4.95 (ISBN 0-686-97516-2, Reward). P-H.
Billnitzer, Harold. Before You Divorce. 1978. pap. 0.95 (ISBN 0-933350-12-0). Morse Pr.
--Chances in a Mixed Marriage. 1978. pap. 1.95 (ISBN 0-933350-11-2). Morse Pr.
--It's Your Death, Make the Most of It. LC 79-88402. 1979. pap. 7.95 (ISBN 0-933350-27-9). wkbk. 0.90 (ISBN 0-933350-28-7). Morse Pr.
Billon, B. M. Death's an End & a Beginning Without. 1981. 15.00x (ISBN 0-7223-1388-8, Pub. by A H Stockwell England). State Mutual Bk.
Bills, Paul. Alaska. LC 80-65307. (Illus.). 160p. (Orig.). 1980. pap. 2.50 (ISBN 0-88243-462-4, 02-0462). Gospel Pub.
Bilnitzer. Check Your Chances of Success in a Mixed Marriage. pap. 1.75 (ISBN 0-686-12318-2). Christs Mission.
Bilson, Elizabeth, jt. ed. see Terzian, Yervant.
Bilson, Thomas. The True Difference Between Christian Subjection & Unchristian Rebellion. LC 70-38154. (English Experience Ser.: No. 434). 854p. 1972. Repr. of 1585 ed. 143.00 (ISBN 90-221-0434-6). Walter J Johnson.
Bimala dasi, ed. see Dasa Goswami, Satvarupa.
Bimala dasi, ed. see Das Goswami, Satsvarupa.
Bimala dasi, ed. see Das Goswami, Satvarupa.
Bimler, Rich. Celebrating Saints. 80p. (Orig.). 1986. pap. 3.95 (ISBN 0-570-04440-5). Concordia.
Bimler, Rich & Brokering, Herb. Lord, I Want to Celebrate. 1980. pap. 2.95 (ISBN 0-570-03069-2, 06-1185). Concordia.
Bimler, Richard. Seventy-Seven Ways of Involving Youth in the Church. (Illus.). 1976. pap. 4.50 (ISBN 0-570-03737-9, 12-2641). Concordia.
Bimler, Richard W. Grand Opening. 1983. 3.75 (ISBN 0-89536-589-8, 0731). CSS of Ohio.
--The Youth Group Meeting Guide. LC 83-82574. 256p. (Orig.). 1984. pap. 11.95 (ISBN 0-936664-17-7). Group Bks.
Bimson, John J. Redating the Exodus & Conquest. 2nd ed. 288p. 1981. pap. text ed. 14.95x (ISBN 0-907459-04-8, Pub. by Almond Pr England). Eisenbrauns.
Binark, Ismet & Eren, Halit. World Bibliography of Translations of the Meanings of the Holy Qur'an: Printed Translations 1515-1980. 600p. 1987. text ed. 125.00 (ISBN 0-7103-0229-0, Kegan Paul). Methuen Inc.
Binder, Louis R. Modern Religious Cults & Society. LC 77-113556. Repr. of 1933 ed. 10.00 (ISBN 0-404-00867-4). AMS Pr.
Bindley, T. Herbert, ed. The Ecumenical Documents of the Faith: The Creed of Nicea; Three Epistles of Cyril; The Tome of Leo; The Chalcedonian Definition. 4th ed. LC 79-8708. viii, 246p. 1980. Repr. of 1950 ed. lib. bdg. 24.75x (ISBN 0-313-22197-9, BIOD). Greenwood.
Binet, Pere. The Divine Favors Granted to St. Joseph. LC 82-50590. 176p. 1983. pap. 3.00 (ISBN 0-89555-187-X). TAN Bks Pubs.
Binford, Helaina, jt. auth. see Binford, Hugh.
Binford, Helaina L. Heart Song: Prophecies, Ponderings & Poetry. (Illus.). 50p. (Orig.). 1986. pap. 5.00 (ISBN 0-939313-11-1). Joshua-I-Minist.
Binford, Hugh & Binford, Helaina. Single? Single Again? A Handbook for Living. 120p. (Orig.). 1986. pap. 7.00 (ISBN 0-939313-22-7). Joshua-I-Minist.
Bingham, Janet, jt. ed. see Bingham, Sam.
Bingham, June. Courage to Change: An Introduction to the Life & Thought of Reinhold Niebuhr. Repr. of 1961 ed. lib. bdg. 27.50x (ISBN 0-678-02766-8). Kelley.
Bingham, Mindy, et al. Challenges: A Young Man's Journal for Self-Awareness & Personal Planning. Greene, Barbara & Peters, Kathleen, eds. LC 84-70108. (Illus.). 240p. 1984. pap. 12.95 (ISBN 0-911655-24-7). Advocacy Pr.
Bingham, Opha & Bingham, Robert E. One Step More, Lord! LC 84-4942. 1984. pap. 7.95 (ISBN 0-8054-5432-2). Broadman.
Bingham, Robert E., jt. auth. see Bingham, Opha.
Bingham, Sam & Bingham, Janet, eds. Between Sacred Mountains: Navajo Stories & Lessons from the Land. LC 82-82827. (Illus.). 296p. 1982. 30.00 (ISBN 0-910675-00-7); pap. 19.95 (ISBN 0-910675-01-5). Rock Point.
Bin-Nun, Aaron. The Language of Faith. LC 78-65723. 1979. 8.95 (ISBN 0-88400-061-3). Shengold.
Bin-Nun, Judy & Cooper, Nancy. Pesach: A Holiday Funtext. (Illus.). 32p. (Orig.). 1983. pap. text ed. 5.00 (ISBN 0-8074-0161-7, 101310). UAHC.
Bin-Nun, Judy & Einhorn, Franne. Rosh Hashana: A Holiday Funtext. (Illus.). 1978. pap. 5.00 (ISBN 0-8074-0010-6, 101300). UAHC.
Bins, John, ed. Building for Justice: A Guide for Social Concerns Committees. 1.77 (ISBN 0-8091-9309-4). Paulist Pr.
Binsbergen, Wim M. J. Van see Van Binsbergen, Wim M. J. & Schoffeleers, J. Matthew.
Binsbergen, Wim M. Van see Van Binsbergen, Wim M.
Binsse, Harry L., tr. see Maritain, Jacques.
Bin Uthman, Ali see Uthman, Ali Bin.
Binyon, Pamela M. The Concepts of Spirit & Demon: A Study in the Use of Different Languages Describing the Same Phenomena. (IC-Studies in the International History of Christianity: Vol. 8). 132p. 1977. pap. 19.60 (ISBN 3-261-01787-2). P Lang Pubs.
Biography of Master Hsuan Hua Publication Committee. Records of the Life of Tripitaka Master Hua, Vol. 1. (Illus.). 90p. (Orig.). 1981. pap. 5.00 (ISBN 0-917512-78-2). Buddhist Text.
--Records of the Life of Tripitaka Master Hua, Vol. 2. (Illus.). 229p. (Orig.). 1976. pap. 8.00 (ISBN 0-917512-10-3). Buddhist Text.
Birch, Bruce C. What Does the Lord Require? The Old Testament Call to Social Witness. LC 85-610. 120p. 1985. pap. 8.95 (ISBN 0-664-24630-3). Westminster.
Birch, Bruce C. & Rasmussen, Larry L. Bible & Ethics in the Christian Life. LC 76-3856. 208p. 1976. pap. 8.95 (ISBN 0-8066-1524-9, 10-0702). Augsburg.
--The Predicament of the Prosperous. LC 78-18412. (Biblical Perspectives on Current Issues). 212p. 1978. pap. 7.95 (ISBN 0-664-24211-1). Westminster.
Birch, David. Early Reformation English Polemics. Hogg, James, ed. (Elizabethan & Renaissance Studies). 181p. (Orig.). 1983. pap. 15.00 (ISBN 0-317-40131-9, Pub by Salzburg Studies). Longwood Pub Group.
Birch, L. C. & Cobb, J. B. The Liberation of Life: From the Cell to the Community. LC 80-42156. 300p. 1982. 42.50 (ISBN 0-521-23787-4). Cambridge U Pr.
Birch, W. J. An Inquiry into the Philosophy & Religion of Shakespeare. LC 72-3660. (Studies in Shakespeare, No. 24). 1972. Repr. of 1848 ed. lib. bdg. 59.95x (ISBN 0-8383-1569-0). Haskell.
Birch, William. Inquiry into the Philosophy & Religion of Shakespeare. LC 76-39446. Repr. of 1848 ed. 15.00 (ISBN 0-404-00868-2). AMS Pr.
Birchall, Christopher, tr. see Holy Transfiguration Monastery.
Birchall, Christopher, tr. see Khrapovitsky, Antony.
Bircher, ed. see Spangenberg, Wolfhart.
Bird, Bob. You Are a Special Person. 16p. (Orig.). 1974. pap. 1.50 (ISBN 0-934804-06-0). Inspiration MI.
Bird, Christopher. The Divining Hand. 1985. pap. 15.00 (ISBN 0-87613-090-2). New Age.
Bird, Malcolm. The Witch's Handbook. (Illus.). 96p. 1985. 10.95 (ISBN 0-312-88458-3). St Martin.
Bird, Michael, jt. ed. see May, John R.
Bird, Phyllis A. The Bible As the Church's Book. LC 82-7049. (Library of Living Faith: Vol. 5). 118p. 1982. pap. 5.95 (ISBN 0-664-24427-0). Westminster.
Bird, Thomas E., ed. Modern Theologians, Christians & Jews. 2nd ed. 1967. 15.95 (ISBN 0-268-00183-9). U of Notre Dame Pr.
Birdsong, Robert E. Adamic Christianity: Questions & Answers, Vol. 1. 1978. pap. 3.75 (ISBN 0-917108-22-1). Sirius Bks.
--The Challenge of the Aquarian Age. (Aquarian Academy Monograph, Ser. A: Lecture No. 7). 1978. pap. 1.25 (ISBN 0-917108-25-6). Sirius Bks.
--Fundamentals of Adamic Christianity. (Aquarian Academy Monograph, Series A: Lecture No. 1). 1974. pap. 1.25 (ISBN 0-917108-00-0). Sirius Bks.
--The Hermetic Commandments in Today's World. (Aquarian Academy Monograph, Ser. F: Lecture No. 7). 1977. pap. 1.25 (ISBN 0-917108-19-1). Sirius Bks.
--Paths to Human Perfection. (Aquarian Academy Supplementary Lecture: No. 3). 1979. pap. 0.75 (ISBN 0-917108-26-4). Sirius Bks.

--Physical Experience & Karmic Liability. (Aquarian Academy Monograph: Ser. A, Lecture No. 6). 38p. 1977. pap. 1.50 (ISBN 0-917108-20-5). Sirius Bks.
--Soul Mates: The Facts & the Fallacies. (Aquarian Academy Supplementary Lecture Ser.: No. 9). 22p. (Orig.). 1980. pap. 1.25 (ISBN 0-917108-32-9). Sirius Bks.
--Way of the Immortal Threefold Self: The Straight Path. (Aquarian Academy Monograph: Ser. E, No. 4). 1980. pap. 1.45 (ISBN 0-917108-29-9). Sirius Bks.
--Way of the Soul: The "Heart Path" to Human Perfection. (Aquarian Academy Monograph: Ser. D, No. 2). 1980. pap. 1.45 (ISBN 0-917108-28-0). Sirius Bks.
--Way of the Spirit: The "Head Path" to Human Perfection, Ser. C, No. 2. (Aquarian Academy Monograph). 1980. pap. 1.45 (ISBN 0-917108-27-2). Sirius Bks.
Bireley, Robert S. J. Religion & Politics in the Age of the Counterreformation: Emperor Ferdinand II, William Lamormaini, S.J., & the Formation of Imperial Policy. LC 80-27334. xiii, 311p. 1981. 30.00x (ISBN 0-8078-1470-9). U of NC Pr.
Birge, John K. The Bektashi Order of Dervishes. LC 77-87662. Repr. of 1937 ed. 35.00 (ISBN 0-404-16400-5). AMS Pr.
Birke, Adolf M. & Kluxen, Kurt, eds. Church, State & Society in the Nineteenth Century. (Prince Albert Studies: Vol. 2). 130p. 1984. lib. bdg. 24.00 (ISBN 3-598-21402-2). K G Saur.
Birkey, Verna. You Are Very Special: A Biblical Guide to Self-Worth. 160p. 1977. pap. 5.95 (ISBN 0-8007-5032-2, Power Bks). Revell.
Birkey, Verna & Turnquist, Jeanette. Building Happy Memories & Family Traditions. (Illus.). 128p. 1983. 4.95 (ISBN 0-8007-5109-4, Power Bks). Revell.
Birkinshaw, Elsye. Turn off Your Age. LC 79-27693. 1980. pap. 7.95 (ISBN 0-912800-77-1). Woodbridge Pr.
Birks, J. S. Across the Savannas to Mecca: The Overland Pilgrimage Route from West Africa. (Illus.). 161p. 1978. 29.50x (ISBN 0-7146-6005-1, F Cass Co). Biblio Dist.
Birks, Walter & Gilbert, R. A. The Treasure of Montsegur. (Crucible Ser.). 176p. 1987. pap. 9.95 (ISBN 0-85030-424-5). Inner Tradit.
Birky, Lela. The Bible Nurture & Reader Ser. 1969. write for info. (ISBN 0-686-05603-5); Span. ed. write for info.; tchr's. ed. avail. (ISBN 0-686-05604-3). Rod & Staff.
--Truth for Life Bible Studies. pap. write for info (ISBN 0-686-15481-9). Rod & Staff.
Birky, Lela & Conley, Lucy. The Building Christian English Series. 1973. write for info. (ISBN 0-686-05606-X); tchr's. ed. avail. (ISBN 0-686-05607-8). Rod & Staff.
Birla, Shri B. Alive in Krishna: Living Memories of the Vedic Quest. (Patterns of World Spirituality Ser.). 160p. 1986. pap. 8.95 (ISBN 0-913757-65-9, Pub. by New Era Bks). Paragon Hse.
Birmingham, Stephen. The Grandees. 384p. 1985. pap. 4.50 (ISBN 0-425-08390-X). Berkley Pub.
--Our Crowd: The Great Jewish Families of New York. 528p. 1985. pap. 4.50 (ISBN 0-425-07557-5). Berkley Pub.
--The Rest of Us: The Rise of America's Eastern European Jews. 384p. 1984. 19.95 (ISBN 0-316-09647-4). Little.
--The Rest of Us: The Rise of America's Eastern European Jews. 432p. 1985. pap. 4.50 (ISBN 0-425-08074-9). Berkley Pub.
Birnbaoum, Philip. Hasiddur Hashalem Daily Prayer Book: Sephardic. 860p. 1969. 17.00 (ISBN 0-88482-053-X). Hebrew Pub.
Birnbaum, Ervin. Politics of Compromise: State & Religion in Israel. LC 70-92557. 348p. 1970. 27.50 (ISBN 0-8386-7567-0). Fairleigh Dickinson.
Birnbaum, Norman. Social Structure & the German Reformation. Zuckerman, Harriet & Merton, Robert K., eds. LC 79-8976. (Dissertation on Sociology Ser.). 1980. lib. bdg. 40.00x (ISBN 0-405-12952-1). Ayer Co Pubs.
Birnbaum, Philim. Hasiddur Hashalem: Daily Prayer Book. 790p. 1977. pap. 9.95 pocket flexible ed. (ISBN 0-88482-054-8). Hebrew Pub.
Birnbaum, Philip. The Birnbaum Haggadah. (Illus.). 160p. 1976. 5.95 (ISBN 0-88482-908-1); pap. 3.95 (ISBN 0-88482-912-X). Hebrew Pub.
--Hasiddur Hashalem (Daily Prayer Book) 790p. 1964. 17.00 (ISBN 0-88482-045-9). Hebrew Pub.
--Mahzor Hashalem: High Holiday Prayer Book, Vol. 1, Rosh Hashahah. 646p. 1960. 14.00 (ISBN 0-88482-246-X). Hebrew Pub.
--Mahzor Hashalem: High Holyday Prayer Book, 5 Vols. 1971. Set. 58.00 (ISBN 0-88482-169-2). Hebrew Pub.
--Mahzor Hashalem: High Holyday Prayer Book, 2 Vols. 1960. Set. 26.50 (ISBN 0-88482-170-6). Hebrew Pub.
--Mahzor Hashalem: High Holyday Prayer Book, 1 Vol. 1042p. 1951. 17.00 (ISBN 0-88482-240-0). Hebrew Pub.
--Mahzor Hashalem: Prayer Book for Pesah, Vol. 4. 459p. 1971. 11.50 (ISBN 0-88482-172-2). Hebrew Pub.
--Mahzor Hashalem: Prayer Book for Shavuot, Vol. 5. 358p. 1971. 11.50 (ISBN 0-88482-173-0). Hebrew Pub.
--Mahzor Hashalem: Prayer Book for Sukkot, Vol. 3. 478p. 1971. 11.50 (ISBN 0-88482-174-9). Hebrew Pub.
--Mahzor Leshalosh Regalim: Prayer Book for Three Festivals. 641p. 1971. 15.00 (ISBN 0-88482-149-8). Hebrew Pub.
--Mazhor Hashalem High Holiday Prayer Book, Vol. 2: Yom Kippur. 770p. 1960. 14.00 (ISBN 0-88482-247-8). Hebrew Pub.
--Siddur Leshabbat Veyom Tov: Prayer Book for Sabbath & Festivals with Torah Readings. 724p. 1950. 14.50 (ISBN 0-88482-062-9). Hebrew Pub.
--The Torah & the Haftarot. 933p. 1983. 19.50 (ISBN 0-88482-456-X). Hebrew Pub.
Birnbaum, Philip, ed. The New Treasury of Judaism. 1977. 15.00 (ISBN 0-88482-410-1, Sanhedrin Pr); pap. 9.95 (ISBN 0-88482-411-X, Sanhedrin Pr). Hebrew Pub.
Birnbaum, Philip, tr. Selihot. 61p. 1952. pap. 1.95 (ISBN 0-88482-344-X). Hebrew Pub.
Birnbaum, Philip, tr. see Maimonides, Moses.
Birner, Herbert A. Marriage Should Be Honored by All. 5.95 (ISBN 0-686-76769-1, 12N1719). Northwest Pub.
Birney, James G. American Churches: The Bulwarks of American Slavery. LC 79-82174. (Anti-Slavery Crusade in America Ser). 1969. Repr. of 1842 ed. 11.00 (ISBN 0-405-00611-X). Ayer Co Pubs.
Birnhack, Sarah. Happy Is the Heart: A Year in the Life of a Jewish Girl. (Illus.). 1976. 7.95 (ISBN 0-87306-131-4); pap. 5.95. Feldheim.
Biro, J. I., jt. ed. see Shahan, Robert W.
Biros, Florence K. With the Ups Comes the Downs. (Illus.). 104p. (Orig.). 1986. pap. 2.95 (ISBN 0-936369-01-9). Son-Rise Pubns.
Biros, Florence K., ed. see Reid, Thomas F., et al.
Birrer, Cynthia & Birrer, William. Song to Demeter. LC 86-20895. (Illus.). 32p. 1987. 11.75 (ISBN 0-688-04040-3); PLB 11.88 (ISBN 0-688-04041-1). Lothrop.
Birrer, William, jt. auth. see Birrer, Cynthia.
Birt, David. The Monastery. (Resource Units: Middle Ages, 1066-1485 Ser.). (Illus.). 1974. pap. text ed. 12.95x 10 copies & tchr's guide (ISBN 0-582-39380-9). Longman.
--The Murder of Becket. (Resource Units: Middle Ages, 1066-1485 Ser.). (Illus.). 24p. 1974. pap. text ed. 12.95 10 copies & tchr's guide (ISBN 0-582-39376-0). Longman.
Birx, H. James. Pierre Teilhard De Chardin's Philosophy of Evolution. 192p. 1972. 21.50x (ISBN 0-398-02466-9). C C Thomas.
Bisagno, John. God Is. 1981. 4.95 (ISBN 0-88207-345-1). Victor Bks.
--Power of Positive Praying. 1965. pap. 3.50 (ISBN 0-310-21212-X, 9238). Zondervan.
--The Secret of Positive Praying. Ruark, Jim, ed. 128p. 1986. pap. 3.95 (ISBN 0-310-21152-2, 9239). Zondervan.
Bisagno, John R. Great Mysteries of the Bible. LC 81-67997. 1982. 7.95 (ISBN 0-8054-1952-7). Broadman.
--How to Build an Evangelistic Church. LC 78-178055. 1972. 8.50 (ISBN 0-8054-2524-1). Broadman.
--Life Without Compromise. LC 81-71253. 1983. 3.95 (ISBN 0-8054-1503-3). Broadman.
--Love Is Something You Do. LC 75-9314. 1979. pap. 6.95 (ISBN 0-06-060793-9, RD-238, HarpR). Har-Row.
--Power of Positive Evangelism: How to Hold a Revival. LC 68-26912. 1968. pap. 3.95 (ISBN 0-8054-2503-9). Broadman.
--Power of Positive Living. LC 70-93913. (Orig.). 1970. pap. 3.95 (ISBN 0-8054-1910-1). Broadman.
Bisagno, Juan. El Poder De la Oracion Tenaz. De Lerin, Olivia S. D., tr. from Eng. Orig. Title: The Power of Positive Praying. (Span.). 96p. 1983. pap. 2.15 (ISBN 0-311-40029-9). Casa Bautista.
Bischoff, Erich. The Kabbala: An Introduction to Jewish Mysticism & Secret Doctrine. LC 84-52262. 96p. 1985. pap. 5.95 (ISBN 0-87728-564-0). Weiser.
Bisen, Malini, tr. see Rajneesh, Acharya.
Bishirjian, Richard. The Nature of Public Philosophy. LC 82-20170. 62p. 1983. pap. text ed. 4.75 (ISBN 0-8191-2861-9). U Pr of Amer.
Bishop, Amelia. The Flame & the Candle. (Orig.). 1987. 7.50 (ISBN 0-8054-5033-5). Broadman.
--The Gift & the Giver. LC 84-2796. 1984. 6.25 (ISBN 0-8054-5106-4). Broadman.
Bishop, Carolyn, jt. auth. see Rife, Carl B.
Bishop, David S. Effective Communication. LC 76-58043. 1977. 5.25 (ISBN 0-87148-285-1); pap. text ed. 4.25 (ISBN 0-87148-286-X). Pathway Pr.
Bishop, Isabella L. The Aspects of Religion in the United States of America. LC 75-38438. (Religion in America, Ser. 2). 200p. 1972. Repr. of 1859 ed. 20.00 (ISBN 0-405-04059-8). Ayer Co Pubs.
Bishop, Jim. The Day Christ Died. LC 57-6125. 1978. pap. 4.95 (ISBN 0-06-060786-6, HJ 38, HarpR). Har-Row.
--The Day Christ Was Born. LC 60-13444. 1978. pap. 2.95i (ISBN 0-06-060785-8, HJ 37, HarpR). Har-Row.
Bishop, John. Methodist Worship: In Relation to Free Church Worship. rev. ed. LC 75-20379. xvii, 173p. 1976. lib. bdg. 6.95 (ISBN 0-89177-001-1). Scholars Studies.
Bishop, Jonathan. Emerson on the Soul. LC 80-2527. Repr. of 1964 ed. 29.50 (ISBN 0-404-19251-3). AMS Pr.
Bishop, Joseph P. The Eye of the Storm. 128p. (Orig.). 1983. pap. 3.95 (ISBN 0-87123-263-4, 210263). Bethany Hse.
--Soul Mending: Letters to Friends in Crisis. 160p. 1986. pap. 8.95 (ISBN 0-8192-1379-9). Morehouse.
Bishop, Morris. Middle Ages. abr. ed. LC 70-95728. 1970. pap. 7.95 (ISBN 0-07-005466-5). McGraw.
Bishop of Exeter, jt. auth. see Hardy, Paul E.
Bishop, Selma L. Isaac Watts's Hymns & Spiritual Songs (1707) A Publishing History & a Bibliography. LC 73-78316. 1974. 29.50 (ISBN 0-87650-033-5). Pierian.
Bishop, Tania E. Born of the Spirit. LC 68-13394. 1968. 7.95 (ISBN 0-8022-0134-2). Philos Lib.
Bishop Ian Shervill. Going It - With God. 4th ed. 94p. 1985. 4.95 (ISBN 0-908175-37-X, Pub. by Boolarong Pubn Australia). Intl Spec Bk.
Bissell, Charles B., III. Letters I Never Wrote, Conversations I Never Had: Dealing with Unresolved Grief & Anger. 58p. (Orig.). 1983. pap. 4.95 (ISBN 0-9612604-0-8). C Bissell.
Bissing, Hurbert. Songs of Submission: On the Practice of Subud. 180p. (Orig.). 1982. pap. 9.50 (ISBN 0-227-67852-4, Pub. by J Clarke UK). Attic Pr.
Bissonnette, Georges. Moscow Was My Parish. LC 78-16489. 1978. Repr. of 1956 ed. lib. bdg. 22.50x (ISBN 0-313-20594-9, BIMM). Greenwood.
Bist, Umrao S. Jaina Theories of Reality & Knowledge. 1985. 6.50x (ISBN 0-8364-1362-8, Pub. by Eastern). South Asia Bks.
Bitney, James. Bright Intervals: Prayers for Paschal People. 96p. 1982. pap. 5.95 (ISBN 0-86683-669-1, HarpR). Har-Row.
Bittinger, Emmet F. Heritage & Promise: Perspectives on the Church of the Brethren. rev. ed. 1983. pap. 6.95 (ISBN 0-87178-357-6). Brethren.
Bittle, Willliam G. James Nayler: The Quaker Indicted by Parliament. 248p. (Orig.). 1987. pap. 14.95x (ISBN 1-85072-015-0). Friends United.
Bittleston, Adam, tr. see Steiner, Rudolf.
Bittner, Vernon J. Make Your Illness Count: A Hospital Chaplain Shows How God's Healing Power Can Be Released in Your Life. LC 76-3862. 128p. (Orig.). 1976. pap. 6.95 (ISBN 0-8066-1532-X, 10-4260). Augsburg.
--You Can Help with Your Healing: A Guide for Recovering Wholeness in Body, Mind, & Spirit. LC 78-66946. 1979. pap. 6.95 (ISBN 0-8066-1698-9, 10-7411). Augsburg.
Bitton, Davis, jt. auth. see Arrington, Leonard J.
Bitton, Davis & Beecher, Maureen U., eds. New Views of Mormon History: A Collection of Essays in Honor of Leonard J. Arrington. 1987. 25.00x (ISBN 0-87480-304-7). U of Utah Pr.
Bitton-Jackson, Livia. Madonna or Courtesan: The Jewish Woman in Christian Literature. 160p. 1983. pap. 7.95 (ISBN 0-8164-2440-3, HarpR). Har-Row.
Bitzer, Heinrich, ed. Light on the Path: Daily Scripture Readings in Hebrew & Greek. 400p. (Orig.). 1982. pap. 9.95 (ISBN 0-8010-0822-0). Baker Bk.
Bivens, Forest & Vallesky, David. New Life in Christ. Fischer, William E., ed. (Bible Class Course Ser.). 120p. (Orig.). 1986. pap. text ed. 4.95 (ISBN 0-938272-07-1). WELS Board.
--New Life in Christ: Teacher's Guide. (Bible Class Course Ser.). 40p. (Orig.). 1986. pap. text ed. 2.50 (ISBN 0-938272-03-9). WELS Board.
Bivens, Ruth. Aunt Ruth's Puppet Scripts, Bk. I. (Orig.). 1986. pap. 19.95 (ISBN 0-89265-096-6). Randall Hse.
--Aunt Ruth's Puppet Scripts, Bk. IV. (Orig.). 1987. three-ring binder & cassette 19.95 (ISBN 0-89265-122-9). Randall Hse.
Biver, Paul. Pere Lamy. O'Connor, John, tr. from Fr. 1973. pap. 5.50 (ISBN 0-89555-055-5). TAN Bks Pubs.
Bivin, David. Understanding the Difficult Words of Jesus. LC 83-61850. (Illus.). 172p. (Orig.). 1983. pap. 8.95 (ISBN 0-918873-00-2). Ctr Judaic-Christ Studies.
Bixler, Julius S. Immortality & the Present Mood. LC 75-3047. Repr. of 1931 ed. 16.00 (ISBN 0-404-59044-6). AMS Pr.
--Religion for Free Minds. LC 75-3048. (Philosophy in America Ser.). 1976. Repr. of 1939 ed. 18.00 (ISBN 0-404-59045-4). AMS Pr.
--Religion in the Philosophy of William James. LC 75-3049. Repr. of 1926 ed. 24.50 (ISBN 0-404-59046-2). AMS Pr.
Bixler, Russell. Learning to Know God As Provider. 96p. 1982. pap. 3.50 (ISBN 0-88368-120-X). Whitaker Hse.
Bizer, Ernst, ed. see Heppe, Heinrich.
Bjerregaard, C. H. The Great Mother: A Gospel of the Eternally Feminine. 1977. lib. bdg. 59.95 (ISBN 0-8490-1900-1). Gordon Pr.
--The Inner Life. Incl. The Tao-Teh-King. 1977. lib. bdg. 49.00 (ISBN 0-8490-2061-1). Gordon Pr.
--Lectures on Mysticism & Nature Worship. 1977. lib. bdg. 59.95 (ISBN 0-8490-2138-3). Gordon Pr.
Bjerregard, Carl H. Jesus: A Poet, Prophet, Mystic & Man of Freedom. 1976. lib. bdg. 59.95 (ISBN 0-8490-2094-8). Gordon Pr.
Bjerring, N., tr. see Basaroff, F.
Bjerring, Nicholas, tr. see Anatolius of Mohilew & Mstislaw.
Bjorge, James R. Forty Ways to Fortify Your Faith. LC 83-72115. 128p. (Orig.). 1984. pap. 5.95 (ISBN 0-8066-2059-5, 10-2358). Augsburg.
--Forty Ways to Say I Love You. LC 78-52179. 1978. pap. 5.95 (ISBN 0-8066-1654-7, 10-2360). Augsburg.
--Forty Ways to Say Thank You, Lord. LC 80-67802. 96p. (Orig.). 1981. pap. 5.95 (ISBN 0-8066-1864-7, 102361). Augsburg.
Bjork, Russell, jt. auth. see Townsley, David.
Bjorkman, Adaline. While It Was Still Dark. (Illus.). 1978. pap. 3.95 (ISBN 0-910452-34-2). Covenant.
Bjorkman, James. Fundamentalism, Revivalists & Violence in South Asia. LC 85-61080. 210p. 1987. 19.00 (ISBN 0-913215-06-6). Riverdale Co.
Bjorling, Joel. The Baha'i Faith: An Historical Bibliography. Melton, J. G, ed. LC 84-49294. (Reference Library of Social Science- Sects & Cults in America: Bibliographic Guides). 250p. 1985. lib. bdg. 35.00 (ISBN 0-8240-8974-X). Garland Pub.
--The Churches of God, Seventh Day: A Bibliography. Meton, J. Gordon, ed. LC 87-67. (Sects & Cults in America Bibliographical Guides Reference Library of Social Sciences Ser.: Vol. 362). 250p. 1987. lib. bdg. 48.00 (ISBN 0-8240-8537-X). Garland Pub.
Bjorn, Thyra F. Once upon a Christmas Time. 1964. 5.95 (ISBN 0-03-047195-8). H Holt & Co.
Bjornstad, James. Counterfeits at Your Door. LC 78-72864. 160p. 1979. pap. text ed. 2.95 (ISBN 0-8307-0610-0, S124254). Regal.
--Sun Myung Moon & the Unification Church. 160p. 1984. pap. 2.95 (ISBN 0-87123-301-0, 210301). Bethany Hse.
Black, Antony. Council & Commune: The Conciliar Movement & the Fifteenth-Century Heritage. LC 79-89220. x, 253p. 1979. 25.95x (ISBN 0-915762-08-0). Patmos Pr.
Black, Daniel. Never A Day Too Much. (Orig.). 1985. pap. text ed. 4.95 (ISBN 0-87148-631-8). Pathway Pr.
Black, David A. Paul, Apostle of Weakness: Astheneia & Its Cognates in the Pauline Literature. LC 83-49515. (American University Studies VII (Theology & Religion): Vol. 3). 340p. (Orig.). 1984. pap. text ed. 27.00 (ISBN 0-8204-0106-4). P Lang Pubs.
Black, Donald. Merging Mission & Unity. LC 86-14847. 180p. (Orig.). 1986. pap. 9.95 (ISBN 0-664-24047-X, A Geneva Press Publication). Westminster.
Black, Doris. Reach for Your Spiritual Potential. 1986. pap. 4.95 (ISBN 0-89137-438-8). Quality Pubns.
Black, Garth. The Holy Spirit. rev. ed. (Way of Life Ser: No. 102). 1967. pap. 3.95 (ISBN 0-89112-102-1, Bibl Res Pr). Abilene Christ U.
Black, George F., ed. Calendar of Cases of Witchcraft in Scotland, 1510-1727. LC 78-137707. (New York Public Library Publications in Reprint Ser.). (Illus.). 1971. Repr. of 1938 ed. 8.00 (ISBN 0-405-01751-0). Ayer Co Pubs.
Black, Glenn D., ed. see Chambers, Oswald.
Black, Ian. Zionism & the Arabs, Nineteen Thirty-Six to Nineteen Thirty-Nine. (Outstanding Theses from the London School of Economics & Political Science Ser.). 500p. 1987. lib. bdg. 75.00 (ISBN 0-8240-1911-3). Garland Pub.
Black, J. B. Reign of Elizabeth, Fifteen Fifty-Eight to Sixteen Three. 2nd ed. (Oxford History of England Ser.). 1959. 45.00x (ISBN 0-19-821701-3). Oxford U Pr.
Black, J. S., jt. ed. see Cheyne, T. K.

Black, James. The Old Testament: Student Text. LC 82-70087. (Illus.). 160p. (Orig.). 1982. pap. 4.95 (ISBN 0-87793-248-4). Ave Maria.
--The Old Testament: Teacher's Manual. 80p. (Orig.). 1982. tchrs. ed. 2.25 (ISBN 0-87793-249-2). Ave Maria.
Black, Jeannette D., ed. see David, Ebenezer.
Black, Matthew. Aramaic Approach to the Gospels & Acts. 3rd ed. 1967. 32.50x (ISBN 0-19-826157-8). Oxford U Pr.
--Romans. (New Century Bible Series). 191p. 1973. 7.50 (ISBN 0-551-00447-9). Attic Pr.
--Romans. rev. ed. (New Century Bible Commentary Ser.). 192p. 1981. pap. 6.95 (ISBN 0-8028-1905-2). Eerdmans.
--The Scrolls & Christian Origins: Studies in the Jewish Background of the New Testament. LC 83-11519. (Brown Judaic Studies). 232p. 1983. pap. 14.00 (ISBN 0-89130-639-0, 14 00 48). Scholars Pr GA.
Black, Matthew & Rowley, H. H. Peake's Commentary on the Bible. 1962. 39.95 (ISBN 0-8407-5019-6). Nelson.
Black, Matthew, ed. see Best, Ernest.
Black, Matthew, ed. see Bruce, F. F.
Black, Matthew, ed. see Grayston, Kenneth.
Black, Matthew, ed. see Guthrie, Donald.
Black, Matthew, ed. see Mitton, C. Leslie.
Black, Matthew, ed. see Neil, William.
Black, Matthew, ed. see Sidebottom, E. M.
Black, R. L. The Church of God of Prophecy: Pastor. 1977. 4.25 (ISBN 0-934942-29-3). White Wing Pub.
--Discerning the Body. 98p. (Orig.). 1984. pap. 3.95 (ISBN 0-934942-42-0, 1264). White Wing Pub.
--Holy Ghost & Speaking in Tongues. 180p. (Orig.). 1983. pap. 4.95 (ISBN 0-934942-35-8, 1869). White Wing Pub.
Black, Robert E. The Books of Chronicles. (The Bible Study Textbook Ser.). (Illus.). 1973. College Pr Pub.
Blackburn, Francis A., ed. Exodus & Daniel. LC 76-144440. (Belles Lettres Ser., Section I: No. 6). Repr. of 1907 ed. 16.50 (ISBN 0-404-53607-7). AMS Pr.
Blackburn, Henry. Art in the Mountains: Story of the Passion Play. LC 77-94544. 1979. Repr. of 1870 ed. lib. bdg. 20.00 (ISBN 0-89341-178-7). Longwood Pub Group.
Blackburn, William M. William Farel & the Story of the Swiss Reform. Date not set. Repr. of 1865 ed. 40.00 (ISBN 0-404-19870-8). AMS Pr.
Blackburn, William W. Young Calvin in Paris: Or, the Scholar & the Cripple. LC 83-45602. Date not set. Repr. of 1868 ed. 30.00 (ISBN 0-404-19869-4). AMS Pr.
Blacker, Carmen. The Catalpa Bow: A Study of Shamanistic Practices in Japan. 2nd ed. (Illus.). 382p. 1986. pap. 14.95 (ISBN 0-04-398008-2). Allen Unwin.
Blacker, Harry see Nero, pseud.
Blackham, H. Moral & Religious Education in County Primary Schools. 6.00x (ISBN 0-85633-115-5, Pub. by NFER Nelson UK). Taylor & Francis.
Blackham, H. J., et al. Objections to Humanism. LC 73-16796. 128p. 1974. Repr. of 1963 ed. lib. bdg. 22.50x (ISBN 0-8371-7235-7, BLOH). Greenwood.
Blackie, W. W. David Livingstone. (Heroes of the Faith Ser.). 1986. 6.95 (ISBN 0-916441-48-2). Barbour & Co.
Blackman, Murray. A Guide to Jewish Themes in American Fiction, 1940-1980. LC 80-24953. 271p. 1981. lib. bdg. 19.00 (ISBN 0-8108-1380-7). Scarecrow.
Blackman, Philip. Ethics of the Fathers. 166p. 1980. pap. 4.95 (ISBN 0-910818-15-0). Judaica Pr.
Blackman, Philip, tr. The Mishnah, 7 vols. with index vol. (Eng. & Hebrew.). 4050p. 1962. 75.00 (ISBN 0-910818-00-2). Judaica Pr.
Blackmer, Rollin C. The Lodge & the Craft. 295p. 1976. text ed. 7.95 s.p. (ISBN 0-88053-043-X). Macoy Pub.
Blackmore, R. W., tr. Duties of Parish Priests in the Russian Orthodox Church. Repr. of 1845 ed. 15.00 (ISBN 0-686-01291-7). Eastern Orthodox.
Blackmore, Susan. The Adventures of a Parapsychologist. 250p. 1986. 19.95 (ISBN 0-87975-360-9). Prometheus Bks.
Blackstone, Harry. Blackstone's Secrets of Magic. pap. 3.00 (ISBN 0-87980-260-X). Wilshire.
Blackstone, Judith & Josipovic, Zoran. Zen for Beginners. (Writers & Readers Documentary Comic Bks.). (Illus.). 176p. (Orig.). 1986. pap. 6.95 (ISBN 0-86316-116-2). Writers & Readers.
Blackwelder, Boyce. The Four Gospels. 1980. 9.95 (ISBN 0-87162-221-1, D3768). Warner Pr.
Blackwell, Elsie, jt. auth. see Adcock, Mabel.
Blackwell, John. The Passion As Story: The Plot of Mark. LC 85-16209. (Fortress Resources for Preaching Ser.). 96p. 1986. pap. 5.95 (ISBN 0-8006-1144-6, 1-1144). Fortress.
Blackwell, Muriel. Peter: The Prince of Apostles. (BibLearn Ser.). (Illus.). 5.95 (ISBN 0-8054-4227-8, 4242-27). Broadman.
Blackwell, Muriel, jt. auth. see Blackwell, William.
Blackwell, Muriel F. Called to Teach Children. LC 82-82954. 1983. 6.95 (ISBN 0-8054-3233-7). Broadman.
--The Dream Lives On. LC 82-73865. 1984. 6.95 (ISBN 0-8054-4808-X, 4248-08). Broadman.
Blackwell, Thomas. Letters Concerning Mythology. LC 75-27887. (Renaissance & the Gods Ser.: Vol. 42). (Illus.). 1976. Repr. of 1748 ed. lib. bdg. 88.00 (ISBN 0-8240-2091-X). Garland Pub.
Blackwell, William & Blackwell, Muriel. Working Partners Working Parents. LC 79-51134. 1979. 5.95 (ISBN 0-8054-5637-6). Broadman.
Blackwood, A. W. La Preparacion de Sermones Biblicos. Crane, Santiago D., tr. (Span.). 255p. 1985. pap. 3.95 (ISBN 0-311-42030-3). Casa Bautista.
Blackwood, Andrew W. Prayers for All Occasions. (Pocket Pulpit Library). pap. 3.95 (ISBN 0-8010-0923-5). Baker Bk.
Blackwood, Andrew W., Jr. When God Came Down. (Pocket Paperback Library Ser.). 1978. pap. 1.45 (ISBN 0-8010-0753-4). Baker Bk.
Blackwood, Cheryl P. & Slattery, Kathryn. A Bright-Shining Place. (Epiphany Ser.). 240p. 1983. pap. 2.75 (ISBN 0-345-30698-8). Ballantine.
Blades, Dudley. Spiritual Healing. 128p. (Orig.). 1980. pap. 4.95 (ISBN 0-85030-130-0). Newcastle Pub.
Blagden, Charles O., jt. auth. see Skeat, Walter W.
Blagrove, Luanna C. Voodoo Lost Arts & Sciences. abr. ed. 250p. 1987. 25.95 (ISBN 0-939776-22-7); text ed. 24.95. Blagrove Pubns.
Blaguy, John. The Foundation of Moral Goodness, 2 vols. in 1. Wellek, Rene, ed. LC 75-11194. (British Philosophers & Theologians of the 17th & 18th Centuries Ser.: Vol. 1). 1976. Repr. of 1729 ed. lib. bdg. 51.00 (ISBN 0-8240-1750-1). Garland Pub.
Blaikie, W. G. & Law, R. The Inner Life of Christ. 459p. 1982. lib. bdg. 17.25 Smythe Sewn (ISBN 0-86524-156-2, 9515). Klock & Klock.
Blaikie, William G. The Book of Joshua. 416p. 1983. lib. bdg. 15.75 (ISBN 0-86524-173-2, 0601). Klock & Klock.
--First Book of Samuel. 440p. 1983. lib. bdg. 16.50 (ISBN 0-86524-174-0, 0901). Klock & Klock.
--Personal Life of David Livingstone. LC 69-19353. (Illus.). 1880. 22.50x (ISBN 0-8371-0518-8, BLL&). Greenwood.
--The Public Ministry of Christ. 356p. 1984. lib. bdg. 13.25 (ISBN 0-86524-167-8, 9517). Klock & Klock.
--Second Book of Samuel. 400p. 1983. lib. bdg. 15.00 (ISBN 0-86524-175-9, 0903). Klock & Klock.
Blaiklock, D. A., ed. Living Is Now. 1972. pap. 1.50 (ISBN 0-8010-0579-5). Baker Bk.
Blaiklock, E. M. The Bible & I. 128p. (Orig.). 1983. pap. 3.95 (ISBN 0-87123-298-7). Bethany Hse.
--Blaiklock's Handbook to the Bible. 256p. 1981. pap. 6.95 (ISBN 0-8007-5055-1, Power Bks). Revell.
--The Pastoral Epistles. 128p. 1972. pap. 4.95 (ISBN 0-310-21233-2, 9232). Zondervan.
--Today's Handbook of Bible Characters. 848p. 1987. 17.95 (ISBN 0-87123-948-5). Bethany Hse.
--World of the New Testament. (Bible Study Commentary Ser.). 127p. 1983. pap. 4.95 (ISBN 0-87508-176-2). Chr Lit.
--Zondervan Pictorial Bible Atlas. (Illus.). 1969. 24.95 (ISBN 0-310-21240-5). Zondervan.
Blaiklock, E. M., commentary by. Living Waters: Psalms for Your Quiet Time with God. (Illus.). 256p. 1985. Repr. 10.95 (ISBN 0-687-22378-4). Abingdon.
Blaiklock, E. M. & Harrison, R. K., eds. The New International Dictionary of Biblical Archaeology. 1986. 24.95 (ISBN 0-310-21250-2, 9277). Zondervan.
Blaiklock, E. M. & Keys, A. C., trs. from Ital. The Little Flowers of St. Francis. 176p. 1985. pap. 3.95 (ISBN 0-89283-300-9). Servant.
Blaiklock, E. M., tr. see Lawrence, Brother.
Blaiklock, E. M., tr. see Thomas a Kempis.
Blair, Alain, tr. see Lagerkvist, Par.
Blair, Allen J. Epistles of John: Living Confidently. LC 82-15196. pap. 4.95 (ISBN 0-87213-028-2). Loizeaux.
Blair, Caroline G. Prayers for Mothers. 1980. pap. 1.95 (ISBN 0-8170-0864-0). Judson.
Blair, Charles & Sherrill, John. The Man Who Could Do No Wrong. 1982. pap. 3.50 (ISBN 0-8423-4002-5). Tyndale.
Blair, Chauncey J. Heat in the Rig Veda & Atharva Veda. (American Oriental Ser.: Vol. 45). 1961. 8.00x (ISBN 0-940490-45-5). Am Orient Soc.
Blair, Edward P. Abingdon Bible Handbook. rev. ed. (Illus.). 528p. 1982. pap. 23.95 (ISBN 0-687-00170-6). Abingdon.
--Deuteronomy, Joshua. LC 59-10454. (Layman's Bible Commentary Ser: Vol. 5). 1964. pap. 4.95 (ISBN 0-8042-3065-X). John Knox.
--Manual Biblico de Abingdon. LC 81-12774. Tr. of Abingdon Bible Handbook. (Span.). 400p. (Orig.). 1982. pap. 12.95 (ISBN 0-687-23170-1). Abingdon.
Blair, Guillermo, tr. see Ford, LeRoy.
Blair, J. Allen. Daniel: Living Courageously. LC 70-140898. 1971. pap. 4.95 (ISBN 0-87213-044-4). Loizeaux.
--First Corinthians: Living Wisely. LC 68-58844. 1969. pap. 5.50 (ISBN 0-87213-057-6). Loizeaux.
--Job: Living Patiently. LC 66-25720. 1966. pap. 5.95 (ISBN 0-87213-051-7). Loizeaux.
--John: Living Eternally. LC 77-28529. 1978. pap. 4.95 (ISBN 0-87213-046-0). Loizeaux.
--Jonah: Living Obediently. LC 63-18265. 1963. pap. 3.95 (ISBN 0-87213-050-9). Loizeaux.
--Living Peacefully: First Peter. 1959. pap. 3.50 (ISBN 0-87213-052-5). Loizeaux.
--Living Reliantly: Twenty-Third Psalm. 1958. pap. 2.75 (ISBN 0-87213-054-1). Loizeaux.
--Living Victoriously: Philippians. LC 62-290. 1962. pap. 2.75 (ISBN 0-87213-056-8). Loizeaux.
--Second Peter: Living Faithfully. LC 61-14600. 1961. pap. 4.95 (ISBN 0-87213-047-9). Loizeaux.
Blair, J. W. Coleccion Navidena, No. 1 & 2. 1980. No. 1. pap. 1.75 (ISBN 0-311-08201-7); No. 2. pap. 1.75 (ISBN 0-311-08202-5). Casa Bautista.
Blair, Joe. When Bad Things Happen, God Still Loves. LC 85-13240. 1986. pap. 4.95 (ISBN 0-8054-5010-6). Broadman.
Blair, Maury & Brendel, Doug. Maury, Hijo Del Dolor. Araujo, Juan S., tr. from Eng. Tr. of Maury, Wednesday's Child. (Span.). 144p. 1986. pap. 3.75 (ISBN 0-88113-204-7). Edit Betania.
Blake, A. G. A Seminar on Time. LC 79-52756. 1980. 5.95 (ISBN 0-934254-00-1). Claymont Comm.
Blake, Nelson M., jt. ed. see Rich, Jane K.
Blake, Nigel & Pole, Kay, eds. Objections to Nuclear Defence: Philosophers on Deterrence. 208p. (Orig.). 1984. pap. 11.95x (ISBN 0-7102-0249-0). Methuen Inc.
Blake, Robert A., jt. auth. see Orbaker, Douglas.
Blake, Viola, jt. auth. see Christenson, Evelyn.
Blake, William. Annotations to Richard Watson: An Apology for the Bible in a Series of Letters Addressed to Thomas Paine, 8th Edition, 1797. James, G. Ingli, ed. (Regency Reprints Ser.: No. III). 144p. (Orig.). 1984. pap. 9.00 (ISBN 0-906449-67-7, Pub. by UC Cardiff Pr). Longwood Pub Group.
--Blake's Job: William Blake's Illustrations of the Book of Job. Damon, S. Foster, ed. LC 82-13585. (Illus.). 76p. 1982. pap. 8.95 (ISBN 0-87451-241-7). U Pr of New Eng.
--The Book of Urizen. LC 78-58217. (Illus.). 102p. 1978. pap. 6.95 (ISBN 0-87773-131-4, 73629-X). Shambhala Pubns.
--Milton. Russell, A. & Maclagan, E., eds. LC 73-16264. 1907. lib. bdg. 15.00 (ISBN 0-8414-3345-3). Folcroft.
--Milton: A Poem. LC 78-58177. (Illus.). 178p. 1978. pap. 17.95 (ISBN 0-87773-129-2). Shambhala Pubns.
Blakely, W. A., ed. American State Papers Bearing on Sunday Legislation. LC 79-122165. (Civil Liberties in American History Ser.). 1970. Repr. of 1911 ed. lib. bdg. 95.00 (ISBN 0-306-71973-8). Da Capo.
Blakemore, Louis B. Masonic Lodge Methods. 320p. 1981. Repr. of 1953 ed. text ed. 11.50 (ISBN 0-88053-027-8, M-76). Macoy Pub.
Blakey, Ronald S. The Man in the Manse, Eighteen Hundred to Nineteen Hundred. 160p. 1979. 10.00x (ISBN 0-905312-05-8, Pub. by Scot Acad Pr). Longwood Pub Group.
Blalock, Jack E., Jr. It's All There If You Want It: And Here Is the Map. LC 80-69519. 200p. (Orig.). 1981. 12.95 (ISBN 0-9605156-0-7); pap. 10.95 (ISBN 0-9605156-1-5). J Blalock.
Blamires, Harry. The Christian Mind. 1978. pap. 4.95 (ISBN 0-89283-049-2). Servant.
--On Christian Truth. 168p. (Orig.). pap. 4.95 (ISBN 0-89283-130-8). Servant.
--Words Made Flesh: God Speaks to Us in the Ordinary Things of Life. 173p. (Orig.). 1985. pap. 6.95 (ISBN 0-89283-235-5). Servant.
Blamires, Harry, et al. Chosen Vessels: Portraits of Ten Outstanding Christian Men. Turner, Charles, ed. 224p. (Orig.). 1985. pap. 10.95 (ISBN 0-89283-226-6, Pub. by Vine Books). Servant.
Blanc, M. Francis Le see Le Blanc, Sr. M. Francis.
Blanch, Jose M., tr. see Dunnett, W. M.
Blanch, Jose M., tr. see Lebar, Lois & Berg, Miguel.
Blanch, Lord S. Way of Blessedness. 272p. 1987. pap. 3.50 (ISBN 0-345-34310-7, Pub. by Ballantine Epiphany). Ballantine.
Blanch, Miguel, tr. see Collins, Gary.
Blanch, Miguel, tr. see Ladd, George E.
Blanch, Miguel, tr. see Morris, Leon.
Blanch, Stuart. For All Mankind: A New Approach to the Old Testament. pap. 4.95 (ISBN 0-19-520025-X). Oxford U Pr.
Blanch, Stuart Y. The Burning Bush. 1979. pap. 5.95 (ISBN 0-8192-1260-1). Morehouse.
--Living by Faith. LC 84-10182. Repr. of 1984 ed. 39.00. Bks Demand UMI.
Blanchard, Charles A. Getting Things from God. (Classic Elective Ser.: No. 1). 168p. 1985. pap. 5.95 (ISBN 0-89693-520-5); pap. 0.95. Victor Bks.
Blanchard, J. Knight Templarism. rev. ed. 9.50x (ISBN 0-685-22013-3). Wehman.
--Standard Freemasonry. 9.00x (ISBN 0-685-22116-4). Wehman.
Blanchard, John. Aceptado Por Dios. 2.95 (ISBN 0-85151-406-5). Banner of Truth.
--Right with God. LC 78-6809. 1978. pap. 3.50 (ISBN 0-8024-7357-1). Moody.
--Right with God. rev. ed. 126p. 1985. pap. 2.95 (ISBN 0-85151-045-0). Banner of Truth.
--What in the World Is a Christian? 1987. pap. 6.95 (ISBN 0-310-20101-2). Zondervan.
Blanchard, Jonathan & Rice, N. L. Debate on Slavery: Is Slavery in Itself Sinful & the Relation Between Master & Slave a Sinful Relation. LC 72-82175. (Anti-Slavery Crusade in America Ser.). 1969. Repr. of 1846 ed. 21.00 (ISBN 0-405-00614-4). Ayer Co Pubs.
Blanchard, Kendall. The Economics of Sainthood: Religious Change among the Rimrock Navajos. LC 75-10141. (Illus.). 244p. 1976. 22.50 (ISBN 0-8386-1770-0). Fairleigh Dickinson.
Blanchard, Tim. A Practical Guide to Finding & Using Your Spiritual Gifts. 1983. pap. 6.95 (ISBN 0-8423-4898-0). Tyndale.
Blanchette, Oliva, tr. see Blondel, Maurice.
Blanco, Miquel A., jt. auth. see Watson, E. W.
Blanco, Tomas. The Child's Gifts: A Twelfth Night Tale. LC 75-46530. (Eng. & Span., Illus.). 32p. 1976. 8.95 (ISBN 0-664-32595-5). Westminster.
Bland, C. C., tr. The Autobiography of Guibert: Abbot of Nogent-Sous-Coucy. 1979. Repr. of 1925 ed. lib. bdg. 30.00 (ISBN 0-8482-0140-X). Norwood Edns.
Bland, C. C., tr. see De Nogent, Guibert.
Bland, Glenn. Success: The Glenn Bland Method. 1983. pap. 3.50 (ISBN 0-8423-6689-X). Tyndale.
Bland, Joan, ed. The Pastoral Vision of John Paul II. 1982. 7.95 (ISBN 0-8199-0839-8). Franciscan Herald.
Bland, Kalman P. Epistle on the Possibility of Conjunction with the Active Intellect by Ibn Rushd with the Commentary of Moses Narboni. LC 81-20788. 314p. 1982. 35.00x (ISBN 0-87334-005-1). Ktav.
Bland, Kalman P., ed. & tr. see Rushd, Ibn.
Bland, Salem. New Christianity. LC 72-95815. (Social History of Canada Ser.). 1973. pap. 6.00 (ISBN 0-8020-6179-6). U of Toronto Pr.
Blandford, Brian. Winners & Losers. LC 84-26709. 1985. pap. 3.95 (ISBN 0-8307-1012-4, S181422). Regal.
Blane, Andrew, ed. The Ecumenical World of Orthodox Civilization: Russia & Orthodoxy, Vol. 3. (Slavistic Printings & Reprintings Ser: No. 260). 1974. text ed. 44.80x (ISBN 90-2792-610-7). Mouton.
Blank, Josef. The Gospel According to St. John, Vol. II. McKenzie, John L., ed. LC 81-605. (The New Testament for Spiritual Reading Ser.). 282p. 1981. pap. 4.95. Crossroad NY.
Blank, Richard. A Christian Passover Celebration. 1981. 2.95 (ISBN 0-89536-477-8, 0317). CSS of Ohio.
Blank, S. H. Prophetic Thought: Essays & Addresses. (Jewish Perspectives Ser: Vol. 2). 15.00x (ISBN 0-87820-501-2, HUC Pr). Ktav.
Blank, Sheldon. Jeremiah, Man & Prophet. 1961. 12.50x (ISBN 0-87820-100-9, Pub. by Hebrew Union). Ktav.
--Understanding the Prophets. 144p. 1983. pap. text ed. 4.00 (ISBN 0-8074-0250-8, 382755). UAHC.
Blanke, Fritz. Brothers in Christ: The History of the Oldest Anabaptist. Nordenhaug, Joseph, tr. LC 61-6723. pap. 20.00 (2029246). Bks Demand UMI.
Blankenbaker, Frances. What the Bible Is All about for Young Explorers. (Illus.). 364p. 1987. pap. 12.95 (ISBN 0-8307-1179-1, 5111647). Regal.
Blanshard, Paul. American Freedom & Catholic Power. LC 84-19141. xii, 402p. 1984. Repr. of 1958 ed. lib. bdg. 47.50x (ISBN 0-313-24620-3, BLAF). Greenwood.

--Communism, Democracy, & Catholic Power. LC 75-156175. 340p. 1972. Repr. of 1952 ed. lib. bdg. 35.00x (ISBN 0-8371-6118-5, BLCD). Greenwood.

--Some of My Best Friends Are Christians. LC 74-744. 200p. 1974. 14.95 (ISBN 0-87548-149-3). Open Court.

Blanton, Alma E. God & Mrs. Adam. (Illus.). 152p. (Orig.). 1978. lib. bdg. 4.95 (ISBN 0-938134-00-0, G-1); pap. 4.95 (ISBN 0-686-73968-X). Loving Pubs.

--Our Gospel's Women. (Illus.). 114p. (Orig.). 1979. pap. 3.00 (ISBN 0-938134-01-9). Loving Pubs.

Blanton, Mary T. Knock on a Door. 32p. 1984. 4.95. Victor Bks.

Blanton, Smiley, jt. auth. see Peale, Norman V.

Blantz, Thomas E. A Priest in Public Service: Francis J. Haas & the New Deal. LC 81-40452. 384p. 1982. 25.00 (ISBN 0-268-01547-3). U of Notre Dame Pr.

Blaquiere, Georgette. The Grace to Be a Woman. Wild, Robert, tr. from Fr. LC 83-15858. 127p. 1983. pap. 6.95 (ISBN 0-8189-0449-6). Alba.

Blase, Betty E. de see De Blase, Betty E.

Blashford-Snell, John. Mysteries: Encounters with the Unexplained. 256p. 1984. 16.95 (ISBN 0-370-30479-9, Pub. by Bodley Head). Salem Hse Pubs.

Blasi, Anthony J. A Phenomenological Transformation of the Social Scientific Study of Religion. LC 85-13303. (American University Studies VII: Theology & Religion: Vol. 10). 195p. 1985. text ed. 27.85 (ISBN 0-8204-0235-4). P Lang Pubs.

Blasi, Anthony J. & Cuneo, Michael W. Issues in the Sociology of Religion: A Bibliography. Chekki, Dan A., ed. (Bibliographies in Sociology-Reference Library of Social Science). 392p. 1986. 53.00 (ISBN 0-8240-8585-X). Garland Pub.

Blasien, Otto Von St. see Otto, Von St. Blasien.

Blasing, Randy. To Continue. 75p. (Orig.). 1983. cancelled 10.95 (ISBN 0-89255-070-8); pap. 5.95 (ISBN 0-89255-071-6). Persea Bks.

Blass, F. & Debrunner, A. Greek Grammar of the New Testament & Other Early Christian Literature. Funk, Robert W., tr. 28.00 (ISBN 0-310-24780-2, 18076). Zondervan.

Blass, Jacqueline, jt. auth. see Hess, Edith.

Blassie, Richard R. de see De Blassie, Richard R. & Anderson, John.

Blate, Michael. The Tao of Health: The Way of Total Well-Being. (Illus., Orig.). 1978. pap. 6.95 (ISBN 0-916878-05-8). Falkynor Bks.

Blattenberger, Ruth, ed. see Leach, Robert J.

Blatter, George J., tr. see Agreda, Mary.

Blattman, George. The Sun. Tr. of Die Sonne. 240p. (Orig.). 1985. pap. text ed. 16.95 (ISBN 0-88010-148-2). Anthroposophic.

Blattner, John. Growing in the Fruit of the Spirit. (Living As A Christian Ser.). 96p. 1984. pap. 3.95 (ISBN 0-89283-177-4). Servant.

Blattner, John, jt. auth. see Manney, James.

Blau, Esther & Deitsch, Cyrel, eds. Spice & Spirit of Kosher-Passover Cooking. LC 77-72116. (Lubavitch Women's Organization Ser.). 1981. 7.95 (ISBN 0-317-14690-4). Lubavitch Women.

Blau, Joseph L. Judaism in America: From Curiosity to Third Faith. LC 75-5069. (Chicago History of American Religion Ser.). 176p. 1976. 6.00x (ISBN 0-226-05727-5). U of Chicago Pr.

--Modern Varieties of Judaism. LC 66-10732. (Lectures on the History of Religion Ser.). 217p. 1966. 24.50x (ISBN 0-231-02867-9); pap. 11.00x (ISBN 0-231-08668-7). Columbia U Pr.

--The Story of Jewish Philosophy. 8.95x (ISBN 0-87068-174-5). Ktav.

Blau, Joseph L., ed. Essays on Jewish Life & Thought. LC 57-11757. 458p. 1959. 31.00x (ISBN 0-231-02171-2). Columbia U Pr.

Blau, Joseph L., ed. see Wayland, Francis.

Blau, Joseph L., et al, eds. The Jews of the United States, 1790-1840: A Documentary History, 3 Vols. LC 64-10108. 1034p. 1964. Set. 140.00x (ISBN 0-231-02651-X). Columbia U Pr.

Blavatsky. Two Books on Stanzas of Dzyan. 4.95 (ISBN 0-8356-7223-9). Theos Pub Hse.

Blavatsky, jt. ed. see Codd, Clara.

Blavatsky, H. P. Key to Theosophy. 7.50 (ISBN 0-8356-5131-2). Theos Pub Hse.

--A Modern Panarion. 504p. 1981. Repr. of 1895 ed. 15.00 (ISBN 0-938998-22-6). Theosophy.

--Theosophical Articles: Reprinted from the Theosophist, Lucifer & other Nineteenth-Century Journals, 3 vols. 1692p. 1982. Set. 37.50 (ISBN 0-938998-26-9). Theosophy.

Blavatsky, H. P., et al. Theosophical Articles & Notes. 300p. 1985. Repr. 10.50 (ISBN 0-938998-29-3). Theosophy.

Blavatsky, Helena P. Abridgement of the Secret Doctrine. Preston, Elizabeth & Humphreys, Christmas, eds. 1968. pap. 5.50 (ISBN 0-8356-0009-2, Quest). Theos Pub Hse.

--The Caves & Jungles of Hindustan. De Zirkoff, Boris, ed. LC 74-26605. (Illus.). 750p. 1975. 18.50 (ISBN 0-8356-0219-2). Theos Pub Hse.

--The Circle of Wisdom. rev ed. Parley, Winifred A., ed. LC 78-8790. 1978. pap. 3.25 (ISBN 0-8356-0516-7, Quest). Theos Pub Hse.

--Collected Writings of H. P. Blavatsky, Vols. 1-11. Incl. Vol. 1. 1874-1878. rev. ed. 16.50 (ISBN 0-8356-0082-3); Vol. 2. 1879-1880 (ISBN 0-8356-0091-2); Vol. 3. 1881-1882 (ISBN 0-8356-0099-8); Vol. 4. 1882-1883 (ISBN 0-8356-0106-4); Vol. 5. 1883 (ISBN 0-8356-0117-X); Vol. 6. 1883-1884-1885 (ISBN 0-8356-0125-0); Vol. 7. 1886-1887 (ISBN 0-8356-0222-2); Vol. 8. 1887 (ISBN 0-8356-7166-6); Vol. 9. 1888 (ISBN 0-8356-0217-6); Vol. 10. 1888-1889 (ISBN 0-8356-0218-4); Vol. 11. 1889. 16.50 (ISBN 0-686-86789-0). (Illus.). 16.50 ea. Theos Pub Hse.

--Dynamics of the Psychic World: Comments by H. P. Blavatsky on Magic, Mediumship, Psychism, & the Powers of the Spirit. LC 72-78193. 150p. (Orig.). 1972. pap. 1.95 (ISBN 0-8356-0429-2, Quest). Theos Pub Hse.

--Esoteric Writings of H. P. Blavatsky. LC 79-6547. (Illus.). 500p. (Orig.). 1980. pap. 8.75 (ISBN 0-8356-0535-3, Quest). Theos Pub Hse.

--H. P. Blavatsky Collected Writings, Vol. XII. De Zirkoff, Boris, ed. LC 80-53953. (Illus.). 849p. 1981. 16.50 (ISBN 0-8356-0228-1). Theos Pub Hse.

--H. P. Blavatsky to the American Conventions: 1888-1891, with a Historical Perspective. LC 78-74256. 1979. pap. 4.00 (ISBN 0-911500-88-X). Theos U Pr.

--Isis Unveiled, 2 Vols. De Zirkoff, Boris, ed. 1971. Set. 30.00 (ISBN 0-8356-0193-5). Theos Pub Hse.

--Isis Unveiled, 2 vols. LC 72-186521. 1976. Set. 20.00 (ISBN 0-911500-02-2); Set. pap. 14.00 (ISBN 0-911500-03-0). Theos U Pr.

--Isis Unveiled: A Master-Key to the Mysteries of Ancient & Modern Science & Theology, 2 vols. in 1. (Illus.). xlix, 1260p. 1931. Repr. of 1877 ed. 17.00 (ISBN 0-938998-01-3). Theosophy.

--The Key to Theosophy. xii, 310p. 1930. Repr. of 1889 ed. 6.00 (ISBN 0-938998-03-X). Theosophy.

--The Key to Theosophy: Verbatim with 1889 Edition. LC 72-95701. 1972. 9.00 (ISBN 0-911500-06-5); pap. 6.00 (ISBN 0-911500-07-3). Theos U Pr.

--The Secret Doctrine, 3 vols. 7th ed. De Zirkoff, Boris, ed. (Illus.). 1980. 45.00 ea. (ISBN 0-8356-7525-4). Theos Pub Hse.

--The Secret Doctrine: The Synthesis of Science, Religion, & Philosophy, 2 vols. in 1. xci, 1474p. 1925. Repr. of 1888 ed. 18.50 (ISBN 0-938998-00-5). Theosophy.

--The Theosophical Glossary: A Photographic Reproduction of the Original Edition, As First Issued at London, England, 1892. Mead, G. R., ed. & intro. by. vi, 389p. 1930. Repr. of 1892 ed. 8.50 (ISBN 0-938998-04-8). Theosophy.

--The Theosophist: Oct. Eighteen Seventy-Nine to Sept. Eighteen Eighty. 2nd ed. (Secret Doctrine Reference Ser.). (Illus.). 320p. 1979. pap. 12.00 (ISBN 0-913510-31-9). Wizards.

--Voice of the Silence. LC 73-7619. 1970. pap. 2.50 (ISBN 0-8356-0380-6, Quest). Theos Pub Hse.

--The Voice of the Silence: Verbatim with 1889 ed. LC 76-25345. 1976. 5.00 (ISBN 0-911500-04-9); pap. 2.75 (ISBN 0-911500-05-7). Theos U Pr.

Blavatsky, Helena P., tr. & intro. by. The Voice of the Silence: Chosen Fragments from the Book of the Golden Precepts. iv, 110p. 1928. Repr. of 1889 ed. 3.00 (ISBN 0-938998-06-4). Theosophy.

Blavatsky, Helena P., et al. Karma Lore: One. 71p. (Orig.). 1983. pap. 3.95 (ISBN 0-912181-02-8). East School Pr.

Blavatsky, Helene P. Theosophical Glossary. LC 74-142546. 1971. Repr. of 1892 ed. 46.00x (ISBN 0-8103-3679-0). Gale.

Blaxland, G. Cuthbert. Mayflower Essays: On the Story of the Pilgrim Fathers, As Told in Governor Bradford's Ms. History of the Plimoth Plantation. LC 78-39713. (Essay Index Reprint Ser.). Repr. of 1896 ed. 13.00 (ISBN 0-8369-2748-6). Ayer Co Pubs.

Blaxland de Lange, Paulamaria, tr. see Udo de Haes, Daniel.

Blaxland de Lange, Simon, tr. see Udo de Haes, Daniel.

Blay, Cecil J. It Is Written. 120p. 1973. text ed. 4.00 (ISBN 0-910424-62-4). Concordant.

Blazer, Howard A. Angels, Their Origin, Nature, Mission & Destiny. 64p. 1974. pap. 2.50x (ISBN 0-88428-034-9). Parchment Pr.

Blazier, Kenneth D. A Growing Church School. 1978. pap. text ed. 2.50 (ISBN 0-8170-0785-7). Judson.

--Workbook for Planning Christian Education. 48p. 1983. pap. 3.95 (ISBN 0-8170-0996-5). Judson.

Blazier, Kenneth D. & Huber, Evelyn M. Planning Christian Education in Your Church. LC 73-19585. 32p. (Orig.). 1974. pap. 1.00 (ISBN 0-8170-0633-8); pap. 2.95 spanish ed (ISBN 0-8170-0685-0). Judson.

Blazier, Kenneth D., ed. The Teaching Church at Work. 64p. 1980. pap. 3.50 (ISBN 0-8170-0879-9). Judson.

Blazquez, Jose M. Diccionario De las Religiones Prerromanas De Hispania. (Span.). 192p. 1975. pap. 9.95 (ISBN 84-7090-071-4, S-50058). French & Eur.

Blecher, Arthur C., ed. see Butwin, Frances.

Blechschmidt, Meinulf. Der Leib und das Heil. (European University Studies: No. 23, Vol. 207). (Ger.). 435p. 1983. 22.10 (ISBN 3-261-03264-2). P Lang Pubs.

Bledsoe, Shirley, jt. auth. see MacKemzie, Joy.

Bledsoe, Shirley, jt. auth. see MacKenzie, Joy.

Bleeck, Arthur H. Avesta: The Religious Books of the Parsees. lib. bdg. 79.95 (ISBN 0-87968-133-0). Krishna Pr.

Blehl, Vincent F. John Henry Newman: A Bibliograhical Catalogue of His Writings. LC 77-12141. 148p. 1978. 20.00x (ISBN 0-8139-0738-1). U Pr of Va.

Bleibtreu, John, ed. see Ichazo, Oscar.

Bleich, D. J. Contemporary Halakhic Problems, Vol. I. (The Library of Jewish Law & Ethics: No. 4). 20.00x (ISBN 0-87068-450-7); pap. 14.95. Ktav.

Bleich, David. With Perfect Faith. 1982. 25.00x (ISBN 0-87068-891-X); pap. 14.95. Ktav.

Bleich, David J. Contemporary Halakhic Problems, Vol.II. 20.00x (ISBN 0-87068-275-X); pap. 14.95. Ktav.

--Judaism & Healing: Halakhic Perspectives. 1981. pap. 9.95 (ISBN 0-87068-890-1). Ktav.

Bleich, J. David. Contemporary Halakhic Problems, Vol. II. (The Library of Jewish Law & Ethics, Volume X). 423p. 1983. 20.00x (ISBN 0-87068-451-5). Ktav.

Bleicher, Josef. Contemporary Hermeneutics: Hermeneutics As Method, Philosophy & Critique. 224p. 1980. 28.00x (ISBN 0-7100-0551-2); pap. 14.00x (ISBN 0-7100-0552-0). Methuen Inc.

Bleick, Roy. Much More Than Giving. 112p. (Orig.). 1985. pap. 6.95 (ISBN 0-570-03951-7, 12-2886). Concordia.

Bleier, Rocky & O'Neil, Terry. Fighting Back. rev. ed. LC 75-12865. (Illus.). 240p. 1980. 14.95 (ISBN 0-8128-2767-8). Stein & Day.

--Fighting Back. (Illus.). 288p. 1976. pap. 2.75 (ISBN 0-446-95704-6). Warner Bks.

Bleiweiss, Robert M., ed. Torah at Brandeis Institute: The Layman Expounds. LC 76-7776. (Illus.). 1976. 8.95 (ISBN 0-916952-00-2). Brandeis-Bardin Inst.

Blench, J. W. Preaching in England in the Late Fifteenth & Sixteenth Centuries. 378p. 1981. Repr. of 1964 ed. lib. bdg. 50.00 (ISBN 0-8495-0604-2). Arden Lib.

Blenkinsopp, J. Gibeon & Israel: The Role of Gibeon & the Gibeonites in the Political and Religious History of Early Israel. LC 74-171672. (Society for Old Testament Studies Monographs). 1972. 34.50 (ISBN 0-521-08368-0). Cambridge U Pr.

Blenkinsopp, Joseph. A History of Prophecy in Israel: From the Settlement in the Land to the Hellenistic Period. LC 83-10178. 288p. (Orig.). 1983. pap. 16.95 (ISBN 0-664-24479-3). Westminster.

--Prophecy & Canon: A Contribution to the Study of Jewish Origins. LC 76-22411. 1977. text ed. 14.95 (ISBN 0-268-01522-8). U of Notre Dame Pr.

--Prophecy & Canon: A Contribution to the Study of Jewish Origins. LC 76-22411. 206p. 1986. pap. 9.95 (ISBN 0-268-01559-7). U of Notre Dame Pr.

--Wisdom & Law in the Old Testament: The Ordering of Life in Israel & Early Judaism. (The Oxford Bible Ser.). (Orig.). 1983. pap. 9.95 (ISBN 0-19-213253-9). Oxford U Pr.

Blenkinsopp, Joseph & Challenor, John. Pentateuch. Bright, Laurence, ed. LC 71-173033. (Scripture Discussion Commentary Ser.: Pt. 1). 248p. 1971. pap. text ed. 4.50 (ISBN 0-87946-000-8). ACTA Found.

Blenkinsopp, Joseph, tr. see Brox, Norbert.

Blessin, Ann M. Sacred Dance with Physically & Mentally Handicapped. Adams, Doug, ed. 1982. pap. 3.00 (ISBN 0-941500-28-4). Sharing Co.

Blessitt, Arthur. Arthur-Peacemaker. LC 85-71322. (Orig.). 1986. pap. 5.00 (ISBN 0-934461-02-3, BP603). Blessitt Pub.

Blevins, James L. Revelation. Hayes, John, ed. LC 84-4387. (Preaching Guides Ser.). 132p. (Orig.). 1984. pap. 6.95 (ISBN 0-8042-3250-4). John Knox.

--Revelation As Drama. LC 84-4986. 1984. pap. 6.95 (ISBN 0-8054-1393-6). Broadman.

Blewett, George J. The Christian View of the World. 1912. 49.50x (ISBN 0-685-89741-9). Elliots Bks.

Bleyker, Merle Den see Hendricks, William C. & Den Bleyker, Merle.

Blidstein, Gerald. Honor Thy Father & Mother. 15.00x (ISBN 0-87068-251-2); pap. 9.95. Ktav.

Blinkenberg, C. The Thunderweapon in Religion & Folklore. xii, 122p. 1985. Repr. of 1911 ed. lib. bdg. 25.00x (ISBN 0-89241-205-4). Caratzas.

--The Thunderweapon in Religion & Folklore. 1977. lib. bdg. 59.95 (ISBN 0-8490-2749-7). Gordon Pr.

Blinkin, Meir. Stories. Rosenfeld, Max, tr. from Yiddish. (Modern Jewish Literature & Culture Ser.). 166p. 1984. 10.95x (ISBN 0-87395-818-7). State U NY Pr.

Blish, James. The Tale That Wags the God. 1986. 15.00 (ISBN 0-911682-29-5). Advent.

Bliss, Eugene F., ed. Diary of David Zeisberger: A Missionary Among the Indians of Ohio, 2 vols. LC 73-108557. 1972. Repr. of 1885 ed. 59.00x (ISBN 0-403-00253-2). Scholarly.

Bliss, Frederick J. Religions of Modern Syria & Palestine. LC 76-39454. Repr. of 1912 ed. 20.00 (ISBN 0-404-00897-6). AMS Pr.

Bliss, Richard. Origins: Two Models. Gish, Duane T. & Moore, John N., eds. LC 76-20178. (Illus.). 1976. 5.95 (ISBN 0-89051-027-X); tchr's. guide avail. Master Bks.

Bliss, Richard B. & Parker, Gary E. Origin of Life. LC 78-58477. (Illus.). 1978. pap. 4.95 (ISBN 0-89051-053-9). Master Bks.

Bliss, Sylvester. Memoirs of William Miller. LC 72-134374. Repr. of 1853 ed. 30.00 (ISBN 0-404-08422-2). AMS Pr.

Blitchington, Evelyn. The Family Devotions Idea Book. LC 82-4252. 139p. (Orig.). 1982. pap. 4.95 (ISBN 0-87123-254-5, 210254). Bethany Hse.

Blitchington, Peter & Cruise, Robert J. Understanding Your Temperament: A Self-Analysis with a Christian Viewpoint. 38p. (Orig.). 1979. pap. 2.95 (ISBN 0-943872-67-7). Andrews Univ Pr.

Blitchington, W. Peter. The Christian Woman's Search for Self-Esteem. LC 81-18963. 168p. 1983. pap. 4.95 (ISBN 0-8407-5830-8). Nelson.

--Sex Roles & the Christian Family. 1983. pap. 5.95 (ISBN 0-8423-5896-X); leader's guide 2.95 (ISBN 0-8423-5897-8). Tyndale.

Blizzard, Roy B., Jr. Let Judah Go up First: A Study in Praise, Prayer, & Worship. 46p. (Orig.). 1984. pap. 3.50 (ISBN 0-918873-01-0). Ctr Judaic-Christ Studies.

Blizzard, Samuel. The Protestant Parish Minister: A Behavioral Science Interpretation. LC 85-50402. (SSSR Monography: No. 5). 1985. pap. 8.00 (ISBN 0-932566-04-9). Soc Sci Stud Rel.

Bloch, ed. Journal of Jewish Bibliography, 4 vols. Set. 35.00 (ISBN 0-685-48593-5). Feldheim.

Bloch, A., ed. see Pope John Paul II.

Bloch, A. P. The Biblical & Historical Background of the Jewish Holy Days. 1978. 20.00x (ISBN 0-87068-338-1); pap. 11.95. Ktav.

Bloch, Abraham P. The Biblical & Historical Backround of Jewish Customs & Ceremonies. 1979. 20.00x (ISBN 0-87068-658-5); pap. 11.95. Ktav.

--A Book of Jewish Ethical Concepts. 1984. 20.00 (ISBN 0-88125-039-2). Ktav.

Bloch, Carl, illus. Jesus, the Son of Man. (Illus.). 80p. 1983. pap. 12.95 (ISBN 0-87973-652-6, 652). Our Sunday Visitor.

Bloch, Chana. Spelling the Word: George Herbert & the Bible. LC 84-123. 375p. 1985. 37.50x (ISBN 0-520-05121-1). U of Cal Pr.

Bloch, Charles E. The First Chanukah. LC 56-12405. (Illus.). 1957. pap. 2.25 (ISBN 0-8197-0450-4). Bloch.

Bloch, Lolla, tr. see Taubes, Hella.

Bloch, Marie H., ed. see Dubovy, Andrew.

Bloch, Maurice & Parry, Jonathan, eds. Death & the Regeneration of Life. LC 82-9467. 256p. 1982. 34.50 (ISBN 0-521-24875-2); pap. 11.95 (ISBN 0-521-27037-5). Cambridge U Pr.

Blocher, Henri. In the Beginning: The Opening Chapters of Genesis. Preston, David G., tr. from Fr. LC 84-12800. 180p. 1984. pap. 8.95 (ISBN 0-87784-325-2). Inter-Varsity.

Block, K. S., ed. Ludus Coventriae, Or, the Place Called Corpus Christi. (Early English Text Society Ser.). 1922. 26.00x (ISBN 0-19-722560-8). Oxford U Pr.

Block, Martin. Gypsies: Their Life & Their Customs. Kuczynski, Barbara & Taylor, Duncan, trs. LC 75-3451. (Illus.). Repr. of 1939 ed. 31.50 (ISBN 0-404-16886-8). AMS Pr.

Blocker, Jack S., Jr. Give to the Winds Thy Fears: The Women Temperance Crusade, 1873-1874. LC 84-15718. (Contributions in Women Studies: No. 55). (Illus.). xix, 280p. 1985. lib. bdg. 35.00 (ISBN 0-313-24556-8, BGW/). Greenwood.

Blodgett, Ralph. Hell: Will the Wicked Burn Forever? (Outreach Ser.). 1981. pap. 0.99 (ISBN 0-8163-0375-4). Pacific Pr Pub Assn.

--How Will It End? (Eighty-Five-Miss Ser). 1984. pap. 1.19 (ISBN 0-8163-0567-6). Pacific Pr Pub Assn.

--Millennium. (Outreach Ser.). 1981. pap. 1.25 (ISBN 0-8163-0398-3). Pacific Pr Pub Assn.

Bloem, Diane. A Womans Workshop on Proverbs. 1978. leader's manual 5.95 (ISBN 0-310-21371-1, 10684); student manual 2.95 (ISBN 0-310-21361-4, 10683). Zondervan.
--A Woman's Workshop on the Beautitudes. (Orig.). 1981. Leader's Manual, 160 Pages. pap. 3.95 (ISBN 0-310-42641-3, 112160); Student's Manual, 96 Pages. pap. 2.95 (ISBN 0-310-42651-0, 11217). Zondervan.

Bloem, Diane B. Into the Midst of Suffering: A Woman's Workshop on Job. (Woman's Workshop Ser.). (Orig.). 1985. Leader's ed., 64pp. pap. 3.95 (ISBN 0-310-42771-1, 11213P); Student's ed., 112pp. pap. 2.95 (ISBN 0-310-42781-9, 11213P). Zondervan.
--Leader's Manual: A Woman's Workshop on Bible Women. 128p. 1983. pap. 3.95 student Manual (ISBN 0-310-23151-5); tchr's. manual avail. (ISBN 0-310-23141-8, 10747). Zondervan.

Bloem, Diane B. & Bloem, Robert C. A Women's Workshop on Bible Marriages. (Woman's Workshop Series of Study Books). 128p. (Orig.). 1980. pap. 2.95 student's manual (ISBN 0-310-21391-6, 10687); pap. 3.95 leader's manual (ISBN 0-310-21401-7, 10688). Zondervan.

Bloem, Robert C., jt. auth. see Bloem, Diane B.

Bloesch, Donald G. Battle for the Trinity: The Debate over Inclusive God-Language. 1985. 8.95 (ISBN 0-89283-230-4, Pub. by Vine Books). Servant.
--Crumbling Foundations: Death & Rebirth in an Age of Upheaval. 160p. (Orig.). 1984. pap. text ed. 6.95 (ISBN 0-310-29821-0, 12740P). Zondervan.
--Jesus Is Victor! Karl Barth's Doctrine of Salvation. LC 76-14360. Repr. of 1976 ed. 33.50 (ISBN 0-8357-9013-4, 2016373). Bks Demand UMI.

Blofeld, John. Bodhisattva of Compassion: The Mystical Tradition of Kuan Yin. LC 77-91352. (Illus.). 155p. 1978. pap. 9.95 (ISBN 0-87773-126-8, 73609-5). Shambhala Pubns.
--Taoism: The Road to Immortality. LC 77-90882. 195p. 1978. pap. 9.95 (ISBN 0-87773-116-0, 73582-X). Shambhala Pubns.

Blofeld, John, tr. see Huang Po.

Blofeld, John E. The Jewel in the Lotus: Outline of Present Day Buddhism in China. LC 74-10096. (China Studies: from Confucius to Mao Ser). 193p. 1986. Repr. of 1948 ed. 20.50 (ISBN 0-88355-161-6). Hyperion Conn.

Blogg, Martin. Dance & the Christian Faith. (Illus.). 283p. 1987. pap. 17.95 (ISBN 0-340-35173-X, Pub. by Hodder & Stoughton UK). David & Charles.

Blom, Dorothea. Art & the Changing World: Uncommon Sense in the Twentieth Century. LC 72-80094. (Illus.). 32p. (Orig.). 1972. pap. 2.50x (ISBN 0-87574-183-5, 183). Pendle Hill.
--Art Imagery & the Mythic Process. LC 77-91636. (Illus.). 31p. (Orig.). 1977. pap. 2.50x (ISBN 0-87574-215-7). Pendle Hill.
--Art Responds to the Bible. LC 74-24006. (Illus.). 32p. (Orig.). 1974. pap. 2.50x (ISBN 0-87574-197-5). Pendle Hill.
--Encounters with Art. 1983. pap. 2.50x (ISBN 0-87574-128-2, 128). Pendle Hill.
--Life Journey of a Quaker Artist. LC 80-80916. 32p. (Orig.). 1980. 2.50x (ISBN 0-87574-232-7). Pendle Hill.
--The Prophetic Element in Modern Art. 1983. pap. 2.50x (ISBN 0-87574-148-7, 148). Pendle Hill.

Blom, John J. Descartes: His Moral Philosophy & Psychology. LC 78-55241. 1978. 35.00 (ISBN 0-8147-0999-0). NYU Pr.

Blom, Paul. Ministry of Welcome: A Guide for Ushers & Greeters. 32p. (Orig.). 1980. pap. 2.95 (ISBN 0-8066-1806-X, 10-4442). Augsburg.

Blomberg, Craig. The Historical Reliability of the Gospels. 288p. 1987. pap. 9.95 (ISBN 0-87784-992-7). Inter-Varsity.

Blomberg, Craig, jt. auth. see Wenham, David.

Blomberg, Don W. Good News of the Kingdom. 1985. 8.75 (ISBN 0-317-13203-2). Carlton.

Blomgren, David K. Bible Survey. (Illus.). 70p. 1979. pap. 6.25 (ISBN 0-914936-39-5). Bible Temple.
--Prophetic Gatherings in the Church. (Illus.). 100p. 1979. pap. 8.95 (ISBN 0-914936-36-0). Bible Temple.
--Song of the Lord. 70p. Date not set. pap. 6.95. Bible Temple.

Blommerde, Anton C. Northwest Semetic Grammar & Job. (Biblica et Orientalia Ser.: Vol. 22). 1969. pap. 13.00 (ISBN 88-7653-322-2). Loyola.

Blondel, Jacques. Milton Poete De la Bible Dans le Paradis Perdu. LC 73-13668. 1959. lib. bdg. 12.50 (ISBN 0-8414-3252-X). Folcroft.

Blondel, Maurice. Action: Essay on a Critique of Life & a Science of Practice. Blanchette, Oliva, tr. from Fr. LC 83-401133. 448p. 1984. text ed. 29.95 (ISBN 0-268-00605-9, 85-06057). U of Notre Dame Pr.

Blood, Benjamin P. Optimism, the Lesson of Ages. LC 75-3055. Repr. of 1860 ed. 18.00 (ISBN 0-404-59053-5). AMS Pr.
--The Philosophy of Justice Between God & Man. LC 75-3056. Repr. of 1851 ed. 20.50 (ISBN 0-404-59054-3). AMS Pr.

Bloodworth, Venice. Key to Yourself. 1986. pap. 4.95 (ISBN 0-87516-296-7). De Vorss.

Bloom, Alexander. Prodigal Sons: The New York Intellectuals & Their World. 461p. 1986. 24.95 (ISBN 0-19-503662-X). Oxford U Pr.

Bloom, Alfred. Shinran's Gospel of Pure Grace. LC 64-8757. (Association for Asian Studies Monograph: No. 20). 97p. 1965. pap. 4.50x (ISBN 0-8165-0405-9). U of Ariz Pr.
--Tannisho: A Resource for Modern Living. LC 80-39523. 112p. (Orig.). 1981. pap. 6.95 (ISBN 0-938474-00-6). Buddhist Study.

Bloom, Alfred, jt. auth. see Baird, Robert D.

Bloom, Alred. Shoshinge: The Heart of Shin Buddhism. Nagatani, T. & Tabrah, Ruth, trs. 108p. (Orig.). 1986. pap. 6.95 (ISBN 0-938474-06-5). Buddhist Study.

Bloom, Anthony. Beginning to Pray. LC 70-169613. 128p. 1982. pap. 4.95 (ISBN 0-8091-1509-3). Paulist Pr.
--Meditations. 3.95 (ISBN 0-87193-010-2). Dimension Bks.

Bloom, Anthony & LeFebvre, George. Courage to Pray. 3rd ed. Livingstone, Dinah, tr. from Fr. 123p. (Orig.). pap. text ed. 4.95 (ISBN 0-88141-031-4). St Vladimirs.

Bloom, Clive. The Occult Experience & the New Criticism: Daemonism, Sexuality & the Hidden in Literature. LC 86-10963. 160p. 1987. 27.50x (ISBN 0-389-20646-6). B&N Imports.

Bloom, Dorothy. Church Doors Open Outward: A Practical Guide to Beginning Community Ministry. 80p. 1987. pap. 6.95 (ISBN 0-8170-1117-X). Judson.

Bloom, Harold. Kabbalah & Criticism. LC 75-12820. 100p. 1975. 8.95 (ISBN 0-8264-0124-4). Continuum.
--Kabbalah & Criticism. LC 82-4674. 126p. 1983. pap. 7.95 (ISBN 0-8245-0487-9). Crossroad NY.

Bloom, Harold, ed. Edmund Spenser. (Modern Critical Views-Medieval & Renaissance Ser.). 1986. 29.50 (ISBN 0-87754-672-X). Chelsea Hse.

Bloom, Harold, ed. & intro. by. Jewish Literature: The Bible Through 1789. (Critical Cosmos--Other European & Latin American Literature Ser.). 1987. 49.95 (ISBN 1-55546-101-8). Chelsea Hse.
--Modern Jewish Literature. (Critical Cosmos--Other European & Latin American Literature Ser.). 1987. 49.95 (ISBN 1-55546-102-6). Chelsea Hse.

Bloom, Irene, jt. ed. see De Bary, W. Theodore.

Bloom, James H. Shakespeare's Church. LC 73-116790. (Studies in Shakespeare, No. 24). 1971. Repr. of 1902 ed. lib. bdg. 49.95x (ISBN 0-8383-1032-X). Haskell.

Bloom, James M. & Sherer, Michael L. A Festival of Lights. (Orig.). 1986. pap. 2.25 (ISBN 0-89536-833-1, 6847). CSS of Ohio.

Bloom, Metropolitan A. Living Prayer. 1975. pap. 6.95 (ISBN 0-87243-054-5). Templegate.

Bloomfield, Arthur. Before the Last Battle-Armageddon. 192p. 1976. pap. 3.95 (ISBN 0-87123-035-6). Bethany Hse.
--The Changing Climate. LC 77-80427. 128p. 1977. pap. 2.50 (ISBN 0-87123-060-7, 200060). Bethany Hse.

Bloomfield, Arthur E. All Things New. LC 42-5300. 1959. pap. 7.95 (ISBN 0-87123-007-0); study guide 1.95 (ISBN 0-87123-520-X). Bethany Hse.
--Antes de la Ultima Batalla-Armagedon. 192p. 1977. 3.75 (ISBN 0-88113-003-6). Edit Betania.
--The End of the Days. LC 51-9505. 288p. 1961. 8.95 (ISBN 0-87123-122-0, 210122). Bethany Hse.
--How to Recognize the Antichrist. LC 75-29424. 160p. 1975. pap. 3.95 (ISBN 0-87123-225-1, 210225). Bethany Hse.
--Signs of His Coming. LC 57-8724. 160p. 1962. pap. 4.95 (ISBN 0-87123-513-7, 210513). Bethany Hse.

Bloomfield, Brynna C. & Moskowitz, Jane M. Traveling Jewish in America: The Complete Guide for 1986 for Business & Pleasure. 407p. (Orig.). 1986. pap. 9.95 (ISBN 0-9617104-0-3). Wandering You Pr.

Bloomfield, Brynna C., et al. Traveling Jewish in America: For Business & Pleasure. rev. ed. 420p. (Orig.). 1987. pap. 9.95 (ISBN 0-9617104-1-1). Wandering You Pr.

Bloomfield, Leonard. Plains Cree Texts. LC 73-3552. (American Ethnological Society. Publications Ser.: No. 16). Repr. of 1934 ed. 36.00 (ISBN 0-404-58166-8). AMS Pr.
--Sacred Stories of the Sweet Grass Cree. LC 74-7933. Repr. of 1930 ed. 34.50 (ISBN 0-404-11821-6). AMS Pr.

Bloomfield, M., tr. Hymns of the Atharva-Veda: Together with Extracts from the Ritual Books & the Commentaries. LC 69-14131. 716p. 1897. Repr. lib. bdg. 32.50x (ISBN 0-8371-1879-4, VEHA). Greenwood.

Bloomfield, Maurice. Religion of the Veda. LC 70-94310. (BCL Ser. II). Repr. of 1908 ed. 18.00 (ISBN 0-404-00912-3). AMS Pr.

Bloomfield, Morton W., ed. Allegory, Myth, & Symbol. (Harvard English Studies: 9). 440p. 1982. text ed. 32.50x (ISBN 0-674-01640-8); pap. text ed. 10.95x (ISBN 0-674-01641-6). Harvard U Pr.

Bloomfield, Samuel T. The Greek Testament: With English Notes, 2 vols. 1986. Repr. of 1843 ed. Set. lib. bdg. 45.00 (ISBN 0-89941-507-5). W S Hein.

Bloore, John. Alternative Views of the Bible. 1978. Repr. of 1925 ed. lib. bdg. 20.00 (ISBN 0-8495-0366-3). Arden Lib.

Blough, Dwight, jt. auth. see Arnold, Heini.

Bloxam, John R., ed. see Heylyn, Peter.

Bloxton, Marian W. Pioneers of Faith. 80p. 1984. pap. 7.95 (ISBN 0-8170-1036-X). Judson.

Bloy, Myron B., Jr., et al. The Recovery of Spirit in Higher Education. Rankin, Robert, ed. 1980. 17.50 (ISBN 0-8164-0469-0, HarpR). Har-Row.

Bluck, R. S., tr. see Plato.

Bludau, August. Die Pilgerreise der Aetheria. pap. 22.00 (ISBN 0-384-04760-2). Johnson Repr.

Blue. Pilgrim Hymnal. 1958. 9.95x (ISBN 0-8298-0460-9). Pilgrim NY.

Blue, Brian, jt. auth. see Strom, Yale.

Blue, Ken, jt. auth. see White, John.

Blue, Lionel. Bright Blue. 96p. 1985. 11.95 (ISBN 0-312-09626-7). St Martin.

Blue, Lionel & Rose, June. A Taste of Heaven: Adventures in Food & Faith. new ed. (Orig.). 1978. pap. 4.50 (ISBN 0-87243-077-4). Templegate.

Bluhm, Heinz. Luther Translator of Paul: Studies in Romans & Galatians. 580p. 1984. text ed. 49.80 bndg. text (ISBN 0-8204-0186-2). P Lang Pubs.

Blum, Jakub & Rich, Vera. The Image of the Jew in Soviet Literature. LC 84-12196. 276p. 1985. 25.00 (ISBN 0-88125-062-7). Ktav.

Blum, Lawrence. Friendship, Altruism & Morality. (International Library of Philosophy). 256p. 1980. 24.95x (ISBN 0-7100-0582-2); pap. 9.95x (ISBN 0-7100-9332-2). Methuen Inc.

Blum, Ralph. The Book of Runes: A Handbook for the Use of an Ancient Oracle-The Viking Runes. 1984. 22.95 (ISBN 0-312-08999-6). St Martin.

Blum, Virgil C. Freedom of Choice in Education. LC 77-8086. 1977. Repr. of 1958 ed. lib. bdg. 22.50x (ISBN 0-8371-9677-9, BLFC). Greenwood.

Blumanthal, David. Understanding Jewish Mysticism: The Philosophic-Mystical Tradition & the Hasidic Tradition, Vol.II. 20.00x (ISBN 0-87068-205-9); pap. 9.95 (ISBN 0-87068-225-3). Ktav.

Blumberg, Harry & Lewittes, Mordecai. Modern Hebrew: Ivrit Hayah, Vol. 1. 3rd ed. 449p. pap. 8.95x (ISBN 0-88482-718-6). Hebrew Pub.

Blume, Clemens, ed. Hymnodia Gotica. Repr. of 1909 ed. 60.00 ea. Vol. 1. (ISBN 0-384-04766-1); Vol. 2. (ISBN 0-384-04767-X). Johnson Repr.
--Thesauri Hymnologica Hymnarium, 2 Vols. Repr. of 1909 ed. 60.00 ea. Johnson Repr.
--Thesauri Hymnologica Prosarium, 2 Vols in 3. (Illus.). Repr. of 1922 ed. 60.00 ea. Johnson Repr.
--Tropi Graduales, 2 Vols. (Illus.). Repr. of 1906 ed. 60.00 ea. Johnson Repr.

Blume, Judy. Are You There God? It's Me, Margaret. 156p. 1986. pap. 2.50 (ISBN 0-440-90419-6, LFL). Dell.

Blumenberg, Hans. Work on Myth. Wallace, Robert M., tr. from Ger. (German Social Thought Ser.). 770p. 1985. text ed. 40.00x (ISBN 0-262-02215-X). MIT Pr.

Blumenberg, Rick. The Prayer Support System: A Plan to Strengthen the Local Church. LC 86-42933. 40p. (Orig.). 1986. pap. 4.00 (ISBN 0-937021-04-0). Sagamore Bks MI.

Blumenthal, D. R. Understanding Jewish Mysticism: A Source Reader, No. I. (Library of Judaic Learning). Vol. II. 20.00x (ISBN 0-87068-334-9); pap. 9.95. Ktav.

Blumenthal, David R. Approaches to Judaism in Medieval Times. LC 83-18886. (Brown Judaic Ser.). 188p. pap. 14.95 (ISBN 0-89130-659-5, 14 00 54). Scholars Pr GA.
--Approaches to Judaism in Medieval Times, Vol. II. (Brown Judaic Studies). 1985. 23.95 (ISBN 0-89130-848-2, 14-00-57); pap. 18.95 (ISBN 0-89130-849-0). Scholars Pr GA.
--The Place of Faith & Grace in Judaism. 29p. (Orig.). 1985. pap. 3.50 (ISBN 0-918873-03-7). Ctr Judaic-Christ Studies.

Blumenthal, David R., ed. And Bring Them Closer to Torah: The Life & Works of Rabbi Aaron H. Blumenthal. 235p. 1986. text ed. 9.95 (ISBN 0-88125-082-1). Ktav.
--Emory Studies on the Holocaust. LC 84-52494. 178p. (Orig.). 1985. pap. 5.00 (ISBN 0-912313-01-3). Witness Holocaust.

Blumenthal, Uta-Renate, ed. Carolingian Essays: Andrew W. Mellon Lectures in Early Christian Studies. LC 83-14562. 249p. 1983. 25.95x (ISBN 0-8132-0579-4). Cath U Pr.

Blumenthal, Warren B. The Creator & Man. LC 80-5843. 139p. 1980. lib. bdg. 20.50 (ISBN 0-8191-1340-9); pap. text ed. 9.50 (ISBN 0-8191-1341-7). U Pr of Amer.

Blumhardt, Christoph, jt. auth. see Blumhardt, Johann C.

Blumhardt, Christoph F., jt. auth. see Blumhardt, Johann C.

Blumhardt, Johann C. & Blumhardt, Christoph. Now Is Eternity. LC 76-10251. 1976. 4.00 (ISBN 0-87486-209-4); pap. 3.00 (ISBN 0-87486-219-1). Plough.

Blumhardt, Johann C. & Blumhardt, Christoph F. Thy Kingdom Come. Eller, Vernard, ed. LC 80-19328. (A Blumhardt Reader Ser.). 180p. 1980. text ed. 5.50 (ISBN 0-8028-3544-9, Pub. by Eerdmans). Plough.

Blumhofer, Edith W. The Assemblies of God: A Popular History. LC 85-70552. 160p. (Orig.). 1985. pap. 2.95 (ISBN 0-88243-469-1, 02-0469). Gospel Pub.

Blunden, Edmund. Edward Gibbon & His Age. 1978. Repr. of 1935 ed. lib. bdg. 12.50 (ISBN 0-8495-0448-1). Arden Lib.

Blunden, Edmund C. Edward Gibbon & His Age. LC 74-14702. 1974. Repr. of 1935 ed. lib. bdg. 7.50 (ISBN 0-8414-3287-2). Folcroft.

Blunt, Anne. Pilgrimage to Nejd, 2 vols. (Illus.). 1968. Repr. of 1881 ed. 85.00x (ISBN 0-7146-1979-5, F Cass Co). Biblio Dist.

Blunt, Anthony. Guide to Baroque Rome. LC 82-47546. (Icon Editions). (Illus.). 256p. 1982. 34.50i (ISBN 0-06-430395-0, HarpT). Har-Row.

Blunt, Hugh F. Great Magdelens. facs. ed. LC 71-86731. (Essay Index Reprint Ser). 1928. 18.50 (ISBN 0-8369-1122-9). Ayer Co Pubs.
--Great Penitents. facs. ed. LC 67-30198. (Essay Index Reprint Ser). 1921. 17.00 (ISBN 0-8369-0220-3). Ayer Co Pubs.

Blunt, J. H., ed. The Myroure of Oure Lady. (EETS, ES Ser.: No. 19). Repr. of 1873 ed. 40.00 (ISBN 0-527-00232-1). Kraus Repr.

Blunt, John H. Dictionary of Sects, Heresies, Ecclesiastical Parties & Schools of Religious Thought. LC 74-9653. 1974. Repr. of 1874 ed. 75.00x (ISBN 0-8103-3751-7). Gale.

Bluth, John V. Concordance to the Doctrine & Covenants. 10.95 (ISBN 0-87747-048-0). Deseret Bk.

Bly, Janet, jt. auth. see Bly, Stephen.

Bly, Stephen & Bly, Janet. Devotions with a Difference. LC 82-8304. 128p. 1982. pap. 5.95 (ISBN 0-8024-1789-2). Moody.
--Questions I'd Like to Ask. LC 82-2252. 1982. 3.50 (ISBN 0-8024-7058-0). Moody.

Blyth, R. H. Buddhist Sermons on Christian Texts. 1976. pap. 2.95 (ISBN 0-89346-000-1). Heian Intl.

Boa, Kenneth. Cults, World Religions, & You. 1977. pap. 6.95 (ISBN 0-88207-752-X). Victor Bks.

Boa, Kenneth & Anders, Max. Drawing Near with Daily Bible Readings & Prayer. 1987. 16.95. Nelson.

Boa, Kenneth & Moody, Larry. I'm Glad You Asked. 1982. pap. 6.95 (ISBN 0-88207-354-0). Victor Bks.

Boa, Kenneth & Proctor, William. The Return of the Star of Bethlehem. 224p. (Orig.). 1985. pap. 7.95 (ISBN 0-310-33631-7, 12770P). Zondervan.

Boa, Kenneth, jt. auth. see Wilkinson, Bruce.

Boadt, Lawrence. Jeremiah One to Twenty-Five. (Old Testament Message Ser.: Vol. 9). 1982. 15.95 (ISBN 0-89453-409-2); pap. 9.95 (ISBN 0-89453-262-6). M Glazier.
--Jeremiah Twenty-Six to Fifty-Two, Habakkuk, Zephaniah, Nahum. (Old Testament Message Ser.: Vol. 10). 1982. 15.95 (ISBN 0-89453-410-6); pap. 9.95 (ISBN 0-89453-244-8). M Glazier.
--Reading the Old Testament: An Introduction. LC 84-60723. 416p. (Orig.). 1984. pap. 7.95 (ISBN 0-8091-2631-1). Paulist Pr.

Boadt, Lawrence, et al, eds. Biblical Studies: Meeting Ground of Jews & Christians. LC 80-82812. (Stimulus Bk). 232p. (Orig.). 1981. pap. 7.95 (ISBN 0-8091-2344-4). Paulist Pr.

Boadt, Lawrence E. Introduction to Wisdom Literature, Proverbs. (Collegeville Bible Commentary: Old Testament Ser.: Vol. 18). 104p. 1986. pap. 2.95 (ISBN 0-8146-1475-2). Liturgical Pr.

Boardman, Elizabeth J. The Phoenix Trip: Notes on a Quaker Mission to Haiphong. LC 84-72319. (Illus.). 192p. 1985. pap. 9.95 (ISBN 0-914064-22-3). Celo Pr.

Boardman, George N. A History of New England Theology. Kuklick, Bruce, ed. (American Religious Thought of the 18th & 19th Centuries Ser.). 314p. 1987. lib. bdg. 45.00 (ISBN 0-8240-6955-2). Garland Pub.

Boardman, Lynda T. The Ministry of Teaching Toddlers. 92p. (Orig.). 1983. pap. 3.95 (ISBN 0-8341-0820-8). Beacon Hill.

--Tending & Teaching Babies. 83p. (Orig.). 1985. pap. 3.50 (ISBN 0-8341-1063-6). Beacon Hill.

Boardman, Robert. A Higher Honor. 197p. 1986. pap. 7.95 (ISBN 0-89109-552-7). NavPress.

Boardman, W. E. The Higher Christian Life. Dayton, Donald W., ed. (Higher Christian Life Ser.). 330p. 1985. PLB 40.00 (ISBN 0-8240-6406-2). Garland Pub.

Boas, Franz. Kwakiutl Culture As Reflected in Mythology. LC 36-6760. (American Folklore Society Memoirs). Repr. of 1935 ed. 19.00 (ISBN 0-527-01080-4). Kraus Repr.

--The Mythology of the Bella Coola Indians. LC 73-3510. (Jesup North Pacific Expedition. Publications: Vol. 1, Pt. 2). Repr. of 1898 ed. 20.00 (ISBN 0-404-58113-7). AMS Pr.

--Religion of the Kwakiutl Indians, 2 Vols. LC 72-82368. (Columbia Univ. Contributions to Anthropology Ser.: No. 10). Repr. of 1930 ed. Set. 60.00 (ISBN 0-404-50560-0); 30.00 ea. AMS Pr.

--The Social Organization & Secret Societies of the Kwakiutl Indians. Based on Personal Observations Notes Made by Mr. George Hunt. (Landmarks in Anthropology Ser). Repr. of 1897 ed. 60.00 (ISBN 0-384-04872-2). Johnson Repr.

--Tsimshian Mythology Based on Texts Recorded by Henry W. Tate. (Landmarks in Anthropology Ser.). (Illus.). Repr. of 1916 ed. 60.00 (ISBN 0-384-04880-3). Johnson Repr.

Boas, George. The Mind's Road to God: Bonaventura. 1953. pap. text ed. write for info. (ISBN 0-02-311250-6). Macmillan.

--Vox Populi: Essays in the History of an Idea. LC 69-13538. (Seminars in the History of Ideas Ser.). (Illus.). pap. 77.00 (ISBN 0-317-41626-X, 2025833). Bks Demand UMI.

Boas, George, tr. see Michaud, Regis.

Boas, Jacob. Boulevard des Miseres: The Story of Transit Camp Westerbork. LC 85-1435. (Illus.). 174p. 1985. lib. bdg. 22.50 (ISBN 0-208-01977-4, Archon Bks). Shoe String.

Boas, Simone B., tr. see Foucher, Alfred C.

Boase, Leonard S. Prayer of Faith. 1985. Repr. 5.95 (ISBN 0-8294-0493-7). Loyola.

Boase, Paul H. The Rhetoric of Christian Socialism. 9.00 (ISBN 0-8446-0501-8). Peter Smith.

Boatman, Don E. Helps from Hebrews. LC 75-1066. (The Bible Study Textbook Ser.). (Illus.). 1960. 14.30 (ISBN 0-89900-044-4). College Pr Pub.

Boatman, Don E. & Boles, Kenny. Galatians. rev. ed. LC 70-1141. (The Bible Study Textbook Ser.). (Illus.). 1976. 12.20 (ISBN 0-89900-039-8). College Pr Pub.

Boatman, Russel. What the Bible Says about End Time. 3rd ed. LC 79-56542. (What the Bible Says Ser.). 1980. 13.95 (ISBN 0-89900-075-4). College Pr Pub.

Boatman, Russell. What the Bible Says about the Church. (What the Bible Says Ser.). text ed. 13.95 (ISBN 0-89900-098-3). College Pr Pub.

Boatright, Mody C., ed. The Sky Is My Tipi. LC 49-1690. (Texas Folklore Society Publications: No. 22). (Illus.). 1966. Repr. of 1949 ed. 13.95 (ISBN 0-87074-010-5). SMU Press.

Bob & Couchman, Win. Ruth & Jonah: People in Process. (Carpenter Studyguide). 80p. 1983. saddle-stiched member's handbk. 1.95 (ISBN 0-87788-736-5); leader's handbook 2.95 (ISBN 0-87788-737-3). Shaw Pubs.

Bobango, Gerald J. Religion & Politics: Bishop Valerian Trifa & His Times. (East European Monograph: No. 92). 299p. 1981. 25.00x (ISBN 0-914710-86-9). East Eur Quarterly.

Bober, Harry, ed. see Male, Emile.

Bobgan, Deidre. Lord of the Dance: The Beauty of the Disciplined Life. 160p. (Orig.). 1987. pap. 5.95 (ISBN 0-89081-583-6). Harvest Hse.

Bobgan, Deidre, jt. auth. see Bobgan, Martin.

Bobgan, Martin & Bobgan, Deidre. How to Counsel from Scripture. 1985. pap. 8.95 (ISBN 0-8024-0373-5). Moody.

--Hypnosis & the Christian. LC 83-21401. 64p. (Orig.). 1984. pap. 2.95 (ISBN 0-87123-402-5, 210402). Bethany Hse.

--The Psychological Way: the Spiritual Way. LC 79-17884. 224p. 1979. pap. 6.95 (ISBN 0-87123-026-7, 210026). Bethany Hse.

Bobik, Joseph. Aquinas on Being & Essence: A Translation & Interpretation. LC 65-23516. pap. 75.50 (ISBN 0-317-26719-1, 2024364). Bks Demand UMI.

Bobosh, Theodore. Am I Saved? 1984. pap. 3.45 (ISBN 0-937032-38-7). Light&Life Pub Co MN.

Bobroff, Alvin & Krishnamurti, U. G. Mystique of Enlightenment. 190p. 1985. pap. 9.95 (ISBN 0-87418-020-1, 156). Coleman Pub.

Bock, Darrell L. Proclamation from Prophecy & Pattern: Lucan Old Testament Christiology. (JSOT Supplement Ser.: No. 12). 350p. 1986. text ed. 28.50x (ISBN 1-85075-000-9, Pub. by JSOT Pr England); pap. text ed. 13.50x (ISBN 1-85075-001-7). Eisenbrauns.

Bock, Emil. Moses: From the Egyptian Mysteries to the Judges of Israel. 208p. (Orig.). 1986. pap. 12.95 (ISBN 0-89281-117-X). Inner Tradit.

Bock, Felicia G. Classical Learning & Taoist Practices in Early Japan, with Translation of Books XVI & XX of the Engi-Shiki. Bock, Felicia G., tr. from Japanese. & intro. by. LC 82-84464. (Occasional Paper Arizona State Univ., Center for Asian Studies: No. 17). 102p. 1985. pap. 8.00 (ISBN 0-939252-13-9). ASU Ctr Asian.

Bock, Fred & Leech, Bryan J., eds. The Hymnal Companion. 1979. 12.95 (ISBN 0-89477-004-7). Paragon Benson.

--Hymns for the Family of God. 1976. 7.95 (ISBN 0-89477-000-4, Dist. by Alexandria House); looseleaf 6.95 (ISBN 0-89477-002-0); pap. 7.95 (ISBN 0-89477-001-2). Paragon Benson.

Bock, Janet L. The Jesus Mystery: Of Lost Years & Unknown Travels. LC 80-67420. (Illus.). 231p. (Orig.). 1980. pap. 6.95 (ISBN 0-937736-00-7). Aura Bks.

Bockelman, A. E. Practical Guide for Altar Guilds. LC 62-16936. (Illus., Orig.). 1962. pap. 4.95 (ISBN 0-8066-0223-6, 10-5050). Augsburg.

Bockelman, Wilfred, ed. Tapestry. 128p. (Orig.). 1985. pap. 3.95 (ISBN 0-8066-2177-X, 10-6201). Augsburg.

Bockemuhl, Jochen, et al. Toward a Phenomenology of the Etheric World: Investigations into the Life of Nature & Man. Gardner, Malcolm, et al, eds. Meeks, John, tr. from Ger. (Illus.). 200p. (Orig.). 1985. pap. 16.95 (ISBN 0-88010-115-6). Anthroposophic.

Bocking, Ronald. History of the London Missionary Society. 256p. 1986. 59.00x (ISBN 0-317-54254-0, Pub. by Elmcrest UK). State Mutual Bk.

Bockl, George. How to Find Something Big to Live for: A Spirital Odyssey. 193p. (Orig.). 1984. pap. 7.95 (ISBN 0-942494-83-0). Coleman Pub.

Bockle, Franz. War, Poverty, Freedom: The Christian Response. (Concilium Ser.: Vol. 15). 7.95 (ISBN 0-8091-0154-8). Paulist Pr.

Bockle, Franz & Beemer, Theo. Dilemmas of Tomorrow's World. LC 78-86974. (Concilium Ser.: No. 45). 188p. 1965. 7.95 (ISBN 0-8091-0030-4). Paulist Pr.

Bockle, Franz, ed. Moral Problems & Christian Personalism. LC 65-24045. (Concilium Ser.: Vol. 5). 191p. 7.95 (ISBN 0-8091-0099-1). Paulist Pr.

--Social Message of the Gospels. LC 68-31249. (Concilium Ser.: Vol. 35). 188p. 7.95 (ISBN 0-8091-0138-6). Paulist Pr.

--Understanding the Signs of the Times. LC 67-25694. (Concilium Ser.: Vol. 25). 176p. 1967. 7.95 (ISBN 0-8091-0152-1). Paulist Pr.

Bockmuehl, Klaus, ed. see Scott, Waldron.

Boddy, A. A. To Kairwan the Holy. 320p. 1985. 49.00x (ISBN 0-317-39199-2, Pub. by Luzac & Co Ltd). State Mutual Bk.

Bode, Carl, ed. see Emerson, Ralph Waldo.

Bode, Frederick A. Protestantism & the New South: North Carolina Baptists & Methodists in Political Crisis, 1894-1903. LC 75-1289. 171p. 1975. 15.00x (ISBN 0-8139-0597-4). U Pr of Va.

Bode, Mabel H. The Pali Literature of Burma. LC 77-87008. Repr. of 1909 ed. 15.00 (ISBN 0-404-16796-9). AMS Pr.

Boden, Evan H. Guide for the Lay Preacher. 1979. pap. 2.95 (ISBN 0-8170-0836-5). Judson.

Boden, Robert. Teen Talks with God. 1980. pap. 3.50 (ISBN 0-570-03812-X, 12-2921). Concordia.

Bodenstedt, Mary I. Praying the Life of Christ. Hogg, James, ed. (Analecta Cartusiana Ser.: No. 15). 184p. (Orig.). 1983. pap. 25.00 (ISBN 3-7052-0017-8, Pub by Salzburg Studies). Longwood Pub Group.

Bodger, Lorraine. Christmas Tree Ornaments. LC 84-52753. (Illus.). 168p. 1985. write for info. (ISBN 0-02-496740-8, Pub by Sedgewood Press). Macmillan.

Bodhi, Bhikkhu, ed. see Thera, Nyanaponika.

Bodin, J. Selected Writings on Philosophy, Religion & Politics. Rose, Paul L., ed. xiv, 94p. (Orig.). 1980. pap. text ed. 18.50x (Pub. by Droz Switzerland). Coronet Bks.

Bodin, Jean. Colloquium of the Seven About Secrets of the Sublime. Daniels, Marion L., tr. from Lat. & intro. by. LC 73-2453. 480p. 1975. 63.00x (ISBN 0-691-07193-4). Princeton U Pr.

Bodine, Walter R. The Greek Text of Judges: Recensional Developments. LC 80-12578. (Harvard Semitic Monographs: No. 23). 15.00x (ISBN 0-89130-400-2, 04-00-23). Scholars Pr GA.

Bodkin, Maud. Studies of Type-Images in Poetry, Religion & Philosophy. LC 74-14665. 1951. lib. bdg. 15.00 (ISBN 0-8414-3273-2). Folcroft.

Bodley, Ronald V. Messenger: The Life of Mohammed. LC 70-92296. Repr. of 1946 ed. lib. bdg. 35.00x (ISBN 0-8371-2423-9, BOTM). Greenwood.

Bodo, John R. Protestant Clergy & Public Issues, Eighteen Twelve to Eighteen Forty-Eight. LC 79-12849. (Perspectives in American History Ser: No. 52). 1980. Repr. of 1954 ed. lib. bdg. 27.50x (ISBN 0-87991-854-3). Porcupine Pr.

Bodo, Murray. Francis: The Journey & the Dream. (Illus.). 1972. pap. 2.95 (ISBN 0-912228-07-5). St Anthony Mess Pr.

--Jesus: A Disciple's Search. 1987. pap. 5.95. St Anthony Mess Pr.

--Juniper: Friend of Francis, Fool of God. 90p. pap. text ed. cancelled (ISBN 0-86716-021-7). St Anthony Mess Pr.

--Song of the Sparrow: Meditations & Poems to Pray by. (Illus.). 187p. (Orig.). 1976. pap. 3.95 (ISBN 0-912228-26-1). St Anthony Mess Pr.

--Through the Year with Francis of Assisi: Daily Meditations from His Words & Life. LC 87-4158. (Illus.). 240p. 1987. pap. 7.95 (ISBN 0-385-23823-1, Im). Doubleday.

--Way of St. Francis: The Challenge of Franciscan Spirituality for Everyone. LC 83-14066. 192p. 1984. 12.95 (ISBN 0-385-19073-5). Doubleday.

--The Way of St. Francis: The Challenge of Franciscan Spirituality for Everyone. LC 83-14066. 1985. 6.95 (ISBN 0-385-19913-9, Im). Doubleday.

Boece, Hector. Hectoris Boetii Murthlacensium Et Aberdonensium Episcoporum Vitae, Iterum in Lucem Editae. LC 76-39462. (Bannatyne Club, Edinburgh. Publications: No. 11). Repr. of 1825 ed. 20.00 (ISBN 0-404-52711-6). AMS Pr.

Boedeker, Deborah. Descent from Heaven: Images of Dew in Greek Poetry & Religion. (American Philological Association, American Classical Studies: No. 13). 154p. 1985. pap. 11.95 (ISBN 0-89130-807-5, 40 04 13). Scholars Pr GA.

Boehlke, Neal A. Man Who Met Jesus at Bethesda. (Arch Bk.). 1981. pap. 0.99 (ISBN 0-570-06143-1, 59-1260). Concordia.

Boehm, Barbara D., tr. see Grodecki, Louis & Brisac, Catherine.

Boehme, Jacob. A Discourse Between Two Souls. pap. 3.95 (ISBN 0-916411-89-3). Sure Fire.

--Jacob Boehme's "The Way to Christ". Stoudt, John J., tr. LC 78-13976. 1979. Repr. of 1947 ed. lib. bdg. 22.50x (ISBN 0-313-21075-6, BOTW). Greenwood.

--Of Heaven & Hell: A Dialogue Between Junius, a Scholar & Theophorus, His Master. 1986. pap. 3.95 (ISBN 0-916411-53-2). Sure Fire.

--Of the Supersensual Life. pap. 4.95 (ISBN 0-916411-90-7). Sure Fire.

--Signature of All Things: & Other Writings. 307p. 1969. pap. 12.95 (ISBN 0-227-67733-1). Attic Pr.

Boehme, Jakob. The Confessions. 69.95 (ISBN 0-87968-258-2). Gordon Pr.

--Works of Jakob Boehme, 4 vols. 1974. lib. bdg. 1500.00 (ISBN 0-87968-465-8). Gordon Pr.

Boehmer, Eduard. Bibliotheca Wiffeniana: Bibliotheca Wiffeniana: Spanish Reformers of Two Centuries from Fifteen Twenty, 3 Vols. 1964. Repr. of 1904 ed. Set. 62.00 (ISBN 0-8337-0330-7). B Franklin.

Boehmer, H. The Jesuits. 69.95 (ISBN 0-87968-199-3). Gordon Pr.

Boehmer, Heinrich. Luther & the Reformation in the Light of Modern Research. LC 83-45639. Date not set. Repr. of 1930 ed. 44.50 (ISBN 0-404-19823-6). AMS Pr.

--Luther in the Light of Recent Research. 1977. lib. bdg. 59.95 (ISBN 0-8490-2189-8). Gordon Pr.

Boehner, Philotheus. Conferences for Franciscan Religious. (Spirit & Life Ser). 1966. 2.00 (ISBN 0-686-11571-6). Franciscan Inst.

--Itinerarium Mentis in Deum. (Works of Saint Bonaventure Ser). 1956. 3.50 (ISBN 0-686-11591-0). Franciscan Inst.

--Walter Burleigh De Puritate Artis Logicae Tractus Langios. Incl. Tractatus Brevior. (Text Ser). 1955. 6.00 (ISBN 0-686-17965-X). Franciscan Inst.

Boehner, Philotheus & Buytaert, Eligius M. Collected Articles on Ockham. (Philosophy Ser). 1958. 23.00 (ISBN 0-686-11542-2). Franciscan Inst.

Boehner, Philotheus, ed. The Tractatus De Successivis Attributed to William Ockham. (Philosophy Ser). 1944. 8.00 (ISBN 0-686-11531-7). Franciscan Inst.

Boehner, Philotheus & Brown, Stephen, eds. Guillelmi de Ockham: Opera Philosophica, Vol. 2. 1978. 40.00 (ISBN 0-686-27930-1). Franciscan Inst.

Boehner, Philotheus, et al, eds. Guillelmi de Ockham: Opera Philosophica, Vol. 1, Summa Philosophica. 1974. 52.00 (ISBN 0-686-11530-9). Franciscan Inst.

Boelhower, Gary, et al. Let Us Give Thanks: Meal Prayers for All Occasions. 42p. (Orig.). 1986. pap. 3.00 (ISBN 0-937997-04-8). Hi-Time Pub.

Boelhower, Gary J. Sacred Times, Timeless Seasons. (Illus.). 76p. 1986. pap. 6.95 (ISBN 0-937997-05-6). Hi-Time Pub.

Boenig, Robert. Biblical Commentaries by Richard Rolle. Hogg, James, ed. (Elizabethan & Renaissance Studies). (Orig.). 1984. pap. 15.00 (ISBN 0-317-40122-X, Pub. by Salzburg Studies). Longwood Pub Group.

Boenzi, Joe, tr. see Aubry, Joseph.

Boer, Charles, tr. from Gr. The Homeric Hymns. rev. ed. (Dunquin Ser.: No. 10). vi, 182p. 1970. pap. 11.50 (ISBN 0-88214-210-0). Spring Pubns.

Boer, Harry R. The Doctrine of Reprobation in the Christian Reformed Church. LC 83-1602. Repr. of 1983 ed. 23.50 (2027537). Bks Demand UMI.

--The Four Gospels & Acts: A Short Introduction. 112p. 1982. pap. 3.95 (ISBN 0-8028-1901-X). Eerdmans.

--A Short History of the Early Church. LC 75-25742. pap. 6.95 (ISBN 0-8028-1339-9). Eerdmans.

Boer, Tjitze J. De. The History of Philosophy in Islam. LC 70-131638. 216p. 1903. Repr. 39.00x (ISBN 0-403-00525-6). Scholarly.

Boerma, Conrad. The Rich, the Poor & the Bible. rev. ed. Bowden, John, tr. from Dutch. LC 80-15337. 120p. 1980. pap. 5.95 (ISBN 0-664-24349-5). Westminster.

Boers, Hendrikus. What Is New Testament Theology? The Rise of Criticism & the Problem of a Theology of the New Testament. Via, Dan O., Jr., ed. LC 79-7372. (Guides to Biblical Scholarship: New Testament Ser.). 96p. 1979. pap. 4.50 (ISBN 0-8006-0466-0, 1-466). Fortress.

Boerstler, Richard W. Letting Go: A Holistic & Meditative Approach to Living & Dying. LC 81-71653. (Illus.). 112p. (Orig.). 1982. pap. 3.95 (ISBN 0-9607928-0-5). Assocs Thanatology.

Boesak, Allan. The Finger of God: Sermons on Faith & Socio-Political Responsibility. Randall, Peter, tr. from Afrikaans. LC 81-16943. Tr. of Die Vinger Van God. 112p. (Orig.). 1982. pap. 5.95 (ISBN 0-88344-135-7). Orbis Bks.

--Walking on Thorns: The Call to Christian Obedience. 80p. (Orig.). 1984. pap. 4.95 (ISBN 0-8028-0041-6). Eerdmans.

Boesak, Allan A. Black & Reformed: Apartheid, Liberation, & the Calvinist Tradition. LC 84-7212. 192p. (Orig.). 1984. pap. 8.95 (ISBN 0-88344-148-9). Orbis Bks.

--Comfort & Protest. LC 86-28076. 120p. (Orig.). 1987. pap. 7.95 (ISBN 0-664-24602-8). Westminster.

Boesak, Allan A. & Villa-Vicencio, Charles, eds. When Prayer Makes News. 192p. (Orig.). 1986. pap. 10.95 (ISBN 0-664-24035-6). Westminster.

Boeschemeyer, Uwe. Die Sinnfrage in Psychotherapie und Theologie: Die Existenzanalyse und Logotherapie Viktor E. Frankls aus theologischer Sicht. (Theologische Bibliothek Toepelmann Ser.: Vol. 32). 1977. 22.80x (ISBN 3-11-006727-7). De Gruyter.

Boethius. The Consolation of Philosophy. Green, Richard H., tr. LC 62-11788. 1962. pap. 5.44 scp (ISBN 0-672-60273-3, LLA86). Bobbs.

--Consolation of Philosophy. Buchanan, James J., ed. LC 57-8649. (Milestones of Thought Ser.). 7.00 (ISBN 0-8044-5149-4); pap. 3.95 (ISBN 0-8044-6057-4). Ungar.

--Theological Tractates. Bd. with Consolation of Philosophy. (Loeb Classical Library: No. 74). 13.95x (ISBN 0-674-99083-8). Harvard U Pr.

Boetie, Etienne de la see La Boetie, Etienne.

Boettner, Loraine. The Christian Attitude Toward War. 104p. 1986. pap. 3.95 (ISBN 0-87552-118-5). Presby & Reformed.

--A Harmony of the Gospels. 1976. pap. 3.95 (ISBN 0-87552-132-0). Presby & Reformed.

--Immortality. 1956. 4.50 (ISBN 0-87552-127-4). Presby & Reformed.

--Reformed Doctrine of Predestination. 1932. 7.95x (ISBN 0-87552-129-0). Presby & Reformed.

--Roman Catholicism. 8.95 (ISBN 0-8010-0685-6). Baker Bk.

--Roman Catholicism. 1962. 8.95 (ISBN 0-87552-130-4). Presby & Reformed.

--Studies in Theology. 1947. 7.95 (ISBN 0-87552-131-2). Presby & Reformed.

Boever, Richard A. Cameos of Church History. 64p. 1986. pap. 1.95 (ISBN 0-89243-249-7). Liguori Pubns.

Boevey, Mateo C. Twenty Holy Hours. 1978. pap. 5.00 (ISBN 0-8198-0563-7). Dghtrs St Paul.

Boewering, Gerhard. The Mystical Vision of Existence in Classical Islam. (Studien zur Sprache, Geschichte und Kultur des islamischen Orients, Beihefte zur "der Islam"). 296p. 1979. text ed. 70.50x (ISBN 3-11-007546-6). De Gruyter.

Boff, Clodovis. Feet-on-the-Ground Theology: Pastoral Ministry in Western Brazil. Berryman, Phillip, tr. from Port. 288p. (Orig.). 1987. 19.95 (ISBN 0-88344-579-4); pap. 8.95 (ISBN 0-88344-554-9). Orbis Bks.

--Theology & Praxis: Epistemological Foundations. Barr, Robert R., tr. LC 86-21671. Tr. of Teologia e Pratica: Teologia do Politico e Suas Mediacoes. (Port.). 416p. (Orig.). 1987. pap. 19.95 (ISBN 0-88344-416-X). Orbis Bks.

Boff, Clodovis & Boff, Leonardo. Salvation & Liberation: In Search of a Balance Between Faith & Politics. Barr, Robert R., tr. from Port. LC 84-7220. Tr. of Da Liberatacas. 128p. (Orig.). 1984. pap. 6.95 (ISBN 0-88344-451-8). Orbis Bks.

Boff, Clodovis, jt. auth. see Boff, Leonardo.

Boff, Leonard. Option for the Poor: Challenge to the Reich. Elizondo, Virgil, ed. (Concilium Nineteen Eighty-Six Ser.). 120p. 1986. pap. 6.95 (ISBN 0-567-30067-6, Pub. by T & T Clark Ltd UK). Fortress.

Boff, Leonardo. Church, Charism, Power. 1986. pap. 10.95 (ISBN 0-8245-0726-6). Crossroad NY.

--Ecclesiogenesis: The Base Communities Reinvent the Church. Barr, Robert R., tr. from Port. LC 85-15600. 128p. (Orig.). 1986. pap. 9.95 (ISBN 0-88344-214-0). Orbis Bks.

--Jesus Christ Liberator: A Critical Christology for Our Time. Hughes, Patrick, tr. from Portuguese. LC 78-969. Tr. of Jesus Cristo Libertador Ensaio de Crista logia Critica para o nosso Tempo. 335p. (Orig.). 1978. pap. 9.95 (ISBN 0-88344-236-1). Orbis Bks.

--Liberating Grace. Drury, John, tr. from Port. LC 79-4206. Tr. of A graca libertadoro no mundo. 256p. (Orig.). 1979. pap. 9.95 (ISBN 0-88344-282-5). Orbis Bks.

--The Lord's Prayer: The Prayer of Integral Liberation. Morrow, Theodore, tr. from Portuguese. LC 82-18811. Tr. of O Pai-nosso: A Oracao da Libertacao. 144p. (Orig.). 1983. pap. 6.95 (ISBN 0-88344-299-X). Orbis Bks.

--Passion of Christ, Passion of the World: The Facts, Their Interpretation & Their Meaning Yesterday & Today. Barr, Robert R., tr. from Port. 160p. (Orig.). 1987. 19.95 (ISBN 0-88344-564-6); pap. 9.95 (ISBN 0-88344-563-8). Orbis Bks.

--Saint Francis: A Model for Human Liberation. 192p. 1984. pap. 9.95 (ISBN 0-8245-0671-5). Crossroad NY.

--The Way of the Cross: Way of Justice. Drury, John, tr. from Port. LC 79-23776. Tr. of Via-Sacra Da Justica. 144p. (Orig.). 1980. pap. 4.95 (ISBN 0-88344-701-0). Orbis Bks.

Boff, Leonardo & Boff, Clodovis. Introducing Liberation Theology. Burns, Paul, tr. from Port. LC 87-5672. Tr. of Como Fazer Teologia da Libertacao. 112p. (Orig.). 1987. 16.95 (ISBN 0-88344-575-1); pap. 7.95 (ISBN 0-88344-550-6). Orbis Bks.

--Liberation Theology: From Dialogue to Confrontation. 120p. (Orig.). 1986. pap. 8.95 (ISBN 0-86683-528-8, HarpR). Har-Row.

Boff, Leonardo, jt. auth. see Boff, Clodovis.

Boff, Leonardo & Elizondo, Virgil, eds. La Iglesia Popular: Between Fear & Hope, Vol. 176. (Concilium Ser.). 128p. 1984. pap. 6.95 (ISBN 0-567-30056-0, Pub. by T & T Clark Ltd UK). Fortress.

Bogan, Mary Inez. Vocabulary & Style of the Soliloquies & Dialogues of St. Augustine, Vol. 42. (Patristic Studies). 238p. 1984. Repr. of 1935 ed. 28.00x (ISBN 0-939738-27-9). Zubal Inc.

Bogart, John L. Orthodox & Heretical Perfectionism in the Johannine Community As Evident in the First Epistle of John. LC 77-5447. (Society of Biblical Literature. Dissertation Ser.). 1977. pap. 9.95 (ISBN 0-89130-138-0, 060133). Scholars Pr GA.

Bogart, Shirley. The New Jewish Homemaker: A Treasury of Tips, Crafts, Foods & Stories. 256p. 16.95t (ISBN 0-940646-20-X). Rossel Bks.

Bogdanos, Theodore. Pearl, Image of the Ineffable: A Study in Medieval Poetic Symbolism. LC 82-42783. 184p. 1983. 22.50x (ISBN 0-271-00339-1). Pa St U Pr.

Boger, Ann C. & DeOreo, Joellen K. Sacred India: Hinduism, Buddhism, Jainism. LC 85-19559. (Illus.). 60p. 1986. pap. 7.95 (ISBN 0-910386-84-6, Pub. by Cleveland Mus Art). Ind U Pr.

Boggs, Sue H. The Secret of Hind's Feet. 2.95 (ISBN 0-89137-537-6). Quality Pubns.

Bogle, Kate C., jt. auth. see Cutler, Katherine N.

Bogolepov, Alexander. Church Reforms in Russia, 1905-1918. 59p. 1966. pap. 1.95 (ISBN 0-913836-01-X). St Vladimirs.

--Orthodox Hymns of Christmas, Easter, & Holy Week. LC 65-16177. 78p. 1965. pap. 1.95 (ISBN 0-913836-02-8). St Vladimirs.

Bogorodskii, N. The Doctrine of St. John Damascene on the Procession of the Holy Spirit. LC 80-2351. Tr. of Uchenie Sv. Ioann Damaskina Ob' Iskhozhdenii Sv. Dukha. Repr. of 1879 ed. 28.50 (ISBN 0-404-18903-2). AMS Pr.

Bogot, Howard. Yoni. 1982. pap. 4.00 (ISBN 0-686-82564-0). UAHC.

Bogot, Howard, jt. auth. see Kipper, Lenore.

Bogue, Robert H. The Dawn of Christianity. 1985. 15.00 (ISBN 0-533-06545-3). Vantage.

Bohannon, Cynthia. The North & South Nodes: The Guideposts of the Spirit. LC 79-55867. 1979. pap. 4.95 (ISBN 0-932782-02-7). Arthur Pubns.

Bohlen, John R. How to Rule the World: Seek First the Kingdom of God. LC 81-90513. (Illus.). 271p. 1982. pap. 3.95 (ISBN 0-9607702-0-8). Kingdom God.

Bohman, James, tr. see Peukert, Helmut.

Bohn, Carol & Getz, Lorine, eds. A Registry of Women in Religious Studies, 1981-1982. (Bohn Ser.). 1981. 9.95 (ISBN 0-88946-277-1). E Mellen.

Bohn, Henry G. Polyglot of Foreign Proverbs. LC 68-55796. (Bohn's Antiquarian Library Ser.). Repr. of 1857 ed. 12.50 (ISBN 0-404-50004-8). AMS Pr.

Bohn, Henry G., ed. Polyglot of Foreign Proverbs - with English Translations. LC 67-23915. (Polyglot Ser.). 1968. Repr. of 1857 ed. 40.00x (ISBN 0-8103-3197-7). Gale.

Bohr, Paul R. Famine in China & the Missionary: Timothy Richard As Relief Administrator & Advocate of National Reform, 1876-1884. LC 72-75828. (East Asian Monographs Ser: No. 48). (Illus.). 1972. pap. 11.00x (ISBN 0-674-29425-4). Harvard U Pr.

Boice, J. Montgomery. God & History. LC 80-24457. (Foundations of the Christian Faith: Vol 4). 292p. (Orig.). 1981. pap. 7.95 (ISBN 0-87784-746-0). Inter-Varsity.

Boice, James M. The Christ of Christmas. 1983. 9.95 (ISBN 0-8024-0337-9). Moody.

--Christ's Call to Discipleship. 1986. text ed. 9.95 (ISBN 0-8024-1397-8). Moody.

--The Epistles of John. 224p. 1983. pap. 7.95 (ISBN 0-310-21531-5, 10421). Zondervan.

--Foundations of the Christian Faith. 2nd ed. 782p. pap. 24.95 (ISBN 0-87784-991-9). Inter-Varsity.

--Genesis, Vol. I. 352p. 1982. Chapter 1-11. 16.95 (ISBN 0-310-21540-4, 10486). Zondervan.

--Genesis: An Expositional Commentary, Vol. 2. 352p. 1985. 16.95 (ISBN 0-310-21560-9, 10487). Zondervan.

--The Gospel of John. 1986. 34.95 (ISBN 0-310-21570-6, 10429). Zondervan.

--How to Live the Christian Life. LC 81-18839. 128p. 1982. pap. 5.95 (ISBN 0-8024-3666-8). Moody.

--The Minor Prophets: An Expositional Commentary (Hosea-Jonah, Vol. 1. 272p. 1983. 12.95 (ISBN 0-310-21550-1, 10423). Zondervan.

--The Minor Prophets: An Expositional Commenatry (Micah-Malachi, Vol. 2. 1986. 14.95 (ISBN 0-310-21580-3, 10424). Zondervan.

--Ordinary Men Called by God: Abraham, Moses, & David. 160p. 1982. pap. 5.95 (ISBN 0-88207-224-2). Victor Bks.

--The Parables of Jesus. 1983. pap. 6.95 (ISBN 0-8024-0163-5). Moody.

--Philippians: An Expositional Commentary. 320p. 1982. pap. 10.95 (ISBN 0-310-21501-3, 10310). Zondervan.

--The Sermon on the Mount. LC 72-83882. 256p. 1972. 14.95 (ISBN 0-310-21510-2). Zondervan.

--The Sovereign God. LC 77-14879. (Foundations of the Christian Faith: Vol. 1). 1978. pap. 7.95 (ISBN 0-87784-743-6). Inter-Varsity.

--Standing on the Rock: The Importance of Biblical Inerrancy. (Orig.). 1984. leader's guide 2.95 (ISBN 0-8423-6604-0); pap. 4.95 (ISBN 0-8423-6603-2). Tyndale.

--Witness & the Revelation in the Gospel of John. 192p. 1970. pap. 4.95 (ISBN 0-85364-099-8). Attic Pr.

Boisard, Marcel. Humanism in Islam. Al-Jarrahi, Abdussamad, tr. from Fr. LC 82-70456. 200p. (Orig.). Date not set. pap. 8.00 (ISBN 0-89259-035-1). Am Trust Pubns.

Boisen, Anton T. Exploration of the Inner World: A Study of Mental Disorder and Religious Experience. 1971. pap. 12.95x (ISBN 0-8122-1020-4, Pa Paperbks). U of Pa Pr.

Boisen, Anton T. & Leary, John. Religion in Crisis & Custom: A Sociological & Psychological Study. LC 72-10977. 271p. 1973. Repr. of 1955 ed. lib. bdg. 22.50x (ISBN 0-8371-6642-X, BORC). Greenwood.

Boissiere, Robert. Meditations With the Hopi. LC 86-70257. (Meditations With Ser.). (Illus.). 144p. (Orig.). 1986. pap. 6.95 (ISBN 0-939680-27-0). Bear & Co.

Boissonet, V. D. Dictionnaire Dogmatique, Moral, Historique, Canonique, Liturgigue et Disciplinaire des Decrets des Diverse Congregations Romaines. Migne, J. P., ed. (Nouvelle Encyclopedie Theologique Ser.: Vol. 26). (Fr.). 646p. Repr. of 1852 ed. lib. bdg. 82.50x (ISBN 0-89241-269-0). Caratzas.

Boiter, Albert. Religion in the Soviet Union. (The Washington Papers: Vol. VIII, No. 78). 88p. (Orig.). 1980. pap. text ed. 7.95 (ISBN 0-8191-6022-9, Pub. by CSIS). U Pr of Amer.

Bojorge, Horacio. The Image of Mary: According to the Evangelists. Owen, Aloysius, tr. from Span. LC 77-15516. (Illus.). 1978. pap. 4.00 (ISBN 0-8189-0362-7). Alba.

Bok, Sissela, jt. ed. see Callahan, Daniel.

Bokenkotter, Thomas. A Concise History of the Catholic Church. LC 78-20269. 1979. pap. 6.50 (ISBN 0-385-13015-5, Im). Doubleday.

--Essential Catholicism: Dynamics of Faith & Belief. LC 86-4390. 456p. 1986. pap. 9.95 (ISBN 0-385-23243-8, Im). Doubleday.

Bokenkotter, Thomas, tr. Essential Catholicism. LC 84-13631. 432p. 1985. 19.95 (ISBN 0-385-18357-7). Doubleday.

Bokser, Baruch M. History of Judaism: The Next Ten Years. Neusner, Jacob, ed. LC 80-25501. (Brown Judaic Studies). 1980. 15.00 (ISBN 0-89130-450-9, 14-00-21); pap. 10.50 (ISBN 0-89130-451-7). Scholars Pr GA.

--Post Mishnaic Judaism in Transition: Samuel in Berakhot & the Beginnings of Gemara. LC 80-19702. (Brown Judaic Studies). 543p. 1980. 19.50 (ISBN 0-89130-432-0, 14 00 17); pap. 15.00 (ISBN 0-89130-433-9). Scholars Pr GA.

Bokser, Ben. Hasiddur: The Prayer Book. 842p. 1957. pap. 9.00 pocket flexible ed. (ISBN 0-88482-069-6). Hebrew Pub.

Bokser, Ben Z. Pharisaic Judaism in Transition. LC 73-2189. (The Jewish People; History, Religion, Literature Ser.). Repr. of 1935 ed. 18.00 (ISBN 0-405-05255-3). Ayer Co Pubs.

Bokser, Ben Z., tr. Minhah & Maariv Service. 45p. 1958. pap. 1.50 (ISBN 0-88482-125-0). Hebrew Pub.

Bokser, Ben Z., tr. from Hebrew. The Prayer Book. 430p. 1983. pap. text ed. 11.95 (ISBN 0-87441-372-9). Behrman.

Bokser, Ben-Zion. The Gifts of Life & Love. 193p. 1975. 7.00 (ISBN 0-88482-894-8). Hebrew Pub.

Bokser, Ben Zion. Judaism & Modern Man. 153p. 1958. 5.95 (ISBN 0-8022-0148-2). Philos Lib.

Bokser, Ben Zion, tr. Abraham Isaac Kook: The Lights of Penitance, Lights of Holiness. the Moral Principles. Essays, Letters & Poems. LC 78-70465. (Classics of Western Spirituality Ser.). 448p. 1978. 13.95 (ISBN 0-8091-0278-1); pap. 10.95 (ISBN 0-8091-2159-X). Paulist Pr.

Boland, T. P. James Duhig. LC 86-15654. (Illus.). 435p. 1987. text ed. 37.50x (ISBN 0-7022-2011-6). U of Queensland Pr.

Bolchazy, Ladislaus J., ed. A Concordance to the Utopia of St. Thomas More & a Frequency Word List. 388p. 1978. lib. bdg. 40.00x (ISBN 3-487-06514-2, Pub. by G Olms BRD). Coronet Bks.

Bolding, Amy. Cheerful Devotions to Give. (Amy Bolding Library). 96p. 1984. pap. 4.50 (ISBN 0-8010-0868-9). Baker Bk.

--Dynamic Fingertip Devotions. (Paperback Program Ser). 1977. pap. 3.95 (ISBN 0-8010-0708-9). Baker Bk.

--Easy Devotions to Give. (Paperback Program Ser.). 96p. (Orig.). 1981. pap. 3.95 (ISBN 0-8010-0794-1). Baker Bk.

--Fingertip Devotions. 1970. 3.95 (ISBN 0-8010-0798-4). Baker Bk.

--I'll Be Glad to Give a Devotion. (Paperback Program Ser). 1978. pap. 3.95 (ISBN 0-8010-0709-7). Baker Bk.

--Inspiring Devotions for Church Groups. 144p. 1985. pap. 4.95 (ISBN 0-8010-0889-1). Baker Bk.

--Installation Services for All Groups. 1984. pap. 4.95 (ISBN 0-8010-0863-8). Baker Bk.

--Please Give a Devotion. 1963. 3.95 (ISBN 0-8010-0819-0). Baker Bk.

--Please Give a Devotion for Active Teens. (Direction Bks). 1974. pap. 3.95 (ISBN 0-8010-0827-1). Baker Bk.

--Please Give a Devotion for All Occasions. 1967. pap. 4.45 (ISBN 0-8010-0519-1). Baker Bk.

--Please Give a Devotion for Church Groups. (Paperback Program Ser.). pap. 3.95 (ISBN 0-8010-0623-6). Baker Bk.

--Please Give a Devotion: For Women's Groups. (Paperback Program Ser.). 108p. 1976. pap. 3.95 (ISBN 0-8010-0583-3). Baker Bk.

--Please Plan a Program. (Paperback Program Ser). (Orig.). 1971. pap. 3.95 (ISBN 0-8010-0527-2). Baker Bk.

--Simple Welcome Speeches & Other Helps. (Pocket Pulpit Library). 1973. pap. 4.50 (ISBN 0-8010-0612-0). Baker Bk.

--Stimulating Devotions for Church Groups. 144p. 1986. pap. 4.95 (ISBN 0-8010-0921-9). Baker Bk.

--Words of Comfort. (Bolding Library). 132p. 1984. pap. 3.95 (ISBN 0-8010-0860-3). Baker Bk.

--Words of Welcome. (Preaching Helps Ser.). (Orig.). 1965. pap. 4.50 (ISBN 0-8010-0550-7). Baker Bk.

Boles, Donald E. Bible, Religion & the Public Schools. 3rd ed. 408p. 1965. 8.95x (ISBN 0-8138-0200-8). Iowa St U Pr.

Boles, H. Leo. Eldership of the Churches of Christ. 1978. pap. 1.50 (ISBN 0-89225-179-4). Gospel Advocate.

--The Holy Spirit. 10.95 (ISBN 0-89225-102-6). Gospel Advocate.

--Questions & Answers: Sermon Outlines & Bible Study Notes. 1985. pap. 8.95 (ISBN 0-89225-274-X). Gospel Advocate.

Boles, H. Leo see Gospel Advocate.

Boles, John B. Religion in Antebellum Kentucky. LC 76-4434. (Kentucky Bicentennial Bookshelf Ser.). 160p. 1976. 6.95 (ISBN 0-8131-0227-8). U Pr of Ky.

Boles, Kenny. Thirteen Lessons on Ephesians. (Bible Student Study Guides). 1978. pap. 2.95 (ISBN 0-89900-159-9). College Pr Pub.

--Thirteen Lessons on Galatians. (Bible Student Study Guides). 1978. pap. 2.95 (ISBN 0-89900-158-0). College Pr Pub.

--Thirteen Lessons on Philippians, Colossians & Philemon. LC 79-53714. (Bible Student Study Guides). (Orig.). 1979. pap. 2.95 (ISBN 0-89900-163-7). College Pr Pub.

Boles, Kenny, jt. auth. see Boatman, Don E.

Bolge, Richard, jt. auth. see Gerlach, Joel.

Bolich, Gregory G. The Christian Scholar: An Introduction to Theological Research. 352p. (Orig.). 1986. lib. bdg. 30.00 (ISBN 0-8191-5135-1, Pub. by Inst Christ Stud); pap. text ed. 15.75 (ISBN 0-8191-5136-X). U Pr of Amer.

--Karl Barth & Evangelicalism. (Orig.). 1979. pap. 6.95 (ISBN 0-87784-615-4). Inter-Varsity.

Bolick, James H. Sermon Outlines for Revival Preaching. (Pulpit Library). 106p. 1986. pap. 2.95 (ISBN 0-8010-0922-7). Baker Bk.

--Sermon Outlines from the Word. (Sermon Outline Ser.). (Orig.). 1980. pap. 2.50 (ISBN 0-8010-0528-0). Baker Bk.

Bolinder, Garth, et al. What Every Pastor Needs to Know about Music, Youth, & Education. (Leadership Library). 192p. 1986. 9.95 (ISBN 0-917463-09-9). Chr Today.

Boling, Robert G. & Wright, Ernest. Joshua, Vol. 6. LC 79-6583. (Anchor Bible Ser.). (Illus.). 432p. 1982. 18.00 (ISBN 0-385-00034-0). Doubleday.

Boling, Robert G., tr. & intro. by. Judges, Vol. 6A. LC 72-96229. (Anchor Bible Ser). (Illus.). 360p. 1975. 18.00 (ISBN 0-385-01029-X). Doubleday.

Bolingbroke, Henry Viscount. The Philosophical Works, 5 vols. Wellek, Rene, ed. LC 75-11198. (British Philosophers & Theologians of the 17th & 18th Centuries: Vol. 5). 1976. Repr. of 1777 ed. Set. lib. bdg. 231.00 (ISBN 0-8240-1754-4); lib. bdg. 254.00. Garland Pub.

Bolitho, Hector. Beside Galilee. 206p. 1981. Repr. of 1933 ed. lib. bdg. 25.00 (ISBN 0-89987-076-7). Darby Bks.

Boll, Lawrence L. Relation of Diu Krone to La Mule Sanz Frain. LC 77-140018. (Catholic University Studies in German Ser.: No. 2). Repr. of 1929 ed. 18.00 (ISBN 0-404-50222-9). AMS Pr.

Boll, Shirley. At Every Gate a Pearl. 1986. 3.25 (ISBN 0-87813-525-1). Christian Light.

Bolle, Jeff, ed. Lay Mission Handbook. 100p. binder 20.00 (ISBN 0-318-21725-2). Intl Liaison.

Bolle, Kees W., ed. Mythology Series, 39 vols. (Illus.). 1978. Set. lib. bdg. 1807.50x (ISBN 0-405-10529-0); Set. lib. bdg. 669.00 (ISBN 0-405-18984-2). Ayer Co Pubs.

--Studies of A. J. Wensinck: An Original Arno Press Anthology. LC 77-82275. (Mythology Ser.). 1978. lib. bdg. 17.00x (ISBN 0-405-10567-3). Ayer Co Pubs.

Bolle, Kees W., ed. see Creuzer, Georg F.

Bolle, Kees W., ed. see De Rebecque, Constant & Benjamin, Henri.

Bolle, Kees W., ed. see Dumezil, Georges.

Bolle, Kees W., ed. see Ehrenreich, Paul.

Bolle, Kees W., ed. see Gorres, Joseph.

Bolle, Kees W., jt. ed. see Jensen, Adolf E.

Bolle, Kees W., ed. see Krappe, Alexandre H.

Bolle, Kees W., ed. see Langer, Fritz.

Bolle, Kees W., ed. see Leenhardt, Maurice.

Bolle, Kees W., ed. see Lessmann, Heinrich.

Bolle, Kees W., ed. see Liebert, Arthur.

Bolle, Kees W., ed. see Lipps, Gottlob F.
Bolle, Kees W., ed. see Mannhardt, Wilhelm.
Bolle, Kees W., ed. see Meyer, Richard M.
Bolle, Kees W., ed. see Muller, Friedrich M.
Bolle, Kees W., ed. see Muller, Karl O.
Bolle, Kees W., ed. see Mus, Paul.
Bolle, Kees W., ed. see Oppert, Gustav.
Bolle, Kees W., ed. see Otto, Walter F.
Bolle, Kees W., jt. ed. see Pettazzoni, Raffaele.
Bolle, Kees W., ed. see Pettazzoni, Rattaele.
Bolle, Kees W., ed. see Pigott, Grenville.
Bolle, Kees W., ed. see Preller, Ludwig.
Bolle, Kees W., ed. see Siecke, Ernst.
Bolle, Kees W., ed. see Wirz, Paul.
Bolle, Kees W., ed. see Ziegler, Leopold.
Bolle, Kees W., tr. & intro. by see De Vries, Jan.
Bollen, J. D. Protestantism & Social Reform in New South Wales 1890-1910. (Illus.). 200p. 1972. 20.00x (ISBN 0-522-84023-X, Pub. by Melbourne U Pr). Intl Spec Bk.
Bollen, Peter D. Nuclear Voices: A Book of Quotations & Perspectives. LC 85-60616. (Illus.). 250p. (Orig.). 1985. pap. 6.95x (ISBN 0-9611350-1-8). Hillside Bks.
Boller, Paul F., Jr. George Washington & Religion. LC 63-9755. 1963. 12.95 (ISBN 0-87074-021-0). SMU Press.
Bollier, John A. The Literature of Theology: A Guide for Students & Pastors. LC 78-10962. 208p. 1979. pap. 5.95 (ISBN 0-664-24225-1). Westminster.
Bollig, Richard Joseph. History of Catholic Education in Kansas: 1836-1932. 131p. 1984. 24.00x (ISBN 0-939738-22-8). Zubal Inc.
Bollinger, Edward E. The Cross & the Floating Dragon: The Gospel in the Ryukyu. LC 82-23540. (Illus.). 368p. 1983. pap. 10.95 (ISBN 0-87808-190-9). William Carey Lib.
Bolshakoff, Serge. Russian Nonconformity: The Story of Unofficial Religion in Russia. Repr. of 1950 ed. 10.00 (ISBN 0-404-00933-6). AMS Pr.
Bolshakoff, Sergius. Russian Mystics. (Cistercian Studies: No. 26). Orig. Title: I Mistici Rusi. 303p. 1981. pap. 6.95 (ISBN 0-87907-926-6). Cistercian Pubns.
Bolt, Christine & Dresher, Seymour, eds. Anti-Slavery, Religion & Reform. LC 79-41532. xi, 377p. 1980. 35.00 (ISBN 0-208-01783-6, Archon). Shoe String.
Bolt, John, ed. see Buchanan, Annette M. & Martin, Kay A.
Bolt, Martin & Myers, David G. The Human Connection. LC 83-20420. 168p. (Orig.). 1984. pap. 6.95 (ISBN 0-87784-913-7). Inter-Varsity.
Bolt, Robert. Man for All Seasons. 1962. 10.95 (ISBN 0-394-40623-0). Random.
--Man for All Seasons. 1966. pap. 2.95 (ISBN 0-394-70321-9, V321, Vin). Random.
Bolten, Thomas A. Finding God in the Space Age. 1987. 14.95 (ISBN 0-533-06954-8). Vantage.
Bolton, Barbara & Smith, Charles. Creative Bible Learning for Children, Grades 1-6. LC 77-74532. 208p. 1977. pap. 3.95 (ISBN 0-8307-0478-7, 9100105). Regal.
Bolton, Brenda. Medieval Reformation. (Foundations of Medieval History). (Illus.). 112p. 1983. text ed. 22.50x (ISBN 0-8419-0879-6); pap. text ed. 14.75x (ISBN 0-8419-0835-4). Holmes & Meier.
Bolton, Charles S. Southern Anglicanism: The Church of England in Colonial South Carolina. LC 81-6669. (Contributions to the Study of Religion: No. 5). (Illus.). 248p. 1982. lib. bdg. 29.95 (ISBN 0-313-23090-0, BOS/). Greenwood.
Bolton, D., tr. see Saurat, Denis.
Bolton, Herbert E. Fray Juan Crespi, Missionary Explorer on the Pacific Coast, 1769-1774. LC 78-158616. Repr. of 1927 ed. 29.50 (ISBN 0-404-01838-6). AMS Pr.
--Padre on Horseback. LC 63-13248. (Illus.). 1963. Repr. of 1962 ed. 3.00 (ISBN 0-8294-0003-6). Loyola.
--Rim of Christendom: A Biography of Eusebio Francisco Kino, Pacific Coast Pioneer. LC 84-8814. 644p. 1984. Repr. of 1960 ed. 40.00x (ISBN 0-8165-0863-1). U of Ariz Pr.
--Wider Horizons of American History. 1967. pap. 5.95x (ISBN 0-268-00301-7). U of Notre Dame Pr.
Bolton, J. Andrew. Restoring Persons in World Community. 1986. pap. 9.00 (ISBN 0-8309-0461-1). Herald Hse.
Bolton, Leonard. China Call. LC 83-82301. 256p. 1984. pap. text ed. 4.95 (ISBN 0-88243-509-4, 02-0509). Gospel Pub.
Bolton, Robert. A Discourse About the State of True Happinesse. LC 79-84089. (English Experience Ser.: No. 909). 184p. 1979. Repr. of 1611 ed. lib. bdg. 14.00 (ISBN 90-221-0909-7). Walter J Johnson.
Bolton, Sarah K. Ralph Waldo Emerson. LC 73-15752. 1973. lib. bdg. 10.00 (ISBN 0-8414-3304-6). Folcroft.
Boman, Thorleif. Hebrew Thought Compared with Greek. Moreau, Jules L., tr. from Ger. 1970. pap. 6.95 (ISBN 0-393-00534-8, Norton Lib). Norton.
Bomely, Steven. Glory to God: A Candlelight Service for Christmas. 1983. pap. 2.75 (ISBN 0-89536-625-8, 0733). CSS of Ohio.
Bomer, Hildegard, tr. see Mayer-Skumanz, Lene.
Bomgren, Marilyn J. Godparents, Why? 1981. 2.50 (ISBN 0-89536-473-5, 0717). CSS of Ohio.
Bomzer, Herbert W. The Kolel in America. LC 85-63012. 184p. 1986. 15.95 (ISBN 0-88400-118-0). Shengold.
Bona, Maurice De see De Bona, Maurice, Jr.
Bonacina, Conrad R., tr. see Von Le Fort, Gertrud.
Bonansea, B. M. Man & His Approach to God in John Duns Scotus. 258p. (Orig.). 1983. lib. bdg. 29.75 (ISBN 0-8191-3299-3); pap. text ed. 13.50 o. p. (ISBN 0-8191-3300-0). U Pr of Amer.
Bonansea, Berbardine, ed. see Bettoni, Efrem.
Bonansea, Bernardine M., ed. see Ryan, John K.
Bonansea, Bernardino M. God & Atheism: A Philosophical Approach to the Problem of God. LC 78-12064. 378p. 1979. 19.95x (ISBN 0-8132-0549-2). Cath U Pr.
Bonar, Andrew. Andrew Bonar Life & Diary. 535p. 1984. Repr. of 1893 ed. 14.95 (ISBN 0-85151-432-4). Banner of Truth.
--Heavenly Springs. 211p. (Orig.). 1986. pap. 4.95 (ISBN 0-85151-479-0). Banner of Truth.
--Leviticus. (Banner of Truth Geneva Series Commentaries). 1978. 15.95 (ISBN 0-85151-086-8). Banner of Truth.
--The Life of R. M. M'Cheyne. 1978. pap. 3.45 (ISBN 0-85151-085-X). Banner of Truth.
Bonar, Andrew, jt. auth. see Tyler, Bennet.
Bonar, Andrew A. Memoir & Remains of R. M. M'cheyne. 1978. 16.95 (ISBN 0-85151-084-1). Banner of Truth.
Bonar, Clayton. Beacon Small-Group Bible Studies, Deuteronomy: Words to Live By. Wolf, Earl C., ed. 100p. (Orig.). 1986. pap. 2.50 (ISBN 0-8341-0959-X). Beacon Hill.
Bonar, Horatius. When God's Children Suffer. LC 80-84441. (Shepherd Illustrated Classics Ser.). (Illus.). 144p. 1981. pap. 5.95 (ISBN 0-87983-221-5). Keats.
--Words to Winners of Souls. (Summit Bks.). 1979. pap. 2.50 (ISBN 0-8010-0773-9). Baker Bk.
Bonaventura. The Problem of God & the Emotional Equilibrium of Man. (Illus.). 78p. 1984. pap. 23.75 (ISBN 0-89266-490-8). Am Classical Coll Pr.
Bonaventure, Saint Bonaventure, Rooted in Faith: Homilies to a Contemporary World. Schumacher, Marigwen, tr. from Lat. 1974. 5.95 (ISBN 0-8199-0465-1). Franciscan Herald.
Bonaventure, St. The Mind's Journey to God (Itinerarium Mentis Ad Deum) Cunningham, Lawrence S., tr. 1979. 6.95 (ISBN 0-8199-0765-0). Franciscan Herald.
Boncore Di Santa Vittoria Staff. Boncore Di Santa Victoria Novus Liber Hymnorum Ac Orationum. Repr. of 1903 ed. 60.00 (ISBN 0-384-12867-X). Johnson Repr.
Bond, Alan. The Sevenfold Path to Peace. 1986. 4.50 (ISBN 0-89536-774-2, 6801). CSS of Ohio.
Bond, E. J. Reason & Value. LC 82-4564. (Cambridge Studies in Philosophy). 220p. 1983. 32.50 (ISBN 0-521-24571-0); pap. 11.95 (ISBN 0-521-27079-0). Cambridge U Pr.
Bond, Francis. An Introduction to English Church Architecture: From the 11th to the 16th Century. LC 77-94546. 1979. Repr. of 1908 ed. lib. bdg. 25.00 (ISBN 0-89341-225-2). Longwood Pub Group.
Bond, George, et al, eds. African Christianity: Patterns of Religious Continuity. LC 79-51668. (AP Studies in Anthropology Ser.). 1979. 29.95 (ISBN 0-12-113450-4). Acad Pr.
Bond, George D., jt. auth. see Carter, John R.
Bond, John J. Handy-Book of Rules & Tables for Verifying Dates with the Christian Era. LC 66-29473. 1966. Repr. of 1889 ed. 10.00x (ISBN 0-8462-1795-3). Russell.
Bondeson, William, et al, eds. New Knowledge in the Biomedical Sciences. 1982. lib. bdg. 29.50 (ISBN 90-277-1319-7, Pub. by Reidel Holland). Kluwer Academic.
Bondi, Richard, jt. auth. see Hauerwas, Stanley.
Boneck, Lenora. Morning Light. (Illus.). 270p. (Orig.). 1986. pap. 12.95 (ISBN 0-940415-00-3). B & K Pub Hse.
Boner, Alice. Vastusutra Upanisad: The Essence of Form in Sacred Art. xii, 192p. 1986. 32.00 (Pub. by Motilal Banarsidass). South Asia Bks.
Boney, F. N. Southerners All. LC 84-9127. x, 218p. 1984. 17.95 (ISBN 0-86554-114-0, MUP-P19); 12.95 (ISBN 0-86554-189-2). Mercer Univ Pr.
Bonham, Tal. D. Humor: God's Gift. 1988. text ed. 9.95 (ISBN 0-8054-5720-8). Broadman.
Bonham, Tal D. The Treasury of Clean Church Jokes. LC 85-26837. 1986. pap. 3.50 (ISBN 0-8054-5719-4). Broadman.
Bonhoeffer, Dietrich. Act & Being. 192p. 1983. Repr. of 1962 ed. 18.50 (ISBN 0-88254-869-7, Octagon). Hippocrene Bks.
--Christ the Center: A New Translation. new ed. LC 78-4747. (Harper's Ministers Paperback Library Ser.). 1978. pap. 5.95 (ISBN 0-06-060815-3, RD 285, HarpR). Har-Row.
--Cost of Discipleship. 1963. pap. 5.95 (ISBN 0-02-083850-6, Collier). Macmillan.
--The Cost of Discipleship. 1983. 14.00 (ISBN 0-8446-5960-6). Peter Smith.
--Creation & Fall. Bd. with Temptation. 1965. pap. 4.95 (ISBN 0-02-083890-5). Macmillan.
--Creation & Fall: Temptation. 1983. 13.00 (ISBN 0-8446-5962-2). Peter Smith.
--Letters & Papers from Prison. enl. ed. 1972. pap. 7.95 (ISBN 0-02-083920-0, Collier). Macmillan.
--Life Together. LC 54-6901. 128p. 1976. pap. 6.95 (ISBN 0-06-060851-X, RD292, HarpR). Har-Row.
--Meditating on the Word. Gracie, David, ed. & tr. from Ger. LC 86-16839. 152p. (Orig.). 1986. 11.95 (ISBN 0-936384-43-3); pap. 6.95 (ISBN 0-936384-41-7). Cowley Pubns.
--Prayers from Prison. Hampe, Johann C., tr. from Ger. LC 77-15228. Tr. of Von guten Machten. 1978. pap. 4.95 (ISBN 0-8006-1334-1, 1-1334). Fortress.
--Psalms: The Prayer Book of the Bible. 2nd ed. Burtness, James H., tr. from Ger. LC 73-101111. Tr. of Das Gebetbuch der Bibel. 88p. 1974. 4.95 (ISBN 0-8066-1439-0, 10-5321). Augsburg.
--Spiritual Care. Rochelle, Jay C., tr. LC 85-47711. 128p. 1985. pap. 4.95 (ISBN 0-8006-1874-2). Fortress.
Bonhoeffer, Dietrich, et al. The Christian Cornerstone Library: The Cost of Discipleship - Mere Christianity - Your God Is Too Small, 3 vols. 672p. 1987. Set. pap. 12.95 (ISBN 0-02-084440-9, Collier). Macmillan.
Boni, Sylvain. The Self & the Other in the Ontologies of Sartre & Buber. LC 82-20130. 202p. (Orig.). 1983. lib. bdg. 27.50 (ISBN 0-8191-2852-X); pap. text ed. 12.50 (ISBN 0-8191-2853-8). U Pr of Amer.
Bonic. The Picture Life of Pope John Paul II. Date not set. lib. bdg. 9.90 (ISBN 0-531-04806-3). Watts.
Boniface, Saint Letters of Saint Boniface. Emerton, Ephraim, ed. 1967. lib. bdg. 21.50x (ISBN 0-374-92584-4, Octagon). Hippocrene Bks.
Bonifacius, Saint Winfrid. Briefe des Heiligen Bonifatius. pap. 23.00 (ISBN 0-384-05025-5). Johnson Repr.
Bonifazi, Conrad. A Theology of Things. LC 76-7549. 1976. Repr. of 1967 ed. lib. bdg. 22.50x (ISBN 0-8371-8838-5, BOTT). Greenwood.
Bonifazi, Flavian. Yearning of a Soul. 1979. 4.95 (ISBN 0-8198-0614-5); pap. 3.50 (ISBN 0-8198-0615-3). Dghtrs St Paul.
Bonilla, Plutarco. Los Milagros Tambien Son Parabolas. LC 78-59240. (Span.). 166p. (Orig.). 1978. pap. 3.95 (ISBN 0-89922-114-9). Edit Caribe.
Bonin, Edmond, ed. see St. Cyprian of Carthage.
Bonin, Edmond, tr. see Evely, Louis.
Bonino, Jose M. Doing Theology in a Revolutionary Situation. Lazareth, William H., ed. LC 74-80424. 208p. 1975. pap. 5.95 (ISBN 0-8006-1451-8, 1-1451). Fortress.
--Room to Be People: An Interpretation of the Message of the Bible for Today's World. Leach, Vickie, tr. from Span. LC 78-14662. 80p. 1979. pap. 4.50 (ISBN 0-8006-1349-X, 1-1349). Fortress.
--Toward a Christian Political Ethics. LC 82-48541. 144p. 1983. pap. 6.95 (ISBN 0-8006-1697-9, 1-1697). Fortress.
Bonk, Jon. Ethiopian Orthodox Church. LC 84-10547. (ATLA Bibliography Ser.: No. 11). 132p. 1984. 15.00 (ISBN 0-8108-1710-1). Scarecrow.
Bonnechose, Emile de. The Reformers Before the Reformation. Mackenzie, Campbell, tr. LC 78-63194. (Heresies of the Early Christian & Medieval Era: Second Ser.). Repr. of 1844 ed. 36.50 set (ISBN 0-404-16190-1). AMS Pr.
Bonnechose, Emile de see Bonnechose, Emile de.
Bonner, Clint. Hymn Is Born. LC 59-9694. 1959. 10.95 (ISBN 0-8054-6801-3). Broadman.
Bonner, Dismas, jt. auth. see Coyle, Alcuin.
Bonner, Dismas, jt. ed. see Mathis, Marcian.
Bonner, Geraldian. St. Augustine of Hippo: Life & Controversies. LC 82-45807. 1985. Repr. of 1963 ed. 42.50 (ISBN 0-404-62376-X). AMS Pr.
Bonnerjea, Biren. Dictionary of Superstitions & Mythology. LC 69-17755. 1969. Repr. of 1927 ed. 43.00x (ISBN 0-8103-3572-7). Gale.
Bonnet, Hans. Reallexikon der aegyptischen Religionsgeschichte. 2nd ed. (Ger., Illus.). 1981. 71.20x (ISBN 3-11-003365-8). De Gruyter.
Bonnet, Jules, ed. see Calvin, Jean.
Bonnet, Jules, ed. see Calvin, John.
Bonnet, L. & Schroeder, A. Epistolas De Pablo Tomo III. Cativiela, A., tr. from Fr. (Comentario del Nuevo Testamento). 538p. 1986. pap. 14.95 (ISBN 0-311-03052-1). Casa Bautista.
Bonnet, L., jt. auth. see Schrolder, A.
Bonney, Charles C. World's Congress Addresses. 88p. 1900. pap. 6.95 (ISBN 0-912050-48-9). Open Court.
Bonney, T. G., et al. Abbeys & Churches of England & Wales. LC 77-23529. 1977. Repr. of 1890 ed. lib. bdg. 40.00 (ISBN 0-89341-203-1). Longwood Pub Group.
Bonnici, Roberta L. I'm Scared to Witness! (Discovery Bks.). (Illus.). 48p. (Orig.). (YA) 1979. pap. 1.50 (ISBN 0-88243-931-6, 02-0931); tchr's ed 3.95 (ISBN 0-88243-330-X, 02-0330). Gospel Pub.
--Your Right to Be Different. (Discovery Bks.). (Illus.). 48p. (YA) 1982. pap. text ed. 1.50 (ISBN 0-88243-842-5, 02-0842); tchr's ed 3.95 (ISBN 0-88243-333-4, 02-0333). Gospel Pub.
Bonniwell, William R. The Life of Blessed Margaret of Castello. LC 83-70524. 113p. 1983. pap. 4.00 (ISBN 0-89555-213-2). TAN Bks Pubs.
Bonnot, Bernard R. Pope John Twenty-Third: A Clever, Pastoral Leader. LC 79-1770. 1980. 9.95 (ISBN 0-8189-0388-0). Alba.
Bono, F. English Cathedrals. 1976. lib. bdg. 234.95 (ISBN 0-8490-1771-8). Gordon Pr.
Bonomi, Patricia U. Under the Cope of Heaven: Religion, Society & Politics in Colonial America. 292p. 1986. 24.95x (ISBN 0-19-504118-6). Oxford U Pr.
Bonpane, Blase. Guerrillas of Peace: Liberation Theology & the Central American Revolution. 120p. (Orig.). 1986. 25.00 (ISBN 0-89608-311-X); pap. 8.00 (ISBN 0-89608-310-1). South End Pr.
Bontier, Pierre & Le Verrier, Jean. The Canarian; or Book of the Conquest & Conversion of the Canarians, in the Year 1402, by Messire Jean de Bethencourt. Major, Richard H., ed. LC 70-286234. (Hakluyt Society Ser.: No. 46). 300p. 1972. lib. bdg. 32.00 (ISBN 0-8337-2188-7). B Franklin.
Bontrager, Frances. Church & the Single Person. (Family Life Ser). 32p. (Orig.). 1969. pap. 1.00 (ISBN 0-8361-1575-9). Herald Pr.
Bontrager, G. Edwin. Divorce & the Faithful Church. LC 78-4671. 224p. 1978. 12.95 (ISBN 0-8361-1850-2); pap. 8.95 (ISBN 0-8361-1851-0). Herald Pr.
Bontrager, G. Edwin & Showalter, Nathan. It Can Happen Today. LC 86-15036. 96p. (Orig.). 1986. pap. 5.95 (ISBN 0-8361-3419-2); pap. 14.95x tchrs. manual (ISBN 0-8361-1286-5). Herald Pr.
Bontrager, Ida B. Ozark Parson. 1978. 5.55 (ISBN 0-87813-512-X). Christian Light.
--Under God's Arrest. 1974. 11.50 (ISBN 0-87813-508-1). Christian Light.
Bonwick, James. Irish Druids & Old Irish Religions. LC 75-36830. (Occult Ser.). 1976. Repr. of 1894 ed. 25.50x (ISBN 0-405-07942-7). Ayer Co Pubs.
Boodin, John E. God & Creation, 2 vols. LC 75-3058. Repr. of 1934 ed. 67.50 set (ISBN 0-404-59057-8). AMS Pr.
--Religion of Tomorrow. LC 75-3062. Repr. of 1943 ed. 14.00 (ISBN 0-404-59061-6). AMS Pr.
--Time & Reality. LC 75-3064. (Philosophy in America Ser.). Repr. of 1904 ed. 20.00 (ISBN 0-404-59063-2). AMS Pr.
Booher, Dianna D. Getting along with People Who Don't Get Along. LC 83-14406. (Orig.). 1984. pap. 3.75 (ISBN 0-8054-5209-5). Broadman.
Book, Doyle C. The Threshold Is High: The Brethren in Christ in Japan. Zercher, Ray M. & Pierce, Glen A., eds. (Illus.). xii, 210p. (Orig.). 1986. pap. 7.95 (ISBN 0-916035-15-8). Evangel Indiana.
Book of the Dead Staff. The Chapters of Coming Forth by Day, 3 vols. LC 73-18833. Repr. of 1910 ed. 49.50 set (ISBN 0-404-11303-6). AMS Pr.
Booker, John. The Dutch Oracle. (Illus.). 224p. 1981. pap. 5.95 (ISBN 0-931116-01-5). Ralston-Pilot.
Booker, Richard. Blow the Trumpet in Zion. LC 85-62152. 208p. (Orig.). 1985. pap. 5.95 (ISBN 0-932081-02-9). Victory Hse.
--Intimacy with God. LC 84-70055. 196p. 1983. pap. 5.95 (ISBN 0-88270-552-0). Bridge Pub.
--The Miracle of the Scarlet Thread. LC 80-84802. (Orig.). 1981. pap. 4.95 (ISBN 0-88270-499-0). Bridge Pub.
--Radical Christian Living. LC 84-90103. (Illus.). 124p. (Orig.). 1985. pap. 4.95 (ISBN 0-932081-03-7). Victory Hse.
--Seated in Heavenly Places. LC 85-72460. 1986. pap. 5.95 (ISBN 0-88270-600-4). Bridge Pub.
Bookidis, Nancy & Stroud, Ronald. Demeter & Persephone in Ancient Corinth. (Corinth Notes Ser.: No. 2). (Illus.). 32p. (Orig.). 1987. pap. 3.00. Am Sch Athens.
Bookser-Feister, John, jt. auth. see Quinn, Bernard.

Bookstaber, Philip D. Judaism & the American Mind: In Theory & Practice. LC 78-26404. 1979. Repr. of 1939 ed. lib. bdg. cancelled (ISBN 0-313-20875-1, BOJU). Greenwood.

Boom. This Day is the Lord's Day. 2.75 (ISBN 0-318-18182-7). WCTU.

Boom, Corrie T. Each New Day. (Christian Library). 1985. Repr. of 1980 ed. 6.95 (ISBN 0-916441-20-2). Barbour & Co.

Boom, Corrie ten. Amazing Love. (Orig.). 1982. pap. 2.50 (ISBN 0-515-06735-0). Jove Pubns.

--Amor, Asombroso Amor. Orig. Title: Amazing Love. 112p. 1980. pap. 2.25 (ISBN 0-311-40035-3, Edit Mundo). Casa Bautista.

--Marching Orders for the End Battle. 1970. pap. 1.95 (ISBN 0-87508-024-3). Chr Lit.

--Plenty for Everyone. 1967. pap. 2.95 (ISBN 0-87508-023-5). Chr Lit.

--Prayers & Promises for Every Day from the Living Bible. 272p. 1985. pap. 9.95 (ISBN 0-8027-2505-8). Walker & Co.

--Prayers & Promises for Every Day: With Corrie Ten Boom. Shaw, Luci, ed. LC 77-92352. (Day Star Devotional). 144p. 1977. pap. 2.95 (ISBN 0-87788-689-X). Shaw Pubs.

--This Day Is the Lord's. 1982. pap. 2.75 (ISBN 0-515-06734-2). Jove Pubns.

--Tramp for the Lord. 1976. pap. 2.95 (ISBN 0-515-08993-1). Jove Pubns.

Boom, Corrie Ten see Graham, Billy & Ten Boom, Corrie.

Boom, Corrie Ten see Ten Boom, Corrie.

Boone, Edna, jt. auth. see Boone, Tom.

Boone, Elizabeth H., ed. Ritual Human Sacrifice in Mesoamerica: A Conference at Dumbarton Oaks, October 13 & 14, 1979. LC 83-14059. (Illus.). 256p. 1984. 18.50x (ISBN 0-88402-120-3). Dumbarton Oaks.

Boone, Jerome. Let There Be Praise. (International Correspondence Program Ser.). 226p. (Orig.). pap. 6.95 (ISBN 0-87148-524-9). Pathway Pr.

Boone, Julia R. Getting to Know Your Bible. LC 81-69259. 176p. 1984. pap. 9.95 (ISBN 0-8054-1140-2). Broadman.

Boone, Pat. My Brothers Keeper? 1975. pap. 1.75 (ISBN 0-89129-028-1). Jove Pubns.

Boone, Tom & Boone, Edna. Prayer & Action. 1974. pap. 1.25x (ISBN 0-8358-0309-0). Upper Room.

Boor, Carl G. De see Nicephorus.

Boorstin, Daniel J., ed. see Ellis, John T.

Boostrom, Paul. The Hostage Game: An Exciting Simulation Game for Junior High Youth Groups. (The Best of Young Teen Action Ser.). 32p. 1985. pap. 4.95 (ISBN 0-89191-382-3). Cook.

--That's Tough: Four Simulation Games on Christian Commitment for Junior High Youth Groups. (The Best of Young Teen Action Ser.). 32p. 1985. pap. 4.95 (ISBN 0-317-39454-1). Cook.

Booth, A. E. Ministry of Peter, John & Paul. 1982. pap. 1.25 (ISBN 0-88172-004-6). Believers Bkshelf.

Booth, Abrh. The Reign of Grace. 5.95 (ISBN 0-685-88390-6). Reiner.

Booth, Catherine. Aggressive Christianity. (Writings of Catherine Booth Ser.). 1986. Repr. of 1880 ed. deluxe ed. 4.95 (ISBN 0-86544-031-X). Salvation Army.

--Highway of Our God. (Writings of Catherine Booth Ser.). 1986. Repr. of 1880 ed. deluxe ed. 4.95 (ISBN 0-86544-033-6). Salvation Army.

--Life & Death. (Writings of Catherine Booth Ser.). 1986. Repr. of 1883 ed. deluxe ed. 4.95 (ISBN 0-86544-034-4). Salvation Army.

--Papers on Godliness. (Writings of Catherine Booth Ser.). 1986. Repr. of 1890 ed. deluxe ed. 4.95 (ISBN 0-86544-032-8). Salvation Army.

--Papers on Practical Religion. (Writings of Catherine Booth Ser.). 1986. Repr. of 1891 ed. deluxe ed. 4.95 (ISBN 0-86544-036-0). Salvation Army.

--Popular Christianity. (Writings of Catherine Booth Ser.). 1986. Repr. of 1888 ed. deluxe ed. 4.95 (ISBN 0-86544-035-2). Salvation Army.

--The Story. pap. 3.95 (ISBN 0-686-27773-2). Schmul Pub Co.

--Writings of Catherine Booth, 6 Vols. 1986. Repr. of 1880 ed. Set. deluxe ed. 19.95 (ISBN 0-86544-038-7). Salvation Army.

--Writings of Catherine Booth. 1101p. 1986. 19.95 (ISBN 0-86544-031-X). Salv Army Suppl South.

Booth, Catherine, et al. The Last Days Collection: A Treasury of Articles from Last Days Ministries. (Illus.). 224p. (Orig.). 1986. pap. text ed. 10.95. Pretty Good TX.

Booth, Edward. Aristotelian Aporetic Ontology in Islamic & Christian Thinkers. LC 82-22068. (Cambridge Studies in Medieval Life & Thought: No. 20). 368p. 1984. 70.00 (ISBN 0-521-25254-7). Cambridge U Pr.

Booth, Howard J. Edwin Diller Starbuck: Pioneer in the Psychology of Religion. LC 80-5731. 304p. 1981. pap. text ed. 15.50 (ISBN 0-8191-1703-X). U Pr of Amer.

Booth, Julianne. Bible Verses to Remember. 1982. pap. 2.95 (ISBN 0-570-04061-2, 56-1364). Concordia.

--Books of the New Testament. (Arch Book Supplement Ser.). 1981. pap. 0.99 (ISBN 0-570-06150-4, 59-1305). Concordia.

--Parables of Jesus. (Arch Bks.). 1982. pap. 0.99 (ISBN 0-570-06163-6, 59-1309). Concordia.

Booth, L. Venchael, ed. Crowned with Glory & Honor: The Life of Rev. Lacey Kirk Williams. 1978. 8.00 (ISBN 0-682-48939-5). Exposition Pr FL.

Booth, Leo. Walking on Water. 180p. (Orig.). 1985. pap. 8.95 (ISBN 0-932194-28-1). Health Comm.

Booth, Mark, ed. see Auden, W. H., et al.

Booth, Newell S. African Religions: A Symposium. LC 73-88062. 390p. 1977. text ed. 21.50x (ISBN 0-88357-012-2). Nok Pubs.

Booth, Peter, ed. see Irani, Adi K.

Booth, Roger P. Jesus & the Laws of Purity: Tradition History & Legal History in Mark 7. (JSoT Supplement Ser.: No. 13). 300p. 1986. text ed. 27.50x (ISBN 1-85075-023-8, Pub. by JSOT Pr England); pap. text ed. 13.50x (ISBN 1-85075-022-X). Eisenbrauns.

Booth, William. How to Preach. 84p. (Orig.). 1979. pap. 3.95 (ISBN 0-89216-026-8). Salv Army Suppl South.

--In Darkest England & the Way Out. 296p. 1984. Repr. of 1890 ed. 6.95 (ISBN 0-86544-024-7). Salv Army Suppl South.

--The Seven Spirits. 128p. 1984. Repr. of 1890 ed. 3.95 (ISBN 0-86544-026-3). Salv Army Suppl South.

Booth-Tucker, Frederick. The Salvation Army in America: Selected Reports, 1899-1903. LC 79-38439. (Religion in America, Ser. 2). 212p. 1972. Repr. of 1972 ed. 19.00 (ISBN 0-405-04060-1). Ayer Co Pubs.

Booty, John. The Christ We Know. LC 87-6779. (Illus.). 174p. 1987. pap. 9.95 (ISBN 0-936384-48-4). Cowley Pubns.

Booty, John E. The Church in History. (Church's Teaching Ser.: Vol. 3). 320p. 1979. 5.95 (ISBN 0-8164-0420-8, HarpR); pap. 3.95 (ISBN 0-8164-2216-8); user guide 0.95 (ISBN 0-8164-2223-0). Har-Row.

--The Servant Church: Diaconal Ministry & the Episcopal Church. LC 82-81429. (Orig.). 1982. pap. 7.95 (ISBN 0-8192-1316-0). Morehouse.

--Three Anglican Divines on Prayer: Jewel, Andrewes & Hooker. vii, 48p. (Orig.). 1978. pap. 3.00 (ISBN 0-936384-00-X). Cowley Pubns.

--What Makes Us Episcopalians? 48p. 1982. pap. 3.50 (ISBN 0-8192-1302-0, 82-80468). Morehouse.

Booty, John E., ed. The Divine Drama in History & Liturgy: Essays Presented to Horton Davies on His Retirement from Princeton University. (Pittsburgh Theological Monographs: New Ser. 10). 1984. pap. 16.50 (ISBN 0-915138-67-0). Pickwick.

--The Godly Kingdom of Tudor England: Great Books of the English Reformation. LC 81-80626. (Illus.). 288p. 1981. 15.95 (ISBN 0-8192-1287-3). Morehouse.

Booty, John E. & Hooker, Richard, eds. Of the Laws of Ecclesiastical Polity: Attack & Response, Vol. IV. (The Folger Library Edition of the Works of Richard Hooker). (Illus.). 320p. 1981. text ed. 45.00 (ISBN 0-674-63216-8). Harvard U Pr.

Booty, John E., ed. see Jewel, John.

Bootz, John, ed. The Book of Common Prayer. LC 75-29330. 1976. 24.95 (ISBN 0-918016-58-4). Folger Bks.

Booz, Gretchen & Holmes, Reed M. Kendra. LC 79-12285. 1979. 2.00 (ISBN 0-8309-0234-1). Herald Hse.

Bopp, Virgil. When the Word Dwells Richly: Baptists in Perspective. 192p. (Orig.). 1987. pap. 5.95 (ISBN 0-87227-119-6). Reg Baptist.

Boraas, Roger S. & Geraty, Lawrence T. Heshbon 1974: The Fourth Campaign at Tell Hesban: A Preliminary Report. (Andrews University Monographs, Studies in Religion: Vol. IX). (Illus.). xii, 232p. 1976. 7.95 (ISBN 0-943872-09-X). Andrews Univ Pr.

--Heshbon 1976: The Fifth Campaign at Tell Hesban: A Preliminary Report. (Andrews University Monographs, Studies in Religion: Vol. X). (Illus.). xi, 328p. 1978. 11.95 (ISBN 0-943872-10-3). Andrews Univ Pr.

Boraas, Roger S. & Horn, Siegfried H. Heshbon 1968: The First Campaign at Tell Hesban: A Preliminary Report. (Andrews University Monographs, Studies in Religion: Vol. II). (Illus.). viii, 239p. 1969. 7.95. Andrews Univ Pr.

--Heshbon 1971: The Second Campaign at Tell Hesban: A Preliminary Report. (Andrews University Monographs, Studies in Religion: Vol. VI). (Illus.). viii, 160p. 7.95 (ISBN 0-943872-06-5). Andrews Univ Pr.

--Heshbon 1973: The Third Campaign at Tell Hesban: A Preliminary Report. (Andrews University Monographs, Studies in Religion: Vol. VIII). (Illus.). viii, 288p. 1975. 7.95 (ISBN 0-943872-08-1). Andrews Univ Pr.

Borchardt, Anne, tr. see Wiesel, Elie.

Borchardt, Lois M. Learning about God's Love: Word-Picture Activities for Children in Grades 1 & 2. 48p. 1986. pap. 2.95 (ISBN 0-570-04354-9). Concordia.

Borchert, Gerald L. Assurance & Warning. (Orig.). 1987. pap. 5.95 (ISBN 0-8054-1011-2). Broadman.

Borchert, Gerald L. & Lester, Andrew D., eds. Spiritual Dimensions of Pastoral Care: Witness to the Ministry of Wayne E. Oates. LC 84-19581. 152p. (Orig.). 1985. pap. 11.95 (ISBN 0-664-24562-5). Westminster.

Bord, Richard J. & Faulkner, Joseph E. The Catholic Charismatics: Anatomy of a Modern Religious Movement. LC 82-42782. 160p. 1983. 19.95x (ISBN 0-271-00340-5). Pa St U Pr.

Borden, Morton. Jews, Turks, & Infidels. LC 83-19863. xii, 163p. 1984. 17.95x (ISBN 0-8078-1592-6). U of NC Pr.

Border, Ross. Church & State in Australia, 1788-1872: A Constitutional Study of the Church of England in Australia. LC 64-56989. 1962. text ed. 15.00x (ISBN 0-8401-0226-7). A R Allenson.

Bordes, Charles, ed. Anthologie Des Maitres Religieux Primirties Des XV, XVI & XVII Siecles, 6 vols. (Music Ser.). 1981. Repr. of 1893 ed. Set. lib. bdg. 250.00 (ISBN 0-306-76089-4); Vol. 1; IV, 184 Pp. lib. bdg. 47.50 (ISBN 0-306-76114-9); Vol. 2; VIII, 194 Pp. lib. bdg. 47.50 (ISBN 0-306-76115-7); Vol. 3; IV, 184 Pp. lib. bdg. 47.50 (ISBN 0-306-76116-5); Vol. 4; IV, 190 Pp. lib. bdg. 47.50 (ISBN 0-306-76117-3); Vol. 5; II, 190 Pp. lib. bdg. 47.50 (ISBN 0-306-76118-1); Vol. 6; II, 202 Pp. lib. bdg. 47.50 (ISBN 0-306-76119-X). Da Capo.

Bordner, Marie S. Marvels & Mysteries. 96p. (Orig.). 1986. pap. 4.95 (ISBN 0-912661-09-7). Woodsong Graph.

Bordow, Sita, compiled by. The Master's Touch: Disciples' Stories. LC 84-28857. 1984. pap. 4.95 (ISBN 0-932040-26-8). Integral Yoga Pubns.

Bordow, Sita, et al. Sri Swami Satchidananda: Apostle of Peace. LC 86-10533. (Illus.). 454p. (Orig.). 1986. pap. 14.95 (ISBN 0-932040-31-4). Integral Yoga Pubns.

Borg, Marcus J. Conflict, Holiness & Politics in the Teachings of Jesus. LC 84-9029. (Studies in the Bible & Early Christianity: Vol. 5). 410p. 1984. 59.95x (ISBN 0-88946-603-3). E Mellen.

Borgatello, Diego, ed. see Ceria, Eugenio.

Borgatello, Diego, tr. see Lemoyne, G. B., et al.

Borgen, Ole E. John Wesley on the Sacraments. 312p. 1986. pap. 12.95 (ISBN 0-310-75191-8, 17085P). Zondervan.

Borhek, Mary V. Coming Out to Parents: A Two-Way Survival Guide for Lesbians & Gay Men & Their Parents. LC 83-3971. 224p. 1983. pap. 9.95 (ISBN 0-8298-0665-2). Pilgrim NY.

Boring, Holland, ed. Songs of Hope. 1979. pap. 2.75 (ISBN 0-88027-059-4). Firm Foun Pub.

Boring, Holland, Sr. & Cox, Bill. Gems for His Crown. 1977. pap. 2.25 (ISBN 0-88027-054-3). Firm Foun Pub.

Boring, M. Eugene. Sayings of the Risen Jesus: Christian Prophecy in the Synoptic Tradition. LC 81-18022. (Society for New Testament Studies Monograph: No. 46). (Illus.). 310p. 1981. 44.50 (ISBN 0-521-24117-0). Cambridge U Pr.

Boring, M. Eugene, tr. see Lohse, Edward.

Boring, W. Eugene. Truly Human-Truly Divine: Christological Language & the Gospel Form. Lambert, Herbert, ed. LC 84-11382. 144p. 1984. pap. 11.95 (ISBN 0-8272-3625-5). CBP.

Bork, Hans. Chronologische Studien Zu Otfrids Evangelienbuch. 27.00 (ISBN 0-685-02224-2); pap. 22.00 (ISBN 0-685-02225-0). Johnson Repr.

Bork, Paul F. The World of Moses. LC 78-5022. (Horizon Ser.). 1978. pap. 5.95 (ISBN 0-8127-0166-6). Review & Herald.

Borland, James A. A General Introduction to the New Testament. (Illus.). viii, 216p. 1986. pap. 14.95x (ISBN 0-936461-00-4). Univ Book Hse.

Bormann, Eugenie. Glauben und Aberglauben. LC 84-70173. 120p. 23.00x (ISBN 0-938100-32-7). Camden Hse.

Borne, Mortimer. Meet Moses: Fifty-Four Drawings in Color. LC 77-74180. (Illus.). 1981. 18.50 (ISBN 0-913870-39-0). Abaris Bks.

Bornhoeft, Theodore P. Prayers Responsively: Responsive Prayers for the Three-Year Lectionary. 1984. pap. 8.95 (ISBN 0-570-03922-3, 12-2861). Concordia.

Bornkamm, Gunther. Jesus of Nazareth. LC 61-5256. 240p. 1975. pap. 6.00 (ISBN 0-06-060932-X, RD113, HarpR). Har-Row.

--The New Testament: A Guide to Its Writings. Fuller, Reginald H. & Fuller, Ilse, trs. from Ger. LC 73-79009. 176p. (Orig.). 1973. pap. 4.95 (ISBN 0-8006-0168-8, 1-168). Fortress.

--Paul. Stalker, D. M., tr. from Ger. LC 70-85068. 1971. short disc 15.95xi (ISBN 0-06-060933-8, HarpR). Har-Row.

Bornkamm, Gunther, et al. Tradition & Interpretation in Matthew. LC 63-10495. 308p. 1963. 13.95 (ISBN 0-664-20453-8). Westminster.

Bornkamm, Heinrich. Luther in Mid-Career, 1521-1530. Bachmann, E. Theodore, tr. from German. LC 82-48591. 736p. 1983. 36.95 (ISBN 0-8006-0692-2, 1-692). Fortress.

Borochov, Ber. Class Struggle & the Jewish Nation: Selected Essays in Marxist Zionism. Cohen, Mitchell, ed. LC 83-4695. 358p. 1983. 29.95 (ISBN 0-87855-479-3). Transaction Bks.

Boroffka, Alexander. Benedict Nta Tanka's Commentary & Dramatized Ideas on Disease & Witchcraft in Our Society: A Schreber Case from Cameroon African on His Mental Illness. (Medical Care in Developing Countries Ser.: Vol. 7). 150p. 1980. 19.45 (ISBN 3-8204-6901-X). P Lang Pubs.

Boros, L. The Hidden God. 132p. 1973. 5.95 (ISBN 0-8245-0313-9). Crossroad NY.

Boros, Ladislaus. Angels & Men. 1976. 6.95 (ISBN 0-8245-0201-9). Crossroad NY.

--Being a Christian Today. Davies, M. Benedict, tr. LC 79-13607. 124p. 1979. 7.95 (ISBN 0-8245-0202-7). Crossroad NY.

--Christian Prayer. 1976. 5.95 (ISBN 0-8245-0208-6). Crossroad NY.

--The Closeness of God. 1978. pap. 3.95 (ISBN 0-8245-0210-8). Crossroad NY.

--The Mystery of Death. 216p. 1973. pap. 3.95 (ISBN 0-8245-0330-9). Crossroad NY.

--Pain & Providence. 132p. 1975. pap. 2.95 (ISBN 0-686-85825-5). Crossroad NY.

Borough, John. Notes of the Treaty Carried on at Ripon Between King Charles First & the Covenanters of Scotland, A. D. 1640. Bruce, John, ed. (Camden Society, London. Publications, First Ser.: No. 100). Repr. of 1869 ed. 19.00 (ISBN 0-404-50200-8). AMS Pr.

--Notes of the Treaty Carried on at Ripon Between King Charles First & the Covenanters of Scotland, A. D. 1640. 1869. 19.00 (ISBN 0-384-05145-6). Johnson Repr.

Borovetz, Fran. Ha Motzi Bracha Kit. (Illus.). 32p. (Orig.). 1985. pap. text ed. 13.95 (ISBN 0-933873-03-4). Torah Aura.

Borowitz, Eugene. Liberal Judaism. LC 83-17997. 468p. (Orig.). 1984. pap. 8.95 (ISBN 0-8074-0264-8, 306050). UAHC.

--Understanding Judaism. 1979. 7.50 (ISBN 0-8074-0027-0, 341800). UAHC.

Borowitz, Eugene B. Choices in Modern Jewish Thought. 352p. 1983. pap. text ed. 9.95x (ISBN 0-87441-343-5). Behrman.

--Choosing a Sex Ethic: A Jewish Inquiry. LC 73-79123. 1970. pap. 5.95 (ISBN 0-8052-0276-5). Schocken.

--Contemporary Christologies: A Jewish Response. LC 80-81051. 208p. (Orig.). 1980. pap. 8.95 (ISBN 0-8091-2305-3). Paulist Pr.

--Reform Judaism Today. 800p. 1983. pap. text ed. 9.95x (ISBN 0-87441-364-8). Behrman.

Borowitz, Eugene B., ed. see Rossel, Seymour.

Borras, Jose. El Inmenso Amor De Dios. (Span.). 96p. 1981. pap. 3.95 (ISBN 0-311-43038-4). Casa Bautista.

Borresen, Kari E. Subordination & Equivalence: The Nature & Role of Women in Augustine & Thomas Aquinas. Talbot, Charles H., tr. from Fr. & Ital. LC 80-67199. 390p. 1981. lib. bdg. 29.25 (ISBN 0-8191-1681-5). U Pr of Amer.

Borri, Christoforo. Cochin-China: Containing Many Admirable Rarities of That Countrey. LC 71-25710. (English Experience Ser.: No. 223). 1970. Repr. of 1633 ed. 9.50 (ISBN 90-221-0223-8). Walter J Johnson.

Borror, Gordon, jt. auth. see Allen, Ronald B.

Borsch, Frederick H. Christian & Gnostic Son of Man. LC 77-131585. (Studies in Biblical Theology, 2nd Ser.: No. 14). (Orig.). 1970. pap. text ed. 10.00x (ISBN 0-8401-3064-3). A R Allenson.

--Introducing the Lessons of the Church Year: A Guide for Lay Readers & Congregations. 240p. (Orig.). 1984. pap. 8.95 (ISBN 0-8164-2496-9, 6102, HarpR). Har-Row.

--Pentecost One. LC 84-18756. (Proclamation Three C Ser.). 64p. 1986. pap. 3.75 (ISBN 0-8006-4130-2, 1-4130). Fortress.

Borsch, Frederick H. & Napier, Davie. Advent-Christmas. Achtemeier, Elizabeth, et al, eds. LC 79-7377. (Proclamation 2: Aids for Interpreting the Lessons of the Church Year, Ser. A). 64p. (Orig.). 1980. pap. 3.75 (ISBN 0-8006-4091-8, 1-4091). Fortress.

Borsch, Frederick H., ed. Anglicanism & the Bible. LC 83-62717. (Anglican Studies). (Orig.). 1984. pap. 8.95 (ISBN 0-8192-1337-3). Morehouse.

Borsh, Frederick H. Power in Weakness: New Hearing for Gospel Stories of Healing & Discipleship. LC 82-15997. 160p. 1983. pap. 8.95 (ISBN 0-8006-1703-7, 1-1703). Fortress.

Borst, James. Contemplative Prayer: A Guide for Today's Catholic. 1979. pap. 1.50 (ISBN 0-89243-106-7). Liguori Pubns.

Borth, Martha. Sitting at His Feet. (Illus.). 85p. (Orig.). 1985. pap. 5.95 (ISBN 0-935993-00-2). Clar Call Bks.

Borthwick, Meredith. Keshub Chunder Sen: A Search for Cultural Synthesis in India. 1978. 13.50x (ISBN 0-88386-904-7). South Asia Bks.

Borthwick, Paul. Any Old Time, Bk. 5. 80p. 1986. pap. 6.95 (ISBN 0-89693-187-0). Victor Bks.

Borton, Samuel L., tr. see Steiner, Rudolf.

Boruch, Behn. Coat of Many Colors. 1959. 3.95 (ISBN 0-88482-728-3). Hebrew Pub.

--In the Beginning. 1958. 4.00 (ISBN 0-88482-727-5). Hebrew Pub.

--The Patriarchs. 28p. 1959. 3.95 (ISBN 0-88482-729-1). Hebrew Pub.

Bos, Alphonse, ed. see Guillaume De Berneville.

Bos, Johanna W. Ruth, Esther, Jonah. LC 85-45793. (Preaching Guides Ser.). 108p. 1986. pap. 4.95 (ISBN 0-8042-3227-X). John Knox.

Bosanquet, Bernard. What Religion Is. LC 78-12709. 1979. Repr. of 1920 ed. lib. bdg. 22.50x (ISBN 0-313-21202-3, BOWR). Greenwood.

Bosch, David J. A Spirituality of the Road. LC 79-10856. (Mennonite Missionary Fellowship: No. 6). 104p. 1979. pap. 4.95 (ISBN 0-8361-1889-8). Herald Pr.

Bosch, H. G., jt. auth. see DeHaan, M. R.

Bosch, Henry G. The Gift of a Thorn. (Solace Ser.). 1984. pap. 1.50 (ISBN 0-8010-0866-2). Baker Bk.

--When Burdens Become Bridges. (Solace Ser.). 1984. pap. 1.50 (ISBN 0-8010-0867-0). Baker Bk.

Bosch, Henry G., jt. auth. see DeHaan, M. R.

Bosch, Henry G., jt. auth. see DeHaan, Richard W.

Bosch, Henry G., jt. ed. see De Haan, Richard W.

Bosch, Paul. The Paschal Cycle. 1979. pap. 6.75 (ISBN 0-570-03796-4, 12-2778). Concordia.

Boschman, LaMar. The Prophetic Song. (Orig.). 1986. pap. 3.95 (ISBN 0-938612-12-3). Revival Press.

Bosco, St. John. St. Dominic Savio. rev. ed. Aronica, Paul, tr. from Ital. LC 78-67221. (Illus.). 1979. pap. 2.95 (ISBN 0-89944-037-1). Don Bosco Multimedia.

Bosco, Ronald A., ed. Lessons for the Children of Godly Ancestors. LC 82-5844. (Sermon in America Ser.). 1982. 60.00x (ISBN 0-8201-1381-6). Schol Facsimiles.

--Puritan Sermon in America, 1630-1750, 4 vols. LC 78-114749. (Sermon in America Ser.). 1978. Repr. 200.00x set (ISBN 0-8201-1320-4). Schol Facsimiles.

Bosco, Ronald A., ed. see Mather, Cotton.

Bose, Abinash C. Three Mystic Poets: A Study of W. B. Yeats, A. E. & Rabindrath Tagore. LC 72-187263. 1945. lib. bdg. 12.50 (ISBN 0-8414-2534-5). Folcroft.

Bose, D. N. Tantras: Their Philosophy & Occult Secrets. rev. 3rd ed. 1981. Repr. of 1956 ed. 12.00x (ISBN 0-8364-0737-7, Pub. by Mukhopadhyay). South Asia Bks.

--The Yoga Vasistha Ramayana. rev. ed. 1984. Repr. of 1954 ed. 12.50x (ISBN 0-8364-1181-1, Pub. by Mukhopadhyaya India). South Asia Bks.

Bose, Ram C. Hindu Philosophy. 420p. 1986. Repr. 28.00X (ISBN 0-8364-1757-7, Pub. by Manohar India). South Asia Bks.

Boshtchanovsky, Basil. Uroki po Pastirskomu Bogosloviju. Tr. of Studies in Pastoral Theology. 100p. 1961. pap. text ed. 5.00 (ISBN 0-317-30267-1). Holy Trinity.

Boskey, James B. & Hughes, Susan C. Teaching about Aging: Religious & Advocacy Perspectives. LC 82-17589. 184p. (Orig.). 1983. lib. bdg. 26.00 (ISBN 0-8191-2802-3); pap. text ed. 11.50 (ISBN 0-8191-2803-1). U Pr of Amer.

Bosmajian, Haig A., ed. The Freedom of Religion. (The First Amendment in the Classroom Ser.: No. 2). 455p. 1987. text ed. 24.95 (ISBN 1-55570-002-0). Neal-Schuman.

Bossart, Donald E. Creative Conflict in Religious Education & Church Administration. LC 80-12704. 284p. (Orig.). 1980. pap. 12.95 (ISBN 0-89135-048-9). Religious Educ.

Bosschere, Jean de & Morris, M. C. Christmas Tales of Flanders. (Illus.). 7.75 (ISBN 0-8446-4516-8). Peter Smith.

Bossert, Gustav. Quellen zur Geshichte der Wiedertaufer. 90.00 (ISBN 0-384-05276-2); pap. 84.00 (ISBN 0-384-05275-4). Johnson Repr.

Bossy, John. Christianity in the West, Fourteen Hundred to Seventeen Hundred. (OPUS). 189p. 1985. 19.95x (ISBN 0-19-219174-8); pap. 7.95 (ISBN 0-19-289162-6). Oxford U Pr.

--The English Catholic Community, 1570-1850. (Illus.). 1976. 39.95x (ISBN 0-19-519847-6); pap. 5.95x (ISBN 0-19-285148-9). Oxford U Pr.

Boster, Gregory, ed. see Ross, Alan.

Bostick, W. F. Jesus & Socrates. 59.95 (ISBN 0-8490-0443-8). Gordon Pr.

Boston, Thomas. The Complete Works of the Late Rev. Thomas Boston, Ettrick: Including His Memoirs, Written by Himself, 12 vols. M'Millan, Samuel, ed. (Puritan Library). (Illus.). 1980. Repr. of 1853 ed. Set. lib. bdg. 225.00 (ISBN 0-940033-00-3). R O Roberts.

Bostrom, Alice. David Livingstone, Missionary to Africa. (Children's Missionary Library: Bk. 7). (Illus.). 32p. (Orig.). 1982. pap. 1.50 (ISBN 0-89323-027-8). Bible Memory.

--Search the Word Bible Puzzles. (Illus.). 48p. 1983. pap. 2.50 (ISBN 0-87239-589-8, 2787). Standard Pub.

Bostrom, Carol, jt. auth. see Burns, Jim.

Bostrom, Christopher J. Philosophy of Religion. 1962. 42.50x (ISBN 0-685-69791-6). Elliots Bks.

Bostrom, Otto H. Alternative Readings in the Hebrew of the Books of Samuel. LC 18-8964. (Augustana College Library Publication Ser.: No. 8). 60p. 1918. pap. 0.75 (ISBN 0-910182-05-1). Augustana Coll.

Boswell, Fred & Boswell, Jeanetta. What Men or Gods Are These? A Genealogical Approach to Classical Mythology. LC 80-13780. 324p. 1980. 27.50 (ISBN 0-8108-1314-9). Scarecrow.

Boswell, Jeanetta, jt. auth. see Boswell, Fred.

Boswell, John. Christianity, Social Tolerance, & Homosexuality: Gay People in Western Europe from the Beginning of the Christian Era to the Fourteenth Century. LC 79-11171. (Illus.). xviii, 424p. 1980. 35.00x (ISBN 0-226-06710-6); pap. 12.95 (ISBN 0-226-06711-4). U of Chicago Pr.

Boswell, Kathryn, jt. auth. see O'Connor, Francine.

Boswell, Kathryn, jt. auth. see O'Connor, Francine M.

Bosworth, C. E. The Islamic Dynasties. 243p. 1980. pap. 10.00 (ISBN 0-85224-402-9, Pub. by Edinburgh U Pr Scotland). Columbia U Pr.

Bosworth, C. E., ed. Iran & Islam. 574p. 1972. 35.00x (ISBN 0-85224-200-X, Pub. by Edinburgh U Pr Scotland). Columbia U Pr.

Bosworth, C. E., jt. ed. see Schacht, Joseph.

Bosworth, F. F. Christ the Healer. 241p. pap. 6.95 (ISBN 0-8007-5124-8, Power Bks). Revell.

Botfield, Beriah. Notes on the Cathedral Libraries of England. LC 68-23138. 1969. Repr. of 1849 ed. 65.00x (ISBN 0-8103-3174-8). Gale.

Bothra, Pushpa. Jaina Theory of Perception. 1976. 11.95 (ISBN 0-89684-229-0). Orient Bk Dist.

Bothwell, Etta K. Alienation in the Jewish American Novel of the Sixties. LC 78-3559. 1979. pap. 10.00 (ISBN 0-8477-3191-X). U of PR Pr.

Bothwell, H. Roger. My First Book about Baptism. (My Church Teaches Ser.). (Illus.). 1978. pap. 1.95 (ISBN 0-8127-0179-8). Review & Herald.

--My First Book About Communion. (My Church Teaches Ser.). (Illus.). 1978. pap. 1.95 (ISBN 0-8127-0180-1). Review & Herald.

Bothwell, Sr. Mary D. We Believe. (Christ Our Life Ser.). (Illus.). 1981. pap. text ed. 4.20 (ISBN 0-8294-0367-1); tchr's ed. 12.95 (ISBN 0-8294-0368-X). Loyola.

--We Worship. (Christ Our Life Ser.). (Illus.). 1982. text ed. 4.20 (ISBN 0-8294-0391-4); tchrs. ed. 12.95 (ISBN 0-8294-0392-2). Loyola.

Bothwell, Sr. Mary. God Guides Us. (Christ Our Life Ser). (Illus.). 1981. pap. text ed. 4.60 (ISBN 0-8294-0365-5); tchr's ed. 12.95 (ISBN 0-8294-0366-3). Loyola.

Bothwell, Roger. For the Umpteenth Time. (Outreach Ser.). 16p. 1983. pap. 0.95 (ISBN 0-8163-0538-2). Pacific Pr Pub Assn.

Botkin-Mayer, Jennifer. Nice Girls Don't Get Raped. 1987. pap. 5.95. Heres Life.

Bott, Victor. Anthroposophical Medicine: Spiritual Science & the Art of Healing. 208p. (Orig.). 1984. pap. 8.95 (ISBN 0-7225-0958-8). Thorsons Pubs.

Botterweck, C. Michael. A Test of Faith: Challenges of Modern Day Christians. 304p. (Orig.). 1983. pap. 8.95 (ISBN 0-911541-01-2). Gregory Pub.

Botterweck, G. Johannes. Diccionario Teologico del Antiguo Testamento, 4 vols. (Span.). 1116p. 1978. Set. pns (S-50106). French & Eur.

Botterweck, G. Johannes & Ringgren, Helmer, eds. Theological Dictionary of the Old Testament, 5 vols. 560p. 1978. Set. 137.50 (ISBN 0-8028-2338-6); Vol. I. 27.50 ea. (ISBN 0-8028-2325-4). Vol. II (ISBN 0-8028-2326-2). Vol. III (ISBN 0-8028-2327-0). Vol. IV (ISBN 0-8028-2328-9). Vol. V (ISBN 0-8028-2329-7). Eerdmans.

Botting, Gary, jt. auth. see Botting, Heather.

Botting, Heather & Botting, Gary. The Orwellian World of Jehovah's Witnesses. (Illus.). 224p. 1984. pap. 10.95 (ISBN 0-8020-6545-7). U of Toronto Pr.

Bottomley, Frank. The Church Explorer's Guide to England, Scotland, & Wales. 1978. pap. 4.95 (ISBN 0-7182-1187-1, Pub. by Kaye & Ward). David & Charles.

Botz, Myrna, jt. auth. see King, Pat.

Botz, Paschal. Runways to God. LC 79-24756. 346p. (Orig.). 1979. pap. 3.50 (ISBN 0-8146-1059-5). Liturgical Pr.

Botz, Paschal, et al. Prayers Before & after Communion. 24p. 1981. pap. 0.50 (ISBN 0-8146-1213-X). Liturgical Pr.

Bouchard, Angeline, tr. see Galot, Jean.

Bouchard, Constance B. Spirituality & Administration: The Role of the Bishop in Twelfth-Century Auxerre. LC 78-55889. 1979. 11.00x (ISBN 0-910956-79-0, SAM5); pap. 5.00x (ISBN 0-910956-67-7). Medieval Acad.

--Sword, Miter, & Cloister: Nobility & the Church in Burgundy, 980-1198. LC 86-29158. (Illus.). 416p. 1987. text ed. 41.50x (ISBN 0-8014-1974-3). Cornell U Pr.

Bouchard, Larry D., jt. ed. see Richesin, L. Dale.

Bouchard, M. Angeline, tr. see Galot.

Bouchard, M. Angeline, tr. see Simonet, Andre.

Bouche-Leclercq, Auguste. Les Pontifes de L'Ancienne Rome: Etudes Historique sur les Institutions Religieuses de Rome. facsimile ed. LC 75-10630. (Ancient Religion & Mythology Ser.). (Fr.). 1976. Repr. of 1871 ed. 33.00x (ISBN 0-405-07006-3). Ayer Co Pubs.

Boucher, Madeleine I. The Parables. (New Testament Message Ser.: Vol. 7). 12.95 (ISBN 0-89453-195-6); pap. 7.95 (ISBN 0-89453-130-1). M Glazier.

Boucher, Therese. Becoming a Sensuous Catechist: Using the Arts in Religion Classes. (Illus.). 80p. 1984. pap. 5.95 (ISBN 0-89622-216-0). Twenty-Third.

Boudard, J. B. Iconologie. LC 75-27888. (Renaissance & the Gods Ser.: Vol. 43). (Illus.). 1976. Repr. of 1766 ed. lib. bdg. 80.00 (ISBN 0-8240-2092-8). Garland Pub.

Boudeaux, Michael. Risen Indeed: Lessons of Faith from the U. S. S. R. (Orig.). 1983. pap. text ed. 5.95 (ISBN 0-88141-021-7). St Vladimirs.

Boudinot, Elias. Star in the West: A Humble Attempt to Discover the Long Lost Ten Tribes of Israel. facs. ed. LC 79-121499. (Select Bibliographies Reprint Ser). 1816. 17.00 (ISBN 0-8369-5457-2). Ayer Co Pubs.

Boudreau, Albert. The Born-Again Catholic. (Illus., Orig.). 1979. pap. 4.95 (ISBN 0-914544-26-8). Living Flame Pr.

Boudreau, Amy. Story of the Christian Year. 1971. 4.50 (ISBN 0-685-27196-X). Claitors.

Boudreau, J. The Happiness of Heaven. LC 83-51548. 258p. 1984. pap. 6.00 (ISBN 0-89555-232-9). TAN Bks Pubs.

Boudreaux, Florentin. God Our Father. LC 65-36485. pap. 55.00 (ISBN 0-317-10042-4, 2001664). Bks Demand UMI.

Bougerol, Guy J. Introduction to the Works of St. Bonaventure. 1964. 7.50 (ISBN 0-8199-0525-9). Franciscan Herald.

Bouhdiba, Abdelwahab. Sexuality in Islam. 288p. 1985. 42.50x (ISBN 0-7100-9608-9). Methuen Inc.

Boulainvilliers, H. De see De Boulainvilliers, H.

Boulden, James. I Am All. (Illus.). 72p. 1982. pap. 2.95 (ISBN 0-87516-481-1). De Vorss.

Bouldin, Don. Ears to Hear, Eyes to See. (Orig.). 1987. pap. 6.95 (ISBN 0-8054-3002-4). Broadman.

Boulding, Elise. Children & Solitude. 1983. pap. 2.50x (ISBN 0-87574-125-8, 125). Pendle Hill.

--The Family As a Way into the Future. 1983. pap. 2.50x (ISBN 0-87574-222-X, 222). Pendle Hill.

Boulding, Kenneth. New Nations for Old. 1983. pap. 2.50x (ISBN 0-87574-017-0, 017). Pendle Hill.

Boulding, Kenneth E. Beyond Economics: Essays on Society, Religion, & Ethics. 1970. pap. 4.95 (ISBN 0-472-06167-4, 167, AA). U of Mich Pr.

--The Evolutionary Potential of Quakerism. 1983. pap. 2.50x (ISBN 0-87574-136-3, 136). Pendle Hill.

--Mending the World: Quaker Insights on the Social Order. LC 86-60283. 1986. pap. 2.50 (ISBN 0-87574-266-1). Pendle Hill.

Boulding, Kenneth E. & Mayer, Milton. Mayer Boulding Dialogue on Peace Research. Murphy, Carol, ed. LC 67-23313. (Orig.). 1967. pap. 2.50x (ISBN 0-87574-153-3). Pendle Hill.

Boulding, Maria. The Coming of God. 224p. 1983. pap. text ed. 9.00 (ISBN 0-8146-1278-4). Liturgical Pr.

Boulding, Maria, ed. A Touch of God: Eight Monastic Journeys. LC 82-24055. 1983. pap. 7.95x (ISBN 0-932506-26-7). St Bedes Pubns.

Boulger, James D. The Calvinistic Temper in English Poetry. (De Proprietatibus Litterarum, Ser. Major: No. 21). 1980. text ed. 71.00x (ISBN 90-279-7575-2). Mouton.

Boult, Pamela, ed. see Newhouse, Flower A.

Boult, Pamela, compiled by. & intro. see Newhouse, Flower A.

Boulton, Roger H., ed. see Heritage Village Church & Missionary Fellowship, Inc. Staff.

Boultwood, Alban. Christ in Us: Reflections on Redemption. LC 81-8371. 144p. (Orig.). 1981. pap. 5.50 (ISBN 0-8146-1234-2). Liturgical Pr.

Bouma, Mary L. The Creative Homemaker. LC 73-17234. 192p. 1973. pap. 3.95 (ISBN 0-87123-078-X, 200084). Bethany Hse.

--The Creative Homemaker. 3.95 (ISBN 0-87123-084-4, 200084). Bethany Hse.

Bouma, Mary La G. Divorce in the Parsonage. LC 79-16157. 160p. 1979. pap. 3.95 (ISBN 0-87123-109-3, 210109). Bethany Hse.

Bouman, H. J., tr. Luther's Works, Vol. 10. 1981. 16.95 (ISBN 0-570-06410-4, 15-1752). Concordia.

Bouman, Herbert, tr. see Schlink, Edmund.

Bouman, Herbert J., tr. Law & Gospel: Selected Writings of C.F.W. Walther. 1981. 12.95 (ISBN 0-570-08275-7, 15-2733). Concordia.

--Luther's Works, Vol. 16. 1968. 14.95 (ISBN 0-570-06416-3, 15-1758). Concordia.

Bouman, Herbert J., tr. see Luther, Martin.

Bouman, Herbert J., tr. see Von Loewenich, Walter.

Bouman, Herbert J., tr. see Walther, C. F.

Bounds, E. M. Catching a Glimpse of Heaven. 150p. 1985. pap. text ed. 3.50 (ISBN 0-88368-167-6). Whitaker Hse.

--The Essentials of Prayer. (Direction Bks Ser.). 1979. pap. 3.95 (ISBN 0-8010-0756-9). Baker Bk.

--Heaven: A Place, a City, a Home. (Direction Bks). 152p. 1975. pap. 3.50 (ISBN 0-8010-0648-1). Baker Bk.

--The Necessity of Prayer. (Direction Bks). 144p. 1976. pap. 2.95 (ISBN 0-8010-0659-7). Baker Bk.

--The Necessity of Prayer. 144p. 1984. pap. 3.50 (ISBN 0-88368-139-0). Whitaker Hse.

--Obtaining Answers to Prayer. 144p. 1984. pap. 3.50 (ISBN 0-88368-142-0). Whitaker Hse.

--The Possibilities of Prayer. (Direction Bks). 1979. pap. 3.95 (ISBN 0-8010-0757-7). Baker Bk.

--Power Through Prayer. 112p. 1983. pap. text ed. 2.95 (ISBN 0-88368-117-X). Whitaker Hse.

--Power Through Prayer. (Moody Classics Ser.). 1985. pap. text ed. 3.50 (ISBN 0-8024-6729-6). Moody.

--Prayer & Praying Men. (Direction Bks). 1977. pap. 3.95 (ISBN 0-8010-0721-6). Baker Bk.

--Reality of Prayer. (Direction Bks). 1978. pap. 3.50 (ISBN 0-8010-0739-9). Baker Bk.

--Satan: His Personality, Power & Overthrow. (Direction Bks). 1972. pap. 2.95 (ISBN 0-8010-0586-8). Baker Bk.

--A Treasury of Prayer. LC 53-9865. 192p. 1981. pap. 5.95 (ISBN 0-87123-543-9, 210543). Bethany Hse.

--The Weapon of Prayer. (Direction Bks.). 57p. 1975. pap. 3.95 (ISBN 0-8010-0634-1). Baker Bk.

--Winning the Invisible War. 160p. 1984. pap. 3.50 (ISBN 0-88368-145-5). Whitaker Hse.

Bounds, Edward M. Power Through Prayer. (Direction Bks). 1972. pap. 3.95 (ISBN 0-8010-0584-1). Baker Bk.

--Power Through Prayer. pap. 2.95 (ISBN 0-310-21612-5, 9237). Zondervan.

--Purpose in Prayer. (Direction Bks). 1978. pap. 3.95 (ISBN 0-8010-0738-0). Baker Bk.

Bouquet, A. C. Everyday Life in New Testament Times. (Hudson River Editions). (Illus.). 1953. lib. rep. ed. 20.00 (ISBN 0-684-14833-1, ScribT). Scribner.

Bouquet, Alan C. Religious Experience: Its Nature, Types, & Validity. LC 75-40997. 140p. 1976. Repr. of 1968 ed. lib. bdg. 22.50x (ISBN 0-8371-8714-1, BORL). Greenwood.

Bourasse, J. J. Dictionnaire d'Archeologie Sacree, 2 vols. Migne, J. P., ed. (Nouvelle Encyclopedie Theologique Ser.: Vols. 11-12). (Fr.). 1236p. Repr. of 1852 ed. lib. bdg. 157.00x (ISBN 0-89241-261-5). Caratzas.

--Dictionnaire d'Epigraphie Chretienne, 2 vols. Migne, J. P., ed. (Nouvelle Encyclopedie Theologique Ser.: Vols. 30-31). (Fr.). 1262p. Repr. of 1852 ed. lib. bdg. 161.00x (ISBN 0-89241-273-9). Caratzas.

Bourbourg, Charles E. Brasseru De see Brasseur De Bourbourg, Charles E.

Bourdillon, A. F. C. The Order of Minoresses in England. 115p. Repr. of 1926 ed. text ed. 33.12x (ISBN 0-576-99212-7, Pub. by Gregg Intl Pubs England). Gregg Intl.

Bourdillon, M. F. C. & Fortes, M. Sacrifices. 1980. 54.50 (ISBN 0-12-119040-4). Acad Pr.

Bourgeois, Henri. On Becoming Christian. 2nd ed. 160p. 1985. pap. 6.95 (ISBN 0-89622-270-5). Twenty-Third.

Bourgeois, Jean-Francois. Los Ninos de la Biblia. Maecha, Alberto, ed. Orig. Title: Les Enfants de la Bible. (Span., Illus.). 40p. 1984. pap. write for info. (ISBN 0-942504-11-9). Overcomer Pr.
Bourgeous, Virginia. Quest for Love & Self-Esteem: New Insights from Psychology & Religion. LC 76-29301. (Illus.). 80p. (Orig.). 1976. pap. 5.95 (ISBN 0-88290-070-6). Horizon Utah.
Bourghei, S. R., et al. Piety. Tavakoli, Amir, tr. from Persian. 1980. pap. 1.00 (ISBN 0-318-03827-7). Book-Dist-Ctr.
Bourguignon, Erika, ed. Religion, Altered States of Consciousness, & Social Change. LC 72-8448. (Illus.). 399p. 1973. 12.50 (ISBN 0-8142-0167-9). Ohio St U Pr.
Bourke, John G. The Medicine Men of the Apache. LC 71-175003. (Illus.). 150p. 13.50 (ISBN 0-87026-049-9). Westernlore.
Bourke, Myles M. Job. (Bible Ser.). Pt. 1. pap. 1.00 (ISBN 0-8091-5073-5); Pt. 2. pap. 1.00 (ISBN 0-8091-5074-3). Paulist Pr.
Bourke, Vernon J. Saint Thomas & the Greek Moralists. (Aquinas Lecture). 1947. 7.95 (ISBN 0-87462-111-9). Marquette.
Bourke, Vernon J., jt. ed. see Miethe, Terry L.
Bourke, Vernon J., commentary by see Saint Augustine.
Bourke, Vernon J. see St. Thomas Aquinas.
Bourne, David L., jt. auth. see Adolph, Harold.
Bourne, Lois. Witch Amongst Us. 208p. 1986. 13.95 (ISBN 0-312-88425-7). St Martin.
Bousset, Wilhelm. The Antichrist Legend: A Chapter in Christian & Jewish Folklore. LC 79-8095. (Satanism Ser.). 344p. Repr. of 1896 ed. 37.50 (ISBN 0-404-18406-5). AMS Pr.
--The Antichrist Legend: A Chapter in Christian & Jewish Folklore. 1977. lib. bdg. 59.95 (ISBN 0-8490-1439-5). Gordon Pr.
Boutas, V., ed. Women in Islam: Social Attitudes & Historical Perspectives. 224p. 1983. 30.00x (ISBN 0-7007-0154-0, Pub. by Curzon England). State Mutual Bk.
Bouterse, Wesley. Scriptural Light on Speaking in Tongues. 1980. pap. 1.25 (ISBN 0-86544-010-7). Salv Army Suppl South.
Bouterwek, K. W. Cademon's Des Angelsachsen Biblishce Dictungen, 2 Vols. 393p. 1983. Repr. of 1854 ed. Set. lib. bdg. 400.00 (ISBN 0-8495-0636-0). Arden Lib.
Boutilier, James A., et al, eds. Mission, Church, & Sect in Oceania. (Asao Monograph: No. 6). (Illus.). 514p. 1984. lib. bdg. 38.25 (ISBN 0-8191-3837-1, Assoc Soc Anthro Oceania); pap. text ed. 20.75 (ISBN 0-8191-3838-X, Assoc Soc Anthro Oceania). U Pr of Amer.
Boutman, Herbert J., et al, trs. see Stiller, Gunther.
Boutroux, Emile. Science & Religion in Contemporary Philosophy. Nield, Jonathan, tr. 1979. Repr. of 1909 ed. lib. bdg. 35.00 (ISBN 0-8495-0540-2). Arden Lib.
--Science & Religion in Contemporary Philosophy. LC 70-102563. 1970. Repr. of 1909 ed. 33.50x (ISBN 0-8046-0723-0, Pub. by Kennikat). Assoc Faculty Pr.
Bouvier, Leon & Rao, Sethu. Socioreligious Factors in Fertility Decline. LC 75-26602. 224p. 1975. text ed. 25.00x prof ref (ISBN 0-88410-352-8). Ballinger Pub.
Bouwsma, William J. Concordia Mundi: The Career & Thought of Guillaume Postel, 1510-1581. LC 57-8622. (Historical Monographs Ser: No. 33). 1957. 22.50x (ISBN 0-674-15950-0). Harvard U Pr.
Bouyer, L. & Cawley, M. Christology. LC 83-4420. (Word & Spirit Ser.: Vol. V). 1983. pap. 7.00 (ISBN 0-932506-28-3). St Bedes Pubns.
Bouyer, Louis. The Church of God. Quinn, Charles U., tr. 1983. 25.00 (ISBN 0-686-45823-0). Franciscan Herald.
--Diccionario De Teologia. 4th ed. (Span.). 672p. 1977. 25.50 (ISBN 84-254-0377-4, S-14671). French & Eur.
--Eucharist: Theology & Spirituality of the Eucharist Prayer. Quinn, Charles U., tr. LC 68-17064. 1968. pap. 13.95 (ISBN 0-268-00498-6). U of Notre Dame Pr.
--Liturgical Piety. (Liturgical Studies Ser). 1965. 10.95x (ISBN 0-268-00158-8). U of Notre Dame Pr.
--Liturgy & Architecture. 1967. 6.95x (ISBN 0-268-00159-6). U of Notre Dame Pr.
--Orthodox Spirituality & Protestant & Anglican Spirituality. (A History of Christian Spirituality Ser.: Vol. 3). 232p. 1982. pap. 9.95 (ISBN 0-8164-2374-1, HarpR). Har-Row.
--Rite & Man: Natural Sacredness & Christian Liturgy. Costelloe, Joseph, tr. 224p. 1985. pap. text ed. 12.25 (ISBN 0-8191-4340-5). U Pr of Amer.
--The Spirituality of the New Testament & the Fathers. (A History of Christian Spirituality Ser.: Vol. 1). 560p. 1982. pap. 13.95 (ISBN 0-8164-2372-5, HarpR). Har-Row.
--Woman in the Church. Teichert, Marilyn, tr. from Fr. LC 79-84878. Orig. Title: Mystere et Ministeres de la femme dans l'Eglise. 132p. (Orig.). 1979. pap. 7.95 (ISBN 0-89870-002-7). Ignatius Pr.
Bovarsky, Abraham & Sarna, Lazar, eds. Canadian Yiddish Writings. LC 77-362060. pap. 37.50 (ISBN 0-317-10945-6, 2022287). Bks Demand UMI.
Bove, Vincent. Playing His Game. LC 84-70985. 1984. pap. 5.95 (ISBN 0-88270-570-9). Bridge Pub.
Bovis, H. Eugene. Jerusalem Question: 1917-1968. LC 73-149796. (Studies Ser.: No. 29). (Illus.). 175p. 1971. 9.95x (ISBN 0-8179-3291-7). Hoover Inst Pr.
Bovon, Francois. Luke the Theologian: Thirty-Five Years of Research (1950-1985) McKinney, Ken, tr. from Fr. (Princeton Theological Monograph Ser.: No. 12). Tr. of Luc la theologien: Vingt-cinq ans de recherches (1950-1975) (Orig.). 1987. pap. price not set (ISBN 0-915138-93-X). Pickwick.
Bovon, Francois & Rouiller, Gregoire, eds. Exegesis: Problems of Method & Exercises in Reading. Miller, Donald G, tr. from Fr. LC 78-27622. (Pittsburgh Theological Monographs: No. 21). Orig. Title: Exegesis; Problemes de Methode et Exercices de Lecture. 1978. pap. 15.00 (ISBN 0-915138-25-5). Pickwick.
Bowden, E. The Imitation of Buddha: Quotations from Buddhist Literature for Each Day. 59.95 (ISBN 0-8490-0386-5). Gordon Pr.
Bowden, Edwin T. & Farmer, David, eds. The Holy Bible at the University of Texas. rev. ed. Orig. Title: The Holy Bible, an Exhibit. (Illus.). 1967. 8.00 (ISBN 0-87959-027-0). U of Tex H Ransom Ctr.
Bowden, Henry S., ed. see Simpson, Richard.
Bowden, Henry W. American Indians & Christian Missions: Studies in Cultural Conflict. LC 80-27840. (Chicago History of American Religion Ser.). 1981. 18.00x (ISBN 0-226-06811-0). U of Chicago Pr.
--American Indians & Christian Missions: Studies in Cultural Conflict. LC 84-27840. (Chicago History of American Religion Ser). xx, 256p. 1985. pap. 7.95 (ISBN 0-226-06812-9). U of Chicago Pr.
--Dictionary of American Religious Biography. Gaustad, Edwin S., ed. LC 76-5258. (Orig.). 1976. lib. bdg. 45.00 (ISBN 0-8371-8906-3, BAR/). Greenwood.
Bowden, J. H. Peter De Vries. (United States Authors Ser.). 1983. lib. bdg. 16.95 (ISBN 0-8057-7388-6, Twayne). G K Hall.
Bowden, James. The History of the Society of Friends in America, 2 vols. in 1. LC 73-38440. (Religion in America, Ser. 2). 870p. 1972. Repr. of 1854 ed. 58.50 (ISBN 0-405-04061-X). Ayer Co Pubs.
Bowden, John. Archeology & the Bible. 24p. 1982. pap. 3.00 (ISBN 0-910309-00-0). Am Atheist.
--Bible Absurdities. 24p. 1982. Repr. of 1968 ed. 2.50 (ISBN 0-911826-45-9, 5036). Am Atheist.
--The Bible Contradicts Itself. 36p. 1982. Repr. of 1968 ed. saddle-stitched 3.00 (ISBN 0-911826-46-7). Am Atheist.
--Edward Schillebeeckx: In Search of the Kingdom of God. 160p. 1983. pap. 8.95 (ISBN 0-8245-0610-3). Crossroad NY.
--Herbert Armstrong & His Worldwide Church of God: An Exposure & an Indictment. 64p. 1982. saddle stitched 3.00 (ISBN 0-911826-24-6). Am Atheist.
Bowden, John, jt. ed. see Richardson, Alan.
Bowden, John, tr. see Beyerlin, Walter.
Bowden, John, tr. see Boerma, Conrad.
Bowden, John, tr. see Grollenberg, Lucas.
Bowden, John, tr. see Gunneweg, A. H.
Bowden, John, tr. see Hengel, Martin.
Bowden, John, tr. see Herrmann, Siegfried.
Bowden, John, tr. see Houtepen, Anton.
Bowden, John, tr. see Jagersma, Henk.
Bowden, John, tr. see Kuitert, H. M.
Bowden, John, tr. see Rendtorff, Rolf.
Bowden, John, tr. see Reventlow, Henning G.
Bowden, John, tr. see Ritschl, Dietrich.
Bowden, John, tr. see Schillebeeckx, Edward.
Bowden, John, tr. see Soggin, J. Albert.
Bowden, John, tr. see Soggin, J. Alberto.
Bowden, John, tr. see Theissen, Gerd.
Bowden, John, tr. see Witvliet, Theo.
Bowden, John, et al, trs. see Jeremias, Joachim.
Bowden, John S., tr. see Grillmeier, Aloys.
Bowden, Malcolm. Rise of the Evolution Fraud. 1982. pap. 8.95 (ISBN 0-89051-085-7). Master Bks.
Bowder, Diana. The Age of Constantine & Julian. (Illus.). 230p. 1978. text ed. 32.50x (ISBN 0-06-490601-9, 06359). B&N Imports.
Bowdle, Donald N., ed. The Promise & the Power. 332p. 1980. 14.95 (ISBN 0-87148-706-3). Pathway Pr.
--La Redencion Lograda y Aplicada. (Span.). 126p. 1979. pap. 3.95 (ISBN 0-87148-521-4). Pathway Pr.
Bowdle, Donald W. Redemption Accomplished & Applied. 1972. 5.25 (ISBN 0-87148-726-8); pap. 4.25 (ISBN 0-87148-727-6). Pathway Pr.
Bowen, Barbara M. Strange Scriptures That Perplex the Western Mind. 1940. pap. 3.95 (ISBN 0-8028-1511-1). Eerdmans.
Bowen, Desmond. The Idea of the Victorian Church: A Study of the Church of England 1833-1889. 1968. 20.00x (ISBN 0-7735-0033-2). McGill-Queens U Pr.
Bowen, E. G. Dewi Sant. Saint David-Patron Saint of Wales. (St. David's Day Bilingual). 90p. 1983. pap. text ed. 6.95x (ISBN 0-7083-0839-2, Pub. by U of Wales). Humanities.
Bowen, Francis A. A Bride's Guide to a Christian Wedding. LC 78-73642. (Illus.). 1979. text ed. 2.95 (ISBN 0-9602830-0-5). F A Bowen.
--How to Produce a Church Newspaper... & Other Ways Churches Communicate. (Illus.). 1974. 5.00 (ISBN 0-9602830-1-3). F A Bowen.
Bowen, Kurt. Protestants in a Catholic State: Ireland's Privileged Minority. 240p. 1983. 27.50x (ISBN 0-7735-0412-5). McGill-Queens U Pr.
Bowen, Patrick G. The Sayings of the Ancient One. lib. bdg. 79.95 (ISBN 0-87968-490-9). Krishna Pr.
Bowen, T. J. Adventures & Missionary Labours in Several Countries in the Interior of Africa from 1849-1856. 2nd rev. ed. 359p. 1968. Repr. of 1857 ed. 32.50x (ISBN 0-7146-1863-2, F Cass Co). Biblio Dist.
Bowen, Van S. A Vestry Member's Guide. rev. ed. 80p. 1983. pap. 3.95 (ISBN 0-8164-2464-0, HarpR). Har-Row.
Bowen, William, Jr. Globalism: America's Demise. LC 84-80408. 222p. (Orig.). 1984. pap. 6.95 (ISBN 0-910311-24-2). Huntington Hse Inc.
Bower, Peter C. Handbook for the Common Lectionary. 300p. (Orig.). 1987. pap. 10.95 (ISBN 0-664-24048-8, A Geneva Press Publication). Westminster.
Bower, Robert K. Administering Christian Education. LC 64-22018. 1964. pap. 8.95 (ISBN 0-8028-1559-6). Eerdmans.
Bower, William C. The Curriculum of Religious Education. (Educational Ser.). 1930. Repr. 30.00 (ISBN 0-8482-7353-2). Norwood Edns.
Bower, William C., ed. Church at Work in the Modern World. facs. ed. LC 67-26717. (Essay Index Reprint Ser). 1935. 18.00 (ISBN 0-8369-0231-9). Ayer Co Pubs.
Bowers, G. M. The Faith & Doctrines of the Early Church. LC 78-60521. 1978. pap. 4.95 (ISBN 0-917182-09-X). Triumph Pub.
Bowers, R. H., ed. Three Middle English Religious Poems. LC 63-63267. (University of Florida Humanities Monographs: No. 12). 1963. pap. 3.50 (ISBN 0-8130-0025-4). U Presses Fla.
Bowes, Betty. Ministry of the Cradle Roll. (Orig.). 1970. pap. 1.95 (ISBN 0-8341-0190-4). Beacon Hill.
Bowes, Paula. The First & Second Samuel. (Bible Commentary Ser.). 128p. 1985. pap. text ed. 2.95 (ISBN 0-8146-1415-9). Liturgical Pr.
Bowker, John. Jesus & the Pharisees. 240p. 1973. 42.50 (ISBN 0-521-20055-5). Cambridge U Pr.
--Problems of Suffering in the Religions of the World. LC 77-93706. 1975. 47.50 (ISBN 0-521-07412-6); pap. 12.95x (ISBN 0-521-09903-X). Cambridge U Pr.
--The Religious Imagination & the Sense of God. 1978. text ed. 32.50x (ISBN 0-19-826646-4). Oxford U Pr.
--Targums & Rabbinic Literature. LC 71-80817. 1969. 67.50 (ISBN 0-521-07415-0). Cambridge U Pr.
Bowker, Margaret. The Henrician Reformation: The Diocese of Lincoln Under John Longland 1521-1547. LC 80-41655. (Illus.). 256p. 1981. 49.50 (ISBN 0-521-23639-8). Cambridge U Pr.
Bowman, Billye G. Had I Known You Better, Lord I'd a Come Runnin' with a Bucket. Goodman, James, ed. 240p. (Orig.). 1986. pap. 10.00 (ISBN 0-89896-140-8, Linolean). Larksdale.
Bowman, Derek. Life into Autobiography: A Study of Goethe's "Dichtung und Wahrheit". (Germanic Studies in America: Vol. 5). 162p. 1972. 19.60 (ISBN 3-261-00311-1). P Lang Pubs.
Bowman, George M. Don't Let Go! An Exposition of Hebrews. 170p. 1982. pap. 4.95 (ISBN 0-87552-121-5). Presby & Reformed.
Bowman, Herbert J., tr. see Oswald, Hilton.
Bowman, Jayne, compiled by. The World of Friendship. (Illus.). 1983. 8.00 (ISBN 0-8378-1801-X). Gibson.
Bowman, John. The Fourth Gospel & the Jews: A Study of R. Akiba, Esther, & the Gospel of John. LC 75-40461. (Pittsburgh Theological Monographs: No. 8). 1975. pap. 9.00 (ISBN 0-915138-10-7). Pickwick.
--The Samaritan Problem: Studies in the Relationship of Samaritanism, Judaism, & Early Christianity. Johnson, Alfred M., Jr., tr. from Ger. LC 75-20042. (Pittsburgh Theological Monographs: No. 4). 1975. pap. 8.75 (ISBN 0-915138-04-2). Pickwick.
Bowman, John, ed. & tr. Samaritans Documents Relating to Their History, Religion & Life. LC 77-4949. (Pittsburgh Original Texts & Translations Ser.: No. 2). 1977. pap. 11.50 (ISBN 0-915138-27-1). Pickwick.
Bowman, John W. Hebrews-Second Peter. LC 59-10454. (Layman's Bible Commentary Ser: Vol. 24). 1962. pap. 4.95 (ISBN 0-8042-3084-6). John Knox.
Bowman, Lea, jt. auth. see Stringer, Leslea.
Bowman, LeRoy E. The American Funeral: A Study in Guilt, Extravagance, & Sublimity. LC 72-14083. 181p. 1973. Repr. of 1959 ed. lib. bdg. 22.50x (ISBN 0-8371-6749-3, BOFU). Greenwood.
Bowman, Mary Ann, compiled by. Western Mysticism: A Guide to the Basic Works. LC 78-18311. vi, 114p. 1979. pap. 9.00 (ISBN 0-8389-0266-9). ALA.
Bowman, Ray, ed. Church Building Sourcebook Two. 264p. 1982. 3-ring vinyl notebook 39.95 (ISBN 0-8341-0759-7). Beacon Hill.
Bowman, Raymond A. Aramaic Ritual Texts from Persepolis. LC 65-55148. (Oriental Institute Pubns. Ser: No. 91). 1970. 35.00x (ISBN 0-226-62194-4). U of Chicago Pr.
Bowman, Rufus D. Church of the Brethren & the War, 1788-1914. LC 75-147667. (Library of War & Peace; Relig. & Ethical Positions on War). 1972. 46.00 (ISBN 0-8240-0425-6). Garland Pub.
Bowman, S. Loren. Power & Polity among the Brethren. (Orig.). 1987. pap. 5.95. Brethren.
Bowman, Steven B. The Jews of Byzantium: Twelve Four to Fourteen Fifty-Three. LC 83-17230. (Judaic Studies Ser.). (Illus.). 400p. 1985. 42.50 (ISBN 0-8173-0198-4). U of Ala Pr.
Bowman, Thea, Sr., ed. Families: Black & Catholic, Catholic & Black, Readings, Resources & Family Activities. 160p. 1985. pap. 14.95 (ISBN 1-55586-890-8). US Catholic.
Bowne, Borden P. The Christian Revelation. LC 75-3069. Repr. of 1898 ed. 20.00 (ISBN 0-404-59068-3). AMS Pr.
--The Essence of Religion. LC 75-3070. Repr. of 1910 ed. 34.50 (ISBN 0-404-59069-1). AMS Pr.
--The Immanence of God. LC 75-3071. Repr. of 1905 ed. 24.50 (ISBN 0-404-59070-5). AMS Pr.
--The Principles of Ethics. LC 75-3073. (Philosophy in America Ser.). Repr. of 1892 ed. 28.00 (ISBN 0-404-59074-8). AMS Pr.
--Studies in Christianity. LC 75-3074. Repr. of 1909 ed. 28.50 (ISBN 0-404-59075-6). AMS Pr.
--Studies in Theism. LC 7-25071. 1968. Repr. of 1907 ed. 28.00 (ISBN 0-527-10450-7). Kraus Repr.
--Theism... Comprising the Deems Lectures for 1902. LC 75-3075. (Philosophy in America Ser.). Repr. of 1902 ed. 37.50 (ISBN 0-404-59076-4). AMS Pr.
Bowness, Charles. The Practice of Meditation 1971. rev. ed. (Paths to Inner Power Ser.). 1979. pap. 3.50 (ISBN 0-85030-182-3). Weiser.
Bowra, C. M. Palladas & Christianity. 1959. pap. 2.25 (ISBN 0-85672-641-9, Pub. by British Acad). Longwood Pub Group.
Bowser, Arthur M. What Every Jehovah's Witness Should Know. 1975. micro book 1.95 (ISBN 0-916406-35-0). Accent Bks.
Bowyer, O. R., et al. Prayer in the Black Tradition. 112p. 1986. pap. 5.95 (ISBN 0-8358-0538-7, ICN 609100, Dist. by Abingdon Press). Upper Room.
Box, Hubert S. The Principles of Canon Law. LC 86-3163. 1986. Repr. of 1949 ed. 32.75x (ISBN 0-313-25204-1, BPRC/). Greenwood.
Boxer, C. R. The Christian Century in Japan: Fifteen Forty-Nine to Sixteen Fifty. (California Library Reprint Ser: No. 51). (Illus.). 552p. 1974. Repr. of 1967 ed. 49.50x (ISBN 0-520-02702-7). U of Cal Pr.
--The Church Militant & Iberian Expansion: 1440-1770. LC 77-18386. (Johns Hopkins Symposia in Comparative History Ser.: No. 10). (Illus.). 1978. text ed. 17.50x (ISBN 0-8018-2042-1). Johns Hopkins.
Boxer, Tim. The Jewish Celebrities Hall of Fame. 1986. pap. 7.95 (ISBN 0-318-21398-2). Shapolsky Pubs.
Boyack, Kenneth, et al. Catholic Faith Inventory. write for info. Paulist Pr.
Boyak, Kenneth. A Parish Guide to Adult Initiation. LC 79-91001. 112p. (Orig.). 1980. pap. 4.95 (ISBN 0-8091-2282-0). Paulist Pr.
Boyarin, Jonathan, jt. auth. see Kugelmass, Jack.

Boyce, Mary. Zoroastrianism. Boyce, Mary, tr. (Textual Sources for the Study of Religion). 224p. 1987. pap. 11.75 (ISBN 0-389-20717-9). B&N Imports.
--Zoroastrians. Hinnells, John, ed. (Library of Religious Beliefs & Practices). 260p. 1986. pap. text ed. 9.95 (ISBN 0-7102-0156-7). Methuen Inc.
Boyce, Mary, ed. Zoroastrianism. LC 84-383. (Textual Sources for the Study of Religion Ser.). 176p. 1984. 23.50x (ISBN 0-389-20478-1, 08040); pap. 11.75x (ISBN 0-389-20717-9). B&N Imports.
Boyce, William D. & Jensen, Larry C. Moral Reasoning: A Psychological-Philosophical Integration. LC 78-5935. xii, 291p. 1978. 22.50x (ISBN 0-8032-0982-7). U of Nebr Pr.
Boyd, Anne. Life in a Fifteenth Century Monastery. LC 76-22452. (Cambridge Topic Bks). (Illus.). 1978. PLB 8.95 (ISBN 0-8225-1208-4). Lerner Pubns.
--The Monks of Durham. LC 74-14438. (Introduction to the History of Mankind Ser). (Illus.). 48p. 1975. text ed. 4.95 (ISBN 0-521-20647-2). Cambridge U Pr.
Boyd, Charles E. At Liberty on Bear Creek, 1835-1985. 1984. 14.95; pap. 9.95. Banner Pr AL.
--Haysop: A Church, A Community, A People of Bibb County, Alabama. (Illus.). 1979. pap. 8.50. Banner Pr AL.
Boyd, Don & Sedano, Maruja. Master Catechist Guide for the Catechist Formation Book. LC 82-60853. 1982. pap. 3.95 (ISBN 0-8091-2471-8). Paulist Pr.
Boyd, Doug. Rolling Thunder. 273p. 1986. pap. 9.95 (ISBN 0-385-28859-X, Delta). Dell.
Boyd, Eric F. see Forbes-Boyd, Eric.
Boyd, Frank M. Ages & Dispensations. 112p. 1955. pap. 1.50 (ISBN 0-88243-463-2, 02-0463). Gospel Pub.
Boyd, Jack. Leading the Lord's Singing. 1981. pap. 5.95 (ISBN 0-89137-603-8). Quality Pubns.
Boyd, James E. Faith Is Sort of Like This. (Illus.). 64p. (Orig.). 1986. pap. 9.95 (ISBN 1-55630-012-3). Brentwood Comm.
Boyd, James P. Boyd's Bible Dictionary. Orig. Title: Vest Pocket Bible Dictionary, Orig. pap. 3.75 (ISBN 0-87981-087-4). Holman Bible Pub.
Boyd, James W., jt. auth. see Kotwal, Firoze M.
Boyd, James W., jt. ed. see Kotwal, Firoze M.
Boyd, Jesse L., III, jt. ed. see Godfrey, W. Robert.
Boyd, Lois A. & Brackenridge, R. Douglas. Presbyterian Women in America: Two Centuries of a Quest for Status. LC 82-15845. (Contributions to the Study of Religion: No. 9). 416p. 1983. lib. bdg. 35.00 (ISBN 0-313-23678-X, BOY/). Greenwood.
Boyd, Malcolm. Gay Priests: An Inner Journey. 208p. 1986. 14.95 (ISBN 0-312-31797-2). St Martin.
--Half Laughing, Half Crying: Songs for Myself. 306p. 1985. 15.95 (ISBN 0-312-35663-3). St Martin.
Boyd, Nancy. Emissaries: The Overseas Work of the American YWCA, 1895-1970. (Illus.). 412p. 16.95 (ISBN 0-9614878-0-1). Woman's Pr.
--Three Victorian Women Who Changed Their World: Josephine Butler, Octavia Hill, Florence Nightingale. 1982. 22.95x (ISBN 0-19-520271-6). Oxford U Pr.
Boyd, R. Vernon. Undying Dedication. 1985. pap. 5.95 (ISBN 0-89225-281-2). Gospel Advocate.
Boyd, Robert H., ed. & tr. see Westermann, Claus.
Boyd, Robert H., tr. see Westermann, Claus.
Boyd, Robert T. Boyd's Bible Handbook. LC 82-81088. 800p. 1983. 26.95 (ISBN 0-89081-352-3). Harvest Hse.
Boyd, Sandra H., jt. auth. see Bass, Dorothy C.
Boyd, Susan J., ed. see Hurst, Jane.
Boyden, Edward A., jt. auth. see Levin, S. I.
Boyden Howes, Elizabeth. Intersection & Beyond, Vol. II. LC 86-3067. 200p. (Orig.). 1986. pap. 8.50 (ISBN 0-917479-07-6). Guild Psy.
Boyer & Zahorski. Visions of Wonders: An Anthology of Christian Fantasy. 1986. pap. 2.50 (ISBN 0-380-78824-1, 78824-1). Avon.
Boyer, Blanche, ed. see Abailard, P.
Boyer, Ernest, Jr. A Way in the World: Family Life as Spiritual Discipline. LC 83-48983. 192p. 1984. 13.45 (ISBN 0-06-061032-8, HarpR). Har-Row.
Boyer, James L. For a World Like Ours: Studies in I Corinthians. pap. 4.95 (ISBN 0-88469-057-1). BMH Bks.
--A Manual of Greek Forms. pap. 4.95 (ISBN 0-88469-007-5). BMH Bks.
--Prophecy, Things to Come. pap. 4.95 (ISBN 0-88469-006-7). BMH Bks.
Boyer, John W. & Kirshner, Julius, eds. University of Chicago Readings in Western Civilization: The Church in the Roman Empire, Vol. 3. LC 85-16328. 1986. lib. bdg. 20.00x (ISBN 0-226-06938-9); pap. text ed. 7.95x (ISBN 0-226-06939-7). U of Chicago Pr.
Boyer, Linda. God Made Me. LC 81-50677. (A Happy Day Bks.). (Illus.). 24p. (Orig.). 1981. pap. 1.59 (ISBN 0-87239-464-6, 3597). Standard Pub.
Boyer, Paul & Nissenbaum, Stephen. Salem Possessed: The Social Origins of Witchcraft. LC 73-84399. 320p. 1974. pap. 6.95x (ISBN 0-674-78526-6). Harvard U Pr.
Boyer, Paul & Nissenbaum, Stephen, eds. The Salem Witchcraft Papers: Verbatim Transcripts, 3 vols. (Civil Liberties in American History Ser.). 1977. Set. lib. bdg. 145.00 (ISBN 0-306-70655-5). Da Capo.
Boyer, Raymond & Brisson, Marie. Miscellanea Cartusiensia, Vol. 3. Hogg, James, ed. (Analecta Cartusiana Ser.: No. 42). (Fr. & Lat.). 101p. (Orig.). 1978. pap. 25.00 (ISBN 3-7052-0058-5, Pub by Salzburg Studies). Longwood Pub Group.
Bo Yin Ra. The Book on Life Beyond. Reichenbach, Bodo A., tr. from Ger. LC 78-51633. 1978. pap. 5.00 (ISBN 0-915034-02-6). Kober Pr.
--The Wisdom of St. John. Reichenbach, Bodo A., tr. from Ger. LC 74-15272. 112p. 1975. 8.00 (ISBN 0-915034-01-8). Kober Pr.
Boykin, James H. Black Jews. LC 81-90626. iv, 98p. (Orig.). 1982. pap. 3.25x (ISBN 0-9603342-1-1). Boykin.
--Political Intrigue in the Establishment of the Identity of Jesus & Mary. LC 86-90957. 286p. 1986. pap. 15.00x (ISBN 0-9603342-6-2). Boykin.
Boykin, John. Circumstances & the Role of God. 224p. 1986. text ed. 12.95 (ISBN 0-317-46020-X). Zondervan.
Boykin, Phyllis. I Like to Go to Church. (Bible-&-Me Ser.). 1987. 5.95 (ISBN 0-8054-4174-3). Broadman.
Boylan, Eugene D. Difficulties in Mental Prayer. 128p. 1984. pap. 5.95 (ISBN 0-87061-105-4). Chr Classics.
Boylan, M. Eugene. This Tremendous Lover. 396p. 1987. pap. 7.95 (ISBN 0-87061-138-0). Chr Classics.
Boyle, Judith, jt. auth. see Saia, Mary J.
Boyle, Marjorie O. Christening Pagan Mysteries: Erasmus in Pursuit of Wisdom. (Erasmus Studies). 168p. 1981. 22.50x (ISBN 0-8020-5525-7). U of Toronto Pr.
--Erasmus on Language & Method in Theology. LC 77-2606. (Erasmus Studies: No. 2). pap. 70.30 (ISBN 0-317-26938-0, 2023596). Bks Demand UMI.
--Rhetoric & Reform: Erasmus' Civil Dispute with Luther. (Harvard Historical Monographs: No. 71). 240p. 1983. text ed. 24.00x (ISBN 0-674-76870-1). Harvard U Pr.
Boyle, Patrick J. Parvitas Materiae in Sexto in Contemporary Catholic Thought. 132p. (Orig.). 1987. lib. bdg. 21.50 (ISBN 0-8191-5790-2); pap. text ed. 9.25 (ISBN 0-8191-5791-0). U Pr of Amer.
Boyle, Robert. James Joyce's Pauline Vision: A Catholic Exposition. LC 78-18901. 133p. 1978. 10.95x (ISBN 0-8093-0861-4). S Ill U Pr.
Boyle, Sarah-Patton. The Desert Blooms: A Personal Adventure in Growing Old Creatively. 208p. (Orig.). 1983. pap. 7.95 (ISBN 0-687-10484-X). Abingdon.
Boynes, Cyril H. Freedom Through the Balisier. LC 83-40235. 148p. (Orig.). 1984. pap. 4.75 (ISBN 0-8356-0584-1, Quest). Theos Pub Hse.
Boynton, Linda L. The Plain People: An Ethnography of the Holdeman Mennonites. (Illus.). 222p. (Orig.). 1986. pap. text ed. 9.95x (ISBN 0-88133-198-8). Sheffield Wisc.
Boynton, Richard W., tr. see Loisy, Alfred F.
Boys, Don. Liberalism: A Rope of Sand. 1979. 4.95 (ISBN 0-686-25591-7). Freedom Univ-FSP.
--Pilgrims, Puritans & Patriots: Our Christian Heritage. 1983. pap. 9.00x (ISBN 0-686-40717-2). Freedom Univ-FSP.
Boys, Mary C. Biblical Interpretation in Religious Education. LC 80-10249. 362p. (Orig.). 1980. pap. 10.95 (ISBN 0-89135-022-5). Religious Educ.
Boys, Mary C., ed. Ministry & Education in Conversation. LC 80-53204. 160p. (Orig.). 1981. pap. 6.95 (ISBN 0-88489-126-7). St Mary's.
Bozarth-Campbell, Alla. Womanpriest: A Personal Odyssey. 229p. 1978. 9.95 (ISBN 0-8091-0243-9). Wisdom House.
Bozeman, Theodore D. Protestants in an Age of Science: The Baconian Ideal & Antebellum Religious Thought. LC 76-25962. xv, 240p. 1977. 22.50x (ISBN 0-8078-1299-4). U of NC Pr.
Braaten, Carl E. The Flaming Center: A Theology of the Christian Mission. LC 76-62605. pap. 44.00 (2026958). Bks Demand UMI.
--Principles of Lutheran Theology. LC 82-16542. 160p. 1983. pap. 8.95 (ISBN 0-8006-1689-8). Fortress.
--The Whole Counsel of God. LC 73-88345. pap. 44.00 (2026840). Bks Demand UMI.
Braaten, Carl E., ed. The New Church Debate: Issues Facing American Lutheranism. LC 83-48008. 176p. 1984. pap. 7.95 (ISBN 0-8006-1715-0, 1-1715). Fortress.
Braaten, Carl E. & Jenson, Robert W., eds. Christian Dogmatics, 2 vols. LC 83-48007. 1984. Volume 1. 24.95 (ISBN 0-8006-0703-1); Volume 2. 24.95 (ISBN 0-8006-0704-X); Set. 45.95 (ISBN 0-8006-0712-0). Fortress.
Braaten, John. Together... Till Death Us Do Part. Sherer, Michael L., ed. (Orig.). 1987. pap. 5.95 (ISBN 0-89536-852-8, 7811). CSS of Ohio.
Brabazon, Francis. In Dust I Sing. 150p. 1974. 8.95 (ISBN 0-940700-08-5); pap. 4.95 (ISBN 0-940700-07-7). Meher Baba Info.
--The Word at World's End. 88p. 1971. 5.95 (ISBN 0-940700-04-2); pap. 3.45 (ISBN 0-940700-03-4). Meher Baba Info.
Brabbs, Derry. English Country Churches. 160p. 1985. 25.00 (ISBN 0-670-80736-2). Viking.
Brace, Beverly W. The Humboldt Years, 1930-39. 1977. pap. 4.50 (ISBN 0-686-19169-2). B W Brace.
Braceland, Lawrence C., tr. see Gilbert.
Braceland, Lawrence C., tr. see Gilbert Of Hoyland.
Bracey, Bertha L., tr. see Otto, Rudolf.
Bracken, et al. Women of the Word: Contemporary Sermons by Women Clergy. Hackett, Charles, ed. LC 84-52656. (Illus.). 144p. (Orig.). 1985. pap. 7.95 (ISBN 0-932419-00-3). Susan Hunter.
Bracken, Carol, illus. The Baby Moses. (Tuck-A-Toy Bks.). (Illus.). 7p. 1985. 3.95 (ISBN 0-8407-6663-7). Nelson.
Bracken, Carolyn, illus. The Baby Jesus. (Tuck-A-Toy Bks.). (Illus.). 7p. 1985. 3.95 (ISBN 0-8407-6666-1). Nelson.
Bracken, Harry M. Berkeley. LC 74-15569. 176p. 1975. 19.95 (ISBN 0-312-07595-2). St Martin.
Bracken, Joseph A. The Triune Symbol: Persons, Process & Community. (Studies in Religion: No. 1). 216p. (Orig.). 1985. lib. bdg. 25.00 (ISBN 0-8191-4440-1, College Theo Soc); pap. text ed. 11.75 (ISBN 0-8191-4441-X). U Pr of Amer.
Brackenridge, Hugh H. & Freneau, Philip. Father Bombo's Pilgrimage to Mecca, 1770. Bell, Michael D., ed. LC 75-5391. (Illus.). 129p. 1975. 10.00 (ISBN 0-87811-020-8). Princeton Lib.
Brackenridge, R. Douglas. Voice in the Wilderness: A History of the Cumberland Presbyterian Church in Texas. LC 68-20136. (Illus.). 192p. 1968. 4.00 (ISBN 0-911536-03-5). Trinity U Pr.
Brackenridge, R. Douglas & Garcia-Treto, Francisco O. Iglesia Presbiteriana: A History of Presbyterians & Mexican Americans in the Southwest. LC 74-76777. (Illus.). 262p. 1974. 8.00 (ISBN 0-911536-53-1). Trinity U Pr.
Brackenridge, R. Douglas, jt. auth. see Boyd, Lois A.
Brackney, William, ed. Baptist Life & Thought: Sixteen Hundred to Nineteen Eighty. 448p. 1983. 12.95 (ISBN 0-8170-0959-0). Judson.
Braden, C. S. Religious Aspects of the Conquest of Mexico. 1976. lib. bdg. 59.95 (ISBN 0-8490-2510-9). Gordon Pr.
Braden, Charles S. Christian Science Today: Power, Policy, Practice. LC 58-11399. 1958. 19.95 (ISBN 0-87074-024-5). SMU Press.
--Religious Aspects of the Conquest of Mexico. LC 74-181914. Repr. of 1930 ed. 37.50 (ISBN 0-404-00925-5). AMS Pr.
Braden, Charles S., ed. Varieties of American Religion. facsimile ed. LC 76-156616. (Essay Index Reprint Ser). Repr. of 1936 ed. 15.50 (ISBN 0-8369-2307-3). Ayer Co Pubs.
Braden, Suzanne G. The First Year: Incorporating New Members. (Pathways to Church Growth Ser.). 80p. (Orig.). Date not set. pap. 5.95 (ISBN 0-88177-046-9, DR046B). Discipleship Res.
Bradfield, Keith, tr. from Swedish. The Testament of Cain. Bradfield, Kieth. cancelled (ISBN 0-86538-019-8); pap. cancelled (ISBN 0-686-32482-X). Ontario Rev NJ.
Bradfield, Kieth see Bradfield, Keith.
Bradford, Brick. Releasing the Power of the Holy Spirit. 32p. 1983. 1.95x (ISBN 0-934421-00-5). Presby Renewal Pubns.
Bradford, Brick, ed. Healing for the Homosexual. 64p. 1983. 1.95 (ISBN 0-934421-06-4). Presby Renewal Pubns.
Bradford, Charles E. The God Between. Coffen, Richard W., ed. 96p. 1984. pap. 4.95 (ISBN 0-8280-0243-6). Review & Herald.
Bradford, Gamaliel. A Prophet of Joy. facsimile ed. LC 77-179506. (Select Bibliographies Reprint Ser.). Repr. of 1920 ed. 17.00 (ISBN 0-8369-6635-X). Ayer Co Pubs.
Bradford, John. A Sermon of Repentance. LC 74-28835. (English Experience Ser.: No. 716). 1975. Repr. of 1553 ed. 6.00 (ISBN 90-221-0716-7). Walter J Johnson.
--Writings of Bradford. 1979. Set. 34.95 (ISBN 0-85151-359-X). Vol. 1 (ISBN 0-85151-283-6). Vol. 2 (ISBN 0-85151-284-4). Banner of Truth.
--Writings of John Bradford...Martyr, 1555, 2 Vols. Repr. of 1853 ed. Set. 92.00 (ISBN 0-384-05440-4). Johnson Repr.
Bradford, Lyle. Building Relationships Through Pastoral Visitation. 64p. 1984. pap. 4.95 (ISBN 0-8170-1006-8). Judson.
Bradford, Mary L., ed. Mormon Women Speak. LC 82-62366. 1982. 9.95 (ISBN 0-913420-94-8). Olympus Pub Co.
Bradford, William. Of Plymouth Plantation: The Pilgrims in America. 18.00 (ISBN 0-8446-1718-0). Peter Smith.
--Of Plymouth Plantation: 1620-1647. Morison, Samuel E., ed. (The American Past Ser). (Illus.). (YA) 1952. 19.95 (ISBN 0-394-43895-7). Knopf.
Bradish, Norman C. John Sergeant: A Forgotten Critic of Descartes & Locke. 65p. 1929. 6.95 (ISBN 0-87548-363-1). Open Court.
Bradlaugh, Charles. Jesus, Shelley, & Malthus. 1978. Repr. of 1877 ed. lib. bdg. 10.00 (ISBN 0-8495-0441-4). Arden Lib.
Bradley, A. C., ed. see Green, Thomas H.
Bradley, Andrew C. Ideals of Religion. LC 77-27218. (Gifford Lectures: 1907). Repr. of 1940 ed. 30.00 (ISBN 0-404-60463-3). AMS Pr.
Bradley, Fred, tr. see Fleck, Ludwig.
Bradley, George G., ed. Lectures on the Book of Job Delivered in Westminster Abbey. 334p. 1981. Repr. of 1888 ed. lib. bdg. 50.00 (ISBN 0-89984-069-8). Century Bookbindery.
Bradley, Gerard T. Face the Light. LC 82-99822. 89p. 1983. 8.95 (ISBN 0-533-05448-6). Vantage.
Bradley, Gerard V. Church-State Relationships in America. LC 86-27149. (Contributions in Legal Studies). 1987. 29.85 (ISBN 0-313-25494-X, BYC). Greenwood.
Bradley, Joshua. Accounts of Religious Revivals in Many Parts of the United States from 1815 to 1818: Collected from Numerous Publications & Letters from Persons of Piety & Correct Information. (Reival Library). 300p. lib. bdg. 11.95 (ISBN 0-940033-13-5). R O Roberts.
Bradley, Richard, ed. see Clary, Linda & Harms, Larry.
Bradley, Ritamary & Lagorio, Valerie M. The Fourteenth Century English Mystics: A Comprehensive Annotated Bibliography. LC 79-7922. (Garland Reference Library of the Humanities). 300p. 1981. lib. bdg. 36.00 (ISBN 0-8240-9535-9). Garland Pub.
Bradley, Ruth, tr. see Arrupe, Pedro.
Bradner, John. Symbols of Church Seasons & Days. (Illus.). 1977. pap. 6.95 (ISBN 0-8192-1228-8). Morehouse.
Bradshaw, Charles. You & Your Teen. (Family Ministry Ser.). (Illus.). 54p. 1985. pap. text ed. 19.95 (ISBN 0-89191-950-3). Cook.
Bradshaw, Charles E. Profile of Faith. 9.95 (ISBN 0-911866-01-9). Advocate.
Bradshaw, Charles O. Faith Development: The Lifelong Process. (Complete Teacher Training Meeting Ser.). 48p. 1985. pap. text ed. 9.95 (ISBN 0-89191-761-6). Cook.
Bradshaw, H. Bradshaw's Life of St. Werburge of Chester. Horstmann, C., ed. (EETS, OS Ser.: No. 88). Repr. of 1887 ed. 20.00 (ISBN 0-527-00085-X). Kraus Repr.
Bradshaw, Henry. Holy Life & History of Saynt Werburg. Repr. of 1848 ed. 28.00 (ISBN 0-384-05450-1). Johnson Repr.
Bradshaw, John. A Concordance to the Poetical Works of John Milton. LC 77-13457. 1977. Repr. of 1894 ed. lib. bdg. 20.00 (ISBN 0-89341-452-2). Longwood Pub Group.
--A Concordance to the Poetical Works of John Milton. LC 70-144894. 412p. 1972. Repr. of 1894 ed. 27.00 (ISBN 0-403-00833-6). Scholarly.
Bradshaw, Marion J. Philosophical Foundations of Faith. LC 78-99248. Repr. of 1941 ed. 10.00 (ISBN 0-404-00968-9). AMS Pr.
Bradshaw, Paul F. Daily Prayer in the Early Church: A Study of the Origins & Early Development of the Divine Office. 1982. 26.00x (ISBN 0-19-520394-1); pap. 9.95x (ISBN 0-19-520395-X). Oxford U Pr.
Bradshaw, William. English Puritanisme & Other Works. 326p. text ed. 62.10 (ISBN 0-576-99738-2, Pub. by Gregg Intl Pub England). Gregg Intl.
Bradsher, Frances. The Preacher Had Ten Kids. 1980. pap. 3.50 (ISBN 0-8423-4886-7). Tyndale.
Brady, Anne. Me & My Mustang. (Illus.). 50p. (Orig.). 1986. pap. 4.95 (ISBN 0-937689-02-5). Chisum Pub.
Brady, Cyrus T. Little Book for Christmas. facsimile ed. LC 73-167443. (Short Story Index Reprint Ser). (Illus.). Repr. of 1917 ed. 17.00 (ISBN 0-8369-3969-7). Ayer Co Pubs.

Brady, David. The Contribution of British writers Between 1560 & 1830 to the Interpretation of Revelation 13. 16-18. 341p. 1983. lib. bdg. 60.00x (ISBN 3-16-144497-3, Pub. by J C B Mohr BRD). Coronet Bks.

Brady, Ignatius, tr. see Clausen, Sophronius.

Brady, Ignatius C., jt. ed. see Armstrong, Regis J.

Brady, Joan, jt. auth. see Koplik, William.

Brady, Jules, ed. An Augustine Treasury: Selections from the Writings of St. Augustine. 1981. 5.00 (ISBN 0-8198-0706-0); pap. 4.00 (ISBN 0-686-73823-3). Dghtrs St Paul.

Brady, Jules M. A Philosopher's Search for the Infinite. 96p. 1983. 10.00 (ISBN 0-8022-2410-5). Philos Lib.

Brady, Sr. M. Rosalie. Thought & Style in the Works of Leon Bloy. LC 70-94176. (Catholic Universtiy of America Studies in Romance Languages & Literatures Ser: No. 30). Repr. of 1945 ed. 19.00 (ISBN 0-404-50330-6). AMS Pr.

Brady, Thomas A. Sarapis & Isis: Collected Essays. Mitchel, Fordyce, ed. 129p. 1978. 25.00 (ISBN 0-89005-253-0). Ares.

Brafman, Morris & Schimel, David. Trade for Freedom. LC 75-26371. 96p. 1975. 6.95 (ISBN 0-88400-043-5). Shengold.

Braga, James. Como Preparar Mensajes. Orig. Title: How to Prepare Bible Messages. (Port.). 1986. write for info. (ISBN 0-8297-1609-2). Life Pubs Intl.

--Como Preparar Mensajes Biblicos. Orig. Title: How to Prepare Bible Messages. Tr. of How to Prepare Bible Messages. (Span.). 320p. 1986. pap. 9.50 (ISBN 0-8254-1072-X). Kregel.

--How to Prepare Bible Messages. rev. ed. LC 81-14132. 1982. pap. 6.95 (ISBN 0-930014-71-5). Multnomah.

--How to Study the Bible. LC 82-6420. (Orig.). 1982. pap. 6.95 (ISBN 0-930014-72-3). Multnomah.

Braga, Meg. Cosas Que Hacer para Navidad. (Editorial Mundo Hispano). (YA) 1981. Repr. of 1980 ed. 3.25 (ISBN 0-311-26607-X). Casa Bautista.

Bragg, George F., Jr. History of the Afro-American Group of the Episcopal Church. (Basic Afro-American Reprint Library). (Illus.). Repr. of 1922 ed. 17.00 (ISBN 0-384-05495-1). Johnson Repr.

Bragg, Juliana. The Nativity. (Golden Storytime Bk.). (Illus.). 24p. 1987. pap. 2.95 (ISBN 0-307-11960-2, Golden Bks.). Western Pub.

Braght, Thieleman J. Van see Van Braght, Thieleman J.

Bragt, Jan Van, tr. see Nishitani, Keiji.

Braham, Randolph L. The Hungarian Jewish Catastrophe: Selected & Annotated Bibliography. 501p. 1984. 45.00x (ISBN 0-88033-054-6). East Eur Quarterly.

--Perspectives on the Holocaust. (Holocaust Studies). 1983. lib. bdg. 20.00 (ISBN 0-89838-124-X). Kluwer Nijhoff.

Braham, Randolph L., ed. Contemporary Views on the Holocaust. 1983. lib. bdg. 31.50 (ISBN 0-89838-141-X). Kluwer Nijhoff.

--The Origins of the Holocaust: Christian Anti-Semitism. (East European Monographs: No. 204). 100p. 1986. 18.00 (ISBN 0-88033-953-5). East Eur Quarterly.

--The Tragedy of the Jews in Hungary: Essays & Documents. (East European Monographs: No. 208). 288p. 1986. 30.00 (ISBN 0-88033-105-4). East Eur Quarterly.

Brahmachari, Dhirenda. Yoga: Yogic Suksma Vyayama. (Illus.). 232p. 1975. 8.95 (ISBN 0-88253-802-0). Ind-US Inc.

Brahmananda, Swami, ed. see Ramakrishna, Sri.

Braidfoot, Larry. Gambling: A Deadly Game. LC 85-19066. (Orig.). 1985. pap. 4.95 (ISBN 0-8054-5664-3). Broadman.

Brailsford, Edward J. The Spiritual Sense in Sacred Legend. 288p. 1983. Repr. of 1910 ed. lib. bdg. 47.50 (ISBN 0-89987-957-8). Darby Bks.

Brailsford, Mabel R. Making of William Penn. facs. ed. LC 77-124227. (Select Bibliographies Reprint Ser.). 1930. 22.00 (ISBN 0-8369-5416-5). Ayer Co Pubs.

Brainerd, David. David Brainerd's Personal Testimony. (Summit Bks.). pap. 3.95 (ISBN 0-8010-8159-9). Baker Bk.

Brainerd, David, ed. Memoirs of the Reverend David Brainerd: Missionary to the Indians on the Border of New York, New Jersey & Pennsylvania. LC 70-108477. (American Indian History Sers). 1970. Repr. of 1822 ed. 49.00x (ISBN 0-403-00233-8). Scholarly.

Brainerd, George W., jt. auth. see Morley, Sylvanus G.

Braithwaite, William C. The Beginnings of Quakerism. (Illus.). 562p. 1981. Repr. of 1923 ed. lib. bdg. 65.00 (ISBN 0-8495-0625-5). Arden Lib.

Braitmichel, Kasper, et al. The Chronicle of the Hutterian Brethren, Vol. 1. Hutterian Brethren, ed. (Ger. & Eng., Illus.). 900p. 1987. 36.00 (ISBN 0-87486-021-0). Plough.

Brakenhelm, C. R. Problems of Religious Experience. 158p. 1985. pap. 23.50x (ISBN 91-554-1657-8, Pub. by Almqvist & Wiksell). Coronet Bks.

Brakhage, Pamela. The Theology of "La Lozana Andaluza". 27.50 (ISBN 0-916379-34-5). Scripta.

Brame, Grace A. Receptive Prayer: A Christian Approach to Meditation. Lambert, Herbert, ed. LC 84-29302. 144p. (Orig.). 1985. pap. 9.95 (ISBN 0-8272-3211-X). CBP.

Bramer, Mary. This Is My Story, This Is My Song. 1984. pap. 6.95 (ISBN 0-570-03923-1, 12-2857). Concordia.

Bramley, William. Jesus & Mary. 450p. 1987. 21.95 (ISBN 0-940291-02-9). Dahlin Family Pr.

Brams, Steven J. Biblical Games: A Strategic Analysis of Stories in the Old Testament. 1980. text ed. 22.00x (ISBN 0-262-02144-7); pap. 7.95 (ISBN 0-262-52074-5). MIT Pr.

Branbsby, Carlos, tr. from Eng. Concordancia Tematica De la Biblia. 199p. 1986. pap. 3.50 (ISBN 0-311-42043-5). Casa Bautista.

Brancaforte, Benito. Guzman de Alfarache: Conversion o Proceso de Degradacion? vi, 230p. 1980. 11.00x (ISBN 0-942260-14-7). Hispanic Seminary.

Branch, Mary. Tell Me a Story. LC 78-53210. (Stories That Win Ser.). 1978. pap. 1.25 (ISBN 0-8163-0210-3, 20079-0). Pacific Pr Pub Assn.

Brand, Irene. Meet Mary & Martha. 144p. 1985. pap. 4.95 (ISBN 0-87239-899-4, 2978). Standard Pub.

--A Year of Programs for Today's Women. 96p. (Orig.). 1984. pap. 3.95 (ISBN 0-87239-744-0, 2975). Standard Pub.

Brand, John. Observations on the Popular Antiquities of Great Britain: Chiefly Illustrating the Origin of Our Vulgar & Provincial Customs, Ceremonies & Superstitions, 3 vols. LC 67-23896. 1969. Repr. of 1849 ed. Set. 68.00x (ISBN 0-8103-3256-6). Gale.

Brand, Paul & Yancey, Philip. Fearfully & Wonderfully Made. (Illus.). 224p. 1980. 11.95 (ISBN 0-310-35450-1, 10241). Zondervan.

--A Imagen de Dios. Delgado, Ady, tr. Tr. of In His Image. 272p. 1987. pap. 4.95 (ISBN 0-88113-128-8). Edit Betania.

--In His Image. 224p. 1984. 12.95 (ISBN 0-310-35500-1, 10242). Zondervan.

Brand, Ralph. Simplified Techniques of Counseling. 132p. 1972. pap. 2.50 (ISBN 0-89114-049-2). Baptist Pub Hse.

Brand, Roy E. De see De Brand, Roy E.

Brand, Sandra. I Dared to Live. LC 78-52142. 1978. pap. 8.95 (ISBN 0-88400-058-3). Shengold.

Brand, William, tr. see Niezabitowska, Malgorzata.

Brandall, William S. The Secret of the Universe: New Discoveries on God, Man & the Eternity of Life. (Illus.). 119p. 1985. 127.45 (ISBN 0-89266-535-1). Am Classical Coll Pr.

Brandeis, Arthur, ed. Jacob's Well, an English Treatise on the Cleansing of Man's Conscience, Pt. 1. (EETS, OS Ser.: No. 115). Repr. of 1900 ed. 54.00 (ISBN 0-527-00114-7). Kraus Repr.

Brandeis, Louis D. Brandeis on Zionism. LC 75-6425. (The Rise of Jewish Nationalism & the Middle East Ser.). 156p. 1975. Repr. of 1942 ed. 17.60 (ISBN 0-88355-312-0). Hyperion Conn.

Brandes, Joseph & Douglas, Martin. Immigrants to Freedom: Jewish Communities in Rural New Jersey Since 1882. LC 76-122384. 1971. 27.50x (ISBN 0-8122-7620-5). U of Pa Pr.

Brandewie, Ernest. Wilhelm Schmidt & the Origin of the Idea of God. 352p. (Orig.). 1983. lib. bdg. 30.00 (ISBN 0-8191-3363-9); pap. text ed. 15.50 (ISBN 0-8191-3364-7). U Pr of Amer.

Brandi, Herman A. Di see Di Brandi, Herman A.

Brandling, Redvers. Christmas in the Primary School. (Ward Lock Educational Ser.). 1985. 29.00x (ISBN 0-7062-4068-5, Pub. by Ward Lock Educ Co Ltd). State Mutual Bk.

Brandon, S. G. Dictionary of Comparative Religions. LC 76-11390. 1970. lib. bdg. 55.00 (ISBN 0-684-15561-3, ScribT). Scribner.

--The Trial of Jesus of Nazareth. LC 68-9206. (Illus.). 1979. pap. 4.95 (ISBN 0-8128-6018-7). Stein & Day.

Brandon, S. G. F. Diccionario de Religiones Comparadas, 2 vols. (Span.). 1553p. 1975. Set. 49.95 (ISBN 8-4705-7188-5). French & Eur.

Brandon, Samuel G., ed. The Saviour God: Comparative Studies in the Concept of Salvation Presented to Edwin Oliver James. LC 80-14924. xxii, 242p. 1980. Repr. of 1963 ed. lib. bdg. 24.75x (ISBN 0-313-22416-1, BRSG). Greenwood.

Brandon, Thomas, jt. auth. see Buzzard, Lynn R.

Brandreth, Henry R. Episcopi Vagantes & the Anglican Church. 80p. Date not set. lib. bdg. 19.95x (ISBN 0-89370-558-6). Borgo Pr.

Brandt, Catharine. The Story of Christmas for Children. LC 74-79366. (Illus.). 20p. (Orig.). 1974. pap. 5.95 (ISBN 0-8066-2030-7, 10-6041). Augsburg.

--You're Only Old Once: Devotions in Large Print. large type ed. LC 76-27085. 1977. pap. 6.95 (ISBN 0-8066-1570-2, 10-7495). Augsburg.

Brandt, Diana, ed. Being Brothers & Sisters. LC 83-83062. (Illus.). 115p. 1984. pap. 7.95 (ISBN 0-87303-091-5). Faith & Life.

Brandt, Edith, jt. auth. see Brandt, Leslie.

Brandt, Frans M. J. The Way to Wholeness: A Guide to Christian Self-Counseling. LC 84-70657. 208p. 1984. pap. 6.95 (ISBN 0-89107-316-7, Crossway Bks). Good News.

Brandt, Geeraert. History of the Reformation & Other Ecclesiastical Transactions in, & about, the Low Countries, from the Beginning of the Eighth Century down to the End of the Famous Synod of Dort, 4 Vols. in 2. LC 70-130625. Repr. of 1733 ed. Set. 285.00 (ISBN 0-404-07960-1). AMS Pr.

Brandt, Gilbert, jt. auth. see Stoesz, Cheryl.

Brandt, Henry R. The Struggle for Inner Peace. rev. ed. 136p. 1984. pap. 4.95 (ISBN 0-88207-245-5). Victor Bks.

Brandt, L. Meditations on a Loving God. LC 12-2812. 1983. 10.95 (ISBN 0-570-03858-8). Concordia.

Brandt, Leslie. Jesus Now. 1978. 8.50 (ISBN 0-570-03268-7, 15-2714). Concordia.

--Psalms-Now. LC 73-78108. 1973. 8.50 (ISBN 0-570-03230-X, 15-2125). Concordia.

Brandt, Leslie & Brandt, Edith. Growing Together: Prayers for Married People. LC 75-2830. 96p. (Orig.). 1975. pap. 5.95 (ISBN 0-8066-1476-5, 10-2903). Augsburg.

Brandt, Leslie F. Bible Reading for the Retired. LC 83-72117. 112p. (Orig.). 1984. pap. 3.95 (ISBN 0-8066-2061-7, 10-0683). Augsburg.

--Bible Readings for Troubled Times. LC 84-18617. 112p. (Orig.). 1984. pap. 3.95 (ISBN 0-8066-2130-3, 10-0686). Augsburg.

--Book of Christian Prayer. LC 73-88603. 96p. (Orig.). 1974. pap. 4.95 (ISBN 0-8066-1406-4, 10-0785). Augsburg.

--Book of Christian Prayer: Gift Edition. rev. ed. LC 73-88603. 160p. 1980. 8.95 (ISBN 0-8066-1751-9, 10-0786). Augsburg.

--Christ in Your Life. 1980. 7.50 (ISBN 0-570-03292-X, 15-2729). Concordia.

--Epistles Now. LC 75-38711. (Illus.). 176p. 1976. 8.50 (ISBN 0-570-03258-X, 15-2166). Concordia.

--God Is Here-Let's Celebrate. LC 73-89877. 1969. pap. 2.95 (ISBN 0-570-03102-8, 12-2320). Concordia.

--Prophets Now. 1979. 8.50 (ISBN 0-570-03278-4, 15-2722). Concordia.

Brandt, Patricia & Jackson, Dave. Just Me & the Kids. (Family Ministry Ser.). (Illus.). 54p. 1985. pap. text ed. 19.95 (ISBN 0-89191-750-0). Cook.

Brandt, Richard B. Philosophy of Schleiermacher: The Development of His Theory of Scientific & Religious Knowledge. LC 68-19265. 1968. Repr. of 1941 ed. lib. bdg. 27.00x (ISBN 0-8371-0027-5, BRPS). Greenwood.

--A Theory of the Good & the Right. 1979. 32.00x (ISBN 0-19-824550-5); pap. 15.95x (ISBN 0-19-824744-3). Oxford U Pr.

Brandt, Robert L. One Way. LC 77-75601. (Radiant Life Ser.). 128p. 1977. pap. 2.50 (ISBN 0-88243-909-X, 02-0909); teacher's ed 3.95 (ISBN 0-88243-179-X, 32-0179). Gospel Pub.

--Pentecostal Promise. (Charismatic Bks.). 47p. 1972. pap. 0.69 (ISBN 0-88243-920-0, 02-0920). Gospel Pub.

Brandt, Walter I. & Lehmann, Helmut T., eds. Luther's Works: The Christian in Society II, Vol. 45. LC 55-9893. 1962. 19.95 (ISBN 0-8006-0345-1, 1-345). Fortress.

Brandwein, Yehuda. Tikune Zohar: Hebrew Text, 2 vols. 1973. Vol. 1. 25.00 (ISBN 0-943688-27-2); Vol. 2. 25.00 (ISBN 0-943688-28-0). Res Ctr Kabbalah.

Branley, Franklyn M. Mystery of Stonehenge. LC 69-11823. (Illus.). 1969. PLB 12.89 (ISBN 0-690-57046-5, Crowell Jr Bks). HarpJ.

Brann, M. & Elbogen, I. Festschrift zu Israel Lewy's Siebzigstem Geburtstag. Katz, Steven, ed. LC 79-7157. (Jewish Philosophy, Mysticism & the History of Ideas Ser.). (Ger. & Hebrew.). 1980. Repr. of 1911 ed. lib. bdg. 51.50x (ISBN 0-405-12242-X). Ayer Co Pubs.

Brann, M. & Rosenthal, F. Gedenkbuch zur Erinnerung an David Kaufmann. Katz, Steven, ed. LC 79-7142. (Jewish Philosophy, Mysticism & History of Ideas Ser.). 1980. Repr. of 1900 ed. lib. bdg. 68.50x (ISBN 0-405-12292-6). Ayer Co Pubs.

Brannan, P. T., tr. from Fr. & see Festugiere, A. J.

Branner, John C., tr. see Herculano, Alexandre.

Branner, Robert, ed. Chartres Cathedral. (Norton Critical Studies in Art History). (Illus.). 1969. pap. 8.95x (ISBN 0-393-09851-6, NortonC). Norton.

Branson, Mark L., ed. The Reader's Guide to the Best Evangelical Books. LC 82-48205. 208p. (Orig.). 1982. pap. 5.95 (ISBN 0-06-061046-8, RD-388, HarpR). Har-Row.

Branson, Mark L. & Padilla, C. Rene, eds. Conflict & Context: Hermeneutics in the Americas. 304p. (Orig.). 1986. pap. 13.95 (ISBN 0-8028-0172-2). Eerdmans.

Branson, Mark L., ed. see Aune, David E.

Branson, Mark L., ed. see Goldingay, John.

Branson, Robert. Beacon Small-Group Bible Studies, Genesis, Pt. I: How It All Began. Wolf, Earl C., ed. 96p. (Orig.). 1984. pap. 2.50 (ISBN 0-8341-0935-2). Beacon Hill.

--Beacon Small-Group Bible Studies, Isaiah: Preparing the Way of the Lord. Wolf, Earl C., ed. 96p. (Orig.). 1985. pap. 2.50 (ISBN 0-8341-0961-1). Beacon Hill.

--God's Word in Man's Language. 83p. (Orig.). 1980. pap. 2.75 (ISBN 0-8341-0659-0). Beacon Hill.

Branston, Brian. Gods & Heroes from Viking Mythology. LC 81-14540. (World Mythologies Ser.). (Illus.). 156p. 1982. 15.95 (ISBN 0-8052-3794-1). Schocken.

Brant, Roxanne. Ministering to the Lord. 80p. (Orig.). 1973. pap. 3.95 (ISBN 0-89228-031-X). Impact Bks MO.

Brantl, George. Catholicism. LC 61-15501. (Great Religions of Modern Man Ser). 1961. 8.95 (ISBN 0-8076-0162-4). Braziller.

Brantley, Richard E. Locke, Wesley & the Method of English Romanticism. LC 83-26026. 311p. 1984. 30.00 (ISBN 0-8130-0783-6). U Presses Fla.

Brasseur De Bourbourg, Charles E. Histoire du Canada, de Son Eglise et De Ses Missions Depuis la Decouverte De L'Amerique Jusqu'a Nos Jours, 2 vols. (Canadiana Before 1867 Ser). (Fr). Repr. of 1852 ed. Set. 50.00 (ISBN 0-384-05570-2). Johnson Repr.

Brasseur De Bourbourg, E. Ch. Histoire de Canada, de Son Eglise et De Ses Missions. (Canadiana Avant 1867: No. 4). 1968. 44.40x (ISBN 90-2796-333-9). Mouton.

Brastow, Lewis O. Representative Modern Preachers. facs. ed. LC 68-57306. (Essay Index Reprint Ser). 1904. 20.00 (ISBN 0-8369-0101-0). Ayer Co Pubs.

Braswell, George W., Jr. Understanding Sectarian Groups in America. 1986. pap. 10.95 (ISBN 0-8054-6607-X). Broadman.

--Understanding World Religions. LC 81-65828. (Orig.). 1983. pap. 7.95 (ISBN 0-8054-6605-3). Broadman.

Bratcher, R. G. Translator's Guide to Paul's First Letter to the Corinthians. LC 82-6951. (Helps for Translators Ser.). 1982. pap. 3.50x (ISBN 0-8267-0185-X, 08566). Am Bible.

--Translator's Guide to the Gospel of Luke. (Helps for Translators Ser.). 388p. 1982. pap. 4.50x (ISBN 0-8267-0181-7, 08712, Pub. by United Bible). Am Bible.

--A Translator's Guide to the Revelation to John. LC 84-8670. (Helps for Translators Ser.). viii, 204p. 1984. flexible bdg. 3.50x (ISBN 0-8267-0195-7, 08790, Pub. by United Bible). Am Bible.

Bratcher, R. G. & Nida, E. A. Translator's Handbook on the Gospel of Mark. LC 61-19352. (Helps for Translators Ser.). 534p. 1961. soft cover 5.90x (ISBN 0-8267-0135-3, 08501, Pub. by United Bible). Am Bible.

Bratcher, R. G., ed. Marginal Notes for the New Testament. 125p. 1980. softcover 2.50x (ISBN 0-8267-0026-8, 08558, Pub. by United Bible). Am Bible.

--Marginal Notes for the Old Testament. 186p. 1980. softcover 5.00x (ISBN 0-8267-0025-X, 08557, Pub. by United Bible). Am Bible.

--New Testament Index. 37p. 1963. pap. 1.15x (ISBN 0-8267-0003-9, 08507, Pub. by United Bible). Am Bible.

--Short Bible Reference System. 148p. 1961. 4.80x (ISBN 0-8267-0030-6, 08506, Pub. by United Bible). Am Bible.

Bratcher, R. G. & Thompson, J. A., eds. Bible Index. 136p. 1970. pap. 2.15x (ISBN 0-8267-0005-5, 08511, Pub. by United Bible). Am Bible.

Bratcher, Robert G. A Translator's Guide to Paul's Letters to Timothy & to Titus. LC 83-4823. (Helps for Translators Ser.). viii, 138p. 1983. softcover 2.30x (ISBN 0-8267-0190-6, 08781, Pub. by United Bible). Am Bible.

--Translator's Guide to Paul's Second Letter to the Corinthians. LC 83-1383. (Helps for Translators Ser.). vii, 160p. 1983. pap. 3.00x (ISBN 0-8267-0186-8, 08571, Pub. by United Bible). Am Bible.

--A Translator's Guide to the Gospel of Mark. (Helps for Translators Ser.). 236p. 1981. pap. 4.50x (ISBN 0-8267-0180-9, 08711, Pub. by United Bible). Am Bible.

--A Translator's Guide to the Gospel of Matthew. LC 82-213977. (Helps for Translators Ser.). 388p. 1981. pap. 4.50x (ISBN 0-8267-0179-5, 08710, Pub. by United Bible). Am Bible.

--A Translator's Guide to the Letters from James, Peter, & Jude. LC 83-18159. (Helps for Translators Ser.). viii, 200p. 1984. 2.30x (ISBN 0-8267-0192-2, 08572, Pub. by United Bible). Am Bible.

Bratcher, Robert G. & Nida, Eugene A. Manuel du Traducteur pour l'Evangile de Marc. Weber, C., tr. (Auxiliaires Du Traducteur Ser.). 542p. 1963. pap. 7.05x (ISBN 0-8267-0250-3, 51972, Pub. by United Bible). Am Bible.

--A Translator's Handbook on Paul's Letters to the Colossians & to Philemon. (Helps for Translators Ser.). 149p. soft cover 3.30x (ISBN 0-8267-0145-0, 08529, Pub. by United Bible). Am Bible.

--A Translator's Handbook on Paul's Letter to the Ephesians. LC 81-19691. (Helps for Translators Ser.). viii, 199p. 1982. pap. 3.50x (ISBN 0-8267-0143-4, 08780, Pub. by United Bible). Am Bible.

Bratcher, Robert G., ed. Old Testament Quotations in the New Testament. 2nd, rev. ed. LC 84-8493. (Helps for Translators Ser.). xii, 80p. 1984. flexible bdg. 2.60x (ISBN 0-8267-0029-2, 08530, Pub. by United Bible). Am Bible.

Bratt, James D. Dutch Calvinism in Modern America: A History of a Conservative Subculture. (Illus.). 368p. (Orig.). 1984. pap. 13.95 (ISBN 0-8028-0009-2). Eerdmans.

Bratt, John H. Final Curtain. (Contemporary Discussion Ser.). 1978. pap. 1.95 (ISBN 0-8010-0748-8). Baker Bk.

Braude, Benjamin & Lewis, Bernard, eds. Christians & Jews in the Ottoman Empire: The Functioning of a Plural Society, 2 vols. LC 80-11337. 1982. Set. text ed. 94.50x. Vol. 1, The Central Lands, 450p (ISBN 0-8419-0519-3). Vol. 2, The Arabic-speaking Lands, 248p (ISBN 0-8419-0520-7). Holmes & Meier.

Braude, William G. & Kapstein, Israel J., trs. from Heb. Tanna Debe Eliyyahu. LC 80-10805. Tr. of The Lore of the School of Elijah. 660p. 1980. 27.50 (ISBN 0-8276-0174-3, 455). Jewish Pubns.

Brauer, Jerald. Religion & the American Revolution. LC 76-9718. pap. 22.30 (2026888). Bks Demand UMI.

Brauer, Jerald C. Protestantism in America: A Narrative History. rev. ed. LC 66-12686. 320p. 1972. Westminster.

Brauer, Jerald C., ed. The Impact of the Church Upon Its Culture: Reappraisals of the History of Christianity. Breen, Quirinus & Drake, George A. LC 67-30155. (Essays in Divinity: Vol. 2). pap. 101.50 (ISBN 0-317-26159-2, 2024085). Bks Demand UMI.

--The Lively Experiment Continued: Essays in Honor of Sidney E. Mead. 288p. 1987. 39.95 (ISBN 0-86554-264-3, H225). Mercer Univ Pr.

--Westminster Dictionary of Church History. LC 69-11071. 900p. 1971. 27.50 (ISBN 0-664-21285-9). Westminster.

Brauer, Jerald C., ed. see Tillich, Paul.

Brauer, Wilhelm. Einleitung Zu Den Werken Des Dom Georgius Schwengel. Hogg, James, ed. (Analecta Cartusiana Ser.: No. 90). 27p. (Orig.). 1982. pap. 25.00 (ISBN 3-7052-0147-6, Pub. by Salzburg Studies). Longwood Pub Group.

--Karthaus Und Sein Kloster "Marienparadies", Ein "Bildband" Zum Heimatbuch Des Kreises Karthaus. Hogg, James, ed. (Analecta Cartusiana Ser.: No. 93). 178p. (Orig.). 1980. pap. 25.00 (ISBN 3-7052-0162-X, Pub. by Salzburg Studies). Longwood Pub Group.

Brauer, Wilhelm, jt. auth. see Hogg, James.

Braun, Eunice. From Strength to Strength: The First Half Century of the Formative Age of the Baha'i Faith. LC 78-9424. 1978. pap. 2.95 (ISBN 0-87743-125-6, 332-030). Baha'i.

--The March of the Institutions: A Commentary on the Interdependence of Rulers & Learned. 112p. 9.95 (ISBN 0-85398-182-5); pap. 5.95 (ISBN 0-85398-183-3). G Ronald Pub.

--A Reader's Guide: The Development of Baha'i Literature in English. 176p. 1986. 14.95 (ISBN 0-85398-228-7); pap. 8.95 (ISBN 0-85398-229-5). G Ronald Pub.

Braun, Eunice & Chance, Hugh E. A Crown of Beauty: The Baha'i Faith & the Holy Land. (Illus.). 104p. 16.95 (ISBN 0-85398-139-6); pap. 11.95 (ISBN 0-85398-140-X). G Ronald Pub.

Braun, Herbert, et al. God & Christ: Existence & Province. Funk, Robert W. & Ebeling, Gerhard, eds. lib. bdg. 17.50x (ISBN 0-88307-042-1). Gannon.

Braun, Hugh. Parish Churches: Their Architectural Development in England. 1970. 12.50 (ISBN 0-571-09045-1). Transatl Arts.

Braun, J. R. The Consequences of Sexual Freedom. 150p. (Orig.). 1980. pap. text ed. 2.95 (ISBN 0-933656-04-1). Trinity Pub Hse.

--Is This My Neighbor? The Union Gospel Mission. (Illus.). 60p. (Orig.). 1980. pap. text ed. 8.95 (ISBN 0-933656-08-4). Trinity Pub Hse.

--Male Sexual Fantasies: The Destruction of the Feminine Personality; The Christian Mandate Against Pornography. 48p. (Orig.). 1980. pap. 1.95 (ISBN 0-933656-05-X). Trinity Pub Hse.

--The Meaning of Sexual Pleasure: A Christian Understanding of Sexuality. 203p. (Orig.). 1976. pap. 4.95 (ISBN 0-933656-02-5). Trinity Pub Hse.

Braun, John A. By His Grace. 1983. pap. 7.95 (ISBN 0-8100-0161-6, 06N0560). Northwest Pub.

Brauner, R. A., ed. Shiv'im: Essays & Studies in Honor of Ira Eisenstein. 20.00x (ISBN 0-87068-442-6). Ktav.

Braunfels, Wolfgang. Monasteries of Western Europe: The Architecture of the Orders. LC 73-2472. (Illus.). 263p. 1973. 55.50 (ISBN 0-691-03896-1); pap. 19.95 (ISBN 0-691-00313-0). Princeton U Pr.

Braunstein, Baruch. The Chuetas of Majorca. rev. ed. 1971. 25.00x (ISBN 0-87068-147-8). Ktav.

Braunthal, Alfred. Salvation & the Perfect Society: The Eternal Quest. LC 79-4705. 448p. 1979. lib. bdg. 25.00x (ISBN 0-87023-273-8). U of Mass Pr.

Brause, Dorsey. Expanded Ministry to Adults: Program Guidelines. 1979. pap. 3.50 (ISBN 0-89367-030-8). Light & Life.

Braver, J. C., ed. see Meland, Bernard E.

Braverman, Eric R. Psalms of the Rabbi Physician. (Illus.). 112p. (Orig.). 1986. pap. 9.95 (ISBN 1-55630-003-4). Brentwood Comm.

Braverman, Jay. Jerome's Commentary on Daniel: A Study of Comparative Jewish & Christian Interpretations of the Hebrew Bible. LC 78-55726. (Catholic Biblical Quarterly Monographs: No. 7). xvi, 162p. 1978. 4.00 (ISBN 0-915170-06-X). Catholic Biblical.

Bravmann, Rene A. African Islam. LC 83-21174. (Illus.). 120p. 1984. pap. 16.95 (ISBN 0-87474-281-1, BRAIP). Smithsonian.

Brawley, Edward M., ed. Negro Baptist Pulpit. facs. ed. LC 74-154072. (Black Heritage Library Collection Ser). 1890. 19.25 (ISBN 0-8369-8783-7). Ayer Co Pubs.

Brawner, Mina R. Woman in the Word. 1.25 (ISBN 0-89985-105-3). Christ Nations.

Bray, F. C. The World of Myths: A Dictionary of Universal Mythology. 75.00 (ISBN 0-8490-1335-6). Gordon Pr.

Bray, Gerald. Creeds, Councils & Christ. LC 83-26443. 220p. 1984. pap. 6.95 (ISBN 0-87784-969-2). Inter-Varsity.

Bray, Gerald L. Holiness & the Will of God: Perspectives on the Theology of Tertullian. LC 79-5211. (New Foundations Theological Library). (Peter Toon & Ralph Martin series editors). 1980. 3.25 (ISBN 0-8042-3705-0). John Knox.

Bray, Thomas. Reverend Thomas Bray: His Life & Selected Works Relating to Maryland. Steiner, Bernard C., ed. LC 72-14420. (Maryland Historical Society. Fund-Publications Ser.: No. 37). Repr. of 1901 ed. 15.00 (ISBN 0-404-57637-0). AMS Pr.

Braybrook, Patrick. Some Thoughts on Hilaire Belloc: Ten Studies. 1973. 17.50 (ISBN 0-8274-1717-9). R West.

Braybrooke, Marcus. Inter-Faith Organizations 1893-1979: An Historical Directory. LC 79-91620. (Texts & Studies in Religion: Vol. 6). xiv, 228p. 1980. 49.95x (ISBN 0-88946-971-7). E Mellen.

Braybrooke, P. Some Catholic Novelists: Their Art & Outlook. 59.95 (ISBN 0-8490-1075-6). Gordon Pr.

Braybrooke, Patrick. G. K. Chesterton. LC 72-6491. (English Biography Ser., No. 31). 130p. 1972. Repr. of 1922 ed. lib. bdg. 35.95x (ISBN 0-8383-1616-6). Haskell.

--Some Catholic Novelists. facs. ed. LC 67-22078. (Essay Index Reprint Ser.). 1931. 19.00 (ISBN 0-8369-1323-X). Ayer Co Pubs.

--Some Thoughts on Hilaire Belloc: Ten Studies. LC 68-1140. (Studies in Irish Literature, No. 16). 1969. Repr. lib. bdg. 48.95x (ISBN 0-8383-0649-7). Haskell.

--Some Victorian & Georgian Catholics. facs. ed. LC 67-22080. (Essay Index Reprint Ser.). 1932. 18.00 (ISBN 0-8369-1325-6). Ayer Co Pubs.

Brayer, Menachem M. The Jewish Woman in Rabbinic Literature: A Psychohistorical Perspective. 400p. 1986. text ed. 20.00x (ISBN 0-88125-073-2); pap. text ed. 11.95x (ISBN 0-88125-072-4). Ktav.

--Jewish Woman in Rabbinic Literature: A Psychosocial Perspective. 300p. 1986. text ed. 20.00x (ISBN 0-88125-071-6); pap. text ed. 11.95x (ISBN 0-88125-070-8). Ktav.

Bready, John W. England, Before & after Wesley: The Evangelical Revival & Social Reform. LC 72-139906. (Illus.). 463p. 1971. Repr. of 1938 ed. 17.00x (ISBN 0-8462-1533-0). Russell.

Bream, Howard N., et al, eds. A Light unto My Path: Old Testament Studies in Honor of Jacob M. Myers. LC 73-85042. (Gettysburg Theological Studies, No. 4). 576p. 1974. 27.95 (ISBN 0-87722-026-3). Temple U Pr.

Breasted, James H. Development of Religion & Thought in Ancient Egypt. LC 58-7111. 406p. 1972. pap. 12.95x (ISBN 0-8122-1045-X, Pa Paperbks). U of Pa Pr.

Breathett, George, ed. The Catholic Church in Haiti 1704-1785: Selected Letters, Memoirs & Documents. 1983. 34.95x (ISBN 0-89712-103-1). Documentary Pubns.

Breault, Joseph. Seeking Purity of Heart: The Gift of Ourselves to God. (Illus.). 96p. (Orig.). 1975. pap. 3.95 (ISBN 0-914544-07-1). Living Flame Pr.

Breault, William. A Voice over the Water. LC 84-73051. 128p. (Orig.). 1985. pap. 4.95 (ISBN 0-87793-281-6). Ave Maria.

Brecheen, Carl & Faulkner, Paul. What Every Family Needs or Whatever Happened to Mom, Dad, & the Kids. LC 78-68726. (Journey Bks.). 1979. pap. 3.95 (ISBN 0-8344-0104-5). Sweet.

Brecht, Martin. Martin Luther: His Road to Reformation, 1483-1521. Schaaf, James L., tr. LC 84-47911. 592p. 1985. 36.95 (ISBN 0-8006-0738-4, 1-738). Fortress.

Breck, Allen D., jt. ed. see Yourgrau, Wolfgang.

Breckenridge, Marilyn S. Jesse Tree Devotions: A Family Activity for Lent. 40p. (Orig.). 1985. pap. 4.95 (ISBN 0-8066-2154-0, 10-3475). Augsburg.

Breckinridge, John, jt. auth. see Hughes, John.

Bredesen, Harald. Yes, Lord. rev. ed. LC 72-91776. 199p. 1982. pap. 4.95 (ISBN 0-910311-00-5). Huntington Hse Inc.

Bredeweg, Frank H. United States Catholic Elementary & Secondary Schools, 1984-85. 1985. 6.60; member 4.95. Natl Cath Educ.

--United States Catholic Elementary & Secondary Schools, 1985-86. 21p. 1986. 6.60. Natl Cath Educ.

Bredin, Eamonn. Rediscovering Jesus: Challenge of Discipleship. 300p. 1986. pap. 9.95 (ISBN 0-89622-300-0). Twenty-Third.

Bredin, Jean-Denis. The Affair: The Case of Alfred Dreyfus. Mehlman, Jeffrey, tr. from Fr. Tr. of L'Affaire. (Illus.). 1987. pap. 12.95 (ISBN 0-8076-1175-1). Braziller.

Bredvold, Louis I. The Brave New World of the Enlightenment. LC 61-10987. pap. 43.00 (ISBN 0-317-08088-1, 2051585). Bks Demand UMI.

Bredweg, Frank H. United States Catholic Elementary & Secondary Schools, 1985-86. 21p. 1986. 7.30 (ISBN 0-318-20578-5). Natl Cath Educ.

--United States Catholic Elementary Schools & their Finances, 1986. 1986. 6.00 (ISBN 0-318-20577-7). Natl Cath Educ.

Breech, James. The Silence of Jesus: The Authentic Voice of the Historical Man. LC 82-71825. 192p. 1983. 14.95 (ISBN 0-8006-0691-4, 1-691). Fortress.

Breed, David K. The Trial of Christ: From a Legal & Scriptural Viewpoint. (Pocket Pulpit Library). 96p. 1982. pap. 2.95 (ISBN 0-8010-0829-8). Baker Bk.

Breed, David R. The History & Use of Hymns & Hymn Tunes. LC 76-39525. Repr. of 1903 ed. 20.00 (ISBN 0-404-09906-8). AMS Pr.

--The History & Use of Hymns & Hymn Tunes. 59.95 (ISBN 0-8490-0313-X). Gordon Pr.

Breeden, Terri. Teaching the Meaning of Church Ordinances to Children. (Orig.). 1986. pap. 5.95 (ISBN 0-89265-097-4). Randall Hse.

Breemen, Peter G. van see Van Breemen, Peter G.

Breen, Quirinus see Brauer, Jerald C.

Breese, Dave. Know the Marks of Cults. LC 74-21907. 128p. 1975. pap. 4.95 (ISBN 0-88207-704-X). Victor Bks.

Breese, David. Satan's Ten Most Believable Lies. 2nd ed. 1987. pap. 6.95 (ISBN 0-8024-7675-9). Moody.

Breffny, Brian de see De Breffny, Brian.

Bregman, Jay. Synesius of Cyrene: Philosopher-Bishop. LC 81-10293. (The Transformation of the Classical Heritage Ser.: Vol. II). 1982. 33.00x (ISBN 0-520-04192-5). U of Cal Pr.

Bregman, Lucy. Through the Landscape of Faith. LC 85-26381. 120p. (Orig.). 1986. pap. 9.95 (ISBN 0-664-24704-0). Westminster.

Bregy, Katherine. Poets Chantry. LC 70-105766. 1970. Repr. of 1912 ed. 21.50x (ISBN 0-8046-1043-6, Pub. by Kennikat). Assoc Faculty Pr.

--The Story of Saint Francis de Sales: Patron of Catholic Writers. 108p. 1982. Repr. of 1958 ed. lib. bdg. 35.00 (ISBN 0-89984-015-9). Century Bookbindery.

Brehaut, Ernest. Encyclopedist of the Dark Ages, Isidore of Seville. (Columbia University. Studies in History, Economics, & Public Law: Vol. 48, No. 1). 1967. Repr. of 1912 ed. 21.50 (ISBN 0-8337-0361-7). B Franklin.

Brehaut, Ernest, tr. see Gregory - Bishop of Tours.

Brehier, Louis. L' Eglise et l'Orient au moyen age: Les croisades. 2nd ed. LC 76-29834. (Fr.). Repr. of 1907 ed. 39.50 (ISBN 0-404-15413-1). AMS Pr.

--La Querelle des Images Huitieme-Neuvieme Siecle. 1969. 14.00 (ISBN 0-8337-0362-5). B Franklin.

--Schisme orientale du onzieme siecle. 1969. Repr. of 1899 ed. 25.50 (ISBN 0-8337-0363-3). B Franklin.

Breidenbach, Monica E., jt. auth. see Hover, Margot K.

Breisch, Francis. Ephesians: A Study Guide. (Revelation Series for Adults). 1976. pap. text ed. 2.50 (ISBN 0-317-39618-8). CRC Pubns.

Breitenkamp, Edward C., jt. auth. see Dabbs, Jack A.

Breiter, Paul, jt. auth. see Kornfield, Jack.

Brem, M. M. La Historia de Maria. (Libros Arco Ser.). Tr. of Mary's Story. (Span., Illus.). 32p. 1979. pap. 0.95 (ISBN 0-89922-145-9). Edit Caribe.

--Mary's Story. (Arch Bks.: Set 4). 1967. laminated bdg. 0.99 (ISBN 0-570-06029-X, 59-1140). Concordia.

Bremer, Maura. And Send the Sun Tomorrow: A Journal of My Father's Last Days. 1979. pap. 2.95 (ISBN 0-03-049396-X, HarpR). Har-Row.

Bremke, Maryann, jt. auth. see Rakel, Michael.

Bremmer, Jan. The Early Greek Concept of the Soul. LC 82-47583. 190p. 1983. 23.00x (ISBN 0-691-03131-2). Princeton U Pr.

Bremmer, Jan & Graf, Fritz, eds. Interpretations of Greek Mythology. LC 86-20638. (Illus.). 304p. 1987. 28.50x (ISBN 0-389-20679-2). B&N Imports.

Bremond, Henri. Prayer & Poetry: Contribution to Poetical Theory. LC 72-188148. 1927. lib. bdg. 25.00 (ISBN 0-8414-9825-3). Folcroft.

Brenan, Gerald. St. John of the Cross: His Life & Poetry. LC 72-83577. pap. 61.30 (ISBN 0-317-26068-5, 2024428). Bks Demand UMI.

Brenchley, Julius, jt. auth. see Remy, Jules.

Brendel, Doug, jt. auth. see Blair, Maury.

Breneman, Mervin, ed. Biblia con Notas. (Span.). 1696p. 1981. black imitation leather 15.95 (ISBN 0-89922-164-5); black imitation leather 19.95 (ISBN 0-89922-364-8); red imitation leather 15.95 (ISBN 0-89922-264-1); red imitation leather 19.95 (ISBN 0-89922-464-4). Edit Caribe.

Brengle, Samuel. God As Strategist. (Illus.). 64p. 1978. pap. 1.50 (ISBN 0-89216-017-9). Salvation Army.

Brengle, Samuel L. Ancient Prophets & Modern Problems. 1978. pap. 3.95 (ISBN 0-86544-000-X). Salv Army Suppl South.

--Guest of the Soul. 1978. pap. 3.95 (ISBN 0-86544-001-8). Salv Army Suppl South.

--Heart Talks on Holiness. 1978. pap. 3.95 (ISBN 0-86544-002-6). Salv Army Suppl South.

--Helps to Holiness. 1978. pap. 3.95 (ISBN 0-86544-003-4). Salv Army Suppl South.

--Love Slaves. 1960. Repr. of 1923 ed. 3.95 (ISBN 0-86544-004-2). Salv Army Suppl South.

--Resurrection Life & Power. 1978. Repr. of 1925 ed. 3.95 (ISBN 0-86544-005-0). Salv Army Suppl South.

--Soul Winner's Secret. 1978. pap. 3.95 (ISBN 0-86544-007-7). Salv Army Suppl South.

--Way of Holiness. 1966. Repr. of 1902 ed. 3.95 (ISBN 0-86544-008-5). Salv Army Suppl South.

--When the Holy Ghost Is Come. 1980. pap. 3.95 (ISBN 0-86544-009-3). Salv Army Suppl South.

Brennan, Anne & Janice, Brewi. Mid-Life Directions, Praying & Playing Sources of New Dynamism. LC 84-62157. 192p. (Orig.). 1985. pap. 7.95 (ISBN 0-8091-2681-8). Paulist Pr.

Brennan, Anne, jt. ed. see Brewi, Janice.

Brennan, J. H. Reincarnation Five Keys to Past Lives. (Paths to Inner Power Ser.). 1981. pap. 3.50 (ISBN 0-85030-275-7). Weiser.

Brennan, John M. The Open Texture of Moral Concepts. LC 74-31826. 171p. 1977. text ed. 26.50x (ISBN 0-06-490656-6, 06364). B&N Imports.

Brennan, Sr. M. Rose. Intellectual Virtues According to the Philosophy of St. Thomas. (Orig.). 1957. pap. text ed. 4.95x (ISBN 0-87015-075-8). Pacific Bks.

Brennan, Patrick. Spirituality for an Anxious Age. 151p. 1985. pap. 7.95 (ISBN 0-88347-194-9). Thomas More.

Brennan, Patrick J. Penance & Reconciliation. (Guidelines for Contemporary Catholics Ser.). (Orig.). 1986. pap. 7.95 (ISBN 0-88347-195-7). Thomas More.

Brennan, Robert E., ed. Essays in Thomism. LC 72-1149. (Essay Index Reprint Ser.). Repr. of 1942 ed. 27.50 (ISBN 0-8369-2834-2). Ayer Co Pubs.

Brennan-Nichols, Patricia. Getting to Know Jesus. (Illus.). 68p. (Orig.). 1984. pap. 3.95 (ISBN 0-89505-130-3). Argus Comm.

--Liturgies & Lessons: Childrens Homilies. 1984. pap. 9.95 (ISBN 0-941850-13-7). Sunday Pubns.

Brenneman, H. G. Meditaciones para la Nueva Madre. 80p. 1982. Repr. of 1978 ed. 2.85 (ISBN 0-311-40032-9). Casa Bautista.

Brenneman, Helen G. But Not Forsaken. 1983. 3.25 (ISBN 0-87813-954-0). Christian Light.
--Meditaciones para la Nueva Madre. La Valle, Maria T., tr. Tr. of Meditations for the New Mother. (Span., Illus.). 80p. 1978. pap. 2.85 (ISBN 0-8361-1212-1). Herald Pr.
--Meditations for the Expectant Mother. LC 68-12025. (Illus.). 80p. (Orig.). 1968. 8.95 (ISBN 0-8361-1639-9); pap. 4.50 (ISBN 0-8361-1567-8). Herald Pr.
--Meditations for the New Mother. LC 53-7585. (Illus.). 78p. (Orig.). 1953. 8.95 (ISBN 0-8361-3400-1); pap. 4.50 (ISBN 0-8361-3399-4). Herald Pr.
--Morning Joy. LC 80-26449. 80p. 1981. pap. 3.95 (ISBN 0-8361-1942-8). Herald Pr.
--My Comforters. LC 66-13156. 80p. (Orig.). 1966. deluxe ed. 3.95 o. p. (ISBN 0-8361-1751-4); pap. 2.50 (ISBN 0-8361-1529-5). Herald Pr.
--Para la Futura Mama. Tr. of Meditations for the Expectant Mother. (Span.). 80p. 1979. pap. 2.85 (ISBN 0-8361-1216-4). Herald Pr.
Brenneman, Walter L., Jr., et al. The Seeing Eye: Hermeneutical Phenomenology in the Study of Religion. LC 81-47174. 168p. 1982. 22.50x (ISBN 0-271-00291-3). Pa St U Pr.
Brenner, Anita. Idols Behind Altars. LC 67-19527. (Illus.). 1929. 18.00 (ISBN 0-8196-0190-X). Biblo.
Brenner, Athalya. Colour Terms in the Old Testament. (Journal for the Study of the Old Testament, Supplement Ser.: No. 21). 296p. 1983. text ed. 29.95x (ISBN 0-905774-42-6, Pub. by JSOT Pr England); pap. text ed. 21.95 (ISBN 0-905774-43-4, Pub. by JSOT Pr England). Eisenbrauns.
--The Israelite Woman: Social Role & Literary Type in Biblical Narrative. (The Biblical Seminar Ser.: No. 2). 144p. 1985. pap. text ed. 7.95x (ISBN 0-905774-83-3, Pub. by JSOT Pr England). Eisenbrauns.
Brenner, Lenni. The Iron Wall: Zionist Revisionism from Jabotinsky to Shamir. 230p. 1984. 26.25x (ISBN 0-86232-216-2, Pub. by Zed Pr England); pap. text ed. 9.25 (ISBN 0-86232-217-0, Pub. by Zed Pr England). Humanities.
--Zionism in the Age of the Dictators. LC 82-23369. 300p. 1983. pap. 8.95 osi (ISBN 0-88208-164-0). Lawrence Hill.
Brenner, Louis. West African Sufi: The Religious Heritage & Spiritual Quest of Cerno Bokar Saalif Taal. LC 83-4803. 215p. 1984. lib. bdg. 24.95x (ISBN 0-520-05008-8). U of Cal Pr.
Brenner, Reeve R. The Faith & Doubt of Holocaust Survivors. LC 79-6764. 1980. 12.95 (ISBN 0-02-904420-0). Free Pr.
Brenner, Robert. Christmas Past. (Illus.). 256p. 1985. 24.95 (ISBN 0-88740-051-5). Schiffer.
--Christmas Revisited. (Illus.). 206p. 1986. pap. 24.95 (ISBN 0-88740-067-1). Schiffer.
Brent, Charles H. Inspiration of Responsibility, & Other Papers. facs. ed. LC 67-22081. (Essay Index Reprint Ser). 1915. 13.00 (ISBN 0-8369-0251-3). Ayer Co Pubs.
Brent, Daniel & Jurkowitz, Carolyn. School Board Study Programs: Board Members Manual, Series I. 1983. 6.00 (ISBN 0-318-00790-8). Natl Cath Educ.
Brentano, Sr. Mary B. Nature in the Works of Fray Luis De Granada. LC 75-94164. (Catholic University. Studies in Romance Languages & Literatures: No. 15). Repr. of 1936 ed. 21.00 (ISBN 0-404-50315-2). AMS Pr.
Brenton, Charles. The Septuagint & Apocrypha in Greek & English. 1390p. 1972. 39.95 (ISBN 0-310-20430-5, 6234). Zondervan.
Breslauer, S. Daniel. The Ecumenical Perspective & the Modernization of Jewish Religion: A Study in the Relationship Between Theology & Myth. 1978. pap. 9.00 (ISBN 0-89130-236-0, 140005). Scholars Pr GA.
--Meir Kahane, Ideologue, Hero, & Thinker. LC 86-21703. (Jewish Studies: Vol. 1). 168p. 1986. text ed. 39.95x (ISBN 0-88946-252-6). E Mellen.
--A New Jewish Ethics. LC 83-23659. (Symposium Ser.: Vol. 9). 136p. 1983. lib. bdg. 19.95x (ISBN 0-88946-700-5). E Mellen.
Breslauer, S. Daniel, compiled by. Contemporary Jewish Ethics: A Bibliographical Survey. LC 85-9895. (Bibliographies & Indexes in Religious Studies: No. 6). xi, 213p. 1985. lib. bdg. 37.50 (ISBN 0-313-24594-0, BCJ/). Greenwood.
--Modern Jewish Morality: A Bibliographical Survey. LC 86-12145. 249p. 1986. 39.95 (ISBN 0-313-24700-5, BJM/). Greenwood.
Breslin, Thomas A. China, American Catholicism, & the Missionary. LC 79-27857. (Illus.). 1980. text ed. 19.75x (ISBN 0-271-00259-X). Pa St U Pr.
Brestin, Dee. Ecclesiastes: God's Wisdom for Evangelism. (Fisherman Bible Studyguide Ser.). 93p. 1980. saddle stitch 2.95 (ISBN 0-87788-212-6). Shaw Pubs.
--Examining the Claims of Jesus. (A Core Study in the Fisherman Bible Studyguides). 48p. 1985. pap. 2.95 (ISBN 0-87788-246-0). Shaw Pubs.
--Finders Keepers: Introducing Your Friends to Christ & Helping Them Grow. LC 83-8522. 180p. 1985. 8.95 (ISBN 0-87788-265-7); pap. 5.95 (ISBN 0-87788-267-3). Shaw Pubs.
--Friendship: Portraits in God's Family Album. (Fisherman Bible Studyguide Ser.). 96p. (Orig.). 1986. pap. 2.95 (ISBN 0-87788-287-8). Shaw Pubs.
--How Should a Christian Live? 1, 2, & 3 John. (A Core Study in the Fisherman Bible Studyguides). 80p. 1985. pap. 2.95 (ISBN 0-87788-351-3). Shaw Pubs.
Brestin, Dee & Brestin, Steve. Proverbs & Parables: God's Wisdom for Living. (Fisherman Bible Studyguide Ser.). 75p. 1975. saddle-stitch 2.95 (ISBN 0-87788-694-6). Shaw Pubs.
Brestin, Dee, jt. auth. see Brestin, Steve.
Brestin, Steve & Brestin, Dee. Higher Ground: For the Believer Who Seeks Joy & Victory. (Fisherman Bible Studyguide Ser.). 58p. 1978. saddle-stitched 2.95 (ISBN 0-87788-345-9). Shaw Pubs.
Brestin, Steve, jt. auth. see Brestin, Dee.
Bretall. Empirical Theology of Henry Nelson Weiman. 1981. pap. 6.95 (ISBN 0-8298-0485-4). Pilgrim NY.
Brethren, Hutterian, ed. see Arnold, Eberhard.
Breton, Denise. This Lie Called Evil. LC 82-80906. 130p. (Orig.). 1983. pap. 8.50 (ISBN 0-942958-02-0). Kappeler Inst Pub.
Breton, Thierry. The Pentecost Project. LC 86-33730. 1987. 17.95 (ISBN 0-8050-0380-0). H Holt & Co.
Breton, Valentine. Life & Prayer. 189p. 1960. 5.95 (ISBN 0-933932-21-9). Scepter Pubs.
Bretscher, Paul G. Cain, Come Home! LC 76-1810. (Illus.). 144p. 1976. pap. text ed. 4.25 (ISBN 0-915644-05-3). Clayton Pub Hse.
Bretschneider, Diana. Bible Puzzle Time, Friends of God. 16p. 1983. pap. 0.60 (ISBN 0-87239-655-X, 2303). Standard Pub.
Brett, Jan, illus. Twelve Days of Christmas. LC 85-46056. (Illus.). 32p. 1986. PLB 12.95 (ISBN 0-396-08821-X). Dodd.
Brett, Laurence. Redeemed Creation: The Sacramentals Today. (Message of the Sacraments Ser.: Vol. 8). 10.95 (ISBN 0-89453-398-3); pap. 6.95 (ISBN 0-89453-234-0). M Glazier.
Brett, Martin, jt. auth. see Whitelock, Dorothy.
Brett, Michael, ed. Northern Africa: Islam & Modernization. 156p. 1973. 28.50x (ISBN 0-7146-2972-3, F Cass Co). Biblio Dist.
Brettschneider, Diana, et al. Twenty-Six Bible Programs for Preschoolers. 96p. 1987. tchr's wkbk. 8.95 (ISBN 0-87403-213-X, 3413). Standard Pub.
Breuer, Isaac. Concepts of Judaism. Levinger, Jacob S., tr. 1974. 10.00 (ISBN 0-87306-058-X). Feldheim.
Breuer, Jacob. Fundamentals of Judaism. 1969. pap. 6.95 (ISBN 0-87306-208-6). Feldheim.
Breuer, Salomon. Chochmo U'Mussar, 3 vols. 1972. Set. 24.00 (ISBN 0-87306-205-1). Feldheim.
Breur, Joseph. The Jewish Marriage. 3.95 (ISBN 0-87306-097-0). Feldheim.
Brewer, Bartholomew F. & Furrell, Alfred W. Peregrinaje Esde Roma. Vargas-Caba, Jose M., tr. from Eng. (Span., Illus.). 194p. 1986. pap. 5.95 (ISBN 0-89084-328-7). Bob Jones Univ Pr.
--Pilgrimage from Rome. rev. ed. (Illus.). 1986. pap. 5.95 (ISBN 0-89084-327-9). Bob Jones Univ Pr.
Brewer, Clifton H. A History of Religious Education in the Episcopal Church to Eighteen Thirty-Five. 1924. 14.50x (ISBN 0-686-51401-7). Elliots Bks.
--History of Religious Education in the Episcopal Church to 1835. LC 73-89152. (American Education Its Men, Institutions & Ideas, Ser. 1). 1969. Repr. of 1924 ed. 16.00 (ISBN 0-405-01390-6). Ayer Co Pubs.
Brewer, Donald R. Dynamic Children's Sermons. (Orig.). 1984. pap. 3.95 (ISBN 0-937172-58-8). JLJ Pubs.
Brewer, E. Cobham. The Dictionary of Miracles, 2 vols. (Illus.). 337p. 1986. Repr. of 1882 ed. Set. 217.50 (ISBN 0-89901-263-9). Found Class Reprints.
--A Dictionary of Miracles, Imitative, Realistic, & Dogmatic. LC 66-29783. 1966. Repr. of 1885 ed. 50.00x (ISBN 0-8103-3000-8). Gale.
Brewer, Earl D. Continuation or Transformation? The Involvement of United Methodism in Social Movements & Issues. (Into our Third Century Ser.). 128p. (Orig.). 1982. pap. 4.95 (ISBN 0-687-09623-5). Abingdon.
Brewer, Ebenezer. A Dictionary of Miracles. 75.00 (ISBN 0-8490-0040-8). Gordon Pr.
Brewer, James W., Jr. Jerome. 15th ed. (Illus.). 1976. pap. 0.50 (ISBN 0-911408-16-9). SW Pks Mnmts.
Brewer, Joan S., compiled by. Sex & the Modern Jewish Woman: Annotated Bibliography - Essays. 128p. 1986. pap. 9.25 (ISBN 0-930395-01-8). Biblio NY.
Brewer, Ralph J. Journey Through the Bible. 167p. (Orig.). 1983. pap. text ed. 5.95 (ISBN 0-87148-450-1); instrs. guide 2.50 (ISBN 0-87148-451-X). Pathway Pr.
Brewer, Tina. Big & Little in the Bible. (Happy Day Bks.). (Illus.). 1.59 (ISBN 0-87403-022-6, 3482). Standard Pub.
Brewi, Janice & Brennan, Anne, eds. Mid Life: Psyhological & Spiritual Perspectives. 224p. 1982. 12.95 (ISBN 0-8245-0417-8); pap. 8.95. Crossroad NY.
Brewster, Earl H., compiled by. The Life of Gotama Buddha (Compiled Exclusively from the Pali Canon) LC 78-72380. Repr. of 1926 ed. 27.50 (ISBN 0-404-17229-6). AMS Pr.
Brewster, Harold P. Saints & Festivals of the Christian Church. LC 73-159869. (Illus.). xiv, 558p. 1975. Repr. of 1904 ed. 48.00x (ISBN 0-8103-3992-7). Gale.
Brewyn, William. A Fifteenth Century Guidebook to the Principal Churches of Rome. Woodruff, C. Eveleigh, tr. LC 78-63451. (The Crusades & Military Orders: Second Ser.). Repr. of 1933 ed. 17.00 (ISBN 0-404-16374-2). AMS Pr.
Breybach, Breyten. Endpapers: Political Essay. 1986. 16.95 (ISBN 0-374-14829-5). FS&G.
Breymayer, Reinhard, jt. ed. see Haeusermann, Friederich.
Brezik, Victor B. About Living. 156p. 1980. 4.95 (ISBN 0-912414-29-4). Lumen Christi.
Brezik, Victor B., ed. One Hundred Years of Thomism: Aeterni Patris & Afterwards - A Symposium. LC 85-14986. 210p. pap. text ed. 9.95 (ISBN 0-9605456-0-3). U of Notre Dame Pr.
--Thomistic Papers, No. I. LC 85-18508. 176p. 1983. text ed. 20.95 (ISBN 0-268-01850-2); pap. text ed. 10.95 (ISBN 0-268-01851-0). U of Notre Dame Pr.
Brianchaninov, Ignatius. Fasting. pap. 0.25 (ISBN 0-686-05642-6). Eastern Orthodox.
--Three Essays: On Reading the Gospel, on Reading the Holy Fathers, on Shunning Reading of Books Containing False Teachings. pap. 0.25 (ISBN 0-686-16365-6). Eastern Orthodox.
Brianchianinov, Ignatius. The Arena. Archimandrite Lazarus Moore, tr. from Rus. 300p. (Orig.). 1982. 15.00 (ISBN 0-88465-009-X); pap. 10.00 (ISBN 0-88465-011-1). Holy Trinity.
--Asketitcheskaya Propovjed, Tom 4. Tr. of Ascetic Sermons. 537p. 25.00 (ISBN 0-317-28962-4); pap. 20.00 (ISBN 0-317-28963-2). Holy Trinity.
--Asketitcheskije Opiti, Tom 2. Tr. of Ascetic Experiences. 332p. 20.00 (ISBN 0-317-28949-7); pap. 15.00 (ISBN 0-317-28950-0). Holy Trinity.
--Asketitcheskije Opiti, tom 3, Tom 3. Tr. of Ascetic Experiences. 315p. 20.00 (ISBN 0-317-28957-8); pap. 15.00 (ISBN 0-317-28958-6). Holy Trinity.
--Prinoshenije Sovremennomu Monashestvu, Vol. 5. Tr. of An Offering to Contemporary Monasticism. 354p. 20.00 (ISBN 0-317-28966-7); pap. 15.00 (ISBN 0-317-28967-5). Holy Trinity.
Brians, Bert. Leoni Meadows Experiences. large print ed. 62p. 1984. pap. 9.00 (ISBN 0-914009-07-9). VHI Library.
--My Wife the Prophetess. large print ed. (Illus.). 55p. 1982. pap. 9.50 (ISBN 0-9608650-7-1). VHI Library.
Brians, Bert, ed. My Wife the Prophetess. rev. ed. (Illus.). 24p. 1985. pap. 4.50 (ISBN 0-914009-73-7). VHI Library.
Brians, Charlene. How I Use Herbs. large print ed. 37p. 1985. pap. 5.50 (ISBN 0-914009-43-5). VHI Library.
Brians, Charlene, jt. auth. see Moss, Michele.
Brians, Charline. Light after Ellen White. large print ed. 32p. 1985. pap. 5.00 (ISBN 0-914009-06-0). VHI Library.
--My Friends the Adventists. large print ed. (Illus.). 57p. 1982. pap. 9.50 (ISBN 0-9608650-6-3). VHI Library.
--Sunday Sister. large print ed. 24p. 1985. pap. 4.00 (ISBN 0-914009-53-2). VHI Library.
--Testing Myself As a Prophet. large print ed. 1985. pap. 5.00 (ISBN 0-914009-10-9). VHI Library.
Brians, Charline, ed. Spirit of Prophecy, Vol. I & II. large print ed. 27p. 1984. pap. 5.00 (ISBN 0-9608650-3-9). VHI Library.
Brians, Pearl. Adventist Evangelist's Diary. large print ed. 1985. pap. 4.00 (ISBN 0-914009-25-7). VHI Library.
--Appetite Control for Christians. large print ed. 28p. 1985. pap. 4.50 (ISBN 0-914009-30-3). VHI Library.
--Carelessness & Indifference. large print ed. 25p. 1985. pap. 5.00 (ISBN 0-914009-39-7). VHI Library.
--Defending the Blind Man. large print ed. 1985. pap. 4.00 (ISBN 0-914009-28-1). VHI Library.
--During My Conversion. large print ed. 44p. 1984. pap. 8.00 (ISBN 0-914009-11-7). VHI Library.
--Indecision about Baptism. large print ed. 34p. 1985. pap. 5.00 (ISBN 0-914009-41-9). VHI Library.
--Ingathering Experience, Vol. 1. large print ed. 33p. 1985. pap. 5.00 (ISBN 0-914009-32-X). VHI Library.
--Mama's Life on a Missouri Farm. large print ed. 86p. pap. 8.00 (ISBN 0-914009-26-5). VHI Library.
--My Appetite Control. large print ed. 1985. pap. 6.00 (ISBN 0-914009-40-0). VHI Library.
--My First SDA Camp Meeting. large print ed. 44p. 1985. pap. 6.00 (ISBN 0-914009-27-3). VHI Library.
--Out of Confusion-into the Light. large print ed. 58p. 1984. pap. 9.50 (ISBN 0-914009-12-5). VHI Library.
--Overeaters Feelings & Faith. large print ed. 40p. 1985. pap. 5.50 (ISBN 0-914009-31-1). VHI Library.
--Pleading with the Father. large print ed. 27p. 1985. pap. 4.50 (ISBN 0-914009-36-2). VHI Library.
--Prayer Changes My Life. large print ed. 23p. 1985. pap. 4.00 (ISBN 0-914009-35-4). VHI Library.
--Prayer Meeting at Our House. large print ed. 25p. 1985. pap. 4.00 (ISBN 0-914009-33-8). VHI Library.
--Recovery from Compulsive Overeating. large print ed. 31p. 1985. pap. 5.00 (ISBN 0-914009-29-X). VHI Library.
Brians, Pearl, ed. Hangups, Health & Heaven. large print ed. 50p. pap. 9.95 (ISBN 0-9608650-0-4). VHI Library.
Brice, Eugene. Books That Bring Life, Vol. II. (Orig.). 1987. pap. price not set (ISBN 0-937462-05-5). Net Pr.
Brice, Joseph. Pentecost. 6.95 (ISBN 0-686-12901-6). Schmul Pub Co.
Bricker, Florence M. Church & Pastoral Records in the Archives of the United Church of Christ. 1982. pap. 6.00 (ISBN 0-910564-01-9). Evang & Ref.
Bricker, George H., ed. see Schaff, Philip.
Bricker, George H, jt. ed. see Yrigoyen, Charles, Jr.
Bricker, Victoria R. The Indian Christ, the Indian King: The Historical Substrate of Maya Myth & Ritual. (Illus.). 382p. 1981. text ed. 45.00x (ISBN 0-292-73824-2). U of Tex Pr.
Bricklin, Mark. The Practical Encyclopedia of Natural Healing. rev. ed. (Illus.). 592p. 1983. 21.95 (ISBN 0-87857-480-8). Rodale Pr Inc.
Brickman, William E., ed. & compiled by. The Jewish Community in America: An Annotated & Classified Bibliographical Guide. (Ethnic Bibliographical Ser: No. 2). 1977. PLB 19.95 (ISBN 0-89102-057-8). B Franklin.
Brickman, William W. & Lehrer, Stanley, eds. Religion, Government & Education. LC 77-24684. 1977. Repr. of 1961 ed. lib. bdg. 22.50x (ISBN 0-8371-9749-X, BRRG). Greenwood.
Brickner, Balfour & Vorspan, Albert. Searching the Prophets for Values. 1981. 6.95 (ISBN 0-8074-0047-5). UAHC.
Bricose, Jill. Here Am I; Send Aaron! 1984. pap. 2.95 (ISBN 0-89693-712-7). Victor Bks.
Bridge, Donald & Phypers, David. Communion: The Meal That Unites? LC 82-62820. 192p. 1983. pap. 5.95 (ISBN 0-87788-160-X). Shaw Pubs.
Bridge, William. A Lifting up for the Downcast. 1979. pap. 5.45 (ISBN 0-85151-298-4). Banner of Truth.
Bridger & Wolk. The New Jewish Encyclopedia. rev. ed. LC 76-15251. (Illus.). 542p. 1976. 14.95 (ISBN 0-87441-120-3). Behrman.
Bridger, David. Hebrew & Heritage, 4 vols. LC 75-1812. (Illus.). 1976. Vol. I. pap. 3.95x (ISBN 0-87441-254-4); Vol. II. pap. 3.95x (ISBN 0-87441-252-8); Vol. III. pap. 3.95x (ISBN 0-87441-259-5); Vol. IV. pap. 3.95x (ISBN 0-87441-274-9). Behrman.
--Programmed Hebrew Series, 2 vols. Incl. Vol. 1. 1971. pap. text ed. 3.50x (ISBN 0-87441-079-7); Vol. 2. 1971. pap. text ed. 3.50x (ISBN 0-87441-080-0). (Reshit Tefillah V'lashon). 62p. (Prog. Bk.). (YA) pap. Behrman.
Bridger, Gordon. First Corinthians-Galatians. (Bible Study Commentaries Ser.). 95p. 1985. pap. 4.95 (ISBN 0-317-43383-0). Chr Lit.
Bridges, C. Exposition of Psalm 119. 504p. 1986. 16.95 (ISBN 0-8254-2257-4). Kregel.
Bridges, Charles. The Christian Ministry. 1980. 13.95 (ISBN 0-85151-087-6). Banner of Truth.
--Ecclesiastes. 319p. 1981. Repr. 12.95 (ISBN 0-85151-322-0). Banner of Truth.
--Proverbs. (Geneva Commentaries Ser.). 1979. 15.95 (ISBN 0-85151-088-4). Banner of Truth.
--Psalm One Hundred Nineteen. 1977. 13.95 (ISBN 0-85151-176-7). Banner of Truth.

Bridges, Geoffrey G. Identity & Distinction in Petrus Thomae. (Philosophy Ser). 1959. 10.00 (ISBN 0-686-11544-9). Franciscan Inst.

Bridges, Horace J. Criticisms of Life. facsimile ed. LC 75-99684. (Essay Index Reprint Ser). 1915. 20.00 (ISBN 0-8369-1342-6). Ayer Co Pubs.

--God of Fundamentalism & Others Studies. facs. ed. LC 79-86733. (Essay Index Reprint Ser.). 1925. 19.00 (ISBN 0-8369-1249-7). Ayer Co Pubs.

Bridges, Horace J., ed. Aspects of Ethical Religion: Essays in Honor of Felix Adler on the Fiftieth Anniversary of His Founding of the Ethical Movement. facs. ed. LC 68-29190. (Essay Index Reprint Ser). 1968. Repr. of 1926 ed. 20.00 (ISBN 0-8369-0161-4). Ayer Co Pubs.

--Aspects of Ethical Religion: Essays in Honor of Felix Adler. 1977. lib. bdg. 59.95 (ISBN 0-8490-1459-X). Gordon Pr.

Bridges, Jacqueline K. Sackcloth & Ashes. LC 84-91345. 99p. 1985. 8.95 (ISBN 0-533-06442-2). Vantage.

Bridges, Jerry. L' Exercice de la Piete. Cosson, Annie L., ed. Claeys, Monique, tr. Tr. of The Practice of Godliness. (Fr.). 240p. 1985. pap. text ed. 2.50 (ISBN 0-8297-1458-8). Life Pubs Intl.

--The Practice of Godliness. LC 83-61499. 272p. 1983. pap. 3.95 (ISBN 0-89109-497-0). NavPress.

--The Practice of Godliness. (Christian Character Library). 272p. 1985. hdbk. 8.95 (ISBN 0-89109-466-0). NavPress.

--The Pursuit of Holiness. LC 78-18109. 158p. 1978. pap. 3.95 (ISBN 0-89109-430-X). NavPress.

--The Pursuit of Holiness. (Christian Character Library). 158p. 1985. hdbk. 8.95 (ISBN 0-89109-467-9). NavPress.

--The Pursuit of Holiness. 192p. 1985. pap. 9.95 (ISBN 0-8027-2507-4). Walker & Co.

--True Fellowship. 150p. 1987. pap. 3.95 (ISBN 0-89109-175-0). NavPress.

Bridges, Julian C. & Estudio, Guias de. Guia De Estudios Sobre Bases Biblicas De la Etica. 96p. 1982. Repr. of 1973 ed. 4.50 (ISBN 0-311-43505-X). Casa Bautista.

Bridges, Ron. Falling in Love with the Lord. 1987. price not set (ISBN 0-89109-143-2). NavPress.

Bridget. The Magnificent Prayers of Saint Bridget of Sweden. (Illus.). 19p. 1983. pap. 1.00 (ISBN 0-89555-220-5). TAN Bks Pubs.

Bridgewater, John. Concerto Ecclesiae Catholicae in Anglia Adversus Calvinopapistas et Puritanos. 886p. Repr. of 1588 ed. text ed. 149.04 (ISBN 0-576-78532-6, Pub. by Gregg Intl Pubs England). Gregg Intl.

Bridgman, J. The Christmas Book: Christmas in the Olden Time: Its Customs & Their Origin. 1978. Repr. of 1859 ed. lib. bdg. 27.50 (ISBN 0-8492-3711-4). R West.

Brief, Richard P., ed. The Institute of Chartered Accountants in England & Wales Library Catalogue, 1913, 2 vols. LC 80-1501. (Dimensions of Accounting Theory & Practice Ser.). 1981. Repr. of 1913 ed. Set. lib. bdg. 92.00x (ISBN 0-405-13526-2). Ayer Co Pubs.

Brien, Robert C. You Are What You Think: Basic Issues in Pastoral Counseling. 182p. (Orig.). 1986. pap. 5.95 (ISBN 0-87227-102-1). Reg Baptist.

Briere, Elizabeth, tr. see Vasileios of Stavronikita.

Briere, Elizabeth, tr. see Yannaras, Christos.

Briffa, Salvino. That I May See: A Prayerful Discovery Through Imagination. 140p. 1986. 6.95 (ISBN 0-87193-251-2). Dimension Bks.

Briggs, Charles & Briggs, Emile G. A Critical & Exegetical Commentary on Psalms, 2 vols. Driver, Samuel R., et al, eds. (International Critical Commentary). 24.95 ea. (Pub. by T & T Clark Ltd UK). Vol. 1, 1906, 580 pgs (ISBN 0-567-05011-4). Vol. 2, 1907, 580 pgs (ISBN 0-567-05012-2). Fortress.

Briggs, Charles, ed. see Driver, Samuel R.

Briggs, Charles A. Inaugural Address & Defense, Eighteen Ninety-One to Eighteen Ninety-Three. LC 70-38442. (Religion in America, Ser. 2). 336p. 1972. Repr. of 1972 ed. 22.00 (ISBN 0-405-04062-8). Ayer Co Pubs.

Briggs, Charles A., ed. see Burton, Ernest De Witt.

Briggs, Charles A., ed. see Charles, R. H.

Briggs, Charles A., ed. see Frame, James E.

Briggs, Charles A., ed. see Plummer, Alfred.

Briggs, Charles A., ed. see Robertson, Archibald & Plummer, Alfred.

Briggs, Charles A., ed. see Vincent, Marvin R.

Briggs, Edward C. A Pilgrim's Guide to Prayer. (Orig.). 1987. pap. 3.25 (ISBN 0-8054-8156-7). Broadman.

Briggs, Emile G., jt. auth. see Briggs, Charles.

Briggs, Freda I. Mom, Can We Still Keep Roger? 96p. 1985. pap. 4.95 (ISBN 0-8010-0888-3). Baker Bk.

Briggs, George S. The Cognizance. 48p. 1984. 7.95 (ISBN 0-533-06100-8). Vantage.

Briggs, John, tr. see Firishtah, Muhammed Kasim.

Briggs, Katherine M. Pale Hecates Team: Examination of the Beliefs on Witchcraft & Magic Among Shakespeare's Contemporaries & His Immediate Succesors. Dorson, Richard M., ed. LC 77-70582. (International Folklore Ser.). (Illus.). 1977. lib. bdg. 24.50x (ISBN 0-405-10083-3). Ayer Co Pubs.

Briggs, Kay. Most Quoted Scriptures. 417p. 1981. Repr. of 1980 ed. 11.95 (ISBN 0-934126-13-5). Randall Bk Co.

Briggs, Lauren Littauer. What You Can Say When You Don't Know What to Say: Reaching out to Those Who Hurt. 176p. (Orig.). 1985. pap. 4.95 (ISBN 0-89081-465-1). Harvest Hse.

Briggs, Martin S. Muhammadan Architecture in Egypt & Palestine. LC 74-1287. (Architecture & Decorative Arts Ser.). (Illus.). 255p. 1974. Repr. of 1924 ed. lib. bdg. 39.50 (ISBN 0-306-70590-7). Da Capo.

Briggs, R. C. Interpreting the New Testament Today. rev. ed. LC 73-8024. 288p. (Orig.). 1973. pap. 9.95 (ISBN 0-687-19327-3). Abingdon.

Briggs, S. R. & Elliott, J. H. Six Hundred Bible Gems & Outlines. LC 75-42955. 200p. 1976. pap. 5.95 (ISBN 0-8254-2255-8). Kregel.

Brigham, Amariah. Observations on the Influence of Religion upon the Health & Physical Welfare of Mankind. LC 73-2389. (Mental Illness & Social Policy; the American Experience Ser.). Repr. of 1835 ed. 21.00 (ISBN 0-405-05197-2). Ayer Co Pubs.

--Observations on the Influence of Religion upon the Health & Physical Welfare of Mankind, 1835: Remarks on the Influence of Mental Cultivation & Mental Excitement Upon Health, 2 vols. in 1. LC 73-17271. (History of Psychology Ser.). 1973. 55.00x (ISBN 0-8201-1125-2). Schol Facsimiles.

Brigham, Frederick, ed. see Schervish, Paul, et al.

Brigham, Judith. A Historical Study of the Educational Agencies of the Southern Baptist Convention, 1845-1945. LC 77-177047. (Columbia University. Teachers College. Contributions to Education Ser.: No. 974). Repr. of 1951 ed. 17.50 (ISBN 0-404-55974-3). AMS Pr.

Bright, Bill. Believing God for the Impossible. LC 78-73565. 1979. 8.95 (ISBN 0-918956-55-2). Campus Crusade.

--Come Help Change Our World. LC 79-53543. 1979. 8.95 (ISBN 0-918956-01-3). Campus Crusade.

--Handbook for Christian Maturity. 360p. (Orig.). 1981. pap. 8.95 (ISBN 0-86605-010-8). Campus Crusade.

--Handbook of Concepts for Living. 545p. (Orig.). 1981. pap. 8.95 (ISBN 0-86605-011-6). Campus Crusade.

--How to Be Filled with the Spirit. (Transferable Concepts Ser.). 58p. 1981. pap. 1.25 (ISBN 0-918956-90-0). Campus Crusade.

--How to Be Sure You Are a Christian. (Transferable Concepts Ser.). 63p. 1981. pap. 1.25 (ISBN 0-918956-88-9). Campus Crusade.

--How to Experience God's Love & Forgiveness. (Transferable Concepts Ser.). 63p. 1981. pap. 1.25 (ISBN 0-918956-89-7). Campus Crusade.

--How to Help Fulfill the Great Commission. (Transferable Concepts Ser.). 64p. 1981. pap. 1.25 (ISBN 0-918956-94-3). Campus Crusade.

--How to Introduce Others to Christ. (Transferable Concepts Ser.). 64p. 1981. pap. 1.25 (ISBN 0-918956-93-5). Campus Crusade.

--How to Love by Faith. (Transferable Concepts Ser.). 64p. 1981. pap. 1.25 (ISBN 0-918956-95-1). Campus Crusade.

--How to Pray. (Transferable Concepts Ser.). 63p. 1981. pap. 1.25 (ISBN 0-918956-96-X). Campus Crusade.

--How to Walk in the Spirit. (Transferable Concepts Ser.). 64p. 1981. pap. 1.25 (ISBN 0-918956-91-9). Campus Crusade.

--How to Witness in the Spirit. (Transferable Concepts Ser.). 64p. 1981. pap. 1.25 (ISBN 0-918956-92-7). Campus Crusade.

--Promises: A Daily Guide to Supernatural Living. LC 82-72302. 365p. 1983. 9.95 (ISBN 0-317-00638-X). Campus Crusade.

--Ten Basic Steps Teachers Manual. 2nd ed. 512p. 1983. pap. 8.95 (ISBN 0-918956-97-8). Campus Crusade.

Bright, John. The Authority of the Old Testament. (Twin Brooks Ser.). 272p. 1975. pap. 6.95 (ISBN 0-8010-0637-6). Baker Bk.

--Covenant & Promise: The Prophetic Understanding of the Future in Pre-Exilic Israel. LC 76-13546. 208p. 1976. 10.00 (ISBN 0-664-20752-9). Westminster.

--A History of Israel. 3rd ed. LC 80-22774. (Illus.). 528p. 1981. 18.95 (ISBN 0-664-21381-2). Westminster.

--Kingdom of God. rev. ed. (Series A). 1957. pap. 7.50 (ISBN 0-687-20908-0, Apex). Abingdon.

Bright, John, tr. Jeremiah. LC 65-13603. (Anchor Bible Ser.: Vol. 21). 1965. 20.00 (ISBN 0-385-00823-6, Anchor Pr). Doubleday.

Bright, Laren. Laughter Is the Best Meditation: The Best of the Inner Jester. LC 78-4491. 1979. pap. 5.00 (ISBN 0-686-10176-6). Baraka Bk.

Bright, Laurence, jt. auth. see Swanston, Hamish.

Bright, Laurence & Clements, Simon, eds. The Committed Church. 1966. 39.50x (ISBN 0-317-27423-6). Elliots Bks.

Bright, Laurence, ed. see Blenkinsopp, Joseph & Challenor, John.

Bright, Laurence, ed. see Freyne, Sean & Wansbrough, Henry.

Bright, Laurence, ed. see Johnston, Leonard & Smith, Michael.

Bright, Laurence, ed. see Macpherson, Ann, et al.

Bright, Laurence, ed. see Macpherson, Duncan, et al.

Bright, Laurence, ed. see Swanston, Hamish.

Bright, Laurence, et al. Paul Two. LC 71-173033. (Scripture Discussion Commentary Ser.: Pt. 11). 224p. 1971. pap. text ed. 4.50 (ISBN 0-87946-010-5). ACTA Found.

Bright, Pamela, tr. see Kannengiesser, Charles.

Bright, Ruth. Grieving: A Handbook for Those Who Care. vi, 229p. 1986. pap. 19.50 (ISBN 0-918812-46-1). MMB Music.

Bright, William. Age of the Fathers, 2 Vols. LC 77-113564. Repr. of 1903 ed. Set. 85.00 (ISBN 0-404-01077-6). Vol. 1 (ISBN 0-404-01078-4). Vol. 2 (ISBN 0-404-01079-2). AMS Pr.

--Chapters in Early English Church History. 3rd ed. 1897. 25.00 (ISBN 0-8337-4005-9). B Franklin.

Brightman, Edgar S. Personality & Religion. LC 75-3084. (Philosophy in America Ser.). Repr. of 1934 ed. 20.00 (ISBN 0-404-59083-7). AMS Pr.

--Philosophy of Religion. LC 72-95112. Repr. of 1940 ed. lib. bdg. 29.75x (ISBN 0-8371-2468-9, BRPR). Greenwood.

--The Problem of God. LC 75-3085. (Philosophy in America Ser.). Repr. of 1930 ed. 27.50 (ISBN 0-404-59084-5). AMS Pr.

--Religious Values. Repr. of 1925 ed. 29.00 (ISBN 0-527-11010-8). Kraus Repr.

--The Spiritual Life. LC 75-3086. (Philosophy in America Ser.). Repr. of 1942 ed. 27.50 (ISBN 0-404-59085-3). AMS Pr.

--Studies in Personalism. Steinkraus, Warren & Beck, Robert, eds. (Signature Series of Philosophy & Religion). Date not set. 16.00 (ISBN 0-86610-067-9). Meridian Pub.

Brightman, Edgar S., ed. Personalism in Theology. LC 75-3088. (Philosophy in America Ser.). Repr. of 1943 ed. 24.50 (ISBN 0-404-59086-1). AMS Pr.

Brightman, Edgare S. The Problem of God. 1979. Repr. of 1930 ed. lib. bdg. 30.00 (ISBN 0-8482-7365-6). Norwood Edns.

Brightman, F. E., tr. & intro. by see Andrewes, Lancelot.

Brill, Abraham A., tr. see Freud, Sigmund.

Brill, E. J. Encyclopedia of Islam. 1983. text ed. write for info. (ISBN 0-02-903770-0). Macmillan.

Brill, Earl H. The Christian Moral Vision. (Church's Teaching Ser.: Vol. 6). 254p. 1979. 5.95 (ISBN 0-8164-0423-2, HarpR); pap. 4.95 (ISBN 0-8164-2219-2). Har-Row.

Brill, Mordecai, et al. Write Your Own Wedding: A Personal Guide for Couples of All Faiths. rev. ed. LC 85-7156. 120p. 1985. pap. 5.95 (ISBN 0-8329-0398-1). New Century.

Brim, Frank M. Satan's Secret Revealed: From the Files of a Christian Exorcist. 176p. 1983. pap. 5.00 (ISBN 0-9612676-0-7). World Wide Mini.

Brin, Herb. ICH Bin Ein Jude. LC 81-15256. 146p. 1983. 9.95 (ISBN 0-8246-0275-7). Jonathan David.

Brin, Ruth. The Shabbat Catalogue. 1971. 5.00x (ISBN 0-87068-636-4). Ktav.

Brin, Ruth F. David & Goliath. (Foreign Lands Bks). (Illus.). 32p. 1977. PLB 5.95 (ISBN 0-8225-0365-4). Lerner Pubns.

Brincat, Matthew De. Salt & Light. 56p. 1983. pap. 3.00 (ISBN 0-911423-00-1). Bible-Speak.

Brindze, Ruth. Story of Our Calendar. (Illus.). 1949. 9.95 (ISBN 0-8149-0278-2). Vanguard.

Bringhurst, Newell G. Saints, Slaves, & Blacks: The Changing Place of Black People Within Mormonism. LC 81-1093. (Contributions to the Study of Religion Ser.: No. 4). (Illus.). 256p. 1981. lib. bdg. 29.95 (ISBN 0-313-22752-7, BSB/). Greenwood.

Bringman, Dale. A Star Is Born. (Orig.). 1987. pap. price not set (ISBN 0-89536-881-1, 7867). CSS of Ohio.

Brink, A. W., ed. see Trosse, George.

Brink, Charles O. Horace on Poetry: Epistles Book II: The Letters to Augustus & Florus, Vol. 3. LC 63-4908. 656p. 1982. 100.00 (ISBN 0-521-20069-5). Cambridge U Pr.

Brink, William P. & DeRidder, Richard R. Manual of Christian Reformed Church Government, 1980. rev. ed. LC 80-24129. 1980. pap. text ed. 7.95 (ISBN 0-933140-19-3). CRC Pubns.

Brinkmann, William & Ditewig, William. Leading Our Children to God. LC 83-72992. (Illus.). 96p. (Orig.). 1984. pap. 4.95 (ISBN 0-87793-310-3). Ave Maria.

Brinkmeyer, Robert H., Jr. Three Catholic Writers of the Modern South. LC 84-19641. 1985. 20.00x (ISBN 0-87805-246-1). U Pr of Miss.

Brinks, Herbert & Heynen, A. James. A Time to Keep: A History of the Christian Reformed Church. text ed. cancelled (ISBN 0-933140-44-4); cancelled leader's guide (ISBN 0-933140-45-2). CRC Pubns.

Brinn, Ruth E. Let's Celebrate: Fifty-Seven Jewish Holiday Crafts for Young Children. (Illus.). 72p. 1977. pap. 4.95 (ISBN 0-930494-02-4). Kar Ben.

Brinner, William M. & Ricks, Stephen D., eds. Studies in Islamic & Judaic Traditions. (Brown Judaic Studies). 287p. 1986. 29.95 (ISBN 1-55540-047-7, 14-01-10); pap. 24.95 (ISBN 1-55540-048-5). Scholars Pr GA.

Brinner, William M., tr. An Elegant Composition Concerning Relief Adversity. LC 49-9495. (Judaica Ser.: No. 20). 1977. 26.50x (ISBN 0-300-01952-1). Yale U Pr.

Brinsmead, Bernard. Galatians: A Dialogical Response to Opponents. LC 81-18535. (SBL Dissertation Ser.). 1982. pap. 17.25 (ISBN 0-89130-549-1, 06 01 65). Scholars Pr GA.

Brinsmead, Hasba. Christmas at Home. (Illus.). 52p. 1986. 12.95 (ISBN 0-207-14543-1). Salem Hse Pubs.

Brintnall, D. E. Revolt Against the Dead: The Modernization of a Mayan Community in the Highlands of Guatemala. (Library of Anthropology). 224p. 1979. 29.00x (ISBN 0-677-05170-0). Gordon & Breach.

Brinton, Anna. Toward Undiscovered Ends. 1983. pap. 5.00x (ISBN 0-87574-062-6, 062). Pendle Hill.

--Wide Horizon. 1983. pap. 2.50x (ISBN 0-87574-038-3, 038). Pendle Hill.

Brinton, Anna, jt. auth. see Penn, William.

Brinton, Anna, ed. Then & Now. facs. ed. LC 72-128214. (Essay Index Reprint Ser). 1960. 21.50 (ISBN 0-8369-1905-X). Ayer Co Pubs.

Brinton, Anna C. The Wit & Wisdom of William Bacon Evans. 1966. pap. 2.50x (ISBN 0-87574-146-0, 146). Pendle Hill.

Brinton, D. G. Myths of the New World: A Treatise on the Symbolism & Mythology of the Red Race of America. LC 68-24972. (American History & Americana Ser., No. 47). 1969. Repr. of 1876 ed. lib. bdg. 75.00x (ISBN 0-8383-0918-6). Haskell.

Brinton, Daniel G. American Hero-Myths: A Study in the Native Religions of the Western Continent. LC 15-7574. (American Studies Ser). Repr. of 1882 ed. 18.00 (ISBN 0-384-05860-4). Johnson Repr.

--The Myths of the New World. LC 71-144901. 331p. 1972. Repr. of 1876 ed. 10.00 (ISBN 0-403-00839-5). Scholarly.

--The Myths of the New World: A Treatise on the Symbolism & Mythology of the Red Race in America. LC 74-1038. 360p. 1974. Repr. of 1896 ed. 30.00x (ISBN 0-8103-3959-5). Gale.

--Myths of the New World: A Treatise on the Symbolism & Mythology of the Red Race of America. 2nd ed. LC 69-13839. 1969. Repr. of 1876 ed. lib. bdg. 22.50x (ISBN 0-8371-2040-3, BRMN). Greenwood.

--Myths of the New World: A Treatise on the Symbolism & Mythology of the Red Race of America. LC 78-31682. 1979. Repr. of 1868 ed. lib. bdg. 30.00 (ISBN 0-89341-326-7). Longwood Pub Group.

--Myths of the New World: The Symbolism & Mythology of the Indians of the Americas. LC 72-81594. (Illus.). 348p. pap. cancelled (ISBN 0-89345-207-6, Steinerbks). Garber Comm.

--Religions of Primitive Peoples. LC 79-88423. Repr. of 1897 ed. 22.50x (ISBN 0-8371-1763-1, BRR&). Greenwood.

Brinton, Daniel G., ed. The Lenape & Their Legends. LC 77-102641. (Library of Aboriginal American Literature Ser.: No. 5). Repr. of 1884 ed. 30.00 (ISBN 0-404-52185-1). AMS Pr.

--Rig Veda Americanus. LC 73-83463. (Library of Aboriginal American Literature Ser.: No. 8). Repr. of 1890 ed. 30.00 (ISBN 0-404-52188-6). AMS Pr.

Brinton, Daniel G., tr. see Olum, Walam.

Brinton, Howard. Ethical Mysticism in the Society of Friends. LC 67-31429. (Orig.). 1983. pap. 2.50x (ISBN 0-87574-156-8). Pendle Hill.

--Light & Life in the Fourth Gospel. LC 76-128679. (Orig.). 1971. pap. 2.50x (ISBN 0-87574-179-7). Pendle Hill.

--The Pendle Hill Idea. LC 50-11234. (Orig.). 1950. pap. 2.50x (ISBN 0-87574-055-3). Pendle Hill.

Brinton, Howard H. Evolution & the Inward Light. LC 77-137101. (Orig.). 1970. pap. 2.50x (ISBN 0-87574-173-8). Pendle Hill.
--Friends for Three Hundred Years. LC 52-5424. (Orig.). 1965. pap. 4.00 (ISBN 0-87574-903-8). Pendle Hill.
--Guide to Quaker Practice. LC 43-11899. (Orig.). 1943. pap. 2.50x (ISBN 0-87574-020-0). Pendle Hill.
--How They Became Friends. LC 61-12670. (Orig.). 1961. pap. 2.50x (ISBN 0-87574-114-2, 114). Pendle Hill.
--Meeting House & Farm House. LC 72-80096. (Orig.). 1972. pap. 2.50x (ISBN 0-87574-185-1). Pendle Hill.
--The Nature of Quakerism. 1983. pap. 2.50x (ISBN 0-87574-047-2, 047). Pendle Hill.
--Prophetic Ministry. 1983. pap. 2.50x (ISBN 0-87574-054-5, 054). Pendle Hill.
--Quaker Doctrine of Inward Peace. LC 64-23230. (Orig.). 1948. pap. 2.50x (ISBN 0-87574-044-8). Pendle Hill.
--Quaker Education in Theory & Practice. rev. ed. LC 58-12843. (Orig.). 1940. pap. 15.00x (ISBN 0-87574-009-X). Pendle Hill.
--Quaker Journals: Varieties of Religious Experience among Friends. LC 78-188399. (Illus., Orig.). 1983. 7.00 (ISBN 0-87574-952-6). Pendle Hill.
--Quakerism & Other Religions. 1983. pap. 2.50x (ISBN 0-87574-093-6, 093). Pendle Hill.
--Reaching Decisions. 1983. pap. 2.50x (ISBN 0-87574-065-0, 065). Pendle Hill.
--Religion of George Fox: As Revealed in His Epistles. LC 68-57978. (Orig.). 1968. pap. 2.50x (ISBN 0-87574-161-4). Pendle Hill.
--A Religious Solution to the Social Problem. 1983. pap. 2.50x (ISBN 0-87574-002-2, 002). Pendle Hill.
--The Society of Friends. 1983. pap. 2.50x (ISBN 0-87574-048-0, 048). Pendle Hill.
--Sources of the Quaker Peace Testimony. 1983. pap. 2.50x (ISBN 0-87574-027-8, 027). Pendle Hill.
Brisac, Catherine. Thousand Years of Stained Glass. LC 85-4506. 200p. 1986. 40.00 (ISBN 0-385-23184-9). Doubleday.
Brisac, Catherine, jt. auth. see Grodecki, Louis.
Brisco, Jill. Caleb's Colt. 1986. pap. 5.95. Ideals.
Briscoe, D. Stuart. Let's Get Moving. LC 77-91773. 160p. 1978. pap. 3.50 (ISBN 0-8307-0538-4, S322102). Regal.
--Patterns for Power. LC 78-68850. (Bible Commentary for Laymen Ser.). 160p. 1979. pap. 3.50 (ISBN 0-8307-0701-8, S331101). Regal.
--Spirit Life. 160p. 1983. pap. 5.95 (ISBN 0-8007-5185-X). Revell.
--When the Going Gets Tough. LC 82-11205. 1982. 5.95 (ISBN 0-8307-0802-2, 5417507). Regal.
Briscoe, Jill. Byttook or Crook: The Life of Peter. 192p. 1987. 12.95 (ISBN 0-8499-0561-3). Word Bks.
--Evergrowing, Evergreen. 96p. 1986. pap. 4.95 (ISBN 0-89693-255-9). Victor Bks.
--Faith Enough to Finish. 108p. 1987. pap. 4.95 (ISBN 0-89693-238-9). Victor Bks.
--How to Follow the Shepherd When You're Being Pushed Around by the Sheep. 192p. 1984. pap. 5.95 (ISBN 0-8007-5166-3, Power Bks). Revell.
--Hush, Hush. 1978. pap. 5.95 (ISBN 0-310-21831-4, 9258P). Zondervan.
--Jonah & the Worm. LC 83-6323. (Illus.). 120p. 1983. 5.95 (ISBN 0-8407-5289-X). Nelson.
--Prime Rib & Apple. 1976. 5.95 (ISBN 0-310-21810-1, 9257P); pap. 4.95 (ISBN 0-310-21811-X). Zondervan.
--Thank You for Being a Friend. 192p. (Orig.). 1981. pap. 5.95 (ISBN 0-310-21851-9, 9261P). Zondervan.
--There's a Snake in My Garden. 1977. pap. 5.95 (ISBN 0-310-21821-7, 9256P). Zondervan.
--Wings. 384p. 1984. 11.95 (ISBN 0-8407-5328-4). Nelson.
--Women in the Life of Jesus. 96p. 1986. pap. 4.95 (ISBN 0-89693-254-0). Victor Bks.
Briscoe, Jill, jt. auth. see Briscoe, Stuart.
Briscoe, Stuart. Bound for Joy. LC 84-17778. (Bible Commentary for Laymen Ser.). 192p. 1984. pap. 3.95 (ISBN 0-8307-1004-3, S383107). Regal.
--Dry Bones. 168p. 1985. pap. 5.95 (ISBN 0-89693-522-1). Victor Bks.
--Genesis (CC) 1986. 18.95 (ISBN 0-8499-0406-4). Word Bks.
--How to Be a Motivated Christian. 192p. 1987. 9.95 (ISBN 0-89693-179-X). Victor Bks.
--Taking God Seriously. 192p. 1986. 10.95 (ISBN 0-8499-0523-0, 0523-0). Word Bks.
--Tough Truths for Today's Living. 178p. 1984. pap. text ed. 5.95 (ISBN 0-8499-2999-7, 2999-7). Word Bks.
--What Works When Life Doesn't. rev. ed. 176p. 1984. pap. 2.95 (ISBN 0-89693-709-7). Victor Bks.
Briscoe, Stuart & Briscoe, Jill. Our Favorite Verse. LC 86-71753. (My Favorite Verse Ser.). 24p. 1987. pap. 4.95 (ISBN 0-89636-224-8). Accent Bks.
--What It Means to Be a Christian. 128p. 1987. pap. 4.95 (ISBN 1-55513-803-9). Cook.
Briscoe, Stuart D. God's Way to Live Successfully. 144p. 1986. pap. 2.95 (ISBN 0-8007-8582-7, Spire Bks). Revell.
Brisette, Claire M. Reflective Living: A Spiritual Approach to Everyday Life. LC 83-21369. (Illus.). 136p. (Orig.). 1983. pap. 8.00 (ISBN 0-89571-019-6). Affirmation.
Brisman, S. A History & Guide to Judaic Bibliography. (Bibliographica Judaica Ser.: No. 7). 35.00x (ISBN 0-87820-900-X, HUC Pr). Ktav.
Brisson, Marie, jt. auth. see Boyer, Raymond.
Brister, C. W. Caring for the Caregivers. LC 85-3793. 1985. pap. 8.95 (ISBN 0-8054-5537-X). Broadman.
--El Cuidado Pastoral De la Iglesia. Tinao, D., et al, trs. Orig. Title: Pastoral Care in the Church. (Span.). 226p. 1982. pap. 5.50 (ISBN 0-311-42040-0). Casa Bautista.
--Pastoral Care in the Church. LC 64-19497. 1977. pap. 6.00 (ISBN 0-06-061051-4, RD 222, HarpR). Har-Row.
--Take Care. LC 76-51022. 1979. pap. 3.95 (ISBN 0-8054-5578-7). Broadman.
Bristol, C. & Sherman, H. TNT: The Power Within You. 1954. pap. 4.95 (ISBN 0-13-922674-5). P-H.
Bristol, Goldie & McGinnis, Carol. When It's Hard to Forgive. 168p. 1982. pap. 5.95 (ISBN 0-88207-311-7). Victor Bks.
Bristol, James E. McCarthyism: The Seed Is in Us. 1983. pap. 2.50x (ISBN 0-87574-076-6, 076). Pendle Hill.
--Stand Fast in Liberty. 1983. pap. 2.50x (ISBN 0-87574-119-3, 119). Pendle Hill.
Bristow, Benny. From Kneepants to Romance. pap. 1.95 (ISBN 0-89137-810-3). Quality Pubns.
--Ten Commandments for Wives. pap. 4.95 (ISBN 0-89137-430-2). Quality Pubns.
Bristow, Edward J. Prostitution & Prejudice: The Jewish Fight Against White Slavery 1870-1939. 368p. 1983. 21.95 (ISBN 0-8052-3866-2). Schocken.
Bristow, Gwen. From Pigtails to Wedding Bells. pap. 1.95 (ISBN 0-89137-811-1). Quality Pubns.
Bristow, Hennie. Something to Think about. pap. 2.50 (ISBN 0-89315-292-7). Lambert Bk.
Britsch, R. Lanier. Unto the Islands of the Sea: A History of the Latter-day Saints in the Pacific. LC 85-27463. (Illus.). 599p. 1986. 16.95 (ISBN 0-87747-754-X). Deseret Bk.
Britsch, R. Lanier & Olson, Terrance D., eds. Counseling: A Guide to Helping Others, Vol. 2. LC 83-72396. 335p. 1985. 9.95 (ISBN 0-87747-737-X). Deseret Bk.
Britt, George, jt. auth. see Broun, Heywood.
Britt, Steuart H., jt. auth. see Graeber, Isacque.
Brittain, Grady B. Platy: The Child in Us. LC 81-6503. (Illus.). 53p. (Orig.). 1981. pap. 0.50 (ISBN 0-86663-761-3). Ide Hse.
Brittain, Mary A., jt. auth. see Williams, Mel.
Brittain, Vera. In the Steps of John Bunyan. (Illus.). 1973. 30.00 (ISBN 0-8274-1456-0). R West.
--Valiant Pilgrim: The Story of John Bunyan & Puritan England. 1950. 30.00 (ISBN 0-8274-3665-3). R West.
Britten, Emma. Nineteenth Century Miracles. 1977. lib. bdg. 59.95 (ISBN 0-8490-2348-3). Gordon Pr.
Britten, James, ed. see Aubrey, John.
Britton, Colleen. Celebrate Communion. 79p. 1984. pap. 9.95 (ISBN 0-940754-26-6). Ed Ministries.
Britton, F. L. Behind Communism: The Jewish Background of Communism. 1982. lib. bdg. 59.95 (ISBN 0-87700-425-0). Revisionist Pr.
Brizee, Robert. Where in the World Is God? God's Presence in Every Moment of Our Lives. 160p. 1987. pap. 6.95 (ISBN 0-8358-0556-5). Upper Room.
Broad, C. D. Berkeley's Argument. LC 75-1069. (Studies in Philosophy: No. 40). 1975. lib. bdg. 22.95x (ISBN 0-8383-0113-4). Haskell.
--Five Types of Ethical Theory. 8th ed. (International Library of Philosophy & Scientific Method). 1930. text ed. 35.00x (ISBN 0-7100-3080-0). Humanities.
Broadbent, Belle B. Where Flowers Grow. 16p. 1982. pap. 1.95 (ISBN 0-939298-04-X). J M Prods.
Broadbent, J., ed. see Milton, John.
Broadbent, John. Introduction to Paradise Lost. (Milton for Schools & Colleges Ser.). (Illus.). 1971. 34.50 (ISBN 0-521-08068-1); pap. 11.95 (ISBN 0-521-09639-1). Cambridge U Pr.
Broadhead, Philip, ed. see Cargill-Thompson, W. D.
Broadus, Boyce. History of First Baptist Church Russellville. 1967. 10.00 (ISBN 0-317-13830-8); pap. 7.00. Banner Pr AL.
Broadus, E. K. Thomas Fuller, Selections: With Essays by Charles Lamb, Leslie Stephen & Co. 1979. Repr. of 1928 ed. lib. bdg. 20.00 (ISBN 0-8492-3742-4). R West.
Broadus, J. A. Tratado Sobre la Predicacion. Barocio, Ernesto, tr. Orig. Title: On the Preparation & Delivery of Sermons. 336p. 1985. pap. 5.50 (ISBN 0-311-42034-6). Casa Bautista.
Broadus, John A. On the Preparation & Delivery of Sermons. 4th ed. Stanfield, Vernon L., rev. by. LC 78-20602. 1979. 7.95 (ISBN 0-06-061112-X, HarpR). Har-Row.
Broadus, Loren. How to Stop Procrastinating & Start Living. LC 82-72641. 128p. 1983. pap. 5.95 (ISBN 0-8066-1947-3, 10-3178). Augsburg.
Broccolo, Gerald T., jt. ed. see Larkin, Ernest.
Broccolo, Gerald T., jt. ed. see Larkin, Ernest E.
Broch, Yitzhak I. The Book of Ruth. 1975. 7.95 (ISBN 0-87306-012-1); pap. 5.95. Feldheim.
Brock, Charles. The Principles & Practice of Indigenous Church Planting. 1981. pap. 4.25 (ISBN 0-8054-6328-3). Broadman.
Brock, Earl E. Devotional Interpretation of Familiar Hymns. facsimile ed. LC 72-93319. (Essay Index Reprint Ser.). 1947. 14.00 (ISBN 0-8369-1395-7). Ayer Co Pubs.
Brock, Horace, ed. Game Theory, Social Choice, & Ethics. 1979. lib. bdg. 31.50 (ISBN 0-686-26826-1, Pub. by Reidel Holland). Kluwer Academic.
Brock, Peter. Pioneers of a Peaceable Kingdom: The Quaker Peace Testimony from the Colonial Era to the First World War. 1970. pap. 12.95x (ISBN 0-691-00573-7). Princeton U Pr.
Brock, Raymond T. The Christ-Centered Family. LC 76-46036. (Radiant Life Ser.). 128p. 1977. pap. 2.50 (ISBN 0-88243-903-0, 02-0903); teacher's ed 3.95 (ISBN 0-88243-173-0, 32-0173). Gospel Pub.
--Into the Highways & Hedges. LC 61-18608. 1961. 1.25 (ISBN 0-88243-533-7, 02-0533). Gospel Pub.
Brock, Raymond T., jt. ed. see Gilbert, Marvin G.
Brock, Sebastian. Syriac Version of the Ps. Nonnos Mythological Scholia. LC 79-139712. (Oriental Publications: No. 20). 1971. 62.50 (ISBN 0-521-07990-X). Cambridge U Pr.
Brock, Sebastian, tr. see Saint Ephrem.
Brockbank, Bernard P. Commandments & Promises of God. LC 82-23629. 667p. 1983. 15.95 (ISBN 0-87747-889-9). Deseret Bk.
Brockelman, Paul. Time & Self. 96p. 1985. pap. 10.95 (ISBN 0-8245-0703-7). Crossroad NY.
--Time & Self: Phenomenological Explorations. (AAR Studies in Religion). 1985. 17.95 (ISBN 0-89130-779-6, 01-00-39); pap. 10.95 (ISBN 0-89130-780-X). Scholars Pr GA.
Brockett, C. W. Antiphons, Responsories & other Chants from the Mozarabic Rite. (Wissenschaftliche Abhandlungen - Musicological Studies Ser.: No. 15). 300p. 1968. lib. bdg. 60.00 (ISBN 0-912024-85-2). Inst Mediaeval Mus.
Brockington, J. L. The Sacred Thread: Hinduism in Continuity & Diversity. 222p. 1981. pap. 10.50x (ISBN 0-85224-393-6, Pub. by Edinburgh U Pr Scotland). Columbia U Pr.
Brockington, L. H. Ezra, Nehemiah & Esther. (New Century Bible Ser). 262p. 1969. text ed. 9.50 (ISBN 0-551-00530-0). Attic Pr.
Brockington, L. H., ed. see Robinson, H. Wheeler.
Brockman, Norbert. Ordained to Service: A Theology of the Permanent Diaconate. 1976. 7.50 (ISBN 0-682-48561-6, University). Exposition Pr FL.
Brockwell, Maurice W. Van Eyck Problem. LC 78-138101. (Illus.). 1971. Repr. of 1954 ed. lib. bdg. 22.50x (ISBN 0-8371-5677-7, BRVE). Greenwood.
Broderick, Carlfred. One Flesh, One Heart: Putting Celestial Love into Your Temple Marriage. LC 85-29329. 101p. 1986. 8.95 (ISBN 0-87579-010-0). Deseret Bk.
Broderick, James. The Economic Morals of the Jesuits. LC 76-38248. (The Evolution of Capitalism Ser.). 168p. 1972. Repr. of 1934 ed. 12.00 (ISBN 0-405-04113-6). Ayer Co Pubs.
Broderick, Robert C. Days of Praise. 1977. 5.50 (ISBN 0-8199-0653-0). Franciscan Herald.
--Parish Council Handbook. 1968. pap. 2.25 (ISBN 0-8199-0083-4, L38623). Franciscan Herald.
--Your Parish - Where the Action Is. 1974. pap. 2.25 (ISBN 0-8199-0486-4). Franciscan Herald.
Broderick, Robert C., ed. The Catholic Encyclopedia. 1983. pap. 14.95 (ISBN 0-87973-700-X). Our Sunday Visitor.
--The Catholic Encyclopedia. rev. & updated ed. 612p. pap. 18.95 (ISBN 0-8407-5787-5). Nelson.
--The Catholic Encyclopedia. rev. ed. 612p. 1987. pap. 18.95 (ISBN 0-8407-5544-9). Nelson.
Brodeur, A. G., tr. see Sturluson, S.
Brodhead, Frank, jt. auth. see Herman, Edward S.
Brodie, Fawn M. No Man Knows My History: The Life of Joseph Smith. (Illus.). 1971. 19.95 (ISBN 0-394-46967-4). Knopf.
Brodman, James W. Ransoming Captives in Crusader Spain: The Order of Merced on the Christian-Islamic Frontier. LC 85-20362. (Middle Ages Ser.). (Illus.). 216p. 1986. text ed. 21.95 (ISBN 0-8122-8001-6). U of PA Pr.
Brodrick, James. Origin of the Jesuits. LC 70-138604. 1971. Repr. of 1940 ed. lib. bdg. 22.50x (ISBN 0-8371-5523-1, BROJ). Greenwood.
--The Origin of the Jesuits. LC 83-45590. Date not set. Repr. of 1940 ed. 33.50 (ISBN 0-404-19883-X). AMS Pr.
--Procession of Saints. LC 72-5436. (Biography Index Reprint Ser). 1972. Repr. of 1949 ed. 20.50 (ISBN 0-8369-8134-0). Ayer Co Pubs.
--Saint Peter Canisius. (Request Reprint). (Illus.). 1962. 19.95 (ISBN 0-8294-0008-7). Loyola.
--Saint Peter Canisius, S. J., 1521-1597. LC 83-45589. Date not set. Repr. of 1935 ed. 65.00 (ISBN 0-404-19882-1). AMS Pr.
Brodsky, Beverley, adapted by. & illus. The Story of Job. LC 85-24303. (Illus.). 40p. 14.95 (ISBN 0-8076-1142-5). Braziller.
Brody, Baruch, ed. Readings in the Philosophy of Religion: An Analytic Approach. LC 73-20485. 608p. 1974. text ed. write for info. (ISBN 0-13-759340-6). P-H.
Brody, Harry. As Once to Birth I Went, Now I Am Taken Back. 1981. 2.00 (ISBN 0-936814-07-1). New Collage.
Brody, Joel, tr. see Lubich, Gino & Lazzarin, Piero.
Brody, Jules, jt. auth. see Spitzer, Leo.
Broeckhover, Egide van. A Friend to All Men. 5.95 (ISBN 0-317-06463-0). Dimension Bks.
Broek, Silvere van den see Van den Broek, Silvere.
Broers, B. C. Mysticism in the Neo-Romanticists. LC 68-767. (Studies in Comparative Literature: No. 35). 1969. Repr. of 1923 ed. text ed. 75.00x (ISBN 0-8383-0514-8). Haskell.
Brohi, A. K. Iqbal & the Concept of Islamic Socialism. pap. 1.00 (ISBN 0-686-18447-5). Kazi Pubns.
Brohl, Noreen, jt. auth. see Fischhoff, Joseph.
Brokamp, Marilyn. Prayer Times for Primary Grades. 1987. pap. 4.95. St Anthony Mess Pr.
Brokamp, Sr. Marilyn, jt. auth. see Brokamp, Sr. Marlene.
Brokamp, Sr. Marlene & Brokamp, Sr. Marilyn. Eucharist: God's Gift of Love. (Illus.). 28p. (Orig.). 1976. pap. 1.95 (ISBN 0-912228-25-3). St Anthony Mess Pr.
Brokering, Herb. The Luther Journey. (Illus.). 96p. (Orig.). 1983. pap. 6.95 (ISBN 0-942562-02-X). Brokering Pr.
--Wholly Holy. 96p. (Orig.). 1981. pap. 3.95 (ISBN 0-942562-00-3). Brokering Pr.
Brokering, Herb & Bainton, Roland. A Pilgrimage to Luther's Germany. 80p. 1983. 14.95 (ISBN 0-86683-629-2, HarpR). Har-Row.
Brokering, Herb & Brokering, Lois. Love Songs: Musical Activities for Christian Celebration. 36p. (Orig.). 1981. pap. 3.95 (ISBN 0-942562-01-1). Brokering Pr.
Brokering, Herb, jt. auth. see Bimler, Rich.
Brokering, Herbert. I Opener. LC 74-4912. (YA) 1974. pap. 2.50 (ISBN 0-570-06472-4, 12-2584). Concordia.
--Lord, If. 1977. pap. 2.95 (ISBN 0-570-03046-3, 6-1171). Concordia.
--The Night Before Jesus. (Continued Applied Christianity Ser.). 1983. 6.50 (ISBN 0-570-04084-1, 56-1439). Concordia.
Brokering, Herbert F. Pilgrimage to Renewal. 96p. (Orig.). 1979. pap. 1.95 (ISBN 0-03-053791-6, HarpR). Har-Row.
--Surprise Me, Jesus. LC 73-83785. 96p. (YA) 1973. pap. 6.95 (ISBN 0-8066-1338-6, 10-6150). Augsburg.
Brokering, Herbert F., ed. Luthers Prayers. Kistler, Charles E., tr. LC 67-25366. 1967. lea. bdg. 7.95 (ISBN 0-8066-0721-1, 10-4231). Augsburg.
Brokering, L. Thirty Six Creative Ideas for Children in the Church School. LC 12-2958. 1982. pap. 4.95 (ISBN 0-570-03865-0). Concordia.
Brokering, Lois, jt. auth. see Brokering, Herb.
Brokhoff, Barbara. Bitter-Sweet Recollections. 1983. 6.50 (ISBN 0-89536-638-X, 0238). CSS of Ohio.
--Trouble on the Mountain! Sherer, Michael L., ed. (Orig.). 1986. pap. 6.25 (ISBN 0-89536-825-0, 6834). CSS of Ohio.
Brokhoff, John. Advent & Event. 88p. (Orig.). 1980. pap. text ed. 3.25 (ISBN 0-89536-453-0, 0147). CSS of Ohio.
--Preaching the Parables: Series B. (Orig.). 1987. pap. price not set (ISBN 0-89536-880-3, 7866). CSS of Ohio.

--This You Can Believe: Participant. (Orig.). 1987. pap. price not set (ISBN 0-89536-893-5, 7879). CSS of Ohio.
Brokhoff, John R. Lent: A Time of Tears. 1984. 4.25 (ISBN 0-89536-649-5, 1267). CSS of Ohio.
Brokke, Harold J. A Guide to Understanding Romans. LC 80-67446. 211p. 1980. pap. 5.95 (ISBN 0-87123-193-X, 210193). Bethany Hse.
--Salvados por Su Vida. 224p. 1978. 2.50 (ISBN 0-88113-317-5). Edit Betania.
--Ten Steps to the Good Life. LC 75-44926. 160p. 1976. pap. 1.95 (ISBN 0-87123-332-0, 200332). Bethany Hse.
Bro. Lawrence, jt. ed. see Demaray, Donald E.
Bromiley, G. W., ed. & tr. Karl Barth: Letters 1961-1968. 288p. Date not set. 21.75 (ISBN 0-567-09321-2, Pub. by T & T Clark Ltd UK). Fortress.
Bromiley, G. W., ed. Zwingli & Bullinger. LC 53-1533. (Library of Christian Classics). 360p. 1979. softcover 8.95 (ISBN 0-664-24159-X). Westminster.
Bromiley, G. W., ed. see Barth, Karl.
Bromiley, G. W., ed. & tr. see Gollwitzer, Helmut.
Bromiley, G. W., tr. see Barth, Karl.
Bromiley, Geoffrey, tr. see Kittel, Gerhard & Friedrich, Gerhard.
Bromiley, Geoffrey W. Children of Promise: The Case for Baptizing Infants. LC 79-10346. 1979. pap. 3.95 (ISBN 0-8028-1797-1). Eerdmans.
--God & Marriage. 96p. (Orig.). 1980. pap. 4.95 (ISBN 0-8028-1851-X). Eerdmans.
--Historical Theology: An Introduction. LC 77-17030. 1978. 14.95 (ISBN 0-8028-3509-0). Eerdmans.
--An Introduction to the Theology of Karl Barth. LC 79-15397. (Orig.). pap. 8.95 (ISBN 0-8028-1804-8). Eerdmans.
Bromiley, Geoffrey W., ed. The International Standard Bible Encyclopedia, Vol. III, K-P. rev. ed. (International Standard Bible Encyclopedia Ser.). (Illus.). 1080p. 1986. 37.50 (ISBN 0-8028-8163-7). Eerdmans.
--International Standard Bible Encyclopedia, Vol. 1, A-D. rev. ed. LC 79-12280. (Illus.). 1979. 37.50 (ISBN 0-8028-8161-0). Eerdmans.
--The International Standard Bible Encyclopedia, Vol. 2: E-J. rev. ed. 1132p. 1981. 37.50 (ISBN 0-8028-8162-9). Eerdmans.
Bromiley, Geoffrey W., ed. see Barth, Karl.
Bromiley, Geoffrey W., ed. see Thielicke, Helmut.
Bromiley, Geoffrey W., tr. see Barth, Karl.
Bromiley, Geoffrey W., tr. see Barth, Karl & Bultmann, Rudolf.
Bromiley, Geoffrey W., tr. see Barth, Karl & Zuckmayer, Carl.
Bromiley, Geoffrey W., tr. see Ellul, Jacques.
Bromiley, Geoffrey W., tr. see Kasemann, Ernst.
Bromiley, Geoffrey W., tr. see Thielicke, Helmut.
Bromilow, William E. Twenty Years Among Primitive Papuans. LC 75-32800. Repr. of 1929 ed. 31.50 (ISBN 0-404-14103-X). AMS Pr.
Bromley, David & Shupe, Anson. A Documentary History of the Anti-Cult Movement. LC 84-25560. (Studies in American Religion: Vol. 13). 420p. 1985. 69.95x_cancelled (ISBN 0-88946-656-4). E Mellen.
--Strange Gods: The Great American Cult Scare. LC 81-65763. 192p. 1982. 21.95x (ISBN 0-8070-3256-5); pap. 8.95 (ISBN 0-8070-1109-6, BP641). Beacon Pr.
Bromley, David G. & Shupe, Anson D., Jr. Moonies in America: Cult, Church, & Crusade. LC 79-16456. (Sage Library of Social Research: Vol. 92). 269p. 1979. 29.00 (ISBN 0-8039-1060-6). Sage.
--New Christian Politics. LC 84-6598. xii, 288p. 1984. 23.95 (ISBN 0-86554-115-9, MUP/H108). Mercer Univ Pr.
Bromley, David G. & Hammond, Philip E., eds. The Future of New Religious Movements. 288p. 1987. 39.95 (ISBN 0-86554-237-6); pap. 19.95 (ISBN 0-86554-238-4). Mercer Univ Pr.
Bronder, Saul E. Social Justice & Church Authority: The Public Life of Archbishop Robert E. Lucey. 215p. 1982. 29.95 (ISBN 0-87722-239-8). Temple U Pr.
Bronner, Edwin B. Quakerism & Christianity. LC 67-18689. (Orig.). 1967. pap. 2.50x (ISBN 0-87574-152-5, 152). Pendle Hill.
--William Penn: 17th Century Founding Father. LC 75-32728. (Illus.). 36p. (Orig.). 1975. pap. 2.50x (ISBN 0-87574-204-1). Pendle Hill.
--William Penn's Holy Experiment; the Founding of Pennsylvania Sixteen Eighty-One to Seventeen Hundred & One. LC 78-5882. (Illus.). 306p. 1978. Repr. of 1963 ed. lib. bdg. 22.50x (ISBN 0-313-20432-2, BRWP). Greenwood.
Bronner, Edwin B., ed. see Robson, Walter.
Bronner, Leah. Biblical Personalities & Archaeology. (Illus.). 216p. 1975. 7.95x (ISBN 0-685-58308-2). Bloch.
Bronowski, Jacob. Science & Human Values. rev. & enl. ed. Bd. with The Abacus & the Rose. (Illus.). 142p. 1972. pap. 3.50 (ISBN 0-06-080269-3, P269, PL). Har-Row.
Bronstein, Daniel J. & Schulweis, Harold M., eds. Approaches to the Philosophy of Religion. facsimile ed. LC 77-93320. (Essay Index Reprint Ser). 1954. 33.00 (ISBN 0-8369-1344-2). Ayer Co Pubs.
Bronstein, Herbert, ed. A Passover Haggadah. (Illus.). 1974. 79.00 set (ISBN 0-916694-66-6); lib. bdg. 27.50 (ISBN 0-916694-06-2); pap. 9.95 (ISBN 0-916694-05-4). Central Conf.
Bronstein, Herbert & Friedlander, Albert, eds. The Five Scrolls. 324p. 1984. 19.95 (ISBN 0-916694-80-1); deluxe ed. 60.00 (ISBN 0-916694-81-X); special ltd. ed., leatherbound 675.00 (ISBN 0-916694-82-8). Central Conf.
Bronte, Patrick. Bronteana: The Rev. Patrick Bronte, His Collected Works & Life. LC 77-148320. Repr. of 1898 ed. 16.00 (ISBN 0-404-08920-8). AMS Pr.
Bronznick, jt. auth. see Uveeler.
Brooke, A. E. A Critical & Exegetical Commentary on the Johannine Epistles. Driver, Samuel R., et al, eds. LC 13-170. (International Critical Commentary Ser.). 336p. 1912. 24.95 (ISBN 0-567-05037-8, Pub. by T & T Clark Ltd UK). Fortress.
Brooke, Avery. Doorway to Meditation. 1976. pap. 6.95 (ISBN 0-8164-0903-X, HarpR). Har-Row.
--Hidden in Plain Sight: The Practice of Christian Meditation. 144p. (Orig.). 1986. pap. 7.95 (ISBN 0-8358-0547-6). Upper Room.
--Plain Prayers for a Complicated World. 124p. 1983. 5.95 (ISBN 0-8164-0501-8, HarpR); pap. 2.95 (ISBN 0-8164-2428-4). Har-Row.
Brooke, C., et al, eds. Church & Government in the Middle Ages. LC 75-41614. (Illus.). 1977. 59.50 (ISBN 0-521-21172-7). Cambridge U Pr.
Brooke, C. N., ed. see Brooke, Christopher.
Brooke, C. N., ed. see Foliot, G.
Brooke, Christopher. The Church & the Welsh Border in the Central Middle Ages. Dunville, D. N. & Brooke, C. N., eds. (Studies in Celtic History). 1986. 40.00 (ISBN 0-85115-175-2, Pub. by Boydell & Bower). Longwood Pub Group.
Brooke, Christopher, jt. auth. see Brooke, Rosalind.
Brooke, Christopher N., et al, eds. Church & Government in the Middle Ages: Essays Presented to C. R. Cheney on His 70th Birthday. LC 75-41614. pap. 83.00 (2027285). Bks Demand UMI.
Brooke, George J. Exegesis at Qumran: Four Q Florilegium in Its Jewish Context. (JSOT Supplement Ser.: No. 29). 370p. 1984. text ed. 28.50x (ISBN 0-905774-76-0, Pub. by JSOT Pr England); pap. text ed. 13.50x (ISBN 0-905774-77-9, Pub. by JSOT Pr England). Eisenbrauns.
Brooke, Odo. Studies in Monastic Theology. (Cistercian Studies Ser.: No. 37). 1980. 8.95 (ISBN 0-87907-837-5). Cistercian Pubns.
Brooke, Roger. Santa's Christmas Journey. LC 85-61188. (Illus.). 32p. 1985. 5.95 (ISBN 0-528-82688-3). Macmillan.
Brooke, Rosalind & Brooke, Christopher. Popular Religion in the Middle Ages. (Illus.). 1985. pap. 10.95 (ISBN 0-500-27381-2). Thames Hudson.
Brooke, Stopford A. Theology in the English Poets. 59.95 (ISBN 0-8490-1189-2). Gordon Pr.
--Theology in the English Poets: Cowper, Coleridge, Wordsworth & Burns. 6th ed. LC 79-129367. Repr. of 1880 ed. 10.00 (ISBN 0-404-01116-0). AMS Pr.
Brooke, Tal. Avatar of Night: The Hidden Side of Sai Baba. 392p. 1982. pap. text ed. 6.95x (ISBN 0-686-91763-4, Pub. by Vikas India). Advent NY.
Brooke-Hunt, Violet. Story of Westminster Abbey. 1977. lib. bdg. 59.95 (ISBN 0-8490-2692-X). Gordon Pr.
Brooker, Wendell, jt. auth. see Andersen, David W.
Brookes, Edgar H. America in Travail. 1983. pap. 2.50x (ISBN 0-87574-159-2, 159). Pendle Hill.
--Three Letters from Africa. LC 65-12948. (Orig.). 1965. pap. 2.50x (ISBN 0-87574-139-8, 139). Pendle Hill.
Brookes, Edgar H. & Vandenbosch, Amry. The City of God & the City of Man in Africa. LC 64-13998. (Illus.). 144p. 1964. 12.00x (ISBN 0-8131-1091-2). U Pr of Ky.
Brookes, James H. Salvation: The Way Made Plain. pap. 4.50 (ISBN 0-685-61831-5). Reiner.
Brookes, Reuben, jt. auth. see Pearl, Chaim.
Brooks. Your Life in Christ. 1.95 (ISBN 0-8054-2520-9). Broadman.
Brooks, Cleanth. Hidden God: Studies in Hemingway, Faulkner, Yeats, Eliot & Warren. (Orig.). 1963. 25.00x (ISBN 0-300-00327-7). Yale U Pr.
Brooks, Cleanth, jt. ed. see Wood, Harriet H.
Brooks, Cyril. Grace Triumphant: Autobiography. 266p. (Orig.). 1985. pap. 9.95 (ISBN 0-937396-66-4). Walterick Pubs.
Brooks, D. P. Bible: How to Understand & Teach It. LC 68-14365. 1969. pap. 4.25 (ISBN 0-8054-1118-6). Broadman.
Brooks, Frances, ed. see Rausch, Robert A.
Brooks, Frances, ed. see Stone, J. David.
Brooks, James A. & Winbery, Carlton L. Syntax of New Testament Greek. LC 78-51150. 1978. pap. text ed. 8.00 (ISBN 0-8191-0473-6). U Pr of Amer.
Brooks, John P. The Divine Church. Dayton, Donald W., ed. (The Higher Christian Life Ser.). 283p. 1985. 35.00 (ISBN 0-8240-6408-9). Garland Pub.
Brooks, Juanita. The History of the Jews in Utah & Idaho, 1853-1950. 252p. 1973. 9.95 (ISBN 0-914740-12-1). Western Epics.
--Jacob Hamblin: Mormon Apostle to the Indians. LC 80-80395. (Illus.). 160p. 1980. pap. 6.95 (ISBN 0-935704-03-5). Howe Brothers.
--John Doyle Lee: Zealot, Pioneer Builder, Scapegoat. LC 84-12849. 406p. 1984. pap. 12.50 (ISBN 0-935704-21-3). Howe Brothers.
--Mountain Meadows Massacre. (Illus.). 342p. 1985. Repr. of 1963 ed. 18.95 (ISBN 0-8061-0549-6). U of Okla Pr.
Brooks, Juanita, ed. On the Mormon Frontier: The Diary of Hosea Stout, 2 Vols. 832p. 1982. Repr. of 1964 ed. 39.95 (ISBN 0-87480-214-8, SET). U of Utah Pr.
Brooks, Juanita, jt. ed. see Cleland, Robert G.
Brooks, Keith. Mark: Gospel of God's Servant. rev. ed. (Teach Yourself the Bible Ser.). 1987. pap. 2.75 (ISBN 0-8024-5200-0). Moody.
Brooks, Keith L. Acts, Adventures of the Early Church. (Teach Yourself the Bible Ser). 1961. pap. 2.75 (ISBN 0-8024-0125-2). Moody.
--Basic Bible Study. (Teach Yourself the Bible Ser.). 1961. pap. 2.75 (ISBN 0-8024-0478-2). Moody.
--Christian Character Course. (Teach Yourself the Bible Ser). 1961. pap. 2.75 (ISBN 0-8024-1301-3). Moody.
--Colossians & Philemon. (Teach Yourself the Bible Ser.). 81p. (Orig.). 1961. pap. 2.75 (ISBN 0-8024-1525-3). Moody.
--Ephesians, the Epistle of Christian Maturity. (Teach Yourself the Bible Ser.). 1944. pap. 2.75 (ISBN 0-8024-2333-7). Moody.
--First & Second Thessalonians. (Teach Yourself the Bible Ser). 1961. pap. 2.75 (ISBN 0-8024-2645-X). Moody.
--First Corinthians. (Teach Yourself the Bible Ser.). 1964. pap. 2.75 (ISBN 0-8024-2649-2). Moody.
--Galatians, the Epistle of Christian Maturity. (Teach Yourself the Bible Ser.). 1963. pap. 2.75 (ISBN 0-8024-2925-4). Moody.
--Great Prophetic Themes. (Teach Yourself the Bible Ser.). 1962. pap. 2.75 (ISBN 0-8024-3320-0). Moody.
--Hebrews: The Beauty of Christ Unveiled. (Teach Yourself the Bible Ser.). 1961. pap. 2.75 (ISBN 0-8024-3507-6). Moody.
--How to Pray. (Teach Yourself the Bible Ser.). 1961. pap. 2.75 (ISBN 0-8024-3708-7). Moody.
--James: Belief in Action. (Teach Yourself the Bible Ser.). 1961. pap. 2.75 (ISBN 0-8024-4227-7). Moody.
--Luke, the Gospel of God's Man. (Teach Yourself the Bible Ser.). 1964. pap. 2.75 (ISBN 0-8024-5047-4). Moody.
--Mark: Gospel of God's Servant. (Teach Yourself the Bible Ser.). 64p. 1961. pap. 2.75 (ISBN 0-8024-5183-7). Moody.
--Matthew, the Gospel of God's King. (Teach Yourself the Bible Ser.). 1963. pap. 2.75 (ISBN 0-8024-5212-4). Moody.
--Philippians, The Epistle of Christian Joy. (Teach Yourself the Bible Ser.). 1964. pap. 2.75 (ISBN 0-8024-6506-4). Moody.
--Practical Bible Doctrine. (Teach Yourself the Bible Ser.). 1962. pap. 2.75 (ISBN 0-8024-6733-4). Moody.
--Revelation, the Future Foretold. (Teach Yourself the Bible Ser.). 1962. pap. 2.75 (ISBN 0-8024-7308-3). Moody.
--Romans: The Gospel for All. (Teach Yourself the Bible Ser.). 1962. pap. 2.75 (ISBN 0-8024-7372-5). Moody.
Brooks, Louise. Early History of Divine Science. 1963. 5.95 (ISBN 0-686-24363-3). Divine Sci Fed.
Brooks, Neil C. The Sepulchre of Christ in Art & Liturgy. pap. 9.00 (ISBN 0-384-05925-2). Johnson Repr.
Brooks, Nicholas. The Early History of the Church at Canterbury. (Studies in the Early History of Britain). 237p. 1983. text ed. 60.00x (ISBN 0-7185-1182-4, Leicester) Humanities.
Brooks, Noel. Ephesians. pap. 5.95 (ISBN 0-911866-02-7). Advocate.
--Scriptural Holiness. 3.95 (ISBN 0-911866-53-1); pap. 2.95 (ISBN 0-911866-54-X). Advocate.
Brooks, Nona. In the Light of Healing: Sermons by Nona L. Brooks. Zarlengo, Patricia, compiled by. (Illus.). 75p. (Orig.). 1986. pap. write for info. First Divine Sci Ch Denver.
Brooks, Oscar S. The Drama of Decision: Baptism in the New Testament. 280p. 1986. 11.95 (ISBN 0-913573-40-X). Hendrickson MA.
--The Sermon on the Mount: Authentic Human Values. 124p. (Orig.). 1985. lib. bdg. 22.00 (ISBN 0-8191-4740-0); pap. text ed. 8.75 (ISBN 0-8191-4741-9). U Pr of Amer.
Brooks, Pat. Healing of the Mind. 4th. ed. Orig. Title: Using Your Spiritual Authority. 1983. pap. text ed. 2.50 (ISBN 0-932050-00-X). New Puritan.
--Out! In the Name of Jesus. 3rd ed. LC 85-72223. 235p. 1986. pap. text ed. 5.00 (ISBN 0-932050-27-1). New Puritan.
Brooks, Phillips. Selected Sermons. facs. ed. Scarlett, William, ed. LC 79-142610. (Essay Index Reprint Ser). 1949. 19.50 (ISBN 0-8369-2146-1). Ayer Co Pubs.
Brooks, R. T. A Place to Start: The Bible As a Guide for Today. 120p. 1983. pap. 4.95 (ISBN 0-86683-708-6, HarpR). Har-Row.
Brooks, R. T., ed. Ask the Bible. LC 83-3841. 400p. 1983. 19.95 (ISBN 0-672-52765-0). Bobbs.
Brooks, Roger. Support for the Poor in the Mishnaic Law of Agriculture: Tractate Peah. LC 83-8719. (Brown Judaic Studies: No. 43). 220p. 1983. pap. 21.00 (ISBN 0-89130-632-3, 14 00 43). Scholars Pr GA.
Brooks, Roger, jt. tr. see Neusner, Jacob.
Brooks, Sandra. I Can Pray to God. LC 82-80031. (Happy Day Bks.). (Illus.). 24p. (Orig.). 1982. pap. 1.59 (ISBN 0-87239-540-5, 3586). Standard Pub.
Brooks, Shirley, jt. auth. see Winters, Sandy.
Brooks, Thomas. Precious Remedies Against Satan's Devices. 253p. 1984. pap. 5.95x (ISBN 0-85151-002-7). Banner of Truth.
--Works of Brooks, 6 vols. 1980. Set. 108.95 (ISBN 0-85151-302-6). Banner of Truth.
Brooks, Van Wyck. Emerson & Others. LC 73-3132. 250p. 1973. Repr. lib. bdg. 20.50x (ISBN 0-374-90998-9, Octagon). Hippocrene Bks.
--The Life of Emerson. LC 80-2528. Repr. of 1932 ed. 37.00 (ISBN 0-404-19252-1). AMS Pr.
Brooks, Vivia. Heritage of the Lord. (Illus.). 96p. 1984. 10.00 (ISBN 0-87770-314-0). Ye Galleon.
Brooks-Davies, Douglas. Pope's Dunciad & the Queen of Night: A Study in Emotional Jacobitism. LC 84-17135. 190p. 1985. 35.00 (ISBN 0-7190-1735-1, Pub. by Manchester Univ Pr); pap. write for info. Longwood Pub Group.
Broome, Connie. Vessels Unto Honor. LC 76-22242. 1977. pap. 3.50 (ISBN 0-87148-879-5). Pathway Pr.
Broomell, Anna P. Poets Walk In. 1983. pap. 2.50x (ISBN 0-87574-077-4, 077). Pendle Hill.
Broomhall, A. J. Hudson Taylor & China's Open Century: Bk. V. Refiner's Fire, Bk. V. 1985. pap. 9.95 (ISBN 0-340-36866-7). OMF Bks.
Broomhall, Marshall. Islam in China: A Neglected Problem. 1980. lib. bdg. 75.00 (ISBN 0-8490-3137-0). Gordon Pr.
Brooten, Bernadette J. Women Leaders in the Ancient Synagogue: Inscriptional Evidence & Background Issues. LC 82-10658. (Brown Judaic Studies). 292p. 1982. pap. 20.00 (ISBN 0-89130-587-4, 14 00 36). Scholars Pr GA.
Brophy, A. Blake. Foundlings on the Frontier: Racial & Religious Conflict in Arizona Territory, 1904-1905. LC 79-187824. (Southwest Chronicles). 129p. 1972. pap. 3.95 (ISBN 0-8165-0319-2). U of Ariz Pr.
Brophy, Don & Westenhaver, Edythe, eds. Story of Catholics in America. 3.95 (ISBN 0-8091-2087-9). Paulist Pr.
Brose, E. F. Twenty New Ways to Get the Minister Out of Moneyraising. 1976. 2.50 (ISBN 0-941500-18-7). Sharing Co.
Brose, Olive J. Frederick Denison Maurice: Rebellious Conformist, 1805-1872. LC 74-141380. xxiii, 308p. 1971. 16.00x (ISBN 0-8214-0092-4). Ohio U Pr.
Brosnan, Barbara. Yoga for Handicapped People. (Human Horizon Ser.). (Illus.). 208p. 1982. pap. 15.95 (ISBN 0-285-64952-3, Pub. by Souvenir Pr England). Brookline Bks.
Brosnan, Cornelius J. Jason Lee: Prophet of the New Oregon. LC 84-71620. (Illus.). 376p. 1985. pap. text ed. 12.00 (ISBN 0-914960-52-0). Academy Bks.
Bross, Olive J. Church & Parliament: The Reshaping of the Church of England, 1828-1860. LC 59-7423. pap. 30.00 (ISBN 0-317-26542-3, 2023992). Bks Demand UMI.
Brosse, La. Diccionario del Cristianismo. (Span.). 1104p. 1976. 53.95 (ISBN 84-254-0777-X, S-50202). French & Eur.
Brosses, Charles de see De Brosses, Charles.
Bro. Stanley. Pure Grace. 96p. 1984. 6.95 (ISBN 0-89962-414-6). Todd & Honeywell.

Brostrom, Kenneth N., ed. Archpriest Avvakum: The Life Written by Himself. (Michigan Slavic Translations Ser.: No. 4). 1979. 20.00 (ISBN 0-930042-33-6); pap. 10.00 (ISBN 0-930042-37-9). Mich Slavic Pubns.

Brother Leonard of Taize. Along an Inner Shore: Echoes from the Gospel. 144p. (Orig.). 1986. pap. 8.95 (ISBN 0-8298-0733-0). Pilgrim NY.

Brother Andrew, et al. God's Smuggler. (Illus.). 224p. 1968. pap. 2.95 (ISBN 0-8007-8016-7, Spire Bks); pap. 0.79 (ISBN 0-8007-8501-0, Spire Comics). Revell.

Brother Bernard Seif. Images of God: Religious Beliefs Given Life Through Counseling, Spiritual Direction, & Prayer. 1987. 7.95 (ISBN 0-533-07239-5). Vantage.

Brotherhood of St. Herman of Alaska Staff. St. Herman Calendar of Orthodox Saints. pap. 5.00 (ISBN 0-686-05410-5). Eastern Orthodox.

Brother John of Taize. The Pilgrim God: A Biblical Journey. (Orig.). 1985. pap. 12.95 (ISBN 0-912405-18-X). Pastoral Pr.

Brother Lawrence. Daily Readings with Brother Lawrence. Llewelyn, Robert, ed. (Daily Readings Ser.). 1986. pap. 4.95 (ISBN 0-87243-144-4). Templegate.

--The God-Illuminated Cook: The Practice of the Presence of God. Dawes, Robin, ed. LC 74-84399. (Illus.). 144p. 1975. pap. 2.50 (ISBN 0-914896-00-8, Strength). East Ridge Pr.

--God-Illuminated Cook: The Practice of the Presence of God. (East Ridge Press Ser.). (Illus.). 142p. 1980. pap. 4.50 (ISBN 0-89345-217-3). Garber Comm.

--Practice of the Presence of God. 64p. pap. 2.75 (ISBN 0-8007-8034-5, Spire Bks). Revell.

Brother Lawrence & Laubach, Frank. Practicing His Presence. 3rd ed. Edwards, Gene, ed. 1973. pap. 5.95 (ISBN 0-940232-01-4). Christian Bks.

Brother Lawrence Of The Resurrection, see Delaney, John J.

Brother Robert J. Kealey. Curriculum in the Catholic School. 61p. 1986. 6.60 (ISBN 0-318-20568-8). Natl Cath Educ.

Brothers, Joan. Religious Institutions. (Aspects of Modern Sociology Ser.). 1971. pap. text ed. 6.95 (ISBN 0-582-48120-1). Humanities.

Brother Terence McLaughlin. Catholic School Finance & Church-State Relations. 81p. 1986. 6.60 (ISBN 0-318-20564-5). Natl Cath Educ.

Broucek, Marcia, ed. see Bankson, Marjory Z.

Broucek, Marcia, ed. see Loder, Ted.

Broucek, Marcia, ed. see O'Connor, Elizabeth.

Brough, R. Clayton. His Servants Speak: Statements by Latter-day Saint Leaders on Contemporary Topics. LC 75-17101. 298p. 1975. 10.95 (ISBN 0-88290-054-4). Horizon Utah.

--The Lost Tribes: History Doctrine, Prophecies & Theories About Israel's Lost Ten Tribes. LC 79-89351. 1979. 7.95 (ISBN 0-88290-123-0). Horizon Utah.

Broughton, Hugh. An Epistle to the Learned Nobility of England: Touching Translating the Bible. LC 77-6862. (English Experience Ser.: No. 855). 1977. Repr. of 1597 ed. lib. bdg. 7.00 (ISBN 90-221-0855-4). Walter J Johnson.

Broughton, Pamela. The Creation. (Golden Bible Stories Ser.). (Illus.). 32p. 1985. 3.95 (ISBN 0-307-11620-4, Pub. by Golden Bks). Western Pub.

--Noah's Ark. (Golden Bible Stories Ser.). (Illus.). 32p. 1985. 3.95 (ISBN 0-307-11621-2, Pub. by Golden Bks). Western Pub.

Broughton, Pamela, retold by. David & Goliath. LC 85-81161. (Golden Bible Stories). (Illus.). 32p. 1986. 3.95 (ISBN 0-307-11625-5, Pub. by Golden Bks). Western Pub.

--Jesus at the Temple. LC 85-81162. (Golden Bible Stories). (Illus.). 32p. 1986. 3.95 (ISBN 0-307-11624-7, Pub. by Golden Bks). Western Pub.

--Joseph & the Coat of Many Colors. LC 85-81156. (Golden Bible Stories). (Illus.). 32p. 1986. 3.95 (ISBN 0-307-11627-1, Pub. by Golden Bks). Western Pub.

--The Life of Jesus. LC 85-51852. (Golden Bible Stories). (Illus.). 32p. 1986. 3.95 (ISBN 0-307-11626-3, Pub. by Golden Bks). Western Pub.

--The Prodigal Son. (Golden Bible Stories Ser.). (Illus.). 32p. 1986. 3.95 (ISBN 0-307-11623-9, Pub. by Golden Bks). Western Pub.

Broughton, Peter. Joshua & Samuel. (Bible Study Commentaries Ser.). 126p. 1984. pap. 4.95 (ISBN 0-317-43371-7). Chr Lit.

Broughton, Richard. English Protestants Plea. LC 76-57380. (English Experience Ser.: No. 798). 1977. Repr. of 1621 ed. lib. bdg. 9.50 (ISBN 90-221-0798-1). Walter J Johnson.

Broun, Heywood & Britt, George. Christians Only: A Study in Prejudice. LC 73-19688. (Civil Liberties in American History Ser). [illegible] 1974. Repr. of 1931 ed. lib. bdg. 39.50 (ISBN 0-306-70599-0). Da Capo.

Brouwer, Arie R. Reformed Church Roots. write for info. (ISBN 0-685-62275-4). Reformed Church.

Browining, Don S., ed. see Anderson, Herbert.

Browman, David L., ed. Spirits, Shamans, & Stars: Perspectives from South America. Scwartz, Ronald A. (World Anthropology Ser.). 1979. text ed. 28.50x (ISBN 90-279-7890-5). Mouton.

Brown, ed. see Townsley, David & Bjork, Russell.

Brown, A. The Christian World. LC 83-50692. (Religions of the World Ser.). 1984. PLB 14.96 (ISBN 0-382-06721-5); 10.75 (ISBN 0-382-06929-3). Silver.

Brown, Alice & Kirk, Pat. Jesus: His Story for Children. (Illus.). 1986. 10.95 (ISBN 0-915720-21-3). Brownlow Pub Co.

Brown, Allen W. The Inner Fire. rev. ed. 1984. pap. 1.95 (ISBN 0-88028-033-6). Forward Movement.

Brown, Angela. Prayers That Avail Much for Children. (Illus.). 32p. (Orig.). 1983. pap. 3.98 (ISBN 0-89274-296-8). Harrison Hse.

Brown, Anna M., jt. auth. see Brown, Oswald E.

Brown, Annice H. Thank You, Lord, for Little Things. 3.95 (ISBN 0-8042-2580-X). John Knox.

Brown, B. The Essence of Chinese Wisdom. (Illus.). 227p. 1986. 117.50 (ISBN 0-89901-279-5). Found Class Reprints.

Brown, Barry F. Accidental Being: A Study in the Metaphysics of St. Thomas Aquinas. LC 85-15653. 440p. (Orig.). 1985. lib. bdg. 32.75 (ISBN 0-8191-4886-5); pap. text ed. 19.50 (ISBN 0-8191-4887-3). U Pr of Amer.

Brown, Beatrice. The Southern Passion. LC 74-10772. 1927. 20.00 (ISBN 0-8414-3122-1). Folcroft.

Brown, Beth, jt. auth. see Thackeray, Helen.

Brown, Bill, jt. auth. see Brown, Joan W.

Brown, Bob W. It's Been One of Those Days, Lord. 144p. (Orig.). 1985. pap. 2.95 (ISBN 0-310-28912-2, 12773P). Zondervan.

Brown, Bonaventure A. The Numerical Distinction of Sins According to the Franciscan School of the Seventeenth & Eighteenth Centuries. 1948. 3.50 (ISBN 0-686-11581-3). Franciscan Inst.

Brown, Brian. The Wisdom of the Hindus. 320p. 1981. pap. 18.00 (ISBN 0-89540-093-6, SB-093). Sun Pub.

Brown, C. C. Philosophy of Hope. 1972. 2.95 (ISBN 0-9600378-0-2); pap. 2.00 (ISBN 0-9600378-3-7). C C Brown Pub.

Brown, Carleton. Religious Lyrics of the Thirteenth, Fourteenth, & Fifteenth Centuries, 3 vols. 300.00 (ISBN 0-8490-0942-1). Gordon Pr.

Brown, Carleton & Robbins, Rossell H. Index of Middle English Verse. xix, 785p. 1943. 40.00x (ISBN 0-87352-017-3, Z2). Modern Lang.

Brown, Carolyn C. Developing Christian Education in a Smaller Church. LC 81-17563. (Griggs Educational Resources Ser.). 96p. (Orig.). 1982. pap. 7.75 (ISBN 0-687-10508-0). Abingdon.

--Youth Ministries: Thinking Big With Small Groups. 96p. 1984. pap. 7.95 (ISBN 0-687-47203-2). Abingdon.

Brown, Charles R., jt. auth. see Gabriel, Ralph H.

Brown, Charles R., jt. auth. see Yale Divinity School Faculty Members Staff.

Brown, Charlotte & Hyman, Paula. The Jewish Woman in America. 1977. pap. 7.95 (ISBN 0-452-25786-7, Z5282, Plume). NAL.

Brown, Christopher K., jt. auth. see Gruner, Mark.

Brown, Clifton F., jt. auth. see Williams, Ethel L.

Brown, Colin. Jesus in European Protestant Thought, 1778-1860. (Studies in Historical Theology: Vol. 1). 380p. 1985. lib. bdg. 35.00x (ISBN 0-939464-18-7). Labyrinth Pr.

--Miracles & the Critical Mind. LC 83-16600. 432p. 1984. 19.95 (ISBN 0-8028-3590-2). Eerdmans.

--The New International Dictionary of New Testament Theology, 3 vols. Set. 109.95 (ISBN 0-310-21928-0, 11137P). Zondervan.

--Philosophy & the Christian Faith. LC 68-58083. (Orig.). 1969. pap. 9.95 (ISBN 0-87784-712-6). Inter-Varsity.

--That You May Believe: Miracles & Faith-Then & Now. 224p. (Orig.). 1985. pap. 8.95 (ISBN 0-8028-0086-6). Eerdmans.

Brown, Colin, ed. The New International Dictionary of New Testament Theology, 4 vols. 1986. 109.95 (ISBN 0-310-33238-9, 11137). Zondervan.

Brown, D. Catherine. Pastor & Laity in the Theology of Jean Gerson. 420p. 1987. 54.50 (ISBN 0-521-33029-7). Cambridge U Pr.

Brown, Dale. Simulations on Brethren History. pap. 6.95 (ISBN 0-87178-794-6). Brethren.

Brown, Dale W. Biblical Pacifism: A Peace Church Perspective. 176p. 1985. pap. 8.95 (ISBN 0-87178-108-5). Brethren.

Brown, Dale W., ed. see Hatfield, Mark, et al.

Brown, David. Choices: Ethics & the Christian. (Faith & the Future Ser.). 176p. 1984. pap. 24.95x (ISBN 0-631-13182-5); pap. 6.95 (ISBN 0-631-13222-8). Basil Blackwell.

--The Four Gospels. 20.95 (ISBN 0-85151-016-7). Banner of Truth.

Brown, David, ed. Bible Wisdom for Modern Living: Arranged by Subject. 400p. 1986. 17.95 (ISBN 0-671-62545-4). S&S.

Brown, David A., jt. auth. see Pedretti, Carlo.

Brown, David C. A Guide to the Salem Witchcraft Hysteria of 1692. LC 84-164658. (Illus.). 130p. (Orig.). 1984. pap. 5.95 (ISBN 0-9613415-0-5). D C Brown.

Brown, Delwin. To Set at Liberty: Christian Faith & Human Freedom. LC 80-21783. 144p. (Orig.). 1981. pap. 6.95 (ISBN 0-88344-501-8). Orbis Bks.

Brown, Diana D. Umbanda: Religion & Politics in Urban Brazil. Kottak, Conrad, ed. LC 85-20962. (Studies in Cultural Anthropology: No. 7). 270p. 1985. 44.95 (ISBN 0-8357-1556-6). UMI Res Pr.

Brown, Douglas E. When Past & Present Meet. 112p. 1986. 4.95 (ISBN 0-913573-46-9). Hendrickson MA.

Brown, Dovid. Mysteries of the Creation. (Illus.). 400p. 1987. 19.99 (ISBN 0-939833-24-7). Mosdos Pubs.

Brown, Earl K. Women of Mr. Wesley's Methodism. LC 83-22010. (Studies in Women & Religion: Vol. 11). 273p. 1984. 49.95x (ISBN 0-88946-538-X). E Mellen.

Brown, Edna M. & Hill, George H. Coloring the Electric Church-Black Religious Broadcaster: A Selected Annotated Bibliography. 60p. 1987. text ed. 15.00X (ISBN 0-933650-31-0); pap. text ed. 7.00 (ISBN 0-933650-30-2). Daystar Co Carson.

Brown, Elizabeth M., et al, eds. Pilgrims & Their Times. rev. ed. (Illus.). 32p. 1973. pap. 2.50 (ISBN 0-87534-121-7). Highlights.

Brown, Eugene. Dreams, Visions & Prophecies of Don Bosco. LC 86-13533. 344p. 1986. lib. bdg. 13.95 (ISBN 0-89944-085-1); pap. 9.95 (ISBN 0-89944-086-X). Don Bosco Multimedia.

Brown, Eugene, ed. see Messori, Vittorio.

Brown, Francis, et al, eds. The New Brown-Driver-Briggs Hebrew - Lexicon of the Old Testament. 1200p. 1979. 34.95 (ISBN 0-913573-20-5). Hendrickson MA.

Brown, Francis, et al, eds. see Gesenius, William.

Brown, Frank B. The Evolution of Darwin's Religious Views. (Special Studies: No. 10). 72p. pap. text ed. 7.95 (ISBN 0-86554-239-2, MUP/M12). NABPR.

--Transfiguration: Poetic Metaphor & the Languages of Religious Belief. LC 82-24714. (Studies in Religion). x, 230p. 1983. 25.00x (ISBN 0-8078-1560-8). U of NC Pr.

Brown, Friedl, tr. see Van Der Meer, Frederik.

Brown, G. Thompson. Christianity in the People's Republic of China. LC 82-49018. 240p. 1983. pap. 7.25 (ISBN 0-8042-1484-0). John Knox.

--Christianity in the People's Republic of China. rev., 2nd ed. LC 86-45554. 256p. 1986. pap. 9.95 (ISBN 0-8042-1485-9). John Knox.

Brown, Gabrielle. The New Celibacy: Why More Men & Women Are Abstaining from Sex & Enjoying It. 300p. 1980. 10.95 (ISBN 0-07-008430-0). McGraw.

Brown, George. The Lady Preacher: Or, the Life & Labors of Mrs. Hannah Reeves, the Late Wife of the Rev. William Reeves of the Methodist Church. De Swarte, Carolyn G. & Dayton, Donald, eds. (Women in American Protestant Religion Series 1800-1930). 341p. 1987. lib. bdg. 50.00 (ISBN 0-8240-0660-7). Garland Pub.

Brown, George H. Bede the Venerable. (Twayne's English Authors Ser.). 144p. 1987. lib. bdg. 19.95 (ISBN 0-8057-6940-4, TEAS 443, Twayne). G K Hall.

Brown, Gerda. Carismas de Dios. (Span., Illus.). 589p. (Orig.). 1983. pap. 8.95 (ISBN 0-939868-98-9). Chr Intl Pubs.

Brown, Handy N. Necromancer, Or, Voo-Doo Doctor. LC 77-39544. Repr. of 1904 ed. 13.50 (ISBN 0-404-00008-8). AMS Pr.

Brown, Harold O. Heresies: The Image of Christ in the Mirror of Heresy & Orthodoxy from the Apostles to the Present. LC 80-2558. (Illus.). 504p. 1984. 17.95 (ISBN 0-385-15338-4). Doubleday.

Brown, Harold O. J. The Bible on Abortion. 1977. 0.50 (ISBN 0-911802-43-6). Free Church Pubns.

Brown, Henry C., Jr., et al. Steps to the Sermon. LC 63-19068. 1963. 12.95 (ISBN 0-8054-2103-3). Broadman.

Brown, Howard, jt. auth. see Keim, Curtis A.

Brown, Hubert L. Black & Mennonite. LC 76-44043. 112p. 1976. pap. 3.95 (ISBN 0-8361-1801-4). Herald Pr.

Brown, Isaac V. Biography of the Reverend Robert Finley. LC 73-82178. (Anti-Slavery Crusade in America Ser). 1969. Repr. of 1857 ed. 18.00 (ISBN 0-405-00617-9). Ayer Co Pubs.

Brown, J. Pilgrim Fathers of New England & Their Puritan Successors. 4th ed. (Illus.). Repr. of 1920 ed. 39.00 (ISBN 0-527-12050-2). Kraus Repr.

Brown, J. Newton. Baptist Church Manual. pap. 1.25 (ISBN 0-8170-0015-1). Judson.

Brown, J. Paul. Counseling with Senior Citizens. LC 64-15217. (Successful Pastoral Counseling Ser.). pap. 36.00 (2027174). Bks Demand UMI.

Brown, Jack & Armbrister, David. The Life & Works of Charles Harmon. 136p. 1986. 16.95; pap. 12.95. Commonwealth Pr.

Brown, James. History of the Origin & Progress of the Sikhs, ISPP Vol. II, No. 4. 74p. 1975. Repr. 2.00 (ISBN 0-88065-068-0, Pub. by Messers Today & Tommorrows Printers & Publishers India). Scholarly Pubns.

Brown, James, et al. The Relationship of the Library to Instructional Systems. Corrigan, John T., ed. (Catholic Library Association Studies in Librarianship: No. 2). 1978. pap. 3.00 (ISBN 0-87507-006-X). Cath Lib Assn.

Brown, James A. The Word & the World: God's Priorities for Today. 64p. 1984. 7.95 (ISBN 0-89962-419-7). Todd & Honeywell.

Brown, James Buchan. Bible Truths with Shakespearian Parallels. 6th ed. LC 74-19106. Repr. of 1886 ed. 15.00 (ISBN 0-404-01136-5). AMS Pr.

Brown, Jamieson-Fausett. Comentario Exegetico y Explicativo de la Biblia Tomo II. Quarles, Jaime C. & Quarles, Lemuel C., trs. from Eng. 382p. 1982. Repr. of 1959 ed. 15.75 (ISBN 0-311-03004-1). Casa Bautista.

Brown, Joan W. Best of Christmas Joys. LC 83-45165. 64p. (Orig.). 1983. pap. 2.95 (ISBN 0-385-19039-5, Galilee). Doubleday.

--Every Knee Shall Bow. 194p. 1984. pap. 5.95 (ISBN 0-89066-054-9). World Wide Pubs.

--Never Alone. 48p. 1985. 6.95 (ISBN 0-8378-5084-3). Gibson.

Brown, Joan W. & Brown, Bill. Together Each Day. 288p. 1980. pap. 7.95 (ISBN 0-8007-5226-0). Revell.

Brown, Joan W., compiled by. Dia-Tras-Dia Con Billy Graham. Orig. Title: Day by Day with Billy Graham. 192p. 1982. Repr. of 1978 ed. 3.95 (ISBN 0-311-40039-6, Edit Mundo). Casa Bautista.

--Day-by-Day with Billy Graham. 1976. pap. 5.95 (ISBN 0-89066-000-X). World Wide Pubs.

Brown, John. The English Puritans. 1978. Repr. of 1910 ed. lib. bdg. 20.00 (ISBN 0-8495-0434-1). Arden Lib.

--The English Puritans. LC 73-12821. 1910. lib. bdg. 22.50 (ISBN 0-8414-3235-X). Folcroft.

--First Peter, 2 vols. 1980. 32.95 (ISBN 0-85151-204-6); Vol. 1, 577 Pp. (ISBN 0-85151-205-4); Vol. 2, 640 Pp. (ISBN 0-85151-206-2). Banner of Truth.

--Galatians. 1982. lib. bdg. 16.00 (ISBN 0-86524-083-3, 4802). Klock & Klock.

--Hebrews. (Geneva Ser.). 329p. 1983. Repr. of 1862 ed. text ed. 15.95 (ISBN 0-85151-099-X). Banner of Truth.

--The History of the English Bible. LC 77-13187. 1977. Repr. lib. bdg. 15.00 (ISBN 0-8414-9929-2). Folcroft.

--I've Got Mixed-Up Feelings, God. 64p. 1984. pap. 3.95 (ISBN 0-8170-1035-1). Judson.

--John Bunyan, (1628-1688) His Life, Times & Work. Harrison, Frank M., ed. (Illus.). xxiv, 515p. 1969. Repr. of 1928 ed. 37.50 (ISBN 0-208-00726-1, Archon). Shoe String.

--Parting Counsels: Exposition of II Peter 1. (Banner of Truth Geneva Series Commentaries). 1980. 13.95 (ISBN 0-85151-301-8). Banner of Truth.

--The Pilgrim Fathers of New England. 352p. 1970. 4.95 (ISBN 0-686-09112-4). Pilgrim Pubns.

--The Resurrection of Life. 1978. 15.50 (ISBN 0-86524-962-8, 4601). Klock & Klock.

--The Sufferings & the Glories of the Messiah. (Giant Summit Bks.). 352p. 1981. pap. 5.95 (ISBN 0-8010-0792-5). Baker Bk.

--Worship Celebrations for Youth. 1980. pap. 4.95 (ISBN 0-8170-0866-7). Judson.

Brown, Joseph E. Spiritual Legacy of American Indian. 160p. 1984. pap. 8.95 (ISBN 0-8245-0618-9). Crossroad NY.

--Spiritual Legacy of the American Indian. LC 64-17425. (Illus., Orig.). 1964. pap. 2.50x (ISBN 0-87574-135-5). Pendle Hill.

Brown, Joseph E., ed. The Sacred Pipe: Black Elk's Account of the Seven Rites of Oglala Sioux. LC 53-8810. (Civilization of the American Indian Ser.: No. 36). (Illus.). 1981. 17.95 (ISBN 0-8061-0272-1). U of Okla Pr.

Brown, Judith C. Immodest Acts: The Life of a Lesbian Nun in Renaissance Italy. (Studies in the History of Sexuality). 221p. 1985. 14.95 (ISBN 0-19-503675-1). Oxford U Pr.

Brown, Judith G. I Sing a Song of the Saints of God. (Illus.). 32p. (Orig.). 1981. pap. 5.95 (ISBN 0-8164-2339-3, HarpR). Har-Row.

Brown, Keven, ed. see Moffet, Ruth.

Brown, L. B. Advances in the Psychology of Religion. (International Series in Experimental Social Psychology: Vol. 11). (Illus.). 236p. 1985. 27.50 (ISBN 0-08-027948-1, Pub by PPL). Pergamon.

--The Psychology of Religious Belief. 1987. 48.00 (ISBN 0-12-136355-4); pap. 24.00 (ISBN 0-12-136356-2). Acad Pr.

Brown, L. David. Take Care: A Guide for Responsible Living. LC 78-52200. 1978. pap. 6.95 (ISBN 0-8066-1665-2, 10-6190). Augsburg.

Brown, Lavonn D. The Life of the Church. 1987. 5.95 (ISBN 0-8054-1643-9). Broadman.

Brown, Leon C., tr. see Al Tunisi, Khayr.

Brown, Les. Keeping Your Eye on Television. LC 79-15828. (Orig.). 1979. pap. 4.95 (ISBN 0-8298-0376-9). Pilgrim NY.

Brown, Leslie. The Indian Christians of St. Thomas: An Account of the Ancient Syrian Church of Malabar. LC 81-21766. (Illus.). 330p. 1982. 39.50 (ISBN 0-521-21258-8). Cambridge U Pr.

Brown, Loren R. Point Loma Theosophical Society: A List of Publications, 1898 - 1942. LC 81-187499. (Illus.). 136p. 1977. pap. 10.00 (ISBN 0-913510-46-7). Wizards.

Brown, Louise F. Political Activities of the Baptists & the Fifth Monarchy Men in England During the Interregnum. 1964. Repr. of 1911 ed. 20.50 (ISBN 0-8337-0399-4). B Franklin.

Brown, Lowell & Haystead, Wes. The Church Computer Manual. 160p. (Orig.). 1985. pap. 12.95 (ISBN 0-8423-0271-9). Tyndale.

Brown, Marcia. Stone Soup. (Illus.). 1947. 12.95 (ISBN 0-684-92296-7, Pub. by Scribner); pap. 5.95 (ISBN 0-684-16217-2, Pub. by Scribner). Macmillan.

Brown, Marguerite. Magnificent Muslims. LC 81-80056. 98p. 1981. 8.00 (ISBN 0-911026-10-X). New World Press NY.

Brown, Marguerite D. Women of Calvary. 1982. pap. 5.25 ea. (ISBN 0-89536-526-X, 2331). CSS of Ohio.

Brown, Marice C. Amen, Brother Ben: A Mississippi Collection of Children's Rhymes. LC 78-32017. 1979. pap. text ed. 5.00 (ISBN 0-87805-094-9). U Pr of Miss.

Brown, Marion E. & Prentice, Marjorie G. Christian Education in the Year Two Thousand. 160p. 1984. pap. 5.95 (ISBN 0-8170-1055-6). Judson.

Brown, Marion M. & Leech, Jane K. Dreamcatcher: The Life of John Neihardt. 144p. (Orig.). 1983. pap. 6.95 (ISBN 0-687-11174-9). Abingdon.

Brown, Marion M., et al. The Silent Storm. 1985. Repr. of 1963 ed. 6.95 (ISBN 0-8010-0884-0). Baker Bk.

Brown, Marion R. Putting Life Back Together. 96p. 1986. 5.95 (ISBN 0-87159-132-4). Unity School.

Brown, Marvin L., Jr. The Wisdom of Christendom. 131p. 1982. pap. 5.95. Edenwood Hse.

Brown, Sr. Mary A., ed. Paul of Pergula: Logica & Tractatus De Sensu Composito et Diviso. (Text Ser). 1961. 11.00 (ISBN 0-686-11558-9). Franciscan Inst.

Brown, Michael. Jew of Juif? Jews in Canada, 1759-1914. (Illus.). 336p. 1987. 16.95 (ISBN 0-8276-0271-5). Jewish Pubns.

Brown, Michael F. Tsewa'a Gift: Magic & Meaning in an Amazonian Society. LC 85-40401. (Ethnographic Inquiry Ser.). (Illus.). 220p. 1986. 19.95x (ISBN 0-87474-294-3, BRTG). Smithsonian.

Brown, Milton P. To Hear the Word: Invitation to Serious Study of the Bible. 256p. 1987. 29.95 (ISBN 0-86554-251-1, MUP H-216); pap. 14.95 (ISBN 0-86554-252-X, MUP P-40). Mercer Univ Pr.

Brown, Milton P., Jr. Authentic Writings of Ignatius: A Study of Linguistic Criteria. LC 63-19458. pap. 33.30 (ISBN 0-8357-9096-7, 2017888). Bks Demand UMI.

Brown, Oswald E. & Brown, Anna M. Life & Letters of Laura Askew Haygood. De Swarte, Carolyn G., ed. (Women in American Protestant Religion Series 1800-1930). 522p. 1987. lib. bdg. 75.00 (ISBN 0-8240-0661-5). Garland Pub.

Brown, Pam. It Was Always Africa. LC 86-2240. (YA) 1986. pap. 4.95 (ISBN 0-8054-4335-5). Broadman.

Brown, Pat. Locating & Preserving Your Church's Records. Deweese, Charles W., ed. (Resource Kit for Your Church's History Ser.). 8p. 1984. 0.50 (ISBN 0-939804-15-8). Hist Comm S Baptist.

Brown, Pean. Gifts of Silence. 84p. 1983. pap. 6.95 (ISBN 0-942494-79-2). Coleman Pub.

Brown, Peter. Augustine of Hippo. 463p. 1987. 22.50 (ISBN 0-88029-098-6, Pub. by Dorset Pr). Hippocrene Bks.

--Augustine of Hippo: A Biography. 1967. pap. 9.95 (ISBN 0-520-01411-1, CAL179). U of Cal Pr.

--The Cult of the Saints: Its Rise & Function in Latin Christianity. LC 80-11210. xvi, 188p. 1982. pap. 7.95 (ISBN 0-226-07622-9, Phoen). U of Chicago Pr.

Brown, Peter, tr. see Van Der Meer, Frederik.

Brown, Philippa, ed. Sibton Abbey Cartularies & Charters: II. (Suffolk Charters VIII). 192p. 1986. 28.95 (ISBN 0-85115-443-3, Pub. by Boydell & Brewer). Longwood Pub Group.

Brown, R. Semitic Influence in Hellenic Mythology. xvi, 228p. Repr. of 1898 ed. lib. bdg. 35.00x (ISBN 0-89241-206-2). Caratzas.

Brown, R. Allen. The Origins of Modern Europe: The Medieval Heritage of Western Civilization. LC 72-11597. 1973. pap. 7.95x (ISBN 0-88295-705-8). Harlan Davidson.

Brown, Ramona A. Memories of Abdu'l-Baha: Recollections of the Early Days of the Baha'i Faith in California. LC 79-16412. (Illus.). 1980. 10.95 (ISBN 0-87743-128-0, 332-010); pap. 6.95 (ISBN 0-87743-139-6, 332-011). Baha'i.

Brown, Raphael. The Roots of St. Francis. 9.50 (ISBN 0-686-45828-1). Franciscan Herald.

--True Joy from Assisi. 276p. 1978. 8.95 (ISBN 0-8199-0688-3). Franciscan Herald.

Brown, Raphael, tr. Little Flower of St. Francis. 1971. pap. 5.50 (ISBN 0-385-07544-8, Im). Doubleday.

Brown, Raphael, tr. see Habig, Marion A.

Brown, Raymond. Let's Read the Old Testament. 1972. pap. 2.95 (ISBN 0-87508-034-0). Chr Lit.

--The Message of Hebrews. Motyer, J. A. & Stott, John R., eds. LC 82-15321. (The Bible Speaks Today Ser.). 272p. (Orig.). 1982. pap. 7.95 (ISBN 0-87784-289-2). Inter-Varsity.

--Timothy-James. 1983. pap. 4.95 (ISBN 0-87508-174-6). Chr Lit.

Brown, Raymond B. Marcos Presenta Al Salvador. Lerin, Olivia Y Alfredo, tr. Orig. Title: Mark - the Saviour for Sinners. 160p. 1982. pap. 4.25 (ISBN 0-311-04346-1). Casa Bautista.

Brown, Raymond E. Biblical Exegesis & Church Doctrine. 5.95 (ISBN 0-8091-2750-4). Paulist Pr.

--Biblical Reflections on Crises Facing the Church. LC 75-19861. 132p. 1975. pap. 4.95 (ISBN 0-8091-1891-2). Paulist Pr.

--The Birth of the Messiah: A Commentary on the Infancy Narratives in Matthew & Luke. LC 76-56271. 1977. pap. 9.95 (ISBN 0-385-05405-X, Im). Doubleday.

--The Churches the Apostles Left Behind. 160p. (Orig.). 1984. pap. 5.95 (ISBN 0-8091-2611-7). Paulist Pr.

--The Community of the Beloved Disciple. LC 78-65894. 204p. 1979. 5.95 (ISBN 0-8091-0274-9); pap. 4.95 (ISBN 0-8091-2174-3). Paulist Pr.

--The Critical Meaning of the Bible. LC 81-82333. 160p. (Orig.). 1981. pap. 5.95 (ISBN 0-8091-2406-8). Paulist Pr.

--Daniel. (Bible Ser.). pap. 1.00 (ISBN 0-8091-5024-7). Paulist Pr.

--The Epistles of John. LC 81-43380. (Anchor Bible Ser.: Vol. 30). 840p. 1982. 20.00 (ISBN 0-385-05686-9). Doubleday.

--Jesus, God & Man. LC 67-29587. (Impact Books). 1967. pap. 4.95 (ISBN 0-02-084000-4, Collier). Macmillan.

--Priest & Bishop. LC 78-139594. 96p. 1970. pap. 4.95 (ISBN 0-8091-1661-8). Paulist Pr.

--Recent Discoveries & the Biblical World. (Background Books Ser.: Vol. 1). 4.95 (ISBN 0-89453-363-0). M Glazier.

--The Virginal Conception & Bodily Resurrection of Jesus. LC 72-97399. 1973. pap. 5.95 (ISBN 0-8091-1768-1). Paulist Pr.

Brown, Raymond E. & Meier, John. Antioch & Rome: New Testament Cradles of Catholic Christianity. 256p. 1983. pap. 5.95 (ISBN 0-8091-2532-3). Paulist Pr.

Brown, Raymond E., tr. Gospel According to John One - Twelve. LC 66-12209. (Anchor Bible Ser.: Vol. 29). 1966. 20.00 (ISBN 0-385-01517-8, Anchor Pr). Doubleday.

--Gospel According to John Thirteen - Twenty-One. LC 66-12209. (Anchor Bible Ser.: Vol. 29A). 1970. 18.00 (ISBN 0-385-03761-9, Anchor Pr). Doubleday.

Brown, Raymond E., et al. Peter in the New Testament. LC 73-83787. 1973. 7.95 (ISBN 0-8066-1401-3, 10-4930). Augsburg.

--Peter in the New Testament. LC 73-84424. (Orig.). 1973. pap. 5.95 (ISBN 0-8091-1790-8). Paulist Pr.

Brown, Raymond E., et al, eds. Jerome Biblical Commentary. 1969. 59.95 (ISBN 0-13-509612-X). P-H.

--Mary in the New Testament. LC 78-8797. 336p. 1978. pap. 6.95 (ISBN 0-8091-2168-9). Paulist Pr.

--Mary in the New Testament: A Collaborative Assessment by Protestant & Roman Catholic Scholars. LC 78-8797. 336p. 1978. pap. 6.95 (ISBN 0-8006-1345-7, 1-1345). Fortress.

Brown, Raymond K. Reach Out to Singles: A Challenge to Ministry. LC 79-15495. 192p. 1979. pap. 7.95 (ISBN 0-664-24270-7). Westminster.

Brown, Rebecca. He Came to Set the Captives Free. 288p. (Orig.). 1986. pap. 7.50 (ISBN 0-937958-25-5). Chick Pubns.

Brown, Richard. Studies in Romans, Vol. 1. (Bible Study Ser.). 1986. pap. 3.50 (ISBN 0-8309-0452-2). Herald Hse.

Brown, Richard A. Studies in Romans, Vol. 2. (Bible Study Ser.). 1986. pap. 3.50 (ISBN 0-8309-0454-9). Herald Hse.

Brown, Robert. Luke: Doctor-Writer. (BibLearn Ser.). (Illus.). 1977. bds. 5.95 (ISBN 0-8054-4233-2, 4242-33). Broadman.

--Semetic Influence in Hellenic Mythology. LC 65-27053. (Library of Religious & Philosophical Thought). 1966. Repr. of 1898 ed. lib. bdg. 25.00x (ISBN 0-678-09952-9, Reference Bk Pubs). Kelley.

--Semitic Influence in Hellentic Mythology. 19.00 (ISBN 0-405-10084-1, 14709). Ayer Co Pubs.

Brown, Robert F. Schelling's Treatise on "the Deities of Samothrace". A Translation & an Interpretation. LC 76-42239. (American Academy of Religion. Studies in Religion). 1977. pap. 9.95 (ISBN 0-89130-087-2, 010012). Scholars Pr GA.

Brown, Robert M. The Bible Speaks to You. LC 84-19578. 324p. 1985. pap. 8.95 (ISBN 0-664-24597-8). Westminster.

--Gustavo Gutierrez. LC 80-82185. (Makers of Contemporary Theology Ser.). 89p. 1981. pap. 3.95 (ISBN 0-8042-0651-1). John Knox.

--Is Faith Obsolete? LC 74-13420. 160p. 1979. pap. 3.95 (ISBN 0-664-24230-8). Westminster.

--Making Peace in the Global Village. LC 80-27213. 118p. 1981. pap. 5.95 (ISBN 0-664-24343-6). Westminster.

--Significance of the Church. LC 56-6172. (Layman's Theological Library). 96p. 1956. pap. 2.45 (ISBN 0-664-24001-1). Westminster.

--Spirit of Protestantism. (YA) 1961. pap. 8.95 (ISBN 0-19-500724-7). Oxford U Pr.

--Theology in a New Key: Responding to Liberation Themes. LC 78-6494. 212p. 1978. pap. 8.95 (ISBN 0-664-24204-9). Westminster.

--Unexpected News: Reading the Bible with Third World Eyes. LC 84-2380. 166p. 1984. pap. 7.95 (ISBN 0-664-24552-8). Westminster.

Brown, Robert M., ed. The Essential Reinhold Niebuhr: Selected Essays & Addresses. LC 85-22798. 272p. 1986. 19.95 (ISBN 0-300-03464-4). Yale U Pr.

Brown, Robert M., tr. see De Dietrich, Suzanne.

Brown, Robert McAfee. Saying Yes & Saying No: On Rendering to God & Caesar. LC 85-29575. 144p. (Orig.). 1986. pap. 7.95 (ISBN 0-664-24695-8). Westminster.

Brown, Ruth A. S. Aureli Augustini: De Beata Vita: A Translation with an Introduction & Commentary, Vol. 72. (Patristic Studies). 211p. 1984. Repr. of 1944 ed. 30.00x (ISBN 0-939738-30-9). Zubal Inc.

Brown, S. W. Secularization of American Education As Shown by State Legislation, State Constitutional Provisions & State Supreme Court Decisions. LC 70-176600. (Columbia University. Teachers College. Contributions to Education: No. 49). Repr. of 1912 ed. 22.50 (ISBN 0-404-55049-5). AMS Pr.

Brown, Sanger. Sex Worship & Symbolism: An Interpretation. LC 72-9624. Repr. of 1922 ed. 27.50 (ISBN 0-404-57419-X). AMS Pr.

Brown, Schuyler. The Origins of Christianity: A Historical Introduction to the New Testament. (Oxford Bible Ser.). (Orig.). 1984. pap. 8.95 (ISBN 0-19-826202-7). Oxford U Pr.

Brown, Schuyler & Saliers, Don E. Pentecost Three. Actemeier, Elizabeth, et al, eds. LC 79-7377. (Proclamation Ser.: No. 2). 64p. 1982. pap. 3.75 (ISBN 0-8006-4099-3, 1-4099). Fortress.

Brown, Stephanie. Religious Painting. LC 78-24454. (Mayflower Gallery). (Illus.). 1979. 12.50 (ISBN 0-8317-7370-7, Mayflower Bks); pap. 6.95 (ISBN 0-8317-7371-5). Smith Pubs.

Brown, Stephen. If God Is in Charge. LC 83-2240. 180p. 1983. pap. 5.95 (ISBN 0-8407-5844-8). Nelson.

--No More Mr. Nice Guy: Saying Goodbye to Doormat Christianity. 224p. 1986. 14.95 (ISBN 0-8407-5539-2). Nelson.

Brown, Stephen, jt. auth. see Masunaga, Shizuto.

Brown, Stephen, jt. ed. see Boehner, Philotheus.

Brown, Stephen F., ed. Guillelmi de Ockham: Scriptum in Librum Primum Sententiarum, Ordinatio, Opera Theologica, Vol. 2, Distinctiones Secunda et Tertia. 1970. 37.00 (ISBN 0-686-11529-5). Franciscan Inst.

Brown, Stewart J. Thomas Chalmers & Godly Commonwealth in Scotland. (Illus.). 1982. 55.00x (ISBN 0-19-213114-1). Oxford U Pr.

Brown, Stuart, ed. Reason & Religion. LC 77-3115. 336p. 1977. pap. 12.95x (ISBN 0-8014-9166-5). Cornell U Pr.

Brown, Stuart G., ed. see Royce, Josiah.

Brown, Theo. The Fate of the Dead: A Study in Folk-Eschatology in the West Country After the Reformation. (Folklore Society Mistletoe Ser.). 118p. 1979. 26.50x (ISBN 0-8476-6214-4). Rowman.

Brown, Thomas. Account of the People Called Shakers. LC 77-17584. Repr. of 1812 ed. 27.00 (ISBN 0-404-08459-1). AMS Pr.

Brown, Thomas K., tr. see Jorns, Auguste.

Brown, Thomas S. The Personal Relevance of Truth. 1983. pap. 2.50x (ISBN 0-87574-081-2, 081). Pendle Hill.

Brown University Dept. of Art Staff. The Survival of the Gods: Classical Mythology in Medieval Art. LC 86-72762. (Illus., Orig.). 1986. pap. text ed. 14.00 (ISBN 0-933519-10-9). D W Bell Gallery.

Brown, Vinson. Tracking the Glorious Lord: Vital Scientific Proofs of the Existence of God. (Paperback Ser.). 96p. (Orig.). 1987. pap. 5.95 (ISBN 0-8022-2519-5). Philos Lib.

--Voices of Earth & Sky. LC 76-41761. (Illus.). 177p. 1976. pap. 6.95 (ISBN 0-87961-060-3). Naturegraph.

Brown, Vinson, et al. Prevent Doomsday! Anti-Nuclear Anthology. new ed. (Illus.). 96p. 1983. pap. 4.95 (ISBN 0-8283-1875-1). Branden Pub Co.

Brown, Virginia P. & Owens, Laurella, eds. Southern Indian Myths & Legends. (Illus.). 160p. 1985. 15.95 (ISBN 0-912221-02-X). Beechwood.

Brown, W. Henry. Charles Kingsley. LC 73-12770. 1924. lib. bdg. 17.50 (ISBN 0-8414-3231-7). Folcroft.

Brown, W. Norman. Man in the Universe: Some Cultural Continuities in Indian Thought. LC 66-12648. (Rabindranath Tagore Memorial Lectures). 1966. 24.00x (ISBN 0-520-00185-0). U of Cal Pr.

Brown, W. S., jt. auth. see Priest, Josiah.

Brown, Walton J. Home at Last. (Discovery Ser.). 96p. pap. 5.95 (ISBN 0-317-01321-1). Review & Herald.

Brown, William A. Christian Theology in Outline. LC 75-41044. (BCL Ser. II). Repr. of 1906 ed. 28.00 (ISBN 0-404-14648-1). AMS Pr.

Brown, William M. Communism & Christianism. 252p. lib. bdg. 24.95 (ISBN 0-88286-046-1); pap. 4.00 (ISBN 0-88286-045-3). C H Kerr.

Brown, William N. The Indian & Christian Miracles of Walking on the Water. LC 78-72381. Repr. of 1928 ed. 16.50 (ISBN 0-404-17243-1). AMS Pr.

Brown, William N., ed. see Sankaracarya.

Brown, Willis M. How I Got Faith. 199p. 2.00 (ISBN 0-686-29117-4). Faith Pub Hse.

Brownback, Paul. Danger of Self-Love. LC 82-12543. 1982. pap. 5.95 (ISBN 0-8024-2068-0). Moody.

Browne. Icons of America. LC 77-84917. 1978. 14.95 (ISBN 0-87972-090-5); pap. 6.95 (ISBN 0-87972-091-3). Bowling Green Univ.

Browne, E. Martin, ed. Religious Drama, Vol. 2: 21 Medieval Mystery & Morality Plays. 17.75 (ISBN 0-8446-2793-3). Peter Smith.

Browne, Edward G., tr. see Abdu'l-Baha.

Browne, G. F. The Venerable Bede: His Life & Writings. LC 76-52505. 1972. Repr. of 1919 ed. lib. bdg. 35.00 (ISBN 0-8414-1652-4). Folcroft.

Browne, Henry J. The Catholic Church & the Knights of Labor. LC 76-6326. (Irish Americans Ser). (Illus.). 1976. Repr. of 1949 ed. 32.00 (ISBN 0-405-09323-3). Ayer Co Pubs.

Browne, Lawrence E. The Eclipse of Christianity in Asia. 1967. Repr. 27.50x (ISBN 0-86527-049-X). Fertig.

Browne, Muriel. Exalt His Name: A Christmas Program. 1984. pap. 0.95 (ISBN 0-8024-3551-3). Moody.

Browne, Peter. Things Divine & Supernatural Conceived by Analogy with Things Natural & Human. Wellek, Rene, ed. LC 75-11203. (British Philosophers & Theologians of the 17th & 18th Centuries: Vol. 9). 1976. Repr. of 1733 ed. lib. bdg. 51.00 (ISBN 0-8240-1758-7). Garland Pub.

Browne, Ray B. Forbidden Fruits: Taboos & Tabooism in Culture. LC 84-71938. 192p. 1984. 21.95 (ISBN 0-317-14769-2); pap. 9.95 (ISBN 0-87972-256-8). Bowling Green Univ.

Browne, Roland A., tr. see Ogier VIII.

Browne, T. & Johnson, Samuel. Christian Morals. 2nd ed. Roberts, S. C., ed. 1927. 20.00 (ISBN 0-527-12200-9). Kraus Repr.

Brownell, Ada N. Confessions of a Pentecostal. LC 77-92887. 112p. 1978. pap. 1.25 (ISBN 0-88243-476-4, 02-0476). Gospel Pub.

Brownell, George B. Reincarnation. 153p. 198[illegible] pap. 9.00 (ISBN 0-89540-107-X, SB-107)[illegible] Pub.

Browneye, Ray. Through African Skies. 136p. 1983. pap. 5.95 (ISBN 0-8010-0853-0). Baker Bk.

Browning, Christopher R. Fateful Months: Essays on the Emergence of the Final Solution, 1941-1942. LC 84-9089. (Illus.). 100p. 1985. text ed. 24.95x (ISBN 0-8419-0967-9). Holmes & Meier.

--The Final Solution & the German Foreign Office. LC 78-8996. 276p. 1978. text ed. 35.00x (ISBN 0-8419-0403-0). Holmes & Meier.

Browning, Don S. The Moral Context of Pastoral Care. LC 76-5858. 144p. 1983. pap. 8.95 (ISBN 0-664-24483-1). Westminster.

--Religious Ethics & Pastoral Care. LC 83-5589. (Theology & Pastoral Care Ser.). 128p. 1983. pap. 7.95 (ISBN 0-8006-1725-8, 1-1725). Fortress.

--Religious Thought & the Modern Psychologies: A Critical Conversation in the Theology of Culture. LC 86-45205. 288p. 1986. 22.50 (ISBN 0-8006-0784-8). Fortress.

Browning, Don S., ed. Practical Theology: The Emerging Field in Theology, Church & World. LC 82-47739. 128p. (Orig.). 1982. pap. 7.95 (ISBN 0-06-061153-7, RD-410, HarpR). Har-Row.

Browning, John & Morton, Richard. Religion in the Eighteenth Century. LC 79-17715. (McMaster University Eighteenth Century Studies). 145p. 1979. lib. bdg. 22.00 (ISBN 0-8240-4005-8). Garland Pub.

Browning, Robert L. & Reed, Roy A. The Sacraments in Religious Education & Liturgy: An Ecumenical Model. LC 84-27536. 313p. (Orig.). 1985. pap. 14.95 (ISBN 0-89135-044-6). Religious Educ.

Browning, William S. The History of the Huguenots During the Sixteenth Century, 2 vols. LC 83-45604. Date not set. Repr. of 1829 ed. Set. 59.50 (ISBN 0-404-19871-6). AMS Pr.

Brownlee, William. Ezekiel: (WBC, Vol. 28. 384p. 1986. 22.95 (ISBN 0-8499-0227-4). Word Bks.

Brownlee, William H. The Midrash Pesher of Habakkuk. LC 76-30560. (Society of Biblical Literature Monograph). 220p. 1979. pap. 9.95 (ISBN 0-89130-147-X, 06 00 24). Scholars Pr GA.

Brownlow, Leroy. Christian's Everyday Problems. 1966. pap. 2.50 (ISBN 0-915720-39-6). Brownlow Pub Co.

--The Fruit of the Spirit. 1982. gift ed. 6.95 (ISBN 0-915720-59-0). Brownlow Pub Co.

--Give Us This Day: A Devotional Guide for Daily Living. 1986. 7.95 (ISBN 0-915720-23-X). Brownlow Pub Co.

--God, the Bible & Common Sense. 1978. pap. 2.50 (ISBN 0-915720-48-5). Brownlow Pub Co.

--Living with the Psalms. 386p. 1976. 7.95 (ISBN 0-915720-17-5). Brownlow Pub Co.

--Thoughts of Gold: Wisdom for Living from the Book of Proverbs. 1974. gift ed. 6.95 (ISBN 0-915720-13-2). Brownlow Pub Co.

--A Time to Laugh - or Grandpa Was a Preacher. 1973. gift ed. 6.95 (ISBN 0-915720-11-6). Brownlow Pub Co.

--Today Is Mine. 1972. gift ed 7.95 (ISBN 0-915720-14-0); leather ed. 12.95 (ISBN 0-915720-57-4). Brownlow Pub Co.

--With the Good Shepherd. 1969. gift ed. 6.95 (ISBN 0-915720-12-4). Brownlow Pub Co.

Brownlow, Paul C., jt. auth. see Baw, Cindy.

Brox, Norbert. Understanding the Message of Paul. Blenkinsopp, Joseph, tr. (Orig.). 1968. pap. 1.45x (ISBN 0-268-00286-X). U of Notre Dame Pr.

Broyles, Craig C. The Conflict of Faith & Experience in the Psalms: A Form-Critical & Theological Study. (JSOT Supplement Ser.: No. 52). 200p. 1986. text ed. 27.50x (ISBN 1-85075-052-1, Pub. by JSOT Pr England); pap. text ed. 19.95x (ISBN 1-85075-053-X, Pub. by JSOT Pr England). Eisenbrauns.

Broyn, Severyn. Quaker Testimonies & Economic Alternatives. LC 80-80915. 35p. pap. 2.50x (ISBN 0-87574-231-9). Pendle Hill.

Brubaber, Zuck & Brubaker, Joanne. Childhood Education in the Church. rev., exp. ed. 1986. text ed. 24.95 (ISBN 0-8024-1251-3). Moody.

Brubaker, Darrel J., jt. ed. see Sider, Ronald J.

Brubaker, J. Lester. Personnel Administration in the Christian School. 168p. (Orig.). 1980. pap. 6.95 (ISBN 0-88469-130-6). BMH Bks.

Brubaker, J. Omar & Clark, Robert E. Understanding People: Children, Youth, Adults. LC 75-172116. 96p. 1981. pap. text ed. 4.95 (ISBN 0-910566-15-1); Perfect bdg. instr's. guide 5.95 (ISBN 0-910566-25-9). Evang Tchr.

Brubaker, Joanne, jt. auth. see Brubaber, Zuck.

Brubaker, Pamela. She Hath Done What She Could. 224p. (Orig.). 1985. pap. 7.95 (ISBN 0-87178-942-6). Brethren.

Bruce, A. B. The Epistle to the Hebrews. 1980. 17.25 (ISBN 0-86524-028-0, 5802). Klock & Klock.

--The Miracles of Christ. 1980. 20.00 (ISBN 0-86524-060-4, 9504). Klock & Klock.

--The Parables of Christ. 1980. 15.50 (ISBN 0-86524-059-0, 9503). Klock & Klock.

Bruce, A. B., jt. auth. see Moulton, Richard G.

Bruce, Alexander B. The Moral Order of the World in Ancient & Modern Thought. LC 77-527224. (Gifford Lectures: 1898). Repr. of 1899 ed. 40.00 (ISBN 0-404-60456-0). AMS Pr.

--The Providential Order of the World. LC 77-27225. (Gifford Lectures: 1897). 1978. Repr. of 1897 ed. 37.50 (ISBN 0-404-60455-2). AMS Pr.

--The Training of the Twelve. LC 79-88121. (Shepherd Illustrated Classics). 1979. pap. 6.95 (ISBN 0-87983-206-1). Keats.

--Training of the Twelve. LC 73-129738. 566p. 1979. 13.95 (ISBN 0-8254-2212-4); pap. 9.95 (ISBN 0-8254-2236-1). Kregel.

Bruce, Calvin E. & Jones, William R., eds. Black Theology II: Essays on the Formation & Outreach of Contemporary Black Theology. LC 75-39113. 285p. 1978. 25.00 (ISBN 0-8387-1893-0). Bucknell U Pr.

Bruce, Carrol. The Commitment Factor. LC 84-5005. 1984. pap. 3.95 (ISBN 0-8054-5541-8). Broadman.

Bruce, Debra F., jt. auth. see Bruce, Robert G.

Bruce, Dickson D., Jr. And They All Sang Hallelujah: Plain-Folk Camp-Meeting Religion, 1800-1845. LC 74-11344. (Illus.). 1974. 13.50x (ISBN 0-87049-157-1); pap. 5.95x (ISBN 0-87049-310-8). U of Tenn Pr.

Bruce, F. F. Acts. 1983. pap. 4.95 (ISBN 0-87508-170-3). Chr Lit.

--Commentary on First & Second Corinthians. Black, Matthew, ed. (New Century Bible Commentary Ser.). 224p. 1980. pap. 8.95 (ISBN 0-8028-1839-0). Eerdmans.

--The Defence of the Gospel in the New Testament. rev. ed. LC 77-2282. 1977. pap. 4.95 (ISBN 0-8028-1024-1). Eerdmans.

--Epistle to the Ephesians. 144p. 1962. 10.95 (ISBN 0-8007-0083-X). Revell.

--The Epistles of John. LC 78-22069. 1978. pap. 5.95 (ISBN 0-8028-1783-1). Eerdmans.

--The Epistles to the Colossians, to Philemon, & to the Ephesians. (New International Commentary on the New Testament Ser.). 464p. 1984. 18.95 (ISBN 0-8028-2401-3). Eerdmans.

--The Gospel of John. 440p. 1984. 13.95 (ISBN 0-8028-3407-8). Eerdmans.

--The Hard Sayings of Jesus. LC 83-10793. (The Jesus Library). 216p. 1983. pap. 7.95 (ISBN 0-87784-927-7). Inter-Varsity.

--History of the Bible in English. 3rd ed. 1978. pap. 8.95 (ISBN 0-19-520088-8). Oxford U Pr.

--Israel y las Naciones. Orig. Title: Israel & the Nations. (Span.). 298p. 1979. 8.95 (ISBN 0-8254-1076-2). Kregel.

--Jesus & Christian Origins Outside the New Testament. 1974. pap. 5.95 (ISBN 0-8028-1575-8). Eerdmans.

--Jesus & Paul: Places They Knew. 128p. 1983. Repr. of 1981 ed. 12.95 (ISBN 0-8407-5281-4). Nelson.

--Jesus: Lord & Savior. Green, Michael, ed. LC 86-7157. (Jesus Library). 228p. 1986. pap. 7.95 (ISBN 0-87784-932-3). Inter-Varsity.

--New Testament History. LC 78-144253. 462p. 1972. pap. 9.95 (ISBN 0-385-02533-5, Anch). Doubleday.

--Paul & His Converts. rev. ed. LC 85-19764. 155p. 1985. pap. 5.95 (ISBN 0-87784-593-X). Inter-Varsity.

--Paul: Apostle of the Heart Set Free. LC 77-26127. 1978. 20.95 (ISBN 0-8028-3501-5). Eerdmans.

--Peter, Stephen, James & John: Studies in Non-Pauline Christianity. (Orig.). 1980. 8.95 (ISBN 0-8028-3532-5). Eerdmans.

--Philippians: A Good News Commentary. LC 82-48919. 176p. (Orig.). 1983. pap. 7.95 (ISBN 0-06-061138-3, RD/446, HarpR). Har-Row.

--Second Thoughts on the Dead Sea Scrolls. 157p. 1986. pap. 7.95 (ISBN 0-85364-017-3, Pub. by Paternoster UK). Attic Pr.

--The Spreading Flame: The Rise & Progress of Christianity from Its Beginnings to the Conversion of the English. 432p. 1980. pap. 14.95 (ISBN 0-8028-1805-6). Eerdmans.

--The Time Is Fulfilled. LC 78-7373. 1978. pap. text ed. 3.95 (ISBN 0-8028-1756-4). Eerdmans.

--What the Bible Teaches about What Jesus Did. 1979. pap. 3.95 (ISBN 0-8423-7885-5). Tyndale.

Bruce, F. F., jt. auth. see Vine, W. E.

Bruce, F. F., ed. International Bible Commentary. rev. ed. 1664p. 1986. text ed. 24.95 (ISBN 0-310-22020-3, 6404). Zondervan.

--Promise & Fulfilment. 216p. 1963. 15.95 (ISBN 0-567-02055-X, Pub. by T & T Clark Ltd UK). Fortress.

Bruce, F. F., ed. see Fee, Gordon D.

Bruce, F. F., ed. see Van Elderen, Bastiaan.

Bruce, Frederick F. The Books & the Parchments. rev. & updated ed. (Illus.). 320p. (Orig.). 13.95 (ISBN 0-8007-1214-5). Revell.

--The Message of the New Testament. 120p. 1973. pap. 4.95 (ISBN 0-8028-1525-1). Eerdmans.

--New Testament Documents: Are They Reliable. pap. 3.95 (ISBN 0-87784-691-X). Inter-Varsity.

Bruce, Frederick F., ed. The Book of the Acts. (New International Commentary on the New Testament). 1954. 16.95 (ISBN 0-8028-2182-0). Eerdmans.

--The Epistle to the Hebrews. (New International Commentary on the New Testament Ser.). 1964. 19.95 (ISBN 0-8028-2183-9). Eerdmans.

--Israel & the Nations. LC 63-22838. 1963. pap. 7.95 (ISBN 0-8028-1450-6). Eerdmans.

--New Testament Development of Old Testament Themes. 1969. pap. 6.95 (ISBN 0-8028-1729-7). Eerdmans.

--New Testament Documents: Are They Reliable? (Orig.). 1959. pap. 2.95 (ISBN 0-8028-1025-X). Eerdmans.

Bruce, Gustav M. Luther As an Educator. LC 77-114482. (Illus.). 318p. Repr. of 1928 ed. lib. bdg. 35.00x (ISBN 0-8371-4771-9, BRLD). Greenwood.

Bruce, John, ed. see Borough, John.

Bruce, Robert G. & Bruce, Debra F. C.A.R.E.S. 1984. 5.50 (ISBN 0-89536-672-X, 0393). CSS of Ohio.

Bruce, S. No Pope of Rome: Militant Protestantism in Modern Scotland. 270p. 1985. text ed. 35.00x (ISBN 0-906391-78-4, Pub. by Mainstream Pubs UK). Humanities.

Bruce, Shelley. Tomorrow Is Today. LC 83-3797. (Illus.). 224p. 1983. 15.95 (ISBN 0-672-52756-1). Bobbs.

Bruce, W. S. The Ethics of the Old Testament. 1909. 17.95 (ISBN 0-567-02058-4, Pub. by T & T Clark Ltd UK). Fortress.

Bruchez, Dardo. Mensaje a la Conciencia. (Span.). 128p. (Orig.). 1979. pap. 3.50 (ISBN 0-89922-143-2). Edit Caribe.

Bruchez, Dardo, tr. see Tozer, A. W.

Bruck, Maria, ed. More Children's Liturgies. LC 81-80877. 256p. (Orig.). 1981. pap. 9.95 (ISBN 0-8091-2362-2). Paulist Pr.

Bruck, Michael von see Schneider, D. Douglas.

Bruckberger, R. L. God & Politics. LC 78-190754. (Howard Greenfield Bk.). 1971. 9.95 (ISBN 0-87955-302-2). O'Hara.

Brueggeman, Walter, ed. see Westermann, Claus.

Brueggemann, Walter. Advent-Christmas: Series B. LC 84-6020. (Proclamation 3: Aids for Interpreting the Lessons of the Church Year Ser.). 64p. 1984. pap. 3.75 (ISBN 0-8006-4101-9). Fortress.

--The Bible Makes Sense. LC 76-29883. (Biblical Foundation Ser.). 1977. pap. 7.95 (ISBN 0-8042-0063-7). John Knox.

--The Bible Makes Sense. LC 76-29883. 1977. pap. 6.95 (ISBN 0-88489-087-2). St Mary's.

--The Creative Word: Canon as a Model for Biblical Education. LC 81-71387. 176p. 1982. pap. 9.95 (ISBN 0-8006-1626-X, 1-1626). Fortress.

--David's Truth: In Israel's Imagination & Memory. LC 85-47717. 128p. 1985. pap. 5.95 (ISBN 0-8006-1865-3). Fortress.

--Genesis. LC 81-82355. (Interpretation: the Bible Commentary for Teaching & Preaching). 432p. 1982. 23.95 (ISBN 0-8042-3101-X). John Knox.

--Hope Within History. LC 86-45353. 144p. (Orig.). 1986. pap. 8.95 (ISBN 0-8042-0918-9). John Knox.

--Hopeful Imagination: Prophectic Voices in Exile. LC 86-45207. 160p. 1986. pap. 7.95 (ISBN 0-8006-1925-0). Fortress.

--In Man We Trust: The Neglected Side of Biblical Faith. LC 72-1761. 144p. 1984. pap. 7.95 (ISBN 0-8042-0198-6). John Knox.

--Kings I. (Knox Preaching Guide Ser.). 132p. 1983. pap. 4.95 (ISBN 0-8042-3212-1). John Knox.

--Kings II. Hayes, John, ed. LC 82-48094. (Knox Preaching Guide Ser.). 120p. 1983. pap. 4.95 (ISBN 0-8042-3214-8). John Knox.

--The Land: Place As Gift, Promise & Challenge in Biblical Faith. Donahue, John R., ed. LC 76-15883. (Overtures to Biblical Theology Ser.: No. 1). 228p. 1977. pap. 8.95 (ISBN 0-8006-1526-3, 1-1526). Fortress.

--Living Toward a Vision: Biblical Reflections on Shalom. rev. ed. LC 76-22172. (Shalom Resource Ser.). 1982. pap. 6.95 (ISBN 0-8298-0613-X). Pilgrim NY.

--The Message of the Psalms: A Theological Commentary. LC 84-21734. (Augsburg Old Testament Studies). 224p. (Orig.). 1984. pap. 11.95 (ISBN 0-8066-2120-6, 10-4370). Augsburg.

--Praying the Psalms. LC 81-86045. (Illus.). 90p. (Orig.). 1982. pap. 6.95 (ISBN 0-88489-143-7). St Mary's.

--The Prophetic Imagination. LC 78-54546. 128p. 1978. pap. 5.95 (ISBN 0-8006-1337-6, 1-1337). Fortress.

--Revelation & Violence: A Study in Contextualization. LC 86-60473. (Pere Marquette Ser.). 72p. 1986. 7.95 (ISBN 0-87462-541-6). Marquette.

Brueggemann, Walter & Wolff, Hans W. The Vitality Old Testament Traditions. 2nd ed. LC 82-7141. pap. 7.95 (ISBN 0-8042-0112-9). John Knox.

Brueggemann, Walter, ed. see Bailey, Lloyd R., Sr.

Brueggemann, Walter, ed. see Fretheim, Terence E.

Brueggemann, Walter, ed. see Hamerton-Kelly, Robert.

Brueggemann, Walter, ed. see Harrelson, Walter.

Brueggemann, Walter, ed. see Harrington, Daniel J.

Brueggemann, Walter, ed. see Johnson, Luke T.

Brueggemann, Walter, ed. see Zimmerli, Walther.

Brueggemann, Walter, tr. see Klein, Ralph W.

Brueggemann, Walter, et al. To Act Justly, Love Tenderly, Walk Humbly: An Agenda for Ministers. 88p. 1986. pap. 3.95 (ISBN 0-8091-2760-1). Paulist Pr.

Bruehl, Charles P. The Pope's Plan for Social Reconstruction. 10.00 (ISBN 0-8159-6507-9). Devin.

Brug, John F. A Study Guide for Ezra, Nehemiah, Esther. (Study Guide for People's Bible Ser.). 60p. (Orig.). 1985. pap. 1.50 (ISBN 0-938272-53-5). Wels Board.

Brugge, David M. Navajos in the Catholic Church Records of New Mexico 1694-1875. LC 84-60510. 1986. 12.50x (ISBN 0-912586-59-1). Navajo Coll Pr.

Bruinsma, Sheryl. Easy-to-Use Object Lessons. (Object Lesson Ser.). 96p. (Orig.). 1983. pap. 3.95 (ISBN 0-8010-0832-8). Baker Bk.

--New Object Lessons for Children of All Ages. (Object Lesson Ser.). 1980. pap. 4.95 (ISBN 0-8010-0775-5). Baker Bk.

--Object Lessons for Special Days. 80p. 1986. 4.50 (ISBN 0-8010-0920-0). Baker Bk.

Bruland, Esther B. & Mott, Stephen C. A Passion for Jesus: A Passion for Justice. 176p. 1983. pap. 9.95 (ISBN 0-8170-0994-9). Judson.

Brumback, Carl. God in Three Persons. 192p. 1959. pap. 4.95 (ISBN 0-87148-354-8). Pathway Pr.

--Like a River. LC 76-58782. (Illus.). 176p. 1977. pap. 2.95 (ISBN 0-88243-564-7, 02-0564). Gospel Pub.

--What Meaneth This? a Pentecostal Answer to a Pentecostal Question. 352p. 1947. pap. 4.95 (ISBN 0-88243-626-0, 02-0624). Gospel Pub.

Brumbaugh, Martin G. A History of the German Baptist Brethren in Europe & America. LC 73-134377. (Communal Societies in America Ser.). (Illus.). Repr. of 1899 ed. 37.50 (ISBN 0-404-08425-7). AMS Pr.

Brumbaugh, Robert S. The Philosophers of Greece. LC 81-9120. (Illus.). 274p. 1981. 34.50x (ISBN 0-87395-550-1); pap. 8.95x (ISBN 0-87395-551-X). State U NY Pr.

Brumbaugh, Thoburn T. My Marks & Scars I Carry: The Story of Ernst Kisch. (Bold Believers Ser.). 1969. pap. 0.95 (ISBN 0-377-84151-X). Friend Pr.

Brumberg, Stephan F. Going to America Going to School: The Jewish Immigrant Public School Encounter in Turn-of-the-Century New York City. LC 85-16791. 300p. 1986. 29.95 (ISBN 0-03-062574-2, C2030). Praeger.

Brumfield, Allaire C. The Attic Festivals of Demeter & Their Relation to the Agricultural Year. Connor, W. R., ed. LC 80-2643. (Monographs in Classical Studies). 1981. lib. bdg. 29.00 (ISBN 0-405-14031-2). Ayer Co Pubs.

Brumfield, J. C. Comfort for Troubled Christians. (Moody Acorn Ser.). 1975. pap. 7.95 package of 10 (ISBN 0-8024-1400-1). Moody.

Brummel, George H. Bible Medicine with Healing Verses. LC 83-91263. 172p. (Orig.). 1984. pap. 9.95 (ISBN 0-9613041-0-3). G Brummel Pub.

Brummelen, Harro W. Van see Van Brummelen, Harro W.

Brummer, Vincent. Theology & Philosophical Inquiry: An Introduction. LC 81-11557. 320p. (Orig.). 1982. pap. 16.95 (ISBN 0-664-24398-3). Westminster.

Brundage, Burr C. The Fifth Sun: Aztec Gods, Aztec World. (Texas Pan American Ser.). (Illus.). 283p. 1979. pap. 8.95 (ISBN 0-292-72438-1). U of Tex Pr.

--The Phoenix of the Western World: Quetzalcoatl & the Sky Religion. LC 81-40278. (The Civilization of the American Indian Ser.: Vol. 160). (Illus.). 320p. 1982. 22.50x (ISBN 0-8061-1773-7). U of Okla Pr.

Brundage, James, jt. ed. see Bullough, Vern.

Bruneau, Thomas C. The Political Transformation of the Brazilian Catholic Church. LC 73-79318. (Perspective on Development Ser.: Vol. 2). pap. 71.00 (ISBN 0-317-28009-0, 2025579). Bks Demand UMI.

Bruneau, Thomas E. The Church in Brazil: The Politics of Religion. LC 81-16391. (University of Texas at Austin, Institute of Latin American Studies-Latin American Monographs: No. 56). pap. 63.30 (2026564). Bks Demand UMI.

Brunelle, Jim, ed. Over to Home & From Away. (Illus.). 340p. (Orig.). 1980. pap. 9.95 (ISBN 0-930096-11-8). G Gannett.

Bruner, Dale. Commentary on Matthew (One) 500p. 1987. 24.95 (ISBN 0-8499-0526-5). Word Bks.

Bruner, Frederick D. Theology of the Holy Spirit. LC 76-103445. 1970. pap. 9.95 (ISBN 0-8028-1547-2). Eerdmans.

Bruner, Frederick D. & Hordern, William E. The Holy Spirit-Shy Member of the Trinity. LC 83-72124. 112p. (Orig.). 1984. pap. 5.95 (ISBN 0-8066-2068-4, 10-3070). Augsburg.

Bruner, Jerome S. The Relevance of Education. LC 74-139376. 192p. 1971. 5.95x (ISBN 0-393-04334-7, Norton Lib.); pap. 4.95x (ISBN 0-393-00690-5, Norton Lib). Norton.

Bruner, William T. The Sex Problem: Its Cause, Its Curse & Its Cure. 1977. 3.00 (ISBN 0-9606566-0-X). Bruner.

--The Truth about Sin: What Does the Bible Say? 1977. 2.00 (ISBN 0-9606566-1-8). Bruner.

Brunet, G. Dictionnaire des Apocryphes, 2 vols. Migne, J. P., ed. (Troisieme et Derniere Encyclopedie Theologique Ser.: Vols. 23-24). (Fr.). 1310p. Repr. of 1858 ed. lib. bdg. 167.50x (ISBN 0-89241-305-0). Caratzas.

Brungardt, Helen. The Mystical Meaning of Jesus the Christ: Significant Episodes in the Life of the Master. 2nd ed. (Illus.). 64p. 1983. pap. 5.00 (ISBN 0-941992-03-9). Los Arboles Pub.

Brunk, George R., ed. Encounter with the Holy Spirit. LC 72-2053. 240p. 1972. pap. 5.95 (ISBN 0-8361-1693-3). Herald Pr.

Brunk, J. D., ed. Church & Sunday School Hymnal with Supplement. LC 72-2053. 384p. (532 hymns & songs, & 50 german songs, words only, 1902; supplement 1911). 1902. 7.95x (ISBN 0-8361-1110-9). Herald Pr.

Brunke, Ottillie S. Chapter Ceremonies & Poems. 60p. pap. text ed. 2.50 (ISBN 0-88053-305-6, S-192). Macoy Pub.

Brunkow, Robert de V., ed. Religion & Society in North America: An Annotated Bibliography. LC 82-24304. (Clio Bibliography Ser.: No. 12). 515p. 1983. lib. bdg. 68.25 (ISBN 0-87436-042-0). ABC-Clio.

Brunn, Emilie Z. St. Augustine: Being & Nothingness in the Dialogs & Confessions. 210p. 1987. 21.95 (ISBN 0-913729-17-5). Paragon Hse.

Brunner, August. New Creation: Towards a Theology of the Christian Life. 143p. 1956. 10.00 (ISBN 0-8022-0189-X). Philos Lib.

Brunner, Emil. The Christian Doctrine of Creation & Redemption. Wyon, Olive, tr. LC 50-6821. (Dogmatic Ser.: Vol. 2). 396p. 1979. pap. 10.95 (ISBN 0-664-24248-0). Westminster.

--The Christian Doctrine of God. Wyon, Olive, tr. LC 50-6821. (Dogmatics Ser.: Vol. 1). 376p. 1980. pap. 11.95 (ISBN 0-664-24304-5). Westminster.

--The Christian Doctrine of the Church, Faith, & the Consummation. LC 50-6821. (Dogmatic Ser., Vol. 3). 472p. 1978. softcover o.s.i. 9.95 (ISBN 0-664-24218-9). Westminster.

--The Divine-Human Encounter. Loos, Amandus W., tr. from Ger. 207p. 1980. Repr. of 1943 ed. lib. bdg. 24.75x (ISBN 0-313-22398-X, BRDH). Greenwood.

--The Divine Imperative. LC 47-2443. 728p. 1979. softcover 9.95 (ISBN 0-664-24246-4). Westminster.

--Man in Revolt: A Christian Anthropology. Wyon, Olive, tr. LC 47-2442. 564p. 1979. softcover 9.95 (ISBN 0-664-24245-6). Westminster.

--Our Faith. 1936. pap. text ed. 7.95 (ISBN 0-684-16856-1, SL87, ScribT). Scribner.

--Our Faith. 153p. 1980. pap. text ed. write for info. (ISBN 0-02-315940-5, Pub. by Scribner). Macmillan.

--Revelation & Reason. 448p. 1984. pap. 14.95 (ISBN 0-913029-01-7). Stevens Bk Pr.

--Scandal of Christianity: The Gospel as Stumbling Block to Modern Man. LC 65-12729. 1965. pap. 5.95 (ISBN 0-8042-0708-9). John Knox.

Brunner, Francis A., tr. see Fellerer, Karl G.

Brunner, Francis A., tr. see Jungmann, Josef A.

Brunner, Francis A., tr. see Jungmann, Joseph A.

Brunner, Heinrich E. Christianity & Civilisation, 2 vols. in one. LC 77-27182. (Gifford Lectures: 1947-48). Repr. of 1949 ed. 35.00 (ISBN 0-404-60530-3). AMS Pr.

--Eternal Hope. Knight, Harold, tr. LC 72-6930. 232p. 1973. Repr. of 1954 ed. lib. bdg. 22.50x (ISBN 0-8371-6508-3, BREH). Greenwood.

--The Philosophy of Religion from the Standpoint of Protestant Theology. LC 78-14106. 1979. Repr. of 1937 ed. 20.35 (ISBN 0-88355-779-7). Hyperion Conn.

Bruno, Giordano. The Ash Wednesday Supper. Jaki, Stanley L., tr. Tr. of La Cena de Le Ceneri. (Illus.). 174p. 1975. text ed. 19.60x (ISBN 90-2797-581-7). Mouton.

Bruno, Soeur & Osb, Barrier. Les Activities Du Solitaire En Chartreuse D'Apres Plus Anciens Temoins. (Analecta Cartusiana: No. 87). 159p. 1981. pap. 25.00 (ISBN 3-7052-0144-1, Pub. by Salzburg Studies). Longwood Pub Group.

Brunsman, Barry. New Hope for Divorced Catholics: A Concerned Pastor Offers Alternatives to Annulment. LC 85-42770. 128p. 1986. 12.95 (ISBN 0-06-061147-2, HarpR). Har-Row.

Brunson, Madelon. Dying, Death & Grief. 1978. pap. 4.50 (ISBN 0-8309-0223-6). Herald Hse.

Brunt, John C. Promise & Present: Adventist Eschatology & Ethics. Coffen, Richard W., ed. 96p. 1987. pap. 5.95 (ISBN 0-8280-0386-6). Review & Herald.

Brunton, Paul. Discover Yourself. rev ed. LC 83-60832. 244p. 1983. pap. 7.95 (ISBN 0-87728-592-6). Weiser.

--Hidden Teaching Beyond Yoga. rev. ed. LC 83-60830. 366p. (Orig.). 1984. pap. 8.95 (ISBN 0-87728-590-X). Weiser.

--The Notebooks of Paul Brunton, Vol. 3: Part 1, Practices for the Quest; Part 2, Relax & Retreat. Cash, Paul & Smith, Timothy, eds. LC 86-81030. 392p. 1986. smyth-sewn bdg, acid-free 22.50 (ISBN 0-943914-15-9, Dist. by Kampmann & Co); pap. 12.50 smyth-sewn bdg, acid free (ISBN 0-943914-16-7, Dist. by Kampmann & Co). Larson Pubns Inc.

--The Notebooks of Paul Brunton, Vol. 4: Pt. 1 - Meditation; Pt. 2 - The Body. Cash, Paul & Smith, Timothy, eds. LC 86-81949. 432p. 1986. smyth-sewn bdg, acid free 22.50 (ISBN 0-943914-18-3, Dist. by Kampmann & Co); Pt. 1: Meditation. pap. 10.95 smyth-sewn bdg (ISBN 0-943914-19-1, Dist. by Kampmann & Co); Pt. 2: The Body. pap. 9.95 smyth-sewn bdg (ISBN 0-943914-20-5, Dist. by Kampmann & Co). Larson Pubns Inc.

--The Notebooks of Paul Brunton, Vol. 7: Healing of the Self; the Negatives, 2 pts. Cash, Paul & Smith, Timothy, eds. (Illus.). 320p. 1987. 22.50 (ISBN 0-943914-26-4, Dist. by Kampmann & Co.); pap. 12.50 (ISBN 0-943914-27-2, Dist. by Kampmann & Co.). Larson Pubns Inc.

--The Notebooks of Paul Brunton, Vol. 8: Reflections on My Life & Writings. Smith, Timothy, ed. (Illus.). 224p. 1987. 22.50 (ISBN 0-943914-28-0); pap. 12.50 (ISBN 0-943914-29-9). Larson Pubns Inc.

--Spiritual Crisis of Man. rev ed. LC 83-60829. 224p. 1984. pap. 7.95 (ISBN 0-87728-593-4). Weiser.

Bruntz, Nelle L. Contemporary Psalms. (Illus.). 64p. 1984. 4.50 (ISBN 0-938462-13-X). Green Leaf Ca.

Brush, Craig B., tr. see Gassendi, Pierre.

Brusius, Ron & Noettl, Margaret. Family Evening Activity Devotions. pap. 4.95 (ISBN 0-570-03803-0, 12-2912). Concordia.

Bruso, Dick. Bible Promises, Help & Hope for Your Finances. 156p. (Orig.). 1985. pap. 2.95 (ISBN 0-89840-075-9). Heres Life.

Brusselmans, C., ed. Jesus Loves Children. 5.95 (ISBN 0-8215-9889-9). Sadlier.

Brusselmans, Christiane & Wakin, Edward. Religion for Little Children: A Parent's Guide. LC 76-140110. 1977. pap. 6.95 (ISBN 0-87973-825-1). Our Sunday Visitor.

Bruster, Bill G. & Dale, Robert D. How to Encourage Others. LC 82-70868. (Orig.). 1983. pap. 6.95 (ISBN 0-8054-2247-1). Broadman.

Bruteau, Beatrice. Evolution Toward Divinity. LC 73-16198. 260p. 1974. 10.00 (ISBN 0-8356-0216-8). Theos Pub Hse.

Bruzelius, Caroline A. The Thirteenth-Century Church at St. Denis. LC 85-3354. 256p. 1986. 30.00 (ISBN 0-300-03190-4). Yale U Pr.

Bryan, Ashley. I'm Going to Sing: Black American Spirituals, Vol. II. (Illus.). 64p. 1982. 10.95 (ISBN 0-689-30915-5, Childrens Bk). Macmillan.

--Walk Together Children. (Illus.). 1981. pap. 2.95 (ISBN 0-689-70485-2, Aladdin). Macmillan.

Bryan, G. McLeod. Dissenter in the Baptist Southland: Fifty Years in the Career of William Wallace Finlator. (Illus.). xi, 198p. 1985. 17.95 (ISBN 0-86554-176-0, MUP-H166). Mercer Univ Pr.

Bryan, G. McLeod, et al. Documents Concerning Baptism & Church Membership: A Controversy Among North Carolina Baptists. LC 76-45687. (Special Studies Ser.: No. 1). vii, 81p. 1977. pap. 2.00 (ISBN 0-932180-00-0). NABPR.

Bryan, Lydia, ed. see Sandifer, Kevin.

Bryan, McLeod G., ed. see Moltmann, Jurgen, et al.

Bryan, William J. In His Image. facsimile ed. LC 73-156618. (Essay Index Reprint Ser). Repr. of 1922 ed. 18.00 (ISBN 0-8369-2270-0). Ayer Co Pubs.

Bryans, J. Lonsdale. The Curve of Fate: From Man-Ape to the Man-God. 1977. lib. bdg. 59.95 (ISBN 0-8490-1696-7). Gordon Pr.

Bryant, Al. Love Songs: Daily Meditations for Married Couples. 8.95 (ISBN 0-8499-3036-7). Word Bks.

--A Pocket Treasury of Daily Devotions. LC 77-82183. 112p. 1978. pap. 3.50 (ISBN 0-87123-464-5, 200464). Bethany Hse.

--Time Out. pap. 2.95 (ISBN 0-310-22122-6). Zondervan.

Bryant, Al, ed. New Every Morning: Three Hundred Sixty-Six Daily Meditations from Your Favorite Christian Writers. 224p. 1985. 9.95 (ISBN 0-8499-0507-9, 0507-9). Word Bks.

Bryant, Al, compiled by. A Pocket Treasury of Devotional Verse. 160p. (Orig.). 1980. pap. 3.50 (ISBN 0-87123-466-1, 200466). Bethany Hse.

Bryant, Charles. Rediscovering the Charismata: Building up the Body of Christ Through Spiritual Gifts. 192p. 1986. 11.95 (ISBN 0-8499-0539-7). Word Bks.

Bryant, Christopher. The Heart in Pilgrimage: Christian Guidelines for the Human Journey. 208p. 1980. 9.95 (ISBN 0-8164-0457-7, HarpR). Har-Row.

--Jung & the Christian Way. 144p. (Orig.). 1984. pap. 7.95 (ISBN 0-86683-872-4, 7917, HarpR). Har-Row.

--The River Within: The Search for God in Depth. 160p. 1983. pap. 5.50 (ISBN 0-8358-0468-2). Upper Room.

Bryant, Darrol, ed. Proceedings of the Virgin Islands' Seminar on Unification Theology. LC 80-52594. (Conference Ser.: No. 6). (Illus.). xv, 323p. (Orig.). 1980. pap. text ed. 9.95 (ISBN 0-932894-06-2). Unif Theol Sem.

--Unification Theology Seminar, Virgin Islands: Proceedings. LC 80-52594. 323p. 1980. pap. 9.95. Rose Sharon Pr.

Bryant, Darrol & Foster, Durwood, eds. Hermeneutics & Unification Theology. LC 80-66201. (Conference Ser.: No. 5). (Illus.). 154p. (Orig.). 1980. pap. 7.95 (ISBN 0-932894-05-4, Pub. by New Era Bks). Paragon Hse.

--Hermeneutics & Unification Theology. LC 80-66201. 154p. (Orig.). 1980. pap. 7.95. Rose Sharon Pr.

Bryant, Darrol & Hodges, Susan, eds. Exploring Unification Theology. LC 78-63274. 168p. (Orig.). 1978. pap. 7.95. Rose Sharon Pr.

Bryant, Darrol, jt. ed. see Sontag, Frederick.

Bryant, David. In the Gap: What It Means to Be a World Christian. LC 84-4880. 280p. 1984. pap. 7.95 (ISBN 0-8307-0952-5, 5418217). Regal.

--With Concerts of Prayer. LC 84-17916. 1985. pap. 6.95 (ISBN 0-8307-0975-4, 5418295). Regal.

Bryant, J. A., Jr. Hippolyta's View: Some Christian Aspects of Shakespeare's Plays. LC 61-6555. 256p. 1961. 24.00x (ISBN 0-8131-1057-2). U Pr of Ky.

Bryant, Jacob. A New System, or, an Analysis of Ancient Mythology, 3 vols. Feldman, Burton & Richardson, Robert, eds. LC 78-60881. (Myth & Romanticism Ser.: Vol. 5). (Illus.). 1979. Set. lib. bdg. 240.00 (ISBN 0-8240-3554-2). Garland Pub.

Bryant, Kenneth E. Poems to the Child-God: Structures & Strategies in the Poetry of Surdas. LC 77-80467. (Center for South & Southeast Asia Studies, UC Berkeley). 1978. 33.00x (ISBN 0-520-03540-2). U of Cal Pr.

Bryant, M. D., ed. The Future of Anglican Theology. LC 84-8983. (Toronto Studies in Theology: Vol. 17). 208p. 1984. 49.95x (ISBN 0-88946-763-3). E Mellen.

Bryant, M. Darrol & Huessy, Hans R. Eugen Rosenstock-Huessy: Studies in His Life & Thought. LC 86-28469. (Toronto Studies in Theology: Vol. 28). 280p. 1987. text ed. 49.95x (ISBN 0-88946-772-2). E Mellen.

Bryant, M. Darrol & Richardson, Herbert W. A Time for Consideration: A Scholarly Appraisal of the Unification Church. 2nd ed. LC 78-61364. (Symposium Ser.: Vol. 3). xi, 332p. 1978. 19.95x (ISBN 0-88946-954-7). E Mellen.

Bryant, M. Darrol & Dayton, Donald W., eds. Coming Kingdom: Essays in American Millennialism & Eschatology. LC 83-82211. xii, 258p. 1984. text ed. 15.95 o. p. (ISBN 0-913757-01-2, Pub. by New Era Bks); pap. text ed. 11.95 (ISBN 0-913757-00-4, Pub. by New Era Bks). Paragon Hse.

Bryant, M. Darrol & Hodges, Susan, eds. Exploring Unification Theology. 2nd ed. LC 78-63274. (Conference Ser.: No. 1). 168p. 1978. pap. text ed. 7.95x (ISBN 0-932894-00-3, Pub. by New Era Bks). Paragon Hse.

Bryant, M. Darrol & Matarágnon, Rita H., eds. The Many Faces of Religion & Society. LC 84-26539. (God Ser.). 208p. (Orig.). 1985. 21.95 (ISBN 0-913757-20-9, Pub. by New Era Bks.); pap. 12.95 (ISBN 0-913757-21-7, Pub. by New Era Bks). Paragon Hse.

Bryant, M. Darrol, jt. ed. see Hodges, Susan.

Bryant, M. Darrol, jt. ed. see Sontag, Frederick.

Bryant, Margaret M. Proverbs & How to Collect Them. (Publications of the American Dialect Society: No. 4). 25p. 1945. pap. 2.35 (ISBN 0-8173-0604-8). U of Ala Pr.

Bryant, Nigel, tr. see De Troyes, Chretien.

Bryant, T. A. New Compact Bible Dictionary. 1967. 9.95 (ISBN 0-310-22080-7, 6726P); pap. 5.95 (ISBN 0-310-22082-3). Zondervan.

Bryant, T. A., compiled by. Today's Dictionary of the Bible. LC 82-12980. 678p. (Orig.). 1982. 15.95 (ISBN 0-87123-569-2, 230569). Bethany Hse.

Bryce, Glendon E. A Legacy of Wisdom: The Egyptian Contribution to the Wisdom of Israel. LC 74-4984. 336p. 1979. 24.50 (ISBN 0-8387-1576-1). Bucknell U Pr.

Bryce, James. The Holy Roman Empire. 1978. Repr. of 1911 ed. lib. bdg. 65.00 (ISBN 0-8495-0333-7). Arden Lib.

--The Holy Roman Empire. 1911. 47.50 (ISBN 0-8482-7383-4). Norwood Edns.

Bryce, James B. The Holy Roman Empire. new enl. rev. ed. LC 75-41045. (BCL Ser. II). Repr. of 1913 ed. 28.50 (ISBN 0-404-14516-7). AMS Pr.

Bryce, Mary C. Place of Pride: The Role of the Bishops in the Development of Catechesis in the United States. LC 84-17065. 227p. 1985. 25.95x (ISBN 0-8132-0595-6). Cath U Pr.

Bryden, W. W. The Christian's Knowledge of God. 278p. 1960. 6.95 (ISBN 0-227-67434-0). Attic Pr.

Bryditzki, Victor V. The Selling of Jesus. (Illus.). 128p. (Orig.). 1985. pap. 3.95 (ISBN 0-937958-22-0). Chick Pubns.

Brym, Robert J., jt. auth. see Zaslavsky, Victor.

Brymer, Harvey P. The Most Memorable Passages of the New Testament Fully & Dramatically Illustrated. (Promotion of the Arts Library). (Illus.). 141p. 1982. 69.85 (ISBN 0-86650-039-1). Gloucester Art.

Brynteson, Donna, jt. auth. see Brynteson, Paul.

Brynteson, Paul & Brynteson, Donna. Fitness & Faith. 224p. 1985. pap. 7.95 (ISBN 0-8407-5920-7). Nelson.

Bryson, Conrey. Winter Quarters. LC 86-2146. (Illus.). 191p. 1986. 9.95 (ISBN 0-87579-011-9). Deseret Bk.

Bryson, Harold, jt. auth. see Leavell, Landrum P.

Bryson, Harold T. How Faith Works. LC 84-17601. 1985. pap. 5.95 (ISBN 0-8054-1394-4). Broadman.

--Increasing the Joy: Studies in I John. LC 81-67200. 1982. pap. 5.95 (ISBN 0-8054-1390-1). Broadman.

--The Reality of Hell & the Goodness of God. LC 83-51674. 192p. 1984. pap. 4.95 (ISBN 0-8423-5279-1). Tyndale.

Bryson, Harold T. & Taylor, James C. Building Sermons to Meet People's Needs. LC 78-74962. 1980. 7.95 (ISBN 0-8054-2109-2). Broadman.

Brzezinski, Zbigniew & Kupperman, Robert H. The International Implications of the Papal Assassination Attempt: A Case of State-Sponsored Terrorism. (Significant Issues Ser.: Vol. VI, No. 20). 23p. 1984. 12.95 (ISBN 0-89206-073-5). CSI Studies.

Buback, Kenneth A. & Grant, Mary K., eds. Quality of Work Life: Health Care Applications. LC 82-12766. 300p. 1985. pap. 24.00 (ISBN 0-87125-074-8). Cath Health.

Bubacz, Bruce. St. Augustine's Theory of Knowledge: A Contemporary Analysis. LC 81-18754. (Texts & Studies in Religion: Vol. 11). 248p. 1982. 39.95x (ISBN 0-88946-959-8). E Mellen.

Bubeck, Mark I. The Adversary. 1975. pap. 5.95 (ISBN 0-8024-0143-0). Moody.

--Overcoming the Adversary. 1984. pap. 5.95 (ISBN 0-8024-0333-6). Moody.

Buber, Martin. Between Man & Man. 15.25 (ISBN 0-8446-6207-0). Peter Smith.

--Eclipse of God: Studies in the Relation Between Religion & Philosophy. 1979. pap. text ed. 7.95x (ISBN 0-391-00902-8). Humanities.

--Ecstatic Confessions: The Heart of Mysticism. Mendes-Flor, Paul, ed. LC 84-48212. 224p. 1985. 16.45 (ISBN 0-06-061154-5, HarpR). Har-Row.

--For the Sake of Heaven. Lewisohn, Ludwig, tr. LC 77-97311. Repr. of 1953 ed. lib. bdg. 60.50x (ISBN 0-8371-2592-8, BUSH). Greenwood.

--For the Sake of Heaven: A Chronicle. Lewisohn, Ludwig, tr. LC 58-8531. (Temple Bks.). 1969. pap. 9.95 (ISBN 0-689-70026-1, T2). Atheneum.

--Good & Evil. 185p. pap. text ed. 7.95 (ISBN 0-684-16990-8). Scribner.

--Good & Evil. 1984. 19.75 (ISBN 0-8446-6121-X). Peter Smith.

--Good & Evil. 143p. 1980. pap. text ed. write for info. (ISBN 0-02-316280-5, Pub. by Scribner). Macmillan.

--Good & Evil: Two Interpretations. 1953. pap. 3.95 (ISBN 0-684-71723-9, SL45, ScribT). Scribner.

--Hasidism & Modern Man. LC 58-10225. 256p. 1972. pap. 5.95 (ISBN 0-8180-1326-5). Horizon.

--I & Thou. 13.50 (ISBN 0-8446-6219-4). Peter Smith.

--Israel & the World: Essays in a Time of Crisis. LC 48-9322. 1963. pap. 6.50 (ISBN 0-8052-0066-5). Schocken.

--The Legend of the Baal-Shem. LC 76-86849. 1969. pap. 7.95 (ISBN 0-8052-0233-1). Schocken.

--Mamre, Essays in Religion. Hort, Greta, tr. LC 72-97271. Repr. of 1946 ed. lib. bdg. 15.00x (ISBN 0-8371-2591-X, BUMA). Greenwood.

--Meetings. Friedman, Maurice, ed. & tr. from Ger. LC 73-82780. 123p. 1973. 9.95 (ISBN 0-87548-085-3). Open Court.

--On Judaism. Glatzer, Nahum, ed. LC 67-28091. 256p. 1972. pap. 7.50 (ISBN 0-8052-0343-5). Schocken.

--On the Bible: Eighteen Studies. Glatzer, Nahum N., ed. LC 81-16555. 288p. 1982. 17.95x (ISBN 0-8052-3796-8); pap. 7.95 (ISBN 0-8052-0691-4). Schocken.

--The Origin & Meaning of Hasidism. LC 60-8161. 256p. 1972. pap. 5.95 (ISBN 0-8180-1315-X). Horizon.

--The Prophetic Faith. 15.75 (ISBN 0-8446-6206-2). Peter Smith.

--The Tales of Rabbi Nachman. LC 56-12330. 214p. 1972. 5.95 (ISBN 0-8180-1325-7). Horizon.

--Tales of the Hasidim, 2 vols. Incl. The Early Masters. pap. 6.95 (ISBN 0-8052-0001-0); The Later Masters. pap. 5.95 (ISBN 0-8052-0002-9). LC 47-2952. 1961. pap. Schocken.

--Ten Rungs: Hasidic Sayings. LC 62-13135. 1962. pap. 3.95 (ISBN 0-8052-0018-5). Schocken.

--To Hallow This Life: An Anthology. Trapp, Jacob, ed. LC 73-11862. 174p. 1974. Repr. of 1958 ed. lib. bdg. 22.50x (ISBN 0-8371-7096-6, BUHL). Greenwood.

--Way of Man. 1966. pap. 2.95 (ISBN 0-87574-106-1, 106). Citadel Pr.

--The Way of Man. 44p. 1985. pap. 3.50 (ISBN 0-8065-0024-7). Citadel Pr.

--The Way of Response: Selections from His Writings. Glatzer, Nahum N., ed. LC 66-26977. 1971. pap. 5.95 (ISBN 0-8052-0292-7). Schocken.

--Writings of Martin Buber. Herberg, Will, ed. (Orig.). pap. 8.95 (ISBN 0-452-00616-3, F616, Mer). NAL.

Buber, Martin, jt. auth. see Magnes, Judah L.

Buber, Martin & Magnes, J. L., eds. Towards Union in Palestine: Essays on Zionism & Jewish-Arab Cooperation. LC 76-97272. (Judaica Ser.). 124p. 1972. Repr. of 1947 ed. lib. bdg. 22.50x (ISBN 0-8371-2564-2, BUUP). Greenwood.

Buber, Martin, et al. I & Thou. Kaufman, Walter & Smith, S. G., trs. LC 72-123845. (Hudson River Edition). 1970. 20.00 (ISBN 0-684-15575-3, ScribT); pap. 6.95 (ISBN 0-684-71725-5, ScribT). Scribner.

Bubis, G. B., ed. Serving the Jewish Family. 25.00x (ISBN 0-87068-439-6). Ktav.

Bubis, Gerald B. & Wasserman, Harry. Synagogue Havurot: A Comparative Study. LC 82-23912. 160p. (Orig.). 1983. lib. bdg. 25.50 (ISBN 0-8191-2969-0, Co-pub. by Ctr Jewish Comm Studies); pap. text ed. 10.50 (ISBN 0-8191-2970-4). U Pr of Amer.

Bublitz, Ruth M. ONE-drous Light. 128p. (Orig.). 1985. pap. 5.95 (ISBN 0-87516-556-7). De Vorss.

Bubna, Donald & Ricketts, Sarah. Building People Through a Caring, Sharing Fellowship. 1982. pap. 5.95 (ISBN 0-8423-0187-9); leader's guide o. p. 2.95 (ISBN 0-8423-0188-7). Tyndale.

Bubna, Paul, frwd. by see Schroeder, David.

Bucaille, Maurice. The Bible, the Quran & Science. Beg, Anwer, ed. Bucaille, Maurice & Pannell, Alastair D., trs. from Fr. LC 77-90336. 253p. 1978. 11.95 (ISBN 0-89259-010-6); pap. 8.50. Am Trust Pubns.

Bucaille, Maurice, tr. see Bucaille, Maurice.

Bucer, Martin. A Briefe Treatise Concerning the Burnynge of Bucer & Phagius at Cambridge. LC 76-57362. (English Experience Ser.: No. 780). 1977. Repr. of 1562 ed. lib. bdg. 14.00 (ISBN 90-221-0780-9). Walter J Johnson.

--Instruction in Christian Love. John Knox.

Buchan, James, et al, eds. Jeddah Old & New. rev. ed. (Illus.). 144p. 1986. Repr. of 1980 ed. 32.50 (ISBN 0-905743-22-9, Pub. by Stacey Intl UK). Humanities.

Buchan, John. Oliver Cromwell. 1957. 25.00 (ISBN 0-8274-3062-0). R West.

Buchanan, Annette M. & Martin, Kay A. The Twelve Months of Christmas. Bolt, John, ed. (Illus.). 192p. 1980. pap. 7.95 (ISBN 0-939114-01-1). Partridge Pair.

Buchanan, Duncan. The Counselling of Jesus. Green, Michael, ed. LC 85-19736. (The Jesus Library). 160p. 1985. pap. 6.95 (ISBN 0-87784-931-5). Inter-Varsity.

Buchanan, Edward A. Broken Jars & Empty Cisterns: Studies in Jeremiah. 32p. 1982. pap. 3.50 (ISBN 0-939298-09-0). J M Prods.

Buchanan, Edward A., jt. auth. see Johnson, L. T.

Buchanan, Emerson, tr. see Ricoeur, Paul.

Buchanan, G. Sidney. Morality, Sex & the Constitution: A Christian Perspective on the Power of Government to Regulate Private Sexual Conduct Between Consenting Adults. LC 85-3249. 242p. (Orig.). 1985. lib. bdg. 26.25 (ISBN 0-8191-4602-1); pap. text ed. 11.75 (ISBN 0-8191-4603-X). U Pr of Amer.

Buchanan, George W. Revelation & Redemption. 1978. text ed. 29.50 (ISBN 0-915948-04-4). Bks Distinction.

Buchanan, George W., tr. To the Hebrews. LC 72-76127. (Anchor Bible Ser.: Vol. 36). 1972. 14.00 (ISBN 0-385-02995-0, Anchor Pr). Doubleday.

Buchanan, George Wesley. Jesus: The King & His Kingdom. LC 83-24939. xx, 348p. 1984. 21.95 (ISBN 0-86554-072-1, H66). Mercer Univ Pr.

Buchanan, James. The Doctrine of Justification. 514p. 1985. Repr. of 1867 ed. 15.95 (ISBN 0-85151-440-5). Banner of Truth.

--Office & Work of the Holy Spirit. 488p. 1984. Repr. of 1843 ed. 11.95 (ISBN 0-85151-089-2). Banner of Truth.

Buchanan, James J., ed. see Boethius.

Buchanan, Jami L. Letters to My Little Sisters. LC 84-27612. (Orig.). 1985. pap. 3.95 (ISBN 0-8307-0999-1, S185100). Regal.

Buchanan, Jim. A Guide to Materials about Public Aid to Religious Schools. (Public Administration Ser.: Bibliography P 1621). 1985. pap. 3.75 (ISBN 0-89028-291-9). Vance Biblios.

Buchanan, Neil, tr. see Harnack, Adolph.

Buchanan, Ray, ed. GLEANINGS: Hunger Meditations for Lent. rev. ed. 112p. pap. 5.50 (ISBN 0-939485-02-8). St Andrew Pr.

Bucheli, J. E., tr. see Clymer, R. Swinburne & Lippard, George.

Bucher, Dorothy, tr. see Bailey, Keith M.

Bucher, Dorothy, tr. see Simpson, A. B.

Buchheim, Durwood. The Power of Darkness. 1985. 6.95 (ISBN 0-89536-746-7, 5852). CSS of Ohio.

Buchholz, Peter, ed. Bibliographie Zur alteuropaeischen Religionsgeschichte, Vol. 1: Nineteen Fifty-Four Bis Nineteen Sixty-Four Literatur zu den antiken Rand-und Nachfolgekulturen im aussermediterranen Europa unter besonderer Beruecksichtigung der nichtchristlichen Religionen. (Arbeitem zur Fruehmittelalterforschung, Vol. 2). (Ger). 1967. 26.80x (ISBN 3-11-000373-2). De Gruyter.

Buchler, Adolf. Types of Jewish-Palestinian Piety from 70 BCE to 70 CE. 264p. Repr. of 1922 ed. text ed. 62.10x (ISBN 0-576-80135-6, Pub by Gregg Intl Pubs England). Gregg Intl.

Buchler, Adolf, jt. auth. see Abrahams, Israel.

Buchner, J. H. The Moravians in Jamaica. facsimile ed. LC 77-178470. (Black Heritage Library Collection Ser.). Repr. of 1854 ed. 17.50 (ISBN 0-8369-8918-X). Ayer Co Pubs.

Buchtal, Hugo. The Miniatures of the Paris Psalter: A Study in Middle Byzantine Painting. (Warburg Institute Studies: Vol. 2). Repr. of 1938 ed. 88.00 (ISBN 0-8115-1379-3). Kraus Repr.

Buchtal, Hugo & Kurz, Otto. Hand List of Illuminated Oriental Christian Manuscripts. (Warburg Institute Studies: Vol. 12). Repr. of 1942 ed. 20.00 (ISBN 0-8115-1389-0). Kraus Repr.

Buck, Carlton C. Communion Thoughts & Prayers. new ed. LC 76-46943. 1977. 5.95 (ISBN 0-8272-0440-X). CBP.

Buck, Dorothy. The Dance of Life. (Patterns of World Spirituality Ser.). 160p. (Orig.). 1987. pap. 8.95 (ISBN 0-913757-52-7, Pub. by New Era Bks). Paragon Hse.

Buck, Dudley. Illustrations in Choir Accompaniment. LC 79-137316. Repr. of 1892 ed. 18.00 (ISBN 0-404-01145-4). AMS Pr.

Buck, Harry M. Spiritual Discipline in Hinduism, Buddhism, & the West. LC 81-12812. (Focus on Hinduism & Buddhism Ser.). 64p. 1981. pap. 4.95x (ISBN 0-89012-022-6). Anima Pubns.

Buck, Jirah D. Symbolism of Freemasonry. 12.00 (ISBN 0-685-19503-1). Powner.

Buck, Mark. Politics, Finance & the Church in the Reign of Edward II: Walter Stapeldon, Treasurer of England. LC 82-17695. (Cambridge Studies in Medieval Life & Thought 19). 248p. 1983. 52.50 (ISBN 0-521-25025-0). Cambridge U Pr.

Buck, P. C., ed. John Taverner: Part 1. (Tudor Church Music Ser.: Vol. 1). 1963. Repr. of 1923 ed. write for info. (ISBN 0-8450-1851-5). Broude.

--John Taverner: Part 2. (Tudor Church Music Ser.: Vol. 3). 1963. Repr. of 1924 ed. 85.00x (ISBN 0-8450-1853-1). Broude.

--Orlando Gibbons. (Tudor Church Music Ser.: Vol. 4). 1963. Repr. of 1925 ed. 85.00x (ISBN 0-8450-1854-X). Broude.

Buck, P. C. & Fellowes, E. H., eds. Tudor Church Music. Incl. Vol. 1. John Taverner - Part One (ISBN 0-8450-1851-5); Vol. 2. William Byrd - English Church Music, Part One (ISBN 0-8450-1852-3); Vol. 3. John Tavernen - Part Two (ISBN 0-8450-1853-1); Vol. 4. Orlando Gibbons (ISBN 0-8450-1854-X); Vol. 5. Robert White (ISBN 0-8450-1855-8); Vol. 6. Tallis, Thomas (ISBN 0-8450-1856-6); Vol. 7. Byrd, William (ISBN 0-8450-1857-4); Vol. 8. Thomas Tomkins (ISBN 0-8450-1858-2); Vol. 9 (ISBN 0-8450-1859-0); Vol. 10. Aston, Hugh & Marbeck, John. (ISBN 0-8450-1860-4). 1963. Repr. of 1922 ed. 750.00x set (ISBN 0-8450-1850-7); 85.00x ea.; appendix 50.00x (ISBN 0-8450-1861-2). Broude.

Buck, P. C., ed. see Byrd, William, et al.

Buck, P. C., ed. see Tallis, Thomas, et al.

Buck, P. C., ed. see Tomkins, Thomas.

Buck, P. C., et al, eds. Robert White. (Tudor Church Music Ser.: Vol. 5). 1963. Repr. of 1926 ed. 85.00x (ISBN 0-8450-1855-8). Broude.

Buck, Pearl S. The Story Bible: New Testament, Vol. 2. 1972. pap. 3.95 (ISBN 0-451-14639-5, AE2694, Sig). NAL.

--The Story Bible: Old Testament, Vol. 1. 1972. pap. 3.95 (ISBN 0-451-13458-3, Sig). NAL.

Buck, Peter & Hiroa, Te Rangi. Arts & Crafts of Hawaii: Religion. (Special Publication Ser.: No. 45 (11)). (Illus.). 77p. 1957. pap. 3.00 (ISBN 0-910240-44-2). Bishop Mus.

Buck, Peter H. Anthropology & Religion. LC 72-121753. viii, 96p. 1970. Repr. of 1939 ed. 16.00 (ISBN 0-208-00950-7, Archon). Shoe String.

--Anthropology & Religion. 1939. 11.50x (ISBN 0-686-83471-2). Elliots Bks.

Buck, William. Mahabarata. 272p. 1979. pap. 3.95 (ISBN 0-451-62347-9, ME1783, Ment). NAL.

--Mahabharata. (Illus.). 1973. pap. 8.95 (ISBN 0-520-04393-6, CAL 491). U of Cal Pr.

Bucke, Richard M. Buddha, Mohammed, Bacon, Whitman & Others & the Theory of Cosmic Consciousness, 2 vols. (Illus.). 291p. 1986. Set. 237.50 (ISBN 0-89901-269-8). Found Class Reprints.

Buckingham, Betty Jo, ed. Women at the Well: Expressions of Faith, Life & Worship Drawn from Our Own Wisdom. Carachei, Maria E., tr. LC 87-6224. (Orig.). (YA) 1987. pap. 7.95 (ISBN 0-9618243-0-1). Womens Caucus Church.

Buckingham, Jamie. Daughter of Destiny. LC 76-12034. 1976. (Pub. by Logos); pap. 2.95 pocket ed. (ISBN 0-88270-318-8). Bridge Pub.

--The Last Word. LC 78-56932. 1978. pap. 4.95 (ISBN 0-88270-303-X). Bridge Pub.

--Risky Living: The Key to Inner Healing. LC 76-12033. 1976. (Pub. by Logos); pap. 4.95 (ISBN 0-88270-177-0). Bridge Pub.

Buckingham, Jamie, jt. auth. see Ortiz, Juan Carlos.

Buckingham, Jamie, jt. auth. see Riley, Jeannie C.

Buckingham, Jamie, jt. auth. see Robertson, Pat.

Buckingham, Jamie, jt. auth. see Ten Boom, Corrie.

Buckingham, Jamie, compiled by see Kuhlman, Kathryn.

Buckland, Augustus R. John Bunyan: The Man & His Work. LC 76-16025. 1976. Repr. of 1928 ed. lib. bdg. 20.00 (ISBN 0-8414-3319-4). Folcroft.

Buckland, Patricia B. Advent to Pentecost-A History of the Church Year. 1979. pap. 4.95 (ISBN 0-8192-1251-2). Morehouse.

Buckland, Raymond. Practical Candle-Burning Rituals. (Illus.). 189p. 1984. pap. 5.95 (ISBN 0-87542-048-6). Llewellyn Pubns.

--Ray Buckland's Complete Book of Witchcraft. Weschcke, Carl L., ed. LC 85-45280. (Sourcebook Ser.). (Illus.). 320p. (Orig.). 1986. wkbk. 12.95 (ISBN 0-87542-050-8). Llewellyn Pubns.

--The Tree: The Complete Book of Saxon Witchcraft. LC 74-79397. (Illus.). 158p. 1974. pap. 5.95 (ISBN 0-87728-258-7). Weiser.

--Witchcraft from the Inside. 2nd ed. (Illus.). 145p. 1975. pap. 3.95 (ISBN 0-87542-085-0). Llewellyn Pubns.

Buckler, William E. On the Poetry of Matthew Arnold: Essays in Critical Reconstruction. (The Gotham Library). 228p. 1982. 35.00x (ISBN 0-8147-1039-5). NYU Pr.

Buckley, Cornelius M., tr. see Gache, Louis-Hippolyte.

Buckley, Francis J. Reconciling. LC 81-68699. 96p. (Orig.). 1981. pap. 2.95 (ISBN 0-87793-237-9). Ave Maria.

Buckley, Francis J., jt. auth. see De la Cruz Aymes, Maria.

Buckley, Frank. Come Worship with Us: Explaining the Mass. 32p. 1987. pap. 1.95 (ISBN 0-89243-263-2). Liguori Pubns.

Buckley, Jorunn J. Female Fault & Fulfilment in Gnosticism. LC 85-29020. (Studies in Religion). xvi, 180p. 1986. 32.50x (ISBN 0-8078-1696-5). U of NC Pr.

Buckley, Mary I., jt. ed. see Klaven, Janet.

Buckley, Michael. Why Are You Afraid. pap. 5.95 (ISBN 0-87061-060-0). Chr Classics.

Buckley, Michael & Castle, Tony, eds. The Catholic Prayer Book. 272p. (Orig.). 1986. pap. 6.95 (ISBN 0-89283-283-5). Servant.

Buckley, Michael J. Motion & Motion's God: Thematic Variations in Aristotle, Cicero, Newton, & Hegel. LC 73-132234. 1971. 30.50 (ISBN 0-691-07124-1). Princeton U Pr.

Buckley, Thomas E. Church & State in Revolutionary Virginia, 1776-1787. LC 77-4283. xii, 217p. 1977. 17.95x (ISBN 0-8139-0692-X). U Pr of Va.

Bucknell, R. S. & Stuart-Fox, Martin. The Twilight Language: Explanations in Buddhist Meditation & Symbolism. 227p. 1986. 27.50 (ISBN 0-312-82540-4). St Martin.

Buckner, John E. Son of Man. 1981. 4.95 (ISBN 0-8062-1796-0). Carlton.

Budapest, Zsuzsanna. The Holy Book of Women's Mysteries, 2 vols. rev. ed. 1986. pap. write for info. (ISBN 0-937081-03-5). SBA Coven.

--The Holy Book of Women's Mysteries, Pt. 1. rev. ed. 1986. pap. text ed. write for info. (ISBN 0-937081-01-9). SBA Coven.

--The Holy Book of Women's Mysteries, Pt. 2. rev. ed. 1986. pap. write for info. (ISBN 0-937081-02-7). SBA Coven.

Buday, George. The History of the Christmas Card. LC 74-174012. (Tower Bks.). (Illus.). xxiii, 304p. 1972. Repr. of 1954 ed. 50.00x (ISBN 0-8103-3931-5). Gale.

Budd, Leonard H. Days Multiplied. 1984. 4.00 (ISBN 0-89536-666-5, 0424). CSS of Ohio.

Budd, Leonard H. & Talbott, Roger G. Resurrection Promises. Sherer, Michael L., ed. (Orig.). 1987. pap. 6.25 (ISBN 0-89536-850-1, 7809). CSS of Ohio.

Buddensieg, Rudolf. John Wycliffe: Patriot & Reformer. Life & Writings. 1979. Repr. of 1884 ed. lib. bdg. 40.00 (ISBN 0-8495-0535-6). Arden Lib.

Buddha, Gautama. Dhammapada. Babbitt, Irving, tr. LC 64-23655. Tr. of The Path of Truth. 1965. pap. 5.95 (ISBN 0-8112-0004-3, NDP188). New Directions.

Buddhadatta. Buddhadatta's Manuals, 2 vols. in 1. Buddhadatta, A. P., ed. LC 78-72382. Repr. of 1928 ed. 47.50 (ISBN 0-404-17244-X). AMS Pr.

Buddhadatta, A. P., ed. see Buddhadatta.

Buddhadharma. Upasaka Two & One. 1981. pap. 3.95 (ISBN 0-87881-078-1). Mojave Bks.

Buddhaghosa. The Atthasalini, Buddhaghosa's Commentary on the Dhammasangani. Muller, Edward, ed. LC 78-72383. Repr. of 1897 ed. 39.50 (ISBN 0-404-17245-8). AMS Pr.

--Buddhaghosa's Parables. Rogers, T., tr. from Burmese. LC 78-72384. Repr. of 1870 ed. 37.50 (ISBN 0-404-17246-6). AMS Pr.

--Expositor (Atthasalini, 2 vols. in 1. rev. ed. Maung Tin, tr. Davis, Carolina A., rev. by. LC 78-72385. Repr. of 1920 ed. 49.50 (ISBN 0-404-17247-4). AMS Pr.

--The Padyacudamani of Buddhaghosacarya. LC 78-72387. Repr. of 1921 ed. 32.50 (ISBN 0-404-17248-2). AMS Pr.

--Papancasudani Majjhimanikayatthakatha of Buddhaghosacariya, 5 vols. in 4. LC 78-72388. Repr. of 1938 ed. Set. 165.00 (ISBN 0-404-17560-0). AMS Pr.

--The Path of Purity, 3 vols. Pe Maung Tin, tr. LC 78-72389. Repr. of 1931 ed. Set. 95.00 (ISBN 0-404-17570-8). AMS Pr.

--The Sumangala-Vilasini, 3 vols. LC 78-72390. Repr. of 1886 ed. Set. 110.00 (ISBN 0-404-17580-5). Vol. 1 (ISBN 0-404-17581-3). Vol. 2 (ISBN 0-404-17582-1). Vol. 3 (ISBN 0-404-17583-X). AMS Pr.

Buddhananda, tr. see Ramprasad.

Buddhavamsa. The Buddavamsa & the Carlya-Pitaka, Pt. 1. Morris, Richard, ed. LC 78-72391. Repr. of 1882 ed. 17.00 (ISBN 0-404-17249-0). AMS Pr.

Buddhist Association of the United States, tr. see Chang, Garma C. C.

Buddhist Books International, tr. see Yamaguchi, Susumu.

Buddhist Text Translation Society, tr. from Chinese. Brahma Net Sutra, Vol. II Commentary by Hui Seng, Elder Master. (Illus.). 210p. (Orig.). 1982. pap. 10.00 (ISBN 0-917512-88-X). Buddhist Text.

--Brahma Net Sutra, text only. 70p. (Orig.). 1982. pap. 5.00 (ISBN 0-917512-56-1). Buddhist Text.

Buddhist Text Translation Society Staff, tr. see Great Master Lyan Chr.

Buddhist Text Translation Society Staff, tr. see National Master Ch'ing Liang.

Buddhist Text Translation Society Staff, tr. see Tripitaka Master Hua.

Buddhist Text Translation Society, tr. see Hua, Tripitaka Master.

Buddhist Text Translation Society, tr. see Hui Seng.

Buddhist Text Translation Society, tr. see Master Hua, Tripitaka.

Buddhist Text Translation Society, tr. see Master Hua, Triptaka.

Buddhist Text Translation Society, tr. see National Master Ch'ing Liang.

Buddhist Text Translation Society, tr. see Tripitaka Master Hua.

Buddhist Text Translation Society, tr. see Vasubhandu, Bodhisattva.

Buddhist Text Translation Society, et al, trs. see Tripitaka Master Hua.

Buddhist Text Translation Society Staff. Cherishing Life, Vol. 2. Bhikshuni Heng Tao & Bhikshuni Heng Ch'ih, trs. from Chinese. (Illus.). 160p. 1983. pap. 7.00 (ISBN 0-88139-015-1). Buddhist Text.

--Filiality, the Human Source, Vol. 1. 132p. 1983. pap. 7.00 (ISBN 0-88139-006-2). Buddhist Text.

--Filiality, the Human Source, Vol. 2. 120p. (Orig.). 1983. pap. 7.00 (ISBN 0-88139-020-8). Buddhist Text.

Buddhist Text Translation Society Staff, tr. Flower Adornment Sutra, Chapter 22: The Ten Inexhaustible Treasuries Commentary by Tripitka Master Hua. (Illus.). 184p. (Orig.). 1983. pap. 7.00 (ISBN 0-917512-38-3). Buddhist Text.

Buddhist Text Translation Society Staff, tr. from Chinese. Flower Adornment Sutra, Chapter 36: Universal Worthy's Conduct. (Illus.). 75p. (Orig.). 1983. pap. 5.00 (ISBN 0-88139-011-9). Buddhist Text.

--Flower Adornment Sutra, Chapter 39: Entering the Dharma Realm, Part VII. 160p. (Orig.). 1983. pap. 9.00 (ISBN 0-88139-050-X). Buddhist Text.

--Flower Adornment Sutra, Chapter 39: Entering the Dharma Realm, Part VI. (Illus.). 320p. (Orig.). 1982. pap. 9.00 (ISBN 0-917512-48-0). Buddhist Text.

--A Pictorial Biography of the Venerable Master Hsu Yun, Vol. 1. (Illus.). 236p. (Orig.). 1983. pap. 8.00 (ISBN 0-88139-008-9). Buddhist Text.

--Pictorial Biography of the Venerable Master Hsu Yun, Vol. 2. (Illus.). 236p. (Orig.). 1985. pap. 8.00 (ISBN 0-88139-116-6). Buddhist Text.

--Sutra of the Past Vows of Earth Store Bodhisattva. (Illus.). 120p. (Orig.). 1982. pap. 6.00 (ISBN 0-88139-502-1). Buddhist Text.

Buddhist Sutra. How One Thousand Buddhas Became Enlightened, 3 Vols. 1986. Set. cancelled (ISBN 0-89800-136-6). Dharma Pub.

--How the Thousand Buddhas Become Enlightened, 3 vols. 1987. 35.00 ea. (ISBN 0-89800-136-6). Dharma Pub.

Budge, A. E., tr. from Syriac. The Paradise of the Fathers, 2 vols. (Illus.). 1984. Set. pap. 25.00 (ISBN 0-913026-56-5). Vol. 1, 386 pp. Vol. 2, 352 pp. St Nectarios.

Budge, E. A. Ancient Egyptian Theology. 1985. pap. 5.95 (ISBN 0-916411-91-5). Holmes Pub.

--Apophthegmata Patrum. 150p. 1975. pap. 5.95 (ISBN 0-686-10938-4). Eastern Orthodox.

--The Book of the Dead. (Illus.). 992p. 1985. pap. 9.95 (ISBN 1-85063-020-8, Ark Paperbks). Methuen Inc.

--Egyptian Book of the Dead: The Papyrus of Ani. 16.25 (ISBN 0-8446-1764-4). Peter Smith.

--Egyptian Heaven & Hell. 1980. lib. bdg. 59.95 (ISBN 0-8490-3203-2). Gordon Pr.

--Gods of the Egyptians or Studies in Egyptian Mythology, 2 Vols. (Illus.). Set. 36.00 (ISBN 0-8446-0520-4). Peter Smith.

--The Gods of the Egyptians: Studies in Egyptian Mythology, 2 Vols. LC 67-28633. (Illus.). 1969. pap. 10.00 ea.; Vol. 1. pap. (ISBN 0-486-22055-9); Vol. 2. pap. (ISBN 0-486-22056-7). Dover.

--Mummy. 2nd ed. LC 64-13391. (Illus.). 1894. 25.00 (ISBN 0-8196-0139-X). Biblo.

--Sayings of the Fathers. 1975. pap. 5.95 (ISBN 0-686-10941-4). Eastern Orthodox.

Budge, E. A., intro. by. The Book of the Dead. 1977. pap. 9.95 (ISBN 0-8065-0591-5). Citadel Pr.

Budge, E. A., tr. see Isho, Anan.

Budge, E. A., tr. see Pachomius, Saint.

Budge, E. A. Wallis. Egyptian Book of the Dead: The Papyrus of Ani in the British Museum. 1967. pap. 8.95 (ISBN 0-486-21866-X). Dover.

Budge, E. Wallis. The Dwellers on the Nile: The Life, History, Religion, & Literature of the Ancient Egyptians. (Illus.). 326p. 1977. pap. 5.95 (ISBN 0-486-23501-7). Dover.

--Egyptian Magic. 1971. pap. 4.00 (ISBN 0-486-22681-6). Dover.

--Egyptian Religion. (Illus.). 1979. pap. 6.95 (ISBN 0-7100-0134-7). Methuen Inc.

--From Fetish to God in Ancient Egypt. LC 72-82206. (Illus.). Repr. of 1934 ed. 33.00 (ISBN 0-405-08317-3, Blom Pubns). Ayer Co Pubs.

--The Liturgy of Funerary Offerings: The Egyptian Texts with English Translations. LC 72-83744. (Illus.). Repr. of 1909 ed. 22.00 (ISBN 0-405-08322-X, Blom Pubns). Ayer Co Pubs.

--Osiris & the Egyptian Resurrection, 2 vols. LC 72-81534. (Illus.). 906p. 1973. Vol. 1. pap. 7.95 (ISBN 0-486-22780-4); Vol. 2. pap. 7.95 (ISBN 0-486-22781-2). Dover.

--Osiris & the Egyptian Resurrection, 2 vols. (Illus.). 30.50 (ISBN 0-8446-4715-2). Peter Smith.

--Tutankhamen: Amenism, Atenism & Egyptain Monotheism. LC 79-160615. (Illus.). Repr. of 1923 ed. 12.75 (ISBN 0-405-08323-8, Blom Pubns). Ayer Co Pubs.

Budge, E. Wallis, tr. see Pachomius, Saint.

Budge, Ernest A. Coptic Texts Edited with Introductions & English Translations, 5 vols. Repr. of 1915 ed. 345.00 set (ISBN 0-404-11550-0); write for info. AMS Pr.

--The Egyptian Heaven & Hell, 3 vols. LC 73-18844. (Illus.). Repr. of 1906 ed. Set. 57.50 (ISBN 0-404-11326-5). AMS Pr.

--The Egyptian Heaven & Hell. (Illus.). 200p. 1974. lib. bdg. 16.95 (ISBN 0-87548-311-9); pap. 5.95 (ISBN 0-87548-298-8). Open Court.

--Egyptian Ideas of the Future Life. LC 73-18839. Repr. of 1899 ed. 14.00 (ISBN 0-404-11330-3). AMS Pr.

--A Hieroglyphic Vocabulary to the Theban Recension of the Book of the Dead. LC 73-18846. Repr. of 1911 ed. 26.50 (ISBN 0-404-11335-4). AMS Pr.

--The Monks of Kublai Khan, Emperor of China. LC 71-38051. Repr. of 1928 ed. 32.50 (ISBN 0-404-56905-6). AMS Pr.

Budge, Ernest A., ed. Baralam & Yewasef - Baralaam & Joasaph, 3 pts. in 2 vols. LC 73-18832. (Illus.). Repr. of 1923 ed. Set. 67.50 (ISBN 0-404-11300-1). AMS Pr.

--Coptic Apocrypha in the Dialect of Upper Egypt. LC 77-3589. (Coptic Texts: Vol. 3). (Illus.). Repr. of 1913 ed. 55.00 (ISBN 0-404-11553-5). AMS Pr.

--Coptic Biblical Texts in the Dialect of Upper Egypt. LC 77-3590. (Coptic Texts: Vol. 2). (Illus.). 1977. Repr. of 1912 ed. 45.00 (ISBN 0-404-11552-7). AMS Pr.

--Coptic Homilies in the Dialect of Upper Egypt. LC 77-3585. (Coptic Texts: Vol. 1). (Illus.). Repr. of 1910 ed. 50.00 (ISBN 0-404-11551-9). AMS Pr.

--Coptic Martyrdoms, Etc. in the Dialect of Upper Egypt. LC 77-3588. (Coptic Texts: Vol. 4). (Illus.). Repr. of 1914 ed. 60.00 (ISBN 0-404-11554-3). AMS Pr.

--Miscellaneous Coptic Texts in the Dialect of Upper Egypt, 2 vols. LC 77-3587. (Coptic Texts: Vol. 5). (Illus.). Repr. of 1915 ed. 135.00 (ISBN 0-404-11555-1). AMS Pr.

Budge, Ernest A., tr. George of Lydda, the Patron Saint of England. LC 77-87668. (Luzac's Semitic Texts & Translations: No. 20). (Eng. & Ethiopic., Illus.). Repr. of 1930 ed. 55.00 (ISBN 0-404-11348-6). AMS Pr.

--The History of the Blessed Virgin Mary & the History of the Likeness of Christ Which the Jews of Tiberius Made to Mock At, 2 vols. LC 73-18848. (Luzac's Semitic Text & Translation Ser.: Nos. 4-5). Repr. of 1899 ed. 45.00 set (ISBN 0-404-11341-9). AMS Pr.

Budge, Ernest A. Wallis see Anan Isho.

Budge, Wallis. Egyptian Magic. 1978. pap. 3.95 (ISBN 0-8065-0629-6). Citadel Pr.

Budhananda. The Saving Challenge of Religion. 272p. (Orig.). 1982. pap. 9.50 (ISBN 0-87481-567-3). Vedanta Pr.

Budhananda, Swami. Can One Be Scientific & Yet Spiritual? 114p. 1973. pap. 2.00 (ISBN 0-87481-145-7). Vedanta Pr.

--The Mind & Its Control. 119p. (Orig.). 1972. pap. 1.75 (ISBN 0-87481-128-7). Vedanta Pr.

Budy, Bertrand. Mary, the Faithful Disciple. 160p. (Orig.). 1985. pap. 6.95 (ISBN 0-8091-2703-2). Paulist Pr.

Bue, F. Lo see Lo Bue, F.

Buechner, Frederick. The Alphabet of Grace. LC 84-48765. 128p. 1985. 12.45 (ISBN 0-06-061173-1, HarpR). Har-Row.

--Love a Feast. LC 84-47714. (Books of Bebb). 380p. 1984. pap. 3.95 (ISBN 0-06-061167-7, P-5009, HarpR). Har-Row.

--Now & Then. LC 82-48413. 128p. 1983. 12.45 (ISBN 0-06-061161-8, HarpR). Har-Row.

--Open Heart. LC 84-47715. (Books of Bebb). 1984. pap. 3.95 (ISBN 0-06-061166-9, P-5008, HarpR). Har-Row.

--Peculiar Treasures: A Biblical Who's Who. Buechner, Katherine A., tr. LC 78-20586. 1979. 12.45 (ISBN 0-06-061157-X, HarpR). Har-Row.

--A Room Called Remember: Uncollected Pieces. LC 83-48457. 192p. 1984. 13.45 (ISBN 0-06-061163-4, HarpR). Har-Row.

--The Sacred Journey. LC 81-47843. 128p. 1982. 12.45 (ISBN 0-06-061158-8, HarpR). Har-Row.

--The Sacred Journey. 224p. 1984. pap. 8.95 large print ed. (ISBN 0-8027-2479-5). Walker & Co.

--Telling the Truth: The Gospel As Tragedy, Comedy, & Fairy Tale. LC 77-7839. 1977. 12.45 (ISBN 0-06-061156-1, HarpR). Har-Row.

--Treasure Hunt. LC 84-47716. (Books of Bebb). 1984. pap. 3.95 (ISBN 0-06-061168-5, P-5010, HarpR). Har-Row.

--Wishful Thinking: A Theological ABC. LC 72-9872. 128p. 1973. 12.45 (ISBN 0-06-061155-3, HarpR). Har-Row.

Buechner, Katherine A., tr. see Buechner, Frederick.

Buehring, David K. Acts Alive. 1986. pap. 7.95 (ISBN 0-935779-10-8). Crown Min.

Buehrle, Marie C. Rafael: Cardinal Merry del Val. 308p. (Orig.). 1980. pap. 7.00 (ISBN 0-912414-28-6). Lumen Christi.

--Who Are You: The Life of St. Cecilia. LC 70-158918. 1971. pap. 2.95 (ISBN 0-913382-07-8, 101-7). Prow Bks-Franciscan.

Buel, J. W. Heroes of the Dark Continent. facs. ed. LC 73-138333. (Black Heritage Library Collection). 1889. 32.75 (ISBN 0-8369-8725-X). Ayer Co Pubs.

Buell, Lawrence. Literary Transcendentalism: Style & Vision in the American Rennaisance. LC 73-8409. 336p. (Orig.). 1975. pap. 9.95x (ISBN 0-8014-9152-5). Cornell U Pr.

Buelow, George, ed. see Tomasello, Andrew.

Buerger, Jane. Growing As Jesus Grew. LC 80-17187. (Illus.). 32p. 1980. PLB 5.95 (ISBN 0-89565-173-4). Childs World.

--Growing as Jesus Grew. (Child's World Books of Understanding). (Illus.). 1985. PLB 5.95 (ISBN 0-89565-173-4, R4924). Standard Pub.

Buerger, Jane & Davis, Jennie. Helping Is. 1984. 4.95 (ISBN 0-89693-218-4). Victor Bks.

--Helping Is-- LC 84-7042. (Illus.). 32p. 1984. lib. bdg. 4.95 (ISBN 0-89693-218-4). Dandelion Hse.

Buerger, Jane, ed. see Baker, Eugene.

Buerger, Jane, ed. see Colina, Tessa.

Buerger, Jane, ed. see Moncure, Jane B.

Buerger, Jane, ed. see Ziegler, Sandy.

Buerlein, Homer K. How to Preach More Powerful Sermons. LC 85-26378. 140p. (Orig.). 1986. pap. 10.95 (ISBN 0-664-24683-4). Westminster.

Buerlen, Wolfgang, tr. see Schubring, Walther.

Buescher, Gabriel. The Eucharistic Teaching of William Ockham. (Theology Ser). 1974. Repr. of 1950 ed. 10.00 (ISBN 0-686-11585-6). Franciscan Inst.

Buess, Bob. Deliverance from the Bondage of Fear. 1972. pap. 2.50 (ISBN 0-934244-03-0). Sweeter Than Honey.

--Discipleship Pro & Con. 1975. pap. 2.50 (ISBN 0-934244-06-5). Sweeter Than Honey.

--Favor the Road to Success. 1982. pap. 2.50 (ISBN 0-934244-17-0). Sweeter Than Honey.

--Implanted Word. 1978. pap. 2.50 (ISBN 0-934244-10-3). Sweeter Than Honey.

--The Laws of the Spirit. 1968. pap. 2.50 (ISBN 0-934244-01-4). Sweeter Than Honey.

--The Race Horse. 1978. pap. 2.50 (ISBN 0-934244-08-1). Sweeter Than Honey.

--Setting the Captives Free. LC 42-1127. 1975. pap. 2.50 (ISBN 0-934244-02-2). Sweeter Than Honey.

--You Can Receive the Holy Ghost Today. 1967. pap. 2.50 (ISBN 0-934244-14-6). Sweeter Than Honey.

Buess, Lynn M. Numerology for the New Age. (Illus.). 1979. pap. 6.95 (ISBN 0-87516-265-7). De Vorss.

Buffam, C. John. The Life & Times of an MK. LC 84-27482. (Mission Candidate Aids Ser.). 224p. (Orig.). 1985. pap. 9.95 (ISBN 0-87808-198-4). William Carey Lib.

Buffington, Albert F., et al. Something for Everyone, Something for You: Essays in Memoriam Albert Franklin Buffington, Vol. 14. (Illus.). 1980. 25.00 (ISBN 0-911122-41-9). Penn German Soc.

Buford, Elizabeth, jt. auth. see Crovitz, Elaine.

Bugg, Charles B. Things My Children Are Teaching Me. LC 81-70409. 1982. pap. 3.95 (ISBN 0-8054-5650-3). Broadman.

Bugg, Leila H. The People of Our Parish. 20.00 (ISBN 0-405-10811-7). Ayer Co Pubs.

Bugge, Sophus. Home of the Eddic Poems. Schofield, William H., tr. LC 74-144524. (Grimm Library: No. 11). Repr. of 1899 ed. 21.00 (ISBN 0-404-53554-2). AMS Pr.

Buhiery, Marwan, ed. The Splendor of the Holy Land. LC 77-5503. 1979. deluxe ed. 500.00x (ISBN 0-88206-019-8). Caravan Bks.

Buhler, G. The Laws of Manu. lib. bdg. 79.95 (ISBN 0-87968-492-5). Krishna Pr.

Buhler, Georg, ed. The Sacred Laws of the Aryas. (Sacred Bks. of the East: Vols. 2 & 14). both vols. 30.00 (ISBN 0-686-97474-3); 15.00 ea. Asian Human Pr.

Buhler, Walther. Living with Your Body. Maloney, L., tr. from Ger. Tr. of Der Leib als Instrument der Seele. 117p. (Orig.). 1979. pap. 9.95 (ISBN 0-85440-345-0, Pub. by Steinerbooks). Anthroposophic.

Buhlmann, Walbert. The Church of the Future: A Model for the Year 2001. Groves, Mary, tr. from Ger. Tr. of Weltkirche-Neue Dimensionen-Model fur das Jahr 2001. 256p. (Orig.). 1986. pap. 10.95 (ISBN 0-88344-253-1). Orbis Bks.

--The Coming of the Third Church: An Analysis of the Present & Future. Woodhall, Ralph & Woodhall, A. N., eds. LC 76-23237. Orig. Title: Es Kommt die dritte Kirche. 430p. 1977. pap. 9.95x (ISBN 0-88344-070-9). Orbis Bks.

--Courage, Church! Essays in Ecclesial Spirituality. Smith, Mary, tr. from Ital. LC 78-1381. Orig. Title: Corragio Chiesa! 149p. (Orig.). 1978. pap. 2.98 (ISBN 0-88344-068-7). Orbis Bks.

--The Missions on Trial. Dolan, A. P., tr. from Fr. & Ger. LC 78-23922. Orig. Title: Missions prozess in Addis Abeba. 160p. (Orig.). 1979. pap. 2.98 (ISBN 0-88344-316-3). Orbis Bks.

--The Search for God: An Encounter with the Peoples & Religions of Asia. Krokosz, B. & Dolan, A. P., trs. from Ger. LC 80-15732. Orig. Title: Alle haben denselben Gott. 221p. (Orig.). 1980. pap. 3.98 (ISBN 0-88344-450-X). Orbis Bks.

Buhring, Gernot, ed. Vaterunser Polyglott: The Lord's Prayer in 42 Languages (Sprachen Mit 75 Text Fassungen) (Ger.). 278p. 1984. 10.00x (ISBN 3-87118-666-X, Pub. by Helmut Buske Verlag Hamburg). Benjamins North AM.

Buhrmann, M. Vera. Living in Two Worlds: Communication Between a White Healer & Her Black Counterparts. 108p. 1986. pap. 9.95 (ISBN 0-933029-10-1). Chiron Pubns.

Buijs, Joseph A., ed. Christian Marriage Today: Growth or Breakdown? LC 85-10466. (Symposium Ser.: Vol. 16). 168p. 1985. 29.95x (ISBN 0-88946-707-2). E Mellen.

Buis, Robert. Religious Beliefs & White Prejudice. 71p. 1975. pap. text ed. 7.95x (ISBN 0-86975-044-5, Pub. by Ravan Pr). Ohio U Pr.

Buitenen, J. A. van see Van Buitenen, J. A.

Buitenen, J. A. van see Dimmitt, Cornelia.

Buitenen, J. A. Van see Van Buitenen, J. A.

Buitenen, J. Van see Van Buitenen, J. A.

Bukhari, Sohail, tr. Abuzar. 200p. 1985. pap. 9.00 (ISBN 0-941724-35-2). Islamic Seminary.

Bukhsh, S. K. Islamic Studies. 16.50 (ISBN 0-686-18357-6). Kazi Pubns.

--The Renaissance of Islam. 1981. 29.00 (ISBN 0-686-97863-3). Kazi Pubns.

Bukhsl, Salahuddin K, tr. see Mez, Adam.

Buksbazen, Lydia. They Looked for a City. 1977. pap. 3.95 (ISBN 0-87508-041-3). Chr Lit.

Buksbazen, Victor. Feasts of Israel. 1976. pap. 2.95 (ISBN 0-87508-043-X). Chr Lit.

Bulfinch, Thomas. Bulfinch's Mythology. abr. ed. Fuller, Edmund, ed. 448p. 1959. pap. 4.50 (ISBN 0-440-30845-3, LE). Dell.

--Bulfinch's Mythology, 3 vols. Incl. Vol. 1. The Age of Fable. 408p. pap. 3.95 (ISBN 0-451-62444-0, ME2230); Vols 2 & 3. The Age of Chivalry & Legends of Charlemagne. 608p. pap. 3.95 (ISBN 0-451-62252-9, ME2252). (YA) pap. (Ment). NAL.

--Bulfinch's Mythology. 2nd rev. ed. LC 69-11314. (Illus.). 1970. 16.45i (ISBN 0-690-57260-3). T Y Crowell.

Bulfinch, Thomas, jt. auth. see Sewell, H.

Bulka, Reuven P. The Coming Cataclysm: The Orthodox-Reform Rift & the Future of the Jewish People. 160p. 1986. pap. 9.95 (ISBN 0-88962-275-2). Riverrun NY.

--The Jewish Pleasure Principle. LC 86-20839. 168p. 1987. text ed. 24.95 (ISBN 0-89885-328-1). Human Sci Pr.

--Sex in the Talmud. (Illus.). 64p. 1979. 5.95 (ISBN 0-88088-488-6). Peter Pauper.

--Torah Therapy: Reflections on the Weekly Sedra & Special Occasions. LC 83-6155. 1983. 15.00x (ISBN 0-88125-033-3). Ktav.

--Wit & Wisdom of the Talmud. 2nd ed. (PPP Gift Editions). (Illus.). 1983. 5.95 (ISBN 0-88088-507-6). Peter Pauper.

Bulka, Reuven P. & Spero, Moshe H. A Psychology-Judaism Reader. (Illus.). 338p. 1982. pap. 27.00x (ISBN 0-398-04582-8). C C Thomas.

Bulka, Reuven P., ed. Mystics & Medics: A Comparison of Mystical & Psychotherapeutic Encounters. LC 79-87593. 120p. 1979. pap. 12.95 (ISBN 0-87705-377-4). Human Sci Pr.

Bulka, Rueven P., ed. Dimensions of Orthodox Judaism. LC 83-260. 471p. 1983. 25.00x (ISBN 0-87068-894-4). Ktav.

Bull, Geoffrey. Love Song in Harvest. 1977. pap. 3.95 (ISBN 0-87508-042-1). Chr Lit.

Bull, George. Harmony on Justification, Defense of the Nicene Creed, Judgement of the Catholic Church, 5 vols. LC 71-39556. (Library of Anglo-Catholic Theology: No. 4). Repr. of 1855 ed. Set. 150.00 (ISBN 0-404-52070-7). AMS Pr.

--Inside the Vatican. 294p. 1983. 13.95 (ISBN 0-312-41884-1). St Martin.

Bull, George, ed. see Sailes, Samuel.

Bull, Henry, ed. Christian Prayers & Holy Meditations. 1842. 21.00 (ISBN 0-384-06285-7). Johnson Repr.

Bull, Norman. Church of Jesus Begins. (Bible Story & Its Background Ser.: Vol. 7). pap. 9.95 (ISBN 0-7175-0983-4). Dufour.

--Church of Jesus Grows. (Bible Story & Its Background Ser.: Vol. 8). pap. 9.95 (ISBN 0-7175-0454-9). Dufour.

--Church of the Jews. (Bible Story & Its Background Ser.: Vol. 4). 9.95 (ISBN 0-7175-0450-6). Dufour.

--Founders of the Jews. (Bible Story & Its Background Ser.: Vol. 1). pap. 9.95 (ISBN 0-7175-0977-X). Dufour.

--One Hundred New Testament Stories. 160p. (Orig.). 1984. pap. 7.95 (ISBN 0-687-29073-2). Abingdon.

--Parables of Jesus. (Bible Story & Its Background Ser.: Vol. 6). 9.95 (ISBN 0-7175-0452-2). Dufour.

--Prophets of the Jews. (Bible Story & Its Background Ser.: Vol. 3). pap. 9.95 (ISBN 0-7175-0979-6). Dufour.

Bulla, Clyde R. Saint Valentine's Day. LC 65-11643. (Holiday Ser.). (Illus.). 1965. PLB 12.89 (ISBN 0-690-71744-X, Crowell Jr Bks). HarpJ.

Bullard, Rayford. Glimpses into Revelation. 5.95 (ISBN 0-911866-74-4). Advocate.

Bullard, Roger A., ed. The Hypostasis of the Archons: The Coptic Text with Translation & Commentary. (Patristische Texte und Studien Ser.: Vol. 10). (Coptic & Eng). 1970. 27.50x (ISBN 3-11-006356-5). De Gruyter.

Bullchild, Percy. The Sun Came Down: The History of the World as My Blackfeet Elders Told It. LC 85-42771. (Illus.). 384p. 1985. 22.45 (ISBN 0-06-250107-0, HarpR). Har-Row.

Bulle, Florence. God Wants You Rich: And Other Enticing Doctrines. 223p. (Orig.). 1983. pap. 5.95 (ISBN 0-87123-264-2, 210264). Bethany Hse.

Bulletin Committee Staff. Fiftieth Anniversary Issue: Kingston Lake Woman's Baptist Educational & Missionary Convention of Horry County, South Carolina. rev. ed. Dozier, Etrulia P., ed. (Illus.). 80p. (Orig.). 1985. pap. text ed. 5.00 (ISBN 0-9615271-2-9). Positive Images.

Bullett, Gerald. The Innocence of G. K. Chesterton. 1973. Repr. of 1923 ed. 17.50 (ISBN 0-8274-1799-3). R West.

Bullett, Gerald W. Sydney Smith: A Biography & a Selection. LC 77-138578. (Illus.). 1971. Repr. of 1951 ed. lib. bdg. 22.50x (ISBN 0-8371-5777-3, BUSS). Greenwood.

Bulliet, Richard W. Conversion to Islam in the Medieval Period: An Essay in Quantitative History. (Illus.). 158p. 1979. text ed. 16.50x (ISBN 0-674-17035-0). Harvard U Pr.

Bullinger, E. W. Critical Lexicon & Concordance to the English & Greek New Testament. 1040p. 1975. text ed. 26.95 (ISBN 0-310-20310-4, 6253P, Pub. by Bagster). Zondervan.

--Figures of Speech Used in the Bible. 24.95 (ISBN 0-8010-0559-0). Baker Bk.

--How to Enjoy the Bible. LC 83-71411. 436p. 1983. 9.95 (ISBN 0-910068-48-8). Am Christian.

Bullinger, Ethelbert W. Commentary on Revelation. LC 83-24917. 768p. 1984. 22.95 (ISBN 0-8254-2239-6). Kregel.

--Great Cloud of Witnesses in Hebrews Eleven. LC 79-14425. 462p. 1986. pap. 12.95 (ISBN 0-8254-2247-7). Kregel.

--Witness of the Stars. LC 68-16762. 212p. 1984. pap. 10.95 (ISBN 0-8254-2245-0). Kregel.

--Word Studies on the Holy Spirit. LC 85-7631. 232p. 1985. pap. 7.95 (ISBN 0-8254-2246-9). Kregel.

Bullinger, Heinrich. The Christian State of Matrimonye. Coverdale, Myles, tr. LC 74-80167. (English Experience Ser.: No. 646). 168p. 1974. Repr. of 1541 ed. 11.50 (ISBN 90-221-0646-2). Walter J Johnson.

--An Holsom Antidotus or Counter-Poysen Agaynst the Pestylent Heresye & Secte of the Anabaptistes. Veron, J., tr. LC 73-6106. (English Experience Ser.: No. 574). 232p. 1973. Repr. of 1548 ed. 13.00 (ISBN 90-221-0574-1). Walter J Johnson.

Bullinger, Henry. The Decades of Henry Bullinger, Minister of the Church of Zurich, 4 vols. 1849-1851. Set. 144.00 (ISBN 0-384-06315-2). Johnson Repr.

Bulloch, James, ed. see Rankin, Eric.

Bullock, C. Hassell. Introduction to Old Testament Poetic Books. 1979. 11.95 (ISBN 0-8024-4143-2). Moody.

--An Introduction to the Old Testament Prophetic Books. 1986. text ed. 19.95 (ISBN 0-8024-4142-4). Moody.

Bullock, C. Hassell, jt. ed. see Inch, Morris A.

Bullock, Charles. Shakespeare's Debt to the Bible. LC 72-187918. 1870. lib. bdg. 10.00 (ISBN 0-8414-2521-3). Folcroft.

Bullough, Edward, tr. see Gilson, Etienne H.

Bullough, Vern & Brundage, James, eds. Sexual Practices & the Medieval Church. LC 80-85227. 289p. 1984. pap. 15.95 (ISBN 0-87975-268-8). Prometheus Bks.

Bulman, Nachman. Reason, Emotion & Habit in the Training of a Torah Personality. (Annual Fryer Memorial Lecture Ser.). 0.75 (ISBN 0-914131-53-2, I34). Torah Umesorah.

Bulman, Nathan, tr. see Kitov, A. E.

Bulman, Nathan, tr. see Kitov, Eliyahu.

Buls, Alfred M. Devotions for New Parents. (Orig.). (YA) 1972. pap. 1.50 (ISBN 0-570-03675-5, 74-1010). Concordia.

Bultema, Harry. Commentary on Isaiah. LC 81-11795. 650p. 1981. 16.95 (ISBN 0-8254-2258-2). Kregel.

Bulter, Paul T. Twenty-Six Lessons on Revelation, Pt. 1. LC 82-71688. (Bible Student Study Guide Ser.). 133p. 1982. pap. 2.95 (ISBN 0-89900-173-4). College Pr Pub.

--Twenty-Six Lessons on Revelation, Pt. 2. LC 82-71688. (Bible Student Study Guide Ser.). 284p. 1982. pap. 4.95 (ISBN 0-89900-176-9). College Pr Pub.

Bulthaupt, Fritz. Milstater Genesis und Exodus: Eine Grammatisch-Stillistische Ist Untersuchung. (Ger). 21.00 (ISBN 0-384-06341-1); pap. 16.00 (ISBN 0-685-02228-5). Johnson Repr.

Bultmann, Rudolf. Faith & Understanding. Funk, Robert W., ed. Smith, Louise P., tr. LC 86-45901. 352p. 1987. pap. 12.95 (ISBN 0-8006-3202-8). Fortress.

--Gospel of John: A Commentary. LC 70-125197. 758p. 1971. 26.50 (ISBN 0-664-20893-2). Westminster.

--History of the Synoptic Tradition. LC 62-7282. 1963. pap. 9.50 (ISBN 0-06-061172-3, RD 187, HarpR). Har-Row.

--Jesus & the Word. (Hudson River Edition). 20.00 (ISBN 0-684-17596-7, ScribT). Scribner.

--Jesus Christ & Mythology. 1958. pap. text ed. 5.95 (ISBN 0-684-17228-3, ScribT). Scribner.

--Jesus Christ & Mythology. 94p. 1981. pap. text ed. write for info. (ISBN 0-02-305570-7, Pub. by Scribner). Macmillan.

--The Johannine Epistles. Funk, Robert W., ed. O'Hara, R. Philip, et al, trs. from Gr. LC 75-171510. (Hermeneia: a Critical & Historical Commentary on the Bible). 158p. 1973. 19.95 (ISBN 0-8006-6003-X, 20-6003). Fortress.

--The New Testament & Mythology & Other Basic Writings. Ogden, Schubert M., ed. & tr. LC 84-47921. 192p. 1984. 12.95 (ISBN 0-8006-0727-9). Fortress.

--Primitive Christianity: In Its Contemporary Setting. Fuller, Reginald H., tr. from Ger. LC 80-8043. 256p. 1980. pap. 8.95 (ISBN 0-8006-1408-9, 1-1408). Fortress.

--The Second Letter to the Corinthians. Linss, Wilhelm C., tr. LC 83-70517. 272p. 1985. pap. 17.95 (ISBN 0-8066-2023-4, 10-5633). Augsburg.

--Theology of the New Testament. (Contemporary Theology Ser.). 278p. 1951. pap. text ed. write for info. (ISBN 0-02-305580-4, Pub. by Scribner). Macmillan.

Bultmann, Rudolf, jt. auth. see Barth, Karl.

Bulwer-Lytton, Edward. Zanoni: A Rosicrucian Tale. 3rd ed. LC 78-157505. (Spiritual Fiction Publications: Vol. 1). 416p. 1985. cancelled (ISBN 0-8334-0000-2, Spiritual Fiction). Garber Comm.

--Zanoni: A Rosicrucian Tale, Vol. 4. LC 78-157505. (Spiritual Science Library). 412p. 1971. lib. bdg. 18.00 (ISBN 0-89345-014-6, Spiritual Sci Lib); pap. 11.50 (ISBN 0-89345-015-4, Steinerbks). Garber Comm.

Bumpus, J. A. Dictionary of Ecclesiastical Terms. 75.00 (ISBN 0-8490-0034-3). Gordon Pr.

Bumpus, John S. Dictionary of Ecclesiastical Terms: Being a History & Explanation of Certain Terms Used in Architecture, Ecclesiology, Liturgiology, Music, Ritual, Cathedral, Constitution, Etc. LC 68-30653. 1969. Repr. of 1910 ed. 35.00x (ISBN 0-8103-3321-X). Gale.

Bunce, William K., ed. Religions in Japan. LC 59-9234. 216p. 1981. pap. 5.25 (ISBN 0-8048-0500-8). C E Tuttle.

Bundschuh, Rick. Glow in the Dark. LC 86-31350. (Illus.). 148p. (Orig.). pap. 4.25 (ISBN 0-8307-1091-4, S182323). Regal.

--A Shadow of a Man. LC 86-22048. (Light Force Ser.). 120p. (Orig.). (YA) 1986. pap. 4.95 (ISBN 0-8307-1143-0, S185116). Regal.

Bundschuh, Rick & Gilbert, Dave. Dating Your Mate. 144p. (Orig.). 1987. pap. 4.95 (ISBN 0-89081-598-4). Harvest Hse.

Bundschuh, Rick, compiled by. Hot Buttons. LC 85-32323. (The Light Force Ser.). (Illus.). 153p. (Orig.). 1986. pap. 4.25 (ISBN 0-8307-1092-2, S182437). Regal.

Bundy, David D. Keswick: A Bibliographic Introduction to the Higher Life Movements. LC 76-369083. (Occasional Bibliographic Papers of the B. L. Fisher Library: No. 3). 89p. 1975. 3.00 (ISBN 0-914368-03-6). Asbury Theological.

Bunger, Robert L. Islamization among the Upper Pokomo. 2nd ed. LC 80-242. (Foreign & Comparative Studies-African Ser.: No. 33). 128p. (Orig.). 1979. pap. 7.00x (ISBN 0-915984-55-5). Syracuse U Foreign Comp.

Bunim. Ethics from Sinai, 3 vols. 1964. Set. 32.95 set (ISBN 0-87306-002-4); Set. pap. 19.95 set (ISBN 0-87306-003-2). Feldheim.

Bunim, Irving M. Ever since Sinai. Wengrov, Charles, ed. 1978. 13.95 (ISBN 0-87306-138-1). Feldheim.

Bunk, Elie. Ascent to Harmony. 180p. 1987. 8.95 (ISBN 0-87306-407-0). Feldheim.

Bunker, Dusty & Knowles, Victoria. Birthday Numerology. 240p. (Orig.). 1982. pap. 11.95 (ISBN 0-914918-39-7). Para Res.

Bunker, Dusty, jt. auth. see Javane, Faith.

Bunnag, Jane. Buddhist Monk, Buddhist Layman: A Study of Urban Monastic Organisation in Central Thailand. LC 72-86420. (Cambridge Studies in Social Anthropology: No. 6). (Illus.). 230p. 1973. 34.50 (ISBN 0-521-08591-8). Cambridge U Pr.

Bunnag, Krachang, tr. see Suriyabongs, Luang.

Bunnett, Fanny E., tr. see Grimm, Herman F.

Bunny, Edmund. Of Divorce for Adulterie & Marrying Againe: That There Is No Sufficient Warrant So to Do. (English Experience Ser.: No. 781). 1977. Repr. of 1612 ed. lib. bdg. 20.00 (ISBN 90-221-0781-7). Walter J Johnson.

Bunsen, Rick, ed. The Golden Christmas Treasury. LC 84-72934. (Illus.). 80p. 1986. 7.95 (ISBN 0-307-15585-4, Pub. by Golden Bks). Western Pub.

Bunson, Maggie. Faith in Paradise. 1977. 8.00 (ISBN 0-8198-0414-2). Dghtrs St Paul.

--Founding of Faith. 1977. 6.00 (ISBN 0-8198-0412-6); pap. 5.00 (ISBN 0-8198-0413-4). Dghtrs St Paul.

Buntain, D. N. The Holy Ghost & Fire. 100p. 1956. 1.25 (ISBN 0-88243-525-6, 02-0525). Gospel Pub.

Buntain, Mark, et al. Miracle in the Mirror. LC 81-70999. (Illus.). 155p. 1982. pap. 3.50 (ISBN 0-87123-352-5, 210352). Bethany Hse.

Bunyan, John. The Acceptable Sacrifice. pap. 1.75 (ISBN 0-685-88365-5). Reiner.

--Advice to Sufferers. pap. 3.25 (ISBN 0-685-19821-9). Reiner.

--Barren Fig Tree. pap. 1.25 (ISBN 0-685-19824-3). Reiner.

--Come & Welcome to Jesus Christ. 1974. pap. 2.50 (ISBN 0-685-52815-4). Reiner.

--Desire of the Righteous Granted. 1974. pap. 1.75 (ISBN 0-685-52816-2). Reiner.

--Doctrine of Law & Grace Unfolded. 1974. pap. 2.95 (ISBN 0-685-52817-0). Reiner.

--Exhortation to Unity & Peace. pap. 0.95 (ISBN 0-685-00744-8). Reiner.

--Fear of God. pap. 3.95 (ISBN 0-685-19828-6). Reiner.

--Grace Abounding to the Chief of Sinners. (Summit Bks). 132p. 1986. pap. 4.95 (ISBN 0-8010-0925-1). Baker Bk.

--The Greatness of the Soul. 1975. pap. 1.95 (ISBN 0-685-54807-4). Reiner.

--Groans of a Lost Soul. LC 68-6571. 1967. pap. 3.25 (ISBN 0-685-19830-8). Reiner.

--Heavenly Footman. pap. 1.25 (ISBN 0-685-19831-6). Reiner.

--Holy Life: The Beauty of Christianity. pap. 1.95 (ISBN 0-685-19832-4). Reiner.

--Holy War. 1975. 12.95 (ISBN 0-685-52819-7). Reiner.

--Holy War. 324p. 1986. pap. 6.95 (ISBN 0-8010-0924-3). Baker Bk.

--House of God. pap. 0.95 (ISBN 0-685-19834-0). Reiner.

--Intercession of Christ. pap. 1.95 (ISBN 0-685-19835-9). Reiner.

--Israel's Hope Encouraged. pap. 1.95 (ISBN 0-685-19836-7). Reiner.

--The Jerusalem Sinner Saved. pap. 3.25 (ISBN 0-685-88378-7). Reiner.

--Justification by an Imputed Righteousness. pap. 2.95 (ISBN 0-685-88380-9). Reiner.

--Light for Them That Sit in Darkness. pap. 3.50 (ISBN 0-685-19838-3). Reiner.

--The Miscellaneous Works of John Bunyan, Vols. 8 & 9. Greaves, Richard L., ed. (Oxford English Texts). 1979. 79.00x (ISBN 0-19-812736-7); Vol. 9, 1981 95.00x, (ISBN 0-19-812737-5). Oxford U Pr.

--My Imprisonment. pap. 1.75 (ISBN 0-686-64391-7). Reiner.

--Paul's Departure & Crown. pap. 0.95 (ISBN 0-685-19839-1). Reiner.

--Pharisee & the Publican. pap. 3.95 (ISBN 0-685-19840-5). Reiner.

--Pictorial Pilgrim's Progress. 1960. pap. 3.95 (ISBN 0-8024-0019-1). Moody.

--The Pilgrim's Progress. (Giant Summit Bks). pap. 8.95 (ISBN 0-8010-0732-1). Baker Bk.

--The Pilgrim's Progress. 1979. Repr. 19.95 (ISBN 0-85151-259-3). Banner of Truth.

--Pilgrim's Progress. (Moody Classics Ser.). 1984. pap. 3.95 (ISBN 0-8024-0012-4). Moody.

--Pilgrim's Progress. 1975. 14.95 (ISBN 0-685-52821-9). Reiner.

--Pilgrim's Progress. 288p. 1965. pap. 3.50 (ISBN 0-8007-8032-9, Spire Bks). Revell.

--Pilgrim's Progress. 416p. 1981. pap. 3.95 (ISBN 0-88368-096-3). Whitaker Hse.

--Pilgrim's Progress. 256p. 1973. pap. 3.95 (ISBN 0-310-22142-0, 6610P). Zondervan.

--Pilgrim's Progress. Helms, Hal M., ed. LC 81-85770. (Living Library Ser.). (Illus.). 270p. 1982. 6.95 (ISBN 0-941478-02-5). Paraclete Pr.

--The Pilgrim's Progress. Helms, Hal M., ed. (Illus.). 268p. pap. 6.95 (ISBN 0-941478-02-5, Pub. by Paraclete Pr). Upper Room.

--Pilgrim's Progress in Today's English. LC 64-25255. 1964. pap. 6.95 (ISBN 0-8024-6520-X). Moody.

--Pilgrims Progress, Sixteen Seventy-Eight. 288p. 1984. 30.00x (ISBN 0-905418-29-8, Pub. by Gresham England). State Mutual Bk.

--El Progreso del Peregrino Ilustrado. Orig. Title: Pilgrim's Progress Illustrated. (Span.). 254p. pap. 4.75 (ISBN 0-8254-1096-7). Kregel.

--Reprobation Asserted. pap. 1.25 (ISBN 0-685-19841-3). Reiner.

--Ruin of Antichrist. pap. 1.95 (ISBN 0-685-19842-1). Reiner.

--Saints Knowledge of Christ's Love. pap. 1.50 (ISBN 0-685-19843-X). Reiner.

--Saved by Grace. pap. 2.25 (ISBN 0-685-88393-0). Reiner.

--The Strait Gate. pap. 2.25 (ISBN 0-685-88394-9). Reiner.

--The Water of Life. pap. 1.50 (ISBN 0-685-88397-3). Reiner.

--Work of Jesus Christ As an Advocate. pap. 3.95 (ISBN 0-685-19844-8). Reiner.

Bunyan, John & Parkhurst, Louis G., Jr. John Bunyan: Pilgrim's Prayer Book. rev. ed. 136p. 1986. pap. 5.95 (ISBN 0-8423-4933-2). Tyndale.

Bunyan, John, et al. How They Found Christ: In Their Own Words. Freeman, Bill, ed. LC 83-62268. 66p. (Orig.). 1983. pap. 1.40 (ISBN 0-914271-00-8). NW Christian Pubns.

Buonarroti, Michelangelo. Michelangelo: A Record of His Life As Told in His Own Letters & Papers. Carden, Robert W., tr. 1976. lib. bdg. 59.95 (ISBN 0-8490-2256-8). Gordon Pr.

Buono, Anthon, tr. see Pope John Paul II.

Buono, Anthony. Liturgy: Our School of Faith. 177p. (Orig.). 1982. pap. 6.95 (ISBN 0-8189-0435-6). Alba.

Buono, Anthony M., tr. see John Paul, II.

Burba, Keith V., jt. auth. see Burba, Linda J.

Burba, Linda. Everybody Ought to Go to Learning Centers. (Teaching Helps Ser.). 80p. 1981. pap. 2.95 (ISBN 0-8010-0811-5). Baker Bk.

Burba, Linda J. & Burba, Keith V. T-R-A-I-N up the Children. 111p. 1985. pap. 4.50 (ISBN 0-8341-1062-8). Beacon Hill.

Burba, Nora, jt. auth. see Litvak, Stuart.

Burbach, Marilyn, jt. auth. see Thiry, Joan.

Burbach, Maur, et al. Our Family: A Love Story. 66p. 1981. 12.50 (ISBN 0-8146-1222-9). Liturgical Pr.

Burbick, Leslie. The Church's Strange Bedfellows. 1986. 6.95 (ISBN 0-8062-2408-8). Carlton.

Burbidge, John. Being & Will: An Essay in Philosophical Theology. LC 76-45934. pap. 40.70 (ISBN 0-8357-9484-9, 2013527). Bks Demand UMI.

Burch, Beverly, jt. auth. see Esau, Truman.

Burch, Francis F., tr. see Henry, Paul.

Burch, George B. Alternative Goals in Religion: Love, Freedom, Truth. 1973. pap. 3.95 (ISBN 0-7735-0163-0). McGill-Queens U Pr.

Burch, George B., ed. see Bhattacharrya, K. C.

Burch, V. Anthropology & the Apocalypse: An Interpretation of "the Book of Revelation" in Relation to the Archaeology, Folklore & Religious Literature & Ritual of the Near East. 1977. lib. bdg. 59.95 (ISBN 0-8490-1437-9). Gordon Pr.

Burckardt, Titus, tr. see Ibn'Arabi.

Burckhardt, John L. Travels in Syria & the Holy Land. LC 77-87614. (Illus.). 720p. 1983. Repr. of 1822 ed. 76.50 (ISBN 0-404-16437-4). AMS Pr.

Burckhardt, T., jt. auth. see Matheson, D. M.

Burd, Gene, jt. auth. see Fontaine, Jacob, III.

Burdick, Donald. Epistles of John. (Everyman's Bible Commentary Ser.). 1970. pap. 5.95 (ISBN 0-8024-2062-1). Moody.

Burdick, Donald W. Letters of John the Apostle. (Orig.). 1985. pap. 13.95 (ISBN 0-8024-2356-6). Moody.

Buren, James Van see Van Buren, James & Dewett, Don.

Buren, Paul M. Van see Van Buren, Paul M.

Burford, A. The Greek Temple Builders at Epidauros. (Liverpool Monographs in Archaeology & Oriental Studies). 274p. 1969. text ed. 25.00x (ISBN 0-85323-080-3, Pub. by Liverpool U Pr). Humanities.

Burg, B. R. Richard Mather of Dorchester. LC 75-41987. 224p. 1976. 21.00x (ISBN 0-8131-1343-1). U Pr of Ky.

Burg, B. Richard. Richard Mather. (United States Authors Ser.). 1982. lib. bdg. 16.50 (ISBN 0-8057-7364-9, Twayne). G K Hall.

Burg, Elizabeth. Midlife: Triumph-Not Crisis. 96p. (Orig.). 1986. pap. 4.50 (ISBN 0-914544-63-2). Living Flame Pr.

Burg, J. B. The Place of St. Patrick in History & His Life. 59.95 (ISBN 0-8490-0839-5). Gordon Pr.

Burger, Harald. Zeit und Ewigkeit: Studien zum Wortschatz der Geistlichen Texte des Alt-und Fruehmittelhochdeutschen. LC 74-174177. (Studia Linguistica Germanica: Vol. 6). 1972. 34.00x (ISBN 3-11-003995-8). De Gruyter.

Burger, Robert, jt. auth. see Morton, Craig.

Burgess, Alan. THe Small Woman: The Story of Gladys Aylward of China. 266p. 1985. pap. 5.95 (ISBN 0-89283-232-0, Pub. by Vine Books). Servant.

Burgess, Allan K. Helping Your Child Stay Morally Clean. LC 84-71705. 100p. 1984. 6.95 (ISBN 0-87747-671-3). Deseret Bk.

--How to Understand & Enjoy the Scriptures. LC 85-29212. (Illus.). 80p. 1986. 5.95 (ISBN 0-87579-030-5). Deseret Bk.

Burgess, Andrew J. Passion, Knowing How, & Understanding: An Essay on the Concept of Faith. LC 75-31550. (American Academy of Religion. Dissertation Ser.). 1975. pap. 9.95 (ISBN 0-89130-044-9, 010109). Scholars Pr GA.

Burgess, Beverly. Three Bears in the Ministry. 32p. (Orig.). 1982. pap. 3.98 (ISBN 0-89274-252-6). Harrison Hse.

Burgess, Beverly C. God Are You Really Real? (Illus.). 30p. (Orig.). 1985. pap. 1.98 (ISBN 0-89274-309-3). Harrison Hse.

--God Is My Best Friend. (Illus.). 32p. (Orig.). 1986. pap. 1.98 (ISBN 0-89274-293-3). Harrison Hse.

--Is Easter Just for Bunnies? (Illus.). 30p. (Orig.). 1985. pap. 1.98 (ISBN 0-89274-310-7). Harrison Hse.

Burgess, E. T. Interesting Men of the Bible. 1970. pap. 0.50 (ISBN 0-89114-007-7). Baptist Pub Hse.

Burgess, Edward E., ed. Christ, the Crown of the Torah. 220p. 1986. pap. 7.95 (ISBN 0-310-41621-3, 9942P). Zondervan.

Burgess, Eric. By Jupiter: Odysseys to a Giant. LC 82-4139. (Illus.). 192p. 1982. 26.50x (ISBN 0-231-05176-X). Columbia U Pr.

Burgess, Harold, ed. see Lawson, John.

Burgess, Harold, ed. see Wood, Laurence W.

Burgess, Harold W. An Invitation to Religious Education. LC 75-14980. 173p. 1975. lib. bdg. 12.95 (ISBN 0-89135-004-7); pap. 10.95 (ISBN 0-89135-019-5). Religious Educ.

Burgess, Harold W., ed. see Kelsey, Morton T.

Burgess, Henry J. Enterprise in Education: The Story of the Work of the Established Church in the Education of the People Prior to 1870. LC 59-1586. 1958. text ed. 15.00x (ISBN 0-8401-0289-5). A R Allenson.

Burgess, James & Fergusson, James. The Cave Temples of India. (Illus.). 1969. text ed. 57.50x. Coronet Bks.

Burgess, Jas. Buddhist Art in India. 240p. 27.00X (ISBN 0-317-52134-9, Pub. by S Chand India). State Mutual Bk.

Burgess, John. Black Gospel, White Church. 128p. 1982. pap. 7.95 (ISBN 0-8164-2380-6, HarpR). Har-Row.

Burgess, John H. Christian Pagan: A Naturalistic Survey of Christian History. (Illus.). 1968. 7.00 (ISBN 0-912084-04-9). Mimir.

Burgess, Joseph A. & Winn, Albert C. Epiphany. Achtemeier, Elizabeth, et al, eds. LC 79-7377. (Proclamation 2: Aids for Interpreting the Lessons of the Church Year, Series A). 64p. (Orig.). 1980. pap. 3.75 (ISBN 0-8006-4092-6, 1-4092). Fortress.

Burgess, Joseph A., jt. auth. see Andrews, James E.

Burgess, Joseph A., ed. The Role of the Augsburg Confession: Catholic & Lutheran Views. LC 79-7373. 224p. 1980. 14.95 (ISBN 0-8006-0549-7, 1-549). Fortress.

Burgess, Mary, jt. auth. see Clarke, Boden.

Burgess, Robert G. Experiencing Comprehensive Education: A Study of Bishop McGregor School. 288p. 1983. 24.00 (ISBN 0-416-35150-6, NO. 4037); pap. 11.95 (ISBN 0-416-35160-3, NO. 4038). Methuen Inc.

Burgess, W. J. Brother Burgess. (Illus.). 121p. 1975. 3.50 (ISBN 0-89114-069-7); pap. 1.50 (ISBN 0-89114-068-9). Baptist Pub Hse.

--Glossolalia. 64p. 1968. pap. 1.00 (ISBN 0-89114-053-0). Baptist Pub Hse.

Burgess, William. Bible in Shakespeare. 79.95 (ISBN 0-87968-728-2). Gordon Pr.

--Bible in Shakespeare. LC 68-24900. (Studies in Shakespeare, No. 24). 1969. Repr. of 1903 ed. lib. bdg. 75.00 (ISBN 0-8383-0921-6). Haskell.

Burghardt, W. J. & Lawler, T. C., eds. St. Gregory of Nyssa, the Lord's Prayer, the Beatitudes. LC 78-62466. (ACW Ser.: No. 18). 216p. 1954. 14.95 (ISBN 0-8091-0255-2). Paulist Pr.

--St. Irenaeus: Proof of the Apostolic Preaching. LC 78-62503. (ACW Ser.: No. 16). 242p. 1952. 12.95 (ISBN 0-8091-0254-4). Paulist Pr.

Burghardt, W. J., ed. see Augustine, St.

Burghardt, W. J., ed. see St. Augustine.

Burghardt, W. J., et al, eds. St. Augustine, Against the Academics. LC 78-62461. (ACW Ser.: No. 12). 220p. 1950. 10.95 (ISBN 0-8091-0252-8). Paulist Pr.

--St. Maximus the Confessor: The Ascetic Life, the Four Centuries on Charity. LC 55-8642. (ACW Ser.: No. 21). 293p. 1955. 13.95 (ISBN 0-8091-0258-7). Paulist Pr.

--Arnobius of Sicca, the Case Against the Pagans, Vol. 1. (ACW Ser.: No. 7). 372p. 1949. 13.95 (ISBN 0-8091-0248-X). Paulist Pr.

--Arnobius of Sicca, the Case Against the Pagans, Vol. 2. LC 78-62458. (ACW Ser.: No. 8). 659p. 1949. 11.95 (ISBN 0-8091-0249-8). Paulist Pr.

--Athenagoras, Embassy for the Christians, the Resurrection of the Dead. LC 56-11421. (Ancient Christian Writers Ser.: No. 23). 193p. 1956. 10.95 (ISBN 0-8091-0036-3). Paulist Pr.

--The Didache, the Epistle of Barnabas, the Epistle & Martyrdom of St. Polycarp, the Fragments of Papias, the Epistle of Diognetus. LC 78-62453. (ACW Ser.: No. 6). 241p. 1948. 13.95 (ISBN 0-8091-0247-1). Paulist Pr.

--Egeria, Diary of a Pilgrimage. LC 70-119159. (ACW Ser.: No. 38). 292p. 1970. 14.95 (ISBN 0-8091-0029-0). Paulist Pr.

--Firmicus Maternus, the Error of the Pagan Religions. (Ancient Christian Writers Ser.: No. 37). 1970. 11.95 (ISBN 0-8091-0039-8). Paulist Pr.

--Julianus Pomerius, the Contemplative Life. LC 78-62457. (ACW Ser.: No. 4). 220p. 1947. 9.95 (ISBN 0-8091-0245-5). Paulist Pr.

--Origen, Prayer, Exhortation to Martyrdom. LC 78-62467. (ACW Ser.: No. 19). 261p. 1954. 14.95 (ISBN 0-8091-0256-0). Paulist Pr.

--Origen, the Song of Songs: Commentary & Homilies. LC 57-11826. (ACW Ser.: No. 26). 491p. 1957. 14.95 (ISBN 0-8091-0261-7). Paulist Pr.

--Rufinus: A Commentary of the Apostles' Creed. LC 78-62468. (ACW Ser.: No. 20). 167p. 1955. 10.95 (ISBN 0-8091-0257-9). Paulist Pr.

--St. Athanasius: The Life of St. Antony. LC 78-62454. (ACW Ser.: No. 10). 155p. 1950. 12.95 (ISBN 0-8091-0250-1). Paulist Pr.

--St. Augustine, the Lord's Sermon on the Mount. LC 78-62451. (ACW Ser.: No. 5). 227p. 1948. 13.95 (ISBN 0-8091-0246-3). Paulist Pr.

--St. Augustine, the Problem of Free Choice. LC 78-62469. (ACW Ser.: No. 22). 298p. 1955. 11.95 (ISBN 0-8091-0259-5). Paulist Pr.

--St. Cyprian, the Lapsed, the Unity of the Catholic Church. LC 57-7364. (Ancient Christian Writers Ser.: No. 25). 132p. 1957. 10.95 (ISBN 0-8091-0260-9). Paulist Pr.

--St. Gregory the Great: Pastoral Care. (ACW Ser.: No. 11). 282p. 1950. 13.95 (ISBN 0-8091-0251-X). Paulist Pr.

--St. John Chrysostom, Baptismal Instructions. LC 62-21489. (Ancient Christian Writers Ser.: No. 31). 381p. 1963. 14.95 (ISBN 0-8091-0262-5). Paulist Pr.

--St. Methodius, the Symposium: A Treatise on Chastity. (Ancient Christian Writers Ser.: No. 27). 256p. 1958. 11.95 (ISBN 0-8091-0143-2). Paulist Pr.

--St. Prosper of Aquitaine, Defense of St. Augustine. LC 78-62463. (Ancient Christian Writers Ser.: No. 32). 235p. 1963. 10.95 (ISBN 0-8091-0263-3). Paulist Pr.

--St. Prosper of Aquitaine, the Call of All Nations. (Ancient Christian Writers Ser.: No. 14). 250p. 1952. 10.95 (ISBN 0-8091-0253-6). Paulist Pr.

--Tertullian, the Treatise Against Hermogenes. LC 56-13257. (Ancient Christian Writers Ser.: No. 24). 179p. 1956. 10.95 (ISBN 0-8091-0148-3). Paulist Pr.

--Tertullian, Treatise on Marriage & Remarriage: To His Wife, an Exhortation to Chastity Monogamy. LC 78-62462. (Ancient Christian Writers Ser.: No. 13). 103p. 1951. 10.95 (ISBN 0-8091-0149-1). Paulist Pr.

--Tertullian, Treatise on Penance: On Penitence & on Purity. LC 58-10746. (Ancient Christian Writers Ser.: No. 28). 138p. 1959. 12.95 (ISBN 0-8091-0150-5). Paulist Pr.

Burghardt, Walter J. Seasons That Laugh or Weep: Musings on the Human Journey. LC 83-60655. 144p. (Orig.). 1983. 4.95 (ISBN 0-8091-2533-1). Paulist Pr.

--Sir, We Would Like to See Jesus: Homilies from a Hilltop. LC 82-60589. 1983. pap. 8.95 (ISBN 0-8091-2490-4). Paulist Pr.

--Still Proclaiming Your Wonders: Homilies for the Eighties. 256p. (Orig.). 1984. pap. 9.95 (ISBN 0-8091-2632-X). Paulist Pr.

--Tell the Next Generation: Homilies & Near Homilies. LC 79-91895. 240p. 1980. pap. 8.95 (ISBN 0-8091-2252-9). Paulist Pr.

Burghardt, Walter J., ed. Religious Freedom, Nineteen Sixty-Five to Nineteen Seventy-Five: A Symposium on a Historic Document. LC 76-45938. 1977. pap. 2.95 (ISBN 0-8091-1993-5). Paulist Pr.

--Woman: New Dimensions. LC 76-50965. 1977. pap. 5.95 (ISBN 0-8091-2011-9). Paulist Pr.

Burghart, Johannes, jt. ed. see Lawler, Thomas C.

Burghart, Richard & Cantlie, Audrey, eds. Indian Religion. LC 84-15115. 320p. 1985. 27.50 (ISBN 0-312-41400-5). St Martin.

Burgt, Robert J. Vanden see Vanden Burgt, Robert J.

Burgus, Jackie. God Given Territory. 96p. 1986. pap. 2.95 (ISBN 0-938612-13-1). Revival Press.

Buri, Fritz. Theology of Existence. Oliver, Harold H, tr. 128p. 1965. 3.95 (ISBN 0-87921-001-X). Attic Pr.

Burkan, Bruce, jt. auth. see Keyes, Ken, Jr.

Burkan, Peggy D. Guiding Yourself into a Spiritual Reality: A Workbook. LC 83-91310. 96p. (Orig.). 1985. pap. 7.95 (ISBN 0-935616-06-3). Reunion Pr.

Burke, Albert L. He That Hath an Ear. 101p. (Orig.). 1982. pap. 3.50 (ISBN 0-9608662-0-5). Eleventh Hour.

Burke, Arthur M. Key to the Ancient Parish Registers of England & Wales. LC 62-6577. (Illus.). 163p. 1981. Repr. of 1908 ed. 15.00 (ISBN 0-8063-0445-6). Genealog Pub.

Burke, Cormac. Conscience & Freedom. 159p. (Orig.). 1977. pap. 4.95x (ISBN 0-933932-39-1). Scepter Pubs.

Burke, David G., ed. The Poetry of Baruch: A Reconstruction & Analysis of the Original Hebrew Text of Baruch 3: 9-5: 9. LC 80-10271. (Society of Biblical Literature, Septuagint & Cognate Studies: No. 10). pap. 15.95 (ISBN 0-89130-382-0, 06-04-10). Scholars Pr GA.

Burke, Dennis. Diligence. 96p. (Orig.). 1983. pap. 2.50 (ISBN 0-89274-307-7, HH307). Harrison Hse.

--How to Meditate God's Word. 64p. 1982. pap. 2.25 (ISBN 0-89274-241-0, HH-241). Harrison Hse.

--Knowing God Intimately. 1985. pap. 2.95 (ISBN 0-89274-349-2). Harrison Hse.

--Understanding the Fear of the Lord. 1982. pap. 2.25 (ISBN 0-89274-265-8, HH-265). Harrison Hse.

Burke, John. Beginners' Guide to Bible Sharing I. 192p. 1985. pap. 8.95 (ISBN 0-697-02014-2). Wm C Brown.

--Beginners' Guide to Bible Sharing II. 240p. 1984. pap. 9.95 (ISBN 0-697-02015-0). Wm C Brown.

--Bible Sharing: How to Grow in the Mystery of Christ. LC 79-15006. (Orig.). 1979. pap. 5.95 (ISBN 0-8189-0386-4). Alba.

--Bible Sharing Youth Retreat: Manual for Retreat Team. 1986. pap. 4.50 (ISBN 0-697-02209-9). Wm C Brown.

--Gospel Power: Toward the Revitalization of Preaching. LC 77-14517. 1978. pap. 4.95 (ISBN 0-8189-0359-7). Alba.

Burke, John, ed. A New Look at Preaching. (Good News Studies Ser.: Vol. 7). 1983. pap. 6.95 (ISBN 0-89453-336-3). M Glazier.

Burke, John B. Studies in Genesis. 1979. pap. 4.95 (ISBN 0-88469-048-2). BMH Bks.

Burke, John J., Jr. & Kay, Donald, eds. The Unknown Samuel Johnson. LC 81-70159. (Illus.). 224p. 1983. 32.50x (ISBN 0-299-09150-3). U of Wis Pr.

Burke, Kenneth. The Rhetoric of Religion: Studies in Logology. 1970. pap. 9.95x (ISBN 0-520-01610-6, CAMPUS 341). U of Cal Pr.

Burke, Marie L. Swami Vivekananda: His Second Visit to the West (New Discoveries) 20.00 (ISBN 0-87481-151-1). Vedanta Pr.

--Swami Vivekananda in the West: New Discoveries: His Prophetic Mission, 2 Vols, Vol. 1. new ed. (Illus.). 515p. text ed. 12.95x (ISBN 0-317-03702-1, Pub. by Advaita Ashrama India). Vedanta Pr.

--Swami Vivekananda in the West: New Discoveries, Vol. II. (Illus.). 457p. 1985. 12.95x (ISBN 0-87481-219-4, Pub. by Advaita Ashrama India). Vedanta Pr.

Burke, Maurice R. The Evolution of the Human Mind: The Passage from Self to Cosmic Consciousness. (Physic Research Library Bks.). (Illus.). 137p. 1981. Repr. of 1905 ed. 69.85 (ISBN 0-89901-033-4). Found Class Reprints.

Burke, O. M. Among the Dervishes. 1973. 11.95 (ISBN 0-900860-17-0, Pub. by Octagon Pr England); pap. 5.95 (ISBN 0-525-47386-6). Ins Study Human.

Burke, Patrick. The Fragile Universe: An Essay in the Philosophy of Religions. LC 78-17885. (Library of Philosophy & Religion). 129p. 1979. text ed. 28.50x (ISBN 0-06-490776-7, 06373). B&N Imports.

Burke, Pratricia A, et al. Adventures from God's Word. rev. ed. Miller, Marge, ed. (Basic Bible Readers Ser.). (Illus.). 128p. 1983. text ed. 7.95 (ISBN 0-87239-663-0, 2953). Standard Pub.

Burke, Richard J. Understanding & Implementing Development. 1985. 4.80 (ISBN 0-318-18573-3). Natl Cath Educ.

Burke, T. Patrick, jt. auth. see Friedman, Maurice S.

Burke, Thomas. Hibernia Dominicana, Sive Historia Provinciae: Hiberniae Ordinis Praedicatorum. 966p. Repr. of 1762 ed. text ed. 124.20x (ISBN 0-576-78541-5, Pub. by Gregg Intl Pubs England). Gregg Intl.

Burke, Thomas P. The Reluctant Vision: An Essay in the Philosophy of Religion. LC 73-88354. pap. 35.50 (2026883). Bks Demand UMI.

Burkert, Walter. Greek Religion. 504p. 1987. pap. text ed. 9.95x (ISBN 0-674-36281-0). Harvard U Pr.

--Homo Necans: Interpretationen altgriechischer Opferriten und Mythen. LC 72-83051. (Religionsgeschichtliche Versuche und Vorarbeiten: Vol. 32). 356p. 1972. 43.20x (ISBN 3-11-003875-7). De Gruyter.

--Lore & Science in Ancient Pythagoreanism. Minar, Edwin L., Jr., tr. from Ger. LC 70-162856. (Illus.). 512p. 1972. 35.00x (ISBN 0-674-53918-4). Harvard U Pr.

--Structure & History in Greek Mythology & Ritual. LC 78-62856. (Sather Classical Lectures Ser.: Vol. 47). 1980. 30.00x (ISBN 0-520-03771-5); pap. 9.95 (ISBN 0-520-04770-2, CAL 581). U of Cal Pr.

Burkert, William. Greek Religion. Raffan, John, tr. from Ger. LC 84-25209. 493p. 1985. text ed. 30.00x (ISBN 0-674-36280-2). Harvard U Pr.

Burkett, Larry. The Financial Planning Workbook. LC 82-7877. (Christian Financial Concepts Ser.). 1982. pap. 6.95 (ISBN 0-8024-2546-1). Moody.

--How to Manage Your Money. LC 82-7904. (Christian Financial Concepts Ser.). 1982. pap. 7.95 (ISBN 0-8024-2547-X). Moody.

--Using Your Money Wisely: Guidelines from Scripture. 1986. pap. 7.95 (ISBN 0-8024-3425-8). Moody.

--What Husbands Wish Their Wives Knew about Money. 1977. pap. 3.95 (ISBN 0-88207-758-9). Victor Bks.

Burkett, Randall K. Garveyism As a Religious Movement: The Institutionalization of a Black Civil Religion. LC 78-15728. (ATLA Monograph Ser.: No. 13). 242p. 1978. 19.00 (ISBN 0-8108-1163-4). Scarecrow.

Burkett, Randall K. & Newman, Richard. Black Apostles: Afro-American Clergy Confront the Twentieth Century. 1978. lib. bdg. 28.50 (ISBN 0-8161-8137-3, Hall Reference). G K Hall.

Burkey, F. T., ed. The Brethren: Growth in Life & Thought. 1975. pap. 3.50x (ISBN 0-934970-00-9). Brethren Ohio.

Burkhardt, John E. Worship. LC 81-23116. 162p. 1982. pap. 8.95 (ISBN 0-664-24409-2). Westminster.

Burkhart, Rob. I Hate Witnessing Leader's Guide. LC 84-18165. 64p. 1985. pap. 3.95 (ISBN 0-8307-1011-6, 6101987). Regal.

--Yet Will I Trust Him. LC 79-91705. (Study & Grow Electives). 64p. 1985. pap. 3.95 (ISBN 0-8307-1016-7, 6102002). Regal.

Burkhart, W. Eugene, Jr. Decorating Christmas Trees. (Illus.). 64p. (Orig.). 1985. pap. 8.95 (ISBN 0-9615199-0-8). Burkharts.

Burkhart, Wanda. Submitting To A Sinning Husband. 64p. 1984. pap. 2.95 (ISBN 0-88144-042-6). Christian Pub.

Burkholder, Byron, ed. They Saw His Glory: Stories of Conversion & Service. 186p. (Orig.). 1984. pap. 5.95 (ISBN 0-919797-40-7). Kindred Pr.

Burkholder, J. Lawrence. To Drink or Not to Drink. 24p. (Orig.). 1981. pap. text ed. 0.75 (ISBN 0-8361-1967-3). Herald Pr.

Burkholder, J. R. & Redekop, Calvin, eds. Kingdom, Cross, & Community. LC 76-29663. 312p. 1976. 14.95 (ISBN 0-317-37847-3). Herald Pr.

Burkill, T. A. Evolution of Christian Thought. LC 76-127775. 518p. 1971. 29.50x (ISBN 0-8014-0581-5). Cornell U Pr.

Burkill, T. A., ed. see Winter, Paul.

Burkitt, F. C. Jewish & Christian Apocalypses. (British Academy, London, Schweich Lectures on Biblical Archaeology Series, 1914). pap. 19.00 (ISBN 0-8115-1255-X). Kraus Repr.

--S. Ephraim's Quotations from the Gospel. (Texts & Studies Ser.: No. 1, Vol. 7, Pt. 2). pap. 13.00 (ISBN 0-8115-1704-7). Kraus Repr.

Burkitt, F. Crawford. The Earliest Sources for the Life of Jesus. 1977. lib. bdg. 59.95 (ISBN 0-8490-1736-X). Gordon Pr.

Burkitt, Francis C. Church & Gnosis: A Study of Christian Thought & Speculation in the Second Century. LC 77-84696. (The Morse Lectures: 1931). Repr. of 1932 ed. 26.00 (ISBN 0-404-16104-9). AMS Pr.

--Early Christianity Outside the Roman Empire: Two Lectures Delivered at Trinity College, Dublin. LC 82-45806. 1983. Repr. of 1899 ed. 18.00 (ISBN 0-404-62375-1). AMS Pr.

--The Religion of the Manichees: Donnellan Lectures for 1924. LC 77-84698. Repr. of 1925 ed. 29.00 (ISBN 0-404-16105-7). AMS Pr.

Burkitt, Lemuel & Read, Jesse. A Concise History of the Kehukee Bapist Association from Its Original Rise to the Present Time. rev. ed. Gaustad, Edwin S., ed. LC 79-52591. (The Baptist Tradition Ser.). 1980. Repr. of 1850 ed. lib. bdg. 28.50x (ISBN 0-405-12458-9). Ayer Co Pubs.

Burkle, Howard R. God, Suffering, & Belief. LC 76-26496. Repr. of 1977 ed. 24.40 (ISBN 0-8357-9010-X, 2016364). Bks Demand UMI.

Burl. The Stone Circles of the British Isles. 1976. 46.00x (ISBN 0-300-01972-6); pap. 22.50x (ISBN 0-300-02398-7, Y-341). Yale U Pr.

Burl, Aubrey. Rites of the Gods. (Illus.). 272p. 1981. text ed. 26.50x (ISBN 0-460-04313-7, BKA 04660, Pub. by J M Dent England). Biblio Dist.

Burland, C. A. Way of the Buddha. (The Way Ser.). pap. 5.95 (ISBN 0-7175-0590-1). Dufour.

Burleigh, Harry T. Negro Spirituals, 2 vols. in 1. LC 74-24262. Repr. of 1922 ed. 45.00 (ISBN 0-404-12874-2). AMS Pr.

Burleigh, John S., ed. Augustine: Earlier Writings. LC 53-13043. (Library of Christian Classics). 410p. 1979. softcover 8.95 (ISBN 0-664-24162-X). Westminster.

Burlingame, E. W. Buddhist Parables. 59.95 (ISBN 0-87968-803-3). Gordon Pr.

--Buddhist Parables. lib. bdg. 79.95 (ISBN 0-87968-494-1). Krishna Pr.

Burman, Ben L. Children of Noah. 5.00 (ISBN 0-685-02658-2). Taplinger.

Burman, Bina R. Religion & Politics in Tibet. 1979. text ed. 17.50x (ISBN 0-7069-0801-5, Pub. by Vikas India). Advent NY.

Burman, Edward. The Templars: Knights of God. (Crucible Ser.). 208p. 1987. pap. 9.95 (ISBN 0-85030-396-6). Thorsons Pubs.

Burman, Madeleine L. Code of the Prophets. LC 84-90888. (Illus.). 100p. (Orig.). 1984. 9.95x (ISBN 0-9613283-0-4); pap. 6.95x. M L Burman.

Burman, Peter. St. Paul's Cathedral. (The New Bell's Cathedral Guides Ser.). 1986. cancelled 24.95 (ISBN 0-918678-15-3). Historical Times.

Burn, A. E. The Athanasian Creed & Its Early Commentaries. (Texts & Studies Ser.: No. 1, Vol. 4, Pt. 1). pap. 19.00 (ISBN 0-8115-1691-1). Kraus Repr.

Burn, Helen J. Better Than the Birds, Smarter Than the Bees. LC 69-12771. (YA) pap. 21.30 (ISBN 0-8357-9000-2, 2016348). Bks Demand UMI.

Burn, Samuel C. Jonah. 1981. lib. bdg. 11.25 (ISBN 0-86524-071-X, 3201). Klock & Klock.

Burnaby, John, ed. Augustine: Later Works. LC 55-5022. (Library of Christian Classics). 356p. 1980. pap. 11.95 (ISBN 0-664-24165-4). Westminster.

Burnaby, Sherrard B. Elements of the Jewish Muhammadan Calendars. 1976. lib. bdg. 59.95 (ISBN 0-8490-1757-2). Gordon Pr.

Burnet, Bishop. History of His Own Times. 409p. 1980. Repr. lib. bdg. 12.50 (ISBN 0-89987-056-2). Darby Bks.

Burnet, David S. & Davis, Moshe, eds. The Jerusalem Mission: Under the Direction of the American Christian Missionary Society. (America & the Holy Land Ser.). 1977. Repr. of 1853 ed. lib. bdg. 26.50x (ISBN 0-405-10233-X). Ayer Co Pubs.

Burnet, Gilbert. The History of the Reformation of the Church of England, 7 vols. rev. ed. LC 83-45575. Date not set. Repr. of 1865 ed. Set. 425.00 (ISBN 0-404-19893-7). Ams Pr.

Burnet, Thomas. Sacred Theory of the Earth. LC 65-10027. (Centaur Classics Ser.). (Illus.). 414p. 1965. 22.50x (ISBN 0-8093-0186-5). S Ill U Pr.

Burnett, Betty. A Time of Favor: The Story of the Catholic Family of Southern Illinois. Franzwa, Gregory M., ed. xvi, 305p. 1987. 10.00 (ISBN 0-935284-48-6). Patrice Pr.

Burnett, Fred W. The Testament of Jesus-Sophia: A Redaction-Critical Study of the Eschatological Discourse in Matthew. LC 80-67211. 491p. (Orig.). 1981. lib. bdg. 35.75 (ISBN 0-8191-1743-9); pap. text ed. 19.75 (ISBN 0-8191-1744-7). U Pr of Amer.

Burnett, J. J. Sketches of Tennessee's Pioneer Baptist Preachers: History of Baptist Beginnings in the Several Associations in the State. (Illus.). 576p. 1985. Repr. of 1919 ed. 21.95 (ISBN 0-932807-11-9). Overmountain Pr.

Burnett, Linda, jt. auth. see Meier, Paul D.

Burnett, V. Compton, tr. see Steiner, Rudolf.

Burney, C. F. The Book of Judges with Introduction & Notes. 528p. Repr. of 1920 ed. lib. bdg. 100.00 (ISBN 0-8495-0481-3). Arden Lib.

--Israel's Settlement in Canaan: The Biblical Tradition & Its Historical Background. 3rd ed. (British Academy, London, Schweich Lectures on Biblical Archaeology Series, 1917). pap. 19.00 (ISBN 0-8115-1259-2). Kraus Repr.

Burney, Joan, jt. auth. see Chandler, Phyllis.

Burnham, Kenneth E. God Comes to America: Father Divine & the Peace Mission Movement. 167p. 1979. 16.95x (ISBN 0-931186-01-3). Lambeth Pr.

Burnham, Sue. Dynamics of Christian Living for Women. LC 81-67598. 50p. (Orig.). (YA) 1981. pap. 2.95 (ISBN 0-940386-00-3). Dynamics Chr Liv.

Burnham, T. Lee. Home & School Connection. 1986. 7.95 (ISBN 0-87579-045-3, Pub. by Shadow Mountain). Deseret Bk.

Burns, et al. The Revival of Religion. 449p. 1984. Repr. of 1840 ed. 13.95 (ISBN 0-85151-435-9). Banner of Truth.

Burns, Allan F., tr. An Epoch of Miracles: Oral Literature of the Yucatec Maya. (Texas Pan American Ser.). (Illus.). 282p. 1983. text ed. 24.50x (ISBN 0-292-72037-8). U of Tex Pr.

Burns, Echo B. Hands that Heal. (Orig.). 1986. pap. 7.95 (ISBN 0-917086-76-7). A C S Pubns Inc.

Burns, J. A. Growth & Development of the Catholic School System in the United States. LC 78-89156. (American Education: Its Men, Institutions & Ideas, Ser. 1). 1969. Repr. of 1912 ed. 21.00 (ISBN 0-405-01394-9). Ayer Co Pubs.

--The Principles, Origin & Establishment of the Catholic School System in the United States. LC 74-89155. (American Education: Its Men, Institutions & Ideas Ser). 1969. Repr. of 1908 ed. 21.00 (ISBN 0-405-01393-0). Ayer Co Pubs.

Burns, J. H. Scottish Churchmen & the Council of Basle. LC 64-7472. 1962. 15.00 (ISBN 0-8023-9034-X). Dufour.

Burns, J. Patout & Fagin, Gerald M. The Holy Spirit. (Message of the Fathers of the Church Ser.: Vol. 3). 16.95 (ISBN 0-89453-343-6); pap. 10.95 (ISBN 0-89453-315-0). M Glazier.

Burns, J. Patout, ed. Theological Anthropology. LC 81-43080. (Sources of Early Christian Thought Ser.). 1981. pap. 7.95 (ISBN 0-8006-1412-7). Fortress.

Burns, J. Patout, ed. see Helgeland, John & Daly, Robert J.

Burns, Jabez. Ninety-One Sermon Outlines on Types & Metaphors. LC 86-27347. 128p. (Orig.). 1987. pap. 5.95 (ISBN 0-8254-2270-1). Kregel.

--One Hundred Fifty-One Sermon Outlines. LC 86-27520. 208p. (Orig.). 1987. pap. 7.95 (ISBN 0-8254-2266-3). Kregel.

--One Hundred Forty-Nine Sermon Outlines. LC 86-27436. 208p. (Orig.). 1987. pap. 7.95 (ISBN 0-8254-2265-5). Kregel.

--One Hundred Ninety-Nine Sermon Outlines. LC 86-27540. 256p. (Orig.). 1987. pap. 8.95 (ISBN 0-8254-2267-1). Kregel.

--Two Hundred One Sermon Outlines. LC 86-27758. 256p. 1987. pap. 8.95 (ISBN 0-8254-2269-8). Kregel.

--Two Hundred Sermon Outlines. LC 75-92502. 128p. 1987. pap. 6.95 (ISBN 0-8254-2264-7). Kregel.

Burns, Jim. Christian Growth Series Leader's Guide. 1986. 7.95 (ISBN 0-89081-555-0). Harvest Hse.

--Getting in Touch with God. 1986. pap. 4.95 (ISBN 0-89081-520-8). Harvest Hse.

--Giving Yourself to God: Pursuing Excellence in Your Christian Life. (Orig.). pap. 3.95; wkbk. 3.95 (ISBN 0-89081-488-0). Harvest Hse.

--Growth Unlimited. 160p. (Orig.). 1987. pap. 5.95 (ISBN 0-89081-580-1). Harvest Hse.

--The Incredible Christ. (LifeSources for Youth Ser.: No. 3). 64p. (Orig.). 1987. wkbk. 3.95 (ISBN 0-89081-575-5). Harvest Hse.

--Jim Burn's Youth Series 1--Leaders' Guide. (Orig.). 1985. pap. 7.95 (ISBN 0-89081-495-3). Harvest Hse.

--Living Your Life... As God Intended. (Illus., Orig.). 1985. pap. 3.95 (ISBN 0-89081-450-3). Harvest Hse.

--Making Your Life Count. (Illus.). 64p. Wkbk 3.95 (ISBN 0-89081-392-2). Harvest Hse.

--The Ninety Day Experience. 112p. 1984. wkbk. 5.95 (ISBN 0-915929-12-0). Merit Bks.

--Putting God First. (Illus.). 64p. 1983. wkbk. 3.95 (ISBN 0-89081-366-3). Harvest Hse.

Burns, Jim & Bostrom, Carol. Handling Your Hormones. (Illus.). 64p. (Orig.). 1984. involvement guide 4.95 (ISBN 0-915929-10-4); leader's guide 1.95 (ISBN 0-915929-14-7). Merit Bks.

Burns, Jim & Fields, Doug. Congratulations! You are Gifted! (Jim Burns Youth Ser.: No. 2). 64p. (Orig.). (YA) 1986. pap. 3.95 (ISBN 0-89081-478-3, 4783). Harvest Hse.

Burns, Jim & Webster, Doug. Building Relationships...With God & Others. (Jim Burns Youth Ser.: No. 2). 64p. (Orig.). 1986. wkbk. 3.95 (ISBN 0-89081-479-1). Harvest Hse.

--Commitment to Growth: Experiencing the Fruit of the Spirit. 64p. (Orig.). 1985. wkbk. 3.95 (ISBN 0-89081-480-5). Harvest Hse.

Burns, Jim & Yaconelli, Mike. High School Ministry. 368p. 1986. 16.95 (ISBN 0-310-34920-6, 10826). Zondervan.

Burns, John, jt. auth. see Twenty-Four Magazine Editors.

Burns, Louis F., ed. Osage Mission Baptisms, Marriages, & Interments, 1820-1886. (Osage Indian & Eng.). 869p. 1986. 35.00 (ISBN 0-942574-08-7). Ciga Pr.

Burns, Marilyn. The Hanukkah Book. (Illus.). 128p. 1981. 9.95 (ISBN 0-02-716140-4, Four Winds). Macmillan.

Burns, Norman T. Christian Mortalism from Tyndale to Milton. LC 72-75406. 224p. 1972. 16.50x (ISBN 0-674-12875-3). Harvard U Pr.

Burns, Patricia H. The Book of Revelation Explained, Vol. 1. LC 82-90898. iv, 57p. 1986. pap. 9.95 (ISBN 0-9611368-0-4). B R E Pub.

Burns, Paul, jt. ed. see Cumming, John.

Burns, Paul, tr. see Boff, Leonardo & Boff, Clodovis.

Burns, Peter, jt. auth. see Connolly, Finbarr.

Burns, R. M. The Great Debate on Miracles: From Joseph Glanvill to David Hume. LC 78-75197. 300p. 1981. 28.50 (ISBN 0-8387-2378-0). Bucknell U Pr.

Burns, Ralph O. Basic Bible Truths for New Converts. 30p. 1978. pap. 0.60 (ISBN 0-87227-007-6). Reg Baptist.

Burns, Ridge & Campbell, Pam. Create in Me a Youth Ministry. 204p. 1986. pap. 11.95 (ISBN 0-89693-636-8). Victor Bks.

Burns, Rita. Exodus, Leviticus, Numbers, with Excursus on Feasts, Ritual, Typology. (Old Testament Message Ser.: Vol. 3). 15.95 (ISBN 0-89453-403-3); pap. 9.95 (ISBN 0-89453-238-3). M Glazier.

--Ezra Nehemiah. (Bible Commentary Ser.). 96p. 1985. pap. 2.95 (ISBN 0-8146-1418-3). Liturgical Pr.

Burns, Rita J. Has the Lord Indeed Spoken Only Through Moses? A Study of the Biblical Portrait of Miriam. (Society of Biblical Literature Dissertation Ser.). 148p. 1987. 16.95 (ISBN 0-89130-964-0, 06-01-84); pap. 12.95 (ISBN 0-89130-965-9). Scholars Pr GA.

Burns, Robert. Jesuits & the Indian Wars of the Northwest. LC 65-22314. 550p. (Orig.). 1985. pap. 12.95 (ISBN 0-89301-110-X). U of Idaho Pr.

Burns, Robert I. Diplomatarium of the Crusader Kingdom of Valencia: The Registered Charters of Its Conqueror, Jaume I, 1257-1276. Volume I: Society & Documentation in Crusader Valencia. LC 84-17828. (Illus.). 288p. 1985. text ed. 40.00x (ISBN 0-691-05435-5). Princeton U Pr.

--Medieval Colonialism: Post-Crusade Exploitation of Islamic Valencia. (Illus.). 432p. 1975. 44.50 (ISBN 0-691-05227-1). Princeton U Pr.

--Muslims, Christians & Jews in the Crusader Kingdom of Valencia: Societies in Symbiosis. LC 83-2007. (Cambridge Iberian & Latin American Studies). 300p. 1984. 65.00 (ISBN 0-521-24374-2). Cambridge U Pr.

Burns, William C. Revival Sermons. 205p. 1981. pap. 4.95 (ISBN 0-85151-316-6). Banner of Truth.

Burnshaw, Stanley. My Friend, My Father. (Galaxy Books). 160p. 1986. pap. 7.95 (ISBN 0-19-503723-5). Oxford U Pr.

Burow, Daniel R. & Greene, Carol, eds. The Little Christian's Songbook. 64p. 1975. pap. 5.50 (56-1266). Concordia.

Burqhardt, ed. see Jerome, Saint.

Burqhardt, ed. see Paulinus of Nola, Saint.

Burr, Angela. I Am Not My Body: A Study of the International Hare Krishna Sect. 352p. 1984. text ed. 35.00x (ISBN 0-7069-2296-4, Pub by Vikas India). Advent NY.

Burr, Anna R. Religious Confessions & Confessants. 1977. lib. bdg. 59.95 (ISBN 0-8490-2511-7). Gordon Pr.

Burr, David. Eucharistic Presence & Conversion in Late Thirteenth Century Franciscan Thought. LC 83-73283. (Transactions Ser.: Vol. 74 Pt. 3). 113p. 1984. 12.00 (ISBN 0-87169-743-2). Am Philos.

Burr, George L. New England's Place in the History of Witchcraft. facsimile ed. LC 71-164592. (Select Bibliographies Reprint Ser). Repr. of 1911 ed. 15.00 (ISBN 0-8369-5876-4). Ayer Co Pubs.

--Persecution & Liberty: Essays in Honor of George Lincoln Burr. facs. ed. LC 68-26467. (Essay Index Reprint Ser). 1968. Repr. of 1931 ed. 17.50 (ISBN 0-8369-0783-3). Ayer Co Pubs.

Burr, Nelson R., compiled by. Religion in American Life. LC 70-136219. (Goldentree Bibliographies in American History Ser.). (Orig.). 1971. 15.95x (ISBN 0-88295-507-1). Harlan Davidson.

Burr, William H. Revelations of Antichrist: Concerning Christ & Christianity. LC 79-161340. (Atheist Viewpoint Ser). 448p. 1972. Repr. of 1879 ed. 29.00 (ISBN 0-405-03801-1). Ayer Co Pubs.

Burrage, Barbara. The Bible Quiz Book. 1979. pap. 2.95 (ISBN 0-8192-1256-3). Morehouse.

--Bible Quizzerama Puzzle Book. 48p. (Orig.). 1981. pap. 1.95 (ISBN 0-87239-446-8, 2836). Standard Pub.

Burrage, Champlin, ed. Answer to John Robinson of Leyden by a Puritan Friend. (Harvard Theological Studies). 1920. pap. 15.00 (ISBN 0-527-01009-X). Kraus Repr.

Burrell, Arthur. Cathedral on the Nile: The History of All Saints Cathedral, Cairo. 120p. 1985. 30.00x (ISBN 0-317-43629-5, Pub. by Amate Pr. Ltd.). State Mutual Bk.

Burrell, David B. Aquinas: God & Action. LC 78-51519. 1979. text ed. 14.95x (ISBN 0-268-00588-5). U of Notre Dame Pr.

--Exercises in Religious Understanding. LC 74-12566. pap. 63.30 (ISBN 0-317-26713-2, 2024366). Bks Demand UMI.

--Knowing the Unknowable God: Ibn-Sina, Maimonides, Aquinas. LC 85-40600. 160p. 1986. text ed. 15.95x (ISBN 0-268-01225-3, 85-12253). U of Notre Dame Pr.

--Knowing the Unknowable God: Ibn-Sina, Maimonides, Aquinas. 130p. 1986. pap. text ed. 8.95x (ISBN 0-268-01226-1, Dist. by Harrow). U of Notre Dame Pr.

Burrell, David B. & Kane, Franzita, eds. Evangelization in the American Context. LC 76-22403. 1976. pap. 2.95x (ISBN 0-268-00902-3). U of Notre Dame Pr.

Burrell, Jill & Burrell, Maurice. Arctic Mission. 1974. 1.60 (ISBN 0-08-017621-6). Pergamon.

Burrell, M. C. & Wright, J. S. Today's Sects. 4.50 (ISBN 0-8010-0855-7). Baker Bk.

Burrell, Maurice, jt. auth. see Burrell, Jill.

Burrell, Maurice C. The Challenge of the Cults. (Direction Bks.). 160p. (Orig.). 1982. pap. 3.95 (ISBN 0-8010-0816-6). Baker Bk.

Burrell, Percival. Suttons Synagogue: Or the English Centurion (A Sermon) LC 74-28822. (English Experience Ser.: No. 647). 1974. Repr. of 1629 ed. 3.50 (ISBN 90-221-0647-0). Walter J Johnson.

Burridge, Kenelm. New Heaven, New Earth: A Study of Millenarian Activities. (Pavilion Ser.). 198p. 1969. pap. text ed. 12.95x (ISBN 0-631-11950-7). Basil Blackwell.

Burris, W. H. Revelations of Antichrist. 59.95 (ISBN 0-8490-0950-2). Gordon Pr.

Burriss, Eli E. Taboo, Magic, Spirits: A Study of Primitive Elements in Roman Religion. LC 72-114489. x, 250p. Repr. of 1931 ed. lib. bdg. 22.50x (ISBN 0-8371-4724-7, BUTA). Greenwood.

Burron, Arnold & Crews, Jerry. Guaranteed Steps to Managing Stress. (Orig.). 1986. pap. 6.95 (ISBN 0-8423-1249-8). Tyndale.

Burron, Arnold, et al. Classrooms in Crisis. LC 85-73068. 196p. (Orig.). 1986. pap. 7.95 (ISBN 0-89636-192-6). Accent Bks.

Burron, Arnold H. Discipline That Can't Fail. 1986. pap. 4.95 (ISBN 0-8010-0940-5). Baker Bk.

Burroughs. The Christian Woman's Resource Book. LC 83-26063. 1987. 9.95 (A Bridgebooks Publication). Westminster.

Burroughs, Jeremiah. The Rare Jewel of Christian Contentment. 1979. pap. 5.45 (ISBN 0-85151-091-4). Banner of Truth.

Burroughs, Melba G. The Christian Woman's Resource Book. LC 83-26063. 202p. (Orig.). 1984. pap. 9.95 (ISBN 0-664-26008-X, A Bridgebooks Publication). Westminster.

Burrow, Dan. When Jesus Was a Baby. LC 84-70244. (Augsburg Open Window Bks.). (Illus.). 12p. (Orig.). 1984. pap. 4.95 (ISBN 0-8066-2078-1, 10-7082). Augsburg.

Burrows, Millart. Founders of Great Religions: Being Personal Sketches of Famous Leaders. LC 72-13272. (Essay Index Reprint Ser.). Repr. of 1931 ed. 16.75 (ISBN 0-8369-8148-0). Ayer Co Pubs.

Burrows, Ruth. Before the Living God. 6.95 (ISBN 0-87193-155-9). Dimension Bks.

--Guidelines for Mystical Prayer. 5.95 (ISBN 0-87193-134-6). Dimension Bks.

--Living Love: Meditations on Texts from the New Testament. 1985. 5.95 (ISBN 0-87193-243-1). Dimension Bks.

--Our Father. (Illus.). 96p. 1986. 5.95 (ISBN 0-87193-255-5). Dimension Bks.

--To Believe in Jesus. 6.95 (ISBN 0-87193-154-0). Dimension Bks.

Burrows, Stephen G. God's Daughter in Nassau. 186p. 1980. 8.50 (ISBN 0-682-49497-6). Exposition Pr FL.
Burrows, William R. New Ministries: The Global Context. LC 80-17261. 192p. (Orig.). 1980. pap. 7.95 (ISBN 0-88344-329-5). Orbis Bks.
Burrus, Ernest. Ducrue's Account of Expulsion of the Jesuits from Lower California. 1967. pap. 20.00 (ISBN 88-7041-502-3). Jesuit Hist.
Burrus, Ernest J., ed. Jesuit Relations, Baja California, 1716-1762. (Baja California Travels Ser.: Vol. 47). (Illus.). 280p. 1984. 60.00 (ISBN 0-87093-243-8). Dawsons.
Burrus, Virginia. Chastity As Autonomy: Women in the Stories of Apocryphal Acts. (Studies in Women & Religion). 184p. 1987. text ed. 39.95 (ISBN 0-88946-526-6). E Mellen.
Burstein, A. Religion, Cults & the Law. 2nd ed. (Legal Almanac Ser.: No. 23). 128p. 1980. 6.95 (ISBN 0-379-11133-0). Oceana.
Burstein, Chaya M. The Jewish Kids Catalog. (Illus.). 224p. 1983. pap. 10.95 (ISBN 0-8276-0215-4, 603). Jewish Pubns.
Burt, Donald X. The Inn of the Samaritan. 96p. (Orig.). 1983. pap. 5.95 (ISBN 0-8146-1315-2). Liturgical Pr.
--The Rush to Resurrection. 112p. 1985. pap. 5.95 (ISBN 0-8146-1440-X). Liturgical Pr.
Burtchaell, James T. For Better, for Worse. 160p. (Orig.). 1985. pap. 5.95 (ISBN 0-8091-2664-8). Paulist Pr.
--Philemon's Problem: The Daily Dilemma of the Christian. LC 73-88935. 1973. pap. 2.95 (ISBN 0-914070-05-3). ACTA Found.
--Rachel Weeping: The Case Against Abortion. LC 83-48986. 400p. 1984. pap. 10.95 (ISBN 0-06-061251-7, RD 517, HarpR). Har-Row.
Burtchaell, James T., et al. Marriage Among Christians: A Curious Tradition. LC 77-81396. (Illus.). 192p. 1977. pap. 3.50 (ISBN 0-87793-139-9). Ave Maria.
Burthogge, Richard. An Essay upon Reason & the Nature of Spirits. LC 75-11204. (British Philosophers & Theologians of the 17th & 18th Centuries: Vol. 10). 1976. Repr. of 1694 ed. lib. bdg. 51.00 (ISBN 0-8240-1759-5). Garland Pub.
Burtis, Warren D. Jesus: The First Human Behaviorist. 128p. 1981. pap. text ed. 5.95 (ISBN 0-939530-00-7). Burtis Ent.
Burtner, Robert W. & Chiles, Robert E., eds. John Wesley's Theology: A Collection from His Works. 304p. 1982. pap. 7.95 (ISBN 0-687-20529-8). Abingdon.
Burtness, James. Shaping the Future: The Ethics of Dietrich Bonhoeffer. LC 85-47723. 208p. 1985. pap. 16.95 (ISBN 0-8006-1869-6, 1-1869). Fortress.
Burtness, James H., tr. see Bonhoeffer, Dietrich.
Burto, William, jt. auth. see Barnet, Sylvan.
Burton, Alma P. Discourses of the Prophet Joseph Smith. LC 77-23977. 399p. 9.95 (ISBN 0-87747-067-7). Deseret Bk.
--Toward the New Jerusalem. LC 85-10203. 172p. 1985. 7.95 (ISBN 0-87747-883-X). Deseret Bk.
Burton, Alma P., jt. auth. see Burton, Clea M.
Burton, Asa. Essays on Some of the First Principles of Metaphysicks, Ethicks, & Theology. LC 73-4839. (History of Psychology Ser.). 432p. 1973. Repr. of 1824 ed. lib. bdg. 60.00x (ISBN 0-8201-1114-7). Schol Facsimiles.
Burton, Clea M. & Burton, Alma P. For They Shall Be Comforted. 5.95 (ISBN 0-87747-091-X). Deseret Bk.
Burton, Earl H., ed. Your Spiritual Deposit. 68p. 1982. pap. 2.00 (ISBN 0-910068-66-6). Am Christian.
Burton, Edward. An Inquiry into the Heresies of the Apostolic Age. LC 78-63166. (Heresies of the Early Christian & Medieval Era: Second Ser.). Repr. of 1829 ed. 62.50 (ISBN 0-404-16179-0). AMS Pr.
Burton, Ella S. God's Word Is Our Only Foundation. 1983. 5.75 (ISBN 0-8062-2164-X). Carlton.
Burton, Ernest D. Syntax of Moods & Tenses of New Testament Greek. 240p. 1898. 11.95 (ISBN 0-567-01002-3, Pub. by T & T Clark Ltd UK). Fortress.
--Syntax of the Moods & Tenses of New Testament Greek. LC 76-25360. 238p. 1976. 12.95 (ISBN 0-8254-2256-6). Kregel.
Burton, Ernest D., jt. auth. see Stevens, William A.
Burton, Ernest De Witt. A Critical & Exegetical Commentary on the Epistle to the Galatians. Driver, Samuel R. & Briggs, Charles A., eds. (International Critical Commentary Ser.). 632p. 1921. 24.95 (ISBN 0-567-05029-7, Pub. by T & T Clark Ltd UK). Fortress.
Burton, Henry. An Apology of Appeale: Also, an Epistle to the True Hearted Nobility. LC 76-57364. (English Experience Ser.: No. 782). 1977. Repr. of 1636 ed. lib. bdg. 5.00 (ISBN 90-221-0782-5). Walter J Johnson.
--For God & the King. LC 76-57365. (English Experience Ser.: No. 783). 1977. lib. bdg. 17.50 (ISBN 90-221-0783-3). Walter J Johnson.
--A Tryall of Private Devotions. LC 77-6863. (English Experience Ser.: No. 856). 1977. Repr. of 1628 ed. lib. bdg. 10.50 (ISBN 90-221-0856-2). Walter J Johnson.
Burton, Isabel, ed. see Burton, Richard F.
Burton, Isadel, ed. see Vetalapancavimsati.
Burton, John. The Collection of the Qur'an. LC 76-27899. 1977. 49.50 (ISBN 0-521-21439-4); pap. 15.95 (ISBN 0-521-29652-8). Cambridge U Pr.
Burton, John H., ed. see Carlyle, Alexander.
Burton, Katherine K. In No Strange Land. facsimile ed. LC 72-99619. (Essay Index Reprint Ser). 1942. 19.50 (ISBN 0-8369-1551-8). Ayer Co Pubs.
Burton, Laurel A. From Hiding to Healing. Sherer, Michael L., ed. (Orig.). 1987. pap. 2.75 participant bk. (ISBN 0-89536-860-9, 7819); pap. 2.25 leader's guide (ISBN 0-89536-861-7, 7820). CSS of Ohio.
Burton, O. E. Study in Creative History. LC 71-105821. (Classics Ser). 1971. Repr. of 1932 ed. 26.00x (ISBN 0-8046-1197-1, Pub. by Kennikat). Assoc Faculty Pr.
Burton, Richard, tr. The Kama Sutra of Vatsyayana. (Hindustani.). 340p. 1986. 16.95 (ISBN 0-88029-089-7, Pub. by Dorset). Hippocrene Bks.
Burton, Richard F. The Jew, the Gypsy & el Islam. 1974. Repr. of 1898 ed. 6.00 (ISBN 0-913022-11-X). Angriff Pr.
--Personal Narrative of a Pilgrimage to Al-Madinah & Meccah, 2 Vols. (Illus.). 1893. Vol. 1. pap. 8.95 (ISBN 0-486-21217-3). Vol. 2. pap. 8.95 (ISBN 0-486-21218-1). Dover.
--Personal Narrative of a Pilgrimage to Al-Madinah & Meccah, 2 Vols. Burton, Isabel, ed. Set. 28.50 (ISBN 0-8446-1781-4). Peter Smith.
--Wit & Wisdom from West Africa: A Book of Proverbial Philosophy, Idioms, Enigmas, & Laconisms. LC 77-79952. 1969. Repr. of 1865 ed. 16.00 (ISBN 0-8196-0243-4). Biblo.
Burton, Richard F., tr. see Vetalapancavimsati.
Burton, Ursula & Dolley, Janice. Christian Evolution. 160p. 1984. pap. 9.95 (ISBN 0-85500-204-2). Newcastle Pub.
Burton, William F. Where to Go with Your Troubles. 80p. 1969. pap. 1.00 (ISBN 0-88243-627-9, 02-0627). Gospel Pub.
Burton, Wilma. Sidewalk Psalms... & Some from Country Lanes. LC 79-92015. 119p. 1980. 8.95 (ISBN 0-89107-165-2). Good News.
--Without a Man in the House. LC 78-68403. pap. 5.95 (ISBN 0-89107-158-X). Good News.
Burtsell, Richard L. & Callahan, Nelson J. The Diary of Richard L. Burtsell, Priest of New York the Early Years, 1865-1868. 37.50 (ISBN 0-405-10813-3). Ayer Co Pubs.
Burtt, Edwin A., ed. Teachings of the Compassionate Buddha. (Orig.). 1955. pap. 3.95 (ISBN 0-451-62450-5, ME2282, Ment). NAL.
Burwick, Ray. Self Esteem: You're Better Than You Think. 1983. pap. 5.95 (ISBN 0-8423-5865-X). Tyndale.
Bury, George W. Pan-Islam. LC 80-1938. Repr. of 1919 ed. 30.00 (ISBN 0-404-18956-3). AMS Pr.
Bury, John B. The Life of St. Patrick: His Place in History. facsimile ed. LC 79-175691. (Select Bibliographies Reprint Ser). Repr. of 1905 ed. 24.50 (ISBN 0-8369-6606-6). Ayer Co Pubs.
Busch, Ernestine G., ed. The Avesta: Major Portions from the Holy Book of the Magi. LC 85-90618. 440p. (Orig.). 1985. pap. 17.50 (ISBN 0-9614750-0-5). E G Busch.
Buschkuhl, Matthias. Great Britain & the Holy See 1746-1870. (Illus.). 260p. 1982. text ed. 40.00x (ISBN 0-7165-0290-9, Pub. by Irish Academic Pr Ireland). Biblio Dist.
Bush, Barbara. Heart Trouble: A Woman's Workshop on Christian Character. Kobobel, Janet, ed. (Woman's Workshop Ser.). (Orig.). 1985. pap. 2.95 (ISBN 0-310-29431-2, 12016P). Zondervan.
--Walking in Wisdom: A Woman's Workshop on Ecclesiastes. (Woman's Workshop Ser.). 128p. (Orig.). 1982. pap. 3.50 (ISBN 0-310-43041-0, 12014P). Zondervan.
Bush, Bernard J. Living in His Love: Essays on Prayer & Christian Living. LC 78-11809. 115p. 1978. pap. 3.95 (ISBN 0-89571-005-6). Affirmation.
Bush, Bernard J., ed. Coping: Issues of Emotional Living in an Age of Stress for Clergy & Religious. LC 76-362761. 83p. 1976. pap. 2.95 (ISBN 0-89571-000-5). Affirmation.
Bush, Charles W. How to Hear God Speak. 128p. (Orig.). 1975. pap. text ed. 1.50 (ISBN 0-89228-028-X). Impact Bks MO.
Bush, Danny E. Invitation to the Feast. LC 85-13314. 1985. pap. 3.75 (ISBN 0-8054-5019-X). Broadman.
Bush, Douglas. Pagan Myth & Christian Tradition in English Poetry. LC 68-8639. (Memoirs Ser.: Vol. 72). 1968. 5.00 (ISBN 0-87169-072-1). Am Philos.
Bush, George. Exodus. 1981. 22.50 (ISBN 0-86524-097-3, 0202). Klock & Klock.
--Genesis, 2 vols. 1981. 29.95 (ISBN 0-86524-094-9, 0103). Klock & Klock.
--Joshua & Judges. 1981. 17.95 (ISBN 0-86524-100-7, 0602). Klock & Klock.
--Leviticus. 1981. 10.50 (ISBN 0-86524-098-1, 0302). Klock & Klock.
--Numbers. 1981. 17.95 (ISBN 0-86524-099-X, 0401). Klock & Klock.
Bush, John C., jt. auth. see Tiemann, William H.
Bush, L. Russ, ed. Classical Readings in Christian Apologetics: A. D. 100-1800. 1986. pap. 11.95 (ISBN 0-310-45641-X, 11622P). Zondervan.
Bush, Lester E. & Mauss, Armand L., eds. Neither White nor Black: Mormon Scholars Confront the Race Issue in a Universal Church. 250p. 1984. pap. 11.95 (ISBN 0-941214-22-2). Signature Bks.
Bush, Marcella. The Community of God. (Illus.). 1975. pap. 3.75x (ISBN 0-8192-4057-5); tchr's guide 4.95x (ISBN 0-8192-4056-7). Morehouse.
Bush, Richard C., et al. Religious Word. 1982. text ed. write for info. (ISBN 0-02-317480-3). Macmillan.
Bush, Russ & Nettles, Tom. Baptists & the Bible. LC 80-11694. 1980. pap. 10.95 (ISBN 0-8024-0474-X). Moody.
Bush, Sargent, Jr. The Writings of Thomas Hooker: Spiritual Adventure in Two Worlds. LC 79-5404. 400p. 1980. 29.50x (ISBN 0-299-08070-6). U of Wis Pr.
Bushman, Claudia L., et al. Mormon Sisters: Women in Early Utah. LC 76-53854. (Illus.). 320p. 1980. pap. 9.95 (ISBN 0-913420-95-6). Olympus Pub Co.
Bushman, Richard L. Joseph Smith & the Beginnings of Mormonism. LC 84-2451. 270p. 1984. 17.95 (ISBN 0-252-01143-0). U of Ill Pr.
Bushman, Richard L., ed. The Great Awakening: Documents on the Revival of Religion, 1740-1745. (Institute of Early American History & Culture Ser.). xiv, 174p. 1970. 15.00x (ISBN 0-8078-1181-5). U of NC Pr.
Bushnell, David L., Jr. Native Cemeteries & Forms of Burial East of the Mississippi. Repr. of 1920 ed. 29.00x (ISBN 0-403-03658-5). Scholarly.
Bushnell, Horace. Christ in Theology: Hartford, 1851. Kuklick, Bruce, ed. (American Religious Thought of the 18th & 19th Centuries Ser.). 348p. 1987. lib. bdg. 50.00 (ISBN 0-8240-6965-X). Garland Pub.
--God in Christ. LC 76-39568. Repr. of 1849 ed. 25.00 (ISBN 0-404-01245-0). AMS Pr.
--God in Christ: Hartford, 1849. Kuklick, Bruce, ed. (American Religious Thought of the 18th & 19th Centuries Ser.). 356p. 1987. lib. bdg. 50.00 (ISBN 0-8240-6964-1). Garland Pub.
--Nature & the Supernatural As Together Constituting the One System of God. LC 70-39569. Repr. of 1858 ed. 29.50 (ISBN 0-404-01246-9). AMS Pr.
--Views of Christian Nurture & Subjects Related Thereto. LC 74-23297. 264p. 1975. Repr. of 1847 ed. lib. bdg. 40.00x (ISBN 0-8201-1147-3). Schol Facsimiles.
Bushong, Ann B. A Guide to the Lectionary. 1978. pap. 5.95 (ISBN 0-8164-2156-0, HarpR). Har-Row.
Bushrui, Suheil. Gibran of Lebanon. 12.00x (ISBN 0-86685-008-2). Intl Bk Ctr.
Busi, Frederick. The Pope of AntiSemitism: The Career & Legacy of Edouard-Adolphe Drumont. 242p. (Orig.). 1986. text ed. 26.50 (ISBN 0-8191-5594-2); pap. text ed. 12.50 (ISBN 0-8191-5595-0). U Pr of Amer.
Buskirk, William R. Van see Van Buskirk, William R.
Busool, A. N. Forty Ahadith: Asqalani. 1981. 4.50 (ISBN 0-686-97860-9). Kazi Pubns.
Buss, Martin J. The Prophetic Words of Hosea: A Morphological Study. (Beiheft 111 Zur Zeitschrift Fuer Die alttestamentliche Wissenschaft). 1969. 30.00- (ISBN 3-11-002579-5). De Gruyter.
Bussard, Paula & Wyrtzen, Christine. Lessons on Love from Critter County. 144p. 1986. wkbk. 9.95 (ISBN 0-87403-000-5, 3340). Standard Pub.
Bussard, Paula J. & Jefferson, Patti. Lessons on Praise from Critter County: Helping Children Praise God. (Critter County Ser.). 144p. 1987. pap. 9.95 (ISBN 0-87403-217-2, 3337). Standard Pub.
Bussell, Harold. Lord, I Can Resist Anything but Temptation. (Orig.). 1985. pap. 5.95 (ISBN 0-310-37271-2, 12389P). Zondervan.
Bussell, Harold L. Unholy Devotion: Why Cults Lure Christians. 160p. 1983. pap. 5.95 (ISBN 0-310-37251-8, 12388P). Zondervan.
Bussmann, Claus. Who Do You Say? Jesus Christ in Latin American Theology. Barr, Robert, tr. from Ger. LC 84-16476. Tr. of Befreiung durch Jesus? 192p. (Orig.). 1985. pap. 9.95 (ISBN 0-88344-711-8). Orbis Bks.
Bustanoby, Andre. Being a Success at Who You Are. 1986. pap. 4.95 (ISBN 0-310-45381-X, 9172P). Zondervan.
--But I Didn't Want a Divorce. 1978. o. p. 5.95 (ISBN 0-310-22170-6, 9207P); pap. 5.95 (ISBN 0-310-22171-4). Zondervan.
--Just Friends? 160p. (Orig.). 1985. pap. 6.95 (ISBN 0-310-45431-X, 9254P). Zondervan.
Buswell, G., tr. see Marxsen, Willi.
Buswell, James O., Jr. Systematic Theology of the Christian Religion. 27.95 (ISBN 0-310-22190-0, 9364P). Zondervan.
Buswell, Robert E., Jr., tr. see Chinul.
Buswell, Sara. Challenge of Old Testament Women Two. 176p. (Orig.). 1987. pap. 5.95 (ISBN 0-8010-0932-4). Baker Bk.
Butani, D. H. The Third Sikh War? Towards or Away from Khalistan? 137p. 1986. 25.00x (ISBN 81-85002-02-9, Pub. by Promilla). South Asia Bks.
Butcher, Edith L. The Story of the Church of Egypt, 2 vols. LC 75-41459. Repr. of 1897 ed. Set. 87.50 (ISBN 0-404-56231-0). AMS Pr.
Butchvarov, Panayot. Being Qua Being: A Theory of Identity, Existence & Predication. LC 78-13812. 288p. 1979. 22.50x (ISBN 0-253-13700-4). Ind U Pr.
Buth, Lenore. The Employed Wife. 176p. (Orig.). 1986. pap. 5.95 (ISBN 0-570-04436-7). Concordia.
Butigan, Ken, jt. ed. see Joranson, Philip N.
Butkovsky-Hewitt, Anna. With Gurdjieff in St. Petersburg. 1978. 9.95 (ISBN 0-7100-8527-3). Weiser.
Butler, Alban. Lives of the Saints, 4 vols. Attwater, Thurston, ed. 1956. Set. 140.00 (ISBN 0-87061-045-7); Set. pap. 95.00 (ISBN 0-87061-137-2). Chr Classics.
Butler, B. C. Prayer: An Adventure in Living. (Ways of Prayer Ser.: Vol. 10). 8.95 (ISBN 0-89453-431-9); pap. 4.95 (ISBN 0-89453-302-9). M Glazier.
Butler, C. Western Mysticism: Neglected Chapters in the History of Religion. 69.95 (ISBN 0-87968-244-2). Gordon Pr.
Butler, Charles. Principles of Musik, in Singing & Setting. LC 68-13273. (Music Ser.). 1970. Repr. of 1636 ed. lib. bdg. 23.50 (ISBN 0-306-70939-2). Da Capo.
--The Principles of Musik, in Singing & Setting. LC 74-25439. (English Experience Ser.: No. 284). 136p. 1971. Repr. of 1636 ed. 14.00 (ISBN 90-221-0284-X). Walter J Johnson.
Butler, Chris. Reincarnation Explained. LC 83-61000. 288p. 1984. 12.95 (ISBN 0-88187-000-5). Science Identity.
Butler, Christopher. The Theology of Vatican II. rev. ed. 238p. 1981. pap. 17.50 (ISBN 0-87061-062-7). Chr Classics.
Butler, E. M. The Myth of the Magus. 283p. 1982. Repr. of 1948 ed. lib. bdg. 65.00 (ISBN 0-89984-084-1). Century Bookbindery.
--The Saint-Simonian Religion in Germany. 1968. Repr. of 1926 ed. 45.00x (ISBN 0-86527-177-1). Fertig.
Butler, Frances J., jt. ed. see Benestace, J. Brian.
Butler, Francis J. & Farrell, Catherine E. Foundation Guide for Religious Grant Seekers. 2nd, rev., updated ed. LC 84-10593. (Handbook Ser.). 150p. 1984. pap. 11.95 (ISBN 0-89130-756-7, 00 15 02). Scholars Pr GA.
Butler, Geoffrey. Studies in Statecraft. LC 79-110899. 1970. Repr. of 1920 ed. 17.00x (ISBN 0-8046-0882-2, Pub. by Kennikat). Assoc Faculty Pr.
Butler, George P., ed. Best Sermons, Nineteen Forty-Nine to Nineteen Fifty. facsimile ed. LC 74-134065. (Essay Index Reprint Ser). Repr. of 1949 ed. 23.50 (ISBN 0-8369-2488-6). Ayer Co Pubs.
--Best Sermons, 1947. facsimile ed. LC 74-134065. (Essay Index Reprint Ser). Repr. of 1947 ed. 23.50 (ISBN 0-8369-2487-8). Ayer Co Pubs.
Butler, J. Donald. The Language of Exixtence & Faith. LC 86-30549. 1987. 19.95 (ISBN 0-8022-2532-2). Philos Lib.
Butler, James T., et al. Understanding the Word: Essays in Honor of Bernhard W. Anderson. (JSOT Supplement Ser.: No. 37). 390p. 1986. text ed. 37.50x (ISBN 0-905774-88-4, Pub. by JSOT Pr England). Eisenbrauns.
Butler, John. Christian Ways to Date, Go Steady, & Break up. (Mini Bible Studies). (Illus.). 1978. pap. 2.95 (ISBN 0-87239-986-9, 39949). Standard Pub.
--TV, Movies & Morality: A Guide for Catholics. LC 84-60753. 144p. 1984. pap. 6.95 (ISBN 0-87973-602-X, 602). Our Sunday Visitor.
Butler, Jonathan M., jt. ed. see Numbers, Ronald L.
Butler, Joseph. The Analogy of Religion. 30.00 (ISBN 0-8274-1862-0). R West.

--The Analogy of Religion. 3rd ed. 1986. lib. bdg. 25.00x (ISBN 0-935005-40-4); pap. text ed. 13.00x (ISBN 0-935005-41-2). Ibis Pub VA.
--Five Sermons. Darwall, Stephen, ed. LC 83-12577. (HPC Philosophical Classics Ser.). 86p. 1983. pap. text ed. 3.45 (ISBN 0-915145-61-8). Hackett Pub.
Butler, Karl D., jt. auth. see Palmer, Richard F.
Butler, L. A. & Morris, R. K., eds. The Anglo-Saxon Church: Papers on History, Architecture, & Archaeology in Honor of Dr. H. M. Taylor. (Research Report Ser.: No. 60). (Illus.). 240p. 1986. pap. 45.00x (ISBN 0-906780-54-3, Pub. by Council British Archaeology). Humanities.
Butler, Mary & Butler, Trent. The John Allen Moores: Good News in War & Peace. LC 85-6656. (Meet the Missionary Ser.). 1985. 5.50 (ISBN 0-8054-4295-2, 4242-95). Broadman.
Butler, P. T. Minor Prophets: The Prophets of the Decline: Hosea-Jonan. LC 79-1493. (Bible Study Textbook). 1968. 15.90 (ISBN 0-317-03548-7). College Pr Pub.
Butler, Paul. The Gospel of John. 3rd ed. LC 78-1789. (The Bible Study Textbook Ser.). (Illus.). 1965. 15.90 (ISBN 0-89900-035-5). College Pr Pub.
--Isaiah, Vol. III. (The Bible Study Textbook). (Illus.). 1978. 14.30 (ISBN 0-89900-022-3). College Pr Pub.
--Isaiah, Vol. I. LC 75-328170. (The Bible Study Textbook Ser.). (Illus.). 1980. cancelled (ISBN 0-89900-020-7). College Pr Pub.
--Isaiah, Vol. II. (The Bible Study Textbook Ser.). (Illus.). 1976. cancelled (ISBN 0-89900-021-5). College Pr Pub.
--Isaiah, Vol. I, II. (Bible Study Textbook). 694p. 1980. 15.90 (ISBN 0-89900-061-4). College Pr Pub.
--Luke. LC 81-68817. (Bible Study Textbook Ser.). 627p. 1981. 17.50 (ISBN 0-89900-062-2). College Pr Pub.
Butler, Paul T. Studies in First Corinthians. (Bible Study Textbook Ser.). 416p. text ed. 14.30 (ISBN 0-89900-063-0). College Pr Pub.
Butler, Paul T., jt. auth. see Ratzlaff, Ruben M.
Butler, Ralph. Out of the Silence. 142p. 1978. pap. 2.95 (ISBN 0-7050-0059-1). Attic Pr.
Butler, Richard O. Religious Vocation: An Unnecessary Mystery. LC 78-14365. 1979. Repr. of 1961 ed. lib. bdg. cancelled (ISBN 0-313-21018-7, BURV). Greenwood.
Butler, Roy F. The Meaning of Agapao & Phileo in the Greek New Testament. 1977. 6.50x (ISBN 0-87291-089-X). Coronado Pr.
Butler, Trent, jt. auth. see Butler, Mary.
Butler, Trent C. Layman's Bible Book Commentary: Isaiah, Vol. 10. LC 80-68890. 1983. 5.95 (ISBN 0-8054-1180-1). Broadman.
Butler, W. E. Magic & the Qabbalah. 1972. pap. 8.95 (ISBN 0-85030-155-6). Weiser.
Butler-Bowdon, W. The Book of Margery Kempe: A Modern Version. 1978. Repr. of 1936 ed. lib. bdg. 25.00 (ISBN 0-8482-3353-0). Norwood Edns.
Butt, Herbert W. Tests of Eternal Life: Studies in First John. pap. 0.50 (ISBN 0-685-00745-6). Reiner.
Buttaci, Salvatore S. & Gerstle, Susan L., eds. Reflections of the Inward Silence. LC 76-19240. 1976. 9.95 (ISBN 0-917398-03-3); pap. 7.95 (ISBN 0-917398-04-1). New Worlds.
Buttenwieser, Moses. The Psalms: Chronologically Treated with a New Translation. rev. ed. (Library of Biblical Studies Ser.). 1969. 59.50x (ISBN 0-87068-044-7). Ktav.
Butterfield, Herbert. Christianity in European History: The Riddel Memorial Lectures, 1951. 1979. Repr. of 1952 ed. lib. bdg. 15.00 (ISBN 0-8482-3440-5). Norwood Edns.
--Herbert Butterfield on History. Winks, Robin W., ed. LC 83-49176. (History & Historiography Ser.). 204p. 1985. lib. bdg. 30.00 (ISBN 0-8240-6352-X). Garland Pub.
--International Conflict in the Twentieth Century. LC 74-6777. 123p. 1974. Repr. of 1960 ed. lib. bdg. 65.00 (ISBN 0-8371-7569-0, BUIC). Greenwood.
--Writing on Christianity & History. 1979. 19.95x (ISBN 0-19-502454-0). Oxford U Pr.
Butterfield, Lyman, jt. auth. see Lumpkin, William L.
Butterly, Daniel R. The Reckless Heart: Meleager & Atalanta. 64p. (Orig.). 1986. 25.00 (ISBN 0-86516-172-0); pap. 15.00 (ISBN 0-86516-173-9). Bolchazy-Carducci.
Butterworth, Adeline M. William Blake: Mystic. LC 74-8017. 1911. lib. bdg. 15.00 (ISBN 0-8414-3186-8). Folcroft.
Butterworth, C. E. & A. Abd Al-Magid Haridi, eds. Averroes's Middle Commentary on Aristotle's Topics. (American Research Center in Egypt, Publications Ser.: Vol. 4). (Arabic & Eng.). 247p. (Orig.). 1979. pap. 5.00x (ISBN 0-686-30893-X, Pub. by Am Res Ctr Egypt). Eisenbrauns.
Butterworth, Charles C. The English Primers, Fifteen Twenty-Nine to Fifteen Forty-Five: Their Publication & Connection with the English Bible & the Reformation in England. 1970. lib. bdg. 26.00x (ISBN 0-374-91131-2, Octagon). Hippocrene Bks.
Butterworth, E. A. Some Traces of the Pre-Olympian World in Greek Literature & Myth. LC 85-21959. (Illus.). 1966. 44.25x (ISBN 3-11-005010-2). De Gruyter.
Butterworth, Eric. Discover the Power Within You. LC 68-17583. 1968. 13.45 (ISBN 0-06-061266-5, HarpR). Har-Row.
--In the Flow of Life. LC 82-50121. 181p. 1982. Repr. 5.95 (ISBN 0-87159-065-4). Unity School.
--Life Is for Loving. LC 73-6326. 128p. 1974. 10.53 (ISBN 0-06-061268-1, HarpR). Har-Row.
--Spiritual Economics--the Prosperity Process. 220p. 1983. 5.95 (ISBN 0-87159-142-1). Unity School.
--Unity: A Quest for Truth. (Orig.). 1965. pap. 3.00 (ISBN 0-8315-0020-4). Speller.
--Unity: A Quest for Truth. 160p. 1985. 5.95 (ISBN 0-87159-165-0, X1965, ROBERT SPELLER & SONS PUB.). Unity School.
Butterworth, F. Edward. Return of the Ancients. (Orig.). 1987. pap. 10.00 (ISBN 0-941227-00-6). Cosmic Pr Chico.
--Roots of the Reorganization: French Polynesia. LC 77-944. (Illus.). 1977. pap. 8.00 (ISBN 0-8309-0176-0). Herald Hse.
Butterworth, H. The Story of the Hymns. 59.95 (ISBN 0-8490-1139-6). Gordon Pr.
Butterworth, Hezekiah. Story of Hymns & Tunes. 1981. Repr. lib. bdg. 79.00x (ISBN 0-403-00107-2). Scholarly.
Butterworth, Nick. Parables, 4 vols. (Illus.). 1986. 6.95 ea. Vol. 1: The House on the Rock (ISBN 0-88070-146-3). Vol. 2: The Lost Sheep (ISBN 0-88070-147-1). The Two Sons (ISBN 0-88070-145-5) (ISBN 0-88070-148-X). Multnomah.
Butterworth, Nick & Inkpen, Mick. The Nativity Play. (Illus.). 32p. 1985. 10.95 (ISBN 0-316-11903-2). Little.
Buttolph, Philip, tr. see Dibelius, Martin & Conzelmann, Hans.
Buttrick, David. Epiphany. LC 84-18756. (Proclamation 3 C Ser.). 64p. 1985. pap. 3.75 (ISBN 0-8006-4126-4). Fortress.
Buttrick, David, jt. auth. see Juel, Donald H.
Buttrick, David G. Homiletic. LC 86-45208. 544p. 1987. 24.95 (ISBN 0-8006-0777-5, 1-777). Fortress.
Buttrick, George A. The Interpreter's Bible, 12 vols. Incl. Vol. 1. General Articles, Genesis, Exodus. 1952 (ISBN 0-687-19207-2); Vol. 2. Leviticus - Samuel. 1953 (ISBN 0-687-19208-0); Vol. 3. Kings - Job. 1954 (ISBN 0-687-19209-9); Vol. 4. Psalms, Proverbs. 1955 (ISBN 0-687-19210-2); Vol. 5. Ecclesiates - Jeremiah. 1956 (ISBN 0-687-19211-0); Vol. 6. Lamentations - Malachi. 1956 (ISBN 0-687-19212-9); Vol. 7. General Articles, Matthew, Mark. 1951 (ISBN 0-687-19213-7); Vol. 8. Luke, John. 1952 (ISBN 0-687-19214-5); Vol. 9. The Acts, Romans. 1954 (ISBN 0-687-19215-3); Vol. 10. Corinthians, Ephesians. 1953 (ISBN 0-687-19216-1); Vol. 11. Philippians - Hebrews. 1955 (ISBN 0-687-19217-X); Vol. 12. James - Revelation. 1957 (ISBN 0-687-19218-8). LC 51-12276. 1957. 22.95 (ISBN 0-686-76914-7); 260.00 (ISBN 0-687-19206-4). Abingdon.
--The Parables of Jesus. (Minister's Paperback Library Ser). 274p. 1973. pap. 6.95 (ISBN 0-8010-0597-3). Baker Bk.
--Prayer in Life: Life in Prayer. 1976. pap. 0.85x (ISBN 0-8358-0346-5). Upper Room.
Buttrick, George A. & Crim, Keith R., eds. The Interpreter's Dictionary of the Bible, 5 vols. LC 62-9387. 1976. Set. 112.00 (ISBN 0-687-19268-4). Abingdon.
Butwin, Frances. Jews of America: History & Sources. Blecher, Arthur C., ed. LC 73-2253. (Illus.). 160p. 1973. pap. text ed. 3.95x (ISBN 0-87441-062-2). Behrman.
Buxbaum, Melvin H. Benjamin Franklin & the Zealous Presbyterians. LC 74-14932. 320p. 1974. 28.75x (ISBN 0-271-01176-9). Pa St U Pr.
Buxton, Clyne. Minister's Service Manual. text ed. 8.95 (ISBN 0-87148-584-2). Pathway Pr.
Buxton, David. The Wooden Churches of Eastern Europe: An Introductory Survey. (Illus.). 384p. 1982. 90.00 (ISBN 0-521-23786-6). Cambridge U Pr.
Buytaert, Eligius M., jt. auth. see Boehner, Philotheus.
Buytaert, Eligius M., ed. Saint John Damascene: De Fide Orthodoxa, Versions of Burgundio & Cerbanus. (Text Ser). 1955. 23.00 (ISBN 0-686-11554-6). Franciscan Inst.
Buytaert, Eligius M., jt. ed. see Hooper, Sr. M. Rachel.
Buzaljko, Grace, ed. see Kroeber, Alfred L. & Gifford, E. W.
Buzzard, Juanita, jt. auth. see Buzzard, Lynn.
Buzzard, Lynn & Buzzard, Juanita. Readiness for Reconciliation. 36p. (Orig.). 1982. wkbk 3.00 (ISBN 0-686-39857-2). Chr Concil Serv.
Buzzard, Lynn & Ericcson, Samuel. The Battle for Religious Liberty. (Issues & Insight Ser.). (Orig.). 1982. pap. 6.95 (ISBN 0-89191-552-4, 55525). Cook.
Buzzard, Lynn R. & Brandon, Thomas. Church Discipline & the Courts. (Pressure Point Ser.). 160p. (Orig.). 1987. pap. 6.95 (ISBN 0-8423-0272-7). Tyndale.
Buzzard, Lynn R. & Eck, Laurence. Tell It to the Church. 192p. (Orig.). 1985. pap. 6.95 (ISBN 0-8423-6986-4). Tyndale.
Byabazaire, Deogratias M. The Contribution of the Christian Churches to the Development of Western Uganda 1894-1974: Theology. (European University Studies: Ser. 23, Vol. 112). 198p. 1979. pap. 21.95 (ISBN 3-261-02553-0). P Lang Pubs.
Byerly, Helen. Growing with Daily Devotions. 20p. 1964. No. 4. 1.50 ea., spiral bd., wkbk. (ISBN 0-87509-337-X). No. 5 (ISBN 0-87509-338-8). No. 6 (ISBN 0-87509-339-6). No. 7 (ISBN 0-87509-340-X). No. 8 (ISBN 0-87509-341-8). No. 9 o.p (ISBN 0-87509-342-6). No. 10 (ISBN 0-87509-343-4). No. 11 (ISBN 0-87509-344-2). No.12 (ISBN 0-87509-345-0). Chr Pubns.
Byers, A. L. Birth of a Reformation: Life & Labours of D. S. Warner. (Illus.). 496p. Repr. 5.50 (ISBN 0-686-29104-2). Faith Pub Hse.
Byers, Carolyn. Mary Andrews: Companion of Sorrow. Wheeler, Gerald, ed. LC 83-21121. (A Banner Bk.). (Illus.). 91p. (Orig.). 1984. pap. 5.95 (ISBN 0-8280-0212-6). Review & Herald.
Byers, David, ed. In the Name of Peace: Collective Statements of the United States Catholic Bishops on War & Peace, 1919-1980. 121p. 1983. pap. 8.95 (ISBN 1-55586-861-4). US Catholic.
--Justice in the Marketplace: Collected Statements of the Vatican & the United States Catholic Bishops on Economic Policy, 1891-1984. 554p. 1985. pap. 14.95 (ISBN 1-55586-933-5). US Catholic.
--The Parish in Transition: Proceedings of a Conference on the American Catholic Parish. 120p. 1986. pap. 8.95 (ISBN 1-55586-967-X). US Catholic.
--Vocations & Church Leadership. 96p. (Orig.). 1986. pap. 5.95 (ISBN 1-55586-108-3). US Catholic.
Byers, David M. & Quinn, Bernard. Readings for Town & Country Church Workers: An Annotated Bibliography. LC 74-77445. 120p. 1974. pap. 2.00x (ISBN 0-914422-00-6). Glenmary Res Ctr.
Byers, J. W. Parent & Child. 60p. pap. 0.50 (ISBN 0-686-29132-8). Faith Pub Hse.
--Sanctification. 96p. 0.75 (ISBN 0-686-29140-9). Faith Pub Hse.
Byers, Paul. Unto Him Be Glory. 220p. 1974. 4.95 (ISBN 0-89114-047-6); pap. 2.95 (ISBN 0-89114-046-8). Baptist Pub Hse.
Byers, Tracy. Martha Berry, the Sunday Lady of Possum Trot. LC 72-159905. 1971. Repr. of 1932 ed. 40.00x (ISBN 0-8103-3783-5). Gale.
Byington, Ezra H. The Puritan As a Colonist & Reformer. LC 75-31115. Repr. of 1899 ed. 34.50 (ISBN 0-404-13601-X). AMS Pr.
--The Puritan in England & New England: With a Chapter on Witchcraft in New England. 4th & enl. ed. LC 70-183241. (Research & Source Works Ser). (Illus.). 457p. 1972. Repr. of 1900 ed. lib. bdg. 29.50 (ISBN 0-8337-4017-2). B Franklin.
Byington, Steven T., tr. The Bible in Living English: Written by an Anarchist. (Men & Movements in the History & Philosophy of Anarchism Ser.). 1979. lib. bdg. 59.95 (ISBN 0-686-59576-9). Revisionist Pr.
Byles, Marie B. Footprints of Gautama the Buddha. LC 68-5855. (Illus.). 1967. pap. 5.95 (ISBN 0-8356-0399-7, Quest). Theos Pub Hse.
Bynum, Bill. Teaching Youth with Confidence. 48p. 1983. pap. 3.95 (ISBN 0-910566-41-0); seminar planbook 3.95 (ISBN 0-910566-42-9). Evang Tchr.
Bynum, Caroline W. Holy Feast & Holy Fast: The Religious Significance of Food to Medieval Women. LC 85-28896. 300p. 1986. 29.95 (ISBN 0-520-05722-8). U of Cal Pr.
--Jesus As Mother: Studies in the Spirituality of the High Middle Ages. LC 81-13137. (Center for Medieval & Renaissance Studies. UCLA Publications: No. 16). 280p. 1982. pap. text ed. 7.95 (ISBN 0-520-05222-6, CAL 697). U of Cal Pr.
Bynum, Caroline W., et al, eds. Gender & Religion: On the Complexity of Symbols. LC 86-47552. 296p. 1986. 25.00 (ISBN 0-8070-1008-1). Beacon Pr.
Byrd & Horton. Keeping Your Balance. 1986. 6.95 (ISBN 0-8499-3056-1). Word Bks.
Byrd, James F., jt. ed. see Carey, Floyd D.
Byrd, Leslie, tr. see Martinez De Toledo, Alfonso.
Byrd, Walter, jt. auth. see Hindson, Edward.
Byrd, William see Buck, P. C. & Fellowes, E. H.
Byrd, William, et al. Gradualia, Bks.1 & 2. Buck, P. C., ed. (Tudor Church Music: Vol. 7). 1963. Repr. of 1927 ed. 85.00x (ISBN 0-8450-1857-4). Broude.
--Masses, Cantiones, Motets. Buck, P. C., ed. (Tudor Church Music Ser.: Vol. 9). 1963. Repr. of 1928 ed. write for info. (ISBN 0-8450-1859-0). Broude.
Byrne, Donald E. No Foot of Land: Folklore of American Methodist Itinerants. LC 75-1097. (ATLA Monograph: No. 6). (Illus.). 370p. 1975. 22.50 (ISBN 0-8108-0798-X). Scarecrow.
Byrne, H. W. Christian Approach to Education. 1986. pap. 9.95 (ISBN 0-8010-0941-3). Baker Bk.
--Improving Church Education. LC 79-10852. 352p. (Orig.). 1979. pap. 12.95 (ISBN 0-89135-017-9). Religious Educ.
Byrne, Patrick. Witchcraft in Ireland. 80p. 1967. pap. 6.95 (ISBN 0-85342-038-6, Pub. by Mercier Pr Ireland). Irish Bk Ctr.
Byrnes, Joseph F. The Psychology of Religion. LC 84-47854. 320p. 1984. 24.95x (ISBN 0-02-903580-5). Free Pr.
Byrt, G. W. John Clifford: A Fighting Free Churchman. 192p. 1947. Repr. 2.95 (ISBN 0-87921-011-7). Attic Pr.
Byrum, E. E. The Secret of Salvation. 264p. pap. 2.50 (ISBN 0-686-29166-2). Faith Pub Hse.
Byrum, Isabel. The Pilot's Voice. (Illus.). 146p. pap. 1.50 (ISBN 0-686-29159-X). Faith Pub Hse.
--The Poorhouse Waif & His Divine Teacher. 223p. pap. 2.00 (ISBN 0-686-29161-1). Faith Pub Hse.
Byrum, R. R. Christian Theology. rev. ed. Newell, Arlo F., ed. 1982. 14.95 (ISBN 0-87162-252-1, D3051). Warner Pr.
--Holy Spirit Baptism & the Second Cleansing. 108p. pap. 0.75 (ISBN 0-686-29114-X); pap. 2.00 3 copies (ISBN 0-686-29115-8). Faith Pub Hse.
--Shadows of Good Things, or the Gospel in Type. (Illus.). 144p. pap. 1.50 (ISBN 0-686-29141-7). Faith Pub Hse.

C

C & MA Home Department Board Staff. The Pastor's Handbook. 102p. 3.95 (ISBN 0-87509-118-0). Chr Pubns.
C, Chester, jt. auth. see O'Brien, Bonnie B.
Cabanis, Pierre J. On the Relations Between the Physical & Moral Aspects of Man, Vol. I. Saidi, Margaret D., tr. LC 80-21694. pap. 112.00 (ISBN 0-317-08229-9, 2019949). Bks Demand UMI.
Cabaniss, Allen, ed. Charlemagne's Cousins: Contemporary Lives of Adalard & Wala. LC 67-26919. 1967. 14.95x (ISBN 0-8156-2115-9). Syracuse U Pr.
Cabasilas, Nicholas. Commentary on the Divine Liturgy. Hussey, J. M. & McNulty, P. A., trs. from Greek. LC 62-53410. 120p. 1977. pap. 6.95 (ISBN 0-913836-37-0). St Vladimirs.
--The Life in Christ. Decatanzaro, Carmino J., tr. 229p. 1974. pap. 8.95 (ISBN 0-913836-12-5). St Vladimirs.
Cabat, Erni. Father Eusebio Francisco Kino & His Missions of the Pimeria Alta: The Side Altars, Bk. I. Polzer, Charles W., ed. Prezelski, Carmen V., tr. LC 82-50219. (Illus.). 36p. (Orig.). 1982. pap. 5.00 (ISBN 0-915076-06-3). SW Mission.
Cabat, Erni & Polzer, Charles W. Father Eusebio Francisco Kino & His Missions of the Pimeria Alta: Bk. II, The Main Altars, Book II. Prezelski, Carmen V., tr. LC 82-50219. (Illus.). 36p. (Orig.). 1983. pap. 5.00 (ISBN 0-915076-08-X). SW Mission.
--Father Eusebio Francisco Kino & His Missions of the Pimeria Alta: Facing the Missions, Bk. II. Prezelski, Carmen V., tr. LC 82-50219. (Illus.). 36p. 1983. pap. 5.00 (ISBN 0-915076-09-8). SW Mission.
Cabestrero, Teofilo. Ministers of God, Ministers of the People: Testimonies of Faith from Nicaragua. Barr, Robert R., tr. from Span. LC 83-6306. Orig. Title: Ministros De Dios, Ministros Del Pueblo. (Illus.). 160p. (Orig.). 1983. pap. 6.95 (ISBN 0-88344-335-X). Orbis Bks.
--Mystic of Liberation: A Portrait of Bishop Pedro Casaldaliga of Brazil. Walsh, Donald D., tr. from Span. & Fr. LC 80-25402. Orig. Title: Dialogos en Mato Grosso con Pedro Casadaliga. (Illus.). 176p. (Orig.). 1981. pap. 7.95 (ISBN 0-88344-324-4). Orbis Bks.
--Revolutionaries for the Gospel: Testimonies of Fifteen Christians in the Nicaraguan Government. Berryman, Phillip, tr. from Spanish. LC 85-25865. Tr. of Revolucionarios por el Evangelico. 176p. (Orig.). 1986. pap. 9.95 (ISBN 0-88344-406-2). Orbis Bks.

Cabestrero, Teofilo, ed. Faith: Conversations with Contemporary Theologians. Walsh, Donald D., tr. from Span. LC 80-1431. Orig. Title: Coversationes sobre la fe. 192p. (Orig.). 1980. pap. 3.98 (ISBN 0-88344-126-8). Orbis Bks.

Cabeza, Susana, tr. see Jones, Chris.

Cabot, Richard C. What Men Live By. 341p. 1985. Repr. of 1941 ed. lib. bdg. 35.00 (ISBN 0-89760-187-4). Telegraph Bks.

Cabrera, Lydia. La Regla Kimbisa del Santo Cristo del Buen Viaje. 2nd ed. (Coleccion del Chichereku en el Exilio Ser.). (Span.). 85p. 1986. pap. 6.95 (ISBN 0-89729-396-7). Ediciones.

Caccamo, Domenico. Eretici Italiani in Moravia, Polonia, Transilvania (1558-1611) LC 72-3474. (Corpus Reformatorum Italicorum & Biblioteca Ser.). (Lat. & Ital., Illus.). 286p. 1970. pap. 17.50 (ISBN 0-87580-511-6). N Ill U Pr.

Cachiaras, D., et al. Twenty-Six Bible Programs for Preschoolers. (Illus.). 96p. 1986. wkbk. 8.95 (ISBN 0-87403-063-3, 3408). Standard Pub.

Cachiaras, Dot. God Created Me Too! (Happy Day Bks.). (Illus.). 32p. 1987. 1.59 (ISBN 0-87403-274-1, 3774). Standard Pub.

--God Gives Us Seasons. (Happy Day Bks.). (Illus.). 24p. 1984. 1.59 (ISBN 0-87239-732-7, 3702). Standard Pub.

Cada, Lawrence, et al. Shaping the Coming Age of Religious Life. 2nd ed. LC 78-25987. 208p. 1985. pap. 7.95 (ISBN 0-89571-023-4). Affirmation.

Cadbury, H. J. Style & Literary Method of Luke, 2 Vols. in 1. (Harvard Theo. Studies: No. 6). 1919-1920. 22.00 (ISBN 0-527-01006-5). Kraus Repr.

Cadbury, Henry J. Behind the Gospels. LC 68-8591. (Orig.). 1968. pap. 2.50x (ISBN 0-87574-160-6). Pendle Hill.

--The Character of a Quaker. 1983. pap. 2.50x (ISBN 0-87574-103-7, 103). Pendle Hill.

--Eclipse of the Historical Jesus. LC 64-12998. (Orig.). 1964. 2.50x (ISBN 0-87574-133-9, 133). Pendle Hill.

--Quaker Relief During the Siege of Boston. 1983. pap. 2.50x (ISBN 0-686-43965-1, 004). Pendle Hill.

Cadbury, Henry J., ed. see Fox, George.

Cadden, John P. The Historiography of the American Catholic Church, 1785-1943. 14.00 (ISBN 0-405-10812-5). Ayer Co Pubs.

Cadden, John Paul. The Historiography of the American Catholic Church: 1785-1943, No. 82. (Studies in Sacred Theology). 134p. 1984. Repr. of 1944 ed. 35.00x (ISBN 0-939738-33-3). Zubal Inc.

Caddy, Eileen. The Spirit of Findhorn. LC 75-36747. (Illus.). 1979. pap. 7.95 (ISBN 0-06-061291-6, RD 296, HarpR). Har-Row.

Cadet, J. M. Ramakien: The Thai Epic. LC 70-128685. (Illus.). 256p. 1970. 35.00 (ISBN 0-87011-134-5). Kodansha.

Cadoux, C. John. The Early Christian Attitude to War: A Contribution to the History of Christian Ethics. 304p. 1982. pap. 9.95 (ISBN 0-8164-2416-0, HarpR). Har-Row.

--The Early Christian Attitude Toward War. 69.95 (ISBN 0-87968-198-5). Gordon Pr.

--The Historic Mission of Jesus: A Constructive Re-Examination of the Eschatological Teaching in the Synoptic Gospels with an Extensive Bibliography. 1977. lib. bdg. 59.95 (ISBN 0-8490-1955-9). Gordon Pr.

Cadoux, Cecil J. Philip of Spain & the Netherlands: An Essay on Moral Judgments in History. LC 69-15788. xv, 251p. 1969. Repr. of 1947 ed. 27.50 (ISBN 0-208-00735-0, Archon). Shoe String.

Cadoux, Cecil J., ed. see Bartlet, James V.

Cadoux, T., pref. by. The Sorrowful & Immaculate Heart of Mary: Message of Berthe Petit, Franciscan Tertiary (1870-1943) 110p. 1966. pap. 3.00 (ISBN 0-913382-02-7, 101-2). Prow Bks-Franciscan.

Cadram, Glenna & Grubbs, Sylvia. The Potter & the Clay. 1986. pap. 9.95 (ISBN 0-87162-446-X). Warner Pr.

Cady, Emilie H. God a Present Help. rev. ed. LC 84-5002010. 1985. 5.95 (ISBN 0-87159-044-1). Unity School.

Cady, Susan A., et al. Sophia: The Future of Feminist Spirituality. 120p. 1986. 14.95 (ISBN 0-06-254200-1, HarpR). Har-Row.

Caemmerer, Richard R., Jr. Visual Art in the Life of the Church: Encouraging Creative Worship & Witness in the Congregation. LC 83-70504. 96p. (Orig.). 1983. pap. 10.95 (ISBN 0-8066-2010-2, 10-6855). Augsburg.

Caes, Charles J. Introduction to the Arguments for God. LC 82-82548. 1983. 8.95 (ISBN 0-87212-162-3). Libra.

Caesarius Of Arles, St. Sermons, Nos. 81-186. LC 56-3628. (Fathers of the Church Ser.: Vol. 47). 495p. 1964. 25.95x (ISBN 0-8132-0047-4). Cath U Pr.

--Sermons, Nos. 187-238. LC 56-3628. (Fathers of the Church Ser.: Vol. 66). 303p. 1973. 17.95x (ISBN 0-8132-0066-0). Cath U Pr.

--Sermons-One to Eighty. (Fathers of the Church Ser.: Vol. 31). 1956. 34.95x (ISBN 0-8132-0031-8). Cath U Pr.

Caffarel, Henri. Being Present to God: Letters on Prayer. LC 83-15459. 202p. 1983. pap. 6.95 (ISBN 0-8189-0462-3). Alba.

Caffrey, Stephanie & Kenslea, Timothy. The Family That Wanted a Home. (Rainbow Books (Bible Story Books for Children)). (Orig.). 1978. pap. 1.00 (ISBN 0-8192-1235-0). Morehouse.

--How the World Began. (Rainbow Books (Bible Story Books for Children)). 16p. 1978. pap. 1.00 (ISBN 0-8192-1233-4). Morehouse.

--The Shepherds Find a King. (Rainbow Books (Bible Story Books for Children)). 16p. 1978. pap. 1.00 (ISBN 0-8192-1232-6). Morehouse.

Caffrey, Stephanie & Kenslea, Timothy, eds. The Boy in the Striped Coat. (Rainbow Books). 1978. pap. 1.00 (ISBN 0-8192-1234-2). Morehouse.

Cagle, Paul R., Jr. & Wallace, Mary H. The Curtain of Time. (Illus., Orig.). 1984. pap. 6.95 (ISBN 0-912315-76-8). Word Aflame.

Cahan, Judah L. Shtudies Vegn Yidisher Folksshafung. Weinreich, ed. 1952. 5.00 (ISBN 0-914512-05-6). Yivo Inst.

Cahill, E. Freemasonry & the Anti-Christian Movement. 59.95 (ISBN 0-8490-0195-1). Gordon Pr.

Cahill, Linda, et al. Successful Single Adult Ministry. 144p. 1987. pap. price not set (ISBN 0-87403-229-6, 3219). Standard Pub.

Cahill, Lisa S. Between the Sexes. 160p. (Orig.). 1985. pap. 7.95 (ISBN 0-8091-2711-3). Paulist Pr.

Cahill, P. Joseph. Mended Speech: The Crisis of Religious Study & Theology. 272p. 1982. 14.95 (ISBN 0-8245-0421-6). Crossroad NY.

Cahn, Stephen M. & Shatz, David, eds. Contemporary Philosophy of Religion. 1982. pap. text ed. 9.95x (ISBN 0-19-503009-5). Oxford U Pr.

Cahn, Walter. Romanesque Bible Illumination. LC 82-71593. (Illus.). 308p. 1982. 95.00x (ISBN 0-8014-1446-6). Cornell U Pr.

--The Romanesque Wooden Doors of Auvergne. LC 74-15391. (College Art Association Monograph Ser.: Vol. 30). (Illus.). 225p. 1985. Repr. of 1974 ed. 30.00x (ISBN 0-271-00400-2). Pa St U Pr.

Caillat, Collette. Jain Cosmology. (Illus.). 192p. 1982. 55.00 (ISBN 0-517-54662-0, Harmony). Crown.

Caillois, Roger. Man & the Sacred. Barash, Meyer, tr. from Fr. LC 79-8709. 190p. 1980. Repr. of 1959 ed. lib. bdg. 22.50x (ISBN 0-313-22196-0, CAMS). Greenwood.

Caine, Hall. Life of Christ. 1310p. 1985. Repr. of 1938 ed. lib. bdg. 45.00 (ISBN 0-89987-194-1). Darby Bks.

Cairas, David, tr. see Althaus, Paul.

Caird, Edward. Evolution of Religion, 2 Vols. in 1. LC 1-17697. (Gifford Lectures 1890-1892). 1968. Repr. of 1893 ed. 46.00 (ISBN 0-527-14120-8). Kraus Repr.

--Evolution of Theology in the Greek Philosophers, 2 Vols in 1. LC 4-16272. (Gifford Lectures 1900-1902). 1968. Repr. of 1904 ed. 46.00 (ISBN 0-527-14130-5). Kraus Repr.

--Evolution of Theology in the Greek Philosophers, the Gifford Lectures, 1900-1902, 2 Vols. 1968. 39.00x (ISBN 0-403-00116-1). Scholarly.

Caird, G. B. The Language & Imagery of the Bible. LC 79-27586. 288p. 1980. 20.00 (ISBN 0-664-21378-2). Westminster.

--Our Dialogue with Rome: The Second Vatican Council & After. 7.25 (ISBN 0-8446-1797-0). Peter Smith.

--The Revelation of St. John the Divine. LC 66-20774. (New Testament Commentaries Ser.). 1966. 17.95 (ISBN 0-06-061296-7, HarpR). Har-Row.

--Saint Luke. LC 77-81622. (Westminster Pelican Commentaries Ser.). 272p. 1978. 10.95 (ISBN 0-664-21345-6). Westminster.

Caird, George B. The Apostolic Age. (Studies in Theology). 222p. 1982. pap. 13.50 (ISBN 0-7156-1680-3, Pub. by Duckworth London). Longwood Pub Group.

--The Gospel of St. Luke: Commentaries. (Orig.). 1964. pap. 7.95 (ISBN 0-14-020490-3, Pelican). Penguin.

--Paul's Letters from Prison (Ephesians, Phillipians, Colossians, Philemon) in the Revised Standard Edition. (New Clarendon Bible). (Orig.). 1976. pap. text ed. 18.95x (ISBN 0-19-836920-4). Oxford U Pr.

Caird, John. The Fundamental Ideas of Christianity, 2 vols. LC 77-27231. (Gifford Lectures: 1892-93, 1895-96). Repr. of 1899 ed. Set. 49.50 (ISBN 0-404-60460-9). AMS Pr.

--Introduction to the Philosophy of Religion. LC 75-113569. (BCL Ser. I). Repr. of 1901 ed. 12.50 (ISBN 0-404-01363-5). AMS Pr.

Cairns, David, tr. see Gollwitzer, Helmut.

Cairns, Earle E. Christianity Through the Centuries. 544p. 1981. 19.95 (ISBN 0-310-38360-9, 9377P). Zondervan.

--An Endless Line of Splendor. 352p. 1986. text ed. 14.95 (ISBN 0-8423-0770-2). Tyndale.

--God & Man in Time. LC 78-73042. 1978. pap. 7.95 (ISBN 0-8010-2426-9). Baker Bk.

Cairns, Earle E., jt. ed. see Douglas, J. D.

Cairns, Thomas H. Preparing Your Church for Ministry to Alcoholics & Their Families. 136p. 1986. 19.75x (ISBN 0-398-05230-1). C C Thomas.

Cairns, Trevor. Barbarians, Christians & Muslims. LC 69-11024. (Cambridge Introduction to the History of Mankind Ser.: Bk. 3). 1970. 8.95 (ISBN 0-521-07360-X). Cambridge U Pr.

--Middle Ages. (Cambridge Introduction to the History of Mankind Ser.: Bk. 4). (Illus.). 1971. 8.95 (ISBN 0-521-07726-5). Cambridge U Pr.

Cairns, Trevor, ed. Barbarians, Christians, & Muslims. LC 73-20213. (Cambridge Introduction to History Ser.). (Illus.). 104p. 1975. PLB 10.95 (ISBN 0-8225-0803-6). Lerner Pubns.

--Life in a Medieval Monastery. (Cambridge Introduction to World History Ser.). (Illus.). 48p. Date not set. pap. 4.95 (ISBN 0-521-33724-0). Cambridge U Pr.

Cairns, William T. Religion of Dr. Johnson. facsimile ed. LC 71-93324. (Essay Index Reprint Ser). 1946. 17.00 (ISBN 0-8369-1279-9). Ayer Co Pubs.

Calcada, Leticia, tr. see Palau, Luis.

Caldarola, Carlo, ed. Religion & Societies: Asia & the Middle East. (Religion & Society: No. 22). 688p. 1982. text ed. 73.75 (ISBN 90-279-3259-X); Pub. 1984. pap. 29.50 (ISBN 3-11-010021-5). Mouton.

Caldecott, Alfred & MacKintosh, H. R. Selections from the Literature of Theism. 1979. Repr. of 1909 ed. lib. bdg. 65.00 (ISBN 0-8495-0932-7). Arden Lib.

Calder, Isabel M., ed. see Davenport, John.

Calderon, Wilfredo, ed. Dinamicas de la Escuela Dominical. (Span.). 108p. 1973. pap. 3.25 (ISBN 0-87148-255-X). Pathway Pr.

Calderwood, David. A Solution of Doctor Resolutus, His Resolutions for Kneeling. LC 79-84093. (English Experience Ser.: No. 913). 60p. 1979. Repr. of 1619 ed. lib. bdg. 8.00 (ISBN 90-221-0913-5). Walter J Johnson.

--The True History of the Church of Scotland: From the Beginnings of the Reform to the End of the Reign of King James VI, 8 vols. Thomson, Thomas, ed. LC 83-45577. Date not set. Repr. of 1842 ed. Set. 525.00 (ISBN 0-404-19894-5). AMS Pr.

Caldwell, Erskine. Deep South: Memory & Observation. LC 80-16013. (Brown Thrasher Bks.). 270p. 1980. pap. 6.95 (ISBN 0-8203-0525-1). U of Ga Pr.

Caldwell, Genevieve. First Person Singular. 180p. 1986. 10.95 (ISBN 0-8407-3072-1). Nelson.

Caldwell, Happy. The Word System. 60p. 1981. pap. 1.50 (ISBN 0-89274-176-7). Harrison Hse.

Caldwell, Louis. The Adventure of Becoming One. (Ultra Bks.). 80p. 1981. 5.95 (ISBN 0-8010-2334-3). Baker Bk.

--After the Tassel Is Moved. (Ultra Bks Ser.). 1968. 4.95 (ISBN 0-8010-2332-7). Baker Bk.

Caldwell, Louis O. Another Tassel Is Moved: Guidelines for College Graduates. (Ultra Books Ser). 1970. 4.95 (ISBN 0-8010-2343-2). Baker Bk.

--A Birthday Remembrance. LC 77-7043. (Illus.). pap. 20.00 (ISBN 0-8357-9001-0, 2016349). Bks Demand UMI.

--Congratulations: A Graduation Remembrance. (Ultra Books). 64p. 1983. 5.95 (ISBN 0-8010-2485-4). Baker Bk.

--Good Morning, Lord: Devotions for College Students. (Good Morning Lord Ser.). 1971. 4.95 (ISBN 0-8010-2324-6). Baker Bk.

--Good Morning, Lord: Meditations for Modern Marrieds. (Good Morning Lord Ser.). 1974. 3.95 (ISBN 0-8010-2351-3). Baker Bk.

--Something Good for Those Who Feel Bad: Positive Solutions for Negative Emotions. 96p. 1985. pap. 6.95 (ISBN 0-8010-2505-2). Baker Bk.

--You Can Develop a Positive Self-Image. (Christian Counseling Aids Ser.). pap. 1.25 (ISBN 0-8010-2503-6). Baker Bk.

--You Can Find Help Through Counseling: Christain Counseling Aids. 1983. pap. 0.95 (ISBN 0-8010-2484-6). Baker Bk.

--You Can Overcome Your Fears, Phobias, & Worries. 1985. pap. 1.25 (ISBN 0-8010-2506-0). Baker Bk.

--You Can Prevent or Overcome a Nervous Breakdown. (Christian Counseling Aids Ser.). 1978. pap. 1.25 (ISBN 0-8010-2415-3). Baker Bk.

--You Can Stop Feeling Guilty. (Christian Counseling Aids Ser.). 1978. pap. 1.25 (ISBN 0-8010-2414-5). Baker Bk.

Caldwell, Louise. Timothy: Young Pastor. (BibLearn Ser..). (Illus.). 1978. 5.95 (ISBN 0-8054-4239-1 4242-39). Broadman.

Caldwell, Martha B. Annals of Shawnee Methodist Mission & Indian Manual Labor School. 2nd ed. LC 39-28738. (Illus.). 120p. 1977. pap. 2.95 (ISBN 0-87726-005-2). Kansas St Hist.

Caldwell, Patricia. The Puritan Conversion Narrative: The Beginnings of American Expression. LC 82-22772. (Cambridge Studies in American Literature & Culture). 192p. 1983. 21.95 (ISBN 0-521-25460-4). Cambridge U Pr.

--The Puritan Conversion Narrative: The Beginnings of American Expression. 224p. 1985. pap. 12.95 (ISBN 0-521-31147-0). Cambridge U Pr.

Caleron, Eduardo, et al. Eduardo el Curandero: The Words of a Peruvian Healer. (Illus.). 200p. 1982. 20.00 (ISBN 0-913028-94-0); pap. 7.95 (ISBN 0-913028-95-9). North Atlantic.

Calfhill, James. An Answer to John Martiall's Treatise of the Cross. 1846. 31.00 (ISBN 0-384-07020-5). Johnson Repr.

Calhoun, Gerald J. Pastoral Companionship: Ministry with Seriously Ill Persons & Their Families. 180p. (Orig.). 1986. pap. 8.95 (ISBN 0-8091-2753-9). Paulist Pr.

Calian, Carnegie S. Today's Pastor in Tomorrow's World. Rev. ed. LC 82-7114. 164p. 1982. pap. 8.95 (ISBN 0-664-24426-2). Westminster.

Caliaro, Marco & Francesconi, Mario. John Baptist Scalabrini: Apostle to Emigrants. Zizzamia, Alba I., tr. from It. LC 76-44922. (Illus.). 580p. 1977. lib. bdg. 15.00x (ISBN 0-913256-24-2). Ctr Migration.

Caligari, Marc, tr. see Pope Paul VI.

Calimani, Riccardo. The Ghetto of Venice. Wolfthal, Katherine, tr. (Illus.). 400p. 1987. 19.95 (ISBN 0-87131-484-3). M Evans.

Calkin, Ruth. Lord, I Keep Running Back to You. 1983. pap. 3.50 (ISBN 0-8423-3819-5). Tyndale.

Calkin, Ruth H. Letters to a Young Bride. 112p. 1985. 10.95 (ISBN 0-8423-2134-9). Tyndale.

--Lord, Could You Hurry a Little. 1983. pap. 2.95 (ISBN 0-8423-3816-0). Tyndale.

--Lord, It Keeps Happening...& Happening. LC 83-91404. 112p. 1984. pap. 2.95 (ISBN 0-8423-3823-3). Tyndale.

--Lord, You Love to Say Yes. (Living Books). 160p. (Orig.). 1985. pap. 2.95 (ISBN 0-8423-3824-1). Tyndale.

--Love Is So Much More, Lord. LC 79-51739. 1979. pap. 2.50 (ISBN 0-89191-187-1). Cook.

--Tell Me Again, Lord, I Forget. (Living Bks.). 160p. (Orig.). 1986. 3.50 (ISBN 0-8423-6990-2). Tyndale.

Calkins & White. Talk to God about The Sabbath. large type ed. 70p. 1984. pap. 8.50x (ISBN 0-914009-22-2). VHI Library.

Calkins, Mary W. The Good Man & the Good: An Introduction to Ethics. LC 75-3093. Repr. of 1918 ed. 24.50 (ISBN 0-404-59090-X). AMS Pr.

Call, Betty & Souther, Sheila. Children Can Worship, Bk. 3. (Orig.). 1983. pap. text ed. 10.95 (ISBN 0-87148-178-2). Pathway Pr.

Call, David M. Within Our Reach. LC 83-26162. 68p. 1984. 5.95 (ISBN 0-87747-975-5). Deseret Bk.

Call, William. The Trial of Faith: Discussions Concerning Mormonism & Neo-Mormonism. 215p. (Orig.). Date not set. pap. write for info. (ISBN 0-916095-11-8). Pubs Pr UT.

Callahan, Annice. Karl Rahner's Spirituality of the Pierced Heart: A Reinterpretation of Devotion to the Sacred Heart. LC 84-29170. 198p. (Orig.). 1985. lib. bdg. 25.25 (ISBN 0-8191-4568-8); pap. text ed. 11.75 (ISBN 0-8191-4569-6). U Pr of Amer.

Callahan, Daniel. Ethics & Population Limitation. LC 78-155736. 45p. (Orig.). 1971. pap. text ed. 3.95 (ISBN 0-87834-002-5). Population Coun.

Callahan, Daniel, ed. The Teaching of Ethics in Higher Education: A Report by the Hastings Center. LC 80-10294. (The Teaching of Ethics Ser.). 103p. 1980. pap. 5.00 xerox form only (ISBN 0-916558-09-6). Hastings Ctr.

Callahan, Daniel & Bok, Sissela, eds. Ethics Teaching in Higher Education. LC 80-24002. (Hastings Center Monograph Ser.). 332p. 1980. 29.50x (ISBN 0-306-40522-9). Plenum Pub.

Callahan, Daniel & Engelhardt, H. Tristram, Jr., eds. The Roots of Ethics. (The Hasting Center Series in Ethics). 464p. 1981. 35.00 (ISBN 0-306-40796-5, Plenum Pr). Plenum Pub.

Callahan, Daniel, jt. ed. see Caplan, Arthur L.

Callahan, John D. Science & Christianity. 2nd ed. (Illus.). 120p. 1986. pap. 5.95 (ISBN 0-9615767-0-7). Callahan CA.

Callahan, Kennon L. Twelve Keys to an Effective Church. LC 83-47718. 1983. pap. 13.45 (ISBN 0-06-061297-5, HarpR). Har-Row.

Callahan, Nelson J., jt. auth. see Burtsell, Richard L.

Callahan, W. J. & Higgs, D. Church & Society in Catholic Europe of the Eighteenth Century. LC 78-12165. 1979. 27.95 (ISBN 0-521-22424-1). Cambridge U Pr.

Callahan, William J. Church, Politics, & Society in Spain, 1750-1874. (Harvard Historical Monographs: No. 73). (Illus.). 336p. 1984. text ed. 25.00x (ISBN 0-674-13125-8). Harvard U Pr.

Callari, Elizabeth S. A Gentle Death: Personal Caregiving to the Terminally Ill. 123p. 1986. 11.95 (ISBN 0-936389-00-1); pap. 7.95 (ISBN 0-936389-01-X). Tudor Pubs.

Callaway, Joseph A. & Adams, J. McKee, eds. Biblical Backgrounds. rev. ed. 1966. 14.95 (ISBN 0-8054-1113-5). Broadman.

Callaway, Tucker N. Zen Way - Jesus Way. LC 76-6032. 1976. 11.00 (ISBN 0-8048-1190-3). C E Tuttle.

Callcott, Wilfrid H. Church & State in Mexico, 1822-1857. 1965. lib. bdg. 27.00x (ISBN 0-374-91235-1, Octagon). Hippocrene Bks.

Callen, Barry. Where Life Begins. 128p. 1973. pap. 2.50 (ISBN 0-87162-146-0, D9026). Warner Pr.

Callen, Barry L., ed. First Century: Church of God Reformation Movement, 2 vols. 1977. Set. 19.95 set. Vol. I (ISBN 0-87162-200-9, D1386). Vol. II (ISBN 0-87162-220-3, D1387). Warner Pr.

Callender, John. Historical Discourse on the Civil & Religious Affairs of the Colony of Rhode Island. facs. ed. LC 79-150172. (Select Bibliographies Reprint Ser.). 1843. 18.00 (ISBN 0-8369-5685-0). Ayer Co Pubs.

Callewaert, Winand M. Bhagavadgitanuvada: A Study in Transcultural Translation. 1984. 26.00x (ISBN 0-8364-1148-X, Pub. by Satya Bharati Pub). South Asia Bks.

Callison, William L., jt. auth. see Iles, Robert H.

Calmann, Marianne. The Carriere of Carpentras. LC 82-48692. (Littman Library of Jewish Civilization). (Illus.). 286p. 1984. 32.50x (ISBN 0-19-710037-6). Oxford U Pr.

Calmet, A. Dictionnaire Historique, Archeologique, Philologique, Chronologique Geographique et Literal de la Bible, 4 vols. Migne, J. P., ed. (Encyclopedie Theologique First Ser.: Vols. 1-4). (Fr.). 2602p. Repr. of 1846 ed. lib. bdg. 332.50x (ISBN 0-89241-231-3). Caratzas.

Caltagirone, Carmen L. The Catechist as a Minister. LC 82-1605. 116p. (Orig.). 1982. pap. 4.95 (ISBN 0-8189-0430-5). Alba.

Calverley, E. E. The Mysteries of Worship in Islam. 1981. 6.50 (ISBN 0-686-97865-X). Kazi Pubns.

Calverley, E. E., tr. see Ghazzali, Al.

Calverley, Edwin E., ed. see Al-Ghazzali.

Calvert, Thomas. The Strange Fibonacci Discoveries in Numerology for Greater Living Achievement. (Illus.). 245p. 1976. 99.15 (ISBN 0-89266-009-0). Am Classical Coll Pr.

Calverton, V. F. The Passing of the Gods. 326p. 1982. Repr. of 1934 ed. lib. bdg. 35.00 (ISBN 0-89987-123-2). Darby Bks.

Calvesi, M. Treasures of the Vatican. 39.95 (ISBN 0-517-62643-8). Outlet Bk Co.

Calvez, J. Y., et al. Conferences on the Chief Decrees of the Jesuit General Congregation XXXII: A Symposium by Some of Its Members. LC 76-2977. (Study Aids on Jesuit Topics Ser.: No. 4). 173p. 1976. smyth sewn 4.50 (ISBN 0-912422-17-3); pap. 3.50 (ISBN 0-912422-13-0). Inst Jesuit.

Calvez, Jean Y. The Social Thought of John Twenty-Third: Mater et Magistra. McKenzie, George J., tr. LC 75-40992. 1977. Repr. of 1965 ed. lib. bdg. 22.50x (ISBN 0-8371-8711-7, CASCJ). Greenwood.

Calvin, Jean. Aphorismes of Christian Religion or a Verie Compendious Abridgement of M. I. Calvins Institutions Set Forth by M I Piscator. Holland, H., tr. LC 73-6107. (English Experience Ser.: No. 575). 1973. Repr. of 1596 ed. 26.00 (ISBN 90-221-0575-X). Walter J Johnson.

--Catechisms or, Manner to Teach-Children the Christian Religion. LC 68-54624. (English Experience Ser.: No. 46). 168p. 1968. Repr. of 1556 ed. 14.00 (ISBN 90-221-0046-4). Walter J Johnson.

--Certain Homilies Containing Profitable Admonition for This Time. LC 73-6108. (English Experience Ser.: No. 576). 120p. 1973. Repr. of 1553 ed. 8.00 (ISBN 90-221-0576-8). Walter J Johnson.

--Letters, Compiled from the Original Manuscripts & Edited with Historical Notes, 4 vols. Bonnet, Jules, ed. Gilchrist, M. R. & Constable, David, trs. from Lat. & Fr. LC 70-185936. 1973. Repr. of 1858 ed. Set. 110.00 (ISBN 0-8337-4021-0). B Franklin.

--Opera Quae Supersunt Omnia, 59 Vols. in 58. Baum, G., et al, eds. 1863-1900. Set. 2600.00 (ISBN 0-384-07195-3); 50.00 ea. Johnson Repr.

Calvin, John. The Best of John Calvin. Dunn, Samuel, compiled by. (Best Ser.). 416p. 1981. pap. 5.95 (ISBN 0-8010-2467-6). Baker Bk.

--Calvin's Commentaries, 22 vols. 1979. Repr. Set. 495.00 (ISBN 0-8010-2440-4). Baker Bk.

--Calvin's Letters. pap. 5.95 (ISBN 0-85151-323-9). Banner of Truth.

--Calvin's New Testament Commentaries, 12 vols. Torrance, David W. & Torrance, Thomas F., eds. Incl. The Gospel According to St. John; Chapters 1-10. Parker, T. H., tr. 10.95 (ISBN 0-8028-2044-1); The Gospel According to St. John; Chapters 11-21. Parker, T. H., tr. 10.95 (ISBN 0-8028-2045-X); Acts of the Apostles, Vol. 1. McDonald, W. J., tr. 10.95 (ISBN 0-8028-2046-8); Acts of the Apostles, Vol. 2. Fraser, John W., tr. 10.95 (ISBN 0-8028-2047-6); The Epistle to the Romans & the Thessalonians. Mackenzie, R., tr. 9.95 (ISBN 0-8028-2048-4); The First Epistle to the Corinthians. Fraser, John W., tr. 10.95 (ISBN 0-8028-2049-2); Galatians, Ephesians, Philippians, Colossians. Parker, T. H., tr. 10.95 (ISBN 0-8028-2051-4); Hebrews and Peter First & Second. Johnson, W. B., tr. 10.95 (ISBN 0-8028-2052-2); Second Corinthians, Timothy, Titus. & Philemon. Smail, T. A. 10.95 (ISBN 0-8028-2050-6); Harmony of the Gospels, 3 Vols. Parker, T. H., tr. 10.95 ea. (ISBN 0-685-22779-0). Vol. 1 (ISBN 0-8028-2038-7). Vol. 2 (ISBN 0-8028-2039-5). Vol. 3 (ISBN 0-8028-2040-9). 1960. Set. 131.40 (ISBN 0-8028-2053-0). Eerdmans.

--Calvin's Selected Works: Tracts & Letters, 7 vols. Beveridge, Henry & Bonnet, Jules, eds. 1983. Repr. 99.95 (ISBN 0-8010-2493-5). Baker Bk.

--The Christian Life. Leith, John A., ed. LC 83-48978. 112p. 1984. 10.45 (ISBN 0-06-061298-3, HarpR). Har-Row.

--Concerning Scandals. Fraser, John W., tr. LC 78-8675. Repr. of 1978 ed. 24.90 (ISBN 0-8357-9126-2, 2012802). Bks Demand UMI.

--Concerning the Eternal Predestination of God. Reid, J. K., tr. 1961. pap. 13.95 (ISBN 0-227-67438-3). Attic Pr.

--Daniel. Myers, Thomas, ed. (Geneva Commentary Ser.). 816p. 1986. Repr. of 1853 ed. 19.95 (ISBN 0-85151-092-2). Banner of Truth.

--Genesis. (Geneva Commentaries Ser.). 1979. 22.95 (ISBN 0-85151-093-0). Banner of Truth.

--Golden Booklet of the True Christian Life: Devotional Classic. (Summit Bks.). 1975. pap. 3.95 (ISBN 0-8010-2366-1). Baker Bk.

--Institutes of the Christian Religion, 1536 Edition. Battles, Ford L., tr. from Lat. 464p. 1986. 25.00 (ISBN 0-8028-2319-X). Eerdmans.

--Institutes of the Christian Religion: Beveridge Translation, 2 Vols. 1953. Set. pap. 16.95 (ISBN 0-8028-8026-6). Eerdmans.

--John Calvin's Sermons on the Ten Commandments. Farley, Benjamin W., ed. 544p. 1980. 12.95 (ISBN 0-8010-2443-9). Baker Bk.

--John Calvin's Treatises Against the Anabaptists & Against the Libertines. Farley, Benjamin W., tr. 360p. (Orig.). 1982. pap. 16.95 (ISBN 0-8010-2476-5). Baker Bk.

--Knowledge of God the Creator. 2.50 (ISBN 0-686-23485-5). Rose Pub MI.

--On God & Man. Strothmann, F. W., ed. LC 56-7500. (Milestones of Thought Ser.). 1965. o.p 6.00 (ISBN 0-8044-5214-8); pap. 3.95 (ISBN 0-8044-6073-6). Ungar.

--Sermons on Ephesians. 1979. 19.95 (ISBN 0-85151-170-8). Banner of Truth.

--Sermons on Timothy & Titus. 1983. 37.95 (ISBN 0-85151-374-3). Banner of Truth.

Calvin, John & Sadoleto, Jacopo, eds. A Reformation Debate. 1976. pap. 4.95 (ISBN 0-8010-2390-4). Baker Bk.

Camara, Dom H. Desert Is Fertile. 1976. pap. 1.50 (ISBN 0-89129-060-5). Jove Pubns.

--Into Your Hands, Lord. 80p. 1987. text ed. 9.95 (ISBN 0-940989-06-9). Meyer Stone Bks.

--Questions for Living. Barr, Robert R., tr. from Fr. Tr. of Des Questions pour Vivre. (Illus.). 112p. (Orig.). 1987. pap. 7.95 (ISBN 0-88344-558-1). Orbis Bks.

--Through the Gospel with Dom Helder. Neame, Alan, tr. from Fr. 160p. (Orig.). 1986. pap. 8.95 (ISBN 0-88344-266-3). Orbis Bks.

Camara, Helder. Hoping Against All Hope. O'Connell, Matthew J., tr. from Ger. LC 83-19348. Orig. Title: Hoffer Wider Alle Hoffnung. 96p. (Orig.). 1984. pap. 4.95 (ISBN 0-88344-192-6). Orbis Bks.

--It's Midnight, Lord. Gallagher, Joseph, et al, trs. (Illus., Orig.). 1984. pap. 7.95 (ISBN 0-912405-02-3). Pastoral Pr.

Cambell, Alexander. The Covenant Story of the Bible. rev. & enl. ed. 256p. 1986. pap. 10.95 (ISBN 0-8298-0734-9). Pilgrim NY.

Cambrai, Fenelon de see Fenelon, Francois D.

Cambridge School Classics Project Foundation Course Staff. Foundation Course Folder III: Greek Religion. 1974. 13.95x (ISBN 0-521-08724-4). Cambridge U Pr.

Cambron, Mark. Come, Lord Jesus. pap. 1.45 (ISBN 0-686-12745-5). Grace Pub Co.

Cameli, Louis. Mary's Journey. 5.95 (ISBN 0-8215-9911-9). Sadlier.

Cameron, Euan. The Reformation of the Heretics: The Waldenses of the Alps, 1480-1580. (Oxford Historical Monographs). (Illus.). 291p. 1984. 48.00x (ISBN 0-19-822930-5). Oxford U Pr.

Cameron, James. The Making of Israel. LC 77-76041. (Illus.). 1977. 7.95 (ISBN 0-8008-5084-X). Taplinger.

Cameron, James M. Images of Authority: A Consideration of the Concepts of "Regnum" & "Sacerdotium". LC 66-12489. pap. 24.30 (ISBN 0-8357-9261-7, 2016769). Bks Demand UMI.

Cameron, Lewis. Opportunity My Ally. (Illus.). 253p. 1965. 10.95 (ISBN 0-227-67706-4). Attic Pr.

Cameron, Nigel. Evolution & the Authority of the Bible. 128p. 1983. pap. 6.95 (ISBN 0-85364-326-1, Pub. by Paternoster UK). Attic Pr.

Cameron, Nigel M. Biblical Higher Criticism & the Defense of Infallibilism in 19th Century Britain. (Texts & Studies in Religion: Vol. 33). 440p. 1987. text ed. 69.96 (ISBN 0-88946-821-4). E Mellen.

Cameron, Ron. Sayings Traditions in the Apocryphon of James. LC 84-45189. (Harvard Theological Studies). 160p. 1984. pap. 12.95 (ISBN 0-8006-7015-9). Fortress.

Cameron, Ron, ed. The Other Gospels: Non-Canonical Gospel Texts. LC 82-8662. 192p. 1982. pap. 11.95 (ISBN 0-664-24428-9). Westminster.

Cameron, Ron & Dewey, Arthur J., trs. The Cologne Mani Codex. LC 79-14743. (Society of Biblical Literature Texts & Translations, 15. Early Christian Literature Ser.: No. 3). 1979. pap. 8.95 (ISBN 0-89130-312-X, 060215). Scholars Pr GA.

Cameron, W. J. Covenant People. 3.00 (ISBN 0-685-08801-4). Destiny.

Cameron, William E. Great Dramas of the Bible. LC 81-71560. 305p. 1982. 5.95 (ISBN 0-87159-047-6). Unity School.

Cammack, Phyllis. Missionary Moments. LC 66-30364. (Illus.). 134p. 1966. 3.50 (ISBN 0-913342-09-2). Barclay Pr.

Cammaerts, Emile. The Childhood of Christ: As Seen by the Primitive Masters. 1978. Repr. of 1922 ed. lib. bdg. 20.00 (ISBN 0-8495-0766-9). Arden Lib.

Camp, Claudia. Wisdom & the Faminine in the Book of Proverbs. (Bible & Literature Ser.: No. II). 360p. 1985. text ed. 29.95x (ISBN 0-907459-42-0, Pub. by Almond Pr England); pap. text ed. 15.95x (ISBN 0-907459-43-9). Eisenbrauns.

Camp Farthest Out Staff. Roots & Fruits of the Camp Farthest Out. 1980. 3.95 (ISBN 0-910924-89-9). Macalester.

Camp, John. Magic, Myth & Medicine. LC 73-18793. 200p. 1974. 8.50 (ISBN 0-8008-5046-7). Taplinger.

Camp, John M. Gods & Heroes in the Athenian Agora. (Excavations of the Athenian Agora Picture Bks.: No. 19). (Illus.). 1980. pap. 3.00x (ISBN 0-87661-623-6). Am Sch Athens.

Camp, Norman. Pensando con Dios. Orig. Title: Thinking with God. (Span.). 128p. 1981. pap. 3.25 (ISBN 0-8254-1100-9). Kregel.

Camp, R. L. Papal Ideology of Social Reform: A Study in Historical Development, 1878-1967. 1969. 30.00 (ISBN 9-0040-4317-9). Heinman.

Camp, Sylvia. I Wonder from Job. pap. 3.50 (ISBN 0-89315-127-0). Lambert Bk.

Campano, Giovanni. Antonio: Opera Omnia. 608p. 1495. Repr. of 1495 ed. text ed. 99.36 (ISBN 0-576-72225-1, Pub. by Gregg Intl Pubs England). Gregg Intl.

Campbell. How to Really Love Your Teenager. LC 81-51515. 1982. 4.95 (ISBN 0-88207-274-9). Victor Bks.

Campbell, Alastair V. Professionalism & Pastoral Care. LC 84-48710. (Theology & Pastoral Care Ser.). 128p. 1985. pap. 7.95 (ISBN 0-8006-1733-9, 1-1733). Fortress.

--Rediscovering Pastoral Care. LC 81-7547. 132p. 1981. pap. 7.95 (ISBN 0-664-24381-9). Westminster.

Campbell, Alastair W. Professional Care: Its Meaning & Practice. LC 84-4081. 160p. 1984. pap. 7.95 (ISBN 0-8006-1812-2). Fortress.

Campbell, Alexander. The Christian System. LC 73-83412. (Religion in America Ser). 1969. Repr. of 1871 ed. 20.00 (ISBN 0-405-00233-5). Ayer Co Pubs.

--Heroes Then, Heroes Now. (Illus.). 89p. (Orig.). 1981. pap. 12.95 (ISBN 0-940754-08-8). Ed Ministries.

--Stories of Jesus, Stories of Now. 80p. (Orig.). 1980. pap. 12.95 (ISBN 0-940754-04-5). Ed Ministries.

Campbell, Alexander & Haff, Gerry. Live with Jesus. 90p. (Orig.). 1984. pap. 12.95 (ISBN 0-940754-20-7). Ed Ministries.

--Live with Moses. 90p. (Orig.). 1982. pap. 12.95 (ISBN 0-940754-13-4). Ed Ministries.

Campbell, Allan. Ten Sails in the Sunrise. 200p. 1986. 14.95 (ISBN 0-317-39595-5). C I L Inc.

Campbell, Anne. Girls in the Gang. (Illus.). 284p. 1984. 16.95 (ISBN 0-631-13374-7). Basil Blackwell.

Campbell, Barbara, tr. see Barreiro, Alvaro.

Campbell, Barbara E., tr. see Richard, Pablo, et al.

Campbell, Benjamin P. No Alien Power. (Orig.). 1985. pap. 1.75 (ISBN 0-88028-050-6). Forward Movement.

Campbell, Bonnie, jt. auth. see Campbell, Will.

Campbell, Bruce F. Ancient Wisdom Revived: A History of the Theosophical Movement. LC 79-64664. 224p. 1980. 18.95x (ISBN 0-520-03968-8). U of Cal Pr.

Campbell, Camille. Meditations With Teresa of Avila. LC 85-71856. (Meditations With Ser.). 142p. (Orig.). 1985. pap. 6.95 (ISBN 0-939680-23-8). Bear & Co.

Campbell, Cathy. Public Relations. 1985. 4.80 (ISBN 0-318-18572-5). Natl Cath Educ.

Campbell, D. Ross. How to Really Love Your Child. LC 77-89470. 132p. 1977. pap. 4.95 (ISBN 0-88207-751-1). Victor Bks.

Campbell, David. The Eternal Sonship: A Refutation According to Adam Clarke. (Illus.). 95p. (Orig.). 1977. pap. 1.95 (ISBN 0-912315-44-X). Word Aflame.

--Yet Not I. 88p. (Orig.). 1978. pap. 1.95 (ISBN 0-912315-39-3). Word Aflame.

Campbell, Don G. Master Teacher: Nadia Boulanger. (Illus.). 151p. 1984. text ed. 19.95 (ISBN 0-912405-03-1). Pastoral Pr.

Campbell, Donald K. Joshua: Leader under Fire. 144p. pap. 5.95 (ISBN 0-89693-502-7). Victor Bks.

--Nehemiah: Man in Charge. 1979. pap. 4.95 (ISBN 0-88207-781-3). Victor Bks.

Campbell, Donald K., ed. Walvoord: A Tribute. LC 81-16888. 396p. 1982. 15.95 (ISBN 0-8024-9227-4). Moody.

Campbell, E. F., Jr., jt. ed. see Freedman, D. N.

Campbell, Edward F. Ruth. LC 74-18785. (Anchor Bible Ser.: Vol. 7). (Illus.). 216p. 1975. 14.00 (ISBN 0-385-05316-9). Doubleday.

Campbell, Eugene E., jt. auth. see Gowans, Fred R.

Campbell, Evelyn, ed. see Becker, Judy.

Campbell, Faith F. Stanley Frodsham: Prophet with a Pen. LC 74-77406. 1974. pap. 1.25 (ISBN 0-88243-603-1, 02-0603). Gospel Pub.

Campbell, G. & Morgan. Studies in the Prophecy of Jeremiah. 288p. 13.95 (ISBN 0-8007-0298-0). Revell.

Campbell, George A. The Knights Templars, Their Rise & Fall. LC 78-63330. (The Crusades & Military Orders: Second Ser.). Repr. of 1937 ed. 35.00 (ISBN 0-404-17005-6). AMS Pr.

Campbell, Helen. Darkness & Daylight: Or, Lights & Shadows of New York Life: A Pictorial Record of Personal Experiences by Day & Night in the Great Metropolis with Hundreds of Thrilling Anecdotes & Incidents. LC 76-81511. 1969. Repr. of 1895 ed. 48.00x (ISBN 0-8103-3566-2). Gale.

Campbell, Horace. Rasta & Resistance: From Marcus Garvey to Walter Rodney. LC 85-73332. 240p. (Orig.). 1987. 32.95 (ISBN 0-86543-034-9); pap. 10.95 (ISBN 0-86543-035-7). Africa World.

Campbell, James. Greek Fathers. LC 63-10279. (Our Debt to Greece & Rome Ser.). 167p. 1963. Repr. of 1930 ed. 18.50x (ISBN 0-8154-0046-2). Cooper Sq.

Campbell, James M. Paul the Mystic. 1977. lib. bdg. 59.95 (ISBN 0-8490-2415-3). Gordon Pr.

Campbell, Jean, ed. see Ridley, Gustave.

Campbell, Joe E. Pentecostal Holiness Church. pap. 6.00 (ISBN 0-911866-55-8). Advocate.

Campbell, John G. Witchcraft & Second Sight in the Highlands & Islands of Scotland. 1976. Repr. 20.00x (ISBN 0-85409-978-6). Charles River Bks.

Campbell, Joseph. The Flight of the Wild Gander. LC 70-183820. 256p. 1972. pap. 7.50 (ISBN 0-89526-914-7). Regnery Bks.

--Hero with a Thousand Faces. rev. ed. LC 49-8590. (Bollingen Ser.: No. 17). (Illus.). 1968. 39.50 (ISBN 0-691-09743-7); pap. 9.95 (ISBN 0-691-01784-0). Princeton U Pr.

--The Inner Reaches of Outer Space: Metaphor As Myth & As Religion. LC 84-40776. (Illus.). 160p. 1986. 16.95 (ISBN 0-912383-09-7). Van der Marck.

--The Masks of God: Creative Mythology. (Illus.). 730p. 1970. pap. 7.95 (ISBN 0-14-004307-1). Penguin.

--The Masks of God: Occidental Mythology. (Illus.). 564p. 1976. pap. 7.95 (ISBN 0-14-004306-3). Penguin.

--The Masks of God: Oriental Mythology. (Illus.). 576p. 1970. pap. 7.95 (ISBN 0-14-004305-5). Penguin.

--The Masks of God: Primitive Mythology. (Illus.). 528p. 1976. pap. 7.95 (ISBN 0-14-004304-7). Penguin.

--The Masks of God 4: Creative Mythology. 1968. 19.95 (ISBN 0-670-46111-3). Viking.

Campbell, Joseph & Abadie, M. J. The Mythic Image. LC 79-166363. (Bollingen Series C). (Illus.). 560p. 1981. pap. 19.95 (ISBN 0-691-01839-1). Princeton U Pr.
Campbell, Joseph, ed. see Zimmer, Heinrich.
Campbell, Keith. A Stoic Philosophy of Life. LC 86-13351. 216p. (Orig.). 1986. lib. bdg. 22.50 (ISBN 0-8191-5529-2); pap. text ed. 12.25 (ISBN 0-8191-5530-6). U Pr of Amer.
Campbell, Kenneth L. The Intellectual Struggle of the English Catholics in the Seventeenth Century: The Catholic Dilemma. LC 86-23893. (Texts & Studies in Religion Ser.: Vol. 30). 256p. 1986. text ed. 49.95 (ISBN 0-88946-818-4). E Mellen.
Campbell, Lewis. Religion in Greek Literature: A Sketch in Outline. facsimile ed. LC 79-148874. (Select Bibliographies Reprint Ser). Repr. of 1898 ed. 22.00 (ISBN 0-8369-5645-1). Ayer Co Pubs.
Campbell, Lucile M. To God Be the Glory. (Orig.). 1981. pap. 1.95 (ISBN 0-9607114-0-6). L M Campbell.
Campbell, Mary J., jt. auth. see Anderson, Emma D.
Campbell, Michael J., jt. auth. see Wees, J. Dustin.
Campbell, Murdoch. From Grace to Glory: Meditations of the Psalms. 1979. pap. 5.45 (ISBN 0-85151-028-0). Banner of Truth.
Campbell, Murry M. Why Denominationalism? LC 84-90492. 140p. 1985. 10.00 (ISBN 0-533-06376-0). Vantage.
Campbell, Oscar J., et al. Studies in Shakespeare, Milton & Donne. McCartney, Eugene S., ed. LC 78-93244. (University of Michigan Publications: Vol. 1). 235p. 1970. Repr. of 1925 ed. 20.00x (ISBN 0-87753-020-3). Phaeton.
Campbell, Pam, jt. auth. see Burns, Ridge.
Campbell, Penelope. Maryland in Africa: The Maryland State Colonization Society, 1831-1857. LC 75-131058. pap. 68.00 (ISBN 0-317-41903-X, 2025915). Bks Demand UMI.
Campbell, Peter A. & McMahon, Edwin M. Bio-Spirituality: Focusing As a Way to Grow. LC 84-21328. 1985. pap. 6.95 (ISBN 0-8294-0478-3). Loyola.
Campbell, R., tr. see Mutahhari, Ayatullah M.
Campbell, R., tr. see Taleghani, Sayyid M.
Campbell, R. J. The Story of Christmas. 1977. lib. bdg. 59.95 (ISBN 0-8490-2677-6). Gordon Pr.
Campbell, R. K. The Church of the Living God. 8.95 (ISBN 0-88172-007-0); pap. 5.95 (ISBN 0-686-13515-6). Believers Bkshelf.
--Divine Principles of Gathering. 40p. pap. 0.45 (ISBN 0-88172-015-1). Believers Bkshelf.
--Essentials of the Christian Life. 46p. pap. 0.50 (ISBN 0-88172-008-9). Believers Bkshelf.
--Our Wonderful Bible. 417p. 12.95 (ISBN 0-88172-009-7); pap. 10.50 (ISBN 0-88172-010-0). Believers Bkshelf.
--Outside the Camp. 16p. pap. 0.30 (ISBN 0-88172-087-9). Believers Bkshelf.
--Parables in Matthew's Gospel. 1978. pap. 1.95 (ISBN 0-915374-42-0, 42-0). Rapids Christian.
--Parables in Matthew's Gospel: Matthew 13. tchr's lesson outline 3.95 (ISBN 0-88172-011-9). Believers Bkshelf.
--Prophetic History of Christendom. 6.95 (ISBN 0-88172-012-7). Believers Bkshelf.
--Things That Accompany Salvation. 40p. pap. 0.45 (ISBN 0-88172-013-5). Believers Bkshelf.
--Woman's Place. 32p. pap. 0.60 (ISBN 0-88172-014-3). Believers Bkshelf.
Campbell, Reginald J. Livingstone. LC 77-138212. (Illus.). 295p. 1972. Repr. of 1930 ed. lib. bdg. 22.50x (ISBN 0-8371-5567-3, CALI). Greenwood.
Campbell, Richard D. Signs of a Lively Congregation. 1984. 3.95 (ISBN 0-89536-701-7, 4886). CSS of Ohio.
Campbell, Richard H. & Pitts, Michael R. The Bible on Film: A Checklist 1897-1980. LC 81-13560. 224p. 1981. 17.50 (ISBN 0-8108-1473-0). Scarecrow.
Campbell, Robert & Sherer, Michael. Turn Us, Lord. 1985. 2.95 (ISBN 0-89536-728-9, 5812). CSS of Ohio.
Campbell, Robert C. Jesus Still Has Something to Say. 192p. 1987. pap. 9.95 (ISBN 0-8170-1114-5). Judson.
Campbell, Roderick. Israel & the New Covenant. LC 82-142978. 364p. 1982. Repr. of 1954 ed. 12.95 (ISBN 0-939404-01-X). Geneva Ministr.
--Israel & the New Covenant. 1982. 12.95 (ISBN 0-87552-161-4). Presby & Reformed.
Campbell, Roger. Let's Communicate. (Orig.). 1979. pap. 3.50 (ISBN 0-87508-060-X). Chr Lit.
--Lord, I'm Afraid. (Orig.). 1980. pap. 2.50 (ISBN 0-87508-056-1). Chr Lit.
--Staying Positive in a Negative World. 132p. 1984. pap. 4.95 (ISBN 0-89693-377-6). Victor Bks.
--You Can Win. 132p. 1985. pap. 4.95 (ISBN 0-89693-317-2). Victor Bks.
Campbell, Roger F. Prosperity in the End Time. 1983. pap. 2.95 (ISBN 0-87508-055-3). Chr Lit.
Campbell, Ross. Si Amas a Tu Adolescente. Araujo, Juan S., tr. from Eng. Tr. of How To Really Love Your Teenager. (Span.). 144p. 1986. pap. 3.95 (ISBN 0-88113-030-3). Edit Betania.
Campbell, Ross & Gray, Randall. How to Keep Going When the Storms Keep Coming. 288p. (Orig.). 1986. pap. 6.95 (ISBN 0-8423-1376-1). Tyndale.
Campbell, Stan. Any Old Time, Bk. 4. 80p. 1985. pap. 6.95 (ISBN 0-89693-640-6). Victor Bks.
Campbell, Stephanie, ed. As We Seek God: International Reflections on Contemporary Benedictine Monasticism. (Cistercian Studies Ser.: No. 70). 1983. pap. 7.95 (ISBN 0-87907-868-5). Cistercian Pubns.
Campbell, Thomas C. & Reierson, Gary B. The Gift of Adminstration. LC 80-24594. 138p. 1981. pap. 6.95 (ISBN 0-664-24357-6). Westminster.
Campbell, Thomas J. The Jesuits, Fifteen Thirty-Four to Nineteen Twenty-One, 2 vols. 1977. lib. bdg. 250.00 (ISBN 0-8490-2093-X). Gordon Pr.
--Jesuits: Fifteen Thirty-Four to Nineteen Twenty-One. LC 77-82144. (Reprints Ser). 1970. Repr. of 1921 ed. lib. bdg. 45.00 (ISBN 0-87821-018-0). Milford Hse.
Campbell, Thomas L., tr. from Gr. Dionysius the Pseudo-Areopagite: The Ecclesiastical Hierarchy. LC 81-40140. 236p. (Orig.). 1981. lib. bdg. 27.50 (ISBN 0-8191-1798-6); pap. text ed. 12.50 (ISBN 0-8191-1799-4). U Pr of Amer.
Campbell, Viola D. Juguemos. (Illus.). 199p. 1983. pap. 3.50 (ISBN 0-311-11006-1). Casa Bautista.
--Recreation Cristiana. (Span., Illus.). 160p. 1986. pap. 4.25 (ISBN 0-311-11037-1). Casa Bautista.
Campbell, Vivian, ed. A Christmas Anthology of Poetry & Painting. LC 79-51963. (Granger Poetry Library). 1980. Repr. of 1947 ed. 27.50x (ISBN 0-89609-181-3). Roth Pub Inc.
Campbell, W. L., ed. see Nagarjuna.
Campbell, Will & Campbell, Bonnie. God on Earth: The Lord's Prayer for Our Time. (Illus.). 128p. 1983. pap. 12.95 (ISBN 0-8245-0586-7). Crossroad NY.
Campbell-Morgan, G. Minor Prophets. 160p. 1960. 10.95 (ISBN 0-8007-0208-5). Revell.
Campderros, Daniel. Bosquejos Biblicos, Tomo III. 96p. 1986. pap. 2.50 (ISBN 0-311-43033-3). Casa Bautista.
--Bosquejos Biblicos Tomo I: Antiguo Testamento. 96p. 1984. pap. 2.50 (ISBN 0-311-43025-2). Casa Bautista.
--Bosquejos Biblicos Tomo II. 96p. 1985. pap. 2.50 (ISBN 0-311-43026-0). Casa Bautista.
Campenhausen, Hans Von. Virgin Birth in the Theology of the Ancient Church. LC 64-55217. (Studies in Historical Theology: No. 2). 1964. pap. 10.00x (ISBN 0-8401-0322-0). A R Allenson.
Campenhausen, Hans von see Von Campenhausen, Hans.
Campenhausen, Hansvon see Von Campenhausen, Hans.
Camphor, Alexander P. Missionary Story Sketches: Folk-Lore from Africa. facsimile ed. LC 79-173603. (Black Heritage Library Collection). Repr. of 1909 ed. 20.00 (ISBN 0-8369-8915-5). Ayer Co Pubs.
Campion, Donald R. & Louapre, Albert C., eds. Documents of the Thirty-Third General Congregation of the Society of Jesus: An English Translation of the Official Latin Texts. LC 84-80080. 116p. pap. 3.00 (ISBN 0-912422-64-5). Inst Jesuit.
Campion, Joan. To Save the Rest of Them: Gisi Fleischmann & the Rescue of Central European Jews. 2nd, rev. ed. (Illus.). 196p. 1985. lib. bdg. 18.95 (ISBN 0-9614649-0-9); pap. text ed. 10.95 (ISBN 0-9614649-1-7). G Hein.
Campion, M. G. Worry: A Maieutic Analysis. 350p. 1986. text ed. 47.50x (ISBN 0-566-05118-4). Gower Pub Co.
Campion, Michael & Zehr, Wilmer. Especially for Grandparents. (When Was the Last Time Ser.). (Illus.). 112p. (Orig.). 1980. pap. 5.95 (ISBN 0-87123-141-7, 210141). Bethany Hse.
--Especially for Husbands. (When Was the Last Time Ser.). (Illus.). 112p. 1978. pap. 5.95 (ISBN 0-87123-136-0, 210136). Bethany Hse.
--Especially for Parents. (When Was the Last Time Ser.). (Illus.). 112p. 1978. pap. 5.95 (ISBN 0-87123-137-9, 210137). Bethany Hse.
Campolo, Anthony. Partly Right. 192p. 1985. 11.95 (ISBN 0-8499-0368-8, 0368-8). Word Bks.
--A Reasonable Faith. 208p. 1985. 8.95 (ISBN 0-8499-3040-5, 3040-5). Word Bks.
--Seven Deadly Sins. 156p. Date not set. 9.95 (ISBN 0-89693-533-7). Victor Bks.
--The Success Fantasy. LC 79-67852. 144p. 1980. pap. 5.95 (ISBN 0-88207-796-1). Victor Bks.
Campolo, Anthony, Jr. The Power Delusion. 168p. 1983. pap. 5.95 (ISBN 0-88207-292-7). Victor Bks.
Campolo, Tony. Who Switched Price Tags? How to Make Life Better in Your Work, Family & Church. 224p. 1986. 11.95 (ISBN 0-8499-0491-9). Word Bks.
Camps, Arnulf. Partners in Dialogue: Christianity & Other World Religions. Drury, John, tr. from Dutch. LC 82-18798. Tr. of Christendom en godsdienstein der wereld. 272p. (Orig.). 1983. pap. 10.95 (ISBN 0-88344-378-3). Orbis Bks.
Campus Crusade for Christ Staff. Discovery II. 1980. pap. 2.95 saddlestitched (ISBN 0-918956-63-3). Campus Crusade.
--Game Plan II. (Illus.). 100p. 1980. pap. text ed. 3.50 (ISBN 0-918956-64-1). Campus Crusade.
--How to Make Your Mark. 540p. (Orig.). 1983. pap. 8.95 (ISBN 0-86605-142-2). Campus Crusade.
Campus Crusade Staff. Insights: Building a Successful Youth Ministry, Vol. I. (Insight Ser.). (Orig.). 1981. pap. text ed. 5.95 (ISBN 0-86605-017-5). Campus Crusade.
Camus, Albert. Homme Revolte: Essai. (Coll. Soleil). 1951. 16.50 (ISBN 0-685-11234-9); pap. 4.95 (ISBN 0-686-66425-6). French & Eur.
Canadian Christian Movement for Peace Staff, et al. Christian Movement for Peace: Militarism & Hope. Huntly, Alyson & Morin, James, eds. 208p. 1983. pap. 29.95 (ISBN 0-697-01919-5). Wm C Brown.
Canadian Christian Movement for Peace Staff. Economic Rights & Human Development. (People Living for Justice Ser.). 240p. 1984. pap. 29.95 (ISBN 0-697-01932-2). Wm C Brown.
--Political & Social Rights & Human Dignity. (People Living for Justice Ser.). 208p. 1984. pap. text ed. 29.95 (ISBN 0-317-19703-7). Wm C Brown.
--Women & Human Wholeness. Huntly, Alyson, et al, eds. (People Living for Justice Ser.). 160p. 1983. pap. text ed. 29.95 (ISBN 0-697-01920-9). Wm C Brown.
--Work & Co-Creation. Huntly, Alyson, et al, eds. (People Living for Justice Ser.). 160p. 1983. pap. text ed. 29.95 (ISBN 0-697-01921-7). Wm C Brown.
Canadian Polish Millenium Fund Staff. Poland's Millenium of Christianity. (Eng. & Fr.). 50p. 1966. 1.00 (ISBN 0-940962-29-2). Polish Inst Art & Sci.
Canale, Andrew. Understanding the Human Jesus: A Journey in Scripture & Imagination. LC 84-61027. 208p. 1985. pap. 7.95 (ISBN 0-8091-2654-0). Paulist Pr.
Canals, Salvatore. Jesus As Friend. 117p. (Orig.). 1979. pap. 6.95 (ISBN 0-906127-11-4, Pub. by Four Courts Pr Ireland). Scepter Pubs.
Canavaggio, Pierre. Dictionnaire Raisonne Des Superstitions et Des Croyances Populaires. (Fr.). 247p. 1977. pap. 19.95 (ISBN 0-686-56937-7, M-6059). French & Eur.
Cancian, F. What Are Norms? A Study of Beliefs & Action in a Maya Community. LC 74-77833. 256p. 1975. 34.50 (ISBN 0-521-20536-0). Cambridge U Pr.
Cancian, Francesca M. What Are Norms? A Study of Beliefs & Action in a Maya Community. LC 74-77833. pap. 55.50 (2027284). Bks Demand UMI.
Canclini, Arnoldo. Cuando la Infidelidad Asoma. (Series on the Family). (Span.). 112p. (Orig.). 1986. pap. 3.50 (ISBN 0-311-46264-2). Casa Bautista.
Canclini, Arnoldo, tr. see Geisler, Norman.
Canclini, Arnoldo, tr. see Humphreys, Fisher.
Canclini, Arnoldo, tr. see Jones, J. Estill.
Canclini, Arnoldo, tr. see Jungel, Eberhard.
Canclini, Arnoldo, tr. see Ladd, George E.
Canclini, Arnoldo, tr. see Stagg, Frank.
Canclini, Santiago. Alzare Mis Ojos. (Span.). 316p. 1984. pap. 7.95 (ISBN 0-311-40047-7). Casa Bautista.
Candlish, Robert S. First Epistle of John. LC 79-14801. (Kregel Bible Study Classics Ser.). 602p. 1979. 22.95 (ISBN 0-8254-2320-1). Kregel.
--Studies in Genesis, 2 vols. in one. LC 79-14084. (Kregel Bible Study Classics Ser.). 854p. 1979. 22.95 (ISBN 0-8254-2315-5). Kregel.
Candolle, Alphonse de see De Candolle, Alphonse.
Candragomin. Difficult Beginnings: Three Works on the Bodhisattva Path. Tatz, Mark, tr. LC 83-2317. Tr. of Sanskrit. 121p. 1985. 22.50 (ISBN 0-87773-317-1, 54530-3). Shambhala Pubns.
Candy, Hugh C. Milton: The Individualist in Metre. 1930. lib. bdg. 7.50 (ISBN 0-8414-3630-4). Folcroft.
Cane, Bill. Through Crisis to Freedom. LC 79-89874. (Orig.). 1980. pap. 3.25 (ISBN 0-914070-14-2). ACTA Found.
Canfield, Anita. Self-Esteem for the Latter-Day Saint Woman. 2nd ed. 135p. 1983. 7.95 (ISBN 0-934126-15-1). Randall Bk Co.
Canfield, Anita, jt. auth. see Flynn, Johanna.
Canfield, Betty M. The Bible World Maps of the Old & New Testaments. (Illus.). 24p. (Orig.). 1983. pap. text ed. 4.95 (ISBN 0-9611756-0-5). Humble Pub Co.
Canfield, Leon H. The Early Persecutions of the Christians. LC 68-54259. (Columbia University Studies in the Social Sciences: No. 136). Repr. of 1913 ed. 14.50 (ISBN 0-404-51136-8). AMS Pr.
Canfield, Muriel. I Wish I Could Say, "I Love You". 204p. (Orig.). 1983. pap. 5.95 (ISBN 0-87123-265-0, 210265). Bethany Hse.
Canfield, Robert L. Faction & Conversion in a Plural Society: Religious Alignments in the Hindu Kush. (Anthropological Papers: No. 50). 1973. 3.00x (ISBN 0-932206-48-4). U Mich Mus Anthro.
Canham, Elizabeth. Pilgrimage to Priesthood. 128p. (Orig.). 1985. pap. 9.95 (ISBN 0-8164-2492-6, 8603, HarpR). Har-Row.
--Praying the Bible: A Parish Life Sourcebook. LC 86-32976. 98p. (Orig.). 1987. pap. 6.95 (ISBN 0-936384-46-8). Cowley Pubns.
Canham, Erwin D. Ethics of United States Foreign Relations. LC 66-14031. 101p. 1966. 6.00x (ISBN 0-8262-0044-3). U of Mo Pr.
Cann, Christian. A Scriptural & Allegorical Glossary to Milton's Paradise Lost. 1978. Repr. of 1828 ed. lib. bdg. 35.00 (ISBN 0-8495-0807-X). Arden Lib.
--Scriptural & Allegorical Glossary to Milton's Paradise Lost. Repr. of 1828 ed. 32.50 (ISBN 0-8414-0566-2). Folcroft.
Cannell, Marian. Caregiver's Handbook. 1986. 46.50 (ISBN 0-939273-00-4). Caregiving Resc.
Canney, Maurice A. Encyclopaedia of Religions. LC 75-123370. 1970. Repr. of 1921 ed. 53.00 (ISBN 0-8103-3856-4). Gale.
Canning, Jeremiah W., ed. Values in an Age of Confrontation: A Symposium Sponsored by the Religion in Education Foundation. LC 72-109054. (Studies of the Person). pap. 41.10 (ISBN 0-317-09226-X, 2055239). Bks Demand UMI.
Canning, Raymond, tr. see Saint Augustine.
Cannon, Anthon S., et al, eds. Popular Beliefs & Superstitions from Utah. 526p. 1984. 45.00x (ISBN 0-87480-236-9). U of Utah Pr.
Cannon, Donald Q., jt. auth. see Cook, Lyndon W.
Cannon, Donald Q. & Cook, Lyndon W., eds. Far West Record. LC 82-23476. 318p. 1983. 10.95 (ISBN 0-87747-901-1). Deseret Bk.
Cannon, George C. The Use of Traditional Materials in Colossians: Their Significance for the Problem of Authenticity. LC 83-8181. viii, 253p. 1983. 17.95 (ISBN 0-86554-074-8, H51). Mercer Univ Pr.
Cannon, George Q. Gospel Truth: Classics Edition. 2nd ed. 1987. 14.95 (ISBN 0-87579-094-1). Deseret Bk.
--Life of Joseph Smith the Prophet. (Classics in Mormon Literature Ser.). 572p. 1986. Repr. of 1964 ed. 14.95 (ISBN 0-87747-148-7). Deseret Bk.
--Writings from the "Western Standard". Repr. of 1864 ed. 25.00 (ISBN 0-404-01379-1). AMS Pr.
Cannon, William R. A Disciple's Profile of Jesus. LC 75-2956. 1975. 2.95x (ISBN 0-8358-0322-8). Upper Room.
--The Gospel of John. 128p. (Orig.). 1985. pap. 4.95 (ISBN 0-8358-0511-5). Upper Room.
--The Gospel of Matthew. LC 82-50948. 128p. (Orig.). 1983. pap. 4.95 (ISBN 0-8358-0450-X). Upper Room.
--History of Christianity in the Middle Ages. (Twin Brooks Ser.). 1983. pap. 9.95 (ISBN 0-8010-2492-7). Baker Bk.
--Jesus the Servant: From the Gospel of Mark. LC 78-62578. 1978. pap. text ed. 2.95x (ISBN 0-8358-0376-7). Upper Room.
--The Theology of John Wesley: With Special Reference to the Doctrine of Justification. 284p. 1984. pap. text ed. 12.75 (ISBN 0-8191-4001-5). U Pr of Amer.
Canon Law Society of America Staff, tr. from Latin. The Code of Canon Law: Latin-English Edition. Orig. Title: Codex Iuris Canonici. xlii, 668p. (Orig.). 1983. 15.00 (ISBN 0-943616-20-4); pap. 12.00 (ISBN 0-943616-19-0). Canon Law Soc.
Canon Law Society of America Staff. Proceedings of the Forty-Sixth Annual Convention. 308p. (Orig.). 1985. pap. 8.00 (ISBN 0-943616-29-8). Canon Law Soc.
Canon Law Society of Great Britain & Ireland Staff, ed. Index to the Code of Canon Law. 104p. (Orig.). 1985. pap. 3.50 (ISBN 0-8028-0067-X). Eerdmans.

Canon Law Society of Great Britain, Ireland Staff, ed. The Code of Canon Law in English Translation. 1983. pap. 9.95 (ISBN 0-8028-1978-8). Eerdmans.

Canright, D. M. El Adventismo Del Septimo Dia. Correa, F. G., tr. 1985. pap. 1.95 (ISBN 0-311-05601-6). Casa Bautista.

--Seventh-Day Adventism in a Nutshell. 2.75 (ISBN 0-89225-162-X). Gospel Advocate.

--Seventh-Day Adventism Renounced. 1982. pap. 5.95. Gospel Advocate.

Canstantopoulos, E. Stories from Greek Mythology. (Illus.). 3.20 (ISBN 0-686-79632-2). Divry.

Cant, R. C., jt. ed. see Aylmer, G. E.

Cantelon, Willard. The Baptism in the Holy Spirit. 34p. 1951. pap. 1.00 (ISBN 0-88243-692-9, 02-0692). Gospel Pub.

--The Day the Dollar Dies: Biblical Prophecy of a New World System in the End Times. LC 72-94186. 190p. 1973. (Haven Bks); pap. 2.95 (ISBN 0-88270-170-3). Bridge Pub.

Cantleberry, Lillian. Jacob: God's Plain Man. 1984. pap. 7.95 (ISBN 0-570-03928-2, 12-2863). Concordia.

--Moses: Prince, Servant, Prophet. 208p. (Orig.). 1985. pap. 7.95 (ISBN 0-570-03970-3, 12-3005). Concordia.

--Sarah's Story. (Continued Applied Christianity Ser.). 1983. pap. 7.95 (ISBN 0-570-03898-7, 12-2980). Concordia.

Cantlie, Audrey, jt. ed. see Burghart, Richard.

Cantoni, Louise. St. Germaine. rev. ed. 1973. 1.75 (ISBN 0-8198-0262-X). Dghtrs St Paul.

Cantoni, Louise B. Leaving Matters to God. (Illus.). 164p. 1984. 3.00 (ISBN 0-8198-4424-1); pap. 2.00 (ISBN 0-8198-4425-X). Dghtrs St Paul.

Cantonwine, Charles R. Science, Religion & Tradition. 1986. 7.95 (ISBN 0-533-06727-8). Vantage.

Cantor, Aviva & Hamelsdorf, Ora, eds. The Jewish Woman: 1900-1985 Bibliography. 2nd ed. 200p. 1987. pap. 8.95 (ISBN 0-930395-04-2). Biblio NY.

Cantor, Norman F. Church, Kingship & Lay Investiture in England, 1089-1135. 1969. lib. bdg. 26.00x (ISBN 0-374-91273-4, Octagon). Hippocrene Bks.

Cantor, Norman F. & Werthman, Michael S., eds. Renaissance, Reformation, & Absolutism: 1450 to 1650. 2nd ed. LC 72-76355. (Structure of European History Ser.: Vol. 3). 319p. 1972. pap. text ed. 7.95x (ISBN 0-88295-712-0). Harlan Davidson.

Cantwell, Mary. Saint Patrick's Day. LC 67-10070. (Holiday Ser.). (Illus.). 1967. PLB 12.89 (ISBN 0-690-71673-7, Crowell Jr Bks). HarpJ.

Capes, William W. English Church in the Fourteenth & Fifteenth Centuries, 1272-1486. LC 2-21441. (History of the English Church: No. 3). Repr. of 1900 ed. 29.50 (ISBN 0-404-50753-0). AMS Pr.

Capetti, Giselda, ed. Cronistoria, 5 vols. LC 80-68484. 400p. (Orig.). 1980. Set. pap. 40.00 (ISBN 0-89944-043-6); Vol. 1. pap. (ISBN 0-89944-044-4); Vol. 2. pap. (ISBN 0-89944-045-2); Vol. 3. pap. (ISBN 0-89944-046-0); Vol. 4. pap. (ISBN 0-89944-047-9); Vol. 5. pap. (ISBN 0-89944-048-7). Don Bosco Multimedia.

Capey, Ernest F. Erasmus. 1902. 25.00 (ISBN 0-8274-2284-9). R West.

Capgrave, J. Lives of St. Augustine & St. Gilbert of Sempringham. (EETS, OS Ser.: No. 140). Repr. of 1910 ed. 40.00 (ISBN 0-527-00137-6). Kraus Repr.

Capgrave, John. The Life of St. Katharine of Alexandria. Horstmann, Carl, ed. (EETS, OS Ser.: No. 100). Repr. of 1893 ed. 70.00 (ISBN 0-527-00102-3). Kraus Repr.

--Ye Solace of Pilgrimes. Mills, C. A., ed. LC 78-63453. (The Crusades & Military Orders: Second Ser.). Repr. of 1911 ed. 25.00 (ISBN 0-404-16375-0). AMS Pr.

Caplan, Arthur L., jt. auth. see Rosen, Bernard.

Caplan, Arthur L. & Callahan, Daniel, eds. Ethics in Hard Times. LC 81-17728. (The Hastings Center Series in Ethics). 312p. 1981. text ed. 29.50 (ISBN 0-306-40790-6, Plenum Pr). Plenum Pub.

Caplan, Harry, tr. & notes by see Pico della Mirandola, Giovanni.

Caplan, Lionel, ed. Studies in Religious Fundamentalism. 240p. 1987. 39.50 (ISBN 0-88706-518-X); pap. 14.95 (ISBN 0-88706-519-8). State U NY Pr.

Caplan, Neil. Futile Diplomacy: Early Arab-Zionist Negotiation Attempts, 1913-1931, Vol. 1. (Illus.). 296p. 1983. text ed. 32.00x (ISBN 0-7146-3214-7, F Cass Co). Biblio Dist.

Caplan, Samuel & Ribalow, Harold. The Great Jewish Books. 1983. pap. 10.95 (ISBN 0-8180-1135-1). Horizon.

Caples, C. B., et al. A Medieval Miscellany. (Rice University Studies: Vol. 62, No. 2). (Illus.). 120p. (Orig.). 1976. pap. 10.00x (ISBN 0-89263-228-3). Rice Univ.

Caplow, Theodore, et al. All Faithful People: Change & Continuity in Middletown's Religion. LC 82-24759. x, 380p. 1983. 19.50 (ISBN 0-8166-1230-7). U of Minn Pr.

Capon, Robert F. Hunting the Divine Fox: Images & Mystery in the Christian Faith. 176p. 1977. pap. 6.95 (ISBN 0-8164-2137-4, AY7359, HarpR). Har-Row.

--An Offering of Uncles: The Priesthood of Adam & the Shape of the World. (The Crossroad Paperback Ser.). 192p. 1982. pap. 5.95 (ISBN 0-8245-0422-4). Crossroad NY.

--The Parables of the Kingdom. 192p. 1985. 10.95 (ISBN 0-310-42670-7, 17040). Zondervan.

--The Supper of the Lamb: A Culinary Reflection. LC 78-14937. 271p. 1979. pap. 3.95 (ISBN 0-15-686893-8, Harv). HarBracej.

--The Third Peacock. 108p. (Orig.). 1986. pap. 7.50 (ISBN 0-86683-497-4, HarpR). Har-Row.

--The Youngest Day: Nature & Grace on Shelter Island. LC 82-48414. (Illus.). 160p. 1983. 11.49 (ISBN 0-06-061309-2, HarpR). Har-Row.

Caponetto, Salvatore, ed. Benedetto Da Mantova: Il Beneficio Di Cristo. LC 72-3471. (Corpus Reformatorum Italicorum & Biblioteca Ser.). (Lat. & Ital., Illus.). 558p. 1972. 40.00 (ISBN 0-87580-035-1). N Ill U Pr.

Caponigri, Aloysius R. Modern Catholic Thinkers: An Anthology. (Essay Index Reprint Ser.). 650p. Repr. of 1960 ed. lib. bdg. 37.50 (ISBN 0-8290-0784-9). Irvington.

Caponigri, Aloysius R., ed. Modern Catholic Thinkers. facs. ed. LC 78-117775. (Essay Index Reprint Ser). 1960. 38.50 (ISBN 0-8369-1787-1). Ayer Co Pubs.

Caporale, Rocco & Grumelli, Antonio, eds. The Culture of Unbelief: Studies & Proceedings from the First International Symposium on Belief, Held in Rome, March 22-27, 1969. LC 75-138513. 1971. 39.50x (ISBN 0-520-01856-7). U of Cal Pr.

Cappa, Alphonse. Fatima: Cove of Wonders. 1980. 4.50 (ISBN 0-8198-0569-6); pap. 3.25 (ISBN 0-8198-0570-X). Dghtrs St Paul.

Cappadelta, Luigi, tr. see Von Funk, Franz X.

Capper, W. M. & Johnson, D., eds. The Faith of a Surgeon: Belief & Experience in the Life of Arthur Rendle Short. 160p. 1976. pap. 5.95 (ISBN 0-85364-198-6). Attic Pr.

Capps, Charles. Angels. 224p. (Orig.). 1984. pap. 3.95 (ISBN 0-89274-308-5, HH-308). Harrison Hse.

--Authority in Three Worlds. 266p. (Orig.). 1980. pap. 3.95 (ISBN 0-89274-281-X). Harrison Hse.

--Can Your Faith Fail? 1978. pap. 1.75 (ISBN 0-89274-105-8). Harrison Hse.

--Changing the Seen & Shaping the Unseen. 1980. pap. 1.75 (ISBN 0-89274-165-1). Harrison Hse.

--Changing the Seen & Shaping the Unseen. 1981. pap. 2.25 (ISBN 0-89274-220-8, HH-220). Harrison Hse.

--Developing Faith in Your Confession. 1986. mini bk. 0.75 (ISBN 0-89274-412-X). Harrison Hse.

--God's Image of You. 1985. 2.95 (ISBN 0-89274-376-X). Harrison Hse.

--Hebrews. 39p. (Orig.). 1985. wkbk. 4.95 (ISBN 0-914307-36-3). Word Faith.

--Hope: A Partner to Faith. 38p. (Orig.). 1986. pap. 1.25 mini-book (ISBN 0-89274-396-4). Harrison Hse.

--How to Have Faith in Your Faith. 1986. pap. 3.95 (ISBN 0-89274-415-4). Harrison Hse.

--Kicking over Sacred Cows. 132p. (Orig.). 1984. pap. 4.95 (ISBN 0-914307-18-5, Dist. by Harrison Hse). Word Faith.

--Releasing the Ability of God Through Prayer. 159p. 1978. pocketbook 3.50 (ISBN 0-89274-075-2). Harrison Hse.

--Righteousness Which Is of Faith. (Orig.). 1986. mini bk. 0.75 (ISBN 0-89274-411-1). Harrison Hse.

--Success Motivation Through the Word. 272p. 1982. pap. 3.95 (ISBN 0-89274-183-X, HH-183). Harrison Hse.

--Why Tragedy Happens to Christians. 187p. (Orig.). 1980. pap. 3.75 (ISBN 0-89274-175-9, HH-175). Harrison Hse.

Capps, Donald. Deadly Sins & Saving Virtues. LC 85-45912. 176p. 1987. pap. text ed. 10.95 (ISBN 0-8006-1948-X, 1-1948). Fortress.

--Life Cycle Theory & Pastoral Care. LC 83-5585. (Theology & Pastoral Care Ser.). 128p. 1983. pap. 7.95 (ISBN 0-8006-1726-6, 1-1726). Fortress.

--Pastoral Care: A Thematic Approach. LC 78-15093. (Illus.). 162p. 1979. softcover 8.95 (ISBN 0-664-24222-7). Westminster.

--Pastoral Care & Hermeneutics. LC 84-47909. (Theology & Pastoral Care Ser.). 128p. 1984. pap. 7.95 (ISBN 0-8006-1732-0). Fortress.

--Pastoral Counseling & Preaching: A Quest for an Integrated Ministry. LC 80-18502. 156p. 1980. pap. 8.95 (ISBN 0-664-24342-8). Westminster.

Capps, Donald, jt. ed. see Reynolds, Frank E.

Capps, Donald, et al. Encounter with Erikson: Historical Interpretation & Religious Biography. LC 76-44434. (American Academy of Religion, Formative Contemporary Thinkers Ser.: No. 2). 1977. pap. 13.50 (010402). Scholars Pr GA.

Capps, Donald, et al, eds. Psychology of Religion: A Guide to Information Sources. LC 73-17530. (Philosophy & Religion Information Guide Ser.: Vol. 1). vii, 380p. 1976. 62.00x (ISBN 0-8103-1356-1). Gale.

Capps, Walter. The Monastic Impulse. LC 82-14866. 224p. 1982. 10.95 (ISBN 0-8245-0490-9). Crossroad NY.

Capps, Walter H., ed. Seeing with a Native Eye: Contributions to the Study of Native American Religion. LC 76-9980. 1976. pap. 6.95xi (ISBN 0-06-061312-2, RD-177, HarpR). Har-Row.

Capps, Walter H. & Wright, Wendy M., eds. Silent Fire. LC 78-3366. (Forum Bk.). 1978. pap. 7.95x (ISBN 0-06-061314-9, RD 290, HarpR). Har-Row.

Capra, Fritjof. The Tao of Physics. 1977. pap. 4.95 (ISBN 0-553-26379-X). Bantam.

--The Tao of Physics. 2nd ed. LC 82-42679. (New Science Library Ser.). (Illus.). 308p. 1975. pap. 10.95 (ISBN 0-87773-246-9, 71612-4). Shambhala Pubns.

Caprio, Betsy. Experiments in Prayer. (Illus.). 192p. 1973. pap. 5.95 (ISBN 0-87793-054-6). Ave Maria.

--The Woman Sealed in the Tower: A Psychological Approach to Feminine Spirituality. 1983. pap. 5.95 (ISBN 0-8091-2486-6). Paulist Pr.

Caprio, Betsy & Hedberg, Thomas. Coming Home: A Handbook for Exploring the Sanctuary Within. (Illus.). 288p. (Orig.). 1986. pap. 9.95 (ISBN 0-8091-2739-3); director's manual 9.95 (ISBN 0-8091-2787-3). Paulist Pr.

Capt, E. Raymond. The Great Pyramid Decoded. rev. ed. LC 78-101677. (Illus.). 96p. 1978. pap. 3.00 (ISBN 0-934666-01-6). Artisan Sales.

--Jacob's Pillar. LC 79-116385. (Illus.). 96p. 1977. pap. 3.00 (ISBN 0-934666-03-2). Artisan Sales.

--King Solomon's Temple. LC 79-54774. (Illus.). 96p. 1979. pap. 3.00 (ISBN 0-934666-05-9). Artisan Sales.

--Lost Chapter of Acts of the Apostles. 32p. 1982. pap. 2.00 (ISBN 0-934666-09-1). Artisan Sales.

--Stonehenge & Druidism. rev. ed. LC 79-54773. (Illus.). 96p. 1979. pap. 3.00 (ISBN 0-934666-04-0). Artisan Sales.

--The Traditions of Glastonbury. LC 82-72525. (Illus.). 128p. (Orig.). 1983. pap. 5.00 (ISBN 0-934666-10-5). Artisan Sales.

Captain, Philip A. Eight Stages of Christian Growth: Human Development in Psycho-Spiritual Terms. (Illus.). 240p. 1984. pap. 6.95 (ISBN 0-13-246661-9). P-H.

Capuchin, John A. Padre Pio. 1983. 9.50 (ISBN 0-8199-0864-9). Franciscan Herald.

Capuchin, Zeno. John Henry Newman: His Inner Life. LC 86-81424. 340p. (Orig.). 1987. 29.95 (ISBN 0-89870-149-X); pap. 12.95 (ISBN 0-89870-112-0). Ignatius Pr.

Caputi, Natalino. Guide to the Unconscious. LC 83-24620. 172p. (Orig.). 1984. pap. 14.95 (ISBN 0-89135-042-X). Religious Educ.

Caputo, John D. The Mystical Element in Heidegger's Thought. LC 77-92251. xvi, 292p. 1978. 28.95x (ISBN 0-8214-0372-9). Ohio U Pr.

--The Mystical Element in Heidegger's Thought. rev. ed. xxviii, 292p. 1986. pap. 12.50 (ISBN 0-8232-1153-3). Fordham.

Carachei, Maria E., tr. see Buckingham, Betty Jo.

Carayon, Jean. Essai sur les rapports du pouvoir politique et du pouvoir religieux chez Montesquieu. LC 75-168919. (Fr.). 1973. Repr. of 1903 ed. lib. bdg. 15.00 (ISBN 0-8337-4024-5). B Franklin.

Carballosa, Evis L. Daniel y el Reino Mesianico. Orig. Title: Daniel & the Messianic Kingdom. 320p. 1979. pap. 7.95 (ISBN 0-8254-1101-7). Kregel.

--La Deidad de Cristo. Orig. Title: The Deity of Christ. (Span.). 168p. 1982. pap. 3.50 (ISBN 0-8254-1102-5). Kregel.

--Filipenses: Un Comentario Exegetico y Practico. Orig. Title: Phillippians: Commentary. (Span.). 140p. 1973. pap. 1.95 (ISBN 0-8254-1105-X). Kregel.

--Santiago: Una Fe en Accion. Orig. Title: James: Faith in Action. (Span.). 352p. (Orig.). 1986. pap. 10.95 (ISBN 0-8254-1112-2). Kregel.

Carberry, John. The Book of the Rosary. LC 83-62424. 120p. (Orig.). 1983. pap. 4.50 (ISBN 0-87973-610-0, 610). Our Sunday Visitor.

--Mary Queen & Mother. 1979. 5.50 (ISBN 0-8198-0584-X); pap. 3.95 (ISBN 0-8198-0585-8). Dghtrs St Paul.

--Reflections & Prayers for Visits with Our Eucharistic King. pap. 0.50 (ISBN 0-8198-0315-4). Dghtrs St Paul.

Card, Orson S. Saintspeak. 64p. (Orig.). 1981. pap. 3.95 (ISBN 0-941214-00-1). Signature Bks.

Cardano, Girolamo. Cardanus Comforte. Bedingfield, T., ed. LC 77-6565. (English Experience Ser.: No. 82). 204p. 1969. Repr. of 1576 ed. 25.00 (ISBN 90-221-0082-0). Walter J Johnson.

Carden, Robert W., tr. see Buonarroti, Michelangelo.

Cardenal, Ernesto. The Gospel in Solentiname, 4 vols. Walsh, Donald D., tr. from Span. LC 76-2681. Orig. Title: El Evangelio en Solentiname. (Orig.). 1982. Vol. 1, 288p. pap. 8.95 (ISBN 0-88344-176-4); Vol. 2, 272p. pap. 8.95 (ISBN 0-88344-175-6); Vol. 3, 320p. pap. 8.95 (ISBN 0-88344-174-8); Vol. 4, 288p. pap. 8.95 (ISBN 0-88344-173-X). Orbis Bks.

--Love. 160p. 1981. pap. 4.95 (ISBN 0-8245-0043-1). Crossroad NY.

--Psalms. 96p. 1981. pap. 3.95 (ISBN 0-8245-0044-X). Crossroad NY.

Carder, David. Promises from Proverbs. 1986. pap. 2.50 (ISBN 0-310-36782-4, 12732P). Zondervan.

Cardiff, Ira D. What Great Men Think of Religion. LC 71-161322. (Atheist Viewpoint Ser). 504p. 1972. Repr. of 1945 ed. 29.00 (ISBN 0-405-03625-6). Ayer Co Pubs.

Cardinale, H. E. Orders of Knighthood, Awards & the Holy See: A Historical Juridical & Practical Compendium. 3rd, rev., enl. ed. 1985. text ed. 55.00x (ISBN 0-905715-26-8). Humanities.

Cardinal Gibbons. Faith of Our Fathers. LC 80-51331. 352p. 1980. pap. 9.00 (ISBN 0-89555-158-6). Tan Bks Pubs.

Cardinal Joseph Bernardin. The Ministry of Service. 40p. 1986. pap. 1.25 (ISBN 0-8146-1485-X). Liturgical Pr.

Cardozo, Arlene. Jewish Family Celebrations. (Illus.). 288p. 1985. pap. 6.95 (ISBN 0-312-44232-7). St Martin.

Cardozo, Arlene R. Jewish Family Celebrations: Shabbat, Festivals & Traditional Ceremonies. LC 82-5566. (Illus.). 288p. 1982. 17.50 (ISBN 0-312-44231-9). St Martin.

Cardozo, Jacob L. The Contemporary Jew in the Elizabethan Drama. (Research & Source Works Ser: No. 175). Repr. of 1925 ed. 15.00 (ISBN 0-8337-0466-4). B Franklin.

Cardwell, Carolyn E., ed. My Heart Speaks to Thee, Vol. 1. (Illus.). 250p. 1985. pap. 8.45 (ISBN 0-916395-02-2, MH-1). Hieroglyphics.

--My Heart Speaks to Thee, Vol. 2. (Illus.). 250p. (Orig.). 1985. pap. 8.45 (ISBN 0-916395-05-7, MH-2). Hieroglyphics.

Cardwell, Jerry D. A Rumor of Trumpets: The Return of God to Secular Society. 118p. (Orig.). 1985. lib. bdg. 22.00 (ISBN 0-8191-4791-5); pap. text ed. 8.75 (ISBN 0-8191-4792-3). U Pr of Amer.

--The Social Context of Religiosity. LC 80-67216. 174p. 1980. pap. text ed. 10.75 (ISBN 0-8191-1136-8). U Pr of Amer.

Cardwell, Julia C. The Moonshine Special. (Illus.). 1983. 5.75 (ISBN 0-8062-1908-4). Carlton.

Carens, Joseph H. Equality, Moral Incentives, & the Market. LC 80-36774. (Illus.). 264p. 1981. lib. bdg. 19.00x (ISBN 0-226-09269-0). U of Chicago Pr.

Carey, Floyd D. Teenagers Pocket Companion, No. 2. 1962. pap. 0.25 (ISBN 0-87148-828-0). Pathway Pr.

--Teenagers Pocket Companion, No. 3. 1962. pap. 0.25 (ISBN 0-87148-829-9). Pathway Pr.

Carey, Floyd D., ed. Sunday School Basics. 1976. 5.25 (ISBN 0-87148-778-0); pap. 4.25 (ISBN 0-87148-777-2). Pathway Pr.

Carey, Floyd D. & Byrd, James F., eds. Manna: A Book of Table Devotions. 1973. pap. 3.95 (ISBN 0-87148-564-8). Pathway Pr.

Carey, Floyd D., Jr. Teen-Agers' Treasure Chest. 100p. 1963. pap. 1.25 (ISBN 0-87148-830-2). Pathway Pr.

Carey, George. A Tale of Two Churches: Can Protestants & Catholics Get Together? LC 84-28858. 180p. (Orig.). 1985. pap. 5.95 (ISBN 0-87784-972-2). Inter-Varsity.

Carey, George W., ed. Freedom & Virtue: The Conservative Libertarian Debate. LC 84-19637. 164p. (Orig.). 1985. lib. bdg. 25.25 (ISBN 0-8191-4334-0, Co-Pub. by Intercollegiate Studies); pap. text ed. 9.50 (ISBN 0-8191-4335-9, Co-pub. by Intercollegiate Studies). U Pr of Amer.

Carey, George W. & Schall, James V., eds. Essays on Christianity & Political Philosophy. (The ISI Roots of Western Culture Ser.). 144p. (Orig.). 1985. 24.00 (ISBN 0-8191-4275-1, Co-pub. by Intercollegiate Studies); pap. text ed. 8.75 (ISBN 0-8191-4276-X). U Pr of Amer.

Carey, Howard R. Journey into Light & Joy. LC 79-53905. (Illus.). 180p. 1979. pap. 4.50 (ISBN 0-87516-380-7). De Vorss.

Carey, John. John Donne: Life, Mind & Art. 1981. 25.00x (ISBN 0-19-520242-2). Oxford U Pr.

Carey, John J. Kairos & Logos: Studies in the Roots & Implications of Tillich Society. LC 84-6738. xxii, 284p. 1984. Repr. of 1978 ed. 15.95 (ISBN 0-86554-106-X, MUP/H100). Mercer Univ Pr.

Carey, John J., ed. Theonomy & Autonomy: Studies in Paul Tillich's Engagement with Modern Culture. LC 83-25847. xxii, 287p. 1984. Repr. of 1978 ed. 21.95 (ISBN 0-86554-105-1, MUP/H99). Mercer Univ Pr.

Carey, Jonathan S., jt. ed. see Ahlstrom, Sydney E.

Carey, Ken. Notes to My Children: A Simplified Metaphysics. 170p. 1987. pap. 8.95 (ISBN 0-913299-36-7, Dist. by NAL). Stillpoint.

--The Starseed Transmissions. 95p. 1986. pap. 6.95 (ISBN 0-913299-29-4, Dist. by NAL). Stillpoint.

--Terra Christa. (Illus.). 237p. 1986. pap. 9.95 (ISBN 0-913299-31-6, Dist. by NAL). Stillpoint.

--Terra Christa: The Global Spiritual Awakening. Gross, Jim, ed. 256p. (Orig.). 1985. pap. 7.95t (ISBN 0-912949-02-3). Uni-Sun.

--Vision. 90p. 1986. pap. 6.95 (ISBN 0-913299-30-8, Dist. by NAL). Stillpoint.

Carey, Patrick. An Immigrant Bishop: John England's Adaptation of Irish Catholicism to American Republicanism. LC 79-63860. (USCHS Monograph: Vol. 36). (Illus.). ix, 236p. 1982. 14.95x (ISBN 0-930060-16-4). US Cath Hist.

Carey, Patrick, ed. American Catholic Religious Thought. 1987. pap. 12.95. Paulist Pr.

Carey, Patrick W. People, Priests, & Prelates: Ecclesiastical Democracy & the Tensions of Trusteeism. LC 86-40243. (Studies in American Catholicism: Vol. 8). 392p. 1987. text ed. 26.95x (ISBN 0-268-01563-5). U of Notre Dame Pr.

Carfardi, Nicholas P., jt. auth. see Maida, Adam J.

Cargas, Harry J. & Corrigan, John T. The Holocaust: An Annotated Bibliography. 1977. pap. text ed. 4.00 (ISBN 0-87507-005-1). Cath Lib Assn.

Cargas, Harry J., ed. Responses to Elie Wiesel. LC 77-94055. 1978. o. p. 15.00 (ISBN 0-89255-031-7); pap. 5.95 (ISBN 0-89255-032-5). Persea Bks.

Cargas, Henry J., ed. When God & Man Failed: Non-Jewish Views of the Holocaust. 320p. 1981. 16.95 (ISBN 0-02-521300-8). Macmillan.

Cargile, Wayne. Bible Melodies Chosen. 1971. pap. 1.00 (ISBN 0-87012-106-5). McClain.

Cargill, Oscar. Drama & Liturgy. LC 73-86272. 1969. Repr. of 1930 ed. lib. bdg. 17.00x (ISBN 0-374-91292-0, Octagon). Hippocrene Bks.

Cargill-Thompson, W. D. The Political Thought of Martin Luther. Broadhead, Philip, ed. LC 83-27521. 204p. 1984. 27.50x (ISBN 0-389-20468-4, 08029). B&N Imports.

Carinat, Alois. The Fully Illustrated Book in Colours of the Crucifixion. (Illus.). 101p. 1983. 275.50x (ISBN 0-86650-078-2). Gloucester Art.

Caris, John. Foundation for a New Consciousness. LC 86-20201. (Illus.). 136p. (Orig.). 1987. pap. 8.95 (ISBN 0-9607320-1-2). Westgate Hse.

Carl, Angela, jt. auth. see Lang, June.

Carl, Angela R. A Matter of Choice. LC 84-7040. (Illus.). 32p. 1984. lib. bdg. 4.95 (ISBN 0-89693-223-0). Dandelion Hse.

Carl, Angela R. & Holmes, Alice C. Growing with Bible Heroes: Grade 4. rev. ed. Miller, Marge, ed. (Basic Bible Readers Ser.). (Illus.). 128p. 1983. text ed. 7.95 (ISBN 0-87239-664-9, 2954). Standard Pub.

Carl, Joseph B. Jesus in Our Affluent Society. 208p. 1981. 9.95 (ISBN 0-938234-01-3); pap. 5.95 (ISBN 0-938234-00-5). Ministry Pubns.

Carl, William J., II. Preaching Christian Doctrine. LC 83-48923. pap. 8.95 (ISBN 0-8006-1788-6). Fortress.

Carl, William J., III, jt. auth. see Pervo, Richard I.

Carl, William J., III, jt. auth. see Vawter, Bruce.

Carlebach, Julius. Karl Marx & the Radical Critique of Judaism. (Littman Library of Jewish Civilization). 478p. 1978. 45.00x (ISBN 0-19-710031-7). Oxford U Pr.

Carlebach, Shlomo. Holy Beggar Teachings: Jewish Hasidic Stories, 1975-1977. Maimes, Steven L. & Rappaport, Elana, eds. 1979. pap. 4.95 (ISBN 0-917246-06-3). Maimes.

Carleton, George. Jurisdiction Regall, Episcopall, Papall. LC 68-54625. (English Experience Ser.: No. 34). 302p. 1968. Repr. of 1610 ed. 30.00 (ISBN 90-221-0034-0). Walter J Johnson.

Carley, Ed. Way of the Cross. 1985. 9.95 (ISBN 0-89837-101-5, Pub. by Pflaum Press). Peter Li.

Carley, K. W. The Book of the Prophet Ezekiel. LC 73-94352. (Cambridge Bible Commentary on the New English Bible Ser.). (Illus.). 340p. (Orig.). 1974. 34.50 (ISBN 0-521-08653-1); pap. 13.95 (ISBN 0-521-09755-X). Cambridge U Pr.

Carley, Keith W. Ezekiel Among the Prophets: A Study of Ezekiel's Place in Prophetic Tradition. (Studies in Biblical Theology, 2nd Ser.: No. 31). 1975. pap. text ed. 10.00x (ISBN 0-8401-3081-3). A R Allenson.

Carley, Ken. Gems & Stones: Scientific Properties & Aspects of Twenty Two-A Comparative Study Based upon the Edgar Cayce Psychic Readings. rev. ed. 1979. pap. 4.95 (ISBN 0-87604-110-1). ARE Pr.

Carlin, Cathy. Jesus, What Are You Doing Tonight? (Outreach Ser.). 32p. 1982. pap. 0.99 (ISBN 0-8163-0492-0). Pacific Pr Pub Assn.

Carlisle, Thomas J. Beginning with Mary: Women of the Gospels in Portrait. 120p. (Orig.). 1986. pap. 5.95 (ISBN 0-8028-0194-3). Eerdmans.

--Eve & after: Old Testament Woman in Portrait. 160p. (Orig.). 1984. pap. 5.95 (ISBN 0-8028-1970-2). Eerdmans.

--Journey with Jonah. rev. ed. 96p. 1984. pap. 1.95 (ISBN 0-88028-035-2). Forward Movement.

Carlozzi, Carl G. The Episcopal Way. 1977. pap. text ed. 4.95x (ISBN 0-8192-4073-7); tchrs ed. 4.95x (ISBN 0-8192-4074-5). Morehouse.

--Promises & Prayers for Healing: Hope for the Future. (Pocketpac Books). 128p. (Orig.). 1985. pap. 2.50 (ISBN 0-87788-336-X). Shaw Pubs.

Carlozzi, Carl G. & Parkes, Ellen. Pocket Parables. 80p. (Orig.). 1985. pap. 2.95 (ISBN 0-8423-4919-7). Tyndale.

Carlsen, Clarence J., tr. see Hallesby, O.

Carlson. A Christmas Lullaby. (Arch Bks.). 24p. 1985. pap. 0.99 (ISBN 0-570-06195-4, 59-1296). Concordia.

Carlson, Bernice W. Listen & Help Tell the Story. (Illus.). 1965. 9.95 (ISBN 0-687-22096-3). Abingdon.

Carlson, Betty. No One's Perfect. LC 76-17669. 1976. pap. 4.95 (ISBN 0-89107-143-1). Good News.

Carlson, Betty, jt. auth. see Smith, Jane S.

Carlson, C. C., jt. auth. see Lindsey, Hal.

Carlson, Carole. A Light in Babylon. 256p. 1985. 12.95 (ISBN 0-8499-0452-8, 0452-8). Word Bks.

Carlson, Carole C. Corrie Ten Boom: Her Life, Her Faith. (Illus.). 224p. 1984. pap. 3.50 (ISBN 0-8007-8490-1, Spire Bks). Revell.

Carlson, Don, ed. Peace Trek: Reclaiming Our Future. Comstock, Craig. (Illus.). 300p. (Orig.). 1985. pap. 19.95 (ISBN 0-317-19166-7). Ark Comm Inst.

Carlson, Don & Comstock, Craig, eds. Citizen Summitry: Keeping the Peace When It Matters Too Much to Be Left to Politicians. (Illus.). 336p. 1986. pap. 10.95 (ISBN 0-87477-406-3). J P Tarcher.

Carlson, Don & Comstock, Craig K., eds. Citizen Summitry. (Ark Reflections: No. 1). (Illus.). 396p. 1986. 11.95 (ISBN 0-934325-01-4). Ark Comm Inst.

--Making the Shift to Peace. (Ark Reflections: No. 2). 368p. 1986. 14.95 (ISBN 0-934325-02-2). Ark Comm Inst.

Carlson, Dwight L. Guiltfree: How to Release the Tension in Your Life. 2nd ed. LC 83-80118. 1985. pap. 4.95 (ISBN 0-89081-375-2, 3752). Harvest Hse.

--Overcoming Hurts & Anger. LC 80-83852. 1981. pap. 4.95 (ISBN 0-89081-277-2). Harvest Hse.

Carlson, Ellsworth C. The Foochow Missionaries, 1847-1880. LC 72-97832. (East Asian Monographs Ser: No. 51). 1973. pap. 20.00x (ISBN 0-674-30735-6). Harvard U Pr.

Carlson, G. Raymond. The Acts Story. LC 78-57178. (Radiant Life Ser.). 128p. (Orig.). 1978. pap. 2.50 (ISBN 0-88243-913-8, 02-0913); tchr's ed. 3.95 (ISBN 0-88243-184-6, 32-0184). Gospel Pub.

--Our Faith & Fellowship. LC 77-75023. (Radiant Life Ser.). 128p. 1977. pap. 2.50 (ISBN 0-88243-908-1, 02-0908); teacher's ed. 3.95 (ISBN 0-88243-178-1, 32-0178). Gospel Pub.

--Prayer & the Christian's Devotional Life. LC 80-83522. (Radiant Life Ser.). 128p. (Orig.). 1981. 2.50 (ISBN 0-88243-878-6, 02-0878); teacher's ed. 3.95 (ISBN 0-88243-190-0, 32-0190). Gospel Pub.

--Preparing to Teach God's Word. LC 75-5221. (Illus.). 128p. 1975. pap. 1.25 (ISBN 0-88243-579-5, 02-0579). Gospel Pub.

--Spiritual Dynamics. LC 76-5633. (Radiant Life Ser.). 128p. 1976. pap. 2.50 (ISBN 0-88243-894-8, 02-0894); teacher's ed 3.95 (ISBN 0-88243-168-4, 32-0168). Gospel Pub.

Carlson, George A. George Carlson: The Spirit of the Tarahumara. Maxon, Gayle & Hopkins, Quincie, eds. LC 85-62063. (Illus.). 27p. (Orig.). 1985. pap. 18.00 (ISBN 0-935037-00-4). Peters Corp NM.

Carlson, Gertrude C. New Age. LC 85-90283. 252p. 1986. 13.95 (ISBN 0-533-06790-1). Vantage.

Carlson, John. Getting More From Your Bible Reading. LC 82-14563. 137p. (Orig.). 1982. pap. 3.95 (ISBN 0-87123-256-1, 210256). Bethany Hse.

Carlson, Lee W., ed. Christian Parenting. 80p. 1984. pap. 6.95 (ISBN 0-8170-1072-6). Judson.

Carlson, Neal. To Die is Gain. (Solace Ser.). 1983. pap. 1.50 (ISBN 0-8010-2487-0). Baker Bk.

Carlson, Paul R. O Christian! O Jew! LC 74-78937. 256p. (Orig.). 1974. pap. 1.95 (ISBN 0-912692-39-1). Cook.

Carlson, R. A. David, the Chosen King: A Traditio-Historical Approach to the 2nd Book of Samuel. 304p. (Orig.). 1964. pap. text ed. 23.50x. Coronet Bks.

Carlson, Roberta. Moments of Grace: Lessons from Grief. 128p. (Orig.). 1987. pap. 4.95 (ISBN 0-8423-4602-3). Tyndale.

Carlston, Charles. Epiphany. Achtemeier, Elizabeth, ed. LC 84-6012. (Proclamation 3: Aids for Interpreting the Lessons of the Church Year Series B). 64p. 1984. pap. 3.75 (ISBN 0-8006-4102-7). Fortress.

Carlton, Eric. Patterns of Belief, 2 vols. Incl. Vol. 1. Peoples & Religion. 130p. pap. 4.95 Vol. 1 (ISBN 0-04-377004-5); Vol. 2. Religions in Society. 140p. pap. 4.95 2 vols. each (ISBN 0-04-377005-3); pap. 4.95 Vol. 2. 1973. pap. 6.95 ea. Attic Pr.

Carlwright, jt. auth. see Rawson.

Carlyle, Alexander. Autobiography of the Rev. Dr. Alexander Carlyle: Containing Memorials of Men & Events of His Time. Burton, John H., ed. LC 78-67649. Repr. of 1860 ed. 44.50 (ISBN 0-404-17179-6). AMS Pr.

Carlyle, Alexander J. Christian Church & Liberty. LC 68-56734. (Research & Source Works Ser.: No. 214). 1968. Repr. of 1924 ed. 14.50 (ISBN 0-8337-0476-1). B Franklin.

Carmack, Derin. Seven Steps to Freedom. 31p. 1986. pap. 3.00 (ISBN 0-937093-25-4). Jewel Pr.

Carmack, Rita J. Image to Image, Vol. II. 155p. 1986. pap. 5.00 (ISBN 0-937093-00-9). Jewel Pr.

--Image to Image, Vol. 1. 146p. 1985. pap. 5.00 (ISBN 0-88144-047-7). Jewel Pr.

--Set My Heart Free. 144p. 1984. pap. 5.00 (ISBN 0-88144-031-0). Jewel Pr.

Carman, George. Science Proves the Bible. De Witt, Mason, ed. 190p. 1986. 12.00 (ISBN 0-936749-00-8). Zytech Western Pub.

Carman, John B., jt. ed. see Dawe, Donald G.

Carman, Stephen & Owen, Robert. Quest. 160p. (Orig.). 1986. pap. 5.95 (ISBN 0-8423-5112-4). Tyndale.

Carmean, E. A., Jr., et al. The Sculpture of Nancy Graves: A Catalogue Raisonne. LC 86-29970. (Illus.). 192p. 1987. 50.00 (ISBN 0-933920-77-6, Dist. by Rizzoli); Museum Distribution Only. pap. 25.00 (ISBN 0-933920-78-4). Hudson Hills.

Carmel, Abraham. So Strange My Path. LC 64-17487. 1977. pap. 5.95 (ISBN 0-8197-0066-5). Bloch.

Carmelite Sisters of Cristo Rey Carmel, San Francisco Staff, tr. see Carmelite Sisters of Noto, Italy Staff.

Carmelite Sisters of Noto, Italy Staff. God's Word to His Church. Carmelite Sisters of Cristo Rey Carmel, San Francisco Staff, tr. from Ital. LC 81-83568. Tr. of Alla Sorgente Della Parola di Dio. 144p. (Orig.). 1982. pap. text ed. 7.95 (ISBN 0-89870-016-7). Ignatius Pr.

Carmell, Aryeh. Aiding Talmud Study. 5th ed. (Illus.). 88p. 1987. 6.95 (ISBN 0-87306-413-5); pap. 4.95 (ISBN 0-87306-428-3). Feldheim.

Carmell, Aryeh & Domb, Cyril, eds. Challenge. 1978. 14.95 (ISBN 0-87306-174-8); pap. 9.95 (ISBN 0-87306-165-9). Feldheim.

Carmell, Aryeh, tr. see Dessler, E. E.

Carmen, D., jt. auth. see Tola, Fernanda.

Carmi, T., ed. The Penguin Book of Hebrew Verse. (Hebrew & Eng.). 448p. (Orig.). 1981. pap. 13.95 (ISBN 0-14-042197-1). Penguin.

Carmichael, Amy. Candles in the Dark. 1982. pap. text ed. 3.50 (ISBN 0-87508-085-5). Chr Lit.

--Figures of the True. 1968. pap. 1.50 (ISBN 0-87508-065-0). Chr Lit.

--Gold Cord. 1957. pap. 5.95 (ISBN 0-87508-068-5). Chr Lit.

--Learning of God. 1986. pap. 4.95 (ISBN 0-87508-086-3). Chr Lit.

--Mimosa. 1958. pap. 2.95 (ISBN 0-87508-074-X). Chr Lit.

--Whispers of His Power. 256p. 1985. pap. 6.95 (ISBN 0-8007-5206-6, Power Bks). Revell.

Carmichael, Bill & Carmichael, Nancie. Answers to the Questions Christian Women Are Asking. 1984. text ed. 10.95 (ISBN 0-89081-446-5); pap. 6.95 (ISBN 0-89081-442-2). Harvest Hse.

Carmichael, C. Women, Law, & the Genesis Tradition. 112p. 1979. 16.50x (ISBN 0-85224-364-2, Pub. by Edinburgh U Pr Scotland). Columbia U Pr.

Carmichael, Calum M. Law & Narrative in the Bible: The Evidence of the Deuteronomic Laws & the Decalogue. LC 85-4214. 352p. 1985. text ed. 35.00x (ISBN 0-8014-1792-9). Cornell U Pr.

Carmichael, Joel. The Death of Jesus. 296p. (Orig.). 1982. pap. 8.95 (ISBN 0-8180-0826-1). Horizon.

--Open Letter to Moses & Mohammed. LC 68-9705. (Open Letter Ser). (Orig.). 1968. pap. 4.95 (ISBN 0-685-11973-4, 18). Heineman.

Carmichael, John P., jt. ed. see Griesbach, Marc F.

Carmichael, Nancie, jt. auth. see Carmichael, Bill.

Carmichael, Ralph. He's Everything to Me: Autobiography. 192p. 1986. 14.95 (ISBN 0-8499-0094-8). Word Bks.

Carmignac, Jean. The Birth of the Synoptic Gospels. Wrenn, Michael J., tr. 1986. 9.50 (ISBN 0-8199-0887-8). Franciscan Herald.

Carmilly-Weinberger, Moshe, ed. The Rabbinical Seminary of Budapest, 1877-1977: A Centennial Volume. (Illus.). 420p. 1986. 35.00 (ISBN 0-87203-148-9). Hermon.

Carmody & Carmody. Shamans, Prophets & Sages: A Concise Intro to World Religion. 1984. write for info. (ISBN 0-534-04263-5). Wadsworth Pub.

Carmody, Denise L. Caring for Marriage. LC 85-60412. 192p. (Orig.). 1985. pap. 7.95 (ISBN 0-8091-2721-0). Paulist Pr.

--Feminism & Christianity: A Two-Way Reflection. LC 82-1709. 192p. (Orig.). 1982. pap. 9.95 (ISBN 0-687-12914-1). Abingdon.

--The Oldest God: Archaic Religion Yesterday & Today. LC 80-25499. 192p. (Orig.). 1981. pap. 7.50 (ISBN 0-687-28813-4). Abingdon.

--Seizing the Apple: A Feminist Spirituality of Personal Growth. 176p. (Orig.). 1984. pap. 10.95 (ISBN 0-8245-0652-9). Crossroad NY.

--What Are They Saying about Non-Christian Faith? (WATSA Ser.). 96p. (Orig.). 1982. pap. 4.95 (ISBN 0-8091-2432-7). Paulist Pr.

Carmody, Denise L. & Carmody, John. Religion: The Great Questions. 176p. 1983. pap. 11.95 (ISBN 0-8164-2476-4, HarpR). Har-Row.

Carmody, Denise L. & Carmody, John T. Becoming One Flesh. LC 84-50841. 160p. (Orig.). 1984. pap. 6.95 (ISBN 0-8358-0486-0). Upper Room.

--Bonded in Christ's Love: Being a Member of the Church. 240p. (Orig.). 1986. pap. 9.95 (ISBN 0-8091-2791-1). Paulist Pr.

--Christianity: An Introduction. 288p. 1982. pap. text ed. write for info (ISBN 0-534-01181-0). Wadsworth Pub.

--Western Ways to the Center: An Introduction to Religions of the West. 272p. 1982. pap. text ed. write for info. (ISBN 0-534-01328-7). Wadsworth Pub.

Carmody, Denise L., jt. auth. see Carmody, John T.

Carmody, Denixe L. Double Cross. 192p. (Orig.). 1986. pap. 10.95 (ISBN 0-8245-0736-3). Crossroad NY.

Carmody, Dennis L. & Carmody, John T. Ways to the Center: An Introduction to World Religions. 432p. 1981. text ed. write for info. (ISBN 0-534-00890-9). Wadsworth Pub.

Carmody, John. Ecology & Religion: Toward a New Christian Theology of Nature. LC 82-62412. 1983. pap. 6.95 (ISBN 0-8091-2526-9). Paulist Pr.

--The Heart of the Christian Matter: An Ecumenical Approach. 304p. (Orig.). 1983. pap. 12.95 (ISBN 0-687-16765-5). Abingdon.

--Holistic Spirituality. 160p. 1984. pap. 7.95 (ISBN 0-8091-2564-1). Paulist Pr.

--How to Make It Through the Day. LC 84-51826. 112p. (Orig.). 1985. pap. 5.95 (ISBN 0-8358-0491-7). Upper Room.

--Maturing a Christian Conscience. 160p. (Orig.). 1985. pap. 6.95 (ISBN 0-8358-0510-7). Upper Room.

--The Quiet Imperative: Meditations on Justice & Peace Based on Readings from the New Testament. 176p. (Orig.). 1986. pap. 6.95 (ISBN 0-8358-0518-2). Upper Room.

--Reexamining Conscience. 144p. (Orig.). 1982. pap. 8.95 (ISBN 0-8164-2405-5, HarpR). Har-Row.

Carmody, John, jt. auth. see Carmody, Denise L.

Carmody, John, et al. Exploring the New Testament. (Illus.). 448p. 1986. text ed. 31.00 (ISBN 0-13-297276-X). P-H.

Carmody, John T. & Carmody, Denise L. Contemporary Catholic Theology. rev. ed. LC 84-48213. 256p. 1985. pap. 9.95 (ISBN 0-06-061316-5, HarpR). Har-Row.

--Interpreting the Religious Experience: A Worldview. 240p. Date not set. text ed. price not set (ISBN 0-13-475609-6). P-H.

Carmody, John T., jt. auth. see Carmody, Denise L.

Carmody, John T., jt. auth. see Carmody, Dennis L.

Carnahan, David H. Prologue in the Old French & Provencal Mystery. LC 68-55160. (Studies in French Literature, No. 45). 1969. Repr. of 1905 ed. lib. bdg. 46.95x (ISBN 0-8383-0519-9). Haskell.

Carnell, Edward J. A Philosophy of the Christian Religion. (Twin Brooks Ser.). 525p. 1981. pap. 10.95 (ISBN 0-8010-2464-1). Baker Bk.

Carnes, John. Axiomatics & Dogmatics. (Theology & Scientific Culture Ser.). 1982. 16.95x (ISBN 0-19-520377-1). Oxford U Pr.

Carnes, Ralph & Carnes, Valerie. The Road to Damascus. 336p. 1986. 16.95 (ISBN 0-312-68517-3, Thomas Dunne Bks). St Martin.

Carnes, Valerie, jt. auth. see Carnes, Ralph.

Carney, Glandion. Creative Urban Youth Ministries. 74p. 1984. pap. 6.95 (ISBN 0-89191-846-9). Cook.

Carney, Mary L. Advent: A Calendar of Devotions, 1987. 48p. pap. 30.00 (ISBN 0-687-00887-5). Abingdon.

--Spiritual Harvest: Reflections on the Fruits of the Spirit. 112p. 1987. pap. 6.95 (ISBN 0-687-39231-4). Abingdon.

--There's an Angel in My Locker. 112p. (Orig.). 1985. pap. 4.95 (ISBN 0-310-28471-6, 11341P). Zondervan.

Carney, Mary Lou. Advent: A Calendar of Devotions, Nineteen Eighty-Six. 48p. (Orig.). 1986. pap. 30.00 (ISBN 0-687-00886-7). Abingdon.

--Heart Cries: Prayers of Biblical Women. 128p. (Orig.). 1986. pap. 5.95 (ISBN 0-687-16762-0). Abingdon.

--A Month of Mondays: Poems & Prayers for the Monday Morning Homemaker Blues. 112p. (Orig.). 1984. pap. 5.95 (ISBN 0-687-27164-9). Abingdon.

Carney, Russell & Moss, Jim. Building Your Youth Ministry. 1986. 4.95 (ISBN 0-931097-09-6). Sentinel Pub.

Carnicelli, Thomas A., ed. King Alfred's Version of St. Augustine's Soliloquies. LC 69-12719. 1969. 7.50x (ISBN 0-674-50360-0). Harvard U Pr.

Carnoy, Albert J; see Keith, A. Berriedale.

Caro, Francis De see De Caro, Francis A.

Carol, J. B. The Absolute Primacy & Predestination of Jesus & His Virgin Mother. 1981. 7.50 (ISBN 0-8199-0848-7). Franciscan Herald.

Carol, Juniper. A History of the Controversy over the "Debitum Peccati". (Theology Ser.). 1978. 7.00 (ISBN 0-686-27935-2). Franciscan Inst.

Carol, Juniper B., tr. see Pancheri, Francesco S.

Carothers, J. Edward. Caring for the World. (Orig.). 1978. pap. 4.95 (ISBN 0-377-00078-7). Friend Pr.

--Living with the Parables: Jesus & the Reign of God. 141p. (Orig.). 1984. pap. 9.95 (ISBN 0-377-00146-5). Friend Pr.

Carothers, Merlin R. Answers to Praise. 169p. (Orig.). 1972. pap. 4.95 (ISBN 0-943026-07-5). Carothers.

--The Bible on Praise. 32p. (Orig.). 1981. pap. 2.25 (ISBN 0-943026-03-2). Carothers.

--Bringing Heaven into Hell. 120p. (Orig.). 1976. pap. 4.95 (ISBN 0-943026-10-5). Carothers.

--Power in Praise. 143p. 1972. pap. 4.95 (ISBN 0-943026-01-6). Carothers.

--Praise Works. 161p. (Orig.). 1973. pap. 4.95. Carothers.

--Prison to Praise. 106p. (Orig.). 1970. pap. 2.95 (ISBN 0-943026-02-4). Carothers.

--Prison to Praise: Giant Print. 106p. (Orig.). 1970. pap. 3.95 (ISBN 0-943026-08-3). Carothers.

--Victory on Praise Mountain. 175p. (Orig.). 1979. pap. 4.95 (ISBN 0-943026-04-0). Carothers.

--Walking & Leaping. 129p. (Orig.). 1974. pap. 4.95 (ISBN 0-943026-05-9). Carothers.

Carpenter, Delburn. The Radical Pietists. LC 72-13586. (Illus.). 19.00 (ISBN 0-404-11008-8). AMS Pr.

Carpenter, Edward. The Art of Creation. 1978. Repr. of 1904 ed. lib. bdg. 45.00 (ISBN 0-8495-0814-2). Arden Lib.

--Pagan & Christian Creeds. 59.95 (ISBN 0-8490-0794-1). Gordon Pr.

Carpenter, Esther B. South County Studies: Of Some Eighteenth Century Persons, Places & Conditions. in That Portion of Rhode Island Called Narragansett. facsimile ed. LC 75-160961. (Select Bibliographies Reprint Ser). Repr. of 1924 ed. 21.00 (ISBN 0-8369-5829-2). Ayer Co Pubs.

Carpenter, George W. Encounter of the Faiths. (Orig.). 1967. pap. 1.75 (ISBN 0-377-37001-0). Friend Pr.

Carpenter, Gilbert C., jt. ed. see Eddy, Mary B.

Carpenter, Gilbert C., Sr. & Carpenter, Gilbert C., Jr. Mary Baker Eddy: Her Spiritual Footsteps. 290p. 1985. pap. 20.00 (ISBN 0-930227-02-6). Pasadena Pr.

Carpenter, Humphrey. Jesus. (Past Masters Ser.). 1980. pap. 4.95 (ISBN 0-19-283016-3). Oxford U Pr.

Carpenter, J. Estlin. Theism in Medieval India. 1977. Repr. of 1921 ed. 22.50x (ISBN 0-89684-457-9). Orient Bk Dist.

--Theism in Medieval India. 564p. Repr. of 1921 ed. text ed. 37.50x. Coronet Bks.

Carpenter, Jan. Turning Sorrow into Song. 154p. 1986. 9.95 (ISBN 0-89066-081-6). World Wide Pubs.

Carpenter, Joel A. & Shipps, Kenneth W., eds. Making Higher Education Christian: The History & Mission of Evangelical Colleges in America. 304p. (Orig.). 1987. pap. 16.95 (ISBN 0-8028-0253-2). Eerdmans.

Carpenter, Joseph E. Theism in Medieval India. LC 77-27152. (Hibbert Lectures: 1919). Repr. of 1921 ed. 48.00 (ISBN 0-404-60419-6). AMS Pr.

Carpenter, K. Theism in Medieval India. 1977. 22.50x (ISBN 0-8364-0100-X). South Asia Bks.

Carpenter, Mark, ed. see Culver, Robert D.

Carpenter, Thomas H. & Gula, Robert J. Mythology: Greek & Roman. (Illus.). 1977. pap. text ed. 6.95x (ISBN 0-88334-089-5). Ind Sch Pr.

Carpenter, Victor, tr. see Lehrmann, Charles C.

Carr & Paquet. God, I've Got to Talk to You Again! LC 59-1315. (Arch Bks.). 24p. (Orig.). 1985. pap. 0.99 (ISBN 0-570-06197-0, 59-1315). Concordia.

Carr, A. W. Angels & Principalities. (Society for the New Testament Studies Monographs: No. 42). 240p. 1982. 32.50 (ISBN 0-521-23429-8). Cambridge U Pr.

Carr, Adrienne, jt. auth. see Carr, John.

Carr, Adrienne, jt. auth. see John.

Carr, Anne. The Theological Method of Karl Rahner. LC 76-51639. (American Academy of Religion, Dissertation Ser.: No. 19). pap. 72.30 (ISBN 0-317-08410-0, 2017556). Bks Demand UMI.

Carr, Anne, ed. Academic Study of Religion: Proceedings. LC 74-14212. (American Academy of Religion. Section Papers). Repr. of 1974 ed. 40.50 (ISBN 0-8357-9563-2, 2017552). Bks Demand UMI.

Carr, Anne, et al. Academic Study of Religion, 1975: Public Schools Religion-Studies. LC 75-26653. (American Academy of Religion. Section Papers). 1975. pap. 9.95 (ISBN 0-89130-023-6, 01-09-17). Scholars Pr Ga.

Carr, Annemarie W. Byzantine Illumination Eleven Fifty to Twelve Fifty: The Study of a Provincial Tradition. (Studies in Medieval Manuscript Illumination Chicago Visual Library: No. 47). (Illus.). 448p. 1987. lib. bdg. 85.00 text-fiche (ISBN 0-226-68863-1). U of Chicago Pr.

Carr, Arthur C., et al, eds. Grief: Selected Readings. 155p. 1974. pap. 7.50 (ISBN 0-930194-76-4). Ctr Thanatology.

Carr, Audrey, jt. auth. see Sohl, Robert.

Carr, Audrey, jt. ed. see Sohl, Robert.

Carr, Clare, ed. The Gathering of Souls. Freelander, Iris. LC 81-69576. 240p. 1981. pap. 11.00 (ISBN 0-910378-17-7). Christward.

Carr, Dan. Cheating. (God I Need to Talk to You About...Ser.). (Illus.). 1984. pap. 0.75 (ISBN 0-570-08725-2, 56-1469). Concordia.

--Hurting Others. (God I Need to Talk to You about...Ser.). (Illus.). 1984. pap. 0.75 (ISBN 0-570-08727-9, 56-1471). Concordia.

--Lying. (God I Need to Talk to You About...Ser.). (Illus.). 1984. pap. 0.75 (ISBN 0-570-08732-5, 56-1476). Concordia.

--My Bad Temper. (God I Need to Talk to You About...Ser.). (Illus.). 1984. pap. 0.75 (ISBN 0-570-08730-9, 56-1474). Concordia.

--Our Savior Is Born. 1984. 6.50 (ISBN 0-570-04092-2, 56-1460). Concordia.

--Paying Attention. (God I Need to Talk to You About...Ser.). (Illus.). 1984. pap. 0.75 (ISBN 0-570-08729-5, 56-1473). Concordia.

--Sharing. (God I Need to Talk to You About...Ser.). (Illus.). 1984. pap. 0.75 (ISBN 0-570-08728-7, 56-1472). Concordia.

--Stealing. (God I Need to Talk to You About...Ser.). (Illus.). 1984. pap. 0.75 (ISBN 0-570-08731-7, 56-1475). Concordia.

--Vandalism. (God I Need to Talk to You About...Ser.). (Illus.). 1984. pap. 0.75 (ISBN 0-570-08726-0, 56-1470). Concordia.

Carr, David, tr. see Husserl, Edmund.

Carr, Dorothy, jt. auth. see Dickens, Arthur G.

Carr, Francis A. Shaker Your Plate: Of Shaker Cooks & Cooking. LC 85-51982. (Illus.). 156p. (Orig.). 1985. pap. 10.95 (ISBN 0-915836-02-5). Shaker Pr ME.

Carr, G. Lloyd & Wiseman, D. J. The Song of Solomon. LC 83-22651. (Tyndale Old Testament Commentaries Ser.). 240p. 1984. 12.95 (ISBN 0-87784-918-8); pap. 6.95 (ISBN 0-87784-268-X). Inter-Varsity.

Carr, Jo & Sorley, Imogene. Bless This Mess & Other Prayers. (Festival Books). 1976. pap. 3.25 (ISBN 0-687-03618-6). Abingdon.

--Plum Jelly & Stained Glass & Other Prayers. 1981. pap. 2.50 (ISBN 0-687-31660-X, Festival). Abingdon.

Carr, Jo, jt. auth. see Norwood, Frederick A.

Carr, John & Carr, Adrienne. Experiment in Practical Christianity: Leader's Guide. rev. ed. 96p. 1985. manual 6.95 (ISBN 0-88177-028-0, DRO28B). Discipleship Res.

--Experiment in Practical Christianity: Participant's Guide. 104p. (Orig.). 1985. pap. 6.95 (ISBN 0-88177-027-2, DRO27B). Discipleship Res.

--The Pilgrimage Project: Participant's Notebook. 48p. (Orig.). 1987. pap. 2.95 (ISBN 0-8358-0549-2). Upper Room.

Carr, Joseph. The Lucifer Connection. 1986. pap. 6.96 (ISBN 0-910311-42-0). Huntington Hse Inc.

Carr, Joseph J. Christian Heroes of the Holocaust. LC 85-70538. 1985. pap. 3.50 (ISBN 0-88270-582-2). Bridge Pub.

Carr, Kermit R. Moments to Live By - Years to Enjoy. 1986. 8.95 (ISBN 0-533-06945-9). Vantage.

Carr, Stephen L. The Historical Guide to Utah Ghost Towns. 166p. 1972. Western Epics.

Carra de Vaux, Bernard. Les Penseurs de l'Islam, 5 vols. LC 80-2197. Repr. of 1926 ed. Set. 200.00 (ISBN 0-404-18990-3). AMS Pr.

Carre, E. G. Praying Hyde. LC 82-73972. 183p. 1983. pap. 4.95 (ISBN 0-88270-541-5). Bridge Pub.

Carreiro, Mary E. The Psychology of Spiritual Growth. 160p. 1987. 24.95 (ISBN 0-89789-123-6); pap. 8.95 (ISBN 0-89789-124-4). Bergin & Garvey.

Carrere, Jean. The Pope: An Analysis of the Office of the Pope & the Roman Church & City. 1977. lib. bdg. 59.95 (ISBN 0-8490-2453-6). Gordon Pr.

Carretto, Carlo. Blessed Are You Who Believed. Wall, Barbara, tr. from Ital. LC 82-22504. Tr. of Beata te Che Hai Creduto. (Illus.). 96p. (Orig.). 1983. pap. 4.95 (ISBN 0-88344-038-5). Orbis Bks.

--The Desert in the City. (The Crossroad Paperback Ser.). 112p. 1982. pap. 4.95 (ISBN 0-8245-0423-2). Crossroad NY.

--I, Francis. Barr, Robert R., tr. from Ital. LC 81-16913. Orig. Title: Io Francesco. 144p. (Orig.). 1982. pap. 6.95 (ISBN 0-88344-200-0). Orbis Bks.

--I Sought & I Found: My Experience of God & of the Church. Barr, Robert R., tr. from Ital. Tr. of Ho Cercato E. Ho Trovato. 144p. 1984. pap. 7.95 (ISBN 0-88344-202-7). Orbis Bks.

--Letters from the Desert. 1976. pap. write for info (ISBN 0-515-09573-7). Jove Pubns.

--Love Is for Living. Moiser, Jeremy, tr. from Ital. LC 76-49878. Orig. Title: Cio Che Conta E Amare. 158p. 1977. pap. 7.95 (ISBN 0-88344-293-0). Orbis Bks.

--Made in Heaven. 4.95 (ISBN 0-87193-135-4). Dimension Bks.

--Summoned by Love. Neame, Alan, tr. from Italian. LC 78-962. Orig. Title: Padre Mio me abbandono a Te. 1978. pap. 5.95 (ISBN 0-88344-472-0). Orbis Bks.

--Why O Lord? The Inner Meaning of Suffering. Barr, Robert R., tr. from Ital. LC 85-29874. Tr. of Perche Signore? Il Dolore: Segreto Nascosto Nei Secoli. 128p. (Orig.). 1986. 10.95 (ISBN 0-88344-224-8); pap. 6.95 (ISBN 0-88344-222-1). Orbis Bks.

Carrez, Maurice & Morel, Francois. Dictionnaire Grec-Francais du Nouveau Testament. (Fr.-Gr.). 276p. 37.50 (ISBN 0-686-56940-7, M-6062). French & Eur.

Carrick, J. C. Wycliffe & the Lollards. 1977. lib. bdg. 59.95 (ISBN 0-8490-2824-8). Gordon Pr.

Carrieri, Mario, photos by. The Vatican & Christian Rome. (Illus.). 522p. 1979. 100.00 (ISBN 0-89860-025-1). Eastview.

Carrigan, Ana. Salvador Witness: The Life & Calling of Jean Donovan. 320p. 1984. 16.95 (ISBN 0-671-47992-X). S&S.

--Salvador Witness: The Life & Calling of Jean Donvan. 320p. 1986. pap. 3.95 (ISBN 0-345-32984-8). Ballantine.

Carrington, Hereward. Death: The Causes & Phenomena with Special Reference to Immortality. Kastenbaum, Robert, ed. LC 76-19563. (Death & Dying Ser.). 1977. lib. bdg. 27.50 (ISBN 0-405-09559-7). Ayer Co Pubs.

Carrington, Patricia. Freedom in Meditation. LC 76-6240. 384p. 1977. pap. 12.00. Pace Educ Systems.

Carrithers, Gale H. Donne at Sermons: A Christian Existential World. LC 74-171183. 1972. 49.50 (ISBN 0-87395-122-0). State U NY Pr.

Carrithers, Michael. The Buddha. LC 83-8004. (Past Masters Ser.). 1983. 13.95x (ISBN 0-19-287590-6); pap. 4.95 (ISBN 0-19-287589-2). Oxford U Pr.

--Forest Monks of Sri Lanka: An Anthropological & Historical Study. (Illus.). 1983. 34.50x (ISBN 0-19-561389-9). Oxford U Pr.

Carritt, E. F. The Theory of Morals: An Introduction to Ethical Philosophy. 144p. 1982. Repr. of 1928 ed. lib. bdg. 30.00 (ISBN 0-89984-118-X). Century Bookbindery.

Carritt, Edgar F. The Theory of Morals. LC 73-3021. 144p. 1974. Repr. of 1928 ed. lib. bdg. 22.50 (ISBN 0-8371-6827-9, CATM). Greenwood.

Carrodeguas, Andy, ed. see Bennett, Dennis & Bennett, Rita.

Carrodeguas, Angel, ed. see Fletcher, William M.

Carrodeguas, Angel, ed. see Hayford, Jack W.

Carrodeguas, Angel A., tr. see Adams, Jay E. & Thompson, Lyle A.

Carrodeguas, Angel A., tr. see Perry, Lloyd M.

Carrol, Frieda, compiled by. Meditation & Yoga Retreats: An International Directory. 200p. 1983. text ed. 4.75 (ISBN 0-913597-06-6, Pub. by Alpha Pyramis). Prosperity & Profits.

Carrol, Michael P. The Cult of the Virgin Mary: Psychological Origins. LC 85-43273. (Illus.). 325p. 1986. 25.00 (ISBN 0-691-09420-9). Princeton U Pr.

Carroll. Learning God's Word, 3 bks. 1971. Bk. 1. pap. 1.75 (ISBN 0-87148-502-8); Bk. 2. pap. 1.35 (ISBN 0-87148-503-6); Bk. 3. pap. 1.35 (ISBN 0-87148-504-4). Pathway Pr.

Carroll, Alexander. Women of Early Christianity. 75.00 (ISBN 0-87968-268-X). Gordon Pr.

Carroll, Anne Kristin. Together Forever. 256p. (Orig.). 1982. pap. 7.95 (ISBN 0-310-45021-7, 6885P). Zondervan.

Carroll, B. H. Sermons. 1986. Repr. of 1893 ed. 19.50 (ISBN 0-317-47643-2). Church History.

Carroll, Carroll. Carroll's First Book of Proverbs or Life Is a Fortune Cookie. (Illus.). 80p. 1981. pap. 4.95 (ISBN 0-87786-004-1). Gold Penny.

Carroll, Frances. A Book of Devotions for Today's Woman. 192p. 1983. pap. 5.95 (ISBN 0-13-080028-7). P-H.

--How to Talk with Your Children about God. 1985. pap. 6.95 (ISBN 0-317-18129-7). P-H.

Carroll, Frances L. Frustration: How Christians Can Deal with It. 156p. 1984. pap. 6.95 (ISBN 0-13-330804-9). P-H.

--Promises: A Guide to Christian Commitment. 228p. 1985. 14.95 (ISBN 0-13-731076-5); pap. 7.95 (ISBN 0-13-731068-4). P H.

--Temptation: How Christians Can Deal with It. 192p. 1984. 13.95 (ISBN 0-13-903229-0); pap. 5.95 (ISBN 0-13-903211-8). P-H.

Carroll, Frank L. Brief Bible Studies for Busy People. LC 85-3470. 144p. 1985. 13.95 (ISBN 0-13-081993-X); pap. 6.95 (ISBN 0-13-081985-9). P-H.

Carroll, Gerry. Creation, Christ & Credibility: How & Why Mankind Has Failed to Discredit the Bible. LC 83-72663. (Illus.). 204p. (Orig.). 1983. pap. 5.95 (ISBN 0-914569-01-5). Creat Pubns B P C M.

Carroll, Jackson & Wilson, Robert. Too Many Pastors? The State of the Clergy Job Market. LC 80-16037. 1980. pap. 6.95 (ISBN 0-8298-0405-6). Pilgrim NY.

Carroll, Jackson W. & Hargrove, Barbara J. Women of the Cloth: New Opportunity for the Churches. LC 82-47740. 288p. 1983. 14.45 (ISBN 0-06-061321-1, HarpR). Har-Row.

Carroll, Jackson W., et al, eds. Handbook for Congregational Studies. 192p. (Orig.). 1986. pap. 16.95 (ISBN 0-687-16562-8). Abingdon.

Carroll, James. Wonder & Worship. LC 70-133469. 168p. 1970. pap. 2.95 (ISBN 0-8091-1871-8). Paulist Pr.

Carroll, Jane. Grace. (Illus.). 28p. 1987. 12.95 (ISBN 1-55523-041-5). Winston-Derek.

Carroll, Joseph. The Cultural Theory of Matthew Arnold. LC 81-23996. 296p. 1982. 25.95x (ISBN 0-520-04616-1). U of Cal Pr.

Carroll, Kenneth. Quakerism on the Eastern Shore. LC 70-112986. (Illus.). 328p. 1970. 15.00x (ISBN 0-938420-15-1). Md Hist.

Carroll, L. Patrick & Dyckman, Katharine M. Inviting the Mystic, Supporting the Prophet: An Introduction to Spiritual Direction. LC 81-80053. 112p. (Orig.). 1981. pap. 5.95 (ISBN 0-8091-2378-9). Paulist Pr.

Carroll, L. Patrick & Dyckman, Katherine M. Chaos or Creation: Spirituality in Mid-Life. 176p. 1986. pap. 8.95 (ISBN 0-8091-2832-2). Paulist Pr.

Carroll, L. Patrick, jt. auth. see Dyckman, Katherine M.

Carroll, Malachy, tr. see De Margerie, Bertrand.

Carroll, Mary A. Catholic History of Alabama & the Floridas. facs. ed. LC 70-124228. (Select Bibliographies Reprint Ser). 1908. 18.00 (ISBN 0-8369-5417-3). Ayer Co Pubs.

Carroll, Peter. Liber Null & Psychonaut. (Illus.). 128p. (Orig.). 1987. pap. 12.50 (ISBN 0-87728-639-6). Weiser.

Carroll, R. Leonard. Stewardship: Total Life Commitment. 144p. 1967. pap. 4.25 (ISBN 0-87148-755-1). Pathway Pr.

Carroll, Robert P. From Chaos to Covenant: Prophecy in the Book of Jeremiah. 288p. 1981. 14.95 (ISBN 0-8245-0106-3). Crossroad NY.
--Jeremiah, a Commentary. LC 85-13655. (Old Testament Library). 880p. 1986. 38.95 (ISBN 0-664-21835-0). Westminster.
Carroll, Thomas K. Preaching the Word. (Message of the Fathers of the Church Ser.: Vol. 11). 15.95 (ISBN 0-89453-351-7); pap. 9.95 (ISBN 0-89453-322-3). M Glazier.
Carroll, Thomas M. The Abomination of Desolation: The Great Persecution. 96p. 1983. pap. 5.95 (ISBN 0-87881-103-6). Mojave Bks.
Carroll, W. H., et al. Reasons for Hope. rev. ed. 254p. 1982. pap. 6.95 (ISBN 0-931888-07-7, Chris. Coll. Pr.). Christendom Pubns.
Carroll, Warren H. The Founding of Christendom. (History of Christendom Ser.: Vol. 1). 605p. 1985. 24.95 (ISBN 0-931888-21-2); pap. 12.95 (ISBN 0-931888-21-2). Christendom Pubns.
--Nineteen Seventeen: Red Banners, White Mantle. 168p. (Orig.). 1981. pap. 4.95 (ISBN 0-931888-05-0). Christendom Pubns.
--Our Lady of Guadalupe & the Conquest of Darkness. 123p. (Orig.). pap. 4.95 (ISBN 0-931888-12-3). Christendom Pubns.
Carrott, Richard G. The Egyptian Revival: Its Sources, Monuments, & Meaning (1808-1858) LC 76-24579. (Illus.). 1978. 44.50x (ISBN 0-520-03324-8). U of Cal Pr.
Carruth, Ella K. She Wanted to Read: The Story of Mary Macleod Bethune. (Illus.). 1966. 6.75 (ISBN 0-687-38353-6). Abingdon.
Carse, James P. The Silence of God: Meditations on Prayer. 128p. 1985. 11.95 (ISBN 0-02-521490-X). Macmillan.
--The Silence of God: Meditations on Prayer. 120p. 1987. pap. 4.95 (ISBN 0-02-084270-8, Collier). Macmillan.
Carson, Alex. Confidence in God in Times of Danger. pap. 2.75 (ISBN 0-685-88371-X). Reiner.
Carson, Alexander. Baptism: It's Mode & Subjects. Young, John, ed. LC 80-8067. 550p. 1981. 18.95 (ISBN 0-8254-2324-4). Kregel.
Carson, D. A. Divine Sovereignty & Human Responsibility: Biblical Perspectives in Tension. Toon, Peter & Martin, Ralph, eds. LC 79-27589. (New Foundations Theological Library). 228p. 1981. 12.95 (ISBN 0-8042-3707-7); pap. 11.95 (ISBN 0-8042-3727-1). John Knox.
--Exegetical Fallacies. 1984. text ed. 7.95p (ISBN 0-8010-2499-4). Baker Bk.
--The Farewell Discourse & the Final Prayer of Jesus: An Exposition of John 14-17. LC 80-68769. 196p. 1981. 9.95 (ISBN 0-8010-2460-9). Baker Bk.
--God with Us. LC 85-10849. (Bible Commentary for Laymen Ser.). 168p. (Orig.). 1985. pap. 3.95 (ISBN 0-8307-1051-5, S392106). Regal.
--King James Version Debate. LC 79-50443. 1978. pap. 4.95 (ISBN 0-8010-2427-7). Baker Bk.
--Sermon on the Mount: An Evangelical Exposition of Matthew 5-7. LC 77-93260. 1978. 4.95 (ISBN 0-8010-2480-3). Baker Bk.
--Showing the Spirit: A Theological Exposition of 1 Corinthians 12-14. 256p. 1987. pap. 12.95 (ISBN 0-8010-2521-4). Baker Bk.
--When Jesus Confronts the World: An Exposition of Matthew 8-10. 240p. 1987. pap. price not set (ISBN 0-8010-2522-2). Baker Bk.
Carson, D. A., ed. Biblical Interpretation & the Church: The Problem of Contextualization. 232p. 1985. pap. 7.95 (ISBN 0-8407-7501-6). Nelson.
--From Sabbath to Lord's Day. 432p. (Orig.). 1982. pap. 10.95 (ISBN 0-310-44531-0, 12035P). Zondervan.
Carson, D. A. & Woodbridge, John D., eds. Hermeneutics, Authority & Canon. 480p. 1986. pap. 14.95 (ISBN 0-310-43991-4, 12644P). Zondervan.
--Scripture & Truth. 1986. pap. 11.95 (ISBN 0-310-43791-1, 12643P). Zondervan.
Carson, D. A., et al. The Expositor's Bible Commentary, Vol. 8. 1986. 29.95 (ISBN 0-88469-188-8). BMH Bks.
Carson, Donald A. From Triumphalism to Maturity: An Exposition of II Corinthians 10-13. 1984. 12.95 (ISBN 0-8010-2489-7). Baker Bk.
Carson, Gerald. Cornflake Crusade. LC 75-39240. (Getting & Spending: the Consumer's Dilemma). (Illus.). 1976. Repr. of 1957 ed. 25.50x (ISBN 0-405-08013-1). Ayer Co Pubs.
Carson, Herbert M. Epistles of Paul to the Colossians & to Philemon. (Tyndale Bible Commentaries). 1960. pap. 3.95 (ISBN 0-8028-1411-5). Eerdmans.
Carson, Karen M., jt. auth. see Kamper, Karl G.
Carson, Patti & Dellosa, Janet. Christmas Readiness Activities. (Stick-Out-Your-Neck Ser.). (Illus.). 32p. 1983. pap. 1.98 (ISBN 0-88724-049-6, CD-8025). Carson-Dellos.
--Christmas Reading & Activity Book. (Stick-Out-Your-Neck Ser.). (Illus.). 32p. 1983. pap. 1.98 (ISBN 0-88724-038-0, CD-8029). Carson-Dellos.
--Easter Preschool-K Practice. (Stick-Out-Your-Neck Ser.). (Illus.). 32p. 1984. pap. 1.98 (ISBN 0-88724-017-8, CD-8032). Carson-Dellos.
--Easter Primary Reading & Art Activities. (Stick-Out-Your-Neck Ser.). (Illus.). 32p. 1984. pap. 1.98 (ISBN 0-88724-027-5, CD-8042). Carson-Dellos.
Carstens, Christopher & Mahedy, William. Right Here, Right Now: Spiritual Exercises for Busy Christians. 1985. 9.95 (ISBN 0-345-31801-3, Pub. by Ballantine Epiphany). Ballantine.
--Right Here, Right Now: Spiritual Exercises for Busy Christians. 1987. pap. 2.95 (ISBN 0-345-34018-3, Pub. by Ballantine Epiphany). Ballantine.
Carstens, Christopher & Mahedy, William P. Starting on Monday: Christian Living in the Workplace. 176p. 1987. 11.95 (ISBN 0-345-32910-4). Ballantine.
Carstens, R. W. Notes on Humanity: Faith, Reason, Certainty. 142p. (Orig.). 1985. pap. text ed. 8.50 (ISBN 0-8191-4885-7). U Pr of Amer.
Carta, Maria, jt. auth. see Beckley, Timothy G.
Cartari, Vincenzo. Le Imagini...Degli Dei. LC 75-27855. (Renaissance & the Gods Ser.: Vol. 12). (Illus.). 602p. 1976. Repr. of 1571 ed. lib. bdg. 88.00 (ISBN 0-8240-2061-8). Garland Pub.
Cartayne, Alice. Irish Saints for Boys & Girls. (Illus.). 96p. 1978. pap. 3.95 (ISBN 0-86167-018-3, Pub. by Educ Co of Ireland). Longwood Pub Group.
Carter. Astrology of Accidents. 3.95 (ISBN 0-7229-5059-4). Theos Pub Hse.
--Symbolic Directions: Modern Astrology. 7.95 (ISBN 0-7229-5145-0). Theos Pub Hse.
Carter, Anne, tr. see Rodinson, Maxime.
Carter, Barbara L. The Copts in Egyptian Politics 1918 - 1952. 256p. 1985. 43.00 (ISBN 0-7099-3417-3, Pub. by Croom Helm Ltd). Methuen Inc.
Carter, Bill. Each One a Minister. LC 86-71722. 72p. (Orig.). 1986. pap. 4.95 (ISBN 0-88177-037-X, DR037B). Discipleship Res.
Carter, C. E. Essays On Foundation of Astrology. 9.95 (ISBN 0-8356-5506-7). Theos Pub Hse.
--Essays on Foundation of Astrology. pap. 5.95 (ISBN 0-8356-5503-2). Theos Pub Hse.
Carter, Charles W. The Wesleyan Bible Commentary, 6 vols. 4484p. 1986. 149.50 (ISBN 0-913573-33-7). Hendrickson MA.
--The Wesleyan Bible Commentary, Vol. 1. 1060p. 1986. 27.95 (ISBN 0-913573-34-5). Hendrickson MA.
--The Wesleyan Bible Commentary, Vol. 2. 660p. 1986. 27.95 (ISBN 0-913573-35-3). Hendrickson MA.
--The Wesleyan Bible Commentary, Vol. 4. 752p. 1986. 27.95 (ISBN 0-913573-37-X). Hendrickson MA.
--The Wesleyan Bible Commentary, Vol. 5. 676p. 1986. 27.95 (ISBN 0-913573-38-8). Hendrickson MA.
--The Wesleyan Bible Commentary, Vol. 6. 528p. 1986. 27.95 (ISBN 0-913573-39-6). Hendrickson MA.
Carter, Charles W., ed. The Wesleyan Bible Commentary, 2 vols. 808p. 1986. 24.95 (ISBN 0-913573-36-1). Hendrickson MA.
Carter, Charles W. & Thompson, Duane R, eds. Contemporary Wesleyan Theology, 2 vols. 1200p. 1986. Set. 39.95 (ISBN 0-310-45650-9, 11626). Zondervan.
Carter, Craig. How to Use the Power of Mind in Everyday Life. 96p. 1976. pap. 4.50 (ISBN 0-911336-65-6). Sci of Mind.
Carter, Curtis I. & Flew, Anthony, eds. Skepticism & Moral Principles: Modern Ethics in Review. 14.95 (ISBN 0-89044-017-4); pap. 8.95. Precedent Pub.
Carter, Curtis L., ed. Skepticism & Moral Principles: Modern Ethics in Review. LC 73-79477. (Studies in Ethics & Society Ser.: Vol. 1). 1973. 9.95 (ISBN 0-89044-017-4); pap. 4.95 (ISBN 0-89044-018-2). New Univ Pr.
Carter, E. R. Biographical Sketches of Our Pulpit. LC 72-99355. 1969. Repr. of 1888 ed. lib. bdg. 14.00 (ISBN 0-8411-0026-8). Metro Bks.
Carter, Edward. Jesus, I Want to Talk with You: Contemporary Prayers. LC 73-75617. (Illus.). 1977. pap. 1.95 (ISBN 0-8189-1142-5, Pub. by Alba Bks). Alba.
--Response to God's Love: A View of the Spiritual Life. 184p. 1984. 9.95 (ISBN 0-317-14585-1). Loyola.
Carter, Edward, ed. Prayer Perspectives. LC 86-28675. 108p. (Orig.). 1987. pap. 5.95 (ISBN 0-8189-0513-1). Alba.
Carter, George. The Story of Milton's Paradise. 1909. lib. bdg. 15.00 (ISBN 0-8414-1590-0). Folcroft.
Carter, George W. Zoroastrianism & Judaism. LC 70-112489. 1970. Repr. of 1918 ed. 14.00 (ISBN 0-404-01396-1). AMS Pr.
Carter, Howard. Questions & Answers on Spiritual Gifts. 127p. 1976. pocket bk. 2.95 (ISBN 0-89274-007-8). Harrison Hse.
--Spiritual Gifts & Their Operation. 96p. 1968. pap. 1.95 (ISBN 0-88243-593-0, 02-0593). Gospel Pub.
Carter, Howard & Mace, A. C. The Discovery of the Tomb of Tutankhamen. LC 77-71042. (Illus.). 382p. 1977. pap. 6.50 (ISBN 0-486-23500-9). Dover.
--Tomb of Tut-Ankh-Amen, 3 Vols. LC 63-17462. (Illus.). Repr. of 1954 ed. Set. 85.00x (ISBN 0-8154-0048-9). Cooper Sq.
Carter, J. R., ed. see Desikachar, T. K.
Carter, James E. Facing the Final Foe. LC 85-19517. 1986. pap. 2.25 (ISBN 0-8054-5433-0). Broadman.
--Help for the Evangelistic Preacher. LC 83-70371. 1985. pap. 6.50 (ISBN 0-8054-6243-0). Broadman.
--Layman's Bible Book Commentary: John, Vol. 18. LC 81-65391. 1984. 5.95 (ISBN 0-8054-1188-7). Broadman.
--A Sourcebook for Stewardship Sermons. LC 78-74768. 1979. pap. 5.95 (ISBN 0-8054-6403-4). Broadman.
Carter, Jesse B. Religious Life of Ancient Rome. 270p. 1972. Repr. of 1911 ed. lib. bdg. 27.50x (ISBN 0-8154-0429-8). Cooper Sq.
Carter, John, jt. auth. see Narramore, Bruce S.
Carter, John D., jt. ed. see Fleck, J. Roland.
Carter, John F. American Messiahs by the Unofficial Observer. LC 68-26232. 1968. Repr. of 1935 ed. 21.50x (ISBN 0-8046-0010-4, Pub by Kennikat). Assoc Faculty Pr.
--Layman's Harmony of the Gospel. 1961. 12.95 (ISBN 0-8054-1326-X). Broadman.
Carter, John R. & Bond, George D. The Threefold Refuge in the Theravada Buddhist Tradition. LC 82-26467. 1982. 4.95x (ISBN 0-89012-030-7). Anima Pubns.
Carter, Lee. Lucifer's Handbook. LC 76-55893. 1977. pap. text ed. 5.95 (ISBN 0-918260-01-9). Acad Assoc.
Carter, Les. Good 'n' Angry. 128p. 1983. 8.95 (ISBN 0-8010-2488-9); pap. 5.95 (ISBN 0-8010-2481-1). Baker Bk.
--The Push-Pull Marriage. 1984. 7.95 (ISBN 0-8010-2497-8); pap. 5.95 (ISBN 0-8010-2490-0). Baker Bk.
Carter, Margaret L. Vampirism in Literature: Shadow of a Shade. 1974. lib. bdg. 69.95 (ISBN 0-87968-225-6). Gordon Pr.
Carter, Mary E. Edgar Cayce on Prophecy. 208p. 1968. pap. 3.50 (ISBN 0-446-32712-3). Warner Bks.
Carter, Nicholas. The Late Great Book: The Bible. McCalden, David, ed. 230p. (Orig.). 1985. pap. 10.00 (ISBN 0-910607-01-X). Truth Missions.
Carter, Pat H. Vivamos En el Espiritu Cada Dia. 160p. 1982. pap. 3.25 (ISBN 0-311-09089-3). Casa Bautista.
Carter, Paul A. The Decline & Revival of the Social Gospel: Social & Political Liberalism in American Protestant Churches, 1920-1940. 2nd ed. LC 70-122413. xxvi, 265p. 1971. Repr. of 1956 ed. 27.50 (ISBN 0-208-01083-1, Archon). Shoe String.
--Spiritual Crisis of the Gilded Age. LC 72-156938. (Illus.). 295p. 1971. 10.00 (ISBN 0-87580-026-2). N Ill U Pr.
Carter, Robert E. Dimensions of Moral Education. 254p. 1984. pap. 11.95 (ISBN 0-8020-6540-6). U of Toronto Pr.
Carter, Stephen & McKinney, Charles. More of a Good Thing. 1982. pap. 3.50 (ISBN 0-570-03840-5, 12-2943). Concordia.
Carter, Stephen J. & McKinney, Charles. Keeping a Good Thing Going. 1979. pap. 3.25 (ISBN 0-570-03787-5, 12-2745). Concordia.
Carter, Stephen J., jt. auth. see Henkelmann, Ervin F.
Carter, Thomas. Shakespeare & Holy Scripture. LC 74-113574. Repr. of 1905 ed. 22.50 (ISBN 0-404-01398-8). AMS Pr.
--Shakespeare, Puritan & Recusant. LC 70-129386. Repr. of 1897 ed. 16.00 (ISBN 0-404-01397-X). AMS Pr.
Carter, Tom. For Members Only: A Guide to Responsible Church Membership. 1986. pap. write for info. (ISBN 0-88270-614-4). Bridge Pub.
Carter, Velma T. & Leavenworth, Lynn J. Caught in the Middle: Children of Divorce. 176p. 1985. pap. 6.95 (ISBN 0-8170-1037-8). Judson.
Carter, Virginia B. I'm Going to Be a Missionary. (Orig.). 1978. pap. 2.95 (ISBN 0-89036-103-7). Hawkes Pub Inc.
Carter, Will. The Accounts to Caesar Tiberius Concerning Jesus of Nazareth. 142p. (Orig.). 1986. pap. 3.99 (ISBN 0-9617190-0-1). Drame Pr.
Cartesius, Hugo. Individual & Society: Nature-Marx-Mao. 158p. 1977. 12.40 (ISBN 3-261-02063-6). P Lang Pubs.
Carthach, St. The Monastic Rule of St. Carthach: St. Mochuda the Younger. pap. 1.50 (ISBN 0-686-05656-6). Eastern Orthodox.
Carthy, Margaret. A Cathedral of Suitable Magnificence: St. Patrick's Cathedral, New York. 1983. 15.00 (ISBN 0-89453-372-X); pap. 6.95 (ISBN 0-89453-373-8). M Glazier.
Carthy, Mary P. Old St. Patrick's: New York's First Cathedral. (Monograph Ser.: No. 23). (Illus.). 1947. 10.00x (ISBN 0-930060-05-9). US Cath Hist.
Cartland, Fernando G. Southern Heroes, or the Friends in Wartime. Bd. with Conscript Quakers. Foster, Ethan. (Library of War & Peace; Conscrip. & Cons. Object.). 1972. lib. bdg. 42.00 (ISBN 0-8240-0424-8). Garland Pub.
Cartlidge, David R. & Dungan, David L. Documents for the Study of the Gospels. LC 79-21341. 300p. (Orig.). 1980. 16.95 (ISBN 0-8006-0640-X, 1-640); pap. 10.95 (ISBN -08006-1640-5, 1-1640). Fortress.
Cartwright & Rawson. Wizards. (Story Books). 1980. 6.95 (ISBN 0-86020-381-6, Usborne-Hayes); PLB 11.96 (ISBN 0-88110-052-8); pap. 2.95 (ISBN 0-86020-380-8). EDC.
Cartwright, Ann & Cartwright, Reg. Norah's Ark. (Illus.). 32p. 1984. PLB 11.97 (ISBN 0-671-52540-9). Messner.
Cartwright, Reg, jt. auth. see Cartwright, Ann.
Cartwright, Thomas. A Briefe Apologie Against M. Sutcliffe. LC 78-25890. (English Experience Ser.: No. 237). 28p. 1970. Repr. of 1596 ed. 7.00 (ISBN 90-221-0237-8). Walter J Johnson.
--The Christian Letter of Certaine English Protestants Unto Mr. R. Hooker. LC 72-180. (English Experience Ser.: No. 202). 50p. 1969. Repr. of 1599 ed. 8.00 (ISBN 90-221-0202-5). Walter J Johnson.
--A Confutation of the Rhemists Translation, Glosses & Annotations on the New Testament. LC 71-171737. (English Experience Ser.: No. 364). 830p. 1971. Repr. of 1618 ed. 114.00 (ISBN 90-221-0364-1). Walter J Johnson.
--Diary. 1843. 19.00 (ISBN 0-384-07815-X). Johnson Repr.
--Diary of Dr. Thomas Cartwright, Bishop of Chester October 1687. (Camden Society, London. Publications. First Ser.: No. 22). Repr. of 1843 ed. 19.00 (ISBN 0-404-50122-2). AMS Pr.
Carty, Charles, jt. auth. see O'Connell, Patrick.
Carty, Charles M. Padre Pio: The Stigmatist. (Illus.). 1971. pap. 8.50 (ISBN 0-89555-054-7, 115). TAN Bks Pubs.
--Stigmata & Modern Science. 31p. 1974. pap. 0.65 (ISBN 0-89555-104-7). TAN Bks Pubs.
--Who Is Teresa Neumann? 1974. pap. 1.25 (ISBN 0-89555-093-8). TAN Bks Pubs.
--Why Squander Illness? 1974. pap. 1.50 (ISBN 0-89555-051-2). TAN Bks Pubs.
Carty, Charles M., jt. auth. see Rumble, Leslie.
Carty, Margaret F. Christmas in Vermont: Three Stories. LC 83-62750. (Illus.). 48p. (Orig.). 1983. pap. 2.95 (ISBN 0-933050-21-6). New Eng Pr VT.
Carus, Paul. Amitabha: A Story of Buddhist Theology. 1977. Repr. 29.00x (ISBN 0-403-07255-7). Scholarly.
--The Bride of Christ. 118p. 1908. 15.95 (ISBN 0-87548-218-X). Open Court.
--Der Buddha. 100p. 1913. pap. 3.95 (ISBN 0-317-40410-5). Open Court.
--Buddhism & Its Christian Critics. 59.95 (ISBN 0-87968-801-7). Gordon Pr.
--The Dawn of a New Religious Era. 131p. 1916. 1.95 (ISBN 0-317-40419-9). Open Court.
--The Dharma; or, the Religious Enlightenment; an Exposition of Buddhism. 5th rev. & enl. ed. LC 78-72393. Repr. of 1907 ed. 24.00 (ISBN 0-404-17253-9). AMS Pr.
--The Ethical Problem: Three Lectures on Ethics As a Science. 2nd enl ed. LC 75-3103. Repr. of 1899 ed. 25.50 (ISBN 0-404-59100-0). AMS Pr.
--God: An Enquiry & a Solution. 253p. 1943. 15.95 (ISBN 0-87548-223-6); pap. 6.95 (ISBN 0-87548-224-4). Open Court.
--Godward: A Record of Religious Progress. 26p. 1898. 0.95 (ISBN 0-317-40417-2). Open Court.
--Gospel of Buddha. (Illus.). 1979. pap. 6.95 (ISBN 0-89744-195-8). Auromere.
--The Gospel of Buddha. 59.95 (ISBN 0-8490-0252-4). Gordon Pr.
--Gospel of Buddha. rev. & enl. ed. LC 17-29837. (Illus.). 331p. 1915. deluxe ed. 24.95 (ISBN 0-87548-226-0); pap. 9.95 (ISBN 0-87548-228-7). Open Court.
--History of the Devil & the Idea of Evil. (Illus.). 496p. 1974. pap. 14.95 (ISBN 0-87548-307-0). Open Court.
--Karma Nirvana: Two Buddhist Tales. LC 73-82781. (Illus.). 160p. 1973. 15.95 (ISBN 0-87548-249-X); pap. 6.95 (ISBN 0-87548-359-3). Open Court.
--Nirvana, a Story of Buddhist Psychology. LC 78-72395. (Illus.). Repr. of 1902 ed. 22.00 (ISBN 0-404-17254-7). AMS Pr.

--Nirvana: A Story of Buddhist Psychology. 93p. 1913. 1.95 (ISBN 0-317-40415-6). Open Court.

--The Pleroma: An Essay on the Origin of Christianity. 163p. 1921. pap. 4.95 (ISBN 0-317-40408-3). Open Court.

--Point of View. Cook, Catherine E., ed. (Illus.). 227p. 1927. 16.95 (ISBN 0-87548-268-6). Open Court.

--The Religion of Science. 3rd ed. 145p. 1913. 6.95 (ISBN 0-912050-68-3). Open Court.

--Sacred Tunes for the Consecration of Life. 48p. 1899. 0.95 (ISBN 0-317-40427-X). Open Court.

--The Soul of Man. 59.95 (ISBN 0-8490-1090-X). Gordon Pr.

--The Story of Samson, & Its Place in the Religious Development of Mankind. 183p. 1907. 1.95 (ISBN 0-317-40420-2). Open Court.

Carus, Paul, ed. Virgil's Prophecy on the Saviour's Birth. 97p. 1918. 2.95 (ISBN 0-317-40414-8). Open Court.

--Yin Chih Wen: The Tract of the Quiet Way. Suzuki, Teitaro & Carus, Paul, trs. from Chinese. 52p. 1950. pap. 0.95 (ISBN 0-87548-245-7). Open Court.

Carus, Paul, tr. Angelus Silesius. 174p. 1909. 1.95 (ISBN 0-317-40418-0). Open Court.

Carus, Paul, tr. see Carus, Paul.

Carus, Paul, tr. see Lao Tze.

Carver, C. C. Church of God Doctrines. 180p. 1948. pap. 2.00 (ISBN 0-686-29106-9). Faith Pub Hse.

Carver, Estelle C. Newness of Life. rev. ed. Helms, Hal M., ed. (Living Library Ser.). 150p. pap. 4.95 (ISBN 0-941478-19-X). Paraclete Pr.

Carver, Everett I. When Jesus Comes Again. 1979. pap. 7.95 (ISBN 0-87552-159-2). Presby & Reformed.

Carver, Frank. Beacon Small-Group Bible Studies, Matthew, Vol. I: To Be a Disciple. Wolf, Earl C., ed. (Beacon Small-Group Bible Study). 80p. (Orig.). 1984. pap. 2.50 (ISBN 0-8341-0870-4). Beacon Hill.

--Matthew, Part 2: Come & Learn from Me. Wolf, Earl, ed. (Small-Group Bible Studies). 84p. 1986. pap. 2.50 (ISBN 0-8341-1076-8). Beacon Hill.

Carver, George. The Catholic Tradition in English Literature. 59.95 (ISBN 0-87968-820-3). Gordon Pr.

--The Catholic Tradition in English Literature. 1977. Repr. lib. bdg. 25.00 (ISBN 0-8492-3819-6). R West.

Carver, Robert C. & Thiess, Susan. The Creator's World. 1978. 4.95x (ISBN 0-8192-4082-6); parent pupil packet 4.95x (ISBN 0-8192-4083-4). Morehouse.

Carville, Geraldine. Norman Splendour: Duiske Abbey, Graignamanagh. (Illus.). 120p. 1979. 11.25 (ISBN 0-85640-171-4, Pub. by Blackstaff Pr). Longwood Pub Group.

--The Occupation of Celtic Sites in Medieval Ireland by the Canons Regular of St Augustine & the Cistercians. (Cistercian Studies Ser.: Nbr. 56). (Illus.). 1983. 13.95 (ISBN 0-87907-856-1). Cistercian Pubns.

Carwardine, Richard. Transatlantic Revivalism: Popular Evangelicalism in Britain & America, 1790-1865. LC 77-94740. (Contributions in American History Ser.: No. 75). 1978. lib. bdg. 35.00 (ISBN 0-313-20308-3, CTR/). Greenwood.

Carwell, L'Ann. Baby's First Bible Story Book. (Illus.). 1979. 1.25 (ISBN 0-570-08003-7, 56-1328). Concordia.

--Baby's First Book About Christmas. (Illus.). 1979. 1.25 (ISBN 0-570-08002-9, 56-1327). Concordia.

--Baby's First Book About Creation. (Illus.). 1979. 1.25 (ISBN 0-570-08000-2, 56-1325). Concordia.

--Baby's First Book About Jesus. (Illus.). 1979. 1.25 (ISBN 0-570-08001-0, 56-1326). Concordia.

Cary, Diane M. Master. 1981. 9.95 (ISBN 0-8062-1763-4). Carlton.

Cary, Joyce. Except the Lord. LC 85-10601. (Second Trilogy Ser.: Bk. 2). 288p. 1985. pap. 7.95 (ISBN 0-8112-0965-2, NDP607). New Directions.

Cary, Margaret M. Are Your Meetings Held in the Life. 1983. pap. 2.50x (ISBN 0-87574-037-5, 037). Pendle Hill.

Cary, Norman R. Christian Criticism in the Twentieth Century. (National University Publications Literary Criticism Ser.). 1976. 17.95x (ISBN 0-8046-9104-5, Pub. by Kennikat). Assoc Faculty Pr.

Cary, Otis. A History of Christianity in Japan: Roman Catholic & Greek Orthodox Missions, 2 vols. LC 75-28972. (Illus.). 1975. Repr. of 1909 ed. boxed 36.95 (ISBN 0-8048-1177-6). C E Tuttle.

--History of Christianity in Japan, Roman Catholic & Greek Orthodox Missions, 2 Vols. 1971. Repr. of 1909 ed. Set. 18.00 (ISBN 0-403-00252-4). Scholarly.

Cary-Elwes, Columbia. Law, Liberty & Love. 1950. 5.00 (ISBN 0-8159-6104-9). Devin.

Casaldaliga, Pedro. Prophets in Combat: The Nicaraguan Journal of Bishop Pedro Casaldaliga. Berryman, Phillip, tr. from Span. 128p. (Orig.). 1987. pap. 8.95 (ISBN 0-940989-02-6). Meyer Stone Bks.

Casalis, George. Correct Ideas Don't Fall from the Skies: Elements for an Inductive Theology. Lyons, Jeanne M. & John, Michael, trs. from Fr. LC 83-19374. Tr. of Les Idees Justes Ne Tombent Pas du Ciel. 240p. (Orig.). 1984. pap. 8.95 (ISBN 0-88344-023-7). Orbis Bks.

Casamada, Jose, tr. see Catoir, John.

Casanova, Humberto, tr. see Erdman, Charles.

Casanova, Viviana, tr. see Erdman, Charles.

Casas, Arnold J., ed. see Wenger, J. C.

Casas, Arnoldo J., ed. see Wenger, J. C.

Casaubon, Meric. The Golden Book of Marcus Aurelius. 1979. Repr. of 1906 ed. lib. bdg. 12.50 (ISBN 0-8482-7564-0). Norwood Edns.

--A Letter of Meric Casaubon to Peter du Moulin Concerning Natural Experimental Philosophie. LC 76-47045. 1976. Repr. of 1669 ed. 90.00x (ISBN 0-8201-1284-4). Schol Facsimiles.

--Treatise Concerning Enthusiasme. LC 77-119864. 1970. Repr. of 1656 ed. 45.00x (ISBN 0-8201-1077-9). Schol Facsimiles.

Cascone, Gina. Pagan Babies & Other Catholic Memories. 160p. 1982. 9.95 (ISBN 0-312-59418-6). St Martin.

--Pagan Babies & Other Catholic Memories. 160p. 1983. pap. 4.95 (ISBN 0-312-59419-4). St Martin.

Case, Charles C. Talking Trees & Singing Whales. Woolsey, Raymond H., ed. (Devotional Ser.). 365p. 1985. 7.95 (ISBN 0-8280-0285-1). Review & Herald.

Case, Charles J. Beyond Time: Ideas of the Great Philosophers on Eternal Existence & Immortality. LC 85-17864. 144p. (Orig.). 1985. lib. bdg. 20.75 (ISBN 0-8191-4933-0); pap. text ed. 8.25 (ISBN 0-8191-4934-9). U Pr of Amer.

Case, Paul F. The True & Invisible Rosicrucian Order. LC 85-3185. (Illus.). 352p. 1985. 22.50 (ISBN 0-87728-608-6). Weiser.

Case, Paul Foster. Tarot: A Key to the Wisdom of the Ages. (Illus.). 215p. 1981. Repr. of 1977 ed. softcover 6.95 (ISBN 0-88053-767-1). Macoy Pub.

Case, Shirley J. Experience with the Supernatural in Early Christian Times. LC 75-174851. Repr. of 1929 ed. 26.50 (ISBN 0-405-08345-9, Blom Pubns). Ayer Co Pubs.

--Jesus, a New Biography. LC 70-95149. (BCL Ser. II). Repr. of 1927 ed. 17.50 (ISBN 0-404-01406-2). AMS Pr.

--Jesus: A New Biography. LC 68-57594. 1968. Repr. of 1927 ed. lib. bdg. 22.50x (ISBN 0-8371-0342-8, CAJE). Greenwood.

--Jesus, a New Biography. 1928. 30.00 (ISBN 0-932062-36-9). Sharon Hill.

--The Social Triumph of the Ancient Church. facsimile ed. LC 76-164596. (Select Bibliographies Reprint Ser). Repr. of 1933 ed. 18.00 (ISBN 0-8369-5880-2). Ayer Co Pubs.

Caselli, Giovanni. A Medieval Monk. LC 86-70451. (The Everyday Life of Ser.). (Illus.). 30p. 1986. 9.95 (ISBN 0-87226-105-0). P Bedrick Bks.

Caselli, Joseph, tr. see Aubry, Joseph.

Casey, Gerard. Natural Reason: A Study of the Notions of Inference, Assent, Intuition, & First Principles in the Philosophy of John Henry Cardinal Newman. (American University Studies V Philosophy: Vol. 4). 345p. 1984. 37.00 (ISBN 0-8204-0078-5). P Lang Pubs.

Casey, Joseph H., ed. see Grisez, Germain & Shaw, Russell.

Casey, Juliana. Hebrews. (New Testament Message Ser.: Vol. 18). 10.95 (ISBN 0-89453-206-5); pap. 6.95 (ISBN 0-89453-141-7). M Glazier.

Casey, Karen. Love Book. (Hazelden Meditation Ser.). (Illus.). 110p. 1986. pap. 7.00 (ISBN 0-86683-505-9, HarpJ). Har-Row.

--The Love Book. (Hazelden Bks.). scp 7.50t (ISBN 0-317-46481-7). Har-Row.

--The Love Book. (Meditation Ser.). 110p. 1985. 7.95 (ISBN 0-89486-339-8). Hazelden.

--The Lovebook. 110p. 1985. pap. 5.95 (ISBN 0-89486-376-2). Hazelden.

Casey, Karen & Vanceburg, Martha. The Promise of a New Day. 400p. (Orig.). 1985. pap. 5.95 (ISBN 0-86683-502-4, HarpR). Har-Row.

--The Promise of a New Day. (Meditation Ser.). 400p. (Orig.). 1983. text ed. 7.95 (ISBN 0-89486-308-8). Hazelden.

Casey, Robert J. Four Faces of Siva. 1929. 25.00 (ISBN 0-8482-3565-7). Norwood Edns.

Casey, Robert P., ed. see Serapion, Saint.

Casgrain, jt. ed. see Laverdiere.

Cash, Paul, ed. see Brunton, Paul.

Cashel Diocesan Library, County Tipperary, Republic of Ireland Staff. Catalogue of the Cashel Diocesan Library. 1973. 100.00 (ISBN 0-8161-1065-4, Hall Library). G K Hall.

Cashen, Richard A. Solitude in the Thought of Thomas Merton. (Cistercian Studies: No. 40). 208p. 1981. 15.50 (ISBN 0-87907-840-5); pap. 5.50 (ISBN 0-87907-940-1). Cistercian Pubns.

Cashman, Greer F. Jewish Days & Holidays. LC 79-66167. (Illus.). 64p. 1979. Repr. of 1976 ed. 10.95 (ISBN 0-89961-000-5). SBS Pub.

Cashman, Greer F. & Frankel, Alona. Jewish Days & Holidays. LC 86-70789. (Illus.). 61p. 1986. 9.95 (ISBN 0-915361-58-2, Dist. by Watts). Adama Pubs Inc.

Cashmore, Ernest. Rastaman: The Rastafarian Movement in England. (Illus.). 272p. 1980. pap. text ed. 9.95x (ISBN 0-04-301116-0). Allen Unwin.

--Rastaman: The Rastafarian Movement in England. (Counterpoint Ser.). 263p. 1983. pap. 9.95 (ISBN 0-04-301164-0). Allen Unwin.

Caskey, Marie. Chariot of Fire: Religion & the Beecher Family. LC 77-5291. (Historical Publications Ser.). (Illus.). 1978. 40.00x (ISBN 0-300-02007-4). Yale U Pr.

Caslow, Dan. Christian Disciple, No. 2. 1984. pap. 1.95 (ISBN 0-8163-0497-1). Pacific Pr Pub Assn.

--Church Fellowship. 1984. pap. 1.95 (ISBN 0-8163-0499-8). Pacific Pr Pub Assn.

--New Life, No. 1. 1984. pap. 1.95 (ISBN 0-317-30423-2). Pacific Pr Pub Assn.

--Personal Ministry, No. 3. 1984. pap. 1.95 (ISBN 0-8163-0498-X). Pacific Pr Pub Assn.

Caslow, Daniel E. Winning. 1981. pap. 5.95 (ISBN 0-8163-0462-9). Pacific Pr Pub Assn.

Caso, Alfonso. Aztecs: People of the Sun, Vol. 50. Dunham, Lowell, tr. (Civilization of the American Indian Ser.: No. 50). (Illus.). 142p. 1978. Repr. of 1958 ed. 24.95 (ISBN 0-8061-0414-7). U of Okla Pr.

Caspary, Gerard E. Politics & Exegesis: Origen & the Two Swords. LC 77-71058. 1979. 42.00x (ISBN 0-520-03445-7). U of Cal Pr.

Caspi, M. M., ed. Jewish Tradition in the Diaspora: Studies in Memory of Professor Walter J. Fischel. 314p. 1981. 19.95 (ISBN 0-943376-16-5). Magnes Mus.

Cass. Negro Freemasonry & Segregation. 11.00 (ISBN 0-685-19494-9). Powner.

Cass, D. A. Negro Freemasonry. 11.00x (ISBN 0-685-22057-5). Wehman.

Cassandre. Life When Jesus Was a Boy. 48p. 1981. pap. 6.95 (ISBN 0-8170-0913-2). Judson.

Cassara, Ernest. Hosea Ballou: The Challenge to Orthodoxy. LC 81-40859. 236p. 1982. lib. bdg. 27.75 (ISBN 0-8191-2271-8); pap. text ed. 12.50 (ISBN 0-8191-2272-6). U Pr of Amer.

Cassara, Ernest, ed. Universalism in America. 1984. pap. 5.95 (ISBN 0-933840-21-7). Unitarian Univ.

Cassara, Ernest, ed. see Ballou, Hosea.

Cass-Beggs, Barbara. A Musical Calender of Festivals: Folk Songs of Feast-Days & Holidays from Around the World. (Ward Lock Educational Ser.). 1985. 25.00x (ISBN 0-7062-4226-2, Pub. by Ward Lock Educ Co Ltd). State Mutual Bk.

Cassel, Russell N. Drug Abuse Education. 1970. 8.95 (ISBN 0-8158-0245-5). Chris Mass.

Cassell, Eric J. The Healer's Art. 240p. 1985. pap. 7.95 (ISBN 0-262-53062-7). MIT Pr.

Cassels, Louis. Christian Primer. 112p. 1981. pap. 1.50 (ISBN 0-88028-012-3). Forward Movement.

Casserley, J. V. Langmead. No Faith of My Own & Graceful Reason: The Contribution of Reason to Theology. 408p. 1984. pap. text ed. 16.75 (ISBN 0-8191-3793-6). U Pr of Amer.

Cassian, John. John Cassian: Conferences. Luibheid, Colm, tr. (Classics of Western Spirituality Ser.). 201p. 1985. 12.95 (ISBN 0-8091-0361-3); pap. 9.95 (ISBN 0-8091-2694-X). Paulist Pr.

Cassian, St. John. Teachings of St. John Cassian. pap. 4.95 (ISBN 0-686-05665-5). Eastern Orthodox.

Cassianus, Joannes. De Institutis Coenobiorum et De Octo Principalium Remediis Liber Xii: De Incarnatione Domini Contra Nestorium Liber Vii, Bk. 12. (Corpus Scriptorum Ecclesiasticorum Latinorum Ser: Vol. 17). (Cat). 1888. 50.00 (ISBN 0-384-07850-8). Johnson Repr.

--Spiritual Life, a Guide for Those Seeking Perfection. 1977. pap. 4.95 (ISBN 0-686-19234-6). Eastern Orthodox.

Cassianus, Johannes. Opera, Pt. 2. Petschenig, M., ed. (Corpus Scriptorum Ecclesiasticorum Latinorum Ser: Vol. 13). 1886. 50.00 (ISBN 0-384-07860-5). Johnson Repr.

Cassidy, Michael. Bursting the Wineskins: Spiritual Odyssey of a Peacemaker. 280p. 1983. pap. 6.95 (ISBN 0-87788-094-8). Shaw Pubs.

Cassidy, Norma C. Favorite Novenas & Prayers. LC 72-91456. 144p. 1972. pap. 3.95 (ISBN 0-8091-1761-4, Deus). Paulist Pr.

Cassidy, Richard J. Jesus, Politics, & Society: A Study of Luke's Gospel. LC 78-735. 238p. (Orig.). 1978. 15.95 (ISBN 0-88344-238-8); pap. 7.95 (ISBN 0-88344-237-X). Orbis Bks.

Cassidy, Richard J. & Scharper, Philip J., eds. Political Issues in Luke-Acts. LC 82-19060. 192p. (Orig.). 1983. 16.95 (ISBN 0-88344-390-2); pap. 9.95 (ISBN 0-88344-385-6). Orbis Bks.

Cassidy, Sheila A. A Prayer for Pilgrims: A Book about Prayer for Ordinary People. (The Crossroad Paperback Ser.). 192p. 1982. pap. 6.95 (ISBN 0-8245-0420-8). Crossroad NY.

Cassie, Dhyan. So Who's Perfect! LC 84-12948. 248p. (Orig.). 1984. pap. 12.95 (ISBN 0-8361-3372-2). Herald Pr.

Cassirer, Ernst. Language & Myth. Langer, Susanne K., tr. 1946. pap. 2.95 (ISBN 0-486-20051-5). Dover.

--Language & Myth. 13.50 (ISBN 0-8446-1820-9). Peter Smith.

--Myth of the State. 1961. pap. 8.95x (ISBN 0-300-00036-7, y33). Yale U Pr.

--Philosophy of Symbolic Forms, Vol. 2, Mythical Thought. Manheim, Ralph, tr. 1955. pap. 11.95x (ISBN 0-300-00038-3, Y147). Yale U Pr.

--Platonic Renaissance in England. LC 71-128186. 207p. 1970. Repr. of 1954 ed. 19.50x (ISBN 0-87752-128-X). Gordian.

Cassizzi, Vic. Overlook: A Castle in the Kingdom. (Illus.). 1981. 3.95 (ISBN 0-686-30374-1). Cassizzi.

Cassuto, Nelda, ed. see Eis, Ruth.

Cassuto, U. Biblical & Oriental Studies: Bible, Vol. 1. Abrahams, Israel, tr. from Hebrew. (Illus.). 298p. 1973. text ed. 29.95x (Pub. by Magnes Pr Israel). Humanities.

--Biblical & Oriental Studies: Bible & Ancient Oriental Texts, Vol. 2. Abrahams, Israel, tr. from Hebrew. 286p. 1975. text ed. 35.00x (Pub. by Magnes Pr Israel). Humanities.

--A Commentary on the Book of Exodus. 2nd ed. Abrahams, Israel, tr. from Hebrew. 509p. 1974. Repr. of 1967 ed. text ed. 35.00x (ISBN 965-223-456-7, Pub. by Magnes Pr Israel). Humanities.

--From Adam to Noah: A Commentary on the Book of Genesis, Part 1. 3rd ed. 323p. 1978. Repr. of 1961 ed. text ed. 35.00x (Pub. by Magnes Pr Israel). Humanities.

--From Noah to Abraham: A Commentary on the Book of Genesis, Pt. 2. 3rd ed. 386p. 1974. Repr. of 1964 ed. text ed. 35.00x (Pub. by Magnes Pr Israel). Humanities.

Castagnola, Lawrence. Parables for Little People. LC 86-62628. (Illus.). 101p. (Orig.). 1982. pap. 5.56 (ISBN 0-89390-034-6); pap. text ed. 7.95. Resource Pubns.

Castaneda, Carlos. Journey to Ixtlan. 1983. pap. 4.95 (ISBN 0-671-60658-1). WSP.

--Tales of Power. 1982. pap. 4.95 (ISBN 0-671-55329-1). WSP.

--The Teachings of Don Juan: A Yaqui Way of Knowledge. LC 68-17303. 1968. pap. 5.95 (ISBN 0-520-02258-0, CAL253). U of Cal Pr.

Castaneda, Carlos E., ed. see Morfi, Fray J.

Castberg, C., jt. auth. see Adler, L. W.

Castel, Christine du see Du Castel, Christine.

Castel, Francois. History of Israel & Judah: From the Beginnings to the Second Century A. D. 288p. (Orig.). 1985. pap. 8.95 (ISBN 0-8091-2701-6). Paulist Pr.

Castelli, Jim. Bishops & the Bomb: Waging Peace in a Nuclear Age. LC 82-48706. 288p. 1983. pap. 7.95 (ISBN 0-385-18760-2, IM). Doubleday.

Castelli, Jim, jt. auth. see Gallup, George, Jr.

Castelli, Jim, et al. The Abortion Issue in the Political Process: A Briefing for Catholic Legislators. Jackman, Paul, ed. 19p. pap. 3.00 (ISBN 0-915365-08-1). Cath Free Choice.

Castellon, Guillermo, tr. see Garbee, Ed & Van Dyke, Henry.

Casteneda, Carlos E. Our Catholic Heritage in Texas, 1519-1936, 7 vols. LC 76-1471. (Chicano Heritage Ser.). (Illus.). 1976. Repr. Set. 248.00 (ISBN 0-405-09488-4). Ayer Co Pubs.

Castillo-Cardenas, Gonzalo. Liberation Theology from Below: The Life & Thought of Manuel Quintin Lame. LC 86-21812. 224p. (Orig.). 1987. pap. 16.95 (ISBN 0-88344-408-9). Orbis Bks.

Castle, Leon W. A Year of Children's Sermons. LC 76-6717. (Illus.). 144p. 1976. pap. 4.95 (ISBN 0-8054-4918-3). Broadman.

Castle, Tony. Celebrations for the Family. 126p. (Orig.). 1986. pap. 5.95 (ISBN 0-89283-270-3). Servant.

--The New Book of Christian Prayers. 364p. 1986. 17.95 (ISBN 0-8245-0781-9). Crossroad NY.

Castle, Tony, ed. The New Book of Christian Quotations. LC 82-25253. 272p. 1983. pap. 9.95 (ISBN 0-8245-0551-4). Crossroad NY.

Castle, Tony, jt. ed. see Buckley, Michael.

Castleman, Robbie. David: Man after God's Own Heart, 2 vols. (Fisherman Bible Studyguide). 1981. saddle stitched 2.95 ea. Vol. 1, 70p (ISBN 0-87788-164-2). Vol. 2, 63p (ISBN 0-87788-165-0). Shaw Pubs.

--Elijah: Obedience in a Threatening World. (Fisherman Bible Studyguide Ser.). 64p. (Orig.). 1986. pap. 2.95 (ISBN 0-87788-218-5). Shaw Pubs.

Castro, Carol C. Welcoming God's Forgiveness. 120p. 1978. pap. text ed. 3.95 (ISBN 0-697-01681-1); leader's guide 4.50 (ISBN 0-697-01682-X); classroom tchr's guide .75 (ISBN 0-697-01907-1); adult resource book, pack/10,10.25 1.05 (ISBN 0-697-01685-4). Wm C Brown.

--Welcoming Jesus. 120p. 1979. pap. 3.95 (ISBN 0-697-01702-8); leader's guide 4.50 (ISBN 0-697-01703-6); classroom teacher's guide .75 (ISBN 0-697-01909-8); adult resource book, pack/10, 10.25 1.05 (ISBN 0-697-01704-4). Wm C Brown.

Castro, Emilio. Sent Free: Mission & Unity in the Perspective of the Kingdom. 112p. (Orig.). 1985. pap. 5.95 (ISBN 0-8028-0068-8). Eerdmans.

Castro, Fidel & Betto, Frei. Fidel & Religion: Castro Talks on Revolution & Religion with Frei Betto. 1987. 19.95 (ISBN 0-671-64114-X). S&S.

Caswall, Henry. America, & the American Church. LC 77-83413. (Religion in America Ser). 1969. Repr. of 1839 ed. 21.00 (ISBN 0-405-00234-3). Ayer Co Pubs.

Caswell, Helen R. God's World Makes Me Feel So Little. (Illus.). 32p. 1985. paper over board 5.95 (ISBN 0-687-15510-X). Abingdon.

Catalano, Joseph S. A Commentary of Jean-Paul Sartre's "Being & Nothingness". LC 79-21234. xvi, 240p. 1985. pap. text ed. 15.00x (ISBN 0-226-09699-8). U of Chicago Pr.

Cataldo, Peter J., ed. The Dynamic Character of Christian Culture: Essays on Dawsonian Themes. 242p. (Orig.). 1984. lib. bdg. 26.00 (ISBN 0-8191-3959-9, Soc Christ Cult); pap. text ed. 11.75 (ISBN 0-8191-3960-2). U Pr of Amer.

Catan, John R., ed. see Owens, Joseph.

Cate, Robert. Help in Ages Past, Hope for Years to Come: Daily Devotions from the Old Testament. 201p. 1983. pap. 5.95 (ISBN 0-13-387431-1). P-H.

Cate, Robert L. An Introduction to the Old Testament & Its Study. (Orig.). 1987. 19.95 (ISBN 0-8054-1233-6). Broadman.

--Layman's Bible Book Commentary: Exodus, Vol. 2. LC 78-59976. 1979. 5.95 (ISBN 0-8054-1172-0). Broadman.

--Old Testament Roots for New Testament Faith. LC 80-70914. 1982. pap. 7.95 (ISBN 0-8054-1220-4). Broadman.

Cater, Douglass, jt. auth. see Childs, Marquis W.

Cates, W. L., tr. see Merle d'Augbine, Jean H.

Cathcart, Dwight. Doubting Conscience: Donne & the Poetry of Moral Argument. LC 74-78985. 1975. 10.00x (ISBN 0-472-08198-5). U of Mich Pr.

Cathcart, Kevin J. Nahum in the Light of Northwest Semetic. (Biblica et Orientalia: Vol. 26). 1973. pap. 20.00 (ISBN 88-7653-326-5). Loyola.

Cather, Willa. Obscure Destinies. LC 74-5323. 1974. pap. 4.95 (ISBN 0-394-71179-3, V-179, Vin). Random.

Catherwood, Christopher. Five Evangelical Leaders. 240p. 1985. pap. 7.95 (ISBN 0-87788-274-6); 12.95 (ISBN 0-87788-257-6). Shaw Pubs.

Catherwood, Christopher, ed. Martyn Lloyd-Jones: Chosen by God. LC 86-70463. 288p. (Orig.). 1986. pap. 7.95 (ISBN 0-89107-404-X, Crossway Bks). Good News.

Catherwood, Fred. On the Job: The Christian Nine to Five. 192p. 1983. pap. 5.95 (ISBN 0-310-37261-5). Zondervan.

Catherwood, Frederick. First Things First: The Ten Commandments in the 20th Century. LC 81-51. 160p. 1981. pap. 5.95 (ISBN 0-87784-472-0). Inter Varsity.

Cathey, Bill V. A New Day in Church Revivals. LC 83-70645. 1984. pap. 7.95 (ISBN 0-8054-6244-9). Broadman.

Catholic Bishops of England & Wales Staff. A Catechism of Christian Doctrine. LC 82-50599. 72p. 1982. pap. 2.00 (ISBN 0-89555-176-4). TAN Bks Pubs.

Catholic Church-Sacred Congregation of Divine Worship Staff. Celebrating the Saints. International Committee on English in the Liturgy, Confraternity of Christian Doctrine for the New American Bible, tr. from Latin. 1978. pap. 10.00 (ISBN 0-916134-30-X). Pueblo Pub Co.

Catholic Church, Sacred Congregation for Divine Worship. Lectionary for Mass: Cycle A, Sundays & Solemnities. Hartdegen, Steven J., ed. International Committee on English in the Liturgy Confraternity of Christian Doctrine for the New American Bible, tr. from Lat. (Lectionary for Mass Ser.). 1974. 14.50 (ISBN 0-916134-01-6). Pueblo Pub Co.

--Lectionary for Mass: Cycle B, Sundays & Solemnities. Hartdegen, Steven J., ed. (Lectionary for Mass Ser.). 1972. 27.50 (ISBN 0-916134-02-4). Pueblo Pub Co.

Catholic Church, Sacred Congregation of Divine Worship Staff. Lectionary for Mass: Cycle C, Sundays & Solemnities. Hartdegen, Steven J., ed. International Committee on English in the Liturgy Confraternity of Christian Doctrine for the New American Bible, tr. from Lat. (Lectionary for Mass). 1973. 27.50 (ISBN 0-916134-03-2). Pueblo Pub Co.

--The Study Edition (Lectors' Guide) of the Lectionary for Mass, Cycle A Sundays & Solemnities. International Committee on English in the Liturgy, Confraternity of Christian Doctrine for the New American Bible, tr. (The Study Edition (Lector's Guide) of the Lectionary for Mass Ser.: Texts from the New American Bible). 1977. pap. 6.95 (ISBN 0-916134-04-0). Pueblo Pub Co.

--The Study Edition (Lectors' Guide) of the Lectionary for Mass, Cycle B Sundays & Solemnities. 1978. pap. 6.95 (ISBN 0-916134-05-9). Pueblo Pub Co.

Catholic Church Staff. The Roman & British Martyrology. 1980. lib. bdg. 79.95 (ISBN 0-8490-3128-1). Gordon Pr.

Catholic Health Association Staff. The Ministry of Healing: Readings in the Catholic Health Care Ministry. LC 81-12201. 120p. 1981. pap. 7.50 (ISBN 0-686-85771-2). Cath Health.

Catholic Heritage Press, jt. auth. see Tiso, Francis.

Catholic Library Association Staff. Guide to Catholic Literature, 6 vols. Romig, Walter, ed. Incl. 20.00 (ISBN 0-685-22623-9); 10.00; Vols. 3-5. 1944-1955. 15.00 ea.; Vol 6. 1956-1959. 17.50 (ISBN 0-685-22626-3); Vol. 7. 1960-1963. 25.00 (ISBN 0-685-22627-1); Vol. 8. 1964-1967. 25.00 (ISBN 0-685-22628-X). Cath Lib Assn.

Catholic University of America Staff. New Catholic Encylopedia, 17 vols. LC 66-22292. 712p. 1981. Repr. of 1967 ed. Set. 750.00 (ISBN 0-07-010235-X). Publishers Guild.

--Studies in American Church History, 25 vols. Repr. of 1942 ed. 662.50 (ISBN 0-404-57750-4). AMS Pr.

Cativiela, A., tr. see Bonnet, L. & Schroeder, A.

Cativiela, A., tr. see Schroeder, L. Bonnet A.

Catlett, Joyce, jt. auth. see Firestone, Robert.

Cato, Sid. Healing Life's Great Hurts. 64p. 5.95 (ISBN 0-914091-51-4). Chicago Review.

Catoir, John. Catholics & Broken Marriage. LC 78-74434. 72p. 1979. pap. 1.95 (ISBN 0-87793-176-3). Ave Maria.

--Family Matters. Thomas, Joseph R., ed. & intro. by. 180p. (Orig.). 1984. pap. 5.00 (ISBN 0-317-46547-3). Chrstphrs NY.

--Gozad del Senor. (Span.). 3.50 (ISBN 0-318-02209-5). Chrstphrs NY.

--Para que Vuestro Gozo Sea colmado. Casamada, Jose, tr. from Eng. (Span.). 158p. (Orig.). 1986. pap. 5.00 (ISBN 0-317-46550-3). Chrstphrs NY.

--World Religions: Beliefs Behind Today's Headlines. rev. ed. xxiii, 148p. pap. 5.00 (ISBN 0-317-46551-1). Chrstphrs NY.

Catoir, John T. Enjoy the Lord. 1979. pap. 2.95 (ISBN 0-88479-023-1). Arena Lettres.

--World Religions: Beliefs Behind Today's Headlines. rev. ed. 160p. 1985. pap. 4.95 (ISBN 0-940518-04-X). Guildhall Pubs.

Caton, Peggy, ed. Equal Circles: Baha'i Views of Women & Men. (Orig.). 1987. pap. 9.95 (ISBN 0-933770-60-X). Kalimat.

Cattaui, Georges & Madaule, Jacques, eds. Entretiens Sur Paul Claudel: Decades Du Centre Culturel International De Cerisy-la-Salle. (Nouvelle Series: No. 11). 1968. pap. 14.00x (ISBN 90-2796-249-9). Mouton.

Cattell, Ann. Dictionary of Esoteric Words. (Orig.). 1967. pap. 1.75 (ISBN 0-8065-0175-8, C205). Citadel Pr.

Cattell, Everett L. Christian Mission: A Matter of Life. 160p. (Orig.). 1981. 11.95 (ISBN 0-913408-76-X); pap. 8.95 (ISBN 0-913408-68-9). Friends United.

Cattell, Raymond B. A New Morality from Science: Beyondism. 1973. 42.00 (ISBN 0-08-016956-2). Pergamon.

Cattermole, Richard, ed. Sacred Poetry of the Seventeenth Century: Including the Whole of Giles Fletcher's Christ's Victory & Triumph, 2 vols. (Research & Source Works Ser.: No. 346). 1969. Repr. of 1835 ed. Set. 44.50 (ISBN 0-8337-0499-0). B Franklin.

Cattley, S. R., ed. see Foxe, John.

Catto, William T. Semi-Centenary Discourse. facs. ed. LC 78-154073. (Black Heritage Library Collection). 1857. 14.25 (ISBN 0-8369-8784-5). Ayer Co Pubs.

Caudill, Paul R. First Corinthians: A Translation with Notes. LC 82-71220. 1983. 4.95 (ISBN 0-8054-1391-X). Broadman.

--Hebrews: A Translation with Notes. LC 84-21415. 1985. pap. 4.95 (ISBN 0-8054-1395-2). Broadman.

--Seven Steps to Peace. LC 81-71254. 1982. pap. 3.95 (ISBN 0-8054-1527-0). Broadman.

Caudill, R. Paul. The Mountain Preacher, Vol. III. LC 84-71992. (Illus.). 165p. (Orig.). 1986. pap. 3.00 (ISBN 0-938980-05-X). Blue Ridge.

--Mountain Preacher, Vol. 3. LC 84-71992. 1986. pap. 3.00 (ISBN 0-938980-05-X). Blue Ridge.

--Philippians: A Translation with Notes. LC 80-70403. (Orig.). 1981. pap. 2.25 (ISBN 0-938980-00-9). Blue Ridge.

Caudwell, Irene. Damien of Molokai, Eighteen Forty to Eighteen Eighty-Nine. 1979. Repr. of 1932 ed. lib. bdg. 20.00 (ISBN 0-8492-4041-7). R West.

Caughlan, Lar. Yoga: The Spirit of Union. 96p. 1981. pap. text ed. 13.00 (ISBN 0-8403-2487-1). Kendall-Hunt.

Caulfield, Sean. The Experience of Praying. LC 79-92428. 88p. 1980. 3.95 (ISBN 0-8091-2358-4). Paulist Pr.

--Under the Broom Tree. LC 82-60593. 80p. 1983. pap. 4.95 (ISBN 0-8091-2493-9). Paulist Pr.

Caussade, Jean-Pierre de see De Caussade, Jean-Pierre.

Caussode, Jean Pierre de see De Caussode, Jean Pierre.

Cauthen, Kenneth. The Impact of American Religious Liberalism. 2nd ed. LC 82-23902. 308p. 1983. pap. text ed. 14.25 (ISBN 0-8191-2762-0). U Pr of Amer.

--Process Ethics: A Constructive System. LC 84-16662. (Toronto Studies in Theology: Vol. 18). 365p. 1985. 59.95x (ISBN 0-88946-764-1). E Mellen.

--Systematic Theology: A Modern Protestant Approach. LC 86-23807. (Toronto Studies in Theology: Vol. 25). 480p. 1986. lib. bdg. 69.95x (ISBN 0-88946-769-2). E Mellen.

Cavaliero, Glen. Charles Williams, Poet of Theology. LC 82-11420. Repr. of 1983 ed. 52.30 (2027538). Bks Demand UMI.

Cavaliero, Roderick. The Last of the Crusaders. LC 78-63337. (The Crusades & Military Orders: Second Ser.). Repr. of 1960 ed. 34.25 (ISBN 0-404-17006-4). AMS Pr.

Cavalletti, Sofia. The Religious Potential of the Child. 224p. 1982. pap. 10.95 (ISBN 0-8091-2389-4). Paulist Pr.

Cavallini, Giuliana. St. Martin de Porres-Apostle of Charity. Holland, Caroline, tr. from It. LC 79-65530. (Cross & Crown Series of Spirituality). 1979. pap. 7.00 (ISBN 0-89555-092-X). TAN Bks Pubs.

Cavanagh, Michael E. The Effective Minister. 160p. (Orig.). 1986. 14.95 (ISBN 0-06-254210-9, HarpR). Har-Row.

--Make Your Tomorrow Better: A Psychological Resource for Singles, Parents & the Entire Family. LC 80-80638. 360p. (Orig.). 1980. pap. 9.95 (ISBN 0-8091-2293-6). Paulist Pr.

Cavanah, Frances. The Truth about the Man Behind the Book That Sparked the War Between the States. LC 75-11566. (Illus.). 188p. 1975. 7.95 (ISBN 0-664-32572-6). Westminster.

Cavanah, Frances, ed. Favorite Christmas Stories. 1948. 5.95 (ISBN 0-448-02376-8, G&D). Putnam Pub Group.

Cavanaugh, Joan & Forseth, Pat. More of Jesus, Less of Me. 1976. pap. 3.95 (ISBN 0-88270-174-6). Bridge Pub.

Cavanaugh, Joseph H. Evidence for Our Faith. 3rd ed. 1959. 8.00x (ISBN 0-268-00092-1). U. of Notre Dame Pr.

Cavanaugh, Michael, ed. God's Call to the Single Adult. 130p. (Orig.). 1986. pap. text ed. 3.95 (ISBN 0-88368-187-0). Whitaker Hse.

Cavarnos, Constantine. Anchored in God. 2nd ed. LC 75-35432. (Illus.). 230p. 1975. 10.00 (ISBN 0-914744-30-5). Inst Byzantine.

--Byzantine Sacred Music. 31p. 1981. pap. 1.00 (ISBN 0-914744-23-2). Inst Byzantine.

--The Classical Theory of Relations. LC 75-2659. 116p. 1975. pap. 3.75 (ISBN 0-914744-28-3). Inst Byzantine.

--A Dialogue Between Bergson, Aristotle, & Philologos. 3rd. enl. ed. 100p. 1986. pap. 4.95 (ISBN 0-914744-77-1). Inst Byzantine.

--A Dialogue on G. E. Moore's Ethical Philosophy: Together with an Account of Three Talks with Moore on Diverse Philosophical Questions. LC 79-65479. 1979. 5.95 (ISBN 0-914744-43-7); pap. 2.95 (ISBN 0-914744-44-5). Inst Byzantine.

--The Future Life According to Orthodox Teaching. Auxentios, Hieromonk & Chrysostomos, Archimandrite, trs. from Gr. 100p. (Orig.). 1985. pap. 6.50 (ISBN 0-911165-06-1). Ctr Trad Orthodox.

--The Holy Mountain. 2nd ed. LC 73-84103. (Illus.). 172p. 1977. pap. 6.50 (ISBN 0-914744-38-0). Inst Byzantine.

--Modern Greek Philosophers on the Human Soul. LC 86-83011. (Illus.). 144p. 1987. pap. 6.95. Inst Byzantine.

--Modern Orthodox Saints: St. Methodia of Kimolos, Vol. 9. (Illus.). 123p. 1987. 8.95 (ISBN 0-914744-75-5); pap. 5.95 (ISBN 0-914744-76-3). Inst Byzantine.

--Modern Orthodox Saints: St. Nikephoros of Chios, Vol. 4. 2nd, rev. ed. LC 86-82207. (Illus.). 124p. 1986. pap. 4.95 (ISBN 0-914744-74-7). Inst Byzantine.

--Modern Orthodox Saints: Vol. 2-St. Macarios of Corinth. 2nd ed. LC 72-85116. (Illus.). 1977. pap. 4.50 (ISBN 0-914744-35-6). Inst Byzantine.

--Modern Orthodox Saints: Vol. 3-St. Nicodemos the Hagiorite. 2nd ed. LC 78-71478. (Illus.). 167p. 1979. 8.00 (ISBN 0-914744-41-0); pap. 4.50. Inst Byzantine.

--Modern Orthodox Saints: Vol. 6-St. Arsenios of Paros. LC 78-54384. (Illus.). 123p. 1978. 8.00 (ISBN 0-914744-39-9); pap. 4.50 (ISBN 0-914744-40-2). Inst Byzantine.

--Modern Orthodox Saints: Vol. 7-St. Nectarios of Aegina. LC 81-82963. (Illus.). 222p. 1981. 10.00 (ISBN 0-914744-53-4); pap. 7.00 (ISBN 0-914744-54-2). Inst Byzantine.

--Modern Orthodox Saints: Vol. 8, St. Savvas the New. LC 85-60117. (Illus.). 144p. 1985. 8.95 (ISBN 0-914744-62-3); pap. 5.95 (ISBN 0-914744-63-1). Inst Byzantine.

--Orthodox Iconography. LC 77-74606. (Illus.). 76p. 1977. pap. 4.50 (ISBN 0-914744-37-2). Inst Byzantine.

--Paths & Means to Holiness. 85p. (Orig.). 1986. pap. 5.00 (ISBN 0-911165-08-8). Ctr Trad Orthodox.

Cavarnos, Constantine, ed. Modern Orthodox Saints, Vol. 1: St. Cosmas Aitolos. 3rd. rev. & enl. ed. LC 85-80440. (Illus.). 118p. 1985. 8.95 (ISBN 0-914744-64-X); pap. 5.95 (ISBN 0-914744-65-8). Inst Byzantine.

Cavarnos, Constantine, compiled by. & t see Kontoglou, Photios.

Cavarnos, Constantine, tr. see Damascene, John & Oecumenical Synod Seventh.

Cavarnos, Constatine & Zeldin, Mary B. Modern Orthodox Saints: Vol. 5-St. Seraphim of Sarov. LC 80-80124. (Illus.). 167p. 1980. 9.00 (ISBN 0-914744-47-X); pap. 6.00 (ISBN 0-914744-48-8). Inst Byzantine.

Cavarnos, John P. St. Gregory of Nyssa on the Origin & Destiny of the Soul. 12p. 1982. pap. 0.90 (ISBN 0-914744-60-7). Inst Byzantine.

Cave, C. H., tr. see Jeremias, Joachim.

Cave, F. H., tr. see Jeremias, Joachim.

Cave, Richard, ed. see Moore, George.

Cave, Sydney. Redemption, Hindu & Christian: The Religious Quest of India. facsimile ed. LC 73-102230. (Select Bibliographies Reprint Ser). 1919. 24.50 (ISBN 0-8369-5115-8). Ayer Co Pubs.

Cavell, Stanley. The Claim of Reason: Wittgenstein, Skepticism, Morality, & Tragedy. 1979. pap. 11.95 (ISBN 0-19-503195-4). Oxford U Pr.

Cavendish, George. The Life of Cardinal Wolsey. 1887. Repr. 15.00 (ISBN 0-8274-2879-0). R West.

Cavendish, George see Sylvester, Richard S. & Harding, Davis P.

Cavendish, Richard. King Arthur & the Grail: The Arthurian Legends & Their Meaning. LC 79-14034. 238p. 1985. pap. 6.95 (ISBN 0-8008-4466-1). Taplinger.

Cavert, Walter D. With Jesus on the Scout Trail. (Orig.). 1970. pap. 3.75 (ISBN 0-687-45849-8). Abingdon.

Cavin, Thomas F. Champion of Youth: Daniel A. Lord, S. J. 1977. 6.50 (ISBN 0-8198-0398-7); pap. text ed. 5.00 (ISBN 0-8198-0399-5). Dghtrs St Paul.

Caviness, Madeline E. & Husband, Timothy. Corpus Vitrearum: Studies on Medieval Stained Glass. (Occasional Papers: No. 1). (Illus.). 160p. 1985. 35.00 (ISBN 0-87099-391-7). Metro Mus Art.

Caviness, Madeline H. The Early Stained Glass of Canterbury Cathedral: 1175-1220. (Illus.). 1978. text ed. 68.50x (ISBN 0-691-03927-5). Princeton U Pr.

Cawley, A. C., ed. Everyman & Medieval Miracle Plays. 10.95x (ISBN 0-460-10381-4, Evman). Biblio Dist.

--The Wakefield Pageants in the Towneley Cycle. (Old & Middle English Texts). 187p. 1975. pap. 10.95x (ISBN 0-06-491013-X, 06392). B&N Imports.

Cawley, M., jt. auth. see Bouyer, L.

Cawte, John, tr. see Grillmeier, Aloys.

Caxton, W., tr. Here Begynneth a Lityll Treatise Spekynge of the Arte & Crafte to Knowe Well to Dye. LC 72-169. (English Experience Ser.: No. 221). 28p. Repr. of 1490 ed. 14.00 (ISBN 90-221-0221-1). Walter J Johnson.

Caxton, W., tr. see Jerome, Saint.

Caxton, William, tr. see Heraclius.

Cayce, Edgar. Revelation: A Commentary on the Book, Based on the Study of Twenty Four Psychic Discourses of Edgar Cayce. (Twenty-Six Interpretive Readings). 1969. pap. 8.95 (ISBN 0-87604-003-2). ARE Pr.

Cayce, Edgar & Cayce, Hugh L. God's Other Door & the Continuity of Life. 1976. pap. 2.95 (ISBN 0-87604-007-5). ARE Pr.

Cayce, H. L. Gifts of Healing. 1976. pap. 1.95 (ISBN 0-87604-070-9). ARE Pr.

Cayce, Hugh L. The Jesus I Knew. 81p. (Orig.). 1984. pap. 4.95 (ISBN 0-87604-156-X). ARE Pr.

--Venture Inward: Edgar Cayce's Story & the Mysteries of the Unconscious Mind. LC 85-42772. 256p. 1985. pap. 4.95 (ISBN 0-06-250131-3, HarpR). Har-Row.

Cayce, Hugh L., jt. auth. see Cayce, Edgar.

Cayce, Hugh L., ed. The Edgar Cayce Reader. 192p. 1969. pap. 3.50 (ISBN 0-446-32561-9). Warner Bks.

Cazden, Elizabeth. Antoinette Brown Blackwell: A Biography. LC 82-4986. (Illus.). 328p. 1983. 24.95 (ISBN 0-935312-00-5); pap. 9.95 (ISBN 0-935312-04-8). Feminist Pr.

Cazelles, Brigitte, jt. auth. see Johnson, Phyllis.

Cazelles, H., et al. Supplement au Dictionnaire de la Bible, 7 vols. (Fr.). 128p. 1967. Set. 595.50 (ISBN 0-686-56943-1, M-6065). French & Eur.

Cazenove, Theophile. Cazenove Journal, 1794: A Journey Through New Jersey & Pennsylvania. Kelsey, Rayner W., ed. (Haverford Coll. Studies: No. 13). 1922. 17.50x (ISBN 0-686-17388-0). R S Barnes.

Cecil, Andrew R., et al. Conflict & Harmony. (Andrew R. Cecil Lectures on Moral Values in a Free Society: Vol. III). 228p. 1982. text ed. 14.50x (ISBN 0-292-71081-X, Pub. by U of Tex. at Dallas). U of Tex Pr.

Cecil, Anthony C., Jr. The Theological Development of Edwards Amasa Park: Last of the "Consistent Calvinists". LC 74-83338. (American Academy of Religion. Dissertation Ser.). 1974. pap. 9.95 (ISBN 0-88420-118-X, 010101). Scholars Pr GA.

Cecil, Martin. Meditations on the Lord's Prayer. 2nd ed. 1982. 10.95 (ISBN 0-686-27652-3). Cole-Outreach.

Cecil, Robert & Rieu, Richard, eds. The King's Son: Readings in the Contemporary Psychologies & Contemporary Thoughts on Man. 181p. 1981. 14.95 (ISBN 0-900860-88-X, Pub. by Octagon Pr England). Ins Study Human.

Cedar, Paul A. The Communicator's Commentary-James First; Second, Peter, Jude, Vol. 2. Ogilvie, Lloyd J., ed. (The Communicator's Commentaries Ser.). 1983. 16.95 (ISBN 0-8499-0164-2). Word Bks.

Cedar Rapids Community School District Staff. Improving Spelling Performance: Student Edition Block IV. 136p. 1981. pap. text ed. 2.55 (ISBN 0-8403-2419-7). Kendall-Hunt.

Cedarbaum, Sophia. A First Book of Jewish Holidays. LC 85-105348. (Illus.). 80p. 1984. pap. text ed. 6.00 (ISBN 0-8074-0274-5, 301500). UAHC.

Cedervall, David. Salvation Army Word Search Puzzles. 75p. (Orig.). 1985. pap. 1.65 (ISBN 0-89216-061-6). Salvation Army.

Cee Cee, pseud. Inside My Head. 1985. 6.50 (ISBN 0-8062-2521-1). Carlton.

Celano, Thomas. St. Francis of Assisi. 1963. pap. 10.50 (ISBN 0-8199-0098-2). Franciscan Herald.

Celeste, Marie. Elizabeth Ann Seton - A Self-Portrait: A Study of Her Spirituality. LC 85-72765. (Illus.). 305p. 1986. 18.95 (ISBN 0-913382-33-7, 101-33). Prow Bks-Franciscan.

Cell, George C. The Rediscovery of John Wesley. LC 83-6505. 438p. 1983. pap. text ed. 15.50 (ISBN 0-8191-3222-5). U Pr of Amer.

Cenker, William. A Tradition of Teachers: Sankara & the Jagadgurus Today. 1983. 18.50 (ISBN 0-8364-0944-2); text ed. 13.00 (ISBN 0-8364-1058-0). South Asia Bks.

Censoni, Bob. Ready-to-Use Christmas Silhouettes. 64p. (Orig.). 1985. pap. 3.50 (ISBN 0-486-24954-9). Dover.

Center for Learning Staff. Classical Literature. 1982. pap. text ed. 34.95 (ISBN 0-697-01884-9). Wm C Brown.

--World Literature I. 1985. pap. text ed. 34.95 (ISBN 0-697-02073-8). Wm C Brown.

--World Literature II. 1985. pap. text ed. 34.95 (ISBN 0-697-02074-6). Wm C Brown.

Center for Self-Sufficiency, Research Division Staff. At Your Own Pace Reference on Meditation & Wholistic Healing. 30p. 1985. pap. text ed. 2.75 (ISBN 0-910811-71-7, Pub. by Center Self Suff). Prosperity & Profits.

Central Commission for the Investigation of German Crimes in Poland Staff. German Crimes in Poland, 2 vols. in one. 1982. Repr. of 1947 ed. 45.00x (ISBN 0-86527-336-7). Fertig.

Central Conference of American Rabbis Staff. A Passover Haggadah. rev. ed. Baskin, Leonard, ed. & illus. (Illus.). 124p. 1978. pap. 14.95 (ISBN 0-14-004871-5). Penguin.

Centre, Michael. In Search of God-the Solar Connection. LC 78-73706. (Illus.). 1978. 9.95x (ISBN 0-932876-00-5); pap. 5.95 (ISBN 0-932876-01-3). Centre Ent.

Ceperley, Gordon. A Promised Land for a Chosen P ple. LC 79-65616. (Illus., Orig.). 1979. pap. 2.50 (ISBN 0-915540-25-8). Friends Israel-Spearhead Pr.

Cerart, Joan. Lord of the Horizon. 300p. 1987. pap. 7.95 (ISBN 0-89804-147-3). Ariel OH.

--Scarlet Feather. 290p. 1988. pap. 7.95 (ISBN 0-89804-148-1). Ariel OH.

--So Moses Was Born. 312p. 1988. pap. 7.95 (ISBN 0-89804-149-X). Ariel OH.

Cerdic Colloquium Staff. Liberation Theology & the Message of Salvation: Proceedings of the Cerdic Colloquium, 4th, Strasbourg, May 10-12, 1973. Metz, Rene & Schlick, Jean, eds. Gelzer, David G., tr. LC 78-7540. (Pittsburgh Theological Monographs: No. 20). 1978. pap. 8.75 (ISBN 0-915138-26-3). Pickwick.

Cerf, Walter, ed. see Hegel, G. W.

Cerf, Walter., tr. see Hegel, G. W.

Ceria, Eugenio. The Biographical Memoirs of Saint John Bosco, Vol. XIV (1879-80) Borgatello, Diego, ed. LC 65-3104. Tr. of Memorie Biografiche di Don Giovanni Bosco. 628p. 1985. 19.95 (ISBN 0-89944-014-2). Don Bosco Multimedia.

Cerling, Charles. The Divorced Christian. 1984. 9.95 (ISBN 0-8010-2495-1); pap. 5.95 (ISBN 0-8010-2486-2). Baker Bk.

--Freedom from Bad Habits. LC 84-62384. 141p. (Orig.). 1984. pap. 5.95 (ISBN 0-89840-079-1). Heres Life.

Cerling, Charles E. Assertiveness & the Christian. 140p. 1983. pap. 4.95 (ISBN 0-8423-0083-X). Tyndale.

Cerling, Chuck. Cleaning Out Your Mental Closet: Transforming Negative Emotions. 150p. 1987. pap. 9.95 (ISBN 0-87788-127-8). Shaw Pubs.

Cerminara, Gina. Insights for the Age of Aquarius. LC 76-6173. 314p. 1976. pap. 6.95 (ISBN 0-8356-0483-7, Quest). Theos Pub Hse.

Cernic, David & Longmire, Linda, eds. Know Thyself: Collected Readings on Identity. 1987. pap. 12.95 (ISBN 0-8091-2872-1). Paulist Pr.

Cerny, Jaroslav. Ancient Egyptian Religion. LC 78-9931. 1979. Repr. of 1957 ed. lib. bdg. 50.00x (ISBN 0-313-21104-3, CEAE). Greenwood.

Cerve, Wishar S. Lemuria, el Continente Perdido del Pacifico. AMORC Staff, tr. from Eng. (Span., Illus.). 191p. (Orig.). 1980. pap. 7.00 (ISBN 0-912057-68-8, GS-512). AMORC.

Cesar, Joseph V. The Teaching of the Master. 120p. (Orig.). pap. text ed. 5.95 (ISBN 0-937816-01-9). Tech Data.

Cesaretti, C. A. & Commins, Stephen, eds. Let the Earth Bless the Lord: A Christian Perspective on Land Use. 160p. (Orig.). 1981. pap. 6.95 (ISBN 0-8164-2296-6, HarpR). Har-Row.

Cesaretti, Charles A. & Vitale, Joseph T., eds. Rumors of War: A Moral & Theological Perspective on the Arms Race. 128p. (Orig.). 1982. pap. 6.95 (ISBN 0-8164-2365-2, HarpR). Har-Row.

Ceserani, Gian P., jt. auth. see Ventura, Piero.

Cessario, Romanus. Christian Satisfaction in Aquinas: Towards a Personalist Understanding. LC 81-43836. 390p. (Orig.). 1982. lib. bdg. 32.00 (ISBN 0-8191-2557-1); pap. text ed. 15.75 (ISBN 0-8191-2558-X). U Pr of Amer.

Cetnar, Jean, jt. auth. see Cetnar, William.

Cetnar, William & Cetnar, Jean. Questions for Jehovah's Witnesses. 1983. pap. 3.95 (ISBN 0-87552-162-2). Presby & Reformed.

Ceynar, Marvin. Writing for the Religious Market. 1986. 2.25 (ISBN 0-89536-804-8, 6822). CSS of Ohio.

Chadbourne, Richard M. Ernest Renan. LC 67-25197. (Twayne's World Authors Ser.). 1968. lib. bdg. 17.95 (ISBN 0-8057-2754-X). Irvington.

Chadda, H. C., ed. Seeing Is Above All: Sant Darshan Singh's First Indian Tour. (Illus.). 1977. pap. 3.00 (ISBN 0-918224-04-7). Sawan Kirpal Pubns.

Chadha, P. N. Hindu Law. 354p. 1982. 60.00x (Pub. by Eastern Bk India). State Mutual Bk.

--Hindu Law: Edition. abr. ed. 354p. 1982. 60.00x (Pub. by Eastern Bk India). State Mutual Bk.

Chadwell, David. Christian Perspectives on Dating & Marriage. 1980. pap. 4.95 (ISBN 0-89137-523-6). Quality Pubns.

Chadwick. Twenty-Five Mornings & Evenings. pap. 3.95 (ISBN 0-686-12924-5). Schmul Pub Co.

Chadwick, Edward W. Pastoral Teaching of Paul. LC 84-7123. 416p. 1984. 11.95 (ISBN 0-8254-2325-2). Kregel.

Chadwick, Enid M. At God's Altar. Schuler, Eugenia, ed. (Illus.). 1978. pap. 1.50x (ISBN 0-934502-00-5). Thursday Pubs.

--At God's Altar: Rite One. Schuler, Eugenia, ed. (Illus.). 1978. pap. 1.50x (ISBN 0-934502-01-3). Thursday Pubs.

Chadwick, H., ed. Origen: Contra Celsum. LC 78-73132. 1980. 80.00 (ISBN 0-521-05866-X); pap. 32.50 (ISBN 0-521-29576-9). Cambridge U Pr.

Chadwick, Henry. Augustine. (Past Masters Ser.). 128p. 1986. 14.95x (ISBN 0-19-287535-3); pap. 4.95 (ISBN 0-19-287534-5). Oxford U Pr.

--Early Christian Thoughts & the Classical Tradition: Studies in Justin, Clement & Origan. 182p. 1984. pap. text ed. 13.95x (ISBN 0-19-826673-1). Oxford U Pr.

--Early Church, Pelican History of the Church, Vol. 1. (Orig.). 1968. pap. 5.95 (ISBN 0-14-020502-0, Pelican). Penguin.

Chadwick, Henry, ed. Boethius: The Consolations of Music, Logic, Theology, & Philosophy. 1981. text ed. 47.00x (ISBN 0-19-826447-X). Oxford U Pr.

Chadwick, Henry, jt. ed. see Oulton, J. E.

Chadwick, Henry, tr. see Lessing, Gotthold.

Chadwick, John W. Theodore Parker: Preacher & Reformer. LC 72-144939. 1971. Repr. of 1900 ed. 39.00x (ISBN 0-403-00925-1). Scholarly.

Chadwick, Nora K., et al. Studies in the Early British Church. LC 73-673. vii, 374p. 1973. Repr. of 1958 ed. 32.50 (ISBN 0-208-01315-6, Archon). Shoe String.

Chadwick, O., jt. ed. see Nuttall, Geoffrey F.

Chadwick, Owen. Britain & the Vatican During the Second World War. 350p. 1987. 39.50 (ISBN 0-521-32242-1). Cambridge U Pr.

--Catholicism & History. LC 77-77740. 1978. 24.95 (ISBN 0-521-21708-3). Cambridge U Pr.

--Hensley Henson: A Study in the Friction Between Church & State. 350p. 1983. text ed. 39.95x (ISBN 0-19-825445-8). Oxford U Pr.

--John Cassian. 2nd ed. 1968. 32.50 (ISBN 0-521-04607-6). Cambridge U Pr.

--Newman. (Past Masters Ser.). 1983. 13.95x (ISBN 0-19-287568-X); pap. 4.95 (ISBN 0-19-287567-1). Oxford U Pr.

--The Popes & European Revolution. (Oxford History of the Christian Church Ser.). 1981. 84.00x (ISBN 0-19-826919-6). Oxford U Pr.

--Reformation, Vol. 3. (History of the Church Ser.). (Orig.). 1964. pap. 5.95 (ISBN 0-14-020504-7, Pelican). Penguin.

Chadwick, Owen, ed. The Mind of the Oxford Movement. 1961. 18.50x (ISBN 0-8047-0342-6). Stanford U Pr.

--Western Asceticism. LC 58-8713. (Library of Christian Classics). 364p. 1979. softcover 8.95 (ISBN 0-664-24161-1). Westminster.

Chadwick, Samuel. Path of Prayer. 1963. pap. 2.95 (ISBN 0-87508-095-2). Chr Lit.

--Way to Pentecost. 1960. pap. 2.95 (ISBN 0-87508-096-0). Chr Lit.

Chafer, Lewis S. Grace. pap. 11.95 (ISBN 0-310-22331-8, 6305P). Zondervan.

--He That Is Spiritual. 1918. 5.95 (ISBN 0-310-22341-5, 6307P, Pub. by Dunham). Zondervan.

--Salvation. 160p. 1972. pap. 5.95 (ISBN 0-310-22351-2, 6309P). Zondervan.

--Satan. 1977. pap. 5.95 (ISBN 0-310-22361-X, 6308P). Zondervan.

--Systematic Theology, 8 vols. 2700p. 1981. Repr. 94.95 (ISBN 0-310-22378-4). Zondervan.

--True Evangelism. pap. 5.95 (ISBN 0-310-22381-4, 6312P). Zondervan.

Chafer, Lewis S. & Walvoord, John F. Major Bible Themes. rev. ed. 11.95 (ISBN 0-310-22390-3, 6203P). Zondervan.

Chaffin, Kenneth L. The Reluctant Witness. LC 74-84548. 1975. 6.95 (ISBN 0-8054-5550-7). Broadman.

Chafin, Kenneth L. Tell All the Little Children. 1976. pap. 0.95 (ISBN 0-8054-6211-2). Broadman.

Chafin, Kenneth L. & Ogilvie, Lloyd J. The Communicator's Commentary: Corinthians First; Second, Vol. 7. 1983. 18.95 (ISBN 0-8499-0347-5). Word Bks.

Chafuen, Alejandro A. Christians for Freedom: Late-Scholastic Economics. LC 86-80784. 200p. 1986. pap. 12.95 (ISBN 0-89870-110-4). Ignatius Pr.

Chai, Ch'U & Chai, Winberg, eds. Li Chi: Book of Rites, 2 Vols. 1966. 25.00 (ISBN 0-8216-0107-5). Univ Bks.

Chai, Winberg, jt. auth. see Ch'u Chai.

Chai, Winberg, jt. ed. see Chai, Ch'U.

Chaigne, Louis. Paul Claudel: The Man & the Mystic. LC 78-5951. 1978. Repr. of 1961 ed. lib. bdg. 24.75x (ISBN 0-313-20465-9, CHCL). Greenwood.

Chaij, Fernando. Preparation for the Final Crisis. LC 66-29118. 1966. pap. 6.95 (ISBN 0-8163-0137-9, 16510-0). Pacific Pr Pub Assn.

Chaikin, Miriam. Exodus. LC 85-27361. (Illus.). 32p. 1987. reinforced bdg. 14.95 (ISBN 0-8234-0607-5). Holiday.

--Light Another Candle: The Story & Meaning of Hanukkah. LC 80-28137. (Illus.). 80p. 1981. 10.50 (ISBN 0-395-31026-1, Clarion); pap. 3.95 (ISBN 0-89919-057-X). HM.

--Make Noise, Make Merry: The Story & Meaning of Purim. LC 82-12926. (Illus.). 96p. 1983. 11.95 (ISBN 0-89919-424-9, Pub. by Clarion); pap. 4.95. Ticknor & Fields.

--Shake a Palm Branch: The Story & Meaning of Sukkot. LC 84-5022. (Illus.). 80p. 1984. PLB 12.95 (ISBN 0-89919-254-8, Clarion). HM.

--Shake a Palm Branch: The Story & Meaning of Sukkot. LC 84-5022. (Illus.). 88p. 1986. pap. 4.95 (ISBN 0-89919-428-1, Pub. by Clarion). Ticknor & Fields.

--Sound the Shofar: The Story & Meaning of Rosh HaShanah & Yom Kippur. LC 86-2651. (Illus.). 96p. 1986. 13.95 (ISBN 0-89919-373-0, Pub. by Clarion); pap. 4.95 (ISBN 0-89919-427-3, Pub. by Clarion). Ticknor & Fields.

Chaikin, Miriam & Frampton, David. The Seventh Day: The Story of the Jewish Sabbath. LC 82-16987. (Illus.). 48p. (Orig.). 1983. pap. 4.95 (ISBN 0-8052-0743-0). Schocken.

Chaim, B., ed. Neturei Karta; Voice of Anti-Zionist Judaism: A Study. 1980. 75.00 (ISBN 0-87700-273-8). Revisionist Pr.

Chaim, Bezalel. Against the Tide: Jewish Nonconformist Views of Israel & Zionism. 1979. lib. bdg. 42.95 (ISBN 0-686-24783-3). M Buber Pr.

Chaim, Chafetz, pseud. Ahavath Chesed: The Love of Kindness As Required by G-D. Oschry, Leonard, tr. from Hebrew. 1978. pap. 6.95 (ISBN 0-87306-167-5). Feldheim.

Chairanya, Krishna. Freedom & Transcendence. 1983. 28.00x (ISBN 0-8364-0953-1, Pub. by Manohar India). South Asia Bks.

Chai-Shin, Yu. Early Buddhism & Christianity. xv, 241p. 1986. Repr. 17.50 (ISBN 81-208-0050-8, Pub. by Motilal Banarsidass). South Asia Bks.

Chait, Baruch, ed. Perek Shira & Zemirot. 100p. (Orig.). 1986. text ed. 4.95 (ISBN 0-88125-095-3). Ktav.

Chaitanya, Swami Christ, ed. see Rajneesh, Bhagwan Shree.

Chaitanya Yati, Guru N. Bhagavad Gita: A Sublime Hymn of Yoga. Nataraja Guru, tr. 550p. 1980. text ed. 50.00x (ISBN 0-7069-1129-6, Pub. by Vikas India). Advent NY.

Chaitow, Boris R. My Healing Secrets. 128p. 1980. 14.95 (ISBN 0-8464-1066-4). Beekman Pubs.

Chaitow, Leon. Relaxation & Meditation Techniques: A Complete Stress-Proofing System. 128p. 1983. pap. cancelled (ISBN 0-7225-0737-2). Thorsons Pubs.

Chaix, Gerald. Reforme et Contre-Reforme Catholiques Recherches Sur la Chartreuse de Cologne au XVI Siecle. Hogg, James, ed. (Analecta Cartusiana Ser.: No. 80,1-3). (Fr.). 1119p. (Orig.). 1981. pap. 85.00 (ISBN 3-7052-0117-4, Pub. by Salzburg Studies). Longwood Pub Group.

Chajes. Student's Guide Through the Talmud. 13.95 (ISBN 0-87306-089-X). Feldheim.

Chakrabarti, Kisor K. The Logic of Gotama. LC 77-13853. (Society for Asian & Comparative Philosophy Monograph: No. 5). 168p. 1978. pap. text ed. 7.00x (ISBN 0-8248-0601-8). UH Pr.

Chakraborty, Bhaktivenode. Platonic Bearings in Rabindranath. 1986. 9.00x (ISBN 0-8364-1580-9, Pub. by KP Bagchi India). South Asia Bks.

Chakravarti, S. C. Bauls: The Spiritual Vikings. 1981. 10.00x (ISBN 0-8364-0671-0, Pub. by Mukhopadhyay India). South Asia Bks.

Chakravarti, Sri S. Be Your Own Guru. 1971. pap. 2.50 (ISBN 0-685-58384-8). Ranney Pubns.

--Samadhi & Beyond. LC 74-79444. 1974. pap. 3.50 (ISBN 0-87707-135-7). Ranney Pubns.

--Scientific Yoga for the Man of Today. 1971. pap. 3.50 (ISBN 0-685-58385-6). Ranney Pubns.

Chakravarti, Sri S., ed. Hidden Treasure of the Gospel of Sri Ramakrishna. 1975. Repr. of 1907 ed. 6.25 (ISBN 0-685-58386-4). Ranney Pubns.

Chakravartinayanan, A., ed. see Kundakunda Acharya.

Chakravarty, Amiya. The Indian Testimony. 1983. pap. 2.50x (ISBN 0-87574-072-3, 072). Pendle Hill.

Chakravarty, Sarat C. Nag Mahasaya: A Saintly Householder Disciple of Sri Ramakrishna. 1978. pap. 2.25 (ISBN 0-87481-481-2). Vedanta Pr.

Chakravarty, Sharat C. Talks with Swami Vivekananda. 6.95 (ISBN 0-87481-156-2). Vedanta Pr.

Chalandon, Ferdinand. Histoire de la premiere croisade jusqu'a l'election de Godefroi de Bouillon. 380p. 1972. Repr. of 1925 ed. lib. bdg. 25.50 (ISBN 0-8337-0515-6). B Franklin.

Chalfant, H. Paul & Beckley, Robert E. Religion in Contemporary Society. 500p. 1986. text ed. 28.95 (ISBN 0-87484-691-9). Mayfield Pub.
Chalfant, Paul H. & Beckley, Robert E. Religion in Contemporary Society. Palmer, C. Eddie, ed. 592p. 1981. Repr. text ed. 28.95 (ISBN 0-87484-691-9). Mayfield Pub.
Chalfant, William B., ed. Ancient Champions of Oneness. Rev. ed. (Illus.). 156p. 1982. pap. 5.95 (ISBN 0-912315-41-5). Word Aflame.
Chalidze, Valery. The Soviet Human Rights Movement: A Memoir. LC 84-72146. xii, 50p. 1984. pap. 2.50 (ISBN 0-87495-064-3). AM Jewish Comm.
Chalk, John A. Jesus' Church. Thomas, J. D., ed. (Twentieth Century Sermons Ser). 1969. 11.95 (ISBN 0-89112-303-2, Bibl Res Pr). Abilene Christ U.
Chalkley, Thomas. The Journal of Thomas Chalkley. LC 75-31088. (Incl. a collection of author's works). Repr. of 1808 ed. 45.00 (ISBN 0-404-13506-4). AMS Pr.
Challenor, John, jt. auth. see Blenkinsopp, Joseph.
Challgren, Patricia, ed. see Lohr, Andrew.
Challoner. Out of Chaos. 6.95 (ISBN 0-8356-5051-0). Theos Pub Hse.
--Regents of Seven Spheres. 8.75 (ISBN 0-8356-5009-X). Theos Pub Hse.
--What of Tomorrow. 5.95 (ISBN 0-8356-5300-5). Theos Pub Hse.
Challoner, H. K. The Path of Healing. LC 76-3660. 175p. 1976. pap. 5.25 (ISBN 0-8356-0480-2, Quest). Theos Pub Hse.
--Path of Healing. 10.50 (ISBN 0-8356-5227-0). Theos Pub Hse.
Chalmers, John I., jt. ed. see Chalmers, Patrick.
Chalmers, Patrick. Ancient Sculptured Monuments of the County of Angus. LC 72-1052. (Bannatyne Club, Edinburgh. Publications: No. 88). Repr. of 1848 ed. 145.00 (ISBN 0-404-52818-X). AMS Pr.
Chalmers, Patrick & Chalmers, John I., eds. Registrum Episcopatus Brechinensis, 2 Vols. LC 72-39524. (Bannatyne Club, Edinburgh. Publications: No. 102). Repr. of 1856 ed. Set. 110.00 (ISBN 0-404-52855-4). AMS Pr.
Chamber, John. A Treatise Against Iudicial Astrologie, 2 pts. LC 77-6872. (English Experience Ser.: No. 860). 1977. Repr. of 1601 ed. lib. bdg. 20.00 (ISBN 90-221-0860-0). Walter J Johnson.
Chamberas, Peter A., tr. see Kalokyris, Constantine D.
Chamberlain. When Can a Child Believe. LC 73-80778. pap. 4.95 (ISBN 0-8054-6208-2). Broadman.
Chamberlain, Eugene. Jesus: God's Son, Saviour, Lord. (BibLearn Ser.). (Illus.). pap. 5.95 (ISBN 0-8054-4226-X, 4242-26). Broadman.
--Loyd Corder: Traveler for God. LC 82-73663. (Meet the Missionary Ser.). 1983. 5.50 (ISBN 0-8054-4284-7, 4242-84). Broadman.
Chamberlain, Gary, tr. The Psalms: A New Translation for Prayer & Worship. LC 84-50842. 192p. (Orig.). 1984. pap. 6.95 (ISBN 0-8358-0485-2). Upper Room.
--Psalms for Singing: Twenty-Six Psalms with Musical Settings for Congregation & Choir. LC 84-50778. 141p. (Orig.). 1984. pap. 7.50 (ISBN 0-8358-0495-X). Upper Room.
Chamberlain, Jonathan M. Eliminate Your SDBS: Self-Defeating Behaviors. LC 77-27634. (Illus.). 1978. pap. 7.95 (ISBN 0-8425-0998-4). Brigham.
Chamberlain, Samuel. Stroll Through Historic Salem. LC 78-79738. (Illus.). 1969. student ed. 9.95 (ISBN 0-8038-6689-5). Hastings.
Chamberlain, Von Del see Von Del Chamberlain.
Chamberlain, William D. Exegetical Grammar of the Greek New Testament. 1979. pap. 7.95 (ISBN 0-8010-2438-2). Baker Bk.
Chamberlane, C. G., ed. The Vestry Book of Petsworth Parish, Glouster County, Virginia, 1670-1793. LC 79-13640. xv, 429p. 1979. Repr. of 1933 ed. 10.00 (ISBN 0-88490-032-0). VA State Lib.
Chamberlayne, C. G. The Vestry Book & Register of St. Peter's Parish, New Kent & James City Counties, Virginia, 1684-1786. xxvi, 840p. 1973. Repr. of 1937 ed. 12.50 (ISBN 0-88490-037-1). VA State Lib.
Chamberlayne, C. G., ed. The Vestry Book of Blisland (Blissland) Parish, New Kent & James City Counties, Virginia, 1721-1786. LC 79-16401. ixii, 277p. 1979. Repr. of 1935 ed. 10.00 (ISBN 0-88490-030-4). VA State Lib.
--The Vestry Book of St. Paul's Parish, Hanover County, Virginia, 1706-1786. xx, 672p. 1973. Repr. of 1940 ed. 12.50 (ISBN 0-88490-038-X). VA State Lib.
Chamberlin, Roxanna, ed. see Shell, Harvey.
Chamberlyne, C. G., ed. The Vestry Book of Stratton Major Parish, King & Queen County, Virginia, 1729-1783. LC 80-14672. xxi, 257p. 1980. Repr. of 1933 ed. 10.00 (ISBN 0-88490-087-8). VA State Lib.
Chambers, B. Bibliography of French Bibles: Fifteenth & Sixteenth Century French Language Editions of the Bible. 572p. (Orig.). 1983. pap. text ed. 67.50x (Pub. by Droz Switzerland). Coronet Bks.
Chambers, Calvin H. In Spirit & in Truth: Charismatic Worship & the Reformed Tradition. 168p. 1980. 7.95 (ISBN 0-8059-2686-0). Dorrance.
Chambers, Catherine, jt. auth. see Morgan, Nell.
Chambers, Claire. The Siecus Circle. LC 75-41650. 1977. pap. 6.95 (ISBN 0-88279-119-2). Western Islands.
Chambers, Joseph E. Micacles, My Father's Delight. 136p. (Orig.). text ed. 8.95 (ISBN 0-87148-585-0); pap. 6.95 (ISBN 0-87148-586-9). Pathway Pr.
Chambers, Oswald. Biblical Ethics. 1964. 2.95 (ISBN 0-87508-102-9). Chr Lit.
--Biblical Psychology. 1973. pap. 3.95 (ISBN 0-87508-099-5). Chr Lit.
--Daily Thoughts-Disciples. 1983. pap. 5.95 (ISBN 0-87508-143-6). Chr Lit.
--Daily Thoughts for Disciples. 1976. 10.95 (ISBN 0-310-22400-4). Zondervan.
--Daily Thoughts for Disciples. 208p. 1985. 8.95 (ISBN 0-310-30470-9). Zondervan.
--Devotions for a Deeper Life. Black, Glenn D., ed. 320p. 1986. 10.95 (ISBN 0-310-38710-8, 17070). Zondervan.
--He Shall Glorify Me. 1965. 3.95 (ISBN 0-87508-111-8). Chr Lit.
--If Thou Wilt Be Perfect. 1962. pap. 2.95 (ISBN 0-87508-113-4). Chr Lit.
--Moral Foundations of Life. 1961. pap. 2.95 (ISBN 0-87508-117-7). Chr Lit.
--Not Knowing Whither. 1957. pap. 2.95 (ISBN 0-87508-118-5). Chr Lit.
--Our Brilliant Heritage. 1965. pap. 2.95 (ISBN 0-87508-120-7). Chr Lit.
--Our Portrait in Genesis. 1973. pap. 2.25 (ISBN 0-87508-135-5). Chr Lit.
--Philosophy of Sin. 1961. pap. 2.25 (ISBN 0-87508-122-3). Chr Lit.
--Place of Help. 1973. pap. 2.95 (ISBN 0-87508-139-8). Chr Lit.
--Psychology of Redemption. 1955. pap. 2.95 (ISBN 0-87508-124-X). Chr Lit.
--Servant As His Lord. 1973. pap. 2.95 (ISBN 0-87508-137-1). Chr Lit.
--Shade of His Hand. 1961. pap. 2.95 (ISBN 0-87508-127-4). Chr Lit.
--So Send I You. 1973. pap. 2.95 (ISBN 0-87508-138-X). Chr Lit.
--Still Higher for His Highest. 192p. 1970. 6.95 (ISBN 0-87508-142-8). Chr Lit.
--Still Higher for His Highest. LC 75-120048. 1970. Repr. of 1970 ed. 8.95 (ISBN 0-310-22410-1, 6494); large print 6.95 (ISBN 0-310-22417-9, 12565L). Zondervan.
--Studies in the Sermon on the Mount. 1973. pap. 2.95 (ISBN 0-87508-136-3). Chr Lit.
--Workmen of God. 1965. pap. 2.95 (ISBN 0-87508-131-2). Chr Lit.
Chambers, R. W. Place of Saint Thomas More in English Literature & History. LC 65-15870. (English Biography Ser., No. 31). 1969. Repr. of 1937 ed. lib. bdg. 75.00x (ISBN 0-8383-0523-7). Haskell.
--Poets & Their Critics: Langland & Milton. 1942. lib. bdg. 10.00 (ISBN 0-685-10478-8). Folcroft.
--The Saga & the Myth of Sir Thomas More. 1978. Repr. of 1927 ed. lib. bdg. 15.00 (ISBN 0-8495-0744-8). Arden Lib.
--Text of Piers Plowman. LC 72-195253. lib. bdg. 10.00 (ISBN 0-8414-3015-2). Folcroft.
Chambers, R. W., jt. ed. see Hitchcock, Elsie V.
Chambers, Raymond W. Saga & Myth of Sir Thomas More. 1926. lib. bdg. 10.00 (ISBN 0-8414-3642-8). Folcroft.
Chambers, Robert, ed. Book of Days: A Miscellany of Popular Antiquities in Connection with the Calendar, Including Anecdote, Biography & History, Curiosities of Literature, & Oddities of Human Life & Character, 2 Vols. LC 67-13009. (Illus.). 1967. Repr. of 1862 ed. 125.00x (ISBN 0-8103-3002-4). Gale.
Chametzky, Jules. Our Decentralized Literature: Cultural Mediations in Selected Jewish & Southern Writers. LC 86-1259. 168p. 1986. lib. bdg. 25.00x (ISBN 0-87023-527-3); pap. text ed. 9.95 (ISBN 0-87023-540-0). U of Mass Pr.
Chamie, Joseph. Religion & Fertility: Arab Christian-Muslim Differentials. LC 80-19787. (ASA Rose Monograph). (Illus.). 176p. 1981. 29.95 (ISBN 0-521-23677-0); pap. 9.95 (ISBN 0-521-28147-4). Cambridge U Pr.
Chamier, Adrian C., ed. Les Actes des Colloques des Eglises Francaises et des Synodes: (Huguenot Society, Vols. 204) Bd. with Register of the Protestant Church at Guisnes. Minet, William, ed. Repr. of 1891 ed; Registre Des Baptesmes, Mariages & Mortz. Marett, Humphrey, ed. Repr. of 1890 ed. 93.00 (ISBN 0-8115-1643-1). Kraus Repr.
Champaklal. Champaklal Speaks. (Illus.). 275p. 1975. pap. 7.25 (ISBN 0-89071-278-6). Matagiri.
--Champaklal's Treasures. (Illus.). 234p. 1976. pap. 5.25 (ISBN 0-89071-279-4). Matagiri.
Champion, Richard G. Go on Singing. LC 76-20889. (Radiant Life). 128p. 1976. tchr's ed 3.95 (ISBN 0-88243-169-2, 32-0169); pap. 2.50 (ISBN 0-88243-895-6, 02-0895). Gospel Pub.
Champion, Selwyn G. The Eleven Religions & Their Proverbial Lore: A Comparative Study. 1979. Repr. of 1945 ed. lib. bdg. 30.00 (ISBN 0-8492-3856-0). R West.
--The Eleven Religions & Their Proverbial Lore: A Comparative Study. 340p. 1985. Repr. of 1945 ed. lib. bdg. 75.00 (ISBN 0-8492-4102-2). R West.
Champlin, David. The Lord Is Present. 7.95 (ISBN 0-87193-175-3). Dimension Bks.
Champlin, Joseph. Healing in the Catholic Church: Mending Wounded Hearts & Bodies. LC 84-62226. 160p. 1985. pap. 5.50 (ISBN 0-87973-719-0, 719). Our Sunday Visitor.
--Special Signs of Grace: The Seven Sacraments & Sacramentals. (Illus.). 160p. 1986. pap. 6.95 (ISBN 0-8146-1466-3). Liturgical Pr.
Champlin, Joseph M. Behind Closed Doors: A Handbook on How to Pray. 240p. (Orig.). 1984. pap. 8.95 (ISBN 0-8091-2637-0). Paulist Pr.
--An Important Office of Immense Love: A Handbook for Eucharistic Ministers. LC 80-80085. 152p. (Orig.). 1980. pap. 4.95 (ISBN 0-8091-2287-1). Paulist Pr.
--Messengers of God's Word: A Handbook for Lectors. 1983. pap. 4.95 (ISBN 0-8091-2484-X). Paulist Pr.
--The Proper Balance. LC 81-68000. 144p. (Orig.). 1981. pap. 3.95 (ISBN 0-87793-233-6). Ave Maria.
--Sharing Treasure, Time, & Talent: A Parish Manual for Sacrificial Giving or Tithing. LC 82-16178. 88p. (Orig.). 1982. pap. 4.95 (ISBN 0-8146-1277-6). Liturgical Pr.
--Through Death to Life. LC 78-74436. 88p. 1979. pap. 1.95 (ISBN 0-87793-175-5). Ave Maria.
--Together by Your Side: A Book for Comforting the Sick & Dying. LC 79-51016. 80p. 1979. pap. 1.95 (ISBN 0-87793-180-1). Ave Maria.
--Together for Life: Regular Edition. rev. ed. (Illus.). 96p. 1970. pap. 1.50 (ISBN 0-87793-018-X). Ave Maria.
--Together for Life: Special Edition for Marriage Outside Mass. rev. ed. (Illus.). 96p. 1972. pap. 1.50 (ISBN 0-87793-118-6). Ave Maria.
--Together in Peace: Penitents Edition. 104p. (Orig.). 1975. pap. 1.50 (ISBN 0-87793-095-3). Ave Maria.
--Together in Peace: Priests Edition. (Illus.). 272p. 1975. pap. 3.95 (ISBN 0-87793-094-5). Ave Maria.
Champlin, Joseph M. & Haggerty, Brian A. Together in Peace for Children. LC 76-26348. (Illus.). 72p. 1976. 1.50 (ISBN 0-87793-119-4). Ave Maria.
Chan, Hok-Lam & DeBary, W. Theodore, eds. Yuan Thought: Chinese Thought & Religion Under the Mongols. LC 82-1259. 512p. 1982. 39.00x (ISBN 0-231-05324-X). Columbia U Pr.
Chan, Silas. A Biographical Sketch of G. Campbell Morgan. (Chinese.). 1984. pap. write for info. (ISBN 0-941598-21-7). Living Spring Pubns.
Chan, Silas, tr. see Allen, R.
Chan, Silas, tr. see Forster, Roger & Marston, Paul.
Chan, Silas, tr. see Morgan, G. Campbell.
Chan, Silas, tr. see Ramm, Bernard.
Chan, Silas, tr. see Stott, John R.
Chan, Sin-wai. Buddhism in Late Ch'ing Political Thought. 191p. 1985. 31.50x (ISBN 0-8133-0256-0). Westview.
Chan, W., ed. see Takakusu, J.
Chan, Wing T. & Alfaruqi, Ismael R. Great Asian Religions. 1969. pap. write for info. (ISBN 0-02-320640-3, 32064). Macmillan.
Chan, Wing-Tsit. The Way of Lao Tzu. 1963. pap. text ed. write for info. (ISBN 0-02-320700-0). Macmillan.
Chan, Wing-Tsit, ed. Chu Hsi & Neo-Confucianism. LC 85-24532. (Illus.). 672p. 1986. 30.00x (ISBN 0-8248-0961-0). UH Pr.
Chan, Wing-Tsit, tr. from Chinese. Neo-Confucian Terms Explained: The Pei-hsi tzu-i. LC 86-5427. (Neo-Confucian Studies Ser.). 288p. 1986. 35.00x (ISBN 0-231-06384-9). Columbia U Pr.
Chan, Wing-Tsit, jt. tr. see Rump, Ariane.
Chan, Wing tsit, tr. see Yang Ming, Wang.
Chan, Wing Tstit, tr. Reflections on Things at Hand: The Neo-Confucian Anthology. LC 65-22548. (Records of Civilization Sources Studies). 441p. 1967. 38.00x (ISBN 0-231-02819-9); pap. 16.00x (ISBN 0-231-06037-8). Columbia U Pr.
Chance, Hugh E., jt. auth. see Braun, Eunice.
Chancellor, John. Flowers & Fruits of the Bible. LC 81-69042. (Illus.). 64p. 1982. 14.95 (ISBN 0-8253-0085-1). Beaufort Bks NY.
Chandler. The Trial of Jesus. (Illus.). 24.95 (ISBN 0-686-90784-1); deluxe ed. 44.95 (ISBN 0-686-90785-X); pap. 9.95 (ISBN 0-686-90786-8). Harrison Co GA.
Chandler, Alfred D., ed. see Urwick, Lyndall.
Chandler, Linda S. When I Talk to God. LC 84-4967. (Illus.). 1984. 5.95 (ISBN 0-8054-4291-X, 4242-91). Broadman.
Chandler, Maggie. Seek Ye First: Song of Solomon. 128p. 1979. pap. 2.50 (ISBN 0-89114-089-1). Baptist Pub Hse.
Chandler, Mary. The Pastoral Associate & the Lay Pastor. 72p. 1986. pap. 3.95 (ISBN 0-8146-1470-1). Liturgical Pr.
Chandler, Phyllis & Burney, Joan. Sharing the Faith with Your Child: From Birth to Age Six. 96p. 1984. pap. 2.25 (ISBN 0-89243-205-5). Liguori Pubns.
Chandler, Robert, et al. The Church Handbook: A Creative Guide for Churches. Gardner, Anna Marie, ed. 224p. (Orig.). 1986. pap. text ed. 16.95 (ISBN 0-9616767-0-1). David Pub MN.
Chandler, Ted E. How to Have Good Health. LC 81-68045. 1982. 7.95 (ISBN 0-8054-5298-2). Broadman.
Chandler, Tertius. Godly Kings & Early Ethics. rev. ed. (Illus.). 220p. 1981. 24.00 (ISBN 0-9603872-4-2). Gutenberg.
--Moses & the Golden Age. (Illus.). 88p. 1986. 9.95 (ISBN 0-8059-3024-8). Dorrance.
Chandler, Walter M. The Trial of Jesus from a Lawyer's Standpoint, 2 vols. LC 83-82312. 1983. Repr. of 1925 ed. 115.00 set (ISBN 0-89941-294-7). W S Hein.
Chandless, William. Visit to Salt Lake. LC 76-134391. Repr. of 1857 ed. 24.50 (ISBN 0-404-08434-6). AMS Pr.
Chandmal, Asit. One Thousand Moons: Krishnamurti at Eighty-Five. (Illus.). 128p. 1985. 25.00 (ISBN 0-8109-1209-0). Abrams.
Chandra, Pramod. Studies in Indian Temple Architecture. LC 75-904089. 1975. 40.00x (ISBN 0-88386-649-8). South Asia Bks.
Chaney, Charles. Church Planting in America at the End of the Twentieth Century. 128p. 1982. pap. 6.95 (ISBN 0-8423-0279-4). Tyndale.
Chaney, Charles L. Birth of Missions in America. LC 75-26500. 352p. 1976. pap. 7.95 (ISBN 0-87808-146-1). William Carey Lib.
Chaney, Charles L. & Lewis, Ron S. Design for Church Growth. LC 77-87364. 1978. pap. 6.95 (ISBN 0-8054-6218-X). Broadman.
--Manual for Design for Church Growth. 1978. pap. text ed. 2.50 (ISBN 0-8054-6219-8). Broadman.
Chaney, Earlyne. The Masters & Astara. 2nd ed. (Illus.). 100p. 1982. pap. 8.95 (ISBN 0-918936-13-6). Astara.
Chaney, Earlyne & Messick, William L. Kundalini & the Third Eye. Chaney, Sita, ed. LC 80-67635. (Illus.). 127p. 1982. pap. 12.95 (ISBN 0-918936-08-X). Astara.
Chaney, Earlyne C. Revelations of Things to Come. (Illus.). 156p. 1982. pap. 13.95 (ISBN 0-918936-12-8). Astara.
Chaney, Robert. Mysticism: The Journey Within. LC 79-52959. 1979. softcover 12.50 (ISBN 0-918936-06-3). Astara.
Chaney, Robert, jt. auth. see Pevarnik, Carrie.
Chaney, Robert G. The Essenes & Their Ancient Mysteries. (Adventures in Esoteric Learning Ser.). 1968. pap. 4.25 (ISBN 0-918936-14-4). Astara.
--Reincarnation: Cycle of Opportunity. LC 84-72387. (Adventures in Esoteric Learning Ser.). (Illus.). 56p. 1984. pap. 4.25 (ISBN 0-918936-13-6). Astara.
Chaney, Sita, ed. see Chaney, Earlyne & Messick, William L.
Chang, C. C. Buddhist Teaching of Totality. LC 70-136965. 1971. 24.50x (ISBN 0-271-01179-3); pap. 14.95x (ISBN 0-271-01142-4). Pa St U Pr.
Chang, Carsun. The Development of Neo-Confucian Thought. LC 77-8338. 1977. Repr. of 1957 ed. lib. bdg. 26.75x (ISBN 0-8371-9693-0, CHDN). Greenwood.
--The Development of Neo-Confucian Thought, Vol. 1. 1957. pap. 10.95x (ISBN 0-8084-0105-X); 14.95x (ISBN 0-8084-0104-1). New Coll U Pr.
Chang, Chung-Li, jt. auth. see Michael, Franz.
Chang, David, tr. see Morgan, G. Campbell.
Chang, Garma C. The Six Yogas of Naropa & Mahamudra. 2nd ed. LC 86-10020. 128p. 1986. pap. 9.95 (ISBN 0-937938-33-5). Snow Lion.
--Teachings of Tibetan Yoga. 128p. 1974. pap. 3.45 (ISBN 0-8065-0460-9). Citadel Pr.
Chang, Garma C., tr. from Tibetan. The Hundred Thousand Songs of Milarepa, 2 Vols. LC 76-55120. 1977. pap. 14.95 ea.; Vol. 1, 356p. (ISBN 0-87773-095-4, 73346-0); Vol. 2, 374p. (ISBN 0-87773-096-2, 72996-X). Shambhala Pubns.

Chang, Garma C. C., ed. A Treasury of Mahayana Sutras: Selections from the Maharatnakuta Sutra. Buddhist Association of the United States, tr. from Chinese. LC 82-42776. (Institute for Advanced Study of World Religions (IASWR) Ser.). 512p. 1983. 26.75x (ISBN 0-271-00341-3). Pa St U Pr.

Chang, Jolan. The Tao of the Loving Couple: True Liberation Through the Tao. (Illus.). 129p. 1983. pap. 8.95 (ISBN 0-525-48042-0, 0869-260). Dutton.

Chang, Lit-Sen. Transcendental Meditation. 1978. pap. 2.95 (ISBN 0-87552-133-9). Presby & Reformed.

--True Gospel vs. Social Activism. 1976. pap. 0.60 (ISBN 0-87552-134-7). Presby & Reformed.

Chang, Stephen T. Complete System of Self-Healing. LC 86-1859. (Illus.). 224p. 1986. 17.00 (ISBN 0-942196-06-6). Tao Pub.

--The Great Tao. (Illus.). 464p. 1985. 26.00 (ISBN 0-942196-01-5). Tao Pub.

--The Tao of Sexology. (Illus.). 224p. 1985. 17.00 (ISBN 0-942196-03-1). Tao Pub.

Chang Cheng-Chi. The Practice of Zen. LC 78-618. 1978. Repr. of 1959 ed. lib. bdg. 29.75x (ISBN 0-313-20264-8, CHPZ). Greenwood.

Chang Chung-Yuan. Creativity & Taoism. (Illus.). 1970. pap. 6.95x (ISBN 0-06-131968-6, TB1968, Torch). Har-Row.

Chang Chung-Yuan, ed. The Original Teachings of Ch'an Buddhism. LC 82-48003. (Grove Press Eastern Philosophy & Religion Ser.). 320p. 1982. pap. 9.95 (ISBN 0-394-62417-3, E813, Ever). Grove.

Chang Po-tuan & Liu I-ming. The Inner Teachings of Taoism. Cleary, Thomas, tr. from Chinese. & intro. by. LC 86-11841. 100p. (Orig.). 1986. pap. 9.95 (ISBN 0-87773-363-5). Shambhala Pubns.

Chanler, Julie. His Messengers Went Forth. facs. ed. LC 77-148209. (Biography Index Reprint Ser.). (Illus.). 1948. 13.00 (ISBN 0-8369-8056-5). Ayer Co Pubs.

Channa, V. C. Hinduism. 1985. 17.50x (ISBN 0-8364-1451-9, Pub. by National Sahitya Akademi). South Asia Bks.

Channer, Burley, tr. see Richter, Gottfried.

Channer, J. H., ed. Abortion & the Sanctity of Human Life. 160p. 1986. pap. 7.50 (ISBN 0-85364-417-9, Pub. by Paternoster UK). Attic Pr.

Channing, William. Character & Writings of John Milton. 1826. lib. bdg. 8.50 (ISBN 0-8414-3465-4). Folcroft.

Channing, William E. Remarks on the Character & Writings of John Milton. 3rd ed. LC 72-966. Repr. of 1828 ed. 12.50 (ISBN 0-404-01448-8). AMS Pr.

--Works of William Ellery Channing, 2 vols. in 1. LC 70-114815. (Research & Source Works Ser.: No. 626). 1971. Repr. of 1882 ed. lib. bdg. 46.50 (ISBN 0-8337-0530-X). B Franklin.

Chanover, Alice, jt. auth. see Chanover, Hyman.

Chanover, Hyman. Haggadah for the School. (Illus.). 1964. pap. 2.25x (ISBN 0-8381-0175-5). United Syn Bk.

Chanover, Hyman & Chanover, Alice. Pesah Is Coming. (Holiday Series of Picture Story Books). (Illus.). 1956. 5.95 (ISBN 0-8381-0713-3, 10-713). United Syn Bk.

--Pesah Is Here. (Holiday Series of Picture Story Books). (Illus.). 1956. 5.95 (ISBN 0-8381-0714-1). United Syn Bk.

Chanover, Hyman & Zusman, Evelyn. A Book of Prayer for Junior Congregations: Sabbath & Festivals. (Eng. & Hebrew.). 256p. 4.50x (ISBN 0-8381-0174-7, 10-174). United Syn Bk.

Chanover, Hyman, adapted by. Service for the High Holy Days Adapted for Youth. new ed. LC 72-2058. 192p. 1972. pap. 3.95x (ISBN 0-87441-123-8). Behrman.

Chanover, Hyman, ed. see Rossel, Seymour.

Chantre, Jean-Claude. Les Considerations Religieuses et Esthetiques D'un "Sturmer und Dranger". (European University Studies: No.1, Vol. 507). (Fr.). 650p. 1982. 62.10 (ISBN 3-261-04989-8). P Lang Pubs.

Chantry, Walter. Signs of the Apostles. 1979. pap. 3.95 (ISBN 0-85151-175-9). Banner of Truth.

--Today's Gospel. 1980. pap. 3.45 (ISBN 0-85151-027-2). Banner of Truth.

Chantry, Walter J. God's Righteous Kingdom. 151p. (Orig.). 1980. pap. 4.95 (ISBN 0-85151-310-7). Banner of Truth.

--Shadow of the Cross: Studies in Self-denial. 79p. (Orig.). 1981. pap. 3.45 (ISBN 0-85151-331-X). Banner of Truth.

Chao, Loran Y., tr. see Cockman, Nelda.

Chao, Lorna, tr. see Morgan, G. Campbell.

Chao, Lorna, tr. see Sanders, J. Oswald.

Chao, Lorna Y., tr. see Clark, Robert.

Chao, Lorna Y., tr. see Dunn, Ronald.

Chao, Lorna Y., tr. see Flynn, Leslie B.

Chao, Lorna Y., tr. see Long, James.

Chao, Lorna Y., tr. see S. P. Publications Editors.

Chao, Lorna Y., tr. see Shelly, Bruce L.

Chao, Samuel, tr. see Sanders, J. Oswald.

Chapian, Marie. Am I the Only One Here with Faded Genes? (Teen Devotionals Ser.). (Illus.). 192p. 1987. pap. 5.95 (ISBN 0-87123-945-0). Bethany Hse.

--Free to Be Thin. LC 79-15656. (Illus.). 192p. 1979. pap. 5.95 (ISBN 0-87123-560-9, 210560); study guide (No. 1) by Neva Coyle 64 pgs. 2.50 (ISBN 0-87123-163-8, 210163). Bethany Hse.

--Love & Be Loved. 192p. 1983. pap. 6.95 (ISBN 0-8007-5092-6, Power Bks). Revell.

--Of Whom the World Was Not Worthy. LC 78-769. (Illus.). 256p. 1978. pap. 6.95 (ISBN 0-87123-250-2, 210417). Bethany Hse.

Chapian, Marie, jt. auth. see Backus, William.

Chapian, Marie, jt. auth. see Coyle, Neva.

Chapin, Alice. Building Your Child's Faith. 144p. (Orig.). 1983. pap. 5.95 (ISBN 0-86605-115-5). Campus Crusade.

Chapin, Edwin H. Humanity in the City. LC 73-11901. (Metropolitan America Ser.). 254p. 1974. Repr. 19.00 (ISBN 0-405-05389-4). Ayer Co Pubs.

Chaplan, Marie, jt. auth. see Backus, William.

Chaplin, Dorothea. Mythological Bonds Between East & West. 1976. lib. bdg. 59.95 (ISBN 0-8490-2325-4). Gordon Pr.

Chapman, Abraham, ed. Jewish-American Literature: An Anthology. 727p. pap. 2.25 (ISBN 0-686-95132-8). ADL.

Chapman, Arthur G. & Wray, Robert D. Christmas Trees for Pleasure & Profit. rev. ed. 220p. 1984. pap. text ed. 14.95 (ISBN 0-8135-1074-0). Rutgers U Pr.

Chapman, Ben, ed. see Harper, Steve.

Chapman, Ben, ed. see Hynson, Leon O.

Chapman, Benjamin. Card-Guide to New Testament Exegesis. 2.95 (ISBN 0-8010-2396-3). Baker Bk.

--Card-Guide to New Testament Greek. 1.95 (ISBN 0-8010-2388-2). Baker Bk.

--Greek New Testament Insert. 1.95 (ISBN 0-8010-2405-6). Baker Bk.

--New Testament Greek Notebook. 1976. looseleaf 19.95 (ISBN 0-8010-2389-0). Baker Bk.

--New Testament: Greek Notebook Exegesis Filler. 1.00 (ISBN 0-8010-2425-0). Baker Bk.

Chapman, Colin. The Case for Christianity. (Illus.). 313p. 1984. pap. 12.95 (ISBN 0-8028-1984-2). Eerdmans.

Chapman, F. Spencer. Lhasa the Holy City. facsimile ed. LC 75-37875. (Select Bibliographies Reprint Ser). Repr. of 1940 ed. 32.00 (ISBN 0-8369-6712-7). Ayer Co Pubs.

Chapman, G. Clarke. Facing the Nuclear Heresy. Eller, David, ed. 224p. (Orig.). 1986. pap. 9.95 (ISBN 0-87178-225-1). Brethren.

Chapman, Gary. Now That You Are Single Again. 80p. 1985. wkbk. 3.95 (ISBN 0-89840-087-2). Heres Life.

--Toward a Growing Marriage. LC 79-21376. 1979. pap. 5.95 (ISBN 0-8024-8787-4). Moody.

Chapman, Gary D. Hope for the Separated. LC 81-18667. 160p. 1982. pap. 5.95 (ISBN 0-8024-3616-1). Moody.

Chapman, Geoffrey. Book of Gospels. (Illus.). 672p. 1985. 95.00 (ISBN 0-225-66351-1, HarpR). Har-Row.

--Lectionary, 3 vols. 3500p. 1985. Vol. 1: The Proper of the Seasons, Sundays in Ordinary Time. 60.00 (ISBN 0-225-66350-3, HarpR). Vol. 2: Weekdays in Ordinary Time, Proper of Saints, Commons. Vol. 3: Rituals Celebrations, Masses for Various Needs & Occasions, Votive Masses, Masses for the Dead. Har-Row.

Chapman, H. John. Studies on the Early Papacy. LC 76-118517. 1971. Repr. of 1928 ed. 23.00x (ISBN 0-8046-1139-4, Pub. by Kennikat). Assoc Faculty Pr.

Chapman, John. Saint Benedict & the Sixth Century. LC 79-109719. 239p. 1972. Repr. of 1929 ed. lib. bdg. 22.50x (ISBN 0-8371-4209-1, CHSB). Greenwood.

Chapman, John J. Letters & Religion. 1977. Repr. 29.00x (ISBN 0-403-07361-8). Scholarly.

Chapman, Marie. Fun with Bible Geography. LC 80-65055. (Teaching Aid Ser.). 65p. 1980. plastic spiral 5.95 (ISBN 0-89636-044-X). Accent Bks.

Chapman, Marie M. Puppet Animals Tell Bible Stories. LC 77-75134. (Illus.). 1977. tchr's ed. spiral bdg. 4.95 (ISBN 0-916406-74-1). Accent Bks.

Chapman, Morris H., compiled by. Jesus: Author & Finisher. 1987. pap. 6.95 (ISBN 0-8054-5047-5). Broadman.

Chappell, Clovis G. The Best of C. G. Chappell. (Best Ser.). 240p. 1984. pap. 5.95 (ISBN 0-8010-2500-1). Baker Bk.

--Chappell's Special Day Sermons. (Pocket Pulpit Library Ser.). 204p. 1983. pap. 4.50 (ISBN 0-8010-2383-1). Baker Bk.

--The Sermon on the Mount. (Pulpit Libaray Ser). 1979. pap. 4.95 (ISBN 0-8010-2363-7). Baker Bk.

--Sermons on Biblical Characters. (Pocket Pulpit Lib.). 192p. 1981. pap. 3.95 (ISBN 0-8010-2330-0). Baker Bk.

--The Seven Words: The Words of Jesus on the Cross Reveal the Heart of the Christian Faith. (Pocket Pulpit Library). 80p. 1976. pap. 2.95 (ISBN 0-8010-2387-4). Baker Bk.

Chappell, David W., ed. Buddhist & Taoist Practice in Medieval Chinese Society: Buddhist & Taoist Studies II. (Asian Studies at Hawaii: No. 34). 256p. 1987. pap. text ed. 18.00x (ISBN 0-8248-0957-2). UH Pr.

Chappell, David W., jt. ed. see Saso, Michael.

Chapple, Christopher. Karma & Creativity. (Religion Ser.). 128p. (Orig.). 1986. 29.50x (ISBN 0-88706-250-4); pap. 9.95x (ISBN 0-88706-251-2). State U NY Pr.

Chapple, Christopher, ed. Samkhya-Yoga: Proceedings of the IASWR Conference, 1981. 181p. 1983. pap. text ed. 10.00 (ISBN 0-915078-04-X). Inst Adv Stud Wld.

Chapple, Christopher, ed. see Sargeant, Winthrop.

Character Research Project Staff, jt. auth. see Ligon, Ernest M.

Chardenal, Valerie, tr. see Dobbins, Richard D.

Chardin, Pierre Teilhard De see Teilhard De Chardin, Pierre.

Chardin, Teilhard de see De Chardin, Teilhard.

Charette, Beverly. Deluxe Story of Easter for Children. (Illus.). 48p. 1985. 5.95 (ISBN 0-8249-8076-X). Ideals.

Chari, S. M. Advaita & Visistadvaita. 2nd ed. 1976. 11.95 (ISBN 0-8426-0886-9). Orient Bk Dist.

--Fundamentals of Visistadvaita Vedanta. 1987. 36.00 (Pub. by Motilal Banarsidass). South Asia Bks.

Charing, Douglas. The Jewish World. LC 83-50693. (Religions of the World Ser.). 48p. 1983. PLB 14.96 (ISBN 0-382-06720-7); 9.25 (ISBN 0-382-06930-7). Silver.

Charish, Chandra B. Sacred City of Anuradhapura. (Illus.). 132p. 1986. Repr. 26.00X (ISBN 0-8364-1746-1, Pub. by Abhinav India). South Asia Bks.

Chariton, Igumen. The Art of Prayer. Kadloubovsky, Palmer, tr. 288p. 1966. 26.95 (ISBN 0-571-06899-5). Faber & Faber.

Charitos, Minas, jt. auth. see Livadeas, Themistocles.

Charity, Alan. Events & Their Afterlife: The Dialectics of Christian Typology in the Bible & Dante. 300p. Date not set. pap. price not set (ISBN 0-521-34923-0). Cambridge U Pr.

Charland, William A., Jr. Decide to Live. LC 79-9563. 156p. 1979. pap. 6.95 (ISBN 0-664-24277-4). Westminster.

Charlebois, Robert, et al. Saints for Kids by Kids. 80p. 1984. pap. 2.95 (ISBN 0-89243-223-3). Liguori Pubns.

Charles, Elizabeth R. Luther: By Those Who Knew Him. 1983. pap. 5.95 (ISBN 0-8024-0314-X). Moody.

Charles, G. J., jt. auth. see Patsavos, L. J.

Charles, Howard H. Alcohol & the Bible. LC 66-10970. 40p. 1981. pap. 1.50 (ISBN 0-8361-1941-X). Herald Pr.

Charles, Pierre. Prayer for All Times. Waterfield, Robin, tr. from Fr. Tr. of La Priere du Toutes Les Heures. 157p. 1983. pap. 5.95 (ISBN 0-87061-090-2). Chr Classics.

Charles, R. H. A Critical & Exegetical Commentary on the Revalation of St. John, 2 vols, Vol. I. Plummer, Alfred & Briggs, Charles A., eds. LC 21-5413. (International Critical Commentary Ser.). 568p. 1920. 24.95x (ISBN 0-567-05038-6, Pub. by T & T Clark Ltd UK). Fortress.

--A Critical & Exegetical Commentary on the Revalation of St. John, 2 vols, Vol. II. LC 21-5413. (International Critical Commentary Ser.). 506p. 1920. 24.95 (ISBN 0-567-05039-4, Pub. by T & T Clark Ltd UK). Fortress.

Charles, R. H., ed. & The Book of Enoch: Or One Enoch. 2nd ed. 331p. pap. 16.95 (ISBN 0-88697-009-1). Life Science.

Charles, R. H., ed. The Book of Jubilees: The Little Genesis. 1984. Repr. of 1902 ed. 39.00x (ISBN 0-403-08996-4, Regency). Scholarly.

--The Book of the Secrets of Enoch. 100p. pap. 11.95 (ISBN 0-88697-010-5). Life Science.

Charles, R. H., intro. by. The Apoclypse of Baruch. 1976. Repr. of 1896 ed. 39.00x (ISBN 0-685-71069-6, Regency). Scholarly.

Charles, R. H., et al. Apocrypha & Pseudepigrapha of the Old Testament, 2 Vols. Vol. 1. 69.00x (ISBN 0-19-826155-1); Vol. 2. 69.00x (ISBN 0-19-826152-7). Oxford U Pr.

Charles, Rodger. Social Teaching of Vatican II: Its Origin & Development. Catholic Social Ethics-an Historical & Comparative Study. LC 81-83567. (Illus.). 597p. 1982. 30.00 (ISBN 0-89870-013-2). Ignatius Pr.

Charles, Ronal. Street Walkin' (Illus.). 120p. (Orig.). 1986. pap. 9.95 (ISBN 1-55630-020-4). Brentwood Comm.

Charles Louis De Bourbon. Bibliotheque liturgique, 2 vols. in 1. Ales, Anatole, ed. LC 72-130592. (Fr). 1970. Repr. of 1898 ed. lib. bdg. 40.50 (ISBN 0-8337-0036-7). B Franklin.

Charlesworth, Arthur R. Paradise Found. LC 72-91109. 1973. 10.00 (ISBN 0-8022-2104-1). Philos Lib.

Charlesworth, J. Old Testament Pseudepigrapha & the New Testament. (Society for New Testament Studies Monographs: No. 54). 213p. 1985. 34.50 (ISBN 0-521-30190-4). Cambridge U Pr.

Charlesworth, James H. The Discovery of a Dead Sea Scroll: It's Importance in the History of Jesus Research. 41p. 1985. pap. 6.00 (ISBN 0-318-18993-3, 85-1). Intl Ctr Arid & Semi-Arid.

--The New Discoveries in St. Catherine's Monastery: A Preliminary Report on the Manuscripts. Freedman, David N., intro. by. LC 81-10992. (American Schools of Oriental Research Monographs: No. 3). (Illus.). 45p. (Orig.). 1982. pap. text ed. 6.00x (ISBN 0-89757-403-6, Am Sch Orient Res). Eisenbrauns.

--The Odes of Solomon. LC 77-21285. (SBL Texts & Translations). 192p. 1983. pap. 8.95 (ISBN 0-89130-202-6, 06 02 13). Scholars Pr GA.

--The Pseudepigrapha & Modern Research, with a Supplement. LC 76-25921. (Society Biblical Literature Septuagint & Cognate Studies). 344p. 1981. pap. 12.75 (ISBN 0-89130-440-1, 06 0707S). Scholars Pr GA.

Charlesworth, James H. & Mueller, James R. The New Testament Apocrypha & Pseudepigrapha: A Guide to Publications, with Excursueses on Apacalypses. LC 85-18350. (ATLA Bibliographer Ser.: No. 17). 468p. 1987. 42.50 (ISBN 0-8108-1845-0). Scarecrow.

Charlesworth, James H., ed. Old Testament Pseudepigrapha, 2 vols. 1056p. 1986. slipcased set 80.00 (ISBN 0-385-19491-9). Doubleday.

--Old Testament Pseudepigrapha: Expansions of the Old Testament & Legends, Wisdom & Philosophical Literature, Prayers, Psalms & Odes, Fragments of Lost Judeo-Hellenistic Words, Vol. II. 1056p. 1985. 40.00 (ISBN 0-385-18813-7). Doubleday.

--Old Testament Pseudepigrapha, Vol. I: Apocalyptic Literature & Testaments. LC 80-2443. 1056p. 1983. 40.00 (ISBN 0-385-09630-5). Doubleday.

Charlesworth, M. J., tr. St. Anselm's Proslogion. LC 78-63300. 1979. text ed. 17.95x (ISBN 0-268-01696-8); pap. text ed. 6.95x (ISBN 0-268-01697-6). U of Notre Dame Pr.

Charlesworth, Max, et al, eds. Religion in Aboriginal Australia: An Anthology. LC 83-23437. (Illus.). 458p. 1984. text ed. 39.50x (ISBN 0-7022-1754-9). U of Queensland Pr.

Charleton, Walter. The Immorality of the Human Soul, Demonstrated by the Light of Nature: In Two Dialogues. LC 83-46043. (Scientific AWakeningin the Restoration Ser.: No. 2). (Illus.). 224p. 1985. Repr. of 1657 ed. 87.50 (ISBN 0-404-63302-1). AMS Pr.

Charley, Julian. Cincuenta Palabras Claves de la Biblia. Diaz, Jorge E. & Diaz, Myriam, trs. from Eng. Orig. Title: Fifty Key Words-The Bible. (Span., Illus.). 80p. Date not set. pap. price not set (ISBN 0-311-04029-2). Casa Bautista.

Charlton, H. B. Shakespeare's Jew. 1934. lib. bdg. 12.50 (ISBN 0-8414-3560-X). Folcroft.

Charlton, Jim & Shulman, Jason. The Family Book of Christmas Songs & Stories. (Illus.). 208p. 1986. pap. 9.95 (ISBN 0-399-51276-4, Perigee). Putnam Pub Group.

Charms, George de see De Charms, George.

Charnock, Stephen. Existence & Attributes of God, 2 vols. 1979. Repr. 29.95 set (ISBN 0-8010-2437-4). Baker Bk.

--Knowledge of God. 598p. 1985. 15.95 (ISBN 0-85151-448-0). Banner of Truth.

Charny, Israel W. & Rapaport, Chanan. Genocide: The Human Cancer. 1983. pap. 10.95 (ISBN 0-87851-313-2). Hearst Bks.

Charon, Jean E., ed. Spirit & Science: Reality & Imagination. (Illus.). 440p. 1987. 24.95 (ISBN 0-89226-027-0, Pub. by ICUS). Paragon Hse.

Charpentier, Etienne. How to Read the Old Testament. LC 82-12728. 128p. 1982. pap. 10.95 (ISBN 0-8245-0540-9). Crossroad NY.

Charpentier, Louis. The Mysteries of Chartres Cathedral. 1980. pap. 1.75 (ISBN 0-380-00386-4, 24596). Avon.

Charry, Dana. Mental Health Skills for Clergy. 160p. 1981. 10.95 (ISBN 0-8170-0886-1). Judson.

Charry, Elias & Segal, Abraham. The Eternal People. (Illus.). 448p. 7.50x (ISBN 0-8381-0206-9, 10-206). United Syn Bk.

Chartier, Emile-Auguste see Alain, pseud.

Chartier, Jan. Developing Leadership in the Teaching Church. 112p. 1985. pap. 5.95 (ISBN 0-8170-1067-X). Judson.

Chartier, Jan & Chartier, Myron. Nurturing Faith in the Family. (Family Life Ser.). 160p. 1986. pap. 6.95 (ISBN 0-8170-1093-9). Judson.
Chartier, Jan, jt. auth. see Chartier, Myron.
Chartier, Janet A. & Chartier, Myron R. Caring Together: Faith, Hope, & Love in Your Family. LC 86-3460. 132p. (Orig.). 1986. pap. 8.95 (ISBN 0-664-24019-4). Westminster.
Chartier, Myron & Chartier, Jan. Trusting Together in God. LC 83-73132. (Illus.). 172p. (Orig.). 1984. pap. 6.95 (ISBN 0-87029-193-9, 20285-3). Abbey.
Chartier, Myron, jt. auth. see Chartier, Jan.
Chartier, Myron R. Preaching As Communication: An Interpersonal Perspective. LC 80-21304. (Abingdon Preacher Library). 128p. (Orig.). 1981. pap. 6.95 (ISBN 0-687-33826-3). Abingdon.
Chartier, Myron R., jt. auth. see Chartier, Janet A.
Chartock, Roselle & Spencer, Jack. The Holocaust Years: Society on Trial. 244p. Repr. 2.95 (ISBN 0-686-95069-0). ADL.
Charukov, Georgy. Bulgarian Monasteries: Monuments of History, Culture & Art. 1981. 89.00x (ISBN 0-569-08507-1, Pub. by Collets UK). State Mutual Bk.
Charvat, William, et al, eds. see Hawthorne, Nathaniel.
Chase, Barbara H. & Man, Martha L., eds. Spirit & Struggle in Southern Asia. 105p. (Orig.). 1986. pap. 5.95 (ISBN 0-377-00157-0). Friend Pr.
Chase, Betty N. Discipline Them, Love Them. 112p. 1982. wkbk. 6.95 (ISBN 0-89191-359-9). Cook.
--How to Discipline & Build Self-Esteem in Your Child. 46p. 1983. pap. text ed. 19.95 (ISBN 0-89191-796-9). Cook.
Chase, Elise, compiled by. Healing Faith: An Annotated Bibliography of Christian Self-Help Books. LC 85-929. (Bibliographies & Indexes in Religious Studies: No. 3). xxxiv, 192p. 1985. lib. bdg. 35.00 (ISBN 0-313-24014-0, DHF/). Greenwood.
Chase, Elizabeth, ed. Pioneer Churches of Florida. LC 77-72276. (Illus.). 74p. 1977. pap. 6.00 (ISBN 0-913122-11-4). Mickler Hse.
Chase, Harry E. Eden in Winter. LC 78-71941. 1978. write for info. (ISBN 0-9601662-2-X). C Schneider.
Chase, Jackson H. Cryptic Masonry. 94p. Repr. of 1981 ed. s.p. soft cover 4.75 (ISBN 0-88053-014-6). Macoy Pub.
Chase, Lewis. A Sense of Values. LC 79-92431. 67p. 1980. 8.95 (ISBN 0-8022-2362-1). Philos Lib.
Chase, Mary E. Bible & the Common Reader. rev. ed. 1962. pap. 4.95 (ISBN 0-02-084390-9, Collier). Macmillan.
Chase, Thornton. In Galilee. Facsimile reprint ed. (Illus.). 98p. 1985. Repr. of 1921 ed. 7.95 (ISBN 0-933770-38-3). Kalimat.
Chase, William D. Chases' Calendar of Annual Events: Special Days, Weeks & Months in 1980. rev. ed. LC 57-14540. (Illus., Orig.). 1979. lib. bdg. 14.95 (ISBN 0-913082-27-9); pap. 9.95 (ISBN 0-913082-26-0). Apple Tree.
Chastain, Jane. Concerned Women Can Make a Difference. 1987. pap. 7.95 (ISBN 0-8307-1185-6, 5418968). Regal.
Chastel, Andre, intro. by. The Vatican Frescoes of Michelangelo, 2 vols. Rosenthal, Raymond, tr. from Fr. LC 80-66646. (Illus.). 528p. 1980. ltd. ed. 7500.00 (ISBN 0-89659-158-1). Abbeville Pr.
Chaston, Gloria, jt. auth. see Jaussi, Laureen.
Chateaubriand, Francois R De see De Chateaubriand, Francois R.
Chateaubriand, Rene de & Guyard, Marius Francois. Vie de Rance. 3.95 (ISBN 0-686-54375-0). French & Eur.
Chateaubriand, Rene de & Mourot, Jean. Itineraire De Paris a Jerusalem. 448p. 1968. 3.50 (ISBN 0-686-54365-3). French & Eur.
Chateaubriand, Viscount de see De Chateaubriand, Viscount.
Chater, A. G., tr. see Undset, Sigrid.
Chater, A. G., tr. see Valentin, Hugo.
Chatfield, Charles. Kirby Page & the Social Gospel: Pacifist & Socialist Aspects. LC 70-147695. (Library of War & Peace: Documentary Anthologies). 1976. lib. bdg. 46.00 (ISBN 0-8240-0451-5). Garland Pub.
Chatfield, Mark. Churches the Victorians Forgot. (Illus.). 1979. 15.00 (ISBN 0-903485-76-1, Pub. by Moorland Pub Co England). Eastview.
Chatham, Joe. Eternal Security Obtained after Completing a Faithful Course. 1978. pap. 1.50 (ISBN 0-934942-05-6). White Wing Pub.
Chatham, Romara. Fasting. LC 85-73212. 1986. pap. cancelled (ISBN 0-88270-604-7). Bridge pub.
Chattalas, Angelos M. Pearls of Wisdom. 1986. 9.50 (ISBN 0-8062-2507-6). Carlton.
Chattapadhyaya. Muhammad, the Prophet of Islam. 1981. 1.25 (ISBN 0-686-97878-1). Kazi Pubns.
Chatterjee, A. N. Sri Krsna Caitanya: A Historical Study of Gaudiya Vaisnavism. 1985. 22.00x (ISBN 0-8364-1321-0, Pub. by Assoc Bks India). South Asia Bks.
Chatterjee, Asim K. A Comprehensive History of Jainism. 1978. 20.00x (ISBN 0-8364-0225-1). South Asia Bks.
Chatterjee, Margaret. Gandhi's Religious Thought. LC 83-5841. 224p. 1984. text ed. 19.95x (ISBN 0-268-01009-9, 85-10091). U of Notre Dame Pr.
--Gandhi's Religious Thought. LC 83-5841. 208p. 1986. pap. 9.95 (ISBN 0-268-01011-0). U of Notre Dame Pr.
--The Religious Spectrum. (Studies in an Indian Context). 196p. 1984. 23.95x (ISBN 0-317-39860-1, Pub. by Allied Pubs India). Asia Bk Corp.
Chatterji, J. C. Kashmir Shaivaism. (Cultural Perspectives Ser.). 176p. (Orig.). 1986. 29.50x (ISBN 0-88706-179-6); pap. 9.95x (ISBN 0-88706-180-X). State U NY Pr.
--Wisdom of the Vedas. LC 80-51550. 100p. 1980. pap. 3.95 (ISBN 0-8356-0538-8, Quest). Theos Pub Hse.
Chatterji, Mohini M. Viveka-Chudamani or the Crest Jewel of Wisdom. 5.75 (ISBN 0-8356-7091-0). Theos Pub Hse.
Chatterton-Hill, Georges. The Sociological Value of Christianity. LC 83-45605. Date not set. Repr. of 1912 ed. 36.00 (ISBN 0-404-19873-2). AMS Pr.
Chatton, Ray, jt. auth. see Mulqueen, Jack.
Chattopadhya, A. Why Have I Accepted Islam? pap. 1.75 (ISBN 0-686-18476-9). Kazi Pubns.
Chattopadhyay, Alaka, tr. see Chattopadhyaya, Debiprasad.
Chattopadhyaya, A., ed. see Taranath.
Chattopadhyaya, Debiprasad, ed. Taranatha's History of Buddhism in India. Chattopadhyay, Alaka, tr. 1980. 28.00x (ISBN 0-8364-1484-5, Pub. by KP Bagchi India). South Asia Bks.
Chattopadhyaya, Debiprsdad, ed. see Taranath.
Chattopadhyaya, S. Evolution of Hindu Sects. 1970. text ed. 18.00x. Coronet Bks.
Chau, Heng, jt. auth. see Sure, Heng.
Chaudhri, A. R. Substance of Muhammahan Law. 1970. 4.25x (ISBN 0-87902-157-8). Orientalia.
Chaudhry, Saida. Call to Prophethood. (Illus.). pap. 4.00. Am Trust Pubns.
--We Are Muslim Children. pap. 4.00 (ISBN 0-89259-050-5). Am Trust Pubns.
Chaudhuri, Dulal. Goddess Durga: The Great Mother. 1985. 7.50x (ISBN 0-8364-1289-3, Pub. by Mrimol). South Asia Bks.
Chaudhuri, Haridas. Being, Evolution & Immortality. rev. ed. LC 74-4821. Orig. Title: Philosophy of Integralism. 224p. 1974. pap. 6.95 (ISBN 0-8356-0449-7, Quest). Theos Pub Hse.
--Evolution of Integral Consciousness. LC 77-4219. 1977. pap. 4.25 (ISBN 0-8356-0494-2, Quest). Theos Pub Hse.
--Integral Yoga. LC 73-17170. 1981. pap. 4.95 (ISBN 0-8356-0444-6, Quest). Theos Pub Hse.
--Mastering the Problems of Living. new ed. LC 75-4172. 222p. 1975. pap. 2.75 (ISBN 0-8356-0463-2, Quest). Theos Pub Hse.
Chaudhuri, J. B., jt. auth. see Natha, Prana.
Chaudhuri, Nirad C. Hinduism: A Religion to Live by. 1979. pap. 9.95. Oxford U Pr.
Chaudhury, Sukomal. Analytical Study of the Abhidharmakosa. 1983. 18.00x (ISBN 0-8364-1017-3, Pub. by Mukhopadyaya). South Asia Bks.
Chauncy, Charles. Mystery Hid from All Ages & Generations. LC 70-83414. (Religion in American, Ser. 1). 1969. Repr. of 1784 ed. 23.50 (ISBN 0-405-00235-1). Ayer Co Pubs.
Chaundler, Christine. The Book of Superstitions. pap. 2.45 (ISBN 0-8065-0302-5). Citadel Pr.
Chautard, Jean-Baptiste. The Soul of the Apostolate. 1977. pap. 6.00 (ISBN 0-89555-031-8). TAN Bks Pubs.
Chavel, C. B., tr. The Commandments of Maimonides, 2 vols. 305p. 1967. 35.00 (ISBN 0-900689-71-4); pap. 25.00. Soncino Pr.
--The Disputation at Barcelona. 48p. 1983. pap. 2.95 (ISBN 0-88328-025-6). Shilo Pub Hse.
Chavel, Charles B. Encyclopedia of Torah Thoughts. Orig. Title: Rabeinu Bachya Ben Asher "Kad Hakemach". 734p. 1980. 19.50 (ISBN 0-88328-016-7); pap. 14.50 (ISBN 0-88328-017-5). Shilo Pub Hse.
--Ramban: His Life & Teachings. LC 63-1543. pap. 5.95 (ISBN 0-87306-037-7). Feldheim.
--Ramban (Nachmanides) Commentary on the Torah, 5 vols. 2575p. 1971. 84.75 set (ISBN 0-686-86743-2); Vol. I, Book Of Genesis. 16.95 ea. (ISBN 0-88328-006-X). Vol. II, Book Of Exodus (ISBN 0-88328-007-8). Vol. III, Book Of Leviticus (ISBN 0-88328-008-6). Vol. IV, Book Of Numbers (ISBN 0-88328-009-4). Vol. V, Book Of Deuteronomy (ISBN 0-88328-010-8). Shilo Pub Hse.
--Ramban (Nachmanides) Writings & Discourses, 2 vols. 768p. 1978. Set. slipcase 33.00 (ISBN 0-88328-013-2). Shilo Pub Hse.
Chavez, Angelico. Coronado's Friars: The Franciscans in the Coronado Expedition. (Monograph Ser.). (Illus.). 1968. 10.00 (ISBN 0-88382-058-7). AAFH.
Chavez, Angelico, ed. The Oroz Codex, or Relation of the Description of the Holy Gospel Province in New Spain, & the Lives of the Founders & Other Note-Worthy Men of Said Province Composed by Fray Pedro Oroz: 1584-1586. (Documentary Ser.). 1972. 25.00 (ISBN 0-88382-011-0). AAFH.
Chavez, Fray A. But Time & Chance: The Biography of Padre Martinez of Taos. LC 81-27. 176p. 1981. 35.00x (ISBN 0-913270-96-2); pap. 11.95 (ISBN 0-913270-95-4). Sunstone Pr.
Chavez, Jose. Santa Maria de Guadalupe. (Span.). 1963. pap. 2.00 (ISBN 0-8198-6825-6). Dghtrs St Paul.
Chavez, Moises. Hebreo Biblico Juego de Dos Tomos, 2 vols. (Span., Vol. I - 568 pgs., Vol. II - 240 pgs.). 1984. Set. pap. 28.95 (ISBN 0-311-42070-2, Edit Mundo). Casa Bautista.
Chavis, Benjamin F., Jr. Psalms from Prison. 192p. 1983. 10.95 (ISBN 0-8298-0661-X); pap. 7.95 (ISBN 0-8298-0666-0). Pilgrim NY.
Chaytor, H. J., tr. see Becker, C. H.
Chazan, Barry. Language of Jewish Education. LC 77-21638. 1978. 10.00 (ISBN 0-87677-146-0). Hartmore.
Chazan, Robert. Church, State & Jew in the Middle Ages. new ed. Kozodoy, Neal, ed. LC 78-27221. (Library of Jewish Studies). 1979. pap. text ed. 9.95x (ISBN 0-87441-302-8). Behrman.
--European Jewry & the First Crusade. 1987. 37.50. U of Cal Pr.
--Medieval Jewry in Northern France: A Poltical & Social History. LC 73-8129. (Johns Hopkins University Studies in Historical & Political Science: 91st; 2). pap. 63.00 (ISBN 0-317-20643-5, 2024132). Bks Demand UMI.
Cheasebro, Margaret. Puppet Scripts by the Month. 1985. pap. 4.95 (ISBN 0-8054-7524-9). Broadman.
Cheesman, John, et al. The Grace of God in the Gospel. 1976. pap. 3.45 (ISBN 0-85151-153-8). Banner of Truth.
Cheesman, Paul R. & Hutchins, Barbara W. Pathways to the Past: A Guide to the Ruins of Mezo-America. LC 83-83236. 210p. 1984. pap. 8.95 (ISBN 0-88290-236-9). Horizon Utah.
Cheesman, Paul R., ed. see Porter, Larry.
Chee Soo. The Tao of Long Life: The Chinese Art of Ch'ang Ming. 176p. 1983. pap. 7.95 (ISBN 0-85030-320-6). Newcastle Pub.
--Taoist Yoga: The Chinese Art of K'ai Men. 160p. 1983. pap. 7.95 (ISBN 0-85030-332-X). Newcastle Pub.
Cheetham, Erika. The Further Prophecies of Nostradamus Nineteen Eighty Five & Beyond. 256p. (Orig.). 1985. pap. 6.95 (ISBN 0-399-51121-0, Perigee). Putnam Pub Group.
Cheetham, Samuel, jt. ed. see Smith, William.
Cheever, George B. God Against Slavery. facs. ed. LC 76-78995. (Black Heritage Library Collection Ser). 1857. 13.00 (ISBN 0-8369-8537-0). Ayer Co Pubs.
--God Against Slavery & the Freedom & Duty of the Pulpit to Rebuke It, As a Sin Against God. LC 79-82182. (Anti-Slavery Crusade in America Ser). 1969. Repr. of 1857 ed. 13.00 (ISBN 0-405-00621-7). Ayer Co Pubs.
--Guilt of Slavery & the Crime of Slaveholding. LC 69-16586. Repr. of 1860 ed. cancelled (ISBN 0-8371-1380-6, CHG&, Pub. by Negro U Pr). Greenwood.
Cheiro. Cheiro's Book of Numbers. LC 64-11269. (Illus., Orig.). 1964. pap. 2.95 (ISBN 0-668-01170-X, 1169). Arco.
Chejne, A. Succession to the Rule in Islam. 1960. 5.30x (ISBN 0-87902-158-6). Orientalia.
Chejne, Anver. Ibn Hazm. 29.00 (ISBN 0-686-83558-1); pap. 19.95. Kazi Pubns.
--Ibn Hazm al Undalasi. 320p. (Orig.). 1982. 29.00x (ISBN 0-935782-03-6); pap. 19.95x (ISBN 0-935782-04-4). Kazi Pubns.
Chejne, Anwar. Succession to the Rule in Muslim. 154p. (Orig.). 1981. pap. 4.75 (ISBN 0-88004-001-7). Sunwise Turn.
Chejne, Anwar G. Islam & the West: The Moriscos. LC 82-703. 368p. 1983. 49.50 (ISBN 0-87395-603-6); pap. 19.95 (ISBN 0-87395-606-0). State U NY Pr.
--Muslim Spain: Its History & Culture. LC 73-87254. (Illus.). 616p. 1974. 32.50 (ISBN 0-8166-0688-9). U of Minn Pr.
Chekki, Dan A., ed. see Blasi, Anthony J. & Cuneo, Michael W.
Chelvam, Reginald T. Einstein Was Wrong: Or the Scroll Theory of Cosmology & of Matter. LC 82-71689. (Illus.). 268p. (Orig.). 1982. pap. 19.95 (ISBN 0-943796-00-8). Penso Pubns.
Chemitz, Martin. Ministry, Word, & Sacraments: An Enchiridion. Poellot, Luther, tr. 1981. pap. 17.50 (ISBN 0-570-03295-4, 15-2730). Concordia.
Chemnitz, Martin. Examination of the Council of Trent. Kramer, Fred, tr. from Lat. LC 79-143693. 1971. 29.95 (ISBN 0-570-03213-X, 15-2113). Concordia.
--Examination of the Council of Trent: Part II. 1979. 29.95 (ISBN 0-570-03272-5, 15-2717). Concordia.
--Justification: The Chief Article of Christian Doctrine. Preus, J. A., tr. 200p. 1986. 16.95 (ISBN 0-570-04227-5, 15-2186). Concordia.
--Two Natures in Christ. Preus, J. A., tr. LC 74-115465. Orig. Title: De Duabus Naturis in Christo. 1970. 24.95 (ISBN 0-570-03210-5, 15-2109). Concordia.
Chen, Fu H., tr. see Torrey, R. A.
Chen, Huan-Chang. The Economic Principles of Confucius & His School, 2 vols. lib. bdg. 250.00 set (ISBN 0-87968-080-6). Krishna Pr.
Ch'en, Kenneth. Buddhism in China: A Historical Survey. (Studies in History of Religion: Vol. 1). 1974. pap. 13.50x (ISBN 0-691-00015-8). Princeton U Pr.
Ch'en, Kenneth K. Buddhism: The Light of Asia. LC 67-30496. 1968. pap. text ed. 5.95 (ISBN 0-8120-0272-5). Barron.
Chen, Liu F. The Confucian Way: A New & Systematic Study of the Four Books. Liu, Shih S., tr. 620p. 1986. text ed. 59.95 (ISBN 0-7103-0171-5). Methuen Inc.
Chen, Ruth T., tr. see Demarest, Bruce A.
Chen, Ruth T., tr. see Nee, Watchman.
Chen, Ruth T., tr. see Spurgeon, Charles.
Chen, Ruth T., tr. see Strauss, Richard L.
Chen, Y. K. T'ai Chi Ch'uan: Its Effects & Practical Applications. 1979. pap. 6.95 (ISBN 0-87877-043-7). Newcastle Pub.
Cheney, C. R. Medieval Texts & Studies. 1973. 55.00x (ISBN 0-19-822399-4). Oxford U Pr.
Cheney, C. R. & Jones, Bridgette A., eds. English Episcopal Acta: Canterbury, 1193-1205, 2 vols, Vols. I & II. (Episcopal Acta). 1984. Set. 165.00x (ISBN 0-19-726022-5). Oxford U Pr.
Cheney, Christopher R. Episcopal Visitation of Monasteries in the Thirteenth Century. 2nd, rev. ed. xxxi, 192p. 1983. lib. bdg. 25.00x (ISBN 0-87991-638-9). Porcupine Pr.
Cheney, Johnston M. The Life of Christ in Stereo. Ellisen, Stanley A., ed. LC 84-8280. 275p. 1984. pap. 6.95 (ISBN 0-88070-068-8). Multnomah.
Cheney, Mary G. Roger, Bishop of Worcestor Eleven Sixty Four to Eleven Seventy Nine: An English Bishop of the Age of Becket. (Oxford Historical Monographs). (Illus.). 1980. 63.00x (ISBN 0-19-821879-6). Oxford U Pr.
Cheney, Ruth G., ed. The Christian Education Catalog. 192p. (Orig.). 1981. pap. 10.95 (ISBN 0-8164-2328-8, HarpR). Har-Row.
Cheney, Thomas E., ed. Mormon Songs from the Rocky Mountains: A Compilation of Mormon Folksong. 224p. 1968. pap. 9.95 (ISBN 0-87480-196-6). U of Utah Pr.
Cheng, Hsueh-li. Empty Logic: Madhyamika Buddhism from Chinese Sources. LC 83-13246. 220p. 1984. 17.95 (ISBN 0-8022-2442-3). Philos Lib.
Cheng, Man-Ch'ing & Smith, Robert W. T'ai-Chi the Supreme Ultimate Exercise for Health, Sport, & Self-Defense. LC 67-23009. (Illus.). 1967. 22.50 (ISBN 0-8048-0560-1). C E Tuttle.
Ch'en Kou-Chun. Studies in Marriage & Funerals of Taiwan Aborigines. (Asian Folklore & Social Life Monograph: No. 4). (Chinese.). 1970. 14.00 (ISBN 0-89986-007-9). Oriental Bk Store.
Chennakesvan, Sarasvati. A Critical Study of Hinduism. 1980. 12.50x (ISBN 0-8364-0614-1). South Asia Bks.
Chenoweth, Linda. God's People: Nursery Leader's Guide. 64p. 1981. 2.95 (ISBN 0-686-74751-8). Westminster.
--God's People Share. Duckert, Mary, ed. 64p. 1981. nursery ldrs. guide 3.95 (ISBN 0-664-24337-1); pap. 1.55 students' book (ISBN 0-664-24336-3); resource Packet 8.95 (ISBN 0-664-24338-X). Westminster.
Chen Wei-Ming. Questions & Answers on T'ai Chi Ch'uan. Pang Jeng Lo, Benjamin & Smith, Robert, trs. from Chinese. Tr. of T'ai Chi Ch'uan Ta Wen. 64p. (Orig.). 1985. 20.00 (ISBN 0-938190-77-6). North Atlantic.
Cherico, Daniel J., jt. auth. see Margolis, Otto S.
Chernaik, Warren L. The Poet's Time: Politics & Religion in the Work of Andrew Marvell. LC 82-4395. 250p. 1983. 37.50 (ISBN 0-521-24773-X). Cambridge U Pr.
Cherne, J. The Learning Disabled Child in Your Church School. LC 12-2818. (09). 1983. pap. 3.25 (ISBN 0-570-03883-9). Concordia.
Chernin, Dennis K. & Manteuffel, Gregory. Health: A Holistic Approach. LC 84-40270. (Illus.). 285p. (Orig.). 1984. pap. 7.50 (ISBN 0-8356-0590-6, Quest). Theos Pub Hse.
Cherniss, Harold F. Platonism of Gregory of Nyssa. 1971. Repr. of 1930 ed. lib. bdg. 18.50 (ISBN 0-8337-0556-3). B Franklin.

Cherniss, Michael D. Ingeld & Christ: Heroic Conceptions & Values in Old English Christian Poetry. (Studies in English Literature: No. 74). 267p. 1972. text ed. 29.60x (ISBN 90-2792-335-3). Mouton.

Cherns, Albert, intro. by see Shoham, S. Giora.

Cherry, C. God's New Israel: Religious Interpretations of American Destiny. 1971. pap. 23.95 (ISBN 0-13-357335-4). P-H.

Cherry, Conrad. Nature & Religious Imagination: From Edwards to Bushnell. LC 79-7374. 256p. 1980. 3.00 (ISBN 0-8006-0550-0, 1-550). Fortress.

Cherry, Conrad, ed. Horace Bushnell: Sermons. LC 85-60410. (Sources of American Spirituality Ser.). 256p. (Orig.). 1985. 12.95 (ISBN 0-8091-0362-1). Paulist Pr.

Cherry, Conrad, ed. see Wyllie, Robert W.

Cherry, Conrad, et al. Jonathan Edwards: His Life & Influence. Angoff, Charles, ed. LC 74-4516. (Leverton Lecture Series II). 65p. 1975. 9.50 (ISBN 0-8386-1571-6). Fairleigh Dickinson.

Cherry, Corbin L. I Have Been Here. 112p. 1987. 6.95 (ISBN 1-55523-050-4). Winston-Derek.

Chertoff, Mordecai, jt. ed. see Alexander, Yona.

Chertoff, Mordecai S., jt. ed. see Leftwich, Joseph.

Chertoff, Mordechai, ed. Zionism: A Basic Reader. 1976. 1.00 (ISBN 0-685-82601-5). Herzl Pr.

Chervin, Ronda. Feminine Free & Faithful. LC 86-80785. 143p. 1986. pap. 7.95 (ISBN 0-89870-103-1). Ignatius Pr.

--Victory over Death. LC 85-8213. (Orig.). 1985. pap. 3.95 (ISBN 0-932506-43-7). St Bedes Pubns.

Chervin, Ronda & Neill, Mary. God-Seekers. 212p. (Orig.). 1986. pap. 4.95 (ISBN 0-914544-65-9). Living Flame Pr.

Chervokas, John. Pinstripe Prayers: Or How to Talk to God While Pursuing Mammon. 48p. (Orig.). 1984. pap. 2.95 (ISBN 0-86683-874-0, 7457, HarpR). Har-Row.

Chesebro, James W., ed. Gayspeak: Gay Male & Lesbian Communication. LC 82-355. 384p. 1981. 17.95 (ISBN 0-8298-0472-2); pap. 9.95 (ISBN 0-8298-0456-0). Pilgrim NY.

Chesham, Sallie. One Hand upon Another. (Illus.). 160p. (Orig.). 1978. pap. 1.50 (ISBN 0-89216-016-0). Salvation Army.

--Peace Like a River. 1981. pap. 5.95 (ISBN 0-86544-014-X). Salv Army Suppl South.

--Preaching Ladies. (Illus.). 179p. (Orig.). 1983. pap. 3.50 (ISBN 0-89216-045-4). Salvation Army.

Chesler, Evan R. The Russian Jewry Reader. 147p. pap. 2.45 (ISBN 0-686-95145-X). ADL.

Chesnut, Glenn F. The First Christian Histories: Eusebius, Socrates, Sozomen, Theodoret, & Evagrius. 2nd, rev. ed. xiv, 296p. 1986. 34.95 (ISBN 0-86554-164-7, MUP/H154); pap. 19.95 (ISBN 0-86554-203-1, MUP-P22). Mercer Univ Pr.

--Images of Christ: An Introduction to Christology. 160p. (Orig.). 1984. pap. 8.95 (ISBN 0-86683-875-9, 7918, HarpR). Har-Row.

Chester, Allan G. Hugh Latimer, Apostle to the English. 1978. Repr. of 1954 ed. lib. bdg. 20.00x (ISBN 0-374-91492-3, Octagon). Hippocrene Bks.

Chester, Allan G., ed. see Latimer, Hugh.

Chester, Andrew, tr. see Schweizer, Edward.

Chesterton, G. K. Collected Works of G. K. Chesterton, Vol. I. LC 85-81511. 1986. 24.95 (ISBN 0-89870-077-9); pap. 15.95 (ISBN 0-89870-079-5). Ignatius Pr.

--Collected Works of G. K. Chesterton II: The Everlasting Man, St. Francis of Assisi, St. Thomas Aquinas. Marlin, George, ed. 480p. 1986. 29.95 (ISBN 0-89870-116-3); pap. 17.95 (ISBN 0-89870-117-1). Ignatius Pr.

--The Collected Works of G. K. Chesterton: The Illustrated London News, Vol. xxvii. Marlin, George, ed. LC 85-81511. 622p. 1986. 29.95 (ISBN 0-89870-118-X); pap. 17.95 (ISBN 0-89870-119-8). Ignatius Pr.

--The Everlasting Man. 320p. 1981. Repr. of 1925 ed. lib. bdg. 37.00 (ISBN 0-8495-0855-X). Arden Lib.

--The Everlasting Man. 344p. 1981. Repr. of 1926 ed. lib. bdg. 20.00 (ISBN 0-89984-115-5). Century Bookbindery.

--The Everlasting Man. 280p. 1974. pap. 4.50 (ISBN 0-385-07198-1, Im). Doubleday.

--The Everlasting Man. LC 72-11233. 344p. 1974. Repr. of 1925 ed. lib. bdg. 22.50x (ISBN 0-8371-6636-5, CEVM). Greenwood.

--G. K. Chesterton Anthology. Kavanagh, P. J., ed. 515p. 1985. 24.95 (ISBN 0-89870-073-6); pap. 14.95 (ISBN 0-89870-096-5). Ignatius Pr.

--The G. K. Chesterton Calendar: A Quotation from the Works of G. K. Chesterton for Every Day in the Year. 75.00 (ISBN 0-87968-325-2). Gordon Pr.

--Napoleon of Notting Hill. LC 77-99307. 228p. 1978. pap. 3.45 (ISBN 0-8091-2096-8). Paulist Pr.

--Orthodoxy. 160p. 1973. pap. 3.50 (ISBN 0-385-01536-4, Im). Doubleday.

--St. Francis of Assisi. 1979. Repr. lib. bdg. 25.00 (ISBN 0-8495-0933-5). Arden Lib.

--Saint Francis of Assisi. LC 57-1230. 1957. pap. 3.95 (ISBN 0-385-02900-4, Im). Doubleday.

--Saint Thomas Aquinas. 200p. 1974. pap. 3.95 (ISBN 0-385-09002-1, Im). Doubleday.

Chesterton, G. K. & More, Thomas. Orthodoxy. (Books to Live Ser.). 1985. Repr. of 1908 ed. 10.95 (ISBN 0-88347-184-1). Thomas More.

Chesterton, G. K., et al. Twelve Modern Apostles & Their Creeds. facs. ed. LC 68-16982. (Essay Index Reprint Ser). 1926. 17.00 (ISBN 0-8369-0955-0). Ayer Co Pubs.

Chesterton, Gilbert K. Heretics. facs. ed. LC 75-128220. (Essay Index Reprint Ser.). 1905. 19.00 (ISBN 0-8369-1869-X). Ayer Co Pubs.

--Orthodoxy. 297p. 1980. Repr. lib. bdg. 39.50 (ISBN 0-89987-125-9). Darby Bks.

Chetanananda, tr. see Avadhuta.

Chetanananda, Swami, jt. auth. see Hatengdi, M. U.

Chetkin, Len. Guess Who's Jewish? (You'll Never Guess) Friedman, Robert S., ed. LC 85-13200. (Illus.). 164p. (Orig.). 1985. pap. 4.95 (ISBN 0-89865-403-3). Donning Co.

Cheve, C. F. Dictionnaire des Apologistes Involontaires, 2 vols. Migne, J. P., ed. (Nouvelle Encyclopedie Theologique Ser.: Vols. 38-39). (Fr.). 1494p. Repr. of 1853 ed. lib. bdg. 189.50x (ISBN 0-89241-279-8). Caratzas.

--Dictionnaire des Bienfaits et Beautes du Christianisme. Migne, J. P., ed. (Troisieme et Derniere Encyclopedie Theologique Ser.: Vol. 9). (Fr.). 732p. Repr. of 1856 ed. lib. bdg. 95.00x (ISBN 0-89241-293-3). Caratzas.

--Dictionnaire des Conversions. Migne, J. P., ed. (Nouvelle Encyclopedie Theologique Ser.: Vol. 33). (Fr.). 836p. Repr. of 1852 ed. lib. bdg. 106.00x (ISBN 0-89241-275-5). Caratzas.

--Dictionnaire des Papes ou Histoire Complete des tous les Souvenirs Pontifes. Migne, J. P., ed. (Troisieme et Derniere Encyclopedie Theologique Ser.: Vol. 32). (Fr.). 706p. Repr. of 1857 ed. lib. bdg. 90.00x (ISBN 0-89241-311-5). Caratzas.

Cheville, Roy A. Scriptures from Ancient America. LC 64-12944. 1964. pap. 10.00 (ISBN 0-8309-0252-X). Herald Hse.

Chevrot, Georges. On the Third Day. 208p. 1961. 5.95 (ISBN 0-933932-10-3); pap. 2.95 (ISBN 0-933932-11-1). Scepter Pubs.

--Simon Peter. 223p. 1980. pap. 4.95x (ISBN 0-933932-43-X). Scepter Pubs.

Chevy Chase Manuscripts Staff, ed. see Johnson, Hubert R.

Chew, Helena M. The English Ecclesiastical Tenants-in-Chief & Knight Service, Especially in the Thirteenth & Fourteenth Centuries. LC 80-2310. Repr. of 1932 ed. 37.50 (ISBN 0-404-18558-4). AMS Pr.

Cheyne, T. K. & Black, J. S., eds. Encyclopedia Biblica, 4 vols. 1977. lib. bdg. 425.95 (ISBN 0-8490-1764-5). Gordon Pr.

Chia, Maneewan, jt. auth. see Chia, Mantak.

Chia, Mantak. Taoist Secrets of Love: Cultivating Male Sexual Energy. 1984. pap. 14.00 (ISBN 0-943358-19-1). Aurora Press.

--Taoist Ways to Transform Stress into Vitality: The Inner Smile - Six Healing Sounds. LC 85-81656. (Illus.). 160p. (Orig.). 1986. pap. 9.95 (ISBN 0-935621-00-8). Heal Tao Bks.

Chia, Mantak & Chia, Maneewan. Healing Love Through the Tao: Cultivating Female Sexual Energy. LC 86-81049. (Illus.). 320p. (Orig.). 1986. 22.50 (ISBN 0-935621-04-0); pap. 12.95 (ISBN 0-935621-05-9). Heal Tao Bks.

Chiampi, Luke. Rebuild My Church. LC 72-87090. 105p. 1972. pap. 0.95 (ISBN 0-8199-0502-X). Franciscan Herald.

Chiarelli, Caterina. Le Attivita Artistiche & il Patrimonio Librario della Certosa di Firenze, 2 vols. Hogg, James, ed. (Analecta Cartusiana Ser.: No. 102). 491p. (Orig.). 1984. pap. 50.00 (ISBN 0-317-42557-9, Pub. by Salzburg Studies). Longwood Pub Group.

Chiari, Joseph. Poetic Drama of Paul Claudel. LC 71-90365. 1969. Repr. of 1954 ed. 15.00x (ISBN 0-87752-018-6). Gordian.

--Reflections on Life & Death. LC 77-4054. 141p. 1977. 12.50x (ISBN 0-87752-212-X). Gordian.

Chiat, Marilyn. Handbook of Synagogue Architecture. LC 81-9419. (Brown Judaic Studies). 1982. pap. 20.00 (ISBN 0-89130-524-6, 14-00-29). Scholars Pr GA.

Chiba, Reiko. Sesshu's Long Scroll: A Zen Landscape Journey. LC 54-14085. (Illus.). 1959. 14.50 (ISBN 0-8048-0677-2). C E Tuttle.

--Seven Lucky Gods of Japan. LC 65-25467. (Illus.). 1966. 12.95 (ISBN 0-8048-0521-0). C E Tuttle.

Chibnall, Majorie, ed. & tr. see Vitalis, Orderic.

Chibnall, Marjorie, ed. Charters & Custumals of the Abbey of Holy Trinity, Caen. (Records of Social & Economic History Ser.). (Illus.). 1982. 37.50x (ISBN 0-19-726009-8). Oxford U Pr.

--The Ecclesiastical History of Orderic Vitalis, Vol. 1. (Oxford Medieval Texts Ser.). (Illus.). 1981. 98.00x (ISBN 0-19-822243-2). Oxford U Pr.

Chibnall, Marjorie, ed. & tr. see Vitalis, Orderic.

Chibnall, Marjorie, et al, eds. Anselm Studies: An Occasional Journal. 273p. (Orig.). 1983. lib. bdg. 35.00x (ISBN 0-527-03662-5). Kraus Intl.

Chick, Jack T. Cortinas de Humo. (Span., Illus., Orig.). 1984. pap. 2.50 (ISBN 0-937958-20-4). Chick Pubns.

--King of Kings. (Sword Ser.: Vol. 1). (Illus.). 64p. (Orig.). 1980. pap. 1.65 (ISBN 0-937958-07-7). Chick Pubns.

--The Last Call. (Illus.). 64p. (Orig.). 1963. pap. 1.95 (ISBN 0-937958-06-9). Chick Pubns.

--The Next Step. (Illus.). 64p. (Orig.). 1978. pap. 1.95 (ISBN 0-937958-04-2). Chick Pubns.

--Smokescreens. (Illus.). 93p. 1982. pap. 2.50 (ISBN 0-937958-14-X). Chick Pubns.

--La Ultima Llamada. (Span., Illus.). 64p. (Orig.). 1972. pap. 1.95 (ISBN 0-937958-02-6). Chick Pubns.

Chiel, Arthur A., ed. Perspectives on Jews & Judaism: Essays in Honor of Wolfe Kelman. 25.00x (ISBN 0-87068-683-6). Ktav.

Chiel, Kinneret. Complete Book of Hanukah. (Illus.). pap. 6.95x (ISBN 0-87068-367-5). Ktav.

Ch'ien, Edward T. Chiao Hung & the Restructuring of Neo-Confucianism in the Late Ming. (Neo-Confucian Studuies). 328p. 1986. 29.00 (ISBN 0-231-06022-X). Columbia U Pr.

Chiera, E. Lists of Personal Names from the Temple School of Nippur: A Syllabary of Personal Names. (Publications of the Babylonian Section: Vol. 11-1). (Illus.). 88p. 1916. soft bound 10.50x (ISBN 0-686-11923-1). Univ Mus of U PA.

--Lists of Personal Names from the Temple School of Nippur: Lists of Akkadian Personal Names. (Publications of the Babylonian Section: Vol. 11-2). (Illus.). 85p. 1916. soft bound 10.50x (ISBN 0-686-11924-X). Univ Mus of U PA.

Chiera, Edward. Lists of Personal Names from the Temple School of Nippur: Lists of Sumerian Personal Names. LC 17-5006. (University of Pennsylvania, University Museum, Publications of the Babylonian Section: Vol. 11, No. 3). pap. 34.00 (ISBN 0-317-28537-8, 2052027). Bks Demand UMI.

Chiesa, Bruno. The Emergence of Hebrew Biblical Pointing, Vol. 1. (Judentum v. Umwelt Ser.: Vol. 1). 92p. 1979. pap. 17.70 (ISBN 3-8204-6419-0). P Lang Pubs.

Chiganos, William S. Preparing to Serve As a God Parent. 1986. pap. 1.25 (ISBN 0-937032-44-1). Light&Life Pub Co MN.

Chigier, Moshe. Husband & Wife in Israeli Law. 281p. 1985. 17.50 (ISBN 0-87203-128-4, Pub. by Harry Fischel Institute for Research in Talmud Jerusalem Israel). Hermon.

Chih-hsu, Ou-i. The Buddhist I Ching. Cleary, Thomas, tr. from Chinese. LC 86-31460. (Dragon Ser.). 290p. 1987. pap. 10.95 (ISBN 0-87773-408-9). Shambhala Pubns.

Chilcote, Paul W. Wesley Speaks on Christian Vocation. 104p. (Orig.). 1987. pap. 6.95 (ISBN 0-88177-041-8, DR041B). Discipleship Res.

Child, Frank S. Colonial Parson of New England. LC 74-19532. 1974. Repr. of 1896 ed. 35.00x (ISBN 0-8103-3667-7). Gale.

Child, Gilbert W. Church & State Under the Tudors. LC 72-183695. 452p. 1974. Repr. of 1890 ed. lib. bdg. 29.50 (ISBN 0-8337-4041-5). B Franklin.

Child, James. Nuclear War: The Moral Dimension. (Studies in Social Philosophy & Policy: No. 6). 150p. 1986. 16.95 (ISBN 0-912051-09-4); pap. 8.95 (ISBN 0-912051-10-8). Soc Phil Pol.

Child, James E., ed. Nuclear War: The Moral Dimension. 160p. (Orig.). 1985. 16.95 (ISBN 0-912051-04-3, Dist. by Transaction Bks); pap. 8.95 (ISBN 0-912051-05-1). Soc Phil Pol.

Child, Mark. Discovering Church Architecture. (Discovering Ser.: No. 214). (Illus., Orig.). 1984. pap. 3.50 (ISBN 0-85263-328-9, Pub. by Shire Pubns England). Seven Hills Bks.

--Discovering Churchyards. (Discovering Ser.: No. 268). (Illus.). 80p. 1983. pap. 3.50 (ISBN 0-85263-603-2, Pub. by Shire Pubns England). Seven Hills Bks.

Childe, V. Gordon, tr. see Moret, A. & Davy, G.

Children at Sunrise Ranch, illus. Songs for the Joy of Living. (Illus.). 50p. 1985. ring-bound 11.95 (ISBN 0-932869-01-7). Eden Valley.

Childress, Harvey. Expanding Outlines of the New Testament Books. 5.95 (ISBN 0-89137-536-8). Quality Pubns.

--My Triumphant Life. 1978. pap. 2.25 (ISBN 0-88027-087-X). Firm Foun Pub.

--My Wonderful Salvation. 1978. pap. 1.75 (ISBN 0-88027-088-8). Firm Foun Pub.

Childress, James F. Civil Disobedience & Political Obligation: A Study in Christian Social Ethics. LC 75-158137. (Yale Publication in Religion Ser.: No. 16). pap. 66.50 (ISBN 0-317-09428-9, 2021988). Bks Demand UMI.

--Moral Responsibility in Conflicts: Essays on Nonviolence, War, & Conscience. LC 82-15197. 224p. 1982. text ed. 25.00x (ISBN 0-8071-1019-1). La State U Pr.

--Priorities in Biomedical Ethics. LC 81-3. 144p. 1981. pap. 8.95 (ISBN 0-664-24368-1). Westminster.

Childress, James F. & Macquarrie, John, eds. The Westminster Dictionary of Christian Ethics. rev. ed. LC 85-22539. 704p. 1986. 34.95 (ISBN 0-664-20940-8). Westminster.

Childs, Brevard S. The Book of Exodus: A Critical, Theological Commentary. LC 73-23120. (Old Testament Library). 686p. 1974. 26.50 (ISBN 0-664-20985-8). Westminster.

--Introduction to the Old Testament As Scripture. LC 78-14665. 688p. 1979. 29.95 (ISBN 0-8006-0532-2, 1-532). Fortress.

--The New Testament as Canon: An Introduction. LC 84-21169. 640p. 1985. 22.95 (ISBN 0-8006-0739-2, 1-739). Fortress.

--Old Testament Books for Pastor and Teacher. LC 76-52457. 120p. 1977. pap. 4.95 (ISBN 0-664-24120-4). Westminster.

--Old Testament Theology in a Canonical Context. LC 85-45503. 272p. 1986. 16.95 (ISBN 0-8006-0772-4, 1-772). Fortress.

Childs, Geoffrey S. The Golden Thread. (Illus.). 200p. 1986. write for info. (ISBN 0-910557-15-2). Acad New Church.

Childs, Marquis W. & Cater, Douglass. Ethics in a Business Society. LC 73-7073. 191p. 1973. Repr. of 1954 ed. lib. bdg. 22.50x (ISBN 0-8371-6905-4, CHBS). Greenwood.

Childs World Editors. Glad or Sad: How Do You Feel? rev. ed. LC 79-12152. (Illus.). 1979. PLB 5.95 (ISBN 0-89565-072-X). Childs World.

Chiles, Robert E. Theological Transition in American Methodism, 1790-1935. LC 83-16666. 238p. 1983. pap. text ed. 11.25 (ISBN 0-8191-3551-8). U Pr of Amer.

Chiles, Robert E., jt. ed. see Burtner, Robert W.

Chill, Abraham. The Minhagim: The Customs & Ceremonies of Judaism, Their Origins & Rationale. 2nd corrected ed. LC 78-62153. (Illus.). 339p. 1980. 14.95 (ISBN 0-87203-076-8); pap. 10.95 (ISBN 0-87203-077-6). Hermon.

Chillingworth, William. Works of William Chillingworth, 3 Vols. Repr. of 1838 ed. Set. lib. bdg. 95.00 (ISBN 0-404-01570-0). Vol. 1 (ISBN 0-404-01571-9). Vol. 3 (ISBN 0-404-01572-7). Vol. 4 (ISBN 0-404-01573-5). AMS Pr.

Chilson, Richard. Catholic Christianity: A Guide to the Way, the Truth, & the Life. 1987. pap. 7.95. Paulist Pr.

--Creed for a Young Catholic. LC 80-2073. 128p. 1981. pap. 2.75 (ISBN 0-385-17436-5, Im). Doubleday.

--Faith of Catholics: An Introduction. rev. ed. LC 72-81229. 320p. 1975. pap. 4.95 (ISBN 0-8091-1873-4, Deus). Paulist Pr.

--Way to Christianity: The Pilgrim. 1980. pap. 8.95 (ISBN 0-03-053426-7, HarpR). Har-Row.

Chilson, Richard W. Full Christianity: A Catholic Response to Fundamental Questions. 144p. (Orig.). 1985. pap. 4.95 (ISBN 0-8091-2669-9). Paulist Pr.

--A Lenten Pilgrimage-Dying & Rising in the Lord: A Manual for Ministry in the Lenten Catechumenate. (Orig.). 1984. pap. 8.95 (ISBN 0-8091-2589-7); handbook 4.95 (ISBN 0-8091-2569-2). Paulist Pr.

Chilstrom, Herbert W. Hebrews: A New & Better Way. LC 83-5600. 80p. 1984. pap. 3.95 (ISBN 0-8006-1717-7, 1-1717). Fortress.

Chilton, Bruce. Beginning New Testament Study. 208p. (Orig.). 1987. pap. 9.95 (ISBN 0-8028-0254-0). Eerdmans.

--Targumic Approaches to the Gospels: Essays in the Mutual Definition of Judaism & Christianity. 200p. (Orig.). 1987. lib. bdg. 24.75 (ISBN 0-8191-5731-7, Pub. by Studies in Judaism); pap. text ed. 12.25 (ISBN 0-8191-5732-5). U Pr of Amer.

Chilton, Bruce, ed. The Kingdom of God in the Teaching of Jesus. LC 83-20569. (Issues in Religion & Theology Ser.). 192p. 1984. pap. 7.95 (ISBN 0-8006-1769-X, 1-769). Fortress.

Chilton, Bruce D. A Galilean Rabbi & His Bible: Jesus' Use of the Interpreted Scripture of His Time. (Good News Studies Ser.: Vol. 8). 7.95 (ISBN 0-89453-374-6). M Glazier.

--The Glory of Israel: The Theology & Provenience of the Isaiah Targum. (JSOT Supplement Ser.: No. 23). ix, 178p. 1984. text ed. 28.00x (ISBN 0-905774-46-9, Pub. by JSOT Pr England); pap. text ed. 18.50 (ISBN 0-905774-47-7, Pub. by JSOT Pr England). Eisenbrauns.

Chilton, David. Productive Christians in An Age of Guilt Manipulators. 3rd ed. 480p. 1985. pap. 12.50 (ISBN 0-930464-04-4). Inst Christian.

China Educational Commission. Christian Education in China: A Study. LC 75-36223. Repr. of 1922 ed. 34.50 (ISBN 0-404-14474-8). AMS Pr.
Ching, Heng, tr. see Hua, Husan.
Ching, Julia. Confucianism & Christianity. LC 77-75962. 234p. 1978. 16.95x (ISBN 0-87011-303-8). Kodansha.
Ching, Julia, ed. see Tsung-Hsi, Huang.
Ching Yee, Janice. God's Busiest Angels. (Illus.). 1975. pap. 3.00 (ISBN 0-931420-09-1). Pi Pr.
--God's Purest Angels. (Illus.). 1976. pap. 3.00 (ISBN 0-931420-11-3). Pi Pr.
Chiniquy, Charles. Fifty Years in the "Church" of Rome. abr. ed. 366p. 1985. pap. 7.95 (ISBN 0-937958-21-2). Chick Pubns.
--The Priest, the Woman, & the Confessional. 144p. 1979. pap. 4.50 (ISBN 0-937958-03-4). Chick Pubns.
Chinitz, Jacob, ed. see Adler, Morris.
Chinmaya, Swami P., ed. see Rajneesh, Bhagwan S.
Chinmaya, Swami Prem, ed. see Rajneesh, Bhagwan Shree.
Chinmoy, Sri. Beauty-Drops. 51p. (Orig.). 1975. pap. 2.00 (ISBN 0-88497-224-0). Aum Pubns.
--Beyond Within. 525p. 1985. pap. 10.95 (ISBN 0-88497-115-5). Aum Pubns.
--A Child's Heart & a Child's Dreams: Growing up with Spiritual Wisdom, a Guide for Parents & Children. 123p. 1986. pap. text ed. write for info. (ISBN 0-88497-862-1). Aum Pubns.
--Death & Reincarnation: Eternity's Voyage. LC 74-81308. (Illus.). 143p. (Orig.). 1974. pap. 3.95 (ISBN 0-88497-038-8). Aum Pubns.
--Eternity's Breadth. 116p. 1975. pap. 5.00 (ISBN 0-88497-235-6). Aum Pubns.
--Everest-Aspiration. 1979. pap. 4.95 (ISBN 0-88497-460-X). Aum Pubns.
--Father's Day: Father with His European Children. 54p. (Orig.). 1976. pap. 2.00 (ISBN 0-88497-297-6). Aum Pubns.
--Fifty Freedom-Boats to One Golden Shore, Pt. 1. 93p. (Orig.). 1974. pap. 3.00 (ISBN 0-88497-087-6). Aum Pubns.
--Fifty Freedom-Boats to One Golden Shore, Pt. 2. 108p. 1974. pap. 3.00 (ISBN 0-88497-101-5). Aum Pubns.
--Fifty Freedom-Boats to One Golden Shore, Pt. 3. 94p. 1974. pap. 3.00 (ISBN 0-88497-071-X). Aum Pubns.
--Fifty Freedom-Boats to One Golden Shore, Pt. 4. 112p. (Orig.). 1974. pap. text ed. 3.00 (ISBN 0-88497-073-6). Aum Pubns.
--Flower-Flames. 208p. 1985. pap. 10.00 (ISBN 0-88497-829-X). Aum Pubns.
--The Garden of Love-Light, Vols 1 & 2. Chinmoy, Sri, tr. from Bengali. (Illus., Orig.). 1973. pap. 2.00 ea.; pap. write for info. (ISBN 0-88497-031-0); pap. write for info. (ISBN 0-88497-032-9); Vol. 1 & 2. pap. write for info. (ISBN 0-88497-030-2). Aum Pubns.
--Giving & Becoming. 50p. (Orig.). 1975. pap. 2.00 (ISBN 0-88497-122-8). Aum Pubns.
--God's Vision Promise. 50p. (Orig.). pap. 2.00 (ISBN 0-88497-125-2). Aum Pubns.
--The Golden Boat, 20 vols. (Illus.). 50p. (Orig.). 1974. pap. 3.00 ea. Aum Pubns.
--I Need Only God. 50p. (Orig.). 1975. pap. 2.00 (ISBN 0-88497-133-3). Aum Pubns.
--Immortality's Dance. 50p. (Orig.). 1974. pap. 2.00 (ISBN 0-88497-132-5). Aum Pubns.
--Inner & Outer Peace. 113p. (Orig.). 1984. pap. 5.95 (ISBN 0-88497-769-2). Aum Pubns.
--Inspiration-Garden & Aspiration-Leaves. 58p. (Orig.). 1977. pap. 2.00 (ISBN 0-88497-379-4). Aum Pubns.
--The Jewel of Humility. (Illus.). 56p. (Orig.). 1980. pap. 2.00 (ISBN 0-88497-493-6). Aum Pubns.
--Justice-Light & Satisfaction-Delight. (Soulful Questions & Fruitful Answers on Law & Justice). 41p. (Orig.). 1977. pap. 2.00 (ISBN 0-88497-338-7). Aum Pubns.
--Light-Delight-Journeys. 67p. (Orig.). 1975. pap. 2.00 (ISBN 0-88497-102-3). Aum Pubns.
--Lord, Receive This Little Undying Cry. 50p. (Orig.). 1975. pap. 2.00. Aum Pubns.
--The Master & the Disciple. LC 85-72172. 115p. (Orig.). 1985. pap. 3.95 (ISBN 0-317-46896-0). Aum Pubns.
--Meditation: Man-Perfection in God-Satisfaction. (Illus.). 1979. pap. 6.95 (ISBN 0-88497-444-8). Aum Pubns.
--Mother India's Lighthouse: India's Spiritual Leaders. LC 74-189998. 288p. 1973. pap. cancelled (ISBN 0-89345-219-X, Steinerbks). Garber Comm.
--My Life-Tree. 50p. (Orig.). 1975. pap. 2.00 (ISBN 0-88497-221-6). Aum Pubns.
--My Lord's Secrets Revealed. 102p. text ed. 10.00 (ISBN 0-88497-793-5); pap. 5.00 (ISBN 0-317-46895-2). Aum Pubns.
--O My Pilot Beloved. 54p. (Orig.). 1980. pap. 2.00 (ISBN 0-88497-502-9). Aum Pubns.
--One Lives, One Dies. 81p. 1974. pap. 2.00 (ISBN 0-88497-072-8). Aum Pubns.
--Perfection in the Head World. 55p. (Orig.). 1980. pap. 2.00 (ISBN 0-88497-492-8). Aum Pubns.
--The Significance of a Smile. 52p. (Orig.). 1977. pap. 2.00 (ISBN 0-88497-367-0). Aum Pubns.
--The Silence of Death. (Illus.). 46p. (Orig.). 1973. pap. 2.00 (ISBN 0-88497-035-3). Aum Pubns.
--Something, Somehow, Somewhere, Someday. 70p. (Orig.). 1973. pap. 2.00 (ISBN 0-88497-025-6). Aum Pubns.
--Songs of the Soul. 96p. (Orig.). 1983. pap. 5.00 (ISBN 0-88497-738-2). Aum Pubns.
--A Soulful Tribute to the Secretary-General: The Pilot Supreme of the United Nations. (Illus.). 1978. pap. 4.95 (ISBN 0-88497-443-X). Aum Pubns.
--Sri Chinmoy Speaks, 10 pts. Incl. Pt. 1. 55p (ISBN 0-88497-282-8); Pt. 2. 58p (ISBN 0-88497-285-2); Pt. 3. 65p (ISBN 0-88497-286-0); Pt. 4. 62p (ISBN 0-88497-288-7); Pt. 5. 56p (ISBN 0-88497-289-5); Pt. 6. 57p (ISBN 0-88497-290-9); Pt. 7. 58p (ISBN 0-88497-294-1); Pt. 8. 56p (ISBN 0-88497-295-X); Pt. 9. 51p (ISBN 0-88497-296-8); Pt. 10. 62p (ISBN 0-88497-335-2). 1976-77. pap. 2.00 ea. Aum Pubns.
--The Summits of God Life: Samadhi & Siddhi. LC 80-65397. 145p. 1984. pap. 3.95 (ISBN 0-88497-145-7). Aum Pubns.
--This Is God's Home. 50p. (Orig.). pap. 2.00 (ISBN 0-88497-233-X). Aum Pubns.
--Union & Oneness. 50p. (Orig.). 1976. pap. 2.00 (ISBN 0-88497-266-6). Aum Pubns.
--Wisdom-Waves in New York, 2 pts. (Orig.). 1979. pap. 2.00 ea. Pt. 1, 53p (ISBN 0-88497-487-1). Pt. 2, 50p (ISBN 0-88497-488-X). Aum Pubns.
--Yoga & Spiritual Life. rev. ed. LC 74-81309. 160p. 1974. pap. 4.95 (ISBN 0-88497-040-X). Aum Pubns.
Chinn, Edward. Questions of the Heart. (Orig.). 1987. pap. price not set (ISBN 0-89536-877-3, 7863). CSS of Ohio.
--The Wonder of Words, Bk. II. Sherer, Michael L., ed. (Orig.). 1987. pap. 7.50 (ISBN 0-89536-867-6, 7826, Co. Pub. by Forward Movement). CSS of Ohio.
--The Wonder of Words, Bk. 2. (Orig.). 1987. pap. 7.50 (ISBN 0-88028-059-X, Co-Pub. by CSS of OH). Forward Movement.
--The Wonder of Words: One Hundred Words & Phrases Shaping How Christians Think & Live. (Orig.). 1985. pap. 5.75 (ISBN 0-89536-737-8, 5822). CSS of Ohio.
Chinn, Wilberta L. & Owyang, Gregory R. Enjoy Your Quiet Time. 52p. 1986. wkbk. 3.00 (ISBN 0-937673-01-3). Peacock Ent LA.
Chinnici, Joseph P. The English Catholic Enlightenment: John Lingard & the Cisalpine Movement, 1780 to 1850. LC 79-20250. (Illus.). xiv, 262p. 1980. 24.95x (ISBN 0-915762-10-2). Patmos Pr.
Chinnici, Joseph P., ed. Devotion to the Holy Spirit in American Catholicism. LC 85-60956. (Sources of American Spirituality Ser.: Vol. 3). 256p. 1985. 12.95 (ISBN 0-8091-0366-4). Paulist Pr.
Chinul. The Korean Approach to Zen: The Collected Works of Chinul. Buswell, Robert E., Jr., tr. LC 82-23873. 484p. 1983. text ed. 29.95x (ISBN 0-8248-0785-5). UH Pr.
Chipa, A. K. Beauty & Wisdom of the Holy Qur'an. 1971. 3.25x (ISBN 0-87902-159-4). Orientalia.
Chippindale, Christopher. Stonehenge Complete: Archaeology, History, Heritage. LC 83-70803. (Illus.). 300p. 1983. 32.50 (ISBN 0-8014-1639-6). Cornell U Pr.
Chippindall, W. H. History of the Parish of Tunstall. 1940. 16.00 (ISBN 0-384-08875-9). Johnson Repr.
Chirban, John T., ed. Coping with Death & Dying: An Interdisciplinary Approach. 108p. 1986. lib. bdg. 22.00 (ISBN 0-8191-4984-5); pap. text ed. 8.75 (ISBN 0-8191-4985-3). U Pr of Amer.
--Marriage & the Family Medicine, Psychology & Religion: New Directions, New Integrations. (Series on Medicine, Psychology & Religion). (Illus.). 94p. (Orig.). 1983. pap. text ed. 4.95 (ISBN 0-916586-63-4). Holy Cross Orthodox.
Chirichigno, G. C., jt. auth. see Archer, Gleason L.
Chirico, Peter. Infallibility: The Crossroads of Doctrine. (Theology & Life Ser.: Vol. 1). pap. 9.95 (ISBN 0-89453-296-0). M Glazier.
Chironna, Mark. The Elisha Principle. 54p. (Orig.). 1985. pap. 2.95 (ISBN 0-938612-11-5). Revival Press.
Chirri, Imam Mohamad Jawad. The Faith of Islam. 24p. Date not set. pap. 3.00 (ISBN 0-317-52358-9). Islamic Ctr.
--The Five Daily Prayers. 24p. Date not set. pap. 3.00 (ISBN 0-317-52360-0). Islamic Ctr.
Chirri, Mohamad J. The Brother of the Prophet Mohammad: The Imam Ali, 2 vols, Vol. II. LC 79-127838. 400p. 1982. 15.00 (ISBN 0-942778-00-6). Islamic Ctr.
Chisholm, Alex & Chisholm, Sarah. Emotions: Can You Trust Them? Leader's Guide. 48p. 1984. pap. 3.95 (ISBN 0-8307-0992-4, 6101926). Regal.
Chisholm, Emily, tr. see Thurian, Max.
Chisholm, Sarah, jt. auth. see Chisholm, Alex.
Chissin, Chaim. A Palestine Diary. 1976. 10.00 (ISBN 0-685-82598-1). Herzl Pr.
Chittick, Donald E. The Controversy: Roots of the Creation-Evolution Conflict. LC 84-22670. (Critical Concern Ser.). 1984. 13.95 (ISBN 0-88070-019-X); pap. 9.95. Multnomah.
Chittick, W. C. & Tabataba'i, Allamah, eds. A Shi'ite Anthology. Chittick, W. C., tr. 152p. 1980. 40.00x (ISBN 0-317-39150-X, Pub. by Luzac & Co Ltd); pap. 29.00x (ISBN 0-317-39151-8). State Mutual Bk.
Chittick, W. C., tr. see Chittick, W. C. & Tabataba'i, Allamah.
Chittick, William & Wilson, Peter, trs. Fakhruddin Iraqi: Divine Flashes. 1982. 12.95 (ISBN 0-8091-0329-X); pap. 7.95 (ISBN 0-8091-2372-X). Paulist Pr.
Chittick, William, tr. see Nurbakhsh, Javad.
Chittick, William, tr. see Tabatabai, Muhammad.
Chittick, William C. The Sufi Path of Love: The Spiritual Teachings of Rumi. LC 82-19511. (SUNY Series in Islam). 400p. 1983. 44.50x (ISBN 0-87395-723-7); pap. 12.95x (ISBN 0-87395-724-5). State U NY Pr.
Chittick, William C., ed. see Tabataba'I, Allamah.
Chittick, William C., tr. see Al-Abidin, Zayn.
Chittick, William C., tr. see Al-Muminin, Amir.
Chittick, William C., tr. see Talib, Ali I.
Chittister, Joan. Women, Ministry, & the Church. LC 82-62418. 1983. pap. 5.95 (ISBN 0-8091-2528-5). Paulist Pr.
Chittister, Joan & Kownacki, Mary L. Psalm Journal. LC 85-50308. 104p. (Orig.). 1985. pap. 6.95 (ISBN 0-934134-28-6, Leaven Pr). Sheed & Ward MO.
Chittister, Joan, et al. Midwives of the Future: American Sisters Tell Their Story. Ware, Ann P., ed. LC 84-82554. 237p. (Orig.). 1984. pap. 8.95 (ISBN 0-934134-11-1, Leaven Pr). Sheed & Ward MO.
Chittister, Joan D. & Marty, Martin E. Faith & Ferment: An Interdisciplinary Study of Christian Beliefs & Practices. Bilheimer, Robert S., ed. 352p. 1983. pap. 15.95 (ISBN 0-8146-1289-X). Liturgical Pr.
Chitty, Derwas J. The Desert a City. 222p. 1977. pap. 8.95 (ISBN 0-913836-45-1). St Vladimirs.
Chiu, Milton M. The Tao of Chinese Religion. (Illus.). 432p. (Orig.). 1985. lib. bdg. 29.50 (ISBN 0-8191-4263-8); pap. text ed. 17.50 (ISBN 0-8191-4264-6). U Pr of Amer.
Chivington, Paul K., jt. auth. see Keyes, Elizabeth.
Chmykhaler, Timothy & Smith, Danny. The Last Christian: Release of the Siberian Seven. 208p. 1985. pap. 7.95 (ISBN 0-310-34021-7, 12411P). Zondervan.
Cho, Paul Y. The Fourth Dimension. LC 79-65588. 1979. pap. 5.95 (ISBN 0-88270-380-3, Pub. by Logos). Bridge Pub.
--The Leap of Faith. 120p. 1984. pap. 2.95 (ISBN 0-88270-574-1). Bridge Pub.
--Solving Life's Problems. LC 80-82787. (Orig.). 1980. pap. 4.95 (ISBN 0-88270-450-8). Bridge Pub.
Cho, Paul Y. & Hostetler, Harold. Successful Home Cell Groups. LC 81-80025. 1981. pap. 5.95 (ISBN 0-88270-513-X, Pub. by Logos). Bridge Pub.
Cho, Paul Y. & Manzano, R. Whitney. The Fourth Dimension, Vol. 2. LC 79-65588. 183p. 1983. pap. 5.95 (ISBN 0-88270-561-X). Bridge Pub.
--Mucho Mas Que Numeros. Bernal, Luis L., ed. Lievano, M. Francisco, tr. Tr. of More Than Numbers. (Span.). 208p. 1985. pap. text ed. 2.95 (ISBN 0-8297-0531-7). Life Pubs Intl.
--La Oracion - Clave del Avivamiento. Araujo, Juan S., tr. from Eng. Tr. of Prayer - Key to Revival. (Span.). 128p. 1987. pap. 3.95 (ISBN 0-88113-241-1). Edit Betania.
--Prayer: Key to Revival. 224p. 1984. 9.95 (ISBN 0-8499-0453-6, 0453-6). Word Bks.
Choate, J. E., jt. auth. see Doran, Adron.
Choate, Joseph H. Ralph Waldo Emerson. 1978. Repr. of 1903 ed. lib. bdg. 8.50 (ISBN 0-8495-0818-5). Arden Lib.
--Ralph Waldo Emerson. LC 73-4034. 1973. lib. bdg. 7.50 (ISBN 0-8414-1831-4). Folcroft.
Chodorow, Stanley, jt. auth. see Hoyt, Robert S.
Cholmeley, Katharine. Margery Kempe, Genius & Mystic. LC 78-7811. 1978. Repr. of 1947 ed. lib. bdg. 17.50 (ISBN 0-8414-0296-5). Folcroft.
Chomsky, Noam. Morphophonemics of Modern Hebrew. Hankamer, Jorge, ed. LC 78-66579. (Outstanding Dissertations in Linguistics Ser.). 1979. 15.00 (ISBN 0-8240-9688-6). Garland Pub.
Chomsky, William. Hebrew: The Eternal Language. LC 57-8140. 322p. 1975. 5.95 (ISBN 0-8276-0077-1, 384). Jewish Pubns.
Chong Sun Kim. Reverend Sun Myung Moon. LC 78-52115. 1978. pap. text ed. 9.50 (ISBN 0-8191-0494-9). U Pr of Amer.
Chophel, Norbu. Folk Culture of Tibet. 105p. 1986. Repr. 7.50X (ISBN 0-8364-1676-7, Pub. by Manohar India). South Asia Bks.
Chopp, Rebecca S. The Praxis of Suffering: An Interpretation of Liberation & Political Theologies. LC 86-824. 192p. (Orig.). 1986. pap. 12.95 (ISBN 0-88344-256-6). Orbis Bks.
Chopra, P. N., ed. Contributions of Buddhism to World Civilization & Culture. 408p. 50.00X (ISBN 0-317-52136-5, Pub. by S Chand India). State Mutual Bk.
--Religions & Communities of India. 1982. 59.00x (ISBN 0-85692-081-9, Pub. by E-W Pubns England). State Mutual Bk.
Choquette, Diane, compiled by. New Religious Movements in the United States & Canada: A Critical Assessment & Annotated Bibliography. LC 85-9964. (Bibliographies & Indexes in Religious Studies Ser.: No. 5). i, 235p. 1985. lib. bdg. 39.95 (ISBN 0-313-23772-7, CRM/). Greenwood.
Chotzinoff, Samuel. A Lost Paradise: Early Reminiscences. facsimile ed. LC 74-27970. (Modern Jewish Experience Ser.). 1975. Repr. of 1955 ed. 31.00x (ISBN 0-405-06700-3). Ayer Co Pubs.
Chou, Peter, tr. see Spurgeon, Charles.
Choudhary, Bani R. The Story of Krishna. (Illus.). 1979. 7.25 (ISBN 0-89744-134-6). Auromere.
--The Story of Ramayan. (Illus.). 1979. 7.50 (ISBN 0-89744-133-8). Auromere.
Choudhary, K. P. Modern Indian Mysticism. 1981. 17.00x (ISBN 0-8364-0744-X, Pub. by Motilal Banarsidass). South Asia Bks.
Choudhury, Bikram & Reynolds, Bonnie J. Bikram's Beginning Yoga Class. new ed. LC 76-29218. (Illus.). 224p. 1977. 13.50 (ISBN 0-87477-081-5); pap. 9.95 (ISBN 0-87477-082-3). J P Tarcher.
Choudhury, Masudul A. Contributions to Islamic Economic Theory: A Study in Social Economics. LC 85-22149. 224p. 1986. 29.95 (ISBN 0-312-16881-0). St Martin.
Chouraqui, Andre. The People & the Faith of the Bible. Gugli, William V., tr. LC 74-21237. 224p. 1975. 15.00x (ISBN 0-87023-172-3). U of Mass Pr.
Chowdharay-Best, George, jt. auth. see Biggs-Davison, John.
Chow Tun Yi. The Book of Universality: A Supplement to the Book of Changes. Hsu, F. G., tr. from Chinese. 70p. 1979. pap. 2.00 (ISBN 0-89071-242-5). Matagiri.
Choy, Leona. Andrew Murray: Apostle of Abiding Love. 1978. 8.95 (ISBN 0-87508-368-4); pap. 6.95 (ISBN 0-87508-367-6). Chr Lit.
Choy, Leona, jt. auth. see Murray, Andrew.
Chretien, Leonard & Chretien, Marjorie. Witnesses of Jehovah. 208p. (Orig.). 1987. pap. 6.95 (ISBN 0-89081-587-9). Harvest Hse.
Chretien, Marjorie, jt. auth. see Chretien, Leonard.
Chrichton, J. D. Christian Celebration: A Three-in-One Textbook. 604p. (Orig.). pap. text ed. 22.50 (ISBN 0-225-66399-6, HarpR). Har-Row.
Chrisci, John. Mysticism: The Search for Ultimate Meaning. 78p. 1986. text ed. 17.50 (ISBN 0-8191-5609-4); pap. text ed. 7.75 (ISBN 0-8191-5610-8). U Pr of Amer.
Chrisman, Miriam & Grundler, Otto, eds. Social Groups & Religious Ideas in the Sixteenth-Century. (Studies in Medieval Culture: No. XIII). 1978. pap. 4.95x (ISBN 0-918720-02-8). Medieval Inst.
Christ, Carol. Diving Deep & Surfacing: Women Writers on Spiritual Quest. 2nd, rev. ed. LC 86-70552. 157p. 1986. pap. 8.95 (ISBN 0-8070-6351-7, BP 722). Beacon Pr.
Christ, Carol P. & Plaskow, Judith. Womanspirit Rising: A Feminist Reader in Religion. LC 78-3363. (Orig.). 1979. pap. 8.95 (ISBN 0-06-061385-8, RD 275, HarpR). Har-Row.
Christ for the Nations, ed. see Lindsay, Gordon.
Christ Foundation Staff. A Spiritual Sex Manual. LC 82-72079. (Illus.). 176p. 1982. pap. 9.95 (ISBN 0-910315-01-9). Christ Found.
Christanand, M. The Philosophy of Indian Monotheism. 1979. 12.00x (ISBN 0-8364-0558-7, Pub. by Macmillan India). South Asia Bks.
Christensen, Alice & Rankin, David. Easy Does It: Yoga for Older People. LC 78-4755. (Illus.). 1979. spiral bdg. 11.95 (ISBN 0-06-250145-3, RD 289, HarpR). Har-Row.
Christensen, Barbara K., jt. auth. see Christensen, Joe J.
Christensen, Bernard, tr. see Steinberger, G.
Christensen, Carl C. Art & the Reformation in Germany. (Studies in the Reformation Ser.: Vol.2). (Illus.). 269p. 1981. 18.95x (ISBN 0-8214-0388-5, 82-82816, Co-Pub by Wayne State U Pr). Ohio U Pr.
Christensen, Chuck & Christensen, Winnie. Acts 1-12: God Moves in the Early Church. rev. ed. (Fisherman Bible Study Guide Ser.). 68p. 1979. saddle stitch 2.95 (ISBN 0-87788-007-7). Shaw Pubs.
--How to Listen When God Speaks. LC 78-73294. 79p. 1979. pap. 2.95 (ISBN 0-87788-355-6). Shaw Pubs.

--James: Faith in Action. LC 75-33442. (Fisherman Bible Studyguide Ser.). 55p. 1975. saddle-stitched 2.95 (ISBN 0-87788-421-8). Shaw Pubs.
--Mark: God in Action. LC 72-88935. (Fisherman Bible Studyguide Ser.). 94p. 1972. saddle-stitched 2.95 (ISBN 0-87788-309-2). Shaw Pubs.
--Paul: Thirteenth Apostle. (Fisherman Bible Studyguide Ser.). 64p. (Orig.). 1987. pap. 2.95 (ISBN 0-87788-652-0). Shaw Pubs.
Christensen, Darrel E. The Search for Concreteness-Reflections on Hegel & Whitehead: A Treatise on Self-Evidence & Critical Method in Philosophy. LC 85-63421. 516p. 1986. 45.00x (ISBN 0-941664-22-8, Pub. by Susquehanna U Pr). Assoc Univ Prs.
Christensen, James L. Communion Reflections & Prayers. Lambert, Herbert, ed. LC 84-29361. 64p. (Orig.). 1985. pap. 4.95 (ISBN 0-8272-0446-9). CBP.
--Contemporary Worship Services. LC 75-137445. Repr. of 1971 ed. 64.00 (ISBN 0-8357-9517-9, 2011444). Bks Demand UMI.
--The Minister's Marriage Handbook. rev. ed. 160p. 1974. Repr. 10.95 (ISBN 0-8007-1424-5). Revell.
Christensen, Joe J. To Grow in Spirit. 81p. 1983. 6.95 (ISBN 0-87747-968-2). Deseret Bk.
Christensen, Joe J. & Christensen, Barbara K. Making Your Home a Missionary Training Center. 140p. 1985. 7.95 (ISBN 0-87747-589-X). Deseret Bk.
Christensen, Leon N. The Little Book: Why I Am a Mormon. 1976. 12.00 (ISBN 0-8283-1606-6). Branden Pub Co.
Christensen, Ronald. The Death of Plato, the Aftermath. vii, 120p. 1983. lib. bdg. 8.95 (ISBN 0-938876-18-X). Entropy Ltd.
Christensen, W. N., jt. auth. see King-Farlow, J.
Christensen, Winnie. Women Who Achieved for God. (Fisherman Bible Studyguide). 80p. 1984. pap. 2.95 (ISBN 0-87788-937-6). Shaw Pubs.
--Women Who Believed God. (Fisherman Bible Studyguide Ser.). 77p. 1983. saddle-stiched 2.95 (ISBN 0-87788-936-8). Shaw Pubs.
Christensen, Winnie, jt. auth. see Christensen, Chuck.
Christenson, Evelyn. Cambiame, Senor! 224p. 1980. 3.25 (ISBN 0-88113-035-4). Edit Betania.
--Gaining Through Losing. LC 80-51630. 180p. 1981. 5.95 (ISBN 0-88207-795-3); pap. 5.95 (ISBN 0-88207-344-3). Victor Bks.
--Lord, Change Me. LC 77-81219. 192p. 1977. pap. 5.95 (ISBN 0-88207-756-2). Victor Bks.
--Perder Para Ganar. 1983. 3.75 (ISBN 0-88113-243-8). Edit Betania.
--What Happens When God Answers. 160p. 1986. 9.95 (ISBN 0-8499-0569-9). Word Bks.
Christenson, Evelyn & Blake, Viola. What Happens When Women Pray. 144p. 1975. pap. 5.95 (ISBN 0-88207-715-5). Victor Bks.
Christenson, Larry. Back to Square One. LC 79-16413. 144p. 1979. pap. 3.95 (ISBN 0-87123-025-9, 210025). Bethany Hse.
--Christ & His Church. (Trinity Bible Ser.). 160p. 1973. pap. 4.95 spiral wkbk. (ISBN 0-87123-550-1, 240550). Bethany Hse.
--The Covenant. (Trinity Bible Ser.). 144p. 1973. pap. 5.95 spiral wkbk. (ISBN 0-87123-551-X, 240551). Bethany Hse.
--La Familia Cristiana. 238p. 1972. 3.95 (ISBN 0-88113-080-X). Edit Betania.
--Family Pocket Promise Book. LC 83-72175. 128p. (Orig.). 1983. pap. 2.95 (ISBN 0-87123-303-7, 200303). Bethany Hse.
--Gift of Tongues. 1963. pap. 1.25 (ISBN 0-87123-184-0, 260184). Bethany Hse.
--Hacia Donde Va la Familia? 32p. 1978. 1.00 (ISBN 0-88113-110-5). Edit Betania.
--How to Have a Daily Quiet Time. 16p. 1979. saddle stitch 0.99 (ISBN 0-87123-235-9, 200235). Bethany Hse.
--The Kingdom. (Trinity Bible Ser.). 160p. 1972. pap. 5.95x (ISBN 0-87123-548-X, 240548). Bethany Hse.
--La Mente Renovada. 128p. 1975. 2.50 (ISBN 0-88113-199-7). Edit Betania.
--La Pareja Cristiana. 1982. 3.75 (ISBN 0-88113-314-0). Edit Betania.
--Speaking in Tongues. LC 97-5595. 1968. pap. 3.95 (ISBN 0-87123-518-8, 200518). Bethany Hse.
--Trinity Teacher Training Workshop Booklet. (Trinity Bible Ser.). 80p. 1975. pap. 2.95 (ISBN 0-87123-552-8, 240552). Bethany Hse.
--What about Baptism? 24p. (Orig.). 1986. pap. 1.35 (ISBN 0-8066-2257-1, 23-3009). Augsburg.
--The Wonderful Way That Babies Are Made. LC 82-12813. 48p. (Orig.). 1982. 8.95 (ISBN 0-87123-627-3, 230627). Bethany Hse.
Christenson, Larry & Christenson, Nordis. The Christian Couple. LC 77-24085. 1977. pap. 5.95 (ISBN 0-87123-051-8); study guide 1.50 (ISBN 0-87123-046-1, 210046). Bethany Hse.
Christenson, Larry, ed. Welcome, Holy Spirit: A Study of Charismatic Renewal in the Church. 400p. (Orig.). 1987. pap. 16.95 (ISBN 0-8066-2273-3, 10-7021). Augsburg.
Christenson, Nordis, jt. auth. see Christenson, Larry.
Christesen, Barbara. The Magic & Meaning of Voodoo. LC 77-12781. (Myth, Magic & Superstition Ser.). (Illus.). 1977. PLB 14.65 (ISBN 0-8172-1030-X). Raintree Pubs.
--Myths of the Orient. LC 77-22199. (Myth, Magic & Superstition). (Illus.). 1977. PLB 14.65 (ISBN 0-8172-1043-1). Raintree Pubs.
Christian Broadcasting Network Staff, ed. The Christian Counselor's Handbook. 240p. 1987. pap. 8.95 (ISBN 0-8423-0255-7). Tyndale.
Christian, C. W. Friedrich Schleiermacher. 157p. 1984. pap. text ed. 8.95 (ISBN 0-8499-3005-7, 3005-7). Word Bks.
Christian Center Staff. Bible Birthday Book. 1983. 5.95t (ISBN 0-911346-06-6). Christianica.
Christian Character Library Staff & Rinehart, Stacy. Living in Light of Eternity. 176p. 1986. 8.95 (ISBN 0-89109-551-9). NavPress.
Christian, Chris. How to Get Started in Christian Music. Styll, John, ed. 167p. 1986. 12.95 (ISBN 0-9616817-0-5). Home Sweet Home.
Christian College Coalition Staff. A Guide to Christian Colleges 1984-85. rev. ed. 160p. 1984. pap. 12.95 (ISBN 0-8028-0010-6). Eerdmans.
Christian Life Magazine Staff & Wagner, C. Peter. Signs & Wonders Today. 1986. write for info. (ISBN 0-8297-0709-3). Life Pubs Intl.
Christian Life Staff. America's Great Revivals. 1970. pap. 3.50 (ISBN 0-87123-003-8). Bethany Hse.
Christian, Mary B. Christmas Reflections. 1980. pap. 3.95 (ISBN 0-570-03494-9, 56-1711). Concordia.
--Grandfathers: God's Gift to Children. 1982. pap. 2.75 (ISBN 0-570-04069-8, 56-1372). Concordia.
--Grandmothers: God's Gift to Children. 1982. pap. 2.75 (ISBN 0-570-04068-X, 56-1371). Concordia.
Christian, Mary B. & Van Woerkom, Dorothy. Bible Heroes, Kings & Prophets. 1982. pap. 3.75 (ISBN 0-570-04066-3, 56-1718). Concordia.
Christian Movement for Peace Staff. Rich World, Poor World: A Curriculum Resource on Youth & Development. (YA) 1986. pap. text ed. 29.95 (ISBN 0-697-02203-X). Wm C Brown.
Christian, Owen L. Faith in Conflict. 192p. 1986. 12.50 (ISBN 0-89962-519-3). Todd & Honeywell.
Christian Publications, Inc. Staff, ed. Fifty-Two Visual Ideas for Opening Assemblies, 3 vols. 2.25 ea. Vol. 1 (ISBN 0-87509-271-3). Vol. 2 (ISBN 0-87509-272-1). Vol. 3 (ISBN 0-87509-273-X). Chr Pubns.
Christian, Robert. Common Sense Renewed. 132p. 1986. 12.50 (ISBN 0-89279-078-4). Graphic Pub.
Christian Science Monitor, jt. auth. see Ladies Home Journal.
Christian, William A. An Interpretation of Whitehead's Metaphysics. LC 77-5619. 1977. Repr. of 1959 ed. lib. bdg. 35.00x (ISBN 0-8371-9638-8, CHIW). Greenwood.
Christian, William A., Jr. Apparitions in Late Medieval & Renaissance Spain. LC 80-8541. (Illus.). 304p. 1981. 34.00x (ISBN 0-691-05326-X). Princeton U Pr.
--Local Religion in 16th Century Spain. LC 80-7513. 296p. 1981. 28.00 (ISBN 0-691-05306-5). Princeton U Pr.
Christian Writers Institute Staff. The Successful Writers & Editors Guidebook. LC 76-62692. 1977. 10.95 (ISBN 0-88419-014-5). Creation Hse.
Christiani, Leon. Evidence of Satan in the Modern World. 1975. pap. 1.50 (ISBN 0-380-00413-5, 25122). Avon.
--St. Francis of Assisi. LC 74-79802. 1975. 4.95 (ISBN 0-8198-0494-0). Dghtrs St Paul.
Christianica Center Staff. Christianica. LC 74-13005. (Illus.). 1975. 5.95 (ISBN 0-911346-02-3). Christianica.
--Rosario Biblico. (Illus.). 1980. 5.95 (ISBN 0-911346-04-X). Christianica.
--Scriptural Rosary. LC 64-66463. (Illus.). 1961. 5.95 (ISBN 0-911346-01-5). Christianica.
Christiansen, Eric. The Northern Crusades: The Baltic & the Catholic Frontier, 1100-1525. (Illus.). xxii, 265p. 1981. 25.00 (ISBN 0-8166-0994-2); pap. 10.95x (ISBN 0-8166-1018-5). U of Minn Pr.
Christianson, Arne. The Future Is Now. 1983. 8.95 (ISBN 0-533-05552-0). Vantage.
Christie, Anthony. Chinese Mythology. LC 85-5975. (The Library of the World's Myths & Legends). (Illus.). 144p. 1985. 18.95 (ISBN 0-87226-015-1). P Bedrick Bks.
Christie, Les. Dating & Waiting: A Chrisitan View of Love, Sex, & Dating. LC 83-1232. (Illus.). 80p. (Orig.). 1983. pap. 2.95 (ISBN 0-87239-643-6, 39972). Standard Pub.
--Getting a Grip on Time Management. 64p. 1984. pap. 5.95 (ISBN 0-88207-192-0). Victor Bks.
--Unsung Heroes: How to Recruit & Train Volunteers. 176p. 1987. text ed. 12.95 (ISBN 0-310-35150-2). Zondervan.
Christie, Richard C., ed. see Copley, Thomas.
Christ-Janer, Albert, et al, eds. American Hymns Old & New: Notes on the Hymns & Biographies of the Authors & Composers, 2 vols. LC 79-4630. (Illus.). 1454p. 1980. 72.00 (ISBN 0-231-05148-4). Columbia U Pr.
Christman, Ronald & Schibilla, Linda. Lessons on Doctrine: For Youth (Teacher) 48p. (Orig.). 1982. pap. 1.95 (ISBN 0-87239-604-5, 3376). Standard Pub.
--Lessons on Doctrine: For Youth (Workbook) (Illus.). 64p. (Orig.). 1982. pap. 3.50 (ISBN 0-87239-603-7, 3377). Standard Pub.
Christoff, Nicholas B. Saturday Night, Sunday Morning: Singles & the Church. LC 77-7841. 160p. 1980. pap. 4.95 (ISBN 0-06-061381-5, RD 341, HarpR). Har-Row.
Christoffel, R. Zwingli or the Rise of the Reformation in Switzerland. 1977. lib. bdg. 59.95 (ISBN 0-8490-2859-0). Gordon Pr.
Christopher. Our New Age: Words for the People. 1st ed. LC 77-72309. (Illus., Orig.). 1977. pap. 2.95 (ISBN 0-916940-01-2). World Light.
--Scott. new ed. (Orig.). 1978. pap. 3.95 (ISBN 0-87243-078-2). Templegate.
Christopher, George, Jr. Jesus of Nazareth: The Man, the Myth, the Enigma. 50p. 1984. 4.95 (ISBN 0-89697-176-7). Intl Univ Pr.
Christopher, J. R. & Ostling, Joan K. C. S. Lewis: An Annotated Checklist. LC 73-76556. (Serif Ser.: No. 30). 402p. 1974. 20.00x (ISBN 0-87338-138-6). Kent St U Pr.
Christopher, Joe R. C. S. Lewis. (Twayne's English Authors Ser.). 160p. 1987. lib. bdg. 16.95 (ISBN 0-8057-6944-7, TEAS 442, Twayne). G K Hall.
Christopher, John B. The Islamic Tradition. (Major Traditions in World Civilization Ser.). 1972. pap. text ed. 11.95 scp (ISBN 0-06-041283-6, HarpC). Har-Row.
Christopher, Joseph P., tr. see Augustine, St.
Christopher, Kenneth. Damien & the Island of Sickness: A Story About Damien. new ed. (Stories About Christian Heroes Ser.). (Illus.). 1979. pap. 1.95 (ISBN 0-86683-768-X, HarpR). Har-Row.
--The Merry Missionary: A Story About Philip Neri. (Stories About Christian Heroes Ser.). (Illus.). 32p. pap. 1.95 (ISBN 0-03-056876-5, HarpR). Har-Row.
--Ten Catholics: Lives to Remember. (Nazareth Bks). 120p. 1983. pap. 3.95 (ISBN 0-86683-715-9, HarpR). Har-Row.
Christophers, Richard A. George Abbot, Archbishop of Canterbury, 1562-1633: A Bibliography. LC 65-27845. pap. 59.00 (ISBN 0-317-10344-X, 2016440). Bks Demand UMI.
Christopherson, Victor A. Child Rearing In Today's Christian Family. (Family Life Ser.). 176p. 1985. pap. 6.95 (ISBN 0-8170-1065-3). Judson.
Christophus, Mike, jt. auth. see Kenyon, Mel.
Christou, Evangelos. The Logos of the Soul. Hillman, James, ed. (Dunquin Ser.: No. 2). 1963. pap. 6.50 (ISBN 0-88214-202-X). Spring Pubns.
Christovale, Cindy. Your Real Beauty. 80p. (Orig.). 1983. pap. 2.95 (ISBN 0-88144-018-3, CPS-018). Christian Pub.
Christy, Arthur. Orient in American Transcendentalism: A Study of Emerson, Thoreau & Alcott. 1963. lib. bdg. 26.00x (ISBN 0-374-91539-3, Octagon). Hippocrene Bks.
--The Transmigration of the Seven Brahmans. Thoreau, Henry D., tr. LC 72-3516. (American Literature Ser., No. 49). Orig. Title: Harivansa. 1972. Repr. of 1931 ed. lib. bdg. 29.95x (ISBN 0-8383-1563-1). Haskell.
Christy, David. Ethiopia: Her Gloom & Glory. LC 73-75550. Repr. of 1857 ed. 22.50x (ISBN 0-8371-1016-5, CHR&, Pub. by Negro U Pr). Greenwood.
Christy, Howard A., ed. see Palmer, Richard F. & Butler, Karl D.
Christy, James. The Puppet Ministry. 78p. 1978. 2.50 (ISBN 0-8341-0532-2). Beacon Hill.
Chrysostom, John. Discourses Against Judaizing Christains. (Fathers of the Church Ser.: Vol. 68). 286p. 1979. 29.95x (ISBN 0-8132-0068-7). Cath U Pr.
--On the Incomprehensible Nature of God. Harkins, Paul W., tr. from Greek. LC 83-1984. (Fathers of the Church Ser.: No. 72). 357p. 1984. 29.95x (ISBN 0-8132-0072-5). Cath U Pr.
--St. John Chrysostom on the Priesthood. 160p. 1977. pap. 4.95 (ISBN 0-913836-38-9). St Vladimirs.
Chrysostom, St. John. Duties of Parents & Children to One Another. pap. 0.25 (ISBN 0-686-17310-4). Eastern Orthodox.
Chrysostomos & Auxentios, Hieromonk. Contemporary Traditionalist Orthodox Thought. 80p. (Orig.). 1986. pap. 5.00 (ISBN 0-911165-07-X). Ctr Trad Orthodox.
Chrysostomos, Archimandrite. The Ancient Fathers of the Church: Translated Narratives from the Evertinos on Passions & Perfection in Christ. (Illus.). 118p. 1980. 7.95 (ISBN 0-916586-77-4); pap. 4.95 (ISBN 0-686-69869-X). Hellenic Coll Pr.
--Orthodox Liturgical Vesture: An Historical Treatment. 76p. 1981. 6.95 (ISBN 0-916586-43-X); pap. 3.95 (ISBN 0-916586-44-8). Holy Cross Orthodox.
--Orthodoxy & Papism. Williams, Theodore M., ed. LC 82-73693. 70p. 1982. pap. 4.50 (ISBN 0-911165-00-2). Ctr Trad Orthodox.
Chrysostomos, Archimandrite & Ambrosios, Hieromonk. Obedience. Young, Alexey & Derugin, Vladimir, eds. (Themes in Orthodox Patristic Psychology Ser.: Vol. 2). 90p. (Orig.). 1984. text ed. write for info. (ISBN 0-916586-88-X); pap. text ed. write for info. (ISBN 0-916586-31-6). Holy Cross Orthodox.
Chrysostomos, Archimandrite & Auxentios, Hieromonk. Scripture & Tradition. 96p. 1984. pap. 5.00 (ISBN 0-911165-04-5). Ctr Trad Orthodox.
Chrysostomos, Archimandrite & Williams, Theodore. Humility, Vol. 1. LC 82-74509. (Themes in Orthodox Patristic Psychology Ser.). 90p. (Orig.). 1983. pap. text ed. 4.50 (ISBN 0-911165-01-0); pap. write for info. (ISBN 0-911165-02-9). Ctr Trad Orthodox.
Chrysostomos, Archimandrite, tr. see Cavarnos, Constantine.
Chrysostomos, Archimandrite, et al. The Old Calendar Orthodox Church of Greece. 116p. 1985. pap. 4.50 (ISBN 0-911165-05-3). Ctr Trad Orthodox.
Chrysostomos, Bishop. Repentance. (Themes in Orthodox Patristic Psychology Ser.: Vol. III). 75p. (Orig.). 1986. pap. 5.00 (ISBN 0-911165-09-6). Ctr Trad Orthodox.
Chrystal, William G. A Father's Mantle: The Legacy of Gustav Niebuhr. LC 81-21108. 160p. (Orig.). 1982. pap. 7.95 (ISBN 0-8298-0494-3). Pilgrim NY.
Chrystal, William G., ed. Young Reinhold Niebuhr: The Early Writings - 1911 to 1931. rev. ed. 256p. 1982. pap. 8.95 (ISBN 0-8298-0607-5). Pilgrim NY.
Chu, John W. Selections from the New Testament in Chinese. 6.00 (ISBN 0-88710-083-X); tapes avail. (ISBN 0-88710-084-8). Far Eastern Pubns.
Chu, Jonathan M. Neighbors, Friends, or Madmen: The Puritan Adjustment to Quakerism in Seventeenth-Century Massachusetts Bay. LC 84-29035. (Contributions to the Study of Religion Ser.: No. 14). xiii, 207p. 1985. lib. bdg. 29.95 (ISBN 0-313-24809-5, CNE/). Greenwood.
Chu, Wen-Djang. Moslem Rebellion in Northwest China, 1862-1878. (Central Asiatic Studies: No. 5). 1966. pap. text ed. 31.20x (ISBN 90-2790-017-5). Mouton.
Chu, Wen Kuan. Tao & Longevity: Mind Body Transformation. LC 82-60164. 192p. (Orig.). 1984. pap. 7.95 (ISBN 0-87728-542-X). Weiser.
Chuang Tsu. Chuang Tsu - Inner Chapters. Gia-Fu Feng, ed. English, Jane, tr. (Giant Ser.). pap. 12.95 (ISBN 0-394-71990-5, V-990, Vin). Random.
Chuang Tzu. Chuang Tzu: Mystic, Moralist, & Social Reformer. 2nd rev. ed. Giles, Herbert A., tr. LC 70-38059. (BCL Ser.: No. II). Repr. of 1926 ed. 44.50 (ISBN 0-404-56915-3). AMS Pr.
Ch'u Chai & Chai, Winberg. Confucianism. LC 73-3977. 1974. pap. text ed. 5.50 (ISBN 0-8120-0303-9). Barron.
Chun-fang Yu. The Renewal of Buddhism in China: Chu-Hung & the Late Ming Synthesis. LC 79-28073. (Buddhist Studies). (Illus.). 1981. 34.00x (ISBN 0-231-04972-2). Columbia U Pr.
Chung-Liang Huang, Al, jt. auth. see Watts, Alan.
Chung-Yuan, Chang. Original Teachings of Cha'an Buddhism. pap. 9.95 (ISBN 0-394-62417-3, V-333, Vin). Random.
Chupco, Lee & Coachman, Ward. Creek (Muscogee) New Testament Concordance. 167p. 1982. spiral bdg. 12.50x (ISBN 0-940392-10-0). Indian U Pr OK.
Chupungco, Anscar J. Cultural Adaptation of the Liturgy. 117p. (Orig.). 1982. pap. 4.95 (ISBN 0-8091-2452-1). Paulist Pr.
Church Administration Department Staff. Illustrating the Gospel of Matthew. LC 81-68044. 1982. pap. 5.25 (ISBN 0-8054-2243-9). Broadman.
Church, Elmer T. Walk with Me in White. LC 86-81184. 154p. 1986. perfect bdg. 9.95 (ISBN 0-318-21723-6). E T Church.
Church, F. Forester. Entertaining Angels: A Guide to Heaven or Atheists & True Believers. 1987. 13.95. Har-Row.

Church, F. J., tr. see Plato.
Church, Gilbert, ed. see Steiner, Rudolf.
Church, Gilbert, et al, eds. see Steiner, Rudolf.
Church, Leslie F., ed. see Henry, Matthew.
Church, Mary C., ed. Life & Letters of Dean Church. 428p. 1981. Repr. of 1897 ed. lib. bdg. 45.00 (ISBN 0-8495-0859-2). Arden Lib.
Church of Christ Staff. What Lack We Yet? Thomas, J. D., ed. LC 74-170920. 319p. 1974. 13.95 (ISBN 0-89112-027-0, Bibl Res Pr). Abilene Christ U.
Church of England, House of Bishops Staff. The Nature of Christian Belief. 60p. (Orig.). 1986. pap. 2.25 (ISBN 0-88028-062-X). Forward Movement.
Church of England Staff. Articles to Be Inquired of, in the First Metropolitical Visitation of the Most Reverend Father Richarde...Archbishop of Canterbury. LC 74-28851. (English Experience Ser.: No. 732). 1975. Repr. of 1605 ed. 3.50 (ISBN 90-221-0732-9). Walter J Johnson.
--A Booke of Certaine Canons, Concernynge Some Parte of the Discipline of the Churche of England. LC 70-26475. (English Experience Ser.: No. 312). 1971. Repr. of 1571 ed. 7.00 (ISBN 9-0221-0312-9). Walter J Johnson.
--Certaine Sermons or Homilies Appointed to Be Read in the Churches in the Time of Elizabeth 1st, 1547-1571, 2 vols. in 1. LC 68-17016. 1968. Repr. of 1623 ed. 50.00x (ISBN 0-8201-1008-6). Schol Facsimiles.
--The Durham Book: Being the First Draft of the Revision of the Book of Common Prayer in 1661. Cuming, G. J., ed. LC 79-12674. 1979. Repr. of 1961 ed. lib. bdg. cancelled (ISBN 0-313-21481-6, CEBC). Greenwood.
--A Parte of a Register, Contayninge Sundrie Memorable Matters, Written by Diuers Godly & Learned in Our Time, Which Stande for the Reformation of Our Church. LC 72-5981. (English Experience Ser.: No. 509). 1973. Repr. of 1593 ed. 67.00 (ISBN 90-221-0509-1). Walter J Johnson.
Church of God Editorial Department. Manual for Editors & Writers. 1976. pap. 4.95 (ISBN 0-87148-568-0). Pathway Pr.
Church of St. Paul the Apostle, New York Staff. Sermons Preached at the Church of St. Paul the Apostle, New York, During the Year, 1863. 32.00 (ISBN 0-405-10851-6, 11854). Ayer Co Pubs.
Church of Scientology Information Service Staff. The Indispensability of Scientology Press, Vol. 1, Pt. 5. 1976. pap. 2.60 (ISBN 0-915598-10-8). Church of Scient Info.
Church of Scientology Information Service Staff & Hubbard, L. Ron. Success with Scientology. 112p. 1976. pap. 8.00 (ISBN 0-915598-01-9). Church of Scient Info.
Church of Scotland, Committee on Public Worship & Aids to Devotion. The Book of Common Order. 1979. 8.95x (ISBN 0-7152-0391-6); leather 14.00 (ISBN 0-686-75148-5). Outlook.
--New Ways to Worship. 1980. pap. 4.95x (ISBN 0-7152-0454-8). Outlook.
Church of Scotland - Committee on Public Worship & Aids to Devotion. Prayers for Contemporary Worship. 1977. pap. 4.95x (ISBN 0-7152-0351-7). Outlook.
--Prayers for Sunday Services. 1980. pap. 6.95x (ISBN 0-7152-0456-4). Outlook.
Church of Scotland - General Assembly - Committee On Public Worship And Aids To Devotion. Prayers for the Christian Year. 2nd ed. 172p. 1952. 10.95x (ISBN 0-19-145602-0). Oxford U Pr.
Church of Scotland Staff. The First & Second Books of Discipline: Together with Some Acts of the General Assemblies. LC 77-7433. (English Experience Ser.: No. 893). 1977. Repr. of 1621 ed. lib. bdg. 6.00 (ISBN 90-221-0893-7). Walter J Johnson.
--Register of Ministers, Exhorters & Readers & of Their Stipends. LC 71-174310. (Maitland Club, Glasgow. Publications: No. 5). Repr. of 1830 ed. 15.00 (ISBN 0-404-52929-1). AMS Pr.
Church of Scotland, the Woman's Guild Staff. Let's Choose Our Worship: Prayers for Women's Meetings. 1980. pap. 1.65 (ISBN 0-7152-0461-0). Outlook.
Church, R. W. The Beginning of the Middle Ages. 1977. lib. bdg. 59.95 (ISBN 0-8490-1484-0). Gordon Pr.
--Occasional Papers, 2 vols. 1973. Repr. of 1897 ed. 20.00 set (ISBN 0-8274-1533-8). R West.
--The Oxford Movement: Twelve Years 1833-1845. 1979. Repr. of 1891 ed. lib. bdg. 35.00 (ISBN 0-8482-7569-1). Norwood Edns.
Church, William F. Richelieu & Reason of State. LC 76-181518. 582p. 1972. 49.00x (ISBN 0-691-05199-2). Princeton U Pr.
--Richelieu & Reason of State. LC 76-181518. pap. 140.50 (ISBN 0-317-42020-8, 2025688). Bks Demand UMI.
Churches Alive, Inc. Staff. Caring. rev. ed. LC 81-66927. 60p. 1981. pap. text ed. 3.95 (ISBN 0-934396-23-X). Churches Alive.
--Communicating. LC 79-52133. (Love One Another Bible Study Ser.). (Illus.). 1979. wkbk. 3.00 (ISBN 0-934396-06-X). Churches Alive.
--Contributing. LC 79-52132. (Love One Another Bible Study Ser.). (Illus.). 1979. wkbk. 3.00 (ISBN 0-934396-05-1). Churches Alive.
--Esteeming. LC 79-52130. (Love One Another Bible Study Ser.). (Illus.). 1979. wkbk. 3.00 (ISBN 0-934396-03-5). Churches Alive.
--Forgiving. LC 79-52128. (Love One Another Bible Study Ser.). (Illus.). 1979. wkbk. 3.00 (ISBN 0-934396-01-9). Churches Alive.
--Growing as a Disciple Conference Notebook. rev. ed. 85p. 1983. pap. write for info. (ISBN 0-934396-37-X). Churches Alive.
--Growing by Discipling Pastor's Handbook. rev. ed. (Illus.). 150p. 1980. pap. text ed. 9.95 (ISBN 0-934396-09-4). Churches Alive.
--Growth Group Leader's Guide. rev. ed. LC 80-52536. (Illus.). 110p. 1980. pap. 7.95 (ISBN 0-934396-10-8). Churches Alive.
--Growth Group Member's Notebook. LC 80-52536. (Illus.). 105p. (Orig.). 1980. pap. text ed. 5.95 (ISBN 0-934396-11-6). Churches Alive.
--Love One Another Leader's Guide. LC 79-52128. (Love One Another Ser.). (Illus.). 85p. (Orig.). 1981. pap. text ed. 4.95 (ISBN 0-934396-13-2). Churches Alive.
--Maintaining Unity. LC 79-52134. (Love One Another Bible Study Ser.). (Illus.). 1979. wkbk. 3.00 (ISBN 0-934396-07-8). Churches Alive.
--Submitting. LC 79-52131. (Love One Another Bible Study Ser.). (Illus.). 1979. wkbk. 3.00 (ISBN 0-934396-04-3). Churches Alive.
--Understanding. LC 79-52129. (Love One Another Bible Study Ser.). (Illus.). 1979. wkbk. 3.00 (ISBN 0-934396-02-7). Churches Alive.
--Visitation Evangelism Leader's Guide. rev. ed. LC 84-73068. (Illus.). 112p. 1985. pap. text ed. 11.95 (ISBN 0-934396-40-X). Churches Alive.
--Visitation Evangelism Member's Notebook. rev. ed. (Illus.). 80p. 1985. pap. text ed. 9.95 (ISBN 0-934396-39-6). Churches Alive.
Churchill, Charles H. The Druzes & the Maronites Under the Turkish Rule from 1840 to 1860. LC 73-6273. (The Middle East Ser.). Repr. of 1862 ed. 20.00 (ISBN 0-405-05329-0). Ayer Co Pubs.
Churchill, J. W., ed. see Harlow, Louis K.
Churchill, John G. What the Bible Tells Me. 60p. 1976. pap. 1.50 (ISBN 0-8341-0412-1). Beacon Hill.
Churchwell, Kay. Baby Jesus. LC 85-24335. (Bible-&-Me Ser.). (Illus.). 1986. 5.95 (ISBN 0-8054-4170-0). Broadman.
Churgin, Pinchas & Smolar, Leivy. Studies in Targum Jonathan to the Prophets. 59.50x (ISBN 0-87068-109-5). Ktav.
Chwolsohn, D. Die Ssabier und der Ssabismus, 2 Vols. 1856. 85.00 (ISBN 0-384-09053-2). Johnson Repr.
Ciampi, Luke. Watering the Seed. 1977. 5.95 (ISBN 0-685-71934-0). Franciscan Herald.
Ciappetta, John T. A Christmas Caring, a Christmas Sharing. 32p. 1987. 6.95 (ISBN 0-89962-646-7). Todd & Honeywell.
Cicco, Philip Di see Krutza, William J. & Dicicco, Philip P.
Cicco, Philip P. Di see Krutza, William J. & DiCicco, Philip P.
Cicero. Nature of the Gods. McGregor, Horace C., tr. (Classics Ser.). 280p. (Orig.). 1972. pap. 6.95 (ISBN 0-14-044265-0). Penguin.
Cihlar, Many. Misticos en Oracion. AMORC Staff, tr. from Eng. (Span.). 59p. (Orig.). 1982. pap. 7.00 (ISBN 0-912057-82-3, GS-509). AMORC.
Cihlar, Many, compiled by. Mystics at Prayer. 19th ed. LC 36-17108. 57p. 1982. 7.95 (ISBN 0-912057-08-4, G-509). AMORC.
Cilento, V., ed. see Marien, Bert.
Cimbolic, Peter, jt. auth. see Hipple, John.
Cinquin, Emmanuelle. To Share with God's Poor: Sister among the Outcasts. LC 83-47735. (Illus.). 458p. 1983. pap. 5.95 (ISBN 0-06-061392-0, RD-485, HarpR). Har-Row.
Cinquino, J., tr. see Francesconi, Mario.
Cionca, John. The Troubleshooting Guide to Christian Education. LC 85-73069. 176p. 1986. pap. 7.95 (ISBN 0-89636-191-8). Accent Bks.
Cioni, Ray & Cioni, Sally. The Droodles Ten Commandments Storybook. (Droodles Adventure Ser.). (Illus.). 64p. 1983. text ed. 8.95 (ISBN 0-89191-636-9). Cook.
Cioni, Sally, jt. auth. see Cioni, Ray.
Cioran, E. M. The Trouble with Being Born. Howard, Richard, tr. from Fr. LC 81-51526. Orig. Title: L' Inconvenient d'etre Ne. Tr. of L' Inconvenient d'Etre Ne. 208p. 1981. pap. 5.95 (ISBN 0-394-17847-5). Seaver Bks.
Cipolla, Carlo M. Faith, Reason & the Plague in Seventeenth-Century Tuscany. Kittel, Muriel, tr. from Ital. LC 79-2479. (Illus.). 140p. 1980. 17.50x (ISBN 0-8014-1230-7). Cornell U Pr.
--Faith, Reason, & the Plague in Seventeenth-Century Tuscany. 128p. 1981. pap. 4.95 (ISBN 0-393-00045-1). Norton.
Cirino, Andre. In the Womb of the Cave. 366p. 1981. 14.00 (ISBN 0-933402-26-0); pap. 9.00 (ISBN 0-933402-25-2). Charisma Pr.
Cirino, Andre & Rogers, Francine. Teens Encounter Christ. LC 77-88321. (Illus., Orig.). 1978. pap. 2.25 (ISBN 0-8189-1156-5, 156, Pub. by Alba Bks). Alba.
Cirner, Randall J., jt. auth. see Scanlan, Michael.
Cirner, Therese. The Facts About Your Feelings: What Every Christian Woman Should Know. 142p. 1982. pap. 4.95 (ISBN 0-89283-103-0). Servant.
Cirou, Joseph, et al. The Johannine Hymnal. LC 75-14542. (Melody ed). 1970. 3.95 (ISBN 0-915866-00-5). Am Cath Pr.
Cisek, James & George, Anthea. Deciding for Yourself Youth Manual. (Illus.). 60p. (Orig.). 1985. pap. 5.95 (ISBN 0-9604510-1-3). Life Skills.
Citrin, Paul J. Joseph's Wardrobe. (Illus.). 1987. pap. 6.95 (ISBN 0-8074-0319-9). UAHC.
Citron, Samuel J. Dramatics for Creative Teaching. (Illus.). 1961. 9.50x (ISBN 0-8381-0212-3). United Syn Bk.
Ciuba, Edward J. Who Do You Say That I Am? An Adult Inquiry into the First Three Gospels. LC 74-10808. 155p. 1974. pap. 5.95 (ISBN 0-8189-0295-7). Alba.
Civrieux, Marc de see De Civrieux, Marc.
Cizik, Richard. The High Cost of Indifference. LC 84-15957. 1984. pap. 6.95 (ISBN 0-8307-1000-0, 5418377). Regal.
Claassen, W. Text & Context: Old Testament & Semitic Studies for F.C. Fensham. (JSOT Supplement Ser.: No. 48). 220p. 1987. text ed. 28.50x (ISBN 1-85075-040-8, Pub. by JSOT Pr England). Eisenbrauns.
Clabaugh, Gary K. Thunder on the Right: The Protestant Fundamentalists. LC 74-9551. 283p. 1974. 19.95x (ISBN 0-88229-108-4). Nelson-Hall.
Claerbaut, David. Urban Ministry. 224p. 1984. pap. 7.95 (ISBN 0-310-45961-3, 12605P). Zondervan.
Claeys, Monique, tr. see Bridges, Jerry.
Clagett, John Y. Christian Conscience. LC 84-9824. 1984. pap. 3.95 (ISBN 0-87227-097-1). Reg Baptist.
Claghorn, Gene. Women Composers & Hymnists: A Concise Biographical Dictionary. LC 83-20429. 288p. 1984. 22.50 (ISBN 0-8108-1680-6). Scarecrow.
Claiborne, Robert. God or Beast: Evolution & Human Nature. (Illus.). 1974. 7.95 (ISBN 0-393-06399-2). Norton.
Clair, Barry St. see St. Clair, Barry.
Clair, Frederic F. Ultimate Defense: A Practical Plan to Prevent Man's Self-Destruction. LC 59-6490. 1959. 3.30 (ISBN 0-8048-0606-3). C E Tuttle.
Clairmonte, Glenn. Truth to Tell. LC 78-66006. 1979. 5.95 (ISBN 0-87159-155-3). Unity School.
Clancy, Bill. Jesus: The Ultimate E.T. Howard, Dick, ed. 40p. (Orig.). 1983. pap. 1.75 (ISBN 0-912573-00-7). Believers Faith.
Clancy, Thomas H. The Conversational Word of God: A Commentary on the Doctrine of St. Ignatius of Loyola Concerning Spiritual Conversation, with Four Early Jesuit Texts. Ganss, George E., frwd. by. LC 78-51343. (Study Aids on Jesuit Topics: No. 8 in Ser. IV). 83p. 1978. 5.00 (ISBN 0-912422-33-5); pap. 2.50 smyth sewn (ISBN 0-912422-34-3). Inst Jesuit.
--English Catholic Books, 1641-1700. LC 74-704. 158p. 1974. pap. 8.00 (ISBN 0-8294-0231-4). Loyola.
--An Introduction to Jesuit Life: The Constitutions & History Through 435 Years. Ganss, George E., ed. LC 75-46080. (Study Aids on Jesuit Topics Ser.: No. 3). 422p. 1976. 12.00 (ISBN 0-912422-15-7). Inst Jesuit.
--Papist Pamphleteers. LC 64-14078. (Jesuit Studies). 1964. 4.95 (ISBN 0-8294-0013-3). Loyola.
Clanton, A. L. The Pentecostal Home: Study Guide. 80p. (Orig.). 1978. pap. 1.00 (ISBN 0-912315-43-1). Word Aflame.
Clanton, A. L., ed. Through the Bible Study Series, 7 vol. set. 2688p. 1982. text ed. 54.95 per set (ISBN 0-912315-51-2). Word Aflame.
--Through the Bible Study Series, Vol. VII. 384p. 1982. text ed. 6.95 (ISBN 0-912315-58-X). Word Aflame.
--Through the Bible Study Series, Vol. VI. 384p. 1981. text ed. 6.95 (ISBN 0-912315-57-1). Word Aflame.
--Through the Bible Study Series, Vol. V. 384p. 1981. text ed. 6.95 (ISBN 0-912315-56-3). Word Aflame.
--Through the Bible Study Series, Vol. IV. 384p. 1981. text ed. 6.95 (ISBN 0-912315-55-5). Word Aflame.
--Through the Bible Study Series, Vol. III. 384p. 1981. text ed. 6.95 (ISBN 0-912315-54-7). Word Aflame.
--Through the Bible Study Series, Vol. 1. 384p. 1981. text ed. 6.95 (ISBN 0-912315-52-0). Word Aflame.
Clanton, Arthur L. United We Stand. (Illus.). 207p. 1970. pap. 5.95 (ISBN 0-912315-42-3). Word Aflame.
Clanton, Arthur L., ed. see Willoughby, David.
Clanton, Bruce. Family Adventures. LC 80-51060. 1980. pap. 4.95 (ISBN 0-89390-018-4). Resource Pubns.
Clanton, Charles, ed. see Freeman, Nona.
Clanton, Charles, ed. see Thompson, Mollie.
Clapham, Alfred W., jt. auth. see Reddan, Minnie.
Clapp, Steve. Christian Education As Evangelism. 154p. (Orig.). 1982. pap. 9.00 (ISBN 0-914527-11-8). C-Four Res.
--Ministerial Competency Report. (Practice of Ministry Ser.). 123p. (Orig.). 1982. pap. 8.00 (ISBN 0-914527-10-X). C-Four Res.
--Retreat Guide I. 20p. (Orig.). 1981. pap. 2.00 (ISBN 0-914527-04-5). C-Four Res.
--Retreat Guide II. (The C-4 Journals). 29p. (Orig.). 1982. pap. 2.00 (ISBN 0-914527-13-4). C-Four Res.
--Sermons on Shalom. 79p. (Orig.). 1982. pap. 8.00 (ISBN 0-914527-37-1). C-Four Res.
--Shalom: Hope for the World. 178p. (Orig.). 1982. pap. 8.00 (ISBN 0-914527-35-5). C-Four Res.
Clapp, Steve & Mauck, Sue I. A Primer for Angry Christians. (Illus.). 138p. (Orig.). 1981. pap. 6.00 (ISBN 0-914527-09-6). C-Four Res.
--Repairing Christian Lifestyles. 2nd ed. (Repairing Christian Lifestyles Ser.). (Illus.). 174p. (YA) 1983. pap. 6.00 (ISBN 0-914527-26-6); pap. 5.00 leader's guide (ISBN 0-914527-27-4). C-Four Res.
--Through the Bible, Vol. I. (C-Four Youth Bible Materials Ser.). (Illus.). 138p. (Orig.). 1982. pap. 10.00 (ISBN 0-914527-15-0). C-Four Res.
Clapp, Steve, jt. auth. see Conn, Robert.
Clapp, Steve, jt. auth. see Davis, Dennis M.
Clapp, Steve, ed. Prayer & the Christian Life: C-4 Devotional Journal II. (The C-4 Journals Ser.). 126p. (Orig.). 1982. pap. 6.00 (ISBN 0-317-11522-7). C-Four Res.
Clapp, Steve, et al. Youth Experiential Annual Resource 1. 122p. (Orig.). 1981. pap. 10.00 (ISBN 0-914527-42-8). C-Four Res.
Clare, Frances. Wow God. 189p. pap. 4.95 (ISBN 0-89221-131-8). New Leaf.
Clare, Francis. Your Move, God. LC 82-81212. 144p. 1982. pap. 4.95 (ISBN 0-89221-102-4). New Leaf.
Clare, Maurice. A Day with Charles Kingsley. Repr. 10.00 (ISBN 0-8274-2148-6). R West.
Claret, Anthony M. The Autobiography of St. Anthony Mary Claret. LC 85-51661. 227p. 1985. pap. 8.00 (ISBN 0-89555-284-1). Tan Bks Pubs.
Clark. Instructions to Christian Converts. pap. 1.95 (ISBN 0-686-12883-4). Schmul Pub Co.
Clark, Barrett H. Blush of Shame: A Few Considerations on Verbal Obscenity in the Theatre. 1932. pap. 1.50 (ISBN 0-910664-01-3). Gotham.
--Great Short Biographies of the World: A Collection of Short Biographies. 1979. Repr. of 1929 ed. lib. bdg. 40.00 (ISBN 0-8492-4037-9). R West.
Clark, C. Shakespeare & the Supernatural. LC 72-92957. (Studies in Shakespeare, No. 24). 1970. Repr. of 1931 ed. lib. bdg. 75.00x (ISBN 0-8383-0966-6). Haskell.
Clark, Carol, jt. auth. see Kownacki, Mary L.
Clark, Carol, jt. auth. see Kownacki, Mary Lou.
Clark, Carol, ed. A Legacy Remembered: The Relief Society Magazine. (Illus.). 1982. 7.95 (ISBN 0-87747-926-7). Deseret Bk.
Clark, Colin. The Myth of Over-Population. 133p. 1975. pap. 3.50 (ISBN 0-912414-26-X). Lumen Christi.
--Population. 30p. 1974. pap. 0.50 (ISBN 0-912414-19-7). Lumen Christi.
Clark, Cumberland. Shakespeare & the Supernatural. LC 72-186985. 1931. lib. bdg. 37.50 (ISBN 0-8414-0341-4). Folcroft.
--Shakespeare & the Supernatural. 346p. Repr. of 1931 ed. 29.00 (ISBN 0-403-04266-6). Somerset Pub.
Clark, D. J. & Mundhenk, N. Translator's Handbook on the Books of Obadiah & Micah. LC 82-8481. (Helps for Translators Ser.). viii, 208p. 1982. pap. 3.50x (ISBN 0-8267-0129-9, 08567, Pub. by United Bible). Am Bible.
Clark, David. Between Pulpit & Pew: Folk Religion in a North Yorkshire Fishing Village. LC 81-18166. (Illus.). 216p. 1982. 32.50 (ISBN 0-521-24071-9). Cambridge U Pr.
Clark, Dennis E. Jesus Christ, His Life & Teaching. 324p. pap. 4.95 (ISBN 0-89191-117-0, 23341). Cook.

Clark, Donald N. Christianity in Modern Korea. LC 86-9092. (Asian Agenda Report: No. 5). 70p. (Orig.). 1986. lib. bdg. 12.75 (ISBN 0-8191-5384-2, Pub. by the Asia Soc); pap. text ed. 4.75 (ISBN 0-8191-5385-0). U Pr of Amer.

Clark, Edward W., jt. ed. see Vaughan, Alden T.

Clark, Elizabeth & Richardson, Herbert W., eds. Women & Religion: Readings in the Western Tradition from Aeschylus to Mary Daly. LC 76-9975. 1976. pap. 9.95 (ISBN 0-06-061398-X, RD-178, HarpR). Har-Row.

Clark, Elizabeth A. Ascetic Piety & Women's Faith: Essays in Late Ancient Christianity. (Studies in Women & Religion: Vol. 20). 1986. 69.95 (ISBN 0-88946-529-0). E Mellen.

--Ascetic Piety & Women's Faith: Essays on Late Ancient Christianity. LC 86-21828. (Studies in Women & Religion: Volume 20). 448p. 1986. lib. bdg. 69.95 (ISBN 0-88946-529-0). E Mellen.

--Clement's Use of Aristotle: The Aristotelian Contribution of Clement of Alexandria's Refutation of Gnosticism. LC 77-93913. (Texts & Studies in Religion: Vol. 1). vii, 192p. 1981. Repr. of 1977 ed. text ed. 49.95x (ISBN 0-88946-984-9). E Mellen.

--Jerome, Chrysostom, & Friends: Essays & Translations. LC 79-66374. (Studies in Women & Religion: Vol. 2). xi, 270p. 1979. soft cover 34.95x (ISBN 0-88946-548-7). E Mellen.

--Jerome, Chrysostom & Friends: Essays & Translations. LC 82-20829. (Studies in Women & Religion: Vol. 2). xi, 270p. 1983. Repr. of 1979 ed. 49.95x (ISBN 0-88946-541-X). E Mellen.

--The Life of Melania the Younger: Introduction, Translation & Commentary. LC 84-20635. (Studies in Women & Religion: Vol. 14). 305p. 1985. 49.95x (ISBN 0-88946-535-5). E Mellen.

--Women in the Early Church. (Message of the Fathers of the Church Ser.: Vol. 13). 17.95 (ISBN 0-89453-353-3); pap. 12.95 (ISBN 0-89453-332-0). M Glazier.

Clark, Elizabeth A. see Shore, Sally R.

Clark, Ella. Guardian Spirit Quest. (Indian Culture Ser.). 1974. pap. 1.95 (ISBN 0-89992-045-4). Coun India Ed.

Clark, Elmer T. The Small Sects in America. 11.75 (ISBN 0-8446-1862-4). Peter Smith.

Clark, Erskine. Wrestlin Jacob: A Portrait of Religion in the Old South. LC 78-52453. 1979. pap. 3.95 (ISBN 0-8042-1089-6). John Knox.

Clark, Fay M. You Will Take It with You. 135p. 1976. pap. 5.00 (ISBN 0-686-12934-2). Hiawatha Bondurant.

Clark, Gertrude M., tr. see Kant, Immanuel.

Clark, Glenn. Beatitudes of Married Life. pap. 0.20 (ISBN 0-910924-02-3). Macalester.

--Come Follow Me. 4.95 (ISBN 0-910924-04-X). Macalester.

--Divine Plan. pap. 0.50 (ISBN 0-910924-05-8). Macalester.

--Fishers of Men. pap. 1.95 (ISBN 0-910924-62-7). Macalester.

--From Crime to Christ. pap. 2.50 (ISBN 0-910924-61-9). Macalester.

--God's Voice in the Folklore. 4.95 (ISBN 0-910924-06-6). Macalester.

--Holy Spirit. pap. 0.50 (ISBN 0-910924-07-4). Macalester.

--I Will Lift up Mine Eyes. 1937. pap. 7.95 (ISBN 0-06-061393-9, RP518, HarpR). Har-Row.

--I Will Lift up Mine Eyes. LC 77-7830. (Illus.). 208p. 1984. pap. 7.95 (ISBN 0-06-061394-7, RD 518, HarpR). Har-Row.

--Living Prayer. 1980. pap. 0.50 (ISBN 0-910924-88-0). Macalester.

--Lord's Prayer. pap. 0.50 (ISBN 0-910924-08-2). Macalester.

--Song of Souls of Men. pap. 0.95 (ISBN 0-910924-14-7). Macalester.

--Three Mysteries of Jesus. 1978. 0.95 (ISBN 0-910924-85-6). Macalester.

--Under the Shelter of His Wings. pap. 0.20 (ISBN 0-910924-50-3). Macalester.

--What Would Jesus Do? pap. 7.95 (ISBN 0-910924-20-1). Macalester.

Clark, Gordon H. The Atonement. (The Trinity Papers: No. 17). 175p. (Orig.). 1987. pap. 8.95 (ISBN 0-940931-17-6). Trinity Found.

--The Biblical Doctrine of Man. (Trinity Papers: No. 7). 95p. (Orig.). 1984. pap. 5.95 (ISBN 0-940931-07-9). Trinity Found.

--Biblical Predestination. 1969. pap. 4.95 (ISBN 0-87552-137-1). Presby & Reformed.

--A Christian Philosophy of Education. 2nd, rev. ed. (Trinity Papers: No. 7). 250p. 1987. pap. 8.95 (ISBN 0-940931-20-6). Trinity Found.

--Clark Speaks from the Grave. (Trinity Papers: No. 12). 77p. (Orig.). 1986. pap. 3.95 (ISBN 0-940931-12-5). Trinity Found.

--Concept of Biblical Authority. 1979. 0.75 (ISBN 0-87552-143-6). Presby & Reformed.

--Dewey. (Modern Thinkers Ser.). 1960. pap. 2.00 (ISBN 0-87552-582-2). Presby & Reformed.

--Ephesians. (Trinity Papers: No. 11). 225p. (Orig.). 1985. pap. 8.95 (ISBN 0-940931-11-7). Trinity Found.

--Faith & Saving Faith. (Trinity Papers: No. 5). 118p. (Orig.). 1983. pap. 5.95 (ISBN 0-940931-05-2). Trinity Found.

--First & Second Peter. 1980. pap. 5.95 (ISBN 0-87552-167-3). Presby & Reformed.

--First & Second Thessolonians. (Trinity Papers: No. 14). 152p. (Orig.). 1986. pap. 5.95 (ISBN 0-940931-14-1). Trinity Found.

--God's Hammer: The Bible & Its Critics. 2nd rev. ed. 200p. 1987. pap. 6.95 (ISBN 0-940931-99-0). Trinity Found.

--In Defense of Theology. 1986. text ed. 12.95 (ISBN 0-8010-2520-6). Baker Bk.

--Language & Theology. 1979. pap. 4.95 (ISBN 0-87552-141-X). Presby & Reformed.

--Logic. (Trinity Papers: No. 9). 123p. (Orig.). 1985. pap. 8.95 (ISBN 0-940931-09-5). Trinity Found.

--Logical Criticisms of Textual Criticism. (Trinity Papers). 49p. (Orig.). 1986. pap. 2.95 (ISBN 0-940931-16-8). Trinity Found.

--The Pastoral Epistles. (Trinity Papers: No. 6). 294p. (Orig.). 1983. pap. 9.95 (ISBN 0-940931-06-0). Trinity Found.

--The Philosophy of Science & Belief in God. 2nd rev. ed. 125p. pap. 5.95 (ISBN 0-940931-18-4). Trinity Found.

--Religion, Reason & Revelation, No. 13. 2nd, rev. ed. (Trinity Papers). 251p. 1986. pap. 7.95 (ISBN 0-940931-13-3). Trinity Found.

--The Trinity. (Trinity Papers: No. 8). 139p. (Orig.). 1985. pap. 8.95 (ISBN 0-940931-08-7). Trinity Found.

--What Do Presbyterians Believe? 1965. pap. 6.95 (ISBN 0-87552-140-1). Presby & Reformed.

Clark, Harold. The New Creationism. LC 79-22250. (Horizon Ser.). 1980. pap. 9.95 (ISBN 0-8127-0247-6). Review & Herald.

Clark, Harold W. Fossils, Flood & Fire. (Illus.). 1968. 8.95 (ISBN 0-911080-16-3). Outdoor Pict.

Clark, Henry. The Church & Residential Desegregation. 1965. 16.95x (ISBN 0-8084-0076-2). New Coll U Pr.

--The Irony of American Morality. 1972. 13.95x (ISBN 0-8084-0036-3); pap. 9.95x (ISBN 0-8084-0037-1). New Coll U Pr.

Clark, Henry B., II. Freedom of Religion in America: Historical Roots, Philosophical Concepts, Contemporary Problems. 143p. 1982. pap. 6.95 (ISBN 0-87855-925-6). Transaction Bks.

Clark, Ira. Christ Revealed: The History of the Neotypological Lyric in the English Renaissance. LC 82-2696. (University of Florida Humanities Monographs: No. 51). xiv, 218p. 1982. pap. 15.00x (ISBN 0-8130-0712-7). U Presses Fla.

Clark, J. Reuben, Jr. Why the King James Version. LC 79-15008. (Classics in Mormon Literature Ser.). 535p. 1979. 7.95 (ISBN 0-87747-773-6). Deseret Bk.

Clark, James M. Great German Mystics: Eckhart, Tauler & Suso. LC 73-81493. 1970. Repr. of 1949 ed. 15.00x (ISBN 0-8462-1351-6). Russell.

Clark, John D. Suffering & the Saints. Goodman, James, ed. 272p. (Orig.). 1987. pap. 9.95 (ISBN 0-89896-129-7, Linolean). Larksdale.

Clark, John H. God of Shelley & Blake. (English Literature Ser., No. 33). 1970. Repr. of 1930 ed. lib. bdg. 39.95x (ISBN 0-8383-0342-0). Haskell.

Clark, John M., jt. auth. see Ward, Alfred D.

Clark, John R. The Great Living System. 1984. pap. 7.95 (ISBN 0-933840-24-1). Unitarian Univ.

Clark, Juan. Religious Repression in Cuba. 115p. (Orig.). 1986. pap. 8.95 (ISBN 0-935501-04-5). U Miami N-S Ctr.

--La Represion Religiosa en Cuba. (Span.). 124p. (Orig.). Date not set. pap. cancelled (ISBN 0-917049-05-5). Saeta.

Clark, Keith. Being Sexual...& Celibate. LC 85-73158. 184p. (Orig.). 1986. pap. 4.95 (ISBN 0-87793-329-4). Ave Maria.

--An Experience of Celibacy. LC 81-69747. (Illus.). 176p. (Orig.). 1982. pap. 4.95 (ISBN 0-87793-240-9). Ave Maria.

--Make Space, Make Symbols. LC 78-73826. (Illus.). 112p. 1979. pap. 2.95 (ISBN 0-87793-173-9). Ave Maria.

Clark, Malcolm, Jr., intro. by see Deady, Matthew P.

Clark, Martha B. Are You Weeping with Me, God? LC 86-17194. (Orig.). 1987. pap. 5.95 (ISBN 0-8054-5436-5). Broadman.

Clark, Martin, jt. auth. see Morris, Henry M.

Clark, Martin E. Choosing Your Career: The Christian's Decision Manual. 1981. pap. 3.95 (ISBN 0-87552-205-X). Presby & Reformed.

--Choosing Your Career: The Christian's Decision Manual. 120p. (Orig.). 1983. pap. 4.95 (ISBN 0-8010-2483-8). Baker Bk.

Clark, Mary E. Thy Kingdom Come. 1.77 (ISBN 0-8091-9315-9). Paulist Pr.

Clark, Mary F. Hiding, Hurting, Healing. 176p. (Orig.). 1985. pap. 6.95 (ISBN 0-310-30551-9, 11612). Zondervan.

Clark, Mary T., ed. An Aquinas Reader. LC 72-76709. pap. 6.95 (ISBN 0-385-02505-X, Im). Doubleday.

Clark, Mary T., tr. see Augustine of Hippo.

Clark, Michael D. Worldly Theologians: The Persistence of Religion in Nineteenth Century American Thought. LC 80-5840. 328p. (Orig.). 1982. lib. bdg. 29.25 (ISBN 0-8191-1778-1); pap. text ed. 14.50 (ISBN 0-8191-1779-X). U Pr of Amer.

Clark, Miles. Glenn Clark: His Life & Writings. LC 75-6877. Repr. of 1975 ed. 30.40 (ISBN 0-8357-9008-8, 2016361). Bks Demand UMI.

Clark, Nancy, ed. see Lodo, Venerable L.

Clark, Nancy, ed. see Lodo, Venerable Larma.

Clark, Ovilene. Heirloom of Memories. 1983. 8.50 (ISBN 0-8062-2137-2). Carlton.

Clark, Peter. Marmaduke Pickthall: British Muslim. (Illus.). 156p. 1987. 19.95 (ISBN 0-7043-2514-4, Pub. by Quartet Bks). Salem Hse Pubs.

Clark, Randolph. Reminiscences, Biographical & Historical. LC 86-1286. 96p. 1986. Repr. of 1919 ed. 25.00x (ISBN 0-87565-064-3). Tex Christian.

Clark, Rebecca. The Rainbow Connection. LC 82-84590. 192p. 1983. 4.95 (ISBN 0-87159-136-7). Unity School.

Clark, Robert. Who Is Jesus? Leader's Guide. Chao, Lorna Y., tr. (Basic Doctrine Ser.). 1986. pap. write for info. (ISBN 0-941598-33-0). Living Spring Pubns.

Clark, Robert A., jt. auth. see Elkinton, Russell J.

Clark, Robert E. Teaching Preschoolers with Confidence. 48p. 1983. pap. 3.95 (ISBN 0-910566-37-2); seminar planbook 3.95 (ISBN 0-910566-38-0). Evang Tchr.

Clark, Robert E., jt. auth. see Brubaker, J. Omar.

Clark, Ruth. Strangers & Sojourners at Port Royal. 1972. lib. bdg. 26.00x (ISBN 0-374-91664-0, Octagon). Hippocrene Bks.

Clark, Sonia T. Life of Rudolf Steiner. (Rudolf Steiner Publications Ser.). 40p. 1985. pap. 4.00 (ISBN 0-89345-905-4, Steiner). Garber Comm.

Clark, Stephen B. Man & Woman in Christ: An Examination of the Roles of Men & Women in Light of Scripture & the Social Sciences. 754p. (Orig.). 1980. 24.95 (ISBN 0-89283-084-0). Servant.

Clark, Stephen B., ed. Patterns of Christian Community. 98p. (Orig.). 1984. pap. 4.95 (ISBN 0-89283-186-3). Servant.

Clark, Stephen R. From Athens to Jerusalem: The Love of Wisdom & the Love God. 1984. 29.95x (ISBN 0-19-824698-6); pap. 11.95x (ISBN 0-19-824697-8). Oxford U Pr.

--The Mysteries of Religion: An Introduction to Philosophy through Religion. 288p. text ed. 45.00 (ISBN 0-631-13419-0); pap. text ed. 12.95 (ISBN 0-631-14295-9). Basil Blackwell.

Clark, Steve B. Baptized in the Spirit & Spiritual Gifts. 1967. pap. 2.95 (ISBN 0-89283-033-6). Servant.

--Growing in Faith. (Living As a Christian Ser.). 1972. pap. 2.25 (ISBN 0-89283-004-2). Servant.

--Knowing God's Will. (Living As a Christian Ser.). 1974. pap. 2.50 (ISBN 0-89283-005-0). Servant.

Clark, Susan L. & Wasserman, Julian N. The Poetics of Conversion: Number Symbolism & Alchemy in Gottfried's "Tristan". (Utah Studies in Literature & Linguistics: Vol. 7). 168p. 1977. pap. 20.90 (ISBN 3-261-02085-7). P Lang Pubs.

Clark, Thomas C., ed. Master of Men. fascimile ed. LC 72-116396. (Granger Index Reprint Ser.). 1930. 15.00 (ISBN 0-8369-6137-4). Ayer Co Pubs.

Clark, Thomas L. A Guide for the Church Usher. LC 83-26211. 1984. pap. 5.50 (ISBN 0-8054-3517-4). Broadman.

--A Yearly Planning Guide for the Church Usher. 1986. pap. 3.95 (ISBN 0-8054-9407-3). Broadman.

Clark, Vivian. God's Remedy for Depression. (Direction Bks.). (Orig.). 1980. pap. 3.50 (ISBN 0-8010-2444-7). Baker Bk.

Clark, Vynomma. So You're a Woman. LC 70-180790. 4.95 (ISBN 0-89112-050-5, Bibl Res Pr). Abilene Christ U.

Clark, W. Joseph. The Holy Land. LC 86-61593. 204p. (Orig.). 1986. pap. 7.95 (ISBN 0-87973-546-5, 546). Our Sunday Visitor.

Clark, Walter H., et al. Religious Experience: Its Nature & Function in the Human Psyche. (Illus.). 168p. 1973. 13.00x (ISBN 0-398-02550-9). C C Thomas.

Clark, Walter J. How to Use New Testament Greek Study Aids. 256p. 1984. pap. 6.95 (ISBN 0-87213-079-7). Loizeaux.

Clark, Wayne C. The Meaning of Church Membership. pap. 4.50 (ISBN 0-8170-0103-4). Judson.

Clark, William R., ed. & tr. see Hefele, Karl J.

Clarke, Adam. Clarke's Commentary, 3 vols. Incl. Vol. 1. Genesis-Esther (ISBN 0-687-09119-5); Vol. 2. Job-Malachi (ISBN 0-687-09120-9); Vol. 3. Matthew-Revelation (ISBN 0-687-09121-7). 1977. Set. 95.00 (ISBN 0-687-09118-7); 34.50 ea. Abingdon.

Clarke, Adam, ed. Adam Clarke's Commentary on the Entire Bible. 29.95 (ISBN 0-8010-2321-1). Baker Bk.

Clarke, Arthur G. Analytical Studies in the Psalms. LC 79-2518. 376p. 1979. 14.95 (ISBN 0-8254-2322-8). Kregel.

Clarke, Basil. The Building of the Eighteenth Century Church. LC 66-37309. (Illus.). 1963. text ed. 20.00x (ISBN 0-8401-0404-9). A R Allenson.

Clarke, Boden. Lords Temporal & Lords Spiritual. LC 80-10979. (Stokvis Studies in Historical Chronology & Thought: No. 1). 160p. 1985. lib. bdg. 19.95x (ISBN 0-89370-800-3); pap. 9.95x (ISBN 0-89370-900-X). Borgo Pr.

Clarke, Boden & Burgess, Mary. Eastern Churches Review: An Index to Volumes One Through Ten, 1966-1978. LC 80-2550. (Borgo Reference Library: Vol. 6). 96p. 1987. lib. bdg. 19.95x (ISBN 0-89370-812-7); pap. text ed. 9.95x (ISBN 0-89370-912-3). Borgo Pr.

Clarke, Bowman & Long, Eugene T., eds. God & Temporality. (God Ser.). 320p. (Orig.). 1986. pap. 12.95 (ISBN 0-913757-10-1, Pub. by New Era Bks). Paragon Hse.

Clarke, Bowman L. Language & Natural Theology. (Janua Linguarum, Ser. Minor: No. 47). (Orig.). 1966. pap. text ed. 18.00 (ISBN 90-2790-580-0). Mouton.

Clarke, C. P. Church History from Nero to Constantine. 1977. lib. bdg. 59.95 (ISBN 0-8490-1626-6). Gordon Pr.

Clarke, E. G. Targum Pseudo-Jonathan of the Pentateuch. 1983. 150.00x (ISBN 0-88125-015-5). Ktav.

--The Wisdom of Solomon. (Cambridge Bible Commentary on the New English Bible, Old Testament Ser.). 148p. 1973. 18.95 (ISBN 0-521-08635-3); pap. 8.95 (ISBN 0-521-09756-8). Cambridge U Pr.

Clarke, Frank, tr. see Kasemann, Ernst.

Clarke, G. W., tr. see Lawler, Thomas C. & Burghart, Johannes.

Clarke, Graehme W., tr. The Letters of St. Cyprian, Vol. 1. (Ancient Christian Writers Ser.: No. 43). 416p. 1983. 24.95 (ISBN 0-8091-0341-9). Paulist Pr.

Clarke, Graeme W., ed. The Letters of St. Cyprian: Vol. 3, Letters 55-66. (ACW Ser.: No. 46). 352p. 1986. 24.95 (ISBN 0-8091-0369-9). Paulist Pr.

Clarke, Graeme W., tr. The Letters of St. Cyprian, Vol. 2. (Ancient Christian Writers Ser.: No. 44). 352p. 1983. 22.95 (ISBN 0-8091-0342-7). Paulist Pr.

Clarke, John & McLoughlin, William G. Colonial Baptists: Massachusetts & Rhode Island. original anthology ed. Gaustad, Edwin S., ed. LC 79-52586. (The Baptist Tradition Ser.). 1980. lib. bdg. 17.00x (ISBN 0-405-12453-8). Ayer Co Pubs.

Clarke, John, tr. Saint Therese of Lisieux General Correspondence: Vol. I, 1877-1890. LC 81-6474. 700p. (Orig.). 1982. pap. 9.95x (ISBN 0-9600876-9-9). ICS Pubns.

Clarke, John, tr. from Fr. St. Therese of Lisieux: Her Last Conversations. LC 76-27207. (Illus.). 1977. pap. 6.95x (ISBN 0-9600876-3-X). ICS Pubns.

--Story of a Soul: The Autobiography of St. Therese of Lisieux. LC 76-43620. 1976. pap. 6.95x (ISBN 0-9600876-4-8). ICS Pubns.

Clarke, John H. God of Shelley & Blake. LC 73-12459. 1973. lib. bdg. 10.00 (ISBN 0-8414-3425-5). Folcroft.

--William Blake on the Lord's Prayer: 1757-1827. LC 70-95421. (Studies in Blake, No. 3). 1971. Repr. of 1927 ed. lib. bdg. 48.95x (ISBN 0-8383-0967-4). Haskell.

Clarke, M. J., et al. Copper, Molybdenum, & Vanadium in Biological Systems: Structure & Bonding, Vol. 53. (Illus.). 166p. 1983. 39.50 (ISBN 0-387-12042-4). Springer-Verlag.

Clarke, M. L. Bangor Cathedral. 125p. 1969. text ed. 6.95x (ISBN 0-900768-23-1, Pub. by U of Wales Pr). Humanities.

Clarke, Peter. A Free Church in a Free Society: The Ecclesiology of John England Bishop of Charleston, 1820-1842. 561p. 1983. (Pub. by John England Stud Inc); pap. 15.95x (ISBN 0-87921-073-7). Attic Pr.

--West Africa & Islam. 280p. 1982. pap. text ed. 19.95 (ISBN 0-7131-8029-3). E Arnold.

Clarke, Peter B. Black Paradise: The Rastafarian Movement. 112p. 1986. pap. 11.95 (ISBN 0-85030-428-8). Newcastle Pub.

--Black Paradise: The Rastafarian Movement. 176p. 1986. lib. bdg. 19.95x (ISBN 0-8095-7021-1). Borgo Pr.

--West Africa & Christianity. 280p. 1986. pap. text ed. 17.95 (ISBN 0-7131-8263-6). E Arnold.

Clarke, Peter S. Complete Guide to Asset-Based Lending. LC 85-9362. 314p. 1986. 69.95 (ISBN 0-13-159831-7, Busn). P-H.

Clarke, Prescott & Gregory, J. S., eds. Western Reports on the Taiping: A Selection of Documents. LC 81-68942. 484p. 1982. text ed. 25.00x (ISBN 0-8248-0807-X); pap. text ed. 15.95x (ISBN 0-8248-0809-6). UH Pr.

Clarke, Rita-Lou. Pastoral Care of Battered Women. LC 86-5604. 132p. (Orig.). 1986. pap. 7.95 (ISBN 0-664-24015-1). Westminster.

Clarke, Samuel. The Works, 4 vols. LC 75-11207. (British Philosophers & Theologians of the 17th & 18th Century Ser.: Vol. 12). 3274p. 1976. Repr. of 1742 ed. Set. lib. bdg. 204.00 (ISBN 0-8240-1762-5). Garland Pub.

Clarke, Sidney M. The Miracle Play in England. LC 65-15874. 1970. Repr. of 1897 ed. text ed. 75.00x (ISBN 0-8383-0529-6). Haskell.

Clarke, Thomas E., ed. Above Every Name: The Lordship of Christ & Social Systems. LC 80-82082. (Woodstock Studies). 312p. (Orig.). 1980. pap. 8.95 (ISBN 0-8091-2338-X). Paulist Pr.

Clarke, Thomas J. People & Their Religions, Part One. (Literacy Volunteers of America Readers Ser.). 48p. (Orig.). 1983. pap. 1.95 (ISBN 0-8428-9609-0). Cambridge Bk.

--People & Their Religions, Part Two. (Literacy Volunteers of America Readers Ser.). 48p. (Orig.). 1983. pap. 1.95 (ISBN 0-8428-9610-4). Cambridge Bk.

Clarke, W. K., tr. & intro. by see Basilius.

Clarke, William. Clarke Papers, 4 Vols. Firth, C. H., ed. 105.00 (ISBN 0-384-09232-2); 27.00 ea. Johnson Repr.

Clarke, William N. Immortality. 1920. 29.50x (ISBN 0-686-83578-6). Elliots Bks.

Clarkson, John F., et al, eds. see St. Mary's College, Kansas, Jesuit Fathers.

Clarkson, Margaret. All Nature Sings. 160p. (Orig.). 1986. pap. 5.95 (ISBN 0-8028-0225-7). Eerdmans.

--Destined for Glory: The Meaning of Suffering. 144p. 1983. pap. 4.95 (ISBN 0-8028-1953-2). Eerdmans.

Clarkson, Thomas. Essay on the Slavery & Commerce of the Human Species. facs. ed. LC 73-93417. (Black Heritage Library Collection Ser). 1786. 15.50 (ISBN 0-8369-8542-7). Ayer Co Pubs.

Clary, Linda & Harms, Larry. Christmas Music for Little People. Bradley, Richard, ed. (Illus.). 32p. 1985. bk & cassette 9.95 (ISBN 0-89748-160-7). Bradley Pubns.

Clasen, Souphronius, ed. Henrici De Werla, O. F. M. Opera Omnia: Tractatus De Immaculata Conceptione Beatae Mariae Virginis. (Text Ser). 1955. 6.00 (ISBN 0-686-11555-4). Franciscan Inst.

Clason, George. The Richest Man in Babylon. 160p. 1985. pap. 3.50 (ISBN 0-553-25345-X). Bantam.

Clasper, Paul. Eastern Paths & the Christian Way. LC 80-13730. 128p. (Orig.). 1980. pap. 5.95 (ISBN 0-88344-100-4). Orbis Bks.

--Theological Ferment: Personal Reflections. 226p. (Orig.). 1982. pap. 6.75 (ISBN 0-686-37687-0, Pub. by New Day Philippines). Cellar.

Clasper, Paul D. The Yogi, the Commissar & the Third World Church. 92p. (Orig.). 1982. pap. 5.00 (ISBN 0-686-37580-7, Pub. by New Day Philippines). Cellar.

Classen, David J. Object Lessons for a Year. 112p. 1986. pap. 4.95 (ISBN 0-8010-2514-1). Baker Bk.

Classen, E., ed. see Backman, Eugene L.

Claudel, Paul. Correspondance avec Andre Gide: 1899-1926. 1949. pap. 7.95 (ISBN 0-686-51967-1). French & Eur.

--Correspondance avec Andre Suares: 1904-1938. 1951. pap. 5.95 (ISBN 0-686-51968-X). French & Eur.

--Correspondance avec Francis Jammes et Gabriel Frizeau: 1897-1938. 1952. pap. 7.95 (ISBN 0-686-51969-8). French & Eur.

--Je Crois en Dieu. 432p. 1961. 8.95 (ISBN 0-686-54394-7). French & Eur.

--Le Symbolisme de la Salette. 64p. 1952. 2.95 (ISBN 0-686-54437-4). French & Eur.

--Une Voix sur Israel. 46p. 1950. 2.95 (ISBN 0-686-54445-5). French & Eur.

--Ways & Crossways. facs. ed. O'Conner, Fr. J., tr. LC 67-28732. (Essay Index Reprint Ser.). 1933. 20.00 (ISBN 0-8369-0313-7). Ayer Co Pubs.

--Ways & Crossways. LC 68-15820. 1968. Repr. of 1933 ed. 21.50 (ISBN 0-8046-0079-1, Pub. by Kennikat). Assoc Faculty Pr.

Claudy, Carl H., ed. Foreign Countries: A Gateway to the Interpretation & Development of Certain Symbols of Freemasonry. 160p. 1971. Repr. of 1925 ed. text ed. 6.00 (ISBN 0-88053-039-1, M-88). Macoy Pub.

Clausen, Sophronius. St. Anthony: Doctor of the Gospel. Brady, Ignatius, tr. from Ger. LC 61-11200. Orig. Title: Antonius. 140p. pap. 2.50 (ISBN 0-8199-0458-9). Franciscan Herald.

Claussen, Evelyn B., jt. auth. see Claussen, Martin P.

Claussen, Martin P. & Claussen, Evelyn B. The Voice of Christian & Jewish Dissenters in America: U. S. Internal Revenue Service Hearings, December 1978. xv, 591p. 1982. pap. 25.00. Piedmont.

Claussen, Russell, ed. The Church's Growing Edge: Single Adults. 1981. pap. 4.95 (ISBN 0-8298-0429-3). Pilgrim NY.

Clawson, Cynthia. My Favorite Verse. LC 86-73189. (My Favorite Verse Ser.). 24p. 1987. pap. 4.95 (ISBN 0-89636-222-1). Accent Bks.

Clawson, Sharalee S. I Feel My Saviour's Love: Themes from LDS Children's Songs in Counted Cross-Stitch. 9p. 1986. pap. 5.00 (ISBN 0-88290-277-6). Horizon Utah.

Clawson, Virginia. The Family Symphony. LC 84-17524. 1984. 7.95 (ISBN 0-8054-5661-9). Broadman.

Clay, A. T. Documents from the Temple Archives of Nippur Dated in the Reigns of Cassite Rulers with Incomplete Dates. (Publications of the Babylonian Section, Ser. A: Vol. 15). (Illus.). xii, 68p. 1906. soft bound 12.00x (ISBN 0-686-11914-2). Univ Mus of U PA.

Clay, Albert T. Documents from the Temple Arhcives of Nippur Dated in the Reigns of Cassite Rulers. LC 13-1106. (University of Pennsylvania, The Museum, Publications of the Babylonian Section: Vol. 2, No. 2). pap. 27.00 (ISBN 0-317-28572-6, 2052022). Bks Demand UMI.

--Epics, Hymns, Omens & Other Texts. LC 78-63519. (Babylonian Records in the Library of J. Pierpont Morgan: 4). Repr. of 1923 ed. 30.00 (ISBN 0-404-60124-3). AMS Pr.

--A Hebrew Deluge Story in Cuneiform. LC 78-63549. (Yale Oriental Ser. Researches: No. 5, Pt. 3). Repr. of 1922 ed. 20.00 (ISBN 0-404-60275-4). AMS Pr.

--Hebrew Deluge Story in Cuneiform. (Yale Oriental Researches Ser.: No. V, Pt. III). 1922. 19.50x (ISBN 0-685-69802-5). Elliots Bks.

--The Origin of Biblical Tradition. LC 78-63556. (Yale Oriental Ser. Researches: No. 12). Repr. of 1923 ed. 37.50 (ISBN 0-404-60282-7). AMS Pr.

Clay, Jenny S. The Wrath of Athena. LC 83-2996. 240p. 1983. 29.00x (ISBN 0-691-06574-8). Princeton U Pr.

Clay, Rotha M. Hermits & Anchorites of England. LC 68-21759. (Illus.). 1968. Repr. of 1914 ed. 40.00x (ISBN 0-8103-3424-0). Gale.

Clay, Walter L. Prison Chaplain: Memoirs of the Rev. John Clay with Selections from His Reports & Correspondence & a Sketch of Prison Discipline in England. LC 69-16232. (Criminology, Law Enforcement, & Social Problems Ser.: No. 90). (Index added). 1969. Repr. of 1861 ed. 25.00 (ISBN 0-87585-090-1). Patterson Smith.

Claypool, John. Glad Reunion. 144p. 1985. 8.95 (ISBN 0-8499-0469-2, 0469-2). Word Bks.

--The Light Within You: Looking at Life Through New Eyes. 1983. 9.95 (ISBN 0-8499-0273-8). Word Bks.

Claypool, John R. Opening Blind Eyes. 144p. (Orig.). 1987. pap. 7.95 (ISBN 0-940989-05-0). Meyer Stone Bks.

Clayton, J. P., jt. auth. see Sykes, S. W.

Clayton, John. Reverend John Clayton: A Parson with a Scientific Mind. Berkeley, Edmund & Berkeley, Dorothy S., eds. LC 65-23459. (Virginia Historical Document: No. 6). (Illus.). 1965. 15.00x (ISBN 0-8139-0067-0). U Pr of Va.

Clayton, John P. The Concept of Correlation: Paul Tillich & the Possibility of a Mediating Theology. (Theologische Bibliothek Topelmann Ser.: No. 37). 427p. 1979. text ed. 44.25x (ISBN 3-11007-914-3). De Gruyter.

Clayton, Peter A., rev. by see Lurker, Manfred.

Clayton, William. The Latter-Day Saints' Emigrants' Guide. Kimball, Stanley B. & Allen, James B., eds. LC 83-2473. (Illus.). vi, 111p. 1983. 12.95 (ISBN 0-935284-27-3). Patrice Pr.

--William Clayton's Journal: A Daily Record of the Journey of the Original Company of Mormon Pioneers from Nauveo, Illinois, to the Valley of the Great Salt Lake. LC 72-9435. (The Far Western Frontier Ser.). 380p. 1973. Repr. of 1921 ed. 26.50 (ISBN 0-405-04965-X). Ayer Co Pubs.

Clayton, William R. Matter & Spirit. LC 80-81694. 136p. 1981. 9.95 (ISBN 0-8022-2368-0). Philos Lib.

Cleary, Edward L. Crisis & Change: The Church in Latin America Today. LC 84-16478. 208p. (Orig.). 1985. pap. 11.95 (ISBN 0-88344-149-7). Orbis Bks.

Cleary, Patrick. The Church & Usury. 1979. lib. bdg. 59.95 (ISBN 0-8490-2884-1). Gordon Pr.

Cleary, Thomas. Entry into the Inconceivable: An Introduction to Hua-yen Buddhism. LC 83-3613. 227p. 1983. text ed. 16.95x (ISBN 0-8248-0824-X). UH Pr.

Cleary, Thomas, ed. The Original Face: An Anthology of Rinzai Zen. LC 77-91354. 1978. pap. 4.95 (ISBN 0-394-17038-5, E707, Ever). Grove.

Cleary, Thomas, tr. The Book of Serenity. 464p. 1986. cancelled (ISBN 0-89281-072-6); pap. cancelled (ISBN 0-89281-074-2). Inner Tradit.

--The Flower Ornament Scripture: A Translation of the Avatamsaka Sutra, Vol. 1. LC 83-2370. 703p. 1984. 40.00 (ISBN 0-87773-767-3, 53690-8). Shambhala Pubns.

--Sayings & Doings of Pai-Chang. LC 78-21228. (Zen Writings Ser.: Vol. 6). 1979. pap. 5.95 (ISBN 0-916820-10-6). Center Pubns.

--Timeless Spring: A Soto Zen Anthology. LC 79-26677. 176p. 1980. pap. 7.95 (ISBN 0-8348-0148-5). Weatherhill.

Cleary, Thomas, tr. from Chines see Chang Po-tuan & Liu I-ming.

Cleary, Thomas, tr. see Chih-hsu, Ou-i.

Cleary, Thomas, tr. see Dogen.

Cleave, Mary E. Van see Van Cleave, Mary E.

Clebsch, William. Christianity in European History. 1979. pap. 8.95x (ISBN 0-19-502472-9). Oxford U Pr.

Clebsch, William & Jaekle, Charles. Pastoral Care in Historical Perspective. LC 84-451130. 344p. 1983. Repr. of 1975 ed. 30.00x (ISBN 0-87668-717-6). Aronson.

Clebsch, William A. American Religious Thought: A History. LC 73-82911. xii, 212p. 1985. pap. text ed. 10.00x (ISBN 0-226-10962-3). U of Chicago Pr.

--England's Earliest Protestants, 1520-1535. LC 80-15226. (Yale Publications in Religion: No. 11). xvi, 358p. 1980. Repr. of 1964 ed. lib. bdg. 22.50x (ISBN 0-313-22420-X, CLEE). Greenwood.

--From Sacred to Profane America: The Role of Religion in American History. LC 81-9142. (Classics & Reprints Series of the American Academy of Religion & Scholars Press). 1981. 9.95 (ISBN 0-89130-517-3, 01 05 02). Scholars Pr GA.

Clebsch, William A., ed. see Donne, John.

Clebsch, William A., ed. see Jastrow, Morris, Jr.

Cleghorn, Spencer. Kabbalistic Discoveries into Hebrew & Aegyptian Mysteries, 2 Vols. (Illus.). 121p. 1983. 177.75 (ISBN 0-89920-057-5). Am Inst Psych.

Cleland, Robert G. & Brooks, Juanita, eds. A Mormon Chronicle: The Diaries of John D. Lee, 1848-1876, 2 vols. (Illus.). xxxii, 824p. 1955. Set. 39.95 (ISBN 0-87480-230-X). U of Utah Pr.

Clemans, E. V. Using Computers in Religious Education. 80p. 1986. pap. 6.95 (ISBN 0-687-43120-4). Abingdon.

Clemen, Carl. Religionsgeschichtliche Erklaerung des Neuen Testamentes: Die Abhaengigkeit des aeltesten Christentums von nichtjuedischen Religionen und philosophischen Systemen. 440p. 1973. Repr. of 1924 ed. text ed. 59.20x (ISBN 3-11-002412-8). De Gruyter.

Clemen, Carl C., et al. Religions of the World. facs. ed. LC 69-17570. (Essay Index Reprint Ser). 1931. 35.50 (ISBN 0-8369-0011-1). Ayer Co Pubs.

Clemen, D. D. Primitive Christianity & Its Non-Jewish Sources. 1977. lib. bdg. 59.95 (ISBN 0-8490-2472-2). Gordon Pr.

Clemen, Otto, ed. see Luther, Martin.

Clemen, Otto see Luther, Martin.

Clemens, Cyril. Chesterton As Seen by His Contemporaries. 1973. 69.95 (ISBN 0-87968-027-X). Gordon Pr.

--Chesterton As Seen by His Contemporaries. LC 76-92958. (English Biography Ser., No. 31). 1969. Repr. of 1938 ed. lib. bdg. 48.95x (ISBN 0-8383-0968-2). Haskell.

Clemens, David A. The Cutting Edge, Vol. 2. LC 79-52420. (Steps to Maturity Ser.). 1975. student's manual 15.95x (ISBN 0-86508-003-8); tchr's. manual 17.95x (ISBN 0-86508-004-6). BCM Intl Inc.

--God Encountered, Vol. 1. LC 79-52420. (Steps to Maturity Ser.). 1973. tchrs'. manual 17.95x (ISBN 0-86508-002-X); student's manual 15.95x (ISBN 0-86508-001-1); visuals packett 4.95x (ISBN 0-86508-007-0). BCM Intl Inc.

Clemens, Frances & Tully, Robert, eds. Recreation & the Local Church. LC 57-18412. pap. 47.80 (ISBN 0-317-28391-X, 2022409). Bks Demand UMI.

Clemens, Paul M., ed. see Nydahl, Ole.

Clemens, Paul M., ed. see Tweedie, Irina.

Clemens, Samuel L. Personal Recollections of Joan of Arc by the Sieur Louis De Conte. LC 80-23663. (Illus.). xiv, 461p. 1980. Repr. of 1906 ed. lib. bdg. 60.50x (ISBN 0-313-22373-4, CLPR). Greenwood.

Clement, Arthur J. Pentecost Or Pretense. 1981. pap. 7.95 (ISBN 0-8100-0118-7, 12N1718). Northwest Pub.

Clement, Clara. A Handbook of Legendary & Mythological Art. 59.95 (ISBN 0-8490-0279-6). Gordon Pr.

Clement, Clara E. Handbook of Legendary & Mythological Art. LC 68-26616. (Illus.). 1969. Repr. of 1881 ed. 45.00x (ISBN 0-8103-3175-6). Gale.

--Saints in Art. LC 77-89303. 1976. Repr. of 1899 ed. 46.00x (ISBN 0-8103-3030-X). Gale.

Clement, George H. The ABC's of the Prophetical Scriptures. pap. 2.25 (ISBN 0-685-61832-3). Reiner.

Clement, Jane T. Sperling. 154p. 1986. pap. 6.00 (ISBN 3-922819-36-2). Plough.

Clemente, Elizabeth M. de see Van Ness, Bethann & De Clemente, Elizabeth M.

Clement Of Alexandria. Christ the Educator. LC 66-20313. (Fathers of the Church Ser.: Vol. 23). 309p. 1954. 16.95x (ISBN 0-8132-0023-7). Cath U Pr.

Clements, Colleen D., jt. auth. see Teichler-Zallen, Doris.

Clements, K. W. The Theology of Ronald Gregor Smith. (Zeitschrift fur Religions- und Geistesgeschichte Ser.: No. 27). xii, 328p. 1986. pap. 49.00 (ISBN 90-04-07298-5, Pub. by E J Brill). Heinman.

Clements, R. E. Isaiah & the Deliverance of Jerusalem. (Journal for the Study of the Old Testament, Supplement Ser.: No. 13). 1980. text ed. 18.95x (ISBN 0-905774-23-X, Pub. by JSOT Pr England); pap. text ed. 10.95 (ISBN 0-905774-62-0). Eisenbrauns.

--New Century Bible Commentary on Isaiah 1-39. rev. ed. 320p. 1980. pap. 8.95 (ISBN 0-8028-1841-2). Eerdmans.

Clements, R. E., ed. Exodus: Cambridge Bible Commentary on the New English Bible. (Old Testament Ser.). 1972. 32.50 (ISBN 0-521-08218-8); pap. 10.95 (ISBN 0-521-09656-1). Cambridge U Pr.

Clements, Ronald, ed. see Grayston, Kenneth.

Clements, Ronald, et al, eds. see Clines, D. J.

Clements, Ronald E. Abraham & David: Genesis 15 & Its Meaning for Israelite Tradition. LC 67-8569. (Studies in Biblical Theology, 2nd Ser.: No. 5). 1967. pap. 10.00x (ISBN 0-8401-3055-4). A R Allenson.

--In Spirit & in Truth: Insights from Biblical Prayers. LC 85-228. 264p. 1985. pap. 9.95 (ISBN 0-8042-0071-8). John Knox.

--One Hundred Years of Old Testament Interpretation. LC 76-23236. 160p. 1976. pap. 7.95 (ISBN 0-664-24747-4). Westminster.

Clements, Ronald E., ed. see Hyatt, J. P.

Clements, Ronald E., ed. see Mayes, A. D.

Clements, Ronald E., ed. see Rowley, H. H.

Clements, Ronald E., ed. see Wevers, John W.

Clements, Ronald E., ed. see Whybray, R. N.

Clements, Simon, jt. ed. see Bright, Laurence.

Clements, Tad, jt. ed. see Horosz, William.

Clements, William M. Care & Counseling of the Aging. Clinebell, Howard J. & Stone, Howard W., eds. LC 78-54547. (Creative Pastoral Care & Counseling Ser). 96p. 1979. pap. 4.50 (ISBN 0-8006-0561-6, 1-561). Fortress.

Clements, William M., ed. Ministry with the Aging: Designs-Challenges-Foundations. LC 80-7739. 1983. pap. 9.95 (ISBN 0-06-061497-8, RD/452, HarpR). Har-Row.

Clemmons, William P. Discovering the Depths. LC 75-22507. 140p. 1976. pap. 7.95 (ISBN 0-8054-5562-0). Broadman.

Cleobury, F. H. From Clerk to Cleric. 64p. 1977. pap. 1.95 (ISBN 0-227-67825-7). Attic Pr.

--Liberal Christian Orthodoxy. 164p. 1963. 9.50 (ISBN 0-227-67668-8). Attic Pr.

--Return to Natural Theology. 246p. 1967. 17.95 (ISBN 0-227-67722-6). Attic Pr.

Clercq, Chretien Le see Le Clercq, Chretien.

Cleveland, Catherine C. The Great Revival in the West, 1797-1805. 11.25 (ISBN 0-8446-1117-4). Peter Smith.

Cleveland, Charles D. Complete Concordance to the Poetical Works of John Milton. LC 76-57784. 1867. lib. bdg. 38.50 (ISBN 0-8414-3459-X). Folcroft.

Cleveland, E. E. The Exodus. Wheeler, Gerald, ed. 1985. write for info. (ISBN 0-8280-0299-1). Review & Herald.

--Milk & Honey. Wheeler, Gerald, ed. 1985. write for info. (ISBN 0-8280-0301-7). Review & Herald.

--One More River. Wheeler, Gerald, ed. 1985. write for info. (ISBN 0-8280-0300-9). Review & Herald.

Cleveland, Harlan & Wilson, Thomas W., Jr. Humangrowth: An Essay on Growth, Values & the Quality of Life. 54p. (Orig.). 1978. pap. text ed. 7.00 (ISBN 0-8191-5904-2, Pub. by Aspen Inst for Humanistic Studies). U Pr of Amer.

Cleveland, Jefferson, jt. ed. see Nix, Verolga.

Cleveland, Ray L. An Ancient South Arabian Necropolis: Objects from the Second Campaign 1951 in the Timna Cemetery. (American Foundation for the Study of Man: Vol. 4). (Illus.). 202p. 1965. 40.00x (ISBN 0-8018-0129-X). Johns Hopkins.

Cleveland, William L. Islam Against the West: Shakib Arslan & the Campaign for Islamic Nationalism. (Modern Middle East Ser.: No. 10). (Illus.). 247p. 1985. 19.95 (ISBN 0-292-77594-6). U of Tex Pr.

Cleven, Harry T., tr. see Jervell, Jacob.

Clevenger & Hill. History of the Bible Church. 1973. pap. 1.50 (ISBN 0-88428-006-3, 171). Parchment Pr.

Clevenger & Hill, eds. Bible Characters. 1973. pap. 1.50 (ISBN 0-88428-008-X, 161). Parchment Pr.

--Bible Geography. 1973. pap. 1.50 (ISBN 0-88428-003-9, 111). Parchment Pr.

--Jesus of the Bible. 1973. pap. 1.50 (ISBN 0-88428-007-1, 101). Parchment Pr.

Clevenger, Ernest A., Jr. The Art of Greeting & Seating: The Church Usher's Guide. (Illus.). 16p. 1983. pap. 0.95 (ISBN 0-88428-000-4). Parchment Pr.

--Bible Characters. (Bible Drill Flash Cards Flipbook Ser.). 1982. pap. 4.25 (ISBN 0-88428-018-7). Parchment Pr.

--The Church. (Bible Drill Flash Card Flipbook Ser.). 104p. 1983. pap. 4.25 (ISBN 0-88428-016-0). Parchment Pr.

--A Pocket Bible Ready Reference for Personal Workers. (Bible Ready Reference Ser.). 24p. (Orig.). 1982. pap. 0.50 (ISBN 0-88428-011-X). Parchment Pr.

Clevenger, Ernest A., Jr. & Clevenger, Glenda W. Comprehensive Topical & Textual Lesson Commentary Index: 1922-1982. 4th ed. 114p. 1981. pap. text ed. 6.95 (ISBN 0-88428-019-5). Parchment Pr.

Clevenger, Ernest, Jr. A Beginning Course in Church Leadership Training for Men. (Illus.). 42p. 1975. 3.25 (ISBN 0-88428-036-5). Parchment Pr.

--Directory Alabama Churches of Christ, 1976. (Illus.). 1976. pap. 2.00 (ISBN 0-88428-039-X). Parchment Pr.

--General Bible Knowledge Bible Drill: Flash Cards Flipbook. (Bible Drill Flash Cards Flipbook Ser.). 104p. 1983. pap. 4.25 (ISBN 0-88428-017-9). Parchment Pr.

Clevenger, Ernest, Jr. & Hill, Samuel G. Bible Evidences. (Bible Centered Studies). (Illus.). 73p. (Orig.). 1973. pap. 1.50 (ISBN 0-88428-009-8). Parchment Pr.

Clevenger, Ernest, Jr., ed. Bible Survey. 1973. pap. 1.50 (ISBN 0-88428-005-5, 141). Parchment Pr.

Clevenger, Glenda W., jt. auth. see Clevenger, Ernest A., Jr.

Clevenot, Michel. Materialist Approaches to the Bible. Nottingham, William, tr. LC 84-14711. 160p. (Orig.). 1985. pap. 8.95 (ISBN 0-88344-343-0). Orbis Bks.

Cleverly, D. W. Preaching Through the Life of Christ. Lambert, Herbert, ed. LC 85-19002. 112p. 1986. pap. 7.95 (ISBN 0-8272-2930-5). CBP.

Cleves, William, et al, trs. see Fuchs, Josef.

Cliffe, A. E. Let Go & Let God. 1951. pap. 5.95 (ISBN 0-13-531509-3). P-H.

Cliffe, J. T. The Puritan Gentry: The Great Puritan Families of Early Stuart England. 300p. 1984. 25.00x (ISBN 0-7102-0007-2). Methuen Inc.

Clifford, Alan. The Middle Ages. Yapp, Malcolm, et al, eds. (World History Ser.). (Illus.). 1980. lib. bdg. 6.95 (ISBN 0-89908-028-6); pap. text ed. 2.45 (ISBN 0-89908-003-0). Greenhaven.

Clifford, Alejandro, tr. see Ten Boom, Corrie.

Clifford, David. The Two Jerusalems in Prophecy. LC 78-14922. (Illus.). 1978. pap. 3.50 (ISBN 0-87213-081-9). Loizeaux.

Clifford, James. Person & Myth: Maurice Leenhardt in the Melanesian World. LC 81-4509. (Illus.). 320p. 1982. 35.00x (ISBN 0-520-04247-6). U of Cal Pr.

Clifford, R. J. Book of Daniel. pap. 1.25 (ISBN 0-317-46870-7). Franciscan Herald.

Clifford, Richard. Deuteronomy, with Excursus on Covenant & Law. (Old Testament Message Ser.: Vol. 4). 1982. 12.95 (ISBN 0-89453-404-1); pap. 7.95 (ISBN 0-89453-239-1). M Glazier.

Clifford, Richard J. Fair-Spoken & Persuading: An Interpretation of Second Isaiah. (Theological Inquiries Ser.). (Orig.). 1984. pap. 8.95. Paulist Pr.

--Psalms 1-72. (Collegeville Bible Commentary: Old Testament Ser.: Vol. 22). 80p. 1986. pap. 2.95. Liturgical Pr.

--Psalms 73-150. (Collegeville Bible Commentary: Old Testament Ser.: Vol. 23). 88p. 1986. pap. 2.95 (ISBN 0-8146-1479-5). Liturgical Pr.

Clifford, Richard J. & Rockwell, Hays H. Holy Week. Achtemeier, Elizabeth, ed. LC 79-7377. (Proclamation 2, Ser. C). 1980. pap. 3.75 (ISBN 0-8006-4088-8, 1-4088). Fortress.

Clift, Jean & Clift, Wallace. Symbols of Transformation in Dreams. 144p. 1986. pap. 9.95 (ISBN 0-8245-0727-4). Crossroad NY.

Clift, Jeannette. Some Run with Feet of Clay. 127p. Repr. of 1978 ed. 7.95 (ISBN 0-318-20047-3). Manor of Grace.

Clift, Wallace, jt. auth. see Clift, Jean.

Clift, Wallace B. Jung & Christianity: The Challenge of Reconciliation. 169p. 1982. 12.95 (ISBN 0-8245-0409-7). Crossroad NY.

--Jung & Christianity: The Challenge of Reconciliation. LC 81-17395. 192p. 1983. pap. 8.95 (ISBN 0-8245-0552-2). Crossroad NY.

Clifton-Taylor, Alec. The Cathedrals of England. (Illus.). 1980. pap. 8.95 (ISBN 0-500-20062-9). Thames Hudson.

Climacus, St. John. Ljestvitsa. Tr. of The Ladder. (Rus.). 266p. (Orig.). 1963. 18.00x (ISBN 0-88465-033-2); pap. 13.00x (ISBN 0-317-38080-X). Holy Trinity.

Clinard, Turner N. Responding to God: The Life of Stewardship. LC 79-24762. 118p. 1980. Westminster.

Clinch, George. Old English Churches: Their Architecture, Furniture, Decorations & Monuments. 1977. lib. bdg. 59.95 (ISBN 0-8490-2368-8). Gordon Pr.

--Old English Churches: Their Architecture, Furniture, Decoration & Monuments. LC 77-94552. 1978. Repr. of 1900 ed. lib. bdg. 30.00 (ISBN 0-89341-221-X). Longwood Pub Group.

Clineball, Howard J., ed. see Clinebell, Charlotte H.

Clinebell, Charlotte H. Counseling for Liberation. Clineball, Howard J. & Stone, Howard W., eds. LC 75-36447. (Creative Pastoral Care & Counseling Ser). 96p. (Orig.). 1976. pap. 4.50 (ISBN 0-8006-0555-1, 1-555). Fortress.

Clinebell, Howard. Basic Types of Pastoral Care & Counseling. 464p. 1984. 17.95 (ISBN 0-687-02492-7). Abingdon.

Clinebell, Howard J. Growth Counseling for Marriage Enrichment: Pre-Marriage & the Early Years. Stone, Howard W., ed. LC 74-26335. (Creative Pastoral Care & Counseling Ser.). 96p. 1975. pap. 4.50 (ISBN 0-8006-0551-9, 1-551). Fortress.

--Growth Counseling for Mid-Years Couples. Stone, Howard W., ed. LC 76-7863. (Creative Pastoral Care & Counseling Ser.). 1977. pap. 0.50 (ISBN 0-8006-0558-6, 1-558). Fortress.

--Growth Counseling for Mid-Years Couples. LC 76-7863. (Creative Pastoral Care & Counseling Ser.). pap. 24.00 (2029607). Bks Demand UMI.

Clinebell, Howard J., ed. see Augsburger, David W.

Clinebell, Howard J., ed. see Clements, William M.

Clinebell, Howard J., ed. see Cobb, John B., Jr.

Clinebell, Howard J., ed. see Colston, Lowell G.

Clinebell, Howard J., ed. see Irwin, Paul B.

Clinebell, Howard J., ed. see Leas, Speed & Kittlaus, Paul.

Clinebell, Howard J., ed. see Oates, Wayne E.

Clinebell, Howard J., ed. see Pattison, E. Mansell.

Clinebell, Howard J., ed. see Stone, Howard W.

Clinebell, Howard J., Jr. Understanding & Counseling the Alcoholic. rev. ed. LC 56-10143. 1968. 13.95 (ISBN 0-687-42803-3). Abingdon.

Clines, D. J. Ezra, Nehemiah, Esther. Clements, Ronald, et al, eds. (New Century Bible Commentary Ser.). 384p. 1984. pap. 8.95 (ISBN 0-8028-0017-3). Eerdmans.

Clines, D. J. & Gunn, D. M. Art & Meaning: Rhetoric in Biblical Literature. (Journal for the Study of the Old Testament, Supplement Ser.: No. 19). viii, 266p. 1982. text ed. 25.00x (ISBN 0-905774-38-8, Pub. by JSOT Pr England); pap. text ed. 13.95x (ISBN 0-905774-39-6). Eisenbrauns.

Clines, David J. The Esther Scroll: Its Genesis, Growth, & Meaning. (JSOT Supplement Ser.: No. 30). 260p. 1984. text ed. 29.50x (ISBN 0-905774-66-3, Pub. by JSOT Pr England); pap. text ed. 13.50x (ISBN 0-905774-67-1, Pub. by JSOT Pr England). Eisenbrauns.

--I, He, We & They: A Literary Approach to Isaiah Fifty-Three. (JSOT Supplement Ser.: No. 1). 65p. 1976. pap. text ed. 4.95x (ISBN 0-905774-00-0, Pub. by JSOT Pr England). Eisenbrauns.

--The Theme of the Pentateuch. (Journal for the Study of the Old Testament Supplement Ser.: No. 10). 152p. 1978. text ed. 22.50 (ISBN 0-905774-14-0, Pub. by JSOT Pr England); pap. text ed. 10.95x (ISBN 0-905774-15-9, Pub. by JSOT Pr England). Eisenbrauns.

Clinton, Henry F. Fasti Romani: The Civil & Literary Chronology of Rome & Constantinople from the Death of Augustus to the Death of Justin the 2nd, 2 Vols. 1965. Repr. of 1850 ed. Set. 105.50 (ISBN 0-8337-0602-0). B Franklin.

Clinton, Iris. Friend of Chiefs, Robert Moffat. (Stories of Faith & Fame). 1975. pap. 2.95 (ISBN 0-87508-608-X). Chr Lit.

--Young Man in a Hurry (William Carey) 1961. pap. 2.95 (ISBN 0-87508-630-6). Chr Lit.

Clinton, Kevin. The Sacred Officials of the Eleusinian Mysteries. LC 73-79573. (Transaction Ser.: Vol. 64, Pt. 3). (Illus.). 1974. pap. 16.00 (ISBN 0-87169-643-6). Am Philos.

Clinton-Tullie, Verna, jt. auth. see Begay, Shirley M.

Clissold, Augustus, tr. see Swedenborg, Emmanuel.

Clissold, Augustus, tr. from Lat. see Swedenborg, Emmanuel.

Clissold, Stephen. St. Teresa of Avila. 288p. (Orig.). 1982. pap. 8.95 (ISBN 0-8164-2621-X, HarpR). Har-Row.

--The Wisdom of the Spanish Mystics. (Wisdom Bks.). 3.95 (ISBN 0-8112-0663-7). New Directions.

Clissold, Stephen, compiled by. The Wisdom of St. Francis & His Companions. LC 78-27504. (Wisdom Books). 1979. pap. 4.95 (ISBN 0-8112-0721-8, NDP477). New Directions.

Cloete, G. D., ed. A Moment of Truth: The Confession of the Dutch Reformed Mission Church, 1982. 176p. (Orig.). 1984. pap. 10.95x (ISBN 0-8028-0011-4). Eerdmans.

Clogan, Paul M., ed. Medieval Hagiography & Romance. LC 75-16872. (Medievalia et Humanistica Ser.: No. 6). pap. 59.30 (2029216). Bks Demand UMI.

Clokey, Joseph W. & Kirk, Hazel J. Childe Jesus: A Christmas Cantata for Mixed Voices. pap. 20.00 (ISBN 0-317-09646-X, 2017838). Bks Demand UMI.

Clorfene, Chaim, jt. auth. see Hecht, Shea.

Clotfelter, Charles T. & Salamon, Lester M. The Federal Government & the Nonprofit Sector: The Impact of the 1981 Tax Act on Individual Charitable Giving. LC 82-113321. cancelled. Urban Inst.

Clothey, Fred & Long, J. Bruce, eds. Experiencing Siva: Encounters with a Hindu Diety. 1983. 24.00x (ISBN 0-8364-1041-6). South Asia Bks.

Cloudsley, Anne. Women of Omdurman: Life, Love & the Cult of Virginity. LC 83-40625. 181p. 1985. 22.50 (ISBN 0-312-88755-8). St Martin.

Clough, Charles W. Madera: The Rich, Colorful & Exciting Historical Heritage of That Area Now Known As Madera County, California. (Illus.). 108p. 1983. casebound 14.95 (ISBN 0-317-44752-1); pap. 9.95 (ISBN 0-317-44753-X). Panorama West.

Clouse, Bonnidell. Moral Development. 368p. 1985. pap. 13.95 (ISBN 0-8010-2507-9). Baker Bk.

Clouse, Robert. Church in an Age of Orthodoxy & Enlightenment. 1980. pap. 4.95 (ISBN 0-570-06273-X, 12-2746). Concordia.

Clouse, Robert, et al. Church in History Series, 6 bks. 1980. pap. 27.95 set (ISBN 0-570-06277-2, 12-2780). Concordia.

Clouse, Robert G. The Meaning of the Millennium. 212p. 1978. pap. 5.95 (ISBN 0-88469-099-7). BMH Bks.

Clouse, Robert G., ed. The Meaning of the Millennium: Four Views. 1977. pap. 7.95 (ISBN 0-87784-794-0). Inter-Varsity.

Clouse, Robert G., ed. see Hoyt, Herman A., et al.

Clouse, Robert G., et al, eds. Protest & Politics: Christianity & Contemporary Affairs. 277p. 1968. 5.95 (ISBN 0-87921-000-1). Attic Pr.

Clouser, K. Danner. Teaching Bioethics: Strategies, Problems & Resources. LC 80-10492. (The Teaching of Ethics Ser.: Vol. IV). 77p. 1980. pap. 4.00 (ISBN 0-916558-07-X). Hastings Ctr.

Clow, W. Bible Reader's Encyclopedia & Concordance. (Illus.). 9.95 (ISBN 0-529-05899-5, RT1). World Bible.

Clower, Jerry. Let the Hammer Down. 1979. pap. 1.95 (ISBN 0-671-82626-3). PB.

Clowers, Don. Chastening of the Lord. 40p. (Orig.). 1986. wkbk 4.95 (ISBN 0-914307-56-8). Word Faith.

--The Power of God's Character. 230p. (Orig.). 1983. pap. text ed. 5.50 (ISBN 0-914307-14-2, Dist. by Harrison Hse). Word Faith.

--Principles of Leadership. 40p. (Orig.). 1985. wkbk. 4.95 (ISBN 0-914307-49-5). Word Faith.

--Spiritual Growth. 164p. (Orig.). 1984. pap. text ed. 3.95 (ISBN 0-914307-31-2). Word Faith.

Clowney, Edmund. Called to the Ministry. 1976. pap. 3.50 (ISBN 0-87552-144-4). Presby & Reformed.

Clowney, Edmund P. Christian Meditation. 1979. pap. 2.50 (ISBN 0-934532-06-0). Presby & Reformed.

--Living in Christ's Church. 1986. pap. text ed. 4.95 (ISBN 0-934688-22-2); leader's guide 3.95 (ISBN 0-934688-24-9). Great Comm Pubns.

--Preaching & Biblical Theology. 1956. pap. 3.95 (ISBN 0-87552-145-2). Presby & Reformed.

Clowney, Paul & Clowney, Tessa. Exploring Churches. LC 82-210857. pap. 23.50 (ISBN 0-317-30134-9, 2025317). Bks Demand UMI.

Clowney, Tessa, jt. auth. see Clowney, Paul.

Cloyd, Betty S. Glory Beyond All Comparison. LC 81-52216. 1981. pap. 4.50x (ISBN 0-8358-0423-2). Upper Room.

Cloyes, Shirley A., jt. auth. see Soelle, Dorothee.

CLSA Staff. Annual Convention Proceedings, 45th: 1983. 354p. 1984. pap. 7.00 (ISBN 0-943616-22-0). Canon Law Soc.

Clutton-Brock, Arthur. Essays on Religion. facs. ed. LC 79-84302. (Essay Index Reprint Ser). 1926. 14.50 (ISBN 0-8369-1078-8). Ayer Co Pubs.

--More Essays on Religion. facsimile ed. LC 76-156632. (Essay Index Reprint Ser). Repr. of 1928 ed. 18.00 (ISBN 0-8369-2349-9). Ayer Co Pubs.

Clymer, R. Swimburne. The Living Christ: Church of Illumination. 58p. 1979. pap. 2.95 (ISBN 0-932785-27-1). Philos Pub.

Clymer, R. Swinborne. The Rosicrucian Fraternity in America, 2 vols. 1935. 75.00 (ISBN 0-686-10446-3). Philos Pub.

Clymer, R. Swinburne. Book of Rosicruciae, 3 Vols. 1948. Set. 27.00 (ISBN 0-686-00809-X). Philos Pub.

--The Book of Rosicruciae, Vol. I. 286p. 1946. 9.95 (ISBN 0-932785-03-4). Philos Pub.

--Ciencia del Alma. Aparis, Fina, tr. (Span.). 272p. (Orig.). 1967. pap. 6.95 (ISBN 0-932785-51-4). Philos Pub.

--La Filosofia del Fuego. Morel, Hector V., tr. Tr. of The Philosophy of Fire. (Span.). 190p. (Orig.). 1980. pap. 5.95 (ISBN 0-932785-54-9). Philos Pub.

--Fraternitas Rosae Crucis. 1929. 9.95 (ISBN 0-932785-11-5). Philos Pub.

--Initiates & the People, 1928-1932, 5 vols. 1933. Repr. Set. 37.95 (ISBN 0-686-15595-5). Vol. I, 204 pp (ISBN 0-932785-18-2). Vol. II, 208 pp (ISBN 0-932785-19-0). Vol. III, 200 pp (ISBN 0-932785-20-4). Vol. IV, 192 pp (ISBN 0-932785-21-2). Vol. V, 207 pp (ISBN 0-932785-22-0). Philos Pub.

--Interpretation of St. John. 266p. 1953. 9.95 (ISBN 0-932785-23-9). Philos Pub.

--La Ley Divina: La Senda Hacia la Maestria. (Span., Orig.). 1972. pap. 6.95 (ISBN 0-932785-55-7). Philos Pub.

--Mysteries of Osiris: Egyptian Initiation. 287p. 1951. 8.95 (ISBN 0-932785-31-X). Philos Pub.

--Mysticism of Masonry. 1924. 4.95 (ISBN 0-686-00820-0). Philos Pub.

--Philosophy of Immortality. 208p. 1960. 6.95 (ISBN 0-932785-39-5). Philos Pub.

--The Rosy Cross: Its Teachings. 287p. 1965. 7.95 (ISBN 0-932785-43-3). Philos Pub.

--Science of Spiritual Alchemy. 235p. 1959. 9.95 (ISBN 0-932785-44-1). Philos Pub.

--The Way to Life & Immortality. 244p. 1948. 7.95 (ISBN 0-932785-48-4). Philos Pub.

Clymer, R. Swinburne & Lippard, George. Cristification: And la Hermanidad de la Rosa Cruz. 2nd ed. Bucheli, J. E., tr. (Span.). 206p. 1980. pap. 6.95 (ISBN 0-932785-52-2). Philos Pub.

Clymer, R. Swinburne, ed. see Randolph, Paschal B.

Clymer, R. Swineburn & Morey, Grace K. Mystic Americanism or the Spiritual Heritage of America Revealed. 328p. 1975. 7.95 (ISBN 0-932785-33-6). Philos Pub.

Coachman, Ward, jt. auth. see Chupco, Lee.

Coakley, Mary L. How to Live Life to the Fullest: A Handbook for Seasoned Citizens. LC 83-63167. 168p. 1984. pap. 4.95 (ISBN 0-87973-628-3, 628). Our Sunday Visitor.

Coalition on Women & Religion Staff. The Women's Bible: Study Guide. 1975. 5.95 (ISBN 0-9603042-2-3). Coalition Women-Relig.

Coalter, Milton J., Jr. Gilbert Tennent, Son of Thunder: A Case Study of Continental Pietism's Impact on the First Great Awakening in the Middle Colonies. LC 86-9967. (Contributions to the Study of Religion: No. 18). 247p. 1986. 35.00 (ISBN 0-313-25514-8, CGI/). Greenwood.

Coates, Austin. Numerology. 128p. 1984. 4.95 (ISBN 0-8065-0892-2). Citadel Pr.

Coates, John. Chesterton & the Edwardian Cultural Crisis. 280p. 1984. text ed. 28.50 (ISBN 0-85958-451-8, Pub. by U of Hull UK); pap. text ed. 19.95 (ISBN 0-85958-444-5). Humanities.

Coates, Sanford E. Psychical Research & Spiritualism. (Illus.). 1980. deluxe ed. 69.75 (ISBN 0-89920-006-0). Am Classical Coll Pr.

Coates, Thomas. The Sermon on the Mount for Today. LC 77-184. 1979. pap. 2.95x (ISBN 0-915644-13-4). Clayton Pub Hse.

Coats, George W. Genesis: With an Introduction to Narrative. (Forms of the Old Testament Literature Ser.: Vol. 1). 368p. (Orig.). 1984. pap. 21.95 (ISBN 0-8028-1954-0). Eerdmans.

--Saga, Legend, Tale, Novella, Fable. (JSOT Supplement Ser.). 159p. 1985. text ed. 18.50x (ISBN 0-905774-84-1, Pub by JSOT Pr England); pap. text ed. 8.95x (ISBN 0-905774-85-X). Eisenbrauns.

Coats, Robert B. John Bunyan. LC 77-9277. 1977. lib. bdg. 15.00 (ISBN 0-8414-1804-7). Folcroft.

Cobb, Alice, jt. auth. see Fahs, Sophia L.

Cobb, Buell E., Jr. The Sacred Harp: A Tradition & Its Music. LC 76-12680. 256p. 1978. 15.00x (ISBN 0-8203-0426-3). U of Ga Pr.

Cobb, J. B., jt. auth. see Birch, L. C.

Cobb, J. E. Cobb's Baptist Church Manual. 193p. 1979. pap. 2.50 (ISBN 0-89114-056-5). Baptist Pub Hse.

Cobb, John B., Jr. Beyond Dialogue: Toward a Mutual Transformation of Christianity & Buddhism. LC 82-8389. 176p. 1982. pap. 8.95 (ISBN 0-8006-1647-2, 1-1647). Fortress.

--Christ in a Pluralistic Age. LC 74-820. 286p. 1984. pap. 11.95 (ISBN 0-664-24522-6). Westminster.

--God & the World. LC 69-11374. 138p. 1969. pap. 5.95 (ISBN 0-664-24860-8). Westminster.

--Living Options in Protestant Theology: A Survey of Methods. 336p. 1986. pap. text ed. 14.75 (ISBN 0-8191-5488-1). U Pr of Amer.

--Process Theology As Political Theology. LC 82-1845. 174p. (Orig.). 1982. pap. 8.95 (ISBN 0-664-24417-3). Westminster.

--The Structure of Christian Existence. 1979. pap. 6.95 (ISBN 0-8164-2229-X, HarpR). Har-Row.

--Theology & Pastoral Care. Clinebell, Howard J. & Stone, Howard W., eds. LC 76-7862. (Creative Pastoral Care & Counseling Ser.). 96p. 1977. pap. 4.50 (ISBN 0-8006-0557-8, 1-557). Fortress.

--To Pray or Not to Pray. 1974. pap. 1.25x (ISBN 0-8358-0310-4). Upper Room.

Cobb, John B., Jr. & Griffin, David R. Process Theology: An Introductory Exposition. LC 76-10352. 192p. 1976. pap. 8.95 (ISBN 0-664-24743-1). Westminster.

Cobb, John B., Jr., jt. auth. see Hough, Joseph C., Jr.

Cobb, John B., Jr., jt. auth. see Tracy, David.

Cobb, John B., Jr., jt. ed. see Robinson, James M.

Cobb, Roger W., jt. auth. see Elder, Charles D.

Cobb, Sanford H. The Rise of Religious Liberty in America. 1978. pap. write for info. (ISBN 0-89102-115-9, Artemis). B Franklin.

--Rise of Religious Liberty in America: A History. LC 68-27517. 541p. 1968. Repr. of 1902 ed. 32.50x (ISBN 0-8154-0051-9). Cooper Sq.

--The Rise of Religious Liberty in America: A History. (American Studies). 1970. Repr. of 1902 ed. 30.00 (ISBN 0-384-09445-7). Johnson Repr.

Cobbe, F. P. The Devil: His Origin, Greatness & Decline. 59.95 (ISBN 0-8490-0022-X). Gordon Pr.

Cobbett, Thomas. Civil Magistrate's Power in Matters of Religion Modestly Debated, London, 1653. LC 74-141104. (Research Library of Colonial Americana). 1972. Repr. of 1653 ed. 24.50 (ISBN 0-405-03318-4). Ayer Co Pubs.

Cobble, James F. Faith & Crisis in the Stages of Life. 128p. 1985. pap. 6.95 (ISBN 0-913573-17-5). Hendrickson MA.

Cober, Kenneth L. Shaping the Church's Educational Ministry. LC 75-139502. (Illus.). 1971. pap. 3.95 (ISBN 0-8170-0519-6); pap. 1.95 spanish ed (ISBN 0-8170-0603-6). Judson.

Cobin, Martin. From Convincement to Conversion. LC 64-17424. (Orig.). 1964. pap. 2.50x (ISBN 0-87574-134-7). Pendle Hill.

Coble, Betty J. The Private Life of the Minister's Wife. LC 81-65385. 1981. pap. 5.95 (ISBN 0-8054-6935-4). Broadman.

--Woman: Aware & Choosing. new ed. LC 75-7943. 156p. 1975. 8.95 (ISBN 0-8054-5613-9). Broadman.

Coburn, Alexander. The Heian Period in the Evolution of Buddhist Architecture in Japan. (Illus.). 176p. 1985. Repr. of 1930 ed. 187.50 (ISBN 0-86650-167-3). Gloucester Art.

Coburn, John. A Life to Live - a Way to Pray. 160p. (Orig.). 1973. pap. 5.95 (ISBN 0-8164-2079-3, SP80, HarpR). Har-Row.

Coburn, John B. Christ's Life, Our Life. LC 77-17172. 112p. 1978. 4.00 (ISBN 0-8164-0384-8, HarpR); pap. 4.95 (ISBN 0-8164-2616-3). Har-Row.

--Deliver Us from Evil: The Prayer of Our Lord. 96p. 1976. pap. 4.95 (ISBN 0-8164-2124-2, HarpR). Har-Row.

--Feeding Fire. LC 80-81103. 62p. 1980. 8.95 (ISBN 0-8192-1281-4). Morehouse.

--Prayer & Personal Religion. LC 57-5397. (Layman's Theological Library). 96p. 1957. pap. 4.95 (ISBN 0-664-24005-4). Westminster.

--Prayer & Personal Religion. LC 85-10477. 160p. 1985. pap. 8.95 (ISBN 0-8027-2509-0). Walker & Co.

Coburn, O., tr. see Lasserre, Jean.

Coburn, Oliver, tr. see Sabet, Huschmand.

Coburn, Oliver, tr. see Schaefer, Udo.

Cochran, Alice C. Miners, Merchants & Missionaries: The Roles of Missionaries & Pioneer Churches in the Colorado Gold Rush & Its Aftermath, 1858-1870. LC 80-16895. (ATLA Monographs: No. 15). x, 287p. 1980. 21.00 (ISBN 0-8108-1325-4). Scarecrow.

Cochran, Louis. The Fool of God. (Heritage of a Movement Book Club Ser.). 416p. Repr. of 1958 ed. 11.95 (ISBN 0-89900-275-7). College Pr Pub.

Cochran, Robert, jt. auth. see Stapleton, Ruth C.

Cochrane, Arthur C. The Church's Confession Under Hitler. 2nd ed. LC 76-57655. (Pittsburgh Reprint Ser.: No. 4). 1977. pap. text ed. 10.75 (ISBN 0-915138-28-X). Pickwick.

--The Mystery of Peace. 224p. 1985. pap. 11.95 (ISBN 0-87178-695-8). Brethren.

Cochrane, Charles C. The Gospel According to Genesis. 96p. (Orig.). 1984. pap. 4.95 (ISBN 0-8028-1971-0). Eerdmans.

--The Gospel According to Genesis: A Guide to Understanding Genesis 1-11. LC 84-4047. Repr. of 1984 ed. 24.00 (2027539). Bks Demand UMI.

Cochrane, Charles N. Christianity & Classical Culture: A Study of Thought & Action from Augustus to Augustine. 1957. pap. 10.95 (ISBN 0-19-500207-5). Oxford U Pr.

--Christianity & Classical Culture: A Study of Thought & Action from Augustus to Augustine. 1984. 18.00 (ISBN 0-8446-6086-8). Peter Smith.

Cochrane, Donald B. & Manley-Casimir, Michael, eds. Development of Moral Reasoning: Practical Approaches. LC 80-17141. 352p. 1980. 44.95 (ISBN 0-03-056209-0). Praeger.

Cochrane, Robert. The Treasury of Modern Biography: A Gallery of Literary Sketches of Eminent Men & Women of the 19th Century. 1881. Repr. 50.00 (ISBN 0-8274-3645-9). R West.

Cockayne, O., ed. Hali Meidenhad, Alliterative Homily of 13th Century. (EETS OS Ser.: No. 18). Repr. of 1922 ed. 11.00 (ISBN 0-527-00020-5). Kraus Repr.

Cocke, Charles F. Parish Lines, Diocese of Southern Virginia. (Virginia State Library Publications: No. 22). 287p. 1979. Repr. of 1964 ed. 5.00 (ISBN 0-88490-049-5). VA State Lib.

--Parish Lines, Diocese of Southwestern Virginia. (Virginia State Library Publications: No. 14). 196p. 1980. Repr. of 1960 ed. 5.00 (ISBN 0-686-74611-2). VA State Lib.

--Parish Lines, Diocese of Virginia. LC 78-19035. (Virginia State Library Publications: No. 28). xv, 321p. 1978. Repr. of 1967 ed. 5.00 (ISBN 0-88490-062-2). VA State Lib.

Cockerham, Allan W. The Apostolic Succession in the Liberal Catholic Church. 2nd ed. (Illus.). 1980. pap. text ed. 2.80 (ISBN 0-918980-09-7). St Alban Pr.

Cockett, M. Bells in Our Lives. 1985. 17.50x (ISBN 0-317-54266-4, Pub. by J Richardson UK). State Mutual Bk.

Cockman, Nelda. Is Bible Reliable? Leader's Guide. Chao, Loran Y., tr. (Basic Doctrine Ser.). (Chinese.). 1986. pap. write for info. (ISBN 0-941598-34-9). Living Spring Pubns.

Cockrell, Marcia W., jt. ed. see Roberts, Anne F.

Cocks, H. Lovell. The Religious Life of Oliver Cromwell. LC 61-47823. 1961. text ed. 6.00x (ISBN 0-8401-0443-X). A R Allenson.

Cockshut, A. O., ed. Religious Controversies of the Nineteenth Century: Selected Documents. LC 66-18225. vi, 265p. 1966. 19.95x (ISBN 0-8032-0019-6). U of Nebr Pr.

Cocoris, G. Michael. Amos: The Message We Dare Not Ignore. 90p. (Orig.). 1985. pap. text ed. 1.00 (ISBN 0-935729-02-X). Church Open Door.

--Colossians. rev. ed. 35p. 1985. pap. 1.00 (ISBN 0-935729-05-4). Church Open Door.

--Colossians, Pt. 1. rev. ed. 41p. 1985. pap. text ed. 1.00 (ISBN 0-935729-04-6). Church Open Door.

--Cults: Deception or Denomination. 53p. (Orig.). 1984. pap. text ed. 1.00 (ISBN 0-935729-11-9). Church Open Door.

--Daniel. rev. ed. 150p. 1985. pap. text ed. 3.00 (ISBN 0-935729-06-2). Church Open Door.

--Ephesians. (Orig.). Date not set. pap. text ed. price not set (ISBN 0-935729-37-2). Church Open Door.

--Evangelism: A Biblical Approach. (Orig.). 1984. pap. 6.95 (ISBN 0-8024-2396-5). Moody.

--Formulas for Family Living. 46p. (Orig.). 1983. pap. text ed. 1.00 (ISBN 0-935729-28-3). Church Open Door.

--Galatians. (Orig.). 1986. pap. text ed. write for info. (ISBN 0-935729-33-X). Church Open Door.

--James, Pt. 1. rev. ed. 51p. 1984. pap. text ed. 1.00 (ISBN 0-935729-12-7). Church Open Door.

--James, Pt. 2. rev. ed. 43p. 1984. pap. text ed. 1.00 (ISBN 0-935729-13-5). Church Open Door.

--John. rev. ed. 181p. 1985. pap. text ed. 3.00 (ISBN 0-935729-07-0). Church Open Door.

--Jonah. 74p. 1986. pap. text ed. 2.00 (ISBN 0-935729-32-1). Church Open Door.

--Joshua. rev. ed. 125p. 1986. pap. text ed. 3.00 (ISBN 0-935729-34-8). Church Open Door.

--Joshua, Pt. 1. 44p. (Orig.). 1984. pap. text ed. 1.00 (ISBN 0-935729-18-6). Church Open Door.

--Joshua, Pt. 2. 42p. (Orig.). 1984. pap. text ed. 1.00 (ISBN 0-935729-19-4). Church Open Door.

--Joshua, Pt. 3. 44p. (Orig.). 1984. pap. text ed. 1.00 (ISBN 0-935729-20-8). Church Open Door.

--The Last Sayings of the Savior from the Cross. 25p. (Orig.). 1985. pap. 1.00 (ISBN 0-935729-01-1). Church Open Door.

--Lordship Salvation-Is It Biblical? 24p. (Orig.). 1983. pap. 1.25 (ISBN 0-9607576-2-7). Redencion Viva.

--Making Evangelism Personal, Pt. 1. 56p. (Orig.). 1984. pap. text ed. 1.00 (ISBN 0-935729-16-X). Church Open Door.

--Making Evangelsim Personal, Pt. 2. 41p. (Orig.). 1984. pap. text ed. 1.00 (ISBN 0-935729-17-8). Church Open Door.

--Nehemiah. rev. ed. 37p. 1984. pap. 1.00 (ISBN 0-935729-14-3). Church Open Door.

--Nehemiah. rev. ed. 37p. 1984. pap. 1.00 (ISBN 0-935729-15-1). Church Open Door.

--Obadiah. 19p. (Orig.). 1983. pap. 1.00 (ISBN 0-935729-29-1). Church Open Door.

--An Outline for Discipling. rev. ed. 9p. 1984. pap. 1.00 (ISBN 0-935729-10-0). Church Open Door.

--Philemon. 22p. (Orig.). 1985. pap. 1.00 (ISBN 0-935729-08-9). Church Open Door.

--Questioning Christianity. 67p. (Orig.). 1985. pap. text ed. 1.00 (ISBN 0-935729-00-3). Church Open Door.

--Seventy Years on Hope Street: A History of the Church of the Open Door 1915-1985. (Illus.). 151p. 1985. text ed. 35.00 (ISBN 0-935729-09-7). Church Open Door.

--Seventy Years on Hope Street: A History of the Church of the Open Door 1915-1985. (Illus.). 151p. 1985. deluxe ed. 195.95 (ISBN 0-935729-30-5). Church Open Door.

--Titus. 99p. (Orig.). 1985. pap. text ed. 2.00 (ISBN 0-935729-31-3). Church Open Door.

--Untangling Bible Doctrine. rev. ed. 107p. 1985. pap. text ed. 2.00 (ISBN 0-935729-03-8). Church Open Door.

Codd. Way of the Disciple. 5.00 (ISBN 0-8356-7049-X). Theos Pub Hse.

Codd, Clara & Blavatsky, eds. Key to Theosophy Simplified. 5.25 (ISBN 0-8356-7060-0). Theos Pub Hse.

Codd, Clara M. Ageless Wisdom of Life. LC 67-8630. 1967. pap. 1.75 (ISBN 0-8356-0145-5, Quest). Theos Pub Hse.

--Ageless Wisdom of Life. 4.95 (ISBN 0-8356-7329-4). Theos Pub Hse.

--Meditation, Its Practice & Results. 4th ed. 1968. 2.25 (ISBN 0-8356-7212-3). Theos Pub Hse.

--Technique of the Spiritual Life. 2nd ed. 1963. 6.95 (ISBN 0-8356-7090-2). Theos Pub Hse.

--Trust Yourself to Life. LC 75-4245. 116p. 1975. pap. 1.75 (ISBN 0-8356-0464-0, Quest). Theos Pub Hse.

Code, Joseph B. Great American Foundresses. facs. ed. LC 68-20291. (Essay Index Reprint Ser). 1929. 21.50 (ISBN 0-8369-0319-6). Ayer Co Pubs.

Coder, Maxwell S. Judas: Los Hechos de los Apostatas (Comentario Biblico Portavoz) Orig. Title: Jude: the Acts of the Apostates (Everyman's Bible Commentary). (Span.). 134p. 1980. pap. 3.95 (ISBN 0-8254-1125-4). Kregel.

Coder, S. Maxwell. The Final Chapter. 318p. 1984. pap. 7.95 (ISBN 0-8423-0866-0). Tyndale.

--Jude: The Acts of the Apostates. (Everyman's Bible Commentary Ser). 1967. pap. 5.95 (ISBN 0-8024-2065-6). Moody.

Coder, S. Maxwell, jt. auth. see Nave, Orville J.

Codman, John T. Mormon Country. LC 70-134392. Repr. of 1874 ed. 18.25 (ISBN 0-404-08481-8). AMS Pr.

Cody, Aelred. Ezekiel: With Excursus on Old Testament Priesthood. (Old Testament Message Ser.: Vol. 11). 1984. 12.95 (ISBN 0-89453-411-4); pap. 9.95 (ISBN 0-89453-245-6). M Glazier.

Coe, Ben. Christian Churches at the Crossroads. LC 80-27624. 160p. (Orig.). 1980. pap. 5.95 (ISBN 0-87808-178-X). William Carey Lib.

Coe, David K. Angst & the Abyss: The Hermeneutics of Nothingness. (Academic Ser.). 1985. 17.95 (ISBN 0-89130-862-8, 01-01-49); pap. 11.95 (ISBN 0-89130-863-6). Scholars Pr GA.

Coe, George A. The Psychology of Religion. LC 75-3113. Repr. of 1916 ed. 40.00 (ISBN 0-404-59109-4). AMS Pr.

--The Psychology of Religion. Repr. of 1916 ed. 25.00 (ISBN 0-89987-046-5). Darby Bks.

--Social Theory of Religious Education. LC 78-89164. (American Education: Its Men, Institutions & Ideas, Ser. 1). 1969. Repr. of 1917 ed. 24.50 (ISBN 0-405-01402-3). Ayer Co Pubs.

Coe, Greg, jt. auth. see Coe, Jolene.

Coe, Jolene & Coe, Greg. The Mormon Experience: A Young Couple's Fascinating Journey to Truth. 176p. (Orig.). 1985. pap. 5.95 (ISBN 0-89081-486-4). Harvest Hse.

Coe, Joyce. The Donkey Who Served the King. (Arch Bk. Ser.: No. 15). (Illus.). 1978. 0.99 (ISBN 0-570-06120-2, 59-1238). Concordia.

--Jesus Rides into Jerusalem. (Illus.). 24p. 1987. pap. 00.99 (ISBN 0-570-09007-5, 59-1435). Concordia.

Coe, Rachel. I Have a Family. LC 86-17629. (Bible-&-Me Ser.). 1987. 5.95 (ISBN 0-8054-4172-7). Broadman.

Coe, Sophie, tr. see Knorozov, Yuri V. & Proskouriakoff, Tatiana.

Coelho, Mary C., jt. ed. see Neufelder, Jerome N.

Coen, Rena N. Old Testament in Art. LC 77-84410. (Fine Art Books). (Illus.). 1970. PLB 5.95 (ISBN 0-8225-0168-6). Lerner Pubns.

Cofer, David B. Saint-Simonism in the Radicalism of Thomas Carlyle. (English Literature Ser., No. 33). 1970. pap. 39.95x (ISBN 0-8383-0017-0). Haskell.

Coffen, Harold G. Origin by Design. Wheeler, Gerald, ed. LC 82-21445. (Illus.). 494p. 1983. text ed. 18.95 (ISBN 0-8280-0131-6). Review & Herald.

Coffen, Richard W., ed. see Bradford, Charles E.

Coffen, Richard W., ed. see Brunt, John C.

Coffen, Richard W., ed. see Heubach, Paul.

Coffen, Richard W., ed. see Johnsson, William G.

Coffen, Richard W., ed. see Liebelt, Gerita G.

Coffen, Richard W., ed. see Moore, Marvin.

Coffen, Richard W., ed. see Orser, Evelyn.

Coffen, Richard W., ed. see Taggart, George.

Coffen, Richard W., ed. see Van Pelt, Nancy L.

Coffen, Richard W., ed. see Vasi, Dianne.

Coffen, Richard W., ed. see Young, Norman.

Coffey, Rosalie L. & Glenn, John S. Completing the Promise. (Religious Awards for Boy Scouts Ser.). 1984. pap. 4.95x (ISBN 0-938758-17-9). MTM Pub Co.

Coffey, Thomas P. A Candle in the Wind: My Thirty Years in Book Publishing. 222p. 1985. pap. 5.95 (ISBN 0-87193-212-1). Dimension Bks.

--There Is a Singing Underneath: Meditations in Central Park. 128p. 1985. pap. 4.95 (ISBN 0-87193-217-2). Dimension Bks.

Coffin, Glenyce. Run to Win: Training for the Overcoming Life. (Cornerstone Ser.). 40p. 1984. pap. 2.50 (ISBN 0-930756-87-8, 533010). Aglow Pubns.

Coffin, Henry S. In a Day of Social Rebuilding: Lectures on the Ministry of the Church. 1919. 29.50x (ISBN 0-686-51402-5). Elliots Bks.

--The Public Worship of God: A Source Book. 16.00 (ISBN 0-8369-7272-4, 8071). Ayer Co Pubs.

--Religion Yesterday & Today. facs. ed. LC 75-117769. (Essay Index Reprint Ser). 1940. 18.00 (ISBN 0-8369-1790-1). Ayer Co Pubs.

--Some Christian Convictions: A Practical Restatement in Terms of Present-Day Thinking. LC 79-167328. (Essay Index Reprint Ser.). Repr. of 1915 ed. 17.00 (ISBN 0-8369-2763-X). Ayer Co Pubs.

--What Men Are Asking. facs. ed. LC 70-117770. (Essay Index Reprint Ser). 1933. 12.50 (ISBN 0-8369-1791-X). Ayer Co Pubs.

Coffin, William S. Living the Truth in a World of Illusions. LC 84-48766. 160p. 1985. 12.45 (ISBN 0-06-061512-5, HarpR). Har-Row.

Coffman, Barbara F. His Name Was John: The Life Story of John S. Coffman, an Early Mennonite Leader. LC 64-18732. (Illus.). 352p. 1964. 12.95 (ISBN 0-8361-1486-8). Herald Pr.

Coffman, Burton. Commentary on James, First & Second; Peter, First, Second & Third, John, Jude. (Firm Foundation Commentary Ser.). 1979. cancelled 10.95 (ISBN 0-88027-075-6). Firm Foun Pub.

Coffman, Carl. Unto a Perfect Man. 4th ed. 209p. 1982. pap. 8.95 (ISBN 0-943872-83-9). Andrews Univ Pr.

Coffman, James B. Commentary on Acts. (Firm Foundation Commentary Ser). 1976. cancelled 10.95 (ISBN 0-88027-069-1). Firm Foun Pub.

--Commentary on Exodus. 1986. 19.95 (ISBN 0-915547-49-X). Abilene Christ U.

--Commentary on First & Second Thessalonians, I & II Timothy, Titus & Philemon. (Firm Foundation Commentary Ser.). 1978. 10.95 (ISBN 0-88027-073-X). Firm Foun Pub.

--Commentary on Galatians, Ephesians, Phillipians, Colossians. (Firm Foundation Commentary Ser.). 1977. cancelled 10.95 (ISBN 0-88027-072-1). Firm Foun Pub.

--Commentary on Genesis. 1986. 19.95 (ISBN 0-915547-48-1). Abilene Christ U.

--Commentary on Hebrews. (Firm Foundation Commentary Ser.). 1971. cancelled 10.95 (ISBN 0-88027-074-8). Firm Foun Pub.

--Commentary on John. (Firm Foundation Commentary Ser.). 1974. cancelled 10.95 (ISBN 0-88027-068-3). Firm Foun Pub.

--Commentary on Leviticus & Numbers. 580p. 1987. 19.95 (ISBN 0-915547-75-9). Abilene Christ U.
--Commentary on Luke. (Firm Foundation Commentary Ser.). 1975. cancelled 10.95 (ISBN 0-88027-067-5). Firm Foun Pub.
--Commentary on Mark. (Firm Foundation Commentary Ser.). 1975. cancelled 10.95 (ISBN 0-88027-066-7). Firm Foun Pub.
--Commentary on Matthew. (Firm Foundation Commentary Ser.). 1968. cancelled 10.95 (ISBN 0-88027-065-9). Firm Foun Pub.
--Commentary on Romans. (Firm Foundation Commentary Ser.). cancelled (ISBN 0-88027-070-5). Firm Foun Pub.
--Commentary on the Minor Prophets, Vol. 1. (Firm Foundation Commentary Ser.). 360p. 1981. cancelled 8.95 (ISBN 0-88027-078-0). Firm Foun Pub.
--Commentary on the Minor Prophets, Vol. 2. (Firm Foundation Commentary Ser.). 383p. 1981. cancelled 8.95 (ISBN 0-88027-079-9). Firm Foun Pub.
--Commentary on the Minor Prophets, Vol. 3. (Commmentary Ser.). 322p. 1983. cancelled 10.95 (ISBN 0-88027-107-8). Firm Foun Pub.
--The Mystery of Redemption. 1976. 5.95 (ISBN 0-88027-089-6). Firm Foun Pub.
--The Ten Commandments Yesterday & Today. pap. 4.50 (ISBN 0-88027-094-2). Firm Foun Pub.
Coffman, S. F., ed. Church Hymnal. 536p. (657 hymns). 1927. 7.95x (ISBN 0-8361-1106-0). Herald Pr.
--Life Songs Number Two. 288p. (With Responsive Readings). 1938. 6.95x (ISBN 0-8361-1116-8). Herald Pr.
Cofone, Charles J., ed. Favorite Christmas Carols. (Illus.). 64p. 1975. pap. 3.50 (ISBN 0-486-20445-6). Dover.
Cogan, Sr. Mary De Paul. Sisters of Maryknoll: Through Troubled Waters. LC 72-167329. (Essay Index Reprint Ser.). Repr. of 1947 ed. 18.00 (ISBN 0-8369-2764-8). Ayer Co Pubs.
Cogan, Morton. Imperialism & Religion: Assyria, Judah & Israel in the Eighth & Seventh Centuries B.C.E. LC 73-83723. (Society of Biblical Literature. Monograph). 1974. 13.50 (ISBN 0-89130-330-8, 060019); pap. 9.95 (ISBN 0-89130-331-6, 00-06-19). Scholars Pr GA.
Cogan, Sara, compiled by. The Jews of San Francisco & the Greater Bay Area: 1849 to 1919. (Western Jewish Americana Ser.: No. 2). 1972. 22.00 (ISBN 0-943376-03-3). Magnes Mus.
--The Jews of Los Angeles, No. 3. (Western Jewish Americana Ser. Publications). 237p. 1980. 24.95 (ISBN 0-943376-12-2); pap. 14.95 (ISBN 0-943376-11-4). Magnes Mus.
Coggan, D. Relevance of the Bible for Today. 1967. pap. 1.75x (ISBN 0-85564-005-7, Pub. by U of W Austral Pr). Intl Spec Bk.
Coggin & Spooner. How to Build a Bus Ministry. 2.25 (ISBN 0-8054-9405-7). Broadman.
Coggins, R. J. The Books of Ezra & Nehemiah. LC 75-26278. (Cambridge Bible Commentary on the New English Bible, Old Testament Ser.). (Illus.). 200p. 1976. 22.95 (ISBN 0-521-08648-5); pap. 9.95x (ISBN 0-521-09759-2). Cambridge U Pr.
--The First & Second Book of the Chronicles. LC 75-17117. (Cambridge Bible Commentary on the New English Bible, Old Testament Ser.). (Illus.). 256p. 1976. 39.50 (ISBN 0-521-08647-7); pap. 16.95x (ISBN 0-521-09758-4). Cambridge U Pr.
--Haggi, Zechariah, Malachi. (Old Testament Guides Ser.). 100p. 1986. pap. text ed. 4.95x (ISBN 1-85075-025-4, Pub. by JSOT Pr England). Eisenbrauns.
Coggins, R. J. & Knibb, M. A. The First & Second Books of Esdras: Cambridge Bible Commentary on the New English Bible. LC 78-16420. (Old Testament Ser.). 1979. pap. 15.95 (ISBN 0-521-09757-6). Cambridge U Pr.
Coggins, R. J. & Phillips, Anthony C., eds. Israel's Prophetic Tradition. LC 81-17065. (Illus.). 290p. 1982. 44.50 (ISBN 0-521-24223-1). Cambridge U Pr.
Coggins, Richard, et al, eds. Israel's Prophetic Tradition: Essays in Honour of Peter Ackroyd. 294p. 1985. 18.95 (ISBN 0-521-31886-6). Cambridge U Pr.
Coggins, Wade T. see Frizen, Edwin L.
Coghlan, Ronan. Pocket Dictionary of Irish Myth & Legend. (Pocket Bk.). (Illus.). 96p. (Orig.). 1985. pap. 3.95 (ISBN 0-86281-152-X, Pub. by Appletree Pr). Irish Bks Media.
Cohen, A. Ezekiel. 350p. 1950. 10.95 (ISBN 0-900689-30-7). Soncino Pr.
--Isaiah One & Two. 330p. 1949. 10.95 (ISBN 0-900689-28-5). Soncino Pr.
--Jeremiah. 369p. 1949. 10.95 (ISBN 0-900689-29-3). Soncino Pr.
--Job. 233p. 1946. 10.95 (ISBN 0-900689-34-X). Soncino Pr.
--Kings One & Two. 337p. 1950. 10.95 (ISBN 0-900689-27-7). Soncino Pr.
--Proverbs. 223p. 1946. 10.95 (ISBN 0-900689-33-1). Soncino Pr.
--The Psalms. 488p. 1945. 10.95 (ISBN 0-900689-32-3). Soncino Pr.
--The Twelve Prophets. 368p. 1948. 10.95 (ISBN 0-900689-31-5). Soncino Pr.
Cohen, A., ed. Chronicles. 358p. 1952. 10.95 (ISBN 0-900689-37-4). Soncino Pr.
--Joshua & Judges. 332p. 1950. 10.95 (ISBN 0-900689-20-X). Soncino Pr.
--Samuel. 361p. 1949. 10.95 (ISBN 0-900689-26-9). Soncino Pr.
Cohen, A., ed. see Nehemiah, Ezra.
Cohen, Abraham. Everyman's Talmud. LC 75-10750. 446p. 1975. pap. 11.25 (ISBN 0-8052-0497-0). Schocken.
Cohen, Adir. The Educational Philosophy of Martin Buber. LC 81-68074. 350p. 1983. 32.50 (ISBN 0-8386-3098-7). Fairleigh Dickinson.
Cohen, Alan. If We Only Have Love. (Illus.). 15p. (Orig.). 1984. pap. 1.00 (ISBN 0-910367-34-5). A Cohen.
--If We Only Have Love. (Illus., Orig.). 1984. pap. 2.00 (ISBN 0-942494-86-5). Coleman Pub.
--The Peace That You Seek. (Illus.). 195p. (Orig.). 1985. pap. 5.95 (ISBN 0-910367-35-3, 157). A Cohen.
Cohen, Alfred S. Halacha & Contemporary Society. LC 84-741. 1985. pap. 9.95 (ISBN 0-88125-043-0). Ktav.
Cohen, Amnon. Jewish Life under Islam: Jerusalem in the Sixteenth Century. (Illus.). 288p. 1984. text ed. 30.00x (ISBN 0-674-47436-8). Harvard U Pr.
Cohen, Amnon & Baer, Gabriel, eds. Egypt & Palestine: A Millennium of Association (868-1948) LC 84-16109. 400p. 1985. 32.50 (ISBN 0-312-23927-0). St Martin.
Cohen, Arthur, jt. auth. see Halverson, Marvin.
Cohen, Arthur A. The Natural & the Supernatural Jew: An Historical and Theological Introduction. LC 79-13038. 1979. pap. text ed. 6.95x (ISBN 0-87441-291-9). Behrman.
Cohen, Arthur A., jt. auth. see Kaplan, Mordecai M.
Cohen, Arthur A. & Mendes-Flohr, Paul, eds. Contemporary Jewish Religious Thought. LC 86-11856. 1986. 75.00 (ISBN 0-684-18628-4). Scribner.
Cohen, Barbara. First Fast. (Illus.). 32p. 1987. 7.95 (ISBN 0-8074-0354-7). UAHC.
Cohen, Bernard. Sociocultural Changes in American Jewish Life As Reflected in Selected Jewish Literature. LC 75-146162. 282p. 1972. 24.50 (ISBN 0-8386-7848-3). Fairleigh Dickinson.
Cohen, Bernard L. Jews Among the Nations. LC 77-79171. 338p. 1978. 10.95 (ISBN 0-8022-2209-9). Philos Lib.
Cohen, Boaz. Jewish & Roman Law, 2 Vols. 1966. Set. 15.00x (ISBN 0-8381-4100-5). United Syn Bk.
--Law & Tradition in Judaism. 1959. 12.50x (ISBN 0-87068-023-4). Ktav.
Cohen, Boaz & Katz, Steven, eds. Saadia Anniversary Volume. LC 79-7168. (Jewish Philosophy, Mysticism & History of Ideas Ser.). 1980. Repr. of 1943 ed. lib. bdg. 28.50x (ISBN 0-405-12244-6). Ayer Co Pubs.
Cohen, Burton I., jt. auth. see Shapiro, Alexander M.
Cohen, Bydr A., ed. The Five Megilloth. 252p. 1946. 10.95 (ISBN 0-900689-35-8). Soncino Pr.
Cohen, Chapman. Religion & Sex. LC 72-9631. Repr. of 1919 ed. 40.00 (ISBN 0-404-57430-0). AMS Pr.
Cohen, Charles. God's Caress: The Psychology of Puritan Religious Experience. 336p. 1986. text ed. 29.95x (ISBN 0-19-503973-4). Oxford U Pr.
Cohen, Daniel. Dealing with the Devil. LC 79-14692. (Illus.). 1979. 11.95 (ISBN 0-396-07700-5). Dodd.
--Famous Curses. (Illus.). pap. 1.95 (ISBN 0-671-41867-X). Archway.
--Famous Curses. LC 79-52039. (High Interest-Low Vocabulary Ser.). (Illus.). 1979. 8.95 (ISBN 0-396-07712-9). Dodd.
--Waiting for the Apocalypse: Doomsday Deferred. rev. ed. LC 83-62189. (Illus.). 260p. 1983. pap. 10.95 (ISBN 0-87975-223-8). Prometheus Bks.
Cohen, Dovid. The Relevancy of Torah to the Social & Ethical Issues of Our Time. (Annual Fryer Memorial Lecture Ser.). 0.50 (ISBN 0-914131-57-5, I36). Torah Umesorah.
Cohen, Edmund D. The Mind of the Bible-Believer. 425p. 1986. 19.95 (ISBN 0-87975-341-2). Prometheus Bks.
Cohen, Eugene J. Guide to Ritual Circumcision & Redemption of the First-Born Son. 210p. 1984. 15.00x (ISBN 0-88125-017-1); pap. 9.95 (ISBN 0-88125-023-6). Ktav.
Cohen, Gary & Kirban, Salem. Israel, Land of Promise, Land of Peace. LC 74-77252. (Illus.). 1974. pap. 5.95 (ISBN 0-912582-16-2). Kirban.
Cohen, Gary, jt. auth. see Kirban, Salem.
Cohen, Gary & Vandermey, H. Ronald, eds. Hosea & Amos. (Everyman's Bible Commentary). 128p. 1981. pap. 5.95 (ISBN 0-8024-2028-1). Moody.
Cohen, Gary G. Biblical Separation Defended. 1966. pap. 3.50 (ISBN 0-87552-147-9). Presby & Reformed.
Cohen, Gerson D., ed. & tr. see Daud, Abraham I.
Cohen, Harold R. Biblical Hapax Legomena in the Light of Akkadian & Ugaritic: Society of Biblical Literature, No.37. LC 77-13422. (Dissertation Ser.). pap. 50.30 (ISBN 0-8357-9565-9, 2017528). Bks Demand UMI.
Cohen, Harry, ed. see Kimchi, David B.
Cohen, Henry. Why Judaism? A Search for Meaning in Jewish Identity. 192p. 1973. pap. 5.00 (ISBN 0-8074-0077-7, 161901). UAHC.
Cohen, Hermann. Hermann Cohen's Judische Schriften, 3 vols. Katz, Steven, ed. LC 79-7128. (Jewish Philosophy, Mysticism & History of Ideas Ser.). 1980. Repr. of 1924 ed. lib. bdg. 103.50x (ISBN 0-405-12245-4). Ayer Co Pubs.
Cohen, I. Bernard. Cotton Mather & American Science & Medicine: With Studies & Documents Concerning the Introduction of Innoculation or Variolation, Vol. 1. 37.50 (ISBN 0-405-12520-8). Ayer Co Pubs.
--Cotton Mather & American Science & Medicine: With Studies & Documents Concerning the Introduction of Inoculation or Variolation, Vol. 2. 37.50 (ISBN 0-405-12521-6). Ayer Co Pubs.
Cohen, I. Bernard, ed. see De Candolle, Alphonse.
Cohen, I. Bernard, ed. see Sayili, Aydin.
Cohen, I. L. Darwin Was Wrong: A Study in Probabilities. Murphy, G., ed. LC 84-22613. (Illus.). 225p. 1985. 16.95 (ISBN 0-910891-02-8). New Research.
--The Secret of Stonehenge. Murphy, G., ed. LC 82-19107. (Illus.). 310p. 1982. 16.95 (ISBN 0-910891-01-X). New Research.
--Urim & Thumim: The Secret of God. Murphy, G., ed. LC 82-24578. (Illus.). 280p. 1983. 16.95 (ISBN 0-910891-00-1). New Research.
Cohen, Israel, ed. The Rebirth of Israel. LC 75-6427. (The Rise of Jewish Nationalism & the Middle East Ser.). 338p. 1975. Repr. of 1952 ed. 25.85 (ISBN 0-88355-314-7). Hyperion Conn.
--Zionist Work in Palestine. LC 75-6428. (The Rise of Jewish Nationalism & the Middle East Ser.). (Illus.). 208p. 1975. Repr. of 1911 ed. 24.75 (ISBN 0-88355-315-5). Hyperion Conn.
Cohen, J. M., tr. see Eliade, Mircea.
Cohen, Jack S. Intermarriage & Conversion: A Halakhic Solution. 1987. 14.95 (ISBN 0-88125-124-0); pap. 9.95 (ISBN 0-88125-125-9). Ktav.
--The Jewish Heart: Essays on Jewish Sensitivities. LC 84-27837. 217p. 1985. 15.00 (ISBN 0-88125-065-1). Ktav.
Cohen, Jeffrey M. Understanding the High Holyday Service. 218p. 1983. 12.50 (ISBN 0-317-26854-6). Hebrew Pub.
Cohen, Jeremy. The Friars & the Jews: The Evolution of Medieval Anti-Judaism. LC 81-15210. 304p. 1984. pap. 10.95x (ISBN 0-8014-9266-1). Cornell U Pr.
Cohen, Kathleen R. Metamorphosis of a Death Symbol: The Transi Tomb in the Late Middle Ages & the Renaissance. LC 78-138511. (California Studies in the History of Art: Vol. 15). 1974. 77.00x (ISBN 0-520-01844-3). U of Cal Pr.
Cohen, Kenneth K. Imagine That! A Child's Guide to Yoga. (Illus.). 48p. 1983. pap. 8.95 (ISBN 0-915520-55-9). Santa Barb Pr.
Cohen, Kitty. The Throne & the Chariot: Studies in Milton's Hebraism. (Studies in English Literature: No. 97). 1975. text ed. 23.20x (ISBN 0-686-22628-3). Mouton.
Cohen, Leonard. Book of Mercy. LC 84-40174. 88p. 1984. 9.95 (ISBN 0-394-53949-4, Pub. by Villard Bks). Random.
Cohen, Lily Y. Lost Spirituals. facsimile ed. LC 74-39081. (Black Heritage Library Collection). (Illus.). Repr. of 1928 ed. 17.25 (ISBN 0-8369-9019-6). Ayer Co Pubs.
Cohen, Mark E. Sumerian Hymnology: The Ersemma. 1981. 18.75x (ISBN 0-87820-601-9). Ktav.
Cohen, Mark R. Jewish Self-Government in Medieval Egypt: The Origins of the Office of the Head of the Jews. LC 80-7514. (Princeton Studies on the Near East). 425p. 1981. 41.00 (ISBN 0-691-05307-3). Princeton U Pr.
Cohen, Martin. Jewish Experience in Latin America, 2 Vols. 1971. Set. 50.00x (ISBN 0-87068-136-2, Pub by Am Jewish Hist Soc). Ktav.
Cohen, Martin S. The Shiur Qomah: Liturgy & Theurgy in Pre-Kabbalistic Jewish Mysticism. 300p. (Orig.). 1983. lib. bdg. 27.50 (ISBN 0-8191-3272-1). U Pr of Amer.
Cohen, Michael J. Churchill & the Jews. (Illus.). 408p. 1985. 25.00x (ISBN 0-7146-3254-6, F Cass Co). Biblio Dist.
Cohen, Mitchell. Zion & State: Nation, Class & the Shaping of Modern Israel. 288p. 1987. 24.95 (ISBN 0-631-15243-1). Basil Blackwell.
Cohen, Mitchell, ed. see Borochov, Ber.
Cohen, Mortimer J. Pathways Through the Bible. rev. ed. (Illus.). 574p. 1946. 10.95 (ISBN 0-8276-0155-7, 167). Jewish Pubns.
Cohen, Naomi. American Jews & the Zionist Idea. pap. 9.95x (ISBN 0-87068-272-5). Ktav.
--Encounter with Emancipation: The German Jews in the United States, 1830 to 1914. (Illus.). 407p. 1984. 25.95 (ISBN 0-8276-0236-7). Jewish Pubns.
Cohen, P. S., ed. Jewish Radicals & Radical Jews. LC 80-41227. 1981. 53.00 (ISBN 0-12-178780-X). Acad Pr.
Cohen, Paul A. China & Christianity: The Missionary Movement & the Growth of Chinese Antiforeignism, 1860-1870. LC 63-19135. (East Asian Ser: No. 11). (Illus.). 1963. 27.50x (ISBN 0-674-11701-8). Harvard U Pr.
Cohen, Paul M. Piety & Politics: Catholic Revival & the Generation of 1905-1914 in France. McNeill, William H. & Pinkney, David H., eds. (Modern European History Ser.). 348p. 1987. lib. bdg. 50.00 (ISBN 0-8240-8034-3). Garland Pub.
Cohen, Paul V., tr. see Count Gobineau, Arthur.
Cohen, R. Dominance & Defiance: A Study of Marital Instability in an Islamic African Society. (Anthropological Studies: No. 6). 1971. pap. 6.00 (ISBN 0-686-36563-1). Am Anthro Assn.
Cohen, Richard I. Burden of Conscience: French Jewry's Response to the Holocaust. (The Modern Jewish Experience Ser.). 351p. 1987. 27.50 (ISBN 0-253-31263-9). Ind U Pr.
Cohen, Richard I., ed. Vision & Conflict in the Holy Land. LC 85-1972. 350p. 1985. 29.95 (ISBN 0-312-84967-2). St Martin.
Cohen, S. J., ed. The Holy Letter: A Study in Medieval Jewish Sexual Morality. pap. 7.95x (ISBN 0-87068-490-6). Ktav.
Cohen, S. S. Advaitic Sadhana. 1976. 8.95 (ISBN 0-8426-0989-X). Orient Bk Dist.
Cohen, Sarah B., ed. Jewish Wry: Essays on Jewish Humor. (Jewish Literature & Culture Ser.). 1987. 27.50 (ISBN 0-253-33185-4). Ind U Pr.
Cohen, Saul B. Jerusalem: A Geopolitical Perspective. 1977. 10.00 (ISBN 0-930832-54-X). Herzl Pr.
--Jerusalem Undivided. 1980. pap. 3.00 (ISBN 0-930832-58-2). Herzl Pr.
Cohen, Seymour. Affirming Life. 350p. 1987. 20.00x (ISBN 0-88125-112-7). Ktav.
Cohen, Shaye J. From the Maccabees to the Mishnah. Meeks, Wayne A., ed. LC 86-28077. (Library of Early Christianity: Vol. 7). 252p. 1987. 20.95 (ISBN 0-664-21911-X). Westminster.
Cohen, Steven M. American Modernity & Jewish Identity. 250p. 1983. 24.00x (ISBN 0-422-77740-4, NO.3467); pap. 9.95 (ISBN 0-422-77750-1, NO.3495). Methuen Inc.
--The National Survey of American Jews, 1984: Political & Social Outlooks. iv, 60p. (Orig.). 1985. pap. 4.00 (ISBN 0-87495-069-4). Am Jewish Comm.
Cohen, Steven M. & Hyman, Paula E., eds. The Jewish Family. 256p. 1986. text ed. 42.50x (ISBN 0-8419-0860-5). Holmes & Meier.
Cohen, Steven M., et al, eds. Perspectives in Jewish Population Research. LC 84-50660. (Replica Edition). 275p. 1984. 22.50x (ISBN 0-86531-853-0). Westview.
Cohen, Stuart A., jt. auth. see Elazar, Daniel J.
Cohn, Emil B. This Immortal People: A Short History of the Jewish People. LC 84-62563. 180p. (Orig.). 1985. pap. 5.95 (ISBN 0-8091-2693-1). Paulist Pr.
Cohn, H. The Trial & Death of Jesus. 14.95x (ISBN 0-87068-432-9). Ktav.
Cohn, Haim H. Human Rights in Jewish Law. LC 83-14846. 266p. 1984. 25.00x (ISBN 0-88125-036-8). Ktav.
Cohn, Marc M. Dictionnaire Francais-Hebreu. (Fr. & Hebrew.). 760p. 1966. 27.50 (ISBN 0-686-56955-5, M-6077). French & Eur.
--Nouveau Dictionnaire Hebreu-Francais. (Fr. & Hebrew.). 792p. 1974. 32.50 (ISBN 0-686-56956-3, M-6078). French & Eur.
Cohn, Norman. Europe's Inner Demons: An Enquiry Inspired by the Great Witch-Hunt. 1977. pap. 8.95 (ISBN 0-452-00761-5, Mer). NAL.
--Pursuit of the Millennium. rev ed. 1970. pap. 11.95 (ISBN 0-19-500456-6). Oxford U Pr.
Cohn, Robert L. The Shape of Sacred Space: Four Biblical Studies. LC 80-11086. (Studies in Religion: No. 23). pap. 8.50 (ISBN 0-89130-384-7, 01-00-23). Scholars Pr GA.
Cohn-Sherbok, Dan. On Earth As It Is in Heaven: Jews, Christians, & Liberation Theology. LC 86-23509. 128p. (Orig.). 1987. pap. 7.95 (ISBN 0-88344-410-0). Orbis Bks.

Coil, Henry W. Coil's Masonic Encyclopedia. LC 60-53289. 749p. cloth w/slipcase 31.50 (ISBN 0-88053-054-5). Macoy Pub.
--A Comprehensive View of Freemasonry. (Illus.). 1985. Repr. of 1954 ed. text ed. 12.50 (ISBN 0-88053-053-7). Macoy Pub.
--Freemasonry Through Six Centuries, 2 vols. 600p. 1976. Repr. of 1966 ed. text ed. 23.50 slipcase (ISBN 0-88053-034-0). Macoy Pub.
Coinci, Gautier De see De Coinci, Gautier.
Cok, Jerry O. Worship Resources for Youth. 133p. (Orig.). 1983. pap. 12.00 (ISBN 0-914527-25-8). C-Four Res.
Colao, Flora & Hosansky, Tamar. Your Children Should Know: Teach Your Children the Strategies That Will Keep Them Safe from Assault & Crime. LC 83-5981. (Illus.). 192p. 1983. 16.95 (ISBN 0-672-52777-4). Bobbs.
Colaw, Emerson. Beliefs of United Methodist Christian. 3rd ed. (Orig.). 1987. pap. 3.95 (ISBN 0-88177-025-6, DRO25B). Discipleship Res.
Colbaugh, Lloyd N. The Gospel Behind Bars. LC 79-53942. (Radiant Life Ser.). 96p. (Orig.). 1979. pap. 1.50 (ISBN 0-88243-503-5, 02-0503). Gospel Pub.
Colbeck, Kay & Harrell, Irene B. The Story of Singing Waters. (Orig.). 1987. pap. 7.00 (ISBN 0-915541-21-1). Star Bks Inc.
Colbert-Thornton, Mollie. God's Purpose for Man: The Spirit & the Flesh. 141p. 1984. 8.95 (ISBN 0-533-05913-5). Vantage.
Colby, Anne & Kohlberg, Lawrence. The Measurement of Moral Judgement, 2 vols, Vols. 1-2. Date not set. Vol. 1: Theoretical Foundations & Research, 425 pgs. price not set (ISBN 0-521-24447-1); Vol. 2: Standard Issue Scoring Manual, 1200 pgs. price not set (ISBN 0-521-32501-3); price not set (ISBN 0-521-32565-X). Cambridge U Pr.
Colby, Benjamin N. & Colby, Lore M. The Daykeeper: The Life & Discource of As Ixtil Dviner. (Illus.). 352p. 1981. text ed. 27.50x (ISBN 0-674-19409-8). Harvard U Pr.
Colby, Elbridge. English Catholic Poets, Chaucer to Dryden. facs. ed. LC 67-28733. (Essay Index Reprint Ser.). 1936. 18.00 (ISBN 0-8369-0321-8). Ayer Co Pubs.
Colby, Lore M., jt. auth. see Colby, Benjamin N.
Colclasure, Chuck. Proverbs, God's Powerhouse of Wisdom. 1981. pap. 2.50 (ISBN 0-8423-4928-6). Tyndale.
Cole, Alan. The Epistle of Paul to the Galatians. (Tyndale Bible Commentaries). 1964. pap. 4.95 (ISBN 0-8028-1408-5). Eerdmans.
--Gospel According to St. Mark. (Tyndale Bible Commentaries Ser.). 1962. pap. 5.95 (ISBN 0-8028-1401-8). Eerdmans.
--Isaiah Forty-Jeremiah. 1983. pap. 4.95 (ISBN 0-87508-161-4). Chr Lit.
Cole, Bruce, jt. ed. see Thompson, Norma H.
Cole, C. Donald. Basic Christian Faith. LC 84-72008. 256p. (Orig.). 1985. pap. 6.95 (ISBN 0-89107-338-8, Crossway Bks). Good News.
--Christian Perspectives on Controversial Issues. 128p. (Orig.). 1983. pap. 3.50 (ISBN 0-8024-0165-1). Moody.
--Have I Committed the Unpardonable Sin? And Other Questions You Were Afraid to Ask about the Christian Faith. LC 84-71421. 128p. 1984. pap. 5.95 (ISBN 0-89107-317-5, Crossway Bks). Good News.
--I Believe... 160p. 1983. pap. 3.95 (ISBN 0-8024-0353-0). Moody.
--Thirsting for God: A Devotional Study of the Psalms in Light of Their Historical Background. LC 85-72918. 350p. 1986. pap. 8.95 (ISBN 0-89107-376-0, Crossway Bks). Good News.
Cole, Carole O., jt. auth. see McIntosh, Carol P.
Cole, Charles C., Jr. Social Ideas of the Northern Evangelists, Eighteen Twenty-Six to Eighteen Sixty. 1966. lib. bdg. 20.50x (ISBN 0-374-91843-0, Octagon). Hippocrene Bks.
Cole, Charles E., ed. Something More Than Human: Biographies of Leaders in American Methodist Higher Education. LC 85-51267. (Illus.). 256p. 1986. 7.95 (ISBN 0-938162-04-7). United Meth Educ.
Cole, Clifford. Studies in Exodus, Vol. 1. (Bible Studies Ser.). 1986. pap. 3.50 (ISBN 0-8309-0460-3). Herald Hse.
Cole, Clifford A. The Mighty Act of God. 192p. 1984. pap. text ed. 12.00 (ISBN 0-8309-0393-3). Herald Hse.
--Studies in Exodus, Vol. 2. (Bible Study Ser.). 1986. pap. 3.50 (ISBN 0-8309-0462-X). Herald Hse.
Cole, Clifford A., jt. auth. see Judd, Peter A.
Cole, Clifford A., ed. The Priesthood Manual. rev. ed. LC 81-7220. 1985. 15.00 (ISBN 0-8309-0420-4). Herald Hse.
Cole, Dan P. Shechem I: Middle Bronze IIB Pottery. (Excavation Reports of the American Schools of Oriental Research). xiv, 203p. 1984. text ed. 30.00 (ISBN 0-89757-047-2, Dist.by Eisenbrauns). Am Sch Orient Res.
Cole, David S. The Wrath of God. 1986. 11.95 (ISBN 0-533-06517-8). Vantage.
Cole, Edwin L. Courage: A Book for Champions. 164p. (Orig.). 1985. pap. 3.95 (ISBN 0-89274-362-X). Harrison Hse.
--Maximized Manhood. 176p. (Orig.). 1982. pap. text ed. 3.95 (ISBN 0-88368-107-2). Whitaker Hse.
--The Potential Principle. 144p. (Orig.). 1984. pap. 3.95 (ISBN 0-88368-144-7). Whitaker Hse.
Cole, Franklin P. They Preached Liberty. LC 76-26327. 1976. 5.95 (ISBN 0-913966-16-9, Liberty Pr); pap. 1.25 (ISBN 0-913966-20-7). Liberty Fund.
Cole, Ginny & Durfey, Carolyn, eds. Come to the Banquet. 200p. 1983. pap. text ed. 7.00 (ISBN 0-913991-00-7). Off Christian Fellowship.
Cole, Henry, tr. see Luther, Martin.
Cole, J. R. Roots of North Indian Shi'ism in Iran & Iraq: Religion & State in Awadh, 1722-1859. 340p. 1987. text ed. 38.00x (ISBN 0-520-05641-8). U of Cal Pr.
Cole, Jeffrey A., ed. The Church & the Society in Latin American. 379p. 1984. pap. 12.00 (ISBN 0-317-43435-7). Tulane U Ctr Lat.
Cole, Joan. A Lenten Journey with Jesus. 48p. 1982. pap. 1.50 (ISBN 0-89243-172-5). Liguori Pubns.
--Our Hearts Wait: Daily Prayer for Advent. 48p. 1984. pap. 1.50 (ISBN 0-89243-215-2). Liguori Pubns.
Cole, Juan R. & Keddie, Nikki R. Shi'ism & Social Protest. LC 85-22780. 352p. 1986. text ed. 40.00 (ISBN 0-300-03550-0); pap. 12.95 (ISBN 0-300-03553-5, Y-584). Yale U Pr.
Cole, Juan R. & Momen, Moojan, eds. Studies in Babi & Baha'i History: Vol. 2: From Iran East & West. (Illus.). 205p. 1984. 19.95 (ISBN 0-933770-40-5). Kalimat.
Cole, Lawrence T. The Basis of Early Christian Theism. lib. bdg. 59.95 (ISBN 0-8490-1478-6). Gordon Pr.
Cole, Myron C. Myron Here. LC 82-61064. (Illus.). 260p. (Orig.). 1983. pap. 5.00 (ISBN 0-935356-04-5). Mills Pub Co.
Cole, R. Alan. Exodus: Tyndale Old Testament Commentary. LC 72-97952. 243p. 1973. 12.95 (ISBN 0-87784-865-3); pap. 6.95 (ISBN 0-87784-252-3). Inter-Varsity.
Cole, Richard L. Love-Feasts: A History of the Christian Agape. 59.95 (ISBN 0-8490-0563-9). Gordon Pr.
Cole, Stewart G. History of Fundamentalism. LC 70-138107. 1971. Repr. of 1931 ed. lib. bdg. 22.50x (ISBN 0-8371-5683-1, COHF). Greenwood.
Cole, W. Douglas. When Families Hurt. LC 79-51133. 1979. 6.50 (ISBN 0-8054-5638-4). Broadman.
Cole, W. Owen. Five Religions in the Twentieth Century. LC 81-68724. (Illus.). 256p. 1981. pap. 11.95 (ISBN 0-8023-1272-1). Dufour.
--The Guru in Sikhism. 1984. pap. 7.00x (ISBN 0-8364-1238-9, Pub. by D Longman & Todd). South Asia Bks.
Cole, W. Owen & Sambhi, Piara S. Sikhism. 1985. 13.00x (ISBN 0-7062-3147-3, Pub. by Ward Lock Educ Co Ltd). State Mutual Bk.
--The Sikhs. (Library of Religious Beliefs & Practices). 210p. 1986. pap. text ed. 14.95 (ISBN 0-7100-8843-4). Methuen Inc.
Colebrooke, H. T. Essays on History, Literature & Religion of Ancient India, 2 vols. 1024p. Repr. of 1873 ed. text ed. 57.50x. Coronet Bks.
Coleman, Bernard & LaBud, Verona. Masinaigans: The Little Book. (Illus.). 368p. 1972. 10.00 (ISBN 0-686-05025-8). North Central.
Coleman, Bill & Coleman, Patty. God's Own Child. rev. ed. 64p. 1983. Parent's Book. pap. text ed. 3.95x (ISBN 0-89622-188-1); Leader's Guide. wkbk. 1.00 (ISBN 0-89622-187-3). Twenty-Third.
--My Confirmation Journal. 95p. 1979. pap. 3.95 (ISBN 0-89622-114-8). Twenty-Third.
--Only Love Can Make It Easy, 2 vols. rev. ed. LC 80-52360. 1981. Couples' Wkbk. pap. 2.95x (ISBN 0-89622-131-8); Leader's Guide. pap. 8.50 (ISBN 0-89622-132-6). Twenty-Third.
Coleman, Charles G. Divine Guidance: That Voice Behind You. LC 77-6796. 1977. pap. 2.50 (ISBN 0-87213-087-8). Loizeaux.
Coleman, Christopher B. Constantine the Great & Christianity. LC 70-155636. (Columbia University Studies in the Social Sciences: No. 146). Repr. of 1914 ed. 18.50 (ISBN 0-404-51146-5). AMS Pr.
Coleman, Edward D. Bible in English Drama: An Annotated Bibliography. rev. ed. 1969. 25.00x (ISBN 0-87068-034-X). Ktav.
--Bible in English Drama: An Annotated List of Plays. 1969. 6.95 (ISBN 0-87104-021-2, Co-Pub by Ktav). NY Pub Lib.
--Jew in English Drama: An Annotated Bibliography. rev. ed. LC 67-11901. 1969. 25.00x (ISBN 0-87068-011-0). Ktav.
--Jew in English Drama: An Annotated Bibliography. LC 67-11901. 1968. Repr. of 1943 ed. with The Jew in Western Drama by Edgar Rosenberg 8.95 (ISBN 0-87104-101-4, Co-Pub by Ktav). NY Pub Lib.
Coleman, F. G., tr. see McDonald, Hope.
Coleman, Gary. A Member Missionary? Hey...I Can Do That! LC 83-80527. 79p. 1983. pap. 4.95 (ISBN 0-88290-220-2). Horizon-Utah.
Coleman, Gary J. A Look at Mormonism. pap. 3.95 (ISBN 0-89036-142-8). Hawkes Pub Inc.
Coleman, Gerald. Homosexuality - an Appraisal. 1978. 0.75 (ISBN 0-685-89391-X). Franciscan Herald.
Coleman, Henry. Church Organist. 2nd ed. 1968. 9.75 (ISBN 0-19-322100-4). Oxford U Pr.
Coleman, John & Baum, Gregory, eds. Youth Without a Future, Vol. 181. (Conciliun Ser.). 128p. 1985. pap. 6.95 (ISBN 0-567-30061-7, Pub. by T&T Clark Ltd UK). Fortress.
Coleman, John, jt. ed. see Baum, Gregory.
Coleman, John, jt. ed. see Baum, Gregory B.
Coleman, John A. An American Strategic Theology. 10.95 (ISBN 0-8091-2469-6). Paulist Pr.
--The Evolution of Dutch Catholicism, Nineteen Fifty-Eight to Nineteen Seventy-Four. LC 74-22958. 1979. 42.50x (ISBN 0-520-02885-6). U of Cal Pr.
Coleman, Lucien E. The Exciting Christian Life: Bible Study on Christian Growth. 36p. 1982. pap. 3.50 (ISBN 0-939298-11-2). J M Prods.
Coleman, Lucien E., Jr. Como Ensenar la Biblia. Diaz, Jorge E., tr. Orig. Title: How to Teach the Bible. (Span.). 265p. 1985. Repr. of 1982 ed. 6.50 (ISBN 0-311-11039-8). Casa Bautista.
--How to Teach the Bible. LC 79-52001. 1980. 9.95 (ISBN 0-8054-3428-3). Broadman.
--Why the Church Must Teach. LC 84-4966. 1984. pap. 6.95 (ISBN 0-8054-3234-5). Broadman.
Coleman, Lyman. Body Building. (Free University Ser.). (Orig.). 1981. pap. 4.95 leader's guide (ISBN 0-687-37306-9); pap. 1.25 student's bk. (ISBN 0-687-37307-7). Abingdon.
--Coping: O God, I'm Struggling. (Serendipity Ser.). (Orig.). 1981. pap. 4.95 leader's guide 64 pgs. (ISBN 0-687-37310-7); pap. 1.25 student's bk. 32 pgs. (ISBN 0-687-37311-5). Abingdon.
--Moral Issues: If Christ Is Lord. (Serendipity Ser.). (Orig.). 1981. pap. 4.95 leader's guide 64 pgs. (ISBN 0-687-37330-1); pap. 1.25 student's bk 32 pgs (ISBN 0-687-37331-X). Abingdon.
--My Calling: Here I Am Lord. (Serendipity Ser.). (Orig.). 1981. pap. 4.95 leader's guide 64 pgs (ISBN 0-687-37336-0); pap. 1.25 student's bk 32 pgs (ISBN 0-687-37337-9). Abingdon.
--Self Profile: The Me Nobody Knows. (Free University - Lay Academy in Christian Discipleship Ser.). (Orig.). 1981. pap. 4.95 leader's guide (ISBN 0-687-37346-8); pap. 1.25 student's bk. (ISBN 0-687-37347-6). Abingdon.
--Serendipity New Testament for Groups: New International Version. 9.95 (ISBN 0-8091-2863-2). Paulist Pr.
--Spiritual Basics: New Life in Christ. (Free University - Lay Academy in Christian Discipleship Ser.). (Orig.). 1981. pap. 1.25 student's bk. (ISBN 0-687-37355-7); pap. 4.95 tchr's bk. (ISBN 0-687-37354-9). Abingdon.
Coleman, Lyman, et al, eds. The Serendipity Group Study Book. 496p. 1986. kivar 9.95 (ISBN 0-310-25081-1, 12032P). Zondervan.
Coleman, Michael C. Presbyterian Missionary Attitudes Toward American Indians, 1837-1893. LC 85-7496. (Illus.). 1985. 25.00x (ISBN 0-87805-278-X). U Pr of Miss.
Coleman, Patty, jt. auth. see Coleman, Bill.
Coleman, Richard J. Issues of Theological Conflict: Evangelicals & Liberals. Rev. ed. LC 79-19494. pap. 74.00 (ISBN 0-317-19816-5, 2023209). Bks Demand UMI.
Coleman, Robert. The New Covenant. 132p. 1985. pap. 4.95 (ISBN 0-89109-524-1). NavPress.
Coleman, Robert E. Dry Bones Can Live Again. pap. 4.95 (ISBN 0-8007-5154-X, Power Bks). Revell.
--Evangelism in Perspective. LC 75-31306. 3.95 (ISBN 0-87509-080-X); pap. 2.00 (ISBN 0-87509-081-8). Chr Pubns.
--Growing in the Word. 272p. 1982. pap. 2.95 (ISBN 0-8007-8448-0, Spire Bks). Revell.
--The Heartbeat of Evangelism. 32p. 1985. pap. 1.95 (ISBN 0-89109-400-8). NavPress.
--The Master Plan of Discipleship. 9.95; pap. 5.95. Revell.
--The Master Plan of Evangelism. 128p. 1978. pap. 5.95 (ISBN 0-8007-5007-1, Power Bks); pap. 2.50 (ISBN 0-8007-8303-4, Spire Bks). Revell.
--Songs of Heaven. 160p. 1982. pap. 5.95 (ISBN 0-8007-5097-7, Power Bks). Revell.
--They Meet the Master. 160p. 1979. pap. 5.95 (ISBN 0-8007-1037-1). Revell.
Coleman, Thomas W. English Mystics of the Fourteenth Century. LC 74-109723. 1971. Repr. of 1938 ed. lib. bdg. 22.50x (ISBN 0-8371-4213-X, COEM). Greenwood.
Coleman, William. Animals That Show & Tell. LC 85-15122. 144p. 1985. pap. 4.95 (ISBN 0-87123-807-1). Bethany Hse.
--Before You Tuck Me In. 128p. (Orig.). 1986. pap. 4.95 (ISBN 0-87123-830-6). Bethany Hse.
--Bouncing Back: Finding Acceptance in the Face of Rejection. (Orig.). 1985. pap. 4.95 (ISBN 0-89081-455-4). Harvest Hse.
--Counting Stars. LC 76-28973. 128p. 1976. 4.95 (ISBN 0-87123-055-0, 210055). Bethany Hse.
--Courageous Christians. LC 81-70519. (Wonderful World of the Bible Ser.). (Illus.). 1983. 9.95 (ISBN 0-89191-558-3). Cook.
--Earning Your Wings. 144p. 1984. pap. 4.95 (ISBN 0-87123-311-8, 210311). Bethany Hse.
--Friends Forever. 160p. (Orig.). 1987. pap. 5.95 (ISBN 0-87123-959-0). Bethany Hse.
--Getting Ready for Our New Baby. LC 84-432. 112p. 1984. pap. 4.95 (ISBN 0-87123-295-2, 210295). Bethany Hse.
--The Good Night Book. LC 79-20002. (Illus.). 128p. 1980. pap. 4.95 (ISBN 0-87123-187-5, 210187). Bethany Hse.
--How, Why, When, Where, Bks. 1 & 2. 23p. 1984. Bk. 1. pap. 2.95 (ISBN 0-89191-717-9, 57174, Chariot Bks.); Bk. 2. pap. 2.95 (ISBN 0-89191-942-2, 59428, Chariot Bks.). Cook.
--Jesus, My Forever Friend. (Wonderful World of the Bible Ser.). (Illus.). 1981. 9.95 (ISBN 0-89191-370-X, 53702). Cook.
--A Measured Pace. 144p. (Orig.). 1986. pap. 4.95 (ISBN 0-87123-671-0, 210671). Bethany Hse.
--On Your Mark. LC 79-16458. 112p. 1979. pap. 4.95 (ISBN 0-87123-490-4, 210490). Bethany Hse.
--The Palestine Herald, 4 vols. (The Palestine Herald Ser.). (Illus.). No. 1. 2.95 (ISBN 0-89191-981-3); No. 2. 2.95 (ISBN 0-89191-982-1); No. 3. 2.95 (ISBN 0-89191-983-X); No. 4. 2.95 (ISBN 0-89191-984-8). Cook.
--Peter. LC 81-85894. 160p. (Orig.). 1982. pap. 4.95 (ISBN 0-89081-305-1). Harvest Hse.
--The Pharisees' Guide To Total Holiness. LC 82-4551. 147p. 1982. 8.95 (ISBN 0-87123-473-4, 210473); pap. 4.95 (ISBN 0-87123-472-6, 210472). Bethany Hse.
--The Warm Hug Book. 128p. (Orig.). 1985. pap. 4.95 (ISBN 0-87123-794-6, 210794). Bethany Hse.
--The Who, What, When, Where Bible Busy Book. 32p. 1984. pap. 1.50 (ISBN 0-89191-853-1). Cook.
--The Who, What, When, Where Book about the Bible. (Illus.). 1980. 11.95 (ISBN 0-89191-291-6). Cook.
--You Can Be Creative. LC 83-80474. 160p. (Orig.). 1984. pap. 3.95 (ISBN 0-89081-387-6, 3876). Harvest Hse.
Coleman, William L. Engaged. 1980. pap. 5.95 (ISBN 0-8423-0693-5). Tyndale.
--Escucha a los Animales. 144p. 1981. 3.25 (ISBN 0-88113-063-X). Edit Betania.
--Listen to the Animals. LC 79-11312. 128p. 1979. pap. 4.95 (ISBN 0-87123-341-X, 210341). Bethany Hse.
--Making TV Work for Your Family. LC 83-11881. 112p. (Orig.). 1983. pap. 4.95 (ISBN 0-87123-322-3, 210322). Bethany Hse.
--Mi Maquina Maravillosa. 144p. 1982. 3.25 (ISBN 0-88113-309-4). Edit Betania.
--More about My Magnificent Machine. LC 79-21140. (Illus.). 128p. (Orig.). 1980. pap. 4.95 (ISBN 0-87123-386-X, 210386). Bethany Hse.
--Singing Penguins & Puffed-up Toads. 125p. 1981. pap. 4.95 (ISBN 0-87123-554-4, 210554). Bethany Hse.
--The Sleep Tight Book. LC 82-12953. (Devotionals for Young Children Ser.). 125p. (Orig.). 1982. pap. 4.95 (ISBN 0-87123-577-3, 210577). Bethany Hse.
--Today I Feel Loved! LC 82-4184. 128p. (Orig.). 1982. pap. 4.95 (ISBN 0-87123-566-8, 210566). Bethany Hse.
--Today's Handbook of Bible Times & Customs. (Illus.). 306p. 1984. 11.95 (ISBN 0-87123-594-3, 230594). Bethany Hse.
Coleman, William V. Finding a Way to Follow. 1977. pap. 4.95 (ISBN 0-8192-1227-X). Morehouse.
--Prayer-Talk: Casual Conversations with God. LC 82-74085. 112p. (Orig.). 1983. pap. 3.95 (ISBN 0-87793-265-4). Ave Maria.
Coleridge, John T. A Memoir of the Rev. John Keble, 2 vols. in 1. 2nd rev. ed. LC 75-30019. Repr. of 1869 ed. 38.50 (ISBN 0-404-14024-6). AMS Pr.
Coleridge-Taylor, S. Twenty-Four Negro Melodies. (Music Reprint Ser.: 1980). 1980. Repr. of 1905 ed. lib. bdg. 35.00 (ISBN 0-306-76023-1). Da Capo.
Colet, John. John Colet's Commentary on First Corinthians. O'Kelly, Bernard, ed. & tr. from Lat. LC 82-12403. (Medieval & Renaissance Texts & Studies: Vol. 21). (Illus.). 352p. 1985. 20.00 (ISBN 0-86698-056-3). Medieval & Renaissance NY.
Colette. Histoire et Absolu: Essai Sur Kierkegaard. 19.95 (ISBN 0-686-54575-3). French & Eur.

Cole-Whittaker, Terry. The Inner Path from Where You Are to Where You Want to Be: A Spiritual Odyssey. LC 84-42930. 239p. 1986. 14.95 (ISBN 0-89256-283-8). Rawson Assocs.
--What You Think of Me Is None of My Business. 194p. (Orig.). 1982. pap. 9.95 (ISBN 0-86679-002-0). Oak Tree Pubns.
Colford, Paul D., jt. auth. see Egan, John P.
Colgrave, Bertram. The Earliest Saint's Lives Written in England. 1978. Repr. of 1958 ed. lib. bdg. 12.50 (ISBN 0-8495-0739-1). Arden Lib.
--Earliest Saints Lives Written in England. LC 72-193175. 1958. lib. bdg. 12.50 (ISBN 0-8414-2353-9). Folcroft.
Colgrave, Bertram, ed. The Earliest Life of Gregory the Great. 192p. 1985. 37.50 (ISBN 0-521-30924-7); pap. 12.95 (ISBN 0-521-31384-8). Cambridge U Pr.
--Two Lives of Saint Cuthbert. 388p. 1985. 44.50 (ISBN 0-521-30925-5); pap. 16.95 (ISBN 0-521-31385-6). Cambridge U Pr.
Colgrave, Bertram, ed. see Bede the Venerable.
Colgrave, Bertram, ed. see Stephanus, Eddius.
Colin, ed. see Townsley, David & Bjork, Russell.
Colina, Tessa. Ark Full of Animals. (Illus.). 1985. comb bdg. 4.95 (ISBN 0-317-30647-2, R2707). Standard Pub.
--You & Me. Buerger, Jane, ed. (Illus.). 112p. 1980. 5.95 (ISBN 0-89565-179-3, 4936). Standard Pub.
Colina, Tessa, ed. Jesus, My Friend. (Jesus & Me Pupil Activities Books: No. 3). (Illus.). 1978. pap. 1.50 (ISBN 0-87239-270-8, 2442). Standard Pub.
--Jesus, My Lord. (Jesus & Me Pupil Activities Books: No. 4). (Illus.). 1978. pap. 1.50 (ISBN 0-87239-271-6, 2443). Standard Pub.
--Jesus, My Saviour. (Jesus & Me Pupil Activities Books: No. 1). (Illus.). 1978. pap. 1.50 (ISBN 0-87239-268-6, 2440). Standard Pub.
--Jesus, My Teacher: (Pupil Activities Book Two) (Jesus & Me Ser.). (Illus.). 16p. 1978. pap. 1.50 (ISBN 0-87239-269-4, 2441). Standard Pub.
Colina, Tessa & Westers, Jacqueline, eds. Jesus & Me Teacher: Primary Study in the Life of Christ. 1978. pap. 7.95 (ISBN 0-87239-165-5, 3243). Standard Pub.
Colkmire, Lance. Reasoning with Juniors for Christs Sake. 1982. pap. 5.95 (ISBN 0-87148-736-5). Pathway Pr.
Coll, Alberto R. The Western Heritage & American Values: Law, Theology & History. Thompson, Kenneth W., ed. LC 81-43761. (American Values Projected Abroad Ser.: Vol. I). 126p. 1982. lib. bdg. 24.00 (ISBN 0-8191-2526-1); pap. text ed. 8.25 (ISBN 0-8191-2527-X). U Pr of Amer.
Coll, Regina. Women & Religion: A Reader for the Clergy. 128p. 1982. pap. 5.95 (ISBN 0-8091-2461-0). Paulist Pr.
Collcutt, Martin. Five Mountains: The Rinzai Zen Monastic Institution in Medieval Japan. (Harvard East Asian Monograph: Vol. 85). (Illus.). 450p. 1980. 27.50x (ISBN 0-674-30497-7). Harvard U Pr.
Colledge, Edmund & Walsh, James. Guigo II: The Ladder of Monks & Twelve Meditations. 14.95; pap. 6.00 (ISBN 0-87907-948-7). Cistercian Pubns.
Colledge, Edmund, tr. see Guigo II.
Colledge, Edmund, et al, eds. Julian of Norwich, "Showings". LC 77-90953. (Classics of Western Spirituality). 384p. 1978. 13.95 (ISBN 0-8091-0234-X); pap. 9.95 (ISBN 0-8091-2091-7). Paulist Pr.
Colledge, Eric, tr. see Tauler, John.
Colledge, M. A. The Parthian Period. (Iconography of Religions XIV Ser.: No. 3). (Illus.). xiv, 47p. 1986. pap. 34.25 (ISBN 90-04-07115-6, Pub. by E J Brill). Heinman.
Colleran, Joseph M., tr. from Latin. see Anselm of Canterbury.
Colleran, Joseph M., tr. see Augustine, St.
Colless, Brian & Donovan, Peter, eds. Religion in New Zealand Society. 216p. 1980. 17.95 (ISBN 0-567-09303-4, Pub. by T & T Clark Uk). Fortress.
Collet's Holdings, Ltd. Staff, ed. Early Russian Painting 11th to Early 13th Centuries: Mosaics, Frescoes & Icons. 308p. 1982. 125.00x (ISBN 0-317-39496-7, Pub. by Collets UK). State Mutual Bk.
Collett, Barry. Italian Benedictine Scholars & the Reformation: The Congregation of Santa Giustina of Padua. (Historical Monographs). 300p. 1985. 48.00x (ISBN 0-19-822934-8). Oxford U Pr.
Colli, Carlo. The Spirit of Mornese. 198p. (Orig.). 1982. pap. 4.95 (ISBN 0-89944-064-9, P-064-9). Don Bosco Multimedia.
Colli, Giorgio, ed. see Nietzsche, Friedrich.
Colliander, Tito. The Way of the Ascetics. 130p. Repr. of 1960 ed. cancelled 5.95 (ISBN 0-913026-22-0). St Nectarios.
Collie, David, ed. see Ssu Shu.
Collier, Arthur. Clavis Universalis: New Inquiry after Truth, Being a Demonstration of the Non-Existence or Impossibility of an External World. Wellek, Rene, ed. LC 75-11208. (British Philosophers & Theologians of the 17th & 18th Centuries Ser.). 150p. 1978. lib. bdg. 51.00 (ISBN 0-8240-1763-3). Garland Pub.
Collier, Howard E. Experiment with a Life. (Orig.). 1953. pap. 2.500784485x (ISBN 0-87574-069-3). Pendle Hill.
--The Quaker Meeting. 1983. pap. 2.50x (ISBN 0-87574-026-X, 026). Pendle Hill.
Collier, Jeremy. A Defence of the Short View off the Profaneness & Immorality of the English Stage. LC 72-170444. (The English Stage Ser.: Vol. 30). 1973. lib. bdg. 61.00 (ISBN 0-8240-0613-5). Garland Pub.
--Short View of the Immorality, & Profaneness of the English Stage. 3rd ed. LC 74-3401. Repr. of 1698 ed. 21.50 (ISBN 0-404-01619-7). AMS Pr.
--Short View of the Profaneness & Immorality of the English Stage. 1969. Repr. of 1730 ed. cancelled (ISBN 3-4870-2589-2). Adlers Foreign Bks.
Collier, John. On the Gleaming Way: Navajos, Eastern Pueblos, Zunis, Hopis, Apaches & Their Land, & Their Meanings to the World. LC 62-12407. 163p. (Photos, Orig). 1962. pap. 5.95 (ISBN 0-8040-0232-0, SB). Ohio U Pr.
Collier, Philip E. It Seems to Me. 1982. 4.95 (ISBN 0-86544-019-0). Salv Army Suppl South.
Collier, Richard. Poetry & Drama in the York Corpus Christi Play. LC 77-21348. 303p. 1977. 27.50 (ISBN 0-208-01611-2, Archon). Shoe String.
Collier, Robert. The Amazing Secrets of the Masters of the Far East. pap. 6.95 (ISBN 0-912576-16-2). R Collier.
--Prayer Works. 1950. pap. 3.95 (ISBN 0-910140-04-9). C & R Anthony.
--Prayer Works! 4.95 (ISBN 0-912576-01-4). R Collier.
Colligan, John & Colligan, Kathleen. Evenings for Parish Ministers: Leader's Guide. LC 84-60266. 53p. (Orig.). 1984. pap. text ed. 2.95 (ISBN 0-911905-20-0); wkbk. 1.95 (ISBN 0-911905-16-2). Past & Mat Rene Ctr.
Colligan, John, et al. Calling Disciples. 54p. (Orig.). 1984. 1.95 (ISBN 0-911905-22-7). Past & Mat Rene Ctr.
--Calling Disciples, Mentality. LC 84-60459. (Calling Disciples Ser.: Bk. 2). 67p. (Orig.). 1984. pap. text ed. 2.95 (ISBN 0-911905-21-9). Past & Mat Rene Ctr.
--The Extended Catholic Family: Rediscovering Our Catholic Identity Through Intimate Relationships with Fellow Catholics. LC 83-62198. 110p. (Orig.). 1983. pap. text ed. 4.95 (ISBN 0-911905-06-5). Past & Mat Rene Ctr.
--A Guide for Using Charisms in the Parish. LC 83-62985. 63p. (Orig.). 1983. pap. text ed. 2.95 (ISBN 0-911905-10-3). Past & Mat Rene Ctr.
--Mission & Ministry: A Vision for the Church. LC 83-62365. 84p. (Orig.). 1983. pap. text ed. 3.95 (ISBN 0-911905-07-3). Past & Mat Rene Ctr.
Colligan, Kathleen, jt. auth. see Colligan, John.
Colligan, Owen A., ed. Saint John Damascene: Dialectica, Version of Robert Grosseteste. (Text Ser.). 1953. 3.50 (ISBN 0-686-11552-X). Franciscan Inst.
Colligan, Owen A., tr. see Faccin, Dominic.
Collin, Rodney. The Mirror of Light. LC 84-22141. 89p. 1985. pap. 6.95 (ISBN 0-87773-314-7, 72996-X). Shambhala Pubns.
--The Theory of Celestial Influence: Man, The Universe, & Cosmic Mystery. LC 83-20286. (Illus.). 392p. (Orig.). 1984. pap. 10.95 (ISBN 0-87773-267-1, 72391-0). Shambhala Pubns.
--The Theory of Conscious Harmony. LC 84-5494. 211p. 1984. pap. 8.95 (ISBN 0-87773-285-X, 72698-7). Shambhala Pubns.
--The Theory of Eternal Life. LC 83-20288. (Illus.). 132p. (Orig.). 1984. pap. 5.95 (ISBN 0-87773-273-6, 72399-6). Shambhala Pubns.
Collingridge, Ruth & Sekowsky, JoAnne. Introduction to Praise. (Workbook Ser.). (Orig.). 1981. pap. 4.95 (ISBN 0-930756-60-6, 581001). Aglow Pubns.
Collingswood, Hermann. A Collection of Fifty-Five Dramatic Illustrations in Full Colours of the Cathedral Cities of Italy. (The Masterpieces of World Architectual Library). (Illus.). 107p. 1983. Repr. of 1911 ed. 287.75 (ISBN 0-89901-081-4). Found Class Reprints.
Collingwood, Guillermo. Las Dos Naturalezas del Creyente. 2nd ed. Bennett, Gordon H., ed. Bautista, Sara, tr. from Eng. (La Serie Diamante). Tr. of The Believer's Two Natures. (Span., Illus.). 52p. 1982. pap. 0.85 (ISBN 0-942504-03-8). Overcomer Pr.
Collini, Stefan. Liberalism & Sociology: L. T. Hobhouse & Political Argument in England, 1880-1914. LC 78-23779. 1979. 37.50 (ISBN 0-521-22304-0). Cambridge U Pr.
Collins. Light on the Path. 1.50 (ISBN 0-8356-7192-5). Theos Pub Hse.
Collins, Adela, ed. Feminist Perspectives on Biblical Scholarship. (Society of Bliblical Literature Centennial Biblical Scholarship in North America Ser.: No. 10). 152p. 13.95_o.s. (ISBN 0-89130-774-5, 06 11 10); pap. 9.50 (ISBN 0-89130-773-7). Scholars Pr GA.
Collins, Adela Y. Apocalypse. (New Testament Message Ser.: Vol. 22). 172p. 1979. 9.95 (ISBN 0-89453-210-3); pap. 6.95 (ISBN 0-89453-145-X). M Glazier.
--Crisis & Catharsis: The Power of the Apocalypse. LC 83-26084. 180p. 1984. pap. 11.95 (ISBN 0-664-24521-8). Westminster.
Collins, Adela Y. & Rice, Charles. Pentecost Two. LC 79-7377. (Proclamation 2: Aids for Interpreting the Lessons of the Church Year, Series B). 64p. 1982. pap. 3.75 (ISBN 0-8006-4090-X, 1-4090). Fortress.
Collins, Anthony. A Disclosure on Free-Thinking. LC 75-11209. (British Philosophers & Theologians of the 17th & 18th Centuries Ser.). 395p. 1976. lib. bdg. 51.00 (ISBN 0-8240-1764-1). Garland Pub.
--A Discourse on the Grounds & Reasons of the Christian Religion. Wellek, Rene, ed. LC 75-11212. (British Philosophers & Theologians of the 17th & 18th Centuries: Vol. 15). 1976. Repr. of 1724 ed. lib. bdg. 51.00 (ISBN 0-8240-1766-8). Garland Pub.
Collins, Charlotte. Not Healed? LC 82-73707. 1983. pap. text ed. 2.50 (ISBN 0-932050-15-8). New Puritan.
Collins, David R. Not Only Dreamers. Eller, David, ed. 160p. (Orig.). 1986. pap. 7.95 (ISBN 0-87178-612-5). Brethren.
Collins, Elma, ed. see Corish, Patrick J.
Collins, Fletcher, Jr. Production of Medieval Church Music-Drama. LC 78-168610. (Illus.). xiii, 356p. 1972. 25.00x (ISBN 0-8139-0373-4). U Pr of Va.
Collins, Fletcher, Jr., ed. Medieval Church Music-Dramas: A Repertory of Complete Plays. LC 75-33896. Repr. of 1976 ed. 128.50 (ISBN 0-8357-9809-7, 2013180). Bks Demand UMI.
Collins, Gary. Beyond Easy Believism. 197p. 1985. pap. 8.95 (ISBN 0-8499-3025-1, 3025-1). Word Bks.
--Helping People Grow. LC 79-6402. (Orig.). 1980. pap. 8.95 (ISBN 0-88449-069-6, A424068). Vision Hse.
--How to Be a People Helper. LC 76-15112. (Orig.). 1976. pap. 5.95 (ISBN 0-88449-055-6, A424076). Vision Hse.
--Innovations in Counseling (RCC) 224p. 1986. 12.95 (ISBN 0-8499-0510-9). Word Bks.
--Orientacion Sicologica Eficaz. Blanch, Miguel, tr. from Eng. Tr. of Effective Counseling. (Span.). 206p. 1979. pap. 4.75 (ISBN 0-89922-136-X). Edit Caribe.
--Overcoming Anxiety. 1975. pap. 2.25 (ISBN 0-88449-017-3, A324101). Vision Hse.
--People Helper Growthbook. LC 76-25752. 1976. pap. 5.95 (ISBN 0-88449-056-4, A424084). Vision Hse.
--Personalidades Quebrantadas. Flores, Jose, tr. from Eng. LC 78-62403. Tr. of Fractured Personalities. (Span.). 215p. 1978. pap. 4.95 (ISBN 0-89922-116-5). Edit Caribe.
--The Rebuilding of Psychology. 1976. pap. 7.95 (ISBN 0-8423-5315-1). Tyndale.
--Spotlight on Stress: Study Guide. 32p. 1983. 1.50 (ISBN 0-88449-100-5, A424650). Vision Hse.
Collins, Gary R. Christian Counseling. 1980. pap. 13.95 (ISBN 0-8499-2889-3). Word Bks.
--Getting Started. 224p. (Orig.). 1984. pap. 5.95 (ISBN 0-8007-5162-0, Power Bks). Revell.
--Getting Your Life Out of Neutral. 1987. 14.95. Revell.
--Give Me a Break with Study Guide. 192p. 1982. pap. 5.95 (Power Bks). Revell.
--The Magnificent Mind. 224p. 1985. 9.95 (ISBN 0-8499-0385-8, 0385-8). Word Bks.
--Psychology & Theology. LC 81-588. 160p. (Orig.). 1981. pap. 7.50 (ISBN 0-687-34830-7). Abingdon.
--The Sixty-Second Christian. 64p. 1984. 5.95 (ISBN 0-8499-0450-1, 0450-1). Word Bks.
Collins, J. H. Ten Miracles. 1975. pap. 0.50 (ISBN 0-8198-0479-7). Dghtrs St Paul.
Collins, James. Pilgrim in Love: An Introduction to Dante & His Spirituality. 312p. 1984. 12.95 (ISBN 0-8294-0453-8). Loyola.
Collins, James D. God in Modern Philosophy. LC 77-25963. 1978. Repr. of 1959 ed. lib. bdg. 32.75x (ISBN 0-313-20079-3, COGM). Greenwood.
Collins, Jodie. Codeword: Catherine. 240p. (Orig.). 1984. pap. 6.95 (ISBN 0-8423-0301-4). Tyndale.
--Codeword Catherine. 384p. cancelled (ISBN 0-8423-0302-2). Tyndale.
Collins, John. Apocalyptic Imagination. 288p. 1984. 24.50x (ISBN 0-8245-0623-5). Crossroad NY.
--Daniel, One-Two Maccabees, with Excursus on Apocalyptic Genre. (Old Testament Message Ser.: Vol. 15). 1982. 15.95 (ISBN 0-89453-415-7); pap. 12.95 (ISBN 0-89453-250-2). M Glazier.
Collins, John A., jt. auth. see Collins, Sheila D.
Collins, John F. A Primer of Ecclesiastical Latin. LC 84-22957. 250p. 1985. 24.95x (ISBN 0-8132-0610-3). Cath U Pr.
Collins, John H. Mystical Body of Christ. 1977. 2.00 (ISBN 0-8198-0435-5); pap. 0.95 (ISBN 0-8198-0436-3). Dghtrs St Paul.
Collins, John J. The Apocalyptic Vision of the Book of Daniel. LC 77-23124. (Harvard Semitic Monograph). 1977. text ed. 11.95 (ISBN 0-89130-133-X, 040016). Scholars Pr GA.
--Between Athens & Jerusalem: Jewish Indentity in the Hellenistic Diaspora. 272p. 1983. 27.50x (ISBN 0-8245-0491-7). Crossroad NY.
--Daniel: With an Introduction to Apocalyptic Literature. Knierim, Rolf, et al, eds. (The Forms of the Old Testament Literature Ser.: Vol. XX). 160p. (Orig.). 1984. pap. 12.95 (ISBN 0-8028-0020-3). Eerdmans.
--Isaiah. (Collegeville Bible Commentary Ser.). 144p. 1986. pap. 2.95 (ISBN 0-8146-1420-5). Liturgical Pr.
--Primitive Religion. (Quality Paperback Ser.: No. 342). 256p. 1978. pap. 4.95 (ISBN 0-8226-0342-X). Littlefield.
--Proverbs & Ecclesiastes. LC 79-92067. (Knox Preaching Guides Ser.). 117p. (Orig., John Hayes series editor). 1980. pap. 4.95 (ISBN 0-8042-3218-0). John Knox.
Collins, John J. & Nickelsburg, George W., eds. Ideal Figures in Ancient Judaism: Profiles & Paradigms. LC 80-19878. 1980. 17.95 (ISBN 0-89130-434-7, 060412); pap. 11.95 (ISBN 0-89130-435-5). Scholars Pr GA.
Collins, Kathleen, tr. see Mars, Louis B.
Collins, Larry & Lapierre, Dominique. O Jerusalem. 1980. pap. 3.95 (ISBN 0-671-83684-6). PB.
Collins, Mabel. Light on the Path. 1970. pap. 1.75 (ISBN 0-8356-0299-0, Quest). Theos Pub Hse.
--When the Sun Moves Northward. LC 86-40402. 195p. (Orig.). 1987. pap. 4.75 (ISBN 0-8356-0614-7). Theos Pub Hse.
Collins, Mabel C. Light on the Path. leatherette 3.00 (ISBN 0-911662-13-8). Yoga.
Collins, Marjorie. Bible Quizzes on Bible Themes. 48p. 1983. pap. 1.95 (ISBN 0-87239-658-4, 3138). Standard Pub.
Collins, Marjorie A. Manual for Missionaries on Furlough. LC 72-92747. 1978. pap. 4.45 (ISBN 0-87808-119-4). William Carey Lib.
--Manual for Today's Missionary: From Recruitment to Retirement. rev. ed. LC 85-27603. (Mission Candidate Aids Ser.). 400p. 1986. pap. 9.95x (ISBN 0-87808-204-2, WCL204-2). William Carey Lib.
Collins, Martin. The French Coast. (Visitor's Guide Ser.). (Illus.). 144p. (Orig.). 1986. pap. 8.95. Hunter Pub NY.
Collins, Mary & Power, David, eds. A Creative Tradition. (Concilium 1983: Vol. 162). 128p. (Orig.). 1983. pap. 6.95 (ISBN 0-8164-2442-X, HarpR). Har-Row.
Collins, Mary, jt. ed. see Fiorenza, Elisabeth S.
Collins, Mary, jt. ed. see Power, David.
Collins, Mary J., ed. A Church Divided: Catholics' Attitudes about Family Planning, Abortion, & Teenage Sexuality. (The Bishops Watch Ser.). (Orig.). 1986. pap. 5.00 (ISBN 0-915365-12-X). Cath Free Choice.
Collins, Myrtle, jt. auth. see Feather, Nevin.
Collins, Patrick W. More Than Meets the Eye: Ritual & Parish Liturgy. LC 82-62920. 160p. (Orig.). 1983. pap. 6.95 (ISBN 0-8091-2539-0). Paulist Pr.
Collins, Raymond F. Christian Morality: Biblical Foundations. LC 85-41020. 256p. 1986. 22.95 (ISBN 0-268-00758-6). U of Notre Dame Pr.
--Christian Morality: Biblical Foundations. LC 85-41020. 258p. 1987. pap. text ed. 10.95x (ISBN 0-268-00759-4, Dist. by Har-Row). U of Notre Dame Pr.
--Introduction to the New Testament. LC 82-45070. (Illus.). 480p. 1983. 24.95 (ISBN 0-385-18126-4). Doubleday.
--Introduction to the New Testament. 480p. 1987. pap. 10.95 (ISBN 0-385-23534-8, Im). Doubleday.
--Models of Theological Reflections. LC 83-21733. (Illus.). 240p. (Orig.). 1984. lib. bdg. 25.75 (ISBN 0-8191-3661-1); pap. text ed. 12.25 (ISBN 0-8191-3662-X). U Pr of Amer.
Collins, Robert E. Theodore Parker: American Transcendentalist: A Critical Essay & a Collection of His Writings. LC 73-9593. 277p. 1973. 17.50 (ISBN 0-8108-0641-X). Scarecrow.
Collins, Ross W. Catholicism & the Second French Republic, 1848-1852. 1980. lib. bdg. 27.50x (ISBN 0-374-91868-6, Octagon). Hippocrene Bks.

Collins, Sheila D. & Collins, John A. In Your Midst: Perspectives on Christian Mission. (Orig.). 1980. pap. 3.25 (ISBN 0-377-00101-5). Friend Pr.
Collins, Steven. Selfless Persons: Imagery & Thought in Theravada Buddhism. LC 81-16998. 1982. 47.50 (ISBN 0-521-24081-6). Cambridge U Pr.
Collins, Varnum L. President Witherspoon. LC 78-83416. (Religion in America, Ser. 1). 1969. Repr. of 1925 ed. 30.00 (ISBN 0-405-00242-4). Ayer Co Pubs.
Collins, Varnum L., ed. see Witherspoon, John.
Collins, Victor, tr. see Gougaud, Dom L.
Collins, Vincent P. Me, Myself & You. rev. ed. LC 74-17734. 1974. pap. 2.95 (ISBN 0-87029-001-0, 20033-7). Abbey.
Collins, W. Lucas. Lucian. 1877. Repr. 25.00 (ISBN 0-8274-3005-1). R West.
Collins, William E., ed. Archbishop Laud Commemoration, 1895. (Bibliography & Reference Ser: No. 257). 1969. Repr. of 1895 ed. 23.50 (ISBN 0-8337-0628-4). B Franklin.
Collinson, Patrick. Archbishop Grindal, 1519-1589: The Struggle for a Reformed Church in England. LC 78-65474. 1979. 46.00x (ISBN 0-520-03831-2). U of Cal Pr.
--The Elizabethan Puritan Movement. (Library Reprints Ser.). 528p. 1982. 60.00x (ISBN 0-416-34000-8, NO. 3701). Methuen Inc.
--Godly People: Essays on English Protestantism & Puritanism. (No. 23). 634p. 1983. 40.00 (ISBN 0-907628-15-X). Hambledon Press.
--The Religion of Protestants: The Church in English Society 1559-1625. 1982. pap. 15.95x (ISBN 0-19-820053-6). Oxford U Pr.
Collis, Johanna, tr. see Grosse, Rudolf.
Collison, Kathleen & Webb, Warren. Forty-Eight Hours More or Less: A Retreat Resource. 111p. (Orig.). pap. 11.00 (ISBN 0-941988-03-1). K Q Assocs.
Colloms, Brenda. Victorian Country Parsons. LC 77-82027. (Illus.). 284p. 1978. 21.50x (ISBN 0-8032-0981-9). U of Nebr Pr.
Colloquium in the Philosophy of Science Staff. Induction, Physics, & Ethics: Proceedings of the Colloquium in the Philosophy of Science, Salzburg, 1969. Weingartner, P. & Zecha, G., eds. LC 78-118137. (Synthese Library: No. 31). 382p. 1970. lib. bdg. 39.50 (ISBN 90-277-0158-X, Pub. by Reidel Holland). Kluwer Academic.
Colloquium on Myth in Literature, Bucknell & Susquehanna Universities, Mar. 21-2, 1974, et al. The Binding of Proteus: Perspectives on Myth & the Literary Process. McCune, Marjorie W. & Orbison, T. Tucker, eds. LC 76-49774. (Illus.). 352p. 1978. 28.50 (ISBN 0-8387-1708-X). Bucknell U Pr.
Colman, Barry, ed. Sex & the Single Christian. LC 85-30138. 120p. (Orig.). 1986. pap. 6.95 (ISBN 0-8307-1107-4, 5418696). Regal.
Colman, Henry, ed. Divine Meditations (Sixteen Forty) 1979. 27.50x (ISBN 0-300-02305-7). Yale U Pr.
Colman, John. John Locke's Moral Philosophy. 280p. 1982. 27.50x (ISBN 0-85224-445-2, Pub. by Edinburgh U Pr Scotland). Columbia U Pr.
Colman, T. S. History of the Parish of Barwick-In-Elmet in the County of York. 1908. 34.00 (ISBN 0-384-09565-8). Johnson Repr.
Colmer, Michael. Executive I Ching: The Business Oracle. 176p. 1987. 17.95 (ISBN 0-7137-1934-6, Pub. by Blandford Pr England). Sterling.
Colombiere, Claude De La see Saint-Jure, Jean B. & De La Colombiere, Claude.
Colombo, Furio. God in America: Religion & Politics in the United States. Jarrat, Kristin, tr. from Ital. LC 84-4278. 208p. 1984. 20.00x (ISBN 0-231-05972-8). Columbia U Pr.
Colonial Williamsburg Staff. Christmas Decorations from Williamsburg's Folk Art Collection: Easy to Follow Instructions for Making 90 Decorations. LC 76-41253. (Illus.). 80p. (Orig.). 1976. pap. 4.95 (ISBN 0-87935-040-7). Williamsburg.
Colquhoun, Frank. Family Prayers. 80p. 1984. pap. 1.35 (ISBN 0-88028-040-9). Forward Movement.
--Four Portraits of Jesus. LC 85-4248. Orig. Title: Fourfold Portrait of Jesus. 84p. 1985. pap. 2.95 (ISBN 0-87784-450-X). Inter-Varsity.
--A Hymn Companion. 288p. 1985. pap. 8.95 (ISBN 0-8192-1368-3). Morehouse.
--Hymns That Live. LC 81-1458. 320p. 1981. pap. 6.95 (ISBN 0-87784-473-9). Inter Varsity.
Colquhoun, Frank, ed. Prayers for Every Occasion. Orig. Title: Parish Prayers. 445p. 1974. Repr. of 1967 ed. kivar 14.95 (ISBN 0-8192-1280-6). Morehouse.
Colson, Charles. Born Again. (Illus.). 352p. 1977. Movie ed. pap. 3.95 (ISBN 0-8007-8290-9, Spire Bks); (Spire Bks). Revell.
--Dare to Be Different, Dare to Be Christian. 48p. 1986. pap. 1.95 (ISBN 0-89693-159-5). Victor Bks.
--Naci de Nuevo. Ward, Rhode, tr. from Eng. LC 77-81645. Tr. of Born Again. (Span.). 419p. 1977. pap. 6.50 (ISBN 0-89922-087-8). Edit Caribe.
--Presenting Belief in an Age of Unbelief. 48p. 1986. 1.95 (ISBN 0-89693-158-7). Victor Bks.
--The Role of the Church in Society. 48p. 1986. 1.95 (ISBN 0-89693-167-6). Victor Bks.
--The Struggle for Men's Hearts & Minds. 48p. 1986. 1.95 (ISBN 0-89693-166-8). Victor Bks.
Colson, Charles, et al. Christianity in Conflict: The Struggle for Christian Integrity & Freedom in Secular Culture. Williamson, Peter S. & Perrotta, Kevin, eds. 180p. (Orig.). 1986. pap. 7.95 (ISBN 0-89283-292-4). Servant.
Colson, Charles W. Life Sentence. (Illus.). 320p. 1981. pap. 7.95 (ISBN 0-8007-5059-4, Power Bks). Revell.
--Loving God. 288p. 1983. 12.95 (ISBN 0-310-47030-7, 11306); study guide 3.95 (ISBN 0-310-47038-2, 11307). Zondervan.
Colson, Howard P. & Rigdon, Raymond M. Understanding Your Church's Curriculum. rev. ed. LC 80-67351. 1981. pap. 5.95 (ISBN 0-8054-3201-9). Broadman.
Colston, Lowell G. Pastoral Care with Handicapped Persons. Clinebell, Howard J. & Stone, Howard W., eds. LC 77-15229. (Creative Pastoral Care & Counseling Ser). 96p. (Orig.). 1978. pap. 4.50 (ISBN 0-8006-0560-8, 1-560). Fortress.
Coltman, Derek, tr. see Eliade, Mircea.
Coltman, Derek, tr. see Varenne, Jean.
Colton, Ann R. Draughts of Remembrance. 177p. 1959. 8.95 (ISBN 0-917187-09-1). A R C Pub.
--Ethical ESP. LC 78-149600. 367p. 1971. 11.50 (ISBN 0-917187-03-2). A R C Pub.
--The Human Spirit. 289p. 1966. 8.95 (ISBN 0-917187-05-9). A R C Pub.
--Islands of Light. 203p. 1953. 6.95 (ISBN 0-917187-14-8). A R C Pub.
--The Jesus Story. 396p. 1969. 10.00 (ISBN 0-917187-04-0). A R C Pub.
--The King. 72p. 1968. 5.00 (ISBN 0-917187-08-3). A R C Pub.
--Kundalini West. (Illus.). 403p. 1978. 12.95 (ISBN 0-917187-01-6). A R C Pub.
--The Lively Oracles. 151p. 1962. 5.95 (ISBN 0-917187-13-X). A R C Pub.
--Men in White Apparel. (Illus.). 202p. 1961. 6.95 (ISBN 0-917187-10-5). A R C Pub.
--Precepts for the Young. 66p. 1959. pap. 2.50 (ISBN 0-917187-15-6). A R C Pub.
--The Soul & the Ethic. 262p. 1965. 7.95 (ISBN 0-917187-07-5). A R C Pub.
--The Third Music. LC 82-71249. (Illus.). 432p. 1982. 15.95 (ISBN 0-917187-00-8). A R C Pub.
--The Venerable One. 166p. 1963. 5.95 (ISBN 0-917187-11-3). A R C Pub.
--Vision for the Future. 139p. 1960. 5.95 (ISBN 0-917187-12-1). A R C Pub.
Colton, Ann R. & Murro, Jonathan. Prophet for the Archangels. (Illus.). 289p. 1964. 8.95 (ISBN 0-917187-06-7). A R C Pub.
Colton, C. E. The Faithfulness of Faith. LC 85-9845. 1985. pap. 4.95 (ISBN 0-8054-1534-3). Broadman.
Colton, Calvin. History & Character of American Revivals of Religion. LC 72-1008. Repr. of 1832 ed. 22.50 (ISBN 0-404-00018-5). AMS Pr.
Colton, G. Q. Shakespeare & the Bible. LC 74-8569. 1888. lib. bdg. 20.00 (ISBN 0-685-45608-0). Folcroft.
Colton, Gary P. Praise & Prayer. 1978. 7.95 (ISBN 0-8198-0593-9). Dghtrs St Paul.
Colton, Harold S. Hopi Kachina Dolls with a Key to Their Identification. rev ed. LC 59-5480. (Illus.). 150p. 1971. pap. 8.95 (ISBN 0-8263-0180-0). U of NM Pr.
Colum, Padraic. The Children of Odin. 1920. 40.00 (ISBN 0-686-18157-3). Havertown Bks.
Columbia University. Spinoza Bibliography. Oko, Adolph S., compiled by. 1964. lib. bdg. 79.00 (ISBN 0-8161-0699-1, Hall Library). G K Hall.
Colver, A. Wayne, ed. see Hume, David.
Colville, Josephine. Growing Up. 1979. 6.25 (ISBN 0-8198-0575-0); pap. 5.00 (ISBN 0-8198-0576-9). Dghtrs St Paul.
Colvin, Mary N., ed. see Guilelmus.
Colwell, Ernest C. The Study of the Bible. rev. ed. LC 64-23411. (Midway Reprint Ser.). pap. 54.50 (2026769). Bks Demand UMI.
Colwell, Ernest C. & Tune, E. W. A Beginner's Reader-Grammar for New Testament Greek. 1965. 11.00 (ISBN 0-06-061530-3, HarpR). Har-Row.
Colwell, Stephen. New Themes for the Protestant Clergy. LC 71-83417. (Religion in America, Ser. 1). 1969. Repr. of 1851 ed. 32.00 (ISBN 0-405-00243-2). Ayer Co Pubs.
--The Position of Christianity in the United States, in Its Relations with Our Political Institutions, & Specially with Reference to Religious Instruction in the Public Schools. LC 78-38444. (Religion in America, Ser. 2). 180p. 1972. Repr. of 1854 ed. 17.00 (ISBN 0-405-04063-6). Ayer Co Pubs.
Colyer-Fergusson, T. C. see Le Fanu, Thomas P.
Coman, Peter. Catholics & the Welfare State. LC 76-49523. pap. 32.00 (ISBN 0-317-08456-9, 2011288). Bks Demand UMI.
Comba, Emilio. History of the Waldenses of Italy: From Their Origin to the Reformation. LC 77-84713. Repr. of 1889 ed. 41.00 (ISBN 0-404-16119-7). AMS Pr.
Combee, Jerry H. & Hall, Cline E. Designed for Destiny. 112p. 1985. 4.95 (ISBN 0-8423-0619-6). Tyndale.
Comblin, Jose. The Church & the National Security State. LC 79-10881. 256p. (Orig.). 1979. pap. 12.95 (ISBN 0-88344-082-2). Orbis Bks.
--Jesus of Nazareth: Meditations on His Humanity. Kabat, Carl, tr. from Port. LC 75-29580. Orig. Title: Jesus De Nazare. 176p. (Orig.). 1976. pap. 3.48 (ISBN 0-88344-239-6). Orbis Bks.
--Sent from the Father: Meditations on the Fourth Gospel. Kabat, Carl, tr. from Port. LC 78-16750. Orig. Title: O Enviado do Pai. 115p. (Orig.). 1979. pap. 2.48 (ISBN 0-88344-453-4). Orbis Bks.
Combs, Diana W. Early Gravestone Art in Georgia & South Carolina. LC 85-1129. (Illus.). 256p. 1986. 35.00x (ISBN 0-8203-0788-2). U of Ga Pr.
Comby, Jean. How to Understand Church History. 208p. 1985. pap. 10.95 (ISBN 0-8245-0722-3). Crossroad NY.
Comeaux, Maureen N., jt. auth. see Ristow, Kate S.
Comerchero, Victor, ed. Values in Conflict: Christianity, Marxism, Psychoanalysis & Existentialism. LC 74-111099. 986p. (Orig., Free booklet, "Suggestions for Instructors," available). 1970. pap. text ed. 19.95x (ISBN 0-89197-463-6). Irvington.
Comes, Natalis. Mythologiae. LC 75-27853. (Renaissance & the Gods Ser.: Vol. 11). (Illus.). 1976. Repr. of 1567 ed. lib. bdg. 88.00 (ISBN 0-8240-2060-X). Garland Pub.
Comfort, William W. William Penn & Our Liberties. (Illus.). 146p. 1976. pap. 3.00 (ISBN 0-941308-02-2). Religious Soc Friends.
Commager, H. S. Theodore Parker: Yankee Crusader. 11.25 (ISBN 0-8446-1884-5). Peter Smith.
Commager, Henry S. The Empire of Reason: How Europe Imagined & America Realized the Enlightenment. 1984. 17.25 (ISBN 0-8446-6088-4). Peter Smith.
--Theodore Parker. 1982. pap. 6.45 (ISBN 0-933840-15-2). Unitarian Univ.
Commager, Steele, ed. see Wagenvoort, Hendrik.
Commins, Stephen, jt. ed. see Cesaretti, C. A.
Commission Christian Lit. Bible Translations. 1981. pap. 0.79 (ISBN 0-8100-0132-2, 04N1212). Northwest Pub.
Commission For Christian Literature, ed. Is Evolutionism the Answer. (Truth Unchanging Series). (Illus.). 1968. pap. 2.50 (ISBN 0-8100-0023-7, 12-0331). Northwest Pub.
Commons, John R. Social Reform & the Church. LC 66-21663. (Illus.). 1967. Repr. of 1894 ed. 22.50x (ISBN 0-678-00286-X). Kelley.
Communication & Learning Innovators, Ltd. Staff, et al, eds. see Patterson, Kathy C. & Niklaus, Phyllis M.
Company for the Propagation of the Gospel in New England & the Parts Adjacent in America, London. Some Correspondence Between the Governors & Treasurers of the New England Company in London & the Commissioners of the United Colonies in America, the Missionaries of the Company & Others Between the Years 1657 & 1712. Ford, John W., ed. LC 73-126413. (Research & Source Works: No. 524). 1970. Repr. of 1896 ed. lib. bdg. 29.50 (ISBN 0-8337-1185-7). B Franklin.
Compayre, Gabriel. Abelard & the Origin & Early History of the Universities. LC 75-90094. (BCL Ser.: II). 1969. Repr. of 1893 ed. 11.50 (ISBN 0-404-01639-1). AMS Pr.
--Abelard & the Origin & Early History of the Universities. 1893. 10.00x (ISBN 0-403-00009-2). Scholarly.
Comper, Frances M. M. & Kastenbaum, Robert, eds. The Book of the Craft of Dying & Other Early English Tracts Concerning Death. LC 76-19564. (Death & Dying Ser.). 1977. Repr. of 1917 ed. lib. bdg. 19.00x (ISBN 0-405-09560-0). Ayer Co Pubs.
Comper, Francis M., ed. see Rolle, Richard.
Compier, Don. Studies in First Corinthians. (Bible Study Ser.). 1987. pap. 3.50 (ISBN 0-8309-0448-4). Herald Hse.
--Studies in Second Corinthians. (Bible Study Ser.). 1987. pap. 3.50 (ISBN 0-8309-0479-4). Herald Hse.
Compton, Al. Armonia Familiar. 32p. 1981. pap. 1.30 (ISBN 0-311-46078-X). Casa Bautista.
Compton, Alan. Comunicacion Cristiana. 168p. 1985. Repr. of 1982 ed. 4.15 (ISBN 0-311-13833-0). Casa Bautista.
Compton, Arthur H. Man's Destiny in Eternity. LC 75-117821. (Essay Index Reprint Ser). 1949. 19.00 (ISBN 0-8369-1762-6). Ayer Co Pubs.
Compton, Everald. Living with Money. 47p. (Orig.). 1983. pap. 5.95 (ISBN 0-340-34299-4, Pub. by Genesis). ANZ Religious Pubns.
Compton, LaNell. Looking Forward to a New Day. 1984. 7.95 (ISBN 0-8158-0418-0). Chris Mass.
Compton, Robert. La Teologia de la Liberacion: Una Introduccion. (Span.). 112p. (Orig.). 1985. pap. 3.75 (ISBN 0-311-09106-7). Casa Bautista.
Compton, W. H. Special Day Sermons. 1972. 3.25 (ISBN 0-87148-752-7). Pathway Pr.
Compton-Burnett, Ivy. A God & His Gifts. 1963. 15.95 (ISBN 0-575-02578-6, Pub by Gollancz England). David & Charles.
Comstock, Craig see Carlson, Don.
Comstock, Craig, jt. ed. see Carlson, Don.
Comstock, Craig K., jt. ed. see Carlson, Don.
Comstock, Susan T., et al, eds. The Apocalypse of Elijah. LC 79-24788. (Society of Biblical Literature Texts & Translations). 126p. 1981. pap. 14.25 (ISBN 0-89130-372-3, 06 02 19). Scholars Pr GA.
Comte, Auguste. The Catechism of Positive Religion. 3rd ed. Congreve, Richard, tr. LC 72-77053. 1973. Repr. of 1891 ed. lib. bdg. 35.00x (ISBN 0-678-00910-4). Kelley.
Conacher, D. J. Aeschylus' "Prometheus Bound". A Literary Commentary. 128p. 1980. 25.00x (ISBN 0-8020-2391-6); pap. 8.50 (ISBN 0-8020-6416-7). U of Toronto Pr.
Conacher, James B., ed. see Du Creux, Francois.
Conant, D. C. The Earnest Man; or the Character & Labors of Adoniram Judson. 1978. Repr. of 1856 ed. lib. bdg. 20.00 (ISBN 0-8492-3943-5). R West.
Conant, Newton. Changed by Beholding Him. 1972. pap. 2.95 (ISBN 0-87508-147-9). Chr Lit.
--Cheating God. 102p. 1985. pap. 3.50 (ISBN 0-317-43393-8). Chr Lit.
Conaway, John. Teaching the Bible. (Complete Teacher Training Meeting ser.). 48p. 1986. tchr's ed 9.95 (ISBN 0-89191-319-X). Cook.
Conaway, Judith. Easy-to-Make Christmas Crafts. LC 85-16475. (Illus.). 48p. 1986. PLB 9.49 (ISBN 0-8167-0674-3); pap. text ed. 1.95 (ISBN 0-8167-0675-1). Troll Assocs.
Concetta. In the Light of the Bible, Vols. 1 & 2. 1976. Vol. 1. 2.00 (ISBN 0-8198-0426-6); Vol. 2. pap. 2.00 (ISBN 0-8198-0427-4). Dghtrs St Paul.
Concordia Historical Institute Staff & Lutheran Historical Conference Staff. Lutheran Historical Conference: Essays & Reports. Suelflow, August R., ed. 7.50 (ISBN 0-318-04799-3). Concordia Hist.
Conde, Jose A. History of the Dominion of the Arabs in Spain, 3 Vols. Foster, Mrs. Jonathan, tr. Repr. of 1855 ed. Set. 55.00 (ISBN 0-404-09270-5); 18.50 ea. Vol. 1 (ISBN 0-404-09271-3). Vol. 2 (ISBN 0-404-09272-1). Vol. 3 (ISBN 0-404-09273-X). AMS Pr.
Condee, Ralph W. Milton's Theories Concerning Epic Poetry. LC 77-861. 1977. lib. bdg. 8.50 (ISBN 0-8414-3421-2). Folcroft.
Conder, Claude R. The Survey of Western Palestine, 3 vols. Palmer, E. H. & Besant, Walter, eds. LC 78-63331. (The Crusades & Military Orders: Second Ser.). (Illus.). Repr. of 1883 ed. Set. 110.00 (ISBN 0-404-17010-2). AMS Pr.
Conder, Claude R., jt. auth. see Warren, Charles.
Condit, Kay, ed. see Owen, Ray.
Condon, R. J. Our Pagan Christmas. 12p. 1982. pap. 1.00 (ISBN 0-911826-47-5). Am Atheist.
Cone, James. God of the Oppressed. 1978. pap. 6.95 (ISBN 0-8164-2607-4, HarpR). Har-Row.
Cone, James H. Black Theology & Black Power. LC 70-76462. (Orig.). 1969. pap. 5.95 (ISBN 0-8164-2003-3, SP59, HarpR). Har-Row.
--A Black Theology of Liberation. 2nd ed. LC 85-18749. 176p. 1986. pap. 9.95 (ISBN 0-88344-245-0). Orbis Bks.
--For My People: Black Theology & the Black Church. LC 84-5195. (Bishop Henry McNeal Turner Studies in North America Black Religion: Vol. 1). 288p. (Orig.). 1984. pap. 9.95 (ISBN 0-88344-106-3). Orbis Bks.
--My Soul Looks Back. 144p. 1986. pap. 8.95 (ISBN 0-88344-355-4). Orbis Bks.
--Speaking the Truth: Ecumenism, Liberation, & Black Theology. 176p. (Orig.). 1986. pap. 8.95 (ISBN 0-8028-0226-5). Eerdmans.
--The Spirituals & the Blues. pap. 5.95 (ISBN 0-8164-2073-4, SP74, HarpR). Har-Row.
Cone, James H., jt. ed. see Wilmore, Gayraud S.
Cone, Molly. About Belonging. (Shema Storybooks: No. 3). (Illus.). 64p. (Orig.). 1972. pap. 5.00 (ISBN 0-8074-0125-0, 101083). UAHC.
--About God. (Shema Storybooks: No. 4). (Illus.). 64p. 1973. pap. 5.00 (ISBN 0-8074-0126-9, 101084). UAHC.

--About Learning. (Shema Primary Ser: No. 2). (Illus., Orig.). 1972. pap. 5.00 (ISBN 0-8074-0127-7, 101082). UAHC.
--First I Say the Shema. (Shema Primary Ser: No. 1). (Illus., Orig.). 1971. pap. text ed. 5.00 (ISBN 0-8074-0134-X, 101081). UAHC.
--Who Knows Ten: Children's Tales of the Ten Commandments. LC 65-24639. (Illus.). 1968. text ed. 6.00 (ISBN 0-8074-0080-7, 102551); record o.p. 5.95 (ISBN 0-8074-0081-5, 102552). UAHC.
Conference of Scientology Ministers. The American Inquisition: U. S. Government Agency Harassment, Religious Persecution & Abuse of Power. 1977. pap. 7.00 (ISBN 0-915598-16-7). Church of Scient Info.
Conference On Jewish Social Studies. Negro-Jewish Relations in the United States. 1966. pap. 1.50 (ISBN 0-8065-0092-1, 218). Citadel Pr.
Conference on Science, Philosophy & Religion in Their Relation to the Democratic Way of Life, 6th. Approaches to Group Understanding: Proceedings. Repr. of 1947 ed. 24.00 (ISBN 0-527-00653-X). Kraus Repr.
Conference on Science-Philosophy & Religion in Their Relation to the Democratic Way of Life - 4th. Approaches to World Peace: Proceedings. 1944. 70.00 (ISBN 0-527-00651-3). Kraus Repr.
Conference on Science-Philosophy & Religion in Their Religion to the Democratic Way of Life, New York. Ethics & Bigness: Proceedings. 1962. 41.00 (ISBN 0-527-00664-5). Kraus Repr.
Conference on Science-Philosophy & Religion in Their Relation to the Democratic Way of Life, 11th. Foundations of World Organization: A Political & Cultural Appraisal: Proceeding. 37.00 (ISBN 0-527-00658-0). Kraus Repr.
Conference on Science-Philosophy & Religion in Their Relation to the Democratic Way of Live, 12th, New York. Freedom & Authority in Our Time: Proceeding. 1953. 51.00 (ISBN 0-527-00659-9). Kraus Repr.
Conference on Science-Philosophy & Religion in Their Relation to the Democratic Way of Life - 9th. Goals for American Education: Proceedings. 1950. 28.00 (ISBN 0-527-00656-4). Kraus Repr.
Conference on Science, Philosophy & Religion in Their Relation to the Democratic Way of Life, 3rd. Science, Philosophy, & Religion: Proceedings. 1943. 37.00 (ISBN 0-527-00650-5). Kraus Repr.
Conference on Science, Philosophy & Religion in Their Relation to the Democratic Way of Life, 2nd. Science, Philosophy, & Religion: Proceedings. 1942. 37.00 (ISBN 0-527-00649-1). Kraus Repr.
Conference on Science, Philosophy & Religion & Their Relation to the Democratic Way of Life, 1st. Science, Philosophy, & Religion: Proceedings. 1941. 37.00 (ISBN 0-527-00648-3). Kraus Repr.
Conference on Science-Philosphy & Religion in Their Relation to the Democratic Way of Life - 5th. Approaches to National Unity: Proceedings. 1945. 70.00 (ISBN 0-527-00652-1). Kraus Repr.
Conference On The Scientific Spirit And Democratic Faith - 3rd. Science for Democracy. facs. ed. LC 70-121459. (Essay Index Reprint Ser.). 1946. 18.00 (ISBN 0-8369-1793-6). Ayer Co Pubs.
Conference On The Scientific Spirit And Democratic Faith-1st-New York-1943. Scientific Spirit & Democratic Faith. facs. ed. LC 72-121457. (Essay Index Reprint Ser). 1944. 14.00 (ISBN 0-8369-1872-X). Ayer Co Pubs.
Conforti, Joseph A. Samuel Hopkins & the New Divinity Movement: Calvinism, the Congregational Ministry, & Reform in New England Between the Great Awakenings. LC 80-28268. pap. 62.30 (ISBN 0-317-08398-8, 2020840). Bks Demand UMI.
Confucius. The Analects. Lau, D. C., tr. 1979. pap. 4.95 (ISBN 0-14-044348-7). Penguin.
--Analects. Waley, Arthur, tr. 1966. pap. 4.95 (ISBN 0-394-70173-9, V173, Vin). Random.
--The Analects of Confucius. (Illus.). 149p. 1986. 88.85 (ISBN 0-89266-538-6). Am Classical Coll Pr.
--Confucian Analects, the Great Learning & the Doctrine of the Mean. Legge, James, ed. 1893. pap. 7.95 (ISBN 0-486-22746-4). Dover.
--The Great Learning & the Doctrine of the Mean. (Illus.). 151p. 1986. 88.85 (ISBN 0-89266-539-4). Am Classical Coll Pr.
--The Most Compelling Sayings by Confucius. Lynall, Leonard D., tr. (Most Meaningful Classics in World Culture Ser.). (Illus.). 166p. 1983. 83.45 (ISBN 0-89266-387-1). Am Classical Coll Pr.
--Sayings of Confucius. Ware, James R., tr. (Orig.). pap. 2.95 (ISBN 0-451-62168-9, Ment). NAL.
--The Wisdom of Confucius. (Illus.). 131p. 1982. 63.45 (ISBN 0-89266-359-6). Am Classical Coll Pr.
--Wisdom of Confucius. 1965. 5.95 (ISBN 0-88088-100-3). Peter Pauper.
--The Wisdom of Confucius. Yutang, Lin, ed. & tr. LC 38-27366. 290p. 1938. 5.95 (ISBN 0-394-60426-1). Modern Lib.
Congar, Yves. Diversity & Communion. Tr. of Diversities et Communion. 240p. 1985. pap. text ed. 9.95 (ISBN 0-89622-275-6). Twenty-Third.
--I Believe in the Holy Spirit, 3 Vols. Smith, David, tr. from Fr. Incl. Vol. I. The Experience of the Spirit. 173p. 24.95 (ISBN 0-8164-0518-2); Vol. 2. Lord & Giver of Life. 230p. 24.95 (ISBN 0-8164-0535-2); Vol. 3. The River of Life Flows in the East & in the West. 274p. 24.95 (ISBN 0-8164-0537-9). 300p. 1983. Set. 70.00 (ISBN 0-8164-0540-9, Winston-Seabury). Har-Row.
--Lay People in the Church. 518p. 1985. pap. 14.95 (ISBN 0-87061-114-3). Chr Classics.
--The Word & the Spirit. 192p. 1986. 15.95 (ISBN 0-86683-538-5, HarpR). Har-Row.
Congdon, Howard K. The Pursuit of Death. LC 76-44308. Repr. of 1977 ed. 36.30 (ISBN 0-8357-9022-3, 2016395). Bks Demand UMI.
Conger, Arthur L., ed. see De Purucker, G.
Conger, George P. Ideologies of Religion. facsimile ed. LC 70-93329. (Essay Index Reprint Ser). 1940. 19.00 (ISBN 0-8369-1283-7). Ayer Co Pubs.
Conger, Margaret. Combined Chronology for Use with the Mahatma Letters to A. P. Sinnett & the Letters of H. P. Blavatsky to A. P. Sinnett. LC 73-92461. 1973. pap. 3.00 (ISBN 0-911500-17-0). Theos U Pr.
Conger, Yves M. After Nine Hundred Years: The Background of the Schism Between the Eastern & Western Churches. LC 78-6154. 1978. Repr. of 1959 ed. lib. bdg. 22.50x (ISBN 0-313-20493-4, COAN). Greenwood.
Congress of Colored Catholics of the United States. Three Catholic Afro-American Congresses. 14.00 (ISBN 0-405-10863-X, 11829). Ayer Co Pubs.
Congreve, Carola, tr. see Van Lysebeth, Andre.
Congreve, Richard, tr. see Comte, Auguste.
Coniaris, A. Crown Them with Glory & Honor: Talks for Weddings. 1985. pap. 4.95 (ISBN 0-937032-40-9). Light&Life Pub Co MN.
--Gems from the Sunday Gospel Lessons in the Orthodox Church, Vol. II. pap. 5.95 (ISBN 0-937032-13-1). Light&Life Pub Co MN.
--Sacred Symbols That Speak, Vol. I. 1986. pap. 7.95 (ISBN 0-937032-39-5). Light&Life Pub Co MN.
Coniaris, A. M. Christ's Comfort for Those Who Sorrow. 1978. pap. 3.95 (ISBN 0-937032-00-X). Light&Life Pub Co MN.
--Eastern Orthodoxy: A Way of Life. 1966. pap. 6.95 (ISBN 0-937032-14-X). Light&Life Pub Co MN.
--Eighty Talks for Orthodox Young People. 1975. pap. 4.95 (ISBN 0-937032-16-6). Light&Life Pub Co MN.
--God Speaks from the Cross. 1984. pap. 4.95 (ISBN 0-937032-33-6). Light&Life Pub Co MN.
--The Great I Came's of Jesus. 1980. pap. 7.95 (ISBN 0-686-27069-X). Light&Life Pub Co MN.
--Introducing the Orthodox Church. 1982. pap. 7.95. Light&Life Pub Co MN.
--Making God Real in the Orthodox Christian Home. 1977. pap. 5.95 (ISBN 0-937032-07-7). Light&Life Pub Co MN.
--The Message of the Sunday Gospel Readings, Vol. 1. 1982. pap. 7.95 (ISBN 0-937032-26-3). Light&Life Pub Co MN.
--The Message of the Sunday Gospels, Vol. 2. 1983. pap. 7.95 (ISBN 0-937032-29-8). Light&Life Pub Co MN.
--No Man Ever Spoke As This Man. 1969. pap. 4.95 (ISBN 0-937032-18-2). Light&Life Pub Co MN.
--Orthodoxy: A Creed for Today. 1972. pap. 7.95 (ISBN 0-937032-19-0). Light&Life Pub Co MN.
--Perspectives on Living the Orthodox Faith. 1985. pap. 7.95 (ISBN 0-937032-36-0). Light&Life Pub Co MN.
--These Are the Sacraments. 1981. pap. 6.95 (ISBN 0-937032-22-0). Light&Life Pub Co MN.
--Treasures from Paul's Letters, Vol. I. 1978. pap. 7.95 (ISBN 0-937032-05-0). Light&Life Pub Co MN.
--Treasures from Paul's Letters, Vol. II. 1979. pap. 7.95 (ISBN 0-937032-06-9). Light&Life Pub Co MN.
--Where Moth & Rust Do Not Consume. 1983. pap. 5.95 (ISBN 0-937032-30-1). Light&Life Pub Co MN.
Coniker, Jerome F. Devotions & Prayers in Honor of St. Joseph. (Living Meditation & Prayer Bklt. Library). (Illus.). 34p. (Orig.). 1978. pap. text ed. 2.50 (ISBN 0-932406-04-1). AFC.
--Peaceful Seed Living, Vols. 1 & 2. 2nd ed. LC 78-66369. (Living Meditation & Prayerbook Ser.). (Illus.). 156p. 1981. pap. text ed. 3.00 ea. (ISBN 0-932406-00-9). AFC.
--Prayers & Recommended Practices. 2nd ed. LC 78-66374. (Living Meditation & Prayerbook Ser.). (Illus.). 91p. pap. text ed. 3.00 (ISBN 0-932406-01-7). AFC.
Coniker, Jerome F., ed. see Seeley, Burns K.
Conkin, Paul K. American Christianity in Crisis. LC 81-80738. (Charles Edmondson Historical Lectures Ser.). 48p. (Orig.). 1981. pap. 4.50 (ISBN 0-918954-24-X). Baylor Univ Pr.
--Puritans & Pragmatists: Eight Eminent American Thinkers. LC 75-34730. (Midland Bks.: No. 197). 512p. 1976. 20.00x (ISBN 0-253-34720-3); pap. 6.95x (ISBN 0-253-20197-7). Ind U Pr.
Conley, Lucy, jt. auth. see Birky, Lela.
Conley, Patrick T. Rhode Island Catholicism: A Historical Guide. 24p. (Orig.). 1984. pap. 2.95 (ISBN 0-917012-56-9). RI Pubns Soc.
Conley, Patrick T. & Smith, Matthew J. Catholicism in Rhode Island: The Formative Era. LC 76-62863. 1976. 12.50 (ISBN 0-917012-13-5). RI Pubns Soc.
Conley, Patrick T., ed. see Foster, Geraldine S.
Conley, Patrick T., ed. see Gelenian, Ara A.
Conn, Charles. Our First One Hundred Years. (Church Training Course Ser.). 1986. cloth 5.75 (ISBN 0-87148-668-7); pap. 4.75 (ISBN 0-87148-669-5). Pathway Pr.
Conn, Charles P. A Faith to Keep. LC 77-70783. pap. 1.99 (ISBN 0-87148-016-6). Pathway Pr.
--Fathercare: What It Means to Be Gods Child. 128p. 1984. pap. 2.95 (ISBN 0-425-08460-4); pap. 3.95 (ISBN 0-8128-8184-2). Berkley Pub.
--The Man from Galilee. LC 74-83547. 1974. pap. 1.99 (ISBN 0-87148-565-6). Pathway Pr.
Conn, Charles P. & Aultman, Donald S. Studies in Discipleship. LC 75-14887. 1975. pap. 1.99 (ISBN 0-87148-772-1). Pathway Pr.
Conn, Charles P. & Conn, Charles W. The Relevant Record. LC 76-2969. (Illus.). 1976. pap. 1.99 (ISBN 0-87148-732-2). Pathway Pr.
--What Is the Church? 1977. pap. 1.99 (ISBN 0-87148-907-4). Pathway Pr.
Conn, Charles P., jt. auth. see DeVos, Richard M.
Conn, Charles P., jt. auth. see Eckerd, Jack.
Conn, Charles P., jt. auth. see Miller, Barbara.
Conn, Charles P., jt. auth. see Walker, Paul L.
Conn, Charles W. The Acts of the Apostles. 1966. pap. 4.25 (ISBN 0-87148-010-7). Pathway Pr.
--Anatomy of Evil. 1984. pap. text ed. 6.95 (ISBN 0-87148-018-2). Pathway Pr.
--A Balanced Church. 1983. pap. 6.95 (ISBN 0-87148-017-4). Pathway Pr.
--The Bible: Books of Books. 1977. pap. 4.25 (ISBN 0-87148-102-2). Pathway Pr.
--A Certain Journey. 152p. 1965. 4.25 (ISBN 0-87148-000-X); pap. 3.25 (ISBN 0-87148-001-8). Pathway Pr.
--Christ & the Gospels. 109p. 1964. pap. 4.25 (ISBN 0-87148-150-2). Pathway Pr.
--The Evangel Reader. 1958. 3.25 (ISBN 0-87148-275-4). Pathway Pr.
--A Guide to the Pentateuch. 109p. 1963. 5.25 (ISBN 0-87148-004-2); pap. 4.25 (ISBN 0-87148-005-0). Pathway Pr.
--Highlights of Hebrew History. 1975. pap. 4.25 (ISBN 0-87148-401-3); instrs. guide 5.25 (ISBN 0-87148-404-8). Pathway Pr.
--Like a Mighty Army. rev. ed. LC 77-82067. 1977. 12.95 (ISBN 0-87148-510-9). Pathway Pr.
--Like a Mighty Army. 1955. 7.95 (ISBN 0-87148-505-2). Pathway Pr.
--Pillars of Pentecost. 148p. 1979. 6.95 (ISBN 0-87148-681-4). Pathway Pr.
--Poets & Prophets of Israel. 1981. 5.25 (ISBN 0-87148-707-1); pap. 4.25 (ISBN 0-87148-708-X). Pathway Pr.
--Rudder & the Rock. 1976. pap. 4.25 (ISBN 0-87148-733-0). Pathway Pr.
--A Survey of the Epistles. 112p. 1969. 5.25 (ISBN 0-87148-007-7); pap. 4.25 (ISBN 0-87148-008-5). Pathway Pr.
--Why Men Go Back. 1983. 6.95 (ISBN 0-87148-902-3); pap. 5.95 (ISBN 0-87148-917-1). Pathway Pr.
Conn, Charles W., jt. auth. see Conn, Charles P.
Conn, Charles W., ed. La Biblia, el Libro de los Libros. (Span.). 116p. 1979. pap. 3.95 (ISBN 0-87148-523-0). Pathway Pr.
--Una Iglesia Blanceada. (Span.). 165p. 1979. pap. 4.95 (ISBN 0-87148-882-5). Pathway Pr.
Conn, Harry. Four Trojan Horses of Humanism. 141p. 1982. pap. 5.95 (ISBN 0-88062-009-9). Mott Media.
Conn, Harvie. Evangelism: Doing Justice & Preaching Grace. 112p. (Orig.). 1982. pap. 4.95 (ISBN 0-310-45311-9, 11646P). Zondervan.
Conn, Harvie M. Contemporary World Theology. 1974. pap. 4.95 (ISBN 0-87552-149-5). Presby & Reformed.
--Eternal Word & Changing Worlds: Theology, Anthropology & Mission in Trialogue. 336p. 1984. pap. 10.95 (ISBN 0-310-45321-6, 11647P). Zondervan.
--Theological Perspectives on Church Growth. 1976. pap. 4.95 (ISBN 0-87552-150-9). Presby & Reformed.
Conn, Harvie M., ed. Reaching the Unreached. (Orig.). 1985. pap. 8.95 (ISBN 0-87552-209-2). Presby & Reformed.
--Reaching the Unreached: The Old-New Challenge. 192p. 1985. 8.95 (ISBN 0-8010-2508-7). Baker Bk.
Conn, Harvie M. & Rowen, Samuel F., eds. Missions & Theological Education in World Perspective. LC 84-72527. 484p. (Orig.). 1984. pap. text ed. 11.95 (ISBN 0-930957-00-8). Assocs Urbanus.
Conn, Joan W., ed. Women's Spirituality: Resources for Christian Development. 336p. (Orig.). 1986. pap. 11.95 (ISBN 0-8091-2752-0). Paulist Pr.
Conn, Robert & Clapp, Steve. Methods of Bible Study. (C-Four Youth Bible Materials Ser.). (Illus.). 91p. (Orig.). 1982. pap. 8.00 (ISBN 0-914527-14-2). C-Four Res.
Conn, Walter E. Conscience: Development & Self-Transcendence. LC 80-24043. 230p. (Orig.). 1981. pap. 12.95 (ISBN 0-89135-025-X). Religious Educ.
--Conversion: Perspectives on Personal & Social Transformation. LC 78-19079. 1978. pap. 10.95 (ISBN 0-8189-0368-6). Alba.
Conn, Walter E., jt. ed. see Swidler, Arlene.
Connally, Andrew M. & Hicks, Olan. Connally-Hicks Debate on Divorce & Remarriage. 1979. pap. 13.00 (ISBN 0-934916-31-4). Natl Christian Pr.
Conne, John. Ignatius His Conclave, or His Inthronisation in a Late Election in Hell. LC 77-6876. (English Experience Ser.: No. 868). 1977. Repr. of 1611 ed. lib. bdg. 11.50 (ISBN 90-221-0868-6). Walter J Johnson.
Connell, Joan. The Roman Catholic Church in England 1780-1850: A Study in Internal Politics. 215p. 1984. 14.00 (ISBN 0-87169-158-2). Am Philos.
Connell, William F. Educational Thought & Influence of Matthew Arnold. LC 74-109305. 1971. Repr. of 1950 ed. lib. bdg. 22.50x (ISBN 0-8371-3580-X, COMA). Greenwood.
Connelly, Douglas. Daniel: Spiritual Living in a Secular World. (LifeBuilder Bible Studies). 64p. (Orig.). 1986. pap. 2.95 (ISBN 0-8308-1031-5). Inter-Varsity.
Connelly, H. W. Forty-Seven Object Lessons for Youth Programs. (Object Lesson Ser). (YA) 1964. pap. 3.95 (ISBN 0-8010-2314-9). Baker Bk.
Connelly, Thomas L. & Bellows, Barbara. God & General Longstreet: The Lost Cause & the Southern Mind. 1982. 14.95 (ISBN 0-8071-1020-5). La State U Pr.
Conner, John T., jt. ed. see Hessel, Dietert T.
Conner, Kevin. Acts. 3rd ed. 136p. 1975. 7.95 (ISBN 0-914936-16-6). Bible Temple.
--The Name of God. (Illus.). 90p. 1975. 8.95 (ISBN 0-914936-15-8). Bible Temple.
--Tabernacle of Moses. 119p. 1974. 7.95 (ISBN 0-914936-08-5). Bible Temple.
Conner, Kevin J. Feasts of Israel. (Illus.). 122p. 1980. pap. 7.95 (ISBN 0-914936-42-5). Bible Temple.
--Foundations of Christian Doctrine. 313p. 1979. pap. 14.95 (ISBN 0-914936-38-7). Bible Temple.
Conner, Kevin J. & Iverson, K. R. Restoring the Church. (Illus.). 92p. 1977. Answer key. pap. 8.95 (ISBN 0-914936-23-9). Bible Temple.
Conner, Kevin J. & Malmin, Ken P. Interpreting the Scriptures. 1976. pap. 9.95 (ISBN 0-914936-20-4). Bible Temple.
Conner, Mona. Christmas at Our House. 64p. 1986. 14.45i (ISBN 0-06-015596-5, HarpT). Har-Row.
Conner, T. Doctrina Cristiana. Robleto, Adolfo, tr. Orig. Title: Christian Doctrine. (Span.). 408p. 1981. pap. 7.50 (ISBN 0-311-09012-5). Casa Bautista.
Conner, Walter T. Christian Doctrine. 1940. 15.95 (ISBN 0-8054-1701-X). Broadman.
Connery, John. Abortion: The Development of the Roman Catholic Perspective. LC 76-51217. 1977. 12.95 (ISBN 0-8294-0257-8). Loyola.
Connery, John, jt. ed. see Malone, Richard.
Connick, C. Milo. Jesus: The Man, the Mission, & the Message. 2nd ed. (Illus.). 512p. 1974. 29.95 (ISBN 0-13-509521-2). P-H.
Connolly, Charles. On Being Catholics. 96p. 1983. pap. 5.00 (ISBN 0-912414-37-5). Lumen Christi.
Connolly, Finbarr. God & Man in Modern Spirituality. 276p. 1984. pap. 9.95 (ISBN 0-87061-108-9). Chr Classics.
Connolly, Finbarr & Burns, Peter. The Ten Commandments & Today's Christian. 48p. 1985. pap. 1.50 (ISBN 0-89243-233-0). Liguori Pubns.

Connolly, J. L. John Gerson: Reformer & Mystic. (Medieval Studies Ser.). (Illus.). Repr. of 1928 ed. lib. bdg. 44.00x (ISBN 0-697-00031-1). Irvington.

Connolly, John R. Dimensions of Belief & Unbelief. LC 80-67241. 373p. 1981. lib. bdg. 30.50 (ISBN 0-8191-1389-1); pap. text ed. 15.75 (ISBN 0-8191-1390-5). U Pr of Amer.

Connolly, Myles. Mister Blue. pap. 3.50 (ISBN 0-385-02866-0, Im). Doubleday.

Connolly, Paul H. Building Family: An Act of Faith. LC 82-74073. 96p. 1982. pap. 4.95 (ISBN 0-87029-186-6, 20277-0). Abbey.

Connolly, Peter. A History of the Jewish People in the Times of Jesus: From Herod the Great to Masada. LC 86-28890. 1987. 15.95. P Bedrick Bks.

--A History of the Jewish People in the Time of Jesus: From Herod the Great to Masada. LC 86-28890. (Illus.). 96p. 1987. 15.95 (ISBN 0-87226-007-0). P Bedrick Bks.

Connolly, Peter, ed. see Werner, Karel.

Connolly, William J., jt. auth. see Barry, William A.

Connor, Elizabeth. Methodist Trail Blazer: Philip Gatch. rev. ed. LC 76-101704. (Illus.). 260p. pap. 12.00 smythsewn (ISBN 0-914960-51-2). Academy Bks.

Connor, Elizabeth, tr. see Aelred of Rievaulx.

Connor, John S. The Spiritual Import of Society. LC 85-91374. 208p. 1987. 10.95 (ISBN 0-533-06881-9). Vantage.

Connor, Paula. Walking in the Garden: Inner Peace from the Flowers of God. (Illus.). 170p. 1984. 14.95 (ISBN 0-13-944280-4); pap. 5.95 (ISBN 0-13-944264-2). P-H.

Connor, W. R., ed. The Acts of the Pagan Martyrs. LC 78-18588. (Greek Texts & Commentaries Ser.). 1979. Repr. of 1954 ed. lib. bdg. 25.50x (ISBN 0-405-11430-3). Ayer Co Pubs.

--Ancient Religion & Mythology, 32 vols. (Illus.). 1976. Set. 1039.00x (ISBN 0-405-07001-2). Ayer Co Pubs.

Connor, W. R., ed. see Brumfield, Allaire C.

Connor, W. R., ed. see Furley, William D.

Connor, W. R., ed. see Philo.

Conomos, Dimitri. Byzantine Hymnography & Byzantine Chant. Vaporis, N. M., intro. by. (Nicholas E. Kulukundis Lectures in Hellenism Ser.). 56p. (Orig.). 1984. pap. text ed. 4.00 (ISBN 0-917653-04-1). Hellenic Coll Pr.

Conomos, Dimitri E. The Late Byzantine & Slavonic Communion Cycle: Liturgy & Music. LC 84-12176. (Dumbarton Oaks Studies: Vol. 21). (Illus.). 222p. 1985. 25.00x (ISBN 0-88402-134-3). Dumbarton Oaks.

Conrad, Edgar W. Fear Not Warrior: A Study of Pericopes in the Hebrew Scriptures. (Brown Judaic Studies). 1985. 30.95 (ISBN 0-89130-864-4, 14-06-75); pap. 25.95 (ISBN 0-89130-865-2). Scholars Pr GA.

Conrad, Geoffrey W. & Demarest, Arthur A. Religion & Empire: The Dynamics of Aztec & Inca Expansionism. LC 83-14414. (New Studies in Archaeology). 256p. 1984. 52.50 (ISBN 0-521-24357-2); pap. 17.95 (ISBN 0-521-31896-3). Cambridge U Pr.

Conrod, John. Computer Bible Games, Bk. 2. LC 83-91269. 160p. (Orig.). (YA) 1984. pap. 6.95 (ISBN 0-89636-141-1). Accent Bks.

Conroy, Charles. First & Second Samuel, First & Second Kings, with Excursus on Davidic Dynasty & Holy City Zion. (Old Testament Message Ser.: Vol. 6). 12.95 (ISBN 0-89453-406-8); pap. 8.95 (ISBN 0-89453-241-3). M Glazier.

Conroy, Michael R. Crusaders. 1975. 19.95 (ISBN 0-915626-02-0). Yellow Jacket.

Conser, Walter H., Jr. Church & Confession: Conservative Theologians in Germany, England, & America, 1815-1866. LC 84-18990. viii, 360p. 1984. 28.95 (ISBN 0-86554-119-1, MUP/H109). Mercer Univ Pr.

Constable, Benjamin. Art, the Metaphysics of Love & Its Universal Mystical Symbols. (Illus.). 1977. 47.25 (ISBN 0-89266-046-5). Am Classical Coll Pr.

--God & the "New" Psychology of Sex. (Illus.). 265p. 1976. 53.75 (ISBN 0-89266-043-0). Am Classical Coll Pr.

--The Mystical Symbolism of Universal Love. (Illus.). 1978. 47.50 (ISBN 0-89266-113-5). Am Classical Coll Pr.

Constable, David, tr. see Calvin, Jean.

Constable, G. & Smith, B., eds. Libellus De Diversis Ordinibus et Professionibus Qui Sunt in Aecclesia: Orders & Callings of the Church. (Oxford Medieval Texts Ser). 1972. 45.00x (ISBN 0-19-822218-1). Oxford u Pr.

Constable, Giles. Attitudes Toward Self-Inflicted Suffering in the Middle Ages. (Stephen J. Brademas Lectures Ser.). 28p. (Orig.). pap. text ed. 2.50 (ISBN 0-916586-87-1). Hellenic Coll Pr.

--Medieval Monasticism: A Select Bibliography. LC 75-42284. 1976. 20.00x (ISBN 0-8020-2200-6). U of Toronto Pr.

Constable, Giles, ed. see Peter The Venerable.

Constandse, William. Why I Became a Buddhist. 130p. (Orig.). 1985. pap. 6.95 (ISBN 0-911527-02-8). Utama Pubns Inc.

Constant, A. L. Dictionnaire de la Litterature Chretienne, Vol. 7. Migne, J. P., ed. (Nouvelle Encyclopedie Theologique Ser.). (Fr.). 626p. Repr. of 1851 ed. lib. bdg. 80.00x (ISBN 0-89241-257-7). Caratzas.

Constant, Gustave L. The Reformation in England. Scantlebury, R. E., tr. LC 83-45576. Date not set. Repr. of 1934 ed. 85.00 (ISBN 0-404-19895-3). AMS Pr.

Constantelos, D. J. Marriage, Sexuality & Celibacy: A Greek Orthodox Perspective. 1975. pap. 4.95 (ISBN 0-937032-15-8). Light&Life Pub Co MN.

Constantelos, Demetrios J. Understanding the Greek Orthodox Church: Its Faith, History & Practice. 214p. 1982. (HarpR); pap. 9.95 (ISBN 0-8164-2367-9). Har-Row.

Constantelos, Demetrios J., intro. by. Orthodox Theology & Diakonia: Trends & Prospects. 398p. 1981. 24.95 (ISBN 0-916586-79-0); pap. 17.95 (ISBN 0-916586-80-4). Hellenic Coll Pr.

Constantine, Archimandrite. Antichrist, Orthodoxy or Heterodoxy. pap. 0.25 (ISBN 0-686-11505-8). Eastern Orthodox.

Constantine I. A Treatise of the Donation of Gyfts & Endowment of Possessyons Gyven & Graunted Unto Sylvester Pope of Rome by Constantyne Emperour of Rome. Marshall, William, tr. LC 79-84096. (English Experience Ser.: No. 916). (Eng.). 152p. 1979. Repr. of 1534 ed. lib. bdg. 24.00 (ISBN 90-221-0916-X). Walter J Johnson.

Conte, Joseph Le see Le Conte, Joseph.

Contemporary Testimony Committee of the Christian Reformed Church. Our World Belongs to God: A Contemporary Testimony (Study Version) 1984. pap. 1.00 (ISBN 0-933140-91-6). CRC Pubns.

Continental Association of Funeral & Memorial Societies, Inc & Memorial Society Association of Canadacompiled by. Handbook for Funeral & Memorial Societies. Fleming, Peggy, ed. LC 72-7963. 1976. pap. 3.50 (ISBN 0-686-18088-7). Continent Assn Funeral.

Contos, Leonidas C. Two Thousand & One the Church in Crisis. 60p. 1981. pap. 2.95 (ISBN 0-916586-46-4). Holy Cross Orthodox.

Contreras, Edgar. Y Despues de la Muerte, Que? Orig. Title: After Death, What. (Span.). 1988. pap. 4.95 (ISBN 0-8254-1130-0). Kregel.

Conway, Anne. The Principles of the Most Ancient & Modern Philosophy. 1982. 35.00 (ISBN 90-247-2671-9, Pub. by Martinus Nijhoff Netherlands). Kluwer Academic.

Conway, Bertrand L., tr. see Vacandard, Elphege.

Conway, Charles A., Jr. The Vita Christi of Ludolph of Saxony & Late Medieval Devotion Centered on the Incarnation: A Descriptive Analysis. Hogg, James, ed. (Analecta Cartusiana Ser.: No. 34). 153p. (Orig.). 1976. pap. 25.00 (ISBN 3-7052-0036-4, Pub. by Salzburg Studies). Longwood Pub Group.

Conway, Flo & Siegelman, Jim. Holy Terror: The Fundamentalist War on America's Freedoms in Religion, Politics, & Our Private Lives. 504p. 1984. pap. 10.95 (ISBN 0-385-29286-4, Delta). Dell.

Conway, Jim. Los Hombres En Su Crisis de Media Vida. Orig. Title: Men in Mid-Life Crisis. (Span.). 256p. 1982. pap. 5.95 (ISBN 0-311-46088-7, Edit Mundo). Casa Bautista.

Conway, Jim & Conway, Sally. La Mujer en su Crisis de Media Vida. De Zorzoli, Alicia, tr. from Span. Tr. of Women in Mid-Life Crisis. 352p. 1985. pap. 6.50 (ISBN 0-311-46105-0). Casa Bautista.

Conway, Moncure D. Demonology & Devil-Lore, 2 vols. Set. 250.00 (ISBN 0-8490-0017-3). Gordon Pr.

--Solomon & Solomonic Literature. LC 72-2032. (Studies in Comparative Literature, No. 35). 1972. Repr. of 1899 ed. lib. bdg. 49.95x (ISBN 0-8383-1478-3). Haskell.

Conway, Robert S. Ancient Italy & Modern Religion. LC 77-27141. (Hibbert Lectures: 1932). Repr. of 1933 ed. 17.00 (ISBN 0-404-60428-5). AMS Pr.

Conway, Sally, jt. auth. see Conway, Jim.

Conwell, Russell H. Acres of Diamonds. 64p. 1975. pap. 2.50 (ISBN 0-8007-8091-4, Spire Bks). Revell.

Conybeare, F. C. & Stock, George, eds. Selections from the Septuagint. (College Classical Ser.). vi, 313p. 1981. lib. bdg. 25.00x (ISBN 0-89241-366-2); pap. 12.50 (ISBN 0-89241-114-7). Caratzas.

Conybeare, Fred C. The Key of Truth. cancelled 93.00 (ISBN 0-686-12403-0). Church History.

Conybeare, Frederick C. & Stock, G. A Grammar of Septuagint Greek. 80p. 1980. pap. 6.95 (ISBN 0-310-43001-1, 6652P). Zondervan.

Conybeare, W. J. & Howson, J. S. Life & Epistles of St. Paul. 1949. 16.95 (ISBN 0-8028-8086-X). Eerdmans.

--The Life & Epistles of St. Paul. 1977. lib. bdg. 59.95 (ISBN 0-8490-2160-X). Gordon Pr.

Conyers, A. J. How to Read the Bible. LC 85-23173. (How to Read Ser.). 216p. (Orig.). 1986. pap. 6.95 (ISBN 0-87784-944-7). Inter-Varsity.

Conze, Edward. Buddha's Law among the Birds. 1986. Repr. 8.00 (ISBN 81-208-0198-9, Pub. by Motilal Banarsidass). South Asia Bks.

--Buddhism: Its Essence & Development. 17.50 (ISBN 0-8446-1889-6). Peter Smith.

--Buddhism: It's Essence & Development. 1982. pap. 6.95x (ISBN 0-06-130058-6, TB 58, Torch). Har-Row.

--Buddhism: Its Essence & Development. 221p. 1975. 25.00x (ISBN 0-317-39041-4, Pub. by Luzac & Co Ltd). State Mutual Bk.

--Buddhist Studies Nineteen Thirty-Four to Nineteen Seventy-Two. 512p. 1977. Repr. 20.00 (ISBN 0-686-48400-2). Wheelwright Pr.

--Buddhist Thought in India. 1967. pap. 8.95 (ISBN 0-472-06129-1, 129, AA). U of Mich Pr.

--Further Buddhist Studies: Selected Essays. 238p. 1975. 40.00x (ISBN 0-317-39071-6, Pub. by Luzac & Co Ltd). State Mutual Bk.

--The Large Sutra on Perfect Wisdom: With the Divisions of the Abhisamayalankara. LC 71-189224. (Center for South & Southeastern Asia Studies, UC Berkeley). 697p. 1985. pap. 12.95 (ISBN 0-520-05321-4, CAL 668). U of Cal Pr.

--The Short Prajnaparamita Texts. 217p. 1973. 35.00x (ISBN 0-317-39153-4, Pub. by Luzac & Co Ltd). State Mutual Bk.

--Thirty Years of Buddhist Studies. 274p. 1967. 40.00x (ISBN 0-317-39172-0, Pub. by Luzac & Co Ltd). State Mutual Bk.

Conze, Edward & Lancaster, Lewis, eds. Buddhist Scriptures: A Bibliography. LC 77-83380. (Reference Library of the Humanities: Vol. 113). 161p. 1982. lib. bdg. 31.00 (ISBN 0-8240-9848-X). Garland Pub.

Conze, Edward, tr. Buddhist Scriptures. (Classics Ser.). (Orig.). 1959. pap. 5.95 (ISBN 0-14-044088-7). Penguin.

Conze, Edward, tr. from Sanskrit. & pref. by. The Perfection of Wisdom in Eight Thousand Lines & Its Verse Summary. LC 72-76540. (Wheel Ser.: No. 1). 348p. 1973. 15.00 (ISBN 0-87704-048-6); pap. 8.95 (ISBN 0-87704-049-4). Four Seasons Foun.

Conze, Edward, et al. Buddhist Texts Through the Ages. 322p. 1985. Repr. of 1964 ed. 20.00x (ISBN 0-317-39042-2, Pub. by Luzac & Co Ltd). State Mutual Bk.

Conzelmann, Hans. Acts. LC 86-45203. 368p. 1987. pap. 37.95 (ISBN 0-8006-6018-8, 20-6018). Fortress.

--First Corinthians. MacRae, George W., ed. Leitch, James W., tr. from Ger. LC 73-88360. (Hermeneia: a Critical & Historical Commentary on the Bible). 352p. 1975. 25.95x (ISBN 0-8006-6005-6, 20-6005). Fortress.

--History of Primitive Christianity. Steely, John E., tr. from Ger. LC 72-8818. Orig. Title: Geschichte Des Unchristentums. 192p. 1973. pap. 8.95 (ISBN 0-687-17252-7). Abingdon.

--Jesus. Reumann, John, ed. Lord, J. Raymond, tr. from Gr. LC 73-79011. 128p. 1973. pap. 4.25 (ISBN 0-8006-1000-8, 1-1000). Fortress.

--The Theology of St. Luke. LC 82-2372. 256p. 1982. pap. 9.95 (ISBN 0-8006-1650-2, 1-1650). Fortress.

Conzelmann, Hans & Lindemann, Andreas. Arbeitsbuch zum Neuen Testament. 8th ed. 474p. (Orig.). 1986. pap. 22.00x (ISBN 3-16-145007-8, Pub. by J C B Mohr BRD). Coronet Bks.

Conzelmann, Hans, jt. auth. see Dibelius, Martin.

Cooey, Paula M. Jonathan Edwards on Nature & Destiny: A Systematic Analysis. LC 85-21499. (Studies in American Religion: Vol. 16). 296p. 1985. lib. bdg. 49.95x (ISBN 0-88946-660-2). E Mellen.

Cook. New Testament Holiness. 4.95 (ISBN 0-686-12895-8). Schmul Pub Co.

--Osiris. 1979. Repr. of 1931 ed. 12.50 (ISBN 0-89005-287-5). Ares.

Cook, A. S. Biblical Quotations in Old English Prose Writers. 59.95 (ISBN 0-87968-731-2). Gordon Pr.

Cook, Albert S. The Bible & English Prose Style. LC 72-192049. Repr. of 1892 ed. lib. bdg. 8.50 (ISBN 0-8414-1134-4). Folcroft.

--Biblical Quotations in Old English Prose Writers. LC 74-2465. 1898. lib. bdg. 40.00 (ISBN 0-8414-3552-9). Folcroft.

--Biblical Quotations in Old English Prose Writers: Second Series. LC 74-7275. 1903. lib. bdg. 40.00 (ISBN 0-686-96720-8). Folcroft.

Cook, Albert S., ed. see Cynewulf.

Cook, Anna. The Isness of Your Life. (Illus.). 56p. 1986. pap. 3.95 (ISBN 0-936029-03-X). Western Bk Journ.

--Powerful Petite Prayers. 3rd ed. LC 85-52398. (Illus.). 112p. 1986. pap. 4.95 (ISBN 0-936029-02-1). Western Bk Journ.

Cook, Arthur B. Zeus: A Study of Ancient Religion, 2 vols. Incl. Vol. 1. Zeus, God of the Bright Sky. LC 64-25839. (Illus.). 885p. Repr. of 1914 ed. 50.00x (ISBN 0-8196-0148-9); Vol. 2. Zeus, God of the Dark Sky: Thunder & Lightning, 2 pts. LC 64-25839. Repr. of 1925 ed. 100.00xset (ISBN 0-8196-0156-X); Vol. 2, Pt. 1. Text & Notes. xliii, 858p; Vol. 2, Pt. 2. Appendixes & Index. (Illus.). 539p. Biblo.

Cook, Barbara. How to Raise Good Kids. LC 78-7844. 192p. 1978. pap. 4.95 (ISBN 0-87123-233-2, 210233). Bethany Hse.

Cook, Bill J. Saints & Sinners. 64p. 1981. pap. 3.95 (ISBN 0-938400-05-3). Donahoe Pubs.

Cook, Blanche, et al. Sermons on War by Theodore Parker. LC 70-149546. (Library of War & Peace; Relig. & Ethical Positions on War). 1973. lib. bdg. 46.00 (ISBN 0-8240-0499-X). Garland Pub.

Cook, Bob. Speaking in Tongues: Is That All There Is? (Discovery Bks.). (Illus.). 48p. (YA) 1982. pap. text ed. 1.50 (ISBN 0-88243-932-4, 02-0932); tchr's ed. 3.95 (02-0935). Gospel Pub.

--Today with the King. 408p. 1985. 12.95 (ISBN 0-89693-364-4). Victor Bks.

Cook, Bruce L., jt. auth. see Oosterveen, Gerald.

Cook, Catherine E., ed. see Carus, Paul.

Cook, Charles, ed. Daily Meditations for Prayer. Gift Ed. 9.95 (ISBN 0-89107-160-1). Good News.

Cook, Charles T, ed. see Spurgeon, Charles H.

Cook, Charles T., ed. see Spurgeon, Charles H.

Cook, Charles T, ed. see Spurgeon, Charles H.

Cook, Charles T., ed. see Spurgeon, Charles H.

Cook, David. Thinking about Faith: An Introductory Guide to Philosophy & Religion. 1986. pap. 8.95 (ISBN 0-310-44131-5). Zondervan.

Cook, David A., tr. see Henrichsen, Walter A.

Cook, David A., tr. see Stott, John R.

Cook, David A., tr. see Wagner, Maurice.

Cook, E. A. Scottish Rite Masonry, 2 vols. Set. 20.00x (ISBN 0-685-22097-4). Wehman.

Cook, E. H. Knight Templarism. 9.50 (ISBN 0-685-19481-7). Powner.

Cook, Ellen. Sharing the Journey. 1986. pap. 6.95 (ISBN 0-697-02208-0). Wm C Brown.

Cook, F. C., ed. The Bible Commentary, 10 vols. 6803p. 1981. Repr. 195.00 (ISBN 0-8010-2431-5). Baker Bk.

Cook, Francis H. Hua-Yen Buddhism: The Jewel Net of Indra. LC 76-43288. (Institute for Advanced Study of World Religions Ser.). 1977. 19.95x (ISBN 0-271-01245-5). Pa St U Pr.

Cook, Gene R. Living by the Power of Faith. 120p. 1985. 8.95 (ISBN 0-87747-745-0). Deseret Bk.

Cook, Gregory D., jt. auth. see Goodwin, Wayne.

Cook, Guillermo. The Expectation of the Poor: Latin American Base Ecclesial Communities in Protestant Perspective. LC 85-5131. 256p. (Orig.). 1985. pap. 13.95 (ISBN 0-88344-209-4). Orbis Bks.

Cook, J. Keith. The First Parish: A Pastor's Survival Manual. LC 83-6940. 154p. (Orig.). 1983. pap. 8.95 (ISBN 0-664-24442-4). Westminster.

Cook, James I., ed. Saved by Hope: Essays in Honor of Richard C. Oudersluys. LC 78-5416. Repr. of 1978 ed. 49.50 (ISBN 0-8357-9132-7, 2016060). Bks Demand UMI.

Cook, Jean T. Hugs for Our New Baby. (Illus.). 1987. 3.95 (ISBN 0-570-04165-1). Concordia.

Cook, Jerry O., ed. see Taylor, Blaine, et al.

Cook, Keningale. The Fathers of Jesus: A Study of the Lineage of the Christian Doctrine & Tradition, 2 vols. 1977. lib. bdg. 250.00 (ISBN 0-8490-1807-2). Gordon Pr.

Cook, Lewis C., ed. see Pollard, Stewart M.

Cook, Lyndon W. Joseph Smith & the Law of Consecration. 100p. 1985. 8.95 (ISBN 0-910523-24-X). E B Grandin.

Cook, Lyndon W. & Cannon, Donald Q. A New Light Breaks Forth. pap. 7.95 (ISBN 0-89036-148-7). Hawkes Pub Inc.

Cook, Lyndon W., jt. ed. see Cannon, Donald Q.

Cook, M. Early Muslim Dogma. 256p. 1981. 54.50 (ISBN 0-521-23379-8). Cambridge U Pr.

Cook, M., jt. auth. see Crone, Patricia.

Cook, Madison D. Biographical Concordance of the New Testament. 216p. 1984. pap. 8.95 (ISBN 0-87213-089-4). Loizeaux.

Cook, Margaret, tr. see Detienne, Marcel.

Cook, Melva, jt. auth. see Hinkle, Joseph.

Cook, Michael. Muhammad. (Past Masters Ser.). (Illus.). 1983. 13.95x (ISBN 0-19-287606-6); pap. 4.95 (ISBN 0-19-287605-8). Oxford U Pr.

Cook, Michael L. The Historical Jesus. (Guidelines for Contemporary Catholics). (Orig.). 1986. pap. 7.95 (ISBN 0-88347-188-4). Thomas More.

--The Jesus of Faith: A Study in Christology. LC 80-84510. 192p. (Orig.). pap. 6.95 (ISBN 0-8091-2349-5). Paulist Pr.

Cook, Paul E. Communion Handbook. 96p. 1980. 5.95 (ISBN 0-8170-0877-2). Judson.

Cook, R. Franklin & Weber, Steve. The Greening: The Story of Nazarene Compassionate Ministries. 104p. (Orig.). 1986. pap. 3.95 (ISBN 0-8341-1130-6). Beacon Hill.

Cook, Robert. Ahora que Creo. Orig. Title: Now That I Believe. (Span.). 128p. 1984. pap. 3.25 (ISBN 0-8254-1137-8). Kregel.

Cook, Robert A. Now That I Believe: New King James Version. 1986. pap. text ed. 2.95 (ISBN 0-8024-5983-8). Moody.

Cook, S. A. The Religion of Ancient Palestine in the Light of Archaeology. (British Academy, London, Schweich Lectures on Biblical Archaeology Series, 1925). pap. 28.00 (ISBN 0-8115-1267-3). Kraus Repr.

Cook, Shirley. The Marriage Puzzle. 128p. (Orig.). 1985. pap. 5.95 (ISBN 0-310-33611-2, 11742P). Zondervan.

Cook, Stanley A. An Introduction to the Bible. LC 78-12762. 1979. Repr. of 1945 ed. lib. bdg. 22.50x (ISBN 0-313-21028-4, COIB). Greenwood.

--The Old Testament. 1936. 39.50 (ISBN 0-8274-3060-4). R West.

--The Religion of Ancient Palestine. 122p. 1921. 0.95 (ISBN 0-317-40429-6). Open Court.

Cook, Walter L. Table Prayers for the Family Circle. 96p. (Orig.). 1982. pap. 3.45 (ISBN 0-8010-2471-4). Baker Bk.

Cook, William H. Success, Motivation, & the Scriptures. new ed. LC 74-82582. 192p. 1975. kivar 6.95 (ISBN 0-8054-5226-5). Broadman.

Cookbook Committee of Holy Trinity Episcopal Church, ed. Not by Bread Alone. (Illus.). 304p. 1985. pap. 11.95 (ISBN 0-9615284-0-0). Holy Episcopal.

Cooke, Bernard. Formation of Faith. LC 65-27619. (Pastoral Ser). 1965. pap. 2.00 (ISBN 0-8294-0014-1). Loyola.

--Ministry to Word & Sacraments: History & Theology. LC 75-36459. 688p. 1980. pap. 16.95 (ISBN 0-8006-1440-2, 1-1440). Fortress.

--Reconciled Sinners: Healing Human Brokenness. 128p. (Orig.). 1986. pap. 4.95 (ISBN 0-89622-284-5). Twenty-Third.

Cooke, Bernard J. Beyond Trinity. (Acquinas Lecutre). 1969. 7.95 (ISBN 0-87462-134-8). Marquette.

Cooke, G. A. A Critical & Exegetical Commentary on Ezekiel. Driver, Samuel R., et al, eds. LC 38-1268. (International Critical Commentary Ser.). 608p. 1936. 24.95 (ISBN 0-567-05016-5, Pub. by T & T Clark Ltd UK). Fortress.

Cooke, George W. Bibliography of Ralph Waldo Emerson. 1908. 32.00 (ISBN 0-527-19250-3). Kraus Repr.

--John Sullivan Dwight: A Biography. LC 79-90210. (Music Reprint Ser). 1969. Repr. of 1898 ed. 39.50 (ISBN 0-306-71818-9). Da Capo.

--The Poets of Transcendentalism: An Anthology. 59.95 (ISBN 0-8490-0868-9). Gordon Pr.

--Ralph Waldo Emerson. LC 74-8996. 1882. lib. bdg. 30.00 (ISBN 0-8414-3367-4). Folcroft.

--Unitarianism in America. LC 72-155153. Repr. of 1902 ed. 12.50 (ISBN 0-404-01699-5). AMS Pr.

Cooke, George W., ed. Poets of Transcendentalism: An Anthology. LC 72-126410. (Literature & Criticism Ser). 1971. Repr. of 1903 ed. lib. bdg. 21.00 (ISBN 0-8337-0652-7). B Franklin.

Cooke, Grace. The Illumined Ones. (Illus.). 1966. pap. 6.95 (ISBN 0-85487-058-X). De Vorss.

--The Jewel in the Lotus. 1973. pap. 5.95 (ISBN 0-85487-032-6). De Vorss.

--Meditation. 1955. pap. 4.95 (ISBN 0-85487-059-8). De Vorss.

--Sun Men of the Americas. pap. 5.95 (ISBN 0-85487-057-1). De Vorss.

Cooke, Grace & Cooke, Ivan. The Light in Britain. (Illus.). 1971. pap. 5.95 (ISBN 0-85487-056-3). De Vorss.

--The Return of Arthur Conan Doyle. (Illus.). 1963. 9.95 (ISBN 0-85487-037-7). De Vorss.

Cooke, Ivan. Healing by the Spirit. 1955. pap. 7.95 (ISBN 0-85487-039-3). De Vorss.

Cooke, Ivan, jt. auth. see Cooke, Grace.

Cooke, John. John Milton: 1608-1674. LC 74-5138. 1973. Repr. of 1908 ed. lib. bdg. 10.00 (ISBN 0-8414-3549-9). Folcroft.

Cooke, M., ed. see Grosseteste, Robert.

Cookson, Catherine. The Glass Virgin. 352p. 1981. pap. 3.95 (ISBN 0-552-08849-8). Bantam.

Coole, Arthur B. A Trouble Shooter for God in China. (Illus.). 1976. 20.00 (ISBN 0-912706-05-8). M Akers.

Cooley, Doris H., ed. Ritual of Music. 12p. 1968. pap. text ed. 1.00 (ISBN 0-88053-318-8, S-79). Macoy Pub.

Cooley, Everett L., ed. Diary of Brigham Young, 1857. 105p. 1980. 17.50 (ISBN 0-941214-37-0). Signature Bks.

Cooley, Frank L., jt. ed. see Haines, Byron L.

Coolidge, Edna M. Celestial Gems Books, Vol. 1. rev. ed. LC 73-88209. 150p. 10.00 (ISBN 0-914154-00-1). Celestial Gems.

--Celestial Gems Books, Vols. 2-3. LC 73-88209. (Illus.). 48p. 1972. spiral bdg. 10.00 ea. Vol. 2 (ISBN 0-914154-01-X). Celestial Gems.

--Celestial Gems Books, Vol. 4. LC 73-88209. 65p. 1974. spiral bdg. 10.00 (ISBN 0-914154-03-6). Celestial Gems.

--Celestial Gems Books, Vols. 5-6. LC 73-88209. (Illus.). 150p. 1975. 10.00 ea.; Vol. 5. (ISBN 0-914154-05-2). Celestial Gems.

Coolidge, Grace. Teepee Neighbors. LC 83-40487. 200p. 1984. pap. 7.95 (ISBN 0-8061-1889-X). U of Okla Pr.

Coolidge, Olivia. Greek Myths. (Illus.). 256p. 1949. 13.95 (ISBN 0-395-06721-9). HM.

Coomara, Swamy M., intro. by. Sutta Nipata: Or Dialogues & Discourses of Gotama Buddha. LC 78-70125. 1980. Repr. of 1874 ed. 23.00 (ISBN 0-404-17384-5). AMS Pr.

Coomaraswamy, A. K. & Noble, M. E. Myths of the Hindus & Buddhists. (Illus.). 15.25 (ISBN 0-8446-1896-9). Peter Smith.

Coomaraswamy, Ananda K. Am I My Brother's Keeper? facs. ed. LC 67-23196. (Essay Index Reprint Ser.). 1947. 12.00 (ISBN 0-8369-0335-8). Ayer Co Pubs.

--Buddha & the Gospel of Buddhism. (Illus.). 1975. text ed. 17.00x. Coronet Bks.

--Christian & Oriental Philosophy of Art. 1957. pap. 3.95 (ISBN 0-486-20378-6). Dover.

--Elements of Buddhist Iconography. (Illus.). 1979. text ed. 23.00x. Coronet Bks.

--Hinduism & Buddhism. LC 78-138215. 1971. Repr. of 1943 ed. lib. bdg. 22.50x (ISBN 0-8371-5570-3, COHB). Greenwood.

--Spiritual Authority & Temporal Power in the Indian Theory of Government. (Amer Oriental Soc Ser.). 1942. pap. 16.00 (ISBN 0-527-02696-4). Kraus Repr.

Coomaraswamy, Ananda K. & Horner, I. B. The Living Thoughts of Gotama, the Buddha. LC 78-72397. Repr. of 1948 ed. 34.50 (ISBN 0-404-17256-3). AMS Pr.

Coomaraswamy, Ananda K. & Nivedita, Sr. Myths of the Hindus & Buddhists. (Illus.). 400p. pap. 6.95 (ISBN 0-486-21759-0). Dover.

Coombe, Jack. The Temptation. 1984. pap. 6.95 (ISBN 0-89896-127-0). Larksdale.

Coombs, H. Samm. Teenage Survival Manual: How to Enjoy the Trip to Twenty. (Illus.). 1978. pap. 5.95 (ISBN 0-87516-277-0). De Vorss.

Coombs, Marie T., jt. auth. see Nemeck, Francis K.

Coombs, Robert S. & Perry, Iris. Of Such Is the Kingdom: Sermons for Children. (Object Lesson Ser.). 96p. (Orig.). 1987. pap. 4.95 (ISBN 0-8010-2518-4). Baker Bk.

Cooney, Barbara. Christmas. LC 67-18510. (Holiday Ser.). (Illus.). 1967. PLB 12.89i (ISBN 0-690-19201-0, Crowell Jr Bks). HarpJ.

Cooney, Ellen. The Quest for the Holy Grail. LC 80-67333. 85p. (Orig.). 1981. pap. 5.95 (ISBN 0-9602912-3-7). Duir Press.

Cooney, John. The American Pope: The Life & Times of Francis Cardinal Spellman. (Illus.). 448p. 1986. pap. 4.50 (ISBN 0-440-10194-8). Dell.

--The American Pope: The Life & Times of Francis Cardinal Spellman 1889-1967. LC 84-40096. (Illus.). 416p. 1984. 19.95 (ISBN 0-8129-1120-2). Times Bks.

Cooney, Nancy H. Sex, Sexuality, & You: A Handbook for Growing Christians. 100p. (Orig.). 1980. pap. text ed. 3.50 (ISBN 0-697-01741-9); tchrs.' resource guide 1.00 (ISBN 0-697-01742-7). Wm C Brown.

Cooney, Randy. Reaching, Touching, Teaching: How to Run Successful Days of Retreat. 1986. pap. 15.95 (ISBN 0-697-02199-8). Wm C Brown.

Cooney, Sean, jt. auth. see Wakin, Edward.

Cooney, Timothy J. Telling Right from Wrong: What Is Moral, What Is Immoral & What Is Neither One Nor the Other. 158p. 1985. 18.95 (ISBN 0-87975-297-1). Prometheus Bks.

Coop, William L. Pacific People Sing Out Strong. (Orig.). 1982. pap. 4.95 (ISBN 0-377-00118-X). Friend Pr.

Cooper & Oakley. Masonry & Medieval Mysticism. pap. 9.25 (ISBN 0-8356-5301-3). Theos Pub Hse.

--Masonry & Medieval Mysticism. 12.95 (ISBN 0-8356-5309-9). Theos Pub Hse.

Cooper, A. A. An Inquiry Concerning Virtue, or Merit. Walford, D. E., ed. 152p. 1977. 23.00 (ISBN 0-7190-0657-0, Pub. by Manchester Univ Pr). Longwood Pub Group.

Cooper, Barry. Michel Foucault: An Introduction to the Study of His Thought. LC 82-8260. (Studies in Religion & Society: Vol. 2). 176p. 1982. 39.95x (ISBN 0-88946-867-2). E Mellen.

--The Political Theory of Eric Voegelin. LC 86-23517. (Toronto Studies in Theology: Vol. 21). 256p. 1986. text ed. 49.95 (ISBN 0-88946-771-4). E Mellen.

Cooper, Brian G. Meeting Famous Christians. (Illus.). 111p. 1977. pap. text ed. 3.50 (ISBN 0-85597-205-X). Attic Pr.

Cooper, Dale. Sermon on the Mount: A Study Guide. (Revelation Series for Adults). 1981. pap. text ed. 2.50 (ISBN 0-933140-22-3). CRC Pubns.

Cooper, Dale J. Psalms: A Study Guide. (Revelation Series for Adults). 1979. pap. text ed. 2.50 (ISBN 0-933140-08-8). CRC Pubns.

Cooper, Darien. How to Be Happy Though Young. (Illus.). 224p. 1979. 5.95 (ISBN 0-8007-5048-9, Power Bks). Revell.

Cooper, Darien B. The Beauty of Beholding God. 168p. 1982. pap. 5.95 (ISBN 0-88207-350-8). Victor Bks.

--The Christian Woman's Planner. 160p. (Orig.). 1986. pap. 8.95 spiral bdg. (ISBN 0-310-44621-X, 11742P). Zondervan.

--You Can Be the Wife of a Happy Husband. LC 74-77450. 156p. 1974. pap. 5.95 (ISBN 0-88207-711-2). Victor Bks.

Cooper, Davis. Daily Devotions for Newlyweds. LC 81-67204. 1983. 8.95 (ISBN 0-8054-5646-5). Broadman.

Cooper, Douglas. Living God's Love. LC 74-27171. (Redwood Ser.). 1975. pap. 4.95 (ISBN 0-8163-0176-X, 12523-7). Pacific Pr Pub Assn.

--Living in Our Finest Hour. Phillips, Max, ed. (RWD Ser.). 112p. 1982. pap. 4.95 (ISBN 0-8163-0465-3). Pacific Pr Pub Assn.

--Living Spirit-Filled Life. (Red Ser.). 1985. pap. 4.95 (ISBN 0-8163-0595-1). Pacific Pr Pub Assn.

--Living We've Just Begun. (Redwood Ser.). 96p. 1983. pap. 4.95 (ISBN 0-8163-0505-6). Pacific Pr Pub Assn.

Cooper, Duff. Talleyrand. 1932. 25.00x (ISBN 0-8047-0616-6). Stanford U Pr.

Cooper, Eli L. Am Seguliah: A Treasured People. LC 82-91010. 148p. 1984. 10.00 (ISBN 0-533-05673-X). Vantage.

--Insights to Scripture. 196p. (Orig.). 1986. lib. bdg. 24.00 (ISBN 0-8191-5121-1); pap. text ed. 10.25 (ISBN 0-8191-5122-X). U Pr of Amer.

Cooper, Elizabeth. Harim & the Purdah: Studies of Oriental Women. LC 68-23147. 312p. 1975. Repr. of 1915 ed. 43.00x (ISBN 0-8103-3167-5). Gale.

Cooper, Guy H. Development & Stress in Navajo Religion. 126p. (Orig.). 1984. pap. text ed. 20.00x (ISBN 91-7146-337-2). Coronet Bks.

Cooper, Harold. Believing Truth about the Church. (Illus.). 122p. 1975. pap. 3.50 (ISBN 0-89114-070-0); P. 64. tchr's ed. 1.00 (ISBN 0-89114-071-9). Baptist Pub Hse.

--Doctrines from the Beloved Disciple: Outlined Gospel of John. 137p. 1972. pap. 1.00 (ISBN 0-89114-054-9). Baptist Pub Hse.

--Living Jesus. (Illus.). 1977. PBK:106. pap. text ed. 1.50 (ISBN 0-89114-077-8); PBK:48. tchrs. ed. 1.00 (ISBN 0-89114-078-6). Baptist Pub Hse.

--Loving Truth about Jesus. 136p. 1976. pap. 1.50 (ISBN 0-89114-100-6); tchr's ed 1.00 (ISBN 0-89114-101-4). Baptist Pub Hse.

--True Service. (Illus.). 111p. 1978. pap. text ed. 1.50 (ISBN 0-89114-081-6); P. 55. tchrs. ed. 1.25 (ISBN 0-89114-082-4). Baptist Pub Hse.

Cooper, Helen. Pastoral: Mediaeval into Renaissance. 257p. 1977. 32.50x (ISBN 0-87471-906-2). Rowman.

Cooper, Irving S. Ceremonies of the Liberal Catholic Rite. 2nd ed. (Illus.). 225p. 1981. Repr. of 1934 ed. 16.50 (ISBN 0-935461-07-8). St Alban Pr CA.

--Reincarnation: A Hope of the World. LC 79-11475. 1979. pap. 3.95 (ISBN 0-8356-0528-0, Quest). Theos Pub Hse.

--Secret of Happiness. LC 75-26815. 75p. 1976. pap. 1.75 (ISBN 0-8356-0469-1, Quest). Theos Pub Hse.

--Theosophy Simplified. 59.95 (ISBN 0-8490-1191-4). Gordon Pr.

--Theosophy Simplified. new ed. LC 78-64905. 1979. pap. 3.25 (ISBN 0-8356-0519-1, Quest). Theos Pub Hse.

Cooper, J. C. An Illustrated Encyclopaedia of Traditional Symbols. LC 78-55429. (Illus.). 208p. 1987. pap. 12.95 (ISBN 0-500-27125-9). Thames Hudson.

--Symbolism: The Universal Language. LC 86-18838. 176p. 1986. lib. bdg. 19.95x (ISBN 0-8095-7001-7). Borgo Pr.

--Taoism: The Way of the Mystic. 1973. pap. 7.95 (ISBN 0-85030-096-7). Weiser.

Cooper, John M. The Northern Algonquian Supreme Being. LC 76-43682. (Catholic University of America Anthropological Ser.: No. 2). Repr. of 1934 ed. 14.00 (ISBN 0-404-15515-4). AMS Pr.

Cooper, John W. The Theology of Freedom: The Legacy of Jacque Maritain & Reinhold Niebuhr. ix, 186p. 1985. text ed. 16.95 (ISBN 0-86554-172-8, MUP-H162). Mercer Univ Pr.

Cooper, Joyce. I Shall Fear No Evil. 1986. 8.95 (ISBN 0-317-43335-0). Vantage.

Cooper, L., ed. Concordance of the Latin, Greek, & Italian Poems of John Milton. Repr. of 1923 ed. 18.00 (ISBN 0-527-19440-9). Kraus Repr.

Cooper, Mildred & Fanning, Martha. What Every Woman Still Knows: A Celebration of the Christian Liberated Woman. LC 78-17182. 182p. 1978. 7.95 (ISBN 0-87131-271-9). M Evans.

Cooper, Nancy, jt. auth. see Bin-Nun, Judy.

Cooper, Neil. The Diversity of Moral Thinking. (CLLP Ser.). (Illus.). 1981. text ed. 45.00x (ISBN 0-19-824423-1). Oxford U Pr.

Cooper, Norman W. Finding Your Self. new ed. 96p. 1974. pap. 4.50 (ISBN 0-87516-183-9). De Vorss.

Cooper, Thomas. An Answer in Defence of the Truth Against the Apology of Private Mass. 1850. 21.00 (ISBN 0-384-09790-1). Johnson Repr.

Cooper, Thomas J. Guidebook to Biblical Truth. Cooper, Willia S., ed. (Make the Path Clear Ser.: Vol. 1). 99p. (Orig.). 1984. pap. 4.95 (ISBN 0-931429-01-3). Cooper & Cooper Pub.

--Guidebook to Biblical Truth. Cooper, Willia S., ed. (The Ministry of Women in God's Plan Ser.: Vol. 6). 50p. (Orig.). 1985. pap. 4.00 (ISBN 0-931429-06-4). Cooper & Cooper Pub.

--Guidebook to Biblical Truth. Cooper, Willia S., ed. (The Master of Light & Darkness Ser.: Vol. 5). 70p. (Orig.). 1985. pap. 4.75 (ISBN 0-931429-05-6). Cooper & Cooper Pub.

Cooper, Thomas J. & Cooper, Willia S. Christian Message for Today. (Guidebook to Biblical Truth Ser.: Vol. 3). 60p. (Orig.). 1984. pap. 4.50 (ISBN 0-931429-03-X, TXU 109-949). Cooper & Cooper Pub.

--Guidebook to Biblical Truth. (Stewardship Ser.: Vol. 4). 60p. (Orig.). 1985. Set. write for info. (ISBN 0-931429-00-5); Vol. 4. pap. 4.50 (ISBN 0-931429-04-8). Cooper & Cooper Pub.

Cooper, W. Norman. Dance with God. LC 81-69932. 128p. (Orig.). 1982. 7.50 (ISBN 0-87516-491-9); pap. 4.50 (ISBN 0-87516-468-4). De Vorss.

--The Ultimate Destination. 95p. 1980. 7.50 (ISBN 0-87516-413-7); pap. 4.50 (ISBN 0-87516-381-5). De Vorss.

Cooper, Willia S., jt. auth. see Cooper, Thomas J.

Cooper, Willia S., ed. see Cooper, Thomas J.

Cooper, William R. Archaic Dictionary. LC 73-76018. 688p. 1969. Repr. of 1876 ed. 75.00x (ISBN 0-8103-3885-8). Gale.

Cooper-Oakley, Isabel. Comte de St. Germain. 15.95 (ISBN 0-7229-5146-9). Theos Pub Hse.

Cooperrider, Edward A., tr. see Rommel, Kurt.

Cooperrider, Edward A., tr. see Steinwede, Dietrich.

Coopersmith, Harry. Companion Volume to the Songs We Sing. 1950. 3.50x (ISBN 0-8381-0210-7). United Syn Bk.

--New Jewish Songbook. LC 65-14593. pap. 9.95x (ISBN 0-87441-060-6). Behrman.

--Songs We Sing. (Illus.). 1950. 22.50x (ISBN 0-8381-0723-0). United Syn Bk.

Cors, Holly. Joy Is the Promise. 1978. pap. 1.50 (ISBN 0-88419-182-6). Creation Hse.

Coote, Robert, jt. auth. see Stott, John R.

Coote, Robert B. Amos among the Prophets: Composition & Theology. LC 80-8054. 144p. 1981. pap. 5.95 (ISBN 0-8006-1400-3, 1-1400). Fortress.

Cope, Lamar. Faith for a New Day. Lambert, Herbert, ed. 128p. (Orig.). 1986. pap. 8.95 (ISBN 0-8272-1013-2). CBP.

Copeland, E. L. El Cristianismo y Otras Religiones. Mora, Abdias A., tr. Orig. Title: Christianity & World Religious. (Span., Illus.). 192p. 1981. pap. 3.50 (ISBN 0-311-05760-8, Edit Mundo). Casa Bautista.

Copeland, E. Luther. World Mission & World Survival. LC 84-14963. 1985. pap. 5.95 (ISBN 0-8054-6335-6). Broadman.

Copeland, Gloria. God's Will Is Prosperity. pap. 2.95 (ISBN 0-89274-090-6, HH-090). Harrison Hse.

Copeland, John A. A Study of Daniel. 1973. pap. 4.50 (ISBN 0-89137-703-4). Quality Pubns.

--A Study of the Revelation. 1971. pap. 4.50 (ISBN 0-89137-702-6). Quality Pubns.

Copeland, Robert M. Spare No Exertions: One Hundred Seventy-Five Years of the Reformed Presbyterian Theological Seminary. LC 86-60501. (Illus.). 144p. 1986. 7.95x (ISBN 0-9616417-0-3). Ref Presby Theo.

Copeland, W. J., et al, eds. Library of Anglo-Catholic Theology, 18 titles in 81 vols. Repr. of 1841 ed. Set. 2627.50 (ISBN 0-404-52010-3); write for info. AMS Pr.

Copinger, H. B., ed. see Merryweather, F. Somner.

Copleston, F. C. Aquinas. 272p. 1956. pap. 5.95 (ISBN 0-14-020349-4, Pelican). Penguin.

Copleston, Frederick. History of Philosophy, 9 vols. Incl. Vol. 1. Greece & Rome (ISBN 0-8091-0065-7); Vol. 2. Medieval Philosophy - Augustine to Scotus (ISBN 0-8091-0066-5); Vol. 3. Ockham to Suarez (ISBN 0-8091-0067-3); Vol. 4. Descartes to Leibniz (ISBN 0-8091-0068-1); Vol. 5. Hobbes to Hume (ISBN 0-8091-0069-X); Vol. 6. Wolff to Kant (ISBN 0-8091-0070-3); Vol. 7. Fichte to Nietzsche (ISBN 0-8091-0071-1); Vol. 8. Bentham to Russell (ISBN 0-8091-0072-X); Vol. 9. Maine de Bira to Sartre. 1976 (ISBN 0-8091-0196-3). Vols. 1-9. 19.95 ea. Paulist Pr.

--Religion & the One: Philosophies East & West. LC 81-5372. (Gifford Lectures, 1980 Ser.). 320p. 1981. 24.50x (ISBN 0-8245-0092-X). Crossroad NY.

Copley, Thomas. Letters of Sir Thomas Copley to Queen Elizabeth & Her Ministers. Christie, Richard C., ed. LC 74-80263. (Research & Source Works Ser.: No. 631). 1971. Repr. lib. bdg. 32.00 (ISBN 0-8337-0655-1). B Franklin.

Coppa, Frank J. Pope Pius IX. (World Leaders Ser.). 1979. lib. bdg. 15.95 (ISBN 0-8057-7727-X, Twayne). G K Hall.

Coppell, William & Flores, Bess, eds. Bibliography of the Cook Islands. 1982. cancelled. Inst Polynesian.

Coppenger, Mark T. A Christian View of Justice. LC 82-70867. 1983. pap. 6.95 (ISBN 0-8054-6126-4). Broadman.

Coppens, Peter R. de see De Coppens, Peter R.

Coppens, Peter Roche de see Winterhalter, Robert.

Coppin, Ezra. Too Proud to Die. LC 82-50238. 168p. (Orig.). 1982. pap. 4.95 (ISBN 0-88449-082-3, A424615). Vision Hse.

Coppin, Ezra M. Slain in the Spirit. LC 75-36001. 96p. 1976. pap. 2.50 (ISBN 0-89221-010-9). New Leaf.

Coppin, Fanny J. Reminiscences of School Life & Hints On Teaching. De Swarte, Carolyn G. & Dayton, Donald, eds. (Women in American Protestant Religion Series 1800-1930). 191p. 1987. lib. bdg. 30.00 (ISBN 0-8240-0662-3). Garland Pub.

Coppolino, Joseph, compiled by. A Book of Devotions. 68p. (Orig.). 1986. pap. 1.75 (ISBN 0-8189-0502-6). Alba.

Coptic Church Staff. Coptic Morning Service for the Lord's Day. Crichton-Stuart, John P., tr. LC 72-39871. Repr. of 1908 ed. 17.25 (ISBN 0-404-01247-7). AMS Pr.

Corbett, James A. & Garvin, Joseph N., eds. Summa Contra Haereticos. (Mediaeval Studies Ser.: No. 15). (Lat). 1968. 23.95 (ISBN 0-268-00268-1). U of Notre Dame Pr.

Corbett, James A. & Moore, Philip S., eds. Petri Pictaviensis Allegoriae Super Tabernaculum Moysi. (Mediaeval Studies Ser.: No. 3). 1938. 17.95 (ISBN 0-268-00207-X). U of Notre Dame Pr.

Corbett, Jan. Creative Youth Leadership. LC 77-778950. 1977. pap. 4.95 (ISBN 0-8170-0761-X). Judson.

Corbett, Julian. Monk. facsimile ed. LC 72-154148. (Select Bibliographies Reprint Ser). Repr. of 1889 ed. 18.00 (ISBN 0-8369-5764-4). Ayer Co Pubs.

Corbett, Patricia, jt. auth. see Eisler, Colin.

Corbett, W. J. Pentecost & the Chosen One. 240p. 1987. 14.95 (ISBN 0-385-29549-9). Delacorte.

Corbin, Henry. Avicenna & the Visionary Recital. Trask, Willard R., tr. from French. (Dunquin Ser.: No. 13). 314p. 1980. pap. 14.50 (ISBN 0-88214-213-5). Spring Pubns.

--The Concept of Comparative Philosophy. Russell, Peter, tr. from Fr. (Orig.). 1985. pap. 3.95 (ISBN 0-933999-29-1). Phanes Pr.

--Creative Imagination in the Sufism of Ibn Arabi. Manheim, R., tr. (Bollingen Ser.: Vol. 91). 1969. 40.00 (ISBN 0-691-09852-2); pap. 12.95 (ISBN 0-691-01828-6). Princeton U Pr.

--Cyclical Time & Ismaili Gnosis. (Islamic Texts & Contexts Ser.). 193p. 1983. 24.95x (ISBN 0-7103-0047-6, Kegan Paul); pap. 13.95 (ISBN 0-7103-0048-4). Methuen Inc.

--Spiritual Body & Celestial Earth: From Mazdean Iran to Shi Ite Iran. Pearson, Nancy, tr. (Bollingen Ser: No. 91). 1977. text ed. 40.00x (ISBN 0-691-09937-5). Princeton U Pr.

Corbin, Linda. Following Jesus. Dys, Pat, ed. (Studies for Kids Ser.: Pt. 1). (Illus.). 48p. 1985. 2.95 (ISBN 0-87239-903-6, 3303). Standard Pub.

Corbin, Linda & Dys, Pat. Following Jesus. (Studies for Kids Ser.: Pt. 2). (Illus.). 48p. 1985. 2.95 (ISBN 0-87239-904-4, 3304). Standard Pub.

--Following Jesus: The Book of Acts, Pt. 1. (Illus.). 48p. 1986. wkbk. 2.95 (ISBN 0-87403-053-6, 3197). Standard Pub.

--Following Jesus: The Book of Acts, Pt. 2. (Illus.). 48p. 1986. wkbk. 2.95 (ISBN 0-87403-054-4, 3308). Standard Pub.

--Jesus Teaches Me. (Discipleship Workbook for Parent & Child Ser.: Bk. 4). (Illus.). 35p. Date not set. wkbk. 3.95 (ISBN 0-87509-389-2). Chr Pubns.

--Together: Jesus Helps Me Grow, Bk. 2. (Orig.). Date not set. pap. 3.95 (ISBN 0-87509-374-4). Chr Pubns.

--Together: Jesus Makes Us New, Bk. 1. (Illus.). 24p. (Orig.). 1986. pap. 3.95 (ISBN 0-87509-373-6). Chr Pubns.

Corbitt, Jackie. Our Lengthened Shadows. 110p. 1970. pap. 1.75 (ISBN 0-89114-015-8). Baptist Pub Hse.

Corcoran, Sr. Mary H., ed. see Hojeda, Diego de.

Corcoran, Paul A. With All Due Respect. 1983. 4.50 (ISBN 0-89536-609-6, 2354). CSS of Ohio.

Cord, Robert L. Separation of Church & State: Historical Fact & Current Fiction. 307p. 1982. 19.95x (ISBN 0-931186-03-X). Lambeth Pr.

Cordasco, Francesco, ed. Protestant Evangelism among Italians in America. LC 74-17943. (Italian American Experience Ser.). (Illus.). 276p. 1975. Repr. 21.00x (ISBN 0-405-06414-4). Ayer Co Pubs.

Cordasco, Francesco, ed. see Lindberg, Duane R.

Cordasco, Francesco, ed. see Schelbert, Leo.

Cordasco, Francesco, ed. see Scourby, Alice.

Cordasco, Francesco, ed. see Ulrich, Robert J.

Cordavero, Moses. Or Nerev: Hebrew Text. 1980. 10.00 (ISBN 0-943688-17-5). Res Ctr Kabbalah.

Cording, Ruth. The Joy of Remembering Our Guests. 1982. gift padded cover 7.95 (ISBN 0-87162-258-0, J1016). Warner Pr.

Cordner, John. Dear Laddie. LC 86-71593. 300p. (Orig.). 1987. pap. 4.50 (ISBN 0-9617224-0-1). J Cordner.

Cordoba, Pedro De see De Cordoba, Pedro.

Cordovano, Steven & Sechi, Stephan M. The Compleat Alchemist. (The Compleat Fantasy Ser.). (Illus.). 45p. 1983. pap. text ed. 7.95 (ISBN 0-9610770-0-X, 4801). Bard Games.

Cordovero, Moses. The Palm Tree of Deborah. Jacobs, Louis, tr. from Heb. LC 80-54594. (The Judaic Studies Library: No. SPH8). 133p. 1981. pap. 7.95 (ISBN 0-87203-097-0). Hermon.

Corduan, Winfried. Handmaid to Theology. 176p. (Orig.). 1981. pap. 7.95 (ISBN 0-8010-2468-4). Baker Bk.

Core, Arthur C. Otterbein (Philip William) 1968. 4.00 (ISBN 0-687-30917-4); pap. 2.25 (ISBN 0-687-30918-2). Abingdon.

Core, Earl L. Morgantown Disciples. (Illus.). 1960. 8.00 (ISBN 0-87012-024-7). McClain.

Coreil, Judith, jt. auth. see Reck, Carleen.

Corelli, Marie. Barabbas. pap. 5.95 (ISBN 0-910122-00-8). Amherst Pr.

--The Master Christian. 604p. 1983. Repr. of 1900 ed. lib. bdg. 45.00 (ISBN 0-8495-0961-0). Arden Lib.

Coretto, Carlo, frwd. by. The Jerusalem Community: Rule of Life. 144p. (Orig.). 1985. pap. 5.95 (ISBN 0-8091-2712-1). Paulist Pr.

Corey, Arthur. Behind the Scenes with the Metaphysicians. 7.50 (ISBN 0-87516-014-X). De Vorss.

--More Class Notes. pap. 2.50 (ISBN 0-87516-016-6). De Vorss.

Corey, Arthur, jt. auth. see Merritt, Robert E.

Corfe, T. St. Patrick & Irish Christianity. LC 73-75862. (Cambridge Introduction to the Hoistory of Mankind Ser.). 48p. 1973. 4.95 (ISBN 0-521-20228-0). Cambridge U Pr.

Corfe, Tom. The Murder of Archbishop Thomas. LC 76-22419. (Cambridge Topic Bks). (Illus.). 1977. PLB 8.95 (ISBN 0-8225-1202-5). Lerner Pubns.

--St. Patrick & Irish Christianity. LC 78-56811. (Cambridge Topic Bks). (Illus.). 1978. PLB 8.95 (ISBN 0-8225-1217-3). Lerner Pubns.

Coriden, James A., et al. The Art of Interpretation: Selected Studies on the Interpretation of Canon Law. v, 79p. (Orig.). 1983. pap. 3.75 (ISBN 0-943616-18-2). Canon Law Soc.

Coriden, James A., et al, eds. The Code of Canon Law: A Text & Commentary. 39.95 (ISBN 0-8091-0345-1). Paulist Pr.

--The Code of Canon Law: A Text & Commentary, Study Edition. 1184p. 1986. pap. text ed. 29.95 (ISBN 0-8091-2837-3). Paulist Pr.

Coriell, Rebekah, jt. auth. see Coriell, Ron.

Coriell, Ron & Coriell, Rebekah. A Child's Book of Character Building, Bk. Two. 128p. 1981. 10.95 (ISBN 0-8007-1265-X). Revell.

Corish, Patrick. The Irish Catholic Experience. 1985. 25.00 (ISBN 0-317-42754-7). M Glazier.

Corish, Patrick J. The Catholic Community in the Seventeenth & Eighteenth Centuries. Cosgrove, Art & Collins, Elma, eds. (Helicon History of Ireland). (Illus.). 156p. 1981. 9.95 (ISBN 0-86167-064-7, Pub. by Educ Co Ireland); pap. 6.95 (ISBN 0-86167-063-9). Longwood Pub Group.

Corl, Heth. Lectionary Worship Aids C (Common) 1985. 9.95 (ISBN 0-89536-760-2, 5867). CSS of Ohio.

Corl, Heth H. Lectionary Worship Aids A: Common Lectionary. rev. ed. Sherer, Michael L., ed. 1986. pap. 9.95 (ISBN 0-89536-814-5, 6843). CSS of Ohio.

Corless, Roger. I Am Food: The Mass in Planetary Perspective. LC 81-7836. 112p. 1981. 8.95 (ISBN 0-8245-0077-6). Crossroad NY.

Corlett, D. Shelby. God in the Present Tense. 176p. 1974. 1.95 (ISBN 0-8341-0248-X). Beacon Hill.

Corlett, William T. The Medicine-Man of the American Indian & His Cultural Background. LC 75-23699. Repr. of 1935 ed. 47.50 (ISBN 0-404-13249-9). AMS Pr.

Corley, Bruce, jt. auth. see Huey, F. B., Jr.

Corley, Bruce, jt. auth. see Vaughan, Curtis.

Corley, Bruce C., ed. Colloquy on New Testament Studies: A Time for Reappraisal & Fresh Approaches. LC 83-8192. xiv, 370p. 1983. 21.50 (ISBN 0-86554-082-9, H54). Mercer Univ Pr.

Corley, Winnie. Echoes from the Hills. 1981. lib. bdg. 14.95x (ISBN 0-934188-06-8). Evans Pubns.

Cormack, Patrick. English Cathedrals. (Illus.). 1984. 14.95 (ISBN 0-517-55409-7, Harmony). Crown.

Cormier, Jay. Giving Good Homilies. LC 84-70383. 96p. 1984. pap. 3.95 (ISBN 0-87793-317-0). Ave Maria.

Cornelison, Isaac J. The Relation of Religion to Civil Government in the United States. LC 75-107409. (Civil Liberties in American History Ser). 1970. Repr. of 1895 ed. lib. bdg. 45.00 (ISBN 0-306-71890-1). Da Capo.

Cornelius, Martin P., III. Til Death Do Us Part: A Basic Education in Total Health: How to Keep Body & Soul Happily Together. 256p. (Orig.). 1981. pap. 15.00 (ISBN 0-9607142-0-0). Health Ed & Life Exp Res.

Cornelius, Peter S. E. K.'s Commentary on the Shepheards Calender. Hogg, James, ed. (Elizabethan & Renaissance Studies). 111p. (Orig.). 1974. pap. 15.00 (ISBN 3-7052-0679-6, Pub. by Salzburg Studies). Longwood Pub Group.

Cornelius, R. M. Christopher Marlowe's Use of the Bible. LC 84-21280. (American University Studies IV (English Language & Literature): Vol. 23). (Illus.). 335p. 1984. text ed. 32.00 (ISBN 0-8204-0193-5). P Lang Pubs.

Cornell, Jean G. Mahalia Jackson: Queen of Gospel Song. LC 73-14713. (Americans All Ser.). (Illus.). 96p. 1974. PLB 7.12 (ISBN 0-8116-4581-9). Garrard.

Cornell University, Libraries Staff. Catalogue of the Witchcraft Collection in Cornell University Library. LC 76-41552. 1977. lib. bdg. 120.00 (ISBN 0-527-19705-X). Kraus Intl.

Cornell, W. L., tr. see Archenti, Augustine & Petrini, Arnold.

Cornell, Wallace L., tr. see Isoardi, Gian C.

Cornfeld & Gaalyah, eds. Josephus: The Jewish War. 560p. 1982. 44.95 (ISBN 0-310-39210-1, 10265). Zondervan.

Cornford, F. M. From Religion to Philosophy. A Study of the Origins of Western Speculation. 275p. 1979. text ed. o. p. (ISBN 0-391-01238-X); pap. text ed. 12.50x (ISBN 0-391-01239-8). Humanities.

Cornford, Francis M., ed. Greek Religious Thought from Homer to the Age of Alexander. LC 79-98637. (Library of Greek Thought: No. 2). Repr. of 1923 ed. 21.50 (ISBN 0-404-01734-7). AMS Pr.

Cornhill, Carl H. History of the People of Israel. 325p. 1943. 4.95 (ISBN 0-317-40441-5); pap. 2.95 (ISBN 0-317-40442-3). Open Court.

--The Prophets of Israel: Popular Sketches from Old Testament History. 1977. Repr. of 1913 ed. lib. bdg. 30.00 (ISBN 0-8482-3453-7). Norwood Edns.

Cornier, Henri. The Humor of Jesus. Heiman, David, tr. from Fr. LC 77-9887. Orig. Title: L Humour De Jesus. 1977. pap. 5.95 (ISBN 0-8189-0356-2). Alba.

Cornils, Stanley. Thirty-Four Two-Minute Talks for Youth & Adults. 64p. 1985. pap. 2.95 (ISBN 0-87239-868-4, 2883). Standard Pub.

--Twenty-Five Two-Minute Talks for Children. 48p. 1985. pap. 2.95 (ISBN 0-87239-867-6, 2882). Standard Pub.

Cornish, Graham. Religious Periodicals Directory. (Clio Periodicals Directories Ser.). 250p. 1986. lib. bdg. 89.00 (ISBN 0-87436-365-9). ABC-Clio.

Cornish, John. The Raising of Lazarus. 1979. pap. 2.95 (ISBN 0-916786-36-6). St George Bk Serv.

Cornish, Patty Jo. The Prayer Primer: A Philosophy Book. Quintero, Roberto, ed. LC 84-81741. 68p. (Orig.). pap. 5.95 (ISBN 0-9613717-0-6). Hilltop Hse.

Cornold, W. The Yoga of Yama. 64p. 1970. pap. 4.95 (ISBN 0-88697-041-5). Life Science.

Cornwall Collective Staff. Your Daughters Shall Prophesy: Feminist Alternatives in Theological Education. LC 80-14891. 155p. 1980. pap. 6.95 (ISBN 0-8298-0404-8). Pilgrim NY.

Cornwall, Judson. La Alabanza Que Libera. 160p. 1976. 2.75 (ISBN 0-88113-002-8). Edit Betania.

--Elements of Worship. LC 85-61459. 1985. pap. 5.95 (ISBN 0-88270-594-6). Bridge Pub.

--Give Me-Make Me. LC 79-64976. 1979. 1.25 (ISBN 0-88270-387-0). Bridge Pub.

--Let Us Abide. LC 77-23143. 155p. 1984. pap. 4.95 (ISBN 0-8007-5065-9). Bridge Pub.

--Let Us Be Holy. LC 87-70993. 1978. pap. 4.95 (ISBN 0-88270-278-5). Bridge Pub.

--Let Us Draw Near. LC 77-24832. 1977. pap. 4.95 (ISBN 0-88270-226-2, Pub. by Logos). Bridge Pub.

--Let Us Enjoy Forgiveness. LC 78-8306. 159p. 1978. pap. 4.95 (ISBN 0-8007-5090-X). Bridge Pub.

--Let Us Praise: A Prominent Charismatic Leader Tells How & Why to Praise God. LC 73-75957. 1973. pap. 4.95 (ISBN 0-88270-039-1). Bridge Pub.

--Let Us See Jesus. LC 80-20645. 160p. 1981. pap. 4.95 (ISBN 0-8007-5052-7). Bridge Pub.

--Let Us Worship. LC 82-74089. 1983. pap. 4.95 (ISBN 0-88270-542-3). Bridge Pub.

--Profiles of a Leader. LC 80-85161. (Orig.). 1980. pap. 4.95 (ISBN 0-88270-503-2). Bridge Pub.

Cornwall, Rebecca & Arrington, Leonard J. Rescue of the Eighteen Fifty-Six Handcart Companies. Alexander, Thomas G., ed. (Charles Redd Monographs in Western History: No. 11). (Illus.). 59p. pap. 4.95 (ISBN 0-941214-04-4, Signature Bks). C Redd Ctr.

Cornwell, Malcolm. Arise & Renew. 96p. 1986. pap. 5.95 (ISBN 0-8146-1441-8). Liturgical Pr.

--Formed by His Word: Patterns of Scriptural Prayer. (Orig.). 1978. pap. 2.95 (ISBN 0-914544-20-9). Living Flame Pr.

Cornwell, Patricia D. A Time for Remembering. 496p. 1985. pap. 16.95 (ISBN 0-8027-2501-5). Walker & Co.

--A Time for Remembering: The Ruth Bell Graham Story. LC 82-48922. (Illus.). 320p. 1983. 13.45 (ISBN 0-06-061685-7, HarpR). Har-Row.

Cornwell, Peter. Church & the Nation: The Case for Disestablishment. (Faith & the Future Ser.). 160p. 1984. 24.95x (ISBN 0-631-13223-6); pap. 8.95x (ISBN 0-631-13224-4). Basil Blackwell.

Corona, Simon, tr. see Yates, K. M.

Corr, Finbarr M. From the Wedding to the Marriage. 1987. 6.95 (ISBN 0-533-07038-4). Vantage.

Corrado, Dennis, jt. ed. see Hinchey, James F.

Corre, Allan. Understanding the Talmud. 1971. pap. 8.95x (ISBN 0-685-22510-0). Ktav.

Correa, F. G., tr. see Canright, D. M.

Correia-Afonso, John, ed. & tr. Letters from the Mughal Court: The First Jesuit Mission to Akbar (1580-1583) LC 81-81766. (Jesuit Primary Sources in English Translation Ser.: No. 4). (Illus.). 150p. 1982. 9.00 (ISBN 0-912422-57-2). Inst Jesuit.

Correu, Larry M., ed. The Best of These Days. LC 82-13415. 132p. 1983. 8.95 (ISBN 0-664-21391-X). Westminster.

Corrie ten Boom. Jesus Is Victor. 288p. 1984. pap. 6.95 (ISBN 0-8007-5176-0, Power Bks). Revell.

Corrigan, Beatrice, ed. see Erasmus, Desiderius.

Corrigan, D. Felicitas, tr. see St. Augustine.

Corrigan, Felicitas. The Nun, the Infidel, & the Superman: The Remarkable Friendships of Dame Laurentia McLachlan. LC 84-52822. (Illus.). viii, 152p. 1985. 14.95 (ISBN 0-226-11589-5). U of Chicago Pr.

Corrigan, Felicitas, tr. see Augustine, St.

Corrigan, John T. Archives: The Light of Faith. (Catholic Library Association Studies in Librarianship: No. 4). 1980. 4.00 (ISBN 0-87507-008-6). Cath Lib Assn.

Corrigan, John T., jt. auth. see Cargas, Harry J.

Corrigan, John T., ed. see Brown, James, et al.

Corrill, John. Brief History of the Church of Christ of Latter Day Saints. 48p. (Orig.). 1983. pap. 1.95 (ISBN 0-942284-05-4). Restoration Re.

Corrin, Sara & Corrin, Stephen, eds. The Faber Book of Christmas Stories. LC 84-13552. (Illus.). 150p. 1984. 9.95 (ISBN 0-571-13348-7). Faber & Faber.

--The Faber Book of Christmas Stories. 9.95 (ISBN 0-317-31393-2). Faber & Faber.

Corrin, Stephen, jt. ed. see Corrin, Sara.

Corry, John. TV News & the Dominant Culture. Media Institute Staff, ed. LC 86-60785. (Media in Society Ser.). 54p. (Orig.). 1986. pap. 12.95 (ISBN 0-937790-34-6). Media Inst.

Corsini, Eugenio. The Apocalypse: The Perennial Revelation of Jesus Christ. Moloney, ed. (Good News Studies: Vol. 5). 1983. pap. 5.95 (ISBN 0-89453-310-X). M Glazier.

Corson-Finnerty, Adam. No More Plastic Jesus: Global Justice & Christian Lifestyle. LC 76-13174. 223p. (Orig.). 1977. pap. 6.95x (ISBN 0-88344-341-4). Orbis Bks.
--World Citizen: Action for Global Justice. LC 81-16918. 178p. (Orig.). 1982. pap. 6.95 (ISBN 0-88344-715-0). Orbis Bks.
Corstanje, Auspicius Van see Van Corstanje, Auspicius.
Cortes, Carlos E., ed. Church Views of the Mexican American. LC 73-14198. (The Mexican American Ser.). (Illus.). 58p. 1974. Repr. 45.00x (ISBN 0-405-05672-9). Ayer Co Pubs.
--Protestantism & Latinos in the United States: An Original Anthology. LC 79-6266. (Hispanics in the United States Ser.). (Illus.). 1981. lib. bdg. 51.50x (ISBN 0-405-13173-9). Ayer Co Pubs.
Cortes, Juan D. & Schramm, Edmund. Ensayo Sobre el Catolicismo, el Liberalismo y el Socialismo & Donoso Cortes, 2 vols. in one. Mayer, J. P., ed. LC 78-67342. (European Political Thought Ser.). (Span. & Ger.). 1979. Repr. of 1935 ed. lib. bdg. 39.00x (ISBN 0-405-11687-X). Ayer Co Pubs.
Corvin, R. O. David & His Mighty Men. facs. ed. LC 74-136646. (Biography Index Reprint Ser.). 1950. 17.00 (ISBN 0-8369-8041-7). Ayer Co Pubs.
Corvin, Raymond O. Great Themes of the Bible. (The Alpha & Omega Bible Studies). 90p. (Orig.). 1986. pap. 5.95 (ISBN 0-89221-138-5). New Leaf.
--Great Truths of the Bible. (The Alpha & Omega Bible Studies). 90p. (Orig.). 1986. pap. text ed. 5.95 (ISBN 0-89221-139-3). New Leaf.
--New Testament Characters. (The Alpha & Omega Studies). 94p. (Orig.). 1986. pap. text ed. 5.95 (ISBN 0-89221-137-7). New Leaf.
--Old Testament Characters. (The Alpha & Omega Bible Studies). 94p. (Orig.). 1986. pap. text ed. 5.95 (ISBN 0-89221-136-9). New Leaf.
Corwin, Judith H. Easter Fun. LC 84-9122. (Messner Holiday Library). (Illus.). 64p. 1984. PLB 9.29 (ISBN 0-671-50798-2); pap. 5.95 (ISBN 0-671-53108-5). Messner.
--Jewish Holiday Fun. 1987. 4.95. Wanderer Bks.
Cory, David M. Faustus Socinus. LC 83-45606. Date not set. Repr. of 1932 ed. 28.50 (ISBN 0-404-19874-0). AMS Pr.
Cory, Lloyd, compiled by. Quotable Quotations. 400p. 1985. pap. 12.95 (ISBN 0-88207-823-2). Victor Bks.
Cosby, Clair. Reflecting the Lord's Radiance. (Orig.). 1987. pap. 5.95 (ISBN 0-8054-5916-2). Broadman.
Cosby, Clair G. Lord, Help Me Love My Sister. LC 86-4831. 80p. (Orig.). 1986. pap. 4.95 (ISBN 0-8361-3413-3). Herald Pr.
Cosby, Michael. Sex in the Bible: An Introduction to What the Scriptures Teach Us about Sexuality. LC 83-16090. 182p. 1984. 12.95 (ISBN 0-13-807280-9); pap. 5.95 (ISBN 0-13-807272-8). P-H.
Coscia, Louis W., pseud. The Promised One. 192p. 1983. 10.95. Todd & Honeywell.
Coser, Lewis A. Refugee Scholars in America: Their Impact & Their Experiences. LC 84-40193. 384p. 1984. 27.50x (ISBN 0-300-03193-9). Yale U Pr.
Coser, Lewis A., ed. see Simmel, Georg.
Cosgrove, Art, ed. see Corish, Patrick J.
Cosgrove, Francis M. Essentials of Discipleship. LC 79-93015. 192p. 1980. pap. 5.95 (ISBN 0-89109-442-3). NavPress.
--Essentials of New Life. LC 78-54949. (Illus.). 180p. (Orig.). 1978. pap. 5.95 (ISBN 0-89109-427-X). NavPress.
Cosgrove, Mark P. The Amazing Body Human. 160p. 1987. pap. 7.95 (ISBN 0-8010-2517-6). Baker Bk.
Coskey, Evelyn. Christmas Crafts for Everyone. LC 76-4916. (Illus.). (YA) 1976. 9.95 (ISBN 0-687-07815-6). Abingdon.
Coslet, Dorothy. Madame Jeanne Guyon: Child of Another World. 219p. (Orig.). 1984. pap. 3.95 (ISBN 0-87508-144-4). Chr Lit.
Cosmao, Vincent. Changing the World: An Agenda for the Churches. Drury, John, tr. LC 84-5153. Tr. of Changer le monde-une tache pour l'eglise. 128p. (Orig.). 1984. pap. 7.95 (ISBN 0-88344-107-1). Orbis Bks.
Coss, Hal, jt. auth. see Wild, Peter.
Cosslett, Tess. Science & Religion in the Nineteenth Century. LC 83-7505. (Cambridge English Prose Texts Ser.). 225p. 1984. 42.50 (ISBN 0-521-24402-1); pap. 14.95 (ISBN 0-521-28668-9). Cambridge U Pr.
Cosson, Annie, ed. see McDowell, Josh.
Cosson, Annie L., ed. see Bridges, Jerry.
Cosson, Annie L., ed. see Dobbins, Richard D.
Cosson, Annie L., ed. see Ladd, George E.
Cosson, Annie L., ed. see Ogilvie, Lloyd J.
Cosson, Annie L., ed. see Robertson, Pat.
Costa, Francis D., ed. see Hopko, T., et al.
Costabel, Eva D. The Pennsylvania Dutch. LC 86-3334. (Illus.). 48p. 1986. 14.95 (ISBN 0-689-31281-4, Children Bk). Macmillan.
Costadoni, A., jt. auth. see Mittarelli, J. H.
Costanza, Mary S. The Living Witness: Art in the Concentration Camps & Ghettos. 1982. 19.95 (ISBN 0-02-906660-3). Free Pr.
Costas, O., et al, eds. Hacia Una Teologia Evangelica Latinoamericana. 154p. 1984. pap. 3.95 (ISBN 0-89922-238-2). Edit Caribe.
Costas, Orlando. Christ Outside the Gate: Mission Beyond Christendom. LC 82-7892. 272p. (Orig.). 1982. pap. 12.95 (ISBN 0-88344-147-0). Orbis Bks.
Costas, Orlando E. Comunicacion Por Medio de la Predicacion. (Span.). 255p. pap. 6.25 (ISBN 0-89922-021-5). Edit Caribe.
--The Integrity of Mission: The Inner Life & Outreach of the Church. LC 79-1759. 1979. pap. 5.95 (ISBN 0-06-061586-9, RD 235, HarpR). Har-Row.
Coste, Rene. Marxist Analysis & Christian Faith. Couture, Roger A., et al, trs. from Fr. LC 85-3119. Tr. of Analyse Marxiste et foi Chretienne. 256p. (Orig.). 1985. pap. 11.95 (ISBN 0-88344-342-2). Orbis Bks.
Costello, Andrew. How to Deal with Difficult People. LC 80-81751. 112p. (Orig.). 1980. pap. 3.95 (ISBN 0-89243-128-8). Liguori Pubns.
--Thank God It's Friday: Meditations For Hard-Working Catholics. 1987. 12.95 (ISBN 0-88347-213-9). Thomas More.
Costello, Don. For Inner Peace & Strength. 1978. 4.00 (ISBN 0-8198-0380-4); pap. 3.00 (ISBN 0-8198-0381-2). Dghtrs St Paul.
Costello, Elaine. Religious Signing. (Illus.). 176p. 1986. pap. 9.95 (ISBN 0-553-34244-4). Bantam.
Costello, Gerald M. Mission to Latin America: The Successes & Failures of a Twentieth-Century Crusade. LC 78-12974. 319p. (Orig.). 1979. pap. 2.49 (ISBN 0-88344-312-0). Orbis Bks.
Costello, Julia G., jt. ed. see Hoover, Robert L.
Costelloe, Joseph, tr. see Bouyer, Louis.
Costelloe, M. Joseph, tr. see Schurhammer, Georg.
Cote, Richard G. Holy Mirth: A Theology of Laughter. 100p. (Orig.). 1985. pap. 8.95 (ISBN 0-89571-031-5). Affirmation.
Cothen, Joe H. Equipped for Good Work: A Guide for Pastors. LC 80-37964. 336p. 1981. 14.95 (ISBN 0-88289-271-1). Pelican.
Cothen, Joe H. & Strange, John O. The Preacher's Notebook on Isaiah. LC 82-24596. 96p. 1983. pap. 6.95 (ISBN 0-88289-365-3). Pelican.
Cotiviela, A., tr. see Schrolder, A. & Bonnet, L.
Cotsforde, Thomas, tr. see Zwingli, Ulrich.
Cott, Allan. Fasting: The Ultimate Diet. 160p. 1986. pap. 3.50 (ISBN 0-553-25967-9). Bantam.
Cotta, John. The Triall of Witch-Craft Shewing the True Methode of the Discovery. LC 68-54629. (English Experience Ser.: No. 39). 128p. 1968. Repr. of 1616 ed. 21.00 (ISBN 90-221-0039-1). Walter J Johnson.
Cotta, Sergio. Why Violence? A Philosophical Interpretation. Gullace, Giovanni, tr. from Ital. LC 84-25779. Orig. Title: Perche la violenza? Una Interpretazione Filosofica. xiv, 150p. 1985. pap. 12.00 (ISBN 0-8130-0824-7). U Presses Fla.
Cotter, George, jt. auth. see Aubin, Pierre.
Cotter, James F. Inscape: The Christology & Poetry of Gerald Manley Hopkins. LC 73-189857. pap. 92.30 (ISBN 0-317-26639-X, 2025436). Bks Demand UMI.
Cotterell, Arthur. A Dictionary of World Mythology. (Illus.). 256p. 1982. pap. 8.95 (ISBN 0-399-50619-5, Perigee). Putnam Pub Group.
Cotterell, M., tr. see Steiner, Rudolf.
Cotterell, Mabel, tr. see Steiner, Rudolf.
Cottingham, John, ed. & tr. Descartes' Conversation with Burman. 1974. 11.95x (ISBN 0-19-824671-4). Oxford U Pr.
Cottle, Ronald E. The Lord's Prayer. 48p. 1980. 0.95 (ISBN 0-88243-566-3, 02-0566). Gospel Pub.
Cottle, Thomas J. Divorce & the Jewish Child. 28p. 1981. pap. 2.50 (ISBN 0-87495-034-1). Am Jewish Comm.
Cotton, Edward H., ed. Has Science Discovered God: A Symposium of Modern Scientific Opinion. facs. ed. LC 68-8452. (Essay Index Reprint Ser). 1931. 21.50 (ISBN 0-8369-0340-4). Ayer Co Pubs.
Cotton, John. Bloudy Tenent, Washed, & Made White in the Bloud of the Lambe. LC 78-141105. (Research Library of Colonial Americana). 1972. Repr. of 1647 ed. 34.00 (ISBN 0-405-03319-2). Ayer Co Pubs.
--Christ the Fountaine of Life, Or, Sundry Choyce Sermons on Part of the Fifth Chapter of the First Epistle of St. John. LC 75-141107. (Research Library of Colonial Americana). 1971. Repr. of 1651 ed. 24.50 (ISBN 0-405-03321-4). Ayer Co Pubs.
--God's Mercie Mixed with His Justice. LC 58-5651. 1977. Repr. of 1641 ed. 30.00x (ISBN 0-8201-1242-9). Schol Facsimiles.
--Two Sermons. LC 79-141108. (Research Library of Colonial Americana). 1971. Repr. of 1642 ed. 22.00 (ISBN 0-405-03322-2). Ayer Co Pubs.
Cottrell, Alan P., tr. see Steiner, Rudolf.
Cottrell, Donald P. Instruction & Instructional Facilities in the Colleges of the United Lutheran Church in America. LC 79-176672. (Columbia University. Teachers College. Contributions to Education: No. 376). Repr. of 1929 ed. 22.50 (ISBN 0-404-55376-1). AMS Pr.
Cottrell, Georgia M. Portrait of Christ in Poetry. (Contemporary Poets of Dorrance Ser.). 100p. 1983. 5.95 (ISBN 0-8059-2888-X). Dorrance.
Cottrell, Jack. The Gospel of Matthew, Vol. IV. LC 85-72877. (Bible Study Textbook Ser.). 996p. text ed. 18.95 (ISBN 0-89900-032-0). College Pr Pub.
--Tough Questions: Biblical Answers Part One. 122p. (Orig.). pap. 3.95 (ISBN 0-89900-208-0). College Pr Pub.
--What the Bible Says about God the Creator. (What the Bible Says Ser.). 1983. 13.95 (ISBN 0-89900-094-0). College Pr Pub.
Cottrell, Stan. To Run & Not Be Weary. (Illus.). 192p. 1985. 12.95 (ISBN 0-8007-1444-X). Revell.
Cottvell, Jack. Tough Questions: Biblical Answers Part Two. Orig. Title: The Bible Says. 128p. 1986. pap. 3.95 (ISBN 0-89900-213-7). College Pr Pub.
--What the Bible Says about God the Ruler. (What the Bible Says about Ser.). 465p. 13.95 (ISBN 0-89900-094-0). College Pr Pub.
Couasnon, C. The Church of the Holy Sepulchre, Jerusalem. (Schweich Lectures on Biblical Archaeology). (Illus.). 62p. 1972. 10.25 (ISBN 0-85672-735-0, Pub. by British Acad). Longwood Pub Group.
Couchman, Bob & Couchman, Win. James: Hear It! Live It! (Carpenter Studyguide Ser.). 1982. saddle-stitched leader's handbook, 61p 2.95 (ISBN 0-87788-423-4); member's handbook, 64p 1.95 (ISBN 0-87788-422-6). Shaw Pubs.
--Small Groups: Timber to Build up God's House. LC 82-798. (Carpenter Studyguide). 83p. 1982. pap. 2.95 (ISBN 0-87788-097-2). Shaw Pubs.
Couchman, Win, jt. auth. see Bob.
Couchman, Win, jt. auth. see Couchman, Bob.
Coudenhove-Kalergi, H. Anti-Semitism Through the Ages. 59.95 (ISBN 0-87968-649-9). Gordon Pr.
Couer de Jesus d' Elbee, Jean du. I Believe In Love. Teichert, Marilyn & Stebbins, Madeline, trs. LC 82-24134. Tr. of Croire a l'amour. (Fr.). 1983. pap. 4.95 (ISBN 0-932506-21-6). St Bedes Pubns.
Coues, Elliott. War & Christianity. 250.00 (ISBN 0-8490-1276-7). Gordon Pr.
Couey, Dick. Happiness Is Being a Physically Fit Christian. LC 84-12746. 1985. 9.95 (ISBN 0-8054-7525-7). Broadman.
Couey, Richard. Lifelong Fitness & Fulfillment. LC 80-65844. 1980. 7.95 (ISBN 0-8054-5426-8). Broadman.
Coughlan, Peter, tr. see Vagaggini, Cipriano.
Coughlin, Charles E. Sermons, 2 vols. Set. 250.00 (ISBN 0-8490-1025-X). Gordon Pr.
Coughlin, Kevin. Finding God in Everyday Life. LC 80-84506. 64p. (Orig.). 1981. pap. 2.95 (ISBN 0-8091-2351-7). Paulist Pr.
Coulling, Sidney. Matthew Arnold & His Critics: A Study of Arnold's Controversies. LC 74-82498. xiv, 351p. 1974. 20.00x (ISBN 0-8214-0161-0). Ohio U Pr.
Coulson, John. Religion & Imagination. 1981. 39.95x (ISBN 0-19-826656-1). Oxford U Pr.
Coulson, John & Allchin, Arthur M., eds. The Rediscovery of Newman: An Oxford Symposium. LC 68-84451. 1967. text ed. 15.00x (ISBN 0-8401-0458-8). A R Allenson.
Coulson, N. J. Succession in the Muslim Family. 1971. 54.50 (ISBN 0-521-07852-0). Cambridge U Pr.
Coulson, Noel. A History of Islamic Law. 264p. 1964. pap. 10.00 (ISBN 0-85224-354-5, Pub. by Edinburgh U Pr Scotland). Columbia U Pr.
Coulter, E. Merton. William G. Brownlow: Fighting Parson of the Southern Highlands. LC 71-136309. (Tennesseana Editions Ser.). (Illus.). pap. 114.50 (ISBN 0-8357-9767-8, 2016173). Bks Demand UMI.
Coulton, G. G. Infant Perdition in the Middle Ages. 1977. lib. bdg. 59.95 (ISBN 0-8490-2058-1). Gordon Pr.
--Scottish Abbeys & Social Life. 1977. lib. bdg. 59.95 (ISBN 0-8490-2573-7). Gordon Pr.
--Two Saints: St. Bernard & St. Francis. 1923. lib. bdg. 15.00 (ISBN 0-8414-3513-8). Folcroft.
Coulton, G. G., ed. & tr. see Salimbene Di Adam.
Coulton, George G. Art & the Reformation. LC 69-15789. (Illus.). xxii, 662p. 1969. Repr. of 1928 ed. 45.00 (ISBN 0-208-00738-5, Archon). Shoe String.
--Inquisition. LC 74-18020. 1974. Repr. of 1929 ed. lib. bdg. 16.50 (ISBN 0-8414-3647-9). Folcroft.
--Life in the Middle Ages. Cambridge U Pr.
Council of Europe Staff, ed. Collected Edition of the "Travaux Preparatoires of the European Convention on Human Rights". Vol. V Legal Committee-Ad Hoc Joint Committee-Committee of Ministers-Consultative Assembly 23 June - 28 August 1950. 356p. 1979. lib. bdg. 131.60 (ISBN 90-247-1970-4). Kluwer Academic.
Council of Trent Staff. The Catechism of the Council of Trent. LC 82-50588. 603p. 1983. pap. 15.00 (ISBN 0-89555-185-3). TAN Bks Pubs.
Council, Raymond. The One Who Made His Cross. 1986. 2.95 (ISBN 0-89536-793-9, 6811). CSS of Ohio.
Counsins, Ewert H. Process Thought on the Eve of the Twenty-First Century. 50p. (Orig.). 1985. pap. 3.95x (ISBN 0-932269-25-7). Wyndham Hall.
Countess, Robert H. The Jehovah's Witnesses' New Testament: A Critical Analysis. 1982. pap. 5.95 (ISBN 0-87552-210-6). Presby & Reformed.
Count Gobineau, Arthur. The Renaissance Savonarola. Levy, Oscar, ed. Cohen, Paul V., tr. (Fr., Illus.). 349p. 1986. Repr. of 1913 ed. lib. bdg. 75.00 (ISBN 0-89760-264-1). Telegraph Bks.
Countryman, Jack. God's Promises for Living. 285p. 1984. leatherbound 19.95 (ISBN 0-937347-01-9). J Countryman Pubs.
--God's Promises for Your Every Need. 334p. 1981. leatherbound 19.95 (ISBN 0-937347-00-0). J Countryman Pubs.
Countryman, L. William. The Mystical Way in the Fourth Gospel: Crossing over into God. LC 86-45913. 160p. 1987. pap. text ed. 9.95 (ISBN 0-8006-1949-8, 1-1949). Fortress.
Countryman, L. Wm. The Rich Christian in the Church of the Early Empire: Contradictions & Accomodations. LC 80-81884. (Texts & Studies in Religion: Vol. 7). viii, 248p. 1980. 49.95x (ISBN 0-88946-970-9). E Mellen.
Countryman, Marsha, ed. see Wilkerson, Ralph.
Countryman, William. Biblical Authority or Biblical Tyranny? Scripture & the Christian Pilgrimage. LC 81-70591. 96p. 1982. pap. 6.95 (ISBN 0-8006-1630-8, 1-1630). Fortress.
Coupland, Susan. Beginning to Pray in Old Age. LC 85-17075. (Parish Life Sourcebks.: Vol. II). xiv, 80p. 1985. pap. 6.95 (ISBN 0-936384-29-8). Cowley Pubns.
Courlander, Harold. The Drum & the Hoe: Life & Lore of the Haitian People. (California Library Reprint: No. 31). (Illus.). 436p. 1981. 40.00x (ISBN 0-520-02364-1); pap. 10.95 (ISBN 0-520-05449-0, CAL 731). U of Cal Pr.
Courlander, Harold & Bastien, Remy. Religion & Politics in Haiti. LC 66-26633. (Illus.). 1970. 3.95 (ISBN 0-911976-00-0). ICR.
Cournand, Andre & Levy, Maurice. Shaping the Future: Gaston Berger & the Concept of Prospective. LC 72-78388. (Current Topics of Contemporary Thought Ser.). 314p. 1973. 72.75 (ISBN 0-677-12550-X). Gordon & Breach.
Coursen, Herbert R., Jr. Christian Ritual & the World of Shakespeare's Tragedies. 441p. 1976. 32.50 (ISBN 0-8387-1518-4). Bucknell U Pr.
Coursen, Virgene. Bulletin Board Ideas for Sunday School & Church. 32p. 1977. pap. 3.50 (ISBN 0-687-04374-3). Abingdon.
Courtade, Anthony E. The Structure of John Webster's Play. Hogg, James, ed. (Jacobean Drama Studies). 172p. (Orig.). 1980. pap. 15.00 (ISBN 0-317-40036-3, Salzburg Studies). Longwood Pub Group.
Courthion, Pierre. Rouault. (Library of Great Painters). (Illus.). 1977. 45.00 (ISBN 0-8109-0459-4). Abrams.
Courthope, W. J. Essays on Milton. 1908. lib. bdg. 10.00 (ISBN 0-8414-3599-5). Folcroft.
Courtin, Robina, ed. see McDonald, Kathleen.
Courtney, Charles, tr. see Dumery, Henry.
Courtney, Ragan. Meditations for the Suddenly Single. pap. 5.95 (ISBN 0-310-70301-8). Zondervan.
Courtright. Ganesa: Lord of Obstacles, Lord of Beginnings. 1985. 29.95x (ISBN 0-19-503572-0). Oxford U Pr.
Cousar, Charles. Galatians: The Bible Commentary for Teaching & Preaching. LC 81-82354. (Interpretation Ser.). 168p. (James Mays General Editor of the series, Paul Achtemeier New Testament editor). 1982. 13.95 (ISBN 0-8042-3138-9). John Knox.
Cousens, Gabriel. Spiritual Nutrition. 232p. 1986. 9.95 (ISBN 0-9615875-2-0). Cassandra Pr.
Cousens, H. The Architectural Antiquities of Western India. (Illus.). 1983. text ed. 34.00x. Coronet Bks.

Cousins, Ewert, ed. Bonaventure: The Soul's Journey into God: the Tree of Life, the Life of Francis. LC 78-60723. (Classics of Western Spirituality). 380p. 1978. 13.95 (ISBN 0-8091-0240-4); pap. 10.95 (ISBN 0-8091-2121-2). Paulist Pr.

Cousins, Ewert, ed. see Green, Arthur.

Cousins, H. James. Irish Mythology. 59.95 (ISBN 0-8490-0425-X). Gordon Pr.

Cousins, Kathryn, et al. How to Read a Spiritual Book. 1.25 (ISBN 0-8091-2415-7). Paulist Pr.

Cousins, L., et al, eds. Buddhist Studies in Honour of I. B. Horner. LC 74-77963. 275p. 1974. lib. bdg. 45.00 (ISBN 90-277-0473-2, Pub. by Reidel Holland). Kluwer Academic.

Cousins, Norman. Albert Schweitzer's Mission: Healing & Peace. 1985. 16.95 (ISBN 0-393-02238-2). Norton.

--Healing & Belief. LC 82-81098. 64p. 1982. 65.00 (ISBN 0-88014-041-0). Mosaic Pr OH.

--The Healing Heart. (General Ser.). 1984. lib. bdg. 14.95 (ISBN 0-8161-3669-6, Large Print Bks). G K Hall.

--The Improbable Triumvirate: John F. Kennedy, Pope John, Nikita Khrushchev. (Illus.). 176p. 1984. pap. 4.95 (ISBN 0-393-30162-1). Norton.

Coussemaker, Edmond de see De Coussemaker, Edmond.

Coustant, Pierre. Epistolae Romanorum Pontificum. 942p. Repr. of 1721 ed. text ed. 207.00x (ISBN 0-576-99106-6, Pub. by Gregg Intl Pubs England). Gregg Intl.

Couture, Roger A., et al, trs. see Coste, Rene.

Covannier, Henry. St. Francis De Sales. 1973. Repr. 5.00 (ISBN 0-8198-0512-2). Dghtrs St Paul.

Cove, Mary & Regan, Jane. Teaching Religion Effectively Program. 96p. 1982. pap. 3.50 (ISBN 0-697-01825-3); program manual 24.95 (ISBN 0-697-01826-1). Wm C Brown.

Cove, Mary K. & Mueller, Mary L. Regarding Religious Education. LC 77-10873. 181p. (Orig.). 1977. pap. 8.95 (ISBN 0-89135-011-X). Religious Educ.

Covell, Alan C. Ecstasy: Shamanism in Korea. LC 83-81487. (Illus.). 107p. 1983. 19.50x (ISBN 0-930878-33-7). Hollym Intl.

Covell, Jon Carter & Yamada, Abbot S. Unraveling Zen's Red Thread: Ikkyu's Controversial Way. LC 80-81040. (Illus.). 341p. 1980. 21.50x (ISBN 0-930878-19-1). Hollym Intl.

Covell, Ralph. W. A. P Martin: Pioneer of Progress in China. LC 77-13321. Repr. of 1978 ed. 59.10 (ISBN 0-8357-9133-5, 2012723). Bks Demand UMI.

Covell, Ralph R. Confucius, the Buddha, & Christ: A History of the Gospel in Chinese. LC 86-8615. 304p. (Orig.). 1986. pap. 14.95 (ISBN 0-88344-267-1, CIP). Orbis Bks.

Coventry, Camilla, tr. see Shestov, Lev.

Coventry, F., tr. see Grotius, Hugo.

Coventry, John. Faith in Jesus Christ. 54p. 1982. pap. 3.95 (ISBN 0-86683-620-9, HarpR). Har-Row.

Coverdale, M., tr. from Dutch. The Original & Sprynge of All Sectes & Orders by Whome, Wha or Where (Sic) They Beganne. LC 79-84127. (English Experience Ser.: No. 946). (Eng.). 140p. 1979. Repr. of 1537 ed. lib. bdg. 11.50 (ISBN 90-221-0946-1). Walter J Johnson.

Coverdale, Myles. Remains of Myles Coverdale, Bishop of Exeter. 1846. 51.00 (ISBN 0-384-09950-5). Johnson Repr.

Coverdale, Myles, tr. see Bullinger, Heinrich.

Covey, Cyclone. Calalus: A Roman Jewish Colony in America from the Time of Charlemagne Through Alfred the Great. 190p. 1975. 10.00 (ISBN 0-533-01209-0). Vantage.

Covey, R. O. Probing Our Problems. 176p. (Orig.). 1986. pap. 5.95 (ISBN 0-934942-59-5, 3950). White Wing Pub.

Covey, Stephen R. How to Succeed with People. 151p. 1971. 6.95 (ISBN 0-87747-439-7). Deseret Bk.

--Spiritual Roots of Human Relations. LC 72-119477. 9.95 (ISBN 0-87747-315-3). Deseret Bk.

Covina, Paul, ed. Celebrating Marriage: Preparing the Wedding Liturgy - A Workbook for the Engaged Couple. 1987. pap. 4.95. Pastoral Pr.

Covington, Jim. Confessions of a Single Father. LC 82-13232. 192p. 1982. 13.95 (ISBN 0-8298-0412-9). Pilgrim NY.

Cowan, Dale H. Human Organ Transplantation: Societal, Medical-Legal, Regulatory, & Reimbursement Issues. LC 86-29478. 1987. price not set (ISBN 0-910701-20-2). Health Admin Pr.

Cowan, Henry. John Knox: The Hero of the Scottish Reformation. LC 70-133817. (Illus.). Repr. of 1905 ed. 27.50 (ISBN 0-404-01788-6). AMS Pr.

--Landmarks of Church History to the Reformation. new rev. & enl. ed. LC 70-144590. Repr. of 1896 ed. 17.00 (ISBN 0-404-01787-8). AMS Pr.

Cowan, I. B., ed. Blast & Counterblast: Contemporary Writings on the Scottish Reformation. 76p. 1985. 22.00x (ISBN 0-317-39400-2, Pub. by Saltire Society). State Mutual Bk.

Cowan, Ian B. The Scottish Reformation. LC 82-5834. 256p. 1982. 25.00x (ISBN 0-312-70519-0). St Martin.

Cowan, Ian B. & Shaw, Duncan, eds. The Renaissance & Reformation in Scotland. 220p. 1983. 20.00x (ISBN 0-7073-0261-7, Scot Acad Pr). Longwood Pub Group.

Cowan, Lyn. Masochism: A Jungian View. LC 82-16957. 137p. (Orig.). 1982. pap. 12.00 (ISBN 0-88214-320-4). Spring Pubns.

Cowan, Marvin W. Los Mormones: Sus Doctrinas Refutadas a la Luz De la Biblia. De La Fuente, Tomas, tr. from Eng. 160p. 1985. pap. 3.50 (ISBN 0-311-05763-2). Casa Bautista.

Cowan, Paul & Cowan, Rachael. Mixed Blessings: Jews & Gentiles Confront Intermarriage. LC 87-480. 288p. 1987. 17.95 (ISBN 0-385-19502-8). Doubleday.

Cowan, Paul & Cowan, Rachel. A Torah Is Written. (Illus.). 32p. 1986. 12.95 (ISBN 0-8276-0270-7). Jewish Pubns.

Cowan, Rachael, jt. auth. see Cowan, Paul.

Cowan, Rachel, jt. auth. see Cowan, Paul.

Cowan, Richard O. Doctrine & Covenants: Our Modern Scripture. rev. ed. LC 78-19190. (Illus.). 1978. pap. 7.95 (ISBN 0-8425-1316-7). Brigham.

Coward, Harold. Pluralism: Challenge to World Religions. LC 84-14737. 144p. (Orig.). 1985. pap. 8.95 (ISBN 0-88344-710-X). Orbis Bks.

Coward, Harold & Kawamura, Leslie, eds. Religion & Ethnicity. 181p. 1978. pap. text ed. 9.95 (ISBN 0-88920-064-5, Pub. by Wilfrid Laurier Canada). Humanities.

Coward, Harold C. Jung & Eastern Thought. (Series in Transpersonal & Humanistic Philosophy). 229p. 1985. 39.50 (ISBN 0-88706-052-8); pap. 12.95 (ISBN 0-88706-051-X). State U NY Pr.

Coward, Harold G. Sphota Theory of Language. 1981. 12.00x (ISBN 0-8364-0692-3). South Asia Bks.

Coward, Harold G., ed. Language in Indian Philosophy & Religion. 98p. 1978. pap. text ed. 9.95x (ISBN 0-919812-07-4, Pub. by Wilfrid Laurier Canada). Humanities.

Coward, Parnell C. Revelation, Systematically Studied. 1983. pap. 6.95 (ISBN 0-87148-739-X). Pathway Pr.

Cowdrey, H. E. The Age of Abbot Desiderius: Montecassino, the Papacy & the Normans in the Eleventh & Early Twelfth Centuries. 1983. 55.00x (ISBN 0-19-821939-3). Oxford U Pr.

--Popes, Monks & Crusaders. (No. 27). 400p. 1983. 40.00 (ISBN 0-907628-34-6). Hambledon Press.

Cowdrey, H. E., ed. see Pope Gregory VII.

Cowell, Barbara, jt. auth. see Wilson, John.

Cowell, E. B. & Muller, F. Max. Buddhist Mahayana Texts. (Sacred Bks. of the East: Vol. 49). 15.00 (ISBN 0-89581-534-6). Asian Human Pr.

Cowell, Sally. Happy Times with Happy Seeds. (Happy Days Bks.). (Illus.). 24p. 1984. 1.59 (ISBN 0-87239-738-6, 3708). Standard Pub.

Cowen, Deborah, ed. The Year of Grace of the Lord. 254p. (Orig.). 1980. pap. 8.95 (ISBN 0-913836-68-0). St Vladimirs.

Cowen, Gerald. Sermon Starters from the Greek New Testament. LC 84-27448. 1985. pap. 5.95 (ISBN 0-8054-1397-9). Broadman.

Cowen, Philip. Memories of an American Jew. facsimile ed. LC 74-27974. (Modern Jewish Experience Ser.). (Illus.). 1975. Repr. of 1932 ed. 37.50x (ISBN 0-405-06703-8). Ayer Co Pubs.

Cowett, Mark. Birmingham's Rabbi: Morris Newfield & Alabama, 1895-1940. LC 85-20897. 379p. 1986. 22.50 (ISBN 0-8173-0284-0). U of Ala Pr.

Cowgill, Carol. Adult Confession: Conversion in Process. 80p. 1984. pap. 3.50 (ISBN 0-697-02030-4). Wm C Brown.

Cowie, Frederick J. Giants of Medieval Church. 175p. Date not set. pap. 7.95 (ISBN 0-87973-586-4, 586). Our Sunday Visitor.

--Pioneers of Catholic Europe. LC 84-62160. 190p. 1985. pap. 6.95 (ISBN 0-87973-713-1, 713). Our Sunday Visitor.

Cowles, C. S. Family Journey into Joy. 168p. 1982. pap. 3.95 (ISBN 0-8341-0803-8). Beacon Hill.

Cowles, H. Robert. Opening the Old Testament. LC 80-65149. (Illus.). 158p. (Orig.). 1980. pap. 4.50 (ISBN 0-87509-279-9); Leader's Guide. 2.95 (ISBN 0-87509-283-7). Chr Pubns.

Cowles, N. Robert. Opening the New Testament. LC 84-72468. 158p. (Orig.). 1985. pap. 4.95 (ISBN 0-87509-357-4); leader's guide 2.95 (ISBN 0-87509-358-2). Chr Pubns.

Cowley, A. E. The Hittites. (British Academy, London; Schweich Lectures on Biblical Archaeology Series, 1918). pap. 19.00 (ISBN 0-8115-1260-6). Kraus Repr.

Cowley, A. E., ed. see Gesunius, William.

Cowley, F. G. The Monastic Order in South Wales: 1066-1349. (Studies in Welsh History: No. 1). 325p. 1977. text ed. 32.50x (ISBN 0-7083-0648-9, Pub. by U of Wales Pr). Humanities.

Cowley, Malcolm, ed. see Emerson, Ralph Waldo.

Cowley, Roger W. The Traditional Interpretation of the Apocalypse of St. John in the Ethiopian Orthodox Church. LC 82-19834. (University of Cambridge Oriental Publications Ser.: No. 33). 480p. 1983. 77.50 (ISBN 0-521-24561-3). Cambridge U Pr.

Cowling, Maurice. Religion & Public Doctrine in Modern England: Assaults, Vol. 2. (Cambridge Studies in the History & Theory of Politics). 403p. 1985. 49.50 (ISBN 0-521-25959-2). Cambridge U Pr.

--Religion & Public Doctrine in Modern England. (Cambridge Studies in the History & Theory of Politics). 498p. 1981. 59.50 (ISBN 0-521-23289-9). Cambridge U Pr.

Cowman, Charles E. Streams in the Desert Sampler. 128p. 1983. pap. 3.95 (ISBN 0-310-37651-3, 6881P). Zondervan.

Cowman, Charles E. & Serrano, Antonio. Manantiales en el Desierto. Orig. Title: Stream in the Desert. 1986. pap. 4.95 (ISBN 0-311-40028-0, Edit Mundo). Casa Bautista.

Cowman, Mrs. Charles E. Cumbres De Inspiracion. Robleto, Adolfo, tr. 1982. pap. 4.25 (ISBN 0-311-40026-4). Casa Bautista.

--Mountain Trailways for Youth: Devotions for Young People. 1979. pap. 6.95 (ISBN 0-310-37641-6, 6880P). Zondervan.

--Springs in the Valley. 1977. large-print ed. kivar 9.95 (ISBN 0-310-22517-5, 12562L). Zondervan.

--Streams in the Desert. 1974. large print kiver 9.95 (ISBN 0-310-22527-2, 12555L). Zondervan.

--Streams in the Desert, Vol. 1. 9.95 (ISBN 0-310-22520-5, 6901, Pub. by Cowman). Zondervan.

--Streams in the Desert, Vol. 2. 1986. 9.95 (ISBN 0-310-22430-6, 6902, Pub. by Cowman). Zondervan.

--Streams in the Desert, Vol. 2. large print ed. 384p. 1976. 9.95 (ISBN 0-310-22537-X, 12557L). Zondervan.

Cowman, Mrs. Charles E., ed. Springs in the Valley. 2nd ed. 384p. 1980. pap. 4.95 (ISBN 0-310-22511-6, 6806P). Zondervan.

Cowper, J. M. & Manning, Robert, eds. Mediations on the Supper of Our Lord. (EETS, OS Ser.: No. 60). Repr. of 1875 ed. 15.00 (ISBN 0-527-00054-X). Kraus Repr.

Cox, Bill, jt. auth. see Boring, Holland, Sr.

Cox, Carol M. Jubilee Time: Celebrating Gods Grace & Justice. 112p. (Orig.). 1984. pap. 8.25 (ISBN 0-687-20609-X). Abingdon.

Cox, Claude E. The Armenian Translation of Deuteronomy. Stone, Michael E., ed. LC 81-5273. 1981. text ed. 16.50 (ISBN 0-89130-491-6, 21-02-02); pap. text ed. 12.00 (ISBN 0-89130-492-4). Scholars Pr GA.

--Hexaplaric Materials Preserved in the Armenian Version. (Septuagint & Cognate Studies). 1986. text ed. 12.95 (ISBN 1-55540-028-0, 06-04-21); pap. 9.95 (ISBN 1-55540-029-9). Scholars Pr GA.

Cox, Clyde C. Apocalyptic Commentary. 1970. 6.95 (ISBN 0-87148-011-5). Pathway Pr.

--Evangelical Precepts of the Revelation. 1972. 5.95 (ISBN 0-87148-278-9). Pathway Pr.

Cox, Dermot. Proverbs, with Introduction to Sapiential Books. (Old Testament Ser.: Vol. 17). 1982. 12.95 (ISBN 0-89453-417-3); pap. 9.95 (ISBN 0-89453-251-0). M Glazier.

Cox, Edward F. Twelve for Twelve. 64p. 1982. pap. 3.50 (ISBN 0-8341-0787-2). Beacon Hill.

Cox, Frank L. According to Luke. 1941. pap. 2.75 (ISBN 0-88027-030-6). Firm Foun Pub.

--Bedside Meditations. 1967. pap. 2.00 (ISBN 0-88027-000-4). Firm Foun Pub.

--One Hundred One Sermon Outlines. 1971. 3.00 (ISBN 0-88027-028-4). Firm Foun Pub.

--Seventy-Seven Sermon Outlines. 1958. pap. 1.75 (ISBN 0-88027-052-7). Firm Foun Pub.

Cox, Frank L., jt. auth. see Showalter, G. H.

Cox, G. W. An Introduction to the Science of Comparative Mythology & Folklore. 69.95 (ISBN 0-8490-0420-9). Gordon Pr.

Cox, George W. The Crusades. Repr. 12.00 (ISBN 0-8482-3560-6). Norwood Edns.

--An Introduction to the Science of Comparative Mythology & Folklore. 1976. lib. bdg. 59.95 (ISBN 0-8490-2071-9). Gordon Pr.

--Latin & Teutonic Christendom: An Historical Sketch. LC 77-94557. 1979. Repr. of 1870 ed. lib. bdg. 30.00 (ISBN 0-89341-259-7). Longwood Pub Group.

--A Manual of Mythology. LC 77-94556. 1979. Repr. of 1867 ed. lib. bdg. 30.00 (ISBN 0-89341-307-0). Longwood Pub Group.

--Tales of the Gods & Heroes. LC 77-94564. 1979. Repr. of 1895 ed. lib. bdg. 25.00 (ISBN 0-89341-309-7). Longwood Pub Group.

Cox, Gray. Bearing Witness: Quaker Process & a Culture of Peace. LC 85-61133. 32p. (Orig.). 1985. pap. 2.50x (ISBN 0-87574-262-9). Pendle Hill.

Cox, Harvey. Feast of Fools: A Theological Essay on Festivity & Fantasy. LC 75-75914. (William Belden Noble Lectures Ser). 1969. 15.00x (ISBN 0-674-29525-0). Harvard U Pr.

--Just As I Am. LC 82-11631. 160p. 1983. 10.95 (ISBN 0-687-20687-1). Abingdon.

--Religion in the Secular City: Toward a Post-Modern Theology. 320p. 1984. 16.95 (ISBN 0-671-45344-0). S&S.

--Religion in the Secular City: Toward a Postmodern Theology. 304p. 1985. pap. 7.95 (ISBN 0-671-52805-X, Touchstone Bks). S&S.

--Turning East: The Promise & Peril of the New Orientalism. 1979. pap. 7.95 (ISBN 0-671-24405-1, Touchstone Bks). S&S.

Cox, Heather & Rickard, Garth. Carols to Sing, Clap & Play: A Companion to the Soprano Recorder Tuition Books. (Illus.). 1984. pap. 4.50 (ISBN 0-918812-36-4). MMB Music.

Cox, J. Charles. The English Parish Church. (Illus.). 1977. Repr. of 1914 ed. 25.00x (ISBN 0-7158-1174-6). Charles River Bks.

Cox, James H. Confessions of a Moonlight Writer: A Freelancer's Guide to the Church Market. LC 80-70315. 97p. (Orig.). 1982. pap. 5.95 (ISBN 0-939298-00-7). J M Prods.

Cox, James W. Preaching: A Comprehensive Approach to the Design & Delivery of Sermons. LC 84-48214. 320p. 1985. 18.45 (ISBN 0-06-061600-8, HarpR). Har-Row.

Cox, James W., ed. Biblical Preaching: An Expositor's Treasury. LC 83-10518. 368p. (Orig.). 1983. 19.95 (ISBN 0-664-21397-9). Westminster.

--The Ministers Manual for Nineteen Eighty-Six. LC 25-21658. 352p. 1985. 14.45 (ISBN 0-06-061595-8, HarpR). Har-Row.

--The Ministers Manual for 1987. 1986. 14.45 (ISBN 0-317-52366-X, HarpR). Har-Row.

Cox, James W. & Cox, Patricia P., eds. Twentieth Century Pulpit, Vol. II. LC 77-21997. 1981. pap. 9.95 (ISBN 0-687-42716-9). Abingdon.

Cox, Jan. Death of Gurdjieff in the Foothills of Georgia: Secret Papers of an American Work Group. 316p. 1980. 9.00 (ISBN 0-936380-03-9). Chan Shal Imi.

Cox, Jeffrey. The English Churches in a Secular Society: Lambeth, 1870-1930. (Illus.). 1982. 45.00x (ISBN 0-19-503019-2). Oxford U Pr.

Cox, Jim, jt. auth. see Robison, James.

Cox, Jimmie, jt. auth. see Robinson, James.

Cox, Michael. Handbook of Christian Spirituality: The Major Figures & Teachings from the New Testament to the 20th Century. LC 84-48236. 288p. 1985. 14.45 (ISBN 0-06-061601-6, HarpR). Har-Row.

--Mysticism: The Direct Experience of God. 256p. 1984. pap. 9.95 (ISBN 0-85030-280-3). Newcastle Pub.

Cox, Montagu H. & Forrest, G. Topham. Parish of St. Margaret, Westminster: Neighbourhood of Whitehall, Vol. 1. LC 70-138272. (London County Council. Survey of London: No. 13). Repr. of 1930 ed. 74.50 (ISBN 0-404-51663-7). AMS Pr.

Cox, Montagu H., ed. The Parish of St. Margaret, Westminster. LC 70-138272. (London County Council. Survey of London: No. 10). (Illus.). Repr. of 1926 ed. 74.50 (ISBN 0-404-51660-2). AMS Pr.

Cox, Norman W., ed. Encyclopedia of Southern Baptists, Vols. I & II. LC 58-5417. (Illus.). 1958. 39.95 (ISBN 0-8054-6501-4). Broadman.

Cox, Patricia. Biography in Late Antiquity: A Quest for the Holy Man. LC 82-4946. (The Transformation of the Classical Heritage Ser.: Vol. 5). 208p. 1983. text ed. 30.00x (ISBN 0-520-04612-9). U of Cal Pr.

Cox, Patricia P., jt. ed. see Cox, James W.

Cox, Richard H. Locke on War & Peace. LC 82-42514. 240p. 1983. pap. text ed. 12.50 (ISBN 0-8191-2662-4). U Pr of Amer.

Cox, Robert G. Do You Mean Me, Lord? The Call to the Ordained Ministry. LC 85-8785. 116p. 1985. pap. 8.95 (ISBN 0-664-24668-0). Westminster.

Cox, S. & Drysdale, A. H. The Epistle to Philemon. 246p. 1982. lib. bdg. 9.25 Smythe Sewn (ISBN 0-86524-134-1, 7108). Klock & Klock.

Cox, S., jt. auth. see Morgan, J.

Cox, Samuel. Commentary on Job. 562p. 1986. 18.95 (ISBN 0-8254-2328-7); pap. 14.95 (ISBN 0-8254-2330-9). Kregel.

--The Pilgrim Psalms: An Exposition of the Songs of Degrees. 255p. 1983. lib. bdg. 9.50 (ISBN 0-86524-159-7, 1903). Klock & Klock.

Cox, Terri, ed. see D'Addio, Janie.

Cox, William E. Biblical Studies in Final Things. 1967. pap. 5.95 (ISBN 0-87552-152-5). Presby & Reformed.

--An Examination of Dispensationalism. 1963. pap. 2.75 (ISBN 0-87552-153-3). Presby & Reformed.

--Sir, I Represent Christian Salesmanship. pap. 1.50 (ISBN 0-686-64392-5). Reiner.

--Why I Left Scofieldism. 1975. pap. 0.50 (ISBN 0-87552-154-1). Presby & Reformed.

Cox, Willis F. Conversations about God from the Journal of Willis F. Cox. LC 85-91148. (Illus., Orig.). 1985. 11.95 (ISBN 0-9610758-2-1); pap. 6.95 (ISBN 0-9610758-3-X); pap. text ed. 6.95 (ISBN 0-9610758-1-3). W F Cox.

Cox-Gedmark, Jan. Coping with Physical Disability. LC 79-28275. (Christian Care Bks.). 118p. 1980. pap. 7.95 (ISBN 0-664-24297-9). Westminster.

Coxhead, Nona. The Relevance of Bliss. 192p. 1986. pap. 6.95 (ISBN 0-312-67055-9). St Martin.

Coy, Genevieve. Counsels of Perfection: A Baha'i Guide to Mature Living. 192p. 1979. 6.95 (ISBN 0-85398-079-9). G Ronald Pub.

Coyle, Alcuin & Bonner, Dismas. The Church Under Tension. 1976. pap. 2.95 (ISBN 0-685-77495-3). Franciscan Herald.

Coyle, Neva. Daily Thoughts on Living Free. LC 82-4495. 174p. (Orig.). 1982. pap. 4.95 (ISBN 0-87123-286-3, 210286). Bethany Hse.

--Free to Be Thin Study Guide Discipline, No. 2. 58p. 1982. pap. 2.25 (ISBN 0-87123-169-7, 210169). Bethany Hse.

--Perseverance for People under Pressure. 64p. (Orig.). 1986. pap. 2.50 saddle stitched (ISBN 0-87123-888-8). Bethany Hse.

--Restoration. 50p. (Orig.). 1985. saddlestitched 2.50 (ISBN 0-87123-851-9). Bethany Hse.

Coyle, Neva & Chapian, Marie. There's More to Being Thin Than Being Thin. 170p. (Orig.). 1984. pap. 5.95 (ISBN 0-87123-443-2, 210443). Bethany Hse.

Coyle, Neva, compiled by. Scriptures for Living Free. 58p. (Orig.). 1982. pap. 5.95 (ISBN 0-87123-576-5, 210576). Bethany Hse.

Coyle, Thomas. This Is Our Mass. 144p. 1985. pap. 3.50 (ISBN 0-89622-233-0). Twenty-Third.

Coyne, John J., tr. see Schutte, Josef F.

Cozort, Dan. Highest Yoga Tantra. 220p. (Orig.). 1986. pap. 10.95 (ISBN 0-937938-32-7). Snow Lion.

Crabb, Jr. & Lawrence, J. Effective Biblical Counseling. 1986. 9.95 (ISBN 0-88469-187-X). BMH Bks.

--Encouragement. 1986. 9.95 (ISBN 0-88469-199-3). BMH Bks.

Crabb, Lawrence J., Jr. Basic Principles of Biblical Counseling. 160p. 1975. 9.95 (ISBN 0-310-22560-4, 10159). Zondervan.

--Basic Principles of Biblical Counseling. 1986. 9.95 (ISBN 0-88469-186-1). BMH Bks.

--Effective Biblical Counseling: A Model for Helping Caring Christians Become Capable Counselors. 1977. 10.95 (ISBN 0-310-22570-1, 10173). Zondervan.

--How to Become One with Your Mate. 1986. write for info. BMH Bks.

--The Marriage Builder: A Blueprint for Couples & Counselors. 176p. 1982. 9.95 (ISBN 0-310-22580-9, 10181). Zondervan.

Crabb, Lawrence J., Jr. & Allender, Dan B. Encouragement: The Key to Caring. 144p. 1984. 9.95 (ISBN 0-310-22590-6, 10182). Zondervan.

Crabtree, Charles T. This I Believe. LC 81-84913. 160p. (Orig.). 1982. pap. 2.95 (ISBN 0-88243-758-5, 02-0758). Gospel Pub.

Crabtree, Ronald. On Wings of Healing. 80p. 1986. 21.00X (ISBN 0-7223-2002-7, Pub. by A H Stockwell England). State Mutual Bk.

Crabtree, T. T. The Zondervan Nineteen Eighty-Seven Pastor's Annual: A Planned Preaching Program for the Year. (Pastor's Annual Ser.). 384p. 1986. 12.95 (ISBN 0-310-22701-1, 11384P). Zondervan.

--The Zondervan Pastor's Annual, 1986. 384p. 1985. pap. 11.95 (ISBN 0-310-22691-0, 11383P). Zondervan.

--Zondervan Pastor's Annual 1988: A Planned Preaching Program. rev. ed. Smith, M., ed. (Zondervan Pastor's Annuals). 384p. 1987. Repr. of 1968 ed. price not set (ISBN 0-310-22711-9). Zondervan.

Cracraft, James. The Church Reform of Peter the Great. 1971. 27.50x (ISBN 0-8047-0747-2). Stanford U Pr.

Craddock, Fred. Philippians: Interpretation: A Bible Commentary for Teaching & Preaching. Mays, James L. & Miller, Patrick D., eds. LC 84-47797. 96p. 1984. 12.95 (ISBN 0-8042-3140-0). John Knox.

Craddock, Fred B. The Gospels. LC 80-26270. 160p. (Orig.). 1981. pap. 8.95 (ISBN 0-687-15655-6). Abingdon.

--John. Hayes, John H., ed. LC 82-48095. (Knox Preaching Guides Ser.). 149p. 1982. pap. 6.95. John Knox.

--Preaching. 224p. 1985. 16.95 (ISBN 0-687-33636-8). Abingdon.

Craddock, Fred B., jt. auth. see Saunders, Ernest W.

Craddock, Fred B., et al. Preaching the New Common Lectionary. 176p. (Orig.). 1984. pap. 8.50 (ISBN 0-687-33845-X). Abingdon.

--Preaching the New Common Lectionary: Year B: Lent, Holy Week, Easter, 2 vols. 256p. (Orig.). 1984. Vol. 2, 256 pgs. pap. 9.95 (ISBN 0-687-33846-8); Vol. 3, 304 pgs. pap. 11.95 (ISBN 0-687-33847-6). Abingdon.

--Preaching the New Common Lectionary: Year C-Advent, Christmas, Epiphany. 176p. (Orig.). 1985. pap. 9.50 (ISBN 0-687-33848-4). Abingdon.

Craddock, Fred B., et al, eds. Preaching the New Common Lectionary: Year C, Lent, Holy Week, Easter. 240p. (Orig.). 1986. pap. 9.95 (ISBN 0-687-33849-2). Abingdon.

Craemer, Willy De see De Craemer, Willy.

Craft, Hazel S. Jesus God's Gift of Peace to You. 100p. (Orig.). 1983. pap. 5.95 (ISBN 0-88144-013-2, CPS-013). Christian Pub.

Cragg, Gerald R. Church & the Age of Reason. (History of the Church: Vol. 4). (Orig.). 1961. pap. 5.95 (ISBN 0-14-020505-5, Pelican). Penguin.

--Puritanism in the Period of the Great Persecution, 1660-1688. LC 76-143557. 1971. Repr. of 1957 ed. 16.00x (ISBN 0-8462-1578-0). Russell.

Cragg, Kenneth. Muhammad & the Christian: A Question of Response. 192p. (Orig.). 1984. pap. 8.95 (ISBN 0-88344-349-X). Orbis Bks.

--The Pen & the Faith: Eight Modern Muslim Writers & the Qur'an. 188p. 1985. text ed. 16.00x (ISBN 0-04-297044-X). Allen Unwin.

--The Wisdom of the Sufis. LC 76-7032. (The Wisdom Books). 1976. pap. 2.75 (ISBN 0-8112-0627-0, NDP424). New Directions.

Craghan, John. Esther, Judith, Tobit, Jonah, Ruth. (Old Testament Message Ser.: Vol. 16). 1982. 12.95 (ISBN 0-89453-416-5); pap. 8.95 (ISBN 0-89453-249-9). M Glazier.

--The Psalms: Prayers for the Ups, Downs & In-Betweens of Life: A Literary Experiential Approach. (Background Bks.: Vol. 2). 1985. pap. 7.95 (ISBN 0-89453-439-4). M Glazier.

Craghan, John F. Exodus. (Bible Commentary Ser.). 112p. 1985. pap. 2.95 (ISBN 0-8146-1371-3). Liturgical Pr.

--Love & Thunder: A Sprituality of the Old Testament. 248p. 1983. pap. text ed. 11.00 (ISBN 0-8146-1279-2). Liturgical Pr.

--Yesterday's Word Today. LC 82-12648. 496p. 1982. pap. 14.95 (ISBN 0-8146-1273-3). Liturgical Pr.

Craig, Barbara. The Evolution of a Mystery Play: Le Sacrifice d'Abraham. 329p. 1983. 24.00 (ISBN 0-917786-30-0). Summa Pubns.

Craig, Diana. Moses & the Flight from Egypt. LC 84-50448. (Bible Stories Ser.). (Illus.). 24p. 1984. 5.45 (ISBN 0-382-06945-5); PLB 6.96 (ISBN 0-382-06797-5). Silver.

--The Young Moses. LC 84-50449. (Bible Stories Ser.). (Illus.). 24p. 1984. PLB 6.96 (ISBN 0-382-06797-5); 5.45 (ISBN 0-382-06946-3). Silver.

Craig, Diana, adapted by. Elijah: Messenger of God. LC 84-51683. (Bible Stories Ser.). (Illus.). 24p. 1984. 5.45 (ISBN 0-382-06943-9); PLB 6.96 (ISBN 0-382-06794-0). Silver.

--Jacob & Esau. LC 84-51684. (Bible Stories Ser.). (Illus.). 24p. 1984. 5.45 (ISBN 0-382-06944-7); PLB 5.96 (ISBN 0-382-06795-9). Silver.

Craig, Floyd. How to Communicate with Single Adults. 1978. pap. 11.95 (ISBN 0-8054-3510-7). Broadman.

Craig, Floyd A. Christian Communicator's Handbook. rev. ed. LC 77-80946. 1977. pap. 8.95 (ISBN 0-8054-3508-5). Broadman.

Craig, Hardin. English Religious Drama of the Middle Ages. LC 78-6893. 1978. Repr. of 1968 ed. lib. bdg. 37.50x (ISBN 0-313-20496-9, CRER). Greenwood.

Craig, James D. Fishers of Men: Group Leader Guide. 3rd rev. ed. 116p. 1981. 4.00 (ISBN 0-88151-016-5). Lay Leadership.

--New Life Studies. 2nd rev. abr. ed. 174p. 1983. pap. text ed. 15.00 (ISBN 0-88151-023-8). Lay Leadership.

--New Life Studies: Group Leader's Guide. 2nd rev. abr. ed. 48p. 1983. 4.00 (ISBN 0-88151-025-4). Lay Leadership.

--New Life Studies: Home Study Guide. 2nd rev. abr. ed. 64p. 1983. 8.00 (ISBN 0-88151-024-6). Lay Leadership.

--Rejoice in the Lord. 32p. 1981. pap. 2.49 (ISBN 0-88151-018-1). Lay Leadership.

Craig, James D. & Hill, Donald E. One Hundred Series Implementation Outline. 38p. 1980. pap. 9.95 inc. cassettes (ISBN 0-88151-020-3). Lay Leadership.

Craig, James D., ed. All about Cells. 2nd rev. ed. 32p. 1981. pap. 2.49 (ISBN 0-88151-017-3). Lay Leadership.

--The Care & Feeding of New Converts. 1st ed. 12p. 1981. pap. text ed. 0.49 (ISBN 0-88151-021-1). Lay Leadership.

Craig, James D. & Hill, Donald E., eds. How to Start a Home Cell Ministry. 1st ed. 32p. 1981. pap. 7.95 includes cassettes (ISBN 0-88151-019-X). Lay Leadership.

Craig, Jonathan. Concepts in Jewish Art. LC 84-263. (Judaic Studies). (Illus.). 165p. 1986. 24.00x (ISBN 0-8046-9355-2, 9355, Pub. by Natl U). Assoc Faculty Pr.

Craig, Katherine T. The Fabric of Dreams, Dream Lore & Dream Interpretation, Ancient & Modern. Repr. of 1918 ed. 20.00 (ISBN 0-89987-048-1). Darby Bks.

Craig, Mary. Mother Teresa. (Profiles Ser.). (Illus.). 64p. 1983. 8.95 (ISBN 0-241-10933-7, Pub. by Hamish Hamilton England). David & Charles.

--Pope John Paul II. (Profiles Ser.). (Illus.). 64p. 1982. 8.95 (ISBN 0-241-10711-3, Pub. by Hamish Hamilton England). David & Charles.

--Pope Paul II. (Illus.). 80p. 1982. pap. 2.50 (ISBN 0-686-40828-4, Pub by Penguin England). Irish Bk Ctr.

Craig, Sidney D. Raising Your Child, Not by Force But by Love. LC 72-10436. 192p. 1982. pap. 6.95 (ISBN 0-664-24413-0). Westminster.

Craig, William L. Apologetics: An Introduction. 1984. 13.95 (ISBN 0-8024-0405-7). Moody.

--The Historical Argument for the Resurrection of Jesus. LC 85-21570. (Texts & Studies in Religion: Vol. 23). 688p. 1985. lib. bdg. 69.95x (ISBN 0-88946-811-7). E Mellen.

--The Kalam Cosmological Argument. LC 77-17232. (Library of Philosophy & Religion Ser.). 216p. 1979. text ed. 28.50x (ISBN 0-06-491308-2). B&N Imports.

--The Only Wise God. 1987. pap. 7.95 (ISBN 0-8010-2519-2). Baker Bk.

Craighead, Meinrad. The Mother's Songs: Images of God the Mother. LC 85-50408. 96p. (Orig.). 1985. pap. 9.95 (ISBN 0-8091-2716-4). Paulist Pr.

Craigie, P. C. Commentary on the Book of Deuteronomy. (New International Commentary of the Old Testament). 520p. 1976. 16.95 (ISBN 0-8028-2355-6). Eerdmans.

Craigie, Peter. Ugarit & the Old Testament. 110p. (Orig.). 1983. pap. 5.95 (ISBN 0-8028-1928-1). Eerdmans.

Craigie, Peter C. Ezekiel. LC 83-7044. (Daily Study Bible-Old Testament). 332p. 1983. 14.95 (ISBN 0-664-21807-5); pap. 7.95 (ISBN 0-664-24574-9). Westminster.

--Problem of War in the Old Testament. LC 78-17698. 1979. pap. 5.95 (ISBN 0-8028-1742-4). Eerdmans.

--Twelve Prophets, Vol. 1. LC 84-2372. (Daily Study Bible-Old Testament Ser.). 1984. 14.95 (ISBN 0-664-21810-5); pap. 7.95 (ISBN 0-664-24577-3). Westminster.

--Twelve Prophets, Vol. 2. LC 84-2372. (The Daily Study Bible-Old Testament). 260p. 1985. 15.95 (ISBN 0-664-21813-X); pap. 8.95 (ISBN 0-664-24582-X). Westminster.

Craigie, W. A. The Religion of Ancient Scandinavia. 59.95 (ISBN 0-8490-0939-1). Gordon Pr.

Craigie, William A. Religion of Ancient Scandinavia. facsimile ed. LC 74-99657. (Select Bibliographies Reprint Ser). 1906. 14.50 (ISBN 0-8369-5086-0). Ayer Co Pubs.

Crain, Steve. Bible Fun Book, No. 7. (Activity Book Ser.). 32p. (Orig.). 1981. oversized saddle stitched .99 (ISBN 0-87123-766-0, 220766). Bethany Hse.

--Bible Fun Book, No. 8. (Activity Book Ser.). 32p. (Orig.). 1981. pap. 0.99 saddle-stitched (ISBN 0-87123-772-5, 220772). Bethany Hse.

Crakanthorp, Richard. Defensio Ecclesiae Anglicanae. LC 72-1027. (Library of Anglo-Catholic Theology: No. 6). Repr. of 1847 ed. 27.50 (ISBN 0-404-52087-1). AMS Pr.

Cram, Mildred. Born in Time: The Christmas Story. (Illus.). 26p. (Orig.). 1972. pap. 2.50 (ISBN 0-913270-10-5). Sunstone Pr.

Cram, R. A. Folio. 1932. 22.00 (ISBN 0-527-01687-X). Kraus Repr.

Cram, Ralph A. The Catholic Church & Art. 59.95 (ISBN 0-87968-817-3). Gordon Pr.

Cramer, Owen, ed. see Rivers, Gloria R.

Cramer, Raymond L. Psicologia de Jesus y la Salud Mental. Vargas, Carlos A., tr. from Eng. LC 76-16438. Tr. of Psychology of Jesus & Mental Health. (Span.). 191p. 1976. pap. 5.95 (ISBN 0-89922-074-6). Edit Caribe.

Cramer, Steven A. Great Shall Be Your Joy. 228p. 1984. 8.95 (ISBN 0-934126-48-8). Randall Bk Co.

--The Worth of a Soul. 127p. 1983. 7.95 (ISBN 0-934126-29-1). Randall Bk Co.

Crandall, Faye E. Into the Copper River Valley. 1983. 9.95 (ISBN 0-8062-2025-2). Carlton.

Crandall, Robert. Ministry to Persons: Organization & Administration. (Illus.). 96p. (Orig.). 1981. pap. 3.50 (ISBN 0-89367-070-7). Light & Life.

Crandall, Ronald & Sells, Ray. There's New Life in the Small Congregation: Why It Happens & How. LC 83-71697. 120p. (Orig.). 1983. pap. 7.50 (ISBN 0-88177-001-9, DR001B). Discipleship Res.

Crane, J. D. El Espiritu Santo en la Experiencia del Cristiano. De Lerin, Olivia, tr. Orig. Title: The Christian's Esperience of the Holy Spirit. Tr. of The Christian Experience of the Holy Spirit. 128p. 1982. Repr. of 1979 ed. 5.95 (ISBN 0-311-09093-1). Casa Bautista.

--Manual para Predicadores Laicos. 122p. 1983. pap. 2.10 (ISBN 0-311-42039-7). Casa Bautista.

Crane, James & Estudios, Guias de. Guia de Estudios Sobre Manual Para Predicadores Laicos. 88p. 1982. pap. 3.50 (ISBN 0-311-43502-5). Casa Bautista.

Crane, James D. El Sermon Eficaz. 308p. 1986. pap. 4.50. Casa Bautista.

Crane, James D. & Diaz, Jorge E. Lecciones Para Nuevos Creyentes Student. 64p. 1984. pap. 1.65 (ISBN 0-311-13835-7); teacher ed. 2.95 (ISBN 0-311-13838-1). Casa Bautista.

Crane, Santiago D., tr. see Blackwood, A. W.

Crane, Thomas E. The Message of St. John: The Spiritual Teachings of the Beloved Disciple. LC 80-11779. 184p. (Orig.). 1980. pap. 5.95 (ISBN 0-8189-0402-X). Alba.

Crane, Thomas F. The Exempla or Illustrative Stories from the Sermones: Vulgares off Jacques de Vitry. (Folk-Lore Society, London, Ser.: Vol. 26). pap. 35.00 (ISBN 0-8115-0512-X). Kraus Repr.

Crane, Thomas F., ed. see Jacobus De Vitriaco.

Cranfield, C. E. Commentary on Romans. abr. ed. 320p. 1985. pap. 10.95 (ISBN 0-8028-0012-2). Eerdmans.

Cranfield, Charles E. The Bible & Christian Life. 256p. 1985. pap. 15.95 (ISBN 0-567-29125-1, Pub. by T&T Clark Ltd UK). Fortress.

--A Critical & Exegetical Commentary on the Epistle to the Romans, 2 vols, Vol. 1 & 2. Emerton, John A., ed. (International Critical Commentary Ser.). 29.95 ea. (Pub. by T & T Clark Ltd UK). Vol. I, 472 pgs., 1975 (ISBN 0-567-05040-8). Vol. II, 476 pgs., 1979 (ISBN 0-567-05041-6). Fortress.

Cranfield, Charles E., ed. see McKane, William.

Crank, David. Godly Finances: The Bible Way to Pay off Your Home. 50p. (Orig.). 1986. pap. 4.95 (ISBN 0-936437-00-6). D Crank Pubns.

Crankshaw, Andrea, ed. see White, Gladyce E.

Cranmer-Byng, J. L., ed. Chinese Buddhist Verse. Robinson, Richard H., tr. from Chinese. LC 79-8725. 1980. Repr. of 1954 ed. lib. bdg. 18.75x (ISBN 0-313-22168-5, ROCB). Greenwood.

Cranmer-Byng, J. L., ed. see Murray, Margaret A.

Cranor, Phoebe. Five Loaves & Two Fishes: New Life Through Inner Healing. 1987. pap. 4.95. Paulist Pr.

--Is Anybody Listening When I Pray? LC 79-27475. 112p. (Orig.). 1980. pap. 3.95 (ISBN 0-87123-200-6, 210200). Bethany Hse.

--Why Did God Let Grandpa Die? LC 76-17737. 128p. 1976. pap. 3.50 (ISBN 0-87123-603-6, 200603). Bethany Hse.

--Why Doesn't God Do Something? LC 78-118. 144p. (YA) 1978. pap. 3.50 (ISBN 0-87123-605-2, 200605). Bethany Hse.

Cranston, Ruth. World Faith. facs. ed. LC 68-58782. (Essay Index Reprint Ser). 1949. 15.00 (ISBN 0-8369-0108-8). Ayer Co Pubs.

Cranston, S. L., jt. auth. see Head, Joseph.

Cranston, Sylvia & Williams, Carey. Reincarnation: A New Horizon in Science, Religion & Society. 1984. 16.95 (ISBN 0-517-55496-8, Harmony). Crown.

Crapanzano, Vincent & Garrison, Vivian, eds. Case Studies in Spirit Possession. LC 76-26653. (Contemporary Religious Movements Ser.). pap. 118.30 (ISBN 0-317-08510-7, 2055396). Bks Demand UMI.

Crapo, Lawrence M., jt. auth. see Fries, James F.

Crapps, Joyce W. Who Made These Things? LC 86-18773. (Bible-&-Me Ser.). 1987. 5.95 (ISBN 0-8054-4178-6). Broadman.

Crapps, Robert W. An Introduction to the Psychology of Religion. 384p. 1986. text ed. 49.95 (ISBN 0-86554-194-9); pap. text ed. 24.95 (ISBN 0-86554-195-7). Mercer Univ Pr.

Crapps, Robert W., et al. Introduction to the New Testament. 566p. 1969. text ed. 25.00 (ISBN 0-394-34415-4, RandC). Random.

Crary, Robert W., jt. auth. see Lorr, Regina E.

Crashaw, W., tr. see Balbani, Niccolo.

Crashaw, William. The Sermon Preached at the Cross, February 14, 1607. Repr. of 1608 ed. 27.00 (ISBN 0-384-10125-9). Johnson Repr.

Craske, Margaret. The Dance of Love: My Life with Meher Baba. LC 80-53859. 180p. (Orig.). 1980. pap. 6.95 (ISBN 0-913078-40-9). Sheriar Pr.

Cratch, Stephen C. & Johansson, Anders B. The Hindu Vedic Master Operations Guide: Astrological Software for the IBM PC. Johansson, Lilian M., ed. (Illus.). 200p. (Orig.). 1985. 30.00 (ISBN 0-914725-12-2); pap. 18.00 (ISBN 0-914725-10-6); spiral 24.00 (ISBN 0-914725-11-4). Astro Dynasty Pub Hse.

Crater, Mildred, ed. see Lohr, Andrew.

Craven, Roy C., Jr. Ceremonial Centers of the Maya. LC 74-2016. (Illus.). 152p. 1974. 20.00 (ISBN 0-8130-0447-0). U Presses Fla.

Craven, Rulon G. The Effective Missionary. LC 82-1471. 106p. 1982. 6.95 (ISBN 0-87747-898-8). Deseret Bk.

Craven, Toni. Artistry & Faith in the Book of Judith. LC 82-25000. (Society of Biblical Literature Dissertation Ser.). 150p. 1983. pap. 11.25 (ISBN 0-89130-612-9, 06 01 70). Scholars Pr GA.

--Ezekiel, Daniel. (Collegeville Bible Commentary Ser.). 144p. 1986. pap. 2.95 (ISBN 0-8146-1423-X). Liturgical Pr.

Cravey, Charles E. Diamonds in the Rough. 64p. (Orig.). 1986. pap. 4.00 (ISBN 0-938645-00-5). Upper Rm Pub.

Crawford, Albert G. & Monson, Rela G. Academy & Community: A Study of the Jewish Identity & Involvement of Professors. LC 80-68432. 40p. 1980. pap. 2.00. Am Jewish Comm.

Crawford, C. C. The Eternal Spirit: His Person & Powers. (The Bible Study Textbook Ser.). 1973. 14.30 (ISBN 0-89900-050-9). College Pr Pub.

--Genesis, Vol. I. LC 77-1140. (The Bible Study Textbook Ser.). 1966. 14.30 (ISBN 0-89900-002-9). College Pr Pub.

--Genesis, Vol. II. (The Bible Study Textbook Ser.). 1968. 15.90 (ISBN 0-89900-003-7). College Pr Pub.

--Genesis, Vol. III. (The Bible Study Textbook Ser.). (Illus.). 1970. 14.30 (ISBN 0-89900-004-5). College Pr Pub.

--Survey Course in Christian Doctrine, Vols. III & IV. LC 71-1388. (The Bible Study Textbook Ser.). 1964. 13.80 (ISBN 0-89900-054-1). College Pr Pub.

--What the Bible Says about Faith. LC 82-72621. (What the Bible Says Ser.). 380p. 1982. cancelled (ISBN 0-89900-089-4). College Pr Pub.

Crawford, Claud C. The End of the Rope. rev. ed. LC 85-90684. 96p. 1985. pap. 6.95 (ISBN 0-933697-00-7). Claud Crawford.

Crawford, Dan R. Evangelife: A Guide to Life-Style Evangelism. LC 84-1805. 1984. pap. 4.95 (ISBN 0-8054-6247-3). Broadman.

--Single Adults: Resource & Recipients for Revival. LC 85-7889. 1985. pap. 5.95 (ISBN 0-8054-3236-1). Broadman.

--Where One Is Gathered in His Name. LC 85-19519. 1986. 6.95 (ISBN 0-8054-5025-4). Broadman.

Crawford, David & Crawford, Leona. Missionary Adventures in the South Pacific. LC 67-15137. 1967. 5.50 (ISBN 0-8048-0403-6). C E Tuttle.

Crawford, Fred R., intro. by see Seventy First Infantry Division, U.S. Army.

Crawford, Fred R., et al. Certain Reactions by the Atlanta Public to the Death of the Rev. Dr. Martin Luther King Jr. LC 73-85669. 1969. pap. 3.00 (ISBN 0-89937-023-3). Ctr Res Soc Chg.

Crawford, George W. Prince Hall & His Followers. LC 74-144591. Repr. of 1914 ed. 16.00 (ISBN 0-404-00145-9). AMS Pr.

Crawford, James L. Catalogue of a Collection of 1500 Tracts by Martin Luther & His Contemporaries, 1511-1598. 1965. Repr. of 1903 ed. 32.00 (ISBN 0-8337-1001-X). B Franklin.

Crawford, Kenneth, jt. auth. see Simmons, Paul D.

Crawford, Leona, jt. auth. see Crawford, David.

Crawford, M. V., tr. see Kurth, Godefried J.

Crawford, Matsu. My Head Is Bloody But Unbowed. 111p. (Orig.). 1983. pap. 5.00 (ISBN 0-9612862-0-2). R E F Typesetting Pub.

Crawford, Richard, jt. auth. see McKay, David.

Crawford, Richard, jt. ed. see Kroeger, Karl.

Crawford, Richard L. Andrew Law, American Psalmodist. (Music Ser.). (Illus.). xix, 424p. 1981. Repr. of 1968 ed. lib. bdg. 42.50 (ISBN 0-306-76090-8). Da Capo.

Crawford, Robert G. The Saga of God Incarnate. 120p. 1985. 13.95 (ISBN 0-86981-309-9, Pub. by T&T Clark Ltd UK). Fortress.

Crawford, S. Cromwell. The Evolution of Hindu Ethical Ideals. (Asian Studies at Hawaii: No. 28). 197p. 1982. pap. text ed. 14.00x (ISBN 0-8248-0782-0). UH Pr.

--Ram Mohan Roy: Social, Political & Religious Reform in 19th Century India. 288p. 1986. 22.95 (ISBN 0-913729-15-9). Paragon Hse.

Crawford, S. Cromwell, ed. World Religions & Global Ethics. (Contemporary Discussion Ser.). 168p. 21.95 (ISBN 0-913757-57-8); pap. 12.95 (ISBN 0-913757-58-6). Paragon Hse.

Crawford, Shirley O. Is God Dead Within You? 112p. 1981. 6.50 (ISBN 0-682-49789-4). Exposition Pr FL.

Crawley, Winston. Global Mission. LC 85-3752. 1985. 11.95 (ISBN 0-8054-6340-2). Broadman.

--Partners Across the Pacific. LC 85-29088. 1986. pap. 4.95 (ISBN 0-8054-6341-0). Broadman.

Crawley-Boevey, Mateo. Jesus King of Love. 1978. 5.50 (ISBN 0-8198-0521-1); pap. 3.95 (ISBN 0-8198-0522-X). Dghtrs St Paul.

--Jesus Rey De Amor. (Span.). 1980. pap. 3.95 (ISBN 0-8198-3909-4). Dghtrs St Paul.

--Meditaciones. (Span.). 1978. plastic bdg. 2.00 (ISBN 0-8198-4706-2). Dghtrs St Paul.

Crazzolara, J. P. Zur Gesellschaft & Religion der Nueer. 1953. 46.00 (ISBN 0-384-10150-X). Johnson Repr.

Creagh, Terry. Give Sorrow Words. 94p. (Orig.). 1982. pap. 9.95 (ISBN 0-85819-341-8, Pub. by JBCE). ANZ Religious Pubns.

Crean, David & Ebbeson, Eric, eds. Living Simply: An Examination of Christian Lifestyles. 128p. (Orig.). 1981. pap. 5.95 (ISBN 0-8164-2340-7, HarpR). Har-Row.

Creegan, Charles C. & Goodnow, Josephine A. Great Missionaries of the Church. facsimile ed. LC 73-37522. (Essay Index Reprint Ser). Repr. of 1895 ed. 24.50 (ISBN 0-8369-2541-6). Ayer Co Pubs.

Creel, Austin. Dharma in Hindu Ethics. 1978. 11.00x (ISBN 0-88386-999-3). South Asia Bks.

Creel, Herrlee G. Confucius, the Man & the Myth. LC 72-7816. 363p. 1973. Repr. of 1949 ed. lib. bdg. 23.00x (ISBN 0-8371-6531-8, CRCO). Greenwood.

--What Is Taoism? And Other Studies in Chinese Cultural History. LC 77-102905. (Midway Reprint Ser.). viii, 192p. 1982. pap. text ed. 11.00x (ISBN 0-226-12047-3). U of Chicago Pr.

Creel, Richard. Religion & Doubt: Toward a Faith of Your Own. 1977. write for info. (ISBN 0-13-771931-0). P-H.

Creel, Richard E. Divine Impassibility: An Essay in Philosophical Theology. 300p. 1985. 39.50 (ISBN 0-521-30317-6). Cambridge U Pr.

Creelman, H. S. History & Literature of the Old Testament, 2 vols. (Illus.). 1987. Set. 189.45 (ISBN 0-89266-573-4). Am Classical Coll Pr.

Creer, Leland H. Mormon Towns in the Region of the Colorado. Incl. The Activities of Jacob Hamblin in the Region of the Colorado. (Glen Canyon Ser.: Nos. 3-4). Repr. of 1958 ed. 20.00 (ISBN 0-404-60633-4). AMS Pr.

Creighton, Mandell. Cardinal Wolsey. 226p. 1982. Repr. of 1888 ed. lib. bdg. 35.00 (ISBN 0-8495-0878-9). Arden Lib.

--History of the Papacy from the Great Schism to the Sack of Rome, 6 Vols. rev. ed. LC 74-77897. Repr. of 1897 ed. Set. 165.00 (ISBN 0-404-01870-X); 27.50 ea. AMS Pr.

Creighton, W., ed. see Wieman, Henry N.

Creme, Benjamin. Messages from Maitreya the Christ, Vol. 1. LC 80-52483. 209p. 1980. pap. 5.00 (ISBN 0-936604-01-8). Tara Ctr.

--The Reappearance of the Christ & the Masters of Wisdom. LC 80-50639. 253p. 1980. pap. 6.00 (ISBN 0-936604-00-X). Tara Ctr.

--Transmission: A Meditation for the New Age. rev. ed. 100p. 1985. pap. 3.50 (ISBN 0-936604-06-9). Tara Ctr.

Cremer, Hermann. Biblico-Theological Lexicon of New Testament Greek. Urwick, William, tr. (Gr.). 960p. 1895. 35.95 (ISBN 0-567-01004-X, Pub. by T & T Clark Ltd UK). Fortress.

Crenshaw, Floyd D. & Flanders, John A., eds. Christian Values & the Academic Disciplines. 224p. (Orig.). 1985. lib. bdg. 23.25 (ISBN 0-8191-4306-5); pap. text ed. 11.75 (ISBN 0-8191-4307-3). U Pr of Amer.

Crenshaw, J. L. & Crenshaw, Willis. Essays on Old Testament Ethics: J. P. Hyatt in Memoriam. 1974. 35.00x (ISBN 0-87068-233-4). Ktav.

Crenshaw, James. Gerhard von Rad. (Makers of the Modern Theological Mind Ser.). 1978. 8.95 (ISBN 0-8499-0112-X). Word Bks.

Crenshaw, James L. Hymnic Affirmation of Divine Justice. LC 75-22349. (Society of Biblical Literature. Dissertation Ser.: No. 24). Repr. of 1975 ed. 36.10 (ISBN 0-8357-9571-3, 2017523). Bks Demand UMI.

--Old Testament Wisdom: An Introduction. LC 80-82183. 262p. 1981. 16.95 (ISBN 0-8042-0143-9); pap. 12.95 (ISBN 0-8042-0142-0). John Knox.

--Prophetic Conflict: Its Effect upon Israelite Religion. (Beiheft 124 zur Zeitschrift fuer die alttestamentliche Wissenschaft). 134p. 1971. 33.00x (ISBN 3-11-003363-1, 3-11-003363-1). De Gruyter.

--Samson: A Secret Betrayed, A Vow Ignored. LC 77-15748. 173p. 1981. text ed. 9.95 (ISBN 0-86554-042-X, MUP-H01). Mercer Univ Pr.

--Story & Faith: A Guide to the Old Testament. 539p. 1986. text ed. write for info. (ISBN 0-02-325600-1). Macmillan.

--Studies in Ancient Israelite Wisdom. 1974. 59.50x (ISBN 0-87068-255-5). Ktav.

--A Whirlpool of Torment: The Oppressive Presence of God in Ancient Israel. LC 83-18479. (Overtures to Biblical Theology Ser.). 144p. 1984. pap. 7.95 (ISBN 0-8006-1536-0, 1-1536). Fortress.

Crenshaw, James L. & Sandmel, Samuel. The Divine Helmsman: Studies on God's Control of Human Events. 1979. 35.00x (ISBN 0-87068-700-X). Ktav.

Crenshaw, James L., ed. Theodicy in the Old Testament. LC 83-8885. (Issues in Religion & Theology Ser.). 176p. 1983. pap. 7.95 (ISBN 0-8006-1764-9). Fortress.

Crenshaw, Willis, jt. auth. see Crenshaw, J. L.

Cresson, Warder. The Key of David: David the True Messiah. Davis, Moshe, ed. LC 77-70671. (America & the Holy Land Ser.). (Illus.). 1977. Repr. of 1852 ed. lib. bdg. 26.50x (ISBN 0-405-10239-9). Ayer Co Pubs.

Creswell, K. Short Account of Early Muslim Architecture. 1968. 18.00x (ISBN 0-86685-010-4). Intl Bk Ctr.

Creswell, K. A. A Bibliography of the Architecture, Arts & Crafts of Islam. 2nd ed. 120.00 (ISBN 0-89410-306-7, Pub. by FP Van Eck Liechtenstein). Three Continents.

--Early Muslim Architecture: Umayyads, Early 'Abbasids, & Tulunids, 2 vols. in 3 pts. LC 75-11057. 1978. Repr. of 1932 ed. lib. bdg. 375.00 (ISBN 0-87817-176-2). Hacker.

--Muslim Architecture of Egypt, 2 vols. LC 75-11056. (Illus.). 1978. Repr. of 1952 ed. lib. bdg. 350.00 (ISBN 0-87817-175-4). Hacker.

Creswell, Mike. Your God, My God. Pennington, Celeste, ed. (Human Touch-Photo Text Ser.). 172p. 1980. 7.95 (ISBN 0-937170-22-4). Home Mission.

Creux, Francois Du see Du Creux, Francois.

Creuzer, Georg F. Symbolik und Mythologie der Alten Volker Besonders der Griechen, 6 vols. Bolle, Kees W., ed. LC 77-79119. (Mythology Ser.). (Ger., Illus.). 1978. Repr. of 1823 ed. lib. bdg. 325.00x (ISBN 0-405-10531-2). Ayer Co Pubs.

Crew, P. Mack. Calvinist Preaching & Iconoclasm in the Netherlands, 1544-1569. LC 77-77013. (Studies in Early Modern History). 1978. 37.50 (ISBN 0-521-21739-3). Cambridge U Pr.

Crewe, Sarah, jt. auth. see Sweeney, Patrick.

Crews, Clyde. English Catholic Modernism: Maude Petre's Way of Faith. LC 83-50747. 156p. 1984. text ed. 16.95x (ISBN 0-268-00912-0, 85-09127). U of Notre Dame Pr.

Crews, Clyde F. An American Holy Land: A History of the Archdiocese of Louisville. 360p. 1987. 29.95 (ISBN 0-89453-622-2). M Glazier.

--Fundamental Things Apply: Reflecting on Christian Basics. LC 83-71005. 104p. (Orig.). 1983. pap. 3.95 (ISBN 0-87793-272-7). Ave Maria.

Crews, Jerry, jt. auth. see Burron, Arnold.

Cribb, C. C. Armageddon-Dead Ahead. LC 77-70212. pap. 2.95 (ISBN 0-932046-03-7). Manhattan Ltd NC.

--The Coming Kingdom. LC 77-70213. pap. 2.95 (ISBN 0-932046-04-5). Manhattan Ltd NC.

--The Devil's Empire. LC 77-70211. pap. 2.95 (ISBN 0-932046-02-9). Manhattan Ltd NC.

--Digging Diamonds Daily. LC 77-70215. Set. (ISBN 0-932046-09-6); Vol. 1. 12.95 (ISBN 0-932046-07-X); Vol. 2. 12.95 (ISBN 0-932046-08-8). Manhattan Ltd NC.

--Flying High Against the Sky: If God Has It I Want It! LC 79-84881. Date not set. pap. 2.95 (ISBN 0-932046-16-9). Manhattan Ltd NC.

--From Now till Eternity. LC 76-21571. 12.95 (ISBN 0-932046-00-2). Manhattan Ltd NC.

--Getting Ready for Heaven. LC 78-60614. (If God Has It I Want It!). 1979. pap. 2.95 (ISBN 0-685-96444-2). Manhattan Ltd NC.

--Getting Ready for the Coming Rapture. LC 79-88232. (If God Has It I Want It! Ser.). Date not set. pap. 2.95 (ISBN 0-932046-19-3). Manhattan Ltd NC.

--Getting Your Share of the Spirit's Outpouring. LC 79-88229. (If God Has It I Want It! Ser.). Date not set. pap. 2.95 (ISBN 0-932046-17-7). Manhattan Ltd NC.

--The Horrified & the Glorified. LC 77-70214. pap. 2.95 (ISBN 0-932046-05-3). Manhattan Ltd NC.

--Man's Earth-Lease Is About to Expire. LC 77-70210. pap. 2.95 (ISBN 0-932046-01-0). Manhattan Ltd NC.

--Moving the Hand That Moves the World. LC 79-88930. (If God Has It I Want It! Ser.). Date not set. pap. 2.95 (ISBN 0-932046-18-5). Manhattan Ltd NC.

--Spinning Straw into Gold. LC 79-84880. (If God Has It I Want It! Ser.). pap. 2.95 (ISBN 0-932046-15-0). Manhattan Ltd NC.

--Staking Your Claim on Healing. LC 79-83919. (If God Has It I Want It!). 1979. pap. 2.95 (ISBN 0-932046-14-2). Manhattan Ltd NC.

Crichton-Stuart, John P., tr. see Coptic Church Staff.

Crider, Charles C. & Kistler, Robert C. The Seventh-Day Adventist Family: An Empirical Study. 296p. 1979. pap. 3.95 (ISBN 0-943872-77-4). Andrews Univ Pr.

Crider, Virginia. Allegheny Gospel Trails. (Illus.). 1971. 7.50 (ISBN 0-87813-502-2). Christian Light.

--Answering the Cry. (Northland Ser.). 1976. pap. 2.50 (ISBN 0-87813-510-3). Christian Light.

--Cry of the Northland. (Northland Ser). 1973. pap. 2.50 (ISBN 0-87813-505-7). Christian Light.

Crilly, Oliver, jt. auth. see Gallagher, Chuck.

Crim, Keith, tr. see Kraus, Hans J.

Crim, Keith, tr. see Pannenberg, Wolfhart.

Crim, Keith, tr. see Westermann, Claus.

Crim, Keith, et al, eds. Abingdon Dictionary of Living Religions. LC 81-1465. 864p. 1981. 17.95 (ISBN 0-687-00409-8). Abingdon.

Crim, Keith R., jt. ed. see Buttrick, George A.

Crim, Keith R., tr. see Wolff, Hans W.

Crim, Keith R., et al, eds. The Interpreter's Dictionary of the Bible, Supplementary Volume. LC 62-9387. (Illus.). 1976. 22.95 (ISBN 0-687-19269-2). Abingdon.

Crimm, Keith, tr. see Rendtorff, Trutz.

Crinzi, Debbie. Principles of Discipleship. 102p. 1984. pap. text ed. 5.00 (ISBN 0-8309-0394-1). Herald Hse.

Crippen, Thomas G. Christmas & Christmas Lore. LC 69-16067. (Illus.). 256p. 1972. Repr. of 1923 ed. 50.00x (ISBN 0-8103-3029-6). Gale.

--Christmas & Christmas Lore. 1976. lib. bdg. 59.95 (ISBN 0-8490-1617-7). Gordon Pr.

Cripps, Richard S. Amos. 1981. lib. bdg. 13.50 (ISBN 0-86524-081-7, 3001). Klock & Klock.

Crisci, Elizabeth. Fifteen Fun-Filled Programs for Adults. (Illus.). 112p. 1986. pap. 4.95 (ISBN 0-87403-078-1, 3198). Standard Pub.

--Ninety-Nine Fun Ideas for Teaching Bible Verses. (Illus.). 112p. 1985. pap. 3.95 (ISBN 0-87239-869-2, 3072). Standard Pub.

Crisler, Janet, jt. auth. see Kinard, Malvina.

Crissey, Clair M. Layman's Bible Book Commentary: Matthew, Vol. 15. LC 79-56691. 1981. 5.95 (ISBN 0-8054-1185-2). Broadman.

Cristenson, Larry. The Renewed Mind. LC 74-12770. 144p. (Orig.). 1974. pap. 4.95 (ISBN 0-87123-479-3, 210479). Bethany Hse.

Cristiani, Leon. A Cross for Napoleon. 1980. 4.00 (ISBN 0-8198-1404-0); pap. 2.00 (ISBN 0-8198-1405-9). Dghtrs St Paul.

--Evidence of Satan in the Modern World. Rowland, Cynthia, tr. from Fr. (Eng.). 1977. pap. 5.50 (ISBN 0-89555-032-6). TAN Bks Pubs.

--Saint Bernadette. LC 65-15727. (Illus.). 181p. 1981. pap. 3.95 (ISBN 0-8189-0421-6). Alba.

--St. Bernard of Clairvaux. 1977. 3.95 (ISBN 0-8198-0463-0); pap. 2.95 (ISBN 0-8198-0464-9). Dghtrs St Paul.

--St. Joan of Arc, Virgin-Soldier. 1977. 3.95 (ISBN 0-8198-0465-7); pap. 2.95 (ISBN 0-8198-0466-5). Dghtrs St Paul.

--St. Margaret Mary Alacoque. 1976. 5.00 (ISBN 0-8198-0456-8). Dghtrs St Paul.

Criswell, W. A. Acts: An Exposition. 948p. 1983. Repr. 19.95 (ISBN 0-310-44150-1, 11666). Zondervan.

--The Baptism, Filling & Gifts of the Holy Spirit. 192p. 1973. pap. 4.95 (ISBN 0-310-22751-8, 18351P). Zondervan.

--Criswell's Guidebook for Pastors. LC 79-7735. 1980. 12.95 (ISBN 0-8054-2536-5). Broadman.

--Expository Sermons on Revelation, 5 Vols. in 1. 1961-66. 24.95 (ISBN 0-310-22840-9, 9442). Zondervan.

--Expository Sermons on the Book of Daniel. 651p. 19.95 (ISBN 0-310-22800-X, 9461). Zondervan.

--Expository Sermons on the Book of Ezekiel. 272p. 1987. 12.95 (ISBN 0-310-23010-1, 18352). Zondervan.

--Great Doctrines of the Bible, Vol. 1. 144p. 1982. 9.95 (ISBN 0-310-43850-0, 9427). Zondervan.

--Great Doctrines of the Bible, Vols. 1, 2, 3, & 4. 192p. 1982. Repr. 44.75 (ISBN 0-310-43868-3, 11663). Zondervan.

--Great Doctrines of the Bible, Vol. 5. 144p. 1985. 9.95 (ISBN 0-310-43930-2). Zondervan.

--Great Doctrines of the Bible, Vol. 7. Ruark, J., ed. 1987. price not set (ISBN 0-310-43960-4). Zondervan.

--Great Doctrines of the Bible: Christology, Vol. 2. 192p. 1982. 9.95 (ISBN 0-310-43860-8, 11660). Zondervan.

--Great Doctrines of the Bible: Ecclesiology, Vol. 3. 128p. 1983. 8.95 (ISBN 0-310-43900-0, 11661). Zondervan.

--Great Doctrines of the Bible, Vol. 4: Pneumatology. 112p. 1984. 7.95 (ISBN 0-310-43910-8, 11662). Zondervan.

--Great Doctrines of the Bible, Vol. 6: Christian Life & Stewardship. 128p. 1986. text ed. 11.95 (ISBN 0-310-43950-7). Zondervan.

--What a Savior! LC 77-82399. 1978. 7.50 (ISBN 0-8054-5155-2). Broadman.

--Why I Preach That the Bible Is Literally True. LC 69-13142. 1969. pap. 3.95 (ISBN 0-8054-5536-1). Broadman.

Critchlow, Keith. The Soul As Sphere & Androgyne. (Illus., Orig.). 1985. pap. 4.95 (ISBN 0-933999-28-3). Phanes Pr.

Croatto, J. Severino. Exodus: A Hermeneutics of Freedom. LC 80-26148. 112p. (Orig.). 1981. pap. 4.95 (ISBN 0-88344-111-X). Orbis Bks.

Croce, Benedetto. What Is Living & What Is Dead of the Philosophy of Hegel. Ainslie, Douglas, tr. from Ital. 268p. 1985. pap. text ed. 10.50 (ISBN 0-8191-4279-4). U Pr of Amer.

Crock, Clement H. No Cross No Crown. 1974. Repr. 3.00 (ISBN 0-8198-0510-6). Dghtrs St Paul.

Crocker, John R. The Student Guide to Catholic Colleges & Universties. LC 82-48923. 468p. (Orig.). 1983. pap. 9.95 (ISBN 0-06-061602-4, RD/459, HarpR). Har-Row.

Crocker, Lester G. An Age of Crisis: Man & World in Eighteenth Century French Thought. LC 59-14233. (Goucher College Ser.). Repr. of 1959 ed. 129.00 (ISBN 0-8357-9260-9, 2011983). Bks Demand UMI.

Crockett, H. Dale. Focus on Watergate: An Examination of the Moral Dilemma of Watergate in the Light of Civil Religion. LC 81-16952. 126p. 1982. 10.95 (ISBN 0-86554-017-9, MUP-H17). Mercer Univ Pr.

Crockett, Maline. More Stories to See & Share. (Illus.). 64p. 1981. pap. 3.95 (ISBN 0-87747-886-4). Deseret Bk.

Crockett, Maline C. Stories to See & Share. 80p. 1980. pap. 4.50 (ISBN 0-87747-828-7). Deseret Bk.

Crockett, Richard H. & Horsch, James E. Jesus Life Songbook. 134p. 1975. pap. 3.95 (ISBN 0-317-37867-8). Herald Pr.

Crockett, Richard H. & Horsch, James E., eds. Jesus Life Songbook. 134p. 1975. pap. 3.95 (ISBN 0-8361-2785-4). Herald Pr.

Crockett, Silvia. Angels in Traditional Design. (International Design Library). (Illus.). 48p. (Orig.). 1987. pap. 3.95 (ISBN 0-88045-086-X). Stemmer Hse.

Crockett, W. David. Promotion & Publicity for Churches. LC 74-80382. 48p. (Orig.). 1974. pap. 3.95 (ISBN 0-8192-1181-8). Morehouse.

Crockett, William D. A Harmony of Samuel, Kings, & Chronicles. 1985. pap. 9.95 (ISBN 0-8010-2511-7). Baker Bk.

Crockett, William J. Faith: Voices from the Heart. 15p. Date not set. pap. 3.00 (ISBN 0-934383-31-6). Pride Prods.

--Friendship: Voices from the Heart. 15p. 1985. pap. 3.00 (ISBN 0-934383-04-9). Pride Prods.

--God's Way: Voices from the Heart. 15p. 1985. pap. 3.00 (ISBN 0-934383-34-0). Pride Prods.

--Life: Voices from the Heart. 15p. 1985. pap. 3.00 (ISBN 0-934383-05-7). Pride Prods.

--Mother's Day: Voices from the Heart. 15p. 1985. pap. 3.00 (ISBN 0-934383-33-2). Pride Prods.

--My Quest: Voices from the Heart. 15p. 1985. pap. 3.00 (ISBN 0-934383-32-4). Pride Prods.

Crockwell, J. H. Pictures & Biographies of Brigham Young & His Wives. 1980. lib. bdg. 59.95 (ISBN 0-8490-3158-3). Gordon Pr.

Croft, Steven J. The Identity of the Individual in the Psalms. (JSOT Supplement Ser.: No. 44). 280p. 1986. text ed. 34.00x (ISBN 1-85075-021-1, Pub. by JSOT Pr England); pap. text ed. 15.95x (ISBN 1-85075-020-3). Eisenbrauns.

Crohn, Joel. Ethnic Identity & Marital Conflict: Jews, Italians & WASPs. LC 86-70084. 44p. (Orig.). 1986. pap. 2.50 (ISBN 0-87495-078-3). Am Jewish Comm.

Croke, B. F. & Harris, J. D. Religious Conflict in Fourth Century Rome. (Sources in Ancient History Ser.). 139p. (Orig.). 1982. pap. 21.00x (ISBN 0-424-00091-1, Pub. by Sydney U Pr Australia). Intl Spec Bk.

Crom, Scott. Encounters with Transcendence: Confessions of a Religious Philosopher. (Orig.). 1986. 2.50 (ISBN 0-87574-267-X). Pendle Hill.

--Obstacles to Mystical Experience. 1983. pap. 2.50x (ISBN 0-87574-132-0, 132). Pendle Hill.

--On Being Real. LC 67-29811. (Orig.). 1967. pap. 2.50x (ISBN 0-87574-155-X, 155). Pendle Hill.

--Quaker Worship & Techniques of Meditation. 1983. pap. 2.50x (ISBN 0-87574-195-9, 195). Pendle Hill.

Cromartie, Michael, jt. ed. see Neuhaus, Richard J.

Cromie, Marguerite. Children Sing. 1975. pap. 1.25 (ISBN 0-8198-0390-1). Dghtrs St Paul.

Cromie, Richard M. Christ Will See You Through. 60p. (Orig.). 1985. pap. 1.50 (ISBN 0-914733-04-4). Desert Min.

--Sometime Before the Dawn. 111p. (Orig.). 1982. 10.00 (ISBN 0-914733-07-9); pap. 6.95 (ISBN 0-914733-08-7). Desert Min.

Cromie, Richard M., jt. auth. see Davis, Warren B.

Crompton, T., illus. The Good Samaritan: Retold by Catherine Storr. (People of the Bible Ser.). (Illus.). 32p. 1984. 10.65 (ISBN 0-8172-1988-9, Raintree Childrens Books Belitha Press Ltd. - London). Raintree Pubs.

Crompton, Yorke. Hinduism. 1985. 13.00 (ISBN 0-7062-3598-3, Pub. by Ward Lock Educ Co Ltd). State Mutual Bk.

Cronbach, Abraham. Stories Made of Bible Stories. 1961. 17.95x (ISBN 0-8084-0386-9). New Coll U Pr.

Crone, Marie-Luise. Untersuchungen Zur Reichskirchenpolitik Lothars III, 1125-1137: Zwischen Reichskirchlicher Tradition Und Reformkurie. (European University Studies: No.3, Vol. 170). 398p. 1982. 40.55 (ISBN 3-8204-7019-0). P Lang Pubs.

Crone, Patricia. Meccan Trade & the Rise of Islam. 320p. 1986. text ed. 30.00 (ISBN 0-691-05480-0). Princeton U Pr.

--Roman, Provincial & Islamic Law: The Origins of the Islamic Patronate. (Cambridge Studies in Islamic Civilization). 200p. Date not set. price not set (ISBN 0-521-32253-7). Cambridge U Pr.

Crone, Patricia & Cook, M. Hagarism: The Making of the Islamic World. LC 75-41714. 1980. pap. 14.95 (ISBN 0-521-29754-0). Cambridge U Pr.

--Hagarism: The Making of the Islamic World. LC 75-41714. 268p. 1977. 37.50 (ISBN 0-521-21133-6). Cambridge U Pr.

Crone, Patricia & Hinds, Martin. God's Caliph: Religious Authority in the First Centuries of Islam. (Oriental Publications Ser.: No. 37). 200p. 1986. 39.50 (ISBN 0-521-32185-9). Cambridge U Pr.

Crone, Robert W. Covenanters Monuments of Scotland. 96p. 1984. 40.00x (ISBN 0-7212-0694-8, Pub. by Regency Pr). State Mutual Bk.

Croner, Helga. More Stepping Stones to Jewish Christian Relations. (Stimulus Bk.). 240p. (Orig.). 1985. pap. 7.95 (ISBN 0-8091-2708-3). Paulist Pr.

--Stepping Stones to Further Jewish-Christian Relations: An Unabridged Collection of Christian Documents. 157p. pap. 10.00 (ISBN 0-686-95183-2). ADL.

Croner, Helga, ed. Issues in the Jewish Christian Dialogue. LC 79-88933. 200p. 1979. pap. 7.95 (ISBN 0-8091-2238-3). Paulist Pr.

--Stepping Stones to Further Jewish Relations. 7.95. Paulist Pr.

Croner, Helga & Klenicki, Leon, eds. Issues in the Jewish-Christian Dialogue: Jewish Perspectives on Covenant Mission & Witness. 190p. 7.95 (ISBN 0-686-95172-7). ADL.

Croner, Helga, tr. see Thoma, Clemens.

Cronin, Gaynell. Sunday Throughout the Week. LC 81-68992. (Illus.). 176p. (Orig.). 1981. pap. 5.95 (ISBN 0-87793-241-7). Ave Maria.

Cronin, Gaynell & Cronin, Jim. Celebrations. 1980. pap. 7.55 (ISBN 0-88479-031-2). Arena Lettres.

--The Mass: Great Common Prayer. 1977. pap. 7.55 (ISBN 0-88479-006-1). Arena Lettres.

--Prayer. 1980. pap. 7.55 (ISBN 0-88479-032-0). Arena Lettres.

Cronin, Gaynell & Gaynell, Jim. The Rosary. 1978. 7.55 (ISBN 0-88479-018-5). Arena Lettres.

Cronin, Gaynell B. Holy Days & Holidays: Prayer Celebrations with Children. rev. ed. 112p. 1985. pap. 7.95 (ISBN 0-86683-226-2, HarpR). Har-Row.

--The Table of the Lord. LC 86-70131. (Illus., Orig.). 1986. Child's Bk, 104 pgs. pap. text ed. 4.50 (ISBN 0-87793-299-9); Director's Manual, 168 pgs. 9.75 (ISBN 0-87793-325-1); Parent's Bk, 96 pgs. 3.50 (ISBN 0-87793-326-X). Ave Maria.

Cronin, Jim, jt. auth. see Cronin, Gaynell.

Cronk, George. The Message of the Bible: An Orthodox Christian Perspective. LC 82-7355. 293p. (Orig.). 1982. pap. 8.95 (ISBN 0-913836-94-X). St Vladimirs.

Crook, B. M., tr. see UNESCO Colloqium, 10th Anniversary of the Death of Albert Einstein & Teilhard De Charden.

Crook, Carol. Step out in Ministry! LC 86-71831. 203p. (Orig.). 1986. pap. 9.95 (ISBN 0-939399-07-5). Bks of Truth.

Crook, Roger H. An Open Book to the Christian Divorcee. LC 73-87064. pap. 4.95 (ISBN 0-8054-5217-6). Broadman.

--Our Heritage & Our Hope: A History of Pullen Memorial Baptist Church 1884-1984. LC 84-62984. (Illus.). 252p. 1985. 10.00 (ISBN 0-9614485-0-4). Pullen Mem Baptist.

Crookall. Next World-& the Next. 7.95 (ISBN 0-8356-5008-1). Theos Pub Hse.

Crooks, Mrs. Boyd. Our Faith Speaks. 62p. 1962. pap. 0.35 (ISBN 0-89114-147-2). Baptist Pub Hse.

Crosbie, Robert. Answers to Questions on the Ocean of Theosophy. 249p. 1933. 5.00 (ISBN 0-938998-12-9). Theosophy.

--The Friendly Philosopher. (Illus.). vii, 415p. 1934. Repr. 6.00 (ISBN 0-938998-13-7). Theosophy.

--The Language of the Soul. (Sangam Texts). 130p. 1986. pap. 8.75 (ISBN 0-88695-026-0). Concord grove.

Crosbie, Robert, jt. auth. see Judge, William Q.

Crosby, Donald A. Horace Bushnell's Theory of Language: In the Context of Other Nineteenth-Century Philosophies of Language. (Studies in Philosophy: No. 22). 300p. 1975. text ed. 33.60x (ISBN 90-2793-044-9). Mouton.

--Interpretive Theories of Religion. (Religion & Reason Ser.: No.20). 336p. 1981. 34.25x (ISBN 90-279-3039-2). Mouton.

Crosby, Everett U., et al. Medieval Studies: A Bibliographical Guide. LC 83-48259. (Reference Library of the Humanities: Vol. 427). 1156p. 1985. 109.00 (ISBN 0-8240-9107-8). Garland Pub.

Crosby, Fanny J. Fanny J. Crosby: Autobiography of Fanny J Crosby. (Christian Biography Ser.). 254p. 1986. Repr. of 1906 ed. 7.95 (ISBN 0-8010-2509-5). Baker Bk.

Crosby, Harold E., jt. auth. see Edgerly, George A.

Crosby, Harriett, ed. see Hart, David.

Crosby, Michael H. The Spirituality of the Beatitudes: Matthew's Challenge for First World Christians. LC 80-24755. 254p. (Orig.). 1981. pap. 7.95 (ISBN 0-88344-465-8). Orbis Bks.

--Thank God Ahead of Time: The Life & Spirituality of Solanus Casey. 1985. 9.50 (ISBN 0-8199-0879-7). Franciscan Herald.

--Thy Will Be Done: Praying the Our Father As Subversive Activity. LC 77-5118. 262p. (Orig.). 1977. pap. 6.95 (ISBN 0-88344-497-6). Orbis Bks.

Crosby, Nina E. & Marten, Elizabeth H. Discovering Philosophy. (Illus.). 72p. (Orig.). 1980. pap. 5.95 (ISBN 0-914634-81-X). DOK Pubs.

--Don't Teach! Let Me Learn about World War II, Adventure, Dreams & Superstition. (The Don't Teach! Let Me Learn Ser.). (Illus.). 72p. (Orig.). 1984. 5.95 (ISBN 0-88047-044-5, 8411). DOK Pubs.

Crosby, Sumner M. The Royal Abbey of Saint-Denis from Its Beginnings to the Death of Suger 475-1151. LC 85-26464. 570p. 1987. text ed. 55.00 (ISBN 0-300-03143-2). Yale U Pr.

Crosby, Sumner M., et al. The Royal Abbey of Saint-Denis in the Time of Abbot Suger (1122-1151) Shultz, Ellen, ed. LC 80-28849. (Illus.). 128p. 1981. pap. 12.95 (ISBN 0-87099-261-9). Metro Mus Art.

Crosby, Thomas. History of the English Baptists: 1740 Ed, 4 vols. in 2 vols. Set. 45.00 (ISBN 0-686-12405-7). Church History.

Croskery, Beverly F. Death Education: Attitudes of Teachers, School Board Members & Clergy. LC 78-68458. 1979. perfect bdg. 9.95 (ISBN 0-88247-559-2). R & E Pubs.

Cross, Arthur L. The Anglican Episcopate & the American Colonies. ix, 368p. 1964. Repr. of 1902 ed. 32.50 (ISBN 0-208-00420-3, Archon). Shoe String.

Cross, Barbara M., ed. see Beecher, Lyman.

Cross, Dorothy. Around the World with Jesus. 0.60 (ISBN 0-88027-102-7). Firm Foun Pub.

Cross, F. L. & Livingstone, Elizabeth A. The Oxford Dictionary of the Christian Church. 1974. 60.00 (ISBN 0-19-211545-6). Oxford U Pr.

Cross, F. W. see Le Fanu, Thomas P.

Cross, Frank M. The Ancient Library of Qumran & Modern Biblical Studies. LC 76-29736. (The Haskell Lectures, 1956-57). (Illus.). 1976. Repr. of 1958 ed. lib. bdg. 22.50x (ISBN 0-8371-9281-1, CRAL). Greenwood.

--Canaanite Myth & Hebrew Epic: Essays in the History of the Religion of Israel. LC 72-76564. 1973. 25.00x (ISBN 0-674-09175-2). Harvard U Pr.

Cross, Frank M. & Talmon, Shemaryahu, eds. Qumran & the History of the Biblical Text. LC 75-12529. 415p. 1975. text ed. 25.00x (ISBN 0-674-74360-1); pap. text ed. 9.95x (ISBN 0-674-74362-8). Harvard U Pr.

Cross, Frank M., Jr., ed. see Zimmerli, Walther.

Cross, Jack L. London Mission: The First Critical Years. x, 180p. 1969. 6.00 (ISBN 0-87013-128-1). Mich St U Pr.

Cross, James A. The Glorious Gospel. 1956. 4.25 (ISBN 0-87148-350-5). Pathway Pr.

--A Study of the Holy Ghost. 1973. pap. 4.25 (ISBN 0-87148-006-9). Pathway Pr.

Cross, James E., jt. ed. see Bazire, Joyce.

Cross, L. S. Paul's Letters Made Easy for Devotions. 120p. (Orig.). 1982. pap. 4.95 (ISBN 0-89221-090-7, Pub by SonLife). New Leaf.

Cross, Luther. Object Lessons for Children. (Object Lesson Ser). (Illus., Orig.). 1967. pap. 3.95 (ISBN 0-8010-2315-7). Baker Bk.

Cross, Luther S. Easy Object Stories. 114p. 1984. pap. 3.95 (ISBN 0-8010-2502-8). Baker Bk.

--Growing in Faith: Devotions for Parent-Child Interaction. 32p. (Orig.). 1984. pap. 2.95 (ISBN 0-8066-2070-6, 23-1606). Augsburg.

--Story Sermons for Children. (Object Lesson Ser.). (Orig.). 1966. pap. 3.50 (ISBN 0-8010-2328-9). Baker Bk.

Cross, Robert A. Emergence of Liberal Catholicism in America. LC 58-5593. 1958. 25.00x (ISBN 0-674-24800-7). Harvard U Pr.

Cross, Robert B., tr. see Rigaud, Milo.

Cross, Robert D., ed. The Church & the City: 1865-1910. LC 66-17273. 1967. 49.50x (ISBN 0-672-50994-6). Irvington.

Cross, Samuel H. Mediaeval Russian Churches. 1949. 10.00x (ISBN 0-910956-27-8). Medieval Acad.

Cross, Whitney R. The Burned-over District: The Social & Intellectual History of Enthusiastic Religion in Western New York, 1800-1850. LC 81-2636. xii, 383p. 1981. Repr. of 1950 ed. lib. bdg. 31.50x (ISBN 0-374-91932-1, Octagon). Hippocrene Bks.

--The Burned-over District: The Social & Intellectual History of Enthusiastic Religion in Western New York, 1800-1850. 400p. 1982. pap. 9.95x (ISBN 0-8014-9232-7). Cornell U Pr.

Crossan, Bettie. Beware! Be Wise. 130p. (Orig.). 1984. pap. 2.95 (ISBN 0-87508-148-7). Chr Lit.

Crossan, John D. The Dark Interval: Towards a Theology of Story. 1975. pap. cancelled (ISBN 0-913592-52-8). Argus Comm.

--Four Other Gospels: Shadows on the Contour of the Canon. 208p. (Orig.). 1985. 15.95 (ISBN 0-86683-959-3, HarpR). Har-Row.

--A Fragile Craft: The Work of Amos Niven Wilder. Richards, Kent, ed. LC 80-19755. 1981. pap. 8.95 (ISBN 0-89130-424-X, 06 11 03). Scholars Pr GA.

--In Fragments: The Aphorisms of Jesus. LC 83-47719. 384p. 1983. 29.45 (ISBN 0-06-061608-3, HarpR). Har-Row.

--In Parables: The Challenge of the Historical Jesus. LC 73-7067. 141p. 1985. pap. 8.95 (ISBN 0-06-061609-1, HarpR). Har-Row.

--Sayings Parallels: A Workbook for the Jesus Tradition. LC 85-16220. (Foundations & Facets Ser.). 256p. 1986. 24.95 (ISBN 0-8006-2109-3, 1-2109); pap. 14.95 (ISBN 0-8006-1909-9, 1-1909). Fortress.

Crossan, John D., ed. Semeia Nineteen: The Book of Job & Ricoeur's Hermeneutics. (Semeia Ser.). pap. 9.95 (06 20 19). Scholars Pr GA.

Crossen, Chaya, ed. see Hecht, Shea & Clorfene, Chaim.

Crossen, Kendra, ed. see Maurana, Humberto R. & Varela, Francisco.

Crossett, John M., jt. tr. see Arieti, James A.

Crossfield, R. C. Book of Onias. LC 70-86503. 1969. 7.95 (ISBN 0-8022-2290-0). Philos Lib.

Crossin, John W. What Are They Saying about Virtue. (WATSA Ser.). pap. 4.95 (ISBN 0-8091-2674-5). Paulist Pr.

Crossley, Alan. Jesus Psychi Super Star. 64p. 1984. 29.00x (ISBN 0-7212-0683-2, Pub. by Regency Pr). State Mutual Bk.

Crossley, Frederick H. The English Abbey: Its Life & Work in the Middle Ages. LC 82-25127. (Illus.). xiv, 114p. 1983. Repr. of 1935 ed. lib. bdg. 45.00x (ISBN 0-313-23849-9, CRFE). Greenwood.

Crossley, Robert. The Trinity. rev. ed. 32p. 1987. pap. 0.75 (ISBN 0-87784-077-6). Inter-Varsity.

Crossley-Holland, Kevin. Axe-Age, Wolf-Age: A Selection for Children from the Norse Myths. (Illus.). 128p. 1985. 11.95 (ISBN 0-233-97688-4). Andre Deutsch.

--The Norse Myths. 1981. pap. 7.95 (ISBN 0-394-74846-8). Pantheon.

Crossman, Eileen. Mountain Rain. 1982. pap. 3.95 (ISBN 9971-972-05-0). OMF Bks.

Crossman, Richard C. Paul Tillich: A Comprehensive Bibliography & Keyword Index of Primary & Secondary Writings in English. LC 83-15026. (ATLA Bibliography Ser.: No. 9). 193p. 1983. 17.50 (ISBN 0-8108-1650-4). Scarecrow.

Crossman, Richard H., ed. see Koestler, Arthur.

Crosson, Fred, ed. The Autonomy of Religious Belief: A Critical Inquiry. LC 81-50461. (Notre Dame Studies in the Philosophy of Religion: Vol. 2). 162p. 1982. pap. text ed. 6.95 (ISBN 0-268-00601-6). U of Notre Dame Pr.

Crosson, Frederick J. The Autonomy of Religious Belief: A Critical Inquiry. 160p. 1981. 14.95 (ISBN 0-268-00596-6). U of Notre Dame Pr.

Crotts, jt. auth. see Schmalenberger.

Crotty, Robert & Manley, Gregory. Commentaries on the Readings of the Lectionary: Cycles A, B, C. 1975. pap. 12.95 (ISBN 0-916134-20-2). Pueblo Pub Co.

Crotty, Robert & Ryan, John B. Commentaries on the Readings of the Rites. (Orig.). 1982. pap. 12.95 (ISBN 0-916134-45-8). Pueblo Pub Co.

Crotty, Robert B., jt. auth. see Hunt, Arnold D.

Crouch, Brodie. The Myth of Mormon Inspiration. 7.50 (ISBN 0-89315-158-0). Lambert Bk.

--Study of Minor Prophets. pap. 2.50 (ISBN 0-89315-291-9). Lambert Bk.

Crouch, Charles E. Principles of New Testament Christianity. 1985. pap. 5.50 (ISBN 0-89137-546-5). Quality Pubns.

Crouch, Owen. Expository Preaching & Teaching-Hebrews. LC 83-71985. 454p. (Orig.). 1983. pap. 9.95 (ISBN 0-89900-197-1). College Pr Pub.

Crouch, W. W. Science & the Bible in a Troubled World. LC 84-90294. 102p. 1985. 8.95 (ISBN 0-533-06326-4). Vantage.

Crovitz, Elaine & Buford, Elizabeth. Courage Knows No Sex. 1978. 8.95 (ISBN 0-8158-0363-X). Chris Mass.

Crow, Martha F. Christ in the Poetry of Today: An Anthology from American Poets. 1978. Repr. of 1917 ed. lib. bdg. 25.00 (ISBN 0-8495-0912-2). Arden Lib.

Crow, Paul A., Jr. Christian Unity: Matrix for Mission. (Orig.). 1982. pap. 4.95 (ISBN 0-377-00115-5). Friend Pr.

Crowe, Frederick E. Method in Theology: An Organon for Our Time. LC 80-81015. (Pere Marquette Ser.). 68p. 1980. 7.95 (ISBN 0-87462-519-X). Marquette.

Crowe, Frederick E., ed. A Third Collection: Papers by Bernard J. F. Longergan, S. J. LC 84-61028. 272p. 1985. pap. 12.95 (ISBN 0-8091-0363-X); pap. 9.95 (ISBN 0-8091-2650-8). Paulist Pr.

Crowe, Jerome. The Acts. (New Testament Message Ser.: Vol. 8). 204p. 1980. 12.95 (ISBN 0-89453-196-4); pap. 8.95 (ISBN 0-89453-131-X). M Glazier.

Crowell, E. B. Buddhist Mahayana Texts. lib. bdg. 79.95 (ISBN 0-87968-499-2). Krishna Pr.

Crowell, Laura I. Speaking His Peace. 160p. 1985. pap. 8.95 (ISBN 0-8192-1359-4). Morehouse.

Crowfoot, J. W. Early Churches in Palestine. (British Academy, London, Schweich Lectures on Biblical Archaeology Series, 1937). pap. 28.00 (ISBN 0-8115-1279-7). Kraus Repr.

Crowley, Aleister. Book of Lies. LC 79-16636. (Illus.). 186p. (Orig.). 1981. pap. 8.95 (ISBN 0-87728-516-0). Weiser.

--Diary of a Drug Fiend. 1973. lib. bdg. 79.95 (ISBN 0-87968-110-1). Krishna Pr.

--Eight Lectures on Yoga. 1972. pap. 5.95 (ISBN 0-87728-122-X). Weiser.

--Eight Lectures on Yoga. 80p. 1985. pap. 5.95 (ISBN 0-941404-36-6). Falcon Pr AZ.

--Seven Seven Seven: A Study of the Kabbalah. 1973. lib. bdg. 80.00 (ISBN 0-87968-105-5). Krishna Pr.

--Seven Seven Seven & Other Qabalistic Writings. rev. ed. LC 73-80056. 336p. 1977. 12.50 (ISBN 0-87728-222-6). Weiser.

Crowley, Aleister & Motta, Marcelo. Equinox: Sex & Religion, Vol. 5. (No. 4). 1981. 44.00 (ISBN 0-933454-04-X, Pub. by Thelema Pub). O T O.

--Oriflamme, Vol. VI, No. 1: Yoga & Magick. 1984. 8.00 (ISBN 0-913735-02-7). O T O.

Crowley, Dale. Soon Coming of Our Lord. 1958. pap. 2.95 (ISBN 0-87213-091-6). Loizeaux.

Crowley, Edward J. Lamentations, Baruch, Sophonia, Nahum, Habacuc. (Bible Ser.). pap. 1.00 (ISBN 0-8091-5078-6). Paulist Pr.

Crowley, Mary C. A Pocketful of Hope. 352p. 1981. 12.50 (ISBN 0-8007-1272-2). Revell.

--You Can Too. 176p. 1980. pap. 5.95 (ISBN 0-8007-5028-4, Power Bks). Revell.

Crowley, Richard. The Way to Wealth, Wherein Is Plainly Taught a Remedy for Sedicion. LC 74-28843. (English Experience Ser.: No. 724). 1975. Repr. of 1550 ed. 3.50 (ISBN 90-221-0724-8). Walter J Johnson.

Crown, W. The Heritage of Buddhist Poetry. 1986. 6.95 (ISBN 0-533-06003-6). Vantage.

Crowson, Elmer T. Life As Revealed Through Early American Court Records, Including the Story of Col. John Custis of Arlington, Queen's Creek & Williamsburg. (Illus.). 1981. 20.00 (ISBN 0-89308-146-9). Southern Hist Pr.

Crowson, Milton. The Epistle to the Hebrews. 1974. pap. 4.95 (ISBN 0-89265-021-4). Randall Hse.

Crowson, Milton, jt. auth. see Fry, Malcolm C.

Crowther, Duane S. Atlas & Outline of the Acts of the Apostles. LC 83-80528. 114p. 1983. pap. 6.95 (ISBN 0-88290-219-9). Horizon-Utah.

--Atlas & Outline of the Life of Christ. LC 83-82414. 120p. (Orig.). 1983. pap. 6.95 (ISBN 0-88290-207-5). Horizon Utah.

--Come unto Christ. LC 70-173393. (Scripture Guide Ser.). 240p. 1971. pap. 5.95 (ISBN 0-88290-007-2). Horizon Utah.

--Gifts of the Spirit. LC 65-29176. 352p. 1983. 10.95 (ISBN 0-88290-210-5). Horizon Utah.

--God & His Church. LC 76-173392. (Scripture Guide Ser.). 244p. 1971. pap. 5.95 (ISBN 0-88290-006-4). Horizon Utah.

--A Guide to Effective Scripture Study. LC 75-5321. (Scripture Guide Ser). 147p. 1975. pap. 4.95 (ISBN 0-88290-004-8). Horizon Utah.

--The Plan of Salvation & the Future in Prophecy. LC 72-173391. (Scripture Guide Ser.). 228p. 1971. pap. 5.95 (ISBN 0-88290-005-6). Horizon Utah.

--The Prophecies of Joseph Smith. LC 83-80664. 413p. 1873. 10.95 (ISBN 0-88290-221-0). Horizon-Utah.

--Prophetic Warnings to Modern America. LC 77-87431. 415p. 1977. 12.95 (ISBN 0-88290-016-1). Horizon Utah.

--Prophets & Prophecies of the Old Testament. 2nd ed. LC 66-25508. (Comprehensive Bible Ser.). (Illus.). 644p. 1973. Repr. of 1967 ed. 12.95 (ISBN 0-88290-022-6). Horizon Utah.

--Reading Guide to the Book of Mormon: A Simplified Program Featuring Brief Outlines & Doctrinal Summaries. LC 75-5322. 169p. 1975. 7.95 (ISBN 0-88290-045-5). Horizon Utah.

Crowther, Jean D. Book of Mormon Puzzles & Pictures for Young Latter-Day Saints. LC 77-74495. (Books for LDS Children). (Illus.). 56p. 1977. pap. 4.95 (ISBN 0-88290-080-3). Horizon Utah.

--Growing Up in the Church: Gospel Principles & Practices for Children. rev. ed. LC 67-25433. (Illus.). 84p. 1973. Repr. of 1965 ed. 6.95 (ISBN 0-88290-024-2). Horizon Utah.

--A Mother's Prayer. 14p. 1978. pap. 1.00 (ISBN 0-88290-099-4). Horizon Utah.

Crowther, M. A. Church Embattled: Religious Controversy in Mid-Victorian England. LC 70-19499. (Library of Politics & Society Ser.). 272p. 1970. 29.50 (ISBN 0-208-01091-2, Archon). Shoe String.

Crowther, Samuel, jt. auth. see Schon, James F.

Crowther-Hunt, Norman. Two Early Political Associations: The Quakers & the Dissenting Deputies in the Age of Sir Robert Walpole. LC 78-23805. 1979. Repr. of 1961 ed. lib. bdg. 24.75x (ISBN 0-313-21036-5, HUTW). Greenwood.

Cruden, Alexander. Cruden's Compact Concordance. 1968. 9.95 (ISBN 0-310-22910-3, 9440). Zondervan.

--Cruden's Complete Concordance. 1949. 14.95 (ISBN 0-310-22920-0, 9441). Zondervan.

--Cruden's Complete Concordance. 1976. pap. 9.95 (ISBN 0-310-22921-9, 9441P). Zondervan.

--Cruden's Complete Concordance. 796p. Date not set. 13.95 (ISBN 0-917006-31-3). Hendrickson MA.

--Cruden's Concordance. 1982. pap. 3.95 (ISBN 0-515-06741-5). Jove Pubns.

--Cruden's Concordance. Eadie, ed. 1982. pap. 7.95 (ISBN 0-89081-362-0). Harvest Hse.

--Cruden's Concordance: Handy Reference Edition. (Baker's Paperback Reference Library). 344p. 1982. pap. 7.95 (ISBN 0-8010-2478-1). Baker Bk.

--Cruden's Handy Concordance. pap. 3.95 (ISBN 0-310-22931-6, 6767P). Zondervan.

--Cruden's Unabridged Concordance. LC 54-11084. 17.95 (ISBN 0-8054-1123-2). Broadman.

Cruden, Alexander, jt. auth. see Tenney, Merrill C.

Cruetz, W. New Light on the Protocols of Zion. 1982. lib. bdg. 69.95 (ISBN 0-87700-366-1). Revisionist Pr.

Cruickshank, John. PASCAL: Pensees. (Critical Guides to French Texts Ser.: No. 23). 79p. 1983. pap. 3.95 (ISBN 0-7293-0154-0, Pub. by Grant & Cutler). Longwood Pub Group.

Cruise, Robert J., jt. auth. see Blitchington, Peter.

Crum, Jesse K. The Art of Inner Listening. LC 74-21643. (Orig.). 1975. pap. 2.25 (ISBN 0-8356-0303-2, Quest). Theos Pub Hse.

Crum, Mary A. A Giggle Goes a Long Way. 96p. 1986. 4.95 (ISBN 0-8010-2510-9). Baker Bk.

Crum, Milton, Jr., jt. auth. see Reid, Richard.

Crummey, Robert O. Old Believers & the World of Antichrist: The Vyg Community & the Russian State, 1694-1855. LC 79-98121. (Illus.). 278p. 1970. 30.00x (ISBN 0-299-05560-4). U of Wis Pr.

Crump, C. G. & Jacob, E. F., eds. Legacy of the Middle Ages. (Legacy Ser.). (Illus.). 1926. 32.50x (ISBN 0-19-821907-5). Oxford U Pr.

Crump, Galbraith M. The Mystical Design of "Paradise Lost". 194p. 1975. 18.00 (ISBN 0-8387-1519-2). Bucknell U Pr.

Crump, Galbraith M., ed. Approaches to Teaching Milton's Paradise Lost. LC 85-21390. (Approaches to Teaching World Literature Ser.: No. 10). 175p. 1986. 30.00x (ISBN 0-87352-493-4); pap. text ed. 16.50x (ISBN 0-87352-494-2). Modern Lang.

Crumrine, N. Ross. The Mayo Indians of Sonora: A People Who Refuse to Die. LC 76-8563. 167p. 1977. 12.50x (ISBN 0-8165-0605-1); pap. text ed. 5.95x (ISBN 0-8165-0473-3). U of Ariz Pr.

Crunlan, Stephen A. & Lambrides, Daniel H. Healing Relationships: A Christian's Manual of Lay Counseling. LC 83-70103. 325p. 1984. pap. 6.45 (ISBN 0-87509-329-9); Leader's Guide. 2.95 (ISBN 0-87509-354-X). Chr Pubns.

Crussell, Leah A., ed. Three Hundred Sixty-Five Devotions, 1986-1987. 1986. pocket ed. 3.95 (ISBN 0-87403-003-X, 3087); pap. 5.95 (ISBN 0-87403-004-8, 4087). Standard Pub.

Cruttwell, Charles T. Literary History of Early Christianity, 2 Vols. LC 76-129369. Repr. of 1893 ed. 65.00 (ISBN 0-404-01877-7). AMS Pr.

Cruttwell, Patrick, ed. see Johnson, Samuel.

Crutwell, Maud. Luca & Andrea Della Robbia. LC 79-155625. (Illus.). Repr. of 1902 ed. 29.50 (ISBN 0-404-01869-6). AMS Pr.

Cruz, Joan C. The Incorruptibles. LC 77-93992. (Illus.). 1977. pap. 8.00 (ISBN 0-89555-066-0). TAN Bks Pubs.

--Relics. LC 84-60744. (Illus.). 352p. 1984. pap. 10.95 (ISBN 0-87973-701-8, 701). Our Sunday Visitor.

Cruz, Nicky. Run Baby Run: The Story of a Gang-Lord Turned Crusader. LC 68-23446. 240p. 1968. pap. 3.50 (ISBN 0-912106-58-1, Pub. by Logos). Bridge Pub.

Cruz, Rodolfo A. Instrucciones Practicas para Nuevos Creyentes. LC 77-71308. (Span.). 78p. (Orig.). 1970. pap. text ed. 1.95 (ISBN 0-89922-002-9). Edit Caribe.

Cruz Aymes, Maria de la see De la Cruz Aymes, Maria & Buckley, Francis J.

Crystal, Richard O., ed. see Schievella, Pasqual S.

CSAA. When Children Ask about Sex. 42p. 1974. pap. 1.50 (ISBN 0-87183-243-7). Jewish Bd Family.

--You, Your Child & Drugs. 1971. pap. 1.75 (ISBN 0-87183-238-0). Jewish Bd Family.

Csoma, Sandor K. The Life & Teachings of Buddha. LC 78-72399. Repr. of 1957 ed. 21.50 (ISBN 0-404-17258-X). AMS Pr.

Cua, A. S. Dimensions of Moral Creativity: Paradigms, Principles, & Ideals. LC 77-16169. 1978. 22.50x (ISBN 0-271-00540-8). Pa St U Pr.

Cubitt, Heather. Luther & the Reformation. Reeves, Marjorie, ed. (Then & There Ser.). (Illus.). 96p. 1976. pap. text ed. 4.75 (ISBN 0-582-20542-5). Longman.

Cuddihy, John M. The Ordeal of Civility: Freud, Marx, Levi-Strauss, & the Jewish Struggle with Modernity. LC 86-47757. 272p. 1987. pap. 9.95 (ISBN 0-8070-3609-9, BP-738). Beacon Pr.

Cudinach, Salvidor, ed. & tr. see Piarist Fathers.

Cudsi, Alex & Dessouki, Ali E. Hillal, eds. Islam & Power in the Contemporary Muslim World. LC 81-47608. 208p. 1981. text ed. 25.00x (ISBN 0-8018-2697-7). Johns Hopkins.

Cudworth, Ralph. A Treatise Concerning Eternal & Immutable Morality. Wellek, Rene, ed. LC 75-11214. (British Philosophers & Theologians of the 17th & 18th Centuries Ser.: Vol. 17). 1976. Repr. of 1731 ed. lib. bdg. 51.00 (ISBN 0-8240-1768-4). Garland Pub.

--The True Intellectual System of the Universe, 2 vols. Wellek, Rene, ed. LC 75-11213. (British Philosophers & Theologians of the 17th & 18th Centuries Ser.: Vol. 16). 1978. Repr. of 1678 ed. Set. lib. bdg. 101.00 (ISBN 0-8240-1767-6). Garland Pub.

Cuffee, James W. Spiritual Automobile. Knickerbocker, Charles, ed. 44p. 1980. 4.75 (ISBN 0-682-48997-2). Exposition Pr FL.

Culbertson, Paul. Living Portraits from the Old Testament. 192p. 1978. pap. 2.95 (ISBN 0-8341-0507-1). Beacon Hill.

Culbertson, William. God's Provision for Holy Living. (Moody Classics Ser.). 1984. pap. 2.95 (ISBN 0-8024-3043-0). Moody.

Culi, Yaakov. The Torah Anthology: Mem Lo'ez, 9 vols. Kaplan, Aryeh, tr. Incl. Vol. 1. Beginnings: From Creation Until Abraham. 540p. 14.95 (ISBN 0-940118-01-7); Vol. 2. The Patriarchs: From Abraham Until Jacob. 600p. 15.95 (ISBN 0-940118-02-5); Vol. 3. The Twelve Tribes: From Jacob Until Joseph. 708p; Vol. 4. Israel in Egypt: Subjugation & Prelude to the Exodus. 280p. 12.95 (ISBN 0-940118-04-1); Vol. 5. Redemption: The Exodus from Egypt. 436p. 15.95 (ISBN 0-940118-05-X); Vol. 6. The Ten Commandments: Revelation at Sinai. 534p.. 16.95 (ISBN 0-940118-06-8); Vol. 7. The Law: The First Codification. 363p. 13.95 (ISBN 0-940118-07-6); Vol. 8. Acceptance: Establishing the Covenant. 250p. 12.95 (ISBN 0-940118-08-4); Vol. 9. The Tabernacle: Plans for the Sanctuary. 413p. 15.95 (ISBN 0-940118-09-2). (MeAm Lo'ez Ser.). (Illus.). 1977-1980. Maznaim.

Culianu, Ioan P. Psychanodia I: A Survey of the Evidence Concerning the Ascension of the Soul & its Relevance. (Etudes Prelimminaires aux Religions Orientales dans l'Empire Romain Ser.: No. 99). 81p. 1983. pap. text ed. 19.95x (ISBN 90-04-06903-8, Pub. by EJ Brill Holland). Humanities.

Cullamar, Evelyn T. Babaylanism in Negros: 1896-1907. (Illus.). 133p. (Orig.). 1986. pap. 8.50x (ISBN 971-10-0293-0, Pub. by New Day Philippines). Cellar.

Cullen, Catherine, tr. see Favret-Saada, Jeanne.

Cullen, Patrick. Spenser, Marvell, & Renaissance Pastoral. LC 76-123566. pap. 42.60 (2014653). Bks Demand UMI.

Culler, A. D., ed. see Newman, John H.

Culler, Arthur D. The Imperial Intellect. LC 55-8700. Repr. of 1955 ed. lib. bdg. 22.50x (ISBN 0-8371-7683-2, CUII). Greenwood.

Culleton, R. Gerald. The Prophets & Our Times. 1974. pap. 6.00 (ISBN 0-89555-050-4). TAN Bks Pubs.

--The Reign of AntiChrist. 1974. pap. 6.00 (ISBN 0-89555-047-4). TAN Bks Pubs.

Culley, Robert C. & Overholt, Thomas W., eds. Semeia Twenty-One: Anthropological Perspectives on Old Testament Prophecy. pap. 9.95 (06 20 21). Scholars Pr GA.

Culley, Thomas D. Jesuits & Music. 401p. 1970. 29.00 (ISBN 88-7041-582-1). Jesuit Hist.

Culligan, Emmett. Fatima Secret. 1975. pap. 1.50 (ISBN 0-89555-052-0). TAN Bks Pubs.

Culligan, Emmett J. The Last World War & the End of Time. (Illus.). 210p. 1981. pap. 6.00 (ISBN 0-89555-034-2). TAN Bks Pubs.

Cullingan, Kevin, intro. by. Spiritual Direction: Contemporary Readings. 237p. (Orig.). 1983. pap. 5.95 (ISBN 0-914544-43-8). Living Flame Pr.

Culliton, Joseph T. Non-Violence-Central to Christian Spirituality: Perspectives from Scriptures to the Present. LC 82-7964. (Toronto Studies in Theology: Vol. 8). 312p. 1982. 49.95x (ISBN 0-88946-964-4). E Mellen.

--Personal Presence: Its Effects on Honesty & Truthfulness. LC 85-6218. 202p. (Orig.). 1985. 24.50 (ISBN 0-8191-4661-7); pap. text ed. 10.75 (ISBN 0-8191-4662-5). U Pr of Amer.

--A Processive World View for Pragmatic Christians. LC 75-3781. 302p. 1975. 13.95 (ISBN 0-8022-2170-X). Philos Lib.

Cullman, Oscar. Christ & Time: The Primitive Christian Conception of Time & History. 1977. lib. bdg. 59.95 (ISBN 0-8490-1614-2). Gordon Pr.

Cullmann, Oscar. Baptism in the New Testament. LC 78-6937. 84p. 1978. pap. 5.95 (ISBN 0-664-24219-7). Westminster.

--The Christology of the New Testament. rev. ed. Guthrie, Shirley C. & Hall, Charles A. M., trs. LC 59-10178. 364p. 1980. pap. 12.95 (ISBN 0-664-24351-7). Westminster.

--Early Christian Worship. LC 78-6636. 126p. 1978. pap. 6.95 (ISBN 0-664-24220-0). Westminster.

--New Testament: An Introduction for the General Reader. LC 68-12796. 138p. 1968. pap. 8.95 (ISBN 0-664-24817-9). Westminster.

Cullmann, Oscar & Leenhardt, Franz J. Essays on the Lord's Supper. LC 58-8979. 1958. pap. 4.95 (ISBN 0-8042-3748-4). John Knox.

Cullum, Charles G. All Things Are Possible: The Charles Cullum Lessons. LC 86-5819. 176p. (Orig.). 1986. pap. 7.95 (ISBN 0-937641-00-6). Stone Canyon Pr.

Cully, Iris V. Christian Child Development. LC 78-19507. 176p. 1983. pap. 6.95 (ISBN 0-06-061654-7, RD/453, HarpR). Har-Row.

--Education for Spiritual Growth. LC 83-48464. 192p. 1984. 14.45 (ISBN 0-06-061655-5, HarpR). Har-Row.

--We Give Thanks. (Illus., Orig.). 1976. pap. text ed. 1.95x (ISBN 0-8192-4070-2); tchr's. ed. 4.50x (ISBN 0-8192-4069-9); guidebk. for parents 1.95x (ISBN 0-8192-4071-0). Morehouse.

Cully, Iris V. & Cully, Kendig B. A Guide to Biblical Resources. LC 81-80625. 160p. (Orig.). 1981. pap. 7.95 (ISBN 0-8192-1286-5). Morehouse.

Cully, Kendig B., jt. auth. see Cully, Iris V.

Cully, Kendig B., ed. Confirmation Re-Examined. LC 82-81428. 144p. (Orig.). 1982. pap. 7.95 (ISBN 0-8192-1304-7). Morehouse.

Culpepper, R. Alan. Anatomy of the Fourth Gospel: A Study in Literary Design. LC 82-16302. (Foundations & Facets Ser.). 256p. 1983. 19.95 (ISBN 0-8006-2102-6, 1-2102). Fortress.

--The Johannine School: An Evaluation of the Johannine-School Hypothesis Based on an Investigation of the Nature of Ancient Schools. LC 75-34235. (Society of Biblical Literature. Dissertation Ser.: No. 26). Repr. of 1975 ed. 62.40 (ISBN 0-8357-9576-4, 2017525). Bks Demand UMI.

--One, Two, Three, John. Hayes, John, ed. LC 85-42821. (Preaching Guides). 132p. 1985. pap. 6.95 (ISBN 0-8042-3248-2). John Knox.

--Pentecost Two. LC 84-18756. (Proclamation Three C Ser.). 64p. 1986. pap. 3.75 (ISBN 0-8006-4131-0, 1-4131). Fortress.

Culpepper, Robert H. Evaluating the Charismatic Movement: A Theology & Biblical Appraisal. 192p. 1987. pap. text ed. 6.95 (ISBN 0-913029-17-3). Stevens Bk Pr.

--Interpreting the Atonement. 170p. 1986. pap. 6.95 (ISBN 0-913029-13-0). Stevens Bk Pr.

Culver, Raymond B. Horace Mann & Religion in the Massachusetts Public Schools. LC 72-89168. (American Education: Its Men, Institutions & Ideas, Ser. 1). 1969. Repr. of 1929 ed. 17.00 (ISBN 0-405-01406-6). Ayer Co Pubs.

Culver, Robert D. A Greater Commission: A Theology of World Missions. (Orig.). 1984. pap. text ed. 9.95 (ISBN 0-8024-3302-2). Moody.

--The Histories & Prophecies of Daniel. 192p. (Orig.). 1980. pap. 4.95 (ISBN 0-88469-131-4). BMH Bks.

--Life of Christ. LC 76-17967. 272p. 1976. pap. 9.95 (ISBN 0-8010-2498-6). Baker Bk.

--The Peacemongers. Carpenter, Mark, ed. 160p. 1985. pap. 5.95 (ISBN 0-8423-4789-5). Tyndale.

Culver, Robert D., jt. auth. see Perry, Lloyd M.

Culver, Sylvia A. Keep the River Flowing. 92p. 1979. pap. 2.50 (ISBN 0-8341-0592-6). Beacon Hill.

Culverwel, Nathanael. An Elegant & Learned Discourse on the Light of Nature, 1652: Nathanael Culverwel (1618-1651) Wellek, Rene, ed. Bd. with Spiritual Opticks. LC 75-11215. (British Philosophers & Theologians of the 17th & 18th Centuries Ser.). 456p. 1978. lib. bdg. 51.00 (ISBN 0-8240-1769-2). Garland Pub.

Cumberland Presbyterian Church, jt. auth. see Office of Worship for the Presbyterian Church (U. S. A.).

Cumbers, Frank, jt. auth. see Meyer, F. B.

Cumbey, Constance. The Hidden Dangers of the Rainbow: The New Age Movement & Our Coming Age of Barbarism. LC 83-80044. 271p. (Orig.). 1983. pap. 6.95 (ISBN 0-910311-03-X). Huntington Hse Inc.

Cumbler, John T. A Moral Response to Industrialism: The Lectures of Reverend Cook in Lynn, Massachusetts. LC 81-9338. (American Social History Ser.). 180p. 1982. 39.50 (ISBN 0-87395-558-7); pap. 10.95 (ISBN 0-87395-559-5). State U NY Pr.

Cuming, G. J., ed. see Church of England Staff.

Cuming, G. J., jt. ed. see Jasper, R. C.

Cuming, Geoffrey. A History of Anglican Liturgy. (Illus.). 450p. 1980. Repr. of 1969 ed. text ed. 55.00x (ISBN 0-333-30661-9). Humanities.

Cumming, Charles G. Assyrian & Hebrew Hymns of Praise. LC 34-3318. (Columbia University. Oriental Studies: No. 12). Repr. of 1934 ed. 16.50 (ISBN 0-404-50502-3). AMS Pr.

Cumming, Diane, tr. see Michaelle.

Cumming, James T. & Moll, Hans G. And, God, What About...? 1980. 4.50 (ISBN 0-570-03806-5, 12-2915). Concordia.

--Hey God, What about...? (Illus.). 1977. pap. 4.50 (ISBN 0-570-03758-1, 12-2666). Concordia.

Cumming, John & Burns, Paul, eds. Prayers for Our Times. 144p. 1983. 10.95 (ISBN 0-8245-0071-7); pap. 6.95 (ISBN 0-8245-0107-1). Crossroad NY.

Cumming, John, tr. see Horkheimer, Max & Adorno, Theodor W.

Cumming, W. P., ed. The Revelations of Saint Birgitta. (EETS, OS Ser.: No. 178). Repr. of 1929 ed. 38.00 (ISBN 0-527-00175-9). Kraus Repr.

Cumming, William K. Follow ME. 6.95 (ISBN 0-917920-01-5); pap. 1.95 (ISBN 0-917920-00-7). Mustardseed.

Cummings. Men in the Sunlight of the Word. pap. 5.95 (ISBN 0-686-27771-6). Schmul Pub Co.

Cummings, A. L. & Fales, D. A., Jr. The Crowninshield-Bentley House. LC 76-16905. (Historic House Booklet Ser.: No. 2). 1976. 2.00 (ISBN 0-88389-060-7). Essex Inst.

Cummings, Calvin K. Confessing Christ. 3rd, rev. ed. (Orig.). 1977. pap. 1.45 (ISBN 0-934688-04-4). Great Comm Pubns.

Cummings, Charles. Monastic Practices. pap. 7.95 (ISBN 0-87907-975-4). Cistercian Pubns.

--The Mystery of the Ordinary: Discovering the Richness of Everyday Experiences. LC 81-47846. 144p. 1982. 9.57 (ISBN 0-06-061652-0, HarpR). Har-Row.

--Songs of Freedom: The Psalter As a School of Prayer. 1986. pap. 6.95 (ISBN 0-87193-245-8). Dimension Bks.

--Spirituality & the Desert Experience. 1976. cancelled (ISBN 0-87193-166-4). Dimension Bks.

Cummings, Charles, tr. see Hausherr, Irenee.

Cummings, D., tr. see Makrakis, Apostolos.

Cummings, D., tr. see Philaretos, S. D.

Cummings, D., tr. see Philaretos, Sotirios D.

Cummings, David, ed. The Purpose of a Christian School. 1979. pap. 4.50 (ISBN 0-87552-157-6). Presby & Reformed.

Cummings, Denver, tr. see Livadeas, Themistocles & Charitos, Minas.

Cummings, Denver, tr. see Makrakis, Apostolos.

Cummings, Des, Jr., jt. auth. see Dudley, Roger L.

Cummings, H. Wayland, ed. see Somervill, Charles.

Cummings, J. T. & Moll, H. Prayers for College Students. LC 12-2962. 1982. pap. 4.95 (ISBN 0-570-03869-3). Concordia.

Cummings, James E. A Handbook on the Holy Spirit. LC 77-79551. 208p. 1977. pap. 3.95 (ISBN 0-87123-541-2, 200541). Bethany Hse.

Cummings, John. Deuteronomy. 1982. lib. bdg. 16.00 (ISBN 0-86524-085-X, 0501). Klock & Klock.

Cummings, Mary. Lives of the Buddha in the Art & Literature of Asia. LC 80-67341. (Michigan Papers on South & Southeast Asia: No. 20). (Illus.). xiii, 225p. 1982. 19.95 (ISBN 0-89148-022-6); pap. 10.95 (ISBN 0-89148-023-4). Ctr S&SE Asian.

Cummings, Mary L., ed. Full Circle: Stories of Mennonite Women. LC 78-66879. 1978. pap. 5.25 (ISBN 0-87303-014-1). Faith & Life.

Cummings, Robert W. Unto You Is the Promise. pap. 0.79 (ISBN 0-88243-750-X, 02-0750). Gospel Pub.

Cummings, Violet. Has Anybody Really Seen Noah's Ark? 416p. 1982. pap. 8.95 (ISBN 0-89051-086-5). Master Bks.

Cummins, D. Duane. A Handbook for Today's Disciples in the Christian Church: Disciples of Christ. LC 81-10029. 64p. (Orig.). 1981. pap. 1.95 (ISBN 0-8272-1419-7, 10H1309). CBP.

--Un Manual para los Discipulos de Hoy. Delgado, Conchita & Sanchez, Zayda N., trs. from Eng. LC 83-15489. Tr. of A Handbook for Today's Disciples. (Span., Illus.). 64p. (Orig.). 1983. pap. 2.25 (ISBN 0-8272-2316-1). CBP.

Cummins, Walter J. Demonstrating God's Power. LC 85-50446. 276p. 1985. 6.95 (ISBN 0-910068-60-7). Am Christian.

Cumnock, Frances, ed. Catalog of the Salem Congregation Music. (Illus.). 682p. 31.50 (ISBN 0-8078-1398-2). Moravian Music.

Cumont, Franz. Astrology & Religion among the Greeks & Romans. 1912. pap. 3.50 (ISBN 0-486-20581-9). Dover.

--The Mysteries of Mithra. 2nd ed. McCormack, Thomas J., tr. (Illus., Fr). 1911. pap. 5.95 (ISBN 0-486-20323-9). Dover.

--Mysteries of Mithra. (Illus.). 14.00 (ISBN 0-8446-1926-4). Peter Smith.

--Oriental Religions in Roman Paganism. 1911. pap. 5.95 (ISBN 0-486-20321-2). Dover.

--Oriental Religions in Roman Paganism. 14.00 (ISBN 0-8446-1925-6). Peter Smith.

--Recherches sur le Symbolisme Funeraire des Romains. facsimile ed. LC 75-10632. (Ancient Religion & Mythology Ser.). (Fr., Illus.). 1976. Repr. of 1942 ed. 57.50x (ISBN 0-405-07007-1). Ayer Co Pubs.

Cundall, A. E. Genesis & Exodus. (Bible Study Commentaries Ser.). 126p. 1980. pap. 4.95 (ISBN 0-87508-150-9). Chr Lit.

Cundall, Arthur E. & Morris, Leon. Judges & Ruth. LC 68-31426. (Tyndale Old Testament Commentary Ser). (Illus.). 1968. 12.95 (ISBN 0-87784-896-3); pap. 6.95 (ISBN 0-87784-257-4). Inter-Varsity.

Cundall, Joseph. The Life & Genius of Rembrandt. LC 77-94567. 1979. Repr. of 1867 ed. lib. bdg. 30.00 (ISBN 0-89341-235-X). Longwood Pub Group.

Cundick, Robert, ed. A First Album for Church Organists. (Illus.). 64p. 1967. pap. 7.95 (ISBN 0-8258-0227-X, 0-4655). Fischer Inc NY.

Cundy, Ian. Ephesians-Thessalonians. 1981. pap. 4.95 (ISBN 0-87508-173-8). Chr Lit.

Cuneo, J. James, jt. ed. see Schumacher, William A.

Cuneo, Michael W., jt. auth. see Blasi, Anthony J.

Cunliffe-Jones, H., ed. Book of Jeremiah. 1961. 8.95 (ISBN 0-02-529260-9). Macmillan.

Cunliffe-Jones, Hubert & Drewery, Benjamin, eds. A History of Christian Doctrine. LC 79-21689. 616p. 1980. 29.95 (ISBN 0-8006-0626-4, 1-626). Fortress.

Cunningham, Agnes. The Bishop in the Church: Patristic Texts on the Role of the Episkopos. (Theology & Life Ser.: Vol. 13). 1985. pap. 3.95 (ISBN 0-89453-469-6). M Glazier.

--The Early Church & the State. LC 81-70666. (Sources of Early Christian Thought Ser.). 128p. 1982. pap. 7.95 (ISBN 0-8006-1413-5, 1-1413). Fortress.

--Prayer: Personal & Liturgical. (Message of the Fathers of the Church Ser.: Vol. 16). 1985. 12.95 (ISBN 0-89453-356-8); pap. 8.95 (ISBN 0-89453-327-4). M Glazier.

Cunningham, Caroline, tr. see Asch, Sholem.

Cunningham, James. A Vanquished Hope: The Church in Russia on the Eve of the Revolution. 1981. pap. 40.00x (Pub. by Mowbrays Pub Div). State Mutual Bk.

Cunningham, James W. A Vanquished Hope: The Movement for Church Renewal in Russia, 1905-1906. LC 81-9077. 384p. 1981. pap. text ed. 10.95 (ISBN 0-913836-70-2). St Vladimirs.

Cunningham, Lawrence. Catholic Experience. 270p. 1987. pap. 10.95 (ISBN 0-8245-0811-4). Crossroad NY.

--Catholic Heritage. 240p. 1985. pap. 9.95 (ISBN 0-8245-0685-5). Crossroad NY.

--Saint Francis of Assisi. LC 81-47419. (Illus.). 128p. 1981. 5.00 (ISBN 0-06-061651-2, HarpR). Har-Row.

Cunningham, Lawrence S. The Catholic Heritage: Martyrs, Ascetics, Pilgrims, Warriors, Mystics, Theologians, Artists, Humanists, Activists, Outsiders & Saints. 256p. 1983. 14.95 (ISBN 0-8245-0592-1). Crossroad NY.

Cunningham, Lawrence S., tr. see Bonaventure, St.

Cunningham, Loren & Rogers, Janice. Eres Tu, Senor? Araujo, Juan S., tr. from Eng. Tr. of Is That Really You, God? (Span.). 176p. 1986. pap. 3.50 (ISBN 0-88113-061-3). Edit Betania.

Cunningham, Philip A. The Apostle Paul: Male Chauvinist or Proponent of Equality? 24p. (Orig.). 1986. pap. 4.25 (ISBN 0-937997-03-X). Hi-Time Pub.

--Jewish Apostle to the Gentiles: Paul As He Saw Himself. 112p. (Orig.). 1986. pap. 5.95 (ISBN 0-89622-302-7). Twenty-Third.

Cunningham, Raymond J., ed. see Mather, Cotton.

Cunningham, Richard B. Creative Stewardship. LC 79-973. (Creative Leadership Ser.). 1979. 6.95 (ISBN 0-687-09844-0). Abingdon.

Cunningham, Richard G. Annotated Bibliography of the Work of the Canon Law Society of America 1965-1980. 121p. (Orig.). 1982. pap. 4.50 (ISBN 0-943616-06-9). Canon Law Soc.

Cunningham, Robert, tr. see Pope John Paul I.

Cunningham, Robert, tr. see Ratzinger, Joseph Cardinal.

Cunningham, Robert, tr. see Schneider, Reinhold.

Cunningham, Robert C. Getting Together with Luke & Acts. 47p. 1972. pap. 0.50 (ISBN 0-88243-930-8, 02-0930). Gospel Pub.

Cunningham, W. J. Agony at Galloway: One Church's Struggle with Social Change. LC 79-56698. 1980. 3.95 (ISBN 0-87805-117-1). U Pr of Miss.

Cunningham, W. P., ed. see Resource Publications, Inc. Staff.

Cunningham, William. Historical Theology, 2 vols. 1979. Set. 38.95 (ISBN 0-85151-058-2); Vol. 1. (ISBN 0-85151-286-0); Vol. 2. (ISBN 0-85151-287-9). Banner of Truth.

--Reformers & the Theology of Reformation. 1979. 19.95 (ISBN 0-85151-013-2). Banner of Truth.

Cupitt, Don. Taking Leave of God. 192p. 1981. 9.95 (ISBN 0-8245-0045-8). Crossroad NY.

Curb, Rosemary & Manahan, Nancy. Lesbian Nuns: Breaking Silence. 400p. 1986. pap. 3.95 (ISBN 0-446-32659-3). Warner Bks.

Curb, Rosemary & Manahan, Nancy, eds. Lesbian Nuns: Breaking Silence. LC 84-29594. 432p. 1985. 16.95 (ISBN 0-930044-63-0); pap. 9.95 (ISBN 0-930044-62-2). Naiad Pr.

Curcic, Slobodan. Gracanica: King Milutin's Church & Its Place in Late Byzantine Architecture. LC 79-11984. (Illus.). 1980. 34.95x (ISBN 0-271-00218-2). Pa St U Pr.

Cureton, Charles T., jt. ed. see Miller, William L.

Cureton, William, ed. Spicilegium Syriacum: Containing Remains of Bardesan, Meliton, Ambrose & Mara Bar Serapion, 1855. 1965. 10.00x (ISBN 0-8401-0493-6). A R Allenson.

Curl, James S. The Egyptian Revival. (Illus.). 256p. 1982. 50.00 (ISBN 0-04-724001-6). Allen Unwin.

--The Victorian Celebration of Death: The Architecture & Planning of the 19th-Century Necropolis. LC 70-184048. 222p. 1972. 35.00x (ISBN 0-8103-2000-2). Gale.

Curlee-Salisbury, Joan. When the Woman You Love Is an Alcoholic. LC 78-73017. (When Bk). (Illus.). 1978. pap. 2.45 (ISBN 0-87029-143-2, 20229-1). Abbey.

Curley, E. M. Descartes Against the Skeptics. LC 77-14366. 1978. 17.50x (ISBN 0-674-19826-3). Harvard U Pr.

Curley, Ed. Church Feasts & Celebrations. 1983. 9.95 (ISBN 0-89837-085-X, Pub. by Pflaum Pr). Peter Li.

--The Mass for Young Catholics. 1978. 9.95 (ISBN 0-686-89575-4, Pub. by Pflaum Pr). Peter Li.

--Morals, Value, & Motivation: Ethics for Today. 1978. 9.95 (ISBN 0-89837-039-6, Pub. by Pflaum Pr). Peter Li.

--Saints for Young Christians. 1983. 9.95 (ISBN 0-89837-088-4, Pub. by Pflaum Pr). Peter Li.

Curley, Edwin, ed. see Spinoza, Baruch.

Curley, Lois, jt. ed. see Hestenes, Roberta.

Curley, Maureen. First Prayers for Young Catholics. (Children of the Kingdom Activities Ser.). 1978. 9.95 (ISBN 0-89837-008-6, Pub. by Pflaum Pr). Peter Li.

--The Sacraments. (Children of the Kingdom Activities Ser.). 1975. 9.95 (ISBN 0-89837-019-1, Pub. by Pflaum Pr). Peter Li.

--The Ten Commandments. (Children of the Kingdom Activities Ser.). 1976. 9.95 (ISBN 0-89837-015-9, Pub. by Pflaum Pr). Peter Li.

Curley, Michael J. Church & State in the Spanish Floridas (1783-1822) LC 73-3584. (Catholic University of America. Studies in American Church History: No. 30). Repr. of 1940 ed. 36.00 (ISBN 0-404-57780-6). AMS Pr.

Curley, Richard T. Elders, Shades, & Women: Ceremonial Change in Lango, Uganda. LC 70-634788. 1973. 32.50x (ISBN 0-520-02149-5). U of Cal Pr.

Curran, Charles, jt. ed. see McCormick, Richard A.

Curran, Charles E. American Catholic Social Ethics: Twentieth Century Approaches. LC 82-4829. 336p. 1982. 24.95 (ISBN 0-268-00603-2). U of Notre Dame Pr.

--American Catholic Social Ethics: Twentieth-Century Approaches. LC 82-4829. 353p. 1984. text ed. 9.95 (ISBN 0-268-00609-1, 85-06099). U of Notre Dame Pr.

--Catholic Moral Theology in Dialogue. LC 76-14906. 1976. text ed. 18.95x (ISBN 0-268-00716-0); pap. 5.95 (ISBN 0-268-00717-9). U of Notre Dame Pr.

--Critical Concerns in Moral Theology. LC 83-40593. 288p. 1984. text ed. 16.95 (ISBN 0-268-00747-0, 85-07477). U of Notre Dame Pr.

--Directions in Catholic Social Ethics. LC 84-28079. 304p. (Orig.). 1985. pap. text ed. 8.95 (ISBN 0-268-00853-1, 85-08533). U of Notre Dame Pr.

--Directions in Fundamental Moral Theology. LC 85-2543. 304p. 1985. pap. text ed. 8.95x (ISBN 0-268-00854-X, 85-08541, Dist. by Har-Row). U of Notre Dame Pr.

--New Perspectives in Moral Theology. LC 76-13206. 293p. 1976. text ed. 18.95 (ISBN 0-268-01449-3); pap. 6.95 (ISBN 0-268-01450-7). U of Notre Dame Pr.

--Toward an American Catholic Moral Theology. LC 86-40583. 256p. 1987. text ed. 18.95x (ISBN 0-268-01862-6, Dist. by Har-Row). U of Notre Dame Pr.

--Transition & Tradition in Moral Theology. LC 78-20877. 272p. 1980. pap. text ed. 6.95 (ISBN 0-268-01838-3). U of Notre Dame Pr.

--Transition & Tradition in Moral Theology. LC 78-20877. 1979. text ed. 18.95x (ISBN 0-268-01837-5, Dist. by Har Row). U of Notre Dame Pr.

Curran, Charles E. & McCormick, Richard. Readings in Moral Theology: No. 1, Moral Norms & Catholic Tradition. LC 79-84237. 1979. pap. 9.95 (ISBN 0-8091-2203-0). Paulist Pr.

Curran, Charles E. & McCormick, Richard A. Readings in Moral Theology, No. 4: The Use of Scripture in Moral Theology. 1984. pap. 9.95 (ISBN 0-8091-2563-3). Paulist Pr.

Curran, Charles E., ed. Absolutes in Moral Theology? LC 75-3988. 320p. 1976. Repr. of 1968 ed. lib. bdg. 25.00x (ISBN 0-8371-7450-3, CUMT). Greenwood.

Curran, Charles E. & McCormick, Richard A., eds. Readings in Moral Theology, No. 2: The Distinctiveness of Christian Ethics. LC 79-84237. 360p. 1980. pap. 7.95 (ISBN 0-8091-2303-7). Paulist Pr.

--Readings in Moral Theology, No. 3: The Magisterium & Morality. LC 81-82436. (Orig.). 1981. pap. 7.95 (ISBN 0-8091-2407-6). Paulist Pr.

Curran, Dolores. Family: A Church Challenge for the 80's. (Orig.). 1980. pap. 3.50 (ISBN 0-86683-640-3, HarpR). Har-Row.

--Family Prayer. rev. ed. 136p. (Orig.). 1983. pap. text ed. 5.95 (ISBN 0-86716-014-4). St Anthony Mess Pr.

--In the Beginning There Were the Parents. 1978. pap. 4.95 (ISBN 0-03-042766-5, HarpR). Har-Row.

--Who, Me Teach My Child Religion? rev. ed. 156p. 1981. pap. 6.95 (HarpR). Har-Row.

Curran, Francis X. Catholics in Colonial Law. 1963. 2.95 (ISBN 0-8294-0016-8). Loyola.

--The Return of the Jesuits. LC 66-29559. 1966. 3.00 (ISBN 0-8294-0018-4). Loyola.

Curran, Michael. The Antiphonary of Bangor. 272p. 1984. 60.00x (ISBN 0-7165-0338-7, BBA 05250, Pub. by Irish Academic Pr Ireland). Biblio Dist.

Curran, Robert E. Michael Augustine Corrigan & the Shaping of Conservative Catholism in America, 1878-1902. 46.50 (ISBN 0-405-10814-1). Ayer Co Pubs.

Curran, Stuart & Wittreich, Joseph A., Jr., eds. Blake's Sublime Allegory: Essays on the "Four Zoas," "Milton," & "Jerusalem". LC 72-1377. (Illus.). 404p. 1973. 35.00x (ISBN 0-299-06180-9). U of Wis Pr.

Currell, R. G. & Hurlbut, E. P. The Ruler of the Kings on the Earth: A Clear Look at Amillennialism for the Lay Person. 126p. 1983. pap. 4.95 (ISBN 0-87552-211-4). Presby & Reformed.

Currey, Cecil B. Reason & Revelation: John Duns Scotus on Natural Theology. LC 77-9614. (Synthesis Ser.). 1977. pap. 0.75 (ISBN 0-8199-0717-0). Franciscan Herald.

Currie, David M. Come, Let Us Worship God: A Handbook of Prayers for Leaders of Worship. LC 77-6808. 132p. 1977. softcover 4.25 (ISBN 0-664-24757-1). Westminster.

Currie, David R. On the Way! LC 81-69403. 1982. pap. 3.95 (ISBN 0-8054-5336-9, 4253-36). Broadman.

Currie, Robert, et al. Churches & Churchgoers: Patterns of Church Growth in the British Isles since 1700. (Illus.). 1978. 42.00x (ISBN 0-19-827218-9). Oxford U Pr.

Currie, Winifred. Creative Classroom Communications. 126p. 1972. pap. 1.25 (ISBN 0-88243-507-8, 02-0507). Gospel Pub.

Currier, Richard L., ed. see Meshorer, Ya'akov.

Currin, Beverly M. The Hope That Never Disappoints. 128p. (Orig.). 1983. pap. 8.75 (ISBN 0-687-17415-5). Abingdon.

Curry, jt. auth. see Augsburger.

Curry, Allen D. Leader's Guide for John W. Sanderson's "The Fruit of the Spirit". A Teaching Manual for Use in Adult Study Groups. (Orig.). 1978. pap. 2.95 (ISBN 0-934688-07-9). Great Comm Pubns.

Curry, Dean C., ed. Evangelicals & the Bishops' Pastoral Letter. LC 84-4005. 254p. (Orig.). 1984. pap. 10.95 (ISBN 0-8028-1985-0). Eerdmans.

Curry, S. E. Vocal & Literary Interpretation of the Bible. 1979. Repr. of 1903 ed. 30.00 (ISBN 0-8414-9988-8). Folcroft.

Curry, S. S. Vocal & Literary Interpretation of the Bible. 1909. 32.50 (ISBN 0-8274-3677-7). R West.

Curry, Thomas J. The First Freedoms: The Establishment of Freedom of Religion in America. 288p. 1986. text ed. 24.95x (ISBN 0-19-503661-1). Oxford U Pr.

Curry, W. Lawrence, ed. Anthems for the Junior Choir, 5 bks. 1.50 ea. Westminster.

--Service Music for the Adult Choir. 3.50 ea. (ISBN 0-664-10059-7). Westminster.

--Songs & Hymns for Primary Children. 1978. softcover 3.95 (ISBN 0-664-10117-8). Westminster.

Curry, Walter C. Milton's Ontology, Cosmogony & Physics. LC 57-5833. (Illus.). 226p. 1957. pap. 6.00x (ISBN 0-8131-0102-6). U Pr of Ky.

Curtas, Ted. Tears of Joy. cancelled (ISBN 0-686-12741-2); pap. 3.95 (ISBN 0-686-12742-0). Grace Pub Co.

Curtayne, Alice. St. Catherine of Siena. LC 80-53745. 1980. pap. 7.50 (ISBN 0-89555-162-4). Tan Bks Pubs.

Curti, Merle E. American Peace Crusade, Eighteen Fifteen to Eighteen Sixty. 1965. lib. bdg. 18.50x (ISBN 0-374-91976-3, Octagon). Hippocrene Bks.

Curtin, Jeremiah. Creation Myths of Primitive America. 1980. 31.00 (ISBN 0-405-13697-8, 1710). Ayer Co Pubs.

--Myths & Folk-Lore of Ireland. 1976. Repr. 18.00x (ISBN 0-7158-1090-1). Charles River Bks.

--Myths & Folk Tales of Ireland. LC 69-18206. 256p. 1975. pap. 4.50 (ISBN 0-486-22430-9). Dover.

--Myths of the Modocs: Indian Legends from the Northwest. LC 74-170711. Repr. of 1912 ed. 20.00 (ISBN 0-405-08415-3, Blom Pubns). Ayer Co Pubs.

Curtin, Rosalie, et al. R. C. I. A. A Practical Approach to Christian Initiation. 136p. (Orig.). 1981. pap. 10.95 (ISBN 0-697-01759-1). Wm C Brown.

Curtis, Adrian H. Ugarit. (Cities of the Biblical World Ser.). 128p. (Orig.). 1985. pap. 8.95 (ISBN 0-8028-0166-8). Eerdmans.

Curtis, Charles, et al. Perspectives on God: Sociological, Theological & Philosophical. LC 78-62943. 1978. pap. text ed. 11.50 (ISBN 0-8191-0605-4). U Pr of Amer.

Curtis, Denis, et al. Dead Martyrs & Living Heroes. LC 83-61651. 260p. 13.95 (ISBN 0-88400-097-4). Shengold.

Curtis, Donald. The Christ-Based Teachings. LC 75-40657. 1976. 5.95 (ISBN 0-87159-016-6). Unity School.

--Your Thoughts Can Change Your Life. pap. 7.00 (ISBN 0-87980-179-4). Wilshire.

Curtis, Edward L. & Madsen, Albert A. A Critical & Exegetical Commentary on Chronicles I & II. Driver, Samuel R., et al, eds. LC 10-14958. (International Critical Commentary Ser.). 560p. 1910. 24.95 (ISBN 0-567-05007-6, Pub. by T & T Clark Ltd UK). Fortress.

Curtis, Helene & Dudley, Cliff. All That I Have. LC 77-81394. 1979. pap. 2.95 (ISBN 0-89221-044-3). New Leaf.

Curtis, June. The Gracious Woman: Developing A Servant's Heart Through Hospitality. 176p. (Orig.). 1985. pap. 4.95 (ISBN 0-89081-489-9). Harvest Hse.

Curtis, Ken & Curtis, Nancy. Tormented? Christians Guide for Spiritual Warfare. rev. ed. (Illus.). 1985. pap. 3.95 (ISBN 0-9615445-0-3, Dist. by Spring Arbor). Spiritual Warfare.

Curtis, Lewis P. Chichester Towers. LC 66-21514. (Illus.). Repr. of 1966 ed. 32.50 (ISBN 0-8357-1319-9, 2013199). Bks Demand UMI.

Curtis, Michael, ed. Antisemitism in the Contemporary World. LC 85-13919. 200p. 1985. 32.50x (ISBN 0-8133-0157-2). Westview.

--Religion & Politics in the Middle East. LC 81-52445. (Westview Special Studies on the Middle East). 406p. 1982. pap. 14.95x (ISBN 0-86531-388-1). Westview.

Curtis, Nancy, jt. auth. see Curtis, Ken.

Curtis, Olin A. The Christian Faith. LC 56-9279. 552p. 1971. 16.95 (ISBN 0-8254-2310-4). Kregel.

Curtis, Thomas C., jt. auth. see Steele, David H.

Curtis, William R. Lambeth Conferences: The Solution for Pan-Anglican Organization. LC 68-58565. (Columbia University Studies in the Social Sciences: No. 488). Repr. of 1942 ed. 24.50 (ISBN 0-404-51488-X). AMS Pr.

Curtiss, Eleanor. For Young Souls. 1941. pap. 1.95 (ISBN 0-87516-303-3). De Vorss.

Curtiss, F. H., jt. auth. see Curtiss, H. A.

Curtiss, F. H., jt. auth. see Curtiss, H. H.

Curtiss, H. A. & Curtiss, F. H. Gems of Mysticism. 83p. Date not set. pap. 5.00 (ISBN 0-89540-143-6, SB-143). Sun Pub.

--The Key to the Universe. 391p. 1981. pap. 21.00 (ISBN 0-89540-069-3, SB-069). Sun Pub.

--The Message of Aquaria. 487p. 1981. pap. 25.00 (ISBN 0-89540-065-0, SB-065). Sun Pub.

Curtiss, H. H. & Curtiss, F. H. Inner Radiance. 369p. Date not set. pap. 20.00 (ISBN 0-89540-149-5, SB-149). Sun Pub.

Curtiss, Harriete & Homer, F. Potent Prayers. 1976p. pap. 1.00 (ISBN 0-87516-362-9). De Vorss.

Curtiss, Harriette & Homer, F. Four-Fold Health. 1936. 4.95 (ISBN 0-87516-304-1). De Vorss.

--The Truth about Evolution & the Bible. 1928. 5.50 (ISBN 0-87516-308-4). De Vorss.

Curtiss, John S. An Appraisal of the Protocols of Zion. LC 78-63661. (Studies in Fascism: Ideology & Practice). Repr. of 1942 ed. 12.50 (ISBN 0-404-16924-4). AMS Pr.

--The Russian Church & the Soviet State, 1917-1950. 1953. 11.75 (ISBN 0-8446-1141-7). Peter Smith.

Curts, Paul. Luther's Variations in Sentence Arrangement From the Modern Literary Usage With Primary Reference to the Position of the Verb. 1910. 39.50x (ISBN 0-686-83611-1). Elliots Bks.

Curts, Paul H., tr. see Hebbel, Friedrich.

Curwen, C. A. Taiping Rebel: The Deposition of Li Hsiu-Ch' eng. LC 76-8292. (Cambridge Studies in Chinese History, Literature & Institutions). (Illus.). 1977. 57.50 (ISBN 0-521-21082-8). Cambridge U Pr.

Curzon, Robert. Visits to Monasteries in the Levant. 400p. 1983. pap. 11.95 (ISBN 0-686-46958-5, 021260104X). Hippocrene Bks.

Cusack, Margaret. The Christmas Carol Sampler. (Illus.). 10.95 (ISBN 0-15-217752-3, HJ). HarBraceJ.

Cushing, Frank H. Outlines of Zuni Creation Myths. LC 74-7947. Repr. of 1896 ed. 20.00 (ISBN 0-404-11834-8). AMS Pr.

--Zuni Fetishes. LC 66-23329. (Illus.). 43p. 1966. pap. 3.00 (ISBN 0-916122-03-4). KC Pubns.

Cushing, John D. Laws of the Pilgrims. 1978. facsimile ed. 8.50 (ISBN 0-940628-00-7). Pilgrim Soc.

Cushing, Richard C. St. Martin de Porres. LC 62-20203. (Illus.). 75p. 1981. 4.00 (ISBN 0-8198-6818-3, STO280); pap. 2.00 (ISBN 0-8198-6819-1). Dghtrs St Paul.

--St. Patrick & the Irish. 1963. 3.50 (ISBN 0-8198-6824-8); pap. 2.00 (ISBN 0-8198-6827-2). Dghtrs St Paul.

Cushing, Richard J. Eternal Thoughts from Christ the Teacher, 2 Vols. 1962. 3.50 ea. Vol. 1 (ISBN 0-8198-0606-4). Vol. 2 (ISBN 0-8198-0607-2). Dghtrs St Paul.

--Meditations for Religious. 1959. 3.00 (ISBN 0-8198-0102-X). Dghtrs St Paul.

Cushman, Joseph D., Jr. Goodly Heritage, the Episcopal Church in Florida, 1821-1892. LC 65-28693. (Illus.). 1965. 7.50 (ISBN 0-8130-0054-8). U Presses Fla.

--Sound of Bells: The Episcopal Church in South Florida, 1892-1969. LC 75-30946. (Illus.). 1976. 15.00 (ISBN 0-8130-0518-3). U Presses Fla.

Cushman, Ralph S., compiled by. Pocket Prayer Book: Large-Type Edition. 1977. 5.00x (ISBN 0-8358-0361-9). Upper Room.

Cushman, Robert E. Faith Seeking Understanding: Essays Theological & Critical. LC 80-69402. xvi, 373p. 1981. 30.25 (ISBN 0-8223-0444-9). Duke.

Cushman, Robert F. Cases in Civil Liberties. 3rd ed. 1979. 18.95. P-H.

Cushman, Rudolf E. Peculiar Forms of Ancient Religious Cults. (Illus.). 1980. deluxe ed. 67.50 (ISBN 0-89266-234-4). Am Classical Coll Pr.

Cushner, Nicholas P. Jesuit Ranches & the Agrarian Development of Colonial Argentina, 1650-1767. 350p. 1982. 49.50x (ISBN 0-87395-707-5); pap. 19.95 (ISBN 0-87395-706-7). State U NY Pr.

Cusick, Lois. Waldorf Parenting Handbook: Useful Information on Child Development & Education from Anthroposophical Sources. 2nd, rev. ed. 1985. pap. 9.95 (ISBN 0-916786-75-7). St George Bk Serv.

Cusin, M. D., ed. see Godet, F. L.

Cuss, Gladys. Hidden Manna Revealed by the Comforter. 200p. 1981. 9.00 (ISBN 0-682-49768-1). Exposition Pr FL.

--I Have Been Before the Judgement Seat of Christ: A Religious Autobiography. 189p. 1980. 7.95 (ISBN 0-682-49521-2). Exposition Pr FL.

Cussen, Joseph A. World Youth & the Family. 1984. pap. 6.95 (ISBN 0-941850-14-5). Sunday Pubns.

Cussianovich, Alejandro. Religious Life & the Poor: Liberation Theology Perspectives. Drury, John, tr. from Sp. LC 78-16740. Orig. Title: Desde los Pobres de la Tiera. 168p. (Orig.). 1979. pap. 1.74 (ISBN 0-88344-429-1). Orbis Bks.

Custance, Arthur C. Doorway Papers: Flood; Local or Global, Vol. 9. 312p. 1985. pap. text ed. 9.95 (ISBN 0-310-23041-1, 10667P). Zondervan.

--Sovereignty of Grace. 1979. 12.95 (ISBN 0-87552-160-6). Presby & Reformed.

--The Virgin Birth & the Incarnation, Vol. 5. 1976. 12.95 (ISBN 0-310-22990-1). Zondervan.

Custer, Stewart. Does Inspiration Demand Inerrancy? 1968. pap. 3.50 (ISBN 0-934532-07-9). Presby & Reformed.

--The Stars Speak: Astronomy in the Bible. (Illus.). 203p. (Orig.). 1977. pap. 6.95 (ISBN 0-89084-059-8). Bob Jones Univ Pr.

--Tools for Preaching & Teaching the Bible. 240p. (Orig.). 1979. pap. 6.95 (ISBN 0-89084-064-4). Bob Jones Univ Pr.

--A Treasury of New Testament Synonyms. 161p. 1975. 7.95 (ISBN 0-89084-025-3). Bob Jones Univ Pr.

Custodio, Sidney & Dudley, Cliff. Love-Hungry Priest. LC 82-61308. 192p. (Orig.). 1983. pap. 2.95 (ISBN 0-89221-099-0). New Leaf.

Cuthbert. The Capuchins: A Contribution to the History of the Counter Reformation, 2 vols. 1977. lib. bdg. 250.00 (ISBN 0-8490-1571-5). Gordon Pr.

Cuthbertson, David. A Tragedy of the Reformation: Being the Authentic Narrative of the History & Burning of the "Christianismi Restitution", 1953, with a Succinct Account of the Theological Controversy Between Michael Servetus, Its Author, & the Reformer, John Calvin. LC 83-45608. Date not set. Repr. of 1912 ed. 20.00 (ISBN 0-404-19826-0). AMS Pr.

Cuthbertson, Duane. Raising Your Child, Not Your Voice. 168p. 1986. pap. 5.95 (ISBN 0-89693-342-3). Victor Bks.

Cutler, Allan H. & Cutler, Helen E. The Jew As Ally of the Muslim: Medieval Roots of Anti-Semitism. LC 84-40295. 594p. 1986. text ed. 50.00 (ISBN 0-268-01190-7, 85-11909). U of Notre Dame Pr.

Cutler, Anthony. Transfigurations: Studies in the Dynamics of Byzantine Iconography. LC 75-1482. (Illus.). 226p. 1975. 32.50x (ISBN 0-271-01194-7). Pa St U Pr.

Cutler, Helen E., jt. auth. see Cutler, Allan H.

Cutler, Julia P., jt. auth. see Cutler, William P.

Cutler, Katherine N. & Bogle, Kate C. Crafts for Christmas. (Illus.). 96p. 1975. pap. 1.95 (ISBN 0-688-46663-X). Lothrop.

Cutler, William P. & Cutler, Julia P. Life, Journals & Correspondence of Rev. Manasseh Cutler, L.L.D, 2 vols. (Illus.). 1032p. 1987. Set. text ed. 40.00x (ISBN 0-8214-0859-3). Ohio U Pr.

Cutrubus, C. Nina, jt. ed. see Hamilton, Charles M.

Cutter, Charles & Oppenheim, Micha F. Jewish Reference Sources: A Select, Annotated Bibliographic Guide. LC 82-15434. (Reference Library of Social Science: Vol. 126). 180p. 1982. lib. bdg. 24.00 (ISBN 0-8240-9347-X). Garland Pub.

Cutting, Edith. Mary, in Bethlehem. (Paper People Ser.). 48p. 1986. wkbk. 4.95 (ISBN 0-86653-370-2). Good Apple.

Cutting, Jorge. La Salvacion: Su Seguridad, Creteza y Gozo. 2nd ed. Daniel, Roger P., ed. Bautista, Sara, tr. from Eng. (La Serie Diamante). Tr. of Safety, Certainity & Enjoyment. (Span., Illus.). 48p. 1982. pap. 0.85 (ISBN 0-942504-05-4). Overcomer Pr.

--La Venida del Senor. 2nd ed. Bennett, Gordon H., ed. Bautista, Sara, tr. from Eng. (La Serie Diamante). Tr. of The Lord's Coming. (Span., Illus.). 48p. 1982. pap. 0.85 (ISBN 0-942504-10-0). Overcomer Pr.

Cutts, A. M. Dios y Sus Ayudantes. (Span., Illus.). 48p. 1981. pap. 1.25 (ISBN 0-311-38548-6). Casa Bautista.

Cutts, Edward L. Parish Priests & Their People in the Middle Ages in England. LC 74-107457. Repr. of 1898 ed. 32.50 (ISBN 0-404-01898-X). Ams Pr.

--Scenes & Characters of the Middle Ages. LC 77-23575. 1977. Repr. of 1922 ed. lib. bdg. 45.00 (ISBN 0-89341-160-4). Longwood Pub Group.

Cuyler, Louise, ed. see Isaac, Heirich.

Cuyler, Margery. The All-Around Christmas Book. LC 82-3104. (Illus.). 96p. 1982. 11.95 (ISBN 0-03-060387-0); pap. 4.95 (ISBN 0-03-062183-6). H Holt & Co.

Cylwicki, Albert. If Today You Hear His Voice: Reflections on the Sunday Readings. LC 81-10966. 553p. (Orig.). 1981. pap. 12.95 (ISBN 0-8189-0418-6). Alba.

Cynewulf. The Christ of Cynewulf; a Poem in Three Parts: The Advent, the Ascension, & the Last Judgement. Cook, Albert S., ed. LC 73-178524. Repr. of 1900 ed. 32.50 (ISBN 0-404-56538-7). AMS Pr.

--Christ of Cynewulf: A Poem in Three Parts, the Advent, the Ascension, & the Last Judgment. facsimile ed. Cook, Albert S., ed. LC 74-114906. (Select Bibliographies Reprint Ser). 1900. 25.50 (ISBN 0-8369-5310-X). Ayer Co Pubs.

Cyprian. De Lapsis & de Ecciesiae Catholicae Unitate. Benevot, Maurice, ed. (Oxford Early Christian Texts Ser.). 1971. 32.50x (ISBN 0-19-826804-1). Oxford U Pr.

Cyprian, Saint A Christian Preparation for Death. pap. 1.50 (ISBN 0-686-25548-8). Eastern Orthodox.

Cyprian, St. Complete Letters. LC 65-12906. (Fathers of the Church Ser.: Vol. 51). 352p. 1964. 19.95x (ISBN 0-8132-0051-2). Cath U Pr.

--The Lapsed & the Unity of the Church. pap. 2.95 (ISBN 0-686-05646-9). Eastern Orthodox.

--Life & Works of St. Cyprian of Carthage, 4 vols. Vols. 1, 2, & 4. pap. 1.50 ea.; Vol. 3. pap. 2.95 (ISBN 0-686-05649-3); pap. 6.95 set (ISBN 0-686-05650-7). Eastern Orthodox.

--On Mortality. pap. 1.50 (ISBN 0-686-05658-2). Eastern Orthodox.

--Selected Treatises. LC 77-81349. (Fathers of the Church Ser.: Vol. 36). 372p. 1958. 19.95x (ISBN 0-8132-0036-9). Cath U Pr.

Cyprianus, Saint Opera Omnia. (Corpus Scriptorum Ecclesiasticorum Latinorum Ser: Vol. 3). 1868-1871. pap. 131.00 (ISBN 0-384-10518-1). Johnson Repr.

Cyres, Viscount St. see St. Cyres, Viscount.

Cyril Of Jerusalem, St. Catecheses Thirteen-Eighteen & Other Works, Vol. 2. (Fathers of the Church Ser.: Vol. 64). 1970. 14.95x (ISBN 0-8132-0064-4). Cath U Pr.

--Procatechesis, Catacheses One - Twelve. LC 68-55980. (Fathers of the Church Ser.: Vol. 61). 279p. 1969. 15.95x (ISBN 0-8132-0061-X). Cath U Pr.

Cyril Of Jerusalem, Saint St. Cyril of Jerusalem on the Sacraments. 83p. 1977. pap. 4.95 (ISBN 0-913836-39-7). St Vladimirs.

Czarnowski, Stefan. Le Culte Des Heros et Ses Conditions Sociales. LC 74-25745. (European Sociology Ser.). 472p. 1975. Repr. 35.50x (ISBN 0-405-06500-0). Ayer Co Pubs.

Czuckza, G. T., ed. see Pope John Paul II.

D

D. C. Cook Editors. Jesus, the Friend of Children. LC 77-72722. (Illus.). 1977. 9.95 (ISBN 0-89191-077-8). Cook.

Daane, James. Freedom of God. 5.95 (ISBN 0-8028-3421-3). Fuller Theol Soc.

Dabas, M. S. & Zarabozo, J. M., trs. from Arabic. Fiqh us-Sunnah Purification & Prayer, Vol. 1. LC 85-73207. 205p. 1986. Repr. of 1985 ed. text ed. 15.00 (ISBN 0-89259-060-2). Am Trust Pubns.

Dabbs, Jack A. & Breitenkamp, Edward C. Records of Salem Lutheran Church, Brenham, Texas 1850-1940. LC 86-72575. (Illus.). 501p. 1986. 35.00 (ISBN 0-911494-10-3). Dabbs.

Dabney, R. L. Lectures in Systematic Theology. 1985. pap. 24.95 (ISBN 0-8010-2956-2). Baker Bk.

--Systematic Theology. 903p. 1985. 19.95 (ISBN 0-85151-453-7). Banner of Truth.

Dabney, Robert L. Dabney Discussions, Vol. 1. 728p. 1982. Repr. of 1891 ed. 19.95 (ISBN 0-85151-348-4). Banner of Truth.

--Dabney Discussions, Vol. 2. (Religious Ser.). 684p. 1982. Repr. of 1891 ed. 19.95 (ISBN 0-85151-349-2). Banner of Truth.

--Dabney Discussions, Vol. 3. (Religious Ser.). 493p. 1982. Repr. of 1892 ed. 17.95 (ISBN 0-85151-350-6). Banner of Truth.

--Discussions, 3 vols. 1982. 51.95 (ISBN 0-85151-395-6). Banner of Truth.

--On Preaching. 1979. 11.95 (ISBN 0-85151-290-9). Banner of Truth.

Dabois, Abee J. State of Christianity in India - During the Early Nineteenth Century. 1977. 11.00x (ISBN 0-686-12059-0). Intl Bk Dist.

Dabovich, Sebastian. Holy Orthodox Church: Its Ritual, Services, & Sacraments. 1898. pap. 2.95 (ISBN 0-686-00253-9). Eastern Orthodox.

--St. Panteleimon. pap. 0.25 (ISBN 0-686-01298-4). Eastern Orthodox.

--True Church of Christ. pap. 0.25 (ISBN 0-686-11506-6). Eastern Orthodox.

Dacio, Juan. Diccionario de los Papas. (Span.). 37.50 (ISBN 84-233-0112-5, S-50110). French & Eur.

DaCosta, I. Noble Families among the Sephardic Jews. 1976. lib. bdg. 134.95 (ISBN 0-8490-2349-1). Gordon Pr.

Dacruz, J. More about Fatima. De Oca, V. Montes, tr. from Port. Tr. of Prodige Prow de Fatima. 1979. pap. 1.00 (ISBN 0-913382-16-7, 102-95). Prow Bks-Franciscan.

Dada. Towards the Unknown: The Journey into New-Dimensional Consciousness. LC 81-65123. (Illus.). 128p. (Orig.). 1981. pap. 8.00 (ISBN 0-930608-02-X). Dada Ctr.

D'Addio, Janie. Every Woman Can. Cox, Terri, ed. (Illus.). 112p. 1983. pap. 9.95 (ISBN 0-914759-00-0). Preferred Pr.

D'Addio, Janie & Bach, Othello. Monicas Hannukah House. (Illus.). 64p. 1983. 14.95 (ISBN 0-914759-01-9). Preferred Pr.

Da Free, John. The Transmission of Doubt. 475p. (Orig.). 1984. pap. 10.95 (ISBN 0-913922-77-3). Dawn Horse Pr.

Da Free John. Conscious Exercise & the Transcendental Sun. 3rd rev. ed. LC 77-83388. (Illus.). 272p. 1977. o. p. (ISBN 0-913922-33-1); pap. 8.95 (ISBN 0-913922-30-7). Dawn Horse Pr.

--Easy Death: Talks & Essays on the Inherent & Ultimate Transcendence of Death & Everything Else. 450p. pap. 10.95 (ISBN 0-913922-57-9). Dawn Horse Pr.

--The Eating Gorilla Comes in Peace. LC 75-24582. 1979. 12.95 (ISBN 0-913922-19-6). Dawn Horse Pr.

--Enlightenment of the Whole Body. LC 77-94504. 600p. 1978. pap. 14.95 (ISBN 0-913922-35-8). Dawn Horse Pr.

--The Way That I Teach. LC 77-94503. 1978. 10.95 (ISBN 0-913922-38-2); pap. 6.95 (ISBN 0-913922-34-X). Dawn Horse Pr.

Dagan, Avigdor, et al, eds. The Jews of Czechoslovakia, Vol. III. (Illus.). 700p. 1984. 29.95 (ISBN 0-8276-0230-8). Jewish Pubns.

Dagg, John L. Manual of Theology... Christian Doctrine... Church Order, 2 vols. in one. Gausted, Edwins., ed. LC 79-52592. (The Baptist Tradition Ser.). 1980. Repr. of 1858 ed. lib. bdg. 57.50x (ISBN 0-405-12459-7). Ayer Co Pubs.

Daglio, S. Daniel, tr. see Yates, Kyle M. & Owens, J. J.

Dagut, Menachem, tr. see Hacohen, David.

Dahl, Dolores. Where Heavens Hide. LC 84-51375. (Illus.). 48p. (Orig.). 1984. pap. 3.95 (ISBN 0-9608960-2-3). Single Vision.

Dahl, Nils A. Studies in Paul. LC 77-84083. 1977. pap. 10.95 (ISBN 0-8066-1608-3, 10-6100). Augsburg.

Dahle, John, ed. Library of Christian Hymns, 3 vols. in 2. LC 72-1649. Repr. of 1928 ed. 74.50 set (ISBN 0-404-13202-2). AMS Pr.

Dahlke, Paul. Buddhism & Its Place in the Mental Life of Mankind. LC 78-72403. Repr. of 1927 ed. 29.00 (ISBN 0-404-17265-2). AMS Pr.

--Buddhist Stories. facsimile ed. Silacara, Bhikkhu, tr. LC 71-106285. (Short Story Index Reprint Ser.). 1913. 19.00 (ISBN 0-8369-3322-2). Ayer Co Pubs.

Dahlquist, Allan. Megasthenes & Indian Religion. 1977. 11.50 (ISBN 0-89684-277-0, Pub. by Motilal Banarsidass India). Orient Bk Dist.

Dahlquist, Anna M. Trailblazers for Translators: The Influence of the "Chichicastenago Twelve". Date not set. pap. price not set (ISBN 0-87808-205-0). William Carey Lib.

Dahlstrom, Daniel O., ed. Practical Reasoning: ACPA Proceedings, 1984, Vol. 58. 250p. 1985. pap. 12.00 (ISBN 0-918090-18-0). Am Cath Philo.

--Realism. (ACPA Proceedings: Vol. 59). 250p. 1985. 15.00 (ISBN 0-918090-19-9). Am Cath Philo.

Dahlstrom, J. & Ryel, D. Promises to Keep: Reading & Writing about Values. 1977. pap. text ed. write for info (ISBN 0-13-731059-5). P-H.

Dahm, Charles & Ghelardi, Robert. Power & Authority in the Catholic Church: Cardinal Cody in Chicago. LC 81-40453. 334p. 1982. text ed. 22.95 (ISBN 0-268-01546-5). U of Notre Dame Pr.

Dahmus, Joseph. The Puzzling Gospels. (Basics of Christian Thought Ser.). 1985. 10.95 (ISBN 0-88347-182-5). Thomas More.

--William Courtenay: Archbishop of Canterbury, 1381-1396. LC 66-18194. 1966. 28.75x (ISBN 0-271-73121-4). Pa St U Pr.

Dahmus, Joseph H. The Prosecution of John Wyclyf. xi, 167p. 1970. Repr. of 1952 ed. 22.50 (ISBN 0-208-00953-1, Archon). Shoe String.

Dahood, Mitchell, ed. Psalms One, One - Fifty. (Anchor Bible Ser.: Vol. 16). 1966. 16.00 (ISBN 0-385-02765-6, Anchor Pr). Doubleday.

--Psalms Three, One Hundred One - One Hundred Fifty. LC 66-11766. (Anchor Bible Ser.: Vol. 17A). 18.00 (ISBN 0-385-00607-1, Anchor Pr). Doubleday.

--Psalms Two, Fifty-One to One Hundred. LC 66-11766. (Anchor Bible Ser.: Vol. 17). 1966. 16.00 (ISBN 0-385-03759-7, Anchor Pr). Doubleday.

Daiches, David. God & the Poets. 232p. 1986. pap. 15.95x (ISBN 0-19-812862-2). Oxford U Pr.

--The King James Version of the English Bible. LC 68-16338. vii, 228p. 1968. Repr. of 1941 ed. 21.50 (ISBN 0-208-00493-9, Archon). Shoe String.

--Milton. (Orig.). 1966. pap. 4.95x (ISBN 0-393-00347-7, Norton Lib). Norton.

Dail, Shirley M. Jesus Said "Leave Her Alone". (Illus.). 1979. pap. 2.95x (ISBN 0-9602440-0-X). Jesus-First.

Dailey, Eva Q. de see Quinones de Dailey, Eva.

Dailey, Janet. For the Love of God. (Nightingale Paperbacks Ser.). 1984. pap. 9.95 (ISBN 0-8161-3697-1, Large Print Bks). G K Hall.

Daille, Jean. Exposition of Colossians. 698p. 1983. lib. bdg. 24.95 (ISBN 0-86524-141-4, 5104). Klock & Klock.

Daily, Jay E. The Anatomy of Censorship. (Books in Library & Information Science: Vol. 6). 424p. 1973. 50.50 (ISBN 0-8247-6065-4). Dekker.

Dakenbing, William F. The Creation Book. LC 75-39840. (Illus.). 70p. 1976. 5.95 (ISBN 0-685-68397-4); pap. 3.95 (ISBN 0-685-68398-2). Triumph Pub.

Dakin, Arthur. Calvinism. LC 72-153211. 1971. Repr. of 1940 ed. 23.00x (ISBN 0-8046-1521-7, Pub. by Kennikat). Assoc Faculty Pr.

Dakin, Edwin F. Mrs. Eddy: The Biography of a Virginal Mind. 13.25 (ISBN 0-8446-0570-0). Peter Smith.

Dalaba, Oliver V. That None Be Lost. LC 77-74553. (Workers' Training Ser.). 128p. 1977. 1.25 (ISBN 0-88243-621-X, 02-621). Gospel Pub.

Dalai Lama. The Opening of the Wisdom Eye. LC 70-152732. 178p. 1981. pap. 6.95 (ISBN 0-8356-0549-3, Quest). Theos Pub Hse.

Dalai Lama, IV. The Opening of the Wisdom-Eye. Rinpoche, Thubten K., et al, trs. from Tibetan. LC 70-152732. (Illus.). 1972. 7.50 (ISBN 0-8356-0202-8). Theos Pub Hse.

Dalal, Nergis. Yoga for Rejuvenation. 128p. (Orig.). 1984. pap. 6.95 (ISBN 0-7225-0948-0). Thorsons Pubs.

Dalby, Joseph, tr. see Grou, Jean-Nicholas.

Dalcho, Frederick. An Historical Account of the Protestant Episcopal Church, in South Carolina, from the First Settlement of the Province, to the War of the Revolution. LC 71-38445. (Religion in America, Ser. 2). 180p. 1972. Repr. of 1820 ed. 42.00 (ISBN 0-405-04064-4). Ayer Co Pubs.

Dale & Larsen, Sandy. Mark: Good News for Today. (Carpenter Studyguide). 80p. 1984. member's handbook 1.95 (ISBN 0-87788-540-0); saddle-stitched leader's handbook 2.95 (ISBN 0-87788-541-9). Shaw Pubs.

Dale, Alan T. The Bible in the Classroom. 96p. (Orig.). 1973. pap. 4.95 (ISBN 0-8192-1151-6). Morehouse.

--The Crowd Is Waiting. (Rainbow Books, Bible Story Books for Children). 1976. pap. 1.00 (ISBN 0-8192-1208-3). Morehouse.

--I've Found the Sheep. (Rainbow Books, Bible Story Books for Children). 1976. pap. 1.00 (ISBN 0-8192-1206-7). Morehouse.

--Jesus Is Really Alive Again! (Rainbow Books, Bible Story Books for Children). 1976. pap. 1.00 (ISBN 0-8192-1209-1). Morehouse.

--New World. (Illus.). 429p. (Orig.). 1973. pap. 9.95 (ISBN 0-8192-1149-4). Morehouse.

--Paul the Traveler. (Rainbow Books, Bible Story Books for Children). 1976. pap. 1.00 (ISBN 0-8192-1211-3). Morehouse.

--Portrait of Jesus. (Illus.). 1979. 6.95 (ISBN 0-8317-7091-0, Mayflower Bks). Smith Pubs.

--Who's My Friend? (Rainbow Books (Bible Story Books for Children)). 16p. 1978. pap. 1.00 (ISBN 0-8192-1236-9). Morehouse.

--The Winding Quest. (Illus.). 432p. (Orig.). 1973. pap. 9.95 (ISBN 0-8192-1150-8). Morehouse.

--God Cares for Everybody, Everywhere. (Rainbow Books (Bible Story Books for Children)). (Orig.). 1978. pap. 1.00 (ISBN 0-8192-1237-7). Morehouse.

Dale, Carrie Kondy, jt. auth. see Dale, Robert D.

Dale, Daryl. Teaching Basics: Adult. (Illus.). 80p. (Orig.). 1985. pap. 2.00 (ISBN 0-87509-369-8). Chr Pubns.

--Teaching Basics: Junior. (Illus.). 73p. (Orig.). 1985. pap. 2.00 (ISBN 0-87509-359-0). Chr Pubns.

--Teaching Basics: Youth. (Illus.). 80p. (Orig.). 1985. pap. 2.00 (ISBN 0-87509-364-7). Chr Pubns.

--Youth Worker's Manual. 95p. 1985. pap. write for info. (ISBN 0-87509-350-7). Chr Pubns.

Dale, Daryl, jt. auth. see Kageler, Len.

Dale, Edgar. Content of Motion Pictures. LC 77-124026. (Literature of Cinema Ser: Payne Fund Studies of Motion Pictures & Social Values). Repr. of 1935 ed. 17.00 (ISBN 0-405-01644-1). Ayer Co Pubs.

Dale, Robert D. Evangelizing the Hard-to-Reach. LC 85-24262. (Broadman Leadership Ser.). 1986. pap. 4.95 (ISBN 0-8054-6251-1). Broadman.

--Ministers As Leaders. LC 84-9501. (Broadman Leadership Ser.). 1984. pap. 4.95 (ISBN 0-8054-3110-1). Broadman.

--Surviving Difficult Church Members. 128p. (Orig.). 1984. pap. 6.95 (ISBN 0-687-40763-X). Abingdon.

--To Dream Again. LC 81-65386. 1981. pap. 5.95 (ISBN 0-8054-2541-1). Broadman.

Dale, Robert D. & Dale, Carrie Kondy. Making Good Marriages Better. LC 78-60052. 1978. 6.95 (ISBN 0-8054-5631-7). Broadman.

Dale, Robert D., jt. auth. see Bruster, Bill G.

Dale, Rodney, ed. Kabbalah Decoded. Sassoon, George, tr. 240p. 1978. 55.00 (ISBN 0-7156-1289-1, Pub. by Duckworth London); pap. 17.00 (ISBN 0-7156-1374-X). Longwood Pub Group.

Dale, Rodney, ed. see Sassoon, George.

Dale, Stephen F. Islamic Society on the South Asian Frontier: The Mappilas of Malabar, 1498 - 1922. (Illus.). 1980. 55.00x (ISBN 0-19-821571-1). Oxford U Pr.

D'Alembert, Jean. An Account of the Destruction of the Jesuits. 59.95 (ISBN 0-87968-575-1). Gordon Pr.

--Eulogies. 59.95 (ISBN 0-8490-0137-4). Gordon Pr.

Dalenburg, Cornelia & De Groot, David. Sharifa. (THe Historical Series of the Reformed Church in America: Vol. 11). (Orig.). 1983. pap. 11.95 (ISBN 0-8028-1973-7). Eerdmans.

Dalglish, Doris N. People Called Quakers. facsimile ed. LC 78-90628. (Essay Index Reprint Ser). 1938. 15.00 (ISBN 0-8369-1254-3). Ayer Co Pubs.

Dalglish, Edward H. Layman's Bible Book Commentary: Jeremiah, Lamentations, Vol. 11. LC 81-65801. 1984. 5.95 (ISBN 0-8054-1181-X). Broadman.

Da Liu. The Tao & Chinese Culture. LC 78-26767. 192p. (Orig.). 1982. pap. 7.95 (ISBN 0-8052-0702-3). Schocken.

Dall, Caroline H. Margaret & Her Friends; or, Ten Conversations with Margaret Fuller Upon the Mythology of the Greeks & Its Expression in Art. LC 72-4961. (The Romantic Tradition in American Literature Ser.). 166p. 1972. Repr. of 1895 ed. 18.00 (ISBN 0-405-04633-2). Ayer Co Pubs.

Dallapiccola, Anna L., jt. ed. see Isacco, Enrico.

Dallas-Damis, Athena, tr. see Kazantzakis, Nikos.

Dallen, James. The Reconciling Community: The Rite of Penance. (Reformed Rites of the Catholic Church Ser.: Vol. III). 400p. (Orig.). 1986. pap. 17.50 (ISBN 0-916134-76-8). Pueblo Pub Co.

Dallimore, Arnold. Forerunner of the Charismatic Movement. (Orig.). 1983. pap. 7.95 (ISBN 0-8024-0286-0). Moody.

Dallison, Dennis. The Apology of John the Baptist. Norman, Ruth, ed. 66p. (Orig.). 1982. pap. 2.50 (ISBN 0-932642-75-6). Unarius Pubns.

--Reflections of My Life: The Apology of John the Baptist. Norman, Ruth, ed. 77p. (Orig.). 1982. pap. text ed. 2.50 (ISBN 0-932642-75-6). Unarius Pubns.

--Yamamoto Returns: A True Story of Reincarnation. (Illus.). 200p. 1985. pap. 5.95 (ISBN 0-932642-98-5). Unarius Pubns.

D'Allonnes, Olivier R. Musical Variations on Jewish Thought. Greenberg, Judith, tr. LC 83-15640. 169p. 1984. 12.95 (ISBN 0-8076-1091-7). Braziller.

Dally, John, jt. ed. see Verdon, Timothy G.

Dalman, Gustaf. Jesus Christ in the Talmud, Midrash, Zohar, & the Liturgy of the Synagogue. LC 73-2190. (The Jewish People; History, Religion, Literature Ser.). Repr. of 1893 ed. 11.00 (ISBN 0-405-05256-1). Ayer Co Pubs.

Dalman, Gustaf H. Words of Christ. 1981. lib. bdg. 13.50 (ISBN 0-86524-080-9, 9509). Klock & Klock.

Dalmases, Candido de. Ignatius of Loyola, Founder of the Jesuits: His Life & Work. Ganss, George E., frwd. by. Aixala, Jerome, tr. from Span. Index. LC 83-80349. (Series II-Scholarly Studies about the Jesuits in English Translations: No. 6). xxii, 362p. 1985. 16.00 (ISBN 0-912422-59-9); pap. 14.00 smyth sewn (ISBN 0-912422-58-0). Inst Jesuit.

Dalmau, Eduardo Martinez see Martinez Dalmau, Eduardo.

Dalpadado, J. Kinglsey. Reading the Gospels. 1975. pap. 4.00 (ISBN 0-8198-0454-1). Dghtrs St Paul.

Dalpadado, J. Kingsley. Reading the Acts, Epistles & Revelations. 1977. 6.95 (ISBN 0-8198-0450-9); pap. 5.95 (ISBN 0-8198-0451-7). Dghtrs St Paul.

--Reading the Bible. 1973. 5.95 (ISBN 0-8198-0338-3); pap. 4.95 (ISBN 0-8198-0339-1). Dghtrs St Paul.

Dalrymple, D., ed. see Hales, John.

Dalrymple, John. Living the Richness of the Cross. LC 83-70945. 128p. (Orig.). 1983. pap. 3.95 (ISBN 0-87793-274-3). Ave Maria.

--Simple Prayer. (Ways of Prayer Ser.: Vol. 9). 118p. 1984. pap. 4.95 (ISBN 0-89453-301-0). M Glazier.

--Toward the Heart of God. 108p. (Orig.). 1981. pap. 3.95 (ISBN 0-86683-602-0, HarpR). Har-Row.

Dalton, A. E. Brief & to the Point: Suggestions for Preachers. 272p. 1973. Repr. of 1961 ed. 17.95 (ISBN 0-227-67419-7). Attic Pr.

Dalton, Lee. When the Brave Ones Cried. 176p. 1986. 8.95 (ISBN 0-88290-282-2). Horizon Utah.

Dalton, Robert C. Tongues Like As of Fire. 127p. 1945. pap. 1.25 (ISBN 0-88243-619-8, 02-0619). Gospel Pub.

Dalton, Roy C. The Jesuits' Estates Question, 1760-1888: A Study of the Background for the Agitation of 1889. LC 74-393033. (Canada Studies in History & Government: No. 11). pap. 53.30 (ISBN 0-317-26918-6, 2023608). Bks Demand UMI.

Dalven, Rachel. The Jews of Jannina. 1986. write for info. (ISBN 0-930685-02-4). Cadmus Press.

Daly, C. P. Settlement of the Jews in North America. 59.95 (ISBN 0-8490-1027-6). Gordon Pr.

Daly, Cahal. Morals, Law & Life. 228p. 1966. 5.95 (ISBN 0-933932-08-1). Scepter Pubs.

Daly, Gabriel. Asking the Father: A Study of the Prayer of Petition. (Ways of Prayer Ser.: Vol. 4). 1982. 8.95 (ISBN 0-89453-428-9); pap. 5.95 (ISBN 0-89453-277-4). M Glazier.

--Transcendence & Immanence: A Study in Catholic Modernism & Integralism. 1980. 37.50x (ISBN 0-19-826652-9). Oxford U Pr.

Daly, James J. Road to Peace. facsimile ed. LC 78-107691. (Essay Index Reprint Ser.). 1936. 17.00 (ISBN 0-8369-1495-3). Ayer Co Pubs.

Daly, John P. An Edition of the Judica Me Deus of Richard Rolle. Hogg, James, ed. (Elizabethan & Renaissance Studies). (Orig.). 1984. pap. 15.00 (ISBN 0-317-40134-3, Pub by Salzburg Studies). Longwood Pub Group.

Daly, Lloyd W. Iohannis Philoponi: De Vocabulis Quae Diversum Significatum Exhibent Secundum Differentiam Accentus. LC 81-72156. (Memoirs Ser.: Vol. 151). 1983. 20.00 (ISBN 0-87169-151-5). Am Philos.

Daly, Lowrie J. The Political Theory of John Wyclif. LC 62-20515. (Jesuit Studies). 1962. 4.95 (ISBN 0-8294-0020-6). Loyola.

Daly, Mary. Beyond God the Father: Toward a Philosophy of Women's Liberation. 2nd rev. ed. LC 84-45067. 257p. 1985. 18.95x (ISBN 0-8070-1502-4); pap. 8.95 (ISBN 0-8070-1503-2, BP681). Beacon Pr.

--Pure Lust: Elemental Feminist Philosophy. LC 83-71944. 488p. 1984. 18.95 (ISBN 0-8070-1504-0); pap. 11.95 (ISBN 0-8070-1505-9, BP 692). Beacon Pr.

Daly, Maura, et al, trs. see Ravier, Andre.

Daly, Robert. God's Altar: The World & the Flesh in Puritan Poetry. LC 77-76182. 1978. 23.00x (ISBN 0-520-03480-5). U of Cal Pr.

Daly, Robert J. Christian Biblical Ethics. (Orig.). 1984. pap. 9.95 (ISBN 0-8091-2592-7). Paulist Pr.

--Christian Sacrifice: The Judaeo-Christian Background Before Origen. LC 78-12004. (Studies in Christian Antiquity: Vol. 18). 587p. 1978. 26.95x (ISBN 0-8132-0530-1). Cath U Pr.

--Origins of the Christian Doctrine of Sacrifices. LC 77-78628. pap. 40.00 (2026875). Bks Demand UMI.

Daly, Robert J., jt. auth. see Helgeland, John.

Daly, Robert J., ed. Rising from History: U. S. Catholic Theology Looks to the future. LC 87-2011. (The Annual Publication of the College Theology Society, 1984: Vol. 30). 234p. (Orig.). 1987. lib. bdg. 24.50 (ISBN 0-8191-6155-1, Pub. by College Theology Society); pap. text ed. 12.75 (ISBN 0-8191-6156-X, Pub. by College Theology Society). U Pr of Amer.

Daly, Robert J., tr. see Von Balthasar, Hans U.

Damascene, John & Oecumenical Synod Seventh. The Icon. Cavarnos, Constantine, tr. from Gr. (Illus.). 11p. 1979. pap. 0.90 (ISBN 0-914744-19-4). Inst Byzantine.

Damascene, John see John Damascene, Saint.

Damian, Peter. Book of Gomorrah: An Eleventh-Century Treatise Against Clerical Homosexual Practices. Payer, Pierre J., tr. 120p. 1982. pap. text ed. 10.50x (ISBN 0-88920-123-4, Pub. by Wilfrid Laurier Canada). Humanities.

Damiani Van Den Eynde & Odulphi Van Den Eynde, eds. Guidonis de Orchellis Tractatus de Sacramentis Ex Eius Summa de Sacramentis et Officiis Ecclesiae. (Text Ser). 1953. 11.00 (ISBN 0-686-11549-X). Franciscan Inst.

Damian-Knight, Guy. Karma & Destiny in the I Ching. 256p. 1987. pap. 12.95 (ISBN 1-85063-038-0, 30380, Ark Paperbks). Methuen Inc.

D'Amico, John F. Renaissance Humanism in Papal Rome: Humanists & Churchmen on the Eve of the Reformation. LC 82-49059. (Studies in Historical & Political Science). 352p. 1983. text ed. 32.50x (ISBN 0-8018-2860-0). Johns Hopkins.

Damle, Shridhar D., jt. auth. see Andersen, Walter K.

Damon, S. Foster, ed. see Blake, William.

Damp, Margaret M. Finding Fulfillment in the Manse. 115p. 1978. pap. 2.95 (ISBN 0-8341-0544-6). Beacon Hill.

Dampier, Joseph H. Workbook on Christian Doctrine. 64p. (Orig.). 1943. pap. 1.95 (ISBN 0-87239-072-1, 3343). Standard Pub.

--Workbook on Christian Doctrine- NIV. rev. ed. 64p. 1986. wkbk. 2.50 (ISBN 0-87403-177-X, 3344). Standard Pub.

Damrell, Joseph. Search for Identity: Youth, Religion, & Culture. LC 78-5887. (Sage Library of Social Research: No. 64). 232p. 24.50 (ISBN 0-8039-0987-X); pap. 14.50 (ISBN 0-8039-0988-8). Sage.

Damrell, Joseph D. Seeking Spiritual Meaning: The World of Vedanta. LC 77-9145. (Sociological Observations Ser.: No. 2). pap. 63.00 (ISBN 0-317-08760-6, 2021885). Bks Demand UMI.

Damsteegt, P. Gerard. Foundations of the Seventh-Day Adventist Message & Mission. LC 76-56799. pap. 91.00 (ISBN 0-317-30135-7, 2025318). Bks Demand UMI.

Dan, Joseph. Gershom Scholem & the Mystical Dimension of Jewish History. 350p. 1987. 50.00x (ISBN 0-8147-1779-9). NYU Pr.

--Jewish Mysticism & Jewish Ethics. LC 85-40358. 158p. 1986. 20.00x (ISBN 0-295-96265-8). U of Wash Pr.

Dan, Joseph, ed. The Teachings of Hasidism. (Orig.). 1983. pap. text ed. 9.95x (ISBN 0-87441-346-X). Behrman.

Dan, Joseph & Kiener, Ronald C., eds. The Early Kabbalah. (Classics of Western Spirituality Ser.: Vol. 51). 224p. 1986. 13.95 (ISBN 0-8091-0373-7); pap. 10.95 (ISBN 0-8091-2769-5). Paulist Pr.

Dan, Joseph & Talmage, Frank, eds. Studies in Jewish Mysticism. 25.00x (ISBN 0-915938-03-0). Ktav.

Dana, H. E. Manual de Eclesiologia. Robleto, Adolfo, tr. Orig. Title: A Manual of Ecclesiology. write for info. (ISBN 0-311-17018-8). Casa Bautista.

--El Mundo Del Nuevo Testamento. Villarello, Ildefonso, tr. 288p. 1982. pap. 4.95 (ISBN 0-311-04342-9). Casa Bautista.

Dana, H. E. & Mantey, J. R. Gramatica Griega Del Nuevo Testamento. Robleto, Adolfo & De Clark, Catalina, trs. 1984. pap. 9.95 (ISBN 0-311-42010-9). Casa Bautista.

Dana, H. E. & Mantey, R. Manual Grammar of the Greek New Testament: With Index. 1957. text ed. write for info. (ISBN 0-02-327070-5, 32707). Macmillan.

Dana, Mark. Lifemating: New Hope for Those Who've Loved & Lost. 1985. 7.75 (ISBN 0-8062-2447-9). Carlton.

Danby, Herbert, tr. see Klausner, Joseph.

Danby, Herbert see Maimonides, Moses.

Dancy, J. C. Shorter Books of the Apochrypha: Cambridge Bible Commentary on the New English Bible. LC 72-76358. (Old Testament Ser.). 224p. (Orig.). 1972. pap. 9.95 (ISBN 0-521-09729-0). Cambridge U Pr.

Dandekar, R. N. The Age of Guptas & Other Essays. 1982. 30.00 (ISBN 0-8364-0916-7, Pub. by Ajanta). South Asia Bks.

Daneel, M. L. Old & New in Southern Shona, Independent Churches, Vol. 1: Background & Rise of the Major Movements. (Change & Continuity in Africa Ser). 1971. text ed. 29.60x (ISBN 0-686-22598-8). Mouton.

--Zionism & Faith-Healing in Rhodesia: Aspects of African Independent Churches. V. A. February Communications, tr. from Dutch. (Illus.). 1970. pap. 6.00x (ISBN 90-2796-278-2). Mouton.

Daner, Francine J. The American Children of Krsna: Case Studies in Cultural Anthrology. LC 75-15616. 1976. pap. text ed. 9.95 (ISBN 0-03-013546-X, HoltC). HR&W.

Dange, S. S. The Bhagavata Purana: Mytho-Social Study. LC 84-900334. 1984. 28.50x (ISBN 0-8364-1132-3, Pub. by Ajanta). South Asia Bks.

Dange, Sindhu S. Hindu Domestic Rituals. 1986. 12.00x (ISBN 81-202-0138-8, Pub. by Ajanta). South Asia Bks.

D'Angelo, Dorie. Living with Angels. 5th ed. 1980. pap. 10.00 (ISBN 0-912216-22-0). Angel Pr.

D'Angelo, Louise. Too Busy for God? Think Again! LC 81-52423. 120p. 1981. pap. 2.50 (ISBN 0-89555-166-7). TAN Bks Pubs.

D'Angelo, Mary R. Moses in the Letter to the Hebrews. LC 78-12917. (Society of Biblical Literature, Dissertation Ser.: No. 42). 1979. pap. 9.95 (ISBN 0-89130-333-2). Scholars Pr GA.

Danich, John, jt. auth. see Ball, Judy.

Daniel, et al. Introduction to Christian Education. 2nd, rev. ed. 352p. 1987. pap. text ed. price not set (ISBN 0-87403-211-3, 88591). Standard Pub.

Daniel, E. Randolph. Abbot Joachim of Fiore Liber De Concordia Noui Ac Veteris Testamenti. LC 82-73832. 455p. 18.00 (ISBN 0-87169-738-6). Am Philos.

Daniel, E. Valentine, jt. auth. see Keyes, Charles F.

Daniel, Eleanor. What the Bible Says about Sexuality Identity. LC 81-71836. (What the Bible Says Ser.). 350p. 1982. 13.95 (ISBN 0-89900-085-1). College Pr Pub.

Daniel, Eleanor, rev. by see Root, Orrin.

Daniel, Eleanor, et al. Introduction to Christian Education. LC 79-92587. (Bible College Textbooks Ser.). 352p. (Orig.). 1980. pap. text ed. 6.95 (ISBN 0-87239-394-1, 88581). Standard Pub.

Daniel, Norman A. Islam & the West. 26.00x (ISBN 0-85224-109-7, Pub. by Edinburgh U Pr Scotland). Columbia U Pr.

Daniel, Orville E. Harmony of the Four Gospels: The New International Version. 1987. pap. price not set (ISBN 0-8010-2974-0). Baker Bk.

Daniel, R. P. Dating, Marriage, Sex & Divorce. 75p. pap. 3.95 (ISBN 0-88172-147-6). Believers Bkshelf.

--Gospel & the Path of Separation. pap. 3.25 (ISBN 0-88172-016-X). Believers Bkshelf.

--Let's Play Bible Detective. 36p. pap. 2.95 (ISBN 0-88172-017-8). Believers Bkshelf.

--Outlines for Christian Youth. pap. 5.95 (ISBN 0-88172-019-4). Believers Bkshelf.

--The Tabernacle Talks Today. pap. 5.25 (ISBN 0-88172-020-8). Believers Bkshelf.

Daniel, R. P., ed. see Dennett, E.

Daniel, R. P., ed. see Grant, F. W.

Daniel, R. P., ed. see Hole, F. B.

Daniel, Rebecca. Abraham. (Our Greatest Heritage Ser.). (Illus.). 32p. 1983. wkbk. 3.95 (ISBN 0-86653-133-5, SS 802). Good Apple.

--Adam & Eve. (Our Greatest Heritage Ser.). (Illus.). 32p. 1983. wkbk. 3.95 (ISBN 0-86653-131-9, SS 800). Good Apple.

--Book VIII-More Parables. (Life of Jesus Ser.). 32p. (YA) 1984. wkbk. 3.95 (ISBN 0-86653-229-3). Good Apple.

--Daniel. (Our Greatest Heritage Ser.). (Illus.). 32p. 1983. wkbk. 3.95 (ISBN 0-86653-140-8, SS 809). Good Apple.

--David. (Our Greatest Heritage Ser.). (Illus.). 1983. wkbk. 3.95 (ISBN 0-86653-138-6, SS 807). Good Apple.

--Jonah. (Our Greatest Heritage Ser.). (Illus.). 32p. 1983. wkbk. 3.95 (ISBN 0-86653-141-6, SS 810). Good Apple.

--Joseph. (Our Greatest Heritage Ser.). (Illus.). 32p. 1983. wkbk. 3.95 (ISBN 0-86653-134-3, SS 803). Good Apple.

--Joshua. (Our Greatest Heritage Ser.). (Illus.). 32p. 1983. wkbk. 3.95 (ISBN 0-86653-136-X, SS 805). Good Apple.

--Moses. (Our Greatest Heritage Ser.). (Illus.). 32p. 1983. wkbk. 3.95 (ISBN 0-86653-135-1, SS 804). Good Apple.

--Noah. (Our Greatest Heritage Ser.). (Illus.). 1983. wkbk. 3.95 (ISBN 0-86653-132-7, SS 801). Good Apple.

--Samson. (Our Greatest Heritage Ser.). (Illus.). 32p. 1983. wkbk. 3.95 (ISBN 0-86653-137-8, SS 806). Good Apple.

--Solomon. (Our Greatest Heritage Ser.). (Illus.). 32p. 1983. wkbk. 3.95 (ISBN 0-86653-139-4, SS 808). Good Apple.

--Women of the Old Testament. (Our Greatest Heritage Ser.). (Illus.). 32p. 1983. wkbk. 3.95 (ISBN 0-86653-142-4, SS 811). Good Apple.

Daniel, Roger P., ed. see Cutting, Jorge.

Daniel, Roger P., ed. see Mackintosh, Carlos H.

Daniel, Samuel, tr. see Giovio, Paolo.

Daniel, William A. Education of Negro Ministers. LC 77-78581. Repr. of 1925 ed. cancelled (ISBN 0-8371-1410-1, DNM&, Pub. by Negro U Pr). Greenwood.

Daniell, G. W. Bishop Wilberforce. 1978. Repr. of 1891 ed. lib. bdg. 20.00 (ISBN 0-8482-0607-X). Norwood Edns.

Danielou, Alain. The Gods of India. (Illus.). 441p. (Orig.). 1985. pap. 18.95 (ISBN 0-89281-101-3). Inner Tradit.

--Shiva & Dionysus. 250p. (Orig.). 1984. pap. 8.95 (ISBN 0-89281-057-2). Inner Tradit.

--While the Gods Play. 352p. (Orig.). 1987. pap. 12.95 (ISBN 0-89281-115-3). Inner Tradit.

Danielou, Jea. God's Life in Us. 2.95 (ISBN 0-317-06464-9). Dimension Bks.

Danielou, Jean. The Dead Sea Scrolls & Primitive Christianity. Attanasio, Salvator, tr. from Fr. LC 78-21516. 1979. Repr. of 1958 ed. lib. bdg. 22.50x (ISBN 0-313-21144-2, DADE). Greenwood.

--A History of Early Christian Doctrine Before the Council of Nicaea. Baker, John A., tr. Incl. Vol. 1. The Theology of Jewish Christianity. 1977; Vol. 2. Gospel Message & Hellenistic Culture. LC 72-7090. 1973; Vol. 3. The Origins of Latin Christianity. LC 76-44380. 528p. 1977. 27.50 (ISBN 0-664-21064-3). Westminster.

--Prayer As a Political Problem. Kirwan, J. R., ed. 1967. 3.50 (ISBN 0-8362-0278-3, Pub. by Sheed). Guild Bks.

--Salvation of the Nations. 1962. pap. 1.25x (ISBN 0-268-00244-4). U of Notre Dame Pr.

Danielou, Jean & Marrou, Henri. Christian Centuries, Vol. 1: First Six Hundred Years. LC 78-55069. (Illus.). 610p. 1969. 22.95 (ISBN 0-8091-0275-7). Paulist Pr.

Danielou, Jean, ed. From Glory to Glory: Texts from Gregory of Nyssa's Mystical Writings. LC 79-38. 304p. 1979. pap. 9.95 (ISBN 0-913836-54-0). St Vladimirs.

Daniel-Rops, Henri. Daily Life in the Time of Jesus. O'Brian, Patrick, tr. from Fr. (Illus.). 518p. 1981. pap. 8.95 (ISBN 0-89283-085-9). Servant.

Daniels, Althea. The Friendship Factor Study Guide. 32p. (Orig.). 1984. pap. 0.95 (ISBN 0-8066-2079-X, 10-2413). Augsburg.

Daniels, Charles B., et al. Towards an Ontology of Number Mind & Sign. (Scots Philosophical Monographs: Vol. 10). 200p. 1986. 29.95x (ISBN 0-391-03397-2, Pub. by Aberdeen U Scotland); pap. 12.50 (ISBN 0-391-03398-0, Pub. by Aberdeen U Scotland). Humanities.

Daniels, Elam J. Como Ser Feliz en el Matrimonio. Orig. Title: How to Be Happily Married. 96p. 1984. pap. 2.10 (ISBN 0-311-46066-6). Casa Bautista.

Daniels, Harold M. What to Do with Sunday Morning. LC 78-21040. 132p. 1979. softcover 4.95 (ISBN 0-664-24237-5). Westminster.

Daniels, Madeline M. Living Your Religion in the Real World. LC 84-18209. 192p. 14.95 (ISBN 0-13-539016-8); pap. 6.95 (ISBN 0-13-539008-7). P-H.

Daniels, Marion L., tr. from Lat. see Bodin, Jean.

Daniels, Rebecca. Bible Teacher Time Savers. (Helping Hand Ser.). 48p. 1984. wkbk. 4.95 (ISBN 0-86653-235-8). Good Apple.

--Book I-His Birth. (Life of Jesus Ser.). 32p. (YA) 1984. wkbk. 3.95 (ISBN 0-86653-213-7). Good Apple.

--Book II-His Boyhood. (Life of Jesus Ser.). 32p. (YA) 1984. wkbk. 3.95 (ISBN 0-86653-223-4). Good Apple.

--Book III-Gathering His Disciples. (Life of Jesus Ser.). 32p. (YA) 1984. wkbk. 3.95 (ISBN 0-86653-224-2). Good Apple.

--Book IV-the Teacher. (Life of Jesus Ser.). 32p. (YA) 1984. wkbk. 3.95 (ISBN 0-86653-225-0). Good Apple.

--Book IX-Prophacies Fulfilled. (Life of Jesus Ser.). 32p. (YA) 1984. wkbk. 3.95 (ISBN 0-86653-230-7). Good Apple.

--Book V-The Healer. (Life of Jesus Ser.). 32p. (YA) wkbk. 3.95 (ISBN 0-86653-226-9). Good Apple.

--Book VI-His Miracles. (Life of Jesus Ser.). 32p. (YA) 1984. wkbk. 3.95 (ISBN 0-86653-227-7). Good Apple.

--Book VII-Parables. (Life of Jesus Ser.). 32p. (YA) 1984. wkbk. 3.95 (ISBN 0-86653-228-5). Good Apple.

--Book X-His Last Days. (Life of Jesus Ser.). 32p. (YA) 1984. wkbk. 3.95 (ISBN 0-86653-231-5). Good Apple.

--Book XI-His Last Hours. (Life of Jesus Ser.). 32p. (YA) 1984. wkbk. 3.95 (ISBN 0-86653-232-3). Good Apple.

--Book XII-His Resurrection. (Life of Jesus Ser.). 32p. (YA) 1984. wkbk. 3.95 (ISBN 0-86653-233-1). Good Apple.

Daniels, Velma S. Patches of Joy. 1979. 7.95 (ISBN 0-88289-101-4); pap. 5.95 (ISBN 0-88289-232-0). Pelican.

Daniels, W. H. Dr. Cullis & His Work. Dayton, Donald W., ed. (The Higher Christian Life Ser.). 364p. 1985. 45.00 (ISBN 0-8240-6410-0). Garland Pub.

--Illustrated History of Methodism. 1977. lib. bdg. 75.00 (ISBN 0-8490-2036-0). Gordon Pr.

Danielson, Dennis. Milton's Good God: A Study in Literary Theodicy. LC 81-15535. 272p. 1982. 39.50 (ISBN 0-521-23744-0). Cambridge U Pr.

Danielson, Edward E. Missionary Kid, MK. rev. ed. LC 84-12655. (Mission Candidate Aids Ser.). (Illus.). 104p. 1985. pap. 5.95 (ISBN 0-87808-745-1). William Carey Lib.

Daniken, Erich von see Von Daniken, Erich.

Daniken, Erich Von see Von Daniken, Erich.

Danjhal, Beryl. Sikhism. (World Religions Ser.). (Illus.). 72p. 1987. 16.95 (ISBN 0-7134-5202-1, Pub. by Batsford England). David & Charles.

Dankenbring, William F. The First Genesis: A New Case for Creation. LC 75-10841. (Illus.). 408p. 1975. 8.95 (ISBN 0-685-54180-0). Triumph Pub.

--The First Genesis: The Saga of Creation Versus Evolution. new ed. LC 79-65131. (Illus.). 1979. 12.00 (ISBN 0-917182-14-6). Triumph Pub.

--The Last Days. LC 77-79265. 1977. 11.95 (ISBN 0-917182-05-7). Triumph Pub.

Danker, Frederick W. Benefactor: Epigraphic Study of a Graeco-Roman & New Testament Semantic Field. LC 81-70419. 1982. 29.95x (ISBN 0-915644-23-1). Clayton Pub Hse.

--Jesus & the New Age According to St. Luke. 1983. pap. text ed. 12.00 (ISBN 0-915644-25-8). Clayton Pub Hse.

--Luke. Krodel, Gerhard, ed. LC 76-5954. (Proclamation Commentaries: the New Testament Witnesses for Preaching Ser.). 128p. 1976. pap. 4.95 (ISBN 0-8006-0583-7, 1-583). Fortress.

--Luke. 2nd, rev. ed. LC 86-45905. (Proclamation Commentary, New Testament Ser.). 144p. 1987. pap. 7.95 (ISBN 0-8006-0598-5, 1-598). Fortress.

--Multipurpose Tools for Bible Study. rev. ed. 1970. pap. 12.50 (ISBN 0-570-03734-4, 12-2638). Concordia.

--No Room in the Brotherhood: The Preus-Otten Purge of Missouri. LC 77-74386. (Illus.). 1977. text ed. 12.95 (ISBN 0-915644-10-X). Clayton Pub Hse.

--Shorter Lexicon of the Greek New Testament. 2nd, rev. ed. Gingrich, F. Wilbur, rev. by. LC 82-10933. 256p. 1983. lib. bdg. 22.00x (ISBN 0-226-13613-2). U of Chicago Pr.

Dann, Bucky. Better Children's Sermons: 54 Visual Lessons, Dialogues, & Demonstrations. LC 83-6851. 124p. (Orig.). 1983. pap. 7.95 (ISBN 0-664-24481-5). Westminster.

--Creating Children's Sermons: Fifty-One Visual Lessons. LC 81-10493. 132p. pap. 7.95 (ISBN 0-664-24383-5). Westminster.

Dannenfeldt, Karl H. Church of the Renaissance & Reformation. LC 77-98300. (Church in History Ser). 1978. pap. 4.95 (ISBN 0-570-06271-3, 12-2726). Concordia.

Danner, Peter L. An Ethics for the Affluent. LC 80-5528. 424p. 1980. lib. bdg. 31.25 (ISBN 0-8191-1163-5); pap. text ed. 15.25 (ISBN 0-8191-1164-3). U Pr of Amer.

Danner, Victor & Thackston, Wheeler. Ibn 'Ata Illah-Kwaja Abdullah Ansari: The Book of Wisdom-Intimate Conversations. LC 78-1022. (Classics of Western Spirituality-Sufi Ser.). 256p. 1978. 12.95 (ISBN 0-8091-0279-X); pap. 8.95 (ISBN 0-8091-2182-4). Paulist Pr.

Dannhauser, Werner J., ed. see Scholem, Gershom.

Danois, Vivian De see De Danois, Vivian.

Dant, Penny. Springs of Joy. (Orig.). 1987. pap. 7.00 (ISBN 0-915541-11-4). Star Bks Inc.

Dante Alighieri. De Monarchia. LC 74-147412. (Library of War & Peace; Proposals for Peace: a History). lib. bdg. 46.00 (ISBN 0-8240-0210-5). Garland Pub.

Danto, Bruce L., et al. Suicide & Bereavement. 17.50 (ISBN 0-405-12505-4). Ayer Co Pubs.

Danton, George H. Nature Sense in the Writings of Ludwig Tieck. LC 78-163673. (Columbia University. Germanic Studies, Old Ser.: No. 9). Repr. of 1907 ed. 15.00 (ISBN 0-404-50409-4). AMS Pr.

D'Antonio, William V. & Aldous, Joan, eds. Families & Religions: Conflict & Change in Modern Society. 320p. 1983. 29.00 (ISBN 0-8039-2075-X); pap. 14.50 (ISBN 0-8039-2468-2). Sage.

Dao, Wong Ming. Stone Made Smooth. 1982. pap. 5.95 (ISBN 0-907821-00-6). OMF Bks.

Dao, Wong Ming see Dao, Wong Ming.

Daoudi, M. S. The Meaning of Kahlil Gibran. 160p. 1982. 9.95 (ISBN 0-8065-0804-3). Citadel Pr.

--The Meaning of Kahlil Gibran. 140p. 1984. pap. 5.95 (ISBN 0-8065-0929-5). Citadel Pr.

D'Aquili, Eugene G., et al. The Spectrum of Ritual: A Biogenetic Structural Analysis. LC 78-19015. 408p. 1979. 35.00x (ISBN 0-231-04514-X). Columbia U Pr.

Dar, B. A. Quranic Ethics. pap. 3.50 (ISBN 0-686-18602-8). Kazi Pubns.

--Qur'anic Ethics. 1970. 5.00x (ISBN 0-87902-160-8). Orientalia.

Daraul, Arkon. Secret Societies. 1983. Repr. of 1961 ed. 14.95 (ISBN 0-86304-024-1, Pub. by Octagon Pr England). Ins Study Human.

Darbishire, Helen. Milton's Paradise Lost. LC 74-3031. 1951. lib. bdg. 15.00 (ISBN 0-8414-3750-5). Folcroft.

Darbishire, Helen, ed. Early Lives of Milton. LC 77-144967. (Illus.). 1971. Repr. of 1932 ed. 49.00x (ISBN 0-403-00935-9). Scholarly.

Darby, J. N. The Collected Writings, 35 vols. Set. 125.00 (ISBN 0-88172-055-0); 4.00 ea. Believers Bkshelf.

--Letters of J. N. Darby, 3 vols. Set. 18.95 (ISBN 0-88172-061-5); 6.95 ea. Believers Bkshelf.

--Notes & Comments on Scripture, 7 vols. Set. 30.00 (ISBN 0-88172-068-2); 4.95 ea. Believers Bkshelf.

--Notes & Jottings on Scripture. 5.95 (ISBN 0-88172-069-0). Believers Bkshelf.

--Synopsis of the Books of the Bible, 5 vols. Set. 27.50 (ISBN 0-88172-070-4). Believers Bkshelf.

D'Arcy, Martin C. Communism & Christianity. 1957. 10.00 (ISBN 0-8159-5208-2). Devin.

--The Nature of Belief. facsimile ed. (Select Bibliographies Reprint Ser). Repr. of 1931 ed. 21.00 (ISBN 0-8369-5930-2). Ayer Co Pubs.

--Of God & Man. 1967. pap. 1.25x (ISBN 0-268-00197-9). U of Notre Dame Pr.

--Revelation & Love's Architecture. 90p. 1976. 8.00 (ISBN 0-89182-010-8). Charles River Bks.

D'Arcy, Mary R. The Saints of Ireland. 241p. 1985. pap. 9.95 (ISBN 0-9614900-0-4). Irish Am Cult.

D'Arcy, Paula. Song for Sarah: A Young Mother's Journey Through Grief, & Beyond. LC 79-14684. 124p. 1979. 6.95 (ISBN 0-87788-778-0); pap. 2.50 (ISBN 0-87788-780-2). Shaw Pubs.

--Where the Wind Begins: Stories of Hurting People Who Said Yes to Life. 144p. 1985. pap. 5.95 (ISBN 0-87788-925-2). Shaw Pubs.

Darcy-Berube, Francoise & Berube, John-Paul. Come, Let Us Celebrate. 64p. 1984. 3.95 (ISBN 0-7773-8007-2, 8514, HarpR). Har-Row.

Darcy-Berube, Francoise & Berube, John P. Someone's There: Paths to Prayer for Young People. LC 86-82055. (Illus.). 80p. (Orig.). 1987. pap. 4.95 (ISBN 0-87793-350-2). Ave Maria.

Darey-Bembe, Francoise & Bembe, John P. Day by Day with God. 1982. 4.95 (ISBN 0-8215-9908-9). Sadlier.

Dargan, Edwin C. History of Preaching, 2 Vols. 1965. lib. bdg. 47.00 (ISBN 0-8337-0772-8). B Franklin.

Dargyay, Eva M. The Rise of Esoteric Buddhism in Tibet. 1977. 14.00 (ISBN 0-8426-0915-6, Pub by Molilal Banarsidass India). Orient Bk Dist.

Darian, Steven G. The Ganges in Myth & History. LC 77-21374. (Illus.). 236p. 1978. text ed. 12.00x (ISBN 0-8248-0509-7). UH Pr.

Dark, Sidney. Five Deans. facsimile ed. LC 71-93332. (Essay Index Reprint Ser.). 1928. 18.00 (ISBN 0-8369-1285-3). Ayer Co Pubs.

--Five Deans: John Colet, John Donne, Jonathan Swift, Arthur Penrhyn Stanley & William Ralph Inge. LC 70-86011. (Essay & General Literature Index Reprint Ser.). 1969. Repr. of 1928 ed. 22.50x (ISBN 0-8046-0555-6, Pub. by Kennikat). Assoc Faculty Pr.

--Seven Archbishops. Repr. of 1944 ed. 25.00 (ISBN 0-686-19840-9). Ridgeway Bks.

Darkes, Anna S. How to Make & Use Overhead Transparancies. LC 77-7888. (Illus.). 1977. pap. 4.50 (ISBN 0-8024-3652-8). Moody.

Darline, R., jt. auth. see Robinson, James H.

Darling, Harold W. Man in His Right Mind. 158p. 1977. pap. 5.95 (ISBN 0-85364-097-1). Attic Pr.

Darmesteter. The Life of Ernest Renan. 1898. Repr. 25.00 (ISBN 0-8274-2884-7). R West.

Darmesteter, J. & Mills, L. H., trs. Zend-Avesta, 3 vols. Repr. 125.00 (ISBN 0-87902-154-3). Orientalia.

Darmesteter, James & Mills, L. H. The Zend-Avesta, 3 vols. 1974. lib. bdg. 300.00 (ISBN 0-87968-509-3). Krishna Pr.

Darmesteter, James, tr. Zend-Avesta: Selections. 1984. pap. 6.95 (ISBN 0-916411-41-9, Near Eastern). Holmes Pub.

Darnall, Jean. Heaven, Here I Come. LC 77-91521. 1978. pap. 2.95 (ISBN 0-88419-148-6). Creation Hse.

Darqyay, Eva. The Rise of Esoteric Buddhism in the Tibet. 272p. 1979. pap. 5.95 (ISBN 0-87728-432-6). Weiser.

Darrah, D. D. History & Evolution of Freemasonry. 12.00x (ISBN 0-685-21969-0). Wehman.

Darrah, Delmore D. History & Evolution of Freemasonry. (Illus.). 1951. 12.00 (ISBN 0-685-19479-5). Powner.

Darrand, Tom C. & Shupe, Anson D. Metaphors of Social Control in a Pentecostal Sect. LC 83-9006. (Studies in Religion & Society: Vol. 6). 232p. 1984. 49.95x (ISBN 0-88946-870-2). E Mellen.

Darrel, Lance H., jt. auth. see Dever, William G.

Darrow, Clarence & Lewis, Arthur. Darrow-Lewis Debate on the Theory of Non-Resistance to Evil. 26p. 1987. pap. write for info. (ISBN 0-911826-48-3). Am Atheist.

Darrow, Clarence S. Resist Not Evil. LC 77-137538. (Peace Movement in America Ser). 179p. 1972. Repr. of 1903 ed. lib. bdg. 14.95x (ISBN 0-89198-065-2). Ozer.

Darrow, Clarence S. & Lewis, Arthur M. Marx Versus Tolstoy: A Debate. LC 73-137537. (Peace Movement in America Ser). 124p. 1972. Repr. of 1911 ed. lib. bdg. 12.95x (ISBN 0-89198-066-0). Ozer.

Darshana Shakti Ma, ed. see Svami Kripalvanananda.

Darst, H. W. Far above Rubies. 128p. (Orig.). 1982. pap. 2.50 (ISBN 0-89114-110-3). Baptist Pub Hse.

Darst, Mrs. H. W. Missions in the Mountains. (Illus.). 116p. 1979. pap. 2.50 (ISBN 0-89114-085-9). Baptist Pub Hse.

Darton, Michael, ed. A Modern Concordance to the New Testament. LC 75-34831. 1977. 12.95 (ISBN 0-385-07901-X). Doubleday.

Darwall, Stephen, ed. see Butler, Joseph.

Daryabadi, A. M. Holy Quaran Arabic-English. 24.50 (ISBN 0-686-83591-3). Kazi Pubns.

Das, Manoj. Sri Aurobindo. 3rd ed. 1982. pap. 4.00x (ISBN 0-8364-1585-X, Pub. by National Sahitya Akademi). South Asia Bks.

Das, Nilima, ed. see The Mother.

Das, S. K. Cynewulf & the Cynewulf Canon. 59.95 (ISBN 0-87968-987-0). Gordon Pr.

Das, Veena. Structure & Cognition: Aspects of Hindu Caste & Ritual. 2nd ed. 1982. 24.95x (ISBN 0-19-561395-3). Oxford U Pr.

Dasa, Mandalesvara, ed. see Dasa Goswami, Satsvarupa.

Dasa, Mandalesvara, ed. see Das Goswami, Satsvarupa.

Dasa, Mandalesvara, ed. see Goswami, Satsvarupa das.

Dasa, Mandalesvara, et al, eds. see Goswami, Satsvarupa D.

Dasa, Mathuresa, ed. see Das Goswami, Satsvarupa.

Dasa Goswaini, Satsvarupa. Living with the Scriptures, Vol. 1. Dattatreya dasa, ed. 120p. 1984. text ed. 5.00 (ISBN 0-911233-26-1). Gita Nagari.

Dasa Goswami, Satsvarupa. Handbook for Krishna Consciousness. 380p. 1983. 5.95 (ISBN 0-318-03098-5). Gita Nagari.

--He Lives Forever. Dasa, Mandalesvara, ed. 80p. 1980. 2.00 (ISBN 0-318-03099-3). Gita Nagari.

Dasa Goswami, Satvarupa. Prabhupada Nectar, Vol. 3. Bimala dasi, ed. 160p. 1985. pap. text ed. 2.00 (ISBN 0-911233-24-5). Gita Nagari.

Dasbach, Fernando L. Blight or Bloom. 198p. 1981. 12.50 (ISBN 0-686-28998-6). Regenbogen-Verlag.

--The Father Has Come. 113p. 1981. 10.00 (ISBN 0-686-28999-4). Regenbogen-Verlag.

Daschbach, Edwin. Interpreting Scripture: A Catholic Response to Fundamentalism. 144p. 1985. pap. 6.95 (ISBN 0-697-02110-6). Wm C Brown.

Das Gosvami, Satsvarupa. Readings in Vedic Literature. 1985. 7.95 (ISBN 0-912776-88-9). Bhaktivedanta.

Das Goswami, Hridayananda. Srimad Bhagavatam. 12.95 (ISBN 0-89213-129-2). Bhaktivedanta.

Das Goswami, Satsvar upa. Reading Reform. Dattatreya dasa, ed. 120p. 1985. pap. text ed. 4.00 (ISBN 0-911233-28-8). Gita Nagari.

Das Goswami, Satsvarupa. Letters from Srila Prabhupada, Vol. 1. Mandalesvara dasa & Gaura Purnima dasa, eds. 274p. (Orig.). 1982. pap. text ed. 3.95 (ISBN 0-911233-03-2). Gita Nagari.

--Life with the Perfect Master. Dasa, Mathuresa, ed. 110p. 1983. pap. text ed. 3.50 (ISBN 0-911233-17-2). Gita Nagari.

--Lilamrta, Vol. 5. (Illus.). 297p. 12.95 (ISBN 0-89213-119-5). Bhaktivedanta.

--Lilmarta, Vol. 6. (Illus.). 12.95 (ISBN 0-89213-120-9). Bhaktivedanta.

--Living with the Scriptures, Vol. 2. Dattatreya dasa, ed. 120p. 1985. text ed. 5.00 (ISBN 0-911233-27-X). Gita Nagari.

--One Hundred & Eight Rosebushes: Preaching in Germany. Mandalesvara dasa & Bimala dasi, eds. (Prabupada-lila Ser.). 44p. (Orig.). 1982. pap. text ed. 2.00 (ISBN 0-911233-04-0). Gita-Nagari.

--Prabhupada: He Built a House in Which the Whole World Could Live. 7.95 (ISBN 0-89213-133-0). Bhaktivedanta.

--Prabhupada Nectar, Bk. 2. Dasi, Bimala, ed. 145p. pap. 4.99 (ISBN 0-911233-23-7). Gita Nagari.

--Prabhupada Nectar, Vol. 4. Bimala dasi, ed. 160p. 1985. pap. text ed. 2.00 (ISBN 0-911233-29-6). Gita Nagari.

--Srila Prbhupada in Latin America. Dasa, Mandalesvara & Dasi, Bimala, eds. (Prabhupada-lila). (Orig.). Vol. 7. pap. text ed. 2.00 (ISBN 0-911233-05-9). Gita-Nagari.

--Vaisnava Behavior: Twenty-Six Qualities of a Devotee. Dasa, Mandalesvara, ed. 201p. 1984. text ed. 5.50 (ISBN 0-911233-18-0). Gita Nagari.

Das Goswami, Satvarupa. Prabhupada Nectar, Vol. 5. Bimala dasi, ed. 160p. 1986. pap. text ed. 4.00 (ISBN 0-911233-31-8). Gita Nagari.

--The Worshipable Deity & Other Poems. Bimala dasi, ed. 140p. 1985. pap. text ed. 4.00 (ISBN 0-911233-30-X). Gita Nagari.

Dasgupta, S. Yoga As Philosophy & Religion. lib. bdg. 79.95 (ISBN 0-87968-104-7). Krishna Pr.

--Yoga As Philosophy & Religion. 1978. Repr. 13.95 (ISBN 0-8426-0488-X). Orient Bk Dist.

Dasgupta, S. N. Hindu Mysticism. 1977. 12.95 (ISBN 0-8426-0929-6). Orient Bk Dist.

--Religion & Rational Outlook. 1974. Repr. 9.95 (ISBN 0-8426-0661-0). Orient Bk Dist.

Dash, Bhagwan & Kashyap, Lalitesh. Basic Principles of Ayurveda. (Illus.). 628p. 1980. 44.95x (ISBN 0-940500-34-5). Asia Bk Corp.

Dash, Vaidya B. Handbook of Ayurveda. 221p. (Orig.). 1983. 28.00 (ISBN 0-317-17437-1, Pub. by Cultural Integration). Auromere.

Dashefsky, Arnold, ed. Contemporary Jewry, Vol. 7. 160p. 1986. 19.95x (ISBN 0-87855-979-5). Transaction Bks.

--Contemporary Jewry, Vol. 8. 160p. 1987. 19.95 (ISBN 0-88738-097-2). Transaction Bks.

Dashti, Ali. Twenty Three Years: A Study of the Prophetic Career of Mohammad. Bagley, F. R., tr. from Persian. 224p. 1985. 17.50 (ISBN 0-04-297048-2). Allen Unwin.

Dasi, Bimala, ed. see Das Goswami, Satsvarupa.

Dasi, Bimala, ed. see Goswami, Satsvarupa das.

Da Silva, Andrew J. Do from the Octave of Man Number Four: The Awakening & Crisis, Vol. 1. Sajkovic, Olivera, ed. LC 85-71128. 128p. 1985. 12.00 (ISBN 0-9614941-0-7). Borderline NY.

Daso, Satyendra Kimar see Das Satyendra Kimar.

Dass, B. Hari. Fire Without Fuel. Ma Renu & Tabachnick, A. Dass, eds. LC 86-60051. (Illus.). 200p. (Orig.). 1986. 35.00 (ISBN 0-918100-09-7); pap. 12.95 (ISBN 0-918100-08-9). Sri Rama.

Dass, Baba Hari. Sweeper to Saint: Stories of Holy India. Renu, Ma, ed. LC 80-52021. (Illus.). 208p. (Orig.). 1980. pap. 6.95 (ISBN 0-918100-03-8). Sri Rama.

Dass, Baba Hari, et al. Silence Speaks--from the Chalkboard of Baba Hari Dass. LC 76-53902. (Illus.). 224p. (Orig.). 1977. pap. 5.95 (ISBN 0-918100-01-1). SRI Rama.

Dass, Ram. Journey of Awakening: A Mediator's Guidebook. 1978. pap. 4.95 (ISBN 0-553-25845-1). Bantam.

--Miracle of Love: Stories About Neem Karoli Baba. (Illus.). 1979. pap. 12.95 (ISBN 0-525-47611-3, 01257-380). Dutton.

--The Only Dance There Is. LC 73-14054. 295p. 1974. pap. 6.95 (ISBN 0-385-08413-7, Anch). Doubleday.

Das Satyendra Kimar. Cynewulf & the Cynewulf Canon. LC 73-17006. 1942. lib. bdg. 27.50 (ISBN 0-8414-7701-9). Folcroft.

Date, V. H. Spiritual Treasures of St. Ramadasa. 1975. 13.50 (ISBN 0-8426-0805-2). Orient Bk Dist.

Datta, V. N. & Gleghorn, B. E., eds. A Nationalist Muslim & Indian Politics. LC 75-902114. 352p. 1974. 14.00 (ISBN 0-333-90023-5). South Asia Bks.

Dattatreya. Avadhuta Gita of Dattatreya. Ashokananda, Swami, tr. from Sanskrit. 1978. pap. 3.95 (ISBN 0-87481-482-0). Vedanta Pr.

Dattatreya dasa, ed. see Dasa Goswaini, Satsvarupa.

Dattatreya dasa, ed. see Das Goswami, Satsvar upa.

Dattatreya dasa, ed. see Das Goswami, Satsvarupa.

Dau, W. H., tr. see Walther, Carl F.

Daube, David. The Exodus Pattern in the Bible. LC 78-9920. 1979. Repr. of 1963 ed. lib. bdg. 24.75 (ISBN 0-313-21190-6, DAEX). Greenwood.

--The New Testament & Rabbinic Judaism. LC 73-2191. (The Jewish People; History, Religion, Literature Ser.). Repr. of 1956 ed. 38.50 (ISBN 0-405-05257-X). Ayer Co Pubs.

D'Aubigne, Merle. History of the Reformation. (Religious Heritage Reprint Library). 1976. Repr. 18.95 (ISBN 0-8010-2859-0). Baker Bk.

--History of the Reformation of the Sixteenth-Century, 1 vol. 1986. pap. 18.95 (ISBN 0-8010-2962-7). Baker Bk.

--The Reformation in England, 2 vols. 1977. Vol. 1. pap. 13.95 (ISBN 0-85151-486-3); Vol. 2. pap. 13.95 (ISBN 0-85151-487-1); Set. o. p. 25.95 (ISBN 0-85151-488-X). Banner of Truth.

Daud, Abraham I. The Book of Tradition: Sefer ha-Qabbalah. Cohen, Gerson D., ed. & tr. from Hebrew. (LLJC Ser.). 486p. 1967. Repr. of 1967 ed. 39.95x (ISBN 0-19-710019-8). Oxford U Pr.

--The Exalted Faith. Weiss, Gershon, ed. Samuelson, Norbert, tr. LC 83-49341. (Hebrew.). 408p. 1986. 75.00x (ISBN 0-8386-3185-1). Fairleigh Dickinson.

Dauer, Dorothea W. Schopenhauer As Transmitter of Buddhist Ideas. (European University Studies: Series 1, German Language & Literature: Vol. 15). 39p. 1969. 6.55 (ISBN 3-261-00014-7). P Lang Pubs.

Daugherty, F. Mark, jt. ed. see Eslinger, Gary S.

Daughters of St. Paul. Adventures of Peter & Paul. (Illus.). 120p. 1984. 10.00 (ISBN 0-8198-0726-5). Dghtrs St Paul.

--Alive in the Spirit. rev. ed. (Way, Truth & Life Ser.). (Illus.). 1974. text ed. 2.75 (ISBN 0-8198-0282-4); tchr's manual 6.25 (ISBN 0-8198-0283-2); activity bk. 1.50 (ISBN 0-8198-0284-0); parents' guide 01.25 (ISBN 0-8198-0285-9). Dghtrs St Paul.

--Always with Jesus. 1973. 3.95 (ISBN 0-8198-0265-4); pap. 2.95 (ISBN 0-8198-0714-1). Dghtrs St Paul.

--Basic Catechism Manual, Vol. I. 1981. pap. 5.95 (ISBN 0-8198-1107-6). Dghtrs St Paul.

--Basic Catechism Manual, Vol. II. 1981. pap. 5.95 (ISBN 0-8198-1106-8). Dghtrs St Paul.

--Boy with a Mission. 1967. 3.00 (ISBN 0-8198-0229-8). Dghtrs St Paul.

--A Brief Catholic Dictionary for Young People. 1977. pap. text ed. 1.00 (ISBN 0-8198-0389-8). Dghtrs St Paul.

--Brief Review for Confirmation. 1973. pap. 0.75 (ISBN 0-8198-0250-6). Dghtrs St Paul.

--Brief Summary of the Ten Commandments. 1976. pap. text ed. 1.75 (ISBN 0-8198-0386-3). Dghtrs St Paul.

--Catherine of Siena. (Encounter Ser.). 1975. 3.00 (ISBN 0-8198-0395-2). Dghtrs St Paul.

--Christ Lives in Me. rev. ed. (Way, Truth & Life Ser.). (Illus.). 1973. text ed. 2.00 (ISBN 0-8198-0308-1); tchr's manual 6.25 (ISBN 0-8198-0309-X); activity bk. 1.00 (ISBN 0-8198-0310-3); parent guide 1.25 (ISBN 0-8198-0311-1). Dghtrs St Paul.

--Christ of Vatican Two. (St. Paul Editions). (Illus.). 1968. 2.00 (ISBN 0-8198-0024-4); pap. 1.00 (ISBN 0-8198-0025-2). Dghtrs St Paul.

--Christ: Our Way to the Father. rev. ed. (Way, Truth & Life Ser.). (Illus.). 1973. text ed. 2.00 (ISBN 0-8198-0300-6); tchrs. manual 6.25 (ISBN 0-8198-0301-4); activity bk. 1.00 (ISBN 0-8198-0302-2); parent guide 0.95 (ISBN 0-8198-0303-0). Dghtrs St Paul.

--Christ's Law of Love. rev. ed. (Way, Truth & Life Ser.). (Illus.). 1973. text ed. 2.50 (ISBN 0-8198-0296-4); tchrs manual 6.25 (ISBN 0-8198-0297-2); activity bk. 1.50 (ISBN 0-8198-0298-0); parent guide 1.25 (ISBN 0-8198-0299-9). Dghtrs St Paul.

--Communicators for Christ. 1973. 5.00 (ISBN 0-8198-0249-2). Dghtrs St Paul.

--The Conscience Game. 1966. 2.00 (ISBN 0-8198-0231-X). Dghtrs St Paul.

--The Daughters of St. Paul: 50 Years of Service in the U. S. A., 1932-1982. (Illus.). 295p. 1982. 15.00 (ISBN 0-8198-1805-4, MS0133). Dghtrs St Paul.

--David. 0.75 (ISBN 0-8198-1800-3). Dghtrs St Paul.

--Drawing Near Him with Confidence. 1976. 3.95 (ISBN 0-8198-0403-7); pap. 2.95 (ISBN 0-8198-0404-5). Dghtrs St Paul.

--Everyman's Challenge. LC 73-89938. 1974. 5.00 (ISBN 0-8198-0294-8). Dghtrs St Paul.

--Faces of Courage. (Illus.). 1974. 5.00 (ISBN 0-8198-0292-1); pap. 4.00 (ISBN 0-8198-0293-X). Dghtrs St Paul.

--Faith We Live By. LC 68-59044. (Divine Master Ser., Vol. 3). (Illus.). 1969. 7.50 (ISBN 0-8198-0039-2); pap. 6.00 (ISBN 0-8198-0040-6); discussion & project manual 0.60 (ISBN 0-8198-0041-4). Dghtrs St Paul.

--Flame in the Night. 1967. 3.00 (ISBN 0-8198-0234-4); pap. 2.00 (ISBN 0-8198-2610-3). Dghtrs St Paul.

--Giae Ly Can Ban. Tueng, Andrew, tr. Orig. Title: Basic Catachism. (Vietnamese.). 202p. (Orig.). 1983. pap. text ed. 2.00 (ISBN 0-8198-3035-6). Dghtrs St Paul.

--God Loves Me. 1982. pap. 1.95 (ISBN 0-8198-3032-1); tchr's. manual 3.95 (ISBN 0-8198-3031-3). Dghtrs St Paul.

--God or Nothing? 222p. 1985. 4.00 (ISBN 0-8198-3039-9); pap. 3.00 (ISBN 0-8198-3040-2). Dghtrs St Paul.

--God the Father Sent His Son. rev. ed. (Way, Truth & Life Ser.). (Illus.). 1973. text ed. 2.00 (ISBN 0-8198-0286-7); tchrs. manual 6.25 (ISBN 0-8198-0287-5); activity bk. 1.00 (ISBN 0-8198-0288-3); parent guide 1.25 (ISBN 0-8198-0289-1). Dghtrs St Paul.
--God's People on the Move. LC 68-59042. (Divine Master Ser.). pap. 2.50 (ISBN 0-8198-0348-0); rev. tchr's. manual 3.95 (ISBN 0-8198-0349-9). Dghtrs St Paul.
--God's Secret Agent. 1967. 3.00 (ISBN 0-8198-0236-0). Dghtrs St Paul.
--Heaven. 1977. 3.50 (ISBN 0-8198-0419-3); pap. 2.50 (ISBN 0-8198-0420-7). Dghtrs St Paul.
--Heroes from Every Walk of Life. 1981. 5.00 (ISBN 0-8198-3303-7); pap. 4.00 (ISBN 0-8198-3304-5). Dghtrs St Paul.
--His Saving Love. rev. ed. (Way, Truth & Life Ser.). (Illus.). 1976. text ed. 2.75 (ISBN 0-8198-0340-5); tchrs. manual 6.95 (ISBN 0-8198-0341-3); activity bk. 1.60 (ISBN 0-8198-0342-1); parent guide 1.50 (ISBN 0-8198-0343-X). Dghtrs St Paul.
--I Learn About Jesus. 1973. 5.50 (ISBN 0-8198-0246-8); pap. 4.00 (ISBN 0-8198-0247-6). Dghtrs St Paul.
--I Learn About Jesus: Projects & Activities for Pre-Schoolers. 1973. pap. 1.00 (ISBN 0-8198-0245-X). Dghtrs St Paul.
--I Pray with Jesus. 1978. deluxe ed. 7.00 (ISBN 0-8198-0535-1); plastic bdg. 3.00 (ISBN 0-8198-0537-8). Dghtrs St Paul.
--Introductions to the Books of the New Testament. 1977. pap. 1.00 (ISBN 0-8198-0421-5). Dghtrs St Paul.
--Joey. 1980. 3.00 (ISBN 0-8198-3907-8); pap. 2.00 (ISBN 0-8198-3908-6). Dghtrs St Paul.
--Karol from Poland. write for info. Dghtrs St Paul.
--Light in the Grotto. 1972. 3.00 (ISBN 0-8198-4409-8); pap. 2.00 (ISBN 0-8198-4410-1). Dghtrs St Paul.
--Live the Mass. rev. ed. (Way, Truth & Life Ser.). (Illus.). text ed. 1.75 (ISBN 0-8198-0272-7); tchr's. manual 6.25 (ISBN 0-8198-0273-5); activity bk. 0.85 (ISBN 0-8198-0274-3); parent guide 0.69 (ISBN 0-8198-0275-1). Dghtrs St Paul.
--Live the Truth-Give the Truth. rev. ed. (Way, Truth & Life Ser.). (Illus.). 1976. text ed. 2.75 (ISBN 0-8198-0304-9); tchr's. manual 8.00 (ISBN 0-8198-0305-7); activity bk. 1.60 (ISBN 0-8198-0306-5); parent guide 1.50 (ISBN 0-8198-0307-3). Dghtrs St Paul.
--Living & Growing Through the Eucharist. 1976. 7.00 (ISBN 0-8198-0432-0); pap. 6.00 (ISBN 0-8198-0433-9). Dghtrs St Paul.
--Master Plan Revealed. (Divine Master Ser.). pap. 3.00 (ISBN 0-8198-0346-4); rev. project & discussion manual o.s.i. 3.95 (ISBN 0-8198-0347-2). Dghtrs St Paul.
--Media Impact & You. 1981. 2.95 (ISBN 0-8198-4702-X); pap. 1.95 (ISBN 0-686-73820-9). Dghtrs St Paul.
--Moments for Prayer. plastic bdg. 1.00 (ISBN 0-8198-0277-8); pap. 0.40 (ISBN 0-8198-0278-6). Dghtrs St Paul.
--More Than a Knight. (Encounter Ser.). (Illus.). 100p. 1982. 3.00 (ISBN 0-8198-4714-3, EN0204); pap. 2.00 (ISBN 0-8198-4715-1). Dghtrs St Paul.
--Mother Cabrini. 1977. 3.50 (ISBN 0-8198-0440-1); pap. 2.50 (ISBN 0-8198-0441-X). Dghtrs St Paul.
--Mother Seton. 1975. 3.95 (ISBN 0-8198-0487-8). Dghtrs St Paul.
--My Favorite Prayers & Reflections. 1973. plastic bdg. 5.00 (ISBN 0-8198-0276-X). Dghtrs St Paul.
--Prayers for Young Adults. 1985. 4.00 (ISBN 0-8198-5822-6). Dghtrs St Paul.
--Preparing to Receive Jesus Christ. (Way, Truth & Life Ser.). 1978. 1.75 (ISBN 0-8198-0548-3); tchr's manual 3.50 (ISBN 0-8198-0549-1); activity book 1.00 (ISBN 0-8198-0550-5). Dghtrs St Paul.
--Really Living. LC 68-59042. (Divine Master Ser.). pap. 3.00 (ISBN 0-8198-0350-2); rev. tchr's. manual 3.95 (ISBN 0-8198-0351-0). Dghtrs St Paul.
--Religion for the People of Today. LC 78-160576. (Illus.). 1971. pap. 1.25 (ISBN 0-8198-0345-6). Dghtrs St Paul.
--Religious Life in the Light of Vatican 2. (Orig.). 4.00 (ISBN 0-8198-0132-1). Dghtrs St Paul.
--St. Paul: A Good Friend of Jesus. 1980. 2.50 (ISBN 0-8198-6811-6); pap. 1.75 (ISBN 0-8198-6810-8). Dghtrs St Paul.
--St. Paul Mass Book for Children. (Illus.). 1973. 1.75 (ISBN 0-8198-0336-7); pap. 1.00 (ISBN 0-8198-0337-5). Dghtrs St Paul.
--St. Rita of Cascia: Saint of the Impossible. LC 73-91992. 1973. 3.95 (ISBN 0-8198-0335-9). Dghtrs St Paul.
--Seven Spiritual Works of Mercy. 1979. 1.75 (ISBN 0-8198-6805-1); pap. 1.00 (ISBN 0-8198-6806-X). Dghtrs St Paul.
--Sixteen Documents of Vatican Two. pap. 3.25 (ISBN 0-8198-0146-1). Dghtrs St Paul.
--Spiritual Life in the Bible. 1980. 5.95 (ISBN 0-686-76825-6); pap. 4.00 (ISBN 0-8198-6813-2). Dghtrs St Paul.
--The Teachings & Miracles of Jesus. 1981. 5.00 (ISBN 0-686-73821-7); pap. 4.00 (ISBN 0-8198-7302-0). Dghtrs St Paul.
--Teenagers Today. 1981. 4.00 (ISBN 0-8198-7303-9); pap. 3.00 (ISBN 0-8198-7304-7). Dghtrs St Paul.
--Thoughts of the Servant of God, Mother Thecla Merlo. LC 68-59045. 1974. flexible plastic 2.25 (ISBN 0-8198-0509-2). Dghtrs St Paul.
--When Jesus Was Born. (Illus.). 1973. plastic bdg. 2.00 (ISBN 0-8198-0326-X); pap. 1.25 (ISBN 0-8198-0327-8). Dghtrs St Paul.
--Where the Gospel Meets the World. 1977. 6.95 (ISBN 0-8198-0482-7); pap. 5.00 (ISBN 0-8198-0483-5). Dghtrs St Paul.
--Wind & Shadows. (Encounter Ser.). 3.00 (ISBN 0-8198-0174-7); pap. 2.00 (ISBN 0-8198-0175-5). Dghtrs St Paul.
--Woman of Faith. (Illus.). 1965. 3.00 (ISBN 0-8198-0179-8). Dghtrs St Paul.
--Women of the Bible. LC 71-145574. (Illus.). 5.95 (ISBN 0-8198-0322-7); pap. 4.95 (ISBN 0-8198-0323-5). Dghtrs St Paul.
--Women of the Gospel. LC 74-32122. 1975. 5.95 (ISBN 0-8198-0495-9); pap. 4.95 (ISBN 0-8198-0496-7). Dghtrs St Paul.
--Yes Is Forever. (Encounter Ser.). (Illus.). 109p. 1982. 3.00 (ISBN 0-8198-8700-5, EN0260); pap. 2.00 (ISBN 0-8198-8702-1). Dghtrs St Paul.
Daughters of St. Paul, ed. Bible Stories for Everyone. 1956. 6.00 (ISBN 0-8198-0008-2); pap. 5.00 (ISBN 0-8198-0009-0). Dghtrs St Paul.
--Catechism of Modern Man. 3rd rev. ed. 1971. 7.95 (ISBN 0-8198-0015-5); pap. 6.95 (ISBN 0-8198-0016-3). Dghtrs St Paul.
--Church's Amazing Story. rev. ed. LC 68-59043. (Divine Master Ser., Vol. 2). 1969. 6.00 (ISBN 0-8198-0028-7); pap. 5.00 (ISBN 0-8198-0029-5); teacher's manual 8.50 (ISBN 0-8198-0030-9). Dghtrs St Paul.
--Dimensions of the Priesthood. new ed. 1973. 5.75 (ISBN 0-8198-0253-0); pap. 4.50 (ISBN 0-8198-0254-9). Dghtrs St Paul.
--Drawing Near Him with Confidence. (Chinese.). 1978. 3.95 (ISBN 0-8198-1801-1); pap. 2.95 (ISBN 0-8198-1802-X). Dghtrs St Paul.
--One Family under God. (Divine Master Ser.). (Orig.). 1968. 3.00 (ISBN 0-8198-0109-7); pap. 2.00 (ISBN 0-8198-0110-0). Dghtrs St Paul.
Daughters of St. Paul, compiled by. Scriptural Meditations on the Rosary. 1981. 3.50 (ISBN 0-8198-6814-0). Dghtrs St Paul.
Daughters of St. Paul, compiled by see Pope John Paul II.
Daughters of St. Paul, tr. Yes to Life. 1977. 6.95 (ISBN 0-8198-0485-1); pap. 5.95 (ISBN 0-8198-0486-X). Dghtrs St Paul.
Daughters Of St. Paul, tr. see Alberione, James.
Daughters of St. Paul, tr. see Alberione, James.
Daughters of St. Paul, tr. see Ricciardi, Antonio.
Daughters of St. Paul Editorial Staff. Looking Ahead to Marriage. (Divine Master Ser.). (Illus.). 1969. 5.25 (ISBN 0-8198-0259-X); pap. 4.25 (ISBN 0-8198-0260-3); discussion & projects manual 2.75 (ISBN 0-8198-0261-1). Dghtrs St Paul.
Daughters of St Paul. Basic Catechism. 1980. 3.00 (ISBN 0-8198-0622-6); pap. 2.00 (ISBN 0-8198-0623-4). Dghtrs St Paul.
--Blessed Kateri Takakwitha: Mohawk Maiden. 1980. 3.75 (ISBN 0-8198-1100-9); pap. 2.25 (ISBN 0-8198-1101-7). Dghtrs St Paul.
--Father Damien of Molokai. 1979. pap. 0.95 (ISBN 0-8198-0640-4). Dghtrs St Paul.
--Moments of Decision. 1976. 5.00 (ISBN 0-8198-0445-2); pap. 4.00 (ISBN 0-8198-0446-0). Dghtrs St Paul.
--Morality Today: The Bible in My Life. 1979. 3.25 (ISBN 0-8198-0620-X); pap. 2.25 (ISBN 0-8198-0621-8). Dghtrs St Paul.
--My Massbook. 1978. plastic bdg. 2.00 (ISBN 0-8198-0361-8); pap. 1.25 (ISBN 0-8198-0362-6). Dghtrs St Paul.
--My Prayer Book. 1978. plastic bdg. 2.00 (ISBN 0-8198-0359-6); pap. 1.25 (ISBN 0-8198-0360-X). Dghtrs St Paul.
--Saint Paul for Every Day of the Year. 1979. 6.00 (ISBN 0-686-63641-4); pap. 4.50 (ISBN 0-8198-0646-3). Dghtrs St Paul.
--Saints for Young People for Every Day of the Year, Vol. 2. (Illus.). 6.00 (ISBN 0-8198-0647-1); pap. 4.50 (ISBN 0-8198-0648-X). Dghtrs St Paul.
--Your Right to Be Informed. LC 68-59042. (Divine Master Ser.: Vol. 1). 1969. 7.95 (ISBN 0-8198-0518-1); pap. 6.50 (ISBN 0-8198-0519-X); teacher manual 8.50 (ISBN 0-8198-0520-3). Dghtrs St Paul.
Daujat, Jean. The Faith Applied. 1963. 5.95x (ISBN 0-933932-22-7). Scepter Pubs.
D'Aulaire, Edgar P., jt. auth. see D'Aulaire, Ingri.
D'Aulaire, Ingri & D'Aulaire, Edgar P. D'Aulaires' Book of Greek Myths. LC 62-15877. (Illus.). 1962. 17.95a (ISBN 0-385-01583-6); PLB o. p. (ISBN 0-385-07108-6); pap. 10.95 (ISBN 0-385-15787-8). Doubleday.
--Norse Gods & Giants. LC 67-19109. (Illus.). 160p. 1967. write for info. (ISBN 0-385-04908-0); o. p. 14.95 (ISBN 0-385-07235-X). Doubleday.
D'Ault-Dumesnil, G. E. Dictionnaire Historique, Geographique et Biographique des Croisades. Migne, J. P., ed. (Nouvelle Encyclopedie Theologique Ser.: Vol. 18). (Fr.). 619p. Repr. of 1852 ed. lib. bdg. 79.00x (ISBN 0-89241-265-8). Caratzas.
Dauphinais, Raymond, tr. see Moran, Hugh.
Dauraul. Witches & Sorcerers. pap. 2.95 (ISBN 0-8065-0286-X). Citadel Pr.
D'Auri, Laura, ed. see Sanadi, Lalita.
Dausey, Gary. The Youth Leader's Sourcebook. 320p. 1983. 15.95 (ISBN 0-310-29310-3, 11633). Zondervan.
Dauw, Dean C. New Educational Methods for Increasing Religious Effectiveness. pap. 0.65 (ISBN 0-8199-0389-2, L38532). Franciscan Herald.
Davanc, G. V., tr. see Neve, Felix.
Davaney, Sheila G. Divine Power: A Study of Karl Barth & Charles Hartshorne. LC 85-45502. (Harvard Dissertions in Religion Ser.). 224p. 1986. pap. 16.95 (ISBN 0-8006-7072-8, 1-7072). Fortress.
Dave, H. T. Life & Philosophy of Shree Swaminarayan. new ed. Shepard, Leslie, ed. (Illus.). 274p. 1974. 8.95 (ISBN 0-04-294082-6). Weiser.
Davenport, F. M. Primitive Traits in Religious Revivals: A Study in Mental & Social Evolution. 1977. lib. bdg. 59.95 (ISBN 0-8490-2478-1). Gordon Pr.
Davenport, Frederick M. Primitive Traits in Religious Revivals. LC 72-163669. Repr. of 1905 ed. 15.00 (ISBN 0-404-01929-3). AMS Pr.
--Primitive Traits in Religious Revivals. LC 68-58053. Repr. of 1905 ed. cancelled (ISBN 0-8371-0378-9, DAR&). Greenwood.
Davenport, John. An Apologetical Reply to a Book Called: An Answer to the Unjust Complaint of W.B. (English Experience Ser.: No. 792). 1977. Repr. of 1636 ed. lib. bdg. 35.00 (ISBN 90-221-0792-2). Walter J Johnson.
--A Just Complaint Against an Unjust Doer, Mr. J. Paget. LC 76-57376. (English Experience Ser.: No. 793). 1977. Repr. of 1634 ed. lib. bdg. 5.00 (ISBN 90-221-0793-0). Walter J Johnson.
--Letters of John Davenport, Puritan Divine. Calder, Isabel M., ed. 1937. 65.00x (ISBN 0-685-69794-0). Elliots Bks.
Davenport, John L., ed. see Mitchell, Roy.
Davenport, R. Edward. Free to Share. LC 82-62743. 183p. (Orig.). 1983. pap. text ed. 6.95 (ISBN 0-87148-337-8). Pathway Pr.
--Person to Person Evangelism. new ed. LC 77-23716. 1978. pap. 2.95 (ISBN 0-87148-691-1). Pathway Pr.
Davey, Cyril. Horseman of the King (John Wesley) 1964. pap. 2.95 (ISBN 0-87508-605-5). Chr Lit.
--John Wesley & the Methodists. 49p. (Orig.). 1986. 6.95 (ISBN 0-687-20434-8). Abingdon.
--Monk Who Shook the World (Martin Luther) 1960. pap. 2.95 (ISBN 0-87508-614-4). Chr Lit.
--Never Say Die: Story of Gladys Aylward. 1964. pap. 2.95 (ISBN 0-87508-616-0). Chr Lit.
--On del Clouds to China (J. Hudson Taylor) 1964. pap. 2.95 (ISBN 0-87508-617-9). Chr Lit.
--Saint in the Slums (Kagawa of Japan) 1968. pap. 2.95 (ISBN 0-87508-620-9). Chr Lit.
Davey, Cyril J. March of Methodism. 1952. 5.95 (ISBN 0-8022-0345-0). Philos Lib.
Davey, James E. Riches of Grace. pap. 0.95 (ISBN 0-87509-127-X). Chr Pubns.
David. The Trilogy of Armageddon. LC 85-90253. 138p. 1986. 10.95 (ISBN 0-533-06739-1). Vantage.
David, A. R. A Guide to Religious Ritual at Abydos. 182p. 1981. pap. text ed. 40.00x (ISBN 0-85668-060-5, Pub. by Aris & Phillips UK). Humanities.
--The Pyramid Builders of Ancient Egypt: A Modern Investigation of Pharoah's Workforce. 258p. 1986. text ed. 34.95 (ISBN 0-7100-9909-6). Methuen Inc.
David, A. Rosalie. The Ancient Egyptians: Religious Beliefs & Practices. (Religious Beliefs & Practices Ser.). 250p. 1982. 26.00x (ISBN 0-7100-0877-5); pap. 10.00 (ISBN 0-7100-0878-3). Methuen Inc.
David, Arthur, tr. see Maimonides, Moses.
David, Charles W. Robert Curthose, Duke of Normandy. LC 78-63356. (The Crusades & Military Orders: Second Ser.). (Illus.). 296p. Repr. of 1920 ed. 32.50 (ISBN 0-404-17007-2). AMS Pr.
David, Ebenezer. Rhode Island Chaplain in the Revolution. Black, Jeannette D. & Roelker, W. Greene, eds. LC 73-159068. 1971. Repr. of 1949 ed. 21.50x (ISBN 0-8046-1662-0, Pub. by Kennikat). Assoc Faculty Pr.
David, Hans T. Music of the Moravians in America from the Archives of the Moravian Church at Bethlehem Pa, 2 vols. Incl. Vol. 1. Ten Sacred Songs. Dencke, J., et al.; Vol. 2. Six Quintets. Peter, John F. write to C. F. Peters Corp., NY for prices (ISBN 0-685-22862-2). NY Pub Lib.
David, Hans T., jt. auth. see Rau, Albert G.
David, Suzy, ed. The Sephardic Kosher Kitchen. LC 84-8150. (Illus.). 228p. 1985. 14.95 (ISBN 0-8246-0303-6). Jonathan David.
David Ben Abraham. The Hebrew-Arabic Dictionary of the Bible, Known As Kitab Jami al-Alfaz (Agron, 2 vols. Skoss, Solomon L., ed. LC 78-63565. (Yale Oriental Ser. Researches: Nos. 20-21). (Hebrew & Arabic.). Repr. of 1945 ed. Set. 97.50 (ISBN 0-404-60290-8). AMS Pr.
Davidheiser, Bolton. Evolution & Christian Faith. 1969. pap. 10.95 (ISBN 0-87552-251-3). Presby & Reformed.
Davidman, Joy. Smoke on the Mountain: An Interpretation of the Ten Commandments. LC 85-7622. 144p. 1985. pap. 7.95 (ISBN 0-664-24680-X). Westminster.
David-Neel, Alexandra. Buddhism. 1979. pap. 3.50 (ISBN 0-380-46185-4, 63594-1, Discus). Avon.
--Buddhism. LC 77-10308. 1978. 8.95 (ISBN 0-312-10680-7). St Martin.
--My Journey to Lhasa. LC 85-47947. (Illus.). 320p. 1986. lib. bdg. 22.00x (ISBN 0-8070-5900-5); pap. 10.95 (ISBN 0-8070-5901-3, BP713). Beacon Pr.
--Secret Oral Teachings in Tibetan Buddhist Sects. 1967. pap. 4.95 (ISBN 0-87286-012-4). City Lights.
Davidovitch, David. The Ketuba: Jewish Marriage Contracts Through the Ages. 2nd ed. (Illus.). 1974. 29.50 (ISBN 0-87203-054-7). Hermon.
--The Ketuba: Jewish Marriage Contracts Through the Ages. LC 82-1247. (Illus.). 120p. 1985. 29.95 (ISBN 0-915361-21-3, 09745-5, Dist. by Watts). Adama Pubs Inc.
Davids, C. Rhys. Gotama, the Man. LC 78-72409. Repr. of 1928 ed. 25.00 (ISBN 0-404-17273-3). AMS Pr.
--What Was the Original Gospel in 'Buddhism'? LC 78-72416. Repr. of 1938 ed. 17.00 (ISBN 0-404-17277-6). AMS Pr.
Davids, C. Rhys, ed. Khuddaka-Nikaya: The Minor Anthologies of the Pali Canon, 4 vols. Repr. of 1931 ed. 105.00 set (ISBN 0-404-17640-2). AMS Pr.
Davids, C. Rhys, intro. by. Stories of the Buddha. LC 78-72444. Repr. of 1929 ed. 30.00 (ISBN 0-404-17316-0). AMS Pr.
Davids, Carolina A. Buddhism: A Study of the Buddhist Norm. LC 78-72408. Repr. of 1912 ed. 25.00 (ISBN 0-404-17269-5). AMS Pr.
--Buddhism: Its Birth & Dispersal. rev. ed. LC 78-72407. Repr. of 1934 ed. 25.00 (ISBN 0-404-17268-7). AMS Pr.
--A Manual of Buddhism for Advanced Students. LC 78-72410. Repr. of 1932 ed. 32.50 (ISBN 0-404-17274-1). AMS Pr.
Davids, Caroline A. Outines of Buddhism: A Historical Sketch. 126p. 1934. Repr. text ed. 12.50x. Coronet Bks.
--Sakya or Buddhist Origins. 444p. 1931. Repr. text ed. 32.50x. Coronet Bks.
Davids, Peter. Commentary on James: New International Greek Testament Commentary. 226p. 1982. 15.95 (ISBN 0-8028-2388-2). Eerdmans.
Davids, Peter H. James: A Good News Commentary. LC 83-47720. (The Good News Commentary Ser.). 176p. (Orig.). 1983. pap. 7.95 (ISBN 0-06-061697-0, RD-499, HarpR). Har-Row.
Davids, Rhys. Buddhist Suttas. lib. bdg. 79.95 (ISBN 0-87968-511-5). Krishna Pr.
--Poems of Cloister & Jungle, a Buddhist Anthology. 59.95 (ISBN 0-8490-0849-2). Gordon Pr.
--Sakya of Buddhist Origins. lib. bdg. 79.95 (ISBN 0-87968-512-3). Krishna Pr.
--Vinaya Texts, 3 vols. lib. bdg. 300.00 (ISBN 0-87968-513-1). Krishna Pr.
Davids, Rhys T., tr. see Fausboll, V.
Davids, Richard C. Man Who Moved a Mountain. LC 75-99609. (Illus.). 270p. 1972. pap. 5.95 (ISBN 0-8006-1237-X, 1-1237). Fortress.
Davids, T. Rhys. Buddhism: Being a Sketch of the Life & Teachings of Guatama, the Buddha. LC 78-72417. Repr. of 1877 ed. 28.00 (ISBN 0-404-17278-4). AMS Pr.

Davids, T. W. Buddhist Suttas. (Sacred Bks. of the East: Vol. 11). 15.00 (ISBN 0-89581-520-6). Asian Human Pr.
--Jaina, Sutras. (Sacred Bks. of the East Ser.: Vol. 22, 45). both vols. 36.00 (ISBN 0-89581-525-7); 15.00 ea. Asian Human Pr.
Davids, T. W. & Oldenberg, H. Vinaya Texts. (Sacred Bks. of the East: Vols. 13, 17, 20). 3 vols. 45.00 (ISBN 0-89581-522-2); 15.00 ea. Asian Human Pr.
Davids, Thomas W. Buddhist India. LC 78-38349. (Select Bibliographies Reprint Ser). Repr. of 1903 ed. 28.00 (ISBN 0-8369-6766-6). Ayer Co Pubs.
Davidson, A. B. The Theology of the Old Testament. Salmond, S. D., ed. 572p. 1904. 16.95 (ISBN 0-567-27206-0, Pub. by T & T Clark Ltd UK). Fortress.
Davidson, A. K. The Art of Zen Gardens: A Guide to Their Creation & Enjoyment. (Illus.). 160p. 1983. 15.95 (ISBN 0-87477-253-2); pap. 9.95 (ISBN 0-87477-254-0). J P Tarcher.
Davidson, Alice J. Christmas Wrapped in Love. 128p. 13.95 (ISBN 0-687-07818-0). Abingdon.
--Prayers & Graces. (Alice in Bibleland Ser.). 32p. 1986. 4.95 (ISBN 0-8378-5078-9). Gibson.
--Psalms & Proverbs. (Alice in Bibleland Ser.). (Illus.). 32p. 1984. 4.95 (ISBN 0-8378-5069-X). Gibson.
--Reflections of Love. (Illus.). 128p. 1982. 12.95 (ISBN 0-8007-1327-3). Revell.
--The Story of Baby Jesus. (Alice in Bibleland Ser.). (Illus.). 32p. 1985. 4.95 (ISBN 0-8378-5072-X). Gibson.
--The Story of Baby Moses. (Alice in Bibleland Ser.). (Illus.). 32p. 1985. 4.95 (ISBN 0-8378-5071-1). Gibson.
--The Story of Creation. (The Alice in Bibleland Storybooks). (Illus.). 32p. 1984. 4.95 (ISBN 0-8378-5066-5). Gibson.
--The Story of Daniel & the Lions. (Alice in Bibleland Ser.). 32p. 1986. 4.95 (ISBN 0-8378-5079-7). Gibson.
--The Story of David & Goliath. (Alice in Bibleland Ser.). (Illus.). 32p. 1985. 4.95 (ISBN 0-8378-5070-3). Gibson.
--The Story of Jonah. (The Alice in Bibleland Storybooks). (Illus.). 32p. 1984. 4.95 (ISBN 0-8378-5068-1). Gibson.
--The Story of Noah. (The Alice in Bibleland Storybooks). (Illus.). 32p. 1984. 4.95 (ISBN 0-8378-5067-3). Gibson.
--The Story of the Loaves & Fishes. (Alice in Bibleland Ser.). (Illus.). 32p. 1985. 4.95 (ISBN 0-8378-5073-8). Gibson.
Davidson, Audrey E. The Quasi-Dramatic St. John Passions from Scandinavia & Their Medieval Background. (Early Drama, Art & Music Monograph: No. 3). (Illus.). viii, 135p. 1981. pap. 8.95 (ISBN 0-918720-14-1). Medieval Inst.
Davidson, Benjamin. Analytical Hebrew & Chaldee Lexicon. (Hebrew.). 27.95 (ISBN 0-310-20290-6, 6263, Pub. by Bagster). Zondervan.
--Analytical Hebrew & Chaldee Lexicon. 784p. Date not set. 24.95 (ISBN 0-913573-03-5). Hendrickson MA.
Davidson, Bernice F. Raphael's Bible: A Study of the Vatican Logge. LC 84-43088. (College Art Association Monographs: Vol. 39). (Illus.). 198p. 1985. 30.00 (ISBN 0-271-00388-X). Pa St U Pr.
Davidson, C. T. Upon This Rock, 3 vols. 692p. 1973. Vol. 1. 11.95 (ISBN 0-934942-16-1); Vol. 2. 14.95 (ISBN 0-934942-17-X); Vol. 3. 13.95 (ISBN 0-934942-18-8). White Wing Pub.
Davidson, C. T., jt. auth. see Willing, Ora M.
Davidson, Charles. Studies in the English Mystery Plays. LC 68-752. (Studies in Drama, No. 39). 1969. Repr. of 1892 ed. lib. bdg. 49.95x (ISBN 0-8383-0536-9). Haskell.
Davidson, Clarissa S. God's Man: The Story of Pastor Niemoeller. LC 78-21065. 1979. Repr. of 1959 ed. lib. bdg. 22.50x (ISBN 0-313-21065-9, DAGM). Greenwood.
Davidson, Donald L. Nuclear War & the American Churches: Ethical Positions on Modern Warfare. 200p. 1983. 21.50x (ISBN 0-86531-706-2). Westview.
Davidson, Edward H. Jonathan Edwards: The Narrative of a Puritan Mind. LC 68-7254. pap. 43.80 (ISBN 0-317-07848-8, 2005489). Bks Demand UMI.
Davidson, Elizabeth H. Establishment of the English Church in Continental American Colonies. (Duke University. Trinity College Historical Society. Historical Papers: No. 20). Repr. of 1936 ed. 24.50 (ISBN 0-404-51770-6). AMS Pr.
Davidson, Glen W. Living with Dying. LC 74-14186. 112p. (Orig.). 1975. pap. 5.95 (ISBN 0-8066-1468-4, 10-3980); study guide 00.30 (10-3981). Augsburg.
--Understanding Mourning: A Guide for Those Who Grieve. LC 84-14527. 112p. (Orig.). 1984. pap. 5.95 (ISBN 0-8066-2080-3, 10-6805). Augsburg.
Davidson, Graeme J. & Macdonald, Mary. Anyone Can Pray: A Guide to Methods of Christian Prayer. LC 82-62921. 208p. (Orig.). 1983. pap. 7.95 (ISBN 0-8091-2542-0). Paulist Pr.
Davidson, H. Ellis. Gods & Myths of Northern Europe. (Orig.). 1965. pap. 5.95 (ISBN 0-14-020670-1, Pelican). Penguin.
Davidson, H. R. Gods & Myths of Northern Europe. 250p. 1986. pap. 3.00 (ISBN 0-317-53026-7). Noontide.
--Scandinavian Mythology. LC 85-22895. (The Library of the World's Myths & Legends). (Illus.). 144p. 1986. 18.95 (ISBN 0-87226-041-0). P Bedrick Bks.
Davidson, Henry M. Good Christian Men. facsimile ed. LC 70-142616. (Essay Index Reprint Ser). Repr. of 1940 ed. 19.00 (ISBN 0-8369-2390-1). Ayer Co Pubs.
Davidson, Herbert. Proofs for Eternity, Creation, & the Existence of God in Medieval Islamic & Jewish Philosophy. (Studies in Northeast Culture & Society: Vol. 7). 500p. 1985. write for info. (ISBN 0-89003-180-0); pap. 62.00x (ISBN 0-89003-181-9). Undena Pubns.
Davidson, Hugh M. The Origins of Certainty: Means & Meanings in Pascal's "Pensees". LC 78-12768. 1979. lib. bdg. 16.00x (ISBN 0-226-13716-3). U of Chicago Pr.
Davidson, Hugh M. & Dube, Pierre H., eds. A Concordance to Pascal's "Pensees". LC 75-16808. (Cornell Concordances Ser.). 1488p. 1975. 85.00x (ISBN 0-8014-0972-1). Cornell U Pr.
Davidson, I., jt. auth. see Ginzberg, L.
Davidson, I. see Ginzberg, L. & Davidson, I.
Davidson, Israel. Parody in Jewish Literature. LC 77-163670. (Columbia University. Oriental Studies: No. 2). Repr. of 1907 ed. 24.50 (ISBN 0-404-50492-2). AMS Pr.
--Thesaurus of Medieval Hebrew Poetry, 4 Vols. rev. ed. (Library of Jewish Classics). 1970. Set. 150.00x (ISBN 0-87068-003-X). Ktav.
Davidson, J. L. Prophets of Deceit. 1960. 5.25 (ISBN 0-88027-016-0). Firm Foun Pub.
Davidson, James. Mobilizing Social Movement Organization: The Formation, Institionalization & Effectiveness of Economical Urban Ministries. (Monograph: No. 6). 1985. pap. 8.00 (ISBN 0-932566-05-7). Soc Sci Stud Rel.
Davidson, Nicholas S. The Counter-Reformation. 96p. 1987. pap. text ed. 7.95 (ISBN 0-631-14888-4). Basil Blackwell.
Davidson, Richard M. Typology in Scripture: A Study of Hermeneutical Tupos Structures. (Andrews University Seminary Doctoral Dissertation Ser.: Vol. 2). 496p. (Orig.). 1981. pap. 10.95 (ISBN 0-943872-34-0). Andrews Univ Pr.
Davidson, Robert. The Bible in Religious Education. 72p. 1980. pap. 5.00x (ISBN 0-905312-10-4, Pub. by Scot Acad Pr). Longwood Pub Group.
--Ecclesiastes & the Song of Solomon. LC 86-15659. (The Daily Study Bible - Old Testament Ser.). 168p. 1986. 14.95 (ISBN 0-664-21838-5); pap. 7.95 (ISBN 0-664-24589-7). Westminster.
--Jeremiah, Vol. 1: Chapters 1 to 20. LC 83-14598. (Daily Study Bible - Old Testament Ser.). 176p. 1983. 12.95 (ISBN 0-664-21394-4); pap. 6.95 (ISBN 0-664-24476-9). Westminster.
Davidson, Robert, ed Creative Ideas for Advent. 114p. (Orig.). 1980. pap. 9.95 (ISBN 0-940754-06-1). Ed Ministries.
--Genesis, Chapters Twelve to Fifty. LC 78-12892. (Cambridge Bible Commentary on the New English Bible, Old Testament Ser.). (Illus.). 1979. 39.50 (ISBN 0-521-22485-3); pap. 14.95x (ISBN 0-521-29520-3). Cambridge U Pr.
--Genesis, Chapters 1-11. LC 72-93675. (Cambridge Bible Commentary on the New English Bible, Old Testament Ser.). 200p. (Orig.). 1973. pap. 8.95x (ISBN 0-521-09760-6). Cambridge U Pr.
Davidson, Robert G. Creative Ideas for Advent, Vol. 2. 100p. (Orig.). 1986. pap. 9.95 (ISBN 0-940754-35-5). Ed Ministries.
--Gathering the Pieces. 88p. (Orig.). 1985. pap. 9.95 (ISBN 0-940754-30-4). Ed Ministries.
--Held in High Value. 65p. (Orig.). 1986. pap. 9.95 (ISBN 0-940754-34-7). Ed Ministries.
--What Do They Expect of Me? 80p. 1986. pap. 9.95 (ISBN 0-940754-32-0). Ed Ministries.
Davidson, Robert G., ed. Creative Ideas for Lent. 120p. (Orig.). 1985. pap. 9.95 (ISBN 0-940754-25-8). Ed Ministries.
Davidson, Sidney, et al. CPA Exam Booklet: Intermediate Accounting. 112p. 1984. pap. 10.95x (ISBN 0-03-071937-2). Dryden Pr.
Davidson, Versa H. The Shadow of God. 320p. 1980. 7.95 (ISBN 0-89962-026-4). Todd & Honeywell.
Davidson, William F. An Early History of Free Will Baptists, Vol. 1. (Free Will Baptist History Ser.). 1974. 7.95 (ISBN 0-89265-037-0); pap. 4.95 (ISBN 0-89265-022-2). Randall Hse.
--The Free Will Baptists in America, 1727-1984. 462p. 1985. text ed. 14.95 (ISBN 0-89265-093-1). Randall Hse.
Davidson, William L. The Stoic Creed. Vlastos, Gregory, ed. LC 78-19341. (Morals & Law in Ancient Greece Ser.). 1979. Repr. of 1907 ed. lib. bdg. 23.00x (ISBN 0-405-11535-0). Ayer Co Pubs.
Davie, Donald. A Gathered Church: The Literature of the English Dissenting Interest, 1700-1930. (The Clark Lectures 1976). 1978. 17.50x (ISBN 0-19-519999-5). Oxford U Pr.
Davie, Donald, ed. The New Oxford Book of Christian Verse. 1982. 27.50x (ISBN 0-19-213426-4). Oxford U Pr.
Davie, Ian. Jesus Purusha. LC 85-23113. 176p. (Orig.). 1985. pap. 8.95 (ISBN 0-89281-069-6, Lindisfarne Pr). Inner Tradit.
Davie, Peter. Pastoral Care & the Parish. 102p. 1984. 24.95x (ISBN 0-631-13225-2); pap. 8.95x (ISBN 0-631-13226-0). Basil Blackwell.
Davies, A. Meaning of the Dead Sea Scrolls. pap. 2.95 (ISBN 0-451-62447-5, ME2097, Ment). NAL.
Davies, Alan T., ed. Antisemitism & the Foundations of Christianity. LC 79-65620. 276p. 1979. pap. 8.95 (ISBN 0-8091-2219-7). Paulist Pr.
Davies, Alfred T. John Calvin: Many Sided Genius. LC 83-45609. Date not set. Repr. of 1947 ed. 18.50 (ISBN 0-404-19827-9). AMS Pr.
Davies, Ann. This Is Truth about the Self. 3rd ed. 1984. 4.50 (ISBN 0-938002-03-1). Builders of Adytum.
Davies, Benedict. Credo: A Catholic Catechism. 300p. 1985. pap. 5.95 (ISBN 0-86683-901-1, HarpR); pap. 3.95 leaders guide (ISBN 0-86683-743-4). Har-Row.
Davies, Benjamin. Baker's Harmony of the Gospels. (Baker's Paperback Reference Library). 192p. 1983. pap. 6.95 (ISBN 0-8010-2928-7). Baker Bk.
Davies, Benjamin & Mitchell, Edward. Hebrew & Lexicon to the Old Testament. 800p. Date not set. 22.95 (ISBN 0-8254-2453-4). Kregel.
Davies, Brian. Thinking about God. 1986. pap. 16.95 (ISBN 0-317-52367-8, HarpR). Har-Row.
Davies, Brian, jt. ed. see Walsh, Michael.
Davies, Chris, et al, eds. Jesus: One of Us. 148p. 1981. pap. 3.95 (ISBN 0-87784-618-9). Inter Varsity.
Davies, D. R. Reinhold Niebuhr: Prophet from America. facs. ed. (Select Bibliographies Reprint Ser). 1945. 13.00 (ISBN 0-8369-5324-X). Ayer Co Pubs.
Davies, Ebenezer T. Episcopacy & the Royal Supremacy in the Church of England in the XVI Century. LC 78-13202. 1978. Repr. of 1950 ed. lib. bdg. 24.75x (ISBN 0-313-20626-0, DAER). Greenwood.
Davies, Edward. Celtic Researches, on the Origin, Traditions & Language, of the Ancient Britons. Feldman, Burton & Richardson, Robert D., eds. LC 78-60902. (Myth & Romanticism Ser.: Vol. 8). (Illus.). 1979. lib. bdg. 80.00 (ISBN 0-8240-3557-7). Garland Pub.
Davies, Eryl. Prophecy & Ethics: Isaiah & the Ethical Traditions of Israel. (Journal for the Study of the Old Testament, Supplement: No. 16). 1981. 19.95 (ISBN 0-905774-26-4, Pub. by JSOT Pr England). Eisenbrauns.
Davies, G. I. The Way of the Wilderness. LC 77-95442. (Society for Old Testament Monographs). (Illus.). 1979. 32.50 (ISBN 0-521-22057-2). Cambridge U Pr.
Davies, Godfrey, jt. ed. see Haller, William.
Davies, Graham I., ed. see Bartlett, John A.
Davies, Horton. The Ecumenical Century: 1900-1965. (Worship & Theology in England Ser.: Vol. 5). 1965. 39.50x (ISBN 0-691-07145-4). Princeton U Pr.
--The English Free Churches. 2nd. ed. LC 85-7684. vii, 208p. 1985. Repr. of 1963 ed. lib. bdg. 37.50x (ISBN 0-313-20838-7, DAEF). Greenwood.
--Great South African Christians. LC 70-104242. Repr. of 1951 ed. lib. bdg. 22.50x (ISBN 0-8371-3916-3, DAGC). Greenwood.
--Like Angels from a Cloud: The English Metaphysical Preachers 1588-1645. 500p. 1986. 30.00 (ISBN 0-87328-088-1). Huntington Lib.
--Mirror of the Ministry in Modern Novels. facsimile ed. LC 70-111824. (Essay Index Reprint Ser.). 1959. 19.00 (ISBN 0-8369-1601-8). Ayer Co Pubs.
Davies, Horton, ed. Studies of the Church in History: Essays Honoring Robert S. Paul on His Sixty-Fifth Birthday, Vol. X. (Pittsburgh Theological Monographs. New Series: No. 5). 276p. (Orig.). 1983. pap. 16.95 (ISBN 0-686-45571-1). Pickwick.
Davies, Horton M. Catching the Conscience. LC 84-71181. 169p. (Orig.). 1984. pap. 7.50 (ISBN 0-936384-21-2). Cowley Pubns.
Davies, J. G. The Early Christian Church. (Twin Brooks Ser.). 1980. pap. 9.95 (ISBN 0-8010-2906-6). Baker Bk.
--Temples, Churches & Mosques: A Guide to the Appreciation of Religious Architecture. LC 82-13130. (Illus.). 256p. 1982. 27.50 (ISBN 0-8298-0634-2). Pilgrim NY.
Davies, J. G. & Van Zyl, P. A Shaker Dance Service Reconstucted. 1984. pap. 3.00 (ISBN 0-941500-34-9). Sharing Co.
Davies, J. G., ed. The New Westminster Dictionary of Liturgy & Worship. LC 86-9219. (Illus.). 560p. 1986. 29.95 (ISBN 0-664-21270-0). Westminster.
--The Westminster Dictionary of Worship. LC 78-25582. (Illus.). 400p. 1979. 18.95 (ISBN 0-664-21373-1). Westminster.
Davies, J. H., ed. Letter to the Hebrews. (Cambridge Bible Commentary on the New English Bible, New Testament Ser.). 1967. 16.95 (ISBN 0-521-04222-4); pap. 9.95x (ISBN 0-521-09408-9). Cambridge U Pr.
Davies, J. K. Mormon Gold: The Story of the Mormon Argonauts. 440p. (Orig.). 1984. pap. 12.95 (ISBN 0-913420-20-4). Olympus Pub Co.
Davies, John. Christians, Politics & Violent Revolution. LC 75-42517. pap. 56.00 (ISBN 0-317-26642-X, 2025118). Bks Demand UMI.
Davies, John D. The Faith Abroad. (Faith & the Future Ser.). 163p. 1984. 24.95x (ISBN 0-631-13183-3); pap. 8.95x (ISBN 0-631-13221-X). Basil Blackwell.
Davies, John G. Daily Life of Early Christians. LC 75-91757. Repr. of 1953 ed. lib. bdg. 22.50x (ISBN 0-8371-2413-1, DAEC). Greenwood.
--The Early Christian Church. LC 75-3989. (Illus.). 314p. 1976. Repr. of 1965 ed. lib. bdg. 24.00x (ISBN 0-8371-7696-4, DAECC). Greenwood.
Davies, Kirk. Earth's Final Hours. 330p. (Orig.). 1982. pap. 9.95 (ISBN 0-9609174-0-3). Pacific Inst.
Davies, M. Benedict, tr. see Boros, Ladislaus.
Davies, Merlin. Priorities in Praying: Learning from the Lord's Prayer. 104p. (Orig.). 1984. pap. 10.95 (ISBN 0-86474-002-6, Pub. by Interface Press). ANZ Religious Pubns.
Davies, Michael. Archbishop Lefebvre & Religious Liberty. 17p. 1980. pap. 1.00 (ISBN 0-89555-143-8). TAN Bks Pubs.
--Communion Under Both Kinds- an Ecumenical Surrender. 1980. pap. 1.00 (ISBN 0-89555-141-1). TAN Bks Pubs.
--Open Lesson to a Bishop. 1980. pap. 1.00 (ISBN 0-89555-142-X). Tan Bks Pubs.
Davies, Norman. The Tomb of Rekh-Mi-Re at Thebes: Metropolitan Museum of Art Egyptian Expedition Publications, 2 vols. in 1, Vol. 11. LC 75-168403. (Metropolitan Museum of Art Publications in Reprint). (Illus.). 374p. 1972. Repr. of 1943 ed. 47.50 (ISBN 0-405-02267-0). Ayer Co Pubs.
Davies, Norman De Garis. The Tomb of Ken-Amun at Thebes: Metropolitan Museum of Art Egyptian Expedition Publications, 2 vols. in 1, Vol. 5. LC 78-168401. (Metropolitan Museum of Art Publications in Reprint). (Illus.). 208p. 1972. Repr. of 1930 ed. 39.00 (ISBN 0-405-02267-0). Ayer Co Pubs.
--The Tomb of Nefer-Hotep at Thebes: Metropolitan Museum of Art Egyptian Expedition Publications, 2 vols in 1, Vol. 9. LC 71-168402. (Metropolitan Museum of Art Publications in Reprint). (Illus.). 192p. 1972. Repr. of 1933 ed. 39.00 (ISBN 0-405-02236-0). Ayer Co Pubs.
Davies, P. C. The Accidental Universe. LC 81-21592. (Illus.). 160p. 1982. 23.95 (ISBN 0-521-24212-6); pap. 11.95 (ISBN 0-521-28692-1). Cambridge U Pr.
Davies, P. R. Daniel. (Old Testament Guides Ser.). 133p. 1985. pap. text ed. 3.95x (ISBN 1-85075-002-5, Pub. by JSOT Pr England). Eisenbrauns.
Davies, Paul. God & the New Physics. 272p. 1984. pap. 7.95 (ISBN 0-671-52806-8, Touchstone Bks). S&S.
Davies, Philip R. The Damascus Covenant: An Interpretation of the "Damascus Document". (Journal for the Study of the Old Testament, Supplement Ser.: No. 25). 267p. 1983. text ed. 28.00x (ISBN 0-905774-50-7, Pub. by JSOT Pr England); pap. text ed. 18.50x (ISBN 0-905774-51-5, Pub. by JSOT Pr England). Eisenbrauns.
--Qumran. (Cities of the Biblical World Ser.). 1983. pap. 6.95 (ISBN 0-8028-1034-9). Eerdmans.
Davies, Phillip R., jt. auth. see Martin, James D.
Davies, R. Trevor. Four Centuries of Witch-Belief. LC 74-180026. Repr. of 1947 ed. 27.50 (ISBN 0-405-08437-4). Ayer Co Pubs.
Davies, Rupert E. The Problems of Authority in the Continental Reformers: A Study of Luther, Zwingli, & Calvin. LC 78-5871. 1978. Repr. of 1946 ed. lib. bdg. cancelled (ISBN 0-313-20487-X, DAPA). Greenwood.
Davies, Rupert E., ed. Approach to Christian Education. 1956. 7.00 (ISBN 0-8022-0352-3). Philos Lib.
Davies, Rupert E., jt. ed. see Flew, Robert N.

Davies, S. L. Peace, Print & Protestantism, Fourteen Fifty to Fifteen Eighty. 1976. 24.50x (ISBN 0-8464-0706-X). Beekman Pubs.

Davies, Stevan L. The Gospel of Thomas & Christian Wisdom. 160p. 1983. pap. 9.95 (ISBN 0-8164-2456-X, HarpR). Har-Row.

--The Revolt of the Widows: The Social World of the Apocryphal Acts. LC 80-11331. 150p. 1980. 12.95x (ISBN 0-8093-0958-0). S Ill U Pr.

Davies, Stevie. Images of Kinship in "Paradise Lost". Milton's Politics & Christian Liberty. LC 82-17485. 256p. 1983. text ed. 21.00x (ISBN 0-8262-0392-2). U of Mo Pr.

Davies, T. L. Bible English: Chapters on Old & Disused Expressions. 1875. 25.00 (ISBN 0-8274-1932-5). R West.

Davies, Tom & Hodder, John. Stained Glass Hours: Modern Pilgrimage. (Illus.). 161p. 1985. 29.95 (ISBN 0-450-06053-5, New Eng Lib). David & Charles.

Davies, W. D. Christian Origins & Judaism. LC 73-2192. (The Jewish People; History, Religion, Literature Ser.). Repr. of 1962 ed. 22.00 (ISBN 0-405-05258-8). Ayer Co Pubs.

--The Gospel & the Land: Early Christianity & Jewish Territorial Doctrine. LC 72-82228. 1974. 32.50x (ISBN 0-520-02278-5). U of Cal Pr.

--Jewish & Pauline Studies. LC 82-48620. 432p. 1983. text ed. 29.95 (ISBN 0-8006-0694-9). Fortress.

--Paul & Rabbinic Judaism: Some Rabbinic Elements in Pauline Theology. LC 80-8049. 448p. 1980. pap. 14.95 (ISBN 0-8006-1438-0, 1-1438). Fortress.

--The Territorial Dimension of Judaism. LC 81-53. (A Quantum Bk.). 160p. 1982. 15.95x (ISBN 0-520-04331-6). U of Cal Pr.

Davies, W. D., ed. Cambridge History of Judaism: Introduction, the Persian Period, Vol. 1. Finkelstein, Louis. LC 77-85704. 461p. 1984. 62.50 (ISBN 0-521-21880-2). Cambridge U Pr.

Davies, Walford, ed. Let's Sing Together. 25.00x (ISBN 0-946095-14-0, Pub. by Gresham England); pap. 20.00x (ISBN 0-946095-13-2, Pub. by Gresham England). State Mutual Bk.

Davies, Walford & Ley, Henry G., eds. Church Anthem Book: One Hundred Anthems. rev. ed. 1959. 17.50x (ISBN 0-19-353106-2). Oxford U Pr.

Davies, William. The Setting of the Sermon on the Mount. LC 64-630. pap. 140.80 (ISBN 0-317-26320-X, 2024449). Bks Demand UMI.

Davies, William D. Sermon on the Mount. (Orig.). 1966. pap. 9.95 (ISBN 0-521-09384-8, 384). Cambridge U Pr.

Davies-Rodgers, Ellen. Heirs Through Hope: The Episcopal Diocese of West Tennessee. LC 83-50733. 1983. 30.00 (ISBN 0-317-05919-X). Plantation.

--The Holy Innocents: The Story of a Historic Church & Country Parish. (Illus.). 12.00 (ISBN 0-685-84990-2). Plantation.

--The Romance of the Episcopal Church in West Tennessee. 12.00 (ISBN 0-685-84991-0). Plantation.

Davies-Rogers, Ellen. A Tree Is Lighted. LC 84-90673. (Illus.). 1984. 5.00 (ISBN 0-317-19588-3). Plantation.

Davila, Mario L., tr. see Abreu Gomez, Emilio.

Davis. Davis Dictionary of the Bible. 24.95 (ISBN 0-8054-1124-0). Broadman.

Davis, et al, eds. Contemporary Issues in Biomedical Ethics. LC 78-71406. (Contemporary Issues in Biomedicine, Ethics, & Society Ser.). 300p. 1979. 29.50 (ISBN 0-89603-002-4). Humana.

Davis, Almond H. The Female Preacher: Memoir of Salome Lincoln, Afterwards the Wife of Elder Junia S. Mowry. LC 72-2599. (American Women Ser.: Images & Realities). (Illus.). 166p. 1972. Repr. of 1843 ed. 13.50 (ISBN 0-405-04489-5). Ayer Co Pubs.

Davis, Billie. Teaching to Meet Crisis Needs. LC 83-82815. 128p. (Orig.). 1984. pap. text ed. 2.95 (ISBN 0-88243-609-0, 02-0609). Gospel Pub.

Davis, Billie C. Dynamic Classroom. LC 86-83084. (Sunday School Staff Training Text for 1988). 144p. (Orig.). 1987. pap. 2.95 (ISBN 0-88243-798-4). Gospel Pub.

Davis, Burnie. How to Activate Miracles in Your Life & Ministry. 125p. 1982. pap. 3.95 (ISBN 0-89274-230-5, HH-230). Harrison Hse.

Davis, Carolina A., rev. by see Buddhaghosa.

Davis, Charles. Theology & Political Society. LC 80-40014. 180p. 1980. 27.95 (ISBN 0-521-22538-8). Cambridge U Pr.

--What Is Living, What Is Dead in Christianity Today. 200p. (Orig.). 1986. 16.95 (ISBN 0-86683-511-3, HarpR). Har-Row.

--Why I Left the Roman Catholic Church. 27p. 1976. 3.00 (ISBN 0-911826-11-4). Am Atheist.

Davis, Clara. The Move of God: Azusa Street to Now. 80p. (Orig.). 1983. pap. 2.95 (ISBN 0-88144-016-7, CPS-016). Christian Pub.

Davis, Creath. Lord, If I Ever Needed You, It's Now! 138p. Date not set. pap. 5.95 (ISBN 0-8010-2968-6). Baker Bk.

Davis, Dennis M. & Clapp, Steve. The Third Wave & the Local Church. 175p. (Orig.). 1983. pap. 8.00 (ISBN 0-914527-54-1). C-Four Res.

Davis, Earl C. Christ at the Door. LC 84-27441. 1985. pap. 5.95 (ISBN 0-8054-6249-X). Broadman.

--Forever, Amen. LC 81-67199. 1982. pap. 4.50 (ISBN 0-8054-1953-5). Broadman.

--Somebody Cares. LC 81-71255. 1983. 7.95 (ISBN 0-8054-5211-7). Broadman.

Davis, F. Hadland. Myths & Legends of Japan. (Illus.). 1978. Repr. of 1912 ed. lib. bdg. 45.00 (ISBN 0-8495-1008-2). Arden Lib.

Davis, Gerald C., ed. Setting Free the Ministry of the People of God. 120p. (Orig.). 1984. pap. 1.75 (ISBN 0-88028-038-7). Forward Movement.

Davis, Gerald L. I Got the Word in Me & I Can Sing It, You Know: A Study of the Performed African American Sermon. LC 85-2544. (Illus.). 272p. 1986. text ed. 24.95 (ISBN 0-8122-7987-5). U of Pa Pr.

Davis, Guillermo H. Gramatica Elemental del Griego del Nuevo Testamento. McKibben, Jorge F., tr. 240p. 1984. Repr. of 1980 ed. 4.75 (ISBN 0-311-42008-7). Casa Bautista.

Davis, H. Grady. Design for Preaching. LC 58-5749. (Orig.). 1958. 9.95 (ISBN 0-8006-0806-2, 1-806). Fortress.

Davis, H. W., ed. Medieval England. new ed. Orig. Title: Bernard's Companion to English History. 1977. Repr. of 1924 ed. lib. bdg. 45.00 (ISBN 0-8495-1006-6). Arden Lib.

Davis, Howard, ed. Ethics & Defence: Power & Responsibility in the Nuclear Age. 224p. 1987. text ed. 39.95 (ISBN 0-631-15174-5); pap. text ed. 19.95 (ISBN 0-631-15175-3). Basil Blackwell.

Davis, Hubert J. Myths & Legends of the Great Dismal Swamp. (Illus.). 112p. 1981. 7.50 (ISBN 0-930230-42-6). Johnson NC.

Davis, Inez S. Story of the Church. new ed. 1981. pap. 18.00 (ISBN 0-8309-0188-4). Herald Hse.

Davis, J. History of the Welsh Baptist: AD Sixty-Three to Seventeen Seventy. 1982. Repr. of 1835 ed. 15.00 (ISBN 0-686-91934-3). Church History.

Davis, J., ed. Religious Organization & Religious Experience. (ASA Monograph). 1982. 42.00 (ISBN 0-12-206580-8). Acad Pr.

Davis, J. E., jt. auth. see Torrey, R. A.

Davis, J. Mearle, ed. see International Missionary Council - Department of Social & Economic Research & Council.

Davis, James A. Wisdom & Spirit: An Investigation of 1 Corinthians 1.18-3.20 Against the Background of Jewish Sapiential. (Traditions in the Greco-Roman Period Ser.). 270p. (Orig.). 1984. lib. bdg. 27.25 (ISBN 0-8191-4210-7); pap. text ed. 13.75 (ISBN 0-8191-4211-5). U Pr of Amer.

Davis, James B. La Quete de Paul Gadenne: Une Morale pour Notre Epoque. (Fr.). 96p. 1979. 9.95 (ISBN 0-917786-18-1). Summa Pubns.

Davis, James H., Jr. Fenelon. (World Authors Ser.). 1979. lib. bdg. 15.95 (ISBN 0-8057-6384-8, Twayne). G K Hall.

Davis, Jennie. Praise Him, Praise Him! 1982. pap. text ed. 4.95 (ISBN 0-89693-208-7, Sonflower Bks). SP Pubns.

Davis, Jennie, jt. auth. see Buerger, Jane.

Davis, John D. Davis Dictionary of the Bible. 1954. 24.95 (ISBN 0-8010-2805-1). Baker Bk.

--Genesis & Semitic Tradition. (Twin Brooks Ser.). 1980. pap. 4.95 (ISBN 0-8010-2902-3). Baker Bk.

Davis, John F. An Audience with Jesus. 134p. 1982. 4.00 (ISBN 0-8198-0721-4, SP0008); pap. 3.00 (ISBN 0-8198-0722-2). Dghtrs St Paul.

Davis, John J. Abortion & the Christian. 128p. 1984. pap. 4.95 (ISBN 0-87552-221-1). Presby & Reformed.

--Biblical Numerology. (Orig.). 1968. pap. 4.50 (ISBN 0-8010-2813-2). Baker Bk.

--Biblical Numerology. pap. 4.95 (ISBN 0-88469-063-6). BMH Bks.

--The Birth of a Kingdom: Studies in I & II Samuel & I Kings I-II. pap. 5.95 (ISBN 0-88469-053-9). BMH Bks.

--Christ's Victorious Kingdom. 144p. 1987. pap. 6.95 (ISBN 0-8010-2970-8). Baker Bk.

--Conquest & Crisis: Studies in Joshua, Judges & Ruth. (Illus.). pap. 5.95 (ISBN 0-88469-052-0). BMH Bks.

--Contemporary Counterfeits. 1979. pap. 1.25 (ISBN 0-88469-003-2). BMH Bks.

--Demons, Exorcism & the Evangelical. 1979. pap. 1.00 (ISBN 0-88469-043-1). BMH Bks.

--Evangelical Ethics: Issues Facing the Church Today. 304p. 1985. 13.95 (ISBN 0-87552-222-X). Presby & Reformed.

--Foundations of Evangelical Theology: A Contextualized Approach. 232p. 1984. pap. 9.95 (ISBN 0-8010-2937-6). Baker Bk.

--Handbook of Basic Bible Texts: Every Key Passage for the Study of Doctrine & Theology. 1986. pap. 6.95 (ISBN 0-310-43711-3, 12103P). Zondervan.

--Moses & Gods of Egypt. (Old Testament Studies). pap. 11.95 (ISBN 0-8010-2957-0). Baker Bk.

--Moses & the Gods of Egypt: Studies in Exodus. Rev. ed. (Illus.). 1985. pap. 11.95 (ISBN 0-88469-177-2). BMH Bks.

--Paradise to Prison: Studies in Genesis. LC 74-30753. (Old Testament Studies). 384p. 1975. 14.95 (ISBN 0-8010-2838-8). Baker Bk.

--Paradise to Prison: Studies in Genesis. 14.95 (ISBN 0-88469-050-4). BMH Bks.

--Perfect Shepherd. (Illus., Orig.). 1980. pap. 4.50 (ISBN 0-8010-2905-8). Baker Bk.

--The Perfect Shepherd: Studies in the Twenty-Third Psalm. pap. 5.50 (ISBN 0-88469-110-1). BMH Bks.

--Theology Primer. LC 81-67093. 128p. (Orig.). 1981. pap. 5.95 (ISBN 0-8010-2912-0). Baker Bk.

--Your Wealth in God's World. 144p. 1984. pap. 4.95 (ISBN 0-87552-219-X). Presby & Reformed.

Davis, John J. & Whitcomb, John C. A History of Israel. (Old Testament Studies). 1980. 17.95 (ISBN 0-8010-2888-4). Baker Bk.

--History of Israel. 17.95 (ISBN 0-88469-061-X). BMH Bks.

Davis, Joy M. A Woman's Song. LC 83-70376. (Orig.). 1984. pap. 5.95 (ISBN 0-8054-5243-5). Broadman.

Davis, Kenneth R. Anabaptism & Asceticism. LC 73-19593. 384p. 1974. 19.95x (ISBN 0-8361-1195-8). Herald Pr.

Davis, Kortright. Mission for Caribbean Change. (IC-Studies in the Intercultural History of Christianity: Vol. 28). 300p. 1982. pap. 32.10 (ISBN 3-8204-5732-1). P Lang Pubs.

Davis, L. Edward, pref. by. The Westminster Confession of Faith: An Authentic Modern Version. rev., 2nd ed. x, 89p. (Orig.). 1985. pap. text ed. write for info. (ISBN 0-9614303-1-1). Summertown.

Davis, Lawrence B. Immigrants, Baptists & the Protestant Mind in America. LC 72-81264. pap. 60.00 (ISBN 0-8357-9682-5, 2019040). Bks Demand UMI.

Davis, Lee E. In Charge. LC 84-4969. 1984. pap. 4.95 (ISBN 0-8054-6404-2). Broadman.

Davis, Lenwood & Hill, George H. Religious Broadcasting, Nineteen Twenty to Nineteen Eighty-Three: A Selectively Annotated Bibliography. (Reference Library of Social Science). 1984. lib. bdg. 40.00 (ISBN 0-8240-9015-2). Garland Pub.

Davis, Linda. How to be the Happy Wife of an Unsaved Husband. 165p. (Orig.). 1986. pap. text ed. 3.50 (ISBN 0-88368-189-7). Whitaker Hse.

Davis, Lola A. Towards a New World Religion. 256p. 1983. pap. 16.00 (ISBN 0-942494-77-6). Coleman Pub.

Davis, Melodie M. For the Next Nine Months: Meditations for Expectant Mothers. 256p. 1983. pap. 3.95 (ISBN 0-310-45542-1, 12477P). Zondervan.

--You Know You're a Mother When... 112p. 1987. pap. 4.95 (ISBN 0-310-44811-5). Zondervan.

Davis, Moshe. America & the Holy Land Series, 72 vols. (Illus.). 1977. Repr. lib. bdg. 2212.50 (ISBN 0-405-10220-8). Ayer Co Pubs.

--From Dependence to Mutuality: The American Jewish Community & World Jewry. (Texts & Studies). (Hebrew.). 1970. 10.00 (ISBN 0-911934-07-3). Am Jewish Hist Soc.

--Mordecai M. Kaplan Jubilee Volume, 2 Vols. 1953. Set. 50.00x (ISBN 0-685-13740-6, Pub. by Jewish Theol Seminary). Ktav.

Davis, Moshe, ed. Call to America to Build Zion: An Original Anthology. LC 77-70723. (America & the Holy Land Ser.). 1977. lib. bdg. 20.00x (ISBN 0-405-10306-9). Ayer Co Pubs.

--Christian Protagonists for Jewish Restoration: An Original Anthology. LC 77-70678. (America & the Holy Land Ser.). 1977. lib. bdg. 20.00x (ISBN 0-405-10221-6). Ayer Co Pubs.

--Holy Land Missions & Missionaries: An Original Anthology. LC 77-70703. (America & the Holy Land Ser.). (Illus.). 1977. lib. bdg. 20.00x (ISBN 0-405-10259-3). Ayer Co Pubs.

--Israel: Its Role in Civilization. LC 77-70673. (America & the Holy Land Ser.). 1977. Repr. of 1956 ed. lib. bdg. 31.00 (ISBN 0-405-10241-0). Ayer Co Pubs.

--Pioneer Settlement in the Twenties: An Original Anthology. LC 77-70699. (America & the Holy Land Ser.). 1977. lib. bdg. 20.00x (ISBN 0-405-10250-X). Ayer Co Pubs.

--World Jewry & the State of Israel. LC 77-72730. (Indivual Publications Ser.). 1977. lib. bdg. 14.00x (ISBN 0-405-10305-0). Ayer Co Pubs.

--Zionism in Transition. LC 80-67905. 1980. lib. bdg. 24.00x (ISBN 0-405-13825-3). Ayer Co Pubs.

--Zionism in Transition. 1980. pap. 8.00 (ISBN 0-930832-61-2). Herzl Pr.

Davis, Moshe, ed. see Adler, Cyrus & Margalith, Aaron M.

Davis, Moshe, ed. see Babcock, Maltbie D.

Davis, Moshe, ed. see Bartlett, Samuel C.

Davis, Moshe, jt. ed. see Burnet, David S.

Davis, Moshe, ed. see Cresson, Warder.

Davis, Moshe, ed. see De Hass, Frank S.

Davis, Moshe, ed. see Field, Frank M.

Davis, Moshe, ed. see Fosdick, Harry E.

Davis, Moshe, ed. see Fulton, John.

Davis, Moshe, ed. see Gordon, Benjamin L.

Davis, Moshe, ed. see Hoofien, Sigfried.

Davis, Moshe, ed. see Intercollegiate Zionist Association of America.

Davis, Moshe, ed. see Johnson, Sarah B.

Davis, Moshe, ed. see Kallen, Horace M.

Davis, Moshe, ed. see Krimsky, Joseph.

Davis, Moshe, ed. see Kyle, Melvin G.

Davis, Moshe, ed. see Lipsky, Louis.

Davis, Moshe, ed. see Macalister, Robert A.

Davis, Moshe, ed. see Merrill, Selah.

Davis, Moshe, ed. see Morris, Robert.

Davis, Moshe, ed. see Morton, Daniel O.

Davis, Moshe, ed. see Odenheimer, William H.

Davis, Moshe, ed. see Palmer, Edward H.

Davis, Moshe, ed. see Prime, William C.

Davis, Moshe, ed. see Rifkind, Simon H., et al.

Davis, Moshe, ed. see Schaff, Philip.

Davis, Moshe, ed. see Sneersohn, Haym Z.

Davis, Moshe, ed. see Talmage, Thomas.

Davis, Moshe, ed. see Vester, Bertha H.

Davis, Moshe, ed. see Wallace, Edwin S.

Davis, Moshe, ed. see Ware, William.

Davis, Myer D. Shetaroth, Hebrew Deeds of English Jews Before 1290. 410p. 1888. text ed. 74.52x (ISBN 0-576-80111-9, Pub. by Gregg Intl Pubs England). Gregg Intl.

Davis, Nancy & Levitt, Joy. The Guide to Everything Jewish in New York. LC 86-10927. 334p. 1986. pap. 14.95 (ISBN 0-915361-47-7, Dist. by Watts). Adama Pubs Inc.

Davis, Nancy M., et al. April & Easter. (Davis Teaching Units Ser.: Vol. 1, No. 8). (Illus.). 45p. (Orig.). 1986. pap. 5.95 (ISBN 0-937103-10-1). DaNa Pubns.

Davis, O. B. Introduction to Biblical Literature. 1976. pap. text ed. 9.25x (ISBN 0-8104-5834-9). Boynton Cook Pubs.

Davis, Patricia A. Suicidal Adolescents. 108p. 1983. 20.50x (ISBN 0-398-04866-5). C C Thomas.

Davis, Patricia T. Together They Built a Mountain. LC 74-14727. (Illus.). 196p. 1974. 6.95 (ISBN 0-915010-00-3). Sutter House.

Davis, R. Dowd. Baptist Distinctives: A Pattern for Service. 64p. (Orig.). 1986. pap. 3.95 (ISBN 0-913029-11-4). Stevens Bk Pr.

Davis, R. M. The Woods: The Human Self & the Realism of Jesus. 79p. 1971. pap. 4.00 (ISBN 0-9600434-0-3, 03). Camda.

Davis, Rebecca M., ed. see Niwano, Nikkyo.

Davis, Richard H., ed. Religion & Aging: The Behavioral & Social Sciences Look at Religion & Aging. 84p. 1967. pap. 3.00 (ISBN 0-88474-009-9). U of S Cal Pr.

Davis, Robert. Great Day in the Morning. (Jesus & His Disciples Ser.: Vol 2). (Illus.). 40p. 1986. 5.40 (ISBN 0-9615877-1-7). Davis Pub.

Davis, Robert W. Jesus Meets Nick. (Jesus & His Disciples Ser.: Vol. I). (Illus.). 24p. 1985. 4.95 (ISBN 0-9615877-0-9). Davis Pub.

Davis, Ron, et al. You Can Teach Adults Successfully. (Training Successful Teachers Ser.). 48p. (Orig.). 1984. pap. 2.95 (ISBN 0-87239-808-0, 3208). Standard Pub.

Davis, Ron L. A Forgiving God in an Unforgiving World. 1984. pap. 5.95 (ISBN 0-89081-431-7). Harvest Hse.

--Gold in the Making. LC 83-21931. 160p. 1984. pap. 5.95 (ISBN 0-8407-5869-3). Nelson.

--The Healing Choice. 160p. 1986. 9.95 (ISBN 0-8499-0466-8, 0466-8). Word Bks.

Davis, Ron L. & Denney, James D. A Time for Compassion. (Crucial Questions Ser.). 224p. 1986. 13.95 (ISBN 0-8007-1492-X). Revell.

Davis, Roy E. Conscious Immortality. 150p. 1978. pap. 2.95 (ISBN 0-87707-216-7). CSA Pr.

--Light on the Spiritual Path. 138p. 1984. pap. 3.95 (ISBN 0-317-20861-6). CSA Pr.

--Miracle Man of Japan: The Life & Work of Masaharu Taniguchi, One of the Most Influential Spiritual Leaders of Our Time. (Illus.). 160p. (Orig.). pap. 3.00 (ISBN 0-87707-048-2). CSA Pr.

--My Personal Fulfillment Plan Workbook. 32p. 1984. pap. 3.95 (ISBN 0-317-20868-3). CSA Pr.

--Philosophy & Practice of Yoga. 192p. 1983. pap. 4.95 (ISBN 0-317-20862-4). CSA Pr.

--Science of Kriya Yoga. 192p. 1984. 7.95 (ISBN 0-317-20860-8). CSA Pr.

--This Is Reality. 160p. 1983. pap. 3.95 (ISBN 0-317-20863-2). CSA Pr.

--Who is the True Guru. 192p. 1981. pap. 4.95 (ISBN 0-317-20864-0). CSA Pr.

Davis, Roy E., ed. The Teachings of Sri Satya Sai Baba. 2.95 (ISBN 0-317-46972-X). CSA Pr.

Davis, S. K. Bible Crossword Puzzle Book. (Quiz & Puzzle Bks). 1969. pap. 2.95 (ISBN 0-8010-2812-4). Baker Bk.

Davis, Stephen. Faith, Skepticism & Evidence: An Essay in Religious Epistemology. 233p. 1978. 20.00 (ISBN 0-8387-2039-0). Bucknell U Pr.

Davis, Stephen T., ed. Encountering Evil: Live Options in Theodicy. LC 80-84647. 1981. pap. 9.95 (ISBN 0-8042-0517-5). John Knox.

Davis, Susan. I Choose to Belong. (My Church Teaches Ser.). 1979. pap. 1.65 (ISBN 0-8127-0237-9). Review & Herald.

--Password to Heaven. (My Church Teaches Ser.). 32p. 1980. pap. 2.50 (ISBN 0-8127-0298-0). Review & Herald.

--A Way to Remember. Davis, Tom, ed. 32p. 1980. pap. 2.95 (ISBN 0-8280-0023-9). Review & Herald.

--When God Lived in a Tent. (My Church Teaches Ser.). (Illus.). 1978. 1.95 (ISBN 0-8127-0181-X). Review & Herald.

Davis, Thomas G. Saved & Certain. (Orig.). 1955. pap. 3.95 (ISBN 0-8054-1611-0). Broadman.

Davis, Thomas M. & Davis, Virginia L., eds. Edward Taylor's "Church Records" & Related Sermons. (American Literary Manuscripts Ser.). 1981. lib. bdg. 36.50 (ISBN 0-8057-9650-9, Twayne). G K Hall.

Davis, Thomas X., tr. see William of St. Thierry.

Davis, Tom, ed. see Davis, Susan.

Davis, Tom, ed. see Hannum, Harold E.

Davis, Vernon P. & Rawlings, James S. The Colonial Churches of Virginia, Maryland, & North Carolina. 1985. pap. 25.00 (ISBN 0-87517-057-9). Dietz.

Davis, Virginia L., jt. ed. see Davis, Thomas M.

Davis, W. A. Another Generation. (Orig.). 1985. text ed. 5.25 (ISBN 0-87148-019-0); pap. 4.25 (ISBN 0-87148-020-4); instr's. guide 7.95 (ISBN 0-87148-021-2). Pathway Pr.

Davis, W. Hersey, jt. auth. see Robertson, A. T.

Davis, W. M. Studies in Revelation. 1976. pap. 2.75 (ISBN 0-88027-044-6). Firm Foun Pub.

--The Way to Get What You Want. 1941. pap. 3.50 (ISBN 0-88027-022-5). Firm Foun Pub.

Davis, W. M., jt. auth. see Showalter, G. H.

Davis, Wade. The Serpent & the Rainbow: A Harvard Scientist Uncovers the Startling Truth about the Secret World of Haitian Voodoo & Zombis. 384p. (Orig.). 1987. pap. 4.95 (ISBN 0-446-34387-0). Warner Bks.

Davis, Warren B. & Cromie, Richard M. The Future Is Now. 110p. (Orig.). 1984. pap. 6.00 (ISBN 0-914733-03-6). Desert Min.

Davis, Willard O. Evolution & Revelation. 6.95 (ISBN 0-88027-097-7). Firm Foun Pub.

Davis, William F. Every Cloud Has One. 1985. 7.95 (ISBN 0-8062-2477-0). Carlton.

Davis, William H. Beginner's Grammar of the Greek New Testament. 1923. 12.45 (ISBN 0-06-061710-1, HarpR). Har-Row.

--Philosophy of Religion. LC 75-92048. (Way of Life Ser: No. 114). (Orig.). 1969. pap. 3.95 (ISBN 0-89112-114-5, Bibl Res Pr). Abilene Christ U.

--Science & Christian Faith. LC 68-21524. (Way of Life Ser: No. 104). 1968. pap. 3.95 (ISBN 0-89112-104-8, Bibl Res Pr). Abilene Christ U.

Davis, Winston. Dojo: Magic & Exorcism in Modern Japan. LC 79-64219. (Illus.). xx, 324p. 1980. 27.50x (ISBN 0-8047-1053-8); pap. 9.95 (ISBN 0-8047-1131-3, SP-7). Stanford U Pr.

Davison, Archibald. Protestant Church Music in America. 59.95 (ISBN 0-8490-0905-7). Gordon Pr.

Davison, Ellen S. Forerunners of Saint Francis & Other Studies. Richards, Gertrude R., ed. LC 77-85270. Repr. of 1927 ed. 49.50 (ISBN 0-404-16120-0). AMS Pr.

Davison, Nigel, ed. see De La Rue, Pierre.

Davison, Peter, ed. Theatrum Redivivum, 17 vols. Repr. 535.00 (ISBN 0-384-59985-0). Johnson Repr.

Davison, Peter, et al, eds. Content & Taste: Religion & Myth. LC 77-90615. (Literary Taste, Culture & Mass Communication: Vol. 7). 338p. 1978. lib. bdg. 47.00x (ISBN 0-85964-042-6). Chadwyck-Healey.

Davison, William T. Mystics & Poets. LC 77-924. 1977. lib. bdg. 25.00 (ISBN 0-8414-3680-0). Folcroft.

--Mystics & Poets. 167p. 1980. Repr. of 1936 ed. lib. bdg. 32.50 (ISBN 0-8482-0639-8). Norwood Edns.

Davisson, A., ed. Kentucky Harmony: A Collection of Psalms, Tunes, Hymns & Anthems. 1976. 16.00 (ISBN 0-8066-1546-X, 11-9249). Augsburg.

Davisson, Emmett D. Art & Mysteries in Tombs, Mummies & Catacombs. (Illus.). 1980. deluxe ed. 97.45 deluxe binding (ISBN 0-930582-63-2). Gloucester Art.

Davitt, Michael. Within the Pale: The True Story of Anti-Semitic Persecutions in Russia. facsimile ed. LC 74-27976. (Modern Jewish Experience Ser.). 1975. Repr. of 1903 ed. 25.50x (ISBN 0-405-06705-4). Ayer Co Pubs.

Davitz, Joel R., jt. auth. see Davitz, Lois L.

Davitz, Lois L. & Davitz, Joel R. How to Live (Almost) Happily with a Teenager. 230p. (Orig.). 1982. pap. 8.95 (ISBN 0-86683-624-1, AY8208, HarpR). Har-Row.

Davy, C. see Steiner, Rudolf.

Davy, C., tr. see Steiner, Rudolf.

Davy, Charles, tr. see Steiner, Rudolf.

Davy, G., jt. auth. see Moret, A.

Davy, Yvonne. Africa's Diamonds. Tyson-Flyn, Juanita, ed. (Daybreak Ser.). 96p. 1983. pap. 4.95 (ISBN 0-8163-0512-9). Pacific Pr Pub Assn.

--Trail of Peril. Wheeler, Gerald, ed. LC 83-17835. (A Banner Bk.). (Illus.). 94p. (Orig.). 1984. pap. 5.95 (ISBN 0-8280-0223-1). Review & Herald.

Dawa-Samdup, Kazi, tr. from Tibetan. Shrichakrasambhara Tantra: A Buddhist Tantra. 255p. 1984. Repr. of 1919 ed. lib. bdg. 22.50x (ISBN 0-88181-000-2). Canon Pubns.

Dawe, Donald G. Jesus: The Death & Resurrection of God. LC 85-5192. 252p. 1985. pap. 15.95 (ISBN 0-8042-0527-2). John Knox.

Dawe, Donald G. & Carman, John B., eds. Christian Faith in a Religiously Plural World. LC 78-50927. 200p. (Orig.). 1978. pap. 7.95 (ISBN 0-88344-083-0). Orbis Bks.

Dawe, Gerald & Longley, Edna, eds. Across a Roaring Hill: The Protestant Imagination in Modern Ireland. 242p. 1985. 16.50 (ISBN 0-85640-334-2, Pub. by Blackstaff Pr). Longwood Pub Group.

Daweewarn, D. Brahamism in Southeast Asia. 322p. 1982. text ed. 40.00x (ISBN 0-391-02581-3, Pub. by Sterling India). Humanities.

Dawes, Elizabeth & Baynes, Norman H., trs. from Greek. Three Byzantine Saints. 275p. 1977. pap. 8.95 (ISBN 0-913836-44-3). St Vladimirs.

Dawes, Jean D. & Magilton, J. R. Cemetery of St. Helen-on-the-Walls, Aldwark, York. (Archaeology of York Ser: Vol. 12). 132p. 1980. pap. text ed. 25.00x (ISBN 0-900312-88-2, Pub. by Coun Brit Archaeology). Humanities.

Dawes, Kathleen A., ed. see Dawes, Walter A.

Dawes, Robin, ed. see Brother Lawrence.

Dawes, Walter A. Christianity Four Thousand Years Before Jesus. Dawes, Kathleen A., ed. (Illus.). 63p. (Orig.). 1982. pap. 4.95 (ISBN 0-938792-17-2). New Capernaum.

--The Ghost of Old Capernaum. (Illus.). 358p. (Orig.). 1980. pap. text ed. 24.95 (ISBN 0-938792-00-8). New Capernaum.

--Impact: The Religion of the Twenty-First Century. (Illus.). 79p. (Orig.). 1980. pap. text ed. 8.95 (ISBN 0-938792-05-9). New Capernaum.

Dawidowicz, L. S., et al, eds. For Max Weinreich on His Seventieth Birthday: Studies in Jewish Language, Literature & Society. 1964. 66.00x (ISBN 0-686-22430-2). Mouton.

Dawidowicz, Lucy. Holocaust Reader. LC 75-33740. pap. 9.95x (ISBN 0-87441-236-6). Behrman.

--The Jewish Presence: Essays on Identity & History. LC 78-6236. 308p. 1978. pap. 3.95 (ISBN 0-15-646221-4, Harv). HarBraceJ.

--The Jewish Presence: Essays on Identity & History. 13.75 (ISBN 0-8446-6217-8). Peter Smith.

Dawidowicz, Lucy S. The Golden Tradition: Jewish Life & Thought in Eastern Europe. LC 84-5560. 512p. 1984. pap. 11.95 (ISBN 0-8052-0768-6). Schocken.

--Holocaust & the Historians. LC 80-29175. (Illus.). 200p. 1983. pap. 16.50x (ISBN 0-674-40566-8); pap. text ed. 6.95 (ISBN 0-674-40567-6). Harvard U Pr.

--On Equal Terms: Jews in America 1881-1981. 1984. pap. 6.95 (ISBN 0-03-071058-8). H Holt & Co.

--The War Against the Jews: 1933-1945. 640p. 1976. pap. 10.95 (ISBN 0-553-34302-5). Bantam.

--The War Against the Jews, 1933-1945. 496p. 1986. 22.95 (ISBN 0-02-908030-4). Free Pr.

Dawisha, Adeed, ed. Islam in Foreign Policy. LC 83-7458. 250p. 1984. 29.95 (ISBN 0-521-25815-4). Cambridge U Pr.

--Islam in Foreign Policy. 202p. 1985. pap. 11.95 (ISBN 0-521-27740-X). Cambridge U Pr.

Dawkins, Lee. The Beast of Revelation Thirteen: The Number of a Man Six Threescore & Six? or Six Threescore to the Power & Six? Equals Nine? 68p. 1982. 5.00 (ISBN 0-682-49887-4). Exposition Pr FL.

Dawkins, R. M., ed. see Machairas, Leontios.

Dawley, Powel M. Our Christian Heritage: Revised & Expanded. 4th ed. LC 78-62062. 1978. pap. 5.50 (ISBN 0-8192-1243-1); leader's guide 3.95x (ISBN 0-8192-4086-9). Morehouse.

Dawn, Marva J. I'm Lonely Lord-How Long? The Psalms for Today. LC 83-47721. 176p. 1984. 12.45 (ISBN 0-06-067201-3, HarpR). Har-Row.

Daws, Gavan. Holy Man: Father Damien of Molokai. 328p. 1984. pap. 8.95 (ISBN 0-8248-0920-3). UH Pr.

Dawsey, James M. The Lukan Voice: Confusion & Irony in the Gospel of Luke. 208p. 1986. 19.50 (ISBN 0-86554-193-0, MUP-H178). Mercer Univ Pr.

Dawson, Carl & Pfordresher, John, eds. Matthew Arnold: Prose Writings. (The Critical Heritage Ser.). 1979. 34.00x (ISBN 0-7100-0244-0). Methuen Inc.

Dawson, Christopher. The Age of the Gods. LC 68-9653. (Illus., Maps, Tabs). 1971. Repr. of 1928 ed. 35.00x (ISBN 0-86527-001-5). Fertig.

--Christianity & the New Age. LC 84-29821. 103p. 1985. 10.95 (ISBN 0-918477-02-6); pap. 7.95 (ISBN 0-918477-01-8). Sophia Inst Pr.

--Christianity in East & West. Mulloy, John J., ed. 224p. 1981. pap. text ed. 5.95 (ISBN 0-89385-015-2). Sugden.

--Mission to Asia. (Medieval Academy Reprints for Teaching Ser.). 228p. 1981. pap. 6.95 (ISBN 0-8020-6436-1). U of Toronto Pr.

--Religion & the Modern State. 1977. Repr. lib. bdg. 20.00 (ISBN 0-8482-0547-2). Norwood Edns.

Dawson, Christopher H. Beyond Politics. facsimile ed. LC 74-111825. (Essay Index Reprint Ser.). 1939. 14.00 (ISBN 0-8369-1603-4). Ayer Co Pubs.

--Enquiries into Religion & Culture. facs. ed. LC 68-29200. (Essay Index Reprint Ser.). 1933. 24.50 (ISBN 0-8369-0367-6). Ayer Co Pubs.

--Medieval Essays. facs. ed. LC 68-58785. (Essay Index Reprint Ser). 1954. 18.00 (ISBN 0-8369-0070-7). Ayer Co Pubs.

--Progress & Religion, an Historical Enquiry. LC 79-104266. Repr. of 1929 ed. lib. bdg. 27.50x (ISBN 0-8371-3917-1, DAPR). Greenwood.

--Religion & Culture. LC 77-27183. (Gifford Lectures Ser.: 1947). 232p. Repr. of 1948 ed. 27.50 (ISBN 0-404-60498-6). AMS Pr.

--Religion & the Rise of Western Culture. LC 77-27181. (Gifford Lectures: 1948-49). Repr. of 1950 ed. 26.50 (ISBN 0-404-60499-4). AMS Pr.

--The Spirit of the Oxford Movement. LC 75-30020. Repr. of 1934 ed. 16.50 (ISBN 0-404-14025-4). AMS Pr.

Dawson, Christopher H., ed. The Mongol Mission. LC 78-63334. (The Crusades & Military Orders: Second Ser.). Repr. of 1955 ed. 33.00 (ISBN 0-404-17008-0). AMS Pr.

Dawson, Frances E., tr. see Steiner, Rudolf.

Dawson, George A. Scripture Scrambles. 48p. 1987. pap. 2.50 (ISBN 0-87403-235-0, 2685). Standard Pub.

Dawson, J. G., tr. see D'Entreves, A. P.

Dawson, John C. Toulouse in the Renaissance: The Floral Games, University & Student Life: Etienne Dolet. (Columbia University. Studies in Romance Philology & Literature: No. 33). Repr. of 1923 ed. 18.50 (ISBN 0-404-50633-X). AMS Pr.

Dawson, John W. The Cancer Patient. LC 78-52192. (Religion & Medicine Ser.). 1978. pap. 5.95 (ISBN 0-8066-1662-8, 10-0960). Augsburg.

Dawson, Joseph M. America's Way in Church, State & Society. LC 79-15522. 1980. Repr. of 1953 ed. lib. bdg. 22.50x (ISBN 0-313-22006-9, DAAW). Greenwood.

--Baptists & the American Republic. Gaustad, Edwin S., ed. LC 79-52584. (The Baptist Tradition Ser.). 1980. Repr. of 1956 ed. lib. bdg. 21.00x (ISBN 0-405-12451-1). Ayer Co Pubs.

--A Thousand Months to Remember: An Autobiography. 306p. 1964. 6.95 (ISBN 0-918954-03-7). Baylor Univ Pr.

Dawson, M. M. The Ethics of Socrates. LC 74-30274. (Studies in Philosophy, No. 40). 1974. lib. bdg. 75.00x (ISBN 0-8383-2042-2). Haskell.

Dawson, Miles M. Ethical Religion of Zoroaster. LC 73-90100. (BCL Ser. I). Repr. of 1931 ed. 22.50 (ISBN 0-404-01999-4). AMS Pr.

Dawson, Patsy R. Appreciating Marriage, Vol I. rev. ed. LC 86-22746. (Marriage: A Taste of Heaven Ser.). (Illus.). 544p. 1987. pap. 12.95 (ISBN 0-938855-40-9); Set. pap. 25.90 (ISBN 0-938855-44-1). Gospel Themes Pr.

--Learning to Love, Vol. II: God's People Make the Best Lovers. LC 86-22746. (Marriage: A Taste of Heaven Ser.). (Illus.). 544p. (Orig.). 1987. pap. 12.95 (ISBN 0-938855-41-7); Set. 25.90 (ISBN 0-938855-44-1). Gospel Themes Pr.

Dawson, Samuel G. & MacArthur, Rod, eds. Handbook of Religious Quotations. 188p. (Orig.). 1987. pap. 5.95 (ISBN 0-938855-16-6). Gospel Themes Pr.

Dawson, W. J. The Man Jesus Christ. 1977. lib. bdg. 59.95 (ISBN 0-8490-2199-5). Gordon Pr.

Dawson, William F. Christmas, Its Origin & Associations, Together with Its Historical Events & Festive Celebrations During Nineteen Centuries. LC 68-54857. 1968. Repr. of 1902 ed. 54.00x (ISBN 0-8103-3351-1). Gale.

Day. If You Fight-Fight Fair. (Out Ser.). 1984. 1.25 (ISBN 0-8163-0597-8). Pacific Pr Pub Assn.

Day, Albert E. An Autobiography of Prayer. 1979. pap. 3.95x (ISBN 0-8358-0384-8). Upper Room.

--Discipline & Discovery. rev. ed. 1977. pap. 4.95x (ISBN 0-8358-0354-6). Upper Room.

Day, Albert E. & Wagner, James K. Letters on the Healing Ministry. 144p. 1986. pap. 6.95 incl. study guide (ISBN 0-317-30215-9, ICN 606462, Dist. by Abingdon Pr). Upper Room.

Day, Dan. Hurting. (Uplook Ser.). 1978. pap. 0.99 (ISBN 0-8163-0088-7, 08889-8). Pacific Pr Pub Assn.

Day, Donald & Trohan, Walter. Onward Christian Soldiers Nineteen Twenty to Nineteen Forty-two: Propaganda, Censorship, & One Man's Struggle to Herald the Truth. 1982. lib. bdg. 69.95 (ISBN 0-87700-450-1). Revisionist Pr.

Day, Donald D. This I Believe. 224p. 1972. pap. 1.95 (ISBN 0-9600500-1-9). Three D Pubs.

Day, Dorothy. From Union Square to Rome. 17.00 (ISBN 0-405-10815-X). Ayer Co Pubs.

--Loaves & Fishes: The Story of the Catholic Worker Movement. LC 82-48433. (Illus.). 240p. 1983. pap. 4.95 (ISBN 0-06-061771-3, RD/434, HarpR). Har-Row.

--The Long Loneliness: An Autobiography. LC 81-4727. (Illus.). 1981. pap. 7.95 (ISBN 0-06-061751-9, RD363, HarpR). Har-Row.

--Therese. 1979. pap. 7.95 (ISBN 0-87243-090-1). Templegate.

Day, Edward. The Catholic Church Story. rev ed. LC 78-73834. (Illus.). 192p. (Orig.). 1975. pap. 3.95 (ISBN 0-89243-105-9, 65300). Liguori Pubns.

Day, Gwynn M. The Joy Beyond. 1979. 3.95 (ISBN 0-8010-2893-0). Baker Bk.

Day, Harvey. Pratical Yoga. pap. cancelled (ISBN 0-7225-0351-2). Thorsons Pubs.

--Yoga Illustrated Dictionary. (Illus.). 1970. 10.95 (ISBN 0-87523-177-2). Emerson.

Day, Heather F. Protestant Theological Education in America: A Bibliography. LC 85-18300. (ATLA Biobliography Ser.: No. 15). 523p. 1985. 42.50 (ISBN 0-8108-1842-6). Scarecrow.

Day, Hughes W. Beside Still Waters. 418p. 1979. 9.95 (ISBN 0-8341-0599-3). Beacon Hill.

Day, James M. & Laufer, William, eds. Crimes, Values & Religion. 280p. 1987. text ed. 37.50 (ISBN 0-89391-411-8). Ablex Pub.

Day, John. God's Conflict with the Dragon & the Sea in the Old Testament: Echoes of a Canaanite Myth. (University of Cambridge Oriental Publications Ser.: No. 35). 208p. 1985. 49.50 (ISBN 0-521-25600-3). Cambridge U Pr.

Day, LeRoy J. Dynamic Christian Fellowship. rev. ed. (Orig.). pap. 2.95 (ISBN 0-8170-0226-X). Judson.

Day, Mark. Yuletide Lost. 1981. 4.95 (ISBN 0-89536-484-0, 2506). CSS of Ohio.

Day, Martin S. The Many Meanings of Myth. 574p. 1984. lib. bdg. 28.75 (ISBN 0-8191-3821-5); pap. text ed. 20.75 (ISBN 0-8191-3822-3). U Pr of Amer.

Day, Millard F. Basic Bible Doctrines. 1953. pap. 3.50 (ISBN 0-8024-0239-9). Moody.

Day, N. R. David's Faithfulness. 85p. (Orig.). 1979. pap. 6.95 (ISBN 0-940754-02-9). Ed Ministries.

--Your Faith Is Growing! 51p. (Orig.). 1981. pap. 5.45 (ISBN 0-940754-10-X). Ed Ministries.

Day, N. Raymond. Energizing Your Faith. 56p. (Orig.). 1985. pap. 5.95 (ISBN 0-940754-28-2). Ed Ministries.

--From Palm Sunday to Easter. 45p. (Orig.). 1979. pap. 5.45 (ISBN 0-940754-01-0). Ed Ministries.

Day, Paul W. Matthew Arnold & the Philosophy of Vico. 1964. 10.00 (ISBN 0-8274-2691-7). R West.

Day, Ralph E. Our Church of God Faith for Children. 1961. pap. 1.25 (ISBN 0-87148-652-0). Pathway Pr.

--Our Church of God Faith: For Young People & Adults. 1959. pap. 1.95 (ISBN 0-87148-651-2). Pathway Pr.

Day, Richard E. Beacon Lights of Grace: Twelve Biographical Vignettes. facs. ed. LC 71-148210. (Biography Index Reprint Ser.). 1947. 17.00 (ISBN 0-8369-8057-3). Ayer Co Pubs.

Day, Thomas I. Dietrich Bonhoeffer on Christian Community & Common Sense. LC 83-25900. (Toronto Studies in Theology: Vol. 11). 248p. 1983. 49.95x (ISBN 0-88946-752-8). E Mellen.

Daya, Sr. The Guru & the Disciple. 1976. pap. 2.95 (ISBN 0-911564-26-8). Vedanta Ctr.

Dayal, Har. The Bodhisattva Doctrine in Buddhist Sanskrit Literature. 1975. Repr. 22.50 (ISBN 0-89684-180-4). Orient Bk Dist.
Day-Lower, Donna C., jt. auth. see Raines, John C.
Dayringer, Richard. God Cares for You. LC 83-70210. (Orig.). 1984. pap. 5.95 (ISBN 0-8054-5232-X). Broadman.
Dayringer, Richard, ed. Pastor & Patient. LC 80-70247. 240p. 1981. 25.00x (ISBN 0-87668-437-1). Aronson.
Dayton, Brandt. The Swami & Sam: A Yoga Book. (Illus.). 95p. (Orig.). pap. 0.95 (ISBN 0-89389-014-6). Himalayan Pubs.
Dayton, Brandt, ed. Practical Vedanta: Of Swami Rama Tirtha. LC 78-10567. 350p. 8.95 (ISBN 0-89389-038-3). Himalayan Pubs.
Dayton, Daonald W., ed. see McPherson, Aimee S.
Dayton, Doanald, tr. see De Swarte, Carolyn G.
Dayton, Donald, ed. see Acornley, John H.
Dayton, Donald, ed. see Andrews, C. W.
Dayton, Donald, ed. see Baker, Frances J.
Dayton, Donald, ed. see Bethune, Joanna.
Dayton, Donald, ed. see Brown, George.
Dayton, Donald, ed. see Coppin, Fanny J.
Dayton, Donald, jt. ed. see De Swarte, Carolyn G.
Dayton, Donald, ed. see Foster, John O.
Dayton, Donald, jt. ed. see Gifford, Carolyn D.
Dayton, Donald, ed. see Holley, Marietta.
Dayton, Donald, ed. see Horton, Isabelle.
Dayton, Donald, ed. see Ingraham, Sarah R.
Dayton, Donald, ed. see MacDonell, Robert W.
Dayton, Donald, ed. see Montgomery, Helen B.
Dayton, Donald, ed. see Prentiss, George L.
Dayton, Donald, ed. see Sexton, Lydia.
Dayton, Donald, ed. see Sleeper, Sarah.
Dayton, Donald, ed. see Smith, Amanda B.
Dayton, Donald, ed. see Starr, Lee A.
Dayton, Donald, ed. see Stevens, Abel.
Dayton, Donald, ed. see Swain, Clara A.
Dayton, Donald, ed. see Utley, Uldine.
Dayton, Donald, ed. see Winslow, Miron.
Dayton, Donald, ed. see Wittenmyer, Annie T.
Dayton, Donald W., ed. The Devotional Writings of Robert Pearsall Smith & Hannah Whitall Smith. (The Higher Christian Life Ser.). 477p. 1985. lib. bdg. 60.00 (ISBN 0-8240-6444-5). Garland Pub.
--Holiness Tracts Defending the Ministry of Women. (The Higher Christian Life Ser.). 304p. 1985. 40.00 (ISBN 0-8240-6411-9). Garland Pub.
--The Sermons of Charles F. Parham. (The Higher Christian Life Ser.). 261p. 1985. lib. bdg. 35.00 (ISBN 0-8240-6413-5). Garland Pub.
--Seven "Jesus Only" Tracts. (The Higher Christian Life Ser.). 379p. 1985. lib. bdg. 45.00 (ISBN 0-8240-6414-3). Garland Pub.
--Three Early Pentecostal Tracts. (The Higher Christian Life Ser.). 441p. 1985. 55.00 (ISBN 0-8240-6415-1). Garland Pub.
--The Work of T. B. Barratt. (The Higher Christian Life Ser.). 435p. 1985. 55.00 (ISBN 0-8240-6404-6). Garland Pub.
Dayton, Donald W. & Robeck, Cecil M., eds. Witness to Pentecost: The Life of Frank Bartleman. (The Higher Christian Life Ser.). 439p. 1985. 55.00 (ISBN 0-8240-6405-4). Garland Pub.
Dayton, Donald W., ed. see Boardman, W. E.
Dayton, Donald W., ed. see Brooks, John P.
Dayton, Donald W., jt. ed. see Bryant, M. Darrol.
Dayton, Donald W., ed. see Daniels, W. H.
Dayton, Donald W., ed. see Fairchild, James H.
Dayton, Donald W., ed. see Figgis, John B.
Dayton, Donald W., ed. see Fleisch, Paul.
Dayton, Donald W., ed. see Girvin, E. A.
Dayton, Donald W., ed. see Gordon, Earnest B.
Dayton, Donald W., ed. see Hills, A. M.
Dayton, Donald W., ed. see Horner, Ralph C.
Dayton, Donald W., ed. see LaBerge, Agnes N.
Dayton, Donald W., ed. see Lee, Luther.
Dayton, Donald W., ed. see McDonald, William & Searless, John E.
Dayton, Donald W., ed. see McLean, A. & Easton, J. W.
Dayton, Donald W., ed. see Mahan, Asa.
Dayton, Donald W., ed. see Montgomery, Carrie J.
Dayton, Donald W., ed. see Palmer, Phoebe.
Dayton, Donald W., jt. ed. see Palmer, Phoebe.
Dayton, Donald W., ed. see Palmer, Phoebe.
Dayton, Donald W., ed. see Palmer, Phoebe & Wheatley, Richard.
Dayton, Donald W., ed. see Pardington, G. P.
Dayton, E. Resources for Christian Leaders. 8th ed. 40p. 1982. pap. 3.95 (ISBN 0-912552-16-6). Missions Adv Res Com Ctr.
Dayton, Ed. Faith That Goes Further: Facing the Contradictions of Life. LC 84-14693. 1984. pap. 5.95 (ISBN 0-88070-062-9). Multnomah.
Dayton, Ed & Wilson, Samuel. The Future of World Evangelization: The Lausanne Movement. 1984. 7.95 (ISBN 0-912552-42-5). Missions Adv Res Com Ctr.
Dayton, Edward & Wagner, C. Peter. Unreached Peoples '80. LC 79-57522. 1980. pap. 8.95 (ISBN 0-89191-837-X). Cook.
Dayton, Edward R. God's Purpose - Man's Plans. 64p. 1982. pap. 5.95 (ISBN 0-912552-11-5). Missions Adv Res Com Ctr.
--That Everyone May Hear: Workbook. pap. 5.75 (ISBN 0-912552-53-0). Missions Adv Res Com Ctr.
--What Ever Happened to Commitment? 224p. 1983. pap. 6.95 (ISBN 0-310-23161-2, 10748P). Zondervan.
Dayton, Edward R. & Engstrom, Ted W. Strategy for Leadership. 240p. 1979. 13.95 (ISBN 0-8007-0994-2). Revell.
--Strategy for Living. LC 76-3935. (Orig.). 1976. pap. 6.95 (ISBN 0-8307-0424-8, 5403405); wkbk. 4.95 (ISBN 0-8307-0476-0, 5202000). Regal.
Dayton, Edward R., ed. That Everyone May Hear. 3rd ed. 91p. 1983. pap. 4.60 (ISBN 0-912552-41-7). Missions Adv Res Com Ctr.
Dayton, Howard. Your Money: Frustration or Freedom? 1979. pap. 5.95 (ISBN 0-8423-8725-0). Tyndale.
D'Costa, Gavin. Theology & Religious Pluralism: The Challenge of Other Religions. (Signposts in Theology Ser.). 160p. 1986. text ed. 39.95 (ISBN 0-631-14517-6); pap. text ed. 14.95 (ISBN 0-631-14518-4). Basil Blackwell.
D-Din-Ahmed, Shemsu see Ahmed, Shemsu-D-Din.
De, Schaps H. see Schutz, Albert & Schaps, Hilda W.
De, Sushil K. Early History of the Vaisnava Faith & Movement in Bengal from Sanskrit & Bengal Sources. 700p. 1986. 54.00X (ISBN 0-8364-1642-2, Pub. by Mukhopadhyay). South Asia Bks.
Deacon, John & Walker, John. Dialogicall Discourses of Spirits & Devils, Declaring Their Proper Essence. LC 76-57377. (English Experience Ser.: No. 795). 1977. Repr. of 1601 ed. lib. bdg. 37.00 (ISBN 90-221-0795-7). Walter J Johnson.
Deacon, Richard. Napoleon's Book of Fate. Orig. Title: The Book of Fate: Its Origins & Uses. 1977. 10.00 (ISBN 0-8065-0564-8); pap. 4.95 (ISBN 0-8065-0577-X). Citadel Pr.
Deady, Matthew P. Pharisee Among Philistines: The Diary of Judge Matthew P. Deady, 1871-1892, 2 vols. Clark, Malcolm, Jr., intro. by. LC 74-75363. (Illus.). 702p. 1975. 27.95 (ISBN 0-87595-046-9); deluxe ed. 30.00 (ISBN 0-686-96825-5); pap. 19.95 (ISBN 0-87595-080-9). Oregon Hist.
Deakins, Roger L., tr. see Heywood, Ellis.
Deal, William S. After Death, What? 1977. 1.75 (ISBN 0-686-19329-6). Crusade Pubs.
--All about Pentacost. 1983. pap. 3.95 (ISBN 0-318-18716-7). Crusade Pubs.
--Christian's Daily Manna. 0.95 (ISBN 0-686-13721-3). Crusade Pubs.
--Daily Christian Living. LC 62-22195. 1962. pap. 0.95 (ISBN 0-686-05840-2). Crusade Pubs.
--Faith, Facts & Feelings. 3rd ed. 1978. pap. 0.95 (ISBN 0-686-05527-6). Crusade Pubs.
--The Furnace of Affliction. 6th ed. 1978. 1.50 (ISBN 0-686-05833-X). Crusade Pubs.
--Happiness & Harmony in Marriage. pap. 2.95 (ISBN 0-686-13723-X). Crusade Pubs.
--Heart Talks on the Deeper Life. 1960. 1.50 (ISBN 0-686-05838-0). Crusade Pubs.
--How May I Know I Am Saved? 1973. pap. 0.60, 3 for 1.50, 5 for 2.50, 10 for 5.00 (ISBN 0-686-05834-8). Crusade Pubs.
--The March of Holiness Through the Centuries. 1978. pap. 2.50 (ISBN 0-686-05528-4). Crusade Pubs.
--New Light on the Shepherd Psalm. 1982. 3.95. Crusade Pubs.
--The Other Shepherd. 1982. 1.95 (ISBN 0-686-38053-3). Crusade Pubs.
--Picking a Partner. 2.95 (ISBN 0-686-13716-7). Crusade Pubs.
--Pictorial Introduction to the Bible. (Baker's Paperback Reference Library). 440p. 1982. pap. 12.95 (ISBN 0-8010-2926-0). Baker Bk.
--Pictorial Introduction to the Bible. large print 12.95 (ISBN 0-686-13725-6); pap. 7.95. Crusade Pubs.
--A Pictorial Introduction to the Bible. LC 67-20517. 438p. 1982. pap. 12.95 (ISBN 0-89081-363-9). Harvest Hse.
--Plain Talks on Parenting. 1984. pap. 3.95 (ISBN 0-318-18715-9). Crusade Pubs.
--Problems of the Spirit-Filled Life. 2.95 (ISBN 0-686-13724-8). Crusade Pubs.
--The Sunday School Teacher's Guide, 1984. 1984. pap. 3.95 (ISBN 0-318-18717-5). Crusade Pubs.
--The Tinker of Bedford: A Historical Fiction on the Life & Times of John Bunyan. 1977. pap. 2.95 (ISBN 0-686-19330-X). Crusade Pubs.
--Unequally Yoked. 2nd ed. LC 80-67387. 112p. 1987. pap. 4.95 (Crossway Bks). Good News.
--What Every Young Christian Should Know. 1982. 1.95. Crusade Pubs.
--Workmen of God. 1975. pap. 0.95 (ISBN 0-686-11025-0). Crusade Pubs.
De Almeida, Abraao. Visiones Profecticas de Daniel. Tr. of Prophetic Visions of Daniel. (Span.). 224p. 1986. pap. 3.95 (ISBN 0-8297-0497-3). Life Pubs Intl.
Dean & Acuff. The S.D.N. Theory of Music. pap. 1.95 (ISBN 0-88027-058-6). Firm Foun Pub.
Dean, Beryl. Embroidery in Religion & Ceremonial. (Illus.). 288p. 1985. pap. 16.50 (ISBN 0-7134-3325-6). Branford.
Dean, Bessie. Aprendamos el Plan de Dios. Balderas, Eduardo, tr. from Eng. LC 80-82256. (Books for LDS Children Ser.). Orig. Title: Let's Learn God's Plan. (Span., Illus.). 64p. (Orig.). 1980. pap. text ed. 3.95 (ISBN 0-88290-135-4). Horizon Utah.
--I'm Happy When I'm Good. (Children's Inspirational Coloring Bk.). (Illus.). 24p. 1979. pap. 1.25 (ISBN 0-88290-109-5). Horizon Utah.
--Lessons Jesus Taught. (Children's Inspirational Coloring Books). (Illus.). 72p. (Orig.). 1980. pap. 2.50 (ISBN 0-88290-146-X). Horizon Utah.
--Let's Go to Church. LC 76-3995. (Books for Lds Children Ser.). (Illus.). 63p. 1976. pap. 3.95 (ISBN 0-88290-062-5). Horizon Utah.
--Let's Learn God's Plan. LC 78-52114. (Illus.). 1978. pap. 3.95 (ISBN 0-88290-092-7). Horizon Utah.
--Let's Learn of God's Love. LC 79-89367. (Books for LDS Children) (Illus.). 64p. 1979. pap. 3.95 (ISBN 0-88290-124-9). Horizon Utah.
--Let's Learn the First Principles. LC 78-70366. (Books for LDS Children). (Illus.). 64p. 1978. pap. 3.95 (ISBN 0-88290-104-4). Horizon Utah.
--Let's Love One Another. LC 77-74492. (Books for Lds Children Ser.). (Illus.). 64p. 1978. pap. 3.95 (ISBN 0-88290-077-3). Horizon Utah.
--Paul, God's Special Missionary. (Story Books to Color.). 72p. (Orig.). 1980. pap. 2.50 (ISBN 0-88290-152-4). Horizon Utah.
Dean, Claire, jt. auth. see Dean, Jay.
Dean, Dave. Now Is Your Time to Win. Vries, Vickie De, ed. 1p. 1985. pap. 2.95 (ISBN 0-8423-4727-5). Tyndale.
Dean, Dave & Hefley, Marti. Now Is Your Time to Win. 1983. 8.95 (ISBN 0-8423-4724-0). Tyndale.
Dean, David M. Defender of the Race: James Theodore Holly, Black Nationalist Bishop. 150p. 1979. 16.95x (ISBN 0-931186-02-1). Lambeth Pr.
Dean, Edith, jt. auth. see Andersen, Georg.
Dean, Elizabeth. Carrie-Ambassador at Large. rev. ed. (Illus.). 269p. 1984. pap. 4.95 (ISBN 0-930033-00-0). Christ Life Revivals.
Dean, Elizabeth P. Jodie: One Little Ewe Lamb. 96p. 1984. pap. 4.95 (ISBN 0-8010-2938-4). Baker Bk.
Dean, Jay & Dean, Claire. How Damage is Done in The Name of Christ! LC 82-90134. 102p. (Orig.). 1982. pap. 3.95 (ISBN 0-943416-00-0). Plus Seven Bks.
Dean, Robert J. Layman's Bible Book Commentary: Luke, Vol. 17. 1983. 5.95 (ISBN 0-8054-1187-9). Broadman.
Dean, Stanley R. Psychiatry & Mysticism. LC 75-8771. (Illus.). 446p. 1975. 30.95x (ISBN 0-88229-189-0). Nelson-Hall.
Dean, Talmage W. Twentieth-Century Protestant Church Music in America. (Orig.). 1987. text ed. 14.95 (ISBN 0-8054-6813-7). Broadman.
Dean, Thomas. Post-Theistic Thinking: The Marxist-Christian Dialogue in Radical Perspective. LC 74-83202. 300p. 1975. 29.95 (ISBN 0-87722-037-9). Temple U Pr.
Dean, William. American Religious Empiricism. (Religious Studies). 126p. (Orig.). 1986. 34.50x (ISBN 0-88706-280-6); pap. 10.95 (ISBN 0-88706-281-4). State U NY Pr.
Dean, William & Axel, Larry E., eds. The Size of God: The Theology of Bernard Loomer in Context. 96p. 1987. 16.95 (ISBN 0-86554-255-4, MUP H-223). Mercer Univ Pr.
Deane, Herbert A. The Political & Social Ideas of St. Augustine. LC 63-9809. 356p. 1963. pap. 14.00x (ISBN 0-231-08569-9). Columbia U Pr.
Deane, John F. High Sacrifice. 61p. 1981. pap. text ed. 6.50x (ISBN 0-85105-382-3, Pub. by Dolmen Pr Ireland). Humanities.
Deane, Sidney M., tr. see Anselm, St.
Deane, W. J. & Kirt, T. Studies in the First Book of Samuel. 509p. 1983. lib. bdg. 19.00 Smythe Sewn (ISBN 0-86524-150-3, 0902). Klock & Klock.
Deanesly, Margaret. History of the Medieval Church, Five Ninety to Fifteen Hundred. 9th ed. 1969. pap. 12.50x (ISBN 0-416-18100-7, NO. 2163). Methuen Inc.
--The Lollard Bible & Other Medieval Biblical Versions. LC 77-84722. Repr. of 1920 ed. 49.50 (ISBN 0-404-16125-1). AMS Pr.
--The Pre-Conquest Church in England. 2nd ed. (Ecclesiastical History of England Ser.). 376p. 1963. text ed. 30.00x (ISBN 0-06-491638-3). B&N Imports.
DeAngeli, Marguerite. The Door in the Wall: Story of Medieval London. LC 64-7025. (Illus.). 111p. 10.95a (ISBN 0-385-07283-X). Doubleday.
DeAngelis, William. Acting Out the Gospels. LC 81-84919. 96p. 1982. pap. 9.95 (ISBN 0-89622-136-9). Twenty-Third.
--School Year Liturgies. (Illus.). 64p. (Orig.). 1985. pap. 9.95 (ISBN 0-89622-218-7). Twenty-Third.
De Angelis Bothwell, Sr. Mary. God Is Good. LC 73-5752. (Christ Our Life Ser.). (Illus.). 138p. 1986. pap. text ed. 4.20 (ISBN 0-8294-0537-2); 12.95 (ISBN 0-8294-0570-4). Loyola.
Dear, John. Disarming the Heart, Toward a Vow of Non-Violence. 144p. (Orig.). 1987. pap. 6.95 (ISBN 0-8091-2842-X). Paulist Pr.
De Aragon, Ray J. Padre Martinez & Bishop Lamy. 3rd ed. LC 78-70565. (History Ser.). (Illus.). 1978. pap. 7.95 (ISBN 0-932906-00-1). Pan-Am Publishing Co.
De Aragon, Ray J., tr. see Sanchez, Pedro.
Dearing, Trevor. Wesleyan & Tractarian Worship. LC 66-72190. 1966. text ed. 15.00x (ISBN 0-8401-0531-2). A R Allenson.
Dearing, Vinton A. A Manual of Textual Analysis. LC 82-20947. ix, 108p. 1983. Repr. of 1959 ed. lib. bdg. 32.50x (ISBN 0-313-23734-4, DEMA). Greenwood.
De Armas, Frederick A. The Return of Astraea: An Astral-Imperial Myth in Calderon. LC 86-7758. (Studies in Romance Languages: No. 32). 272p. 1986. 27.00 (ISBN 0-8131-1570-1). U Pr of Ky.
Dearmer, Percy. Songs of Praise. Vaughan Williams, Ralph & Shaw, Martin, eds. Incl. Music Ed. rev. & enl. ed. 1932. 19.95x (ISBN 0-19-231207-3). Oxford U Pr.
--A Subject Index of Hymns in the English Hymnal & Songs of Praise. 59.95 (ISBN 0-8490-1159-0). Gordon Pr.
Dearmer, Percy, et al, eds. Oxford Book of Carols. 1928. 21.00 (ISBN 0-19-353314-6); pap. 13.95 (ISBN 0-19-353315-4); Words & Melody. pap. 6.95 (ISBN 0-19-313118-8). Oxford U Pr.
--Oxford Book of Carols for Schools. 1956. piano ed. 6.75 (ISBN 0-19-330830-4); melody ed. 2.50 (ISBN 0-19-330831-2). Oxford U Pr.
DeArteaga, William. Past Life Visions: A Christian Exploration. 256p. 1983. pap. 9.95 (ISBN 0-8164-2414-4, HarpR). Har-Row.
Deason, Dee & Deason, Velma. World Outreach Intercessory Prayer Warriors. 1983. pap. 2.50 (ISBN 0-910709-40-8). PTL Repro.
Deason, Velma, jt. auth. see Deason, Dee.
De Aspurz-Iriarte, Lazaro. The Franciscan Calling. Kelly, Sr. Marie, tr. 300p. 1975. 6.95 (ISBN 0-8199-0538-0). Franciscan Herald.
Deats, Paul & Robb, Carol S., eds. The Boston Personalist Tradition in Philosophy, Social Ethics, & Theology. (Illus.). xiv, 295p. 1986. text ed. 28.95 (ISBN 0-86554-177-9, MUP-H167). Mercer Univ Pr.
De Azevedo, Carlos. Churches of Portugal. LC 85-50365. (Illus.). 196p. 1985. 35.00 (ISBN 0-935748-66-0). Scala Books.
De Azevedo, Marcello C. Basic Ecclesiastical Communities. Drury, John, tr. 1987. write for info. (ISBN 0-87840-430-9); pap. write for info. (ISBN 0-87840-448-1). Georgetown U Pr.
Debahy, Moses. Dictionary Hebrew Verbs. (Hebrew & Arabic.). 1974. 15.00x (ISBN 0-86685-123-2). Intl Bk Ctr.
DeBand, Roy E., jt. auth. see Bess, C. W.
DeBardeleben, Martha G. Fear's Answer: A Case History in Nouthetic Counseling. 1981. pap. 3.75 (ISBN 0-87552-236-X). Presby & Reformed.
De Bargh, David J. Christ in My Life. 1977. 4.50 (ISBN 0-8198-0396-0); pap. text ed. 3.50 (ISBN 0-8198-0397-9). Dghtrs St Paul.
De Bary, W. Theodore, ed. The Unfolding of Neo-Confucianism. LC 74-10929. (Neo-Confucian Series & Studies in Oriental Culture: No. 10). 593p. 1975. 38.00x (ISBN 0-231-03828-3); pap. 18.50x (ISBN 0-231-03829-1). Columbia U Pr.
De Bary, W. Theodore & Bloom, Irene, eds. Principle & Practicality: Essays in Neo-Confucianism & Practical Learning. LC 78-11530. (Neo-Confucian Series & Studies in Oriental Culture). 1979. 38.00x (ISBN 0-231-04612-X); pap. 19.00x (ISBN 0-231-04613-8). Columbia U Pr.
DeBary, W. Theodore, jt. ed. see Chan, Hok-Lam.
De Bary, William T. Neo-Confucian Orthodoxy & the Learning of the Mind-&-Heart. LC 81-3809. (Neo-Confucian Studies). 267p. 1986. pap. 15.00x (ISBN 0-231-05229-4). Columbia U Pr.
De Bary, William T., ed. The Buddhist Tradition: In India, China & Japan. 448p. 1972. pap. 4.76 (ISBN 0-394-71696-5, V702, Vin). Random.
De Bary, William T. & Haboush, Jahyun K., eds. The Rise of Neo-Confucianism in Korea. 512p. 1985. 40.00x (ISBN 0-231-06052-1). Columbia U pr.

Debate Study Group & Tharchin, Sermey G., eds. Logic & Debate Tradition of India, Tibet & Mongolia: History, Reader & Sources. 281p. (Orig.). 1979. pap. 9.50 (ISBN 0-918753-00-7, Pub by Rashi Gempil Ling). Mahayana.

De Beausobre, Isaac see Beausobre, Isaac de.

De Bedoian, Adriana P., tr. see Engstrom, Ted W.

De Beer, Francis. We Saw Brother Francis. 1983. 12.00 (ISBN 0-8199-0803-7). Franciscan Herald.

De Bellefonds, Y. Linant see Linant De Bellefonds, Y.

DeBellis, Robert, et al, eds. Medical Care of the Dying Patient. 30.00 (ISBN 0-405-13947-0). Ayer Co Pubs.

--Continuing Care: For the Dying Patient, Family & Staff. LC 85-19165. (The Foundation of Thanatology Ser.: Vol. 5). 190p. 1985. 37.95 (ISBN 0-03-000357-1, C1334). Praeger.

--Suffering: Psychological & Social Aspects in Loss, Grief, & Care. LC 85-31744. (Loss, Grief & Care Ser.: Vol. 1(1-2)). 196p. 1986. text ed. 32.95 (ISBN 0-86656-558-2). Haworth Pr.

--The House Staff & Thanatology. 15.00 (ISBN 0-405-14211-0). Ayer Co Pubs.

DeBenedictis, Matthew M. The Social Thought of Saint Bonaventure: A Study in Social Philosophy. LC 73-138108. 276p. 1946. Repr. lib. bdg. 22.50x (ISBN 0-8371-5684-X, DESB). Greenwood.

De Benedittis, Suzanne M. Teaching Faith & Morals. 200p. (Orig.). 1981. pap. 8.95 (ISBN 0-86683-621-7, HaprsR). Har-Row.

Debevec, et al, eds. United States Documents in the Propaganda Fide Archives, Vol. 9. 1982. 40.00 (ISBN 0-88382-210-5). AAFH.

De Beze, Theodore. A Discourse Conteyning the Life & Death of John Calvin. LC 77-38153. (English Experience Ser.: No. 433). 80p. 1972. Repr. of 1564 ed. 11.50 (ISBN 90-221-0433-8). Walter J Johnson.

De Blase, Betty E. Survivor of a Tarnished Ministry. 176p. (Orig.). 1983. pap. text ed. 6.95 (ISBN 0-913621-00-5). Truth CA.

DeBlassie, Paul, III. Inner Calm: A Christian Answer to Modern Stress. LC 84-52377. 128p. 1985. pap. 3.95 (ISBN 0-89243-229-2). Liguori Pubns.

De Blassie, Richard R. & Anderson, John. Helping the Troubled. 179p. 1981. pap. 3.95 (ISBN 0-8189-1163-8). Alba.

De Bles, Arthur. How to Distinguish the Saints in Art by Their Costumes, Symbols & Attributes. LC 68-18018. 1975. Repr. of 1925 ed. 70.00x (ISBN 0-8103-4125-5). Gale.

De Bles, Arthur see De Bles, Arthur.

DeBoer, John C. Let's Plan: A Guide to the Planning Process for Voluntary Organizations. LC 72-124329. (Illus., Orig.). 1970. pap. 3.95 (ISBN 0-8298-0177-4). Pilgrim NY.

De Bona, Maurice, Jr. God Rejected: A Summary of Atheistic Thought. LC 75-46088. 1976. 4.95 (ISBN 0-916698-00-9); pap. 2.95 (ISBN 0-916698-01-7). Desserco Pub.

De Boor, Carl G., ed. see Nicephorus.

Debor, Jane & Isabel, Linda. Banner Designs for Celebrating Christians. 1984. pap. 5.95 (ISBN 0-570-03931-2, 12-2865). Concordia.

De Bosschere, Jean see Bosschere, Jean de & Morris, M. C.

De Boulainvilliers, H. The Life of Mahomet. Luzac & Co. Ltd. Staff, ed. 400p. 1985. 60.00 (ISBN 0-317-39040-6, Pub. by Luzac & Co Ltd). State Mutual Bk.

De Bourbourg, Charles E. Brasseru see Brasseur De Bourbourg, Charles E.

DeBoy, James J., Jr. Getting Started in Adult Religious Education: A Practical Guide. LC 79-88932. 128p. 1979. pap. 5.95 (ISBN 0-8091-2222-7). Paulist Pr.

De Brand, Roy E. Children's Sermons for Special Occasions. LC 82-72228. (Orig.). 1983. pap. 3.95 (ISBN 0-8054-4927-2). Broadman.

--The Cross & Beyond. LC 83-70374. 1984. pap. 4.95 (ISBN 0-8054-2250-1). Broadman.

De Breffny, Brian. In the Steps of St. Patrick. (Illus.). 1982. 9.98 (ISBN 0-500-24110-4). Thames Hudson.

De Brincat, Matthew see Brincat, Matthew De.

De Brosses, Charles. Du Culte Des Dieux Fetiches, Ou Parallele de l'Ancienne Religion de l'Egypte Avec la Religion Actuelle de Nigrittie. 286p. Repr. of 1760 ed. text ed. 62.10 (ISBN 0-576-12101-0, Pub. by Gregg Intl Pubs England). Gregg Intl.

Debrunner, A., jt. auth. see Blass, F.

DeBurgh, David. The Maturing Salesian. 1977. pap. 3.95 (ISBN 0-89944-028-2). Don Bosco Multimedia.

DeBurgh, David, tr. see Wirth, Morand.

DeBurgh, W. G. From Morality to Religion. LC 70-102568. 1970. Repr. of 1938 ed. 31.50x (ISBN 0-8046-0728-1, Pub. by Kennikat). Assoc Faculty Pr.

De Burgh, W. G. From Morality to Religion. 352p. 1985. Repr. of 1938 ed. lib. bdg. 85.00 (ISBN 0-89984-042-6). Century Bookbindery.

De Candolle, Alphonse. Histiore Des Sciences et Des Savants Depuis Deux Siecles. Cohen, I. Bernard, ed. LC 80-2116. (Development of Science Ser.). (Illus.). 1981. lib. bdg. 50.00x (ISBN 0-405-13836-9). Ayer Co Pubs.

Decard, Bob. The California Connection. 90p. (Orig.). 1986. pap. 6.95 (ISBN 0-9616620-1-8). Constellation Pr.

De Caro, Francis A., compiled by. Women & Folklore: A Bibliographic Survey. LC 83-12837. xiv, 170p. 1983. lib. bdg. 35.00 (ISBN 0-313-23821-9, DWF/). Greenwood.

De Catanzaro, C. J. Symeon, the New Theologian: The Discourses. LC 80-82414. (Classics of Western Spirituality Ser.). 416p. 1980. 13.95 (ISBN 0-8091-0292-7); pap. 9.95 (ISBN 0-8091-2230-8). Paulist Pr.

Decatanzaro, Carmino J., tr. see Cabasilas, Nicholas.

De Caussade, Jean-Pierre. Abandonment to Divine Providence. LC 74-2827. 120p. 1975. pap. 3.50 (ISBN 0-385-02544-0, Im). Doubleday.

--The Joy of Full Surrender. (Living Library Ser.). 160p. 1986. pap. 5.95 (ISBN 0-941478-49-1). Paraclete Pr.

De Caussode, Jean Pierre. Daily Readings with Jean-Pierre de Caussade. LLewelyn, Robert, ed. (Daily Readings Ser.). 1986. pap. 4.95 (ISBN 0-87243-145-2). Templegate.

DeCelles, Charles. The Unbound Spirit: God's Universal, Sanctifying Work. LC 85-20047. 367p. (Orig.). 1985. pap. 9.95 (ISBN 0-8189-0486-0). Alba.

Dechanet, Jean M. William of St. Thierry: The Man & His Work. Strachen, Richard, tr. from Fr. LC 73-152485. (Cistercian Studies: No. 10). Tr. of Guillaume de Saint-Thierry. 192p. 1972. 10.95 (ISBN 0-87907-810-3). Cistercian Pubns.

De Chardin, Pierre T. see Teilhard de Chardin, Pierre.

De Chardin, Pierre Teilhard see Teilhard De Chardin, Pierre.

De Chardin, Teilhard. Building the Earth. 7.95 (ISBN 0-87193-078-1). Dimension Bks.

--Le Groupe Zoologique Humain, Structure et Directions Evolutives. (Coll. les Savants et le Monde Ser.). pap. 6.95 (ISBN 0-685-36591-3). French & Eur.

De Charms, George. Lectures on the Philosophy of Swedenborg's Principia. 68p. 1970. pap. 3.00 (ISBN 0-915221-39-X). Swedenborg Sci Assn.

De Chateaubriand, Francois R. The Genius of Christianity. LC 75-25532. 1975. Repr. of 1856 ed. 40.00x (ISBN 0-86527-254-9). Fertig.

De Chateaubriand, Viscount. The Genius of Christianity, 2 vols. White, Charles I., tr. 245p. 1985. 117.35 (ISBN 0-89901-223-X). Found Class Reprints.

Dechevrens, Antoine. Composition Musicale et Composition Litteraire a Propos du Chant Gregorrien. 373p. 1910. Repr. lib. bdg. 62.50x (Pub. by G Olms BRD). Coronet Bks.

De Civrieux, Marc. Watunna: An Orinoco Creation Cycle. Guss, David, ed. LC 80-82440. (Illus.). 216p. 1980. 20.00 (ISBN 0-86547-002-2); pap. 12.50 (ISBN 0-86547-003-0). N Point Pr.

Deck, Gladys E. Bits of Solace, Guidance & Consolation. 97p. 1984. 7.50 (ISBN 0-913382-30-2, 101-30). Prow Bks-Franciscan.

--Meet the Holy Family. 139p. 1978. 7.50 (ISBN 0-913382-24-8, 101-24). Prow Bks-Franciscan.

--A Mother's Soliloquy. 115p. 1986. 7.50 (ISBN 0-913382-38-8, 101-38). Prow Bks-Franciscan.

Deck, John N. Nature, Contemplation, & the One: A Study in the Philosophy of Plotinus. LC 67-98055. pap. 36.30 (ISBN 0-317-08774-6, 2014184). Bks Demand UMI.

Decker, Ed & Hunt, Dave. Los Fabricantes de Dioses. Powell, Adriana, tr. from Eng. Tr. of The Godmakers. (Span.). 240p. 1987. pap. 4.95 (ISBN 0-88113-088-5). Edit Betania.

--The God Makers. LC 83-82319. 192p. 1984. pap. 6.95 (ISBN 0-89081-402-3). Harvest Hse.

Decker, Harold A. & Herford, Julius, eds. Choral Conducting: A Symposium. LC 72-94347. (Illus.). 320p. 1973. 34.00 (ISBN 0-13-133355-0). P-H.

Decker, Marjorie A. The Christian Mother Goose Trilogy, 3 Vols. (Illus.). 336p. 1983. PLB 35.50 (ISBN 0-933724-14-4). Decker Pr Inc.

De Clark, Catalina, tr. see Dana, H. E. & Mantey, J. R.

De Clemente, Elizabeth M., jt. auth. see Van Ness, Bethann.

De Coinci, Gautier. Tumbler of Our Lady & Other Miracles. Kemp-Welch, A., tr. (Medieval Library). (Illus.). Repr. of 1926 ed. 17.50x (ISBN 0-8154-0076-4). Cooper Sq.

De Coppens, Peter R. The Nature & Use of Ritual. 1977. pap. text ed. 9.75 (ISBN 0-8191-0341-1). U Pr of Amer.

--Spiritual Perspective II: The Spiritual Dimension & Implications of Love, Sex, & Marriage. LC 80-6302. 175p. (Orig.). 1981. pap. text ed. 10.75 (ISBN 0-8191-1512-6). U Pr of Amer.

De Cordoba, Pedro. Christian Doctrine for the Instruction & Information of the Indians. Stoudemire, Sterling A., tr. LC 79-121681. 1970. 7.95x (ISBN 0-87024-159-1). U of Miami Pr.

De Coussemaker, Edmond, ed. Drames liturgiques du moyen age, texte et musique. (Fr., Lat., Illus.). 370p. 1964. Repr. of 1860 ed. 57.50x (ISBN 0-8450-1004-2). Broude.

De Craemer, Willy. The Jamaa & the Church: A Bantu Catholic Movement in Zaire. (Oxford Studies in African Affairs). 1977. 58.00x (ISBN 0-19-822708-6). Oxford U Pr.

De Danois, Vivian. Abortion & the Moral Degeneration of the American Medical Profession. (A Science of Man Library Bk). 92p. 1975. 81.50 (ISBN 0-913314-56-0). Am Classical Coll Pr.

--God & Abortion. (A Science of Man Library Bk). 1979. 51.50 (ISBN 0-89266-160-7). Am Classical Coll Pr.

Dede, Vivian H. Elizabeth's Christmas Story. LC 59-1430. (Arch Bks.). (Illus.). 24p. 1987. pap. 0.99 (ISBN 0-570-09002-4, 59/1430). Concordia.

De Deguilleville, Guillaume. The Pilgrimage of the Life of Man, Pts. 1-3. Furnivall, F. J. & Locock, K. B., eds. (EETS, ES Ser.: Nos. 77, 83, & 92). Repr. of 1904 ed. 90.00 (ISBN 0-527-00279-8). Kraus Repr.

De Deiros, Norma H. C. Dramatizaciones Infantiles Para Dias Especiales. 96p. 1985. pap. 2.50 (ISBN 0-311-07606-8). Casa Bautista.

De Dietrich, Suzanne. God's Unfolding Purpose: A Guide to the Study of the Bible. Brown, Robert M., tr. LC 60-6169. 1960. Westminster.

--The Witnessing Community: The Biblical Record of God's Purpose. LC 58-5020. 180p. 1978. pap. 3.95 (ISBN 0-664-24199-9). Westminster.

De Djunkovskoy, E., jt. auth. see Lacroix.

Deedat, A. Is Bible God's Word? 1981. 2.75 (ISBN 0-686-97857-9). Kazi Pubns.

--Quran, the Ultimate Miracle. pap. 2.95 (ISBN 0-686-63913-8). Kazi Pubns.

--Was Jesus Crucified? pap. 1.50 (ISBN 0-686-63916-2). Kazi Pubns.

--What the Bible Says about Muhammad? 1.75 (ISBN 0-686-63917-0). Kazi Pubns.

Deedy, John. The Catholic Fact Book. 1986. 23.95 (ISBN 0-88347-186-8). Thomas More.

Deegan, Paul J. Stickhandling & Passing. LC 76-8444. (Sports Instruction Ser.). (Illus.). 1976. PLB 8.95 (ISBN 0-87191-520-0); pap. 3.95 (ISBN 0-686-67437-5). Creative Ed.

Deekken, Alfons S. J. Growing Old & How to Cope with it. LC 86-80786. 192p. 1986. pap. 7.95 (ISBN 0-89870-104-X). Ignatius Pr.

Deems, Betty. Easy-to-Make Felt Ornaments for Christmas & Other Occasions. LC 76-18405. (Dover Needlework Ser). (Illus.). 32p. (Orig.). 1976. pap. 3.50 (ISBN 0-486-23389-8). Dover.

Deems, Edward M., ed. Holy-Days & Holidays: A Treasury of Historical Material, Sermons in Full & in Brief, Suggestive Thoughts & Poetry, Relating to Holy Days & Holidays. LC 68-17940. 1968. Repr. of 1902 ed. 65.00x (ISBN 0-8103-3352-X). Gale.

Deen, Edith. All of the Women of the Bible. LC 55-8621. 1955. 18.45 (ISBN 0-06-061810-8, HarpR). Har-Row.

--Great Women of the Christian Faith. (The Christian Library). 410p. 1986. Repr. of 1959 ed. 6.95 (ISBN 0-916441-46-6). Barbour & Co.

Deer, John. Bigamy, Polygamy & Polyandry: A Comprehensive Bibliography. 108p. (Orig.). 1986. pap. 11.95 (ISBN 0-940519-08-9). Res Discover Pubns.

Deerfield, William. Stretching Your Faith. 48p. 1985. 4.95 (ISBN 0-8378-5401-6). Gibson.

Deerforth, Daniel. Knock Wood! Superstition Through the Ages. LC 79-164220. 200p. 1974. Repr. of 1928 ed. 43.00x (ISBN 0-8103-3964-1). Gale.

De Faye, Eugene. Origen & His Work. LC 78-16959. 1926. 27.50 (ISBN 0-8414-3684-3). Folcroft.

De Felice, Renzo. Jews in an Arab Land: Libya, 1835-1970. Roumani, Judith, tr. 436p. 1985. 27.50x (ISBN 0-292-74016-6). U of Tex Pr.

Defeller, F. X. & Perennes, F. Dictionnaire de Biographie Chretienne, 3 vols. Migne, J. P., ed. (Nouvelle Encyclopedie Theologique Ser.: Vols. 1-3). (Fr.). 2352p. Repr. of 1851 ed. lib. bdg. 298.00x (ISBN 0-89241-254-2). Caratzas.

Deferrari, R. J., tr. see Hugh of St. Victor.

Deferrari, Roy J., ed. Essays on Catholic Education in the U. S. facsimile ed. LC 71-90629. (Essay Index Reprint Ser.). 566p. Repr. of 1942 ed. lib. bdg. 32.00 (ISBN 0-8290-0814-4). Irvington.

Deffner, Donald. I Hear Two Voices, God! LC 12-2817. 1983. pap. 4.95 (ISBN 0-570-03882-0). Concordia.

--Please Talk to Me, God! (Continued Applied Christianity). 1983. pap. 4.95 (ISBN 0-570-03899-5, 12-2981). Concordia.

--You Promised Me God. LC 12-2792. (Illus.). 1981. pap. 4.95 (ISBN 0-570-03827-8). Concordia.

Deffner, Donald, jt. auth. see Andersen, Richard.

Deffner, Donald L. Come Closer to Me, God! 1982. pap. 4.95 (ISBN 0-570-03851-0, 12-2806). Concordia.

Deffner, Wenonah S. Scripture Word Search. (Quiz & Puzzle Bks.). 1980. pap. 2.45 (ISBN 0-8010-2897-3). Baker Bk.

De Fleury, C. Rohault. La Sainte Vierge: Etudes Archeologiques et Iconographiques, 2 vols. (Fr., Illus.). Repr. of 1878 ed. Set. 325.00x (ISBN 0-89241-154-6). Caratzas.

De Forest, Grant E. God in the American Schools: Religious Education in a Pluralistic Society. (Illus.). 1979. 49.50 (ISBN 0-89266-181-X). Am Classical Coll Pr.

De Foucauld, Charles. Come, Let Us Sing a Song Unknown. 2.95 (ISBN 0-87193-080-3). Dimension Bks.

De Gaury, Gerald. Rulers of Mecca. LC 78-63458. (Pilgrimages Ser.). (Illus.). 1982. Repr. of 1954 ed. 34.50 (ISBN 0-404-16517-6). AMS Pr.

De Gayangos, P., tr. see Al-Maqqari, Ahmed.

Degeest, Achille. Saint Joseph Commentary on the Sunday Readings, 3 vols. 3.95 ea. Year A (ISBN 0-89942-341-8, 341/04). Year B (ISBN 0-89942-342-6, 342/04). Year C (ISBN 0-89942-343-4, 343/04). Catholic Bk Pub.

De George, R. T. & Scanlan, J. P., eds. Marxism & Religion in Eastern Europe. LC 75-33051. (Sovietica Ser: No. 36). 180p. 1976. lib. bdg. 39.50 (ISBN 90-277-0636-0, Pub. by Reidel Holland). Kluwer Academic.

Degering, Etta B. Once upon a Bible Time. Van Dolson, Bobbie J., ed. LC 76-14118. (Illus.). 1976. 7.95 (ISBN 0-8280-0052-2). Review & Herald.

DeGidio, Sandra. R. C. I. A: The Rites Revisited. 144p. (Orig.). 1984. pap. 7.95 (ISBN 0-86683-837-6, 8436, HarpR). Har-Row.

De Gidio, Sandra. Re-Treat Your Family to Lent. 50p. (Orig.). 1983. pap. text ed. 1.95 (ISBN 0-86716-022-5). St Anthony Mess Pr.

Degler, Lois. Man & God. LC 74-28943. (Illus.). 1975. pap. 3.00 (ISBN 0-930422-04-X). Dennis-Landman.

DeGolia. Object Lessons Using Common Things. 1954. 3.50 (ISBN 0-88207-026-6). Victor Bks.

De Gonzalez, Nelly, jt. ed. see Diaz, Jorge.

De Goscinny, Rene. The Mansion of the Gods. (Asterix Ser.). (Illus.). 1976. 7.95x (ISBN 0-340-17719-5); pap. 4.95x (ISBN 2-2050-6916-0). Intl Learn Syst.

De Grandmaison, C. Dictionnaires Heraldique. Migne, J. P., ed. (Nouvelle Encyclopedie Theologique Ser.: Vol. 13). (Fr.). 688p. Repr. of 1852 ed. lib. bdg. 90.00x (ISBN 0-89241-262-3). Caratzas.

De Grauwe, Jan. Histoire de la Chartreuse Sheen Anglorum au Continent: Bruges, Louvain, Malines, Nieuport (1559-1783) Hogg, James, ed. (Analecta Cartuaiana Ser.: No. 48). (Fr.). 254p. (Orig.). 1985. pap. 25.00 (ISBN 3-7052-0068-2, Pub by Salzburg Studies). Longwood Pub Group.

--Historia Cartusiana Belgica: Esquisse Historique et Apercu des Archives, des Bibliotheques et des Oeuvres D'Art. Hogg, James, ed. (Analecta Cartusiana: No. 51). (Orig.). 1985. pap. 25.00 (ISBN 3-7052-0071-2, Pub. by Salzburg Studies). Longwood Pub Group.

--Prosopographia Cartuaiana Belgica: 1314-1796. Hogg, James, ed. (Analecta Cartusiana Ser.: No. 28). (Flemish & Fr.). 360p. (Orig.). 1976. pap. 25.00 (ISBN 3-7052-0029-1, Pub by Salzburg Studies). Longwood Pub Group.

De Grazia, Alfred see Grazia, Alfred de.

Degrelle, Leon. Letter to the Pope on His Visit to Auschwitz. 1982. lib. bdg. 59.95 (ISBN 0-87700-346-7). Revisionist Pr.

Degrijse, Omer. Going Forth: Missionary Consciousness in Third World Catholic Churches. LC 83-19337. 112p. (Orig.). 1984. pap. 6.95 (ISBN 0-88344-427-5). Orbis Bks.

DeGroat, Florence. Resurrection. LC 81-67782. (Universal Man Ser.: Vol. 2). (Illus.). 168p. (Orig.). 1981. pap. text ed. 6.50 (ISBN 0-87516-456-0). De Vorss.

--Tales from Galilee. 96p. (Orig.). 1982. pap. 4.50 (ISBN 0-87516-485-4). De Vorss.

--This Drama Called Life: An Introduction to Advanced Christianity. (Illus.). 49p. 1984. pap. 6.95 (ISBN 0-942494-89-X). Coleman Pub.

--Universal Man. LC 80-69413. 117p. 1981. pap. 6.50 (ISBN 0-87516-428-5). De Vorss.

De Groot, David, jt. auth. see Dalenburg, Cornelia.

De Groot, J. J. Le Cope du Mahayana en Chine: Amsterdam, 1892. LC 78-74288. (Oriental Religions Ser.: Vol. 15). 281p. 1980. lib. bdg. 40.00 (ISBN 0-8240-3917-3). Garland Pub.

DeGroot, J. J. The Religious System of China, 6 vols. 1982. Repr. of 1892 ed. 130.00 (ISBN 0-89986-346-9). Oriental Bk Store.

De Groot, J. J. Sectarianism & Religious Persecution in China: A Page in the History of Religions, 2 vols. 872p. 1972. Repr. of 1903 ed. 60.00x (ISBN 0-7165-2034-6, Pub. by Irish Academic Pr Ireland). Biblio Dist.

De Groot, Jeanne L. Man & Mind. ix, 441p. 1985. text ed. 45.00x (ISBN 0-8236-3087-0). Intl Univs Pr.

De Groot, John H. Shakespeares-'The Old Faith.' facs. ed. LC 68-57315. (Essay Index Reprint Ser.). 1946. 18.00 (ISBN 0-8369-0368-4). Ayer Co Pubs.

DeGrote-Sorensen, Barbara. Everybody Needs a Friend: A Young Christian Book for Girls. LC 86-32152. 112p. (Orig.). 1987. pap. 4.95 (ISBN 0-8066-2247-4, 10-2120). Augsburg.

DeGruchy, John W. Bonhoeffer & South Africa: Theology in Dialogue. 128p. (Orig.). 1984. pap. 9.95 (ISBN 0-8028-0042-4). Eerdmans.

De Gruchy, John W. The Church Struggle in South Africa. 2nd ed. 300p. 1986. pap. 10.95 (ISBN 0-8028-0243-5). Eerdmans.

--Cry Justice! Prayers, Meditations & Readings from South African Christians in a Time of Crisis. LC 86-667. (Illus.). 264p. (Orig.). 1986. pap. 6.95 (ISBN 0-88344-223-X). Orbis Bks.

DeGruchy, John W. Theology & Ministry in Context & Crisis: A South African Perspective. 182p. (Orig.). 1987. pap. 9.95 (ISBN 0-8028-0290-7). Eerdmans.

De Gruchy, John W. & Villa-Vicencio, Charles, eds. Apartheid Is a Heresy. 208p. (Orig.). 1983. pap. 5.95 (ISBN 0-8028-1972-9). Eerdmans.

De Gubernatis, Angelo see Gubernatis, Angelo De.

De Guibert, Joseph. The Jesuits: Their Spiritual Doctrine & Practice. Young, W. J., tr. LC 64-21430. 717p. 1964. pap. 15.00 (ISBN 0-912422-09-2). Inst Jesuit.

Deguilleville, Guillaume De see De Deguilleville, Guillaume.

De Gutierrez, Edna L., tr. see Ton, Mary E.

De Gutierrez, Edna L., tr. see Wood, Fred M.

De Guzman, Domingo see Domingo De Guzman, Saint.

DeHaan, Dan. The God You Can Know. (Moody Press Electives Ser.). 1985. pap. text ed. 3.95 (ISBN 0-8024-0697-1); leader's guide 2.50 (ISBN 0-8024-0698-X). Moody.

--Steve Bartkowski: Intercepted: A Game Plan for Spiritual Growth. (Illus.). 160p. 1981. pap. 5.95 (ISBN 0-8007-5075-6, Power Bks). Revell.

DeHaan, Daniel F. The God You Can Know. LC 81-16948. 180p. 1982. pap. 5.95 (ISBN 0-8024-3008-2). Moody.

DeHaan, Dennis J., ed. Windows on the World. 1984. pap. 4.95 (ISBN 0-8010-2946-5). Baker Bk.

De Haan, M. J., jt. ed. see Gumbert, J. P.

DeHaan, M. R. The Chemistry of the Blood. 160p. 1983. pap. 5.95 (ISBN 0-310-23291-0, 9282P). Zondervan.

--Daniel the Prophet. 340p. 1983. pap. 8.95 (ISBN 0-310-23321-6). Zondervan.

De Haan, M. R. Days of Noah. 5.95 (ISBN 0-310-23331-3, 9512P). Zondervan.

DeHaan, M. R. Five Hundred Eight Answers to Bible Questions. 1979. pap. 7.95 (ISBN 0-310-23341-0, 9495P). Zondervan.

--The Jew & Palestine in Prophecy. 1978. pap. 5.95 (ISBN 0-310-23381-X, 9497P). Zondervan.

--Portraits of Christ in Genesis. 1978. pap. 6.95 (ISBN 0-310-23431-X, 9516P). Zondervan.

De Haan, M. R. Revelation. 1956. 13.95 (ISBN 0-310-23440-9, 9498P). Zondervan.

DeHaan, M. R. The Tabernacle. 1979. pap. 6.95 (ISBN 0-310-23491-3, 9502P). Zondervan.

DeHaan, M. R. & Bosch, H. G. Bread for Each Day. large print ed. 1979. Kivar 10.95 (ISBN 0-310-23267-8, 1257L); 13.95 (ISBN 0-310-23260-0, 9510). Zondervan.

DeHaan, M. R. & Bosch, Henry G. Our Daily Bread. 1986. 13.95 (ISBN 0-310-23410-7, 9505). Zondervan.

De Haan, Martin R. Coming Events in Prophecy. 5.95 (ISBN 0-310-23301-1). Zondervan.

DeHaan, Martin R. Religion o Cristo? Orig. Title: Religion or Christ. (Span.). 64p. 1970. pap. 2.25 (ISBN 0-8254-1153-X). Kregel.

--Second Coming of Jesus. 1978. pap. 6.95 (ISBN 0-310-23461-1, 9498P). Zondervan.

De Haan, Mr. R. Hebrews. pap. 6.95 (ISBN 0-310-23371-2, 9506P). Zondervan.

DeHaan, R. F. Return Unto Me. pap. 2.00 (ISBN 0-686-14199-7). Rose Pub MI.

DeHaan, Richard W. Como Ser Feliz. Orig. Title: How to Be Happy. (Span.). 64p. 1978. pap. 2.25. Kregel.

--Pray: God Is Listening. 80p. (Orig.). 1980. pap. 2.50 (ISBN 0-310-23542-1). Zondervan.

--The Secret of a Happy Home. (Direction Bks.). 88p. 1982. pap. 2.95 (ISBN 0-8010-2916-3). Baker Bk.

DeHaan, Richard W. & Bosch, Henry G. Our Daily Bread Favorites. rev. ed. 384p. 1986. pap. 9.95 large print ed. (ISBN 0-310-25877-4, 12587L). Zondervan.

De Haan, Richard W. & Bosch, Henry G., eds. Our Daily Bread Favorites. 384p. 1971. 10.95 (ISBN 0-310-23590-1). Zondervan.

Deharbe, Joseph. A Full Catechism of the Catholic Religion. 1979. lib. bdg. 59.95 (ISBN 0-8490-2924-4). Gordon Pr.

De Hartmann, Olga, jt. auth. see De Hartmann, Thomas.

De Hartmann, Thomas. Our Life with Mister Gurdjieff. LC 64-22661. (Illus.). 1964. 17.50x (ISBN 0-8154-0058-6). Cooper Sq.

De Hartmann, Thomas & De Hartmann, Olga. Our Life with Mr. Gurdjieff. rev. ed. LC 83-47722. 160p. 1983. pap. 7.95 (ISBN 0-06-061865-5, RD 469, HarpR). Har-Row.

De Hartog, Jan. Adopted Children. rev. ed. 268p. 1987. pap. 13.95 (ISBN 0-915361-65-5, Dist. by Watts). Adama Pubs Inc.

De Hass, Frank S. Buried Cities Recovered: Explorations in Bible Lands. Davis, Moshe, ed. LC 77-70774. (America & the Holy Land). (Illus.). 1977. lib. bdg. 40.00x (ISBN 0-405-10242-9). Ayer Co Pubs.

Dehejia, Vidya. Early Buddhist Rock Temples. LC 75-158835. (Studies in Ancient Art & Archaeology Ser.). (Illus.). 193p. 1972. 42.50x (ISBN 0-8014-0651-X). Cornell U Pr.

--Early Stone Temples of Orissa. LC 78-54434. (Illus.). 217p. 1979. 37.75 (ISBN 0-89089-092-7). Carolina Acad Pr.

--Living & Dying: An Inquiry into the Enigma of Death & After-Life. 1979. 8.95x (ISBN 0-7069-0815-5, Pub. by Vikas India). Advent NY.

De Hernandez Carrera, Armida O., ed. El Vuela del Triunfador. (Span.). Date not set. pap. 3.95 (ISBN 0-87148-306-8). Pathway Pr.

Dehlvi, A. M. The Finality of Prophethood. pap. 1.25 (ISBN 0-686-18424-6). Kazi Pubns.

De Hojeda, Diego see Hojeda, Diego de.

Dehoney, Wayne. An Evangelical's Guidebook to the Holy Land. LC 73-85698. pap. 9.95 (ISBN 0-8054-5701-1). Broadman.

DeHoyos, Genieve. Stewardship, the Divine Order. LC 81-82055. 200p. 1982. 6.95 (ISBN 0-88290-191-5, 1065). Horizon Utah.

De Hucck Doherty, Catherine see Doherty, Catherine de Hucck.

De Hueck Doherty, Catherine. Soul of My Soul: Reflections from a Life of Prayer. LC 85-72271. 128p. (Orig.). 1985. pap. 4.95 (ISBN 0-87793-298-0). Ave Maria.

Deikman, Arthur J. The Observing Self: Mysticism & Psychotherapy. LC 81-70486. 208p. 1983. pap. 8.95 (ISBN 0-8070-2951-3, BP 652). Beacon Pr.

Deiros, P. A. Que Paso con Estos Pecados? 144p. 1979. pap. 2.50 (ISBN 0-311-42063-X). Casa Bautista.

Deiros, Pablo. El Cristiano y los Problemas Eticos. 112p. 1982. pap. 3.50 (ISBN 0-311-46064-X). Casa Bautista.

Deiros, Pablo A., jt. auth. see Lewis, John M.

Deiss, Lucien. Springtime of the Liturgy: Liturgical Texts of the First Four Centuries. rev. ed. O'Connell, Matthew J., tr. from Fr. LC 79-15603. 307p. 1979. pap. 10.00 (ISBN 0-8146-1023-4). Liturgical Pr.

Deissman, Adolph. Paul: A Study in Social & Religious History. Wilson, William W., tr. 1958. 12.75 (ISBN 0-8446-1965-5). Peter Smith.

Deitering, Carolyn. Actions, Gestures & Bodily Attitudes. LC 80-51058. 1980. pap. 10.95 (ISBN 0-89390-021-4). Resource Pubns.

--The Liturgy As Dance & the Liturgical Dancer. (Illus.). 144p. 1984. pap. 8.95 (ISBN 0-8245-0654-5). Crossroad NY.

Deitrick, Bernard E. A Basic Book List for Church Libraries. 2nd rev ed. LC 77-4093. 1983. pap. 3.95x (ISBN 0-915324-10-5); pap. 3.00 members. CSLA.

--Know Your Neighbor's Faith. LC 83-7259. (Orig.). 1983. pap. 3.95x (ISBN 0-915324-19-9); pap. 3.00 members. CSLA.

Deitsch, Cyrel, jt. ed. see Blau, Esther.

De Jaegher, Paul, ed. An Anthology of Christian Mysticism. 1977. 7.95 (ISBN 0-87243-073-1). Templegate.

De Jesus, Gonzalo. Fray Jose de Guadalupe Mojica: Mi Guia y Mi Estrella. (Illus.). 100p. 1976. 2.00 (ISBN 0-8199-0570-4). Franciscan Herald.

De Jim, Strange. Visioning. LC 79-66208. (Illus.). 112p. (Orig.). 1979. pap. 5.95 (ISBN 0-9605308-0-0). Ash-Kar Pr.

De Joinville, Jean. Histoire de Saint Louis. De Wailly, N., ed. 1868. 38.00 (ISBN 0-384-27721-7); pap. 32.00 (ISBN 0-384-27720-9). Johnson Repr.

De Joinville, Jean, jt. auth. see De Villehardouin, Geoffrey.

DeJong. The Dutch Reformed Church in the American Colonies. LC 78-17216. 1978. pap. 8.95 (ISBN 0-8028-1741-6). Eerdmans.

De Jong, Benjamin R. Uncle Ben's Instant Clip Quotes. 128p. 1985. pap. 5.95 (ISBN 0-8010-2954-6). Baker Bk.

--Uncle Ben's Quotebook. 1976. 11.95 (ISBN 0-8010-2851-5). Baker Bk.

De Jong, J. W., ed. Mi la Ras Pa'i Rnam Thar: Texte Tibetian De la Vie De Milarepa. (Indo-Iranian Monographs: No. 4). 1959. 22.00x (ISBN 90-2790-052-3). Mouton.

De Jong, James. Into His Presence: Perspectives on Reformed Worship. 1985. pap. 7.95 (ISBN 0-933140-99-1); pap. text ed. 3.95 leader's guide (ISBN 0-930265-08-4). CRC Pubns.

DeJong, James A. & Van Dyke, Louis Y., eds. Building the House: Essays on Christian Education. 153p. (Orig.). 1981. pap. 5.95 (ISBN 0-932914-05-5). Dordt Coll Pr.

De Jong, Norman. Christian Approaches to Learning Theory: A Symposium; Major Papers Delivered at the First Annual Conference at Trinity Christian College, November 11-12, 1983. 234p. 1985. 25.00 (ISBN 0-8191-4319-7, Pub. by Trinity Christ Coll). U Pr of Amer.

--Christian Approaches to Learning Theory: A Symposium; Major Papers Delivered at the First Annual Conference at Trinity Christian College, November 11-12, 1983. 234p. (Orig.). 1985. pap. 12.25 (ISBN 0-8191-4320-0, Pub. by Trinity Christ Coll). U Pr of Amer.

--Christianity & Democracy. 1978. pap. 4.95 (ISBN 0-934532-08-7). Presby & Reformed.

DeJong, Norman, ed. Christian Approaches to Learning Theory: The Nature of the Learner - Major Papers Delivered at the Second Annual Conference, Trinity Christian College, Palos Heights, Illinois, Nov. 2-3, 1984, Vol. II. 174p. (Orig.). 1986. lib. bdg. 25.00 (ISBN 0-8191-5004-5, Pub. by Trinity Christ Coll); pap. text ed. 11.75 (ISBN 0-8191-5005-3). U Pr of Amer.

DeJong, Peter & Smit, William. Family Planning: How To Decide What's Best for You. 208p. 1987. pap. 6.95 (ISBN 0-310-37961-X). Zondervan.

De Jong, Ralph. The Life of Mary Magdalene in the Paintings of the Great Masters, 2 vols. (Illus.). 1979. deluxe ed. 117.45 (ISBN 0-930582-30-6). Gloucester Art.

De Jonge, Joanne E. My Listening Ears. LC 85-7372. (My Father's World Ser.). (Illus.). 144p. 1985. pap. 3.95 (ISBN 0-930265-09-2). CRC Pubns.

DeJonge, M. Christology in Context. price not set. Westminster.

De Jonge, Marinus. Jesus: Stranger from Heaven & Son of God. Steely, John E., ed. LC 77-9984. (Soceity of Biblical Literature. Sources for Biblical Studies: No. 11). Repr. of 1977 ed. 61.50 (ISBN 0-8357-9575-6, 2017532). Bks Demand UMI.

--Outside the Old Testament. (Camridge Commentaries on the Writings of the Jewish & Christian World 200 B.C. to 200 A.D. Ser.: No. 4). 264p. 1985. 49.50 (ISBN 0-521-24249-5); pap. 18.95 (ISBN 0-521-28554-2). Cambridge U Pr.

Dekar, Paul R. & Ban, Joseph D., eds. In the Great Tradition. 240p. 1982. 25.00 (ISBN 0-8170-0972-8). Judson.

De Kemeseye, Johannes. Roll of the Household Expenses of Richard De Swinfield, Bishop of Hereford, 1289-1290, 2 Vols. 1854-1855. 65.00 (ISBN 0-384-29130-9). Johnson Repr.

Dekker, James C., tr. see Hanks, Thomas D.

De Kleen, Tyra. Mudras: The Ritual Hand-Poses of the Buddha Priests & the Shiva Priests of Bali. 1970. 5.00 (ISBN 0-8216-0119-9). Univ Bks.

DeKlerk, Peter & DeRidder, Richard R., eds. Perspectives on the Christian Reformed Church. 1983. 14.95 (ISBN 0-8010-2934-1). Baker Bk.

Dekmejian, R. Hrair. Islam in Revolution: Fundamentalism in the Arab World. (Contemporary Issues in the Middle East Ser.). 224p. 1985. text ed. 28.00x (ISBN 0-8156-2329-1); pap. text ed. 13.95x (ISBN 0-8156-2330-5). Syracuse U Pr.

De Kort, Kees, illus. What the Bible Tells Us: Third Series, 4 bks. Incl. A Baby Called John. 28p (ISBN 0-8066-1770-5, 10-0538); Jesus & a Little Girl. 28p (ISBN 0-8066-1771-3, 10-3479); The Son Who Left Home. 28p (ISBN 0-8066-1773-X, 10-5852); Jesus Goes Away. 28p (ISBN 0-8066-1774-8, 10-3510). 1980. pap. 2.95 ea. Augsburg.

DeKosky, Robert K. Knowledge & Cosmos: Development & Decline of the Medieval Perspective. LC 79-66226. 1979. text ed. 26.00 (ISBN 0-8191-0814-6); pap. text ed. 15.25 (ISBN 0-8191-0815-4). U Pr of Amer.

DeKoster, Lester, jt. auth. see Berghoef, Gerard.

De la Barca, Pedro C. Celos Aun Del Aire Matan. Stroud, Matthew D., tr. LC 80-54543. (Span. & Eng., Illus.). 219p. 1981. 15.00 (ISBN 0-911536-90-6); pap. 10.00 (ISBN 0-939980-01-0). Trinity U Pr.

De LaBrosse, Olivier see Henry, Antonir Marie & LaBrosse, Olivier De.

De Lacey, D. R. Expansion of Christianity. (Discovering the Bible Ser.). pap. 8.95 (ISBN 0-7175-1163-4). Dufour.

--Jesus & the Gospels. (Discovering the Bible Ser.). pap. 8.95 (ISBN 0-7175-1162-6). Dufour.

De La Colombiere, Claude, jt. auth. see Saint-Jure, Jean B.

Delacour, Jean. Dictionnaire des Mots d'Esprit. (Fr.). 352p. 1976. pap. 15.95 (ISBN 0-686-56849-4, M-6627). French & Eur.

De la Cruz Aymes, Maria & Buckley, Francis J. Fe y Cultura: Manual de Direccion. 112p. (Orig.). 1986. pap. 8.95 (ISBN 0-8091-2749-0); apuntes 5.95; leader's manual 8.95 (ISBN 0-8091-2748-2). Paulist Pr.

De la Cruz Aymes, Maria, et al. Growing with God. (God with Us Program). 112p. (Orig.). 1983. pap. text ed. 3.69 (ISBN 0-8215-1121-1); tchr's ed. 10.86 (ISBN 0-8215-1131-9); wkbk. 1.65 (ISBN 0-8215-1151-3); compact ed 3.18 (ISBN 0-8215-1101-7). Sadlier.

--Growing with God's Forgiveness & I Celebrate Reconcilation. (Sacrament Program Ser.). 72p. 1985. pap. text ed. 3.30 (ISBN 0-8215-2371-6); tchr's. ed. 4.50 (ISBN 0-8215-2373-2); Parent Pack (10 booklets) 5.04 (ISBN 0-8215-2377-5). Sadlier.

--Growing with Jesus. 144p. (Orig.). 1983. pap. text ed. 3.69 (ISBN 0-8215-1122-X); 10.86 (ISBN 0-8215-1132-7); wkbk. 1.65 (ISBN 0-8215-1152-1); compact ed. 3.18 (ISBN 0-8215-1102-5). Sadlier.

--Growing with the Bread of Life & My Mass Book. (Sacrament Program Ser.). 72p. 1985. pap. text ed. 3.30 (ISBN 0-8215-2370-8); tchr's. ed. 4.50 (ISBN 0-8215-2372-4); Parent Pack (10 booklets) 5.04 (ISBN 0-8215-2376-7). Sadlier.

Delafield, E. Love Prescription. (Stories That Win Ser.). 64p. 1980. pap. 0.95 (ISBN 0-8163-0410-6). Pacific Pr Pub Assn.

Delaforge, Gaetan. The Templar Tradition in the Age of Aquarius. (Illus.). 175p. (Orig.). 1987. pap. 10.00 (ISBN 0-939660-20-2). Threshold VT.

De La Fuente, Tomas. Abraham y Jose el Patriarca: Personas Importantes de la Biblia. (Span., Illus.). 76p. 1982. pap. 2.50 (ISBN 0-940048-03-5). Austin Bilingual Lang Ed.

--La Hermosa Historia de Jesus: Ordenada, Simplificada y Brevemente Explicada. 1983. pap. 4.95 (ISBN 0-311-04658-4). Casa Bautista.

De La Fuente, Tomas, tr. see Cowan, Marvin W.

De La Fuente, Tomas R. Jesus Nos Habla Por Medio De Sus Parabolas. 160p. 1978. 2.95 (ISBN 0-311-04344-5). Casa Bautista.

DeLage, Ida. What Does a Witch Need? LC 76-143305. (Old Witch Bks.). (Illus.). 48p. 1971. PLB 6.69 (ISBN 0-8116-4058-2). Garrard.

Delahoyde, Melinda. Fighting for Life. 96p. (Orig.). 1984. pap. 3.95 (ISBN 0-89283-138-3). Servant.

De la Mare, Walter. Stories from the Bible. (Illus.). 418p. 1985. pap. 6.95 (ISBN 0-571-11086-X). Faber & Faber.

De Lamartine, Alphonse see Lamartine, Alphonse de.

Delaney, C. F., ed. Rationality & Religious Belief. LC 79-63359. (Studies in the Philosophy of Religion: No. 1). 1979. text ed. 12.95x (ISBN 0-268-01602-X, 85-16023); pap. text ed. 5.95x (ISBN 0-268-01603-8, 85-16031). U of Notre Dame Pr.

Delaney, Howard L., jt. auth. see Stauter, Patrick C.

Delaney, John J. Dictionary of American Catholic Biography. LC 83-25524. 624p. 1984. 24.95 (ISBN 0-385-17878-6). Doubleday.

--Dictionary of Saints. LC 79-7783. (Illus.). 648p. 1980. 24.95 (ISBN 0-385-13594-7). Doubleday.

--Pocket Dictionary of Saints. LC 82-45479. 528p. 1983. pap. 6.95 (ISBN 0-385-18274-0, Im). Doubleday.

--Saints Are Now: Eight Portraits of Modern Sanctity. LC 82-45866. 224p. 1983. pap. 4.50 (ISBN 0-385-17356-3, Im). Doubleday.

Delaney, John J., ed. Saints for All Seasons. LC 77-81438. 1978. pap. 3.95 (ISBN 0-385-12909-2, Im). Doubleday.

--Woman Clothed with the Sun. LC 60-5922. 1961. pap. 4.50 (ISBN 0-385-08019-0, Im). Doubleday.

Delaney, John J., tr. The Practice of the Presence of God. LC 77-70896. 1977. pap. 2.95 (ISBN 0-385-12861-4, Im). Doubleday.

Delaney, Sue. The Lord, the Lion & Mutn. pap. 0.95 (ISBN 0-89985-995-X). Christ Nations.

--Mutu Finds the Way to Heaven. pap. 0.95 (ISBN 0-89985-996-8). Christ Nations.

De Lange, N. R. Origen & the Jews. LC 75-36293. (Oriental Publications Ser.: No. 25). 160p. 1977. 39.50 (ISBN 0-521-20542-5). Cambridge U Pr.

De Lange, Nicholas. Judaism. 224p. 1986. 14.95 (ISBN 0-19-219198-5). Oxford U Pr.

Delanghe, Jules A. The Philosophy of Jesus: Real Love. LC 72-96805. 1973. 4.95 (ISBN 0-8059-1821-3). Dorrance.

Delanglez, Jean. The French Jesuits in Lower Louisiana (1700-1763) LC 73-3576. (Catholic University of America. Studies in American Church History: No. 21). Repr. of 1935 ed. 46.00 (ISBN 0-404-57771-7). AMS Pr.

De Langre, Jacques. Food Consciousness for Spiritual Development. LC 80-84993. (Illus., Orig.). 1986. pap. 6.00 (ISBN 0-916508-05-6). Happiness Pr.

Delano, Lucile. Charles de Lannoy: Victor of Pavia. 144p. 1983. 9.75 (ISBN 0-8158-0442-3). Chris Mass.

Delano, Sterling F. The Harbinger & New England Transcendentalism: A Portrait of Associationism in America. 224p. 1983. 27.50 (ISBN 0-8386-3138-X). Fairleigh Dickinson.

Delany, Selden P. Married Saints. facs. ed. LC 69-17573. (Essay Index Reprint Ser). 1935. 18.00 (ISBN 0-8369-0071-5). Ayer Co Pubs.

Delaporte. The Devil: Does He Exist & What Does He Do? 212p. 1982. pap. 4.00 (ISBN 0-89555-173-X). TAN Bks Pubs.

De La Rue, Pierre. Magnificat Quinti Toni. Davison, Nigel, ed. LC 65-26095. (Penn State Music Series, No. 8). 19p. 1965. pap. 3.00x (ISBN 0-271-73081-1). Pa St U Pr.

De La Saussaye, P. Chantepie. The Religion of the Teutons. LC 76-27519. 1976. Repr. of 1902 ed. lib. bdg. 50.00 (ISBN 0-89341-030-6). Longwood Pub Group.

De La Touche, Louise M. The Book of Infinite Love. O'Connell, E. Patrick, tr. from Fr. LC 79-90488. 1979. pap. 3.00 (ISBN 0-89555-129-2). TAN Bks Pubs.

--The Little Book of the Work of Infinite Love. LC 79-90490. 1979. pap. 1.50 (ISBN 0-89555-130-6). TAN Bks Pubs.

--The Sacred Heart & the Priesthood. LC 79-90487. 1979. pap. 5.00 (ISBN 0-89555-128-4). TAN Bks Pubs.

Delattre, Floris. La Literature De L'angleterre Puritaine 1603-1660. 1978. Repr. lib. bdg. 25.00 (ISBN 0-8492-0692-8). R West.

Delaughter, Thomas J. Malachi: Messenger of Divine Love. LC 75-40410. 160p. (Orig.). 1976. 6.00 (ISBN 0-914520-08-3); pap. text ed. 5.00 (ISBN 0-914520-07-5). Insight Pr.

DeLaura, David, ed. see Newman, John H.

Delaville Le Roulx, Joseph. La France en Orient au XIVe Siecle, 2 vols. LC 78-63335. (The Crusades & Military Orders: Second Ser.). Repr. of 1886 ed. Set. 37.50 (ISBN 0-404-17020-X). AMS Pr.

Delbanco, Nicholas, jt. ed. see Heimert, Alan.

DelBene, Ron & Montgomery, Herb. Alone with God: A Place for Your Time Together. 120p. (Orig.). 1984. pap. 4.95 (ISBN 0-86683-856-2, 8434, HarpR). Har-Row.

--Breath of Life: Discovering Your Breath Prayer. 108p. (Orig.). 1981. pap. 3.95 (ISBN 0-86683-639-X, HarpR). Har-Row.

--Hunger of the Heart. 96p. (Orig.). 1983. pap. 4.95 (ISBN 0-86683-801-5, HarpR). Har-Row.

Del Caro, Adrian. Dionysian Aesthetics: The Role of Destruction in Creation as Reflected in the Life & Works of Friedrich Nietzsche. (European University Studies: Series 20, Philosophy: Vol. 69). 157p. 1980. 20.65 (ISBN 3-8204-6819-6). P Lang Pubs.

Delehaye, Hippolyte. The Legends of the Saints. LC 77-26797. 1907. 30.00 (ISBN 0-8414-3657-6). Folcroft.

--Les Origines du Culte des martyrs. 2nd, rev. ed. LC 78-63459. (The Crusades & Military Orders: Second Ser.). Repr. of 1933 ed. 40.00 (ISBN 0-404-16518-4). AMS Pr.

DeLellis, Leatrice, ed. see Portilla, Lorraine.

De Leon, Daniel. Abolition of Poverty. 8th ed. 1969. pap. text ed. 0.50 (ISBN 0-935534-00-8). NY Labor News.

--The Vatican in Politics. 4th ed. 1962. pap. text ed. 0.50 (ISBN 0-935534-31-8). NY Labor News.

De Lerin, O. S. D., tr. see Hudson, R. Lofton.

De Lerin, Olivia, tr. see Crane, J. D.

De Lerin, Olivia S. Enviame a Mi: Aventuras de los esposos Davis, fundadores de la C. B. P. 64p. 1980. pap. 1.75 (ISBN 0-311-01062-8). Casa Bautista.

De Lerin, Olivia S. D., tr. see Bisagno, Juan.

De Leu, Barbara, jt. auth. see Walters, Julie.

Delfeld, Paula. The Indian Priest: Philip B. Gordon, 1885-1948. 1977. 5.95 (ISBN 0-8199-0650-6). Franciscan Herald.

Delgado, Ady, tr. see Brand, Paul & Yancey, Philip.

Delgado, Conchita, tr. see Cummins, D. Duane.

Delgado, Gabriel. A Love Story. 64p. (Orig.). pap. 1.25 (ISBN 0-89228-046-8). Impact Bks MO.

D'Elia, Donald. The Spirits of Seventy-Six: A Catholic Inquiry. 182p. (Orig.). pap. 6.95 (ISBN 0-931888-10-7). Christendom Pubns.

De Liguori, Alphonse. How to Converse Continually & Familiarly with God. Aubin, tr. 2.95 (ISBN 0-8198-0062-7). Dghtrs St Paul.

De Lint, J. G. Rembrandt. Repr. 20.00 (ISBN 0-8482-3695-5). Norwood Edns.

De Lion, Gwoffrey, et al. Chronicles of the Crusades. Giles, John A. & Johnes, Thomas, trs. LC 73-84862. (Bohn's Antiquarian Library Ser.). Repr. of 1848 ed. 41.50 (ISBN 0-404-50014-5). AMS Pr.

Delisle, Leopold V., ed. Rouleaux Des Morts Du IXe Au XVe Siecle. 1866. 43.00 (ISBN 0-384-11361-3); pap. 37.00 (ISBN 0-384-11360-5). Johnson Repr.

Delitzsch, F., jt. auth. see Gloag, P. J.

Delitzsch, Franz. Commentary on the Epistle to the Hebrews, 2 vols. 1978. Set. 31.50 (ISBN 0-86524-110-4, 5801). Klock & Klock.

--A New Commentary on Genesis, 2 vols. 1978. Set. 30.50 (ISBN 0-86524-131-7, 0101). Klock & Klock.

Delitzsch, Franz, jt. auth. see Keil, Carl F.

Dell, David J., et al. Guide to Hindu Religion. 1981. lib. bdg. 47.00 (ISBN 0-8161-7903-4, Hall Reference). G K Hall.

Della Mirandola, Giovanni Pico see Pico Della Mirandola, Giovanni.

Della Mirandola, Giovanni Pico see Pico della Mirandola, Giovanni.

Dellinger, Annetta. Chuckles & Challenges. 96p. 1986. pap. 4.95 (ISBN 0-8010-2960-0). Baker Bk.

--Happy Talk. 1982. pap. 5.95 (ISBN 0-570-03859-6, 12-2953). Concordia.

--You Are Special to Jesus. 1984. pap. 4.95 (ISBN 0-570-04089-2, 56-1457). Concordia.

Dellinger, Annetta E. Adopted & Loved Forever. (Illus.). 1987. 3.95 (ISBN 0-570-04167-8). Concordia.

--Angels Are My Friends. LC 85-7858. 32p. 1985. 4.95 (ISBN 0-570-04120-1, 56-1531). Concordia.

--I Talk to God. LC 84-50287. (Little Happy Day Bks.). (Illus.). 24p. (Orig.). 1984. pap. 0.49 (ISBN 0-87239-802-1, 2162). Standard Pub.

Delliquadri, Lyn, ed. Drawings: Eighty-First Exhibition by Artists of Chicago & Vicinity. 32p. (Orig.). 1985. pap. 6.95 (ISBN 0-86559-071-0). Art Inst Chi.

Dell'Isola, Frank. Thomas Merton: A Bibliography. rev. ed. LC 74-79148. (Serif Ser.: No. 31). 200p. 1975. 13.50x (ISBN 0-87338-156-4). Kent St U Pr.

Delloff, Linda M., ed. see Sittler, Joseph A.

Delloff, Linda Marie, ed. see Sittler, Joseph.

Dellosa, Janet, jt. auth. see Carson, Patti.

Delmage, Lewis, tr. see Ignatius, Saint.

Del Mastro, M. L., tr. Revelations of Divine Love: Juliana of Norwich. LC 76-52004. 1977. pap. 4.95 (ISBN 0-385-12297-7, Im). Doubleday.

Del Mastro, M. L., jt. tr. see Meisel, Anthony C.

Del Mazza, Valentino. Good News for the Liturgical Community: Cycle B. 1980. 5.95 (ISBN 0-8198-3004-6); pap. 4.95 (ISBN 0-8198-3005-4). Dghtrs St Paul.

--Good News for the Liturgical Community: Cycle C. rev. ed. 1981. 5.95 (ISBN 0-8198-0573-4); pap. 4.95 (ISBN 0-8198-3003-8). Dghtrs St Paul.

--Our Lady among Us. 1978. 4.00 (ISBN 0-8198-0363-4); pap. 3.00 (ISBN 0-8198-0364-2). Dghtrs St Paul.

Delnay, Robert G. Teach As He Taught: How to Apply Jesus' Teaching Methods. (Orig.). 1987. pap. 5.95 (ISBN 0-8024-4340-0). Moody.

DeLoach, Clarence, Jr., ed. The Faith Once Delivered. (Illus.). 170p. 1974. 6.95 (ISBN 0-88428-033-0). Parchment Pr.

Deloe, Jesse B. Sweeter Than Honey. pap. 4.95 (ISBN 0-88469-105-5). BMH Bks.

De Lopez, Mary W., tr. see Granjon, Henry.

Deloria, Vine, Jr. God Is Red. 1983. pap. 3.95 (ISBN 0-440-33044-0, LE). Dell.

--The Metaphysics of Modern Existence. LC 76-8708. (Native American Publishing Program Ser.). 1978. 8.45 (ISBN 0-06-450250-3, HarpR). Har-Row.

Delp, Paul S. The Life of Mind. LC 82-61238. (Illus.). 125p. (Orig., PB). 1983. pap. 10.00 (ISBN 0-935356-05-3). Mills Pub Co.

Del Punta, Francesco, ed. Guillelmi de Ockham: Opera Philosophica, Vol. 3. 1979. 29.00 (ISBN 0-686-27931-X). Franciscan Inst.

--Paul of Venice, Logica Magna, Part II, Fasc. 6. Adams, Marilyn M., tr. from Latin. 288p. 1978. 27.00 (ISBN 0-85672-695-8, Pub. by British Acad). Longwood Pub Group.

De Lubac, Henri. A Brief Catechesis on Nature & Grace. Arnandez, Richard, tr. from Fr. LC 83-82108. Tr. of Petite Catechese sur Nature et Grace. 308p. (Orig.). 1984. pap. 10.95 (ISBN 0-89870-035-3). Ignatius Pr.

--Christian Faith. Arnandez, Richard, tr. from Fr. LC 84-80903. Orig. Title: La Foi Chretienne. 353p. (Orig.). 1986. pap. 12.95 (ISBN 0-89870-053-1). Ignatius Pr.

--Christian Faith. 1986. pap. 12.95 (ISBN 0-317-52368-6, HarpR). Har-Row.

De Lubac, Henry. Paradoxes & Further Paradoxes. Simon, Paule, et al, trs. LC 86-62928. Orig. Title: Paradoxes, Nuveaux Paradoxes. (Fr.). 222p. (Orig.). 1986. pap. 11.95 (ISBN 0-89870-132-5). Ignatius Pr.

De Lubicz, Isha S. The Opening of the Way. Gleadow, Rupert, tr. LC 81-782. 256p. 1981. pap. 9.95 (ISBN 0-89281-015-7). Inner Tradit.

De Lubicz, R. A. Schwaller see Schwaller de Lubicz, R. A.

De Luca, Anthony J. Freud & Future Religious Experience. (Quality Paperback Ser: No. 330). 263p. 1977. pap. 4.95 (ISBN 0-8226-0330-6). Littlefield.

Delumeau, Jean. Catholicism Between Luther & Voltaire: A New View of the Counter-Reformation. Moiser, Jeremy, tr. LC 77-4005. 314p. 1977. 21.50 (ISBN 0-664-21341-3). Westminster.

Delve, Eric. To Boldly Go. 132p. 1986. pap. 4.95 (ISBN 0-89693-275-3). Victor Bks.

Del Vecchio, Anthony & Del Vecchio, Mary. Preparing for the Sacrament of Marriage. LC 80-67721. (Illus.). 144p. (Orig.). 1980. pap. 3.95 (ISBN 0-87793-208-5). Ave Maria.

Del Vecchio, Mary, jt. auth. see Del Vecchio, Anthony.

DeLys, Claudia. Giant Book of Superstitions. 1979. pap. 5.95 (ISBN 0-8065-0721-7). Citadel Pr.

De Maillard, Benjamin. Hindu Theology, Egyptian Civilization & the Growth of European Culture. (Illus.). 156p. 1986. 137.50 (ISBN 0-89266-548-3). Am Classical Coll Pr.

De Maistre, Joseph M. see Maistre, Joseph M. De.

DeMallie, Raymond J., ed. see Walker, James R.

De Manhar, Nurho. The Zohar: Bereshith. rev.,3rd ed. (Secret Doctrine Reference Ser.). 432p. 1985. 21.00 (ISBN 0-913510-53-X). Wizards.

Demaray, Donald. How Are You Praying? 176p. (Orig.). 1985. pap. 5.95 (ISBN 0-310-23841-2, 6801P). Zondervan.

--Near Hurting People: The Pastoral Ministry of Robert Moffat Fine. (Illus.). 1978. pap. 3.50 (ISBN 0-89367-024-3). Light & Life.

Demaray, Donald E. Basic Beliefs. 1958. pap. 4.50 (ISBN 0-8010-2827-2). Baker Bk.

--Introduction to Homiletics. 140p. 1978. pap. 5.95 (ISBN 0-8010-2892-2). Baker Bk.

--Laughter, Joy, & Healing. 160p. 1987. pap. 7.95 (ISBN 0-8010-2969-4). Baker Bk.

--Proclaiming the Truth. 1980. pap. 6.95 (ISBN 0-8010-2898-1). Baker Bk.

Demaray, Donald E. & Bro. Lawrence, eds. The Practice of the Presence of God. (Devotional Classics Ser). 64p. 1975. pap. 2.45 (ISBN 0-8010-2844-2). Baker Bk.

Demaray, Kathleen. Instruye al Nino. Orig. Title: Train up a Child. (Span., Illus.). 24p. 1982. Spiral Wire Bound 5.95 (ISBN 0-89367-085-5). Light & Life.

De Marchi, Attilio. Il Culto Privato di Roma Antica, 2 vols. in 1. facsimile ed. LC 75-10641. (Ancient Religion & Mythology Ser.). (Ital., Illus.). 1976. Repr. 40.00x (ISBN 0-405-07011-X). Ayer Co Pubs.

DeMarco, Donald. The Anesthetic Society. 182p. (Orig.). 1982. pap. 6.95 (ISBN 0-931888-09-3). Christendom Pubns.

Demaree, Doris C. Bible Boys & Girls. (Bible Stories for Children Ser.). (Illus.). 1970. pap. 1.50 (ISBN 0-87162-002-2, D1443). Warner Pr.

--Bible Heroes. (Bible Stories for Children Ser.). 1970. pap. 1.50 (ISBN 0-87162-004-9, D1444). Warner Pr.

--Exciting Adventures. (Bible Stories for Children Ser.). 1974. pap. 1.50 (ISBN 0-87162-235-1, D1445). Warner Pr.

--Followers of God. (Bible Stories for Children Ser.). 1974. pap. 1.50 (ISBN 0-87162-236-X, D1446). Warner Pr.

--Helping Others. (Bible Stories for Children Ser.). 1970. pap. 1.50 (ISBN 0-87162-237-8, D1447). Warner Pr.

--Living for Jesus. (Bible Stories for Children Ser.). 1974. pap. 1.50 (ISBN 0-87162-238-6, D1448). Warner Pr.

Demarest, Arthur A., jt. auth. see Conrad, Geoffrey W.

Demarest, Bruce. A HIstory of Interpretation of Hebrews 7, 1-10 from the Reformation to the Present. 154p. 1976. pap. text ed. 28.50x (Pub. by J C B Mohr BRD). Coronet Bks.

Demarest, Bruce, jt. ed. see Lewis, Gordon R.

Demarest, Bruce A. General Revelation: Historical Views & Contemporary Issues. 320p. 1982. 14.95 (ISBN 0-310-44550-7, 12706). Zondervan.

--Who Is Jesus? 132p. 1983. pap. 4.50 (ISBN 0-88207-103-3). SP Pubns.

--Who Is Jesus. Chen, Ruth T., tr. (Basic Doctrine Ser.: Bk. 1). 1985. pap. write for info. (ISBN 0-941598-26-8). Living Spring Pubns.

Demarest, Bruce A., jt. auth. see Lewis, Gordon R.

Demarest, Victoria B. God, Woman & Ministry. rev. ed. LC 76-42915. (Illus.). 1978. 6.95 (ISBN 0-912760-61-3). Valkyrie Pub Hse.

--Sex & Spirit: God, Woman, & the Ministry. LC 76-42915. (Illus.). 1977. 6.95 (ISBN 0-912760-38-9); pap. 4.95 (ISBN 0-912760-29-X). Valkyrie Pub Hse.

De Margerie, Bertrand. Christ for the World. Carroll, Malachy, tr. from Fr. Tr. of Christ Pour le Monde. write for info (ISBN 0-8199-0460-0); pap. 3.95 (ISBN 0-8199-0485-6). Franciscan Herald.

--The Christian Trinity in History. Fortman, E. J., tr. from Fr. LC 81-8735. Tr. of La Trinite Christienne dans l'histoire. 1982. cloth 29.95 (ISBN 0-932506-14-3). St Bedes Pubns.

--Human Knowledge of Christ. 1980. 2.95 (ISBN 0-8198-3301-0); pap. 1.50 (ISBN 0-8198-3302-9). Dghtrs St Paul.

--Remarried Divorcees & Eucharistic Communion. 1980. pap. 1.95 (ISBN 0-8198-6401-3). Dghtrs St Paul.

--A Theological Retreat. 280p. 1977. 8.95 (ISBN 0-8199-0584-4). Franciscan Herald.

De Maria, Richard. Communal Love at Oneida: A Perfectionist Vision of Authority, Property & Sexual Order. LC 78-60958. (Texts & Studies in Religion: Vol. 2). xiii, 248p. 1978. soft cover 19.95x (ISBN 0-88946-986-5). E Mellen.

DeMaria, Richard. Communal Love at Oneida: A Perfectionist Vision of Authority, Property & Sexual Order. 2nd. ed. LC 78-60958. (Texts & Studies in Religion: Vol. 2). 248p. 1983. 49.95x (ISBN 0-88946-988-1). E Mellen.

De Martinez, Violeta S., tr. see Stowell, Gordon.

DeMartini, Rodney J. Be with Me Lord: Prayers for the Sick. LC 82-71881. 96p. (Orig.). 1982. pap. 2.95 (ISBN 0-87793-256-5). Ave Maria.

Dembitz, Lewis N. Jewish Services in Synagogue & Home. facs. ed. LC 74-27977. (Modern Jewish Experience Ser.). 1975. Repr. of 1898 ed. 40.00x (ISBN 0-405-06706-2). Ayer Co Pubs.

De Mello, Anthony. One-Minute Wisdom. LC 85-29003. 216p. 1986. 14.95 (ISBN 0-385-23585-2). Doubleday.

DeMello, Anthony. Sadhana: A Way to God. LC 84-6735. 144p. 1984. pap. 5.50 (ISBN 0-385-19614-8, Im). Doubleday.

De Mello, Anthony. Sadhana: A Way to God, Christian Exercises in Eastern Form. LC 78-70521. (Study Aids on Jesuit Topics: No. 9). 146p. 1978. pap. 4.95 (ISBN 0-912422-46-7). Inst Jesuit.

DeMello, Anthony. Song of the Bird. LC 84-10105. (Illus.). 192p. 1984. pap. 6.95 (ISBN 0-385-19615-6, Im). Doubleday.

--Wellsprings: A Book of Spiritual Exercises. LC 84-13655. 216p. 1985. 13.95 (ISBN 0-385-19616-4). Doubleday.

--Wellsprings: A Book of Spiritual Exercises. LC 86-4478. 240p. 1986. pap. 7.95 (ISBN 0-385-19617-2, Im). Doubleday.

DeMena, Henry F. How to Increase Parish Income. 144p. 1982. pap. 12.95 (ISBN 0-89622-160-1). Twenty-Third.

De Menil, Dominique, intro. by. Constant Companions: An Exhibition of Mythological Animals, Demons, & Monsters. (Illus.). 1964. pap. 6.00 (ISBN 0-914412-19-1). Inst for the Arts.

De Merchant, Joan see Merchant, Joan de & Gallagher, Merchant.

Demetrio, Francisco R. Christianity in Context. 134p. 1981. pap. 5.50x (ISBN 0-686-32576-1, Pub. by New Day Phillipines). Cellar.

DeMile, James W. Tao of E Wing Chun Do, 2 pts, Vol. 1, pt. 1. 4th ed. (Illus.). 1983. 6.95 ea. (ISBN 0-918642-01-9); Pt. 1. Pt. 2. Tao of Wing.

Deming, Doris R. Touch of Infinity. 1984. 6.75 (ISBN 0-8062-2224-7). Carlton.

DeMolen, Richard L., ed. Erasmus. LC 73-89992. (Documents of Modern History Ser.). 208p. 1974. 18.95 (ISBN 0-312-25795-3). St Martin.

--Erasmus of Rotterdam: A Quincentennial Symposium. LC 76-125264. 151p. 1971. text ed. 29.00x (ISBN 0-8290-0170-0). Irvington.

--Leaders of the Reformation. LC 83-51423. 360p. 1984. 39.50 (ISBN 0-941664-05-8, Pub. Susquehanna U Pr). Assoc Univ Prs.

De Molina, Sara Pais, tr. see Haas, Harold I.

De Monfort, St. Louis. The Secret of the Rosary. Barbour, Mary, tr. from Fr. 1976. pap. 1.00 (ISBN 0-89555-056-3). TAN Bks Pubs.

De Monstrelet, Enguerrend. Chronique D'Enguerrand De Monstrelet, 6 Vols. Douet D'Arcq, L., ed. 1857-62. Set. 255.00 (ISBN 0-384-39781-6); Set. pap. 220.00 (ISBN 0-384-39780-8). Johnson Repr.

De Montault, X. Barbier. Traite d'Iconographie Chretienne. (Fr., Illus.). 972p. Repr. of 1890 ed. lib. bdg. 200.00x (ISBN 0-89241-137-6). Caratzas.

De Montfort, Louis. True Devotion. LC 63-12679. 1973. 3.50 (ISBN 0-8198-0517-3); pap. 2.50. Dghtrs St Paul.

De Montfort, St. Louis. Love of Eternal Wisdom. 4.95 (ISBN 0-910984-51-4); pap. 2.95 (ISBN 0-910984-05-0). Montfort Pubns.

De Montfort, St. Louis Marie. True Devotion to the Blessed Virgin. 4.95 (ISBN 0-910984-49-2); pap. 3.95 (ISBN 0-910984-50-6). Montfort Pubns.

De Montmorency, J. E. Thomas A'Kempis: His Age & Book. LC 73-103183. 1970. Repr. of 1906 ed. 30.00x (ISBN 0-8046-0820-2, Pub by Kennikat). Assoc Faculty Pr.

De Montrond, M. Dictionnaire des Abbayes et Monasteres ou Histoire Des Establissements Religieux. Migne, J. P., ed. (Troisieme et Derniere Encyclopedie Theologique Ser.: Vol. 16). (Fr.). 614p. Repr. of 1856 ed. lib. bdg. 81.00x (ISBN 0-89241-299-2). Caratzas.

De Mornay, Charlotte A. Memoires, 2 vols. 1869. Set. 67.00 (ISBN 0-384-40148-1); Set. pap. 55.00 (ISBN 0-384-40149-X). Johnson Repr.

Demos, Jean, tr. see Tsatsos, Ioanna.

Demos, John. Little Commonwealth: Family Life in Plymouth Colony. (Illus.). 1970. pap. 6.95x (ISBN 0-19-501355-7). Oxford U Pr.

Demos, John P. Entertaining Satan: Witchcraft & the Culture of Early New England. LC 81-22463. 558p. 1982. 29.95x (ISBN 0-19-503131-8); pap. 12.95 (ISBN 0-19-503378-7). Oxford U Pr.

DeMott, Harold. Beacon Small-Group Bible Studies, Daniel: Daring to Live by Faith. Wolf, Earl C., ed. 96p. (Orig.). 1985. pap. 2.50 (ISBN 0-8341-0962-X). Beacon Hill.

Dempsey, Elbert A. God's Other Books. 1987. pap. 12.75 (ISBN 0-8309-0464-6). Herald Hse.

Dempsey, T. Delphic Oracle: Its Early History, Influence & Fall. LC 69-13234. Repr. of 1918 ed. 15.00 (ISBN 0-405-08442-0). Ayer Co Pubs.

Demus, Otto. Byzantine Mosaic Decoration: Aspects of Monumental Art in Byzantium. (Illus.). 162p. 1976. 25.00 (ISBN 0-89241-018-3). Caratzas.

Den Bleyker, Merle, jt. auth. see Hendricks, William C.

Dencher, Ted. Why I Left Jehovah's Witnesses. 1966. pap. 5.95 (ISBN 0-87508-183-5). Chr Lit.

Dencke, J., et al see David, Hans T.

De Nebesky-Wojkowitz, Rene see Nebesky-Wojkowitz, Rene De.

Denef, Lawrence W., tr. see Lapide, Pinchas & Stuhlmacher, Peter.

Denef, Lawrence W., tr. see Loewenich, Walther von.

DeNevi, Don & Moholy, Noel. Junipero Serra: The Illustrated Story of the Franciscan Founder of California's Missions. LC 84-47718. (Illus.). 256p. 1985. 14.45 (ISBN 0-06-061876-0, HarpR). Har-Row.

Dengevin, K. The Idea of Justice in Christian Perspective. 1978. pap. 2.95 (ISBN 0-88906-102-5). Radix Bks.

Dengler, Sandy. D. L. Moody: God's Salesman. (Preteen Biography Ser.). (Orig.). 1986. pap. 3.50 (ISBN 0-8024-1786-8). Moody.

--Susanna Wesley: Servant of God. (Preteen Biographies Ser.). (YA) 1987. pap. text ed. 3.95 (ISBN 0-8024-8414-X). Moody.

--To Die in the Queen of Cities: A Story of the Christian Courage & Love in the Face of Roman Persecution. 256p. 1986. pap. 6.95 (ISBN 0-8407-5996-7). Nelson.

Deng Ming-Dao. The Wandering Taoist. LC 82-48925. (Illus.). 272p. 1986. pap. 6.95 (ISBN 0-06-250226-3, HarpR). Har-Row.

Den Haag, Ernest Van see Van Den Haag, Ernest.

De Nicolas, Antonio. Powers of Imagining: Ignatius de Loyola: A Philosophical Hermeneutic of Imagining through the Collected Works of Ignatius de Loyola with a Translation of These Works. 416p. 1986. 44.50x (ISBN 0-88706-109-5); pap. 19.95x (ISBN 0-88706-110-9). State U NY Pr.

De Nicolas, Antonio T. Avatara: The Humanization of Philosophy Through the Bhagavad Gita. LC 76-152. 1976. 12.50 (ISBN 0-89254-001-X); pap. 8.50 (ISBN 0-89254-002-8). Nicolas-Hays.

--Meditations Through the Rg Veda: Four-Dimensional Man. LC 76-39692. 1976. 12.95 (ISBN 0-89254-004-4). Nicolas-Hays.

De Nicolas, Antonio T. & Moutsopolous, Evanghelos, eds. God: Experience or Origin? (God Ser.). 256p. (Orig.). 1986. 21.95 (ISBN 0-913757-24-1, Pub. by New Era Bks); pap. 12.95 (ISBN 0-913757-25-X, Pub. by New Era Bks). Paragon Hse.

De Nicolas, Antonio T., ed. see Lincoln, Victoria.

Denim, B. C. Different Is Not the Same As Wrong. 1982. pap. 1.95 (ISBN 0-570-08408-3, 39-1083). Concordia.

Denis, Ernest. Huss et les guerres hussites. LC 77-8424. Repr. of 1930 ed. 46.50 (ISBN 0-404-16126-X). AMS Pr.

Denis, Gabriel. Reign of Jesus Thru Mary. 5.50 (ISBN 0-910984-03-4). Montfort Pubns.

Denlinger, Martha. Real People. rev. ed. LC 74-16966. (Illus.). 96p. 1975. pap. 3.95 (ISBN 0-8361-1960-6). Herald Pr.

Dennehy, Raymond. Reason & Dignity. LC 81-40364. 152p. 1982. lib. bdg. 25.00 (ISBN 0-8191-1898-2); pap. text ed. 9.75 (ISBN 0-8191-1899-0). U Pr of Amer.

Dennehy, Raymond, ed. see Muggeridge, Malcolm, et al.

Dennett, E. The Step I Have Taken. Daniel, R. P., ed. 53p. pap. 3.50 (ISBN 0-88172-140-9). Believers Bkshelf.

Denney, James. The Biblical Doctrine of Reconciliation. 348p. 1985. smythe sewn 14.00 (ISBN 0-86524-192-9, 8806). Klock & Klock.

--The Death of Christ. LC 81-81100. (The Shephard Illustrated Classics Ser.). (Illus.). 372p. 1981. pap. 6.95 (ISBN 0-87983-258-4). Keats.

Denney, James D., jt. auth. see Davis, Ron L.

Denney, Reuel. In Praise of Adam. LC 61-18887. (Phoenix Poets Ser). 1961. pap. 1.50 (ISBN 0-226-14301-5, PP3, Phoen). U of Chicago Pr.

Denning, Dennis. We Are One in the Lord: Developing Caring Groups in the Church. LC 81-14958. 96p. (Orig.). 1982. pap. 5.50 (ISBN 0-687-44281-8). Abingdon.

Denning, Melita & Phillips, Osborne. Voudoun Fire: The Living Reality of the Mystical Religions. LC 79-3375. (Mystery Religions Series: No. 1). (Illus.). 172p. (Orig.). 1979. pap. 9.95 (ISBN 0-87542-699-9). Llewellyn Pubns.

Denninger, Richard. Anatomy of the Pure & of the Impure Love. (Intimate Life of Man Library Bk.). (Illus.). 1979. 97.95 (ISBN 0-89266-177-1); spiral bdg. 37.95 (ISBN 0-685-67718-4). Am Classical Coll Pr.

Dennis, Joe. Spreading Truth. 64p. 1979. pap. text ed. 1.95 (ISBN 0-89114-086-7); P. 78. tchrs. ed. 1.95 (ISBN 0-89114-087-5). Baptist Pub Hse.

Dennis, Lane T., ed. The Letters of Francis A. Schaeffer: Spiritual Reality in the Personal Christian Life. LC 85-70473. 264p. (Orig.). 1986. 15.95 (ISBN 0-89107-361-2, Crossway Bks); pap. 7.95 (ISBN 0-89107-409-0, Crossway Bks). Good News.

Dennis, Mildred. Short Talks for Special Occasions, Bk. 1. 64p. 1987. pap. 2.95 (ISBN 0-87403-069-2, 2880). Standard Pub.

--Short Talks for Special Occasions, Bk. 2. 64p. 1987. pap. 2.95 (ISBN 0-87403-070-6, 2881). Standard Pub.

Dennis, Muriel, ed. Chosen Children. 150p. 1978. 6.95 (ISBN 0-89107-154-7). Good News.

Dennison, James T., Jr. The Market Day of the Soul: The Puritan Doctrine of the Sabbath in England, 1532-1700. LC 83-6990. (Illus.). 188p. (Orig.). 1983. lib. bdg. 25.00 (ISBN 0-8191-3204-7); pap. text ed. 11.25 (ISBN 0-8191-3205-5). U Pr of Amer.

Dennison, Mark A. Preparing for the Greatest Two Years of Your Life. pap. 3.95 (ISBN 0-89036-128-2). Hawkes Pub Inc.

Dennison, William D. Paul's Two-Age Construction & Apologetics. LC 85-20272. 144p. (Orig.). 1986. lib. bdg. 19.50 (ISBN 0-8191-5011-8); pap. text ed. 8.75 (ISBN 0-8191-5012-6). U Pr of Amer.

Denniston, Denise, jt. auth. see Goldhaber, Nat.

Denny, Barbara. Kings Bishop. 376p. 1986. 49.00 (ISBN 0-946619-16-6, Pub. by Alderman Pr). State Mutual Bk.

Denny, Don. The Annunciation from the Right: From Early Christian Times to the Sixteenth Century. LC 76-23611. (Outstanding Dissertations in the Fine Arts - 2nd Ser. - Fifteenth Century). (Illus.). 1977. Repr. of 1965 ed. lib. bdg. 55.00 (ISBN 0-8240-2683-7). Garland Pub.

Denny, Frederick M. An Introduction to Islam. 368p. 1985. text ed. write for info. (ISBN 0-02-328520-6). Macmillan.

Denny, Frederick M. & Taylor, Rodney L. The Holy Book in Comparative Perspective. LC 85-8473. (Studies in Comparative Religion). 244p. 1985. 19.95 (ISBN 0-87249-453-5). U of SC Pr.

Denny, James. Death of Christ. 1982. lib. bdg. 12.50 (ISBN 0-86524-090-6, 9507). Klock & Klock.

--Jesus & the Gospel. 1977. lib. bdg. 59.95 (ISBN 0-8490-2095-6). Gordon Pr.

Denny, Randal. The Habit of Happiness. 102p. 1976. 2.50 (ISBN 0-8341-0399-0). Beacon Hill.

Denny, Randal E. Personal Devotions. (Christian Living Ser.). 32p. (Orig.). 1987. pap. write for info. (ISBN 0-8341-1186-1). Beacon Hill.

--Wind in the Rigging. 120p. 1985. pap. 4.50 (ISBN 0-8341-0937-9). Beacon Hill.

De Nogent, Guibert. The Autobiography of Guibert, Abbot of Nogent-Sous-Coucy. Bland, C. C., tr. from Lat. LC 79-11248. 1980. Repr. of 1926 ed. lib. bdg. 24.75x (ISBN 0-313-21460-3, GUAU). Greenwood.

Denslow, Jamin. The Day the Lion Roars. Graves, Helen, ed. LC 86-40284. 286p. (Orig.). 1987. pap. 8.95 (ISBN 1-55523-029-6). Winston-Derek.

Densmore, Frances. Menominee Music. LC 72-1882. (Music Ser.). (Illus.). 286p. 1972. Repr. of 1932 ed. lib. bdg. 29.50 (ISBN 0-306-70510-9). Da Capo.

Dent, Arthur. The Plaine Mans Path-Way to Heaven. LC 74-80173. (English Experience Ser.: No. 652). 430p. 1974. Repr. of 1601 ed. 29.00 (ISBN 90-221-0652-7). Walter J Johnson.

Dent, C. M. Protestant Reformers in Elizabethan England. (Oxford Theological Monographs). 1985. 39.95x (ISBN 0-19-826723-1). Oxford U Pr.

Dent, George, jt. auth. see Sims, Albert E.

Dent, N. J. The Moral Psychology of the Virtues. LC 83-26208. (Cambridge Studies in Philosophy). 240p. 1984. 37.50 (ISBN 0-521-25726-3). Cambridge U Pr.

Den Tak Richard, Van see Van Den Tak, Richard.

Dentan, Robert C. First, Second Kings & First, Second Chronicles. LC 59-10454. (Layman's Bible Commentary Ser., Vol. 7). 1964. pap. 4.95 (ISBN 0-8042-3067-6). John Knox.

--Holy Scriptures: A Survey. (Orig.). 1949. pap. 5.95 (ISBN 0-8164-2031-9, SP1, HarpR). Har-Row.

Denton, Juanita H., jt. auth. see Denton, Wallace.

Denton, Wallace & Denton, Juanita H. Creative Couples: The Growth Factor in Marriage. LC 82-17439. 154p. 1983. pap. 8.95 (ISBN 0-664-24453-X). Westminster.

D'Entreves, A. P., ed. Thomas Aquinas: Selected Political Writings. Dawson, J. G., tr. 136p. 1981. 26.50x; pap. 9.95x (ISBN 0-389-20244-4). B&N Imports.

D'Entreves, Alexander P. Medieval Contribution to Political Thought: Thomas Aquinas, Marsilius of Padua, Richard Hooker. 1959. Repr. of 1939 ed. text ed. 12.50x (ISBN 0-391-00513-8). Humanities.

Denwood, Philip & Piatigorsky, Alexander. Buddhist Studies: Ancient & Modern. 220p. 1981. 30.00x (ISBN 0-7007-0153-2, Pub. by Curzon England). State Mutual Bk.

Denwood, Philip & Piatigorsky, Alexander, eds. Buddhist Studies: Ancient & Modern. (Collected Papers on South Asia: No. 4). (Illus.). 206p. 1983. 24.50x (ISBN 0-389-20264-9, 07082). B&N Imports.

Denyer, C. P., tr. see Halley, Henry H.

Denyer, Carlos. Concordancia de las Sagradas Escrituras. LC 74-21722. (Span.). 936p. 1969. 28.95 (ISBN 0-89922-004-5); pap. 21.95 (ISBN 0-89922-121-1). Edit Caribe.

De Oca, V. Montes, tr. see Dacruz, J.

De Oliveira, Joseph see Oliveira, Joseph De.

DeOreo, Joellen K., jt. auth. see Boger, Ann C.

DePalma, David J. & Foley, Jeanne M. Moral Development: Current Theory & Research. LC 75-14211. 206p. 1975. text ed. 24.95x (ISBN 0-89859-116-3). L Erlbaum Assocs.

De Paola, Tomie. The Family Christmas Tree Book. LC 80-12081. (Illus.). 32p. 1980. reinforced bdg. 11.95 (ISBN 0-8234-0416-1). Holiday.

--Francis: The Poor Man of Assisi. LC 81-6984. (Illus.). 48p. 1982. reinforced 14.95 (ISBN 0-8234-0435-8). Holiday.

--The Friendly Beasts: An Old English Christmas Carol. (Illus.). 32p. 1981. 10.95 (ISBN 0-399-20739-2); pap. 4.95 (ISBN 0-399-20777-5). Putnam Pub Group.

DePaola, Tomie. The Miracles of Christ. LC 86-18297. (Illus.). 1987. price not set reinforced bdg. (ISBN 0-8234-0635-0). Holiday.

--Noah & the Ark. (Illus.). 40p. (Orig.). 1983. 12.95 (ISBN 0-86683-699-3, AY8268, HarpR); pap. 5.95. Har-Row.

--Noah & the Ark. (Illus.). 32p. 1983. 12.95 (ISBN 0-86683-819-8, AY8451, HarpR). Har-Row.

De Paola, Tomie. Things to Make & Do for Valentine's Day. (Things to Make & Do Ser.). (Illus.). 48p. 1976. PLB 8.90 (ISBN 0-531-01187-9). Watts.

DePaola, Tomie, illus. David & Goliath. (Bible Story Cutout Bks.). (Illus., Orig.). 1984. 32 pages 12.95, (ISBN 0-86683-820-1, 8452, HarpR); pap. 5.95, 40 pages (ISBN 0-86683-700-0, 8469). Har-Row.

--Queen Esther. (Bible Story Cutout Bks.). (Illus., Orig.). 1984. 32p 12.95, (ISBN 0-86683-822-8, 8454, HarpR); pap. 4.95, 40p (ISBN 0-86683-702-7, 8271). Har-Row.

Department of Education, USCC Staff. Serve Together: With Generosity & Love. 1987. pap. 4.95. US Catholic.

De Patterson, Paulina G. Te Damos Gracias, Dios. (Illus.). 28p. 1981. pap. 0.60 (ISBN 0-311-38508-7). Casa Bautista.

De Paul, Vincent. Correspondence, Conferences, Documents, Vol. 1. Law, Helen M., et al, trs. from Fr. & Lat. Kilar, Jacqueline, ed. LC 83-63559. 675p. 1985. 28.00 (ISBN 0-317-27157-1). New City.

De Pauley, William C. Candle of the Lord. facsimile ed. LC 75-107693. (Essay Index Reprint Ser). 1937. 16.00 (ISBN 0-8369-1496-1). Ayer Co Pubs.

--The Candle of the Lord: Studies in the Cambridge Platonists. (Church Historical Society, London, New Ser.: No. 28). pap. 23.00 (ISBN 0-8115-3152-X). Kraus Repr.

De Petri, Catharose. Golden Rosycross. Lectorium Rosicrucianum Staff, tr. from Dutch. Orig. Title: Het Gouden Rozenkruis. Date not set. pap. 8.00. Rosycross Pr.

--Seven Voices Speak. Lectorium Rosicrucianum, ed. Orig. Title: Zeven Stemmen Spreken. (Dutch.). 79p. Date not set. pap. 8.00. Rosycross Pr.

--Transfiguracion. (Span.). 1987. pap. 6.00. Rosycross Pr.

De Petri, Catharose, jt. auth. see Van Rijckenborgh, Jan.

Depew, David J., ed. The Greeks & the Good Life. 280p. lib. bdg. 25.00 (ISBN 0-937622-00-1); pap. text ed. 7.95 (ISBN 0-937622-01-X). CSU Fullerton.

D'Epinay, Christian L. Haven of the Masses: A Study of the Pentecostal Movement in Chile. Sandle, Marjorie, tr. (World Studies of Churches in Mission). 1969. pap. 4.95 (ISBN 0-377-82931-5, Pub. by Lutterworth England). Friend Pr.

De Planhol, Xavier see Planhol, Xavier de.

De Plou, Dafne C., tr. see Drakeford, John W.

De Plou, Dafne C., tr. see Harty, Robert & Harty, Annelle.

De Pomiane, Edouard. The Jews of Poland: Recollections & Recipes. Bacon, Josephine, tr. from Fr. (Jewish Cookery Classics Ser.). Tr. of Cuisine Juive: Ghettos Modernes. (Illus.). 256p. 1985. 9.95 (ISBN 0-910231-02-8); pap. 9.95. Pholiota.

De Poncins, Leon. Freemasonry & the Vatican. 1982. lib. bdg. 69.95 (ISBN 0-87700-351-3). Revisionist Pr.

--Judaism & the Vatican. 1982. lib. bdg. 65.00 (ISBN 0-87700-381-5). Revisionist Pr.

DePoncins, Leon V. Freemasonry & the Vatican. 59.95 (ISBN 0-8490-0196-X). Gordon Pr.

--Judaism & the Vatican. 59.95 (ISBN 0-8490-0466-7). Gordon Pr.

De Pons, Beatriz. Crecer Contigo. 80p. 1978. pap. 2.50 (ISBN 0-311-40037-X). Casa Bautista.

De Pontlarcy, Y., jt. auth. see Picard, J. M.

De Poor, Betty M., tr. Dios, Tu y Tu Familia. (Dios, Tu y la Vida). Orig. Title: Deus, Voce E Sua Familia. 1981. Repr. of 1978 ed. 0.95 (ISBN 0-311-46202-2). Casa Bautista.

Deppermann, Klaus. Melchior Hoffman: Social Unrest & Apocalyptic Visions in the Age of Reformation. Wren, Malcolm, tr. 450p. 1986. 38.95 (ISBN 0-567-09338-7, Pub. by T & T Clark Ltd UK). Fortress.

DePree, Gladis. Festival! An Experiment in Living. 208p. 1985. 12.95 (ISBN 0-310-44110-2, 9488). Zondervan.

DePree, Gladis, jt. auth. see DePree, Gordon.

De Pree, Gladis, jt. auth. see De Pree, Gordon.

De Pree, Gordon & De Pree, Gladis. Blade of Grass. LC 65-19504. 1971. pap. 4.95 (ISBN 0-310-23641-X). Zondervan.

DePree, Gordon & DePree, Gladis. Faces of God. LC 80-14384. 128p. 1980. pap. 5.95 (ISBN 0-664-24350-9). Westminster.

De Pressense, E. Jesus Christ: His Times, Life & Work. 1978. Repr. of 1898 ed. lib. bdg. 50.00 (ISBN 0-8495-1032-5). Arden Lib.

De Purucker, G. Clothed with the Sun: The Mystery-Tale of Jesus the Avatara. rev. ed. Small, Emmett & Todd, Helen, eds. Orig. Title: The Story of Jesus. (Illus.). 56p. 1972. pap. 1.00 (ISBN 0-913004-06-5). Point Loma Pub.

--Dialogues of G. de Purucker, 3 vols. Conger, Arthur L., ed. LC 79-65630. 1948. Set. 25.00 (ISBN 0-911500-59-6). Theos U Pr.

--The Four Sacred Seasons. LC 79-63565. 1979. 5.00 (ISBN 0-911500-83-9); pap. 2.75 (ISBN 0-911500-84-7). Theos U Pr.

--Fundamentals of the Esoteric Philosophy. 2nd, rev. ed. Knoche, Grace F., ed. LC 78-74258. 1979. 14.00 (ISBN 0-911500-63-4); pap. 8.00 (ISBN 0-911500-64-2). Theos U Pr.

--Golden Precepts of Esotericism. 3rd, rev. ed. LC 78-74257. 1979. 5.00 (ISBN 0-911500-85-5); pap. 3.00 (ISBN 0-911500-86-3). Theos U Pr.

--Man in Evolution. 2nd rev. ed. Knoche, Grace F., ed. LC 76-45503. 1977. pap. 6.00 (ISBN 0-911500-55-3). Theos U Pr.

--Occult Glossary. LC 53-37086. (A Compendium of Oriental & Theosophical Terms). 1972. 7.50 (ISBN 0-911500-50-2); pap. 4.00 (ISBN 0-911500-51-0). Theos U Pr.

--The Path of Compassion: Time-honored Principles of Spiritual & Ethical Conduct. 84p. 1986. pap. 4.00 (ISBN 0-911500-69-3). Theos U Pr.
--Wind of the Spirit. 2nd, rev. ed. LC 84-50118. 328p. 1984. 10.00 (ISBN 0-911500-67-7); pap. 5.00 (ISBN 0-911500-68-5). Theos U Pr.
De Purucker, G. & Tingley, Katherine. H. P. Blavatsky: The Mystery. rev. ed. Small, W. Emmett & Todd, Helen, eds. (Illus.). 256p. 1974. pap. 5.25 (ISBN 0-913004-14-6). Point Loma Pub.
De Purucker, G. De see De Purucker, G.
De Rebecque, Constant & Benjamin, Henri. Dupolytheisme Romain: Considere dans ses rapports avec la philosophie grecque et la religion chertienne. Bolle, Kees W., ed. LC 77-79118. (Mythology Ser.). (Fr.). 1978. Repr. of 1833 ed. lib. bdg. 59.50 (ISBN 0-405-10530-4). Ayer Co Pubs.
Derenbourg, Joseph. Essai Sur L'Histoire et la Geographie de la Palestine, D'Apres les Autres Sources Rabbiniques. Premiere Partie, Hisoire Depuis Cyrun Jusqu' a Adrien. 490p. Repr. of 1867 ed. text ed. 99.36x (ISBN 0-576-80155-0). Gregg Intl.
Derham, William. Physico-Theology: A Demonstration of the Being & Attributes of God, from His Works of Creation. Egerton, Frank N., 3rd, ed. LC 77-74212. (History of Ecology Ser.). 1978. Repr. of 1716 ed. lib. bdg. 37.50 (ISBN 0-405-10383-2). Ayer Co Pubs.
DeRidder, Richard R., jt. auth. see Brink, William P.
DeRidder, Richard R., jt. ed. see DeKlerk, Peter.
Dering, Edward. M. Derings Workes: More at Large Than Ever Hath Heer-to-Fore Been Printed, 3 pts. LC 74-38171. (English Experience Ser.: No. 448). 692p. 1972. Repr. of 1597 ed. 95.00 (ISBN 90-221-0448-6). Walter J Johnson.
Derk, Francis H. Names of Christ: A Pocket Guide. LC 75-44928. 176p. 1976. pap. 3.95 (ISBN 0-87123-390-8, 210390). Bethany Hse.
Der Lans, J. M. van see Van Belzen, J. A. & Van Der Lans, J. M.
Der Leeuw, J. J. Van see Van Der Leeuw, J. J.
Derman, Sylvia, ed. see Tarthang Tulku.
Der Mehden, Fred R. Von see Von der Mehden, Fred R.
Dermenghem, Emile. Muhammad & the Islamic Tradition. Watt, Jean M., tr. from Fr. LC 81-47412. (Spiritual Masters Ser.). (Illus.). 192p. 1981. 18.95 (ISBN 0-87951-130-3). Overlook Pr.
--Muhammad & the Islamic Tradition. Watt, Jean M., tr. LC 81-47412. 192p. pap. 9.95 (ISBN 0-87951-170-2). Overlook Pr.
De Robeck, Nesta. Praise the Lord. 1967. 4.50 (ISBN 0-8199-0086-9, L38643). Franciscan Herald.
DeRocco, Jovan. Legend of the Truant Tree. (Illus.). 112p. 1982. 6.50 (ISBN 0-682-49804-1). Exposition Pr FL.
De Rosa Villarosa, Carlantonio. Memorie Degli Scrittori Filippini o Siano Della Congregazione Dell' Oratorio de S. Filippo Neri, 2 vols. 1380p. Date not set. Repr. of 1842 ed. text ed. 74.52x (ISBN 0-576-72217-0, Pub. by Gregg Intl Pubs England). Gregg Intl.
De Rosny, Eric. Healers in the Night. Barr, Robert R., tr. from Fr. LC 85-5659. Tr. of Les Yeaux de Ma Chevre sur les Pas des Maitres de la Nuit en Pays Douala. 304p. (Orig.). 1985. pap. 13.95 (ISBN 0-88344-199-3). Orbis Bks.
Der Osten-Sacken, Peter Von see Von Der Osten-Sacken, Peter.
Derr, Thomas S. Barriers to Ecumenism: The Holy See & the World Council on Social Questions. LC 82-18761. 112p. (Orig.). 1983. pap. 7.95 (ISBN 0-88344-031-8). Orbis Bks.
Derrick, Christopher. Church Authority & Intellectual Freedom. LC 81-80209. 113p. (Orig.). 1981. pap. 7.95 (ISBN 0-89870-011-6). Ignatius Pr.
--Joy Without a Cause: Selected Essays of Christopher Derrick. 254p. 1979. pap. 5.95 (ISBN 0-89385-004-7). Sugden.
--That Strange Divine Sea: Reflections on Being a Catholic. LC 83-80190. 189p. (Orig.). 1983. pap. 8.95 (ISBN 0-89870-029-9). Ignatius Pr.
--Too Many People? A Problem in Values. LC 85-60469. 116p. (Orig.). 1986. pap. 6.95 (ISBN 0-89870-071-X, 85-60469). Ignatius Pr.
--Words & the Word. 134p. 1987. pap. 6.95 (ISBN 0-89870-130-9). Ignatius Pr.
--Words & the Word: Notes on Our Catholic Vocabulary. 1987. pap. 6.95. Ignatius Pr.
Derrida, Jacques. Glas. Leavey, John P., Jr. & Rand, Richard, trs. from Fr. LC 85-28877. vi, 262p. 1986. 50.00x (ISBN 0-8032-1667-X). U of Nebr Pr.
Derstine, Gerald. Destined to Mature. 144p. (Orig.). 1984. pap. 3.50 (ISBN 0-88368-147-1). Whitaker Hse.
Dertinger, Charles J. Reflections. 1983. write for info. (ISBN 0-8062-2043-0). Carlton.
Derugin, Vladimir, ed. see Chrysostomos, Archimandrite & Ambrosios, Hieromonk.
Desai, Amrit. Kripalu Yoga: Meditation-in-Motion, - Focusing Inward, Bk. II. Tennen, Laura, ed. (Illus.). 120p. 1987. wkbk. 9.95 (ISBN 0-940258-16-1). Kripalu Pubns.
Desai, Devangana. Erotic Sculpture of India: A Socio-Cultural Study. (Illus.). 290p. 1984. text ed. 55.00x. Coronet Bks.
Desai, Mahadev. A Righteous Struggle. 105p. 1983. pap. 1.25 (ISBN 0-934676-34-8). Greenlf Bks.
Desai, Mahadev, ed. see Gandhi, M. K.
Desai, Mahadev, tr. see Gandhi, M. K.
Desai, Moraji. A View of the Gita. 1974. text ed. 10.00x. Coronet Bks.
Desai, Santosh N. Hinduism in Thai Life. 163p. 1980. 23.95x (ISBN 0-940500-66-3, Pub by Popular Prakashan India). Asia Bk Corp.
Desai, Yogi A. Journal of the Spirit. (Illus.). 160p. 1985. pap. 4.95 (ISBN 0-940258-18-8). Kripalu Pubns.
--Love Is an Awakening. Sarasohn, Lisa, ed. (Illus.). 40p. (Orig.). 1985. pap. 2.00 (ISBN 0-940258-14-5). Kripalu Pubns.
--Loving Each Other. Sarasohn, Lisa, ed. (Illus.). 40p. 1985. pap. 2.00 (ISBN 0-940258-19-6). Kripalu Pubns.
--The Wisdom of the Body. Sarasohn, Lisa, ed. (Illus.). 40p. (Orig.). 1984. pap. 2.00 (ISBN 0-940258-13-7). Kripalu Pubns.
--Working Miracles of Love: A Collection of Teachings. LC 85-50126. (Illus.). 184p. 1985. pap. text ed. 5.95 (ISBN 0-940258-15-3). Kripalu Pubns.
De Sainte-Beuve, Charles-Augustin. Port-Royal, 3 tomes. 1953-1955. Set. 79.95 (ISBN 0-685-11502-X). French & Eur.
De Sainte Marthe, Denis. Gallia Christiana, 16 vols. 12462p. Repr. of 1715 ed. text ed. 1863.00x (ISBN 0-576-78556-3, Pub. by Gregg Intl Pubs England). Gregg Intl.
De Saint-Martin, Louis-Claude. Of Errors & Truth. Vadenais, Philip & Vadenais, Antoinette, trs. from Fr. LC 86-63353. 435p. (Orig.). 1987. pap. write for info. (ISBN 0-912057-47-5, G-651). AMORC.
De Saint Pierre, Michel. The New Priests. 209p. 1966. pap. 1.95 (ISBN 0-912414-18-9). Lumen Christi.
De Sales, Francis. The Sermons of St. Francis de Sales on Prayer. Fiorelli, Lewis, ed. Visitation Nuns, tr. LC 84-52310. 51p. 1985. pap. 3.00 (ISBN 0-89555-258-2). Tan Bks Pubs.
De Sales, Saint Francoise. Treatise on the Love of God. Mackey, Henry B., tr. LC 71-156190. xiiv, 555p. Repr. of 1942 ed. lib. bdg. 31.75x (ISBN 0-8371-6139-8, FRLG). Greenwood.
De Salignac de la Mothe-Fenelon, Francoise. Along the Royal Way. Helms, Hal M., ed. LC 83-61406. (Living Library Ser.). 152p. (Orig.). 1984. pap. 5.95 (ISBN 0-941478-20-3). Paraclete Pr.
DeSalvo, John A., ed. see Adams, Frank O.
De Santa Ana, Julio, ed. Separation Without Hope? LC 80-12831. 198p. (Orig.). 1980. pap. 2.24 (ISBN 0-88344-456-9). Orbis Bks.
De Santis, Zerlina. A Child's Story of Saints, Past & Present. 1979. 1.75 (ISBN 0-8198-0567-X); pap. 1.00 (ISBN 0-8198-0568-8). Dghtrs St Paul.
--Journeys with Mary. (Encounter Ser.). 155p. 1982. 3.00 (ISBN 0-8198-3900-0, EN0165); pap. 2.00 (ISBN 0-8198-3910-8). Dghtrs St Paul.
De Santo, Charles. Dear Tim. LC 81-23744. 200p. (Orig.). 1982. pap. 7.95 (ISBN 0-8361-1991-6). Herald Pr.
DeSaulniers, Lawrence B. The Response in American Catholic Periodicals to the Crises of the Great Depression, 1930-1935. LC 83-23603. 198p. (Orig.). 1984. lib. bdg. 24.75 (ISBN 0-8191-3786-3); pap. text ed. 11.75 (ISBN 0-8191-3787-1). U Pr of Amer.
Desautels, Joseph. Manuel des cures pour le bon Gouvernement Temporel Des Paroisses et des Fabriques dans le Bas-Canada. 1864. 24.00 (ISBN 0-384-11480-6). Johnson Repr.
Descartes, Rene. Oeuvres, 11 tomes. Adam & Tannery, eds. Incl. Tome I. Correspondance (Avril 1622-Fevrier 1638) 36.95 (ISBN 0-685-34212-3); Tome II. Correspondance (Mars 1638 - Decembre 1639) 32.95 (ISBN 0-685-34213-1); Tome III. Correspondance (Janvier 1640-Juin 1643) 37.95 (ISBN 0-685-34214-X); Tome IV. Correspondance (Juillet 1643-Avril 1647) 37.95 (ISBN 0-685-34215-8); Tome V. Correspondance (Mai 1647 - Fevrier 1650) 36.95 (ISBN 0-685-34216-6); Tome VI. Discours de la Methode et Essais. 32.95 (ISBN 0-685-34217-4); Tome VII. Meditationes de Prima Philosophia. 27.95 (ISBN 0-685-34218-2); Tome VIII, Pt. 1. Principia Philosophiae. 15.95 (ISBN 0-685-34219-0); Tome VIII, Pt. 2. Epistola ad Voetium, Lettre Apologetique, Notas in Programma. 20.95 (ISBN 0-685-34220-4); Tome IX, Pt. 1. Meditations. 12.95 (ISBN 0-685-34221-2); Tome IX, Pt. 2. Principes. 14.95 (ISBN 0-685-34222-0); Tome X. Physico-Mathematica, Compendium Musicae, Regulea ad Directionem Ingenii, Recherche de la Verite, Supplement a **la Correspondance. 37.95 (ISBN 0-685-34223-9); Tome XI. Le Monde, Description du Corps Humain, Passions de l'Ame, Anatomica, Varia. 37.95 (ISBN 0-685-34224-7). French & Eur.**
--Oeuvres et Lettres: Avec: Discours de la Methode. 1424p. 1937. 42.95 (ISBN 0-686-55676-3). French & Eur.
--Philosophical Essays: Discourse on Method; Meditations; Rules for the Direction of the Mind. Lafleur, Laurence J., tr. LC 63-16951. (Orig.). 1964. pap. 7.87 scp (ISBN 0-672-60292-X, LLA99). Bobbs.
--Philosophical Works, 2 Vols. Haldane, E. S. & Ross, G. R., eds. 1967. Vol. 2. 57.50 (ISBN 0-521-06944-0); Vol. 1. pap. 14.95 (ISBN 0-521-09416-X); Vol. 2. pap. 14.95 (ISBN 0-521-09417-8). Cambridge U Pr.
--Philosophical Writings. Anscombe, Elizabeth & Geach, Peter T., eds. Anscombe, Elizabeth & Geach, Peter T., trs. LC 79-171798. 1971. pap. 7.20 scp (ISBN 0-672-61274-7, LLA198). Bobbs.
--Principes de la Philosophie, Vol. 1. 3rd ed. 158p. 1970. 9.95 (ISBN 0-686-55678-X). French & Eur.
Deschner, John. Wesley's Christology: An Interpretation. LC 85-2274. 244p. pap. 12.95x (ISBN 0-87074-200-0). SMU Press.
Deselm, Joel, jt. auth. see Fishel, Kent.
Desgranges, ed. see Pascal, Blaise.
Deshen, Shlomo & Zenner, Walter P. Jewish Societies in the Middle East: Community, Culture & Authority. LC 80-6285. (Illus.). 328p. (Orig.). 1982. lib. bdg. 30.50 (ISBN 0-8191-2578-4); pap. text ed. 14.25 (ISBN 0-8191-2579-2). U Pr of Amer.
Deshimaru, Taisen. Questions to a Zen Master. Amphoux, Nancy, tr. 160p. 1985. pap. 8.95 (ISBN 0-525-48141-9, 0869-260). Dutton.
Deshmukh, C. D., ed. see Baba, Meher.
Deshon, George. Guide for Catholic Young Women. 24.50 (ISBN 0-405-10816-8). Ayer Co Pubs.
Desikachar, T. K. Religiousness in Yoga: Lectures on Theory & Practice. Skelton, Mary L. & Carter, J. R., eds. LC 79-9643. (Illus.). 314p. 1980. text ed. 27.00 (ISBN 0-8191-0966-5); pap. text ed. 11.75 (ISBN 0-8191-0967-3). U Pr of Amer.
De Silva, Padmasiri. An Introduction to Buddhist Psychology. (Library of Philosophy & Religion Ser.). 134p. 1979. text ed. 28.50x (ISBN 0-06-491666-9). B&N Imports.
De Simoni, Felix. Mary Magdalene & the Theory of Sin, 2 vols. LC 72-84832. (Illus.). 35p. 1972. 179.50 (ISBN 0-913314-04-8). Am Classical Coll Pr.
De Sivry, L. Dictionnaire Geographique, Historique, Descriptif, Archeologique des Pelegrinages, 2 vols. Migne, J. P., ed. (Encyclopedie Theologique Ser.: Vols. 43-44). (Fr.). 1328p. Repr. of 1851 ed. lib. bdg. 169.00x (ISBN 0-89241-248-8). Caratzas.
Des Mas-Latrie, L. Dictionnaire de Statistique Religieuse. Migne, J. P., ed. (Nouvelle Encyclopedie Theologique Ser.: Vol. 9). (Fr.). 538p. Repr. of 1851 ed. lib. bdg. 69.00x (ISBN 0-89241-259-3). Caratzas.
De Smet, Pierre J. Life, Letters & Travels of Father Pierre Jean de Smet, 4 vols. LC 75-83418. (Religion in America Ser. I). 1969. Repr. of 1905 ed. 88.00 set (ISBN 0-405-00237-8); Vols. 1-2. 22.00 ea. Vol. 1 (ISBN 0-405-00238-6). Vol. 2 (ISBN 0-405-00239-4). Vols. 3-4. 22.00 ea. Vol. 3 (ISBN 0-405-00240-8). Vol. 4 (ISBN 0-405-00241-6). Ayer Co Pubs.
DeSmet, Pierre-Jean. Indian Missions. 67p. 1985. 10.95. Ye Galleon.
De Smet, Pierre-Jean. Origin, Progress & Prospects of the Catholic Mission to the Rocky Mountains. 1971. pap. 1.00 (ISBN 0-87770-044-3). Ye Galleon.
De Smith, Josie. El Hogar Que Dios Me Dio. 80p. 1986. pap. 2.25 (ISBN 0-311-46082-8). Casa Bautista.
De Smith, Josie see Smith, Josie De.
Desmond, Cecelia. Blessed James Salomoni. 1970. 2.00 (ISBN 0-8198-0000-7); pap. 1.00 (ISBN 0-8198-0001-5). Dghtrs St Paul.
Desmond, Humphrey. A. P. A. Movement: A Sketch. LC 69-18772. (American Immigration Collection Ser., No. 1). 1969. Repr. of 1912 ed. 10.00 (ISBN 0-405-00519-9). Ayer Co Pubs.
De Sola, Carla. The Spirit Moves: A Handbook of Dance & Prayer. Adams, Doug, ed. & intro. by. LC 77-89743. (Illus.). 152p. 1986. pap. 9.95 (ISBN 0-941500-38-1). Sharing Co.
De Sola Pinto, Vivan see Pinto, Vivan De Sola.
De Soto, Domingo. De Natura et Gratia. 612p. Repr. of 1549 ed. text ed. 99.36 (ISBN 0-576-99423-5, Pub. by Gregg Intl Pubs England). Gregg Intl.
De Souza, Allan. Sikhs in Britain. (Communities in Britain Ser.). (Illus.). 72p. 1986. 16.95 (ISBN 0-7134-5100-9, Pub. by Batsford England). David & Charles.
Despland, Michel. The Education of Desire: Plato & the Philosophy of Religion. 400p. 1985. 25.00 (ISBN 0-8020-6524-4). U of Toronto Pr.
Despot, Maggi, tr. see Matura, Thaddee.
Desramaut, Francis. Don Bosco & the Spiritual Life. Luna, Roger M., tr. from Fr. LC 79-52674. (Orig.). 1979. pap. text ed. 10.95 (ISBN 0-89944-022-3). Don Bosco Multimedia.
Desroche, Henri. The American Shakers: From Neo-Christianity to Presocialism. Savacool, John K., ed. LC 78-123537. 368p. 1971. 20.00x (ISBN 0-87023-063-8). U of Mass Pr.
--Jacob & the Angel: An Essay in Sociologies of Religion. Savacool, John K., ed. & tr. from Fr. LC 72-77575. 196p. 1973. 15.00x (ISBN 0-87023-109-X). U of Mass Pr.
Desroche, Henri, et al. Dieux D'hommes: Dictionnaire Des Messianismes & Millenarismes De L'ere Chretienne. 1969. 30.40x (ISBN 90-2796-415-7). Mouton.
Desroches-Noblecourt, Christiane. Tutankhamen. LC 63-15145. 312p. 1976. pap. 8.95 (ISBN 0-8212-0695-8, 857017). NYGS.
Dessain, Charles S. John Henry Newman. 2nd ed. 1971. 17.50x (ISBN 0-8047-0778-2). Stanford U Pr.
Dessain, Charles S., ed. see Newman, John H.
Dessain, Stephen, ed. see Newman, John H.
Desseaux, Jacques. Twenty Centuries of Ecumenism. 1984. pap. 4.95 (ISBN 0-8091-2617-6). Paulist Pr.
Dessem, Ralph. Celebrating Advent in the Sanctuary. 1983. pap. 2.50 (ISBN 0-89536-635-5, 0384). CSS of Ohio.
Dessem, Ralph E., jt. auth. see Tozer, Tom.
Dessler, E. E. Strive for the Truth: The World of Rav Dessler. Carmell, Aryeh, tr. from Hebrew. Tr. of Michtav M'Eliyahu. 1978. 9.95 (ISBN 0-87306-139-X); pap. 7.95 (ISBN 0-87306-177-2). Feldheim.
Dessler, Eliyahu. Strive for Truth, Vol. 2. 1985. 12.95 (ISBN 0-87306-395-3); pap. 9.95 (ISBN 0-87306-396-1). Feldheim.
Dessler, N. W. Suggested Curriculum for the Day School. 7.00 (ISBN 0-914131-63-X, C01). Torah Umesorah.
Dessouki, Ali E. Hillal. Islamic Resurgence in the Arab World. LC 81-12135. 286p. 1982. 40.95 (ISBN 0-03-059673-4). Praeger.
Dessouki, Ali E. Hillal, jt. ed. see Cudsi, Alex.
Destang, Francoise, jt. auth. see Paschos, Jacqueline.
DeStefano, Patricia. Interlude of Widowhood. (Greeting Book Line Ser.). 48p. (Orig.). 1983. pap. 1.50 (ISBN 0-89622-200-4). Twenty-Third.
De Suassure, Eric, ed. Taize Picture Bible. LC 69-11860. (Illus.). 298p. 1968. 9.95 (ISBN 0-8006-0005-3, 1-5). Fortress.
De Summers, Jessica. Gozo Al Grecer. 48p. 1981. pap. 1.10 (ISBN 0-311-38550-8, Edit Mundo). Casa Bautista.
De Surgy, Paul. Mystery of Salvation. Sheed, Rosemary, tr. 1966. pap. 6.95 (ISBN 0-268-00185-5). U of Notre Dame Pr.
De Swarte, Carolyn G., ed. The Nineteenth-Century American Methodist Itinerant Preacher's Wife. Dayton, Doanald, tr. (Women in American Protestant Religion Series 1800-1930). 276p. 1987. lib. bdg. 40.00 (ISBN 0-8240-0656-9). Garland Pub.
De Swarte, Carolyn G. & Dayton, Donald, eds. The Defense of Women's Rights to Ordination in the Methodist Episcopal Church. (Women in American Protestant Religion Series 1800-1930). 230p. 1987. lib. bdg. 35.00 (ISBN 0-8240-0654-2). Garland Pub.
--The Ideal of "The New Woman" According to the Woman's Christian Temperance Union. (Women in American Protestant Religion 1800-1930). 394p. 1987. lib. bdg. 55.00 (ISBN 0-8240-0655-0). Garland Pub.
De Swarte, Carolyn G., ed. see Acornley, John H.

De Swarte, Carolyn G., ed. see Andrews, C. W.
De Swarte, Carolyn G., ed. see Baker, Frances J.
De Swarte, Carolyn G., ed. see Bethune, Joanna.
De Swarte, Carolyn G., ed. see Brown, George.
De Swarte, Carolyn G., ed. see Brown, Oswald E. & Brown, Anna M.
De Swarte, Carolyn G., ed. see Coppin, Fanny J.
De Syrmia, Edmond. At the Head of Nations: The Rise of the Papal & Princely House of Odescalchi. LC 76-44029. (Illus.). 116p. 1978. 10.00 (ISBN 0-914226-05-3). Cyclopedia.
Detacuden, Nam U. The Simplest Explanation of God Ever Explained. 230p. 1983. 13.50 (ISBN 0-682-49951-X). Exposition Pr FL.
Deterding, Paul E. Echoes of Pauline Concepts in the Speech at Antioch. (Concordia Student Journal Monograph Ser.: No. 1). (Illus.). 50p. (Orig.). 1980. pap. 2.50 (ISBN 0-911770-51-8). Concordia Schl Grad Studies.
De Thomasis, Louis. My Father's Business: Creating a New Future for the People of God. 168p. (Orig.). 1984. pap. 6.95 (ISBN 0-87061-107-0). Chr Classics.
Detienne, Marcel. The Creation of Mythology. Cook, Margaret, tr. LC 85-24658. 192p. 1986. 25.00x (ISBN 0-226-14350-3); pap. 10.95x (ISBN 0-226-14348-1). U of Chicago Pr.
De Tolnay, Charles Q. Michelangelo, 6 vols. Incl. Vol. 1. The Youth of Michelangelo. 1969. 90.00x (ISBN 0-691-03858-9); Vol. 2. The Sistine Ceiling. 1969. 90.00x (ISBN 0-691-03856-2); Vol. 3. The Medeci Chapel. 1970. 90.00 (ISBN 0-691-03854-6); Vol. 4. The Tomb of Julius Two. 1970. 91.50x (ISBN 0-691-03857-0); Vol. 5. The Final Period. 1970. 90.00x (ISBN 0-691-03855-4); Vol. 6. Michelangelo, Architect. 68.00x (ISBN 0-691-03853-8); Michelangelo: Sculpter-Painter-Architect. (One vol. condensation). 52.50 (ISBN 0-691-03876-7); pap. 20.50 (ISBN 0-691-00337-8). Princeton U Pr.
De Trevino, Elizabeth B. see Trevino, Elizabeth B. De.
Detrich, Richard L. & Steele, Nicola. How to Recover from Grief. 128p. 1983. pap. 7.95 (ISBN 0-8170-0989-2). Judson.
Detrick, R. Blaine. Favorite Men of the Bible. Sherer, Michael L., ed. (Orig.). 1987. pap. 7.25 (ISBN 0-89536-855-2, 7814). CSS of Ohio.
--Golf & the Gospel. 1985. 4.95 (ISBN 0-89536-766-1, 5873). CSS of Ohio.
De Troyes, Chretien. Perceval: The Story of the Grail. Bryant, Nigel, tr. 320p. 1986. pap. 16.25 (ISBN 0-85991-224-8, Pub. by Boydell & Brewer). Longwood Pub Group.
De Tryon, Charles F. see Montalembert, Charles, pseud.
Detweiler, Richard C. Mennonite Statements on Peace. 80p. (Orig.). 1968. pap. 2.95 (ISBN 0-8361-1581-3). Herald Pr.
Detweiler, Robert. Four Spiritual Crises in Mid-Century American Fiction. facs. ed. LC 78-121461. (Essay Index Reprint Ser). 1964. 12.00 (ISBN 0-8369-1799-5). Ayer Co Pubs.
--Four Spiritual Crises in Mid-Century American Fiction. LC 64-63316. (University of Florida Humanities Monographs: No. 14). 1963. pap. 3.50 (ISBN 0-8130-0058-0). U Presses Fla.
--Story, Sign, & Self: Phenomenology & Structuralism As Literary-Critical Methods. Beardslee, William A., ed. LC 76-9713. (Semeia Studies). 240p. 1978. pap. 9.95 (ISBN 0-8006-1505-0, 1-1505). Fortress.
Detweiler, Robert, ed. Art, Literature, Religion: Life on the Borders. LC 82-3319. (AAR Thermatic Studies). 208p. 1983. 22.50 (ISBN 0-89130-578-5, 01 24 92). Scholars Pr GA.
--Semeia Thirty-One: Reader Response Approaches to Biblical & Secular Texts. (Semeia Ser.). 1985. pap. 9.95 (ISBN 0-317-38640-9, 06-20-31). Scholars Pr GA.
--Semeia Twenty-Three: Derrida & Biblical Studies. (Semeia Ser.). pap. 9.95 (06 20 23). Scholars Pr GA.
Detwiler, Donald S., jt. auth. see Mendelsohn, John.
Detwiler-Zapp, Diane & Dixon, William C. Lay Caregiving. LC 81-66519. (Creative Pastoral Care & Counseling Ser.). 1982. pap. 4.50 (ISBN 0-8006-0567-5, 1-567). Fortress.
Detzler, Wayne. New Testament Words in Today's Language. 408p. 1986. 14.95 (ISBN 0-89693-528-0). Victor Bks.
Deudon, Eric H. Nietzsche en France: L'antichristianisme et la Critique, 1891-1915. LC 81-43820. 176p. (Orig.). 1982. lib. bdg. 27.50 o. p. (ISBN 0-8191-2339-0); pap. text ed. 11.75 (ISBN 0-8191-2340-4). U Pr of Amer.
Deuink, James W. Christian School Finance. (Illus.). 160p. 1985. pap. 6.60 (ISBN 0-89084-304-X). Bob Jones Univ Pr.
--The Ministry of the Christian School Guidance Counselor. (Illus.). 175p. (Orig.). 1984. pap. 6.60 (ISBN 0-89084-273-6). Bob Jones Univ Pr.
Deuink, James W. & Herbster, Carl D. Effective Christian School Management. 2nd ed. (Illus.). 291p. 1986. pap. 8.95 (ISBN 0-89084-319-8). Bob Jones Univ Pr.
Deuink, James W., ed. Some Light on Christian Education. (Illus.). 195p. (Orig.). 1984. pap. 4.95 (ISBN 0-89084-262-0). Bob Jones Univ Pr.
De Unamuno, Miguel. Tragic Sense of Life. 14.00 (ISBN 0-8446-3100-0). Peter Smith.
Deursen, A. Van see Van Deursen, A.
Deursen, A. van see Van Deursen, A.
Deussen, Paul. Philosophy of the Upanishads. Geden, A. S., tr. (Orig.). 1966. pap. 8.50 (ISBN 0-486-21616-0). Dover.
Deutsch, Alfred H. Still Full of Sap, Still Green. LC 79-21558. 130p. 1979. pap. 2.50 (ISBN 0-8146-1051-X). Liturgical Pr.
Deutsch, Eliot. Advaita Vedanta: A Philosophical Reconstruction. LC 69-19282. 1969. pap. text ed. 5.95x (ISBN 0-8248-0271-3, Eastwest Ctr). UH Pr.
--Humanity & Divinity: An Essay in Comparative Metaphysics. LC 76-128081. 1970. 14.00x (ISBN 0-87022-190-6). UH Pr.
--On Truth: An Ontological Theory. LC 79-12754. 1979. text ed. 14.00x (ISBN 0-8248-0615-8). UH Pr.
Deutsch, Eliot & Van Buitenen, J. A. A Source Book of Advaita Vedeanta. LC 75-148944. pap. 65.60 (ISBN 0-317-12996-1, 2017216). Bks Demand UMI.
Deutsch, Otto. Handel: A Documentary Biography. LC 74-3118. (Music Ser.). 942p. 1974. Repr. of 1954 ed. lib. bdg. 85.00 (ISBN 0-306-70624-5). Da Capo.
Deutsch, Vera, tr. see Heidegger, Martin.
Deutscher, Isaac. The Non-Jewish Jew. 170p. 1982. pap. 5.95 (ISBN 0-932870-18-X). Alyson Pubns.
Deutscher, Thomas B., jt. ed. see Bietenholz, Peter G.
Deutschle, Phil. The Two-Year Mountain. LC 86-4026. 256p. 1986. 15.95 (ISBN 0-87663-471-4). Universe.
Devadutt, Vinjamuri E. Bible & the Faiths of Men. (Orig.). 1967. pap. 1.25 (ISBN 0-377-37011-8). Friend Pr.
De Valle, Francisca J. About the Holy Spirit. 120p. 5.00 (ISBN 0-912414-31-6). Lumen Christi.
Devaraja, N. K. The Mind & Spirit of India. 1967. 5.95 (ISBN 0-89684-281-9). Orient Bk Dist.
Devas, Dominic. Treatise on Prayer & Meditation. Repr. of 1926 ed. lib. bdg. 25.00 (ISBN 0-8495-1026-0). Arden Lib.
Devasthali, G., ed. Glimpses of Veda & Vyakarana. 1985. 26.00x (ISBN 0-8364-1408-X, Pub. by Popular Prakashan). South Asia Bks.
Devault, Joseph J. Josue. (Bible Ser.). pap. 1.00 (ISBN 0-8091-5075-1). Paulist Pr.
Devaux, Augustin. La Chartreuse de Selignac. Hogg, James, ed. (Analecta Cartusiana Ser.: No. 24). (Fr.). 313p. (Orig.). 1975. pap. 25.00 (ISBN 3-7052-0024-0, Pub by Salzburg Studies). Longwood Pub Group.
De Vaux, R. Archaeology & the Dead Sea Scrolls. 2nd & rev. ed. (Schweich Lectures on Biblical Archaeology). (Illus.). 142p. 1977. 13.50 (ISBN 0-85672-725-3, Pub. by British Acad). Longwood Pub Group.
De Vaux, R. & Milik, J. T. Discoveries in the Judaean Desert: Qumran Grotte 4-11, Vol. 6. (Illus.). 1977. text ed. 52.00x (ISBN 0-19-826317-1). Oxford U Pr.
De Vaux, Roland. The Early History of Israel. LC 78-1883. 914p. 1978. Westminster.
Devavrata Basu Ray, tr. see Swami Vishwashrayananda.
De V. Brunkow, Robert see Brunkow, Robert de V.
DeVeer, Donald Van see Regan, Tom & Van DeVeer, Donald.
Devendra Gani. Davva-Samgaha (Dravya-Samgaha) Goshal, Sarat C., ed. & intro. by. LC 73-3835. Repr. of 1917 ed. 27.50 (ISBN 0-404-57701-6). AMS Pr.
--Gommatsara Jiva-Kanda (the Soul) Jaini, Rai B., ed. & intro. by. LC 73-3839. Repr. of 1927 ed. 48.00 (ISBN 0-404-57705-9). AMS Pr.
--Gommatsara Karma-Kanda, Pts. 1 & 2. Jaini, Rai B. & Ji, Brachmachari S., eds. LC 73-3840. Repr. of 1927 ed. Set. 72.50 (ISBN 0-404-57712-1). AMS Pr.
Dever, William G. Gezer One: Preliminary Report of the 1964-1966 Seasons. 1971. 35.00x (ISBN 0-87820-300-1, Pub. by Hebrew Union). Ktav.
--Gezer Two. 1974. 35.00x (ISBN 0-685-56198-4). Ktav.
Dever, William G. & Darrel, Lance H. A Manual of Field Excavation. 1979. 15.00x (ISBN 0-87820-303-6). Ktav.
Devereux, E. J. Renaissance English Translations of Erasmus: A Bibliography to 1700. (Erasmus Ser.). 256p. 1983. 35.00x (ISBN 0-8020-2411-4). U of Toronto Pr.
Devereux, James, ed. see Williams, Shirley & Zalaquett, Jose.
Devers, Dorothy. Faithful Friendship. 1980. 2.40 (ISBN 0-88028-011-5). Forward Movement.
Devi, Indira & Roy, Dilip K. Pilgrims of the Stars. 2nd ed. (Illus.). 406p. 1985. pap. 14.95 (ISBN 0-931454-10-7). Timeless Bks.
Devi, Indra. Yoga for Americans. 1971. pap. 2.25 (ISBN 0-451-09869-2, E9869, Sig). NAL.
DeVille, Jard. Pastor's Handbook on Interpersonal Relationships. 145p. 1986. pap. 8.95 (ISBN 0-8010-2961-9). Baker Bk.
De Villehardouin, Geoffrey & De Joinville, Jean. Chronicles of the Crusades. Shaw, Margaret R., tr. (Classics Ser.). (Orig.). 1963. pap. 5.95 (ISBN 0-14-044124-7). Penguin.
De Villehardouin, Geoffroi. De la Conqueste de Constantinoble. Paris, Paulin, ed. 1965. 39.00 (ISBN 0-685-92799-7); pap. 33.00 (ISBN 0-384-64581-X). Johnson Repr.
De Villehardouin, Geoffroi & Joinville. Memoirs of the Crusades. LC 83-1515. (Everyman's Library: History: No. 333). xli, 340p. 1983. Repr. of 1908 ed. lib. bdg. 45.00x (ISBN 0-313-23856-1, VIME). Greenwood.
De Villehardouin, Geoffroy. Conqueste de Constantinople. White, Julian E., Jr., ed. LC 68-16196. (Medieval French Literature Ser). (Fr., Orig.). 1968. pap. text ed. 5.95x (ISBN 0-89197-102-5). Irvington.
Devin-Adair Staff. Dogmatic Canons & Decrees of the Council of Trent, Vatican Council I, Plus the Decree on the Immaculate Conception & the Syllabus of Errors. LC 79-112469. (Eng.). 1977. pap. 5.00 (ISBN 0-89555-018-0). TAN Bks Pubs.
Devin, Robert. A History of the Grassy Creek Baptist Church. Repr. 15.00 (ISBN 0-686-12337-9); vinyl back 8.00 (ISBN 0-686-12338-7). Church History.
DeVine, Bob. Uncle Bob Talks with My Digestive System. LC 85-4737. (Designed by God Ser.). (Illus.). 48p. 1985. pap. 4.95 (ISBN 0-89191-944-9, 59444, Chariot Bks). Cook.
Devine, George. Transformation in Christ. LC 70-39884. 125p. 1972. pap. 3.95 (ISBN 0-8189-0240-X). Alba.
Devine, George, ed. That They May Live: Theological Reflections on the Quality of Life. 314p. 1984. pap. text ed. 10.50 (ISBN 0-8191-3852-5, College Theo Soc). U Pr of Amer.
--A World More Human: A Church More Christian. 204p. 1984. pap. text ed. 9.50 (ISBN 0-8191-3851-7, College Theo Soc). U Pr of Amer.
Devine, Mary. Brujeria: A Study of Mexican American Folk-Magic. Weschcke, Carl L., ed. LC 82-83427. (Illus.). 266p. (Orig.). 1982. pap. 7.95 (ISBN 0-87542-775-8). Llewellyn Pubns.
De Vio, Tommaso. Cajetan Responds: A Reader in Reformation Controversy. Wicks, Jared, ed. LC 77-22606. pap. 75.00 (2029507). Bks Demand UMI.
De Visme Williamson, Rene see Williamson, Rene De Visme.
De Visser, Marinus W. The Arhats in China & Japan. LC 78-70136. Repr. of 1923 ed. 27.50 (ISBN 0-404-17406-X). AMS Pr.
De Vito, Albert. Christmas Songs for Piano. 1968. pap. 2.95 (ISBN 0-934286-53-1). Kenyon.
DeVito, Michael. The Church's Faith, Bk. I. pap. 3.95 (ISBN 0-941850-06-4). Sunday Pubns.
De Vito, Michael J. The New York Review, 1905-1908. LC 77-75637. (Monograph Ser.: No. 34). (Illus.). 1977. 13.95x (ISBN 0-930060-14-8). US Cath Hist.
Devlin, Christopher. Hamlet's Divinity & Other Essays. facs. ed. (Essay Index Reprint Ser). 1963. 15.00 (ISBN 0-8369-1915-7). Ayer Co Pubs.
De Vogue, Adalbert. The Rule of Saint Benedict: A Doctrinal & Spiritual Commentary. Hasbrouck, John B., tr. from Fr. (Cistercian Studies: No. 54). Tr. of La Regle de saint Benoit, VII, Commentaire doctrinal et spirituel. 1983. pap. 25.95 (ISBN 0-87907-845-6). Cistercian Pubns.
De Voltaire, M. Essays & Criticisms: Containing Letters on the Christian Religion, The Philosophy of History, The Ignorant Philosopher, & the Chinese Catechism. 120p. 1983. Repr. of 1982 ed. lib. bdg. 65.00 (ISBN 0-89987-878-4). Darby Bks.
DeVos, Richard M. & Conn, Charles P. Believe! 128p. 1975. pap. 2.95 (ISBN 0-8007-8267-4, Spire). Revell.
De Vries, Anne. Story Bible for Young Children. (Illus.). 1986. pap. 9.95 (ISBN 0-8010-2963-5). Baker Bk.
DeVries, Betty. Bible Activity Capsule. (Pelican Activity Ser.). pap. 0.89 (ISBN 0-8010-2896-5). Baker Bk.
--Bible Treasures Activity Book. (Pelican Activity Ser.). pap. 0.89 (ISBN 0-8010-2895-7). Baker Bk.
--One Hundred One Bible Activity Sheets. 144p. 1983. pap. 5.95 (ISBN 0-8010-2931-7). Baker Bk.
De Vries, Dawn. Servant of the Word. LC 86-45902. 240p. 1987. pap. 14.95 (ISBN 0-8006-3203-6). Fortress.
DeVries, Henri. Incarnate Son of God. pap. 2.75 (ISBN 0-87509-095-8). Chr Pubns.
DeVries, J. Hendrick, tr. see Kuyper, Abraham.
DeVries, James. The Kingdom of Christ. LC 84-90313. 155p. (Orig.). 1984. pap. 3.50 (ISBN 0-9613181-0-4). Kingdom Bks.
De Vries, James E. You Can Live with a Heartache: Hope for Long-Term Heartaches. (Christian Counseling Aids Ser.). 1977. pap. 0.95 (ISBN 0-8010-2876-0). Baker Bk.
De Vries, Jan. Do Miracles Exist? 176p. 1986. 39.75x (ISBN 1-85158-029-8, Pub. by Mainstream Scotland); pap. 24.75x (ISBN 1-85158-030-1). State Mutual Bk.
--Perspectives in the History of Religions. Bolle, Kees W., tr. & intro. by. LC 76-20154. 1977. pap. 3.65 (ISBN 0-520-03300-0, CAL 352). U of Cal Pr.
DeVries, Janet M. Learning the Pacific Way: A Guide for All Ages. (Orig.). 1982. pap. 3.95 (ISBN 0-377-00119-8). Friend Pr.
De Vries, Simon J. The Achievements of Biblical Religion: A Prolegomenon to Old Testament Theology. LC 83-3614. 558p. (Orig.). 1983. lib. bdg. 40.75 (ISBN 0-8191-3140-7); pap. text ed. 22.25 (ISBN 0-8191-3141-5). U Pr of Amer.
DeVries, Thomas D. Discovering Our Gifts. 1.50 (ISBN 0-8091-9328-0). Paulist Pr.
De Vries, Vickie see Dean, Dave.
De Waal, Esther. God under My Roof. 40p. (Orig.). 1985. pap. 1.50 (ISBN 0-941478-42-4). Paraclete Pr.
--Seeking God: The Way of St. Benedict. 160p. 1984. pap. 4.95 (ISBN 0-8146-1388-8). Liturgical Pr.
De Waal, Esther see Allchin, A. M. & Waal, Esther de.
De Waal, Hugo, tr. see Faber, Heije.
De Waal Malefijt, Anne X. see Malefijt, Anne M.
De Waard, J. & Nida, E. A. Translator's Handbook on the Book of Ruth. (Helps for Translators Ser.). 111p. 1973. 3.30x (ISBN 0-8267-0107-8, 08518, Pub. by United Bible). Am Bible.
De Waard, J. & Smalley, W. A. Translator's Handbook on the Book of Amos. LC 80-490970. (Helps for Translators Ser.). 274p. 1979. 4.00x (ISBN 0-8267-0128-0, 08577, Pub. by United Bible). Am Bible.
De Waard, Jan see Waard, Jan de & Nida, Eugene A.
De Wailly, N., ed. see De Joinville, Jean.
Dewan, Wilfred F. Catholic Belief & Practice in an Ecumenical Age. (Orig.). 1966. pap. 1.95 (ISBN 0-8091-1510-7, Deus). Paulist Pr.
Dewar, Diana. All for Christ: Some Twentieth Century Martyrs. 1980. pap. 8.95x (ISBN 0-19-283024-4). Oxford U Pr.
--The Saint of Auschwitz: The Story of Maximilian Kolbe. LC 82-48926. (Illus.). 160p. (Orig.). 1983. pap. 5.95 (ISBN 0-06-061901-5, RD/460, HarpR). Har-Row.
Dewart, Joanne. The Theology of Grace of Theodore of Mopsuestia. LC 65-18319. (Studies in Christian Antiquity: Vol. 16). 160p. 1971. 12.95x (ISBN 0-8132-0523-9). Cath U Pr.
Dewart, Leslie. Foundations of Belief. LC 69-17777. 1970. pap. 4.95 (ISBN 0-8164-2549-3, HarpR). Har-Row.
De Waters, Lillian. The Christ Within. 5.95 (ISBN 0-686-05717-1). L De Waters.
--The Finished Kingdom. 5.95 (ISBN 0-686-05716-3). L De Waters.
--God & Oneself. pap. 3.00 (ISBN 0-686-05705-8). L De Waters.
--God Is All. pap. 0.95 (ISBN 0-686-05711-2). L De Waters.
--Voice of Revelation. 5.95 (ISBN 0-686-05714-7). L De Waters.
--The Word Made Flesh. (Practical Demonstration Ser.). pap. 0.95 (ISBN 0-686-05718-X). L De Waters.
Dewdney, Selwyn. Sacred Scrolls of the Southern Ojibway. LC 73-90150. 1974. 27.50x (ISBN 0-8020-3321-0). U of Toronto Pr.
Deweese, Charles W. The Emerging Role of Deacons. LC 79-50337. 1980. pap. 3.75 (ISBN 0-8054-3512-3). Broadman.
--Prayer in Baptist Life. LC 85-21301. 1986. pap. 4.95 (ISBN 0-8054-6941-9). Broadman.
Deweese, Charles W., ed. Resource Kit for Your Church's History. 1984. 11.95 (ISBN 0-939804-12-3). Hist Comm S Baptist.
Deweese, Charles W., ed. see Brown, Pat.
Deweese, Charles W., ed. see Sumners, Bill.
DeWelt, Don. Acts Made Actual. rev. ed. LC 59-20263. (The Bible Study Textbook Ser.). (Illus.). 1975. 14.30 (ISBN 0-89900-036-3). College Pr Pub.
--If You Want to Preach. 2nd ed. LC 56-13226. 1964. pap. 3.95 (ISBN 0-89900-111-4). College Pr Pub.
--Leviticus. LC 75-328945. (The Bible Study Textbook Ser.). (Illus.). 1975. 14.95 (ISBN 0-89900-007-X). College Pr Pub.
--Nine Lessons on the Holy Spirit. 187p. 1978. cancelled (ISBN 0-89900-116-5). College Pr Pub.

--The Power of the Holy Spirit, Vol. III. 3rd ed. 1972. pap. 3.95 (ISBN 0-89900-125-4). College Pr Pub.
--Power of the Holy Spirit, Vol. IV. 2nd ed. (Orig.). 1976. pap. 6.95 (ISBN 0-89900-126-2). College Pr Pub.
--Power of the Holy Spirit, Vol. II. 5th ed. (Orig.). 1971. pap. 3.95 (ISBN 0-89900-124-6). College Pr Pub.
--Power of the Holy Spirit, Vol. I. 8th ed. (Orig.). 1963. pap. 3.95 (ISBN 0-89900-123-8). College Pr Pub.
--Romans Realized. LC 72-1068. (The Bible Study Textbook Ser.). (Illus.). 1959. 12.20 (ISBN 0-89900-037-1). College Pr Pub.
--Ten Timely Truths. 1949. pap. 2.00 (ISBN 0-89900-135-1). College Pr Pub.
DeWelt, Don & Baird, John. What the Bible Says about Fasting. LC 79-57087. (What the Bible Says Ser.). 1984. 13.95 (ISBN 0-89900-077-0). College Pr Pub.
DeWelt, Don, jt. auth. see Johnson, B. W.
DeWelt, Don, jt. auth. see Kidwell, R. J.
DeWelt, Don, ed. see Rotherham, Joseph B.
Dewett, Don, jt. auth. see Van Buren, James.
Dewey, Arthur J. The Word in Time. 204p. (Orig.). 1986. pap. 14.95 (ISBN 0-941850-18-8). Sunday Pubns.
Dewey, Arthur J., jt. tr. see Cameron, Ron.
Dewey, Barbara. As You Believe. LC 85-7370. 208p. 1985. 18.95 (ISBN 0-933123-01-9). Bartholomew Bks.
--The Creating Cosmos. LC 85-70369. 128p. 1985. 16.95 (ISBN 0-933123-00-0). Bartholomew Bks.
Dewey, Joanna. Markan Public Debate: Literary Technique, Concentric Structure & Theology in Mark 2: 1-3: 6. LC 79-17443. (Society of Biblical Literature Ser.: No. 48). 14.95 (ISBN 0-89130-337-5, 06-01-48); pap. 9.95 (ISBN 0-89130-338-3). Scholars Pr GA.
Dewey, John. Common Faith. (Terry Lectures Ser.). 1934. pap. 3.95x (ISBN 0-300-00069-3, Y18). Yale U Pr.
--Outlines of a Critical Theory of Ethics. LC 71-92299. Repr. of 1957 ed. lib. bdg. 22.50x (ISBN 0-8371-2707-6, DETE). Greenwood.
Dewey, Melvil. Two Hundred (Religion) Class. LC 79-55849. 1980. Repr. saddlewire pap. 4.95 (ISBN 0-8054-3107-1). Broadman.
Dewey, Robert E. & Hurlbutt, Robert H. Introduction to Ethics. 1977. write for info. (ISBN 0-02-329480-9, 32948). Macmillan.
De Wheat, Gaye, jt. auth. see Wheat, Ed.
Dewhurst, C. Kurt, et al. Religious Folk Art in America: Reflections of Faith. (Illus.). 163p. 1983. 29.95 (ISBN 0-525-93300-X, 02908-870). Dutton.
De Winter, Patrick M. The Sacral Treasure of the Guelphs. LC 85-3820. (Illus.). 160p. 1985. pap. 14.95X (ISBN 0-910386-81-1, Pub. by The Cleveland Museum of Art). Ind U Pr.
De Winter, Patrick M. see De Winter, Patrick M.
Dewitt, David. Answering the Tough Ones. 160p. 1980. pap. 5.95 (ISBN 0-8024-8971-0). Moody.
--Beyond the Basics. 1983. pap. 5.95 (ISBN 0-8024-0178-3). Moody.
DeWitt, J. Richard, tr. see Ridderbos, Herman N.
Dewitt, John R. Amazing Love. 160p. (Orig.). 1981. pap. text ed. 5.45 (ISBN 0-85151-328-X). Banner of Truth.
--What Is the Reformed Faith? (Orig.). 1981. pap. text ed. 1.45 (ISBN 0-85151-326-3). Banner of Truth.
De Witt, Mason, ed. see Carman, George.
DeWitt, Robert H. Arise, Thy Light Is Come. (Orig.). 1957. pap. 1.95 (ISBN 0-8054-9703-X). Broadman.
De Witt, Roy L. Teaching from the Tabernacle. LC 86-60046. (Illus.). 168p. (Orig.). pap. 8.95 (ISBN 0-9616360-0-9). Revival Teach.
De Wohl, Louis. Founded on a Rock: A History of the Catholic Church. LC 81-6557. 248p. 1981. Repr. lib. bdg. 23.50x (ISBN 0-313-23168-0, DEFO). Greenwood.
DeWolf, Carol. Object Talks from A to Z. (Illus.). 64p. 1987. 5.95 (ISBN 0-87403-237-7, 2867). Standard Pub.
DeWolf, L. Harold. Eternal Life: Why We Believe. LC 79-21670. 112p. 1980. pap. 6.95 (ISBN 0-664-24288-X). Westminster.
Dexter, Anne. View the Land. 1986. pap. 3.50 (ISBN 0-88270-609-8). Bridge Pub.
Dexter, Henry M. Congregationalism of the Last Three Hundred Years As Seen in Its Literature, 2 Vols. LC 65-58213. (Research & Source Ser.: No. 519). 1970. Repr. of 1880 ed. Set. lib. bdg. 53.00 (ISBN 0-8337-0851-1). B Franklin.
--The Congregationalism of the Last Three Hundred Years As Seen in Its Literature. 1072p. Date not set. Repr. of 1879 ed. text ed. 99.36x (Pub. by Gregg Intl Pubs England). Gregg Intl.
Dexter, Henry M. & Dexter, Morton. The England & Holland of the Pilgrims. LC 77-90433. (Illus.). 673p. 1978. Repr. of 1906 ed. 28.50 (ISBN 0-8063-0794-3). Genealog Pub.
Dexter, Morton, jt. auth. see Dexter, Henry M.
Dexter, W. Mr. Pickwick's Pilgrimages. 59.95 (ISBN 0-8490-0645-7). Gordon Pr.
Dey, J. N., tr. see Jnanatmananda, Swami.
Dey, J. N., tr. see Saradeshananda.
Dey, Lala K. The Intermediary World & Patterns of Perfection in Philo & Hebrews. LC 75-22457. (Society of Biblical Literature Dissertation Ser.: No.25). pap. 62.80 (ISBN 0-317-12981-3, 2017524). Bks Demand UMI.
DeYoung, Donald B., jt. auth. see Whitcomb, John C.
De Young, Garry. The Meaning of Christianity. 96p. 1982. pap. 7.95x (ISBN 0-936128-02-X). tchrs' ed. o. p. 7.95. De Young Pr.
DeYoung, Gordon. Dial-a-Word from the Bible. (Quiz & Puzzle Bks). 1977. pap. 0.95 (ISBN 0-8010-2862-0). Baker Bk.
DeYoung, Mary. Call to Reason: An Introduction to Atheism. 3rd ed. 1979. pap. 7.50 (ISBN 0-936128-01-1). De Young Pr.
De Zirkoff, Boris. The Dream That Never Dies: Boris de Zirkoff Speaks Out on Theosophy. Small, W. Emmett, ed. (Illus.). 242p. 1983. pap. 11.50 lexitone (ISBN 0-913004-45-6). Point Loma Pub.
De Zirkoff, Boris, ed. H. P. Blavatsky: Collected Writings, Vol. XIV. LC 84-50694. (Illus.). 750p. 1985. text ed. 16.50 (ISBN 0-8356-0234-6). Theos Pub Hse.
De Zirkoff, Boris, ed. see Blavatsky, Helena P.
De Zorzoli, Alicia, tr. see Conway, Jim & Conway, Sally.
DH - TE Research Studies. The Vatican & the Third World: Diplomacy & the Future. LC 75-14400. 1975. pap. 3.50 (ISBN 0-686-11971-1). Bks Intl DH-TE.
Dhaky, M. A., jt. ed. see Meister, Michael W.
Dhalla, M. N. Zoroastrian Civilization from the Earlist Times to the Downfall of the Last Zoroastrian Empire, 651 A. D. 1976. lib. bdg. 59.95 (ISBN 0-8490-2857-4). Gordon Pr.
--Zoroastrian Theology. lib. bdg. 79.95 (ISBN 0-87968-516-6). Krishna Pr.
Dhalla, Maneckji N. History of Zoroastrianism. LC 74-21256. Repr. of 1938 ed. 40.00 (ISBN 0-404-12806-8). AMS Pr.
--Our Perfecting World: Zarathushtra's Way of Life. LC 74-21257. Repr. of 1930 ed. 27.50 (ISBN 0-404-12807-6). AMS Pr.
--Zoroastrian Civilization: From the Earliest Times to the Downfall of the Last Zoroastrian Empire, 651 A.D. LC 74-21258. Repr. of 1922 ed. 30.00 (ISBN 0-404-12808-4). AMS Pr.
--Zoroastrian Theology from the Earliest Times to the Present Day. LC 70-131038. Repr. of 1914 ed. 30.00 (ISBN 0-404-02123-9). AMS Pr.
Dhammapada. The Buddha's Path of Virtue. 2nd ed. Woodward, F. L., tr. LC 78-72419. Repr. of 1929 ed. 21.50 (ISBN 0-404-17283-0). AMS Pr.
--Texts from the Buddhist Canon. Beal, Samuel, tr. from Chin. LC 78-72420. Repr. of 1878 ed. 22.50 (ISBN 0-404-17284-9). AMS Pr.
Dhammapadatthakatha. The Commentary on the Dhammapada, 5 vols. in 4. Norman, H. C., ed. LC 78-72423. Repr. of 1915 ed. Set. 155.00 (ISBN 0-404-17620-8). AMS Pr.
Dhar, Niranjan. Aurobindo, Gandhi & Roy: A Yogi, a Mahatma & a Rationalist. 1986. 13.50x (ISBN 0-8364-1578-7, Pub. by Minerva India). South Asia Bks.
--Vedanta & the Bengal Renaissance: Progress or Reaction. LC 76-52210. 1977. 11.00x (ISBN 0-88386-837-7). South Asia Bks.
Dharma Realm Buddhist Association Staff. World Peace Gathering. (Illus.). 128p. (Orig.). pap. 5.00 (ISBN 0-917512-05-7). Buddhist Text.
Dharma Realm Buddhist University Faculty. Human Roots: Buddhist Stories for Young Readers, Vol. 2. (Illus.). 140p. (Orig.). 1984. pap. 6.00 (ISBN 0-88139-017-8). Buddhist Text.
Dhavamony, Mariasusai, ed. Evangelization, Dialogue & Development. (Documenta Missionalia Ser.: No. 5). 1972. pap. 20.00 (ISBN 0-8294-0323-X, Pub. by Gregorian U Pr). Loyola.
Dhavamony, Mariasusai, et al. Revelation in Christianity & Other Religions. (Studia Missionalia: Vol. 20). (Eng., Fr., & Ital.). 1971. pap. 15.00 (ISBN 0-8294-0324-8, Pub. by Gregorian U Pr). Loyola.
Dhawan, Y. P. Beyond the Guru. 227p. 1980. pap. 4.25 (ISBN 0-86578-060-9). Ind-US Inc.
Dheilly, Joseph. Dictionnaire Biblique. (Fr.). 1284p. 1964. 22.50 (ISBN 0-686-57092-8, M-6114). French & Eur.
D'hert, Ignace. Wittgenstein's Relevance for Theology. (European University Studies: Ser. 23, Vol. 44). 237p. 1978. pap. 27.15 (ISBN 3-261-03092-5). P Lang Pubs.
Dhiegh, Khigh, ed. The Golden Oracle: The Ancient Chinese Way to Prosperity. LC 82-18471. (Illus.). 176p. 1983. 15.95 (ISBN 0-668-05661-4); pap. 8.95 (ISBN 0-668-05913-3). Arco.
Dhiravamsa. The Dynamic Way of Meditation. 160p. 1983. pap. 8.95 (ISBN 0-85500-163-1). Newcastle Pub.
--A New Approach to Buddhism. LC 74-81623. 1974. pap. 3.95 (ISBN 0-913922-08-0). Dawn Horse Pr.
--The Way of Non-Attachment: The Practice of Insight Meditation. 160p. 1984. pap. 9.95 (ISBN 0-85500-210-7). Newcastle Pub.
D'Holbach, Paul H. Christianity Unveiled. 69.95 (ISBN 0-87968-068-7). Gordon Pr.
D'Holbach, Paul H. & Meslier, Jean. Superstition in All Ages. 69.95 (ISBN 0-87968-108-X). Gordon Pr.
Diachenko, Gregory. Dukhovnija Posjevi. Tr. of Spiritual Sowing. (Illus.). 475p. 1977. 20.00 (ISBN 0-317-30414-3); pap. 15.00 (ISBN 0-317-30415-1). Holy Trinity.
Diamant, Alfred. Austrian Catholics & the First Republic: Democracy, Capitalism, & the Social Order, 1918-1934. LC 60-5745. pap. 84.30 (ISBN 0-317-09404-1, 2015226). Bks Demand UMI.
--Austrian Catholics & the Social Question, 1918-1933. LC 59-62692. (University of Florida Social Sciences Monographs: No. 2). 1959. pap. 3.50 (ISBN 0-8130-0059-9). U Presses Fla.
Diamant, Anita. The New Jewish Wedding. LC 84-24102. (Illus.). 1985. 16.95 (ISBN 0-671-49527-5). Summit Bks.
--New Jewish Wedding. 272p. 1986. 8.95 (ISBN 0-671-62882-8). Summit Bks.
Diamond, A. R. The Confessions of Jeremiah in Context: Scenes of Prophetic Drams. (JSOT Supplement Ser.: No. 45). 250p. 1987. text ed. 29.50x (ISBN 1-85075-032-7, Pub. by JSOT Pr England); pap. text ed. 19.95x (ISBN 1-85075-033-5, Pub. by JSOT Pr England). Eisenbrauns.
Diamond, Carlin J. Love It, Don't Label It: A Practical Guide for Using Spiritual Principles in Everyday Life. Peterson, Kim, ed. (Illus.). 200p. (Orig.). 1986. pap. 10.00 (ISBN 0-911761-03-9). Fifth Wave Pr.
Diamond, Eugene & Diamond, Rosemary. The Positive Values of Chastity. 1983. 7.50 (ISBN 0-8199-0829-0). Franciscan Herald.
Diamond, James S. Barukh Kurzweil & Modern Hebrew Literature. LC 82-16770. (Brown Judaic Studies). 232p. 1983. pap. 18.00 (ISBN 0-89130-595-5, 14 00 39). Scholars Pr GA.
Diamond, Lucy. Jesus by the Sea of Galilee. (Ladybird Ser). (Illus.). 1958. bds. 2.50 (ISBN 0-87508-840-6). Chr Lit.
--Jesus Calls His Disciples. (Ladybird Ser). (Illus.). 1959. bds. 2.50 (ISBN 0-87508-842-2). Chr Lit.
--Moses, Prince & Shepherd. (Ladybird Ser). (Illus.). 1954. bds. 2.50 (ISBN 0-87508-850-3). Chr Lit.
--Naaman & the Little Maid. (Ladybird Ser). (Illus.). 1959. bds. 2.50 (ISBN 0-87508-852-X). Chr Lit.
--Story of Daniel. (Ladybird Ser). (Illus.). 1958. bds. 2.50 (ISBN 0-87508-866-X). Chr Lit.
--Story of Joseph. (Ladybird Ser). (Illus.). 1954. bds. 2.50 (ISBN 0-87508-868-6). Chr Lit.
--Two Stories Jesus Told. (Ladybird Ser). (Illus.). 1959. bds. 2.50 (ISBN 0-87508-870-8). Chr Lit.
Diamond, Malcolm L. Martin Buber: Jewish Existentialist. 1968. lib. bdg. 17.50x (ISBN 0-88307-077-4). Gannon.
Diamond, Michael J. & Gowing, Peter G. Islam & Muslims: Some Basic Information. 100p. 1981. pap. 3.75x (ISBN 0-686-30367-9, Pub. by New Day Publishers Philippines). Cellar.
Diamond, Rosemary, jt. auth. see Diamond, Eugene.
Diara, Agadem L. Islam & Pan-Africanism. LC 72-91318. (Illus.). 120p. 1973. pap. 3.75 (ISBN 0-913358-04-5). El-Shabazz Pr.
Diaz, Alfredo, tr. see Lima, Tiago.
Diaz, Jorge & De Gonzalez, Nelly, eds. La Biblia lo Dice. (Span., Illus.). 120p. 1986. Repr. of 1984 ed. spiral bdg. 3.95 (ISBN 0-311-11453-9). Casa Bautista.
Diaz, Jorge E. Guia De Estudios Sobre Doctrina Cristiana. (Guias De Estudio). 88p. pap. 3.25 (ISBN 0-311-43500-9). Casa Bautista.
Diaz, Jorge E., jt. auth. see Crane, James D.
Diaz, Jorge E., tr. see Charley, Julian.
Diaz, Jorge E., tr. see Coleman, Lucien E., Jr.
Diaz, Jorge E., tr. see Ford, LeRoy.
Diaz, Myriam, tr. see Charley, Julian.
Diaz, Olimpia, tr. see Balado, Jose L.
Diaz, Olimpia, tr. see McPhee, John.
Diaz, Olimpia, tr. see Norquist, Marilyn.
Diaz, Olimpia, tr. see Ruhnke, Robert.
Diaz, Olimpia, tr. see Tickle, John.
Diaz, Olimpia, Sr., tr. see Tickle, John.
Dibbert, Michael T., et al. Growth Groups: A Key to Christian Fellowship & Spiritual Maturity in the Church. 160p. (Orig.). 1985. pap. 5.95 (ISBN 0-310-23121-3, 11673P). Zondervan.
Dibble, Charles E., tr. see Leon-Portilla, Miguel.
Dibble, Charles E., tr. see Sahagun, Bernardino de.
Dibelius, Martin. Fresh Approach to the New Testament & Early Christian Literature. LC 78-32096. 1979. Repr. of 1936 ed. lib. bdg. 24.75x (ISBN 0-8371-4219-9, DINT). Greenwood.
--From Tradition to Gospel. Wooff, Bertram L., tr. 328p. 1971. 27.50 (ISBN 0-227-67752-8). Attic Pr.
--James. Koester, Helmut, ed. Willims, Michael A., tr. LC 74-80428. (Hermeneia: a Critical & Historical Commentary on the Bible). 308p. 1975. 24.95 (ISBN 0-8006-6006-4, 20-6006). Fortress.
Dibelius, Martin & Conzelmann, Hans. The Pastoral Epistles. Koester, Helmut, ed. Buttolph, Philip & Yarbro, Adela, trs. from Ger. LC 71-157549. (Hermeneia: a Critical & Historical Commentary on the Bible). 1972. 19.95 (ISBN 0-8006-6002-1, 20-6002). Fortress.
Di Berardino, Angelo, jt. ed. see Quasten, Johannes.
Dibinga wa Said. The Unification Church Policy on South Africa. (Christian Churches Policies on South Africa Ser.). 14p. (Orig.). 1986. pap. write for info. (ISBN 0-943324-26-2). Omenana.
Di Brandi, Herman A. Introduction to Christian Doctrine. 128p. (Orig.). 1976. pap. 4.95 (ISBN 0-8192-1194-X). Morehouse.
DiCarlo, Joseph, Jr. Following Christ. (Faith & Life Ser.). (Illus.). 142p. (Orig.). 1985. pap. 6.20 (ISBN 0-89870-065-5). Ignatius Pr.
Di Cesare, Mario A., jt. auth. see Mignani, Rigo.
Dicharry, Warren. To Live the Word Inspired & Incarnate: An Integral Biblical Spirituality. LC 85-7386. 464p. (Orig.). 1985. pap. 12.95 (ISBN 0-8189-0476-3). Alba.
Dicharry, Warren F. Greek Without Grief: An Outline Guide to New Testament Greek. 5th ed. (Illus.). 1985. pap. 8.95 (ISBN 0-9608630-3-6). Vincentian.
DiCicco, Philip P., jt. auth. see Krutza, William J.
Dicicco, Philip P., jt. auth. see Krutza, William J.
DiCicco, Philip P., jt. auth. see Krutza, William J.
Dicicco, Philip P., jt. auth. see Krutza, William J.
Dick, Lois H. Amy Carmichael: Let the Little Children Come. (Orig.). 1984. pap. 3.95 (ISBN 0-8024-0433-2). Moody.
Dick, Louise L., ed. Clips from Tom M. Olson: Nuggets from the Writings of Tom M. Olson Provide the Only-Way to View Events. LC 86-90141. (One-Way Ser.: Vol. 10). 251p. (Orig.). 1986. pap. 6.95 (ISBN 0-935899-06-5). LeTourneau Pr.
Dickason, C. Fred. Angels, Elect & Evil. 256p. 1975. pap. 6.95 (ISBN 0-8024-0222-4). Moody.
Dickens, A. G. The Counter-Reformation. (Library of World Civilization). (Illus.). 1979. pap. 7.95x (ISBN 0-393-95086-7). Norton.
--Lollards & Protestants in the Diocese of York. (No. 10). 280p. 1983. 27.00 (ISBN 0-907628-05-2); pap. 12.00 (ISBN 0-907628-06-0). Hambledon Press.
--Reformation & Society in Sixteenth Century Europe. (History of European Civilization Library). (Illus., Orig.). 1966. pap. text ed. 11.95 (ISBN 0-15-576455-1, HC). HarBraceJ.
--Reformation Studies. 624p. 1983. 40.00 (ISBN 0-907628-04-4). Hambledon Press.
Dickens, A. G., et al. The Reformation in Historical Thought. 456p. 1985. text ed. 33.50x (ISBN 0-674-75311-9). Harvard U Pr.
Dickens, Arthur G. English Reformation. LC 64-22987. (Fabric of British History Ser). 1968. pap. 8.95 (ISBN 0-8052-0177-7). Schocken.
Dickens, Arthur G. & Carr, Dorothy. Reformation in England to the Accession of Elizabeth 1. (Documents of Modern History Ser). (Orig.). 1968. pap. 11.95 (ISBN 0-312-66815-5). St Martin.
Dickens, Charles. A Christmas Carol: Retold by A. Sweaney. (Oxford Progressive English Readers Ser.). 1975. pap. text ed. 3.75x (ISBN 0-19-580724-3). Oxford U Pr.
--The Life of Our Lord. LC 80-22131. (Illus.). 128p. 1981. Repr. of 1934 ed. 10.95 (ISBN 0-664-21382-0). Westminster.
Dicker, Gordon S., ed. Homosexuality & the Church. 71p. (Orig.). 1985. pap. 6.95 (ISBN 0-85819-505-4, Pub. by Uniting Church). ANZ Religious Pubns.
Dicker, Herman. Creativity, Holocaust, Reconstruction: Jewish Life in Wuertemberg, Past & Present. (Illus.). 1984. 18.50 (ISBN 0-87203-118-7). Hermon.

Dickerhoff, Heinrich. Wege ins Alte Testament - und Zurueck: Vom Sinn und den Moeglichkeiten einer "Theologie mit dem Alten Testament" in der Arbeit mit Erwachsenen, Vol 211. (European University Studies: No. 23). (Ger.). 409p. 1983. 40.55 (ISBN 3-8204-7734-9). P Lang Pubs.

Dickerson, Grace. Jesus. 1985. 5.50 (ISBN 0-533-03936-3). Vantage.

Dickey, Adam H. Memoirs of Mary Baker Eddy. 51p. 1985. pap. 6.00 (ISBN 0-930227-04-2). Pasadena Pr.

Dickey, C. R. One Man's Destiny. 1942. 8.00 (ISBN 0-685-08811-1). Destiny.

Dickey, James. God's Images: A New Vision. LC 78-17465. (Illus.). 110p. (Orig.). 1978. pap. 7.95 (ISBN 0-8164-2194-3, HarpR). Har-Row.

Dickinson, E. Music in the History of the Western Church. LC 68-25286. (Studies in Music, No. 42). 1969. Repr. of 1902 ed. lib. bdg. 49.95x (ISBN 0-8383-0301-3). Haskell.

Dickinson, Edward. Music in the History of the Western Church. LC 77-127454. Repr. of 1902 ed. 14.50 (ISBN 0-404-02127-1). AMS Pr.

--Music in the History of the Western Church, with an Introduction in Religious Music Among the Primitive & Ancient Peoples. LC 69-13884. Repr. of 1902 ed. lib. bdg. 22.50x (ISBN 0-8371-1062-9, DIMW). Greenwood.

--Music in the History of the Western Church, with an Introduction in Religious Music Among the Primitive & Ancient Peoples. 1977. Repr. 19.00 (ISBN 0-403-08194-7). Scholarly.

Dickinson, George T. Jeremiah: The Iron Prophet. (Horizon Ser.). 1978. pap. 5.95 (ISBN 0-8127-0183-6). Review & Herald.

Dickinson, Helena. A Treasury of Worship. 59.95 (ISBN 0-8490-1230-9). Gordon Pr.

Dickinson, J. C. The Later Middle Ages: From the Norman Conquest to the Eve of the Reformation. (Ecclesiastical History of England Ser.). 487p. 1979. text ed. 30.00x (ISBN 0-06-491678-2). B&N Imports.

Dickinson, John C. Monastic Life in Medieval England. LC 78-25804. (Illus.). 1979. Repr. of 1961 ed. lib. bdg. 24.75x (ISBN 0-313-20774-7, DIML). Greenwood.

Dickman, R. Thomas. In God We Should Trust. LC 76-53146. 1977. 6.95 (ISBN 0-87212-071-6). Libra.

--Of Sex & Sin. LC 85-91068. 1986. 10.00 (ISBN 0-87212-195-X). Libra.

Dickson, Albert A. Fascination of Faith. Keith, Gerald, ed. 268p. (Orig.). 1980. pap. 4.95x (ISBN 0-9604080-0-2). Gloria Pubs.

Dickson, David. A Commentary on the Psalms, 2 vols. 1980. 32.50 (ISBN 0-86524-017-5, 1901). Klock & Klock.

--Matthew. (Geneva Ser. Commentaries). Orig. Title: A Brief Exposition of the Evangel of Jesus Christ According to Matthew. 416p. 1981. 15.95 (ISBN 0-85151-319-0). Banner of Truth.

--Psalms. (Geneva Commentary Ser.). 1064p. 1985. Repr. of 1653 ed. 21.95 (ISBN 0-85151-481-2). Banner of Truth.

Dickson, Elaine. Say No, Say Yes to Change. LC 81-67375. 1982. 6.95 (ISBN 0-8054-5210-9). Broadman.

Dickson, Kwesi A. Theology in Africa. LC 84-5154. 240p. (Orig.). 1984. pap. 9.95 (ISBN 0-88344-508-5). Orbis Bks.

Dickson, Nicholas. The Bible in Waverley. 1973. Repr. of 1884 ed. write for info. (ISBN 0-8274-1586-9). R West.

--Bible in Waverley: Or, Sir Walter Scott's Use of the Sacred Scripture. 311p. 1980. Repr. of 1884 ed. lib. bdg. 30.00 (ISBN 0-8495-1123-2). Arden Lib.

--Or, Sir Walter Scott's Use of Sacred Scriptures. 1979. Repr. of 1884 ed. lib. bdg. 30.00 (ISBN 0-8414-3830-7). Folcroft.

Dickson, Roger. Millennial Mistake. 2.50 (ISBN 0-89315-160-2). Lambert Bk.

DiCrescenza, Frances. Annihilation or Salvation? 1986. 8.95 (ISBN 0-8062-2505-X). Carlton.

Diddee, Dolly, tr. see Rajneesh, Bhagwan S.

Didi, Dolli, tr. see Rajneesh, Bhagwan S.

Didion, Joan. A Book of Common Prayer. 288p. 1983. pap. 3.95 (ISBN 0-671-49589-5). PB.

Dieckmann, Ed, Jr. The Secret of Jonestown: The Reason Why. 176p. (Orig.). 1982. pap. 6.00 (ISBN 0-939482-02-9). Noontide.

Diefenbach, Gabriel. Common Mystic Prayer. 1978. 2.50 (ISBN 0-8198-0527-0); pap. 1.95 (ISBN 0-8198-0528-9). Dghtrs St Paul.

Diefenthaler, Jon. H. Richard Niebuhr: A Lifetime of Reflections on the Church & the World. 144p. (Orig.). 1986. 24.95 (ISBN 0-86554-214-7, MUP-H193); pap. 9.95 (ISBN 0-86554-235-X, MUP-P33). Mercer Univ Pr.

Diehl & Morris. Physical Fitness & the Christian. 212p. 1986. pap. text ed. 14.95 (ISBN 0-8403-4200-4). Kendall-Hunt.

Diehl, Charles F., jt. auth. see Stevenson, Dwight E.

Diehl, Helmut. Atheismus Im Religionsunterricht. (European University Studies Thirty-Three: Vol. 6). (Ger.). 622p. 1982. 46.30 (ISBN 3-8204-6280-5). P Lang Pubs.

Diehl, Huston. An Index of Icons in English Emblem Books, 1500-1700. LC 85-40950. (Illus.). 288p. 1986. 35.00x (ISBN 0-8061-1989-6). U of Okla Pr.

Diehl, Judith R. A Woman's Place: Equal Partnership in Daily Ministry. LC 84-47915. 128p. 1985. pap. 5.95 (ISBN 0-8006-1791-6, 1-1791). Fortress.

Diehl, Katharine S. Hymns & Tunes: An Index. LC 66-13743. 1242p. 1979. lib. bdg. 65.00 (ISBN 0-8108-0062-4). Scarecrow.

--Jesuits, Lutherans, & the Printing Press in South India. (Printers & Printing in the East Indies to 1850 Ser.: Vol. III). write for info. Caratzas.

Diehl, Patrick S. The Medieval Religious Lyric: An Ars Poetria. LC 83-6557. 475p. 1984. text ed. 40.00x (ISBN 0-520-04673-0). U of Cal Pr.

Diehl, William E. Christianity & Real Life. LC 76-7860. 128p. 1976. pap. 4.50 (ISBN 0-8006-1231-0, 1-1231). Fortress.

--Thank God, It's Monday! LC 81-71390. 192p. 1982. pap. 6.95 (ISBN 0-8006-1656-1, 1-1656). Fortress.

Diehm, William J. Criticizing. LC 86-17372. (Christian Growth Bks). 128p. (Orig.). 1986. pap. 6.95 (ISBN 0-8066-2211-3, 10-1722). Augsburg.

--Finding Your Life Partner. 128p. 1984. pap. 4.95 (ISBN 0-8170-1028-9). Judson.

Diel, Paul. The God-Symbol. 240p. 1985. 17.95 (ISBN 0-86683-475-3, HarpR). Har-Row.

--Symbolism in the Bible. 1986. 17.95 (ISBN 0-317-52369-4, HarpR). Har-Row.

Dieleman, Dale. Our Life & Times. 1985. pap. 5.95 (ISBN 0-8010-2951-1). Baker Bk.

Dieleman, Dale, compiled by. The Go Book. (Good Things for Youth Leaders). 64p. 1982. pap. 4.50 (ISBN 0-8010-2929-5). Baker Bk.

--The Praise Book. 1984. pap. 5.95 (ISBN 0-8010-2947-3). Baker Bk.

--Taking Charge. (Good Things for Youth Leaders Ser.). pap. 3.45 (ISBN 0-8010-2911-2). Baker Bk.

Diem, Hermann. Kierkegaard's Dialectic of Existence. Knight, Harold, tr. from German. LC 77-18886. 1978. Repr. of 1959 ed. lib. bdg. 22.50x (ISBN 0-313-20220-6, DIKD). Greenwood.

Diemer, J. Nature & Miracle. 1977. pap. 1.95 (ISBN 0-88906-015-0). Wedge Pub.

Dienstag, J. I., ed. Studies in Maimonidean Medicine. (Texts, Studies & Translations in Maimonidean Thought & Scholarship: Vol.2). 35.00x (ISBN 0-87068-449-3). Ktav.

--Studies in Maimonides & Spinoza. (Texts, Studies & Translations in Maimonidean Thought & Scholarship: Vol. 3). 35.00x (ISBN 0-87068-330-6). Ktav.

Dienstag, Jacob I. Eschatology in Maimonidean Thought: Messianism, Resurrection, & the World to Come-Jacob I. LC 82-17303. cxx, 281p. 1982. 59.50x (ISBN 0-87068-706-9). Ktav.

--Maimonides & St. Thomas Aquinas. 1974. 39.50x (ISBN 0-87068-249-0). Ktav.

Diercksmeier, John, jt. auth. see Larranaga, Ignacio.

Dieten, Ioannes Van see Van Dieten, Ioannes.

Dieten, Jan-Louis Van see Van Dieten, Jan-Louis.

Dieter, Hallie, ed. see Smith, Hannah W.

Dieter, Melvin, ed. see Smith, Hannah W.

Dieter, Melvin E. The Holiness Revival of the Nineteenth Century. LC 80-17259. (Studies in Evangelicalism: No. 1). 366p. 1980. 26.00 (ISBN 0-8108-1328-9). Scarecrow.

Dieter, Melvin E. & Berg, Daniel N., eds. Church. (Wesleyan Theological Perspectives Ser.: Vol. IV). 1984. 14.95 (ISBN 0-87162-406-0, D4853). Warner Pr.

Dieterlen, Germaine, ed. see International African Seminar - 3rd - Salisburg - Southern Rhodesia.

Dietrich, B. C. The Origins of Greek Religion. 314p. 1973. 84.00x (ISBN 3-11-003982-6). De Gruyter.

Dietrich, Bernard C. Tradition in Greek Religion. xvi, 213p. 1986. 66.00x (ISBN 3-11-010695-7). De Gruyter.

Dietrich, Donald J. Catholic Citizens in the Third Reich: Psyco-Social Principles & Moral Reasoning. 385p. 1987. 39.95 (ISBN 0-88738-131-6). Transaction Bks.

--The Goethezeit & the Metamorphosis of Catholic Theology in the Age of Idealism: Theology, Vol. 128. (European University Studies: Ser. 23). 261p. 1979. pap. 26.25 (ISBN 3-261-04703-8). P Lang Pubs.

Dietrich, Martin O. & Lehmann, Helmut T., eds. Luther's Works: Devotional Writings I, Vol. 42. LC 55-9893. (Prog. Bk.). 1969. 19.95 (ISBN 0-8006-0342-7, 1-342). Fortress.

Dietrich, Suzanne. Matthew. LC 59-10454. (Layman's Bible Commentary Ser.: Vol. 16). 1961. pap. 4.95 (ISBN 0-8042-3076-5). John Knox.

Dietrich, Suzanne De see De Dietrich, Suzanne.

Dietrich, Wendell, ed. see Kane, John F.

Dietrich, Wendell, ed. see Orr, Robert P.

Dietrich, Wendell S. Cohen & Troeltsch: Ethical Monotheistic Religion & Theory of Culture. (Brown Judaic Studies). 1986. text ed. 23.95 (ISBN 1-55540-017-5, 14-01-20); pap. 18.95 (ISBN 1-55540-018-3). Scholars Pr GA.

Dietrich, Wendell S., ed. see Smith, David L.

Dietz, Sarah S. Easter Activity Book. (Stick-Out-Your Neck Ser.). (Illus.). 32p. 1984. pap. 1.98 (ISBN 0-88724-067-4, CD-8051). Carson-Dellos.

Dietzen, John J. The New Question Box. rev. ed. 606p. 1987. pap. 9.95 (ISBN 0-940518-01-5). Guildhall Pubs.

DiFederico, Frank. The Mosaics of Saint Peter's: Decorating the New Basilica. LC 82-42777. (Illus.). 176p. 1983. 42.50x (ISBN 0-271-00344-8). Pa St U Pr.

--The Mosaics of the National Shrine of the Immaculate Conception. (Illus.). 96p. 1981. 16.95 (ISBN 0-916276-09-0). Decatur Hse.

DiFranco, Anthony. Pope John Paul II: Bringing Love to a Troubled World. LC 82-23618. (Taking Part Ser.). (Illus.). 48p. 1983. PLB 8.95 (ISBN 0-87518-241-0). Dillon.

Digan, Parig. Churches in Contestation: Asian Christian Social Protest. LC 83-19338. 224p. (Orig.). 1984. pap. 10.95 (ISBN 0-88344-102-0). Orbis Bks.

DiGangi, Mariano. I Believe in Mission. 1979. pap. 2.95 (ISBN 0-87552-255-6). Presby & Reformed.

Di Gangi, Mariano. Twelve Prophetic Voices. 168p. 1985. pap. 5.95 (ISBN 0-89693-536-1). Victor Bks.

Digby, John, tr. see Epicurus.

Digby, Sir Kenelme. Two Treatises: In the One of Which the Nature of Bodies; In the Other the Nature of Man's Soule is Look'd into the Way of Discovery of the Immortality of Reasonable Souls. Wellek, Rene, ed. LC 75-11217. (British Philosophers & Theologians of the 17th & 18th Centuries Ser.). 514p. 1978. lib. bdg. 51.00 (ISBN 0-8240-1771-4). Garland Pub.

Diggle, John W. Religious Doubt: Its Nature, Treatment, Causes, Difficulties, Consequences & Dissolution. 1978. Repr. of 1895 ed. lib. bdg. 25.00 (ISBN 0-8495-1030-9). Arden Lib.

Diggs, Bernard J. Love & Being: An Investigation into the Metaphysics of St. Thomas Aquinas. 180p. 1947. 6.75 (ISBN 0-913298-45-X). S F Vanni.

Diggs, Dorothy C. Working Manual for Altar Guilds. rev. ed. (Orig.). 1957. pap. 3.95 (ISBN 0-8192-1028-5). Morehouse.

Di Giacomo, James. When Your Teenager Stops Going to Church. LC 80-65401. (When Books). (Illus.). 96p. (Orig.). 1980. pap. 2.45 (ISBN 0-87029-165-3, 20260-6). Abbey.

DiGiacomo, James, jt. auth. see Walsh, John.

Digiacomo, James, et al. The Longest Step: Searching for God. (The Encounter Ser.). (Illus.). 1977. pap. text ed. 4.50 (ISBN 0-86683-180-0, 315, HarpR); resource manual 1.95 (ISBN 0-86683-181-9, 316). Har-Row.

--Meet the Lord: Encounters with Jesus. (The Encounter Ser.). 1977. pap. 3.98 (ISBN 0-03-021281-2, 317, HarpR); resource manual 1.95 (ISBN 0-03-021866-7, 318). Har-Row.

Dignan, Patrick J. A History of the Legal Incorporation of Catholic Church Property in the United States (1784-1932) LC 73-3569. (Catholic University of America. Studies in American Church History: No. 14). Repr. of 1933 ed. 31.00 (ISBN 0-404-57764-4). AMS Pr.

Dijk, Jan van see Van Dijk, Jan, et al.

Dikshit, Sudhakar S., ed. see Nisargadatta Maharaj.

Dilday, Russell H., Jr. Personal Computer: A New Tool for Ministers. LC 84-20360. 1985. pap. 8.95 (ISBN 0-8054-3111-X). Broadman.

Di Lella, Alexander A., jt. auth. see Hartman, Louis F.

Dilke, Emilia F. Book of the Spiritual Life. LC 70-37689. (Illus., With a memoir of the author by the Rt. Hon. Sir Charles W. Dilke). Repr. of 1905 ed. 26.00 (ISBN 0-404-56743-6). AMS Pr.

Dill, S. Roman Society in the Last Century of Western Empire. 75.00 (ISBN 0-87968-060-1). Gordon Pr.

Dillaway, Newton. Gospel of Emerson. 1968. Repr. 5.95 (ISBN 0-87159-046-8). Unity School.

Dillenberger, Jane. Style & Content in Christian Art. 320p. 1986. pap. 17.95 (ISBN 0-8245-0782-7). Crossroad NY.

--Style & Content in Christian Art: From the Catacombs to the Chapel Designed by Matisse at Vence, France. LC 65-22293. pap. 80.50 (ISBN 0-317-10399-7, 2001274). Bks Demand UMI.

Dillenberger, Jane, ed. see Tillich, Paul.

Dillenberger, John. Benjamin West: The Context of His Life's Work. LC 76-42004. (Illus.). 238p. 1977. 25.00 (ISBN 0-911536-65-5). Trinity U Pr.

--Protestant Thought & Natural Science: A Historical Interpretation. LC 77-7200. 1977. Repr. of 1960 ed. lib. bdg. 22.75x (ISBN 0-8371-9670-1, DIPT). Greenwood.

--A Theology of Artistic Sensibilities: The Visual Arts & the Church. 280p. 1986. 22.50 (ISBN 0-8245-0783-5). Crossroad NY.

--The Visual Arts & Christianity in America: The Colonial Period Through the Nineteenth Century. LC 84-3897. (Scholars Press Studies in the Humanities). 1984. 29.25 (ISBN 0-89130-734-6, 00 01 05); pap. 19.50 (ISBN 0-89130-761-3). Scholars Pr GA.

Dillenberger, John & Welch, Claude. Protestant Christianity. 340p. 1976. pap. text ed. write for info. (ISBN 0-02-330470-7, Pub. by Scribner). Macmillan.

Dillenberger, John, ed. John Calvin: Selections from His Writings. LC 75-26875. (American Academy of Religion. Aids for the Study of Religion). 590p. 1975. pap. 10.95 (ISBN 0-89130-025-2, 010302). Scholars Pr GA.

Dillenberger, John, ed. see Luther, Martin.

Dillenberger, John, ed. see Tillich, Paul.

Diller, Jerry V. Ancient Roots & Modern Meanings. LC 77-99196. 1978. 12.50 (ISBN 0-8197-0457-1); pap. 7.95 (ISBN 0-685-27177-3). Bloch.

Dillett, Eric S. What Is Man? 80p. 1985. 6.50 (ISBN 0-682-40254-0). Exposition Pr FL.

Dilley, Romilda. Silhouette Crafts. (Illus.). 24p. (YA) 1987. wkbk. 2.95 (ISBN 0-87403-238-5, 2148). Standard Pub.

Dilling, E. The Plot Against Christianity: A Study of the Talmud. 1982. lib. bdg. 69.95 (ISBN 0-87700-359-9). Revisionist Pr.

Dilling, Elizabeth. The Jewish Religion: Its Influence Today. (Illus.). 300p. 1983. pap. 8.00 (ISBN 0-939482-07-X). Noontide.

--Plot Against Christianity. 310p. 12.00 (ISBN 0-913022-33-0). Angriff Pr.

Dillion, John M., jt. auth. see Morrow, Glenn R.

Dillistone, F. W. The Power of Symbols in Religion & Culture. 176p. 1986. 14.95 (ISBN 0-8245-0784-3). Crossroad NY.

Dillon, E. J. Sceptics of the Old Testament. LC 73-16064. (Studies in Comparative Literature, No. 35). 1974. Repr. of 1895 ed. lib. bdg. 51.95x (ISBN 0-8383-1723-5). Haskell.

Dillon, George E. Freemasonry Unmasked. Fuhley, Denis, pref. by. 114p. 1984. pap. 6.00 (ISBN 0-89562-095-2). Sons Lib.

Dillon, John, jt. auth. see Winston, David.

Dillon, Valerie V., ed. A Positive Vision for Family Life: A Resource Guide for Pope John Paul II's Apostolic Exhortation Familiaris Consortio. 56p. 1985. pap. 3.95 (ISBN 1-55586-938-6). US Catholic.

Dillow, Linda. Creative Counterpart. rev. & updated ed. 228p. 1986. pap. 7.95 (ISBN 0-8407-3067-5). Nelson.

--La Esposa Virtuosa. 160p. 1981. 2.95 (ISBN 0-88113-064-8). Edit Betania.

Dilsaver, Paul. Encounters with the Antichrist. 4.00 (ISBN 0-317-52034-2). Jelm Mtn.

Dilthey, Wilhelm. Leben Schleiermachers, 2 vols. Incl. Vol. 1, Pt. 1. 1768-1802. 3rd ed. Redeker, Martin, ed. xlvi, 567p. 1970. 48.00x (ISBN 3-11-006348-4); Vol. 1, Pt. 2. 1803-1807. Mulert, H., ed. xxiv, 251p. 1970. 24.00x (ISBN 3-11-006437-5); Vol. 2. Schleiermachers System als Philosophie und Theologie, 2 vols. in 1. Redeker, Martin, ed. lxxx, 811p. 1966. 72.00x (ISBN 3-11-001266-9). (Ger.). De Gruyter.

Dilthey, Wilthelm. Philosophy of Existence: Introduction to Weltanschauugslehre. LC 78-5673. 1978. Repr. of 1957 ed. lib. bdg. 22.50x (ISBN 0-313-20460-8, DIPH). Greenwood.

DiLustre, Tawny. A Compilation of Thoughts, I Think?! 104p. 1985. 6.95 (ISBN 0-8059-2962-2). Dorrance.

Dilworth, David A., tr. see Kitaro, Nishida.

Di Marchi, John. Fatima from the Beginning. (Illus.). 1980. pap. 5.95 (ISBN 0-911218-16-5). Ravengate Pr.

DiMaria-Kuiper, Johannes W. Hot under the Collar: Self-Portrait of a Gay Pastor. LC 83-60016. 177p. (Orig.). 1983. pap. 7.95 (ISBN 0-912393-00-9). Mercury Pr.

DiMauro, Joseph & Tumulty, Sharon A. Together: A Process for Parish Family Ministry. 1985. Envisioning. pap. 2.50 (ISBN 0-697-02024-X); Listening. pap. 3.50 (ISBN 0-697-02025-8); Responding. pap. 3.50 (ISBN 0-697-02026-6); Enabling. pap. 3.50 (ISBN 0-697-02027-4); Administering. pap. 3.50 (ISBN 0-697-02028-2); Administrator manual. 20.00 (ISBN 0-697-02023-1). Wm C Brown.

Di Meglio, Clara, jt. auth. see Valentini, Norberto.

Dimermanas, Alon, ed. see Rabbi Nachman of Breslov & Rabbi Nathan of Breslov.

Dimermanas, Alon, tr. see Rabbi Nachman.

Dimier. Recueil de Plans d'Eglises Cisterciennes, 2 tomes. Set. 100.75 (ISBN 0-685-34012-0). French & Eur.

Dimitry of Rostov, St. Angels & the Other Heavenly Bodiless Powers. pap. 0.25 (ISBN 0-686-05638-8). Eastern Orthodox.

Dimmitt, Cornelia, ed. Classical Hindu Mythology: A Reader in the Sanskrit Puranas. Van Buitenen, J. A., tr. LC 77-92643. 388p. 1978. 34.95 (ISBN 0-87722-117-0); pap. 12.95x (ISBN 0-87722-122-7). Temple U Pr.

Dimock, Edward C., Jr. & Levertov, Denise, trs. In Praise of Krishna: Songs from the Bengali. (Illus.). xii, 96p. 1981. 6.95 (ISBN 0-226-15231-6, Phoen). U of Chicago Pr.

Dimock, Giles, jt. ed. see Alexander, Jon.

Dimond, Jasper. Noah's Ark. (Illus.). 48p. 1983. 8.95 (ISBN 0-13-622951-4). P-H.

Dimont, Max. The Jews in America. 1980. 6.95 (ISBN 0-671-25412-X, Touchstone). S&S.

Dimont, Max I. The Amazing Adventures of the Jewish People. LC 84-16806. 175p. (YA) 1984. pap. 3.95 (ISBN 0-87441-391-5). Behrman.

--The Indestructible Jews. 480p. 1973. pap. 4.95 (ISBN 0-451-13878-3, Sig). NAL.

--Jews, God & History. 1972. pap. 4.95 (ISBN 0-451-14694-8, AE2181, Sig). NAL.

Dimsdale, Joel E., ed. Survivors, Victims & Perpetrators: Essays on the Nazi Holocaust. LC 79-24834. (Illus.). 474p. 1980. text ed. 42.50 (ISBN 0-89116-145-7); pap. text ed. 32.95 (ISBN 0-89116-351-4). Hemisphere Pub.

Din, M. R., jt. auth. see Malik, Imam.

Dinda, R. J., tr. Luther's Works, Vol. 18. 1980. 16.95 (ISBN 0-570-06418-X, 15-1760). Concordia.

Dinda, R. J., jt. tr. see Miller, W. M.

Dingley, Thomas. History from Marble, 2 Vols. LC 70-164834. (Camden Society, London. Publications, First Ser.: Nos. 94 & 97). Repr. of 1868 ed. Set. 74.00 (ISBN 0-404-50210-5). AMS Pr.

Dinin, Samuel. Judaism in a Changing Civilization. LC 70-176722. (Columbia University. Teachers College. Contributions to Education: No. 563). Repr. of 1933 ed. 22.50 (ISBN 0-404-55563-2). AMS Pr.

Dinnerstein, Dorothy. The Mermaid & the Minotaur: Sexual Arrangements & Human Malaise. LC 72-23879. 1977. pap. 7.95 (ISBN 0-06-090587-5, CN 587, PL). Har-Row.

Dinnerstein, Leonard. Uneasy at Home: Antisemitism & the American Jewish Experience. LC 87-521. 272p. 1987. 25.00 (ISBN 0-231-06252-4). Columbia U Pr.

Dinnerstein, Leonard & Palsson, Mary D., eds. Jews in the South. LC 72-89114. viii, 392p. 1973. 32.50x (ISBN 0-8071-0226-1). La State U Pr.

Di Nola, Alfonso, ed. Prayers of Man. 1960. 27.95 (ISBN 0-8392-1152-X). Astor-Honor.

Dinsmore, Charles A. The English Bible as Literature. 1931. Repr. 30.00 (ISBN 0-8274-3832-X). R West.

Dinsmore, M. H. What Really Happened When Christ Died. LC 79-52539. 1979. pap. 4.95 (ISBN 0-89636-025-3). Accent Bks.

DiNunzio, Sylvester L. The Priesthood & Humanity. 1984. 8.50 (ISBN 0-8062-2379-0). Carlton.

Dionne, J. Robert. The Papacy & the Church: A Study of Praxis & Reception in Ecumenical Perspective. LC 85-9319. 524p. 1987. 29.95 (ISBN 0-8022-2494-6). Philos Lib.

Dionne, James R. Pascal & Nietzche: Etude Historique & Comparee. LC 74-3300. (Fr.). 1976. lib. bdg. 18.00 (ISBN 0-89102-032-2). B Franklin.

Dionysius Of Fourna. Manuel d'iconographie Chretienne, Grecque et Latine. Durand, Paul, tr. 1963. Repr. of 1845 ed. 32.00 (ISBN 0-8337-0868-6). B Franklin.

Diorio, MaryAnn L. Dating Etiquette for Christian Teens. (Illus.). 48p. (Orig.). 1984. pap. 3.95 (ISBN 0-930037-00-6). Daystar Comm.

DiOrio, Ralph A. Called to Heal: Releasing the Transforming Power of God. LC 82-45354. (Illus.). 264p. 1984. pap. 7.95 (ISBN 0-385-19704-7, Im). Doubleday.

Di Orio, Ralph A. Healing Love. LC 86-1572. 216p. 1987. 14.95 (ISBN 0-385-23694-8). Doubleday.

--Healing Power of Affirmation. LC 85-4400. 216p. 1986. pap. 6.95 (ISBN 0-385-23592-5, Im). Doubleday.

Diorio, Ralph A. Miracle to Proclaim: First-Hand Experience of Healing. LC 83-18218. 224p. 1984. pap. 4.50 (ISBN 0-385-19241-X, Im). Doubleday.

DiOrio, Ralph A. & Gropman, Donald. The Man Beneath the Gift: The Story of My Life. LC 80-17619. (Illus.). 239p. 1981. 9.95 (ISBN 0-688-03740-2); pap. 7.95 (ISBN 0-688-00795-3). Morrow.

Dioszegi, V., ed. Popular Beliefs & Folklore Tradition in Siberia. (Uralic & Altaic Ser.: No. 57). 1968. text ed. 40.80x (ISBN 0-686-22621-6). Mouton.

DiPaolo-Healey, Antonette, ed. The Old English Vision of St. Paul. LC 77-89928. 1978. 11.00x (ISBN 0-910956-76-6, SAM 2); pap. 5.00x (ISBN 0-910956-62-6). Medieval Acad.

Dircks, Henry. Naturalistic Poetry, Selected from Psalms & Hymns of the Last Three Centuries: In Four Essays, Developing the Progress of Nature-Study, in Connection with Sacred Song. 1979. Repr. of 1872 ed. lib. bdg. 20.00 (ISBN 0-8482-0622-3). Norwood Edns.

Dirscherl, Denis. Dostoevsky & the Catholic Church. 179p. 1986. 12.95 (ISBN 0-8294-0502-X). Loyola.

Dirvin, Joseph I. St. Catherine Laboure of the Miraculous Medal. LC 84-50466. 245p. 1984. pap. 7.50 (ISBN 0-89555-242-6). TAN Bks Pubs.

DiSalvo, Jackie. War of Titans: Blake's Critique of Milton & the Politics of Religion. LC 82-11136. 403p. 1983. 38.95x (ISBN 0-8229-3804-9). U of Pittsburgh Pr.

Disciples of Donato the Christ. Healing: A Thought Away, Vol. 2. 438p. 1981. pap. 10.00 (ISBN 0-935146-61-X). Morningland.

Disciples of Morningland. The Way to Oneness. 4th ed. 1979. pap. 3.95 (ISBN 0-935146-00-8). Morningland.

Disciples of the Master Donato the Christ. Healing: As It Is, Vol. 4. 418p. (Orig.). pap. 10.00 (ISBN 0-935146-65-2). Morningland.

Diskalkar, D. B. Selections from Sanskrit Inscriptions. 1977. 18.00x (ISBN 0-686-22673-9). Intl Bk Dist.

Distad, N. Merrill. Guessing at Truth: The Life of Julius Charles Hare 1795-1855. LC 78-11625. xiv, 258p. 1979. 23.50x (ISBN 0-915762-07-2). Patmos Pr.

Ditchfield, P. H. The Cathedrals of Great Britain: Their History & Architecture. (Illus.). 1979. Repr. of 1916 ed. lib. bdg. 45.00 (ISBN 0-8495-1112-7). Arden Lib.

--The Old-Time Parson. 342p. 1980. Repr. of 1908 ed. lib. bdg. 35.00 (ISBN 0-89760-130-0). Telegraph Bks.

Ditewig, William, jt. auth. see Brinkmann, William.

Ditmore, Esteban, tr. see Sisson, Richard, et al.

Ditsky, John. The Onstage Christ: Studies in the Persistence of a Theme. (Critical Studies Ser.). 188p. 1980. 28.50x (ISBN 0-389-20059-X). B&N Imports.

Dittes, James E. Minister on the Spot. LC 79-114051. 1970. pap. 3.95 (ISBN 0-8298-0155-3). Pilgrim NY.

--When Work Goes Sour. 120p. (Orig.). 1987. pap. 6.95 (ISBN 0-664-24045-3). Westminster.

Dittmer, Bernice. Let There Be Light... Date not set. 40.00 (ISBN 0-930208-23-4). Mangan Bks.

Dittmer, Terry. Creating Contemporary Worship. 80p. (Orig.). 1985. pap. 6.95 (ISBN 0-570-03954-1, 12-2889). Concordia.

Divett, Robert T. Medicine & the Mormons: An Introduction to the History of Latter-day Saint Health Care. LC 81-84588. 230p. 1981. pap. 9.95 (ISBN 0-88290-194-X, 2050). Horizon Utah.

Diwakar, R. R. Mahayogi: Life, Sadhana & Teachings of Sri Aurobindo. 292p. 1976. pap. 6.00 (ISBN 0-89744-240-7, Pub. by Bharatiya Vidya Bhavan India). Auromere.

Dix, Dom G. The Shape of the Liturgy. 816p. 1982. 24.50 (ISBN 0-8164-2418-7, HarpR). Har-Row.

Dix, Gregory, ed. Apostoliki Paradosis: The Treatise on the Apostolic Tradition of St. Hippolytus of Rome, Bishop & Martyr, Vol. 1. (Church Historical Society, London, New Ser.: No. 24). Repr. of 1937 ed. 40.00 (ISBN 0-8115-3148-1). Kraus Repr.

Dix, Griffin, jt. ed. see Kendall, Laurel.

Dixon, Abd'al-Ameer'Abd. The Umayyad Caliphate: A Political Study. 222p. 1971. 95.00x (ISBN 0-317-39182-8, Pub. by Luzac & Co Ltd). State Mutual Bk.

Dixon, Christa K. Negro Spirituals: From Bible to Folk Song. LC 75-364444. pap. 31.80 (2026874). Bks Demand UMI.

Dixon, Gregory L. Noteworthy: A Believer's Companion. 116p. 1986. 9.95 (ISBN 0-9616294-0-1). Joi Prod Enter.

Dixon, James W. Reading the Bible As History. 605p. 1986. 21.90 (ISBN 0-533-06192-X). Vantage.

Dixon, John W., Jr. Art & Theological Imagination. (Illus.). 1978. 12.95 (ISBN 0-8164-0397-X, HarpR). Har-Row.

Dixon, Laurinda S. Alchemical Imagery in Bosch's "Garden of Delights". Seidel, Linda, ed. LC 81-14673. (Studies in Fine Arts: Iconography: No. 2). 250p. 1981. 49.95 (ISBN 0-8357-1247-8). UMI Res Pr.

Dixon, Roland B. Oceanic Mythology, Vol. 9. LC 63-19094. (Mythology of All Races Ser). (Illus.). 1964. Repr. of 1932 ed. 30.00x (ISBN 0-8154-0059-4). Cooper Sq.

Dixon, Trudy, ed. see Suzuki, Shunryu.

Dixon, W. Macneile. The Human Situation. 75.00 (ISBN 0-87968-062-8). Gordon Pr.

Dixon, William C. Pointed Tales. LC 80-81102. 98p. (Orig.). 1980. pap. 5.95 (ISBN 0-8192-1270-9). Morehouse.

Dixon, William C., jt. auth. see Detwiler-Zapp, Diane.

Djunkovskoy, E. De see Lacroix & De Djunkovskoy, E.

Djuric, Mihailo. Nietzsche und Die Metaphysik. (Monographien und Texte zur Nietsche-Forschung: Band 16). (Ger.). viii, 326p. 1985. 61.60x (ISBN 3-11-010169-6). De Gruyter.

D'Mar Shimun, Surma. Assyrian Church Customs & the Murder of Mar Shimun. Wigram, W. A., ed. (Illus.). 128p. 1983. pap. 5.00 (ISBN 0-931428-02-5). Vehicle Edns.

Do, ed. see Malyala, Panduranga R.

Doan, Ruth A. The Miller Heresy, Millenialism, & Amercian Culture. 270p. 1987. price not set (ISBN 0-87722-481-1). Temple U Pr.

Doane, T. W. Bible Myths & Their Parallels in Other Religions. 589p. spiral bdg. 12.00. Truth Seeker.

Dobbert, John A. If Being a Christian Is So Great, Why Do I Have the Blahs? LC 79-65420. 160p. 1980. pap. 4.95 (ISBN 0-8307-0729-8, 5413206). Regal.

Dobbin, Christine. Islamic Revivalism in a Changing Peasant Economy: Central Sumatra, 1784-1847. 328p. 1981. 40.00x (ISBN 0-7007-0155-9, Pub. by Curzon England). State Mutual Bk.

Dobbin, Muriel. Going Live. Engelson, Joyce, ed. 432p. 1987. 17.95 (ISBN 0-525-24473-5). Dutton.

Dobbins, Austin C. Milton & the Book of Revelation: The Heavenly Cycle. LC 73-22715. (Studies in the Humanities: No. 7). 176p. 1975. o. p. 12.50 (ISBN 0-8173-7320-9); pap. 4.95 (ISBN 0-8173-7321-7). U of Ala Pr.

Dobbins, Frank A. The Contributions of Mohammedanism to the Historical Growth of Mankind & Its Future Prospects. (Illus.). 103p. Repr. of 1883 ed. 97.75 (ISBN 0-89901-111-X). Found Class Reprints.

Dobbins, G. S. Aprenda a Ser Lider. Molina, S. P., tr. from Eng. Orig. Title: Learning to Lead. (Span.). 126p. 1986. pap. 2.50 (ISBN 0-311-17013-7). Casa Bautista.

Dobbins, Gaines S. Ministering Church. LC 60-9530. 1960. 9.95 (ISBN 0-8054-2505-5). Broadman.

Dobbins, John, ed. see Hegel, G. W.

Dobbins, Richard D. Su Poder Espiritual Y Emocional. Oyola, Eliezer, tr. from Eng. Orig. Title: Your Spiritual & Emotional Power. (Span.). 171p. 1985. pap. 2.95 (ISBN 0-8297-0705-0). Life Pubs Intl.

--Votre Force Spirituelle et Emotionnelle. Cosson, Annie L., ed. Chardenal, Valerie, tr. from Eng. Tr. of Your Spiritual & Emotional Power. (Fr.). 188p. 1985. pap. text ed. 2.25 (ISBN 0-8297-0703-4). Life Pubs Intl.

--Your Spiritual & Emotional Power. 160p. (Orig.). 1984. pap. 4.95Bks (ISBN 0-8007-5136-1, Power Bks). Revell.

Doberstein, J. W., tr. see Thielicke, Helmut.

Doberstein, John W., ed. Minister's Prayer Book: An Order of Prayers & Readings. LC 85-16212. 512p. 1986. 12.95 (ISBN 0-8006-0760-0, 1-760). Fortress.

Doberstein, John W., jt. ed. see Lehmann, Helmut T.

Doberstein, John W., tr. see Lehmann, Helmut T. & Doberstein, John W.

Doberstein, John W., tr. see Schubert, Kurt.

Doberstein, John W., tr. see Thielicke, Helmut.

Dobie, J. Frank, ed. Spur-Of-The-Cock. LC 34-1434. (Texas Folklore Society Publications: No. 11). 1965. Repr. of 1933 ed. 11.95 (ISBN 0-87074-043-1). SMU Press.

Dobie, M. R., tr. see Grenier, Albert.

Dobin, Joel C. The Astrological Secrets of the Hebrew Sages: To Rule Both Day & Night. LC 77-8288. 256p. 1983. pap. 9.95 (ISBN 0-89281-052-1). Inner Tradit.

Doble, G. H. Lives of the Welsh Saints. Evans, D. Simon, ed. 258p. 1984. text ed. 15.00x (ISBN 0-7083-0870-8, Pub. by U of Wales). Humanities.

Dobneck, Johann. Commentaria. 372p. 1549. text ed. 124.40x (ISBN 0-576-72201-4, Pub. by Gregg Intl Pubs England). Gregg Intl.

Dobosiewicz, Hanna, tr. see Niezabitowska, Malgorzata.

Dobracyynski, J. Before the Earth Arose. 1981. 8.95 (ISBN 0-317-46868-5). Franciscan Herald.

Dobree, Bonamy. John Wesley. LC 74-7428. 1973. lib. bdg. 17.50 (ISBN 0-8414-3739-4). Folcroft.

--Three Eighteenth Century Figures: Sarah Churchill, John Wesley, Giacomo Casanova. LC 80-19398. xi, 248p. 1981. Repr. of 1962 ed. lib. bdg. 25.00x (ISBN 0-313-22682-2, DOTF). Greenwood.

--William Penn, Quaker & Pioneer. LC 78-15258. 1978. Repr. of 1932 ed. lib. bdg. 35.00 (ISBN 0-8414-3790-4). Folcroft.

--William Penn, Quaker & Pioneer. 346p. 1983. Repr. of 1932 ed. lib. bdg. 35.00 (ISBN 0-8492-4227-4). R West.

Dobrin, Arthur. Little Heroes. (Ethical Humanist Society Monograph: No. 1). (Illus.). 1977. pap. 2.50x (ISBN 0-89304-200-5, CCC111). Cross Cult.

Dobrinsky, Hebert. A Treasury of Sephardic Laws & Customs. 500p. 1986. 29.50x (ISBN 0-88125-031-7); pap. text ed. 16.95. Ktav.

Dobroczcki, L. & Kirshenblatt-Gimblett, B. Image Before My Eyes: A Photographic History of Jewish Life in Poland, 1864-1939. (Illus.). 1977. 25.00; pap. text ed. 15.00 (ISBN 0-914512-38-2). Yivo Inst.

Dobroszycki, Lucjan & Kirshenblatt-Gimblett, Barbara. Image Before My Eyes: A Photographic History of Jewish Life in Poland, 1864-1939. LC 75-35448. (Illus.). 1977. 29.95 (ISBN 0-8052-3607-4). Schocken.

--Image Before My Eyes: A Photographic History of Jewish Life in Poland, 1864-1939. LC 75-35448. (Illus.). 1979. pap. 19.95 (ISBN 0-8052-0634-5). Schocken.

Dobroszycki, Lucjan, ed. The Chronicle of the Lodz Ghetto, 1941-1944. LC 84-3614. (Illus.). 603p. 1984. 37.50x (ISBN 0-300-03208-0). Yale U Pr.

Dobschutz, Ernst Von. Christian Life in the Primitive Church. 1977. lib. bdg. 59.95 (ISBN 0-8490-1615-0). Gordon Pr.

Dobson Books Ltd., ed. The Sacred Bridge: Supplementary Volume. 256p. 1981. 75.00x (ISBN 0-234-77038-4, Pub. by Dobson Bks England). State Mutual Bk.

Dobson, Ed, et al. The Fundamentalist Phenomenon: The Resurgence of Conservative Christianity. 2nd ed. pap. 7.95 (ISBN 0-8010-2958-9). Baker Bk.

Dobson, Edward. What the Bible Really Says about Marriage, Divorce & Remarriage. 160p. 1986. 9.95 (ISBN 0-8007-1493-8). Revell.

Dobson, James. Dare to Discipline. 1973. pap. 6.95 (ISBN 0-8423-0631-5). Tyndale.

--Dare to Discipline. 1977. pap. 3.50 mass (ISBN 0-8423-0635-8). Tyndale.

--Emotions: Can You Trust Them? LC 79-91703. 144p. 1980. text ed. 7.95 (ISBN 0-8307-0730-1, 5109108). Regal.

--Esto Es Ser Hombre: Conversaciones Francas Con los Hombres y Sus Esposas. Almanza, Francisco, tr. from Eng. Orig. Title: Straight Talk to Men & Wives. 240p. 1986. pap. 7.50 (ISBN 0-311-46096-8, Edit Mundo). Casa Bautista.

--Hide or Seek. expanded & updated ed. 192p. 1974. 11.95 (ISBN 0-8007-1070-3); pap. 6.95 (ISBN 0-8007-5146-9). Revell.

--Love Must Be Tough. 1986. write for info. Word Bks.

--Preparemonos para la Adolescencia. 192p. 1981. 3.25 (ISBN 0-88113-253-5). Edit Betania.

--Preparing for Adolescence. LC 78-57673. 192p. 1980. 5.95 (ISBN 0-88449-111-0, A424717); pap. 2.95 (ISBN 0-88449-045-9, A324551). Vision Hse.

--What Wives Wish Their Husbands Knew about Women. 1975. 9.95 (ISBN 0-8423-7890-1). Tyndale.

--What Wives Wish Their Husbands Knew about Women. 1977. pap. 5.95 (ISBN 0-8423-7889-8); pap. 3.50 (ISBN 0-8423-7896-0, Living Bobks). Tyndale.

Dobson, James C. Love for a Lifetime: Wise Words from Those Who've Gone Before. Date not set. price not set (ISBN 0-88070-174-9). Multnomah.

--Straight Talk to Men & Their Wives. 1980. 12.95 (ISBN 0-8499-0260-6). Word Bks.

--The Strong-Willed Child. 1978. 10.95 (ISBN 0-8423-0664-1). Tyndale.

Dobson, R. & Donaghey, S. The History of Clementhorpe Nunnery. (The Archaeology of York-Historical Sources for York Archaeology after AD 1100,). 40p. 1984. pap. text ed. 10.50x (ISBN 0-906780-40-3, Pub. by Council British Archaeology England). Humanities.

Dobson, R. B., ed. The Church, Politics & Patronage in the Fifteenth Century. LC 84-15102. 245p. 1985. 25.00 (ISBN 0-312-13481-9). St Martin.

Dobson, Shirley & Gaither, Gloria. Let's Make a Memory. 1986. pap. write for info. Word Bks.

Dobson, Theodore. How to Pray for Spiritual Growth: A Practical Handbook of Inner Healing. LC 81-83182. 176p. (Orig.). 1982. pap. 7.95 (ISBN 0-8091-2419-X). Paulist Pr.

--Inner Healing: God's Great Assurance. LC 78-65129. 216p. 1978. pap. 7.95 (ISBN 0-8091-2161-1). Paulist Pr.

Dobson, Theodoree. Inner Healing. 384p. 1985. 12.95 (ISBN 0-8027-2488-4). Walker & Co.

Dockrey, Karen. Dating: Making Your Own Choices. LC 86-30985. (Orig.). (YA) 1987. pap. 4.95 (ISBN 0-8054-5345-8). Broadman.

--Friends: Finding & Keeping Them. LC 85-12783. 1985. pap. 4.50 (ISBN 0-8054-5343-1). Broadman.

--Getting to Know God. LC 84-1702. (Orig.). 1984. pap. 4.50 (ISBN 0-8054-5341-5, 4253-41). Broadman.

--Getting to Know God: Study Guide. LC 86-8272. (Orig.). 1986. pap. 3.25 (ISBN 0-8054-3240-X). Broadman.

Dr. Clem Davies Ministry Inc., et al. Immortality: The Next Giant Step for Mankind. LC 83-90890. 138p. 1985. 10.00 (ISBN 0-533-05910-0). Vantage.

Dr. Williams' Library, London. Early Nonconformity, 1566-1800: A Catalogue of Books in Dr. Williams' Library, London, 3 pts. Incl. Pt. 1. Author Catalogue, 5 vols. Set. 495.00 (ISBN 0-8161-0797-1); Pt. 2. Subject Catalogue, 5 vols. Set. 495.00 (ISBN 0-8161-0174-4); Pt. 3. Chronological Catalogue, 2 vols. Set. 198.00 (ISBN 0-8161-0173-6). 1968 (Hall Library). G K Hall.

Dodd, C. H. A Course of Study Outlines for Bible Class Leaders. 59.95 (ISBN 0-87968-954-4). Gordon Pr.

--Founder of Christianity. 1970. pap. 5.95 (ISBN 0-02-084640-1, Collier). Macmillan.

--The Parables of the Kingdom. 176p. 1977. pap. text ed. write for info. (ISBN 0-02-330460-X, Pub. by Scribner). Macmillan.

Dodd, Charles. Dodd's Church History of England, 1500-1688, 5 Vols. Tierney, M. A., ed. LC 75-119152. Repr. of 1843 ed. Set. 262.00 (ISBN 0-404-02150-6); 52.50 ea. Vol. 1 (ISBN 0-404-02151-4). Vol. 2 (ISBN 0-404-02152-2). Vol. 3 (ISBN 0-404-02153-0). Vol. 4 (ISBN 0-404-02154-9). Vol. 5 (ISBN 0-404-02155-7). AMS Pr.

Dodd, Charles H. Historical Tradition in the Fourth Gospel. 1975. pap. 17.95x (ISBN 0-521-29123-2). Cambridge U Pr.

--Interpretation of the Fourth Gospel. 67.50 (ISBN 0-521-04848-6); pap. text ed. 18.95 (ISBN 0-521-09517-4). Cambridge U Pr.

Dodd, Damon C. The Book of Revelation, Study Guide. 1973. pap. 2.95 (ISBN 0-89265-013-3). Randall Hse.

Dodd, Erica C. & Khairallah, Shereen. The Image of the Word: A Study of Quranic Verses in Islamic Architecture, 2 vols. (Illus.). 434p. 1982. 95.00x (ISBN 0-8156-6061-8, Am U Beirut). Syracuse U Pr.

Dodd, Robert V. Helping Children Cope with Death. LC 84-6713. 56p. (Orig.). 1984. pap. 1.95 (ISBN 0-8361-3368-4). Herald Pr.

--Praying the Name of Jesus. 96p. (Orig.). 1985. pap. 4.95 (ISBN 0-8358-0514-X). Upper Room.

--Your Church's Ministry of Prayer. 1981. 3.00 (ISBN 0-89536-476-X, 2501). CSS of Ohio.

Doddridge, John. A Compleat Parson: Or, a Description of Advowsons. LC 73-6119. (English Experience Ser.: No. 586). 95p. 1973. Repr. of 1630 ed. 10.50 (ISBN 90-221-0586-5). Walter J Johnson.

Doddridge, Philip. Exposition of the Gospels, 2 vol. 1986. Set. 37.50 (ISBN 0-8254-2456-9). Vol. I, 472pgs. Vol. II, 492pgs. Kregel.

Dodds, E. R. Pagan & Christian in an Age of Anxiety: Some Aspects of Religious Experience from Marcus Aurelius to Constantine. 1970. pap. 5.95 (ISBN 0-393-00545-3, Norton Lib). Norton.

Dodds, James E. The Gentleman from Heaven. 123p. 1962. Repr. of 1948 ed. 3.50 (ISBN 0-87516-464-1). De Vorss.

Dodge, David L. War Inconsistent with the Religion of Jesus Christ. LC 75-137540. (Peace Movement in America Ser). xxiv, 168p. 1972. Repr. of 1905 ed. lib. bdg. 15.95x (ISBN 0-89198-067-9). Ozer.

Dodge, Ralph E. The Revolutionary Bishop: Who Saw God at Work in Africa. LC 85-29092. (Illus.). 216p. (Orig.). 1986. pap. 7.95 (ISBN 0-87808-203-4, WCL203-4). William Carey Lib.

Dods, Marcus. The Prayer That Teaches to Pray. LC 80-82323. (Shepherd Illustrated Classics Ser.). (Illus.). 1980. pap. 5.95 (ISBN 0-87983-232-0). Keats.

Dods, Marcus, tr. see St. Augustine.

Dodson, E. O. The Phenomenon of Man Revisited: A Biological Viewpoint on Teilhard de Chardin. LC 83-20959. (Illus.). 288p. 1984. 26.50x (ISBN 0-231-05850-0). Columbia U Pr.

Dodu, Gaston J. Histoire des institutions monarchiques dans le Royaume latin de Jerusalem, 1099-1291. LC 76-29820. (Fr.). Repr. of 1894 ed. 32.50 (ISBN 0-404-15415-8). AMS Pr.

Doebler, Bettie A. The Quickening Seed: Death in the Sermons of John. (Elizabethan & Renaissance Studies). 297p. (Orig.). 1974. pap. 15.00 (ISBN 3-7052-0678-8, Pub. by Salzburg Studies). Longwood Pub Group.

Doellinger, Johann J. Beitrage Zur Sektengenchichte des Mittelalter, 2 vols in 1. LC 91-26634. (Social Science Ser). (Ger). 1970. Repr. of 1890 ed. Set. lib. bdg. 57.50 (ISBN 0-8337-0880-5). B Franklin.

Doerblin, Alfred. The Living Thoughts of Confucius. 182p. 1983. Repr. of 1940 ed. lib. bdg. 25.00 (ISBN 0-89987-173-9). Darby Bks.

Doerffler, Alfred. God at My Sickbed. 1966. 1.50 (ISBN 0-570-03062-5, 6-1114). Concordia.

--The Mind at Ease. rev. ed. LC 75-43869. (Large Print Ser.). 104p. 1976. pap. 5.50 (ISBN 0-570-03040-4, 6-1163). Concordia.

--Open the Meeting with Prayer. LC 55-7442. 1955. 3.50 (ISBN 0-570-03147-8, 12-2531). Concordia.

Doering, Bernard. Jacques Maritain & the French Catholic Intellectuals. LC 82-40377. 288p. 1983. text ed. 22.95. U of Notre Dame Pr.

Doering, Jeanne. The Power of Encouragement. 176p. (Orig.). 1983. pap. 5.95 (ISBN 0-8024-0146-5). Moody.

--Your Power of Encouragement. (Moody Press Electives Ser.). (Orig.). 1985. pap. text ed. 3.95 (ISBN 0-8024-0687-4); leader's guide 2.50 (ISBN 0-8024-0688-2). Moody.

Doerksen, Vernon C., rev. by see Thiessen, Henry C.

Doerkson, Vernon. James. (Everyman's Bible Commentaries Ser.). (Orig.). 1983. pap. 5.95 (ISBN 0-8024-0242-9). Moody.

Doerries, Hermann. Constantine & Religious Liberty. 1960. 39.50x (ISBN 0-686-51363-0). Elliots Bks.

Dogen. A Primer of Soto Zen: A Translation of Dogen's Shobogenzo Zuimonki. Masunaga, Reiho, tr. from Japanese. LC 76-126044. 128p. 1975. pap. text ed. 5.95x (ISBN 0-8248-0357-4, Eastwest Ctr). UH Pr.

--Shobogenzo: Zen Essays by Dogen. Cleary, Thomas, tr. LC 85-20979. 136p. 1986. 14.00x (ISBN 0-8248-1014-7). UH Pr.

Dohanian, Diran D. The Mahayana Buddhist Sculpture of Ceylon. LC 76-23613. (Outstanding Dissertations in the Fine Arts). (Illus.). 1977. Repr. of 1964 ed. lib. bdg. 58.00 (ISBN 0-8240-2685-3). Garland Pub.

Doherty, Barbara. I Am What I Do: Contemplation & Human Experience. 226p. 1982. pap. 9.95 (ISBN 0-88347-129-9). Thomas More.

--Make Yourself an Ark. 1984. 10.95 (ISBN 0-88347-162-0). Thomas More.

Doherty, Catherine D. Dear Father: A Message of Love to Priests. LC 78-31389. 1979. pap. 3.50 (ISBN 0-8189-0377-5). Alba.

--Doubts, Loneliness & Rejection. LC 81-19115. (Illus.). 93p. 1982. pap. 4.50 (ISBN 0-8189-0419-4). Alba.

--The Gospel of a Poor Woman. 6.95 (ISBN 0-87193-151-6). Dimension Bks.

--Journey Inward: Interior Conversations 1960 to the Present. LC 84-443. 116p. (Orig.). 1984. pap. 6.95 (ISBN 0-8189-0468-2). Alba.

--Molchanie: The Silence of God. 112p. 1982. 8.95 (ISBN 0-8245-0407-0). Crossroad NY.

--Poustinia. LC 74-19961. 216p. 1975. pap. 3.95 (ISBN 0-87793-083-X). Ave Maria.

Doherty, Catherine de Hucck. Molchanie: The Silence of God. 128p. 1984. pap. 7.95 (ISBN 0-8245-0672-3). Crossroad NY.

Doherty, Catherine de Hueck. Coming Home. 3.95 (ISBN 0-87193-081-1). Dimension Bks.

--Fragments of My Life. LC 79-56889. (Illus.). 208p. (Orig.). 1979. pap. 4.95 (ISBN 0-87793-194-1). Ave Maria.

--Urodivoi: Fools for Good. LC 82-23530. 112p. 1983. 9.95 (ISBN 0-8245-0553-0). Crossroad NY.

Doherty, Catherine de Hueck see De Hueck Doherty, Catherine.

Doherty, Catherine de Hueck see Doherty, Catherine D.

Doherty, Eddie. True Devotion to Mary. pap. 2.00 (ISBN 0-910984-02-6). Montfort Pubns.

--Wisdom's Fool. 4.95 (ISBN 0-910984-08-5); pap. 2.95 (ISBN 0-910984-09-3). Montfort Pubns.

Doherty, Ivy D. Rainbows of Promise. Wheeler, Gerald, ed. (A Banner Bk.). (Illus.). 92p. (Orig.). 1984. pap. 5.95 (ISBN 0-8280-0213-4). Review & Herald.

Doherty, John. Praying in the Home. 2nd. ed. LC 83-61212. 54p. 1984. pap. text ed. 1.95 (ISBN 0-911905-04-9). Past & Mat Rene Ctr.

Doi, A. R. Hadith: An Introduction. 1980. pap. 6.50 (ISBN 0-686-64661-4). Kazi Pubns.

--Non-Muslims Under Shari'ah. 1981. 6.50 (ISBN 0-686-97861-7). Kazi Pubns.

--Quran, an Introduction. pap. 5.50 (ISBN 0-686-63911-1). Kazi Pubns.

Doig, Desmond. Mother Teresa: Her Work & Her People. LC 75-39857. (Illus.). 176p. 1980. pap. 11.95 (ISBN 0-06-061941-4, RD336, HarpR). Har-Row.

Dolan, A. P., tr. see Buhlmann, Walbert.

Dolan, Edward F., Jr. Anti-Semitism. LC 85-8820. (Illus.). 135p. 1985. PLB 11.90 (ISBN 0-531-10068-5). Watts.

Dolan, Jay P. American Catholic Experience: A History from Colonial Times to the Present. LC 84-26026. 504p. 1985. 19.95 (ISBN 0-385-15206-X). Doubleday.

--American Catholic Experience: A History from Colonial Times to the Present. 504p. 1987. pap. 10.95 (ISBN 0-385-15207-8, Im). Doubleday.

--Catholic Revivalism: The American Experience, 1830-1900. LC 77-89755. 1979. pap. text ed. 4.95x (ISBN 0-268-00729-2). U of Notre Dame Pr.

--Catholic Revivalism: The American Experience, 1830-1900. LC 77-89755. 1978. text ed. 19.95x (ISBN 0-268-00722-5). U of Notre Dame Pr.

--The Immigrant Church: New York's Irish & German Catholics. LC 75-12552. pap. 59.30 (ISBN 0-317-08406-2, 2019817). Bks Demand UMI.

--The Immigrant Church: New York's Irish & German Catholics, 1815-1865. LC 82-23827. (Illus.). xiv, 221p. 1983. pap. text ed. 7.95x (ISBN 0-268-01151-6, 85-11511). U of Notre Dame Pr.

Dolan, Jay P., ed. The American Catholic Parish: A History from 1850 to the Present. Vol. I: The Northeast, Southeast & South Central States. 19.95t; Vol. II: The Pacific States, Intermountain West & Midwest States. 19.95t (ISBN 0-8091-2854-3). Paulist Pr.

--The American Catholic Tradition. 1893.50 (ISBN 0-405-10810-9). Ayer Co Pubs.

Dolan, John, jt. ed. see Jedin, Hubert.

Dolan, John P. Catholicism. LC 67-28536. (Orig.). 1968. pap. text ed. 5.95 (ISBN 0-8120-0273-3). Barron.

Dolan, John P., jt. ed. see Jedin, Hubert.

Dolan, Walter. The Classical World Bibliography of Philosophy, Religion, & Rhetoric. LC 76-52512. (Library of Humanities Reference Bks.: No. 95). 396p. 1978. lib. bdg. 51.00 (ISBN 0-8240-9878-1). Garland Pub.

Dolbeare, Kenneth M. & Hammond, Philip E. School Prayer Decisions: From Court Policy to Local Practice. LC 70-140461. 1971. 8.00x (ISBN 0-226-15515-3). U of Chicago Pr.

Dolch, Edward W. & Dolch, M. P. Gospel Stories. (Pleasure Reading Ser.). 176p. 1951. PLB 6.57 (ISBN 0-8116-2608-3). Garrard.

--Greek Stories. (Pleasure Reading Ser.). 176p. 1955. PLB 6.57 (ISBN 0-8116-2607-5). Garrard.

Dolch, M. P., jt. auth. see Dolch, Edward W.

Dole, Anita S. Bible Study Notes, Vols. 1-3. Woofenden, William R., ed. LC 76-24081. 1976-78. lib. bdg. write for info. (ISBN 0-685-92171-9). Vol 1 (ISBN 0-917426-01-0). Vol. 2 (ISBN 0-917426-02-9). Vol. 3 (ISBN 0-917426-03-7). Am New Church Sunday.

--Bible Study Notes, Vol. 4. Woofenden, William R., ed. LC 76-24081. 1979. write for info. (ISBN 0-917426-04-5). Am New Church Sunday.

--Bible Study Notes, Vol. 5. Woofenden, William R., ed. LC 76-24081. 1979. write for info (ISBN 0-917426-05-3). Am New Church Sunday.

--Bible Study Notes, Vol. 6. Woofenden, William R., ed. LC 76-24081. 1979. write for info (ISBN 0-917426-06-1). Am New Church Sunday.

Dole, George, tr. see Swedenborg, Emanuel.

Doleski, Teddi. A Present for Jessica. (Illus.). 48p. (Orig.). 1986. pap. 2.50 (ISBN 0-8091-6557-0). Paulist Pr.

Dolger, Franz J. Der Exorzismus Im Altchristlichen Taufritual. 1909. pap. 15.00 (ISBN 0-384-12090-3). Johnson Repr.

Dolinsky, Benjamin. Our Miracle. LC 86-43253. 116p. 1987. pap. 5.95 (ISBN 0-88400-126-1). Shengold.

Dollarhide, Kenneth. Nichiren's Senji-sho: An Essay on the Selection of the Proper Time. LC 82-21687. (Studies in Asian Thought & Religion: Vol. 1). 184p. 1983. 39.95x (ISBN 0-88946-051-5). E Mellen.

Dollen, Charles. The Book of Catholic Wisdom. LC 86-60327. 205p. (Orig.). 1986. pap. 7.95 (ISBN 0-87973-535-X, 535). Our Sunday Visitor.

--Jesus Lord. (Orig.). 1964. 3.00 (ISBN 0-8198-0066-X); pap. 2.00 (ISBN 0-8198-0067-8). Dghtrs St Paul.

--Prayer Book of the Saints. LC 84-60749. 1984. pap. 6.95 (ISBN 0-87973-717-4, 717). Our Sunday Visitor.

--Prayers for the Third Age: A Devotion for Mature Catholics. LC 85-60889. 200p. (Orig.). 1985. pap. 7.95 (ISBN 0-87973-837-5, 837). Our Sunday Visitor.

--Ready or Not. LC 67-29164. 1969. 3.00 (ISBN 0-8198-0130-5). Dghtrs St Paul.

Dolley, Janice, jt. auth. see Burton, Ursula.

Dollinger, Johann J. Von. Lectures on the Reunion of the Churches. LC 74-131579. (Sources in the History of Interpretation: No. 2). 1973. 15.00x (ISBN 0-8401-0567-3). A R Allenson.

Dollinger, John J. The First Age of Christianity & the Church. 1977. lib. bdg. 59.95 (ISBN 0-8490-1840-4). Gordon Pr.

Dolman, Dirk H. The Tabernacle. 525p. 1982. Repr. lib. bdg. 19.75 smythe sewn (ISBN 0-86524-152-X, 0203). Klock & Klock.

Dolson, Bobbie J. Van see Aaen, Bernhard.

Dolson, Bobbie J. Van see Degering, Etta B.

Dolson, Bobbie J. Van see Hills, Desmond B.

Dolson, Bobbie J. Van see Irland, Nancy B.

Dolson, Bobbie J. Van see Todd, Sharon.

Dolson, Bobbie J. Van see Willis, Mary.

Dolson, Leo Van see Van Dolson, Leo.

Domanska, Janina, illus. The First Noel. LC 85-27084. (Illus.). 24p. 1986. 11.75 (ISBN 0-688-04324-0); PLB 11.88 (ISBN 0-688-04325-9). Greenwillow.

Domaszewski, Alfred von see Von Domaszewski, Alfred.

Domb, Cyril, jt. ed. see Carmell, Aryeh.

Dombrowski, James. Early Days of Christian Socialism in America. 1966. lib. bdg. 19.50x (ISBN 0-374-92223-3, Octagon). Hippocrene Bks.

Domingo De Guzman, Saint The Life of St. Dominie in Old French Verse. Manning, Warren F., ed. (Harv Studies in Romance Languages). 1944. 32.00 (ISBN 0-527-01118-5). Kraus Repr.

Dominian, J. Marital Breakdown. 1969. 5.95 (ISBN 0-8199-0151-2, L38436). Franciscan Herald.

Dominian, Jack. The Capacity to Love. 174p. (Orig.). 1985. text ed. 6.95 (ISBN 0-8091-2726-1). Paulist Pr.

--Make or Break: A Guide to Marriage Counselling. (Pastoral Help Bks.: Vol. 1). 1985. pap. 8.95 (ISBN 0-89453-473-4). M Glazier.

--Marriage, Faith & Love. 288p. 1982. 14.95 (ISBN 0-8245-0425-9). Crossroad NY.

Dominican Fathers of the Province of St. Joseph, ed. The Maritain Volume of "The Thomist", Dedicated to Jacques Maritain on the Occasion of His 60th Anniversary. LC 77-92509. (Essay Index in Reprint Ser.). 1978. Repr. 24.50x (ISBN 0-8486-3003-3). Roth Pub Inc.

Dominican Nuns of the Perpetual Rosary, tr. see Alonso, Joaquin M.

Domino, Ruth. Search. 1983. pap. 2.50x (ISBN 0-87574-052-9, 052). Pendle Hill.

Dominy, Bert. God's Work of Salvation. LC 83-71264. (Layman's Library of Christian Doctrine Ser.). 1986. 5.95 (ISBN 0-8054-1638-2). Broadman.

Domnitz, Myer. Judaism. 1985. 13.00 (ISBN 0-7062-3596-7, Pub. by Ward Lock Educ Co Ltd). State Mutual Bk.

--Judaism. (Religions of the World Ser.). (Illus.). 48p. 1986. PLB 10.90 (ISBN 0-531-18066-2, Pub. by Bookwright). Watts.

Donagan, Alan. Theory of Morality. LC 76-25634. 1979. pap. 10.00x (ISBN 0-226-15567-6, P838, Phoen); 20.00x (ISBN 0-226-15566-8). U of Chicago Pr.

Donaghey, S., jt. auth. see Dobson, R.

Donaghy, John A. Peacemaking & the Community of Faith: A Handbook for Congregations. 2.95 (ISBN 0-8091-5181-2). Paulist Pr.

Donahue, Bob & Donahue, Marilyn. Don't Be a Puppet on a String. 1983. pap. 3.95 (ISBN 0-8423-0610-2). Tyndale.

--Getting Your Act Together. (No. 4). 108p. 1983. pap. 3.95 (ISBN 0-8423-1005-3). Tyndale.

--How to Make People Like You When You Know They Don't. 1982. pap. 4.95 (ISBN 0-8423-1531-4). Tyndale.

Donahue, John R. The Theology & Setting of Discipleship in the Gospel of Mark. LC 83-60749. (Pere Marquette Lecture Ser.). 1983. 7.95 (ISBN 0-87462-538-6). Marquette.

Donahue, John R., ed. see Bailey, Lloyd R., Sr.

Donahue, John R., ed. see Brueggemann, Walter.

Donahue, John R., ed. see Hamerton-Kelly, Robert.

Donahue, John R., ed. see Harrelson, Walter.

Donahue, John R., ed. see Harrington, Daniel J.

Donahue, John R., ed. see Johnson, Luke T.

Donahue, John R., ed. see Westermann, Claus.

Donahue, John R., tr. see Klein, Ralph W.

Donahue, Lois. Dear Moses: Letters to Saints & Other Prominent People. LC 84-60743. (Illus.). 104p. 1984. pap. 4.95 (ISBN 0-87973-699-2, 699). Our Sunday Visitor.

Donahue, Marilyn, jt. auth. see Donahue, Bob.

Donald, G. H. Cooking for Your Children Cookbook. 17.50 (ISBN 0-87559-125-6). Shalom.

Donald, Gertrude. Men Who Left the Movement. facs. ed. LC 67-23207. (Essay Index Reprint Ser). 1933. 20.00 (ISBN 0-8369-0385-4). Ayer Co Pubs.

Donaldson, Augustas B. Five Great Oxford Leaders: Keble, Newman, Pusey, Liddon & Church. 1978. Repr. of 1900 ed. lib. bdg. 35.00 (ISBN 0-8495-1036-8). Arden Lib.

Donaldson, Christopher. Martin of Tours: Parish Priest, Mystic & Exorcist. (Illus.). 171p. 1985. pap. 8.95 (ISBN 0-7102-0682-8). Methuen Inc.

Donaldson, Dwight M. The Shi, Its Religion: A History of Islam in Persia & Iraq. 1976. lib. bdg. 59.95 (ISBN 0-8490-2598-2). Gordon Pr.

--The Shi'ite Religion: A History of Islam in Persia & Irak. LC 80-1933. 49.50 (ISBN 0-404-18959-8). AMS Pr.

Donaldson, G. The Scottish Reformation. 49.50 (ISBN 0-521-08675-2). Cambridge U Pr.
Donaldson, J., ed. see Ante-Nicene Fathers.
Donaldson, James & Roberts, Alexander, trs. Martyrdom of St. Polycarp: The Encyclical Epistle of the Church at Smyrna Concerning the Martyrdom of the Holy Polycarp. pap. 1.50 (ISBN 0-317-11392-5). Eastern Orthodox.
Donaldson, Joseph C., et al. How To Manual for Volunteer Youth Leaders. LC 86-80688. (Equipping Ser.). (Illus.). 136p. (Orig.). 1986. pap. 6.96 (ISBN 0-935797-22-X). Harvest IL.
Donaldson, Terence L. Jesus on the Mountain: A Study in Matthean Theology. (JSNT Supplement Ser.: No. 8). 326p. 1985. text ed. 28.50x (ISBN 0-905774-74-4, Pub. by JSOT Pr England); pap. text ed. 13.50x (ISBN 0-905774-75-2, Pub. by JSOT Pr England). Eisenbrauns.
Donat, Alexander. The Holocaust Kingdom. LC 77-89067. 361p. (Orig.). 1963. pap. 12.95 (ISBN 0-89604-001-1). Holocaust Pubns.
--The Holocaust Kingdom: A Memoir. 368p. pap. 5.95 (ISBN 0-686-95070-4). ADL.
Donat, Alexander, ed. The Death Camp Treblinka. LC 79-53471. (Illus.). 320p. (Orig.). 1979. 16.95 (ISBN 0-89604-008-9); pap. 12.95 (ISBN 0-89604-009-7). Holocaust Pubns.
Donato, Gopi G., jt. auth. see Donato, Sri.
Donato, Sri. The Day of Brahma. Morningland Publications, Inc., ed. (Illus.). 377p. 1981. pap. 10.00 (ISBN 0-935146-20-2). Morningland.
--The Unicorn. Morningland Publications, Inc., ed. (Illus.). 207p. (Orig.). 1981. pap. 10.00 (ISBN 0-935146-16-4). Morningland.
Donato, Sri & Donato, Gopi G. Oneness, Vol. III. Morningland Publications, Inc., ed. 167p. 1981. pap. 7.95 spiral bdg. (ISBN 0-935146-58-X). Morningland.
Doncaster, Hugh L. The Quaker Message: A Personal Affirmation. 1983. pap. 2.50x (ISBN 0-87574-181-9, 181). Pendle Hill.
Donceel, Joseph F. The Searching Mind: An Introduction to a Philosophy of God. LC 79-18166. 1979. text ed. 6.95 (ISBN 0-268-01700-X). U of Notre Dame Pr.
Donde, Antoine. The Life, Death & Miracles of Saint Francois De Paule. (Printed Sources of Western Art Ser.). (Fr., Illus.). 258p. 1981. pap. 40.00 slipcase (ISBN 0-915346-64-8). A Wofsy Fine Arts.
Dondero, John P. & Frary, Thomas D. New Pressures, New Responses in Religious Life. LC 76-26585. 1979. pap. 5.95 (ISBN 0-8189-0332-5). Alba.
Donders, Joseph G. Beyond Jesus: Reflections on the Gospel for the B-Cycle. LC 84-5088. 320p. (Orig.). 1984. 10.95 (ISBN 0-88344-049-0). Orbis Bks.
--Christ, the Divine Network: Reflections on the Gospel for the A-Cycle. LC 86-718. 256p. (Orig.). 1986. pap. 10.95 (ISBN 0-88344-254-X). Orbis Bks.
--Creation & Human Dynamism: A Spirituality for Life. 112p. (Orig.). 1985. pap. 5.95 (ISBN 0-89622-227-6). Twenty-Third.
--The Global Believer: Toward a New Imitation of Christ. 144p. (Orig.). 1986. pap. 5.95 (ISBN 0-89622-294-2). Twenty-Third.
--Jesus, Hope Drawing Near: Reflections on the Gospels for the C-Cycle. LC 85-5125. 272p. (Orig.). 1985. pap. 10.95 (ISBN 0-88344-244-2). Orbis Bks.
--Jesus, the Stranger. LC 77-21783. 298p. (Orig.). 1978. pap. 8.95x (ISBN 0-88344-235-3). Orbis Bks.
--Liberation, the Jesus Mode: Reflections on the Gospels for the B-Cycle. LC 87-5700. 228p. (Orig.). 1987. pap. 10.95 (ISBN 0-88344-553-0). Orbis Bks.
--Non-Bourgeois Theology: An African Experience of Jesus. LC 84-16677. 224p. (Orig.). 1985. pap. 10.95 (ISBN 0-88344-352-X). Orbis Bks.
Donders, Josephs G. Empowering Hope. 112p. (Orig.). 1986. pap. 5.95 (ISBN 0-89622-281-0). Twenty-Third.
Donehoo, Paris. Prayer in the Life of Jesus. (Orig.). 1984. pap. 3.95 (ISBN 0-8054-5101-3). Broadman.
Donelson, Lewis R. Pseudoepigraphy & Ethical Arguments in the Pastoral Epistles. 260p. 1986. lib. bdg. 52.50x (ISBN 3-16-145009-4, Pub. by J C B Mohr BRD). Coronet Bks.
Doney, Meryl. The Kind Stranger. (Illus.). 16p. 1982. pap. 0.99 (ISBN 0-86683-666-7, AY8244, HarpR). Har-Row.
--The Lost Sheep. (Illus.). 16p. 1982. pap. 0.99 (ISBN 0-86683-663-2, AY8243, HarpR). Har-Row.
--The Loving Father. (Illus.). 16p. 1982. pap. 0.99 (ISBN 0-86683-665-9, AY8245, HarpR). Har-Row.
--The Two Houses. (Illus.). 16p. 1982. pap. 0.99 (ISBN 0-86683-664-0, AY8246, HarpR). Har-Row.
Doney, Willis, ed. see Koyre, Alexandre.
Donfried, Karl P. The Dynamic Word: New Testament Insights for Contemporary Christians. LC 80-8905. 244p. 1981. 12.95 (ISBN 0-06-061945-7, HarpR). Har-Row.
Donfried, Karl P., ed. The Romans Debate: Essays on the Origin & Purpose on the Epistle. LC 77-84082. 1977. pap. 10.95 (ISBN 0-8066-1607-5, 10-5542). Augsburg.
Dong, Paul. The Four Major Mysteries of Mainland China. (Illus.). 204p. 1984. 16.95 (ISBN 0-13-330572-4); pap. 8.95 (ISBN 0-13-330556-2). P-H.
Donia, Robert J. Islam Under the Double Eagle: The Muslims of Bosnia & Hercegovina, 1878-1914. (East European Monographs: No. 78). 237p. 1981. 22.00x (ISBN 0-914710-72-9). East Eur Quarterly.
Donicht, Mark. Chrysalis: A Journey into the New Spiritual America. (Illus.). 192p. 1978. pap. 4.95 (ISBN 0-89496-011-3). Ross Bks.
Doniger, Simon, ed. The Nature of Man in Theological & Psychological Perspective. LC 72-10819. (Essay Index Reprint Ser.). 1973. Repr. of 1962 ed. 18.00 (ISBN 0-8369-7213-9). Ayer Co Pubs.
Donin, Hayim. To Be a Jew. LC 72-89175. 1972. 17.95 (ISBN 0-465-08624-1). Basic.
Donin, Hayim H. To Pray As a Jew. LC 80-50554. 384p. 1980. 17.95 (ISBN 0-465-08628-4). Basic.
--To Raise a Jewish Child: A Guide for Parents. LC 76-7679. 1977. 15.95 (ISBN 0-465-08626-8). Basic.
Donin, Hayyim H., ed. Sukkot. 128p. pap. 4.50 (ISBN 0-686-95148-4). ADL.
Donne, Brian K. Christ Ascended: A Study in the Significance of the Ascension of Jesus Christ in the New Testament. 1983. pap. text ed. 7.95 (ISBN 0-85364-336-9). Attic Pr.
Donne, John. Devotions upon Emergent Occasions. Bd. with Death's Duel. 1959. pap. 7.95 (ISBN 0-472-06030-9, 30, AA). U of Mich Pr.
--Devotions upon Emergent Occasions. Raspa, Anthony, ed. LC 76-361973. pap. 62.00 (ISBN 0-317-26281-5, 2024263). Bks Demand UMI.
--John Donne's Sermons on the Psalms & Gospels: With a Selection of Prayers & Meditations. Simpson, Evelyn M., ed. & intro. by. LC 63-16249. 1963. pap. 7.95 (ISBN 0-520-00340-3, CAL84). U of Cal Pr.
--The Prayers of John Donne. Umbach, Herbert H., ed. (Orig.). 1962. 11.95x; pap. 7.95x (ISBN 0-8084-0252-8). New Coll U Pr.
--Pseudo-Martyr. LC 74-16215. 450p. 1974. 60.00x (ISBN 0-8201-1140-6). Schol Facsimiles.
--The Sermons of John Donne: In Ten Volumes. Simpson, Evelyn M. & Potter, George R., eds. LC 52-7179. 4365p. 1984. lib. bdg. 450.00x set (ISBN 0-520-05255-2). U of Cal Pr.
--Suicide. Clebsch, William A., ed. LC 83-4466. (SP Studies in the Humanities). 134p. 1983. pap. 8.95 (ISBN 0-89130-624-2). Scholars Pr GA.
Donnell, Nils. It's Not the Same Old Me. 1975. pap. 2.00 (ISBN 0-88027-007-1). Firm Foun Pub.
Donnelly, Dody. Team. LC 77-74584. 168p. (Orig.). 1977. pap. 5.95 (ISBN 0-8091-2013-5). Paulist Pr.
Donnelly, Doris. Learning to Forgive. (Festival Ser.). 144p. 1982. pap. 4.95 (ISBN 0-687-21324-X). Abingdon.
--Putting Forgiveness into Practice. LC 82-71967. 192p. 1982. 5.95 (ISBN 0-89505-087-0). Argus Comm.
Donnelly, Dorothy. God & the Apple of His Eye. LC 72-96114. 1973. pap. 2.50 (ISBN 0-913382-05-1, 101-6). Prow Bks-Franciscan.
--The Witness of Little Things. (Orig.). Date not set. pap. price not set (ISBN 0-913382-37-X, 101-37). Prow Bks-Franciscan.
Donnelly, Dorothy H. Radical Love: Toward a Sexual Spirituality. 144p. 1984. pap. 6.95 (ISBN 0-86683-817-1, AY8407, HarpR). Har-Row.
Donnelly, Ignatius. Atlantis: The Antediluvian World. lib. bdg. 100.00 (ISBN 0-87968-055-5). Krishna Pr.
Donnelly, John & Lyons, Leonard, eds. Conscience. new ed. LC 72-6720. 249p. (Orig.). 1973. pap. 4.95 (ISBN 0-8189-0259-0). Alba.
Donnelly, Joseph P. Pierre-Gibault, Missionary, Seventeen Thirty-Seven to Eighteen Hundred Two. LC 77-156371. 1971. 8.95 (ISBN 0-8294-0203-9). Loyola.
--Thwaites' Jesuit Relations, Errata & Addenda. LC 66-27701. (The American West Ser). 1967. 6.95 (ISBN 0-8294-0025-7). Loyola.
Donnelly, Mark & Fenton, Nina. Search Heaven & Hell. Rappaport, Jon, ed. LC 86-81968. 500p. 1986. pap. 10.95 (ISBN 1-55666-001-4). Authors Unltd.
Donnelly, Morwenna. Founding the Life Divine. 176p. 1976. Repr. of 1976 ed. write for info. Auromere.
--Founding the Life Divine: An Introduction to the Integral Yoga of Sri Aurobindo. LC 74-2430. 250p. 1976. pap. 7.95 (ISBN 0-913922-13-7). Dawn Horse Pr.
Donner, Fred M. The Early Islamic Conquests. LC 80-8544. (Princeton Studies on the Near East). (Illus.). 328p. 1981. 19.95x (ISBN 0-691-10182-5). Princeton U Pr.
Donner, Henry W. Introduction to Utopia. LC 78-94268. (Select Bibliographies Reprint Ser). 1946. 18.00 (ISBN 0-8369-5042-9). Ayer Co Pubs.
Donoghue, Quentin & Shapiro, Linda. Bless Me, Father, for I Have Sinned: Catholics Speak Out about Confession. LC 84-81332. 303p. 1984. 17.95 (ISBN 0-917657-02-0). D I Fine.
--Bless Me Father, for I Have Sinned: Catholics Speak Out about Confession. LC 84-81332. 303p. 1985. pap. 8.95 (ISBN 0-917657-44-6). D I Fine.
Donohue, John, ed. see Wright, Bonnie L., et al.
Donohue, John J. & Esposito, John L., eds. Islam in Transition: Muslim Perspectives. 1982. 28.00x (ISBN 0-19-503022-2); pap. 12.95x (ISBN 0-19-503023-0). Oxford U Pr.
Donoso Cortes, Juan. An Essay on Catholicism, Authority & Order Considered in Their Fundamental Principles. Goddard, Madeleine V., tr. LC 78-59018. 1979. Repr. of 1925 ed. 28.00 (ISBN 0-88355-692-8). Hyperion Conn.
Donovan, John B. The Family Book of Bible Stories. 120p. 1986. pap. 8.95 (ISBN 0-8192-1381-0). Morehouse.
Donovan, Joseph P. Pelagius & the Fifth Crusade. LC 76-29822. Repr. of 1950 ed. 29.00 (ISBN 0-404-15416-6). AMS Pr.
Donovan, Mary S. A Different Call: Women's Ministries in the Episcopal Church. 216p. (Orig.). 1986. text ed. 19.95 (ISBN 0-8192-1396-9). Morehouse.
Donovan, Peter, jt. ed. see Colless, Brian.
Donovan, Robert K. No Popery & Radicalism: Opposition to Roman Catholic Relief in Scotland, 1778-1782. McNeill, Willaim H. & Stansky, Peter, eds. (Modern European History Ser.). 425p. 1987. lib. bdg. 65.00 (ISBN 0-8240-7804-7). Garland Pub.
Donovan, Robert O. The Bible Back in Our Schools. LC 72-80782. 80p. 1972. pap. 2.50 (ISBN 0-913748-01-3). Orovan Bks.
--Her Door of Faith. LC 79-172385. (Illus.). 112p. 1971. pap. 2.95 (ISBN 0-913748-02-1). Orovan Bks.
Donovan, Suzanne & Bannon, William J. Volunteers & Ministry: A Manual for Developing Parish Volunteers. LC 82-62963. 112p. 1983. pap. 6.95 (ISBN 0-8091-2545-5). Paulist Pr.
Donovan, Vincent J. Christianity Rediscovered. rev. ed. LC 81-18992. 208p. 1982. pap. 8.95 (ISBN 0-88344-096-2). Orbis Bks.
Don-Yehiya, Eliezer, jt. auth. see Liebman, Charles S.
Donze, Sr. M. Terese. The Kingdom Lost & Found: A Fable for Everyone. LC 82-71983. (Illus.). 64p. (Orig.). 1982. pap. 3.95 (ISBN 0-87793-253-0). Ave Maria.
Donze, Mary T. Down Gospel Byways: Eighteen Stories of People Who Met Jesus. 80p. 1984. pap. 2.95 (ISBN 0-89243-198-9). Liguori Pubns.
--In My Heart Room. 64p. 1982. pap. 1.50 (ISBN 0-89243-161-X). Liguori Pubns.
--Touching a Child's Heart: An Innovative Guide to Becoming a Good Storyteller. LC 85-71557. 88p. (Orig.). 1985. pap. 3.95 (ISBN 0-87793-290-5). Ave Maria.
Doohan, Helen. Leadership in Paul. (Good News Studies Ser.: Vol. 11). 1984. pap. 7.95 (ISBN 0-89453-435-1). M Glazier.
--The Minister of God: Effective & Fulfilled. LC 86-14099. 127p. (Orig.). 1986. pap. 6.95 (ISBN 0-8189-0507-7). Alba.
Doohan, Leonard. The Laity: A Bibliography. LC 87-45006. (Theological & Biblical Resources). 160p. (Orig.). 1987. pap. 8.95 (ISBN 0-89453-617-6). M Glazier.
--Laity's Mission in the Local Church. 204p. (Orig.). 1986. pap. 8.95 (ISBN 0-86683-490-7, HarpR). Har-Row.
--The Lay-Centered Church: Theology & Spirituality. 204p. 1984. pap. 8.95 (ISBN 0-86683-808-2, AY8403, HarpR). Har-Row.
--Luke: The Perennial Spirituality. LC 85-71858. 214p. (Orig.). 1985. pap. 9.95 (ISBN 0-939680-24-6). Bear & Co.
--Mark: Visionary of Early Christianity. LC 86-72485. 192p. (Orig.). 1986. pap. 9.95 (ISBN 0-939680-33-5). Bear & Co.
--Matthew: Spirituality for the 80's & 90's. LC 85-70838. 199p. (Orig.). 1985. pap. 9.95 (ISBN 0-939680-19-X). Bear & Co.
Dooley, Kate. The Saints Book: Stories for Children. LC 80-82814. 48p. (Orig.). 1981. pap. 2.95 (ISBN 0-8091-6547-3). Paulist Pr.
Dooley, Kate C. The Jesus Book. LC 82-61422. 48p. (Orig.). 1983. pap. 2.95 (ISBN 0-8091-2514-5). Paulist Pr.
Dooley, L. M. That Motherly Mother of Guadalupe. 2.25 (ISBN 0-8198-0634-X); pap. 1.25 (ISBN 0-8198-0635-8). Dghtrs St Paul.
Doolittle, H. D. Priest & A Dead Priestess Speaks. (Illus.). 38p. 1983. 90.00x (ISBN 0-914742-79-5). Copper Canyon.
Doonan, Gladys. From My Jewel Box. LC 83-4439. 1983p. pap. 3.95 (ISBN 0-87227-092-0). Reg Baptist.
Doongaji, Damayanti. Law of Crime & Punishment in Ancient Hindu Society. 310p. 1986. 48.50X (ISBN 81-202-0168-X, Pub. by Ajanta). South Asia Bks.
Doornik, N. Van see Van Doornik, N.
Dooyeweerd, Herman. In the Twilight of Western Thought. 1960. pap. 3.95 (ISBN 0-934532-09-5). Presby & Reformed.
Doran, Adron & Choate, J. E. The Christian Scholar. 1985. 14.95 (ISBN 0-89225-279-0); pap. 8.95 (ISBN 0-89225-282-0). Gospel Advocate.
Doran, Robert M. Psychic Conversion & Theological Foundations: Toward a Reorientation of the Human Sciences. LC 81-9360. (American Academy of Religion Studies in Religion Ser.). 1981. pap. 9.95 (ISBN 0-89130-522-X, 01-00-25). Scholars Pr GA.
Doran, Verda C., tr. see Philippe, Thomas.
Doray, S. J. Gateway to Islam, 4. pap. 9.50 (ISBN 0-686-18395-9). Kazi Pubns.
Dorcy, Mary J. Saint Dominic. LC 82-50978. 173p. 1982. pap. 5.00 (ISBN 0-89555-195-0). TAN Bks Pubs.
--St. Dominic's Family. LC 83-70219. 631p. 1983. pap. 20.00 (ISBN 0-89555-208-6). TAN Bks Pubs.
Dore, Clement. Theism. 1984. lib. bdg. 34.50 (ISBN 0-318-00886-6, Pub. by Reidel Holland). Kluwer Academic.
Dore, Gustave. Dore Bible Illustrations. (Illus.). 256p. 1974. pap. 8.95 (ISBN 0-486-23004-X). Dover.
Dore, Henri. Researches into Chinese Superstitions, 5 vols. (vols. I-X & XIII) Repr. of 1914 ed. Set. text ed. 97.00x (ISBN 0-89644-108-3, Pub. by Chinese Matl Ctr). Coronet Bks.
Doren, Carl Van see Van Doren, Carl.
Doren, Mark Van see Van Doren, Mark.
Doren, W. H. Van see Van Doren, W. H.
Doress, Irvin, jt. auth. see Porter, Jack N.
Doresse, Jean. The Secret Books of the Egyptian Gnostics. (Illus.). 446p. 1986. pap. 14.95 (ISBN 0-89281-107-2). Inner Tradit.
Dorff, Elliot. Jewish Law & Modern Ideology. 1970. pap. 6.50x (ISBN 0-8381-0209-3). United Syn Bk.
Dorff, Elliot N. & Rosett, Arthur. A Living Tree: Materials on the Jewish Legal Tradition with Comparative Notes. 680p. 1987. 49.50x (ISBN 0-88706-459-0); pap. 19.95x (ISBN 0-88706-460-4). State U NY Pr.
Dorian, Emil. The Quality of Witness: A Romanian Diary, 1937-1944. Dorian, Marguerite, ed. Vamos, Mara S., tr. from Romanian. 352p. 1983. 19.95 (ISBN 0-8276-0211-1). Jewish Pubns.
Dorian, Marguerite, ed. see Dorian, Emil.
Doris. Listen...The Speaking Heart. LC 79-50254. 1979. pap. 3.75 (ISBN 0-87516-361-0). De Vorss.
D'Orleans, Pierre J. History of the Two Tartar Conquerors of China. LC 75-162706. 1963. Repr. of 1668 ed. 26.00 (ISBN 0-8337-3630-2). B Franklin.
Dorman, Harry G. Toward Understanding Islam: Contemporary Apologetic of Islam & Missionary Policy. LC 79-176727. (Columbia University. Teachers College. Contributions to Education: No. 940). Repr. of 1948 ed. 22.50 (ISBN 0-404-55940-9). AMS Pr.
Dorn, Edwin. Rules & Racial Equality. LC 79-64228. 1979. 24.50x (ISBN 0-300-02362-6). Yale U Pr.
Dornblatt, Leah. Tova's Happy Purim: In Yerusholayim. (Illus.). cancelled (ISBN 0-87306-989-7). Feldheim.
Dornbusch, Sanford M., jt. auth. see Schneider, Louis.
Dorner, Isaak A. Geschichte Der Protestantischen Theologie. 1867. 55.00 (ISBN 0-384-12385-6). Johnson Repr.
--History of Protestant Theology, 2 Vols. LC 72-133823. Repr. of 1871 ed. Set. 87.50 (ISBN 0-404-02147-6). AMS Pr.
Dorner, Rita C., ed. From Ashes to Easter. 1979. pap. 9.95 (ISBN 0-918208-99-8). Liturgical Conf.
Doron, Pinchas. Interpretations of Difficult Passages in Rashi, Vol. I. (Hebrew.). 1985. text ed. 20.00x (ISBN 0-88125-080-5). Ktav.
Dorotheus Of Gaza. Dorotheos of Gaza: Discourses & Sayings. LC 77-4295. (Cistercian Studies Ser: No. 33). 1977. 7.00 (ISBN 0-87907-933-9). Cistercian Pubns.
Dorr, Donal. Option for the Poor: A Hundred Years of Vatican Social Teaching. 333p. (Orig.). 1983. pap. 11.95 (ISBN 0-88344-365-1). Orbis Bks.

--Spirituality & Justice. 264p. (Orig.). 1985. pap. 10.95 (ISBN 0-88344-449-6). Orbis Bks.

Dorr, Roberta. David & Bathsheba. 1982. pap. 4.95 (ISBN 0-8423-0618-8). Tyndale.

Dorris, C. E see Gospel Advocate.

Dorrough, Ardith. The Real Christmas Tree. 48p. (Orig.). 1983. pap. 2.50 (ISBN 0-88144-020-5, CPS/020). Christian Pub.

Dorsen, Norman & Law, Sylvia. Emerson, Haber & Dorsen's Political & Civil Rights in the United States, Vol. 2. 4th ed. 1979. text ed. 34.00 student ed. (ISBN 0-316-19049-7); lawyers ed. 55.00 (ISBN 0-316-23627-6). Little.

Dorsett, Judy. Bulletin Board Builders, No. 3. (Illus.). 64p. 1986. 3.95 (ISBN 0-87403-020-X, 3240). Standard Pub.

--Handbook of Creativity. (Illus.). 128p. 1985. pap. 7.95 (ISBN 0-87239-729-7, 3226). Standard Pub.

Dorsett, Lyle W. And God Came In: The Extraordinary Story of Joy Davidman-Her life & Marriage to C.S. Lewis. (Illus.). 192p. 1983. 14.95 (ISBN 0-02-532250-8). Macmillan.

--And God Came In: The Extraordinary Story of Joy Davidman; Her Life & Marriage to C. S. Lewis. (Illus.). 192p. 1984. pap. 2.95 (ISBN 0-345-31787-4). Ballantine.

Dorsey, G. A. & Voth, H. R. Oraibi Soyal Ceremony, & Oraibi Powamu Ceremony, & Mishongnovi Ceremonies of the Snake & Antelope Fraternities, & Oraibi Summer Snake Ceremony, 4 wks. in 1 vol. 1901-03. (Chicago Field Museum of Natural History). 70.00 (ISBN 0-527-01863-5). Kraus Repr.

Dorsey, John M. Psychology of Ethics. 261p. 1974. 18.95 (ISBN 0-8143-1639-5). Wayne St U Pr.

Dorson, Richard, ed. see Hector, Lee H.

Dorson, Richard, ed. see Palmer, Abram S.

Dorson, Richard M., ed. see Briggs, Katherine M.

Dorson, Richard M., ed. see Gill, William W.

Dorson, Richard M., ed. see McPherson, Joseph M.

Dorson, Richard M., ed. see Muller, Friedrich Max.

Dorson, Richard M., ed. see Ricks, George R.

Dorson, Richard M., ed. see Stern, Stephen.

D'Ortigue, J. L. Dictionnaire Liturgique, Historique, et Theorique de Plain Chante de Musique Religieuse. Migne, J. P., ed. (Nouvelle Encyclopedie Theologique Ser.: Vol. 29). (Fr.). 782p. Date not set. Repr. of 1860 ed. lib. bdg. 99.00x (ISBN 0-89241-272-0). Caratzas.

D'Ortigue, M. J. Dictionnaire Liturgique, Historique et Theorique de Plainchant et de Musique d'Eglise. LC 79-155353. (Music Ser). (Fr.). 1971. Repr. of 1854 ed. lib. bdg. 110.00 (ISBN 0-306-70165-0). Da Capo.

Doshi, Nagin. Guidance from Sri Aurobindo: Letters to a Young Disciple, Vol. 2. 1976. pap. 4.50 (ISBN 0-89071-265-4). Matagiri.

Doshi, Nagin, ed. see Sri Aurobindo.

Dosker, Henry E., ed. The Dutch Anabaptists: Stone Lectures Delivered at Princeton Theological Seminary, 1918-1919. LC 83-45610. Date not set. Repr. of 1921 ed. 36.50 (ISBN 0-404-19828-7). AMS Pr.

Doskow, Minna. William Blake's Jerusalem. LC 81-65463. (Illus.). 388p. 1982. 37.50 (ISBN 0-8386-3090-1). Fairleigh Dickinson.

Dostoyevsky, Fyodor. The Grand Inquisitor. LC 56-7503. (Milestones of Thought Ser.). pap. 2.95x (ISBN 0-8044-6125-2). Ungar.

--Grand Inquisitor on the Nature of Man. Garnett, Constance, tr. 1948. pap. 4.79 scp (ISBN 0-672-60237-7, LLA63). Bobbs.

Doswald, Beverly J. Learning about God & Jesus: An Overview of the Gospel in Simple English. LC 86-81297. 50p. (Orig.). 1986. pap. 3.25 (ISBN 0-938783-00-9). Helpful Beginnings.

Dotts, Maryann J. When Jesus Was Born. LC 79-3958. (Illus.). 1979. 9.95 (ISBN 0-687-45020-9). Abingdon.

Dotts, Maryann J., jt. auth. see Franklin, M.

Doty, Brant L. Numbers. (The Bible Study Textbook Ser.). 1973. 14.30 (ISBN 0-89900-008-8). College Pr Pub.

Doty, Harry. Prayer Meetings. LC 78-10622. 1979. pap. 6.00 (ISBN 0-8309-0228-7). Herald Hse.

Doty, William G. Letters in Primitive Christianity. Via, Dan O., Jr., ed. LC 72-87058. (Guides to Biblical Scholarship: New Testament Ser.). 96p. 1973. pap. 4.50 (ISBN 0-8006-0170-X, 1-170). Fortress.

--Mythography: The Study of Myths & Rituals. LC 85-991. 384p. 1986. 28.50 (ISBN 0-8173-0269-7). U of Ala Pr.

Doty, William G., tr. see Guttgemanns, Erhard T.

Doty, William L. One Season Following Another: A Cycle of Faith. LC 68-54394. 141p. 1968. 4.50 (ISBN 0-8199-0152-0, L38573). Franciscan Herald.

Douais, Celestin. Les Albigeois. 2nd ed. LC 78-63182. (Heresies of the Early Christian & Medieval Era: Second Ser.). Repr. of 1879 ed. 64.50 (ISBN 0-404-16221-5). AMS Pr.

Double, Don. Life in a New Dimension. 1979. pap. 2.95 (ISBN 0-88368-083-1). Whitaker Hse.

Douet D'Arcq, L., ed. see De Monstrelet, Enguerrend.

Dougherty, Flavian, ed. The Deprived, the Disabled & the Fullness of Life. 1984. pap. 4.95 (ISBN 0-89453-442-4). M Glazier.

--The Meaning of Human Suffering. LC 81-6267. 349p. 1982. 39.95 (ISBN 0-89885-011-8). Human Sci Pr.

Dougherty, James. The Fivesquare City. 178p. 1980. 15.95 (ISBN 0-268-00946-5). U of Notre Dame Pr.

Dougherty, James E. The Bishops & Nuclear Weapons: The Catholic Pastoral Letter on War & Peace. LC 84-2994. 255p. 1984. 22.50 (ISBN 0-208-02051-9, Archon Bks). Shoe String.

Dougherty, Jude P., jt. ed. see McLean, George F.

Dougherty, Raymond P. The Shirkutu of Babylonian Deities. LC 78-63548. (Yale Oriental Ser. Researches: 5, Pt. 2). Repr. of 1923 ed. 25.00 (ISBN 0-404-60295-9). AMS Pr.

Doughty, Stephen. Answering Love's Call: Christian Love & a Life of Prayer. LC 86-81809. 128p. (Orig.). 1986. pap. 4.95 (ISBN 0-87793-348-0). Ave Maria.

Doughty, Stephen V. Ministry of Love: A Handbook for Visiting the Aged. LC 84-71674. 96p. (Orig.). 1984. pap. 3.95 (ISBN 0-87793-324-3). Ave Maria.

Doughty, W. L. Studies in Religious Poetry of the Seventeenth Century: Essays on Henry Vaughn, Francis Quarles, Richard Crawshaw, John Davies, Henry More & Thomas Traherne. LC 68-26278. Repr. of 1946 ed. 21.00x (ISBN 0-8046-0113-5, Pub. by Kennikat). Assoc Faculty Pr.

Doughty, W. L., ed. The Prayers of Susanna Wesley. 80p. 1984. pap. 3.95 (ISBN 0-310-36351-9, 12368P, Clarion Class). Zondervan.

Douglas, C. E. When All Hell Breaks Loose. 1974. pap. 4.95 (ISBN 0-9601124-0-5). Tusayan Gospel.

Douglas, C. H. The Land for the Chosen People Racket. 1982. lib. bdg. 55.00 (ISBN 0-87700-415-3). Revisionist Pr.

Douglas, D. C., ed. Feudal Documents from the Abbey of Bury St. Edmunds. (British Academy, London, Records of the Social & Economic History of England & Wales: Vol. 8). pap. 45.00 (ISBN 0-8115-1248-7). Kraus Repr.

Douglas, J. D., ed. The New Bible Dictionary. 1344p. 1982. 24.95 (ISBN 0-8423-4667-8). Tyndale.

Douglas, J. D. & Cairns, Earle E., eds. The New International Dictionary of the Christian Church. rev. ed. 1978. 29.95 (ISBN 0-310-23830-7, 11100). Zondervan.

Douglas, J. D. & Van der Maas, E., eds. The New Zondervan Pictorial Bible Dictionary. rev. ed. 1000p. 1987. price not set. Zondervan.

Douglas, John. Milton on Plagiary; Or a Detection of the Forgeries. LC 72-187954. Repr. of 1756 ed. lib. bdg. 10.00 (ISBN 0-8414-0508-5). Folcroft.

Douglas, Kenneth, tr. see Tsogyal, Yeshe.

Douglas, Leonora M., ed. World Christianity: Oceania. pap. 15.00 (ISBN 0-912552-48-4). Missions Adv Res Com Ctr.

Douglas, Lloyd C. Big Fisherman. 1948. 15.95 (ISBN 0-395-07630-7). HM.

--Robe. 1942. 12.95 (ISBN 0-395-07635-8). HM.

Douglas, Mark, jt. auth. see Moore, Marcia.

Douglas, Martin, jt. auth. see Brandes, Joseph.

Douglas, Mary. Natural Symbols: Explorations in Cosmology. 1982. pap. 5.95 (ISBN 0-394-71105-X). Pantheon.

--Purity & Danger: An Analysis of the Concepts of Pollution & Taboo. 196p. 1984. pap. 6.95 (ISBN 0-7448-0011-0, Ark Paperbks). Methuen Inc.

Douglas, Mary & Tipton, Steven M., eds. Religion & America: Spirituality in a Secular Age. LC 82-72500. 256p. 1983. 25.00x (ISBN 0-8070-1106-1); pap. 13.95x (ISBN 0-8070-1107-X, BP648). Beacon Pr.

Douglas, N. & White, M. Karmapa the Black Hat Lama of Tibet. 248p. 1976. 40.00x (ISBN 0-317-39097-X, Pub. by Luzac & Co Ltd). State Mutual Bk.

Douglas, R. Confucianism & Taoism. 59.95 (ISBN 0-87968-930-7). Gordon Pr.

Douglas, Robert C. Freedom in Christ. Thomas, J. D., ed. LC 72-140290. (Twentieth Century Sermons Ser). 1970. 11.95 (ISBN 0-89112-305-9, Bibl Res Pr). Abilene Christ U.

Douglas, Robert W. John Paul II: The Pilgrim Pope. LC 79-24930. (Picture-Story Biographies Ser.). (Illus.). 32p. 1980. PLB 10.60 (ISBN 0-516-03563-0). Childrens.

Douglass, H. E. Hello Neighbor. (Outreach Ser.). 16p. 1983. pap. 0.25 (ISBN 0-8163-0523-4). Pacific Pr Pub Assn.

Douglass, James W. Lightning East to West: Jesus, Gandhi & the Nuclear Age. 112p. 1983. pap. 6.95 (ISBN 0-8245-0587-5). Crossroad NY.

Douglass, Jane D. Women, Freedom, & Calvin. LC 85-8778. 156p. 1985. pap. 11.95 (ISBN 0-664-24663-X). Westminster.

Douglass, R. Bruce, et al. The Deeper Meaning of Economic Life: Critical Essays on the U. S. Bishops' Pastoral Letter on the Economy. (Studies in Ethics). Orig. Title: Forging a New Public Philosophy. 296p. 1987. 19.95 (ISBN 0-87840-440-6); pap. 12.95 (ISBN 0-87840-441-4). Georgetown U Pr.

Douglass, Stephen B. & Roddy, Lee. Making the Most of Your Mind. 250p. (Orig.). 1982. pap. 6.95 (ISBN 0-86605-109-0). Heres Life.

Douglass, William. Sermons Preached in the African Protestant Episcopal Church of St. Thomas' Philadelphia. facs. ed. LC 79-157366. (Black Heritage Library Collection Ser). 1854. 20.00 (ISBN 0-8369-8804-3). Ayer Co Pubs.

Douhet, J. Dictionnaire des Legendes du Christianisme. Migne, J. P., ed. (Troisieme et Derniere Encyclopedie Theologique Ser.: Vol. 14). (Fr.). 764p. Repr. of 1855 ed. lib. bdg. 97.50x (ISBN 0-89241-297-6). Caratzas.

--Dictionnaire des Mysteres. Migne, J. P., ed. (Nouvelle Encyclopedie Theologique Ser.: Vol. 43). (Fr.). 788p. Repr. of 1854 ed. lib. bdg. 100.00x (ISBN 0-89241-282-8). Caratzas.

Douie, Decima L. The Nature & the Effect of the Heresy of the Fraticelli. LC 77-84715. Repr. of 1932 ed. 36.50 (ISBN 0-404-16121-9). AMS Pr.

Douie, Decima L. & Farmer, David H., eds. Magna Vita Sancti Hugonis: The Life of St. Hugh of Lincoln. (Medieval Texts Ser.). (Illus.). 1985. Vol. I. 45.00x (ISBN 0-19-822207-6); Vol. II. 45.00x (ISBN 0-19-822208-4). Oxford U Pr.

Doukhan, Jacques. Drinking at the Sources. 1981. 7.95 (ISBN 0-8163-0407-6). Pacific Pr Pub Assn.

--Ellen G. White & the Jews: An Interpretative Analysis of Her Writings & Their Significance for Our Time. Adar Publications, ed. LC 85-70340. 35p. (Orig.). 1985. pap. 1.75x (ISBN 0-916169-01-4). Adar Pubns.

Doukhan, Jacques B. The Genesis Creation Story: Its Literary Structure. (Andrews University Seminary Doctoral Dissertation Ser.: Vol. 5). xii, 303p. 1982. pap. 10.95 (ISBN 0-943872-37-5). Andrews Univ Pr.

Doulatram, J., et al, eds. The Collected Works of Mahatma Gandhi, 90 Vols. 48000p. 1983. 950.00 (ISBN 0-934676-35-6). Greenlf Bks.

Doulis, T. Journeys to Orthodoxy. 1986. pap. 6.95 (ISBN 0-937032-42-5). Light&Life Pub Co MN.

Douma, George. Encouragement. pap. 0.45 (ISBN 0-686-23477-4). Rose Pub MI.

--My Doctrine Book. pap. 2.25 (ISBN 0-686-23469-3). Rose Pub MI.

--Together with God. pap. 0.45 (ISBN 0-686-23478-2). Rose Pub MI.

Douty, Norman. Loving Kindness of the Sovereign God. pap. 0.50 (ISBN 0-685-88383-3). Reiner.

--Union with Christ. 10.95 (ISBN 0-685-36792-4). Reiner.

Dov ben Khayyim. The Telling: A Loving Hagadah for Passover (Non-Sexist, Yet Traditional) rev. ed. (Illus.). 48p. 1984. pap. 4.00 (ISBN 0-9612500-0-3). Rakhamim Pubns.

Dow, James. The Shaman's Touch: Otomi Indian Symbolic Healing. (Illus.). 180p. (Orig.). 1986. 13.95 (ISBN 0-87480-257-1). U of Utah Pr.

Dow, James L., ed. World's Handy Dictionary of the Bible. 640p. 1986. pap. 4.95 (ISBN 0-529-06320-4). World Bible.

Dow, T. I. Confucianism vs. Marxism. 200p. 1977. pap. text ed. 12.50 (ISBN 0-8191-0183-4). U Pr of Amer.

Dow, T. W. Truth of Creation. LC 67-31148. (Illus.). 1968. 5.00 (ISBN 0-910340-04-8). Celestial Pr.

Doward, Jan S. The Moment to Decide. Woolsey, Raymond H., ed. (Daily Devotional Ser.). 384p. 1984. 7.95 (ISBN 0-8280-0234-7). Review & Herald.

Dowd, John C. You Cannot Hold Back the Dawn. LC 74-75619. 1974. 4.95 (ISBN 0-8198-0320-0); pap. 3.95 (ISBN 0-8198-0321-9). Dghtrs St Paul.

Dowell, Spright. Columbus Roberts: Christian Steward Extraordinary. LC 83-887. xvi, 171p. 13.95 (ISBN 0-86554-071-3, H67). Mercer Univ Pr.

Dowley, Tim. Eerdmans' Handbook to the History of Christianity. LC 77-5616. 1977. 24.95 (ISBN 0-8028-3450-7). Eerdmans.

--The Moody Guide to Bible Lands. 1987. text ed. 7.95 (ISBN 0-8024-5563-8). Moody.

--The Moody Guide to the Bible. 1986. Repr. text ed. 7.95 (ISBN 0-8024-5562-X). Moody.

Dowley, Tim, ed. Discovering the Bible. (Illus.). 144p. 1986. 14.95 (ISBN 0-8028-3624-0). Eerdmans.

Dowley, Tom. High above the Holy Land. Roe, Earl O., ed. LC 86-6422. (Illus.). 64p. 1986. 15.95 (ISBN 0-8307-1153-8, 5111590). Regal.

Dowling, Theodore E. Armenian Church. LC 71-131511. Repr. of 1910 ed. 16.00 (ISBN 0-404-02167-0). AMS Pr.

Dowman, Keith. Masters of Mahamudra: Songs & Histories of Eighty-Four Siddhas. (Buddhist Studies). 320p. 1986. 44.50x (ISBN 0-88706-158-3); pap. 10.95x (ISBN 0-88706-160-5). State U NY Pr.

Dowman, Kieth, tr. The Divine Madman: The Sublime Life & Songs of Drukpa Kunley. (Illus.). 180p. 1982. pap. 8.95 (ISBN 0-913922-75-7). Dawn Horse Pr.

Down, Goldie. Saga of an Ordinary Man. (Dest Two Ser.). 1984. pap. 4.95 (ISBN 0-8163-0554-4). Pacific Pr Pub Assn.

Downame, John. The Christian Warfare. LC 74-80174. (English Experience Ser.: No. 653). 674p. 1974. Repr. of 1604 ed. 67.00 (ISBN 90-221-0653-5). Walter J Johnson.

Downes, David A. Hopkins' Sanctifying Imagination. LC 85-11071. 134p. (Orig.). 1985. lib. bdg. 22.00 (ISBN 0-8191-4755-9); pap. text ed. 8.75 (ISBN 0-8191-4756-7). U Pr of Amer.

--Ruskin's Landscape of Beatitude. LC 83-48767. (American University Studies IV (English Language & Literature): Vol. 4). 247p. 1984. pap. text ed. 24.75 (ISBN 0-8204-0049-1). P Lang Pubs.

Downey, David G. Modern Poets & Christian Teaching: Richard Watson Gilder, Edwin Markham, Edward Rowland Sill. 1973. Repr. of 1906 ed. 25.00 (ISBN 0-8274-1700-4). R West.

--Modern Poets & Christian Teaching: Richard Watson Gilder, Edwin Markham, Edward Rowland Sill. 183p. 1982. Repr. lib. bdg. 40.00 (ISBN 0-89984-013-2). Century Bookbindery.

Downey, John K. Beginning at the Beginning: Wittgenstein & Theological Conversation. 166p. (Orig.). 1986. lib. bdg. 23.50 (ISBN 0-8191-5650-7); pap. text ed. 12.50 (ISBN 0-8191-5651-5). U Pr of Amer.

Downey, Michael. Clothed in Christ. 160p. 1987. pap. 9.95 (ISBN 0-8245-0812-2). Crossroad NY.

Downey, Murray W. Art of Soul Winning. 1957. pap. 5.95 (ISBN 0-8010-2820-5). Baker Bk.

Downing, Charles. The Messiahship of Shakespeare. LC 76-57998. (Studies in Shakespeare, No. 24). 1977. lib. bdg. 39.95x (ISBN 0-8383-2172-0). Haskell.

Downing, Christine. The Goddess: Mythological Images of the Feminine. 256p. 1984. pap. 9.95 (ISBN 0-8245-0624-3). Crossroad NY.

Downing, David C., compiled by. Two Hundred Twenty Misconceptions about the Bible: A Handbook of Misinformation, Misquotation, & Misinterpretations of the Bible. 1987. pap. price not set (ISBN 0-8010-2975-9). Baker Bk.

Downing, Francis G. Church & Jesus. LC 78-3050. (Studies in Biblical Theology, 2nd Ser.: No. 10). 1968. pap. 10.00x (ISBN 0-8401-3060-0). A R Allenson.

Downs, Barry. Sacred Places: Religious Architecture of the 18th & 19th Centuries in British Columbia. LC 81-670050. (Illus.). 160p. 1980. 29.95 (ISBN 0-295-95774-3, Pub. by Douglas & McIntyre Canada). U of Wash Pr.

Downs, Thomas. The Parish As Learning Community. LC 78-70816. 128p. 1979. pap. 3.95 (ISBN 0-8091-2172-7). Paulist Pr.

Dowsett, Dick. Is God Really Fair? 1985. pap. 3.95 (ISBN 0-8024-3277-8). Moody.

Dowsett, Norman & Jayaswal, Sita R. Dimensions of Spiritual Education. (Integral Education Ser.: No.4). (Illus.). 91p. 1975. pap. 2.50 (ISBN 0-89071-216-6). Matagiri.

Dowson, John. A Classical Dictionary of Hindu Mythology & Religion, Geography, History & Literature. 11th ed. 26.95 (ISBN 0-7100-1302-7). Methuen Inc.

Dox, Victor L. What the World Needs. LC 67-31068. 3.50 (ISBN 0-8198-0328-6); pap. 2.50 (ISBN 0-8198-0329-4). Dghtrs St Paul.

Doyle, Aileen A. Youth Retreats: Creating Sacred Space for Young People. (Illus.). 107p. 1986. spiral bdg. 12.95 (ISBN 0-88489-177-1). St Mary's.

Doyle, Alfreda C. The Creator or Almighty Always Has an Answer. Date not set. 7.95 (Pub. by Biblio Pr GA); pap. text ed. 2.95 (ISBN 0-939476-23-1, Pub. by Biblio Pr GA). Prosperity & Profits.

Doyle, Brendan. Meditations with TM Julian of Norwich. LC 82-73955. (Meditations with TM). (Illus.). 135p. (Orig.). 1983. pap. 6.95 (ISBN 0-939680-11-4). Bear & Co.

Doyle, Charles H. Fifty Funeral Homilies. 110p. 1984. pap. 10.00 spiral bdg. (ISBN 0-87061-094-5). Chr Classics.

Doyle, Derek. Coping With a Dying Relative. 1983. 30.00x (ISBN 0-86334-028-8, Pub. by Macdonald Pub UK); pap. 20.00x (ISBN 0-86334-026-1). State Mutual Bk.

Doyle, Eric. The Disciple & the Master: St. Bonaventure's Sermons on St. Francis of Assisi. 220p. 1983. 15.00 (ISBN 0-8199-0842-8). Franciscan Herald.
--Saint Francis & the Song of Brotherhood. 1981. pap. 5.95 (ISBN 0-8164-2300-8, HarpR). Har-Row.
Doyle, I. A., intro. by. The Vernon Manuscript: Bodleian Library MS. English Poet a.1. (Illus.). 704p. 1987. facsimile 695.00 (ISBN 0-85991-200-0, Pub. by Boydell & Brewer). Longwood Pub Group.
Doyle, James A. Catholic Press Directory. 184p. 1985. pap. 25.00 (ISBN 0-686-30366-0). Cath Pr Assn.
Doyle, Mary L., ed. see Mead, Sidney E.
Doyle, Sr. Rosa. Catholic Atmosphere in Marie Von Ebner Eschenbach: Its Use As a Literary Device. LC 70-140040. (Catholic University Studies in German Ser.: No. 6). Repr. of 1936 ed. 18.00 (ISBN 0-404-50226-1). AMS Pr.
Doyle, Stephen. The Pilgrim's New Guide to the Holy Land. 1985. pap. 7.95 (ISBN 0-89453-440-8). M Glazier.
--Thessalonians & Galations. (Read & Pray Ser.). 1980. 1.75 (ISBN 0-8199-0635-2). Franciscan Herald.
Doyle, Stephen C. Covenant Renewal in Religious Life: Biblical Reflections. 140p. 1976. 6.95 (ISBN 0-8199-0585-2). Franciscan Herald.
Doyle, Teresa A., ed. see Adams, Daniel J.
Doyle, Thomas P. Rights & Responsibilities. 64p. (Orig.). 1983. pap. 2.50 (ISBN 0-916134-58-X). Pueblo Pub Co.
Doyle, Thomas P., ed. Marriage Studies: Reflections in Canon Law & Theology, Vol. 1. 155p. (Orig.). 1980. pap. 4.00 (ISBN 0-943616-03-4). Canon Law Soc.
--Marriage Studies: Reflections in Canon Law & Theology, Vol. 2. 202p. (Orig.). 1982. pap. 4.50 (ISBN 0-943616-04-2). Canon Law Soc.
--Marriage Studies, Vol. 3: Reflections in Canon Law & Theology. 207p. (Orig.). 1985. pap. 6.00 (ISBN 0-943616-25-5). Canon Law Soc.
Dozier, Etrulia P., ed. see Bulletin Committee Staff.
Dozy, Reinhart. Spanish Islam: History of the Moslems in Spain. 770p. 1972. Repr. of 1913 ed. 45.00x (ISBN 0-7146-2128-5, F Cass Co). Biblio Dist.
Drachman, A. Atheism In Pagan Antiquity. 178p. 1977. 12.50 (ISBN 0-89005-201-8). Ares.
Drachman, Bermard, tr. see Hirsch, Samson R.
Drachman, Bernard. From the Heart of Israel. LC 72-110183. (Short Story Index Reprint Ser.). 1905. 23.50 (ISBN 0-8369-3334-6). Ayer Co Pubs.
Drachman, Bernard, tr. see Hirsch, Somson R.
Drachmann, A. B. Atheism in Pagan Antiquity. 69.95 (ISBN 0-87968-675-8). Gordon Pr.
Drahmann, Theodore. The Catholic School Principal: An Outline for Action. 50p. 1981. 4.80 (ISBN 0-686-39893-9). Natl Cath Educ.
--Governance & Administration in the Catholic School. 45p. 1986. 6.60 (ISBN 0-318-20563-7). Natl Cath Educ.
Drahos, Mary. To Touch the Hem of His Garment. 224p. (Orig.). 1983. pap. 7.95 (ISBN 0-8091-2548-X). Paulist Pr.
Drake, Benjamin. Life of Tecumseh & of His Brother the Prophet: With a Historical Sketch of the Shawanoe Indians. LC 78-90173. (Mass Violence in America Ser). Repr. of 1841 ed. 14.00 (ISBN 0-405-01307-8). Ayer Co Pubs.
Drake, Durant. Problems of Religion: An Introductory Survey. LC 68-19268. Repr. of 1916 ed. lib. bdg. 22.50x (ISBN 0-8371-0062-3, DRPR). Greenwood.
Drake, George A. see Brauer, Jerald C.
Drake, Gertrude C., ed. see Vida, Marco G.
Drake, H. A. In Praise of Constantine: A Historical Study & New Translation of Eusebius' Tricennial Orations. LC 75-62009. (UC Publications in Classical Studies: Vol. 15; California Library Reprint Ser.: No. 93). 1976. Repr. of 1975 ed. 22.50x (ISBN 0-520-03694-8). U of Cal Pr.
Drake, Marsha. The Proverbs Thirty-One Lady & Other Impossible Dreams. LC 84-6453. 192p. (Orig.). 1984. pap. 5.95 (ISBN 0-87123-595-1, 210595). Bethany Hse.
--The Submissive Wife & other Legends. 176p. (Orig.). 1987. pap. 5.95 (ISBN 0-87123-926-4). Bethany Hse.
Drake, Marvia, jt. auth. see Drake, Terrance.
Drake, Maurice. Saints & Their Emblems. (Illus.). 1971. Repr. of 1916 ed. lib. bdg. 24.50 (ISBN 0-8337-0902-X). B Franklin.
Drake, Samuel G. Annals of Witchcraft in New England & Elsewhere in the United States from Their First Settlement. LC 67-13327. 1967. Repr. of 1869 ed. 20.00 (ISBN 0-405-08466-8, Blom Pubns). Ayer Co Pubs.
--Annals of Witchcraft in New England, & Elsewhere in the United States. LC 73-161683. (Woodward's Historical Ser.: No. 8). 306p. 1972. Repr. of 1869 ed. lib. bdg. 23.50 (ISBN 0-8337-0898-8). B Franklin.
--Annals of Witchcraft in New England & Elsewhere in the United States. 69.95 (ISBN 0-87968-641-3). Gordon Pr.
--Witchcraft Delusion in New England, 3 vols. LC 79-120720. (Research & Source Works Ser.: No. 471). 1970. Repr. of 1866 ed. lib. bdg. 62.00 (ISBN 0-8337-0908-9). B Franklin.
Drake, Terrance & Drake, Marvia. Teaching Your Child about Sex. LC 83-71726. 60p. 1983. 6.95 (ISBN 0-87747-951-8). Deseret Bk.
Drakeford, J. W. Psicologia y Religion. 384p. 1980. pap. 8.95 (ISBN 0-311-46035-6, Edit Mundo). Casa Bautista.
Drakeford, John W. The Awesome Power of the Healing Thought. LC 80-70915. 1981. 8.95 (ISBN 0-8054-5294-X). Broadman.
--A Christian View of Homosexuality. LC 76-41474. 1977. pap. 3.95 (ISBN 0-8054-5620-1). Broadman.
--Counseling for Church Leaders. LC 61-12412. 1961. 9.25 (ISBN 0-8054-2405-9). Broadman.
--Growing Old-Feeling Young. LC 84-21341. 1985. pap. 7.95 (ISBN 0-8054-5009-2). Broadman.
--Hechos el Uno Para el Otro. De Plou, Dafne C., tr. (Sexo en la Vida Cristiana Ser.). 1983. pap. 3.50 (ISBN 0-311-46256-1). Casa Bautista.
--Humor in Preaching. 160p. 1986. pap. 6.95 (ISBN 0-310-20121-7). Zondervan.
--Psychology in Search of a Soul. LC 64-15096. 1964. 11.95 (ISBN 0-8054-6701-7). Broadman.
--Wisdom for Today's Family. LC 77-94449. 1978. pap. 5.50 (ISBN 0-8054-5592-2). Broadman.
Drakeford, John W. & Drakeford, Robina. Mothers Are Special. LC 78-73137. 1979. 8.95 (ISBN 0-8054-5636-8). Broadman.
Drakeford, Robina, jt. auth. see Drakeford, John W.
Drakeman, Donald, jt. ed. see Wilson, John.
Drane, James. Your Emotional Life & What You Can Do about It. 204p. 1984. 9.95 (ISBN 0-88347-157-4). Thomas More.
Drane, James F. A New American Reformation: A Study of Youth Culture & Religion. (Quality Paperback Ser.: No. 293). 166p. 1974. pap. 2.95 (ISBN 0-8226-0293-8). Littlefield.
--The Possibility of God. (Quality Paperback Ser.: No. 321). 194p. 1976. pap. 3.50 (ISBN 0-8226-0321-7). Littlefield.
Drane, John. The Early Christians: Life in the First Years of the Church, an Illustrated Documentary. LC 81-47835. (Illus.). 144p. (Orig.). 1982. pap. 9.95 (ISBN 0-06-062067-6, RD 378, HarpR). Har-Row.
--Jesus & the Gospels. LC 77-20448. 1979. pap. 9.95 (ISBN 0-06-062066-8, RD264, HarpR). Har-Row.
--Paul: An Illustrated Documentary on the Life & Writings. LC 76-62918. (Illus.). 1977. pap. text ed. 9.95 (ISBN 0-06-062065-X, RD 208, HarpR). Har-Row.
Drane, John W. Old Testament Faith. LC 86-45075. (Illus.). 224p. (Orig.). 1986. pap. 10.95 (ISBN 0-06-062064-1, HarpR). Har-Row.
Draper, Edgar. Psychiatry & Pastoral Care. LC 65-23861. (Successful Pastoral Counseling Series). pap. 34.50 (2026894). Bks Demand UMI.
Draper, Edythe. Cool: How a Kid Should Live. 1974. kivar 6.95 (ISBN 0-8423-0435-5). Tyndale.
--In Touch. 1983. deluxe ed. 8.95 gift ed. (ISBN 0-8423-1711-2); christmas ed. 8.95 (ISBN 0-8423-1712-0); deluxe graduation ed. 8.95 (ISBN 0-8423-1713-9); kivar 5.95 (ISBN 0-8423-1710-4). Tyndale.
--Living Light. Incl. Large Print Edition. 1976. kivar 8.95 (ISBN 0-8423-2652-9). 1972. leatherette o.p. 8.95 (ISBN 0-8423-2651-0). Tyndale.
--Stretch. 1983. kivar, girls' ed. 5.95 (ISBN 0-8423-6673-3). Tyndale.
--Stretch. 1983. kivar, boys' ed. 5.95 (ISBN 0-8423-6668-7). Tyndale.
--Wonder. 448p. 1984. 5.95 (ISBN 0-8423-8385-9). Tyndale.
Draper, James T. The Conscience of a Nation. LC 82-73420. 1983. pap. 7.95 (ISBN 0-8054-1530-0). Broadman.
Draper, James T., Jr. Discover Joy: Studies in Philippians. 1983. pap. 4.95 (ISBN 0-8423-0606-4); leader's guide 2.95 (ISBN 0-8423-0607-2). Tyndale.
--Faith that Works: Studies in James. 1983. pap. 5.95 (ISBN 0-8423-0872-5); Leader's Guide 2.95 (ISBN 0-8423-0873-3). Tyndale.
--Foundations of Biblical Faith. LC 78-67001. 1979. 8.95 (ISBN 0-8054-1951-9). Broadman.
--Live up to Your Faith: Studies in Titus. 1983. pap. 3.95 (ISBN 0-8423-3687-7); leader's guide 2.95 (ISBN 0-8423-3688-5). Tyndale.
--Proverbs: Practical Directions for Living. (Living Studies). pap. 4.95 (ISBN 0-8423-4922-7); leader's guide 2.95 (ISBN 0-8423-4923-5). Tyndale.
Draper, Maurice L. Isles & Continents. (Orig.). 1982. pap. 14.00 (ISBN 0-8309-0343-7). Herald Hse.
--Restoration Studies, Vol. II. 1983. pap. 13.00 (ISBN 0-8309-0362-3). Herald Hse.
Draper, Maurice L., ed. Restoration Studies III. 1986. pap. 15.00 (ISBN 0-8309-0432-8, Pub. by Reidel Holland). Kluwer Academic.
--Restoration Studies, Vol.1. 1980. pap. 13.00 (ISBN 0-8309-0292-9). Herald Hse.
Dravida dasa, ed. see Svarupa dasa, Ravindra.
Draxe, Thomas. Bibliotheca Scholastica Instructissima: Or a Treasure of Ancient Adagies. LC 76-57378. (English Experience Ser.: No. 796). 1977. Repr. lib. bdg. 24.00 (ISBN 90-221-0796-5). Walter J Johnson.
Drazin, Israel. Targum Onkelos on Deuteronomy. 1981. 45.00x (ISBN 0-87068-755-7). Ktav.
Drazin, Nathan. History of Jewish Education from 515 B. C. E. to 220 C. E. 1979. 16.00 (ISBN 0-405-10598-3). Ayer Co Pubs.
Dreckamer, John M., tr. see Walther, C. F.
Dregni, Meredith S. Experiencing More with Less. LC 83-80954. 88p. (Orig.). 1983. pap. 4.95 (ISBN 0-8361-3334-X). Herald Pr.
Dreher, G. K., ed. see Peele, George.
Dreier, Patricia, compiled by. The Gold of Friendship: A Bouquet of Special Thoughts. (Illus.). 1980. 6.95 (ISBN 0-8378-1707-2). Gibson.
--Happiness Is a Journey. (Illus.). 1983. boxed 8.00 (ISBN 0-8378-1804-4). Gibson.
Dreikurs, Rudolf. Character Education & Spiritual Values in an Anxious Age. (AAI Monograph Ser.: No. 1). 1971. pap. 2.00x (ISBN 0-918560-16-0). A Adler Inst.
Drekmeier, Charles. Kingship & Community in Early India. LC 62-9565. 1962. 27.50x (ISBN 0-8047-0114-8). Stanford U Pr.
Drescher, Betty, jt. auth. see Drescher, John.
Drescher, John & Drescher, Betty. If We Were Starting Our Marriage Again. 96p. (Orig.). 1985. pap. 6.50 (ISBN 0-687-18672-2). Abingdon.
Drescher, John M. If I Were Starting My Family Again. LC 78-13278. (Festival Ser.). (Illus.). 1979. pap. 2.95 (ISBN 0-687-18674-9). Abingdon.
--Meditations for the Newly Married. LC 69-10835. 142p. 1969. gift-boxed 9.95 (ISBN 0-8361-1571-6). Herald Pr.
--Now Is the Time to Love. LC 73-123411. 144p. 1970. pap. 1.50 (ISBN 0-8361-1641-0). Herald Pr.
--Spirit Fruit. rev. ed. LC 73-21660. 352p. 1978. pap. 8.95 (ISBN 0-8361-1867-7). Herald Pr.
--When Opposites Attract. LC 79-53272. (When Bks.). (Illus., Orig.). 1979. pap. 2.45 (ISBN 0-87029-153-X, 20239-0). Abbey.
Drescher, John M., et al. When Your Child... LC 86-4831. 144p. (Orig.). 1986. pap. 7.95 (ISBN 0-8361-3416-8). Herald Pr.
Drescher, Sandra. Dear Jesus, Love Sandy. 112p. 1982. pap. 3.95 (ISBN 0-310-44841-7, 18235P); gift ed. o. p. cancelled 7.95 (ISBN 0-310-44840-9). Zondervan.
--Just Between God & Me. 1977. girls o.p. 9.95 (ISBN 0-310-23940-0); boys gift ed. o.p. 9.95 (ISBN 0-310-23950-8, 18111B); pap. 4.95 (ISBN 0-310-23941-9, 18111P). Zondervan.
Dresher, Seymour, jt. ed. see Bolt, Christine.
Dresner, Samuel. Prayer, Humility & Compassion. 4.95 (ISBN 0-87677-006-5). Hartmore.
Dresner, Samuel & Sherwin, Byron. Judaism: The Way of Sanctification. 1978. text ed. 6.50 (ISBN 0-8381-0222-0). United Syn Bk.
Dresner, Samuel & Siegel, Seymour. Jewish Dietary Laws. rev. ed. LC 83-235401. 110p. pap. 2.95x (ISBN 0-8381-2105-5). United Syn Bk.
Dresner, Samuel H. Between the Generations. pap. 1.75 (ISBN 0-87677-042-1). Hartmore.
--God, Man & Atomic War. 6.95 (ISBN 0-87677-007-3). Hartmore.
--Portraits of a Hasidic Master: Levi Yitzhak of Berditchev. 1986. pap. 8.95 (ISBN 0-933503-59-8). Shapolsky Pubs.
--Sabbath. 1970. pap. 2.95 (ISBN 0-8381-2114-4). United Syn Bk.
--Zaddik: The Doctrine of the Zaddik According to the Writings of Rabbi Yaakov Yosef of Polnoy. LC 60-7228. 312p. 1974. pap. 4.95 (ISBN 0-8052-0437-7). Schocken.
Dresner, Samuel H., ed. see Heschel, Abraham J.
Dresselhaus, Richard. Your Sunday School at Work. 78p. 1980. pap. 2.95 (ISBN 0-88243-793-3, 02-0793). Gospel Pub.
Dresselhaus, Richard L. The Deacon & His Ministry. LC 77-73518. 1977. pap. 2.25, 2.00 for 6 or more (ISBN 0-88243-493-4, 02-0493). Gospel Pub.
--The Joy of Belonging. LC 78-66868. (Radiant Life Ser.). 128p. 1978. pap. 2.50 (ISBN 0-88243-526-4, 02-0526); tchr's ed. 3.95 (ISBN 0-88243-186-2, 32-0186). Gospel Pub.
--Teaching for Decision. LC 73-75502. 124p. 1973. pap. 1.25 (ISBN 0-88243-616-3, 02-0616). Gospel Pub.
Dretke, James P. A Christian Approach to Muslims: Reflections from West Africa. LC 79-11912. (Islamic Studies). 1979. pap. 3.95 (ISBN 0-87808-432-0). William Carey Lib.
Dreves, Guido M., ed. Cantiones Bohemicae. 1886. 60.00 (ISBN 0-384-12860-2). Johnson Repr.
--Cantiones et Muteti, 3 vols. (Illus.). 1895-1904. 60.00 ea. (ISBN 0-384-12865-3). Johnson Repr.
--Historiae Rhythmicae, 8 Vols. 1889-1904. 60.00 ea. (ISBN 0-384-12880-7). Johnson Repr.
--Hymni Inediti, 7 Vols. 1888-1903. 60.00 ea. Johnson Repr.
--Hymnodia Hiberica: Liturgische Reimofficien, Aus Spanischen Brevieren. (Illus.). 1894. 60.00 (ISBN 0-384-12915-3). Johnson Repr.
--Hymnodia Hiberica: Spanische Hymnen Des Mittelalters. 1894. 60.00 (ISBN 0-384-12920-X). Johnson Repr.
--Pia Dictamina, 7 Vols. 1893-1905. 60.00 ea. (ISBN 0-384-12950-1). Johnson Repr.
--Psalteria Rhythmica, 2 Vols. 1900-01. 60.00 ea. (ISBN 0-384-12960-9) (ISBN 0-384-12961-7). Johnson Repr.
Dreves, Guido M., ed. see Stocklin, Ulrich V.
Drew, George. The Beatitudes: Attitudes for a Better Future. 63p. (Orig.). 1980. pap. 6.95 (ISBN 0-940754-03-7). Ed Ministries.
--Making the Bible Our Own. 65p. 1985. pap. 6.95 (ISBN 0-940754-29-0). Ed Ministries.
--The Original Ideas of Jesus That Are Changing the World. 45p. (Orig.). 1980. pap. 5.45 (ISBN 0-940754-05-3). Ed Ministries.
--The Parables in Depth. 55p. (Orig.). 1982. pap. 6.95 (ISBN 0-940754-18-5). Ed Ministries.
--The Prophets Speak to Our Time. 62p. (Orig.). 1981. pap. 6.95 (ISBN 0-940754-09-6). Ed Ministries.
--St. Paul. 60p. (Orig.). 1984. pap. 6.95 (ISBN 0-940754-22-3). Ed Ministries.
--The Ten Commandments in Today's World. 48p. (Orig.). 1979. pap. 6.95 (ISBN 0-940754-00-2). Ed Ministries.
Drew, George E. What Kind of God Is God? 65p. (Orig.). 1986. pap. 6.95 (ISBN 0-940754-33-9). Ed Ministries.
Drew, Joseph W. & Hague, W. Creation of Full Human Personality. pap. 0.75 (ISBN 0-8199-0247-0, L38115). Franciscan Herald.
Drew, Katherine F. & Lear, Floyd S., eds. Perspectives in Medieval History. LC 63-20902. Repr. of 1963 ed. 26.30 (ISBN 0-8357-9653-1, 2015753). Bks Demand UMI.
Drew, Louise C., jt. ed. see Miller, Max B.
Drew, Naomi. Learning the Skills of Peacemaking. Lovelady, Janet, ed. 200p. (Orig.). 1987. pap. 17.95x (ISBN 0-915190-46-X). Jalmar Pr.
Drewery, Benjamin. Origen & the Doctrine of Grace. LC 61-19395. 1960. text ed. 17.50x (ISBN 0-8401-0579-7). A R Allenson.
Drewery, Benjamin, jt. ed. see Cunliffe-Jones, Hubert.
Drewery, Benjamin, jt. ed. see Rupp, E. G.
Drewes, C. F. Introduction to the Books of the Bible. 1929. 4.95 (ISBN 0-570-03185-0, 12-2110). Concordia.
Drews, Arthur. The Witnesses to the Historicity of Jesus. McCabe, Joseph, tr. LC 70-161327. (Atheist Viewpoint Ser.). 332p. 1972. Repr. of 1912 ed. 23.50 (ISBN 0-405-03811-9). Ayer Co Pubs.
--The Witnesses to the Historicity of Jesus. 69.95 (ISBN 0-8490-1313-5). Gordon Pr.
Drews, Robert. In Search of the Shroud of Turin: New Light on Its History & Origins. LC 83-24586. (Illus.). 148p. 1984. 19.95x (ISBN 0-8476-7349-9, Rowman & Allanheld). Rowman.
Drews, Toby R. Getting Them Sober, Vol. 3. LC 85-73330. 1986. pap. 3.95 (ISBN 0-88270-610-1). Bridge Pub.
Drexelius, Jeremias. Heliotropium: Conformity of the Human Will to the Divine. LC 84-51597. 416p. 1985. pap. 8.50 (ISBN 0-89555-245-0). Tan Bks Pubs.
Dreyfus, Francois. Did Jesus Know He Was God? Date not set. price not set (ISBN 0-8199-0899-1). Franciscan Herald.
Driljvers, H. J., jt. ed. see Van Baaren, T. P.
Drillock, David & Erickson, John, eds. The Divine Liturgy. 368p. 1982. text ed. 30.00 (ISBN 0-913836-95-8); pap. 20.00 (ISBN 0-913836-93-1). St Vladimirs.
Drillock, David, et al. Pascha: The Resurrection of Christ. (Music Ser.). 274p. 1980. pap. 15.00 (ISBN 0-913836-50-8); 20.00 (ISBN 0-913836-65-6). St Vladimirs.
--Holy Week. (Music Ser.: Vol. I). 186p. (Orig.). 1980. 18.00 (ISBN 0-913836-67-2); pap. 14.00 (ISBN 0-913836-66-4). St Vladimirs.
Drinan, Robert F. God & Caesar on the Potomac: A Pilgrimage of Conscience. 1985. 15.00 (ISBN 0-89453-458-0). M Glazier.
--Religion, the Courts, & Public Policy. LC 78-6124. 261p. 1978. Repr. of 1963 ed. lib. bdg. 22.50x (ISBN 0-313-20444-6, DRRE). Greenwood.
Driscoll, J. Walter, jt. auth. see Gurdjieff Foundation of California.
Driver, John. Community & Commitment. LC 76-41463. 96p. 1976. pap. 3.95 (ISBN 0-8361-1802-2). Herald Pr.

--Kingdom Citizens. LC 80-16171. 160p. (Orig.). 1980. pap. 6.95 (ISBN 0-8361-1935-5). Herald Pr.
--Understanding the Atonement for the Mission of the Church. LC 86-3133. 288p. (Orig.). 1986. pap. 19.95 (ISBN 0-8361-3403-6). Herald Pr.
Driver, John, jt. auth. see Escobar, Samuel.
Driver, S. R. An Introduction to the Literature of the Old Testament. 640p. 1913. 19.95 (ISBN 0-567-07205-3, Pub. by T & T Clark Ltd UK). Fortress.
--Introduction to the Literature of the Old Testament. 16.50 (ISBN 0-8446-1998-1). Peter Smith.
--Modern Research As Illustrating the Bible. (British Academy, London, Schweich Lectures on Biblical Archaeology, 1908). pap. 19.00 (ISBN 0-8115-1250-9). Kraus Repr.
--Notes on the Hebrew Text of Samuel. 1986. 24.95 (ISBN 0-88469-163-2). BMH Bks.
Driver, Samuel R. A Critical & Exegetical Commentary on Deuteronomy. LC 2-25926. (International Critical Commentary Ser.). 556p. 1902. 24.95 (ISBN 0-567-05003-3, Pub. by T & T Clark Ltd UK). Fortress.
--A Critical & Exegetical Commentary on Job. Plummer, Alfred & Briggs, Charles, eds. LC 21-15647. (International Critical Commentary Ser.). 816p. 1921. 24.95 (ISBN 0-567-05010-6, Pub. by T & T Clark Ltd UK). Fortress.
Driver, Samuel R., ed. see Barton, George A.
Driver, Samuel R., ed. see Bernard, J. H.
Driver, Samuel R., ed. see Burton, Ernest De Witt.
Driver, Samuel R., ed. see Frame, James E.
Driver, Samuel R., ed. see Gray, G. Buchanan.
Driver, Samuel R., ed. see Moffatt, James.
Driver, Samuel R., ed. see Montgomery, James A.
Driver, Samuel R., ed. see Plummer, Alfred.
Driver, Samuel R., ed. see Robertson, Archibald & Plummer, Alfred.
Driver, Samuel R., ed. see Sanday, William & Headlam, Arthur C.
Driver, Samuel R., ed. see Smith, John M., et al.
Driver, Samuel R., ed. see Vincent, Marvin R.
Driver, Samuel R., et al, eds. see Abbott, T. K.
Driver, Samuel R., et al, eds. see Batten, Loring W.
Driver, Samuel R., et al, eds. see Bigg, Charles.
Driver, Samuel R., et al, eds. see Briggs, Charles & Briggs, Emile G.
Driver, Samuel R., et al, eds. see Brooke, A. E.
Driver, Samuel R., et al, eds. see Cooke, G. A.
Driver, Samuel R., et al, eds. see Curtis, Edward L. & Madsen, Albert A.
Driver, Samuel R., et al, eds. see Gould, Ezra P.
Driver, Samuel R., et al, eds. see Gray, George B.
Driver, Samuel R., et al, eds. see Harper, William R.
Driver, Samuel R., et al, eds. see Lock, Walter.
Driver, Samuel R., et al, eds. see Montgomery, James A.
Driver, Samuel R., et al, eds. see Moore, George F.
Driver, Samuel R., et al, eds. see Paton, Lewis B.
Driver, Samuel R., et al, eds. see Skinner, John.
Driver, Samuel R., et al, eds. see Smith, Henry P.
Driver, Samuel R., et al, eds. see Toy, Crawford H.
Driver, Tom F. Christ in a Changing World: Toward an Ethical Christology. LC 81-5552. 224p. 1981. 12.95 (ISBN 0-8245-0105-5). Crossroad NY.
--Patterns of Grace: Human Experience As Word of God. 214p. 1985. pap. text ed. 9.75 (ISBN 0-8191-4637-4). U Pr of Amer.
Drobena, Thomas J. & Kucharek, Wilma S. Heritage of the Slavs: The Christianization of the Great Moravian Empire. (Illus.). xviii, 174p. 1979. pap. 5.95 (ISBN 0-915887-01-0). Kosovo Pub Co.
Droege, Thomas A. Faith Passages & Patterns. LC 82-48544. (Lead Bks.). 128p. 1983. pap. 4.95 (ISBN 0-8006-1602-2, 1-1602). Fortress.
Droel, William & Pierce, Gregory. Confident & Competent: A Challenge for the Lay Church. LC 86-72789. 112p. (Orig.). 1987. pap. 3.95 (ISBN 0-87793-351-0). Ave Maria.
Drohan, Francis B. Jesus Who? The Greatest Mystery Never Told. LC 84-16654. 270p. 1985. 15.00 (ISBN 0-8022-2475-X). Philos Lib.
Droogers, Andre. The Dangerous Journey: Symbolic Aspects of Boys' Initiation Among the Wagenia of Kisangani, Zaire. (Change & Continuity in Africa Ser.). 1979. pap. text ed. 23.60x (ISBN 90-279-3357-X). Mouton.
Drotts, Wallace D. Take up Your Cross: Invitation to Abundant Life. LC 84-61032. 80p. (Orig.). 1985. pap. 3.95 (ISBN 0-8091-2655-9). Paulist Pr.
Droubie, Riadh El see El Droubie, Riadh.
Drower, Ethel S. Peacock Angel: Being Some Account of Votaries of a Secret Cult & Their Sanctuaries. LC 77-87643. Repr. of 1941 ed. 20.00 (ISBN 0-404-16425-0). AMS Pr.
--Water into Wine: A Study of Ritual Idiom in the Middle East. LC 77-87663. Repr. of 1956 ed. 23.50 (ISBN 0-404-16401-3). AMS Pr.
Drown, Ruth B. Wisdom from Atlantis. 153p. 1981. pap. 9.00 (ISBN 0-686-78074-4, SB-098). Sun Pub.
Dru, Alexander, ed. & tr. see Kierkegaard, Soren.
Drucker, Malka. Celebrating Life: Jewish Rites of Passage. LC 84-4684. (Illus.). 112p. 1984. reinforced bdg. 11.95 (ISBN 0-8234-0539-7). Holiday.
--Eliezer Ben-Yehuda: The Father of Modern Hebrew. LC 86-15213. (Jewish Biography Ser.). (Illus.). 128p. 1987. 13.95 (ISBN 0-525-67184-6, 01354-410). Lodestar Bks.
--Hanukkah: Eight Nights, Eight Lights. LC 80-15852. (A Jewish Holidays Book). (Illus.). 96p. 1980. reinforced bdg. 12.95 (ISBN 0-8234-0377-7). Holiday.
--Shabbat: A Peaceful Island (a Jewish Holidays Book) LC 83-7900. (Illus.). 96p. 1983. reinforced bdg. 11.95 (ISBN 0-8234-0500-1). Holiday.
--Sukkot: A Time to Rejoice. LC 82-80814. (A Jewish Holidays Bk.). (Illus.). 96p. 1982. Reinforced bdg. 10.95 (ISBN 0-8234-0466-8). Holiday.
Druffel, Ann & Marcotte, Armand. Past Lives Future Growth. (Inner Visions Ser.). (Orig.). 1987. pap. 12.95 (ISBN 0-917086-88-0). A C S Pubns Inc.
Druks, Herbert. Jewish Resistance During the Holocaust. LC 83-14. 132p. 1983. text ed. 14.95x (ISBN 0-8290-1295-8). Irvington.
--Not in Vain: A Holocaust Documentary. 125p. 1984. text ed. 14.95x (ISBN 0-8290-1499-3). Irvington.
Drummond, Andrew L. The Churches in English Fiction. 1950. 30.00 (ISBN 0-8495-6277-5). Arden Lib.
Drummond, Audrey. Honor Thy Womanself. 1982. pap. 7.50 (ISBN 0-933840-12-8). Unitarian Univ.
Drummond, Henry. Greatest Thing in the World. 1959. 3.95 (ISBN 0-399-12828-X, G&D). Putnam Pub Group.
--Greatest Thing in the World. 64p. 1968. pap. 2.50 (ISBN 0-8007-8018-3, Spire Bks). Revell.
--The Greatest Thing in the World. 64p. 1981. pap. 2.95 (ISBN 0-88368-100-5). Whitaker Hse.
--Natural Law in the Spiritual World. 371p. 1981. pap. 20.00 (ISBN 0-89540-082-0, SB-082). Sun Pub.
--Peace Be with You. (Illus.). 1978. 4.95 (ISBN 0-915720-44-2). Brownlow Pub Co.
Drummond, James. Via, Veritas, Vita: Lectures on "Christianity in Its Most Simple & Intelligible Form". 2nd ed. LC 77-27160. (Hibbert Lectures: 1894). Repr. of 1895 ed. 31.50 (ISBN 0-404-60412-9). AMS Pr.
Drummond, Lewis. Leading Your Church in Evangelism. LC 75-30135. 168p. 1976. pap. 5.50 (ISBN 0-8054-6210-4). Broadman.
--The Life & Ministry of Charles Finney. 272p. 1985. pap. 5.95 (ISBN 0-87123-818-7, 210818). Bethany Hse.
Drummond, Lewis A. The Awakening That Must Come. LC 78-59239. 1979. pap. 4.50 (ISBN 0-8054-6535-9). Broadman.
--The Revived Life. LC 82-71217. 1982. pap. 6.50 (ISBN 0-8054-5205-2). Broadman.
Drummond, Richard H. Toward a New Age in Christian Theology. LC 85-5155. 272p. 1985. pap. 12.95 (ISBN 0-88344-514-X). Orbis Bks.
--Unto the Churches: Jesus Christ, Christianity, & the Edgar Cayce Readings. 1978. pap. 7.95 (ISBN 0-87604-102-0). ARE Pr.
Drummond, William. Flowres of Sion: To Which Is Adjoyned His Cypresse Grove. LC 73-6124. (English Experience Ser.: No. 590). 80p. 1973. Repr. of 1623 ed. 8.00 (ISBN 90-221-0590-3). Walter J Johnson.
Drumwright, Huber L. An Introduction to New Testament Greek. 2nd ed. LC 78-59982. 1980. 11.95 (ISBN 0-8054-1368-5). Broadman.
Drumwright, Huber L. & Vaughan, Curtis, eds. New Testament Studies: Essays in Honor of Ray Summers in His Sixty-fifth Year. LC 75-29815. 195p. 1975. 7.95 (ISBN 0-918954-15-0). Baylor Univ Pr.
Drury, Clifford M. Marcus & Narcissa Whitman & the Opening of Old Oregon. (Illus.). 911p. 1986. pap. 21.84 (ISBN 0-914019-08-2). Pacif NW Natl Pks.
Drury, John. Parables in Gospels. LC 84-27652. 192p. 1985. 14.95 (ISBN 0-8245-0655-3). Crossroad NY.
Drury, John, ed. & tr. see Bellini, Enzo, et al.
Drury, John, ed. & tr. see Bellini, Enzo.
Drury, John, ed. & tr. see Bellini, Enzo, et al.
Drury, John, tr. see Alves, Rubem.
Drury, John, tr. see Biffi, Inos.
Drury, John, tr. see Boff, Leonardo.
Drury, John, tr. see Camps, Arnulf.
Drury, John, tr. see Cosmao, Vincent.
Drury, John, tr. see Cussianovich, Alejandro.
Drury, John, tr. see De Azevedo, Marcello C.
Drury, John, tr. see Fierro, Alfredo.
Drury, John, tr. see Gibellini, Rosino.
Drury, John, tr. see Miranda, Jose P.
Drury, John, tr. see Motte, Gonzague.
Drury, John, tr. see Perez-Esclarin, Antonio.
Drury, John, tr. see Segundo, Jean L.
Drury, John, tr. see Segundo, Juan L.
Drury, John, tr. see Sobrino, Jon.
Drury, John, tr. see Stella, Pietro.
Drury, John, tr. see Torres, Sergio & Eagleson, John.
Drury, Michael. The Adventure of Spiritual Healing. 304p. 1985. pap. 9.95 large print ed. (ISBN 0-8027-2493-0). Walker & Co.
Drury, Naama. The Sacrificial Ritual in the Satapatha Brahmana. 137p. 1981. text ed. 8.25 (ISBN 0-8426-1759-0). Verry.
Drury, Nevill. Don Juan, Mescalito & Modern Magic: The Mythology of Inner Space. 256p. 1985. pap. 8.95 (ISBN 1-85063-015-1, Ark Paperbks). Methuen Inc.
--Encyclopedia of Mysticism & the Occult. LC 84-48215. (Illus.). 544p. (Orig.). 1985. 24.45 (ISBN 0-06-062093-5, HarpR); pap. 12.95 (ISBN 0-06-062094-3). Har-Row.
Drury, Ronan, ed. New Testament as Personal Reading. 158p. 1983. pap. 7.95 (ISBN 0-87243-122-3). Templegate.
Drysdale. Holiness in the Parables. pap. 2.50 (ISBN 0-686-12879-6). Schmul Pub Co.
Drysdale, A. H., jt. auth. see Cox, S.
D'Souza, Dinesh. The Catholic Classics. LC 86-61500. 168p. (Orig.). 1986. pap. 6.95 (ISBN 0-87973-545-7, 545). Our Sunday Visitor.
Duane, Priebe A., tr. see Ebeling, Gerhard.
Dubash, P. N. Hindoo Art in Its Social Setting. (Illus.). 278p. 1986. Repr. 30.00X (ISBN 0-8364-1752-6, Pub. by Usha). South Asia Bks.
Dubay, Thomas. Authenticity. 4.95 (ISBN 0-87193-143-5). Dimension Bks.
--Dawn of a Consecration. 1964. 4.00 (ISBN 0-8198-0034-1). Dghtrs St Paul.
--Faith & Certitude. LC 84-80910. 266p. (Orig.). 1985. pap. 9.95 (ISBN 0-89870-054-X). Ignatius Pr.
--Happy Are You Poor. 5.95 (ISBN 0-87193-141-9). Dimension Bks.
--What is Religious Life? 5.95 (ISBN 0-87193-116-8). Dimension Bks.
Dube, Pierre H., jt. ed. see Davidson, Hugh M.
Dube, S. N. Cross Currents in Early Buddhism. 1981. 22.50x (ISBN 0-8364-0686-9, Pub. by Manohar India). South Asia Bks.
Dubitsky, Cora M. Building the Faith Community. LC 74-12632. 192p. 1975. pap. 2.95 (ISBN 0-8091-1848-3). Paulist Pr.
Dubnov, Simon. History of the Jews, Vol. 1. 18.00 (ISBN 0-8453-6410-3, Cornwall Bks). Assoc Univ Prs.
--History of the Jews, Vol. 2. 18.00 (ISBN 0-8453-6659-9, Cornwall Bks). Assoc Univ Prs.
--History of the Jews, Vol.3. 18.00 (ISBN 0-8453-6822-2, Cornwall Bks). Assoc Univ Prs.
--History of the Jews, Vol. 4. 18.00 (ISBN 0-8453-7537-7, Cornwall Bks). Assoc Univ Prs.
--History of the Jews, Vol. 5. 18.00 (ISBN 0-8453-7691-8, Cornwall Bks). Assoc Univ Prs.
Dubnow, Semen M. Jewish History: An Essay in the Philosophy of History. LC 72-5481. (Select Bibliographies Reprint Ser.). 1972. Repr. of 1903 ed. 16.00 (ISBN 0-8369-6903-0). Ayer Co Pubs.
Dubois, Aberic. Conversations in Umbria. 1980. 7.95 (ISBN 0-8199-0784-7). Franciscan Herald.
Dubois, J. A. & Beauchamp, Henry K. Hindu Manners, Customs & Ceremonies. 800p. 1986. Repr. 17.50X (ISBN 0-8364-1760-7, Pub. by Manohar India). South Asia Bks.
Dubois, W. E. B. Darkwater: Voices from Within the Veil. LC 70-91785. Repr. of 1920 ed. 12.50 (ISBN 0-404-00151-3). AMS Pr.
--Prayers for Dark People. Aptheker, Herbert, ed. LC 80-12234. 88p. 1980. lib. bdg. 12.00x (ISBN 0-87023-302-5); pap. 6.95 (ISBN 0-87023-303-3). U of Mass Pr.
--The Souls of Black Folk. (Great Illustrated Classics). 1979. 10.95 (ISBN 0-396-07757-9). Dodd.
--Souls of Black Folk. (Classic Ser). (Orig.). 1969. pap. 3.95 (ISBN 0-451-51953-1, CE1820, Sig Classics). NAL.
--Souls of Black Folk. (Illus.). 1970. pap. 1.25 (ISBN 0-671-47833-8). WSP.
Dubos, Rene. A God Within. LC 76-37224. 320p. 1973. pap. 8.95 (ISBN 0-684-13506-X, SL 458, ScribT). Scribner.
DuBose, Francis M. God Who Sends. LC 83-70002. 1983. 10.95 (ISBN 0-8054-6331-3). Broadman.
Dubose, Francis M., ed. Classics of Christian Missions. LC 78-53147. 1979. pap. 12.95 (ISBN 0-8054-6313-5). Broadman.
DuBose, William P. A DuBose Reader. Armentrout, Donald S., ed. LC 84-51878. 256p. 1984. pap. 10.95 (ISBN 0-918769-06-X). Univ South.
--The Ecumenical Councils. 1977. lib. bdg. 59.95 (ISBN 0-8490-1751-3). Gordon Pr.
Dubovy, Andrew. Pilgrims of the Prairie: Pioneer Ukrainian Baptists in North Dakota. Bloch, Marie H., ed. (Illus.). 72p. (Orig.). 1983. lib. bdg. 8.50; pap. 4.50. Ukrainian Cult Inst.
Du Boys, Albert. Catherine of Aragon & the Sources of the English Reformation, 2 vols in 1. Yonge, Charlotte M., ed. 1969. Repr. of 1881 ed. 35.50 (ISBN 0-8337-0931-3). B Franklin.
Dubs, Homer H. Hsuntze, the Moulder of Ancient Confucianism. 339p. Repr. of 1927 ed. text ed. 22.50x (ISBN 0-89644-006-0, Pub. by Chinese Matl Ctr). Coronet Bks.
Duby, Georges. The Age of the Cathedrals: Art & Society, 980-1420. Levieux, Eleanor & Thompson, Barbara, trs. LC 80-22769. (Illus.). vi, 312p. 1981. 26.00x (ISBN 0-226-16769-0); pap. 11.95 (ISBN 0-226-16770-4). U of Chicago Pr.
Ducasse, C. J. Critical Examination of the Belief in a Life after Death. 336p. 1974. pap. 39.50x spiral (ISBN 0-398-03037-5). C C Thomas.
--Nature, Mind & Death. (Paul Carus Lecture Ser.). 533p. 1951. 19.95 (ISBN 0-87548-102-7). Open Court.
Du Castel, Christine. The Morale Proberbes of Christyne. LC 73-25783. (English Experience Ser.: No. 241). 8p. 1970. Repr. of 1478 ed. 14.00 (ISBN 90-221-0241-6). Walter J Johnson.
Ducey, Michael H. Sunday Morning: Aspects of Urban Ritual. LC 76-25342. 1977. 17.00 (ISBN 0-02-907640-4). Free Pr.
Du Charme, Jerome, tr. see Roguet, A. M.
DuCharme, Jerome J. The Reader's Guide to Proclamation: For Sundays & Major Feasts in Cycle A. 160p. 1974. pap. 2.95 (ISBN 0-8199-0577-1). Franciscan Herald.
Duchesne-Guillemin, J. The Western Response to Zoroaster. LC 72-9593. 112p. 1973. Repr. of 1958 ed. lib. bdg. 27.50x (ISBN 0-8371-6590-3, DUWR). Greenwood.
Du Choul, Guillaume. Discours de la Religion des Anciens Romains Illustre. LC 75-27851. (Renaissance & the Gods Ser.: Vol. 9). (Illus.). 1976. Repr. of 1556 ed. lib. bdg. 88.00 (ISBN 0-8240-2058-8). Garland Pub.
Duck, Ruth, jt. auth. see Bausch, Michael.
Duck, Ruth C. Bread for the Journey: Resources for Worship Based on the New Ecumenical Lectionary. LC 81-5046. 96p. 1981. pap. 4.95 (ISBN 0-8298-0423-4). Pilgrim NY.
--Flames of the Spirit. (Orig.). 1985. pap. 6.95 (ISBN 0-8298-0537-0). Pilgrim NY.
Duckert, Mary. Help: I'm a Sunday School Teacher. LC 77-83133. (Illus.). 126p. 1969. pap. 3.95 (ISBN 0-664-24862-4). Westminster.
Duckert, Mary, ed. see Chenoweth, Linda.
Duckert, Mary, ed. see Helm, Janet.
Duckert, Mary J., ed. see Fogle, Jeanne S.
Ducket, Mary Jean, ed. see Fogle, Jeanne S.
Duckett, Eleanor S. Anglo-Saxon Saints & Scholars. x, 484p. 1967. Repr. of 1947 ed. 35.00 (ISBN 0-208-00200-6, Archon). Shoe String.
Duckworth, Henry T. The Church of the Holy Sepulchre. LC 78-63361. (BCL Ser.). (Illus.). Repr. of 1922 ed. 32.00 (ISBN 0-404-17014-5). AMS Pr.
Duckworth, John & Duckworth, Liz. The No-Frills Guide to Youth Group Drama. 64p. 1985. pap. 5.95 (ISBN 0-88207-574-8). Victor Bks.
Duckworth, John, et al. Muhammad & the Arab Empire. Yapp, Malcolm & Killingray, Margaret, eds. (World History Ser.). (Illus.). 1980. lib. bdg. 6.95 (ISBN 0-89908-036-7); pap. text ed. 2.45 (ISBN 0-89908-011-1). Greenhaven.
Duckworth, John, et al, eds. The Battle. (Pacesetter Ser.). 64p. 1987. tchr's. ed. 7.95. Cook.
--The Bible. (Pacesetter Ser.). 64p. 1987. tchr's. ed. 7.95 (ISBN 0-318-21517-9). Cook.
--The Family. (Pacesetter Ser.). 64p. 1987. tchr's. ed. 7.95. Cook.
--Give It Away! (Pacesetter Ser.). 64p. 1987. tchr's. ed. 7.95. Cook.
--Identity Search. (Pacesetter Ser.). 64p. 1987. tchr's. ed. 7.95. Cook.
--Rites of Passage. (Pacesetter Ser.). 64p. 1987. tchr's. ed. 7.95. Cook.
Duckworth, Liz, jt. auth. see Duckworth, John.
Duckworth, Marion. Becoming Complete: Embracing Your Biblical Image. LC 85-10465. 1985. pap. 5.95 (ISBN 0-88070-099-8). Multnomah.
--The Strong Place. 1983. pap. 4.95 (ISBN 0-8423-6663-6). Tyndale.
Duckworth, Rita L. see Lucy, Reda, pseud.
Duckworth, Robin. This Is the Word of the Lord: Year B., the Year of the Mark. 1981. pap. 9.95 (ISBN 0-19-826662-6). Oxford U Pr.
--This Is the Word of the Lord: Year C. the Year of Luke. (Orig.). 1982. pap. 9.95 (ISBN 0-19-826666-9). Oxford U Pr.
Duckworth, Robin, ed. This Is the Word of the Lord: Year A: The Year of Matthew. 1980. pap. 9.95 (ISBN 0-19-213248-2). Oxford U Pr.

Duclaux, Mary. Portrait of Pascal. 1927. Repr. 25.00 (ISBN 0-8274-3188-0). R West.
Ducote, Darryl, jt. auth. see McKenna, Megan.
Du Creux, Francois. History of Canada, or New France, 2 Vols. Conacher, James B., ed. Robinson, Percy J., tr. LC 69-14507. 1969. Repr. of 1951 ed. Vol. 1. lib. bdg. 26.75x (ISBN 0-8371-5070-1, DUHI); Vol. 2. lib. bdg. 25.75x (ISBN 0-8371-5071-X, DUHJ). Greenwood.
Ducrocq, Marie-Pascale. Therese of Lisieux: A Vocation of Love. LC 81-20512. 77p. (Orig.). 1982. pap. 3.95 (ISBN 0-8189-0431-3). Alba.
Duda, William J. The Last Testament. 1987. 7.95 (ISBN 0-533-07114-3). Vantage.
Duddington, Natalie, tr. see Berdiaev, Nikolai.
Dudley, Carl S. Making the Small Church Effective. LC 78-2221. 1983. pap. 7.95 (ISBN 0-687-23044-6). Abingdon.
--Where Have All Our People Gone? New Choices for Old Churches. LC 79-525. (Illus.). 1979. pap. 6.95 (ISBN 0-8298-0359-9). Pilgrim NY.
Dudley, Carl S., ed. Building Effective Ministry: Theory & Practice in the Local Church. LC 82-48411. 256p. 1983. pap. 8.95 (ISBN 0-06-062102-8, RD-418, HarpR). Har-Row.
Dudley, Cliff. The Hidden Christian. LC 80-80657. 160p. 1980. 7.95 (ISBN 0-89221-074-5). New Leaf.
Dudley, Cliff, jt. auth. see Bakker, Tammy.
Dudley, Cliff, jt. auth. see Curtis, Helene.
Dudley, Cliff, jt. auth. see Custodio, Sidney.
Dudley, Cliff, jt. auth. see Hill, Elsie Isensce.
Dudley, Cliff, jt. auth. see Kilpatrick, Paula.
Dudley, Cliff, jt. auth. see Steer, John L.
Dudley, Cliff, jt. auth. see Tari, Mel.
Dudley, Gwenyth, et al. Human Sexuality. (Illus.). 55p. (Orig.). 1984. pap. 5.95 (ISBN 0-85819-465-1, Pub. by JBCE). ANZ Religious Pubns.
Dudley, Roger L. Passing on the Torch. Woolsey, Raymond H., ed. 192p. 1986. 12.95 (ISBN 0-8280-0348-3). Review & Herald.
--The World Love It or Leave It. (Anchor Ser.). 80p. (Orig.). 1987. pap. 5.95 (ISBN 0-8163-0665-6). Pacific Pr Pub Assn.
Dudley, Roger L. & Cummings, Des, Jr. Adventures in Church Growth. Wheeler, Gerald, ed. LC 83-16089. (Illus.). 160p. (Orig.). 1983. pap. 8.95 (ISBN 0-8280-0228-2). Review & Herald.
Dudley-Smith, Timothy. Someone Who Beckons. LC 78-18548. 1978. pap. 3.95 (ISBN 0-87784-731-2). Inter-Varsity.
Dudon, Paul. St. Ignatius of Loyola. Young, William J., tr. LC 83-45591. Date not set. Repr. of 1949 ed. 49.50 (ISBN 0-404-19884-8). AMS Pr.
Dueck, A. J., et al, eds. see Toews, John A.
Dueland, Joy. The Blessings of Jesus. (Illus.). 1979. 8.95 (ISBN 0-931942-02-0). Phunn Pubs.
--What Is Christmas? (Illus.). 9p. 1978. pap. 1.50. Phunn Pubs.
Duerlinger, James P., ed. Ultimate Reality & Spiritual Discipline. (God Ser.). 240p. (Orig.). 1984. text ed. 21.95 (ISBN 0-913757-09-8, Pub. by New Era Bks); pap. text ed. 12.95 (ISBN 0-913757-08-X, Pub. by New Era Bks). Paragon Hse.
Dueuker, R. Sheldon. Tensions in the Connection. 128p. 1983. pap. 4.95 (ISBN 0-687-41243-9). Abingdon.
Duewel, Wesley L. Touch the World Through Prayer. 240p. 1986. pap. 3.95 (ISBN 0-310-36271-7, 17093P). Zondervan.
Dufau, Micheline, tr. see Quinn, Esther C.
Duff, Clarence W. God's Higher Ways. 1978. pap. 7.50 (ISBN 0-87552-257-2). Presby & Reformed.
Duff, E. Gordon, ed. Information for Pilgrims Unto the Holy Land. LC 78-63464. Repr. of 1893 ed. 16.50 (ISBN 0-404-16536-2). AMS Pr.
Duff, Frank. Miracles on Tap. 5.00 (ISBN 0-910984-14-X); pap. 3.50 (ISBN 0-910984-15-8). Montfort Pubns.
Duff, Robert A. Spinoza's Political & Ethical Philosophy. LC 71-108858. 1920. Repr. of 1903 ed. lib. bdg. 37.50x (ISBN 0-678-00615-6). Kelley.
--Spinoza's Political & Ethical Philosophy. 1973. Repr. of 1903 ed. 14.00 (ISBN 0-8274-1391-2). R West.
Duffer, H. F., Jr., tr. see Maston, T. B.
Duffield, Guy P. Handbook of Bible Lands. 192p. 1985. pap. 7.95 (ISBN 0-8010-2948-1). Baker Bk.
Duffield, Samuel W. English Hymns: Their Authors & History. 1980. Repr. of 1886 ed. lib. bdg. 60.00 (ISBN 0-89341-441-7). Longwood Pub Group.
--The Latin Hymn-Writers & Their Hymns. 1980. Repr. of 1889 ed. lib. bdg. 50.00 (ISBN 0-89341-440-9). Longwood Pub Group.
Duffy, John. Under the Goldwood Tree. 64p. 1982. 5.00 (ISBN 0-682-49869-6). Exposition Pr FL.
Duffy, John, ed. Synodicon Vetus. Parker, John. LC 79-52935. (Dumbarton Oaks Texts: Vol. 5). 209p. 1979. 35.00x (ISBN 0-88402-088-6). Dumbarton Oaks.
Duffy, Regis. Real Presence: Worship, Sacraments, & Commitment. LC 81-47877. 192p. 1982. pap. 8.95 (ISBN 0-06-062105-2, RD 383, HarpR). Har-Row.
Duffy, Regis, et al. Initiation & Conversion. Johnson, Lawrence, ed. 96p. 1985. pap. 4.95 (ISBN 0-8146-1431-0). Liturgical Pr.
Duffy, Regis A. On Becoming a Catholic: The Challenge of Christian Initiation. LC 84-47721. 176p. (Orig.). 1984. pap. 7.95 (ISBN 0-06-062106-0, RD 525, HarpR). Har-Row.
--A Roman Catholic Theology of Pastoral Care. LC 83-48006. (Theology & Pastoral Care Ser.). 128p. 1983. pap. 7.95 (ISBN 0-8006-1727-4, 1-1727). Fortress.
Dufour, Leon. Vocabulario de Teologila Biblica. 9th ed. (Span.). 976p. 1977. 35.95 (ISBN 84-254-0809-1, S-50205); pap. 29.95 (ISBN 84-254-0808-3, S-50204). French & Eur.
Dufresne, Ed. Faithfulness. 57p. 1981. pap. 0.75 (ISBN 0-89274-378-6). Harrison Hse.
--Praying God's Word. 96p. (Orig.). 1983. pap. 2.75 (ISBN 0-89274-276-3). Harrison Hse.
Dugan, Albert. The Masses Are Asses. 256p. (Orig.). 1987. pap. 9.95 (ISBN 0-89896-047-9). Larksdale.
Dugan, Dick. How To Know You'll Live Forever. LC 84-70727. 176p. 1984. pap. 3.95 (ISBN 0-87123-312-6, 200312). Bethany Hse.
Dugan, LeRoy. Help Yourself to a Healthier Mind. 112p. (Orig.). 1980. 5.95 (ISBN 0-87123-205-7, 210205). Bethany Hse.
--Heroes of the Old Testament. 96p. (Orig.). 1981. No. 1. pap. 1.95 oversized, saddle stitched (ISBN 0-87123-704-0, 220704); No. 2. pap. 2.95 (ISBN 0-87123-705-9, 220705). Bethany Hse.
--The Uncomplicated Christian. LC 78-66886. 128p. 1978. pap. 2.50 (ISBN 0-87123-572-2, 200572). Bethany Hse.
Dugan, LeRoy, illus. Heroes of the New Testament Coloring Book. (Illus.). 96p. (Orig.). 1981. saddle-stitched 2.95 (ISBN 0-87123-701-6). Bethany Hse.
--Heroes of the Old Testament, No. 3. (Illus.). 96p. (Orig.). 1981. pap. 2.95 saddle stitched (ISBN 0-87123-703-2). Bethany Hse.
Dugan, Richard L. Building Christian Commitment. (Trinity Bible Ser.). 107p. (Orig.). 1982. wkbk. 3.95 (ISBN 0-87123-280-4, 240280). Bethany Hse.
Dugard, Marie. Ralph Waldo Emerson: Sa Vie et Son Oeuvre. LC 76-100530. (Illus.). Repr. of 1907 ed. 37.50 (ISBN 0-404-02215-4). AMS Pr.
--Ralph Waldo Emerson: Sa Vie et Son Oeuvre. 1973. 16.45 (ISBN 0-8274-0066-7). R West.
Duggan, Anne. Thomas Becket: A Textual History of His Letters. 1980. 56.00x (ISBN 0-19-822486-9). Oxford U Pr.
Duggan, Robert, ed. Conversion & the Catechumenate. 1984. pap. 7.95 (ISBN 0-8091-2614-1). Paulist Pr.
Duggar, Gordon E. Jehovah's Witness: Not Just Another Denomination. (Illus.). 144p. 1982. 8.00 (ISBN 0-682-49874-2). Exposition Pr FL.
--Jehovah's Witnesses: Watchout for the Watchtower! 144p. 1985. pap. 5.95 (ISBN 0-8010-2955-4). Baker Bk.
Duggar, John W. Girl with a Missionary Heart. (Illus.). 104p. 1975. pap. 1.95 (ISBN 0-89114-074-3). Baptist Pub Hse.
Duhem, Pierre. Medieval Cosmology: Theories of Infinity, Place, Time, Void, & the Plurality of Worlds. Ariew, Roger, ed. LC 85-8115. 642p. 1986. lib. bdg. 35.00x (ISBN 0-226-16922-7). U of Chicago Pr.
Dujarier, Michel. A History of the Catechumenate. 144p. 1982. pap. 5.95 (ISBN 0-8215-9327-7). Sadlier.
--The Rites of Christian Initiation. 244p. 1982. pap. 5.95 (ISBN 0-8215-9328-5). Sadlier.
Duke, David N. The Biblical View of Reality: The Bible & Christian Ethics. ii, 59p. 1985. pap. text ed. 6.95x (ISBN 0-932269-05-2). Wyndham Hall.
Duke, James, tr. see Schleiermacher, Friedrich.
Duke, James A. Medicinal Plants of the Bible. (Traditional Healing Ser.: No. 10). (Illus.). 300p. 1983. lib. bdg. 49.95 (ISBN 0-932426-23-9). Trado-Medic.
Duke, James O. Horace Bushnell: On the Vitality of Biblical Language. LC 83-16312. (SBL-Biblical Schlolarship in North America). 138p. 1984. pap. 13.50 (ISBN 0-89130-650-1, 06 11 09). Scholars Pr GA.
Duke, Paul D. Irony in the Fourth Gospel. LC 85-42822. 228p. 1985. pap. 11.95 (ISBN 0-8042-0242-7). John Knox.
Duke, Robert W. The Sermon As God's Word: Theologies for Preaching. LC 80-18094. (Abingdon Preacher's Library). 128p. (Orig.). 1980. pap. 6.95 (ISBN 0-687-37520-7). Abingdon.
Dukes, H. N. The Bible: Fact, Fiction, Fantasy, Faith. 178p. (Orig.). 1987. pap. 8.00 (ISBN 0-682-40337-7). Exposition Pr Fl.
Dukore, Bernard F., ed. see Shaw, Bernard.
Dulack, Tom, jt. auth. see Patrick, Ted.
Dulaure, Jacques-Antoine. The Gods of Generation. LC 72-9635. Tr. of De Divinites Generatrices. Repr. of 1934 ed. 42.00 (ISBN 0-404-57433-5). AMS Pr.
Duling, Dennis C. Jesus Christ Through History. 324p. 1979. pap. text ed. 13.95 (ISBN 0-15-547370-0, HC). HarBraceJ.
Duling, Dennis C., jt. auth. see Perrin, Norman.
Dull, Elaine & Sekowsky, Jo Anne. Teach Us to Pray. (Aglow Bible Study Book Enrichment). 64p. 1980. pap. 2.95 (ISBN 0-930756-49-5, 522002). Aglow Pubns.
Dulles, Avery. Apologetics & the Biblical Christ. LC 63-22027. 88p. (Orig.). 1963. pap. 4.95 (ISBN 0-8091-1505-0). Paulist Pr.
--The Catholicity of the Church & the Structure of Catholicism. 210p. 1985. 22.50 (ISBN 0-19-826676-6). Oxford U Pr.
--A Church to Believe In: Discipleship & the Dynamics of Freedom. LC 81-17520. 208p. 1983. pap. 8.95 (ISBN 0-8245-0593-X). Crossroad NY.
--Models of Revelation. LC 82-45243. 360p. 1983. 16.95 (ISBN 0-385-17975-8). Doubleday.
--Models of Revelation. LC 82-45243. 360p. 1985. pap. 8.95 (ISBN 0-385-23235-7, Im). Doubleday.
--Models of the Church. LC 77-11246. 1987. pap. 4.95 (ISBN 0-385-13368-5, Im). Doubleday.
--The Survival of Dogma: Faith, Authority & Dogma in a Changing World. (Crossroad Paperback Ser.). 240p. 1982. pap. 7.95 (ISBN 0-8245-0427-5). Crossroad NY.
Dulles, Avery & Granfield, Patrick. The Church: A Bibliography. (Theology & Biblical Resources Ser: Vol. 1). 1985. 15.00 (ISBN 0-89453-449-1); pap. 8.95 (ISBN 0-89453-470-X). M Glazier.
Dulong, Marthe, jt. auth. see Moore, Philip S.
Dumas, Edith B. The Least of These. 128p. 1982. 7.95 (ISBN 0-89962-261-5). Todd & Honeywell.
Dumbrell, W. J. Covenant & Creation: A Theology of Old Testament Covenants. 220p. 1986. pap. 8.95 (ISBN 0-8407-3053-5). Nelson.
Dumery, Henry. Phenomenology & Religion: Structures of the Christian Institution. Barrett, Paul, tr. LC 73-94443. (Hermeneutics Series: Studies in the History of Religion). 1975. 27.50x (ISBN 0-520-02714-0). U of Cal Pr.
--The Problem of God in Philosophy of Religion: A Critical Examination of the Category of the Absolute & the Scheme of Transcendence. Courtney, Charles, tr. (Studies in Phenomenology & Existential Philosophy). 135p. 1964. 14.95 (ISBN 0-8101-0083-5); pap. 8.95 (ISBN 0-8101-0606-X). Northwestern U Pr.
Dumezil, Georges. Archaic Roman Religion, 2 Vols. Krapp, Philip, tr. from Fr. LC 76-116981. 1971. Set. 45.00x (ISBN 0-226-16968-5). U of Chicago Pr.
--Camillus: A Study of Indo-European Religion As Roman History. Strutynski, Udo, ed. Aronowicz, Annette, et al, trs. from Fr. LC 80-36771. 250p. 1980. 24.00x (ISBN 0-520-02841-4). U of Cal Pr.
--Deesses Latines et Mythes Vediques. Bolle, Kees W., ed. LC 77-79121. (Mythology Ser.). (Fr.). 1978. Repr. of 1956 ed. lib. bdg. 17.00x (ISBN 0-405-10533-9). Ayer Co Pubs.
--Destiny of a King. Hiltebeitel, Alf, tr. 1973. 15.00x (ISBN 0-226-16975-8). U of Chicago Pr.
--The Destiny of the Warrior. Hiltebeitel, Alf, tr. LC 75-113254. 184p. 1971. pap. write for info. (ISBN 0-226-16971-5). U of Chicago Pr.
--Gods of the Ancient Northmen. Haugen, Einar, ed. & tr. (Center for the Study of Comparative Folklore & Mythology, UCLA Ser.: No. 3). 1974. 34.00x (ISBN 0-520-02044-8); pap. 8.95 (ISBN 0-520-03507-0, CAL 371). U of Cal Pr.
--Horace et les Curiaces. Bolle, Kees W., ed. (Mythology Ser.). (Fr.). 1978. Repr. of 1942 ed. lib. bdg. 17.00x (ISBN 0-405-10534-7). Ayer Co Pubs.
Dumia, Mariano A. The Ifugao World. Edades, Jean, ed. (Illus.). 1979. pap. 6.00x (ISBN 0-686-24953-4, Pub. by New Day Pub). Cellar.
Dumitriu, Petru. To the Unknown God. Kirkup, James, tr. from Fr. LC 82-5722. 256p. 1982. pap. 11.95 (ISBN 0-8164-2424-1, HarpR). Har-Row.
Dumke, Edward J. The Serpent Beguiled Me & I Ate: A Heavenly Diet for Saints & Sinners. LC 86-4445. (Illus.). 1986. pap. 8.95 (ISBN 0-385-23671-9). Doubleday.
Dummelow, John R. Commentary on the Holy Bible. 1909. 19.95 (ISBN 0-02-533770-X). Macmillan.
Dumont, L. On Value. (Radcliffe-Brown Lectures on Social Anthropology). 1980. pap. 4.00 (ISBN 0-85672-239-1, Pub. by British Acad). Longwood Pub Group.
Dumont, Louis. Une Sous-Caste de L'Inde du Sud: Organisation Sociale et Religion des Pramalai Kallar. (Le Monde D'outre Mer Passe et Present Etudes: No. 1). (Fr.). 1957. pap. text ed. 21.60x (ISBN 0-686-22530-9). Mouton.
Dumont, Theron. Art & Science of Personal Magnetism. 8.00 (ISBN 0-911662-38-3). Yoga.
Dumoulin, Heinrich. Christianity Meets Buddhism. Maraldo, John C., tr. from Ger. LC 73-82783. 212p. 1974. 19.95 (ISBN 0-87548-121-3). Open Court.
--Zen Enlightenment: Origins & Meaning. LC 78-27310. 188p. 1979. pap. 7.95 (ISBN 0-8348-0141-8). Weatherhill.
Dunaway, Patricia. Beyond the Distant Shadows. 208p. (Orig.). 1984. pap. 4.95 (ISBN 0-87123-446-7). Bethany Hse.
Dunbar, Newell. Phillip Brooks: The Man, the Preacher, & the Author. 1978. Repr. of 1893 ed. lib. bdg. 35.00 (ISBN 0-8492-0668-5). R West.
Duncan, Alistair. The Noble Heritage: Jerusalem & Christianity - a Portrait of the Church of the Resurrection. 1974. 12.95x (ISBN 0-86685-011-2). Intl Bk Ctr.
Duncan, Anthony. Jesus: Essential Readings. (Crucible Ser.). 176p. 1987. pap. 9.95 (ISBN 0-85030-395-8). Thorsons Pubs.
Duncan, David D. The World of Allah. 1982. 40.00 (ISBN 0-395-32504-8). HM.
Duncan, Denis. The Way of Love: A Thought & a Prayer a Day at a Time. LC 81-15925. 96p. 1982. Westminster.
Duncan, Elmer H. Soren Kierkegaard. Patterson, Bob E., ed. LC 76-2862. (Markers of the Modern Theological Mind Ser.). 1976. 8.95 (ISBN 0-87680-463-6, 80463). Word Bks.
Duncan, George. Every Day with Jesus. 288p. 1984. pap. 6.95 (ISBN 0-89066-059-X). World Wide Pubs.
Duncan, George B. Preacher among the Prophets. 176p. 1985. pap. 5.95 (ISBN 0-930577-00-0). N Burleson.
Duncan, Judith A., illus. The Sermon on the Mount: From the Translation Prepared at Cambridge in 1611 for King James I. LC 81-211201. (Illus.). 1978. 15.00 (ISBN 0-9606844-0-9). Mac Col MN.
Duncan, M. C. Masonic Ritual. rev. ed. 12.50x (ISBN 0-685-22033-8). Wehman.
Duncan, Malcolm. Masonic Ritual & Monitor, 2 Pts. 1946. 8.50 ea.; 1 vol. ed. 12.50 (ISBN 0-685-19489-2). Powner.
Duncan, Malcolm C. Duncan's Masonic Ritual & Monitor. new ed. 288p. 1976. 10.95 (ISBN 0-679-50979-8); pap. 5.95. McKay.
Duncan, Paul. Who Is Sun Myung Moon? 21p. (Orig.). 1981. pap. text ed. 1.25 (ISBN 0-87148-914-7). Pathway Pr.
Duncan, R. S. A History of the Baptists in Missouri. 1981. Repr. of 1882 ed. 38.00 (ISBN 0-686-77695-X). Church History.
Duncan, Tannis. Reaching for Excellence. 67p. (Orig.). 1982. pap. text ed. 2.50 (ISBN 0-87148-737-3). Pathway Pr.
Duncan-Jones, Arthur S. The Struggle for Religious Freedom in Germany. LC 78-63664. (Studies in Fascism: Ideology & Practice). Repr. of 1938 ed. 34.00 (ISBN 0-404-16927-9). AMS Pr.
Duncombe, Alice E. Handbook for Telephone Ministry. Rev. ed. 7.95 (ISBN 0-89985-110-X). Christ Nations.
Dundes, Alan, ed. Sacred Narrative: Reading in the Theory of Myth. LC 83-17921. (Illus.). ix, 352p. 1984. 42.00x (ISBN 0-520-05156-4); pap. 11.95x (ISBN 0-520-05192-0, CAL 362). U of Cal Pr.
Dundes, Alan, jt. ed. see Hasan-Rokem, Galit.
Dundes, Alan, ed. see Samuelson, Sue.
Dungan, David L., jt. auth. see Cartlidge, David R.
Dunham, Craig R. Women Ministers?! Women in Paul & Adventchristendom. 98p. (Orig.). 1986. pap. 4.95 (ISBN 0-913439-04-5). Henceforth.
Dunham, James H. Religion of Philosophers. facs. ed. LC 78-80386. (Essay Index Reprint Ser). 1947. 21.50 (ISBN 0-8369-1059-1). Ayer Co Pubs.
Dunham, Lowell, tr. see Caso, Alfonso.
Dunigan, Jack. How to Prepare Sermons. 1986. pap. 3.95 (ISBN 0-932943-02-0). Life Lines.
--The Pastor's Handbook. (Orig.). 1985. pap. 6.95 (ISBN 0-932943-00-4). Life Lines.
Dunker, Marilee P. Days of Glory, Seasons of Night. rev. ed. 176p. 1984. pap. text ed. 6.95 (ISBN 0-310-45501-4, 12040P). Zondervan.
Dunkin, Steve. Church Advertising: A Practical Guide. LC 81-17562. (Creative Leadership Ser.). 128p. (Orig.). 1982. pap. 6.95 (ISBN 0-687-08140-8). Abingdon.
Dunlap, Knight. Mysticism, Freudianism & Scientific Psychology. facsimile ed. (Select Bibliographies Reprint Ser). Repr. of 1920 ed. 17.00 (ISBN 0-8369-5838-1). Ayer Co Pubs.

Dunlap, Shirlee. Circle of Light. (Illus.). 183p. (Orig.). 1982. pap. 7.95 (ISBN 0-942494-19-9). Coleman Pub.

Dunlavy, John. Manifesto, or a Declaration of the Doctrines & Practice of the Church of Christ. LC 74-134416. Repr. of 1818 ed. 34.50 (ISBN 0-404-08460-5). AMS Pr.

Dunlop, Ian. The Cathedrals' Crusade. LC 81-14431. (Illus.). 256p. 1982. 20.00 (ISBN 0-8008-1316-2). Taplinger.

Dunlop, Laurence. Patterns of Prayer in the Psalms. 160p. (Orig.). 1982. pap. 9.95 (ISBN 0-8164-2377-6, HarpR). Har-Row.

Dunn, Charles W. American Political Theology: Historical Perspective & Theoretical Analysis. LC 84-13308. 208p. 1984. 31.95 (ISBN 0-03-071843-0); pap. 13.95 (ISBN 0-03-071844-9, B1603). Praeger.

Dunn, Charles W., Sr. How to Be Happy in an Unhappy World. 141p. (Orig.). 1986. pap. 6.95 (ISBN 0-89084-318-X). Bob Jones Univ Pr.

Dunn, Dennis J. The Catholic Church & the Soviet Government. (East European Monographs: No. 30). 267p. 1977. 25.00x (ISBN 0-914710-23-0). East Eur Quarterly.

Dunn, Dennis J., ed. Religion & Communist Society: Selected Papers from the Second World Congress for Soviet & East European Studies. 165p. (Orig.). 1983. pap. 14.00 (ISBN 0-933884-29-X). Berkeley Slavic.

Dunn, Frank E. The Ministering Teacher. 112p. 1982. pap. 4.95 (ISBN 0-8170-0958-2). Judson.

Dunn, Frank G. Building Faith in Families: Using the Sacraments in Pastoral Ministry. 160p. (Orig.). 1987. pap. 8.95 (ISBN 0-8192-1394-2). Morehouse.

Dunn, Frederick S. War & the Minds of Men. LC 79-131371. xvi, 115p. 1971. Repr. of 1950 ed. 15.00 (ISBN 0-208-00945-0, Archon). Shoe String.

Dunn, James D. Baptism in the Holy Spirit: A Re-Examination of the New Testament Teaching on the Gift of the Spirit in Relation to Pentacostalism Today. LC 77-3995. 256p. 1977. pap. 8.95 (ISBN 0-664-24140-9). Westminster.

--Christology in the Making: A New Testament Inquiry into the Origins of the Doctrine of the Incarnation. LC 80-16968. 462p. 1980. pap. 24.50 (ISBN 0-664-24356-8). Westminster.

--The Evidence for Jesus. LC 85-22540. 128p. (Orig.). 1986. pap. 8.95 (ISBN 0-664-24698-2). Westminster.

--Jesus & the Spirit: A Study of the Religious & Charismatic Experience of Jesus & the First Christians as Reflected in the New Testament. LC 75-9802. 528p. 1979. pap. 15.95 (ISBN 0-664-24290-1). Westminster.

--Unity & Diversity in the New Testament: An Inquiry into the Character of Earliest Christianity. LC 77-22598. 488p. 1984. pap. 14.95 (ISBN 0-664-24525-0). Westminster.

Dunn, Jean, ed. see Nisargadatta Maharaj.

Dunn, Jerry G. God Is for the Alcoholic. Tr. of Deus e a Favor do Alcoolatra. 1986. write for info. (ISBN 0-8297-1610-6). Life Pubs Intl.

Dunn, Jerry G. & Palmer, Bernard. God Is for the Alcoholic. rev. ed. pap. 6.95 (ISBN 0-8024-3284-0). Moody.

Dunn, Joseph, jt. auth. see Wilkins, Skip.

Dunn, Richard S. Age of Religious Wars, Fifteen Fifty-Nine to Seventeen Fifteen. 2nd ed. (Illus.). 1979. pap. text ed. 7.95x (ISBN 0-393-09021-3). Norton.

Dunn, Richard S., jt. ed. see Soderlund, Jean R.

Dunn, Robert. The Possibility of Weakness of Will. LC 85-24784. 192p. 1986. lib. bdg. 25.00 (ISBN 0-915145-99-5); pap. 14.50 (ISBN 0-915145-98-7). Hackett Pub.

Dunn, Ronald. The Faith Crisis. Chao, Lorna Y., tr. (Chinese.). 1985. pap. write for info. (ISBN 0-941598-30-6). Living Spring Pubns.

Dunn, Samuel, compiled by see Calvin, John.

Dunn, Sharon, ed. The Agni Review. 1985. 4.00. Agni Review.

Dunn, Stephen P., ed. see Klibanov, A. I.

Dunnam, Maxie. Exodus: (CC, Vol. 2. 320p. 1987. 18.95 (ISBN 0-8499-0407-2). Word Bks.

--Jesus' Claims-Our Promise: A Study of the "I Am" Sayings of Jesus. LC 84-51831. 128p. (Orig.). 1984. pap. 5.95 (ISBN 0-8358-0502-6). Upper Room.

--The Sanctuary for Lent, 1985. 48p. (Orig.). 1985. pap. 30.00 per 100 (ISBN 0-687-36847-2). Abingdon.

--The Workbook on Becoming Alive in Christ. 160p. (Orig.). 1986. pap. 5.50 (ISBN 0-8358-0542-5). Upper Room.

--Workbook on Spiritual Disciplines. LC 83-51402. 160p. 1984. wkbk. 4.50 (ISBN 0-8358-0479-8). Upper Room.

Dunnam, Maxie D. Alive in Christ: The Dynamic Process of Spiritual Formation. LC 81-20631. 160p. 1982. 8.75 (ISBN 0-687-00993-6). Abingdon.

--The Christian Way. 112p. 1987. pap. 4.95 (ISBN 0-310-20741-X). Zondervan.

--Workbook of Intercessory Prayer. LC 78-65617. 1979. pap. 4.50x (ISBN 0-8358-0382-1). Upper Room.

--The Workbook of Living Prayer. 1975. 4.50x (ISBN 0-8358-0323-6). Upper Room.

Dunne, Carrin. Buddha & Jesus: Conversations. 1975. pap. 4.95 (ISBN 0-87243-057-X). Templegate.

Dunne, George H. Generation of Giants. 1962. 19.95 (ISBN 0-268-00109-X). U of Notre Dame Pr.

Dunne, John. The House of Wisdom. LC 84-48767. 224p. 1985. 15.45 (ISBN 0-317-18550-0, HarpR). Har-Row.

--How God Created. pap. 2.00 (ISBN 0-268-00120-0). U of Notre Dame Pr.

Dunne, John S. The Church of the Poor Devil: Reflections on a Riverboat Voyage & a Spiritual Journey. LC 83-14548. 1983. pap. text ed. 6.95 (ISBN 0-268-00746-2, 85-07469). U of Notre Dame Pr.

--The City of the Gods: A Study in Myth & Mortality. LC 78-2588. 1978. Repr. of 1965 ed. text ed. 7.95 (ISBN 0-268-00725-X). U of Notre Dame Pr.

--The Reasons of the Heart: A Journey into Solitude & Back Again into the Human Circle. 1979. pap. 5.95 (ISBN 0-268-01606-2). U of Notre Dame Pr.

--A Search for God in Time & Memory. LC 76-20165. 1977. text ed. 15.95x (ISBN 0-268-01689-5); pap. 6.95 (ISBN 0-268-01673-9). U of Notre Dame Pr.

--Time & Myth. LC 74-32289. 128p. 1975. pap. 4.95 (ISBN 0-268-01828-6). U of Notre Dame Pr.

--The Way of All the Earth: Experiments in Truth & Religion. LC 78-1575. 1978. text ed. 19.95x (ISBN 0-268-01927-4); pap. 7.95 (ISBN 0-268-01928-2). U of Notre Dame Pr.

Dunne, Tad. We Cannot Find Words. casebound 8.95 (ISBN 0-87193-138-9). Dimension Bks.

Dunne, Thomas A. Do This in Memory of Me. LC 81-67927. (Illus.). 237p. (Orig.). 1981. pap. text ed. 4.95x (ISBN 0-89944-056-8); tchr's manual 2.95x (ISBN 0-89944-057-6). Don Bosco Multimedia.

Dunne, William P. Is It a Saint's Name? 1977. pap. 1.25 (ISBN 0-89555-024-5). TAN Bks Pubs.

Dunner, Peter M. Pioneer Jesuits in Northern Mexico. LC 78-10566. (Illus.). 1979. Repr. of 1944 ed. lib. bdg. 24.75x (ISBN 0-313-20653-8, DUPJ). Greenwood.

Dunnett, W. M. Sintesis del Nuevo Testamento. Blanch, Jose M., tr. from Eng. (Curso Para Maestros Cristianos: No. 3). (Span.). 128p. 1972. pap. 3.50 (ISBN 0-89922-012-6). Edit Caribe.

Dunnett, Walter. Outline of New Testament Survey. (Orig.). 1960. pap. 5.95 (ISBN 0-8024-6245-6). Moody.

Dunnett, Walter M. The Book of Acts. (Shield Bible Study Ser.). 144p. (Orig.). 1981. pap. 3.95 (ISBN 0-8010-2915-5). Baker Bk.

--New Testament Survey. LC 63-7410. 96p. 1963. pap. text ed. 4.95 (ISBN 0-910566-03-8); Perfect bdg. instr's. guide 5.95 (ISBN 0-910566-19-4). Evang Tchr.

Dunnett, Walter M., rev. by see Tenney, Merrill C.

Dunney, Joseph A. Church History in the Light of the Saints. LC 74-2196. (Essay Index Reprint Ser.). Repr. of 1944 ed. 25.00 (ISBN 0-518-10162-2). Ayer Co Pubs.

Dunnhaupt, Gerhard, ed. The Martin Luther Quincentennial. LC 84-15239. 329p. 1984. 29.95x (ISBN 0-8143-1774-X). Wayne St U Pr.

Dunning, H. Ray. Fruit of the Spirit. 38p. 1982. pap. 1.95 (ISBN 0-8341-0806-2). Beacon Hill.

Dunning, H. Ray, jt. auth. see Greathouse, William.

Dunning, James B. Ministries: Sharing God's Gifts. LC 80-52058. (Illus.). 136p. (Orig.). 1980. pap. 5.95 (ISBN 0-88489-123-2). St Marys.

--New Wine: New Wineskins. 128p. (Orig.). 1981. pap. 5.95 (ISBN 0-8215-9807-4). Sadlier.

Dunning, Stephen N. The Tongues of Men: Hegel & Hamann on Religious Language & History. LC 79-10729. (American Academy of Religion, Dissertation Ser.: No. 27). 1979. 14.00 (ISBN 0-89130-283-2, 010127); pap. 9.95 (ISBN 0-89130-302-2). Scholars Pr GA.

Dunstan, Alan. Interpreting Worship. 102p. 1985. pap. 5.95 (ISBN 0-8192-1357-8). Morehouse.

Dunstan, G. R., ed. see Kirk, Kenneth E.

Dunstan, J. Leslie, ed. Protestantism. LC 61-15497. (Great Religions of Modern Man Ser). 1961. 8.95 (ISBN 0-8076-0161-6). Braziller.

Dunville, D. N., ed. see Brooke, Christopher.

Dupin, Louis E. Bibliotheque Des Auteurs Ecclesiastiques Du 18e Siecle, 5 vols, Ser. 4. 2100p. Date not set. Repr. of 1736 ed. text ed. 517.50x (ISBN 0-576-72789-X, Pub. by Gregg Intl Pubs England). Gregg Intl.

--Bibliotheque Des Auteurs Separes De la Communion De L'Eglise Romaine Du 16e et 17e Siecles, 5 vols, Ser. III. 1910p. Date not set. Repr. of 1719 ed. text ed. 517.50x (ISBN 0-576-72788-1, Pub. by Gregg Intl Pubs England). Gregg Intl.

--Nouvelle Bibliotheque des Auteurs Ecclesiastiques du Premier au 173 Siecle, 36 vols, Ser. I. 18798p. Date not set. Repr. of 1723 ed. text ed. 3720.00 (ISBN 0-576-72786-5, Pub. by Gregg Intl Pubs England). Gregg Intl.

Dupleix, Joseph F., tr. see Pillai, Ananda R., et al.

DuPlessis, David. A Man Called Mr. Pentecost. LC 76-53322. 1977. pap. 5.95 (ISBN 0-88270-184-3). Bridge Pub.

Du Plessis, David. Simple & Profound. 1986. pap. 7.95 (ISBN 0-941478-51-3). Paraclete Pr.

Du Plou, Dafne C., tr. see Edens, David.

Dupont, Dom P. Sermons Capitulaires de la Chartreuse de Mayence du Debut du XV Siecle. Hogg, James, ed. (Analecta Cartusiana Ser.: No. 46). (Fr.). 193p. (Orig.). 1978. pap. 25.00 (ISBN 3-7052-0062-3, Pub by Salzburg Studies). Longwood Pub Group.

Du Pont, Guigo. Della Contemplazione. Hogg, James, ed. Piovesan, Emilio, tr. & intro. by. (Analecta Cartusiana Ser.: No. 45). (Ital. & Lat.). 123p. (Orig.). 1979. pap. 25.00 (ISBN 3-7052-0061-5, Pub by Salzburg Studies). Longwood Pub Group.

DuPont, Philippe. Guigues Du Pont: Traite Sur la Contemplation, 2 vols. Hogg, James, ed. (Analecta Cartusiana Ser.: No. 72). (Orig.). 1984. pap. 50.00 (ISBN 3-7052-0107-7, Pub. by Salzburg Studies). Longwood Pub Group.

DuPont, Yves. Catholic Prophecy. (Eng.). 1977. pap. 2.50 (ISBN 0-89555-015-6). TAN Bks Pubs.

Dupont-Sommer, A. The Essene Writings from Qumran. Vermes, G., tr. 13.50 (ISBN 0-8446-2012-2). Peter Smith.

Dupre, Louis. The Deeper Life: A Meditation on Christian Mysticism. 128p. (Orig.). 1981. pap. 4.95 (ISBN 0-8245-0007-5). Crossroad NY.

--Transcendent Selfhood: The Loss & Rediscovery of the Inner Life. 1976. 8.95 (ISBN 0-8164-0306-6, HarpR). Har-Row.

Dupre, Wilhelm. Religion in Primitive Cultures: A Study in Ethnophilosophy. (Religion & Reason: No. 9). 366p. 1975. text ed. 39.00x (ISBN 0-686-22610-0). Mouton.

DuPree, Sherry S. & Noble, E. Myron, eds. Bible Lessons for Youth, Bk. I. 40p. (Orig.). 1987. pap. text ed. 2.95 (ISBN 0-9616056-4-2). Mid Atl Reg Pr.

Du Prel, Carl. The Philosophy of Mysticism, 2vols. in 1. Massey, C. C., tr. LC 75-36838. (Occult Ser.). 1976. Repr. of 1889 ed. 51.00x (ISBN 0-405-07951-6). Ayer Co Pubs.

--The Philosophy of Mysticism, 2 vols. 1977. lib. bdg. 250.00 (ISBN 0-8490-2434-X). Gordon Pr.

Dupuis, Charles. The Origin of All Religious Worship. Feldman, Burton & Richardson, Robert D., eds. LC 78-60897. (Myth & Romanticism Ser.). 1984. lib. bdg. 80.00 (ISBN 0-8240-3558-5). Garland Pub.

Dupuis, J., jt. ed. see Neuner, J.

Duquoc, Christian. Opportunities for Belief & Behavior. LC 67-31523. (Concilium Ser: Vol. 29). 186p. 1967. 7.95 (ISBN 0-8091-0106-8). Paulist Pr.

--Secularization & Spirituality. LC 76-103390. (Concilium Ser.: Vol. 49). 187p. 7.95 (ISBN 0-8091-0136-X). Paulist Pr.

Duquoc, Christian & Floristan, Casiano. Job & the Silence of God. (Concilium Ser. 1983: Vol. 169). 128p. (Orig.). 1983. pap. 6.95 (ISBN 0-8164-2449-7, HarpR). Har-Row.

Duquoc, Christian, jt. auth. see Floristan, Casiano.

Duquoc, Christian, ed. Spirituality in Church & World. LC 65-28868. (Concilium Ser.: Vol. 9). 174p. 7.95 (ISBN 0-8091-0139-4). Paulist Pr.

--Spirituality in the Secular City. LC 66-30366. (Concilium Ser.: Vol. 19). 192p. 7.95 (ISBN 0-8091-0140-8). Paulist Pr.

DuQuoc, Christian, jt. ed. see Floristan, Casiano.

Duraiswami, Pandit M. Sri Pancaratra-Raksha of Vedanta Desika. 2nd ed. 1967. 6.00 (ISBN 0-8356-7482-7, ALS 36). Theos Pub Hse.

Duran, Fr. Diego. Book of the Gods & Rites & the Ancient Calendar. Horcasitas, Fernando & Heyden, Doris, trs. LC 73-88147. (Civilization of the American Indian Ser.: No. 102). (Illus.). 1977. pap. 12.95 (ISBN 0-8061-1201-8). U of Okla Pr.

Duran, Manuel & Kluback, William, trs. Luis de Leon: Names of Christ. (Classics of Western Spirituality Ser.). 1984. 14.95 (ISBN 0-8091-0346-X); pap. 11.95 (ISBN 0-8091-2561-7). Paulist Pr.

Durand, Eugene. The Biggest Little Church in the World. Wheeler, Gerald, ed. (Better Living Ser.). 32p. (Orig.). 1986. pap. 1.25 (ISBN 0-8280-0320-3). Review & Herald.

Durand, Paul, tr. see Dionysius Of Fourna.

Durand, Ursin, jt. auth. see Martene, Edmond.

Durant, John, ed. Darwinism & Divinity: Essays on Evolution & Religious Belief. 224p. 1986. pap. text ed. 14.95 (ISBN 0-631-15101-X). Basil Blackwell.

Durant, Will. Age of Faith. (Story of Civilization: Vol. 4). (Illus.). 1950. 32.95 (ISBN 0-671-01200-2). S&S.

--Caesar & Christ: A History of Roman Civilization from Its Beginnings to A.D. 337. (Story of Civilization: Vol. 3). 1944. 29.95 (ISBN 0-671-11500-6). S&S.

--Reformation. (Story of Civilization: Vol. 6). (Illus.). 1957. 29.95 (ISBN 0-671-61050-3). S&S.

Durantel, J. Saint Thomas et le Pseudo-Denis. (Medieval Studies Ser.). (Fr.). Repr. of 1919 ed. lib. bdg. 45.00x (ISBN 0-697-00036-2). Irvington.

Durantis, Gulielmus. The Symbolism of Churches & Church Ornaments. 1980. lib. bdg. 64.95 (ISBN 0-8490-3166-4). Gordon Pr.

--Symbolism of Churches & Church Ornaments: A Translation of the First Book of the Rationale Divinorum Officiorum. Neale, John M. & Webb, Benjamin, eds. Repr. of 1843 ed. 28.00 (ISBN 0-404-04653-3). AMS Pr.

Durasoff, Steve. The Russian Protestants: Evangelicals in the Soviet Union. LC 72-76843. (Illus.). 312p. 1969. 27.50 (ISBN 0-8386-7465-8). Fairleigh Dickinson.

Durckheim, Karlfried von see Von Duerckheim, Karlfried.

Durepo, Martha. Our Bible. LC 86-17571. (Bible-&-Me Ser.). 1987. 5.95 (ISBN 0-8054-4175-1). Broadman.

Durfey, Carolyn, jt. ed. see Cole, Ginny.

Durfey, Thomas C. & Ferrier, James A. Religious Broadcast Management Handbook. 1986. pap. 14.95 (ISBN 0-310-39741-3). Zondervan.

Durfield, Richard. How Shall We Escape. 1983. pap. 3.95 (ISBN 0-938612-07-7). Revival Press.

Durham, Charles. Temptation: Help for Struggling Christians. LC 82-153. 164p. (Orig.). 1982. pap. 4.95 (ISBN 0-87784-382-1). Inter-Varsity.

--When You Are Feeling Lonely. LC 84-10499. 180p. (Orig.). 1984. pap. 5.95 (ISBN 0-87784-915-3). Inter-Varsity.

Durham, G. Homer. N. Eldon Tanner: His Life & Service. LC 82-9681. (Illus.). 370p. 1982. 9.95 (ISBN 0-87747-913-5). Deseret Bk.

Durham, Jackie. In Search of Energy. Pennington, Celeste, ed. (Home Mission Study). (Illus., Orig.). 1984. pap. 1.75 (ISBN 0-937170-27-5). Home Mission.

Durham, James. Song of Solomon. 1981. lib. bdg. 17.25 (ISBN 0-86524-075-2, 2201). Klock & Klock.

--Song of Solomon. (Geneva Ser.). 460p. 1982. Repr. of 1840 ed. 13.95 (ISBN 0-85151-352-2). Banner of Truth.

Durham, John. Exodus (WBC, Vol. 3. 448p. 1986. 25.95 (ISBN 0-8499-0202-9). Word Bks.

Durham, John I., ed. Southeastern Studies: Toward A.D. 2000. LC 77-80400. (Emerging Directions in Christian Ministry Ser.: Vol. 1). viii, 146p. 1981. 8.95 (ISBN 0-86554-026-8, MUP-H004). Mercer Univ Pr.

Durham, John I. & Porter, J. R., eds. Proclamation & Presence: Old Testament Essays in Honor of Gwynne Henton Davies. LC 83-17445. xx, 315p. 1983. 17.95 (ISBN 0-86554-101-9, MUP/H93). Mercer Univ Pr.

Durham, Ken. Speaking from the Heart. LC 86-61523. 1986. 10.95 (ISBN 0-8344-0136-3, BA120H). Sweet.

Durka, Gloria & Smith, Joanmarie. Aesthetic Dimensions of Religious Education. LC 78-65903. 252p. 1979. pap. 8.50 (ISBN 0-8091-2164-6). Paulist Pr.

--Family Ministry. 216p. (Orig.). 1980. pap. 7.95 (ISBN 0-86683-762-0, HarpR). Har-Row.

Durken, Daniel, ed. Blow the Trumpet at the New Moon: A Sisters Today Jubilee. LC 79-27505. xi, 480p. (Orig.). 1980. pap. 3.00 (ISBN 0-8146-1016-1). Liturgical Pr.

Durken, Daniel, ed. & pref. by. Sin, Salvation, & the Spirit. LC 79-20371. (Illus.). 368p. 1979. text ed. 6.00 (ISBN 0-8146-1078-1); pap. text ed. 10.00 (ISBN 0-8146-1079-X). Liturgical Pr.

Durkheim, Emile. Elementary Forms of the Religious Life. Swain, Joseph W., tr. 1965. pap. text ed. 14.95 (ISBN 0-02-908010-X). Free Pr.

--The Elementary Forms of the Religious Life. 2nd ed. Swain, Joseph W., tr. LC 76-369730. pap. 117.80 (ISBN 0-317-20057-7, 2023276). Bks Demand UMI.

Durkin, Henry P. Forty-Four Hours to Change Your Life: Marriage Encounter. (Orig.). pap. write for info (ISBN 0-515-09442-0). Jove Pubns.

Durkin, Mary. Sexuality. (Guidelines for Contemporary Catholics Ser.). (Orig.). 1987. pap. 7.95 (ISBN 0-88347-211-2). Thomas More.

Durkin, Mary, jt. auth. see Anzia, Joan.

Durkin, Mary, jt. auth. see Greeley, Andrew.

Durkin, Mary G. Feast of Love. 248p. 1984. 9.95 (ISBN 0-8294-0443-0). Loyola.
Durland, Frances C. Coping with Widowhood. 1979. pap. 1.50 (ISBN 0-89243-098-2). Liguori Pubns.
Durland, William R. No King But Caesar? LC 74-30093. (Christian Peace Shelf Ser.). 184p. 1975. o. p. 6.95 (ISBN 0-8361-1757-3); pap. 4.95 (ISBN 0-8361-1927-4). Herald Pr.
Durnbaugh, Donald F. The Believers' Church. LC 85-7599. 328p. (Orig.). 1985. pap. 12.95x (ISBN 0-8361-1271-7). Herald Pr.
--The Brethren in Colonial America. (Illus.). 659p. (YA) 1967. 15.95 (ISBN 0-87178-110-7). Brethren.
--The Church of the Brethren Yesterday & Today. Eller, David, ed. 192p. (Orig.). 1986. pap. 9.95 (ISBN 0-87178-151-4). Brethren.
--European Origins of the Brethren. 463p. 1958. 13.95 (ISBN 0-87178-256-1). Brethren.
Durnbaugh, Donald F., ed. Every Need Supplied: Mutual Aid & Christian Community in Free Churches, 1525-1675. LC 73-94279. (Documents in Free Church History Ser.: No. 1). (Illus.). 258p. 1974. 19.95 (ISBN 0-87722-031-X). Temple U Pr.
--Meet the Brethren. (Illus.). 120p. 1984. pap. 2.95 (ISBN 0-936693-11-8). Brethren Encyclopedia.
--On Earth Peace. 1978. pap. 9.95 (ISBN 0-87178-660-5). Brethren.
Durnbaugh, Hedwig. The German Hymnody of the Brethren, 1720-1903. Eberly, William R., ed. (Monograph). (Illus.). 336p. 1986. 25.00x (ISBN 0-936693-21-5). Brethren Encyclopedia.
Duro, Carol J., jt. auth. see Duro, Peter A.
Duro, Peter A. & Duro, Carol J. You Don't Know My God. LC 85-81388. 238p. (Orig.). 1985. pap. 5.95 (ISBN 0-9615955-0-7). Emmanuel Christian.
Durodola, James I. Scientific Insights into Yoruba Traditional Medicine. (Traditional Healing Ser.). 1985. 27.50 (ISBN 0-686-85813-1). Conch Mag.
Durr, Ruth E. A Shelter from Compassion. LC 56-6375. (Orig.). 1956. pap. 2.50x (ISBN 0-87574-087-1). Pendle Hill.
Durrant, Michael. The Logical Status of God. LC 72-93886. (New Studies in the Philosophy of Religion). 132p. 1973. 18.95 (ISBN 0-312-49455-6). St Martin.
Durrant, Stephen, jt. auth. see Nowak, Margaret.
Durrett, Deane. My New Sister, the Bully. 128p. 1985. 7.95 (ISBN 0-687-27551-2). Abingdon.
Durst, Mose. To Bigotry, No Sanction: The Reverend Sun Myung Moon & the Unification Church. LC 84-60571. (Illus.). 196p. 1984. pap. 6.95 (ISBN 0-89526-829-9). Regnery Bks.
Durstewitz, Claire W. Conscience Plays. 1982. pap. 4.95 (ISBN 0-89536-527-8, 0340). CSS of Ohio.
Duryea, John S. & Bartlett, Oso. Alive into the Wilderness: The Story of An Excommunicated Priest. (Illus.). 300p. (Orig.). 1984. pap. 9.50 (ISBN 0-9606288-3-5). Coastlight Pr.
Dusen, Wilson Van see Van Dusen, Wilson.
Dushkin, Alexander M. Jewish Education: Selected Writings. 180p. 1980. text ed. 10.00x (ISBN 965-223-353-6, Pub. by Magnes Pr Israel). Humanities.
Duska, Ronald & Whelan, Mariellen. Moral Development: A Guide to Piaget & Kohlberg. LC 75-20863. 136p. 1975. pap. 5.95 (ISBN 0-8091-1892-0). Paulist Pr.
Dussel, Enrique. The History of the Church in Latin America: Colonialism to Liberation. Neely, Alan, tr. 368p. 1981. 21.95 (ISBN 0-8028-3548-1). Eerdmans.
Duthie, Alan S. Bible Translations & How to Choose Between Them. 127p. 1986. pap. 10.95 (ISBN 0-85364-400-4, Pub. by Paternoster UK). Attic Pr.
Duthie, Alexander. The Greek Mythology: A Reader's Handbook. 2nd ed. LC 78-12988. 1979. Repr. of 1949 ed. lib. bdg. 22.50x (ISBN 0-313-21077-2, DUGM). Greenwood.
Dutt, N. Buddhist Sects in India. 2nd ed. 1977. 9.00x (ISBN 0-88386-971-3). South Asia Bks.
Dutt, Nalinaksha. Buddhist Sects in India. 1978. (Pub. by Motilal Banarsidas India); pap. 7.50 (ISBN 0-89684-044-1). Orient Bk Dist.
--Early Monastic Buddhism. 1981. Repr. of 1971 ed. 12.50x (ISBN 0-8364-0815-2, Pub. by Mukhopadhyay). South Asia Bks.
--Mahayana Buddhism. rev. ed. 1978. 12.95 (ISBN 0-89684-032-8, Pub. by Motilal Banarsidass India). Orient Bk Dist.
--Mahayana Buddhism. 1976. Repr. of 1973 ed. 11.00x (ISBN 0-8364-0430-0). South Asia Bks.
Dutt, Romesh C., tr. The Ramayana. Bd. with The Mahabharata. 1972. 12.95x (ISBN 0-460-00403-4, Evman). Biblio Dist.
Dutton, Bertha P. & Olin, Caroline. Myths & Legends of the Indian Southwest. (Bk 2). (Illus.). 1978. pap. 2.95 (ISBN 0-88388-062-8). Bellerophon Bks.
Dutton, Charles J. The Samaritans of Molokai. facsimile ed. (Select Bibliographies Reprint Ser). Repr. of 1932 ed. 23.50 (ISBN 0-8369-5733-4). Ayer Co Pubs.
Duty, Guy. Divorce & Remarriage. LC 96-2485. 160p. 1983. 8.95 (ISBN 0-87123-097-6, 230097). Bethany Hse.
--Divorcio y Nuevo Matrimonio. 176p. 1975. 2.95 (ISBN 0-88113-060-5). Edit Betania.
--Escape from the Coming Tribulation. LC 75-17979. 160p. (Orig.). 1975. pap. 4.95 (ISBN 0-87123-131-X, 210131). Bethany Hse.
--If Ye Continue. LC 82-2314. 192p. 1966. pap. 4.95 (ISBN 0-87123-243-X, 210243). Bethany Hse.
Duvall, D. C., jt. auth. see Wissler, Clark.
Duvall, Lindsay O. James City County, Virginia 1634-1659, Vol. 4. (Virginia Colonial Abstracts, Series II). 1979. Repr. of 1957 ed. 20.00 (ISBN 0-89308-065-9). Southern Hist Pr.
--Lancaster County, Virginia Records, Vol. 2. (Virginia Colonial Abstracts, Series II). 1979. Repr. 20.00 (ISBN 0-89308-063-2). Southern Hist Pr.
--Northumberland County, Virginia 1678-1713, Vol. 1. (Virginia Colonial Abstracts, Series II). 160p. 1979. pap. 20.00 (ISBN 0-89308-062-4). Southern Hist Pr.
--Prince George County, Virginia, Vol. 6. (Virginia Colonial Abstracts, Series II). 80p. 1978. pap. 20.00 (ISBN 0-89308-067-5). Southern Hist Pr.
Duvall, Sylvanus M. Methodist Episcopal Church & Education up to 1869. LC 79-176735. (Columbia University. Teachers College. Contributions to Education: No. 284). Repr. of 1928 ed. 22.50 (ISBN 0-404-55284-6). AMS Pr.
Duverger, Christian. L' Esprit du Jeu Chez les Azteques. (Civilisations et Societes Ser.: No. 59). (Illus.). 1978. pap. 26.00 (ISBN 90-279-7664-3). Mouton.
Duvernoy, Claude. Controversy of Zion. LC 86-6386. 232p. 1987. pap. 6.96 (ISBN 0-89221-144-X). New Leaf.
Dvornik, Francis. Early Christian & Byzantine Political Philosophy: Origins & Background, 2 vols. LC 67-4089. (Dumbarton Oaks Studies: Vol. 9). 975p. 1966. 50.00x (ISBN 0-88402-016-9). Dumbarton Oaks.
--The Idea of Apostolicity in Byzantium & the Legend of the Apostle Andrew. (Dumbarton Oaks Studies: Vol. 4). 342p. (LC A58-8640). 1958. 25.00x (ISBN 0-88402-004-5). Dumbarton Oaks.
--Legendes de Constantin et de methode vues de Byzance. (Russian Ser: No. 12). 1969. Repr. of 1933 ed. 35.00 (ISBN 0-87569-009-2). Academic Intl.
Dwiggins, Gwen, jt. auth. see Hughes, Barbara.
Dwight, Henry Otis, et al, eds. Encyclopedia of Missions: Descriptive, Historical, Biographical, Statistical. 2nd ed. LC 74-31438. 851p. 1975. Repr. of 1904 ed. 80.00x (ISBN 0-8103-3325-2). Gale.
Dwight, Timothy. Theology, 5 vols. LC 75-3132. Repr. of 1819 ed. 200.00 set (ISBN 0-404-59136-1). AMS Pr.
Dwivedi, A. N. Essentials of Hinduism, Jainism & Buddhism. 148p. 1979. 12.00 (ISBN 0-88065-083-4, Pub. by Messers Today & Tomorrows Printers & Publishers India). Scholarly Pubns.
Dwivedi, R. C. Contributions of Jainism to Indian Culture. 1975. 12.95 (ISBN 0-8426-0953-9). Orient Bk Dist.
Dwyer, John C. Church History: Twenty Centuries of Catholic Christianity. 424p. (Orig.). 1985. pap. 9.95 (ISBN 0-8091-2686-9). Paulist Pr.
--Son of Man & Son of God: A New Language for Faith. 160p. 1983. pap. 7.95 (ISBN 0-8091-2505-6). Paulist Pr.
Dwyer, Judith A., ed. The Catholic Bishops & Nuclear War: A Critique & Analysis of the Pastoral, the Challenge of Peace. 120p. 1984. pap. 6.50 (ISBN 0-87840-409-0). Georgetown U Pr.
--Questions of Special Urgency: The Church in the Modern World Twenty Years after Vatican II. 200p. (Orig.). 1986. 17.95 (ISBN 0-87840-434-1); pap. 9.95 (ISBN 0-87840-425-2). Georgetown U Pr.
Dwyer, Paulinus, jt. auth. see MacKenthun, Carole.
Dyck, C. J. An Introduction to Mennonite History. rev. ed. LC 81-1958. 400p. 1981. 12.95 (ISBN 0-8361-1955-X). Herald Pr.
Dyck, C. J., ed. Something Meaningful for God. LC 80-10975. (MCC Story Ser.: Vol. 4). 408p. (Orig.). 1981. pap. 7.95x (ISBN 0-8361-1244-X). Herald Pr.
Dyck, Cornelius J. From the Files of the MCC. LC 80-10975. (MCC Story Ser.: Vol. 1). 168p. 1980. pap. 3.95x (ISBN 0-8361-1229-6). Herald Pr.
--Responding to Worldwide Needs. LC 80-10975. (MCC Story Ser.: Vol. 2). 168p. 1980. pap. 3.95x (ISBN 0-8361-1230-X). Herald Pr.
--Twelve Becoming, Biographies of Mennonite Disciples from the Sixteenth to the Twentieth Century. LC 73-75174. 1973. pap. 4.50 (ISBN 0-87303-865-7). Faith & Life.
--Witness & Service in North America. LC 80-10975. (MCC Story Ser.: Vol. 3). 1980. pap. 3.95x (ISBN 0-8361-1231-8). Herald Pr.
Dyck, Peter, tr. see Gerber, Samuel.
Dyckman, Katharine M., jt. auth. see Carroll, L. Patrick.
Dyckman, Katherine M. & Carroll, L. Patrick. Solitude to Sacrament. LC 82-252. 128p. (Orig.). 1982. pap. 2.95 (ISBN 0-8146-1255-5). Liturgical Pr.
Dyckman, Katherine M., jt. auth. see Carroll, L. Patrick.
Dyczkowski, Mark S. The Canon of the Saivagama & the Kubjika: Tantras of the Western Kaula Tradition. (Kashmir Shaivism Ser.). 256p. 1987. text ed. 34.50x (ISBN 0-88706-494-9). State U NY Pr.
Dye, Dwight L. A Kingdom of Servants. 1979. 3.95 (ISBN 0-87162-218-1, D5050). Warner Pr.
Dye, Harold. The Touch of Friendship. LC 79-51138. 1979. pap. 4.25 large type (ISBN 0-8054-5422-5). Broadman.
Dye, Harold E. A Daily Miracle. (Orig.). 1986. pap. 3.25 (ISBN 0-8054-5026-2). Broadman.
Dye, Joseph M. Ways to Shiva: Life & Ritual in Hindu India. LC 80-25113. (Illus.). 94p. (Orig.). 1980. pap. 4.95 (ISBN 0-87633-038-3). Phila Mus Art.
Dye, William M. Moslem Egypt & Christian Abyssinia. LC 78-97365. Repr. of 1880 ed. 23.00x (ISBN 0-8371-2432-8, DYM&, Pub. by Negro U Pr). Greenwood.
Dyer, Alvin R. The Refiner's Fire. 8.95 (ISBN 0-87747-222-X). Deseret Bk.
Dyer, Charles, jt. ed. see Toussaint, Stanley D.
Dyer, George, ed. An American Catholic Catechism. LC 75-7786. 320p. 1975. (HarpR); pap. 7.95 (ISBN 0-8164-2588-4). Har-Row.
Dyer, Heather. Stories Jesus Told. Incl. The Good Samaritan (ISBN 0-89191-286-X); The Good Shepherd (ISBN 0-89191-283-5); The Great Feast (ISBN 0-89191-284-3); The House Built on Sand (ISBN 0-89191-288-6); The Prodigal Son (ISBN 0-89191-285-1); The Rich Man (ISBN 0-89191-287-8). (Illus.). 1980. Repr. 2.50 ea. Cook.
Dyer, Wayne W. Happy Holidays: How to Enjoy the Christmas & Chanukkah Season to the Fullest. Nast, Thomas, tr. LC 86-2448. (Illus.). 96p. 1986. 9.95 (ISBN 0-688-06466-3). Morrow.
Dyer, William G. Creating Closer Families: Principles of Positive Family Interaction. LC 75-20169. (Illus.). 144p. 1975. pap. 6.95 (ISBN 0-8425-0726-4). Brigham.
Dyer, William G. & Kunz, Phillip R. Effective Mormon Families. 1986. text ed. 9.95 (ISBN 0-87579-059-3). Deseret Bk.
Dyet, James T. Getting Through to Adults. LC 79-53294. (Accent Teacher Training Ser.). (Orig.). 1980. pap. 4.95 (ISBN 0-89636-037-7). Accent Bks.
--Paul: Apostle of Steel & Velvet. 3rd. ed. LC 76-9579. 1976. pap. 3.50 (ISBN 0-916406-30-X). Accent Bks.
Dyke, Henry Van see Van Dyke, Henry.
Dyke, Henry van see Van Dyke, Henry.
Dyke, Van Henry. First Christmas Tree. 76p. 1984. 2.95 (ISBN 0-89783-034-2). Larlin Corp.
Dykstra, Craig. Vision & Character: A Christian Educator's Alternative to Kohlberg. LC 81-82340. 160p. (Orig.). 1981. pap. 5.95 (ISBN 0-8091-2405-X). Paulist Pr.
Dykstra, Craig & Parks, Sharon, eds. Faith Development & Fowler. 322p. (Orig.). 1986. pap. 14.95 (ISBN 0-89135-056-X). Religious Educ.
Dymond, Jonathan. Inquiry into the Accordancy of War with the Principles of Christianity. LC 79-147432. (Library of War & Peace; Proposals for Peace: a History). 1973. lib. bdg. 46.00 (ISBN 0-8240-0222-9). Garland Pub.
Dyne, Glen Van see Van Dyne, Glen.
Dynes, Wayne. The Illuminations of the Stavelot Bible. LC 77-94693. (Outstanding Dissertations in the Fine Arts Ser.). (Illus.). 1978. lib. bdg. 44.00 (ISBN 0-8240-3225-X). Garland Pub.
Dyorak, Max. Idealism & Naturalism in Gothic Art. Klawiter, Randolph J., tr. LC 67-22143. (Illus.). pap. 70.50 (ISBN 0-317-10425-X, 2022072). Bks Demand UMI.
Dyrness, W. A. Christian Art in Asia. 1979. pap. text ed. 11.50x (ISBN 0-391-01157-X). Humanities.
Dyrness, William A. Christian Apologetics in a World Community. LC 82-21383. 180p. 1983. pap. 6.95 (ISBN 0-87784-399-6). Inter-Varsity.
--Let the Earth Rejoice! 192p. (Orig.). 1983. pap. 6.95 (ISBN 0-89107-282-9, Crossway Bks). Good News.
--Themes in Old Testament Theology. LC 79-2380. 1979. pap. 8.95 (ISBN 0-87784-726-6). Inter-Varsity.
Dyrud, Keith P., et al. The Other Catholics. 33.00 (ISBN 0-405-10820-6). Ayer Co Pubs.
Dys, Pat. He Obeyed God: A Child's Life of A. B. Simpson. 55p. 1986. pap. 3.95 (ISBN 0-87509-382-5). Chr Pubns.
Dys, Pat, jt. auth. see Corbin, Linda.
Dys, Pat, ed. see Corbin, Linda.
Dyson, W. H. Studies in Christian Mysticism. 1977. lib. bdg. 69.95 (ISBN 0-8490-2702-0). Gordon Pr.

E

Eade, Alfred T. Expanded Panorama Bible Study Course. (Illus.). 192p. 12.95 (ISBN 0-8007-0086-4). Revell.
--The New Panorama Bible Study Course. Incl. No. 1. A Study of Dispensational Truth. (Illus.). 28p (ISBN 0-8007-0221-2); No. 2. The Study of Angelology. 32p (ISBN 0-8007-0222-0); No. 3. The Second Coming of Christ. 36p (ISBN 0-8007-0223-9); No. 4. The Book of Revelation. (Illus.). 28p (ISBN 0-8007-0434-7). pap. 6.95 ea. Revell.
--Panorama de la Biblia. Orig. Title: New Panorama Bible Study Course. 32p. 1986. pap. 3.75 (ISBN 0-311-03657-0). Casa Bautista.
Eadie, ed. see Cruden, Alexander.
Eadie, John. Colossians. 1981. 10.50 (ISBN 0-86524-067-1, 5103). Klock & Klock.
--The Words of the Apostle Paul. 462p. 1985. smythe sewn 18.50 (ISBN 0-86524-191-0, 4405). Klock & Klock.
Eadie, John W., ed. The Conversion of Constantine. LC 76-25480. (European American Studies). 120p. 1977. pap. text ed. 5.95 (ISBN 0-88275-453-X). Krieger.
Eadmer. The Life of St. Anselm, Archbishop of Canterbury. Southern, R. W., ed. & tr. from Latin. (Oxford Medieval Texts Ser.). 1972. 49.00x (ISBN 0-19-822225-4). Oxford U Pr.
Eaford & Ajaz. Judaism or Zionism? What Difference for the Middle East? 320p. 1986. 32.50 (ISBN 0-86232-475-0, Pub. by Zed Pr England); pap. 12.50 (ISBN 0-86232-476-9, Pub. by Zed Pr England). Humanities.
Eager, George B. How to Succeed in Winning Children to Christ. 190p. 1979. pap. 3.95 (ISBN 0-9603752-0-1). Mailbox.
--Love, Dating & Marriage. LC 86-90552. (Illus.). 136p. (Orig.). 1987. pap. 5.95 (ISBN 0-9603752-5-2). Mailbox.
--The New Life in Christ. LC 86-62669. (Illus.). 163p. 1987. pap. text ed. 4.95 (ISBN 0-9603752-6-0). Mailbox.
--Wake up World! Jesus Is Coming Soon! 40p. (Orig.). 1980. pap. 1.00 (ISBN 0-9603752-3-6). Mailbox.
Eagleson, John & Scharper, Philip J., eds. Puebla & Beyond. LC 79-24098. 370p. (Orig.). 1979. pap. 9.95 (ISBN 0-88344-399-6). Orbis Bks.
Eagleson, John, jt. ed. see Torres, Sergio.
Eagleson, John, ed. see Torres, Sergio.
Eagleson, John, tr. see Miranda, Jose P.
Eakin, Frank E., Jr. We Believe in One God: Creed & Scripture. LC 85-51755. 165p. 1985. pap. text ed. 21.95 (ISBN 0-932269-64-8). Wyndham Hall.
Eakin, Mary M. Scuffy Sandals: A Guide for Church Visitation in the Community. LC 81-15824. 96p. (Orig.). 1982. pap. 5.95 (ISBN 0-8298-0490-0). Pilgrim NY.
Eakin, Patsy. God Said, Part I. 65p. (Orig.). 1981. pap. 2.95 (ISBN 0-931097-06-1). Sentinel Pub.
--God Said, Part II. 89p. 1981. pap. text ed. 2.95 (ISBN 0-931097-11-8). Sentinel Pub.
Eames, Wilberforce. The Bay Psalm Book. 1978. pap. 53.95 (ISBN 0-89102-098-5, Artemis). B Franklin.
--Early New England Catechisms. 1898. 16.00 (ISBN 0-8337-0989-5). B Franklin.
--Early New England Catechisms. LC 68-31081. 1969. Repr. of 1898 ed. 35.00x (ISBN 0-8103-3478-X). Gale.
Eames, Wilberforce, ed. A List of Editions of the Bay Psalm Book or New England Version of the Psalms, 2 vols. in 1. Incl. Bible. O. T. Psalms. English. Paraphrases. 1912 Bay Psalm Book. facsimile ed. New England Society. 1912. Repr. LC 1-538. 1885. Repr. 23.50 (ISBN 0-8337-0987-9). B Franklin.
Eareckson, Joni & Estes, Steve. A Step Further. 2nd ed. (Illus.). 192p. 1980. pap. 5.95 (ISBN 0-310-23971-0, 12007P). Zondervan.
--A Step Further. 192p. 1982. pap. 3.95 (ISBN 0-310-23972-9, 12008P). Zondervan.
Eareckson, Joni & Musser, Joe. Joni. 1984. pap. 2.95 (ISBN 0-553-22886-2). Bantam.
--Joni. (Illus.). 256p. 1980. pap. 3.95 (ISBN 0-310-23982-6, 12009P). Zondervan.
--Joni. 1976 (12563L). kivar, large print o.p. 7.95 (ISBN 0-310-23967-2); pap. 6.95 (ISBN 0-310-23961-3, 12005P). Zondervan.
Eareckson-Tada, Joni. Choices, Changes. 1986. write for info. Zondervan.

Earhart, H. Byron. Japanese Religion: Unity & Diversity. 3rd ed. 288p. 1982. pap. text ed. write for info. (ISBN 0-534-01028-8). Wadsworth Pub.
Earhart, H. Byron, tr. see Murakami, Shigeyoshi.
Earl, Gloria. The Book. 1984. 6.75 (ISBN 0-8062-1572-0). Carlton.
Earle, Alice M. Sabbath in Puritan New England. 335p. 1969. Repr. of 1891 ed. 20.00 (ISBN 0-87928-005-0). Corner Hse.
--Sun Dials & Roses of Yesterday. LC 79-75790. 1969. Repr. of 1902 ed. 37.00x (ISBN 0-8103-3830-0). Gale.
Earle, Arthur. The Bible Dates Itself. LC 73-88548. 1974. 12.50 (ISBN 0-9600788-1-9). A Earle.
Earle, Edwin & Kennard, Edward A. Hopi Kachinas. 2nd ed. LC 71-139867. (Illus.). 1971. 12.50 (ISBN 0-934490-11-2). Mus Am Ind.
Earle, John. Facsimile of Some Leaves in Saxon Handwriting on Saint Swidhun. 1861. lib. bdg. 35.00 (ISBN 0-8414-3989-3). Folcroft.
Earle, Ralph. How to Study the Bible. (Christian Living Ser.). 32p. (Orig.). 1987. pap. write for info. (ISBN 0-8341-1187-X). Beacon Hill.
--How We Got Our Bible. 119p. 1972. 2.95 (ISBN 0-8341-0226-9). Beacon Hill.
--Mark: Gospel of Action. LC 73-15084. (Everyman's Bible Commentary Ser.). 1970. pap. 5.95 (ISBN 0-8024-2041-9). Moody.
--Peloubet's Sunday School Notes, 1987-1988. 1987. pap. 7.95 (ISBN 0-8010-3439-6). Baker Bk.
--Word Meanings in the New Testament. 374p. 1987. text ed. 24.95 (ISBN 0-8010-3434-5). Baker Bk.
--Word Meanings in the New Testament: Hebrews-Revelation, Vol. 6. 174p. 1984. 9.95 (ISBN 0-8341-0943-3). Beacon Hill.
--Word Meanings in the New Testament: I & II Corinthians, Galatians & Ephesians, Vol. 4. 1979. 9.95 (ISBN 0-8010-3349-7). Baker Bk.
--Word Meanings in the New Testament: Romans, Vol. 3. 9.95 (ISBN 0-8010-3322-5). Baker Bk.
--Word Meanings in the New Testament, Vol. 3: Romans. 264p. 1974. 9.95 (ISBN 0-8341-0512-8). Beacon Hill.
--Word Meanings in the New Testament, Vol. 1: Matthew, Mark, Luke. 285p. 1980. 9.95 (ISBN 0-8341-0683-3). Beacon Hill.
--Word Meanings in the New Testament, Vol. 5: Philemon-Philippians. 1977. 9.95 (ISBN 0-8341-0493-8). Beacon Hill.
--Word Meanings in the New Testament: 1 & 2 Corinthians, Ephesians, Vol. 4. 350p. 1979. 9.95 (ISBN 0-8341-0567-5). Beacon Hill.
--Word Meanings: Matthew-Luke, Vol. 1. 9.95 (ISBN 0-8010-3362-4). Baker Bk.
--Word Meanings: Philippians-Philemon, Vol. 5. 9.95 (ISBN 0-8010-3330-6). Baker Bk.
Earle, William, et al, eds. Christianity & Existentialism. (Studies in Phenomenology & Existential Philosophy). 1963. pap. 7.95 (ISBN 0-8101-0084-3). Northwestern U Pr.
Earles, Brent D. Bouncing Back. (Life Enrichment Ser.). 144p. Date not set. pap. 5.95 (ISBN 0-8010-3435-3). Baker Bk.
--The Dating Maze. pap. 3.95 (ISBN 0-8010-3424-8). Baker Bk.
--The Gospels for Graduates. 160p. 1987. text ed. 5.95 (ISBN 0-8010-3438-8). Baker Bk.
--Perfect "10". 112p. 1986. 5.95 (ISBN 0-8010-3431-0). Baker Bk.
--Proverbs for Graduates. 1984. 5.95 (ISBN 0-8010-3415-9). Baker Bk.
--Psalms for Graduates. 5.95 (ISBN 0-8010-3426-4). Baker Bk.
--You're Worth It! But Do You Believe It? 112p. 1985. pap. 5.95 (ISBN 0-8010-3427-2). Baker Bk.
Early, Sarah J. Life & Labors of Rev. Jordan W. Early: One of the Pioneers of African Methodism in the West & South. facsimile ed. LC 72-164386. (Black Heritage Library Collection). Repr. of 1894 ed. 16.00 (ISBN 0-8369-8845-0). Ayer Co Pubs.
Earnest, James D. & Tracey, Gerard. John Henry Newman: An Annotated Bibliography of His Tract & Pamphlet Collection. LC 84-48069. (Reference Library of Social Science). 600p. 1984. lib. bdg. 78.00 (ISBN 0-8240-8958-8). Garland pub.
Earp, Frank R. Way of the Greeks. LC 75-136393. Repr. of 1929 ed. 21.50 (ISBN 0-404-02234-0). AMS Pr.
Eash, John E. Bring an Offering. 1985. pap. 1.95 (ISBN 0-317-38498-8). Brethren.
Easson, Roger R., ed. see Jones, Margaret W.
Easson, Roger R., ed. see Olsen, Sue.
East, Reginald. Heal the Sick. LC 77-80678. 160p. (Orig.). 1977. pap. 2.95 (ISBN 0-87123-232-4, 200232). Bethany Hse.
Eastcott, Michal J. I: The Story of the Self. LC 80-51552. (Illus.). 201p. (Orig.). 1980. pap. 5.50 (ISBN 0-8356-0541-8, Quest). Theos Pub Hse.
Easter, Frances. Bible Studies Series. (Studies in Luke: Vol. 1). 1985. pap. 3.50 (ISBN 0-8309-0424-7). Herald Hse.
--Bible Studies Series. (Studies in Luke Ser.: Vol. II). 1985. pap. 3.50 (ISBN 0-8309-0430-1). Herald Hse.
--Bible Study. (Studies in Acts: vol. I). 1986. pap. 3.50 (ISBN 0-8309-0436-0). Herald Hse.
--Studies in Acts, Vol. II. (Bible Study Ser.). 1986. pap. 3.50 (ISBN 0-8309-0442-5). Herald Hse.
Easterling, P. E. & Muir, J. V., eds. Greek Religion & Society. (Illus.). 264p. 1985. 39.50 (ISBN 0-521-24552-4); pap. 12.95 (ISBN 0-521-28785-5). Cambridge U Pr.
Easterly, Frederick J. The Life of Rt. Rev. Joseph Rosati, D. M., First Bishop of St. Louis, 1789-1843. LC 73-3587. (Catholic University of America. Studies in American Church History: No. 33). Repr. of 1942 ed. 27.00 (ISBN 0-404-57783-0). AMS Pr.
Easterly, Lane, ed. Great Bible Stories for Children. (Illus.). 7.95 (ISBN 0-8407-5351-9). Nelson.
Eastern & Western Disciples of Vivekananda. The Life of Swami Vivekananda, 2 Vols. rev. ed. Vol. 1, 1980, 629p. 12.95x (ISBN 0-87481-196-1); Vol. 2. 16.00x (ISBN 0-87481-197-X). Vedanta Pr.
Eastham, Scott T. Nucleus: Reconnecting Science & Religion in the Nuclear Age. LC 86-22265. 223p. (Orig.). 1986. pap. 9.95 (ISBN 0-939680-31-9). Bear & Co.
Eastlake, A. The Oneida Community. 69.95 (ISBN 0-8490-0769-0). Gordon Pr.
Eastlake, Charles. History of the Gothic Revival. LC 71-96937. (Library of Victorian Culture). 1975. pap. text ed. 12.00 (ISBN 0-89257-035-0). Am Life Foun.
Eastman, A. Theodore. The Baptizing Community: Christian Initiation & the Local Congregation. 144p. (Orig.). 1982. pap. 9.95 (ISBN 0-8164-2419-5, HarpR). Har-Row.
Eastman, Addison J. A Handful of Pearls: The Epistle of James. LC 78-5797. 106p. 1978. pap. 5.50 (ISBN 0-664-24202-2). Westminster.
Eastman, Charles A. The Soul of the Indian: An Interpretation. LC 79-26355. xvi, 170p. 1980. pap. 5.95 (ISBN 0-8032-6701-0, BB 735, Bison). U of Nebr Pr.
Eastman, Dick. A Celebration of Praise: Exciting Prospects for Extraordinary Praise. pap. 4.95 (ISBN 0-8010-3420-5). Baker Bk.
--Hour That Changes the World. (Direction Bks.). pap. 2.50 (ISBN 0-8010-3337-3). Baker Bk.
--No Easy Road: Inspirational Thoughts on Prayer. new ed. (Direction Bks.). 1973. pap. 2.50 (ISBN 0-8010-3259-8). Baker Bk.
--La Universidad de la Palabra. Silva, Jose D., tr. from English. (Span.). 239p. 1986. pap. text ed. 3.50 (ISBN 0-8297-0443-4). Life Pubs Intl.
--The University of the Word. LC 83-17763. 1983. pap. 3.95 (ISBN 0-8307-0903-7, 5018301). Regal.
Eastman, Fred. Christ in the Drama: A Study of the Influence of Christ on the Drama of England & America. facsimile ed. LC 79-167336. (Essay Index Reprints - Shaffer Lectures of Northwestern University, 1946). Repr. of 1947 ed. 15.00 (ISBN 0-8369-2647-1). Ayer Co Pubs.
--Men of Power: Benjamin Franklin, Ralph Waldo Emerson, George Fox, Charles Darwin, Vol. 3. facs. ed. LC 74-128236. (Essay Index Reprint Ser). 1939. 18.00 (ISBN 0-8369-1993-9). Ayer Co Pubs.
--Men of Power: Francis of Assisi, Leonardo Da Vinci, Oliver Cromwell, John Milton, Vol. 2. facs. ed. LC 74-128236. (Essay Index Reprint Ser). 1938. 18.00 (ISBN 0-8369-1992-0). Ayer Co Pubs.
--Men of Power: Nicolai Lenin, Mahatma Gandhi, Edward Livingston Trudeau, Robest Louis Stevenson, Vol. 5. facs. ed. LC 74-128236. (Essay Index Reprint Ser). 1940. 18.00 (ISBN 0-8369-1995-5). Ayer Co Pubs.
Eastman, Hubbard. Noyesism Unveiled. LC 72-134402. Repr. of 1849 ed. 30.00 (ISBN 0-404-08446-X). AMS Pr.
Eastman, Moira & Poussard, Wendy. The Christmas Book. LC 80-68368. (Illus.). 40p. 1980. 5.95 (ISBN 0-87793-214-X). Ave Maria.
Eastman, Roger, ed. The Ways of Religion. 608p. 1975. pap. text ed. 21.95 scp (ISBN 0-06-382595-3, CP, HarpC). Har-Row.
Easton, Emily. Roger Williams, Prophet & Pioneer. LC 76-101266. Repr. of 1930 ed. 40.00 (ISBN 0-404-02236-7). AMS Pr.
--Roger Williams, Prophet & Pioneer. LC 71-102235. (Select Bibliographies Reprint Ser). 1930. 32.00 (ISBN 0-8369-5120-4). Ayer Co Pubs.
--Roger Williams: Prophet & Pioneer. LC 78-144994. 399p. 1972. Repr. of 1930 ed. 17.00x (ISBN 0-403-00793-3). Scholarly.
Easton, J. W., jt. auth. see McLean, A.
Easton, M. G. Illustrated Bible Dictionary. (Baker's Paperback Reference Library). 760p. 1983. pap. 12.95 (ISBN 0-8010-3386-1). Baker Bk.
Easton, Stewart. The Way of Anthroposophy: Answers to Modern Questions. 102p. (Orig.). 1986. pap. 7.00 (ISBN 0-85440-464-3, Pub. by Steinerbooks). Anthroposophic.
Easton, Stewart, ed. see Steiner, Rudolf.
Easton, Stewart, tr. see Glas, Norbert.
Easton, Stewart C. Man & World in the Light of Anthroposophy. Rev. ed. 536p. 1982. pap. 11.95 (ISBN 0-88010-006-0). Anthroposophic.
--Man & World in the Light of Anthroposophy. 2nd ed. 543p. 1982. pap. 21.00 (ISBN 0-88010-077-X). Anthroposophic.
--Rudolf Steiner: Herald of a New Epoch. LC 80-67026. (Illus.). 1980. pap. 10.95 (ISBN 0-910142-93-9). Anthroposophic.
Easton, Stewart C., et al, eds. see Steiner, Rudolf.
Eastwick, Edward. Sadi: The Rose Garden. 1979. 16.95 (ISBN 0-900860-65-0). Ins Study Human.
Eastwood, J. & Wright, W. Aldis. A Glossary of the English Bible Words. 564p. 1981. Repr. of 1866 ed. lib. bdg. 75.00 (ISBN 0-89760-210-2). Telegraph Bks.
Easu & Rodehaver, Gladys K., eds. Book II of Revelations for the Aquarian Age. 1983. pap. 7.00 (ISBN 0-930208-14-5). Mangan Bks.
Easwaran, Eknath. Formulas for Transformation: A Mantram Handbook. 264p. 1977. 15.00 (ISBN 0-915132-41-9); pap. 8.00. Nilgiri Pr.
--Instrucciones En la Meditacion. 1980. pap. 2.00 (ISBN 0-915132-23-0). Nilgiri Pr.
--Love Never Faileth: The Inspiration of St. Francis, St. Augustine, St. Paul & Mother Teresa. (Illus.). 208p. (Orig.). 1985. 15.00 (ISBN 0-915132-31-1); pap. 8.00 (ISBN 0-915132-32-X). Nilgiri Pr.
--A Man to Match His Mountains: Badshah Khan, Nonviolent Soldier of Islam. (Illus.). 1985. 15.95 (ISBN 0-915132-33-8); pap. 7.95 (ISBN 0-915132-34-6). Nilgiri Pr.
--Meditation: An Eight-Point Program. LC 78-10935. 240p. 1978. 15.00 (ISBN 0-915132-15-X); pap. 8.00. Nilgiri Pr.
Easwaran, Eknath, ed. God Makes the Rivers to Flow: Passages for Meditation. (Illus.). 96p. 1982. 12.00 (ISBN 0-915132-28-1); pap. 7.00 (ISBN 0-915132-29-X). Nilgiri Pr.
Easwaran, Eknath, tr. from Pali. The Dhammapada. 1986. 13.95 (ISBN 0-915132-38-9); pap. 6.95 (ISBN 0-915132-37-0). Nilgiri Pr.
Eaton, Arthur W. The Famous Mather Byles: Noted Boston Tory Preacher, Poet, & Wit 1707-1788. facsimile ed. LC 74-165626. (Select Bibliographies Reprint Ser). Repr. of 1914 ed. 33.00 (ISBN 0-8369-5933-7). Ayer Co Pubs.
--The Famous Mather Byles, the Noted Boston Tory Preacher, Poet, & Wit. facsimile ed. LC 72-8697. (American Revolutionary Ser.). Repr. of 1914 ed. lib. bdg. 19.00x (ISBN 0-8398-0458-X). Irvington.
Eaton, Bili. A Love So Amazing... Memories of Meher Baba. LC 84-23597. 144p. 1984. pap. 8.95 (ISBN 0-913078-55-7). Sheriar Pr.
Eaton, Charles L. see Le Gai Eaton, Charles.
Eaton, Dave. How Do We Get to Heaven? (Questions, Questions Ser.). 32p. 1986. 2.95 (ISBN 0-89081-549-6). Harvest Hse.
Eaton, Evelyn. I Send a Voice. LC 78-7273. (Illus., Orig.). 1978. 10.95 (ISBN 0-8356-0513-2). Theos Pub Hse.
Eaton, Evelyn E. & Whitehead, James. Seasons of Strength: New Visions of Adult Christian Maturing. LC 84-4199. 240p. 1986. pap. 7.95 (ISBN 0-385-19680-6, Im). Doubleday.
Eaton, Hugh Van see Van Eaton, Hugh.
Eaton, J. H. Job. (Old Testament Guides Ser.). 69p. 1985. pap. text ed. 3.95x (ISBN 0-905774-97-3, Pub by. JSOT Pr England). Eisenbrauns.
Eaton, Jeffrey C., ed. For God & Clarity: New Essays in Honor of Austin Farrer. Loades, Ann. (Pittsburgh Theological Monographs New Series: No. 4). 206p. 1983. pap. 12.00 (ISBN 0-915138-52-2). Pickwick.
Eaton, John. Kingship & the Psalms. (The Biblical Seminar Ser.: No. 3). 240p. 1986. pap. text ed. 9.95x (ISBN 0-905774-89-2, Pub. by JSOT Pr England). Eisenbrauns.
Eaton, John H. The Psalms Come Alive: Capturing the Voice & the Art of Israel's Songs. LC 86-20115. (Illus.). 180p. 1986. pap. 6.95 (ISBN 0-87784-387-2). Inter-Varsity.
Eaton, Michael A. Ecclesiastes. Wiseman, D. J., ed. (Tyndale Old Testament Commentary Ser.). 1983. 12.95 (ISBN 0-87784-963-3); pap. 6.95 (ISBN 0-87784-267-1). Inter-Varsity.
Eaton, Richard M. Sufis of Bijapur, 1300-1700 Social Roles of Sufis in Medieval India. LC 77-71978. (Illus.). 1978. 42.00x (ISBN 0-691-03110-X). Princeton U Pr.
Eaton, Thomas R. Shakespeare & the Bible. LC 77-144601. Repr. of 1860 ed. 19.00 (ISBN 0-404-02237-5). AMS Pr.
Eaves, Mary L. The Truth Will Make You Free. LC 83-90380. 59p. 1985. 7.95 (ISBN 0-533-05883-X). Vantage.
Eavey, C. B. Chapel Talks. (Pocket Pulpit Library). 120p. 1981. pap. 2.95 (ISBN 0-8010-3365-9). Baker Bk.
Eavey, Louise. A Child's Shining Pathway. (Illus.). 1976. pap. 1.35 (ISBN 0-915374-08-0, 08-0). Rapids Christian.
--Happiness Rhymes for Children. 1969. pap. 1.35 (ISBN 0-915374-09-9, 09-0). Rapids Christian.
Eban, Abba. Heritage: Civilization & the Jews. (Illus.). 352p. 1984. 32.95 (ISBN 0-671-44103-5). Summit Bks.
--Heritage: Civilization & the Jews. 356p. 1986. pap. 16.95 (ISBN 0-671-62881-X). Summit Bks.
--My People: The Story of the Jews. LC 68-27328. (Illus.). 1968. 25.00 (ISBN 0-87441-294-3). Behrman.
Ebaugh, Helen R. Out of the Cloister: A Study of Organizational Dilemmas. 177p. 1977. text ed. 12.50x (ISBN 0-292-76007-8). U of Tex Pr.
Ebbeson, Eric, jt. ed. see Crean, David.
Ebel, Henry. After Dionysus: An Essay on Where We Are Now. LC 70-156321. 136p. 1972. 15.00 (ISBN 0-8386-7958-7). Fairleigh Dickinson.
Ebel, Holly. Christmas in the Air: A New Fashioned Book for An Old Fashioned Christmas. (Illus.). 96p. (Orig.). 1982. pap. 7.95 (ISBN 0-943786-00-2). HollyDay.
Ebeling, Gerhard. Luther: An Introduction to His Thought. Wilson, R. A., tr. from Ger. LC 77-99612. 288p. 1970. pap. 6.95 (ISBN 0-8006-1162-4, 1-1162). Fortress.
--The Nature of Faith. Smith, Ronald G., ed. LC 62-7194. pap. 47.80 (2026871). Bks Demand UMI.
--On Prayer: The Lord's Prayer in Today's World. Leitch, James W., tr. LC 78-5079. pap. 27.80 (2026853). Bks Demand UMI.
--The Study of Theology. Duane, Priebe A., tr. LC 78-5393. pap. 76.50 (2026983). Bks Demand UMI.
--Truth of the Gospel: An Exposition of Galatians. LC 84-47918. 288p. 1985. 19.95 (ISBN 0-8006-0728-7, 1-728). Fortress.
Ebeling, Gerhard, ed. see Braun, Herbert, et al.
Ebeling, Gerhard, ed. see Kasemann, Ernst, et al.
Ebeling, Gerhard, ed. see Robinson, James M., et al.
Ebeling, Gerhard, et al. The Bible As a Document of the University. Betz, H. D., ed. 1981. pap. 10.00 (ISBN 0-89130-422-3, 00-03-03). Scholars Pr GA.
Eber, Irene. Confucianism: The Dynamics of Tradition. 264p. 1986. text ed. 27.50x (ISBN 0-02-908780-5). Macmillan.
Eberhard, Arnold. Gemeinsamesleben-Wozu? (Ger.). 44p. 1978. pap. 2.50 (ISBN 3-87630-406-7, Pub. by Prasenz-Verlag, West Germany). Plough.
Eberhart, E. T. Burnt Offerings: Parables for Twentieth Century Christians. LC 77-23158. 1977. pap. 3.95 (ISBN 0-687-04375-1). Pilgrim Hse.
Eberhart, George M. Monsters: A Guide to Information on Unaccounted for Creatures, Including Bigfoot, Many Water Monsters, & Other Irregular Animals. LC 82-49029. (Supernatural Studies). 358p. 1983. lib. bdg. 28.00 (ISBN 0-8240-9213-9). Garland Pub.
Eberhart, Stephen, tr. see Adams, George.
Eberle, Luke, tr. from Latin. & The Rule of the Master: Regula Magistri. LC 77-3986. (Cistercian Studies Ser: No. 6). 1977. 12.95 (ISBN 0-87907-806-5). Cistercian Pubns.
Eberle, Luke, tr. see Heufelder, Emmanuel.
Eberle, Sarah, rev. by see Grogg, Evelyn.
Eberly, William R., ed. see Durnbaugh, Hedwig.
Ebersole, Robert. Black Pagoda. LC 57-12929. (Illus.). 1957. 8.50 (ISBN 0-8130-0070-X). U Presses Fla.
Ebersole, Stella. Go Ye to Burma. 432p. 1986. 24.95 (ISBN 0-89962-556-8). Todd & Honeywell.
Ebert, Barbara. God's World. 1985. pap. 0.98 (ISBN 0-317-30757-6, 2695). Standard Pub.
Eberts, Harry W., Jr. We Believe: A Study of the Book of Confessions for Church Officers. LC 87-2097. 120p. (Orig.). 1987. pap. price not set (ISBN 0-664-24063-1, A Geneva Press Publication). Westminster.
Ebner, James H. God Present As Mystery: A Search for Personal Meaning in Contemporary Theology. LC 76-13750. 1976. pap. 5.95 (ISBN 0-88489-084-8). St Marys.
Ebner, Louise. Exploring Truths Through. pap. 3.95 (ISBN 0-89957-602-8). AMG Pubs.
Eboussi Boulaga, F. Christianity Without Fetishes: An African Critique & Recapture of Christianity. Barr, Robert R., tr. from Fr. LC 84-5807. Tr. of Christianisme sans Fetiche. 256p. (Orig.). 1984. pap. 11.95 (ISBN 0-88344-432-1). Orbis Bks.

Eby, Louise S. Quest for Moral Law. facsimile ed. LC 78-37849. (Essay Index Reprint Ser). Repr. of 1944 ed. 20.00 (ISBN 0-8369-2588-2). Ayer Co Pubs.

Eby, Ray. Bakers Bible Atlas Study Guide. 1977. 4.95 (ISBN 0-686-25535-6); test 1.75 (ISBN 0-686-31725-4); map 1.55 (ISBN 0-686-31726-2). Rod & Staff.

Eby, Richard E. Caught up into Paradise. pap. 3.50 (ISBN 0-8007-8489-8, Spire Bks). Revell.

--Tell Them I Am Coming. 1980. pap. 5.95 (ISBN 0-8007-5045-4, Power Bks). Revell.

--Tell Them I Am Coming. 160p. 1984. pap. 2.50 (ISBN 0-8007-8496-0, Spire Bks). Revell.

Eccles, Sir John. The Human Mystery. LC 78-12095. (Illus.). 1978. 25.00 (ISBN 0-387-09016-9). Springer-Verlag.

Eccles, Mark, ed. Macro Plays: The Castle of Perseverance, Wisdom, Mankind. (Early English Text Society Ser.). 1969. 17.95x (ISBN 0-19-722265-X). Oxford U Pr.

Eccles, Robert S. Erwin Ramsdell Goodenough: A Personal Pilgrimage. (SBL-Biblical Scholarship in North America). 1985. 22.95 (ISBN 0-89130-907-1, 01-11-11); pap. 16.95 (ISBN 0-89130-908-X). Scholars Pr GA.

Ecclestone, Alan. A Staircase for Silence. 158p. 1977. pap. 6.50 (ISBN 0-232-51364-3). Attic Pr.

Echegaray, Hugo. The Practice of Jesus. O'Connell, Matthew J., tr. from Span. LC 83-19341. Orig. Title: La Practica de Jesus. 176p. (Orig.). 1984. pap. 7.95 (ISBN 0-88344-397-X). Orbis Bks.

Echlin, Edward P. Deacon in the Church. LC 75-158571. 1971. 4.95 (ISBN 0-8189-0213-2). Alba.

Echols, Evaline. Climb up Through Your Valleys. 1980. 6.95 (ISBN 0-87148-174-X); pap. 5.95 (ISBN 0-87148-173-1). Pathway Pr.

Eck, Diana L. Banaras: City of Light. LC 81-48134. (Illus.). 1982. 25.00 (ISBN 0-394-51971-X). Knopf.

--Darsan: Seeing the Divine Image in India. 2nd, enl. ed. 97p. 1985. pap. 5.95 (ISBN 0-89012-042-0). Anima Pubns.

Eck, Ellen, tr. from Eng. Himnos de la Vida Cristiana. 1980. 3.95 (ISBN 0-87509-277-2); pap. 2.25 (ISBN 0-87509-275-6); With music. pap. 4.50. Chr Pubns.

Eck, John. Enchiridion of Commonplaces of John Eck. (Twin Brooks Ser.). pap. 9.95 (ISBN 0-8010-3352-7). Baker Bk.

Eck, Laurence, jt. auth. see Buzzard, Lynn R.

Eck, Margaret. Lest We Forget. 72p. pap. 0.75 (ISBN 0-686-29125-5); pap. 2.00 3 copies (ISBN 0-686-29126-3). Faith Pub Hse.

Eckardt, A. R., ed. Your People, My People: The Meeting of Jews & Christians. 212p. 7.95 (ISBN 0-686-95188-3). ADL.

Eckardt, A. Roy. For Righteousness' Sake: Contemporary Moral Philosophies. 1987. 29.95 (ISBN 0-253-32241-3). Ind U Pr.

--Jews & Christians: The Contemporary Meeting. LC 85-45327. 192p. 1986. 19.95x (ISBN 0-253-33162-5). Ind U Pr.

Eckardt, A. Roy & Eckardt, Alice L. Long Night's Journey into Day - Life & Faith After the Holocaust. LC 81-14788. 206p. 1982. 19.50x (ISBN 0-8143-1692-1). Wayne St U Pr.

Eckardt, Alice L., jt. auth. see Eckardt, A. Roy.

Eckel, Malcolm D. Jnanagarbha's Commentary on the Distinction Between the Two Truths. (Buddhist Studies). 196p. (Orig.). 1986. 39.50x (ISBN 0-88706-301-2); pap. 12.95x (ISBN 0-88706-302-0). State U NY Pr.

Eckelmann, Herman J., Jr., jt. auth. see Newman, Robert C.

Eckenrode, Hamilton J. Separation of Church & State in Virginia. LC 75-122164. (Civil Liberties in American History Ser). 1971. Repr. of 1910 ed. lib. bdg. 22.50 (ISBN 0-306-71969-X). Da Capo.

Eckenstein, Lina. A History of the Sinai. LC 78-63461. (The Crusades & Military Orders: Second Ser.). Repr. of 1921 ed. 22.50 (ISBN 0-404-16533-8). AMS Pr.

--Woman Under Monasticism. 59.95 (ISBN 0-8490-1318-6). Gordon Pr.

--Woman Under Monasticism: Chapters on Saint-Lore & Convent Life Between A. D. 500 & A. D. 1500. LC 63-11028. 1963. Repr. of 1896 ed. 10.00x (ISBN 0-8462-0363-4). Russell.

Eckerd, Jack & Conn, Charles P. Eckerd. (Illus.). 1987. 12.95 (ISBN 0-8007-1532-2). Revell.

Eckermann, Willigis. Der Physikkommentar Hugolins von Orvieto Oesa: Ein Beitrag zur Erkenntnislehre des spaetmittelalterlichen Augustinismus. (Spaetmittelalter und Reformation, Vol. 5). 160p. 1972. 23.60x (ISBN 3-11-003714-9). De Gruyter.

Eckhart, Meister. Breakthrough: Meister Eckhart's Creation Spirituality. LC 80-909. 600p. 1980. pap. 10.95 (ISBN 0-385-17034-3, Im). Doubleday.

--Meister Eckhart: A Modern Translation. pap. 8.95x (ISBN 0-06-130008-X, TB8, Torch). Har-Row.

--Meister Eckhart: Mystic & Philosopher. Schurmann, Reiner, tr. LC 76-26416. (Studies in Phenomenology & Existential Philosophy Ser.). 320p. 1978. 22.50x (ISBN 0-253-35183-9). Ind U Pr.

Eckman, Lester. Jewish Tradition & Corporate Morality. LC 85-63013. 96p. 1986. 10.95. Shengold.

Eckstein, Jerome. The Deathday of Socrates: Living, Dying & Immortality-The Theater of Ideas in Plato's "Phaedo". 1981. 17.95 (ISBN 0-914366-19-X); pap. 12.95 (ISBN 0-914366-20-3). Vanguard.

Eckstein, Stephen D., Jr. A History of Churches of Christ in Texas, 1824-1950. 1963. 6.95 (ISBN 0-88027-098-5); 4.95. Firm Foun Pub.

--The Purpose of Genesis. 1976. pap. 2.75 (ISBN 0-88027-037-3). Firm Foun Pub.

Eckstorm, Fannie H. Old John Neptune & Other Maine Indian Shamans. 209p. 1980. pap. 5.95 (ISBN 0-89101-044-0). U Maine Orono.

Eclov, Lee. The Church: Pictures of Christ's Body. (Fisherman Bible Studyguide Ser.). 55p. 1981. saddle stitched 2.95 (ISBN 0-87788-155-3). Shaw Pubs.

Ecole Biblique et Archeologique Francaise. Jerusalem. Catalogue de la Bibliotheque de l'ecole Biblique et Archeologique Francaise (Catalog of the Library of the French Biblical & Archaeological School, 13 vols. 1975. lib. bdg. 1405.00 (ISBN 0-8161-1154-5, Hall Library). G K Hall.

Ed Dufresne Ministries. Praying God's Word. 1979. pap. 1.50 (ISBN 0-89274-126-0). Harrison Hse.

Edades, Jean, ed. see Dumia, Mariano A.

Eddleman, H. Leo. By Life or By Death: A Practical Commentary on Paul's Letter to the Philippians. 176p. (Orig.). 1981. pap. 3.75 (ISBN 0-682-49700-2, Testament). Exposition Pr FL.

--Hail Mary. rev. ed. 134p. 1983. pap. 4.00 (ISBN 0-682-40143-9). Exposition Pr FL.

--Hail Mary, Are You Heeding the Blessed Virgin? In Defense of Public Schools. (Orig.). 1982. pap. 4.00 (ISBN 0-682-49899-8). Exposition Pr FL.

--Schools & Churches in American Democracy: In Defense of Public Schools. 135p. 1983. pap. 4.00 (ISBN 0-682-40144-7). Exposition Pr FL.

Eddy, George S. Man Discovers God. facs. ed. LC 68-24849. (Essay Index Reprint Ser). 1968. Repr. of 1942 ed. 18.00 (ISBN 0-8369-0401-X). Ayer Co Pubs.

--Pathfinders of the World Missionary Crusade. facs. ed. LC 76-84304. (Essay Index Reprint Ser). 1945. 20.25 (ISBN 0-8369-1127-X). Ayer Co Pubs.

Eddy, Mary B. Christian Science. pap. 2.00 (ISBN 0-87516-021-2). De Vorss.

--A Complete Concordance to the Writings of Mary B. Eddy. 33.50 (ISBN 0-87952-092-2). First Church.

--Concordance to Other Writings. 1984. 35.00 (ISBN 0-87952-089-2). First Church.

--Concordance to Science & Health. 1982. 22.50 (ISBN 0-87952-093-0). First Church.

--The First Church of Christ, Scientist, & Miscellany. German Ed. pap. 8.50 (ISBN 0-87952-155-4). First Church.

--The First Church of Christ, Scientist & Miscellany. 1982. pap. 4.50 (ISBN 0-87952-041-8). First Church.

--Manual of the Mother Church, 11 vols. Incl. Vol. 1. Danish. 12.50 (ISBN 0-87952-104-X); Vol. 2. Dutch. 12.50 (ISBN 0-87952-110-4); Vol. 3. French. 12.50 (ISBN 0-87952-118-X); Vol. 4. German. 12.50 (ISBN 0-87952-153-8); Vol. 5. Italian. 12.50 (ISBN 0-87952-181-3); Vol. 6. Norwegian. 12.50 (ISBN 0-87952-196-1); Vol. 7. Portuguese. 12.50 (ISBN 0-87952-206-2); Vol. 8. Spanish. 12.50 (ISBN 0-87952-228-3); Vol. 9. Swedish. 12.50 (ISBN 0-87952-251-8); Vol. 10. Greek. 12.50 (ISBN 0-87952-171-6); Vol. 11. Japanese. 12.50 (ISBN 0-87952-191-0). First Church.

--Manual of the Mother Church, The First Church of Christ, Scientist, in Boston, Massachusetts. standard ed. 9.50 (ISBN 0-87952-061-2); century ed. 11.00 (ISBN 0-87952-063-9); leather 35.00 (ISBN 0-87952-064-7). First Church.

--Miscellaneous Writings, Eighteen Eighty-Three to Eighteen Ninety-Six. 1982. pap. 5.50 (ISBN 0-87952-229-1). First Church.

--The People's Idea of God, Christian Healings No & Yes. pap. 4.50 (ISBN 0-87952-042-6). First Church.

--Prose Works. new type ed. 32.50 (ISBN 0-87952-074-4); brown new type ed. o.p. 70.00 (ISBN 0-87952-076-0); standard ed. 25.00 (ISBN 0-87952-070-1); new type bonded lea. ed. o.p. 47.00 (ISBN 0-87952-075-2). First Church.

--Pulpit & Press. pap. 4.50 (ISBN 0-87952-046-9). First Church.

--Retrospection & Introspection. pap. 4.50 (ISBN 0-87952-044-2). First Church.

--Retrospection & Introspection. French 12.50 (ISBN 0-87952-122-8); German 12.50 (ISBN 0-87952-157-0); Italian 12.50 (ISBN 0-87952-182-1); Portugese 12.50 (ISBN 0-87952-207-0); Spanish 7.50 (ISBN 0-87952-231-3); Swedish 12.50 (ISBN 0-87952-252-6). First Church.

--Rudimental Divine Science & No & Yes. Danish 12.50 (ISBN 0-87952-105-8); German 12.50 (ISBN 0-87952-158-9); Italian 12.50 (ISBN 0-87952-183-X); Portugese 12.50 (ISBN 0-87952-208-9); Swedish 12.50 (ISBN 0-87952-253-4); Spanish 12.50 (ISBN 0-87952-232-1). First Church.

--Rudimental Divine Science: No & Yes. 1976. lib. bdg. 69.95 (ISBN 0-8490-2546-X). Gordon Pr.

--Science & Health with Key to the Scriptures. (Pol.). 25.00 (ISBN 0-87952-200-3). First Church.

--Science & Health with Key to the Scriptures. pap. 10.50 Spanish ed. (ISBN 0-87952-225-9); pap. 10.50 German ed. (ISBN 0-87952-150-3); pap. 10.50 French ed. (ISBN 0-87952-116-3). First Church.

--Science & Health with Key to the Scriptures. Indonesian 25.00 (ISBN 0-87952-175-9); Japanese 25.00 (ISBN 0-87952-190-2). First Church.

--Science & Health with Key to the Scriptures. Incl. Vol. 1. Danish Ed. 25.00 (ISBN 0-87952-103-1); Vol. 2. Dutch Ed. 25.00 (ISBN 0-87952-109-0); Vol. 3. French Ed. 25.00 (ISBN 0-87952-117-1); Vol. 4. German Ed. 25.00 (ISBN 0-87952-151-1); Vol. 5. Norwegian Ed. 25.00 (ISBN 0-87952-195-3); Vol. 6. Swedish Ed. 25.00 (ISBN 0-87952-250-X); Vol. 7. Russian Ed. 25.00 (ISBN 0-87952-220-8); Vol. 8. Greek Ed. 25.00 (ISBN 0-87952-170-8); Vol. 9. Italian Ed. 25.00 (ISBN 0-87952-180-5); Vol. 10. Spanish Ed. 25.00 (ISBN 0-87952-226-7). First Church.

--Seven Messages to the Mother Church. pap. 4.50 (ISBN 0-87952-045-0). First Church.

--Unity of Good. Indonesian ed. 12.50 (ISBN 0-87952-177-5); French Ed. 7.50 (ISBN 0-87952-123-6). First Church.

--Unity of Good, Rudimental Divine Science. pap. 4.50 (ISBN 0-87952-043-4). First Church.

--Unity of Good, Two Sermons. Danish 12.50 (ISBN 0-87952-106-6); Norwegian 12.50 (ISBN 0-87952-197-X); German o.p. 6.00 (ISBN 0-87952-159-7). First Church.

Eddy, Mary B. & Carpenter, Gilbert C., eds. Watches, Prayers, Arguments. 100p. 1985. pap. 12.00 (ISBN 0-930227-01-8). Pasadena Pr.

Eddy, Robert L. Minister's Saturday Night. LC 79-23819. (Orig.). 1980. pap. 6.95 (ISBN 0-8298-0382-3). Pilgrim NY.

Ede, David, et al. Guide to Islam. 265p. 1983. lib. bdg. 59.50 (ISBN 0-8161-7905-0, Hall Reference). G K Hall.

Edel, Wilbur. Defenders of the Faith: Religion & Politics from Pilgrim Fathers to Ronald Reagan. LC 87-2367. 280p. 1987. lib. bdg. 38.95 (ISBN 0-275-92662-1, C2662). Praeger.

Edelby, Neophytos. Future of Canon Law. LC 78-100004. (Concilium Ser.: No. 48). 188p. 7.95 (ISBN 0-8091-0049-5). Paulist Pr.

Edelby, Neophytos & Urresti, Teodoro-J., eds. Religious Freedom. LC 66-29260. (Concilium Ser.: Vol. 18). 191p. 7.95 (ISBN 0-8091-0124-6). Paulist Pr.

Edelby, Neophytos, jt. ed. see Urresti, Teodoro-J.

Edelby, Neophytos, ed. see Urresti, Teodoro J., et al.

Edelby, Neophytos, et al, eds. Sacraments in Theology & Canon Law. LC 68-58308. (Concilium Ser.: Vol. 38). 191p. 1968. 7.95 (ISBN 0-8091-0132-7). Paulist Pr.

Edelestein, Leonard. We Are Accountable. pap. 2.50x (ISBN 0-87574-024-3, 024). Pendle Hill.

Edelman, Lily. Israel. 1958. 20.00 (ISBN 0-686-17232-9). Scholars Ref Lib.

--Sukkah & the Big Wind. (Holiday Series of Picture Story Books). (Illus.). 1956. 5.95 (ISBN 0-8381-0716-8). United Syn Bk.

Edelman, Murray. The Symbolic Uses of Politics: With a New Afterword. LC 84-16195. 232p. 1985. pap. 6.95 (ISBN 0-252-01202-X). U of Ill Pr.

Edelmann, Martin, ed. see Mekhilta, Munich.

Edelstein, Alan. An Unacknowledged Harmony: Philo-Semitism & the Survival of European Jewry. LC 81-1563. (Contributions in Ethnic Studies: No. 4). xii, 235p. 1982. lib. bdg. 29.95 (ISBN 0-313-22754-3, EDP/). Greenwood.

Edelstein, Dov B. Worlds Torn Asunder. 1985. 12.95 (ISBN 0-88125-040-6). Ktav.

Edelstein, Emma J. & Edelstein, Ludwig. Asclepius: A Collection & Interpretation of the Testimonies, 2 vols. in 1. facsimile ed. LC 75-10635. (Ancient Religion & Mythology Ser.). (Eng. & Gr.). 1976. Repr. of 1945 ed. 57.50x (ISBN 0-405-07009-8). Ayer Co Pubs.

Edelstein, Ludwig, jt. auth. see Edelstein, Emma J.

Edens, David. Estoy Creciendo Estoy Cambiando. Du Plou, Dafne C., tr. (Sexo en la Vida Cristiana Ser). (Illus.). 1985. pap. 1.75 (ISBN 0-311-46252-9). Casa Bautista.

Edersheim, Alfred. Jesus the Messiah. 1959. pap. 10.95 (ISBN 0-8028-8131-9). Eerdmans.

--Life & Times of Jesus the Messiah. 1972. 25.95 (ISBN 0-8028-8027-4). Eerdmans.

--The Life & Times of Jesus the Messiah. 1568p. Date not set. 24.95 (ISBN 0-917006-12-7). Hendrickson MA.

--Old Testament Bible History. 1972. 24.95 (ISBN 0-8028-8028-2). Eerdmans.

--Practical Truths from Elisha. LC 82-18702. 368p. 1983. 14.95 (ISBN 0-8254-2511-5). Kregel.

--Temple, Its Ministry & Services. 1950. 5.95 (ISBN 0-8028-8133-5). Eerdmans.

Edersheim, Alfred, et al. Practical Truth Series, 6 Vols. Incl. Elisha; Jonah; Thessalonians; Pastoral Epistles; Israel's Wanderings; Judges. 1940p. 1986. Set. 74.70 (ISBN 0-8254-3529-3). Kregel.

Edgar, Carlson M. The Classic Christian Faith: Chapel Meditations Based on Luther's Small Catechism. LC 59-9093. pap. 42.80 (2026912). Bks Demand UMI.

Edgar, Ellen, jt. auth. see Edgar, James.

Edgar, James & Edgar, Ellen. A Chrismon Service. 20p. 1981. pap. text ed. 2.95 (ISBN 0-89536-500-6, 0341). CSS of Ohio.

Edgar, Thomas R. Miraculous Gifts: Are They for Today? 384p. 1983. 11.95 (ISBN 0-87213-133-5). Loizeaux.

Edgar, William. In Spirit & in Truth: Ten Bible Studies on Worship. 72p. (Orig.). 1976. pap. 2.25 (ISBN 0-87784-458-5). Inter-Varsity.

Edge, Findley B. Helping the Teacher. 1959. 10.95 (ISBN 0-8054-3403-8). Broadman.

--Metodologia Pedagogica. Mendoza, Celia & Molina, Sara P., trs. from Eng. Orig. Title: Helping the Teacher. 155p. 1982. pap. 3.75 (ISBN 0-311-11026-6). Casa Bautista.

--Pedagogia Fructifera. Lopez, Alberto, tr. from Eng. Tr. of Teaching for Results. (Span.). 192p. 1985. pap. 3.95 (ISBN 0-311-11025-8). Casa Bautista.

--Teaching for Results. 1956. 10.95 (ISBN 0-8054-3401-1). Broadman.

Edge, Henry T. Esoteric Keys to the Christian Scriptures. rev. 2nd ed. Small, W. Emmett & Todd, Helen, eds. Bd. with The Universal Mystery-Language of Myth & Symbol. Orig. Title: The Universal Mystery-Language & Its Interpretations. Orig. Title: Theosophical Light on the Christian Bible. 1973. pap. 3.00 (ISBN 0-913004-12-X, 913004-12). Point Loma Pub.

--Evolution: Who & What Is Man. Small, W. Emmett & Todd, Helen, eds. (Theosophical Manual: No. 6). 78p. 1975. pap. 2.00 (ISBN 0-913004-22-7, 913004-22). Point Loma Pub.

--Theosophy & Christianity. rev. ed. Small, W. Emmett & Todd, Helen, eds. (Theosophical Manual: No. 12). 80p. 1974. pap. 2.00 (ISBN 0-913004-17-0). Point Loma Pub.

Edge, Henry T., et al. Mirrors of the Hidden Wisdom: Threads of Theosophy in Literature - I. (Study Ser.: No. 7). 122p. 1981. pap. 5.95 (ISBN 0-913004-42-1). Point Loma Pub.

Edgerly, George A. & Crosby, Harold E. Strategies for Sunday School Growth. LC 83-80404. (Worker's Training Ser.). 128p. (Orig.). 1983. pap. 2.50 (ISBN 0-88243-591-4, 02-0591). Gospel Pub.

Edgerton, Dorothy. Walk on in Peace. LC 82-73133. 64p. (Orig.). 1982. pap. 1.45 (ISBN 0-87029-187-4, 20278-8). Abbey.

Edgerton, Franklin, ed. Buddhist Hybrid Sanscrit Reader. 1953. 49.50x (ISBN 0-685-69814-9). Elliots Bks.

Edgerton, R. B., ed. see Langness, L. L. & Frank, Gelya F.

Ediger, Max. A Vietnamese Pilgrimage. LC 78-53650. (Illus.). 1978. pap. 5.25 (ISBN 0-87303-007-9). Faith & Life.

Ediger, Peter J. The Prophets' Report on Religion in North America. rev. ed. LC 78-150650. 1978. pap. 2.00 (ISBN 0-87303-686-7). Faith & Life.

Edington, David W. Christians & the Third World. 160p. 1982. pap. text ed. 7.95 (ISBN 0-85364-286-9). Attic Pr.

Edkins, Joseph. Chinese Buddhism: A Volume of Sketches, Historical, Descriptive & Critical. 2nd, rev. ed. 487p. Repr. of 1893 ed. text ed. 27.50x (Pub. by Chinese Matl Ctr). Coronet Bks.

Edman, David. Once upon an Eternity. LC 83-62515. 108p. 1984. pap. 6.95 (ISBN 0-89390-052-4). Resource Pubns.

Edman, Irwin. Contemporary & His Soul. LC 66-25907. Repr. of 1931 ed. 18.50x (ISBN 0-8046-0129-1, Pub. by Kennikat). Assoc Faculty Pr.

Edman, V. E. & Laidlaw, R. A. The Fullness of the Spirit. 36p. pap. 0.95 (ISBN 0-87509-083-4). Chr Pubns.

Edman, V. Raymond. Finney Lives On. 256p. 1970. pap. 4.95 (ISBN 0-87123-150-6, 210150). Bethany Hse.

--They Found the Secret: Twenty Lives that Reveal a Touch of Eternity. 176p. 1984. pap. 5.95 (ISBN 0-310-24051-4, 9564P, Clarion Class). Zondervan.

Edmonds, Cyrus R. John Milton: A Biography. LC 72-194753. 1851. lib. bdg. 20.00 (ISBN 0-8414-3886-2). Folcroft.

Edmonds, Irene, tr. see Bernard Of Clairvaux.

Edmonds, Irene, jt. tr. see Walsh, Kilian.

Edmonds, Rosemary, tr. see Sophrony, Archimandrite.

Edmonson, Munro S., tr. from Maya. Heaven Born Merida & Its Destiny: The Book of Chilam Balam of Chumayel. (Texas Pan American Ser.). (Illus.). 304p. 1986. 37.50x (ISBN 0-292-73027-6). U of Tex Pr.

Edmunds, C. C. & Hatch, W. H. Gospel Manuscripts of the General Theological Seminary. (Harv Theol Studies). 1918. pap. 15.00 (ISBN 0-527-01004-9). Kraus Repr.

Edmunds, L. Francis. Anthroposophy as a Healing Force. 14p. pap. 2.25 (ISBN 0-88010-037-0, Pub.by Rudolf Steiner Pr). Anthroposophic.

Edmundson, George. The Church in Rome in the First Century. 1976. lib. bdg. 59.95 (ISBN 0-8490-1627-4). Gordon Pr.

Edsman, C. M., jt. auth. see Hartman, Sven S.

Edstrom, Lois. Contemporary Object Lessons for Children's Church. (Object Lessons Ser.). 112p. 1986. 4.50 (ISBN 0-8010-3432-9). Baker Bk.

--Object Talks on the Parables of Jesus. (Illus.). 48p. (Orig.). 1984. pap. 2.95 (ISBN 0-87239-721-1, 2857). Standard Pub.

Edvardsen, Aril & Harris, Madalene. Dreaming & Achieving the Impossible. 1984. pap. 5.95 (ISBN 0-88419-192-3). Creation Hse.

Edward, Gene. A Tale of Three Kings. 120p. 1980. pap. 5.95 (ISBN 0-940232-03-0). Christian Bks.

Edward, Herbert. First Baron Herbert of Cherbury. Wellek, Rene, ed. (British Philosophers & Theologians of the 17th & 18th Centuries Ser.). 1979. 51.00 (ISBN 0-8240-1779-X). Garland Pub.

Edwards, Anne, jt. auth. see Steen, Shirley.

Edwards, Bob. Anybody Who Needs to Be Sure Is in Trouble. LC 82-81009. 72p. 1982. pap. 5.45 (ISBN 0-941780-11-2, Parkhurst-Little). August Hse.

Edwards, Bruce & Fudge, Edward. A Journey Toward Jesus. 1.50 (ISBN 0-686-12687-4). E Fudge.

Edwards, Carolyn P. Promoting Social & Moral Development in Young Children: Creative Approaches for the Classroom. (Early Childhood Education Ser.). 192p. 1986. text ed. 25.95x (ISBN 0-8077-2831-4); pap. text ed. 13.95x (ISBN 0-8077-2820-9). Tchrs Coll.

Edwards, Charles G. Stress. (Outreach Ser.). 32p. 1982. pap. 1.25 (ISBN 0-8163-0468-8). Pacific Pr Pub Assn.

Edwards, Charles L. Understanding Biblical Symbols. 96p. 1981. 6.00 (ISBN 0-682-49704-5). Exposition Pr FL.

Edwards, Dale. Founded Upon a Rock. 1977. pap. 3.95 (ISBN 0-89265-043-5). Randall Hse.

Edwards, David L. What Anglicans Believe. 128p. 1975. pap. 1.90 (ISBN 0-88028-003-4, 503). Forward Movement.

Edwards, Deborah. Opening Devotions for Womens Groups. 96p. 1985. pap. 4.95 (ISBN 0-8010-3428-0). Baker Bk.

Edwards, Denis. Human Experience of God. 1984. pap. 7.95 (ISBN 0-8091-2559-5). Paulist Pr.

--What Are They Saying about Salvation? 100p. 1986. pap. 4.95 (ISBN 0-8091-2793-8). Paulist Pr.

Edwards, E. H. Fire & Sword in Shansi: The Story of the Martyrdom of Foreigners & Chinese Christians. LC 74-111738. (American Imperialism: Viewpoints of United States Foreign Policy, 1898-1941). 1970. Repr. of 1903 ed. 21.00 (ISBN 0-405-02014-7). Ayer Co Pubs.

Edwards, F. H. Life & Ministry of Jesus. 1982. pap. 14.00 (ISBN 0-686-95353-3). Herald Hse.

Edwards, F. Henry. God Our Help. 1981. pap. 11.00 (ISBN 0-8309-0310-0). Herald Hse.

--History of the Reorganized Church of Jesus Christ of Latter Day Saints Vol. 5: 1890-1902. 1969. 22.50 (ISBN 0-8309-0019-5). Herald Hse.

--The History of the Reorganized Church of Jesus Christ of Latter Day Saints, Vols. 6 & 7. Incl. Vol. 6. 1903-1914. 1970 (ISBN 0-8309-0030-6); Vol. 7. 1915-1925. 1973 (ISBN 0-8309-0075-6). 22.50 ea. Herald Hse.

--History of the Reorganized Church of Jesus Christ of the Latter Day Saints, Vol. 8: 1926-1946. 1976. 22.50 (ISBN 0-8309-0157-4). Herald Hse.

--Meditation & Prayer. LC 79-23708. 1980. pap. 12.00 (ISBN 0-8309-0271-6). Herald Hse.

--The Power That Worketh in Us. 1987. pap. 16.00 (ISBN 0-8309-0481-6). Herald Hse.

--A Students Guide to the Doctrine & Covenants. 1980. pap. 9.00 (ISBN 0-8309-0267-8). Herald Hse.

Edwards, F Henry. Studies in Genesis, Vol. 1. 1987. pap. 3.50 (ISBN 0-8309-0482-4). Herald Hse.

Edwards, Francis. The Jesuits in England from 1850 to the Present Day. LC 85-12048. 333p. text ed. cancelled (ISBN 0-268-01204-0, Pub. by Burns & Oates London). U of Notre Dame Pr.

Edwards, Fred E. The Role of the Faith Mission: A Brazilian Case Study. LC 79-152406. (Illus.). 76p. 1971. pap. 3.45 (ISBN 0-87808-406-1). William Carey Lib.

Edwards, Gene. Church Life. 132p. 1987. text ed. 8.95 (ISBN 0-940232-25-1). Christian Bks.

--The Early Church. 1974. pap. text ed. 5.95 (ISBN 0-940232-02-2). Christian Bks.

--How to Have a Soul Winning Church. 1963. pap. 3.95 (ISBN 0-88243-524-8, 02-0524). Gospel Pub.

--Inward Journey. 250p. 1982. pap. 5.95 (ISBN 0-940232-06-5). Christian Bks.

--Letters to a Devastated Christian. 68p. 1983. pap. 3.95 (ISBN 0-940232-13-8). Christian Bks.

--Our Mission. (Orig.). 1984. pap. 7.95 (ISBN 0-940232-11-1). Christian Bks.

--Preventing a Church Split. 1987. 8.95 (ISBN 0-940232-26-X). Christian Bks.

--The Purpose. 1987. pap. 5.95 (ISBN 0-940232-27-8). Christian Bks.

Edwards, Gene, ed. The Divine Romance. 1984. 10.95 (ISBN 0-940232-24-3); pap. 7.95. Christian Bks.

Edwards, Gene, ed. see Brother Lawrence & Laubach, Frank.

Edwards, Gene, ed. see Fenelon.

Edwards, Gene, ed. see Guyon, Jeanne.

Edwards, Gene, ed. see Guyon, Jeanne M.

Edwards, Gene, ed. see Molinos, Michael.

Edwards, George R. Gay-Lesbian Liberation: A Biblical Perspective. 144p. (Orig.). 1984. pap. 9.95 (ISBN 0-8298-0725-X). Pilgrim NY.

Edwards, I. E. S. The Pyramids of Egypt. 368p. 1987. 25.00 (ISBN 0-670-80153-4). Viking.

Edwards, James R., jt. ed. see Knight, George.

Edwards, James R., jt. ed. see Knight, George W.

Edwards, John. Some Thoughts Concerning the Several Causes & Occasions of Atheism, Especially in the Present Age. LC 80-48568. (The Philosophy of John Locke Ser.). 268p. 1984. lib. bdg. 35.00 (ISBN 0-8240-5603-5). Garland Pub.

Edwards, Jonathan. Apocalyptic Writings. LC 57-2336. (The Works of Jonathan Edwards: Vol. 5). (Illus.). 1977. 50.00x (ISBN 0-300-01945-9). Yale U Pr.

--A Dissertation Concerning Liberty & Necessity. LC 73-21786. 1974. Repr. of 1797 ed. lib. bdg. 22.50 (ISBN 0-8337-1003-6). B Franklin.

--Freedom of the Will. Kaufman, Arnold S. & Frankena, William K., eds. LC 82-18742. 300p. 1982. pap. text ed. 14.95x (ISBN 0-8290-1264-8). Irvington.

--Freedom of the Will. Ramsey, Paul, ed. (Works of Jonathan Edwards Ser.: Vol. 1). (Illus.). 1957. 50.00x (ISBN 0-300-00848-1). Yale U Pr.

--The Great Awakening. Goen, C. C., ed. LC 75-179472. (Works of Johathan Edwards Ser.: Vol. 4). 1972. 50.00x (ISBN 0-300-01437-6). Yale U Pr.

--Images or Shadows of Divine Things. Miller, Perry, ed. LC 73-8157. 1977. Repr. of 1948 ed. lib. bdg. 29.75x (ISBN 0-8371-6952-6, EDIS). Greenwood.

--The Life & Character of the Late Reverend, Learned, & Pious Mr. Jonathan Edwards, President of the College in New Jersey. LC 75-31090. Repr. of 1804 ed. 28.50 (ISBN 0-404-13508-0). AMS Pr.

--The Life of David Brainerd: The Works of Jonathan Edwards, Vol. 7. Pettit, Norman, ed. LC 83-23445. (Illus.). 640p. 1984. text ed. 50.00x (ISBN 0-300-03004-5). Yale U Pr.

--Nature of True Virtue. 1960. pap. 5.95 (ISBN 0-472-06037-6, 37, AA). U of Mich Pr.

--Original Sin. Holbrook, Clyde A., ed. (Works of Jonathan Edwards Ser.: Vol. 3). 1970. 50.00x (ISBN 0-300-01198-9). Yale U Pr.

--Religious Affections. Smith, John E., ed. LC 59-12702. (Works of Jonathan Edwards Ser.: Vol. 2). (Illus.). 1959. 50.00x (ISBN 0-300-00966-6). Yale U Pr.

--Religious Affections. Houston, James M., ed. LC 84-14863. (Classics of Faith & Devotion Ser.). 1984. 11.95 (ISBN 0-88070-064-5). Multnomah.

--Religious Affections. 382p. 1986. pap. 9.45 (ISBN 0-85151-485-5). Banner of Truth.

--Selected Writings of Jonathan Edwards. Simonson, Harold P., ed. LC 78-115064. (Milestones of Thought Ser.). 1970. pap. 7.95 (ISBN 0-8044-6132-5). Ungar.

--Sinners in the Hands of an Angry God. pap. 0.50 (ISBN 0-685-00746-4). Reiner.

--Treatise on Grace & Other Posthumous Published Writings Including Observations on the Trinity. Helm, Paul, ed. 141p. 1971. 13.95 (ISBN 0-227-67739-0). Attic Pr.

--The Works of Jonathan Edwards, 2 vols. 1979. Set. 66.95 (ISBN 0-85151-397-2); Vol. 1. 36.95 (ISBN 0-85151-216-X); Vol. 2. 36.95 (ISBN 0-85151-217-8). Banner of Truth.

--Works of President Edwards, 10 Vols. Williams, Edward & Parsons, Edward, eds. LC 68-56782. (Research & Source Works Ser.: No. 271). 1968. Repr. of 1847 ed. 245.00 (ISBN 0-8337-1019-2). B Franklin.

Edwards, Judson. Dancing to Zion: How to Harvest Joy on the Road to Heaven. Sloan, John, ed. 180p. 1986. pap. 5.95 avail. (ISBN 0-310-34511-1, 12066P). Zondervan.

--Running the Race. LC 85-4700. 1985. pap. 5.95 (ISBN 0-8054-5711-9). Broadman.

--With Love from Dad. 208p. 1986. pap. 5.95 (ISBN 0-89081-501-1). Harvest Hse.

Edwards, Katherine. A House Divided. 144p. 1984. pap. 4.95 (ISBN 0-310-43501-3, 11169P). Zondervan.

Edwards, LaVell. Achieving. 77p. 1985. 7.95 (ISBN 0-934126-79-8). Randall Bk Co.

Edwards, Maria. Total Youth Ministry: A Handbook for Parishes. LC 76-29885. 1976. pap. 4.50 (ISBN 0-88489-085-6). St Mary's.

Edwards, Mark & Tavard, George. Luther: A Reformer for the Churches. 1983. pap. 4.95 (ISBN 0-8091-2575-7). Paulist Pr.

Edwards, Mark & Tavard, George H. Luther: A Reformer for the Churches; An Ecumenical Study Guide. LC 83-48005. 96p. 1983. pap. 5.50 (ISBN 0-8006-1718-5, 1-1718). Fortress.

Edwards, Mark U., Jr. Luther & the False Brethren. LC 75-181. 1975. 20.00x (ISBN 0-8047-0883-5). Stanford U Pr.

--Luther's Last Battles: Politics & Polemics, 1531-1546. LC 82-72363. (Illus.). 272p. 1986. pap. text ed. 9.95x (ISBN 0-8014-9393-5). Cornell U Pr.

--Luther's Last Battles: Politics & Polemics, 1531-46. 272p. 1983. 24.95x (ISBN 0-8014-1564-0). Cornell U Pr.

Edwards, Mark U., Jr., ed. see Moeller, Bernd.

Edwards, Michael. Towards a Christian Poetics. 260p. 13.95x (ISBN 0-8028-3596-1). Eerdmans.

Edwards, Morgan. Materials Toward a History of the Baptists, 2 vols. 1984. 36.00 (ISBN 0-317-38301-9). Church History.

Edwards, O. C. How It All Began: Origins of the Christian Church New Edition with Study Guide. 1978. pap. 6.95 (ISBN 0-8164-2164-1, HarpR). Har-Row.

--The Living & Active Word: A Way to Preach from the Bible Today. 166p. 1975. 1.50 (ISBN 0-8164-0265-5, HarpR). Har-Row.

Edwards, O. C., jt. auth. see Bennett, Robert A.

Edwards, O. C., et al. Anglican Theology & Pastoral Care. Griffiss, James, ed. 160p. (Orig.). 1985. pap. 8.95 (ISBN 0-8192-1364-0). Morehouse.

Edwards, O. C., Jr. Elements of Homiletic. LC 84-157333. 110p. (Orig.). 1982. pap. 7.95 (ISBN 0-916134-55-5). Pueblo Pub CO.

--Luke's Story of Jesus. LC 81-43076. 96p. 1981. pap. 4.50 (ISBN 0-8006-1611-1, 1-1611). Fortress.

Edwards, O. C., Jr. & Taylor, Gardner C. Pentecost 3. Achtemeier, Elizabeth, et al, eds. LC 79-7377. (Proclamation 2: Aids for Interpreting the Lessons of the Church Year, Ser. C). 64p. (Orig.). 1980. pap. 3.75 (ISBN 0-8006-4084-5, 1-4084). Fortress.

Edwards, O. C., Jr. & Westerhoff, John H., 3rd, eds. A Faithful Church: Issues in the History of Catechesis. LC 80-81099. 320p. (Orig.). 1981. pap. 14.95 (ISBN 0-8192-1278-4). Morehouse.

Edwards, R. B. Kadmos the Phoenician: A Study in Greek Legends & the Mycenaen Age. xiv, 258p. 1979. pap. text ed. 67.50x (Pub. by A. M. Hakkert). Coronet Bks.

Edwards, R. Dudley. Church & State in Tudor Ireland: A History of Penal Laws Against Irish Catholics 1534-1603. LC 76-180608. (Illus.). xliiii, 352p. 1972. Repr. of 1935 ed. 18.00x (ISBN 0-8462-1641-8). Russell.

Edwards, Rem B. Reason & Religion: An Introduction to the Philosophy of Religion. LC 78-66278. 1979. pap. text ed. 12.50 (ISBN 0-8191-0690-9). U Pr of Amer.

Edwards, Richard & Wild, Robert. The Sentences of Sextus. LC 81-13770. (Society of Biblical Literature Texts & Translations Ser.). 1981. pap. text ed. 12.00 (ISBN 0-89130-528-9, 06-02-22). Scholars Pr GA.

Edwards, Richard A. A Concordance to Q. LC 75-6768. (Society of Biblical Literature. Sources for Biblical Study). iv, 186p. 1975. pap. 13.95 (ISBN 0-89130-880-6, 060307). Scholars Pr GA.

--A Concordance to Q. LC 75-6768. (Society of Biblical Literature. Sources for Biblical Study: No. 7). Repr. of 1975 ed. 36.90 (ISBN 0-8357-9568-3, 2017677). Bks Demand UMI.

--Matthew's Story of Jesus. LC 84-48711. 96p. 1985. pap. 4.50 (ISBN 0-8006-1619-7, 1-1619). Fortress.

--Sign of Jonah in the Theology of the Evangelists & Q. LC 74-153931. (Studies in Biblical Theology, 2nd Ser.: No. 18). 1971. pap. text ed. 10.00x (ISBN 0-8401-3068-6). A R Allenson.

Edwards, Robert. The Montecassino Passion & the Poetics of Medieval Drama. LC 75-22655. 1977. 36.50x (ISBN 0-520-03102-4). U of Cal Pr.

Edwards, Rosemary W. Cut & Color Patterns for Young Children. rev. ed. (Illus.). 112p. 1985. pap. 4.95 (ISBN 0-912315-93-8). Word Aflame.

Edwards, Ruth. Answer Me. LC 83-61453. (Illus., Orig.). 1983. pap. 7.95 (ISBN 0-89390-041-9); pap. text ed. 6.95. Resource Pubns.

Edwards, Sarah A., jt. ed. see Berkey, Robert F.

Edwards, Steve L. Connections. 112p. 1986. pap. 7.95x (ISBN 0-8170-1110-2). Judson.

Edwards, Steven A. Interior Acts: Teleology, Justice, & Friendship in the Religious Ethics of Thomas Aquinas. LC 85-29530. 184p. (Orig.). 1986. lib. bdg. 24.75 (ISBN 0-8191-5212-9); pap. text ed. 11.75 (ISBN 0-8191-5213-7). U Pr of Amer.

Edwards, Thomas C. A Commentary on the First Epistle to the Corinthians. 1979. 18.00 (ISBN 0-86524-013-2, 4602). Klock & Klock.

--The Epistle to the Hebrews. 394p. 1982. lib. bdg. 13.00 Smythe Sewn (ISBN 0-86524-154-6, 5803). Klock & Klock.

Edwards, Tilden. Living Simply Through the Day. 444p. 1985. pap. 9.95 large print ed. (ISBN 0-8027-2492-2). Walker & Co.

--Sabbath Time: Understanding & Practice for Contemporary Christians. 144p. 1984. pap. 8.95 (ISBN 0-8164-0526-3, AY7883, HarpR). Har-Row.

--Spiritual Friend: Reclaiming the Gift of Spiritual Direction. LC 79-91408. 272p. 1980. pap. 9.95 (ISBN 0-8091-2288-X). Paulist Pr.

Eeden, Frederik Van see Van Eeden, Frederik.

Eells, Hastings. The Attitudes of Martin Bucer Toward the Bigamy of Philip of Hesse. LC 83-45611. Date not set. Repr. of 1924 ed. 32.50 (ISBN 0-404-19829-5). AMS Pr.

Eells, John S. Touchstones of Matthew Arnold. LC 76-136388. Repr. of 1955 ed. 22.50 (ISBN 0-404-02263-4). AMS Pr.

Eeningenburg, Dennis. Workbook on Morality: A Biblical View of Sexuality. 74p. (Orig.). 1981. pap. 4.95 (ISBN 0-8341-0717-1). Beacon Hill.

Effendi, Shoghi. The Advent of Divine Justice. rev. ed. LC 84-436. x, 104p. 1984. 14.95 (ISBN 0-87743-195-7); pap. 8.95 (ISBN 0-87743-196-5). Baha'i.

--Call to the Nations: Extracts from the Writings of Shoghi Effendi. LC 79-670140. 1978. 6.95 (ISBN 0-85398-068-3, 108-050); pap. 3.00 o. s. i. (ISBN 0-85398-069-1, 108-051). Baha'i.

--The Promised Day Is Come. rev. ed. 1980. 10.95 (ISBN 0-87743-132-9, 108-017); pap. 5.50 (ISBN 0-87743-138-8, 108-018). Baha'i.

--Selected Writings of Shoghi Effendi. rev. ed. 1975. pap. 1.95 (ISBN 0-87743-079-9, 308-043). Baha'i.

--The World Order of Baha'u'llah. 2nd rev. ed. LC 56-17685. 1974. 16.95 (ISBN 0-87743-031-4, 108-020); pap. 8.95 (ISBN 0-87743-004-7, 108-021). Baha'i.

Effendi, Shoghi, tr. see Abdu'l-Baha.

Effendi, Shoghi, tr. see Baha'u'llah.

Effendi, Shoghi, tr. see Bahaullah.

Effron, Benjamin, ed. see Karp, Deborah.

Efird, James M. Biblical Books of Wisdom. 96p. 1983. pap. 4.95 (ISBN 0-8170-0999-X). Judson.

--End-Times: Rapture, Antichrist, Millennium. 96p. (Orig.). 1986. pap. 5.95 (ISBN 0-687-11787-9). Abingdon.

--How to Interpret the Bible. LC 83-49051. 144p. 1984. pap. 7.95 (ISBN 0-8042-0069-6). John Knox.

--Marriage & Divorce: What the Bible Says. (Contemporary Christian Concerns Ser.). 96p. (Orig.). 1985. pap. 4.95 (ISBN 0-687-23619-3). Abingdon.

--The New Testament Writings: History, Literature, Interpretation. LC 79-87750. (Biblical Foundation Ser.). 1980. pap. 7.95 (ISBN 0-8042-0246-X). John Knox.

--The Old Testament Prophets Then & Now. 128p. 1982. pap. 4.95 (ISBN 0-8170-0960-4). Judson.

--Old Testament Writings: History, Literature, Interpretation. LC 81-82352. (Biblical Foundations Ser.). (Illus.). 324p. 1982. pap. 11.95 (ISBN 0-8042-0145-5). John Knox.

--These Things Are Written: An Introduction to the Religious Ideas of the Bible. LC 77-15749. (Biblical Foundations Ser.). 1978. pap. 8.95 (ISBN 0-8042-0073-4). John Knox.

Efron, Benjamin & Rubin, Alvan D. Coming of Age: Your Bar or Bat Mitzvah. LC 77-78031. (Illus.). 1977. 5.00 (ISBN 0-8074-0084-X, 142530). UAHC.

Efron, Marshall & Olsen, Alfa B. Bible Stories You Can't Forget No Matter How Hard You Try. (Illus.). 1976. 9.95 (ISBN 0-525-26500-7, 0966-290). Dutton.

Efros, Israel I. Ancient Jewish Philosophy. 1976. pap. 5.95x (ISBN 0-8197-0014-2). Bloch.

--Philosophical Terms in the Moreh Nebukim. LC 73-164764. (Columbia University. Oriental Studies: No. 22). Repr. of 1924 ed. 17.00 (ISBN 0-404-50512-0). AMS Pr.

--Problem of Space in Jewish Medieval Philosophy. LC 77-164765. (Columbia University. Oriental Studies: No. 11). Repr. of 1917 ed. 14.75 (ISBN 0-404-50501-5). AMS Pr.

--Problem of Space in Jewish Medieval Philosophy. facsimile ed. lib. bdg. 37.50x (ISBN 0-697-00037-0); pap. 7.95 (ISBN 0-89197-904-2). Irvington.

Egan, Eileen. Such a Vision of the Street: Mother Teresa; The Spirit & The Work. LC 81-43570. (Illus.). 456p. 1985. 16.95 (ISBN 0-385-17490-X). Doubleday.

--Such a Vision of the Street: Mother Teresa-The Spirit & the Work. LC 81-43570. (Illus.). 528p. 1986. pap. 9.95 (ISBN 0-385-17491-8, Im). Doubleday.

Egan, Harvey D. Christian Mysticism. 300p. (Orig.). 1984. pap. 14.95 (ISBN 0-916134-63-6). Pueblo Pub Co.

--The Spiritual Exercises & the Ignatian Mystical Horizon. LC 76-5742. (Study Aids on Jesuit Topics, Series 4: No. 5). xii, 216p. 1976. smyth sewn 7.00 (ISBN 0-912422-18-1); pap. 6.00 (ISBN 0-912422-14-9). Inst Jesuit.

--What Are They Saying about Mysticism? (WATSA Ser.). 128p. 1982. pap. 4.95 (ISBN 0-8091-2459-9). Paulist Pr.

Egan, John P. & Colford, Paul D. Baptism of Resistance-Blood & Celebration: A Road to Wholeness in the Nuclear Age. 1983. pap. 5.95 (ISBN 0-89622-164-4). Twenty-Third.

Egan, Katherine. Beginnings: The Orientation of New Teachers. 20p. 1981. 2.40 (ISBN 0-686-39892-0). Natl Cath Educ.

Egan, M. Winston, jt. auth. see Landau, Elliott D.

Egan, Maurice F. The Life of St. Francis & the Soul of Modern Man. (Illus.). 131p. 1983. 88.85 (ISBN 0-89266-427-4). Am Classical Coll Pr.

Egbert, Elaine. Hardly an Angel in Sight. Woolsey, Raymond H., ed. (Banner Ser.). 128p. (Orig.). 1987. pap. 6.50 (ISBN 0-8280-0369-6). Review & Herald.

Ege, Arvia M. The Experience of the Christmas Foundation Meeting, 1923. 14p. 1981. pap. 2.50 (ISBN 0-932776-03-5). Adonis Pr.

Egelkraut, Helmuth L. Jesus' Mission to Jerusalem: Theology, Vol. 80. (European University Studies: Ser. 23). x, 258p. 1977. pap. 28.70 (ISBN 3-261-02133-0). P Lang Pubs.

Egenter, Richard. Desecration of Christ. 1967. 4.50 (ISBN 0-8199-0018-4, L38133). Franciscan Herald.

Egenter, Richard & Matussek, Paul. Moral Problems & Mental Health. 1967. 4.95 (ISBN 0-8189-0095-4). Alba.

Egenton, Judy, intro. by. Stubbs: Portraits in Detail. (Illus.). 48p. 1985. pap. 8.95 (ISBN 0-946590-17-6). Salem Hse Pubs.

Egermeier, Elsie E. Egermeier's Bible Story Book. 5th ed. LC 68-23397. (Illus.). 1969. 14.95 (ISBN 0-87162-006-5, D2005); deluxe ed. 15.95 (ISBN 0-87162-007-3, D2006); pap. 8.95 (ISBN 0-87162-229-7, D2008). Warner Pr.

--Egermeier's Favorite Bible Stories. 1965. 7.95 (ISBN 0-87162-014-6, D3695). Warner Pr.

--Egermeier's Picture-Story Life of Jesus. (Illus.). 1969. 7.95 (ISBN 0-87162-008-1, D2015). Warner Pr.

--Picture Story Bible ABC Book. rev. ed. (Illus.). 1963. 5.95 (ISBN 0-87162-262-9, D1703). Warner Pr.

Egerton, Frank N., 3rd, ed. see Derham, William.

Egerton, Frank N., 3rd, ed. see Ray, John.

Eggeling, Julius. The Satapatha Brahmana. (Sacred Bks. of the East: Vols. 12, 26, 41, 43, 44). 5 vols. 75.00 (ISBN 0-686-97483-2); 15.00 ea. Asian Human Pr.

Eggeling, Julius, ed. The Satapatha Brahmana, 5 vols. 1974. lib. bdg. 500.00 (ISBN 0-8490-0994-4). Gordon Pr.

Eggenstein, Kurt. The Unknown Prophet Jakob Lorber. LC 79-89530. 78p. (Orig.). 1979. pap. 3.50 (ISBN 0-912760-99-0). Valkyrie Pub Hse.

Eggleton, John E. Discovering the Old Testament. 306p. 1980. pap. text ed. 7.95 (ISBN 0-933656-07-6). Trinity Pub Hse.

Eggold, Henry J. Preaching Is Dialogue. 144p. 1980. pap. 5.95 (ISBN 0-8010-3358-6). Baker Bk.

Eggstein, Kurt. The Prophet Jakob Lorber Predicts Coming Catastrophies & the True Christianity. Schuck, Marjorie M., ed. Meuss, A. R., tr. from Ger. LC 85-51354. 480p. 1985. pap. 12.00 (ISBN 0-934616-40-X). Valkyrie Pub Hse.

Ehlen-Miller, Margaret, et al. The Gift of Time: Family Activities for Advent, Christmas, Epiphany. (Illus.). 1977. pap. 4.95 (ISBN 0-8192-1224-5). Morehouse.

--A Time of Hope: Family Celebrations & Activities for Lent & Easter. (Illus., Orig.). 1979. pap. 4.95 (ISBN 0-8192-1247-4). Morehouse.

Ehmann, Wilhelm. Choral Directing. Wiebe, George D., tr. 1968. 15.95 (ISBN 0-8066-0832-3, 11-9130). Augsburg.

Ehrenburg, Iiya & Grossman, Vasily. The Black Book. LC 81-81519. 595p. 1980. 24.95 (ISBN 0-89604-031-3); pap. 14.95 (ISBN 0-89604-032-1). Holocaust Pubns.

Ehrenpreis, Andreas & Felbinger, Claus. Brotherly Community, the Highest Command of Love: Two Anabaptist Documents of 1650 & 1560. LC 78-21065. 1979. pap. 5.00 (ISBN 0-87486-190-X). Plough.

Ehrenreich, Paul. Die Allgemeine Mythologie und Ihre Ethnologischen Grundlagen. Bolle, Kees W., ed. LC 77-79125. (Mythology Ser.). 1978. Repr. of 1915 ed. lib. bdg. 34.50x (ISBN 0-405-10536-3). Ayer Co Pubs.

Ehrensperger, Harold A. & Lehrer, Stanley. Religious Drama: Ends & Means. LC 77-22986. (Illus.). 1977. Repr. of 1962 ed. lib. bdg. 32.50x (ISBN 0-8371-9744-9, EHRD). Greenwood.

Ehret, Walter & Evans, George K. International Book of Christmas Carols. LC 80-13105. (Illus.). 352p. 1980. pap. 14.95 (ISBN 0-8289-0378-6). Greene.

Ehrhardt, Arnold A. Framework of the New Testament Stories. LC 65-79. 1964. 22.50t (ISBN 0-674-31700-9). Harvard U Pr.

Ehrlich, Leonard H. Karl Jaspers: Philosophy As Faith. LC 73-79505. 292p. 1975. 20.00x (ISBN 0-87023-153-7). U of Mass Pr.

Ehrmann, E. L. Readings in Jewish History: From the American Revolution to the Present. 9.95x (ISBN 0-87068-447-7). Ktav.

Ehrmann, Naftali H. The Rav. Paritzky, Karen, tr. from Ger. Tr. of Der Rav. (Illus.). 1978. 7.95 (ISBN 0-87306-137-3); pap. 5.95. Feldheim.

Eichenbaum, Sharon & Goldin, Alice. Jewish Awareness Worksheets, 2 vols. pap. 2.95x ea. Vol. 1 (ISBN 0-87441-266-8). Vol. 2 (ISBN 0-87441-270-6). Behrman.

Eichenberg, Fritz. Art & Faith. (Illus., Orig.). 1952. pap. 2.50x (ISBN 0-87574-068-5). Pendle Hill.

Eichhorn. Evangelizing the American Jew. LC 77-28975. 1978. 12.50 (ISBN 0-8246-0225-0). Jonathan David.

Eichhorn, David M. Cain: Son of the Serpent. (Limited Editions Reprints). 160p. 1985. 14.95 (ISBN 0-940646-24-2); pap. 8.95 (ISBN 0-940646-19-6). Rossel Bks.

--Conversion to Judaism: A History & Analysis. 1966. 12.50x (ISBN 0-87068-019-6). Ktav.

Eichhorn, David M., ed. Joys of Jewish Folklore. LC 80-13936. 534p. 1981. 16.95 (ISBN 0-8246-0254-4). Jonathan David.

Eichrodt, Walther. Ezekiel: A Commentary. LC 71-117646. (Old Testament Library). 608p. 1970. 18.95 (ISBN 0-664-20872-X). Westminster.

--Theology of the Old Testament, 2 Vols. Baker, J., tr. LC 61-11867. (Old Testament Library). 1967. 22.95 ea. Vol. 1, 542p (ISBN 0-664-20352-3). Vol. 2, 574p (ISBN 0-664-20769-3). Westminster.

Eichstadt, V. Bibliographie zur Geschichte der Judenfrage, BD 1, 1750-1848. 278p. Date not set. Repr. of 1939 ed. text ed. 66.24x (ISBN 0-576-80137-2, Pub. by Gregg Intl Pubs England). Gregg Intl.

Eickelman, Dale F. Knowledge & Power in Morocco: The Education of a Twentieth-Century Notable. LC 85-3444. (Princeton Studies on the Near East). (Illus.). 325p. 1985. text ed. 32.50x (ISBN 0-691-09415-2). Princeton U Pr.

--Moroccan Islam: Tradition & Society in a Pilgrimage Center. (Modern Middle East Ser.: No. 1). 323p. 1976. pap. text ed. 12.95x (ISBN 0-292-75062-5). U of Tex Pr.

Eidelberg, Shlomo, ed. Jews & the Crusaders: The Hebrew Chronicles of the First & Second Crusades. (Illus.). 200p. 1977. 24.95x (ISBN 0-299-07060-3). U of Wis Pr.

Eidsmoe, John. Christian Legal Advisor. 1987. pap. 14.95 (ISBN 0-8010-3441-8). Baker Bk.

--Christianity & the Constitution. 442p. 1987. pap. price not set (ISBN 0-8010-3444-2). Baker Bk.

--God & Caesar: Christian Faith & Political Action. LC 84-71423. 226p. 1984. (Crossway Bks); pap. 7.95 (ISBN 0-89107-313-2). Good News.

Eifert, Frank & Stenbock, Evelyn. They Sang with the Spirit. 104p. 1983. pap. 3.95 (ISBN 0-8341-0824-0). Beacon Hill.

Eighmy, John L. Churches in Cultural Captivity: A History of the Social Attitudes of Southern Baptists. LC 70-111047. 1972. 22.50x (ISBN 0-87049-115-6). U of Tenn Pr.

--Churches in Cultural Captivity: A History of the Social Attitudes of Southern Baptists. Hill, Samual S., Jr., intro. by. LC 70-111047. pap. 67.00 (2029374). Bks Demand UMI.

Eijndhoven, J. van see Van Eijndhoven, J.

Eikner, Allen V., ed. Religious Perspectives & Problems: An Introduction to the Philosophy of Religion. LC 80-67265. 368p. 1980. lib. bdg. 29.75 (ISBN 0-8191-1215-1); pap. text ed. 15.25 (ISBN 0-8191-1216-X). U Pr of Amer.

Eilberg-Schwartz, Howard. The Human Will in Judaism: The Mishnah's Philosophy of Intention. (Brown Judaic Studies). 164p. 1986. 31.95 (ISBN 0-89130-938-1, 14-01-03). Scholars Pr GA.

Eims, Leroy. Be the Leader You Were Meant to Be. LC 75-5392. 132p. 1975. pap. 4.95 (ISBN 0-88207-723-6). Victor Bks.

--Keeping off the Casualty List. 132p. 1986. pap. 4.95 (ISBN 0-89693-152-8). Victor Bks.

--Laboring in the Harvest. 108p. 1985. pap. 4.95 (ISBN 0-89109-530-6). NavPress.

--The Lost Art of Disciple Making. pap. 6.95 (ISBN 0-310-37281-X, 9233P). Zondervan.

--Prayer: More Than Words. LC 82-61301. 162p. 1983. pap. 3.95 (ISBN 0-89109-493-8). NavPress.

--What Every Christian Should Know about Growing. LC 75-44842. 168p. 1976. pap. 5.95 (ISBN 0-88207-727-9). Victor Bks.

--Winning Ways. LC 74-77319. 160p. 1974. pap. 4.50 (ISBN 0-88207-707-4). Victor Bks.

Einem, Herbert Von. Michelangelo. 2nd ed. 1973. 43.00x (ISBN 0-416-15140-X, NO. 2183). Methuen Inc.

Einenkel, E., ed. Catharina, Saint, of Alexandria: The Life of St. Katherine. (EETS, OS Ser.: No. 80). Repr. of 1884 ed. 20.00 (ISBN 0-527-00080-9). Kraus Repr.

Einhorn, David. Seventh Candle & Other Folk Tales of Eastern Europe. Pashin, Gertrude, tr. LC 68-10968. (Illus.). 1968. 7.95x (ISBN 0-87068-369-1). Ktav.

Einhorn, Franne, jt. auth. see Bin-Nun, Judy.

Einspahr, Bruce, compiled by. Index to the Brown, Driver & Briggs Hebrew Lexicon. LC 76-25479. (Hebrew.). 1976. 25.95 (ISBN 0-8024-4082-7). Moody.

Einstein, Albert. Essays in Humanism. 130p. 1983. pap. 4.95 (ISBN 0-8022-2417-2). Philos Lib.

--The World As I See It. 1979. pap. 2.95 (ISBN 0-8065-0711-X). Citadel Pr.

Eipper, Chris. The Ruling Trinity: A Community Study of Chruch, State & Business in Ireland. 1986. text ed. 42.00 (ISBN 0-566-05173-7, Pub. by Gower Pub England). Gower Pub Co.

Eire, Carlos M. War Against the Idols: The Reformation of Worship from Erasmus to Calvin. 320p. 1986. 37.50 (ISBN 0-521-30685-X). Cambridge U Pr.

Eis, Ruth. Ornamented Bags for Tallit & Tefllin. Cassuto, Nelda, ed. LC 83-83059. (The Magnes Museum Collection Ser.). 99p. (Orig.). 1984. pap. text ed. 22.50 (ISBN 0-318-01125-5). Magnes Mus.

--Torah Binders of the Judah L. Magnes Museum. LC 79-83877. 80p. 1979. pap. 18.00 (ISBN 0-943376-15-7). Magnes Mus.

Eisel, J. The Bells of Hereford Cathedral. 1985. 12.50x (ISBN 0-317-54268-0, Pub. by J Richardson UK). State Mutual Bk.

Eisele, Carol. Christ in You. (Aglow Bible Study Basic Ser.: Bk. 10). 64p. 1977. 2.95 (ISBN 0-930756-22-3, 521010). Aglow Pubns.

Eiselen, Frederick Carl, et al, eds. The Abingdon Bible Commentary. 1979. pap. 19.95 (ISBN 0-385-14877-1, Galilee). Doubleday.

Eisemann, Moshe. Yechezkel-Ezekiel, 3 vols. (Art Scroll Tanach Ser.). (Illus.). 832p. 1980. Set. 55.95 (ISBN 0-89906-085-4); Set. pap. 45.95 (ISBN 0-89906-086-2). Mesorah Pubns.

--Yechezkel-Ezekiel, Vol. 2. (Art Scroll Tanach Ser.). 272p. 1980. 17.95 (ISBN 0-89906-077-3); pap. 14.95 (ISBN 0-89906-078-1). Mesorah Pubns.

--Yechezkel-Ezekiel, Vol. 3. (Art Scroll Tanach Ser.). (Illus.). 208p. 1980. 17.95 (ISBN 0-89906-083-8); pap. 14.95 (ISBN 0-89906-084-6). Mesorah Pubns.

Eisen, Arnold M. The Chosen People in America: A Study in Jewish Religious Ideology. LC 82-49296. (Modern Jewish Experience Ser.). 254p. 1983. 20.00x (ISBN 0-253-31365-1). Ind U Pr.

--Galut: Modern Jewish Reflections on Homelessness & Homecoming. LC 85-45763. (Modern Jewish Experience Ser.). 224p. 1986. pap. 27.50x (ISBN 0-253-32550-1). Ind U Pr.

Eisen, Sydney & Lightman, Bernard V. Victorian Science & Religion: A Bibliography of Works on Ideas & Institutions with Emphasis on Evolution, Belief & Unbelief, Published from 1900 to 1975. LC 82-24497. xix, 696p. 1984. lib. bdg. 49.50 (ISBN 0-208-02010-1, Archon Bks). Shoe String.

Eisen, William. The English Cabalah, 2 vols, Vol. 1. (Illus.). 608p. 1980. text ed. 16.95 (ISBN 0-87516-390-4). De Vorss.

--The English Cabalah Volume 2: The Mysteries of Phi. LC 79-57053. (Agashan Teachings Ser.). 652p. 1982. 26.95 (ISBN 0-87516-459-5). De Vorss.

--The Essence of the Cabalah. (Illus.). 480p. 1984. 22.95 (ISBN 0-87516-524-9). De Vorss.

Eisenbeis, Walter. The Key Ideas of Paul Tillich's Systematic Theology. LC 82-21834. (Ger. & Eng.). 268p. (Orig.). 1983. lib. bdg. 27.50 (ISBN 0-8191-2948-8); pap. text ed. 13.25 (ISBN 0-8191-2949-6). U Pr of Amer.

--A Translation of the Greek Expressions in the Text of The Gospel of John, A Commentary by Rudolf Bultmann. 160p. (Orig.). 1984. lib. bdg. 22.00 (ISBN 0-8191-3884-3); pap. text ed. 11.25 (ISBN 0-8191-3885-1). U Pr of Amer.

Eisenberg, Azriel. The Book of Books. 163p. 1976. pap. 9.95 (ISBN 0-900689-77-3). Soncino Pr.

--The Book of Books: The Story of the Bible Text. 1976. 9.95x (ISBN 0-685-84453-6). Bloch.

--Eyewitnesses to American Jewish History, Pt. 4: The American Jew 1915 to 1969. 1979. 6.00 (ISBN 0-8074-0018-1, 044062). UAHC.

--Jewish Historical Treasures. LC 68-57432. (Illus.). 300p. 1969. 12.50 (ISBN 0-8197-0076-2). Bloch.

--Modern Jewish Life in Literature, 2 Vols. 1952-1968. Vol. 1. 4.50x (ISBN 0-8381-0201-8); Vol. 2. 4.50x (ISBN 0-8381-0207-7). United Syn Bk.

--The Synagogue Through the Ages: An Illustrated History of Judaism's Houses of Worship. LC 73-77284. (Illus.). 1973. 15.00 (ISBN 0-8197-0290-0). Bloch.

Eisenberg, Azriel & Arian, Philip. The Story of the Prayer Book. pap. 5.95x (ISBN 0-87677-017-0). Hartmore.

Eisenberg, Azriel & Robinson, Jessie B. My Jewish Holidays. 208p. 3.95x (ISBN 0-8381-0176-3, 10-176). United Syn Bk.

Eisenberg, Azriel, ed. The Lost Generation: Children in the Holocaust. 384p. 1982. 17.95 (ISBN 0-8298-0498-6). Pilgrim NY.

Eisenberg, Azriel, jt. ed. see Shoshuk, Levi.

Eisenberg, Azriel, et al, eds. Eyewitnesses to American Jewish History: East European Immigration 1881-1920, Pt. 3. (Illus.). 1978. pap. 5.00 (ISBN 0-8074-0017-3, 144061); tchrs'. guide 5.00 (ISBN 0-8074-0021-1, 204063). UAHC.

--Eyewitnesses to American Jewish History: 1492-1793, Pt. 1. 1976. pap. 5.00 (ISBN 0-686-77106-0, 144060); tchrs'. guide 5.00 (ISBN 0-8074-0019-X, 204061). UAHC.

--Eyewitnesses to American Jewish History: The German Immigration 1800-1875, Pt. 2. (Illus.). 1977. pap. 5.00 (ISBN 0-8074-0016-5, 144059); tchrs'. guide 5.00 (ISBN 0-8074-0020-3, 204062). UAHC.

Eisenberg, C. G. History of the First Dakota-District of the Evangelical-Lutheran Synod of Iowa & Other States. Richter, Anton H., tr. from Ger. LC 82-17645. 268p. (Orig.). 1983. lib. bdg. 29.25 (ISBN 0-8191-2798-1); pap. text ed. 13.75 (ISBN 0-8191-2799-X). U Pr of Amer.

Eisenberg, Gary. Smashing the Idols: A Jewish Inquiry into the Cults. 325p. 1987. 25.00 (ISBN 0-87668-974-8). Aronson.

Eisenberg, Helen & Eisenberg, Larry. More Bulletin Boards-ers. 1984. 5.25 (ISBN 0-89536-704-1, 4887). CSS of Ohio.

--Programs & Parties for Christmas. 160p. 1980. pap. 4.50 (ISBN 0-8010-3359-4). Baker Bk.

Eisenberg, Helen, jt. auth. see Eisenberg, Larry.

Eisenberg, Larry & Eisenberg, Helen. Fun with Skits, Stunts, & Stories. (Game & Party Books). 64p. 1975. pap. 3.95 (ISBN 0-8010-3367-5). Baker Bk.

Eisenberg, Larry, jt. auth. see Eisenberg, Helen.

Eisenhart, E. J., jt. ed. see Hills, M. T.

Eisenhower, David & Murray, John. Warwords: U. S. Militarism the Catholic Right & the Bulgarian Connection. Smith, Betty, ed. 138p. 1987. pap. 3.95 (ISBN 0-7178-0650-2). Intl Pubs Co.

Eisenman, Robert H. James the Just in the Habakkuk Pesher. (Studia Post-Biblica Ser.: Vol. 35). x, 110p. 1986. pap. 17.25 (ISBN 90-04-07587-9, Pub. by E J Brill). Heinman.

Eisenman, Tom. Big People, Little People. (Family Ministry Ser.). (Illus.). 54p. 1985. pap. text ed. 19.95 (ISBN 0-89191-968-6). Cook.

--Everyday Evangelism. 180p. (Orig.). 1987. pap. 5.95 (ISBN 0-87784-997-8). Inter-Varsity.

--On My Own. (Family Ministry Ser.). (Illus.). 54p. 1985. pap. text ed. 19.95 (ISBN 0-89191-978-3). Cook.

Eisenstadt, S. N., et al, eds. Orthodoxy, Heterodoxy & Dissent in India. LC 83-26910. (Religion & Society Ser.: No. 23). viii, 179p. 1984. 42.00x (ISBN 3-11-009659-5). Mouton.

Eisenstein, Ira. Judaism under Freedom. LC 56-12814. 262p. 1956. pap. 6.95 (ISBN 0-935457-05-4). Reconstructionist Pr.

--Reconstructing Judaism: An Autobiography. 1986. 17.95 (ISBN 0-935457-37-2). Reconstructionist Pr.

--What We Mean by Religion. Rev., 3rd ed. LC 57-14413. 173p. 1958. pap. 7.95 (ISBN 0-935457-06-2). Reconstructionist Pr.

Eisenstein, Ira & Kohn, Eugene, eds. Mordecai M. Kaplan: An Evaluation. 324p. 1952. 12.00 (ISBN 0-935457-11-9). Reconstructionist Pr.

Eisermann, Moshe. Yechezkel-Ezekiel, Vol. 1. (The Art Scroll Tanach Ser.). 352p. 1977. 17.95 (ISBN 0-89906-075-7); pap. 14.95 (ISBN 0-89906-076-5). Mesorah Pubns.

Eishenberg, Fritz. Artist on the Witness Stand. LC 84-61828. (Orig.). 1984. pap. 2.50x (ISBN 0-87574-257-2). Pendle Hill.

Eisikovits, Max. Songs of the Martyrs: Hassidic Melodies of Maramures. LC 79-67624. 1980. pap. 7.95 (ISBN 0-87203-089-X). Hermon.

Eisler, Colin & Corbett, Patricia. The Prayer Book of Michelino Da Besozzo. LC 81-68186. (Illus.). 1981. 50.00 (ISBN 0-8076-1016-X). Braziller.

Eisler, Moritz. Vorlesungen ueber die Juedischen Philosophen des Mittelalters, 3vols in 2. 1965. Repr. of 1884 ed. 39.50 (ISBN 0-8337-4086-5). B Franklin.

Eisler, Robert. Man into Wolf: An Anthropological Interpretation of Sadism, Masochism, & Lycanyhropy. LC 77-2497. 264p. 1978. lib. bdg. 11.95 (ISBN 0-915520-16-8); pap. text ed. 5.95 (ISBN 0-915520-06-0). Ross-Erikson.

Eisner, Robert. The Road to Daulis: Psychoanalysis, Psychology & Classical Mythology. 284p. 1987. 32.50 (ISBN 0-8156-0210-3). Syracuse U Pr.

Eisner, Will. A Contract with God. 136p. 1985. signed ed. o.p. 25.00 (ISBN 0-87816-017-5); pap. 7.95 (ISBN 0-87816-018-3). Kitchen Sink.

Eissfeldt, Otto. The Old Testament: An Introduction. LC 65-15399. 1965. 14.95xi (ISBN 0-06-062171-0, RD162, HarpR). Har-Row.

Eister, Allan W., ed. Changing Perspectives in the Scientific Study of Religion. LC 74-2092. 370p. 1974. 25.50 (ISBN 0-471-23476-1, Pub. by Wiley). Krieger.

Eitan, Israel. Contribution to Biblical Lexicography. (Columbia University. Contributions to Oriental History & Philology: No. 10). Repr. of 1924 ed. 12.50 (ISBN 0-404-50540-6). AMS Pr.

Eitel, Alta W. Yon Mountain: A Doctor of Faith Walks with God. LC 85-90286. 101p. 1986. 10.95 (ISBN 0-533-06783-9). Vantage.

Eitel, Lorraine, compiled by. The Treasury of Christian Poetry. 192p. 1982. 12.95 (ISBN 0-8007-1291-9). Revell.

Eitzen, Ruth. Fun to Do All Year Through. 32p. 1982. pap. 2.95 (ISBN 0-8170-0969-8). Judson.

Eker, Dorothy. Reflections of Him. LC 75-393402. 1976. 4.95 (ISBN 0-87212-053-8). Libra.

Eklund, Emmet E. Peter Fjellstedt: Missionary Mentor to Three Continents. LC 83-71472. (Augustana Historical Society Publication Ser.: No. 30). 197p. 1983. 20.00x (ISBN 0-910184-30-5). Augustana.

Ekstrom, Rosemary, jt. auth. see Reynolds, R.

Ekvall, Robert B. The Lama Knows: A Tibetan Legend Is Born. LC 81-4160. (Illus.). 144p. 1981. pap. 5.95 (ISBN 0-88316-541-4). Chandler & Sharp.

Ela, Jean-Marc. African Cry. Barr, Robert R., tr. from Fr. LC 86-12429. Tr. of Le Cri de l'homme Africain. 176p. (Orig.). 1986. pap. 10.95 (ISBN 0-88344-259-0). Orbis Bks.

El-Amin, Mustafa. Al-Islam, Christianity, & Freemasonry. 214p. (Orig.). 1985. pap. 6.95 (ISBN 0-933821-05-0). New Mind Prod.

El-Awa, M. S. On the Political System of the Islamic State. pap. 4.50. Am Trust Pubns.

El Awa, M. S. Punishment in Islamic Law. 162p. Date not set. pap. 6.00 (ISBN 0-89259-015-7). Am Trust Pubns.

Elazar, Daniel J. Community & Polity: The Organizational Dynamics of American Jewry. LC 75-8167. (Illus.). 448p. 1976. pap. 9.95 (ISBN 0-8276-0068-2, 377). Jewish Pubns.

--Kinship & Consent: The Jewish Political Tradition & Its Contemporary Uses. LC 82-21851. 412p. 1983. lib. bdg. 29.50 (ISBN 0-8191-2800-7, Co-pub. by Ctr Jewish Comm Studies); pap. text ed. 14.50 (ISBN 0-8191-2801-5). U Pr of Amer.

Elazar, Daniel J. & Aviad, Janet. Religion & Politics in Israel: The Interplay of Judaism & Zionism. 32p. 1981. pap. 2.50 (ISBN 0-87495-033-3). Am Jewish Comm.

Elazar, Daniel J. & Cohen, Stuart A. The Jewish Polity: Jewish Political Organization from Biblical Times to the Present. LC 83-48648. (Jewish Political & Social Studies). (Illus.). 384p. 1984. 27.50x (ISBN 0-253-33156-0). Ind U Pr.

Elazar, Daniel J. & Friedenreich, Harriet P. The Balkan Jewish Communities: Yugoslavia, Bulgaria, Greece, & Turkey. (Illus.). 208p. (Orig.). 1984. lib. bdg. 22.00 (ISBN 0-8191-3473-2, Co-Pub. by Ctr Jewish Comm Studies); pap. text ed. 10.25 (ISBN 0-8191-3474-0). U Pr of Amer.

Elbert, John A. Newman's Concept of Faith. 59.95 (ISBN 0-8490-0729-1). Gordon Pr.

Elbert, Paul. Essays on Apostolic Themes. 252p. 1985. 14.95 (ISBN 0-913573-14-0). Hendrickson MA.

Elbin, Paul N. Improvement of College Worship. LC 72-176744. (Columbia University. Teachers College. Contributions to Education: No. 530). Repr. of 1932 ed. 22.50 (ISBN 0-404-55530-6). AMS Pr.

--Making Happiness a Habit. (Festival Ser.). 192p. 1981. pap. 2.75 (ISBN 0-687-23030-6). Abingdon.

Elbogen, I., jt. auth. see Brann, M.

Elchaninov, Alexander. The Diary of a Russian Priest. 2nd ed. Ware, Kallistos T., ed. LC 82-16795. (Illus.). 225p. (Orig.). 1982. pap. 8.95 (ISBN 0-88141-000-4). St Vladimirs.

Elder, Carl A. Youth & Values: Getting Self Together. LC 76-58063. 1978. 6.75 (ISBN 0-8054-5326-1, 4253-26). Broadman.

Elder, Charles D. & Cobb, Roger W. The Political Uses of Symbols. Rockwood, Irving, ed. LC 82-12722. (Professional Studies in Political Communication). (Illus.). 192p. 1983. text ed. 22.50x (ISBN 0-582-28392-2); pap. text ed. 10.95 (ISBN 0-582-28393-0). Longman.

Elder, Dorothy. Revelation: For a New Age. LC 81-65477. 320p. (Orig.). 1981. pap. 11.50 (ISBN 0-87516-446-3). De Vorss.

--Women of the Bible Speak to Women of Today. LC 86-70873. (Illus.). 288p. (Orig.). 1986. pap. 12.00 (ISBN 0-87516-574-5). De Vorss.

Elder, E. R., ed. Heaven on Earth: Studies in Medieval Cistercian History, IX. (Cistercian Studies: No. 68). (Orig.). 1982. pap. 7.95 (ISBN 0-87907-868-5). Cistercian Pubns.

--The Roots of the Modern Christian Tradition. 1984. 24.95 (ISBN 0-87907-855-3); pap. 10.00. Cistercian Pubns.

Elder, E. R., ed. see William of St. Thierry.

Elder, E. Rozanne, ed. The Spirituality of Western Christendom. LC 76-22615. (Cistercian Studies Ser.: No. 30). (Illus.). 1976. pap. 6.95 (ISBN 0-87907-987-8). Cistercian Pubns.

--The Way of Love. (Cistercian Fathers Ser.: No. 16). (Illus.). 1977. 7.95 (ISBN 0-87907-616-X); pap. 4.50 (ISBN 0-87907-966-5). Cistercian Pubns.

Elder, E. Rozanne, ed. see William of St. Thierry.

Elder, E. Rozanne, et al, eds. Cistercians in the Late Middle Ages: Studies in Medieval Cistercian History. (Cistercian Studies: No. VI). 161p. (Orig.). 1981. pap. 8.95 (ISBN 0-87907-865-0). Cistercian Pubns.

Elder, John. Belief in God in the Twentieth Century. LC 82-81671. 70p. 1982. pap. 3.25 (ISBN 0-9608440-0-7). Nur Pubns.

--A Goodly Heritage - Pioneers for God: Devotional Readings. Armajani, Yahya, tr. from Farsi. LC 83-62806. viii, 141p. (Orig.). 1983. pap. 3.50 (ISBN 0-9608440-1-5). Nur Pubns.

Elder, Lloyd. Blueprints. LC 84-7634. 1984. 7.50 (ISBN 0-8054-6581-2). Broadman.

Elder, Rozanne, ed. From Cloister to Classroom: The Spirituality of Western Christendom III. (Cistercian Studies: No. 90). 1986. 26.95 (ISBN 0-87907-890-1); pap. 10.95 (ISBN 0-87907-990-8). Cistercian Pubns.

Elder, Rozanne E., ed. The Spirituality of Western Christendom II: The Roots of Modern Christian Spirituality. (Cistercian Studies: Nbr. 55). pap. write for info. (ISBN 0-87907-855-3). Cistercian Pubns.

Elder, Sam. A Christmas Celebration. LC 84-47709. (Illus.). 1984. 5.00 (ISBN 0-06-015359-8, HarpT). Har-Row.

Elderen, Bastiaan Van see Van Elderen, Bastiaan.

Elders of Bible Temple & Iverson, Dick. Restoring the Family. 3rd ed. 143p. Date not set. pap. price not set. Bible Temple.

Eldridge, Charlotte. The Watcher. (Orig.). 1981. pap. write for info. Shamar Bk.

Eldridge, Paul. Kingdom Without God. 15p. 1951. pap. cancelled (ISBN 0-911826-50-5). Am Atheist.

Eldridge, Paul, jt. auth. see Viereck, George S.

El Droubie, Riadh. Islam. 1985. 13.00 (ISBN 0-7062-3595-9, Pub. by Ward Lock Educ Co Ltd). State Mutual Bk.

Eleen, Luba. The Illustration of the Pauline Epistles in French & English Bibles of the Twelfth & Thirteenth Century. (Illus.). 1982. 89.00x (ISBN 0-19-817344-X). Oxford U Pr.

Elert, Werner. Structure of Lutheranism: The Theology & Philosophy of Life of Lutheranism, 16th & 17th Centuries, Vol. 1. Hansen, Walter A., tr. LC 62-19955. 1974. pap. 15.95 (ISBN 0-570-03192-3, 12-2588). Concordia.

El Farra, Muhammad. Years of No Decision. 350p. 1987. 37.50 (ISBN 0-7103-0215-0, Kegan Paul). Methuen Inc.

El-Helbawy, Kamal, tr. see Ali-Nadawi, Abul H.

Eliach, Yaffa. Hasidic Tales of the Holocaust. 1982. 17.95 (ISBN 0-19-503199-7). Oxford U Pr.

--Hasidic Tales of the Holocaust. 336p. 1983. pap. 4.95 (ISBN 0-380-64725-7, Discus). Avon.

Eliade, Mircea. From Primitives to Zen: A Thematic Sourcebook in the History of Religions. LC 66-20775. 1978. 12.00 (ISBN 0-06-062134-6, RD 249, HarpR). Har-Row.

--A History of Religious Ideas: From the Stone Age to the Eleusinian Mysteries, Vol. 1. Trask, Willard R., tr. from Fr. LC 77-16784. xviii, 490p. 1979. 25.00x (ISBN 0-226-20400-6); pap. 16.95 (ISBN 0-226-20401-4). U of Chicago Pr.

--History of Religious Ideas, Vol. II: From Gautama Buddha to the Triumph of Christianity. Trask, Willard, tr. from Fr. LC 77-16784. vi, 564p. 1982. 27.50x (ISBN 0-226-20402-2). U of Chicago Pr.

--A History of Religious Ideas, Vol. 2: From Gautama Buddha to the Triumph of Christianity. Trask, Willard R., tr. LC 77-16784. vi, 564p. 1984. pap. 15.95 (ISBN 0-226-20403-0). U of Chicago Pr.

--A History of Religious Ideas, Vol. 3: From Muhammad to the Age of Reforms. Hiltebeiten, Alf & Apostolos-Cappadona, Diane, trs. LC 77-16784. xii, 352p. 1985. 27.50 (ISBN 0-226-20404-9). U of Chicago Pr.

--Myth & Reality. pap. 5.95x (ISBN 0-06-131369-6, TB1369, Torch). Har-Row.

--Myth of the Eternal Return. Trask, Willard R., tr. (Bollingen Ser.: Vol. 46). 1954. 24.00 (ISBN 0-691-09798-4); pap. 8.50 (ISBN 0-691-01777-8). Princeton U Pr.

--Myths, Dreams & Mysteries: The Encounter Between Contemporary Faiths & Archaic Realities. pap. 5.95x (ISBN 0-06-131943-0, TB 1943, Torch). Har-Row.

--No Souvenirs, Journal, Nineteen Fifty-Seven to Nineteen Sixty-Nine. 1983. 16.00 (ISBN 0-8446-6030-2). Peter Smith.

--Occultism, Witchcraft, & Cultural Fashion: Essays in Comparative Religions. LC 75-12230. 1978. pap. 9.00 (ISBN 0-226-20392-1, P755, Phoen). U of Chicago Pr.

--Ordeal by Labyrinth: Conversations with Claude-Henri Rocquet. Coltman, Derek, tr. from Fr. LC 81-21796. (Illus.). 1982. 17.50x (ISBN 0-226-20387-5). U of Chicago Pr.

--Patanjali & Yoga. LC 75-10785. (Illus.). 224p. 1975. pap. 5.95 (ISBN 0-8052-0491-1). Schocken.

--Patterns in Comparative Religion. pap. 9.95 (ISBN 0-452-00728-3, Mer). NAL.

--Patterns in Comparative Religion. 16.00 (ISBN 0-8446-6226-7). Peter Smith.

--The Quest: History & Meaning in Religion. LC 68-19059. (Midway Reprint Ser.). xii, 180p. 1984. pap. text ed. 10.00x (ISBN 0-226-20386-7). U of Chicago Pr.

--Rites & Symbols of Initiation: The Mysteries of Birth & Rebirth. Orig. Title: Birth & Rebirth. pap. 5.95x (ISBN 0-06-131236-3, TB1236, Torch). Har-Row.

--Rites & Symbols of Initiation: The Mysteries of Birth & Rebirth. 16.75 (ISBN 0-8446-2027-0). Peter Smith.

--The Sacred & the Profane: The Nature of Religion. Trask, Willard, tr. LC 58-10904. 1968. pap. 4.95 (ISBN 0-15-679201-X, Harv). HarBraceJ.

--The Sacred & the Profane: The Nature of Religion. 1983. 13.75 (ISBN 0-8446-6080-9). Peter Smith.

--Shamanism: Archaic Techniques of Ectasy. Trask, Willard R., tr. (Bollingen Ser.: Vol. 76). 1964. 50.00x (ISBN 0-691-09827-1); pap. 11.95x (ISBN 0-691-01779-4). Princeton U Pr.

--The Two & the One. Cohen, J. M., tr. LC 79-2268. 1979. pap. 7.00 (ISBN 0-226-20389-1, P811). U of Chicago Pr.

--Yoga: Immortality & Freedom. 2nd ed. Trask, Willard R., tr. LC 58-8986. (Bollingen Ser.: Vol. 56). 1970. 45.00x (ISBN 0-691-09848-4); pap. 11.50x (ISBN 0-691-01764-6). Princeton U Pr.

--Zalmoxis: The Vanishing God. LC 72-76487. (Comparative Studies in the Religions & Folklore of Dacia & Eastern Europe). x, 260p. 1986. pap. text ed. 16.00x (ISBN 0-226-20385-9, Midway Reprint). U of Chicago Pr.

Eliade, Mircea & Kitagawa, Joseph. History of Religions: Essays in Methodology. LC 59-11621. 1959. 12.50x (ISBN 0-226-20394-8). U of Chicago Pr.

Eliade, Mircea, ed. Encyclopedia of Religion, 16 vols. 8000p. 1986. Set. reference 1100.00x (ISBN 0-02-909480-1). Macmillan.

Eliade, Mircea & Kitagawa, Joseph, eds. The History of Religions: Essays in Methodology. LC 59-11621. 1973. pap. 3.50 (ISBN 0-226-20395-6, P549, Phoen). U of Chicago Pr.

Eliade, Mircea & Tracy, David, eds. What Is Religion? An Inquiry for Christian Theology, Concilium 136. (New Concilium 1980). 128p. 1980. pap. 5.95 (ISBN 0-8164-2278-8, HarpR). Har-Row.

Elias, Esther. The Queening of Ceridwen. 1982. 6.95 (ISBN 0-8158-0409-1). Chris Mass.

Elias, John L. The Foundations & Practice of Adult Religious Education. LC 81-19327. 312p. 1982. 18.50 (ISBN 0-89874-339-7). Krieger.

--Psychology & Religious Education. 3rd ed. LC 83-7061. 154p. 1984. text ed. 11.50 (ISBN 0-89874-615-9). Krieger.

Elias, Joseph. The Haggadah. (The Art Scroll Mesorah Ser.). 224p. 1977. 10.95 (ISBN 0-89906-150-8); pap. 7.95 (ISBN 0-89906-151-6). Mesorah Pubns.

Eliopoulos, Nicholas C. Oneness of Politics & Religion. 126p. (Orig.). 1970. pap. 3.00x (ISBN 0-9605396-1-1). Eliopoulos.

Eliot, Alexander. Zen Edge. 1979. 3.95 (ISBN 0-8264-0177-5). Continuum.

Eliot, George. Scenes of Clerical Life. Lodge, David, ed. (English Library). (Orig.). 1973. pap. 4.95 (ISBN 0-14-043087-3). Penguin.

Eliot, George, tr. see Feuerbach, Ludwig.

Eliot, John. Christian Commonwealth: Or, the Civil Policy of the Rising Kingdom of Jesus Christ. LC 77-141110. (Research Library of Colonial Americana). 1972. Repr. of 1659 ed. 18.00 (ISBN 0-405-03323-0). Ayer Co Pubs.

Eliot, T. S. Christianity & Culture. Incl. The Idea of a Christian Society; Notes Towards the Definition of Culture. 202p. 1960. pap. 5.95 (ISBN 0-15-617735-8, HB32, Harv). HarBraceJ.

Elipoulos, Nicholas C. Oneness of Politics & Religion. rev. ed. 169p. 1979. text ed. 6.95 (ISBN 0-9605396-3-8). Eliopoulos.

Eliseo, Vivas L. Creation & Discovery. LC 81-85511. 460p. 1982. pap. 4.95 (ISBN 0-89526-952-X). Regnery Bks.

Elison, George. Deus Destroyed: The Image of Christianity in Early Modern Japan. LC 72-97833. (East Asian Ser: No. 72). 704p. 1974. 40.00x (ISBN 0-674-19961-8). Harvard U Pr.

Elizondo, Virgil & Greinacher, Norbert, eds. Church & Peace. (Concilium 1983: Vol. 164). 128p. (Orig.). 1983. pap. 6.95 (ISBN 0-8164-2444-6, HarpR). Har-Row.

--Religion & Churches in Eastern Europe. (Concilium Ser.: Vol. 154). 128p. (Orig.). 1982. pap. 6.95 (ISBN 0-8164-2385-7, HarpR). Har-Row.

--Tensions Between the Churches of the First World & the Third World, Vol. 144. (Concilium 1981). 128p. (Orig.). 1981. pap. 6.95 (ISBN 0-8164-2311-3, HarpR). Har-Row.

--The Transmission of Faith to the Next Generation, Vol. 174. (Concilium Ser.). 128p. pap. 6.95 (ISBN 0-567-30054-4, Pub. by T & T Clark Ltd UK). Fortress.

--Women in a Man's Church, Concilium 134. (New Concilium 1980: Vol. 134). 128p. 1980. pap. 5.95 (ISBN 0-8164-2276-1, HarpR). Har-Row.

Elizondo, Virgil, ed. see Boff, Leonard.

Elizondo, Virgil, jt. ed. see Boff, Leonardo.

Elizondo, Virgilio P. Creemos en Jesucristo. (Span.). 128p. 1982. pap. 2.95 (ISBN 0-89243-153-9). Liguori Pubns.

--La Morenita: Evangelizadora de las Americas. (Span.). 96p. 1981. pap. 2.50 (ISBN 0-89243-145-8). Liguori Pubns.

Elkholy, Abdo A. The Arab Moslems in the United States. 1966. 12.95x (ISBN 0-8084-0052-5); pap. 8.95x (ISBN 0-8084-0053-3). New Coll U Pr.

Elkin, Adolphus P. Studies in Australian Totemism. LC 76-44712. Repr. of 1933 ed. 31.50 (ISBN 0-404-15857-9). AMS Pr.

Elkin, Judith L. Krishna Smiled: Assignment in Southeast Asia. LC 72-737. pap. 63.30 (2027638). Bks Demand UMI.

Elkin, Judith L. & Merkx, Gilbert, eds. The Jewish Presence in Latin America. (Thematic Studies in Latin America). 256p. 1987. text ed. 34.95x (ISBN 0-04-497012-9); pap. text ed. 13.95x (ISBN 0-04-497013-7). Allen Unwin.

Elkin, Judith L., ed. see Niehaus, Thomas, et al.

Elkins, Chris. Heavenly Deception. 1980. pap. 3.95 (ISBN 0-8423-1402-4). Tyndale.

--Heavenly Deception. 1981. pap. 9.95 incl. cassette (ISBN 0-8423-1403-2). Tyndale.

Elkins, Dov P. Clarifying Jewish Values: Clarification Strategies for Jewish Groups. LC 77-83774. 1977. softbound 10.00 (ISBN 0-918834-02-3). Growth Assoc.

--God's Warriors: Dramatic Adventures of Rabbis in Uniform. LC 74-226. (Illus.). 92p. 1974. 7.95 (ISBN 0-8246-0168-8). Jonathan David.

--Jewish Consciousness Raising: A Handbook of 50 Experiential Exercises for Jewish Groups. LC 77-83775. 1977. softbound 10.00 (ISBN 0-918834-03-1). Growth Assoc.

Elkins, Dov P., ed. Being Jewish, Being Human: A Gift Book of Poems & Readings. LC 79-88298. Date not set. pap. 16.50 (ISBN 0-918834-07-4). Growth Assoc.

--Rejoice with Jerusalem. 1972. pap. 1.95 (ISBN 0-87677-065-0). Prayer BK.

Elkins, Garland, jt. ed. see Warren, Thomas B.

Elkins, Hervey. Fifteen Years in the Senior Order of Shakers: A Narration of Facts, Concerning That Singular People. LC 72-2984. Repr. of 1853 ed. 16.00 (ISBN 0-404-10746-X). AMS Pr.

Elkins, Phillip W. Church Sponsored Missions. 1974. pap. 3.00 (ISBN 0-88027-003-9). Firm Foun Pub.

Elkinton, Russell J. & Clark, Robert A. The Quaker Heritage in Medicine. (Illus.). 1978. pap. 3.95 (ISBN 0-910286-68-X). Boxwood.

Ellacombe, H. T., jt. ed. see Hale, William H.

Ellam, J. B. Buddhism & Lamaism. 1984. pap. 6.95 (ISBN 0-916411-79-6, Oriental Classics). Holmes Pub.

Ellam, J. E. The Religion of Tibet: Study of Lamaism. 59.95 (ISBN 0-8490-0940-5). Gordon Pr.

Ellard, G. Ordination Anointings in the Western Church Before 1000 A. D. (Med Acad of Amer Pubns). 1932. 18.00 (ISBN 0-527-01688-8). Kraus Repr.

Ellard, Gerald. Christian Life & Worship. 35.50 (ISBN 0-405-10819-2). Ayer Co Pubs.

--Master Alcuin, Liturgist. LC 56-8943. (Jesuit Studies). 1956. 2.95 (ISBN 0-8294-0027-3). Loyola.

Ellebracht, Mary P. Easter Passage: The RCIA Experience. 204p. 1983. pap. 11.95 (ISBN 0-86683-693-4, HarpR). Har-Row.

Elledge, Scott, ed. see Milton, John.

Ellenbogen, M. Foreign Words in the Old Testament: Their Origin & Terminology. 190p. 1972. 50.00x (ISBN 0-317-39068-6, Pub. by Luzac & Co Ltd). State Mutual Bk.

Ellens, J. Harold. God's Grace & Human Health. 1982. pap. 8.75 (ISBN 0-687-15326-3). Abingdon.

Eller, David, ed. see Chapman, G. Clarke.

Eller, David, ed. see Collins, David R.

Eller, David, ed. see Durnbaugh, Donald F.

Eller, David, ed. see Tengbom, Mildred.

Eller, David, ed. see Welliver, Dotsey.

Eller, David, ed. see Ziegler, Edward K.

Eller, Meredith F. The Beginnings of the Christian Religion: A Guide to the History & Literature of Judaism & Christianity. 1958. 16.95x (ISBN 0-8084-0392-3); pap. 12.95x (ISBN 0-8084-0393-1). New Coll U Pr.

Eller, Vernard. Christian Anarchy: Jesus' Primacy Over the Powers. 304p. (Orig.). 1987. pap. 13.95 (ISBN 0-8028-0227-3). Eerdmans.

--The Language of Canaan & the Grammar of Feminism: An Exercise in Wittgensteinian Analysis. 64p. 1982. pap. 2.95 (ISBN 0-8028-1902-8). Eerdmans.

--The Most Revealing Book of the Bible: Making Sense Out of Revelation. 1974. pap. 4.95 (ISBN 0-8028-1572-3). Eerdmans.

--Towering Babble: God's People Without God's Word. LC 83-4621. (Illus.). 192p. (Orig.). 1983. pap. 7.95 (ISBN 0-87178-855-1). Brethren.

--War & Peace from Genesis to Revelation. LC 80-26280. (Christian Peace Shelf Ser.). 232p. 1981. pap. 9.95 (ISBN 0-8361-1947-9). Herald Pr.

Eller, Vernard, ed. see Blumhardt, Johann C. & Blumhardt, Christoph F.

Ellicott, Charles. Ellicott's Commentaries, Critical & Grammatical on the Epistles of Saint Paul, 2 vol. 1986. Repr. of 1879 ed. lib. bdg. 45.00 (ISBN 0-89941-506-7). W S Hein.

Ellict, George R. Dramatic Providence in Macbeth: A Study of Shakespeare's Tragic Theme of Humanity & Grace, with a Supplementary Essay on King Lear. LC 70-90501. Repr. of 1960 ed. lib. bdg. 27.50x (ISBN 0-8371-3091-3, ELMA). Greenwood.

Elliff, Thomas D. Praying for Others. LC 79-52341. 1979. pap. 3.95 (ISBN 0-8054-5273-7). Broadman.

Elliger, K., ed. Twelve Prophets. (Biblia Hebraica Stuttgartensia Ser.). x, 96p. 1970. pap. 2.50x (ISBN 3-438-05210-5, 61261, Pub. by German Bible Society). Am Bible.

Ellingsen, Mark. Doctrine & Word: Theology in the Pulpit. LC 82-21311. pap. 51.00 (2027152). Bks Demand UMI.

Ellingston, Jenefer. We Are the Mainstream. McKenna, Constance, ed. (Illus.). 16p. 1981. pap. 1.00 (ISBN 0-915365-02-2). Cath Free Choice.

Ellington, James W., tr. see Kant, Immanuel.

Ellingworth, P. & Nida, E. A. Translator's Handbook on Paul's Letter to the Thessalonians. (Helps for Translators Ser.). 229p. 1975. 4.50x (ISBN 0-8267-0146-9, 08526, Pub. by United Bible). Am Bible.

Ellingworth, Paul & Hatton, Howard. A Translator's Handbook on Paul's First Letter to the Corinthians. LC 85-1142. (Helps for Translators Ser.). viii, 352p. 1985. flexible 4.20x (ISBN 0-8267-0140-X, 08578, Dist. by American Bible Society). United Bible.

Ellingworth, Paul & Nida, Eugene A. A Translator's Handbook on the Letter to the Hebrews. LC 83-17947. (Helps for Translators Ser.). viii, 364p. 1983. 5.00x (ISBN 0-8267-0150-7, 08782, Pub. by United Bible). Am Bible.

Ellinwood, Leonard. History of American Church Music. LC 69-12683. (Music Reprint Ser.). 1970. Repr. of 1953 ed. lib. bdg. 32.50 (ISBN 0-306-71233-4). Da Capo.

Elliot, Betsy R. How to Help a Missionary. 32p. (Orig.). 1984. pap. 0.75 (ISBN 0-87784-069-5). Inter-Varsity.

Elliot, Delber H. Doom of the Dictators. LC 59-14581. pap. 23.00 (ISBN 0-317-07875-5, 2012820). Bks Demand UMI.

Elliot, Elisabeth. As We Forgive Those. 16p. 1982. pap. 1.25 (ISBN 0-89107-255-1). Good News.

--Discipline: The Glad Surrender. 1985. pap. 5.95 (ISBN 0-8007-5195-7, Power Bks). Revell.

--A Lamp for My Feet: The Bible's Light for Daily Living. 210p. (Orig.). 1985. pap. 9.95 (ISBN 0-89283-234-7, Pub. by Vine Books). Servant.

--Love Has a Price Tag. 152p. 1982. pap. 5.95 (ISBN 0-89283-153-7, Pub. by Vine Books). Servant.

--The Mark of a Man. LC 80-25108. 176p. 1981. pap. 5.95 (ISBN 0-8007-5121-3, Power Bks). Revell.

--No Graven Image. LC 81-71346. 256p. 1982. pap. 5.95 (ISBN 0-89107-235-7, Crossway Bks). Good News.

--Notes on Prayer. 1982. pap. 0.95 (ISBN 0-89107-254-3). Good News.

--Passion & Purity. 160p. (Orig.). 1984. pap. 6.95 (ISBN 0-8007-5137-X, Power Bks). Revell.

--The Savage My Kinsman. (Illus.). 149p. 1981. pap. 5.95 (ISBN 0-89283-099-9, Pub. by Vine Books). Servant.

--A Slow & Certain Light: Thoughts on the Guidance of God. (Festival Ser.). 128p. 1982. pap. 1.95 (ISBN 0-687-38700-0). Abingdon.

--These Strange Ashes. LC 74-25684. 132p. 1979. pap. 6.95 (ISBN 0-06-062234-2, RD 488, HarpR). Har-Row.

--Through Gates of Splendor. 1981. 3.95 (ISBN 0-8423-7151-6). Tyndale.

--What God Has Joined. 32p. 1983. Repr. 1.50 (ISBN 0-89107-276-4). Good News.

Elliot, Elisabeth, ed. see Elliot, Jim.

Elliot, Elizabeth. Shadow of the Almighty: The Life & Testament of Jim Elliot. LC 58-10365. 1979. pap. 6.95 (ISBN 0-06-062211-3, RD 488, HarpR). Har-Row.

Elliot, Jim. The Journals of Jim Elliot. Elliot, Elisabeth, ed. 416p. 1978. 7.95 (Power Bks). Revell.

--The Journals of Jim Elliot. Elliot, Elisabeth, ed. 416p. 1983. pap. 7.95 (ISBN 0-8007-5147-7, Power Bks). Revell.

Elliot, John. Peter One, Estrangement & Community. (Herald Biblical). 1979. 1.25 (ISBN 0-8199-0728-6). Franciscan Herald.

Elliot, John H. A Home for the Homeless: A Sociological Exegesis of 1 Peter, Its Solution & Strategy. LC 80-2394. 320p. 1981. 24.95 (ISBN 0-8006-0659-0, 1-659). Fortress.

Elliot, Malinda, ed. see Lad, Vasant.

Elliot, Norman K. God Really Loves You. 0.50, 3 for 1.00 (ISBN 0-910924-25-2). Macalester.

Elliot, Paula. Performing Arts Information, Nineteen Seventy-Five to Nineteen Eighty: A Bibliography of Reference Works. 1982. pap. 4.00. KSU.

Elliott, Alan J. Chinese Spirit-Medium Cults in Singapore. 1981. Repr. of 1955 ed. 15.00 (ISBN 0-89986-347-7). Oriental Bk Store.

Elliott, Albert P. Fatalism in the Works of Thomas Hardy. LC 74-10791. 1972. lib. bdg. 17.50 (ISBN 0-8414-3950-8). Folcroft.

Elliott, Alison G. Roads to Paradise: Reading the Lives of the Early Saints. LC 86-40384. 272p. 1987. 27.50 (ISBN 0-87451-389-8). U Pr of New Eng.

Elliott, Ann. Christian Folk Art: Crafts & Activities. (Illus.). 1979. pap. 4.95 (ISBN 0-8192-1250-4). Morehouse.

Elliott, Brian, tr. see Levy-Bruel, Lucien.

Elliott, Charles. The Bible & Slavery: In Which the Abrahamic & Mosaic Discipline is Considered. 17.25 (ISBN 0-8369-9167-2, 9042). Ayer Co Pubs.

--Praying the Kingdom: Towards A Political Spirituality. 160p. (Orig.). 1986. pap. 6.95 (ISBN 0-8091-2820-9). Paulist Pr.

Elliott, Charles, ed. see McConnaughey, Bayard & McConnaughey, Evelyn.

Elliott, Dietlinde, tr. see Stegemann, Wolfgang.

Elliott, Douglas. As You Recover. 32p. 1984. pap. 1.25 (ISBN 0-8010-3414-0). Baker Bk.

Elliott, Elisabeth. Let Me Be a Woman. 1977. pap. 5.95 (ISBN 0-8423-2161-6); pap. 3.95 (ISBN 0-8423-2162-4). Tyndale.

Elliott, Emory. Power & the Pulpit in Puritan New England. 256p. 1975. 27.00x (ISBN 0-691-07206-X). Princeton U Pr.

Elliott, Hugh, jt. auth. see Hancock, James.

Elliott, J. E. Once Saved Always Saved. 74p. (Orig.). 1986. pap. 2.25 (ISBN 0-934942-62-5, 4115). White Wing Pub.

Elliott, J. H., jt. auth. see Briggs, S. R.

Elliott, John H. & Martin, R. A. Augsburg Commentary on the New Testament. LC 82-70962. 192p. (Orig.). 1982. 8.95 (ISBN 0-8066-1937-6, 10-9042). Augsburg.

Elliott, John H., ed. Social-Scientific Criticism of the New Testament. (Semeia Ser.: No. 35). pap. 9.95 (06 20 35). Scholars Pr GA.

Elliott, John R., Jr. & Runnalls, Graham A., eds. The Baptism & Temptation of Christ: The First Day of a Medieval French Passion Play. LC 78-6564. 1978. 24.50x (ISBN 0-300-02199-2). Yale U Pr.

Elliott, Maurice. The Psychic Life of Jesus. 69.95 (ISBN 0-87968-185-3). Gordon Pr.

--Spiritualism in the Old Testament. 59.95 (ISBN 0-8490-1117-5). Gordon Pr.

Elliott, Norman. How to Be the Lord's Prayer. pap. 2.95 (ISBN 0-910924-26-0). Macalester.

Elliott, Ralph H. Church Growth That Counts. 128p. 1982. pap. 5.95 (ISBN 0-8170-0943-4). Judson.

Elliott, Scott. Story of Atlantis & the Lost Lemuria. 8.95 (ISBN 0-8356-5509-1). Theos Pub Hse.

Elliott, Walter. The Life of Father Hecker. LC 75-38446. (Religion in America, Ser. 2). 456p. 1972. Repr. of 1891 ed. 28.00 (ISBN 0-405-04065-2). Ayer Co Pubs.

Elliott-Binns, L. The Development of English Theology in the Later Nineteenth Century. LC 72-122411. ix, 137p. 1971. Repr. of 1952 ed. 17.50 (ISBN 0-208-01045-9, Archon). Shoe String.

--Innocent III. LC 68-15343. xi, 212p. 1968. Repr. of 1931 ed. 19.50 (ISBN 0-208-00393-2, Archon). Shoe String.

Elliott-Binns, Leonard E. From Moses to Elisha: Israel to the End of the Ninth Century B. C. LC 78-10639. (Illus.). 1979. Repr. of 1929 ed. lib. bdg. 27.50x (ISBN 0-313-21015-2, EBFM). Greenwood.

Elliott-Binns, Leonard E., ed. Erasmus the Reformer: A Study in Restatement. LC 83-45655. Date not set. Repr. of 1923 ed. 24.50 (ISBN 0-404-19805-8). AMS Pr.

Ellis, Albert. The Case Against Religion: A Psychotherapist's View & the Case Against Religiousity. 57p. 1985. saddle stiched 4.00 (ISBN 0-910309-18-3). Am Atheist.

Ellis, Bruce T. Bishop Lamy's Santa Fe Cathedral. LC 85-8551. (Historical Society of New Mexico Publication Ser.). (Illus.). 208p. 1985. 19.95 (ISBN 0-8263-0824-4); pap. 10.95 (ISBN 0-8263-0850-3). U of NM Pr.

Ellis, C. The Christ in Shakespeare's Dramas & Sonnets. 59.95 (ISBN 0-87968-860-2). Gordon Pr.

Ellis, Carl, Jr. Beyond Liberation. LC 83-18561. (Illus.). 200p. (Orig.). 1983. pap. 6.95 (ISBN 0-87784-914-5). Inter-Varsity.

Ellis, Charles & Ellis, Norma. Wells of Salvation: Meditations of Isaiah. 224p. (Orig.). 1986. pap. 5.95 (ISBN 0-85151-457-X). Banner of Truth.

Ellis, Charles M. Essay on Transcendentalism. LC 70-91761. Repr. of 1954 ed. lib. bdg. 22.50x (ISBN 0-8371-3092-1, ELTR). Greenwood.

Ellis, Dorsey D. Look unto the Rock: A History of the Presbyterian Church, in West Virginia from 1719 to 1974. LC 82-60889. (Illus.). 372p. (Orig.). 1982. pap. 14.95 (ISBN 0-9609076-0-2). McClain.

Ellis, E. Earle. Prophecy & Hermeneutics in Early Christianity: New Testament Essays. 306p. 1978. lib. bdg. 54.00x. Coronet Bks.

--The World of St. John: The Gospels & the Epistles. 96p. (Orig.). 1984. pap. 4.95 (ISBN 0-8028-0013-0). Eerdmans.

Ellis, George E. Puritan Age & Rule in the Colony of the Massachusetts Bay, 1629-1685. LC 75-122838. (Research & Source Ser.: No. 522). 1970. Repr. of 1888 ed. lib. bdg. 32.00 (ISBN 0-8337-1054-0). B Franklin.

Ellis, Harry B. The Dilemma of Israel. 1970. pap. 5.25 (ISBN 0-8447-1041-5). Am Enterprise.

Ellis, Henry, ed. Pylgrymage of Sir Richard Guylforde to the Holy Land, A. D. 1506. LC 75-166023. (Camden Society, London. Publications, First Ser.: No. 51). Repr. of 1851 ed. 19.00 (ISBN 0-404-50151-6). AMS Pr.

Ellis, Hilda R. Road to Hell: A Study of the Conception of the Dead in Old Norse Literature. LC 68-23286. (Illus.). 1968. Repr. of 1943 ed. lib. bdg. 22.50x (ISBN 0-8371-0070-4, ELRH). Greenwood.

Ellis, James J. Charles Kingsley. 1890. Repr. 25.00 (ISBN 0-8274-3799-4). R West.

Ellis, Jane. The Russian Orthodox Church: A Contemporary History. LC 85-45884. 700p. 1986. 39.95x (ISBN 0-253-35029-8). Ind U Pr.

Ellis, Joe. The Church on Purpose: Keys to Effective Church Leadership. LC 82-3175. (Illus.). 112p. (Orig.). 1982. pap. 6.95 (ISBN 0-87239-441-7, 88584). Standard Pub.

--The Church on Target. 128p. 1986. pap. 5.95 (ISBN 0-87403-005-6, 3019). Standard Pub.

Ellis, John T. American Catholicism. 2nd ed. Boorstin, Daniel J., ed. LC 69-19274. (Chicago History of American Civilization Ser.). 1969. pap. 10.00x (ISBN 0-226-20556-8, CHAC5). U of Chicago Pr.

--Catholic Bishops: A Memoir. 1983. pap. 6.95 (ISBN 0-89453-463-7). M Glazier.

Ellis, John T. & Trisco, Robert. A Guide to American Catholic History. 2nd, rev. ed. LC 81-17585. 265p. 1982. lib. bdg. 29.85 (ISBN 0-87436-318-7). ABC-Clio.

Ellis, John T., ed. Documents of American Catholic History, 3 vols. LC 86-80801. 1200p. 1987. Set. 65.00; 25.00 ea. Vol. 1: 1494-1865 (ISBN 0-89453-611-7). Vol. 2: 1866-1966 (ISBN 0-89453-612-5). Vol. 3: 1967-1986 (ISBN 0-89453-588-9). M Glazier.

Ellis, Joyce. Plug into a Rainbow. 144p. (Orig.). 1984. pap. 3.95 (ISBN 0-310-47192-3, 12495P). Zondervan.

Ellis, Joyce & Lynn, Claire. Bible Bees. (Illus.). 36p. 1981. 1.25 (ISBN 0-89323-049-9). Bible Memory.

Ellis, Judith M., jt. auth. see Ellis, Peter F.

Ellis, Loudell O. Church Treasurer's Handbook. LC 77-10433. 1978. 6.95 (ISBN 0-8170-0762-8). Judson.

Ellis, Marc. A Year of the Catholic Worker. LC 78-61722. 144p. 1978. pap. 3.50 (ISBN 0-8091-2140-9). Paulist Pr.

Ellis, Marc H. Toward a Jewish Theology of Liberation. LC 86-23553. 160p. (Orig.). 1987. pap. 9.95 (ISBN 0-88344-358-9). Orbis Bks.

Ellis, Mark H., ed. In an Age of Holocaust. (A Chrysalis Bk). 128p. (Orig.). 1986. pap. 14.95 (ISBN 0-916349-13-6). Amity House Inc.

Ellis, Norma, jt. auth. see Ellis, Charles.

Ellis, Peter F. The Genius of John: A Composition-Critical Commentary on the Fourth Gospel. (Orig.). 1984. pap. 10.95 (ISBN 0-8146-1328-4). Liturgical Pr.

--Jeremiah, Baruch. (Collegeville Bible Commentary Ser.). 136p. 1986. pap. 2.95 (ISBN 0-8146-1421-3). Liturgical Pr.

--Seven Pauline Letters. LC 82-15252. (Orig.). 1982. pap. 8.95 (ISBN 0-8146-1245-8). Liturgical Pr.

Ellis, Peter F. & Ellis, Judith M. John: An Access Guide for Scripture Study. 174p. 1983. pap. 3.95 (ISBN 0-8215-5936-2); leader's guide 3.25 (ISBN 0-8215-5918-4). Sadlier.

Ellis, Roger, jt. auth. see Hogg, James.

Ellis, William E. A "Man of Books & a Man of the People". E. Y. Mullins & the Crisis Moderate Southern Baptist Leadership. xi, 228p. 1985. text ed. 18.95 (ISBN 0-86554-175-2, MUP-H165). Mercer Univ Pr.

Ellis, William T. Billy Sunday. (Golden Oldies Ser.). 1959. pap. 3.95 (ISBN 0-8024-0042-6). Moody.

Ellisen, Stanley A. Divorce & Remarriage in the Church. 1977. pap. 5.95 (ISBN 0-310-35561-3, 11256P). Zondervan.

Ellisen, Stanley A., ed. see Cheney, Johnston M.

Ellison, Craig. The Urban Mission: Essays on the Building of a Comprehensive Model for Evangelical Urban Ministry. LC 82-23764. 230p. 1983. pap. text ed. 12.50 (ISBN 0-8191-2968-2). U Pr of Amer.

Ellison, Craig W., ed. Your Better Self: Christianity, Psychology, & Self-Esteem. LC 82-47742. 224p. (Orig.). 1982. pap. 8.95 (ISBN 0-686-97230-9, RD/408, HarpR). Har-Row.

Ellison, H. L. Exodus. LC 81-12917. (Daily Study Bible Old Testament Ser.). 216p. 1982. 12.95 (ISBN 0-664-21803-2); pap. 7.95 (ISBN 0-664-24570-6). Westminster.

--From Babylon to Bethlehem: The People of God from the Exile to the Messiah. LC 78-24504. 144p. 1984. pap. 5.95 (ISBN 0-8010-3412-4). Baker Bk.

--The Household Church. 120p. 1979. pap. 4.95 (ISBN 0-85364-239-7). Attic Pr.

--The Mystery of Israel: An Exposition of Romans 9-11. 3rd ed. 117p. 1976. pap. 4.95 (ISBN 0-85364-169-2). Attic Pr.

--The Servant of Jehovah. 32p. 1983. pap. 2.50 (ISBN 0-85364-254-0, Pub. by Paternoster UK). Attic Pr.

Ellison, Harold. Portavoces del Eterno. Orig. Title: Old Testament Prophets. (Span.). 214p. 1982. pap. 7.50 (ISBN 0-8254-1201-3). Kregel.

Ellison, John W. Nelson's Complete Concordance of the Revised Standard Version. 2nd ed. 1136p. 1985. 29.95 (ISBN 0-8407-4954-6). Nelson.

Ellison, Marvin M. The Center Cannot Hold: The Search for a Global Economy of Justice. LC 82-23795. 330p. (Orig.). 1983. lib. bdg. 31.00 (ISBN 0-8191-2963-1); pap. text ed. 15.50 (ISBN 0-8191-2964-X). U Pr of Amer.

Ellrod, Frederick E., jt. ed. see McLean, George F.

Ellsberg, Margaret. Created to Praise: The Language of Gerard Manley Hopkins. 160p. 1987. 15.95x (ISBN 0-19-504098-8). Oxford U Pr.

Ellspermann, Gerald L. The Attitude of the Early Christian Latin Writers Toward Pagan Literature & Learning. 295p. 1984. Repr. of 1949 ed. 45.00x (ISBN 0-939738-26-0). Zubal Inc.

Ellsworth, Donald P. Christian Music in Contemporary Witness: Historical Antecedents & Contemporary Practices. LC 79-52359. 1980. 7.95 (ISBN 0-8010-3338-1). Baker Bk.

Ellsworth, Irene B. I Met Angels in the Tangles of Life. LC 84-52166. 118p. (Orig.). 1985. pap. 4.95 (ISBN 0-9614165-0-5). Terhell Bks.

Ellsworth, Paul. Direct Healing. LC 83-3920. 1983. lib. bdg. 15.95x (ISBN 0-89370-658-2). Borgo Pr.

--Direct Healing. 1982. pap. 5.95 (ISBN 0-87877-058-5). Newcastle Pub.

Ellsworth, S. George, ed. Dear Ellen: Two Mormon Women & Their Letters. 92p. 1974. 12.00 (ISBN 0-941214-33-8). Signature Bks.

Ellul, Jacques. In Season Out of Season. 1983. 16.00 (ISBN 0-8446-6029-9). Peter Smith.

--Money & Power. Neff, LaVonne, tr. from Fr. LC 83-22647. Orig. Title: L Homme et l'Argent. 216p. 1984. pap. 7.95 (ISBN 0-87784-916-1). Inter-Varsity.

--Perspectives on Our Age: Jacques Ellul Speaks on His Life & Work. Vanderburg, William H., ed. Neugroschel, Joachim, tr. 1981. 10.95 (ISBN 0-8164-0485-2, HarpR). Har-Row.

--Prayer & Modern Man. Hopkins, C. Edward, tr. from Fr. 192p. 1973. pap. 6.95 (ISBN 0-8164-2081-5, HarpR). Har-Row.

--The Subversion of Christianity. Bromiley, Geoffrey W., tr. from Fr. 224p. (Orig.). 1986. pap. 9.95 (ISBN 0-8028-0049-1). Eerdmans.

--To Will & to Do. Hopkin, C. Edward, tr. LC 70-91166. 1969. 12.50 (ISBN 0-8298-0137-5). Pilgrim NY.

Ellwood, Rober S., ed. Eastern Spirituality in America: Selected Writings. (Sources of American Spirituality Ser.). 256p. 1987. pap. 16.95 (ISBN 0-8091-0388-5). Paulist Pr.

Ellwood, Robert. Finding Deep Joy. LC 84-40167. 156p. (Orig.). 1984. pap. 4.50 (ISBN 0-8356-0586-8). Theos Pub Hse.

--Finding the Quiet Mind. LC 83-615. 155p. (Orig.). 1983. pap. 4.50 (ISBN 0-8356-0576-0, Quest). Theos Pub Hse.

--Theosophy. LC 85-40843. (Illus.). 236p. (Orig.). 1986. pap. 6.50 (ISBN 0-8356-0607-4, Quest). Theos Pub Hse.

Ellwood, Robert S. Alternative Altars: Unconventional & Eastern Spirituality in America. LC 78-15089. (Chicago History of American Religion Ser.). 1979. lib. bdg. 12.95x (ISBN 0-226-20618-1); pap. 5.50x (ISBN 0-226-20620-3). U of Chicago Pr.

Ellwood, Robert S. & Pilgrim, Richard. Japanese Religion: A Cultural Perspective. (Illus.). 192p. 1985. pap. text ed. 16.00 (ISBN 0-13-509282-5). P-H.

Ellwood, Robert S., Jr. Introducing Religion: From Inside & Outside. (Illus.). 240p. 1983. pap. text ed. write for info. (ISBN 0-13-477497-3). P-H.

--Many Peoples, Many Faiths. 2nd ed. (Illus.). 416p. 1982. 27.95 (ISBN 0-13-556001-2). P-H.

--Religious & Spiritual Groups in Modern America. 352p. 1973. pap. 24.33 (ISBN 0-13-773309-7). P-H.

--Words of the World's Religion. 1977. pap. text ed. 24.33x (ISBN 0-13-965004-0). P-H.

Ellwood, Robert S., Jr., ed. Readings on Religion: From Inside & Outside. 1978. pap. text ed. write for info. (ISBN 0-13-760942-6). P-H.

Elmen, Paul, ed. The Anglican Moral Choice. LC 82-62391. 274p. (Orig.). 1983. pap. 10.95 (ISBN 0-8192-1322-5). Morehouse.

Elmer, Irene & Mathews. Boy Who Ran Away. LC 63-23143. (Arch Bks: Set 1). (Illus.). 1964. laminated bdg. 0.99 (ISBN 0-570-06001-X, 59-1104). Concordia.

Elmessiri, Abdelwahab M. The Land of Promise: A Critique of Political Zionism. LC 77-83664. 1977. text ed. 11.95x (ISBN 0-930244-02-8); pap. text ed. 7.95x (ISBN 0-930244-01-X). North American Inc.

Elmo, Francis, tr. from Span. I, in Christ Arisen. LC 81-85745. Orig. Title: Yo, en Cristo Resucitado. 100p. 1982. pap. 4.00 (ISBN 0-9607590-0-X). Action Life Pubns.

El Morya. Encyclical on World Good Will. 1963. 1.50 (ISBN 0-685-79130-0). Summit Univ.

--Morya. Prophet, Elizabeth C., ed. LC 81-85570. 412p. 1982. pap. 9.95 (ISBN 0-916766-52-7). Summit Univ.

--The Sacred Adventure. LC 81-85464. 148p. 1981. 7.95 (ISBN 0-916766-53-5). Summit Univ.

Elmslie, W. A., ed. The Mishna of Idolatry Aboda Zara. (Texts & Studies Ser.: No. 1, Vol. 8, Pt. 2). pap. 19.00 (ISBN 0-8115-1709-8). Kraus Repr.

Elon, Amos. Herzl. (Illus.). 496p. 1986. pap. 12.95 (ISBN 0-8052-0790-2). Schocken.

--Understanding Israel: A Social Studies Approach. Sugarman, Morris J., ed. LC 76-18282. (Illus.). 256p. 1976. pap. text ed. 6.95x (ISBN 0-87441-234-X). Behrman.

Elon, Menachem, ed. The Principles of Jewish Law. 866p. 1975. 50.00 (ISBN 0-87855-188-3). Transaction Bks.

Elrington, G. A., ed. see Gilson, Etienne H.

El Saadawi, Nawal. The Hidden Face of Eve: Women in the Arab World. Hetata, Sherif, tr. from Egyptian. LC 81-68358. 212p. 1982. pap. 9.95 (ISBN 0-8070-6701-6, BP 627). Beacon Pr.

Elsas, Christoph. Neuplatonische und gnostische Weltablehnung in der Schule Plotins. (Religionsgeschichtliche Versuche und Vorarbeiten Ser., Vol. 34). 1975. 45.60 (ISBN 3-11-003941-9). De Gruyter.

Elsbree, Oliver W. The Rise of the Missionary Spirit in America 1790-1815. LC 79-13028. (Perspectives in American History Ser.: No. 55). 1980. Repr. of 1928 ed. 22.50x (ISBN 0-87991-376-2). Porcupine Pr.

Elsdon, Ronald. Bent World. LC 81-8261. 200p. (Orig.). 1981. pap. 4.95 (ISBN 0-87784-834-3). Inter-Varsity.

Elser, Otto, ed. The Ministry of Health & Healing. 1986. pap. 7.50 (ISBN 0-8309-0451-4). Herald Hse.

El-Shakhs, Salah S., jt. auth. see Lutz, Jesse G.

Elson, Edward. Wide Was His Parish. 320p. 1986. 12.95 (ISBN 0-8423-8205-4). Tyndale.

Elspeth. Victorian Christmas: 1876. 1974. pap. 1.50 (ISBN 0-87588-106-8). Hobby Hse.

Elton, G. R. F. W. Maitland. LC 85-40439. 128p. 1985. 15.00x (ISBN 0-300-03528-4). Yale U Pr.

--Policy & Police: The Enforcement of the Reformation in the Age of Thomas Cromwell. 458p. 1985. pap. 14.95 (ISBN 0-521-31309-0). Cambridge U Pr.

--Reform & Reformation: England, 1509-1558. LC 77-6464. (Harvard Paperback Ser.: No. 146, The New History of England). 1979. 27.50x (ISBN 0-674-75245-7); pap. 8.95x (ISBN 0-674-75248-1). Harvard U Pr.

Elton, Gelffrey R. Renaissance & Reformation, Thirteen Hundred to Sixteen Forty-Eight. 3rd ed. (Ideas & Institutions in Western Civilization: Vol. 3). 1976. pap. text ed. write for info. (ISBN 0-02-332840-1). Macmillan.

Elton, Geoffrey R. Reform & Renewal, Thomas Cromwell & the Common Weal. (Wiles Lectures, 1972). 230p. 1973. pap. 11.95 (ISBN 0-521-09809-2). Cambridge U Pr.

Elvey, Linda B. Where Do I Go from Here. 1983. 6.00 (ISBN 0-8062-2194-1). Carlton.

Elvy, Peter. Buying Time: The Foundation of the Electronic Church. (Illus.). 1987. pap. 5.95 (ISBN 0-89622-325-6). Twenty-Third.

Elwell, Clarence E. Influence of the Enlightenment on the Catholic Theory of Religious Education in France, 1750-1850. LC 66-27064. 1967. Repr. of 1944 ed. 10.00x (ISBN 0-8462-0980-2). Russell.

Elwell, Sue L., compiled by. The Jewish Women's Studies Guide. 2nd ed. 1987. pap. 19.75 (Co-Pub by U Press of America); pap. 9.75 (Co-Pub. by U Press of America). Biblio NY.

Elwell, Walter, intro. by see Bagster, Samuel.

Elwell, Walter A. Evangelical Dictionary of Theology. LC 84-71575. 1984. 29.95 (ISBN 0-8010-3413-2). Baker Bk.

Elwell, Walter A., ed. The Shaw Pocket Bible Handbook. 400p. 1984. 9.95 (ISBN 0-87788-683-0). Shaw Pubs.

Elwes, tr. see Spinoza, Benedict D.

Elwes, R. H., tr. see Spinoza, Benedict.

Elwood, Douglas. Faith Encounters Ideology: Christian Discernment & Social Change. xvi, 318p. (Orig.). 1985. pap. 16.00 (ISBN 971-10-0201-9, Pub. by New Day Philippines). Cellar.

Elwood, Douglas J. & Magdamo, Patricia L. Christ in the Philippine Context. 1971. newsprint 6.75 (ISBN 0-686-18694-X). Cellar.

Elwood, Douglas J. see Nacpil, Emerito.

Elwood, Douglas J., ed. The Humanities in Christian Higher Education in Asia: Ethical & Religious Perspectives. 1978. pap. 7.50x (ISBN 0-686-23913-X, Pub. by New Day Pub.). Cellar.

Elwood, Douglas J., jt. ed. see Nacpil, Emerito.

Elwood, Roger. Historias Extranas de Brujeria. Lockward, George, tr. from Eng. (Span.). 112p. 1974. pap. 1.95 (ISBN 0-89922-028-2). Edit Caribe.

Elworthy, Frederick T. The Evil Eye: An Account of This Ancient & Widespread Superstition. (Illus.). 1986. pap. 7.95 (ISBN 0-517-55971-4, Julian). Crown.

Ely, Evelyn & Hughes, Phyllis. Ojos de Dios. (Illus.). 1972. pap. 2.50 (ISBN 0-89013-056-6). Museum NM Pr.

Ely, R. Unto God & Caesar: Religious Issues in the Emerging Commonwealth 1891-1906. 1976. 22.00x (ISBN 0-522-84093-0, Pub. by Melbourne U Pr). Intl Spec Bk.

Elzas, Barnett A. The Jews of South Carolina, from the Earliest Times to the Present Day. LC 77-187364. (Illus.). 352p. 1972. Repr. of 1905 ed. 23.50 (ISBN 0-87152-092-3). Reprint.

El-Zein, Abdul H. The Sacred Meadows: A Structural Analysis of Religious Symbolism in an East African Town. LC 73-91310. (Studies in African Religion). 1974. text ed. 19.95x (ISBN 0-8101-0443-1). Northwestern U Pr.

E Maung. Burmese Buddhist Law. LC 77-87483. Repr. of 1937 ed. 25.00 (ISBN 0-404-16812-4). AMS Pr.

Embree, Ainslie, ed. Alberuni's India. abr. ed. Sachau, Edward C., tr. 1971. pap. 2.75x (ISBN 0-393-00568-2, Norton Lib). Norton.

Embree, Ainslie T., ed. The Hindu Tradition. 448p. 1972. pap. 5.95 (ISBN 0-394-71702-3, V696, Vin). Random.

Embree, Esther. Now Rings the Bell. (Illus.). 1978. pap. 2.95 (ISBN 0-89367-023-5). Light & Life.

Embry, Jessie L., ed. see Shipps, Jan, et al.

Emerson, Ellen. Indian Myths. 59.95 (ISBN 0-8490-0400-4). Gordon Pr.

Emerson, Everett. Puritanism in America. (World Leaders Ser.). 1977. lib. bdg. 12.50 (ISBN 0-8057-7692-3, Twayne). G K Hall.

Emerson, Everett H. John Cotton. (Twayne's United States Authors Ser). 1965. pap. 8.95x (ISBN 0-8084-0180-7, T80, Twayne). New Coll U Pr.

Emerson, James C., ed. The Life of Christ in the Conception & Expression of Chinese & Oriental Artists. (The Great Art Masters of the World Ser.). (Illus.). 117p. 1983. 97.50 (ISBN 0-86650-054-5). Gloucester Art.

Emerson, James G. Suffering: Its Meaning & Ministry. 176p. (Orig.). 1986. pap. 8.95 (ISBN 0-687-40573-4). Abingdon.

Emerson, Nathaniel B. Pele & Hiiaka: A Myth from Hawaii. LC 75-35190. Repr. of 1915 ed. 29.50 (ISBN 0-404-14218-4). AMS Pr.

--Unwritten Literature of Hawaii: The Sacred Songs of the Hula. LC 65-12971. (Illus.). 1965. pap. 6.75 (ISBN 0-8048-1067-2). C E Tuttle.

--Unwritten Literature of Hawaii; the Sacred Songs of the Hula. Repr. of 1909 ed. 39.00x (ISBN 0-403-03720-4). Scholarly.

Emerson, Ralph Waldo. The Portable Emerson. Bode, Carl & Cowley, Malcolm, eds. 664p. 1981. pap. 7.95 (ISBN 0-14-015094-3). Penguin.

Emerson, Ralph Waldo, ed. Parnassus. facsimile ed. LC 73-116400. (Granger Index Reprint Ser). 1874. 25.50 (ISBN 0-8369-6141-2). Ayer Co Pubs.

Emerson, W. A., jt. auth. see Irwin, James B., Jr.

Emert, Joyce R. Louis Martin: Father of a Saint. LC 83-2728. 208p. (Orig.). 1983. pap. 9.95 (ISBN 0-8189-0446-1). Alba.

Emerton, E. Erasmus of Rotterdam. 59.95 (ISBN 0-8490-0122-6). Gordon Pr.

Emerton, E., tr. see Gregory Seventh, Pope.

Emerton, Ephraim. Desiderius Erasmus of Rotterdam. 1900. 35.00 (ISBN 0-8274-2167-2). R West.

--An Introduction to the Study of the Middle Ages: 375-814. 1979. Repr. of 1895 ed. lib. bdg. 30.00 (ISBN 0-8495-1325-1). Arden Lib.

--An Introduction to the Study of the Middle Ages (375-814) 1978. Repr. of 1900 ed. lib. bdg. 35.00 (ISBN 0-8482-0713-0). Norwood Edns.

Emerton, Ephraim, ed. see Boniface, Saint.

Emerton, J. A. & Reif, Stefan C., eds. Interpreting the Hebrew Bible. LC 81-21668. (University of Cambridge Oriental Publication Ser.: No. 32). 1982. 52.50 (ISBN 0-521-24424-2). Cambridge U Pr.

Emerton, John A., ed. see Cranfield, Charles E.

Emerton, John A., ed. see McKane, William.

Emery, Andree, tr. see Von Balthasar, Has U.

Emery, Helen F. The Puritan Village Evolves: A History of Wayland, Massachusetts. LC 81-5185. (Illus.). 384p. 1981. 15.00x (ISBN 0-914016-78-4). Phoenix Pub.

Emery, Richard W. Heresy & Inquisition in Narbonne. LC 75-166031. (Columbia University Studies in the Social Sciences: No. 480). 17.50 (ISBN 0-404-51480-4). AMS Pr.

Emhardt, William C. Eastern Church in the Western World. LC 74-131039. Repr. of 1928 ed. 15.75 (ISBN 0-404-02329-0). AMS Pr.

Emhardt, William C. & Lamsa, G. M. Oldest Christian People. LC 71-126651. Repr. of 1926 ed. 14.50 (ISBN 0-404-02339-8). AMS Pr.

Emilsen, William W. & Irvine, A. D., eds. Remodelling God. 125p. (Orig.). 1983. pap. 7.95 (ISBN 0-85819-418-X, Pub. by JBCE). ANZ Religious Pubns.

Emiot, Israel. The Birobidzhan Affair: A Yiddish Writer in Siberia. Rosenfeld, Max, tr. from Yiddish. LC 81-2511. 220p. 1981. 13.95 (ISBN 0-8276-0191-3, 477). Jewish Pubns.

Emmens, Carol A. & Maglione, Harry, eds. An Audio-Visual Guide to American Holidays. LC 78-6230. 284p. 1978. lib. bdg. 20.00 (ISBN 0-8108-1140-5). Scarecrow.

Emmerich, Anne C. Dolorous Passion of Our Lord Jesus Christ. 1980. lib. bdg. 64.95 (ISBN 0-8490-3100-1). Gordon Pr.

--The Dolorous Passion of Our Lord Jesus Christ. LC 83-70406. 382p. 1983. pap. 10.00 (ISBN 0-89555-210-8). TAN Bks Pubs.

--Life of Jesus Christ & Biblical Revelations, 4 vols. Schmoeger, C. E., ed. LC 79-90066. 1979. Set. pap. 30.00 (ISBN 0-89555-127-6); Vol. 1. (ISBN 0-89555-123-3); Vol. 2. pap. (ISBN 0-89555-124-1); Vol. 3. (ISBN 0-89555-125-X); Vol. 4. (ISBN 0-89555-126-8). TAN Bks Pubs.

--The Life of Jesus Christ & Biblical Revelations. Schmoger, Carl E., ed. LC 86-50154. 1986. Repr. of 1914 ed. Set. 67.00 (ISBN 0-89555-293-0); Vol. 1, 486 p. 16.75 ea (ISBN 0-89555-289-2). Vol. 2, 481 p (ISBN 0-89555-290-6). Vol. 3, 594 p (ISBN 0-89555-291-4). Vol. 4, 476 p (ISBN 0-89555-292-2). TAN Bks Pubs.

--The Life of the Blessed Virgin Mary. Palairet, Michael, tr. from Ger. 1970. pap. 10.00 (ISBN 0-89555-048-2). TAN Bks Pubs.

Emmerick, A. C. Life of the Blessed Virgin Mary. (Roman Catholic Ser.). 1979. lib. bdg. 69.95 (ISBN 0-8490-2959-7). Gordon Pr.

Emmerick, R. E. The Sutra of Golden Light: A Mahayana Text. 1980. write for info. Dharma Pub.

Emmerson, Grace I. Hosea: An Israelite Prophet in Judean Perspective. (JSOT Supplement Ser.: No. 28). 224p. 1984. text ed. 28.50x (ISBN 0-905774-68-X, Pub. by JSOT Pr England); pap. text ed. 11.95x (ISBN 0-905774-69-8, Pub. by JSOT Pr England). Eisenbrauns.

Emmerson, Richard K. Antichrist in the Middle Ages: A Study of Medieval Apocalypticism, Art, & Literature. LC 79-3874. (Illus.). 320p. 1981. 35.00x (ISBN 0-295-95716-6). U of Wash Pr.

Emmerson, Walter L. Reformation & the Advent Movement. 224p. pap. 9.95 (ISBN 0-8280-0168-5). Review & Herald.

Emmichoven, F. W. The Anthroposophical Understanding of the Soul. Schwarzkopf, Friedemann, tr. from Ger. 170p. (Orig.). 1983. pap. 8.95 (ISBN 0-88010-019-2). Anthroposophic.

Emmons, Michael & Richardson, David. The Assertive Christian. Frost, Miriam, ed. 144p. (Orig.). 1981. pap. 6.95 (ISBN 0-86683-755-8, HarpR). Har-Row.

Emmons, Viva. Roots of Peace. LC 73-78911. (Orig.). 1969. pap. 1.75 (ISBN 0-8356-0505-1, Quest). Theos Pub Hse.

Emory, K. P. Tuamotuan Religious Structures & Ceremonies. (BMB Ser.). Repr. of 1947 ed. 14.00 (ISBN 0-527-02299-3). Kraus Repr.

Empereur, James. Worship: Exploring the Sacred. 1987. pap. 11.95. Pastoral Pr.

Empereur, James L. Prophetic Anointing: God's Call to the Sick, the Elderly, & the Dying. (Message of the Sacraments Ser.: Vol. 7). 1982. text ed. 15.95 (ISBN 0-89453-397-5); pap. 10.95 (ISBN 0-89453-233-2). M Glazier.

Empie, Paul C. Lutherans & Catholics in Dialogue: Personal Notes for a Study. Tiemeyer, Raymond, ed. LC 80-69754. pap. 40.00 (2029612). Bks Demand UMI.

Empie, Paul C., et al, eds. Lutherans & Catholics in Dialogue I-III. LC 74-83330. 1974. pap. 8.95 (ISBN 0-8066-1451-X, 10-4190). Augsburg.

--Papal Primacy & the Universal Church. LC 74-83329. 1974. pap. 7.95 (ISBN 0-8066-1450-1, 10-4870). Augsburg.

--Teaching Authority & Infallibility in the Church, No. 6. LC 79-54109. (Lutherans & Catholics in Dialogue). 352p. (Orig.). 1979. pap. 8.95 (ISBN 0-8066-1733-0, 10-6222). Augsburg.

Empson, Ralph H. The Cult of the Peacock Angel: A Short Account of the Yezidi Tribes of Kurdistan. LC 77-87646. Repr. of 1928 ed. 21.00 (ISBN 0-404-16416-1). AMS Pr.

Empson, William. Milton's God. LC 80-40109. 320p. 1981. pap. 18.95 (ISBN 0-521-29910-1). Cambridge U Pr.

--Milton's God. LC 78-14409. 1978. Repr. of 1961 ed. lib. bdg. 27.50x (ISBN 0-313-21021-7, EMMG). Greenwood.

Emswiler, James P. Using a Computer in Church Ministry. 1986. pap. 6.95 (ISBN 0-87193-248-2). Dimension Bks.

Emswiler, James P. & Moore, Joseph. Handbook for Peer Ministry. LC 81-84351. 128p. (Orig.). 1982. pap. 4.95 (ISBN 0-8091-2427-0). Paulist Pr.

Emswiler, Sharon & Neufer, Thomas. Women & Worship. rev., expanded ed. LC 83-48459. 144p. 1984. pap. 5.95 (ISBN 0-06-066101-1, RD 507, HarpR). Har-Row.

Emswiler, Tom N. The Click in the Clock: Meditations for Junior Highs. LC 81-11875. 128p. (Orig.). 1981. pap. 5.95 (ISBN 0-8298-0470-6). Pilgrim NY.

Emswiler, Tom N., jt. auth. see Neufer, Sharon.

Emswiler, Tom N., et al. A Complete Guide to Making the Most of Video in Religious Settings: How to Produce, Find, Use & Distribute Video in the Church & Synagogue. LC 85-50019. 128p. (Orig.). 1985. pap. 9.95 (ISBN 0-9606652-1-8). Wesley Found.

Emurian, Ernest K. Living Stories of Famous Hymns. (Interlude Bks). 1971. pap. 4.95 (ISBN 0-8010-3260-1). Baker Bk.

--Stories of Christmas Carols. (Paperback Program Ser). 1969. pap. 4.95 (ISBN 0-8010-3265-2). Baker Bk.

Ende, Richard C. von see Von Ende, Richard C.

Endelman, Judith E. The Jewish Community of Indianapolis, 1849 to the Present. LC 83-49513. (The Modern Jewish Experience Ser.). (Illus.). 316p. 1985. 17.50x (ISBN 0-253-33150-1). Ind U Pr.

Endelman, Judith E., jt. auth. see Rudolph, L. C.

Endelman, Todd M., ed. Jewish Apostasy in the Modern World. 300p. 1987. 34.50 (ISBN 0-8419-1029-4). Holmes & Meier.

Endemann, Carl T. Voyage into the Past: Continuous Life Through 35 Centuries. LC 81-81554. (Illus.). 1981. 9.95 (ISBN 0-931926-10-6). Alta Napa.

Endo, Shusaku. A Life of Jesus. Schuchert, Richard, tr. from Japanese. LC 78-61721. 192p. 1979. pap. 3.95 (ISBN 0-8091-2319-3). Paulist Pr.

Endres, John C. Biblical Interpretation in the Book of Jubilees. Karris, Robert J., ed. LC 86-6845. (Catholic Biblical Quarterly-Monograph: no. 18). 284p. (Orig.). 1987. pap. 8.50 (ISBN 0-915170-17-5). Catholic Bibl Assn.

Endress, Gerhard. An Introduction to Islamic History. 220p. 1986. cancelled (ISBN 0-85224-496-7, Pub. by Edinburgh U Pr Scotland). Columbia U Pr.

--Islam: A Historical Introduction. Hillenbrand, Carole, tr. from Ger. 205p. 1987. text ed. 25.00 (ISBN 0-231-06580-9); pap. text ed. 12.00 (ISBN 0-231-06579-5). Columbia U Pr.

Enelow, H. G., ed. see Kohler, Kaufmann.

Engblom, Philip C., tr. see Mokashi, D. B.

Engel, James F. & Norton, Wilbert H. What's Gone Wrong with the Harvest? 192p. 1975. pap. 7.95 (ISBN 0-310-24161-8, 18417P). Zondervan.

Engelbrecht, A., ed. see Faustus, Saint.

Engelbrecht, A., ed. see Mamertus, Claudianus.

Engelbrecht, A., ed. see Rufinius, Tyrannius.

Engelder, Theodore, et al, trs. see Pieper, Francis.

Engelhardt, H. Tristram, Jr., jt. ed. see Callahan, Daniel.

Engelhardt, Zephyrin. Mission Santa Ines. LC 85-23977. (Missions & Missionaries of California Ser.). (Illus.). 202p. (Orig.). 1986. 16.50 (ISBN 0-87461-063-X); pap. 7.50 (ISBN 0-87461-062-1). McNally & Loftin.

--Missions & Missionaries of California, 4 Vols. (Illus.). lib. bdg. 185.00 (ISBN 0-87821-019-9). Milford Hse.

Engelman, Uriah Z. The Rise of the Jew in the Western World. LC 73-2194. (The Jewish People; History, Religion, Literature Ser.). Repr. of 1944 ed. 22.00 (ISBN 0-405-05260-X). Ayer Co Pubs.

Engels, Friedrich, jt. auth. see Marx, Karl.

Engelson, Joyce, ed. see Dobbin, Muriel.

Engelzakis, Benedict. New & Old in God's Revelation. (Studies in Relations Between Spirit & Tradition in the Bible). 128p. 1982. text ed. 12.95 (ISBN 0-913836-89-3). St Vladimirs.

Engen, John Van see Van Engen, John.

Engineer, Asghar A. Indian Muslims: A Study of Minority Problems in India. 1986. 28.00x (ISBN 81-202-0139-6, Pub. by Ajanta). South Asia Bks.

--The Origin & Development of Islam. 248p. 1980. 18.95x (ISBN 0-940500-33-7). Asia Bk Corp.

--The Origin & Development of Islam: An Essay on Its Socio-Economic Growth. 248p. 1980. text ed. 18.95x (ISBN 0-86131-174-4, Pub. by Orient Longman Ltd India). Apt Bks.

England, Eugene. Dialogues with Myself: Personal Essays on Mormon Experience. 205p. (Orig.). 1984. pap. 7.50 (ISBN 0-941214-21-4, Orion). Signature Bks.

England, John C., ed. Living Theology in Asia. LC 82-2288. 256p. (Orig.). 1982. pap. 9.95 (ISBN 0-88344-298-1). Orbis Bks.

England, Kathleen. Why We Are Baptized. LC 78-19180. (Illus.). 1978. 5.95 (ISBN 0-87747-893-7). Deseret Bk.

England, Kathy. What Is Faith? (Illus.). 27p. 1981. pap. 4.95 (ISBN 0-87747-876-7). Deseret Bk.

Englander, Lois, et al. The Jewish Holiday Do-Book. new ed. 1977. 9.95x (ISBN 0-685-76976-3). Bloch.

Engle, Jon. Servants of God: The Lives of the 10 Gurus of the Sikhs. LC 79-63457. (Illus.). 192p. 1980. pap. 6.00 (ISBN 0-89142-035-5). Sant Bani Ash.

Engle, Paul. The Governor Drove Us up the Wall: A Guide to Nehemiah. 1985. pap. text ed. 4.95 (ISBN 0-934688-11-7); pap. text ed. 3.95 leader's guide (ISBN 0-934688-13-3). Great Comm Pubns.

Engle, Paul E. Discovering the Fullness of Worship. (Illus.). 129p. (Orig.). 1978. pap. 4.95 (ISBN 0-934688-01-X). Great Comm Pubns.

--Worship Planbook. (Orig.). 1981. pap. 3.95 (ISBN 0-934688-03-6). Great Comm Pubns.

Englebert, Omer. Hero of Molokai. (Illus.). 1977. 4.00 (ISBN 0-8198-0057-0); pap. 3.00 (ISBN 0-8198-0058-9). Dghtrs St Paul.

--Saint Francis of Assisi: A Biography. abr. ed. 1979. pap. 3.95 (ISBN 0-89283-071-9). Servant.

Englert, Robert W. Scattering & Oneing: A Study of Conflict in the Works of the Author of the Cloud of Unknowing. Hogg, James, ed. (Analecta Cartusiana Ser.: No. 105). 184p. (Orig.). 1983. pap. 25.00 (ISBN 0-317-42594-3, Pub. by Salzburg Studies). Longwood Pub Group.

English Benedictine Congregation Members & Rees, Daniel. Consider Your Call. (Cistercian Studies Ser.: No. 20). 447p. 1980. 17.95 (ISBN 0-87907-820-0). Cistercian Pubns.

English, E. Schuyler. A Companion to the New Scofield Reference Bible. 1972. 6.95 (ISBN 0-19-526872-5). Oxford U Pr.

--Ordained of the Lord: H. A. Ironside. LC 76-13873. (Illus.). 1976. pap. 4.95 (ISBN 0-87213-143-2). Loizeaux.

--The Rapture. 1954. pap. 5.95 (ISBN 0-87213-144-0). Loizeaux.

--Things Surely to Be Believed. 1970. Repr. of 1946 ed. 4.95 (ISBN 0-87213-146-7). Loizeaux.

English, Jane, tr. see Chuang Tsu.

English, Jane, tr. see Lao Tsu.

English, Raymond, jt. auth. see Norman, Edward R.

Englund, Sergia, tr. see Balthasar, Hans Urs Von.

Englund, Sergia, tr. see Muggeridge, Malcolm, et al.

Englund, Sr. Sergia, tr. see Lubac, Henri De.

Engman, Suzy, jt. auth. see Grossman, Cheryl S.

Engnell, Ivan. Rigid Scrutiny: Critical Essays on the Old Testament. Willis, John T., tr. LC 70-76166. 1969. 15.00x (ISBN 0-8265-1133-3). Vanderbilt U Pr.

--A Rigid Scrutiny: Critical Essays on the Old Testament. Willis, John T., ed. (Vanderbilt University Press Bks.). 303p. 1969. 15.00 (ISBN 0-8265-1133-3). U of Ill Pr.

Engstrom, Barbie. Faith to Know. LC 77-94207. (Christian Guidebook Ser.). (Illus., Orig.). Date not set. pap. 10.50 (ISBN 0-932210-01-5). Kurios Found.

--Faith to See: Reflections & Photographs. LC 74-25540. (Illus.). 64p. 1979. pap. 3.00 (ISBN 0-932210-00-7). Kurios Found.

Engstrom, Ted. Your Gift of Administration: How to Discover & Use It. LC 83-8327. 192p. 1983. 9.95 (ISBN 0-8407-5297-0). Nelson.

Engstrom, Ted & Larson, Robert C. A Time for Commitment. 112p. 1987. padded gift ed. 9.95 (ISBN 0-310-51010-4); pap. 4.95 (ISBN 0-310-51011-2). Zondervan.

Engstrom, Ted W. Desafio del Liderazgo. De Bedoian, Adriana P., tr. from Eng. Tr. of Your Gift of Administration. (Span.). 128p. 1987. pap. 3.25 (ISBN 0-88113-058-3). Edit Betania.

--Un Lider No Nace, Se Hace. 256p. 1980. 4.25 (ISBN 0-88113-330-2). Edit Betania.

--The Making of a Christian Leader. 1976. pap. 6.95 (ISBN 0-310-24221-5, 9573P). Zondervan.

--Motivation to Last a Lifetime. 96p. 1983. gift ed. 8.95 (ISBN 0-310-24250-9, 9570L); pap. 4.95 (ISBN 0-310-24251-7, 9570P). Zondervan.

Engstrom, Ted W. & Larson, Robert C. The Fine Art of Friendship. 176p. 1985. 9.95 (ISBN 0-8407-5419-1). Nelson.

Engstrom, Ted W., jt. auth. see Dayton, Edward R.

Enlart, Camille. Les Monuments des Croises dans le Royaume de Jerusalem, 4 vols. LC 78-63336. (The Crusades & Military Orders: Second Ser.). Repr. of 1927 ed. Set. 495.00 (ISBN 0-404-17050-1). AMS Pr.

Enloe, Eilene, jt. auth. see Smelser, Georgia.

Enlow, David R. Church Usher: Servant of God. LC 80-66769. 64p. (Orig.). 1980. pap. 1.95 (ISBN 0-87509-284-5). Chr Pubns.

Enlow, David R., jt. auth. see Parker, Paul E.

Enlow, Jack. Glosario de Nombres Biblicos. 96p. 1981. pap. 2.25 (ISBN 0-311-03655-4). Casa Bautista.

Ennodius, Magnus F. Opera Omnia. (Corpus Scriptorum Ecclesiasticorum Latinorum Ser.: Vol. 6). 1882. pap. 60.00 (ISBN 0-384-14370-9). Johnson Repr.

Enns, Herman. This We Believe, Leader's Guide. LC 78-130643. 1970. pap. 1.75 (ISBN 0-87303-846-0). Faith & Life.

Enns, Paul P. Ezekiel. (Bible Study Commentary Ser.). 224p. 1986. pap. 7.95 (ISBN 0-310-44071-8). Zondervan.

--Joshua: Bible Study Commentary. (Bible Study Commentary). 160p. (Orig.). 1981. pap. 4.95 (ISBN 0-310-44041-6, 11830P). Zondervan.

--Judges: A Bible Study Commentary. (Bible Study Commentary Ser.). 160p. (Orig.). 1982. pap. 5.95 (ISBN 0-310-44051-3, 11831P). Zondervan.

--Ruth: A Bible Study Commentary. 96p. (Orig.). 1982. pap. 3.95 (ISBN 0-310-44061-0, 11832P). Zondervan.

Enns, Peter & Forsberg, Glen. Adam & Eve & Five Other Stories. (Stories that Live Ser.: Bk. 1). (Illus.). 24p. 1985. book & Cassette 4.95 (ISBN 0-936215-01-1). STL Intl.

--Daniel & the Lions & Five Other Stories. (Stories that Live Ser.: Bk. 4). (Illus.). 24p. 1985. book & cassette 4.95 (ISBN 0-936215-04-6). STL Intl.

--David & Goliath & Five Other Stories. (Stories that Live Ser.: Bk. 3). (Illus.). 24p. 1985. book & Cassette 4.95 (ISBN 0-936215-03-8). STL Intl.

--Jesus Is Alive! & Five Other Stories. (Stories that Live Ser.: Bk. 6). 24p. 1985. book & cassette 4.95 (ISBN 0-936215-06-2). STL Intl.

--Joseph the Dreamer & Five Other Stories. (Stories that Live Ser.: Bk. 2). (Illus.). 24p. 1985. book & cassette 4.95 (ISBN 0-936215-02-X). STL Intl.

--Six Stories of Jesus. (Stories that Live Ser.: Bk. 5). (Illus.). 24p. 1985. 4.95 (ISBN 0-936215-05-4); cassette incl. STL Intl.

--Stories That Live, 6 vols. (Series I). (Illus.). 144p. 1985. books & cassettes 29.70 (ISBN 0-936215-00-3). STL Intl.

Enright, Michael J. Iona, Tara, & Soissons: The Origin of the Royal Anointing Ritual in Francia. (Arbeiten zur Fruehmittelalterforschung: Vol. 17). x, 198p. 1985. 67.25x (ISBN 3-11-010628-0). De Gruyter.

Enriquez, Edmund C. The Golden Gospel: A Pictorial History of the Restoration. (Illus.). 96p. 1981. pap. 5.95 (ISBN 0-88290-198-2). Horizon Utah.

Enrody, Ladislaus. Hope Unlimited. 1962. 2.50 (ISBN 0-8198-0060-0); pap. 1.50 (ISBN 0-8198-0061-9). Dghtrs St Paul.

Enroth, Ronald. The Lure of the Cults. rev. ed. 130p. 1987. pap. 5.95 (ISBN 0-87784-994-3). Inter-Varsity.

Enroth, Ronald, et al. A Guide to Cults & New Religions. LC 83-44. 200p. (Orig.). 1983. pap. 6.95 (ISBN 0-87784-837-8). Inter-Varsity.

Enroth, Ronald M. & Melton, Gordon J. Why Cults Succeed Where the Church Fails. 128p. 1985. 6.95 (ISBN 0-87178-932-9). Brethren.

Enroth, Ronald M., et al. The Story of the Jesus People: A Factual Survey. (Illus.). 256p. 1972. pap. 3.95 (ISBN 0-85364-131-5). Attic Pr.

Ensley, Francis G. Leader's Guide for Use with Persons Can Change, by Francis Gerald Ensley. LC 69-101739. pap. 20.00 (ISBN 0-317-10063-7, 2001430). Bks Demand UMI.

Enswiler, James P. The Religious Education Handbook: A Practical Parish Guide. LC 79-26008. 108p. (Orig.). 1980. pap. 4.95 (ISBN 0-8189-0398-8). Alba.

Entrevernes Group. Signs & Parables: Semiotics & Gospel Texts. Phillips, Gary, tr. from Fr. LC 78-12840. (Pittsburgh Theological Monographs: No. 23). Orig. Title: Signes et Paraboles. 1978. pap. 10.00 (ISBN 0-915138-35-2). Pickwick.

Entwisle, Doris R., jt. auth. see Huggins, William H.

Entz, Angeline J. Elijah: Brave Prophet. (BibLearn Ser.). (Illus.). 1978. 5.95 (ISBN 0-8054-4244-8, 4242-44). Broadman.

Enuma Elish. Le Poeme Babylonien de la Creation. LC 78-72734. (Ancient Mesopotamian Texts & Studies). Repr. of 1935 ed. 24.50 (ISBN 0-404-18173-2). AMS Pr.

--The Seven Tablets of Creation, 2 vols. LC 73-18850. (Luzac's Semitic Text & Translation Ser.: Nos. 12 & 13). (Illus.). Repr. of 1902 ed. Set. 45.00 (ISBN 0-404-11344-3). AMS Pr.

Enyart, David K. Applying for Your Church. LC 84-71852. 72p. (Orig.). pap. 2.95 (ISBN 0-89900-192-0). College Pr Pub.

Enyi, Donatus O. Thirty Seconds with Your Bible: Learn How to Chart Your Horoscope, Predict Your Destiny, Luck, Fortune... LC 86-70272. (Illus.). 80p. 1986. 9.95 (ISBN 0-937171-00-X); pap. 6.95 (ISBN 0-937171-01-8). D Enyi.

Enz, Jacob J. The Christian & Warfare: The Old Testament, War & the Christian. (Christian Peace Shelf Ser.). 104p. 1972. pap. 2.95 (ISBN 0-8361-1684-4). Herald Pr.

Enzler, Clarence. In the Presence of God. pap. 4.95 (ISBN 0-87193-055-2). Dimension Bks.

--My Other Self. pap. 5.95 (ISBN 0-87193-056-0). Dimension Bks.

Enzler, Clarence J. Let Us Be What We Are. 5.95 (ISBN 0-87193-136-2). Dimension Bks.

Eogan, George. Knowth: And the Passage Tombs of Ireland. LC 86-50218. (New Aspects of Antiquity Ser.). (Illus.). 248p. 1987. 29.95 (ISBN 0-500-39023-1). Thames Hudson.

Ephraem, Saint Repentance. pap. 1.95 (ISBN 0-686-18718-0). Eastern Orthodox.

Epictetus. The Most Meaningful Writings by Epictetus. Roswell, Steve C., tr. (The Most Meaningful Classics in World Culture Ser.). (Illus.). 1979. 49.75 (ISBN 0-89266-183-6). Am Classical Coll Pr.

Epicurus. Epicurus's Morals. Digby, John, tr. LC 74-158299. Tr. of Le Morale d'Epicure. Repr. of 1712 ed. 28.00 (ISBN 0-404-54114-3). AMS Pr.

Epigraphic Survey. The Temple of Khonsu: Vol. 2, Scenes & Inscriptions in the Court & the First Hypostyle Hall. LC 80-82999. (Oriental Institute Publications Ser.: Vol. 103). 1981. pap. 95.00x incl. 96 plates in portfolio (ISBN 0-918986-29-X). Oriental Inst.

Episcopal Church. Prayer Book Guide to Christian Education. 224p. 1983. pap. 9.95 (ISBN 0-8164-2422-5, HarpR). Har-Row.

Episcopal Church Center. The Work You Give Us to Do: A Mission Study. 179p. (Orig.). 1982. pap. 4.95 (ISBN 0-8164-7116-9, HarpR); study guide 1.25 (ISBN 0-8164-7117-7). Har-Row.

Episcopal Society for Ministry on Aging, compiled by. Affirmative Aging: A Resource for Ministry. 192p. (Orig.). 1986. pap. 8.95 (ISBN 0-86683-786-8, HarpR). Har-Row.

Epp, Eldon J. & Gordon, Fee D., eds. New Testament Textual Criticism: Its Significance for Exegesis. (Illus.). 94.00x (ISBN 0-19-826175-6). Oxford U Pr.

Epp, Frank H. Mennonites in Canada, Nineteen Twenty to Nineteen Forty, Vol. II. LC 82-81339. 640p. 1982. text ed. 21.95x (ISBN 0-8361-1255-5). Herald Pr.

--The Palestinians. LC 76-12976. 240p. 1976. 10.00 (ISBN 0-8361-1338-1). Herald Pr.

Epp, Margaret. The Earth is Round. 228p. (Orig.). pap. 4.00 (ISBN 0-919797-00-8). Kindred Pr.

--Eight, Tulpengasse: A Church Blossom's in Vienna. 276p. (Orig.). 1978. pap. 4.95 (ISBN 0-919797-01-6, Dist. by Herald Pr.). Kindred Pr.

Eppenstein, Simon, et al. Festschriftum, 3 vols. Katz, Steven, ed. LC 79-7161. (Jewish Philosophy, Mysticism & History of Ideas Ser.). 1980. Repr. of 1914 ed. Set. lib. bdg. 69.00x (ISBN 0-405-12247-0); lib. bdg. 23.00x ea. Vol. 1 (ISBN 0-405-12248-9). Vol. 2 (ISBN 0-405-12249-7). Vol. 3 (ISBN 0-405-12304-3). Ayer Co Pubs.

Eppler, Elizabeth E., ed. International Bibliography of Jewish Affairs 1966-1967: A Select List of Books & Articles Published in the Diaspora. LC 74-84654. 365p. 1976. 35.00x (ISBN 0-8419-0177-5). Holmes & Meier.

Eppsteiner, Fred & Maloney, Dennis, eds. The Path of Compassion: Contemporary Writings on Engaged Buddhism. 1985. 9.95 (ISBN 0-934834-52-0). White Pine.

Epstein, David & Stutman, Suzanne. Torah with Love: A Guide for Strengthening Jewish Values Within the Family. (Illus.). 208p. 1986. 16.95 (ISBN 0-13-925371-8). P-H.

Epstein, Dena J. Sinful Tunes & Spirituals: Black Folk Music to the Civil War. LC 77-6315. (Music in American Life Ser.). (Illus.). 1981. pap. 10.95 (ISBN 0-252-00875-8). U of Ill Pr.

Epstein, Ellen R., jt. auth. see Lewit, Jane.

Epstein, I. Minor Tractates. 480p. 1965. write for info. (ISBN 0-900689-86-2). Soncino Pr.

--Tractate Nedarim. 1985. 22.95 (ISBN 0-900689-90-0). Soncino Pr.

--Tractate Yevamoth. 1984. 22.95 (ISBN 0-900689-92-7). Soncino Pr.

Epstein, I., ed. Tractate Baba Kamma. 1977. 22.95 (ISBN 0-900689-59-5). Soncino Pr.

--Tractate Baba Kamma. 1964. student's ed. 15.00 (ISBN 0-900689-67-6). Soncino Pr.

--Tractate Berakoth. 1960. 22.95 (ISBN 0-900689-56-0). Soncino Pr.

--Tractate Erubin. 1983. 22.95 (ISBN 0-900689-80-3). Soncino Pr.

--Tractate Gitten. 1973. 22.95 (ISBN 0-900689-58-7). Soncino Pr.

--Tractate Hullin. 1980. 22.95 (ISBN 0-900689-17-X). Soncino Pr.

--Tractate Kethuboth. 1971. 22.95 (ISBN 0-900689-06-4). Soncino Pr.

--Tractate Pesachim. 1983. 22.95 (ISBN 0-900689-81-1). Soncino Pr.

--Tractate Sanhedrin. 1969. 22.95 (ISBN 0-900689-04-8). Soncino Pr.

--Tractate Shabbath, 2 vols. 1972. Set. 45.95 (ISBN 0-900689-62-5). Soncino Pr.

--Tractate Yoma. 1974. 22.95 (ISBN 0-900689-63-3). Soncino Pr.

--Tractates Baba Bathra, 2 Vols. 1976. Set. write for info. (ISBN 0-900689-64-1). Soncino Pr.

Epstein, Isadore. The Faith of Judaism. 418p. 1954. pap. 8.75 (ISBN 0-900689-13-7). Soncino Pr.

--Step by Step in the Jewish Religion. 143p. 1958. pap. 4.95 (ISBN 0-900689-12-9). Soncino Pr.

Epstein, Isidore. Faith of Judaism. pap. 8.75x (ISBN 0-900689-13-7). Bloch.

--Judaism. (Orig.). 1959. pap. 6.95 (ISBN 0-14-020440-7, Pelican). Penguin.

--Step by Step in the Jewish Religion. PLB 4.95x. Bloch.

Epstein, Ita. Ba'sha'ar: Yahadus & Middos Text & Workbook. (Illus.). text ed. 4.00 (ISBN 0-914131-02-8, A10). Torah Umesorah.

Epstein, Jane G. The Jewish Working Parent: Determining Priorities. 4.95. United Synagogue.

Epstein, Lawrence J. Zion's Call: Christian Contributions to the Origins & Development of Israel. LC 84-15184. 176p. (Orig.). 1984. lib. bdg. 23.00 (ISBN 0-8191-4185-2); pap. text ed. 11.25 (ISBN 0-8191-4186-0). U Pr of Amer.

Epstein, Leslie. King of the Jews. 352p. 1986. pap. 7.95 (ISBN 0-452-25823-5, Plume). NAL.

Epstein, Louis M. The Jewish Marriage Contract: A Study in the Status of the Woman in Jewish Law. LC 73-2195. (The Jewish People; History, Religion, Literature Ser.). Repr. of 1927 ed. 33.00 (ISBN 0-405-05261-8). Ayer Co Pubs.

--Marriage Laws in the Bible & the Talmud. 1942. 25.00 (ISBN 0-384-14535-3). Johnson Repr.

Epstein, Melech. Jewish Labor in the U. S. A., 1882-1952. rev. ed. 1969. 45.00x (ISBN 0-87068-042-0). Ktav.

Epstein, Morris. All about Jewish Holidays & Customs. rev. ed. 1969. pap. 7.95x (ISBN 0-87068-500-7). Ktav.

--My Holiday Story Book. rev. ed. 1958. pap. 4.50x (ISBN 0-87068-368-3). Ktav.

--A Picture Parade of Jewish History. 1977. pap. 4.95 (ISBN 0-8197-0024-X). Bloch.

Epstein, Simon. Cry of Cassandra: The Resurgence of European Anti-Semitism. Posel, Norman S., tr. from Fr. Tr. of Antisemitism Francais. 256p. 1986. 15.95 (ISBN 0-915765-13-6, Pub. by Zenith Edit); pap. 7.95 (ISBN 0-915765-14-4, Pub. by Zenith Edit). Natl Pr Inc.

Erasmus. Christian Humanism & the Reformation: Selected Writings with the Life of Erasmus by Beatus Rhenanus. Olin, John C., ed. 11.25 (ISBN 0-8446-2035-1). Peter Smith.

--Enchiridion Militis Christiani. O'Donnell, Anne M., ed. (Early English Text Society Ser.). (Illus.). 1981. text ed. 47.00x (ISBN 0-19-722284-6). Oxford U Pr.

--Enchiridion of Erasmus. Himelick, Raymond, tr. 16.50 (ISBN 0-8446-0614-6). Peter Smith.

--Inquistio De Fide: A Colloquy by Desiderius Erasmus Roterodamus, 1524. 2nd ed. Thompson, Craig, ed. LC 74-31476. xiii, 137p. 1975. Repr. of 1950 ed. 20.00 (ISBN 0-685-51693-8, Archon). Shoe String.

Erasmus, Desiderius. A Booke Called in Latyn Enchiridian & in Englysshe the Manuell of the Christen Knyght. LC 70-25758. (English Experience Ser.: No. 156). 340p. 1969. Repr. of 1533 ed. 28.00 (ISBN 90-221-0156-8). Walter J Johnson.

--The Censure & Judgement of Erasmus: Whyther Dyuorsemente Stondeth with the Lawe of God. Lesse, N., tr. LC 76-38177. (English Experience Ser.: No. 452). 160p. 1972. Repr. of 1550 ed. 15.00 (ISBN 90-221-0452-4). Walter J Johnson.

--De Contemptu Mundi. Paynell, Thomas, tr. LC 67-18715. 1967. 30.00x (ISBN 0-8201-1016-7). Schol Facsimiles.

--The Correspondence of Erasmus, Letters, 1501-1514, Vol. 2. Corrigan, Beatrice, ed. LC 72-47422. (Collected Works of Erasmus: Vol. 2). (Illus.). 1975. 75.00x (ISBN 0-8020-1983-8). U of Toronto Pr.

--The Correspondence of Erasmus. Vol. 1: Letters 1-141: 1484-1500. Corrigan, Beatrice, ed. LC 72-97422. (Collected Works of Erasmus: Vol. 1). (Illus.). 1974. 75.00x (ISBN 0-8020-1981-1). U of Toronto Pr.

--Correspondence of Erasmus, Vol. 3: Letters 298-445 (1514-1516) Mynors, Mynors, R. A. & Thomson, D. F., trs. LC 72-97422. (Collected Works of Erasmus: Vol. 3). (Illus.). 1976. 75.00x (ISBN 0-8020-2202-2). U of Toronto Pr.

--The Correspondence of Erasmus, Vol. 4: Letters 446-593. Mynors, R. A. & Thomson, D. F., trs. LC 72-97422. (Collected Works of Erasmus: Vol. 4). 1977. 75.00x (ISBN 0-8020-5366-1). U of Toronto Pr.

--The Correspondence of Erasmus, Vol. 5: Letters 594-841 (July 1517 - April 1518) Mynors, R. A. & Thomson, D. F., trs. LC 78-6904. (Collected Works of Erasmus: Vol. 5). 1979. 75.00x (ISBN 0-8020-5429-3). U of Toronto Pr.

--The Correspondence of Erasmus, Vol. 6: Letters 842-992 (May 1518 - June 1519) Mynors, R. A. & Thomson, D. F., trs. (Collected Works of Erasmus: Vol. 6). 1981. 75.00x (ISBN 0-8020-5500-1). U of Toronto Pr.

--The Critical Writing by Desiderius Erasmus on the Spiritual Conditions of His Times & the Psychological Impulses Motivating the Actions of Men. (Illus.). 123p. 1984. 89.45 (ISBN 0-89920-106-7). Am Inst Psych.

--Erasmus on His Times: A Shortened Version of the Adages of Erasmus. Phillips, Margaret M., ed. 1967. pap. 9.95 (ISBN 0-521-09413-5). Cambridge U Pr.

--An Exhortation to the Diligent Studye of Scripture. Roy, W., tr. LC 72-5983. (English Experience Ser.: No. 510). 156p. 1973. Repr. of 1529 ed. 11.50 (ISBN 90-221-0510-5). Walter J Johnson.

--The First Tome or Volume of the Paraphrase of Erasmus Upon the Newe Testamente. LC 75-23361. 1350p. 1975. Repr. of 1548 ed. lib. bdg. 100.00x (ISBN 0-8201-1159-7). Schol Facsimiles.

--The Historical Significance of Desiderius Erasmus in the Light of the Protesant Revolution & the Catholic Church As Revealed by His Most Famous Pronouncements, 2 vols. (Illus.). 396p. 1985. Set. 207.50. Am Classical Coll Pr.

--A Lytle Treatise of the Maner & Forme of Confession. LC 79-39487. (English Experience Ser.: No. 553). (Illus.). 232p. 1973. Repr. of 1535 ed. 16.00 (ISBN 90-221-0553-9). Walter J Johnson.

--Paraphrases on Romans & Galatians. Sider, Robert D., ed. Payne, John B., et al, trs. (Collected Works of Erasmus Ser.: Vol. 42). 232p. 1984. 29.50x (ISBN 0-8020-2510-2). U of Toronto Pr.

--The Praise of Folly. Miller, Clarence H., intro. by. LC 78-13575. 1979. text ed. 25.00 (ISBN 0-300-02279-4); pap. 7.95x (ISBN 0-300-02373-1). Yale U Pr.

--Preparation to Deathe: A Boke As Devout As Eloquent. LC 74-28852. (English Experience Ser.: No. 733). 1975. Repr. of 1538 ed. 6.00 (ISBN 90-221-0762-0). Walter J Johnson.

--Proverbs or Adages. Taverner, Richard, tr. LC 55-11634. 1977. Repr. of 1569 ed. 35.00x (ISBN 0-8201-1232-1). Schol Facsimiles.

--Proverbs or Adagies with Newe Addicions, Gathered Out of the Chiliades of Erasmus. LC 73-264117. (English Experience Ser.: No. 124). 1969. Repr. of 1539 ed. 13.00 (ISBN 90-221-0124-X). Walter J Johnson.

Erb, Paul. El Alfa & la Omega. 230p. 1968. pap. 3.30x (ISBN 0-8361-1111-7). Herald Pr.

--South Central Frontiers. LC 74-12108. (Studies in Anabaptist & Mennonite History, No. 17). (Illus.). 448p. 1974. 19.95x (ISBN 0-8361-1196-6). Herald Pr.

--We Believe. LC 69-15831. 112p. (Orig.). 1969. pap. 3.95 (ISBN 0-8361-1587-2). Herald Pr.

Erb, Peter. Johann Arndt: True Christianity. LC 78-72046. (Classics of Western Spirituality). 320p. 1979. 12.95 (ISBN 0-8091-0281-1); pap. 9.95 (ISBN 0-8091-2192-1). Paulist Pr.

Erb, Peter C. Jacob Boehme, "The Way to Christ". LC 77-95117. (Classics of Western Spirituality). 336p. 1978. 13.95 (ISBN 0-8091-0237-4); pap. 7.95 o. p. (ISBN 0-8091-2102-6). Paulist Pr.

--Schwenckfeld & Early Schwenkfeldianism. 428p. (Orig.). 1986. pap. 10.00 (ISBN 0-935980-05-9). Schwenkfelder Lib.

Erb, Peter C., ed. The Pietists: Selected Writings. (Classics of Western Spirituality Ser.). 1983. 13.95 (ISBN 0-8091-0334-6); pap. 9.95 (ISBN 0-8091-2509-9). Paulist Pr.

Erb, Peter C., tr. see Weigelt, Horst.

Erbe, T. Mirk's Festial: A Collection of Homilies. (EETS ES Ser.: No. 96). Repr. of 1905 ed. 28.00 (ISBN 0-527-00296-8). Kraus Repr.

Erdahl, Lowell. Ten for Our Time. 1986. 5.50 (ISBN 0-89536-786-6, 6804). CSS of Ohio.

Erdahl, Lowell O. The Lonely House: Strength for Times of Loss. LC 77-1907. Repr. of 1977 ed. 21.30 (ISBN 0-8357-9015-0, 2016377). Bks Demand UMI.

--Pro-Life, Pro-Peace: Life Affirming Alternatives to Abortion, War, Mercy Killing, & the Death Penalty. LC 86-3552. 160p. (Orig.). 1986. pap. 8.95 (ISBN 0-8066-2209-1, 10-5240). Augsburg.

Erdman, Charles. El Pentateuco. Casanova, Humberto & Casanova, Viviana, trs. Tr. of The Pentateuch. 396p. 1986. 12.95 (ISBN 0-939125-14-5). Evangelical Lit.

Erdman, Charles R. Deuteronomy. 96p. 1982. pap. 3.50 (ISBN 0-8010-3379-9). Baker Bk.

--Genesis. 128p. 1982. pap. 4.95 (ISBN 0-8010-3375-6). Baker Bk.

--Isaiah. 160p. 1982. pap. 4.50 (ISBN 0-8010-3380-2). Baker Bk.

--Numbers. 144p. 1982. pap. 4.50 (ISBN 0-8010-3378-0). Baker Bk.

Erdman, David V. Blake: Prophet Against Empire. rev. ed. LC 69-18055. 1969. pap. 17.00x (ISBN 0-691-01329-2). Princeton U Pr.

Erdman, V. R. Signs of Christ's Second Coming. 29p. pap. 0.95 (ISBN 0-87509-130-X). Chr Pubns.

Erdmann, Carl. The Origin of the Idea of Crusade. Baldwin, Marshall W. & Goffart, Walter, trs. from Ger. 1977. 55.50x (ISBN 0-691-05251-4). Princeton U Pr.

Erdoes, Richard, jt. auth. see John Lame Deer.

Erdozain, Placido. Archbishop Romero: Martyr of Salvador. McFadden, John & Warner, Ruth, trs. from Sp. LC 81-2007. Orig. Title: Monsenor Romero: Martis de la Iglesia Popular. (Illus.). 128p. (Orig.). 1981. pap. 4.95 (ISBN 0-88344-019-9). Orbis Bks.

Eren, Halit, jt. auth. see Binark, Ismet.

Ericcson, Samuel, jt. auth. see Buzzard, Lynn.

Ericksen, Ephraim E. The Psychological & Ethical Aspects of Mormon Group Life. LC 75-310523. (A Bonneville Books Reprint Edition). pap. 30.80 (ISBN 0-317-41838-6, 2025900). Bks Demand UMI.

Ericksen, Robert P. Theologians under Hitler: Gerhard Kittel, Paul Althaus, & Emanuel Hirsch. LC 84-40731. (Illus.). 256p. 1985. 20.00x (ISBN 0-300-02926-8). Yale U Pr.

Erickson, Craig D. Under the Shadow of Your Wings. Sherer, Michael L., ed. (Orig.). 1987. pap. 6.75 (ISBN 0-89536-844-7, 7803). CSS of Ohio.

Erickson, Gary D. The Conversion Experience: A Biblical Study of the Blood, Water & Spirit. Bernard, David, ed. (Illus.). 160p. (Orig.). 1987. pap. 5.95 (ISBN 0-932581-13-7). Word Aflame.

Erickson, J. Irving. Sing It Again! 1985. 12.95 (ISBN 0-910452-58-X). Covenant.

Erickson, John, jt. ed. see Drillock, David.

Erickson, Joyce. In Straw & Story: Christmas Resources for Home & Church. rev. ed. (Illus.). 192p. 1983. pap. 10.95 (ISBN 0-87178-417-3). Brethren.

Erickson, K. Please, Lord, Untie My Tongue. LC 12-2816. 1983. pap. 2.50 (ISBN 0-570-03881-2). Concordia.

Erickson, Kenneth. The Power of Praise. 1984. pap. 4.95 (ISBN 0-570-03925-8, 12-2859). Concordia.

Erickson, Kenneth A. Christian Time Management. 128p. (Orig.). 1985. pap. 4.95 (ISBN 0-570-03972-X, 12-3007). Concordia.

--The Power of Communication. 112p. (Orig.). 1986. pap. 4.95 (ISBN 0-570-04435-9). Concordia.

Erickson, Lois J., tr. Songs from the Land of Dawn. facs. ed. LC 68-58828. (Granger Index Reprint Ser). 1949. 14.00 (ISBN 0-8369-6014-9). Ayer Co Pubs.

Erickson, Lonni R. Creation vs. Evolution: A Comparison. 30p. write for info. Scandia Pubs.

Erickson, Mae. Quiz for Christian Wives. 32p. 1976. pap. 0.95 (ISBN 0-930756-20-7, 541003). Aglow Pubns.

Erickson, Mary. Don't Cry for Anna. LC 85-10975. (Jesus, the Wonder Worker Ser.). 48p. 1985. pap. 3.95 (ISBN 0-89191-683-0, 56838, Chariot Bks). Cook.

Erickson, Millard J. Christian Theology, Vol. 1. 432p. 1983. 19.95 (ISBN 0-8010-3391-8). Baker Bk.

--Christian Theology, Vol. 2. 432p. 1984. 19.95 (ISBN 0-8010-3419-1). Baker Bk.

--Christian Theology, Vol. 3. 1985. 19.95 (ISBN 0-8010-3425-6). Baker Bk.

--Concise Dictionary of Christian Theology. 1986. 9.95 (ISBN 0-8010-3436-1). Baker Bk.

--Contemporary Options in Eschatology: A Study of the Millennium. LC 77-89406. 1977. 9.95 (ISBN 0-8010-3262-8). Baker Bk.

Erickson, Millard J., ed. Christian Theology, 1 vol. 1986. 39.95 (ISBN 0-8010-3433-7). Baker Bk.

--Man's Need & God's Gift: Readings in Christian Theology. LC 76-17965. 512p. 1976. pap. 12.95 (ISBN 0-8010-3324-1). Baker Bk.

--New Life: Readings in Christian Theology. LC 79-53903. 1979. pap. 11.95 (ISBN 0-8010-3340-3). Baker Bk.

--Readings In Christian Theology. 1973. pap. 12.95 (ISBN 0-8010-3305-5). Baker Bk.

Erickson, Milton H., et al. Healing in Hypnosis. Rossi, Ernest L. & Sharp, Florence A., eds. 1984. 19.95 (ISBN 0-8290-0739-3). New Horizon NJ.

Erickson, Robert P. Theologians under Hitler. LC 84-40731. 256p. 1987. pap. 8.95 (ISBN 0-300-03889-5, Y-618). Yale U Pr.

Ericson, Donald E. The Portuguese Letters: Love Letters of a Nun to a French Officer. 2nd ed. LC 86-71957. 78p. 1986. pap. 5.95 (ISBN 0-9617271-0-1). Bennett-Edwards.

Ericson, Jack T., ed. Missionary Society of Connecticut Papers, 1759-1948: A Guide to the Microform Edition. 49p. 1976. pap. 15.00 (ISBN 0-667-00289-8). Microfilming Corp.

--Shaker Collection of the Western Reserve Historical Society. 77p. 1977. pap. 7.50 (ISBN 0-667-00522-6). Microfilming Corp.

Erikson, Erik H. Young Man Luther. 1962. pap. 5.95 (ISBN 0-393-00170-9). Norton.

Erikson, Joan M. Saint Francis & His Four Ladies. LC 71-127178. (Illus.). 1970. 6.95 (ISBN 0-393-05427-6). Norton.

--Universal Bead. LC 68-20819. (Illus.). 1969. 13.95 (ISBN 0-393-04233-2). Norton.

Erikson, Kai T. Wayward Puritans: A Study in the Sociology of Deviance. LC 66-16140. (Deviance & Criminology Ser.). 228p. 1968. pap. text ed. write for info. (ISBN 0-02-332200-4). Macmillan.

Erman, Adolf. A Handbook of Egyptian Religions. LC 76-27517. (Illus.). 1976. Repr. of 1907 ed. lib. bdg. 30.00 (ISBN 0-89341-032-2). Longwood Pub Group.

--Life in Ancient Egypt. Tirard, H. M., tr. (Illus.). pap. 8.50 (ISBN 0-486-22632-8). Dover.

Erman, Adolph. Life in Ancient Egypt. LC 68-56523. (Illus.). Repr. of 1894 ed. 25.00 (ISBN 0-405-08488-9, Blom Pubns). Ayer Co Pubs.

--Life in Ancient Egypt. 16.75 (ISBN 0-8446-0090-3). Peter Smith.

Ernst, Carl W. Words of Ecstasy in Sufism. (SUNY Series in Islam). 230p. 1985. 44.50x (ISBN 0-87395-917-5); pap. 16.95x (ISBN 0-87395-918-3). State U NY Pr.

Ernst, Eldon. Moment of Truth for Protestant America: Interchurch Campaigns Following World War I. LC 74-16567. (American Academy of Religion. Dissertation Ser.). 1974. pap. 9.95 (010103). Scholars Pr GA.

Ernst, James E. Roger Williams: New England Firebrand. LC 76-90097. (BCL Ser.: I). Repr. of 1932 ed. 24.50 (ISBN 0-404-02355-X). AMS Pr.

Ernst, John. Sadhana in Our Daily Lives: A Handbook for the Awakening of the Spiritual Self. LC 81-51360. 320p. (Orig.). 1981. pap. 9.95 (ISBN 0-9606482-0-8). Valley Lights.

Ernst, M. L. & Lindey, A. The Censor Marches on. LC 73-164512. (Civil Liberties in American History Ser.). 346p. 1971. Repr. of 1940 ed. lib. bdg. 39.50 (ISBN 0-306-70295-9). Da Capo.

Erny, Ed, jt. auth. see Steel, Valetta.

Erodes, Richard & Ortiz, Alfonso. American Indian Myth & Legends. LC 84-42669. (Illus.). 504p. 1984. 19.45 (ISBN 0-394-50796-7). Pantheon.

Errico, Rocco A. The Ancient Aramaic Prayer of Jesus. (Illus.). 82p. 1978. pap. 4.95 (ISBN 0-911336-69-9). Sci of Mind.

--Let There Be Light: The Seven Keys. 180p. (Orig.). 1985. pap. 9.95 (ISBN 0-87516-555-9). De Vorss.

Erskine, John T. Millionaire for God (C. T. Studd) 1968. pap. 2.95 (ISBN 0-87508-611-X). Chr Lit.

Erskine, Noel L. Decolonizing Theology: A Caribbean Perspective. LC 80-21784. 144p. (Orig.). 1981. pap. 6.95 (ISBN 0-88344-087-3). Orbis Bks.

Ervin, Howard M. Conversion-Initiation & the Baptism in the Holy Spirit. 108p. 1985. pap. 9.95 (ISBN 0-913573-12-4). Hendrickson MA.

Ervin, Paula. Women Exploited: The Other Victims of Abortion. 200p. (Orig.). 1985. pap. 6.95 (ISBN 0-87973-847-2, 847). Our Sunday Visitor.

Erwin, Gayle D. The Jesus Style. 211p. 1985. 9.95 (ISBN 0-8499-0509-5, 0509-5). Word Bks.

Esau, Truman & Burch, Beverly. Partners in Process. 156p. 1986. pap. 5.95 (ISBN 0-89693-372-5). Victor Bks.

Escandon, R. Como Llegar a Ser Vencedor. (Span.). 128p. 1982. pap. 3.95 (ISBN 0-311-46092-5, Edit Mundo). Casa Bautista.

Esco Foundation For Palestine Inc. Palestine: A Study of Jewish, Arab, & British Policies, 2 Vols. LC 47-2569. Repr. of 1947 ed. Set. 192.00 (ISBN 0-527-27750-9). Kraus Repr.

Escobar, Samuel & Driver, John. Christian Mission & Social Justice. LC 78-6035. (Mennonite Missionary Study Ser.: No. 5). 112p. 1978. pap. 4.95 (ISBN 0-8361-1855-3). Herald Pr.

Escobar, Thyrza. The Star Wheel Technique. pap. 12.00 (ISBN 0-912368-04-7). Golden Seal.

Escriva, Josemaria. The Way of the Cross. (Illus.). 123p. 1983. 10.95 (ISBN 0-906138-05-1); pap. 6.95 (ISBN 0-906138-06-X); pocket size 3.95 (ISBN 0-906138-07-8). Scepter Pubs.

Escriva de Balaguer, Josemaria. Christ Is Passing by. LC 74-78783. 276p. (Foreign language editions avail). 1977. pap. 6.95 (ISBN 0-933932-04-9). Scepter Pubs.
--Friends of God. Tr. of Amigos de Dios. 301p. 1981. 14.50 (ISBN 0-906138-03-5); deluxe ed. 24.00 (ISBN 0-906138-04-3); pap. 7.95 (ISBN 0-906138-02-7). Scepter Pubs.
--Holy Rosary. (Illus.). 49p. 1979. 5.95 (ISBN 0-933932-45-6); pap. 2.95 (ISBN 0-933932-44-8). Scepter Pubs.
--The Way. (Foreign language editions avail.). 1965. 9.95 (ISBN 0-933932-00-6). Scepter Pubs.
--The Way. Orig. Title: Camino. 1979. pap. 4.95 (ISBN 0-933932-01-4). Scepter Pubs.
Eshbaugh, Howard. Hear the Good News. 1984. 3.50 (ISBN 0-89536-656-8, 0805). CSS of Ohio.
--Hearing the Word: Scripture in Worship. 1980. 4.50 (ISBN 0-89536-413-1, 0833). CSS of Ohio.
Eshleman, Clayton. Visions of the Fathers of Lascaux. 44p. (Orig.). 1983. pap. 5.00 (ISBN 0-915572-70-2). Panjandrum.
Eshleman, H. Frank. Historic Background & Annals of the Swiss & German Pioneer Settlers of Southeastern Pennsylvania & of Their Remote Ancestors. LC 77-86809. 386p. 1982. Repr. of 1917 ed. 20.00 (ISBN 0-8063-0105-8). Genealog Pub.
Eshleman, Paul. I Just Saw Jesus, Still Doing Miracles, Still Touching Lives. 224p. (Orig.). 1985. pap. 6.95 (ISBN 0-89840-100-3). Heres Life.
Eskelin, Neil. Pat Robertson: A Biography. 192p. (Orig.). 1987. pap. 7.95 (ISBN 0-910311-47-1). Huntington Hse Inc.
Esler, Philip S. Community & Gospel in Luke-Acts: The Social & Political Motivations of Lucan Theory. (Society for New Testament Studies Monographs: No. 57). 224p. Date not set. price not set (ISBN 0-521-32965-5). Cambridge U Pr.
Eslinger, Elise S., compiled by. The Upper Room Worshipbook. 208p. (Orig.). 1985. pap. 7.50 (ISBN 0-8358-0515-8). Upper Room.
Eslinger, Gary S. & Daugherty, F. Mark, eds. Sacred Choral Music in Print, 2 vols. 2nd ed. LC 85-15368. (Music in Print Ser.: Vol. 1). 1312p. 1985. lib. bdg. 180.00 (ISBN 0-88478-017-1). Musicdata.
Eslinger, Lyle. The Ringship of God in Crisis: A Close Reading of 1 Samuel 1-12. (Bible & Literature Ser.: No. 35). 515p. 1985. text ed. 29.95x (ISBN 0-907459-40-4, Pub. by Almond Pr England); pap. text ed. 15.95 (ISBN 0-907459-41-2). Eisenbrauns.
Eslinger, Richard. Prepare in the Wilderness. 1984. 5.25 (ISBN 0-89536-680-0, 4856). CSS of Ohio.
Esmein, Adhemar. Mariage En Droit Canonique, 2 Vols. (Fr). 1969. Repr. of 1891 ed. Set. 47.00 (ISBN 0-8337-1072-9). B Franklin.
Espada-Matta, Alberto. Church & State in the Social Context of Latin America. LC 85-90067. 79p. 1986. 7.95 (ISBN 0-533-06592-5). Vantage.
Espeland, Pamela. The Story of Baucis & Philemon. LC 80-27674. (A Myth for Modern Children Ser.). (Illus.). 32p. 1981. PLB 6.95 (ISBN 0-87614-140-8). Carolrhoda Bks.
--The Story of Cadmus. LC 80-66795. (Myths for Modern Children Ser.). (Illus.). 32p. 1980. PLB 6.95 (ISBN 0-87614-128-9). Carolrhoda Bks.
--The Story of King Midas. LC 80-66794. (Myths for Modern Children Ser.). (Illus.). 32p. 1980. PLB 6.95 (ISBN 0-87614-129-7). Carolrhoda Bks.
--Theseus & the Road to Athens. LC 80-27713. (Myths for Modern Children Ser.). (Illus.). 32p. 1981. PLB 6.95 (ISBN 0-87614-141-6). Carolrhoda Bks.
Espenschied, Steven. Historical Review: St. Paul's Family Parish, North Canton, Ohio, Pt. II. LC 85-29277. 240p. (Orig.). 1986. 14.95 (ISBN 0-938936-52-2). Daring Bks.
Espina, Noni. Vocal Solos for Christian Churches: A Descriptive Reference of Solo Music for the Church Year. 3rd ed. LC 84-51398. 256p. 25.00 (ISBN 0-8108-1730-6). Scarecrow.
Espinasse, Francis. Life of Ernest Renan. 1895. Repr. 20.00 (ISBN 0-8274-2925-8). R West.
Espinosa, Carmen G. The Freeing of the Deer & Other New Mexico Indian Myths. LC 85-16406. (Illus.). 83p. 1985. 9.95 (ISBN 0-8263-0840-6). U of NM Pr.
Esposito, Donna J., ed. Printed Circuit Board Basics. 92p. (Orig.). 1986. 14.95 (ISBN 0-931463-00-9). PMS Indus.
Esposito, John L. Women in Muslim Family Law. LC 81-18273. (Contemporary Issues in the Middle East Ser.). 172p. 1982. pap. text ed. 10.95X (ISBN 0-8156-2278-3). Syracuse U Pr.
Esposito, John L., ed. Islam & Development: Religion & Sociopolitical Change. LC 80-25119. (Contemporary Issues in the Middle East Ser.). 292p. 1980. pap. text ed. 9.95x (ISBN 0-8156-2230-9). Syracuse U Pr.
--Voices of Resurgent Islam. 1983. 27.00x (ISBN 0-19-503339-6); pap. 12.95x (ISBN 0-19-503340-X). Oxford U Pr.
Esposito, John L., jt. ed. see Donohue, John J.
Esquivel, Julia. Threatened with Resurrection: Amenazado de Resurreccion. (Eng. & Span.). 128p. 1982. pap. 4.95 (ISBN 0-87178-844-6). Brethren.
Ess, Dorothy Van see Van Ess, Dorothy.
Ess, Josef Von. Zwischen Hadit und Theologie: Studien Zum Entstehen Praedestinatianischer Ueberlieferung. LC 73-91809. (Studien Zur Sprache, Geschichte und Kultur Des Islamischen Orients, N.F. Vol. 7). (Ger.). 1974. 53.20x (ISBN 3-11-004290-8). De Gruyter.
Esser, Cajetan. Origins of the Order of Friars Minor. (Orig.). 1970. 12.50 (ISBN 0-8199-0414-7). Franciscan Herald.
Esslemont, J. E. Baha'u'llah & the New Era: An Introduction to the Baha'i Faith. 5th rev. ed. LC 80-24305. 1980. pap. 4.50 (ISBN 0-87743-160-4, 231-005). Baha'i.
--Baha'u'llah & the New Era: An Introduction to the Baha'i Faith. 4th rev. ed. LC 79-21937. 1980. 16.95 (ISBN 0-87743-136-1, 231-004). Baha'i.
Essrig, Harry. Judaism. 1984. Barron.
Essrig, Harry & Segal, Abraham. Israel Today. rev. ed. LC 77-7536. (Illus.). (YA) 1977. text ed. 8.50 (ISBN 0-8074-0007-6, 142601); tchr's guide o.p. 5.00 (ISBN 0-686-83000-8, 202601). UAHC.
Estelami, Mohammad, ed. see Mowlana Jalal ud-Din Mohammad Rumi.
Estep, William R. The Anabaptist Story. 1975. pap. 7.95 (ISBN 0-8028-1594-4). Eerdmans.
--Renaissance & Reformation. 320p. (Orig.). pap. text ed. 21.95 (ISBN 0-8028-0050-5). Eerdmans.
Esterer, Arnulf K. Towards a Unified Faith. LC 62-20870. 1963. 5.95 (ISBN 0-8022-0459-7). Philos Lib.
Estes, D. Timothy. A Humanizing Ministry. LC 84-15669. 160p. 1984. pap. 7.95 (ISBN 0-8361-3365-X). Herald Pr.
Estes, James M. Christian Magistrate & State Church: The Reforming Career of Johannes Brenz. 208p. 1982. 30.00x (ISBN 0-8020-5589-3). U of Toronto Pr.
Estes, Steve & Estes, Verna. Called to Die: The Story of American Linguist Chet Bitterman, Slain by Terrorists. Sloan, John, ed. 208p. pap. 6.95 (ISBN 0-310-28381-7, 12197P). Zondervan.
Estes, Steve, jt. auth. see Eareckson, Joni.
Estes, Verna, jt. auth. see Estes, Steve.
Estevez, Kent. The Untold Story of Jesus Christ. LC 86-81086. 100p. (Orig.). 1986. pap. 10.00 (ISBN 0-9616660-0-5). Holland Pub Hse.
Estlake, Allan. The Oneida Community: A Record of an Attempt to Carry Out the Principles of Christian Unselfishness & Scientific Race-Improvement. LC 72-4179. Repr. of 1900 ed. 11.50 (ISBN 0-404-10758-3). AMS Pr.
Estrada, Jose R. Dias Sin Gloria. (Span.). 64p. 1982. pap. 1.95 (ISBN 0-311-08213-0, Edit Mundo). Casa Bautista.
Estrada, Leobardo. Grandes Hombres de la Biblia. 235p. 1975. pap. 5.25 (ISBN 0-311-04656-8). Casa Bautista.
Estreicher, Donna G., jt. auth. see Arnold, L. Eugene.
Estrello, Francisco E. Senderos de Comunion. 1.75 (ISBN 0-8358-0416-X). Upper Room.
Estrello, Francisco E., tr. see White, D. M.
Estudio, Guias de, jt. auth. see Bridges, Julian C.
Estudio, Guias de, jt. auth. see Price, J. M.
Estudios, Guias de, jt. auth. see Allen, Carlos.
Estudios, Guias de, jt. auth. see Crane, James.
Esway, Judy. Prayers of a Working Mother. (Getting Book Line Ser.). 32p. (Orig.). 1985. pap. 1.50 (ISBN 0-89622-269-1). Twenty-Third.
Etchison, Birdie L. Don't Drop the Sugar Bowl in the Sink! LC 84-80057. 144p. 1984. pap. 4.50 (ISBN 0-88243-485-3, 02-0485). Gospel Pub.
Eterovich, Adam S. Orthodox Church Directory of the United States. 1968. softcover 5.00 (ISBN 0-88247-126-0). Ragusan Pr.
Etheridge, J. W. Targums of Onkelos & Jonathan Ben Uzziel on the Pentateuch with the Fragments of the Jerusalem Targum from the Chaldee. 1969. Repr. of 1865 ed. 59.50x (ISBN 0-87068-045-5). Ktav.
Etheridge, Myrna L. Break Forth into Joy. 179p. (Orig.). 1985. pap. 5.00x (ISBN 0-937417-01-7). Etheridge Minist.
--Fearing No Evil. (Illus.). 119p. (Orig.). 1984. pap. 5.00x (ISBN 0-937417-00-9). Etheridge Minist.
--Spring Wind of the Silent Administrator. 80p. (Orig.). Date not set. pap. 4.00 (ISBN 0-937417-02-5). Etheridge Minist.
Etheridge, Sanford G., tr. see Sextus Empiricus Staff.
Etheridge, Sanford G., tr. see Sextus Empiricus.
Etheridge, Truman H. Rightly Dividing. 1955. 6.00 (ISBN 0-88027-017-9). Firm Foun Pub.
Etherington, Charles L. Protestant Worship Music: Its History & Practice. LC 77-15990. (Illus.). 1978. Repr. of 1962 ed. lib. bdg. 35.00x (ISBN 0-313-20024-6, ETPW). Greenwood.
Ethics, Humanisms & Medicine Conference, University of Michigan, Ann Arbor, MI. 1981 & Basson, Marc D. Troubling Problems in Medical Ethics: The Third Volume in a Series on Ethics, Humanism & Medicine, Proceedings. LC 81-20723. (Progress in Clinical & Biological Research: Vol. 76). 306p. 1981. 28.00 (ISBN 0-8451-0076-9). A R Liss.
Etling, Harold H. Emmanuel, God with Us: Studies in Matthew. pap. 4.95 (ISBN 0-88469-107-1). BMH Bks.
--Our Heritage: Brethren Beliefs & Practices. pap. 4.95 (ISBN 0-88469-022-9). BMH Bks.
Ettin, Andrew V. Literature & the Pastoral. LC 83-26052. 212p. 1984. 22.50x (ISBN 0-300-03160-2). Yale U Pr.
Etzenhouser, R. From Palmyra, New York, Eighteen Thirty to Independence, Missouri, Eighteen Ninety-Four. LC 73-134393. Repr. of 1894 ed. 29.50 (ISBN 0-404-08435-4). AMS Pr.
Etzkorn, Girard J., ed. Guillelmi de Ockham: Scriptum in Librum Primum Sententiarum, Ordinatio, Opera Theologica, Vol. 3, Distinctiones 4-18. 1977. 46.00 (ISBN 0-686-27929-8). Franciscan Inst.
Etzkorn, Girard J. & Kelley, Francis E., eds. Guillelmi de Ockham: Scriptum in Librum Primum Sententiarum, Ordinatio, Opera Theologica, Vol. 4, Distinctiones 19-48. 1979. 48.00 (ISBN 0-686-27932-8). Franciscan Inst.
Eubanks, David L. & Shannon, Robert C. Hebrews. (Standard Bible Studies). 128p. 1986. pap. text ed. 5.95 (ISBN 0-87403-171-0, 40111). Standard Pub.
Eudaly, Maria S. De. El Cuidado de Dios. Villasenor, Emma Z., tr. (Illus.). 1983. pap. 0.95 (ISBN 0-311-38555-9). Casa Bautista.
Eugene, P. Marie. I Want to See God - I Am a Daughter of the Church, 2 vols. in 1. 1216p. 1986. pap. 39.95 (ISBN 0-87061-134-8). Chr Classics.
Eugippius. Leben Des Heiligen Severin. 3rd ed. Rodenbery, C., tr. (Ger.). Repr. of 1912 ed. 12.00 (ISBN 0-384-14820-4). Johnson Repr.
--Life of Saint Severin & Other Minor Works. LC 65-12908. (Fathers of the Church Ser: Vol. 55). 132p. 1965. 14.95x (ISBN 0-8132-0055-5). Cath U Pr.
Euler, Robert C., jt. auth. see Smithson, Carma L.
Euripides. Hippolytus in Drama & Myth. Sutherland, Donald, tr. LC 60-13112. vi, 124p. 1960. pap. 4.50x (ISBN 0-8032-5195-5, BB 103, Bison). U of Nebr Pr.
Eusden, John. Zen & Christian: The Journey Between. 224p. 1981. 10.95 (ISBN 0-8245-0099-7). Crossroad NY.
Eusden, John, jt. auth. see Westerhoff, John H.
Eusden, John D., ed. & tr. see Ames, William.
Eusebeius. The History of the Church: From Christ to Constantine. Williamson, G. A., tr. from Latin. LC 75-22726. Orig. Title: Historia Ecclesiastica. 432p. 1975. pap. 12.95 (ISBN 0-8066-1509-5, 10-3045). Augsburg.
Eusebius. Ecclesiastical History. (Twin Brooks Ser). pap. 11.95 (ISBN 0-8010-3306-3). Baker Bk.
--The History of the Church from Christ to Constantine. Williamson, G. A., tr. (Classics Ser.). 1981. pap. 5.95 (ISBN 0-14-044138-7). Penguin.
--History of the Church (From Christ to Constantine) Williamson, G. A., tr. 1985. Repr. of 1965 ed. 16.95 (ISBN 0-317-19661-8, Pub. by Dorset Pr). Hippocrene Bks.
--Preparation for the Gospel, 2 vols. Gifford, Edwin H., tr. from Gr. (Twin Brooks Ser.). 948p. 1982. pap. 24.95 (ISBN 0-8010-3369-1). Baker Bk.
Eusebius Pamphili. Ecclesiastical History, 2 Vols. (Loeb Classical Library: No. 153, 265). 13.95x ea. Vol. 1 (ISBN 0-674-99169-9). Vol. 2 (ISBN 0-674-99293-8). Harvard U Pr.
--Ecclesiastical History, Bks. 6-10. (Fathers of the Church Ser: Vol. 29). 325p. 1955. 17.95x (ISBN 0-8132-0029-6). Cath U Pr.
--Ecclesiastical History: Books 1-5. LC 65-27501. (Fathers of the Church Ser: Vol. 19). 347p. 1953. 18.95x (ISBN 0-8132-0019-9). Cath U Pr.
Eustace, C. J. Infinity of Questions: Studies in the Art of Religion & the Religion of Art in the Lives of Helen Foley, Katherine Mansfield, et al. 170p. 1946. 10.00 (ISBN 0-87556-595-6). Saifer.
Eustace, Cecil J. Infinity of Questions. facs. ed. LC 70-84356. (Essay Index Reprint Ser). 1946. 16.50 (ISBN 0-8369-1080-X). Ayer Co Pubs.
Eustace, Herbert W. Christian Science, Its "Clear, Correct Teaching" & Complete Writings. 2nd ed. 1037p. 1985. 16.00 (ISBN 0-9611156-0-2). Eustace CSB.
--Letter Excerpts, Statements on Christian Science. 36p. 1976. pap. 3.00 (ISBN 0-9611156-1-0). Eustace CSB.
Evangelical Sisterhood of Mary, tr. see Schlink, Basilea.
Evangelical Teacher Training Association. More Training When Meeting. 32p. 1982. pap. 2.95 (ISBN 0-317-02858-8); leader's planbook 3.95 (ISBN 0-910566-36-4). Evang Tchr.
--Training When Meeting. 32p. 1981. pap. text ed. 2.95 (ISBN 0-910566-33-X); planbook 3.95 (ISBN 0-910566-34-8). Evang Tchr.
--Video Seminar Planbook for Dynamic Bible Teaching. 64p. 1983. pap. 5.95 (ISBN 0-910566-60-7). Evang Tchr.
Evangelicals for Social Action Staff & Sider, Ronald J. Completely Pro-Life. 160p. (Orig.). 1987. pap. 5.95 (ISBN 0-87784-496-8). Inter-Varsity.
Evans & Matilal, eds. Buddhist Logic & Epistemology. 1986. lib. bdg. 59.50 (ISBN 90-277-2222-6, Pub. by Reidel Holland). Kluwer Academic.
Evans, Alice F. & Evans, Robert A. Introduction to Christianity: A Case Method Approach. pap. 3.99 (ISBN 0-8042-1314-3). John Knox.
Evans, Alice F., jt. auth. see Evans, Robert A.
Evans, Alice Frazer & Evans, Robert A. Pedagogies for the Non-Poor. LC 86-21831. 272p. (Orig.). 1987. pap. 13.95 (ISBN 0-88344-409-7). Orbis Bks.
Evans, Arthur. Witchcraft: The Gay Counterculture. 1977. pap. 5.95 (ISBN 0-915480-01-8). Fag Rag.
Evans, Austin P. Episode in the Struggle for Religious Freedom. LC 74-130618. Repr. of 1924 ed. 19.00 (ISBN 0-404-02357-6). AMS Pr.
Evans, Austin P., ed. see Scott, Ernest F.
Evans, B. The Early English Baptists, 2 vols. (Illus.). 1977. Repr. of 1862 ed. Vol. 1, 298 pp. 9.50 (ISBN 0-87921-041-9); Vol. 2, 362 pp. 9.50 (ISBN 0-87921-045-1). Attic Pr.
Evans, C. Stephen. Existentialism: The Philosophy of Despair & the Quest for Hope. LC 83-11198. (Orig.). 1984. pap. 6.95 (ISBN 0-310-43741-5, 11198P). Zondervan.
--Philosophy of Religion. LC 84-25198. (Contours of Christian Philosophy Ser.). 180p. (Orig.). 1985. pap. 6.95 (ISBN 0-87784-343-0). Inter-Varsity.
Evans, C. Stephen, ed. see Ratzsch, Del.
Evans, C. Stephen, ed. see Wolfe, David L.
Evans, C. Stephens. The Quest for Faith. LC 86-7436. 144p. (Orig.). 1986. pap. 4.95 (ISBN 0-87784-511-5). Inter-Varsity.
Evans, Carl D., et al, eds. Scripture in Context: Essays on the Comparative Method. LC 80-10211. (Pittsburgh Theological Monograph Ser.: No. 34). 1980. pap. 15.00 (ISBN 0-915138-43-3). Pickwick.
Evans, Charles W., Jr. Babylon: The Oldest & Most Corrupt Harlot. 1984. 12.95 (ISBN 0-533-05914-3). Vantage.
Evans, Christmas. Sermons & Memoirs of Christmas Evans. LC 86-7108. 320p. 1986. Repr. 12.95 (ISBN 0-8254-2522-0). Kregel.
Evans, Coleen. Living True. 132p. 1985. pap. 4.95 (ISBN 0-89693-321-0). Victor Bks.
Evans, Colin. The Mirror & the Skylight. 1986. 40.00x (ISBN 0-317-54255-9, Pub. by Elmcrest Uk). State Mutual Bk.
Evans, Colleen T. Give Us This Day Our Daily Bread: Asking for & Sharing Life's Necessities. 160p. 1982. pap. 3.50 (ISBN 0-687-14743-3). Abingdon.
--Love Is an Everyday Thing. rev. ed. 128p. 1984. pap. 4.95 (ISBN 0-8007-5157-4, Power Bks). Revell.
--A New Joy. (Orig.). 1975. pap. 1.50 (ISBN 0-89129-015-X). Jove Pubns.
Evans, D. Simon, ed. see Doble, G. H.
Evans, David, ed. see Batten, Adrian.
Evans, David M. The Pastor in a Teaching Church. 96p. 1983. pap. 4.95 (ISBN 0-317-00688-6). Judson.
--Shaping the Church's Ministry with Youth. (Orig.). pap. 2.95 (ISBN 0-8170-0342-8). Judson.
Evans, Debra. The Mystery of Womanhood. LC 86-72262. 256p. (Orig.). 1987. pap. 8.95 (ISBN 0-89107-426-0, Crossway Bks). Good News.
Evans, Donald. Faith, Authenticity, & Morality. 1980. 30.00x (ISBN 0-8020-5424-2). U of Toronto Pr.
Evans, E. P. Animal Symbolism in Ecclesiastical Architecture. 59.95 (ISBN 0-87968-638-3). Gordon Pr.
Evans, Eifion. Daniel Rowland & the Great Evangelical Awakening in Wales. 383p. 1985. 22.95 (ISBN 0-85151-446-4). Banner of Truth.
Evans, Elizabeth C. The Cults of the Sabine Territory. LC 39-25699. (American Academy in Rome. Papers & Monographs: Vol. 11). pap. 71.00 (2026727). Bks Demand UMI.

Evans, Frederick W. Autobiography of a Shaker, & Revelation of the Apocalypse. enl. ed. LC 72-2986. Repr. of 1888 ed. 10.00 (ISBN 0-404-10748-6). AMS Pr.

--Shaker Communism: Or, Tests of Divine Inspiration. LC 72-2987. Repr. of 1871 ed. 14.50 (ISBN 0-404-10749-4). AMS Pr.

--Shaker Music: Inspirational Hymns & Melodies Illustrative of the Resurection, Life & Testimony of the Shakers. LC 72-2988. Repr. of 1875 ed. 27.50 (ISBN 0-404-10750-8). AMS Pr.

--Shakers: Compendium of the Origin, History, Principles, Rules & Regulations, Government & Doctrines of the United Society of Believers in Christ's Second Appearing. 4th ed. LC 72-2985. (Communal Societies in America). Repr. of 1867 ed. 14.00 (ISBN 0-404-10747-8). AMS Pr.

Evans, G. Nesta. Religion & Politics in Mid-Eighteenth Century Anglesey. 251p. 1953. text ed. 17.50x (ISBN 0-7083-0071-5, Pub. by U of Wales). Humanities.

Evans, G. R. Alan of Lille: The Frontiers of Theology in the Twelfth Century. LC 83-1834. 240p. 1983. 54.50 (ISBN 0-521-24618-0). Cambridge U Pr.

--Augustine on Evil. LC 81-21793. 220p. 1983. 34.50 (ISBN 0-521-24526-5). Cambridge U Pr.

--The Language & Logic of the Bible: The Road to Reformation. 200p. 1985. 32.50 (ISBN 0-521-30548-9). Cambridge U Pr.

Evans, G. R. & Singer, C. C. The Church & the Sword. 2nd ed. LC 82-50234. 1983. pap. text ed. 5.00 (ISBN 0-932050-20-4). New Puritan.

Evans, G. Rosemary. Anselm & a New Generation. 1980. 32.50x (ISBN 0-19-826651-0). Oxford U Pr.

--Anselm & Talking About God. 1978. 29.95x (ISBN 0-19-826647-2). Oxford U Pr.

--The Mind of St. Bernard of Clairvaux. 1983. text ed. 37.00x (ISBN 0-19-826667-7). Oxford U Pr.

--Old Arts & New Theology: The Beginnings of Theology As an Academic Discipline. 1980. text ed. 34.95x (ISBN 0-19-826653-7). Oxford U Pr.

Evans, Gary T. & Hayes, Richard E. Equipping God's People. (Church's Teaching Ser.: Introductory). 80p. 1979. pap. 1.25 (ISBN 0-86683-896-1, HarpR). Har-Row.

Evans, George K., jt. auth. see Ehret, Walter.

Evans, Gillian, ed. St. Anselm, Archbishop of Canterbury: A Concordance to the Works of St. Anselm, 4 vols. LC 82-48973. (Orig.). 1985. Set. lib. bdg. 400.00 (ISBN 0-527-03661-7). Kraus Intl.

Evans, Gillian R., tr. see Alan Of Lille.

Evans, H. Sherwood, ed. see Thurman, Thomas D.

Evans, Hiram W. The Rising Storm: An Analysis of the Growing Conflict Over the Political Dilemma of Roman Catholics in America. Grob, Gerald, ed. LC 76-46075. (Anti-Movements in America). 1977. lib. bdg. 27.50x (ISBN 0-405-09948-7). Ayer Co Pubs.

Evans, Hubert, tr. see Petrushevsky, I. P.

Evans, Ivor H. The Religion of the Tempusak Dusuns of North Borneo. LC 77-86972. Repr. of 1953 ed. 40.00 (ISBN 0-404-16707-1). AMS Pr.

Evans, J. M., ed. see Milton, John.

Evans, Jean. Make Ready the Way: An Advent-Christmas Journal Book. LC 81-52596. 64p. (Orig.). 1981. pap. text ed. 4.95 (ISBN 0-89390-030-3). Resource Pubns.

Evans, Joan. Magical Jewels of the Middle Ages & the Renaissance Particularly in England. LC 75-26288. (Illus.). 288p. 1976. pap. 5.95 (ISBN 0-486-23367-7). Dover.

--Monastic Iconography in France from the Renaissance to the Revolution. LC 67-12317. (Illus.). 1969. 80.00 (ISBN 0-521-06960-2). Cambridge U Pr.

Evans, John Whitney. The Newman Movement. 264p. 1980. 16.95 (ISBN 0-268-01453-1). U of Notre Dame Pr.

Evans, Joseph W., tr. see Maritain, Jacques.

Evans, Louis H., Jr. Covenant to Care. 120p. 1982. pap. 4.95 (ISBN 0-88207-355-9). Victor Bks.

Evans, M. J. Progress of God's People. (Discovering the Bible Ser.). pap. 8.95 (ISBN 0-7175-1161-8). Dufour.

Evans, M. J., tr. see Loserth, Johann.

Evans, Malcolm. Signifying Nothing: Truth's True Contents in Shakespeare's Text. LC 85-28945. 256p. 1986. 25.00x (ISBN 0-8203-0837-4). U of GA Pr.

Evans, Marian, tr. see Strauss, David F.

Evans, Mary J. Woman in the Bible. LC 84-4641. 160p. 1984. pap. 6.95 (ISBN 0-87784-978-1). Inter-Varsity.

Evans, Maurice. G. K. Chesterton. LC 72-3187. (English Literature Ser., No. 33). 1972. Repr. of 1939 ed. lib. bdg. 39.95x (ISBN 0-8383-1504-6). Haskell.

Evans, R. C. Forty Years in the Mormon Church: Why I Left It. 1976. Repr. of 1920 ed. 6.95 (ISBN 0-89315-054-1). Lambert Bk.

Evans, Richard I. Dialogue with C. G. Jung. LC 81-15371. 256p. 1981. 36.95 (ISBN 0-03-059927-X). Praeger.

--Dialogue with Erik Erikson: And Reactions from Ernest Jones. LC 81-15379. 188p. 1981. 33.95 (ISBN 0-03-059923-7). Praeger.

Evans, Robert A. & Evans, Alice F. Human Rights: A Dialogue Between the First & Third Worlds. LC 82-18780. 236p. (Orig.). 1983. pap. 9.95 (ISBN 0-88344-194-2). Orbis Bks.

Evans, Robert A., jt. auth. see Evans, Alice F.

Evans, Robert A., jt. auth. see Evans, Alice Frazer.

Evans, Robert A. & Parker, Thomas D., eds. Christian Theology: A Case Method Approach. LC 76-9963. 1976. pap. 9.95xi (ISBN 0-06-062252-0, HarpR, RD 176, HarpR). Har-Row.

Evans, Robert A., et al. Casebook for Christian Living: Value Formation for Families & Congregations. pap. 6.95 (ISBN 0-8042-2032-8). John Knox.

Evans, Robert F. Four Letters of Pelagius: On the Grounds for Authenticity of 4 of the 20 Works Ascribed by De Plinval to Pelagius. LC 68-11594. 1968. text ed. 12.00x (ISBN 0-685-00379-5). A R Allenson.

Evans, Sabastian, tr. High History of the Holy Graal. (Illus.). 395p. 1969. 16.95 (ISBN 0-227-67727-7). Attic Pr.

Evans, Shirlee. A Life in Her Hands. 192p. (Orig.). 1987. pap. 5.95 (ISBN 0-8361-3441-9). Herald Pr.

--Tree Tall to the Rescue. (Tree Tall Ser.: No. 3). (Illus.). 144p. (Orig.). 1987. pap. 4.50 (ISBN 0-8361-3444-3). Herald Pr.

Evans, Stanley G., ed. Return to Reality: Some Essays on Contemporary Christianity. 1954. 39.50x (ISBN 0-317-07644-2). Elliots Bks.

Evans, Stephens. Subjectivity & Religious Belief. LC 82-40062. 238p. 1982. pap. text ed. 12.50 (ISBN 0-8191-2665-9). U Pr of Amer.

Evans, Thomas G. & Wright, Toblas A., eds. Baptisms from Sixteen Thirty-Nine to Eighteen Hundred in the Reformed Dutch Church, New York, 2 Vols. 1298p. 1968. Repr. of 1902 ed. 75.00 (ISBN 0-8398-0152-1). Parnassus Imprints.

Evans, W. Glyn. Beloved Adversary: Our Complex Relationship with a Loving God. Link, Julie A., ed. 96p. 1985. pap. 5.95 (ISBN 0-310-29371-5, 10462P). Zondervan.

--Daily with the King. LC 79-21970. 1979. pap. 5.95 (ISBN 0-8024-1739-6). Moody.

--A Healing Mind. 160p. 1987. pap. 6.95 (ISBN 0-310-29381-2). Zondervan.

Evans, William. Las Grandes Doctrinas de la Biblia. Orig. Title: Great Doctrines of the Bible. (Span.). 1986. pap. 4.75 (ISBN 0-8254-1222-6). Kregel.

--The Great Doctrines of the Bible. rev. ed. 350p. 1974. enlarged edition 11.95 (ISBN 0-8024-3301-4). Moody.

--How to Prepare Sermons. 1964. 9.95 (ISBN 0-8024-3725-7). Moody.

Evans, William A. Management Ethics: An Intercultural Perspective. (Dimensions in International Business Ser.). 256p. 1981. lib. bdg. 15.00 (ISBN 0-89838-055-3). Kluwer-Nijhoff.

Evans-Pritchard, E. E. Theories of Primitive Religion. LC 85-22003. (Sir D. Owens Evan Lectures, 1962). 138p. 1985. Repr. of 1965 ed. lib. bdg. 29.75x (ISBN 0-313-24978-4, EPTP). Greenwood.

Evans-Pritchard, Edward E. Kinship & Marriage among the Nuer. (Illus.). 1951. 32.50x (ISBN 0-19-823104-0). Oxford U Pr.

--Nuer Religion. (Illus.). 1956. 10.95x (ISBN 0-19-874003-4). Oxford U Pr.

--The Political System of the Anuak of the Anglo-Egyptian Sudan. LC 74-15036. (London School of Economics & Political Science Monographs on Social Anthropology: No. 4). Repr. of 1940 ed. 27.50 (ISBN 0-404-12041-5). AMS Pr.

--Theories of Primitive Religion. 1965. pap. 9.95x (ISBN 0-19-823131-8). Oxford U Pr.

Evans-Wentz, W. Y. Cuchama & Sacred Mountains. Waters, Frank & Adams, Charles L., eds. LC 81-8749. (Illus.). xxxii, 196p. 1982. 22.95 (ISBN 0-8040-0411-0, Pub. by Swallow). Ohio U Pr.

Evans-Wentz, W. Y., ed. Tibetan Book of the Great Liberation. 1954. 24.95x (ISBN 0-19-501437-5). Oxford U Pr.

--Tibetan Book of the Great Liberation. (Illus.). 1968. pap. 9.95 (ISBN 0-19-500293-8). Oxford U Pr.

--Tibetan Yoga & Secret Doctrines. 2nd ed. 1958. 24.95x (ISBN 0-19-501438-3). Oxford U Pr.

--Tibetan Yoga & Secret Doctrines. (Illus.). 1967. pap. 11.95 (ISBN 0-19-500278-4). Oxford U Pr.

--Tibet's Great Yogi, Milarepa. 2nd ed. (Illus.). 1969. pap. 9.95 (ISBN 0-19-500301-2). Oxford U Pr.

Evdokimov, Paul. The Sacrament of Love: The Nuptial Mystery in the Light of the Orthodox Tradition. Gythiel, Anthony P. & Steadman, Victoria, trs. from Fr. LC 85-2261. 192p. (Orig.). 1985. pap. 8.95 (ISBN 0-88141-042-X). St Vladimirs.

Evelan, R. R. How to Read the Bible: A Step by Step Manual. 1984. 5.95 (ISBN 0-89536-700-9, 4883). CSS of Ohio.

--How to Read the Bible: Leader's Guide. 1984. 2.25 (ISBN 0-89536-716-5, 4891). CSS of Ohio.

Evely, Louis. Faith of a Modern Man. 1.95 (ISBN 0-317-06468-1). Dimension Bks.

--That Man Is You. Bonin, Edmond, tr. LC 63-23494. 297p. 1964. pap. 4.95 (ISBN 0-8091-1697-9). Paulist Pr.

Even, Charles. The Lost Tribes of Israel: Or, the First of the Red Men. 26.50 (ISBN 0-405-10243-7, 14436). Ayer Co Pubs.

Evenhouse, Bill. Reasons One, Sects & Cults with Non-Christian Roots. 120p. (Orig.). 1981. pap. text ed. 4.10 (ISBN 0-933140-23-1); tchr's manual, 61 pgs. 4.10 (ISBN 0-933140-24-X). CRC Pubns.

--Reasons Two, Sects & Cults with Christian Roots. (Orig.). 1981. pap. text ed. 4.10 (ISBN 0-933140-25-8); tchr's manual, 67 pgs. 4.10 (ISBN 0-933140-26-6). CRC Pubns.

Evennett, H. Outram. Spirit of the Counter-Reformation. LC 68-11282. 1970. pap. 4.95x (ISBN 0-268-00425-0). U of Notre Dame Pr.

Evennett, Henry O. The Cardinal of Lorraine & the Council of Trent: A Study in the Counter-Reformation. LC 83-45592. Date not set. Repr. of 1940 ed. 57.50 (ISBN 0-404-19885-6). AMS Pr.

Evensen, Ken L. Healing Love: The Inner Power of All Things. 9.95 (ISBN 0-533-04807-9). Vantage.

Even-Shoshan, Abraham, ed. A New Concordance of the Old Testament: Using the Hebrew & Aramaic Text. 1328p. 51.00 (ISBN 0-8010-3417-5). Baker Bk.

Everding, H. Edward, Jr. & Wilbanks, Dana M. Decision Making & the Bible. LC 75-11656. 160p. 1975. pap. 5.95 (ISBN 0-8170-0668-0). Judson.

Everett, Betty S. I Want to Be Like You, Lord: Bible Devotion for Girls. LC 84-21563. (Young Readers Ser.). 112p. (Orig.). 1984. pap. 3.95 (ISBN 0-8066-2112-5, 10-3196). Augsburg.

--Who Am I, Lord? LC 82-72645. (Young Readers Ser.). 112p. (Orig.). 1983. pap. 3.95 (ISBN 0-8066-1951-1, 10-7072). Augsburg.

Everett, Charles C. Theism & the Christian Faith. Hale, Edward, ed. LC 75-3139. Repr. of 1909 ed. 34.00 (ISBN 0-404-59148-5). AMS Pr.

Everett, Donald E. Trinity University: A Record of One Hundred Years. LC 68-24632. (Illus.). 1968. 5.00 (ISBN 0-911536-21-3). Trinity U Pr.

Everett, J. Rutherford. Religion in Economics: A Study of John B. Clark, Richard T. Ely & Simon N. Patten. 1982. Repr. of 1946 ed. lib. bdg. 22.50x (ISBN 0-87991-866-7). Porcupine Pr.

Everett, William J. Blessed Be the Bond: Christian Perspectives on Marriage & Family. LC 84-48712. 144p. 1985. pap. 6.95 (ISBN 0-8006-1831-9, 1-1831). Fortress.

Everett, William W. & Bachmeyer, T. J. Disciplines in Transformation: A Guide to Theology & the Behavioral Sciences. LC 78-68570. 1979. pap. text ed. 11.75 (ISBN 0-8191-0692-5). U Pr of Amer.

Everist, Burton. The Christian Family Craftbook. LC 78-62064. (Illus.). 1978. pap. 5.95 (ISBN 0-8192-1239-3). Morehouse.

Everist, Norma J. Education Ministry in the Congregation: Eight Ways We Learn from One Another. LC 83-70515. 240p. (Orig.). 1983. pap. 11.95 (ISBN 0-8066-2021-8, 10-2006). Augsburg.

Every, George. Byzantine Patriarchate, Four Hundred Fifty-One to Twelve Hundred Four. 2nd rev. ed. LC 78-63340. (The Crusades & Military Orders: Second Ser.). Repr. of 1962 ed. 27.50 (ISBN 0-404-17015-3). AMS Pr.

--Christian Legends. LC 86-22242. (Library of the World's Myths & Legends). (Illus.). 144p. 1987. 18.95 (ISBN 0-87226-046-1). P Bedrick Bks.

Every, George, et al, eds. Time of the Spirit. LC 84-10696. 256p. (Orig.). 1984. pap. text ed. 9.95 (ISBN 0-88141-035-7). St Vladimirs.

Evola, Julius. Metaphysics of Sex. Ormrod, J. A., tr. from Ital. LC 82-11909. (Illus.). 384p. 1983. pap. 9.95 (ISBN 0-89281-025-4). Inner Tradit.

Evslin, Bernard. Signs & Wonders: Tales from the Old Testament. (Illus.). 352p. 1982. 17.95 (ISBN 0-02-734100-3, Four Winds). Macmillan.

Evslin, Bernard, et al. The Greek Gods. 1972. pap. 2.25 (ISBN 0-590-06350-2, Schol Pap). Scholastic Inc.

--The Greek Gods. (Illus.). 120p. 1984. pap. 2.25 (ISBN 0-590-33456-5, Point). Scholastic Inc.

--Heroes & Monsters of Greek Myth. (Illus.). 112p. 1984. pap. 2.25 (ISBN 0-590-33457-3, Point). Scholastic Inc.

Ewart, Frank J. The Phenomenon of Pentecost. 208p. (Orig.). 1947. pap. 4.95 (ISBN 0-912315-32-6). Word Aflame.

Ewens, Mary. The Role of the Nun in Nineteenth Century America. 36.50 (ISBN 0-405-10828-1). Ayer Co Pubs.

Ewer, Mary A., tr. see Arsen'ev, Nicolai S.

Ewers, John C., ed. see Wildschut, William.

Ewert, Christian. Islamische Funde in Balaguer und die Aljaferia in Zaragoza. (Madrider Forschungen, Vol. 7). (Illus.). 281p. 1971. 96.00 (ISBN 3-11-003613-4). De Gruyter.

Ewert, David. And Then Comes the End. LC 79-28410. 216p. 1980. pap. 7.95 (ISBN 0-8361-1921-5). Herald Pr.

--From Ancient Tablets to Modern Translations: A General Introduction to the Bible. 1986. 15.95 (ISBN 0-310-45370-4, 12384). Zondervan.

--The Holy Spirit in the New Testament. LC 82-95089. 336p. 1983. pap. 12.95 (ISBN 0-8361-3309-9). Herald Pr.

--Stalwart for the Truth: The Life & Legacy of A. H. Unruh. (Trailblazer Ser.). 148p. (Orig.). 1975. pap. 6.95 (ISBN 0-919797-18-0). Kindred Pr.

Ewin, R. E. Cooperation & Human Values: A Study of Moral Reasoning. 1981. 22.50 (ISBN 0-312-16956-6). St Martin.

Ewing, A. C. A Short Commentary on Kant's "Critique of Pure Reason". viii, 278p. Date not set. pap. text ed. 16.00 (ISBN 0-226-22779-0, Midway Reprint). U of Chicago Pr.

Ewing, Alfred C. The Definition of Good. LC 78-59021. 1979. Repr. of 1947 ed. 20.25 (ISBN 0-88355-695-2). Hyperion Conn.

--Ethics. 1965. pap. text ed. 9.95 (ISBN 0-02-910030-5). Free Pr.

Ewing, Upton C. The Essene Christ. LC 61-10608. (Illus.). 456p. 1977. pap. 12.95 (ISBN 0-8022-0461-9). Philos Lib.

--The Essene Christ. 438p. pap. 12.95 (ISBN 0-317-07627-2). Edenite.

--Prophet of the Dead Sea Scrolls. 148p. pap. 6.95 (ISBN 0-317-07628-0). Edenite.

Exeler, Adolf & Mette, Norbert, eds. A People's Theology. 192p. pap. 9.95 cancelled (ISBN 0-8245-0477-1). Crossroad NY.

Exell, Joseph S. Practical Truths from Jonah. LC 82-18671. 240p. 1983. 11.95 (ISBN 0-8254-2525-5). Kregel.

Exell, Joseph S., jt. ed. see Spence, H. D.

Exell, T. S., jt. auth. see Spence, H. D.

Exley, Helen, jt. auth. see Exley, Richard.

Exley, Richard & Exley, Helen. A Child's View of Christmas. (Illus.). 64p. 1981. 7.50 (ISBN 0-8298-0463-3). Pilgrim NY.

Exline, Barbara. Beyond the Battlefield. (Illus.). 78p. (Orig.). (YA) 1986. pap. 3.25 (ISBN 0-89216-063-2). Salvation Army.

Exman, Gary. Get Ready... Get Set... Grow! Sherer, Michael L., ed. (Orig.). 1987. pap. 8.75 (ISBN 0-89536-865-X, 7824). CSS of Ohio.

Exum, J. Cheryl, ed. Tragedy & Comedy in the Bible. (Semeia Ser.: No. 32). pap. 9.95 (06 20 32). Scholars Pr GA.

Exupery, Antoine de Saint see Saint-Exupery, Saint Antoine De.

Ey, Henri. Consciousness: A Phenomenological Study of Being Conscious & Becoming Conscious. Flodstrom, John H., tr. LC 76-26429. (Studies in Phenomenology & Existential Philosophy Ser.). (Illus.). 448p. 1978. 29.50x (ISBN 0-253-31408-9). Ind U Pr.

Eyer, Mary S. He Restoreth My Soul. LC 82-1363. 98p. 1982. 6.95 (ISBN 0-87747-908-9). Deseret Bk.

--Reflection of a Soul. 83p. 1986. 7.95 (ISBN 0-934126-66-6). Randall Bk Co.

Eyer, Richard C. Devotions of Hope. 1984. 1.95 (ISBN 0-89536-653-3, 0418). CSS of Ohio.

Eynon, Dana. Adventures Through the Bible. rev. ed. LC 79-1031. 176p. 1980. pap. 7.95 tchr's book (ISBN 0-87239-378-X, 3234). Standard Pub.

--My New Life with Christ: Baptismal Certificate. (Certificate Booklets Ser.). (Illus.). 16p. 1982. pap. 0.95 self-cover (ISBN 0-87239-529-4, 1177). Standard Pub.

--Through the Bible in a Year: Pupil Workbook. 64p. 1975. wkbk. 1.95 (ISBN 0-87239-011-X, 3239). Standard Pub.

--Through the Bible in a Year: Teacher. LC 74-27239. 176p. 1975. tchr's manual 7.95 (ISBN 0-87239-028-4, 3237). Standard Pub.

Eyre, Jackie, jt. auth. see Eyre, Stephen.

Eyre, Linda & Eyre, Richard. Teaching Children Charity: A Program to Help Teens & Preteens Forget Themselves. LC 85-27468. (Illus.). 280p. 1986. 9.95 (ISBN 0-87579-024-0). Deseret Bk.

--Teaching Children Joy. 203p. pap. 8.95 (ISBN 0-87747-888-0, Pub. by Shadow Mountain). Deseret Bk.

--Teaching Children Joy. LC 84-201498. 240p. 1986. pap. 3.50 (ISBN 0-345-32704-7). Ballantine.

Eyre, Margery. The Sacred Mirror: A Spiritual Diary. 94p. 9.95 (ISBN 0-86140-068-2). Dufour.
Eyre, Richard, jt. auth. see Eyre, Linda.
Eyre, Stephen & Eyre, Jackie. Matthew: Being Discipled by Jesus. (LifeBuilder Bible Studies). 64p. (Orig.). 1987. pap. 2.95 (ISBN 0-8308-1003-X). Inter-Varsity.
Eyres, Lawrence. The Elders of the Church. 1975. pap. 2.50 (ISBN 0-87552-258-0). Presby & Reformed.
Eyrich, Howard A. Three to Get Ready: A Christian Premarital Counselor's Manual. 1978. pap. 4.95 (ISBN 0-87552-259-9). Presby & Refomed.
Eyring, Henry. Reflections of a Scientist. LC 83-7109. (Illus.). 101p. 1983. 7.95 (ISBN 0-87747-944-5). Deseret Bk.
Ezcurra, Ana M. The Vatican & the Reagan Administration. New York CIRCUS Publications, Inc. Staff, ed. Tr. of El Vaticano y la Administracion Reagan. 220p. (Orig.). 1986. pap. text ed. 6.95 (ISBN 0-318-20240-9). NY Circus Pubns.
Ezell, Lee. The Cinderella Syndrome: Discovering God's Plan When Your Dreams Don't Come True. 176p. (Orig.). 1985. pap. 4.95 (ISBN 0-89081-475-9). Harvest Hse.
Ezra, Kate, tr. see Zahan, Dominique.
Ezrahi, Sidra D. By Words Alone: The Holocaust in Literature. LC 79-56908. 1980. 19.00x (ISBN 0-226-23335-9). U of Chicago Pr.

F

F. A. R. M. S. Staff. Book of Mormon Critical Text: A Tool for Scholarly Reference, 3 vols. LC 85-137843. (F. A. R. M. S. Critical Text Project). (Illus.). 1100p. (Orig.). 1986. Set. 55.00x (ISBN 0-934893-00-4, STF-84A); Vol. 3: Helaman - Moroni April 1987. pap. text ed. 20.00x (ISBN 0-934893-03-9). FARMS.
F. A. R. M. S. Staff, ed. Book of Mormon Critical Text: A Tool for Scholarly Reference, Vol. 1, I Nephi-Words of Mormon. rev., 2nd ed. (F. A. R. M. S. Critical Text Project Ser.: No. 4). (Illus.). 382p. 1986. Set of 3 Vols. 55.00 (ISBN 0-934893-07-1); pap. 20.00 (ISBN 0-934893-04-7). FARMS.
Faase, Thomas P. Making the Jesuits More Modern. LC 81-40388. (Illus.). 478p. (Orig.). 1981. lib. bdg. 31.50 o. p. (ISBN 0-8191-1761-7); pap. text ed. 18.75 (ISBN 0-8191-1762-5). U Pr of Amer.
Fabel, Arthur. Cosmic Genesis. (Tielhard Studies). 1981. 2.00 (ISBN 0-89012-028-5). Anima Pubns.
Fabella, Virginia, ed. Asia's Struggle for Full Humanity: Towards a Relevant Theology. LC 80-14923. 229p. (Orig.). 1980. pap. 8.95 (ISBN 0-88344-015-6). Orbis Bks.
Fabella, Virginia & Torres, Sergio, eds. Doing Theology in a Divided World. LC 84-14712. 224p. (Orig.). 1985. pap. 11.95 (ISBN 0-88344-197-7). Orbis Bks.
--Irruption of the Third World: Challenge to Theology. LC 82-18851. 304p. (Orig.). 1983. pap. 10.95 (ISBN 0-88344-216-7). Orbis Bks.
Fabella, Virginia, jt. ed. see Torres, Sergio.
Faber, Doris. The Perfect Life: The Shakers in America. LC 73-90968. (Illus.). 224p. 1974. 10.95 (ISBN 0-374-35819-2). FS&G.
Faber, Federick W. Bethlehem. LC 78-66306. 1978. pap. 10.00 (ISBN 0-89555-080-6). TAN Bks Pubs.
Faber, Frederick. Self-Deceit. 1983. pap. 2.50x (ISBN 0-87574-050-2, 050). Pendle Hill.
Faber, Frederick W. The Blessed Sacrament. LC 78-66302. 1978. pap. 11.00 (ISBN 0-89555-077-6). TAN Bks Pubs.
--The Creator & Creature. LC 78-66301. 1978. pap. 9.50 (ISBN 0-89555-076-8). TAN Bks Pubs.
--The Foot of the Cross: The Sorrows of Mary. LC 78-66303. 1978. pap. 10.00 (ISBN 0-89555-078-4). TAN Bks Pubs.
--Spiritual Conferences. LC 78-66304. 1978. pap. 9.00 (ISBN 0-89555-079-2). TAN Bks Pubs.
Faber, Fredrick W. Hymns. 1977. Repr. of 1881 ed. 20.00 (ISBN 0-8274-4295-5). R West.
Faber, Geoffrey. Oxford Apostles. 467p. 1974. 7.95 (ISBN 0-571-10495-9). Faber & Faber.
--Oxford Apostles: A Character Study of the Oxford Movement. 1979. Repr. of 1933 ed. lib. bdg. 35.00 (ISBN 0-8482-3953-9). Norwood Edns.
Faber, Geoffrey C. Oxford Apostles: A Character Study of the Oxford Movement. LC 75-30022. Repr. of 1933 ed. 34.50 (ISBN 0-404-14027-0). AMS Pr.
Faber, George S. The Origin of Pagan Idolatry, 3 vols. Feldman, Burton & Richardson, Robert D., eds. LC 78-60891. (Myth & Romanticism Ser.). 1984. Set. lib. bdg. 240.00 (ISBN 0-8240-3559-3). Garland Pub.
Faber, Heije. Pastoral Care in the Modern Hospital. De Waal, Hugo, tr. LC 70-168632. 160p. 1972. 10.95 (ISBN 0-664-20922-X). Westminster.
--Psychology of Religion. LC 75-43721. 348p. 1976. 13.95 (ISBN 0-664-20748-0). Westminster.
--Striking Sails: A Pastoral View of Growing Older in Our Society. Mitchell, Kenneth R., tr. 160p. 1984. pap. 10.95 (ISBN 0-687-39941-6). Abingdon.
Faber, M. D. Culture & Consciousness: The Social Meaning of Altered Awareness. LC 80-36683. 296p. 1981. text ed. 34.95 (ISBN 0-8, ,05-505-X); professional 32.95. Human Sci Pr.
Faber, Stuart J. How to Get Rid of Your Wife: And No Court Will Ever Convict You. 200p. 1974. 7.95 (ISBN 0-685-50674-6). Good Life.
Fabian, Larry L. & Schiff, Ze'ev, eds. Israelis Speak: About Themselves & the Palestinians. LC 75-51150. 1977. text ed. 10.00 (ISBN 0-87003-007-8); pap. text ed. 5.00 (ISBN 0-87003-008-6). Carnegie Endow.
Fabiny, T. Martin Luther's Last Will & Testament: A Facsimile of the Original Document, with an Account of Its Origins, Composition & Subsequent History. 51p. 1984. text ed. 25.00x (ISBN 0-904720-15-2, Pub. by Ussher Pr Ireland). Humanities.
Fabrega, Horacio, Jr. & Silver, Daniel B. Illness & Shamanistic Curing in Zinacantan: An Ethnomedical Analysis. LC 73-80621. 304p. 1973. 22.50x (ISBN 0-8047-0844-4). Stanford U Pr.
Fabro, Cornelio. God in Exile: Modern Atheism. Gibson, Arthur, tr. LC 68-20846. 1272p. 1968. slipcase 35.00 (ISBN 0-8091-0053-3). Paulist Pr.
Fabry, Joseph, tr. see Lukas, Elisabeth.
Fabry, Joseph B., et al, eds. Logotherapy in Action. LC 79-51917. 379p. 1979. 19.95 (ISBN 0-317-06212-3). Inst Logo.
Faccin, Dominic. Spiritual Exercises According to Saint Bonaventure. Colligan, Owen A., tr. (Spirit & Life Ser). 1955. 3.00 (ISBN 0-686-11568-6). Franciscan Inst.
Facione, Peter A., et al. Values & Society: An Introduction to Ethics & Social Philosophy. 1978. pap. text ed. write for info (ISBN 0-13-940338-8). P-H.
Fackenheim, Emil, jt. ed. see Morgan, Michael L.
Fackenheim, Emil L. Encounters Between Judaism & Modern Philosophy: A Preface to Future Jewish Thought. LC 80-16437. 288p. 1980. pap. 7.95 (ISBN 0-8052-0656-6). Schocken.
--God's Presence in History. 1972. pap. 5.95x (ISBN 0-06-131690-3, TB1690, Torch). Har-Row.
--The Jewish Return into History: Reflections in the Age of Auschwitz & a New Jerusalem. LC 77-87861. 1978. 14.95 (ISBN 0-8052-3677-5). Schocken.
Fackenheim, Emil. L. Quest for Past & Future: Essays in Jewish Theology. LC 83-12692. 336p. 1983. Repr. of 1968 ed. lib. bdg. 39.75x (ISBN 0-313-22738-1, FAQP). Greenwood.
Fackenhein, Emil L. To Mend the World: Foundations of Future Jewish Thought. LC 81-16614. 352p. (Orig.). 1982. pap. 12.95 (ISBN 0-8052-0699-X). Schocken.
Fackler, Mark. Ride the Hot Wind. LC 77-78850. 1978. pap. 2.95 (ISBN 0-88419-126-5). Creation Hse.
Fackler, Mark, jt. auth. see Katterjohn, Arthur.
Fackre, Gabriel. The Christian Story. rev. ed. 304p. 1985. pap. 12.95 (ISBN 0-8028-1989-3). Eerdmans.
--The Religious Right & the Christian Faith. 1982. 8.95 (ISBN 0-8028-3565-2); pap. 4.95 (ISBN 0-8028-1983-4). Eerdmans.
Fader, Herbert L., ed. see Kaung, Stephen.
Fader, Herbert L., ed. see Nee, Watchman.
Fader, Herbert L., ed. see Watchman, Nee.
Fader, Herbert L., et al, eds. see Nee, Watchman.
Fadness, Arley. Blueprint for Lent. 1983. 10.00 (ISBN 0-89536-603-7, 0219). CSS of Ohio.
Faerber, W. Catholic Catechism. LC 78-68498. 122p. 1978. pap. 3.00 (ISBN 0-89555-086-5, 307). TAN Bks Pubs.
Fagan, Harry. Empowerment: Skills for Parish Social Action. LC 79-52106. 64p. 1979. pap. 4.95 (ISBN 0-8091-2210-3). Paulist Pr.
Fagerberg, Holsten. A New Look at the Lutheran Confession. Lund, Gene J., tr. 336p. 1981. 15.50 (ISBN 0-570-03223-7, 15-2121). Concordia.
Fages, Martine, tr. see Sunim, Kusan.
Fagin, Gerald M., jt. auth. see Burns, J. Patout.
Fagin, Gerald M., ed. Vatican II: Open Questions & New Horizons. (Theology & Life Ser.: Vol. 8). pap. 6.95 (ISBN 0-89453-366-5). M Glazier.
Faherty, William B. Dream by the River. rev. ed. (Illus.). 1981. Repr. of 1973 ed. 4.95 (ISBN 0-933150-21-0). River City MO.
Fahey, Charles J. & Wakin, Edward. The Catholic Guide to the Mature Years. LC 84-60747. 144p. 1984. pap. 6.95 (ISBN 0-87973-603-8, 603). Our Sunday Visitor.
Fahey, Frank J., jt. auth. see Vrga, Djuro J.
Fahey, Michael A. Cyprian & the Bible: A Study of Third-Century Exegesis. 701p. 1971. lib. bdg. 65.00 (Pub. by J C B Mohr BRD). Coronet Bks.
Fahey, Michael A., ed. Catholic Perspectives on Baptism, Eucharist & Ministry: A Study Commissioned by the Catholic Theological Society of America. 240p. (Orig.). 1986. lib. bdg. 24.50 (ISBN 0-8191-5431-8, Pub. by Catholic Theological Soc of Amer); pap. text ed. 11.75 (ISBN 0-8191-5432-6). U Pr of Amer.
Fahie, J. J. Galileo: His Life & Work. (Illus.). Repr. of 1903 ed. lib. bdg. 57.00x (ISBN 0-697-00003-6). Irvington.
Fahrner, R. Wortsinn und Wortschoepfung Bei Meister Eckehart. pap. 9.00 (ISBN 0-384-15090-X). Johnson Repr.
Fahs, Sophia L. & Cobb, Alice. Old Tales for a New Day: Early Answers to Life's Eternal Questions. LC 80-84076. (Library of Liberal Religion). (Illus.). 1980. 11.95 (ISBN 0-87975-138-X); tchr's manual 9.95 (ISBN 0-87975-131-2). Prometheus Bks.
Fa-hsien, Fl. The Travels of Fa-hsien, 399 to 144 A.D. Or Record of the Buddhistic Kingdoms. Giles, M. A. & Giles, H. A., trs. from Fr. LC 81-13362. xx, 96p. 1982. Repr. of 1956 ed. lib. bdg. 22.50x (ISBN 0-313-23240-7, FATR). Greenwood.
Fahy, B., tr. see Habig, Marion A.
Failing, George E. Did Christ Die for All? 1980. 1.25 (ISBN 0-937296-02-3, 222-B). Presence Inc.
--Secure & Rejoicing. 1980. 0.95 (ISBN 0-937296-03-1, 223-A). Presence Inc.
Fair, Harold L. Class Devotions, 1986-1987: For Use with the 1986-1987 International Lesson Annual. 128p. (Orig.). 1986. pap. 6.50 (ISBN 0-687-08626-4). Abingdon.
--Class Devotions, 1987-1988. 128p. 1987. pap. 6.50 (ISBN 0-687-08627-2). Abingdon.
Fairbairn, Patrick. The Pastoral Epistles. 1980. 17.25 (ISBN 0-86524-053-1, 7107). Klock & Klock.
Fairbank, John K., ed. The Missionary Enterprise in China & America. LC 74-82191. (Studies in American-East Asian Relations: No. 6). 442p. 1974. text ed. 25.00x (ISBN 0-674-57655-1). Harvard U Pr.
Fairbank, John K., jt. ed. see Barnett, Suzanne W.
Fairbanks, Henry G. Towards Acceptance--the Ultimates: Aging, Pain, Fear & Death from an Integral Human View. 1986. pap. 8.95 (ISBN 0-8158-0433-4). Chris Mass.
Fairbanks, Lebron. Beacon Small-Group Bible Studies, Acts, Pt. II: The Continuing Mission of the Church. Wolf, Earl C., ed. 90p. (Orig.). 1985. pap. 2.50 (ISBN 0-8341-0947-6). Beacon Hill.
--Beacon Small-Group Bible Studies, Philippians, Colossians, Experiencing His Peace. 100p. 1982. pap. 2.50 (ISBN 0-8341-0778-3). Beacon Hill.
Fairbridge, Maurice H. Studies in Biblical & Semitic Symbolism. 1977. lib. bdg. 59.95 (ISBN 0-8490-2700-4). Gordon Pr.
Fairchild, Hoxie N. Religious Trends in English Poetry, 6 vols. Incl. Vol. 1. Protestantism & the Cult of Sentiment: 1700-1740 (ISBN 0-231-08821-3); Vol. 2. Religious Sentimentalism in the Age of Johnson: 1740-1780. 1942 (ISBN 0-231-08822-1); Vol. 3. Romantic Faith: 1780-1830. 1949 (ISBN 0-231-08823-X); Vol. 4. Christianity & Romanticism in the Victorian Era: 1830-1880. 1957 (ISBN 0-231-08824-8); Vol. 5. Gods of a Changing Poetry: 1880-1920. 1962 (ISBN 0-231-08825-6); Vol. 6. Valley of Dry Bones: 1920-1965. 1968 (ISBN 0-231-08826-4). LC 39-12839. 45.00x ea. Columbia U Pr.
Fairchild, James H. Oberlin: The Colony & the College. Dayton, Donald W., ed. (The Higher Christian Life Ser.). 377p. 1985. 45.00 (ISBN 0-8240-6416-X). Garland Pub.
Fairchild, Johnson E., ed. Basic Beliefs: The Religious Philosophies of Mankind. 11.50x (ISBN 0-911378-03-0). Sheridan.
Fairchild, Roy W. Finding Hope Again: A Pastor's Guide to Counseling Depressed Persons. LC 79-2988. 160p. 1980. 9.45 (ISBN 0-06-062325-X, HarpR). Har-Row.
Fairclough, Adam. To Redeem the Soul of America: The Southern Christian Leadership Conference & Martin Luther King, Jr. (Illus.). 456p. 1987. 35.00 (ISBN 0-8203-0898-6); pap. 17.95 (ISBN 0-8203-0938-9). U of Ga Pr.
Fairfield, James G. All That We Are We Give. LC 77-14510. 192p. 1977. pap. 5.95 (ISBN 0-8361-1839-1). Herald Pr.
Fairfield, Leslie P. John Bale: Mythmaker for the English Reformation. LC 75-19953. 250p. 1976. 9.75 (ISBN 0-911198-42-3). Purdue U Pr.
Fairlie, Henry. The Seven Deadly Sins Today. LC 79-893. (Illus.). 1979. pap. 5.95 (ISBN 0-268-01698-4, 85-16981). U of Notre Dame Pr.
Fairman, Marion A. Biblical Patterns in Modern Literature. LC 72-85235. 128p. 1972. 2.95 (ISBN 0-913228-04-4). Dillon-Liederbach.
Fairweather, A. M., ed. Aquinas on Nature & Grace. LC 54-10259. (Library of Christian Classics). 382p. 1978. pap. 10.95 softcover (ISBN 0-664-24155-7). Westminster.
Fairweather, Alan M. The Word As Truth: A Critical Examination of the Christian Doctrine of Revelation in the Writings of Thomas Aquinas & Karl Barth. LC 78-26040. 1979. Repr. of 1944 ed. lib. bdg. cancelled (ISBN 0-313-20808-5, FAWT). Greenwood.
Fairweather, Eugene R., et al, eds. A Scholastic Miscellany: Anselm to Ockham. LC 56-5104. (Library of Christian Classics). 454p. 1982. pap. 11.95 (ISBN 0-664-24418-1). Westminster.
Fairweather, William. Among the Mystics. facs. ed. LC 68-20298. (Essay Index Reprint Ser.). 1936. 14.00 (ISBN 0-8369-0437-0). Ayer Co Pubs.
--Among the Mystics. 150p. 1936. 4.95 (ISBN 0-567-02104-1, Pub. by T & T Clark Ltd UK). Fortress.
--Background of the Epistles. 1977. 16.50 (ISBN 0-86524-118-X, 8002). Klock & Klock.
--The Background of the Gospels. 464p. 1916. 15.95 (ISBN 0-567-02101-7, Pub. by T & T Clark Ltd UK). Fortress.
--Background of the Gospels. 1977. 17.00 (ISBN 0-86524-117-1, 8001). Klock & Klock.
--From Exile to Advent. Moffatt, J., ed. (Handbooks for Bible Classes & Private Students Ser.). 210p. 1894. 8.95 (ISBN 0-567-28128-0, Pub. by T & T Clark Ltd Uk). Fortress.
--Jesus & the Greeks. 1977. lib. bdg. 59.95 (ISBN 0-8490-2096-4). Gordon Pr.
Faizi, A. Q. Milly: A Tribute to Amelia E. Collins. 52p. pap. 2.95 (ISBN 0-85398-074-8). G Ronald Pub.
--The Prince of Martyrs: A Brief Account of Imam Husayn. 74p. 1977. pap. 3.50 (ISBN 0-85398-073-X). G Ronald Pub.
--Stories from The Delight of Hearts: The Memoirs of Haji Mirza Haydar-'Ali. LC 79-91219. (Illus.). 176p. 1980. 11.95 (ISBN 0-933770-11-1). Kalimat.
Fakes, Dennis. Points with Punch. 1982. pap. 5.00 (ISBN 0-89536-534-0, 1616). CSS of Ohio.
Fakhry, Ahmed. The Pyramids. 2nd ed. LC 61-8645. 272p. 1974. pap. 9.95 (ISBN 0-226-23473-8, P571, Phoen). U of Chicago Pr.
Fakhry, Majid. A History of Islamic Philosophy. 2nd ed. LC 81-21781. 450p. 1983. 29.50x (ISBN 0-231-05532-3). Columbia U Pr.
--A History of Islamic Philosophy. 2nd ed. (Studies in Oriental Culture: No. 5). 394p. 1987. pap. text ed. 16.00 (ISBN 0-231-05533-1). Columbia U Pr.
Fakhry, Tamer. The Gospel Unified. 1984. 15.00 (ISBN 0-533-05126-6). Vantage.
Fakkema, Robert, jt. auth. see Bannerman, Glenn.
Falardeau, Ernest. One Bread & Cup: Source of Communion. 1987. pap. 7.95. M Glazier.
Falaturi, Abdoldjavad & Petuchowski. Three Ways to One God. 160p. 1987. 14.95 (ISBN 0-8245-0818-1). Crossroad NY.
Falcione, Raymond L., jt. auth. see Greenbaum, Howard H.
Falco, Giorgio. The Holy Roman Republic: A Historic Profile of the Middle Ages. Kent, K. V., tr. from Italian. LC 80-19696. Orig. Title: La Santa Romana Republica. 336p. 1980. Repr. of 1965 ed. lib. bdg. 42.50x (ISBN 0-313-22395-5, FAHR). Greenwood.
Falcon, C., et al. Diccionario de la Mitologia Clasica. (Span.). 633p. 1980. pap. 25.00 (ISBN 84-206-1961-2, S-32723). French & Eur.
Falcon, Rafael. The Hispanic Mennonite Church in North America, 1932-1982. LC 85-30220. (Span.). 224p. 1986. 17.95x (ISBN 0-8361-1282-2). Herald Pr.
--La Iglesia Menonita Hispana en Norte America: 1932-1982. LC 85-61020. (Span.). 208p. 1985. 14.95x (ISBN 0-8361-1272-5). Herald Pr.
Falconar, A. E. Gardens of Meditation. 128p. 9.95 (ISBN 0-86140-057-7). Dufour.
Fales, D. A., Jr., jt. auth. see Cummings, A. L.
Falk, Cathy. Action Rhymes: Bible Learning Through Movement. 48p. 1985. pap. 2.50 (ISBN 0-87239-920-6, 3202). Standard Pub.
--God's Care. (Bible Activities for Little People Ser.: Bk. 1). 24p. (Orig.). 1983. pap. 1.50 (ISBN 0-87239-676-2, 2451). Standard Pub.
--God's Friends. (Bible Activities for Little People Ser.: BK. 2). 24p. (Orig.). 1983. pap. 1.50 (ISBN 0-87239-677-0, 2452). Standard Pub.
--God's Son. (Bible Activities for Little People Ser.: Bk. 3). 24p. (Orig.). 1983. pap. 1.50 (ISBN 0-87239-678-9, 2453). Standard Pub.

--We Love God. (Bible Lessons for Little People Ser.: Bk. 2). 144p. (Orig.). 1983. pap. 7.95 (ISBN 0-87239-613-4, 3360). Standard Pub.

--We Please God. (Bible Activities Ser.: Bk. 4). 24p. (Orig.). 1983. pap. 1.50 (ISBN 0-87239-679-7, 2454). Standard Pub.

Falk, Esther, tr. see Segal, Yocheved.

Falk, Harvey. Jesus the Pharisee: New Look at the Jewishness of Jesus. (Orig.). 1985. pap. 8.95 (ISBN 0-8091-2677-X). Paulist Pr.

Falk, Marcia. Love Lyrics from the Bible: A Translation & Literary Study of the Song of Songs. (Bible & Literature Ser.: No. 4). 1981. text ed. 19.95x (ISBN 0-907459-06-4, Pub. by Almond Pr England); pap. text ed. 9.95x (ISBN 0-907459-07-2, Pub. by Almond Pr England). Eisenbrauns.

Falk, Nancy A. & Gross, Rita M., eds. Unspoken Worlds. LC 79-2989. (Women's Religious Lives Ser.). 304p. (Orig.). 1980. pap. text ed. 5.95x (ISBN 0-06-063492-8, RD 308, HarpR). Har-Row.

Falla, Terry, ed. Be Our Freedom, Lord: Responsive Prayers & Readings for Contemporary Worship. 376p. (Orig.). 1985. pap. 11.95 (ISBN 0-8028-0014-9). Eerdmans.

Fallis, William J. Points for Emphasis, Nineteen Eighty-Seven to Eighty-Eight. (Orig.). 1987. pap. 3.95 (ISBN 0-8054-1560-2). Broadman.

--Points for Emphasis, Nineteen Eighty-Seven to Eighty-Eight. 1987. pap. 2.95 (ISBN 0-8054-1559-9). Broadman.

Fallon, Dennis J. & Wolbers, Mary J., eds. Religion & Dance. LC 83-189712. (Focus on Dance Ser.: No. 10). pap. 24.00 (2029558). Bks Demand UMI.

Fallon, Francis T. Second Corinthians. (New Testament Message Ser.: Vol. 11). 12.95 (ISBN 0-89453-199-9); pap. 7.95 (ISBN 0-89453-134-4). M Glazier.

Fallon, Michael. The Winston Commentary on the Gospels. 470p. 1982. pap. 12.95 (ISBN 0-86683-680-2, JHarpR). Har-Row.

Fallon, Timothy P. & Riley, Philip B., eds. Religion & Culture: Essays in Honor of Bernard Lonergan, S.J. 512p. 1987. 44.50x (ISBN 0-88706-289-X). State U NY Pr.

Fallowell, Duncan & Ashley, April. April Ashley's Odyssey. (Illus.). 287p. 1983. 15.95 (ISBN 0-224-01849-3, Pub. by Jonathan Cape). Salem Hse Pubs.

Falvan, Michael, et al, eds. Faith & Culture: A Multicultural Catechetical Resource. 96p. (Orig.). 1987. pap. 5.95 (ISBN 1-55586-994-7). US Catholic.

Falwell, Jerry. Champions for God. 132p. 1985. pap. 4.95 (ISBN 0-89693-534-5). Victor Bks.

--Fasting. 1981. pap. 2.50 (ISBN 0-8423-0849-0). Tyndale.

--My Favorite Verse. LC 86-72750. (My Favorite Verse Ser.). 24p. 1987. pap. 4.95 (ISBN 0-89636-235-3). Accent Bks.

--When It Hurts Too Much to Cry. 160p. 1984. 9.95 (ISBN 0-8423-7993-2). Tyndale.

--Wisdom for Living. 156p. 1984. pap. 5.95 (ISBN 0-89693-370-9). Victor Bks.

Falwell, Jerry, jt. auth. see Towns, Elmer.

Falwell, Jerry & Hindson, Edward E., eds. The Liberty Bible Commentary. LC 83-7280. (Illus.). 2736p. 1983. 29.95 (ISBN 0-8407-5295-4). Nelson.

Family Cirle & Hadda, Ceri, eds. The Family Circle Christmas Treasury. 1986. 19.95 (ISBN 0-933585-02-0). Family Circle Bks.

Fancy, Robert & Rooney, Lucy. The Contemplative Way of Prayer: Deepening Your Life with God. 112p. (Orig.). 1986. pap. 4.95 (ISBN 0-89283-308-4). Servant.

Fandel, John. God's Breath in Man. LC 77-76604. 1977. pap. 1.50 (ISBN 0-87957-005-9). Roth Pub.

--A Morning Answer. 1984. pap. 3.35 (ISBN 0-88028-041-7). Forward Movement.

Fanfani, Amintore. Catholicism, Protestantism & Capitalism. LC 78-38251. (The Evolution of Capitalism Ser.). 234p. 1972. Repr. of 1935 ed. 23.50 (ISBN 0-405-04119-5). Ayer Co Pubs.

--Catholicism, Protestantism, & Capitalism. LC 84-40363. 272p. 1984. pap. text ed. 8.95 (ISBN 0-268-00752-7, 85-07527). U of Notre Dame Pr.

Fang, Carl, tr. see Morgan, G. Campbell.

Fang, Chaoying, ed. see Tsung-Hsi, Huang.

Fangmeier, Jurgen, ed. see Barth, Karl.

Fankhauser, Jerry. Everybody Is Your Teacher. 58p. 1986. pap. 7.00 (ISBN 0-9617006-2-9). J Fankhauser.

--The Power of Affirmations. 56p. 1979. pap. 8.00 (ISBN 0-9617006-1-0). J Fankhauser.

Fanning, Martha, jt. auth. see Cooper, Mildred.

Fant, Clyde. Preaching for Today. 1977. pap. 8.95 (ISBN 0-06-062332-2, RD-204, HarpR). Har-Row.

Fant, Clyde, compiled by. The Best of Open Windows. LC 81-67201. 1981. 7.95 (ISBN 0-8054-5290-7). Broadman.

Fant, David J., Jr. A. W. Tozer: A Twentieth Century Prophet. LC 64-21945. (Illus.). 180p. 1964. pap. 3.95 (ISBN 0-87509-048-6). Chr Pubns.

Fant, Louie J., Jr. Noah. new ed. (Illus.). 14p. 1973. pap. text ed. 5.00 (ISBN 0-917002-70-9). Joyce Media.

Fant, Louie, Jr., ed. Noah-in Sign Language. pap. 5.00 (ISBN 0-917002-10-5). Joyce Media.

Fanthorpe, Lionel, jt. auth. see Fanthorpe, Patricia.

Fanthorpe, Patricia & Fanthorpe, Lionel. The Holy Grail Revealed: The Real Secret of Rennes-le-Chateau. LC 82-4303. 128p. 1982. Repr. lib. bdg. 19.95x (ISBN 0-89370-660-4). Borgo Pr.

Fantin, Mario. Mani Rimdu-Nepal: The Buddhist Dance Drama of Tengpoche (1976) (Illus.). 1978. 40.00. Heinman.

Fanu, Thomas P. le see Le Fanu, Thomas P.

Fanu, Thomas P. le see Peet, Henry.

Faqih, I. Glimpses of Islamic History. 16.50 (ISBN 0-686-63900-6). Kazi Pubns.

Far West Editions. Material for Thought, No.7. LC 77-89507. 76p. 1977. pap. 2.50 (ISBN 0-914480-03-0). Far West Edns.

--Material for Thought, No. 8. LC 79-56899. 88p. 1979. pap. 2.95 (ISBN 0-914480-05-7). Far West Edns.

--Material for Thought, No. 9. LC 81-68048. 94p. 1981. pap. 3.95 (ISBN 0-914480-07-3). Far West Edns.

--Material for Thought, Vol.74 & 76, Nos. 7 & 8. Bound Vol. pap. 7.95 (ISBN 0-686-47075-3). Far West Edns.

--Material For Thought: Spring 1976. LC 73-94407. 1976. pap. 2.95 (ISBN 0-914480-02-2). Far West Edns.

--Material for Thought: 1970. 31p. 1970. pap. 0.50 (ISBN 0-686-47079-6). Far West Edns.

--Material for Thought: 1971. 47p. 1971. pap. 0.50 (ISBN 0-686-47081-8). Far West Edns.

--Material for Thought: 1972. 63p. 1972. pap. 0.50 (ISBN 0-686-47082-6). Far West Edns.

--Material for Thought: 1974. LC 73-94407. 114p. 1974. pap. 2.00 (ISBN 0-914480-01-4). Far West Edns.

--Speaking of My Life. 149p. 1979. pap. 4.95 (ISBN 0-686-47084-2). Far West Edns.

Faraday, Lucy W. Edda I: The Divine Mythology of the North, 2: The Heroic Mythology of the North, 2 Vols. in 1. (Popular Studies in Mythology, Romance & Folklore: Nos. 12 & 13). Repr. of 1902 ed. 11.00 (ISBN 0-404-53512-7). AMS Pr.

Farah, Caesar E. Islam: Beliefs & Observances. rev. ed. LC 72-135505. (Orig.). (YA) 1970. pap. 6.50 (ISBN 0-8120-0277-6). Barron.

Farah, Charles, Jr. From the Pinnacle of the Temple. LC 79-89218. 1979. pap. 4.95 (ISBN 0-88270-462-1). Bridge Pub.

Farah, Madelain. Marriage & Sexuality in Islam: A Translation of al-Ghazali's Book on the Etiquette of Marriage from the Ihya' 192p. 1984. 20.00 (ISBN 0-87480-231-8). U of Utah Pr.

Farah, Nadia R. Religious Strife in Egypt: Crisis & Ideological Conflict in the Seventies. 144p. 1986. text ed. 42.00 (ISBN 2-88124-092-5). Gordon & Breach.

Faraone, Joseph J. & Stewart, Jane L. Paraclete Power: A Study Guide for the Acts of the Apostles. LC 77-16475. 1978. pap. 3.50 (ISBN 0-8189-0361-9). Alba.

Faraud, Henri J. Dix-Huit Ans Chez Les Sauvages: Voyages Et Missions De Monseigneur Henry Faraud. Repr. of 1866 ed. 28.00 (ISBN 0-384-15135-3). Johnson Repr.

--Dix-Huit Ans Chez les Sauvages: Voyages et Missions De Mgr. Henry Faraud Paris-Bruxelles 1866. (Canadiana Avant 1867: No.12). 1966. 26.00x (ISBN 90-2796-329-0). Mouton.

Farber, Anne & Rogler, LLoyd H. Unitas: Hispanic & Black Children in a Healing Community. 128p. 1982. 18.95 (ISBN 0-87073-505-5); pap. 8.95 (ISBN 0-87073-506-3). Schenkman Bks Inc.

Farber, Norma. All Those Mothers at the Manger. LC 85-42610. (Illus.). 32p. 1985. 11.25i (ISBN 0-06-021869-X); PLB 10.89g (ISBN 0-06-021870-3). HArpJ.

--How the Hibernators Came to Bethlehem. LC 80-7685. (Illus.). 32p. 1980. PLB 7.85 (ISBN 0-8027-6353-7). Walker & Co.

Farber, Paul L., jt. ed. see Osler, Margaret J.

Fardan, Dorothy B. Understanding Self & Society. LC 80-81696. 232p. 1981. 14.95 (ISBN 0-8022-2370-2). Philos Lib.

Fardjadi, Homa, tr. see Shariati, Ali.

Fares, Lawrence T., tr. see Geagea, Nilo.

Faria, S., et al. The Emerging Christian Woman. 292p. 1986. 8.50x (ISBN 0-8364-1810-7, Pub. by Macmillan India). South Asia Bks.

Faricy, Robert. The End of the Religious Life. 96p. 1983. pap. 6.95 (ISBN 0-86683-690-X, HarpR). Har-Row.

--Praying for Inner Healing. LC 79-92857. 94p. (Orig.). 1979. pap. 3.95 (ISBN 0-8091-2250-2). Paulist Pr.

Faricy, Robert & Wicks, Robert J. Contemplating Jesus. 48p. (Orig.). 1986. pap. 2.95 (ISBN 0-8091-2757-1). Paulist Pr.

Faricy, Robert, jt. auth. see Rooney, Lucy.

Faricy, Robert S. The Spirituality of Teilhard de Chardin. 128p. (Orig.). 1981. pap. 5.95 (ISBN 0-86683-608-X, HarpR). Har-Row.

Faricy, Robert S. J. Praying. 120p. 1980. pap. 3.50 (ISBN 0-03-056661-4, HarpR). Har-Row.

Farid, A. H. Prayers of Muhammad. 1969. 10.75x (ISBN 0-87902-050-4). Orientalia.

Farina, John. An American Experience of God: The Spirituality of Isaac Hecker. LC 81-80875. 240p. 1981. 11.95 (ISBN 0-8091-0321-4). Paulist Pr.

--Hecker Studies: Essays on the Thought of Isaac Hecker. LC 83-60654. 196p. (Orig.). 1983. pap. 7.95 (ISBN 0-8091-2555-2). Paulist Pr.

Farina, Richard. Been Down So Long It Looks Like up to Me. 1983. pap. 6.95 (ISBN 0-14-006536-9). Penguin.

Faris. My Bible Story Reader, 5 vols. pap. 2.95 ea. Schmul Pub Co.

Faris, N. A. Foundation of Articles of Faith. 9.50 (ISBN 0-686-18607-9). Kazi Pubns.

--The Mysteries of Almsgiving. pap. 4.50 (ISBN 0-686-18616-8). Kazi Pubns.

--The Mysteries of Fasting. pap. 3.75 (ISBN 0-686-18615-X). Kazi Pubns.

--The Mysteries of Purity. pap. 4.75 (ISBN 0-686-18614-1). Kazi Pubns.

Faris, Nabih A., ed. The Arab Heritage. LC 79-2856. 279p. 1981. Repr. of 1944 ed. 30.00 (ISBN 0-8305-0030-8). Hyperion Conn.

--The Arab Heritage. LC 84-27929. (Illus.). xii, 279p. 1985. Repr. of 1944 ed. lib. bdg. 55.00x (ISBN 0-313-23371-3, FAAH). Greenwood.

Faris, Nabik A., tr. see Al-Ghazzali.

Farish, Hunter D. Circuit Rider Dismounts, a Social History of Southern Methodism 1865-1900. LC 77-87534. (American Scene Ser). 1969. Repr. of 1938 ed. 45.00 (ISBN 0-306-71450-7). Da Capo.

Farish, Starr. Voice of Silence. 5th ed. (Illus.). 119p. 1983. pap. 6.95 (ISBN 0-9605492-2-6). Touch Heart.

Farish, Starr, ed. see Gittner, Louis.

Farkas, Mary, ed. see Sasaki, Sokei-an.

Farkasfalvy, Denis, jt. auth. see Farmer, William R.

Farley, Benjamin W., ed. see Calvin, John.

Farley, Benjamin W., tr. see Calvin, John.

Farley, Edward. Ecclesial Reflection: An Anatomy of Theological Method. LC 81-43088. 1982. 29.95 (ISBN 0-8006-0670-1). Fortress.

--Theologia: The Fragmentation & Unity of Theological Education. LC 82-48621. 224p. 1983. pap. 14.95 (ISBN 0-8006-1705-3). Fortress.

Farley, G. M. & Pelton, Robert W. Satan Unmasked: Principles & Practice of Christian Exorcism. LC 78-70632. (Illus.). 1979. 7.50 (ISBN 0-916620-24-7). Portals Pr.

Farley, S. Brent. Spiritually Yours: Applying Gospel Principles for Personal Progression. LC 81-82054. 160p. 1982. 6.95 (ISBN 0-88290-192-3, 1068). Horizon Utah.

Farmer, David, jt. ed. see Bowden, Edwin T.

Farmer, David H. Saint Hugh of Lincoln. (Cistercian Studies: No. 87). xi, 114p. 1987. pap. 7.95 (ISBN 0-87907-887-1). Cistercian Pubns.

Farmer, David H., ed. The Oxford Dictionary of Saints. 1978. pap. 8.95 (ISBN 0-19-283036-8). Oxford U Pr.

Farmer, David H., jt. ed. see Douie, Decima L.

Farmer, Herbert H. Revelation & Religion: Studies in the Theological Interpretation of Religious Types. LC 77-27177. (Gifford Lectures: 1950). (Illus.). 256p. Repr. of 1954 ed. 31.00 (ISBN 0-404-60505-2). AMS Pr.

--Servant of the Word. LC 64-20405. 128p. (Orig.). 1964. pap. 3.95 (ISBN 0-8006-4001-2, 1-4001). Fortress.

Farmer, Richard, ed. see Morano, Roy W.

Farmer, Richard, ed. see Safranski, Scott R.

Farmer, William R. Jesus & the Gospel. LC 81-43078. 320p. 1982. 22.95 (ISBN 0-8006-0666-3). Fortress.

--The Synoptic Problem: A Critical Analysis. LC 76-13764. xi, 308p. 1981. 18.95 (ISBN 0-915948-02-8, MUP-H005). Mercer Univ Pr.

Farmer, William R. & Farkasfalvy, Denis. The Formation of the New Testament Canon: An Ecumenical Approach. LC 82-62417. (Theological Inquiries Ser.). 1983. pap. 8.95 (ISBN 0-8091-2495-5). Paulist Pr.

Farmer, William R., ed. New Synoptic Studies: The Cambridge Gospel Conference & Beyond. LC 83-13396. xii, 533p. 1983. 32.95 (ISBN 0-86554-087-X, MUP/H76). Mercer Univ Pr.

--Synopticon. 1969. 80.00 (ISBN 0-521-07464-9). Cambridge U Pr.

Farmer, William R. & Moule, C. F., eds. Christian History & Interpretation: Studies Presented to John Knox. LC 67-15306. pap. 116.00 (ISBN 0-317-08479-8, 2022449). Bks Demand UMI.

Farnell, L. R. The Higher Aspects of Greek Religion. vii, 155p. 1977. 10.00 (ISBN 0-89005-206-9). Ares.

Farnell, Lewis R. The Attributes of God. LC 77-27205. (Gifford Lectures Ser.: 1924-25). 296p. Repr. of 1925 ed. 34.50 (ISBN 0-404-60475-7). AMS Pr.

--The Cults of the Greek States, 5 vols. Incl. Vol. 1. Cronos, Zeus, Hera, Athena. 50.00 (ISBN 0-89241-029-9); Vol. 2. Artemis, Aphrodite. 50.00 (ISBN 0-89241-030-2); Vol. 3. Cults of the Mother of the Gods, Raeh, Cybele. 50.00 (ISBN 0-89241-031-0); Vol. 4. Poseidon, Apollo. 60.00 (ISBN 0-89241-032-9); Vol. 5. Hermes, Dionysos, Hestia Hephaistos, Ares, the Minor Cults. 60.00 (ISBN 0-89241-033-7). (Illus.). 1977. Repr. 250.00x set (ISBN 0-89241-049-3). Caratzas.

--Greece & Babylon: A Comparative Sketch of Mesopatamian, Anatolian, & Hellenic Religions. 1977. lib. bdg. 59.95 (ISBN 0-8490-1906-0). Gordon Pr.

--The Higher Aspects of Greek Religion. LC 77-27158. (Hibbert Lectures Ser.: 1911). Repr. of 1912 ed. 20.00 (ISBN 0-404-60413-7). AMS Pr.

--Outline History of Greek Religion. 160p. (Orig.). 1986. 10.00 (ISBN 0-89005-025-2); pap. 10.00 (ISBN 0-89005-442-8). Ares.

Farnsworth, Kenneth C. Journey to Healing. Lambert, Herbert, ed. LC 85-3838. (Orig.). 1985. pap. 8.95 (ISBN 0-8272-1706-4). CBP.

Farnsworth, Kirk E. Integrating Psychology & Theology: Elbows Together but Hearts Apart. LC 81-40100. 94p. 1982. lib. bdg. 23.50 (ISBN 0-8191-1851-6); pap. text ed. 8.25 (ISBN 0-8191-1852-4). U Pr of Amer.

--Wholehearted Integration: Harmonizing Psychology & Christianity Through Word & Deed. 160p. 1986. 6.95 (ISBN 0-8010-3513-9). Baker Bk.

Farnsworth, Kirk E. & Lawhead, Wendell H. Life Planning. 96p. (Orig.). 1981. pap. 7.95 (ISBN 0-87784-840-8). Inter-Varsity.

Farook, Omar & Rauf, A. Quran for Children. pap. 5.95 (ISBN 0-686-63912-X). Kazi Pubns.

Farquhar, J. N. An Outline of Religious Literature of India. 1984. Repr. 30.00 (ISBN 0-89684-287-8). Orient Bk Dist.

Farr, Edward, ed. Select Poetry, Chiefly Devotional, of the Reign of Queen Elizabeth, 2 Vols. 1845. Vol. 1. 41.00 (ISBN 0-384-15165-5); Vol. 2. 41.00 (ISBN 0-384-15166-3). Johnson Repr.

Farra, L. Genesis Seven. 1987. 8.95 (ISBN 0-533-07034-1). Vantage.

Farrar, Austin. Rebirth of Images: The Making of St. John's Apocalypse. 13.25 (ISBN 0-8446-0617-0). Peter Smith.

Farrar, Dean. Ruskin As a Religious Teacher. 1978. Repr. of 1904 ed. lib. bdg. 15.00 (ISBN 0-8495-1616-1). Arden Lib.

--Ruskin As a Religious Teacher. LC 73-2834. 1973. lib. bdg. 8.50 (ISBN 0-8414-1957-4). Folcroft.

Farrar, F. W. The Life & Work of St. Paul. 1980. 2 vol. set 43.95 (ISBN 0-86524-055-8, 8402). Klock & Klock.

Farrar, Frederic W. Life of Christ. 1980. 15.00 (ISBN 0-911376-01-1). Fountain Publications Oregon.

--Life of Christ. 1982. lib. bdg. 24.95 (ISBN 0-86524-089-2, 9508). Klock & Klock.

Farrar, Janet & Farrar, Stuart. A Witches Bible, 2 vols. (Illus., Orig.). 1984. Vol. I - The Sabbats. pap. 10.95 (ISBN 0-939708-06-X); Vol. II - The Rituals. pap. 10.95 (ISBN 0-939708-07-8); pap. 21.90 boxed set (ISBN 0-939708-08-6). Magickal Childe.

Farrar, Stuart, jt. auth. see Farrar, Janet.

Farrell, Catherine E., jt. auth. see Butler, Francis J.

Farrell, Christopher & Artz, Thomas. The Sacraments Today: Their Meaning & Celebration. LC 78-69750. 1978. pap. 3.95 (ISBN 0-89243-087-7). Liguori Pubns.

Farrell, Edward. Can You Drink This Cup? pap. 4.95 (ISBN 0-87193-179-6). Dimension Bks.

--The Father Is Very Fond of Me. 6.95 (ISBN 0-87193-029-3). Dimension Bks.

--Prayer Is a Hunger. 4.95 (ISBN 0-87193-031-5). Dimension Bks.

--Surprised by the Spirit. 4.95 (ISBN 0-87193-030-7). Dimension Bks.

Farrell, Gerald J., jt. auth. see Kosicki, George W.

Farrell, Melvin L. Getting to Know the Bible: An Introduction to Sacred Scripture for Catholics. 112p. 1986. pap. 5.95 (ISBN 0-937997-01-3). HI-Time Pub.

Farrell, Michael. Arming the Protestants: The Formation of the Ulster Special Constabulary & the Royal Ulster Constabulary, 1920-1927. 274p. (Orig.). 1983. pap. 15.00 (ISBN 0-86104-705-2, Pub by Pluto Pr). Longwood Pub Group.

Farrell, Pat. Time for Me. (Everyday Ser.). (Illus.). 26p. (Orig.). 1983. pap. 3.00 (ISBN 0-915517-01-9). Everyday Ser.

Farrell, Robert T., jt. auth. see Hill, Thomas D.

Farrelly, John. God's Work in a Changing World. 346p. (Orig.). 1985. lib. bdg. 28.50 (ISBN 0-8191-4523-8); pap. text ed. 14.50 (ISBN 0-8191-4524-6). U Pr of Amer.

Farrer, Austin. Finite & Infinite: A Philosophical Essay. 312p. (Orig.). 1979. pap. 8.95 (ISBN 0-8164-2001-7, HarpR). Har-Row.

--A Rebirth of Images: The Making of St. John's Apocalypse. 352p. (Orig.). 1986. 39.50 (ISBN 0-88706-271-7); pap. 12.95 (ISBN 0-88706-272-5). State U NY Pr.

Farrer, Claire R., ed. Women & Folklore: Images & Genres. (Illus.). 100p. 1986. pap. text ed. 6.95x (ISBN 0-88133-227-5). Waveland Pr.

Farrer, S. Christianity Without the Myths. 39.00x (ISBN 0-317-43636-8, Pub. by Regency pr). State Mutual Bk.

--The Evolution of Christianity Leading to Christianity Without the Myths. 1986. 40.00x (ISBN 0-7212-0740-5, Pub. by Regency Pr). State Mutual Bk.

Farris, Kenna. Christianity Is a Bridge. Date not set. price not set. Port Love Intl.

Farris, Stephen. The Hymns of Luke's Infancy Narratives: Their Origin, Meaning & Significance. (JSoT Supplement Ser.: No. 44). 225p. 1985. text ed. 32.50x (ISBN 0-905774-91-4, Pub. by JSOT Pr England); pap. text ed. 13.95x (ISBN 0-905774-92-2). Eisenbrauns.

Farrow, John. Damien the Leper. 1954. pap. 3.95 (ISBN 0-385-02918-7, D3, Im). Doubleday.

Farrow, Stephen S. Faith, Fancies & Fetish or Yoruba Paganism. LC 76-98718. (Illus.). Repr. of 1926 ed. 22.50x (ISBN 0-8371-2759-9, FFF&, Pub. by Negro U Pr). Greenwood.

Farschman, Marc W. Setting the Captives Free! A Practical Guide to Breaking the Power of Satan over Your Life. LC 85-61138. 146p. (Orig.). 1985. pap. 4.95 (ISBN 0-934285-00-4). New Life Faith.

Farstad, Arthur L. & Hodges, Zane C., eds. The Greek New Testament According to the Majority Text. 78p. 1982. 14.95 (ISBN 0-8407-4963-5). Nelson.

Farthing. When We Die. 3.25 (ISBN 0-8356-5118-5). Theos Pub Hse.

Farthing, Geoffrey. Theosophy: What's It All About. 1967. 5.25 (ISBN 0-8356-5075-8). Theos Pub Hse.

Faruqi, I. Azad. The Tarjuman Al-Qura'n: A Critical Analysis of Maulana Abul Kalam Azad's Approach to the Understanding of the Qura'n. 128p. 1983. text ed. 15.95x (ISBN 0-7069-1342-6, Pub. by Vikas India). Advent NY.

Faruqi, R. I., tr. see Haykal, M. H.

Farwell, Beatrice. Manet & the Nude, a Study in Iconography in the Second Empire. LC 79-57509. (Outstanding Dissertations in the Fine Arts Ser.: No. 5). 290p. 1981. lib. bdg. 61.00 (ISBN 0-8240-3929-7). Garland Pub.

Fasching, Darrell J. The Thought of Jacques Ellul: A Systematic Exposition. LC 81-22529. (Toronto Studies in Theology: Vol. 7). 272p. 1982. 49.95x (ISBN 0-88946-961-X). E Mellen.

Faso, Charles N., jt. auth. see Shannon, Thomas A.

Fasol, Al. A Guide to Self-Improvement in Sermon Delivery. 128p. 1983. pap. 5.95 (ISBN 0-8010-3507-4). Baker Bk.

Fast, Bette, jt. auth. see Fast, Howard.

Fast, H. A. Jesus & Human Conflict. LC 58-10315. 215p. 1959. 7.95 (ISBN 0-8361-1382-9). Herald Pr.

Fast, Heinhold. Quellen zur Geschichte der Taufer in der Schweiz, Vol. 2: Ostschweiz. (Ger.). 1974. 59.00x (ISBN 0-8361-1197-4). Herald Pr.

Fast, Howard. The Jews: Story of a People. 384p. 1978. pap. 3.95 (ISBN 0-440-34444-1). Dell.

Fast, Howard & Fast, Bette. The Picture Book History of the Jews. 60p. 1942. 5.95 (ISBN 0-88482-771-2). Hebrew Pub.

Fatemi, Faramarz S., jt. auth. see Fatemi, Nasrollah S.

Fatemi, Nasrollah S. & Fatemi, Faramarz S. Love, Beauty, & Harmony in Sufism. 12.95 (ISBN 0-8453-2248-6, Cornwall Bks). Assoc Univ Prs.

Fath, Gerald. Health Care Ministries. 2nd ed. LC 80-12620. 1980. pap. 8.50 (ISBN 0-87125-061-6). Cath Health.

Father Sheedy. Questions Catholics Ask. LC 78-58466. 1978. pap. 4.95 (ISBN 0-87973-738-7). Our Sunday Visitor.

Father Andrew. The Life & Letters of Father Andrew. LC 82-80473. (Treasures from the Spiritual Classics Ser.). 64p. 1982. pap. 2.95 (ISBN 0-8192-1310-1). Morehouse.

Father Augustine. Some Loves of the Seraphic Saint. 1979. 5.95 (ISBN 0-8199-0776-6). Franciscan Herald.

Father Benedict. The Daily Cycle of Services of the Orthodox Church: An Historical Synopsis. 30p. (Orig.). 1986. pap. 4.95x (ISBN 0-936649-09-7, TX 1-781-934). St Anthony Orthodox.

Father Benedict, ed. Wondrous Is God in His Saints. LC 85-63506. (Illus.). 190p. (Orig.). 1985. pap. 6.95 (ISBN 0-936649-00-3). St Anthony Orthodox.

Father Edwin J. McDermott. Distinctive Qualities of the Catholic School. 78p. 1986. 6.60 (ISBN 0-318-20560-2). Natl Cath Educ.

Father Harold A. Buetow. A History of Catholic Schooling in the United States. 89p. 1986. 6.60 (ISBN 0-318-20561-0). Natl Cath Educ.

Father James F. Hawker. Catechetics in the Catholic School. 61p. 1986. 6.60 (ISBN 0-318-20569-6). Natl Cath Educ.

Fathers of the Company of Mary, ed. see Louis.

Fator, Sue. The Adventures of Timoteo. pap. 1.25 (ISBN 0-89985-992-5). Christ Nations.

Faulder, Carolyn. Whose Body Is It? The Troubling Issue of Informed Consent. 168p. (Orig.). 1986. pap. 6.95 (ISBN 0-86068-645-0, Pub. by Virago Pr). Salem Hse Pubs.

Faulhaber. Judaism, Christianity & Germany. Smith, George D., tr. from Ger. 116p. 1981. Repr. of 1934 ed. lib. bdg. 30.00 (ISBN 0-89987-263-8). Darby Bks.

Faulhaber, Clare W., tr. see Peyret, Raymond.

Faulkner, Brooks R. Burnout in Ministry. LC 81-67752. 1981. pap. 5.95 (ISBN 0-8054-2414-8). Broadman.

--Forced Termination. LC 86-6122. (Orig.). 1986. pap. 4.95 (ISBN 0-8054-5435-7). Broadman.

Faulkner, Harold U. Chartism & the Churches. LC 79-76712. (Columbia University. Studies in the Social Sciences: No. 173). Repr. of 1916 ed. 12.50 (ISBN 0-404-51173-2). AMS Pr.

--Chartism & the Churches: A Study in Democracy. 152p. 1970. Repr. of 1916 ed. 32.50x (ISBN 0-7146-1308-8, F Cass Co). Biblio Dist.

Faulkner, John A. Cyprian: The Churchman. 1977. lib. bdg. 59.95 (ISBN 0-8490-1698-3). Gordon Pr.

Faulkner, Joseph E., jt. auth. see Bord, Richard J.

Faulkner, Paul. Making Things Right, When Things Go Wrong. LC 86-61405. 1986. 11.95 (ISBN 0-8344-0137-1, BA130H). Sweet.

Faulkner, Paul, jt. auth. see Brecheen, Carl.

Faulkner, R. O., tr. see Andrews, Carol.

Faulkner, Robert K. Richard Hooker & the Politics of a Christian England. LC 79-65776. 195p. 1981. 31.00x (ISBN 0-520-03993-9). U of Cal Pr.

Faupel, David W. The American Pentecostal Movement: A Bibliographic Essay. LC 76-361994. (Occasional Bibliographic Papers of the B. L. Fisher Library: No. 2). 56p. 1972. 3.00 (ISBN 0-914368-01-X). Asbury Theological.

Faur, Jose. Golden Doves with Silver Dots: Semiotics & Textuality in Rabbinic Tradition. LC 84-47967. (Jewish Literature & Culture Ser.). 256p. 1986. 27.50x (ISBN 0-253-32600-1). Ind U Pr.

Faure, Sebastian. Does God Exist? lib. bdg. 59.95 (ISBN 0-8490-0054-8). Gordon Pr.

Faurisson, Robert. The Holocaust Debate: Revisionist Historians Versus Six Million Jews. 1980. lib. bdg. 59.95 (ISBN 0-686-62797-0). Revisionist Pr.

Fausboll, V., ed. Buddhist Birth Stories; or Jataka Tales, Vol. 1. Davids, Rhys T., tr. LC 78-72443. Repr. of 1880 ed. 42.50 (ISBN 0-404-17309-8). AMS Pr.

Fauset, Arthur H. Black Gods of the Metropolis, Negro Religious Cults of the Urban North. LC 73-120251. 1970. Repr. lib. bdg. 16.00x (ISBN 0-374-92714-6, Octagon). Hippocrene Bks.

--Black Gods of the Metropolis: Negro Religious Cults of the Urban North. LC 75-133446. 1971. pap. 9.95x (ISBN 0-8122-1001-8, Pa Paperbks). U of Pa Pr.

Fauss, O. F. What God Hath Wrought: The Complete Works of O. F. Fauss. Wallace, Mary H., ed. (Illus.). 300p. (Orig.). 1985. pap. 6.95 (ISBN 0-912315-84-9). Word Aflame.

Fausset, A. R. Fausset's Bible Dictionary. (Illus.). 1970. 9.95 (ISBN 0-310-24311-4, 9616P). Zondervan.

Fausset, H. L'Anson. The Flame & the Light: Vedanta & Buddhism. 59.95 (ISBN 0-8490-0173-0). Gordon Pr.

Fausset, High I. Studies in Idealism. 278p. 1982. Repr. of 1923 ed. lib. bdg. 30.00 (ISBN 0-89760-230-7). Telegraph Bks.

Fausset, Hugh A. Flame & the Light: Meanings in Vedanta & Buddhism. LC 69-10089. Repr. of 1969 ed. lib. bdg. 22.50x (ISBN 0-8371-0996-5, FAVB). Greenwood.

Faust, Candy, jt. auth. see Faust, David.

Faust, Clarence H. & Johnson, Thomas H. Jonathan Edwards. 1981. Repr. of 1935 ed. lib. bdg. 40.00 (ISBN 0-89760-234-X). Telegraph Bks.

Faust, David & Faust, Candy. Puppet Plays with a Point. rev. ed. 160p. 1979. pap. 7.95 (ISBN 0-87239-248-1, 3364). Standard Pub.

Faust, Harriet. Enough of Christmas. (Orig.). 1980. pap. 2.95 (ISBN 0-937172-08-1). JLJ Pubs.

Faustus, Saint Praeter Sermones Pseudo-Eusebianos Opera. Engelbrecht, A., ed. (Corpus Scriptorum Ecclesiasticorum Latinorum Ser: Vol. 21). 1891. unbound 50.00 (ISBN 0-384-15200-7). Johnson Repr.

Fauth, Roy D. Prayers for All Reasons. 1980. 3.50 (ISBN 0-89536-448-4, 1642). CSS of Ohio.

Favour, John. Antiquitie Triumphing over Noveltie. LC 76-171757. (English Experience Ser.: No. 325). 602p. 1971. Repr. of 1619 ed. 72.00 (ISBN 90-221-0325-0). Walter J Johnson.

Favret-Saada, Jeanne. Deadly Words. Cullen, Catherine, tr. from Fr. LC 79-41607. (Illus.). 1981. o. p. 57.50 (ISBN 0-521-22317-2); pap. text ed. 15.95 o. p. (ISBN 0-521-29787-7). Cambridge U Pr.

Fawcett, Benjamin. A Compassionate Address to the Christian Negroes in Virginia. LC 72-168011. Repr. of 1756 ed. 11.50 (ISBN 0-404-00258-7). AMS Pr.

Fawcett, Cheryl. Know & Grow, Vol. 1. LC 82-21567. 1983. pap. 4.95 (ISBN 0-87227-086-6). Reg Baptist.

--Know & Grow, Vol. 2. LC 82-21567. 1983. pap. 4.95 (ISBN 0-87227-090-4). Reg Baptist.

Fawcett, John. Christ Precious to Those That Believe. 1979. 10.00 (ISBN 0-86524-026-4, 8901). Klock & Klock.

Faxon, Alicia C. Women & Jesus. LC 72-11868. 1973. 4.95 (ISBN 0-8298-0244-4). Pilgrim NY.

Fazio, Sue A., ed. see Ramtha.

Feagins, Mary E. Tending the Light. 1984. pap. 2.50x (ISBN 0-87574-255-6, 255). Pendle Hill.

Fear, Leona K. New Ventures-Free Methodist Missions Nineteen Sixty to Nineteen Seventy-Nine. (Orig.). 1979. pap. 1.50 (ISBN 0-89367-036-7). Light & Life.

Fearon, Mary & Hirstein, Sandra. Celebrating Our Sacraments. 1985. Boxed Set. 84.95 (ISBN 0-697-02066-5); program director's guide 4.95 (ISBN 0-697-02058-4); write for info. tchr's. guide & student leaflets. Wm C Brown.

Fearon, Mary & Hirstein, Sandra J. Celebrating the Gift of Forgiveness. 64p. 1982. pap. 3.50 (ISBN 0-697-01792-3); program manual 6.95 (ISBN 0-697-01793-1). Wm C Brown.

--Celebrating the Gift of Jesus. 64p. 1982. pap. 3.50 (ISBN 0-697-01794-X); program manual 6.95 (ISBN 0-697-01795-8). Wm C Brown.

--The Eucharist Makes Us One. 1983. box set 84.95 (ISBN 0-697-01843-1); program dir. guide 4.95 (ISBN 0-697-01844-X); tchr's. manual, pre-school to junior levels 3.25 (ISBN 0-697-01845-8); write for info. student leaflets; attendance certificates 6.95 (ISBN 0-697-01973-X). Wm C Brown.

Fearon, Mary & Tully, Mary J. Wonder-Filled. 1983. pap. 4.00 (ISBN 0-697-01853-9); tchr's. manual 6.00 (ISBN 0-697-01854-7); parent book 3.50 (ISBN 0-697-01855-5). Wm C Brown.

Fearon, Mary, jt. auth. see Tully, Mary Jo.

Fears, J. R. Princeps a Diis Electus: The Divine Election of the Emperor as a Political Concept at Rome. 353p. 1977. 38.00x (ISBN 0-271-00474-6). Pa St U Pr.

Feather, Nevin & Collins, Myrtle. Come Holy Spirit. 1986. 4.75 (ISBN 0-89536-790-4, 6808). CSS of Ohio.

Featherstone, Vaughn J. Charity Never Faileth. LC 80-10528. 121p. 1980. 7.95 (ISBN 0-87747-806-6). Deseret Bk.

--The Disciple of Christ. LC 84-71706. 100p. 7.95 (ISBN 0-87747-910-0). Deseret Bk.

--Purity of Heart. LC 82-72728. 103p. 1982. 8.95 (ISBN 0-87747-914-3). Deseret Bk.

Febvre, Lucien. The Problem of Unbelief in the Sixteenth Century: The Religion of Rabelais. Gottlieb, Beatrice, tr. from Fr. (Illus.). 528p. 1982. text ed. 40.00x (ISBN 0-674-70825-3). Harvard U Pr.

--The Problem of Unbelief in the Sixteenth Century: The Religion of Rabelais. Gottlieb, Beatrice, tr. 552p. 1985. pap. 9.95x (ISBN 0-674-70826-1). Harvard U Pr.

Febvre, Lucien P. Martin Luther: A Destiny. Tapley, Roberts, tr. LC 83-45640. Date not set. Repr. of 1929 ed. 37.50 (ISBN 0-404-19850-3). AMS Pr.

Fecher, Charles A. Philosophy of Jacques Maritain. LC 70-90705. Repr. of 1953 ed. lib. bdg. 22.50x (ISBN 0-8371-2287-2, FEJM). Greenwood.

Fecher, Vincent J. Religion & Aging: An Annotated Bibliography. LC 82-81019. 119p. 1982. 16.00 (ISBN 0-911536-96-5); pap. 9.00 (ISBN 0-911536-97-3). Trinity U Pr.

Fechner, Gustav T. The Little Book of Life After Death. Kastenbaum, Robert, ed. LC 76-19570. (Death & Dying Ser.). 1977. Repr. of 1904 ed. lib. bdg. 15.00x (ISBN 0-405-09565-1). Ayer Co Pubs.

Feder, A., ed. see Hilarius, Saint.

Feder, Lillian. Ancient Myth in Modern Poetry. LC 70-154994. 1972. 38.50x (ISBN 0-691-06207-2); pap. 11.50x (ISBN 0-691-01336-5). Princeton U Pr.

Federn, Karl. Richelieu. LC 72-132440. (World History Ser., No. 48). 1970. Repr. of 1928 ed. lib. bdg. 38.95x (ISBN 0-8383-1222-5). Haskell.

Federspiel, Howard. Persatuan Islam: Islamic Reform in Twentieth Century Indonesia. (Monograph Ser.). (Orig.). 1970. pap. 7.50 (ISBN 0-87763-013-5). Cornell Mod Indo.

Fee, Gordon & Stuart, Douglas. How to Read the Bible for All it's Worth. 272p. 1982. pap. 7.95 (ISBN 0-310-37361-1, 11146P). Zondervan.

Fee, Gordon D. The First Epistle to the Corinthians. Bruce, F. F., ed. (New International Commentary on the New Testament Ser.). 736p. 1987. pap. 27.95 (ISBN 0-8028-2288-6). Eerdmans.

--New Testament Exegesis: A Handbook for Students & Pastors. LC 82-24829. (Illus.). 154p. (Orig.). 1983. pap. 8.95 (ISBN 0-664-24469-6). Westminster.

Fee, John G. Anti-Slavery Manual, Being an Examination, in the Light of the Bible, & of Facts, into the Moral & Social Wrongs of American Slavery. LC 74-82189. (Anti-Slavery Crusade in America Ser). 1969. Repr. of 1848 ed. 14.00 (ISBN 0-405-00627-6). Ayer Co Pubs.

Feeley, Kathleen. Flannery O'Connor: Voice of the Peacock. 2nd ed. LC 76-163958. xviii, 198p. 1982. pap. 9.00 (ISBN 0-8232-1093-6). Fordham.

Feeley-Harnik, Gillian. The Lord's Table: Eucharist & Passover in Early Christianity. 1981. text ed. 23.50x (ISBN 0-8122-7786-4). U of Pa Pr.

Feeney, James H. Divorce & Marriage. 1980. pap. 1.75 (ISBN 0-911739-06-8). Abbott Loop.

Feeney, Leonard. Mother Seton: Saint Elizabeth of New York. LC 75-23224. 212p. 1975. 6.95 (ISBN 0-911218-05-X); pap. 3.95 (ISBN 0-911218-06-8). Ravengate Pr.

Fegan, W. R. Becoming a Church Member. 1979. pap. 3.50 (ISBN 0-89536-389-5, 0232). CSS of Ohio.

Feher, Ferenc, jt. auth. see Heller, Agnes.

Fehl, Jim, ed. Standard Lesson Commentary, 1986-87. 450p. 1986. text ed. 9.50 (ISBN 0-87403-010-2, 74017); pap. text ed. 7.95 (ISBN 0-87403-009-9, 1987). Standard Pub.

Fehlauer, Adolph. Catechism Lessons: Pupil's Book. Grunze, Richard, ed. (Illus.). 336p. 1981. 6.95 (ISBN 0-938272-09-8). WELS Board.

--Life & Faith of Martin Luther. 1981. pap. 5.95 (ISBN 0-8100-0125-X, 15N0376). Northwest Pub.

Fehlauer, Adolph F. Bible Reader's Guide. 1981. 5.95 (ISBN 0-8100-0146-2, 06N0558). Northwest Pub.

Fehr, Terry, jt. auth. see Petersen, W. P.

Fehr, Wayne L. The Birth of the Catholic Tubingen School: The Dogmatics of Johann Sebastian Drey. Raschke, Carl, ed. LC 81-14645. (American Academy of Religion, Dissertation Ser.). 1981. text ed. 14.95 (ISBN 0-89130-544-0, 01-01-37). Scholars Pr GA.

Fehren, Henry, ed. see Liturgical Prayer Magazine.

Feibleman, James K. Christianity, Communism & the Ideal Society: A Philosophical Approach to Modern Politics. LC 75-3140. Repr. of 1937 ed. 38.00 (ISBN 0-404-59149-3). AMS Pr.

--Religious Platonism. LC 78-161628. 236p. Repr. of 1959 ed. lib. bdg. 22.50x (ISBN 0-8371-6184-3, FERP). Greenwood.

Feider, Paul A. The Journey to Inner Peace. LC 84-71863. 112p. (Orig.). 1984. pap. 3.95 (ISBN 0-87793-275-1). Ave Maria.

--The Sacraments: Encountering the Risen Lord. LC 85-73569. 128p. (Orig.). 1986. pap. 4.95 (ISBN 0-87793-327-8). Ave Maria.

Feifel, Herman. New Meanings of Death. (Illus.). 1977. 25.00 (ISBN 0-07-020350-4); pap. 18.95 (ISBN 0-07-020349-0). McGraw.

Feil, Ernst. The Theology of Dietrich Bonhoeffer. Rumscheidt, H. Martin, tr. LC 84-47919. 272p. 1985. 19.95 (ISBN 0-8006-0696-5, 1-696). Fortress.

Feild, Reshad. The Invisible Way: A Sufi Love Story. LC 78-19501. 176p. 1983. pap. 7.95 (ISBN 0-06-062588-0, RD/457, HarpR). Har-Row.

--The Last Barrier. LC 75-9345. 1977. pap. 8.95 (ISBN 0-06-062586-4, RD 202, HarpR). Har-Row.

Fein, Helen. Accounting for Genocide: National Response & Jewish Victimization During the Holocaust. LC 78-53085. (Illus.). 1979. 17.95 (ISBN 0-02-910220-0). Free Pr.

--Accounting for Genocide: National Responses & Jewish Victimization During the Holocaust. LC 83-24219. (Illus.). xxii, 469p. 1984. pap. 13.95 (ISBN 0-226-24034-7). U of Chicago Pr.

--Congregational Sponsorship of Indochinese Refugees in the United States, 1979-1981: Helping Beyond Borders: A Study of Collective Altruism. LC 85-45952. 168p. 1987. 26.50x (ISBN 0-8386-3279-3). Fairleigh Dickinson.

Feinberg, Charles. Millennialism: The Two Major Views. 1985. 12.95 (ISBN 0-88469-166-7). BMH Bks.

Feinberg, Charles L. Daniel, the Kingdom of the Lord. 1984. 9.95 (ISBN 0-88469-157-8). BMH Bks.

--God Remembers: A Study of Zechariah. 4th ed. LC 79-88530. 1979. 8.95 (ISBN 0-930014-33-2). Multnomah.

--The Minor Prophets. rev ed. LC 76-44088. 384p. 1976. 17.95 (ISBN 0-8024-5306-6). Moody.

--Prophecy of Ezekiel. 1984. 11.95 (ISBN 0-8024-6908-6). Moody.

--Revelation. 1985. 9.95 (ISBN 0-88469-162-4). BMH Bks.

Feinberg, John S. & Feinberg, Paul D. Tradition & Testament. LC 81-11223. 1982. 14.95 (ISBN 0-8024-2544-5). Moody.

Feinberg, Paul D., jt. auth. see Feinberg, John S.

Feiner, Johannes & Vischer, Lukas, eds. The Common Catechism: A Book of Christian Faith. LC 75-1070. 690p. 1975. 10.95 (ISBN 0-8245-0211-6). Crossroad NY.

Feingold, Henry L. The Politics of Rescue. LC 80-81713. (Illus.). 432p. (Orig.). 1970. pap. 12.95 (ISBN 0-89604-019-4). Holocaust Pubns.

--The Politics of Rescue: The Roosevelt Administration & the Holocaust, 1938-1945. LC 75-127049. 1970. 40.00 (ISBN 0-8135-0664-6). Rutgers U Pr.

--Zion in America. rev. ed. (American Immigrant Ser.). 1981. pap. 10.95 (ISBN 0-88254-592-2). Hippocrene Bks.

Feinsilver, A. Aspects of Jewish Belief. 1973. pap. 5.95x (ISBN 0-87068-225-3). Ktav.

Feinsilver, Alexander, ed. The Talmud Today. 320p. 1980. 14.95 (ISBN 0-312-78479-1). St Martin.

Feiring, Evolyn B. Concatenation: Enoch's Prophecy Fulfilling! Hebrew-Christian Metaphysics Supported by Modern Science. LC 72-96989. 5.00x (ISBN 0-9603386-0-8); pap. 2.00x (ISBN 0-9603386-1-6). Rocky Mtn Bks.

Feitelson, Rose, jt. auth. see Salomon, George.

Feiwel, R. J., tr. see Ruppin, Arthur.

Felbinger, Claus, jt. auth. see Ehrenpreis, Andreas.

Feld, Lipman G. Harassment & Other Collection Taboos. 156p. 1976. pap. 8.95 (ISBN 0-934914-08-7). NACM.

Feldblum, E. Y. The American Catholic Press & the Jewish State: 1917-1959. 25.00x (ISBN 0-87068-325-X). Ktav.

Felder, Hilaron. The Ideals of St. Francis of Assisi. 1983. 12.50 (ISBN 0-8199-0845-2). Franciscan Herald.

Felderhof, M. C. Religious Education in a Pluralistic Society. 160p. 1985. pap. text ed. 18.95 (ISBN 0-340-35413-5). Princeton Bk Co.

Feldhaus, Anne. The Religious Systems of the Mahanubhava Sect. 1983. 26.00x (ISBN 0-8364-1005-X). South Asia Bks.

Feldhaus, Anne, ed. The Deeds of God in Rddhipur. LC 83-21949. 1984. 27.00x (ISBN 0-19-503438-4). Oxford U Pr.

Feldman, Abraham J. The American Jew: A Study of Backgrounds. LC 78-26254. 1979. Repr. of 1937 ed. lib. bdg. cancelled (ISBN 0-313-20876-X, FEAJ). Greenwood.

Feldman, Aharon, tr. see Ha-Cohen, Yisroel Meir.

Feldman, Asher. The Parables & Similes of the Rabbis, Agricultural & Pastoral. LC 75-23127. 1975. Repr. of 1927 ed. lib. bdg. 27.50 (ISBN 0-8414-4229-0). Folcroft.

Feldman, Burton & Richardson, Robert D. The Rise of Modern Mythology, Sixteen Hundred Eighty to Eighteen Hundred Sixty. LC 71-135005. pap. 147.80 (2056249). Bks Demand UMI.

Feldman, Burton, ed. see Anquetil-Duperron, A. H.

Feldman, Burton, ed. see Beausobre, Isaac de.

Feldman, Burton, ed. see Bell, John.

Feldman, Burton, ed. see Bryant, Jacob.

Feldman, Burton, ed. see Davies, Edward.

Feldman, Burton, ed. see Dupuis, Charles.

Feldman, Burton, ed. see Faber, George S.

Feldman, Burton, ed. see Godwin, William.

Feldman, Burton, ed. see Maurice, Thomas.

Feldman, Burton, ed. see Moor, Edward.

Feldman, Burton, ed. see Owen, William.

Feldman, Burton, ed. see Rowlands, Henry.

Feldman, Burton, ed. see Stukeley, William.

Feldman, Burton, ed. see Volney, C. F.

Feldman, David M. Birth Control in Jewish Law: Marital Relations, Contraception, & Abortion As Set Forth in the Classic Texts of Jewish Law. LC 79-16712. 1980. Repr. of 1968 ed. lib. bdg. 27.50x (ISBN 0-313-21297-X, FEBC). Greenwood.

--Health & Medicine in the Jewish Tradition: The Pursuit of Wholeness. 176p. 1986. 15.95x (ISBN 0-8245-0707-X). Crossroad NY.

--Marital Relations, Birth Control, & Abortion in Jewish Law. LC 68-15338. 336p. 1974. pap. 8.95 (ISBN 0-8052-0438-5). Schocken.

Feldman, Emanuel, ed. The Biblical Echo: Reflection on Bible, Jews & Judaism. 1986. text ed. 17.50x (ISBN 0-88125-104-6). Ktav.

Feldman, Fred. Introductory Ethics. 1978. text ed. write for info. (ISBN 0-13-501783-1). P-H.

Feldman, Jacob. The Jewish Experience in Western Pensylvania, 1755-1945. (Illus.). 1986. 9.95 (ISBN 0-936340-03-7). Hist Soc West Pa.

Feldman, Louis, ed. Josephus, Judaism & Christianity. Hata, Gohei, tr. from Japanese. 336p. 1987. 39.95X (ISBN 0-8143-1831-2); pap. 13.95X (ISBN 0-8143-1832-0). Wayne St U Pr.

Feldman, Louis H. Josephus & Modern Scholarship: 1937-1980. LC 84-1879. xvi, 1055p. 1984. 248.00x (ISBN 3-11-008138-5). De Gruyter.

Feldman, Seymour, intro. by see Spinoza, Baruch.

Feldman, Seymour, tr. see Gershom, Levi B.

Feldman, Seymour, tr. see Gersonides.

Feldman, Steven, et al, eds. Guide to Jewish Boston & New England. LC 85-90430. 235p. (Orig.). pap. text ed. 10.95 (ISBN 0-9615649-0-3). Genesis Two.

Feldmeth, Joanne, jt. auth. see Larson, Jim.

Feldstein, Leonard C. The Dance of Being: Man's Labyrinthe Rhythms, the Natural Ground of the Human. LC 77-75799. xvi, 302p. 1979. 30.00 (ISBN 0-8232-1032-4). Fordham.

Feldstein, Mark D., ed. see Ortiz, Joe.

Felice, Renzo De see De Felice, Renzo.

Feliks, Yehuda. Nature & Man in the Bible. 294p. 1981. 25.00 (ISBN 0-900689-19-6). Soncino Pr.

Felins, Yehuda. Nature & Man in the Bible: Chapters in Biblical Ecology. 1982. 25.00x (ISBN 0-900689-19-6). Bloch.

Fell, Edgar T. Recent Problems in Admiralty Jurisdiction. LC 78-63977. (Johns Hopkins University. Studies in the Social Sciences. Fortieth Ser. 1922: 3). Repr. of 1922 ed. 16.50 (ISBN 0-404-61222-9). AMS Pr.

Fellerer, Karl G. The History of Catholic Church Music. Brunner, Francis A., tr. LC 78-21637. 1979. Repr. of 1951 ed. lib. bdg. 22.50x (ISBN 0-313-21147-7, FECC). Greenwood.

Fellers, Pat. Peace-ing It Together: Peace & Justice Activities for Youth. (The Learning Connection Ser.). 160p. (Orig.). 1984. pap. 9.95 (ISBN 0-86683-836-8, 8440, HarpR). Har-Row.

Fellowes, E. H., jt. ed. see Buck, P. C.

Fellowes, Edmund H. Appendix with Supplementary Notes. (Tudor Church Music Ser.). 1963. Repr. of 1948 ed. 50.00x (ISBN 0-8450-1861-2). Broude.

--English Cathedral Music. 5th, rev. ed. Westrup, J. A., ed. LC 80-24400. (Illus.). xi, 283p. 1981. Repr. of 1973 ed. lib. bdg. 27.50x (ISBN 0-313-22643-1, FEEC). Greenwood.

Fellows, Carmen, et al. Twenty-Six Programs for Preschoolers (Spring & Summer) 96p. 1986. wkbk. 8.95 (ISBN 0-87403-011-0, 3404). Standard Pub.

Fellows, Ward J. Religions East & West. LC 78-27721. 1979. text ed. 31.95 (ISBN 0-03-019441-5, HoltC). H Holt & Co.

Fellowship of Catholic Scholars. Christian Faith & Freedom: Proceedings. Williams, Paul L., ed. LC 82-81072. 128p. (Orig.). 1982. pap. text ed. 4.50 (ISBN 0-686-97454-9). NE Bks.

--Faith & the Sources of Faith: The Sixth Convention of the Fellowship of Catholic Scholars. Williams, Paul L., ed. 120p. (Orig.). 1985. pap. 5.95 (ISBN 0-937374-00-8). NE Bks.

Fellucci, Mario. The Masterpieces of the Vatican. (A Science of Man Library Bk). (Illus.). 40p. 1975. 97.45 (ISBN 0-913314-54-4). Am Classical Coll Pr.

Feltham, Owen. Resolves, a Duple Century. 3rd ed. LC 74-28853. (English Experience Ser.: No. 734). 1975. Repr. of 1628 ed. 35.00 (ISBN 90-221-0734-5). Walter J Johnson.

Fenelon. Fenelon's Spiritual Letters. Edwards, Gene, ed. 139p. pap. 5.95 (ISBN 0-940232-09-X). Christian Bks.

--Let Go! 1973. pap. 3.50 (ISBN 0-88368-010-6). Whitaker Hse.

Fenelon, et al. A Guide to True Peace, or the Excellency of Inward & Spiritual Prayer. LC 78-78157. 1979. pap. 6.95x (ISBN 0-87574-905-4). Pendle Hill.

Fenelon, Archbishop. The Royal Way of the Cross. Helms, Hal M., ed. LC 80-67874. (Living Library Ser.). 1982. 5.95 (ISBN 0-941478-00-9). Paraclete Pr.

Fenelon, Francois. Christian Perfection. Whiston, Charles F., ed. Stillman, Mildred W., tr. from Fr. LC 75-22545. 208p. 1976. pap. 4.95 (ISBN 0-87123-083-6, 200083). Bethany Hse.

--Spiritual Letters to Women. 224p. 1984. pap. 5.95 (ISBN 0-310-36371-3, 12366P, Clarion Class). Zondervan.

Fenelon, Francois D. Spiritual Letters to Women. LC 80-82327. (Shepherd Illustrated Classics Ser.). 1980. pap. 5.95 (ISBN 0-87983-233-9). Keats.

Fenerstein, Georg, tr. see Schumann, Hans W.

Fenhagen, James C. Invitation to Holiness. LC 85-42774. 128p. 1985. 12.45 (ISBN 0-06-062351-9, HarpR). Har-Row.

--Ministry & Solitude: The Ministry of Laity & Clergy in Church & Society. 128p. 1981. 9.95 (ISBN 0-8164-0498-4, HarpR). Har-Row.

--More Than Wanderers: Spiritual Disciplines for Christian Ministry. 1985. pap. 7.95 (ISBN 0-86683-978-X, HarpR). Har-Row.

--Mutual Ministry: New Vitality for the Local Church. 1986. 7.95 (ISBN 0-8164-0332-5, HarpR). Har-Row.

Fenn, Carl. The Church & the Disabled. 1985. pap. 5.00 (ISBN 0-8309-0414-X). Herald Hse.

Fenn, Richard K. Liturgies & Trials: The Secularization of Religious Language. LC 81-19250. 256p. 1982. 15.95 (ISBN 0-8298-0495-1). Pilgrim NY.

--The Spirit of Revolt: Anarchism & the Cult of Authority. LC 86-15430. 192p. 1986. 27.95x (ISBN 0-8476-7522-X). Rowman.

Fenn, William P. Christian Higher Education in Changing China, 1880-1950. LC 75-43741. (Illus.). pap. 64.00 (ISBN 0-317-07969-7, 2012769). Bks Demand UMI.

Fenn, William W. Theism: The Implication of Experience. 1969. 10.00 (ISBN 0-87233-005-2). Bauhan.

Fennema, Jack. Nurturing Children in the Lord. 1978. pap. 4.95 (ISBN 0-87552-266-1). Presby & Reformed.

Fenner, Dudley. A Counter-Poyson..., to the Objections & Reproaches, Wherewith the Aunswerer to the Abstract, Would Disgrace the Holy Discipline of Christ. LC 74-28854. (English Experience Ser.: No. 735). 1975. Repr. of 1584 ed. 10.50 (ISBN 90-221-0735-3). Walter J Johnson.

--A Short Treatise of Lawfull & Unlawfull Recreations. LC 77-6740. (English Experience Ser.: No. 870). 1977. Repr. of 1590 ed. lib. bdg. 3.50 (ISBN 90-221-0870-8). Walter J Johnson.

Fenocketti, Mary M. Coping with Discouragement. 64p. 1985. pap. 1.50 (ISBN 0-89243-226-8). Liguori Pubns.

--Learning from Little Ones: Insights from the Gospel. 48p. 1984. pap. 1.95 (ISBN 0-89243-203-9). Liguori Pubns.

Fensham, F. Charles. The Books of Ezra & Nehemiah. (The New International Commentary on the Old Testament Ser.). 288p. 1983. 14.95 (ISBN 0-8028-2362-9). Eerdmans.

Fenske, Elizabeth W., ed. Spiritual Insights for Daily Living: A Daybook of Reflections on Ancient Spiritual Truths of Relevance for Our Contemporary Lives. (Illus.). 416p. (Orig.). pap. 7.50 (ISBN 0-914071-09-2). Spirit Front Fellow.

Fenske, S. H. My Life in Christ: A Momento of My Confirmation. LC 76-5729. 1976. pap. 2.50 (ISBN 0-8100-0056-3, 16N0514). Northwest Pub.

Fenton, Ann D., jt. auth. see Peterson, Carolyn S.

Fenton, Geoffrey. A Forme of Christian Pollicie. LC 78-38180. (English Experience Ser.: No. 454). 424p. 1972. Repr. of 1574 ed. 42.00 (ISBN 90-221-0454-0). Walter J Johnson.

Fenton, Geoffrey, tr. A Form of Christian Policy Gathered Out of French. 504p. Repr. of 1574 ed. 50.00 (ISBN 0-384-15483-2). Johnson Repr.

Fenton, J. C. Saint Matthew. LC 77-81620. (Westminster Pelican Commentaries Ser.). 488p. 1978. Westminster.

Fenton, John. The Gospel of St. Matthew: Commentaries. (Orig.). 1964. pap. 7.95 (ISBN 0-14-020488-1, Pelican). Penguin.

Fenton, Nina, jt. auth. see Donnelly, Mark.

Fenton, Paul, tr. see Maimonides, Obadyah.

Fenton, William N. The False Faces of the Iroquois. (Illus.). 1987. 75.00. U of Okla Pr.

Fenwick, Agnes M. My Journey into God's Realm of Light. 1974. 3.50 (ISBN 0-682-47865-2). Exposition Pr FL.

Fenwick, Benedict J. Memoirs to Serve for the Future Ecclesiastical History of the Diocese of Boston. McCarthy, Joseph M., ed. LC 77-64366. (Monograph: No. 35). (Illus.). 270p. 1979. 10.95x (ISBN 0-686-65388-2). US Cath Hist.

Ferber, Stanley, ed. Islam & the Medieval West. (Illus.). 1979. pap. 29.50x (ISBN 0-87395-802-0). State U NY Pr.

Ferch, Arthur. In the Beginning. Wheeler, Gerald, ed. LC 85-1946. 128p. (Orig.). 1985. pap. 5.95 (ISBN 0-8280-0282-7). Review & Herald.

Ferch, Arthur J. The Son of Man in Daniel Seven. (Andrews University Seminary Doctoral Dissertation Ser.: Vol. 6). x, 237p. 1983. pap. 9.95 (ISBN 0-943872-38-3). Andrews Univ Pr.

Ferder, Fran. Words Made Flesh: Scripture, Psychology & Human Communication. LC 85-73255. 184p. (Orig.). 1986. pap. 5.95 (ISBN 0-87793-331-6). Ave Maria.

Ferencz, Benjamin B. Less Than Slaves: Jewish Forced Labor & the Quest for Compensation. LC 79-10690. 1979. 17.50x (ISBN 0-674-52525-6). Harvard U Pr.

Ferguson, Adam. Institutes of Moral Philosophy. 2nd rev. ed. LC 75-11219. (British Philosophers & Theologians of the 17th & 18th Centuries Ser.: Vol. 22). 1978. Repr. of 1773 ed. lib. bdg. 51.00 (ISBN 0-8240-1773-0). Garland Pub.

--Principles of Moral & Political Science, 2 Vols. LC 71-147970. Repr. of 1792 ed. Set. 85.00 (ISBN 0-404-08222-X). AMS Pr.

--Principles of Moral & Political Science, 2 vols. Wellek, Rene, ed. LC 75-11218. (British Philosophers & Theologians of the 17th & 18th Centuries Ser.: Vol. 21). 1978. Repr. of 1792 ed. Set. lib. bdg. 101.00 (ISBN 0-8240-1772-2). Garland Pub.

Ferguson, Charles W. Methodists & the Making of America. 480p. 1983. 17.95 (ISBN 0-89015-424-4); pap. 12.95 (ISBN 0-89015-405-8). Eakin Pr.

Ferguson, Charles W., compiled by. Great Themes of the Christian Faith, As Presented by G. C. Morgan. facs. ed. LC 68-58788. (Essay Index Reprint Ser). 1930. 17.50 (ISBN 0-8369-1034-6). Ayer Co Pubs.

Ferguson, Duncan S. Biblical Hermeneutics: An Introduction. LC 85-45456. 204p. 1986. pap. 12.95 (ISBN 0-8042-0050-5). John Knox.

Ferguson, Everett. Backgrounds of Early Christianity. 464p. (Orig.). 1987. pap. 22.95 (ISBN 0-8028-0292-3). Eerdmans.

--A Cappella Music in the Public Worksip of the Church. LC 72-76963. (Way of Life Ser: No. 125). 1972. pap. text ed. 3.95 (ISBN 0-89112-125-0, Bibl Res Pr). Abilene Christ U.

--Church History, Early & Medieval. 2nd ed. (Way of Life Ser: No. 106). (Orig.). 1966. pap. 3.95 (ISBN 0-89112-106-4, Bibl Res Pr). Abilene Christ U.

--Church History, Reformation & Modern. (Way of Life Ser: No. 107). 1967. pap. 3.95 (ISBN 0-89112-107-2, Bibl Res Pr). Abilene Christ U.

--Demonology of the Early Christian World. LC 84-16681. (Symposium Ser.: Vol. 12). 190p. 1984. 19.95 (ISBN 0-88946-703-X). E Mellen.

--Early Christians Speak. LC 81-68871. 258p. 1981. pap. text ed. 9.95 (ISBN 0-89112-044-0, Bibl Res Pr). Abilene Christ U.

--Message of the New Testament: The Letters of John. (Way of Life Ser.: No. 175). 1984. pap. 3.95 (ISBN 0-89112-175-7, Bibl Res Pr). Abilene Christ U.

--The New Testament Church. LC 68-55790. (Way of Life Ser: No. 108). 1968. pap. 3.95 (ISBN 0-89112-108-0, Bibl Res Pr). Abilene Christ U.

Ferguson, Franklin C. A Pilgrimage in Faith: An Introduction to the Episcopal Church. rev. ed. LC 75-5220. 180p. (Orig.). 1979. pap. 6.95 (ISBN 0-8192-1277-6). Morehouse.

Ferguson, George. Signs & Symbols in Christian Art. (Illus.). 1966. pap. 7.95 (ISBN 0-19-501432-4). Oxford U Pr.

Ferguson, Henry. Essays in American History. LC 68-26266. 1969. Repr. of 1894 ed. 21.50x (ISBN 0-8046-0144-5, Pub. by Kennikat). Assoc Faculty Pr.

Ferguson, Howard E. The Edge. (Illus.). 340p. 1983. text ed. 29.95x (ISBN 0-9611180-0-8). H E Ferguson.

Ferguson, John. Encyclopedia of Mysticism & Mystery Religions. (Crossroad Paperback Ser.). (Illus.). 228p. 1982. pap. 9.95 (ISBN 0-8245-0429-1). Crossroad NY.

--Pelagius: A Historical & Theological Study. LC 77-84700. Repr. of 1956 ed. 27.00 (ISBN 0-404-16107-3). AMS Pr.

--The Place of Suffering. 137p. 1972. 7.95 (ISBN 0-227-67803-6). Attic Pr.

--The Religions of the Roman Empire. LC 71-110992. (Aspects of Greek & Roman Life Ser.). (Illus.). 296p. (Orig.). 1985. 29.95x (ISBN 0-8014-0567-X); pap. text ed. 8.95x (ISBN 0-8014-9311-0). Cornell U Pr.

--War & Peace in the World's Religions. 1978. pap. 5.95 (ISBN 0-19-520074-8). Oxford U Pr.

Ferguson, John, jt. auth. see Lawrence, Joy.

Ferguson, John & Nelson, William, eds. The United Church of Christ Hymnal. LC 74-12571. 1974. Pew Edition. spiral bound 12.50x (ISBN 0-8298-0300-9); 9.95x. Pilgrim NY.

Ferguson, John C. Chinese Mythology. Bd. with Japanese Mythology. Anesaki, Masaharu. LC 63-19093. (Mythology of All Races Ser.: Vol. 8). (Illus.). Repr. of 1932 ed. 30.00x (ISBN 0-8154-0068-3). Cooper Sq.

Ferguson, John P., ed. see Mendelson, E. Michael.

Ferguson, Larry & Jackson, Dave. The Freedom Years. (Family Ministry Ser.). (Illus.). 54p. 1985. pap. text ed. 19.95 (ISBN 0-89191-966-X). Cook.

Ferguson, Mable L. God's High Country. 384p. (Orig.). pap. 14.95 (ISBN 0-930161-09-2). State of the Art Ltd.

Ferguson, Nina. In the Beginning God. 1985. 6.95 (ISBN 0-8062-2430-4). Carlton.

Ferguson, Roger. Experiencing Fullness in Christian Living: Studies in Colossians. 36p. 1982. pap. 3.50 (ISBN 0-939298-08-2). J M Prods.

Ferguson, Sinclair. A Heart for God. (Christian Character Library). 150p. 1985. hdbk. 8.95 (ISBN 0-89109-507-1). NavPress.

--Man Overboard. 1982. pap. 3.95 (ISBN 0-8423-4015-7); leader's guide 2.95 (ISBN 0-8423-4016-5). Tyndale.

Ferguson, Sinciair B. Children of the Living God. LC 86-63652. 168p. (Orig.). 1987. pap. price not set (ISBN 0-89109-137-8). NavPress.

--Discovering God's Will. 125p. (Orig.). 1981. pap. 3.95 (ISBN 0-85151-334-4). Banner of Truth.

--Heart for God. 150p. 1987. pap. 3.95 (ISBN 0-89109-176-9). NavPress.

--Kingdom Life in a Fallen World: Living out the Sermon on the Mount. (Christian Character Library). 224p. 1986. 8.95 (ISBN 0-89109-492-X). NavPress.

Ferguson, Walter W. Living Animals of the Bible. (Encore Edition). 1974. 3.95 (ISBN 0-684-15245-2, ScribT). Scribner.

Fergusson, James, jt. auth. see Burgess, James.

Ferlita, Ernest. Gospel Journey. 120p. (Orig.). 1983. pap. 5.95 (ISBN 0-86683-685-3, HarpR). Har-Row.

Ferm, Dean W. Alternative Lifestyles Confront the Church. 144p. 1983. pap. 8.95 (ISBN 0-8164-2394-6, HarpR). Har-Row.

Ferm, Deane W. Contemporary American Theologies: A Critical Survey. 192p. (Orig.). 1981. pap. 8.95 (ISBN 0-8164-2341-5, HarpR). Har-Row.

--Contemporary American Theologies II: A Book of Readings. 214p. (Orig.). 1982. pap. 15.95 (ISBN 0-8164-2407-1, HarpR). Har-Row.

--Third World Liberation Theologies: An Introductory Survey. LC 85-15534. pap. 10.95 (ISBN 0-88344-515-8). Orbis Bks.

Ferm, Deane W., ed. Third World Liberation Theologies: A Reader. LC 85-15302. 400p. (Orig.). 1986. pap. 16.95 (ISBN 0-88344-516-6). Orbis Bks.

Ferm, Robert L., ed. Issues in American Protestantism: A Documentary History from the Puritans to the Present. 15.25 (ISBN 0-8446-2052-1). Peter Smith.

Ferm, Vergilius. An Encyclopedia of Religion. LC 75-36508. 844p. 1976. Repr. of 1945 ed. lib. bdg. 55.00x (ISBN 0-8371-8638-2, FEEOR). Greenwood.

--Philosophy Beyond the Classroom. 411p. 1974. 12.95 (ISBN 0-8158-0314-1). Chris Mass.

--Toward an Expansive Christian Theology. LC 64-16359. 201p. 1964. 5.95 (ISBN 0-8022-0496-1). Philos Lib.

--What Can We Believe. 1952. 5.95 (ISBN 0-8022-0497-X). Philos Lib.

Ferm, Vergilius, ed. Encyclopedia of Morals. LC 70-90504. Repr. of 1956 ed. lib. bdg. 40.00x (ISBN 0-8371-2138-8, FEEM). Greenwood.

--Encyclopedia of Religion. LC 62-18535. 86p. 1962. 19.95 (ISBN 0-8022-0490-2). Philos Lib.

Ferm, Vergilius T., ed. Contemporary American Theology. LC 78-86749. (Essay Index Reprint Ser). 1933. 21.50 (ISBN 0-8369-1181-4). Ayer Co Pubs.

--Forgotten Religions. facs. ed. LC 70-128240. (Essay Index Reprint Ser). 1950. 22.00 (ISBN 0-8369-1922-X). Ayer Co Pubs.

--Religion in the Twentieth Century. Repr. of 1948 ed. lib. bdg. 22.50x (ISBN 0-8371-2290-2, FERT). Greenwood.

--Religion in Transition. facs. ed. LC 68-29204. (Essay Index Reprint Ser). 1937. 15.50 (ISBN 0-8369-0074-X). Ayer Co Pubs.

Ferm, Virgiulius. Protestant Credo. 1953. 5.95 (ISBN 0-8022-0494-5). Philos Lib.

Ferme, Deane W., ed. Restoring the Kingdom. LC 83-82671. 226p. 1984. pap. 11.95 (ISBN 0-913757-06-3). Rose Sharon Pr.

Fern, Deane W., ed. Restoring the Kingdom. 240p. (Orig.). 1984. pap. text ed. 10.95 (ISBN 0-913757-06-3, Pub. by New Era Bks). Paragon Hse.

Fern, Vergilus. Concise Dictionary of Religion. 1956. 7.95 (ISBN 0-8022-0488-0). Philos Lib.

Fernandez, D. S. Los Falsos Testigos De Jehova. 46p. 1985. pap. 1.25 (ISBN 0-311-06351-9). Casa Bautista.

Fernandez, David, jt. auth. see Hamilton, Gavin.

Fernandez, Domingo. El Mormonismo Revelacion Divina o Invencion Humana. 32p. 1984. pap. 1.00 (ISBN 0-311-05762-4). Casa Bautista.

--Por Que Guardamos el Domingo? 87p. 1984. pap. 2.00 (ISBN 0-311-05603-2). Casa Bautista.

Fernandez, Domingo S. Una Interpretacion Del Apocalipsis. (Span.). 234p. 1985. pap. 3.50 (ISBN 0-311-04312-7). Casa Bautista.

Fernandez, James W. Bwiti: An Ethnography of the Religious Imagination in Africa. LC 81-47125. (Illus.). 708p. 1982. 97.50x (ISBN 0-691-09390-3); pap. 28.00x LPE (ISBN 0-691-10122-1). Princeton U Pr.

Fernandez, Manuel. Religion y Revolucion en Cuba. (Realidades Ser.). (Span., Illus.). 250p. 1984. pap. 14.95 (ISBN 0-917049-00-4). Saeta.

Fernandez, Sergio, tr. see Ziglar, Zig.

Fernando, Ajith. The Christian's Attitude Toward World Religions. 160p. (Orig.). 1987. pap. 5.95 (ISBN 0-8423-0292-1). Tyndale.

--Leadership Lifestyles: A Study of 1 Timothy. (Living Studies). 224p. 1985. pap. 6.95 (ISBN 0-8423-2130-6); leader's guide 2.95 (ISBN 0-8423-2131-4). Tyndale.

Fernando, Antony & Swidler, Leonard. Buddhism Made Plain: An Introduction for Christians & Jews. LC 84-18880. 176p. (Orig.). 1985. pap. 9.95 (ISBN 0-88344-198-5). Orbis Bks.

Fernea, Elizabeth W. & Bezirgan, Basima Q., eds. Middle Eastern Muslim Women Speak. (Illus.). 452p. 1977. 23.50x (ISBN 0-292-75033-1); pap. 12.50x (ISBN 0-292-75041-2). U of Tex Pr.

Ferntheil, Carol. Bible Adventures Basic Bible Reader. 128p. 1985. pap. 4.95 (2757). Standard Pub.

Ferntheil, Carol, ed. Songs of Cheer. (Illus.). 16p. (Orig.). 1979. pap. 0.85 (ISBN 0-87239-345-3, 7948). Standard Pub.

Ferrar, William J. The Early Christian Books. 1919. Repr. 20.00 (ISBN 0-8274-2211-3). R West.

--The Early Christian Books: A Short Introduction to Christian Literature to the Middle of the Second Century. 1979. Repr. of 1919 ed. lib. bdg. 20.00 (ISBN 0-8495-1637-4). Arden Lib.

Ferrara, J. A. Living Love. (Illus.). 142p. 1961. 9.45 (ISBN 0-933961-04-9). Mystic Jhamom.

Ferrari, Raffaella, tr. see Meredith, Peter & Tailby, John.

Ferraro, John. Ten Series of Meditations on the Mysteries of the Rosary. (Illus., Orig.). 1964. 5.00 (ISBN 0-8198-0157-7); pap. 4.00 (ISBN 0-8198-0158-5). Dghtrs St Paul.

Ferrarotti, Franco. A Theology for Nonbelievers: Post-Christian & Post-Marxist Reflections. LC 86-10782. (Studies in Social Thought: Polity & Civil Society). Tr. of Una Teologia per Atei. 208p. 1987. text ed. 21.50x (ISBN 0-8046-9401-X, 9401). Assoc Faculty Pr.

Ferre, Frederick. Language, Logic, & God. LC 81-27305. viii, 184p. 1987. pap. text ed. 10.00 (ISBN 0-226-24457-1, Midway Reprint). U of Chicago Pr.

Ferre, Frederick P. & Mataragnon, Rita H., eds. God & Global Justice: Religion & Poverty in an Unequal World. LC 84-26538. (God Ser.). 224p. (Orig.). 1985. text ed. 21.95 (ISBN 0-913757-36-5, Pub. by New Era Bks.); pap. text ed. 12.95 (ISBN 0-913757-37-3, Pub. by New Era Bks.). Paragon Hse.

Ferre, Nels. The Christian Understanding of God. LC 78-12234. 1979. Repr. of 1951 ed. lib. bdg. 22.50x (ISBN 0-313-21183-3, FECU). Greenwood.

Ferre, Nels F. Christianity & Society. facs. ed. LC 78-117791. (Essay Index Reprint Ser). 1950. 19.00 (ISBN 0-8369-1924-6). Ayer Co Pubs.

--Evil & the Christian Faith. facsimile ed. LC 71-134075. (Essay Index Reprints - Reason & the Christian Faith Ser.: Vol. 2). Repr. of 1947 ed. 18.00 (ISBN 0-8369-2393-6). Ayer Co Pubs.

--Faith & Reason. facsimile ed. LC 78-142626. (Essay Index Reprints - Reason & the Christian Faith Ser.: Vol. 1). Repr. of 1946 ed. 19.00 (ISBN 0-8369-2392-8). Ayer Co Pubs.

--The Finality of Faith, & Christianity Among the World Religions. LC 78-11979. 1979. Repr. of 1963 ed. lib. bdg. 22.50x (ISBN 0-313-21182-5, FEFF). Greenwood.

--Swedish Contributions to Modern Theology: With Special Reference to Lundensian Thought. 1967. lib. bdg. 17.50x (ISBN 0-88307-092-8). Gannon.

Ferreira, M. Jamie. Doubt & Religious Commitment: The Role of the Will in Newman's Thought. 1980. 29.95x (ISBN 0-19-826654-5). Oxford U Pr.

Ferreira, Ruth V., tr. see Getz, Gene.

Ferreira-Ibarra, Dario C., ed. The Canon Law Collection of the Library of Congress: A General Bibliography with Selective Annotations. LC 81-607964. (Illus.). xiv, 210p. 1981. 11.00 (ISBN 0-8444-0367-9). Lib Congress.

Ferrell, Frank, et al. Trevor's Place: The Story of the Boy Who Brings Hope to the Homeless. LC 84-48768. (Illus.). 138p. 1985. 12.45 (ISBN 0-06-062531-7, HarpR). Har-Row.

Ferrell, John & Ferrell, MaryAnn. Coaching Flag Football. 56p. 1980. pap. 3.25x (ISBN 0-88035-027-X). Human Kinetics.

Ferrell, MaryAnn, jt. auth. see Ferrell, John.

Ferrer, Cornelio M. Pastor to the Rural Philippines: an Autobiography. 1974. wrps. 2.50x (ISBN 0-686-18697-4). Cellar.

Ferrerio, Giovanni. Ferrerii Historia Abbatum De Kynlos. LC 78-168018. (Bannatyne Club, Edinburgh. Publications: No. 63). Repr. of 1839 ed. 15.00 (ISBN 0-404-52774-4). AMS Pr.

Ferrero, Guglielmo. Peace & War. facs. ed. Pritchard, B., tr. LC 69-18927. (Essay Index Reprint Ser). 1933. 18.00 (ISBN 0-8369-0041-3). Ayer Co Pubs.

Ferretti, Paolo A. Estetica Gregoriana. LC 77-5498. (Music Reprint Ser.). 1977. Repr. of 1934 ed. lib. bdg. 45.00 (ISBN 0-306-77414-3). Da Capo.

Ferrier, James A., jt. auth. see Durfey, Thomas C.

Ferrin, Martha. Moments with Martha. LC 83-60477. 1983. pap. text ed. 2.50 (ISBN 0-932050-18-2). New Puritan.

Ferris, B. G. Mormons at Home. LC 70-134395. Repr. of 1856 ed. 24.00 (ISBN 0-404-08437-0). AMS Pr.

--Utah & the Mormons. LC 77-134394. Repr. of 1856 ed. 27.00 (ISBN 0-404-08436-2). AMS Pr.

Ferris, Theodore P. Prayers. 1981. 6.95 (ISBN 0-8164-0483-6, HarpR). Har-Row.

--This Is the Day: Selected Sermons. 2nd ed. LC 76-39640. 368p. 1980. pap. 10.00 (ISBN 0-911658-16-5). Yankee Bks.

Ferrone, Frank, jt. auth. see Baker, Thomas.

Ferrucci, Piero. What We May Be: Techniques for Psychological & Spiritual Growth. LC 81-51107. (Illus.). 256p. 1982. 6.95 (ISBN 0-87477-262-1). J P Tarcher.

Ferry, Anne D. Milton & the Miltonic Dryden. LC 68-25608. 1968. 16.50x (ISBN 0-674-57576-8). Harvard U Pr.

Ferster, J. Chaucer on Interpretation. LC 84-23188. 194p. 1985. 29.95 (ISBN 0-521-26661-0). Cambridge U Pr.

Fesperman, Francis I. From Torah to Apocalypse: An Introduction to the Bible. 334p. 1983. pap. text ed. 15.25 (ISBN 0-8191-3555-0). U Pr of Amer.

Fesquet, Henri. Has Rome Converted. Salemson, Harold J., tr. 1968. 9.50 (ISBN 0-685-11959-9). Heineman.

Fessio, Joseph, ed. see Von Balthasar, Hans U.

Festugiere, A. J. Freedom & Civilization among the Greeks. Brannan, P. T., tr. from Fr. & intro. by. (Princeton Theological Monograph: No. 10). Tr. of Liberte et Civilisation chez les Grecs. (Orig.). 1987. pap. price not set (ISBN 0-915138-98-0). Pickwick.

Festugiere, Andre-Jean. Personal Religion among the Greeks. (Sather Classical Lecture Ser.: No. 26). 186p. 1984. Repr. of 1954 ed. lib. bdg. 25.00 (ISBN 0-313-23209-1, FERG). Greenwood.

Fetterhoff, Dean. Dynamics of Evangelism. pap. 1.00 (ISBN 0-88469-019-9). BMH Bks.

--The Making of a Man of God: Studies in I & II Timothy. pap. 4.95 (ISBN 0-88469-030-X). BMH Bks.

Fettke, Steven M. Messages to a Nation in Crisis: An Introduction to the Prophecy of Jeremiah. LC 82-19997. (Illus.). 72p. (Orig.). 1983. pap. text ed. 7.75 (ISBN 0-8191-2839-2). U Pr of Amer.

Feucht, O. E. Everyone a Minister. 160p. pap. 2.95 (ISBN 0-570-03184-2, 12-2587). Concordia.

Feucht, Oscar E. Guidelines for Women's Groups in the Congregation. 1981. pap. 3.95 (ISBN 0-570-03828-6, 12-2793). Concordia.

Feucht, Oscar E., ed. see Norden, Rudolph F.

Feuchtwanger, Lion. Josephus: A Historical Romance. LC 32-28823. (Temple Bks). 1972. pap. 12.95 (ISBN 0-689-70345-7, T25). Atheneum.

Feuer, A. C. Tehillim: Psalms, 2 vols. 1985. 39.95 (ISBN 0-317-38548-8); pap. 29.95 (ISBN 0-317-38549-6). Mesorah Pubns.

Feuer, Avrohom C. Tashlich. (Art Scroll Mesorah Ser.). 64p. 1979. 6.95 (ISBN 0-89906-158-3); pap. 4.95 (ISBN 0-89906-159-1). Mesorah Pubns.

Feuer, Lewis S. Psychoanalysis & Ethics. LC 73-1433. 134p. 1973. Repr. of 1955 ed. lib. bdg. 45.00x (ISBN 0-8371-6795-7, FEPE). Greenwood.

Feuerbach, Ludwig. Essence of Christianity. pap. 7.95x (ISBN 0-06-130011-X, TB11, Torch). Har-Row.

--Essence of Christianity. Eliot, George, tr. 1958. 18.25 (ISBN 0-8446-2055-6). Peter Smith.

--The Essence of Christianity. Waring, E. Graham & Strothmann, F. W., eds. LC 57-8650. (Milestones of Thought Ser.). 1975. pap. 3.45 (ISBN 0-8044-6145-7). Ungar.

--Thoughts on Death & Immortality: From the Pages of a Thinker, along with an Appendix of Theological Satirical Epigrams, Edited by One of His Friends. Massey, James A., tr. from Ger. LC 80-25259. 263p. 1980. 33.00x (ISBN 0-520-04051-1); pap. 6.95 (ISBN 0-520-04062-7, CAL 486). U of Cal Pr.

Feuerlight, M. M. Where the Jews Fail. 1984. lib. bdg. 79.95 (ISBN 0-87700-569-9). Revisionist Pr.

Feuerstein, Georg. Bhagavad Gita: An Introduction. LC 82-42702. 191p. 1983. pap. 6.75 (ISBN 0-8356-0575-2, Quest). Theos Pub Hse.

--Crazy Wisdom. 140p. 1987. pap. 7.95 (ISBN 0-941255-37-9). Integral Pub.

--The Essence of Yoga. LC 75-42897. 1976. pap. 3.95 (ISBN 0-394-17902-1, E671, Ever). Grove.

Feuerstein, Georg, ed. see John, Da F.

Feuillet, Andre. Jesus & His Mother. Maluf, Leonard, tr. from Fr. LC 84-6790. (Studies in Scripture Ser.: Vol. I). Tr. of Jesus et sa Mere. 266p. (Orig.). 1984. pap. 19.95 (ISBN 0-932506-27-5). St Bedes Pubns.

Feunte, Tomas de La see De La Fuente, Tomas.

Feuser, W. F., tr. see Mbiti, John S.

Fever, Avrohom C. Tehillim (Psalms, 3 vols. Incl. Vol. 1. Psalms 1-30. 368p. 1977. (ISBN 0-89906-050-1); pap. (ISBN 0-89906-051-X); Vol. 2. Psalms 31-55. 352p. 1978. (ISBN 0-89906-052-8); pap. (ISBN 0-89906-053-6); Vol. 3. Psalms 56-85. 384p. 1979. (ISBN 0-89906-054-4); pap. (ISBN 0-89906-055-2). (Art Scroll Tanach Ser.). 15.95 ea.; pap. 12.95 ea. Mesorah Pubns.

Fewkes, Jesse W. Hopi Snake Ceremonies: An Eyewitness Account. LC 86-1127. (Bureau of American Ethnology Ser.). (Illus.). 160p. 1986. Repr. of 1897 ed. 16.95 (ISBN 0-936755-00-8). Avanyu Pub.

Fewkes, Jesse W. & Owens, John G. A Few Summer Ceremonials at the Tusayon Pueblos: Natal Ceremonies of the Hopi Indians,& a Report on the Present Condition of a Ruin in Arizona Called Casa Grande. LC 76-21217. (A Journal of American Ethnology & Archaeology: Vol. 2). 1977. Repr. of 1892 ed. 30.00 (ISBN 0-404-58042-4). AMS Pr.

Fewkes, Jesse W., et al. The Snake Ceremonials at Walpi. LC 76-17497. (A Journal of American Ethnology & Archaeology: Vol. 4). Repr. of 1894 ed. 25.00 (ISBN 0-404-58044-0). AMS Pr.

Fewkes, Jessie W. & Gilman, Benjamin I. A Few Summer Ceremonials at Zuni Pueblo: Zuni Melodies, Reconnaissance of Ruins in or Near the Zuni Reservation. LC 76-21216. (A Journal of American Ethnology & Archaeology: Vol. 1). Repr. of 1891 ed. 25.00 (ISBN 0-404-58041-6). AMS Pr.

Fey, Harold E., ed. How My Mind Has Changed. 7.00 (ISBN 0-8446-2056-4). Peter Smith.

Fey, Harold E. & Frakes, Margaret, eds. The Christian Century Reader: Representative Articles, Editorials, & Poems Selected from More Than Fifty Years of the Christian Century. LC 72-331. (Essay Index Reprint Ser.). Repr. of 1962 ed. 24.50 (ISBN 0-8369-2786-9). Ayer Co Pubs.

Fey, William R. Faith & Doubt: The Unfolding of Newman's Thought on Certainty. LC 75-38101. xxii, 229p. 1976. 22.95x (ISBN 0-915762-02-1). Patmos Pr.

Feyerabend, Paul. Against Method. (Illus.). 1978. pap. 7.95 (ISBN 0-8052-7008-6, Pub by NLB). Schocken.

Feys, J. Sri Aurobindo's Treatment of Hindu Myth. 1984. 7.50x (ISBN 0-8364-1109-9, Pub. by Mukhopadhyay India). South Asia Bks.

Ffinch, Michael. G. K. Chesterton: A Biography. 1987. 18.95 (ISBN 0-06-252576-X, HarpR). Har-Row.

Ffrench-Beytagh, Gonville. A Glimpse of Glory. 128p. 1987. pap. 7.95 (ISBN 0-8091-2903-5). Paulist Pr.

Fiacc, Saint, jt. auth. see Patrick, Saint.

Fiand, Barbara. Releasement: Spirituality for Ministry. 112p. 1987. 11.95 (ISBN 0-8245-0813-0). Crossroad NY.

Fichte, J. G. Fichte's Critique of All Revelation. Green, G. D., tr. LC 77-77756. 1978. 34.50 (ISBN 0-521-21707-5). Cambridge U Pr.

Fichte, Johann G. The Vocation of Man. Smith, William, tr. LC 56-44104. 1956. pap. 5.99 scp (ISBN 0-672-60220-2, LLA50). Bobbs.

--Vocation of Man. Smith, William, tr. from Ger. 190p. 1965. 12.95 (ISBN 0-87548-074-8); pap. 5.95 (ISBN 0-87548-075-6). Open Court.

Fichter, Joseph H. Autobiographies of Conversion. LC 87-1634. (Studies in Religion & Society: Vol. 17). 232p. 1987. 49.95 (ISBN 0-88946-857-5). E Mellen.

--Dynamics of a City Church. 26.50 (ISBN 0-405-10829-X, 11836). Ayer Co Pubs.

--Healing Ministries: Conversations on the Spiritual Dimensions of Health Care. 224p. 1986. pap. 9.95 (ISBN 0-8091-2807-1). Paulist Pr.

--The Holy Family of Father Moon. LC 84-82549. 155p. (Orig.). 1985. pap. 7.95 (ISBN 0-934134-13-8, Leaven Pr). Sheed & Ward MO.

--The Rehabilitation of Clergy Alcoholics: Ardent Spirits Subdued. LC 80-28447. 203p. 1982. 26.95 (ISBN 0-89885-009-6). Human Sci Pr.

--Religion & Pain: The Spiritual Dimensions of Health Care. 128p. 1981. 9.95 (ISBN 0-8245-0102-0). Crossroad NY.

--Religion As an Occupation. (Orig.). 1966. pap. 3.95x (ISBN 0-268-00229-0). U of Notre Dame Pr.

--Social Relations in the Urban Parish. LC 54-11207. pap. 68.00 (ISBN 0-317-07856-9, 2020061). Bks Demand UMI.

Fichtl, Frank. The Great Day of the Lord. 256p. 1986. 12.95 (ISBN 0-89962-510-X). Todd & Honeywell.

Fichtner, Joseph. Proclaim His Word: Homiletic Themes for Sundays & Holy Days - Cycle C, Vol. 1. new ed. LC 73-5726. 238p. (Orig.). 1973. pap. 3.95 (ISBN 0-8189-0274-4). Alba.

--Proclaim His Word: Homiletic Themes for Sundays & Holy Days-Cycle A, Vol. 2. new ed. LC 73-5726. 239p. (Orig.). 1974. pap. 4.95 (ISBN 0-8189-0292-2). Alba.

--To Stand & Speak for Christ. LC 81-10975. 166p. 1981. pap. 6.95 (ISBN 0-8189-0415-1). Alba.

Fick, Mike & Richardson, Jim. Control Your Thoughts. 1983. pap. 1.75 (ISBN 0-911739-01-7). Abbott Loop.

Ficken, Carl. God's Story & Modern Literature: Reading Fiction in Community. LC 84-48705. 176p. 1985. pap. 9.95 (ISBN 0-8006-1823-8, 1-1823). Fortress.

Fickett, Harold, jt. auth. see Rover, Dave.

Fickett, Harold L., Jr. Keep on Keeping on. LC 75-23517. 160p. (Orig.). 1977. pap. 3.50 (ISBN 0-8307-0371-3, S311100). Regal.

Fickett, John D. Confess It, Possess It: Faith's Formula? 40p. 1984. 1.95 (ISBN 0-934421-04-8). Presby Renewal Pubns.

Fiday, Beverly. Jeff's Happy Day. (Happy Day Bks.). (Illus.). 24p. 1984. 1.59 (ISBN 0-87239-740-8, 3710). Standard Pub.

Field, A. N. The Evolution Hoax Exposed. 1971. pap. 3.00 (ISBN 0-89555-049-0). TAN Bks Pubs.

Field, Claud H. Jewish Legends of the Middle Ages. LC 76-48141. 1976. Repr. of 1930 ed. lib. bdg. 25.00 (ISBN 0-8414-6771-4). Folcroft.

Field, David. Marriage Personalities. 192p. (Orig.). 1986. pap. 5.95 (ISBN 0-89081-476-7). Harvest Hse.

Field, Faye. Women Who Encountered Jesus. LC 81-65798. 1982. 4.50 (ISBN 0-8054-5182-X). Broadman.

Field, Filip. W. Norman Cooper - a Prophet for Our Time. LC 79-52443. 1979. 7.50 (ISBN 0-87516-417-X); pap. 4.50 (ISBN 0-87516-372-6). De Vorss.

Field, Frank M. Where Jesus Walked: Through the Holy Land with the Master. Davis, Moshe, ed. LC 77-70681. (America & the Holy Land Ser.). (Illus.). 1977. Repr. of 1951 ed. lib. bdg. 20.00x (ISBN 0-405-10244-5). Ayer Co Pubs.

Field, Frederick V. From Right to Left: An Autobiography. LC 82-23407. 336p. 1983. 16.95 (ISBN 0-88208-162-4); pap. 8.95 (ISBN 0-88208-161-6). Lawrence Hill.

Field, G. Memoirs, Incidents, Reminiscences of the Early History of the New Church in Michigan, Indiana, Illinois, & Adjacent States, & Canada. LC 70-134423. 1972. Repr. of 1879 ed. 27.00 (ISBN 0-404-08463-X). AMS Pr.

Field, John. A Godly Exhortation. Incl. Sermon Preached at Pawles Crosse, 3 November 1577. White, Thomas. Repr. of 1578 ed. Repr. of 1583 ed. 28.00 (ISBN 0-384-15680-0). Johnson Repr.

Field, Kent A. Test Your Salvation. 0.60 (ISBN 0-89137-531-7). Quality Pubns.

Field, Margaret J. Religion & Medicine of the Ga People. LC 76-44718. 1977. Repr. of 1937 ed. 37.50 (ISBN 0-404-15923-0). AMS Pr.

Field, Marilyn J. The Comparative Politics of Birth Control: Determinants of Policy Variation & Change in the Developed Nations. (Landmark Dissertations in Women's Studies). (Illus.). 320p. 1983. 42.95 (ISBN 0-03-069527-9). Praeger.

Field, Rachel. Prayer for a Child. LC 44-47191. (Illus.). 32p. 1968. 8.95 (ISBN 0-02-735190-4). Macmillan.

Field, Stephen, tr. from Chinese. Tian Wen: A Chinese Book of Origins. LC 86-12737. 128p. (Orig.). 1986. 22.95 (ISBN 0-8112-1010-3); pap. 8.95 (ISBN 0-8112-1011-1, NDP624). New Directions.

Fielding-Hall, A. The Theory of the World Soul. (Illus.). 161p. 1985. Repr. of 1910 ed. 88.85 (ISBN 0-89901-235-3). Found Class Reprints.

Fielding-Hall, Harold. The Inward Light. LC 78-72431. Repr. of 1908 ed. 27.00 (ISBN 0-404-17294-6). AMS Pr.

Fields, Doug, jt. auth. see Burns, Jim.

Fields, Harvey J. With All Your Heart: Bechol Levavcha, 2 vols. (Illus.). 1977. Set. 10.00 (ISBN 0-8074-0197-8, 142611). UAHC.

Fields, Mary E. Foundations of Truth. LC 80-67931. 275p. 1980. 10.00 (ISBN 0-87516-423-4). De Vorss.

Fields, Rick, et al. Chop Wood, Carry Water: A Guide to Finding Spiritual Fulfillment in Everyday Life. LC 84-23942. 304p. 1984. pap. 11.95 (ISBN 0-87477-209-5). J P Tarcher.

Fields, Rona M. Northern Ireland: Society under Siege. LC 80-80316. 267p. 1980. pap. 5.95 (ISBN 0-87855-806-3). Transaction Bks.

Fields, Wilbur. Exploring Exodus. LC 78-301089. (The Bible Study Textbook Ser.). (Illus.). 1977. 18.95 (ISBN 0-89900-006-1). College Pr Pub.

--The Glorious Church-Ephesians. 2nd ed. LC 71-1065. (The Bible Study Textbook Ser.). (Illus.). 1960. 10.60 (ISBN 0-89900-040-1). College Pr Pub.

--New Testament Backgrounds. 2nd ed. (Bible Student Study Guides Ser). 1977. pap. 5.95 (ISBN 0-89900-156-4). College Pr Pub.

--Philippians, Colossians, Philemon. LC 78-8763. (The Bible Study Textbook Ser.). (Illus.). 1969. 10.60 (ISBN 0-89900-041-X). College Pr Pub.

--Thinking Through Thessalonians. LC 77-1794. (The Bible Study Textbook Ser.). (Illus.). 1963. 12.20 (ISBN 0-89900-042-8). College Pr Pub.

Fields, Wilbur, ed. see Smith, William.

Fiensy, David A. Prayers Alleged to Be Jewish: An Examination of the Constitutiones Apostolorum. (Brown Judaic Studies). 1985. 29.95 (ISBN 0-89130-795-8, 14-00-65); pap. 21.95 (ISBN 0-89130-796-6). Scholars Pr GA.

Fiering, Norman. Jonathan Edward's Moral Thought & Its British Context. LC 80-26755. (Institute of Early American History & Culture Ser.). xi, 391p. 1981. 32.50x (ISBN 0-8078-1473-3). U of NC Pr.

--Moral Philosophy at Seventeenth-Century Harvard: A Discipline in Transition. LC 80-18282. (Institute of Early American History & Culture Ser.). xiii, 323p. 1981. 27.50x (ISBN 0-8078-1459-8). U of NC Pr.

Fierman, Floyd S. Guts & Ruts: The Jewish Pioneer on the Trail in the American Southwest. (Illus.). 1985. 20.00 (ISBN 0-88125-061-9). Ktav.

--Roots & Boots: From Crypto-Jew in New Spain to Community Leader in the American Southwest. 1987. 20.00 (ISBN 0-88125-114-3). KTAV.

Fierro, Alfredo. The Militant Gospel: A Critical Introduction to Political Theologies. Drury, John, tr. from Span. LC 77-1652. Orig. Title: El Evangelio Beligerente. 459p. (Orig.). 1977. pap. 3.48 (ISBN 0-88344-311-2). Orbis Bks.

Fiester, Mark. Look for Me in Heaven: The Life of John Lewis Dyer. LC 80-14913. (Illus.). 400p. 1980. 19.95 (ISBN 0-87108-564-X). Pruett.

Fife, Alta, jt. auth. see Fife, Austin.

Fife, Austin & Fife, Alta. Saints of Sage & Saddle: Folklore Among the Mormons. 375p. 1980. pap. 14.95 (ISBN 0-87480-180-X). U of Utah Pr.

Fife, Robert H. Young Luther. LC 79-131040. 1970. Repr. of 1928 ed. 19.50 (ISBN 0-404-02385-1). AMS Pr.

Figgis, John B. Keswick from Within. Dayton, Donald W., ed. (The Higher Christian Ser.). 192p. 1985. 25.00 (ISBN 0-8240-6417-8). Garland Pub.

Figgis, John N. The Divine Right of Kings. 14.00 (ISBN 0-8446-0621-9). Peter Smith.

Figueras, P. Decorated Jewish Ossuaries. (Documenta et Monumenta Orientis Antiqui Ser.: No. 20). (Illus.). 119p. 1983. text ed. 39.95x (ISBN 90-04-06579-2, Pub. by EJ Brill Holland). Humanities.

Figueroa Y Miranda, Miguel. La Pintura Cristiana En los Tres Primeros Siglos. (UPREX, Humanidades: No. 12). pap. 1.85 (ISBN 0-8477-0012-7). U of PR Pr.

Figurski, Leszek. Finality & Intelligence. LC 78-62252. 1978. pap. text ed. 11.25 (ISBN 0-8191-0565-1). U Pr of Amer.

Filbeck, David. The First Fifty Years. LC 80-65966. 336p. 1980. pap. cancelled (ISBN 0-89900-060-6). College Pr Pub.

--Social Context & Proclamation: A Socio-Cognitive Study in Proclaiming the Gospel Cross-Culturally. LC 84-28539. (Illus.). 192p. 1985. pap. text ed. 8.95X (ISBN 0-87808-199-2). William Carey Lib.

Filby, P. Gwyn. Stories of Jesus, Tell Them to Me. 200p. 1986. 45.00x (ISBN 0-947939-01-6, Pub. by Elmcrest UK). State Mutual Bk.

--Tell Them to Me. 200p. 1986. 40.00x (ISBN 0-947939-01-6, Pub. by Elmcrest Uk). State Mutual Bk.

Filipi, Emily. One Hundred & One Word Puzzles on the Bible. LC 84-21445. 1985. pap. 2.95 (ISBN 0-8054-9110-4). Broadman.

--One Hundred Word Puzzles on the Bible. LC 81-68367. 1982. pap. 2.95 (ISBN 0-8054-9107-4). Broadman.

--Scripture Facts the Easy Way. (Quiz & Puzzle Books). 1980. pap. 1.95 (ISBN 0-8010-3491-4). Baker Bk.

Filley, Dorothy M. Recapturing Wisdom's Valley: The Watervliet Shaker Heritage, 1775-1975. Richmond, Mary L., ed. LC 75-27133. (Illus.). 128p. 1975. 10.00 (ISBN 0-89062-010-5, Pub. by Town of Colonie); pap. 5.00 (ISBN 0-89062-029-6). Pub Ctr Cult Res.

Fillingham, Patricia. John Calvin. (Illus.). 42p. 1983. pap. 5.00 (ISBN 0-942292-04-9). Warthog Pr.

Fillmore, Charles. Charles Fillmore Concordance. 1975. 5.95 (ISBN 0-87159-015-8). Unity School.

--Christian Healing. 1909. 5.95 (ISBN 0-87159-017-4). Unity School.

--Curacion Cristiana. LC 84-52152. Tr. of Christian Healing. (Span.). 160p. 5.95 (ISBN 0-87159-020-4). Unity School.

--Dynamics for Living. 1967. 5.95 (ISBN 0-87159-025-5). Unity School.

--Guarda una Cuaresma Verdadera. (Span.). 214p. 1983. 5.95 (ISBN 0-87159-048-4). Unity School.

--Jesucristo Sana (Jesus Christ Heals) (Span.). 200p. 1984. 5.95 (ISBN 0-87159-071-9). Unity School.

--Jesus Christ Heals. 1939. 5.95 (ISBN 0-87159-070-0). Unity School.

--Keep a True Lent. 1982. 5.95 (ISBN 0-87159-076-X). Unity School.

--Mysteries of Genesis. 1936. 5.95 (ISBN 0-87159-104-9). Unity School.

--Mysteries of John. 1946. 5.95 (ISBN 0-87159-105-7). Unity School.

--Revealing Word. 1959. 5.95 (ISBN 0-87159-137-5). Unity School.

Fillmore, Charles & Fillmore, Cora. Teach Us to Pray. 1976. 5.95 (ISBN 0-87159-152-9). Unity School.

Fillmore, Cora, jt. auth. see Fillmore, Charles.

Fillmore, Cora D. Christ Enthroned in Man. 1981. 4.95. Unity School.

Fillmore, Donna, ed. Leading Children in Worship, Vol. 1, 2, 3. 216p. 1982. Vol. 2. pap. 7.95 each (ISBN 0-8341-0767-8). Vol. 1 (ISBN 0-8341-0677-9). Vol. 3 (ISBN 0-8341-0676-0). Beacon Hill.

Fillmore, Lowell. Health, Wealth & Happiness. 1964. 5.95 (ISBN 0-87159-055-7). Unity School.

Fillmore, Myrtle. Come Dejar Que Dios Te Ayude. Tr. of How to Let God Help You. 1984. 5.95 (ISBN 0-87159-019-0). Unity School.

--How to Let God Help You. 1956. 5.95 (ISBN 0-87159-057-3). Unity School.

Filmore, Charles. Descubre Tu Poder Interno. LC 81-69933. Orig. Title: Discover the Power Within You. (Eng.). 448p. 1983. 5.95 (ISBN 0-87159-026-3). Unity School.

Filson, F. V., jt. ed. see Wright, G. Ernest.

Filson, Floyd V. John. LC 59-10454. (Layman's Bible Commentary Ser: Vol. 19). 1963. pap. 4.95 (ISBN 0-8042-3079-X). John Knox.

--A New Testament History: The Story of the Emerging Church. LC 64-15360. (Illus.). 464p. 1964. 12.95 (ISBN 0-664-20525-9). Westminster.

--Yesterday: A Study of Hebrews in the Light of Chapter 13. LC 67-7015. (Studies in Biblical Theology: 2nd Ser., No. 4). 1967. pap. text ed. 10.00x (ISBN 0-8401-3054-6). A R Allenson.

Filson, Floyd V., jt. ed. see Wright, G. Ernest.

Filson, Wright. Atlas Historico Westminster de la Biblia. 134p. 1981. pap. 19.95 (ISBN 0-311-15030-6). Casa Bautista.

Finamore, John. Iamblichus & the Theory of the Vehicle of the Soul. (APA-American Classical Studies). 1985. pap. 12.95 (ISBN 0-89130-883-0, 40-04-14). Scholars Pr GA.

Financial Publishing Co. Staff. Daily Compounding Savings Certificate Tables: Five Percent to Ten Percent. 319p. 1982. pap. write for info. (ISBN 0-87600-582-2). Finan Pub.

Finazzo, Giancarlo. The Notion of Tao in Lao Tzu & Chuang Tsu. 240p. 1980. 11.95 (ISBN 0-89955-146-7, Pub. by Mei Ya China). Intl Spec Bk.

Finberg, H. P. Tavistock Abbey. LC 69-10850. (Illus.). 1969. Repr. of 1951 ed. 35.00x (ISBN 0-678-05597-1). Kelley.

Finch, John G. Nishkamakarma. LC 82-83498. (Orig.). 1982. pap. 8.50 (ISBN 0-9609928-0-4). Integ Pr.

Findeisen, Barbara. A Course in Miracles Concordance. 457p. 15.00 (ISBN 0-942494-45-8). Coleman Pub.

Findhorn Community. The Findhorn Garden. 1976. pap. 10.95 (ISBN 0-06-090520-4, CN520, PL). Har-Row.

Findlay, G. G. The Epistles of Paul the Apostle to the Thessalonians. (Thornapple Commentaries Ser.). 319p. 1982. pap. 9.95 (ISBN 0-8010-3503-1). Baker Bk.

Findlay, J. N., tr. see Hegel, G. W.

Findly, Ellison B., jt. ed. see Haddad, Yvonne Y.

Fine, Ellen S. Legacy of Night: The Literary Universe of Elie Wiesel. LC 81-14601. (Modern Jewish Literature & Culture Ser.). 276p. 1982. 44.50 (ISBN 0-87395-589-7); pap. 14.95 (ISBN 0-87395-590-0). State U NY Pr.

Fine, Helen. At Camp Kee Tov: Ethics for Jewish Juniors. (Illus.). text ed. 6.95 (ISBN 0-8074-0128-5, 121711). UAHC.

--G'Dee. (Illus.). 1958. text ed. 4.50 (ISBN 0-8074-0137-4, 123702). UAHC.

--G'Dee's Book of Holiday Fun. (Illus.). 1961. pap. 3.00 (ISBN 0-685-20737-4, 121701). UAHC.

Fine, Irene. Educating the New Jewish Woman: A Dynamic Approach. LC 85-51215. 80p. (Orig.). 1985. pap. 8.95 (ISBN 0-9608054-4-3). Womans Inst-Cont Jewish Ed.

Fine, Jo Renee & Wolfe, Gerard R. The Synagogues of New York's Lower East Side. LC 75-15126. (Illus.). 1978. 27.50 (ISBN 0-8147-2559-7). NYU Pr.

Fine, John V. The Bosnian Church: A Study of the Bosnian Church & Its Place in State & Society from the 13th to 15th Centuries. (East European Monographs: No. 10). 447p. 1975. 30.00x (ISBN 0-914710-03-6). East Eur Quarterly.

Fine, Lawrence, tr. see Safed.

Fine, Leon. Will the Real Israel Please Stand Up? 2nd ed. (Illus.). 278p. (Orig.). 1984. pap. 10.95 (ISBN 965-10-0003-1, Pub. by Massada Israel). Hermon.

Fine, Robert. Great Todays - Better Tomorrows. 1976. pap. 2.95 (ISBN 0-89367-001-4). Light & Life.

Finegan, Jack. The Archaeology of the New Testament: The Mediterranean World of the Early Christian Apostles. (Illus.). 400p. 1981. 40.00x (ISBN 0-86531-064-5). Westview.

--Archeology of the New Testament: The Life of Jesus & the Beginning of the Early Church. LC 69-18059. (Illus.). 1970. 60.00x (ISBN 0-691-03534-2); pap. 10.50x (ISBN 0-691-02000-0). Princeton U Pr.

--Light from the Ancient Past, 2 vols. 2nd ed. (Illus.). 1959. Vol. 1 2nd Ed. 52.50 (ISBN 0-691-03550-4); Vol. 1 2nd Edition. pap. 16.50 (ISBN 0-691-00207-X); Vol. 2. 50.00 (ISBN 0-691-03551-2); Vol. 2. pap. 15.50x (ISBN 0-691-00208-8); Set. 90.00 (ISBN 0-686-76901-5). Princeton U Pr.

Finegold, Julius J. & Thetford, William N., eds. Choose Once Again. LC 76-20363. (Illus.). 112p. 1981. 6.95 (ISBN 0-89087-413-1). Celestial Arts.

Fing, Wing F. Fuck, YES! A Guide to the Happy Acceptance of Everything. (Illus.). 270p. (Orig.). 1987. pap. 8.50 (ISBN 0-940183-21-8). Shepherd Bks.

Fingarette, Herbert. Confucius: The Secular As Sacred. 160p. 1972. pap. 6.95x (ISBN 0-06-131682-2, TB1682, Torch). Har-Row.

Finger, Alan & Guber, Lynda. Yoga Moves with Alan Finger. (Illus.). 160p. (Orig.). 1984. pap. 9.95 (ISBN 0-671-50064-3, Wallaby). S&S.

Finger, Seymour M. American Jewry During the Holocaust. 1984. pap. 14.95x (ISBN 0-9613537-3-2). Am Jewish Holo.

--American Jewry During the Holocaust. 412p. (Orig.). 1984. pap. text ed. 17.95 (ISBN 0-8419-7506-X). Holmes & Meier.

--Their Brother's Keepers: American Jewry & the Holocaust. 300p. 1988. text ed. 34.50x (ISBN 0-8419-1036-7). Holmes & Meier.

Finger, Thomas. Christian Theology: An Eschatological Approach, Vol. 1. 320p. 1985. text ed. 18.95 (ISBN 0-8407-7505-9). Nelson.

Fink, Benjamin. Life of John Kline. 7.95 (ISBN 0-87178-516-1). Brethren.

Fink, Reuben & Moshe, Davis, eds. America & Palestine: The Attitude of Official America & of the American People Toward the Rebuilding of Palestine As a Free & Democratic Jewish Commonwealth. LC 77-70680. (America & the Holy Land Ser.). 1977. Repr. of 1944 ed. lib. bdg. 40.00x (ISBN 0-405-10245-3). Ayer Co Pubs.

Finkel, Asher & Frizzell, Lawrence. Standing Before God: Studies on Prayer in Scripture & in Essays in Honor of John M. Oesterreicher. 1981. 39.50x (ISBN 0-87068-708-5). Ktav.

Finkel, Nosson. Chessed as an Expression of Emunah: A Schmuess. Kaminetsky, Joseph, ed. 0.50 (ISBN 0-914131-10-9, I30). Torah Umesorah.

Finkelstein, et al. Religions of Democracy. 1941. 9.50 (ISBN 0-8159-6708-X). Devin.

Finkelstein, Adrian. Your Past Lives & the Healing Process. 233p. (Orig.). 1985. pap. 9.95x (ISBN 0-87418-001-5). Coleman Pub.

--Your Past Lives & the Healing Process. 233p. (Orig.). 1985. pap. 9.95x. A Finkelstein.

Finkelstein, Jacob J., ed. see Speiser, Ephraim A.

Finkelstein, Louis. Akiba: Scholar, Saint & Martyr. LC 62-12354. (Temple Bks). 1970. pap. text ed. 6.95x (ISBN 0-689-70230-2, T11). Atheneum.

--Sifre on Deuteronomy. 1969. 25.00x (ISBN 0-685-31422-7, Pub. by Jewish Theol Seminary). Ktav.
--Social Responsibility in an Age of Revolution. 1971. 10.00x (ISBN 0-685-31421-9, Pub. by Jewish Theol Seminary). Ktav.

Finkelstein, Louis see Davies, W. D.

Finkelstein, Louis, ed. Thirteen Americans. LC 68-26190. (Essay & General Literature Index Reprint Ser.). 1969. Repr. of 1953 ed. 23.50x (ISBN 0-8046-0219-0, Pub by Kennikat). Assoc Faculty Pr.

Finkelstein, Louis & Katz, Steven, eds. Rab Saadia Gaon: Studies in His Honor. LC 79-7169. (Jewish Philosophy, Mysticism & History of Ideas Ser.). 1980. Repr. of 1944 ed. lib. bdg. 19.00x (ISBN 0-405-12250-0). Ayer Co Pubs.

Finkelstein, Louis, ed. see Kimchi, David B.

Finker, Kaja. Spiritualist Healers in Mexico: Successes & Failures of Alternative Therapies. 256p. 1984. 29.95 (ISBN 0-03-063912-3, C1156). Praeger.

Finkler, Kaja. Spiritualist Healers in Mexico: Successes & Failures of Alternative Therapeutics. (Illus.). 272p. 1983. text ed. 29.95x (ISBN 0-03-063912-3); pap. text ed. 14.95 (ISBN 0-89789-092-2). Bergin & Garvey.

Finks, P. David. Radical Vision of Saul Alinsky. (Orig.). 1984. pap. 9.95 (ISBN 0-8091-2608-7). Paulist Pr.

Finlan, Stephen. The Forgotten Teachings of Jesus. (Illus.). 49p. (Orig.). 1984. pap. 3.00 perfect bound (ISBN 0-9614275-0-7). Spiritual.
--The Forgotten Teachings of Jesus. rev. ed. (Illus.). 46p. 1985. pap. 4.50 (ISBN 0-9615301-1-1). Dilman Pr.

Finlayson, Michael G. Historians, Puritanism & the English Revolution: The Religious Factor in English Politics before & after the Interregnum. LC 83-215172. pap. 54.50 (2026454). Bks Demand UMI.

Finley, Harvey E. & Isbell, Charles D. Biblical Hebrew. 213p. 1975. pap. text ed. 13.95 (ISBN 0-8341-0350-8). Beacon Hill.

Finley, James. The Awakening Call. LC 84-72094. 160p. (Orig.). 1985. pap. 4.95 (ISBN 0-87793-278-6). Ave Maria.
--Merton's Palace of Nowhere. LC 78-58738. 160p. 1978. pap. 3.95 (ISBN 0-87793-159-3). Ave Maria.
--Your Future & You. LC 81-65228. (Illus.). 176p. (Orig.). 1981. pap. 4.50 (ISBN 0-87793-223-9); tchrs. ed. 2.25 (ISBN 0-87793-224-7). Ave Maria.

Finley, James, jt. auth. see Pennock, Michael.

Finley, James B. Sketches of Western Methodism: Biographical, Historical & Miscellaneous Illustrative of Pioneer Life. LC 79-83419. (Religion in America, Ser. 1). 1969. Repr. of 1954 ed. 30.00 (ISBN 0-405-00244-0). Ayer Co Pubs.

Finley, James F. Wake up & Preach. LC 85-26667. 111p. (Orig.). 1986. pap. 5.95 (ISBN 0-8189-0492-5). Alba.

Finley, Jean D., tr. see Perrin, Joseph-Marie.

Finley, Kathy, jt. auth. see Finley, Mitch.

Finley, Merrill. Christ & the Colonel. 120p. 1987. pap. write for info. (ISBN 0-911826-51-3). Am Atheist.

Finley, Mitch & Finley, Kathy. Christian Families in the Real World. 1984. pap. 8.95 (ISBN 0-88347-192-2). Thomas More.

Finley, Moses, ed. see Klima, Otakar.

Finley, Moses, ed. see Krauss, Samuel.

Finley, Tom. Good Clean Fun: Fifty Nifty Bible Games for Junior Highers. 112p. 1986. pap. 8.95 (ISBN 0-310-31251-5, 18389). Zondervan.
--The World Is Not Enough. Parrish, Annette, ed. LC 86-22049. 252p. (Orig.). (YA) 1986. pap. 4.25 (ISBN 0-8307-1151-1, S183329). Regal.

Finn, Daniel R. & Pemberton, Prentiss L. Toward a Christian Economic Ethic: Stewardship & Social Power. LC 83-25409. 266p. 1985. pap. 10.95 (ISBN 0-86683-876-7, 7919, HarpR). Har-Row.

Finn, Edward E. These Are My Rites: A Brief History of the Eastern Rites of Christianity. LC 79-24937. (Illus.). 104p. 1980. pap. 4.95 (ISBN 0-8146-1058-7). Liturgical Pr.

Finn, James, ed. Global Economics & Religion. 277p. 1983. 26.95 (ISBN 0-87855-477-7). Transaction Bks.

Finn, Virginia S. Pilgrim in the Parish: Spirituality for Lay Ministers. 208p. (Orig.). 1986. pap. 8.95 (ISBN 0-8091-2742-3). Paulist Pr.

Finnegan, Edward G. Children's Bible Stories. LC 75-18758. (Treasure House Bks). (Illus.). 256p. 1978. 7.95 (ISBN 0-8326-1803-9, 3602); deluxe ed. 8.95 (ISBN 0-686-66397-7). World Bible.
--Historias De la Biblia. LC 75-18758. (Treasure House Bks). (Span., Illus.). 1978. 9.95 (ISBN 0-8326-2601-5, 5180). World Bible.

Finnegan, Edward G., ed. Windsor Bible Dictionary. (Illus.). 1979. pap. 1.25 (ISBN 0-685-02398-2). World Bible.

Finnegan, Robert E. Christ & Satan: A Critical Edition. 169p. 1977. pap. text ed. 15.95x (ISBN 0-88920-041-6, Pub. by Wilfrid Laurier Canada); pap. text ed. 10.50 (ISBN 0-88920-040-8). Humanities.

Finnell, Kathy B., jt. auth. see Kishpaugh, Charles R.

Finney, Charles. Principles of Devotion. rev. ed. Parkhurst, Louis, ed. 288p. 1987. pap. 6.95 (ISBN 0-87123-873-X). Bethany Hse.

Finney, Charles & Parkhurst, Louis. Principles of Sanctification. rev. ed. 240p. 1986. pap. 5.95 (ISBN 0-87123-859-4). Bethany Hse.

Finney, Charles G. Answers to Prayer. Parkhurst, Louis G., Jr., ed. LC 83-12253. 122p. (Orig.). 1983. pap. 3.95 (ISBN 0-87123-296-0). Bethany Hse.
--The Autobiography of Charles G. Finney. Wessel, Helen S., ed. LC 77-2813. 1977. pap. 5.95 (ISBN 0-87123-010-0). Bethany Hse.
--Charles G. Finney: An Autobiography. 480p. 16.95 (ISBN 0-8007-0095-3). Revell.
--Charles G. Finney Memorial Library, 8 vols. 1975. Set. pap. 31.50 (ISBN 0-8254-2623-5). Kregel.
--Crystal Christianity: A Vital Guide to Personal Revival. Orig. Title: Lectures to Professing Christians. 330p. 1986. pap. 3.95 (ISBN 0-88368-171-4). Whitaker Hse.
--Finney on Revival. Shelhamer, E. E., ed. 128p. 1974. pap. 3.50 (ISBN 0-87123-151-4, 200151). Bethany Hse.
--Finney's Systematic Theology. LC 76-3500. Orig. Title: Finney's Lectures on Systematic Theology. 448p. 1976. pap. 9.95 (ISBN 0-87123-153-0, 210153). Bethany Hse.
--God's Love for a Sinning World. LC 66-19200. (Charles G. Finney Memorial Library). 122p. 1975. pap. 4.50 (ISBN 0-8254-2620-0). Kregel.
--Guilt of Sin. LC 65-25845. (Charles G. Finney Memorial Library). 124p. 1975. pap. 4.50 (ISBN 0-8254-2616-2). Kregel.
--The Heart of Truth: Finney's Outlines of Theology. LC 75-46128. Orig. Title: Skeletons of a Course of Theological Lectures. 256p. 1976. pap. 6.95 (ISBN 0-87123-226-X, 210226). Bethany Hse.
--How to Experience Revival. 143p. 1984. pap. text ed. 3.50 (ISBN 0-88368-140-4). Whitaker Hse.
--How to Experience Revival. 1986. write for info. (ISBN 0-8297-0798-0). Life Pubs Intl.
--Lectures to Professing Christians. (The Higher Christian Life Ser.). 348p. 1985. lib. bdg. 45.00 (ISBN 0-8240-6418-6). Garland Pub.
--Love Is Not a Special Way of Feeling. Orig. Title: Attributes of Love. 144p. 1963. pap. 3.50 (ISBN 0-87123-005-4, 200005). Bethany Hse.
--Prevailing Prayer. LC 65-25846. (Charles G. Finney Memorial Library). 1975. pap. 3.50 (ISBN 0-8254-2603-0). Kregel.
--Principles of Holiness. LC 83-25769. 274p. 1984. pap. 5.95 (ISBN 0-87123-403-3, 210403). Bethany Hse.
--Principles of Love. Parkhurst, Louis G., ed. 200p. 1986. pap. 5.95 (ISBN 0-87123-866-7, 210866). Bethany Hse.
--Principles of Prayer. Parkhurst, L. G., ed. LC 80-17856. 112p. (Orig.). 1980. pap. 3.95 (ISBN 0-87123-468-8, 210468). Bethany Hse.
--Principles of Union with Christ. Parkhurst, Louis G., ed. 128p. 1985. pap. 4.95 (ISBN 0-87123-447-5, 210447). Bethany Hse.
--Principles of Victory. Parkhurst, G., ed. LC 81-15464. 201p. (Orig.). 1981. pap. 5.95 (ISBN 0-87123-471-8, 210471). Bethany Hse.
--The Promise of the Spirit. Smith, Timothy L., ed. LC 79-26286. 272p. (Orig.). 1980. pap. 6.95 (ISBN 0-87123-207-3, 210207). Bethany Hse.
--Reflections on Revival. LC 78-26527. 160p. 1979. pap. 4.95 (ISBN 0-87123-157-3, 210157). Bethany Hse.
--Revival Lectures. 544p. 15.95 (ISBN 0-8007-0272-7). Revell.
--Sanctification. Allen, W. E., ed. 1963. pap. 2.50 (ISBN 0-87508-191-6). Chr Lit.
--So Great Salvation. LC 65-25844. (Charles G. Finney Memorial Library). 128p. 1975. pap. 4.50 (ISBN 0-8254-2621-9). Kregel.
--True & False Repentance. LC 66-10576. (Charles G. Finney Memorial Library). 122p. 1975. pap. 4.50 (ISBN 0-8254-2617-0). Kregel.
--True Saints. LC 66-24880. (Charles G. Finney Memorial Library). 120p. 1975. pap. 4.50 (ISBN 0-8254-2622-7). Kregel.
--True Submission. LC 66-24881. (Charles G. Finney Memorial Library). 128p. 1975. pap. 4.50 (ISBN 0-8254-2618-9). Kregel.
--Victory Over the World. LC 66-24879. (Charles G. Finney Memorial Library). 124p. 1975. pap. 4.50 (ISBN 0-8254-2619-7). Kregel.

Finney, Charles G. & Parkhurst, L. B. Principles of Liberty. rev. ed. LC 82-20705. (Finney's Sermons on Romans Ser.). 194p. (Orig.). 1983. pap. 5.95 (ISBN 0-87123-475-0, 210475). Bethany Hse.

Finney, Theodore M., ed. James Warrington: Short Titles of Books, Relating to or Illustrating the History & Practice of Psalmody in the United States,1620-1820. LC 70-18250. (Bibliographia Tripotamopolitana: No.1). 1970. 6.00x (ISBN 0-931222-00-1). Pitts Theolog.

Finotti, Joseph. Bibliographia Catholica Americana: A List of Works by Catholic Authors & Published in the United States. LC 74-149232. (Bibliography & Reference Ser.: No. 401). 1971. Repr. of 1872 ed. lib. bdg. 23.50 (ISBN 0-8337-1128-8). B Franklin.

Finsaas, Clarence B. They Marched to Heaven's Drumbeat. 1985. pap. 5.95 (ISBN 0-88419-193-1). Creation Hse.

Finucane, Ronald C. Soldiers of the Faith: Crusaders & Moslems at War. (Illus.). 256p. 1984. 19.95 (ISBN 0-312-74256-8). St Martin.

Finzel, Hans. Opening the Book. 352p. 1986. pap. 11.95 (ISBN 0-89693-277-X). Victor Bks.
--Unlocking the Scriptures. 144p. 1986. 7.95 (ISBN 0-89693-276-1). Victor Bks.

Fiore, Edith. Unquiet Dead: A Psychologist Works with Spirit Possession. LC 86-29096. 192p. 1987. 15.95 (ISBN 0-385-23904-1, Dolp). Doubleday.

Fiorelli, Lewis, ed. see De Sales, Francis.

Fiorelli, Lewis S., ed. see St. Francis of Sales.

Fiorenza, Elisabeth S. The Book of Revelation: Justice & Judgment. LC 84-47920. 224p. 1984. pap. 11.95 (ISBN 0-8006-1793-2). Fortress.
--Bread Not Stone: The Challenge of Feminist Biblical Interpretation. LC 84-14669. 208p. 1986. pap. 8.95 (ISBN 0-8070-1103-7, BP 717). Beacon Pr.
--In Memory of Her: A Feminist Theological Reconstruction of Christian Origins. LC 82-19896. 275p. 1983. 22.50 (ISBN 0-8245-0493-3). Crossroad NY.

Fiorenza, Elisabeth S. & Holmes, Urban T. Lent. Achtemeier, Elizabeth & Krodel, Gerhard, eds. LC 79-7377. (Proclamation 2: Aids for Interpreting the Lessons of the Church Year, Ser. B). 64p. 1981. pap. 3.75 (ISBN 0-8006-4070-5, 1-4070). Fortress.

Fiorenza, Elisabeth S., ed. In Memory of Her: A Feminist Theological Reconstruction of Christian Origins. 384p. 1984. pap. 12.95 (ISBN 0-8245-0667-7). Crossroad NY.

Fiorenza, Elisabeth S. & Collins, Mary, eds. Women: Invisible In Church & Theology. (Concilium Ser.: Vol. 182). 128p. 1985. pap. 6.95 (Pub. by T & T Clark Ltd UK). Fortress.

Fiorenza, Elizabeth S. The Apocalypse. (Read & Pray Ser.). 64p. 1976. pap. 1.25 (ISBN 0-8199-0726-X). Franciscan Herald.
--Bread Not Stone: The Challenge of Feminist Biblical Interpretation. LC 84-14669. 207p. 1985. 17.95 (ISBN 0-8070-1100-2). Beacon Pr.

Fiorenza, Elizabeth S., ed. Aspects of Religious Propaganda in Judaism & Early Christianity. LC 74-27890. (University of Notre Dame. Center for the Study of Judaism & Christianity in Antiquity Ser: No. 2). pap. 51.30 (2029308). Bks Demand UMI.

Fiorenza, Francis S. Foundational Theology: Jesus & the Church. 320p. 1984. 22.50 (ISBN 0-8245-0494-1). Crossroad NY.
--Foundational Theology: Jesus & the Church. rev. ed. 352p. 1985. pap. 14.95 (ISBN 0-8245-0706-1). Crossroad NY.

Fiorenza, Francis S., tr. see Schleiermacher, Friedrich.

Firas, Shihab. Healer, Ash-Shafuja, an Ismaili Treatise. Makarem, Sami N., ed. 1966. pap. 15.95x (ISBN 0-8156-6026-X, Am U Beirut). Syracuse U Pr.

Fireside, Harvey. Icon & Swastika: The Russian Orthodox Church Under Nazi & Soviet Control. LC 70-123567. (Harvard University, Russian Research Center Studies: Vol. 62). pap. 67.00 (ISBN 0-317-08921-8, 2021595). Bks Demand UMI.

Firestone, Robert & Catlett, Joyce. The Truth: A Psychological Curse. 234p. 1981. 13.95 (ISBN 0-02-538380-9). Macmillan.

Firishtah, Muhammad. History of the Rise of the Mahomedan Power in India until AD 1612, 4 vols. Biggs, John, tr. Repr. of 1910 ed. Set. text ed. 125.00x. Coronet Bks.

Firishtah, Muhammed Kasim. History of the Rise of the Mahomedan Power in India till the Year A.D. 1612, 4 Vols. Briggs, John, tr. LC 79-154112. Repr. of 1910 ed. Set. 225.00 (ISBN 0-404-56300-7). AMS Pr.

Firkins, Oscar W. Ralph Waldo Emerson. LC 80-2532. Repr. of 1915 ed. 44.50 (ISBN 0-404-19258-0). AMS Pr.

Firth, C. H., ed. see Clarke, William.

Firth, Charles H. John Bunyan. LC 74-11062. 1911. lib. bdg. 10.00 (ISBN 0-8414-4212-6). Folcroft.

Firth, John B. Constantine the Great: The Reorganization of the Empire & the Triumph of the Church. facsimile ed. LC 77-152983. (Select Bibliographies Reprint Ser). Repr. of 1904 ed. 27.50 (ISBN 0-8369-5735-0). Ayer Co Pubs.

Firth, Katherine R. The Apocalyptic Tradition in Reformation Britain 1530-1645. (Historical Monographs). (Illus.). 1979. 45.00x (ISBN 0-19-821868-0). Oxford U Pr.

Firth, Robert E., jt. ed. see Phillips, Harold R.

Fisch, Dov A. Jews for Nothing: On Cults, Assimilation & Intermarriage. 368p. 1984. 13.95 (ISBN 0-87306-347-3). Feldheim.

Fisch, H. Zionist Revolution. LC 78-424. 1978. 19.95x (ISBN 0-312-89886-X). St Martin.

Fisch, Harold. A Remembered Future: A Study in Literary Mythology. LC 83-48899. 208p. 1985. 22.50x (ISBN 0-253-35003-4). Ind U Pr.

Fischel, H. A., intro. by. The First Book of Maccabees. 124p. 1985. pap. 4.95 (ISBN 0-8052-0793-7). Schocken.

Fischel, Jack, jt. ed. see Pinsker, Sanford.

Fischel, Jack R. & Pinsker, Sanford, eds. The Churches' Response to the Holocaust. (Holocaust Studies Annual: Vol. II). 200p. 1986. 20.00 (ISBN 0-913283-12-6). Penkevill.

Fischel, Walter. Jews in the Economic & Political Life of Medieval Islam. rev. ed. LC 68-25719. 1969. Repr. of 1937 ed. 15.00x (ISBN 0-87068-047-1). Ktav.

Fischer, Balthasar. Signs, Words & Gestures. O'Connell, Matthew J., tr. from Ger. 1981. pap. 5.95 (ISBN 0-916134-48-2). Pueblo Pub Co.

Fischer, Bernhard, ed. Healing Education Based on Anthroposophy's Image of Man: Living, Learning, Working with Children & Adults in Need of Special Soul Care. Mier, C. A. & Mier, G. F., trs. from Ger. (Illus.). 227p. 1974. pap. 11.00 (ISBN 3-772506-39-9). Anthroposophic.

Fischer, Carl, ed. see Holmberg, Kathleen.

Fischer, Carl, ed. see Schrieber, Angela.

Fischer, Eberhard & Jain, Jyotindra. Art & Rituals: Twenty Five Hundred Years of Jainism in India. LC 78-670055. (Illus.). 1977. 20.00 (ISBN 0-89684-369-6). Orient Bk Dist.

Fischer, Edward. Everybody Steals from God: Communication as Worship. LC 77-3711. 1977. text ed. 10.95x (ISBN 0-268-00904-X). U of Notre Dame Pr.
--Fiji Revisited: A Columbian Father's Memories of Twenty-Eight Years in the Islands. LC 81-5365. (Illus.). 1981. 10.95 (ISBN 0-8245-0097-0). Crossroad NY.
--Japan Journey: The Columban Fathers in Nippon. LC 84-14228. 208p. 1984. pap. 9.95 (ISBN 0-8245-0656-1). Crossroad NY.
--Journeys Not Regreeted. 1986. pap. 10.95 (ISBN 0-317-42448-3). Crossroad NY.

Fischer, Gretl K. In Search of Jerusalem: Religion & Ethics in the Writings of A. M. Klein. LC 76-367083. pap. 66.50 (ISBN 0-317-26452-4, 2023858). Bks Demand UMI.

Fischer, James A. How to Read the Bible. rev. ed. 1987. 14.95 (ISBN 0-396-08986-0); pap. 8.95 (ISBN 0-396-09028-1). Dodd.
--Song of Songs, Ruth, Lamentations, Ecclesiastes, Esther. (Collegeville Bible Commentary Ser.). 112p. 1986. pap. 2.95 (ISBN 0-8146-1480-9). Liturgical pr.

Fischer, John. Dark Horse: The Story of a Winner. LC 83-11411. 100p. 1983. pap. 3.95 (ISBN 0-88070-016-5). Multnomah.
--The Olive Tree Connection: Sharing Israel's Messiah. LC 83-12645. 192p. (Orig.). 1983. pap. 8.95 (ISBN 0-87784-848-3). Inter-Varsity.

Fischer, Kathleen R. The Inner Rainbow: The Imagination in Christian Life. 160p. 1983. pap. 6.95 (ISBN 0-8091-2498-X). Paulist Pr.
--Winter Grace, Spirituality for the Later Years. LC 84-61975. 1985. pap. 7.95 (ISBN 0-8091-2675-3). Paulist Pr.

Fischer, Maximiliano, ed. Codex Traditionum Ecclesiae Collegiatae Claustroneoburgensis Continens Donationes, Fundationes Commutationesque Hanc Ecclesiam Attinentes Ab Anno Domin: MCCLX Usque Circiter MCCLX. Repr. of 1851 ed. 23.00 (ISBN 0-384-29873-7). Johnson Repr.

Fischer, P. C., ed. see Schutte, Josef F.

Fischer, Robert H. & Lehmann, Helmut T., eds. Luther's Works: Word & Sacrament III, Vol. 37. LC 55-9893. 1961. 19.95 (ISBN 0-8006-0337-0, 1-337). Fortress.

Fischer, Robert H., tr. see Luther, Martin.

Fischer, Ulrich. Eschatologic & Jenseitserwartung Im Hellenistischen Diasporajudentum. (Beiheft 44 Zur Zeitschrift Fuer Die Alttestamentliche Wissenschaft). 1978. 29.20x (ISBN 3-11-007595-4). De Gruyter.

Fischer, William, ed. see Kelm, Paul.

Fischer, William E., jt. auth. see Aderman, James.

Fischer, William E., ed. see Aderman, James.

Fischer, William E., ed. see Aderman, James A.

Fischer, William E., ed. see Bivens, Forest & Vallesky, David.

Fischer, William E., ed. see Kuschel, Harlyn J.

Fischer, William E., ed. see Lauersdorf, Richard E.

Fischer, William E., ed. see Stadler, Richard H.

Fischer, William E., ed. see Wendland, Ernst H.

Fischer, William E., ed. see Witt, James G., III.

Fischer, William L. Alternatives. LC 79-67005. 1980. 5.95 (ISBN 0-87159-000-X). Unity School.

Fischhoff, Joseph & Brohl, Noreen. Before & After My Child Died: A Collection of Parents' Experiences. 247p. (Orig.). 1981. pap. 7.95x (ISBN 0-9607956-0-X). Emmons-Fairfield Pub.

Fischman, Joyce. Bible Work & Play, 3 vols. (Illus., Orig.). 1966. pap. text ed. 2.50 ea. Vol. 1 o.p (102610). Vol. 2 o.p (102620). Vol. 3 (102640). UAHC.

--Bible Work & Play, Vol. 1. rev. ed. (Illus.). 80p. (Orig.). 1985. pap. text ed. 5.00 (ISBN 0-8074-0304-0). UAHC.

--Bible Work & Play, Vol. 2. rev. ed. (Illus.). 80p. 1984. wkbk. 5.00 (ISBN 0-8074-0256-7). UAHC.

Fischoff, Ephraim, tr. see Weber, Max.

Fish, Roy J. Every Member Evangelism for Today. rev. ed. LC 75-12289. 128p. 1976. pap. 6.95 (ISBN 0-06-061551-6, RD125, HarpR). Har-Row.

--Giving a Good Invitation. LC 74-18043. 1975. pap. 3.50 (ISBN 0-8054-2107-6). Broadman.

Fish, Sharon & Shelly, Judith A. Spiritual Care: The Nurse's Role. 2nd ed. LC 83-12604. (Illus.). 192p. 1983. pap. 7.95 (ISBN 0-87784-878-5). Inter-Varsity.

Fish, Sharon, jt. auth. see McCormick, Thomas.

Fish, Simon. A Supplicacyon for the Beggers. LC 72-5989. (English Experience Ser.: No. 515). 16p. 1973. Repr. of 1529 ed. 6.00 (ISBN 90-221-0515-6). Walter J Johnson.

Fish, Stanley E. Surprised by Sin: The Reader in Paradise Lost. 1971. pap. 9.95 (ISBN 0-520-01897-4, CAL228). U of Cal Pr.

Fishbane, Michael. Biblical Interpretation in Ancient Israel. 1985. 49.95x (ISBN 0-19-826325-2). Oxford U Pr.

--Judaism. LC 85-42775. (Religious Traditions of the World Ser.). 128p. (Orig.). 1985. 6.95 (ISBN 0-06-062655-0, HarpR). Har-Row.

--Text & Texture: Close Readings of Selected Biblical Texts. LC 79-14083. 154p. 1982. pap. 7.95 (ISBN 0-8052-0726-0). Schocken.

Fishbein, Morris. Fads & Quackery in Healing. LC 75-23708. Repr. of 1932 ed. 45.00 (ISBN 0-404-13260-X). AMS Pr.

Fishberg, Maurice. Materials for the Physical Anthropology of the Eastern European Jews. LC 6-2111. (American Anthro. Association Memoirs). 1905. 14.00 (ISBN 0-527-00500-2). Kraus Repr.

Fishburn, Janet F. The Fatherhood of God & the Victorian Family: The Social Gospel in America. LC 81-43090. 220p. 1982. 4.95 (ISBN 0-8006-0671-X). Fortress.

Fishel, Kent. Cornerstones: Believing the Bible. 112p. 1987. pap. 4.95 (ISBN 0-310-39761-8). Zondervan.

Fishel, Kent & Deselm, Joel. Breakthrough No. 1: Christian Assurances. 1986. pap. 2.95 (ISBN 0-310-45981-8, 12629P). Zondervan.

--Breakthrough No. 2: Christian Growth. 1986. pap. 2.95 (ISBN 0-310-45971-0, 12628P). Zondervan.

--Breakthrough No. 3: Christian Living. 1986. pap. 2.95 (ISBN 0-310-45941-9, 12627P). Zondervan.

Fishel, Kent & Rayds, John. Resurrection Evidences. (Cornerstone Ser.). 1985. pap. 2.95 (ISBN 0-310-46102-2, 12675P). Zondervan.

Fishelis, Avraham. Bastion of Faith. 3rd ed. 256p. 1980. 9.00 (ISBN 0-9605560-1-X). A Fishelis.

--Kol Rom, Vol. I. 3rd ed. (Hebrew.). 208p. 5.50 (ISBN 0-9605560-0-1). A Fishelis.

--Kol Rom, Vol. II. (Hebrew.). 292p. 6.50 (ISBN 0-9605560-2-8). A Fishelis.

--Kol Rom, Vol. III. (Hebrew.). 431p. 12.00 (ISBN 0-9605560-3-6). A Fishelis.

Fisher, Aileen. Easter. LC 67-23666. (Holiday Ser.). (Illus.). 1968. PLB 12.89 (ISBN 0-690-25236-6, Crowell Jr Bks). HarpJ.

Fisher, Ben C., ed. New Pathways: A Dialogue in Christian Higher Education. LC 80-80255. x, 110p. 1980. pap. 4.95 (ISBN 0-86554-000-4, MUP-P01). Mercer Univ Pr.

Fisher, Betty J., ed. see Hatcher, John S.

Fisher, Betty J., jt. ed. see Paine, Mabel H.

Fisher, Carl, jt. ed. see Baumgartner, Aline.

Fisher, Carl, ed. see Mitchell, Joan & O'Neill, Irene.

Fisher, Carl, ed. see Mitchell, Joan & Sherlock, Therese.

Fisher, Clay C. New Concepts of Bible Mysteries & Eschatologies. LC 76-96074. 1969. pap. 2.50 (ISBN 0-686-00510-4). C C Fisher.

Fisher, Constance. Dancing Festivals of the Church Year. Adams, Doug, ed. (Illus.). 120p. (Orig.). 1986. pap. 8.95 (ISBN 0-941500-42-X). Sharing Co.

Fisher, Constance & Adams, Doug. Dancing with Early Christians. (Illus.). 176p. 1983. pap. 6.95 (ISBN 0-941500-30-6). Sharing Co.

Fisher, Constance L. Dancing the Old Testament: Christian Celebrations of Israelite Heritage for Worship & Education. Adams, Doug, ed. (Illus.). 1980. pap. 5.95 (ISBN 0-941500-07-1). Sharing Co.

--Music & Dance: In the Worship Program of the Church. (Orig.). 1981. pap. 2.50 (ISBN 0-941500-20-9). Sharing Co.

Fisher, David. Morality & the Bomb: An Ethical & Assessment of Nuclear Deterrence. LC 85-2210. 136p. 1985. 25.00 (ISBN 0-312-54784-6). St Martin.

Fisher, David, jt. ed. see Barrett, Eric C.

Fisher, Doug, ed. Why We Serve: Personal Stories of Catholic Lay Ministers. 176p. (Orig.). 1984. pap. 6.95 (ISBN 0-8091-2640-0). Paulist Pr.

Fisher, Douglas. Peacemaking. homily bk. 1.50 (ISBN 0-8091-9321-3); group discussion guide 2.95 (ISBN 0-8091-9326-4); participants' bks. 1.00 (ISBN 0-8091-9341-8). Paulist Pr.

Fisher, Eugene. Faith Without Prejudice: Rebuilding Christian Attitudes Toward Judaism. LC 77-83550. 196p. 1977. pap. 3.95 (ISBN 0-8091-2064-X). Paulist Pr.

Fisher, Eugene J. Seminary Education & Christian-Jewish Relationss. 100p. 1983. 4.80 (ISBN 0-318-20615-3). Natl Cath Educ.

Fisher, Eugene J. & Polish, Daniel F., eds. The Formation of Social Policy in the Catholic & Jewish Tradition. new ed. LC 80-50268. 208p. text ed. 17.95 (ISBN 0-268-00953-8); pap. text ed. 8.95 (ISBN 0-268-00951-1). U of Notre Dame Pr.

--Liturgical Foundations of Social Policy in the Catholic & Jewish Traditions. LC 82-40378. 180p. 1983. text ed. 16.95 (ISBN 0-268-01267-9); pap. text ed. 9.95 (ISBN 0-268-01268-7). U of Notre Dame Pr.

Fisher, George P. Discussions in History & Theology. Kuklick, Bruce, ed. (American Religious Thought of the 18th & 19th Centuries Ser.). 565p. 1987. lib. bdg. 75.00 (ISBN 0-8240-6963-3). Garland Pub.

--History of Christian Doctrine. LC 75-41095. Repr. of 1901 ed. 41.50 (ISBN 0-404-14663-5). AMS Pr.

--History of the Christian Church. LC 75-41094. 48.50 (ISBN 0-404-14662-7). AMS Pr.

--The Reformation. LC 83-45660. Date not set. Repr. of 1906 ed. 54.50 (ISBN 0-404-19810-4). AMS Pr.

Fisher, J. M. Mystic Gnosis. 1977. lib. bdg. 59.95 (ISBN 0-8490-2316-5). Gordon Pr.

Fisher, James E. Democracy & Mission Education in Korea. LC 70-176773. (Columbia University. Teachers College. Contributions to Education Ser.: No. 306). Repr. of 1928 ed. 22.50 (ISBN 0-404-55306-0). AMS Pr.

Fisher, Joe. The Case for Reincarnation. 208p. 1985. pap. 3.95 (ISBN 0-553-24868-5). Bantam.

Fisher, John. This Treatise Concernynge the Fruytfull Saynges of Davyd..Was Made & Compyled by..John Fyssher..Bysshop of Rochester. LC 79-84106. (English Experience Ser.: No. 925). 296p. 1979. Repr. of 1509 ed. lib. bdg. 28.00 (ISBN 90-221-0925-9). Walter J Johnson.

Fisher, Kathleen R. & Hart, Thomas N. Christian Foundations: An Introduction to Faith in Our Time. 240p. 1986. pap. 9.95 (ISBN 0-8091-2817-9). Paulist Pr.

Fisher, Leonard E. Symbol Art: Thirteen Squares, Circles & Triangles from Around the World. LC 85-42805. (Illus.). 64p. 1986. 12.95 (ISBN 0-02-735270-6, Four Winds). Macmillan.

Fisher, Lizette A. Mystic Vision in the Grail Legend & in the Divine Comedy. LC 79-168029. Repr. of 1917 ed. 16.50 (ISBN 0-404-02389-4). AMS Pr.

Fisher, Mary P. Heart of Gold: The Light Within Life. LC 85-81211. (Illus.). 72p. (Orig.). 1985. pap. 6.00 (ISBN 0-9615149-5-7). Fenton Valley Pr.

Fisher, Neal F. Context for Discovery. LC 81-7929. (Into Our Third Century Ser.). (Orig.). 1981. pap. 4.95 (ISBN 0-687-09620-0). Abingdon.

Fisher, Phyllis K. Los Alamos Experience. (Illus.). 240p. 1985. 12.95 (ISBN 0-87040-623-X, Dist. by Harper & Row). Japan Pubns USA.

Fisher, Robert. En Espiritu y en Verdad. (Span., Orig.). pap. text ed. 5.95 (ISBN 0-87148-313-0). Pathway Pr.

--The Family & the Church. LC 77-99163. 1978. 5.25 (ISBN 0-87148-334-3); pap. 4.25 (ISBN 0-87148-335-1). Pathway Pr.

Fisher, Robert, ed. In Spirit & in Truth. (Orig.). pap. text ed. 5.95 (ISBN 0-87148-438-2). Pathway Pr.

--Pressing Toward the Mark. LC 83-63384. 176p. 1983. pap. text ed. 8.95 (ISBN 0-87148-714-4). Pathway Pr.

Fisher, Sara E. & Stahl, Rachel K. The Amish School. LC 84-81142. (People's Place Booklet: No. 6). (Illus.). 96p. (Orig.). 1985. pap. 4.50 (ISBN 0-934672-17-2). Good Bks PA.

Fisher, Sidney G. Quaker Colonies. 1919. 8.50x (ISBN 0-686-83720-7). Elliots Bks.

Fisher, Vardis. Children of God. 1977. 12.95 (ISBN 0-918522-50-1). O L Holmes.

Fisher, Wallace E. All the Good Gifts: On Doing Bible Stewardship. LC 79-50077. 1979. pap. 5.95 (ISBN 0-8066-1702-0, 10-0227). Augsburg.

Fisher, William A. Seventy Negro Spirituals, for High Voice. LC 72-1637. Repr. of 1926 ed. 29.00 (ISBN 0-404-09921-1). AMS Pr.

Fishler, Stanley A. In the Beginning: A Navaho Creation Myth. (Utah Anthropological Papers: No. 13). Repr. of 1953 ed. 26.50 (ISBN 0-404-60613-X). AMS Pr.

Fishman, Charles, jt. auth. see Vinecour, Earl.

Fishman, Hertzel. American Protestantism & a Jewish State. LC 72-3746. (Schaver Publication Fund for Jewish Studies Ser). 250p. 1973. 24.95x (ISBN 0-8143-1481-3). Wayne St U Pr.

Fishman, Isidore. Remember the Days of Old. LC 79-100058. 1969. 4.95 (ISBN 0-87677-000-6). Hartmore.

Fishman, Joshua A. Yiddish in America: Socio-Linguistic Description & Analysis. LC 65-63395. (General Publications Ser: Vol. 36). (Orig.). 1965. pap. text ed. 9.95x (ISBN 0-87750-110-6). Res Ctr Lang Semiotic.

Fishman, Priscilla. Learn Mishnah Notebook. 128p. 1983. pap. 3.50x (ISBN 0-87441-369-9). Behrman.

Fishwick, Nina M. Liberated for Life a Christian Declaration of Indepence. (Study & Grow Electives Ser.). 64p. 1985. pap. 3.95 (ISBN 0-8307-1039-6, 6102095). Regal.

Fishwick, Nina M., jt. auth. see Stewart, Ed.

Fisk, Milton. Ethics & Society: A Marxist Interpretation of Value. LC 79-3513. 1980. 20.00x (ISBN 0-8147-2564-3). NYU Pr.

Fisk, Samuel. Divine Healing Under the Searchlight. LC 78-15083. 1978. pap. 2.25 (ISBN 0-87227-057-2). Reg Baptist.

--Divine Sovereignty & Human Freedom. LC 73-81550. 1973. pap. 5.95 (ISBN 0-87213-166-1). Loizeaux.

Fiske, Charles. Confessions of a Puzzled Parson, & Other Pleas for Reality. facs. ed. LC 68-54345. (Essay Index Reprint Ser). 1968. Repr. of 1928 ed. 18.00 (ISBN 0-8369-0442-7). Ayer Co Pubs.

Fiske, John. Myths & Myth-Makers: Old Tales & Superstitions Interpreted by Comparative Mythology. LC 77-85618. 1977. Repr. of 1890 ed. lib. bdg. 30.00 (ISBN 0-89341-304-6). Longwood Pub Group.

Fison, J. E. Understanding the Old Testament: The Way of Holiness. LC 78-21116. 1979. Repr. of 1952 ed. lib. bdg. 24.75x (ISBN 0-313-20839-5, FIUO). Greenwood.

Fitch, Alger M., Jr. Afterglow of Christ's Resurrection. LC 75-14692. (New Life Bks). (Illus.). 136p. 1975. pap. 3.95 (ISBN 0-87239-055-1, 40030). Standard Pub.

--Revelation. (Standard Bible Studies). 112p. 1986. pap. 5.95 (ISBN 0-87403-173-7, 40113). Standard Pub.

Fitch, Ed & Renee, Janine. Magical Rites from the Crystal Well. Weschcke, Carl L., ed. LC 83-80134. (Practical Magick Ser.). (Illus.). 166p. 1984. pap. 9.95 (ISBN 0-87542-230-6, L-230). Llewellyn Pubns.

Fitch, George H. Great Spiritual Writers of America. 1977. lib. bdg. 59.95 (ISBN 0-8490-1904-4). Gordon Pr.

Fitchen, John. The Construction of Gothic Cathedrals: A Study of Medieval Vault Erection. LC 80-26291. (Illus.). 1977. pap. 12.95 (ISBN 0-226-25203-5, Phoen). U of Chicago Pr.

Fitt, A. P. Life of D. L. Moody. pap. 3.50 (ISBN 0-8024-4727-9). Moody.

Fittbogen, Gottfried. Die Religion Lessings. 1967. 36.00; pap. 31.00 (ISBN 0-685-13575-6). Johnson Repr.

Fitti, Charles J. Between God & Man. LC 78-50527. 49p. 1978. 10.00 (ISBN 0-8022-2225-0). Philos Lib.

Fittipaldi, Silvio. How to Pray Always: Without Always Praying. LC 85-80599. (Orig.). 1985. pap. 2.95 (ISBN 0-89243-237-3). Liguori Pubns.

Fittro, Pat, compiled by. Easter Programs for the Church, No. 11. (Illus.). 64p. 1987. pap. 3.50 (ISBN 0-87403-283-0, 8723). Standard Pub.

--Standard Easter Program Book, No. 37. 48p. 1986. pap. 1.95 (ISBN 0-87403-083-8, 8707). Standard Pub.

Fitts, Bob. When You Pray - Things Happen. LC 82-82018. 144p. 1982. 2.95 (ISBN 0-89221-089-3). New Leaf.

Fitzell, John. Hermit in German Literature: From Lessing to Eichendorff. LC 74-168033. (North Carolina. University. Studies in the Germanic Languages & Literatures: No. 30). Repr. of 1961 ed. 27.00 (ISBN 0-404-50930-4). AMS Pr.

Fitzer, Joseph. Moehler & Baur in Controversy Eighteen Thirty-Two to Thirty-Eight: Romantic-idealist Assesment of the Reformation & Counter-Reformation. LC 74-77619. (American Academy of Religion. Studies in Religion). 1974. 9.95 (ISBN 0-88420-111-2, 010007). Scholars Pr GA.

Fitzgerald. Rainbow. (Dear God Kids Ser.). Date not set. 3.95 (ISBN 0-671-50681-1). S&S.

Fitzgerald, Annie. Dear God, Bless Our Food. LC 84-71372. (Dear God Bks.). 16p. (Orig.). 1984. pap. 1.50 (ISBN 0-8066-2108-7, 10-1859). Augsburg.

--Dear God, Good Morning. LC 84-71377. (Dear God Bks.). 16p. (Orig.). 1984. pap. 1.50 (ISBN 0-8066-2104-4, 10-1860). Augsburg.

--Dear God, Good Night. LC 84-71374. (Dear God Bks.). 16p. 1984. pap. 1.50 (ISBN 0-8066-2105-2, 10-1861). Augsburg.

--Dear God, I Just Love Birthdays. LC 84-71371. (Dear God Bks.). 16p. (Orig.). 1984. pap. 1.50 (ISBN 0-8066-2107-9, 10-1862). Augsburg.

--Dear God, Let's Play. LC 83-70495. 16p. (Orig.). 1983. pap. 1.50 (ISBN 0-8066-2001-3, 10-1852). Augsburg.

--Dear God, Thanks for Friends. LC 84-71873. (Dear God Bks.). 16p. (Orig.). 1984. pap. 1.50 (ISBN 0-8066-2109-5, 10-1863). Augsburg.

--Dear God, Thanks for Making Me. LC 83-71368. (Dear God Bks.). 16p. (Orig.). 1984. pap. 1.50 (ISBN 0-8066-2106-0, 10-1864). Augsburg.

--Dear God, Thanks for Thinking up Love. LC 83-70499. 16p. 1983. pap. 1.50 (ISBN 0-8066-2005-6, 10-1853). Augsburg.

--Dear God, Thanks for Your Help. LC 83-70496. 16p. 1983. pap. 1.50 (ISBN 0-8066-2002-1, 10-1854). Augsburg.

--Dear God, We Just Love Christmas. LC 83-70494. 16p. (Orig.). 1983. pap. 1.50 (ISBN 0-8066-2000-5, 10-1855). Augsburg.

--Dear God, Where Do You Live? LC 83-70497. 16p. 1983. pap. 1.50 (ISBN 0-8066-2003-X, 10-1856). Augsburg.

--Dear God, Your World Is Wonderful. LC 83-70498. 16p. 1983. pap. 1.50 (ISBN 0-8066-2004-8, 10-1857). Augsburg.

Fitzgerald, Ernest A. Diamonds Everywhere: Appreciating God's Gifts. 112p. (Orig.). 1983. pap. 7.75 (ISBN 0-687-10734-2). Abingdon.

FitzGerald, G. M. Sixth Century Monastery at Beth-Shan (Scythopolis) (Publications of the Palestine Section Ser.: Vol. 4). (Illus.). xiv, 66p. 1939. 18.75 (ISBN 0-686-24094-4). Univ Mus of U.

Fitzgerald, George. Handbook of the Mass. 128p. 1982. pap. 4.95 (ISBN 0-8091-2401-7). Paulist Pr.

--A Practical Guide to Preaching. LC 79-67742. 160p. (Orig.). 1980. pap. 5.95 (ISBN 0-8091-2281-2). Paulist Pr.

Fitzgerald, John & White, Michael. The Tabula of Cebes. LC 82-19118. (SBL Texts & Translations). 236p. 1983. pap. 14.25 (ISBN 0-89130-601-3, 06 02 24). Scholars Pr GA.

FitzGerald, Paul A. Governance of Jesuit Colleges in the United States, 1920-1970. LC 83-25927. 328p. 1984. text ed. 20.00 (ISBN 0-268-01010-2, 85-10109). U of Notre Dame Pr.

Fitzgerald, Sally, ed. The Habit of Being: Letters of Flannery O'Connor. LC 79-23319. 1980. pap. 10.95 (ISBN 0-394-74259-1, Vin). Random.

Fitzgerald, Sally, ed. & intro. by see O'Connor, Flannery.

Fitzgibbon, John F. Ethics: Fundamental Principles of Moral Philosophy. LC 83-1178. 92p. (Orig.). 1983. lib. bdg. 22.25 (ISBN 0-8191-3064-8); pap. text ed. 8.75 (ISBN 0-8191-3065-6). U Pr of Amer.

Fitzhardinge, L. F. The Spartans. LC 79-66136. (Ancient Peoples & Places Ser.). (Illus.). 180p. 1985. pap. 10.95f (ISBN 0-500-27364-2). Thames Hudson.

Fitzmyer, J. A. To Advance the Gospel: New Testament Essays. 320p. 1981. 19.50x (ISBN 0-8245-0008-3). Crossroad NY.

Fitzmyer, Joseph A. A Christological Catechism: New Testament Answers. 160p. (Orig.). 1982. pap. 4.95 (ISBN 0-8091-2453-X). Paulist Pr.

--The Dead Sea Scrolls: Major Publications & Tools for Study. LC 75-5987. (Society of Biblical Literature. Sources for Biblical Study Ser.). xiv, 171p. 1975. pap. 10.50 (ISBN 0-88414-053-9, 060308). Scholars Pr GA.

--Essays on the Semitic Background of the New Testament. LC 74-83874. (Society of Biblical Literature. Sources for Biblical Study). 1974. pap. 13.50 (060305). Scholars Pr GA.

--Gospel According to Luke I-IX, Vol. 28. LC 80-702. (Anchor Bible Ser.). 1981. 20.00 (ISBN 0-385-00515-6). Doubleday.

Fitzmyer, Joseph F. Pauline Theology: A Brief Sketch. (Orig.). 1967. pap. text ed. write for info. (ISBN 0-13-654525-4). P-H.

Fitzpatrick, Brian. Catholic Royalism in the Department of the Gard: 1814-1852. LC 82-14564. (Illus.). 224p. 1983. 49.50 (ISBN 0-521-22454-3). Cambridge U Pr.

Fitzpatrick, Clare L., ed. see Thomas a Kempis.

Fitzpatrick, Daniel J. Confusion, Call, Commitment: The Spiritual Exercises & Religious Education. LC 76-3801. 178p. 1976. pap. 4.95 (ISBN 0-8189-0327-9). Alba.

Fitzpatrick, James M., jt. auth. see Simon, Thomas G.

Fitzpatrick, Kathryn. Commandments: Twenty-Eight Family Times to Respond in Love. (Familytime - Faithtime: A Home-Based Approach to Religious Education Ser.). (Illus.). 52p. (Orig.). 1982. pap. text ed. 3.50 (ISBN 0-86716-013-6). St Anthony Mess Pr.

--Creed: Twenty-Nine Family Times to Explore Belief, 3 Vols. (Family Time - Faith Time: A Home-Based Approach to Religious Education Ser.). (Illus.). 70p. (Orig.). 1982. pap. text ed. 3.50 (ISBN 0-86716-012-8). St Anthony Mess Pr.

--Family Time, Faith Time, 3 Vols. (Illus.). 307p. (Orig.). 1982. Set. pap. text ed. 8.95 (ISBN 0-86716-030-6). St Anthony Mess Pr.

--Sacraments: Twenty-Eight Family Times to Celebrate Life. (Family Time - Faith Time: A Home-Based Approach to Religious Education Ser.). (Illus.). 70p. (Orig.). 1982. pap. 3.50 (ISBN 0-86716-010-1). St Anthony Mess Pr.

Fitzpatrick, Mary C., tr. see St. Thomas Aquinas.

Fitzpatrick, Nancy J., ed. Creative Ideas for Christmas, 1986. (Illus.). 160p. 1986. 17.95 (ISBN 0-8487-0683-8). Oxmoor Hse.

Fitzpatrick, T. A. Catholic Secondary Education in South-West Scotland Before 1972: Its Contributions to the Change in Status of the Catholic Community of the Area. (Illus.). 248p. 1986. 19.00 (ISBN 0-08-032439-8, Pub. by AUP). Pergamon.

Fitzsimmons, John, ed. Manning: Anglican & Catholic. LC 78-11571. 1979. Repr. of 1951 ed. lib. bdg. cancelled (ISBN 0-313-21005-5, FIMA). Greenwood.

Fitzwater, Perry B. La Mujer: Su Mision, Posicion y Ministerio. Orig. Title: Woman: Mission, Position, Ministry. (Span.). 76p. 1972. pap. 2.25 (ISBN 0-8254-1233-1). Kregel.

Fix, Janet & Levitt, Zola. For Singles Only. 128p. 1978. pap. 5.95 (ISBN 0-8007-5034-9, Power Bks). Revell.

Flachman, Leonard. Christmas: The Annual of Christmas Literature & Art, Vol. 55. 64p. 1985. text ed. 14.50 (ISBN 0-8066-8967-6, 17-0131); pap. text ed. 6.95 (ISBN 0-8066-8966-8, 17-0130). Augsburg.

Flachman, Leonard, ed. Christmas: The Annual of Christmas Literature & Art, Vol. 57. (Illus.). 64p. 1987. text ed. 14.50 (ISBN 0-8066-8971-4, 17-0135); pap. 6.95 (ISBN 0-8066-8970-6, 17-0134). Augsburg.

Flack, Elmer E., ed. see Melanchthon, Philipp.

Flaherty, Cornelia M. Go with Haste into the Mountains. 230p. (Orig.). 1984. 9.95 (ISBN 0-934318-42-5); pap. write for info. Falcon Pr MT.

Flake, Carol. Redemptorama. LC 82-45356. 288p. 1984. 15.95 (ISBN 0-385-18241-4, Anchor Pr). Doubleday.

--Redemptorama: Culture, Politics & the New Evangelicalism. (Nonfiction Ser.). 320p. 1985. pap. 7.95 (ISBN 0-14-008265-4). Penguin.

Flake, Chad J., ed. A Mormon Bibliography, 1830-1930: Books, Pamphlets, Periodicals, & Broadsides Relating to the First Century of Mormonism. LC 74-22639. (Illus.). 1978. 80.00x (ISBN 0-87480-016-1). U of Utah Pr.

Flamma, Thomas. Metaphysics, a Bridge to ECKANKAR. LC 81-80177. 232p. 1981. pap. 3.95 (ISBN 0-914766-65-1, 0193). IWP Pub.

Flammanc, Solveng, tr. see McDowell, Josh.

Flamming, Peter J. God & Creation. LC 85-6647. (Layman's Liberty of Christian Doctrine Ser.). 1985. 5.95 (ISBN 0-8054-1635-8). Broadman.

Flammonde, Paris. Mystic Healers. LC 73-91856. (Illus.). 256p. 1974. 8.95 (ISBN 0-8128-1680-3). Stein & Day.

Flanagan, Donal. Evolving Church. 1966. 4.95 (ISBN 0-8189-0047-4). Alba.

Flanagan, Neal. Jeremiah, 2 pts. (Bible Ser.). Pt. 1. pap. 1.00 (ISBN 0-8091-5071-9); Pt. 2. pap. 1.00 (ISBN 0-8091-5072-7). Paulist Pr.

Flanagan, Neal M. The Gospel According to John VII the Johannine Epistles, No. 4. Karris, Robert J., ed. LC 82-22908. (Collegeville Bible Commentary Ser.). 128p. 1983. pap. 2.95 (ISBN 0-8146-1304-7). Liturgical Pr.

Flanagan, Padraig, ed. A New Missionary Era. LC 81-9595. 192p. (Orig.). 1982. pap. 2.49 (ISBN 0-88344-331-7). Orbis Bks.

Flanders, Henry J., Jr., et al. Introduction to the Bible. 588p. 1973. text ed. 25.75 (ISBN 0-394-34416-2, RandC). Random.

Flanders, John A., jt. ed. see Crenshaw, Floyd D.

Flanders, Robert B. Nauvoo: Kingdom on the Mississippi. LC 65-19110. (Illus.). 374p. 1975. pap. 8.95 (ISBN 0-252-00561-9). U of Ill Pr.

Flannery, Austin. Vatican Council II: The Conciliar & Post Conciliar Documents, Vol. 2. 994p. 1983. pap. 9.95 (ISBN 0-8146-1299-7). Liturgical Pr.

Flannery, Austin, ed. Vatican Council II. 1976. pap. 7.95 (ISBN 0-685-77498-8). Franciscan Herald.

Flannery, Austin P. Document of Vatican 11. 1975. pap. 7.95 (ISBN 0-8028-1623-1). Eerdmans.

Flannery, Austin P., ed. Vatican II: More Postconciliar Documents. 944p. (Orig.). 1983. pap. 9.95 (ISBN 0-8028-1638-X). Eerdmans.

Flannery, Edward. The Anguish of the Jews: Twenty-Three Centuries of Antisemitism. rev. ed. LC 85-60298. 384p. 1985. pap. 12.95 (ISBN 0-8091-2702-4). Paulist Pr.

Flasche, Rainer. Die Religionswissenschaft Joachim Wachs. (Theologische Bibliothek Toeelmann: Vol. 35). 1978. 35.20x (ISBN 3-11-007238-6). De Gruyter.

Flatt, Bill, et al. Counseling the Homosexual. 11.00 (ISBN 0-934916-49-7). Natl Christian Pr.

Flattery, George M. Teaching for Christian Maturity. 126p. 1968. 1.50 (ISBN 0-88243-618-X, 02-0618). Gospel Pub.

Flaubert, Gustave. The Temptation of Saint Anthony. Mrosovsky, Kitty, tr. LC 80-70452. (Illus.). 288p. 1981. 29.95x (ISBN 0-8014-1239-0). Cornell U Pr.

Flavel, John. The Mystery of Providence. 1976. pap. 3.95 (ISBN 0-85151-104-X). Banner of Truth.

Flaviux, Josephus see Josephus, Flavius.

Fleck, G. Peter. The Mask of Religion. LC 79-9644. (Library of Liberal Religion). 204p. 1980. 12.95 (ISBN 0-87975-125-8). Prometheus Bks.

Fleck, J. Roland & Carter, John D., eds. Psychology & Christianity: Integrative Readings. LC 81-7911. 400p. (Orig.). 1981. pap. 15.95 (ISBN 0-687-34740-8). Abingdon.

Fleck, Ludwig. Genesis & Development of a Scientific Fact. Trenn, Thaddeus J. & Merton, Robert K., eds. Bradley, Fred, tr. from Ger. LC 79-12521. 224p. 1981. pap. 8.00x (ISBN 0-226-25325-2). U of Chicago Pr.

Fleece, Isabel. Not by Accident. 1987. pap. 1.95 (ISBN 0-317-54045-9). Moody.

Fleg, Edmond. The Jewish Anthology. Samuel, Maurice, tr. LC 72-142934. 399p. 1975. Repr. of 1925 ed. lib. bdg. 22.50x (ISBN 0-8371-5824-9, FLJA). Greenwood.

--Why I Am a Jew. 2nd facsimile ed. Wise, Louise W., tr. from Fr. LC 74-27984. (Modern Jewish Experience Ser.). (Eng.). 1975. Repr. of 1945 ed. 13.00 (ISBN 0-405-06711-9). Ayer Co Pubs.

--Why I Am a Jew. Wise, Louise W., tr. from Fr. LC 75-4124. 1985. pap. 4.95 (ISBN 0-8197-0009-6). Bloch.

Fleisch, Paul. Die Moderne Gemeinschaftsbewegung in Deutschland. Dayton, Donald W., ed. (The Higher Christian Life Ser.). 605p. 1985. 75.00 (ISBN 0-8240-6419-4). Garland Pub.

Fleischner, E., ed. Auschwitz - Beginning of a New Era? Reflections on the Holocaust. 35.00x (ISBN 0-87068-499-X); pap. 16.95. Ktav.

Fleischner, Eva. Judaism in German Christian Theology since 1945: Christianity & Israel Considered in Terms of Mission. LC 75-22374. (ATLA Monograph: No. 8). 205p. 1975. 17.50 (ISBN 0-8108-0835-8). Scarecrow.

Fleisher, David & Freedman, David M. Death of an American: The Killing of John Singer. (Illus.). 248p. 1983. 15.95 (ISBN 0-8264-0231-3). Crossroad NY.

Fleming, Austin. Yours Is a Share: The Call of Liturgical Ministry. 1985. pap. 4.95 (ISBN 0-317-38558-5). Pastoral Pr.

Fleming, Austin H. Preparing for Liturgy: A Theology & Sprituality. (Orig.). 1985. pap. 6.95 (ISBN 0-912405-16-3). Pastoral Pr.

Fleming, Bruce C. E. Contextualization of Theology: An Evangelical Assessment. 1981. pap. 5.95 (ISBN 0-87808-431-2). William Carey Lib.

Fleming, David A., ed. Religious Life at the Crossroads. 200p. (Orig.). 1985. pap. 8.95 (ISBN 0-8091-2709-1). Paulist Pr.

Fleming, David H., ed. The Reformation in Scotland, Causes, Characteristics, Consequences: Stone Lectures at Princeton Theological Seminary, 1907-1908. LC 83-45579. Date not set. Repr. of 1910 ed. 67.50 (ISBN 0-404-19897-X). AMS Pr.

Fleming, David L. A Contemporary Reading of the Spiritual Exercises: A Companion to St. Ignatius' Text. 2nd ed. Ganss, George E., ed. LC 80-81812. (Study Aids on Jesuit Topics Ser.:. No.2). 112p. 1980. pap. 3.00 (ISBN 0-912422-47-5); smyth sewn 4.00 (ISBN 0-912422-48-3). Inst Jesuit.

--Modern Spiritual Exercises: A Contemporary Reading of the Spiritual Exercises of St. Ignatius. LC 82-46055. 152p. 1983. pap. 3.95 (ISBN 0-385-18853-6, Im). Doubleday.

--The Spiritual Exercises of St. Ignatius: A Literal Translation & a Contemporary Reading. Ganss, George E., ed. LC 77-93429. (Study Aids on Jesuit Topics Ser.: No. 7). 290p. 1978. smyth sewn 9.00 (ISBN 0-912422-31-9). Inst Jesuit.

Fleming, Gerald. Hitler & the Final Solution. LC 83-24535. (Illus.). 219p. 1984. 25.00 (ISBN 0-520-05103-3). U of Cal Pr.

Fleming, Jean. Between Walden & the Whirlwind. (Christian Character Library). 133p. 1985. hdbk. 8.95 (ISBN 0-89109-520-9). NavPress.

--El Corazon de Una Madre. Araujo, Juan S., tr. from Eng. Tr. of A Mother's Heart. (Span.). 144p. 1987. pap. 4.25 (ISBN 0-88113-029-X). Edit Betania.

Fleming, Jean M. Between Walden & the Whirlwind. 133p. 1987. pap. 3.95. NavPress.

Fleming, John V. From Bonaventure to Bellini: An Essay in Franciscan Exegesis. LC 82-47593. (Princeton Essays on the Arts Ser.: No. 14). (Illus.). 192p. 1982. 28.00x (ISBN 0-691-07270-1); pap. 14.50 L.P.E. (ISBN 0-691-10143-4). Princeton U Pr.

--An Introduction to the Franciscan Literature of the Middle Ages. 274p. 1977. 10.95 (ISBN 0-8199-0651-4). Franciscan Herald.

Fleming, Peggy, ed. see Continental Assocation of Funeral & Memorial Societies, Inc.

Fleming, Peter. Bayonets to Lhasa. LC 73-16737. (Illus.). 1974. Repr. of 1961 ed. lib. bdg. 22.50x (ISBN 0-8371-7216-0, FLBL). Greenwood.

Fleming, Sanford. Children & Puritanism: The Place of Children in the Life & Thought of the New England Churches, 1620-1847. LC 70-89178. (American Education: Its Men, Institutions & Ideas Ser). 1969. Repr. of 1933 ed. 15.00 (ISBN 0-405-01416-3). Ayer Co Pubs.

Fleming, Stuart, et al. The Egyptian Mummy: Secrets & Science. (University Museum Handbook Ser.: No. 1). (Illus.). x, 93p. (Orig.). 1980. pap. 10.00x (ISBN 0-934718-38-5). Univ Mus of U Pa.

Flender, Harold. Rescue in Denmark. LC 80-81716. (Illus.). 281p. (Orig.). 1963. pap. 10.95 (ISBN 0-89604-018-6). Holocaust Pubns.

Flesseman-Van Leer, E. A Faith for Today. Steely, John E., tr. LC 79-56514. (Special Studies Ser.: No. 7). vii, 148p. 1980. pap. 6.95 (ISBN 0-932180-06-X). NABPR.

Fletcher, Alice C. Indian Games & Dances with Native Songs. LC 75-136369. Repr. of 1915 ed. 14.50 (ISBN 0-404-07229-1). AMS Pr.

Fletcher, Angus. The Prophetic Moment: An Essay on Spenser. LC 73-130587. 1971. 20.00x (ISBN 0-226-25332-5). U of Chicago Pr.

Fletcher, Anthony. The Outbreak of the English Civil War. 480p. 1985. pap. text ed. 19.95 (ISBN 0-7131-6454-9). E Arnold.

Fletcher, Charles R. Gustavus Adolphus & the Struggle of Protestantism for Existence. LC 73-14441. (Heroes of the Nations Ser.). Repr. of 1892 ed. 30.00 (ISBN 0-404-58260-5). AMS Pr.

Fletcher, Cynthia H. My Jesus Pocketbook of ABC's. LC 81-80218. (Illus.). 32p. (Orig.). 1981. pap. 0.49 (ISBN 0-937420-01-8). Stirrup Assoc.

Fletcher, Ella A. The Law of the Rhythmic Breath. LC 80-19750. 372p. 1980. Repr. of 1979 ed. lib. bdg. 19.95x (ISBN 0-89370-644-2). Borgo Pr.

Fletcher, George. Predestination. pap. 0.50 (ISBN 0-686-64389-5). Reiner.

Fletcher, H. Use of the Bible in Milton's Prose. LC 75-95425. (Studies in Milton, No. 22). 1970. Repr. of 1929 ed. lib. bdg. 39.95x (ISBN 0-8383-0974-7). Haskell.

Fletcher, Harris F. Milton Studies in Honor of Harris Francis Fletcher. LC 74-16488. 1974. Repr. of 1961 ed. lib. bdg. 30.00 (ISBN 0-8414-4247-9). Folcroft.

--Milton's Rabbinical Readings. LC 67-30701. 344p. 1967. Repr. of 1930 ed. 29.50x (ISBN 0-87752-034-8). Gordian.

--Milton's Rabbinical Readings. LC 67-22303. 344p. 1967. Repr. of 1930 ed. 29.50 (ISBN 0-208-00335-5, Archon). Shoe String.

--Milton's Semitic Studies. LC 74-18236. 1973. lib. bdg. 27.50 (ISBN 0-8414-4249-5). Folcroft.

--Milton's Semitic Studies & Some Manifestations of Them in His Poetry. LC 66-29575. 155p. 1966. Repr. of 1926 ed. 14.50x (ISBN 0-87752-035-6). Gordian.

--Use of the Bible in Milton's Prose. 1973. lib. bdg. 59.95 (ISBN 0-87968-014-8). Gordon Pr.

--The Use of the Bible in Milton's Prose. Repr. of 1929 ed. 15.00. Johnson Repr.

Fletcher, J. S. Reformation in Northern England. LC 71-118469. 1971. Repr. of 1925 ed. 23.50x (ISBN 0-8046-1218-8, Pub. by Kennikat). Assoc Faculty Pr.

Fletcher, John. The Painted Churches of Romania: A Visitor's Impressions. (Illus.). 52p. 1971. 22.95 (ISBN 0-88010-062-1, Pub. by Steinerbooks). Anthroposophic.

--Portrait of a Preacher. 8.95 (ISBN 0-686-12902-4). Schmul Pub Co.

Fletcher, Joseph. Moral Responsibility: Situation Ethics at Work. LC 67-14515. 256p. (Orig.). 1967. pap. 4.95 (ISBN 0-664-24770-9). Westminster.

--Situation Ethics: The New Morality. LC 66-11917. 176p. 1966. pap. 6.95 (ISBN 0-664-24691-5). Westminster.

Fletcher, Joseph & Montgomery, John W. Situation Ethics: True or False. 90p. (Orig.). 1972. pap. 2.95 (ISBN 0-87123-525-0, 200525). Bethany Hse.

Fletcher, Joseph F. William Temple, Twentieth-Century Christian. LC 63-12587. 1963. text ed. 15.00x (ISBN 0-8401-0741-2). A R Allenson.

Fletcher, Mary. My Very First Prayer-Time Book. (Very First Bible Stories Ser.). 1984. 1.59 (ISBN 0-87162-274-2, D8503). Warner Pr.

Fletcher, R. A. The Episcopate in the Kingdom of Leon in the Twelfth Century. (Historical Monographs). (Illus.). 1978. 42.00x (ISBN 0-19-821869-9). Oxford U Pr.

Fletcher, Robert S. History of Oberlin College: From Its Foundation Through the Civil War, 2 vols. in 1. LC 75-165716. (American Education Ser, No. 2). 1971. Repr. of 1943 ed. 60.50 (ISBN 0-405-03705-8). Ayer Co Pubs.

Fletcher, Sarah. Bible Story Book: New Testament. LC 56-1427. (Continued Applied Christianity Ser.). 1983. 10.50 (ISBN 0-570-04080-9). Concordia.

--Bible Story Book: Old Testament. LC 83-1801. (Continued Applied Christianity Ser.). 1983. 10.50 (ISBN 0-570-04079-5, 56-1426). Concordia.

--Christian Babysitter's Handbook. 1985. pap. 3.95 (ISBN 0-570-03948-7, 12-2881). Concordia.

--Stewardship: Taking Care of God's World. (Illus.). 1984. pap. 3.95 (ISBN 0-570-04106-6, 56-1498). Concordia.

Fletcher, William. The Second Greatest Commandment. LC 83-62501. 156p. 1983. pap. 4.95 (ISBN 0-89109-502-0). NavPress.

--Soviet Believers: The Religious Sector of the Population. LC 80-25495. 276p. 1981. 27.50x (ISBN 0-7006-0211-9). U Pr of KS.

--The Triumph of Surrender: Responding to the Greatness of God. (Christian Character Library). 190p. Date not set. 8.95 (ISBN 0-89109-538-1). NavPress.

Fletcher, William c. Soviet Charismatics: The Pentecostals in the U. S. S. R. (American University Studies VII (Theology & Religion): Vol. 9). 287p. 1985. text ed. 25.15 (ISBN 0-8204-0226-5). P Lang Pubs.

Fletcher, William M. El Segundo de los Grandes Mandamientos. Carrodeguas, Angel, ed. Romanenghi de Powell, Elsie R., tr. from Eng. Tr. of The Second Greatest Commandment. (Span.). 192p. Date not set. pap. text ed. 2.95 (ISBN 0-8297-0722-0). Life Pubs Intl.

Fleure, H. F. & Peake, Harold. Priests & Kings. (Corridors of Time Ser.: No. 4). 1927. 29.50x (ISBN 0-686-83710-X). Elliots Bks.

Fleury, C. Rohault. La Messe: Etudes Archeologiques sur ses Monuments, 8 vols. (Fr., Illus.). 1722p. Repr. of 1889 ed. lib. bdg. 600.00x (ISBN 0-89241-153-8). Caratzas.

Fleury, C. Rohault de see De Fleury, C. Rohault.

Fleury, C. Rohault de see Fleury, C. Rohault.

Flew, A. G. N., jt. ed. see Warren, Thomas B.

Flew, Anthony, jt. auth. see Habermas, Gary.

Flew, Anthony, jt. ed. see Carter, Curtis I.

Flew, Antony. God: A Critical Enquiry. 210p. 1984. pap. 8.95 (ISBN 0-87548-371-2). Open Court.

--God, Freedom & Immortality: A Critical Analysis. LC 84-42543. 183p. 1984. pap. text ed. 10.95 (ISBN 0-87975-251-3). Prometheus Bks.

Flew, Robert N. & Davies, Rupert E., eds. The Catholicity of Protestantism: Being a Report Presented to His Grace the Archbishop of Canterbury by a Group of Free Churchmen. LC 80-29108. 159p. 1981. Repr. of 1950 ed. lib. bdg. 22.50x (ISBN 0-313-22825-6, FLCAT). Greenwood.

Flewelling, Ralph T. The Reason in Faith. LC 75-3148. Repr. of 1924 ed. 24.00 (ISBN 0-404-59155-8). AMS Pr.

Flick, Alexander C. Decline of the Medieval Church, 2 vols. (Bibliography & Reference Ser.: No. 133). 1968. Repr. of 1930 ed. Set. 48.00 (ISBN 0-8337-1158-X). B Franklin.

--Rise of the Medieval Church & Its Influence on the Civilization of Western Europe from the 1st to the 13th Century. 636p. 1973. Repr. of 1909 ed. lib. bdg. 33.50 (ISBN 0-8337-1159-8). B Franklin.

Flick, Maurizio, jt. auth. see Alszeghy, Zoltan.

Fliegel, Carl J., compiled by. Index to the Records of the Moravian Mission among the Indians of North America, 2 vols. 1407p. 1970. Set. 400.00 (ISBN 0-89235-018-0). Res Pubns CT.

Flinder, Alexander. Secrets of the Bible Seas: An Underwater Archaeologist in the Holy Land. (Illus.). 192p. 1986. 17.95 (ISBN 0-7278-2047-8). Salem Hse Pubs.

Flinn, Frank, ed. Christology: The Center & the Periphery. 256p. 1987. 21.95 (ISBN 0-913757-75-6). Paragon Hse.

--Hermeneutics & Horizons: The Shape of the Future. LC 82-50053. 445p. (Orig.). 1982. pap. 12.95. Rose Sharon Pr.

Flinn, Frank K., ed. Hermeneutics & Horizons: The Shape of the Future. LC 82-50053. (Conference Ser.: No. 11). xvii, 445p. (Orig.). 1982. pap. text ed. 11.95 (ISBN 0-932894-11-9, Pub. by New Era Bks). Paragon Hse.

Flinn, Frank K. & Hendricks, Tyler, eds. Religion in the Pacific Era. 244p. (Orig.). 1985. (Pub. by New Era Bks.); pap. text ed. 12.95 (ISBN 0-913757-19-5, Pub. by New Era Bks.). Paragon Hse.

Flint, Carol. Flat in Bliss. 1980. 2.00 (ISBN 0-936814-06-3). New Collage.

Flint, Tommy & Griffin, Neil. Gospel Guitar. 48p. 1976. wkbk 2.95 (ISBN 0-89228-018-2). Impact Bks MO.

Flint, W. Russell, tr. see Thomas a Kempis.

Flint, William W. Use of Myth to Create Suspense. (Studies in Comparative Literature, No. 35). 1970. pap. 24.95x (ISBN 0-8383-0030-8). Haskell.

Flitch, J. Crawford, tr. see Unamuno, Miguel.

Floding, Mathew, jt. auth. see Nystrom, Carolyn.

Floding, Matthew, jt. auth. see Nystrom, Carolyn.

Flodstrom, John H., tr. see Ey, Henri.

Flood, Bob. The Story of Moody Church. (Orig.). 1985. pap. 5.95 (ISBN 0-8024-0539-8). Moody.

Flood, David. Franciscan Women. 64p. 1976. pap. 0.95 (ISBN 0-8199-0593-3). Franciscan Herald.

Flood, David & Matura, Thadee. The Birth of a Movement. LaChance, Paul & Schwartz, Paul, trs. 168p. 1975. 6.95 (ISBN 0-8199-0567-4). Franciscan Herald.

Flood, Edmund. The Laity Today & Tomorrow. 120p. (Orig.). 1987. pap. 4.95 (ISBN 0-8091-2848-9). Paulist Pr.

--Making More of Holy Week. 1984. pap. 3.95 pamphlet (ISBN 0-8091-5184-7). Paulist Pr.

--More Parables For Now. 4.95 (ISBN 0-87193-192-3). Dimension Bks.

--Parables for Now. 4.95 (ISBN 0-87193-186-9). Dimension Bks.

Flood, Gregory. I'm Looking for Mr. Right, But I'll Settle for Mr. Right Away: AIDS, True Love, the Perils of Safe Sex, & Other Spiritual Concerns of the Gay Male. 136p. (Orig.). 1987. pap. 6.95 (ISBN 0-938407-00-7). Brob Hse Bks.

Flood, Robert. Faith for All Generations. LC 86-70628. Orig. Title: Up with America. 96p. 1986. pap. 4.95 (ISBN 0-89636-214-0). Accent Bks.

Flood, Robert G. The Christian's Vacation & Travel Guide. 224p. 1982. pap. 9.95 (ISBN 0-8423-0260-3). Tyndale.

--Thirty Minute Panorama of the Bible. (Orig.). 1984. pap. 1.95 (ISBN 0-8024-8747-5). Moody.

Flood, Robert G. & Jenkins, Jerry B. Teaching the Word, Reaching the World. 1985. text ed. 14.95 (ISBN 0-8024-8567-7). Moody.

Flora, Cornelia B. Pentecostalism in Colombia: Baptism by Fire & Spirit. LC 74-4974. 288p. 1976. 26.50 (ISBN 0-8386-1578-3). Fairleigh Dickinson.

Flora, Steven R., jt. auth. see Barnett, Timothy L.

Flores, Bess, jt. ed. see Coppell, William.

Flores, Jose. Profecia y Carisma, Que de las Lenguas? Orig. Title: Prophecy & Charisma. (Span.). 68p. 1974. pap. 2.25 (ISBN 0-8254-1238-2). Kregel.

Flores, Jose, tr. see Collins, Gary.

Flores, Jose, tr. see Karo, Nancy & Mickelson, Alvera.

Floridi, Alexis. Moscow & the Vatican. 365p. 1986. 23.50 (ISBN 0-88233-647-9). Ardis Pubs.

Florinsky, N. I. Soslasno li c Evangelijem Dejstvoval i uchil Ljuter? Tr. of Were the Actions & Teachings of Luther in Accord with the Gospel? 166p. 1975. pap. text ed. 6.00 (ISBN 0-317-30257-4). Holy Trinity.

Florio, Anthony. You Can Make Your Marriage Stronger. (Christian Counseling Aids Ser). 1978. pap. 1.25 (ISBN 0-8010-3484-1). Baker Bk.

Florisoone, Michel. Dictionnaire des Cathedrales de France. (Fr.). 256p. 1971. pap. 6.95 (ISBN 0-686-56834-6, M-6612). French & Eur.

Floristan, Casiano & Duquoc, Christian. Francis of Assisi Today, Vol. 149. (Concilium 1981). 128p. (Orig.). 1981. pap. 6.95 (ISBN 0-8164-2349-0, HarpR). Har-Row.

Floristan, Casiano, jt. auth. see Duquoc, Christian.

Floristan, Casiano & DuQuoc, Christian, eds. Forgiveness. (Concilium Nineteen Eighty-Six Ser.). 120p. 1986. pap. 6.95 (ISBN 0-567-30064-1, Pub. by T & T Clark Ltd UK). Fortress.

Flournoy, Richard L., et al. One Hundred Ways to Obtain Peace: Overcoming Anxiety. (Life Enrichment Ser.). 1986. pap. 4.95 (ISBN 0-8010-3528-7). Baker Bk.

Flower, Margaret. The Wonderful Discoveries of the Witchcrafts of M. & P. Flower. LC 72-5992. (English Experience Ser.: No. 517). 50p. 1972. Repr. of 1619 ed. 6.00 (ISBN 90-221-0517-2). Walter J Johnson.

Flowers, Ronald B., jt. ed. see Miller, Robert T.

Floyd, Carol M. Anybody Listening? 1982. 2.50 (ISBN 0-89536-572-3, 0119). CSS of Ohio.

Floyd, Diane, ed. see Ward, Harvey.

Floyd, Mary K. Abortion Bibliography for 1970. LC 72-78877. (Abortion Bibliography Ser.: No. 2). 120p. 1972. 7.50x (ISBN 0-87875-024-X). Whitston Pub.

--Abortion Bibliography for 1971. LC 72-78877. (Abortion Bibliography Ser.: No. 3). 125p. 1973. 11.00x (ISBN 0-87875-030-4). Whitston Pub.

--Abortion Bibliography for 1972. LC 72-78877. (Abortion Bibliography Ser.: No. 4). xx, 223p. 1973. 11.00x (ISBN 0-87875-044-4). Whitston Pub.

--Abortion Bibliography for 1973. LC 72-78877. (Abortion Bibliography Ser.: No. 5). xxiii, 237p. 1974. 11.00x (ISBN 0-87875-056-8). Whitston Pub.

--Abortion Bibliography for 1974. LC 72-78877. (Abortion Bibliography Ser.: No. 6). 1975. 15.00x (ISBN 0-87875-079-7). Whitston Pub.

--Abortion Bibliography for 1976. LC 72-78877. (Abortion Bibliography Ser.: Vol. 7). 1978. 17.00x (ISBN 0-87875-126-2). Whitston Pub.

Floyd, Tim. Welcome to the Real World. LC 84-5876. 1984. pap. 5.95 (ISBN 0-8054-5001-7). Broadman.

Floyd, Tony. United to Christ. (Illus.). 80p. (Orig.). 1983. pap. 5.95 (ISBN 0-85819-420-1, Pub. by JBCE). ANZ Religious Pubns.

Floyer, A. M. Evolution of Ancient Buddhism. 59.95 (ISBN 0-8490-0143-9). Gordon Pr.

Fluckiger, W. Lynn. Unique Advantages of Being a Mormon. pap. 3.95 (ISBN 0-89036-138-X). Hawkes Pub Inc.

Fluehr-Lobban, Carolyn. Islamic Law & Society in the Sudan. 275p. 1986. 32.50x (ISBN 0-7146-3280-5, F Cass Co). Biblio Dist.

Flumiani, C. M. The Philosophy of Life & the Philosophy of Death. 89p. 1987. pap. 8.50 (ISBN 0-86650-223-8). Gloucester Art.

Flumiani, Carlo M. What a Teenager Ought to Know About God. (Illus.). 1978. 42.50 (ISBN 0-89266-140-2). Am Classical Coll Pr.

Flynn, Eileen P. Human Fertilization "In Vitro". A Catholic Moral Perspective. LC 83-27343. 202p. (Orig.). 1984. lib. bdg. 25.00 (ISBN 0-8191-3819-3); pap. text ed. 12.25 (ISBN 0-8191-3820-7). U Pr of Amer.

--My Country Right or Wrong? Selective Conscientious Objection in the Nuclear Age. 1985. pap. 3.95 (ISBN 0-317-18110-6). Loyola.

Flynn, George Q. Roosevelt & Romanism: Catholics & American Diplomacy, 1937-1945. LC 75-35343. (Contributions in American History: No. 47). 272p. 1976. lib. bdg. 29.95 (ISBN 0-8371-8581-5, FRR/). Greenwood.

Flynn, J. G., tr. see Shahrastani, Muhammad B.

Flynn, Johanna & Canfield, Anita. Visiting Teaching: A Call to Serve. 80p. (Orig.). 1984. pap. 3.95 (ISBN 0-934126-42-9). Randall Bk Co.

Flynn, John S. Influence of Puritanism. LC 72-102569. 1970. Repr. of 1920 ed. 23.00x (ISBN 0-8046-0729-X, Pub. by Kennikat). Assoc Faculty Pr.

Flynn, Leslie. The Twelve. 156p. 1982. pap. 5.95 (ISBN 0-88207-310-9). Victor Bks.

Flynn, Leslie B. Holy Contradictions. 156p. 1987. pap. 5.95 (ISBN 0-89693-239-7). Victor Bks.

--Nineteen Gifts of the Spirit. LC 74-91027. 204p. 1974. pap. 6.95 (ISBN 0-88207-701-5). Victor Bks.

--The Sustaining Power of Hope. 132p. 1985. pap. 4.95 (ISBN 0-89693-600-7). Victor Bks.

--What Is Man. Chao, Lorna Y., tr. (Chinese.). 1985. pap. write for info. (ISBN 0-941598-27-6). Living Spring Pubns.

--You Don't Have to Go It Alone. LC 80-66722. 160p. (Orig.). 1981. pap. 4.95 (ISBN 0-89636-058-X). Accent Bks.

Flynn, Robert. And Holy Is His Name. 1983. 5.95 (ISBN 0-87193-197-4). Dimension Bks.

Focsa, Marcela, jt. auth. see Irimie, Cornel.

Foege, Richard H. Stewardship Preaching: Series C. 56p. (Orig.). 1985. pap. 4.95 (ISBN 0-8066-2152-4, 10-6003). Augsburg.

Foerster, Werner. From the Exile to Christ: Historical Introduction to Palestinian Judaism. Harris, Gordon E., ed. LC 64-18151. 264p. 1964. pap. 10.95 (ISBN 0-8006-0978-6, 1-978). Fortress.

Fogarty, Gerald P. The Vatican & the American Hierarchy from 1870 to 1965. 1985. pap. 16.95 (ISBN 0-317-42752-0). M Glazier.

Fogarty, Michael P. Christian Democracy in Western Europe, 1820-1953. LC 73-11997. (Illus.). 448p. 1974. Repr. of 1957 ed. lib. bdg. 26.75x (ISBN 0-8371-7114-8, FOCH). Greenwood.

Fogelklou, Emilia. Reality & Radiance: Selected Autobiographical Works of Emilia Fogelklou. Lutz, Howard T., ed. & tr. from Swedish. 196p. (Orig.). 1986. pap. 10.95 (ISBN 0-913408-89-1). Friends United.

Fogelklou-Norlind, Emilia. Atonement of George Fox. Mather, Eleanore P., ed. LC 75-84675. (Orig.). 1969. pap. 2.50x (ISBN 0-87574-166-5). Pendle Hill.

Fogle, Jeanne S. Signs of God's Love. pap. 4.50. Westminster.

--Signs of God's Love: Baptism & Communion. Duckert, Mary J. & Lane, W. Ben, eds. (Illus.). 32p. (Orig.). 1984. pap. 4.50 (ISBN 0-664-24636-2). Geneva Pr.

--Symbols of God's Love: Codes & Passwords. Ducket, Mary Jean & Lane, W. Benson, eds. LC 86-12014. (Illus.). 32p. (Orig.). 1986. pap. 4.95 (ISBN 0-664-24050-X, A Geneva Press Publication). Westminster.

Fogle, Sonja, jt. auth. see Harpers, Ferry W.

Fogle, Willa. Beside the Still Waters. 1979. pap. 4.00 (ISBN 0-87516-282-7). De Vorss.

Foglio, Frank. Hey God! A Large Italian Family's Amazing Experience with God. LC 72-87328. 1972. pap. 4.95 (ISBN 0-88270-007-3). Bridge Pub.

Foh, Susan. Women & the Word of God. pap. 6.95 (ISBN 0-87552-268-8). Presby & Reformed.

Fohr, S. D. Adam & Eve: The Spiritual Symbolism of Genesis & Exodus. LC 86-1497. 162p. (Orig.). 1986. lib. bdg. 25.75 (ISBN 0-8191-5267-6); pap. text ed. 10.25 (ISBN 0-8191-5268-4). U Pr of Amer.

Fohrer, Georg. Geschichte der Israelitischen Religion. (Ger.). xvi, 367p. 1969. 20.80x (ISBN 3-11-002652-X). De Gruyter.

--Theologische Grundstrukturen des Alten Testaments. (Theologische Bibliothek Toepelmann, 24). 1972. pap. 23.20x (ISBN 3-11-003874-9). De Gruyter.

Fohrer, Georg, et al, eds. Hebrew & Aramaic Dictionary of the Old Testament. Johnstone, W. A., tr. from Ger. LC 73-82430. (Hebrew & Aramaic.). viii, 344p. 1973. text ed. 16.75 (ISBN 3-11-004572-9). De Gruyter.

Fokkelman, J. P. Narrative & the Poetry in the Books of Samuel; Vol. 2: The Crossing Fates. (Studia Semitica Neerlandica: No. 20). 744p. 1986. 50.00 (ISBN 90-232-2175-3, Pub. by Van Gorcum Holland). Longwood Pub Group.

--Narrative Art & Poetry in the Books of Samuel: A Full Interpretation on Stylistic & Structural Analysis, Volume 1. (King David-Studia Semitica Neerlandica: No. 20). 534p. 1981. text ed. 50.00 (ISBN 90-232-1852-3). Longwood Pub Group.

Folda, Jaroslav. Crusader Manuscript Illumination at Saint-Jean D'Acre, 1275-1291. LC 75-2991. (Illus.). 646p. 1975. 70.50x (ISBN 0-691-03907-0). Princeton U Pr.

Foley, Albert S. Bishop Healy: Beloved Outcaste. LC 79-94130. (American Negro: His History & Literature, Ser. No. 3). 1970. Repr. of 1954 ed. 17.00 (ISBN 0-405-01925-4). Ayer Co Pubs.

--God's Men of Color: The Colored Catholic Priest of the U. S. 1854-1954. LC 69-18569. (American Negro: His History & Literature, Ser. No. 2). 1969. Repr. of 1955 ed. 14.00 (ISBN 0-405-01864-9). Ayer Co Pubs.

Foley, Grover, tr. see Barth, Karl.

Foley, Helen S. Bible Records, Barbour County, Ala, Vol. 1. 80p. 1983. pap. 10.00 (ISBN 0-89308-180-9). Southern Hist Pr.

--Bible Records, Barbour County, Ala, Vol. 2. 84p. 1983. pap. 10.00 (ISBN 0-89308-181-7). Southern Hist Pr.

Foley, Henry. Records of the English Province of the Society of Jesus, 7 Vols. in 8. (Illus.). Repr. of 1883 ed. Set. 690.00 (ISBN 0-384-16310-6). Johnson Repr.

Foley, Jeanne M., jt. auth. see DePalma, David J.

Foley, Leonard. Believing in Jesus: A Popular Overview of the Catholic Faith. (Illus.). 185p. (Orig.). 1981. pap. text ed. 5.95 (ISBN 0-912228-79-2). St Anthony Mess Pr.

--From Eden to Nazareth: Finding Our Story in the Old Testament. (Illus.). 103p. (Orig.). 1983. pap. text ed. 3.50 (ISBN 0-86716-020-9). St Anthony Mess Pr.

--Saint of the Day: A Life & Lesson for Each of the 173 Saints of the New Missal, Vol. 2. (Illus.). 160p. 1975. pap. 3.50 (ISBN 0-912228-20-2). St Anthony Mess Pr.

--Signs of Love: The Sacraments of Christ. (Illus.). 1976. pap. 1.95 (ISBN 0-912228-32-6). St Anthony Mess Pr.

Foley, Leonard, ed. Saint of the Day. (Illus.). 354p. 1981. text ed. 10.95 (ISBN 0-912228-96-2). St Anthony Mess Pr.

--Saint of the Day: A Life & Lesson for Each of the 173 Saints of the New Missal, Vol. 1. (Illus.). 1974. pap. 3.50 (ISBN 0-912228-16-4). St Anthony Mess Pr.

Foley, N. Nadine, intro. by. Preaching & the Non-Ordained: An Interdisciplinary Study. 1983. pap. 6.95 (ISBN 0-8146-1291-1). Liturgical Pr.

Foley, Rita. Create! 2nd ed. (Catechist Training Ser.). 1982. 3.95 (ISBN 0-8215-1230-7). Sadlier.

Foley, Stepehn, ed. see More, Thomas.

Foliot, G. The Letters & Charters of Gilbert Foliot. Morey, A. & Brooke, C. N., eds. 1967. Cambridge U Pr.

Folk, Jerry L., jt. auth. see Lutz, Charles P.

Folkening, John. Handbells in the Liturgical Service. (Illus.). 52p. (Orig.). 1984. pap. 3.00 (ISBN 0-570-01328-3, 99-1254). Concordia.

Follett, Barbara L. Checklist for a Perfect Wedding. rev. & expanded ed. LC 85-29206. (Illus.). 160p. 1986. pap. 3.95 (ISBN 0-385-23588-7). Doubleday.

Follette, John W. Broken Bread: Sermons & Poems. 216p. 1957. pap. 4.95 (ISBN 0-88243-474-8, 02-0474). Gospel Pub.

Follette, Marcel la. Creationism, Science, & the Law: Arkansas Case Documents & Commentaries. LC 82-21646. 232p. (Orig.). 1983. pap. 11.95x (ISBN 0-262-62041-3). MIT Pr.

Folliet, Joseph. The Evening Sun. 183p. 1983. 12.50 (ISBN 0-8199-0817-7). Franciscan Herald.

Follis, Elaine R. Directions in Biblical Hebrew Poetry. (JSOT Supplement Ser.: No. 40). 340p. 1986. text ed. 33.50x (ISBN 1-85075-013-0, Pub. by JSOT Pr England); pap. text ed. 15.95x (ISBN 1-85075-012-2). Eisenbrauns.

Folsom, James K., jt. ed. see Slotkin, Richard.

Foltz, Nancy T., ed. Handbook of Adult Religious Education. 272p. (Orig.). 1986. pap. 14.95 (ISBN 0-89135-052-7). Religious Educ.

Foner, Philip S. & Pacheco, Josephine F. Three Who Dared: Prudence Crandall, Margaret Douglass, Myrtilla Miner-Champions of Antebellum Black Education. LC 83-12830. (Contributions in Women's Studies: No. 47). xviii, 234p. 1984. lib. bdg. 32.95 (ISBN 0-313-23584-8, FTH/). Greenwood.

Fontaine, Carol R. Traditional Sayings in the Old Testament: A Contextual Study. (Bible & Literature Ser.: No. 5). 1982. text ed. 24.95x (ISBN 0-907459-08-0, Pub. by Almond Pr England); pap. text ed. 14.95x (ISBN 0-907459-09-9, Pub. by Almond Pr England). Eisenbrauns.

Fontaine, Jacob, III & Burd, Gene. Jacob Fontaine: From Slavery to the Greatness of the Pulpit, Press, & Public Service. 96p. 1984. pap. 6.95 (ISBN 0-89015-438-4). Eakin Pr.

Fontaine, Patrick. Little Talks About Life. 1956. 4.50 (ISBN 0-8198-0082-1). Dghtrs St Paul.

Fontana, John M. Mankind's Greatest Invention. LC 64-5232. 112p. 1964. 4.95 (ISBN 0-9600034-1-X). J M Fontana.

Fontein, J. Pilgrimage of Sudhana. 1967. text ed. 35.60x (ISBN 90-2796-387-8). Mouton.

Fontenay, Charles L. The Keyen of Fu Tze: The Wise Sayings of Confucious. 1977. 5.95 (ISBN 0-900306-50-5, Pub. by Coombe Springs Pr). Claymont Comm.

Fontenrose, Joseph. Python. 1959. 25.00 (ISBN 0-8196-0285-X). Biblo.

--Python: A Study of Delphic Myth & Its Origins. (California Library Reprint Ser.: No. 108). 637p. 1981. 40.00x (ISBN 0-520-04106-2); pap. 8.95 (ISBN 0-520-04091-0, CAL 449). U of Cal Pr.

Fontes, M. E. Existentialism & Its Implications for Counseling. pap. 0.75 (ISBN 0-8199-0382-5, L38138). Franciscan Herald.

Fontinell, Eugene. Self, God & Immortality: A Jamesian Investigation. 320p. 1986. 34.95 (ISBN 0-87722-428-5). Temple U Pr.

Foont, Ronnie, jt. auth. see Kustanowitz, Shulamit.

Foose, Sandra L. Scrap Saver's Christmas Stitchery. (Illus.). 160p. 1986. 19.95 (ISBN 0-8487-0646-3). Oxmoor Hse.

Foot, Philippa, ed. Theories of Ethics. (Oxford Readings in Philosophy Ser.). 1967. pap. 8.95x (ISBN 0-19-875005-6). Oxford U Pr.

Foot, Philippa R. Virtues & Vices, & Other Essays in Moral Philosophy. LC 78-54794. 1979. 32.50x (ISBN 0-520-03686-7); pap. 5.95 (ISBN 0-520-04396-0, CAL 494). U of Cal Pr.

Foote, Evelyn C. Time with God: Devotional Readings for Youth. LC 72-97604. 1978. pap. 2.75 (ISBN 0-8054-5164-1, 4251-64). Broadman.

Foote, G. W. & Ball, W. P. The Bible Handbook. 372p. 1983. pap. 7.00 (ISBN 0-910309-26-4). Am Atheist.

Foote, G. W. & Ball, W. P., eds. The Bible Handbook: For Freethinkers & Inquiring Christians. 11th ed. LC 71-161330. (Atheist Viewpoint Ser). 176p. 1972. Repr. of 1961 ed. 20.00 (ISBN 0-405-03797-X). Ayer Co Pubs.

Foote, G. W. & Wheeler, J. M., eds. The Jewish Life of Christ: Being Sepher Tolduth Jeshu. (Illus.). 49p. 1982. pap. 3.00 (ISBN 0-910309-02-7). Am Atheist.

Foote, P. G., tr. see Winsnes, Andreas H.

Foote, Samuel. A Treatise on the Passions, So Far As They Regard the Stage. LC 72-144608. Repr. of 1747 ed. 11.50 (ISBN 0-404-02448-3). AMS Pr.

Foote, William H. Sketches of North Carolina. 3rd ed. 593p. 1965. 12.00. Synod NC Church.

Forbes, A. Dean, jt. auth. see Andersen, Francis I.

Forbes, Cheryl. Imagination: Embracing a Theology of Wonder. LC 86-811. (Critical Concern Bks.). 1986. 12.95 (ISBN 0-88070-136-6). Multnomah.

--The Religion of Power. 176p. 1983. 9.95 (ISBN 0-310-45770-X, 12396). Zondervan.

Forbes, Clarence A., ed. see Vida, Marco G.

Forbes, Harrison. Reflections from the Son: For Men. (Orig.). 1986. pap. 5.00 (ISBN 0-915541-07-6). Star Bks Inc.

Forbes-Boyd, Eric. In Crusader Greece. (Illus.). 10.00 (ISBN 0-87556-091-1). Saifer.

Forbes-Leith, W., tr. from Latin. Life of Saint Cuthbert. pap. 6.95 (ISBN 0-317-52092-X). Eastern Orthodox.

Forbush, Bliss. Elias Hicks: Quaker Liberal. LC 56-6250. pap. 95.80 (ISBN 0-317-08431-3, 2050181). Bks Demand UMI.

Forbush, W. B., ed. Fox's Book of Martyrs. 11.95 (ISBN 0-310-24390-4, 9636); pap. 6.95 (ISBN 0-310-24391-2, 9636P). Zondervan.

Forchheimer, Paul. Maimonides' Commentary on Avoth. pap. 5.95 (ISBN 0-87306-332-5). Feldheim.

Forchheimer, Paul, tr. see Hoffmann, David.

Ford, Alice E. Edward Hicks, Painter of the Peaceable Kingdom. LC 52-13392. (Illus.). 1973. Repr. of 1952 ed. 63.00 (ISBN 0-527-30400-X). Kraus Repr.

Ford, Bruce E. Notes on the Celebration of the Eucharist: A Supplement to the Ceremonial Directions of the Book of Common Prayer, 1979. LC 86-21523. 48p. (Orig.). 1986. pap. 7.50 (ISBN 0-942466-10-1). Hymnary Pr.

Ford, Bud & Ford, Donna. The Dulcimer Hymn Book. 72p. 1979. wkbk 4.95 (ISBN 0-89228-054-9). Impact Bks MO.

Ford, Charles W. How to Study the Bible. LC 77-99213. (Radiant Life Ser.). 128p. 1978. pap. text ed. 2.50 (ISBN 0-88243-912-X, 02-0912); tchr's ed. 3.95 (ISBN 0-88243-183-8, 32-0183). Gospel Pub.

--The Inspired Scriptures. LC 78-60267. (Radiant Life Ser.). 128p. 1978. pap. 2.50 (ISBN 0-88243-914-6, 02-0914); tchr's ed. 3.95 (ISBN 0-88243-185-4, 32-0185). Gospel Pub.

--Learning from Hebrews. LC 80-67467. (Radiant Life Ser.). 127p. (Orig.). 1980. 2.50 (ISBN 0-88243-915-4, 02-0915); teacher's ed 3.95 (ISBN 0-88243-188-9, 32-0188). Gospel Pub.

Ford, David F., jt. auth. see Hardy, Daniel W.

Ford, Desmond. The Abomination of Desolation in Biblical Eschatology. LC 79-64195. 1979. pap. text ed. 14.25 (ISBN 0-8191-0757-3). U Pr of Amer.

Ford, Donna, jt. auth. see Ford, Bud.

Ford, Harold W. A History of the Restoration Plea. 2nd ed. 1967. pap. 3.95 (ISBN 0-89900-110-6). College Pr Pub.

Ford, Henry. The International Jew. 59.95 (ISBN 0-8490-0418-7). Gordon Pr.

--The International Jew. 1978. pap. 5.00x (ISBN 0-911038-45-0). Noontide.

--The International Jew, 4 vols. 1984. lib. bdg. 500.95 (ISBN 0-87700-586-9). Revisionist Pr.

Ford, Herschel W. Simple Sermons for Funeral Services. 54p. 1985. pap. 2.95 (ISBN 0-8010-3514-7). Baker Bk.

Ford, J. Massingberd. Trilogy on Wisdom & Celibacy. 1967. 16.95x (ISBN 0-268-00285-1). U of Notre Dame Pr.

Ford, J. Massyngbaerd. My Enemy Is My Guest. LC 84-5812. 192p. 1984. pap. 9.95 (ISBN 0-88344-348-1). Orbis Bks.

Ford, J. Massyngberd. Pentecostal Experience. LC 72-116869. 64p. (Orig.). 1970. pap. 1.95 (ISBN 0-8091-1655-3). Paulist Pr.

Ford, J. Massyngberde, tr. Revelation. LC 74-18796. (Anchor Bible Ser.: Vol. 38). (Illus.). 504p. 1975. 18.00 (ISBN 0-385-00895-3). Doubleday.

Ford, John W., ed. see Company for the Propagation of the Gospel in New England & the Parts Adjacent in America, London.

Ford, L. The Christian Persuader. LC 66-22043. 160p. 1976. pap. 6.00 (ISBN 0-06-062679-8, RD/157, HarpR). Har-Row.

Ford, Lauren. Little Book about God. LC 81-43749. (Illus.). 48p. 1985. 9.95 (ISBN 0-385-17691-0). Doubleday.

Ford, Leighton. Good News Is for Sharing. LC 77-78496. 1977. 6.95 (ISBN 0-89191-083-2). Cook.

Ford, LeRoy. Capacitese Como Lider. Blair, Guillermo, tr. Tr. of Developing Skills for Church Leaders. (Span.). 64p. 1986. pap. 3.75 (ISBN 0-311-17023-4, Edit Mundo). Casa Bautista.

--Modelos Para el Proceso de Ensenanza-Aprendizaje. Gaydou, Nelda B. de & Diaz, Jorge E., trs. from Eng. Tr. of Design for Teaching & Training. (Span., Illus.). 320p. (Orig.). 1986. pap. 5.95 (ISBN 0-311-11042-8). Casa Bautista.

--Pedagogia Ilustrada: Tomo I Principios Generales. Orig. Title: A Primer for Teachers & Leaders. (Illus.). 144p. 1982. pap. 3.95 (ISBN 0-311-11001-0, Edit Mundo). Casa Bautista.

--Using Problem Solving in Teaching & Training. LC 77-178060. (Multi-Media Teaching & Training Ser.). (Orig.). 1972. pap. 5.50 (ISBN 0-8054-3415-1). Broadman.

Ford, Lewis S. The Lure of God: A Biblical Background for Process Theism. 158p. 1985. Repr. of 1978 ed. lib. bdg. 8.75 (ISBN 0-8191-4902-0). U Pr of Amer.

Ford, Sallie R. Mary Bunyan: Blind Daughter of John Bunyan. 9.95 (ISBN 0-685-00748-0). Reiner.

Ford, W. Herschel. Sermons You Can Preach. (Simple Sermon Ser.). 384p. 1983. pap. 10.95 (ISBN 0-310-46971-6). Zondervan.

--Sermons You Can Preach on Acts. 352p. Date not set. pap. 10.95 (ISBN 0-310-38461-3). Zondervan.

--Sermons You Can Preach on John: Simple Sermons. 432p. pap. 12.95 (ISBN 0-310-38451-6, 9835P). Zondervan.

--Sermons You Can Preach on Matthew. 240p. (Orig.). 1985. pap. 8.95 (ISBN 0-310-45521-9, 9834P). Zondervan.

--Simple Sermons for Saints & Sinners. 152p. 1986. pap. 3.95 (ISBN 0-8010-3522-8). Baker Bk.

--Simple Sermons for Special Days & Occasions. 140p. 1985. pap. 4.50 (ISBN 0-8010-3515-5). Baker Bk.

--Simple Sermons for Sunday Morning. 128p. 1986. pap. 3.95 (ISBN 0-8010-3523-6). Baker Bk.

--Simple Sermons for Time & Eternity. 120p. 1985. pap. 3.95 (ISBN 0-8010-3516-3). Baker Bk.

--Simple Sermons of Great Christian Doctrines. 138p. 1985. pap. 4.50 (ISBN 0-8010-3519-8). Baker Bk.

--Simple Sermons on Conversion & Commitment. (W. Herschel Ford Sermon Library). 128p. 1986. pap. 3.95 (ISBN 0-8010-3524-4). Baker Bk.

--Simple Sermons on Evangelistic Themes. 128p. 1986. pap. 3.95 (ISBN 0-8010-3525-2). Baker Bk.

--Simple Sermons on Grace & Glory. 92p. 1986. pap. 3.50 (ISBN 0-8010-3526-0). Baker Bk.

--Simple Sermons on Prayer. 88p. 1985. pap. 3.50 (ISBN 0-8010-3520-1). Baker Bk.

--Simple Sermons on Salvation & Service. 136p. 1986. pap. 4.50 (ISBN 0-8010-3527-9). Baker Bk.

--Simple Sermons on the New Testament Texts. 112p. 1985. pap. 3.95 (ISBN 0-8010-3517-1). Baker Bk.

Forde, Gerhard O. Justification by Faith: A Matter of Death & Life. LC 81-70663. 112p. 1982. pap. 5.95 (ISBN 0-8006-1634-0, 1-1634). Fortress.

--Where God Meets Man: Luther's Down-to-Earth Approach to the Gospel. LC 72-78569. 128p. 1972. pap. 6.95 (ISBN 0-8066-1235-5, 10-7060). Augsburg.

Fordyce, C. J. & Knox, T. M. The Library of Jesus College, Oxford: With an Appendix on the Books Bequeathed Thereto by Lord Herbert of Cherbury. rev. ed. (Oxford Bible Society Ser.: Vol. 5, Pt. 2). Repr. of 1937 ed. 13.00 (ISBN 0-8115-1238-X). Kraus Repr.

Fore, William F. Television & Religion: The Shaping of Faith & Value. 208p. (Orig.). 1987. pap. 11.95 (ISBN 0-8066-2268-7, 10-6229). Augsburg.

Forehand, Mary A. Love Lives Here. (Orig.). 1975. pap. 1.95 (ISBN 0-377-00028-0). Friend Pr.

Forehand, Mary A., jt. auth. see Schirer, Marshall E.

Foreign Service Institute. Hebrew Basic Course. (Hebrew.). 552p. 1980. plus 24 cassettes 215.00x (ISBN 0-88432-040-5, H345). J Norton Pubs.

Forell, Betty & Wind, Betty. Little Benjamin & the First Christmas. (Arch Bks: Set 1). (Illus.). 1964. laminated bdg. 0.99 (ISBN 0-570-06005-2, 59-1113). Concordia.

Forell, George W. Augsburg Confession: A Contemporary Commentary. LC 68-25798. (Orig.). 1968. pap. 6.95 (ISBN 0-8066-0815-3, 10-0518). Augsburg.

--Christian Social Teachings. LC 71-159003. 1971. pap. 7.95 (ISBN 0-8066-1126-X, 10-1179). Augsburg.

--Ethics of Decision: An Introduction to Christian Ethics. LC 55-7767. 176p. 1955. pap. 4.50 (ISBN 0-8006-1770-3, 1-1770). Fortress.

--Faith Active in Love. LC 15-5702. 1954. kivar 7.95 (ISBN 0-8066-0186-8, 10-2165). Augsburg.

--History of Christian Ethics: From the New Testament to Augustine, Vol. 1. LC 79-50096. 248p. 1979. 15.95 (ISBN 0-8066-1715-2, 10-3042). Augsburg.

--The Luther Legacy: An Introduction to Luther's Life & Thought for Today. LC 83-72106. 80p. 1983. pap. 5.95 (ISBN 0-8066-2050-1, 10-4142). Augsburg.

--The Proclamation of the Gospel in a Pluralistic World: Essays on Christianity & Culture. LC 73-79354. pap. 36.00 (2026865). Bks Demand UMI.

--The Protestant Faith. LC 74-26341. 320p. 1975. pap. 9.95 (ISBN 0-8006-1095-4, 1-1095). Fortress.

Forell, George W. & McCue, James F. Confessing One Faith: A Joint Commentary on the Augsburg Confession by Lutheran & Catholic Theologians. LC 80-65557. 368p. 1981. pap. 16.95 (ISBN 0-8066-1802-7, 10-1637). Augsburg.

Forell, George W., ed. & tr. from Ger. Zinzendorf: Nine Public Lectures on Important Subjects in Religion. LC 74-93784. 170p. 1973. text ed. 15.00 (ISBN 0-87745-036-6). U of Iowa Pr.

Forell, George W. & Lehmann, Helmut T., eds. Luther's Works: Career of the Reformer II, Vol. 32. LC 55-9893. 1958. 19.95 (ISBN 0-8006-0332-X, 1-332). Fortress.

Foreman, Kenneth J. From This Day Forward: Thoughts about a Christian Marriage. pap. 2.95x (ISBN 0-685-02584-5). Outlook.

--Romans, First & Second Corinthians. LC 59-10454. (Layman's Bible Commentary Ser: Vol. 21). 1961. pap. 4.95 (ISBN 0-8042-3081-1). John Knox.

Foreman, Kenneth J., et al. Introduction to the Bible. Kelly, Balmer H., et al, eds. LC 59-10454. (Layman's Bible Commentary, Vol. 1). 1959. pap. 4.95 (ISBN 0-8042-3061-7). John Knox.

Foreman, Kenneth J., Jr., ed. see Marshall, James W.

Foreman, Max L. Rx for Living: Take as Needed. 1982. 20.00x (ISBN 0-8197-0490-3). Bloch.

Foresi, Pascal. Celibacy Put to the Gospel Test. 33p. 1969. pap. 1.15 (ISBN 0-911782-16-8). New City.

--Reaching for More. Moran, Hugh J., tr. from Ital. Tr. of Conversazioni con i Focolarini. 128p. (Orig.). 1982. pap. 4.95 (ISBN 0-911782-40-0). New City.

Forest, Grant E. De see De Forest, Grant E.

Forest, James H. Thomas Merton: A Pictorial Biography. LC 80-82249. (Illus.). 112p. (Orig.). 1980. pap. 5.95 (ISBN 0-8091-2284-7). Paulist Pr.

Forestell, J. T. Targumic Traditions. LC 79-19293. (Society of Biblical Literature Aramaic Studies: No. 4). 151p. 1984. pap. 12.00 (ISBN 0-89130-352-9, 06-13-04). Scholars Pr GA.

Forestell, J. Terrence. Proverbs. (Bible Ser.). 1.00 (ISBN 0-8091-5122-7). Paulist Pr.

Forester, Bruce. Signs & Omens. 256p. 1984. 15.95 (ISBN 0-396-08392-7). Dodd.

Forlines, F. Leroy. Christian Standards & Convictions Without Legalism. 1981. pap. 2.25 (ISBN 0-89265-074-5). Randall Hse.

--The Doctrine of Perseverance. 2nd ed. 24p. 1987. pap. price not set. Randall Hse.

--Randall House Bible Commentary: Romans. (Bible Commentary Ser.). 350p. 1986. 19.95 (ISBN 0-89265-116-4). Randall Hse.

Forlines, Leroy. Biblical Ethics. 1973. pap. 5.95 (ISBN 0-89265-014-1). Randall Hse.

--Biblical Systematics. 1975. 7.95 (ISBN 0-89265-025-7); pap. 4.95 (ISBN 0-89265-038-9). Randall Hse.

--Evolution. 1973. pap. 0.95 (ISBN 0-89265-105-9). Randall Hse.

--Inerrancy & the Scriptures. 26p. 1978. pap. 0.95 (ISBN 0-89265-107-5). Randall Hse.

Forlines, Leroy & Picirilli, Robert. A Survey of the Pauline Epistles. 1976. pap. 3.75 (ISBN 0-89265-035-4). Randall Hse.

Forliti, John E. Program Planning for Youth Ministry. LC 75-143. 1975. pap. 4.50 (ISBN 0-88489-061-9). St Marys.

--Reverence for Life & Family Program: Parent-Teacher Resource. 1981. pap. 4.50 176 pp (ISBN 0-697-01789-3); tchr. training tape 9.95 (ISBN 0-697-01837-7). Wm C Brown.

Forman, Charles C. Four Early Bibles in Pilgrim Hall. (Pilgrim Society Notes: No. 9). 1959. 1.00 (ISBN 0-940628-17-1). Pilgrim Soc.

Forman, Charles W. A Faith for the Nations. LC 57-9601. (Layman's Theological Library). 1957. pap. 1.00 (ISBN 0-664-24007-0). Westminster.

--The Island Churches of the South Pacific: Emergence in the Twentieth Century. LC 81-18666. 304p. (Orig.). 1982. pap. 17.50 (ISBN 0-88344-218-3). Orbis Bks.

Forman, Charles W., ed. Christianity in the Non-Western World. facs. ed. LC 71-117792. (Essay Index Reprint Ser). 1967. 17.00 (ISBN 0-8369-1806-1). Ayer Co Pubs.

Formstecher, Salomon. Die Religion des Geistes. Katz, Steven, ed. LC 79-7129. (Jewish Philosophy, Mysticism & History of Ideas Ser.). 1980. Repr. of 1841 ed. lib. bdg. 40.00x (ISBN 0-405-12251-9). Ayer Co Pubs.

Forrer, Richard. Theodicies in Conflict: A Dilemma in Puritan Ethics & Nineteenth-Century American Literature. LC 85-27220. (Contributions to the Study of Religion: No. 17). 302p. 1986. lib. bdg. 37.95 (ISBN 0-313-25191-6, FTS/). Greenwood.

Forrest, Diane. The Adventurers: Ordinary People with Special Callings. 1984. pap. 5.95 (ISBN 0-317-13951-7). Upper Room.

Forrest, Earle R. The Snake Dance of the Hopi Indians. LC 61-15835. (Illus.). 9.25 (ISBN 0-87026-018-9). Westernlore.

Forrest, G. Topham, jt. auth. see Cox, Montagu H.

Forrest, Linn A., jt. auth. see Garfield, Viola E.

Forrest, M. D. Chats with Converts: Complete Explanation of Catholic Belief. 31st ed. LC 78-56979. 1978. pap. 5.00 (ISBN 0-89555-069-5). TAN Bks Pubs.

Forrest, Tom, ed. Be Holy: God's First Call to Priests Today. Orig. Title: A Call to Holiness: World Retreat for Priests. (Illus.). 132p. 1987. pap. 5.95 (ISBN 0-937779-04-0). Greenlawn Pr.

Forrester, Duncan, et al. Encounter with God. 192p. 1983. pap. 13.95 (ISBN 0-567-29346-7, Pub. by T&T Clark Ltd UK). Fortress.

Forrester, Duncan B. Theology & Practice. 1986. 32.00x (Pub. by Hesketh UK). State Mutual Bk.

Forrester, Duncan B. & Murray, Douglas M., eds. Studies in the History of Worship in Scotland. 190p. 1984. pap. 15.95 (ISBN 0-567-29349-1, Pub. by T&T Clark Ltd UK). Fortress.

Forrester, Mary G. Moral Language. 240p. 1982. 27.50x (ISBN 0-299-08630-5). U of Wis Pr.

Forrester, T., tr. see Ordericus Vitalis.

Forsberg, Glen, jt. auth. see Enns, Peter.

Forseth, Pat, jt. auth. see Cavanaugh, Joan.

Forstemann, E. Commentary on the Maya Manuscript in the Royal Public Library of Dresden. (HU PMP). 1906. 25.00 (ISBN 0-527-01202-5). Kraus Repr.

Forster, Arnold. Report from Israel. 72p. pap. 1.25 (ISBN 0-686-74976-6). ADL.

Forster, Roger & Marston, Paul. That's a Good Question. 2nd ed. Sun, Hugo S. & Chan, Silas, trs. (Chinese.). 204p. 1982. pap. write for info (ISBN 0-941598-01-2). Living Spring Pubns.

Forster, Roger T. & Marston, V. Paul. God's Strategy in Human History. Tseng, Chen C., tr. from Eng. (Chinese.). 1986. write for info. (ISBN 0-941598-92-6); pap. write for info. (ISBN 0-941598-09-8). Living Spring Pubns.

--God's Strategy in Human History. 304p. 1984. pap. 7.95 (ISBN 0-87123-434-3, 210434). Bethany Hse.

Forstman, H. Jackson. Word & Spirit: Calvin's Doctrine of Biblical Authority. 1962. 20.00x (ISBN 0-8047-0070-2). Stanford U Pr.

Forstman, Jack, tr. see Schleiermacher, Friedrich.

Forsyth, George H. & Weitzmann, Kurt. The Monastery of Saint Catherine at Mount Sinai: The Church & Fortress of Justinian: Plates. LC 68-29257. (Illus.). 236p. 1973. 65.00 (ISBN 0-472-33000-4). U of Mich Pr.

Forsyth, Ilene H. The Throne of Wisdom: Wood Sculptures of the Madonna in Romanesque France. LC 72-166372. pap. 77.30 (ISBN 0-317-41726-6, 2052061). Bks Demand UMI.

Forsyth, Peter T. The Cruciality of the Cross. 104p. 1983. pap. 5.95 (ISBN 0-913029-00-9). Stevens Bk Pr.

--Religion in Recent Art. 3rd ed. LC 73-148780. Repr. of 1905 ed. 24.50 (ISBN 0-404-02515-3). AMS Pr.

Forsyth, William H. Entombment of Christ: French Sculptures of the Fifteenth & Sixteenth Centuries. LC 70-99523. (Illus., Pub. for the Metropolitan Museum of Art). 1970. 22.50x (ISBN 0-674-25775-8). Harvard U Pr.

Forsythe, Sidney A. An American Missionary Community in China, 1895-1905. LC 70-178077. (East Asian Monographs Ser: No. 43). 1971. pap. 11.00x (ISBN 0-674-02626-8). Harvard U Pr.

Fort, Gertrud von Le see Von Le Fort, Gertrud.

Fort, Gertrud Von Le see Von Le Fort, Gertrud.

Fort, Timothy L. Law & Religion. LC 86-43082. 153p. 1987. pap. 13.95 (ISBN 0-89950-265-2). McFarland & Co.

Fortenbaugh, William. Quellen zur Ethik Theophrasts. 380p. 1983. 48.00x (ISBN 90-6032-218-5, Pub by B R Gruener Amsterdam). Benjamins North Am.

Fortes, M., jt. auth. see Bourdillon, M. F. C.

Fortes, Meyer. Oedipus & Job in West African Religion. 1980. Repr. of 1959 ed. lib. bdg. 15.50x (ISBN 0-374-92820-7, Octagon). Hippocrene Bks.

Fortes, Meyer & Horton, Robin. Oedipus & Job in West African Religion. LC 83-7587. (Cambridge Studies in Social Anthropology: No. 48). 128p. 1984. 32.50 (ISBN 0-521-26208-9); pap. 9.95 (ISBN 0-521-27719-1). Cambridge U Pr.

Fortes, Meyer, ed. see International African Seminar - 3rd - Salisbury - Southern Rhodesia.

Fortescue, Adrian. Lesser Eastern Churches. LC 79-168124. Repr. of 1913 ed. 31.50 (ISBN 0-404-02517-X). AMS Pr.

--The Orthodox Eastern Church. 3rd facsimile ed. LC 70-179520. (Select Bibliographies Reprint Ser). Repr. of 1920 ed. 26.50 (ISBN 0-8369-6649-X). Ayer Co Pubs.

--Orthodox Eastern Church. (Illus.). 1969. 25.50 (ISBN 0-8337-1217-9). B Franklin.

Fortescue, Edward F. Armenian Church: Founded by Saint Gregory the Illuminator. 1970. Repr. of 1872 ed. 21.50 (ISBN 0-404-02518-8). AMS Pr.

Fortini, Arnaldo. Francis of Assisi. Moak, Helen, tr. 900p. 1980. 39.50x (ISBN 0-8245-0003-2). Crossroad NY.

Fortman, E. J., tr. see De Margerie, Bertrand.

Fortman, Edmund. Activities of the Holy Spirit. LC 84-13786. 199p. 1984. 12.00 (ISBN 0-8199-0881-9). Franciscan Herald.

Fortman, Edmund J. Everlasting Life: Towards a Theology of the Future Life. LC 85-30720. 369p. (Orig.). 1986. pap. 9.95 (ISBN 0-8189-0495-X). Alba.

--The Triune God: A Historical Study of the Doctrine of the Trinity. (Twin Brooks Ser.). 408p. 1982. pap. 10.95 (ISBN 0-8010-3505-8). Baker Bk.

Fortuna, James L., Jr. The Unsearchable Wisdom of God: A Study of Providence in Richardson's Pamela. LC 80-14919. (University of Florida Humanities Monographs: No. 49). vii, 130p. 1980. pap. 6.50 (ISBN 0-8130-0676-7). U Presses Fla.

Fortunato, Connie. Children's Music Ministry. 222p. 1981. pap. 6.95 (ISBN 0-89191-341-6). Cook.

Fortunato, John. Embracing the Exile: Healing Journeys of Gay Christians. 156p. (Orig.). 1984. pap. 7.95 (ISBN 0-8164-2637-6, 6338, HarpR). Har-Row.

Fortunato, John E. AIDS, the Spiritual Dilemma. 1987. pap. 7.95. Har-Row.

Fortune, Dion. Goat-Foot God. (Orig.). 1980. pap. 7.95 (ISBN 0-87728-500-4). Weiser.

--Mystical Qabalah. 311p. 1984. 8.95 (ISBN 0-87728-596-9). Weiser.

--Sane Occultism. 192p. 1973. pap. 7.95 (ISBN 0-85030-105-X). Weiser.

--Winged Bull. 328p. (Orig.). 1980. pap. 6.95 (ISBN 0-87728-501-2). Weiser.

Fortune, Dion, ed. The Esoteric Orders & Their Work. 144p. 1983. pap. 7.95 (ISBN 0-85030-310-9). Newcastle Pub.

Fortune, Katie. Receive All God Has to Give. 1971. pap. write for info. color booklet (ISBN 0-930756-01-0, 541001); pap. 0.95 color booklet (ISBN 0-317-03288-7). Aglow Pubns.

Fortune, Marie M. Sexual Violence: The Unmentionable Sin: An Ethical & Pastoral Perspective. 256p. (Orig.). 1983. pap. 9.95 (ISBN 0-8298-0652-0). Pilgrim NY.

Fortune, Nigel & Lewis, Anthony, eds. New Oxford History of Music, Vol. 5: Opera & Church Music 1630-1750. (Illus.). 1975. 49.95x (ISBN 0-19-316305-5). Oxford U Pr.

Fosdick, Harry E. As I See Religion. LC 75-11835. 201p. 1975. Repr. of 1932 ed. lib. bdg. 45.00x (ISBN 0-8371-8142-9, FOAI). Greenwood.

--Great Time to Be Alive: Sermons on Christianity in Wartime. LC 78-167341. (Essay Index Reprint Ser.). Repr. of 1944 ed. 18.00 (ISBN 0-8369-2688-9). Ayer Co Pubs.

--The Man from Nazareth: As His Contemporaries Saw Him. LC 78-16469. 1978. Repr. of 1949 ed. lib. bdg. 24.25x (ISBN 0-313-20603-1, FOMN). Greenwood.

--The Meaning of Faith. (Festival Bks). 352p. 1982. pap. 3.95 (ISBN 0-687-23959-1). Abingdon.

--The Meaning of Prayer. 1982. pap. 2.95 (ISBN 0-687-23960-5, Festival). Abingdon.

--The Meaning of Prayer. LC 76-50560. 1976. Repr. of 1946 ed. lib. bdg. 18.50 (ISBN 0-8414-4159-6). Folcroft.

--The Meaning of Service. 224p. 1983. pap. 4.35 (ISBN 0-687-23961-3). Abingdon.

--The Modern Use of the Bible. 1925. 35.00 (ISBN 0-8274-2758-1). R West.

--A Pilgrimage to Palestine. Davis, Moshe, ed. LC 77-70688. (America & the Holy Land Ser.). 1977. Repr. of 1927 ed. lib. bdg. 30.00x (ISBN 0-405-10247-X). Ayer Co Pubs.

Foshee, Howard. Broadman Church Manual. LC 72-94629. 192p. 1973. 8.95 (ISBN 0-8054-2525-X). Broadman.

Foshee, Howard B. Now That You're a Deacon. LC 74-79488. 128p. 1975. 7.95 (ISBN 0-8054-3506-9). Broadman.

Fossum, Jarl E. The Name of God & the Angel of the Lord: Samaritan & Jewish Concepts of Intermeditation & the Origin of Gnosticism. 400p. 1985. lib. bdg. 54.00x (ISBN 3-16-144789-1, Pub. by J C B Mohr BRD). Coronet Bks.

Foster, ed. see Nee, Watchman.

Foster, Ann T. Theodore Roethke's Meditative Sequences: Contemplation & the Creative Process. LC 85-3041. (Studies in Art & Religious Interpretation: Vol. 4). 210p. 1985. 49.95x (ISBN 0-88946-555-X). E Mellen.

Foster, Arthur L., ed. The House Church Evolving. LC 76-4198. (Studies in Ministry & Parish Life). 126p. 1976. 13.95x (ISBN 0-913552-04-6); pap. 6.95x (ISBN 0-913552-05-4). Exploration Pr.

Foster, Betty J., jt. auth. see Krahn, John.

Foster, Betty J., jt. auth. see Krahn, John H.

Foster, Birket, illus. Christmas with the Poets. (Illus.). 1978. Repr. of 1851 ed. 50.00 (ISBN 0-8492-0090-3). R West.

Foster, Bruce D., jt. auth. see Stark, Rodney.

Foster, Charles K. The Unknown History of the Jewish People, 2 vols. (Illus.). 247p. 1986. Set. 187.45. Found Class Reprints.

Foster, Charles R. The Ministry of the Volunteer Teacher. 96p. 1986. pap. 6.95 (ISBN 0-687-27040-5). Abingdon.

--Teaching in the Community of Faith. 160p. (Orig.). 1982. pap. 8.75 (ISBN 0-687-41086-X). Abingdon.

Foster, Claude R., et al, trs. see Roehrich, Gustave G.

Foster, Durwood, jt. ed. see Bryant, Darrol.

Foster, Durwood, jt. ed. see Mojzes, Paul.

Foster, Ellwood. Inspirationally Yours. LC 80-53330. 1984. 5.95 (ISBN 0-533-04843-5). Vantage.

Foster, Elvie L. The Most Important Thing in Our Lives Is... LC 86-90082. 47p. 1986. 5.95 (ISBN 0-533-07047-3). Vantage.

Foster, Ethan see Cartland, Fernando G.

Foster, Frank H. A Genetic History of the New England Theology. Kuklick, Bruce, ed. (American Religious Thought of the 18th & 19th Centuries Ser.). 56p. 1987. lib. bdg. 75.00 (ISBN 0-8240-6956-0). Garland Pub.

--Modern Movement in American Theology. facs. ed. LC 76-86751. (Essay Index Reprint Ser). 1939. 14.50 (ISBN 0-8369-1131-8). Ayer Co Pubs.

Foster, Fred B. & Foster, Linda. Guardian I: The Answers. 224p. 1984. pap. 9.95 (ISBN 0-9613762-0-1). F B Foster Pubns.

Foster, Fred J. Their Story: Twentieth Century Pentecostals. Wallace, Mary H., ed. LC 86-26718. (Illus.). 192p. 1983. pap. 4.95 (ISBN 0-912315-05-9). Word Aflame.

Foster, Genevieve & Hufford, David J. The World Was Flooded with Light: A Mystical Experience Remembered. LC 84-22013. 216p. 1985. 14.95 (ISBN 0-8229-3512-0). U of Pittsburgh Pr.

Foster, Geraldine S. The Jews in Rhode Island: A Brief History. Conley, Patrick T., ed. (Rhode Island Ethnic Heritage Pamphlet Ser.). (Illus.). 48p. (Orig.). 1985. pap. 2.75 (ISBN 0-917012-80-1). RI Pubns Soc.

Foster, H. Normal Christian Life: Study Guide. rev ed. 52p. 1985. pap. 2.25 (ISBN 0-317-43399-7). Chr Lit.

Foster, Harry. Daily Thoughts on Bible Characters. 2nd ed. Living Spring Publications Staff, tr. (Chinese.). 1982. write for info. (ISBN 0-941598-99-3); pap. write for info (ISBN 0-941598-00-4). Living Spring Pubns.

Foster, J. & Robinson, H., eds. Essays on Berkeley: A Tercentennial Celebration. 1985. 38.00x (ISBN 0-19-824734-6). Oxford U Pr.

Foster, J. R., tr. see Frossard, Andre & Pope John Paul II.

Foster, John & Goldsborough, June. Christian ABC Book. (Illus.). 1982. 6.95 (ISBN 0-911346-05-8). Christianica.

Foster, John O. Life & Labors of Mrs. Maggie Newton Van Cott, the First Lady Licensed to Preach in the Methodist Episcopal Church in the United States. Gifford, Carolyn & Dayton, Donald, eds. (Women in American Protestant Religion 1800-1930 Ser.). 339p. 1987. lib. bdg. 50.00 (ISBN 0-8240-0663-1). Garland Pub.

Foster, Mrs. Jonathan, tr. see Conde, Jose A.

Foster, Julia A., jt. auth. see Lund, Shirley.

Foster, K. The Idea of Truth in Manzoni & Leopardi. (Italian Lectures). 1967. pap. 2.25 (ISBN 0-85672-283-9, Pub. by British Acad). Longwood Pub Group.

Foster, K. Neill. The Discerning Christian. 104p. (Orig.). 1982. 6.95 (ISBN 0-87509-312-4); pap. 3.95 (ISBN 0-87509-316-7). Chr Pubns.

Foster, Lawrence. Religion & Sexuality: Three American Communal Experiments of the Nineteenth Century. 1981. 24.95x (ISBN 0-19-502794-9). Oxford U Pr.

Foster, Lee. Beautiful California Missions. Shangle, Robert D., ed. LC 78-102341. (Illus.). 72p. 1986. pap. 8.95 (ISBN 0-915796-22-8). Beautiful Am.

Foster, Lewis. John. (Standard Bible Studies). (Illus.). 272p. 1987. pap. price not set (ISBN 0-87403-164-8, 40104). Standard Pub.

--The Only Way. LC 77-83658. 96p. (Orig.). 1978. pap. 2.25 (ISBN 0-87239-193-0, 40048). Standard Pub.

--The True Life. LC 77-83656. 96p. (Orig.). 1978. pap. 2.25 (ISBN 0-87239-192-2, 40047). Standard Pub.

Foster, Lewis & Stedman, Jon. Selecting a Translation of the Bible. LC 83-4689. (Illus.). 128p. (Orig.). 1983. pap. 3.95 (ISBN 0-87239-645-2, 39975). Standard Pub.

Foster, Lewis A. Luke. (Standard Bible Studies). 336p. 1986. pap. text ed. 9.95 (ISBN 0-87403-163-X, 40103). Standard Pub.

Foster, Linda, jt. auth. see Foster, Fred B.

Foster, Marshall E. & Swanson, Mary E. The American Covenant: The Untold Story. rev. ed. (Illus.). 186p. (Orig.). 1982. limited, signed 19.95; pap. text ed. 9.95 (ISBN 0-941370-00-3). Mayflower Inst.

Foster, Michael B. Mystery & Philosophy. LC 79-8721. (The Library of Philosophy & Theology). 96p. 1980. Repr. of 1957 ed. lib. bdg. 24.75x (ISBN 0-313-20792-5, FOMP). Greenwood.

Foster, Myles B. Anthems & Anthem Composers. LC 76-125047. (Music Ser.). 1970. Repr. of 1901 ed. lib. bdg. 32.50 (ISBN 0-306-70012-3). Da Capo.

Foster, Nancy H. The Alamo & Other Texas Missions to Remember. LC 84-647. (Illus.). 96p. (Orig.). 1984. pap. 9.95x (ISBN 0-88415-033-X, Lone Star Bks). Gulf Pub.

Foster, R. C. Studies in the Life of Christ. 1979. Repr. 29.95 (ISBN 0-8010-3452-3). Baker Bk.

Foster, Richard. Alabanza a la Disciplina. Lievano, M. Francisco, tr. from Eng. Tr. of Celebration of Discipline. (Span.). 224p. 1986. pap. 4.95 (ISBN 0-88113-012-5). Edit Betania.

--Discovering English Churches: A Beginner's Guide to the Story of the Parish Church from Before the Conquest to the Gothic Revival. (Illus.). 1982. 30.00x (ISBN 0-19-520366-6). Oxford U Pr.

Foster, Richard J. The Celebration of Discipline: Paths to Spiritual Growth. LC 77-20444. 1978. 13.45 (ISBN 0-06-062831-6, HarpR). Har-Row.

--Celebration of Discipline Study Guide. LC 77-20444. 96p. (Orig.). 1983. pap. 5.95 (ISBN 0-06-062833-2, RD/390, HarpR). Har-Row.

--Freedom of Simplicity. LC 80-8351. 192p. 1981. 13.45 (ISBN 0-06-062832-4, HarpR). Har-Row.

--Money, Sex & Power: Study Guide. LC 84-48785. 96p. (Orig.). 1985. pap. 4.95 (ISBN 0-06-062827-8, HarpR). Har-Row.

--Money, Sex & Power: The Challenge of the Disciplined Life. LC 84-48769. 192p. 1985. 13.45 (ISBN 0-06-062826-X, HarpR). Har-Row.

Foster, Robert D. The Navigator. LC 83-60287. 240p. 1983. pap. 3.95 (ISBN 0-89109-495-4). NavPress.

Foster, Stephen. Their Solitary Way: The Puritan Social Ethic in the First Century of Settlement in New England. LC 76-151573. (Yale Historical Publications Miscellany Ser.: No. 94). pap. 59.50 (ISBN 0-317-29587-X, 2021997). Bks Demand UMI.

Foster, Stephen, ed. see Howe, Jeffery W.

Foster, Stephen S. Brotherhood of Thieves: Or, A True Picture of the American Church & Clergy. LC 79-82190. (Anti-Slavery Crusade in America Ser). 1969. Repr. of 1886 ed. 9.00 (ISBN 0-405-00628-4). Ayer Co Pubs.

Foster, Theodora C. Women, Religion, & Development in the Third World. LC 83-13670. 288p. 1984. 30.95 (ISBN 0-03-064108-X). Praeger.

Foster, Timothy. How to Deal with Depression. 132p. 1984. pap. 4.95 (ISBN 0-88207-610-8). Victor Bks.

Foster, W. The Church Before Covenants. 1975. 12.50x (ISBN 0-7073-0184-X, Pub. by Scot Acad Pr). Longwood Pub Group.

Foster, Warren D., ed. Heroines of Modern Religion. LC 77-107700. (Essay Index Reprint Ser.). 1913. 20.00 (ISBN 0-8369-1572-0). Ayer Co Pubs.

Foth, Margaret. Life Is Too Short. 144p. (Orig.). 1985. pap. 5.95 (ISBN 0-310-42681-2, 12779P). Zondervan.

Fotion, N. Moral Situations. LC 68-31034. 135p. 1968. 8.00x (ISBN 0-87338-076-2); pap. 4.95x (ISBN 0-87338-077-0). Kent St U Pr.

Foucart, Paul F. Des Associations Religieuses chez les Grecs: Thiases, Eranes, Orgeons. facsimile ed. LC 75-10637. (Ancient Religion & Mythology Ser.). (Fr.). 1976. Repr. of 1873 ed. 20.00x (ISBN 0-405-07014-4). Ayer Co Pubs.

--Les Mysteres d'Eleusis. facsimile ed. LC 75-10636. (Ancient Religion & Mythology Ser.). (Fr.). 1976. Repr. of 1914 ed. 37.50x (ISBN 0-405-07013-6). Ayer Co Pubs.

Foucher, A. The Beginnings of Buddhist Art. 1972. 20.00 (ISBN 0-89684-370-X). Orient Bk Dist.

Foucher, Alfred C. The Life of the Buddha. Boas, Simone B., tr. LC 72-6195. 272p. 1972. Repr. of 1963 ed. lib. bdg. 22.50x (ISBN 0-8371-6476-1, FOLB). Greenwood.

Foucher De Chartres. Chronicle of the First Crusade. McGinty, Martha E., tr. LC 76-29823. Repr. of 1941 ed. 22.50 (ISBN 0-404-15417-4). AMS Pr.

Fouere, Rene. Krishnamurti: The Man & His Teaching. 1974. lib. bdg. 69.95 (ISBN 0-8490-0477-2). Gordon Pr.

Foulds, Elfrida V. The Candle of the Lord. pap. 2.50x (ISBN 0-87574-248-3, 248). Pendle Hill.

--Let Your Lives Speak. 1983. pap. 2.50x (ISBN 0-87574-071-5, 071). Pendle Hill.

Foulke, Arthur T. Picture-Book for Proud Lovers of Danville, Montour County & Riverside, PA. LC 75-32061. (Illus.). 320p. 1976. 15.00 (ISBN 0-8158-0334-6). Chris Mass.

Foulkes, Francis. Pocket Guide to the New Testament. LC 77-27742. 1978. pap. 2.95 (ISBN 0-87784-580-8). Inter-Varsity.

Foulks, Frances, ed. La Oracion Eficaz. Tr. of Effectual Prayer. (Span.). 160p. 5.95 (ISBN 0-87159-089-1). Unity School.

Foulks, Frances W. Effectual Prayer. 1979. 5.95 (ISBN 0-87159-031-X). Unity School.

Fountain, Thomas. Claves de Interpretacion Biblica. 148p. 1985. pap. 4.25 (ISBN 0-311-03653-8). Casa Bautista.

Fouquet, Jean. The Hours of Etienne Chevalier. LC 78-160131. (Illus.). 128p. 1971. slipcased 40.00 (ISBN 0-8076-0618-9). Braziller.

Fourez, Gerard. Sacraments & Passages: Celebrating the Tensions of Modern Life. LC 83-71164. 168p. (Orig.). 1983. pap. 4.95 (ISBN 0-87793-301-4). Ave Maria.

Fournel, Henri. Bibliographie Saint-Simonienne: De 1802 au 31 December 1832. LC 70-131405. (Fr.). 130p. 1973. Repr. of 1833 ed. lib. bdg. 21.00 (ISBN 0-8337-1222-5). B Franklin.

Fournier, Edouard, ed. Theatre Francais Avant La Renaissance, 1430-1550. 1965. Repr. of 1872 ed. 32.00 (ISBN 0-8337-1225-X). B Franklin.

Fourteenth Dalai Lama His Holiness Tenzin Gyatso. Kindness, Clarity & Insight. Hopkins, Jeffrey & Napper, Elizabeth, eds. LC 84-51198. (Illus.). 250p. (Orig.). 1984. pap. 10.95 (ISBN 0-937938-18-1). Snow Lion.

Foust, Paul. Reborn to Multiply. LC 73-9110. 1973. pap. 2.75 (ISBN 0-570-03170-2, 12-2573). Concordia.

Foust, Paul & Kortals, Richard. Reach Out. 1984. pap. 3.95 (ISBN 0-570-03933-9, 12-2868). Concordia.

Fowler, Albert. Two Trends in Modern Quaker Thought. 1983. pap. 2.50x (ISBN 0-87574-112-6, 112). Pendle Hill.

Fowler, David C. The Bible in Early English Literature. LC 76-7786. (Illus.). 274p. 1976. 18.95x (ISBN 0-295-95438-8). U of Wash Pr.

Fowler, Everett W. Evaluating Versions of the New Testament. LC 80-81607. (Illus.). 80p. (Orig.). 1981. pap. 2.95 (ISBN 0-937136-03-4). Maranatha Baptist.

Fowler, Harlan D. Behold the Flaming Sword: A Biography of John & Jesus. (Illus.). 1983. 35.00 (ISBN 0-533-05059-6). Vantage.

Fowler, Harold. The Gospel of Matthew, Vol. I. LC 78-1064. (The Bible Study Textbook Ser.). (Illus.). 1975. 14.30 (ISBN 0-89900-029-0). College Pr Pub.

--The Gospel of Matthew, Vol. II. (The Bible Study Textbook Ser.). (Illus.). 1972. 17.50 (ISBN 0-89900-030-4). College Pr Pub.

--The Gospel of Matthew, Vol. III. (The Bible Study Textbook Ser.). (Illus.). 1978. 18.95 (ISBN 0-89900-031-2). College Pr Pub.

Fowler, Henry T. The History & Literature of the New Testament. LC 78-12516. 1979. Repr. of 1925 ed. lib. bdg. cancelled (ISBN 0-313-21188-4, FOHL). Greenwood.

Fowler, J. B., Jr. Illustrated Sermon Outlines. LC 86-2674. 1987. 4.95 (ISBN 0-8054-2261-7). Broadman.

--Living Illustrations. LC 85-4175. 1985. pap. 5.95 (ISBN 0-8054-2260-9). Broadman.

Fowler, James W. Becoming Adult, Becoming Christian: Adult Development & Christian Faith. LC 83-48987. 144p. 1984. 14.45 (ISBN 0-06-062841-3, HarpR). Har-Row.

--Faith Development & Pastoral Care. LC 86-45904. 128p. 1987. pap. 7.95 (ISBN 0-8006-1739-8). Fortress.

--Stages of Faith: The Psychology of Human Development & the Quest for Meaning. LC 80-7757. 224p. 1981. 18.45 (ISBN 0-06-062840-5, HarpR). Har-Row.

--To See the Kingdom: The Theological Vision of H. Richard Niebuhr. LC 85-17878. 304p. 1985. pap. text ed. 13.75 (ISBN 0-8191-4938-1). U Pr of Amer.

Fowler, Jeaneane D. Theophoric Personal Names in Ancient Hebrew: A Comparative Study. (JSOT Supplement Ser.: No. 49). 400p. 1987. text ed. 37.50x (ISBN 1-85075-038-6, Pub. by JSOT Pr England); pap. text ed. 18.95x (ISBN 1-85075-039-4, Pub. by JSOT Pr England). Eisenbrauns.

Fowler, Lea. Precious in the Sight of God. 1983. pap. 4.95 (ISBN 0-89137-428-0). Quality Pubns.

Fowler, Paul. Abortion: Toward an Evangelical Consensus. (Critical Concern Ser.). 1987. 11.95 (ISBN 0-88070-173-0). Multnomah.

Fowler, Richard A. Winning by Losing: Eleven Biblical Paradoxes That Can Change Your Life. (Orig.). 1986. pap. 6.95 (ISBN 0-8024-9564-8). Moody.

Fowler, Richard A. & House, H. Wayne. The Christian Confronts His Culture. 228p. (Orig.). 1983. pap. 7.95 (ISBN 0-8024-0232-1). Moody.

Fowler, Robert B. A New Engagement: Evangelical Political Thought, 1966-1976. 298p. (Orig.). 1983. pap. 13.95 (ISBN 0-8028-1929-X). Eerdmans.

--A New Engagement: Evangelical Political Thought, 1966-1976. LC 82-11389. Repr. of 1982 ed. 77.00 (2027453). Bks Demand UMI.

Fowler, Robert Booth. Religion & Politics in America. LC 84-20237. (Atla Monograph: No. 21). 365p. 1984. 25.00 (ISBN 0-8108-1752-7). Scarecrow.

Fowler, Robert M. Loaves & Fishes: The Function of the Feeding Stories in the Gospel of Mark. Baird, William, ed. LC 81-2749. (Society of Biblical Literature Dissertation Ser.). 1981. pap. 15.00 (ISBN 0-89130-486-X, 06-01-54). Scholars Pr GA.

Fowler, Roe. Christmas Was. 88p. 1982. pap. 6.95 (ISBN 0-686-38093-2). Fig Leaf Pr.

Fowler, Thomas B., Jr., tr. see Zubiri, Xavier.

Fowler, William W. Roman Ideas of Deity in the Last Century Before the Christian Era. LC 75-102236. (Select Bibliographies Reprint Ser). 1914. 19.00 (ISBN 0-8369-5121-2). Ayer Co Pubs.

Fox, Alistair. Thomas More: History & Providence. LC 82-11178. 288p. 1985. pap. text ed. 10.95x (ISBN 0-300-03415-6, Y-536). Yale U Pr.

Fox, David. Saint George: The Saint with Three Faces. (Illus.). 188p. 1986. 42.00 (ISBN 0-946041-13-X). Salem Hse Pubs.

Fox, Donald H., ed. see Fox, Frederic E.

Fox, Donald S. The White Fox of Andhra. 216p. 1978. 6.95 (ISBN 0-8059-2432-9). Dorrance.

Fox, Douglas. Meditation & Reality: A Critical View. LC 85-45459. 192p. 1986. pap. 12.95 (ISBN 0-8042-0662-7). John Knox.

Fox, Douglas A. The Heart of Buddhist Wisdom: A Translation of the Heart Sutra with Historical Introduction & Commentary. (Studies in Asian Thought & Religion: Vol. 3). 195p. 1986. lib. bdg. 39.95x (ISBN 0-88946-053-1). E Mellen.

--What Do You Think about God. 96p. 1985. pap. 4.95 (ISBN 0-8170-1077-7). Judson.

Fox, Douglas J. The Matthew-Luke Commentary of Philoxenus. LC 78-12852. 1979. 14.50 (ISBN 0-89130-350-2); pap. 9.95 (ISBN 0-89130-266-2, 060143). Scholars Pr GA.

Fox, Edward. The True Differences Between the Regal Power & the Ecclesiastical Power. LC 73-6129. (English Experience Ser.: No. 595). 108p. 1973. Repr. of 1548 ed. 9.50 (ISBN 90-221-0595-4). Walter J Johnson.

Fox, Emmet. Alter Your Life. 1950. 12.45 (ISBN 0-06-062850-2, HarpR). Har-Row.

--Around the Year with Emmet Fox. LC 58-13248. 1958. 12.45 (ISBN 0-06-062870-7, HarpR). Har-Row.

--Diagrams for Living: The Bible Unveiled. LC 69-10475. 1968. 12.45 (ISBN 0-06-062851-0, HarpR). Har-Row.

--Find & Use Your Inner Power. 1941. 11.60 (ISBN 0-06-062890-1, HarpR). Har-Row.

--Make Your Life Worthwhile. LC 83-48456. 256p. 1984. pap. 7.95 (ISBN 0-06-062913-4, RD 508, HarpR). Har-Row.

--Power Through Constructive Thinking. 1940. 12.45 (ISBN 0-06-062930-4, HarpR). Har-Row.

--El Sermon del Monte. Tr. of Sermon on the Mount. 1984. 5.95 (ISBN 0-87159-034-4). Unity School.

--Sermon on the Mount. 1934. 12.45 (ISBN 0-06-062950-9, HarpR). Har-Row.

--Stake Your Claim. LC 52-11683. 1952. 8.95 (ISBN 0-06-062970-3, HarpR). Har-Row.

--The Ten Commandments. LC 53-8369. 1953. 12.45 (ISBN 0-06-062990-8, HarpR). Har-Row.

Fox, Everett. In the Beginning: A New English Rendition of the Book of Genesis. 288p. 1983. 14.95 (ISBN 0-8052-3870-0). Schocken.

Fox, Frank, et al. Beginner's Guide to Zen & the Art of Windsurfing. 3rd ed. (Illus.). 160p. 1985. pap. 6.95 (ISBN 0-934965-02-1). Amber Co Pr.

Fox, Frank W. J. Reuben Clark: The Public Years. LC 80-17903. (J. Reuben Clark Three Vol. Ser.). (Illus.). 706p. 1980. 10.95 (ISBN 0-8425-1832-0). Brigham.

Fox, Frederic E. Seven Sermons & One Eulogy As Preached in the Chapel of Princeton University from 1965 to 1980. Fox, Donald H., ed. LC 82-90693. 88p. (Orig.). 1982. pap. 5.95 (ISBN 0-910521-02-6). Fox Head.

Fox, George. George Fox's Book of Miracles. Cadbury, Henry J., ed. LC 73-735. 161p. 1973. Repr. of 1948 ed. lib. bdg. 16.50x (ISBN 0-374-92825-8, Octagon). Hippocrene Bks.

--The Works of George Fox, Vols. 1-8. Incl. Vols. 1 & 2. A Journal or Historical Account of the Life, Travels, Sufferings, Christian Experiences & Labour of Love in the Work of the Ministry, of That Ancient, Eminent, & Faithful Servant of Jesus Christ, George Fox. LC 75-16194. Vol. 1 (ISBN 0-404-09351-5). Vol. 2 (ISBN 0-404-09352-3); Vol. 3. The Great Mystery of the Great Whore Unfolded. LC 75-16195. 616p (ISBN 0-404-09353-1); Vols. 4-6. Gospel Truth Demonstrated, in a Collection of Doctrinal Books, Given Forth by That Faithful Minister of Jesus Christ, George Fox. LC 75-16199. Vol. 4 (ISBN 0-404-09354-X). Vol. 5 (ISBN 0-404-09355-8). Vol. 6 (ISBN 0-404-09356-6); Vols. 7 & 8. A Collection of Many Select & Christian Epistles, Letters & Testimonies. LC 75-16207. Vol. 7 (ISBN 0-404-09357-4). Vol. 8 (ISBN 0-404-09358-2). Repr. of 1831 ed. Set. 320.00 (ISBN 0-404-09350-7); 40.00 ea. AMS Pr.

Fox, H. E., jt. auth. see Morris, George E.

Fox, H. Eddie & Morris, George E. Faith-Sharing. 144p. 1987. pap. 7.95 (ISBN 0-310-38381-1). Zondervan.

Fox, Helen, tr. see Steiner, Rudolf.

Fox, James J. Religion & Morality: Their Nature & Mutual Relations. 334p. 1983. Repr. of 1899 ed. 20.00x (ISBN 0-939738-09-0). Zubal Inc.

Fox, John. Foxe's Christian Martyrs of the World. 1985. 6.95 (ISBN 0-916441-12-1). Barbour & Co.

Fox, Marvin, ed. Modern Jewish Ethics: Theory & Practice. LC 74-28395. 274p. 1975. 14.50 (ISBN 0-8142-0192-X). Ohio St U Pr.

Fox, Matt & Swimme, Brian. Manifesto for a Global Civilization. LC 82-71450. 54p. (Orig.). 1982. pap. 3.95 (ISBN 0-939680-05-X). Bear & Co.

Fox, Matthew. Meditations with TM Meister Eckhart. LC 82-71451. (Meditations with TM Ser.). (Illus.). 131p. (Orig.). 1982. pap. 6.95 (ISBN 0-939680-04-1). Bear & Co.

--On Becoming a Musical Mystical Bear: Spirituality American Style. LC 75-34842. 192p. 1976. pap. 4.95 (ISBN 0-8091-1913-7). Paulist Pr.

--A Spirituality Named Compassion, & the Healing of the Global Village, Humpty Dumpty, & Us. 1979. pap. 7.95 (ISBN 0-86683-751-5, HarpR). Har-Row.

--Western Spirituality: Historical Roots, Ecumenical Routes. LC 81-67364. 440p. 1981. pap. 11.95 (ISBN 0-939680-01-7). Bear & Co.

--Whee! We, Wee All the Way Home: A Guide to a Sensual Prophetic Spirituality. LC 81-67365. 257p. 1981. pap. 8.95 (ISBN 0-939680-00-9). Bear & Co.

Fox, Matthew, ed. see Hildegard of Bingen.

Fox, Paul. Reformation in Poland. LC 72-136395. Repr. of 1924 ed. 24.50 (ISBN 0-404-02544-7). AMS Pr.

--Reformation in Poland, Some Social & Economic Aspects. LC 71-104272. Repr. of 1924 ed. lib. bdg. 22.50x (ISBN 0-8371-3924-4, FORP). Greenwood.

Fox, Robert. Teenagers & Purity, Teenagers & Going Steady, Teenagers & Looking Ahead to Marriage. 1978. pap. 0.75 (ISBN 0-8198-0370-7). Dghtrs St Paul.

Fox, Robert F. Catechism of the Catholic Church. 1979. 8.95 (ISBN 0-685-94958-3). Franciscan Her.

Fox, Robert J. Call of Heaven: Brother Gino, Stigmatist. (Illus.). 206p. (Orig.). 1982. pap. 3.95 (ISBN 0-931888-06-9). Christendom Pubns.

--Call of Heaven: Father Gino, Stigmatist. 2nd ed. (Illus.). 232p. pap. 5.95 (ISBN 0-931888-22-0). Christendom Pubns.

--The Catholic Faith. LC 83-61889. 360p. (Orig.). 1983. pap. 7.95 (ISBN 0-87973-614-3, 614). Our Sunday Visitor.

--A Catholic Prayer Book. LC 74-75133. 128p. 1974. pap. 3.95 (ISBN 0-87973-771-9). Our Sunday Visitor.

--Catholic Truth for Youth. LC 78-104309. (Illus.). 448p. 1978. pap. 5.95 (ISBN 0-911988-05-X). AMI Pr.

--Fatima Today. (Illus.). 263p. (Orig.). pap. 6.95 (ISBN 0-931888-11-5). Christendom Pubns.

--Francisco of Fatima: His Life As He Might Tell It. 14p. 1982. pap. 1.00 (ISBN 0-911988-53-X). Ami Pr.

--The Immaculate Heart of Mary: True Devotion. 200p. (Orig.). 1986. pap. 7.50 (ISBN 0-87973-550-3, 550). Our Sunday Visitor.

--Jacinta of Fatima: Her Life as She Might Tell It. 22p. 1982. pap. 1.00 (ISBN 0-911988-52-1). Ami Pr.

--Opus Sanctorum Angelorum: Work of the Holy Angels. 1.50 (ISBN 0-911988-49-1). AMI Pr.

--A Prayer Book for Young Catholics. LC 82-81318. 168p. 1982. pap. 5.50 Leatherette (ISBN 0-87973-370-5, 370). Our Sunday Visitor.

--Prayerbook for Catholics. 112p. (Orig.). 1982. 6.00 (ISBN 0-931888-08-5); pap. 3.95. Christendom Pubns.

--Rediscovering Fatima. LC 82-60667. (Illus.). 144p. (Orig.). 1982. pap. 4.50 (ISBN 0-87973-657-7, 657). Our Sunday Visitor.

--Religious Education: Its Effects, Its Challenges Today. 1972. pap. 0.95 (ISBN 0-8198-0344-8). Dghtrs St Paul.

--St. Joseph: His Life As He Might Tell It. 1983. pap. 1.00 (ISBN 0-911988-55-6). AMI Pr.

--St. Louis Marie Grignon de Montfort: His Life As He Might Tell It. 20p. 1983. 1.00 (ISBN 0-911988-62-9). Ami Pr.

--St. Therese of Lisieux: Her Life As She Might Tell It. 20p. 1982. pap. 1.00 (ISBN 0-911988-54-8). AMI Pr.

--Saints & Heroes Speak. 512p. 1983. 7.95 (ISBN 0-911988-43-2). Ami Pr.

--A World at Prayer. LC 78-74623. 1979. pap. 3.95 (ISBN 0-87973-633-X). Our Sunday Visitor.

Fox, Robin L. Pagans & Christians. 1987. 35.00 (ISBN 0-394-55495-7). Knopf.

Fox, Sanford J. Science & Justice: The Massachusetts Witchcraft Trials. LC 68-18771. (Illus.). Repr. of 1968 ed. 27.40 (ISBN 0-8357-9285-4, 2016570). Bks Demand UMI.

Fox, Zeni, et al. Leadership for Youth Ministry. (Illus.). 200p. (Orig.). 1984. pap. 8.95 (ISBN 0-88489-157-7). St Mary's.

Fox-Ashrei, Meir, tr. see Zevin, Shlomo Y.

Foxe, John. Acts & Monuments, 8 Vols. Cattley, S. R. & Townsend, George, eds. LC 79-168132. Repr. of 1849 ed. Set. 400.00 (ISBN 0-404-02590-0). AMS Pr.

--The English Sermons of John Foxe. LC 77-29100. 1978. Repr. of 1578 ed. 60.00x (ISBN 0-8201-1267-4). Schol Facsimiles.

--Foxe's Book of Martyrs. Berry, W. Grinton, ed. (Giant Summit Bks). 1978. pap. 7.95 (ISBN 0-8010-3483-3). Baker Bk.

--Foxe's Book of Martyrs. 400p. pap. 3.95 (ISBN 0-8007-8013-2, Spire Bks). Revell.

--Foxe's Book of Martyrs. 400p. 1981. pap. 3.95 (ISBN 0-88368-095-5). Whitaker Hse.

Foxglove, Lady. We've got the Power: Witches among Us. LC 81-11098. (A Jem Book Ser.). (Illus.). 64p. (Teens reading on a 2-3rd grade level). 1981. lib. bdg. 9.29 (ISBN 0-671-43604-X). Messner.

Foy, Felician A. & Avato, Rose, eds. Concise Guide to the Catholic Church. LC 83-63170. 80p. (Orig.). 1984. pap. 6.95 (ISBN 0-87973-616-X, 616). Our Sunday Visitor.

Foy, Felician A. & Avato, Rose M., eds. Catholic Almanac, 1986. LC 73-64101. 650p. (Orig.). 1985. pap. 13.95 (ISBN 0-87973-256-3, 256). Our Sunday Visitor.

--Catholic Almanac 1987. LC 73-64101. 600p. (Orig.). 1986. pap. 13.95 (ISBN 0-87973-257-1, 257). Our Sunday Visitor.

--Concise Guide to the Catholic Church, Vol. II. 165p. (Orig.). 1986. pap. 6.95 (ISBN 0-87973-585-6, 585). Our Sunday Visitor.

Foy, Thomas. Richard Crashaw Poet & Saint. LC 74-9797. 1933. lib. bdg. 10.00 (ISBN 0-8414-4204-5). Folcroft.

Fraade, Steven D. Enosh & His Generation: Pre-Israelite Hero & History in Post-Biblical Interpretation. LC 83-27137. (Society of Biblical Literature-Monograph Ser.). 1984. 29.95 (ISBN 0-89130-724-9, 06 00 30); pap. 19.95 (ISBN 0-89130-725-7). Scholars Pr GA.

Fraenckelscher, Stiftung. Festschrift Seventy-Five Jahrigen Bestehen Des Judich-Theologischen Seminars, 2 vols. Katz, Steven, ed. LC 79-7159. (Jewish Philosophy, Mysticism & History of Ideas Ser.). 1980. Repr. of 1929 ed. Set. lib. bdg. 80.00x (ISBN 0-405-12243-8). Ayer Co Pubs.

Fraile, Peter A. God Within Us: Movements, Powers, & Joys. 110p. 1986. 6.95 (ISBN 0-8294-0503-8). Loyola.

Frakes, Jerold C., tr. see Berschin, Walter.

Frakes, Margaret, jt. ed. see Fey, Harold E.

Frame, James E. A Critical & Exegetical Commentary on the Epistles of St. Paul to the Thessalonians. Driver, Samuel R. & Briggs, Charles A., eds. (International Critical Commentary Ser.). 336p. 1912. 22.95 (ISBN 0-567-05032-7, Pub. by T & T Clark Ltd UK). Fortress.

Frampton, David, jt. auth. see Chaikin, Miriam.

Franasiak, Edwin J., ed. Belonging: Issues of Emotional Living in an Age of Stress for Clergy & Religious. LC 79-11482. 127p. 1979. pap. 4.95 (ISBN 0-89571-007-2). Affirmation.

Francaviglia, Richard V. The Mormon Landscape: Existence, Creation & Perception of a Unique Image in the American West. LC 77-83791. (Studies in Social History: No. 2). (Illus.). 39.50 (ISBN 0-404-16020-4). AMS Pr.

France, Lillian E. Challenge, I Dare You. 1984. 5.75 (ISBN 0-8062-1803-7). Carlton.

France, Peter, et al. An Encyclopedia of Bible Animals. (Illus.). 168p. 1986. 26.95 (ISBN 0-7099-3737-7). Salem Hse Pubs.

France, R. T. The Evidence for Jesus. Green, Michael, ed. LC 86-20927. (The Jesus Library). 144p. 1986. pap. 6.95 (ISBN 0-87784-986-2). Inter-Varsity.

France, R. T., ed. A Bibliographical Guide to New Testament Research. 56p. (Orig.). 1979. pap. text ed. 3.95x (ISBN 0-905774-19-1, Pub. by JSOT Pr England). Eisenbrauns.

France, R. T. & Wenham, David, eds. Gospel Perspectives: Studies of History & Tradition in the Four Gospels, Vol. II. 375p. 1981. text ed. 14.75x (ISBN 0-905774-31-0, Pub. by JSOT Pr England). Eisenbrauns.

--Gospel Perspectives: Studies of History & Tradition in the Four Gospels, Vol. 1. 263p. 1980. text ed. 14.75x (ISBN 0-905774-21-3, Pub. by JSOT Pr England). Eisenbrauns.

--Gospel Perspectives, Vol. III: Studies of History & Tradition in the Four Gospels. 299p. 1983. text ed. 14.75x (ISBN 0-905774-56-6, Pub. by JSOT Press England). Eisenbrauns.

Francesconi, Mario. Bishop John B. Scalabrini: An Insight into His Spirituality. Cinquino, J. & Monaco, Vincent, trs. from It. LC 73-75230. (Illus.). 107p. 1973. pap. 3.00 (ISBN 0-913256-50-1). Ctr Migration.

Francesconi, Mario, jt. auth. see Caliaro, Marco.

Frances D'Assisi, Saint The Writings of Saint Francis of Assisi. Robinson, Paschal, tr. 1977. lib. bdg. 59.95 (ISBN 0-8490-2822-1). Gordon Pr.

Francis, Anne F. Hieronimus Bosch: The Temptation of Saint Anthony. (Illus.). 1980. 15.00 (ISBN 0-682-48910-7, University). Exposition Pr FL.

--Voyage of Re-Discovery: The Veneration of St. Vincent. 1978. 15.00 (ISBN 0-682-48429-6, University). Exposition Pr FL.

Francis, Convers. Life of John Eliot: The Apostle to the Indians. 1972. Repr. of 1854 ed. lib. bdg. 29.00 (ISBN 0-8422-8049-9). Irvington.

Francis, Dale, ed. see Seeley, Burns K.

Francis, Dorothy B. Promises & Turtle Shells: And Forty-Nine Other Object Lessons for Children. 112p. (Orig.). 1984. pap. 7.50 (ISBN 0-687-34337-2). Abingdon.

Francis, Fred O. & Sampley, J. Paul. Pauline Parallels. rev. ed. LC 83-48920. (Foundations & Facets: New Testament Ser.). 416p. 1984. 29.95 (ISBN 0-8006-2103-4, 1-2103). Fortress.

Francis, Fred O. & Wallace, Raymond P., eds. Tradition As Openness to the Future: Essays in Honor of Willis W. Fisher. (Illus.). 236p. (Orig.). 1984. lib. bdg. 25.00 (ISBN 0-8191-3722-7); pap. text ed. 12.25 (ISBN 0-8191-3723-5). U Pr of Amer.

Francis, George. She Died, She Lives: In Search of Maria Orsola. 176p. 1977. pap. 3.95 (ISBN 0-232-51392-9). Attic Pr.

Francis, J. R. The Encyclopedia of Death. large type ed. (Illus.). pap. 7.00 (ISBN 0-910122-47-4). Amherst Pr.

Francis, Mary. But I Have Called You Friends. 1974. 4.95 (ISBN 0-8199-0500-3). Franciscan Herald.

--How to Pray. 84p. 1985. 1.50 (ISBN 0-8199-0931-9). Franciscan Herald.

Francis, Sr. Mary. Variations on a Theme. 1977. 5.00 (ISBN 0-8199-0664-6). Franciscan Herald.

Francis, R. Mabel. Filled with the Spirit-Then What? 1974. 2.50 (ISBN 0-87509-082-6). Chr Pubns.

Francis, Thomas, tr. see Staeglich, Wilhelm.

Franciscan Friars of Marytown, ed. The Hero of Auschwitz. (Illus.). 47p. 1979. pap. 0.75 (ISBN 0-913382-11-6, 105-29). Prow Bks-Franciscan.

Franciscan Friars of Marytown Staff, ed. Kolbe Novena in Honor of the Immaculate Conception & Novena in Honor of St. Maximilin Kolbe. (Illus.). 31p. 1983. pap. 0.50 (ISBN 0-913382-14-0, 105-38). Prow Bks-Franciscan.

Francisco, C. T. Introduccion Al Antiguo Testamento. Lacue, Juan J., tr. from Eng. Tr. of Introducing the Old Testament. (Span.). 350p. 1983. pap. 5.25 (ISBN 0-311-04010-1). Casa Bautista.

Francisco, Clyde T. Introducing the Old Testament. rev. ed. LC 76-24060. 1977. bds. 13.95 (ISBN 0-8054-1213-1, 4212-13). Broadman.

--Un Varon Llamado Job. Glaze, Jack A., tr. from Eng. (Reflexiones Teologicas Ser.). Orig. Title: A Man Called Job. 64p. 1981. pap. 1.95 (ISBN 0-311-04659-2). Casa Bautista.

Franck, Adolf. The Kabbalah & the Philosophy of Plato. (Illus.). 81p. 1986. 98.85 (ISBN 0-89901-288-4). Found Class Reprints.

Franck, Adolph. The Kabbalah or the Religious Philosophy of the Hebrews. LC 73-2199. (The Jewish People; History, Religion, Literature Ser.). Repr. of 1926 ed. 30.00 (ISBN 0-405-05264-2). Ayer Co Pubs.

Franck, Adolphe. The Kabbalah. 1979. pap. 5.95 (ISBN 0-8065-0708-X). Citadel Pr.

Franck, Eskil. Revelation Taught: The Paraclete in the Gospel of John. (New Testament Ser.: No. 14). 168p. (Orig.). 1985. pap. text ed. 27.50x (ISBN 91-40-05114-5, Pub. by Liber Utbildning (Stockholm Sweden)). Coronet Bks.

Franck, Frederick. Art As a Way: A Return to the Spiritual Roots. LC 81-7853. (Illus.). 160p. (Orig.). 1981. pap. 9.95 (ISBN 0-8245-0076-8). Crossroad NY.

--The Book of Angelus Silesius. LC 85-70839. 145p. 1985. pap. 10.95 (ISBN 0-939680-20-3). Bear & Co.

--The Buddha Eye: An Anthology of the Kyoto School. 256p. 1982. 14.95 (ISBN 0-8245-0410-0). Crossroad NY.

--Exploding Church. pap. 2.95 (ISBN 0-440-52432-6). Dell.

--The Supreme Koan: An Artist's Spiritual Journey. LC 81-22037. (Illus.). 1982. pap. 12.95 (ISBN 0-8245-0430-5). Crossroad NY.

--Zen of Seeing. 1973. pap. 8.95 (ISBN 0-394-71968-9, V968, Vin). Random.

Franck, Frederick, ed. Zen & Zen Classics: Selections from R. H. Blyth. (Illus.). 1978. pap. 7.95 (ISBN 0-394-72489-5, Vin). Random.

Franck, Sebastian. Sebastian Franck: Two Hundred Eighty Paradoxes or Wondrous Sayings. Furcha, E. J., tr. (Texts & Studies in Religion: 26). 562p. 1986. lib. bdg. 79.95 (ISBN 0-88946-814-1). E Mellen.

Francklyn, G. Answer to the Rev. Mr. Clarkson's Essay on the Slavery & Commerce of the Human Species. facs. ed. LC 74-83963. (Black Heritage Library Collection Ser). 1789. 13.50 (ISBN 0-8369-8574-5). Ayer Co Pubs.

Francois De Sales. Oeuvres: Introduction a la Vie Devote & Traite de l'Amour de Dieu, etc. (Saint). 2024p. 46.95 (ISBN 0-686-56512-6). French & Eur.

Francuch, Peter D. Four Concepts of the Spiritual Structure of Creation. LC 82-62630. 119p. 1983. pap. 3.95 (ISBN 0-939386-05-4). TMH Pub.

--Fundamentals of Human Spirituality. LC 81-16660. 483p. 1982. 9.95x (ISBN 0-939386-01-1). TMH Pub.

--Major Ideas of the New Revelation. LC 84-51914. 266p. 1985. pap. 8.95 (ISBN 0-939386-08-9). TMH Pub.

--Messages from Within. LC 82-60513. 220p. 1982. pap. 7.95 (ISBN 0-939386-03-8). TMH Pub.

--Reality, Myths & Illusions. LC 83-51193. 513p. 1984. 9.95 (ISBN 0-939386-06-2). TMH Pub.

--Who Are You & Why Are You Here? LC 83-51781. 256p. (Orig.). 1984. pap. 4.95 (ISBN 0-939386-07-0). TMH Pub.

Francuch, Peter D. & Jones, Arthur E. Intensive Spiritual Hypnotherapy. LC 82-62015. 543p. 1983. 9.95 (ISBN 0-939386-04-6). TMH Pub.

Frandsen, Katherine, jt. auth. see Hafen, Brent.

Frank, Anne. Anne Frank: The Diary of a Young Girl. rev. ed. Mooyaart, B. M., tr. 312p. (YA) 1967. 16.95 (ISBN 0-385-04019-9). Doubleday.

--Diary of a Young Girl. LC 58-11474. 1958. o.s. 5.95 (ISBN 0-394-60451-2). Modern Lib.

--The Works of Anne Frank. LC 73-16643. (Illus.). 332p. 1974. Repr. of 1959 ed. lib. bdg. 32.50x (ISBN 0-8371-7206-3, FRWO). Greenwood.

Frank, C. P., tr. see Robert, Charles.

Frank, Diane, ed. see Fries, Michael, et al.

Frank, Douglas W. Less Than Conquerors. 336p. (Orig.). 1986. pap. 14.95 (ISBN 0-8028-0228-1). Eerdmans.

Frank, Edgar. Talmudic & Rabbinical Chronology. 1978. 6.95 (ISBN 0-87306-050-4). Feldheim.

Frank, Erich. Philosophical Understanding & Religious Truth. LC 82-8476. 220p. 1982. pap. text ed. 11.75 (ISBN 0-8191-2510-5). U Pr of Amer.

Frank, Gelya F., jt. auth. see Langness, L. L.

Frank, Grace. Medieval French Drama. 1954. 34.95x (ISBN 0-19-815317-1). Oxford U Pr.

Frank, Harry T. Atlas of the Bible Lands. rev. ed. LC 77-6292. (Illus.). 48p. 1984. 7.95 (ISBN 0-8437-7056-2); pap. 4.99 (ISBN 0-8437-7055-4). Hammond Inc.

--Discovering the Biblical World. rev. ed. LC 74-7044. (Illus.). 228p. 1977. 19.95 (ISBN 0-8437-3624-0). Hammond Inc.

Frank, Harry T. & Strange, James F. Discovering the Biblical World. rev. ed. (Illus.). 288p. 1987. pap. 14.95 (ISBN 0-8437-3626-7). Hammond Inc.

Frank, Harry T., ed. Atlas of the Bible Lands. 1979. pap. 4.95 (ISBN 0-8054-1136-4). Broadman.

Frank, Loraine C. My Book of Gold & Other Writings. 1987. 6.95 (ISBN 0-533-07072-4). Vantage.

Frank, Luanne T. & George, Emery E., eds. Husbanding the Golden Grain: Studies in Honor of Henry W. Nordmeyer. 337p. 1973. 12.50x (ISBN 0-913950-01-7). M S Rosenberg.

Frank, P. El Alcohol y la Familia. 1981. pap. 1.50 (ISBN 0-89243-139-3). Liguori Pubns.

Frank, Penny. Daniel in the Lion's Den. Alexander, P., ed. (Lion Story Bible Ser.). 24p. 1987. 2.95 (ISBN 0-85648-752-X). Lion USA.

--Jesus on Trial. Alexander, P., ed. (Lion Story Bible Ser.). 24p. 1987. 2.95. Lion USA.

--Jesus the Teacher. Alexander, P., ed. (Lion Story Bible Ser.). 24p. 1987. 2.95 (ISBN 0-85648-760-0). Lion USA.

--King David. Alexander, P., ed. (Lion Story Bible Ser.). 24p. 1987. 2.95 (ISBN 0-85648-744-9). Lion USA.

--Naaman's Dreadful Secret. Alexander, P., ed. (Lion Story Bible Ser.). 24p. 1987. 2.95 (ISBN 0-85648-748-1). Lion USA.

--Paul & His Friends. Alexander, P., ed. (Lion Story Bible Ser.). 24p. 1987. 2.95 (ISBN 0-85648-776-7). Lion USA.

--The Story of the Two Brothers. Alexamder, P., ed. (Lion Story Bible Ser.). 24p. 1987. 2.95 (ISBN 0-85648-765-1). Lion USA.

Frank, Richard M. Beings & Their Attributes: The Teaching of the Bastian School of the Matzzila in the Classical Period. LC 78-6957. 1978. 49.50x (ISBN 0-87395-378-9). State U NY Pr.

Frank, Ruth S. & Wolheim, William. The Book of Jewish Books: A Readers' Guide to Judaism. LC 86-45014. (Illus.). 272p. (Orig.). 1986. 15.95 (ISBN 0-06-063008-6, HarpR); pap. 8.95 (ISBN 0-06-063009-4, HarpR). Har-Row.

Frank, S. L. God with Us. 1946. 29.50x (ISBN 0-686-83560-3). Elliots Bks.

--The Unknowable: An Ontological Introduction to the Philosophy of Religion. Jakim, Boris, tr. from Russian. xxii, 313p. 1983. text ed. 26.95x (ISBN 0-8214-0676-0, 82-84440). Ohio U Pr.

Franke, Merle G. It Came upon the Midnight Clear: Christmas Photo Sermon. 1977. pap. 9.50 (ISBN 0-89536-291-0, 0916). CSS of Ohio.

--Lord, Where Are You? I'm Hip-Deep in Alligators. 1985. 4.95 (ISBN 0-89536-740-8, 5824). CSS of Ohio.

--Who Tarnished My Saints? 1984. 5.95 (ISBN 0-89536-986-9, 7534). CSS of Ohio.

Frankel, Alona, jt. auth. see Cashman, Greer F.

Frankel, Charles. Faith of Reason. LC 71-86277. 1969. Repr. of 1948 ed. lib. bdg. 17.00x (ISBN 0-374-92850-9, Octagon). Hippocrene Bks.

Frankel, Jonathan. Prophecy & Politics: Socialism, Nationalism, & the Russian Jews, 1862-1917. LC 80-14414. 686p. 1984. pap. 19.95 (ISBN 0-521-26919-9). Cambridge U Pr.

Frankel, William, ed. Survey of Jewish Affairs 1983. 320p. 1985. 25.00 (ISBN 0-8386-3244-0). Fairleigh Dickinson.

--Survey of Jewish Affairs, 1985. 280p. 1985. 25.00x (ISBN 0-8386-3269-6). Fairleigh Dickinson.

Frankena, William K. Ethics. 2nd ed. (Foundations of Philosophy Ser.). 144p. 1973. pap. text ed. write for info. (ISBN 0-13-290478-0). P-H.

--Thinking about Morality. (Michigan Faculty Ser.). 112p. 1980. pap. 4.95 (ISBN 0-472-06316-2). U of Mich Pr.

Frankena, William K. & Granrose, John T. Introductory Readings in Ethics. 496p. 1974. text ed. write for info. (ISBN 0-13-502112-X). P-H.

Frankena, William K., ed. see Edwards, Jonathan.

Frankfort, Henri. Ancient Egyptian Religion: An Interpretation. pap. 7.95x (ISBN 0-06-130077-2, TB77, Torch). Har-Row.

--Ancient Egyptian Religion: An Interpretation. 16.00 (ISBN 0-8446-2084-X). Peter Smith.

--Cylinder Seals, A Documentary Essay on the Art & Religion of the Ancient Near East. 427p. Repr. of 1939 ed. text ed. 74.52x (ISBN 0-576-19456-5). Gregg Intl.

--Kingship & the Gods: A Study of Ancient Near Eastern Religion As the Integration of Society & Nature. LC 48-5158. 1978. pap. 12.95 (ISBN 0-226-26011-9, P766, Phoen). U of Chicago Pr.

Frankforter, A. Daniel. A History of the Christian Movement: The Development of Christian Institutions. LC 77-8071. 332p. 1978. text ed. 22.95x (ISBN 0-88229-292-7); pap. 11.95x (ISBN 0-88229-568-3). Nelson-Hall.

Frankiel, Sandra S. Christianity: A Way of Salvation. LC 84-48770. 144p. (Orig.). 1985. pap. 6.95 (ISBN 0-06-063015-9, RD 498, HarpR). Har-Row.

Frankl, Ludwig A. The Jews in the East, 2 vols. Beaton, P., tr. LC 78-97278. 1975. Repr. of 1859 ed. Set. lib. bdg. 28.50x (ISBN 0-8371-2596-0, FRJE). Greenwood.

Frankl, Razelle. Televangelism: The Marketing of Popular Religion. (Illus.). 224p. 1987. 19.95 (ISBN 0-8093-1299-9). S Ill U Pr.

Frankl, Victor. The Unconscious God. 1976. pap. 5.95 (ISBN 0-671-22426-3, Touchstone Bks). S&S.

Frankl, Viktor. The Unconscious God. 1985. pap. 3.50 (ISBN 0-671-54728-3). WSP.

Franklin, Alexander. Seven Miracle Plays. 1963. pap. 8.95x (ISBN 0-19-831391-8). Oxford U Pr.

Franklin, H. Bruce. The Wake of the Gods: Melville's Mythology. 1963. pap. 16.95x (ISBN 0-8047-0137-7). Stanford U Pr.

Franklin, J. E. Black Girl from Genesis to Revelations. LC 74-30386. 1977. 9.95 (ISBN 0-88258-019-1). Howard U Pr.

Franklin, James. Present State of Hayti: Saint Domingo-with Remarks on Its Agriculture, Commerce, Laws, Regligion, Finance & Population. LC 79-109325. Repr. of 1828 ed. 25.00x (ISBN 0-8371-3591-5, FRH&). Greenwood.

Franklin, James C. Mystical Transformations: The Imagery of Liquids in the Work of Mechthild Von Magdeburg. LC 75-5248. 192p. 1976. 18.50 (ISBN 0-8386-1738-7). Fairleigh Dickinson.

Franklin, Karl, ed. & intro. by. Current Concerns of Anthropologists & Missionaries. LC 86-81558. (International Museum of Cultures Ser.: No. 22). 174p. (Orig.). 1987. pap. text ed. 14.00 (ISBN 0-88312-176-X); microfiche (3) 6.00 (ISBN 0-88312-259-6). Summer Inst Ling.

Franklin, M. & Dotts, Maryann J. Clues to Creativity, Vol. 2: J-P. (Orig.). 1975. pap. 4.95 (ISBN 0-377-00041-8). Friend Pr.

--Clues to Creativity, Vol. 3: R-Z. (Orig.). 1976. pap. 4.95 (ISBN 0-377-00042-6). Friend Pr.

Franklin, Margaret A., ed. The Force of the Feminine: Women, Men & the Church. 232p. 1986. text ed. 29.95x (ISBN 0-86861-930-2); pap. text ed. 12.95x (ISBN 0-86861-914-0). Allen Unwin.

Franklin, R. W. Nineteenth-Century Churches: The History of a New Catholicism in Wurttemberg, England & France. McNeill, William H., ed. 700p. 1987. lib. bdg. 105.00 (ISBN 0-8240-8067-X). Garland Pub.

Franklin, R. W., ed. see Williams, George H.

Frankl-Lundborg, Otto. What Is Anthroposophy? Wetzl, Joseph, tr. 1977. pap. 2.95 (ISBN 0-916786-14-5). St George Bk Serv.

Franks, Judith, jt. auth. see Samskriti.

Fransen, P. Intelligent Theology, Vol. 1: The Trinity Lives in Us As We Celebrate Life. LC 77-85505. 148p. pap. 2.50 (ISBN 0-8199-0400-7). Franciscan Herald.

--Intelligent Theology, Vol. 2: Confirmation & Priesthood. 157p. pap. 2.50 (ISBN 0-8199-0401-5). Franciscan Herald.

--Intelligent Theology, Vol. 3: A Universal Theology. 183p. pap. 2.50 (ISBN 0-8199-0402-3). Franciscan Herald.

Fransen, Paul. Effective Church Councils: Leadership Styles & Decision Making in the Church. (Administration Series for Churches). 56p. (Orig.). 1985. pap. 3.95 (ISBN 0-8066-2198-2, 10-2023). Augsburg.

Frantz, Alison. The Church of the Holy Apostles. LC 76-356003. (Athenian Agora Ser: Vol. 20). (Illus.). xiii, 45p. 1972. 15.00x (ISBN 0-87661-220-6). Am Sch Athens.

Franz, Marie-Louise Von see Jung, Emma & Von Franz, Marie-Louise.

Franz, Marie-Louise von see Von Franz, Marie-Louise.

Franz, Raymond. Crisis of Conscience: The Struggle between Loyalty to God & Loyalty to One's Religion. LC 83-62637. (Illus.). 384p. 1983. 10.95 (ISBN 0-914675-00-1); pap. 7.95 (ISBN 0-914675-03-6). Comment Pr.

Franzblau, Abraham N. Religious Belief & Character among Jewish Adolescents. LC 78-176783. (Columbia University. Teachers College. Contributions to Education: No. 634). Repr. of 1934 ed. 22.50 (ISBN 0-404-55634-5). AMS Pr.

Franzen, Lavern G. Good News from Luke: Visual Messages for Children. LC 76-3869. 112p. (Orig.). 1976. pap. 6.95 (ISBN 0-8066-1528-1, 10-2813). Augsburg.

Franzmann, jt. auth. see Roehrs.

Franzmann, Martin H. The Revelation to John. 148p. 1986. pap. 7.95 (ISBN 0-570-03728-X, 12-2630). Concordia.

--Romans. 288p. 1986. pap. 8.95 (ISBN 0-570-04426-X, 12-3036). Concordia.

Franzmann, Werner H. Bible History Commentary: Old Testament. LC 80-53145. (Illus.). 616p. 1981. 15.95 (ISBN 0-938272-04-7). WELS Board.

Franzos, Karl E. The Jews of Barnow. facsimile ed. Macdowall, M. W., tr. from Ger. LC 74-27985. (Modern Jewish Experience Ser.). (Eng.). 1975. Repr. of 1883 ed. 30.00x (ISBN 0-405-06712-7). Ayer Co Pubs.

Franzwa, Gregory M. The Old Cathedral. 2nd ed. LC 80-15885. (Illus.). 1980. 14.95 (ISBN 0-935284-18-4). Patrice Pr.

Franzwa, Gregory M., ed. see Burnett, Betty.

Frary, Thomas D., jt. auth. see Dondero, John P.

Fraser, Alexander C. Berkeley. 1899. 12.50 (ISBN 0-8274-1926-0). R West.

--Philosophy of Theism. LC 77-27228. (Gifford Lectures: 1894-95). Repr. of 1895 ed. 24.50 (ISBN 0-404-60453-6). AMS Pr.

--Philosophy of Theism: Second Series. LC 77-27227. (Gifford Lectures: 1895-96). Repr. of 1896 ed. 30.00 (ISBN 0-404-60454-4). AMS Pr.

Fraser, Amy S. The Hills of Home. (Illus.). 250p. 1973. pap. 8.95 (ISBN 0-7102-0540-6). Methuen Inc.

Fraser, Donald. The Metaphors of Christ. 384p. 1985. smythe sewn 15.25 (ISBN 0-86524-188-0, 9523); lib. bdg. 15.25 smythe sewn (ISBN 0-317-40599-3). Klock & Klock.

Fraser, Gordon H. Is Mormonism Christian? 1977. pap. 3.95 (ISBN 0-8024-4169-6). Moody.

Fraser, Hilary. Beauty & Belief: Aesthetics & Religion in Victorian Literature. 306p. 1986. 34.50 (ISBN 0-521-30767-8). Cambridge U Pr.

Fraser, J. O. & Allbutt, Mary E., eds. Prayer of Faith. pap. 1.00 (ISBN 0-85363-106-9). OMF Bks.

Fraser, James W. Cremation: Is It Christian? 1965. pap. 1.50 (ISBN 0-87213-180-7). Loizeaux.

--Pedagogue for God's Kingdom: Lyman Beecher & the Second Great Awakening. LC 85-17794. 248p. 1985. lib. bdg. 27.50 (ISBN 0-8191-4905-5); pap. text ed. 12.75 (ISBN 0-8191-4906-3). U Pr of Amer.

Fraser, John W. see Calvin, John.

Fraser, John W., tr. see Calvin, John.

Fraser, Mitchell W. English Pulpit Oratory from Andrews to Tillotson: A Study of Its Literary Aspects. 516p. 1982. Repr. of 1932 ed. lib. bdg. 85.00 (ISBN 0-89760-564-0). Telegraph Bks.

Fraser, Ralph S., tr. see Talbert, Charles H.

Fraser, Ronald, tr. see Schwaller De Lubicz, Isha.

Fraser, Theodore P. & Kopp, Richard L. The Moralist Tradition in France. LC 81-69245. 286p. (Orig.). 1982. text ed. 22.50x (ISBN 0-86733-017-1). Assoc Faculty Pr.

Fraser-Harris, D. Shakespeare & the Influence of the Stars. 69.95 (ISBN 0-8490-1031-4). Gordon Pr.

Frasier, Carl. Inspiring Poems. 6.00 (ISBN 0-8062-2493-2). Carlton.

Fraunce, Abraham see Batman, Stephen.

Frawley, David. Hymns from the Golden Age: Selected Hymns from the Rig Veda with Yogic Interpretation. 256p. 1986. 22.00 (ISBN 81-208-0072-9, Pub. by Motilal Banarsidass). South Asia Bks.

Frazee, Charles A. Catholics & Sultans: The Church & the Ottoman Empire 1453-1923. LC 82-4562. 384p. 1983. 67.50 (ISBN 0-521-24676-8). Cambridge U Pr.

--Orthodox Church in Independent Greece 1821-52. LC 69-10488. 1969. 42.50 (ISBN 0-521-07247-6). Cambridge U Pr.

Frazel, J. G. The Fear of the Dead in Primitive Religion. LC 66-15215. 1933. 10.00 (ISBN 0-8196-0167-5). Biblo.

Frazen, Lavern G. Good News from Matthew: Visual Messages for Children. LC 77-72463. 1977. pap. 6.95 (ISBN 0-8066-1597-4, 10-2814). Augsburg.

Frazer, J. G. Psyche's Task: A Discourse Concerning the Influence of Superstition on the Growth of Institutions. 2nd ed. 1979. Repr. of 1913 ed. lib. bdg. 27.50 (ISBN 0-8495-1636-6). Arden Lib.

Frazer, James. The New Golden Bough. rev. ed. Gaster, Theodore, ed. 832p. 1975. pap. 5.95 (ISBN 0-451-62208-1, ME2208, Ment). NAL.

Frazer, James G. The Fear of the Dead in Primitive Religion, 3 vols. in one. Kastenaum, Robert, ed. LC 76-19571. (Death & Dying Ser.). 1977. Repr. of 1936 ed. lib. bdg. 57.50x (ISBN 0-405-09566-X). Ayer Co Pubs.

--Golden Bough. rev., abr ed. 1985. pap. 10.95 (ISBN 0-02-095570-7, Collier). Macmillan.
--The Worship of Nature. LC 73-21271. (Gifford Lectures: 1924-25). Repr. of 1926 ed. 41.50 (ISBN 0-404-11427-X). AMS Pr.
Frazier, Allie M., ed. Readings in Eastern Religious Thought, 3 vols. Incl. Vol. 1. Hinduism; Vol. 2. Buddhism; Vol. 3. Chinese & Japanese Religions. (ISBN 0-664-24848-9). LC 69-14197. 1969. Westminster.
Frazier, E. Franklin & Lincoln, C. Eric. The Negro Church in America. Bd. with The Black Church Since Frazier. LC 72-96201. (Sourcebooks in Negro History Ser.). 1973. pap. 4.95 (ISBN 0-8052-0387-7). Schocken.
Fream, Donald. A Chain of Jewels from James & Jude. LC 71-1073. (The Bible Study Textbook Ser.). (Illus.). 1965. 12.20 (ISBN 0-89900-045-2). College Pr Pub.
--Thirteen Lessons on James & Jude. (Bible Student Study Guides). 1979. pap. 2.95 (ISBN 0-89900-161-0). College Pr Pub.
Freburger, William. Baptism. 1970. pap. 0.95 (ISBN 0-8189-0425-9). Alba.
--This Is the Word of the Lord. rev. ed. LC 83-72480. 176p. 1984. spiral bound 6.95 (ISBN 0-87793-309-X). Ave Maria.
Freburger, William J. Birthday Blessings. (Greeting Book Line Ser.). 32p. (Orig.). 1985. pap. 1.50 (ISBN 0-89622-242-X). Twenty-Third.
--Liturgy: Work of the People. 112p. (Orig.). 1984. pap. 4.95 (ISBN 0-89622-214-4). Twenty-Third.
Freddoso, Alfred J., ed. The Existence & Nature of God. LC 83-47521. (Notre Dame Studies in Philosophy of Religion). 190p. 1984. 16.95x (ISBN 0-268-00910-4, 85-09119); pap. text ed. 9.95x (ISBN 0-268-00911-2). U of Notre Dame Pr.
Frederic, Harold. New Exodus: A Study of Israel in Russia. LC 71-115538. (Russia Observed, Series I). 1970. Repr. of 1892 ed. 19.00 (ISBN 0-405-03027-4). Ayer Co Pubs.
Frederick, Filis, ed. see Schloss, Malcolm & Purdom, Charles.
Frederick, John T. The Darkened Sky: Nineteenth-Century American Novelists & Religion. LC 69-14811. pap. 72.50 (ISBN 0-317-29688-4, 2022068). Bks Demand UMI.
Frederick, Peter J. Knights of the Golden Rule: The Intellectual As Christian Social Reformer in the 1890s. LC 76-9497. 344p. 1976. 28.00x (ISBN 0-8131-1345-8). U Pr of Ky.
Fredericq, Paul see McIlvain, James W.
Fredman, Ruth G. The Passover Seder. 1982. pap. 5.95 (ISBN 0-452-00606-6, Mer). NAL.
--The Passover Seder: Afikoman in Exile. 1981. 22.00x (ISBN 0-8122-7788-0). U of Pa Pr.
--The Passover Seder: Afikoman in Exile. 192p. 19.00 (ISBN 0-686-95143-3). ADL.
Fredman, Ruth G., ed. Jewish Life on Campus: A Directory of B'nai B'rith Hillel Foundations & Other Campus Agencies. 1986. pap. 8.95 (ISBN 0-9603058-5-8). B'nai B'rith Hillel.
Fredrickson, Carl, ed. Church Soloists Favorites, 2 bks. (Illus.). 1963. Bk. 1, High Voice, 64p. pap. 6.95 (ISBN 0-8258-0228-8, RB-65); Bk. 2, Low Voice, 85p. pap. 6.95 (ISBN 0-8258-0229-6, RB-66). Fischer Inc NY.
Fredrikson, Roger L. The Communicator's Commentary-John, Vol. 4. Ogilvie, Lloyd J., ed. (The Communicator's Commentaries Ser.). 1983. 18.95 (ISBN 0-8499-0157-X). Word Bks.
Free Church. Ministers Service Manual. 1981. 5.95 (ISBN 0-911802-48-7). Free Church Pubns.
--You & Your Church. 3rd ed. 1978. pap. 1.95. Free Church Pubns.
Free, John Da see Da Free, John.
Free, John Da see John, Da Free.
Freedberg, David. Rubens: The Life of Christ after the Passion, Pt. VII. (Corpus Rubenianum Ludwig Burchand). (Illus.). 1983. 74.00 (ISBN 0-19-921032-2). Oxford U Pr.
Freedberg, S. J., ed. see Martone, Thomas.
Freedberg, S. J., ed. see Sheppard, Jennifer M.
Freedberg, Sydney J., ed. see Sale, J. Russell.
Freedland, Michael. So Let's Hear the Applause: The Story of the Jewish Entertainer. (Illus.). 250p. 1986. 16.50x (ISBN 0-85303-215-7, Pu. by Valentine Mitchell England). Biblio Dist.
Freedman, D. N. Pottery, Poetry & Prophecy: Studies in Early Hebrew Poetry. 1980. text ed. 20.00 (ISBN 0-931464-04-8). Eisenbrauns.
Freedman, D. N. & Mathews, K. A. The Paleo-Hebrew Leviticus Scroll. (Illus.). xii, 135p. 1985. text ed. 19.95x (ISBN 0-89757-007-3). Am Sch Orient Res.
Freedman, D. N. & Campbell, E. F., Jr., eds. The Biblical Archaeologist Reader, No. 4. (Illus.). xiii, 390p. 1983. text ed. 24.95x (ISBN 0-907459-34-X, Pub. by Almond Pr England); pap. text ed. 9.95x (ISBN 0-907459-35-8). Eisenbrauns.
Freedman, David, ed. see Morton, A. Q., et al.
Freedman, David, ed. see Parunak, Van Dyke H.
Freedman, David, ed. see Radday, Yehuda & Levi, Yaakov.
Freedman, David M., jt. auth. see Fleisher, David.
Freedman, David N., jt. auth. see O'Connor, M.
Freedman, David N., intro. by see Charlesworth, James H.
Freedman, David N., ed. see Morton, A. Q. & Michaelson, S.
Freedman, David Noel, ed. see Morton, A. Q. & Michaelson, Sidney.
Freedman, David Noel, ed. see Tyson, Joseph B. & Longstaff, Thomas R. W.
Freedman, Jacob. Polychrome Historical Prayerbook: Siddur 'Bet Yosef' (Illus.). 400p. 1984. 125.00x (ISBN 0-686-12113-9). J Freedman Liturgy.
Freedman, Maurice, tr. see Granet, Marcel.
Freehof, Lillian S. Bible Legends: An Introduction to Midrash. rev. ed. Schwartz, Howard, ed. 1987. pap. text ed. 6.95 (ISBN 0-8074-0357-1). UAHC.
--Bible Legends: An Introduction to Midrash. Schwartz, Howard, ed. (YA) Date not set. pap. text ed. 6.95 (ISBN 0-8074-0357-1). UAHC.
--Stories of King David. (Illus.). 1952. 5.95 (ISBN 0-8276-0162-X, 263). Jewish Pubns.
Freehof, S. Reform Jewish Practice. 9.95x (ISBN 0-685-55600-X). Ktav.
Freehof, S. B. Reform Responsa for Our Time. 15.00x (ISBN 0-87820-111-4, HUC Pr). Ktav.
Freehof, Solomon B. The Book of Jeremiah: A Commentary. LC 77-8259. 1977. 15.00 (ISBN 0-8074-0008-4, 381610). UAHC.
--Contemporary Reform Response. 15.00x (ISBN 0-87820-108-4, Pub. by Hebrew Union College Press). Ktav.
--Current Reform Responsa. 1969. 15.00x (ISBN 0-87820-102-5, Pub. by Hebrew Union). Ktav.
--Ezekiel: A Commentary. 1979. 15.00 (ISBN 0-8074-0033-5, 380010). UAHC.
--Isaiah: A Commentary. 1972. 15.00 (ISBN 0-8074-0042-4, 383015). UAHC.
--Modern Reform Response. 1971. 15.00x (ISBN 0-87820-101-7, Pub. by Hebrew Union). Ktav.
--Preaching the Bible. 1974. 12.50x (ISBN 0-87068-244-X). Ktav.
Free John, Da. The Method of the Siddhas. rev. ed. LC 78-53869. (Illus.). 364p. 1978. pap. 9.95 (ISBN 0-913922-44-7). Dawn Horse Pr.
--The Paradox of Instruction: An Introduction to the Esoteric Spiritual Teaching of Da Free John. LC 77-81836. 9.95 (ISBN 0-913922-32-3). Dawn Horse Pr.
Freelander, Iris see Carr, Clare.
Freeman. Handbook of Bible Manners & Customs. Repr. of 1870 ed. cancelled. Guildhall Pubs.
Freeman, Arnold, tr. see Steiner, Rudolf.
Freeman, Bill. Gaining Christ in Daily Life. 12p. 1983. pap. 0.25 (ISBN 0-914271-02-4). NW Christian Pubns.
--God's Eternal Purpose. (Illus.). 14p. 1983. pap. 0.25 (ISBN 0-914271-01-6). NW Christian Pubns.
Freeman, Bill, ed. see Bunyan, John, et al.
Freeman, Carroll B. The Senior Adult Years. LC 79-51137. 1979. 7.95 (ISBN 0-8054-5421-7). Broadman.
Freeman, David. Know Your Self. 1976. pap. 3.95 (ISBN 0-934532-11-7). Presby & Reformed.
Freeman, David H. Tillich. (Modern Thinkers Ser.). 1960. pap. 2.00 (ISBN 0-87552-589-X). Presby & Reformed.
Freeman, Dorothy. From Copper to Gold: The Life of Dorothy Baker. (Illus.). 368p. 17.50 (ISBN 0-85398-177-9); pap. 10.95 (ISBN 0-85398-178-7). G Ronald Pub.
Freeman, Edward A. The Epoch of Negro Baptists & the Foreign Mission Board. Gaustad, Edwin S., ed. LC 79-52593. (The Baptist Tradition Ser.). 1980. Repr. of 1953 ed. lib. bdg. 26.50x (ISBN 0-405-12460-0). Ayer Co Pubs.
Freeman, Eileen E. The Holy Week Book. new ed. LC 78-73510. (Illus.). 1979. pap. 19.95 (ISBN 0-89390-007-9). Resource Pubns.
Freeman, Eugene, jt. ed. see Reese, William L.
Freeman, Gordon M. The Heavenly Kingdom: Aspects of Political Thought in the Talmud & Midrash. 196p. (Orig.). 1986. lib. bdg. 24.75 (ISBN 0-8191-5139-4, Co-pub. by Ctr Jewish Comm Studies); pap. text ed. 11.75 (ISBN 0-8191-5140-8). U Pr of Amer.
Freeman, Grace & Sugarman, Joan. Inside the Synagogue. rev. ed. (Illus.). 64p. 1984. pap. 6.00 (ISBN 0-8074-0268-0, 301785). UAHC.
Freeman, Harold. Variety in Biblical Preaching. 192p. 1986. 12.95 (ISBN 0-8499-0562-1). Word Bks.
Freeman, Hobart. Nahum, Sofonias, Habacuc (Comentario Biblico Portavoz) Orig. Title: Nahum, Zephaniah & Habakkuk (Everyman's Bible Commentary) (Span.). 112p. 1980. pap. 3.50 (ISBN 0-8254-1246-3). Kregel.
Freeman, James D. The Case for Reincarnation. 320p. 1986. 5.95 (ISBN 0-87159-021-2). Unity School.
--Of Time & Eternity. LC 81-51069. 200p. 1981. 5.95 (ISBN 0-87159-122-7). Unity School.
--Once upon a Christmas. LC 78-53345. (Illus.). 1978. 6.95 (ISBN 0-87159-119-7). Unity School.
--Prayer: The Master Key. 1975. 5.95 (ISBN 0-87159-128-6). Unity School.
--The Story of Unity. rev. ed. (Illus.). 1978. 5.95 (ISBN 0-87159-145-6). Unity School.
--Tu Puedes! LC 82-70490. 256p. 1982. 5.95 (ISBN 0-87159-158-8). Unity School.
Freeman, James M. Manners & Customs of the Bible. (Illus.). 515p. 1972. (Pub. by Logos); pap. 8.95 (ISBN 0-88270-022-7). Bridge Pub.
Freeman, Joanna M. How to Minister in Nursing Homes. 40p. 1983. pap. text ed. 3.95 (ISBN 0-87148-410-2). Pathway Pr.
Freeman, Kathleen. God, Man & State. LC 79-101039. 1969. Repr. of 1952 ed. 27.50x (ISBN 0-8046-0705-2, Pub. by Kennikat). Assoc Faculty Pr.
--God, Man & State: Greek Concepts. Repr. of 1952 ed. lib. bdg. 27.50x (ISBN 0-8371-2821-8, FRGM). Greenwood.
Freeman, Laurence. Light Within: The Inner Path of Meditation. 112p. 1987. pap. 7.95 (ISBN 0-8245-0785-1). Crossroad NY.
Freeman, Lucy, ed. Listening to the Inner Self. LC 83-9988. 206p. 1984. 20.00 (ISBN 0-87668-640-4). Aronson.
Freeman, Lucy C. & Strean, Herbert S. Guilt: Letting Go. LC 86-15873. 288p. 1987. 14.95 (ISBN 0-471-83636-2). Wiley.
Freeman, Margaret. Hidden Treasure: Parables for Kids. LC 81-16669. (Illus.). 96p. (Orig.). 1982. pap. 3.95 (ISBN 0-87239-499-9, 2728). Standard Pub.
Freeman, Nona. The Adventures of Bug & Me. Clanton, Charles, ed. 128p. (Orig.). 1977. pap. 4.95 (ISBN 0-912315-28-8). Word Aflame.
--Box 44, Monrovia. Wallace, Mary H., ed. (Illus.). 224p. 1983. pap. 5.95 (ISBN 0-912315-09-1). Word Aflame.
--Bug & Nona on the Go. Clanton, Charles, ed. LC 86-9845. 176p. (Orig.). 1979. pap. 4.95 (ISBN 0-912315-27-X). Word Aflame.
--Shoutin' on the Hills. LC 85-22521. (Illus.). 320p. (Orig.). 1985. pap. 6.95 (ISBN 0-912315-94-6). Word Aflame.
--This Is the Day. Clanton, Charles, ed. 256p. (Orig.). 1978. pap. 4.95 (ISBN 0-912315-36-9). Word Aflame.
Freeman, Robert N. Franz Schneider (Seventeen Thirty-Seven to Eighteen Twelve) A Thematic Catalogue of His Works. LC 79-15260. (Thematic Catalogues Ser.: No. 5). 1979. lib. bdg. 24.00x (ISBN 0-918728-13-4). Pendragon NY.
Freeman, Sean. Parables, Psalms, Prayers. 1985. 10.95 (ISBN 0-88347-185-X). Thomas More.
Freemesser, George F. Learning to Live from Within: A Glimpse of Jesus As Healer. 1985. 8.95 (ISBN 0-87193-242-3). Dimension Bks.
Freer, Coburn. Music for a King: George Herbert's Style & the Metrical Psalms. LC 76-179136. pap. 67.50 (ISBN 0-317-42332-0, 2025815). Bks Demand UMI.
Frees, John Da see John, Da Free.
Freese, Doris. Children's Church: A Comprehensive How-to. LC 81-22426. 128p. 1982. pap. 6.95 (ISBN 0-8024-1250-5). Moody.
--Vacation Bible School. LC 77-76179. 96p. 1977. pap. text ed. 4.95 (ISBN 0-910566-11-9); Perfect bdg. instr's. guide by Werner Graendorf 5.95 (ISBN 0-910566-27-5). Evang Tchr.
Freesoul, John Redtail. Breath of the Invisible. LC 86-40124. (Illus.). 226p. (Orig.). 1986. pap. 6.95 (ISBN 0-8356-0611-2). Theos Pub Hse.
Freeze, Gregory L. The Parish Clergy in Nineteenth-Century Russia: Crisis, Reform, Counter-Reform. LC 82-61361. 552p. 1983. 52.50x (ISBN 0-691-05381-2). Princeton U Pr.
--The Russian Levites: Parish Clergy in the Eighteenth Century. (Russian Research Center Studies: 78). 1977. 22.50x (ISBN 0-674-78175-9). Harvard U Pr.
Freeze, Gregory L., ed. see Belliustin, I. S.
Frei, Hans W. The Eclipse of Biblical Narrative: A Study in Eighteenth & Nineteenth-Century Hermeneutics. LC 73-86893. 384p. 1974. pap. 10.95x (ISBN 0-300-02602-1). Yale U Pr.
Freiday, Dean. Nothing Without Christ. LC 84-70040. (Orig.). 1984. pap. 3.95 (ISBN 0-913342-44-0). Barclay Pr.
Freiman, A., et al, eds. Festschrift zum Siebzigsten Geburtstage A. Berliner's. LC 79-7165. (Jewish Philosophy, Mysticism & History of Ideas Ser.). 1980. Repr. of 1903 ed. lib. bdg. 45.00x (ISBN 0-405-12252-7). Ayer Co Pubs.
Freligh, H. M. Studies in Revelation, 4 Vols. Schroeder, E. H., ed. 327p. 1969. pap. text ed. 2.50 ea.; Vol. 1. (ISBN 0-87509-140-7); Vol. 2. (ISBN 0-87509-141-5); Vol. 3. (ISBN 0-87509-142-3); Vol. 4. (ISBN 0-87509-143-1). Chr Pubns.
Freligh, H. M., ed. see Pardington, G. P.
Freligh, Harold M. Job. pap. 1.95 (ISBN 0-87509-097-4). Chr Pubns.
Fremantle, Ann & Fremantle, Christopher. In Love with Love: One Hundred of the World's Greatest Spiritual Poems. LC 78-64360. (Spiritual Masters Ser.). 1978. pap. 2.95 (ISBN 0-8091-2136-0). Paulist Pr.
Fremantle, Anne, tr. see Schamoni, Wilhelm.
Fremantle, Christopher, jt. auth. see Fremantle, Ann.
Fremantle, Francesca & Trungpa, Chogyam, trs. from Tibetan. The Tibetan Book of the Dead: The Great Liberation Through Hearing in the Bardo. LC 74-29615. (Clear Light Ser.). (Illus.). 256p. 1975. pap. 7.95 (ISBN 0-87773-074-1). Shambhala Pubns.
French, Curtis. Winning Words: Devotions for Athletes. LC 77-75467. 1983. pap. 5.95 (ISBN 0-8499-2805-2). Word Bks.
French, Hajjar. Christiarisme en Orient. 9.00x (ISBN 0-86685-172-0). Intl Bk Ctr.
French, Hal W. & Sharma, Arvind. Religious Ferment in Modern India. 1982. 19.95x (ISBN 0-312-67134-2). St Martin.
French, Harold W. The Swan's Wide Waters: Ramakrishna & Western Culture. new ed. LC 74-77657. (National University Publications Ser.). 214p. 1974. 23.50x (ISBN 0-8046-9055-3, Pub by Kennikat). Assoc Faculty Pr.
French, J. Milton, ed. Life Records of John Milton, 1608-1674, 5 Vols. LC 66-20024. 2368p. 1966. Repr. of 1958 ed. Set. 150.00x (ISBN 0-87752-039-9). Gordian.
French, Jane, jt. auth. see French, Joel.
French, Joel & French, Jane. War Beyond the Stars. LC 79-90267. (Illus.). 128p. 1979. pap. 4.95 (ISBN 0-89221-067-2). New Leaf.
French, Peter. The Scope of Morality. 1980. 25.00 (ISBN 0-8166-0837-7); pap. 9.95 (ISBN 0-8166-0900-4). U of Minn Pr.
French, Peter A. Ethics in Government. 176p. 1983. pap. write for info. (ISBN 0-13-290908-1). P-H.
French, Peter A., et al, eds. Studies in Ethical Theory. (Midwest Studies in Philosophy: Vol. 3). 1980. 25.00x (ISBN 0-8166-0968-3); pap. 12.95 (ISBN 0-8166-0971-3). U of Minn Pr.
French, R. M., tr. The Way of the Pilgrim & the Pilgrim Continues His Way. 256p. pap. 7.95 (ISBN 0-86683-898-8, AY7444, HarpR). Har-Row.
French, R. M., tr. see Berdiaev, Nikolai A.
French, Reginald M., tr. from Rus. Way of a Pilgrim. (Illus.). 242p. 1974. (HarpR); pap. 7.95 (ISBN 0-86683-898-8, SP18). Har-Row.
Frend, W. H. The Donatist Church: A Movement of Protest in Roman North Africa. 384p. 1985. 42.00x (ISBN 0-19-826408-9). Oxford U Pr.
--The Early Church. LC 81-43085. 1982. pap. 11.95 (ISBN 0-8006-1615-4). Fortress.
--The Rise of Christianity. LC 83-48909. (Illus.). 1042p. 1984. pap. 24.95 (ISBN 0-8006-1931-5, 1-1931). Fortress.
--The Rise of the Monophysite Movement: Chapters in the History of the Church in the Fifth & Sixth Centuries. LC 72-75302. (Illus.). 400p. 1972. 74.50 (ISBN 0-521-08130-0). Cambridge U Pr.
--Saints & Sinners in the Early Church: Differing & Conflicting Traditions in the First Six Centuries. (Theology & Life Ser.: Vol. 11). 1985. pap. 8.95 (ISBN 0-89453-451-3). M Glazier.
Frendo, J. D., tr. from Lat. Agathias: The Histories. (Corpus Fontium Historiae Byzantinae: Vol. 2a). Tr. of Agathiae Myrinaei Historiarum libri quinque. iv, 170p. 1975. 51.00x (ISBN 3-11-003357-7). De Gruyter.
Freneau, Philip, jt. auth. see Brackenridge, Hugh H.
Frensdorff, Salomon. Massora Magna. rev. ed. LC 67-11896. (Library of Biblical Studies). (Heb). 1968. 35.00x (ISBN 0-87068-052-8). Ktav.
--Ochlah W'Ochlah. 35.00x (ISBN 0-87068-194-X). Ktav.
Frere, Walter H. The Anaphora or Great Eucharistic Prayer: An Eirenical Study in Liturgical History. (Church Historical Society, London, New Ser.: No. 26). Repr. of 1938 ed. 50.00 (ISBN 0-8115-3150-3). Kraus Repr.
--Antiohonale Sarisburiense, 6 Vols. 115p. 1923. text ed. 310.50 (ISBN 0-576-28701-6, Pub. by Gregg Intl Pubs England). Gregg Intl.
--English Church in the Reigns of Elizabeth & James First, 1558-1625. (History of the English Church: No. 5). Repr. of 1904 ed. 29.50 (ISBN 0-404-50755-7). AMS Pr.
--The English Church in the Reigns of Elizabeth & James I: 1558-1625. 1977. lib. bdg. 59.95 (ISBN 0-8490-1773-4). Gordon Pr.
--Puritan Manifestoes. 1907. 20.50 (ISBN 0-8337-4119-5). B Franklin.
Frerichs, Ernest S., jt. ed. see Neusner, Jacob.
Fretheim, Terence E. Deuteronomic History. Bailey, Lloyd R. & Furnish, Victory P., eds. 160p. (Orig.). 1983. pap. 9.95 (ISBN 0-687-10497-1). Abingdon.
--The Message of Jonah: A Theological Commentary. LC 77-72461. pap. 8.95 (ISBN 0-8066-1591-5, 10-4350). Augsburg.

--The Suffering of God: An Old Testament Perspective. Bruegemann, Walter, ed. LC 84-47921. (Overtures to Biblical Theology Ser.). 224p. 1984. pap. 10.95 (ISBN 0-8006-1538-7). Fortress.

Fretz, Clarence Y. Story of God's People. (Christian Day School Ser). pap. 5.90x (ISBN 0-87813-900-1); tchrs. guide 6.95x (ISBN 0-87813-901-X). Christian Light.

--You & Your Bible-You & Your Life. (Christian Day School Ser). pap. 4.10x (ISBN 0-87813-902-8); teachrs guide 13.75x (ISBN 0-87813-903-6). Christian Light.

Freud, Sigmund. The Future of an Illusion. Strachey, James, ed. 1975. 10.95 (ISBN 0-393-01120-8); pap. 2.95 (ISBN 0-393-00831-2). Norton.

--Moses & Monotheism. Jones, Katherine, ed. 1955. pap. 4.95 (ISBN 0-394-70014-7, V14, Vin). Random.

--Totem & Taboo. Strachey, James, tr. 1962. pap. 3.95 (ISBN 0-393-00143-1, Norton Lib.). Norton.

--Totem & Taboo. Brill, Abraham A., tr. 1960. pap. 2.95 (ISBN 0-394-70124-0, Vin, V124). Random.

Freudenberger, C. Dean. Food for Tomorrow. LC 83-72119. 176p. 1984. pap. 9.95 (ISBN 0-8066-2063-3, 10-2333). Augsburg.

Freudenberger, C. Dean & Minus, Paul M., Jr. A Christian Responsibility in a Hungry World. LC 75-43764. 1976. pap. 3.25 (ISBN 0-687-07567-X). Abingdon.

Freudenberger, Elsie. Reference Works in the Field of Religion 1977-1985. (Orig.). 1986. pap. 15.00 (ISBN 0-87507-037-X). Cath Lib Assn.

Freund, John, jt. auth. see Hunter, JoAnn H.

Freund, Ronald. What One Person Can Do to Help Prevent Nuclear War. 2nd ed. 144p. 1983. pap. 5.95 (ISBN 0-89622-192-X). Twenty-Third.

Frey, Arthur. Cross & Swastika, the Ordeal of the German Church. McNab, J. Strathearn, tr. LC 78-63668. (Studies in Fascism: Ideology & Practice). 224p. Repr. of 1938 ed. 24.50 (ISBN 0-404-16526-5). AMS Pr.

Frey, Conrad I. Handbook for Church Officers & Boards. 1985. pap. 1.50 (ISBN 0-8100-0187-X, 15N0414). Northwest Pub.

Frey, Jean B. Corpus Inscriptionum Judaicarum. rev. ed. (Library of Biblical Studies). 1970. 100.00x (ISBN 0-87068-103-6). Ktav.

Frey, John A. Motif Symbolism in the Disciples of Mallarme. LC 73-94193. (Catholic University of America Studies in Romance Languages & Literatures Ser: No. 55). Repr. of 1957 ed. 23.00 (ISBN 0-404-50355-1). AMS Pr.

Frey, Kessler. Satsang Notes of Swami Amar Jyoti. LC 77-89524. (Illus.). 1977. 4.95 (ISBN 0-933572-01-8); pap. 2.95 (ISBN 0-933572-02-6). Truth Consciousness.

Frey, Louis. Analyse Ordinale Es Evangiles Synoptiques. (Mathematiques et Sciences De L'homme: No. 11). 1972. 46.50 (ISBN 0-686-21228-2); pap. 27.20x (ISBN 0-686-21229-0). Mouton.

Frey, Robert S. & Thompson-Frey, Nancy. The Imperative of Response: The Holocaust in Human Context. 186p. 1985. lib. bdg. 24.25 (ISBN 0-8191-4633-1); pap. text ed. 10.75 (ISBN 0-8191-4634-X). U Pr of Amer.

Freyne, Sean. The World of the New Testament. (New Testament Message Ser.: Vol. 2). 12.95 (ISBN 0-89453-190-5); pap. 8.95 (ISBN 0-89453-125-5). M Glazier.

Freyne, Sean & Wansbrough, Henry. Mark & Matthew. Bright, Laurence, ed. LC 71-173033. (Scripture Discussion Commentary Ser.: Pt. 7). 256p. 1971. pap. text ed. 4.50 (ISBN 0-87946-006-7). ACTA Found.

Freytag, Gustav. Doctor Luther. Reimer, G. C., tr. LC 83-45642. Date not set. Repr. of 1916 ed. 27.50 (ISBN 0-404-19851-1). AMS Pr.

--Martin Luther. LC 78-144612. Repr. of 1897 ed. 27.50 (ISBN 0-404-02577-3). AMS Pr.

Freze, Mike. Questions & Answers: The Gospel of Matthew. 144p. 1987. pap. 4.95 (ISBN 0-8010-3534-1). Baker Bk.

Friar, Kimon, tr. see Kazantzakis, Nikos.

Friberg, Barbara, jt. ed. see Friberg, Timothy.

Friberg, Timothy & Friberg, Barbara, eds. Analytical Greek New Testament. 1000p. 1981. 24.95 (ISBN 0-8010-3496-5). Baker Bk.

Frick, Frank S. The Formation of the State in Ancient Israel: A Survey of Models & Theories. (The Social World of Biblical Antiquity Ser.). 219p. 1985. text ed. 24.95x (ISBN 0-907459-51-X, Pub. by Almond Pr England); pap. text ed. 10.95 (ISBN 0-907459-52-8). Eisenbrauns.

Fricker, E. G. God Is My Witness: The Story of the World-Famous Healer. LC 76-50557. 1977. pap. 2.75 (ISBN 0-8128-7068-9). Stein & Day.

Friebel, Otto. Fulgentius, der Mythograph und Bischof. pap. 15.00 (ISBN 0-384-16880-9). Johnson Repr.

Fried, Charles. An Anatomy of Values: Problems of Personal & Social Choice. LC 78-111483. 1970. 18.50x (ISBN 0-674-03151-2). Harvard U Pr.

Fried, Jacob L. Jews & Divorce. 1968. 12.50x (ISBN 0-87068-049-8). Ktav.

Fried, Jerome, jt. ed. see Leach, Maria.

Fried, Martha N. & Fried, Morton H. Transitions: Four Rituals in Eight Cultures. 1980. 14.95 (ISBN 0-393-01350-2). Norton.

Fried, Morton H., jt. auth. see Fried, Martha N.

Fried, Vilem, tr. see Macek, Josef.

Friedenberg, Albert M. The Sunday Laws of the United States & Leading Judicial Decisions Having Special Reference to the Jews. LC 12-23685. 42p. 1986. pap. 12.50 (ISBN 0-89941-475-3). W S Hein.

Friedenreich, Harriet P., jt. auth. see Elazar, Daniel J.

Friedenwald, Harry. Jews & Medicine & Jewish Luminaries in Medical History, 3 Vols. rev. ed. 1967. 50.00x (ISBN 0-87068-053-6). Ktav.

Friederichsen, Kay. God's Word Made Plain. 1958. pap. 4.95 (ISBN 0-8024-3041-4). Moody.

Friederichsen, Kay H. Las Profundas Verdades de la Biblia. Orig. Title: God's World Made Plain. (Span.). 256p. 1958. pap. 4.75 (ISBN 0-8254-1248-X). Kregel.

Friederichsen, Kay H. de see Friederichsen, Kay H.

Friedlander, Albert. Out of the Whirlwind. 1968. 10.95 (ISBN 0-8074-0043-2, 959065). UAHC.

Friedlander, Albert, jt. ed. see Bronstein, Herbert.

Friedlander, Dov & Goldscheider, Calvin. The Population of Israel: Growth, Policy & Implications. LC 78-13139. 264p. 1979. 31.00x (ISBN 0-231-04572-7). Columbia U Pr.

Friedlander, G. Shakespeare & the Jew. 59.95 (ISBN 0-8490-1032-2). Gordon Pr.

Friedlander, Gerald. Jewish Fairy Tales & Stories. LC 78-67711. (The Folktale). (Illus.). Repr. of 1919 ed. 20.00 (ISBN 0-404-16088-3). AMS Pr.

--Jewish Sources of the Sermon on the Mount. 1976. lib. bdg. 59.95 (ISBN 0-8490-2102-2). Gordon Pr.

--Jewish Sources of the Sermon on the Mount. rev. ed. (Library of Biblical Studies). 1969. 14.95x (ISBN 0-87068-054-4). Ktav.

--Shakespeare & the Jew. LC 74-168084. Repr. of 1921 ed. 18.00 (ISBN 0-404-02579-X). AMS Pr.

Friedlander, Gerald, tr. from Heb. Pirke De Rabbi Eliezer (The Chapters of Rabbi Eliezer the Great) LC 80-545920. (The Judaic Studies Library: No. SPH6). 552p. 1981. pap. 14.95 (ISBN 0-87203-095-4). Hermon.

Friedlander, Henry, jt. ed. see Milton, Sybil.

Friedlander, Ira. The Ninety-Nine Names of Allah. (Orig.). 1978. pap. 6.95 (ISBN 0-06-090621-9, CN 621, PL). Har-Row.

Friedlander, Ira, jt. auth. see Speeth, Kathleen R.

Friedlander, Ira, ed. Submission Sayings of the Prophet Muhammad. 1977. pap. 5.95 (ISBN 0-06-090592-1, CN592, PL). Har-Row.

Friedlander, M. Jewish Religion: Describing & Explaining the Philosophy & Rituals of the Jewish Faith. 35.00 (ISBN 0-87559-117-5). Shalom.

Friedlander, M., tr. see Maimonides, Moses.

Friedlander, Michael, tr. see Ibn Ezra.

Friedlander, Saul. Pius XII & the Third Reich. LC 80-12830. 238p. 1980. Repr. of 1966 ed. lib. bdg. 21.50x (ISBN 0-374-92930-0, Octagon). Hippocrene Bks.

--When Memory Comes. Lane, Helen, tr. from Fr. 192p. 1979. 9.95 (ISBN 0-374-28898-4). FS&G.

Friedlander, Saul, et al, eds. Visions of Apocalypse: End or Rebirth? 272p. 1985. text ed. 28.50x (ISBN 0-8419-0673-4); pap. text ed. 15.50x (ISBN 0-8419-0755-2). Holmes & Meier.

Friedlander, Shems. When You Hear Hoofbeats, Think of a Zebra Talks on Sufism. LC 86-45657. 128p. (Orig.). 1987. pap. 5.95 (ISBN 0-06-096128-7, PL 6128, PL). Har-Row.

Friedling, Sheila, ed. The Pit & the Trap: Leyb Rochman. Kohn, Moshe, tr. (Yiddish., Illus.). 288p. (Orig.). 1983. 16.95 (ISBN 0-8052-5044-1); pap. 10.95 (ISBN 0-8052-5045-X). Holocaust Pubns.

Friedman, Ada J., ed. see Friedman, Philip.

Friedman, Alexander Z. Wellsprings of Torah. Hirschler, Gertrude, tr. from Yiddish. 584p. 1980. slipcased 18.95 (ISBN 0-910818-20-7); pap. 16.95 (ISBN 0-910818-04-5). Judaica Pr.

Friedman, Audrey, jt. auth. see Zwerin, Raymond A.

Friedman, Audrey M. & Zwerin, Raymond. High Holy Day Do It Yourself Dictionary. (Illus.). 32p. 1983. pap. 5.00 (ISBN 0-8074-0162-5, 101100). UAHC.

Friedman, Bob, jt. auth. see Schlamm, J. Vera.

Friedman, Clarence W. Prefigurations in Meistergesang. LC 75-140020. (Catholic University of America Studies in German Ser.: No. 18). Repr. of 1943 ed. 22.00 (ISBN 0-404-50238-5). AMS Pr.

Friedman, David L., tr. see Maitreya, Sthiramati.

Friedman, Edwin H. Generation to Generation: Family Process in Church & Synagogue. (Family Therapy Ser.). 319p. 1986. Repr. of 1985 ed. lib. bdg. 25.00 (ISBN 0-89862-059-7). Guilford Pr.

Friedman, Elizabeth. Colonialism & After: An Algerian Jewish Community. (Critical Studies in Work & Community). 288p. 1987. text ed. 34.95 (ISBN 0-89789-095-7). Bergin & Garvey.

Friedman, Greg. It Begins with Friendship: A Fresh Approach to Prayer. 73p. (Orig.). 1984. pap. text ed. 3.95 (ISBN 0-86716-038-1). St Anthony Mess Pr.

Friedman, Ina, tr. see Almog, Shmuel.

Friedman, Ina, tr. see Golan, Matti.

Friedman, Ina, tr. see Gutman, Yisrael.

Friedman, Irving. The Book of Creation. 64p. 1977. pap. 2.95 (ISBN 0-87728-289-7). Weiser.

Friedman, Isaiah. Germany, Turkey, & Zionism, 1897-1918. 1977. 59.00x (ISBN 0-19-822528-8). Oxford U Pr.

Friedman, J. Michael Servetus: A Case Study in Total Heresy. 154p. (Orig.). 1978. pap. text ed. 34.00x (Pub. by Droz Switzerland). Coronet Bks.

Friedman, Jerome. The Most Ancient Testimony: Sixteenth-Century Christian-Hebraica in the Age of Renaissance Nostalgia. LC 82-18830. x, 279p. 1983. text ed. 26.95x (ISBN 0-8214-0700-7). Ohio U Pr.

Friedman, Lee M. Pilgrims in a New Land. LC 78-26208. (Illus.). 1979. Repr. of 1948 ed. lib. bdg. 32.50x (ISBN 0-313-20877-8, FRPI). Greenwood.

Friedman, Lester D. Hollywood's Image of the Jew. LC 81-70118. (Illus.). 408p. 1982. pap. 8.95 (ISBN 0-8044-6160-0). Ungar.

Friedman, Lionel J. Text & Iconography of Joinville's Credo. LC 58-7918. 1958. 12.00x (ISBN 0-910956-42-1). Medieval Acad.

Friedman, Maurice. The Covenant of Peace. 1983. pap. 2.50x (ISBN 0-87574-110-X, 110). Pendle Hill.

--The Human Way. LC 81-8011. (Religion & Human Experience Ser.). 168p. 1982. 13.95 (ISBN 0-89012-025-0). Anima Pubns.

--Martin Buber: The Life of Dialogue. 3rd, rev. ed. 1976. pap. 13.00x (ISBN 0-226-26356-8). U of Chicago Pr.

--Modern Promethean: A Dialogue with Today's Youth. LC 73-104050. (Orig.). 1969. pap. 2.50x (ISBN 0-87574-168-1). Pendle Hill.

Friedman, Maurice, ed. & tr. see Buber, Martin.

Friedman, Maurice, jt. ed. see Schilpp, Paul A.

Friedman, Maurice S. & Burke, T. Patrick. Searching in the Syntax of Things: Experiments in the Study of Religion. LC 70-171494. pap. 40.00 (2026864). Bks Demand UMI.

Friedman, Melvin J. The Added Dimension: The Art of Mind of Flannery O'Connor. 2nd ed. LC 66-11070. xviii, 263p. 1977. pap. 9.00 (ISBN 0-8232-0711-0). Fordham.

Friedman, Melvin J., ed. Vision Obscured: Perceptions of Some Twentieth-Century Catholic Novelists. LC 72-126130. 1970. 25.00 (ISBN 0-8232-0890-7). Fordham.

Friedman, Michael. Passages of Observation: A Guru's Guide to Salvation. Jacobsen, Liz, ed. (Illus.). 1983. pap. 4.95 (ISBN 0-912561-00-9). Counsel & Stress.

Friedman, Murray. Solving Ethical Problems. 0.50 (ISBN 0-914131-58-3, I38). Torah Umesorah.

--The Utopian Dilemma: American Judaism & Public Policy. LC 85-7068. 125p. (Orig.). 1985. 12.00 (ISBN 0-89633-092-3); pap. 7.95 (ISBN 0-89633-093-1). Ethics & Public Policy.

Friedman, Murray, ed. Jewish Life in Philadelphia, 1830-1940. LC 83-10763. (Illus.). 360p. 1983. 19.95 (ISBN 0-89727-050-9). ISHI PA.

Friedman, Natalie & Rogers, Theresa F. The Jewish Community & Children of Divorce: A Pilot Study of Perceptions & Responses. 32p. 1983. pap. 2.00 (ISBN 0-87495-051-1). Am Jewish Comm.

Friedman, Nathalie & Rogers, Theresa F. The Divorced Parent & the Jewish Community. LC 85-61859. 58p. (Orig.). 1985. pap. 5.00 (ISBN 0-87495-074-0). Am Jewish Comm.

Friedman, Philip. Roads to Extinction: Essays on the Holocaust. Friedman, Ada J., ed. LC 79-89818. 616p. 1980. 27.50 (ISBN 0-8276-0170-0, 446). Jewish Pubns.

--Their Brothers' Keepers. LC 57-8773. 232p. 1978. pap. 12.95 (ISBN 0-89604-002-X). Holocaust Pubns.

--Their Brothers' Keepers: The Christian Heroes & Heroines Who Helped the Oppressed Escape the Nazi Terror. LC 57-8773. 1978. pap. 8.95 (ISBN 0-8052-5002-6, Pub. by Holocaust Library). Schocken.

--Their Brothers' Keepers: The Christian Heroes & Heroines Who Helped the Oppressed Escaper the Nazi Terror. 232p. Repr. 4.95 (ISBN 0-686-95090-9). ADL.

Friedman, Philip, jt. auth. see Gar, Josef.

Friedman, Richard E. The Exile & Biblical Narrative: The Formation of the Deuteronomistic & Priestly Works. LC 80-28836. 1981. 12.00 (ISBN 0-89130-457-6, 04 00 22). Scholars Pr GA.

--The Poet & the Historian: Essays in Literary & Historical Biblical Criticism. LC 83-9035. (Harvard Semitic Studies). 172p. 1983. 13.50 (ISBN 0-89130-629-3, 04 04 26). Scholars Pr GA.

--Who Wrote The Bible. 1987. 16.95. Summit Bks.

Friedman, Richard E., ed. The Creation of Sacred Literature: Composition & Redaction of the Biblical Text. (U.C. Publications in Near Eastern Studies: Vol. 22). 1981. pap. 21.50x (ISBN 0-520-09637-1). U of Cal Pr.

Friedman, Robert, ed. see Summer Rain, Mary.

Friedman, Robert S., ed. see Chetkin, Len.

Friedman, Saul S. No Haven for the Oppressed: United States Policy Toward Jewish Refugees, 1938-1945. LC 72-2271. 315p. 1973. 25.00x (ISBN 0-8143-1474-0). Wayne St U Pr.

Friedman, Susan S. Psyche Reborn: The Emergence of H. D. LC 80-8378. (Illus.). 352p. 1981. 22.50x (ISBN 0-253-37826-5). Ind U Pr.

Friedmann, Herbert. A Bestiary for St. Jerome: Animal Symbolism in European Religious Art. LC 79-607804. (Illus.). 378p. 1980. 39.95x (ISBN 0-87474-446-6, FRBJ). Smithsonian.

Friedmann, Hope, jt. auth. see Gribble, Mercedes.

Friedmann, Robert. Glaubenszeugnisse Oberdeutscher Taufgesinnter, Band Zwei. (Tauferakten Kommission Ser., Vol. 12). 318p. (Ger). 9.50x (ISBN 0-8361-1186-9). Herald Pr.

--The Theology of Anabaptism. LC 73-7886. (Studies in Anabaptist & Mennonite History, No. 15). 176p. 1973. 12.95x (ISBN 0-8361-1194-X). Herald Pr.

Friedmann, Yohanan. Prophecy Continuous: Aspects of Ahmadi Religious Thoughts & Its Medieval Background. 370p. 1987. text ed. 35.00x. U of Cal Pr.

Friedrich, Carl J. Inevitable Peace. Repr. of 1948 ed. lib. bdg. 22.50x (ISBN 0-8371-2397-6, FRIN). Greenwood.

--Transcendent Justice: The Religious Dimensions of Constitutionalism. LC 64-20097. ix, 116p. 1964. 13.75 (ISBN 0-8223-0061-3). Duke.

Friedrich, Dick, jt. ed. see Harris, Angela.

Friedrich, Elizabeth. The Story of God's Love. 144p. 1985. 9.95 (ISBN 0-570-04122-8, 56-1533). Concordia.

Friedrich, Gerhard. In Pursuit of Moby Dick. 1983. pap. 2.50x (ISBN 0-87574-098-7, 098). Pendle Hill.

Friedrich, Gerhard, jt. ed. see Kittel, Gerhard.

Friedson, Anthony M., ed. New Directions in Biography. (Biography Monographs: No. 2). 125p. 1982. pap. text ed. 7.95x (ISBN 0-8248-0783-9). UH Pr.

Frieman, Donald G. Milestones in the Life of a Jew. LC 65-15710. 1980. pap. 3.95 (ISBN 0-8197-0002-9). Bloch.

Fries, Heinrich & Rahner, Karl. Unity of the Churches: An Actual Possibility. Gritsch, E. & Gritsch, R., trs. LC 84-8122. 160p. pap. 6.95 (ISBN 0-8006-1820-3). Fortress.

--Unity of the Churches: An Actual Possibility. 1985. pap. 6.95 (ISBN 0-8091-2671-0). Paulist Pr.

Fries, Jakob F. Dialogues on Morality & Religion. Phillips, D. Z., et al, eds. LC 82-13787. (Values & Philosophical Inquiry Ser.). (Illus.). 268p. 1982. text ed. 28.95x (ISBN 0-389-20326-2). B&N Imports.

Fries, James F. & Crapo, Lawrence M. Vitality & Aging: Implications of the Rectangular Curve. LC 81-4566. (Illus.). 172p. 1981. text ed. 23.95 (ISBN 0-7167-1308-X); pap. text ed. 13.95 (ISBN 0-7167-1309-8). W H Freeman.

Fries, Michael, et al. A Christian Guide to Prosperity. 2nd ed. Frank, Diane, ed. LC 83-46178. (Illus.). 523p. 1984. pap. 9.95 (ISBN 0-9611910-5-8). Comm Res.

Fries, Paul R. & Nersoyan, Tiran, eds. Christ in East & West. 240p. 1987. 31.95 (ISBN 0-86554-267-8, MUP H-228); pap. 14.95 (ISBN 0-86554-277-5). Mercer Univ Pr.

Friesel, Evyatar, ed. see Simon, Julius.

Friesen, Abraham. P. M. Friesen & His History: Understanding Mennonite Brethren Beginnings. (Perspective on Mennonite Life & Thought Ser.: Vol. 2). 176p. (Orig.). 1979. pap. 5.95 (ISBN 0-318-18906-2). Kindred Pr.

Friesen, Duane. Moral Issues in the Control of Birth. new ed. LC 74-76587. (Illus.). 64p. 1974. pap. 1.95 (ISBN 0-87303-561-5). Faith & Life.

Friesen, Duane K. Christian Peacemaking & International Conflict. LC 85-24803. 320p. (Orig.). 1986. pap. 19.95x (ISBN 0-8361-1273-3). Herald Pr.

Friesen, Evelyn & Phu, Sam. Freedom Isn't Free. 165p. (Orig.). 1985. pap. 6.65 (ISBN 0-318-18903-8). Kindred Pr.

Friesen, Garry & Maxson, J. Robin. Decision Making & the Will of God. LC 80-24592. (Critical Concern Bks.). 1981. 13.95 (ISBN 0-930014-47-2). Multnomah.

--Decision Making & the Will of God: A Biblical Alternative to the Traditional View. LC 80-24592. (Critical Concern Ser.). 252p. 1983. pap. 9.95 (ISBN 0-88070-024-6); study guide 2.95 (ISBN 0-88070-021-1). Multnomah.

--Decision Making & the Will of God: A Biblical Alternative to the Traditional View. expanded ed. (Critical Concern Bks.). pap. cancelled (ISBN 0-88070-100-5). Multnomah.

Friesen, Ivan & Frieson, Rachel. How Do You Decide? (Shalom Ser.: No. 6). (Illus.). 16p. pap. 0.50 (ISBN 0-8361-1975-4). Herald Pr.

Friesen, P. M. The Mennonite Brotherhood in Russia (1789-1910) rev. ed. LC 78-52664. 1065p. 1980. 24.95 (ISBN 0-919797-19-9). Kindred Pr.

Frieson, Rachel, jt. auth. see Friesen, Ivan.

Friess, Horace L. & Schneider, Herbert W. Religion in Various Cultures. (Illus.). Repr. of 1932 ed. 24.00 (ISBN 0-384-16990-2). Johnson Repr.

Friess, Horace L., tr. see Schleiermacher, Friedrich E.

Frings, Manfred S., tr. see Scheler, Max.

Frisbie, Charlotte J., ed. Southwestern Indian Ritual Drama. LC 79-2308. (School of American Research Advanced Seminar Ser.). (Illus.). 384p. 1980. 30.00x (ISBN 0-8263-0521-0). U of NM Pr.

Frischauer, A. S. Altspanischer Kirchenbau. (Studien zur spaetantiken Kunstgeschichte, Vol. 3). (Illus.). x, 100p. 1978. Repr. of 1930 ed. 58.80x (ISBN 3-11-005703-4). De Gruyter.

Frischwasser-Ra' Anan, H. F. The Frontiers of a Nation. LC 75-6433. (The Rise of Jewish Nationalism & the Middle East Ser). 168p. 1976. Repr. of 1955 ed. 18.15 (ISBN 0-88355-320-1). Hyperion Conn.

Frisk, Donald C. Covenant Affirmations: This We Believe. 196p. (Orig.). 1981. pap. 6.95 (ISBN 0-910452-48-2). Covenant.

--New Life in Christ. 1969. pap. 2.95 (ISBN 0-910452-03-2). Covenant.

Friskney, Tom. Thirteen Lessons on I & II Thessalonians. LC 82-71253. (Bible Student Study Guide Ser.). 122p. 1982. pap. 2.95 (ISBN 0-89900-172-6). College Pr Pub.

Frist, Betty. My Neighbors, the Billy Grahams. LC 83-70368. 1983. 8.95 (ISBN 0-8054-7229-0). Broadman.

Fristedt, Sven L. The Wycliffe Bible, 2 vols. LC 78-63195. (Heresies of the Early Christian & Medieval Era: Second Ser.). Repr. of 1953 ed. 45.00 set (ISBN 0-404-16370-X). AMS Pr.

Fritchman, Stephen. Heretic. pap. 6.95 (ISBN 0-933840-19-5). Unitarian Univ.

Frith, Francis. Egypt & the Holy Land in Historic Photographs. White, Jon. E., selected by. 16.50 (ISBN 0-8446-5887-1). Peter Smith.

--Egypt & the Holy Land in Historic Photographs: Seventy-Seven Views. Van Haaften, Julia, ed. 112p. 1981. pap. 7.95 (ISBN 0-486-24048-7). Dover.

Fritsch, Charles T. Genesis. LC 59-10454. (Layman's Bible Commentary Ser: Vol. 2). 1959. pap. 4.95 (ISBN 0-8042-3062-5). John Knox.

--The Qumran Community: Its History & Scrolls. 1973. Repr. of 1956 ed. 18.00 (ISBN 0-8196-0279-5). Biblo.

Fritscher, John. Popular Witchcraft. 224p. 1973. 6.95 (ISBN 0-8065-0380-7). Citadel Pr.

Fritz, Jean. Early Thunder. LC 67-24217. (Illus.). 1967. 9.95 (ISBN 0-698-20036-5, Coward). Putnam Pub Group.

Fritz, Mary. Take Nothing for the Journey: Solitude as the Foundation for Non-Possessive Life. 88p. (Orig.). 1985. pap. 3.95 (ISBN 0-8091-2722-9). Paulist Pr.

Fritz, Patricia. Te Alabamos Senor: We Praise You O Lord. Sarre, Alicia, tr. from Span. 112p. 1984. pap. 3.95 (ISBN 0-8091-2641-9). Paulist Pr.

--We Praise You, O Lord! 2.95 (ISBN 0-8091-2518-8). Paulist Pr.

Frizen, Edwin L., ed. Christ & Caesar in Christian Missions. Coggins, Wade T. LC 79-17124. (Orig.). 1979. pap. 5.95 (ISBN 0-87808-169-0). William Carey Lib.

Frizzell, Lawrence, jt. auth. see Finkel, Asher.

Frizzell, Lawrence, tr. see Thoma, Clemens.

Frodsham, Stanley H. Smith Wigglesworth: Apostle of Faith. 160p. 1948. pap. 2.50 (ISBN 0-88243-586-8, 02-0586). Gospel Pub.

--With Signs Following. 188p. 1946. pap. 5.95 (ISBN 0-88243-635-X, 02-0635). Gospel Pub.

Froehlich, Karlfried, ed. & tr. Biblical Interpretation in the Early Church. LC 84-47922. (Sources of Early Christian Thought Ser.). 128p. 1985. pap. 7.95 (ISBN 0-8006-1414-3, 1-1414). Fortress.

Froese, J. A. Witness Extraordinary: A Bibliography of Elder Heinrich Voth, 1851-1918. (Trailblazer Ser.). 60p. (Orig.). 1975. pap. 1.00 (ISBN 0-919797-20-2). Kindred Pr.

Frohlich, Margaret, tr. see Richter, Gottfried.

Fromer, Margaret & Fromer, Paul. Putting Christ First: A Woman's Workshop on Colossians. Kobobel, Janet, ed. (Woman's Workshop Ser.). 128p. 1986. pap. 5.95 (ISBN 0-310-44801-8, 11313P). Zondervan.

--A Woman's Workshop on Philippians. (Woman's Workshop Ser.). 128p. 1982. pap. 2.95 (ISBN 0-310-44771-2, 11312P). Zondervan.

Fromer, Margaret & Keyes, Sharrel. Genesis I Through 25: Walking with God. rev. ed. (Fisherman Bible Studyguide Ser.). 80p. 1979. saddle-stitched 2.95 (ISBN 0-87788-297-5). Shaw Pubs.

--Genesis 26 through 50: Called by God. rev. ed. (Fisherman Bible Studyguide Ser.). 66p. 1979. pap. 2.95 saddle-stitched (ISBN 0-87788-298-3). Shaw Pubs.

--Jonah, Habakkuk, Malachi: Living Responsibly. (Fisherman Bible Studyguide Ser.). 68p. 1982. saddle-stitch 2.95 (ISBN 0-87788-432-3). Shaw Pubs.

--Let's Pray Together: Studies in Prayer. LC 74-76160. (Fisherman Bible Studyguide Ser.). 63p. 1974. saddle-stitched 2.95 (ISBN 0-87788-801-9). Shaw Pubs.

--Letters to the Thessalonians. LC 75-33441. (Fisherman Bible Studyguide Ser.). 47p. 1975. saddle-stitched 2.95 (ISBN 0-87788-489-7). Shaw Pubs.

--Letters to Timothy: Discipleship in Action. LC 74-19763. (Fisherman Bible Study Guide Ser.). 80p. 1974. saddle-stitched 2.95 (ISBN 0-87788-490-0). Shaw Pubs.

Fromer, Margaret & Nystrom, Carolyn. James: Roadmap for Down-to-Earth Christians. (Young Fisherman Bible Studyguide Ser.). (Illus.). 89p. 1982. saddle-stiched tchr's. ed. 4.95 (ISBN 0-87788-420-X); student ed. 2.95 (ISBN 0-87788-419-6). Shaw Pubs.

Fromer, Margaret, jt. auth. see Nystrom, Carolyn.

Fromer, Paul, jt. auth. see Fromer, Margaret.

Fromm, Erich. The Heart of Man: Its Genius for Good & Evil. LC 64-18053. 1980. pap. 6.95 (ISBN 0-06-090795-9, CN 795, PL). Har-Row.

--Psychoanalysis & Religion. (Terry Lectures Ser.). 1950. pap. 5.95 (ISBN 0-300-00089-8, Y12). Yale U Pr.

--You Shall Be As Gods: A Radical Interpretation of the Old Testament & Its Tradition. 1977. pap. 2.50 (ISBN 0-449-30763-8, Prem). Fawcett.

Fromm, Erich, et al. Zen Buddhism & Psychoanalysis. LC 60-5293. 1970. pap. 6.95 (ISBN 0-06-090175-6, CN175, PL). Har-Row.

Fromm, Herbert. Herbert Fromm on Jewish Music: A Composers View. LC 78-60716. 1979. 10.00x (ISBN 0-8197-0465-2). Bloch.

Frommer, Eva A., tr. see Steiner, Rudolf.

Frossard, Andre & Pope John Paul II. Be Not Afraid! John Paul II Speaks Out on His Life, His Beliefs & His Inspiring Vision for Humanity. Foster, J. R., tr. from Fr. 252p. 1984. 13.95 (ISBN 0-312-07021-7). St Martin.

Frossard, Andre, jt. auth. see Pope John Paul II.

Frost & Frost. Magic Power of Witchcraft. 1977. 14.95 (ISBN 0-13-545376-3, Reward); pap. 5.95 (ISBN 0-13-545368-2). P-H.

Frost, Bede. Saint John of the Cross: Doctor of Divine Love, an Introduction to His Philosophy, Theology & Spirituality. 1977. lib. bdg. 59.95 (ISBN 0-8490-2559-1). Gordon Pr.

Frost, Christopher J. Religious Melancholy or Psychological Depression: Some Issues Involved in Relating Psychology & Religion As Illustrated in a Study of Elie Wiesel. 274p. (Orig.). 1985. lib. bdg. 27.75 (ISBN 0-8191-4496-7); pap. text ed. 13.50 (ISBN 0-8191-4497-5). U Pr of Amer.

Frost, Gerhard. Homing in the Presence: Meditations for Daily Living. 125p. 1978. pap. 5.95 (ISBN 0-86683-756-6, HarpR). Har-Row.

Frost, Gerhard E. Bless My Growing: For Parents, Teachers, & Others Who Learn. LC 74-77680. (Illus.). 96p. 1975. pap. 5.95 (ISBN 0-8066-1431-5, 10-0770). Augsburg.

--Blessed Is the Ordinary. (Illus.). 96p. pap. 4.95 (ISBN 0-86683-606-3, HarpR). Har-Row.

--Color of the Night: Reflections on the Book of Job. LC 77-72458. 1977. pap. 5.95 (ISBN 0-8066-1583-4, 10-1520). Augsburg.

--Kept Moments. 96p. (Orig.). 1982. pap. 5.95 (ISBN 0-86683-668-3, HarpR). Har-Row.

--A Second Look. (Orig.). 1984. pap. 6.95 (ISBN 0-86683-935-6, 8513, HarpR). Har-Row.

Frost, Gerhard E., ed. see Bickel, Margot & Steigert, Hermann.

Frost, Joseph H., jt. auth. see Lee, Daniel.

Frost, Marie H. Fifty-Two Nursery Patterns. (Illus.). 48p. (Orig.). 1979. pap. 4.95 (ISBN 0-87239-341-0, 42046). Standard Pub.

--Fifty-Two Primary Crafts. 48p. (Orig.). 1984. pap. 2.95 (ISBN 0-87239-726-2, 2106). Standard Pub.

--Frankly Feminine: Leader's Guide. 48p. (Orig.). 1984. pap. 2.95 (ISBN 0-87239-746-7, 2970). Standard Pub.

--I Thank God. (First Happy Day Bks.). (Illus.). 20p. 1986. casebound 1.29 (ISBN 0-87403-134-6, 2004). Standard Pub.

--Jesus Is Born. (First Happy Day Bks.). (Illus.). 20p. 1986. casebound 1.29 (ISBN 0-87403-131-1, 2001). Standard Pub.

--Listen to Your Children. LC 80-50320. 144p. (Orig.). 1980. pap. 2.95 (ISBN 0-87239-396-8, 3000). Standard Pub.

--Listen to Your Children: Leader's Guide. 48p. (Orig.). 1984. pap. 2.95 (ISBN 0-87239-747-5, 2999). Standard Pub.

--Love Is God. (First Happy Day Bks.). (Illus.). 20p. 1986. casebound 1.29 (ISBN 0-87403-133-8, 2003). Standard Pub.

--Our Christmas Handbook, No. 4. (Illus.). 112p. 1986. 7.95 (ISBN 0-87403-081-1, 3044). Standard Pub.

Frost, Miriam, ed. see Emmons, Michael & Richardson, David.

Frost, Miriam, ed. see Pilch, John J.

Frost, Robert. Our Heavenly Father. LC 77-95191. 1978. pap. 3.95 (ISBN 0-88270-266-1). Bridge Pub.

--Set My Spirit Free. LC 73-84475. 234p. 1973. pap. 4.95 (ISBN 0-88270-058-8). Bridge Pub.

Frost, Robert C. Aglow with the Spirit: How to Receive the Baptism in the Holy Spirit. 1965. pap. 2.95 (ISBN 0-912106-64-6). Bridge Pub.

Frost, S. E., Jr., ed. Favorite Stories from the Bible. 176p. 1986. pap. 2.95 (ISBN 0-345-33125-7, Pub. by Ballantine Epiphany). Ballantine.

--The Sacred Writings of the Worlds Great Religions. 416p. 1972. pap. 6.95 (ISBN 0-07-022520-6). McGraw.

--The Sacred Writings of the World's Great Religions. 410p. 1983. Repr. of 1951 ed. lib. bdg. 40.00 (ISBN 0-89760-241-2). Telegraph Bks.

Frost, Siegmund. The Question Is the Answer. cancelled (ISBN 0-87306-075-X). Feldheim.

Frost, Stanley B. Patriarchs & Prophets. 232p. 1963. 10.00 (ISBN 0-7735-0010-3). McGill-Queens U Pr.

--Standing & Understanding: A Re-Appraisal of the Christian Faith. LC 68-59095. pap. 46.80 (ISBN 0-317-26033-2, 2023834). Bks Demand UMI.

Frothingham, O. C. Transcendentalism in New England: A History. 11.25 (ISBN 0-8446-1191-3). Peter Smith.

Frothingham, Octavius B. George Ripley. LC 75-101910. Repr. of 1883 ed. 24.50 (ISBN 0-404-02625-7). AMS Pr.

--Transcendentalism in New England: A History. LC 59-10346. 1972. pap. 14.95x (ISBN 0-8122-1038-7, Pa. Paperbacks). U of Pa Pr.

Froude, J. A. The Life & Letters of Erasmus & the Unknown Historical Significance of the Protestant Reformation, 2 vols. (Illus.). 157p. 1984. 147.55x set (ISBN 0-89266-469-X). Am Classical Coll Pr.

Froude, James A. Bunyan. Morley, John, ed. LC 68-58379. (English Men of Letters). Repr. of 1888 ed. lib. bdg 12.50 (ISBN 0-404-51711-0). AMS Pr.

--Bunyan. LC 73-11369. 1880. lib. bdg. 12.00 (ISBN 0-8414-1985-X). Folcroft.

--A Comparative Analysis of the Philosophies of Erasmus & Luther. (Illus.). 133p. 1981. Repr. of 1868 ed. 69.85 (ISBN 0-89901-038-5). Found Class Reprints.

--Divorce of Catherine of Aragon. 2nd ed. LC 68-58379. Repr. of 1891 ed. 31.50 (ISBN 0-404-02626-5). AMS Pr.

--Lectures on the Council of Trent, Delivered at Oxford 1892-3. LC 68-8244. 1969. Repr. of 1901 ed. 27.00x (ISBN 0-8046-0159-3, Pub. by Kennikat). Assoc Faculty Pr.

--Life & Letters of Erasmus. LC 70-155628. Repr. of 1895 ed. 24.50 (ISBN 0-404-02627-3). AMS Pr.

--Spanish Story of the Armada & Other Essays. LC 71-144613. Repr. of 1892 ed. 24.50 (ISBN 0-404-02628-1). AMS Pr.

Fruchtenbaum, Arnold G. Biblical Lovemaking: A Study of the Song of Solomon. 70p. 1983. pap. 3.50 (ISBN 0-914863-03-7). Ariel Pr CA.

--Footsteps of the Messiah: A Study of the Sequence of Prophetic Events. (Illus.). 468p. 1982. 20.00 (ISBN 0-914863-02-9). Ariel Pr CA.

--Hebrew Christianity: Its Theology, History & Philosophy. Rev. ed. 142p. 1983. pap. 3.50 (ISBN 0-8010-3497-3). Ariel Pr CA.

--Jesus Was a Jew. Rev. ed. LC 74-75670. 156p. 1981. pap. 2.95 (ISBN 0-8054-6209-0). Ariel Pr CA.

Frueh, Erne & Frueh, Florence. Chicago Stained Glass. (Illus.). 160p. 1983. 19.95 (ISBN 0-8294-0435-X). Loyola.

Frueh, Florence, jt. auth. see Frueh, Erne.

Fry, Barbara, et al, eds. Eastern Churches Review, Vols. I-X, 1966-1978. 2000p. 1985. pap. text ed. 80.00x (ISBN 0-89370-095-9). Borgo Pr.

Fry, C. George, jt. auth. see Arnold, Duane W.

Fry, Caroline. Christ Our Example. 155p. 1976. pap. 3.95 (ISBN 0-685-53618-1). Reiner.

Fry, Christopher, tr. see Anouilh, Jean.

Fry, D. B. The Nature of Religious Man. 1982. 15.95 (ISBN 0-900860-67-7, Pub. by Octagon Pr England). Ins Study Human.

Fry, Eldon E., et al. Now We Are Three. (Family Ministry Ser.). (Illus.). 54p. 1985. pap. text ed. 19.95 (ISBN 0-89191-977-5). Cook.

Fry, George C., et al. Great Asian Religions. 228p. 1984. pap. 9.95 (ISBN 0-8010-3511-2). Baker Bk.

Fry, L. An Analysis of Zionism. 1982. lib. bdg. 59.00 (ISBN 0-87700-416-1). Revisionist Pr.

Fry, Mae. Faith Is the Victory. (Orig.). 1986. pap. 1.95 (ISBN 0-89265-098-2). Randall Hse.

Fry, Malcolm C. Discipling & Developing. (Sunday School Workers Training Course Ser.: No. 4). 1971. pap. 3.95 (ISBN 0-89265-006-0, Free Will Baptist Dept). Randall Hse.

--Discipling & Developing: Teachers Guide. 1979. pap. 1.50 (ISBN 0-89265-062-1). Randall Hse.

--Precepts for Practice. (Way of Life Ser.). 1971. pap. 3.95 (ISBN 0-89265-004-4, Free Will Baptist Dept); tchrs' guide 4.95 (ISBN 0-89265-005-2). Randall Hse.

Fry, Malcolm C. & Crowson, Milton. The Ministry of Ushering: Leader's Guide. 1980. pap. 2.50 (ISBN 0-89265-066-4). Randall Hse.

Fry, P. Spirits of Protest. LC 75-20832. (Cambridge Studies in Social Anthropology: No. 14). 134p. 1976. 27.95 (ISBN 0-521-21052-6). Cambridge U Pr.

Fry, Timothy & Baker, Imogene, eds. The Rule of St. Benedict in English. 96p. (Orig.). 1982. pap. 2.25 (ISBN 0-8146-1272-5). Liturgical Pr.

Fry, Timothy, et al, eds. RB Nineteen Eighty. LC 81-1013. 627p. 1981. 24.95 (ISBN 0-8146-1211-3); pap. 17.50 (ISBN 0-8146-1220-2). Liturgical Pr.

--RB Nineteen-Eighty: The Rule of St. Benedict in Latin & English with Notes & Thematic Index. abr. ed. LC 81-12434. xii, 198p. 1981. pap. 8.95 (ISBN 0-8146-1243-1). Liturgical Pr.

Frydman, Maurice, tr. see Nisargadatta Maharaj.

Frye, Northrop. The Great Code: The Bible in Literature. LC 81-47303. 261p. 1983. pap. 5.95 (ISBN 0-15-636480-8, Harv). HarBraceJ.

--The Return of Eden: Five Essays on Milton's Epics. 1975. 15.00x (ISBN 0-8020-1353-8). U of Toronto Pr.

--The Secular Scripture: A Study of the Structure of Romance. (Charles Eliot Norton Lectures Ser.). 192p. 1976. 15.00x (ISBN 0-674-79675-6); pap. 5.95x (ISBN 0-674-79676-4, HP 127). Harvard U Pr.

Frye, Roland M. Is God a Creationist? The Religious Case Against Creation Science. 256p. 1983. pap. text ed. write for info. (ISBN 0-02-339560-5, Pub. by Scribner). Macmillan.

--Milton's Imagery & the Visual Arts: Iconographic Tradition in the Epic Poems. LC 77-24541. 1978. 83.00x (ISBN 0-691-06349-4). Princeton U Pr.

Frye, Roland M., ed. Is God a Creationist? Religious Arguments Against Creation-Science. 256p. 1983. 15.95 (ISBN 0-684-17993-8, ScribT). Scribner.

--The Reader's Bible, A Narrative: Selections from the King James Version. LC 77-311. 638p. 1979. pap. 13.50 (ISBN 0-691-01995-9). Princeton U Pr.

Fryer, Alfred C. The Religious Thoughts of Some of Our Poets. 1911. Repr. 17.50 (ISBN 0-8274-3263-1). R West.

Fryer, Charles. A Hand in Dialogue. 128p. 1983. 17.95 (ISBN 0-227-67841-9, Pub. by J Clarke UK). Attic Pr.

Fryman, Sarah. The Measure of a Woman. LC 77-74533. (The Measure of... Ser.). 64p. 1985. pap. 3.95 (ISBN 0-8307-0988-6, 6101888). Regal.

Frymer, Berl. Jewish Horizons. LC 81-65057. 256p. 1982. 12.95 (ISBN 0-8453-4705-5, Cornwall Bks). Assoc Univ Prs.

Fu, Charles W. & Spiegler, Gerhard E., eds. Movements & Issues in World Religions: A Sourcebook & Analysis of Developments since 1945; Religion, Ideology, & Politics. LC 86-4634. 576p. 1987. lib. bdg. 75.00 (ISBN 0-313-23238-5, FUR). Greenwood.

Fuchs, Daniel. Israel's Holy Days: In Type & in Prophecy. LC 85-13172. 96p. 1985. pap. 3.95 (ISBN 0-87213-198-X). Loizeaux.

Fuchs, Emil. Christ in Catastrophe. 1983. pap. 2.50x (ISBN 0-87574-049-9, 049). Pendle Hill.

Fuchs, Esther. Encounters with Israeli Authors. LC 82-62086. (Illus.). 95p. 1983. pap. 7.50 (ISBN 0-916288-14-5). Micah Pubns.

Fuchs, Harald. Augustin und der Antike Friendensgedanke. LC 72-147669. (Library of War & Peace; Relig. & Ethical Positions on War). 1973. lib. bdg. 46.00 (ISBN 0-8240-0427-2). Garland Pub.

Fuchs, Josef. Christian Ethics in a Secular Arena. Hoose, Bernard & McNeil, Brian, trs. from Ital. & Ger. LC 84-7964. 164p. (Orig.). 1984. pap. 9.95 (ISBN 0-87840-411-2). Georgetown U Pr.

--Personal Responsibility & Christian Morality. Cleves, William, et al, trs. from Ger. LC 83-1548. 240p. (Orig.). 1983. pap. 10.95 (ISBN 0-87840-405-8). Georgetown U Pr.

Fudge, Edward. Christianity Without Ulcers. pap. 5.00 (ISBN 0-686-12686-6). E Fudge.

--Expository Outlines on Ephesians. 2.00 (ISBN 0-686-12688-2). E Fudge.

--Ezekiel: Prophet of Jehovah's Glory. 1.00 (ISBN 0-686-12692-0). E Fudge.

--Gold from the Gospels. pap. 2.00 (ISBN 0-686-12679-3). E Fudge.

--Preaching with Power. pap. 2.00 (ISBN 0-686-12680-7). E Fudge.

--Sermons That Demand a Decision. pap. 2.00 (ISBN 0-686-12681-5). E Fudge.

--Sermons That Strengthen. pap. 2.00 (ISBN 0-686-12682-3). E Fudge.

--Sermons to Grow on. pap. 2.00 (ISBN 0-686-12683-1). E Fudge.

--Simple Sermons That Demand a Decision. 2.00 (ISBN 0-686-12689-0). E Fudge.

--Simple Sermons That Say Something. pap. 2.00 (ISBN 0-686-12684-X). E Fudge.

--Sunday Night Sermons. pap. 2.00 (ISBN 0-686-12685-8). E Fudge.

Fudge, Edward, jt. auth. see Edwards, Bruce.

Fudge, Edward W. The Fire That Consumes: A Biblical & Historical Study of Final Punishment. 1983. 19.95 (ISBN 0-89890-018-2). Providential Pr.

Fuellenbach, John. Ecclesiastical Office & the Primacy of Rome: An Evaluation of Recent Theological Discussion of First Clement. LC 79-17574. (Catholic University of America. Studies in Christian Antiquity Ser.: No. 20). pap. 72.00 (2029502). Bks Demand UMI.

Fuente, Tomas De La see Cowan, Marvin W.

Fuente, Tomas de La see De La Fuente, Tomas.

Fuerst, W. J. Ruth, Esther, Ecclesiastes, the Song of Songs, Lamentations. LC 74-82589. (Cambridge Bible Commentary on the New English Bible, Old Testament Ser.). 250p. 1975. 32.50 (ISBN 0-521-20651-0); pap. 11.95 (ISBN 0-521-09920-X). Cambridge U Pr.

Fugate, J. Richard. What the Bible Says About Child Training. (What the Bible Says about...Ser.). (Illus.). 287p. 1980. pap. 5.95 (ISBN 0-86717-000-X). Aletheia Pubs.

Fugett, Albert F. Spokesman for the Devil. (Illus.). 165p. 1985. 14.95 (ISBN 0-9614870-0-3). Triple Seven.

Fugita, Neil. Introducing the Bible. LC 81-80874. 224p. (Orig.). 1981. pap. 5.95 (ISBN 0-8091-2392-4). Paulist Pr.

Fuhley, Denis, pref. by see Dillon, George E.

Fujian Sheng Museum Staff. Thirteenth-Century Tomb Near Fuzhou. 145p. 1982. 100.00x (ISBN 0-317-43751-8, Pub. by Han-Shan Tang Ltd). State Mutual Bk.

Fujioka, Michio. Angkor Wat. LC 71-158641. (This Beautiful World Ser.: Vol. 29). (Illus.). 138p. (Orig.). 1972. pap. 4.95 (ISBN 0-87011-156-6). Kodansha.

Fujisawa, Chikao. Zen & Shinto: The Story of Japanese Philosophy. LC 78-139133. 92p. Repr. of 1959 ed. lib. bdg. 22.50x (ISBN 0-8371-5749-8, FUZS). Greenwood.

Fukuyama, Yoshio. The Ministry in Transition: A Case Study of Theological Education. LC 72-1395. 200p. 1973. 22.50x (ISBN 0-271-01129-7). Pa St U Pr.

Fulbecke, William. A Booke of Christian Ethicks or Moral Philosophie. LC 74-28856. (English Experience Ser.: No. 737). 1975. Repr. of 1587 ed. 6.00 (ISBN 90-221-0737-X). Walter J Johnson.

Fulbright, Robert G. Old Testament Friends: Men of Courage. (BibLearn Ser.). (Illus.). 1979. 5.95 (ISBN 0-8054-4251-0, 4242-51). Broadman.

Fulbrook, Mary. Piety & Politics: Religion & the Rise of Absolutism in England, Wurttemberg & Prussia. LC 83-5316. 224p. 1984. 37.50 (ISBN 0-521-25612-7); pap. 13.95 (ISBN 0-521-27633-0). Cambridge U Pr.

Fulder, Stephen. Tao of Medicine: Ginseng, Oriental Remedies & the Pharmacology of Harmony. LC 82-1066. (Illus.). 328p. 1982. text ed. 9.95 (ISBN 0-89281-027-0, Destiny Bks). Inner Tradit.

Fulke, William. Defence of the Sincere & True Translations of the Holy Scriptures into the English Tongue. Repr. of 1843 ed. 51.00 (ISBN 0-384-17230-X). Johnson Repr.

--Stapleton's Fortress Overthrown: A Rejoinder to Martiall's Reply. Repr. of 1848 ed. 31.00 (ISBN 0-384-17240-7). Johnson Repr.

Fullam, Everett L. How to Walk with God. 192p. 1987. pap. 8.95 (ISBN 0-8407-9514-9). Oliver-Nelson.

Fuller, Andrew R. Psychology & Religion: Eight Points of View. 143p. 1977. pap. text ed. 8.75 (ISBN 0-8191-0143-5). U Pr of Amer.

--Psychology & Religion: Eight Points of View. 2nd ed. 286p. 1986. pap. text ed. 9.75 (ISBN 0-8191-5336-2). U Pr of Amer.

Fuller, Clifford. Let's Try This Way. pap. 1.00 (ISBN 0-87516-196-0). De Vorss.

Fuller, Daniel P. Gospel & Law: Contrast or Continuum? the Hermeaneutics of Dispensationalism & Covenant Theology. (Orig.). 1980. pap. 8.95 (ISBN 0-8028-1808-0). Eerdmans.

Fuller, David O., ed. A Treasury of Evangelical Writings. LC 61-9768. 472p. 1974. pap. 11.95 (ISBN 0-8254-2613-8). Kregel.

--Which Bible? 6th, rev. ed. LC 70-129737. 360p. 1975. pap. 8.95 (ISBN 0-8254-2612-X). Kregel.

Fuller, David O., ed. see Spurgeon, Charles H.

Fuller, Edmund, ed. see Bulfinch, Thomas.

Fuller, Elizabeth. The Touch of Grace. (Illus.). 256p. 1986. 14.95 (ISBN 0-396-08667-5). Dodd.

Fuller, Ilse, tr. see Bornkamm, Gunther.

Fuller, J. F. C. Secret Wisdom of Qabalah. 1976. Repr. 7.00 (ISBN 0-911662-63-4). Yoga.

--Yoga. 180p. 1975. 7.00 (ISBN 0-911662-55-3). Yoga.

Fuller, Joy. The Glorious Presence. LC 81-65753. 168p. (Orig.). 1981. pap. 2.95 (ISBN 0-87516-449-8). De Vorss.

Fuller, Millard. Bokotola. LC 77-1277. 1978. pap. 5.95 (ISBN 0-8329-1179-8). New Century.

Fuller, R. C. Alexander Geddes: A Forerunner of Biblical Criticism. (Historic Texts & Interperters Ser.: No. 3). 186p. 1985. text ed. 25.95x (ISBN 0-907459-26-9, Pub. by Almond Pr England); pap. text ed. 12.95x (ISBN 0-907459-27-7). Eisenbrauns.

Fuller, Reginald & Perkins, Pheme. Who Is This Christ? Gospel Christology & Contemporary Faith. LC 82-48590. 176p. 1983. pap. 8.95 (ISBN 0-8006-1706-1, 1-1706). Fortress.

Fuller, Reginald C., et al, eds. A New Catholic Commentary on Holy Scripture. rev. ed. 1378p. 1984. 34.95 (ISBN 0-8407-5017-X). Nelson.

Fuller, Reginald H. Advent-Christmas. Achtemeier, Elizabeth, et al, eds. LC 79-7377. (Proclamation 2: Aids for Interpreting the Lessons of the Church Year, Ser. C). 64p. 1979. pap. 3.75 (ISBN 0-8006-4079-9, 1-4079). Fortress.

--A Critical Introduction to the New Testament. 221p. 1979. pap. 9.95 (ISBN 0-7156-0582-8, Pub. by Duckworth London). Longwood Pub Group.

--The Formation of the Resurrection Narratives. LC 79-8885. 240p. 1980. pap. 7.95 (ISBN 0-8006-1378-3, 1-1378). Fortress.

--Foundations of New Testament Christology. 1965. lib. bdg. 25.00x (ISBN 0-684-15532-X, ScribT); pap. 1.50 (ISBN 0-684-15537-0, SL772, ScribT). Scribner.

--Holy Week. Achtemeier, Elizabeth, ed. LC 84-6011. (Proclamation 3: Aids for Interpreting the Lessons of the Church Year Ser. B). 64p. 1984. pap. 3.75 (ISBN 0-8006-4104-3). Fortress.

--New Testament in Current Study. (Hudson River Editions). 1976. 15.00x (ISBN 0-684-14843-9, ScribT). Scribner.

--Preaching the Lectionary: The Word of God for the Church Today. rev. ed. 672p. 1984. pap. 16.95 (ISBN 0-8146-1351-9). Liturgical Pr.

--The Use of the Bible in Preaching. LC 80-2377. 80p. (Orig.). 1981. pap. 3.95 (ISBN 0-8006-1447-X, 1-1447). Fortress.

Fuller, Reginald H., tr. see Bornkamm, Gunther.

Fuller, Reginald H., tr. see Bultmann, Rudolf.

Fuller, Reginald H., tr. see Schweitzer, Albert.

Fuller, Reginald H., et al. Hebrews, James, 1 & 2 Peter, Jude, Revelation. Krodel, Gerhard, ed. LC 76-7864. (Proclamation Commentaries). 132p. 1977. pap. 4.95 (ISBN 0-8006-0584-5, 1-584). Fortress.

Fuller, Thoams. The Church History of Britain, from the Birth of Jesus Christ Until the Year 1648, 6 Vols. 3202p. 1845. text ed. 621.00x (ISBN 0-576-78882-1, Pub. by Gregg Intl Pubs England). Gregg Intl.

Fuller, Thomas, jt. auth. see Walten, Maximilian G.

Fullerton, Kemper. Essays & Sketches: Oberlin, 1904-1934. facsimile ed. LC 70-156644. (Essay Index Reprint Ser). Repr. of 1938 ed. 17.00 (ISBN 0-8369-2361-8). Ayer Co Pubs.

Fullerton, Sheryl, ed. see McGuire.

Fullerton, Sheryl, ed. see Neusner, Jacob.

Fullerton, W. Y. Charles Spurgeon. (Golden Oldies Ser.). 288p. 1980. pap. 4.95 (ISBN 0-8024-1236-X). Moody.

Fullington, James F., ed. The Bible: Prose & Poetry from the Old Testament. LC 50-9988. (Crofts Classics Ser.). 1950. pap. text ed. 4.95x (ISBN 0-88295-013-4). Harlan Davidson.

Fullman, Everett L. Living the Lord's Prayer. (Epiphany Ser.). 128p. 1983. pap. 2.50 (ISBN 0-345-30432-2). Ballantine.

Fulop-Miller, Rene. The Power & Secret of the Jesuits. 1930. 29.50 (ISBN 0-8414-4288-6). Folcroft.

--Rasputin the Holy Devil. 1977. Repr. of 1928 ed. lib. bdg. 30.00 (ISBN 0-8414-4308-4). Folcroft.

--Saints That Moved the World: Anthony, Augustine, Francis, Ignatius, Theresa. LC 72-13293. (Essay Index Reprint Ser.). Repr. of 1945 ed. 32.00 (ISBN 0-8369-8159-6). Ayer Co Pubs.

Fulton, Alvenia M. The Fasting Primer. 2nd & rev. ed. Williams, James C., ed. LC 78-60661. 1978. pap. 5.95 (ISBN 0-931564-04-2). JBR Pub.

Fulton, Ginger A. God Made Me Special Even Before I Was Born. (Illus., Orig.). 1986. pap. 2.95 (ISBN 0-8024-3011-2). Moody.

--When I'm a Daddy. 1985. pap. 2.95 (ISBN 0-8024-0387-5). Moody.

--When I'm a Mommy: A Little Girl's Paraphrase of Proverbs 31. (Illus.). 1984. pap. 2.95 (ISBN 0-8024-0367-0). Moody.

Fulton, John. Beautiful Land: Palestine: Historical, Geographical & Pictorial. Davis, Moshe, ed. LC 77-70694. (America & the Holy Land Ser.). (Illus.). 1977. Repr. of 1891 ed. lib. bdg. 52.00x (ISBN 0-405-10248-8). Ayer Co Pubs.

Fulton, John F. & Stanton, Madeline E. Michael Servetus, Humanist & Martyr. (Illus.). 99p. 40.00 (ISBN 0-8139-1089-7). H Reichner.

Fulton, Justin D. The Fight with Rome. LC 76-46077. (Anti-Movements in America). 1977. Repr. of 1889 ed. lib. bdg. 30.00x (ISBN 0-405-09950-9). Ayer Co Pubs.

Fulton, Robert. Death, Grief & Bereavement: A Bibliography, 1845-1975. Kastenbaum, Robert, ed. LC 76-19572. (Death and Dying Ser.). 1976. PLB 27.50 (ISBN 0-405-09570-8). Ayer Co Pubs.

Fumagalli, M. Beonio-Brocchieri see Beonio-Brocchieri Fumagalli, M. T.

Funchion, Michael F., ed. Irish American Voluntary Organizations. LC 83-6712. (Ethnic American Voluntary Organizations Ser.). xviii, 323p. 1983. lib. bdg. 45.00 (ISBN 0-313-22948-1, FIA/). Greenwood.

Funderburk, James. Science Studies Yoga. 270p. (Orig.). pap. 8.95 (ISBN 0-89389-026-X). Himalayan Pubs.

Fung, Raymond, compiled by. Households of God on China's Soil. LC 82-18974. 84p. (Orig.). 1983. pap. 5.95 (ISBN 0-88344-189-6). Orbis Bks.

Funk, Franz X. Von see Von Funk, Franz X.

Funk, Nancy. Two Christmas Plays. 1984. 4.50 (ISBN 0-89536-695-9, 4872). CSS of Ohio.

Funk, Robert W. New Gospel Parallels, Vol. 1. LC 84-48727. (Foundations & Facets Ser.). 512p. 1985. 29.95 (ISBN 0-8006-2104-2, 1-2104). Fortress.

--New Gospel Parallels, Vol. 2. LC 84-48727. (Foundations & Facets Ser.). 384p. 1986. 24.95 (ISBN 0-8006-2106-9, 1-2106). Fortress.

--Parables & Presence. LC 82-71827. 224p. 1982. 3.00 (ISBN 0-8006-0688-4, 1-688). Fortress.

Funk, Robert W., ed. Greek Grammar of the New Testament & Other Early Christian Literature. LC 61-8077. 1961. 32.00x (ISBN 0-226-27110-2). U of Chicago Pr.

Funk, Robert W., ed. see Braun, Herbert, et al.

Funk, Robert W., ed. see Bultmann, Rudolf.

Funk, Robert W., ed. see Haenchen, Ernst.

Funk, Robert W., ed. see Kasemann, Ernst, et al.

Funk, Robert W., ed. see Robinson, James M., et al.

Funk, Robert W., tr. see Blass, F. & Debrunner, A.

FUnk, Robert W., tr. see Haenchen, Ernst.

Funk, Roger L., tr. see Scheler, Max.

Fuqua, E. C., jt. auth. see Warren, Thomas B.

Furcha, E., tr. Huldrych Zwingli Writings in Defense of the Reformed Faith: Writings in the Defense of the Reformed Faith, Vol. 1. (Pittsburgh Theological Monographs: No. 12). 1984. pap. 19.95 (ISBN 0-915138-58-1). Pickwick.

Furcha, E. J., ed. & tr. Selected Writings of Hans Denck. LC 76-7057. (Pittsburgh Original Texts & Translations Ser.: No. 1). 1976. 5.50 (ISBN 0-915138-15-8). Pickwick.

Furcha, E. J., ed. Spirit within Structure: Essays in Honor of George Johnston on the Occasion of His Seventieth Birthday. (Pittsburgh Theological Monographs: New Ser.: No. 3). xvi, 194p. 1983. pap. 12.50 (ISBN 0-915138-53-0). Pickwick.

Furcha, E. J., tr. see Franck, Sebastian.

Furchs, E. J. & Pipkin, H. Wayne, eds. Prophet, Pastor, Protestant: The Work of Huldrych Zwingli after Five Hundred Years. LC 84-14723. (Pittsburgh Theological Monographs (New Series): No. 11). (Orig.). 1984. pap. 15.00 (ISBN 0-915138-64-6). Pickwick.

Furer-Haimendorf, Christoph von see Von Furer-Haimendorf, Christoph.

Furer-Haimendorf, Christoph Von, ed. see Nebesky-Wojkowitz, Rene De.

Furey, Robert J. So I'm Not Perfect: A Psychology of Humility. 131p. (Orig.). 1986. pap. 6.95 (ISBN 0-8189-0499-2). Alba.

Furfey, Paul H. Fire on the Earth. 17.00 (ISBN 0-405-10830-3, 11837). Ayer Co Pubs.

Furfine, Sandy S. & Nowak, Nancy C. The Jewish Preschool Teachers Handbook. LC 81-67023. (Illus.). 132p. (Orig.). 1981. pap. 13.50 (ISBN 0-86705-004-7). AIRE.

Furley, William D. Studies in the Use of Fire in the Ancient Greek Religion. rev. ed. Connor, W. R., ed. LC 80-2650. (Monographs in Clasical Studies). (Illus.). 1981. lib. bdg. 29.00 (ISBN 0-405-14037-1). Ayer Co Pubs.

Furlong, Monica. Christian Uncertainties. LC 82-72129. xii, 124p. 1982. pap. 6.95 (ISBN 0-936384-06-9). Cowley Pubns.

--Contemplating Now. LC 83-70991. 128p. 1983. pap. 6.00 (ISBN 0-936384-13-1). Cowley Pubns.

--Merton: A Biography. LC 84-48218. (Illus.). 368p. 1985. pap. 8.95 (ISBN 0-06-063078-7, RD 529, HarpR). Har-Row.

--Travelling in. LC 84-71182. 125p. 1984. pap. 6.00 (ISBN 0-936384-20-4). Cowley Pubns.

--Zen Effects: The Life of Alan Watts. 1986. 17.95 (ISBN 0-395-35344-0). HM.

Furlong, William B. Shaw & Chesterton: The Metaphysical Jesters. LC 77-114616. 1970. 21.95 (ISBN 0-271-00110-0). Pa St U Pr.

Furlow, Elaine. Love with No Strings: The Human Touch in Christian Social Ministries. Hullum, Everett, ed. (The Human Touch Photo-Text Ser.: Volume IV). (Illus.). 1977. 6.95 (ISBN 0-937170-15-1). Home Mission.

Furlow, Elaine, et al. Light upon the Land. (Home Mission Study). 110p. (Orig.). 1984. pap. 2.85 (ISBN 0-937170-28-3). Home Mission.

Furlow, Elaine S., jt. auth. see Rutledge, Don.

Furlow, Elaine S., ed. see Loucks, Celeste, et al.

Furlow, Elaine S., ed. see Loucks, Celeste & Hullum, Everett.

Furlow, Elaine S., ed. see Nicholas, Tim & Touchton, Ken.

Furman, D. Religion & Social Conflicts in the U. S. A. 254p. 1985. 7.95 (ISBN 0-8285-2975-2, Pub. by Progress Pubs USSR). Imported Pubns.

Furman, Frida K. Beyond Yiddishkeit: The Struggle for Jewish Identity in a Reform Synagogue. (Anthropology & Judaic Studies). 152p. 1987. text ed. 29.50x (ISBN 0-88706-513-9); pap. 9.95x (ISBN 0-88706-514-7). State U NY Pr.

Furman, Richard. The Intimate Husband. 1986. pap. 8.95 (ISBN 0-89081-557-7). Harvest Hse.

--Reaching Your Full Potential. 1984. pap. 6.95 (ISBN 0-89081-443-0). Harvest Hse.

Furneaux, Philip. The Palladium of Conscience. LC 74-122161. (Civil Liberties in American History Ser). 267p. 1974. Repr. of 1773 ed. lib. bdg. 35.00 (ISBN 0-306-71972-X). Da Capo.

Furness, C. J. Lotus Petals: The Life & Work of Rudolf Steiner. 59.95 (ISBN 0-8490-0557-4). Gordon Pr.

Furnish, Dorothy J. Exploring the Bible with Children. LC 74-34486. 176p. 1975. pap. 6.95 (ISBN 0-687-12426-3). Abingdon.

Furnish, Victor. Lent. LC 84-18756. (Proclamation 3A Ser.). 64p. 1986. pap. 3.75 (ISBN 0-8006-4119-1, 1-4119). Fortress.

Furnish, Victor P. Theology & Ethics in Paul. LC 68-17445. 1978. pap. 12.95 (ISBN 0-687-41499-7). Abingdon.

Furnish, Victor P. & Thulin, Richard L. Pentecost 3. Achtemeier, Elizabeth, et al, eds. LC 79-7377. (Proclamation 2: Aids for Interpreting the Lessons of the Church Year, Ser. A). 64p. (Orig.). 1981. pap. 3.75 (ISBN 0-8006-4098-5, 1-4098). Fortress.

Furnish, Victor P., intro. by. Corinthians II, Vol 32A. LC 83-2056. (Anchor Bible Ser.). (Illus.). 648p. 1984. 18.00 (ISBN 0-385-11199-1). Doubleday.

Furnish, Victor P., ed. see Murphy, Roland E.

Furnish, Victory P., ed. see Fretheim, Terence E.

Furniss, Norman F. The Mormon Conflict, 1850-1859. LC 77-5424. (Illus.). 1977. Repr. of 1960 ed. lib. bdg. 23.75x (ISBN 0-8371-9636-1, FUMC). Greenwood.

Furnivall, F. J. Adam Davy's Five Dreams about Edward 2nd. Incl. The Life of St. Alexius; Solomon's Book of Wisdom; St. Jeremies Fifteen Tokens Before Doomsday; The Lamentacion of Souls. (EETS, OS Ser.: No. 69). Repr. of 1878 ed. 10.00 (ISBN 0-527-00068-X). Kraus Repr.

Furnivall, F. J., ed. The Gild of St. Mary & Other Documents. (EETS, ES Ser.: No. 114). Repr. of 1920 ed. 10.00 (ISBN 0-527-00316-6). Kraus Repr.

Furnivall, F. J., ed. see De Deguilleville, Guillaume.

Furnivall, F. J., ed. see Lovelich, Henry.

Furnivall, Frederick J., ed. Political, Religious & Love Poems. 348p. 1981. Repr. of 1866 ed. lib. bdg. 75.00 (ISBN 0-89987-276-X). Darby Bks.

Furrell, Alfred W., jt. auth. see Brewer, Bartholomew F.

Furrey, Donna M. God, Where's My Daddy? 32p. 1985. pap. 3.50 (ISBN 0-570-04130-9, 56-1542). Concordia.

Furse, Margaret L. Mysticism - Window on a World View: Introduction to Mysticism As a Pattern of Thought & Practice. LC 76-56816. Repr. of 1977 ed. 55.00 (ISBN 0-8357-9018-5, 2016384). Bks Demand UMI.

--Nothing but the Truth: What It Takes to Be Honest. LC 81-3501. 128p. 1981. 8.75 (ISBN 0-687-28130-X). Abingdon.

Furse, Margaret L., et al. The Problem of Religious Knowledge. (Rice University Studies: Vol. 60, No. 1). 129p. 1974. pap. 10.00x (ISBN 0-89263-219-4). Rice Univ.

Furst, Gesenius. Hebrew-English Dictionary: Hebrew & Chaldee Lexicon to the Old Testament. rev. ed. Mitchell, Edward C., ed. (Hebrew & Eng.). 47.50 (ISBN 0-87559-021-7); thumb indexed 52.50 (ISBN 0-87559-022-5). Shalom.

Furst, Jeffrey, ed. Edgar Cayce's Story of Attitudes & Emotions. 1983. pap. 3.50 (ISBN 0-425-08194-X). Berkley Pub.

--Edgar Cayce's Story of Jesus. 1984. pap. 3.95 (ISBN 0-425-09534-7, Medallion). Berkley Pub.

Furst, Walther, ed. see Barth, Karl.

Furutan, A. Mothers, Fathers, & Children: Practical Advice to Parents. 280p. pap. 8.95 (ISBN 0-85398-095-0). G Ronald Pub.

Furutan, Ali A. The Story of My Heart. (Illus.). 272p. 14.95 (ISBN 0-85398-114-0); pap. 8.95 (ISBN 0-85398-115-9). G Ronald Pub.

Furutan, Ali-Akbar. Stories of Baha'u'llah. 128p. 1986. 12.95; pap. 5.95. G Ronald Pub.

Fuss, Abraham, ed. Studies in Jewish Jurisprudence. (Studies in Jewish Jurisprudence Ser.: Vol. 4). 320p. 1975. 14.50 (ISBN 0-87203-058-X). Hermon.

Fuss, Peter, ed. see Hegel, G. W.

Fuss, Werner. Die Deuteronomistische Pentateuchredaktion in Exodus 3-17. (Beiheft 126 zur Zeitschrift fuer die alttestamentliche Wissenschaft). xii, 406p. 1972. 48.40x (ISBN 3-11-003854-4). De Gruyter.

Fussell, Paul. The Rhetorical World of Augustan Humanism: Ethics & Imagery from Swift to Burke. LC 66-1724. pap. 80.80 (ISBN 0-317-29155-6, 2055599). Bks Demand UMI.

Fusselle, Warner E. Scenes with the Savior. LC 84-11389. 1984. pap. 3.75 (ISBN 0-8054-1532-7). Broadman.

Futrell, John C. Making an Apostolic Community of Love: The Role of the Superior According to St. Ignatius of Loyola. LC 73-139365. (Original Studies Composed in English Ser.). 239p. 1970. smyth sewn 5.00 (ISBN 0-912422-19-X); pap. 4.00 (ISBN 0-912422-08-4). Inst Jesuit.

Fyzee, Asaf A. Outlines of Muhammadan Law. 5th ed. Pearl, David, ed. 520p. 1986. pap. 13.95x (ISBN 0-19-561393-7). Oxford U Pr.

G

G-Jo Institute. Meditative Relaxation. 1980. pap. 4.50 (ISBN 0-916878-13-9). Falkynor Bks.

Gaalyah, jt. ed. see Cornfeld.

Gabbott, Mabel J. Have a Very Merry Christmas! Skits for Elementary Schools & Families. LC 80-83034. 56p. (Orig.). 1981. pap. 4.95 (ISBN 0-88290-163-X, 2044). Horizon Utah.

Gabel, John B. & Wheeler, Charles. The Bible As Literature: An Introduction. 320p. 1986. 24.50x (ISBN 0-19-503993-9); pap. 9.95x (ISBN 0-19-503994-7). Oxford U Pr.

Gabel, Leona C. Benefit of Clergy in England in the Later Middle Ages. 1969. lib. bdg. 17.00x (ISBN 0-374-92964-5, Octagon). Hippocrene Bks.

Gabert, Glen, Jr. In Hoc Signo? A Brief History of Catholic Parochial Education in America. LC 72-89992. 1973. 19.95x (ISBN 0-8046-9028-6, Pub. by Kennikat). Assoc Faculty Pr.

Gabhart, Herbert C. Meeting the Challenge. 1984. 6.95 (ISBN 0-8054-5340-7, 4253-40). Broadman.

Gabirol, Solomon I. Fountain of Life. pap. 1.45 (ISBN 0-685-19402-7, 104, WL). Citadel Pr.

Gabler, Ulrich. Huldrych Zwingli: His Life & Work. Gritsch, Ruth C., tr. LC 85-16199. 208p. 1986. 24.95 (ISBN 0-8006-0761-9, 1-761). Fortress.

Gabriel. Divine Intimacy, Vol. III. 1983. 12.95 (ISBN 0-87193-203-2). Dimension Bks.

--Divine Intimacy, Vol. II. 1983. 12.95 (ISBN 0-87193-201-6). Dimension Bks.

--Divine Intimacy, Vol. IV. 12.95 (ISBN 0-87193-204-0). Dimension Bks.

--Divine Intimacy, Vol. 1. 12.95 (ISBN 0-87193-194-X). Dimension Bks.

Gabriel, Astrik L. Student Life in Ave Maria College, Medieval Paris. (Mediaeval Studies Ser.: No. 14). (Illus.). 1955. 26.95 (ISBN 0-268-00265-7). U of Notre Dame Pr.

Gabriel, George, tr. see Kalomiros, Alexander.

Gabriel, Milley, ed. see Ornitz, Samuel.

Gabriel, Ralph H. Religion & Learning at Yale: Church of Christ in the College & University, 1757-1957. 1958. 39.50x (ISBN 0-685-69820-3). Elliots Bks.

Gabriel, Ralph H. & Brown, Charles R. Christianity & Modern Thought. 11.00 (ISBN 0-8369-7217-1, 8016). Ayer Co Pubs.

Gabrieli, Francesco, ed. Arab Historians of the Crusades. LC 68-23783. 1978. 40.00x (ISBN 0-520-03616-6); pap. 9.95 (ISBN 0-520-05224-2, CAL 699). U of Cal Pr.

Gabriel of St. Mary Magdalen. Divine Intimacy: A Celebration of Prayer and the Joy of Christian Life, 4 vols. 2nd ed. LC 86-83132. (Orig.). 1987. pap. 12.95 ea. Vol. 1, 285 p (ISBN 0-89870-142-2). Vol. 2, 285 p (ISBN 0-89870-143-0). Vol. 3, 285 p (ISBN 0-89870-144-9). Vol. 4, 285 p (ISBN 0-89870-145-7). Ignatius Pr.

Gache, Louis-Hippolyte. A Frenchman, a Chaplain, a Rebel: The War Letters of Pere Louis-Hippolyte Gache, S. J. Buckley, Cornelius M., tr. 282p. 1981. 8.95 (ISBN 0-8294-0376-0). Loyola.

Gadamer, Hans-Georg. Truth & Method. 516p. 1982. pap. 16.95x (ISBN 0-8264-0431-6). Continuum.

Gade, Richard E. Historical Survey of Anti-Semitism. pap. 5.95 (ISBN 0-8010-3747-6). Baker Bk.

Gadolin, A. A. A Theory of History & Society, with Special Reference to the Chronographia of Michael Psellus: Eleventh Century Byzantium. 2nd ed. (Illus.). 244p. 1986. lib. bdg. 45.00x (ISBN 90-256-0906-6, Pub. by A M Hakkert). Coronet Bks.

Gaebelein, A. C. What the Bible Says About Angels. (Direction Bks). 120p. 1975. pap. 4.95 (ISBN 0-8010-3810-3). Baker Bk.

--What the Bible Says about Angels. 116p. 1987. pap. 4.95 (ISBN 0-8010-3810-3). Baker Bk.

Gaebelein, Arno C. Acts of the Apostles. rev. ed. LC 61-17224. 1965. 10.95 (ISBN 0-87213-215-3). Loizeaux.

--The Conflict of the Ages. x ed. (Illus.). 171p. pap. 5.50 (ISBN 0-9609260-1-1). Exhorters.

--Ezekiel. LC 72-88419. 9.95 (ISBN 0-87213-217-X). Loizeaux.

--Gaebelein's Concise Commentary on the Whole Bible. rev. ed. 1237p. 1985. Repr. of 1970 ed. 29.95 (ISBN 0-87213-209-9). Loizeaux.

--Gospel of John. rev. ed. LC 65-26586. 1965. 9.95 (ISBN 0-87213-220-X). Loizeaux.

--Gospel of Matthew. LC 61-17223. 1961. Repr. of 1910 ed. 12.95 (ISBN 0-87213-221-8). Loizeaux.

--The Prophet Daniel. LC 55-9465. 218p. 1968. pap. 5.95 (ISBN 0-8254-2701-0). Kregel.

--Psalms. 1939. 10.95 (ISBN 0-87213-222-6). Loizeaux.

--Revelation. LC 61-17225. 1960. 7.95 (ISBN 0-87213-223-4). Loizeaux.

Gaebelein, Frank E. The Christian, the Arts, & Truth: Regaining the Vision of Greatness. Lockerbie, D. Bruce, frwd. by. LC 85-9005. (Critical Concern Bks.). 1985. 12.95 (ISBN 0-88070-114-5). Multnomah.

--The Expositor's Bible Commentary, 5 vols. 1979. Set. 107.75 (ISBN 0-310-36568-6, 11183). Zondervan.

--Pattern of God's Truth. LC 54-6908. 1968. pap. 5.95 (ISBN 0-8024-6450-5). Moody.

--The Pattern of God's Truth. 1985. pap. 5.95 (ISBN 0-88469-170-5). BMH Bks.

Gaebelein, Frank E., ed. Expositor's Bible Commentary, Vol. 1. (Introductory Actilces). 1979. 22.95 (ISBN 0-310-36430-2, 11170). Zondervan.

--Expositor's Bible Commentary, Vol. 6. 1986. text ed. 29.95 (ISBN 0-88469-182-9). BMH Bks.

--Expositor's Bible Commentary, Vol. 9. (John & Acts). 464p. 1980. 19.95 (ISBN 0-310-36510-4, 11178). Zondervan.

--The Expositor's Bible Commentary, Vol. 12. (Hebrews - Revelation). 624p. 1981. 19.95 (ISBN 0-310-36540-6, 11181). Zondervan.

--Expositor's Bible Commentary: Daniel & the Minor Prophets, Vol. 7. 752p. 1985. text ed. 24.95 (ISBN 0-310-36490-6, 11176). Zondervan.

--The Expositor's Bible Commentary: Isaiah, Jeremiah, Lamentations, Ezekiel, Vol. 6. 1088p. 1986. 29.95 (ISBN 0-310-36480-9, 11175). Zondervan.

--The Expositors' Bible Commentary: Matthew, Mark, Luke, Vol. 8. LC 83-11177. 1056p. (Orig.). 1984. 29.95 (ISBN 0-310-36500-7, 11177). Zondervan.

--The Expositor's Bible Commentary, (Romans - Galatians, Vol. 10. 600p. 1976. 19.95 (ISBN 0-310-36520-1, 11179). Zondervan.

--The Expositor's Bible Commentary Vol. 11 (Ephesians-Philemon) 1978. 19.95 (ISBN 0-310-36530-9, 11180). Zondervan.

--Expositor's Bible Commentary, Vol. 4: Kings-Job. (Expositor's Bible Commentary Ser.). 1987. 29.95 (ISBN 0-310-36460-4). Zondervan.

Gaeddert, John, jt. ed. see Hartzler, Arlene.

Gaede, S. D. Belonging: Our Need for Community in Church & Family. LC 85-17987. 288p. (Orig.). 1985. pap. 9.95 (ISBN 0-310-36891-X, 12294P). Zondervan.

--Where Gods May Dwell: Understanding the Human Condition. 168p. (Orig.). 1985. pap. 7.95 (ISBN 0-310-42971-4, 12756P). Zondervan.

Gaeng, Paul A. An Inquiry into the Local Variations in Vulgar Latin As Reflected in the Vocalism of Christian Inscriptions. (Studies in the Romance Languages & Literatures: No. 77). 300p. 1968. pap. 16.50x (ISBN 0-8078-9077-4). U of NC Pr.

Gaer, Joseph. How the Great Religions Began. LC 81-7764. 1981. pap. 6.95 (ISBN 0-396-08013-8). Dodd.

--What the Great Religions Believe. pap. 3.95 (ISBN 0-451-14320-5, AE1978, Sig). NAL.

Gaer, Joseph, ed. The Torah for Family Reading. LC 86-70620. 559p. 1986. Repr. 30.00 (ISBN 0-87668-915-2). Aronson.

Gaffin, Richard B. Perspectives on Pentecost. 1979. pap. 3.95 (ISBN 0-87552-269-6). Presby & Reformed.

Gaffin, Richard B., Jr., ed. Redemptive History & Biblical Interpretation: The Shorter Writings of Geerhardus Vos. 1980. 17.50 (ISBN 0-87552-270-X). Presby & Reformed.

Gaffin, Richard B., Jr., ed. see Vos, Geerhardus.

Gaffney, Edward M., jt. auth. see Moots, Philip R.

Gaffney, J. Patrick. Inexhaustible Presence: The Mystery of Jesus. 210p. 1986. 11.95 (ISBN 0-87193-249-0). Dimension Bks.

Gaffney, James. Newness of Life: A Modern Introduction to Catholic Ethics. LC 79-84404. 360p. 1979. pap. 6.95 (ISBN 0-8091-2202-2). Paulist Pr.

--Sin Reconsidered. LC 82-61424. 96p. (Orig.). 1983. pap. 3.95 (ISBN 0-8091-2516-1). Paulist Pr.

Gaffney, Patrick. Mary's Spiritual Maternity. 4.95 (ISBN 0-910984-18-2); pap. 2.95 (ISBN 0-910984-19-0). Montfort Pubns.

Gafni, Shlomo S. & Van der Heyden, A. The Glory of Jerusalem: An Explorer's Guide. LC 81-17053. 128p. 1982. o. p. 16.95 (ISBN 0-521-24613-X). Cambridge U Pr.

--The Glory of the Holy Land. LC 81-17054. (Illus.). 256p. 1982. o. p. 21.95 (ISBN 0-521-24612-1). Cambridge U Pr.

Gafni, Shlomo S., ed. The Glory of the New Testament. LC 83-840322. 1984. 25.00 (ISBN 0-394-53659-2, Pub. by Villard Bks). Random.

--The Glory of the Old Testament. LC 83-848323. 256p. 1984. 25.00 (ISBN 0-394-53658-4, Pub. by Villard Bks). Random.

Gagarin, Jean X. Russian Clergy. LC 70-131035. Repr. of 1872 ed. 21.00 (ISBN 0-404-02666-4). AMS Pr.

Gage, Gloria. A Season for Glory. 144p. (Orig.). 1984. pap. 4.95 (ISBN 0-89636-143-8). Accent Bks.

Gage, Joy. Every Woman's Privilege: Taking Responsibility for Your Spiritual Growth. (Touch of Grace Ser.). 1986. pap. 6.95 (ISBN 0-88070-177-3). Multnomah.

Gage, Joy, jt. auth. see Gage, Ken.

Gage, Ken & Gage, Joy. Restoring Fellowship: Judgement & Church Discipline. (Orig.). 1984. pap. 4.50 (ISBN 0-8024-4440-7). Moody.

Gage, Matilda J. Woman, Church, & State: A Historical Account of the Status of Woman Through the Christian Ages, with Reminiscenses of the Matriarchate. 2nd ed. LC 72-2602. (American Women Ser.: Images & Realities). 558p. 1972. Repr. of 1900 ed. 32.00 (ISBN 0-405-04458-5). Ayer Co Pubs.

Gage, Richard L., tr. see Niwano, Nichiko.

Gage, Richard L., tr. see Niwano, Nikkyo.

Gage, Robert C. Cultivating Spiritual Fruit. 144p. (Orig.). 1986. pap. 5.25 (ISBN 0-87227-114-5). Reg Baptist.

Gage, William L., tr. see Ritter, Karl.

Gager, Dorthy. It's My Move: Older Adults Choose How to Live. 80p. (Orig.). 1987. pap. 7.95 (ISBN 0-88177-045-0, DR045B). Discipleship Res.

Gager, John G. Kingdom & Community: The Social World of Early Christianity. 160p. 1975. pap. text ed. write for info. (ISBN 0-13-516203-3). P-H.

--Moses in Graeco-Roman Paganism. (SBL Monograph). 8.95 (ISBN 0-89130-323-5, 06-00-16). Scholars Pr GA.

Gagiati, Annie. Peace Where Is It? LC 73-91996. 1974. pap. 1.95 (ISBN 0-8198-0507-6). Dghtrs St Paul.

Gagliardo, John G. Reich & Nation: The Holy Roman Empire As Idea & Reality, 1763-1806. LC 79-2170. 384p. 1980. 25.00x (ISBN 0-253-16773-6). Ind U Pr.

Gagne, Ronald, et al. Introducing Dance in Christian Worship. (Illus.). 184p. 1984. pap. 7.95 (ISBN 0-912405-04-X). Pastoral Pr.

Gail, Marzieh. Khanum: The Greatest Holy Leaf. (Illus.). 48p. 6.95 (ISBN 0-85398-112-4); pap. 3.50 (ISBN 0-85398-113-2). G Ronald Pub.

--Other People, Other Places. 288p. 14.95 (ISBN 0-85398-122-1); pap. 8.95 (ISBN 0-85398-123-X). G Ronald Pub.

--The Sheltering Branch. 101p. 1959. 7.95 (ISBN 0-87743-022-5). G Ronald Pub.

Gail, Marzieh, tr. see Abdu'l-Baha.

Gail, Marzieh, tr. see Muhammad-'Aliy-Salmani, Ustad.

Gailey, James H., Jr. Micah-Malachi. LC 59-10454. (Layman's Bible Commentary Ser: Vol. 15). 1962. pap. 4.95 (ISBN 0-8042-3075-7). John Knox.

Gainer, Lucia A. The Hidden Garden. LC 84-61580. 128p. 1985. pap. 4.95 (ISBN 0-87973-598-8, 598). Our Sunday Visitor.

Gainer, Patrick W. Witches, Ghosts & Signs, Folklore of the Southern Appalachians. LC 75-29893. 192p. 1975. 7.95 (ISBN 0-89092-006-0). Seneca Bks.

Gaines, David P. The World Council of Churches. 1966. 18.50 (ISBN 0-87233-816-9). Bauhan.

Gaines, M. C., ed. Picture Stories from the Bible: The Old Testament in Full-Color Comic-Strip Form. LC 79-66064. (Illus.). 224p. 1979. Repr. of 1943 ed. 9.95 (ISBN 0-934386-01-3). Scarf Pr.

Gaines, Wesley J. African Methodism in the South: Or Twenty-Five Years of Freedom. LC 71-99379. 1969. Repr. of 1890 ed. lib. bdg. 16.00 (ISBN 0-8411-0050-0). Metro Bks.

Gainet, J. C. Dictionnaire d'Ascetisme, 2 vols. Migne, J. P., ed. (Nouvelle Encyclopedie Theologique Ser.: Vols. 45-46). (Fr.). 1520p. Repr. of 1854 ed. lib. bdg. 192.50x (ISBN 0-89241-284-4). Caratzas.

Gairdner, Canon W. H. T. Theories, Practices & Training Systems of a Sufi School. (Sufi Research Ser.). 1980. pap. 5.95 (ISBN 0-86304-003-9, Pub. by Octagon Pr England). Ins Study Human.

Gairdner, James. English Church in the Sixteenth Century, from the Accession of Henry Eighth to the Death of Mary, 1509-1558. LC 72-168089. (History of the English Church Ser.: No. 4). Repr. of 1902 ed. 29.50 (ISBN 0-404-50754-9). AMS Pr.

--Lollardy & the Reformation in England: An Historical Survey, 4 Vols. 1965. Repr. of 1913 ed. 141.00 (ISBN 0-8337-1268-3). B Franklin.

Gaitan, Elizabeth M. From Demon Deliverance to Divine Healing. 1985. 5.95 (ISBN 0-8062-2394-4). Carlton.

Gaither, Gloria. Fully Alive! 208p. 1984. pap. 4.95 (ISBN 0-8407-5945-2). Nelson.

Gaither, Gloria, jt. auth. see Dobson, Shirley.

Gakpe-Ntrsi, Theodore. Church As a Sacrament of Salvation. 112p. 1987. 9.95 (ISBN 0-89962-577-0). Todd & Honeywell.

Gal, Allon. Socialist Zionism: Theory & Issues in Contemporary Jewish Nationalism. 225p. 1973. pap. 5.50 (ISBN 0-87073-669-8). Transaction Bks.

Gal, Gedeon, ed. Guillelmi de Ockham: Scriptum in Librum Primum Sententiarum, Ordinatio, Opera Theologica, Vol. 1, Prologues et Distinctio Prima. 1967. 35.00 (ISBN 0-686-11528-7). Franciscan Inst.

Galambos, Edith P. Loving Hands for Jesus. (Little Learner Ser.). 24p. 1985. 5.95 (ISBN 0-570-08951-4, 56-1543). Concordia.

Galanter, Patricia, ed. see Reverend Mother Ruth.

Galas, Yechiel. Halacha. 192p. 1973. pap. 4.95 (ISBN 0-910818-13-4). Judaica Pr.

Galavaris, George. Bread & the Liturgy: The Symbolism of Early Christian & Byzantine Bread Stamps. LC 75-98120. pap. 63.30 (ISBN 0-317-07859-3, 2015361). Bks Demand UMI.

Galbreath, Naomi. The Story of Passover for Children. (Illus.). 32p. pap. 2.95 (ISBN 0-8249-8084-0). Ideals.

Galdamez, Pablo. Faith of a People: The Life of a Basic Christian Community in El Salvador. Barr, Robert R., tr. from Span. LC 85-30981. Tr. of La Fe de un Pueblo: Historia de una Comunidad Cristiana en El Salvador. 112p. (Orig.). 1986. pap. 7.95 (ISBN 0-88344-270-1). Orbis Bks.

Galde, Dorothy. You Write the Ticket, Lord. 144p. 1983. pap. 5.95 (ISBN 0-89840-047-3). Heres Life.

Galde, Phyllis, ed. see Llewellyn Publications Staff.

Galdston, Iago, ed. see New York Academy Of Medicine.

Gale, Elizabeth W. Children Together, Vol. 2. 128p. 1982. pap. 9.95 (ISBN 0-8170-0974-4). Judson.

Gale, Rodney. The Natural Path to Genuine Lasting Happiness. 1976. 6.50 (ISBN 0-533-02131-6). H R Gale.

Gale, Van, jt. auth. see Harrison, Buddy.

Gale, William. I Sat Where They Sat. pap. 2.50 (ISBN 0-686-12884-2). Schmul Pub Co.

Galeone, Victor. The Great Drama of Jesus: A Life of Christ for Teens Who Want to be Challenged. (Illus.). 207p. (Orig.). 1979. pap. 5.95 (ISBN 0-913382-31-0, 101-28). Prow Bks-Franciscan.

Galey, John. Sinai & the Monastery of St. Catherine. 191p. 1986. 45.00 (ISBN 977-424-118-5, Pub. by Am Univ Cairo Pr); pap. 24.00x (ISBN 977-424-118-5). Columbia U Pr.

Galfridus Anglicus. Promptorium Parvulorum Sive Clericorum, Dictionarius Anglolatinus Princeps, 3 Pts. Repr. of 1865 ed. 37.00 ea. Johnson Repr.

Galilea, Segundo. The Beatitudes: To Evangelize as Jesus Did. Barr, Robert R., tr. from Span. LC 83-19342. Tr. of La Mision Segun Las Bienaventuranzas. 128p. (Orig.). 1984. pap. 5.95 (ISBN 0-88344-344-9). Orbis Bks.

--Following Jesus. Phillips, Helen, tr. from Span. LC 80-24802. Orig. Title: El Seguimiento de Cristo. 128p. (Orig.). 1981. pap. 6.95 (ISBN 0-88344-136-5). Orbis Bks.

--The Future of Our Past: The Spanish Mystics Speak to Contemporary Spirituality. LC 85-71822. 96p. (Orig.). 1985. pap. 4.95 (ISBN 0-87793-296-4). Ave Maria.

--The Way of Living Faith. 12.45 (ISBN 0-317-52400-3, HarpR). Har-Row.

Gall, A. Von, ed. Der Hebraeische Pentateuch der Samaritaner, 5 pts. (Ger.). xciv, 440p. 1966. Repr. of 1918 ed. Set. 45.60x (ISBN 3-11-009258-1). De Gruyter.

Gall, E. Mysticism Through the Ages. 59.95 (ISBN 0-8490-0697-X). Gordon Pr.

Gall, James. Bible Student's English-Greek Concordance & Greek-English Dictionary. (Paperback Reference Library). 376p. 1983. pap. 9.95 (ISBN 0-8010-3795-6). Baker Bk.

Gallagher, Charles A. & Maloney, George A. Embodied in Love: The Sacramental Spirituality of Sexual Intimacy. 176p. (Orig.). 1983. pap. 9.95 (ISBN 0-686-46141-X). Crossroad NY.

Gallagher, Chuch & Vandenburg, Thomas. Celibacy Myth. 144p. 1987. 12.95 (ISBN 0-8245-0814-9). Crossroad NY.

Gallagher, Chuck & Crilly, Oliver. Prayer, Saints, Scripture & Ourselves. LC 83-60189. 162p. (Orig.). 1983. pap. text ed. 6.95 (ISBN 0-911905-03-0). Past & Mat Rene Ctr.

Gallagher, Chuck, et al. Calling Disciples: Outlines. LC 84-60459. (Calling Disciples Ser.: Bk. 1). 64p. (Orig.). 1984. pap. text ed. 2.95 (ISBN 0-911905-23-5). Past & Mat Rene Ctr.

Gallagher, Eric. Christians in Ulster, Nineteen Sixty-Eight to Nineteen Eighty. 1982. 19.95x (ISBN 0-19-213237-7). Oxford U Pr.

Gallagher, Eugene V. Divine Man or Magician? Celsus & Origin on Jesus. (SBL Dissertation Ser.). 1982. pap. 13.50 (ISBN 0-89130-542-4, 06 01 64). Scholars Pr GA.

Gallagher, John. The Basis for Christian Ethics. 240p. (Orig.). 1985. pap. 9.95 (ISBN 0-8091-2690-7). Paulist Pr.

Gallagher, John, ed. Homosexuality & the Magisterium: Documents from the Vatican & U. S. Bishops, 1975-1985. 109p. 1986. 9.95 (ISBN 0-935877-00-2). New Ways Min.

Gallagher, Joseph. Pain & the Privilege: Diary of a City Priest. LC 82-1766. 384p. 1983. pap. 7.95 (ISBN 0-385-19019-0, Im). Doubleday.

Gallagher, Joseph, et al, trs. see Camara, Helder.

Gallagher, Joseph V. Para Ser Catolico: Un Catecismo Para Hoy. new, spanish ed. 1976. pap. 1.50 (ISBN 0-8091-1939-0). Paulist Pr.

--To Be a Catholic. LC 73-137884. 96p. 1970. pap. 1.95 (ISBN 0-8091-5143-X). Paulist Pr.

Gallagher, Maureen. The Cathedral Book. LC 82-60592. 1983. pap. 2.95 (ISBN 0-8091-2485-8). Paulist Pr.

--God's Love for Us. 1983. 3.95 (ISBN 0-89837-090-6, Pub. by Pflaum Pr); 3.95 (ISBN 0-89837-091-4). Peter Li.

Gallagher, Maureen, ed. Christian Parenting Handbook. 2.95 (ISBN 0-8091-2262-6). Paulist Pr.

Gallagher, Maureen, et al. Praying with Scripture Handbook. LC 82-62923. 176p. (Orig.). 1984. pap. 7.95 (ISBN 0-8091-2544-7); leader's manual with slides 22.95 (ISBN 0-8091-7751-X). Paulist Pr.

Gallagher, Merchant, jt. auth. see Merchant, Joan de.

Gallagher, Neil. Don't Go Overseas until You've Read This Book. LC 77-2643. 128p. 1977. pap. 5.95 (ISBN 0-87123-105-0, 210105). Bethany Hse.

--The Porno Plague. LC 77-21992. (Illus.). 256p. 1977. pap. 5.95 (ISBN 0-87123-231-6, 210231). Bethany Hse.

Gallagner, Chuck, jt. auth. see Rousseau, Mary.

Gallardo, Jose. El Concepto Biblico de Justicia. LC 86-80343. (Title from Mennonite Faith Ser.). 80p. (Orig.). 1986. pap. 1.50X (ISBN 0-8361-1285-7). Herald Pr.

--The Way of Biblical Justice. LC 82-83386. (Mennonite Faith Ser.: Vol. 11). 80p. (Orig.). 1983. pap. 1.50 (ISBN 0-8361-3321-8). Herald Pr.

Gallaway, Ira. Drifted Astray: Returning the Church to Witness & Ministry. 160p. (Orig.). 1983. pap. 6.95 (ISBN 0-687-11186-2). Abingdon.

Gallen, John, ed. Christians at Prayer. LC 76-22407. 1977. text ed. 14.95x (ISBN 0-268-00718-7). U of Notre Dame Pr.

--Christians at Prayer. LC 76-22407. (Liturgical Studies). 1977. pap. text ed. 5.95 (ISBN 0-268-00719-5). U of Notre Dame Pr.

Gallen, Joseph F. Cannon Law for Religious: An Explanation. LC 83-15883. 218p. (Orig.). 1983. pap. 9.95 (ISBN 0-8189-0461-5). Alba.

--Conforming Constitutions to the New Code. 58p. 1984. pap. 2.00 (ISBN 0-317-18638-8). Dghtrs St Paul.

Galley, Howard, ed. The Burial of the Dead: Rite One. 1977. pap. 0.95 (ISBN 0-8164-2152-8, HarpR). Har-Row.

--The Burial of the Dead: Rite Two. 1977. pap. 0.95 (ISBN 0-8164-2153-6, HarpR). Har-Row.

--The Prayer Book Office. 800p. 1980. 39.95 (ISBN 0-8164-0370-8, HarpR). Har-Row.

Galli, Mario Von see Von Galli, Mario.

Galligan, Michael. God & Evil. LC 75-36172. 96p. 1976. pap. 2.95 (ISBN 0-8091-1925-0). Paulist Pr.

Galloway. Twelve Ways to Develop a Positive Attitude. 1975. pap. 1.95 (ISBN 0-8423-7550-3). Tyndale.

Galloway, Dale. Rebuild Your Life. 1981. pap. 4.95 (ISBN 0-8423-5323-2). Tyndale.

--You Can Win with Love. LC 76-15129. 176p. 1980. pap. 2.95 (ISBN 0-89081-233-0). Harvest Hse.

Galloway, Dale E. Expect a Miracle. 1982. pap. 4.95 (ISBN 0-8423-0822-9). Tyndale.

--Una Nueva Ilusion. Ward, Rhode F., tr. Tr. of Dream a New Dream. (Span.). 169p. 1982. pap. 3.95 (ISBN 0-89922-158-0). Edit Caribe.

Galloway, John, Jr. How to Stay Christian. 144p. 1984. pap. 4.95 (ISBN 0-8170-1038-6). Judson.

Gallup, George, Jr. & Castelli, Jim. American Catholic People: Their Beliefs, Practices, & Values. LC 86-16576. 216p. 1987. 15.95 (ISBN 0-385-23122-9). Doubleday.

Gallup, George, Jr. & O'Connell, George. Who Do Americans Say That I Am? LC 85-26383. 130p. (Orig.). 1986. pap. 10.95 (ISBN 0-664-24685-0). Westminster.

Gallwey, Peter, ed. The Legend of St. Dismas & Other Poems. LC 83-82115. 126p. (Orig.). 1984. pap. 6.95 (ISBN 0-89870-034-5). Ignatius Pr.

Gallyon, Margaret. The Early Church in Eastern England. 1979. 30.00x (ISBN 0-900963-19-0, Pub. by Terence Dalton England). State Mutual Bk.

Galot. Who Is Christ? A Theology of the Incarnation. Bouchard, M. Angeline, tr. 423p. 1981. 10.00 (ISBN 0-8199-0813-4). Franciscan Herald.

Galot, Jean. The Mystery of Christian Hope. LC 77-1222. 1977. 4.95 (ISBN 0-8189-0346-5). Alba.

--The Person of Christ: Covenant Between God & Man. Bouchard, Angeline, tr. LC 84-5982. 102p. 1983. 7.50 (ISBN 0-8199-0832-0). Franciscan Herald.

Galpern, A. N. The Religions of the People in Sixteenth Century Champagne. (Historical Studies: No. 92). 1976. 22.50x (ISBN 0-674-75836-6). Harvard U Pr.

Galt, Tom. The World Has a Familiar Face. 85p. 1981. pap. 5.00 (ISBN 0-938050-03-6). Shearwater.

Galton, Arthur H. Church & State in France, 1300-1907. LC 70-185939. xxiv, 290p. 1972. Repr. of 1907 ed. lib. bdg. 21.00 (ISBN 0-8337-4124-1). B Franklin.

Galupkin, Esther. Kindergarten Curriculum for the Day School. 1.50 (ISBN 0-914131-39-7, C05). Torah Umesorah.

Galusha, David. The First Christmas. LC 81-82147. (Illus.). 32p. 1981. wkbk. 3.95 (ISBN 0-87973-662-3, 662). Our Sunday Visitor.

Galvin, John P., tr. see Lohfink, Gerhard.

Galvin, John P., tr. see Theissen, Gerd.

Gama, Roberto, tr. from Eng. Diccionario Biblico Arqueologico. Pfeiffer, Charles F., ed. Tr. of The Biblical World - A Dictionary of Biblical Archaelolgy. (Span.). 768p. 1982. 29.95 (ISBN 0-311-03667-8). Casa Bautista.

Gama, Roberto, tr. see Graham, Ruth B.

Gamache, H. Eighth, Ninth & Tenth Books of Moses. 4.95x (ISBN 0-685-21888-0). Wehman.

Gamanovitch, Hieromonk A. Grammatika Tserkovno-Slavjanskago Jazika. Tr. of Church Slavonic Grammer. 264p. 1984. pap. text ed. 9.00 (ISBN 0-317-30313-9). Holy Trinity.

Gambaci, Elio. Religious Life. 25.00 (ISBN 0-8198-6416-1). Dghtrs St Paul.

Gambari, Elio. Updating of Religious Formation. LC 75-98171. 1969. pap. 2.00 (ISBN 0-8198-0168-2). Dghtrs St Paul.

Gambhirananda, tr. from Sanskrit. Sruti Gita: The Song of the Srutis. 99p. 1982. pap. 4.95 (ISBN 0-87481-510-X). Vedanta Pr.

Gambhirananda, Swami. History of the Ramakrishna Math & Mission. rev. ed. 344p. 1983. 10.00 (ISBN 0-87481-215-1, Pub. by Advaita Ashram India). Vedanta Pr.

--Holy Mother, Sri Sarada Devi. (Illus.). 8.95 (ISBN 0-87481-434-0). Vedanta Pr.

Gambhirananda, Swami, ed. Apostles of Ramakrishna. (Illus.). 6.95x (ISBN 0-87481-098-1). Vedanta Pr.

Gambhirananda, Swami, tr. from Sanskrit. Aitereya Upanishad. (Upanishads with Shankara's Commentary Ser.). 75p. 1980. pap. 1.25 (ISBN 0-87481-200-3). Vedanta Pr.

--Katha Upanishad. (Upanishads with Shankara's Commentary Ser.). 136p. pap. 2.95 (ISBN 0-87481-201-1). Vedanta Pr.

--Mandukya Upanishad. (Upanishads with Shankara's Commentary Ser.). 240p. 1980. pap. 3.50 (ISBN 0-87481-202-X). Vedanta Pr.

--Mundaka Upanishad with Commentary of Shankara. 100p. pap. 1.25 (ISBN 0-87481-203-8). Vedanta Pr.

--Prasna Upanishad. (Upanishads with Shankara's Commentary Ser.). 104p. 1980. pap. 2.25 (ISBN 0-87481-204-6). Vedanta Pr.

Gambhirananda, Swami, tr. see Shankara.

Gambhirananda, Swami, tr. see Shivananda, Swami.

Gambill, Henrietta. Are You Listening? LC 84-7026. (Illus.). 32p. 1984. lib. bdg. 7.45 (ISBN 0-89693-221-4). Dandelion Hse.

--Are You Listening? LC 85-10349. (A New Values Ser.). (Illus.). 32p. 1985. PLB 7.45 (ISBN 0-89565-332-X). Childs World.

--How God Gives Us Popcorn. (Happy Days Bks.). (Illus.). 24p. 1984. 1.59 (ISBN 0-87239-739-4, 3709). Standard Pub.

Gambill, Henrietta D. Seven Special Days. (Happy Day Bks.). (Illus.). 32p. 1987. 1.59 (ISBN 0-87403-281-4, 3781). Standard Pub.

Gambill, Sandra & Ashley, Clara. Missions Studies: Mexico. pap. 1.00 (ISBN 0-89114-095-6). Baptist Pub Hse.

--Missions Studies: Taiwan. pap. 1.00 (ISBN 0-89114-123-5). Baptist Pub Hse.

--Missions Studies: The Philippines. (Vacation Bible School Ser.). (Illus.). 32p. (Orig.). 1981. pap. 1.00 (ISBN 0-89114-105-7). Baptist Pub Hse.

Gamble, Eliza B. The God-Idea of the Ancients: Or Sex in Religion. LC 79-66997. 339p. 1981. Repr. of 1897 ed. 30.00 (ISBN 0-8305-0110-X). Hyperion Conn.

Gamble, Harry Y. The New Testament Canon: Its Making & Meaning. LC 85-4509. (Guides to Biblical Scholarship Ser.). 96p. 1985. pap. 4.50 (ISBN 0-8006-0470-9). Fortress.

Gamblin, Eleanor & Morehouse, Joyce M. The Sparrow's Song. Wallace, Mary H., ed. 192p. (Orig.). 1984. pap. 5.95 (ISBN 0-912315-68-7). Word Aflame.

Gambrell, Mary L. Ministerial Training in Eighteenth-Century New England. (Columbia University. Studies in the Social Sciences: No. 428). Repr. of 1937 ed. 16.50 (ISBN 0-404-51428-6). AMS Pr.

Gamer, Helena M., jt. auth. see McNeill, John T.

Gamm, David. Child's Play. LC 78-51069. (Illus.). 96p. 1978. pap. 4.95 (ISBN 0-87793-150-X). Ave Maria.

Gammie, John G. Daniel. (Preaching Guides Ser.). 116p. 1983. pap. 5.95 (ISBN 0-8042-3224-5). John Knox.

Gammie, John G., ed. Israelite Wisdom: Theological & Literary Essays in Honor of Samuel Terrien. LC 77-17862. 1978. pap. 18.00 (ISBN 0-89130-208-5, 00-16-03). Scholars Pr GA.

Gamoran, Emanuel. Changing Conceptions in Jewish Education. facsimile ed. LC 74-27986. (Modern Jewish Experience Ser.). 1975. Repr. of 1924 ed. 36.50x (ISBN 0-405-06713-5). Ayer Co Pubs.

Gamoran, Mamie G. Fun Ways to Holidays. 1951. pap. 2.00 (ISBN 0-8074-0136-6, 321400). UAHC.

Gamshirananda, Swami, tr. from Sanskrit. Chandogya Upanishad. 690p. 1987. 16.00 (ISBN 0-87481-416-2, Pub. by Advaita Ashram India). Vedanta Pr.

Gandhi, Kishore. The Evolution of Consciousness: A Contemporary Mythic Journey into the Roots of Global Awareness. (Patterns of World Spirituality Ser.). 272p. 1986. pap. 11.95 (ISBN 0-913757-50-0, Pub. by New Era Bks). Paragon Hse.

Gandhi, M. K. All Men Are Brothers. (Modern Classics of Peace Ser). pap. 7.95 (ISBN 0-912018-15-1). World Without War.

--Ashram Observances in Action. 151p. 1983. pap. 1.00 (ISBN 0-934676-36-4). Greenlf Bks.

--An Autobiography: Or, the Story of My Experiments with Truth. 2nd ed. Desai, Mahadev, tr. from Gujarati. 432p. 1983. 8.00 (ISBN 0-934676-40-2). Greenlf Bks.

--Delhi Diary: Daily Talks at Prayer Meetings, 1947-1948. 426p. 1982. 7.50 (ISBN 0-934676-56-9). Greenlf Bks.

--Discourses on the Gita. 73p. (Orig.). 1983. pap. 1.50 (ISBN 0-934676-55-0). Greenlf Bks.

--The Gospel of Selfless Action or the Gita According to Gandhi. Desai, Mahadev, ed. 1985. pap. 11.00x (ISBN 0-8364-1397-0, Pub. by Navajivan). South Asia Bks.

--My Religion. Kumarappa, B., ed. 178p. (Orig.). 1983. pap. 5.00 (ISBN 0-934676-54-2). Greenlf Bks.

Gandhi, M. K. & Tagore, Rabindranath. Tagore-Gandhi Controversy. Prabhu, R. K., ed. 155p. (Orig.). 1983. pap. 2.00 (ISBN 0-934676-52-6). Greenlf Bks.

Gandhi, M. K., pref. by. The Bhagavadgita. 14.50 (ISBN 0-86516-179-8). Bolchazy-Carducci.

Gandhi, Mohandas K. The Bhagavad Gita: An Interpretation. Parikh, Narahari D., ed. 309p. (Orig.). 1984. pap. 8.00 (ISBN 0-934676-65-8). Greenlf Bks.

--The Message of Jesus Christ. Hingorani, A. T., ed. 64p. (Orig.). 1980. pap. 1.25 (ISBN 0-934676-20-8). Greenlf Bks.

Gandhi, Rajmohan. Eight Lives: A Study of the Hindu-Muslim Encounter. 320p. 1986. 39.50x (ISBN 0-88706-196-6); pap. 14.95x (ISBN 0-88706-197-4). State U NY Pr.

Gandolfo, Joseph B. Spiritual Psychic Healing: A Comparative Psychological & Biblical Study. 1986. 6.95 (ISBN 0-533-06839-8). Vantage.

Gandy, Tillie H. Of Cabbages & Kings. 1983. 6.50 (ISBN 0-8062-2138-0). Carlton.

Gandy, Tilly H. Ears to Hear. 1984. 6.95 (ISBN 0-8062-2293-X). Carlton.

--Ten True Tales of Reincarnation. 1984. 6.00 (ISBN 0-8062-2292-1). Carlton.

Gandz, Solomon, tr. see Maimonides, Moses.

Ganesan, K., tr. see Muhaiyaddeen, Bawa.

Ganesan, R., tr. see Muhaiyaddeen, Bawa.

Gang, Arthur, jt. auth. see Gang, Miriam.

Gang, Miriam & Gang, Arthur. The Gang's Weigh. 88p. (Orig.). 1986. pap. 9.95 (ISBN 0-941850-24-2). Sunday Pubns.

Gangadharan, N., tr. from Sanskirt. Agnipurana, 4 pts, Pt. III. (Ancient Indian Tradition & Mythology: Vol. 29). 210p. 1986. 18.50 (ISBN 81-208-0174-1, Pub. by Motilal Banarsidass India). Orient Bk Dist.

Gange, Robert. Origins & Destiny: A Scientist Examines God's Handiwork. 192p. 1986. 12.95 (ISBN 0-8499-0447-1, 0447-1). Word Bks.

Gangel, Elizabeth & McDaniel, Elsiebeth. You Can Reach Families Through Their Babies. 64p. 1976. pap. 3.50 (ISBN 0-88207-140-8). Victor Bks.

Gangel, Elizabeth, jt. auth. see Gangel, Kenneth.

Gangel, Kenneth. You Can Be an Effective Sunday School Superintendent. 64p. 1981. pap. 3.50 (ISBN 0-88207-141-6). Victor Bks.

Gangel, Kenneth & Gangel, Elizabeth. Building a Christian Family: A Guide for Parents. (Orig.). 1987. pap. 6.95 (ISBN 0-8024-1506-7). Moody.

Gangel, Kenneth O. Building Leaders for Church Education. 1981. 21.95 (ISBN 0-8024-1592-X). Moody.

--The Church Education Handbook. 300p. 1985. pap. 9.95 (ISBN 0-89693-602-3). Victor Bks.

--The Family First. pap. 3.50 (ISBN 0-88469-106-3). BMH Bks.

--Lessons in Leadership from the Bible. 1980. pap. 5.95 (ISBN 0-88469-109-8). BMH Bks.

--So You Want to Be a Leader. pap. 2.95 (ISBN 0-87509-131-8); leaders guide 2.00 (ISBN 0-87509-298-5). Chr Pubns.

--Understanding Teaching. LC 68-24579. 96p. 1979. pap. text ed. 4.95 (ISBN 0-910566-14-3); Perfect bdg. instr's. guide 5.95 (ISBN 0-910566-26-7). Evang Tchr.

--Unwrap Your Spiritual Gifts. 120p. 1983. pap. 4.95 (ISBN 0-88207-102-5). Victor Bks.

Gangel, Kenneth O. & Benson, Warren S. Christian Education: Its History & Philosophy. 1983. 18.95 (ISBN 0-8024-3561-0). Moody.

Gangopadhyaya, M., tr. Nyaya: Gautama's Nyaya Sutra with Vatsyayana's Commentary. 1983. 28.50x (ISBN 0-8364-1000-9, Pub. by Indian Stud). South Asia Bks.

Gangstad, John E. Great Pyramid: Signs in the Sun (Pyramid Design & Prophecy: Second Advent) LC 76-24077. (Illus.). 200p. 1976. 1980-86 supplement 3.00 (ISBN 0-9603374-2-3). Di-Tri Bks.

Ganin, Zvi. Truman, American Jewry, & Israel, 1945-1948. 238p. 1979. text ed. 34.50x (ISBN 0-8419-0401-4); pap. 22.50 (ISBN 0-8419-0497-9). Holmes & Meier.

Gannett, William C. Ezra Stiles Gannett: Unitarian Minister in Boston, 1824-1871. 1979. Repr. of 1875 ed. lib. bdg. 30.00 (ISBN 0-8492-4932-5). R West.

Gannon, Michael V. Cross in the Sand: The Early Catholic Church in Florida, 1513-1870. LC 83-10498. 1965. pap. 12.00 (ISBN 0-8130-0776-3). U Presses Fla.

Gannon, Thomas M. & Traub, George W. The Desert & the City: An Interpretation of the History of Christian Spirituality. 338p. 1984. 8.95 (ISBN 0-8294-0452-X). Loyola.

Gannon, Thomas M., ed. The Catholic Challenge to the American Economy: Reflections on the Bishops Pastoral Letter on Catholic Social Teaching & the U. S. Economy. 352p. 24.95 (ISBN 0-02-911260-5). Macmillan.

Gannon, Thomas S., ed. The Catholic Challenge to the American Economy: Reflections on the Bishops' Pastoral Letter on Catholic Social Teaching & the U. S. Economy. 352p. 1987. pap. 14.95 (ISBN 0-02-911270-2, Collier). Macmillan.

Gannon, Timothy J. Emotional Development & Spiritual Growth. pap. 0.75 (ISBN 0-8199-0386-8, L38135). Franciscan Herald.

Ganoczy, Alexandre. An Introduction to Catholic Sacramental Theology. 1984. pap. 8.95 (ISBN 0-8091-2568-4). Paulist Pr.

Ganong, William F., ed. see Le Clercq, Chretien.

Gans, Manfred, ed. Yeshiva Children Write Poetry: From the Heart We Sing. 6.95 (ISBN 0-914131-76-1, D43). Torah Umesorah.

Gans, Mozes Heiman. Memorbook: Pictorial History of Dutch Jewry from the Renaissance to 1940. (Illus.). 852p. 1983. 125.00x (ISBN 0-8143-1749-9). Wayne St U Pr.

Ganss, G. E., frwd. by see Pousset, Edouard.

Ganss, G. E., ed. see Schutte, Josef F.

Ganss, G. E., et al, trs. see Arrupe, Pedro.

Ganss, George E. The Jesuit Educational Tradition & Saint Louis University: Some Bearings for the University's Sesquicentennial, 1818-1968. LC 75-87922. (Illus.). 70p. 1969. 3.25 (ISBN 0-912422-02-5). Inst Jesuit.

--Saint Ignatius' Idea of a Jesuit University. 2nd ed. (Illus.). 1956. pap. 16.95 (ISBN 0-87462-437-1). Marquette.

Ganss, George E., ed. Jesuit Religious Life Today: The Principal Features of its Spirit, in Excerpts... from Official Documents. LC 77-78816. (Jesuit Primary Sources in English Translation Ser.: No. 3). 190p. 1977. pap. 3.00 (ISBN 0-912422-27-0). Inst Jesuit.

Ganss, George E., frwd. by see Arrupe, Pedro.

Ganss, George E., ed. see Bangert, William V.

Ganss, George E., frwd. by see Clancy, Thomas H.

Ganss, George E., ed. see Clancy, Thomas H.

Ganss, George E., frwd. by see Dalmases, Candido de.

Ganss, George E., ed. see Fleming, David L.

Ganss, George E., ed. see Gruenberg, Gladys W.

Ganss, George E., ed. see Iparraguirre, Ignacio.

Ganss, George E., ed. see Mason, Sr. M. Elizabeth.

Ganss, George E., ed. see Stanley, David M.

Ganss, George E., frwd. by see Stanley, David M.

Ganss, George E., ed. see Toner, Jules J.

Ganss, George E., tr. & commentary by see Ignatius Of Loyola, St.

Ganstad, Edwin S., ed. see Olson, Adolf.

Gantz, Jeffrey. Early Irish Myths & Sagas. (Pengiun Classic Ser.). 1982. pap. 4.95 (ISBN 0-14-044397-5). Penguin.

--Early Irish Myths & Sagas. 250p. 1985. 14.95 (ISBN 0-88029-038-2, Pub. by Dorset Pr). Hippocrene Bks.

Ganz, Yaffa. Follow the Moon: A Journey Through the Jewish Year. 1984. 8.95 (ISBN 0-87306-369-4). Feldheim.

--The Gift That Grew. 1986. 8.95 (ISBN 0-87306-422-4). Feldheim.

--Our Jerusalem. (Illus.). 1979. pap. 3.50x (ISBN 0-87441-308-7). Behrman.

--Who Knows One? A Book of Jewish Numbers. 1981. 8.95 (ISBN 0-87306-285-X). Feldheim.

Ganzfried, Solomon. Code of Jewish Law: Kitzur Shulhan Arukh, 4 vols. Goldin, Hyman E., tr. (Eng. & Hebrew.). 1961. Set. 49.50 (ISBN 0-88482-412-8). Hebrew Pub.

GAP Committee on Psychiatry & Religion. Mysticism: Spiritual Quest or Psychic Disorder, Vol. 9. LC 76-45931. (Report: No. 97). 1976. pap. 5.00 (ISBN 0-87318-134-4, Pub. by GAP). Brunner-Mazel.

--The Psychic Function of Religion in Mental Illness & Health, Vol. 6. LC 62-2872. (Report: No. 67). 1968. pap. 5.00 (ISBN 0-87318-092-5, Pub. by GAP). Brunner-Mazel.

Gar, Josef. Biblyografye Fun Artiklen Vegn Khurbn un Gvure. Incl. Vol. 1. LC 67-2416. (Yad Vashem-Yivo Joint Documentary Projects Bibliographical Ser.: No.). 306p. 1966. 10.00 (ISBN 0-914512-22-6); Vol. 2. (Yad Vashem-Yivo Joint Documentary Projects Bibliographical Ser.: No. 10). 338p. 1969. 15.00 (ISBN 0-914512-10-2). Yivo Inst.

Gar, Josef & Friedman, Philip. Biblyografye Fun Yidishe Bikher Vegn Khurbn un Gvure. (Yad Vashem-Yivo Joint Documentary Projects Bibliographical Ser.: No. 3). (Yiddish.). 330p. 1962. 10.00 (ISBN 0-914512-12-9, HE-65-1134). Yivo Inst.

Gara, Larry. War Resistance in Historical Perspective. 1983. pap. 2.50x (ISBN 0-87574-171-1, 171). Pendle Hill.

Garbe, Richard. India & Christendom: The Historical Connections Between Their Religions. Robinson, Lydia, tr. from Ger. 321p. 1959. 22.95 (ISBN 0-87548-232-5). Open Court.

Garbee, Ed & Van Dyke, Henry. Dramas De Navidad. Prince, Soledad G. & Castellon, Guillermo, trs. 1981. pap. 1.50 (ISBN 0-311-08214-9). Casa Bautista.

Garber, Bernard J. Shards from the Heart: A Spiritual Odyssey in Twentieth Century America. LC 64-13358. (Freedeeds Library). 160p. 1965. 8.00 (ISBN 0-89345-004-9, Freedeeds Bks). Garber Comm.

Garber, Bernard J., ed. see Steiner, Rudolf.

Garber, Bernard J., ed. see Steiner, Rudolf & Schure, Edward.

Garber, Marjorie, ed. Cannibals, Witches, & Divorce: Estranging the Renaissance. LC 86-45472. (Selected Papers from the English Institute, 1985 New Ser.: No. 11). 256p. 1987. text ed. 19.50x (ISBN 0-8018-3405-8). Johns Hopkins.

Garber, Zev, ed. Methodology in the Academic Teaching of Judaism. (Studies in Judaism). 308p. (Orig.). 1987. lib. bdg. 28.00 (ISBN 0-8191-5723-6, Pub. by Studies in Judaism); pap. text ed. 15.75 (ISBN 0-8191-5724-4). U Pr of Amer.

Garcia, Jo, ed. Walking on the Water: Women Talk about Spirituality. Maitland, Sara. (Illus.). 224p. 1984. pap. 5.95 (ISBN 0-86068-381-8, Pub by Virago Pr). Salem Hse Pubs.

Garcia Icazbalceta, Joaquin. Obras de Joaquin Garcia Icazbalceta, 10 vols. LC 68-58758. (Span). 1969. Repr. of 1898 ed. Set. 225.00 (ISBN 0-8337-1798-7). B Franklin.

Garcia-Treto, Francisco O., jt. auth. see Brackenridge, R. Douglas.

Gard, Richard A., ed. Buddhism. LC 61-15499. (Great Religions of Modern Man Ser). 1976. 8.95 (ISBN 0-8076-0166-7). Braziller.

Gardella, Peter. Innocent Ecstasy: How Christianity Gave America an Ethic of Sexual Pleasure. LC 84-27253. (Illus.). 1985. 17.95 (ISBN 0-19-503612-3). Oxford U Pr.

Gardiner, George E. La Catastrofe de Corinto. Orig. Title: The Corinthian Catastrophe. (Span.). 64p. 1976. pap. 2.25 (ISBN 0-8254-1254-4). Kregel.

--The Corinthian Catastrophe. LC 74-75106. 64p. 1975. pap. 2.95 (ISBN 0-8254-2708-8). Kregel.

Gardiner, Harold C. Mysteries' End: An Investigation of the Last Days of the Medieval Religious Stage. LC 67-26652. (Yale Studies in English Ser.: No. 103). xiv, 139p. 1967. Repr. of 1946 ed. 21.50 (ISBN 0-208-00385-1, Archon). Shoe String.

Gardiner, James J. & Roberts, J. Deotis, eds. Quest for a Black Theology. LC 76-151250. 128p. 1971. 6.95 (ISBN 0-8298-0196-0). Pilgrim NY.

Gardiner, M. James. Program Evaluation in Church Organization. LC 77-80070. (Management Ser.). (Illus.). 1977. pap. 4.50 (ISBN 0-89305-017-2). Anna Pub.

Gardiner, Samuel R. Cromwell's Place in History. LC 76-94270. (Select Bibliographies Reprint Ser). 1897. 15.00 (ISBN 0-8369-5044-5). Ayer Co Pubs.

--The First Two Stuarts & the Puritan Revolution: 1603-1660. 1977. Repr. of 1891 ed. lib. bdg. 25.00 (ISBN 0-8495-1911-X). Arden Lib.

--Oliver Cromwell. 1977. Repr. of 1909 ed. 25.00x (ISBN 0-7158-1181-9). Charles River Bks.

Gardiner, Samuel R., ed. Documents Relating to the Proceedings Against William Prynne, in 1634 & 1637. Repr. of 1877 ed. 27.00 (ISBN 0-384-17635-6). Johnson Repr.

Gardiner, Stephen. Obedience in Church & State: Three Political Tracts. Janelle, Pierre, ed. LC 68-19272. 1968. Repr. of 1930 ed. lib. bdg. 22.50x (ISBN 0-8371-0081-X, GABW). Greenwood.

Gardner, A. Synesius of Cyrene: Philosopher & Bishop. 1977. lib. bdg. 59.95 (ISBN 0-8490-2697-0). Gordon Pr.

Gardner, Alice. Theodore of Studium, His Life & Times 759-826. 1905. 19.50 (ISBN 0-8337-1280-2). B Franklin.

Gardner, Anna Marie, ed. see Chandler, Robert, et al.

Gardner, Dame H. Religion & Literature. 1983. pap. text ed. 9.95x (ISBN 0-19-812824-X). Oxford U Pr.

Gardner, Daniel K. Chu Hsi & the Ta-hsueh: Neo-Confucian Reflection on the Confucian Canon. (Harvard East Asian Monographs: No. 118). 300p. 1985. text ed. 20.00x (ISBN 0-674-13065-0, Pub. by Coun East Asian Stud). Harvard U Pr.

Gardner, Dudley. Angel with a Bushy Beard. 1980. pap. 8.95x (ISBN 0-7152-0425-4). Outlook.

Gardner, E. Saint Catherine of Siena: A Study in the Religion, Literature & History of the Fourteenth Century in Italy. 1976. lib. bdg. 59.95 (ISBN 0-8490-2557-5). Gordon Pr.

Gardner, E. Clinton. Biblical Faith & Social Ethics. 1960. text ed. 23.50 scp (ISBN 0-06-042240-8, HarpC). Har-Row.

--Christocentrism in Christian Social Ethics: A Depth Study of Eight Modern Protestants. LC 82-21843. 264p. (Orig.). 1983. lib. bdg. 28.50 (ISBN 0-8191-2954-2); pap. text ed. 13.50 (ISBN 0-8191-2955-0). U Pr of Amer.

Gardner, E. G. Dante & the Mystics: A Study of the Mystical Aspect of the Divina Commedia. LC 68-24952. (Studies in Italian Literature, No. 46). 1969. Repr. of 1913 ed. lib. bdg. 49.95x (ISBN 0-8383-0271-8). Haskell.

Gardner, E. G., ed. see Richard Of St. Victor, et al.

Gardner, Edmund G. Dukes & Poets of Ferrara: A Story in the Poetry, Religion & Politics of Fifteenth & Early Sixteenth Centuries. LC 78-145033. xiv, 578p. 1972. Repr. of 1904 ed. 39.00x (ISBN 0-403-00776-3). Scholarly.

Gardner, Edward L. The Play of Consciousness in the Web of the Universe. LC 86-30006. (Illus.). 224p. 1987. pap. 7.25 (ISBN 0-8356-0236-2). Theos Pub Hse.

Gardner, Esmond, jt. ed. see Gardner, Nancy.

Gardner, Gerald B. Witchcraft Today. 1970. pap. 2.45 (ISBN 0-8065-0002-6). Citadel Pr.

Gardner, Gerard B. Witchcraft Today. (Illus.). 184p. pap. 9.95 (ISBN 0-939708-03-5). Magickal Childe.

Gardner, Helen. Limits of Literary Criticism. LC 74-16242. 1956. lib. bdg. 8.00 (ISBN 0-8414-4558-3). Folcroft.

Gardner, Hope C. & Gunnell, Sally. Teach Me in My Way: A Collection for L.D.S. Children. LC 80-84147. 1980. soft cover 5.95 (ISBN 0-913420-85-9). Olympus Pub Co.

Gardner, Johann V. Aljeksjej Theodorovich L'vov-director Imperatorskoj pridvornoj pevcheskoj kapelli i dukhovnij kompozitor. Tr. of Alexei Feodorovitch Lvov-Director of the Emperors Court Capella & Composer of Sacred Music. 90p. 1970. pap. 3.00 (ISBN 0-317-30387-2). Holy Trinity.

--Alliluija (Liturgijnaja), 8-mi Glasov. Tr. of Alleluia (for Divine Liturgy) Eight Tones. 1966. pap. 3.00 (ISBN 0-317-30391-0). Holy Trinity.

--Bogosluzhebncje Penije Russkoj Pravoslavnoj Tserkvi: Suschnost' Sistema I Istoria: Liturgical Chant of the Russian Orthodox Church: Its Essence, Structure & History, Vol. 1. LC 77-77086. (Rus., Illus., Orig.). 1979. text ed. 30.00 (ISBN 0-88465-008-1); pap. text ed. 25.00 (ISBN 0-686-50014-8). Holy Trinity.

--Bogosluzhebnoje Penije Russkoj Pravoslavnoj Tserkvi: Istorija, Vol. 2. LC 77-77086. Tr. of Liturgical Chant of the Russian Orthodox Church; History. (Illus.). 1981. text ed. 30.00 (ISBN 0-88465-010-3); pap. text ed. 25.00 (ISBN 0-317-30384-8). Holy Trinity.

--Dostojino Jest', 8-mi glasov, znamennago rospjeva. Tr. of It is Truly Meet, Eight Tones, Znamenny Chant. 1967. pap. 3.00 (ISBN 0-317-30397-X). Holy Trinity.

Gardner, Johannes von see Von Gardner, Johann.

Gardner, John C. The Construction of the Wakefield Cycle. LC 74-5191. (Literary Structures Ser.). 173p. 1974. 8.95x (ISBN 0-8093-0668-9). S Ill U Pr.

Gardner, Leonard. Genesis: The Teacher's Guide. 1966. pap. 6.50 (ISBN 0-8381-0401-0). United Syn Bk.

Gardner, Lynn, ed. see Wilson, Seth.

Gardner, Malcolm, et al, eds. see Bockemuhl, Jochen, et al.

Gardner, Nancy & Gardner, Esmond, eds. Five Great Healers Speak Here. LC 82-50164. (Illus.). 138p. (Orig.). 1982. pap. 6.25 (ISBN 0-8356-0567-1, Quest). Theos Pub Hse.

Gardner, Percy. Principles of Christian Art. 1977. lib. bdg. 59.95 (ISBN 0-8490-2479-X). Gordon Pr.

Gardyne, Alexander. A Theatre of Scottish Worthies, & the Lyf, Doings & Deathe of William Elphinston, Bishop of Aberdee. Repr. of 1878 ed. 40.00 (ISBN 0-384-17655-0). Johnson Repr.

Garfield, Leon. The King in the Garden. LC 84-10064. (Illus.). 32p. 1985. 11.75 (ISBN 0-688-04106-X). Lothrop.

Garfield, Samuel. The Immortality of the Soul & the Perfectibility of Man. (Illus.). 1977. 45.00 (ISBN 0-89266-026-0). Am Classical Coll Pr.

--The Life of the Spirit: The Immortality of the Soul & the Perfectibility of Man. (Illus.). 1978. deluxe bdg. 41.45 (ISBN 0-930582-04-7). Gloucester Art.

Garfield, Viola E. & Forrest, Linn A. Wolf & the Raven: Totem Poles of Southeastern Alaska. 2nd ed. LC 49-8492. (Illus.). 161p. 1961. pap. 8.95 (ISBN 0-295-73998-3). U of Wash Pr.

Garin, Eugenio. Astrology in the Renaissance. Jackson, Carolyn & Allen, June, trs. from Ital. Tr. of Lo Zodiaco Della Vita. 160p. 1983. 21.95 (ISBN 0-7100-9259-8). Methuen Inc.

Garis, M. R. Martha Root: Lioness at the Threshold. LC 83-3913. (Illus.). 500p. 1983. 22.95 (ISBN 0-87743-184-1); pap. 15.95 (ISBN 0-87743-185-X). Baha'i.

Garland, D. David. Amos: Bible Study Commentary. 96p. 1973. pap. 4.95 (ISBN 0-310-24833-7, 9696P). Zondervan.

--Hosea: Bible Study Commentary. 128p. 1975. pap. 4.95 (ISBN 0-310-24843-4, 10234P). Zondervan.

--Isaiah: Bible Study Commentary. (Orig.). 1968. pap. 4.95 (ISBN 0-310-24853-1, 9672P). Zondervan.

--Job: Bible Study Commentary. 160p. 1971. pap. 4.95 (ISBN 0-310-24863-9, 9671P). Zondervan.

Garland, David E., jt. auth. see Richmond-Garland, Diana S.

Garland, Robert. The Greek Way of Death. LC 85-470. (Illus.). 208p. 1985. text ed. 22.50x (ISBN 0-8014-1823-2). Cornell U Pr.

Garlett, Marti W. Who Will Be My Teacher? The Christian Way to Stronger Schools. 256p. 1985. 12.95 (ISBN 0-8499-0471-4, 0471-4). Word Bks.

Garlock, H. B. Before We Kill & Eat You. 1.95 (ISBN 0-89985-109-6). Christ Nations.

Garlow, James. Partners in Ministry. (Illus.). 195p. (Orig.). 1981. pap. 4.95 (ISBN 0-8341-0693-0). Beacon Hill.

Garlow, James L. LITE Manual. 177p. 1982. pap. 6.95 spiral binding (ISBN 0-8341-0883-6, S-2000); Leader's Guide 14.95. Beacon Hill.

Garlow, Willa R. Jesus Is a Special Person. LC 85-24361. (Bible & Me Ser.). (Illus.). 1986. 5.95 (ISBN 0-8054-4166-2). Broadman.

Garner, Robert H. The Way of St. Francis. 1984. 6.95 (ISBN 0-8062-1605-0). Carlton.

Garnett, Constance, tr. see Dostoyevsky, Fyodor.

Garnett, Constance, tr. see Tolstoy, Leo.

Garnett, Lucy M. Mysticism & Magic in Turkey: An Account of the Religious Doctrines, Monastic Organisation & Ecstatic Powers of the Dervish Orders. LC 77-87628. (Illus.). Repr. of 1912 ed. 22.00 (ISBN 0-404-16453-6). AMS Pr.

Garnett, Paul. Salvation & Atonement in the Qumran Scrolls. 160p. 1977. pap. 24.00x (Pub. by J C B Mohr BRD). Coronet Bks.

Garnett, R. The Age of Dryden. 1977. Repr. of 1909 ed. lib. bdg. 17.50 (ISBN 0-8495-1902-0). Arden Lib.

Garnett, Richard. The Age of Dryden. facsimile ed. LC 70-164601. (Select Bibliographies Reprint Ser). Repr. of 1895 ed. 20.00 (ISBN 0-8369-5885-3). Ayer Co Pubs.

--The Age of Dryden. 1973. Repr. of 1895 ed. 17.50 (ISBN 0-8274-1280-0). R West.

--Life of Emerson. LC 73-21630. (American Biography Ser., No. 32). 1974. lib. bdg. 49.95x (ISBN 0-8383-1775-8). Haskell.

--Life of John Milton. LC 77-112638. Repr. of 1890 ed. 10.00 (ISBN 0-404-02686-9). AMS Pr.

--Life of John Milton. 1890. lib. bdg. 9.75 (ISBN 0-8414-4638-5). Folcroft.

--Life of Ralph Waldo Emerson. LC 73-12352. 1972. Repr. of 1888 ed. lib. bdg. 12.50 (ISBN 0-8414-4404-8). Folcroft.

--Prose of Milton. 1894. Repr. 20.00 (ISBN 0-8274-3214-3). R West.

Garnier, Freres. Catalogue General des Ouvrages Edites Par l'Abbe Migne. LC 71-168926. 1967. Repr. of 1885 ed. 22.50 (ISBN 0-8337-2386-3). B Franklin.

Garnier, H. L' Idee du Juste Prix Chez les Theologiens et Cannonistes du Moyen Age. LC 79-122228. (Fr.). 164p. 1973. Repr. of 1900 ed. lib. bdg. 20.50 (ISBN 0-8337-1286-1). B Franklin.

Garnier, J. Worship of the Dead: The Origin & Nature of Pagan Idolatry & Its Bearing Upon the Early History of Egypt & Babylonia. LC 77-85617. 1977. Repr. of 1904 ed. lib. bdg. 50.00 (ISBN 0-89341-300-3). Longwood Pub Group.

Garnier, J. C., jt. auth. see Poussin, J. C.

Garraghan, Gilbert J. The Jesuits of the Middle United States, 3 vols. 162.00 (ISBN 0-405-10831-1, 11838). Ayer Co Pubs.

--Prose Studies in Newman. 1915. Repr. 25.00 (ISBN 0-8274-3216-X). R West.

Garrand, Victor. Augustine Laure, S. J., Missionary to the Yakimas. 36p. 1977. 8.00_o.s.i (ISBN 0-87770-176-8); pap. 5.95 (ISBN 0-87770-187-3). Ye Galleon.
Garret-Jones, John. Tales & Teaching of the Buddha. 1979. 18.95 (ISBN 0-04-294104-0). Allen Unwin.
Garrett, Arthur. The Folk of Christendom. LC 79-92433. 500p. 1981. 49.95 (ISBN 0-8022-2363-X). Philos Lib.
--The Noble Romans. LC 86-30240. 550p. 1987. 34.95 (ISBN 0-8022-2528-4). Philos Lib.
Garrett, Clarke. Respectable Folly: Millenarians and the French Revolution in France and England. LC 74-24378. 252p. 1975. 26.00x (ISBN 0-8018-1618-1). Johns Hopkins.
--Spirit Possession & Popular Religion: From the Camisards to the Shakers. LC 86-46284. 288p. 1987. text ed. 29.50x (ISBN 0-8018-3486-4). Johns Hopkins.
Garrett, James L., Jr. & Hinson, E. Glenn. Are Southern Baptists "Evangelicals"? LC 82-18870. 247p. 1983. 14.95 (ISBN 0-86554-033-0, MUP-H44). Mercer Univ Pr.
Garrett, Leroy. The Stone-Campbell Movement. LC 80-65965. 739p. 1981. 21.95 (ISBN 0-89900-059-2). College Pr Pub.
Garrett, Paul D. St. Innocent: Apostle to America. LC 79-19634. 345p. 1979. pap. 8.95 (ISBN 0-913836-60-5). St Vladimirs.
Garrett, Shirley. Social Reformers in Urban China: The Chinese Y. M. C. A., Eighteen Ninety-Five to Nineteen Twenty-Six. LC 74-133218. (East Asian Ser.: No. 56). 1970. 16.50x (ISBN 0-674-81220-4). Harvard U Pr.
Garrett, Willis O. Church Ushers' Manual. 64p. pap. 2.50 (ISBN 0-8007-8456-1, Spire Bks.). Revell.
Garrigou-Lagrange, R. The Three Ways of the Spiritual Life. 1977. pap. 3.00 (ISBN 0-89555-017-2). TAN Bks Pubs.
Garrison, Eileen & Albanese, Gayle. Eucharistic Manual for Children. LC 84-60217. (Illus.). 28p. (Orig.). 1984. pap. 3.95 (ISBN 0-8192-1343-8). Morehouse.
Garrison, James. The Darkness of God: Theology after Hiroshima. LC 83-1415. pap. 62.00 (ISBN 0-317-30139-X, 2025322). Bks Demand UMI.
Garrison, Jayne. The Christian Working Mother's Handbook. 144p. 1986. pap. 7.95 (ISBN 0-8423-0258-1). Tyndale.
Garrison, Omar V. The Hidden Story of Scientology. 8.50 (ISBN 0-8065-0440-4). Church of Scient Info.
--Jesus Loved Them. (Illus.). 133p. 1983. 19.95 (ISBN 0-931116-06-6). Ralston-Pilot.
--Playing Dirty: The Secret War Against Beliefs. 13.95 (ISBN 0-931116-04-X). Church of Scient Info.
--Playing Dirty: The Secret War Against Beliefs. LC 80-51315. (Illus.). 288p. 1980. 10.50 (ISBN 0-931116-04-X); pap. 4.95 (ISBN 0-931116-05-8). Ralston-Pilot.
--The Secret World of Interpol. 13.95 (ISBN 0-686-74638-4). Church of Scient Info.
Garrison, Vivian, jt. ed. see Crapanzano, Vincent.
Garrison, Winfred E. March of Faith: The Story of Religion in America Since 1865. LC 79-138112. 1971. Repr. of 1933 ed. lib. bdg. 22.50x (ISBN 0-8371-5688-2, GAMF). Greenwood.
Garrone, Gabriel-Marie. Poor in Spirit: Awaiting All from God. 1978. pap. 2.95 (ISBN 0-232-51337-6). Living Flame Pr.
Garrotto, Alfred J. Christ in Our Lives. (Orig.). 1980. pap. text ed. 4.95 (ISBN 0-03-056979-6, HarpR). Har-Row.
--Christians & Prayer. (Orig.). 1980. pap. text ed. 4.95 (ISBN 0-03-056981-8, HarpR). Har-Row.
--Christians Reconciling. 96p. (Orig.). 1982. pap. 4.95 (ISBN 0-86683-170-3, HarpR). Har-Row.
Garsee, Lee. New Dimensions in Puppet Ministry. 1983. pap. 5.95 (ISBN 0-89137-607-0). Quality Pubns.
Garsoian, N. G. Paulician Heresy: A Study of the Origin & Development of Paulicianism in Armenia & the Eastern Provinces of the Byzantine Empire. (Publications in Near & Middle East Ser.: No. 6). 1967. text ed. 32.80x (ISBN 90-2790-096-5). Mouton.
Garsoian, Nina & Mathews, Thomas, eds. East of Byzantium: Syria & Armenia in the Formative Period. LC 82-9665. (Dumbarton Oaks Symposium). (Illus.). 266p. 1982. 35.00x (ISBN 0-88402-104-1). Dumbarton Oaks.
Garstang, John. Joshua-Judges. LC 78-9518. (Kregel Limited Edition Library). 464p. 1978. 19.95 (ISBN 0-8254-2719-3). Kregel.
--Joshua Judges: The Foundations of Bible History. 1977. lib. bdg. 59.95 (ISBN 0-8490-2109-X). Gordon Pr.
Garth, et al, trs. see Ovid.
Garth, Helen M. Saint Mary Magdalene in Medieval Literature. LC 78-64210. (Johns Hopkins University. Studies in the Social Sciences. Sixty-Seventh Ser. 1949: 3). Repr. of 1950 ed. 15.50 (ISBN 0-404-61315-2). AMS Pr.
Garver. At Wit's End Corner. (Illus.). pap. 1.25 (ISBN 0-686-12326-3). Christs Mission.
--Our Christian Heritage. (Illus.). 4.50 (ISBN 0-935120-00-9). Christs Mission.
--Stars in the Night. pap. 2.50 (ISBN 0-935120-01-7). Christs Mission.
--Watch Your Teaching: Home Study. pap. 4.95 (ISBN 0-935120-03-3). Christs Mission.
Garver, Newton. Jesus, Jefferson & the Task of Friends. 1983. pap. 2.50x (ISBN 0-87574-251-3, 251). Pendle Hill.
Garver, William L. Brother of the Third Degree. 14.95 (ISBN 0-87505-089-1). Borden.
Garvey, Edwin C. Process Theology & Secularization. 21p. 1972. pap. 0.75 (ISBN 0-912414-14-6). Lumen Christi.
Garvey, John. The Prematurely Saved. 1986. pap. 8.95 (ISBN 0-87243-150-9). Templegate.
Garvey, John, ed. Modern Spirituality: An Anthology. 156p. 1985. 12.95 (ISBN 0-87243-132-0). Templegate.
Garvey, Sr. M. Patricia, tr. see Saint Augustine.
Garvey, Robert. First Book of Jewish Holidays. (Illus.). 1954. pap. 4.50x (ISBN 0-87068-362-4). Ktav.
Garvie, A. E. Studies in the Inner Life of Jesus. 1977. lib. bdg. 69.95 (ISBN 0-8490-2705-5). Gordon Pr.
Garvin, Harry. Literature, Arts & Religion. LC 80-70270. (Bucknell Review Ser.: Vol. 26, No. 2). (Illus.). 192p. 1982. 16.50 (ISBN 0-8387-5021-4). Bucknell U Pr.
Garvin, Joseph N., jt. ed. see Corbett, James A.
Garvy, John W., Jr. Yin & Yang: Two Hands Clapping. Liebermann, Jeremiah, ed. (Five Phase Energetics Ser.: No. 2). (Illus.). 1985. pap. 3.00 (ISBN 0-943450-01-2). Wellbeing Bks.
Gary, Barbara S. Seeking Foundation Grants. 1985. 5.65 (ISBN 0-318-18574-1). Natl Cath Educ.
Gasche, Rodolphe. The Tain of the Mirror. LC 86-4673. 384p. 1986. text ed. 25.00x (ISBN 0-674-86700-9). Harvard U Pr.
Gascoigne, Bamber. The Christians. (Illus.). 304p. 1986. pap. 15.95 (ISBN 0-224-02863-4, Pub. by Jonathan Cape). Salem Hse Pubs.
Gaskin, J. C. The Quest for Eternity: An Outline of the Philosophy of Religion. (Pelican Ser.). 192p. 1984. pap. 5.95 (ISBN 0-14-022538-2). Penguin.
Gaskin, Stephen. This Season's People: A Book of Spiritual Teachings. LC 86-159636. (Illus.). 1976. 3.00 (ISBN 0-913990-05-1). Book Pub Co.
Gasnick, Roy. Francis: Brother of the Universe. (Illus.). 1.00. Paulist Pr.
--Mother Teresa of Calcutta. 1.25. Paulist Pr.
Gasnick, Roy M., compiled By. The Francis Book: A Celebration of the Universal Saint. (Illus.). 320p. 1980. (Collier); pap. 15.95 (ISBN 0-02-003200-5). Macmillan.
Gaspar, Karl. How Long? Prison Reflections from the Philippines. Graham, Helen & Noonan, Breda, eds. LC 85-25851. 176p. (Orig.). 1986. pap. 9.95 (ISBN 0-88344-226-4). Orbis Bks.
Gaspard, Perry A. The Baptism with the Holy Spirit. 1983. pap. 1.00 (ISBN 0-931867-02-9). Abundant Life Pubns.
--The Basic Principles of Prayer. 1984. pap. 2.00 (ISBN 0-931867-07-X). Abundant Life Pubns.
--The Different Kinds of Prayer. 88p. 1984. pap. text ed. 3.00 (ISBN 0-931867-08-8). Abundant Life Pubns.
--Freedom from Fear. 1980. pap. 2.00 (ISBN 0-931867-06-1). Abundant Life Pubns.
--The Power of God's Word. 60p. 1981. pap. 2.00 (ISBN 0-931867-05-3). Abundant Life Pubns.
--The Power of the Tongue. 1983. pap. 1.50 (ISBN 0-931867-04-5). Abundant Life Pubns.
--Redeemed from the Curse. 64p. 1983. pap. 2.00 (ISBN 0-931867-03-7). Abundant Life Pubns.
--Salvation. 1983. pap. 1.00 (ISBN 0-931867-00-2). Abundant Life Pubns.
Gasper, Louis. The Fundamentalist Movement. (Twin Brooks Ser.). 181p. (Orig.). 1981. pap. 6.95 (ISBN 0-8010-3769-7). Baker Bk.
Gasperson, David. Seek-the-Verses Bible Puzzles. 48p. 1986. pap. 2.50 (ISBN 0-87403-045-5, 2689). Standard Pub.
Gasque, Ward. A History of the Criticism of the Acts of the Apostles. 334p. 1975. lib. bdg. 52.00x (Pub. by J C B Mohr BRD). Coronet Bks.
Gasquet, Cardinal. Monastic Life in the Middle Ages. 59.95 (ISBN 0-8490-0657-0). Gordon Pr.
Gasquet, Cardinal, ed. see Teresa, Saint.
Gasquet, Cardinal, tr. see Benedict, Saint.
Gasquet, Francis A. English Monastic Life. fascimile ed. LC 77-157336. (Select Bibliographies Reprint Ser.). Repr. of 1904 ed. 32.00 (ISBN 0-8369-5796-2). Ayer Co Pubs.
--English Monastic Life. LC 76-118470. 1971. Repr. of 1904 ed. 29.50x (ISBN 0-8046-1219-6, Pub. by Kennikat). Assoc Faculty Pr.
--Eve of the Reformation. LC 75-118522. 1971. Repr. of 1900 ed. 35.00x (ISBN 0-8046-1144-0, Pub. by Kennikat). Assoc Faculty Pr.
--Henry the Eighth & the English Monasteries, 2 vols. LC 74-39467. (Select Bibliography Reprint Ser.). 1972. Repr. of 1888 ed. 56.75 (ISBN 0-8369-9905-3). Ayer Co Pubs.
--Henry VIII & the English Monasteries, 2 vols. (Select Bibliographies Reprint Ser.). Repr. of 1888 ed. lib. bdg. 55.00 set (ISBN 0-8290-0849-7). Irvington.
--Monastic Life in the Middle Ages, 1792-1806. facs. ed. LC 76-137377. (Select Bibliographies Reprint Ser). 1922. 16.00 (ISBN 0-8369-5578-1). Ayer Co Pubs.
Gasquet, Francis C. Old English Bible & Other Essays. LC 68-26209. 1969. Repr. of 1897 ed. 28.50x (ISBN 0-8046-0166-6, Pub. by Kennikat). Assoc Faculty Pr.
Gassendi, Pierre. Selected Works. Brush, Craig B., tr. 1972. Repr. 45.00 (ISBN 0-384-17685-2). Johnson Repr.
Gaster, M. The Origin of the Kabbala. 1976. lib. bdg. 69.95 (ISBN 0-8490-2386-6). Gordon Pr.
--The Samaritans: History, Doctrine & Literature. 1976. lib. bdg. 134.95 (ISBN 0-8490-2563-X). Gordon Pr.
--The Samaritans: Their History, Doctrines & Literature. (British Academy, London, Schweich Lectures on Biblical Archaeology Series, 1923). pap. 28.00 (ISBN 0-8115-1265-7). Kraus Repr.
Gaster, Moses. The Chronicles of Jerahmeel. rev. ed. 1971. 35.00x (ISBN 0-87068-162-1). Ktav.
--Exempla of the Rabbis. rev. ed. 1968. 25.00x (ISBN 0-87068-055-2). Ktav.
--The Samaritan Oral Law & Ancient Traditions. LC 77-87609. Repr. of 1932 ed. 22.00 (ISBN 0-404-16433-1). AMS Pr.
--Studies & Texts in Folklore, Magic, Medieval Romance, Hebrew Apocrypha & Samaritan Archaeology, 3 Vols. rev. ed. 1970. Set. 45.00x (ISBN 0-87068-056-0). Ktav.
Gaster, Moses, tr. from Judeo-German. Ma'aseh Book: Book of Jewish Tales & Legends. LC 81-80356. 694p. 1981. pap. 10.95 (ISBN 0-8276-0189-1, 471). Jewish Pubns.
Gaster, Theodor H. The Dead Sea Scriptures. 2nd ed. LC 76-2840. 1976. pap. 7.95 (ISBN 0-385-08859-0, Anchor Pr). Doubleday.
--Festivals of the Jewish Year: A Modern Interpretation & Guide. 1971. pap. 7.95 (ISBN 0-688-06008-0). Morrow.
--Passover, Its History & Tradition. LC 83-22678. (Illus.). 102p. 1984. Repr. of 1949 ed. lib. bdg. 22.50x (ISBN 0-313-24372-7, GAPA). Greenwood.
Gaster, Theodore, ed. see Frazer, James.
Gaster, Theodore H. Myth, Legend & Custom in the Old Testament: A Comparative Study with Chapters from Sir James G. Frazer's Folklore in the Old Testament, 2 vols. Set. 36.00 (ISBN 0-8446-5189-3). Peter Smith.
Gaston, Anne-Marie. Siva in Dance, Myth & Iconography. (Illus.). 1982. 45.00x (ISBN 0-19-561354-6). Oxford U Pr.
Gaston, Hugh. A Complete Common-Place Book to the Holy Bible; or, a Scriptural Account of the Faith & Practices of Christians: Comprehending a Thorough Arrangement of the Various Texts of Scripture Bearing upon the Doctrines, Duties, & C., of Revealed Religion. 1979. Repr. of 1847 ed. lib. bdg. 15.00 (ISBN 0-8482-4186-X). Norwood Edns.
Gastoue, Amedee. L' Art Gregorien. 3rd ed. LC 77-178576. (Fr.). Repr. of 1920 ed. 21.50 (ISBN 0-404-56607-3). AMS Pr.
--Musique et Liturgie: Le Graduel et l'Antiphonaire Romains; Histoire et Description. LC 70-178577. (Fr.). Repr. of 1913 ed. 32.50 (ISBN 0-404-56608-1). AMS Pr.
--Les Origines du chant romain: L'antiphonaire Gregorien. (Fr.). Repr. of 1907 ed. 32.50 (ISBN 0-404-56609-X). AMS Pr.
Gastrell, Francis. Notitia Cestriensis, 2 Vols. in 4. Repr. of 1850 ed. Set. 92.00 (ISBN 0-384-17700-X). Johnson Repr.
Gastwirt, Harold P. Fraud Corruption & Holiness: The Controversy over the Supervision of Jewish Dietary Practice in New York City. LC 74-77649. 1974. 23.95x (ISBN 0-8046-9056-1, Pub. by Kennikat). Assoc Faculty Pr.
Gataker, Thomas. A Sparke Towards the Kindling of Sorrow for Zion. LC 76-57382. (English Experience Ser.: No. 800). 1977. Repr. of 1621 ed. lib. bdg. 7.00 (ISBN 90-221-0800-7). Walter J Johnson.
Gatens, William J. Victorian Cathedral Music in Theory & Practice. 300p. 1986. 39.50 (ISBN 0-521-26808-7). Cambridge U Pr.
Gater, George H. & Hiorns, F. R. The Parish of St. Martin-in-the Fields: Trafalgar Square & Neighborhood, Pt. 3. LC 70-37852. (London County Council. Survey of London: No. 20). Repr. of 1940 ed. 74.50 (ISBN 0-404-51670-X). AMS Pr.
Gates, Brian, ed. Afro-Caribbean Religions. 1985. 30.00x (ISBN 0-686-81323-5, Pub. by Ward Lock Educ Co Ltd). State Mutual Bk.
Gates, John E. An Analysis of the Lexicographic Resources Used by American Biblical Scholars Today. LC 72-88670. (Society of Bibical Literature. Dissertation Ser.: No. 8). pap. 49.00 (ISBN 0-317-10146-3, 2017664). Bks Demand UMI.
Gates, Larry W. Dwelling in Scullerland. LC 85-40200. 105p. (Orig.). 1985. pap. text ed. 8.95 (ISBN 0-938232-68-1). Winston-Derek.
Gates, Rebecca L. The Beauty of a Disciplined Life. 96p. 1987. pap. 4.95 (ISBN 0-89693-248-6). Victor Bks.
Gates, Susa Y. & Widtsoe, Leah D. The Life Story of Brigham Young. facsimile ed. LC 74-164602. (Select Bibliographies Reprint Ser). Repr. of 1930 ed. 24.00 (ISBN 0-8369-5886-1). Ayer Co Pubs.
Gathorne-Hardy, Robert & Williams, William P., eds. Bibliography of the Writings of Jeremy Taylor to 1700: With a Section of Tayloriana. LC 71-149932. 159p. 1971. 20.00 (ISBN 0-87580-023-8). N Ill U Pr.
Gatta, Julia. Three Spiritual Directors for Our Time: Julian of Norwich, the Cloud of Unknowing Walter Hilton. LC 86-29169. 137p. (Orig.). 1987. pap. 8.95 (ISBN 0-936384-44-1). Cowley Pubns.
Gatti, Enzo. Rich Church-Poor Church? O'Connell, Matthew, tr. from It. LC 74-77432. Orig. Title: Couli che Sa Il Dolore Dell'uomo. 138p. (Orig.). 1974. 4.95 (ISBN 0-88344-437-2). Orbis Bks.
Gattin, Dana. God Is the Answer. 1984. 5.95 (ISBN 0-317-03625-4). Unity School.
Gattinoni, C. T., tr. see Jones, E. Stanley.
Gatwood, Lynn E. Devi & the Spouse Goddess: Women, Sexuality & Marriage in India. LC 85-61077. 206p. 1985. 18.00 (ISBN 0-913215-01-5). Riverdale Co.
Gaub, Ken, ed. God's Got Your Number. 150p. (Orig.). 1986. pap. text ed. 3.95 (ISBN 0-88368-185-4). Whitaker Hse.
Gauba, Om P. Sandarbh-MulAK Shabd-Kosh: Hindi-English-Hindi Dictionary of Phrase & Fable Including Symbolic & Idiomatic Expressions. viii, 258p. 1986. text ed. 35.00x (ISBN 81-7018-363-4, Pub. by B. R. Pub Corp Delhi). Apt Bks.
Gauchat, Dorothy & Lyons, Arthur. All God's Children. 224p. 1985. pap. 2.50 (ISBN 0-345-31988-5). Ballantine.
Gauchhwal, B. S. Concept of Perfection in the Teachings of Kant & the Gita. 1967. 4.95 (ISBN 0-89684-186-3). Orient Bk Dist.
Gaudefroy-Demombynes, Maurice. Muslim Institutions. LC 84-12953. 216p. 1984. Repr. of 1950 ed. lib. bdg. 35.00x (ISBN 0-313-24287-9, GAMU). Greenwood.
--Le Pelerinage a la Mekke: Etude D'histoire Religieuse. LC 77-10690. (Studies in Islamic History: No. 7). viii, 332p. 1978. Repr. of 1923 ed. lib. bdg. 35.00x (ISBN 0-87991-456-4). Porcupine Pr.
Gaudin, Thierry. The Secret Code: The Lost & Hidden Language of the Bible, Vol. 1. LC 85-70031. 300p. (Orig.). 1985. pap. 12.95 (ISBN 0-933357-05-2). Bret Pubns.
Gaudiose, Dorothy. Prophet of the People: A Biography of Padre Pio. LC 74-7123. 1977. pap. 5.95 (ISBN 0-8189-0351-1). Alba.
Gauhar, Altaf. Translation from the Quran. 16.95 (ISBN 0-686-18511-0). Kazi Pubns.
Gaulke, Earl H. You Can Have a Family Where Everybody Wins. LC 75-23574. 104p. 1975. pap. 3.50 (ISBN 0-570-03723-9, 12-2625). Concordia.
Gaultier, Andre P., jt. auth. see Lasne, Sophie.
Gaura Purnima dasa, ed. see Das Goswami, Satsvarupa.
Gauri Modi, tr. see Svami Kripalvananda.
Gaury, Gerald De see De Gaury, Gerald.
Gause, R. H. Church of God Polity: With Supplement. 1958. 9.95 (ISBN 0-87148-158-8). Pathway Pr.
Gause, R. Hollis. Living in the Spirit. 136p. 1980. pap. 5.25 (ISBN 0-87148-515-X). Pathway Pr.
--Revelation: God's Stamp of Sovereignty. LC 83-63383. 286p. 1983. pap. text ed. 9.95 (ISBN 0-87148-740-3). Pathway Pr.
Gaussen, L. Divine Inspiration of the Bible. LC 75-155249. (Kregel Reprint Library). 382p. 1971. 12.95 (ISBN 0-8254-2707-X). Kregel.
Gaustad, Edwin, ed. A Documentary History of Religion in America, Vol. 1. 1982. pap. 19.95 (ISBN 0-8028-1871-4). Eerdmans.
Gaustad, Edwin S. Baptist Piety: The Last Will & Testimony of Obadiah Holmes. LC 79-52570. (The Baptist Tradition Ser.). 1980. lib. bdg. 17.00x (ISBN 0-405-12439-2). Ayer Co Pubs.
--Dissent in American Religion. (Chicago History of American Religion Ser). 1973. 12.95x (ISBN 0-226-28436-0). U of Chicago Pr.
--Dissent in American Religion. LC 73-77131. xii, 184p. 1975. pap. 3.95x (ISBN 0-226-28437-9, P637, Phoen). U of Chicago Pr.

--A Documentary History of Religion in America Since 1865, Vol. 2. (Illus.). 640p. 1983. pap. 19.95 (ISBN 0-8028-1874-9). Eerdmans.
--The Great Awakening in New England. 13.75 (ISBN 0-8446-1491-2). Peter Smith.
--Religion in America: History & Historiography. LC 73-91240. (AHA Pamphlets: No. 260). 60p. 1974. pap. text ed. 1.50 (ISBN 0-87229-016-6). Am Hist Assn.
--Religious History of America. 1974. pap. 10.95 (ISBN 0-06-063093-0, RD/66, HarpR). Har-Row.
Gaustad, Edwin S., ed. Baptists: The Bible, Church Order & the Churches. original anthology ed. LC 79-52587. (The Baptist Tradition Ser.). 1980. lib. bdg. 46.00x (ISBN 0-405-12454-6). Ayer Co Pubs.
--Baptists Tradition Series, 40 bks, Vols. 1-22. (Illus.). 1980. Repr. Set. lib. bdg. 1323.00x (ISBN 0-405-12437-6). Ayer Co Pubs.
--Religion in America, 38 vols. 1969. Repr. Set. 2510.50 (ISBN 0-405-00229-7). Ayer Co Pubs.
--Religion in America: Ser. 2, 40 vols. 1972. Repr. 830.00 set (ISBN 0-405-04050-4). Ayer Co Pubs.
Gaustad, Edwin S., ed. see Allison, William H. & Barnes, W. W.
Gaustad, Edwin S., ed. see Asplund, John.
Gaustad, Edwin S., ed. see Bacote, Samuel W.
Gaustad, Edwin S., ed. see Baker, J. C.
Gaustad, Edwin S., ed. see Baker, Robert A.
Gaustad, Edwin S., ed. see Bowden, Henry W.
Gaustad, Edwin S., ed. see Burkitt, Lemuel & Read, Jesse.
Gaustad, Edwin S., ed. see Clarke, John & McLoughlin, William G.
Gaustad, Edwin S., ed. see Dawson, Joseph M.
Gaustad, Edwin S., ed. see Freeman, Edward A.
Gaustad, Edwin S., ed. see Howe, Claude L., Jr.
Gaustad, Edwin S., ed. see Jeter, Jeremiah B.
Gaustad, Edwin S., ed. see Knight, Richard.
Gaustad, Edwin S., ed. see Lambert, Byron C.
Gaustad, Edwin S., ed. see Lewis, James K.
Gaustad, Edwin S., ed. see Lumpkin, William L. & Butterfield, Lyman.
Gaustad, Edwin S., ed. see McBeth, H. Leon.
Gaustad, Edwin S., ed. see Macintosh, Douglas C.
Gaustad, Edwin S., ed. see McKibbens, Thomas R., Jr. & Smith, Kenneth.
Gaustad, Edwin S., ed. see Morris, Elias C.
Gaustad, Edwin S., ed. see Pitman, Walter G.
Gaustad, Edwin S., ed. see Powell, Adam C., Sr.
Gaustad, Edwin S., ed. see Purefoy, George W.
Gaustad, Edwin S., ed. see Robinson, H. Wheeler & Payne, Ernest A.
Gaustad, Edwin S., ed. see Seventh-Day Baptist General Conference.
Gaustad, Edwin S., ed. see Smith, Elias.
Gaustad, Edwin S., jt. ed. see Stealey, Sydnor L.
Gaustad, Edwin S., ed. see Stiansen, Peder.
Gaustad, Edwin S., ed. see Taylor, John.
Gaustad, Edwin S., ed. see Tull, James E.
Gaustad, Edwin S., jt. ed. see Valentine, Foy D.
Gaustad, Edwin S., ed. see Wayland, Francis.
Gaustad, Edwin S., ed. see Whitsitt, William H.
Gaustad, Edwin S., ed. see Wood, Nathan E.
Gausted, Edwin S., ed. see Jordan, Lewis G.
Gaustad, Edwins., ed. see Dagg, John L.
Gautama. Gautama: The Nyaya Philosophy. Junankar, N. S., tr. from Sanskrit. 1978. 25.50 (ISBN 0-89684-002-6, Pub. by Motilal Banarsidass India). Orient Bk Dist.
Gautama Buddha. The Diamond Sutra. (Sacred Texts Ser.). viii, 72p. 1983. pap. 8.75 (ISBN 0-88695-004-X). Concord Grove.
Gautrey, R. Moffat. The Burning Cataracts of Christ: An Evangelical Interpretation of John Mosefield's "The Ever-Lasting Mercy". LC 78-23716. 1933. lib. bdg. 20.00 (ISBN 0-8414-4483-8). Folcroft.
Gautrey, Robert M. The Burning Cataracts of Christ. 1980. Repr. of 1933 ed. lib. bdg. 30.00 (ISBN 0-8482-4193-2). Norwood Edns.
Gauvin, Marshall, jt. auth. see Teller, Woolsey.
Gauvin, Marshall J. Case Against Religion. 500p. 10.00 (ISBN 0-318-19200-4). Truth Seeker.
Gavaert, Francois A. Les Origines du Chant Litturgique de l'Eglise Latin. 93p. Repr. of 1890 ed. lib. bdg. 30.00x (Pub. by G. Olms BRD). Coronet Bks.
Gavalda, A. Diccionario Mitologico. (Span.). 900p. 29.95 (ISBN 0-686-92532-7, S-37663). French & Eur.
Gaventa, Beverly R. From Darkness to Light: Aspects of Conversion in the New Testament. LC 85-16309. (Overtures to Biblical Theology Ser.). 176p. 1986. pap. 8.95 (ISBN 0-8006-1545-X, 1-1545). Fortress.
Gavigan, John J., tr. see Oliverus.
Gavin, Frank. Seven Centuries of the Problem of Church & State. 1938. 22.50x (ISBN 0-86527-180-1). Fertig.
Gavin, Frank S. Aphraates & the Jews. LC 77-168102. (Columbia University. Contributions to Oriental History & Philology: No. 9). Repr. of 1923 ed. 12.50 (ISBN 0-404-50539-2). AMS Pr.
--Some Aspects of Contemporary Greek Orthodox Thought. LC 73-133818. Repr. of 1923 ed. 29.00 (ISBN 0-404-02687-7). AMS Pr.
Gavriilova, Alexandra. Zapiski Palomnitsi. Tr. of Diary of a Pilgrim. 175p. (Orig.). 1968. pap. 6.00 (ISBN 0-317-30250-7). Holy Trinity.
Gawain, Shakti. Creative Visualization. LC 79-13760. (Illus.). 158p. 1978. pap. 7.95 (ISBN 0-931432-02-2). Whatever Pub.
Gawle, Barbara. How to Pray: Discovering Spiritual Growth Through Prayer. (Illus.). 204p. 1984. pap. 6.95 (ISBN 0-13-430463-2). P-H.
Gawryn, Marvin. Reaching High: The Psychology of Spiritual Living. LC 80-24306. 200p. 1981. 11.95 (ISBN 0-938380-00-1); pap. 7.95 (ISBN 0-938380-01-X). Highreach Colorado.
Gay, David. Voyage to Freedom: Story of the Pilgrim Fathers. pap. 5.45 (ISBN 0-85151-384-0). Banner of Truth.
Gay, Jules. Papes Du Onzieme Siecle et la Chretiente. 2nd ed. 1970. 21.00 (ISBN 0-8337-1302-7). B Franklin.
Gay, Marcina. The Bible Puzzle Book. 128p. (Orig.). 1984. pap. 2.25 (ISBN 0-8007-8487-1, Spire Bks). Revell.
--Bible Quizzes for Kids. 48p. (Orig.). 1982. pap. 1.95 (ISBN 0-87239-594-4, 3136). Standard Pub.
Gay, Peter. The Enlightenment: An Interpretation-the Rise of Modern Paganism, Vol. 1. 1977. pap. 10.95x (ISBN 0-393-00870-3, N870, Norton Lib). Norton.
Gay, Volney P. Freud on Ritual: Reconstruction & Critique. LC 79-11385. (American Academy of Religion, Dissertation Ser.: No. 26). 1979. 14.00 (ISBN 0-89130-282-4, 010126); pap. 9.95 (ISBN 0-89130-301-4). Scholars Pr Ga.
--Reading Freud: Psychology, Neurosis, & Religion. LC 83-2917. (AAR Studies in Religion). 142p. 1983. pap. 8.25 (ISBN 0-89130-613-7, 01 00 32). Scholars Pr GA.
--Reading Jung: Science, Psychology, & Religion. LC 84-1322. (AAR-Studies in Religion). 166p. 1984. pap. 8.25 (ISBN 0-89130-731-1, 01 00 34). Scholars Pr GA.
Gayangos, P. De see Al-Maqqari, Ahmed.
Gaydos, Michael. Eyes to Behold. LC 73-77531. 1982. pap. 4.95 (ISBN 0-89221-069-9). New Leaf.
Gaydou, Nelda B. de, tr. see Ford, LeRoy.
Gayley, Charles M. The Classic Myths in English Literature & Art. LC 77-6986. 1977. Repr. of 1911 ed. lib. bdg. 45.00 (ISBN 0-89341-163-9). Longwood Pub Group.
Gaylor, Anne N. Lead Us Not into Penn Station. 1983. 5.00 (ISBN 0-318-00995-1). Freedom Rel Found.
Gaynell, Jim, jt. auth. see Cronin, Gaynell.
Gaynor, Frank. Dictionary of Mysticism. 211p. 1973. pap. 2.45 (ISBN 0-8065-0172-3). Citadel Pr.
Gaynor, John S. Life of St. Vincent Pallotti. 1980. 4.00 (ISBN 0-8198-4401-2); pap. 3.00 (ISBN 0-8198-4402-0). Dghtrs St Paul.
Gaytan, C. Diccionario Mitologico. (Span.). 3.75 (ISBN 0-686-56651-3, S-25775). French & Eur.
Gbadamosi, Bakare & Beier, Ulli. Not Even God Is Ripe Enough. (African Writers Ser.). 1968. pap. text ed. 4.00x (ISBN 0-435-90048-X). Heinemann Ed.
Geach, P. T. Providence & Evil. LC 76-28005. 1977. 24.95 (ISBN 0-521-21477-7). Cambridge U Pr.
Geach, P. T., ed. see Prior, Arthur N.
Geach, Peter T., ed. see Descartes, Rene.
Geach, Peter T., tr. see Descartes, Rene.
Geagea, Nilo. Mary of the Koran: A Meeting Point Between Islam & Christianism. Fares, Lawrence T., tr. LC 82-3804. 324p. 1984. 17.50 (ISBN 0-8022-2395-8). Philos Lib.
Gealy, Fred D., et al. Companion to the Hymnal. 1970. 19.95 (ISBN 0-687-09259-0). Abingdon.
Geanakoplos, Deno J. Western Medieval Civilization. 1979. text ed. 23.95 (ISBN 0-669-00868-0). Heath.
Geaney, Dennis J. The Prophetic Parish: A Center for Peace & Justice. 144p. (Orig.). 1983. pap. 6.95 (ISBN 0-86683-807-4, HarpR). Har-Row.
Geaney, Dennis J. & Sokol, Dolly. Parish Celebrations: A Reflective Guide for Liturgy Planning. (Orig.). 1983. pap. 5.95 (ISBN 0-89622-190-3). Twenty-Third.
Geankoplos, Deno J. Byzantine East & Latin West: Two Worlds of Christendom in Middle Ages & Renaissance. LC 76-20685. (Illus.). xii, 206p. 1976. Repr. of 1966 ed. 17.50 (ISBN 0-208-01615-5, Archon). Shoe String.
Gear, Felix B. Our Presbyterian Belief. LC 79-23421. 90p. (Orig.). 1980. pap. 6.95 (ISBN 0-8042-0676-7). John Knox.
Geary, Gerald J. The Secularization of the California Missions (1810-1846) LC 73-3572. (Catholic University of America. Studies in American Church History: No. 17). Repr. of 1934 ed. 26.00 (ISBN 0-404-57767-9). AMS Pr.
Geary, Patrick J. Furta Sacra: Thefts of Relics in the Central Middle Ages. LC 77-85538. 1978. 26.50 (ISBN 0-691-05261-1). Princeton U Pr.
Gebauer, Victor. Manual for Altar Guilds. 72p. (Orig.). 1986. pap. 9.50 (ISBN 0-8066-2203-2, 10-4267). Augsburg.
Gebhardt, Gunther, ed. see World Conference on Religion & Peace Staff.
Gebhardt, Mattie L. Meatless Recipes. LC 75-4315. (Illus.). 130p. (Orig.). 1975. pap. 2.50 (ISBN 0-8356-0304-0, Quest). Theos Pub Hse.
Gebhardt, Richard F. & Armstrong, Mark. Object Lessons from Science Experiments. (Object Lesson Ser.). 128p. 1987. pap. 5.95 (ISBN 0-8010-3811-1). Baker Bk.
Gebhart, E. Mystics & Heretics in Italy at the End of the Middle Ages. 1977. lib. bdg. 59.95 (ISBN 0-8490-2321-1). Gordon Pr.
Gebler, Karl Von. Galileo Galilei & the Roman Curia from Authentic Sources. Sturge, Jane, tr. LC 76-1124. 1977. Repr. of 1897 ed. lib. bdg. 28.50x (ISBN 0-915172-11-9). Richwood Pub.
Gecseq, F. & Steinby, M. Tree Automata. 1984. 99.00x (ISBN 0-569-08794-5, Pub. by Collets (UK)). State Mutual Bk.
Gedde, Palmer. One Plus One Equals. Kujath, Mentor, ed. 1979. pap. 4.95 (ISBN 0-8100-0103-9, 12-1712). Northwest Pub.
--While You Can. (Orig.). 1987. pap. price not set (ISBN 0-89536-891-9, 7877). CSS of Ohio.
Geddes, Jim. The Better Half of Life. (Orig.). 1987. pap. 7.95 (ISBN 0-8054-5732-1). Broadman.
--The Bright Side of Depression. LC 85-17123. (Orig.). 1985. pap. 5.95 (ISBN 0-8054-5016-5). Broadman.
Geddes, Joseph A. The United Order Among the Mormons (Missouri Phase) An Unfinished Experiment in Economic Organization. LC 72-8247. Repr. of 1924 ed. 19.50 (ISBN 0-404-11001-0). AMS Pr.
Geden, A. S., tr. see Deussen, Paul.
Gedney, William J., ed. see Anuman, Rajadhon Phraya.
Gee, Donald. Concerning Spiritual Gifts. rev. ed. LC 80-83784. 144p. 1972. pap. 2.95 (ISBN 0-88243-486-1, 02-0486). Gospel Pub.
--The Fruit of the Spirit. 80p. 1975. pap. 1.95 (ISBN 0-88243-501-9, 02-0501, Radiant Bks). Gospel Pub.
--Fruitful or Barren? 90p. 1961. pap. 1.35 (ISBN 0-88243-502-7, 02-0502). Gospel Pub.
--Is It God? (Charismatic Bks.). 30p. 1972. pap. 0.69 (ISBN 0-88243-916-2, 02-0916). Gospel Pub.
--A New Discovery. Orig. Title: Pentecost. 96p. 1932. pap. 1.00 (ISBN 0-88243-569-8, 02-0569). Gospel Pub.
--Now That You've Been Baptized in the Spirit. 176p. 1972. pap. 1.50 (ISBN 0-88243-461-6, 02-0461). Gospel Pub.
--Spiritual Gifts in the Work of the Ministry Today. 102p. 1963. pap. 1.25 (ISBN 0-88243-592-2, 02-0592). Gospel Pub.
--This Is the Way. (Radiant Bks.). Orig. Title: Studies in Guidance. 64p. 1975. pap. 0.95 (ISBN 0-88243-630-9, 02-0630). Gospel Pub.
--Toward Pentecostal Unity. Orig. Title: All with One Accord. 62p. 1961. pap. 0.60 (ISBN 0-88243-689-9, 02-0689). Gospel Pub.
--A Word to the Wise. (Radiant Bks.). Orig. Title: Proverbs for Pentecost. 80p. 1975. pap. 0.95 (ISBN 0-88243-632-5, 02-0632). Gospel Pub.
Gee, Edward. The Divine Right & Original of the Civil Magistrate from God. LC 75-31092. Repr. of 1658 ed. 30.00 (ISBN 0-404-13510-2). AMS Pr.
Gee, Henry. The Elizabethan Clergy & the Settlement of Religion, 1558-64. LC 83-45581. Date not set. Repr. of 1898 ed. 39.50 (ISBN 0-404-19899-6). AMS Pr.
Gee, Henry & Hardy, William J., eds. Documents Illustrative of English Church History. LC 83-45580. Date not set. Repr. of 1896 ed. 62.50 (ISBN 0-404-19898-8). AMS Pr.
Geer, Russell. Letters, Principal Doctrines, & Vatican Sayings: Epicurus. 1964. pap. text ed. write for info. (ISBN 0-02-341200-3). Macmillan.
Geer, Thelma. Mormonism & Me: A True Story. 1986. pap. 6.95 (ISBN 0-8024-5633-2). Moody.
--Mormonism, Mama & Me. 3rd, rev. ed. LC 81-146846. (Illus.). 228p. 1983. pap. 3.95 (ISBN 0-912375-00-0). Calvary Miss Pr.
--Mormonism, Mama, & Me. 1983. pap. 4.95 (ISBN 0-87508-192-4). Chr Lit.
Geer, Thelma, ed. Mormonism, Mama & Me. 4th ed. (Illus.). 252p. 1984. pap. 4.95 (ISBN 0-912375-01-9). Calvary Miss Pr.
Geertz, Armin W. & Lomatuway'ma, Michael. Children of Cottonwood: Piety & Ceremonialism in Hopi Indian Puppetry. (American Tribal Religions Ser.: Vol. 12). (Illus.). viii, 412p. 1987. 24.95x (ISBN 0-8032-2127-4); pap. 14.95x (ISBN 0-8032-7021-6). U of Nebr Pr.
Geertz, Clifford. Islam Observed: Religious Development in Morocco & Indonesia. 1971. pap. 6.00x (ISBN 0-226-28511-1, P439, Phoen). U of Chicago Pr.
Geffcken, J. The Last Days of Greco-Roman Paganism. (Europe in the Middle Ages Selected Studies: Vol. 8). 344p. 1978. 74.50 (ISBN 0-444-85005-8, North-Holland). Elsevier.
Geffre, Claude & Jossua, Jean-Pierre. Indifference to Religion. (Concilium 1983: Vol. 165). 128p. (Orig.). 1983. pap. 6.95 (ISBN 0-8164-2445-4, HarpR). Har-Row.
Geffre, Claude & Jossua, Jean-Pierre, eds. The Human, Criterion of Christian Existence? (Concilium Ser.: Vol. 155). 128p. (Orig.). 1982. pap. 6.95 (ISBN 0-8164-2386-5, HarpR). Har-Row.
--Monotheism, Vol. 177. (Concilium Ser.). 128p. pap. 6.95 (ISBN 0-567-30057-9, Pub. by T & T Clark Ltd UK). Fortress.
--Nietzsche & Christianity, Vol. 145. (Concilium 1981). 128p. (Orig.). 1981. pap. 6.95 (ISBN 0-8164-2312-1, HarpR). Har-Row.
--True & False Universality of Christianity. (Concilium Ser.: Vol. 135). 128p. (Orig.). 1980. pap. 5.95 (ISBN 0-8164-2277-X, HarpR). Har-Row.
Geffre, Claude, et al, eds. Different Theologies, Common Responsibilities. (Concilium Ser.: Vol. 171). 116p. 1984. pap. 6.95 (ISBN 0-567-30051-X, Pub. by T & T Clark Ltd Uk). Fortress.
Gehman, Henry S., ed. The New Westminster Dictionary of the Bible. LC 69-10000. (Illus.). 1064p. 1982. thumb indexed 25.95 (ISBN 0-664-21388-X); 22.95. Westminster.
Gehrig, Gail. American Civil Religion: An Assessment. LC 81-82801. (Society for the Scientific Study of Religion Monograph: No. 3). (Orig.). 1981. pap. 5.50 (ISBN 0-932566-02-2). Soc Sci Stud Rel.
Gehris, Kathy, jt. auth. see Gehris, Paul.
Gehris, Paul & Gehris, Kathy. The Teaching Church: Active in Mission. 80p. 1987. pap. 5.95 (ISBN 0-8170-1080-7). Judson.
Gehrke, Ralph D., tr. see Westermann, Claus.
Gehrke, Ralph D., tr. see Wolff, Hans W.
Geiermann, Peter. The Convert's Catechism of Catholic Doctrine. 1977. pap. 2.00 (ISBN 0-89555-029-6). TAN Bks Pubs.
Geiger, Abraham. Judaism & It's History: In Two Parts. Newburgh, Charles, tr. from Ger. LC 85-9043. (Brown Classics in Judaica Ser.). 414p. 1985. pap. text ed. 17.50 (ISBN 0-8191-4491-6). U Pr of Amer.
--Nachgelassene Schriften, 5 vols. in 3. Katz, Steven, ed. LC 79-7132. (Jewish Philosophy, Mysticism & History of Ideas Ser.). 1980. Repr. of 1875 ed. Set. lib. bdg. 172.50x (ISBN 0-405-12255-1); lib. bdg. 57.50x ea. Vol. 1 (ISBN 0-405-12256-X). Vol. 2 (ISBN 0-405-12257-8). Vol. 3 (ISBN 0-405-12228-4). Ayer Co Pubs.
--Salomo Gabirol und seine Dichtungen. Katz, Steven, ed. LC 79-7130. (Jewish Philosophy, Mysticism & History of Ideas Ser.). 1980. Repr. of 1867 ed. lib. bdg. 14.00x (ISBN 0-405-12254-3). Ayer Co Pubs.
Geiger, Bernard M., ed. see Manteau-Bonamy, H. M.
Geiger, Gail. The Carafa Chapel, Renaissance Art in Rome. (Sixteenth Century Essays & Studies Ser.: Vol. V). (Illus.). 210p. 1985. smyth sewn 50.00x (ISBN 0-940474-05-0). Sixteenth Cent.
Geiger, Linda M. God Loves Me! 8 Lessons, Vol. 1. (Steps of Faith for Special Children Ser.). 1981. kit 19.95x (ISBN 0-86508-045-3); text ed. 4.95x (ISBN 0-86508-046-1). BCM Intl Inc.
Geiger, Lura J. Astonish Me, Yahweh! Leader's Guide. (Illus.). 101p. (Orig.). 1984. 12.95 (ISBN 0-931055-02-4). LuraMedia.
--Healing: Drawing on God's Strength. (Orig.). 1987. pap. 34.50; cassette incl. LuraMedia.
--Inner Peace: Finding Serenity Within. 1987. pap. 34.50; cassette incl. LuraMedia.
--Spiritual Renewal: Tapping Your Inner Resources. (Orig.). 1987. pap. 34.50 (ISBN 0-931055-37-7); cassette incl. LuraMedia.
Geiger, Lura J., jt. auth. see Backman, Pat.
Geiger, Lura J., et al. Astonish Me, Yahweh! (Illus.). 106p. (Orig.). 1983. wkbk. 11.95 (ISBN 0-931055-01-6). LuraMedia.
Geiger, Maynard. Franciscan Missionaries in Hispanic California 1769-1848: A Biographical Dictionary. LC 74-79607. Repr. of 1969 ed. 60.50 (ISBN 0-8357-9191-2, 2015007). Bks Demand UMI.
Geiger, Wilhelm & Windischmann, Friedrich, eds. Zarathushtra in the Gathas & in the Greek & Roman Classics. 2nd ed. LC 74-21260. Repr. of 1899 ed. 24.50 (ISBN 0-404-12810-6). AMS Pr.
Geisebrecht, Wilhel M Von see Gregorius, Saint.
Geiseman, O. A. Make Yours a Happy Marriage. 1981. pap. 3.95 (ISBN 0-570-03133-8, 12-2383). Concordia.

Geisendorfer, James. Religion in America. 175p. 1983. pap. text ed. 19.95x (ISBN 90-04-06910-0, Pub. by Magnes Pr Israel). Humanities.

Geisendorfer, James V., jt. auth. see Melton, James G.

Geisler, Norm. False Gods of Our Time. (Orig.). 1985. pap. 5.95 (ISBN 0-89081-494-5). Harvest Hse.

Geisler, Norman. Ethics: Alternatives & Issues. 256p. 1971. 14.95 (ISBN 0-310-24930-9, 18079). Zondervan.

--La Etica Cristiana del Amor. Canclini, Arnoldo, tr. from Eng. LC 77-15813. Tr. of The Christian Ethic of Love. (Span.). 126p. 1977. pap. 3.95 (ISBN 0-89922-103-3). Edit Caribe.

--Inerrancy. 1980. pap. 11.95 (ISBN 0-310-39281-0, 18157P). Zondervan.

Geisler, Norman L. Christian Apologetics. LC 76-24706. 464p. 1976. 15.95 (ISBN 0-8010-3704-2). Baker Bk.

--Creator in the Courtroom "Scopes II". 1987. pap. 5.95 (ISBN 0-8010-3814-6). Baker Bk.

--Miracles & Modern Thought. 208p. (Orig.). 1982. pap. 7.95 (ISBN 0-310-44681-3, 12560P). Zondervan.

--Options in Contemporary Christian Ethics. LC 80-69431. 128p. (Orig.). 1981. pap. 4.95 (ISBN 0-8010-3757-3). Baker Bk.

--A Popular Survey of the Old Testament. LC 77-78578. 1977. pap. 8.95 (ISBN 0-8010-3684-4). Baker Bk.

--The Roots of Evil. (Christian Free University Curriculum Ser.). 1978. pap. 4.95 (ISBN 0-310-35751-9, 12655P). Zondervan.

Geisler, Norman L. & Amano, J. Yutaka. The Reincarnation Sensation. 224p. 1986. pap. 6.95 (ISBN 0-8423-5404-2). Tyndale.

Geisler, Norman L. & Anderson, J. Kerby. Origin Science. 1987. pap. 8.95 (ISBN 0-8010-3808-1). Baker Bk.

Geisler, Norman L. & Nix, William E. From God to Us. 302p. (Orig.). 1974. pap. 9.95 (ISBN 0-8024-2878-9). Moody.

--General Introduction to the Bible. rev. ed. LC 68-18890. 1968. 29.95 (ISBN 0-8024-2916-5). Moody.

Geisler, Norman L., ed. see Augustine, Aurelius.

Geisler, Ruth. The Christian Family Prepares for Easter. 96p. (Orig.). 1985. pap. 6.95 (ISBN 0-570-03977-0, 12-2893). Concordia.

Geissbuhler, Elisabeth C., tr. see Rodin, Auguste.

Geissler, Eugene S., ed. Bible Prayer Book. LC 80-71052. 528p. (Orig.). 1981. pap. 4.95 (ISBN 0-87793-218-2). Ave Maria.

Geissler, Eugene S., compiled by. The Spirit Bible. LC 73-88004. 272p. 1973. pap. 2.25 (ISBN 0-87793-062-7). Ave Maria.

Geissler, Suzanne B. Jonathan Edwards to Aaron Burr, Jr. From Great Awakening to Democratic Politics. LC 81-38353. (Studies in American Religion: Vol. 1). xii, 298p. 1981. 49.95x (ISBN 0-88946-906-7). E Mellen.

Gelberg. The Hare Krishna Movement. 1985. lib. bdg. 23.00 (ISBN 0-8240-8751-8). Garland Pub.

Gelberg, Steven, ed. Hare Krishna Hare Krishna: Five Distinguished Scholars in Religion Discuss the Krishna Movement in the West. LC 82-21055. (Press Eastern Philosophy & Literature Ser.). 224p. (Orig.). 1983. pap. 7.95 (ISBN 0-394-62454-8, E845, Ever). Grove.

Gelberman, Joseph. To Be Fully Alive. 89p. pap. 5.95 (ISBN 0-942494-49-0). Coleman Pub.

Gelberman, Joseph H. Haggadah: The Story of Thanksgiving. 35p. (Orig.). 1983. pap. 4.00 (ISBN 0-942494-55-5). Coleman Pub.

Geldenhuys, J. Norval. Commentary on Luke. (New International Commentary on the New Testament). 1951. 17.95 (ISBN 0-8028-2184-7). Eerdmans.

Gelenian, Ara A. The Armenians in Rhode Island: Ancient Roots to Present Experiences. Conley, Patrick T., ed. (Rhode Island Ethnic Heritage Ser.). (Illus.). 36p. (Orig.). 1985. pap. 2.75 (ISBN 0-917012-73-9). RI Pubns Soc.

Gelesnoff, Vladimir M. Paul's Epistle to the Galatians. 1977. pap. text ed. 3.00 (ISBN 0-910424-73-X). Concordant.

Gelfond, Renee. Discover a New Beginning. LC 83-20079. (Illus.). 100p. (Orig.). 1983. pap. 6.95 (ISBN 0-914789-00-7). Serenity Hse.

Gelin, Albert. Key Concepts of the Old Testament. Lamb, George, tr. 96p. pap. 2.95 (ISBN 0-8091-1610-3, Deus). Paulist Pr.

Gelineau, Joseph. Learning to Celebrate: The Mass & Its Music. 1985. pap. 6.95 (ISBN 0-317-38557-7). Pastoral Pr.

--Psalms: A Singing Version. 256p. 1968. pap. 3.95 (ISBN 0-8091-1669-3, Deus). Paulist Pr.

Geller, Ernest. Muslim Society. LC 80-41103. (Cambridge Studies in Social Anthropology: No. 32). 267p. 1983. pap. 12.95 (ISBN 0-521-27407-9). Cambridge U Pr.

Geller, L. D. Between Concord & Plymouth: The Transcendentalists & the Watsons. (Illus.). 1973. 6.00 (ISBN 0-685-42210-0). Thoreau Found.

Geller, Lawrence D. & Gomes, Peter J. The Books of the Pilgrims. LC 74-30056. (Reference Library of the Humanities: No. 13). (Illus.). 100p. 1975. lib. bdg. 25.00 (ISBN 0-8240-1065-5). Garland Pub.

Geller, Norman. Color Me Happy: It's Rosh Hashannah & Yom Kippur. (Illus.). 36p. 1986. pap. 2.50 (ISBN 0-915753-10-3). N Geller Pub.

--Color Me Kosher for Passover. (Illus.). 23p. 1985. pap. 1.00 (ISBN 0-915753-06-5). N Geller Pub.

--David's Seder. (Illus.). 16p. 1983. pap. 4.95 (ISBN 0-915753-01-4). N Geller Pub.

--The First Seven Days. (Illus.). 32p. 1983. pap. 6.95 (ISBN 0-915753-00-6). N Geller Pub.

--It's Not the Jewish Christmas. (Illus.). 20p. 1985. pap. 4.95 (ISBN 0-915753-09-X). N Geller Pub.

--Talk to God...I'll Get the Message: Catholic Version. (Illus.). 23p. 1983. pap. 4.95 (ISBN 0-915753-03-0). N Geller Pub.

--Talk to God...I'll Get the Message: Jewish Version. (Illus.). 23p. 1983. pap. 4.95 (ISBN 0-915753-02-2). N Geller Pub.

--Talk to God...I'll Get the Message: Protestant Version. (Illus.). 23p. 1983. pap. 4.95 (ISBN 0-915753-04-9). N Geller Pub.

Geller, Stephen A. Parallelism in Early Biblical Poetry. LC 78-27255. (Harvard Semitic Monographs: No. 20). 1979. 12.00 (ISBN 0-89130-275-1, 040020). Scholars Pr GA.

Geller, Stephen A., et al. A Sense of Text: The Art of Language in the Study of Biblical Literature. 113p. 1983. pap. text ed. 12.50 (ISBN 0-9602686-1-8). Dropsie Coll.

Gellhorn, Walter & Greenawalt, R. Kent. Sectarian College & the Public Purse: Fordham: a Case Study. LC 74-111415. 212p. 1970. 10.00 (ISBN 0-379-00456-9). Oceana.

Gellman, Ellie. It's Chanukah. LC 85-80782. (Illus.). 12p. 1985. bds. 4.95 (ISBN 0-930494-51-2). Kar Ben.

--It's Rosh-Hashanah. LC 85-80783. (Illus.). 12p. 1985. bds. 4.95 (ISBN 0-930494-50-4). Kar Ben.

--Shai's Shabbat Walk. LC 85-80780. (Illus.). 12p. 1985. bds. 4.95 (ISBN 0-930494-49-0). Kar Ben.

Gelpi, Donald L. The Divine Mother: A Trinitarian Theology of the Holy Spirit. LC 84-11921. 260p. (Orig.). 1984. lib. bdg. 27.25 (ISBN 0-8191-4034-1); pap. text ed. 12.50 (ISBN 0-8191-4035-X). U Pr of Amer.

Gelpke, R., ed. & tr. see Nizami.

Gelser, David, tr. see Stickelberger, E.

Gelsinger, Michael, tr. from Greek see Vaporis, Nomikos M.

Gelston, A. The Peshitta of the Twelve Prophets. 272p. 1985. 34.50x (ISBN 0-19-826179-9). Oxford U Pr.

Gelwick, Richard. Way of Discovery: An Introduction to the Thought of Michael Polanyi. 1977. pap. 4.95 (ISBN 0-19-502193-2). Oxford U Pr.

Gelzer, David G., tr. see Cerdic Colloquium Staff.

Gendrot, Marcel, ed. Make Way for Jesus Christ. pap. 4.95 (ISBN 0-910984-52-2). Montfort Pubns.

Genequand, C. F. The Metaphysics of Ibn Rushd: Averroes. LC 83-15428. (Studies in Islamic Philosophy & Science). write for info. cancelled (ISBN 0-88206-059-7). Caravan Bks.

General Conference Sabbath School Department. Sabbath School Manual. rev. ed. 1982. pap. 5.50 (ISBN 0-8127-0228-X). Review & Herald.

General Conference Youth Department. Church Heritage: A Course in Church History. pap. 2.50 (ISBN 0-686-82636-1). Review & Herald.

General Episcopal Synod. The Holy Eucharist, Longer Form & Other Services. rev. ed. 44p. 1986. pap. 1.50 (ISBN 0-935461-12-4). St Alban Pr CA.

--The Liturgy According to the Use of the Liberal Catholic Church, Prepared for the Use of English-Speaking Congregations. 3rd ed. 421p. 1987. Repr. of 1942 ed. price not set (ISBN 0-935461-11-6). St Alban Pr CA.

Genne, Elizabeth & Genne, William. Church Family Camps & Conferences. LC 78-24395. 1979. pap. 2.95 (ISBN 0-8170-0818-7). Judson.

Genne, Elizabeth S. & Genne, William H. First of All Persons: A New Look at Men-Women Relationships. (Orig.). 1973. pap. 1.95 (ISBN 0-377-03041-4). Friend Pr.

Genne, William, jt. auth. see Genne, Elizabeth.

Genne, William H., jt. auth. see Genne, Elizabeth S.

Genoud, C. & Inoue, T. Buddhist Wall-Painting of Ladakh. (Illus.). 116p. 1981. text ed. 75.00x (ISBN 2-88086-001-6, Pub. by Editions Olizane Holland). Humanities.

Genovesi, Vincent. In Pursuit of Love: Catholic Morality & Human Sexuality. 1987. pap. 16.95. M Glazier.

Genovesi, Vincent J. Expectant Creativity: The Action of Hope in Christian Ethics. LC 81-43807. 172p. (Orig.). 1982. lib. bdg. 27.75 (ISBN 0-8191-2407-9); pap. text ed. 11.50 (ISBN 0-8191-2408-7). U Pr of Amer.

Gent, Barbara & Sturges, Betty. The Altar Guild Book. LC 82-80469. (Illus.). 104p. (Orig.). 1982. pap. 5.95 (ISBN 0-8192-1305-5, 82-80469). Morehouse.

Gentile, Ernest B. The Charasmatic Catechism. LC 76-22255. 1977. pap. 4.95 (ISBN 0-89221-025-7). New Leaf.

Gentle, Jimmie & Richard, Dwight Peter. Programmed Guide to Increasing Church Attendance. 1980. 10.75 (ISBN 0-89536-446-8, 1641). CSS of Ohio.

Gentry, Kenneth L., Jr. The Christian & Alcoholic Beverages: A Biblical Perspective. 1986. pap. 4.95 (ISBN 0-8010-3807-3). Baker Bk.

Gentry, Marshall B. Flannery O'Connor's Religion of the Grotesque. LC 85-20267. 216p. 1986. 22.50x (ISBN 0-87805-285-2). U Pr of Miss.

Gentry, Peter W. Heritage in the Warmed Heart. 63p. 1986. pap. 2.50 (ISBN 0-8341-0955-7). Beacon Hill.

Gentz, William H. The World of Philip Potter. 1974. pap. 2.95 (ISBN 0-377-00006-X). Friend Pr.

Gentz, William H., ed. The Dictionary of Bible & Religion. (Illus.). 1152p. 1986. 26.95 (ISBN 0-687-10757-1). Abingdon.

--Religious Writer's Marketplace: The Definitive Sourcebook. rev. ed. LC 84-27691. 221p. 1985. pap. 17.95 (ISBN 0-89471-305-1). Running Pr.

Genzburg, Carlo. The Cheese & the Worms: The Cosmos of a Sixteenth-Century Miller. LC 79-3654. pap. 51.80 (2026706). Bks Demand UMI.

Geoffrey of Auxerre. Geoffrey of Auxerre: On the Apocalypse, No. 42. Gibbons, Joseph, tr. from Latin. (Cistercian Fathers Ser.). write for info (ISBN 0-87907-642-9). Cistercian Pubns.

Geoghegan, Vincent. Reason & Eros: The Social Theory of Herbert Marcuse. 122p. 1981. pap. 6.75 (ISBN 0-86104-335-9, Pub. by Pluto Pr). Longwood Pub Group.

George, Anthea, jt. auth. see Cisek, James.

George, Augustine, et al. Gospel Poverty: Essays in Biblical Theology. Guinan, Michael D., tr. LC 76-44548. 167p. 1977. 6.95 (ISBN 0-8199-0610-7). Franciscan Herald.

George, Bill. His Story: The Life of Christ. LC 76-53630. 1977. pap. text ed. 3.95 (ISBN 0-87148-406-4). Pathway Pr.

George, Charles & George, Katherine. The Protestant Mind of the English Reformation, 1570-1640. LC 77-130746. pap. 116.00 (ISBN 0-317-08472-0, 2000986). Bks Demand UMI.

George, Christopher S., ed. Candramaharosana Tantra. (American Oriental Ser.: Vol. 56). 1974. pap. 15.00x (ISBN 0-940490-56-0). Am Orient Soc.

George, David C. Layman's Bible Book Commentary: Second Corinthians, Galatians, Ephesians, Vol. 21. LC 78-74202. 1980. 5.95 (ISBN 0-8054-1191-7). Broadman.

George, Denise. The Christian As a Consumer. LC 83-26062. (Potentials: Guides for Productive Living Ser.; Vol. 3). 114p. (Orig.). 1984. pap. 7.95 (ISBN 0-664-24518-8). Westminster.

--The Student Marriage. LC 82-72230. (Orig.). 1983. pap. 4.95 (ISBN 0-8054-6939-7, 4269-39). Broadman.

George, Denise & George, Timothy. Dear Unborn Child. LC 83-71714. 1984. pap. 4.95 (ISBN 0-8054-5658-9). Broadman.

George, Denise, compiled by. When Night Becomes as Day. LC 86-6887. (Orig.). 1986. pap. 5.95 (ISBN 0-8054-5434-9). Broadman.

George, Emery. Holderlin's "Ars Poetica". A Part-Rigorous Analysis of Information Structure in the Late Hymns. (De Proprietatibu Litterarum Ser. Practica: No. 32). text ed. 60.80x (ISBN 90-2792-381-7). Mouton.

George, Emery E., jt. ed. see Frank, Luanne T.

George, Katherine, jt. auth. see George, Charles.

George, Malcom F. Introduction to Christian Counseling. (Parchment Psychology Ser.). 64p. 1975. pap. 2.25 (ISBN 0-88428-038-1). Parchment Pr.

George, Timothy, jt. auth. see George, Denise.

George, Timothy F. John Robinson & the English Separatist Tradition. LC 82-14201. (National Association of Baptist Professors of Religion Dissertation Ser.: No. 1). ix, 263p. 1982. text ed. 18.50 (ISBN 0-86554-043-8, MUP-P006). Mercer Univ Pr.

--John Robinson & the English Separatist Tradition. (Dissertation Ser.: No. 1). ix, 263p. 1982. pap. 18.50 (ISBN 0-86554-043-8). NABPR.

George, William T. Lo Que Dios Espera de Mi. LC 82-60829. (Illus.). 157p. (Orig.). 1983. pap. text ed. 6.95 (ISBN 0-87148-517-6). Pathway Pr.

--What God Expects of Me. LC 82-60828. 175p. (Orig.). 1982. pap. text ed. 6.95 (ISBN 0-87148-918-X). Pathway Pr.

Georgi, D. De Liturgia Romani Pontificis in Solemni Celebratione Missarum, 3 vols. 1822p. Repr. of 1731 ed. text ed. 372.60 (ISBN 0-576-99174-0, Pub. by Gregg Intl Pubs England). Gregg Intl.

Georgi, Dieter. The Opponents of Paul in Second Corinthians: A Study of Religious Propaganda in Late Antiquity. LC 84-47917. 464p. 1985. 32.95 (ISBN 0-8006-0729-5, 1-729). Fortress.

Georgiades, Thrysbulos. Music & Language: The Rise of Western Music Exemplified in Settings of the Mass. Gollner, Marie-Louise, tr. LC 82-4246. (Illus.). 150p. 1983. 29.95 (ISBN 0-521-23309-7); pap. 9.95 (ISBN 0-521-29902-0). Cambridge U Pr.

Geotchius, Eugene Van Ness see Van Ness Goetchius, Eugene.

Gerard, Francois C. The Future of the Church: The Theology of Renewal of Willem Adolf Visser't Hooft. LC 74-26564. (Pittsburgh Theological Monographs: No. 2). 1974. pap. 6.00 (ISBN 0-915138-01-8). Pickwick.

Gerardi, Natalie, tr. see Poliakov, Leon.

Geraty, Lawrence T., jt. auth. see Boraas, Roger S.

Gerber, Aaron. Abraham: The First Hebrew. 180p. 1981. 12.50 (ISBN 0-89962-208-9). Todd & Honeywell.

--Biblical Attitudes on Human Sexuality. 176p. 1982. 15.95 (ISBN 0-89962-301-8). Todd & Honeywell.

Gerber, Bobbie. Shelter: A Work of Ministry. 160p. 1983. pap. 8.95 (ISBN 0-8164-2622-8, HarpR). Har-Row.

Gerber, David A., ed. Anti-Semitism in American History. 440p. 1986. 29.95 (ISBN 0-252-01214-3). U of Ill Pr.

Gerber, Irwin, et al, eds. Perspectives on Bereavement. (Thanatology Ser.). 1978. 14.95x (ISBN 0-8422-7304-2); pap. text ed. 7.95x (ISBN 0-8290-1878-6). Irvington.

Gerber, Isreal J. Job on Trial: A Book for Our Time. 217p. 1982. 14.95 (ISBN 0-318-01102-6). E P Press.

Gerber, Samuel. Learning to Die. Dyck, Peter, tr. from Ger. LC 84-10809. 104p. (Orig.). 1984. pap. 5.95 (ISBN 0-8361-3369-2). Herald Pr.

Gerberding, Kieth A. How to Respond to Transcendental Meditation. (The Response Ser.). 1977. 1.95 (ISBN 0-570-07676-5, 12-2659). Concordia.

Gerberich, Albert H. Luther & the English Bible. LC 83-45643. Date not set. Repr. of 1933 ed. 17.50 (ISBN 0-404-19852-X). AMS Pr.

Gerbrandt, Gerald. Better Than Rivers of Oil. LC 85-81305. (Faith & Life Bible Studies). 78p. (Orig.). pap. 4.95 (ISBN 0-87303-105-9). Faith & Life.

Gerbrandt, Gerald E. Kingship According to Deuteronomistic History. (Society of Biblical Literature Dissertation Ser.). 1986. 17.95 (ISBN 0-89130-968-3, 06 01 87); pap. 12.95 (ISBN 0-89130-969-1). Scholars Pr GA.

Gerchick, Elias. The Role of the Community Hospital in the Care of the Dying Patient, & the Bereaved. 16.50 (ISBN 0-405-12506-2). Ayer Co Pubs.

Gereboff, Joel. Rabbi Tarfon: The Tradition, the Man & Early Rabbinic Judaism. LC 78-15220. (Brown Judaic Studies: No. 7). 1979. 16.50 (ISBN 0-89130-257-3, 140007); pap. 12.00 (ISBN 0-89130-299-9). Scholars Pr GA.

Geres, Paul. Prayers for Impossible Days. Hjelm, Ingalill H., tr. from Fr. LC 75-36442. 64p. 1976. pap. 2.95 (ISBN 0-8006-1214-0, 1-1214). Fortress.

Gergely, Tibor, illus. Noah's Ark. (Illus.). 24p. 1983. 3.50 (ISBN 0-307-11482-1, 10391, Golden Bks). Western Pub.

Gerhardsson, Birger. The Origins of the Gospel Traditions. LC 78-19634. pap. 23.80 (2029615). Bks Demand UMI.

Gerhart, Mary & Russell, Allan M. Metaphoric Process: The Creation of Scientific & Religious Understanding. LC 83-15614. 217p. 1984. 16.95x (ISBN 0-912646-82-9); pap. 10.95x (ISBN 0-912646-86-1). Tex Christian.

Gericke, Paul. Crucial Experiences in the Life D. L. Moody. LC 78-7570. 72p. (Orig.). 1978. pap. 3.00 (ISBN 0-914520-12-1). Insight Pr.

Gerig, Donald. Leadership in Crisis. LC 81-51741. 128p. 1981. pap. 3.95 (ISBN 0-8307-0797-2, 5415304). Regal.

Gerke, Friedrich. Die Christlichen Sarkophage der vorkonstantinischen Zeit. (Studien Zur Spaetantiken Kunstgeschichte: Vol. 11). (Illus.). viii, 432p. 1978. Repr. of 1940 ed. 140.00x (ISBN 3-11-004999-6). De Gruyter.

Gerkin, Charles V. The Living Human Document: Re-Visioning Pastoral Counseling in a Hermeneutical Mode. 224p. 1984. pap. 10.95 (ISBN 0-687-22372-5). Abingdon.

--Widening the Horizons: Pastoral Responses to a Fragmented Society. LC 86-7832. 154p. (Orig.). 1986. pap. 11.95 (ISBN 0-664-24037-2). Westminster.

Gerlach, Barbara. The Things That Make for Peace: Biblical Meditations. (Illus.). 64p. (Orig.). 1983. pap. 4.95 (ISBN 0-8298-0664-4). Pilgrim NY.

Gerlach, Joel & Bolge, Richard. Preach the Gospel. 1982. 8.95 (ISBN 0-8100-0153-5, 15NO387). Northwest Pub.

Gerlach, Luther P. & Hine, Virginia H. People, Power, Change: Movements of Social Transformation. LC 70-109434. 1970. pap. 9.63 scp (ISBN 0-672-60613-5). Bobbs.

Gerlitz, Menaham. The Heavenly City. Weinbach, Sheindel, tr. from Hebrew. Tr. of Yerushalayim Shel Ma'ala. 1978. 6.95 (ISBN 0-87306-147-0). Feldheim.

Germain, Walter M. Magic Power of Your Mind. pap. 7.00 (ISBN 0-87980-093-3). Wilshire.

German, Terence J. Hamann on Language & Religion. (Oxford Theological Monographs). 1981. text ed. 34.95x (ISBN 0-19-826717-7). Oxford U Pr.

Germany, Lucille, jt. auth. see Sumrall, Velma.

Germino, Dante. Beyond Ideology: The Revival of Political Theory. (Midway Reprint Ser.). 1976. pap. 14.00x (ISBN 0-226-28849-8). U of Chicago Pr.

Gernet, Jacques. China & the Christian Impact: A Conflict of Cultures. LLoyd, Janet, tr. 280p. 1985. 49.50 (ISBN 0-521-26681-5); pap. 17.95 (ISBN 0-521-31319-8). Cambridge U Pr.

Gerostergios, Asterios. Justinian the Great: The Emperor & Saint. LC 82-82095. (Illus.). 312p. 1982. 15.95 (ISBN 0-914744-58-5); pap. 11.95 (ISBN 0-914744-59-3). Inst Byzantine.

--On the Divine Liturgy: Orthodox Homilies, Vol. 1. Kantiotes, Augoustinos N., tr. LC 85-81949. (Illus.). 274p. 1986. 13.95 (ISBN 0-914744-72-0). Inst Byzantine.

--St. Photios the Great. LC 80-82285. (Illus.). 125p. 1980. 8.50 (ISBN 0-914744-50-X); pap. 5.50 (ISBN 0-914744-51-8). Inst Byzantine.

Gerostergios, Asterios, tr. see Kantiotes, Angoustinos N.

Gerould, G. H. Saints' Legends. 59.95 (ISBN 0-8490-0987-1). Gordon Pr.

Gerould, Gordon H. Saints' Legends. 1980. Repr. of 1916 ed. lib. bdg. 37.00 (ISBN 0-8414-4627-X). Folcroft.

Gerrick, David J. God Stories to Scare the Hell Out of You. 1979. pap. text ed. 4.95 (ISBN 0-916750-24-8). Dayton Labs.

Gerrish, B. A. The Old Protestantism & the New: Essays on the Reformation Heritage. LC 82-2730. 400p. 1983. lib. bdg. 38.00x (ISBN 0-226-28869-2). U of Chicago Pr.

--A Prince of the Church: Schleiermacher & the Beginnings of Modern Theology. LC 83-48924. 80p. 1984. pap. 4.95 (ISBN 0-8006-1787-8, 1-1787). Fortress.

--Tradition & the Modern World: Reformed Theology in the Nineteenth Century. LC 78-4982. 1978. lib. bdg. 20.00x (ISBN 0-226-28866-8). U of Chicago Pr.

Gerrish, Brian, ed. Reformatio Perennis: Essays on Calvin & the Reformation in Honor of Ford Lewis Battles. (Pittsburgh Theological Monograph Ser.: No. 32). 1981. pap. 15.00 (ISBN 0-915138-41-7). Pickwick.

Gersh, Harry. Sacred Books of the Jews. LC 68-17320. 1972. pap. 4.95 (ISBN 0-8128-1528-9). Stein & Day.

--When a Jew Celebrates. LC 70-116678. (Jewish Values Ser.). (Illus.). 256p. 1971. pap. text ed. 6.95x (ISBN 0-87441-091-6). Behrman.

Gersh, Harry & Platzner, Robert S. Mishnah, the Oral Law. 64p. 1984. pap. 2.95 (ISBN 0-87441-390-7); tchr's 6.95 (ISBN 0-317-15397-8). Behrman.

Gersh, Harry, et al. Story of the Jew. rev. ed. LC 64-22514. (Illus.). 1965. 5.95x (ISBN 0-87441-019-3). Behrman.

Gershator, Phillis. Honi & His Magic Circle. LC 79-84931. (Illus.). 1979. 6.95 (ISBN 0-8276-0167-0, 443). Jewish Pubns.

Gershom, Levi B. The Wars of the Lord: Immortality of the Soul, Vol. I: Book 1. Feldman, Seymour, tr. from Hebrew. 256p. 1984. 23.95 (ISBN 0-8276-0220-0, 605). Jewish Pubns.

Gershom, Levi ben see Gersonides, pseud.

Gershon, Levi, tr. see Alon, Gedaliah.

Gersonides, pseud. The Wars of the Lord, Vol. 2, bks. 2, 3, & 4. Feldman, Seymour, tr. from Hebrew. 288p. 1987. 23.95 (ISBN 0-8276-0275-8). Jewish Pubns.

Gerstenberger, Erhard, ed. Psalms: With Introduction to Cultic Poetry, Prt. I. (The Forms of the Old Testament Literature Ser.: Vol. XIV). 224p. (Orig.). 1987. pap. 21.95 (ISBN 0-8028-0255-9). Eerdmans.

Gerstenberger, Erhard S. & Schrage, Wolfgang. Woman & Man: Biblical Encounter Ser. Stott, Douglas W., tr. from Ger. LC 81-10898. 256p. (Orig.). 1982. pap. 10.95 (ISBN 0-687-45920-6). Abingdon.

Gerstle, Susan L., jt. ed. see Buttaci, Salvatore S.

Gerstner, John. Bible Inerrancy Primer. 1981. pap. 2.50 (ISBN 0-88469-144-6). BMH Bks.

Gerstner, John H. Predestination Primer. 1981. pap. 2.50 (ISBN 0-88469-145-4). BMH Bks.

--A Primer on Dispensationalism. 1982. pap. 1.75 (ISBN 0-87552-273-4). Presby & Reformed.

--A Primer on Free Will. 1982. pap. 1.50 (ISBN 0-87552-272-6). Presby & Reformed.

--A Primer on Justification. 32p. 1983. pap. 1.50 (ISBN 0-87552-276-9). Presby & Reformed.

--A Primer on the Deity of Christ. 40p. 1984. pap. 1.75 (ISBN 0-87552-277-7). Presby & Reformed.

--The Problem of Pleasure. 1983. pap. 1.50 (ISBN 0-87552-275-0). Presby & Reformed.

--Teachings of Jehovah's Witnesses. pap. 1.95 (ISBN 0-8010-3718-2). Baker Bk.

--Teachings of Mormonism. pap. 1.95 (ISBN 0-8010-3719-0). Baker Bk.

--Teachings of Seventh-Day Adventism. pap. 1.75 (ISBN 0-8010-3720-4). Baker Bk.

--Theology of the Major Sects. (Twin Brooks Ser). 1960. pap. 6.95 (ISBN 0-8010-3656-9). Baker Bk.

Gertel, Elliot, jt. auth. see Siegel, Seymour.

Gerth, Hans H., tr. see Weber, Max.

Gertiz, Albert J., ed. see Rastell, John.

Gertsch, Alfred. Der Steigende Ruhm Miltons. Repr. of 1927 ed. 54.00 (ISBN 0-384-18230-5). Johnson Repr.

Gervais, Marcel, ed. Journey: A Home & Group Bible Study Program. (Illus.). Set. 60.00; Old Testament, Set 20 Bklts. 30.00 (ISBN 0-8091-9279-9); New Testament Set, 20 Bklts. 30.00 (ISBN 0-8091-9280-2); bklt. 1.50 ea. Paulist Pr.

Gervers, Michael, ed. The Cartulary of the Knights of St. John of Jerusalem in England. (Records of Social & Economic History Ser.). 1982. 195.00x (ISBN 0-19-725996-0). Oxford U Pr.

Gesch, Roy. Made for Each Other: Devotions for Newly Married Couples. 112p. 1987. pap. 4.95 (ISBN 0-570-04453-7, 12-3059). Concordia.

--To Love & to Cherish. 1985. 4.95 (ISBN 0-570-04214-3, 15-2174). Concordia.

Gesch, Roy C. Confirmed in Christ. 1983. pap. 2.25 (ISBN 0-570-03911-8, 12-2852). Concordia.

Gesch, Roy G. Help, I'm in College. LC 70-77282. 1969. pap. 3.50 (ISBN 0-570-03100-1, 12-2663). Concordia.

Gesellschaft zur Forderung der Wissenschaft des Judentums. Festschrift Siebzigsten Geburtstage Jakob Guttmanns. Katz, Steven, ed. LC 79-7155. (Jewish Philosophy, Mysticism & History of Ideas Ser.). 1980. Repr. of 1915 ed. lib. bdg. 25.50x (ISBN 0-405-12253-5). Ayer Co Pubs.

Gesenius, Wilhelm. Hebrew & Chaldee Lexicon: Keyed to Strong's Exhaustive Concordance. Tregelles, Samuel P., tr. (Hebrew & Chaldee.). kivar 24.95 (ISBN 0-8010-3801-4); pap. 19.95 (ISBN 0-8010-3736-0). Baker Bk.

Gesenius, William. Hebrew & English Lexicon to the Old Testament. 2nd ed. Brown, Francis, et al, eds. Robinson, Edward, tr. (Hebrew & Eng.). 1959. Repr. of 1907 ed. 34.95x (ISBN 0-19-864301-2). Oxford U Pr.

Geshe, Dhargyey, jt. auth. see Geshe, Rabten.

Geshe, Rabten & Geshe, Dhargyey. Advice from a Spiritual Friend. rev. ed. Beresford, Brian, ed. (A Wisdom Basic Book, Orange Ser.). (Illus.). 160p. 1984. pap. 8.95 (ISBN 0-86171-017-7, Wisdom Pubns). Great Traditions.

Gesswein, Armin R. With One Accord in One Place. 93p. (Orig.). 1978. pap. 1.75 (ISBN 0-87509-161-X). Chr Pubns.

Gestwicki, Ronald. Santa Claus: The Tooth Fairy & Other Stories - A Child's Introduction to Religion. Ashton, Sylvia, ed. LC 77-80276. 1977. 15.95 (ISBN 0-87949-108-6). Ashley Bks.

Gesualda Of The Holy Spirit, Sr. Saint Theresa, the Little Flower. (Illus.). 1960. 4.95 (ISBN 0-8198-0142-9); pap. 3.95. Dghtrs St Paul.

Gesunius, William. Gesenius' Hebrew Grammar. 2nd ed. Kautzsch, E. & Cowley, A. E., eds. 1910. 29.95x (ISBN 0-19-815406-2). Oxford U Pr.

Gettings, Fred. How to Interpret Dreams, Omens & Fortune Telling Signs. pap. 5.00 (ISBN 0-87980-399-1). Wilshire.

Getty, Alice. The Gods of Northern Buddhism. LC 62-15617. (Illus.). 1962. 39.50 (ISBN 0-8048-1129-6). C E Tuttle.

Getty, Mary A. Ephesians, Philippians, Colassians. (Read & Pray Ser.). 1980. pap. 1.95 (ISBN 0-8199-0636-0). Franciscan Herald.

--Philippians & Philemon. (New Testament Message Ser.: Vol. 14). 10.95 (ISBN 0-89453-202-2); pap. 5.95 (ISBN 0-89453-137-9). M Glazier.

Getty, Mary A. & Karris, Robert J. First Corinthians, Second Corinthians, No. 7. (Collegeville Bible Commentary Ser.). 128p. 1983. pap. 2.95 (ISBN 0-8146-1307-1). Liturgical Pr.

Gettys, Joseph M. How to Study Acts. 219p. 1976. pap. 4.50x (ISBN 0-87921-028-1). Attic Pr.

--How to Study Ephesians. rev. ed. 64p. 1976. pap. 4.00x (ISBN 0-87921-056-7). Attic Pr.

--How to Study I Corinthians. 128p. 1968. pap. 4.50x (ISBN 0-8042-3532-5). Attic Pr.

--How to Study John. 153p. 1960. pap. 4.50x (ISBN 0-8042-3568-6). Attic Pr.

--How to Study Luke. rev. ed. 153p. 1975. pap. 4.50x (ISBN 0-87921-027-3). Attic Pr.

--How to Study Philippians, Colossians, & Philemon. 87p. 1964. pap. text ed. 4.50x (ISBN 0-8042-3472-8). Attic Pr.

--How to Study the Revelation. rev. ed. 117p. 1973. pap. 4.50x (ISBN 0-87921-029-X). Attic Pr.

--Surveying the Historical Books. 164p. 1963. pap. 4.00x (ISBN 0-8042-3664-X). Attic Pr.

--Surveying the Pentateuch. 147p. 1962. pap. 4.50x (ISBN 0-8042-3676-3). Attic Pr.

Getz, Gene. A Estatura de Uma Mulher. Batista, Jaoa, ed. Ferreira, Ruth V., tr. (Port.). 144p. 1981. pap. 1.60 (ISBN 0-8297-1075-2). Life Pubs Intl.

--God's Plan for Building a Good Reputation. 144p. 1987. pap. 5.95 (ISBN 0-89693-010-6). Victor Bks.

--Joshua: Defeat to Victory. LC 78-53358. 176p. 1979. pap. 5.95 (ISBN 0-8307-0643-7, 5410509). Regal.

--Loving One Another. LC 79-63450. 143p. 1979. pap. 5.95 (ISBN 0-88207-786-4). Victor Bks.

--Praying for One Another. 132p. 1982. pap. 5.50 (ISBN 0-88207-351-6). Victor Bks.

--Serving One Another. 156p. 1984. pap. 5.95 (ISBN 0-88207-612-4). Victor Bks.

Getz, Gene A. Bajo Presion. Tr. of When the Pressure Is On. (Span.). 1986. pap. 3.25 (ISBN 0-8297-0898-7). Life Pubs Intl.

--Believeing God When You Are Tempted To Doubt. LC 83-4440. (The Measure of...Ser.). 160p. 1983. pap. 5.95 (ISBN 0-8307-0881-2, 5417930). Regal.

--Believing God When You Are Tempted to Doubt: The Measure of a Christian; Studies in James I. LC 84-27543. 160p. pap. 5.95 (ISBN 0-8307-1021-3, 5418416). Regal.

--Building up One Another. LC 76-19918. 120p. 1976. pap. 4.95 (ISBN 0-88207-744-9). Victor Bks.

--Doing Your Part When You'd Rather Let God Do It All: The Measure of a Christian Based on James 2-5. LC 84-17749. 1985. pap. 5.95 (ISBN 0-8307-1002-7, 5418395). Regal.

--Encouraging One Another. 1981. pap. 5.95 (ISBN 0-88207-256-0). Victor Bks.

--Joseph: From Prison to Palace. LC 82-18571. 1983. pap. 5.95 (ISBN 0-8307-0870-7, 5417907). Regal.

--Living for Others When You'd Rather Live for Yourself. LC 85-24283. (Biblical Renewal Ser.). 126p. 1985. pap. write for info. (ISBN 0-8307-1125-2, 5418606). Regal.

--Looking up When You Feel Down Based on Ephesians 1-3. LC 85-2041. 158p. 1985. pap. 5.95 (ISBN 0-8307-1028-0, 5418463). Regal.

--Measure of a Church. LC 75-17160. (Orig.). 1975. pap. 3.50 (ISBN 0-8307-0398-5, 5014700). Regal.

--Measure of a Man. LC 74-175983. 224p. (Orig.). 1974. pap. 4.95 (ISBN 0-8307-0291-1, 5012104). Regal.

--The Measure of a Marriage. LC 78-53356. 144p. 1980. pap. 3.50 (ISBN 0-8307-0638-0, 5017203). Regal.

--Moses: Moments of Glory...Feet of Clay. LC 75-23519. 160p. (Orig.). 1976. pap. 4.95 (ISBN 0-8307-0400-0, 5403200). Regal.

--Nehemiah: A Man of Prayer & Persistence. LC 80-53102. 1981. pap. 4.95 (ISBN 0-8307-0778-6, 5414500). Regal.

--Pressing on When You'd Rather Turn Back: Philippians. rev. ed. (Biblical Renewal Ser.). 200p. 1985. pap. 5.95 (ISBN 0-8307-1089-2, 5418561). Regal.

--Saying "No" When You'd Rather Say "Yes". LC 83-2939. (A Measure of...Ser.). 200p. 1983. pap. 5.95 (ISBN 0-8307-0882-0, 5419099). Regal.

--Sharpening the Focus of the Church. 360p. 1984. pap. 8.95 (ISBN 0-89693-393-8). Victor Bks.

--Standing Firm When You'd Rather Retreat. LC 86-429. (Biblical Renewal Ser.). 168p. (Orig.). 1986. pap. 5.95 (ISBN 0-8307-1093-0, 5418594). Regal.

--Vivendo Sob Pressao. Orig. Title: When the Pressure Is on. (Port.). 1986. write for info. (ISBN 0-8297-0897-9). Life Pubs Intl.

--When You Feel You Haven't Got It. rev. ed. LC 86-540. (Biblical Renewal Ser.). 160p. 1986. pap. 5.95 (ISBN 0-8307-1123-6, 5418757). Regal.

--When You're Confused & Uncertain. rev. ed. LC 86-477. (Biblical Renewal Ser.). 160p. 1986. pap. 5.95 (ISBN 0-8307-1122-8, 5418749). Regal.

Getz, Gene A., jt. auth. see Zuck, Roy B.

Getz, Lorine, jt. ed. see Bohn, Carol.

Getz, William L. & Allen, David B. Brief Counseling with Suicidal Persons. LC 80-8375. 288p. 1982. 29.00x (ISBN 0-669-04090-8). Lexington Bks.

Gevirtz, Eliezer. Shmittah: What It's All About. (Orig.). 1987. write for info. Torah Umesorah.

Gewirth, Alan. Reason & Morality. LC 77-13911. 1978. pap. text ed. 9.95x (ISBN 0-226-28876-5). U of Chicago Pr.

Gewurz, Elias. Hidden Treasures of the Ancient Qabalah. 1922. 4.50 (ISBN 0-911662-31-6). Yoga.

--Mysteries of the Qabalah. 1922. 4.50 (ISBN 0-911662-32-4). Yoga.

Geyer, Alan. The Idea of Disarmament, Rethinking the Unthinkable. 256p. 1982. 17.95 (ISBN 0-87178-397-5); pap. 11.95 (ISBN 0-87178-396-7). Brethren.

--Idea of Disarmament, Rethinking the Unthinkable. 256p. 1985. 11.95. Brethren.

Geyer, Paul, ed. Itinera Hierosolymitana, Saeculi 3-8. (Corpus Scriptorum Ecclesiasticorum Latinorum Ser: Vol. 39). Repr. of 1898 ed. 40.00 (ISBN 0-384-18270-4). Johnson Repr.

Gfollner, Adelheid. John Masefields Stellung Zum Religiosen. Hogg, James, ed. (Poetic Drama & Poetic Theory). 129p. (Orig.). 1979. pap. 15.00 (ISBN 3-7052-0880-2, Pub. by Salzburg). Longwood Pub Group.

Ghai, O. P., ed. Unity in Diversity. 132p. 1986. text ed. 15.95x (ISBN 0-86590-762-5, Pub. by Sterling Pubs India). Apt Bks.

Ghai, S. K., ed. see Powell, James N.

Ghanananda, Swami & Steward-Wallace, John, eds. Women Saints of East & West. LC 79-65731. 1979. pap. 7.95 (ISBN 0-87481-036-1). Vedanta Pr.

Ghanoonparvar, M. R., tr. see Kasravi, Ahmad.

Ghanoonparvar, Mohammed R., tr. see Banisadr, Abolhassan.

Gharib, Georges, jt. ed. see Berselli, Costante.

Ghasemy, A. Asghar, tr. see Shariati, Ali.

Ghasemy, Ali A., tr. see Shariati, Ali.

Ghatan, H. Yedidiah. Our Invaluable Pearl: The Unique Status of Women in Judaism. LC 85-73454. 200p. (Orig.). 1986. pap. 9.95x (ISBN 0-8197-0502-0). Bloch.

Ghazi, A. Mercy for the Mankind, Vol. II. 1981. 4.00 (ISBN 0-686-97848-X). Kazi Pubns.

--Messenger of Allah, Vol. II. 1981. 4.50 (ISBN 0-686-97851-X). Kazi Pubns.

--Our Prophet, Vol. II. 1981. 3.50 (ISBN 0-686-97846-3). Kazi Pubns.

Ghazzali, Al. Mysteries of Worship in Islam: The Book of the Ihya' on Worship Translated with Commentary & Introduction. Calverley, E. E., tr. pap. 11.00 (ISBN 0-87902-200-0). Orientalia.

Ghelardi, Robert, jt. auth. see Dahm, Charles.

Ghezzi, Bert. The Angry Christian: How to Control & Use Your Anger. (Living As a Christian Ser.). 108p. (Orig.). 1980. pap. 2.95 (ISBN 0-89283-086-7). Servant.

--Becoming More Like Jesus. LC 86-63424. 160p. 1987. pap. 5.95 (ISBN 0-87973-518-X, 518). Our Sunday Visitor.

--Facing Your Feelings: How to Get Your Emotions to Work for You. (Living as a Christian Ser.). 112p. 1983. pap. 2.95 (ISBN 0-89283-133-2). Servant.

--Getting Free: How Christians Can Overcome the Flesh & Conquer Persistent Personal Problems. (Living As a Christian Ser.). 112p. 1982. pap. 2.95 (ISBN 0-89283-117-0). Servant.

--Transforming Problems. 140p. (Orig.). 1986. pap. 4.95 (ISBN 0-89283-294-0). Servant.

Ghezzi, Bert & Kinzer, Mark. Emotions As Resources: A Biblical & Pastoral Perspective. 110p. 1983. pap. 6.95 (ISBN 0-89283-158-8). Servant.

Ghose, Jogendra C., ed. see Rammohun Roy, R.

Ghose, Sisirkumar. The Mystic As a Force for Change. rev. ed. LC 80-53954. 144p. 1980. pap. 4.75 (ISBN 0-8356-0547-7, Quest). Theos Pub Hse.

Ghosh, A. Jaina Art & Architecture, 3 vols. (Illus.). 1974. Set. text ed. 110.00x. Coronet Bks.

--The Koran & the Kafir: Islam & the Infidel. (Illus.). 190p. 1983. pap. 5.95 (ISBN 0-9611614-0-X). Ghosh A.

--The Koran & the Kafir: Islam & the Infidel. rev., 2nd ed. (Illus.). 200p. (Orig.). 1983. pap. 7.35 (ISBN 0-9611614-1-8). Ghosh A.

Ghosh, Jajneshwar. A Study of Yoga. 2nd rev. ed. 1977. 16.95 (ISBN 0-89684-014-X, Pub. by Motilal Banarsidass India); pap. 12.50 (ISBN 0-89684-015-8). Orient Bk Dist.

Ghosh, Mallar. Development of Buddhist Iconography in Eastern India. (Illus.). 1980. text ed. 44.00x. Coronet Bks.

Ghosh, Oroon K. Science, Society & Philosophy: A New Radical Humanist Approach. 1986. 28.00x (ISBN 0-8364-1563-9, Pub. by Ajanta). South Asia Bks.

Ghosh, Prabodh C. Poetry & Religion As Drama. 1979. Repr. of 1965 ed. lib. bdg. 25.00 (ISBN 0-8492-4940-6). R West.

Ghosh, S. K. Muslim Politics in India. 1986. 18.50 (ISBN 81-7024-070-0, Pub. by Ashish India). South Asia Bks.

Ghosh, S. P. Hindu Religious Art & Architecture. (Illus.). 148p. 1983. text ed. 30.00x (ISBN 0-86590-124-4). Apt Bks.

Ghosh, Sananda L. Mejda: The Family & the Early Life of Paramahansa Yogananda. LC 80-54206. (Illus.). 330p. 1980. 8.50 (ISBN 0-87612-265-9). Self Realization.

Ghoshal, Sarat C., ed. The Sacred Books of the Jainas (Bibliotheca Jainica, 11 vols. Repr. of 1940 ed. 324.00 (ISBN 0-404-19549-0). AMS Pr.

Ghougassian, Joseph P. Kahlil Gibran: Wings of Thought. LC 73-77402. (Illus.). 255p. 1973. 7.50 (ISBN 0-8022-2115-7). Philos Lib.

Ghurye, G. S. Gods & Men. 1962. 39.50x (ISBN 0-317-27474-0). Elliots Bks.

--Vedic India. 1979. 46.00 (ISBN 0-89684-061-1, Pub. by Motilal Banarsidass India). Orient Bk Dist.

Giachery, Ugo. Shoghi Effendi: Recollections. (Illus.). 248p. 1973. 16.95 (ISBN 0-85398-050-0). G Ronald Pub.

Giacometti, Mario. Pregare in Certosa Oggi. Hogg, James, ed. (Analecta Cartusiana Ser.: No. 97). 141p. (Orig.). 1980. pap. 25.00 (ISBN 3-7052-0168-9, Pub. by Salzburg Studies). Longwood Pub Group.

Giacomo, James Di see Di Giacomo, James.

Gia-Fu Feng, ed. see Chuang Tsu.

Gia-Fu Feng, ed. see Lao Tsu.

Giancotti, Emilia, ed. Proceedings of the First Italian International Congress on Spinoza. (Illus.). 556p. 1985. 60.00x (ISBN 88-7088-121-0, Pub. by Bibliopolis Italy). Humanities.

Giannella, Donald A., ed. Religion & the Public Order: An Annual Review of Church & State & of Religion, Law, & Society. LC 64-17164. pap. 72.00 (ISBN 0-317-20699-0, 2024114). Bks Demand UMI.

Gianotti, Charles R. The New Testament & the Mishnah. 1983. pap. 3.50 (ISBN 0-8010-3791-3). Baker Bk.

Gibb, C. C. More Than Enough. 83p. pap. 4.95 (ISBN 0-88172-071-2). Believers Bkshelf.

Gibb, Christopher. Richard the Lionheart & the Crusades. (Life & Times Ser.). (Illus.). 64p. 1985. s&l 11.40 (ISBN 0-531-18011-5, Pub. by Bookwright Pr). Watts.

Gibb, H. A. & Kramers, J. H., eds. Shorter Encyclopaedia of Islam. (Illus.). 678p. 1957. 85.00x (ISBN 0-8014-0150-X). Cornell U Pr.

Gibb, H. A., tr. see Ibn Al-Qalanisi.

Gibb, H. A., et al see Lewis, B., et al.

Gibb, Hamilton A. Mohammedanism: An Historical Survey. 2nd ed. 1953. pap. 5.95x (ISBN 0-19-500245-8, 90). Oxford U Pr.

Gibb, Hamilton A., ed. Whither Islam? A Survey of Modern Movements in the Moslem World. LC 73-180338. Repr. of 1932 ed. 27.00 (ISBN 0-404-56263-9). AMS Pr.

Gibb, John & Montgomery, William. The Confessions of Augustine. 2nd ed. LC 78-66639. (Ancient Philosophy Ser.). 554p. 1980. lib. bdg. 67.00 (ISBN 0-8240-9597-9). Garland Pub.

Gibbany, Etta M. Star Beams. 24p. 1958. pap. 1.50 (ISBN 0-88053-323-4, S-304). Macoy Pub.

Gibble, Kenneth L. The Preacher as Jacob: A Paradigm for Pulpit Ministry. 144p. (Orig.). 1985. pap. 8.95 (ISBN 0-8164-2633-3, AY8587, HarpR). Har-Row.

--Yeast, Salt & Secret Agents. 1979. pap. 4.95 (ISBN 0-87178-968-X). Brethren.

Gibbon, Edward. Autobiography. (World's Classics Ser., No. 139). 16.95 (ISBN 0-19-250139-9). Oxford U Pr.

--The Early Growth of Christianity & the History of the First Christians. (Illus.). 177p. 1986. 137.45 (ISBN 0-89266-557-2). Am Classical Coll Pr.

--History of Christianity. LC 79-169227. (Atheist Viewpoint Ser.). (Illus.). 912p. 1972. Repr. of 1883 ed. 51.00 (ISBN 0-405-03796-1). Ayer Co Pubs.

--History of Christianity. 59.95 (ISBN 0-8490-0319-9). Gordon Pr.

--Mahomet & the Political Theory of the Arab Empire, 2 vols. (Illus.). 328p. 1984. Repr. of 1901 ed. 217.85 set (ISBN 0-89901-181-0). Found Class Reprints.

Gibbons, Francis. Joseph F. Smith. LC 84-70071. (Illus.). 1984. 10.95 (ISBN 0-87747-988-7). Deseret Bk.

Gibbons, Francis M. David O. McKay: Apostle to the World, Prophet of God. LC 86-4564. (Illus.). 455p. 1986. 13.95 (ISBN 0-87579-036-4). Deseret Bk.

--Heber J. Grant: Man of Steel, Prophet of God. LC 79-11649. 252p. 1979. 8.95 (ISBN 0-87747-755-8). Deseret Bk.

--John Taylor: Mormon Philosopher, Prophet of God. LC 84-73532. 312p. 1985. 10.95 (ISBN 0-87747-714-0). Deseret Bk.

Gibbons, Gail. Christmas Time. LC 82-1038. (Illus.). 32p. 1982. Reinforced bdg. 12.95 (ISBN 0-8234-0453-6). Holiday.

--Christmas Time. (Illus.). 32p. 1985. pap. 5.95 (ISBN 0-8234-0575-3). Holiday.

Gibbons, James. The Faith of Ours Fathers: Being a Plain Exposition & Vindication of the Church Founded by Our Lord Jesus Christ. 33.00 (ISBN 0-405-10832-X, 11839). Ayer Co Pubs.

Gibbons, James C. A Retrospect of Fifty Years, 2 vols. in 1. LC 79-38447. (Religion in America, Ser. 2). 720p. 1972. Repr. of 1916 ed. 47.50 (ISBN 0-405-04066-0). Ayer Co Pubs.

Gibbons, John. Road to Nazareth: Through Palestine Today. LC 77-180339. Repr. of 1936 ed. 26.00 (ISBN 0-404-56264-7). AMS Pr.

Gibbons, Joseph, tr. see Geoffrey of Auxerre.

Gibbons, Joseph C. Whatever Happened to Friday? & Other Questions Catholics Ask. LC 79-91275. (Orig.). 1980. pap. 3.95 (ISBN 0-8091-2278-2). Paulist Pr.

Gibbons, Sherry, et al. Evenings of Joy & Inspiration for Parish Leaders. LC 83-62197. 64p. (Orig.). 1983. pap. text ed. 2.95 (ISBN 0-911905-08-1). Past & Mat Rene Ctr.

Gibbs, A. P. Christian Baptism. 1982. pap. 5.00 (ISBN 0-937396-62-1). Walterick Pubs.

--The Preacher & His Preaching. 16.95 (ISBN 0-937396-31-1); pap. 10.95 (ISBN 0-937396-30-3). Walterick Pubs.

--Scriptural Principles of Gathering. pap. 1.95 (ISBN 0-937396-37-0). Walterick Pubs.

--Through the Scriptures. pap. 5.95 (ISBN 0-937396-45-1). Walterick Pubs.

--Worship: The Christian's Highest Occupation. pap. 5.95 (ISBN 0-937396-57-5). Walterick Pubs.

Gibbs, E., jt. auth. see Gibbs, M.

Gibbs, Ellen & Gibbs, Mary. The Bible References of John Ruskin. 310p. 1973. Repr. of 1898 ed. 20.00 (ISBN 0-8274-0652-5). R West.

Gibbs, Lee W., tr. see Ames, William.

Gibbs, M. Christians with Secular Power. LC 80-8048. (Laity Exchange). 144p. (Orig.). 1981. pap. 5.95 (ISBN 0-8006-1389-9, 1-1389). Fortress.

Gibbs, M. & Gibbs, E. The Bible References of John Ruskin. 59.95 (ISBN 0-87968-729-0). Gordon Pr.

Gibbs, Margaret. Saints Beyond the White Cliffs: Stories of English Saints. facs. ed. LC 75-148211. (Biography Index Reprint Ser.). (Illus.). 1947. 20.00 (ISBN 0-8369-8058-1). Ayer Co Pubs.

Gibbs, Mark, ed. see Mouw, Richard J.

Gibbs, Mary, jt. auth. see Gibbs, Ellen.

Gibbs, Tam, tr. see Men-Ching, Cheng.

Gibellini, Rosino, ed. Frontiers of Theology in Latin America. Drury, John, tr. from Ital. LC 78-9147. Orig. Title: La nuova frontiera della Teologia in Latina America. 333p. (Orig.). 1979. pap. 10.95 (ISBN 0-88344-144-6). Orbis Bks.

Giblin, James C. The Truth about Santa Claus. LC 85-47541. (Illus.). 96p. 1985. 11.70 (ISBN 0-690-04483-6, Crowell Jr Bks); PLB 11.89 (ISBN 0-690-04484-4). HarpJ.

Gibran, Kahlil. Jesus the Son of Man. (Illus.). 1928. 14.95 (ISBN 0-394-43124-3). Knopf.

--Lazarus & His Beloved. 64p. 1973. 5.95 (ISBN 0-8464-1165-2). Beekman Pubs.

--Sand & Foam. (Illus.). 1926. 9.95 (ISBN 0-394-44369-1). Knopf.

Gibson, Agnes C., tr. see Grunwedel, Albert.

Gibson, Alan G. Eight Years in Kaffraria, 1882-1890. LC 79-82052. (Illus.). Repr. of 1891 ed. cancelled (ISBN 0-8371-1573-6, GIK&, Pub. by Negro U Pr). Greenwood.

Gibson, Arthur. Biblical Semantic Logic. 1981. 32.50 (ISBN 0-312-07796-3). St Martin.

--The Silence of God: Creative Response to the Films of Ingmar Bergman. LC 81-18754. 171p. 1978. soft cover 9.95x (ISBN 0-88946-951-2). E Mellen.

Gibson, Arthur, tr. see Fabro, Cornelio.

Gibson, Boyce. Religion of Dostoevsky. 214p. 6.95 (ISBN 0-664-20989-0). Brown Bk.

Gibson, Dennis L. Live, Grow & Be Free: A Guide to Self-Parenting. LC 82-82412. 136p. 1982. pap. 5.95 (ISBN 0-89840-030-9). Here's Life.

Gibson, Edgar C. The Book of Job. 266p. 1983. lib. bdg. 10.00 (ISBN 0-86524-170-8, 1801). Klock & Klock.

Gibson, Edmund. Codex Juris Ecclesiastici Anglicani, 2 Vols. 1761. text ed. 372.60x (ISBN 0-576-99471-5, Pub. by Gregg Intl Pubs England). Gregg Intl.

Gibson, Elsie. Honest Prayer. LC 80-39570. 120p. (Orig.). 1981. pap. 7.95 (ISBN 0-664-24348-7). Westminster.

Gibson, Eva. Intimate Moments: Teaching Your Child to Walk with God. 1987. pap. 5.95. Heres Life.

--Melissa. 137p. (Orig.). 1982. pap. 2.95 (ISBN 0-87123-575-7, 200575). Bethany Hse.

Gibson, Eva & Price, Steven. Building Christian Confidence. (Building Bks.). 64p. (Orig.). 1987. tchr's. guide 4.95 (ISBN 0-87123-935-3). Bethany Hse.

--Building Christian Confidence. (Building Bks.). 76p. (Orig.). 1987. student wkbk. 3.95 (ISBN 0-87123-934-5). Bethany Hse.

Gibson, George M. Story of the Christian Year. LC 71-142635. (Essay Index Reprint Ser.). (Illus.). Repr. of 1945 ed. 25.00 (ISBN 0-8369-2770-2). Ayer Co Pubs.

Gibson, J. Paul. Shakespeare's Use of the Supernatural. LC 79-144615. Repr. of 1908 ed. 15.00 (ISBN 0-404-02719-9). AMS Pr.

Gibson, Jean. Advanced Christian Training. (Orig.). 1986. pap. 7.00 (ISBN 0-937396-04-4). Walterick Pubs.

--Basic Christian Training. (Believer's Bible Lessons Ser.). 1980. pap. 5.95 (ISBN 0-937396-06-0). Walterick Pubs.

--Intermediate Christian Training. 1981. pap. 7.50 (ISBN 0-937396-60-5). Walterick Pubs.

--Survey in Basic Christianity. (Believer's Bible Lessons Ser.). 1979. pap. 5.50 (ISBN 0-937396-41-9). Walterick Pubs.

Gibson, John. The Book of Hu & the Book of Tyana. LC 84-19096. (Illus.). 136p. 1984. 15.00 (ISBN 0-8022-2449-0). Philos Lib.

Gibson, John C. Canaanite Myths & Legends. (Illus.). 208p. 1978. 32.95 (ISBN 0-567-02351-6, Pub. by T & T Clark Ltd UK). Fortress.

--Job. LC 85-13652. (Daily Study Bible - Old Testament). 294p. 1985. 16.95 (ISBN 0-664-21815-6); pap. 8.95 (ISBN 0-664-24584-6). Westminster.

Gibson, John C. L. Genesis, Vol. 1 chs. 1-11. LC 81-7477. (Daily Study Bible-Old Testament Ser.). 224p. 1981. 12.95 (ISBN 0-664-21801-6); pap. 6.95 (ISBN 0-664-24568-4). Westminster.

--Genesis, Vol. 2, chs. 12-50. LC 81-7477. (Daily Study Bible-Old Testament Ser.). 336p. 1982. 12.95 (ISBN 0-664-21804-0); pap. 7.95 (ISBN 0-664-24571-4). Westminster.

Gibson, Katherine. The Tall Book of Bible Stories. LC 57-10952. (Tall Bks.). (Illus.). 128p. 1980. 5.70i (ISBN 0-06-021935-1); PLB 7.89 (ISBN 0-06-021936-X). HarpJ.

Gibson, McGuire. Excavations at Nippur. LC 75-9054. (Oriental Institute Communications Ser.: No. 22). 1976. pap. 15.00x (ISBN 0-226-62339-4). U of Chicago Pr.

Gibson, McGuire, et al. Excavations at Nippur: Twelfth Season. LC 78-59117. (Oriental Institute Communications Ser.: No. 23). (Illus.). 1978. pap. 22.00x (ISBN 0-918986-22-2). Oriental Inst.

Gibson, Margaret. Lanfranc of Bec. 1978. 47.00x (ISBN 0-19-822462-1). Oxford U Pr.

Gibson, Margaret, jt. auth. see Hunt, R. W.

Gibson, Margaret W. Emma Smith: Elect Lady. LC 54-7910. 1954. pap. 8.00 (ISBN 0-8309-0256-2). Herald Hse.

Gibson, Michael. Gods, Men & Monsters from the Greek Myths. LC 81-14542. (World Mythologies Ser.). (Illus.). 156p. 1982. 15.95 (ISBN 0-8052-3793-3). Schocken.

Gibson, Morgan. Among Buddhas of Japan. 1987. 10.00. White Pine.

Gibson, Morgan & Murakami, Hiroshi, trs. Tantric Poetry of Kukai. 1985. 7.00 (ISBN 0-934834-67-9). White Pine.

Gibson, Roxie C. Hey, God! Hurry! LC 82-60193. (Illus.). 52p. 1982. 3.95 (ISBN 0-938232-08-8, 32534). Winston-Derek.

--Hey, God! Listen! LC 82-60195. (Illus.). 68p. 1982. 3.95 (ISBN 0-938232-06-1, 32466). Winston-Derek.

--Hey, God! What Is America? LC 81-71025. (Illus.). 52p. 1982. 3.95 (ISBN 0-938232-05-3, 32795). Winston-Derek.

--Hey, God! What Is Christmas. LC 82-60192. (Illus.). 64p. 3.95 (ISBN 0-938232-09-6, 32752). Winston-Derek.

--Hey, God! Where are You? LC 82-60194. (Illus.). 64p. 1982. 3.95 (ISBN 0-938232-07-X, 32485). Winston-Derek.

Gibson, Ruth E. In Search of Young Parents. 120p. (Orig.). 1984. pap. 4.95 (ISBN 0-8341-0911-5). Beacon Hill.

Gick, Georg J. & Swinger, Marlys. Shepherd's Pipe Songs from the Holy Night: A Christmas Cantata for Children's Voices or Youth Choir. Choral ed. LC 71-85805. (Illus.). 64p. 1969. pap. 2.50 choral ed. (ISBN 0-87486-011-3); cassette 6.00 (ISBN 0-686-66331-4). Plough.

Gide, Andre P. Dostoevsky. LC 78-14443. 1979. Repr. of 1961 ed. lib. bdg. 22.50x (ISBN 0-313-21178-7, GIDO). Greenwood.

Gideon, Virtus E. Luke: Study Guide Commentary. (Orig.). 1967. pap. 4.95 (ISBN 0-310-24973-2, 9084P). Zondervan.

Gideon, Virtus E., jt. auth. see Vaughan, Curtis.

Gidio, Sandra de see De Gidio, Sandra.

Gidlow, Elsa. Makings for Meditation. (Illus.). 1973. 2.00 (ISBN 0-9606568-0-4). Druid Heights.

Gier, Nicholas F. God, Reason & the Evangelicals: The Case Against Evangelical Rationalism. 404p. (Orig.). 1987. lib. bdg. 34.50 (ISBN 0-8191-5812-7); pap. text ed. 19.75 (ISBN 0-8191-5813-5). U Pr of Amer.

Gies, Frances. The Knight in History. LC 84-47571. (Illus.). 192p. 1984. 16.45 (ISBN 0-06-015339-3, HarpT). Har-Row.

Giesbrecht, Herbert. The Mennonite Brethren Church: A Bibliographic Guide. 99p. (Orig.). 1983. pap. 7.95 (ISBN 0-919797-28-8). Kindred Pr.

Giese, Vincent J. Youth for Peace: A Handbook for Young Christian Peacemakers. LC 84-60751. 120p. 1984. pap. 5.95 (ISBN 0-87973-596-1, 596). Our Sunday Visitor.

Giesey, R. E. The Royal Funeral Ceremony in Renaissance France. viii, 240p. (Orig.). 1960. pap. text ed. 40.00x (Pub. by Droz Switzerland). Coronet Bks.

Giesey, Ralph. If Not, Not: The Oath of the Aragonese & the Legendary Laws of the Sobrarbe. LC 67-21023. 1968. 30.50 (ISBN 0-691-05128-3). Princeton U Pr.

Gietzen, Jean J. A People Set Apart. LC 83-61452. 1983. pap. 6.95 (ISBN 0-89390-047-8). Resource Pubns.

Giff, Patricia R. Mother Teresa: A Sister to the Poor. LC 85-40885. (Illus.). 64p. 1986. 9.95 (ISBN 0-670-81096-7, Viking Kestrel). Viking.

Giffin, Rodney & Giffin, Sara. In the Catacombs of Rome. 1982. pap. 3.00 (ISBN 0-89536-524-3, 0902). CSS of Ohio.

Giffin, Sara, jt. auth. see Giffin, Rodney.

Gifford, Carolyn, ed. see Foster, John O.

Gifford, Carolyn, ed. see Holley, Marietta.

Gifford, Carolyn, ed. see Horton, Isabelle.

Gifford, Carolyn, ed. see Ingraham, Sarah R.

Gifford, Carolyn, ed. see Montgomery, Helen B.

Gifford, Carolyn, tr. see Gifford, Carolyn D. & Dayton, Donald.

Gifford, Carolyn D. & Dayton, Donald, eds. The American Deaconess Movement in the Early Twentieth Century. (Women in American Protestant Religion 1800-1930 Ser.). 288p. 1987. lib. bdg. 40.00 (ISBN 0-8240-0650-X). Garland Pub.

--The American Ideal of the "True Woman" As Reflected in Advice Books to Young Women. Gifford, Carolyn, tr. (Women in American Protestant Religion 1800-1930 Ser.). 431p. 1987. lib. bdg. 60.00 (ISBN 0-8240-0651-8). Garland Pub.

Gifford, Carolyn D., ed. see MacDonell, Robert W.

Gifford, Carolyn D., ed. see Prentiss, George L.

Gifford, Carolyn D., ed. see Sexton, Lydia.

Gifford, Carolyn D., ed. see Sleeper, Sarah.

Gifford, Carolyn D., ed. see Smith, Amanda B.

Gifford, Carolyn D., ed. see Starr, Lee A.

Gifford, Carolyn D., ed. see Stevens, Abel.

Gifford, Carolyn D., ed. see Swain, Clara A.

Gifford, Carolyn D., ed. see Utley, Uldine.

Gifford, Carolyn D., ed. see Winslow, Miron.

Gifford, Carolyn D., ed. see Wittenmyer, Annie T.

Gifford, Douglas. Warriors, Gods & Spirits from Central & South American Mythology. (World Mythologies Ser.). (Illus.). 132p. 1983. 15.95 (ISBN 0-8052-3857-3). Schocken.

Gifford, E. H., jt. auth. see Andrews, Samuel J.

Gifford, E. W. Tongan Myths & Tales. (BMB). Repr. of 1924 ed. 25.00 (ISBN 0-527-02111-3, BMB, NO. 8). Kraus Repr.

Gifford, E. W., jt. auth. see Kroeber, Alfred L.

Gifford, Edwin H., tr. see Eusebius.

Gifford, George. A Discourse of the Subtill Practises of Devilles by Witches & Sorcerers. LC 77-6745. (English Experience Ser.: No. 871). 1977. Repr. of 1587 ed. lib. bdg. 8.00 (ISBN 90-221-0871-6). Walter J Johnson.

--A Plaine Declaration That Our Brownists Be Full Donatists. LC 74-80180. (English Experience Ser.: No. 661). 1974. Repr. of 1590 ed. 14.00 (ISBN 90-221-0661-6). Walter J Johnson.

Gignac, Francis T. An Introductory New Testament Greek Course. 4.20 (ISBN 0-8294-0223-3). Loyola.

Gilani, A. Maududi, Thought & Movements. 25.00 (ISBN 0-317-46091-9). Kazi Pubns.

Gilbert. Gilbert of Hoyland: Treasties, Epistles, & Sermons. Braceland, Lawrence C., tr. (Fathers Ser.: No. 34). 1981. 12.95 (ISBN 0-87907-434-5). Cistercian Pubns.

Gilbert, Allan H. Dante's Conception of Justice. LC 76-166199. (BCL Ser.: I). Repr. of 1925 ed. 15.00 (ISBN 0-404-02757-1). AMS Pr.

Gilbert, Arthur. The Passover Seder. (Illus.). 1965. pap. 2.95x (ISBN 0-87068-504-X). Ktav.

--Your Neighbor Worships. 31p. 1.50 (ISBN 0-686-74968-5). ADL.

Gilbert, Arthur & Tarcov, Oscar. Your Neighbor Celebrates. 38p. 0.75 (ISBN 0-686-74967-7). ADL.

--Your Neighbor Celebrates. 6.00x (ISBN 0-87068-364-0, Pub. by Friendly Hse). Ktav.

Gilbert, Dave, jt. auth. see Bundschuh, Rick.

Gilbert, David. Some Ancient Christmas Carols with the Tunes to Which They Were Formally Sung in the West of England. LC 72-6976. 1972. lib. bdg. 12.50 (ISBN 0-88305-249-0). Norwood Edns.

Gilbert, Dennis A., jt. auth. see Weber, Paul J.

Gilbert, Donald. Jellyfish Bones the Humor of Zen. Angilly, Richard, ed. (Illus.). 168p. (Orig.). 1980. pap. 7.95x (ISBN 0-931290-25-2). Blue Dragon.

Gilbert, Felix. The Pope, His Banker & Venice. LC 80-13062. (Illus.). 167p. 1980. text ed. 12.50x (ISBN 0-674-68975-5). Harvard U Pr.

Gilbert, George. The Sixty Dramatic Illustrations in Full Colours of the Cathedral Cities of England. (A Promotion of the Arts Library). (Illus.). 99p. 1983. 297.85 (ISBN 0-86650-046-4). Gloucester Art.

Gilbert, John R. Pastor As Shepherd of the School Community. 52p. 1983. 4.80 (ISBN 0-318-00788-6). Natl Cath Educ.

Gilbert, Martin. Exile & Return: The Struggle for a Jewish Homeland. (Illus.). 364p. 1978. 12.95 (ISBN 0-397-01249-7). Brown Bk.

--The Final Journey: The Fate of the Jews in Nazi Europe. (Illus.). 1980. 12.50 (ISBN 0-8317-3325-X, Mayflower Bks). Smith Pubs.

--The Holocaust. 64p. 1979. pap. 6.95 (ISBN 0-8090-1389-4). Hill & Wang.

--The Holocaust: A History of the Jews of Europe during the Second World War. LC 85-5523. (Illus.). 900p. 1986. 19.45 (ISBN 0-317-44733-5). H Holt & Co.

--The Holocaust: The History of the Jews of Europe During the Second World War. LC 85-5523. (Illus.). 488p. 1985. 24.95 (ISBN 0-03-062416-9). H Holt & Co.

--The Jews of Hope. (Nonfiction Ser.). 272p. 1985. pap. 7.95 (ISBN 0-14-008510-6). Penguin.

--The Jews of Hope: The Plight of Soviet Jewry Today. LC 84-40461. (Illus.). 237p. 1985. 15.95 (ISBN 0-670-80377-4, E. Sifton Bks). Viking.

--Macmillan Atlas of the Holocaust. (Quality Paperbacks Ser.). (Illus.). 256p. 1984. pap. 13.95 (ISBN 0-306-80218-X). Da Capo.

--Scharansky: Hero of our Time. 512p. 1986. 24.95 (ISBN 0-317-46605-4). Viking.

--Shcharansky: Hero of Our Time. (Illus.). 512p. 1986. 24.95 (ISBN 0-670-81418-0). Viking.

Gilbert, Marvin. God, Me, & Thee. (Discovery Bks.). 1980. 1.50 (ISBN 0-88243-841-7, 02-0841); tchr's ed 3.95 (ISBN 0-88243-331-8, 02-0331). Gospel Pub.

Gilbert, Marvin G. & Brock, Raymond T., eds. The Holy Spirit & Counseling: Theology & Theory. 248p. 1985. pap. 12.95 (ISBN 0-913573-41-8). Hendrickson MA.

Gilbert, O. & Whittaker, R. The Historical Meaning of Savonarola As a Religious, Moral & Political Prophet & the Progress of the Reformation in Italy. 189p. 1985. 88.45 (ISBN 0-89266-514-9). Am Classical Coll Pr.

Gilbert, R. A. The Golden Dawn: Twilight of the Magicians. 128p. 1983. pap. 7.95 (ISBN 0-85030-278-1). Newcastle Pub.

Gilbert, R. A., jt. auth. see Birks, Walter.

Gilbert, Richard. The Prophetic Imperative. 1980. pap. 6.75 (ISBN 0-933840-16-0). Unitarian Univ.

Gilbert, Stuart, tr. see Saint-Exupery, Saint Antoine De.

Gilbert, Timothy D., jt. auth. see Tillman, William M., Jr.

Gilbert Of Hoyland. Gilbert of Hoyland: Sermons on the Song of Songs, 1. Braceland, Lawrence C., tr. from Latin. LC 77-23026. (Fathers Ser.: No. 14). 1978. 15.95 (ISBN 0-87907-414-0). Cistercian Pubns.

--Gilbert of Hoyland, Sermons on the Song of Songs, II. (Fathers Ser.: No. 20). 1979. 8.95 (ISBN 0-87907-420-5). Cistercian Pubns.

--Gilbert of Hoyland: Sermons on the Song of Songs, III. Braceland, Lawrence C., tr. (Fathers Ser.: No. 26). 1979. 8.95 (ISBN 0-87907-426-4). Cistercian Pubns.

--Sermons on the Song of Songs, 3 vols, Vols. 1-3. Set. 30.00. Cistercian Pubns.

Gilbertson, Merrill T. Way It Was in Bible Times. LC 59-10759. (Illus.). 1959. pap. 6.95 (ISBN 0-8066-1442-0, 10-7000). Augsburg.

Gilboa, Yehoshuna A. A Language Silenced: Hebrew Culture in the Soviet Union. LC 80-70920. 320p. 1982. 25.00 (ISBN 0-8386-3072-3). Fairleigh Dickerson.

Gilby, Thomas, ed. see St. Thomas Aquinas.

Gilchrist, Alexander. Life of William Blake: With Selections from His Poems & Other Writings, 2 vols. enl. ed. (Illus.). 993p. 1969. Set. 75.00x (ISBN 0-87753-017-3). Phaeton.

Gilchrist, John & Andrews, Judy. Matthew's Gospel. 1.77 (ISBN 0-8091-9335-3). Paulist Pr.

Gilchrist, John, jt. auth. see McDowell, Josh.

Gilchrist, M. R., tr. see Calvin, Jean.

Gildea, Joseph, ed. see Gregory the Great.

Gildea, Sr. Marianna. Expressions of Religious Thought & Feeling in the Chansons De Geste. LC 75-94172. (Catholic University of America Studies in Romance Languages & Literatures Ser: No. 25). 1969. Repr. of 1943 ed. 30.00 (ISBN 0-404-50325-X). AMS Pr.

Gildon, Charles. The Deist's Manual; or a Rational Enquiry into the Christian Religion. Wellek, Rene, ed. LC 75-11220. (British Philosophers & Theologians of the 17th & 18th Centuries Ser.: Vol. 23). 1976. Repr. of 1705 ed. lib. bdg. 51.00 (ISBN 0-8240-1774-9). Garland Pub.

Gildrie, Richard P. Salem, Massachusetts, Sixteen Twenty-Six to Sixteen Eighty-Three: A Covenant Community. LC 74-20841. (Illus.). 187p. 1975. 20.00x (ISBN 0-8139-0532-X). U Pr of Va.

Gileadi, Avraham. The Apocalyptic Book of Isaiah: A New Translation with Interpretative Key. Gileadi, Avraham, tr. (Hebrew.). 207p. 1982. 10.95 (ISBN 0-910511-00-4). Hebraeus Pr.

--The Book of Isaiah. 264p. 1987. 12.95 (ISBN 0-87579-076-3). Deseret Bk.

Gileadi, Avraham, ed. Israel's Apostasy & Restoration in Prophetic Thought: Essays in Honor of Roland Kenneth Harrison. 336p. 1986. 26.95 (ISBN 0-8407-7532-6). Nelson.

Giles, Edward, ed. Documents Illustrating Papal Authority, A.D. 96-454. LC 78-59023. 1979. Repr. of 1952 ed. 28.00 (ISBN 0-88355-696-0). Hyperion Conn.

Giles, H. A. Confucianism & Its Rivals. lib. bdg. 79.95 (ISBN 0-87968-520-4). Krishna Pr.

--The Religions of Ancient China. 59.95 (ISBN 0-8490-0941-3). Gordon Pr.

Giles, H. A., tr. see Fa-hsien, Fl.

Giles, Herbert A. Confucianism & Its Rivals. LC 77-27155. (Hibbert Lectures: 1914). Repr. of 1915 ed. 30.00 (ISBN 0-404-60416-1). AMS Pr.

--Religions of Ancient China. LC 79-95067. (Select Bibliographies Reprint Ser). 1905. 17.00 (ISBN 0-8369-5069-0). Ayer Co Pubs.

--Religions of Ancient China. LC 76-20524. 1976. Repr. of 1905 ed. lib. bdg. 17.00 (ISBN 0-8414-4518-4). Folcroft.

Giles, Herbert A., ed. & tr. from Chinese. Musings of a Chinese Mystic: Selections from the Philosophy of Chuang Tzu. 112p. Repr. of 1926 ed. text ed. 17.50x (ISBN 0-89644-497-X, Pub. by Chinese Matl Ctr). Coronet Bks.

Giles, Herbert A., tr. see Chuang Tzu.

Giles, J. A., ed. see Alan of Tewkesbury.

Giles, J. E. Bases Biblicas De la Etica. 1983. Repr. of 1979 ed. 4.25 (ISBN 0-311-46028-3). Casa Bautista.

Giles, James E. Esto Creemos los Bautistas. 111p. 1981. pap. 2.50 (ISBN 0-311-09091-5). Casa Bautista.

--Pastoral Care & Counselling. pap. text ed. 10.95 (ISBN 0-311-72535-X). Casa Bautista.

--La Psicologia y el Ministerio Cristiano. 384p. 1982. Repr. of 1978 ed. 3.20 (ISBN 0-311-42059-1). Casa Bautista.

Giles, John A., ed. Benedicti Abbatis Petriburgenis De Vita et Miraculis S. Thomae Cantuar. Repr. of 1850 ed. 24.00 (ISBN 0-8337-1341-8). B Franklin.

--Chronicon Angliae Petriburgense. 1966. Repr. of 1845 ed. 24.00 (ISBN 0-8337-1342-6). B Franklin.

Giles, John A., ed. see Bede the Venerable.

Giles, John A., tr. see De Lion, Gwoffrey, et al.

Giles, Lionel, jt. tr. see Johnston, Charles.

Giles, M. A., tr. see Fa-hsien, Fl.

Giles, Mary. Francisco de Osuna: The Third Spiritual Alphabet, Vol 1. (Classics of Western Spirtuality Ser.). 1982. 16.95 (ISBN 0-8091-0266-8); pap. 11.95 (ISBN 0-8091-2145-X). Paulist Pr.

Giles, Mary E. The Feminist Mystic & Other Essays on Women & Spirituality. 208p. 1982. pap. 8.95 (ISBN 0-8245-0432-1). Crossroad NY.

--The Poetics of Love: Meditations with John of the Cross. (American University Studies VII-Theology & Religion). 177p. 1987. text ed. 20.00 (ISBN 0-8204-0321-0). P Lang Pubs.

--When Each Leaf Shines: Voices of Women's Ministry. 1986. pap. 4.95 (ISBN 0-87193-246-6). Dimension Bks.

Gilhodes, Abbe L. La Chartreuse Saint-Sauveur de Villefranche-de-Rouergue 1459-1791. Hogg, James, ed. (Analecta Cartusiana Ser.: No. 14). (Fr.). 236p. (Orig.). 1973. pap. 25.00 (ISBN 3-7052-0016-X, Pub by Salzburg Studies). Longwood Pub Group.

Gilhooley, Leonard. Contradiction & Dilemma: Orestes Brownson & the American Idea. LC 78-158738. xvi, 231p. 1972. 25.00 (ISBN 0-8232-0930-X). Fordham.

Gilkey, Helen L., jt. auth. see Greenburg, Samuel A.

Gilkey, Langdon. Creationism on Trial: Evolution & God at Little Rock. LC 85-50256. 301p. (Orig.). 1985. pap. 12.95 (ISBN 0-86683-780-9, HarpR). Har-Row.

--Maker of Heaven & Earth: The Christian Doctrine of Creation in the Light of Modern Knowledge. 392p. 1986. pap. text ed. 14.75 (ISBN 0-8191-4976-4). U Pr of Amer.

--Message & Existence: An Introduction to Christian Theology. 272p. 1980. 12.95 (ISBN 0-8164-0450-X, HarpR); pap. 7.95 (ISBN 0-8164-2023-8). Har-Row.

--Reaping the Whirlwind: A Christian Interpretation of History. 1977. (HarpR); pap. 12.95 (ISBN 0-8164-2317-2). Har-Row.

--Religion & the Scientific Future. LC 81-18934. (Reprints of Scholarly Excellence (ROSE)). xii, 193p. Repr. of 1970 ed. text ed. 13.95 (ISBN 0-86554-030-6, MUP-H21). Mercer Univ Pr.

--Society & the Sacred: Toward a Theology of Culture in Decline. LC 81-9775. 225p. 1981. 14.95 (ISBN 0-8245-0089-X). Crossroad NY.

Gill, Clinton. Hereby We Know: I, II, III John. LC 70-1464. (The Bible Study Textbook Ser.). (Illus.). 1966. 10.60 (ISBN 0-89900-047-9). College Pr Pub.

Gill, Clinton R. Minor Prophets: A Study of Micah Through Malachi. (The Bible Study Textbook Ser.). (Illus.). 1971. 15.90 (ISBN 0-89900-027-4). College Pr Pub.

Gill, David. Peter the Rock: Extraordinary Lessons from an Ordinary Man. LC 86-7383. 192p. (Orig.). 1986. pap. 6.95 (ISBN 0-87784-609-X). Inter-Varsity.

Gill, David, ed. see World Council of Churches, Assembly (6th: 1983: Vancouver, BC).

Gill, David W. The Word of God in the Ethics of Jacques Ellul. LC 83-20165. (ATLA Monograph Ser.: No. 20). 231p. 1984. 19.00 (ISBN 0-8108-1667-9). Scarecrow.

Gill, Eric. Christianity & the Machine Age. 59.95 (ISBN 0-87968-864-5). Gordon Pr.

Gill, Frederick C. The Romantic Movement & Methodism: A Study of English Romanticism & the Evangelical Revival. 1978. Repr. of 1937 ed. lib. bdg. 25.00 (ISBN 0-8492-4910-4). R West.

Gill, Jean. Images of My Self: Meditation & Self-Exploration Through the Imagery of the Gospels. 128p. 1982. pap. 3.95 (ISBN 0-8091-2463-7). Paulist Pr.

--Unless You Become Like a Little Child. 88p. (Orig.). 1985. pap. 4.95 (ISBN 0-8091-2717-2). Paulist Pr.

Gill, Jerry H. On Knowing God. LC 81-10481. 174p. 1981. pap. 9.95 (ISBN 0-664-24380-0). Westminster.

--Philosophy & Religion: Some Contemporary Perspectives. LC 68-54894. pap. 95.50 (ISBN 0-317-08950-1, 2003459). Bks Demand UMI.

--Toward Theology. LC 82-45009. 130p. (Orig.). 1982. PLB 24.00 (ISBN 0-8191-2429-X); pap. text ed. 9.25 (ISBN 0-8191-2430-3). U Pr of Amer.

Gill, John, ed. Notices of the Jews & Their Country by the Classic Writers of Antiquity. LC 70-97281. (Judaica Ser). 180p. 1972. Repr. of 1872 ed. lib. bdg. 22.50x (ISBN 0-8371-2603-7, GINJ). Greenwood.

Gill, Joseph. The Council of Florence. LC 78-63345. (The Crusades & Military Orders: Second Ser.). (Illus.). 480p. Repr. of 1959 ed. 37.50 (ISBN 0-404-17016-1). AMS Pr.

Gill, Pritam S. Concepts of Sikhism. 183p. 1979. 10.00x (ISBN 0-89684-379-3). Orient Bk Dist.

Gill, Robin. A Textbook of Christian Ethics. 571p. 1986. pap. 19.95 (ISBN 0-567-29127-8, Pub. by T & T Clark Ltd UK). Fortress.

Gill, Rowland, ed. see Sandifer, Kevin.

Gill, Rowland P., ed. Public Relations Are an Asset for Archives & Museums. (No. 6). 32p. (Orig.). 1985. pap. text ed. 5.15 (ISBN 0-910653-12-7, 8101-L). Archival Servs.

Gill, Rowland P., ed. see Sandifer, Kevin.

Gill, Rowland P., ed. see Sandifer, Kevin W.

Gill, Sam. Beyond the "Primitive". Religions of Nonliterate Peoples. (Illus.). 200p. 1982. pap. 14.95 (ISBN 0-13-076034-X). P-H.

--Native American Religions. 208p. 1981. pap. text ed. write for info. (ISBN 0-534-00973-5). Wadsworth Pub.

Gill, Sam D. Sacred Words: A Study of Navajo Religion & Prayer. LC 80-659. (Contributions in Intercultural & Comparative Studies: No. 4). (Illus.). xxvi, 257p. 1981. lib. bdg. 29.95 (ISBN 0-313-22165-0, GSW/). Greenwood.

Gill, William W. Myths & Songs from the South Pacific. Dorson, Richard M., ed. LC 77-70596. (International Folklore Ser.). 1977. Repr. of 1876 ed. lib. bdg. 25.50x (ISBN 0-405-10095-7). Ayer Co Pubs.

Gillard, John T. The Catholic Church & the Negro. (Basic Afro-American Reprint Library). 1969. Repr. of 1929 ed. 19.00 (ISBN 0-384-18550-9). Johnson Repr.

Gillen, Ann, jt. ed. see Rudin, A. James.

Gillerman, Dorothy. The Cloture of Notre-Dame & Its Role in the 14th Century Choir Program. LC 76-23623. (Outstanding Dissertations in the Fine Arts - 2nd Series - Medieval). (Illus.). 292p. 1977. Repr. of 1973 ed. lib. bdg. 69.00 (ISBN 0-8240-2693-4). Garland Pub.

Gilles, Anthony E. Fundamentalism: What Every Catholic Needs to Know. (Illus.). 72p. (Orig.). 1985. pap. text ed. 3.75 (ISBN 0-86716-043-8). St Anthony Mess Pr.

--People of the Book: The Story Behind the Old Testament. (Illus.). 178p. (Orig.). 1983. pap. text ed. 5.95 (ISBN 0-86716-026-8). St Anthony Mess Pr.

--People of the Creed: The Story Behind the Early Church. (The People Ser.: Vol. 3). (Illus., Orig.). 1985. pap. text ed. 5.95 (ISBN 0-86716-046-2). St Anthony Mess Pr.

--The People of the Way: The Story Behind the New Testament. (Illus.). 142p. (Orig.). 1984. pap. 5.95 (ISBN 0-86716-036-5). St Anthony Mess Pr.

Gillet, Charles R., tr. see Krueger, Gustav.

Gillet, Lev. In Thy Presence. LC 77-1040. 144p. 1977. pap. 3.95 (ISBN 0-913836-34-6). St Vladimirs.

--On the Invocation of the Name of Jesus. 1985. pap. 4.95 (ISBN 0-87243-133-9). Templegate.

Gillett, Ezra H. The Life & Times of John Huss: The Bohemian Reformation of the Fifteenth Century, 2 vols. LC 77-85271. Repr. of 1863 ed. Set. 94.50 (ISBN 0-404-16150-2). AMS Pr.

Gilley, Robert. God's Plan for the World, New Testament Survey. (International Correspondence Program Ser.). 169p. (Orig.). 1984. pap. 6.95 (ISBN 0-87148-362-9). Pathway Pr.

Gilliam, Olive. Qumran & History: The Place of the Teachers in Religion. 3.95 (ISBN 0-533-01167-1). Vantage.

Gillies, George & Gillies, Harriet. Scriptural Outline of the Baptism of the Holy Spirit. 32p. 1972. pap. 1.50 (ISBN 0-88368-062-9). Whitaker Hse.

Gillies, Harriet, jt. auth. see Gillies, George.

Gilliland, Dean S. African Religion Meets Islam: Religious Change in Northern Nigeria. 250p. (Orig.). 1986. lib. bdg. 24.50 (ISBN 0-8191-5634-5); pap. text ed. 12.75 (ISBN 0-8191-5635-3). U Pr of Amer.

--Pauline Theology & Mission Practice. 304p. 1983. pap. 12.95 (ISBN 0-8010-3788-3). Baker Bk.

Gilliland, Dolores S. Selected Women of the Scriptures of Stamina & Courage. (Illus.). 1978. pap. 3.95 (ISBN 0-931446-02-3). Honor Bks.

Gilliland, Hap. Coyote's Pow-Wow. (Indian Culture Ser.). 1972. 1.95 (ISBN 0-89992-022-5). Coun India Ed.

Gillingham, E. Leonard. Dealing with Conflict. LC 81-20662. 144p. 1982. 8.75 (ISBN 0-687-10329-0). Abingdon.

Gillingham, John, tr. see Mayer, Hans E.

Gillingham, Peter N., jt. auth. see Schumacher, E. F.

Gillington, Alice E. Old Christmas Carols of the Southern Counties. LC 76-25121. 1976. Repr. of 1910 ed. lib. bdg. 17.50 (ISBN 0-8414-4534-6). Folcroft.

Gillispie, Charles C. Genesis & Geology: A Study in the Relations of Scientific Thought, Natural Theology & Social Opinion in Great Britain, 1790-1850. LC 51-10449. (Historical Monographs Ser: No. 58). 1951. 22.50x (ISBN 0-674-34480-4). Harvard U Pr.

Gillman, Neil. Gabriel Marcel on Religious Knowledge. LC 80-5061. 315p. 1980. text ed. 26.75 (ISBN 0-8191-1034-5); pap. text ed. 14.25 (ISBN 0-8191-1035-3). U Pr of Amer.

Gillon, Edmund. Shaker Village. (Illus.). 56p. 1986. pap. 5.95 (ISBN 0-88740-077-9). Schiffer.

Gillon, Edmund V., jt. auth. see Sanders, Ronald.

Gillon, Edmund V., Jr. Early New England Gravestone Rubbings. (Illus., Orig.). 1966. pap. 7.95 (ISBN 0-486-21380-3). Dover.

Gillow, Joseph. Literary & Biographical History; or Bibliographical Dictionary of English Catholics from the Breach with Rome, in 1534, to the Present Time, 5 Vols. 1962. Repr. of 1892 ed. 205.00 (ISBN 0-8337-1356-6). B Franklin.

Gillquist, Peter. Designed for Holiness: God's Plan to Shape & Use You for His Kingdom. rev. ed. 210p. 1986. pap. 5.95 (ISBN 0-89283-286-X). Servant.

Gillquist, Peter E. Love Is Now. new ed. 1970. 4.95 (ISBN 0-310-36941-X, 18054P). Zondervan.

Gillum, Perry. The Christian Life. (Whole Man Whole World Bible Lessons Ser.). 151p. (Orig.). 1983. pap. 3.95 (ISBN 0-934942-46-3, 2418). White Wing Pub.

--History of Christianity. (Whole Man Whole World Bible Lessons Ser.). 140p. (Orig.). 1984. pap. 3.95 (ISBN 0-934942-48-X); text ed. 2.95 (ISBN 0-934942-49-8); tchr's. ed. 2.95 (ISBN 0-934942-47-1). White Wing Pub.

Gillum, Perry & Allen, Rob, eds. Getting a Grip: Bible Study for Young Teens. 41p. (Orig.). (YA) 1986. pap. 3.95 (ISBN 0-934942-55-2); tchr's. ed. 2.95 (ISBN 0-934942-56-0). White Wing Pub.

--Issues: A Biblical Perspective on Current Social Themes. 128p. (Orig.). 1986. pap. 3.95 (ISBN 0-934942-57-9); discussion kit 2.95 (ISBN 0-934942-83-8). White Wing Pub.

Gilman, Arthur. Library of Religious Poetry. 59.95 (ISBN 0-8490-0521-3). Gordon Pr.

Gilman, Benjamin I., jt. auth. see Fewkes, Jessie W.

Gilman, Charlotte P. His Religion & Hers: A Study of the Faith of Our Fathers & the Work of Our Mothers. LC 75-29509. (Pioneers of the Woman's Movement: An International Perspective Ser.). xi, 300p. 1976. Repr. of 1923 ed. 26.50 (ISBN 0-88355-377-5). Hyperion-Conn.

Gilman, Ernest B. Iconoclasm & Poetry in the English Reformation: Down Went Dragon. LC 85-28837. (Illus.). 240p. 1986. lib. bdg. 19.00x (ISBN 0-226-29382-3). U of Chicago Pr.

Gilman, Nicholas P. Socialism & the American Spirit. facsimile ed. LC 70-150183. (Select Bibliographies Reprint Ser). Repr. of 1893 ed. 23.50 (ISBN 0-8369-5696-6). Ayer Co Pubs.

Gilman, Sander L. Jewish Self-Hatred: Anti-Semitism & the Hidden Language of the Jews. LC 85-45050. 480p. 1986. text ed. 28.50x (ISBN 0-8018-3276-4). Johns Hopkins.

Gilmartin, Richard J., ed. see Struzzo, John A., et al.

Gilmer, Arden E. Romans: The Gospel According to Paul. LC 85-72274. 1985. pap. 4.50x (ISBN 0-934970-05-X). Brethren Ohio.

Gilmer, Harry. The If-You Form an Israelite Law. LC 75-23136. (Society of Biblical Literature. Dissertation Ser.: No. 15). Repr. of 1975 ed. 36.80 (ISBN 0-8357-9572-1, 2017518). Bks Demand UMI.

Gilmore, David B. The Essence & the Vocation of Man. (Illus.). 123p. 1980. deluxe ed. 57.50 (ISBN 0-89920-009-5). Am Inst Psych.

Gilmore, Donald R. Stepping Stones of Faith. rev. ed. 88p. 1987. price not set (ISBN 0-9617810-0-9). D R Gilmore.

Gilmore, G. Don. Angels, Angels, Everywhere. LC 81-8525. 180p. 1981. 11.95 (ISBN 0-8298-0477-3); pap. 6.95 (ISBN 0-8298-0479-X). Pilgrim NY.

--No Matter How Dark, the Valley: The Power of Faith in Times of Need. LC 81-48208. 141p. 1982. pap. 7.64 (ISBN 0-06-063121-X, RD-391, HarpR). Har-Row.

Gilmore, Haydn. Jog for Your Life. new ed. (Illus.). 1979. pap. 1.95 (ISBN 0-310-25022-6). Zondervan.

Gilmore, J. Herbert. They Chose to Live: The Racial Agony of an American Church. LC 72-75577. pap. 51.50 (ISBN 0-317-07872-0, 2012911). Bks Demand UMI.

Gilmour, Peter. Praying Together. LC 77-91623. (Illus.). 1978. pap. 1.95 (ISBN 0-88489-097-X); leader's manual 1.00 (ISBN 0-88489-120-8). St Mary's.

Gilmovsky, Norman. My Life, My Destiny. LC 82-46083. (Illus.). 320p. 1984. 22.50 (ISBN 0-317-02674-7, Cornwall Bks). Assoc Univ Prs.

Gilpin, R. Biblical Demonology: A Treatise on Satan's Temptations. 1982. lib. bdg. 20.00 (ISBN 0-86524-093-0, 9805). Klock & Klock.

Gilpin, Robert G., Jr. American Scientists & Nuclear Weapons Policy. 1962. 37.00x (ISBN 0-691-07501-8). Princeton U Pr.

Gilpin, W. Clark. The Millenarian Piety of Roger Williams. LC 78-20786. 1979. lib. bdg. 19.00x (ISBN 0-226-29397-1). U of Chicago Pr.

Gilroy, Caroline. Song of the Soul Set Free. 103p. (Orig.). 1986. pap. 3.95 (ISBN 0-8341-1138-1). Beacon Hill.

Gilsdorf, Helen M., ed. Modern Liturgy Index. 2nd ed. 1984. pap. 6.95 (ISBN 0-89390-040-0). Resource Pubns.

Gilsenan, Michael. Saint & Sufi in Modern Egypt: An Essay in the Sociology of Religion. (Monographs in Social Anthropology). (Illus.). 1973. 42.00x (ISBN 0-19-823181-4). Oxford U Pr.

Gilson, Etienne. The Christian Philosophy of St. Augustine. xii, 398p. 1983. Repr. of 1960 ed. lib. bdg. 35.00 (ISBN 0-88254-873-5, Octagon). Hippocrene Bks.

--The Christian Philosophy of St. Thomas Aquinas. x, 502p. 1983. Repr. of 1956 ed. lib. bdg. 45.00 (ISBN 0-88254-874-3, Octagon). Hippocrene Bks.

--God & Philosophy. (Powell Lectures Ser.). 1941. pap. 6.95x (ISBN 0-300-00097-9, Y8). Yale U Pr.

--History of Philosophy & Philosophical Education. (Aquinas Lecture). 1947. 7.95 (ISBN 0-87462-112-7). Marquette.

--The Philosophy of St. Bonaventure. 1965. 7.50 (ISBN 0-8199-0526-7). Franciscan Herald.

--Thomist Realism. Wauck, Mark A., tr. LC 86-80104. 215p. 1986. pap. 12.95 (ISBN 0-89870-094-9). Ignatius Pr.

--Wisdom & Love in Saint Thomas Aquinas. (Aquinas Lecture). 1951. 7.95 (ISBN 0-87462-116-X). Marquette.

Gilson, Etienne H. Elements of Christian Philosophy. LC 78-10231. 1978. Repr. of 1960 ed. lib. bdg. 35.00 (ISBN 0-313-20734-8, GIEL). Greenwood.

--The Philosophy of St. Thomas Aquinas. facsimile ed. Elrington, G. A., ed. Bullough, Edward, tr. from Fr. LC 70-157337. (Select Bibliographies Reprint Ser). Repr. of 1937 ed. 26.50 (ISBN 0-8369-5797-0). Ayer Co Pubs.

Giltner, Fern M., ed. Women's Issues in Religious Education. 190p. 1985. pap. 12.95 (ISBN 0-89135-051-9). Religious Educ.

Gimbutas, Marija. Goddesses & Gods of Old Europe, 7000 to 3500 B.C. Myths, Legends, & Cult Images. 1982. pap. 14.95 (ISBN 0-520-04655-2, CAL 565). U of Cal Pr.

Gimello, Robert M. & Gregory, Peter N., eds. Studies in Ch'an & Hua-Yen. (Studies in East Asian Buddhism: No. 1). 406p. 1983. pap. text ed. 14.95x (ISBN 0-8248-0835-5). UH Pr.

Gimenez, Anne, tr. see Robertson, Pat.

Gimpel, Jean. The Cathedral Builders. Waugh, Teresa, tr. LC 84-47572. (Illus.). 192p. 1984. pap. 8.95 (ISBN 0-06-091158-1, CN 1158, PL). Har-Row.

Ginat, Joseph. Women in Muslim Rural Society. LC 79-66432. 259p. 1981. 29.95 (ISBN 0-87855-342-8). Transaction Bk.

Gindele, Egon, ed. Bibliographie zur Geschichte und Theologie des Augustiner Eremiten Ordens bis zum Beginn der Reformation. (Spaetmittelalter und Reformation: Texte und Untersuchungen, Vol. 1). 1977. text ed. 74.00x (ISBN 3-11-004949-X). De Gruyter.

Gingerich, Melvin. The Christian & Revolution. LC 68-12028. (Conrad Grebel Lecture, No. 12). 1968. 12.95 (ISBN 0-8361-1573-2). Herald Pr.

Gingerich, Orland. The Amish of Canada. LC 72-94800. 248p. 1978. pap. 4.95 (ISBN 0-8361-1856-1). Herald Pr.

Gingrich, F. Wilbur. Shorter Lexicon of the Greek New Testament. 2nd ed. 256p. 1983. 22.00 (ISBN 0-310-25030-7, 18075). Zondervan.

Gingrich, F. Wilbur, rev. by see Danker, Frederick W.

Gingrich, Raymond E. The Epistles of the Blessed Hope: First & Second Thessalonians. 1986. pap. 5.95 (ISBN 0-88469-176-4). BMH Bks.

--Fellowship with the Word of Life: Studies in I, II, III John. pap. 4.95 (ISBN 0-88469-042-3). BMH Bks.

Gingrich, Wilbur F., et al. Greek-English Lexicon of the New Testament & Other Early Christian Literature. rev 2nd. ed. 1979. 45.00 (ISBN 0-310-20570-0, 6768). Zondervan.

Giniger, Ken S., compiled by. Compact Treasury of Inspiration. 320p. (Orig.). 1983. pap. 3.50 (ISBN 0-515-07442-X). Jove Pubns.

Ginn, Roman. Adventure in Spiritual Direction: A Prophetic Pattern. (Orig.). 1979. pap. 2.95 (ISBN 0-914544-27-6). Living Flame Pr.

--Jonah: The Spirituality of a Reluctant Prophet. (Orig.). pap. 2.95 (ISBN 0-914544-21-7). Living Flame Pr.

Ginsberg, Louis H. The Israelian Heritage of Judaism. 15.00x (ISBN 0-87334-013-2). Ktav.

Ginsberg, Mitchell. The Far Shore. 100p. 1984. 21.00x (ISBN 0-7212-0577-1, Pub. by Regency Pr). State Mutual Bk.

Ginsburg, Christian D. Introduction to the Massoretico Critical Edition of the Hebrew Bible. rev. ed. 1966. 79.50x (ISBN 0-87068-060-9). Ktav.

Ginsburg, David C. Coheleth & Song of Songs, with a Commentary Historical & Critical, 2 Vols. in 1. rev. ed. (Library of Biblical Studies Ser). 1970. 59.50x (ISBN 0-87068-059-5). Ktav.

Ginzberg, Asher see Ha-am, Achad, pseud.

Ginzberg, Asher, et al. Maimonides Octocentennial Series, No. I-IV. (Jewish People; History, Religion, Literature Ser.). Repr. of 1935 ed. 15.00 (ISBN 0-405-05278-2). Ayer Co Pubs.

Ginzberg, Eli. Agenda for American Jews. 90p. 1964. pap. 4.50 (ISBN 0-935457-12-7). Reconstructionist Pr.

Ginzberg, L. & Davidson, I. Genizah Studies in Memory of Solomon Schechter, 3 vols. Incl. Vol. 1. Midrash & Haggadah. Ginzberg, L. 1969. Repr. of 1928 ed. 17.50 (ISBN 0-87203-015-6); Vol. 2. Geonic & Early Karaitic Halakah. Ginzberg, L. Repr. of 1929 ed. 17.50 (ISBN 0-87203-016-4); Vol. 3. Liturgical & Secular Poetry. Davidson, I. Repr. of 1928 ed. 17.50 (ISBN 0-87203-017-2). LC 73-76172. Hermon.

Ginzberg, Louis. Legends of the Bible. LC 56-9915. 620p. 1956. 14.95 (ISBN 0-8276-0036-4, 168). Jewish Pubns.

--Legends of the Jews, 7 Vols. LC 76-58650. 1956. Set. 80.00 (ISBN 0-8276-0148-4); 11.95 ea. Vol. 1 (172). Vol. 2 (173). Vol. 3 (174). Vol. 4 (175). Vol. 5 (176). Vol. 6 (177). Vol. 7 (178). Jewish Pubns.

--Of Jewish Law & Lore. LC 55-6707. (Temple Bks). 1970. pap. 5.95 (ISBN 0-689-70231-0, T12). Atheneum.

--Students Scholars & Saints. LC 85-9089. (Brown Classics in Judaica Ser.). 312p. 1985. pap. text ed. 12.75 (ISBN 0-8191-4490-8). U Pr of Amer.

Ginzburg, Carlo, ed. I Costituti Di Don Pietro Manelfi. LC 72-3473. (Corpus Reformatorum Italicorum & Biblioteca Ser.). (Illus.). 101p. 1970. pap. 10.00 (ISBN 0-87580-510-8). N Ill U Pr.

Giordani, Igino. Diary of Fire. Tr. of Diario di Fuoco. 127p. (Orig.). 1982. pap. 3.95 (ISBN 0-911782-41-9). New City.

--Mary of Nazareth. (Orig.). 1965. 6.00 (ISBN 0-8198-0092-9); pap. 5.00 (ISBN 0-8198-0093-7). Dghtrs St Paul.

--Saint Catherine of Siena. 1981. 8.00 (ISBN 0-8198-0493-2); pap. 7.00 (ISBN 0-8198-6809-4). Dghtrs St Paul.

--St. Paul Apostle & Martyr. (Obelisk Ser.). 1961. 8.00 (ISBN 0-8198-0138-0); pap. 7.00 (ISBN 0-8198-0139-9). Dghtrs St Paul.

--Social Message of Jesus. 1977. 4.50 (ISBN 0-8198-0467-3); pap. 3.50 (ISBN 0-8198-0468-1). Dghtrs St Paul.

--Social Message of the Early Church Fathers. 1977. 3.95 (ISBN 0-8198-0469-X); pap. 2.95 (ISBN 0-8198-0470-3). Dghtrs St Paul.

Giorgi, Louis P. Windows of St. Justin Martyr. LC 80-67119. (Illus.). 136p. 1982. 25.00 (ISBN 0-87982-034-9). Art Alliance.

Giovio, Paolo. The Worthy Tract of Paulus Iovius. Daniel, Samuel, tr. LC 76-13497. 300p. 1976. Repr. of 1585 ed. lib. bdg. 50.00x (ISBN 0-8201-1272-0). Schol Facsimiles.

Gipson, Leland F. How to Use the Tremendous Power of Creative Prayer. LC 80-85276. 114p. (Orig.). 1981. pap. 2.95 (ISBN 0-9605014-0-1). Levada.

Giran, Etienne. A Modern Job: An Essay on the Problem of Evil. 92p. 1916. 1.95 (ISBN 0-317-40399-0). Open Court.

Girard, Raphael. Esotericism of the Popol Vuh. LC 78-74712. (Illus.). 1979. 14.00 (ISBN 0-911500-13-8); pap. 8.50 (ISBN 0-911500-14-6). Theos U Pr.

Girardot, N. J. Myth & Meaning in Early Taoism: The Themes of Chaos (hun-tun) LC 81-21964. (Hermeneutics Studies in the History of Religions). (Illus.). 430p. 1983. 39.50x (ISBN 0-520-04330-8). U of Cal Pr.

Girdlestone, Robert B. Synonyms of the Old Testament. 1948. pap. 6.95 (ISBN 0-8028-1548-0). Eerdmans.

--Synonyms of the Old Testament: Numerically Coded to Strong's Exhaustive Concordance. White, Donald R., ed. 400p. 1983. deluxe ed. 22.95 (ISBN 0-8010-3798-0); pap. 17.95 kivar bdg. (ISBN 0-8010-3789-1). Baker Bk.

Girod, Gordon H. The Deeper Faith: An Exposition of the Canons of Dort. 1978. pap. 1.95 (ISBN 0-8010-3725-5). Baker Bk.

Giroux, Paul L. God's Plan for the Human Race. 1980. 5.00 (ISBN 0-682-49270-1). Exposition Pr FL.

Girvin, E. A. Phineas F. Bresse: A Prince in Israel. Dayton, Donald W., ed. (The Higher Christian Life Ser.). 464p. 55.00 (ISBN 0-8240-6407-0). Garland Pub.

Girzone, Joseph F. Joshua. 320p. 1983. 12.00 (ISBN 0-911519-03-3). Richelieu Court.

--Who Will Teach Me? 61p. 1982. 6.00 (ISBN 0-911519-00-9). Richelieu Court.

Gise, Wayne T. Biblical Personality Puzzlebook. LC 86-14720. (Orig.). 1987. pap. 2.95 (ISBN 0-8054-9112-0). Broadman.

--Searching for Answers. LC 85-14993. (Orig.). 1985. pap. 2.95 (ISBN 0-8054-9111-2). Broadman.

Gish, Arthur G. Beyond the Rat Race. rev. ed. LC 73-9336. 208p. 1973. pap. 6.95 (ISBN 0-8361-1985-1). Herald Pr.

--Living in Christian Community. LC 79-11848. 384p. 1979. pap. 9.95 (ISBN 0-8361-1887-1). Herald Pr.

Gish, Duane T. Speculations & Experiments Related to the Origin of Life: A Critique. (ICR Technical Monograph: No. 1). (Illus.). 41p. 1972. pap. 5.95 (ISBN 0-89051-010-5). Master Bks.

--Up with Creation! Acts, Facts, Impacts, Vol. 3. LC 78-55612. (Illus.). 1978. pap. 6.95 (ISBN 0-89051-048-2). Master Bks.

Gish, Duane T., jt. auth. see Morris, Henry M.

Gish, Duane T., ed. see Bliss, Richard.

Gispen, W. H. The Bible Student's Commentary: Exodus. (The Bible Student's Commentary). 352p. 1982. 16.95 (ISBN 0-310-43970-1). Zondervan.

Gitenstein, R. Barbara. Apocalyptic Messianism & Contemporary Jewish-American Poetry. (Modern Jewish Literature & Culture Ser.). 128p. (Orig.). 1986. 39.50x (ISBN 0-88706-154-0); pap. 12.95x (ISBN 0-88706-155-9). State U NY Pr.

Gittelsohn, Roland B. The Extra Dimension. 228p. 1983. pap. 7.95 (ISBN 0-8074-0170-6, 168500). UAHC.

--Love, Sex & Marriage: A Jewish View. (Illus.). 1980. pap. 7.95x (ISBN 0-8074-0046-7, 142683). UAHC.

Gittings, James A. Bread, Meat & Raisins after the Dance. LC 77-83883. 1977. 10.00 (ISBN 0-89430-006-7). Palos Verdes.

Gittleman, Sol. From Shtetl to Suburbia: The Family in Jewish Literary Imagination. LC 78-53646. 1978. 12.95x (ISBN 0-8070-6364-9); pap. 5.95 o. p. (ISBN 0-8070-6365-7). Beacon Pr.

--Sholom Aleichem: A Non-Critical Introduction. (De Proprietatibus Litterarum Ser. Didactica: No. 3). 1974. pap. text ed. 13.60x (ISBN 90-2792-606-9). Mouton.

Gittner, Louis. Listen Listen Listen. Farish, Starr, ed. 320p. (Orig.). 1980. pap. 8.95 (ISBN 0-9605492-0-X). Touch Heart.

--There Is a Rainbow. (Illus.). 65p. (Orig.). 1981. pap. 5.95 (ISBN 0-9605492-1-8). Touch Heart.

Giuseppi, Montague S. Naturalization of Foreign Protestants in the American & West Indian Colonies, Etc. LC 64-19759. 196p. 1979. Repr. of 1921 ed. 14.00 (ISBN 0-8063-0157-0). Genealog Pub.

Givens, Lula P. Christiansburg Montgomery County, Virginia in the Heart of the Alleghenies. LC 80-68026. (Illus.). 256p. 1981. 12.00 (ISBN 0-9614765-1-6). Pat G Johnson.

Givet, Jacques. The Anti-Zionist Complex. Abel, Evelyn, tr. from Fr. LC 81-16693. Tr. of Israel et le Genocide Inacheve. 192p. 1982. 11.95 (ISBN 0-89961-019-6). SBS Pub.

Glacken, Clarence J. Traces on the Rhodian Shore: Nature & Culture in Western Thought from Ancient Times to the End of the Eighteenth Century. LC 67-10970. 1973. pap. 15.50x (ISBN 0-520-03216-0, CAMPUS 170). U of Cal Pr.

Glad, John, tr. see Alexeyeva, Ludmilla.

Gladden, Lee & Gladden, Vivianne C. Heirs of the Gods: A Space Age Interpretation of the Bible. LC 78-53852. (Illus.). 324p. Repr. of 1979 ed. 15.95 (ISBN 0-686-37960-8). Bel-Air.

Gladden, Vivianne C., jt. auth. see Gladden, Lee.

Gladden, Washington. Being a Christian. LC 72-4168. (Select Bibliographies Reprint Ser.). 1972. Repr. of 1876 ed. 14.00 (ISBN 0-8369-6880-8). Ayer Co Pubs.

--Ruling Ideas of the Present Age. 1971. Repr. of 1895 ed. 23.00 (ISBN 0-384-18865-6). Johnson Repr.

--Tools & the Man: Property & Industry under the Christian Law. LC 75-353. (The Radical Tradition in America Ser). 308p. 1975. Repr. of 1893 ed. 23.65 (ISBN 0-88355-222-1). Hyperion Conn.

--Who Wrote the Bible? A Book for the People. LC 72-5435. (Select Bibliographies Reprint Ser.). 1972. Repr. of 1891 ed. 22.00 (ISBN 0-8369-6909-X). Ayer Co Pubs.

--Witnesses of the Light. facs. ed. LC 77-84307. (Essay Index Reprint Ser). 1903. 17.75 (ISBN 0-8369-1081-8). Ayer Co Pubs.

Gladden, Washington T. Working People & Their Employers. LC 75-89734. (American Labor: From Conspiracy to Collective Bargaining Ser., No. 1). 1969. Repr. of 1876 ed. 15.00 (ISBN 0-405-02123-2). Ayer Co Pubs.

Gladish, Richard R. Bishop William Henry Benade: Founder & Reformer. (Illus.). 400p. 1983. 15.00 (ISBN 0-910557-07-1). Acad New Church.

Gladman, Donna. It's Sunday Night Again? Zapel, Arthur L., ed. LC 79-84726. (Illus.). 1979. pap. text ed. 4.95 (ISBN 0-916260-04-6). Meriwether Pub.

Gladson, Jerry. Who Said Life Is Fair? Wheeler, Gerald, ed. 128p. 1985. pap. 6.95 (ISBN 0-8280-0242-8). Review & Herald.

Gladstone, J. W. Protestant Christianity & People's Movements in Kerala, 1850-1936. 470p. 1986. 12.50x (ISBN 0-8364-1821-2, Pub. by Somaiya). South Asia Bks.

Gladstone, William E. The State in Its Relations with the Church. 1196p. Repr. of 1841 ed. text ed. 62.10x (ISBN 0-576-02192-X, Pub. by Gregg Intl Pubs England). Gregg Intl.

Glaesner, Kay M. Miracle of Christmas. (Orig.). 1982. pap. 2.95 (ISBN 0-937172-39-1). JLJ Pubs.

Glanvill, Joseph. Essays on Several Important Subjects in Philosophy & Religion. Repr. of 1676 ed. 32.00 (ISBN 0-384-18880-X). Johnson Repr.

--Saducismus Triumphatus: Or, Full & Plain Evidence Concerning Witches & Apparitions. LC 66-60009. 1966. Repr. of 1689 ed. 75.00x (ISBN 0-8201-1021-3). Schol Facsimiles.

--Scepsis Scientifics: Or Confest Ignorance, the Way to Science, 2 vols. in 1. Wellek, Rene, ed. LC 75-11222. (British Philosophers & Theologians of the 17th & 18th Centuries Ser.). 330p. 1978. lib. bdg. 51.00 (ISBN 0-8240-1776-5). Garland Pub.

--Two Choice & Useful Treatises: The One, One Lux Orientalis,...the Other, A Discourse of Truth by the Late Reverend Dr. Rust. Wellek, Rene, ed. LC 75-11223. (British Philosophers & Theologians of the 17th & 18th Centuries Ser.). 532p. 1978. lib. bdg. 51.00 (ISBN 0-8240-1777-3). Garland Pub.

Glanville, Joan P. Not a Sparrow Shall Fall. 184p. (Orig.). 1984. pap. 6.35 (ISBN 0-919797-38-5). Kindred Pr.

Glanville, Joseph. Some Discourse, Sermons & Remains. Wellek, Rene, ed. LC 75-11221. (British Philosophers & Theologians of the 17th & 18th Centuries Ser.). 1979. lib. bdg. 51.00 (ISBN 0-8240-1775-7). Garland Pub.

Glanville, Stephen R. The Legacy of Egypt. LC 76-44448. (Illus.). 1976. Repr. of 1942 ed. lib. bdg. 34.00x (ISBN 0-8371-9092-4, GLLE). Greenwood.

Glanz, Rudolf. Aspects of the Social, Political, & Economic History of the Jews in America. 1984. 29.50x (ISBN 0-87068-463-9). Ktav.

--The German Jewish Women, Vol. 2. 25.00x (ISBN 0-87068-462-0). Ktav.

--The Jewish Female in America: Two Female Generations, 1820-1929, Vol. 1. The Eastern European Jewish Woman 25.00x (ISBN 0-87068-461-2). Ktav.

Glanz, Rudolph. German Jew in America: An Annotated Bibliography Including Books, Pamphlets & Articles of Special Interest. 1969. 39.50x (ISBN 0-87068-061-7). Ktav.

Glanzman, George S. Deuteronomy. Pt. 1. pap. 1.00 (ISBN 0-8091-5028-X); Pt. 2. pap. 1.00 (ISBN 0-8091-5029-8). Paulist Pr.

Glaphre. Talking with God: A Woman's Workshop on Prayer. (Woman's Workshop Ser.). 160p. (Orig.). 1985. pap. 3.95 (ISBN 0-310-45301-1, 12240P). Zondervan.

--When the Pieces Don't Fit... God Makes the Difference. 176p. 1984. pap. 5.95 (ISBN 0-310-45341-0, 12239P). Zondervan.

Glas, Norbert. Fulfillment of Old Age. Easton, Stewart, tr. from Fr. Tr. of Lichtvolles Alter. 141p. 1987. pap. 9.95 (ISBN 0-88010-161-X). Anthroposophic.

Glas, Werner, ed. see Asten, Dietrich V.

Glaser, John W. Caring for the Special Child. LC 84-82551. 97p. (Orig.). 1985. pap. 6.95 (ISBN 0-934134-14-6, Leaven Pr). Sheed & Ward MO.

Glashouwer, Willem J. How the Bible Came to Be. 1980. cancelled (ISBN 0-310-42130-6). Zondervan.

Glass, Bill & McEachern, James E. Plan to Win. 160p. 1984. 8.95 (ISBN 0-8499-0431-5, 0431-5). Word Bks.

Glass, Dorlis B. Children, Children! A Ministry Without Boundries. LC 86-50509. 72p. (Orig.). 1986. pap. 4.95 (ISBN 0-88177-033-7, DR033B). Discipleship Res.

Glass, Henry A. Story of the Psalters. LC 72-1635. Repr. of 1888 ed. 18.50 (ISBN 0-404-08308-0). AMS Pr.

Glass, Hiram B. Science & Ethical Values. LC 81-13170. ix, 101p. 1981. Repr. of 1965 ed. lib. bdg. 22.50x (ISBN 0-313-23141-9, GLSE). Greenwood.

Glass, Justine. Witchcraft-the Sixth Sense. pap. 7.00 (ISBN 0-87980-174-3). Wilshire.

Glass, Mrs. Quintard. Cemetery Inscriptions from Dyer County, Tennessee. 240p. 1978. 15.00 (ISBN 0-89308-095-0). Southern Hist Pr.

Glasse, James D. Profession: Minister. LC 68-17447. Repr. of 1968 ed. 33.50 (ISBN 0-8357-9021-5, 2011670). Bks Demand UMI.

Glasser, Arthur F. & McGavran, Donald A. Contemporary Theologies of Mission. 320p. (Orig.). 1983. pap. 12.95 (ISBN 0-8010-3790-5). Baker Bk.

Glassie, Henry. All Silver & No Brass: An Irish Christmas Mumming. 1983. 9.95 (ISBN 0-8122-1139-1). U of Pa Pr.

Glassman, Bernard. Anti-Semitic Stereotypes Without Jews: Images of the Jews in England, 1290-1700. LC 75-16391. 218p. 1975. 22.50x (ISBN 0-8143-1545-3). Wayne St U Pr.

Glassman, Bernard T., jt. auth. see Maezumi, Hakuyu T.

Glassman, Bernard T., jt. ed. see Maezumi, Hakuyu T.

Glassman, Eugene H. The Translation Debate. LC 80-29286. 128p. (Orig.). 1981. pap. 4.25 (ISBN 0-87784-467-4). Inter Varsity.

Glassman, Samuel. Epic of Survival: The Story of Anti-Semitism. LC 80-69018. 400p. 20.00x (ISBN 0-8197-0481-4). Bloch.

Glasson, T. Francis. Moses in the Fourth Gospel. LC 63-5666. (Studies in Biblical Theology: No. 40). 1963. pap. 10.00x (ISBN 0-8401-3040-6). A R Allenson.

Glasson, Thomas F., ed. Revelation of John. (Cambridge Bible Commentary on the New English Bible, New Testament Ser.). (Orig.). 1965. 16.95 (ISBN 0-521-04208-9); pap. 9.95x (ISBN 0-521-09256-6). Cambridge U Pr.

Glatfelter, Charles H. Pastors & People: German & Lutheran Reformed Churches in the Pennsylvania Field, 1717-1793, Vol. II, The History. LC 80-83400. (Penn. German Ser.: Vol. 15). (Illus.). 25.00 (ISBN 0-911122-44-3). Penn German Soc.

--Pastors & People: German Lutheran & Reformed Churches in the Pennsylvania Field, 1717-1793. LC 80-83400. (Penn. German Ser.: Vol. 13). (Illus.). 1979. 30.00 (ISBN 0-911122-40-0). Penn German Soc.

Glathorn, Allan A. & Shields, Carmel R. Differentiated Supervision for Catholic Schools. 72p. 1983. 5.75 (ISBN 0-318-00781-9). Natl Cath Educ.

Glatstein, Jacob, et al. Anthology of Holocaust Literature. LC 68-19609. (Temple Bks). 1972. pap. text ed. 6.95x (ISBN 0-689-70343-0, T23). Atheneum.

Glatzer, Nahum. The Judaic Tradition. 352p. 1982. pap. text ed. 9.95x (ISBN 0-87441-344-3). Behrman.

Glatzer, Nahum, ed. see Buber, Martin.

Glatzer, Nahum N. The Dimensions of Job: A Study & Selected Readings. LC 69-11936. 320p. 1973. pap. 7.95 (ISBN 0-8052-0378-8). Schocken.

Glatzer, Nahum N., ed. Modern Jewish Thought: A Source Reader. LC 76-9139. 1976. pap. 7.50 (ISBN 0-8052-0542-X). Schocken.

--Passover Haggadah: Including Readings on the Holocaust, with English Translation, Introduction & Commentary. 3rd ed. LC 69-10846. (Illus., Bilingual ed). 1979. pap. 3.95 (ISBN 0-8052-0624-8). Schocken.

Glatzer, Nahum N., ed. see Buber, Martin.

Glatzer, Nahum N., ed. see Schurer, Emil.

Glaze, Jack A., tr. see Francisco, Clyde T.

Glaze, R. E., Jr. No Easy Salvation. LC 66-10708. 72p. 1984. pap. 4.00 (ISBN 0-914520-06-7). Insight Pr.

Glazer, Nathan. American Judaism. rev. ed. LC 57-8574. (Chicago History of American Civilization Ser). 1972. 12.50x (ISBN 0-226-29839-6); pap. 7.50 (ISBN 0-226-29841-8, CHAC7). U of Chicago Pr.

Glazier, Michael, ed. Where We Are: American Catholics in the 1980's. 1985. pap. 7.95 (ISBN 0-89453-471-8). M Glazier.

Glazier, Stephen D. Marchin' the Pilgrims Home: Leadership & Decision-Making in an Afro-Caribbean Faith. LC 82-24179. (Contributions to the Study of Religion Ser.: No. 10). (Illus.). xx, 165p. 1983. lib. bdg. 29.95 (ISBN 0-313-23464-7, GPI/). Greenwood.

Glazier, Stephen D., ed. Perspectives on Pentecostalism: Case Studies from the Caribbean & Latin America. LC 80-7815. 207p. 1980. lib. bdg. 25.25 (ISBN 0-8191-1071-X); pap. text ed. 12.25 (ISBN 0-8191-1072-8). U Pr of Amer.

Gleadow, Rupert, tr. see De Lubicz, Isha S.

Gleason, Elisabeth G. Reform Thought in Sixteenth Century Italy. Massey, James A., ed. LC 81-5648. (American Academy of Religion Texts & Translations Ser.). 1981. pap. text ed. 10.95 (ISBN 0-89130-498-3, 01-02-04). Scholars Pr GA.

Gleason, John J., Jr. Consciousness & the Ultimate. LC 80-21397. 192p. (Orig.). 1981. pap. 7.75 (ISBN 0-687-09470-4). Abingdon.

Gleason, Philip. Conservative Reformers: German-American Catholics & the Social Order. 1968. 22.95x (ISBN 0-268-00061-1). U of Notre Dame Pr.

--Documentary Reports on Early American Catholicism. 17.00 (ISBN 0-405-10833-8, 11825). Ayer Co Pubs.

--Keeping the Faith: American Catholicism Past & Present. LC 86-40579. 320p. 1987. text ed. 24.95x (ISBN 0-268-01227-X, Dist. by Har-Row). U of Notre Dame Pr.

Gleaves, Les. Building Your Bible School. 1986. 4.95 (ISBN 0-931097-10-X). Sentinel Pub.

Gleckner, Robert F. Blake's Prelude: "Poetical Sketches". LC 82-47976. 216p. 1983. text ed. 20.00x (ISBN 0-8018-2850-3). Johns Hopkins.

Gleeson, John R., III. Sportscape. LC 84-52105. (Illus.). 176p. (Orig.). 1984. pap. 12.95 (ISBN 0-912661-04-6). Woodsong Graph.

Gleghorn, B. E., jt. ed. see Datta, V. N.

Glen, Irma, ed. Religious Science Hymnal. 3rd ed. 225p. 1982. Repr. of 1956 ed. 8.00 (ISBN 0-87516-489-7). De Vorss.

Glen, Thomas L. Rubens & the Counter Reformation: Studies in His Religious Paintings Between 1609 & 1620. LC 76-23621. (Outstanding Dissertations in the Fine Arts Ser.). 1977. lib. bdg. 68.00 (ISBN 0-8240-2692-6). Garland Pub.

Glendinning, O. N., tr. see Baroja, Julio C.

Glenn, Alfred A. Taking Your Faith to Work. (Orig.). 1980. pap. 4.95 (ISBN 0-8010-3748-4). Baker Bk.

Glenn, Jim, jt. auth. see McMillin, John.

Glenn, John S., jt. auth. see Coffey, Rosalie L.

Glenn, Menachem. Jewish Tales & Legends. 441p. 1929. 6.95 (ISBN 0-88482-857-3). Hebrew Pub.

Glenn, Paul J. Apologetics. LC 80-51330. 303p. 1980. pap. 6.00 (ISBN 0-89555-157-8). TAN Bks Pubs.

--Tour of the Summa. LC 78-66307. 1978. pap. 12.50 (ISBN 0-89555-081-4). TAN Bks Pubs.

Glennie, Alexander. Sermons Preached on Plantations to Congregations of Negroes. facsimile ed. LC 75-161260. (Black Heritage Library Collection). Repr. of 1844 ed. 16.25 (ISBN 0-8369-8819-1). Ayer Co Pubs.

Glennon, Canon J. Your Healing Is Within You. LC 80-82616. 1980. pap. 4.95 (ISBN 0-88270-457-5). Bridge Pub.

Glennon, Jim. How Can I Find Healing? LC 84-73039. 1985. pap. 3.50 (ISBN 0-88270-580-6). Bridge Pub.

Gleysteen, Jan. Mennonite Tourguide to Western Europe. LC 84-683. 340p. (Orig.). 1984. pap. 17.95 (ISBN 0-8361-3360-9). Herald Pr.

Glick, Ferne P. & Pellman, Donald R. Breaking Silence: A Family Grows with Deafness. LC 82-6067. 208p. (Orig.). 1982. pap. 6.95 (ISBN 0-8361-3300-5). Herald Pr.

Glick, Joel, jt. auth. see Lorusso, Julia.

Glick, Thomas, compiled by. Darwinism in Texas. LC 72-185614. (Illus.). 38p. 1972. 7.00 (ISBN 0-87959-032-7). U of Tex H Ransom Ctr.

Glick, Thomas F. Islamic & Christian Spain in the Early Middle Ages: Comparative Perspectives on Social & Cultural Formation. LC 78-70296. 1978. 41.50 (ISBN 0-691-05274-3). Princeton U Pr.

Glickman, S. Craig. A Song for Lovers. LC 75-21454. 204p. (Orig.). 1976. pap. 6.95 (ISBN 0-87784-768-1). Inter-Varsity.

Glicksberg, Charles I. Literature & Religion: A Study in Conflict. LC 77-23753. 1977. Repr. of 1960 ed. lib. bdg. 22.50x (ISBN 0-8371-9753-8, GLLR). Greenwood.

Gliner, Bob. Beyond Coping. 273p. (Orig.). 1982. pap. 5.95x (ISBN 0-910029-01-6). Dell.

Glinsky, Vladimir. Confessionary Questions: A Preparation for the Sacrament of Penitence with Text of the Office. pap. 0.25 (ISBN 0-686-05391-5). Eastern Orthodox.

Gliozzo, Charles A. Bibliography of Ecclesiastical History of the French Revolution. LC 73-154506. (Bibliographia Tripotamopolitana: No. 6). 1972. 8.00x (ISBN 0-931222-05-2). Pitts Theolog.

Glisson, Jerry. Knowing & Doing God's Will. LC 86-2617. (Orig.). 1986. pap. 5.95 (ISBN 0-8054-5027-0). Broadman.

Glisson, Jerry & Taylor, Jack R. The Church in a Storm. LC 82-74208. (Orig.). 1983. pap. 5.95 (ISBN 0-8054-5522-1). Broadman.

Gloag, P. J. & Delitzsch, F. The Messiahship of Christ. 628p. 1983. lib. bdg. 23.50 Smythe Sewn (ISBN 0-86524-146-5, 9514). Klock & Klock.

Gloag, Paton J. A Critical & Exegetical Commentary on the Acts of the Apostles, 2 vols. 1979. 29.95 (ISBN 0-86524-006-X, 4402). Klock & Klock.

Globus, Gordon, et al, eds. Consciousness & the Brain: A Scientific & Philosophical Inquiry. LC 75-44478. (Illus.). 378p. 1976. 45.00x (ISBN 0-306-30878-9, Plenum Pr). Plenum Pub.

Glock, Charles & Bellah, Robert N., eds. The New Religious Consciousness. 391p. 29.50 (ISBN 0-686-95181-6); pap. 6.95 (ISBN 0-686-99471-X). ADL.

Glock, Charles Y. & Stark, Rodney. Christian Beliefs & Anti-Semitism. LC 78-31750. (Univ. of California Five-Year Study of Anti-Semitism). 1979. Repr. of 1966 ed. lib. bdg. 24.75x (ISBN 0-313-20969-3, GLCB). Greenwood.

--Northern California Church Member Study, 1963. LC 79-63206. 1979. codebk. write for info. (ISBN 0-89138-980-6). ICPSR.

Glock, Charles Y., jt. auth. see Quinley, Harold E.

Glock, Charles Y., jt. auth. see Stark, Rodney.

Glock, Charles Y. & Bellah, Robert N., eds. The New Religious Consciousness. LC 75-17295. 1976. 36.50x (ISBN 0-520-03083-4); pap. 11.95x (ISBN 0-520-03472-4, CAMPUS 329). U of Cal Pr.

Gloer, Hulitt, ed. see Schweizer, Eduard.

Glover, Elsa M. Science & Religion. 1987. 8.95 (ISBN 0-533-07048-1). Vantage.

Glover, T. R. Jesus in the Experience of Men. LC 78-23617. 1921. 30.00 (ISBN 0-8414-4616-4). Folcroft.

--The Jesus of History. LC 78-25986. 30.00 (ISBN 0-8414-4488-9). Folcroft.

Glover, Terrot R. Life & Letters in the Fourth Century. LC 68-10923. 1968. Repr. of 1901 ed. 11.00x (ISBN 0-8462-1065-7). Russell.

--Springs of Hellas. LC 74-122878. (Essay & General Literature Index Reprint Ser). 1971. Repr. of 1945 ed. 21.00x (ISBN 0-8046-1333-8, Pub. by Kennikat). Assoc Faculty Pr.

Glover, Willis B. Biblical Origins of Modern Secular Culture. LC 84-14868. xx, 300p. 1984. 23.95 (ISBN 0-86554-138-8, MUP-H129). Mercer Univ Pr.

Glubb, Faris. Zionist Relations with Nazi Germany. LC 79-90569. 6.00 (ISBN 0-911026-11-8). New World Press NY.

Glubokovsky, N. N. Blagovjestije Khristikanskoj Slavi v Apokalipsisje. Tr. of The Good News of Christian Glory in the Apocalypse. 116p. 1966. pap. 5.00 (ISBN 0-317-29139-4). Holy Trinity.

Gluckel. The Memoirs of Gluckel of Hameln. Lowenthal, Marvin, tr. from Ger. LC 77-75290. 1977. pap. 7.95 (ISBN 0-8052-0572-1). Schocken.

Glueck, Nelson. Hesed in the Bible. 1968. 12.50x (ISBN 0-87820-104-1, Pub. by Hebrew Union). Ktav.

Glunz, Hans. Britannien und Bibeltext. Repr. of 1930 ed. 16.00 (ISBN 0-384-18950-4). Johnson Repr.

--Die Lateinische Vorlage der Westsaechsischen Evangelienversion. pap. 8.00 (ISBN 0-384-18955-5). Johnson Repr.

Glustrom, Simon. Language of Judaism. rev. ed. 1973. pap. 9.95x (ISBN 0-87068-224-5). Ktav.

Gnaneswarananda, Swami. Yoga for Beginners. Gupta, Mallika C., ed. LC 74-29557. 200p. 1975. pap. 4.95 (ISBN 0-9600826-1-1). Vivekananda.

Gnilka, Joachim & Mussner, Franz. The Epistle to the Phillipians & the Epistle to the Colossians. McKenzie, John L., ed. LC 81-605. (New Testament for Spiritual Reading Ser.). 180p. 1981. pap. 4.95 (ISBN 0-8245-0126-8). Crossroad NY.

Gnuse, Robert. Authority of the Bible, Theories of Inspiration Revelation & the Canon of Scripture. (Theological Inquirers Ser.). 160p. (Orig.). 1985. pap. 6.95 (ISBN 0-8091-2692-3). Paulist Pr.

--You Shall Not Steal: Community & Property in the Biblical Tradition. LC 85-4810. 176p. (Orig.). 1985. pap. 9.95 (ISBN 0-88344-799-1). Orbis Bks.

Goar, R. J. Cicero & the State Religion. 141p. (Orig.). 1972. pap. text ed. 30.00x (Pub. by A M Hakkert). Coronet Bks.

Gobbel, A. Roger & Huber, Phillip C. Creative Designs with Children at Worship. LC 80-82225. 96p. (Orig.). 1981. pap. 6.95 (ISBN 0-8042-1526-X). John Knox.

Gobbel, A. Roger, et al. Helping Youth Interpret the Bible: A Teaching Resource. LC 84-3916. 204p. 1984. pap. 9.95 (ISBN 0-8042-1580-4). John Knox.

Gobbel, Gertrude G., jt. auth. see Gobbel, Roger A.

Gobbel, Roger A. & Gobbel, Gertrude G. The Bible: A Child's Playground. LC 85-45501. 192p. 1986. pap. 9.95 (ISBN 0-8006-1887-4). Fortress.

Gobbell, Phyllis C. Like a Promise. LC 83-71490. 1983. 8.95 (ISBN 0-8054-7319-X). Broadman.

Gober, Lasley F. The Christmas Lover's Handbook. LC 85-13450. (Illus.). 256p. 1985. pap. 12.95 (ISBN 0-932620-53-1). Betterway Pubns.

Goberna, M. Regina. Our Father Saint Benedict. Green, Maurus, tr. from Catalan. Tr. of El Pare Sant Benet. (Illus.). 128p. (Orig.). 1983. pap. 4.95 (ISBN 0-911782-45-1). New City.

Gobineau, Arthur. The Renaissance, Savonarola - Cesare - Borgia -Julius II - Leo X - Michael Angelo. Levy, Oscar, ed. 349p. 1981. Repr. of 1903 ed. lib. bdg. 50.00 (ISBN 0-89984-235-6). Century Bookbindery.

Gobineau, Arthur Count see Count Gobineau, Arthur.

Gobineau, Joseph A. Golden Flower. facsimile ed. Redman, B. R., tr. LC 68-54347. (Essay Index Reprint Ser). 1924. 15.00 (ISBN 0-8369-0477-X). Ayer Co Pubs.

Goble, Phillip E. Everything You Need to Grow a Messianic Synagogue. LC 74-28017. (Illus., Orig.). 1974. pap. 3.95 (ISBN 0-87808-421-5). William Carey Lib.

Goble, Phillip E., ed. Everything You Need to Grow a Messianic Yeshiva. LC 81-1032. 312p. (Orig.). 1981. pap. 10.95 (ISBN 0-87808-181-X). William Carey Lib.

Goblet D'Alviella, Eugene F. Lectures on the Origin & Growth of the Conception of God as Illustrated by Anthropology & History. Wicksteed, P. H., tr. LC 77-27163. (Hibbert Lectures: 1887). Repr. of 1892 ed. 34.00 (ISBN 0-404-60409-9). AMS Pr.

Gocek, Matilda A. Love Is a Challenge. LC 78-12327. (Keepers of the Light Ser.). (Illus.). 72p. 1978. pap. 3.95 (ISBN 0-912526-22-X). Lib Res.

Gockel, Herman W. Daily Walk with God. 1982. 15.95 (ISBN 0-570-03298-9, 15-2171); pap. 10.95 (ISBN 0-570-03855-3, 12YY2810). Concordia.

--My Hand in His. rev. ed. LC 60-15577. 1975. pap. 6.50 (12-2613). Concordia.

--What Jesus Means to Me. 1956. 4.95 (ISBN 0-570-03021-8, 6-1008). Concordia.

Gockel, Herman W. & Saleska, Edward J., eds. Child's Garden of Prayer. (Illus.). 1981. pap. 1.50 (ISBN 0-570-03412-4, 56-1016). Concordia.

Goddard. On the Trail of the UCC. 1981. pap. 8.95 (ISBN 0-8298-0353-X). Pilgrim NY.

Goddard, Dwight. The Buddha's Golden Path. 2nd rev. ed. LC 78-72435. Repr. of 1931 ed. 27.00 (ISBN 0-404-17296-2). AMS Pr.

--The Buddha's Golden Path. 214p. 1981. pap. 12.00 (ISBN 0-89540-074-X, SB-074). Sun Pub.

Goddard, Dwight, ed. A Buddhist Bible. LC 72-105327. 677p. 1970. pap. 11.95 (ISBN 0-8070-5951-X, BP357). Beacon Pr.

Goddard, E., tr. see Steiner, Rudolf.

Goddard, H. C. Studies in New England Transcendentalism. 1978. Repr. of 1960 ed. lib. bdg. 30.00 (ISBN 0-8492-4906-6). R West.

Goddard, Harold C. Blake's Fourfold Vision. LC 56-7354. (Orig.). 1956. pap. 2.50x (ISBN 0-87574-086-3). Pendle Hill.

Goddard, Madeleine V., tr. see Donoso Cortes, Juan.

Goddard, Pliny E. Myths & Tales from the San Carlos Apache. LC 76-43715. (AMNH. Anthropological Pap.: Vol. 29, Pt. 1). Repr. of 1918 ed. 16.50 (ISBN 0-404-15548-0). AMS Pr.

Godden, Malcolm, ed. see Aelfric.

Goddu, A. The Physics of William of Ockham. (Studies und Texte zur Geistesgeschichte des Mittelalters: No. 16). 310p. 1984. text ed. 50.00x (ISBN 90-04-06912-7, Pub. by EJ Brill Holland). Humanities.

Gode, Alexander, tr. see Petersen, Carol.

Godet, F. L. Commentary on the Gospel of Saint Luke, 2 vols, Vol. 1. Shalders, E. W., ed. 448p. 1870. 13.95 (ISBN 0-567-27445-4, Pub. by T & T Clark Ltd UK). Fortress.

--Commentary on the Gospel of St. Luke, 2 vols, Vol. 2. Cusin, M. D., ed. 472p. 1870. 13.95 (ISBN 0-567-27446-2, Pub. by T&T Clark Ltd UK). Fortress.

Godet, Frederic L. Commentary John's Gospel, 2 vols. in 1. LC 78-59145. (Kregel Reprint Library). 1132p. 1980. Repr. of 1885 ed. 34.95 (ISBN 0-8254-2714-2). Kregel.

--Commentary on First Corinthians. LC 77-79190. (Kregel Reprint Library). 928p. 1977. 29.95 (ISBN 0-8254-2716-9). Kregel.

--Commentary on Luke. 3rd ed. LC 81-18614. (Kregel Reprint Library). 586p. 1981. Repr. of 1887 ed. 24.95 (ISBN 0-8254-2720-7). Kregel.

--Commentary on Romans. LC 77-79189. (Kregel Reprint Library). 542p. 1977. 24.95 (ISBN 0-8254-2715-0). Kregel.

--Studies in Paul's Epistles. LC 84-7138. 352p. 1984. 14.95 (ISBN 0-8254-2723-1). Kregel.

Godfrey, John. Twelve Hundred & Four-the Unholy Crusade. (Illus.). 1980. 39.95x (ISBN 0-19-215834-1). Oxford U Pr.

Godfrey, Laurie R., ed. Scientists Confront Creationism. 352p. 1984. pap. 8.95 (ISBN 0-393-30154-0). Norton.

Godfrey, W. Robert & Boyd, Jesse L., III, eds. Through Christ's Word: A Festschrift for Philip E. Hughes. 272p. (Orig.). 1985. pap. 10.95 (ISBN 0-87552-274-2). Presby & Reformed.

Godfrey, Walter H., ed. Parish of Chelsea, Pt. 1. LC 71-138271. (London County Council. Survey of London: No. 2). Repr. of 1909 ed. 74.50 (ISBN 0-404-51652-1). AMS Pr.

Godin, Andre. The Psychology of Religious Vocations: Problems of the Religious Life. Wauck, LeRoy A., ed. LC 82-24708. 136p. (Orig.). 1983. lib. bdg. 24.00 (ISBN 0-8191-3007-9); pap. text ed. 9.50 (ISBN 0-8191-3008-7). U Pr of Amer.

--Psycological Dynamics of Religious Experience. Turton, Mary, tr. from Fr. Orig. Title: Psychologie des Experiences Religieuses. 279p. 1985. pap. 13.95 (ISBN 0-89135-039-X). Religious Educ.

Godman, David, ed. Be As You Are: The Teachings of Sri Ramana Maharshi. 256p. 1985. pap. 8.95 (ISBN 1-85063-006-2, Ark Paperbks). Methuen Inc.

Godolphin, F. R., ed. & intro. by. Great Classical Myths. LC 64-10293. 7.95 (ISBN 0-394-60417-2). Modern Lib.

Godoretzky, N. T. The Humiliated Christ in Modern Russian Thought. 59.95 (ISBN 0-8490-0376-8). Gordon Pr.

Godsey, John D. Preface to Bonhoeffer: The Man & Two of His Shorter Writings. LC 79-7378. 80p. 1979. pap. 3.50 (ISBN 0-8006-1367-8, 1-1367). Fortress.

Godsey, John D., jt. ed. see Kelly, Geffrey B.

Godshall, C. David. Prayers in Dialogue. (Common & Lutheran Ser. C). 1985. 7.95 (ISBN 0-89536-759-9, 5866). CSS of Ohio.

--Prayers in Dialogue B: (Con-Luth) 1984. 7.95 (ISBN 0-89536-692-4, 4869). CSS of Ohio.

--Prayers in Dialogue: Series A. rev. ed. Sherer, Michael L., ed. 1986. pap. 7.95 (ISBN 0-89536-813-7, 6842). CSS of Ohio.

Godwin, David. Godwin's Practical Encyclopedia of Cabalistic Magick. 2nd, rev. & expanded ed. Weschcke, Carl L., ed. (Sourcebook Ser.). 500p. 1987. pap. 15.00 (ISBN 0-87542-292-6, L-292). Llewellyn Pubns.

Godwin, Don & Godwin, Vi. Faith vs. Fear. 257p. 1986. pap. 7.95 (ISBN 0-317-52284-1). Christian Pub.

Godwin, George. The Great Mystics. LC 74-2430. (St. Paul, Plotinus, St. Augustine, St. Francis, St. Teresa, Martin Luther, Jacob Boehme, George Fox, Emanuel Swedenborg, William Blake). 1945. lib. bdg. 27.50 (ISBN 0-8414-4499-4). Folcroft.

Godwin, Jeff. The Devil's Disciples. (Illus.). 352p. (Orig.). 1986. pap. 7.95 (ISBN 0-937958-23-9). Chick Pubns.

Godwin, Johnnie C. Layman's Bible Book Commentary: Mark, Vol. 16. LC 78-54774. 1979. 5.95 (ISBN 0-8054-1186-0). Broadman.

Godwin, Joscelyn. Music, Mysticism & Magic: A Source Book. 384p. 1986. text ed. 50.00 (ISBN 0-7102-0904-5, 0905W, Pub. by Routledge UK). Methuen Inc.

--Mystery Religions: In the Ancient World. LC 81-47423. (Illus.). 180p. (Orig.). 1981. pap. 9.95 (ISBN 0-06-063140-6, CN4020, HarpR). Har-Row.

Godwin, Shiri. Christian Social Thought in India, 1962-77. (Orig.). 1983. pap. 6.00 (ISBN 0-8364-0988-4, Pub. by Christian Lit Soc India). South Asia Bks.

Godwin, Vi, jt. auth. see Godwin, Don.

Godwin, William. Essays. LC 77-23245. 1977. Repr. of 1873 ed. lib. bdg. 35.00 (ISBN 0-8414-4502-8). Folcroft.

--The Pantheon: or, Ancient History of the Gods of Greece & Rome. Feldman, Burton & Richardson, Robert D., eds. LC 78-60886. (Myth & Romanticism Ser.). 1984. lib. bdg. 80.00 (ISBN 0-8240-3560-7). Garland Pub.

--St. Leon: A Tale of the Sixteenth Century. LC 74-162884. (Illus.). Repr. of 1835 ed. 32.50 (ISBN 0-404-54405-3). AMS Pr.

Goebbels, Joseph. Communism with the Mask Off: The Jewish Origin of Communism. 1982. lib. bdg. 59.95 (ISBN 0-87700-406-4). Revisionist Pr.

Goebel, Patrice, ed. see Molnar, Paul J.

Goedicke, Hans. Near Eastern Studies: In Honor of William Foxwell Albright. LC 70-142817. 504p. 1971. 42.50x (ISBN 0-8018-1235-6). Johns Hopkins.

Goedicke, Hans & Roberts, J. J., eds. Unity & Diversity: Essays in the History, Literature, & Religion of the Ancient Near East. LC 74-24376. (Johns Hopkins University Near Eastern Studies). pap. 60.00 (ISBN 0-317-11301-1, 2016572). Bks Demand UMI.

Goehri Ethridge, Myrna L. Fearing No Evil: One Woman's Life of Tragedy & Victory. (Illus.). 108p. (Orig.). 1984. pap. 5.95 (ISBN 0-941018-12-1). Martin Pr CA.

Goehring, James E., jt. ed. see Pearson, Birger A.

Goell, Yohai. Bibliography of Modern Hebrew Literature in English Translation. 132p. 1968. casebound 14.95x (ISBN 0-87855-187-5). Transaction Bks.

Goen, C. C. Broken Churches, Broken Nation: Denominational Schism & the Coming of the American Civil War. 208p. 1985. 17.95 (ISBN 0-86554-166-3, MUP-H156). Mercer Univ Pr.

Goen, C. C., ed. see Edwards, Jonathan.

Goenner, M. E. Mary-Verse of the Teutonic Knights. LC 72-140022. (Catholic University of America Studies in German: No. 19). Repr. of 1943 ed. 20.00 (ISBN 0-404-50239-3). AMS Pr.

Goergen, Don. The Sexual Celibate. 272p. 1975. 5.00 (ISBN 0-8164-0268-X, HarpR). Har-Row.

Goering, Gladys V. Women in Search of Mission. LC 80-66787. (Illus.). 136p. 1980. pap. 3.95 (ISBN 0-87303-062-1). Faith & Life.

Goerner, H. Cornell. All Nations in God's Purpose. LC 78-50360. 1979. pap. 4.95 (ISBN 0-8054-6312-7). Broadman.

Goertz, Hans J. Profiles of Radical Reformers. Tr. of Radikale Reformatoren. 228p. 1982. pap. 9.95x (ISBN 0-8361-1250-4). Herald Pr.

Goertz, Hans-Jurgen, ed. Umstrittenes Taufertum 1525-1975. 1975. 22.50x (ISBN 0-8361-1128-1). Herald Pr.

Goetchius, Eugene V. & Price, Charles P. The Gifts of God. LC 84-60627. 128p. (Orig.). 1984. pap. 4.95 (ISBN 0-8192-1349-7). Morehouse.

Goethe, J. W. Von see Von Goethe, J. W. & Steiner, Rudolf.

Goettelmann, Paul A. The Baptistry of Frejus: A Restoration Based on the Architectural & Historical Evidence. (Illus.). 75p. 1984. Repr. of 1933 ed. 25.00x (ISBN 0-939738-23-6). Zubal Inc.

Goetz, Delia, jt. tr. see Recinos, Adrian.

Goetz, Joan. El Amor y la Juventud. Montero, Lidia D., tr. from Eng. Tr. of Let's Look at Love. (Illus.). 96p. 1984. pap. 2.25 (ISBN 0-311-46058-5). Casa Bautista.

Goetz, Joseph. Mirrors of God. 1984. pap. 4.95 (ISBN 0-86716-031-4). St Anthony Mess Pr.

Goetze, Albrecht. Old Babylonian Omen Texts. LC 79-3537. (Yale Oriental Series: Babylonian Texts: No. 10). (Illus.). 176p. Repr. of 1966 ed. 37.50 (ISBN 0-404-60265-7). AMS Pr.

Goff, Guillermo. El Matrimonio y la Familia en la Vida Cristiana. (Span.). 240p. 1985. pap. 7.00 (ISBN 0-311-46097-6). Casa Bautista.

Goff, Jacques Le see Le Goff, Jacques.

Goff, James & Goff, Margaret. In Every Person Who Hopes... (Orig.). 1980. pap. 3.75 (ISBN 0-377-00096-5). Friend Pr.

Goff, Margaret, jt. auth. see Goff, James.

Goffart, Walter, tr. see Erdmann, Carl.

Goffart, Walter A. Le Mans Forgeries: A Chapter from the History of Church Property in the Ninth Century. LC 66-18246. (Historical Studies: No. 76). 1966. 25.00x (ISBN 0-674-51875-6). Harvard U Pr.

Goffen, Rona. Piety & Patronage in Renaissance Venice: Bellini, Titian, & Franciscans. LC 85-91280. 320p. 1986. 40.00 (ISBN 0-300-03455-5). Yale U Pr.

Goffstein, M. B. Your Lone Journey. LC 86-45107. (Illus.). 32p. 12.45 (ISBN 0-06-015659-7, HarpT). Har-Row.

Goforth, Rosalind. Goforth of China. 384p. 1969. pap. 4.95 (ISBN 0-87123-181-6, 200181). Bethany Hse.

--Jonathan Goforth. (Men of Faith Ser.). 3.95 (ISBN 0-87123-842-X, 200842). Bethany Hse.

Gogol, Nikolai. Meditations on the Divine Liturgy. 58p. (Orig.). 1985. pap. 3.00 (ISBN 0-317-30300-7). Holy Trinity.

--Razmishljenije o Bozhestvennoj Liturgii. Tr. of Meditations on the Divine Liturgy. 48p. pap. 2.00 (ISBN 0-317-29135-1). Holy Trinity.

Goguel, Maurice. The Life of Jesus. Wyon, Olive, tr. LC 75-41114. Repr. of 1933 ed. 32.50 (ISBN 0-404-14546-9). AMS Pr.

Gohdes, Clarence. Periodicals of American Transcendentalism. LC 77-136380. Repr. of 1931 ed. 16.00 (ISBN 0-404-02854-3). AMS Pr.

Gohdes, Clarence L. Periodicals of American Transcendentalism. LC 76-107803. (Select Bibliographies Reprint Ser). 1931. 19.00 (ISBN 0-8369-5206-5). Ayer Co Pubs.

Goitein, S. D. Jews & Arabs: Their Contacts Through the Ages. 3rd ed. LC 74-9141. 271p. 1974. pap. 6.95 (ISBN 0-8052-0464-4). Schocken.

--A Mediterranean Society: The Jewish Communities of the Arab World As Portrayed in the Documents of the Cairo Geniza. Bd. with Vol. I. Economic Foundations. 1968; Vol. 2. The Community. 1971; Vol. 3. The Family. 1978. 48.50x (ISBN 0-520-03265-9); Vol. 4. Daily Life. 1983. 42.00x (ISBN 0-520-04869-5). LC 67-22430. (Near Eastern Center, UCLA). U of Cal Pr.

Goitein, S. D., ed. Religion in a Religious Age. 10.00x (ISBN 0-87068-268-7, Pub. by an Academic Inst); pap. 8.95. Ktav.

Gokak, Vinayak K. Narahari: Prophet of New India. 298p. 1972. pap. 7.95 (ISBN 0-317-20882-9). CSA Pr.

--Sri Aurobindo-Seer & Poet. LC 73-900907. 185p. 1974. 8.00x (ISBN 0-89684-454-4). Orient Bk Dist.

Gokhale, Balkrishna G. Buddhism & Asoka. LC 78-72443. Repr. of 1948 ed. 41.50 (ISBN 0-404-17298-9). AMS Pr.

Golan, Matti. Shimon Peres: A Biography. Friedman, Ina, tr. LC 82-7354. (Hebrew., Illus.). 275p. 1982. 25.00 (ISBN 0-312-71736-9). St Martin.

Golann, Cecil P. Mission on a Mountain: The Story of Abraham & Isaac. LC 73-7498. (Foreign Lands Ser.). (Illus.). 32p. 1975. PLB 5.95 (ISBN 0-8225-0363-8). Lerner Pubns.

Golb, Norman & Pritsak, Omeljan. Khazarian Hebrew Documents of the Tenth Century. 152p. 1982. 45.00x (ISBN 0-8014-1221-8). Cornell U Pr.

Golbitz, Pat, ed. see Hyman, B. D. & Hyman, Jeremy.

Golbitz, Pat, ed. see Mickey, Paul & Proctor, William.

Golbitz, Pat, ed. see Noorbergen, Rene.

Golby, J. M. & Purdue, A. W. The Making of the Modern Christmas. LC 86-7083. (Illus.). 144p. 1986. 19.95 (ISBN 0-8203-0879-X). U of GA Pr.

Gold, Avie. Hoshanos. (Art Scroll Mesorah Ser.). 160p. 1980. 11.95 (ISBN 0-89906-162-1); pap. 8.95 (ISBN 0-89906-163-X). Mesorah Pubns.

Gold, E. J. Creation Story Verbatim. 278p. (Orig.). 1986. pap. 11.95 (ISBN 0-89556-047-X). Gateways Bks & Tapes.

--The Human Biological Machine As a Transformational Apparatus. Lourie, Iven, pref. by. LC 85-60946. 176p. (Orig.). 1985. pap. 12.50 (ISBN 0-89556-046-1). Gateways Bks & Tapes.

--The Joy of Sacrifice: Secrets of the Sufi Way. LC 78-54140. (Illus.). 1978. pap. 5.95 (ISBN 0-89556-003-8, Pub. by IDHHB & HOHM Press). Gateways Bks & Tapes.

--Shakti. (Illus.). 1973. pap. 4.95 (ISBN 0-89556-005-4). Gateways Bks & Tapes.

Gold, Leonard, tr. see Shaham, Nathan.

Gold, Penny S. The Lady & the Virgin: Image, Attitude & Experience in Twelfth-Century France. LC 84-23701. (Women in Culture & Society Ser.). (Illus.). 228p. 1985. lib. bdg. 20.00x (ISBN 0-226-30087-0). U of Chicago Pr.

Gold, Peter. Tibetan Reflections. (Illus.). 112p. (Orig.). 1984. pap. 11.95 (ISBN 0-86171-022-3, Wisdom Pubns). Great Traditions.

Goldberg, B. Z. The Sacred Fire. 285p. 1974. pap. 3.95 (ISBN 0-8065-0456-0). Citadel Pr.

--Sacred Fire. (Illus.). 1958. 7.50 (ISBN 0-8216-0146-6). Univ Bks.

Goldberg, Ben Z. The Jewish Problem in the Soviet Union: Analysis & Solution. LC 82-15842. (Illus.). x, 374p. 1982. Repr. of 1961 ed. lib. bdg. 45.00x (ISBN 0-313-23692-5, GOJE). Greenwood.

Goldberg, George. Church, State & the Constitution. rev. ed. LC 87-4566. 160p. 1987. 14.95 (ISBN 0-89526-794-2). Regnery Bks.

--Reconsecrating America. 160p. 1984. 9.95 (ISBN 0-8028-3607-0). Eerdmans.

Goldberg, Harvey E., ed. Judaism Viewed from Within & from Without: Anthropological Studies. (Anthropolgy & Judaic Studies). 348p. 1986. 44.50X (ISBN 0-88706-354-3); pap. 16.95X (ISBN 0-88706-356-X). STate U NY Pr.

Goldberg, Hillel. Israel Salanter: Text, Structure, Idea. 1982. 25.00x (ISBN 0-87068-709-3). Ktav.

--Wherever I Go, I Go to Jerusalem. 240p. 1986. 12.95 (ISBN 0-940646-09-9); pap. 8.95 (ISBN 0-940646-10-2). Rossel Bks.

Goldberg, Israel. Israel: A History of the Jewish People. LC 72-162629. 715p. 1949. Repr. lib. bdg. 29.50x (ISBN 0-8371-6196-7, GOIS). Greenwood.

Goldberg, Ivan K., et al, eds. Pain, Anxiety & Grief: Pharmacotherapeutic Care of the Dying Patient & the Bereaved. 224p. 1985. 24.00x (ISBN 0-231-04742-8). Columbia U Pr.

Goldberg, Louis. Deuteronomy. (Bible Study Commentary Ser.). 208p. 1986. pap. 7.95 (ISBN 0-310-20201-9, 11412P). Zondervan.

--Ecclesiastes: Bible Study Commentary. 1986. pap. 4.95 (ISBN 0-310-41823-2, 18199P). Zondervan.

--Leviticus: Bible Study Commentary. (A Study Guide Commentary Ser.). 128p. (Orig.). 1980. pap. 4.95 (ISBN 0-310-41813-5, 18198P). Zondervan.

--Our Jewish Friends. Rev. ed. 1983. pap. text ed. 4.95 (ISBN 0-87213-239-0). Loizeaux.

--Turbulence over the Middle East: Israel & the Nations in Confrontation & the Coming Kingdom of Peace on Earth. (Illus.). 320p. 1982. pap. 7.95 (ISBN 0-87213-240-4). Loizeaux.

Goldberg, M. Hirsch. The Jewish You Wouldn't Believe It Book. (Illus.). 252p. 1986. pap. 7.95 (ISBN 0-933503-51-2). Shapolsky Pubs.

Goldberg, M. Hirsh. Just Because They're Jewish. 1978. 9.95 (ISBN 0-8128-2518-7). Stein & Day.

Goldberg, Michael. Jews & Christians, Getting Our Stories Straight: The Exodus & the Passion...Resurrection. 240p. (Orig.). 1985. pap. 12.95 (ISBN 0-687-20330-9). Abingdon.

--Theology & Narrative: A Critical Introduction. 304p. (Orig.). 1982. pap. 11.95 (ISBN 0-687-41503-9). Abingdon.

Goldberg, Nathan. New Functional Hebrew-English, English-Hebrew Dictionary. (Hebrew & Eng.). 1958. 5.00x (ISBN 0-87068-379-9). Ktav.

--New Illustrated Hebrew-English Dictionary for Young Readers. (Hebrew & Eng., Illus.). 1958. pap. 6.95x (ISBN 0-87068-370-5). Ktav.

Goldberg, Nathan, et al. The Classification of Jewish Immigrants & Its Implications: A Survey of Opinion. LC 45-6587. (Yivo English Translation Ser.). 154p. 1945. pap. 2.00 (ISBN 0-914512-13-7). Yivo Inst.

Goldberg, Robert A. Back to the Soil: The Jewish Farmers of Clarion, Utah, & Their World. (Utah Centennial Ser.: Vol. 2). (Illus.). 208p. 1986. 19.95 (ISBN 0-87480-263-6). U of Utah Pr.

Goldblatt, Harvey, jt. ed. see Picchio, Riccardo.

Goldbrunner, Josef. Cure of Mind, Cure of Soul: Depth Psychology & Pastoral Care. 1962. pap. 2.50x (ISBN 0-268-00067-0). U of Notre Dame Pr.

--Realization: The Anthropology of Pastoral Care. 1966. 18.95 (ISBN 0-268-00227-4). U of Notre Dame Pr.

Golden, Jerry & Lestarjette, Steve. Burned Alive! 176p. 1987. pap. text ed. 5.95 (ISBN 0-939079-01-1). Christlife Pubs.

Golden, Robert & Sullivan, Mary C. Flannery O'Connor & Caroline Gordon: A Reference Guide. 1977. lib. bdg. 28.50 (ISBN 0-8161-7845-3, Hall Reference). G K Hall.

Goldenberg, Naomi R. Changing of the Gods: Feminism & the End of Traditional Religions. LC 78-19602. 1979. pap. 7.95 (ISBN 0-8070-1111-8, BP600). Beacon Pr.

Goldenberg, Robert. The Sabbath-Law of R. Meir. LC 78-14370. (Brown University. Brown Judaic Studies: No. 6). 1978. pap. 9.00 (ISBN 0-89130-249-2, 140006). Scholars Pr GA.

Goldenweiser, Alexander. Totemism. 59.95 (ISBN 0-8490-1223-6). Gordon Pr.

Goldfield, Lea N. An Inquiry into the Authenticity of Moses Maimonides' Treatise on Resurrection. 1985. text ed. 19.95x (ISBN 0-88125-088-0). Ktav.

Goldfrank, D. Rule of Iosif of Volokolamsk. (Cistercian Studies: No. 36). pap. 14.95 (ISBN 0-87907-836-7). Cistercian Pubns.

Goldfrank, David, ed. The Monastic Rule of Losif Volotsky. 1983. pap. 14.95 (ISBN 0-87907-936-3). Cistercian Pubns.

Goldhaber, Nat & Denniston, Denise. TM: An Alphabetical Guide to the Transcendental Meditation Program. (Illus.). 1976. pap. 3.95 (ISBN 0-345-24096-0). Ballantine.

Goldhammer, Arthur, tr. see Le Goff, Jacques.

Goldhammer, Arthur, tr. see LeGoff, Jacques.

Goldhammer, Arthur, tr. see Schnapper, Dominique.
Goldhammer, Arthur, tr. see Sergent, Bernard.
Goldin, Alice, jt. auth. see Eichenbaum, Sharon.
Goldin, Hyman E. Jew & His Duties. 246p. 1953. pap. 6.95 (ISBN 0-88482-429-2). Hebrew Pub.
Goldin, Hyman E., tr. see Ganzfried, Solomon.
Goldin, Judah. The Living Talmud. 1957. pap. 3.95 (ISBN 0-451-62344-4, Ment). NAL.
Goldin, Judah, ed. & The Jewish Expression. LC 75-27866. 512p. 1976. pap. 10.95 (ISBN 0-300-01975-0). Yale U Pr.
Goldingay, John. God's Prophet God's Servant: A Study in Jeremiah & Isaiah 40-56. 160p. 1986. pap. 11.95 (ISBN 0-85364-338-5, Pub. by Paternoster UK). Attic Pr.
--Old Testament Commentary Survey. 2nd ed. Hubbard, Robert & Branson, Mark L., eds. 66p. 1981. pap. 3.50 (ISBN 0-8308-5499-1). Inter-Varsity.
--Theological Diversity & the Authority of the Old Testament. 240p. (Orig.). 1987. pap. 14.95 (ISBN 0-8028-0229-X). Eerdmans.
Goldman, Alan H. The Moral Foundations of Professional Ethics. LC 80-11696. (Philosophy & Society Ser.). 305p. 1980. 28.95x (ISBN 0-8476-6274-8); pap. 11.95x (ISBN 0-8476-6285-3). Rowman.
Goldman, Alex J. Child's Dictionary of Jewish Symbols. (Illus.). 5.00 (ISBN 0-685-09470-7). Feldheim.
--A Handbook for the Jewish Family: Understanding & Enjoying the Sabbath & Other Holidays. LC 58-12938. (Illus.). 1983. Repr. of 1958 ed. 14.95 (ISBN 0-8197-0085-1). Bloch.
Goldman, Bernard. The Sacred Portal: A Primary Symbol in Ancient Judaic Art. LC 86-10983. (Brown Classics in Judaica Ser.). (Illus.). 260p. 1986. pap. text ed. 15.75 (ISBN 0-8191-5269-2). U Pr of Amer.
Goldman, Edward A., ed. Jews in a Free Society: Challenges & Opportunities. 12.50x (ISBN 0-87820-112-2). Ktav.
Goldman, Robert P. God's Priests & Warriors: The Bhrgus of the Mahabharata. LC 76-41255. (Studies in Oriental Culture). 195p. 1977. 23.00x (ISBN 0-231-03941-7). Columbia U Pr.
Goldman, Ronald. Readiness for Religion. 1970. pap. 4.95 (ISBN 0-8164-2060-2, SP70, HarpR). Har-Row.
--Religious Thinking from Childhood to Adolescence. 1968. pap. text ed. 6.95 (ISBN 0-8164-2061-0, SP53, HarpR). Har-Row.
Goldman, Solomon. The Jew & the Universe. LC 73-2200. (The Jewish People; History, Religion, Literature Ser.). Repr. of 1936 ed. 23.50 (ISBN 0-405-05265-0). Ayer Co Pubs.
Goldman, W. Darryl. Stand in the Door. LC 80-65309. 176p. 1980. pap. 2.95 (ISBN 0-88243-599-X, 02-0599). Gospel Pub.
Goldmann, Lucien. The Philosophy of the Enlightenment: The Burgess & the Enlightenment. Maas, Henry, tr. from Fr. 1973. 17.50x (ISBN 0-262-07060-X). MIT Pr.
Goldmark, Josephine. Pilgrims of Forty-Eight. facsimile ed. LC 74-27989. (Modern Jewish Experience Ser.). (Illus.). 1975. Repr. of 1930 ed. 29.00x (ISBN 0-405-06716-X). Ayer Co Pubs.
Goldreich, Gloria, ed. A Treasury of Jewish Literature: From Biblical Times to Today. LC 81-6967. 256p. 1982. 13.45 (ISBN 0-03-053831-9). H Holt & Co.
Goldsborough, June, jt. auth. see Foster, John.
Goldscheider, Calvin. The American Jewish Community: Social Science Research & Policy Implications. (Brown Judaic Studies). 183p. 1986. 27.95 (ISBN 1-55540-081-7, 14-50-03). Scholars Pr GA.
--American Jewish Fertility. (Brown Studies on Jews & Their Societies). 1986. text ed. 23.95 (ISBN 0-89130-919-5, 14-50-01); pap. 18.95 (ISBN 0-89130-920-9). Scholars Pr GA.
--Jewish Continuity & Change: Emerging Patterns in America. LC 84-48746. (Jewish Political & Social Studies). (Illus.). 214p. 1986. 24.95x (ISBN 0-253-33157-9). Ind U Pr.
Goldscheider, Calvin, jt. auth. see Friedlander, Dov.
Goldscheider, Calvin, jt. auth. see Goldstein, Sidney.
Goldsmith, D., jt. auth. see Wagoner, R.
Goldsmith, Dale. New Testament Ethics. 196p. (Orig.). 1987. pap. 9.95 (ISBN 0-87178-605-2). Brethren.
Goldsmith, E. E. The Psychological Meaning of the Sacred Symbols in Art, 2 vols. (Illus.). 311p. 1987. Set. 167.50 (ISBN 0-89920-149-0). Am Inst Psych.
Goldsmith, Earl A. Counseling with Confidence. 155p. 1984. pap. 5.95 (ISBN 0-916945-01-4). V I Pr.
Goldsmith, Elizabeth. God Can Be Trusted. 1974. pap. 3.95 (ISBN 0-903843-85-4). OMF Bks.
Goldsmith, Emanuel S. Architects of Yiddishism at the Beginning of the Twentieth Century: A Study in Jewish Cultural History. LC 73-2894. 309p. 1976. 27.50 (ISBN 0-8386-1384-5). Fairleigh Dickinson.
Goldsmith, Emanuel S., ed. see Kaplan, Mordecai M.
Goldsmith, Joel. Beyond Words & Thoughts. 6.00 (ISBN 0-8216-0041-9). Univ Bks.
--Conscious Union with God. 6.00 (ISBN 0-8216-0050-8). Univ Bks.
--The Master Speaks. 192p. 1984. pap. 5.95 (ISBN 0-8065-0912-0). Citadel Pr.
Goldsmith, Joel S. The Altitude of Prayer. Sinkler, Lorainne, ed. LC 74-25082. 160p. 1975. 9.45 (ISBN 0-06-063171-6, HarpR). Har-Row.
--Art of Meditation. LC 56-13258. 1957. 12.45 (ISBN 0-06-063150-3, HarpR). Har-Row.
--Art of Spiritual Healing. LC 59-14532. 1959. 11.45 (ISBN 0-06-063170-8, HarpR). Har-Row.
--Beyond Words & Thoughts. 200p. 1974. pap. 4.95 (ISBN 0-8065-0447-1). Citadel Pr.
--Conscious Union with God. 1977. pap. text ed. 5.95 (ISBN 0-8065-0578-8). Citadel Pr.
--Consciousness Is What I Am. Sinkler, Lorraine, ed. LC 76-9967. 160p. 1976. 11.45 (ISBN 0-06-063173-2, HarpR). Har-Row.
--The Contemplative Life. 212p. 1976. pap. 5.95 (ISBN 0-8065-0523-0). Citadel Pr.
--I Am the Vine. 1972. pap. 1.00 (ISBN 0-87516-138-3). De Vorss.
--The Infinite Way. pap. 5.95 (ISBN 0-87516-309-2). De Vorss.
--Joel Goldsmith's Gift of Love. LC 82-11891. 96p. 1983. 8.95 (ISBN 0-686-92026-0, HarpR). Har-Row.
--The Letters. 299p. 1980. pap. 5.95 (ISBN 0-87516-386-6). De Vorss.
--Living Between Two Worlds. LC 73-18679. 1974. 8.95 (ISBN 0-06-063191-0, HarpR). Har-Row.
--Living Now. Sinkler, Lorraine, ed. 192p. 1984. pap. 5.95 (ISBN 0-8065-0911-2). Citadel Pr.
--Living the Infinite Way. rev. ed. LC 61-9646. 1961. 11.45 (ISBN 0-06-063190-2, HarpR). Har-Row.
--Love & Gratitude. 1972. pap. 1.75 (ISBN 0-87516-139-1). De Vorss.
--Man Was Not Born to Cry. 1984. pap. 5.95 (ISBN 0-8065-0915-5). Citadel Pr.
--The Mystical I. Sinkler, Lorraine, ed. LC 73-149745. 1971. 10.45 (ISBN 0-06-063195-3, HarpR). Har-Row.
--Our Spiritual Resources. LC 78-16010. 192p. 1983. pap. 3.50 (ISBN 0-06-063212-7, RD 478, HarpR). Har-Row.
--Parenthesis in Eternity. LC 64-10368. 1963. pap. 11.95 (ISBN 0-06-063230-5, HarpR). Har-Row.
--Parenthesis in Eternity: Living the Mystical Life. LC 85-45354. 1986. pap. 11.95 (ISBN 0-06-063231-3, PL 4125, PL). Har-Row.
--Practicing the Presence. LC 58-7474. 1958. 11.95 (ISBN 0-06-063250-X, HarpR). Har-Row.
--Realization of Oneness: The Practice of Spiritual Healing. 200p. 1974. pap. 5.95 (ISBN 0-8065-0453-6). Citadel Pr.
--Secret of the Twenty-Third Psalm. 1972. pap. 1.50 (ISBN 0-87516-140-5). De Vorss.
--Thunder of Silence. LC 61-7340. 1961. 12.45 (ISBN 0-06-063270-4, HarpR). Har-Row.
--Truth. 1972. pap. 1.00 (ISBN 0-87516-141-3). De Vorss.
--The World Is New. LC 62-7953. 1978. 8.95 (ISBN 0-06-063291-7, HarpR). Har-Row.
Goldsmith, M. Leviticus-Deuteronomy. (Bible Study Commentary Ser.). 126p. 1980. pap. 4.95 (ISBN 0-87508-151-7). Chr Lit.
Goldsmith, Martin. Islam & Christian Witness. LC 83-6112. 160p. 1983. pap. 4.95 (ISBN 0-87784-809-2). Inter-Varsity.
Goldsmith, Michael, et al. Today's Father: A Guide to Understanding, Enjoying & Making Things for the Growing Family. (Winston Family Handbooks). 96p. (Orig.). 1984. pap. 9.95 (ISBN 0-86683-849-X, AY8494, HarpR). Har-Row.
Goldsmith, Oliver, tr. see Marteilhe, Jean.
Goldstein, Charles. Bunker. Malkin, Esther, tr. from Fr. LC 74-116978. (Temple Bks). 1973. pap. 3.95 (ISBN 0-689-70347-3, T27). Atheneum.
Goldstein, David. The Ashkenazi Haggadah. (Illus.). 140p. 1985. 75.00 (ISBN 0-8109-1819-6). Abrams.
--Hebrew Incunables in the British Isles: A Preliminary Census. (Illus.). 50p. (Orig.). 1985. pap. 14.25 (ISBN 0-7123-0047-3, Pub. by British Lib). Longwood Pub Group.
--Hebrew Manuscript Painting. LC 85-18995. (Illus.). 80p. (Orig.). 1985. pap. 8.95 (ISBN 0-7123-0054-6, Pub. by British Lib). Longwood Pub Group.
Goldstein, David, ed. see Weiss, Joseph.
Goldstein, David, tr. see Tishby, Isaiah.
Goldstein, David I. Dostoyevsky & the Jews. (University of Texas Press Slavic Ser.: No. 3). 256p. 1981. 20.00x (ISBN 0-292-71528-5). U of Tex Pr.
Goldstein, Doris. Trial of Faith: Religion & Politics in Tocqueville's Thought. 144p. 1975. 21.00 (ISBN 0-444-99001-1). Elsevier.
Goldstein, Doris S. Trial of Faith: Religion & Politics in Tocqueville's. LC 75-4753. pap. 39.00 (2026263). Bks Demand UMI.
Goldstein, Eleanor C., ed. Ethics, Vol. 1 (incl. 1979 & 1981 Supplement) (Social Issues Resources Ser.). 1982. 70.00 (ISBN 0-89777-026-9). Soc Issues.
--Religion, Vol. 1 (incl. 1978-1980 Supplements) (Social Issues Resources Ser.). 1981. 70.00 (ISBN 0-89777-021-8). Soc Issues.
--Religion, Vol. 2 (incl. 1981-1985 Supplements) 1986. 70.00 (ISBN 0-89777-053-6). Soc Issues.
Goldstein, Israel. My World as a Jew, Vol. 1. LC 82-42721. (Illus.). 352p. 1984. 27.50 (ISBN 0-8453-4765-9, Cornwall Bks). Assoc Univ Prs.
--My World as a Jew, Vol. 2. LC 82-42621. (Illus.). 416p. 1984. 27.50 (ISBN 0-8453-4780-2, Cornwall Bks). Assoc Univ Prs.
--Toward a Solution. facs. ed. LC 79-128248. (Essay Index Reprint Ser). 1940. 21.00 (ISBN 0-8369-1877-0). Ayer Co Pubs.
Goldstein, Jonathan A., tr. & intro. by. Maccabees One. LC 75-32719. (Anchor Bible Ser.: Vol. 41). (Illus.). 18.00 (ISBN 0-385-08533-8, Anchor Pr). Doubleday.
Goldstein, Joseph. The Experience of Insight: A Simple & Direct Guide to Buddhist Meditation. LC 82-42682. 185p. (Orig.). 1983. pap. 7.95 (ISBN 0-87773-226-4). Shambhala Pubns.
--The Experience of Insight: A Simple & Direct Guide to Buddhist Meditation. 1987. pap. 9.95. Shambhala Pubns.
Goldstein, Rose. Time to Pray. LC 72-91792. 10.00 (ISBN 0-87677-141-X). Hartmore.
Goldstein, Sidney & Goldscheider, Calvin. Jewish Americans: Three Generations in a Jewish Community. (Brown Classics in Judaica Ser.). (Illus.). 294p. 1985. pap. text ed. 13.50 (ISBN 0-8191-4721-4). U Pr of Amer.
Goldstein-Alpern, Neva G. Beginning of the World. (Board Bks.). (Illus.). 12p. 1987. 5.95. Judaica Pr.
Goldsworthy, Graeme. Gospel & Kingdom: A Christian Interpretation of the Old Testament. pap. cancelled (ISBN 0-85364-218-4, Pub. by Paternoster U K). Attic Pr.
--Gospel & Kingdom: A Christian's Guide to the Old Testament. 128p. 1983. pap. 6.95 (ISBN 0-86683-686-1, HarpR). Har-Row.
Goldwasser, M., tr. see Weinreich, Uriel.
Goldwert, Marvin. Psyche & History. 85p. (Orig.). 1985. pap. 6.95x (ISBN 0-932269-41-9). Wyndham Hall.
Goldworm, Hersh. Mishnah-Moed, Vol. 2. (Artscroll Mishnah Ser.). 416p. 1981. 16.95 (ISBN 0-89906-254-7); pap. 13.95 (ISBN 0-89906-255-5). Mesorah Pubns.
Goldwurm, Hersh. Daniel. (The Art Scroll Tanach Ser.). 352p. 1979. 16.95 (ISBN 0-89906-079-X); pap. 13.95 (ISBN 0-89906-080-3). Mesorah Pubns.
Goldwurm, Hersh, et al. Mishnah-Moed, Vol. 3. (Art Scroll Mishnah Ser.). 1980. 16.95 (ISBN 0-89906-256-3); pap. 13.95 (ISBN 0-89906-257-1). Mesorah Pubns.
Goldziher, Ignac. Muslim Studies. Stern, S. M., ed. & tr. Incl. Vol. 1. Muhammedanische Studien. LC 67-20745. 1967. 44.50 (ISBN 0-87395-234-0); Vol. 2. Hadith: The 'Traditions', Ascribed to Muhammed. LC 72-11731. 1972. State U NY Pr.
Goldziher, Ignaz. Introduction to Islamic Theology & Law. Lewis, Bernard, ed. Hamori, Andras & Hamori, Ruth, trs. from Ger. LC 80-7523. (Modern Classics in Near Eastern Studies). 325p. 1981. 32.00 (ISBN 0-691-07257-4); pap. 14.50 LPE (ISBN 0-691-10099-3). Princeton U Pr.
Golikhere, Vasanti R., ed. see Pandit, M. P.
Golinkin, Noah. Ayn Keloheynu. LC 81-51960. (Illus.). 128p. 1981. pap. 7.95x (ISBN 0-88400-076-1). Shengold.
--Shalom Aleichem. 77p. 1978. pap. 4.95x (ISBN 0-88482-696-1). Hebrew Pub.
Golka, F. W., ed. see Westerman, Claus.
Gollancz, Victor. A Year of Grace. 1950. 15.95 (ISBN 0-575-00982-9, Pub. by Gollancz England). David & Charles.
Gollancz, Victor, jt. ed. see Greene, Barbara.
Gollin, Gillian L. Moravians in Two Worlds: A Study of Changing Communities. LC 67-19653. 302p. 1967. 31.00x (ISBN 0-231-03033-9). Columbia U Pr.
Gollner, Marie-Louise, tr. see Georgiades, Thrysbulos.
Gollomb, Joseph. Albert Schweitzer: Genius in the Jungle. (Illus.). 149p. 1949. 10.95 (ISBN 0-8149-0308-8). Vanguard.
Gollwitzer, Gerhard. Sex, Eros & Marital Love. pap. 0.75 (ISBN 0-87785-104-2). Swedenborg.
Gollwitzer, Helmut. An Introduction to Protestant Theology. Cairns, David, tr. LC 82-4798. 236p. 1982. pap. 12.95 (ISBN 0-664-24415-7). Westminster.
--Karl Barth: Church Dogmatics - A Selection with Introduction. Bromiley, G. W., ed. & tr. 272p. Date not set. pap. 8.50 (ISBN 0-567-29051-4, Pub. by T & T Clark Ltd UK). Fortress.
--The Way to Life. Cairns, David, tr. from Ger. Tr. of Wendung Zum Leben. 232p. 1981. 21.95 (ISBN 0-567-09322-0, Pub. by T&T Clark Ltd UK); pap. 11.95 (ISBN 0-567-29322-X). Fortress.
Golomb, Morris. Know Jewish Living & Enjoy It. LC 78-54569. (Illus.). 1981. 11.95 (ISBN 0-88400-054-0). Shengold.
Golphenee, Lucille B. Isaac's Chosen Wife. (Arch Book Ser.: No. 21). 1984. pap. 0.99 (59-1282). Concordia.
Golubinskii, E. E. O Reforme v Byte Russkoi Tserkvi: Sbornik Statei. 142p. Repr. of 1913 ed. text ed. 33.12x (ISBN 0-576-99237-2, Pub. by Gregg Intl Pubs England). Gregg Intl.
Gomara, Francisco Lopez de. Cortes: The Life of the Conqueror of Mexico by His Secretary, Francisco Lopez de Gomara. Simpson, Lesley B., ed. & tr. LC 64-13474. 1964. pap. 5.95 (ISBN 0-520-00493-0, CAL 126). U of Cal Pr.
Gombrich, E. H. Symbolic Images: Studies in the Art of the Renaissance, No. II. LC 84-28111. (Illus.). xii, 356p. 1985. pap. 14.95 (ISBN 0-226-30217-2). U of Chicago Pr.
Gombrich, Richard, jt. ed. see Bechert, Heinz.
Gomes, Peter. Lent. LC 84-18756. (Proclamation 3 C Ser.). 64p. 1985. pap. 3.75 (ISBN 0-8006-4127-2). Fortress.
Gomes, Peter J., jt. auth. see Geller, Lawrence D.
Gomes, Peter J., jt. auth. see Kee, Howard C.
Gomez, Ildefonso. La Cartuja en Espana. Hogg, James, ed. (Analecta Cartusiana Ser.: No. 114). 499p. (Orig.). 1984. pap. 25.00 (ISBN 0-317-42560-9, Pub. by Salzburg Studies). Longwood Pub Group.
Gomez, Ildefonso M. & Hogg, James. La Cartuja de el Paular. Hogg, James, ed. (Analecta Cartusiana Ser.: No. 77). 100p. (Orig.). 1982. pap. 25.00 (ISBN 3-7052-0113-1, Pub. by Salzburg Studies). Longwood Pub Group.
Gompertz, Helen. First Prayers. (Illus.). 32p. 1983. 5.95 (ISBN 0-8170-1013-0). Judson.
--My Book of Prayers. (Illus.). 32p. 1986. pap. 3.95 (ISBN 0-8170-1104-8). Judson.
Gompertz, Rolf. A Celebration of Life: With Menachem. LC 83-50872. 160p. 1983. velo binding 10.00 (ISBN 0-918248-06-X). Word Doctor.
--The Messiah of Midtown Park. LC 83-50871. 136p. 1983. velo binding 10.00 (ISBN 0-918248-05-1). Word Doctor.
--My Jewish Brother Jesus. LC 76-55591. 200p. 1977. 15.00 (ISBN 0-918248-03-5); pap. 10.00 (ISBN 0-918248-02-7). Word Doctor.
--Sparks of Spirit: A Handbook for Personal Happiness. LC 83-50870. 168p. 1983. velo binding 10.00 (ISBN 0-918248-04-3). Word Doctor.
Gomperz, Heinrich. Philosophical Studies by Heinrich Gomperz. Robinson, Daniel S., ed. 1953. 9.50 (ISBN 0-8158-0100-9). Chris Mass.
Gonda, J. Change & Continuity in Indian Religion. 1984. text ed. 30.00x. Coronet Bks.
--Vision of the Vedic Poets. (Disputationes Rheno-Trajectinae Ser.: No. 8). (Orig.). 1963. pap. text ed. 28.80x (ISBN 90-2790-034-5). Mouton.
--Visnuism & Sivaism: A Comparison. LC 71-545904. 1976. 12.50x (ISBN 0-89684-465-X). Orient Bk Dist.
Gonda, Jan. Epithets in the Rgveda. (D. R. T. Ser: No. 3). 1959. pap. text ed. 29.60x (ISBN 90-2790-030-2). Mouton.
--Some Observations on the Relations Between Gods & Powers in the Veda, a Propos of the Phrase, Sunah Sahasah. (Disputationes Rheno-Trajectinae Ser.: No. 1). (Orig.). 1957. pap. text ed. 12.80x (ISBN 90-2790-027-2). Mouton.
Gonen, Rivka. Biblical Holy Places. (Illus.). 192p. pap. cancelled (ISBN 0-915361-67-1). Adama Pubs Inc.
Gonsalves, Carol. Sermon on the Mountain. (Arch Bk. Supplement Ser.). 1981. pap. 0.99 (ISBN 0-570-06149-0, 59-1304). Concordia.
Gonter, Janet. Choosing Is... (I'm Growing Up Ser.). (Illus.). 1986. casebound 3.95 (ISBN 0-87403-123-0, 3603). Standard Pub.
Gonzales, Bertha, tr. from Span. The Bible & the Message to the Men of the "New Earth". (Illus.). 144p. (Orig.). 1986. pap. write for info. (ISBN 0-9607590-5-0). Action Life Pubns.
Gonzales, F. Jose. He Reigns from the Cross. Lemon, tr. 1962. 3.00 (ISBN 0-8198-0054-6). Dghtrs St Paul.
Gonzalez, Ananias, ed. see Sisemore, J. T.
Gonzalez, Bertha, tr. from Span. A World According to the Heart of God. LC 85-73186. 176p. (Orig.). 1986. pap. 5.00 (ISBN 0-9607590-1-8). Action Life Pubns.
Gonzalez, Catherine, jt. auth. see Gonzalez, Justo.
Gonzalez, Catherine G., jt. auth. see Gonzalez, Justo L.
Gonzalez, Jose L. & Playfoot, Jane, eds. My Life for the Poor: Mother Teresa of Calcutta. 1987. pap. 2.95 (ISBN 0-345-33780-8, Pub. by Ballantine Epiphany). Ballantine.

Gonzalez, Juan G. The New Libertarian Gospel: Pitfalls of the Theology of Liberation. 1977. 7.95 (ISBN 0-8199-0682-4). Franciscan Herald.

Gonzalez, Justo. The Story of Christianity. LC 83-49187. (Reformation to the Present Day Ser.: Vol. II). (Illus.). 448p. (Orig.). 1984. pap. 13.95 kivar cover (ISBN 0-06-063316-6, RD 511, HarpR). Har-Row.

Gonzalez, Justo & Gonzalez, Catherine. In Accord-Let Us Worship. (Orig.). 1981. pap. 3.95 (ISBN 0-377-00110-4). Friend Pr.

Gonzalez, Justo L. La Era de las Tinieblas. (Y Hasta Lo Ultimo de la Tierra: una Historia Ilustrada del Christianismo Ser.: Tomo III). (Span., Illus.). 199p. (Orig.). 1978. pap. 5.95 (ISBN 0-89922-128-9). Edit Caribe.

--La Era de los Altos Ideales. (Y Hasta Lo Ultimo de la Tierra: una Historia Ilustrada Del Cristianismo Ser.: Tomo IV). (Span., Illus.). 197p. (Orig.). 1979. pap. 5.95 (ISBN 0-89922-135-1). Edit Caribe.

--La Era de los Conquistadores. (Y Hasta Lo Ultimo de la Tierra: una Historia Ilustrada del Cristianismo: Tomo VII). (Span., Illus.). 218p. (Orig.). 1981. pap. 5.95 (ISBN 0-89922-162-9). Edit Caribe.

--La Era de los Dogmas y las Dudas. (Y hasta lo ultimo de la tierra Ser.: Tomo No. 8). (Illus.). 224p. (Orig.). 1983. pap. 5.95 (ISBN 0-89922-171-8). Edit Caribe.

--La Era de los Gigantes. (Y Hasta Lo Ultimo de la Tierra: una Historia Ilustrada del Cristianismo Ser.: Tomo II). (Span., Illus.). 184p. (Orig.). 1978. pap. 5.95 (ISBN 0-89922-117-3). Edit Caribe.

--La Era de los Martires. (Y Hasta Lo Ultimo de la Tierra: una Historia Ilustrada del Christianismo Ser.: Tomo I). (Span., Illus.). 189p. (Orig.). 1978. pap. 5.95 (ISBN 0-89922-109-2). Edit Caribe.

--La Era de los Reformadores. (Y Hasta Lo Ultimo de la Tierra: una Historia Ilustrada del Cristianismo Ser.: Tomo VI). (Span., Illus.). 219p. (Orig.). 1980. pap. 5.95 (ISBN 0-89922-154-8). Edit Caribe.

--La Era de los Suenos Frustrados. (Y Hasta Lo Ultimo de la Tierra: una Historia Ilustrada del Cristianismo Ser.: Tomo V). (Span., Illus.). 182p. (Orig.). 1979. pap. 5.95 (ISBN 0-89922-139-4). Edit Caribe.

--History of Christian Thought, 3 vols. rev. ed. LC 74-109679. 1975. Set. 56.00 (ISBN 0-687-17181-4). Abingdon.

--A History of Christian Thought. rev. ed. 1987. Set. 59.95 (ISBN 0-687-17185-7). Abingdon.

--The History of Christian Thought: From the Beginnings to the Council of Chalcedon in A. D. 451. rev. ed. LC 74-109679. Set. text ed. 56.00 (ISBN 0-687-17181-4); Vol. II. text ed. 18.75; Vol. I. text ed. 20.00 (ISBN 0-687-17150-4); Vol. III. text ed. 20.00. Abingdon.

--Luces Bajo el Almud. LC 77-11753. (Span.). 76p. (Orig.). 1977. pap. 2.50 (ISBN 0-89922-102-5). Edit Caribe.

--The Story of Christianity, Volume 1: The Early Church to the Reformation. LC 83-48430. (Illus.). 448p. (Orig.). 1983. pap. 13.95 (ISBN 0-317-01107-3, RD 510, HarpR). Har-Row.

Gonzalez, Justo L. & Gonzalez, Catherine G. Liberation Preaching: The Pulpit & the Oppressed. LC 79-27858. (Abingdon Preacher's Library). 1980. pap. 6.95 (ISBN 0-687-21700-8). Abingdon.

Gonzalez, Justo, Sr. Historia de un Milagro. (Span.). 166p. 1984. pap. 3.95 (ISBN 0-89922-144-0). Edit Caribe.

Gonzalez, Mari, jt. auth. see Harvey, Adell.

Gonzalez, Nelly de see Diaz, Jorge & De Gonzalez, Nelly.

Gonzalez-Balado, Jose L. & Playfoot, Janet, eds. My Life for the Poor: The Story of Mother Teresa in Her Own Words. LC 85-42787. 128p. 1985. 10.95 (ISBN 0-06-068237-X, HarpR). Har-Row.

Gonzalez-Ruiz, Jose-Maria. The New Creation: Marxist & Christian? O'Connell, Mathew J., tr. from Spanish. LC 76-10226. Orig. Title: Marximo y Cristianismo Frente Al Hombre Nuevo. 160p. (Orig.). 1976. 1.74 (ISBN 0-88344-327-9). Orbis Bks.

Gonzalez-Wippler, Migene. The Complete Book of Spells, Ceremonies, & Magic. (Illus.). 1977. 12.95 (ISBN 0-517-52885-1). Crown.

--A Kabbalah for the Modern World. 2nd, rev. & expanded ed. LC 83-80133. (New Age Ser.). 250p. 1987. pap. 9.95 (ISBN 0-87542-294-2). Llewellyn Pubns.

Gooch, Paul W. Partial Knowledge: Philosophical Studies in Paul. LC 86-40589. 224p. 1987. text ed. 22.95x (ISBN 0-268-01567-8, Dist. by Har-Row). U of Notre Dame Pr.

Good, Edwin M. Irony in the Old Testament. (Bible & Literature Ser.: No. 3). (Orig.). 1981. pap. text ed. 9.95x (ISBN 0-907459-05-6, Pub. by Almond Pr England). Eisenbrauns.

Good Housekeeping Magazine Editors. Good Housekeeping American Family Christmas. (Brownstone Library Book). (Illus.). 168p. 1985. 19.95 (ISBN 0-916410-29-3). A D Bragdon.

Good, John W. Studies in the Milton Tradition. LC 73-144619. Repr. of 1915 ed. 16.00 (ISBN 0-404-02862-4). AMS Pr.

--Studies in the Milton Tradition. Repr. of 1915 ed. 22.00 (ISBN 0-384-19150-9). Johnson Repr.

Good, Lou-Ann. Bible Readings for Office Workers. 112p. (Orig.). 1987. pap. 3.95 (ISBN 0-8066-2250-4, 10-0693). Augsburg.

Good, Mrs. Marvin. How God Made the World. 1978. pap. 1.95 (ISBN 0-686-24050-2). Rod & Staff.

--A Shepherd Boy. 1978. pap. 1.95 (ISBN 0-686-24054-5). Rod & Staff.

Good, Merle. Who Are the Amish? LC 85-70283. (Illus.). 128p. (Orig.). 1985. 24.95 (ISBN 0-934672-28-8); pap. 15.95 (ISBN 0-934672-26-1). Good Bks PA.

Good, Phyllis P., jt. auth. see Kraybill, Donald B.

Good, Robert M. The Sheep of His Pasture: A Study of the Hebrew Noun 'AM(M) & its Semitic Cognates. LC 83-90934. (Harvard Semitic Monographs). 214p. 1984. 15.00 (ISBN 0-89130-628-5, 04 00 29). Scholars Pr GA.

Goodall, Blake. The Homilies of St. John Chrysostom on the Letters of St. Paul to Titus & Philemon. (Univ. of California Publications in Classical Studies: Vol. 20). 1979. 19.95x (ISBN 0-520-09596-0). U of Cal Pr.

Goodard, Dwight, ed. see Asvaghosa.

Goodboy, Eadie. God's Daughter. rev. ed. (Bible Study: Basic Ser.). 60p. (Orig.). 1985. pap. 2.95 (ISBN 0-932305-45-8, 521002). Aglow Pubns.

Goodboy, Eadie, jt. auth. see Lawless, Agnes.

Gooddard, Harold C. Atomic Peace. 1983. pap. 2.50x (ISBN 0-87574-057-X, 057). Pendle Hill.

Goode, Erich. Social Class & Church Participation. Zuckerman, Harriet & Merton, Robert K., eds. LC 79-9001. (Dissertations on Sociology Ser.). 1980. lib. bdg. 22.00x (ISBN 0-405-12970-X). Ayer Co Pubs.

Goode, Francis. The Better Covenant. 408p. 1986. 14.95 (ISBN 0-8254-2726-6). Kregel.

Goode, Teresa C. Gonzalo De Berceo. (Carl Ser.: No. 7). Repr. of 1933 ed. 21.00 (ISBN 0-404-50307-1). AMS Pr.

Goodell, John. The Triumph of Moralism in New England Piety: A Study of Lyman Beecher, Harriet Beecher Stowe & Henry Ward Beecher. 50.00 (ISBN 0-405-14113-0). Ayer Co Pubs.

Goodenough, Caroline L. High Lights on Hymnists & Their Hymns. LC 72-1626. Repr. of 1931 ed. 32.50 (ISBN 0-404-08310-2). AMS Pr.

Goodenough, Daniel W. Providence & Free Will in Human Actions. 132p. 1986. pap. 5.95 (ISBN 0-915221-63-2). Swedenborg Sci Assn.

Goodenough, E. R. Jewish Symbols in the Greco-Roman Period, 13 vols. Incl. Vols. 1-3. Archeological Evidence from Palestine & the Diaspora. 1953; Vol. 4. The Problem of Method; Symbols from Jewish Cult. 1954; Vols. 5 & 6. Fish, Bread, & Wine, 2 vols. 1956; Vols. 7 & 8. Pagan Symbols in Judaism. 1958. o.p. (ISBN 0-691-09755-0); Vols. 9-11. Symbolism in the Dura Synagogue. 1964; Vol. 12. Summary & Conclusions. 1965. 34.00x (ISBN 0-691-09757-7); Vol. 13. General Index & Maps. 1969. (Bollingen Ser.). Princeton U Pr.

Goodenough, Erwin R. Church in the Roman Empire. LC 77-122754. 1970. Repr. of 1931 ed. lib. bdg. 23.50x (ISBN 0-8154-0337-2). Cooper Sq.

--The Psychology of Religious Experiences. (Brown Classics in Judaica Ser.). 214p. 1986. pap. text ed. 10.75 (ISBN 0-8191-4489-4). U Pr of Amer.

Goodenough, Simon. The Country Parson. (Illus.). 192p. 1983. 19.95 (ISBN 0-7153-8238-1). David & Charles.

Goodgame, Louis R. Delightful Discipline. Date not set. pap. 3.00 (ISBN 0-8010-3815-4). Baker Bk.

Goodich, Michael. The Unmentionable Vice: Homosexuality in the Later Medieval Period. LC 78-13276. 179p. 1980. pap. 7.95 (ISBN 0-87436-300-4). Ross-Erikson.

Goodier, A. Public Life of Our Lord Jesus Christ, 2 vols. 1978. Set. 15.95 (ISBN 0-8198-0551-3); Set. pap. 13.95 (ISBN 0-8198-0552-1). Dghtrs St Paul.

Goodier, Alban. The Crown of Sorrow. 156p. 1982. 3.25 (ISBN 0-8198-1422-9, SP0093); pap. 2.25 (ISBN 0-8198-1423-7). Dghtrs St Paul.

--The Prince of Peace. 152p. 1982. 3.25 (ISBN 0-8198-5807-2, SP0585); pap. 2.25 (ISBN 0-8198-5808-0). Dghtrs St Paul.

--Saints for Sinners. LC 70-99637. (Essay Index Reprint Ser.). 1930. 18.00 (ISBN 0-8369-1504-6). Ayer Co Pubs.

Gooding, D. W. The Account of the Tabernacle. (Texts & Studies, New Ser.: Vol. 6). Repr. of 1959 ed. 28.00 (ISBN 0-8115-1719-5). Kraus Repr.

Gooding, D. W., ed. see Katz, Peter.

Gooding, David. Un Reino Inconmovible. Orig. Title: An Unshakeable Kingdom. (Span.). 196p. 1983. pap. 4.95 (ISBN 0-8254-1275-7). Kregel.

Goodis, Karen L. The Learning Center Book of Bible People. LC 81-67026. (Learning Center Book Ser.). (Illus.). 123p. (Orig.). 1981. pap. 14.50 (ISBN 0-86705-005-5). AIRE.

Goodland, Roger. A Bibliography of Sex Rites & Customs. LC 72-9839. Repr. of 1931 ed. 42.50 (ISBN 0-404-57445-9). AMS Pr.

--A Bibliography of Sex Rites & Customs. LC 77-11605. 1977. Repr. of 1931 ed. lib. bdg. 60.00 (ISBN 0-89341-193-0). Longwood Pub Group.

Goodman, Allan E., jt. ed. see Abramowski, Luise.

Goodman, Arnold M. A Plain Pine Box: A Return to Simple Jewish Funerals & Eternal Traditions. 7.95x (ISBN 0-87068-895-2). Ktav.

Goodman, Clarke E. Preaching the Gospel of Jesus Christ. LC 84-90077. 101p. 1985. 8.95 (ISBN 0-533-06156-3). Vantage.

Goodman, Don. Cory Hears with His Heart. LC 82-12272. (A Cory Story Ser.). 32p. 1982. pap. 2.95 (ISBN 0-8307-0858-8, 5608318). Regal.

Goodman, Hanna see Goodman, Philip.

Goodman, Hannah G. Story of Prophecy. LC 65-24925. 1965. 5.95x (ISBN 0-87441-017-7). Behrman.

Goodman, James, ed. see Bowman, Billye G.

Goodman, James, ed. see Clark, John D.

Goodman, L. Ringing in Hertfordshire. 1985. 15.00x (ISBN 0-317-54314-8, Pub. by J Richardson UK). State Mutual Bk.

Goodman, Lenn E. Monotheism: A Philosophic Inquiry into the Foundations of Theology & Ethics. LC 79-24818. (Publications of the Oxford Centre for Postgraduate Hebrew Study). 228p. 1981. 22.50x (ISBN 0-86598-068-3). Allanheld.

Goodman, Lori, jt. auth. see Baker, Andrew.

Goodman, Marguerite. Christmas Comes in Assorted Sizes. Ashton, Sylvia, ed. LC 77-80303. 1977. 14.95 (ISBN 0-87949-111-6). Ashley Bks.

Goodman, Mark N. The Ninth Amendment: History, Interpretation & Meaning. 74p. 1981. 5.00 (ISBN 0-682-49630-8, University). Exposition Pr FL.

Goodman, Martin, tr. see Reuchlin, Johann.

Goodman, Michael H. The Last Dalai Lama. LC 85-27906. 400p. 1987. pap. 14.95 (ISBN 0-87773-400-3). Shambhala Pubns.

Goodman, Morris C. Modern Numerology. pap. 5.00 (ISBN 0-87980-102-6). Wilshire.

Goodman, Philip, ed. The Hanukkah Anthology. LC 75-44637. (Illus.). xxxiv, 466p. 1976. 15.95 (ISBN 0-8276-0080-1, 392). Jewish Pubns.

--Jewish Marriage Anthology. Goodman, Hanna. LC 65-17045. (Illus.). 1965. 13.95 (ISBN 0-8276-0145-X, 236). Jewish Pubns.

--Passover Anthology. LC 61-11706. (Illus.). 196p. 1961. 14.95 (ISBN 0-8276-0019-4, 250). Jewish Pubns.

--Purim Anthology. (Illus.). 525p. 1949. 7.50 (ISBN 0-8276-0022-4, 248). Jewish Pubns.

--Rosh Hashanah Anthology. LC 74-105069. (Illus.). 379p. 1970. 10.95 (ISBN 0-8276-0023-2, 246). Jewish Pubns.

--The Shavuot Anthology. LC 74-25802. (Illus.). 369p. 1975. 9.95 (ISBN 0-8276-0057-7, 366). Jewish Pubns.

--Yom Kippur Anthology. LC 72-151312. (Illus.). 399p. 1971. 9.95 (ISBN 0-8276-0026-7, 245). Jewish Pubns.

Goodman, Robert. A Teacher's Guide to Jewish Holidays. LC 83-70197. 224p. 1983. pap. text ed. 15.00 (ISBN 0-86705-036-5). AIRE.

Goodman, S. L. The Faith of Secular Jews. (Library of Judaic Learning). 25.00x (ISBN 0-87068-489-2); pap. 11.95. Ktav.

Goodman, Wolf, tr. see Michelson, Frida.

Goodnow, Josephine A., jt. auth. see Creegan, Charles C.

Goodrich, Frances C. Third Adam. LC 66-22003. 1967. 5.95 (ISBN 0-8022-0608-5). Philos Lib.

Goodrich, Norma L. Ancient Myths. 256p. pap. 3.95 (ISBN 0-451-62361-4, Ment). NAL.

--Medieval Myths. rev. ed. 224p. (YA) 1977. pap. 3.95 (ISBN 0-451-62359-2, Ment). NAL.

Goodrick, Edward W. Do It Yourself Hebrew & Greek. 2nd ed. LC 79-25463. 1980. pap. text ed. 9.95 (ISBN 0-930014-35-9); with cassette 14.95 (ISBN 0-930014-42-1). Multnomah.

--Do It Yourself Hebrew & Greek: Everybody's Guide to the Language Tools. 256p. (Orig.). 1980. pap. 11.95 (ISBN 0-310-41741-4, 6245P). Zondervan.

Goodrick, Edward W. & Kohlenberger, John P. The NIV Complete Concordance. 1056p. 1981. 22.95 (ISBN 0-310-43650-8, 12100). Zondervan.

Goodrick, Edward W. & Kohlenberger, John R., III. The NIV Handy Concordance. 384p. (Orig.). 1982. pap. 5.95 (ISBN 0-310-43662-1, 12101P). Zondervan.

Goodsell, Willystine. Conflict of Naturalism & Humanism. LC 74-176814. (Columbia University. Teachers College. Contributions to Education: No. 33). Repr. of 1910 ed. 22.50 (ISBN 0-404-55033-9). AMS Pr.

Goodson, Millie S. Sunday School Growth & Renewal: How to Reach, Teach, Care, Share. LC 84-71642. 76p. (Orig.). DR014B. pap. 3.75 (ISBN 0-88177-014-0). Discipleship Res.

Goodspeed, Edgar J. Full History of the Wonderful Career of Moody & Sankey, in Great Britain & America. LC 70-168154. (Illus.). Repr. of 1876 ed. 39.00 (ISBN 0-404-07227-5). AMS Pr.

--History of Early Christian Literature. rev. & enl. ed. Grant, Robert M., ed. LC 66-13871. (Midway Reprint Ser.). 1966. pap. 13.00x (ISBN 0-226-30386-1). U of Chicago Pr.

--How Came the Bible ? (Festival Books). 1976. pap. 1.95 (ISBN 0-687-17524-0). Abingdon.

--Index Patristicus, Sive Clavis Patrum Apostolicorum Operum. LC 60-52358. 1960. 18.00x (ISBN 0-8401-0863-X). A R Allenson.

--A Life of Jesus. LC 78-21540. 1979. Repr. of 1950 ed. lib. bdg. 24.75x (ISBN 0-313-20728-3, GOLJ). Greenwood.

--Story of the Bible. LC 36-21666. Repr. of 1967 ed. 44.00 (ISBN 0-8357-9657-4, 2013612). Bks Demand UMI.

--Strange New Gospels. 1979. Repr. of 1931 ed. lib. bdg. 22.50 (ISBN 0-8495-2000-2). Arden Lib.

--Strange New Gospels. facsimile ed. LC 70-156652. (Essay Index Reprint Ser). Repr. of 1931 ed. 12.00 (ISBN 0-8369-2364-2). Ayer Co Pubs.

--The Student's New Testament: The Greek Text & the American Translation. pap. 160.00 (ISBN 0-317-20700-8, 2024115). Bks Demand UMI.

--The Student's New Testament: The Greek Text & the American Translation, 2 vols. (Midway Reprint Ser.). Vol. 1. pap. 121.80 (2026775); Vol. 2. pap. 146.00. Bks Demand UMI.

Goodspeed, Edgar J., ed. Apocrypha. 1959. pap. 5.95 (ISBN 0-394-70163-1, V163, Vin). Random.

Goodspeed Publishing Company. History of Giles, Lincoln, Franklin & Moore Counties, Tennessee. 1979. Repr. of 1886 ed. 26.50 (ISBN 0-89308-116-7). Southern Hist Pr.

--History of Northeast Arkansas. 1978. Repr. of 1884 ed. 42.50 (ISBN 0-89308-081-0). Southern Hist Pr.

--History of South Arkansas. 1978. Repr. of 1884 ed. 47.50 (ISBN 0-89308-083-7, Goodspeed Pub Co). Southern Hist Pr.

--History of Western Arkansas. 1978. Repr. of 1884 ed. 37.50 (ISBN 0-89308-084-5). Southern Hist Pr.

--Memorial & Genealogical Record of Southwest Texas. 661p. 1978. Repr. of 1894 ed. 40.00 (ISBN 0-89308-122-1). Southern Hist Pr.

Goodwin, Bennie E. How to Be a Growing Christian. LC 86-33737. 40p. (Orig.). 1986. pap. 1.95 (ISBN 0-87784-573-5). Inter-Varsity.

Goodwin, Frank J. Harmony of the Life of St. Paul. 1951. pap. 8.95 (ISBN 0-8010-3797-2). Baker Bk.

Goodwin, George L. The Ontological Argument of Charles Hartshorne. LC 78-2821. 1978. pap. 9.95 (ISBN 0-89130-228-X, 01-01-20). Scholars Pr GA.

Goodwin, Grenville, ed. Myths & Tales of the White Mountain Apache. LC 39-33959. (AFS M). Repr. of 1939 ed. 29.00 (ISBN 0-527-01085-5). Kraus Repr.

Goodwin, Robert P., tr. see St. Thomas Aquinas.

Goodwin, Thomas. Holy Spirit in Salvation. 1979. 15.95 (ISBN 0-85151-279-8). Banner of Truth.

--Justifying Faith. 593p. 1985. 15.95 (ISBN 0-85151-447-2). Banner of Truth.

Goodwin, Wayne & Cook, Gregory D. The Serving Sunday School. (Complete Teacher Training Meeting Ser.). 48p. 1986. tchr's ed 9.95 (ISBN 0-89191-315-7). Cook.

Goody, Jack. Death, Property, & the Ancestors: A Study of the Mortuary Customs of the LoDagaa of West Africa. (Illus.). 1962. 32.50x (ISBN 0-8047-0068-0). Stanford U Pr.

Goodyear, Imogene, ed. The Beauty of Wholeness: Program Resource for Women 1981. 1980. pap. 5.00 (ISBN 0-8309-0294-5). Herald Hse.

--Daily Bread, Nineteen Eighty-Six. 1985. pap. 7.50 (ISBN 0-8309-0407-7). Herald Hse.

--Daily Bread, 1987. 1986. pap. 8.00 (ISBN 0-8309-0435-2). Herald Hse.

Gookenough, Erwin R. An Introduction to Philo Judaeus. 2nd ed. (Brown Classics in Judaica Ser.). 194p. 1986. pap. text ed. 12.75 (ISBN 0-8191-5335-4). U Pr of Amer.

Gooneratne, Edmund R., ed. The Dhatu Katha Pakarana & Its Commentary. LC 78-72426. Repr. of 1892 ed. 21.50 (ISBN 0-404-17287-3). AMS Pr.
Goossen, Rachel W. Meetingplace: A History of the Mennonite Church of Normal 1912-1987. Stutzman, Terry, ed. LC 86-63769. (Illus.). 192p. 1987. text ed. 25.00 (ISBN 0-9617978-0-0); pap. text ed. 18.00 (ISBN 0-9617978-1-9). Mennonite Church.
Goossens, Mathias, ed. With the Church. 6.95 (ISBN 0-8199-0148-2, L39000). Franciscan Herald.
Goot, Henry V. Vander see Vander Goot, Henry V.
Goot, Mary Vander see Vander Goot, Mary.
Gopi Krishna. The Inner World. 12p. 1978. pap. 3.95 (ISBN 0-88697-001-6). Life Science.
--To Those Concerned Citizens. (Illus.). 16p. 1978. pap. 3.95 (ISBN 0-88697-002-4). Life Science.
Goppelt, Leonard. Theology of the New Testament: Jesus & the Gospels, Vol I. Alsup, John E., tr. LC 80-28947. 316p. 1981. 15.95 (ISBN 0-8028-2384-X). Eerdmans.
Goppelt, Leonhard. Theology of the New Testament: The Variety & Unity of the Apostolic Witness to Christ, Vol. II. 248p. 1983. 17.95 (ISBN 0-8028-2385-8). Eerdmans.
Gorbachev, Mikail S. The Coming Century of Peace. Richardson, Stewart, ed. 304p. 1986. 17.95 (ISBN 0-931933-22-6). Richardson & Steirman.
Gorce, Pierre F. La see La Gorce, Pierre F.
Gorday, Peter. Principles of Patristic Exegesis: Romans 9-11 in Origen, John Chrysostom & Augustine. LC 83-20588. (Studies in the Bible & Early Christianity: Vol. 4). 424p. 1984. 69.95x (ISBN 0-88946-602-5). E Mellen.
Gordis, Robert. The Biblical Text in the Making: A Study of the Kethibh-Qere. rev. ed. 1971. 29.95x (ISBN 0-87068-157-5). Ktav.
--The Book of God & Man. LC 65-25126. 1978. pap. 12.95x (ISBN 0-226-30410-8, P771, Phoen). U of Chicago Pr.
--The Book of Job: Commentary, New Translation & Special Studies. LC 78-2305. (Moreshet Ser.: No. 2). 1977. 45.00 (ISBN 0-87334-003-5). Ktav.
--Faith for Moderns. 2nd rev. ed. LC 76-136424. 1971. pap. 8.95x (ISBN 0-8197-0001-0, 10001). Bloch.
--Judaic Ethics for a Lawless World. 185p. 1986. 20.00. Ktav.
--Koheleth: The Man & His World: A Study of Ecclesiastes. rev. ed. LC 67-26988. 1968. pap. 10.95 (ISBN 0-8052-0166-1). Schocken.
--Love & Sex: A Modern Jewish Perspective. 290p. 1978. 8.95 (ISBN 0-374-19252-9). FS&G.
--Megillat Esther: The Mascretic Hebrew Text with Introduction, New Translation & Commentary. 1977. 3.95x (ISBN 0-87068-763-8). Ktav.
--Poets, Prophets, & Sages: Essays in Biblical Interpretation. LC 79-98984. pap. 111.50 (ISBN 0-317-37273-4, 2055498). Bks Demand UMI.
--Root & the Branch: Judaism & the Free Society. LC 62-17133. 1962. 20.00x (ISBN 0-226-30411-6). U of Chicago Pr.
--The Song of Songs & Lamentations: A Commentary & Translation. 1974. 25.00x (ISBN 0-87068-256-3). Ktav.
--Understanding Conservative Judaism. 15.00x (ISBN 0-87068-680-1). Ktav.
Gordon, A. D. Selected Essays. LC 73-2201. (The Jewish People; History, Religion, Literature Ser.). Repr. of 1938 ed. 25.50 (ISBN 0-405-05266-9). Ayer Co Pubs.
Gordon, A. J. The Ministry of the Spirit. 160p. 1986. pap. 3.95 (ISBN 0-87123-843-8, 210843). Bethany Hse.
Gordon, Adoniram J. Holy Spirit in Missions. pap. 2.25 (ISBN 0-87509-094-X). Chr Pubns.
Gordon, Albert I. Jews in Suburbia. LC 73-11749. 264p. 1973. Repr. of 1959 ed. lib. bdg. 15.00x (ISBN 0-8371-7088-5, COJS). Greenwood.
Gordon, Alexander, ed. Milton on the Son of God & the Holy Spirit (From the Treatise on Christian Doctrine) LC 73-4827. 1973. lib. bdg. 15.00 (ISBN 0-8414-2028-9). Folcroft.
Gordon, Arthur. A Song Called Hope. 48p. 1985. 6.95 (ISBN 0-8378-5081-9). Gibson.
--Through Many Windows. 192p. 1985. pap. 6.95 (ISBN 0-8007-5207-4, Power Bks). Revell.
--Touch of Wonder. (Orig.). pap. 2.95 (ISBN 0-515-08987-7). Jove Pubns.
Gordon, Benjamin L. New Judea: Jewish Life in Modern Palestine & Egypt. Davis, Moshe, ed. LC 77-70697. (America & the Holy Land Ser.). (Illus.). 1977. Repr. of 1919 ed. lib. bdg. 30.00x (ISBN 0-405-10251-8). Ayer Co Pubs.
Gordon, Cyrus. The Pennsylvania Tradition of Semitics: A Century of Near Eastern & Biblical Studies at the University of Pennsylvania. (Biblical Scholarship in North America Ser.). 85p. 1987. 13.95 (ISBN 1-55540-022-1); pap. 11.95 (ISBN 1-55540-023-X). Scholars Pr GA.
Gordon, Cyrus H. Ancient Near East. 1965. pap. 8.95 (ISBN 0-393-00275-6, Norton Lib). Norton.
--Before the Bible. LC 72-10828. (Essay Index Reprint Ser.). 1973. Repr. of 1962 ed. 24.00 (ISBN 0-8369-7219-8). Ayer Co Pubs.
--Common Background of Greek & Hebrew Civilizations. (Illus.). 1965. pap. 7.95 (ISBN 0-393-00293-4, Norton Lib). Norton.
--Homer & Bible: The Origin & Character of East Mediterranean Literature. 1967. pap. 4.95 (ISBN 0-911566-03-1). Ventnor.
Gordon, Dane R. The Old Testament: A Beginning Survey. (Illus.). 400p. 1985. pap. text ed. 23.33 (ISBN 0-13-634031-8). P-H.
Gordon, Earnest B. Adoniram Judson Gordon. Dayton, Donald W., ed. (The Higher Christian Life Ser.). 386p. 1985. 55.00 (ISBN 0-8240-6421-6). Garland Pub.
Gordon, Edmund F., jt. auth. see Harrington, Daniel J.
Gordon, Edmund F., jt. auth. see Meier, John P.
Gordon, Fee D., jt. ed. see Epp, Eldon J.
Gordon, Frank J. Growing in Grace. (Illus.). 111p. (Orig.). 1981. pap. 6.00 (ISBN 0-686-34382-4). G Lutheran Foun.
Gordon, George N. Erotic Communications: Studies in Sex, Sin & Censorship. new ed. (Humanistic Studies in the Communication Arts). (Illus.). 352p. 1980. 21.00x (ISBN 0-8038-1959-5, Communication Arts); pap. 13.00x (ISBN 0-8038-1960-9). Hastings.
Gordon, Gregory S. Impeach the Anti-Christ. 96p. (Orig.). 1986. pap. 4.95 (ISBN 0-9616971-5-6). Dynamic Reflections.
Gordon, Haim. Martin Buber: A Centenary Volume. 1983. 49.50x (ISBN 0-88125-026-0). Ktav.
Gordon, Haim & Grob, Leonard, eds. Education for Peace: Testimonies from World Religions. LC 86-31083. 224p. (Orig.). 1987. pap. 14.95 (ISBN 0-88344-359-7). Orbis Bks.
Gordon, Harold H. Chaplain on Wings. Zahavy, Zev, ed. LC 81-51749. (Illus.). 192p. 1981. 12.95 (ISBN 0-88400-075-3). Shengold.
Gordon, Joel R. Focus on Growth in the Church. rev. ed. (To Live in Christ Ser.). 1980. pap. write for info. (ISBN 0-697-01724-9); instrs.' manual avail. (ISBN 0-697-01722-2). Wm C Brown.
Gordon, John. Englands & Scotlands Happiness in Being Reduced to Unitie of Religion. LC 75-38190. (English Experience Ser.: No. 461). 50p. 1972. Repr. of 1604 ed. 7.00 (ISBN 90-221-0461-3). Walter J Johnson.
Gordon, John D. Ralph Waldo Emerson Eighteen Hundred Three to Eighteen Eighty-Two. LC 73-16267. 1973. lib. bdg. 10.00 (ISBN 0-8414-4481-1). Folcroft.
Gordon, Judith, jt. auth. see Gordon, Sol.
Gordon, Linda. Woman's Body, Woman's Right: Birth Control in America. 1977. pap. 8.95 (ISBN 0-14-004683-6). Penguin.
Gordon, Paul A. The Sanctuary, Eighteen Forty-Four & the Pioneers. Wheeler, Gerald, ed. LC 83-17611. 160p. (Orig.). 1984. pap. 9.95 (ISBN 0-8280-0217-7). Review & Herald.
Gordon, R., ed. Yiddish Literature, 10 Vols, No. IV. 1986. lib. bdg. 975.00 (ISBN 0-8490-3859-6). Gordon Pr.
--Yiddish Literature, 10 Vols, No. III. 1986. lib. bdg. 950.95 (ISBN 0-8490-3858-8). Gordon Pr.
--Yiddish Literature, 10 Vols, No. II. 1986. lib. bdg. 975.00 (ISBN 0-8490-3857-X). Gordon Pr.
Gordon, R. L., ed. Myth, Religion & Society: Structuralist Essays by M. Detienne, L. Gernet, J. P. Vernant & P. Vidal-Naquet. (Illus.). 250p. 1982. text ed. 44.50 (ISBN 0-521-22780-1); pap. text ed. 15.95 (ISBN 0-521-29640-4). Cambridge U Pr.
Gordon, Robert P. One & Two Samuel. (Old Testament Guides Ser.). 102p. 1984. pap. text ed. 3.95x (ISBN 0-905774-64-7, Pub. by JSOT Pr England). Eisenbrauns.
Gordon, S. D. The Healing Christ. rev. ed. 160p. (Orig.). 1985. pap. 3.95 (ISBN 0-89283-271-1, Pub. by Vine Books). Servant.
--Quiet Talks on Prayer. (S. D. Gordon Library). 1980. pap. 4.95 (ISBN 0-8010-3754-9). Baker Bk.
Gordon, Sarah. Hitler, Germans, & the "Jewish Question". LC 83-43073. 416p. 1984. 42.00 (ISBN 0-691-05412-6); pap. 15.00 (ISBN 0-691-10162-0). Princeton U Pr.
Gordon, Sol. When Living Hurts. 1985. pap. 8.95 (ISBN 0-8074-0310-5). UAHC.
Gordon, Sol & Gordon, Judith. Raising a Child Conservatively in a Sexually Permissive World. 224p. 1986. pap. 7.95 (ISBN 0-671-62797-X, Fireside). S&S.
Gordon, Thomas, jt. auth. see Trenchard, John.
Gordon, William C. Bible Word Search. (Quiz & Puzzle Bks.). 112p. 1983. 2.95 (ISBN 0-8010-3679-8). Baker Bk.
Gordon-Smith, Eileen L. In His Time. 1984. pap. 2.25 (ISBN 9971-972-04-2). OMF Bks.
Gore, Charles. Philosophy of Good Life. 1963. Repr. of 1935 ed. 12.95x (ISBN 0-460-00924-9, Evman). Biblio Dist.
--The Philosophy of the Good Life. LC 77-27197. (Gifford Lectures: 1929-30). Repr. of 1930 ed. 24.00 (ISBN 0-404-60484-6). AMS Pr.
--The Social Doctrine of the Sermon on the Mount. 59.95 (ISBN 0-8490-1063-2). Gordon Pr.
Gore, G. The Scientific Basis of National Progress, Including That of Morality. 218p. 1970. Repr. of 1882 ed. 26.00x (ISBN 0-7146-2407-1, BHA-02407, F Cass Co). Biblio Dist.
Gore, Tipper. Raising PG Kids in an X-Rated Society. 240p. 1987. 12.95 (ISBN 0-687-35283-5); pap. 8.95 (ISBN 0-687-35282-7). Abingdon.
Goreau, Eloise K. Integrity of Life: Allegorical Imagery in the Plays of John Webster. Hogg, James, ed. (Jacobean Drama Studies). 194p. (Orig.). 1974. pap. 15.00 (ISBN 0-317-40056-8, Pub. by Salzburg Studies). Longwood Pub Group.
Gorecki, Danuta M. & Wajenberg, Arnold. Cannon Law: History, Sources, & a Proposed Classification Scheme. Date not set. price not set. Am Assn Law Libs.
Gorelick, L. & Williams-Forte, E., eds. Ancient Seals & the Bible. (Occasional Papers on the Near East: Vol. 2, Issue 1). (Illus.). 84p. 1984. pap. 13.00x (ISBN 0-89003-045-6). Undena Pubns.
Goren, Arthur A. New York Jews & the Quest for Community. LC 76-129961. 1979. 34.00x (ISBN 0-231-03422-9); pap. 17.00x (ISBN 0-231-08368-8). Columbia U Pr.
Goren, Arthur A., ed. Dissenter in Zion: From the Writings of Judah L. Magnes. (Illus.). 576p. 1982. text ed. 32.50X (ISBN 0-674-21283-5). Harvard U Pr.
Goren, Leyla. Elements of Brahmanism in the Transcendentalism of Emerson. LC 80-2534. Repr. of 1959 ed. 18.50 (ISBN 0-404-19260-2). AMS Pr.
Gorer, Geoffrey. Death, Grief, & Mourning. Kastenbaum, Robert, ed. LC 76-19573. (Death & Dying Ser.). (Illus.). 1977. Repr. of 1965 ed. lib. bdg. 24.50x (ISBN 0-405-09571-6). Ayer Co Pubs.
Gorges, A., tr. see Bacon, Francis.
Gorges, Arthur see Bacon, Francis.
Gorham, Melvin. The Pagan Bible. 296p. 1982. 8.95 (ISBN 0-914752-22-7). Sovereign Pr.
--Pagan Reality. 201p. 1970. pap. 5.00 (ISBN 0-914752-02-2). Sovereign Pr.
Goricheva, Tatiana. Talking about God Is Dangerous: The Diary of a Russian Dissident. 144p. 1987. 11.95 (ISBN 0-8245-0798-3). Crossroad NY.
Gorion, Emanuel bin, jt. ed. see Gorion, Micha J. bin.
Gorion, Micha J. bin & Gorion, Emanuel bin, eds. Mimekor Yisrael: Classical Jewish Folktales, 3 vols. Lask, I. M., tr. from Heb. LC 74-15713. 1666p. 1976. 100.00 (ISBN 0-253-15330-1). Ind U Pr.
Gorman, G. E. & Gorman, Lyn. Theological & Religious Reference Materials: Systematic Theology & Church History. LC 83-22759. (Bibliographies & Indexes in Religious Studies: No. 2). xiv, 401p. 1985. lib. bdg. 47.50 (ISBN 0-313-24779-X, GOS/). Greenwood.
Gorman, G. E., et al, eds. Theological & Religious Reference Materials: Practical Theology. LC 86-380. (Bibliographies & Indexes in Religious Studies: No. 7). 402p. 1986. lib. bdg. 49.95 (ISBN 0-313-25397-8, GPA/). Greenwood.
Gorman, George. The Society of Friends. 1978. pap. 3.15 (ISBN 0-08-021412-6). Pergamon.
Gorman, Hugh. Beacon Small-Group Bible Studies: Hosea, "The Triumph of God". 88p. (Orig.). 1984. pap. 2.50 (ISBN 0-8341-0914-X). Beacon Hill.
Gorman, Lyn, jt. auth. see Gorman, G. E.
Gorman, Margaret, ed. Psychology & Religion: A Reader. pap. 11.95 (ISBN 0-8091-2684-2). Paulist Pr.
Gorman, Michael J. Abortion & the Early Church: Christian, Jewish, & Pagan Attitudes. 120p. (Orig.). 1982. pap. 4.95 (ISBN 0-87784-397-X). Inter-Varsity.
--Abortion & the Early Church: Christian, Jewish, & Pagan Attitudes in the Greco-Roman World. 4.95 (ISBN 0-8091-2511-0). Paulist Pr.
Gorman, Ralph. Last Hours of Jesus. 1960. 4.50 (ISBN 0-8362-0221-X, Pub. by Sheed). Guild Bks.
Gorman, Robert. Catholic Apologetical Literature in the United States (1784-1858) LC 73-3582. (Catholic University of America. Studies in American Church History: No. 28). Repr. of 1939 ed. 23.00 (ISBN 0-404-57778-4). AMS Pr.
Gornall, Thomas, ed. see Newman, John H.
Gorny, Joseph. The British Labour Movement & Zionism 1917-1948. 270p. 1983. text ed. 30.00x (ISBN 0-7146-3162-0, F Cass Co). Biblio Dist.
Gorodetsky, Benjamin. Light in the Darkness. Schreiber, Mordecai, tr. LC 85-63010. (Illus.). 224p. 1986. 14.95 (ISBN 0-88400-120-2). Shengold.
Gorodetzky, Nadejda. The Humiliated Christ in Modern Russian Thought. LC 79-168159. Repr. of 1938 ed. 18.75 (ISBN 0-404-02883-7). AMS Pr.
Goronwy, Jessica. The Tree of Hope. 1985. 20.00x (ISBN 0-7223-1827-8, Pub. by A H Stockwell England). State Mutual Bk.
Gorospe, Vitaliano R. The Four Faces of Asia: A Summary Report on the Asian Bishops' Meeting, Manila 1971. 1971. wrps. 3.00x (ISBN 0-686-09496-4). Cellar.
Gorr, Samuel, ed. see Berniker, Bernard.
Gorres, Joseph. Mythengeschichte der Asiatischen Welt: Mit einen Anhang: Beitrage aus den Heidelberger Jahrbuchern. Bolle, Kees W., ed. (Mythology Ser.). (Ger.). 1978. Repr. of 1935 ed. lib. bdg. 54.00x (ISBN 0-405-10538-X). Ayer Co Pubs.
Goshal, Sarat C., ed. & intro. by see Devendra Gani.
Goshen-Gottstein, Moshe H. Syriac Manuscripts in the Harvard College Library: A Catalogue. LC 77-13132. (Harvard Semitic Studies: No. 23). 1979. 15.00 (ISBN 0-89130-189-5, 040423). Scholars Pr GA.
Goslinga, C. J. Bible Student's Commentary: Joshua, Judges, Ruth. Tr. of Korte Verklaring. 544p. 1986. 24.95 (ISBN 0-310-45280-5). Zondervan.
Gospel Advocate. Commentaries on the New Testament. Incl. Matthew. Boles, H. Leo (ISBN 0-89225-001-1); Mark. Dorris, C. E (ISBN 0-89225-002-X); Luke. Boles, H. Leo (ISBN 0-89225-003-8); John. Dorris, C. E (ISBN 0-89225-004-6); Acts. Boles, H. Leo (ISBN 0-89225-005-4); Romans. Lipscomb, David & Shepherd, J. W. (ISBN 0-89225-006-2); Corinthians I. Lipscomb, David & Shepard, J. W. (ISBN 0-89225-007-0); Corinthians II - Galatians. Lipscomb, David & Shepherd, J. W. (ISBN 0-89225-008-9); Ephesians - Colossians. Shepherd, J. W (ISBN 0-89225-009-7); Thess. I, II; Tim. I, II; Titus; Philomen. Shepherd, J. W (ISBN 0-89225-010-0); Hebrews. Milligan, Robert (ISBN 0-89225-011-9); James. Woods, Guy N (ISBN 0-89225-012-7); Peter I, II; John I, II, III; Jude. Woods, Guy N (ISBN 0-89225-013-5); Revelation. Hinds, John T (ISBN 0-89225-014-3). Set. 135.00 (ISBN 0-89225-000-3); 10.95 ea. Gospel Advocate.
Goss, Agnes G., jt. auth. see Grenell, Zelotes.
Goss, Ethel E. The Winds of God. 2nd ed. (Illus.). 288p. 1958. pap. 5.95 (ISBN 0-912315-26-1). Word Aflame.
Goss, James, jt. ed. see Martin, Luther H.
Goss, Leonard G., jt. auth. see Aycock, Don M.
Goss, Leonard G., ed. see Payne, Franklyn E., Jr.
Goss, Leonard G., ed. see Redmond, Howard.
Gosse, Carol A., jt. auth. see Rother, Kathleen.
Gosse, Edmund. Jeremy Taylor. 1904. Repr. 9.50 (ISBN 0-8274-2609-7). R West.
Gosse, Edmund W. Jeremy Taylor. LC 4-1683. 1969. Repr. of 1904 ed. 11.00x (ISBN 0-403-00088-2). Scholarly.
Gossen, Gary. Chamulas in the World of the Sun: Time & Space in a Maya Oral Tradition. (Illus.). 382p. 1984. pap. text ed. 10.95x (ISBN 0-88133-091-4). Waveland Pr.
Gossett, Don. How to Conquer Fear. Orig. Title: How You Can Rise Above Fear. 160p. 1981. pap. 2.95 (ISBN 0-88368-092-0). Whitaker Hse.
--If Nobody Reaches, Nobody Gets Touched. 128p. (Orig.). 1983. pap. 2.95 (ISBN 0-88368-127-7). Whitaker Hse.
--I'm Sold on Being Bold. 1979. pap. 2.25 (ISBN 0-88368-085-8). Whitaker Hse.
--Praise Avenue. 128p. 1976. pap. 3.50 (ISBN 0-88368-059-9). Whitaker Hse.
--There's Dynamite in Praise. rev. ed. 1974. pap. 3.50 (ISBN 0-88368-048-3). Whitaker Hse.
--What You Say Is What You Get. 192p. 1976. pap. 3.95 (ISBN 0-88368-066-1). Whitaker Hse.
Gossip, A. J. Experience Worketh Hope. (A Scholar As Preacher Ser.). 208p. 1945. 10.95 (ISBN 0-567-04423-8, Pub. by T & T Clark Ltd UK). Fortress.
Gossman, Lionel. Orpheus Philologus Bachofen versus Mommsen on the Study of Antiquity. 90p. 1983. 8.00 (ISBN 0-87169-735-1). Am Philos.
Goswami, B. S., ed. see Sridhara, Swami B.
Goswami, Chitta R. Sri Aurobindo's Concept of the Superman. 260p. 1976. 8.00 (ISBN 0-89071-211-5). Matagiri.
Goswami, Hridayananda das see Das Goswami, Hridayananda.
Goswami, Satavarupa das see Das Goswami, Satsvarupa.

Goswami, Satsvarupa D. Opening a Temple in Los Angelos: A Visit to Boston. Dasa, Mandalesvara, et al, eds. (Prabhupada-lila Ser.). 72p. 1981. pap. 2.25 (ISBN 0-911233-01-6). Gita Nagari.

Goswami, Satsvarupa das. Japa Reform Notebook. Dasi, Bimala & Dasa, Mandalesvara, eds. 144p. (Orig.). 1982. pap. text ed. 3.95 (ISBN 0-911233-07-5). Gita Nagari.

Goswami, Satsvarupa das see Das Goswami, Satsvarupa.

Goswami, Satsvarupa Das see Das Goswami, Satsvarupa.

Goswami, Satsvarupa das see Das Goswami, Satsvarupa.

Goswami, Satsvarupa das see Goswami, Satsvarupa das.

Goswami, Satsvarupa Dasa see Dasa Goswami, Satsvarupa.

Goswami, Shrivatsa & Shinn, Larry, eds. In Search of the Divine: Some Unexpected Consequences of Interfaith Dialogue. (God Ser.). 240p. (Orig.). 1987. text ed. 22.95 (ISBN 0-913757-28-4, Pub. by New Era Bks.); pap. text ed. 12.95 (ISBN 0-913757-29-2, Pub. by New Era Bks). Paragon Hse.

Goswami, Srila Hridayananda dasa, ed. The Glories of Sri Caitanya Mahaprabhu. Kusakratha dasa, tr. LC 83-7078. 64p. (Orig.). 1984. pap. 6.00 (ISBN 0-89647-018-0). Bala Bks.

Gotaas, Mary C. Bossuet & Vieira. LC 75-128929. (Catholic Univ. of American Studies in Romance Lang. & Lit. Ser.: No. 46). Repr. of 1953 ed. 21.00 (ISBN 0-404-50346-2). AMS Pr.

Gotama. The Nyaya Sutras of Gotama. Satisa Chandra Vidyabhusana, tr. LC 73-3795. (Sacred Books of the Hindus: No. 8). Repr. of 1913 ed. 29.00 (ISBN 0-404-57808-X). AMS Pr.

Gotlieb, Randie & Gotlieb, Steven. Once to Every Man & Nation: Stories about Becoming a Baha'i. 160p. 1985. pap. 5.95 (ISBN 0-85398-211-2). G Ronald Pub.

Gotlieb, Steven, jt. auth. see Gotlieb, Randie.

Gottcent, John H. The Bible: A Literary Study. 120p. 1986. 10.50 (ISBN 0-8057-7951-5, Twayne); pap. 5.95 (ISBN 0-8057-8003-3). G K Hall.

--The Bible As Literature: A Selective Bibliography. 1979. lib. bdg. 26.00 (ISBN 0-8161-8121-7, Hall Reference). G K Hall.

Gotte, Johannes. Augustine's Concept of Providence. 1.00 (ISBN 0-686-23373-5). Classical Folia.

Gottemoller, Bartholomew. Why Good People Suffer: A Practical Treatise on the Problem of Evil. 1987. 9.95 (ISBN 0-533-07107-0). Vantage.

Gottesman, Meir U. Shpeter: Book One. (Judaica Youth Ser.). (Illus.). 1981. 5.95 (ISBN 0-910818-35-5); pap. 4.95 (ISBN 0-910818-36-3). Judaica Pr.

--Shpeter: Book Two. (Judaica Youth Ser.). (Illus.). 1981. 5.95 (ISBN 0-910818-39-8); pap. 4.95 (ISBN 0-910818-40-1). Judaica Pr.

Gottfried, Robert S. Bury St. Edmunds & the Urban Crisis, 1290-1539. LC 81-11984. (Illus.). 324p. 1981. 34.00x (ISBN 0-691-05340-5). Princeton U Pr.

Gottheil, Richard J., ed. Fragments from the Cairo Genizah in the Freer Collection. Repr. of 1927 ed. 37.00 (ISBN 0-384-38813-2). Johnson Repr.

Gottheil, Richard J., intro. by. Persian Literature (Comprising of the Shan Nameth, the Rubaiyat, the Divan & the Gulistan, 2 vols. 1986. Repr. of 1900 ed. Set. PLB 150.00 (ISBN 0-89760-246-3). Telegraph Bks.

Gottlieb, Beatrice, tr. see Febvre, Lucien.

Gottlieb, Malke, jt. auth. see Mlotek, Eleanor G.

Gottlieb, Malke, jt. ed. see Mlotek, Chane.

Gottlieb, Robert & Wiley, Peter. America's Saints: The Rise of Mormon Power. LC 84-3304. 1984. 16.95 (ISBN 0-399-12924-3, Putnam). Putnam Pub Group.

--America's Saints: The Rise of Mormon Power. LC 85-24879. 288p. 1986. pap. 5.95 (ISBN 0-15-605658-5, Harv). HarBraceJ.

Gottschalk, Herbert. Lexikon der Mythologie der Eurpaeischen Voelker. (Ger.). 42.00 (ISBN 3-7934-1184-2, M-7246). French & Eur.

Gottschalk, Stephen. The Emergence of Christian Science in American Religious Life. LC 72-85530. 1974. 20.95 (ISBN 0-520-02308-0); pap. 4.95 (ISBN 0-520-03718-9, CAL 398). U of Cal Pr.

Gottwald, Norman K. The Hebrew Bible-A Socio-Literary Introduction. LC 84-48719. (Illus.). 736p. 1985. 34.95 (ISBN 0-8006-0853-4, 1-853); pap. 19.95 (ISBN 0-8006-1853-X, 1-1853). Fortress.

--The Tribes of Yahweh: A Sociology of the Religion of Liberated Israel, 1250-1050 B.C. LC 78-24333. 944p. (Orig.). 1979. pap. 19.95 (ISBN 0-88344-499-2). Orbis Bks.

Gottwald, Norman K., ed. SEMEIA: Social Scientific Criticism of the Hebrew Bible & Its Social World: The Israelite Monarchy. 152p. 1986. pap. 9.95 (ISBN 0-317-52980-3, 06-20-37). Scholars Pr GA.

Gotwald, William K. Ecclesiastical Censure at the End of the Fifteenth Century. LC 78-64124. (Johns Hopkins University. Studies in the Social Sciences. Forty-Fifth Ser. 1927: 3). Repr. of 1927 ed. 13.50 (ISBN 0-404-61238-5). AMS Pr.

Goubet, jt. auth. see Aubert.

Goudard, Sr. M. Lucien. Etude Sur les Epistres Morales D'Honore D'Urfe. LC 70-94204. (Catholic University of America Studies in Romance Languages & Literatures Ser: No. 8). (Fr). Repr. of 1933 ed. 21.00 (ISBN 0-404-50308-X). AMS Pr.

Goudoever, H. D. von see Van Goudoever, H. D.

Goudriaan, T., tr. Kasyapa's Book of Wisdom: A Ritual Handbook of the Vaikhanasas. (Disputationes Rheno-Trajectinae Ser.: No. 10). 1965. pap. text ed. 37.60 (ISBN 90-2790-036-1). Mouton.

Goudriaan, Teun. Maya Divine & Human. 1978. 19.95 (ISBN 0-89684-040-9, Pub. by Motilal Banarsidass India). Orient Bk Dist.

--Maya, Divine & Human. 1979. 26.00x (ISBN 0-685-95754-3). South Asia Bks.

Goudzwaard, B. Aid for the Overdeveloped West. 1975. pap. 3.50 (ISBN 0-88906-100-9). Wedge Pub.

Goudzwaard, Bob. Idols of Our Time. Vennen, Mark V., tr. from Dutch. LC 84-652. Tr. of Genoodzaakt Goed te Wezen: Christelijke Hoop in Een Bezetenwereld. 120p. (Orig.). 1984. pap. 6.95 (ISBN 0-87784-970-6). Inter-Varsity.

Gougaud, Dom L. Gaelic Pioneers of Christianity: The Work & Influence of Irish Monks & Saints in Continental Europe. Collins, Victor, tr. from Fr. 166p. 1983. lib. bdg. 85.00 (ISBN 0-89984-223-2). Century Bookbindery.

Gouge, William. Of Domesticall Duties. LC 76-57385. (English Experience Ser.: No. 803). 1977. Repr. of 1622 ed. lib. bdg. 66.00 (ISBN 90-221-0803-1). Walter J Johnson.

Gough, Edward. The Philosophy of the Upanishads. 268p. 1979. Repr. of 1882 ed. 19.95 (ISBN 0-89684-158-8). Orient Bk Dist.

Goulaeff, E. E., tr. see Saint John of Kronstadt.

Gould, Dana, jt. auth. see Sanders, J. Oswald.

Gould, Eric. Mythical Intentions in Modern Literature. LC 81-47132. 304p. 1981. 30.50 (ISBN 0-691-06482-2). Princeton U Pr.

Gould, Ezra P. A Critical & Exegetical Commentary on the Gospel According to St. Mark. Driver, Samuel R., et al, eds. (International Critical Commentary Ser.). 376p. 1896. 24.95 (ISBN 0-567-05022-X, Pub. by T & T Clark Ltd UK). Fortress.

Gould, Karen. The Psalter & Hours of Yolande of Soissons. LC 78-55888. 1978. 11.00x (ISBN 0-910956-78-2, SAM4); pap. 5.00x (ISBN 0-910956-64-2). Medieval Acad.

Gould, Nathaniel D. Church Music in America. 1980. lib. bdg. 59.75 (ISBN 0-8490-3192-3). Gordon Pr.

--Church Music in America, Comprising Its History & Its Peculiarities at Different Periods. LC 78-144620. Repr. of 1853 ed. 19.25 (ISBN 0-404-02888-8). AMS Pr.

Gould, Toby, et al. We Don't Have Any Here. 52p. 1986. pap. 4.95 (ISBN 0-88177-030-2, DR030B). Discipleship Res.

Goulder, Michael D. The Psalms of the Sons of Korah. (Journal for the Study of the Old Testament, Supplement Ser.: No. 20). xiv, 302p. 1983. 27.50x (ISBN 0-905774-40-X, Pub. by JSOT Pr England); pap. text ed. 14.95x (ISBN 0-905774-41-8). Eisenbrauns.

--The Song of Fourteen Songs. (JSOT Supplement Ser.: No. 36). viii, 94p. 1986. text ed. 18.00x (ISBN 0-905774-86-8, Pub. by JSOT Pr England); pap. text ed. 7.50x (ISBN 0-905774-87-6). Eisenbrauns.

Goulding, Dorothy J. Three Christmas Plays. 20p. Repr. of 1955 ed. 3.00 (ISBN 0-88020-103-7). Coach Hse.

Goulding, F. J., tr. see Musavi, Sayyed M.

Goulooze, William. Comfort for the Sorrowing. pap. 0.45 (ISBN 0-686-23474-X). Rose Pub MI.

--The Shepherd's Care. pap. 0.45 (ISBN 0-686-23475-8). Rose Pub MI.

Gour, Hari S. The Spirit of Buddhism. LC 78-72432. Repr. of 1929 ed. 57.50 (ISBN 0-404-17299-7). AMS Pr.

Gover, Robert. Voodoo Contra. LC 84-52293. 128p. (Orig.). 1985. pap. 6.95 (ISBN 0-87728-619-1). Weiser.

Govinda A., intro. by see Winkler, Kenneth D.

Govinda, L. Anagarika. Foundations of Tibetan Mysticism. (Illus.). 331p. 1969. pap. 7.95 (ISBN 0-87728-064-9). Weiser.

Govinda, Lama A. Psycho-Cosmic Symbolism of the Buddhist Stupa. LC 76-797. (Illus.). 144p. 1976. pap. 6.95 (ISBN 0-913546-36-4). Dharma Pub.

--Psycho-Cosmic Symbolism of the Buddhist Stupa. 102p. 1976. 20.00x (ISBN 0-317-39141-0, Pub. by Luzac & Co Ltd). State Mutual Bk.

--The Way of the White Clouds. (Illus.). 305p. 1970. pap. 10.95 (ISBN 0-87773-007-5). Shambhala Pubns.

Govoroff, Theofan, tr. see St. Nicodemos the Hagiorite.

Govoroff, Theophan, tr. see St. Nicodemos the Hagiorite.

Gow, Bonar A. Madagascar & the Protestant Impact. LC 78-11216. (Dalhousie African Studies). 256p. 1980. text ed. 49.50x (ISBN 0-8419-0463-4, Africana). Holmes & Meier.

--Madagascar & the Protestant Impact: The Work of the British Missions, 1818-95. (Dalhousie African Studies Ser.). pap. 71.00 (ISBN 0-317-27749-9, 2025229). Bks Demand UMI.

Gow, Kathleen M. Yes, Virginia, There Is Right & Wrong. 255p. 1985. 12.95 (ISBN 0-8423-8558-4); pap. 6.95 (ISBN 0-8423-8561-4). Tyndale.

Gowan, Donald E. Eschatology in the Old Testament. LC 85-4550. 160p. 1985. pap. 9.95 (ISBN 0-8006-1906-4, 1-1906). Fortress.

--Reclaiming the Old Testament for the Christian Pulpit. 176p. Date not set. pap. 10.95 (ISBN 0-567-29106-5, Pub. by T & T Clark Ltd UK). Fortress.

--When Man Becomes God: Humanism & Hybris in the Old Testament. LC 75-17582. (Pittsburgh Theological Monographs: No. 6). 1975. pap. 8.75 (ISBN 0-915138-06-9). Pickwick.

Gowan, Donald E., ed. Bridge Between the Testaments: Reappraisal of Judaism from the Exile to the Birth of Christianity. 3rd, rev. ed. LC 86-9327. (Pittsburgh Theological Monographs: No. 14). 1986. text ed. 32.95 (ISBN 0-915138-88-3). Pickwick.

Gowans, Fred R. & Campbell, Eugene E. Fort Supply: Brigham Young's Green River Experiment. 1976. pap. 2.95 (ISBN 0-8425-0248-3). Brigham.

Gowen, Herbert H. Five Foreigners in Japan. facs. ed. LC 67-28735. (Essay Index Reprint Ser). 1936. 20.00 (ISBN 0-8369-0491-5). Ayer Co Pubs.

Gower, Joseph F. & Leliaert, Richard M., eds. The Brownson-Hecker Correspondence. LC 76-20160. 1979. text ed. 25.00x (ISBN 0-268-00656-3). U of Notre Dame Pr.

Gower, Ralph, jt. auth. see Wight, Fred H.

Gowing, Peter G. Muslim Filipinos: Heritage & Horizon. (Illus.). 1979. pap. 11.00x (ISBN 0-686-25217-9, Pub. by New Day Pub). Cellar.

Gowing, Peter G., jt. auth. see Diamond, Michael J.

Gowland, D. A. Methodist Secessions. 192p. 1979. 40.00 (ISBN 0-7190-1335-6, Pub. by Manchester Univ Pr). Longwood Pub Group.

Gowland, D. A., jt. auth. see Hayes, A. J.

Gowland, D. A., jt. ed. see Hayes, A. J.

Goy, Joseph. Les Fluctuations Du Produit De la Dime: Conjoncture Decimale et Domaniale De la Fin Dumoyen Age Au XV111e Siecle. (Cahiers Des Etudes Rurales: No. 3). 1972. pap. 34.40x (ISBN 90-2797-000-9). Mouton.

Goyet. L' Humanisme de Bossuet. 48.25 (ISBN 0-685-34207-7). French & Eur.

Grabar, Andre. Christian Iconography: A Study of Its Origins. LC 67-31114. (A. W. Mellon Lectures in the Fine Arts No. 10, Bollingen Ser: No. Xxxv). (Illus.). 432p. (Orig.). 1980. 66.00x (ISBN 0-691-09716-X); pap. 15.95x (ISBN 0-691-01830-8). Princeton U Pr.

Grabar, Oleg, ed. Muqarnas: An Annual on Islamic Art & Architecture: The Art of the Mamluks, Vol. II. LC 83-643765. (Illus.). 240p. 1984. 35.00x (ISBN 0-300-03137-8). Yale U Pr.

Grabbe, George. Dogmat Tserkvi v Sovrjemjennom Mire. Tr. of The Dogma of the Church in the Modern World. 1975. pap. 1.50 (ISBN 0-317-30381-3). Holy Trinity.

--Orthodox Christian Education of Children in Our Days. 30p. 1976. pap. 1.00x (ISBN 0-913026-17-4). St Nectarios.

--Otritsanije vmesto utverzhdenije. Tr. of Denial Instead of Affirmation. 48p. 1971. pap. 2.00 (ISBN 0-317-30377-5). Holy Trinity.

--Pravda o Russkoj Tserkvi na Rodinje i za Rubjezhom. Tr. of The Truth of the Russian Church at Home & Abroad. 216p. 1961. pap. 8.00 (ISBN 0-317-30359-7). Holy Trinity.

Grabbe, Lester L. Comparative Philology & the Text of Job: A Study in Methodology. LC 77-23489. (Society of Biblical Literature. Dissertation Ser.). 1977. pap. 9.95 (ISBN 0-89130-139-9, 060134). Scholars Pr GA.

Graber, David, ed. Tsese-Ma'Heone-Nemeototse: Cheyenne Spiritual Songs. LC 82-83401. (Eng. & Cheyenne.). 227p. 1982. 29.95 (ISBN 0-87303-078-8). Faith & Life.

Grabner Haider, Anton. Vocabulario Practico De la Biblia. (Span.). 892p. 1975. 41.95 (ISBN 84-254-0964-0, S-50206). French & Eur.

Grace, James H. God, Sex, & the Social Project: The Glassboro Papers on Religion & Human Sexuality. LC 78-65496. (Symposium Ser.: Vol. 2). x, 203p. 1978. 19.95x (ISBN 0-88946-900-8). E Mellen.

--Sex & Marriage in the Unification Movement: A Sociological Study. LC 85-2961. (Studies in Religion & Society: Vol. 13). 304p. 1985. 49.95x (ISBN 0-88946-861-3). E Mellen.

Grace, V. V., ed. The Most Memorable Utterances of Our Lord & Master Jesus Christ. (Illus.). 98p. 1987. 97.85 (ISBN 0-89266-580-7). Am Classical Coll Pr.

Grace, William J. Ideas in Milton. LC 68-12290. 1969. Repr. of 1968 ed. 6.95x (ISBN 0-268-00126-X). U of Notre Dame Pr.

Gracey, Colin B., jt. auth. see Ames, David A.

Gracie, David, ed. & tr. see Bonhoeffer, Dietrich.

Gracie, David M., tr. see Harnack, Adolf.

Grad, Eli & Roth, Bette. Congregation Shaarey Zedek: 5622-5742 1861-1981. LC 82-48650. (Illus.). 198p. 1982. 25.00x (ISBN 0-8143-1713-8). Wayne St U Pr.

Grade, Chaim. Rabbis & Wives. LC 83-5855. 320p. 1983. pap. 5.95 (ISBN 0-394-71647-7, Vin). Random.

Gradel, Morris, tr. see Yahil, Leni.

Grady, John L. Abortion: Yes or No? LC 79-53228. 32p. 1968. pap. 1.00 (ISBN 0-89555-117-9). TAN Bks Pubs.

Graeber, Charlotte. Jonah, Speak for God. (Speak for Me Ser.). (Illus.). 24p. 1986. 3.95 (ISBN 0-8407-6702-1). Nelson.

--Moses, Speak for God! (Speak for Me Ser.). (Illus.). 24p. 1986. 3.95 (ISBN 0-8407-6704-8). Nelson.

--Paul, Speak for God. (Speak for Me Ser.). (Illus.). 24p. 1986. 3.95 (ISBN 0-8407-6700-5). Nelson.

--Peter, Speak for God. (Speak for Me Ser.). (Illus.). 24p. 1986. 3.95 (ISBN 0-8407-6701-3). Nelson.

Graeber, Isacque & Britt, Steuart H. Jews in a Gentile World: The Problem of Anti-Semitism. LC 78-26329. (Illus.). 1979. Repr. of 1942 ed. lib. bdg. 32.50x (ISBN 0-313-20878-6, GRJE). Greenwood.

Graebner, Alan. Uncertain Saints. LC 75-1573. (Contributions in American History: No. 42). 320p. 1975. lib. bdg. 29.95 (ISBN 0-8371-7963-7, GUS/). Greenwood.

Graef, H. C. The Way of the Mystics. 1977. lib. bdg. 59.95 (ISBN 0-8490-2811-6). Gordon Pr.

Graendorf, Werner, jt. auth. see Mattson, Lloyd.

Graendorf, Werner, ed. Introduction to Biblical Christian Education. LC 81-1608. 1981. 16.95 (ISBN 0-8024-4128-9). Moody.

Graesser, Erich. Das Problem der Parusieverzoegerung in den Synoptischen Evangelien und in der Apostelgeschichte. 3rd ed. (Beihefte zur Zeitschrift fuer die Alttestamentliche Wissenschaft 22). 1977. 36.40x (ISBN 3-11-007512-1). De Gruyter.

Graesser, Erich, et al. Jesus in Nazareth. (Beiheft 40 zur Zeitschrift fuer die alttes tamentliche Wissenschaft). 153p. 1972. 41.50x (ISBN 3-11-004004-2). De Gruyter.

Graetz, Heinrich. The Structure of Jewish History & Other Essays. 20.00x (ISBN 0-87068-466-3); pap. 14.95x (ISBN 0-685-56206-9). Ktav.

Graf, Fritz. Eleusis und die Orphische Dichtung Athens in Vorhellenistischer Zeit. (Religionsgeschichtliche Versuche und Vorarbeiten, Vol. 33). xii, 224p. 1974. 33.60x (ISBN 3-11-004498-6). De Gruyter.

Graf, Fritz, jt. ed. see Bremmer, Jan.

Graff, Gil. Separation of Church & State: Dina de-Malkhuta Dina in Jewish Law, 1750-1848. LC 84-24061. (Judaic Studies Ser.). ix, 224p. 1985. 29.50 (ISBN 0-8173-0264-6). U of Ala Pr.

Gragg, Alan. George Burman Foster: Religious Humanist. LC 77-92499. (Special Studies Ser.: No. 3). v, 79p. 1978. pap. 3.50 (ISBN 0-932180-02-7). NABPR.

Gragg, Florence A., ed. The Latin Writings of the Italian Humanists. (College Classical Ser.). xxxvi, 434p. 1981. lib. bdg. 30.00 (ISBN 0-89241-356-5); pap. text ed. 17.50 (ISBN 0-89241-110-4). Caratzas.

Gragg, Gerald R., ed. see Wesley, John.

Gragg, Rod. Bobby Bagley POW. 1978. pap. 3.95 (ISBN 0-89728-022-9, 678434). Omega Pubns OR.

Graham, Billy. Los Angeles: Agentes Secretos de Dios. Rojas, Juan, tr. from Eng. LC 76-20259. Tr. of Angels: God's Secret Agents. (Span.). 168p. 1976. pap. 4.95 (ISBN 0-89922-069-X). Edit Caribe.

--Angels. 1984. pap. 3.50 (ISBN 0-671-54147-1). PB.

--Angels: God's Secret Agents. 176p. 1986. 9.95 (ISBN 0-8499-0542-7, 0542-7); pap. 7.95 (ISBN 0-8499-3049-9). Word Bks.

--Approaching Hoofbeats: The Four Horsemen of the Apocalypse. 288p. 1985. pap. 3.95 (ISBN 0-380-69921-4). Avon.

--A Biblical Standard for Evangelists. LC 84-51639. 144p. 1984. pap. 5.95 (ISBN 0-89066-057-3). World Wide Pubs.

--Billy Graham Christian Worker's Handbook. 240p. 1982. write for info. (ISBN 0-89066-042-5); pap. 7.95. World Wide Pub.
--El Espiritu Santo. Sipowicz, A. Edwin, tr. from Eng. Orig. Title: The Holy Spirit. (Span.). 252p. 1981. pap. 6.25 (ISBN 0-311-09096-6). Casa Bautista.
--Hasta el Armagedon. Sipowicz, Edwin, tr. from Eng. Orig. Title: Till Armageddon. 272p. 1983. pap. 5.95 (ISBN 0-311-09097-4). Casa Bautista.
--The Holy Spirit. 1978. 3.95 (ISBN 0-8499-4153-9). Word Bks.
--How to Be Born Again. LC 77-76057. 1977. 3.95 (ISBN 0-8499-4119-9). Word Bks.
--El Mundo en Llamas. Orig. Title: World Aflame. (Span.). 272p. 1983. pap. 5.25 (ISBN 0-311-46091-7). Casa Bautista.
--Nacer a Una Nueva Vida. Ward, Rhode, tr. from Eng. LC 78-52622. Tr. of How to Be Born Again. (Span.). 191p. 1978. pap. 4.95 (ISBN 0-89922-110-6). Edit Caribe.
--Paz con Dios. Muntz, Carrie, tr. from Eng. Orig. Title: Peace with God. 272p. 1981. pap. 3.75 (ISBN 0-311-43037-6). Casa Bautista.
--Paz con Dios. rev. & enl. ed. Tr. of Peace with God. (Span.). 220p. 1987. pap. 7.50 (ISBN 0-311-46109-3). Casa Bautista.
--Peace with God. rev. ed. 288p. 1985. 10.95 (ISBN 0-8499-0464-1, 0464-1); pap. text ed. 7.95 (ISBN 0-8499-2991-1, 2991-1). Word Bks.
--The Secret of Happiness. rev. & enl. ed. 160p. 1985. 11.95 (ISBN 0-8499-0508-7, 0508-7); pap. 9.95 (ISBN 0-8499-3034-0, 3034-0). Word Bks.
--El Secreto de la Felicidad. Orig. Title: The Secret of Happiness. (Span.). 192p. 1981. pap. 2.75 (ISBN 0-311-04352-6). Casa Bautista.
--Till Armageddon. 224p. 1984. pap. 6.95 (ISBN 0-8499-2998-9, 2998-9). Word Bks.
--Unto the Hills: A Devotional Treasury from Billy Graham. 384p. 1986. 14.95 (ISBN 0-8499-0603-2). Word Bks.

Graham, Billy & Ten Boom, Corrie. To God Be the Glory. 62p. 1985. pap. text ed. 4.95 large print ed. (ISBN 0-8027-2473-6). Walker & Co.

Graham, Billy, Center Staff, ed. An Evangelical Agenda: Nineteen Eighty-Four & Beyond. LC 79-15889. 1979. pap. 5.95 (ISBN 0-87808-171-2). William Carey Lib.

Graham, Carolyn. Jazz Chants for Children. (Illus.). 1979. pap. text ed. 7.50x (ISBN 0-19-502496-6); tchrs ed. 10.95x (ISBN 0-19-502497-4); cassette 12.00x (ISBN 0-19-502575-X); tchrs' ed & cassette 16.00x (ISBN 0-19-502576-8). Oxford U Pr.

Graham, Franklinn & Lockerbie, Jeanette. Bob Pierce: This One Thing I Do. 1983. 10.95 (ISBN 0-8499-0097-2). Word Bks.

Graham, Helen, ed. see Gaspar, Karl.

Graham, Henry G. What Faith Really Means. LC 82-74243. 94p. 1982. pap. 2.00 (ISBN 0-89555-204-3). TAN Bks Pubs.
--Where We Got the Bible... Our Debt to the Catholic Church. 153p. 1977. pap. 3.00 (ISBN 0-89555-137-3). TAN Bks Pubs.

Graham, James R. The Planting of the Presbyterian Church in Northern Virginia Prior to the Organization of Winchester Presbytery, December Fourth, Seventeen Ninenty Four. LC 26-22114. 168p. 1904. 15.00x (ISBN 0-685-65067-7). Va Bk.

Graham, John K. God's Gift: The Secrets of Financial Freedom, No. 1. LC 83-83273. (God's Gift Ser.). (Illus.). 112p. 1984. 12.95 (ISBN 0-916333-00-0). King's Hse Pub.

Graham, John W. Conscription & Conscience: A History 1916-1919. LC 78-81509. 1969. Repr. of 1922 ed. 35.00x (ISBN 0-678-00507-9). Kelley.

Graham, Kathy. Hope for a Troubled Nation. (Bible Puzzle Time). (Illus.). 16p. (Orig.). 1982. pap. 0.60 (ISBN 0-87403-016-1, 2176). Standard Pub.

Graham, Loren R. Between Science & Values. LC 81-4436. 448p. 1981. 28.00 (ISBN 0-231-05192-1); pap. 14.00x (ISBN 0-231-05193-X). Columbia U Pr.

Graham, R. B. A Brazilian Mystic: Life & Miracles of Antonio Conselheiro. 1976. lib. bdg. 59.95 (ISBN 0-87968-786-X). Gordon Pr.

Graham, Robert A. Vatican Diplomacy: A Study of Church & State on the International Plane. LC 59-13870. pap. 113.00 (ISBN 0-317-08423-2, 2015012). Bks Demand UMI.

Graham, Robert B. Vanished Arcadia: Being Some Account of the Jesuits in Paraguay. LC 68-25238. (Studies in Spanish Literature, No. 36). 1969. Repr. of 1901 ed. lib. bdg. 50.95x (ISBN 0-8383-0949-6). Haskell.

Graham, Roy E. Ellen G. White: Co-Founder of the Seventh-Day Adventist Church. (American University Studies VII: Theology & Religion: Vol 12). 506p. 1985. text ed. 41.00 (ISBN 0-8204-0255-9). P Lang Pubs.

Graham, Ruth B. Navidad en Nuestra Familia. Gama, Roberto, tr. from Eng. Orig. Title: Our Christmas Story. (Span., Illus.). 128p. (Orig.). pap. 5.25 (ISBN 0-311-08225-4). Casa Bautista.
--Sitting by My Laughing Fire. LC 77-75457. 1977. 10.95 (ISBN 0-8499-2933-4). Word Bks.

Graham, Stephen. Peter the Great: A Life of Peter I of Russia. LC 75-138241. (Illus.). 1971. Repr. of 1950 ed. lib. bdg. 39.75x (ISBN 0-8371-5598-3, GRPG). Greenwood.
--Soul of John Brown. LC 70-109915. Repr. of 1920 ed. 25.00 (ISBN 0-404-00162-9). AMS Pr.

Graham, Terry, tr. see Nurbakhsh, Javad.

Graham, Terry, tr. see Nurbakhsh, Dr. Javad.

Graham, Terry, tr. see Nurbakhsh, Jawad.

Graham, Terry, et al, trs. see Javad, Nurbakhsh.

Graham, Terry, et al, trs. see Nurbakhsh, Iavad.

Graham, Thomas E., ed. & intro. by see Jones, Jenkin L.

Graham, William A. Divine Word & Prophetic Word in Early Islam: A Reconsideration of the Sources, with Special Reference to the Divine Saying or Hadith Qudsi. (Religion & Society Ser.). 1977. text ed. 37.50x (ISBN 90-279-7612-0). Mouton.

Graham, William C., jt. ed. see Sprengling, Martin.

Grahame, Kenneth. Pagan Papers. LC 72-3427. (Essay Index Reprint Ser.). Repr. of 1898 ed. 15.00 (ISBN 0-8369-2903-9). Ayer Co Pubs.

Grainger, Roger. The Language of the Rite. 192p. 1984. pap. 8.95 (ISBN 0-232-51246-9). Chr Classics.

Gram, Moltke S. The Transcendental Turn: The/Foundation of Kant's Idealism. LC 84-22047. xii, 260p. 1985. 30.00 (ISBN 0-8130-0787-9). U Presses Fla.

Gram, Moltke S., ed. Interpreting Kant. LC 82-13627. 1982. text ed. 18.00 (ISBN 0-87745-118-4). U of Iowa Pr.

Gram, Robert L. An Enemy Disguised: Unmasking the Illusion of Meaningful Death. 224p. 1985. 10.95 (ISBN 0-8407-5942-8). Nelson.

Gramelsbach, Helen. Seventy-One Creative Bible Story Projects: Patterns for Crafts, Visuals, & Learning Centers. (Illus.). 64p. 1983. pap. 4.95 (ISBN 0-87239-607-X, 2103). Standard Pub.

Gramick, Jeannine, ed. Homosexuality & the Catholic Church. 176p. 1985. 8.95 (ISBN 0-88347-149-3). New Ways Min.

Grams, Betty J. Families Can Be Happy. LC 81-82420. 128p. (Orig.). 1981. pap. 2.50 (ISBN 0-88243-759-3, 02-0759); tchr's ed 3.95 (ISBN 0-88243-334-2, 02-0334). Gospel Pub.
--Women of Grace. LC 77-93409. 128p. 1978. pap. 3.95 (ISBN 0-88243-751-8, 02-0751, Radiant Books); tchr's. ed 3.95 (ISBN 0-88243-336-9, 02-0336). Gospel Pub.

Grana, Janice, ed. Images: Women in Transition. LC 75-46441. 1977. pap. 4.95 (ISBN 0-88489-092-5). St Mary's.

Granberg-Michaelson, Karin. In the Land of the Living: Health Care & the Church. 1984. pap. 4.95 (ISBN 0-310-27491-5, 6897P). Zondervan.

Granberg-Michaelson, Wes, ed. Tending the Garden: Essays on the Gospel & the Earth. 176p. (Orig.). 1987. pap. 8.95 (ISBN 0-8028-0230-3). Eerdmans.

Granberg-Michaelson, Wesley. A Wordly Spirituality: The Call to Take Care of the Earth. LC 83-48997. 224p. 1984. 13.45 (ISBN 0-06-063380-8, HarpR). Har-Row.

Granberry, Nola, tr. see Woggon, Guillermo.

Grand, Samuel, jt. auth. see Grand, Tamar.

Grand, Tamar & Grand, Samuel. Children of Israel. (Illus.). 1972. text ed. 5.50 (ISBN 0-8074-0131-5, 121320); tchr's guide 2.25 (ISBN 0-8074-0132-3, 201320); fun & act bk. 4.50 (ISBN 0-8074-0133-1, 121322). UAHC.

Grandaur, Georg, ed. & tr. Leben Des Abtes Eigil Von Fulda und der Aebtissin Hathumoda Von Gandersheim Nebst der Uebertragung Des Hl. Liborius und Des Hl. Vitus. (Ger). pap. 10.00 (ISBN 0-384-19640-3). Johnson Repr.

Grandmaison, C. De see De Grandmaison, C.

Grane, Leif, ed. The Augsburg Confession: A Commentary. Rasmussen, John H., tr. from Ger. LC 86-28832. Tr. of Die Confessio Augustana. 272p. (Orig.). 1987. pap. 14.95 (ISBN 0-8066-2252-0, 10-0519). Augsburg.

Granet, Marcel. The Religion of the Chinese People. Freedman, Maurice, tr. from Fr. 1977. pap. 5.95x (ISBN 0-06-131905-8, TB 1905, Torch). Har-Row.

Granfield, Patrick, jt. auth. see Dulles, Avery.

Grangewood, W., tr. see Rabbi Yehoshja Y. Neuwirth.

Granjon, Henry. Along the Rio Grande: A Pastoral Visit to Southern New Mexico in 1902. Taylor, Michael R., ed. De Lopez, Mary W., tr. from Fr. LC 86-11390. (Illus.). 153p. 1986. 17.50x (ISBN 0-8263-0903-8); pap. 8.95 (ISBN 0-8263-0904-6, Co-pub. by Historical Society of New Mexico). U of NM Pr.

Grannis, Chandler B., et al. Century of a Modern Church. LC 83-4800. (Illus.). 120p. (Orig.). 1983. pap. 5.00 (ISBN 0-9610366-0-5). Union Cong Church.

Grannis, J. Christopher, et al. The Risk of the Cross: Christian Discipleship in the Nuclear Age. 128p. (Orig.). 1981. pap. 5.95 (ISBN 0-8164-2305-9, HarpR). Har-Row.

Granqvist, Hilma N. Birth & Childhood Among the Arabs. LC 72-9643. Repr. of 1947 ed. 36.00 (ISBN 0-404-57447-5). AMS Pr.

Granrose, John T., jt. auth. see Frankena, William K.

Granskou, D., jt. ed. see Richardson, P.

Grant, Amy, et al. Amy Grant's Heart to Heart Bible Stories. LC 85-62143. (Illus.). 96p. 1985. 9.95x (ISBN 0-8344-0130-4, BB500C). Sweet.

Grant, Arthur J. The Huguenots. LC 69-11552. 255p. 1969. Repr. of 1934 ed. 27.50 (ISBN 0-208-00745-8, Archon). Shoe String.

Grant, Brian W. From Sin to Wholeness. LC 81-16122. 174p. 1982. pap. 8.95 (ISBN 0-664-24399-1). Westminster.
--Reclaiming the Dream: Marriage Counseling in the Parish Context. 176p. (Orig.). 1986. pap. 9.95 (ISBN 0-687-35729-2). Abingdon.

Grant, C. David. God the Center of Value: Value Theory in the Theology of H. Richard Niebuhr. LC 84-40232. 185p. 1984. 16.95x (ISBN 0-912646-92-6). Tex Christian.

Grant, Christian P. The Syrian Desert. LC 78-63341. (The Crusades & Military Orders: Second Ser.). (Illus.). Repr. of 1937 ed. 41.00 (ISBN 0-404-17017-X). AMS Pr.

Grant, Dave. The Great Lover's Manifesto. 160p. (Orig.). 1986. 9.95 (ISBN 0-89081-481-3). Harvest Hse.

Grant, E., jt. auth. see Wood, Irving F.

Grant, F. C. Hellenistic Religions: Grant. 1953. pap. text ed. write for info. (ISBN 0-02-345640-X). Macmillan.

Grant, F. C., ed. see Weiss, Johannes.

Grant, F. W. The Crowned Christ. pap. 4.25 (ISBN 0-88172-073-9). Believers Bkshelf.
--Lessons from Exodus. 6.25 (ISBN 0-88172-074-7). Believers Bkshelf.
--Nicolaitanism, the Rise & Growth of the Clergy. Daniel, R. P., ed. pap. 2.95 (ISBN 0-88172-139-5). Believers Bkshelf.
--Numerical Structure of Scripture. 1956. pap. 4.95 (ISBN 0-87213-269-2). Loizeaux.
--Witness the Witness of Arithmetic to Christ. 64p. 1980. pap. 2.25 (ISBN 0-87213-272-2). Loizeaux.

Grant, F. W., ed. The Numerical Bible, 7 vols. Incl. Vol. 1. Genesis to Deuteronomy (ISBN 0-87213-262-5); Vol. 2. Joshua to Second Samuel (ISBN 0-87213-263-3); Vol. 3. Psalms (ISBN 0-87213-264-1); Vol. 4. Ezekiel (ISBN 0-87213-265-X); Vol. 5. Matthew to John (ISBN 0-87213-266-8); Vol. 6. Acts to Philemon (ISBN 0-87213-267-6); Vol. 7. Hebrews to Revelation (ISBN 0-87213-268-4). 1890-1932. Set. 79.95 (ISBN 0-87213-261-7); 12.95 ea. Loizeaux.

Grant, Frederick C. Ancient Judaism & the New Testament. LC 77-18848. 1978. Repr. of 1959 ed. lib. bdg. cancelled (ISBN 0-313-20204-4, GRAJ). Greenwood.
--The Gospels: Their Origin & Their Growth. vii, 216p. 1983. Repr. of 1957 ed. lib. bdg. 19.00 (ISBN 0-88254-870-0, Octagon). Hippocrene Bks.

Grant, Frederick C., ed. Hellenistic Religions: The Age of Syncretism. 1953. pap. 13.24 scp (ISBN 0-672-60342-X, LLA134). Bobbs.

Grant, George. The Dispossessed: Homelessness in America. LC 86-71355. 256p. 1986. pap. 8.95 (ISBN 0-89107-411-2, Crossways Bks). Good News.
--In the Shadow of Plenty. 1986. pap. 6.95 (ISBN 0-8407-3095-0). Nelson.

Grant, Gi-Gi. Thirty-Three Prayers. 1986. 6.95 (ISBN 0-533-05468-0). Vantage.

Grant, Harold, et al. From Image To Likeness: A Jungian Path in the Gospel Journey. 224p. (Orig.). 1983. pap. 8.95 (ISBN 0-8091-2552-8). Paulist Pr.

Grant, J. M. J. M. Grant's Rigdon. 16p. (Orig.). 1984. pap. 1.95 (ISBN 0-942284-06-2). Restoration Re.

Grant, James. The Mysteries of All Nations. LC 79-150243. 1971. Repr. of 1880 ed. 70.00x (ISBN 0-8103-3391-0). Gale.

Grant, James M., jt. auth. see Lee, Mark.

Grant, Joan M. So Moses Was Born. 21.00 (ISBN 0-405-11791-4). Ayer Co Pubs.

Grant, Junior. I Have Seen the Lord. 48p. 1982. 5.95 (ISBN 0-8059-2845-6). Dorrance.

Grant, Kenneth. Ponderings. 48p. 1986. 6.95 (ISBN 0-8378-5087-8). Gibson.

Grant, L. Comments on the Book of Romans. pap. 3.95 (ISBN 0-88172-078-X). Believers Bkshelf.

Grant, L. M. The Bible: It's Sixty Six Books in Brief. 70p. pap. 3.95 (ISBN 0-88172-160-3). Believers Bkshelf.
--First & Second Corinthians. 194p. pap. 7.25 (ISBN 0-88172-154-9). Believers Bkshelf.
--First & Second Thessalonians. 46p. pap. 2.95 (ISBN 0-88172-079-8). Believers Bkshelf.
--God's Order: Is It Possible Today? pap. 0.95 (ISBN 0-88172-153-0). Believers Bkshelf.

Grant, Mary K., jt. ed. see Buback, Kenneth A.

Grant, Michael. The History of Ancient Israel. (Illus.). 360p. 1984. pap. 14.95 (ISBN 0-684-18084-7, ScribT); 19.95 (ISBN 0-684-18081-2). Scribner.
--The History of Ancient Israel. 360p. 1984. pap. text ed. write for info. (ISBN 0-02-345620-5, Pub. by Scribner). Macmillan.
--Jesus: An Historian's Review of the Gospels. LC 77-70218. 1978. text ed. 12.50 (ISBN 0-684-14889-7, ScribT); pap. text ed. 9.95 (ISBN 0-684-17439-1). Scribner.
--Jesus: An Historian's View of the Gospels. 261p. 1978. pap. text ed. write for info. (ISBN 0-02-345630-2, Pub. by Scribner). Macmillan.
--Jews in the Roman World. LC 72-11118. 1973. lib. rep. ed. 20.00x (ISBN 0-684-15494-3, ScribT). Scribner.
--Myths of the Greeks & Romans. (Illus.). 1964. pap. 4.95 (ISBN 0-451-62267-7, ME2267, Ment). NAL.
--Saint Paul. (Crossroad Paperback Ser.). 256p. pap. 7.95 (ISBN 0-686-85826-3). Crossroad NY.
--Saint Paul. 272p. 1976. 5.95 (ISBN 0-684-14682-7, ScribT); pap. 5.95 (ISBN 0-684-17746-3). Scribner.

Grant, Michael & Hazel, John. Gods & Mortals in Classic Mythology: Dictionary. 320p. 1985. 19.95 (ISBN 0-88029-036-6, Pub. by Dorset Pr). Hippocrene Bks.

Grant, Myrna. La Jornada. 208p. 1980. 1.00 (ISBN 0-88113-200-4). Edit Betania.
--Vanya. 208p. 1976. 3.25 (ISBN 0-88113-310-8). Edit Betania.

Grant, Patrick. The Literature of Mysticism in Western Tradition. LC 83-5789. 200p. 1983. 22.50x (ISBN 0-312-48808-4). St Martin.
--Six Modern Authors & Problems of Belief. LC 79-14511. 175p. 1979. text ed. 28.50x (ISBN 0-06-492515-3). B&N Imports.
--The Transformation of Sin: Studies in Donne, Herbert, Vaughan & Traherne. LC 73-93174. 308p. 1974. 20.00x (ISBN 0-87023-158-8). U of Mass Pr.
--The Transformation of Sin: Studies in Donne, Herbert, Vaughan & Traherne. LC 73-93174. pap. 63.50 (ISBN 0-317-26444-3, 2023850). Bks Demand UMI.

Grant, Patrick, ed. A Dazzling Darkness: An Anthology of Western Mysticism. (Orig.). 1985. pap. 9.95 (ISBN 0-8028-0088-2). Eerdmans.

Grant, Peter. The Power of Intecession. 108p. (Orig.). 1984. pap. 4.95 (ISBN 0-89283-132-4). Servant.

Grant, Ray, jt. auth. see Iverson, Dick.

Grant, Robert M. Eusebius As Church Historian. 1980. 36.00x (ISBN 0-19-826441-0). Oxford U Pr.
--Gods & the One God. LC 85-11443. (Library of Early Christianity: Vol. 1). 212p. 1986. 16.95 (ISBN 0-664-21905-5). Westminster.

Grant, Robert M. & Tracy, David. A Short History of the Interpretation of the Bible. 2nd, rev. & enlarged ed. LC 83-18485. 224p. 1984. pap. 10.95 (ISBN 0-8006-1762-2, 1-1762). Fortress.

Grant, Robert M., ed. Gnosticism: A Source Book of Heretical Writings from the Early Christian Period. LC 77-85274. Repr. of 1961 ed. 32.50 (ISBN 0-404-16108-1). AMS Pr.

Grant, Robert M., ed. see Goodspeed, Edgar J.

Grant, Sandy. Celebrate the Church. 80p. 1987. pap. 5.95 (ISBN 1-55513-826-8). Cook.
--Share the Gospel. 80p. 1987. pap. 5.95 (ISBN 1-55513-825-X). Cook.

Grant, Wilson W. The Caring Father. LC 82-72990. (Orig.). 1983. pap. 5.95 (ISBN 0-8054-5654-6). Broadman.
--De Padres a Hijos Acerca del Sexo. La Valle, Maria T., et al, trs. from Eng. (Sexo en la Vida Cristiana Ser.). (Span., Illus.). 192p. 1982. pap. 3.95 (ISBN 0-311-46255-3). Casa Bautista.
--The Power of Affirming Touch. LC 86-10830. (Christian Growth Bks). 128p. (Orig.). 1986. pap. 6.95 (ISBN 0-8066-2210-5, 10-5028). Augsburg.

Grant Duff, Mountstuart. Ernest Renan in Memoriam. 1893. Repr. 25.00 (ISBN 0-8274-2285-7). R West.

Grantham, Rudolph E. Lay Shepherding. 1980. pap. 5.95 (ISBN 0-8170-0863-2). Judson.

Grassi, Joseph A. Broken Bread & Broken Bodies: The Eucharist & World Hunger. LC 84-18888. 128p. (Orig.). 1985. pap. 6.95 (ISBN 0-88344-193-4). Orbis Bks.
--Changing the World Within: The Dynamics of Personal & Spiritual Growth. 128p. (Orig.). 1986. pap. 5.95 (ISBN 0-8091-2755-5). Paulist Pr.
--Healing the Heart: The Power of Biblical Heart Imagery. (Orig.). 1987. 7.95 (ISBN 0-8091-2862-4). Paulist Pr.

--Teaching the Way: Jesus, the Early Church & Today. LC 82-7054. 176p. 1982. lib. bdg. 26.75 (ISBN 0-8191-2501-6); pap. text ed. 11.50 (ISBN 0-8191-2502-4). U Pr of Amer.

Grassian, Victor. Moral Reasoning: Ethical Theory & Some Contemporary Moral Problems. 400p. 1981. pap. text ed. write for info. (ISBN 0-13-600759-7). P-H.

Grater, Fred A., tr. see Schwenckfeld, Caspar.

Gratian Of Paris. I Know Christ. (Spirit & Life Ser). 1957. 2.00 (ISBN 0-686-11569-4). Franciscan Inst.

Gration, John. Steps to Getting Overseas. 38p. (Orig.). 1986. pap. 1.95 (ISBN 0-87784-203-5). Inter-Varsity.

Gratsch, Edward, et al. Principles of Catholic Theology: A Synthesis of Dogma & Morals. LC 80-26272. 401p. (Orig.). 1981. pap. 12.95 (ISBN 0-8189-0407-0). Alba.

Gratsch, Edward J. Aquinas' Summa: An Introduction & Interpretation. LC 85-15842. 305p. (Orig.). 1985. pap. 12.95 (ISBN 0-8189-0485-2). Alba.

Gratton, Carolyn. Guidelines for Spiritual Direction. 8.95 (ISBN 0-87193-130-3). Dimension Bks.

--Trusting: Theory & Practice. LC 82-9760. 240p. 1982. 17.50 (ISBN 0-8245-0496-8). Crossroad NY.

--Trusting: Theory & Practice. LC 82-9760. 256p. 1983. pap. 9.95 (ISBN 0-8245-0548-4). Crossroad NY.

Gratus, Jack. The False Messiahs: Prophets of the Millennium. LC 75-29890. 284p. 1976. 10.95 (ISBN 0-8008-2588-8). Taplinger.

Gratz, Rebecca. Letters of Rebecca Gratz. facsimile ed. LC 74-27987. (Modern Jewish Experience Ser.). 1975. Repr. of 1929 ed. 38.50x (ISBN 0-405-06714-3). Ayer Co Pubs.

Grau, Joseph A. Morality & the Human Future in the Thought of Teilhard De Chardin: A Critical Study. LC 74-4976. 389p. 1976. 28.50 (ISBN 0-8386-1579-1). Fairleigh Dickinson.

Graumann, Nicholas S. A Representational Outline of the Philosophy of Buddhism. (Illus.). 151p. 1982. 77.85 (ISBN 0-89266-331-6). Am Classical Coll Pr.

Graupe, Heinz M. The Rise of Modern Judaism: An Intellectual History of German Jewry 1650-1942. LC 77-9059. 344p. 1979. lib. bdg. 24.00 (ISBN 0-88275-395-9); pap. text ed. 10.50 (ISBN 0-89874-562-4). Krieger.

Grauwe, Jan de see De Grauwe, Jan.

Graver, Jane. Please, Lord, Don't Put Me on Hold! 1979. pap. 2.25 (ISBN 0-570-03790-5, 12-2753). Concordia.

--Single But Not Alone. LC 12-2815. 1983. pap. 2.50 (ISBN 0-570-03880-4). Concordia.

Graves, Helen, ed. see Armstrong, William.

Graves, Helen, ed. see Denslow, Jamin.

Graves, Helen, ed. see Hamada, Louis.

Graves, Helen, ed. see Kazemi, Hassan.

Graves, Helen, ed. see Lyons, Harold D.

Graves, Helen, ed. see Matthews, Narvella.

Graves, Helen, ed. see Ramsey, Russell.

Graves, Helen, ed. see Robbins, Edward M.

Graves, Helen, ed. see Schwing, Sally A.

Graves, Helen, ed. see Westmoreland, Tony.

Graves, Kersey. The World's Sixteen Crucified Saviors. 436p. spiral bdg. 8.50. Truth Seeker.

Graves, Robert. Claudius the God. 1977. pap. 4.95 (ISBN 0-394-72537-9, Vin). Random.

--Greek Gods & Heroes. 125p. pap. 2.50 (ISBN 0-440-93221-1, LFL). Dell.

--Greek Myths. (Illus.). 244p. 1982. 25.00 (ISBN 0-385-17790-9). Doubleday.

--Greek Myths, 2 Vols. (Orig.). (YA) 1955. Vol. 1. pap. 4.95 (ISBN 0-14-020508-X, Pelican); Vol. 2. pap. 4.95 (ISBN 0-14-020509-8). Penguin.

--King Jesus. 356p. 1983. Repr. of 1946 ed. lib. bdg. 25.00 (ISBN 0-8495-2139-4). Arden Lib.

--The White Goddess: A Historical Grammar of Poetic Myth. rev. & enl. ed. 511p. 1966. pap. 9.95 (ISBN 0-374-50493-8). FS&G.

--The White Goddess (amended & enlarged edition) 1983. 16.50 (ISBN 0-8446-5983-5). Peter Smith.

Graves, Robert & Patai, Raphael. Hebrew Myths. 1966. pap. 5.95 (ISBN 0-07-024125-2). McGraw.

Graves, William W. The Church Teaching & Training. Viertel, Weldon & Viertel, Joyce, eds. 152p. 1982. Repr. of 1975 ed. 11.50 (ISBN 0-311-72681-X, Carib Pubns). Casa Bautista.

Gravrock, Mark. Stewardship Preaching. (Ser. B). 56p. (Orig.). 1984. pap. 4.95 (ISBN 0-8066-2076-5, 10-6002). Augsburg.

Gray, Alice & McAuley, Marilyn. Mirror, Mirror. 144p. (Orig.). 1985. pap. 5.95 (ISBN 0-310-42951-X, 11344). Zondervan.

Gray, Betty, jt. auth. see Gray, William B.

Gray, Clifton D., ed. The Samas Religious Texts Classified in the British Museum Catalogue As Hymns, Prayers, & Incantations. LC 78-72728. (Ancient Mesopotamian Texts & Studies). Repr. of 1901 ed. 17.50 (ISBN 0-404-18176-7). AMS Pr.

Gray, D. Dodson, jt. auth. see Gray, E. Dodson.

Gray, David F. Questions Pentecostals Ask. Bernard, David, ed. LC 86-26784. 304p. (Orig.). 1986. pap. 6.95 (ISBN 0-932581-07-2). Word Aflame.

Gray, Donald. Finding God among Us. 2nd ed. LC 77-89322. 1977. pap. 3.95 (ISBN 0-88489-090-2). St Mary's.

Gray, Donald P. Jesus: The Way to Freedom. LC 79-66823. (Illus.). 1979. pap. text ed. 4.95 (ISBN 0-88489-112-7). St Mary's.

--A New Creation Story: The Creative Sprituality of Teilhard de Chardin. (Teilhard Studies). 1979. pap. 2.00 (ISBN 0-89012-014-5). Anima Pubns.

Gray, E. Dodson & Gray, D. Dodson. Children of Joy: Raising Your Own Home-Grown Christians. LC 74-80259. xviii, 258p. (Orig.). 1975. pap. 7.95 (ISBN 0-934512-03-5). Roundtable Pr.

Gray, Elizabeth Dodson. Green Paradise Lost. LC 79-89193. x, 166p. 1979. pap. 8.95 (ISBN 0-934512-02-7). Roundtable Pr.

--Why the Green Nigger? Re-Mything Genesis. LC 79-89193. x, 166p. 1979. 12.95 (ISBN 0-934512-01-9). Roundtable Pr.

Gray, Elizabeth J. Contributions of the Quakers. 1983. pap. 2.50x (ISBN 0-87574-034-0, 034). Pendle Hill.

Gray, Elma E. & Gray, Leslie R. Wilderness Christians: The Moravian Mission to the Delaware Indians. LC 72-84988. (Illus.). xiv, 354p. 1973. Repr. of 1956 ed. 22.00x (ISBN 0-8462-1701-5). Russell.

Gray, G. Buchanan. A Critical & Exegetical Commentary on Numbers. Driver, Samuel R. & Plummer, Alfred, eds. LC 3-31887. (International Critical Commentary Ser.). 544p. 1903. 24.95 (ISBN 0-567-05002-5, Pub. by T & T Clark Ltd UK). Fortress.

Gray, G. Franklin & Woods, Charles A. Welcome, Blessed Morning! Sherer, Michael L., ed. (Orig.). 1987. pap. 3.50 (ISBN 0-89536-849-8, 7808). CSS of Ohio.

Gray, George B. A Critical & Exegetical Commentary on Isaiah. Driver, Samuel R., et al, eds. (International Critical Commentary Ser.). 567p. 1912. 24.95 (ISBN 0-567-05015-7, Pub. by T & T Clark Ltd UK). Fortress.

--A Critical Introduction to the Old Testament. 1978. Repr. of 1936 ed. lib. bdg. 25.00 (ISBN 0-8495-1939-X). Arden Lib.

Gray, James, ed. see Johnson, Samuel.

Gray, James M. Home Bible Study Commentary. LC 85-9750. 448p. 1985. pap. 12.95 (ISBN 0-8254-2727-4). Kregel.

Gray, Janet G. The French Huguenots. LC 81-67172. 200p. (Orig.). 1981. pap. 8.95 (ISBN 0-8010-3758-1). Baker Bk.

Gray, Joan S. & Tucker, Joyce C. Presbyterian Polity for Church Officers. LC 86-2797. 228p. (Orig.). 1986. pap. 7.95 (ISBN 0-8042-1406-9). John Knox.

Gray, John. The Biblical Doctrine of the Reign of God. 414p. 29.95 (ISBN 0-567-09300-X, Pub. by T & T Clark Ltd UK). Fortress.

--First & Second Kings, a Commentary. rev. ed. 2nd ed. LC 73-134271. (Old Testament Library). (Illus.). 826p. 1978. 27.50 (ISBN 0-664-20898-3). Westminster.

--I & II Kings: A Commentary. 2nd rev. ed. (The Old Testament Library Ser.). 27.50. Westminster.

--Joshua, Judges & Ruth. rev. ed. (New Century Bible Ser). 337p. 1977. 14.50 (ISBN 0-551-00784-2). Attic Pr.

--Joshua, Judges, Ruth. rev. ed. (New Century Bible Commentary Ser.). 432p. 1986. pap. 12.95 (ISBN 0-8028-0018-1). Eerdmans.

--Near Eastern Mythology. LC 84-45599. (The Library of the World's Myths & Legends). (Illus.). 144p. 1985. 18.95 (ISBN 0-87226-004-6). P Bedrick Bks.

Gray, Leslie R., jt. auth. see Gray, Elma E.

Gray, Margaret. The Donkey's Tale. (Illus.). 32p. 1984. casebound 3.95 (ISBN 0-8307-0963-0, 5111209). Regal.

Gray, Nicolette, ed. Jacob's Ladder: Bible Picture Book from Anglo-Saxon & 12th Century English MSS. 1978. Repr. of 1949 ed. lib. bdg. 25.00 (ISBN 0-8495-1948-9). Arden Lib.

Gray, Randall, jt. auth. see Campbell, Ross.

Gray, Robert. Cardinal Manning: A Biography. LC 85-10687. 366p. 1985. 29.95 (ISBN 0-312-12032-X). St Martin.

Gray, Ronald. Christopher Wren & St. Paul's Cathedral. LC 81-13696. (Cambridge Topic Bks.). (Illus.). 52p. 1982. PLB 8.95 (ISBN 0-8225-1222-X). Lerner Pubns.

Gray, William B. & Gray, Betty. Episcopal Church Welcomes You: An Introduction to Its History, Worship & Mission. rev. ed. LC 73-17898. 168p. 1974. (HarpR); pap. 3.95 (ISBN 0-8164-2087-4). Har-Row.

Gray, William G. Concepts of Qabalah. LC 82-62848. (The Sangreal Sodality Ser.: Vol.3). 384p. 1984. pap. 9.95 (ISBN 0-87728-561-6). Weiser.

--The Sangreal Sacrament. LC 82-62847. (The Sangreal Sodality Ser.: Vol. 2). 224p. 1983. pap. 8.95 (ISBN 0-87728-562-4). Weiser.

--A Self Made by Magic. LC 76-15547. 198p. (Orig.). 1984. pap. 8.95 (ISBN 0-87728-556-X). Weiser.

--Western Inner Workings. LC 82-62846. (The Sangreal Sodality Ser.: Vol. 1). 188p. 1983. pap. 8.95 (ISBN 0-87728-560-8). Weiser.

Grayling, Anthony C. Refutation of Scepticism. LC 85-5032. 150p. 1985. cloth 22.95 (ISBN 0-87548-314-3). Open Court.

Grayson, Donald K., ed. The Establishment of Human Antiquity (Monograph) LC 82-11571. 280p. 1983. 29.50 (ISBN 0-12-297250-3). Acad Pr.

Grayston, Donald. Thomas Merton: The Development of a Spiritual Theologian. LC 84-27299. (Toronto Studies in Theology: Vol. 20). 225p. 1985. 49.95x (ISBN 0-88946-758-7). E Mellen.

Grayston, Kenneth. The Johannine Epistles. Clements, Ronald & Black, Matthew, eds. (New Century Bible Commentary Ser.). 180p. (Orig.). 1984. pap. 5.95 (ISBN 0-8028-1981-8). Eerdmans.

--Philippians & Thessalonians. (Cambridge Bible Commentary on the New English Bible, New Testament Ser.). 1967. 16.95 (ISBN 0-521-04224-0); pap. 8.95 (ISBN 0-521-09409-7, 409). Cambridge U Pr.

Grayzel, Solomon. History of the Jews. rev. ed. (Illus.). 908p. 1968. Repr. of 1947 ed. 12.95 (ISBN 0-8276-0142-5, 190). Jewish Pubns.

--A History of the Jews. 768p. 1968. pap. 4.95 (ISBN 0-452-00694-5, Mer). NAL.

Grazia, Alfred de. God's Fire: Moses & the Management of Exodus. (Quantavolution Ser.). (Illus.). 340p. 1983. pap. 20.00 (ISBN 0-940268-03-5). Metron Pubns.

Greathouse, M., ed. see Martin, T. E.

Greathouse, Willam M. Beacon Bible Expositions: Vol. 6, Romans. Taylor, Willard H., ed. (Beacon Bible Exposition Ser.). 1975. 8.95 (ISBN 0-8341-0317-6). Beacon Hill.

Greathouse, William & Dunning, H. Ray. An Introduction to Wesleyan Theology. 128p. 1982. 4.95 (ISBN 0-8341-0762-7). Beacon Hill.

Greathouse, William, et al, eds. Beacon Bible Expositions, 12 vols. 1984. Set. 89.95 (ISBN 0-8341-0323-0). Beacon Hill.

Greathouse, William H., ed. see Knight, John A.

Greathouse, William M. From the Apostles to Wesley. 124p. 1979. pap. 3.50 (ISBN 0-8341-0588-8). Beacon Hill.

Greathouse, William M., jt. auth. see Bassett, Paul M.

Greathouse, William M., jt. auth. see Sanner, A. Elwood.

Greathouse, William M., ed. see Airhart, Arnold E.

Greathouse, William M, ed. see Martin, Sydney.

Greathouse, William M., ed. see Purkiser, W. T.

Greathouse, William M., ed. see Reed, Oscar F.

Greathouse, William M., ed. see Welch, Reuben.

Greathouse, William M., ed. see Young, Samuel.

Great Master Lyan Chr, commentary by. Essentials of the Shramanera Vinaya & Rules of Deportment: A General Explanation. Buddhist Text Translation Society Staff, tr. from Chinese. (Eng., Illus.). 112p. (Orig.). 1975. pap. 5.00 (ISBN 0-917512-04-9). Buddhist Text.

Greaves, Richard L. Society & Religion in Elizabethan England. LC 81-2530. pap. 160.00 (2056201). Bks Demand UMI.

Greaves, Richard L., compiled by. Annotated Bibliography of John Bunyan Studies. LC 72-177693. 1972. 7.00 (ISBN 0-318-03615-0). Pitts Theolog.

Greaves, Richard L., ed. Triumph over Silence: Women in Protestant History. LC 85-961. (Contributions to the Study of Religion Ser.: No. 15). xii, 295p. 1985. lib. bdg. 35.00 (ISBN 0-313-24799-4, GTS/). Greenwood.

Greaves, Richard L., ed. see Bunyan, John.

Greaves, Roger, tr. see Kaltenmark, Max.

Greeley, Andrew. The Bottom Line Catechism for Contemporary Catholics. 304p. 1982. pap. 10.95 (ISBN 0-88347-135-3). Thomas More.

--The Catholic Why? Book. 167p. 1983. 10.95 (ISBN 0-88347-154-X). Thomas More.

--How to Save the Catholic Church. 288p. 1984. 16.95 (ISBN 0-670-38475-5, Elizabeth Sifton Bks). Viking.

Greeley, Andrew & Durkin, Mary. Angry Catholic Women. 1984. pap. 15.95 (ISBN 0-88347-165-5). Thomas More.

Greeley, Andrew M. The American Catholic: A Social Portrait. LC 76-7683. (Illus.). 1978. pap. 9.95x (ISBN 0-465-09733-2, TB-5058). Basic.

--American Catholics Since the Council: An Unauthorized Report. (Illus.). 240p. (Orig.). 1985. pap. 14.95 (ISBN 0-88347-191-4). Thomas More.

--Catholic High Schools & Minority Students. LC 81-23131. (Illus.). 125p. 1982. 14.95 (ISBN 0-87855-452-1). Transaction Bks.

--Changing Catholic College. LC 67-27393. (NORC Monographs in Social Research Ser.: No. 13). 1967. 8.95x (ISBN 0-202-09011-6). NORC.

--Confessions of a Parish Priest. 448p. 1986. 18.95. S&S.

--The Great Mysteries: An Essential Catechism. 192p. (Orig.). 1976. pap. 8.95x (ISBN 0-8164-0309-0, AY7823, HarpR). Har-Row.

--The Great Mysteries: An Essential Catechism. rev. ed. 192p. 1985. pap. 6.95 (ISBN 0-86683-871-6, HarpR). Har-Row.

--The Mary Myth: On the Femininity of God. 240p. 1977. 9.95 (ISBN 0-8164-0333-3, HarpR). Har-Row.

--Religion: A Secular Theory. 144p. 1982. text ed. 19.95 (ISBN 0-02-912870-6); pap. text ed. 8.95x (ISBN 0-02-912880-3). Free Pr.

--Unsecular Man. LC 85-2459. 297p. 1985. pap. 8.95 (ISBN 0-8052-0794-5). Schocken.

Greeley, Andrew M. & Rossi, Peter H. Education of Catholic Americans. LC 66-10867. (NORC Monographs in Social Research Ser.: No. 6). 1966. 8.95x (ISBN 0-202-09003-5). NORC.

Green, Arnold H., ed. In Quest of an Islamic Humanism: Arabic & Islamic Studies in Memory of Mohamed al-Nowaihi. 288p. 1986. pap. 27.50 (ISBN 977-424-027-8, Pub. by Am Univ Cairo Pr). Columbia U Pr.

Green, Arthur. Jewish Spirituality: Vol 1. Cousins, Ewert, ed. (World Spirituality Ser.). 496p. 1985. 49.50x (ISBN 0-8245-0762-2). Crossroad NY.

--Tormented Master: A Life of Rabbi Nahman of Bratslav. LC 78-16674. (Judaic Studies: No. 9). (Illus.). 400p. 1979. 30.00 (ISBN 0-8173-6907-4). U of Ala Pr.

Green, Calvin C. Counseling: With the Pastor & CPE Student in Mind. 1984. 12.95 (ISBN 0-533-05923-2). Vantage.

Green, David, tr. see Zimmerli, Walther.

Green, David E., tr. see Becker, Joachim.

Green, David E., tr. see Hahn, Ferdinand.

Green, David E., tr. see Ringgren, Helmer.

Green, David E., tr. see Schrage, Wolfgang.

Green, David E., tr. see Schweizer, Eduard.

Green, David E., tr. see Westermann, Claus.

Green, Eise F. Now We Can Face the Day. 1975. 2.25 (ISBN 0-87509-112-1). Chr Pubns.

Green, G. D., tr. see Fichte, J. G.

Green, H. Benedict. The Gospel According to Matthew in the Revised Standard Version. (New Clarendon Bible Ser). 1975. pap. 9.95x (ISBN 0-19-836911-5). Oxford U Pr.

Green, Harry L. Echoes of Thunder. LC 80-66322. 167p. 1980. 10.95 (ISBN 0-936958-00-6); pap. 5.95 (ISBN 0-936958-01-4). Emerald Hse.

Green, Henry A. The Economic & Social Origins of Gnosticism. (SBL Dissertation). 1985. 26.95 (ISBN 0-89130-842-3, 06-01-77); pap. 17.95 (ISBN 0-89130-843-1). Scholars Pr GA.

Green, Hollis. Why Churches Die. 224p. (Orig.). 1972. pap. 5.95 (ISBN 0-87123-642-7, 210642). Bethany Hse.

Green, Hollis L. Dynamics of Christian Discipleship. 112p. 1962. 5.25 (ISBN 0-87148-251-7); pap. 4.25 (ISBN 0-87148-252-5). Pathway Pr.

Green, Holly W. Turning Fear to Hope: Help for Marriages Troubled by Abuse. 228p. (Orig.). 1984. pap. 5.95 (ISBN 0-8407-5937-1). Nelson.

Green, I. M. The Re-Establishment of the Church of England, 1660-1663. (Oxford Historical Monographs). 1978. 42.00x (ISBN 0-19-821867-2). Oxford U Pr.

Green, Jay P., ed. The Pocket Interlinear New Testament. 1981. pap. 5.95 (ISBN 0-8010-3777-8). Baker Bk.

Green, Jay P., Sr. The Interlinear Bible, 4 vols. 2952p. 1986. 89.95 (ISBN 0-913573-31-0). Hendrickson MA.

--The Interlinear Bible. 736p. 1986. 21.95 (ISBN 0-913573-29-9). Hendrickson MA.

--The Interlinear Bible. 960p. 1986. 44.95 (ISBN 0-913573-25-6). Hendrickson MA.

Green, Joel B. How to Read Prophecy. LC 84-12838. 150p. (Orig.). 1984. pap. 6.95 (ISBN 0-87784-936-6). Inter-Varsity.

--How to Read the Gospels & Acts. LC 87-5572. (The How to Read Ser.). 180p. (Orig.). 1987. pap. 6.95 (ISBN 0-87784-940-4). Inter-Varsity.

Green, John L. Pioneer Evangelists of the Church of God in the Pacific Northwest. 164p. pap. 2.00 (ISBN 0-686-29135-2). Faith Pub Hse.

Green, Julien. God's Fool: The Life of Francis of Assisi. LC 84-48771. 256p. 1985. 16.95 (ISBN 0-06-063462-6, HarpR). Har-Row.

Green, Lowell C. How Melanchthon Helped Luther Discover the Gospel: The Doctrine of Justification in the Reformation. 274p. 1980. 7.95 (ISBN 0-89890-010-7). Attic Pr.

Green, M. Second Epistle Peter & Epistle of Jude. (Tyndale Bible Commentaries: Vol. 18). 1968. pap. 4.95 (ISBN 0-8028-1417-4). Eerdmans.

Green, Maurus, tr. see Goberna, M. Regina.

Green, Michael. Choose Freedom. 1987. pap. 5.95 (ISBN 0-310-46361-0). Zondervan.

--Creo en el Espiritu Santo. Vilela, Ernesto S., tr. from Eng. LC 77-164. (Serie Creo). Tr. of I Believe in the Holy Spririt. (Span.). 267p. 1977. pap. 5.95 (ISBN 0-89922-090-8). Edit Caribe.

--The Empty Cross of Jesus. LC 84-19312. (The Jesus Library). 224p. 1984. pap. 7.95 (ISBN 0-87784-930-7). Inter-Varsity.
--Evangelism in the Early Church. 1970. pap. 7.95 (ISBN 0-8028-1612-6). Eerdmans.
--Evangelism: Now & Then. 150p. 1982. pap. 3.50 (ISBN 0-87784-394-5). Inter-Varsity.
--I Believe in Satan's Downfall. (I Believe Ser.). 256p. (Orig.). 1981. pap. 6.95 (ISBN 0-8028-1892-7). Eerdmans.
--I Believe in the Holy Spirit. (I Believe Ser). 224p. 1975. pap. 8.95 (ISBN 0-8028-1609-6). Eerdmans.
--New Life, New Lifestyle: A Fresh Look at the World. LC 84-25390. 159p. 1985. pap. 5.95 (ISBN 0-88070-073-4). Multnomah.
--Second Peter & Jude. rev. ed. (Tyndale New Testament Commentaries Ser.). 1987. pap. 5.95 (ISBN 0-8028-0078-5). Eerdmans.
--What Is Christianity? 64p. 1982. 10.95 (ISBN 0-687-44650-3). Abingdon.

Green, Michael, ed. see Bruce, F. F.

Green, Michael, ed. see Buchanan, Duncan.

Green, Michael, ed. see France, R. T.

Green, Michael, ed. see Harper, Michael.

Green, Milton. The Great Falling Away Today. (Orig.). 1986. pap. 6.95 (ISBN 0-910311-40-4). Huntington Hse Inc.

Green, Miranda. The Gods of the Celts. LC 86-22135. (Illus.). 224p. 1986. 27.50x (ISBN 0-389-20672-5). B&N Imports.

Green, Miranda J. The Gods of Roman Britain. (Shire Archeaology Ser.: No. 34). (Illus.). 64p. (Orig.). 1983. pap. 5.95 (ISBN 0-85263-634-2, Pub. by Shire Pubns England). Seven Hills Bks.

Green, N. W. Mormonism: Its Rise, Progress & Present Condition. LC 79-134401. Repr. of 1870 ed. 32.50 (ISBN 0-404-08445-1). AMS Pr.

Green, Nancy L. Pletzl of Paris: Jewish Immigrant Workers in the Belle Epoque. 278p. 1985. 39.55 (ISBN 0-8419-0995-4). Holmes & Meier.

Green, R. L. The Tale of Thebes. LC 76-22979. (Illus.). 1977. o. p. 14.95 (ISBN 0-521-21410-6); pap. 6.95 (ISBN 0-521-21411-4). Cambridge U Pr.

Green, Richard. Anti-Methodist Publications Issued During the 18th Century. LC 71-83701. 175p. 1974. Repr. of 1902 ed. lib. bdg. 22.50 (ISBN 0-8337-1436-8). B Franklin.
--The Works of John & Charles Wesley. 2nd rev. ed. LC 74-26049. Repr. of 1906 ed. 23.00 (ISBN 0-404-12924-2). AMS Pr.

Green, Richard H., tr. see Boethius.

Green, Richard J. Dissolving Depression & Finding Peace. pap. 2.50 (ISBN 0-87516-278-9). De Vorss.
--Meditation, The Highway to Happiness. 3rd ed. 40p. 1980. pap. 3.00 (ISBN 0-87516-407-2). De Vorss.

Green, Robert W., ed. Protestantism & Capitalism & Social Science: The Webster Thesis Controversy. 2nd ed. (Problems in American Civilization Ser). 1973. pap. text ed. 5.50 (ISBN 0-669-81737-6). Heath.

Green, Roberta. Joshua: Promises to Keep. (Young Fisherman Bible Studyguide Ser.). (Illus.). 70p. 1982. tchr's ed. 4.95 (ISBN 0-87788-434-X); student ed. 2.95 (ISBN 0-87788-433-1). Shaw Pubs.

Green, Roger L. Tales of Greek Heroes. (Orig.). 1974. pap. 2.95 (ISBN 0-14-030119-4, Puffin). Penguin.

Green, Roger L. & Hooper, Walter. C. S. Lewis: A Biography. LC 75-29425. 320p. 1976. pap. 7.95 (ISBN 0-15-623205-7, Harv). HarBraceJ.

Green, Ronald M. Religious Reason: The Rational & Moral Basis of Religious Belief. 1978. text ed. 18.95x (ISBN 0-19-502388-9); pap. text ed. 7.95x (ISBN 0-19-502389-7). Oxford U Pr.

Green, Rosalie B., jt. ed. see Ragusa, Isa.

Green, Ruth H. The Book of Ruth. 1982. 7.00. Freedom Rel Found.
--The Born Again Skeptic's Guide to the Bible. 1979. 9.00. Freedom Rel Found.

Green, Shirlee, ed. see Tompkins, Iverna.

Green, T. H., ed. see Hume, David.

Green, Thomas. Weeds among the Wheat: Discernment: Where Prayer & Action Meet. LC 84-70663. 208p. (Orig.). 1984. pap. 4.95 (ISBN 0-87793-318-9). Ave Maria.

Green, Thomas H. Darkness in the Marketplace. LC 81-67559. 128p. (Orig.). 1981. pap. 3.95 (ISBN 0-87793-230-1). Ave Maria.
--Opening to God. (Religion Ser.). 128p. 1987. pap. 2.95 (ISBN 0-553-26666-7). Bantam.
--Opening to God: A Guide to Prayer. LC 77-83197. 144p. 1977. pap. 3.95 (ISBN 0-87793-136-4). Ave Maria.
--Prolegomena to Ethics. 5th ed. Bradley, A. C., ed. LC 32-3225. 1968. Repr. of 1929 ed. 42.00 (ISBN 0-527-35800-2). Kraus Repr.
--A Vacation with the Lord: A Personal, Directed Retreat. LC 86-71143. 176p. (Orig.). 1986. pap. 4.95 (ISBN 0-87793-343-X). Ave Maria.
--When the Well Runs Dry: Prayer Beyond the Beginnings. LC 79-52404. 176p. (Orig.). 1979. pap. 4.95 (ISBN 0-87793-182-8). Ave Maria.

Green, V. H. Renaissance & Reformation: A Survey of European History Between 1450 & 1660. 2nd ed. 462p. 1964. pap. text ed. 17.95 (ISBN 0-7131-5617-1). E Arnold.

Green, Vivian H. From St. Augustine to William Temple. facsimile ed. LC 72-148213. (Biography Index Reprint Ser.). 1948. 18.00 (ISBN 0-8369-8060-3). Ayer Co Pubs.
--Renaissance & Reformation. 2nd ed. (Illus.). 1974. pap. text ed. 16.95 (ISBN 0-312-67305-1). St Martin.

Green, William H. General Introduction to the Old Testament: The Canon. (Twin Brooks Ser.). 1980. pap. 6.95 (ISBN 0-8010-3755-7). Baker Bk.
--The Higher Criticism of the Pentateuch. (Twin Brooks Ser.). 1978. pap. 4.95 (ISBN 0-8010-3723-9). Baker Bk.

Green, William S. Approaches to Ancient Judaism, Vol. IV. (Brown Judaic Studies). 208p. 1983. pap. 17.00 (ISBN 0-89130-673-0, 14 00 27). Scholars Pr GA.
--Approaches to Ancient Judaism II. LC 76-57656. (Brown Judaic Studies). 1980. 15.00 (ISBN 0-89130-447-9, 14-00-09); pap. 10.50 (ISBN 0-89130-448-7). Scholars Pr GA.
--Approaches to Ancient Judaism: Theory & Practice. LC 76-57656. 1978. pap. 16.50 (ISBN 0-89130-130-5, 14-00-01). Scholars Pr GA.

Green, William S., ed. Approaches to Ancient Judaism, Vol. V. (Brown Judaic Studies: No. 32). 1985. 20.95 (ISBN 0-89130-797-4, 14 00 32); pap. 17.25 (ISBN 0-89130-798-2). Scholars Pr GA.
--Approaches to Ancient Judaism III. LC 76-57656. (Brown Judaic Studies). 220p. 1981. pap. 15.00 (ISBN 0-89130-553-X, 14 00 11). Scholars Pr GA.
--Persons & Institutions in Early Rabbinic Judaism. LC 79-20712. (Brown University, Brown Judaic Studies: No. 3). 1977. pap. 13.50 (ISBN 0-89130-131-3, 14 00 03). Scholars Pr GA.

Greenawalt, R. Kent, jt. auth. see Gellhorn, Walter.

Greenbaum, Avraham, tr. see Nachman of Breslov.

Greenbaum, Avraham, tr. see Nachman of Breslov & Nathan of Breslov.

Greenbaum, Avraham, tr. see Nathan of Breslov.

Greenbaum, Avraham, tr. see Nathan, Rabbi.

Greenbaum, Avraham, tr. see Rabbi Nachman of Breslov.

Greenbaum, Howard H. & Falcione, Raymond L. Organizational Communication Nineteen Seventy-Seven: Abstracts, Analysis, & Overview. new ed. 1979. pap. 9.00 (ISBN 0-931874-08-4). Assn Busn Comm.

Greenberg, Blu. On Women & Judaism: A View from Tradition. LC 81-11779. 192p. 1983. pap. 5.95 (ISBN 0-8276-0195-6, 482). Jewish Pubns.

Greenberg, David & Bernards, Solomon S. The Living Heritage of Hanukkah. 47p. 1.50 (ISBN 0-686-74963-4). ADL.

Greenberg, Eliezer, jt. ed. see Howe, Irving.

Greenberg, Irving, jt. ed. see Rosenfeld, Alvin H.

Greenberg, Judith, tr. see D'Allonnes, Olivier R.

Greenberg, Louis. Jews in Russia: The Struggle for Emancipation, 2 Vols. in 1. LC 79-161769. Repr. of 1965 ed. 27.50 (ISBN 0-404-09023-0). AMS Pr.
--The Jews in Russia: The Struggle for Emancipation, 1772-1917, 2 vols. in 1. Wishnitzer, Mark, ed. LC 75-36489. 234p. 1976. pap. 11.95 (ISBN 0-8052-0525-X). Schocken.

Greenberg, Marian. The Down Side of Up. LC 86-80657. (Illus.). 264p. 1986. pap. 8.95 (ISBN 0-941404-40-4). Falcon Pr AZ.

Greenberg, Martin. The Hamlet Vocation of Coleridge & Wordsworth. LC 85-18189. 232p. 1986. 22.50x (ISBN 0-87745-131-1). U of Iowa Pr.

Greenberg, Martin H. & Waugh, Charles G., eds. Cults! An Anthology of Secret Societies, Sects, & the Supernatural. 368p. 1983. 17.95 (ISBN 0-8253-0159-9). Beaufort Bks NY.

Greenberg, Moshe. Biblical Prose Prayer: As a Window to the Popular Religion of Ancient Israel. LC 83-47662. (Taubman Lectures in Jewish Studies: No. 6). 78p. 1983. 16.50x (ISBN 0-520-05011-8); pap. 3.95 (ISBN 0-520-05012-6, CAL 680). U of Cal Pr.
--Ezekiel, 1-20: A New Translation with Introduction & Commentary. LC 77-12855. (Anchor Bible Ser.: Vol. 22). (Illus.). 408p. 1983. 16.00 (ISBN 0-385-00954-2, Anchor Pr). Doubleday.
--Introduction to Hebrew. 1964. text ed. write for info. (ISBN 0-13-484469-6). P-H.
--Understanding Exodus. 214p. 1969. pap. 9.95x (ISBN 0-87441-265-X). Behrman.

Greenberg, Moshe, ed. see Speiser, Ephraim A.

Greenberg, Moshe, tr. see Kaufmann, Yehezkel.

Greenberg, Noah & Auden, W. H., eds. Play of Daniel, a Thirteenth-Century Musical Drama. (Illus.). 1959. pap. 5.95 (ISBN 0-19-385195-4). Oxford U Pr.

Greenberg, Noah & Smoldon, W. L., eds. Play of Herod: A Twelfth-Century Musical Drama. (Illus.). 1965. pap. 4.25 (ISBN 0-19-385196-2). Oxford U Pr.

Greenberg, S. The Ethical in the Jewish & American Heritage. (Moreshet Ser: No. 4). 25.00x (ISBN 0-87334-002-7, Pub. by Jewish Theol Seminary). Ktav.

Greenberg, Sidney. Lessons for Living: Reflections on the Weekly Bible Readings & on the Festivals. 236p. 1985. 15.95x (ISBN 0-87677-157-6). Hartmore.

Greenberg, Sidney & Levine, Jonathan. Likrat Shabbat. LC 78-669313. 10.00 (ISBN 0-87677-076-6); large type ed. 14.95; 10.95. Prayer Bk.

Greenberg, Sidney & Levine, Jonathan D. Mahzor Hadash. rev. ed. 12.50 (ISBN 0-87677-075-8); simulated leather 14.95. Prayer Bk.

Greenberg, Sidney & Sugarman, Allan S. Junior Contemporary Prayer Book for the High Holidays. pap. 4.95 (ISBN 0-87677-054-5). Prayer Bk.

Greenberg, Sidney, ed. Contemporary Prayers & Readings. 1972. pap. 3.95 (ISBN 0-87677-050-2). Prayer BK.
--Light from Jewish Lamps: A Modern Treasury of Jewish Thoughts. LC 86-71270. 465p. 1986. 30.00 (ISBN 0-87668-918-7). Aronson.
--New Model Seder. pap. 1.95 (ISBN 0-87677-058-8). Prayer Bk.

Greenberg, Sidney S., ed. Treasury of Comfort. pap. 5.00 (ISBN 0-87980-167-0). Wilshire.

Greenberg, Simon. A Jewish Philosophy & Pattern of Life. LC 81-2153. (Moreshet Series, Studies in Jewish History, Literature & Thought: Vol. 9). 550p. 1982. 25.00x (ISBN 0-87334-012-4, Pub. by Jewish Theol Seminary). Ktav.

Greenburg, S. Thomas, jt. ed. see O'Rourke, John J.

Greenburg, Samuel A. & Gilkey, Helen L. Guests in My House, Bk. 1. 212p. 1984. 10.95 (ISBN 0-533-05727-2). Vantage.

Greene, Barbara & Gollancz, Victor, eds. God of a Hundred Names: Prayers & Meditations from Many Faiths & Cultures. 304p. 1985. pap. 7.95 (ISBN 0-575-03645-1, Pub. by Gollancz England). David & Charles.

Greene, Barbara, ed. see Bingham, Mindy, et al.

Greene, Carol. The Easter Women. (Arch Bks.). (Illus.). 24p. 1987. pap. 0.99 (ISBN 0-570-09003-2, 59-1432). Concordia.
--I Am One: Prayers for Singles. LC 85-23015. 112p. (Orig.). 1985. pap. 5.95 (ISBN 0-8066-2186-9, 10-3191). Augsburg.
--Kiri & the First Easter. (Arch Bks: Set 9). (Illus.). 32p. 1972. pap. 0.99 (ISBN 0-570-06064-8, 59-1182). Concordia.
--Mother Teresa: Friend of the Friendless. LC 83-7386. (Picture-Story Biographies Ser.). (Illus.). 32p. 1983. PLB 10.60 (ISBN 0-516-03559-2). Childrens.
--Proverbs-Important Things to Know. 1980. pap. 0.99 (ISBN 0-570-06140-7, 59-1303, Arch Bk). Concordia.
--Welcome the Stranger. (Illus.). 1984. 7.95 (ISBN 0-570-04105-8, 561497). Concordia.
--Wendy & the Whine. (Illus.). 32p. 1987. pap. 3.95 (ISBN 0-570-04157-0, 56-1615). Concordia.

Greene, Carol, jt. ed. see Burow, Daniel R.

Greene, Douglas, ed. Diaries of the Popish Plot. LC 77-938. 1977. 50.00x (ISBN 0-8201-1288-7). Schol Facsimilies.

Greene, Ella L., jt. auth. see Williams, Herman.

Greene, Evarts B. Religion & the State: The Making & Testing of an American Tradition. LC 75-41122. Repr. of 1941 ed. 17.25 (ISBN 0-404-14548-5). AMS Pr.

Greene, Jacqueline D. A Classroom Hanukah. (Illus.). 32p. (Orig.). 1980. pap. 3.00 (ISBN 0-938836-01-3). Pascal Pubs.

Greene, John C. Darwin & the Modern World View. LC 61-15489. (Rockwell Lectures Ser.). 152p. 1973. pap. text ed. 6.95x (ISBN 0-8071-0062-5). La State U Pr.

Greene, Joshua, retold by. Krishna, Master of All Mystics. (Illus.). 16p. 1981. pap. 4.00 (ISBN 0-89647-010-5). Bala Bks.

Greene, Joshua M., ed. see Rosen, Steven.

Greene, Liz, jt. auth. see Arroyo, Stephen.

Greene, M. Louise. Development of Religious Liberty in Connecticut. facs. ed. LC 79-126235. (Select Bibliographies Reprint Ser). 1905. 26.50 (ISBN 0-8369-5461-0). Ayer Co Pubs.
--Development of Religious Liberty in Connecticut. LC 74-99858. (Civil Liberties in American History Ser). 1970. Repr. of 1905 ed. lib. bdg. 59.50 (ISBN 0-306-71861-8). Da Capo.

Greene, Michael H. Program Your Own Life. 230p. 1982. 10.00 (ISBN 0-9610136-0-5). Behavorial Sys Inc.

Greene, Norman N. Jean-Paul Sartre: The Existentialist Ethic. LC 80-12203. vii, 213p. 1980. Repr. of 1960 ed. lib. bdg. 22.50x (ISBN 0-313-22422-6, GRJP). Greenwood.

Greene, Ralph L. Dynamic & Inspirational Sermons for Today. 128p. 1980. 7.95 (ISBN 0-89962-021-3). Todd & Honeywell.

Greene, Richard L. The Early English Carols. LC 76-161945. 461p. 1935. Repr. 79.00x (ISBN 0-403-01342-9). Scholarly.

Greene, Richard L., ed. The Early English Carols. 2nd ed. 1977. 129.00x (ISBN 0-19-812715-4). Oxford U Pr.
--A Selection of English Carols. LC 77-13760. 1978. Repr. of 1962 ed. lib. bdg. 24.75x (ISBN 0-313-20002-5, GREC). Greenwood.

Greene, Roberta M. & Heavenrich, Elaine. A Question in Search of an Answer: Understanding Learning Disability in Jewish Education. LC 8-18059. (Illus.). 262p. 1981. pap. 5.00 (ISBN 0-8074-0029-7). UAHC.

Greene, Ruth A. Hsiang-Ya Journal. LC 76-28526. Repr. of 1977 ed. 36.70 (2011504). Bks Demand UMI.

Greene, William B. The Blazing Star, with an Appendix Treating of the Jewish Kabbala. 1977. lib. bdg. 59.95 (ISBN 0-8490-1516-2). Gordon Pr.
--Transcendentalism; bd. with Equality. LC 81-8972. (Repr. of 1849 eds.). 1981. 35.00x (ISBN 0-8201-1366-2). Schol Facsimiles.

Greenfeld, Howard. Bar Mitzvah. LC 81-5104. (Illus.). 32p. 1981. 7.95 (ISBN 0-03-053861-0). H Holt & Co.
--Chanukah. LC 76-6527. 1976. 6.95 (ISBN 0-03-015566-5). H Holt & Co.
--Chanukah, Passover, Rosh Hashanah, Yom Kippur. 1982. boxed set 20.00 (ISBN 0-03-057626-1). H Holt & Co.
--Passover. LC 77-13910. (Illus.). 32p. 1978. 6.95 (ISBN 0-03-039921-1). H Holt & Co.
--Purim. LC 82-3058. (Illus.). 32p. 1983. 9.95 (ISBN 0-03-061478-3). H Holt & Co.
--Rosh Hashanah & Yom Kippur. LC 79-4818. (Illus.). 1979. 6.95 (ISBN 0-03-044756-9). H Holt & Co.

Greenfield, Eloise. Mary McLeod Bethune. LC 76-11522. (Biography Ser.). (Illus.). 1977. PLB 12.89 (ISBN 0-690-01129-6, Crowell Jr Bks). HarpJ.

Greenfield, Guy. We Need Each Other. 1984. 8.95 (ISBN 0-8010-3799-9); pap. 5.95 (ISBN 0-8010-3800-6). Baker Bk.
--The Wounded Parent. LC 82-70463. 128p. 1982. pap. 4.95 (ISBN 0-8010-3779-4). Baker Bk.

Greengrass, M., jt. ed. see Potter, G. R.

Greengrass, Mark. The French Reformation. 96p. 1987. pap. text ed. 7.95 (ISBN 0-631-14516-8). Basil Blackwell.

Greenham, Richard. The Works, Examined, Corrected & Published: By H. Holland. LC 72-5999. (English Experience Ser.: No. 524). 496p. 1973. Repr. of 1599 ed. 70.00 (ISBN 90-221-0524-5). Walter J Johnson.

Greenleaf, Richard E. The Roman Catholic Church in Colonial Latin America. LC 77-76836. 284p. 1977. pap. 6.50x (ISBN 0-87918-034-X). ASU Lat Am St.
--Zumarraga & the Mexican Inquisition: 1536-1543. (Monograph Ser.). (Illus.). 1962. 20.00 (ISBN 0-88382-053-6). AAFH.

Greenleaf, Robert K. Servant Leadership: A Journey into the Nature of Legitimate Power & Greatness. LC 76-45678. 348p. 1977. 9.95 (ISBN 0-8091-2527-7). Paulist Pr.

Greenleaf, Simon. The Testimony of the Evangelists. 640p. 1984. Repr. of 1874 ed. 19.95 (ISBN 0-8010-3803-0). Baker Bk.

Greenlee, J. Harold. Concise Exegetical Grammar of New Testament Greek. (Orig.). 1963. pap. 3.95 (ISBN 0-8028-1092-6). Eerdmans.
--A Concise Exegetical Grammar of New Testament Greek. 5th, rev. ed. 88p. (Orig.). 1987. pap. text ed. 5.95 (ISBN 0-8028-0173-0). Eerdmans.
--Introduction to New Testament Textual Criticism. 1964. pap. 7.95 (ISBN 0-8028-1724-6). Eerdmans.
--Scribes, Scrolls, & Scripture: A Layperson's Guide to Textual Criticism. 112p. (Orig.). 1985. pap. 6.95 (ISBN 0-8028-0082-3). Eerdmans.

Greenlees. Gospel of Guru Granth Sahib. 8.95 (ISBN 0-8356-7132-1). Theos Pub Hse.
--Gospel of Islam. 7.25 (ISBN 0-8356-7158-5). Theos Pub Hse.
--Gospelof Zarathustra. 7.95 (ISBN 0-8356-7239-5). Theos Pub Hse.

Greenman, Bill. How to Find Your Purpose in Life. 200p. (Orig.). 1987. pap. text ed. 3.95 (ISBN 0-88368-192-7). Whitaker Hse.

Greenshields, R. S., tr. see Arif of Herat.

Greenslade, Philip. Leadership, Greatness, & Servanthood. 208p. (Orig.). 1986. pap. 5.95 (ISBN 0-87123-871-3, 210871). Bethany Hse.

Greenslade, S. L. Early Latin Theology. LC 56-5229. (The Library of Christian Classics). 412p. 1978. pap. 8.95 (ISBN 0-664-24154-9). Westminster.

Greenslade, Stanley L. Church & State from Constantine to Theodosius. LC 79-8712. 93p. 1981. Repr. of 1954 ed. lib. bdg. 22.50x (ISBN 0-313-20793-3, GRCS). Greenwood.

Greenspahn, Frederick, jt. auth. see Bellah, Robert.

Greenspahn, Frederick E. Hapax Legomena in Biblical Hebrew. LC 83-20021. (SBL Dissertation Ser.). 274p. 1984. 10.50 (ISBN 0-89130-660-9, 06 01 74); pap. 10.95 (ISBN 0-89130-785-0). Scholars Pr GA.

--The Human Condition in the Jewish & Christian Conditions. 1985. text ed. 25.00x (ISBN 0-88125-084-8). Ktav.

Greenspahn, Frederick E., ed. Scripture in the Jewish & Christian Traditions: Authority, Interpretation, Relevance. 240p. 1982. pap. 11.95 (ISBN 0-687-37065-5). Abingdon.

Greenspahn, Frederick E., jt. ed. see Bellah, Robert N.

Greenspahn, Frederick E., et al, eds. Nourished with Peace: Studies in Hellenistic Judaism in Memory of Samuel Sandmel. (Scholars Press Homage Ser.: No. 9). 23.95 (ISBN 0-89130-740-0, 00 16 09). Scholars Pr GA.

Greenspan, Alice. What God Gave Me. LC 84-50286. (Little Happy Day Bks.). (Illus.). 24p. (Orig.). 1984. pap. 0.49 (ISBN 0-87239-804-8, 2164). Standard Pub.

Greenspan, Ezra. The Schlemiel Comes to America. LC 83-14399. 258p. 1983. 20.00 (ISBN 0-8108-1646-6). Scarecrow.

Greenspan, Jay Seth. Hebrew Calligraphy: A Step-by-Step Guide. LC 79-12718. (Illus.). 1980. pap. 8.95 (ISBN 0-8052-0664-7). Schocken.

Greenspoon, Leonard. Textual Studies in the Book of Joshua. LC 83-3434. (Harvard Semitic Monographs). 412p. 1983. 21.75 (ISBN 0-89130-622-6, 04 00 28). Scholars Pr GA.

Greenstein, Edward L. & Preminger, Alex, eds. Hebrew Bible in Literary Criticism. (Library of Literary Criticism). 635p. 1986. 65.00x (ISBN 0-8044-3266-X). Ungar.

Greenstein, Howard. Turning Point: Zionism & Reform Judaism. LC 81-8996. (Brown BJS Ser.). 1981. pap. 12.00 (ISBN 0-89130-512-2, 140012). Scholars Pr GA.

Greenstein, Howard R. Judaism: An Eternal Covenant. LC 82-17601. 176p. 1983. pap. 10.95 (ISBN 0-8006-1690-1, 1-1690). Fortress.

Greenstone, Julius H. The Messiah Idea in Jewish History. LC 70-97284. 347p. 1972. Repr. of 1906 ed. lib. bdg. 22.50x (ISBN 0-8371-2606-1, GRMI). Greenwood.

Greenwalt, Emmett A. The Point Loma Community in California, 1897-1942: A Theosophical Experiment. LC 76-42802. Repr. of 1955 ed. 22.00 (ISBN 0-404-60068-9). AMS Pr.

Greenway, John. The Primitive Reader: An Anthology of Myths, Tales, Songs, Riddles, & Proverbs of Aboriginal Peoples Around the World. LC 65-21986. viii, 211p. Repr. of 1965 ed. 35.00x (ISBN 0-8103-5014-9). Gale.

Greenway, John L. The Golden Horns: Mythic Imagination & the Nordic Past. LC 74-30676. 232p. 1977. 20.00x (ISBN 0-8203-0384-4). U of Ga Pr.

Greenway, Roger S. Apostles to the City: Biblical Strategies for Urban Missions. 1978. pap. 4.95 (ISBN 0-8010-3724-7). Baker Bk.

--Discipling the City. LC 78-67165. 1979. pap. 9.95 (ISBN 0-8010-3727-1). Baker Bk.

Greenwood, David C. Structuralism & the Biblical Text. (Religion & Reason Ser.: No. 32). xi, 155p. 1985. 37.75x (ISBN 0-89925-103-X). Mouton.

Greenwood, John O. Henry Hodgkin: The Road to Pendle Hill. LC 79-91958. 1980. pap. 2.50x (ISBN 0-87574-229-7). Pendle Hill.

Greer, Clark. Multi-Media Methods for Christian Ministries. LC 82-16132. 1982. pap. 2.95 (ISBN 0-87227-085-8). Reg Baptist.

Greer, Rowan. The Captain of Our Salvation: A Study in the Patristic Exegesis of Hebrews. 325p. 1973. lib. bdg. 52.00x (Pub. by J C B Mohr BRD). Coronet Bks.

Greer, Rowan A. Broken Lights & Mended Lives: Theology & Common Life in the Early Church. LC 85-21823. 251p. 1986. 19.50x (ISBN 0-271-00422-3). Pa St U Pr.

Greer, Rowan A., jt. auth. see Kugel, James L.

Greer, Rowan A., ed. Origen: Selected Writings. LC 79-84886. (Classics of Western Spirituality Ser.). 334p. 1979. 13.95 (ISBN 0-8091-0283-8); pap. 9.95 (ISBN 0-8091-2198-0). Paulist Pr.

Greetings Etc. by Alfreda. Meeting Challenges: Scripture References. 1984. pap. text ed. 2.95 (ISBN 0-318-04372-6, Pub. by Greetings). Prosperity & Profits.

Greever, Jack. Marcos: Estudios Para un Joven En Busca De Identidad. Orig. Title: Mark: an Inductive Bible Study. (Span.). 64p. 1982. pap. 2.50 (ISBN 0-311-12325-2, Edit Mundo). Casa Bautista.

Greg, William R. Enigmas of Life. LC 72-323. (Essay Index Reprint Ser.). Repr. of 1879 ed. 21.00 (ISBN 0-8369-2794-X). Ayer Co Pubs.

Gregg, Edward. The Protestant Succession in International Politics, 1710-1716. (Outstanding Theses from the London School of Economics & Political Science Ser.). 475p. 1987. lib. bdg. 75.00 (ISBN 0-8240-1918-0). Garland Pub.

Gregg, Richard B. A Discipline for Non-Violence. 1983. pap. 2.50x (ISBN 0-87574-011-1, 011). Pendle Hill.

--Pacifist Program. 1983. pap. 2.50x (ISBN 0-686-43957-0, 005). Pendle Hill.

--The Value of Voluntary Simplicity. 1983. pap. 2.50x (ISBN 0-87574-003-0, 003). Pendle Hill.

Gregg, Robert C. & Groh, Dennis E. Early Arianism: A View of Salvation. LC 79-7379. 224p. 1981. 5.00 (ISBN 0-8006-0576-4, 1-576). Fortress.

Gregg, Robert C., ed. & intro. by. Arianism: Historical & Theological Reassessments. LC 85-81654. (Patristic Monograph Ser.: No. 11). viii, 380p. 1985. pap. 12.00 (ISBN 0-915646-10-2). Phila Patristic.

Gregg, Robert C., ed. Athanasius: The Life of Antony & the Letter to Marcellinus. LC 79-56622. (Classics of Western Spirituality Ser.). 192p. 1980. 12.95 (ISBN 0-8091-0309-5); pap. 8.95 (ISBN 0-8091-2295-2). Paulist Pr.

Gregoire, Reginald, et al. The Monastic Realm. LC 85-43046. (Illus.). 288p. 1985. 75.00 (ISBN 0-8478-0664-2). Rizzoli Intl.

Gregorian, Juanita L. Glorious Thunder. 144p. 1986. 10.95 (ISBN 0-89962-498-7). Todd & Honeywell.

Gregorich, Barbara. Colors. Hoffman, Joan, ed. (A Get Ready! Bk.). (Illus.). 32p. 1983. pap. text ed. 1.95 (ISBN 0-938256-64-5). Sch Zone Pub Co.

Gregorius, Saint Histoire Ecclesiastique Des Francs, 4 vols. 1967. 154.00 (ISBN 0-384-19875-9); pap. 130.00 (ISBN 0-384-19874-0). Johnson Repr.

--Les Livres des Miracles & Autres Opuscules, 4 Vols. 1863. Set. 149.00 (ISBN 0-384-19888-0); 38.00 ea.; pap. 32.00 ea.; Set. pap. 125.00 (ISBN 0-384-19889-9). Johnson Repr.

--Zehn Bucher Frankischer Geschichte, 3 vols. 4th ed. Hellmann, S., ed. Von Geisebrecht, Wilhel M, tr. 1911-1913. 34.00 ea. (ISBN 0-384-19908-9). Johnson Repr.

Gregorius I. Life & Miracles of Saint Benedict: Book Two of Dialogues. Zimmermann, Odo J. & Avery, Benedict R., trs. from Latin. LC 80-19624. xv, 87p. 1980. Repr. of 1949 ed. lib. bdg. 22.50x (ISBN 0-313-22766-7, GRLI). Greenwood.

Gregory. Teaching of Saint Gregory: An Early Armenian Catechism. Thomson, Robert W., et al, trs. from Arm. LC 78-115482. (Armenian Texts & Studies: No. 3). 1971. 14.00x (ISBN 0-674-87038-7). Harvard U Pr.

Gregory - Bishop of Tours. History of the Franks. Brehaut, Ernest, tr. (Columbia University Records of Civilization Ser). 1969. pap. 7.95x (ISBN 0-393-09845-1, NortonC). Norton.

Gregory, Christelle E. Creative Parables for Christian Teachers. LC 86-62626. 100p. 1987. pap. 9.95 (ISBN 0-89390-096-6). Resource Pubns.

Gregory, Dick. Dick Gregory's Bible Tales. 1978. pap. 2.95 (ISBN 0-06-080445-9, P 445, PL). Har-Row.

Gregory, Hamilton, ed. The Religious Case for Abortion. LC 82-61786. 96p. (Orig.). 1983. pap. 9.95 (ISBN 0-910915-00-8). Madison Polk.

Gregory, Isabella A. Gods & Fighting Men. LC 76-115243. 1971. Repr. of 1904 ed. 23.00x (ISBN 0-403-00400-4). Scholarly.

Gregory, J. S., jt. ed. see Clarke, Prescott.

Gregory, Joel, jt. auth. see Allen, R. Earl.

Gregory, John M. Seven Laws of Teaching. 1954. 7.95 (ISBN 0-8010-3652-6). Baker Bk.

--The Seven Laws of Teaching. (Orig.). 1886. 1.95x (ISBN 0-9606952-1-4). PBBC Pr.

Gregory, John W. Foundation of British East Africa. LC 78-88412. Repr. of 1901 ed. cancelled (ISBN 0-8371-1727-5, GRB&, Pub. by Negro U Pr). Greenwood.

Gregory, Peter N., ed. Traditions of Meditation in Chinese Buddhism. LC 86-19243. (Studies in East Asian Buddhism: No. 4). 272p. 1987. pap. text ed. 16.00x (ISBN 0-8248-1088-0). UH Pr.

Gregory, Peter N., jt. ed. see Gimello, Robert M.

Gregory, Ruth W. Special Days: The Book of Anniversaries & Holidays. 1978. pap. 5.95 (ISBN 0-8065-0659-8). Citadel Pr.

Gregory, Sadie. A New Dimension in Old Testament Study. 103p. (Orig.). 1980. pap. 5.00 (ISBN 0-917479-05-X). Guild Psy.

Gregory, St. Life of St. Macrina. 1974. pap. 2.95 (ISBN 0-686-10202-9). Eastern Orthodox.

Gregory, Sally. Poems, Prayers & Graces. (Illus.). 28p. 1987. 12.95 (ISBN 0-340-34873-9, Pub. by Hodder & Stoughton UK). David & Charles.

Gregory, Timothy E. Vox Populi: Popular Opinion & Violence in the Religious Controversies of the Fifth Century A.D. LC 79-16885. 257p. 1979. 25.00x (ISBN 0-8142-0291-8). Ohio St U Pr.

Gregory Nazianzen, St. & Ambrose, St. Funeral Orations. LC 67-28586. (Fathers of the Church Ser: Vol. 22). 344p. 1953. 18.95x (ISBN 0-8132-0022-9). Cath U Pr.

Gregory Of Nyssa, St. Ascetical Works. LC 64-13360. (Fathers of the Church Ser: Vol. 58). 288p. 1967. 16.95x (ISBN 0-8132-0058-X). Cath U Pr.

Gregory of Tours. The History of the Franks: Gregory of Tours. Thorpe, Lewis, tr. 720p. 1976. pap. 6.95 (ISBN 0-14-044295-2). Penguin.

Gregory Of Tours see Peters, Edward.

Gregory Seventh, Pope The Correspondence of Pope Gregory VII. Emerton, E., tr. (Columbia University Records of Civilization Ser.). 1969. pap. 5.95x (ISBN 0-393-09859-1). Norton.

Gregory The Great. The Life of Saint Benedict: Book II of the Dialogues of Gregory the Great. Uhlfelder, Myra L., tr. LC 66-30611. (Orig.). 1967. pap. 3.56 scp (ISBN 0-672-60468-X, LLA216). Bobbs.

--Remediarium Conversorum: A Synthesis in Latin of "Moralia in Job". Peter of Waltham & Gildea, Joseph, eds. LC 84-3693. 504p. 1984. 25.00 (ISBN 0-8453-4507-9). Assoc Univ Prs.

Gregory The Great, St. Dialogues. (Fathers of the Church Ser.: Vol. 39). 287p. 1959. 29.95x (ISBN 0-8132-0039-3). Cath U Pr.

Gregson, Stephen, ed. Arthur Oakman's Radio Sermons, Vol. 2. 193p. 1984. pap. 11.00 (ISBN 0-8309-0400-X). Herald Hse.

Gregson, Vernon. Lonergan, Spirituality, & the Meeting of Religions. LC 85-3312. (College Theology Society-Studies in Religion: No. 2). 170p. (Orig.). 1985. lib. bdg. 24.50 (ISBN 0-8191-4619-6, Co-Pub by College Theo Soc); pap. text ed. 10.75 (ISBN 0-8191-4620-X). U Pr of Amer.

Greidanus, Morris, et al. Welcome. LC 82-12907. 71p. 1982. pap. 3.50 (ISBN 0-933140-48-7); pap. 3.50 leader's guide (ISBN 0-933140-49-5). CRC Pubns.

Greif, Martin. The St. Nicholas Book. LC 76-5089. (Illus.). 60p. 1976. 5.95 (ISBN 0-87663-554-0). Universe.

Greif, Martin, jt. auth. see Schorsch, Anita.

Greif, Martin, ed. The Saint Nicholas Book: A Celebration of Christmas Past. 3rd, rev. ed. LC 86-21706. (Illus.). 96p. (Orig.). 1986. pap. 7.95 (ISBN 1-55562-006-X). Main Street.

Greig, Doris W. We Didn't Know They Were Angels. Beckwith, Mary, ed. 300p. (Orig.). 1987. pap. 7.95 (ISBN 0-8307-1145-7, 5418802). Regal.

Greig, James, tr. see Hubner, Hans.

Grein, Janny. Called, Appointed, Annointed. 95p. (Orig.). 1985. pap. 4.00 (ISBN 0-89274-354-9). Harrison Hse.

Greinacher, Norbert, ed. Evangelization in the World Today. (Concilium Ser.: Vol. 114). 1979. pap. 6.95 (ISBN 0-8245-0274-4). Crossroad NY.

Greinacher, Norbert & Mette, Norbert, eds. Popular Religion. (Concilium Nineteen Eighty-Six Ser.). 120p. 1986. pap. 6.95 (ISBN 0-567-30066-8, Pub. by T & T Clark Ltd UK). Fortress.

Greinacher, Norbert, jt. ed. see Elizondo, Virgil.

Greive, Hermann. Studien zum juedischen Neuplatonismus: Die Religionsphilosophie des Abraham Ibn Ezra. (Studia Judaica Vol. 7). 225p. 1973. 35.60x (ISBN 3-11-004116-2). De Gruyter.

Grelle, Bruce & Krueger, David A., eds. Christianity & Capitalism: Perspectives on Religion, Liberalism, & the Economy. LC 85-73375. (Studies in Religion & Society Ser.). 189p. 1986. text ed. 25.95x (ISBN 0-913348-23-6); pap. 14.95x (ISBN 0-913348-24-4). Ctr Sci Study.

Gremillion, Joseph. Church & Culture since Vatican II: The Experience of North & Latin America. LC 84-40364. 350p. 1985. pap. text ed. 12.95 (ISBN 0-268-00753-5, 85-07535). U of Notre Dame Pr.

Gremillion, Joseph, ed. Food-Energy & the Major Faiths. LC 77-17975. 302p. (Orig.). 1978. pap. 2.49 (ISBN 0-88344-138-1). Orbis Bks.

--The Gospel of Peace & Justice: Catholic Social Teaching Since Pope John. LC 75-39892. 637p. (Orig.). 1976. pap. 14.95 (ISBN 0-88344-166-7). Orbis Bks.

Grendler, Paul F. The Roman Inquisition & the Venetian Press, 1540-1605. LC 76-45900. 1978. text ed. 42.00x (ISBN 0-691-05245-X). Princeton U Pr.

Grene, Marjorie. Introduction to Existentialism. LC 84-2725. (Midway Ser.). x, 150p. 1984. pap. text ed. 7.00x (ISBN 0-226-30823-5). U of Chicago Pr.

Grene, Nails, ed. Spinoza & the Sciences. 1986. lib. bdg. 54.50 (ISBN 90-277-1976-4, Pub. by Reidel Holland). Kluwer-Academic.

Grenell, Zelotes & Goss, Agnes G. The Work of the Clerk. 1967. pap. 3.95 (ISBN 0-8170-0383-5). Judson.

Grenier, Albert. Roman Spirit in Religion, Thought & Art. Dobie, M. R., tr. LC 76-118639. (Illus.). 423p. 1970. Repr. of 1926 ed. lib. bdg. 32.50x (ISBN 0-8154-0330-5). Cooper Sq.

--The Roman Spirit in Religion, Thought & Art. (Illus.). 423p. 1986. Repr. of 1926 ed. lib. bdg. 100.00 (ISBN 0-89760-448-2). Telegraph Bks.

Grenier, M. Special Day Prayers for the Very Young Child. LC 56-1719. 1983. 7.95 (ISBN 0-570-04076-0). Concordia.

Grenz, Stanley. Isaac Backus - Puritan & Baptist. (Dissertation Ser.: No. 4). vii, 346p. 1983. pap. 21.95 (ISBN 0-86554-067-5). NABPR.

--Isaac Backus: Puritan & Baptist; His Place in History, His Thought, & the Implications for Modern Baptist Theology. LC 83-12140. vii, 346p. pap. 21.95 (ISBN 0-86554-067-5, P12). Mercer Univ Pr.

Grenz, Stanley J. The Baptist Congregation. 128p. 1985. pap. 7.95 (ISBN 0-8170-1083-1). Judson.

Grenz, Stanley J., jt. ed. see Wozniak, Kenneth W.

Gresham, Charles R. Preach the Word. LC 83-71917. 200p. (Orig.). 1983. pap. 3.95 (ISBN 0-89900-198-X). College Pr Pub.

--What the Bible Says about Resurrection. LC 82-7411. (What the Bible Says Ser.). 351p. 1983. 13.95 (ISBN 0-89900-090-8). College Pr Pub.

Gresk, Grace E. Come Holy Spirit-I Need Thee. 48p. 1985. 5.95 (ISBN 0-533-06177-6). Vantage.

Greville, Brooke R. The Nature of Truth, It's Union & Unity with the Soule. 210p. Repr. of 1640 ed. text ed. 33.12x (ISBN 0-576-02144-X, Pub. by Gregg Intl Pubs England). Gregg Intl.

Grey, George. Polynesian Mythology & Ancient Traditional History of the New Zealanders As Furnished by Their Priests & Chiefs. LC 75-35253. Repr. of 1906 ed. 20.50 (ISBN 0-404-14425-X). AMS Pr.

Grgic, Bob. Journey to the Father. (YA) 1987. pap. text ed. write for info. (ISBN 0-697-02225-0); write for info. tchr's. ed. (ISBN 0-697-02226-9). Wm C Brown.

Griaule, Marcel. Conversations with Ogotemmeli: An Introduction to Dogon Religious Ideas. (Illus.). 1975. pap. 8.95x (ISBN 0-19-519821-2). Oxford U Pr.

--Conversations with Ogotemmeli: An Introduction to Dogon Religious Ideas. LC 65-3614. pap. 62.00 (ISBN 0-317-28624-2, 2055384). Bks Demand UMI.

Gribbin, John. Genesis: The Origins of Man & the Universe. (Illus., Orig.). 1982. pap. 8.95 (ISBN 0-385-28321-0, Delta). Dell.

Gribbin, William. The Churches Militant: The War of 1812 & American Religion. LC 72-91313. pap. 55.00 (ISBN 0-317-29581-0, 2022000). Bks Demand UMI.

Gribble, Mercedes & Friedmann, Hope. Two Hundred Rooms in the Inn: The Story of Providence Mission Homes. LC 83-15367. (Illus.). 112p. (Orig.). 1983. pap. 3.95 (ISBN 0-87808-195-X). William Carey Lib.

Gribbon, R. T. Students, Churches & Higher Education. 128p. 1981. pap. 6.95 (ISBN 0-8170-0931-0). Judson.

Grider, J. Kenneth. Born Again & Growing. 118p. 1982. pap. 3.50 (ISBN 0-8341-0758-9). Beacon Hill.

Grier, Rosey. Rosey: The Gentle Giant. 1986. 17.95 (ISBN 0-89274-406-5). Harrison Hse.

Grier, W. J. The Momentous Event. 1976. pap. 2.95 (ISBN 0-85151-020-5). Banner of Truth.

Grierson, Denham. Transforming a People of God. 161p. (Orig.). 1984. pap. 11.95 (ISBN 0-85819-464-3, Pub. by JBCE). ANZ Religious Pubns.

Grierson, Denham, et al. Discovering the Needs & Interests of Young People. (Youth Work Guides Ser.). (Illus.). 88p. (Orig.). 1977. pap. 8.95 (ISBN 0-85819-177-6, Pub. by JBCE). ANZ Religious Pubns.

Grierson, Francis. Modern Mysticism. 1977. lib. bdg. 59.95 (ISBN 0-8490-2271-1). Gordon Pr.

--Modern Mysticism. LC 77-102570. 1970. Repr. of 1899 ed. 22.50x (ISBN 0-8046-0730-3, Pub. by Kennikat). Assoc Faculty Pr.

Grierson, Herbert. Criticism & Creation. LC 73-733. 1949. lib. bdg. 17.50 (ISBN 0-8414-1603-6). Folcroft.

Grierson, Herbert J. Cross-Currents in Seventeenth Century English Literature: The World, the Flesh & the Spirit, Their Actions & Reactions. 1959. 11.25 (ISBN 0-8446-6247-X). Peter Smith.

Griesbach, Marc F., jt. auth. see Jones, John D.

Griesbach, Marc F. & Carmichael, John P., eds. The ACPA in Today's Intellectual World: Proceedings, 1983, Vol. 57. LC 82-73233. 250p. 1984. pap. 15.00 (ISBN 0-918090-17-2). Am Cath Philo.

Griese, Orville N. Catholic Identity in Health Care: Principles & Practice. 400p. (Orig.). 1987. pap. 17.95 (ISBN 0-935372-19-9). Pope John Ctr.

Griesinger, Theodor. The Jesuits: A Complete History of Their Open & Secret Proceedings, 2 vols. 1977. Set. lib. bdg. 200.00 (ISBN 0-8490-2092-1). Gordon Pr.

Griffen, William B. Indian Assimilation in the Franciscan Area of Nueva Vizcaya. LC 78-14546. (Anthropological Papers: No. 33). 122p. 1979. pap. 10.95x (ISBN 0-8165-0584-5). U of Ariz Pr.

Griffhorn, Thelma. Things for Kids to Do. 132p. 1985. pap. 6.95 (ISBN 0-89693-525-6). Victor Bks.

Griffin, Bobby. The Search. pap. 1.75 (ISBN 0-686-12739-0). Grace Pub Co.

Griffin, Bryan F. Panic among the Phillistines. (Christian Activist Ser.). 259p. 1985. pap. 5.95 (ISBN 0-89526-817-5). Regnery Bks.

Griffin, David R., jt. auth. see Cobb, John B., Jr.

Griffin, Edward M. Jonathan Edwards. (Pamphlets on American Writers Ser: No. 97). (Orig.). 1971. pap. 1.25x (ISBN 0-8166-0601-3, MPAW97). U of Minn Pr.

Griffin, Em. Making Friends & Making Them Count. LC 87-2619. (Illus.). 220p. (Orig.). 1987. pap. 7.95 (ISBN 0-87784-996-X). Inter-Varsity.

--The Mind Changers. 1976. pap. 7.95 (ISBN 0-8423-4290-7). Tyndale.

Griffin, Emilie. Clinging: The Experience of Prayer. LC 83-48989. 96p. 1984. 11.95 (ISBN 0-06-063461-8); 11.45i. Har-Row.

--Turning: Reflections on the Experience of Conversion. LC 79-6652. 224p. 1982. 8.95 (ISBN 0-385-15823-8, Im); pap. 4.50 (ISBN 0-385-17892-1). Doubleday.

Griffin, Frances. Old Salem in Pictures. (Illus.). 64p. 1986. pap. 5.95 (ISBN 0-914875-10-8). Bright Mtn Bks.

Griffin, Gayle. Food for Temple & Table. 1981. spiral bdg. 9.95 (ISBN 0-89323-018-9). Bible Memory.

Griffin, Graeme M., ed. Bereavement. (Illus.). 59p. (Orig.). 1977. pap. 5.95 (ISBN 0-85819-314-0, Pub. by JBCE). ANZ Religious Pubns.

Griffin, Henry E., Jr. Brethern, I Would Not Have You Ignorant. 64p. (Orig.). 1986. pap. 2.25 (ISBN 0-934942-63-3, 2262). White Wing Pub.

Griffin, Henry W. Jesus for Children. (Illus.). 132p. 1985. 12.95 (HarpR); pap. 4.95 (ISBN 0-86683-866-X). Har-Row.

Griffin, James A. The Priestly Heart. LC 83-26611. 149p. (Orig.). 1984. pap. 6.95 (ISBN 0-8189-0460-7). Alba.

--Sackcloth & Ashes: Liturgical Reflections for Lenten Weekdays. LC 74-44463. 1976. pap. 4.00 (ISBN 0-8189-0336-8). Alba.

Griffin, John H. The Hermitage Journals. LC 82-45833. (Illus.). 240p. 1983. pap. 6.95 (ISBN 0-385-18470-0, Im). Doubleday.

Griffin, John H. & Simon, Yves R. Jacques Maritain: Homage in Words & Pictures. LC 73-85056. (Illus.). 1974. 12.95x (ISBN 0-87343-046-8). Magi Bks.

Griffin, John R. John Keble, Saint of Anglicanism. 128p. 1987. 24.95 (ISBN 0-86554-249-X). Mercer Univ Pr.

Griffin, Joseph A. The Contribution of Belgium to the Catholic Church in America (1523-1857) LC 73-3568. (Catholic University of America. Studies in American Church History: No. 13). Repr. of 1932 ed. 28.00 (ISBN 0-404-57763-6). AMS Pr.

Griffin, Kathryn. Teaching Teens the Truth. LC 78-58567. 1978. pap. 4.95 (ISBN 0-8054-3425-9, 4234-25). Broadman.

Griffin, LaDean. Escape the Drug Scene. pap. 3.95 (ISBN 0-89036-141-X). Hawkes Pub Inc.

Griffin, Michael D., tr. from Span. Lingering with my Lord: Post-Communion Experiences of St. Teresa of Avila. LC 84-18590. Orig. Title: Obras Completas de Teresa de Jesus Doctora de la Iglesia. 79p. 1985. pap. 3.95 (ISBN 0-317-19366-X). Alba.

Griffin, Neil, jt. auth. see Flint, Tommy.

Griffin, Nigel. Jesuit School Drama: Critical Literature. (Research Bibliographies & Checklists Ser.: 12). 54p. 1976. pap. 6.50 (ISBN 0-7293-0003-X, Pub. by Grant & Cutler). Longwood Pub Group.

Griffin, Paul R. Black Theology As the Foundation of Three Methodist Colleges: The Educational Views & Labors of Daniel Payne, Joseph Price, Isaac Lane. LC 84-13070. 148p. (Orig.). 1984. lib. bdg. 20.75 (ISBN 0-8191-4160-7); pap. text ed. 9.50 (ISBN 0-8191-4161-5). U Pr of Amer.

Griffin, Robert. I Never Said I Didn't Love You. LC 76-24442. (Emmuas Book Ser.). 128p. 1977. pap. 2.95 (ISBN 0-8091-1989-7). Paulist Pr.

Griffin, Robert F. The Continuing Conversation. LC 85-80352. 200p. (Orig.). 1985. pap. 7.50 (ISBN 0-87973-828-6, 828). Our Sunday Visitor.

Griffin, Robert P. John Webster: Politics & Tragedy. Hogg, James, ed. (Jacobean Drama Studies). 179p. (Orig.). 1972. pap. 15.00 (ISBN 3-7052-0311-8, Pub. by Salzburg Studies). Longwood Pub Group.

Griffin, Steve. Children's Guitar Hymnal. 32p. 1978. wkbk 1.95 (ISBN 0-89228-052-2). Impact Bks MO.

Griffin, Ted, ed. see Stafford, Bill.

Griffis, William E. Religions of Japan: From the Dawn of History to the Era of Meiji. facsimile ed. LC 70-37469. (Essay Index Reprint Ser). Repr. of 1895 ed. 21.00 (ISBN 0-8369-2550-5). Ayer Co Pubs.

Griffiss, James, ed. see Edwards, O. C., et al.

Griffiss, James E. Church, Ministry & Unity: A Divine Commission. 118p. 1984. 24.95x (ISBN 0-631-13185-X); pap. 8.95x (ISBN 0-631-13227-9). Basil Blackwell.

--A Silent Path to God. LC 79-8903. pap. 27.50 (2029620). Bks Demand UMI.

Griffith, Anna. Balance: A Modern Christian Challenge. pap. 4.95 (ISBN 0-89137-425-6). Quality Pubns.

Griffith, Carol F., ed. Christianity & Politics: Catholic & Protestant Perspectives. LC 81-19412. 124p. 1981. pap. 6.00 (ISBN 0-89633-050-8). Ethics & Public Policy.

Griffith, Earle G. The Pastor As God's Minister. LC 76-50694. 1978. 7.95 (ISBN 0-87227-054-8). Reg Baptist.

Griffith, Elisabeth. In Her Own Right: The Life of Elizabeth Cady Stanton. LC 83-25120. (Illus.). 1984. 19.95 (ISBN 0-19-503440-6). Oxford U Pr.

Griffith, Gwilym O. Interpreters of Reality: Lao-Tse, Heraclitus & the Christian Faith. 1977. lib. bdg. 59.95 (ISBN 0-8490-2065-4). Gordon Pr.

--John Bunyan. 1973. Repr. of 1927 ed. lib. bdg. 20.00 (ISBN 0-8414-4623-7). Folcroft.

Griffith, Harry C. The Ways of God: Paths into the New Testament. 149p. 1986. pap. 7.95 (ISBN 0-8192-1377-2). Morehouse.

Griffith, Leonard. Take Hold of the Treasure. 128p. 1983. pap. 5.95 (ISBN 0-8170-0997-3). Judson.

Griffith, Nancy S. & Person, Laura. Albert Schweitzer: An International Bibliography. 1981. lib. bdg. 47.00 (ISBN 0-8161-8531-X, Hall Reference). G K Hall.

Griffith, R. T. The Hymns of the Rigveda. rev. ed. 1976. 39.95 (ISBN 0-8426-0592-4). Orient Bk Dist.

Griffith, Ralph T., tr. from Sanskrit. Sam-Veda Sanhita. 338p. 1978. Repr. of 1907 ed. 22.00 (ISBN 0-89684-160-X). Orient Bk Dist.

Griffiths, A. Philips, ed. Knowledge & Belief. 1967. pap. 9.95x (ISBN 0-19-875003-X). Oxford U Pr.

Griffiths, Bede. Christ in India. pap. 8.95 (ISBN 0-87243-134-7). Templegate.

--The Cosmic Revelation: The Hindu Way to God. 128p. 1983. pap. 7.95 (ISBN 0-87243-119-3). Templegate.

--Return to the Center. 1976. pap. 7.95 (ISBN 0-87243-112-6). Templegate.

--River of Compassion. (Wellspring Bk.). 224p. (Orig.). pap. 11.95 (ISBN 0-916349-08-X). Amity Hous Inc.

--Vedanta & Christian Faith. LC 73-88179. 85p. 1973. pap. 3.95 (ISBN 0-913922-04-8). Dawn Horse Pr.

Griffiths, Brian. The Creation of Wealth. LC 85-5210. 160p. 1985. pap. 6.95 (ISBN 0-87784-566-2). Inter-Varsity.

Griffiths, J. G. The Conflict of Horus & Seth - A study in Ancient Mythology from Egyptian & Classical Sources. 194p. 1960. text ed. 19.95x (ISBN 0-85323-071-4, Pub. by Liverpool U Pr). Humanities.

Griffiths, John, ed. A Letter of Private Direction. LC 81-126. (The Spiritual Classics Ser.). 176p. 1981. 9.95 (ISBN 0-8245-0081-4). Crossroad NY.

--The Mirror of Simple Souls. LC 81-126. (The Spiritual Classics Ser.). 176p. 1981. 9.95 (ISBN 0-8245-0083-0). Crossroad NY.

Griffiths, John, ed. see John Of Landsburg.

Griffiths, John, ed. see Kempe, Margery, et al.

Griffiths, John, ed. see Rahner, Karl.

Griffiths, Michael. Encouraging New Christians. pap. 0.75 (ISBN 0-87784-106-3). Inter-Varsity.

--The Example of Jesus. LC 84-6739. (The Jesus Library). 180p. 1985. pap. 6.95 (ISBN 0-87784-929-3). Inter-Varsity.

--Get Your Church Involved in Missions. 1972. pap. 1.00 (ISBN 9971-83-784-6). OMF Bks.

--God Is Great, God Is Good: I'd Believe Him If I Could. LC 86-62368. Orig. Title: Down to Earth God. 170p. 1987. pap. 4.50 (ISBN 0-89109-468-7). NavPress.

--God's Forgetful Pilgrims: Recalling the Church to Its Reason for Being. LC 75-16166. Repr. of 1975 ed. 44.00 (2027545). Bks Demand UMI.

--What on Earth Are You Doing? 1983. pap. 4.95 (ISBN 0-8010-3792-1). Baker Bk.

Grigg, Richard. Symbol & Empowerment: Paul Tillich's Post-Theistic System. xvi, 148p. 1985. text ed. 14.50 (ISBN 0-86554-163-9, MUP H153). Mercer Univ Pr.

Griggs, Donald & Griggs, Patricia. Teaching & Celebrating Advent. rev. ed. (Griggs Educational Resources Ser.). (Illus.). 1980. pap. 6.95 (ISBN 0-687-41080-0). Abingdon.

Griggs, Donald, jt. auth. see Griggs, Patricia.

Griggs, Donald L. Basic Skills for Church Teachers. (Griggs Educational Resources Ser.). 112p. 1985. pap. 7.95 (ISBN 0-687-02488-9). Abingdon.

--Planning for Teaching Church School. LC 85-12588. 64p. 1985. pap. 5.95 (ISBN 0-8170-1079-3). Judson.

--Teaching Teachers to Teach: A Basic Manual for Church Teachers. (Griggs Educational Resources Ser.). 1983. pap. 7.95 (ISBN 0-687-41120-3). Abingdon.

--Twenty New Ways of Teaching the Bible. (Griggs Educational Resources Ser.). 1979. pap. 7.25 (ISBN 0-687-42740-1). Abingdon.

Griggs, Patricia. Creative Activities in Church Education. (Griggs Educational Resources Ser.). 1980. pap. 6.95 (ISBN 0-687-09812-2). Abingdon.

--Opening the Bible with Children: Beginning Bible Skills. 64p. (Orig.). 1986. pap. 7.50 (ISBN 0-687-29210-7). Abingdon.

Griggs, Patricia & Griggs, Donald. Teaching & Celebrating Lent-Easter. (Griggs Educational Resources Ser.). 1980. pap. 6.95 (ISBN 0-687-41081-9). Abingdon.

Griggs, Patricia, jt. auth. see Griggs, Donald.

Griggs, Patricia, jt. auth. see Williams, Doris.

Griggs, Patricia R. Using Storytelling in Christian Education. LC 80-26468. 64p. (Orig.). 1981. pap. 7.25 (ISBN 0-687-43117-4). Abingdon.

Grigor, Jean C. Grow to Love. 1977. pap. 5.75x (ISBN 0-7152-0437-8). Outlook.

Grigsby, Daryl R. Reflections on Liberation. LC 84-72421. (Illus.). 176p. (Orig.). 1985. pap. 5.95 (ISBN 0-9614210-0-2). Asante Pubns.

Grigulevich, I. Historia de la Inquisicion. (Span.). 414p. 1980. 8.95 (ISBN 0-8285-1813-0, Pub. by Progress Pubs USSR). Imported Pubns.

--Papado Siglo XX. 354p. 1982. 5.95 (ISBN 0-8285-2323-1, Pub. by Progress Pubs USSR). Imported Pubns.

Grijalva, Josue, tr. see Sisemore, J. T.

Grillmeier, Aloys. Christ in Christian Tradition: From the Apostolic Age to Chalcedon, Vol. 1. rev. ed. Bowden, John S., tr. from Ger. LC 75-13456. 451p. 1975. 29.95 (ISBN 0-8042-0492-6). John Knox.

--Christ in the Christian Tradition, Vol. 2, Pt. 1. Allen, Pauline & Cawte, John, trs. 1987. 34.95 (ISBN 0-8042-0493-4). John Knox.

Grim, John. Reflections on Shamanism: The Tribal Healer & the Technological Trance. (Teilhard Studies: No. 6). 20p. (Orig.). 1981. pap. 2.00 (ISBN 0-89012-029-3). Anima Pubns.

Grim, John A. The Shaman: Patterns of Siberian & Ojibway Healing. LC 83-47834. (Civilization of the American Indian Ser.: Vol. 165). (Illus.). 264p. 1983. pap. 19.95 (ISBN 0-8061-1809-1). U of Okla Pr.

Grimal, Pierre. The Dictionary of Classical Mythology. 580p. 1985. 34.95x (ISBN 0-631-13209-0). Basil Blackwell.

--Dictionnaire de la Mythologie Grecque et Romaine. 5th ed. (Fr.). 612p. 1969. 59.95 (ISBN 0-686-57316-1, M-6299). French & Eur.

Grimaldi, Nuzzo, jt. auth. see Lorit, Sergius C.

Grimbol, William. The Darkest Day. 1986. 1.75 (ISBN 0-89536-789-0, 6807). CSS of Ohio.

--Passion Paths. Sherer, Michael L., ed. (Orig.). 1987. pap. 3.95 (ISBN 0-89536-842-0, 7801). CSS of Ohio.

--Perspectives on the Passion. 1984. 5.95 (ISBN 0-89536-665-7, 1645). CSS of Ohio.

Grimbol, William R. The Communion Clown Circle. 1985. 3.25 (ISBN 0-89536-734-3, 5818). CSS of Ohio.

Grimes, Bobbie M. The Parable of Jesus & Santa. LC 84-90331. (Illus.). 40p. 1984. 14.95 (ISBN 0-9613328-0-8). B & D Pub.

Grimes, Ronald L. Beginnings in Ritual Studies. LC 81-40521. 312p. (Orig.). 1982. lib. bdg. 32.00 (ISBN 0-8191-2210-6); pap. text ed. 14.00 (ISBN 0-8191-2211-4). U Pr of Amer.

--Research in Ritual Studies: A Programmatic Essay & Bibliography. LC 84-23474. (ATLA Bibliography Ser.: No. 14). 177p. 1985. 15.00 (ISBN 0-8108-1762-4). Scarecrow.

Grimke, Angelina E. Appeal to the Christian Women of the South. LC 77-82195. (Anti-Slavery Crusade in America Ser). 1969. Repr. of 1836 ed. 9.50 (ISBN 0-405-00635-7). Ayer Co Pubs.

Grimke, Thomas S. Address on the Truth, Dignity, Power & Beauty of the Principles of Peace, & on the Unchristian Character & Influence of War & the Warrior. LC 72-137542. (Peace Movement in America Ser). 56p. 1972. Repr. of 1832 ed. lib. bdg. 11.95x (ISBN 0-89198-070-9). Ozer.

Grimley, Mildred H. Mattie Loves All. (Illus.). 22p. 1985. 5.95 (ISBN 0-87178-552-8). Brethren.

Grimm, G. Doctrine of the Buddha. 2nd ed. 1984. Repr. 32.00 (ISBN 0-8426-0489-8). Orient Bk Dist.

Grimm, George. Buddhist Wisdom: The Mystery of the Self. 2nd, rev. ed. Keller-Grimm, M., ed. Aikins, Carrol, tr. from Ger. 1982. 11.50 (ISBN 0-89684-041-7, Pub. by Motilal Banarsidass India). Orient Bk Dist.

Grimm, H. Life of Michaelangelo, 2 vols. 200.00 (ISBN 0-8490-0533-7). Gordon Pr.

Grimm, Hans. Tradition & History of the Early Churches of Christ in Central Europe. pap. 1.00 (ISBN 0-88027-095-0). Firm Foun Pub.

Grimm, Harold J. Lazarus Spengler: A Lay Leader of the Reformation. LC 78-13508. (Illus.). 249p. 1979. 22.50x (ISBN 0-8142-0290-X). Ohio St U Pr.

--The Reformation. LC 72-76717. (AHA Pamphlets: No. 403). 1972. pap. text ed. 1.50 (ISBN 0-87229-003-4). Am Hist Assn.

--The Reformation Era: 1500-1650. 2nd ed. (Illus.). 700p. 1973. text ed. write for info. (ISBN 0-02-347270-7, 34727). Macmillan.

Grimm, Harold J. & Lehmann, Helmut T., eds. Luther's Works: Career of the Reformer I, Vol. 31. LC 55-9893. 1957. 19.95 (ISBN 0-8006-0331-1, 1-331). Fortress.

Grimm, Harold J., ed. see Luther, Martin.

Grimm, Herman F. Life of Michael Angelo, 2 Vols. Bunnett, Fanny E., tr. Repr. of 1900 ed. Set. lib. bdg. 48.00x (ISBN 0-8371-2750-5, GRMA). Greenwood.

--Life of Michael Angelo, 2 Vols. 45.00x (ISBN 0-403-00399-7). Scholarly.

Grimm, Jacob & Grimm, Wilhelm K. Lucky Hans. LC 86-2520. (Illus.). 32p. 1986. 12.45 (ISBN 0-8050-0009-7, North South Bks). H Holt & Co.

Grimm, Werner, tr. see Althoff, Karl F.

Grimm, Wilhelm K., jt. auth. see Grimm, Jacob.

Grimme, Hubert. Israelitische Pfingstfest und der Plejadenkult. 1907. pap. 12.00 (ISBN 0-384-20060-5). Johnson Repr.

--Texte und Untersuchungen Zur Safatenisch - Arabischen Religion. 1929. pap. 15.00 (ISBN 0-384-20070-2). Johnson Repr.

Grimshaw, William H. Official History of Free Masonry among the Colored People in North America. LC 74-91257. (Illus.). Repr. of 1903 ed. 22.50x (ISBN 0-8371-2051-9, GRF&, Pub. by Negro U Pr). Greenwood.

--Official History of Freemasonry among the Colored People in North America. facs. ed. LC 74-157370. (Black Heritage Library Collection). 1903. 22.50 (ISBN 0-8369-8808-6). Ayer Co Pubs.

Grimsley, R. W. The Church That Jesus Built. 1969. pap. 2.75 (ISBN 0-88027-031-4). Firm Foun Pub.

Grimsrud, Ted. Triumph of the Lamb. LC 87-409. 192p. (Orig.). 1987. pap. 14.95 (ISBN 0-8361-3438-9). Herald Pr.

Grimstad, William. Antizion: The Jewish & Zionist Question Through the Ages. 1982. lib. bdg. 69.95 (ISBN 0-686-97529-4). Revisionist Pr.

Grimstad, William, compiled by. Antizion. 2nd rev. ed. 1980. pap. 6.00 (ISBN 0-911038-20-5). Noontide.

Grimstad, William N., ed. see Truth in History Committee.

Grimstone, A. V., ed. Two Zen Classics: Mumonkan & Hekiganroku. Sekida, Katsuki, tr. from Chinese. LC 77-2398. 1977. 13.50 (ISBN 0-8348-0131-0); pap. 8.95 (ISBN 0-8348-0130-2). Weatherhill.

Grimstone, A. V., ed. see Sekida, Katsuki.

Grindal, Harald. Telecare Ministry: Using the Telephone in a Care Ministry. 40p. 1984. pap. 3.95 (ISBN 0-8066-2099-4, 23-1899). Augsburg.

Grindall, Irene V. Teaching Gifts. LC 85-71784. 64p. (Orig.). 1985. pap. 3.50 (ISBN 0-88177-020-5, DR020B). Discipleship Res.

Grindel, John. Joshua, Judges. (Bible Commentary Ser.). 120p. 1985. pap. 2.95 (ISBN 0-8146-1414-0). Liturgical Pr.

Grindel, John A. First Book of Chronicles. (Bible Ser.: No. 17). (Orig.). 1974. pap. 1.00 (ISBN 0-8091-5170-7). Paulist Pr.

--Second Book of Chronicles. (Bible Ser.: Vol. 18). (Orig.). 1974. pap. 1.00 (ISBN 0-8091-5171-5). Paulist Pr.

Grinnell, Isabel H. Greek Temples. LC 79-168420. (Metropolitan Museum of Art Publications in Reprint Ser.). (Illus.). 138p. 1972. Repr. of 1943 ed. 35.50 (ISBN 0-405-02258-1). Ayer Co Pubs.

Grinspoon, Lester, ed. & intro. by. The Long Darkness: Psychological & Moral Perspectives on Nuclear Winter. LC 85-40986. 224p. 1986. text ed. 25.00 (ISBN 0-300-03663-9); pap. 7.95 (ISBN 0-300-03664-7, YF-31). Yale U Pr.

Grinstead, Wayne. The Ross Hannas: Living, Laughing, Loving. LC 86-6807. (Meet the Missionary Ser.). 1986. 5.50 (ISBN 0-8054-4325-8). Broadman.

Grinstein, Hyman. A Short History of the Jews in the United States. 208p. 1980. 20.00 (ISBN 0-900689-50-1). Soncino Pr.

Gripkey, Sr. M. Vincentine. Blessed Virgin Mary As Mediatrix in the Latin & Old French Legend Prior to the Fourteenth Century. LC 72-94166. (Catholic University of America Studies in Romance Languages & Literatures Ser: No. 17). 1969. Repr. of 1938 ed. 26.00 (ISBN 0-404-50317-9). Ams Pr.

Gripper, Clinton. Words of Inspiration. 32p. 1987. 5.95 (ISBN 0-89962-569-X). Todd & Honeywell.

Grisar, Hartmann. History of Rome & the Popes in the Middle Ages, 3 vols. LC 70-154115. Tr. of Geschichte Roms und der Papste Immittelater. (Illus.). Repr. of 1912 ed. Set. 120.00 (ISBN 0-404-09370-1). AMS Pr.

--Martin Luther: His Life & Work. Preuss, Arthur, ed. LC 71-137235. Repr. of 1930 ed. 29.50 (ISBN 0-404-02935-3). AMS Pr.

Grisbrooke, Jardine W., ed. Spiritual Counsels of Father John of Kronstadt: Select Passages from "My Life in Christ". 256p. 1983. pap. 10.95 (ISBN 0-227-67856-7, Pub. by J Clarke UK). Attic Pr.

Grisbrooke, W. Jardine. The Spiritual Counsels of Father John of Kronstadt. 230p. (Orig.). 1982. pap. 8.95 (ISBN 0-913836-92-3). St Vladimirs.

Grisell, R. Sufism. 120p. 1983. pap. 4.95 (ISBN 0-89496-038-5). Ross Bks.

Grisez, Germain. Beyond the New Theism: A Philosophy of Religion. LC 74-27885. 444p. 1975. text ed. 22.95x (ISBN 0-268-00567-2); pap. text ed. 8.95x (ISBN 0-268-00568-0). U of Notre Dame Pr.

Grisez, Germain & Shaw, Russell. Beyond the New Morality: The Responsibilities of Freedom. rev. ed. LC 80-18293. 240p. 1980. text ed. 14.95 (ISBN 0-268-00663-6); pap. 6.95 (ISBN 0-268-00665-2). U of Notre Dame Pr.

--A Grisez Reader for Beyond the New Morality. Casey, Joseph H., ed. LC 81-43481. 218p. (Orig.). 1982. lib. bdg. 29.00 (ISBN 0-8191-2243-2); pap. text ed. 11.50 (ISBN 0-8191-2244-0). U Pr of Amer.

Grishaver, Joel L. Being Torah. LC 85-50219. (Illus.). 224p. (Orig.). 1985. pap. text ed. 7.95 (ISBN 0-933873-00-X). Torah Aura.

--Being Torah Student Commentary, 2 Vols. (Illus.). 72p. (Orig.). 1986. pap. text ed. 3.25 ea. Vol. 1 (ISBN 0-933873-09-3). Vol. 2 (ISBN 0-933873-10-7). Torah Aura.

--Torah Toons I. (Illus.). 115p. (Orig.). 1985. pap. text ed. 5.50 (ISBN 0-933873-01-8). Torah Aura.

--Torah Toons II. (Illus.). 114p. (Orig.). 1985. pap. text ed. 5.50 (ISBN 0-933873-02-6). Torah Aura.

Grissen, Lillian V. & Spykman, Gordon J. Men & Women: Partners in Service. 100p. (Orig.). 1981. pap. text ed. 4.50 (ISBN 0-933140-36-3). CRC Pubns.

Grissom, Mary A. Negro Sings a New Heaven. LC 70-168209. Repr. of 1930 ed. 11.50 (ISBN 0-404-08311-0). AMS Pr.

Griswold, Charles L., Jr. Self-Knowledge in Plato's Phaedrus. LC 86-5506. 328p. 1986. text ed. 29.50x (ISBN 0-300-03594-2). Yale U Pr.

Griswold, H. D. Religion of the Rigveda. 1971. 8.50 (ISBN 0-89684-305-X). Orient Bk Dist.

Griswold, Roland. The Winning Church. 144p. 1986. pap. 4.95 (ISBN 0-89693-527-2). Victor Bks.

Gritsch, E., tr. see Fries, Heinrich & Rahner, Karl.

Gritsch, Eric W. Born Againism: Perspectives on a Movement. LC 81-70595. 112p. 1982. pap. 6.95 (ISBN 0-8006-1625-1, 1-1625). Fortress.

--Martin - God's Court Jester: Luther in Retrospect. LC 83-48004. 304p. 1983. pap. 15.95 (ISBN 0-8006-1753-3, 1-1753). Fortress.

Gritsch, Eric W. & Jenson, Robert W. Lutheranism: The Theological Movement & Its Confessional Writings. LC 76-7869. 228p. 1976. pap. 8.95 (ISBN 0-8006-1246-9, 1-1246). Fortress.

Gritsch, Eric W., jt. auth. see Bainton, Roland H.

Gritsch, Eric W. & Lehmann, Helmut T., eds. Luther's Works: Church & Ministry I, Vol. 39. LC 55-9893. 1970. 19.95 (ISBN 0-8006-0339-7, 1-339). Fortress.

Gritsch, Eric W., ed. see Haendler, Gert.

Gritsch, Eric W., jt. ed. see Lehmann, Helmut T.

Gritsch, R., tr. see Fries, Heinrich & Rahner, Karl.

Gritsch, Ruth, tr. see Moltmann-Wendel, Elizabeth.

Gritsch, Ruth C., tr. see Gabler, Ulrich.

Gritsch, Ruth C., tr. see Haendler, Gert.

Gritter, George. Communion Mediations. 80p. 1984. pap. 5.95 (ISBN 0-8010-3805-7). Baker Bk.

--When God Was at Calvary: Messages on the Seven Words. (Pocket Pulpit Library). 144p. 1982. pap. 3.50 (ISBN 0-8010-3785-9). Baker Bk.

Grob, Gerald, jt. auth. see Monk, Maria.

Grob, Gerald, ed. Anti-Catholicism in America, 1841-1851. Three Sermons: An Original Anthology. (Anti-Movements in America Ser.). 1977. Repr. of 1977 ed. lib. bdg. 17.00x (ISBN 0-405-09980-0). Ayer Co Pubs.

--A Course of Lectures on the Jews: By Ministers of the Established Church in Glasgow. LC 76-46095. (Anti-Movements in America). 1977. lib. bdg. 37.50x (ISBN 0-405-09968-1). Ayer Co Pubs.

--Pope, or President? Startling Disclosures of Romanism As Revealed by Its Own Writers: Facts for Americans. LC 76-46094. (Anti-Movements in America). 1977. lib. bdg. 27.50x (ISBN 0-405-09967-3). Ayer Co Pubs.

Grob, Gerald, ed. see Beecher, Lyman.

Grob, Gerald, ed. see Evans, Hiram W.

Grob, Gerald, ed. see Hendrick, Burton J.

Grob, Gerald, ed. see King, James M.

Grob, Gerald, ed. see Murray, Nicholas.

Grob, Gerald, ed. see Nevins, William.

Grob, Gerald, ed. see Timayenis, Telemachus T.

Grob, Leonard, jt. ed. see Gordon, Haim.

Grobel, Kendrick, tr. The Gospel of Truth. LC 78-63167. (Heresies of the Early Christian & Medieval Era: Second Ser.). Repr. of 1960 ed. 26.00. AMS Pr.

Grobman, Alex, ed. Simon Wiesenthal Center Annual, Vol. 1. (Illus.). 256p. 1984. text ed. 17.95x (ISBN 0-940646-30-7). Rossel Bks.

Grobman, Alex, et al, eds. Genocide: Critical Issues of the Holocaust. LC 83-3052. (Illus.). 502p. 1983. 19.95 (ISBN 0-940646-04-8, Co-pub. by Simon Wiesenthal Center); pap. 12.95 (ISBN 0-940646-38-2). Rossel Bks.

--Genocide: Critical Issues of the Holocaust. 1986. pap. 12.95 (ISBN 0-317-42656-7). Shapolsky Pubs.

Grocott, Allan M. Convicts, Clergymen & Churches. 356p. 1980. 38.00x (ISBN 0-424-00072-5, Pub. by Sydney U Pr Australia). Intl Spec Bk.

Grodecki, Louis & Brisac, Catherine. Gothic Stained Glass: 1200-1300. Boehm, Barbara D., tr. from Fr. LC 85-71277. (Illus.). 288p. 1985. text ed. 75.00x (ISBN 0-8014-1809-7). Cornell U Pr.

Grodon, R., ed. Yiddish Literature, 10 Vols, Series I. 1986. lib. bdg. 975.95 (ISBN 0-8490-3856-1). Gordon Pr.

Groen, Jim, jt. auth. see Hensley, Dennis E.

Groenhoff, Edwin. Care & Concern of the Churches. LC 81-69760. (Heritage Ser.: Vol. 8). 1984. 8.95 (ISBN 0-911802-59-2). Free Church Pubns.

Groenhoff, Edwin L. It's Your Choice. 1975. pap. 1.75 (ISBN 0-911802-38-X). Free Church Pubns.

Groeschel, Benedict J. The Courage to Be Chaste. 128p. (Orig.). 1985. pap. 4.95 (ISBN 0-8091-2705-9). Paulist Pr.

--Listening at Prayer. 80p. (Orig.). 1984. 4.95 (ISBN 0-8091-2582-X). Paulist Pr.

--Spiritual Passages. LC 82-17139. 176p. 1983. 12.95 (ISBN 0-8245-0497-6). Crossroad NY.

Grof, Christina, jt. auth. see Grof, Stanislav.

Grof, Stanislav. East & West: Ancient Wisdom & Modern Science. (Broadside Ser.). 30p. 1985. pap. 2.95 (ISBN 0-931191-00-9). Rob Briggs.

Grof, Stanislav & Grof, Christina. Beyond Death: The Gates of Consiousness. (Art & Imagination Ser.). (Illus.). 1980. pap. 10.95 (ISBN 0-500-81019-2). Thames Hudson.

Grof, Stanislav, ed. Ancient Wisdom & Modern Science. 360p. 1984. 39.50 (ISBN 0-87395-848-9); pap. 12.95x (ISBN 0-87395-849-7). State U NY Pr.

Groff, Cora M. Crown of Jewels. 144p. 1985. pap. 6.00 (ISBN 0-682-40210-9). Exposition Pr FL.

Groff, Warren F. God's Story-& Ours! 148p. (Orig.). 1986. pap. 7.95 (ISBN 0-317-52618-9). Brethren.

--Prayer: God's Time & Ours! 144p. (Orig.). 1984. pap. 6.95 (ISBN 0-87178-714-8). Brethren.

Grogan, Geoffrey W. What the Bible Teaches about Jesus. 1979. pap. 3.95 (ISBN 0-8423-7884-7). Tyndale.

Grogg, Evelyn. Bible Lessons for Little People: Revised with Learning Centers. rev. ed. Eberle, Sarah, rev. by. LC 80-53878. 144p. 1981. pap. 7.95 (ISBN 0-87239-430-1, 3368). Standard Pub.

Groh, Dennis E. In Between Advents: Biblical & Spiritual Arrivals. LC 86-45199. (The Bible for Christian Life Ser.). 64p. 1986. pap. 3.95 (ISBN 0-8006-2025-9). Fortress.

Groh, Dennis E., jt. auth. see Gregg, Robert C.

Groh, Dennis E. & Jewett, Robert, eds. The Living Text: Essays in Honor of Ernest W. Saunders. (Illus.). 272p. (Orig.). 1985. lib. bdg. 27.50 (ISBN 0-8191-4584-X); pap. text ed. 14.25 (ISBN 0-8191-4585-8). U Pr of Amer.

Groh, John E. & Smith, Robert H., eds. The Lutheran Church in North American Life: 1776-1976, 1580-1980. LC 78-71233. 1979. 5.95 (ISBN 0-915644-17-7, Clayton). Luth Acad.

Grollenberg, Luc H. The Penguin Shorter Atlas of the Bible. Hedlund, Mary F., tr. (Reference Ser). (Illus.). 1978. pap. 7.95 (ISBN 0-14-051056-7). Penguin.

Grollenberg, Lucas. Paul. Bowden, John, tr. LC 78-14372. 186p. 1979. pap. 4.50 (ISBN 0-664-24234-0). Westminster.

Grollman, Earl A. Living When a Loved One Has Died. LC 76-48508. (Illus.). 1977. pap. 6.95 (ISBN 0-8070-2741-3, BP560). Beacon Pr.

--Time Remembered: A Journal for Survivors. LC 86-47753. 98p. 1987. 10.00 (ISBN 0-8070-2704-9). Beacon Pr.

Grollman, Earl A., ed. Concerning Death: A Practical Guide for the Living. LC 73-17117. 384p. 1974. pap. 9.95 (ISBN 0-8070-2765-0, BP484). Beacon Pr.

--Explaining Death to Children. LC 67-4891. 1969. pap. 8.95 (ISBN 0-8070-2385-X, BP317). Beacon Pr.

--What Helped Me When My Loved One Died. LC 80-68166. 168p. 1982. pap. 7.95 (ISBN 0-8070-3229-8, BP 626). Beacon Pr.

Gromacki, Robert G. Are These the Last Days? LC 75-42165. 1975. pap. 3.50 (ISBN 0-87227-019-X). Reg Baptist.

--Called to Be Saints. 1977. pap. 5.95 (ISBN 0-87227-014-9). Reg Baptist.

--Called to Be Saints (I Corinthians) 1977. pap. 5.95 (ISBN 0-8010-3715-8). Baker Bk.

--Modern Tongues Movement. pap. 4.95 (ISBN 0-8010-3708-5). Baker Bk.

--Modern Tongues Movement. 1967. pap. 4.95 (ISBN 0-87552-304-8). Presby & Reformed.

--New Testament Survey. 16.95 (ISBN 0-8010-3677-1). Baker Bk.

--New Testament Survey. LC 74-83793. 1974. 9.95 (ISBN 0-87227-018-1). Reg Baptist.

--Stand Perfect in Wisdom: Colossians & Ephesians. 1981. pap. 5.95 (ISBN 0-8010-3767-0). Baker Bk.

--The Virgin Birth of Christ. 200p. 1981. pap. 5.95 (ISBN 0-8010-3765-4). Baker Bk.

Gronbech, Vilhelm. Religious Currents in the Nineteenth Century. Mitchell, P. M. & Paden, W. D., trs. from Danish. LC 72-11829. (Arcturus Bks. Paperbacks). 206p. 1973. lib. bdg. 7.00x (ISBN 0-8093-0629-8); pap. 2.45x (ISBN 0-8093-0630-1). S Ill U Pr.

Grondahl, Calvin. Freeway to Perfection: A Collection of Mormon Cartoons. (Illus.). 96p. (Orig.). 1980. pap. 4.50 (ISBN 0-9606760-1-5). Sunstone Found.

Groner, Judyth S. & Wikler, Madeline. My Very Own Jewish Community. LC 83-22215. (Illus.). 40p. 1984. pap. 4.95 (ISBN 0-930494-32-6). Kar Ben.

Gronlund, Laurence. Our Destiny: The Influence of Socialism on Morals & Religion; an Essay on Ethics. LC 75-321. (The Radical Tradition in America Ser.). 170p. 1975. Repr. of 1890 ed. 19.25 (ISBN 0-88355-225-6). Hyperion Conn.

Groom, Bernard. On the Diction of Tennyson, Browning & Arnold. LC 79-138975. 57p. 1970. Repr. of 1939 ed. 14.50 (ISBN 0-208-01027-0, Archon). Shoe String.

Groom, Olive. Yasmin Meets a Yak. 1973. pap. 1.95 (ISBN 0-87508-806-6). Chr Lit.

Groome, Thomas H. Christian Religious Education: Sharing Our Story & Vision. LC 81-47847. 320p. 1982. pap. text ed. 12.95 (ISBN 0-06-063494-4, RD 371, HarpR). Harper Row.

Groomer, Vera. Good Friends Again: Two - Three. (Come Unto Me Ser.: Year 2, Bk. 3). 32p. 1980. pap. 1.65 (ISBN 0-8127-0272-7). Review & Herald.

--Growing Stronger: Two - Two. (Come Unto Me Ser.: Year 2, Bk. 2). 32p. 1980. pap. 1.65 (ISBN 0-8127-0271-9). Review & Herald.

--Kind Kristy. (Come Unto Me Library). 1979. pap. 1.65 (ISBN 0-8127-0209-3). Review & Herald.

--Obedience Brings Happiness. (Come Unto Me Ser.). 16p. 1979. pap. 1.65 (ISBN 0-8127-0251-4). Review & Herald.

--Quiet Because. (Come Unto Me Ser.). 1979. pap. 1.65 (ISBN 0-8127-0253-0). Review & Herald.

--Talking to My Friend Jesus: Two - Four. (Come Unto Me Ser.: Year 2, Bk. 4). 32p. 1980. pap. 1.65 (ISBN 0-8127-0273-5). Review & Herald.

Groot, David de see Dalenburg, Cornelia & De Groot, David.

Groot, J. J. De see De Groot, J. J.

Groot, Jan J. The Religion of the Chinese. LC 79-2824. 230p. 1981. Repr. of 1910 ed. 21.50 (ISBN 0-8305-0004-9). Hyperion Conn.

Groot, Jeanne L. De see De Groot, Jeanne L.

Groot, John H. De see De Groot, John H.

Groothuis, Douglas R. The New Age Movement. 32p. (Orig.). 1986. pap. 0.75 (ISBN 0-87784-079-2). Inter-Varsity.

--Unmasking the New Age. LC 85-23832. 200p. (Orig.). 1986. pap. 6.95 (ISBN 0-87784-568-9). Inter-Varsity.

Gropman, Donald, jt. auth. see DiOrio, Ralph A.

Grose, Peter. Israel & the Mind of America. 1983. 17.95 (ISBN 0-394-51658-3). Random.

Grose, T. H., ed. see Hume, David.

Groseclose, Kel. Coming up Short in a Tall World. (Illus.). 144p. 1984. pap. 3.95 (ISBN 0-87123-435-1). Bethany Hse.

--Three-Speed Dad in a Ten-Speed World. LC 83-2765. 176p. (Orig.). 1983. pap. 4.95 (ISBN 0-87123-585-4, 210585). Bethany Hse.

Grosheide, Frederick W. Commentary on First Corinthians. (New International Commentary on the New Testament). 1953. 14.95 (ISBN 0-8028-2185-5). Eerdmans.

Gross, Alexander, jt. auth. see Kaminetsky, Joseph.

Gross, Arthur W. Child's Garden of Bible Stories. (Concordia Primary Religion Ser.). 1981. 9.95 (ISBN 0-570-03414-0, 56-1001); pap. 5.95 (ISBN 0-570-03402-7, 56-1012). Concordia.

--Stories Jesus Told. 1981. 6.95 (ISBN 0-570-04059-0, 56YY1352). Concordia.

Gross, Arthur W. & Jahsmann, Allan H. Little Children Sing to God! 1960. 8.95 (ISBN 0-570-03471-X, 56-1036). Concordia.

Gross, Darwin. The Ancient Teachings of the Masters. (Illus.). 45p. (Orig.). 1987. pap. 10.00 (ISBN 0-931689-06-6). SOS Pub OR.

--The Atom. 130p. (Orig.). 1984. pap. 3.95 (ISBN 0-931689-01-5). SOS Pub OR.

--The Key to the Universe. 75p. (Orig.). 1986. pap. 3.00 (ISBN 0-931689-08-2). SOS Pub OR.

Gross, Jim, ed. see Carey, Ken.

Gross, Kenneth. Spenserian Poetics: Idolatry, Iconoclasm & Magic. LC 85-47701. 256p. 1986. text ed. 24.95x (ISBN 0-8014-1805-4). Cornell U Pr.

Gross, Leonard. The Golden Years of the Hutterites. LC 80-10711. (Studies in Anabaptist & Mennonite History: Vol. 23). 1980. 17.95x (ISBN 0-8361-1227-X). Herald Pr.

--Golden Years of the Hutterites, 1565-1578. LC 80-10711. 280p. 1980. 15.00 (ISBN 0-317-47160-0). Plough.

Gross, Ralph. Praise the Lord & Rub It Out. (Illus.). 30p. (Orig.). 1981. pap. 5.00 (ISBN 0-686-32010-7). Karma Pub.

Gross, Raphael H., ed. Century of the Catholic Essay. facs. ed. LC 76-134087. (Essay Index Reprint Ser). 1946. 19.00 (ISBN 0-8369-2190-9). Ayer Co Pubs.

Gross, Rita M., ed. Beyond Androcentrism: New Essays on Women & Religion. LC 77-13312. (AAR Aids for the Study of Religion: No. 6). 1981. pap. 9.95 (ISBN 0-89130-196-8, 010306). Scholars Pr GA.

Gross, Rita M., jt. ed. see Falk, Nancy A.

Gross, Sukey. How & What to Teach: A Pre-School & Kindergarten Curriculum Guide for the Day School. 8.00 (ISBN 0-914131-33-8, C04). Torah Umesorah.

Gross, Theodore L. Literature of American Jews. LC 72-93311. 1973. 14.95 (ISBN 0-02-913190-1). Free Pr.

Gross, Theodore L. & Wertheim, S. Hawthorne, Melville, Stephen Crane: A Critical Bibliography. LC 75-142364. 1971. 14.95 (ISBN 0-02-913220-7). Free Pr.

Grosse, David G. Beacon Small-Group Bible Studies, Job: The Trial & Triumph of Faith. Wolf, Earl C., ed. 88p. (Orig.). 1986. pap. 2.50 (ISBN 0-8341-1109-8). Beacon Hill.

--Job: The Trial & Triumph of Faith. (Small Group Bible Studies). 88p. (Orig.). 1986. pap. 2.50 (ISBN 0-8341-1138-1). Beacon Hill.

Grosse, E. Dictionnaire d'Antiphilosophisme ou Refutation des Erreurs du 18e Siecle. Migne, J. P., ed. (Troisieme et Derniere Encyclopedie Theologique Ser.: Vol. 18). (Fr.). 770p. Repr. of 1856 ed. lib. bdg. 97.50x (ISBN 0-89241-301-8). Caratzas.

Grosse, Rudolf. The Christmas Foundation Meeting: Beginning of a New Cosmic Age. Collis, Johanna, tr. from Ger. Tr. of Die Weihnachtstagung als Zeitenwende. 158p. (Orig.). 1984. pap. 14.00 (ISBN 0-919924-23-9, Steiner Bk Ctr). Anthroposophic.

Grosser, Paul E. & Halpern, Edwin G. Anti-Semitism: Causes & Effects of a Prejudice. 1979. pap. 5.95 (ISBN 0-8065-0703-9). Citadel Pr.

Grosseteste, Robert. Carmina Anglo-Normannica: Chasteau d'Amour, to Which Is Added La Vie de Saint-Marie Egyptienne & an English Version of the Chasteau d'Amour. Cooke, M., ed. 1852. 24.00 (ISBN 0-8337-1467-8). B. Franklin.

Grossfeld, B. Bibliography of Targum Literature: Supplement, Vol. 2. (Bibliographica Judaica Ser: No. 8). 39.50x (ISBN 0-87820-905-0, HUC Pr). Ktav.

Grossfeld, B., jt. auth. see Aberbach, M.

Grossfeld, Bernard. Concordance of the First Targum to the Book of Esther. LC 83-11550. (SBL Aramaic Studies). 186p. 1984. pap. 11.25 (ISBN 0-89130-635-8, 06 13 05). Scholars Pr GA.

--A Critical Commentary on Targum Neofiti I to Genesis. Schiffman, L. H., ed. 75.00x (ISBN 0-87068-333-0). Ktav.

--The First Targum to Esther. (Aramaic & Eng., Illus.). xiv, 224p. 1983. pap. 19.50 (ISBN 0-87203-112-8). Hermon.

Grossfield, B. A Bibliography of Targum Literature, Vol. 1. 1972. 39.50x. Ktav.

Grossinger, Richard. Early Field Notes from the All-American Revival Church. 1973. pap. 3.50 (ISBN 0-913028-19-3). North Atlantic.

Grossinger, Richard & Hough, Lindy, eds. Nuclear Strategy & the Code of the Warrior: Faces of Mars & Shiva in the Crisis of Human Survival. (Io Ser.: No. 33). 320p. (Orig.). 1984. 25.00 (ISBN 0-938190-50-4); pap. 12.95 (ISBN 0-938190-49-0). North Atlantic.

Grossman, Bob. The New Chinese-Kosher Cookbook. rev. ed. LC 77-79248. (Illus.). 1978. 5.95 (ISBN 0-8397-6308-5); pap. 4.95 (ISBN 0-8397-6309-3). Eriksson.

Grossman, Brigite S. Experiencing Jewish Boston. LC 80-85316. (Illus.). 54p. (Orig.). 1981. pap. 3.50 (ISBN 0-9605624-0-0). Jewish Comm Ctr.

Grossman, Cheryl S. & Engman, Suzy. Jewish Literature for Children: A Teaching Guide. 230p. (Orig.). 1985. text ed. 19.00 (ISBN 0-86705-018-7); pap. text ed. 15.00. AIRE.

Grossman, Joan A., jt. auth. see Isaacman, Clara.

Grossman, Philip see Maimonides, Moses.

Grossman, Richard L. Salvation. (Literary Chapbook Ser.). 48p. 1977. pap. 3.00 (ISBN 0-916300-05-6). Gallimaufry.

Grossman, Richard L., jt. auth. see Kazis, Richard.

Grossman, Siegfried. Stewards of God's Grace. 192p. (Orig.). 1981. pap. text ed. 8.95 (ISBN 0-85364-287-7). Attic Pr.

Grossman, Vasily, jt. auth. see Ehrenburg, Iiya.

Grossman, Walter. Johann Christian Edelmann: From Orthodoxy to Enlightenment. (Religion & Society Ser: No. 3). 209p. 1976. text ed. 22.25x (ISBN 90-2797-691-0). Mouton.

Grosso, Stephan. Harry, My Friend. LC 85-82391. 80p. 1986. pap. 2.95 (ISBN 0-89243-247-0). Liguori Pubns.

Grote, Jim, jt. ed. see Mitcham, Carl.

Groten, Dallas. Will the Real Winner Please Stand Up. 160p. 1985. pap. 4.95 (ISBN 0-87123-819-5, 210819). Bethany Hse.

Grotenhuis, Elizabeth Ten see Rosenfield, John M. & Ten Grotenhuis, Elizabeth.

Groth, J. L. Prayer: Learning How to Talk to God. LC 56-1395. (Concept Books Series Four). 1983. pap. 3.95 (ISBN 0-570-07799-0). Concordia.

Groth, Jeanette. Little Journeys Through the Old Testament. 128p. (Orig.). 1986. pap. 5.95 (ISBN 0-570-03985-1, 12-3012). Concordia.

--Thank You for My Spouse. LC 12-2826. 1983. pap. 2.50 (ISBN 0-570-03885-5). Concordia.

Groth, Jeanette L. Little Journeys with Jesus. pap. 5.95 (ISBN 0-570-03924-X, 12-2858). Concordia.

Groth, Lynn. God Cares for Me. (A Cradle Roll Program Ser.). 8p. (Orig.). pap. 1.25 (ISBN 0-938272-75-6). Wels Board.

--Jesus Loves Children. (A Cradle Roll Program Ser.). 16p. (Orig.). 1985. pap. 1.25 (ISBN 0-938272-78-0). Wels Board.

--A Very Special Baby-Jesus. (A Cradle Roll Program Ser.). 8p. (Orig.). 1985. pap. 1.25 (ISBN 0-938272-76-4). Wels Board.

--With You, Dear Child, in Mind. (A Cradle Roll Program Ser.). 16p. (Orig.). 1985. pap. 1.25 (ISBN 0-938272-77-2). Wels Board.

Grotius, Hugo. True Religion Explained & Defended. Coventry, F., tr. LC 72-201. (English Experience Ser.: No. 318). 350p. 1971. Repr. of 1632 ed. 28.00 (ISBN 90-221-0318-8). Walter J Johnson.

Grott, J. J. De see De Groot, J. J.

Grou, Jean-Nicholas. How to Pray. Dalby, Joseph, tr. 154p. 1982. pap. 6.95 (ISBN 0-227-67485-5). Attic Pr.

Grounds, Vernon. Radical Commitment: Getting Serious about Christian Growth. LC 84-3344. 1984. pap. 5.95 (ISBN 0-88070-051-3). Multnomah.

Grousset, Rene. In the Footsteps of the Buddha. facs. ed. Leon, Mariette, tr. from Fr. LC 77-124235. (Select Bibliographies Reprint Ser). 1932. 19.50 (ISBN 0-8369-5423-8). Ayer Co Pubs.

Grover, Satish. The Architecture of India: Islamic. (Illus.). 280p. 1981. text ed. 45.00x (ISBN 0-7069-1130-X, Pub. by Vikas India). Advent NY.

Grover, Veronica, jt. auth. see Wilkins, Ronald.

Groves, Mary, tr. see Buhlmann, Walbert.

Groves, Norris A. Christian Devotedness. pap. 1.95 (ISBN 0-937396-63-X). Walterick Pubs.

Grow, Douglas, jt. auth. see Barnidge, Thomas.

Grubb, L. L. How to Discover God. 1979. pap. write for info. (ISBN 0-88469-002-4). BMH Bks.

Grubb, Norman P. C. T. Studd. 1972. 7.95 (ISBN 0-87508-201-7); pap. 5.95 (ISBN 0-87508-202-5). Chr Lit.

--Deep Things of God. 1970. pap. 4.95 (ISBN 0-87508-209-2). Chr Lit.

--Law of Faith. 1969. pap. 3.95 (ISBN 0-87508-223-8). Chr Lit.

--Spontaneous You. 1970. pap. 3.50 (ISBN 0-87508-224-6). Chr Lit.

--Summit Living. 368p. 1985. 9.95 (ISBN 0-317-43397-0); pap. 7.95 (ISBN 0-87508-267-X). Chr Lit.

--Who Am I? 1975. pap. 2.95 (ISBN 0-87508-227-0). Chr Lit.

--Yes, I Am. 1982. pap. text ed. 4.95 (ISBN 0-87508-206-8). Chr Lit.

Grubbs, Jerry C. Continuing Education: A Hedge Against Boredom in Ministry. LC 86-42931. 40p. (Orig.). 1986. pap. 4.00 (ISBN 0-937021-03-2). Sagamore Bks MI.

Grubbs, Sylvia, jt. auth. see Cadram, Glenna.

Grube, G. M., tr. see Plato.

Grube, G. M. A., ed. & tr. see Aurelius, Marcus.

Grube, Joel W., jt. auth. see Ball-Rokeach, Sandra.

Gruber, Joachim. Kommmentar Zu Boethius De Consolatione Philosophiae. (Texte und Kommentare: Vol. 9). 1978. 62.00x (ISBN 3-11-007223-8). De Gruyter.

Gruchy, John W. de see De Gruchy, John W.

Gruchy, John W. de see De Gruchy, John W. & Villa-Vicencio, Charles.

Grudem, Wayne A. The Gift of Prophecy in One Corinthians. LC 81-40583. 358p. (Orig.). 1982. lib. bdg. 32.00 (ISBN 0-8191-2083-9); pap. text ed. 15.75 (ISBN 0-8191-2084-7). U Pr of Amer.

Gruen, Ernest J. Freedom to Choose. 224p. 1976. pap. 2.95 (ISBN 0-88368-072-6). Whitaker Hse.

--Touching the Heart of God. (Orig.). 1986. pap. 3.95 (ISBN 0-88368-175-7). Whitaker Hse.

Gruenberg, Gladys W. Labor Peacemaker: The Life & Works of Father Leo. C. Brown, S. J. Ganss, George E., ed. LC 80-83552. (Original Studies Composed in English Ser.: No. 4). (Illus.). 176p. 1981. 8.50 (ISBN 0-912422-54-8); pap. 7.00 smythsewn paperbound (ISBN 0-912422-53-X); pap. 6.00 (ISBN 0-912422-52-1). Inst Jesuit.

Gruenler, Royce G. The Inexhaustible God: Biblical Faith & the Challenge of Process Theism. 176p. 1983. pap. 11.95 (ISBN 0-8010-3794-8). Baker Bk.

--The Trinity in the Gospel of John. 1986. pap. 9.95 (ISBN 0-8010-3806-5). Baker Bk.

Gruffydd, W. J. Folklore & Myth in the Mabinogion. LC 75-34083. 1958. lib. bdg. 15.00 (ISBN 0-8414-4522-2). Folcroft.

Gruhn, Albert. Die Byzantinische Politik Zur der Zeit Kreuzzuege. 1904. 12.50 (ISBN 0-8337-1479-1). B Franklin.

Gruman, Gerald J. A History of Ideas about the Prolongation of Life: The Evolution of Prolongevity Hypotheses to 1800. Kastenbaum, Robert, ed. LC 76-19574. (Death & Dying Ser.). (Illus.). 1977. Repr. of 1966 ed. lib. bdg. 17.00x (ISBN 0-405-09572-4). Ayer Co Pubs.

Grumelli, Antonio, jt. ed. see Caporale, Rocco.

Grunblatt, Joseph. Golus Ugeuloh: Exile & Redemption--21 Shiurim on the Meaning of Jewish History. 1987. 16.95 (ISBN 0-88125-130-5); pap. 9.95 (ISBN 0-88125-135-6). Ktav.

Grundler, Otto, jt. ed. see Chrisman, Miriam.

Grundtvig, N. F. What Constitutes Authentic Christianity? Nielsen, Ernest D., ed. & tr. from Ger. LC 84-48728. 128p. 1985. pap. 6.95 (ISBN 0-8006-1844-0, 1-1844). Fortress.

Grundy, Julia M. Ten Days in the Light of 'Akka. rev. ed. LC 79-12177. 1979. pap. 6.95 (ISBN 0-87743-131-0, 332-040). Baha'i.

Grunebaum, G. E. von see Von Grunebaum, G. E.

Grunebaum, G. E. Von see Von Grunebaum, G. E.

Grunebaum, Gustave E. von see Abel, Armand, et al.

Grunebaum, Gustave Von see Von Grunebaum, Gustave E.

Gruner, Mark & Brown, Christopher K. Mark Gruner's Numbers of Life: An Introduction to Numerology. LC 78-57560. 1979. 9.95 (ISBN 0-8008-5639-2); pap. 3.95 (ISBN 0-8-805640-6). Taplinger.

Grunfeld. The Jewish Dietary Laws, 2 vols. 1973. Set. 32.95x (ISBN 0-900689-09-9). Bloch.

Grunfeld, Dayan I. The Jewish Dietary Laws, 2 vols. 246p. 1972. Vol. 1, 246 pgs. pap. 29.95 (ISBN 0-900689-10-2); Vol. 2, 285 pgs. pap. 32.95 slipcased (ISBN 0-900689-11-0). Soncino Pr.

Grunfeld, I. The Sabbath: A Guide to Its Understanding & Observance. 6.95; pap. 4.95 (ISBN 0-87306-099-7). Feldheim.

Grunfeld, Joseph. Science & Values. 210p. (Orig.). 1973. pap. 22.00x (ISBN 90-6032-016-6, Pub. by B R Gruener). Benjamins North AM.

Grunlan, Stephen A. Marriage & the Family: A Christian Perspective. 384p. 1984. pap. 10.95 (ISBN 0-310-36341-1, 11282P). Zondervan.

--Serving with Joy: A Study in Philippians. LC 85-71352. 107p. (Orig.). 1985. pap. 4.95 (ISBN 0-87509-371-X); leader's guide 2.95 (ISBN 0-87509-372-8). Chr Pubns.

Grunlan, Stephen A. & Mayers, Marvin K. Cultural Anthropology: A Christian Perspective. 1979. 9.95 (ISBN 0-310-36321-7, 11280P). Zondervan.

Grunwald, Stefan, ed. see Nau, Erika S.

Grunwedel, Albert. Buddhist Art in India. Gibson, Agnes C., tr. (Ger., Illus.). 236p. Repr. of 1901 ed. text ed. 37.50x. Coronet Bks.

Grunze, Richard. Bible History: Teachers' Manual. 228p. 1985. suedene vinyl 3-ring binder 12.95 (ISBN 0-938272-15-2). WELS Board.

--Paul: An Example for Christian Teachers. 1979. pap. text ed. 3.50 (ISBN 0-8100-0108-X, 07N0740). Northwest Pub.

--Searching in God's Word-New Testament. (Lutheran Elementary Schools' Religion Curriculum Ser.). 142p. 1986. 4.95 (ISBN 0-938272-41-1). WELS Board.

--Searching in God's Word-Old Testament. (Lutheran Elementary Schools' Religion Curriculum Ser.). 140p. 1986. 4.95 (ISBN 0-938272-40-3). WELS Board.

--The Young Christian's Life. 1979. 9.95 (ISBN 0-8100-0104-7, 06N0557). Northwest Pub.

Grunze, Richard, ed. Bible History. (WELS Lutheran Elementary Schools' Religion Curriculum Ser.). (Illus.). 556p. 1984. 11.95 (ISBN 0-938272-14-4). WELS Board.

Grunze, Richard, ed. see Fehlauer, Adolph.

Gruppe, Otto. Griechische Mythologie und Religionsgeschichte, 2 vols. facsimile ed. LC 75-10638. (Ancient Religion & Mythology Ser.). (Ger.). 1976. Repr. of 1906 ed. 144.00x set (ISBN 0-405-07015-2). Ayer Co Pubs.

Grupper, David & Klein, David G. The Paper Shtetl: A Complete Model of an East European Jewish Town. LC 83-42714. (Illus., Orig.). 1984. pap. 11.95 (ISBN 0-8052-0749-X). Schocken.

Gruss, Edmond C. Apostles of Denial. 1970. pap. 8.95 (ISBN 0-87552-305-6). Presby & Reformed.

--Jehovah's Witnesses & Prophetic Speculation. pap. 5.95 (ISBN 0-8010-3710-7). Baker Bk.

--Jehovah's Witnesses & Prophetic Speculation. 1972. pap. 5.95 (ISBN 0-87552-306-4). Presby & Reformed.

--We Left Jehovah's Witnesses. pap. 5.95 (ISBN 0-8010-3696-8). Baker Bk.

--We Left Jehovah's Witnesses: A Non-Prophet Organization. 1974. pap. 5.95 (ISBN 0-87552-307-2). Presby & Reformed.

--What Every Mormon Should Know. (Orig.). 1975. micro book 1.95 (ISBN 0-916406-34-2). Accent Bks.

Gruzen, Lee F. Raising Your Jewish-Christian Child: Wise Choices for Interfaith Parents. 1987. 16.95 (ISBN 0-396-08551-2). Dodd.

Gryczka, Mary, jt. auth. see Wilkins, Ronald.

Gryn, Tom. Growing Closer to God. 100p. (Orig.). 1982. pap. 2.50 (ISBN 0-89283-160-X). Servant.

Gryson, R. Le Receuil Arien de Verone. 1983. 46.00 (ISBN 90-247-2705-7, Pub. by Martinus Nijhoff Netherlands). Kluwer Academic.

Gualtieri, Antonio R. The Vulture & the Bull: Religious Responses to Death. 194p. (Orig.). 1984. lib. bdg. 26.00 (ISBN 0-8191-3963-7); pap. text ed. 11.75 (ISBN 0-8191-3964-5). U Pr of Amer.

Guangzhou Municipal Museum. Guangzhou Hanmu Excavation of the Han Tombs at Guangzhou. 526p. 1981. 150.00x (ISBN 0-317-44071-3, Pub. by Han-Shan Tang Ltd). State mutual Bk.

Guardini, Romano. Lord. 1978. pap. 9.95 (ISBN 0-89526-909-0). Regnery Bks.

Guareschi, Giovanni. Little World of Don Camillo. LC 86-8845. (Illus.). 144p. 1986. pap. 5.95 (ISBN 0-385-23242-X, Im). Doubleday.

Guber, Lynda, jt. auth. see Finger, Alan.

Guber, Rivka. Village of the Brothers. LC 78-54568. (Illus.). 1979. 10.00 (ISBN 0-88400-059-1). Shengold.

Gubernatis, Angelo De. Zoological Mythology, 2 Vols. LC 68-58904. 1968. Repr. of 1872 ed. Set. 56.00x (ISBN 0-8103-3527-1). Gale.

Gudemann, Moritz. Judische Apologetik. Katz, Steven, ed. LC 79-7133. (Jewish Philosophy, Mysticism & History of Ideas Ser.). 1980. Repr. of 1906 ed. lib. bdg. 23.00x (ISBN 0-405-12258-6). Ayer Co Pubs.

Guder, Darrell L., tr. see Weber, Otto.

Guder, Darrell L. Be My Witnesses: The Church's Mission, Message, & Messengers. LC 85-10129. 256p. (Orig.). 1985. pap. 10.95 (ISBN 0-8028-0051-3). Eerdmans.

Guder, Darrell L., tr. see Jungel, Eberhard.

Guder, Darrell L., tr. see Weber, Otto.

Gudorf, Christine E. Catholic Social Teaching on Liberation Themes. LC 80-5382. 394p. 1980. lib. bdg. 29.00 (ISBN 0-8191-1080-9); pap. text ed. 15.50 (ISBN 0-8191-1081-7). U Pr of Amer.

Gueber, H. A. The Myths of Greece & Rome. 1986. 27.50x (ISBN 0-245-56918-9, Pub. by Harrap Ltd England). State Mutual Bk.

Guedalla, Philip. Super & Superman. 1924. Repr. 20.00 (ISBN 0-8274-3554-1). R West.

Guelich, Robert. The Sermon on the Mount. 448p. 1982. 19.95 (ISBN 0-8499-0110-3). Word Bks.

Guelinboin, Marie T., illus. Krishna & the Demons. (Illus.). 16p. 1978. pap. 2.50 (ISBN 0-89647-005-9). Bala Bks.

Guenebault, L. J. Dictionnaire Iconographique des Figures Legendes et Actes des Saints. Migne, J. P., ed. (Encyclopedie Theologique Ser.: Vol. 45). (Fr.). 716p. Repr. of 1850 ed. lib. bdg. 91.00x (ISBN 0-89241-249-6). Caratzas.

Guenon, Rene. Studies in Hinduism. 1986. 18.50x (ISBN 0-8364-1548-5, Pub. by Navrang). South Asia Bks.

--The Symbolism of the Cross. 134p. 1975. 35.00x (ISBN 0-317-39165-8, Pub. by Luzac & Co Ltd); pap. 19.00x (ISBN 0-317-39166-6). State Mutual Bk.

Guentert, Kenneth. The Server's Book of the Mass. LC 86-60894. 64p. 1985. pap. 4.95 (ISBN 0-89390-078-8). Resource Pubns.

--Young Server's Book of the Mass. LC 86-60894. 1987. pap. 4.95 (ISBN 0-89390-078-8). Resource Pubns.

Guenther, H. V. Philosophy & Psychology in the Abhidharma. 2nd rev. ed. 1974. 18.00 (ISBN 0-87773-048-2). Orient Bk Dist.

Guenther, Heinz O. The Footprints of Jesus' Twelve in Early Christian Traditions: A Study in the Meaning of Religious Symbolism. LC 84-48032. (American University Studies VII (Theology & Religion): Vol. 7). 156p. 1984. text ed. 20.90 (ISBN 0-8204-0164-1). P Lang Pubs.

Guenther, Herbert, et al. Questions & Answers on Guru & Disciple. (Illus.). 1978. pap. text ed. 3.00 (ISBN 0-931454-02-6). Timeless Bks.

Guenther, Herbert V. Matrix of Mystery: Scientific & Humanistic Aspects of rDzogs-chen Thought. LC 83-2306. (Illus.). 317p. 1984. 22.50 (ISBN 0-87773-291-4, 54073-5). Shambhala Pubns.

--Tibetan Buddhism in Western Perspective. LC 76-47758. (Illus.). 1977. pap. 8.95 (ISBN 0-913546-50-X). Dharma Pub.

Guenther, Herbert V. & Trungpa, Chogyam. The Dawn of Tantra. LC 74-10250. (Illus.). 92p. pap. 6.95 (ISBN 0-87773-059-8). Shambhala Pubns.

Guenther, Herbert V., tr. see Klong-chen rab-byams pa.

Guenther, Herbert V., tr. see SGam po pa.

Guenther, Herbert V., tr. see Ye-Shes Rgyal-Mtshan.

Guerard, Albert, tr. see Michelet, Jules.

Guerard, Albert J. Andre Gide. rev. ed. LC 74-88805. 1969. 20.00x (ISBN 0-674-03525-9). Harvard U Pr.

Guerber, H. A. Myths of Greece & Rome: Narrated with Special Reference to Literature & Art. 428p. 1985. Repr. of 1893 ed. 40.00 (ISBN 0-8495-2102-5). Arden Lib.

--Myths of Norsemen. 69.95 (ISBN 0-87968-280-9). Gordon Pr.

Guerin, L. F. Dictionnaire de l'Histoire Universelle de l'Eglise, 6 vols. Migne, J. P., ed. (Troisieme et Derniere Encyclopedie Theologique Ser.: Vols. 51-56). (Fr.). 4187p. Repr. of 1873 ed. lib. bdg. 532.50x (ISBN 0-89241-322-0). Caratzas.

Guernsey, Alfred H. Ralph Waldo Emerson. 1978. Repr. of 1901 ed. lib. bdg. 30.00 (ISBN 0-8492-0969-2). R West.

Guernsey, Dennis. Thoroughly Married. 145p. 1984. pap. text ed. 5.95 (ISBN 0-8499-3000-6, 3000-6). Word Bks.

Guernsey, Dennis B. The Family Covenant: Students Manual. 113p. 1984. pap. text ed. 3.95 (ISBN 0-89191-843-4). Cook.

--A New Design for Family Ministry. LC 82-72793. 126p. 1982. pap. 6.95 (ISBN 0-89191-650-4). Cook.

Guernsey, Dennis B., jt. auth. see Anderson, Ray S.

Guerra, Michael J., jt. auth. see Benson, Peter L.

Guerrero, Andres G. A Chicano Theology. LC 86-23561. 192p. (Orig.). 1987. pap. 11.95 (ISBN 0-88344-407-0). Orbis Bks.

Guerry, Herbert, ed. Philosophy & Mysticism. Dell.

Guest, Charlotte. The Mabinogion. (Illus.). 504p. 1978. pap. 9.95 (ISBN 0-89733-000-5). Academy Chi Pubs.

Guest, Dean. Discovering the Word of God. 64p. (Orig.). 1980. pap. 1.95 (ISBN 0-89841-011-8). Zoe Pubns.

--Tabernacle, God's Dwelling Place. 64p. (Orig.). 1979. pap. 1.95 (ISBN 0-89841-012-6). Zoe Pubns.

--Trees of Restoration. cancelled (ISBN 0-533-05752-3). Vantage.

Guest, John. In Search of Certainty. LC 83-19273. (In Search of...Ser.). 1984. 9.95 (ISBN 0-8307-0919-3, 5111001). Regal.

--Only a Prayer Away. 140p. (Orig.). 1985. pap. 6.95 (ISBN 0-89283-273-8, Pub. by Vine Books). Servant.

Guest, Lisa, jt. auth. see Smoke, Jim.

Gugli, William V., tr. see Chouraqui, Andre.

Guha, D. C. Navya Nyaya System of Logic. 3rd enlarged ed. 1979. 15.50 (ISBN 0-89684-059-X, Pub. by Motilal Banarsidass India). Orient Bk Dist.

Guibert, Joseph De see De Guibert, Joseph.

Guicciradi, Francesco. Catholic Rome & Its Most Beautiful Paintings. (The Institute for the Promotion of the Arts Ser.). (Illus.). 1978. deluxe bdg. 75.65 (ISBN 0-930582-01-2). Gloucester Art.

Guigo II. Guigo II: The Ladder of Monks & Twelve Meditations. Colledge, Edmund & Walsh, James, trs. (Cistercian Studies: No. 48). (Illus.). 1981. pap. write for info. (ISBN 0-87907-748-4). Cistercian Pubns.

Guilday, Peter K. History of the Councils of Baltimore, 1791-1884. LC 77-83421. (Religion in America, Ser. 1). 1969. Repr. of 1932 ed. 25.50 (ISBN 0-405-00246-7). Ayer Co Pubs.

--Life & Times of John England. LC 70-83422. (Religion in America, Ser. 1). 1969. Repr. of 1927 ed. 54.00 (ISBN 0-405-00247-5). Ayer Co Pubs.

Guilelmus. Godeffroy of Boloyne; or, the Siege & Conquest of Jerusalem. Colvin, Mary N., ed. (EETS, ES Ser.: No. 64). Repr. of 1893 ed. 29.00 (ISBN 0-527-00269-0). Kraus Repr.

Guiles, Cecil R. Ministering to Youth. 1973. 5.25 (ISBN 0-87148-551-6); pap. 4.25 (ISBN 0-87148-552-4); instrs. guide 4.95 (ISBN 0-87148-834-5). Pathway Pr.

Guilfoile, Elizabeth. Valentine's Day. LC 65-10086. (Holiday Bks.). (Illus.). 1965. PLB 7.56 (ISBN 0-8116-6556-9). Garrard.

Guillaume, A., jt. auth. see Arnold, T. W.

Guillaume, A., intro. by see Ishaq, I.

Guillaume, Alfred. Islam. 1954. pap. 6.95 (ISBN 0-14-020311-7, Pelican). Penguin.

--The Traditions of Islam. LC 79-52552. (Islam Ser.). 1980. Repr. of 1924 ed. lib. bdg. 16.00x (ISBN 0-8369-9260-1). Ayer Co Pubs.

Guillaume De Berneville. La Vie De Saint Gilles. Paris, Gaston & Bos, Alphonse, eds. 34.00 (ISBN 0-384-20300-0); pap. 28.00 (ISBN 0-384-20285-3). Johnson Repr.

Guillemette, Pierre. The Greek New Testament Analyzed. LC 86-81317. 480p. 1986. 29.95 (ISBN 0-8361-3418-4). Herald Pr.

Guillemin. Le Converti Paul Claudel. 25.95 (ISBN 0-685-37276-6). French & Eur.

Guinan, Michael D. Covenant in the Old Testament. (Biblical Booklets Ser). 68p. 1975. pap. 1.25 (ISBN 0-8199-0520-8). Franciscan Herald.

--Gospel Poverty: Witness to the Risen Christ. LC 81-80051. 96p. (Orig.). 1981. pap. 4.95 (ISBN 0-8091-2377-0). Paulist Pr.

--Job. (Collegeville Bible Commentary: Old Testament Ser.: Vol. 19). 88p. 1986. pap. 2.95 (ISBN 0-8146-1476-0). Liturgical Pr.

Guinan, Michael D., tr. see George, Augustine, et al.

Guindon, Andre. The Sexual Creators: An Ethical Proposal for Concerned Christians. 256p. (Orig.). 1986. lib. bdg. 28.00 (ISBN 0-8191-5239-0); pap. text ed. 13.00 (ISBN 0-8191-5240-4). U Pr of Amer.

Guiness, Os. The Gravedigger File. LC 83-10666. (Illus.). 204p. (Orig.). 1983. pap. 7.95 (ISBN 0-87784-817-3). Inter-Varsity.

Guinness, Michele. Child of the Covenant. 160p. 1985. pap. 2.95 (ISBN 0-345-32715-2). Ballantine.

Guiraud, Jean. The Medieval Inquisition. Messenger, E. C., tr. LC 78-63181. (Heresies of the Early Christian & Medieval Era: Second Ser.). Repr. of 1929 ed. 31.00 (ISBN 0-404-16222-3). AMS Pr.

Guirdham, Arthur. Cathars & Reincarnation. LC 77-17012. (Illus.). 1978. pap. 3.75 (ISBN 0-8356-0506-X, Quest). Theos Pub Hse.

Guirguis, Fouad. The Difficult Years of Survival. LC 83-90921. 89p. 1985. 7.95 (ISBN 0-533-05937-2). Vantage.

Guissani, Luigi. Morality: Memory & Desire. Whitehead, Kenneth D., tr. LC 86-80476. Tr. of Italian. 174p. 1986. pap. 8.95 (ISBN 0-89870-090-6). Ignatius Pr.

Guitton, Jean. Human Love. LC 66-17110. 253p. 1966. 4.50 (ISBN 0-8199-0046-X). Franciscan Herald.

Gula, Richard M. To Walk Together Again: The Sacrament of Reconciliation. LC 83-82021. (Orig.). 1984. pap. 8.95 (ISBN 0-8091-2603-6). Paulist Pr.

--What Are They Saying about Moral Norms? LC 81-83188. 128p. (Orig.). 1982. pap. 4.95 (ISBN 0-8091-2412-2). Paulist Pr.

Gula, Richard S. What Are They Saying about Euthenasia? (W. A. T. S. A. Ser.). 192p. (Orig.). 1986. pap. 5.95 (ISBN 0-8091-2766-0). Paulist Pr.

Gula, Robert J., jt. auth. see Carpenter, Thomas H.

Gularte, Frank & Richardson, Jim. Prophecy. pap. 2.95 (ISBN 0-911739-23-8). Abbott Loop.

Gulati, S. P. Quintessence of Islamic History & Culture. 225p. 1986. 23.00X (ISBN 81-85061-44-0, Pub. by Manohar India). South Asia Bks.

Gulick, Edward V. Peter Parker & the Opening of China. LC 73-82628. (Harvard Studies in American-East Asian Relations: No. 3). 228p. 1974. text ed. 17.50x (ISBN 0-674-66326-8). Harvard U Pr.

Gullace, Giovanni, tr. see Cotta, Sergio.

Gulledge, Dennis & McWhirter, David. An Index to the Evangelist & the Christian. LC 83-70079. 160p. (Orig.). 1983. pap. 3.95 (ISBN 0-89900-231-5). College Pr Pub.

Gulledge, Jack. Ideas & Illustrations for Inspirational Talks. LC 85-24268. (Orig.). 1985. pap. 4.95 (ISBN 0-8054-5017-3). Broadman.

Gullery, Jonathan G., ed. The Path of a Pioneer: The Early Days of Sun Myung Moon & the Unification Church. (Illus.). 88p. (Orig.). 1986. pap. 3.95 (ISBN 0-910621-50-0). HSA Pubns.

Gulleserian, Papken. Armenian Church. Poladian, Vartapet T., tr. LC 70-131508. Repr. of 1939 ed. 11.50 (ISBN 0-404-02949-3). AMS Pr.

Gulley, Hal & Gulley, Nadine. I Tell You Truly. LC 81-82218. 192p. 1983. pap. 4.95 (ISBN 0-89900-194-7). College Pr Pub.

Gulley, Nadine, jt. auth. see Gulley, Hal.

Gulston, Charles. Jerusalem: The Tragedy & the Triumph. 1977. 12.95 (ISBN 0-310-35510-9). Zondervan.

Gumbert, J. P. & De Haan, M. J., eds. Texts & Manuscripts: Litterae Textuales. (Illus.). 110p. 1972. 46.50 (ISBN 0-8390-0105-3). Abner Schram Ltd.

--Varia Codicologica: Litterae Textuales. (Illus.). 110p. 1972. 46.50 (ISBN 0-8390-0106-1). Abner Schram Ltd.

Gumbley, Walter. Parish Priests among the Saints. facs. ed. LC 76-148214. (Biography Index Reprint Ser.). 1947. 15.00 (ISBN 0-8369-8061-1). Ayer Co Pubs.

Gummere, Amelia M. Quaker: A Study in Costume. LC 68-56494. (Illus.). 1968. Repr. of 1901 ed. 20.00 (ISBN 0-405-08585-0, Blom Pubns). Ayer Co Pubs.

Gun, Guneli. The Adventures of Huru on the Road to Baghdad. 352p. 1987. 19.95 (ISBN 0-89793-033-9). Hunter Hse.

Gunabhadra Acharya. Atmanushasana (Discourse to the Soul) Jaini, Rai B., ed. & tr. LC 73-3841. (Sacred Books of the Jainas: No. 7). Repr. of 1928 ed. 18.00 (ISBN 0-404-57707-5). AMS Pr.

Gunaratna, Henepola. The Path of Serenity & Insight. 1984. 22.50x (ISBN 0-8364-1149-8). South Asia Bks.

Gunderson, Vivian. Bible Learn & Do: Exodus. (Illus.). 1981. pap. 1.25 (ISBN 0-8323-0394-1); tchr's manual 2.50 (ISBN 0-8323-0435-2). Binford-Metropolitan.

--Bible Learn & Do: Genesis, Pt. I. (Illus.). 1979. pap. 1.25 (ISBN 0-8323-0368-2); tchr's. manual 2.50 (ISBN 0-8323-0376-3). Binford-Metropolitan.

--Bible Learn & Do: Genesis, Pt. II. (Illus.). 1980. pap. 1.25 (ISBN 0-8323-0369-0); tchr's. manual 2.50 (ISBN 0-8323-0377-1). Binford-Metropolitan.

--Bible Learn & Do: Gospel of Mark. (Illus.). 1982. pap. 1.25 (ISBN 0-8323-0412-3); pap. 2.50 tchr's manual (ISBN 0-8323-0439-5). Binford-Metropolitan.

--Bible Learn & Do: Numbers. (Illus.). 1981. pap. 1.25 (ISBN 0-8323-0393-3); tchr's. manual 2.50 (ISBN 0-8323-0436-0). Binford-Metropolitan.

--Bible Learn & Do: The Bible Is the Best Book, Why? 1985. pap. 1.25 (ISBN 0-8323-0442-5). Binford-Metropolitan.

--What's the Bible Like: New Testament. (Illus.). 1983. pap. 1.25 (ISBN 0-8323-0418-2). Binford-Metropolitan.

Gunderson, Vivian D. The Enemy Guest. 1964. pap. 1.75 (ISBN 0-915374-11-0, 11-0). Rapids Christian.

--Over the Cliff. 1974. pap. 1.75 (ISBN 0-915374-13-7, 13-7). Rapids Christian.

--Saved on Monday. 1964. pap. 1.75 (ISBN 0-915374-14-5, 14-5). Rapids Christian.

--The Wrong Road. 1964. pap. 1.75 (ISBN 0-915374-15-3, 15-3). Rapids Christian.

Gundry, D. W. Teacher & the World's Religions. 160p. 1968. 6.50 (ISBN 0-227-67456-1). Attic Pr.

Gundry, Patricia, jt. ed. see Gundry, Stanley.

Gundry, R. Soma, in Biblical Theology, with Emphasis on Pauline Anthropology. LC 75-22927. (Society for New Testament Studies: No. 29). 300p. 1976. o. p. 54.50 (ISBN 0-521-20788-6). Cambridge U Pr.

Gundry, Robert. Matthew: A Commentary on His Literary & Theological Art. 600p. 1982. 24.95 (ISBN 0-8028-3549-X). Eerdmans.

Gundry, Robert H. The Church & the Tribulation. 224p. 1973. pap. 7.95 (ISBN 0-310-25401-9, 18097P). Zondervan.

--Soma in Biblical Theology: With Emphasis on Pauline Anthropology. LC 75-22975. (Society for New Testament Studies. Monograph: 29). pap. 69.50 (ISBN 0-317-41736-3, 2025584). Bks Demand UMI.

--Somain Biblical Theology: With Emphasis on Pauline Anthropology. LC 75-22975. (Society for New Testament Studies: No. 29). pap. 69.50 (ISBN 0-317-28002-3, 2025584). Bks Demand UMI.

--A Survey of the New Testament. (Illus.). 432p. 1982. 17.95 (ISBN 0-310-25410-8, 18280). Zondervan.

Gundry, Stanley & Gundry, Patricia, eds. The Wit & Wisdom of D. L. Moody. (Direction Bks.). 78p. 1982. pap. 2.95 (ISBN 0-8010-3780-8). Baker Bk.

Gundry, Stanley N. Love Them In: The Proclamation Theology of D. L. Moody. 252p. 1982. pap. 8.95 (ISBN 0-8010-3783-2). Baker Bk.

Gundry, Stanley N., jt. auth. see Thomas, Robert L.

Gundry, Stanley N. & Johnson, Alan F., eds. Tensions in Contemporary Theology. 2nd ed. 478p. 1983. pap. 15.95 (ISBN 0-8010-3796-4). Baker Bk.

Gunkel, Carroll R. They Met the Master: Sermons on Contemporary Saints. 1980. 4.50 (ISBN 0-89536-388-7, 2035). CSS of Ohio.

Gunkel, Hermann. The Folktale in the Old Testament. (Historic Texts & Interpreters Ser.: No. 5). 224p. 1985. text ed. 24.95x (ISBN 1-85075-031-9, Pub. by Almond Pr England); pap. text ed. 10.95x (ISBN 1-85075-030-0). Eisenbrauns.

--The Influence of the Holy Spirit: The Popular View of the Apostolic Age & the Teaching of the Apostle Paul. Harrisville, Roy A. & Quanbeck, Philip A., II, trs. LC 78-20022. 144p. 1979. 3.00 (ISBN 0-8006-0544-6, 1-544). Fortress.

--The Legends of Genesis: The Biblical Saga & History. LC 64-22609. 1984. pap. 5.50 (ISBN 0-8052-0086-X). Schocken.

--Psalms: A Form-Critical Introduction. Reumann, John, ed. Horner, Thomas M., tr. from Ger. LC 67-22983. (Facet Bks.). 64p. (Orig.). 1967. pap. 2.50 (ISBN 0-8006-3043-2, 1-3043). Fortress.

Gunn, D. M. The Fate of King Saul. (Journal for the Study of the Old Testament, Supplement Ser.: No. 14). 1980. text ed. 18.95x (ISBN 0-905774-24-8, Pub. by JSOT Pr England); pap. text ed. 10.95 (ISBN 0-905774-63-9). Eisenbrauns.

--The Story of King David: Genre & Interpretation. (Journal for the Study of the Old Testament Supplement Ser.: No. 6). 164p. 1978. (Pub. by JSOT Pr England); pap. text ed. 16.95x (ISBN 0-905774-05-1, Pub. by JSOT Pr England). Eisenbrauns.

Gunn, D. M., jt. auth. see Clines, D. J.

Gunn, George S. Indispensable Christ: Sermons. 266p. 1962. 6.50 (ISBN 0-227-67661-0). Attic Pr.

--This Gospel of the Kingdom: Dilemmas in Evangelism. 167p. 1964. 5.95 (ISBN 0-227-67660-2). Attic Pr.

Gunn, Giles. The Bible & American Arts & Letters. LC 83-5634. (SBL Bible in American Culture Ser.). 256p. 1983. 15.95 (ISBN 0-89130-625-0, 06 12 03). Scholars Pr GA.

--The Interpretation of Otherness: Literature Religion & the American Imagination. 1979. 24.95x (ISBN 0-19-502453-2). Oxford U Pr.

Gunn, Giles, ed. New World Metaphysics: Readings on the Religious Meaning of the American Experience. 1981. pap. text ed. 10.95x (ISBN 0-19-502874-0). Oxford U Pr.

Gunn, James. Christ: The Fullness of the Godhead, a Study in New Testament Christology. 256p. 1983. pap. 5.50 (ISBN 0-87213-283-8). Loizeaux.

Gunn, Rodger S. Mormonism: Challenge & Defense. 1979. pap. 8.95 (ISBN 0-89036-126-6). Hawkes Pub Inc.

Gunnell, Sally, jt. auth. see Gardner, Hope C.

Gunnemann, Louis H. The Shaping of the United Church of Christ: An Essay in the History of American Christianity. LC 77-4900. 1977. 6.95 (ISBN 0-8298-0335-1). Pilgrim NY.

Gunneweg, A. H. Understanding the Old Testament. Bowden, John, tr. LC 78-6696. (Old Testament Library). 272p. 1978. Westminster.

Gunnin, Gerry C. John Wheatley, Catholic Socialism, & Irish Labour in the West of Scotland, 1906-1924. McNeil, William H. & Stansky, Peter, eds. (Modern European History Ser.). 375p. 1987. lib. bdg. 55.00 (ISBN 0-8240-7811-X). Garland Pub.

Gunning, Peter. Paschal or Lent Fast. LC 70-168214. (Library of Anglo-Catholic Theology: No. 7). Repr. of 1845 ed. 27.50 (ISBN 0-404-52088-X). AMS Pr.

Gunnison, John W. The Mormons: Or, Latter-Day Saints, in the Valley of the Great Salt Lake; a History of Their Rise & Progress, Peculiar Doctrines, Present Condition & Prospects, Derived from Personal Observation During a Residence Among Them. LC 70-38355. (Select Bibliographies Reprint Ser.). Repr. of 1852 ed. 16.00 (ISBN 0-8369-6772-0). Ayer Co Pubs.

Gunson, Niel. Messengers of Grace: Evangelical Missionaries in the South Seas 1797-1860. (Illus.). 1978. 49.95x (ISBN 0-19-550517-4). Oxford U Pr.

Gunstone, Don & Gunstone, Gail. Home Fellowship Meetings: Creative Ideas. 47p. 1986. pap. 3.25 (ISBN 0-914936-99-9). Bible Temple.

Gunstone, Gail, jt. auth. see Gunstone, Don.

Gunstone, John. Healing Power: What It Is & What to Do with It. 168p. (Orig.). 1987. pap. 4.95 (ISBN 0-89283-318-1, Pub. by Vine Books). Servant.

Gunter, Christopher L. The Intelligent Understanding of Sculptures & Mosaics in the Early Church. (Illus.). 138p. 1982. 75.45 (ISBN 0-86650-037-5). Gloucester Art.

Gunther, Bernard. Energy Ecstasy & Your Seven Vital Shakras. LC 83-8822. 200p. 1983. lib. bdg. 21.95x (ISBN 0-89370-666-3). Borgo Pr.

Gunther, Peter F., ed. Great Sermons of the Twentieth Century. LC 86-70286. 224p. (Orig.). 1986. pap. 7.95 (ISBN 0-89107-397-3, Crossway Bks). Good News.

--Sermon Classics by Great Preachers. LC 81-16899. 1982. pap. 4.95 (ISBN 0-8024-3328-6). Moody.

Gunton, Colin. Yesterday & Today: Continuites in Christology. 240p. (Orig.). 1983. pap. 7.95 (ISBN 0-8028-1974-5). Eerdmans.

Gunton, Colin E. Becoming & Being: The Doctrine of God in Charles Hartshorne & Karl Barth. (Theological Monographs). 1978. text ed. 39.95x (ISBN 0-19-826713-4). Oxford U Pr.

Gunzburg, D., et al, eds. Festschrift zu Ehren des Dr. A. Harkavy. LC 79-7160. (Jewish Philosophy, Mysticism & History of Ideas Ser.). 1980. Repr. of 1908 ed. lib. bdg. 60.00x (ISBN 0-405-12259-4). Ayer Co Pubs.

Gupta, Bina, ed. Sexual Archetypes: East & West. (God: The Contemporary Discussion Ser.). (Illus.). 344p. 1986. 22.95 (ISBN 0-913757-59-4, Pub. by New Era Bks); pap. 12.95 (ISBN 0-913757-68-3, Pub. by New Era Bks). Paragon Hse.

Gupta, Mallika C., jt. auth. see Ray, Irene R.

Gupta, Mallika C., ed. see Gnaneswarananda, Swami.

Gupta, Ram C. Sri Krishna: A Socio-Political & Philosophical Study. xiv, 188p. 1984. text ed. 30.00x (ISBN 0-86590-376-X, Pub. by B R Pub Corp Delhi). Apt Bks.

Gupta, S. K. Madhusudan Saraswati on the Bhagavaddita. 1977. 28.00 (ISBN 0-89684-246-0, Pub. by Motilal Banarsidass India). Orient Bk Dist.

Gupta, Sunil K., ed. Insights into Buddhism. 212p. 1986. 15.00 (ISBN 81-7030-022-3, Pub. by Sri Satguru Pubns India). Orient Bk Dist.

Gupta, Yogi. Yoga & Yogic Powers. LC 63-14948. (Illus.). 1963. 20.00 (ISBN 0-911664-02-5). Yogi Gupta.

Gupte, R. S. Iconography of the Hindus, Buddhists & Jains. 2nd ed. (Illus.). xviii, 201p. 1981. text ed. 45.00x (ISBN 0-86590-028-0, Pub. by Taraporevala India). Apt Bks.

Gura, Carol. Ministering to Young Adults. (Illus.). 200p. 1987. spiralbound 28.95 (ISBN 0-88489-179-8). St Mary's.

Gura, Philip F. A Glimpse of Sion's Glory. Incl. 1984. 30.00x (ISBN 0-8195-5095-7); Puritan Radicalism in New England,1620-1660. (Illus.). 399p. 1986. pap. 12.95 (ISBN 0-8195-6154-1). 1984. 30.00. Wesleyan U Pr.

--The Wisdom of Words: Language, Theology & Literature in the New England Renaissance. x, 203p. 1985. pap. 12.95 (ISBN 0-8195-6120-7). Wesleyan U Pr.

Guraya, M. Y. Origins of Islamic Jurisprudence. 18.00 (ISBN 0-317-46093-5). Kazi Pubns.

Gurbachan Singh Talib. Japuji: The Immortal Prayer-Chant. 1977. 7.00x (ISBN 0-88386-967-5). South Asia Bks.

Gurdjieff Foundation of California & Driscoll, J. Walter. Gurdjieff: An Annotated Bibliography. LC 83-49296. (Reference Library of Social Science). 390p. 1985. lib. bdg. 50.00 (ISBN 0-8240-8972-3). Garland Pub.

Gurdjieff, G. I. Life Is Real Only Then, When "I Am". 177p. 1981. 17.50 (ISBN 0-525-14547-8, 01699-510). Dutton.

Gurdus, Luba K. The Death Train. LC 78-54657. (Illus.). 1979. 12.95 (ISBN 0-8052-5005-0, Pub. by Holocaust Library). Schocken.

--The Death Train. LC 78-54657. (Illus.). 165p. (Orig.). 1978. 12.95 (ISBN 0-89604-005-4). Holocaust Pubns.
--Painful Echoes: From the Diary of Luba Krugman Gurdus. pap. 12.95 (ISBN 0-89604-059-3). Holocaust Pubns.
Gurganus, Gene. The Great Omission: Fruit That Remains. (Illus.). 104p. 1983. pap. 3.95 (ISBN 0-89084-191-8). Bob Jones Univ Pr.
Gurganus, George P., ed. Guidelines for World Evangelism. 1977. 11.95 (ISBN 0-89112-040-8, Bibl Res Pr). Abilene Christ U.
Gurian, Waldemar. Hitler & the Christians. Peeler, E. F., tr. LC 78-63675. (Studies in Fascism: Ideology & Practice). 184p. Repr. of 1936 ed. 22.00 (ISBN 0-404-16937-6). AMS Pr.
Gurley, Ralph R. Life of Jehudi Ashmun. facs. ed. LC 73-149867. (Black Heritage Library Collection Ser). 1835. 22.50 (ISBN 0-8369-8749-7). Ayer Co Pubs.
Gurnall, William. The Christian in Complete Armour. 1979. 26.95 (ISBN 0-85151-196-1). Banner of Truth.
--Christian in Complete Armour: A Modernised Abridgement, Vol. 1. rev., abr. ed. 320p. 1986. pap. 5.95 (ISBN 0-85151-456-1). Banner of Truth.
Gurney, O. R. Some Aspects of Hittite Religion. (Schweich Lectures on Biblical Archaeology). (Illus.). 80p. 1976. 10.25 (ISBN 0-85672-740-7, Pub. by British Acad). Longwood Pub Group.
Gurock, Jeffrey S. American Jewish History: A Bibliograhical Guide. 1983. 6.95 (ISBN 0-88464-037-X). ADL.
Guroian, Vigen. Incarnate Love: Essays in Orthodox Ethics. LC 86-40591. 208p. 1987. text ed. 22.95x (ISBN 0-268-01162-1, Dist. by Har-Row). U of Notre Dame Pr.
Gursan-Salzmann, Ayse & Salzmann, Laurence. Last Jews of Radauti. LC 82-22176. (Illus.). 192p. 1983. 29.95 (ISBN 0-385-27808-X, Dial). Doubleday.
Gurteen, S. Humphreys. Epic of the Fall of Man. LC 65-15879. (Studies in Comparative Literature, No. 35). 1969. Repr. of 1896 ed. lib. bdg. 75.00x (ISBN 0-8383-0561-X). Haskell.
Guru, R. H. Talk Does Not Cook the Rice: The Teachings of Agni Yoga. LC 81-70390. (Vol. 2). 198p. (Orig.). 1985. pap. 8.95 (ISBN 0-87728-535-7). Weiser.
Gurudas. Flower Essences & Vibrational Healing. 2nd ed. 314p. 1985. pap. 12.95 (ISBN 0-914732-09-9). Bro Life Inc.
Gusmer, Charles W. And You Visited Me. (Studies in the Reformed Rites of the Catholic Church: Vol. VI). 160p. (Orig.). 1984. pap. 9.95 (ISBN 0-916134-61-X). Pueblo Pub Co.
Guss, David, ed. see De Civrieux, Marc.
Gust, Dodie. As I Take Christ: Daily Prayer & Reflection with Paul. LC 86-72439. 136p. (Orig.). 1987. pap. 4.95 (ISBN 0-87793-352-9). Ave Maria.
Gustafson, Dana, ed. Food from Afar. spiral 3.95 (ISBN 0-686-12747-1). Grace Pub Co.
Gustafson, Gus. I Was...Called To Be a Layman. 176p. (Orig.). 1982. pap. 7.95 (ISBN 0-687-18604-8). Abingdon.
Gustafson, J. Louise & Poziemski, Christine L. Step-by-Step Through the Bible: Puzzles, Quizzes & Writing Experiences for Teaching Important Biblical Passages. (The Learning Connections Ser.). 160p. (Orig.). 1984. pap. 9.95 (ISBN 0-86683-835-X, 8442, HarpR). Har-Row.
Gustafson, James M. Can Ethics Be Christian? LC 74-11622. 1977. pap. 7.00x (ISBN 0-226-31102-3, P734, Phoen). U of Chicago Pr.
--Christ & the Moral Life. 1979. 8.00x (ISBN 0-226-31109-0, P830, Phoen). U of Chicago Pr.
--Ethics from a Theocentric Perspective: Theology & Ethics, Vol. 1. LC 81-11603. 284p. 1981. 27.50x (ISBN 0-226-31110-4). U of Chicago Pr.
--Ethics from a Theocentric Perspective: Theology & Ethics, Vol. 1. LC 81-11603. xiv, 346p. 1983. pap. 12.00x (ISBN 0-226-31111-2). U of Chicago Pr.
--Ethics from a Theocentric Perspective, Vol. 2: Ethics & Theology. LC 81-11603. 370p. 1984. lib. bdg. 25.00x (ISBN 0-226-31112-0). U of Chicago Pr.
--Protestant & Roman Catholic Ethics: Prospects for Rapprochement. LC 77-21421. 1980. pap. 8.00x (ISBN 0-226-31108-2, P868); 15.00 (ISBN 0-226-31107-4). U of Chicago Pr.
Gustafson, Robert R. Authors of Confusion. pap. 1.45 (ISBN 0-686-12743-9). Grace Pub Co.
Gustaveson, David. Personal Life Notebook. 192p. 1980. pap. 8.95 spiral bdg. (ISBN 0-87123-467-X, 210467). Bethany Hse.
Guste, Bob. Mary at My Side. 64p. (Orig.). 1985. pap. 3.95 (ISBN 0-89622-247-0). Twenty-Third.
Guterman, Simeon L. Religious Toleration & Persecution in Ancient Rome. LC 70-104269. 160p. Repr. of 1951 ed. lib. bdg. 22.50x (ISBN 0-8371-3936-8, GURT). Greenwood.
Gutherie, Shirley C., Jr. Diversity in Faith-Unity in Christ. LC 86-9157. 144p. (Orig.). 1986. pap. 10.95 (ISBN 0-664-24013-5). Westminster.
Guthmann, Robert F., Jr. & Womack, Sharon K. Death, Dying & Grief: A Bibliography. LC 77-82084. 1978. pap. text ed. 5.50 (ISBN 0-918626-01-3, Pied Publications). Word Serv.
Guthrie, et al. Nuevo Comentario Biblico. Orig. Title: The New Bible Commentary Revised. 972p. 1986. pap. 39.95 (ISBN 0-311-03001-7). Casa Bautista.
Guthrie, Donald. The Apostles. 432p. 1981. pap. 12.95 (ISBN 0-310-25421-3, 12235P). Zondervan.
--The Epistle to the Hebrews: An Introduction & Commentary. (Tyndale New Testament Commentaries: Vol. 15). 288p. 1983. pap. 5.95 (ISBN 0-8028-1427-1). Eerdmans.
--Exploring God's Word: A Guide to John's Gospel. 232p. (Orig.). pap. 7.95 (ISBN 0-8028-0256-7). Eerdmans.
--Exploring God's World: A Guide to Ephesians, Philippians, & Colossians. 224p. (Orig.). 1985. pap. 6.95 (ISBN 0-8028-0084-X). Eerdmans.
--Galatians. rev. ed. Black, Matthew, ed. (New Century Bible Commentary Ser.). 176p. 1981. pap. 5.95 (ISBN 0-8028-1906-0). Eerdmans.
--Jesus the Messiah. 400p. 1981. pap. 12.95 (ISBN 0-310-25431-0, 12223P). Zondervan.
--New Bible Commentary. rev. ed. 1970. 24.95 (ISBN 0-8028-2281-9). Eerdmans.
--New Testament Introduction. rev. ed. 1971. 34.95 (ISBN 0-87784-953-6). Inter-Varsity.
--New Testament Theology. 1056p. 1981. text ed. 34.95 (ISBN 0-87784-965-X). Inter-Varsity.
--Pastoral Epistles. (Tyndale Bible Commentary). 1957. pap. 4.95 (ISBN 0-8028-1413-1). Eerdmans.
--Shorter Life of Christ. LC 71-120039. (Contemporary Evangelical Perspectives Ser). 1970. kivar 8.95 (ISBN 0-310-25441-8, 6500P). Zondervan.
--Teaching of the New Testament. 1983. pap. 4.95 (ISBN 0-87508-179-7). Chr Lit.
Guthrie, Gary D. The Wisdom Tree. 56p. (Orig.). Date not set. pap. price not set (ISBN 0-9612980-0-6). Gary Guthrie.
Guthrie, Harvey H., Jr. Israel's Sacred Songs: A Study of Dominant Themes. 256p. 1984. pap. text ed. 11.50 (ISBN 0-8191-4027-9, Co-Pub. by Episcopal Div Sch). U Pr of Amer.
--Theology As Thanksgiving: From Israel's Psalms to the Church's Eucharist. 1981. 15.95 (ISBN 0-8164-0486-0, HarpR). Har-Row.
Guthrie, Kenneth S., tr. The Life of Zoroaster: In the Words of His Own Hymns the "Gathas". LC 73-131036. Repr. of 1914 ed. 14.50 (ISBN 0-404-02964-7). AMS Pr.
Guthrie, LaWanda. His Strange Ways. LC 81-10854. 1986. pap. 10.95 (ISBN 0-87949-212-0). Ashley Bks.
Guthrie, Lula. The Sunshine Basket. (Illus.). 1986. pap. 1.95 (ISBN 0-89265-112-1). Randall Hse.
Guthrie, Ramon, tr. see Rousset, David.
Guthrie, Shirley C., tr. see Cullmann, Oscar.
Guthrie, Shirley C., Jr. Christian Doctrine: Teachings of the Christian Church. (Illus., Orig.). 1969. pap. 7.95 (ISBN 0-8042-9051-2). John Knox.
Guthrie, Stewart E. A Japanese New Religion: Rissho Kosei-Kai in a Mountain Hamlet. LC 86-33446. (Michigan Papers in Japanese Studies: No. 16). 1987. text ed. 20.00 (ISBN 0-939512-33-5); pap. 10.00 (ISBN 0-939512-34-3). U Mi Japan.
Guthrie, William K. Greeks & Their Gods. (Orig.). 1955. pap. 8.95x (ISBN 0-8070-5793-2, BPA16). Beacon Pr.
Gutierrez, Edna L., tr. see Mandeville, Sylvia.
Gutierrez, Edna L., tr. see Mandeville, Sylvia & Pierson, Lance.
Gutierrez, Edna L. de see Ton, Mary E.
Gutierrez, Edna L. de see Wood, Fred M.
Gutierrez, Gustavo. On Job: God-Talk & the Suffering of the Innocent. O'Connell, Matthew, tr. from Span. LC 87-5661. Tr. of Hablar de Dios desde el Sufrimento del Inocente. 144p. (Orig.). 1987. 10.95 (ISBN 0-88344-577-8); pap. 8.95 (ISBN 0-88344-552-2). Orbis Bks.
--We Drink from Our Own Wells: The Spiritual Journey of a People. O'Connell, Matthew J., tr. from Span. LC 83-22008. Orig. Title: Beber en Supropio Pozo: En el Itinerario Espiritual de un Pueblo. 208p. (Orig.). 1984. pap. 7.95 (ISBN 0-88344-707-X). Orbis Bks.
Gutierrez, Rolando C. Mensaje de los Salmos, Tomo III. 160p. 1983. pap. 5.95 (ISBN 0-311-04028-4). Casa Bautista.
--El Mensaje de los Salmos en Nuestro Contexto, Tomo II. 160p. 1980. pap. 4.95 (ISBN 0-311-04025-X). Casa Bautista.
--El Mensaje de los Salmos en Nuestro Contexto Tomo I. 160p. 1984. Repr. of 1979 ed. 5.95 (ISBN 0-311-04023-3). Casa Bautista.
Gutierrez-Cortes, Rolando. Cuando la Familia Enfrenta Problemas. (Serie de la Familia). (Span.). 96p. 1985. pap. 3.50 (ISBN 0-311-46261-8). Casa Bautista.
Gutman, Y. & Rothkirchen, L., eds. The Catastrophe of European Jewry: Antecedents, History, Reflections. 25.00x (ISBN 0-87068-336-5). Ktav.
Gutman, Y. & Zuroff, E., eds. Rescue Attempts During the Holocaust. 25.00x (ISBN 0-87068-345-4). Ktav.
Gutman, Yisrael. The Jews of Warsaw, 1939-1943: Ghetto, Underground, Revolt. Friedman, Ina, tr. LC 81-47570. (Illus.). 512p. 1982. 24.95x (ISBN 0-253-33174-9). Ind U Pr.
Gutman, Yisrael, ed. The Holocaust in Documents. 1982. 22.50 (ISBN 0-686-85569-8). ADL.
Gutman, Yisrael & Krakowski, Shmuel, eds. The Angel of Death: The Untold Story of Josef Mengele. 1986. 16.95 (ISBN 0-933503-62-8). Shapolsky Pubs.
Gutmanis, June. Na Pule Kahiko: Ancient Hawaiian Prayers. LC 83-80256. (Illus.). 136p. 1983. 17.50 (ISBN 0-9607938-6-0); deluxe ed. 100.00 (ISBN 0-9607938-7-9). Editions Ltd.
Gutmann, Joseph. Beauty in Holiness: Studies in Jewish Ceremonial Art & Customs. 1970. 50.00x (ISBN 0-87068-012-9). Ktav.
--Hebrew Manuscript Painting. (Magnificent Paperback Art Ser.). 1978. 22.95 (ISBN 0-8076-0890-4); pap. 12.95 (ISBN 0-8076-0891-2). Braziller.
--The Jewish Sanctuary. (Inconography of Religions, Section Ser.: Vol. 23). (Illus.). 33p. 1983. pap. text ed. 32.50x (ISBN 90-04-06893-7, Pub. by EJ Brill Holland). Humanities.
--No Graven Images: Studies in Art & the Hebrew Bible. (Library of Biblical Studies). 1970. 50.00x (ISBN 0-87068-063-3). Ktav.
--The Synagogue: Studies in Origins, Archeology, & Architecture. 1974. 35.00x (ISBN 0-87068-265-2). Ktav.
Gutmann, Joseph, ed. Ancient Synagogues: The State of Research. LC 81-5252. (Brown Univ. BJS Ser.). 1981. pap. 14.00 (ISBN 0-89130-467-3, 140022). Scholars Pr GA.
--The Temple of Solomon: Archaeological Fact & Medieval Tradition in Christian, Islamic & Jewish Art. LC 75-19120. 1976. 9.00 (ISBN 0-89130-013-9, 090103). Scholars Pr GA.
Guttgemans, Erhard T. Candid Questions Concerning Gospel Form Criticism: A Methodological Sketch of Fundamental Problematics of Form & Redaction Criticism. 2nd ed. Doty, William G., tr. LC 79-10167. (Pittsburgh Theological Monographs: No. 26). 1979. pap. 15.00 (ISBN 0-915138-24-7). Pickwick.
Gutting, Gary. Religious Belief & Religious Skepticism. LC 82-50287. 192p. 1982. text ed. 15.95 (ISBN 0-268-01613-5). U of Notre Dame Pr.
--Religious Belief & Religious Skepticism. LC 82-50287. xi, 192p. 1983. pap. text ed. 9.95x (ISBN 0-268-01618-6, 85-16189). U of Notre Dame Pr.
Guttman, Alexander. Struggle over Reform in Rabbinic Literature. LC 75-45046. 1977. 13.50 (ISBN 0-8074-0005-X, 382790). UAHC.
Guttman, Julius. Philosophies of Judaism: The History of Jewish Philosophy from Biblical Times to Franz Rosenzweig. LC 63-11875. 560p. 1973. pap. 13.50 (ISBN 0-8052-0402-4). Schocken.
Guttman, Julius W., ed. see Maimonides, Moses.
Guttmann, Jacob. Die Religionsphilosophischen Lehren des Isaak Abravanel. Katz, Steven, ed. LC 79-7134. (Jewish Philosophy, Mysticism & History of Ideas Ser.). 1980. Repr. of 1916 ed. lib. bdg. 14.00x (ISBN 0-405-12260-8). Ayer Co Pubs.
Guttmann, Yitzhak J. On the Philosophy of Religion. Herman, David V., tr. from Hebrew. 134p. 1976. text ed. 25.00x (Pub. by Magnes Pr Israel). Humanities.
Guttschuss, Heather. Growing More Like Jesus. 128p. 1985. pap. 6.95 (ISBN 0-8163-0486-6). Pacific Pr Pub Assn.
Gutwirth, Israel. The Kaballah & Jewish Mysticism. 1987. 15.00. Philos Lib.
--Kabbalah & Jewish Mysticism. LC 86-18693. 288p. 1986. 15.00 (ISBN 0-8022-2516-0). Philos Lib.
Gutzke, Manford G. Plain Talk on Acts. 224p. 1972. pap. 7.95 (ISBN 0-310-25501-5, 9725P). Zondervan.
--Plain Talk on Corinthians. 1978. pap. 7.95 (ISBN 0-310-25641-0, 9858P). Zondervan.
--Plain Talk on Ephesians. 224p. 1973. pap. 6.95 (ISBN 0-310-25511-2, 9729P). Zondervan.
--Plain Talk on Hebrews. 160p. 1976. pap. 5.95 (ISBN 0-310-25541-4, 9852P). Zondervan.
--Plain Talk on Isaiah. 1977. pap. 6.95 (ISBN 0-310-25551-1, 9854P). Zondervan.
--Plain Talk on James. 1969. pap. 5.95 (ISBN 0-310-25561-9, 9728P). Zondervan.
--Plain Talk on John. LC 69-11646. (Prog. Bk.). 1969. pap. 7.95 (ISBN 0-310-25571-6, 9726P). Zondervan.
--Plain Talk on Luke. 1966. pap. 5.95 (ISBN 0-310-25581-3, 9097P). Zondervan.
--Plain Talk on Mark. 295p. 1975. pap. 6.95 (ISBN 0-310-25591-0, 9762P). Zondervan.
--Plain Talk on Matthew. pap. 6.95 (ISBN 0-310-25601-1, 9727P). Zondervan.
--Plain Talk on Revelation. (Orig.). 1979. pap. 5.95 (ISBN 0-310-25681-X, 9863P). Zondervan.
--Plain Talk on the Epistles of John. 1977. pap. 5.95 (ISBN 0-310-25631-3, 9857P). Zondervan.
--Plain Talk on Timothy, Titus, & Philemon. (Plain Talk Ser.). 1978. pap. 6.95 (ISBN 0-310-25661-5, 9861P). Zondervan.
Guy, B. Domestic Correspondance of Dominique-Marie Varlet: Bishop of Babylon 1678-1742. (Studies in the History of Christian Thought: No. 36). ix, 150p. 1986. 22.00 (ISBN 90-04-07671-9, Pub. by E J Brill). Heinman.
Guy, J. A. The Public Career of Sir Thomas More. LC 80-5391. 224p. 1980. 34.00x (ISBN 0-300-02546-7). Yale U Pr.
Guyard, Marius Francois, jt. auth. see Chateaubriand, Rene de.
Guyon, Jeanne. The Book of Job. 1985. pap. 7.95 (ISBN 0-940232-23-5). Christian Bks.
--Christ Our Revelation. (Orig.). 1985. pap. 7.95 (ISBN 0-940232-21-9). Christian Bks.
--Final Steps in Christian Maturity. 1985. pap. 6.95 (ISBN 0-940232-22-7). Christian Bks.
--Genesis. 1983. pap. 5.95 (ISBN 0-940232-15-4). Christian Bks.
--Song of Songs. 1983. pap. 5.95 (ISBN 0-940232-16-2). Christian Bks.
--Union with God. Edwards, Gene, ed. 117p. 1981. pap. 5.95 (ISBN 0-940232-05-7). Christian Bks.
--The Way Out. (Orig.). 1985. pap. 6.95 (ISBN 0-940232-20-0). Christian Bks.
Guyon, Jeanne M. Experiencing the Depths of Jesus Christ. 3rd ed. Edwards, Gene, ed. 1975. pap. 5.95 (ISBN 0-940232-00-6). Christian Bks.
Guyon, Madame. Experiencing God Through Prayer. (Experiencing the Depths of Jesus Christ Ser.). 176p. 1984. pap. text ed. 3.50 (ISBN 0-88368-153-6). Whitaker Hse.
Guzie, Noreen M., jt. auth. see Guzie, Tad.
Guzie, Tad. The Book of Sacramental Basics. LC 81-83189. 160p. (Orig.). 1982. pap. 6.95 (ISBN 0-8091-2411-4). Paulist Pr.
Guzie, Tad & Guzie, Noreen M. About Men & Women: How Your Great Story Shapes Your Destiny. 176p. (Orig.). 1986. pap. 7.95 (ISBN 0-8091-2813-6). Paulist Pr.
Guzie, Tad W. Jesus & the Eucharist. LC 73-90069. 168p. 1974. pap. 5.95 (ISBN 0-8091-1858-0). Paulist Pr.
Guzman, Domingo De see Domingo De Guzman, Saint.
Guzman, Juan P., tr. see Taylor, Jack R.
Gvillo, Doris. Musing, Meditations, & Meanderings. 1984. 5.95 (ISBN 0-89536-982-6, 7531). CSS of Ohio.
Gwatkin, Henry M. The Arian Controversy. new ed. LC 77-84702. Repr. of 1903 ed. 27.50 (ISBN 0-404-16109-X). AMS Pr.
--Early Church History to A. D. 313, 2 vols. 1977. lib. bdg. 200.00 (ISBN 0-8490-1738-6). Gordon Pr.
--Early Church History to A.D. 313, 2 Vols. LC 77-168216. Repr. of 1909 ed. 52.50 (ISBN 0-404-02966-3). AMS Pr.
--The Knowledge of God & Its Historical Development, 2 vols. LC 77-27219. (Gifford Lectures: 1904-05). 1978. Repr. of 1906 ed. Set. 49.50 (ISBN 0-404-60490-0). AMS Pr.
--Studies of Arianism: Chiefly Referring to the Character & Chronology of the Reaction Which Followed the Council of Nicaea. 2nd ed. LC 77-84703. Repr. of 1900 ed. 38.00 (ISBN 0-404-16110-3). AMS Pr.
Gwyn, Douglas. Apocalypse of the Word: The Life & Message of George Fox (1624-1690) 240p. (Orig.). 1986. pap. 14.95 (ISBN 0-913408-91-3). Friends United.
Gwynn, Robin D. Huguenot Heritage: The History & Contribution of the Huguenots in England. (Illus.). 256p. 1985. 34.95x (ISBN 0-7102-0420-5). Methuen Inc.
Gwynn, Stephen. Henry Grattan & His Times. facsimile ed. LC 78-175699. (Select Bibliographies Reprint Ser.). Repr. of 1939 ed. 26.50 (ISBN 0-8369-6614-7). Ayer Co Pubs.
--Thomas Moore. LC 73-13838. 1905. Repr. lib. bdg. 15.00 (ISBN 0-8414-4448-X). Folcroft.
Gwynne, H. The Cause of World Unrest: The Jews. 1982. lib. bdg. 69.95 (ISBN 0-87700-340-8). Revisionist Pr.
Gwynne, H. A., intro. by. The Cause of World Unrest. 1978. pap. 5.00x (ISBN 0-911038-40-X). Noontide.
Gwynne, Walker. The Christian Year; Its Purpose & Its History. LC 74-89269. xiv, 143p. 1972. Repr. of 1917 ed. 43.00x (ISBN 0-8103-3814-9). Gale.

Gyalpo, Tangtong. A Technique for Developing Enlightened Consciousness: A Traditional Buddhist Meditation on Avalokiteshvara. Gyatso, Janet, tr. from Tibetan. (Basic Buddhism Ser.). 26p. (Orig.). 1980. pap. 1.50 (ISBN 0-915078-02-3, P-01). Buddhist Assn US.

Gyalsten, Khenpo K. The Garland of Mahamudra Practices. 140p. 1986. pap. 9.95 (ISBN 0-937938-35-1). Snow Lion.

--Prayer Flags: The Spiritual Life & Songs of Jigten Sumgon. 96p. (Orig.). 1986. pap. 6.95 (ISBN 0-937938-37-8). Snow Lion.

Gyan, Gopi. Morningland Color Book. 1979. pap. 7.95 (ISBN 0-935146-09-1). Morningland.

Gyan, Gopi, jt. auth. see Patricia.

Gyan, Gopi, jt. auth. see Patricia, Sri.

Gyatsho, Tenzin see Dalai Lama, IV.

Gyatso, Geshe K. Buddhism in the Tibetan Tradition: A Guide. (Illus.). 144p. (Orig.). 1984. pap. 9.95 (ISBN 0-7102-0242-3). Methuen Inc.

--Clear Light of Bliss. Landaw, Jonathan, ed. Norbu, Tenzin, tr. from Tibetan. (Wisdom Advanced Book: Blue Ser.). (Illus.). 264p. (Orig.). 1982. pap. 10.95 (ISBN 0-86171-005-3, Pub. by Wisdom Pubns). Great Traditions.

Gyatso, Janet, tr. see Gyalpo, Tangtong.

Gyatso, Tenzin. My Land & My People. 3rd ed. (Illus.). 271p. 1983. Repr. of 1962 ed. 6.95. Potala.

Gyatso, Tenzin, jt. auth. see Nagarjuna.

Gyekye, Kwame, ed. & tr. Arabic Logic: Ibn al-Tayyib on Porphyry's "Eisagoge". LC 76-4071. 1979. 49.50x (ISBN 0-87395-308-8). State U NY Pr.

Gyldenvand, Lily M. Joy in His Presence: Christian Reflections on Everyday Life. LC 81-67806. 112p. (Orig.). 1981. pap. 4.95 (ISBN 0-8066-1896-5, 10-3596). Augsburg.

Gysi, Lydia. Platonism & Cartesianism in the Philosophy of Ralph Cudworth. 163p. 1962. 14.35 (ISBN 3-261-00648-X). P Lang Pubs.

Gythiel, Anthony P., tr. see Evdokimov, Paul.

Gythiel, Anthony P., tr. see Spidlik, Tomas.

H

Ha, Ta. Al-Dhabh. 3.95 (ISBN 0-686-83897-1). Kazi Pubns.

Haaften, Julia Van see Frith, Francis.

Haag. La France Protestante: Biographies Historiques, 12 tomes. Set. 113.75 (ISBN 0-685-36098-9). French & Eur.

Haag, Herbert. Diccionario De la Biblia. 7th ed. (Span.). 1080p. 1977. 50.00 (ISBN 84-254-0077-5, S-50196). French & Eur.

Haak, B. Rembrandt Drawings. Willems-Treeman, Elizabeth, tr. LC 76-10073. (Illus.). 1976. 22.50 (ISBN 0-87951-047-1). Overlook Pr.

--Rembrandt Drawings. Willems-Treeman, Elizabeth, tr. LC 76-10073. (Illus.). 1977. pap. 10.95 (ISBN 0-87951-051-X). Overlook Pr.

Ha-am, Achad, pseud. Ten Essays on Zionism & Judaism. LC 73-2202. (The Jewish People; History, Religion, Literature Ser.). Repr. of 1922 ed. 26.50 (ISBN 0-405-05267-7). Ayer Co Pubs.

Haan, M. J. De see Gumbert, J. P. & De Haan, M. J.

Haan, M. R. see De Haan, Martin R.

Haan, M. R. see DeHaan, Martin R.

Haan, Martin R. De see De Haan, M. R.

Haan, Martin R. De see De Haan, Mr. R.

Haan, Richard W. De see De Haan, Richard W. & Bosch, Henry G.

Haan, Sheri D. Good News for Children. 1969. pap. 5.95 (ISBN 0-8010-4073-6). Baker Bk.

Haas, C., et al. Translator's Handbook on the Letters of John. LC 74-102407. (Helps for Translators Ser.). 171p. 1972. 3.30x (ISBN 0-8267-0154-X, 08516, Pub. by United Bible). Am Bible.

Haas, Dorothy. My First Communion. Tucker, Kathleen, ed. (Illus.). 48p. 1987. PLB 9.25 (ISBN 0-8075-5331-X). A Whitman.

Haas, Harold I. El Cristiano Frente a los Problemas Mentales. De Molina, Sara Pais, tr. 110p. 1977. Repr. of 1975 ed. 2.50 (ISBN 0-311-42500-3). Casa Bautista.

--Pastoral Counseling with People in Distress. LC 77-99316. 1969. pap. 6.95 (ISBN 0-570-03794-8, 12-2776). Concordia.

Haas, James & Haas, Lynne. Make a Joyful Noise! (Illus.). 40p. (Orig.). 1973. pap. 1.95 (ISBN 0-8192-1146-X). Morehouse.

Haas, James E. Praise the Lord! LC 74-80388. 1974. pap. 3.95 (ISBN 0-8192-1176-1). Morehouse.

--Rainbow Songs. 40p. (Orig.). 1975. pap. 3.95 (ISBN 0-8192-1201-6). Morehouse.

Haas, Joseph S. The Northeast Retreat of 1759 & 1981. LC 81-90691. (Cathedral of the Beechwoods Ser.: No. 1). (Illus.). 148p. (Orig.). 1981. per copy 7.00 (ISBN 0-9605552-0-X). Haas Ent NH.

Haas, Lois J. Tell Me about God: 12 Lessons, Vol. 1. (Tiny Steps of Faith Ser.). 1966. complete kit 12.95 (ISBN 0-86508-011-9); text only 2.95 (ISBN 0-86508-012-7); color & action book 0.90 (ISBN 0-86508-013-5). BCM Intl Inc.

--Tell Me about Jesus: 16 Lessons, Vol. 2. (Tiny Steps of Faith Ser.). 1967. complete kit 12.95 (ISBN 0-86508-014-3); text only 2.95 (ISBN 0-86508-015-1); color & action book 0.90 (ISBN 0-86508-016-X). BCM Intl Inc.

--Tell Me How to Please God: 16 Lessons, Vol. 4. (Tiny Steps of Faith Ser.). 1974. complete kit 10.95 (ISBN 0-86508-020-8); text only 2.95 (ISBN 0-86508-021-6); color & action book 0.90 (ISBN 0-86508-022-4). BCM Intl Inc.

--Tell Me How to Trust God: 16 Lessons, Vol. 3. (Tiny Steps of Faith Ser.). 1970. complete kit 12.95 (ISBN 0-86508-017-8); text only 2.95 (ISBN 0-86508-018-6); color & action book 0.90 (ISBN 0-86508-019-4). BCM Intl Inc.

Haas, Lynne, jt. auth. see Haas, James.

Haas, Peter, ed. Biblical Hermeneutics in Jewish Moral Discourse. (Semeia Ser.: No. 34). pap. 9.95 (06 20 34). Scholars Pr GA.

Haas, Peter J., tr. from Hebrew-Aramaic. The Talmud of Babylonia: An American Translation XXXV: Meilah & Tamid. (Brown Judaic Studies). 180p. 1986. 29.95 (ISBN 1-55540-086-8, 14-01-09). Scholars Pr GA.

Haas, Wayne. Your Crocodile Is Ready. 1984. 6.25 (ISBN 0-89536-620-7, 4888). CSS of Ohio.

Haase, Felix A. Die Koptischen Quellen Zum Konzil Von Nicaa. 12.00 (ISBN 0-384-20630-1). Johnson Repr.

Haase, Wolfgang, ed. see Aveling, J. C., et al.

Haase, Wolfgang, jt. ed. see Temporini, Hildegard.

Habeck, Irwin J. Ephesiana. 1985. 7.95 (ISBN 0-8100-0171-3, 15N0404). Northwest Pub.

Habel, N. C. Book of Job. LC 74-82588. (Cambridge Bible Commentary on the New English Bible, Old Testament Ser.). 250p. 1975. 27.95 (ISBN 0-521-20653-7); pap. 12.95 (ISBN 0-521-09943-9). Cambridge U Pr.

Habel, Norman C. The Book of Job, a Commentary. LC 84-21580. (The Old Testament Library). 586p. 1985. 39.95 (ISBN 0-664-21831-8). Westminster.

--Create in Me: A Form of the Eucharist in a Modern Idiom. 1978. 0.95 (ISBN 0-915644-14-2). Clayton Pub Hse.

--Job. LC 80-82193. (Knox Preaching Guides). 100p. (Orig., John Hayes series editor). 1981. pap. 4.95 (ISBN 0-8042-3216-4). John Knox.

--Literary Criticism of the Old Testament. Rylaarsdam, Coert, ed. LC 78-157548. (Guides to Biblical Scholarship: Old Testament Ser.). 96p. 1971. pap. 4.50 (ISBN 0-8006-0176-9, 1-176). Fortress.

--Yahweh vs. Baal. 128p. 1964. write for info. Concordia Schl Grad Studies.

Haber, Francis C. The Age of the World: Moses to Darwin. LC 77-13854. 1978. Repr. of 1959 ed. lib. bdg. 22.50x (ISBN 0-8371-9898-4, HAAW). Greenwood.

Haberman, Jacob. Maimonides & Aquinas: A Contemporary Appraisal. 25.00x (ISBN 0-87068-685-2). Ktav.

Habermas, Gary & Flew, Anthony. Did Jesus Rise from the Dead? 1987. 14.95 (HarpR). Har-Row.

Habermas, Gary B., jt. auth. see Stevenson, Kenneth.

Habermas, Gary R. Ancient Evidence for the Life of Jesus: Historical Records of His Death & Resurrection. 1985. pap. 6.95 (ISBN 0-8407-5919-3). Nelson.

--The Resurrection of Jesus: An Apologetic. 188p. 1984. pap. text ed. 11.50 (ISBN 0-8191-3750-2). U Pr of Amer.

Habermas, Jurgen. Theory & Practice. Viertel, John, tr. from Ger. LC 72-6227. 320p. 1973. pap. 10.95x (ISBN 0-8070-1527-X, BP489). Beacon Pr.

Habershon, Ada R. Hidden Pictures in the Old Testament. LC 82-18676. 304p. 1983. pap. 8.95 (ISBN 0-8254-2855-6). Kregel.

--Outline Study of the Tabernacle. LC 73-85298. 1974. pap. 2.95 (ISBN 0-8254-2820-3). Kregel.

--Study of the Miracles. LC 62-19174. 336p. 1967. 12.95 (ISBN 0-8254-2801-7); pap. 9.95 (ISBN 0-8254-2851-3). Kregel.

--Study of the Parables. LC 62-19175. 392p. 1967. 12.95 (ISBN 0-8254-2802-5); pap. 9.95 (ISBN 0-8254-2852-1). Kregel.

--Study of the Types. LC 67-24340. 240p. 1975. pap. 7.95 (ISBN 0-8254-2850-5). Kregel.

Habert, Isaac. Liber Pontificalis Graecae. 790p. Repr. of 1643 ed. text ed. 124.20x (ISBN 0-576-99140-6, Pub. by Gregg Intl Pubs England). Gregg Intl.

Habezk, Irwin J., jt. auth. see Schuetze, Armin W.

Habig, M. A. Francis of Assisi: Writer. 1981. 2.00 (ISBN 0-8199-0844-4). Franciscan Herald.

Habig, Marion. Christ the Prisoner. 1976. pap. 0.50 (ISBN 0-685-77502-X). Franciscan Herald.

--Franciscan Book of Saints. 988p. 1980. 30.00 (ISBN 0-8199-0751-0). Franciscan Herald.

Habig, Marion A. Franciscan Crown Rosary. 1977. 3.00 (ISBN 0-8199-0605-0). Franciscan Herald.

--In Journeyings Often: Franciscan Pioneers in the Orient. (Spirit & Life Ser). 1953. 6.50 (ISBN 0-686-11564-3). Franciscan Inst.

--My God & My All. 1977. 4.50 (ISBN 0-685-77278-0). Franciscan Herald.

--Spanish Texas Pilgrimage: The Old Franciscan Missions & Other Spanish Settlements of Texas, 1632-1821. 1985. 12.50 (ISBN 0-8199-0883-5). Franciscan Herald.

Habig, Marion A., ed. English Omnibus of Sources: St. Francis of Assisi. new ed. 1977. 30.00 (ISBN 0-8199-0658-1). Franciscan Herald.

--The Marian Era, Vol. 11. (Illus.). 132p. 1973. 6.95 (ISBN 0-8199-0215-2). Franciscan Herald.

--St. Francis of Assisi: Omnibus of Sources of the Life of St.Francis. Brown, Raphael & Fahy, B., trs. (Illus.). 1828p. 1975. 35.00 (ISBN 0-8199-0440-6). Franciscan Herald.

--Vitam Alere, Franciscan Readings. (Tau Ser.). 1979. 5.95 (ISBN 0-8199-0769-3). Franciscan Herald.

Haboush, Jahyun K., jt. ed. see De Bary, William T.

Hachey, Thomas, ed. Anglo-Vatican Relations, 1914-1939: Confidential Annual Reports of the British Ministers to the Holy See. 1972. lib. bdg. 23.00 (ISBN 0-8161-0991-5, Hall Reference). G K Hall.

Hack, John. How to Make Audiovisuals. rev. ed. LC 78-72847. 1980. pap. 5.95 (ISBN 0-8054-3427-5). Broadman.

--How to Operate a Cassette Tape Ministry. LC 81-66822. 1981. pap. 4.25 (ISBN 0-8054-3429-1). Broadman.

Hack, Roy K. God in Greek Philosophy to the Time of Socrates. 1970. Repr. of 1931 ed. lib. bdg. 12.50 (ISBN 0-8337-1514-3). B Franklin.

Hackel, Sergei. The Byzantine Saint. LC 83-8738. 245p. 1982. lib. bdg. 23.95x (ISBN 0-89370-081-9); pap. text ed. 15.95x (ISBN 0-7044-0451-6). Borgo Pr.

--Pearl of Great Price: The Life of Mother Maria Skobtsova 1891-1945. rev. ed. LC 81-21356. 192p. 1982. pap. 6.95 (ISBN 0-913836-85-0). St Vladimirs.

Hackel, Sergei, ed. The Byzantine Saint. (Illus.). 245p. (Orig.). 1981. pap. 6.95 (ISBN 0-7044-0451-6). St Vladimirs.

Hacker, Paul. Ego in Faith: Martin Luther & the Origins of Anthropocentric Religion. Wicks, Jared, ed. LC 70-85506. (Das Ich Im Glauben Bei Martin Luther). 1971. 6.50 (ISBN 0-8199-0406-6). Franciscan Herald.

Hacker, Richard C. The Christmas Pipe: A Collector's Celebration of Pipe Smoking at Yuletide. LC 86-70905. (Illus.). 156p. 1986. 27.95 (ISBN 0-931253-01-2). Autumngold Pub.

Hackett, Allen, tr. see Schmidt, Elisabeth.

Hackett, Charles, ed. see Bracken, et al.

Hackett, Charles D., jt. auth. see Harrisville, Roy A.

Hackett, Jo Ann. The Balaam Text from Deir Alla. LC 83-27125. (Harvard Semitic Museum - Monograph). 160p. 1984. 11.95 (ISBN 0-89130-723-0, 04 00 31). Scholars Pr GA.

Hackett, John. A History of the Orthodox Church of Cyprus from the Coming of the Apostles Paul & Barnabas to the Commencement of the British Occupation (A.D. 45-A.D. 1878) Together with Some Account of the Latin & Other Churches Existing in the Island. LC 79-185941. (Illus.). 760p. 1972. Repr. of 1901 ed. lib. bdg. 35.50 (ISBN 0-8337-1515-1). B Franklin.

Hackett, Rosalind I., ed. New Religious Movements in Nigeria. LC 86-31080. (African Studies: Vol. 5). 1987. 59.95 (ISBN 0-88946-180-5). E Mellen.

Hackett, Stuart C. Reconstruction of the Christian Revelation Claim: A Philosophical & Critical Apologetic. 560p. 1984. pap. 19.95 (ISBN 0-8010-4283-6). Baker Bk.

--The Resurrection of Theism: Prolegomena to Christian Apology. (Twin Brooks Ser.). 381p. 1982. pap. 11.95 (ISBN 0-8010-4263-1). Baker Bk.

Hacking, W. Smith Wigglesworth Remembered. 107p. 1981. pap. 3.95 (ISBN 0-89274-203-8). Harrison Hse.

Hackman, George G., ed. Temple Documents of the Third Dynasty of Ur from Umma. LC 78-63524. (Babylonian Inscriptions in the Collection of James B. Nies: No. 5). Repr. of 1937 ed. 28.50 (ISBN 0-404-60135-9). AMS Pr.

Hackman, Ruth. God in the Midst of Every Day: Reflections on Life's Simple Gifts. LC 86-7888. (Illus.). 128p. 1986. kivar paper 6.50 (ISBN 0-8066-2207-5, 10-2643). Augsburg.

Hackstaff, L. H., jt. auth. see Benjamin, A.

Hackstaff, L. H., tr. see Saint Augustine.

Hackwood, F. W. Christ Lore. 59.95 (ISBN 0-87968-861-0). Gordon Pr.

Hackwood, Frederick W. Christ Lore: Being the Legends, Traditions, Myths, Symbols, Customs, & Superstitions of the Christian Church. LC 69-16064. (Illus.). 1971. Repr. of 1902 ed. 34.00x (ISBN 0-8103-3528-X). Gale.

Hacohen, David. Time to Tell. Dagut, Menachem, tr. LC 84-45243. 256p. 1985. 18.50 (ISBN 0-8453-4789-6, Cornwall Bks). Assoc Univ Prs.

HaCohen, Israel M. see Chaim, Chafetz, pseud.

HaCohen, Israel M. see Hayyim, Hafetz, pseud.

Hacohen, Menachem. The Haggadah of Legends & Customs. (Illus.). 128p. 1987. 29.95 (ISBN 0-915361-78-7, Dist. by Watts). Adama Pubs Inc.

Ha-Cohen, Yisroel Meir. Mishnah Bervrah, Vol. 3C. Orenstein, Aviel, tr. from Herbrew. 1984. 13.95 (ISBN 0-87306-351-1); large type ed. 17.95 (ISBN 0-87306-350-3). Feldheim.

--Mishnah Bervrah, Vol. 3B. Feldman, Aharon & Orenstein, Aviel, trs. 402p. 1981. 12.95 (ISBN 0-87306-276-0); large type ed. 15.95 (ISBN 0-87306-275-2). Feldheim.

Hadar, Eric. No Reason to Die. 32p. 1983. pap. 5.00 (ISBN 0-942494-76-8). Coleman Pub.

Hadas, Moses & Smith, Morton. Heroes & Gods: Spiritual Biographies in Antiquity. facsimile ed. LC 77-117800. (Essay Index Reprints - Religious Perspectives Ser.: Vol. 13). Repr. of 1965 ed. 19.00 (ISBN 0-8369-1880-0). Ayer Co Pubs.

Hadas, Moses, ed. see Maimon, Solomon.

Hadas, Pamela W. In Light of Genesis. LC 80-13129. (Jewish Poetry Ser.). 128p. 1980. 10.95 (ISBN 0-8276-0177-8, 462); pap. 6.95 (ISBN 0-8276-0178-6, 461). Jewish Pubns.

Hadassah Magazine Staff. Jewish Traveler. Tigay, Alan M., ed. LC 86-8917. (Illus.). 416p. 1987. 19.95 (ISBN 0-385-23811-8); pap. 12.95 (ISBN 0-385-23451-1). Doubleday.

Hadaway, C. Kirk, jt. ed. see Rose, Larry L.

Hadaway, C. KIrk, et al. Home Cell Groups & House Churches. 1987. 9.95 (ISBN 0-8054-6944-3). Broadman.

Hadawi, S. The Jews, Zionism & the Bible. 1984. lib. bdg. 79.95 (ISBN 0-87700-572-9). Revisionist Pr.

Hadcock, R. Neville, jt. auth. see Knowles, David.

Hadda, Ceri, jt. ed. see Family Circle.

Haddad, Hassan & Wagner, Donald, eds. All in the Name of the Bible. 2nd ed. 130p. 1986. pap. 7.95 (ISBN 0-915597-42-X). Amana Bks.

Haddad, Heskel M. The Jews of Arab & Islamic Countries: History, Problems & Solutions. LC 83-5065. 168p. 1984. 12.95 (ISBN 0-88400-100-8). Shengold.

Haddad, Robert M. Syrian Christians in Muslim Society: An Interpretation. LC 81-6202. (Princeton Studies on the Near East). viii, 118p. 1981. Repr. of 1970 ed. lib. bdg. 22.50x (ISBN 0-313-23054-4, HASYC). Greenwood.

Haddad, Yvonne Y. Contemporary Islam & the Challenge of History. LC 81-8732. 272p. 1982. 49.50 (ISBN 0-87395-543-9); pap. 19.95 o. s. i. (ISBN 0-87395-544-7). State U NY Pr.

Haddad, Yvonne Y., jt. auth. see Smith, Jane I.

Haddad, Yvonne Y. & Findly, Ellison B., eds. Women, Religion, & Social Change. (Illus.). 564p. 1985. 49.00x (ISBN 0-88706-068-4); pap. 19.50x (ISBN 0-88706-069-2). State U NY Pr.

Haddad, Yvonne Y., et al, eds. The Islamic Impact. (Contemporary Issues in the Middle East Ser.). (Illus.). 264p. 1983. text ed. 30.00x o. p. (ISBN 0-8156-2304-6); pap. text ed. 13.95x (ISBN 0-8156-2299-6). Syracuse U Pr.

Hadden, James C. Life of Handel: The Kelkel Edition. LC 74-24096. Repr. of 1904 ed. 15.00 (ISBN 0-404-12941-2). AMS Pr.

Hadden, Jeffrey K., ed. Religion in Radical Transition. 166p. 1973. 9.95 (ISBN 0-87855-070-4); pap. 3.95x (ISBN 0-87855-567-6). Transaction Bks.

Hadden, Jeffrey K. & Long, Theodore E., eds. Religion & Religiosity in America. LC 82-23605. (Studies in Honor of Joseph H. Fichter). 192p. 1983. 15.95 (ISBN 0-8245-0555-7). Crossroad NY.

Hadden, Jeffrey K. & Shupe, Anson, eds. Prophetic Religions & Politics: Religion & the Political Order. 408p. 1986. 24.95 (ISBN 0-913757-63-2, Pub. by New Era Bks); pap. 12.95 (ISBN 0-913757-53-5, Pub. by New Era Bks). Paragon Hse.

Haddon, David. Transcendental Meditation. new ed. 32p. (Orig.). 1975. pap. 0.75 (ISBN 0-87784-155-1). Inter-Varsity.

Haddon, David & Hamilton, Vail. TM Wants You. (Direction Bks). 160p. 1976. pap. 1.95 (ISBN 0-8010-4151-1). Baker Bk.

Hadfield, J. A. Psychology & Morals. 245p. 1980. Repr. of 1926 ed. lib. bdg. 30.00 (ISBN 0-8492-5282-2). R West.

Hadfield, P. Traits of Divine Kingship in Africa. LC 78-32120. 1979. Repr. of 1949 ed. lib. bdg. 22.50x (ISBN 0-8371-5189-9, HDK&, Pub. by Negro U Pr). Greenwood.

Hadfield, Percival. The Savage & His Totem. LC 75-32825. Repr. of 1938 ed. 20.00 (ISBN 0-404-14129-3). AMS Pr.

Hadidian, Allen. Discipleship: Helping Other Christians Grow. 1987. pap. 6.95 (ISBN 0-8024-3362-6). Moody.

Hadidian, Dikran Y., ed. Bibliography of British Theological Literature 1850-1940. (Bibliographia Tripotampolitana Ser.: No. 12). (Illus.). 500p. 1985. pap. 35.00 (ISBN 0-931222-11-7). Pitts Theolog.

--From Faith to Faith, Essays in Honor of Donald G. Miller, on His Seventieth Birthday. LC 79-23408. (Pittsburgh Theological Monographs: No. 31). 1979. 18.00 (ISBN 0-915138-38-7). Pickwick.

Hadingham, Evan. Lines to the Mountain Gods: Nazca & the Mysteries of Peru. LC 86-10137. (Illus.). 256p. 1986. 22.50 (ISBN 0-394-54235-5). Random.

Hadley, E. C. Prophetic Events. 74p. pap. 4.25 (ISBN 0-88172-146-8). Believers Bkshelf.

--The Song of Solomon. pap. 3.95 (ISBN 0-88172-080-1). Believers Bkshelf.

Hadley, Eric & Hadley, Tessa. Legends of Earth, Air, Fire & Water. (Illus.). 32p. 1985. 10.95 (ISBN 0-521-26311-5). Cambridge U Pr.

Hadley, Tessa, jt. auth. see Hadley, Eric.

Hadwin, M. R. The Role of New Testament Examples As Related to Biblical Authority. 1974. pap. 2.75 (ISBN 0-88027-038-1). Firm Foun Pub.

Haeberlin, Herman K. The Idea of Fertilization in the Culture of the Pueblo Indians. LC 16-25723. (American Anthro. Association Memoirs). pap. 15.00 (ISBN 0-527-00512-6). Kraus Repr.

Haeckel, Ernst. Riddle of the Universe at the Close of the 19th Century. LC 6403. 1900. 18.00x (ISBN 0-403-00117-X). Scholarly.

Haefeli, Leo. Stilmittel Bei Afrath, Dem Perischen Weisen. (Ger). 1932. 19.00 (ISBN 0-384-20710-3). Johnson Repr.

Haenchen, Ernst. The Acts of the Apostles, A Commentary. LC 78-161218. 762p. 1971. 29.95 (ISBN 0-664-20919-X). Westminster.

--The Gospel of John. FUnk, Robert W., tr. from Ger. LC 82-48756. (Hermeneia). 1984. 34.95 (ISBN 0-8006-6013-7, 20-6013). Fortress.

Haenchen, Ernst, tr. from Ger. The Gospel of John, Vol. 2. Funk, Robert W., ed. LC 82-48756. (Hermeneia Ser.). 384p. 34.95 (ISBN 0-8006-6015-3). Fortress.

Haendler, Gert. Luther on Ministerial Office & Congregational Function. Gritsch, Eric W., ed. Gritsch, Ruth C., tr. from Ger. LC 81-43075. Tr. of Amt und Gemeinde bei Luther im Kontext der Kirchengeschichte. 112p. 1981. 9.95 (ISBN 0-8006-0665-5, 1-665). Fortress.

Haeri, Shaykh F. Beams of Illumination from the Divine Revelation. 340p. 1987. pap. 18.95 (ISBN 0-7103-0219-3, 02193, Kegan Paul). Methuen Inc.

--Heart of Qu'ran & Perfect Mizan. 140p. 1987. pap. 18.95 (ISBN 0-7103-0222-3, Kegan Paul). Methuen Inc.

--Journey of the Universe As Expounded in the Qur'an. 120p. 1985. 29.95x (ISBN 0-7103-0149-9, Kegan Paul). Methuen Inc.

--Man in Qur'an & the Meaning of Furqan. 210p. 1987. pap. 18.95 (ISBN 0-7103-0223-1, Pub. by Routledge UK). Methuen Inc.

Haeri, Shykh F. The Mercy of Qur'an & the Advent of Zaman. 164p. 1987. pap. 18.95 (ISBN 0-7103-0224-X, 02231, Kegan Paul). Methuen Inc.

Haerle, Wilfried. Sein und Gnade: Die Ontologie in Karl Barths Kirchlicher Dogmatik. (Theologische Bibliothek Toepelmann, Vol. 27). (Ger.). 428p. 1975. 45.60x (ISBN 3-11-005706-9). De Gruyter.

Haessly, Jacqueline. Peacemaking: Family Activities for Peace & Justice. 2.95 (ISBN 0-8091-2269-3). Paulist Pr.

Haeusermann, Friederich & Breymayer, Reinhard, eds. Die Lehntafel der Prinzessin Antonia, 2 Vol. (Texte Zur Geschichte Des Pietismus: Sec. 7, Vol. 1). 1977. 112.00x (ISBN 3-11-004130-8). De Gruyter.

Hafen, Brent & Frandsen, Katherine. From Acupuncture to Yoga: Alternative Methods of Healing. (Illus.). 136p. 1983. 12.95 (ISBN 0-13-330845-6). P-H.

Haff, Gerry, jt. auth. see Campbell, Alexander.

Haffert, John M. Dear Bishop: Memoirs of the Author Concerning the History of the Blue Army. (Illus.). 352p. 1981. 8.95 (ISBN 0-911988-44-0); pap. 5.95 (ISBN 0-911988-42-4). AMI Pr.

--Meet the Witnesses. (Illus.). 160p. 1981. pap. 3.25 (ISBN 0-911988-39-4). AMI Pr.

--Who Is the Woman of the Apocalypse? 104p. 1982. pap. 1.95 (ISBN 0-911988-47-5). AMI Pr.

Haffey, Richard. Thank You, Dad. (Greeting Book Line Ser.). 24p. (Orig.). 1986. pap. 1.50 (ISBN 0-89622-305-1). Twenty-Third.

--Thank You, Mom. (Greeting Book Line Ser.). 24p. (Orig.). 1986. pap. 1.50 (ISBN 0-89622-306-X). Twenty-Third.

Hafiz, M. Virtues of the Holy Quran. pap. 7.50 (ISBN 0-686-18508-0). Kazi Pubns.

Haft, Cynthia J. The Bargain & the Bridle: The General Union of the Israelites of France, 1941-1944. 150p. (Orig.). 1983. pap. 14.95 (ISBN 0-914153-00-5). Dialog.

Hagan, Lowell & Westerhof, Jack. Theirs Is the Kingdom. LC 86-11679. (Illus.). 336p. 1986. 16.95 (ISBN 0-8028-5013-8). Eerdmans.

Hagans, Marilyn T. All Good Gifts: Crafts for Christian Gift-Giving. LC 82-62924. 128p. (Orig.). 1983. pap. 5.95 (ISBN 0-8091-2543-9). Paulist Pr.

Hagedorn, Dieter, ed. Der Hiobkommentar Des Arianers Julian. LC 73-75486. (Patristische Texte und Studien, Vol. 14). 410p. 1973. 45.60x (ISBN 3-11-004244-4). De Gruyter.

Hagedorn, Maria. Reformation und Spanische Andachtsliteratur. 1934. 12.00 (ISBN 0-384-20770-7). Johnson Repr.

Hagelganz, James W., jt. auth. see Biehl, Bobb.

Hageman, Howard G. Lily Among the Thorns. 1978. write for info. (ISBN 0-916466-00-0). Reformed Church.

Hagemeyer, Stanley, jt. auth. see Richards, Sue.

Hagen, Lyman B., ed. see Simon, Charlie M.

Hager, Wesley H. Consider the Grass: God Cares for You. (Contempo Ser.). pap. 0.95 (ISBN 0-8010-4102-3). Baker Bk.

Hagerty, Cornelius. The Authenticity of the Sacred Scriptures. 339p. 1969. 10.00 (ISBN 0-912414-00-6). Lumen Christi.

--The Holy Eucharist. 77p. 1967. pap. 1.50 (ISBN 0-912414-12-X). Lumen Christi.

--The Problem of Evil. LC 77-3022. 1978. 9.95 (ISBN 0-8158-0352-4). Chris Mass.

Hagerty, Cornelius J. The Holy Trinity. 362p. 1976. 8.95 (ISBN 0-8158-0316-8). Chris Mass.

Haggai, John E. How to Win Over Worry. 1967. pap. 3.95 (ISBN 0-310-25712-3, 9740P). Zondervan.

Haggart, James A. Stories of Lost Israel in Folklore. LC 80-65735. 144p. 1981. pap. 5.00 (ISBN 0-934666-08-?). Artisan Sales.

Haggerty, Brian A. & Walters, Thomas P. We Receive the Spirit of Jesus (Confirmation Program) wkbk. 3.50 (ISBN 0-8091-9532-1); parent's notes 2.45 (ISBN 0-8091-9533-X); celebration's bk. 9.95 (ISBN 0-8091-9531-3); director's manual 7.50 (ISBN 0-8091-9530-5). Paulist Pr.

--We Receive the Spirit of Jesus Filmstrips. with guidebook & cassette 49.95 (ISBN 0-8091-7664-5). Paulist Pr.

Haggerty, Brian A., jt. auth. see Champlin, Joseph M.

Haggerty, Brian A., et al. We Share New Life (Baptism Program) Reflections & Activities for Families. 2.95 (ISBN 0-8091-9183-0); Activities for Children. 2.75 (ISBN 0-8091-9182-2); director's manual 7.95 (ISBN 0-8091-9181-4); celebrations bk. 4.95 (ISBN 0-8091-9184-9). Paulist Pr.

Hagin, Kenneth. His Name Shall Be Called Wonderful. 1983. pap. 0.50 mini bk. (ISBN 0-89276-260-8). Hagin Ministries.

--Obedience in Finances. 1983. pap. 0.50 mini bk. (ISBN 0-89276-259-4). Hagin Ministries.

--Paul's Revelation: The Gospel of Reconciliation. 1983. pap. 0.50 mini bk. (ISBN 0-89276-261-6). Hagin Ministries.

--Understanding the Anointing. 1983. pap. 3.50 (ISBN 0-89276-507-0). Hagin Ministries.

Hagin, Kenneth E. The Art of Intercession. 1980. pap. 3.50 (ISBN 0-89276-503-8). Hagin Ministries.

--La Autoridad Del Creyente. 2nd ed. (Span.). 1982. pap. 1.00 (ISBN 0-89276-106-7). Hagin Ministries.

--The Believer's Authority. 2nd ed. 1985. pap. 2.50 (ISBN 0-89276-406-6). Hagin Ministries.

--A Better Covenant. 1981. pap. 0.50 mini bk. (ISBN 0-89276-251-9). Hagin Ministries.

--Bible Answers to Man's Questions on Demons. 1983. pap. 1.00 (ISBN 0-89276-028-1). Hagin Ministries.

--Bible Faith Study Course. 1974. pap. 5.00 (ISBN 0-89276-080-X). Hagin Ministries.

--Bible Prayer Study Course. 1974. pap. 5.00 (ISBN 0-89276-081-8). Hagin Ministries.

--The Bible Way to Receive the Holy Spirit. 1981. pap. 0.50 mini bk. (ISBN 0-89276-255-1). Hagin Ministries.

--Casting Your Cares Upon the Lord. 1981. pap. 1.00 (ISBN 0-89276-023-0). Hagin Ministries.

--The Coming Restoration. 1985. mini bk. 0.50 (ISBN 0-89276-267-5). Hagin Ministries.

--A Commonsense Guide to Fasting. 1981. pap. 1.50 (ISBN 0-89276-403-1). Hagin Ministries.

--Como Desatar Su Fe. 2nd ed. (Span.). 1982. pap. 1.00 (ISBN 0-89276-107-5). Hagin Ministries.

--Como Retener Su Sanidad. (Span.). 1983. pap. 0.50 mini bk. (ISBN 0-89276-159-8). Hagin Ministries.

--Concerning Spiritual Gifts. 2nd ed. 1974. pap. 2.50 (ISBN 0-89276-072-9). Hagin Ministries.

--El Cristiano Intercesor. 1985. 1.00 (ISBN 0-89276-118-0). Hagin Ministries.

--Demons & How to Deal With Them. 2nd ed. 1983. pap. 1.00 (ISBN 0-89276-026-5). Hagin Ministries.

--Los Dones Del Ministerio. 1983. study guide 10.00 (ISBN 0-89276-192-X). Hagin Ministries.

--Don't Blame God. 1979. pap. 0.50 mini bk. (ISBN 0-89276-056-7). Hagin Ministries.

--El Shaddai. 1980. pap. 1.50 (ISBN 0-89276-401-5). Hagin Ministries.

--En El. (Span.). 1983. pap. 0.50 mini bk. (ISBN 0-89276-152-0). Hagin Ministries.

--Exceedingly Growing Faith. 1983. pap. 3.50 (ISBN 0-89276-506-2). Hagin Ministries.

--Faith Food for Autumn. 2nd ed. (Illus.). 1978. pap. 1.95 (ISBN 0-89276-040-0). Hagin Ministries.

--Faith Food for Spring. 2nd ed. (Illus.). 1978. pap. 1.95 (ISBN 0-89276-042-7). Hagin Ministries.

--Faith Food for Summer. 2nd ed. (Illus.). 1978. pap. 1.95 (ISBN 0-89276-043-5). Hagin Ministries.

--Faith Food for Winter. 2nd ed. (Illus.). 1977. pap. 1.95 (ISBN 0-89276-041-9). Hagin Ministries.

--La Fe, Lo Que Es. 2nd ed. (Span.). 1982. pap. 1.00 (ISBN 0-89276-102-4). Hagin Ministries.

--Five Hindrances to Growth in Grace. 1981. pap. 0.50 mini bk (ISBN 0-89276-253-5). Hagin Ministries.

--The Gift of Prophecy. 1969. pap. 1.00 (ISBN 0-89276-015-X). Hagin Ministries.

--The Gifts & Calling of God. 1986. pap. 0.50 (ISBN 0-89276-268-3). Hagin Ministries.

--Godliness Is Profitable. 1982. pap. 0.50 mini bk. (ISBN 0-89276-256-X). Hagin Ministries.

--Growing up, Spiritually. 1976. pap. 3.50 (ISBN 0-89276-504-6). Hagin Ministries.

--Having Faith in Your Faith. 1981. pap. 0.50 mini bk. (ISBN 0-89276-252-7). Hagin Ministries.

--Healing Belongs to Us. 1969. pap. 1.00 (ISBN 0-89276-016-8). Hagin Ministries.

--The Holy Spirit & His Gifts. 1974. pap. 5.00 (ISBN 0-89276-082-6). Hagin Ministries.

--How God Taught Me About Prosperity. 1985. mini bk. 0.50 (ISBN 0-89276-265-9). Hagin Ministries.

--How to Keep Your Healing. 1980. pap. 0.50 mini bk (ISBN 0-89276-059-1). Hagin Ministries.

--How to Turn Your Faith Loose. 2nd ed. 1983. pap. 1.00 (ISBN 0-89276-007-9). Hagin Ministries.

--How to Walk in Love. 1983. pap. 0.50 mini bk. (ISBN 0-89276-262-4). Hagin Ministries.

--How to Write Your Own Ticket with God. 1979. mini bk. .50 (ISBN 0-89276-055-9). Hagin Ministries.

--How You Can Be Led by the Spirit of God. 1978. pap. 3.50 (ISBN 0-89276-500-3). Hagin Ministries.

--How You Can Know the Will of God. 2nd ed. 1983. pap. 1.00 (ISBN 0-89276-019-2). Hagin Ministries.

--I Believe in Visions. 2nd ed. 1984. pap. 3.50 (ISBN 0-89276-508-9). Hagin Ministries.

--I Went to Hell. 1982. pap. 0.50 mini bk. (ISBN 0-89276-257-8). Hagin Ministries.

--In Him. 1975. pap. 0.50 mini bk. (ISBN 0-89276-052-4). Hagin Ministries.

--The Interceding Christian. 2nd ed. 1983. pap. 1.00 (ISBN 0-89276-018-4). Hagin Ministries.

--Kenneth E. Hagin's Fifty Years in the Ministry, 1934-1984. 1984. pap. write for info. (ISBN 0-89276-093-1). Hagin Ministries.

--The Key to Scriptural Healing. 2nd ed. 1983. pap. 1.00 (ISBN 0-89276-008-7). Hagin Ministries.

--Laying on of Hands. 1980. pap. 0.50 mini bk. (ISBN 0-89276-250-0). Hagin Ministries.

--Learning to Forget. 1985. mini bk. 0.50 (ISBN 0-89276-266-7). Hagin Ministries.

--Love Never Fails. 1984. pap. 0.50 mini bk. (ISBN 0-89276-264-0). Hagin Ministries.

--Man on Three Dimensions. 1973. pap. 1.00 (ISBN 0-89276-020-6). Hagin Ministries.

--La Medicina De Dios. (Span.). 1982. pap. 0.50 mini bk. (ISBN 0-89276-153-9). Hagin Ministries.

--Ministering to the Oppressed. 2nd ed. 1983. pap. 1.00 (ISBN 0-89276-027-3). Hagin Ministries.

--The Ministry Gifts Study Guide. 1981. pap. 10.00 spiral bdg. (ISBN 0-89276-092-3). Hagin Ministries.

--The Ministry of a Prophet. 1968. pap. 1.00 (ISBN 0-89276-009-5). Hagin Ministries.

--Must Christians Suffer? 1982. pap. 1.50 (ISBN 0-89276-404-X). Hagin Ministries.

--The Name of Jesus. 1979. pap. 3.50 (ISBN 0-89276-502-X). Hagin Ministries.

--The New Birth. 1975. pap. 0.50 mini bk. (ISBN 0-89276-050-8). Hagin Ministries.

--New Thresholds of Faith. 2nd ed. 1972. pap. 2.50 (ISBN 0-89276-070-2). Hagin Ministries.

--No Culpe a Dios! (Span.). 1983. pap. 0.50 mini bk. (ISBN 0-89276-156-3). Hagin Ministries.

--El Nuevo Nacimiento. (Span.). 1983. pap. 0.50 mini bk. (ISBN 0-89276-150-4). Hagin Ministries.

--La Oracion Que Prevalece. (Span.). 1986. pap. 2.50 (ISBN 0-89276-186-5). Hagin Ministries.

--The Origin & Operation of Demons. 2nd ed. 1983. pap. 1.00 (ISBN 0-89276-025-7). Hagin Ministries.

--Palabras. (Span.). 1983. pap. 0.50 mini bk. (ISBN 0-89276-157-1). Hagin Ministries.

--El Pensar Bien y Mal. 2nd ed. (Span.). 1983. pap. 1.00 (ISBN 0-89276-104-0). Hagin Ministries.

--Plead Your Case. 1979. pap. 0.50 mini bk. (ISBN 0-89276-058-3). Hagin Ministries.

--El Porque De Las Lenguas. (Span.). 1983. pap. 0.50 (ISBN 0-89276-151-2). Hagin Ministries.

--Prayer Secrets. 2nd ed. 1983. pap. 1.00 (ISBN 0-89276-005-2). Hagin Ministries.

--The Precious Blood of Jesus. 1984. pap. 0.50 mini bk. (ISBN 0-89276-263-2). Hagin Ministries.

--The Present-Day Ministry of Jesus Christ. 2nd ed. 1983. pap. 1.00 (ISBN 0-89276-014-1). Hagin Ministries.

--Prevailing Prayer to Peace. 2nd ed. 1973. pap. 2.50 (ISBN 0-89276-071-0). Hagin Ministries.

--The Real Faith. 1970. pap. 1.00 (ISBN 0-89276-017-6). Hagin Ministries.

--Redeemed from Poverty, Sickness, & Death. 1966. pap. 1.00 (ISBN 0-89276-001-X). Hagin Ministries.

--Redimido De La Pobreza, La Enfermedad, La Muerte. 2nd ed. 1982. pap. 1.00 (ISBN 0-89276-101-6). Hagin Ministries.

--Right & Wrong Thinking. 2nd ed. 1966. pap. 1.00 (ISBN 0-89276-004-4). Hagin Ministries.

--Seven Steps for Judging Prophecy. 1982. pap. 1.00 (ISBN 0-89276-024-9). Hagin Ministries.

--Seven Things You Should Know about Divine Healing. 1979. pap. 2.50 (ISBN 0-89276-400-7). Hagin Ministries.

--Seven Vital Steps to Receiving the Holy Spirit. 2nd ed. 1980. pap. 1.00 (ISBN 0-89276-003-6). Hagin Ministries.

--Siete Pasos Para Recibir El Espiritu Santo. 2nd ed. 1983. pap. 1.00 (ISBN 0-89276-103-2). Hagin Ministries.

--Sign of the Times. 1986. pap. 0.50 (ISBN 0-89276-269-1). Hagin Ministries.

--Three Big Words. 1983. pap. 0.50 mini bk. (ISBN 0-89276-258-6). Hagin Ministries.

--Turning Hopeless Situations Around. 1981. pap. 1.00 (ISBN 0-89276-022-2). Hagin Ministries.

--Usted Puede Tener lo Que Diga. (Span.). 1983. pap. 0.50 mini bk. (ISBN 0-89276-154-7). Hagin Ministries.

--What Faith Is. 2nd ed. 1966. pap. 1.00 (ISBN 0-89276-002-8). Hagin Ministries.

--What to Do When Faith Seems Weak & Victory Lost. 1979. pap. 3.50 (ISBN 0-89276-501-1). Hagin Ministries.

--Why Do People Fall under the Power? 1981. pap. 0.50 mini bk (ISBN 0-89276-254-3). Hagin Ministries.

--Why Tongues? 1975. pap. 0.50 mini bk (ISBN 0-89276-051-6). Hagin Ministries.

--The Woman Question. 2nd ed. 1983. pap. 2.50 (ISBN 0-89276-405-8). Hagin Ministries.

--Words. 1979. pap. 0.50 mini bk. (ISBN 0-89276-057-5). Hagin Ministries.

--You Can Have What You Say. 1978. mini bk. 0.50 (ISBN 0-89276-054-0). Hagin Ministries.

--ZOE: The God-Kind of Life. 1981. pap. 2.50 (ISBN 0-89276-402-3). Hagin Ministries.

Hagin, Kenneth E. & Hagin, Kenneth, Jr. Ministering to Your Family. 1986. pap. 1.50 (ISBN 0-89276-407-4). Hagin Ministries.

Hagin, Kenneth, Jr. The Answer for Oppression. 1983. pap. 0.50 mini bk. (ISBN 0-89276-717-0). Hagin Ministries.

--Because of Jesus. 2nd ed. 1979. 1.00 (ISBN 0-89276-701-4). Hagin Ministries.

--Blueprint for Building Strong Faith. 1980. pap. 0.50 mini bk. (ISBN 0-89276-704-9). Hagin Ministries.

--Commanding Power. 1985. pap. 0.50 (ISBN 0-317-40350-8). Hagin Ministries.

--Faith Takes Back What the Devil's Stolen. 1982. pap. 0.50 mini bk (ISBN 0-89276-709-X). Hagin Ministries.

--Faith Worketh by Love. 1979. pap. 0.50 mini bk. (ISBN 0-89276-703-0). Hagin Ministries.

--La Fe Obra Por El Amor. (Span.). 1983. pap. 0.50 mini bk. (ISBN 0-89276-173-3). Hagin Ministries.

--Get Acquainted with God. 1983. pap. 0.50 mini bk. (ISBN 0-89276-714-6). Hagin Ministries.

--Healing: A Forever-Settled Subject. 1981. pap. 0.50 mini bk. (ISBN 0-89276-707-3). Hagin Ministries.

--How to Make the Dream God Gave You Come True. 1981. pap. 1.00 (ISBN 0-89276-708-1). Hagin Ministries.
--Las Imposibilidades Del Hombre-Posibilidades Para Dios. (Span.). 1983. pap. 2.50 (ISBN 0-89276-170-9). Hagin Ministries.
--Is Your Miracle Passing You By? 1985. mini bk. 0.50 (ISBN 0-89276-718-9). Hagin Ministries.
--Itching Ears. 1982. pap. 0.50 mini bk. (ISBN 0-89276-711-1). Hagin Ministries.
--The Life of Obedience. 1986. pap. 1.00 (ISBN 0-89276-720-0). Hagin Ministries.
--Man's Impossibility, God's Possibility. 1978. pap. 2.50 (ISBN 0-89276-700-6). Hagin Ministries.
--The Past Tense of God's Word. 1980. pap. 0.50 mini bk. (ISBN 0-89276-706-5). Hagin Ministries.
--The Prison Door Is Open: What Are You Still Doing Inside? 1982. pap. 0.50 mini bk (ISBN 0-89276-710-3). Hagin Ministries.
--Seven Hindrances to Healing. 1980. pap. 0.50 mini bk. (ISBN 0-89276-705-7). Hagin Ministries.
--Showdown with the Devil. 1983. pap. 0.50 mini bk. (ISBN 0-89276-715-4). Hagin Ministries.
--Siete Impedimentos Para Recibir Sanidad. (Span.). 1983. pap. 0.50 mini bk. (ISBN 0-89276-175-X). Hagin Ministries.
--El Tiempo Pasada De La Palabra De Dios. (Span.). 1983. pap. 0.50 mini bk. (ISBN 0-89276-176-8). Hagin Ministries.
--Unforgiveness. 1983. pap. 0.50 (ISBN 0-89276-716-2). Hagin Ministries.
--Where Do We Go from Here? 1982. pap. 0.50 mini bk (ISBN 0-89276-712-X). Hagin Ministries.

Hagin, Kenneth, Jr., jt. auth. see Hagin, Kenneth E.

Hagner, Donald & Harris, Murray, eds. Pauline Studies: Essays Presented to Prof. F. F. Bruce on His 70th Birthday. LC 80-16146. 336p. 1981. 19.95 (ISBN 0-8028-3531-7). Eerdmans.

Hagner, Donald A. Hebrews: A Good News Commentary. LC 82-48410. (Good News Commentary Ser.). 288p. 1983. pap. 9.95 (ISBN 0-06-063555-X, RD-425, HarpR). Har-Row.

Hagood, L. M. Colored Man in the Methodist Episcopal Church. facs. ed. LC 77-149868. (Black Heritage Library Collection Ser). 1890. 19.50 (ISBN 0-8369-8631-8). Ayer Co Pubs.

Hagood, Lewis M. Colored Man in the Methodist Episcopal Church. LC 73-111577. Repr. of 1890 ed. cancelled (ISBN 0-8371-4602-X, HCM&, Pub. by Negro U Pr). Greenwood.

Hagstrom, Jane. The Young Witness: Evangelism to & by Children & Youth. LC 23-3036. 56p. (Orig.). 1986. pap. 4.95 (ISBN 0-8066-2233-4). Augsburg.

Hagstrum, Jean H., ed. see Johnson, Samuel.

Hague, Michael. A Child's Book of Prayers. LC 85-8380. (Illus.). 32p. 1985. 11.95 (ISBN 0-03-001412-3). H Holt & Co.

Hague, Rene, tr. see Teilhard de Chardin, Pierre.

Hague, W., jt. auth. see Drew, Joseph W.

Hahn, Ferdinand. Historical Investigation & New Testament Faith. Krentz, Edgar, ed. Maddox, Robert, tr. from Ger. LC 82-48547. 112p. 1983. pap. 7.50 (ISBN 0-8006-1691-X, 1-1691). Fortress.
--The Worship of the Early Church. Reumann, John, ed. Green, David E., tr. from Ger. LC 72-87063. 144p. 1973. pap. 4.95 (ISBN 0-8006-0127-0, 1-127). Fortress.

Hahn, Galdys, ed. see Steiner, Rudolf.

Hahn, Gladys, tr. see Steiner, Rudolf.

Haich, Elisabeth. The Day with Yoga. pap. 3.95 (ISBN 0-943358-12-4). Aurora Press.
--Sexual Energy & Yoga. 160p. 1983. 7.95 (ISBN 0-943358-03-5). Aurora Press.

Haich, Elisabeth, jt. auth. see Yesudian, Selvarajan.

Haig, Alan. The Victorian Clergy. 380p. 1984. 33.00 (ISBN 0-7099-1230-7, Pub. by Croom Helm Ltd). Methuen Inc.

Haig, J. A. Headmaster. LC 80-52617. 270p. 1982. 5.95 (ISBN 0-941478-06-8). Paraclete Pr.

Haig, J. Alastair. Al Who? LC 80-52617. 270p. (Orig.). 1980. pap. cancelled (ISBN 0-932260-05-5). Paraclete Pr.

Haigh, C. Last Days of the Lancashire Monasteries & the Pilgrimage of Grace. 182p. 1969. 30.00 (ISBN 0-7190-1150-7, Pub. by Manchester Univ Pr). Longwood Pub Group.

Haight, Grace W., ed. see Jones, Bob, Sr.

Haight, Roger. The Experience & Language of Grace. LC 79-84403. 192p. 1979. pap. 7.95 (ISBN 0-8091-2200-6). Paulist Pr.

Haight, Roger S. An Alternative Vision: An Interpretation of Liberation Theology. (Orig.). 1985. 10.95 (ISBN 0-8091-2679-6). Paulist Pr.

Haigler, Anne M. The Church Records of Saint Matthews Lutheran Church, Orangeburg, Co., S. C. Beginning in 1799, Giving Births, Christenings, Confirmations, Marriages, & Burials & "the Red Church", 1767-1838. (Illus.). 126p. 1985. 15.00 (ISBN 0-89308-563-4). Southern Hist Pr.

Haile, Berard. Cathechism & Guide: Navaho-English. (Orig.). 1937. pap. 3.00 (ISBN 0-686-32657-1). St Michaels.
--Head & Face Masks in Navaho Ceremonialism. LC 76-43722. Repr. of 1947 ed. 17.50 (ISBN 0-404-15565-0). AMS Pr.
--Love-Magic & Butterfly People: The Slim Curly Version of the Ajilee & Mothway Myths. LC 78-59705. (American Tribal Religions Ser.: Vol. 2). (Illus.). xii, 172p. 1978. pap. 13.95x (ISBN 0-89734-026-4, Pub by Mus Nothern Ariz). U of Nebr Pr.
--Starlore among the Navaho. LC 76-53085. 1977. lib. bdg. 15.00x (ISBN 0-88307-532-6). Gannon.
--The Upward Moving & Emergence Way: The Gishin Biye Version. Luckert, Karl W., ed. LC 81-7441. (American Tribal Religions Ser.: Vol. 7). xvi, 239p. 1981. 19.95x (ISBN 0-8032-2320-X); pap. 11.95x (ISBN 0-8032-7212-X, BB 786, Bison). U of Nebr Pr.
--Waterway. LC 79-66605. (American Tribal Religions Ser.: Vol. 5). (Illus.). vi, 153p. 1979. pap. 12.95x (ISBN 0-89734-030-2, Pub. by Mus Northern Ariz). U of Nebr Pr.
--Women versus Men: A Conflict of Navajo Emergence. Luckert, Karl W., ed. LC 81-7433. (American Tribal Religions Ser.: Vol. 6). viii, 119p. 1981. 14.95x (ISBN 0-8032-2319-6); pap. 9.95x (ISBN 0-8032-7211-1, BB 785, Bison). U of Nebr Pr.

Haile, H. G. Luther: An Experiment in Biography. LC 82-48569. 460p. 1983. 31.50x (ISBN 0-691-05374-X); pap. 10.50x (ISBN 0-691-00798-5). Princeton U Pr.

Hailey, Homer. A Commentary on Isaiah. 544p. 1985. 17.95 (ISBN 0-8010-4292-5). Baker Bk.
--Commentary on the Minor Prophets. 1972. 14.95 (ISBN 0-8010-4049-3). Baker Bk.
--From Creation to the Day of Eternity. (Illus.). 1982. 11.95 (ISBN 0-913814-42-3). Nevada Pubns.
--Revelation. LC 78-62441. 1979. 14.95 (ISBN 0-8010-4201-1). Baker Bk.
--That You May Believe: Studies in the Gospel of John. (Illus.). 1982. 9.95 (ISBN 0-913814-51-2). Nevada Pubns.

Haim, Sylvia G., jt. ed. see Kedourie, Elie.

Haim, Yehoyada. Abandonment of Illusions: Zionist Political Attitudes Toward Palestinian Arab Nationalism, 1936-1939. (Relica Edition Ser.). 170p. 1983. softcover 22.50x (ISBN 0-86531-971-5). Westview.

Haiman, Franklyn S., ed. see Pfeffer, L.

Haimowitz, Morris L. & Haimowitz, Natalie R. Suffering Is Optional! The Myth of the Innocent Bystander. LC 77-72839. (Illus.). 1977. pap. 6.00 (ISBN 0-917790-01-4). Haimowoods.

Haimowitz, Natalie R., jt. auth. see Haimowitz, Morris L.

Haines, Byron L. & Cooley, Frank L., eds. Christians & Muslims Together: An Exploration by Presbyterians. LC 87-218. 120p. (Orig.). 1987. pap. 7.95 (ISBN 0-664-24061-5). Westminster.

Haines, Charles R. Christianity & Islam in Spain, A. D. 756-1031. LC 76-144625. Repr. of 1889 ed. 17.50 (ISBN 0-404-03024-6). AMS Pr.

Haines, Denise, jt. auth. see Spong, John.

Haines, J. Harry. I'm Only One Person, What Can I Do? (Orig.). 1985. pap. 5.95 (ISBN 0-8358-0521-2). Upper Room.
--Ten Hands for God. 80p. (Orig.). 1983. pap. 3.50 (ISBN 0-8358-0449-6). Upper Room.

Haines, Leland M. The Unfolding Plan of Redemption. 1982. 3.50 (ISBN 0-87813-517-0). Christian Light.

Haines, Madge. You, Too, Can Find Peace. Woolsey, Raymond H., ed. (Banner Ser.). 128p. (Orig.). 1987. pap. 6.50 (ISBN 0-8280-0366-1). Review & Herald.

Haines, R. M. The Church & Politics in Fourteenth Century England. LC 76-54062. (Studies in Medieval Life & Thought: No. 10). 1978. 49.50 (ISBN 0-521-21544-7). Cambridge U Pr.

Haines, Richard C., jt. auth. see McCown, Donald E.

Haines, Victor Y. The Fortunate Fall of Sir Gawain: The Typology of Sir Gawain & the Green Knight. LC 80-5847. (Illus.). 240p. (Orig.): 1982. PLB 29.00 (ISBN 0-8191-2437-0); pap. text ed. 12.75 (ISBN 0-8191-2438-9). U Pr of Amer.

Haining, Peter. The Witchcraft Papers. 1974. 7.95 (ISBN 0-8216-0223-3). Univ Bks.

Hainsworth, Phillip & Perkins, Mary. The Baha'i Faith. 1985. 13.00x (ISBN 0-7062-3939-3, Pub. by Ward Lock Educ Co Ltd). State Mutual Bk.

Haire, James. The Character & Theological Struggle of the Church in Halmahera, Indonesia, 1941-1979. (IC-Studies in the Intercultural History of Christianity: Vol. 26). xii, 382p. 1981. pap. 42.05 (ISBN 3-8204-5888-3). P Lang Pubs.

Haiven, Judith. Faith, Hope, No Charity: An Inside Look at the Born Again Movement in Canada & the United States. (Illus.). 221p. 1984. lib. bdg. 14.95 (ISBN 0-919573-32-0); pap. 7.95 (ISBN 0-919573-33-9). Left Bank.

Hajos, Mary. Removing the Stones. 1976. pap. 2.95 (ISBN 0-87508-264-5). Chr Lit.

Hake, Edward. A Touchstone for This Time Present. LC 74-80182. (English Experience Ser.: No. 663). 96p. 1974. Repr. of 1574 ed. 7.00 (ISBN 90-221-0663-2). Walter J Johnson.

Hakeda, Yoshita S., tr. from Japanese. Kukai: Major Works, Translated with an Account of His Life & a Study of His Thought. LC 72-3124. (Records of Civilization, Sources, Studies & Translations of the Oriental Classics Ser.). 303p. 1972. 30.00x (ISBN 0-231-03627-2); pap. 14.00x (ISBN 0-231-05933-7). Columbia U Pr.

Hakeda, Yoshito S., ed. Bankei Zen. Haskel, Peter, tr. LC 83-81372. (Eastern Bks.). 240p. 1985. 27.50 (ISBN 0-394-53524-3, GP 886). Grove.
--Bankei Zen. Haskel, Peter, tr. LC 83-81372. (Eastern Bks.). 1985. pap. 8.95 (ISBN 0-394-62493-9, E-272, Ever). Grove.

Hakeda, Yoshito S., tr. The Awakening of Faith, Attributed to Asvaghosha. LC 67-13778. 128p. 1974. 24.00x (ISBN 0-231-03025-8); pap. 10.00x (ISBN 0-231-08336-X). Columbia U Pr.

Hakenewerth, Quentin. The Grain of Wheat. 88p. 1966. pap. 1.75 (ISBN 0-9608124-0-7). Marianist Com Ctr.
--In His Likeness: A Manual of Direction for the Spiritual Life. 88p. (Orig.). 1977. pap. 1.75 (ISBN 0-9608124-1-5). Marianist Com Ctr.
--Mary in Modern Spirituality. 52p. (Orig.). 1966. pap. 1.25 (ISBN 0-9608124-2-3). Marianist Com Ctr.
--The Prayer of Faith. 76p. (Orig.). 1969. pap. 1.75 (ISBN 0-9608124-3-1). Marianist Com Ctr.

Hakes, Thomas L. Where Have All the Little Angels Gone? (Illus.). 10p. 1985. pap. 2.00x (ISBN 0-915020-58-0). Bardic.

Hakes, Thomas L., ed. Mother Nature & Beauty, Vol. 1. 16p. 1984. pap. 3.25x (ISBN 0-915020-17-3). Bardic.

Hakim, K. A. Islam & Communism. pap. 15.95 (ISBN 0-686-18576-5). Kazi Pubns.
--Islamic Ideology. 16.50 (ISBN 0-686-18571-4). Kazi Pubns.
--Metaphysics of Rumi. 1959. 3.95x (ISBN 0-87902-061-X). Orientalia.
--The Prophet & His Message. 8.50 (ISBN 0-686-18422-X). Kazi Pubns.

Hakim, Khalifa A. The Metaphysics of Rumi. 157p. 1981. pap. 3.95 (ISBN 0-88004-004-1). Sunwise Turn.

Hakuin. The Zen Master Hakuin: Selected Writings. Yampolsky, Philip B., tr. from Japanese. 253p. 1985. 29.00 (ISBN 0-231-03463-6); pap. 14.00x (ISBN 0-231-06041-6). Columbia U Pr.

Halbritter, Irving J. How to Master the Miracle of Introspection for the Better Knowledge of Yourself, the Broader Dimensions of Your Intellectual Life & the Gaining of Maximal Success in Your Field of Endeavour. (Illus.). 136p. 1982. 69.75 (ISBN 0-89920-044-3). Am Inst Psych.

Halbrook, Becky, jt. auth. see Halbrook, D. L.

Halbrook, D. L. & Halbrook, Becky. Wait Guys & Girls. pap. 4.25 (ISBN 0-89137-805-7). Quality Pubns.

Hald, Marie M. Jesus Jewels. 118p. 1983. pap. 5.00 (ISBN 0-682-49963-3). Exposition Pr FL.

Haldane, E. S., ed. see Descartes, Rene.

Haldane, John B. Possible Worlds: And Other Papers. facsimile ed. LC 75-167351. (Essay Index Reprint Ser). Repr. of 1928 ed. 18.00 (ISBN 0-8369-2452-5). Ayer Co Pubs.

Haldane, Robert. The Authenticity & Inspiration of the Holy Scriptures. 210p. 1985. Repr. lib. bdg. 9.00 (ISBN 0-86524-182-1, 8604). Klock & Klock.

Haldeman, I. M. Second Coming of Christ. 326p. 1986. 12.95 (ISBN 0-8254-2844-0). Kregel.
--Tabernacle, Priesthood & Offerings. 408p. 14.95 (ISBN 0-8007-0303-0). Revell.

Haldeman-Julius, E. What Can a Free Man Believe. 55p. pap. cancelled (ISBN 0-911826-99-8). Am Atheist.

Halder, J. R. Early Buddhist Mythology. 1977. 15.00x (ISBN 0-88386-998-5). South Asia Bks.

Hale, Anita. My Room at Church. LC 85-24344. (Bible & Me Ser.). (Illus.). 1986. 5.95 (ISBN 0-8054-4168-9). Broadman.

Hale, Annie R. These Cults. 1981. 8.95 (ISBN 0-686-76751-9). B of A.

Hale, Charles. Russian Missions in China & Japan. 1974. pap. 1.50 (ISBN 0-686-10198-7). Eastern Orthodox.

Hale, Charles R. Metropolitan Innocent of Moscow, the Apostle of Alaska. pap. 1.25 (ISBN 0-686-05655-8). Eastern Orthodox.

Hale, Clarence B. Let's Study Greek. rev. ed. LC 82-3619. 1982. 14.95 (ISBN 0-8024-4666-3). Moody.

Hale, Donald, jt. auth. see Robicsek, Francis.

Hale, Edward, ed. see Everett, Charles C.

Hale, Edward E. Ralph Waldo Emerson. LC 72-8439. 1972. Repr. of 1902 ed. lib. bdg. 20.00 (ISBN 0-8414-0295-7). Folcroft.

Hale, Edward W. Asura in Early Vedic Religion. 275p. 1986. 16.00 (ISBN 81-208-0061-3, Pub. by Motilal Banarsidass). South Asia Bks.

Hale, Frederick. Trans-Atlantic Conservative Protestantism in the Evangelical Free & Mission Covenant Traditions. Scott, Franklyn D., ed. LC 78-15183. (Scandinavians in America Ser.). 1979. lib. bdg. 30.50x (ISBN 0-405-11638-1). Ayer Co Pubs.

Hale, Frederick, jt. ed. see Sandeen, Ernest R.

Hale, Horatio E., ed. Iroquois Book of Rites. LC 74-83458. (Library of Aboriginal American Literature: No. 2). Repr. of 1883 ed. 30.00 (ISBN 0-404-52182-7). AMS Pr.

Hale, J. Russell. The Unchurched: Who They Are & Why They Stay Away. LC 79-2993. 192p. 1980. 12.00 (ISBN 0-06-063560-6, HarpR). Har-Row.
--Who Are the Unchurched? An Exploratory Study. LC 77-81922. 1977. pap. 2.00x (ISBN 0-914422-06-5). Glenmary Res Ctr.

Hale, Mabel. Emma Bailey Seeks Truth. 24p. 1982. pap. 0.25 (ISBN 0-686-36258-6); pap. 1.00 5 copies (ISBN 0-686-37283-2). Faith Pub Hse.
--The Hero of Hill House. 224p. pap. 2.00 (ISBN 0-686-29148-4). Faith Pub Hse.
--Stories of Home Folks. 160p. pap. 1.50 (ISBN 0-686-29143-3). Faith Pub Hse.

Hale, Robert. Canterbury & Rome, Sister Churches: A Roman Catholic Monk Reflects on Reunion in Diversity. 7.95 (ISBN 0-8091-2480-7). Paulist Pr.
--Christ & the Universe. Meilach, Michael, ed. (Theilhard de Chardin & the Universe Ser). 5.50 (ISBN 0-8199-0449-X). Franciscan Herald.

Hale, Sara A., tr. see Mullins, Edgar Y.

Hale, Sara A., tr. see Robertson, A. T.

Hale, Thomas, Jr. Don't Let the Goats Eat the Loquat Trees. 304p. pap. 9.95 (ISBN 0-310-21301-0, 18318P). Zondervan.

Hale, William H. & Ellacombe, H. T., eds. Account of the Executors of Richard Bishop of London 1303, & of the Executors of Thomas Bishop of Exeter 1310. 1874. 27.00 (ISBN 0-384-20950-5). Johnson Repr.

Halecki, Oscar. From Florence to Brest, Fourteen Thirty-Nine to Fifteen Ninety-Six. 2nd ed. LC 68-26103. 456p. 1968. 35.00 (ISBN 0-208-00702-4, Archon). Shoe String.

Hales, John. The Works of the Ever Memorable Mr. John Hales of Eaton, 3 vols. in 2. Dalrymple, D., ed. LC 77-131037. Repr. of 1765 ed. 82.50 (ISBN 0-404-03050-5). AMS Pr.

Hales, John W., et al, eds. see Percy, Bishop.

Halevi, Judah. The Kuzari: An Argument for the Faith of Israel. LC 64-15222. 1966. pap. 6.95 (ISBN 0-8052-0075-4). Schocken.

Halevi, Yehudah. Book of Kuzari. (Hebrew & Eng.). 37.50 (ISBN 0-87559-077-2). Shalom.

Halevi, Z'ev B. The Work of the Kabbalist. (Illus.). 223p. (Orig.). 1985. pap. 9.95 (ISBN 0-87728-637-X). Weiser.

Halevi, Z'ev Ben Shimon. Kabbalah & Psychology. (Illus.). 260p. (Orig.). 1986. pap. 12.50 (ISBN 0-87728-671-X). Weiser.
--School of Kabbalah. LC 85-50635. (Illus.). 288p. (Orig.). 1985. pap. 8.95 (ISBN 0-87728-648-5). Weiser.
--The Way of the Kabbalah. 1976. pap. 6.50 (ISBN 0-87728-305-2). Weiser.

Haley, Jay. The Power Tactics of Jesus Christ, & Other Essays. 2nd ed. 160p. 1986. 14.95 (ISBN 0-931513-04-9, Dist. by W. W. Norton, Inc). Triang Pr.

Haley, John W. Alleged Discrepancies of the Bible. (Direction Bks.). 1977. pap. 7.95 (ISBN 0-8010-4171-6). Baker Bk.
--Alleged Discrepancies of the Bible. 480p. 1984. pap. text ed. 3.95 (ISBN 0-88368-157-9). Whitaker Hse.

Haliczer, Stephen, ed. Inquisition & Society in Early Modern Europe. LC 86-26493. 208p. 1987. 28.50x (ISBN 0-389-20700-4). B&N Imports.

Haliel. The Book of the New Age, Bk. 1. 50p. (Orig.). 1985. pap. 3.00. Westgate Pr.

Halifax, Joan. Shaman: The Wounded Healer. Purce, Jill, ed. LC 81-67705. (The Illustrated Library of Sacred Imagination Ser.). (Illus.). 96p. 1982. pap. 9.95 (ISBN 0-8245-0066-0). Crossroad NY.
--Shamanic Voices: A Survey of Visionary Narratives. 1979. pap. 11.95 (ISBN 0-525-47525-7, 01160-350). Dutton.

Halivni, David W. Midrash, Mishnah & Gemara: The Jewish Predilection for Justified Law. 176p. 1986. text ed. 22.50x (ISBN 0-674-57370-6). Harvard U Pr.

Halkin, Abraham, tr. see Hartman, David.

Halkin, Hillel. Letters to an American Jewish Friend: A Zionist's Polemic. LC 76-58650. 246p. 1977. pap. 6.95 (ISBN 0-8276-0207-3, 402). Jewish Pubns.

Halkin, Hillel, tr. from Hebrew. see Agnon, S. Y.

Hall. Getting More from Your Bible. 1984. 5.95 (ISBN 0-88207-300-1). Victor Bks.

--Off the Shelf & Into Your Self. 1982. 3.95 (ISBN 0-88207-589-6). Victor Bks.

Hall, Barbara. Joining the Conversation: Jesus, Matthew, Luke & Us. LC 84-72480. (Parish Life Sourcebooks: Vol. 1). 103p. (Orig.). 1985. pap. 6.95 (ISBN 0-936384-25-5). Cowley Pubns.

Hall, Barbara Y. Born Amish. (Illus.). 100p. (Orig.). 1980. pap. 6.95 (ISBN 0-9606154-0-7). Jacbar Pubns.

Hall, Brian. The Development of Consciousness: A Confluent Theory of Values. LC 75-34843. 288p. 1976. 9.95 (ISBN 0-8091-0201-3); pap. 8.95 (ISBN 0-8091-1894-7). Paulist Pr.

--Shepherds & Lovers. LC 81-84352. 144p. (Orig.). 1982. pap. 6.95 (ISBN 0-8091-2425-4). Paulist Pr.

Hall, Brian & Tonna, Benjamin. God's Plan for Us: A Practical Strategy for Communal Discernment of Spirits. LC 80-81439. 128p. 1980. pap. 8.95 (ISBN 0-8091-2311-8). Paulist Pr.

Hall, Brian, et al. Readings in Value Development. 1982. pap. 11.95 (ISBN 0-8091-2448-3). Paulist Pr.

Hall, Brian P. The Genesis Effect: Personal & Organizational Transformations. (Illus.). 376p. (Orig.). 1986. pap. 14.95 (ISBN 0-8091-2741-5). Paulist Pr.

--Leadership Through Values: A Study in Personal & Organizational Development. LC 80-81438. (Illus.). 112p. (Orig.). 1980. pap. 8.95 (ISBN 0-8091-2313-4). Paulist Pr.

--The Personal Discernment Inventory: An Instrument for Spiritual Guides. pap. 5.95 (ISBN 0-8091-2312-6). Paulist Pr.

Hall, Brian P. & Tonna, Benjamin. The Hall-Tonna Inventory of Values. write for info. Paulist Pr.

Hall, Cameron P. Lay Action: The Church's Third Force. (Orig.). 1974. pap. 3.50 (ISBN 0-377-00018-3). Friend Pr.

Hall, Carolyn. Does God Give Interviews? 56p. 1985. 7.95 (ISBN 0-533-06644-1). Vantage.

Hall, Charles A. M., tr. see Cullmann, Oscar.

Hall, Charles C. Christ & the Eastern Soul: Oriental Consciousness & Jesus. 1977. lib. bdg. 59.95 (ISBN 0-8490-1613-4). Gordon Pr.

Hall, Clarence. Miracle on the Sepik. 2nd ed. (Illus.). 100p. 1980. pap. 3.95. Full Gospel.

--Miracle on the Sepik. 2nd ed. (Illus.). 100p. 1981. pap. 3.95. Gift Pubns.

Hall, Clarence W. Portrait of a Builder: William A. McIntyre. 1983. pap. 5.95 (ISBN 0-86544-020-4). Salv Army Suppl South.

--Samuel Logan Brengle: Portrait of a Prophet. 1978. Repr. of 1933 ed. 3.95 (ISBN 0-86544-006-9). Salv Army Suppl South.

Hall, Clement. Collection of Many Christian Experiences, Sentences, & Several Places of Scripture Improved. xxv, 51p. 1961. Repr. of 1753 ed. 5.00 (ISBN 0-86526-019-2). NC Archives.

Hall, Cline E., jt. auth. see Combee, Jerry H.

Hall, David D. The Faithful Shepherd: A History of the New England Ministry in the Seventeenth Century. 320p. 1974. pap. 3.45x (ISBN 0-393-00719-7, Norton Lib). Norton.

--The Faithful Shepherd: A History of the New England Ministry in the Seventeenth Century. LC 72-81326. (Institute for Early American History & Culture Ser.). xvi, 301p. 1972. 27.50x (ISBN 0-8078-1193-9). U of NC Pr.

Hall, David L. & Ames, Roger T. Thinking Through Confucius. (Systematic Philosophy Ser.). 320p. 1987. 39.50X (ISBN 0-88706-376-4); pap. 12.95x (ISBN 0-88706-377-2). State U NY Pr.

Hall, Douglas J. God & Human Suffering: An Excercise in the Theology of the Cross. LC 86-7964. 224p. 1986. text ed. 16.95 (ISBN 0-8066-2223-7, 10-2640). Augsburg.

--Has the Church a Future? LC 79-29647. 192p. 1980. pap. 8.95 (ISBN 0-664-24308-8). Westminster.

--Imaging God: Dominion As Stewardship. 272p. (Orig.). 1986. pap. 8.95 (ISBN 0-8028-0244-3). Eerdmans.

--Lighten Our Darkness: Toward an Indigenous Theology of the Cross. LC 75-38963. 252p. 1980. pap. 9.95 (ISBN 0-664-24359-2). Westminster.

--When You Pray: Thinking Your Way Into God's World. 176p. 1987. pap. 9.95 (ISBN 0-8170-1105-6). Judson.

Hall, Eugene E. & Heflin, James L. Proclaim the Word. LC 84-17458. 1985. 9.95 (ISBN 0-8054-2102-5). Broadman.

Hall, Eugene J. The Language of Mining & Metallurgy in English. (English for Careers Ser.). 1978. pap. text ed. 4.25 (ISBN 0-88345-307-X, 18521). Regents Pub.

Hall, Fitzedward, ed. Vishnu Purana. Wilson, Horace M., tr. from Sanskrit. LC 74-78004. (Secret Doctrine Reference Ser.). 2150p. Date not set. lib. bdg. 95.00 (ISBN 0-913510-14-9). Wizards.

Hall, Frederic T. The Pedigree of the Devil. LC 76-173108. (Illus.). Repr. of 1883 ed. 27.50 (ISBN 0-405-08594-X, Blom Pubns). Ayer Co Pubs.

Hall, Frederick. Bible Quizzes for Everybody. (Quiz & Puzzle Bks.). 150p. 1980. pap. 3.95 (ISBN 0-8010-4032-9). Baker Bk.

Hall, George F. The Missionary Spirit in the Augustana Church. LC 84-72945. (Publications Ser.: No. 32). 166p. 1985. 7.50 (ISBN 0-910184-32-1). Augustana.

Hall, Henry R. A. D. Nineteen Ninety-One: The Genesis of Holocaust. (Prophetic Ser.). 375p. (Orig.). 1985. pap. 4.95 (ISBN 0-930351-01-0). Spirit Prophecy.

Hall, Isaac. The Growth & the Essence of Buddhism. (Illus.). 148p. 1982. Repr. of 1883 ed. 89.75 (ISBN 0-89901-060-1). Found Class Reprints.

Hall, J. L., ed. Through the Bible Study Series, Vol. II. 384p. 1981. text ed. 6.95 (ISBN 0-912315-53-9). Word Aflame.

Hall, J. L., jt. ed. see United Pentecostal Church Int.

Hall, James. Knowledge, Belief, & Trancendence: Philosophical Problems in Religion. LC 82-21757. 254p. 1983. pap. text ed. 12.25 (ISBN 0-8191-2912-7). U Pr of Amer.

Hall, Jean. Out of Easter, the Gospels. (YA) 1979. pap. text ed. 4.25 (ISBN 0-03-021301-0, 321, HarpR); tchr's ed 2.95 (ISBN 0-03-021306-1, 322). Har-Row.

Hall, Jim. Pressings from the Vine. (Orig.). 1987. pap. 7.00 (ISBN 0-915541-18-1). Star Bks Inc.

Hall, John R. Gone from the Promised Land: Jonestown As American Cultural History. 435p. 1987. 29.95 (ISBN 0-88738-124-3). Transaction Bks.

Hall, Joseph. An Humble Remonstrance to the High Court of Parliament. LC 72-203. (English Experience Ser.: No. 255). 44p. 1970. Repr. of 1640 ed. 8.00 (ISBN 90-221-0255-6). Walter J Johnson.

--Works of Bishop Joseph Hall, 10 Vols. Wynter, P., ed. LC 76-86830. Repr. of 1863 ed. Set. 375.00 (ISBN 0-404-03070-X); 37.50 ea. AMS Pr.

Hall, Linda B. Making Eucharistic Vestments on a Limited Budget. 2nd ed. Barrett, James E., ed. (Illus.). 48p. 1985. pap. text ed. 8.50 (ISBN 0-942466-07-1). Hymnary Pr.

Hall, Louis B. The Perilous Vision of John Wyclif. LC 82-18890. 288p. 1983. lib. bdg. 23.95X (ISBN 0-8304-1006-6). Nelson-Hall.

Hall, Manly P. Apocalypse Attributed to St. John. pap. 2.95 (ISBN 0-89314-810-5). Philos Res.

--Arhats of Buddhism. pap. 3.95 (ISBN 0-89314-529-7). Philos Res.

--Buddha's Sermon on the Mount. pap. 2.50 (ISBN 0-89314-307-3). Philos Res.

--Buddhism & Psychotherapy. pap. 7.95 (ISBN 0-89314-394-4). Philos Res.

--Cabalistic Keys to Prayer. pap. 2.50 (ISBN 0-89314-308-1). Philos Res.

--Codex Rosae Crucis - DOMA. 20.00 (ISBN 0-89314-404-5). Philos Res.

--Dark Night of the Soul. pap. 2.50 (ISBN 0-89314-311-1). Philos Res.

--Death & After. pap. 2.50 (ISBN 0-89314-312-X). Philos Res.

--Death to Rebirth. pap. 4.95 (ISBN 0-89314-395-2). Philos Res.

--E. A. Gordon - Pioneer in East-West Religious Understanding. pap. 2.50 (ISBN 0-89314-377-4). Philos Res.

--Four Seasons of the Spirit. pap. 2.50 (ISBN 0-89314-315-4). Philos Res.

--Freemasonry of the Ancient Egyptians. 10.50 (ISBN 0-89314-803-2). Philos Res.

--From Death to Rebirth. pap. 3.50 (ISBN 0-89314-316-2). Philos Res.

--Great Books on Religion & Esoteric Philosophy. pap. 5.50 (ISBN 0-89314-821-0). Philos Res.

--Healing: Divine Art. 10.00 (ISBN 0-89314-510-6); pap. 6.95 (ISBN 0-89314-390-1). Philos Res.

--Is Each Individual Born with a Purpose? pap. 2.50 (ISBN 0-89314-325-1). Philos Res.

--Koyasan: Sanctuary of Buddhism. pap. 2.50 (ISBN 0-89314-326-X). Philos Res.

--Light of the Vedas. (Adepts Ser.). pap. 3.95 (ISBN 0-89314-530-0). Philos Res.

--Lone Traveler. pap. 2.50 (ISBN 0-89314-329-4). Philos Res.

--Lord Giveth & Taketh. pap. 2.50 (ISBN 0-89314-330-8). Philos Res.

--Lost Keys of Freemasonry. 8.95 (ISBN 0-89314-500-9). Philos Res.

--The Lost Keys of Freemasonry: Or, the Secret of Hiram Abiff. rev. and enl. ed. 190p. 1981. Repr. text ed. 8.95 (ISBN 0-88053-044-8). Macoy Pub.

--Masonic Orders of Fraternity. 5.95 (ISBN 0-89314-536-X). Philos Res.

--Meditation Disciplines. pap. 3.50 (ISBN 0-89314-800-8). Philos Res.

--Mystery of Holy Spirit. pap. 2.50 (ISBN 0-89314-333-2). Philos Res.

--Mystical Christ. 10.95 (ISBN 0-89314-514-9). Philos Res.

--Mysticism & Mental Healing. pap. 2.50 (ISBN 0-89314-336-7). Philos Res.

--Mystics of Islam. pap. 3.95 (ISBN 0-89314-532-7). Philos Res.

--Noble Eightfold Path. pap. 2.50 (ISBN 0-89314-337-5). Philos Res.

--Orders of the Great Work - Alchemy. 5.95 (ISBN 0-89314-534-3). Philos Res.

--Orders of the Quest - the Holy Grail. 5.95 (ISBN 0-89314-533-5). Philos Res.

--Psychology of Religious Ritual. pap. 2.50 (ISBN 0-89314-347-2). Philos Res.

--Reincarnation: The Cycle of Necessity. 1978. 8.50 (ISBN 0-89314-519-X); pap. 4.95 (ISBN 0-89314-387-1). Philos Res.

--Research on Reincarnation. pap. 2.50 (ISBN 0-89314-349-9). Philos Res.

--Science & Immortality. pap. 2.50 (ISBN 0-89314-351-0). Philos Res.

--The Secret Teachings of All Ages: An Encyclopedic Outlines of Masonic, Hermetic, Quabbalistic & Rosicrucian Symbolical Philosophy. (Illus.). 1978. pap. 24.95 (ISBN 0-89314-540-8). Philos Res.

--Sermon on the Mount. pap. 2.50 (ISBN 0-89314-353-7). Philos Res.

--Soul in Egyptian Metaphysics. pap. 2.50 (ISBN 0-89314-355-3). Philos Res.

--Story of Christmas. pap. 2.50 (ISBN 0-89314-379-0). Philos Res.

--Twelve World Teachers. pap. 6.50 (ISBN 0-89314-816-4). Philos Res.

--Value of Prayer in Psychological Integration. pap. 2.50 (ISBN 0-89314-366-9). Philos Res.

--Visions & Metaphysical Experiences. pap. 2.50 (ISBN 0-89314-378-2). Philos Res.

--White Bird of Tao. pap. 4.00 (ISBN 0-89314-371-5). Philos Res.

--Wisdom Beyond the Mind. pap. 2.50 (ISBN 0-89314-372-3). Philos Res.

--Zen of the Bright Virtue. pap. 4.00 (ISBN 0-89314-374-X). Philos Res.

Hall, Marie B. The Christ Principle & True Christianity to Be. (Illus.). 1973. 8.50 (ISBN 0-938760-03-3). Veritat Found.

Hall, Marion P. The Healing Coin. 86p. 1984. pap. 5.50 (ISBN 0-87516-542-7). De Vorss.

Hall, Marjorie W., jt. auth. see Hall, Robert B.

Hall, Mary. The Impossible Dream: The Spirituality of Dom Helder Camara. LC 79-26888. 96p. (Orig.). 1980. pap. 2.48 (ISBN 0-88344-212-4). Orbis Bks.

--A Quest for the Liberated Christian. (IC-Studies in the Intercultural History of Christianity: Vol. 19). 341p. 1978. pap. 37.25 (ISBN 3-261-02668-5). P Lang Pubs.

Hall, Michael. The Last American Puritan: The Life of Increase Mather. 1987. 35.00 (ISBN 0-8195-5128-7). Wesleyan U Pr.

Hall, Miriam J. Jesus, the Children's Friend. 64p. (Orig.). 1983. pap. 1.95 (ISBN 0-8341-0815-1). Beacon Hill.

Hall, R. Henry. Revelations of Brimstone: Ominous Portents of the Parousia of Christ. (Illus.). 374p. (Orig.). 1984. pap. 6.95 (ISBN 0-930351-00-2). Spirit Prophecy.

Hall, Renee, et al, eds. see Sandifer, Kevin W.

Hall, Robert B. Anyone Can Prophesy. 1977. pap. 3.95 (ISBN 0-686-23219-4). Episcopal Ctr.

--Church Growth for Episcopalians. 1982. pap. 4.95 (ISBN 0-686-37069-4). Episcopal Ctr.

--Receiving the Holy Spirit. 1964. pap. 1.00 (ISBN 0-686-14948-3). Episcopal Ctr.

--Sharing Your Faith. 1981. pap. 4.95 (ISBN 0-686-14949-1). Episcopal Ctr.

Hall, Robert B. & Hall, Marjorie W. Prayer, Responding to God. 1985. pap. 5.95 (ISBN 0-318-04676-8). Episcopal Ctr.

Hall, Roger L. The Stoughton Musical Society's Centennial Collection of Sacred Music. (Earlier American Music Ser.: No. 23). 304p. 1980. Repr. of 1878 ed. lib. bdg. 37.50 (ISBN 0-306-79618-X). Da Capo.

Hall, Roger L., ed. The Happy Journey: Thirty-Five Shaker Spirituals Compiled by Miss Clara Endicott Sears. LC 81-69875. (Illus.). 60p. (Orig.). 1982. 8.00 (ISBN 0-941632-00-8). Fruitlands Mus.

Hall, Ruth. Three Steps to Heaven. 1981. 4.95 (ISBN 0-8062-1560-7). Carlton.

Hall, Ruthann. That's Life. 1974. pap. 2.25 (ISBN 0-89265-020-6). Randall Hse.

Hall, Sandra. Christ & His Church: Teacher Guide. 96p. (Orig.). 1985. pap. 6.95 (ISBN 0-87123-801-2). Bethany Hse.

--The Kingdom: Teacher's Guide. 96p. (Orig.). 1985. pap. 6.95. Bethany Hse.

Hall, Stanley G. Adolescence-Its Psychology & Its Relation to Physiology, Anthropology, Sociology, Sex, Crime, Religion & Education, 2 vols. LC 79-89183. (American Education: Its Men, Institutions & Ideas Ser). 1970. Repr. of 1905 ed. Set. 65.00 (ISBN 0-405-01421-X); Vol. 1. 38.50 (ISBN 0-405-01422-8); Vol. 2. 35.00 (ISBN 0-405-01423-6). Ayer Co Pubs.

Hall, Stuart G., ed. see Melito.

Hall, T. William, ed. Introduction to the Study of Religion. LC 78-4427. (Orig.). 1978. pap. text ed. 10.95xi (ISBN 0-06-063572-X, RD 281, HarpR). Har-Row.

Hall, T. William, et al. Religion: An Introduction. LC 85-42777. 288p. (Orig.). 1986. pap. 14.45 (ISBN 0-06-063573-8, HarpR). Har-Row.

Hall, Terry. Bible Panorama. 1983. text ed. 9.95 (ISBN 0-88207-273-0). Victor Bks.

--Dynamic Bible Teaching with Overhead Transparencies. 80p. 1985. pap. 9.95 (ISBN 0-89191-584-2). Cook.

--Finally, Family Devotions That Work. (Orig.). 1986. pap. 5.95 (ISBN 0-8024-2538-0). Moody.

--How to Be the Best Sunday School Teacher You Can Be. (Orig.). 1986. pap. 6.95 (ISBN 0-8024-3631-5). Moody.

--New Testament Express. 160p. 1986. pap. 3.95 (ISBN 0-88207-598-5). Victor Bks.

--Old Testament Express. 160p. 1985. pap. 3.95 (ISBN 0-88207-599-3). Victor Bks.

Hall, Theodore. The Mysterious Fundamental Option. (Synthesis Ser.). 1979. 0.75 (ISBN 0-8199-0746-4). Franciscan Herald.

Hall, Thor. Anders Nygren. (Makers of the Modern Theological Mind Ser.). 1978. 8.95 (ISBN 0-8499-0098-0). Word Bks.

--Anders Nygren. 230p. 1984. pap. text ed. 8.95 (ISBN 0-8499-3004-9, 3004-9). Word Bks.

--The Evolution of Christology. LC 81-14838. 128p. (Orig.). 1982. pap. 6.50 (ISBN 0-687-12190-6). Abingdon.

--The Future Shape of Preaching. LC 77-157537. pap. 40.00 (2026899). Bks Demand UMI.

Hall, Willard S. The Lamb of God; the Theme Eternal. 35p. 1974. 4.95 (ISBN 0-87881-033-1). Mojave Bks.

Hall, William C. Milton & His Sonnets. LC 73-4268. 1973. lib. bdg. 12.50 (ISBN 0-8414-2071-8). Folcroft.

Hall, Wilmer L., ed. The Vestry Book of the Upper Parish, Nansemond County, Virginia, 1793-1943. LC 50-9492. ixxiv, 328p. 1949. 10.00 (ISBN 0-88490-039-8). VA State Lib.

Hallam, Arthur F. Christian Capitalism. 182p. (Orig.). 1981. pap. 14.95 (ISBN 0-938770-00-4). Capitalist Pr OH.

--Christian Capitalist Sermons One Thru Twenty-Six. 232p. 1983. pap. 30.00 (ISBN 0-938770-02-0). Capitalist Pr OH.

--Concurrences Between Dio Chrysostom's First Discourse & the New Testament. 91p. (Orig.). 1985. pap. 9.95 (ISBN 0-938770-04-7). Capitalist Pr OH.

--Total Surrender to God. 236p. (Orig.). 1985. pap. 19.95 (ISBN 0-938770-05-5). Capitalist Pr OH.

--William Lloyd's Life of Pythagoras, with a New Thesis on the Origin of the New Testament. 84p. (Orig.). 1982. pap. 8.50 (ISBN 0-938770-01-2). Capitalist Pr OH.

Halle, Anna S. Thoughts Are Free: A Quaker Youth in Nazi Germany. LC 85-61843. (Orig.). 1985. pap. 2.50 (ISBN 0-87574-265-3). Pendle Hill.

Hallen, Barry & Sodipo, J. O. Knowledge, Belief & Witchcraft. 144p. 1986. text ed. 24.95x (ISBN 0-936508-19-1, Ethnographica). Barber Pr.

Haller, William. Elizabeth One & the Puritans. LC 64-7541. 1965. pap. 3.95 (ISBN 0-918016-24-X). Folger Bks.

--Liberty & Reformation in the Puritan Revolution. LC 54-6482. 410p. 1955. pap. 14.00x (ISBN 0-231-08547-8). Columbia U Pr.

--The Rise of Puritanism. LC 57-10117. 479p. 1972. pap. 14.95x (ISBN 0-8122-1048-4, Pa Paperbks). U of Pa Pr.

Haller, William & Davies, Godfrey, eds. The Leveller Tracts: 1647-1653. 1964. 11.75 (ISBN 0-8446-1218-9). Peter Smith.

Hallesby, O. God's Word for Today: A Daily Devotional for the Whole Year. Carlsen, Clarence J., tr. LC 78-67940. 1979. pap. 5.95 (ISBN 0-8066-1682-2, 10-2741). Augsburg.

--Prayer. LC 75-2846. 176p. 1975. pap. 3.95 (ISBN 0-8066-1473-0, 10-5067). Augsburg.

--Temperament & the Christian Faith. LC 62-9093. 106p. 1978. pap. 3.95 (ISBN 0-8066-1660-1, 10-6237). Augsburg.

Hallett, Paul. Witness to Permanence. LC 86-82637. 279p. (Orig.). 1986. pap. 11.95 (ISBN 0-89870-134-1). Ignatius Pr.

Halley, Henry H. Compendio Manual de la Biblia. Denyer, C. P., tr. (Span., Illus.). 768p. 1985. Repr. of 1984 ed. 14.95 (ISBN 0-311-03666-X). Casa Bautista.

--Compendio Manual de la Biblia. Orig. Title: Halley's Bible Handbook. (Span.). 768p. 1955. 14.95 (ISBN 0-8254-1300-1); pap. 12.95. Kregel.
--Halley's Bible Handbook. 1976. 9.95 (ISBN 0-310-25720-4, 9744); pap. 13.95 Large print (ISBN 0-310-25727-1, 12564L); large print Kivar 19.95 (ISBN 0-310-41390-7, 9840). Zondervan.
Halliburton, John, tr. see Klauser, Theodor.
Halliburton, Warren J. & Katz, William L. American Majorities & Minorities: A Syllabus of United States History for Secondary Schools. 6.95 (ISBN 0-405-18855-2, 19424). Ayer Co Pubs.
Hallick, Mary P. The Book of Saints. 1984. pap. 5.95 (ISBN 0-937032-31-X). Light&Life Pub Co MN.
Halliday, W. R. The Pagan Background of Christianity. 59.95 (ISBN 0-8490-0795-X). Gordon Pr.
Hallie, Philip P., ed. see Sextus Empiricus.
Hallie, Phillip P., ed. see Sextus Empiricus Staff.
Halligan, Nicholas. The Sacraments & Their Celebration. LC 85-23031. 284p. (Orig.). 1986. pap. 14.95 (ISBN 0-8189-0489-5). Alba.
Halliwell, William J. The Style of Pope St. Leo the Great, No. 59. (Patristic Studies). 114p. 1984. 26.00x (ISBN 0-939738-25-2). Zubal Inc.
Hallman, Barbara M. Italian Cardinals, Reform, & the Church As Property, 1492-1563. LC 84-8501. (Center for Medieval & Renaissance Studies, UCLA Publications: No. 22). 1985. 35.00x (ISBN 0-520-04937-3). U of Cal Pr.
Hallo, W. W., et al, eds. Scripture in Context II: More Essays on the Comparative Method. 1983. text ed. 17.50 (ISBN 0-931464-14-5). Eisenbrauns.
Hallo, William & Ruderman, David. Heritage: Civilization & the Jews; a Study Guide. 302p. 1984. 34.95 (ISBN 0-03-000484-5); pap. 12.95 (ISBN 0-03-000483-7). Praeger.
Hallo, William & Ruderman, David, eds. Heritage: Civilization & the Jews; a Source Reader. 332p. 1984. 34.95 (ISBN 0-03-000479-9); pap. 13.95 (ISBN 0-03-000482-9). Praeger.
Hallo, William W., tr. see Rosenzweig, Franz.
Hallowell, Richard P. The Quaker Invasion of Massachusetts. 13.50 (ISBN 0-8369-7139-6, 7970). Ayer Co Pubs.
Halls, W. D., tr. see Hubert, Henri & Mauss, Marcel.
Halm, Carolus, ed. see Severus, Sulpicius.
Halper, Roe. Passover Haggadah. (Illus.). 40p. (Orig.). 1986. pap. 5.00 (ISBN 0-916326-03-9). Bayberry Pr.
Halperin, D. A. Psychodynamic Perspectives on Religion, Sect & Cult. 416p. 1983. pap. text ed. 46.50 (ISBN 0-7236-7029-3). PSG Pub Co.
Halperin, David. Merkabah in Rabbinic Literature. (American Oriental Ser.: Vol. 62). 1980. 14.00x (ISBN 0-940490-62-5). Am Orient Soc.
Halperin, Don A. Ancient Synagogues of the Iberian Peninsula. LC 78-62577. (University of Florida Social Sciences Monographs: No. 38). (Illus.). 1969. pap. 3.50 (ISBN 0-8130-0272-9). U Presses Fla.
--The Old Synagogues of Turkey: A Pictorial Narrative. LC 86-50586. (Illus.). 73p. (Orig.). 1987. pap. text ed. 9.95x (ISBN 0-932269-89-3). Wyndham Hall.
Halperin, S. William. Separation of Church & State in Italian Thought from Cavour to Mussolini. LC 71-120623. 1970. Repr. lib. bdg. 15.00x (ISBN 0-374-93412-6, Octagon). Hippocrene Bks.
Halperin, Samuel W. Italy & the Vatican at War: A Study of Their Relations from the Outbreak of the Franco-Prussian War to the Death of Pius 9th. LC 68-57606. (Illus.). 1968. Repr. of 1939 ed. lib. bdg. 22.50x (ISBN 0-8371-0461-0, HAIV). Greenwood.
Halpern, Baruch. The Emergence of Israel in Canaan. LC 82-24030. (Society of Biblical Literature Monographic Ser.: No. 29). 352p. 1984. 36.75 (ISBN 0-89130-649-8, 06 00 29); pap. 24.50 (ISBN 0-89130-609-9). Scholars Pr GA.
Halpern, Baruch & Levenson, Jon D., eds. Traditions in Transformation: Turning Points in Biblical Faith. 1981. 22.50 (ISBN 0-931464-06-4). Eisenbrauns.
Halpern, Ben. The American Jew: A Zionistic Analysis. LC 82-16875. 192p. 1983. pap. 6.95 (ISBN 0-8052-0742-2). Schocken.
--Idea of the Jewish State. rev. ed. LC 71-89969. (Middle Eastern Studies: No. 3). (Illus.). 1969. 30.00x (ISBN 0-674-44201-6). Harvard U Pr.
Halpern, Edwin G., jt. auth. see Grosser, Paul E.
Halpern, Joel M., ed. Bibliography of Judaic Cultures, Nos. 749-750. 1975. 8.00 (ISBN 0-686-20342-9). CPL Biblios.
Halpert, Herbert & Story, G. M., eds. Christmas Mumming in Newfoundland: Essays in Anthropology, Folklore, & History. LC 71-391290. pap. 64.50 (ISBN 0-317-42289-8, 2055819). Bks Demand UMI.
Halpin, Marlene. Imagine That! 144p. 1982. pap. 4.95 (ISBN 0-697-01812-1); videotapes avail. Wm C Brown.
Halsell, Grace. Prophecy & Politics: Militant Evangelists on the Road to Nuclear War. (Illus.). 256p. 1986. 14.95 (ISBN 0-88208-210-8). Lawrence Hill.
Halsema, Thea B. Van see Van Halsema, Thea B.
Halsey, Alexandra, ed. see Riggins, John & Winter, Jack.
Halsey, William M. The Survival of American Innocence: Catholicism in An Era of Disillusionment, 1920-1940. LC 79-63360. (Studies in American Catholicism: No. 2). 1979. 19.95x (ISBN 0-268-01699-2, 85-16999). U of Notre Dame Pr.
Halton, Thomas. The Church. (Message of the Fathers of the Church Ser.: Vol. 4). 1985. 15.95 (ISBN 0-89453-344-4); pap. 10.95 (ISBN 0-89453-316-9). M Glazier.
Halton, Thomas, ed. see Hamman, Adelbert.
Halverson, Delia T. Helping Your Child Discover Faith. 128p. 1982. pap. 5.95 (ISBN 0-8170-0957-4). Judson.
--Helping Your Teen Develop Faith. 112p. 1985. pap. 5.95 (ISBN 0-8170-1046-7). Judson.
Halverson, K. & Hess, Karen. The Wedded Unmother. LC 79-54123. 128p. 1980. pap. 5.95 (ISBN 0-8066-1768-3, 10-7015). Augsburg.
Halverson, Marvin & Cohen, Arthur. Handbook of Christian Theology. (Fount Paperback Ser.). pap. 7.95 (ISBN 0-687-16567-9). Abingdon.
Halverson, Marvin, ed. Religious Drama, Vol. 1: Five Plays. 11.25 (ISBN 0-8446-2792-5). Peter Smith.
--Religious Drama, Vol. 3. 11.25 (ISBN 0-8446-2794-1). Peter Smith.
Halverson, Richard C. A Living Fellowship. 195p. 1985. pap. 5.95 (ISBN 0-310-25781-6, Pub. by Pyranee). Zondervan.
--Somehow Inside of Eternity. LC 80-21687. (Illus., Orig.). 1981. pap. 8.95 (ISBN 0-930014-51-8). Multnomah.
--The Timelessness of Jesus Christ. LC 82-80008. 1982. 8.95 (ISBN 0-8307-0838-3, 5109902). Regal.
--The Word of a Gentleman: Meditations for Modern Man. 208p. 1983. pap. 5.95 (ISBN 0-310-25811-1, 6878P). Zondervan.
Halverson, Sandy. Book of Mormon Activity Book: Creative Scripture Learning Experiences for Children 4-12. (Illus.). 80p. 1982. pap. 2.95 (ISBN 0-88290-188-5, 4521). Horizon Utah.
--Church History Activity Book: Creative Learning Experiences About the Restoration for Children 4-12. 36p. (Orig.). 1983. pap. 2.95 (ISBN 0-88290-213-X). Horizon Utah.
--Preparing for Baptism. 48p. 1983. pap. 3.95 (ISBN 0-88290-233-4). Horizon-Utah.
Halverstadt, Robert. God's Word for Your Healing. 1982. pap. 1.95 (ISBN 0-88144-003-5, CPS-003). Christian Pub.
--God's Word for Your Prosperity. 1982. pap. 1.95 (ISBN 0-88144-002-7, CPS-002). Christian Pub.
--Your New Birth. 1982. pap. 0.75 (ISBN 0-88144-001-9, CPS-001). Christian Pub.
Halvorson, Loren E. Grace at Point Zero. (Orig.). 1972. pap. 1.75 (ISBN 0-377-02111-3). Friend Pr.
Halvorson, Peter L. & Newman, William M. Atlas of Religious Change in America: 1952-1971. LC 78-67653. (Illus.). 1978. pap. 6.50 (ISBN 0-914422-09-X). Glenmary Res Ctr.
Halvorson, Peter L., jt. auth. see Newman, William M.
Ham, Ken. The Lie: Evolution. 188p. 1987. 10.95 (ISBN 0-89051-117-9). Master Bks.
Ham, Marlene, jt. auth. see Ham, Wayne.
Ham, Wayne. More Than Burnt Offerings. LC 78-17646. 1978. pap. 7.00 (ISBN 0-8309-0217-1). Herald Hse.
--Studies in Genesis, Vol. 2. (Bible Study Ser.). 1987. pap. 3.50 (ISBN 0-8309-0483-2). Herald Hse.
Ham, Wayne & Ham, Marlene. My Million Faces. (World Religion Ser.). 74p. 1985. Set. pap. 3.00 (ISBN 0-8309-0415-8); Faces from India. pap. 3.00 (ISBN 0-8309-0416-6); Faces from the Orient. pap. 3.00 (ISBN 0-8309-0417-4); Faces fron the Eternal. pap. 3.00 (ISBN 0-8309-0418-2). Herald Hse.
Hamad, Khalil M., tr. see Al-Qaradawl, Yusuf.
Hamada, Louis. God Loves the Arabs Too. Graves, Helen, ed. LC 85-40888. 174p. 1986. 13.95 (ISBN 1-55523-044-X); pap. 10.95 (ISBN 1-55523-000-8). Winston-Derek.
Hamann, H. P. A Popular Guide to New Testament Criticism. 1977. pap. 4.75 (ISBN 0-570-03760-3, 12-2671). Concordia.
Hamann, Henry P. Justification by Faith in Modern Theology. 114p. 1957. write for info. Concordia Schl Grad Studies.
Hamar, Paul. The Book of First Corinthians. LC 80-65305. 192p. (Orig.). 1980. 6.95 (ISBN 0-88243-316-4, 02-0316). Gospel Pub.
Hamblen, Emily S. The Interpretaton of William Blake's Job. LC 70-100759. 1970. pap. 39.95x (ISBN 0-8383-0037-5). Haskell.
Hamblin, Henry T. Dynamic Thought. limited ed. 8.00 (ISBN 0-911662-22-7). Yoga.
Hamblin, Robert L. Triumphant Strangers: A Contemporary Look at First Peter. LC 81-67206. 1982. pap. 5.95 (ISBN 0-8054-1389-8). Broadman.
Hambly, W. D. Serpent Worship in Africa - the Ovimbundu of Angola: Culture Areas of Nigeria. (Chicago Field Museum of Natural History Fieldiana Anthropology Ser). Repr. of 1935 ed. 51.00 (ISBN 0-527-01881-3). Kraus Repr.
Hambrick, John. The High Cost of Indifference: Leader's Guide. (Study & Grow Electives). 64p. 1985. pap. 3.95 (ISBN 0-8307-1019-1, 6102038). Regal.
Hambrick-Stowe, Charles E. The Practice of Piety: Puritan Devotional Disciplines in Seventeenth Century New England. LC 81-19806. (Published for the Institute of Early American History & Culture, Williamsburg, Virginia Ser.). xvi, 298p. 1986. pap. 10.95x (ISBN 0-8078-4145-5). U of Nc Pr.
Hambrick-Stowe, Elizabeth A. Your Baby... Gift of God. (Looking Up Ser.). (Orig.). 1985. pap. 1.25 (ISBN 0-8298-0549-4). Pilgrim NY.
Hamburger, Roberta, jt. ed. see Sayre, John L.
Hameed, Hakeem A., ed. Islam at a Glance. 125p. 1981. (Pub. by Vikas India); pap. 4.95x (ISBN 0-7069-1413-9). Advent NY.
Hameedullah, M. Introduction to Islam. pap. 14.95 (ISBN 0-686-18488-2). Kazi Pubns.
--Islam, a General Picture. pap. 4.50 (ISBN 0-686-63903-0). Kazi Pubns.
Hameedullah, Muhammad. Introduction to Islam. 276p. (Orig.). 1977. pap. 6.50 (ISBN 0-939830-13-2, Pub. by IIFSO Kuwait). New Era Pubns MI.
Hamel, Mike, jt. auth. see MacDonald, William.
Hamelin, Leonce. Reconciliation in the Church. O'Connell, Matthew J., tr. from Fr. LC 80-29328. Orig. Title: La Reconciliation en Eglise. 111p. 1980. pap. text ed. 5.50 (ISBN 0-8146-1215-6). Liturgical Pr.
Hamell, Patrick J. Handbook of Patrology. 1968. pap. 5.95 (ISBN 0-8189-0057-1). Alba.
Hamelsdorf, Ora, et al, eds. Jewish Women & Jewish Law: Bibliography. 60p. 1981. pap. 3.00 (ISBN 0-9602036-2-1). Biblio NY.
Hamelsdorf, Ora, jt. ed. see Cantor, Aviva.
Hamerton-Kelly, Robert. God the Father: Theology & Patriarchy in the Teaching of Jesus, No. 4. Brueggemann, Walter & Donahue, John R., eds. LC 78-54551. (Overtures to Biblical Theology Ser.). 144p. 1979. pap. 8.95 (ISBN 0-8006-1528-X, 1-1528). Fortress.
Hamerton-Kelly, Robert G. Sprung Time: Seasons of the Christian Year. LC 79-56162. 144p. (Orig.). 1980. pap. 4.50 (ISBN 0-8358-0397-X). Upper Room.
Hamerton-Kelly, Robert G., ed. Violent Origins: Walter Burkert, Rene Girard, & Jonathan Z. Smith on Ritual Killing & Cultural Formation. LC 86-23009. 296p. 1987. 32.50x (ISBN 0-8047-1370-7). Stanford U Pr.
Hames. Deeper Things. pap. 2.95 (ISBN 0-686-12864-8). Schmul Pub Co.
Hamidullah, D. M. Holy Quran, 2 vols. (Arabic, Fr.). 1981. Set. french & arabic 69.00 (ISBN 0-686-77430-2). Kazi Pubns.
Hamill, James E. Pastor to Pastor. LC 85-60248. 192p. 1985. 5.50 (ISBN 0-88243-600-7, 02-0600). Gospel Pub.
Hamill, Paul, ed. Introits & Responses for Contemporary Worship. (Orig.). 1983. pap. 2.95 (ISBN 0-8298-0649-0). Pilgrim NY.
Hamilton, Alastair. The Family of Love. 185p. 1981. text ed. 29.95 (ISBN 0-227-67845-1). Attic Pr.
Hamilton, Bernard. The Medieval Inquisition. 112p. 1981. 25.00x (ISBN 0-7131-6251-1, Pub. by E Arnold England). State Mutual Bk.
--Medieval Inquisition: Foundations of Medieval History. LC 80-27997. 110p. (Orig.). 1981. 24.50x (ISBN 0-8419-0718-8); pap. text ed. 14.95x (ISBN 0-8419-0695-5). Holmes & Meier.
--Religion in the Medieval West. 224p. 1986. pap. text ed. 14.95 (ISBN 0-7131-6461-1). E Arnold.
Hamilton, C. The Hedaya: A Commentary on the Muslim Laws. 1963. 130.00 (ISBN 0-87902-163-2). Orientalia.
Hamilton, Charles G. You Can't Steal First Base. LC 74-164909. 1972. 6.95 (ISBN 0-8022-2057-6). Philos Lib.
Hamilton, Charles M. & Cutrubus, C. Nina, eds. The Salt Lake Temple: A Monument to a People. (Illus.). 208p. 1983. write for info. (ISBN 0-913535-01-X); pap. write for info. (ISBN 0-913535-02-8); Ltd. Ed. 250.00 (ISBN 0-913535-00-1). Univ Servs Inc.
Hamilton, Dan, ed. see MacDonald, George.
Hamilton, Dorothy. Last One Chosen. LC 82-3150. (Illus.). 112p. (Orig.). 1982. pap. 3.95 (ISBN 0-8361-3306-4). Herald Pr.
Hamilton, Edith. Greek Way. (YA) 1948. 19.95 (ISBN 0-393-04162-X). Norton.
--The Greek Way. 1983. pap. 3.95 (ISBN 0-393-00230-6). Norton.
--Mythology. (Illus.). 1942. 15.45 (ISBN 0-316-34114-2). Little.
--Mythology. 336p. (YA) 1971. pap. 3.50 (ISBN 0-451-62523-4, Ment). NAL.
--Spokesmen for God. 1962. pap. 3.95 (ISBN 0-393-00169-5, Norton Lib). Norton.
Hamilton, Elizabeth. I Stay in the Church. 183p. 1973. 4.95 (ISBN 0-85478-053-X). Attic Pr.
--Letters Addressed to the Daughter of a Nobleman on the Formation of the Religious & the Moral Principle, 2 vols. Luria, Gina, ed. (The Feminist Controversy in England, 1788-1810 Ser.). 1974. Set. lib. bdg. 121.00 (ISBN 0-8240-0865-0). Garland Pub.
--The Life of Saint Teresa of Avila. 190p. 1982. pap. 6.95 (ISBN 0-87061-089-9, Pub. by A Clarke Bks UK). Chr Classics.
Hamilton, G. Rostrevor. Hero or Fool. LC 70-98995. (Studies in Milton, No. 22). 1970. pap. 19.95x (ISBN 0-8383-0038-3). Haskell.
--Hero or Fool: A Study of Milton's Satan. LC 74-16136. 1944. lib. bdg. 17.50 (ISBN 0-8414-4860-4). Folcroft.
Hamilton, Gavin & Fernandez, David. Donde Estan los Muertes? Orig. Title: Where Are the Dead? (Span.). 64p. 1983. pap. 2.25 (ISBN 0-8254-1301-X). Kregel.
Hamilton, Iva. The Story of Albert J. (Illus., Orig.). 1985. pap. 6.95 (ISBN 0-87418-028-7, 162). Coleman Pub.
Hamilton, James. Moses, the Man of God. 388p. 1985. Repr. lib. bdg. 14.75 (ISBN 0-86524-187-2, 8407). Klock & Klock.
Hamilton, James D. The Faces of God. 100p. 1985. pap. 3.95 (ISBN 0-8341-0940-9). Beacon Hill.
--Ministry of Pastoral Counseling. (Source Books for Ministers Ser). 1972. pap. 5.95 (ISBN 0-8010-4069-8). Baker Bk.
Hamilton, James E. The Liturgical Coordinator. 64p. (Orig.). 1984. pap. text ed. 10.00 (ISBN 0-942466-06-3); Looseleaf 9.50 (ISBN 0-942466-05-5). Hymnary Pr.
Hamilton, James E., jt. auth. see Madden, Edward H.
Hamilton, Joan K. Patterns. (Illus.). 1977. tchrs'. manual 5.25x (ISBN 0-8192-4078-8); parents' letters & pupils' leaflets package 5.75x (ISBN 0-8192-4077-X). Morehouse.
Hamilton, John A. The Life of John Milton, Englishman. LC 74-16133. 1974. Repr. lib. bdg. 9.50 (ISBN 0-8414-4874-4). Folcroft.
Hamilton, John T. A History of the Church Known As the Moravian Church. LC 70-134379. Repr. of 1900 ed. 37.50 (ISBN 0-404-08427-3). AMS Pr.
Hamilton, Kenneth. What's New in Religion? A Critical Study of New Theology, New Morality & Secular Christianity. 176p. 1969. pap. 3.95 (ISBN 0-85364-092-0). Attic Pr.
Hamilton, LeRoy L. Jogging with God. 56p. 1985. 5.95 (ISBN 0-8059-2983-5). Dorrance.
Hamilton, M. J. Adam of Dryburgh: Six Christmas Sermons (Introduction & Translation) Hogg, James, ed. (Analecta Cartusiana Ser.: No. 16). (Orig.). 1974. pap. 25.00 (ISBN 3-7052-0018-6, Pub by Salzburg Studies). Longwood Pub Group.
Hamilton, Michael. God's Plan for the Church-Growth! LC 81-82021. (Radiant Life Ser.). 128p. (Orig.). 1981. 2.50 (ISBN 0-88243-885-9, 02-0885); teacher's ed. 3.95 (ISBN 0-88243-194-3, 32-0194). Gospel Pub.
Hamilton, Michael P. & Reid, Helen F. A Hospice Handbook. (Orig.). 1980. pap. 7.95 (ISBN 0-8028-1820-X). Eerdmans.
Hamilton, Neill Q. Maturing in the Christian Life: A Pastor's Guide. LC 83-20661. 192p. (Orig.). 1984. pap. 10.95 (ISBN 0-664-24515-3). Westminster.
Hamilton, Ronald R. Reluctant Followers: A Chosen People? Sherer, Michael L., ed. (Orig.). 1986. pap. 6.25 (ISBN 0-89536-824-2, 6833). CSS of Ohio.
Hamilton, Vail, jt. auth. see Haddon, David.
Hamilton, Victor P. Handbook on the Pentateuch. LC 82-70466. 392p. 1982. 15.95 (ISBN 0-8010-4259-3). Baker Bk.
Hamilton, W. Douglas. Original Papers Illustrative of the Life & Writings of John Milton. LC 76-29043. 1859. lib. bdg. 25.00 (ISBN 0-8414-4935-X). Folcroft.
Hamilton, Wallace. Clash by Night. 1983. pap. 2.50x (ISBN 0-87574-023-5, 023). Pendle Hill.
Hamilton, William. The Christian Man. LC 56-8666. (Layman's Theological Library). 94p. 1956. pap. 1.00 (ISBN 0-664-24003-8). Westminster.
--Melville & the Gods. (Scholars Press Studies in the Humanities: No. 7). 1985. pap. 13.25 (ISBN 0-89130-741-9, 00 01 07). Scholars Pr GA.

Hamilton, William D., ed. Original Papers Illustrative of the Life & Writings of John Milton. (Camden Society, London. Publications, First Ser.: No. 75). Repr. of 1859 ed. 28.00 (ISBN 0-404-50175-3). AMS Pr.
--Original Papers Illustrative of the Life & Writings of John Milton. 1859. 28.00 (ISBN 0-384-21220-4). Johnson Repr.

Hamlin, E. J. The International Theological Commentary on Joshua. Holmgren, Frederick & Knight, George A., eds. (The International Theological Commentary Ser.). 200p. (Orig.). 1983. pap. 8.95 (ISBN 0-8028-1041-1). Eerdmans.

Hamlin, E. J. see Holmgren, Frederick & Knight, George A.

Hamm, Jack. Custom Clip Art for Churches, Vol. 2. 48p. (Orig.). 1985. pap. 9.95 (ISBN 0-933545-00-2). Knight Media.
--Handy Clip Art for Church Bulletin Covers. 48p. (Orig.). 1985. pap. 9.95 (ISBN 0-933545-02-9). Knight Media.
--Illustrated Clip Art Bible Verses. 48p. (Orig.). 1985. pap. 9.95 (ISBN 0-933545-01-0). Knight Media.

Hamm, Peter M. Continuity & Change among Canadian Mennonite Brethren. (Social Scientific Studies in Religion: Religion & Identity). 304p. 1986. 35.00 (ISBN 0-88920-189-7, Pub. by Wilfrid Laurier Canada). Humanities.

Hammack, Mary L. A Dictionary of Women in Church History. LC 84-14710. 1984. 11.95 (ISBN 0-8024-0332-8). Moody.
--How to Organize Your Church Library & Resource Center. 128p. 1985. pap. 5.95 (ISBN 0-8170-1066-1). Judson.

Hamman, Adelbert. Mass: Ancient Liturgies & Patristic Texts. Halton, Thomas, ed. LC 67-15202. 1967. 5.95 (ISBN 0-8189-0086-5). Alba.
--Paschal Mystery: Ancient Liturgical & Patristic Texts. Halton, Thomas, ed. LC 78-77646. Orig. Title: Mystere De Paques. 1969. 5.95 (ISBN 0-8189-0108-X). Alba.

Hammar, Richard R. Pastor, Church & Law. LC 83-80245. 448p. 1983. 16.95 (ISBN 0-88243-580-9, 02-0580). Gospel Pub.
--Pastor, Church & Law Supplement. LC 85-82192. 208p. (Orig.). 1986. 6.95 (ISBN 0-88243-582-5, 02-0582). Gospel Pub.

Hammarskjold, Dag. Markings. (Epiphany Bks.). 1985. pap. 3.50 (ISBN 0-345-32741-1). Ballantine.

Hammel, W. W. So Great Salvation. 1972. pap. 2.95 (ISBN 0-87148-751-9). Pathway Pr.

Hammer, Gottlieb. Good Faith & Credit. LC 85-13962. (Illus.). 280p. 1986. 17.95 (ISBN 0-8453-4798-5, Cornwall Bks). Assoc Univ Prs.

Hammer, Raymond. Japan's Religious Ferment: Christian Presence Amid Faiths Old & New. LC 85-14867. (Christian Presence Ser.). 207p. 1985. Repr. of 1962 ed. lib. bdg. 39.75x (ISBN 0-313-24921-0, HAJR). Greenwood.

Hammer, Reuven, tr. from Hebrew. & Sifre: A Tannaitic Commentary on the Book of Deuteronomy. LC 85-29556. (Yale Judaica Ser.: No. 24). 560p. 1986. text ed. 45.00x (ISBN 0-300-03345-1). Yale U Pr.

Hammerich, Angul. Mediaeval Musical Relics of Denmark. LC 74-24104. Repr. of 1912 ed. 24.50 (ISBN 0-404-12952-8). AMS Pr.

Hammer-Purgstall, Joseph Von see Von Hammer-Purgstall, Joseph.

Hammes, John A. Ascend to Your Father: An Introduction to Marian Meditation. (Orig.). 1987. pap. 5.95 (ISBN 0-913382-36-1, 101-36). Prow Bks-Franciscan.
--Humanistic Psychology: A Christian Interpretation. LC 76-110448. 224p. 1971. 49.50 (ISBN 0-8089-0650-X, 791865). Grune.
--In Praise of God: The Rosary in Scriptural Meditation. 154p. 1983. 1.98 (ISBN 0-911988-51-3). Ami Pr.

Hammett, Jenny. Woman's Transformation: A Psychological Theology. LC 82-14287. (Symposium Ser.: Vol. 8). 112p. 1982. pap. 19.95x (ISBN 0-88946-918-0). E Mellen.

Hammond, Beth. Lord, Help Me! The Desperate Dieter. (Continued Applied Christianity Ser.). 1983. pap. 4.50 (ISBN 0-570-03896-0, 12-2978). Concordia.

Hammond, Edmund J. Methodist Episcopal Church in Georgia. 1935. 10.00 (ISBN 0-88289-286-X). Pelican.

Hammond, Frank & Hammond, Ida M. Pigs in the Parlor. 153p. (Orig.). 1973. pap. 4.95 (ISBN 0-89228-027-1). Impact Bks MO.

Hammond, Frank & Hammond, Ida Mae. Kingdom Living for the Family. 175p. (Orig.). 1985. pap. 4.95 (ISBN 0-89228-100-6). Impact Bks MO.

Hammond, Gerald. The Making of the English Bible. LC 83-13264. 249p. 1983. 19.95 (ISBN 0-8022-2419-9). Philos Lib.

Hammond, Heather. Preparing for God's Gift: Devotions for Families Using the Advent Wreath. 40p. (Orig.). 1986. pap. 2.50 (ISBN 0-8066-2260-1, 23-1809). Augsburg.

Hammond, Henry. Practical Catechism, 3 Vols. LC 79-168238. (Library of Anglo-Catholic Theology: No. 8). Repr. of 1850 ed. Set. 87.50 (ISBN 0-404-52090-1). AMS Pr.

Hammond, Ida M., jt. auth. see Hammond, Frank.

Hammond, Ida Mae, jt. auth. see Hammond, Frank.

Hammond, Jane. Daniel the Dog. (God's Animals Story Bks.). 1983. pap. 1.50 (ISBN 0-87162-287-4, D5601). Warner Pr.
--Debra the Donkey. (God's Animals Story Bks.). 1983. pap. 1.50 (ISBN 0-87162-288-2, D5602). Warner Pr.
--Larry the Lamb. (God's Animals Story Bks.). 1983. pap. 1.50 (ISBN 0-87162-286-6, D5600). Warner Pr.

Hammond, Philip E. The Sacred in a Secular Age: Toward Revision in the Scientific Study of Religion. LC 84-16470. 380p. 1985. 37.50x (ISBN 0-520-05342-7); pap. 8.95 (ISBN 0-520-05343-5, CAL 726). U of Cal Pr.

Hammond, Philip E., jt. auth. see Dolbeare, Kenneth M.

Hammond, Philip E., jt. ed. see Bromley, David G.

Hammond, Phillip E. The Role of Ideology in Church Participation. Zuckerman, Harriet & Merton, Robert K., eds. LC 79-9003. (Dissertations on Sociology Ser.). 1980. lib. bdg. 27.50x (ISBN 0-405-12972-6). Ayer Co Pubs.

Hammond, William E. What Masonry Means. 1978. Repr. of 1939 ed. 5.50 (ISBN 0-88053-051-0, M-311). Macoy Pub.

Hamori, Andras, tr. see Goldziher, Ignaz.

Hamori, Ruth, tr. see Goldziher, Ignaz.

Hampe, Johann C., tr. see Bonhoeffer, Dietrich.

Hampsch, John H. & Kelly, Clint. Faith: Key to the Heart of God. LC 84-62433. (Keyhole Ser.: No. 1). 102p. (Orig.). 1985. pap. 6.95 (ISBN 0-9613575-1-7). Perf Pr.
--The Key to Inner Peace. LC 85-61758. (Keyhole Ser.: No. 2). 112p. (Orig.). 1985. pap. 6.95 (ISBN 0-9613575-2-5). Perf Pr.

Hampshire, Annette P. Mormonism in Conflict: The Nauvoo Years. LC 84-27263. (Studies in Religion & Society: Vol. II). 350p. 1985. 59.95x (ISBN 0-88946-874-5). E Mellen.

Hampshire, Stuart. Morality & Conflict. 176p. 1987. pap. text ed. 9.50x (ISBN 0-674-58732-4). Harvard U Pr.
--Spinoza. (Orig.). 1952. pap. 4.95 (ISBN 0-14-020253-6, Pelican). Penguin.

Hampton, Diane. The Diet Alternative. Orig. Title: Scriptural Eating Patterns. 144p. (Orig.). 1984. pap. 3.95 (ISBN 0-88368-148-X). Whitaker Hse.

Hampton, Larry D. Commissioned to Communicate: Teacher's Guide. 1978. pap. 1.50 (ISBN 0-89265-056-7). Randall Hse.
--Pupil Profiles: Teacher's Guide. 1978. pap. 1.50 (ISBN 0-89265-057-5). Randall Hse.

Hampton, Ralph, Jr., jt. auth. see O'Donnell, J. D.

Hampton, Ralph, Jr., jt. auth. see Picirilli, Robert.

Hamre, James S. Georg Sverdrup: Educator, Theologian, Churchman. 194p. 1986. 15.00 (ISBN 0-87732-071-3). Norwegian-Am Hist Assn.

Hamroque, John & Krastel, Joseph. Guilt: How to Deal with It. 48p. 1986. pap. 1.50 (ISBN 0-89243-256-X). Liguori Pubns.

Hamsa, Bhagwan. The Holy Mountain: Being the Story of a Pilgrimage to Lake Manas & of Initiation on Mount Kailas in Tibet. LC 78-72437. Repr. of 1934 ed. 27.50 (ISBN 0-404-17303-9). AMS Pr.

Hamsher, Paul. Pulpit Preparation. (Orig.). 1981. pap. 5.95 (ISBN 0-937172-29-4). JLJ Pubs.

Hamson, Robert L. Signature of God: A Positive Identification of Christ & His Prophets by Computer Wordprints. LC 81-51809. (Illus.). 111p. 1982. 8.95 (ISBN 0-940356-01-5). Sandpiper CA.

Han, Maung Ba see Ba Han, Maung.

Han, Nathan E. A Parsing Guide to the Greek New Testament. LC 77-158175. 496p. 1971. pap. 17.95 (ISBN 0-8361-1653-4). Herald Pr.

Hanauer, James E. Folk-Lore of the Holy Land: Moslem, Christian & Jewish. LC 77-22030. 1977. Repr. of 1935 ed. lib. bdg. 25.00 (ISBN 0-8414-4955-4). Folcroft.
--Folklore of the Holy Land. 280p. 1980. Repr. of 1935 ed. lib. bdg. 35.00 (ISBN 0-8492-5272-5). R West.

Hance, Lilian. Sowing & Reaping. 1981. 14.00x (ISBN 0-7223-1418-3, Pub. by A H Stockwell England). State Mutual Bk.

Hanchey, Howard. Creative Christian Education: Teaching the Bible Through the Church Year. 224p. 1986. pap. 10.95 (ISBN 0-8192-1380-2). Morehouse.

Hancock, James & Elliott, Hugh. The Herons Handbook. LC 84-47576. (Illus.). 288p. 1984. 24.45i (ISBN 0-06-015331-8, HarpT). Har-Row.

Hancock, Jim, ed. Resource Directory for Youth Workers 1986. rev. ed. 128p. pap. 9.95 (ISBN 0-310-35161-8, 10785P). Zondervan.

Hancock, Maxine. Living on Less & Liking It More. 160p. 1982. pap. 4.95 (ISBN 0-89081-414-7). Harvest Hse.

Hancock, Robert L., jt. ed. see Henry, Carl F.

Hancock, Steve. Discovering My Gifts for Service: Leader's Guide. rev. ed. 48p. 1984. pap. 2.95 (ISBN 0-87239-811-0, 39979). Standard Pub.

Hancock, Thomas. Principles of Peace: Exemplified by the Conduct of the Society of Friends in Ireland, 1798. LC 70-147620. (Library of War & Peace; Non-Resis. & Non-Vio.). lib. bdg. 46.00 (ISBN 0-8240-0377-2). Garland Pub.

Hand, Marcus V. Put Your Arms Around the World. LC 78-66976. 112p. (Orig.). 1978. pap. text ed. 1.25 (ISBN 0-87148-698-9). Pathway Pr.

Hand, Phyllis. Breaking into Bible Games. (Helping Hand Ser.). 48p. (YA) 1984. wkbk. 4.95 (ISBN 0-317-43001-7). Good Apple.
--Celebrate God & Country. (Celebrate Ser.). 144p. 1987. pap. 9.95 (ISBN 0-86653-390-7). Good Apple.

Hand, Thomas A. Augustine on Prayer. rev. ed. (Orig.). 1986. pap. 3.95 (ISBN 0-89942-171-7, 171-04). Catholic BK Pub.

Handberg, Ejner. Shop Drawings of Shaker Furniture & Woodenware, Vol. 2. LC 73-83797. 1975. pap. 5.95 (ISBN 0-912944-29-3). Berkshire Traveller.

Handel, George F. Complete Concerti Grossi in Full Score. 20.25 (ISBN 0-8446-5890-1). Peter Smith.
--Look Down, Harmonious Saint. Stevens, Denis, ed. LC 63-21369. (Penn State Music Series, No. 1). 22p. 1963. pap. 3.00x (ISBN 0-271-73079-X). Pa St U Pr.

Handelman, Susan A. The Slayers of Moses: The Emergence of Rabbinic Interpretation in Modern Literary Theory. LC 81-16522. (Modern Jewish Literature & Culture Ser.). 284p. 1982. 49.50x (ISBN 0-87395-576-5); pap. 18.95 (ISBN 0-87395-577-3). State U NY Pr.

Handford, Elisabeth R. Yo? Obedecer a Mi Marido? Orig. Title: Me? Obey Him? Tr. of Me? Obey Him. (Span.). 128p. 1984. pap. 3.25 (ISBN 0-8254-1302-8). Kregel.

Handford, Elizabeth R. Forgiving the Unforgivable. (The "Joyful Living" Ser.). 31p. (Orig.). 1985. pap. 1.50 (ISBN 0-912623-02-0). Joyful Woman.

Handford, Elizabeth R. & Martin, Joy R. Fatigue: Satan's Secret Weapon against Women. 23p. (Orig.). 1986. pap. 1.00 (ISBN 0-912623-03-9). Joyful Woman.
--The Mysterious Alabaster Bottle. 28p. (Orig.). 1987. pap. 1.50 (ISBN 0-912623-04-7). Joyful Woman.

Handler, Andrew. Dori: The Life & Times of Theodor Herzl in Budapest, 1860-1878. LC 82-8509. (Judaic Studies). (Illus.). 176p. 1983. text ed. 16.95 (ISBN 0-8173-0125-9). U of Ala Pr.

Handler, Andrew, ed. & tr. Ararat: A Collection of Hungarian-Jewish Short Stories. LC 75-5244. 153p. 1978. 18.00 (ISBN 0-8386-1733-6). Fairleigh Dickinson.

Handlin, Mimi & Layton, Marilyn S. Let Me Hear Your Voice: Portraits of Aging Immigrant Jews. LC 83-47974. (Illus.). 112p. 1984. 19.95 (ISBN 0-295-96039-6). U of Wash Pr.

Handlin, Oscar. American Jews: Their Story. 48p. 2.50 (ISBN 0-88464-011-6). ADL.

Handy, Carol. The Dragons of Rizvania. (Illus.). 64p. 1984. 8.95 (ISBN 0-85398-192-2). G Ronald Pub.

Handy, E. S. Polynesian Religion. (Bayard Dominick Expedition Publication Ser: No. 12). Repr. of 1927 ed. 56.00 (ISBN 0-527-02137-7). Kraus Repr.

Handy, Robert T. A Christian America: Protestant Hopes & Historical Realities. 2nd & enl. ed. 1983. 27.00x (ISBN 0-19-503386-8); pap. 10.95x (ISBN 0-19-503387-6). Oxford U Pr.
--A History of the Churches in the United States & Canada. 1977. 29.95x (ISBN 0-19-826910-2). Oxford U Pr.
--A History of the Churches in the United States & Canada. 1977. pap. 8.95 (ISBN 0-19-502531-8). Oxford U Pr.
--A History of Union Theological Seminary in New York, 1836-1986. (Illus.). 388p. 1987. 30.00 (ISBN 0-231-06454-3). Columbia U Pr.

Handy, Robert T., ed. The Holy Land in American Protestant Life, 1800 to 1948: A Documentary History. LC 79-1052. (Illus.). 1980. lib. bdg. 22.00x (ISBN 0-405-13466-5). Ayer Co Pubs.

Handy, Robert T., rev. by see Walker, Williston.

Handy, Rollo. The Measurement of Values. LC 79-110107. 232p. 1970. 12.50 (ISBN 0-87527-040-9). Fireside Bks.

Haneef, S. What Everyone Should Know about Islam & Muslims. pap. 9.95 (ISBN 0-686-63919-7). Kazi Pubns.

Hanes, Mari. The Child Within. 1983. pap. 2.95 (ISBN 0-8423-0219-0). Tyndale.

Haney, Anita. Battling Anorexia. (Orig.). 1986. pap. 5.95 (ISBN 0-89265-111-3). Randall Hse.

Haney, David. El Ministerio de Todo Creyente. Martinez, Jose Luis, ed. Kratzig, Guillermo, tr. 200p. 1984. pap. 4.75 (ISBN 0-311-09099-0). Casa Bautista.
--Renueva Mi Iglesia. Martinez, Jose Luis, ed. Kratzig, Guillermo, tr. Orig. Title: Renew My Church. (Span.). 104p. 1983. pap. 3.75 (ISBN 0-311-17025-0). Casa Bautista.
--El Senor y Sus Laicos. Martinez, Jose Luis, ed. (Span.). 84p. 1986. pap. 2.50 (ISBN 0-311-09095-8). Casa Bautista.

Haney, John, jt. ed. see Hansen, William P.

Haney, Joy. The Carpenter. Wallace, Mary, ed. LC 85-26498. (Illus.). 96p. (Orig.). 1985. pap. 5.00 (ISBN 0-912315-97-0). Word Aflame.

Haney, Kenneth F. Latter Day Shepherds & Sheepfolds. Wallace, Mary, ed. (Illus.). 78p. 1984. pap. 4.50 (ISBN 0-912315-72-5). Word Aflame.

Haney, Kristine E. The Winchester Psalter: An Iconographic Study. (Illus.). 204p. 1986. text ed. 60.00x (ISBN 0-7185-1260-X, Pub. by Leicester U Pr). Humanities.

Haney, Thomas R. Reach Out & Touch. 1980. pap. 3.95 (ISBN 0-88479-027-4). Arena Lettres.

Haney, William R. From the Backwoods to Bethel. Jones, Amos, Jr., ed. LC 84-50332. 95p. (Orig.). 1985. pap. cancelled. Sunday School.

Hanfmann, George M. The Season Sarcophagus in Dumbarton Oaks. LC 71-146800. (Dumbarton Oaks Studies: Vol. 2). (Illus.). 518p. 1951. Repr. 35.00x (ISBN 0-88402-001-0). Dumbarton Oaks.
--Season Sarcophagus in Dumbarton Oaks, 2 Vols. Repr. of 1951 ed. Set. 60.00 (ISBN 0-384-21290-5); 30.00 ea. Johnson Repr.

Hanh, Thich N. The Miracle of Mindfulness! A Manual on Meditation. LC 76-7747. (Illus.). 1976. pap. 7.95 (ISBN 0-8070-1119-3, BP546). Beacon Pr.

Hanigan, James. What Are They Saying about Sexual Morality? (WATSA Ser.). 128p. (Orig.). 1982. pap. 4.95 (ISBN 0-8091-2451-3). Paulist Pr.

Hanigan, James P. As I Have Loved You: Challenge of Christian Ethics. 240p. (Orig.). 1986. pap. 9.95 (ISBN 0-8091-2734-2). Paulist Pr.

Hanisch, jt. auth. see Ronan.

Hankamer, Jorge, ed. see Chomsky, Noam.

Hanke, Howard. The Thompson Chain Reference Bible Survey. 1981. 19.95 (ISBN 0-8499-0272-X). Word Bks.

Hanks, Darla & Bascom, Arlene. To Parents, with Love: Practical Pointers for Family Success. 341p. 1978. 10.95 (ISBN 0-88290-090-0). Horizon Utah.

Hanks, Geoffrey. Children of Naples. 1974. 1.60 (ISBN 0-08-017619-4). Pergamon.

Hanks, Joyce M. Ronsard & Biblical Tradition. (Etudes litteraires francaises: 17). 199p. (Orig.). 1982. pap. 19.00x (ISBN 3-87808-896-5). Benjamins North Am.

Hanks, Thomas D. God So Loved the Third World: The Bible, the Reformation & Liberation Theologies. Dekker, James C., tr. from Span. LC 83-8076. Tr. of Opresion, Podreza y Liberacion: Reflexiona Biblicas. 176p. (Orig.). 1983. pap. 8.95 (ISBN 0-88344-152-7). Orbis Bks.

Hanley, Boniface. No Greater Love: Maximilian Kolbe. LC 82-72656. (Illus.). 80p. (Orig.). 1982. pap. 3.95 (ISBN 0-87793-257-3). Ave Maria.
--No Strangers to Violence, No Strangers to Love. LC 83-71608. (Illus.). 224p. (Orig.). 1983. pap. 6.95 (ISBN 0-87793-302-2). Ave Maria.
--Ten Christians: By Their Deeds You Shall Know Them. LC 79-53836. (Illus.). 272p. (Orig.). 1979. pap. 6.95 (ISBN 0-87793-183-6). Ave Maria.

Hanley, Thomas O. Their Rights & Liberties. 160p. 1984. 9.95 (ISBN 0-8294-0471-6). Loyola.

Hanlon. Into the Fourth Dimension. 3.95 (ISBN 0-8356-7529-7). Theos Pub Hse.

Hann, Robert R. The Bible: An Owner's Manual, What You Need to Know Before You & Read Your Own Bible. 160p. 1983. pap. 6.95 (ISBN 0-8091-2503-X). Paulist Pr.
--The Manuscript History of the Psalms of Solomon. LC 81-21212. (SBL Septuagint & Cognate Studies). 1982. pap. 15.00 (ISBN 0-89130-557-2, 06-04-13). Scholars Pr GA.

Hanna, Barbara & Hoover, Janet. Teaching Preschoolers. 3.95 (ISBN 0-89137-608-9). Quality Pubns.

Hanna, Ken. In Search of Spiritual Leadership. 144p. 1987. pap. 5.95 (ISBN 0-89693-246-X). Victor Bks.

Hanna, Mary. Catholics & American Politics. LC 79-11035. 1979. text ed. 16.50x (ISBN 0-674-10325-4). Harvard U Pr.
Hanna, Robert. A Grammatical Aid to the Greek New Testament. 1983. 16.95 (ISBN 0-8010-4272-0). Baker Bk.
Hanna-Barbera, illus. Daniel & the Lion's Den. (The Greatest Adventure: Ser.Stories from the Bible.). (Illus., Orig.). Date not set. 5.95 (ISBN 0-687-15746-3). Abingdon.
--David & Goliath. (The Greatest Adventure Ser.Stories from the Bible). (Illus., Orig.). 1986. 5.95 (ISBN 0-687-15741-2). Abingdon.
--Joshua & the Battle of Jericho. (The Greatest Adventure: Stories from the Bible). (Illus., Orig.). Date not set. 5.95 (ISBN 0-687-15743-9). Abingdon.
--Moses Let My People Go. (The Greatest Adventure: Stories from the Bible). (Illus.). 48p. (Orig.). Date not set. 5.95 (ISBN 0-687-15740-4). Abingdon.
--Noah's Ark. (The Greatest Adventure: Stories from the Bible). (Illus., Orig.). Date not set. 5.95 (ISBN 0-687-15744-7). Abingdon.
--Samson & Delilah. (The Greatest Adventure: Stories from the Bible). (Illus., Orig.). Date not set. 5.95 (ISBN 0-687-15745-5). Abingdon.
Hannaford, Claudia. The ABC's of Financing Church & Synagogue Libraries, No. 13. LC 85-13286. (CSLA Guide Ser.). (Illus.). 36p. (Orig.). 1985. pap. 5.95X (ISBN 0-915324-23-7). CSLA.
Hannah, John, ed. Inerrancy & the Church. (Orig.). 1984. pap. 14.95 (ISBN 0-8024-0327-1). Moody.
Hannah, Kenneth. Soon Coming World Emperor. 48p. (Orig.). pap. 2.95 (CPS-012). Christian Pub.
Hannay, James B. Symbolism in Relation to Religion. LC 79-118523. (Illus.). 1971. Repr. of 1915 ed. 28.50x (Pub by Kennikat). Assoc Faculty Pr.
Hanne, Tony. A New Old Testament. LC 84-90178. 105p. 1986. 8.95 (ISBN 0-533-06228-4). Vantage.
Hannemann, Manfred. The Diffusion of the Reformation in Southwestern Germany, 1518-1534. LC 75-14120. (Research Papers Ser.: No. 167). (Illus.). 1975. pap. 10.00 (ISBN 0-89065-074-8). U Chicago Dept Geog.
Hannon, Ruth. Children's Bible Stories from the Old Testament. (Illus.). 1978. 4.95 (ISBN 0-307-13740-6, 13740, Golden Bks). Western Pub.
Hannum, Harold E. Let the People Sing. Davis, Tom, ed. 112p. 1981. pap. 7.95 (ISBN 0-8280-0029-8). Review & Herald.
Hanon, Bill. The Eternal Church. 398p. (Orig.). 1981. 12.95 (ISBN 0-939868-01-6); pap. 8.95 (ISBN 0-939868-00-8). Chr Intl Pubs.
Hansadutta. The Book: What the Black Sheep Said. LC 85-5636. (Illus.). 1160p. (Orig.). 1985. pap. text ed. 9.95 (ISBN 0-933593-03-1). Hansa Pub.
--Fool's Paradise. LC 85-5839. (Illus.). 190p. (Orig.). 1985. pap. 5.95 (ISBN 0-933593-05-8). Hansa Pub.
Hansburg, Mary E. Myth, Faith & Hermeneutics. 85p. (Orig.). 1985. pap. 6.95x (ISBN 0-932269-23-0). Wyndham Hall.
Hansel, G. Understanding the Living Word. 1980. pap. 8.95 (ISBN 0-8163-0372-X). Pacific Pr Pub Assn.
Hansel, Tim. What Kids Need Most in a Dad. LC 83-22902. 192p. 1984. 10.95 (ISBN 0-8007-1390-7). Revell.
--When I Relax I Feel Guilty. LC 78-73460. 1979. pap. 6.95 (ISBN 0-89191-137-5). Cook.
--You Gotta Keep Dancin' LC 85-11298. 150p. 1985. pap. 6.95 (ISBN 0-89191-722-5, 57224). Cook.
Hansen, Bent S., jt. ed. see Parpola, Asko.
Hansen, Carlton D. Beacon Small-Group Bible Studies: Proverbs, Wisdom for Today's Challenges. 80p. (Orig.). 1984. pap. 2.50 (ISBN 0-8341-0905-0). Beacon Hill.
Hansen, Chadwick. Witchcraft at Salem. LC 69-15825. (Illus.). 1969. 11.95 (ISBN 0-8076-0492-5). Braziller.
--Witchcraft at Salem. LC 99-943950. 252p. (YA) pap. 3.95 (ISBN 0-451-62214-6, ME2214, Ment). NAL.
--Witchcraft at Salem. (Illus.). 252p. 1985. pap. 7.95 (ISBN 0-8076-1137-9). Braziller.
Hansen, Cindy S., ed. Group Magazine's Best Youth Group Programs, Vol. 1. LC 86-313. (Illus.). 224p. 1986. 17.95 (ISBN 0-931529-11-5). Group Bks.
Hansen, H. B. Mission, Church & State in a Colonial Setting: Uganda 1890-1925. LC 84-16052. 608p. 1985. 39.95 (ISBN 0-312-53474-4). St Martin.
Hansen, James. The Ministry of the Cantor. (Ministry Ser.). 40p. 1985. pap. 1.25 (ISBN 0-8146-1387-X). Liturgical Pr.
Hansen, Klaus J. Mormonism & the American Experience. LC 80-19312. (History of American Religion Ser.). 224p. 1981. 15.00x (ISBN 0-226-31552-5). U of Chicago Pr.
--Mormonism & the American Experience. LC 80-19312. (Chicago History of American Religions Ser.). xx, 258p. 1983. pap. 8.50 (ISBN 0-226-31553-3). U of Chicago Pr.
Hansen, Lillian E. The Double Yoke. (Illus.). 268p. 1979. pap. 2.95 (ISBN 0-89216-020-9). Salvation Army.
Hansen, Paul G. Portraits of the Passion. 1983. 6.25 (ISBN 0-89536-582-0, 1624). CSS of Ohio.
Hansen, Paul H. All God's Children Got Dreams. (Orig.). 1980. pap. 2.95 (ISBN 0-937172-03-0). JLJ Pubs.
Hansen, Vee & Shaw, Opal. Macoy's Short Addresses for Matron: Forty-Five Sentiments. 28p. 1975. pap. 1.50 (ISBN 0-88053-329-3, S-83). Macoy Pub.
Hansen, Vee, et al. Macoy's Short Addresses & Ceremonies for Matron's Use. 24p. 1983. pap. 1.50 (ISBN 0-88053-330-7). Macoy Pub.
Hansen, Walter A., tr. see Elert, Werner.
Hansen, William P. & Haney, John, eds. Calvin. (World's Leaders--Past & Present Ser.). (Illus.). 112p. 1987. lib. bdg. 16.95 (ISBN 0-87754-515-4). Chelsea Hse.
--Judas Maccabeus. (World Leaders--Past & Present Ser.). (Illus.). 112p. 1987. lib. bdg. 16.95 (ISBN 0-87754-539-1). Chelsea Hse.
--Luther. (World Leaders--Past & Present Ser.). (Illus.). 112p. 1986. lib. bdg. 16.95 (ISBN 0-87754-538-3). Chelsea Hse.
--Pope John XXIII. (World Leaders--Past & Present Ser.). (Illus.). 112p. 1987. lib. bdg. 16.95 (ISBN 0-87754-535-9). Chelsea Hse.
Hanson, Anthony & Hanson, Richard. Reasonable Belief: A Funny of the Christian Faith. 1980. pap. 11.95x (ISBN 0-19-213238-5). Oxford U Pr.
Hanson, Anthony T., ed. Pastoral Letters. (Cambridge Bible Commentary on the New English Bible, New Testament Ser.). (Orig.). 1966. 17.95 (ISBN 0-521-04214-3); pap. 7.50x (ISBN 0-521-09380-5, 380). Cambridge U Pr.
Hanson, Calvin B. The Trinity Story. LC 83-81575. 1983. 8.95 (ISBN 0-911802-58-4). Free Church Pubns.
Hanson, Eric O. The Catholic Church in World Politics. (Illus.). 468p. 1987. 24.95 (ISBN 0-691-07729-0). Princeton U Pr.
--Catholic Politics in China & Korea. LC 79-27206. 160p. (Orig.). 1980. pap. 2.49 (ISBN 0-88344-084-9). Orbis Bks.
Hanson, Fred. The Old Time Religion. 1986. pap. 1.00 (ISBN 0-89265-099-0). Randall Hse.
Hanson, Grant W. Foundations for the Teaching Church. 96p. 1986. pap. 5.95 (ISBN 0-8170-1096-3). Judson.
Hanson, Handt. Spirit Touching Spirit, A Contemporary Hymnal. 240p. 1986. 10.95 (ISBN 0-933173-01-6). Prince Peace Pub.
Hanson, James E. If I'm a Christian Why Be a Catholic? The Biblical Roots of a Catholic Faith. (Orig.). 1984. pap. 5.95 (ISBN 0-8091-2633-8). Paulist Pr.
Hanson, Joanna K. The Civilian Population & the Warsaw Uprising of 1944. LC 81-15545. (Illus.). 375p. 1982. 39.50 (ISBN 0-521-23421-2). Cambridge U Pr.
Hanson, John & Horsley, Richard A. Bandits, Prophets, & Messiahs: Popular Movements at the Time of Jesus. 220p. 1985. 28.35 (ISBN 0-86683-992-5, HarpR). Har-Row.
Hanson, John A. Roman Theater-Temples. LC 78-5510. (Illus.). 1978. Repr. of 1959 ed. lib. bdg. 27.50x (ISBN 0-313-20477-2, HATT). Greenwood.
Hanson, Judith, tr. see Kongtrul, Jamgon.
Hanson, Karen. The Self Imagined: Philosophical Reflections on the Social Character of Psyche. 160p. 1986. 26.95 (ISBN 0-7102-0559-7, 05597). Methuen Inc.
Hanson, Muriel. Honey & Salt. 2nd ed. LC 78-185512. 1971. pap. text ed. 1.50 (ISBN 0-911802-26-6). Free Church Pubns.
Hanson, Paul D. The Dawn of Apocalyptic: The Historical & Sociological Roots of Jewish Apocalyptic Eschatology. rev. ed. LC 79-17099. 464p. 1979. 16.95 (ISBN 0-8006-0285-4, 1-285); pap. 12.95 (ISBN 0-8006-1809-2). Fortress.
--The Diversity of Scripture: Trajectories in the Confessional Heritage. LC 81-43079. (Overtures to Biblical Theology Ser.: No. 11). 1982. pap. 8.95 (ISBN 0-8006-1535-2, 1-1535). Fortress.
--Dynamic Transcendence: The Correlation of Confessional Heritage & Contemporary Experience in Biblical Model of Divine Activity. LC 78-54552. pap. 27.30 (2026940). Bks Demand UMI.
--The People Called: The Growth of Community in the Bible. LC 84-47725. 448p. 1986. 29.45 (ISBN 0-06-063700-5, HarpR). Har-Row.
Hanson, Paul D., ed. Visionaries & Their Apocalypses. LC 83-5488. (Issues in Religion & Theology Ser.). 176p. 1983. pap. 7.95 (ISBN 0-8006-1765-7). Fortress.
Hanson, Paul D., ed. see Wolff, Hans W.
Hanson, R. P. The Continuity of Christian Doctrine. 112p. 1981. 9.95 (ISBN 0-8164-0504-2, HarpR). Har-Row.
--The Life & Writings of the Historical St. Patrick. 144p. 1983. 11.95 (ISBN 0-8164-0523-9, HarpR). Har-Row.
Hanson, Richard. Studies in Christian Antiquity. 376p. 1986. 32.95 (ISBN 0-567-09363-8, Pub. by T & T Clark Ltd UK). Fortress.
Hanson, Richard, jt. auth. see Hanson, Anthony.
Hanson, Richard S. The Comings of God: Meditations for the Advent Season. LC 81-65645. 128p. (Orig.). 1981. pap. 5.95 (ISBN 0-8066-1881-7, 10-1590). Augsburg.
--Journey to Resurrection. 81p. (Orig.). 1986. pap. 4.95 (ISBN 0-8091-2737-7). Paulist Pr.
--The Sunday Church School Teacher. 1986. 5.95 (ISBN 0-89536-796-3, 6814); leader's guide 1.75 (ISBN 0-89536-806-4, 6824). CSS of Ohio.
Hanson, Robert W., ed. Science & Creation: Geological, Theological & Educational Perspectives. LC 83-50822. (AAAS Ser. on Issues in Science & Technology). 288p. 1985. text ed. 24.95x (ISBN 0-02-949870-8). Macmillan.
Hanson, Virginia. Gifts of the Lotus. LC 74-5130. 192p. (Orig.). 1974. pap. 3.50 (ISBN 0-8356-0450-0, Quest). Theos Pub Hse.
Hanson, Virginia, ed. H. P. Blavatsky & the Secret Doctrine Commentaries on Her Contributions to World Thought. LC 71-112039. (Orig.). 1971. pap. 2.25 (ISBN 0-8356-0031-9, Quest). Theos Pub Hse.
--Karma. 2nd rev. ed. Stewart, Rosemarie. LC 80-53951. 200p. 1980. pap. 4.95 (ISBN 0-8356-0543-4, Quest). Theos Pub Hse.
--The Silent Encounter. LC 74-4168. 240p. (Orig.). 1974. pap. 4.75 (ISBN 0-8356-0448-9, Quest). Theos Pub Hse.
Hanson, William G. The Early Monastic Schools of Ireland, Their Missionaries, Saints & Scholars. 1927. 18.00 (ISBN 0-8337-4580-8). B Franklin.
Hans-Ulrich, Rieker. The Yoga of Light: The Classic Esoteric Handbook of Kundalini Yoga. Becherer, Elsy, tr. LC 79-167868. (Illus.). 1974. pap. 7.95 (ISBN 0-913922-07-2). Dawn Horse Pr.
Hantschk, Rolanda. Die Geschichte der Kartause Mauerbach. Hogg, James, ed. (Analecta Cartusiana Ser.: No. 7). (Ger.). 164p. (Orig.). 1972. pap. 25.00 (ISBN 3-7052-0008-9, Pub by Salzburg Studies). Longwood Pub Group.
Han-ung Yang, et al, eds. The Hye Ch'o Diary: Memoir of the Pilgrimage to the Five Regions of India. (Religions of Asia Ser.). 118p. 1984. 20.00 (ISBN 0-89581-024-7). Asian Human Pr.
Hanus, Jerome J. & Schall, James V., eds. Studies on Religion & Politics. LC 86-9166. 120p. (Orig.). 1986. lib. bdg. 28.50 (ISBN 0-8191-5391-5); pap. text ed. 12.75 (ISBN 0-8191-5392-3). U Pr of Amer.
Hapgood, Hutchins. Spirit of the Ghetto. facsimile ed. Rischin, Moses, ed. LC 67-12099. (The John Harvard Library). (Illus.). 1967. 22.50x (ISBN 0-674-83265-5). Harvard U Pr.
Happe, Peter, intro. by. Four Morality Plays. 1987. pap. 6.95 (ISBN 0-14-043119-5). Penguin.
Happel, Stephen. Coleridge's Religious Imagination: Three Volume Set, 3 vol. set, No. 100. (Salzburg-Romantic Reassessment). 943p. 1983. Set. pap. text ed. 80.00x (ISBN 0-391-03042-6, Pub. by Salzburg Austria). Vol.1 (ISBN 0-391-03039-6). Vol.2 (ISBN 0-391-03040-X). Vol.3 (ISBN 0-391-03041-8). Humanities.
Happel, Stephen & Tracy, David. A Catholic Vision. LC 83-5687. 196p. 1984. pap. 10.95 (ISBN 0-8006-1719-3). Fortress.
Happel, Stephen & Walter, James J. Conversion & Discipleship: A Christian Foundation for Ethics & Doctrine. LC 85-45499. 240p. 1986. pap. 14.95 (ISBN 0-8006-1908-0, 1-1908). Fortress.
Happold, F. C. Religious Faith & Twentieth Century Man. 192p. 1981. 6.95 (ISBN 0-8245-0046-6). Crossroad NY.
Happold, Frank C. Mysticism. (Orig.). 1963. pap. 6.95 (ISBN 0-14-020568-3, Pelican). Penguin.
Haq, M. Fazal, tr. Islamic Teaching, V. 102p. 1985. pap. 6.00 (ISBN 0-317-19682-0). Islamic Seminary.
--Islamic Teachings, VI. 140p. 1985. pap. 6.00 (ISBN 0-317-19685-5). Islamic Seminary.
--Islamic Teachings, VII. 192p. 1985. pap. 9.00 (ISBN 0-941724-33-6). Islamic Seminary.
Haq, M. Fazal, tr. see Al-Askari, Allama M.
Haq, M. Fazal, tr. see Al-Gita, Kashif.
Haq, M. Fazal, tr. see Al-Khui, Ayatullah A.
Haq, M. Fazal, tr. see Jordac, George.
Haq, M. Fazal, tr. see Sharafuddin, Sadruddin.
Haq, M. Fazal, tr. see Subhani, Jafar.
Haque, Muhammad S. Al-Qur'anal-Karim, The Holy Qur'an: Surah Al-Fatiha, Section 1 of Surah Baqarah, Ayatul Kursi, Surah Nas thru Surah Naba with Modern English Translations, & Reading Guide, Prayer modes & Qaidah, Pt. 30. LC 84-63148. (Arabic & Eng., Illus.). viii, 80p. (Orig.). 1985. pap. text ed. 3.00 (ISBN 0-933057-02-4). Namuk Intl Inc.
--The Holy Qur'an (With Modern English Translations & Annotations) 800p. 1987. text ed. 20.00 (ISBN 0-933057-05-9). Namuk Intl Inc.
Hara, O. Hashnu. Practical Yoga: Thoroughly Practical Lessons upon the Philosophy & Practice of Yoga. 6th ed. 79p. 1970. pap. 4.95 (ISBN 0-88697-032-6). Life Science.
Harakas, Emily. Daily Lenten Meditations for Orthodox Christians. 1983. pap. 2.95 (ISBN 0-937032-27-1). Light&Life Pub Co MN.
--Through the Year with the Church Fathers. 1985. pap. 8.95 (ISBN 0-937032-37-9). Light&Life Pub Co MN.
Harakas, S. Guidelines for Marriage in the Orthodox Church. 1980. pap. 1.45 (ISBN 0-937032-21-2). Light&Life Pub Co MN.
--Living the Liturgy. 1974. pap. 4.95 (ISBN 0-937032-17-4). Light&Life Pub Co MN.
--Something Is Stirring in World Orthodoxy. 1978. pap. 3.25 (ISBN 0-937032-04-2). Light&Life Pub Co MN.
--Toward Transfigured Life. 1983. pap. 12.95 (ISBN 0-937032-28-X). Light&Life Pub Co MN.
Harakas, S. S. Contemporary Moral Issues Facing the Orthodox Christian. 1982. pap. 6.95 (ISBN 0-937032-24-7). Light&Life Pub Co MN.
Harakas, Stanley. Melody of Prayer: How to Personally Experience the Divine Liturgy. pap. 1.95 (ISBN 0-686-27068-1). Light&Life Pub Co MN.
Harakas, Stanley S. For the Health of Body & Soul. 48p. (Orig.). 1980. pap. 1.95 (ISBN 0-916586-42-1). Hellenic Coll Pr.
--Let Mercy Abound: Social Concern in the Greek Orthodox Church. 188p. 1983. text ed. 18.95 (ISBN 0-686-90967-4); pap. text ed. 12.95 (ISBN 0-686-90968-2). Holy Cross Orthodox.
Haraldsson, Erlendur, jt. auth. see Osis, Karlis.
Haran, Menahem. Temples & Temple-Service in Ancient Israel. 416p. 1985. Repr. of 1978 ed. text ed. 20.00x (ISBN 0-931464-18-8). Eisenbrauns.
Harap, Louis. Creative Awakening: The Jewish Presence in Twentieth-Century American Literature, 1900-1940s-Published in Cooperation with the American Jewish Archives. LC 86-14986. (Contributions in Ethnic Studies: No. 17). 216p. 1987. lib. bdg. 29.95 (ISBN 0-313-25386-2, HFI). Greenwood.
--The Image of the Jew in American Literature. LC 74-12887. 608p. 1975. 10.00 (ISBN 0-8276-0054-2, 357). Jewish Pubns.
Harari, Josue V. Scenarios of the Imaginary: Theorizing the French Englightenment. LC 86-24247. 240p. 1987. text ed. 24.95x (ISBN 0-8014-1842-9). Cornell U Pr.
Harbaugh, Gary L. The Faith-Hardy Christian: How to Face the Challenges of Life with Confidence. LC 86-7966. (Christian Growth Ser.). 128p. 1986. pap. 6.95 (ISBN 0-8066-2212-1, 10-2184). Augsburg.
--Pastor As Person. LC 84-24259. 176p. (Orig.). 1984. pap. 9.95 (ISBN 0-8066-2115-X, 10-4889). Augsburg.
Harbhajan, Khalsa S. The Teachings of Yogi Bhajan: The Power of the Spoken Word. LC 85-22347. 196p. 1985. Repr. of 1977 ed. lib. bdg. 19.95x (ISBN 0-89370-878-X). Borgo Pr.
Harbin, E. O. The New Fun Encyclopedia: Vol. 1: Games. 256p. (Orig.). 1983. pap. 9.95 (ISBN 0-687-27754-X). Abingdon.
Harbin, J. William. When a Pastor Search Committee Comes... or Doesn't. LC 85-13541. 1985. pap. 4.95 (ISBN 0-8054-2545-4). Broadman.
Harbison, E. Harris. The Age of Reformation. LC 76-10816. (Development of Western Civilization Ser). (Illus.). 145p. (Orig.). (YA) 1955. 5.95x (ISBN 0-8014-9844-9). Cornell U Pr.
--The Age of Reformation. LC 82-2985. (The Development of Western Civilization Ser.). xiv, 145p. 1982. Repr. of 1955 ed. lib. bdg. 22.50x (ISBN 0-313-23555-4, HAAGR). Greenwood.
Harbison, Elmore H. The Christian Scholar in the Age of the Reformation. LC 83-16511. Repr. of 1983 ed. 46.80 (2027546). Bks Demand UMI.
Harbour, Brian L. Famous Couples of the Bible. LC 78-60053. 1979. pap. 4.95 (ISBN 0-8054-5630-9). Broadman.
--Famous Parents of the Bible. LC 82-73079. 1983. pap. 4.95 (ISBN 0-8054-5655-4). Broadman.

--Famous Singles of the Bible. LC 79-56309. 1980. pap. 4.95 (ISBN 0-8054-5640-6). Broadman.
--From Cover to Cover. LC 81-67197. 1982. pap. 7.50 (ISBN 0-8054-2241-2). Broadman.
--A New Look at the Book. LC 84-27479. 1985. pap. 5.95 (ISBN 0-8054-1535-1). Broadman.
Hard, Larry. Contemporary Altar Prayers, Vol. 7. 1983. 5.95 (ISBN 0-89536-576-6, 0383). CSS of Ohio.
Hard, Larry & Watts, Mark P. Preparing for Marriage. 1984. 2.95 (ISBN 0-89536-673-8, 1638). CSS of Ohio.
Hardacre, Helen. Kurozumikyo & the New Religions of Japan. LC 85-43287. (Illus.). 232p. 1986. text ed. 28.00 (ISBN 0-691-06675-2). Princeton U Pr.
--Lay Buddhism in Contemporary Japan. LC 83-43075. (Illus.). 328p. 1984. 35.00x (ISBN 0-691-07284-1). Princeton U Pr.
--The Religion of Japan's Korean Minority: The Preservation of Ethnic Identity. (Korea Research Monographs: No. 9). (Illus.). 155p. (Orig.). 1984. pap. text ed. 12.00x (ISBN 0-912966-67-X). IEAS.
Harder, Bertha F. Twelve Becoming: Leader's Guide for Juniors. new ed. (Illus.). 61p. 1973. pap. 2.00x (ISBN 0-87303-866-5). Faith & Life.
Harder, Geraldine G. When Apples Are Ripe. LC 73-160722. (Illus.). 224p. 1972. pap. 3.95 (ISBN 0-8361-1694-1). Herald Pr.
Harder, Helmut. Guide to Faith. LC 79-50682. 1979. pap. 3.95 (ISBN 0-87303-022-2). Faith & Life.
--Living As God's People. LC 86-80675. (Faith & Life Bible Studies). 64p. (Orig.). 1986. pap. 4.95 (ISBN 0-87303-108-3). Faith & Life.
Harder, Johannes H. Observations on Some Tendencies of Sentiment & Ethics in 18th Century Poetry. LC 68-886. (Studies in Poetry, No. 38). 1969. Repr. of 1933 ed. lib. bdg. 49.95x (ISBN 0-8383-0564-4). Haskell.
Harder, Leland, jt. auth. see Kauffman, J. H.
Harder, Leland, ed. The Sources of Swiss Anabaptism. LC 85-5520. (Classics of the Radical Reformation: No. 4). 816p. 1985. 69.00x (ISBN 0-8361-1251-2). Herald Pr.
Hardesty. Great Women of Faith. 2.95 (ISBN 0-318-18173-8). WCTU.
Hardesty, Nancy A. Great Women of Faith. (Festival Ser.). 144p. 1982. pap. 3.25 (ISBN 0-687-15728-5). Abingdon.
--Inclusive Language in the Church. LC 86-46036. 108p. (Orig.). 1987. pap. 7.95 (ISBN 0-8042-1686-X). John Knox.
--Women Called to Witness: Evangelical Feminism in the Nineteenth Century. LC 83-45959. 176p. (Orig.). 1984. pap. 8.95 (ISBN 0-687-45959-1). Abingdon.
Hardick, Lothar, et al. The Admonitions of St. Francis of Assisi. Smith, David, tr. 399p. 1983. 12.50 (ISBN 0-8199-0869-X). Franciscan Herald.
Hardie, Frank & Herrman, Irwin. Britain & Zion: The Fateful Entanglement. 192p. 1980. 11.95 (ISBN 0-85640-229-X, Pub. by Blackstaff Pr). Longwood Pub Group.
Hardie, W. F. Aristotle's Ethical Theory. 2nd ed. 1981. pap. 29.95x (ISBN 0-19-824633-1). Oxford U Pr.
Hardin, Garrett. Mandatory Motherhood: The True Meaning of "Right to Live". LC 74-4880. 136p. 1974. 6.95 (ISBN 0-8070-2176-8). Beacon Pr.
--Prometean Ethics: Living with Death, Competition, & Triage. LC 79-56592. (The Jesse & John Danz Lecture Ser.). 92p. 1980. 10.00x (ISBN 0-295-95717-4). U of Wash Pr.
Hardin, Garrett, ed. Population, Evolution, & Birth Control: A Collage of Controversial Ideas. 2nd ed. LC 69-16921. (Biology Ser.). (Illus.). 386p. 1969. pap. text ed. 13.95x (ISBN 0-7167-0670-9). W H Freeman.
Hardin, H. Grady. The Leadership of Worship. LC 79-26863. 1980. 6.95 (ISBN 0-687-21160-3). Abingdon.
Hardin, Joyce. Three Steps Behind. 320p. (Orig.). 1986. pap. 10.95 (ISBN 0-915547-91-0). Abilene Christ U.
Hardin, Russell, et al, eds. Nuclear Deterrence: Ethics & Strategy. LC 85-8423. viii, 396p. 1985. 25.00x (ISBN 0-226-31702-1); pap. 10.95 (ISBN 0-226-31704-8). U of Chicago Pr.
Harding, D. E. On Having No Head: Zen & the Rediscovery of the Obvious. rev. ed. (Illus.). 96p. 1986. pap. 4.95 (ISBN 0-317-40544-6). Methuen Inc.
Harding, David P. Milton & the Renaissance Ovid. LC 76-47466. 1977. Repr. of 1946 ed. lib. bdg. 17.50 (ISBN 0-8414-4941-4). Folcroft.
Harding, Davis P., jt. ed. see Sylvester, Richard S.
Harding, Frank J. Matthew Arnold, the Critic & France. LC 76-50106. 1977. Repr. of 1964 ed. lib. bdg. 25.00 (ISBN 0-8414-4721-7). Folcroft.
Harding, M. Esther. Woman's Mysteries. 1976. pap. 6.95 (ISBN 0-06-090525-5, CN525, PL). Har-Row.
Harding, Richard W. John Bunyan: His Life & Times. LC 76-27749. 1976. Repr. of 1928 ed. lib. bdg. 20.00 (ISBN 0-8414-4933-3). Folcroft.
Harding, Vincent, ed. see Thurman, Howard.
Harding, William H. John Bunyan, Pilgrim & Dreamer. LC 77-9369. 1977. 25.00 (ISBN 0-8414-4782-9). Folcroft.
--The Life of George Muller. (Heroes of the Faith Ser.). 384p. 1985. Repr. of 1914 ed. 6.95 (ISBN 0-916441-13-X). Barbour & Co.
Hardinge, Leslie. The Conquerors. (Anchor Ser.). 112p. 1983. pap. 5.95 (ISBN 0-8163-0509-9). Pacific Pr Pub Assn.
--The Victors. (Anchor Ser.). 112p. 1982. pap. 5.95 (ISBN 0-8163-0490-4). Pacific Pr Pub Assn.
Hardison, Amy. How to Feel Great about Being a Mother. LC 86-29349. 1987. 8.95 (ISBN 0-87579-073-9). Deseret Bk.
Hardisty, Margaret. Forever My Love. LC 74-32644. 1979. pap. 3.25 (ISBN 0-89081-140-7, 1407). Harvest Hse.
--Your Husband & Your Emotional Needs. LC 80-81471. 176p. 1982. pap. text ed. 2.95 (ISBN 0-89081-312-4). Harvest Hse.
Hardman, Keith J. Charles Grandison Finney, Seventeen Ninety-Two to Eighteen Seventy-Five: Revivalist & Reformer. (Illus.). 536p. 1987. text ed. 45.00x (ISBN 0-8156-2397-6). Syracuse U Pr.
Hardon, John. Spiritual Life in the Modern World. 1982. 3.50 (ISBN 0-8198-6839-6, SP0708); pap. 2.50 (ISBN 0-8198-6840-X). Dghtrs St Paul.
Hardon, John A. American Judaism. LC 72-148264. 1971. 5.95 (ISBN 0-8294-0199-7). Loyola.
--The Catholic Catechism. LC 73-81433. 1973. pap. 10.95 (ISBN 0-385-08045-X). Doubleday.
--Christianity in the Twentieth Century. 1978. 5.95 (ISBN 0-8198-0356-1); pap. 2.95 (ISBN 0-8198-0357-X). Dghtrs St Paul.
--Holiness in the Church. 1976. 3.50 (ISBN 0-8198-0417-7); pap. 2.50 (ISBN 0-8198-0418-5). Dghtrs St Paul.
--Modern Catholic Dictionary. LC 77-82945. 624p. 1980. 22.95 (ISBN 0-385-12162-8). Doubleday.
--Pocket Catholic Dictionary. LC 85-5790. 528p. 1985. pap. 6.95 (ISBN 0-385-23238-1, Im). Doubleday.
--Question & Answer Catholic Catechism. LC 80-2961. 408p. 1981. (Im); pap. 9.95 (ISBN 0-385-13664-1). Doubleday.
--Religions of the Orient: A Christian View. LC 71-108377. pap. 55.30 (ISBN 0-317-30169-1, 2025351). Bks Demand UMI.
--Religious Life Today. 1977. 3.00 (ISBN 0-8198-0452-5). Dghtrs St Paul.
--Salvation & Santification. 1978. 3.50 (ISBN 0-8198-0366-9); pap. 2.50 (ISBN 0-8198-0367-7). Dghtrs St Paul.
--Treasury of Catholic Wisdom. LC 86-19648. 768p. 1987. 27.50 (ISBN 0-385-23079-6). Doubleday.
Hardon, Reverend John. Theology of Prayer. 1979. 3.75 (ISBN 0-8198-7311-X); pap. 2.50 (ISBN 0-8198-7312-8). Dghtrs St Paul.
Hardy, Alister. The Spiritual Nature of Man. 1979. 27.00x (ISBN 0-19-824618-8); pap. 12.95x (ISBN 0-19-824732-X). Oxford U Pr.
Hardy, Daniel W. & Ford, David F. Praising & Knowing God. LC 84-25756. 226p. (Orig.). 1985. pap. 12.95 (ISBN 0-664-24624-9). Westminster.
Hardy, Edward R., ed. Christology of the Later Fathers. LC 54-9949. (Library of Christian Classics). 396p. 1977. pap. 10.95 (ISBN 0-664-24152-2). Westminster.
Hardy, Evelyn. Donne, a Spirit in Conflict. LC 72-187484. 1942. lib. bdg. 35.00 (ISBN 0-8414-4993-7). Folcroft.
Hardy, Friedhelm E. Viraha-Bhakti: The Early History of Krsna Devotion in South India. (Illus.). 1983. 55.00x (ISBN 0-19-561251-5). Oxford U Pr.
Hardy, Linda C. Boys Who Became Prophets. LC 82-2373. (Illus.). 72p. 1982. 6.95 (ISBN 0-87747-900-3). Deseret Bk.
Hardy, P. Muslims of British India. LC 77-184772. (South Asian Studies: No. 13). (Illus.). 300p. 1973. pap. 15.95 o. p. (ISBN 0-521-09783-5). Cambridge U Pr.
Hardy, Paul E. & Bishop of Exeter. A Guide to the Preservation of Medieval Cathedrals & Churches. LC 82-14257. (Illus.). 160p. 1983. pap. text ed. 16.95 (ISBN 0-582-30514-4, Construction Press). Longman.
Hardy, Peter. The Muslims of British India. LC 77-184772. (Cambridge South Asian Studies: No. 13). pap. 79.30 (ISBN 0-317-27996-3, 2025585). Bks Demand UMI.
Hardy, Richard P. Search for Nothing: Life of John of the Cross. 160p. 1987. pap. 8.95 (ISBN 0-8245-0815-7). Crossroad NY.
--The Search for Nothing: The Life of John of the Cross. LC 82-13081. 160p. 1982. 10.95 (ISBN 0-8245-0499-2). Crossroad NY.
Hardy, Robert S. Eastern Monachism: An Account of the Origin, Laws, Discipline, Sacred Writings, Mysterious Rites, Religious Ceremonies, & Present Circumstances, of the Order of Mendicants Founded by Gotama Budha. LC 78-72438. Repr. of 1850 ed. 40.00 (ISBN 0-404-17304-7). AMS Pr.
--A Manual of Buddhism in Its Modern Development. LC 78-72439. Repr. of 1853 ed. 46.50 (ISBN 0-404-17305-5). AMS Pr.
Hardy, William J., jt. ed. see Gee, Henry.
Hare, D. S. Story of Peter the Fisherman. (Ladybird Ser). 1970. 2.50 (ISBN 0-87508-867-8). Chr Lit.
--The Story of St. Paul. (Ladybird Ser.). (YA) 1969. pap. 2.50 (ISBN 0-87508-869-4). Chr Lit.
Hare, Douglas R., ed. see Knox, John.
Hare, Eric B. Fullness of Joy. 1985. pap. 5.95 (ISBN 0-8163-0586-2). Pacific Pr Pub Assn.
--Fulton's Footprints in Fiji. 1985. pap. 5.95 (ISBN 0-8163-0583-8). Pacific Pr Pub Assn.
Hare, F. Kenneth, ed. The Experiment of Life: Science & Religion. 192p. 1983. 25.00x (ISBN 0-8020-2486-6); pap. 9.95 (ISBN 0-8020-6506-6). U of Toronto Pr.
Hare, Lloyd C. Thomas Mayhew, Patriarch to the Indians, 1593-1682. LC 76-104347. (Illus.). Repr. of 1932 ed. 20.00 (ISBN 0-404-03108-0). AMS Pr.
Hare, R. M. Essays on the Moral Concepts. LC 70-187322. (New Studies in Practical Philosophy). 150p. 1972. 18.50x (ISBN 0-520-02231-9). U of Cal Pr.
--Moral Thinking: Its Levels, Methods, & Point. 1981. 27.00x (ISBN 0-19-824659-5); pap. 9.95x (ISBN 0-19-824660-9). Oxford U Pr.
Hare, Richard M. Freedom & Reason. (Oxford Paperbacks Ser.: No. 92). 1965. pap. text ed. 8.95x (ISBN 0-19-881092-X). Oxford U Pr.
Haresign, Gordon. Innocence: The Story of Steve Linscott, the Emmaus Bible School Student Convicted of Murder. 224p. 1986. 7.95 (ISBN 0-310-43801-2, 12056P). Zondervan.
Hargrave, Vessie D. The Church & World Missions. 128p. 1970. 5.25 (ISBN 0-87148-152-9); pap. 4.25 (ISBN 0-87148-153-7). Pathway Pr.
Hargrove, Barbara. The Emerging New Class of Experts: Implications for Church & Society. 160p. (Orig.). 1986. pap. 8.95 (ISBN 0-8298-0578-8). Pilgrim NY.
--The Sociology of Religion: Classical & Contemporary Approaches. LC 79-50879. 1979. pap. text ed. 16.95x (ISBN 0-88295-211-0). Harlan Davidson.
Hargrove, Barbara & Jones, Stephen D. Reaching Youth Today: Heirs to the Whirlwind. 1983. pap. 5.95 (ISBN 0-8170-0977-9). Judson.
Hargrove, Barbara, ed. Religion & the Sociology of Knowledge: Modernization & Pluralism in Christian Thought & Structure. LC 83-22149. (Studies in Religion & Society: Vol. 8). 412p. 1984. 59.95x (ISBN 0-88946-872-9). E Mellen.
Hargrove, Barbara J., jt. auth. see Carroll, Jackson W.
Hargrove, Eugene C., ed. Religion & Environmental Crisis. LC 86-7019. 248p. 1986. 25.00x (ISBN 0-8203-0845-5); pap. 12.00x (ISBN 0-8203-0846-3). U of GA Pr.
Hari Dass, Baba. Ashtanga Yoga Primer. Ault, Karuna K., ed. LC 81-51052. (Illus.). 72p. (Orig.). 1981. pap. 4.95 (ISBN 0-918100-04-6). Sri Rama.
--A Child's Garden of Yoga. Ault, Karuna, ed. LC 80-80299. (Illus.). 108p. 1980. pap. 6.95 (ISBN 0-918100-02-X). Sri Rama.
Haring, Bernard. Blessed Are the Pure in Heart: The Beatitudes. (Illus.). 1977. pap. 4.95 (ISBN 0-8245-0204-3). Crossroad NY.
--Dare to Be Christian: Developing a Social Conscience. 160p. 1983. pap. 4.25 (ISBN 0-89243-180-6). Liguori Pubns.
--Eucharistic Devotion: New Meanings for a Timeless Tradition. 48p. 1987. pap. 1.95 (ISBN 0-89243-261-6). Liguori Pubns.
--Free & Faithful in Christ: General Moral Theology. (Free & Faithful in Christ Ser.: Vol. 1). 506p. 1987. pap. 19.50 (ISBN 0-8245-0308-2). Crossroad NY.
--Free & Faithful in Christ: Light to the World, Vol. 3. 500p. 1981. 19.50 (ISBN 0-8245-0009-1). Crossroad NY.
--Free & Faithful in Christ: The Truth Will Set You Free. (Free & Faithful in Christ Ser.: Vol. 2). 592p. pap. 14.95 (ISBN 0-8245-0501-8). Crossroad NY.
--Free & Faithful in Christ: The Truth Will Set You Free, Vol. 2. 560p. 1979. 19.50 (ISBN 0-8245-0309-0). Crossroad NY.
--Heart of Jesus: Symbol of Redeeming Love. 160p. 1983. pap. 4.25 (ISBN 0-89243-191-1). Liguori Pubns.
--In Pursuit of Wholeness: Healing in Today's Church. LC 85-80000. 128p. 1985. pap. 3.50 (ISBN 0-89243-236-5). Liguori Pubns.
--Law of Christ, 3 vols. 646p. Vol. 1. 17.95 (ISBN 0-8091-0084-3). Paulist Pr.
--Mary & Your Everyday Life. LC 77-92897. 1978. pap. 4.95 (ISBN 0-89243-075-3). Liguori Pubns.
--Toward a Christian Moral Theology. 1966. 12.95x (ISBN 0-268-00281-9). U of Notre Dame Pr.
Haris, Althea, ed. see Harris, Clarence.
Hark, J. Max, tr. see Lamech.
Harkavy, Alexander, ed. Yiddish-English-Hebrew Dictionary. LC 86-31414. 624p. 1987. Repr. 29.95 (ISBN 0-8052-4027-6). Schocken.
Harker, Herbert. Turn Home Again. 245p. 1984. 6.95 (ISBN 0-934126-57-7). Randall Bk Co.
Harkins, Conrad L., ed. Franciscan Studies. (Annual review). 16.00 (ISBN 0-686-12038-8). Franciscan Inst.
Harkins, Conrad L., jt. ed. see Almagno, Romano S.
Harkins, Paul W., tr. see Chrysostom, John.
Harkness, Georgia. Understanding the Christian Faith. (Festival Ser.). 192p. 1981. pap. 1.95 (ISBN 0-687-42955-2). Abingdon.
Harkness, Georgia E. John Calvin: The Man & His Ethics. 1977. lib. bdg. 59.95 (ISBN 0-8490-2106-5). Gordon Pr.
--John Calvin: The Man & His Ethics. LC 83-45612. Date not set. Repr. of 1931 ed. 32.50 (ISBN 0-404-19830-9). AMS Pr.
--The Modern Rival of Christian Faith: An Analysis of Secularism. LC 77-27000. 1978. Repr. of 1952 ed. lib. bdg. 20.50x (ISBN 0-313-20174-9, HAMR). Greenwood.
Harkovy, Alexander. Family Bible Holy Scriptures Commentary, 2 vols. Set. 62.50 (ISBN 0-317-30501-8). Shalom.
--The Holy Scriptures Holy Bible Commentary. 32.50 (ISBN 0-317-30500-X). Shalom.
Harland, Henry. Yoke of the Thorah, by Sidney Luska. Repr. of 1887 ed. 23.00 (ISBN 0-384-21370-7). Johnson Repr.
Harland, Marion. John Knox. 1900. 25.00 (ISBN 0-686-19912-X). Quaker City.
Harle, J. C. Temple Gateways of South India: The Architecture & Iconography of the Cidammaram Gopuras. (Illus.). 179p. 1963. 65.00x (ISBN 0-317-39167-4, Pub. by Luzac & Co Ltd). State Mutual Bk.
Harless, Dan. Discoveries. 1982. pap. 4.95 (ISBN 0-89225-207-3). Gospel Advocate.
Harley, Gary K. A Scriptural Guide to a Fulfilling Marriage: Two Shall Become One. 168p. (Orig.). 1987. cancelled (ISBN 0-932990-01-0). Ideals.
Harley, George W. Notes on the Poro in Liberia. (HU PMP). 1941. 12.00 (ISBN 0-527-01248-3). Kraus Repr.
Harley, Marta P. A Revelation of Purgatory by an Unknown, 15th Century Woman Visionary: Introduction, Critical Text & Translation. (Studies in Women & Religion: Vol. 18). 160p. 1986. lib. bdg. 49.95x (ISBN 0-88946-531-2). E Mellen.
Harley, Timothy. Moon Lore. 1976. Repr. 13.00x (ISBN 0-85409-828-3). Charles River Bks.
Harlow, Joanne. Patterns & Instructions for a Child's Quiet Book. 27p. 1977. 3.50 (ISBN 0-317-03553-3). Randall Bk Co.
Harlow, Jules. Lessons from Our Living Past. LC 72-2055. (Illus.). 128p. 1972. text ed. 6.95x (ISBN 0-87441-085-1). Behrman.
Harlow, Jules, ed. see Prose, Francine.
Harlow, Jules, ed. see Simms, Laura & Kozodoy, Ruth.
Harlow, Louis K. The World's Best Hymms. Churchill, J. W., ed. 1978. Repr. of 1893 ed. lib. bdg. 25.00 (ISBN 0-8495-2323-0). Arden Lib.
Harm, Frederick R. How to Respond to the Science Religions. 1981. pap. 1.75 (ISBN 0-570-07686-2, 12-2787). Concordia.
Harman, A. M., jt. auth. see Renwick, A. M.
Harman, Alec, tr. see Palestrina, Giovanni P.
Harman, Gilbert. The Nature of Morality: An Introduction to Ethics. 1977. pap. text ed. 10.95x (ISBN 0-19-502143-6). Oxford U Pr.
Harman, Shirley. Retreat Planning Made Easy: A Resource for Christian Retreats. 40p. (Orig.). pap. 4.95 (ISBN 0-8066-2155-9, 10-5488). Augsburg.
Harmelink, Herman. Ecumenism & the Reformed Church. 1969. pap. 3.95 (ISBN 0-8028-1281-3). Eerdmans.
Harmer, J. R., ed. see Lightfoot, J. B.
Harmon, Beatrice E. Mosaics. LC 74-144725. (Yale Ser. of Younger Poets: No. 18). Repr. of 1923 ed. 18.00 (ISBN 0-404-53818-5). AMS Pr.
Harmon, Frances A. The Social Philosophy of the St. Louis Hegelians. LC 75-3159. 1976. Repr. of 1943 ed. 20.00 (ISBN 0-404-59164-7). AMS Pr.
Harmon, Rebecca L. Susanna: Mother of the Wesleys. rev. ed. 1968. 7.50 (ISBN 0-687-40766-4). Abingdon.
Harms, Larry, jt. auth. see Clary, Linda.

Harms, Orlando. Pioneer Publisher: The Life & Times of J. F. Harms. LC 84-82050. 116p. (Orig.). 1984. pap. 5.95 (ISBN 0-919797-33-4). Kindred Pr.

Harms, Paul. Seek Good, Not Evil (That You May Live) 1985. 6.25 (ISBN 0-89536-754-8, 5860). CSS of Ohio.

Harn, Roger E. Van see Van Harn, Roger E.

Harn, Roger van see Van Harn, Roger.

Harnack, Adolf. Expansion of Christianity in the First Three Centuries, 2 vols. Moffatt, James, tr. LC 72-4163. (Select Bibliographies Reprint Ser.). 1972. Repr. of 1905 ed. Set. 64.00 (ISBN 0-8369-6882-4). Ayer Co Pubs.

--The Expansion of Christianity in the First Three Centuries, Vol. I. Moffatt, James, ed. LC 72-4163. 494p. Repr. of 1904 ed. 56.00 (ISBN 0-8290-0530-7). Irvington.

--Militia Christi: The Christian Religion & the Military in the First Three Centuries. Gracie, David M., tr. from Ger. LC 81-43089. Tr. of Militia Christi: Die christliche Religion und der Soldatenstand in den ersten drei Jahrhunderten. 112p. 1981. 3.00 (ISBN 0-8006-0673-6, 1-673). Fortress.

--What Is Christianity? LC 78-15359. 1978. Repr. lib. bdg. 32.50 (ISBN 0-8414-4869-8). Folcroft.

Harnack, Adolf Von. What Is Christianity? 301p. 1980. Repr. of 1901 ed. lib. bdg. 35.50 (ISBN 0-8482-1228-2). Norwood Edns.

--What Is Christianity? LC 86-45209. (Texts in Modern Theology Ser.). Tr. of Das Wesen des Christentums. 320p. 1986. pap. 12.95 (ISBN 0-8006-3201-X, 1-3201). Fortress.

Harnack, Adolf von see Von Harnack, Adolf.

Harnack, Adolph. History of Dogma, 2 vols. in 1, Vols. 2 & 3. Buchanan, Neil, tr. from Ger. Set. 18.00 (ISBN 0-8446-2207-9). Peter Smith.

--What Is Christianity. 1958. 17.50 (ISBN 0-8446-2208-7). Peter Smith.

Harner, Michael J., ed. Hallucinogens & Shamanism. (Illus.). 1973. pap. 9.95x (ISBN 0-19-501649-1). Oxford U Pr.

Harner, Nevin C. Factors Related to Sunday School Growth & Decline in the Eastern Synod of the Reformed Church in the U. S. LC 71-176839. (Columbia University. Teachers College. Contributions to Education Ser.: No. 479). Repr. of 1931 ed. 22.50 (ISBN 0-404-55479-2). AMS Pr.

--I Believe. (Orig.). 1950. 3.95 (ISBN 0-8298-0066-2); pap. 2.95 (ISBN 0-8298-0067-0). Pilgrim NY.

Harner, Philip B. An Inductive Approach to Biblical Study. LC 82-40213. 132p. (Orig.). 1982. lib. bdg. 24.00 (ISBN 0-8191-2608-X); pap. text ed. 7.75 (ISBN 0-8191-2609-8). U Pr of Amer.

Harney, Martin. Legacy of St. Patrick. 1972. 3.50 (ISBN 0-8198-4407-1); pap. 2.25 (ISBN 0-8198-4408-X). Dghtrs St Paul.

Harney, Martin P. Catholic Church Through the Ages. LC 73-76312. 1974. 12.00 (ISBN 0-8198-0500-9); pap. 11.00 (ISBN 0-8198-0501-7). Dghtrs St Paul.

--Good Father in Brittany. (Illus.). 1964. pap. 4.00 (ISBN 0-8198-0049-X). Dghtrs St Paul.

--Medieval Ties Between Italy & Ireland. 1963. 1.50 (ISBN 0-8198-0101-1). Dghtrs St Paul.

Harnish, James A. Jesus Makes the Difference! The Gospel in Human Experience. 144p. (Orig.). 1987. pap. 6.95 (ISBN 0-8358-0554-9). Upper Room.

--What Will You Do with King Jesus. 128p. (Orig.). 1986. pap. 5.95 (ISBN 0-8358-0530-1, ICN 613108, Dist. by Abingdon Pr). Upper Room.

Harold Shaw Publishers. Bible Index Pocketbook. LC 81-8940. 192p. 1981. pap. 2.95 (ISBN 0-87788-077-8). Shaw Pubs.

Haron, jt. auth. see Amery.

Haroutunian, Joseph, ed. Calvin: Commentaries. LC 58-5060. (Library of Christian Classics). 410p. 1979. softcover 8.95 (ISBN 0-664-24160-3). Westminster.

Harp, Grace. Handbook of Christian Puppetry. LC 83-73204. 128p. (Orig.). 1984. pap. 5.95 plastic comb bdg. (ISBN 0-89636-125-X). Accent Bks.

Harp, Richard L. Thomas Percy's 'Life of Dr. Oliver Goldsmith' Hogg, James, ed. (Romantic Reassessment Ser.). 205p. (Orig.). 1976. pap. 15.00 (ISBN 3-7052-0507-2, Pub. by Salzburg Studies). Longwood Pub Group.

Harper, A. F. Beacon Small-Group Bible Studies, I & II Samuel: David-A Man after God's Own Heart". Wolf, Earl C., ed. 102p. (Orig.). 1985. pap. 2.50 (ISBN 0-8341-0934-4). Beacon Hill.

--Beacon Small-Group Bible Studies, James: Does God Want Faith or Obedience. 80p. (Orig.). 1980. pap. 2.50 (ISBN 0-8341-0625-6). Beacon Hill.

Harper, A. F., jt. auth. see Sanner, A. E.

Harper, Albert F. God Speaks Through His Word. 432p. 1985. pap. 11.95 (ISBN 0-8341-1067-9). Beacon Hill.

Harper, Alfred F. Beacon Small-Group Bible Studies, Acts, Pt, I: The Spirit-Filled Church. 96p. 1982. pap. 2.50 (ISBN 0-8341-0800-3). Beacon Hill.

Harper, Frances E. Idylls of the Bible. LC 75-168245. Repr. of 1901 ed. 11.50 (ISBN 0-404-00058-4). AMS Pr.

Harper, G. M. The Legend of the Holy Grail. 59.95 (ISBN 0-8490-0502-7). Gordon Pr.

Harper, George. Jesus: A Whole in One Down. (H. B. & His-Her Adventures Ser.). 224p. (Orig.). 1986. pap. 5.95 (ISBN 0-937959-12-X). Falcon Pr Mt.

--Kings on the Hill. (H. B. Bible Adventures Ser.). 224p. (Orig.). 1985. pap. 5.95 (ISBN 0-934318-70-0). Falcon Pr MT.

--The Race to Grace. (H. B. Bible Adventures Ser.). 216p. (Orig.). 1986. pap. 5.95 (ISBN 0-934318-74-3). Falcon Pr MT.

Harper, George H. A God in the Bush is Worth Two in the Hand. (Bible Adventure Ser.). 216p. (Orig.). 1985. pap. 5.95 (ISBN 0-934318-48-4). Falcon Pr MT.

Harper, H. B. Prophet Potpourri: H. B. & His-Her Bible Adventures, Vol. 6. LC 86-81422. 216p. (Orig.). 1986. pap. 5.95 (ISBN 0-934318-91-3). Falcon Pr MT.

Harper, Howard. Evangelism in My Parish. 1972. pap. 3.00 (ISBN 0-686-14947-5). Episcopal Ctr.

Harper, Howard V. Profiles of Protestant Saints. LC 67-24071. 1968. 9.95 (ISBN 0-8303-0037-6). Fleet.

Harper, Mary-Angela. Ascent to Excellence in Catholic Education: A Guide to Effective Decision-Making. 278p. 1980. 9.55 (ISBN 0-318-00777-0). Natl Cath Educ.

--Developing Performance Excellence in Catholic Educational Policymaking: A Handbook of Training Programs. 82p. 1982. 6.00 (ISBN 0-686-39917-X). Natl Cath Educ.

--Let Peace & Justice Prevail. 10p. 1977. 1.55 (ISBN 0-686-39920-X). Natl Cath Educ.

Harper, Michael. The Healings of Jesus. Green, Michael, ed. LC 86-20971. (The Jesus Library). 228p. 1986. pap. 6.95 (ISBN 0-87784-987-0). Inter-Varsity.

--Poder para Vencer. 1982. 2.95 (ISBN 0-88113-245-4). Edit Betania.

--Spiritual Warfare. 120p. 1984. pap. 4.95 (ISBN 0-89283-175-8). Servant.

--Walking in the Spirit. 112p. (Orig.). 1983. pap. 3.95 (ISBN 0-87123-614-1, 210614). Bethany Hse.

Harper, Ralph. Human Love: Existential & Mystical. LC 66-24410. pap. 48.00 (2026322). Bks Demand UMI.

Harper, Steve. Devotional Life in the Wesleyan Tradition. 80p. (Orig.). 1983. pap. 3.95 (ISBN 0-8358-0467-4). Upper Room.

--John Wesley's Message for Today. Chapman, Ben, ed. 1983. pap. 4.95 (ISBN 0-310-45711-4, 12382P). Zondervan.

Harper, Tommie F. From the Plow to the Pulpit. Neeld, Elizabeth H., ed. LC 86-9656. (Illus.). 360p. (Orig.). 1986. pap. 9.95 (ISBN 0-937897-77-9). Centerpoint Pr.

Harper, Vessa. Suddenly It's Springtime. 1967. pap. 3.50 (ISBN 0-88027-050-0). Firm Foun Pub.

Harper, Wilhelmina, ed. Easter Chimes: Stories for Easter & the Spring. (Illus.). 1967. 8.95 (ISBN 0-525-29037-0). Dutton.

Harper, William R. A Critical & Exegetical Commentary on Amos & Hosea. Driver, Samuel R., et al, eds. LC 5-7893. (International Critical Commentary Ser.). 608p. 1905. 24.95 (ISBN 0-567-05018-1, Pub. by T & T Clark Ltd UK). Fortress.

--Elements of Hebrew by an Inductive Method. LC 59-7625. (Midway Reprint Ser.). 204p. 1974. pap. 9.00x (ISBN 0-226-31681-5). U of Chicago Pr.

--Introductory Hebrew: Method & Manual. rev. ed. Smith, James M., ed. LC 59-7624. (Midway Reprint Ser.). 1974. pap. 15.00x (ISBN 0-226-31683-1). U of Chicago Pr.

Harpers, Ferry W. & Fogle, Sonja. Recent Advances in Leather Conservation: Proceedings of a Refresher Course Sponsored by FAIC, June,1984. 15.00 (ISBN 0-318-18700-0). Am Inst Conser Hist.

Harpsfield, Nicholas. Treatise on the Pretended Divorce Between Henry Eighth & Catharine of Aragon. Pocock, N., ed. LC 78. 27.00 (ISBN 0-384-21420-7). Johnson Repr.

Harpur, Tom. For Christ's Sake. LC 86-47866. 118p. 1987. 17.95 (ISBN 0-8070-1012-X); pap. 8.95 (ISBN 0-8070-1013-8, BP 756). Beacon Pr.

Harralson, David M. Jesus of Nazareth. (Literacy Volunteers of America Readers Ser.). 48p. (Orig.). 1983. pap. 1.95 (ISBN 0-8428-9608-2). Cambridge Bk.

--Stories from the Old Testament. (Literacy Volunteers of America Readers Ser.). 48p. (Orig.). 1983. pap. 1.95 (ISBN 0-8428-9607-4). Cambridge Bk.

Harran, Marilyn J. Luther & Learning: The Wittenberg University Luther Symposium. LC 84-40810. (Illus.). 144p. 1985. 19.50 (ISBN 0-941664-13-9, Pub. by Susquehanna U Pr). Assoc Univ Prs.

--Luther on Conversion: The Early Years. LC 83-7194. 224p. 1983. 29.95x (ISBN 0-8014-1566-7). Cornell U Pr.

Harre, Alan F. Close the Back Door. 1984. pap. 6.50 (ISBN 0-570-03932-0, 12-2867). Concordia.

Harrell, David E., Jr. All Things Are Possible: The Healing & Charismatic Revivals in Modern America. LC 75-1937. (Midland Bks.: No. 221). (Illus.). 320p. 1976. 20.00x (ISBN 0-253-10090-9); pap. 8.95x (ISBN 0-253-20221-3). Ind U Pr.

Harrell, David E., Jr., ed. Varieties of Southern Evangelicalism. LC 81-11312. xii, 114p. 1981. 9.95 (ISBN 0-86554-015-2, MUP-H18). Mercer Univ Pr.

Harrell, Irene, jt. auth. see Hill, Harold.

Harrell, Irene B. A Prayerable a Day. (Orig.). 1987. pap. 7.00 (ISBN 0-915541-15-7). Star Bks Inc.

Harrell, Irene B., jt. auth. see Colbeck, Kay.

Harrell, Irene B., jt. auth. see Hill, Harold.

Harrell, Irene B., jt. auth. see Jordan, Mickey.

Harrell, Irene B., jt. auth. see Lam, Nora.

Harrell, Irene B., jt. auth. see Lewis, Tommy.

Harrell, Irene B., jt. auth. see Phillips, Gloria.

Harrell, Irene B. & Benson, Alie H., eds. The Manufacturer's Handbook. (Orig.). 1987. pap. 7.00 (ISBN 0-915541-04-1). Star Bks Inc.

Harrell, John. To Tell of Gideon: The Art of Storytelling in the Church. 1975. 8.00x (ISBN 0-9615389-4-5); cassette 6.95x (ISBN 0-9615389-5-3). York Hse.

Harrelson, Walter. The Ten Commandments & Human Rights. Brueggemann, Walter & Donahue, John R., eds. LC 77-15234. (Overtures to Biblical Theology Ser.). 240p. 1980. pap. 10.95 (ISBN 0-8006-1527-1, 1-1527). Fortress.

Harrelson, Walter J. From Fertility Cult to Worship: A Reassessment for the Modern Church. LC 66-14929. (Scholars Press Reprint Ser.: No. 4). pap. 10.25x (ISBN 0-89130-379-0, 00 07 04). Scholars Pr GA.

Harries, John. Discovering Churches. (Discovering Ser.: No. 137). 1984. pap. 4.50 (ISBN 0-85263-471-4, Pub. by Shire Pubns England). Seven Hills Bks.

Harries, Karsten. The Bavarian Rococo Church: Between Faith & Aestheticism. LC 82-1116. (Illus.). 304p. 1983. text ed. 42.00x (ISBN 0-300-02720-6). Yale U Pr.

Harries, Richard. Prayer & the Pursuit of Happiness. 160p. (Orig.). 1985. pap. 6.95 (ISBN 0-8028-0089-0). Eerdmans.

--What Christians Believe. 176p. 1982. pap. 4.95 (ISBN 0-86683-677-2, HarpR). Har-Row.

Harries, Richard, ed. Reinhold Niebuhr & the Issues of Our Time. 216p. (Orig.). 1986. pap. 9.95 (ISBN 0-8028-0232-X). Eerdmans.

Harrilchak, Paul N. The Divine Liturgy of the Great Church with Melodies for Congregational Sin. (Illus.). x, 221p. (Orig.). 1984. 15.00x (ISBN 0-930055-00-4). Holy Trinity Ortho.

Harriman, Joseph B. A Harmony of Paul's Life & Letters. 77p. (Companion vol. to A Harmony of the Four gospels). 1969. 2.50 (ISBN 0-910840-13-X). Kingdom.

Harrington, Arthur. What the Bible Says about Leadership. (What the Bible Says Ser.). 425p. text ed. 13.95 (ISBN 0-89900-250-1). College Pr Pub.

Harrington, Daniel. Light of All Nations: Essays on the Church in New Testament Research. (Good News Studies Ser.: Vol. 3). 1982. pap. 7.95 (ISBN 0-89453-291-X). M Glazier.

Harrington, Daniel, ed. The Bible in the Churches: How Different Christians Interpret the Scriptures. 1985. pap. 8.95 (ISBN 0-8091-2676-1). Paulist Pr.

Harrington, Daniel J. God's People in Christ: New Testament Perspectives on the Church & Judaism, No. 7. Brueggemann, Walter & Donahue, John R., eds. LC 79-7380. (Overtures to Biblical Theology Ser.). 144p. 1980. pap. 8.95 (ISBN 0-8006-1531-X, 1-1531). Fortress.

--The Gospel According to Matthew, No. 1. Karris, Robert J., ed. LC 82-20333. (Collegeville Bible Commentary Ser.). (Illus.). 128p. 1983. pap. 2.95 (ISBN 0-8146-1301-2). Liturgical Pr.

--Interpreting the New Testament: A Practical Guide. (New Testament Message Ser.: Vol. 1). 1979. 10.95 (ISBN 0-89453-189-1); pap. 6.95 (ISBN 0-89453-124-7). M Glazier.

--Interpreting the Old Testament: A Practical Guide. (Old Testament Message Ser.: Vol. 1). 1981. 10.95 (ISBN 0-89453-401-7); pap. 6.95 (ISBN 0-89453-236-7). M Glazier.

--The New Testament: A Bibliography. (Theological & Biblical Resources Ser.: Vol. 2). 1985. pap. 8.95 (ISBN 0-89453-535-8). M Glazier.

--Pentecost Two: Proclamation 3B. LC 84-18756. (Proclamation Ser.). 64p. 1985. pap. 3.75 (ISBN 0-8006-4107-8, 1-4107). Fortress.

Harrington, Daniel J. & Gordon, Edmund F. Luke: An Access Guide for Scripture Study. (Access Guides for Scripture Study). 1983. pap. 3.20 (ISBN 0-8215-5929-X); leader's ed. 3.45 (ISBN 0-8215-5934-6). Sadlier.

--Mark: An Access for Scripture Study. (Access Guide for Scripture Study). 128p. 1983. pap. 3.45 (ISBN 0-8215-5928-1); leader's ed. 4.20 (ISBN 0-8215-5933-8). Sadlier.

Harrington, Daniel J., ed. & tr. from Heb. The Hebrew Fragments of Pseudo-Philo. LC 73-89170. (Socity of Biblical Literature. Texts & Translation-Psuedepigrapha Ser.). 1974. pap. 7.50_o.s. (ISBN 0-88414-036-9, 060203). Scholars Pr GA.

Harrington, Jeremy, ed. The Way of the Cross for Congregational Use. (Illus.). 28p. (Orig.). 1976. pap. text ed. 0.65 (ISBN 0-912228-24-5). St Anthony Mess Pr.

Harrington, M. R. Sacred Bundles of the Sac & Fox Indians. (Anthropological Publications Ser.: Vol. 4-2). (Illus.). 142p. 1914. 10.50x (ISBN 0-686-24093-6). Univ Mus of U.

Harrington, Mark R. Religion & Ceremonies of the Lenape. LC 76-43731. (MAI Indian Notes & Monographs. Miscellaneous). Repr. of 1921 ed. 31.50 (ISBN 0-404-15572-3). AMS Pr.

--Sacred Bundles of the Sac & Fox Indians. LC 76-43732. (Univivesity of Pennsylvania Museum Anthropological Publications: Vol. 4, No. 1). (Illus.). 192p. Repr. of 1914 ed. 30.00 (ISBN 0-404-15573-1). AMS Pr.

Harrington, Michael. The Politics at God's Funeral: The Spiritual Crisis of Western Civilization. (Penguin Nonfiction Ser.). 320p. 1985. pap. 7.95 (ISBN 0-14-007689-1). Penguin.

Harrington, Norman W. Shaping of Religion in America. (Illus.). 168p. 1980. 29.95 (ISBN 0-937692-01-8). Queen Anne Pr.

Harrington, W., et al. The Saving Word, Years A, B & C. 370p. 1982. pap. 12.00 ea. (ISBN 0-89453-266-9); Set. pap. 30.00. M Glazier.

Harrington, Wilfrid. The Bible's Ways of Prayer. 164p. (Orig.). 1981. pap. 5.95 (ISBN 0-89453-182-4, Pub. by Dominican Pubns Ireland). M Glazier.

--Christ & Life. 160p. 1976. 7.95 (ISBN 0-8199-0571-2). Franciscan Herald.

--Mark. (New Testament Message Ser.: Vol. 4). 270p. 1979. 14.95 (ISBN 0-89453-192-1); pap. 9.95 (ISBN 0-89453-127-1). M Glazier.

--The New Guide to Reading & Studying the Bible. enl. ed. pap. 7.95 (ISBN 0-89453-092-5). M Glazier.

Harrington, Wilfrid J. Parables Told by Jesus: Contemporary Approach. LC 74-12395. 135p. (Orig.). 1974. pap. 3.95 (ISBN 0-8189-0296-5). Alba.

--The Rosary: A Gospel Prayer. LC 75-44676. (Illus.). 160p. 1976. pap. 2.95 (ISBN 0-8189-1129-8, Pub. by Alba Bks). Alba.

Harris. Applying Moral Theories. 1985. pap. text ed. write for info. (ISBN 0-534-05898-1). Wadsworth Pub.

Harris, Alan. Teaching Morality & Religion. 104p. 1975. 14.95x (ISBN 0-8464-1274-8). Beekman Pubs.

Harris, Anastas. Journal of Holistic Health: Vol. VI. (Illus.). 144p. 1981. pap. 12.00 (ISBN 0-939410-07-9). Mandala Holistic.

Harris, Angela & Friedrich, Dick, eds. A Priest for All Reason: William B. Faherty 50 Years a Jesuit. LC 81-52127. (Illus., Orig.). 1981. pap. 6.95 (ISBN 0-933150-27-X). River City MO.

Harris, Charles. The Proofs of Christianity. LC 77-77215. (Radiant Life Ser.). 128p. 1977. pap. 2.50 (ISBN 0-88243-911-1, 02-0911); teacher's ed 3.95 (ISBN 0-88243-181-1, 32-0181). Gospel Pub.

--What's Ahead? LC 80-84173. (Radiant Life Ser.). 128p. (Orig.). 1982. pap. 2.50 (ISBN 0-88243-897-2, 02-0897); teacher's ed. 3.95 (ISBN 0-88243-195-1, 32-0195). Gospel Pub.

Harris, Christina. Nationalism & Revolution in Egypt: The Role of the Muslim Brotherhood. LC 79-2861. 276p. 1987. Repr. of 1964 ed. 25.00 (ISBN 0-8305-0034-0). Hyperion Conn.

Harris, Clarence. Without Controversy Great Is the Mystery of Godliness. rev. ed. Haris, Althea, ed. (Illus.). 185p. 1982. pap. 4.95 (ISBN 0-686-39817-3). Gospel Place.

Harris, Dale L. Jesus Christ's World Utopia. rev. ed. (Illus.). 1984. pap. text ed. 4.95 (ISBN 0-318-00118-7). Christian Freedom.

Harris, Daniel A. Inspirations Unbidden: The "Terrible Sonnets" of Gerard Manley Hopkins. LC 81-11497. 200p. 1982. 26.50x (ISBN 0-520-04539-4). U of Cal Pr.

Harris, Dixie L. Twenty Stories of Bible Women. 1980. 12.50 (ISBN 0-682-49526-3). Exposition Pr FL.

Harris, Ellen T. Handel & The Pastoral Tradition. (Illus.). 1980. 47.00x (ISBN 0-19-315236-3). Oxford U Pr.

Harris, Errol E. Revelation Through Reason: Religion in the Light of Science & Philosophy. 1958. 39.50x (ISBN 0-317-27547-X). Elliots Bks.
Harris, Errol E. & Litt, D. The Problem of Evil. LC 77-72325. (Aquinas Lecture Ser.). 1977. 7.95 (ISBN 0-87462-142-9). Marquette.
Harris, F. Donald & Harris, Ronald A. The Trinity: Is the Doctrine Biblical-Is It Important? LC 77-123613. 1971. pap. 1.50 (ISBN 0-87213-310-9). Loizeaux.
Harris, George E. A Treatise on Sunday Laws: The Sabbath-the Lord's Day, Its History & Observance, Civil & Criminal. xxiii, 338p. 1980. Repr. of 1892 ed. lib. bdg. 32.50x (ISBN 0-8377-2232-2). Rothman.
Harris, Gerladine. Gods & Pharaohs from Egyptian Mythology. (World Mythologies Ser.). (Illus.). 132p. 1983. 15.95 (ISBN 0-8052-3802-6). Schocken.
Harris, Gordon E., ed. see Foerster, Werner.
Harris, Grace G. Casting Out Anger: Religion among the Taita of Kenya. (Illus.). 193p. 1986. pap. text ed. 7.95x (ISBN 0-88133-233-X). Waveland Pr.
Harris, H. S., ed. see Hegel, G. W.
Harris, H. S., tr. see Hegel, G. W.
Harris, Huffman T. Open the Door Wide to Happy Living. 1985. 12.95 (ISBN 0-8062-2523-8). Carlton.
Harris, Irving. He Touched Me: Conversion Stories of Norman Vincent Peale, Bruce Larson, Ernest Gordon, Bill Wilson, & Others. 144p. (Orig.). pap. 8.95 (ISBN 0-687-16680-2). Abingdon.
Harris, Ishwar C. Radhakrishna: Profile of a Universalist. 1982. 17.50x (ISBN 0-8364-0778-4). South Asia Bks.
Harris, Iverson L. Theosophy under Fire: A Miniature Key to Theosophy As Recorded in a Legal Deposition. 2nd ed. 120p. (Orig.). 1970. pap. 3.00 (ISBN 0-913004-03-0). Point Loma Pub.
--The Wisdom of Laotse. 36p. 1972. pap. 0.75 (ISBN 0-913004-05-7). Point Loma Pub.
Harris, J. D., jt. auth. see Croke, B. F.
Harris, J. R. Codex Bezae: A Study of the So-Called Western Text of the New Testament. (Texts & Studies Ser.: No. 1, Vol. 2, Pt. 1). pap. 19.00 (ISBN 0-8115-1684-9). Kraus Repr.
Harris, J. R., ed. Legacy of Egypt. 2nd ed. (Legacy Ser.). (Illus.). 1971. 35.00x (ISBN 0-19-821912-1). Oxford U Pr.
Harris, James H. Black Ministers & Laity in the Urban Church: An Analysis of Political & Social Expectations. LC 86-28151. (Illus.). 146p. 1987. lib. bdg. 23.50 (ISBN 0-8191-5823-2); pap. text ed. 9.75 (ISBN 0-8191-5824-0). U Pr of Amer.
Harris, Jesse W. John Bale. facs. ed. LC 72-119958. (Select Bibliographies Reprint Ser). 1940. 17.00 (ISBN 0-8369-5401-7). Ayer Co Pubs.
--John Bale. LC 73-12898. 1940. Repr. lib. bdg. 20.00 (ISBN 0-8414-4742-X). Folcroft.
Harris, Joel C. Nights with Uncle Remus: Myths & Legends of the Old Plantation. LC 70-164329. 1971. Repr. of 1883 ed. 42.00x (ISBN 0-8103-3866-1). Gale.
Harris, John. The Teaching Methods of Christ: Characteristics of Our Lord's Ministry. 444p. 1984. lib. bdg. 16.75 (ISBN 0-86524-161-9, 9516). Klock & Klock.
--Violence & Responsibility. 1980. 20.00x (ISBN 0-7100-0448-6). Methuen Inc.
Harris, John, ed. see Saalman, Howard.
Harris, Kaasa, tr. see Molland, Einar.
Harris, Kenneth M. Carlyle & Emerson: Their Long Debate. LC 77-28036. 1978. 14.00x (ISBN 0-674-09755-6). Harvard U Pr.
Harris, Kevin. Sex, Ideology & Religion: The Representation of Women in the Bible. LC 84-12413. 144p. 1984. 22.50x (ISBN 0-389-20509-5, BNB08067). B&N Imports.
Harris, Leon. Night Before Christmas-in Texas, that Is. (Illus.). 1977. Repr. of 1952 ed. 7.95 (ISBN 0-88289-175-8). Pelican.
Harris, Lis. Holy Days: The World of a Hasidic Family. 272p. 1986. pap. 8.95 (ISBN 0-02-020970-3, Collier). Macmillan.
Harris, Lorie K. Tlingit Tales: Potlach & Totem Pole. (Illus.). 64p. 11.95 (ISBN 0-87961-152-9); pap. 5.95 (ISBN 0-87961-153-7). Naturegraph.
Harris, Madalene, jt. auth. see Edvardsen, Aril.
Harris, Maria. Portrait of Youth Ministry. LC 80-84512. 232p. (Orig.). 1981. pap. 8.95 (ISBN 0-8091-2354-1). Paulist Pr.
Harris, Maria, ed. The DRE Reader: A Sourcebook in Education & Ministry. LC 80-52059. 192p. (Orig.). 1980. pap. 6.95 (ISBN 0-88489-124-0). St Marys.
Harris, Marvin. Cows, Pigs, Wars, & Witches: The Riddles of Culture. 1974. pap. 2.36 (ISBN 0-394-71372-9, Vin) (ISBN 0-394-48338-3). Random.
Harris, Murray, jt. ed. see Hagner, Donald.
Harris, Murray J. Easter in Durham: Bishop Jenkins & the Resurrection of Jesus. 32p. 1986. pap. 1.95 (ISBN 0-85364-419-5, Pub. by Paternoster UK). Attic Pr.
--Raised Immortal: Resurrection & Immortality in the New Testament. 320p. (Orig.). 1985. pap. 10.95 (ISBN 0-8028-0053-X). Eerdmans.
Harris, Paula. Scorpio. (Sun Signs). (Illus.). 1978. pap. 3.95 (ISBN 0-89812-078-0). Creative Ed.
Harris, R. Laird. Inspiration & Canonicity of the Bible. (Contemporary Evangelical Perspectives Ser.). kivar 8.95 (ISBN 0-310-25891-X, 9766P). Zondervan.
--Your Bible: An Introduction to the Word. rev. ed. 96p. 1976. pap. text ed. 4.95 (ISBN 0-910566-12-7); instr's. guide 5.95 (ISBN 0-910566-29-1). Evang Tchr.
Harris, R. Laird, et al, eds. Theological Wordbook of the Old Testament, 2 Vols. LC 80-28047. 1800p. 1980. text ed. 39.95 (ISBN 0-8024-8631-2). Moody.
Harris, Rabia, tr. see Arabi, Ibn.
Harris, Ralph W. The Incomparable Story. LC 77-75602. (Radiant Life Ser.). 128p. 1977. pap. 2.50 (ISBN 0-88243-907-3, 02-0907); tchr's ed. 3.95 (ISBN 0-88243-177-3, 32-0177). Gospel Pub.
--Now What? A Guidebook for the New Christian. 24p. 1964. pap. 0.35 (ISBN 0-88243-558-2, 02-0558). Gospel Pub.
--Pictures of Truth. LC 76-58081. (Radiant Life Ser.). 128p. 1977. pap. 2.50 (ISBN 0-88243-905-7, 02-0905); teacher's ed 3.95 (ISBN 0-88243-175-7, 32-0175). Gospel Pub.
--Spoken by the Spirit. LC 73-87106. 128p. 1973. pap. 2.50 (ISBN 0-88243-725-9, 02-0725). Gospel Pub.
Harris, Rendel. Boanerges. 1978. Repr. of 1913 ed. lib. bdg. 50.00 (ISBN 0-8482-4381-1). Norwood Edns.
Harris, Ronald A., jt. auth. see Harris, F. Donald.
Harris, Stephen L. Understanding the Bible. 2nd ed. 1985. pap. 19.95 (ISBN 0-87484-696-X). Mayfield Pub.
Harris, Thomas L. Arcana of Christianity, 3 pts. in 2 vols. LC 72-2955. Repr. of 1867 ed. Set. 92.00 (ISBN 0-404-10720-6). AMS Pr.
Harris, W. Melville. John Milton: Puritan, Patriot, Poet. LC 77-3593. lib. bdg. 5.00 (ISBN 0-8414-4919-8). Folcroft.
Harris, W. T. The Mythology of Plato & Dante & the Future Life. (The Essential Library of the Great Philosophers). (Illus.). 107p. 1983. Repr. of 1896 ed. 71.85 (ISBN 0-89901-091-1). Found Class Reprints.
Harris, William L. Constitutional Powers of the General Conference: With a Special Application to the Subject of Slave Holding. facs. ed. LC 74-146265. (Black Heritage Library Collection Ser). 1860. 12.25 (ISBN 0-8369-8740-3). Ayer Co Pubs.
Harris, Zellig S., jt. auth. see Montgomery, James A.
Harrison, Beverly W. Making the Connections: Essays in Feminist Social Ethics. Robb, Carol S., intro. by. LC 84-45718. (Illus.). 352p. 1985. 22.95 (ISBN 0-8070-1524-5). Beacon Pr.
--Our Right to Choose: Toward a New Ethic of Abortion. LC 81-70488. 256p. 1983. 18.95x (ISBN 0-8070-1508-3). Beacon Pr.
--Our Right to Choose: Toward a New Ethic of Abortion. LC 81-70488. 356p. 1984. pap. 10.95 (ISBN 0-8070-1509-1, BP673). Beacon Pr.
Harrison, Beverly W., et al. The Public Vocation of Christian Ethics. 400p. (Orig.). 1987. pap. 12.95 (ISBN 0-8298-0582-6). Pilgrim NY.
Harrison, Buddy. Maintaining a Spirit Filled Life. 1985. 0.75 (ISBN 0-89274-383-2). Harrison Hse.
Harrison, Buddy & Gale, Van. Count It All Joy. rev. ed. 32p. 1981. pap. 2.50 (ISBN 0-89274-198-8). Harrison Hse.
Harrison, Doyle. Understanding Authority for Effective Leadership. rev. ed. 122p. (Orig.). 1985. pap. 3.50 (ISBN 0-89274-379-4). Harrison Hse.
Harrison, Doyle & Landsman, Michael. Mercy: The Gift Before & Beyond Faith. 64p. (Orig.). 1984. pap. 2.25 (ISBN 0-89274-305-0). Harrison Hse.
Harrison, Everett. Colossians. (Everyman's Bible Commentary Ser). 128p. (Orig.). 1971. pap. 5.95 (ISBN 0-8024-2051-6). Moody.
--A Short Life of Christ. (Highlights in the Life of Christ). 1968. pap. 8.95 (ISBN 0-8028-1824-2). Eerdmans.
Harrison, Everett & Pfeiffer, Charles F. Wycliffe Bible Commentary. (Affordables Ser.). 1525p. 16.95 (ISBN 0-8024-0420-0). Moody.
Harrison, Everett & Pfeiffer, Charles F., eds. Wycliffe Bible Commentary. 29.95 (ISBN 0-8024-9695-4). Moody.
Harrison, Everett F. El Comentario Biblico Moody: Nuevo Testamento. Orig. Title: Wycliffe Bible Commentary: N. T. (Span.). 568p. 1965. 16.95 (ISBN 0-8254-1307-9). Kregel.
--Interpreting Acts. (Interpreting Ser.: No. 2). 352p. 1986. pap. 14.95 (ISBN 0-310-31850-5). Zondervan.
--Introduction to the New Testament. 1964. 22.95 (ISBN 0-8028-3106-0). Eerdmans.
--John: The Gospel of Faith. (Everyman's Bible Commentary Ser.). 1967. pap. 5.95 (ISBN 0-8024-2043-5). Moody.
--Juan: El Evangelio de la Fe (Comentario Biblico Portavoz) Orig. Title: John: The Gospel of Faith (Everyman's Bible Commentary) (Span.). 128p. 1981. pap. 3.50 (ISBN 0-8254-1304-4). Kregel.
Harrison, Everett F., ed. Baker's Dictionary of Theology. pap. 12.95 (ISBN 0-8010-4289-5). Baker Bk.
Harrison, Everett F., et al. The Expositor's Bible Commentary, Vol. 10. 1986. 19.95 (ISBN 0-88469-196-9). BMH Bks.
Harrison, Frank M. Bibliography of the Works of John Bunyan. LC 76-28174. 1932. lib. bdg. 12.50 (ISBN 0-8414-4934-1). Folcroft.
--A Bibliography of the Works of John Bunyan. 1977. lib. bdg. 59.95 (ISBN 0-8490-1502-2). Gordon Pr.
Harrison, Frank M., ed. see Brown, John.
Harrison, Frederic. Oliver Cromwell. 228p. 1980. Repr. of 1915 ed. lib. bdg. 25.00 (ISBN 0-8495-2293-5). Arden Lib.
--Oliver Cromwell. LC 78-39196. (Select Bibliographies Reprint Ser.). Repr. of 1888 ed. 18.00 (ISBN 0-8369-6798-4). Ayer Co Pubs.
--Oliver Cromwell. 1973. Repr. of 1888 ed. lib. bdg. 25.00 (ISBN 0-8414-5006-4). Folcroft.
--Positive Evolution of Religion. facs. ed. LC 74-142641. (Essay Index Reprint Ser). 1913. 18.00 (ISBN 0-8369-2053-8). Ayer Co Pubs.
Harrison, Frederick. Practical Church Financing. 128p. 1970. pap. 5.95 (ISBN 0-912522-58-5). Aero Medical.
Harrison, G. B. & McCabe, John. Proclaiming the Word. 2nd ed. 1976. pap. 4.95 (ISBN 0-916134-00-8). Pueblo Pub Co.
Harrison, G. B., ed. Bible for Students of Literature & Art. LC 64-13820. 1964. pap. 8.50 (ISBN 0-385-04475-5, A394, Anch). Doubleday.
Harrison, G. E. Haworth Parsonage: Study of Wesley & the Brontes. 1937. lib. bdg. 16.50 (ISBN 0-8414-5008-0). Folcroft.
Harrison, G. Elsie. Son to Susanna: The Private Life of John Wesley. 1937. Repr. 35.00 (ISBN 0-8274-3468-5). R West.
Harrison, G. T. Mormonism, Now & Then. 357p. cancelled (ISBN 0-686-96149-8). Am Atheist.
Harrison, Graham, tr. see Pieper, Josef.
Harrison, Graham, tr. see Ratzinger, Cardinal J.
Harrison, Graham, tr. see Ratzinger, Joseph.
Harrison, Graham, tr. see Ratzinger, Joseph, et al.
Harrison, Graham, tr. see Ratzinger, Joseph & Messori, Vittorio.
Harrison, Graham, tr. see Scheffczyk, Leo.
Harrison, Graham, tr. see Urs von Balthasar, Hans.
Harrison, Graham, tr. see Von Balthasar, Hans U.
Harrison, Graham, tr. see Von Speyr, Adrienne.
Harrison, H. D. Christian Education: Total Task of the Church. 28p. 1976. pap. 0.75 (ISBN 0-89265-101-6). Randall Hse.
--How to Start a Bible Institute. 1978. pap. 2.95 (ISBN 0-89265-051-6). Randall Hse.
Harrison, H. D., ed. Who's Who among Free Will Baptists. 1978. 18.95 (ISBN 0-89265-052-4). Randall Hse.
Harrison, H. D., ed. see Picirilli, Robert E.
Harrison, Hank. The Holy Grail. (The Grail Trilogy). (Illus.). 325p. (Orig.). 1987. 24.95 (ISBN 0-918501-18-0). Archives Pr.
Harrison, Harrold D. Commissioned to Communicate. (Sunday School Workers Training Course Ser.: No. 2). 1969. pap. 3.95 (ISBN 0-89265-003-6, Free Will Baptist Dept). Randall Hse.
Harrison, Harrold D., ed. see Outlaw, et al.
Harrison, Helen R. Values to Cherish. (Orig.). 1978. pap. 4.50 (ISBN 0-87881-071-4). Mojave Bks.
Harrison House Staff. Confessions for Kids. (Illus.). 29p. (Orig.). 1984. pap. 0.75 (ISBN 0-89274-322-0). Harrison Hse.
Harrison, Jane. Prolegomena to the Study of Greek Religion. 682p. 1981. text ed. 27.50x (ISBN 0-85036-262-8, Pub. by Merlin Pr UK); pap. 17.50x. Humanities.
Harrison, Jane E. Myths of Greece & Rome. LC 76-46570. 1976. Repr. of 1927 ed. lib. bdg. 20.00 (ISBN 0-8414-4907-4). Folcroft.
--Prolegomena to the Study of Greek Religion. facsimile ed. LC 75-10639. (Ancient Religion & Mythology Ser.). (Illus.). 1976. Repr. of 1922 ed. 57.50x (ISBN 0-405-07018-7). Ayer Co Pubs.
--The Religion of Ancient Greece. 1979. Repr. of 1905 ed. lib. bdg. 27.00 (ISBN 0-8495-2325-7). Arden Lib.
--The Religion of Ancient Greece. 66p. 1921. 0.95 (ISBN 0-317-40433-4). Open Court.
Harrison, John F. The Second Coming: Popular Millenarianism 1780-1850. 1979. 32.00x (ISBN 0-8135-0879-7). Rutgers U Pr.
Harrison, Marc, illus. The Alphabet Book. (Bible Look 'N Learn Bks.). (Illus.). 24p. 1985. bds. 3.95 (ISBN 0-8407-6685-8). Nelson.
--The Animal Book. (Bible Look-n-Learn Ser.). 1986. 3.95 (ISBN 0-8407-6708-0). Nelson.
--The Color Book. (Bible Look 'N Learn Bks.). (Illus.). 24p. 1985. bds. 3.95 (ISBN 0-8407-6687-4). Nelson.
--The Counting Book. (Bible Look 'N Learn Bks.). (Illus.). 24p. 1985. bds. 3.95 (ISBN 0-8407-6686-6). Nelson.
--The Opposite Book. (Bible Look-n-Learn Ser.). 1986. 3.95 (ISBN 0-8407-6710-2). Nelson.
--The Shape Book. (Bible Look-n-Learn Ser.). 1986. 3.95 (ISBN 0-8407-6709-9). Nelson.
Harrison, Matthew W., Jr., ed. see Ressler, Martin E., et al.
Harrison, Michael. The Roots of Witchcraft. 280p. 1974. 7.95 (ISBN 0-8065-0444-7). Citadel Pr.
Harrison, Norman B. His Comfort. 1973. pap. 0.75 (ISBN 0-911802-32-0). Free Church Pubns.
--His Joy. 1973. pap. 0.75 (ISBN 0-911802-35-5). Free Church Pubns.
--His Peace. 1972. pap. 0.75 (ISBN 0-911802-29-0). Free Church Pubns.
--New Testament Living. 1972. pap. 1.25 (ISBN 0-911802-30-4). Free Church Pubns.
--Suffering. 1965. pap. 0.75 (ISBN 0-911802-34-7). Free Church Pubns.
Harrison, Paul M. Authority & Power in the Free Church Tradition: A Social Case Study of the American Baptist Convention. (Arcturus Bks.). 267p. 1971. lib. bdg. 7.00x (ISBN 0-8093-0503-8); pap. 2.45x (ISBN 0-8093-0499-6). S Ill U Pr.
Harrison, R. K. Jeremiah & Lamentations. LC 72-97951. 240p. 1973. 12.95 (ISBN 0-87784-864-5); pap. 6.95 (ISBN 0-87784-271-X). Inter-Varsity.
Harrison, R. K. & Wiseman, D. J. Leviticus: An Introduction & Commentary. LC 80-7985. (Tyndale Old Testament Commentaries Ser.). 180p. 1980. 12.95 (ISBN 0-87784-890-4); pap. 6.95 (ISBN 0-87784-253-1). Inter-Varsity.
Harrison, R. K., ed. Major Cities of the Biblical World. 320p. 1985. 15.95 (ISBN 0-8407-7520-2). Nelson.
Harrison, R. K., jt. ed. see Blaiklock, E. M.
Harrison, R. K., ed. see Verhoef, Pieter A.
Harrison, Roland K. Old Testament Times. (Illus.). 1970. 16.95 (ISBN 0-8028-3334-9). Eerdmans.
--Teach Yourself Biblical Hebrew. (Teach Yourself Ser.). pap. 6.95 (ISBN 0-679-10180-2). McKay.
Harrison, Russell F. More Brief Prayers for Bread & Cup. Lambert, Herbert, ed. LC 86-6076. 80p. (Orig.). 1986. pap. 4.95 (ISBN 0-8272-2319-6). CBP.
Harrison, Shirley. Who Is Father Christmas? (Illus.). 64p. 1983. 7.50 (ISBN 0-7153-8222-5). David & Charles.
Harrison, Stanley M. & Taylor, Richard C., eds. The Life of Religion: A Marquette University Symposium on the Nature of Religious Belief. 124p. (Orig.). 1986. lib. bdg. 22.50 (ISBN 0-8191-5558-6); pap. text ed. 8.75 (ISBN 0-8191-5559-4). U Pr of Amer.
Harrison, Ted. Much Beloved Daughter: The Story of Florence Li. 110p. 1986. pap. 6.95 (ISBN 0-8192-1378-0). Morehouse.
Harrison, William H. Mother Shipton Investigated. LC 77-3412. 1977. Repr. of 1881 ed. lib. bdg. 17.00 (ISBN 0-8414-4911-2). Folcroft.
Harrison, William P. Gospel Among the Slaves. LC 70-168249. Repr. of 1893 ed. 27.50 (ISBN 0-404-00263-3). AMS Pr.
Harrisville, Roy. Holy Week. LC 84-18756. (Proclamation 3 C Ser.). 64p. 1985. pap. 3.75 (ISBN 0-8006-4128-0). Fortress.
Harrisville, Roy A. Augsburg Commentary on the New Testament-Romans. LC 80-65550. 246p. (Orig.). 1980. pap. 9.95 (ISBN 0-8066-8864-5, 10-9022). Augsburg.
--Benjamin Wisner Bacon: Pioneer in American Biblical Criticism. LC 76-16178. (Society of Biblical Literature. Studies in Biblical Scholarship). 1976. pap. 8.95 (ISBN 0-89130-110-0, 061102). Scholars Pr GA.
--Frank Chamberlain Porter: Pioneer in American Biblical Interpretation. LC 76-4498. (Society of Biblical Literature. Study in Biblical Scholarship). 1976. pap. 8.95 (ISBN 0-89130-104-6, 061101). Scholars Pr GA.
Harrisville, Roy A. & Hackett, Charles D. Holy Week. Achtemeier, Elizabeth, et al, eds. LC 79-7377. (Proclamation 2: Aids for Interpreting the Lessons of the Church Year, Ser. B). 64p. 1981. pap. 3.75 (ISBN 0-8006-4086-1, 1-4086). Fortress.
Harrisville, Roy A., tr. see Gunkel, Hermann.
Harrisville, Roy A., tr. see Kasemann, Ernst.

Harrod, Howard L. The Human Center: Moral Agency in the Social World. LC 80-2392. 160p. 1981. 3.50 (ISBN 0-8006-0657-4, 1-657). Fortress.
--Renewing the World: Northern Plains Indian Religion. LC 87-5010. 210p. 1987. 22.50x (ISBN 0-8165-0958-1). U of Ariz Pr.
Harrold, Charles F., ed. see Newman, John H.
Harrold, Robert. Cassadaga: An Inside Look at the South's Oldest Psychic Community with True Experiences of People Who Have Been There. (Illus.). 1979. pap. 4.95 (ISBN 0-916224-49-X). Banyan Bks.
Harrop, Clayton. History of the New Testament in Plain Language. 192p. 1984. 9.95 (ISBN 0-8499-0432-3, 0432-3). Word Bks.
Harshananda, Swami. Hindu Gods & Goddesses. (Illus., Orig.). 1985. pap. 4.25 (ISBN 0-87481-522-3, Pub. by Ramakrishna Math Madras India). Vedanta Pr.
Harshbarger, Luther H. & Mourant, John A. Judaism & Christianity: Perspectives & Traditions. 490p. Date not set. text ed. price not set (ISBN 0-8290-0294-4); pap. text ed. price not set (ISBN 0-8290-0295-2). Irvington.
Harsin, L. D. Our Caring Fellowship. 1983. pap. 8.50 (ISBN 0-8309-0373-9). Herald Hse.
Harsley, F., ed. Eadwine's Canterbury Psalter from Ms of Trinity College. (EETS, OS Ser.: No. 92). Repr. of 1889 ed. 50.00 (ISBN 0-527-00091-4). Kraus Repr.
Hart, A. Tindal. The Country Priest in English History. 1959. Repr. 30.00 (ISBN 0-8274-2107-9). R West.
--The Parson & the Publican. 1984. 9.50 (ISBN 0-533-05730-2). Vantage.
Hart, Archibald. Counseling the Depressed. 224p. 1987. 12.95 (ISBN 0-8499-0582-6). Word Bks.
Hart, Archibald D. The Success Factor. 160p. 1984. pap. 5.95 (ISBN 0-8007-5138-8, Power Bks). Revell.
Hart, David. The Psychology of a Fairy Tale. Crosby, Harriett, ed. LC 76-56563. (Orig.). 1976. pap. 2.50x (ISBN 0-87574-210-6). Pendle-Hill.
Hart, David M., jt. ed. see Ahemd, Akbar S.
Hart, H. The Challenge of Our Age. LC 68-9843. 1974. pap. 3.25 (ISBN 0-686-11982-7). Wedge Pub.
Hart, H. L., jt. auth. see Bentham, Jeremy.
Hart, Hendrik & Van Der Hoeven, Johan, eds. Rationality in the Calvinian Tradition. LC 83-19672. (Christian Studies Today). 420p. (Orig.). 1984. lib. bdg. 32.25 (ISBN 0-8191-3616-6); pap. text ed. 16.75 (ISBN 0-8191-3617-4). U Pr of Amer.
Hart, James G., jt. ed. see Laycock, Steven W.
Hart, Joanna. Fifty-Two Preschool Crafts. 48p. (Orig.). 1984. pap. 2.95 (ISBN 0-87239-725-4, 2105). Standard Pub.
Hart, John. Regard the Lilies, Regard the Blood: Poems to the Blessed Virgin. 79p. 1983. pap. 6.00 (ISBN 0-682-49941-2). Exposition Pr FL.
--The Spirit of the Earth. 1984. pap. 8.95 (ISBN 0-8091-2581-1). Paulist Pr.
Hart, Joseph L., ed. see Sammon, Sean D., et al.
Hart, Kathleen, jt. auth. see Hart, Thomas.
Hart, Lee. Adult Ministries in the Church & the World. LC 76-773. 1976. 11.00 (ISBN 0-8309-0160-4). Herald Hse.
Hart, Patrick, ed. The Legacy of Thomas Merton. (Cistercian Studies: No. 92). 1985. 25.95 (ISBN 0-87907-892-8); pap. 7.95 (ISBN 0-87907-992-4). Cistercian Pubns.
--The Message of Thomas Merton. (Cistercian Studies: No. 42). (Illus.). 1981. 15.95 (ISBN 0-87907-842-1); pap. 5.50 (ISBN 0-87907-942-8). Cistercian Pub.
Hart, Patrick, ed. see Merton, Thomas.
Hart, Ray. Unfinished Man & the Imagination: Toward an Ontology & a Rhetoric of Revelation. (Reprints & Translations Ser.). 1985. pap. text ed. 12.95 (ISBN 0-89130-937-3, 00-07-15). Scholars Pr GA.
Hart, Ray L., ed. Trajectories in the Study of Religion: Addresses at the Seventy-Fifth Anniversary of the American Academy of Religion. (Studies in Religion & Theological Scholarship (American Academy of Religion)). 333p. 25.95 (ISBN 1-55540-064-7, 00-08-03). Scholars Pr GA.
Hart, Reed L. Key Thoughts for Talks. (Orig.). 1978. pap. 3.50 (ISBN 0-89036-105-3). Hawkes Pub Inc.
Hart, Roderick P. The Political Pulpit. LC 76-12290. 160p. 1977. 7.95 (ISBN 0-911198-44-X). Purdue U Pr.
Hart, S. L. Lifetime of Love. LC 67-29163. 1969. 6.50 (ISBN 0-8198-0076-7); pap. 5.50 (ISBN 0-8198-4426-8). Dghtrs St Paul.
Hart, Thomas. Living Happily Ever after: Toward a Theology of Christian Marriage. LC 79-89475. 96p. 1979. pap. 3.95 (ISBN 0-8091-2213-8). Paulist Pr.
Hart, Thomas & Hart, Kathleen. The First Two Years of Marriage: Foundations for a Life Together. 144p. (Orig.). 1983. pap. 5.95 (ISBN 0-8091-2553-6). Paulist Pr.
Hart, Thomas N. The Art of Christian Listening. LC 80-82810. 132p. (Orig.). 1981. pap. 4.95 (ISBN 0-8091-2345-2). Paulist Pr.
--To Know & Follow Jesus: Contemporary Christology. 160p. (Orig.). 1984. pap. 6.95 (ISBN 0-8091-2636-2). Paulist Pr.
Hart, Thomas N., jt. auth. see Fisher, Kathleen R.
Hartbauer, Roy E. Pastoral Care of the Handicapped. LC 82-74357. (Illus.). xvi, 183p. 1983. pap. 11.95 (ISBN 0-943872-87-1). Andrews Univ Pr.
Hartdegen, Steven J., ed. see Catholic Church, Sacred Congregation for Divine Worship.
Hartdegen, Steven J., ed. see Catholic Church, Sacred Congregation of Divine Worship Staff.
Harte, B. Bell Ringer of Angel's. 1985. 10.00x (Pub. by J Richardson UK). State Mutual Bk.
Harte, Thomas. Papal Social Principles: A Guide & Digest. 12.00 (ISBN 0-8446-1225-1). Peter Smith.
Hartfeld, Hermann. Irina's Story. 318p. 1983. pap. 5.95 (ISBN 0-87123-261-8, 210261). Bethany Hse.
Hartfield, Hermann. Faith Despite the KGB. 248p. 1980. pap. 5.95 (ISBN 0-88264-156-5). Diane Bks.
Hartigan, Richard S. The Forgotten Victim: A History of the Civilian. 173p. 1982. 16.95x (ISBN 0-913750-19-0). Transaction Bks.
Hartill, J. Edwin. Principles of Biblical Hermeneutics. 13.95 (ISBN 0-310-25900-2, 9774). Zondervan.
Hartingsveld, L. Van see Van Hartingsveld, L.
Hartland, Edwin S. Mythology & Folktales: Their Relation & Interpretation. LC 75-144519. (Popular Studies in Mythology, Romance & Folklore: No. 7). Repr. of 1900 ed. 5.50 (ISBN 0-404-53507-0). AMS Pr.
Hartley, Elda. Perennial Wisdom. (Chrysalis Bk). (Illus.). 80p. (Orig.). 1986. pap. 4.95 (ISBN 0-916349-09-8). Amity Hous Inc.
Hartley, Fred. Dare to Be Different. 128p. 1980. pap. 5.95 (ISBN 0-8007-5041-1, Power Bks). Revell.
--One Hundred Percent: Beyond Mediocrity. (Illus.). 160p. 1983. pap. 5.95 (ISBN 0-8007-5112-4, Power Bks). Revell.
--Update. 160p. 1982. pap. 2.95 (ISBN 0-8007-8431-6, Spire Bks). Revell.
Hartley, Jan. Family Ideas for Prayers. (Together with God Ser.). (Illus.). 80p. (Orig.). 1984. pap. 5.95 (ISBN 0-85819-495-3, Pub. by JBCE). ANZ Religious Pubns.
--Sharing Faith at Home. (SPAN Ser.). (Illus.). 31p. (Orig.). 1983. pap. 3.95 (ISBN 0-85819-450-3, Pub. by JBCE). ANZ Religious Pubns.
Hartley, John E. & Shelton, R. L., eds. Salvation. (Wesleyan Theological Perspectives Ser.: Vol. I). 1981. 14.95 (ISBN 0-87162-240-8, D4850). Warner Pr.
Hartley, Loyde H. Understanding Church Finances: The Economics of the Local Church. LC 83-23769. 192p. (Orig.). 1984. pap. 10.95 (ISBN 0-8298-0708-X). Pilgrim NY.
Hartley, William. In the Beginning God: Jottings from Genesis. 96p. 1975. pap. 1.45 (ISBN 0-8010-4132-5). Baker Bk.
Hartman, Charles. Han Yu & the T'ang Search for Unity. LC 85-16885. 448p. 1986. text ed. 50.00 (ISBN 0-691-06665-5). Princeton U Pr.
Hartman, Charles S., ed. see Luccock, Halford E.
Hartman, Charles S., ed. & intro. by see Luccock, Halford E.
Hartman, David. Joy & Responsibility: Israel, Modernity & the Renewal of Judaism. 286p. 12.50 (ISBN 0-686-95138-7). ADL.
--A Living Covenant: The Innovative Spirit in Traditional Judaism. 384p. 1985. 21.60x (ISBN 0-02-914140-0). Free Pr.
--Maimonides-Torah & Philosophic Quest. LC 76-6305. 288p. 1977. pap. 7.95 (ISBN 0-8276-0089-5, 392). Jewish Pubns.
Hartman, David, ed. Crisis & Leadership: Epistles of Maimonides. Halkin, Abraham, tr. from Hebrew. 292p. 1985. 15.95 (ISBN 0-8276-0238-3). Jewish Pubns.
Hartman, Edwin. Substance, Body & Soul: Aristotelian Investigations. LC 77-71984. 1977. text ed. 34.50x (ISBN 0-691-07223-X). Princeton U Pr.
Hartman, Franz. Rosicrucian Symbols. 1983. 2.95 (ISBN 0-916411-15-X). Sure Fire.
Hartman, Geoffrey. Midrash & Literature. LC 85-17898. 424p. 1986. 28.50 (ISBN 0-300-03453-9). Yale U Pr.
Hartman, Grover L. Militarism for America. 1983. pap. 2.50x (ISBN 0-87574-025-1, 025). Pendle Hill.
Hartman, Jane E. Hoku & the Precious Stones. 1985. pap. 4.95 (ISBN 0-87613-087-2). New Age.
Hartman, Louis F. & Di Lella, Alexander A. The Book of Daniel: A New Translation with Introduction & Commentary. LC 77-82762. (Anchor Bible Ser.: Vol. 23). 1978. 18.00 (ISBN 0-385-01322-1, Anchor Pr). Doubleday.
Hartman, Robert H., ed. Poverty & Economic Justice: A Philosophical Approach. 1984. pap. 10.95 (ISBN 0-8091-2597-8). Paulist Pr.
Hartman, Sven S. & Edsman, C. M. Mysticism. (Illus.). 258p. (Orig.). 1970. pap. text ed. 16.95x (Pub. by Almqvist & Wiksell). Coronet Bks.
Hartman, Thomas, ed. see Zanzucchi, Annamaria.
Hartmann, Angelika. An-Nasir Li-Din Allah (1180-1225) Politik, Religion, Kultur in der Spaeten Abbasidenzeit. (Studien Zur Sprache, Geschichte und Kultur Des Islamischen Orients, N. F.: Vol. 8). 1975. 88.00x (ISBN 3-11-004179-0). De Gruyter.
Hartmann, Franz. Life of Jacob Boehme. 1985. pap. 4.95 (ISBN 0-916411-97-4, Pub by Sure Fire). Holmes Pub.
Hartmann, Heinz. Once a Doctor, Always a Doctor: The Memoirs of a German-Jewish Immigrant Physician. 130p. Date not set. 18.95 (ISBN 0-87975-342-0). Prometheus Bks.
--Psychoanalysis & Moral Values. LC 58-9230. (The New York Psychoanalytic Institute Freud Anniversary Lecture Ser.). 121p. 1960. text ed. 17.50 (ISBN 0-8236-5240-8). Intl Univs Pr.
Hartmann, Jacob W., tr. see Kautsky, Karl.
Hartmann, Olga De see De Hartmann, Thomas & De Hartmann, Olga.
Hartmann, Thomas De see De Hartmann, Thomas.
Hartmann, Thomas De see De Hartmann, Thomas & De Hartmann, Olga.
Hartnack, Justus. From Radical Empiricism to Absolute Idealism. LC 86-8603. (Studies in the History of Philosophy: Vol. 1). 222p. 1986. 49.95x (ISBN 0-88946-304-2). E Mellen.
Hartnett, William, tr. see Lubich, Chiara.
Hartog, Jan de see De Hartog, Jan.
Hartog, John. Enduring to the End: Jehovah's Witnesses & Bible Doctrine. 200p. 1987. pap. write for info. (ISBN 0-87227-118-8). Reg Baptist.
Hartsaw, John W. End Time-God's Glory. 112p. 1982. 6.50 (ISBN 0-682-49848-3). Exposition Pr FL.
Hartshorn, Leon R. Classic Stories from the Lives of Our Prophets. LC 73-155235. 384p. 1975. 9.95 (ISBN 0-87747-438-9). Deseret Bk.
--A Mother's Love. LC 80-81506. 76p. 1980. 5.95 (ISBN 0-88290-143-5). Horizon Utah.
Hartshorne, Charles. Anselm's Discovery: A Re-Examination of the Ontological Proof for God's Existence. LC 65-20278. 349p. 1973. 23.95 (ISBN 0-87548-216-3); pap. 11.95 (ISBN 0-87548-217-1). Open Court.
--Aquinas to Whitehead: Seven Centuries of Metaphysics of Religion. LC 76-5156. (Aquinas Lectures Ser.). 1976. 7.95 (ISBN 0-87462-141-0). Marquette.
--The Divine Relativity: A Social Conception of God. LC 48-7802. (The Terry Lectures Ser.). 184p. 1982. pap. 7.95x (ISBN 0-300-02880-6, Y-430). Yale U Pr.
--The Logic of Perfection & Other Essays in Neoclassical Metaphysics. LC 61-11286. 351p. 1973. pap. 8.95 (ISBN 0-87548-037-3). Open Court.
--A Natural Theology for Our Time. LC 66-14722. 145p. 1967. pap. 9.95 (ISBN 0-87548-239-2). Open Court.
--Omnipotence & Other Theological Mistakes. LC 83-6588. 144p. 1983. 34.50 (ISBN 0-87395-770-9); pap. 9.95x (ISBN 0-87395-771-7). State U NY Pr.
Hartshorne, Charles & Reese, William L. Philosophers Speak of God. LC 53-10041. (Midway Reprint Ser.). 1976. 24.00x (ISBN 0-226-31862-1). U of Chicago Pr.
Hartshorne, Hugh & Lotz, Elsa. Case Studies of Present-Day Religions Teaching. (Educational Ser.). 1932. Repr. 15.00 (ISBN 0-8482-4454-0). Norwood Edns.
Hartshorne, Hugh & Miller, J. Q. Community Organization in Religious Education. 1932. 49.50x (ISBN 0-686-51356-8). Elliots Bks.
Hartsoe, Colleen I. Dear Daughter: Letters from Eve & Other Women of the Bible. LC 81-80627. 1981. pap. 4.95 (ISBN 0-8192-1288-1). Morehouse.
Hartstein, Jacob I. & Miller, Benjamin. Jews in America: Heritage & History. (Illus.). 1978. 6.50 (ISBN 0-686-26239-5). Board Jewish Educ.
Hartt, Frederick, ed. Michelangelo. (Library of Great Painters). 1965. 45.00 (ISBN 0-8109-0299-0). Abrams.
Hartt, Julian N., ed. The Critique of Modernity: Theological Reflections on Contemporary Culture. (Virginia Lectures on Individual & Society). 160p. 1987. text ed. 16.95x (ISBN 0-8139-1118-4). U Pr of VA.
Hartweg, Judy. Faithful Followers. (Helping Hand Ser.). 48p. 1984. wkbk. 4.95 (ISBN 0-86653-237-4). Good Apple.
Hartwell, Herbert. The Theology of Karl Barth: An Introduction. (Studies in Theology). 201p. 1964. pap. 13.50 (ISBN 0-7156-0356-6, Pub. by Duckworth London). Longwood Pub Group.
Hartwell, Kathleen. Lactantius & Milton. LC 74-17014. (Studies in Milton, No. 22). 1974. lib. bdg. 46.95x (ISBN 0-8383-1743-X). Haskell.
Harty, Annelle & Harty, Robert. Made to Grow. (Sexuality in Christian Living Ser.). 32p. 1973. 6.95 (ISBN 0-8054-4222-7). Broadman.
Harty, Annelle, jt. auth. see Harty, Robert.
Harty, Robert & Harty, Annelle. Creados Para Crecer. De Plou, Dafne C., tr. (Sexo en la Vida Cristiana Ser.). (Illus.). 1985. pap. 1.50 (ISBN 0-311-46251-0). Casa Bautista.
Harty, Robert, jt. auth. see Harty, Annelle.
Hartzler, Arlene & Gaeddert, John, eds. Children's Hymnary. LC 67-24327. 1967. 5.95 (ISBN 0-87303-095-8). Faith & Life.
Hartzler, Jonas S. Mennonites in the World War: Or, Nonresistance under Test. LC 76-137543. (Peace Movement in America Ser). 246p. 1972. Repr. of 1922 ed. lib. bdg. 18.95x (ISBN 0-89198-071-7). Ozer.
Harupa, Gisela & Nold, Liselotte. Advent Day by Day in the Home. Kaste, Omar, tr. LC 62-17507. 1962. pap. 2.95 (ISBN 0-8066-0209-0, 10-0160). Augsburg.
Harvard University Dumbarton Oaks Research Library. Dictionary Catalogue of the Byzantine Collection of the Dumbarton Oaks Research Library, 12 vols. 1975. Set. lib. bdg. 1390.00 (ISBN 0-8161-1150-2, Hall Library). G K Hall.
Harvard University Library. Catalogue of Hebrew Books, 6 Vols. LC 68-22146. (Yiddish & Heb). 1968. Set. 225.00x (ISBN 0-674-10150-2). Harvard U Pr.
--Catalogue of Hebrew Books: Supplement I, 3 vols. LC 68-22416. 1972. Set. 185.00x (ISBN 0-674-10173-1). Harvard U Pr.
Harvard University, Phillips Brooks House Association. Religion & Modern Life. LC 75-39104. (Essay Index Reprint Ser.). Repr. of 1927 ed. 21.00 (ISBN 0-8369-2713-3). Ayer Co Pubs.
Harvey. The King's Diamond. 3.95 (ISBN 0-686-27782-1). Schmul Pub Co.
Harvey, A. E. Companion to the New Testament: The New English Bible. 858p. 1970. 49.50x (ISBN 0-19-826160-8); pap. 24.95x (ISBN 0-19-213229-6). Oxford U Pr.
--New English Bible Companion to the New Testament. 1979. 65.00 (ISBN 0-521-07705-2). Cambridge U Pr.
--New English Bible Companion to the New Testament: The Gospels. 400p. 1972. pap. 9.95 (ISBN 0-521-09689-8). Cambridge U Pr.
--The New English Bible Companion to the New Testament: The Gospels. (Orig.). 1972. pap. 13.95x (ISBN 0-19-826168-3). Oxford U Pr.
Harvey, Adell & Gonzalez, Mari. Sacred Chow. 176p. 1987. pap. 9.95 (ISBN 0-687-36713-1). Abingdon.
Harvey, Barbara. Westminster Abbey & Its Estates in the Middle Ages. (Illus.). 1977. text ed. 55.00x (ISBN 0-19-822455-9). Oxford U Pr.
Harvey, Bonnie C., ed. see Lee, Laurel.
Harvey, Bonnie C., jt. ed. see Phillips, Cheryl.
Harvey, Bonnie C., jt. ed. see Phillips, Cheryl M.
Harvey, Bonnie C., ed. see Stirrup Associates, Inc.
Harvey, Bonnie C., ed. see Stirrup Associates Inc.
Harvey, Charles H. Matthew Arnold: A Critic of the Victorian Period. LC 69-18273. 256p. 1969. Repr. of 1931 ed. 27.50 (ISBN 0-208-00732-6, Archon). Shoe String.
Harvey, Edwin D. The Mind of China. LC 73-874. (China Studies: from Confucius to Mao Ser). x, 321p. 1973. Repr. of 1933 ed. 25.50 (ISBN 0-88355-069-5). Hyperion Conn.
Harvey, George L., ed. Church & the Twentieth Century. facs. ed. LC 67-26747. (Essay Index Reprint Ser). 1936. 21.50 (ISBN 0-8369-0517-2). Ayer Co Pubs.
Harvey, H. El Pastor. Trevino, Alejandro, tr. Orig. Title: The Pastor. (Span.). 232p. 1984. pap. 3.95 (ISBN 0-311-42025-7). Casa Bautista.
Harvey, J. D. Faith Plus - Search for the Holy Life. 1976. pap. 1.75 (ISBN 0-89367-002-2). Light & Life.
Harvey, J. Glenn. How to Go to Heaven. 104p. (Orig.). 1982. pap. 2.95 (ISBN 0-915059-00-2). Ind Christ Pubns.
--Now That You're a Christian. 127p. (Orig.). 1983. pap. 3.95 (ISBN 0-915059-01-0). Ind Christ Pubns.
--Therefore. (Orig.). 1984. pap. 3.95 (ISBN 0-915059-02-9). Ind Christ Pubns.
Harvey, James M., ed. A Letter: The Crucifixion by an Eye Witness. 7th ed. LC 70-186124. (Supplemental Harmonic Ser.: Vol. 4). 107p. 1972. pap. 3.95 (ISBN 0-686-01242-9). Harvey J M.
Harvey, John, jt. auth. see May, William.

Harvey, John F., ed. Church & Synagogue Libraries. LC 80-11736. 299p. 1980. 20.00 (ISBN 0-8108-1304-1). Scarecrow.

Harvey, John W., tr. see Otto, Rudolf.

Harvey, Van A. Handbook of Theological Terms. 1964. pap. 4.95 (ISBN 0-02-085430-7, Collier). Macmillan.

--The Historian & the Believer: The Morality of Historical Knowledge & Christian Belief. LC 80-27941. 320p. 1981. Westminster.

Harvey, William L. Christianity in Action. 232p. 1954. pap. 1.95 (ISBN 0-88243-487-X, 02-0487). Gospel Pub.

Harwell, Delores T., jt. auth. see Harwell, Henry O.

Harwell, Henry O. & Harwell, Delores T. The Creek Verb. 57p. 1981. 6.00x (ISBN 0-940392-03-8). Indian U Pr OK.

Harwood, A. C. Recovery of Man in Childhood. 2nd ed. (Illus.). 212p. 1981. pap. 8.95 (ISBN 0-88010-001-X). Anthroposophic.

Harwood, A. C., tr. & intro. by see Schoer, Karl J.

Has, Von Balthasar U. see Von Balthasar, Has U.

Hasan-Rizvi, S. Muhammad, tr. see Al-Kulayni Ar-Razi.

Hasan-Rokem, Galit & Dundes, Alan, eds. The Wandering Jew: Essays in the Interpretation of a Christian Legend. LC 84-48248. (Illus.). 288p. 1986. 27.50x (ISBN 0-253-36340-3). Ind U Pr.

Hasbrouck, Hypatia. Handbook of Positive Prayer. 160p. 1984. 5.95 (ISBN 0-87159-051-4). Unity School.

Hasbrouck, John B., tr. see De Vogue, Adalbert.

Hasegawa, Sam. Terry Bradshaw. (Sports Superstars Ser.). (Illus.). 1977. pap. 3.95 (ISBN 0-89812-212-0). Creative Ed.

Hasel, Gerhard. New Testament Theology. pap. 5.95 (ISBN 0-8028-1733-5). Eerdmans.

Hasel, Gerhard F. Old Testament Theology: Basic Issues in the Current Debate. rev. ed. 168p. 1975. pap. 5.95 (ISBN 0-8028-1478-6). Eerdmans.

--The Remnant: The History & Theology of the Remnant Idea from Genesis to Isaiah. 3rd ed. (Andrews University Monographs, Studies in Religion: Vol. V). x, 474p. 1980. pap. 10.95 (ISBN 0-943872-05-7). Andrews Univ Pr.

Haselmayer, Louis A. Medieval English Episcopal Registers. (Church Historical Society, London, New Ser.: No. 33). pap. 16.00 (ISBN 0-8115-3157-0). Kraus Repr.

Hashim, A. S. Eleven Surahs Explained. (Islamics Books for Children: Bk. 3). pap. 4.95 (ISBN 0-686-18412-2); pap. 45.00 entire ser. (ISBN 0-686-18413-0). Kazi Pubns.

--Ibadat. (Islamic Books for Children: Bk. 2). pap. 4.95 (ISBN 0-686-18414-9); pap. 40.00 entire ser. (ISBN 0-686-18415-7). Kazi Pubns.

--Iman, Basic Beliefs. (Islamic Books for Children: Bk. 1). pap. 4.95 (ISBN 0-686-18416-5); pap. 45.00 entire ser. (ISBN 0-686-18417-3). Kazi Pubns.

--Islamic Ethics. (Islamic Books for Children: Bk. 7). pap. 4.95 (ISBN 0-686-18404-1); pap. 45.00 entire set (ISBN 0-686-18405-X). Kazi Pubns.

--Life of Prophet Muhammad-I. (Islamic Books for Children: Bk. 4). pap. 4.95 (ISBN 0-686-18410-6); pap. 45.00 entire ser. (ISBN 0-686-18411-4). Kazi Pubns.

--Life of Prophet Muhammad-II. (Islamic Books for Children: Bk 5). pap. 4.95 (ISBN 0-686-18408-4); pap. 45.00 entire ser. (ISBN 0-686-18409-2). Kazi Pubns.

--Stories of Some of the Prophets, Vol. I. (Islamic Books for Children: Bk. 8). pap. 4.95 (ISBN 0-686-18402-5); pap. 45.00 entire series (ISBN 0-686-18403-3). Kazi Pubns.

--Stories of Some of the Prophets, Vol II. (Islamic Books for Children: Bk. 9). pap. 4.95 (ISBN 0-686-18400-9); pap. 45.00 entire series (ISBN 0-686-18401-7). Kazi Pubns.

Hashim Amir-Ali. Message of the Qur'an: Presented in Perspective. LC 73-84906. 1974. 25.00 (ISBN 0-8048-0976-3). C E Tuttle.

Hashmi, A. H. Nationalism, Islam & Pakistan. pap. 14.95 (ISBN 0-317-46108-7). Kazi Pubns.

Hasime, Tanabe. Philosophy As Metanoetics. 224p. 1987. text ed. 40.00 (ISBN 0-520-05490-3). U of Cal Pr.

Haskel, Peter, tr. see Hakeda, Yoshito S.

Haskelevich, B., ed. Introduction to Talmud Study. (Rus.). 400p. 1982. pap. 6.00x (ISBN 0-938666-01-0). CHAMAH Pubs.

Haskelevich, B., tr. from Hebrew. Disputation at Barcelona, Nachmanides(Ramban) With Introduction & Commentaries. Tr. of Vikkuakh Hazamban. (Rus.). (1982) 6.00 (ISBN 0-938666-03-7); pap. 3.75 (1981) (ISBN 0-938666-00-2). CHAMAH Pubs.

Haskell, Edward, ed. Full Circle: The Moral Force of Unified Science. LC 72-84271. (Current Topics of Contemporary Thought Ser.). (Illus.). 270p. (Orig.). 1972. 57.75 (ISBN 0-677-12480-5). Gordon & Breach.

Haskett, M. R., ed. see Haskett, William P.

Haskett, William P. Grandpa Haskett Presents: Original New Christmas Stories for the Young & Young-at-Heart. Haskett, M. R., ed. (Illus.). 20p. (Orig.). 1982. pap. 3.00g (ISBN 0-9609724-0-4). Haskett Spec.

Haskins, David G. Ralph Waldo Emerson. LC 76-122656. 1971. Repr. of 1887 ed. 26.50x (ISBN 0-8046-1305-2, Pub. by Kennikat). Assoc Faculty Pr.

Haslam, Gerald M. Clash of Cultures: The Norwegian Experience with Mormonism, 1842-1920. LC 83-49362. (American University Studies IX (History): Vol. 7). 350p. 1984. text ed. 39.80 (ISBN 0-8204-0179-X). P Lang Pubs.

Hasler, J. Ireland. The Message of Life: Studies in the Epistle of St. John (Missionary Message of the New Testament) 96p. 1949. 3.95 (ISBN 0-87921-013-3). Attic Pr.

Hass, Frank S. De see De Hass, Frank S.

Hassall, Arthur. Mazarin. facs. ed. LC 73-137379. (Select Bibliographies Reprint Ser.). 1903. 17.00 (ISBN 0-8369-5580-3). Ayer Co Pubs.

Hassall, Phillip. I Cannot Hear You, But I Can Hear God. Mandeville, Sylvia, ed. 144p. 1987. pap. 3.95 (ISBN 0-340-38268-6, Pub. by Hodder & Stoughton UK). David & Charles.

Hassan, Farooq. The Concept of State & Law in Islam. LC 80-69038. 321p. (Orig.). 1981. lib. bdg. 29.25 (ISBN 0-8191-1426-X); pap. text ed. 13.75 (ISBN 0-8191-1427-8). U Pr of Amer.

Hassel, David J. City of Wisdom: A Christian View of the American University. 461p. 1983. 18.50 (ISBN 0-8294-0433-3). Loyola.

--Dark Intimacy: Hope for Those in Difficult Prayer Experiences. 176p. (Orig.). 1986. pap. 8.95 (ISBN 0-8091-2818-7). Paulist Pr.

--Radical Prayer. 160p. 1983. 5.95 (ISBN 0-8091-2649-4). Paulist Pr.

Hassel, R. Chris, Jr. Renaissance Drama & the English Church Year. LC 78-24233. (Illus.). xii, 215p. 1979. 18.95x (ISBN 0-8032-2304-8). U of Nebr Pr.

Hassey, Janette. No Time for Silence: Evangelical Women in Public Ministry Around the Turn of the Century. 176p. 1986. pap. 7.95 (ISBN 0-310-29451-7, 12786P). Zondervan.

Hassig, Ross, ed. see Ruiz de Alarcon, Hernando.

Hassing, Arne. Religion & Power: The Case of Methodism in Norway. (Jesse Lee Prize Ser.). (Illus.). 300p. 1980. 15.00 (ISBN 0-915466-03-1). United Meth Archives.

Hastie, W., ed. see Kant, Immanuel.

Hastings, A. A History of African Christianity: 1950-1975. LC 78-16599. (Illus.). 1979. o. p. 49.50 (ISBN 0-521-22212-5); pap. 17.95 (ISBN 0-521-29397-9). Cambridge U Pr.

Hastings, A. W. & Hastings, E., eds. Important Moral Issues. 128p. 1966. pap. 6.95 (ISBN 0-567-22302-7, Pub. by T & T Clark Ltd UK). Fortress.

--Theologians of Our Time. LC 66-73626. 224p. pap. 7.95 (ISBN 0-567-22301-9, Pub. by T & T Clark Ltd UK). Fortress.

Hastings, Adrian. African Christianity. 12p. 1977. 9.95 (ISBN 0-8164-0336-8, AY6700, HarpR). Har-Row.

--Church & Mission in Modern Africa. LC 67-30321. (Orig.). 1967. 25.00 (ISBN 0-8232-0770-6). Fordham.

Hastings, C. B. Introducing Southern Baptists. LC 81-80052. 168p. (Orig.). 1981. pap. 7.95 (ISBN 0-8091-2364-9). Paulist Pr.

Hastings, E., jt. ed. see Hastings, A. W.

Hastings, Edward, jt. ed. see Hastings, James.

Hastings, Gerald L. Publish Good News: A Resource Guide for Self-Publishing Church Groups. (Illus.). 80p. (Orig.). 1986. pap. 6.50 (ISBN 0-937641-01-4). Stone Canyon Pr.

Hastings, James, ed. Dictionary of the Bible. 1963. lib. bdg. 55.00x (ISBN 0-684-15556-7, ScribT). Scribner.

--The Encyclopedia of Religion & Ethics, 12 vols. 1926. Set. 599.95 (ISBN 0-567-06514-6, Pub. by T&T Clark Ltd Uk). Fortress.

Hastings, James & Hastings, Edward, eds. Speaker's Bible, 18 vols. 1979. 275.00 (ISBN 0-8010-4036-1). Baker Bk.

Hastings, Robert J. Glorious Is Thy Name! LC 85-26948. 1986. 7.95 (ISBN 0-8054-7230-4). Broadman.

Hastings, Thomas. Dissertation on Musical Taste. LC 68-16237. (Music Ser.). 228p. 1974. Repr. of 1822 ed. lib. bdg. 35.00 (ISBN 0-306-71085-4). Da Capo.

--Dissertation on Musical Taste. LC 6-18360. (American Studies). 1968. Repr. of 1853 ed. 24.00 (ISBN 0-384-21750-8). Johnson Repr.

--The History of Forty Choirs. LC 72-1620. Repr. of 1854 ed. 18.50 (ISBN 0-404-08313-7). AMS Pr.

Hata, Gohei, tr. see Feldman, Louis.

Hatch, Edwin. The Influence of Greek Ideas & Usages Upon the Christian Church. 384p. 1972. Repr. of 1891 ed. lib. bdg. 21.50 (ISBN 0-8337-1595-X). B Franklin.

--The Influence of Greek Ideas on Christianity. 11.75 (ISBN 0-8446-0683-9). Peter Smith.

--The Organization of the Early Christian Churches: Eight Lectures Delivered Before the University of Oxford in the Year 1880 on the Foundation of the Late Rev. John Bampton, M. A., Canon of Salisbury. LC 77-183696. (Research & Source Works Ser). 222p. 1972. Repr. of 1881 ed. lib. bdg. 18.50 (ISBN 0-8337-4163-2). B Franklin.

Hatch, Edwin & Redpath, Henry A. A Concordance to the Septuagint & Other Greek Versions of the Old Testament (Including the Apocryphal Books), 3 vols. in 2. 1088p. 1983. Repr. of 1906 ed. Set. 75.00 (ISBN 0-8010-4270-4). Baker Bk.

Hatch, Jane M., ed. American Book of Days. LC 78-16239. 1212p. 1978. 73.00 (ISBN 0-8242-0593-6). Wilson.

Hatch, Nathan O. & Noll, Mark A., eds. The Bible in America: Essays in Cultural History. LC 81-18751. 1982. 22.50x (ISBN 0-19-503099-0); pap. 6.95 (ISBN 0-19-503100-8). Oxford U Pr.

Hatch, W. H. Pauline Idea of Faith in Its Relation to Jewish & Hellenistic Religion. (Harvard Theological Studies). 1917. 11.00 (ISBN 0-527-01002-2). Kraus Repr.

Hatch, W. H., jt. auth. see Edmunds, C. C.

Hatch, William H. Greek & Syrian Miniatures in Jerusalem. (Illus.). 1931. 15.00x (ISBN 0-910956-04-9). Medieval Acad.

Hatchell, L. F. Apocalypse: World War III, Vol. I. (Illus.). 160p. 1980. pap. 3.95x (ISBN 0-940532-02-6). AOG.

Hatcher, John. Ali's Dream: The Story of Baha'u'llah. (Illus.). 260p. 14.95 (ISBN 0-85398-092-6); pap. 8.95 (ISBN 0-85398-093-4). G Ronald Pub.

--From the Auroral Darkness: The Life & Poetry of Robert Hayden. (Illus.). 368p. 23.50 (ISBN 0-85398-188-4); pap. 12.95 (ISBN 0-85398-189-2). G Ronald Pub.

Hatcher, John S. The Purpose of Physical Reality: The Kingdom of Names. Fisher, Betty J. & Hill, Richard A., eds. 250p. 1987. pap. 12.00 (ISBN 0-87743-208-2). Baha'i.

Hatcher, W. John Jasper: Negro Philosopher & Preacher. 59.95 (ISBN 0-8490-0452-7). Gordon Pr.

Hatcher, William & Martin, James D. The Baha'i Faith: The Emerging Global Religion. LC 84-42743. 224p. 1985. 14.45 (ISBN 0-06-065441-4, HarpR). Har-Row.

Hatcher, William E. John Jasper, the Unmatched Negro Philosopher & Preacher. LC 71-88413. Repr. of 1908 ed. 22.50x (ISBN 0-8371-1842-5, HAJ&, Pub. by Negro U Pr). Greenwood.

Hatchett, Marion. Commentary on the American Prayer Book. 608p. 1981. 32.50 (ISBN 0-8164-0206-X, HarpR). Har-Row.

Hatchett, Marion J. The Making of the First American Book of Common Prayer. 224p. 1982. 19.95 (ISBN 0-8164-0512-3, HarpR). Har-Row.

--Sanctifying Life, Time & Space: An Introduction to Liturgical Study. 1976. (HarpR); pap. 8.95 (ISBN 0-8164-2396-2). Har-Row.

Hatchett, Marion J., jt. auth. see LeCroy, Anne K.

Hateley, B. J. Telling Your Story, Exploring Your Faith. Lambert, Herbert, ed. LC 85-13307. 120p. (Orig.). 1985. pap. 8.95 (ISBN 0-8272-3626-3). CBP.

Hatengdi, M. U. Nityananda: The Divine Presence. Navarro, Aurelia, ed. LC 84-60099. (Illus.). 192p. (Orig.). 1984. pap. 10.95 (ISBN 0-915801-00-0). Rudra Pr.

Hatengdi, M. U. & Chetanananda, Swami. Nitya Sutras: The Revelations of Nityananda from the Chidakash Gita. (Illus.). 224p. (Orig.). 1985. pap. 11.95 (ISBN 0-915801-02-7). Rudra Pr.

Hater, Robert J. The Ministry Explosion. 96p. (Orig.). 1979. pap. 3.25 (ISBN 0-697-01709-5). Wm C Brown.

Hatfield, Edwin F. The Poets of the Church. LC 77-91533. 1977. Repr. of 1884 ed. lib. bdg. 45.00 (ISBN 0-89341-195-7). Longwood Pub Group.

--Poets of the Church: A Series of Biographical Sketches of Hymn-Writers, with Notes on Their Hymns. 1979. Repr. of 1884 ed. 110.00x (ISBN 0-8103-4291-X). Gale.

Hatfield, Mark, et al. Confessing Christ & Doing Politics. Skillen, James, ed. LC 80-71233. 100p. (Orig.). 1982. pap. 3.95 (ISBN 0-936456-02-7). Assn Public Justice.

--What about the Russians? A Christian Approach to US-Soviet Conflict. Brown, Dale W., ed. 144p. 1984. pap. 6.95 (ISBN 0-87178-751-2). Brethren.

Hathaway, Richard D. Sylvester Judd's New England. LC 81-17854. (Illus.). 362p. 1982. 24.95x (ISBN 0-271-00307-3). Pa St U Pr.

Hatherly, S. G. Treatise on Byzantine Music. LC 77-75226. 1977. Repr. of 1892 ed. lib. bdg. 20.00 (ISBN 0-89341-071-3). Longwood Pub Group.

Hathorn, Richmond. Greek Mythology. 1977. 22.00x (ISBN 0-8156-6048-0, Am U Beirut). Syracuse U Pr.

Hathrill, Robert. The Bell Ringer. 1983. 8.95 (ISBN 0-533-05631-4). Vantage.

Hati, Aten. Astro-Change. 53p. 1981. pap. 5.00 (ISBN 0-935146-64-4). Morningland.

Hattenberg, Ludwig Van see Van Hattenberg, Ludwig.

Hatton, Howard, jt. auth. see Ellingworth, Paul.

Hatton, Thomas J. Joseph of Arimathea: An Easter Play. 1980. 4.25 (ISBN 0-89536-417-4, 1013). CSS of Ohio.

--A Quiet Night: A Play for Christmas. 24p. (Orig.). 1980. pap. text ed. 5.25 (ISBN 0-89536-438-7, 1703). CSS of Ohio.

--Rabbit Christmas. (Orig.). 1982. pap. 2.95 (ISBN 0-937172-40-5). JLJ Pubs.

Hatzfeld, Adolphe. Saint Augustine. LC 71-168252. 155p. 1975. Repr. of 1903 ed. 16.00 (ISBN 0-404-03155-2). AMS Pr.

Hatznung, Ruth. Martin Luther: Man for Whom God Had Great Plans. 1974. pap. 1.95 (ISBN 0-8100-0060-1, 16-0757). Northwest Pub.

Hauber, Anajean. A Way of the Cross for the Separated & Divorced. (Illus.). 45p. (Orig.). 1985. pap. text ed. 2.95 (ISBN 0-86716-050-0). St Anthony Mess Pr.

Hauck, Karl, ed. Fruehmittelaterliche Studien, Vol. 11. (Illus.). 1977. 89.60x (ISBN 3-11-007076-6). De Gruyter.

Hauck, Paul A. Marriage Is a Loving Business. LC 77-2202. 116p. 1977. pap. 6.95 (ISBN 0-664-24137-9). Westminster.

--Overcoming Worry & Fear. LC 74-20629. 112p. 1975. pap. 6.95 (ISBN 0-664-24811-X). Westminster.

--The Three Faces of Love. LC 83-10468. 174p. 1984. pap. 8.95 (ISBN 0-664-24486-6). Westminster.

Hauer, Christian E. & Young, William A. An Introduction to the Bible: A Journey into Three Worlds. (Illus.). 400p. 1985. text ed. 29.67 (ISBN 0-13-478488-X). P-H.

Hauerwas, Stanley. Against the Nations: War & Survival in a Liberal Society. 240p. (Orig.). 1985. 19.95 (ISBN 0-86683-957-7, AY8549, HarpR). Har-Row.

--Character & the Christian Life: A Study in Theological Ethics. LC 85-5873. (Monograph Series in Religion). 265p. 1985. pap. text ed. 10.95 (ISBN 0-939980-10-X). Trinity U Pr.

--A Community of Character: Toward a Constructive Christian Social Ethic. LC 80-53072. 320p. 1981. pap. text ed. 7.95 (ISBN 0-268-00735-7, NDP 265). U of Notre Dame Pr.

--A Community of Character: Toward a Constructive Christian Social Ethic. LC 80-53072. 320p. 1981. text ed. 20.00 (ISBN 0-268-00733-0). U of Notre Dame Pr.

--The Peaceable Kingdom: A Primer in Christian Ethics. LC 83-14711. 224p. 1983. text ed. 17.95x (ISBN 0-268-01553-8, 85-15538); pap. text ed. 7.95x (ISBN 0-268-01554-6, 85-15546). U of Notre Dame Pr.

--Should War Be Eliminated? Philosophical & Theological Investigations. LC 84-60236. (Pere Marquette Lecture Ser.). 75p. 1984. 7.95 (ISBN 0-87462-539-4). Marquette.

--Suffering Presence: Theological Reflections on Medicine, the Mentally Handicapped & the Church. LC 85-40603. 224p. (Orig.). 1986. text ed. 19.95x (ISBN 0-268-01721-2, 85-17211, Dist. by Har-Row); pap. text ed. 9.95 (ISBN 0-268-01722-0, 85-17229). U of Notre Dame Pr.

--Vision & Virtue: Essays in Christian Ethical Reflection. LC 80-54877. 264p. 1981. text ed. 7.95 (ISBN 0-268-01921-5). U of Notre Dame Pr.

Hauerwas, Stanley & Bondi, Richard. Truthfulness & Tragedy: Further Investigations in Christian Ethics. LC 76-30425. 1977. 18.95x (ISBN 0-268-01831-6); pap. text ed. 9.95 (ISBN 0-268-01832-4). U of Notre Dame Pr.

Hauerwas, Stanley & MacIntyre, Alasdair, eds. Revisions: Changing Perspectives in Moral Philosophy. (Revisions Ser.). 320p. 1983. text ed. 24.95 (ISBN 0-268-01614-3); pap. text ed. 9.95 (ISBN 0-268-01617-8). U of Notre Dame Pr.

Haug, Martin. The Parsis. 427p. 1978. Repr. of 1878 ed. 25.00 (ISBN 0-89684-157-X). Orient Bk Dist.

Haug, Martin, ed. & tr. The Aitareya Brahmanam of Rigveda: Containing the Earliest Speculations of the Brahmans on the Meaning of the Sacrificial Prayers, & on the Origin, Performance & Sense of the Rites of the Vedic Religion. LC 73-3830. (Sacred Books of the Hindus: Extra Vol. 4). Repr. of 1922 ed. 27.50 (ISBN 0-404-57848-9). AMS Pr.

Haugan, Randolph, ed. Christmas, Vol. 47. LC 32-30914. 64p. 1977. 14.50 (ISBN 0-8066-8951-X, 17-0115); pap. 6.95 (ISBN 0-8066-8950-1, 17-0114). Augsburg.

Haugan, Randolph E. My Confirmation Book. (Illus.). 1942. pap. 2.50 ea. (ISBN 0-8066-0078-0, 10-4631). Augsburg.

Haugan, Randolph E., ed. Christmas: An American Annual of Christmas Literature & Art, Vol. 46. LC 32-30914. 64p. 1976. 14.50 (ISBN 0-8066-8948-X, 17-0113); pap. 6.95 (ISBN 0-8066-8947-1, 17-0112). Augsburg.

--Christmas: An American Annual of Christmas Literature & Art, Vol. 48. LC 32-30914. (Illus.). 64p. 1978. 14.50 (ISBN 0-8066-8953-6, 17-0117); pap. 6.95 (ISBN 0-8066-8952-8, 17-0116). Augsburg.

--Christmas: An American Annual of Christmas Literature & Art, Vol. 49. LC 32-30914. (Illus.). 64p. 1979. 14.50 (ISBN 0-8066-8955-2, 17-0119); pap. 6.95 (ISBN 0-8066-8954-4, 17-0118). Augsburg.

Haugen, Einar, ed. & tr. see Dumezil, Georges.

Haugerud, Joann. The Word for Us, Gospels of John & Mark, Epistles to the Romans, & the Galations. LC 77-83418. 1977. 7.95 (ISBN 0-9603042-3-1). Coalition Women-Relig.

Haugh, Kenneth & McKay, William J. Christian Caregiving: A Way of Life, Leaders Guide. LC 86-10931. 128p. (Orig.). 1986. pap. 8.95 (ISBN 0-8066-2224-5, 10-1104). Augsburg.

Haughey, John. Personal Values in Public Policy. LC 79-84401. (Woodstock Studies: No. 3). 288p. (Orig.). 1979. pap. 6.95 (ISBN 0-8091-2201-4). Paulist Pr.

Haughey, John C. Conspiracy of God: The Holy Spirit in Men. LC 73-80730. 120p. 1976. pap. 2.95 (ISBN 0-385-11558-X, Im). Doubleday.

--The Faith That Does Justice: Examining the Christian Sources for Social Change. LC 77-74578. 312p. (Orig.). 1977. pap. 8.95 (ISBN 0-8091-2026-7). Paulist Pr.

--Holy Use of Money: Personal Finance in Light of Christian Faith. LC 85-29213. 288p. 1986. 16.95 (ISBN 0-385-23448-1). Doubleday.

Haught, John F. The Cosmic Adventure: Science, Religion & the Quest for Purpose. LC 83-82026. (Orig.). 1984. pap. 7.95 (ISBN 0-8091-2599-4). Paulist Pr.

--Religion & Self-Acceptance: A Study of the Relationship Between Belief in God & the Desire to Know. LC 80-5872. 195p. 1980. lib. bdg. 24.75 (ISBN 0-8191-1296-8); pap. text ed. 10.50 (ISBN 0-8191-1297-6). U Pr of Amer.

--What Is God? How to Think about the Divine. 160p. (Orig.). 1986. pap. 7.95 (ISBN 0-8091-2754-7). Paulist Pr.

Haughton, Rosemary. The Catholic Thing. 1980. pap. 8.95 (ISBN 0-87243-116-9). Templegate.

--The Passionate God. LC 81-80049. 352p. 1981. pap. 9.95 (ISBN 0-8091-2383-5). Paulist Pr.

--The Re-Creation of Eve. 1985. pap. 8.95 (ISBN 0-87243-135-5). Templegate.

Haugk, Kenneth C. Christian Caregiving: A Way of Life. LC 84-24341. (Orig.). 1984. pap. 7.95 (ISBN 0-8066-2123-0, 10-1103). Augsburg.

Hauglid, R. Norwegian Stave Churches. (Illus.). 1977. 22.00x (ISBN 8-2090-0937-0, N497). Vanous.

Haupt, Garry E., ed. see More, St. Thomas.

Haureau, Barthelemy. Bernard Delicieux et l'Inquisition Albigeoise, 1300-1320. LC 78-63180. (Heresies of the Early Christian & Medieval Era: Second Ser.). Repr. of 1877 ed. 31.00 (ISBN 0-404-16223-1). AMS Pr.

Haury, Samuel S. Letters Concerning the Spread of the Gospel. 50p. 1982. pap. 3.95 (ISBN 0-8361-1252-0). Herald Pr.

Hausdorff, David M. A Book of Jewish Curiosities. LC 55-11366. 1979. pap. 5.95 (ISBN 0-8197-0466-0). Bloch.

Hauser, Judith A. Jesuit Rings from Fort Michilimackinac & Other European Contact Sites. LC 83-100548. (Archaeological Completion Report Ser.: No. 5). (Illus.). 69p. (Orig.). 1983. pap. 5.00 (ISBN 0-911872-45-0). Mackinac Island.

Hauser, Richard J. In His Spirit. LC 81-83187. 128p. (Orig.). 1982. pap. 5.95 (ISBN 0-8091-2421-1). Paulist Pr.

Hauser, Roger L. Activities with Senior Adults. 1987. 7.95 (ISBN 0-8054-3901-3). Broadman.

Hauser, Walter, jt. auth. see White, Hugh G.

Hauser, Walter see White, Hugh G. & Hauser, Walter.

Hausherr, I. Penthos. 24.95 (ISBN 0-87907-853-7); pap. 7.95 (ISBN 0-87907-953-3). Cistercian Pubns.

Hausherr, Irenee. The Name of Jesus. Cummings, Charles, tr. LC 77-10559. (Cistercian Studies: No. 44). 358p. 1978. 15.95 (ISBN 0-87907-844-8); pap. 8.00 (ISBN 0-87907-944-4). Cistercian Pubns.

Hausman, Gerald. Meditations With Animals: A Native American Bestiary. LC 86-70259. (Meditations With Ser.). (Illus.). 141p. (Orig.). 1986. pap. 6.95 (ISBN 0-939680-26-2). Bear & Co.

Hausmann, William J. Karl Barth's Doctrine of Election. LC 74-81812. 1969. 5.95 (ISBN 0-8022-2281-1). Philos Lib.

Hausmann, Winifred W. A Guide to Love-Powered Living. LC 85-72282. 192p. (Orig.). 1986. pap. 7.95 (ISBN 0-87516-560-5). De Vorss.

--How to Live Life Victoriously. 160p. 1982. 5.95 (ISBN 0-87159-060-3). Unity School.

--Your God-Given Potential. LC 77-80458. 1978. 5.95 (ISBN 0-87159-182-0). Unity School.

Hausner, John H. Sebastian: The Essence of My Soul. (Illus.). 1982. 5.95 (ISBN 0-533-05510-5). Vantage.

Haussleiter, I., ed. see Victorinus, Saint.

Haut, Irwin H. Divorce in Jewish Law & Life. (Studies in Jewish Jurisprudence Ser.: Vol. 5). 160p. 1983. 12.50 (ISBN 0-87203-110-1); pap. 9.75 (ISBN 0-87203-114-4). Hermon.

--The Talmud As Law Or Literature: An Analysis of David W. Halivni's Mekorot Umasorot. x, 83p. pap. 6.95 (ISBN 0-87203-107-1). Hermon.

Havell, Ernest B. The History of Aryan Rule in India. LC 72-900073. (Illus.). 613p. 1972. Repr. of 1918 ed. 22.50x (ISBN 0-89684-400-5). Orient Bk Dist.

Haven, Gilbert. Sermons, Speeches, Letters on Slavery & Its War 1850-1868. LC 74-82197. (Anti-Slavery Crusade in America Ser). 1969. Repr. of 1869 ed. 26.00 (ISBN 0-405-00637-3). Ayer Co Pubs.

Havener, Ivan & Karris, Robert J. First Thessalonians, Philippians, Philemon, Second Thessalonians, Colossians, Ephesians, No. 8. (Collegeville Bible Commentary Ser.). (Illus.). 112p. 1983. pap. 2.95 (ISBN 0-8146-1308-X). Liturgical Pr.

Havener, Ivan, et al, trs. Early Monastic Rules: The Rules of the Fathers & the Regula Orientalis. LC 82-51. 88p. (Orig.). 1982. pap. 5.95 (ISBN 0-8146-1251-2). Liturgical Pr.

Havens, Joseph. The Journal of a College Student. LC 65-19208. (Orig.). pap. 2.50x (ISBN 0-87574-141-X). Pendle Hill.

Havens, Teresina R. Standards of Success. 1983. pap. 2.50x (ISBN 0-87574-043-X, 043). Pendle Hill.

Haver, Ted. Throw Away Society. 140p. (Orig.). 1986. pap. write for info. (ISBN 0-914981-13-7). Paradigm ID.

Havergal, F. R. Morning Bells. pap. 2.25 (ISBN 0-685-88387-6). Reiner.

--My King. pap. 2.25 (ISBN 0-685-88388-4). Reiner.

--Royal Bounty. pap. 1.95 (ISBN 0-685-88391-4). Reiner.

Havergal, Frances R. Kept for the Master's Use. (Large Print Christian Classic Ser.). 1982. 11.95 (ISBN 0-87983-290-8). Keats.

--Opened Treasures. LC 62-21063. 1962. 7.95 (ISBN 0-87213-320-6). Loizeaux.

Havergel, Frances. Kept for the Master's Use. 120p. 1986. pap. 4.95 (ISBN 0-89693-279-6). Victor Bks.

Havner, Vance. Best of Vance Havner. (Best Ser.). pap. 3.95 (ISBN 0-8010-4234-8). Baker Bk.

--Consider Jesus. 104p. 1987. pap. 4.95 (ISBN 0-8010-4306-9). Baker Bk.

--Day by Day: With Vance Havner. 272p. 1984. pap. 5.95 (ISBN 0-8010-4279-8). Baker Bk.

--Don't Miss Your Miracle. 74p. 1984. pap. 4.95 (ISBN 0-8010-4280-1). Baker Bk.

--Lord of What's Left. rev. ed. 124p. 1985. pap. 4.95 (ISBN 0-8010-4286-0). Baker Bk.

--Messages on Revival. (Pulpit Library). 128p. 1983. pap. 4.50 (ISBN 0-8010-4275-5). Baker Bk.

--Moments of Decision. 128p. 1980. 8.95 (ISBN 0-8007-1091-6). Revell.

--Moments of Decision: Guidelines for the Most Important Choices of Your Life. 128p. 1985. pap. 4.95 (ISBN 0-8010-4287-9). Baker Bk.

--On This Rock I Stand. 160p. 1986. pap. 5.95 (ISBN 0-8010-4296-8). Baker Bk.

--Pepper & Salt. (Pulpit Library). 128p. 1983. pap. 4.95 (ISBN 0-8010-4276-3). Baker Bk.

--Playing Marbles with Diamonds: And Other Messages for America. 80p. 1985. text ed. 7.95 (ISBN 0-8010-4290-9). Baker Bk.

--Pleasant Paths. (Direction Bks.). 96p. 1983. pap. 2.95 (ISBN 0-8010-4268-2). Baker Bk.

--The Vance Havner Devotional Treasury: Daily Meditations for a Year. (Direction Books). 192p. 1981. pap. 4.50 (ISBN 0-8010-4257-7). Baker Bk.

--The Vance Havner Quotebook. 208p. 1986. 9.95 (ISBN 0-8010-4299-2). Baker Bk.

--Vance Havner Treasury. Hester, Dennis, compiled by. 264p. Date not set. 9.95 (ISBN 0-8010-4315-8). Baker Bk.

--When God Breaks Through: And Other Challenging Talks. 96p. 1987. Repr. price not set. Baker Bk.

Havran, Martin J. The Catholics in Caroline England. 1962. 17.50x (ISBN 0-8047-0112-1). Stanford U Pr.

Hawkes, John D. Art of Achieving Success. 128p. 1971. pap. 2.95 (ISBN 0-89036-008-1). Hawkes Pub Inc.

--Book of Mormon Digest. 240p. 1966. pap. 4.95 (ISBN 0-89036-010-3). Hawkes Pub Inc.

--Doctrine & Covenants & Pearl of Great Price Digest. 1977. pap. text ed. 4.95 (ISBN 0-89036-100-2). Hawkes Pub Inc.

--New Testament Digest. 160p. 1968. pap. 3.95 (ISBN 0-89036-014-6). Hawkes Pub Inc.

Hawkes, Laura M. Favorite Christmas Stories. 64p. 1973. pap. 2.50 (ISBN 0-89036-015-4). Hawkes Pub Inc.

Hawkes, Peter, tr. see Ishii, Yoneo.

Hawkin, David. Christ & Modernity: Christian Self-Understanding in a Technological Age. (Studies in Religion: Vol. 17). 200p. 1985. pap. text ed. 12.95x (ISBN 0-88920-193-5, Pub. by Wilfrid Laurier Canada). Humanities.

Hawkins, tr. see St Jerome.

Hawkins, Anne O. Archetypes of Conversion: The Spiritual Autobiographies of St. Augustine, John Bunyan, & Thomas Merton. LC 83-46156. 192p. 1985. 25.00 (ISBN 0-8387-5079-6). Bucknell U Pr.

Hawkins, C. The Mind of Whittier: A Study of Whittier's Fundamental Religious Ideas. LC 73-6984. (American Literature Ser., No. 49). 1973. Repr. of 1904 ed. lib. bdg. 39.95x (ISBN 0-8383-1700-6). Haskell.

Hawkins, C. S., jt. auth. see Taylor, Jack R.

Hawkins, Colin. Witches. LC 85-40425. (Illus.). 32p. 1985. 7.45 (ISBN 0-382-09132-9). Silver.

Hawkins, Denis J. The Essentials of Theism. LC 72-9373. 151p. 1973. Repr. of 1949 ed. lib. bdg. 22.50x (ISBN 0-8371-6579-2, HAET). Greenwood.

Hawkins, Elza M. From Now to Pentecost: A Mirrored View of Development in Christianity. 260p. (Orig.). 1982. pap. 11.00 (ISBN 971-10-0038-5, Pub. by New Day Philippines). Cellar.

Hawkins, Judith, jt. auth. see Rogers, Maggie.

Hawkins, O. S. After Revival Comes. LC 81-66090. 1981. pap. 4.95 (ISBN 0-8054-6231-7). Broadman.

--Clues to a Successful Life. LC 82-71561. (Orig.). 1982. pap. 6.95 (ISBN 0-8054-5515-9). Broadman.

--Tracing the Rainbow Through the Rain. LC 85-6610. 1985. 7.95 (ISBN 0-8054-5020-3). Broadman.

--Where Angels Fear to Tread. LC 83-24022. 1984. pap. 4.95 (ISBN 0-8054-5538-8). Broadman.

Hawkins, Peter S. Getting Nowhere: Christian Hope & Utopian Dream. LC 85-12758. 133p. (Orig.). 1985. pap. 8.95 (ISBN 0-936384-28-X). Cowley Pubns.

Hawkins, Peter S., ed. Civitas: Christian Ideas of the City. (Scholars Press Studies in the Humanities). 143p. 1986. 20.95 (ISBN 0-89130-987-X, 00-01-10). Scholars Pr GA.

Hawkins, Robert L. A Pastor's Primer for Premarital Guidance. 1978. pap. 3.95 (ISBN 0-9607764-0-0). R L Hawkins.

Hawkins, Robert O., Jr., jt. auth. see Moses, A. Elfin.

Hawkins, Thomas R. The Unsuspected Power of the Psalms. LC 84-51828. 128p. (Orig.). 1985. pap. 5.95 (ISBN 0-8358-0499-2). Upper Room.

Hawkins, Tomas. Homiletica Practica. 1986. Repr. of 1985 ed. 1.95 (ISBN 0-311-42041-9). Casa Bautista.

Hawkinson, Eric G. Images in Covenant Beginnings. (Illus.). 1968. 3.95 (ISBN 0-910452-04-0). Covenant.

Hawkinson, James R., ed. Bound to Be Free. 150p. 1975. 6.95 (ISBN 0-910452-40-7); pap. 5.45 (ISBN 0-910452-25-3). Covenant.

--Come, Let Us Praise Him. 1985. pap. 3.95 (ISBN 0-910452-57-1). Covenant.

Hawkridge, Emma. Indian Gods & Kings: The Story of a Living Past. facs. ed. LC 68-24853. (Essay Index Reprint Ser.). 1935. 21.50 (ISBN 0-8369-0521-0). Ayer Co Pubs.

--Wisdom Tree. LC 72-128257. (Essay Index Reprint Ser.). 1945. 33.00 (ISBN 0-8369-1881-9). Ayer Co Pubs.

Hawley. The True Confessions of a Sunday School Teacher. 1983. 3.95 (ISBN 0-88207-285-4). Victor Bks.

Hawley, Charles A. Critical Examination of the Peshitta Version of the Book of Ezra. LC 24-1925. (Columbia University. Contributions to Oriental History & Philology: No. 8). Repr. of 1922 ed. 12.50 (ISBN 0-404-50538-4). AMS Pr.

Hawley, Gloria H. Frankly Feminine: God's Idea of Womanhood. LC 81-50348. 128p. (Orig.). 1981. pap. 3.50 (ISBN 0-87239-455-7, 2969). Standard Pub.

Hawley, John S. At Play with Krishna: Pilgrimage Dramas from Brindavan. LC 80-8552. (Illus.). 360p. 1985. 37.00x (ISBN 0-691-06470-9); pap. 10.95x (ISBN 0-691-01419-1). Princeton U Pr.

Hawley, John S. & Wulff, Donna M., eds. The Divine Consort: Radha & the Goddesses of India. LC 86-47759. (Illus.). 432p. 1987. pap. 11.95 (ISBN 0-8070-1303-X, BP-734). Beacon Pr.

Hawley, Monroe E. Searching for a Better Way. 1980. pap. 5.50 (ISBN 0-89137-525-2). Quality Pubns.

Haworth, Peter. English Hymns & Ballads. 1927. lib. bdg. 16.50 (ISBN 0-8414-4975-9). Folcroft.

Hawthorne, Minnie. Here We Go Again Lord. 1982. 4.50 (ISBN 0-8062-1659-X). Carlton.

Hawthorne, Nathaniel. Tanglewood Tales. (Classics Ser.). (Illus.). 1968. pap. 1.25 (ISBN 0-8049-0175-9, CL-175). Airmont.

--Wonder Book. (Classics Ser.). pap. 1.25 (ISBN 0-8049-0118-X, CL-118). Airmont.

--A Wonder Book & Tanglewood Tales. Charvat, William, et al, eds. LC 77-150221. (Centenary Edition of the Works of Nathaniel Hawthorne Ser.: Vol. 7). (Illus.). 476p. 1972. 25.00 (ISBN 0-8142-0158-X). Ohio St U Pr.

Hawthorne, Steven C., jt. ed. see Winter, Ralph D.

Hawting, G. R. The First Dynasty of Islam: The Umayyad Caliphate A.D. 661-750. 160p. 1986. text ed. 24.95x (ISBN 0-8093-1324-3). S Ill U Pr.

Hay, Denys. The Church in Italy in the Fifteenth Century. LC 76-47409. (Birkbeck Lectures: 1971). 1977. 37.50 (ISBN 0-521-21532-3). Cambridge U Pr.

Hay, Hope. The Quakers. 1985. 13.00x (ISBN 0-7062-4025-1, Pub. by Ward Lock Educ Co Ltd). State Mutual Bk.

Hay, Louise L. Heal Your Body. rev. ed. 48p. 1984. pap. 3.00 (ISBN 0-937611-00-X). Hay House.

--I Love My Body. 80p. 1985. pap. 5.00 (ISBN 0-937611-02-6). Hay House.

--You Can Heal Your Life. 224p. (Orig.). 1984. lib. bdg. 10.00 (ISBN 0-317-52419-4); pap. 10.00 (ISBN 0-937611-01-8). Hay House.

Hay, Malcolm. The Roots of Christian Anti-Semitism. 356p. 10.00 (ISBN 0-686-95112-3). ADL.

Hayden, Amos S. Early History of the Disciples in the Western Reserve, Ohio; with Biographical Sketches of the Principal Agents in Their Religious Movement. LC 76-38449. (Religion in America, Ser. 2). 480p. 1972. Repr. of 1875 ed. 32.00 (ISBN 0-405-04068-7). Ayer Co Pubs.

Hayden, Edwin. Beloved Sufferer. 144p. 1987. pap. 5.95 (ISBN 0-87403-236-9, 3178). Standard Pub.

Hayden, Edwin V. Preaching Through the Bible. 2nd ed. LC 81-82987. 557p. 1981. pap. 8.95 (ISBN 0-89900-145-9). College Pr Pub.

Hayden, Eric. God's Answer for Fear. LC 85-70873. 1986. pap. 2.95 (ISBN 0-88270-581-4). Bridge Pub.

--A History of Spurgeons Tabernacle. 1971. 5.95 (ISBN 0-686-09091-8). Pilgrim Pubns.

Hayden, Eric W. All-Occasion Sermon Outlines. (Sermon Outline Ser.). pap. 2.50 (ISBN 0-8010-4206-2). Baker Bk.

--Letting the Lion Loose. 1984. pap. 3.95 (ISBN 0-907927-05-X). Pilgrim Pubns.

--Searchlight on Spurgeon: Spurgeon Speaks for Himself. 1973. pap. 3.50 (ISBN 0-686-09108-6). Pilgrim Pubns.

--Traveller's Guide to Spurgeon Country. 1974. pap. 1.95 (ISBN 0-686-10527-3). Pilgrim Pubns.

Hayden, Marshall. God's Plan for Church Leadership: Leader's Guide. LC 82-3378. 64p. (Orig.). 1982. pap. 1.95 (ISBN 0-87239-567-7, 39986). Standard Pub.

--Two Hundred Stewardship Meditations. 112p. (Orig.). 1984. pap. 3.95 (ISBN 0-87239-780-7, 3034). Standard Pub.

Haydon, Albert E. Biography of the Gods. LC 74-37848. (Essay Index Reprint Ser.). Repr. of 1941 ed. 19.00 (ISBN 0-8369-2595-5). Ayer Co Pubs.

Haydon, Albert E., ed. Modern Trends in World-Religions. facs. ed. LC 68-29214. (Essay Index Reprint Ser). 1934. 18.00 (ISBN 0-8369-0522-9). Ayer Co Pubs.

Haye, Beverly La see La Haye, Beverly.

Haye, Tim La see LaHaye, Tim.

Hayes & Hook. Meu Livro de Historias Biblicas. (Portugese Bks.). Tr. of My Book of Bible Stories. (Port.). 1979. 3.00 (ISBN 0-8297-0758-1). Life Pubs Intl.

Hayes, A. J. & Gowland, D. A. Scottish Methodism in the Early Victorian Period: The Scottish Correspondence of the Reverend Jabez Bunting, 1800-1857. 143p. 1981. 20.00x (ISBN 0-85224-412-6, Pub. by Edinburgh U Pr Scotland). Columbia U Pr.

Hayes, A. J. & Gowland, D. A., eds. Scottish Methodism in the Early Victorian Period: The Scottish Correspondence of the Rev. Jabez Bunting 1800-57. 1981. 40.00x (ISBN 0-85224-412-6, Pub. by Edinburgh Univ England). State Mutual Bk.

Hayes, Albert & Laughlin, J., eds. A Wreath of Christmas Poems. LC 72-80975. 32p. 1972. pap. 1.95 (ISBN 0-8112-0459-6, NDP347). New Directions.

Hayes, Bartlett. Tradition Becomes Innovation: Modern Religious Architecture in America. LC 82-18581. (Illus.). 176p. 1982. 27.50 (ISBN 0-8298-0635-0); pap. 12.95 (ISBN 0-8298-0624-5). Pilgrim NY.

Hayes, Bernard. Love in Action: Reflections on Christian Service. 120p. (Orig.). pap. 5.95 (ISBN 0-914544-57-8). Living Flame Pr.

--To Live As Jesus Did. new ed. 128p. (Orig.). 1981. pap. 2.95 (ISBN 0-914544-35-7). Living Flame Pr.

--Who Is This God You Pray To. 96p. (Orig.). 1981. pap. 2.95 (ISBN 0-914544-41-1). Living Flame Pr.

Hayes, Carlton J. Christianity & Western Civilization. LC 83-5680. vii, 63p. 1983. Repr. of 1954 ed. lib. bdg. 22.50x (ISBN 0-313-23962-2, HACW). Greenwood.

Hayes, Dan. Fireseeds of Spiritual Awakening. 144p. 1983. pap. 5.95 (ISBN 0-86605-130-9). Campus Crusade.

Hayes, Edward J., et al. Catholicism & Reason. (Catholicism Catechism Ser.). 256p. (YA) 1981. pap. 5.95 (ISBN 0-913382-23-X, 103-14); tchr's manual 3.00 (ISBN 0-913382-25-6, 103-15). Prow Bks-Franciscan.

--Catholicism & Society. (Catholicism Catechism Ser.). 1982. pap. 5.95 (ISBN 0-913382-26-4, 103-16); tchr's manual 3.00 (ISBN 0-913382-27-2, 103-17). Prow Bks-Franciscan.

Hayes, Edward L. The Focused Life. 96p. 1986. 4.95 (ISBN 0-8010-4297-6). Baker Bk.

Hayes, Gloria L. God Provides. 64p. 1986. 6.95 (ISBN 0-89962-523-1). Todd & Honeywell.

Hayes, Helen. A Gathering of Hope. LC 83-1728. 112p. 1983. 9.95 (ISBN 0-8006-0705-8). Fortress.

--A Gathering of Hope. 222p. 1985. pap. 7.95 large print ed. (ISBN 0-8027-2467-1). Walker & Co.

Hayes, James D., ed. see Nawsome, James D.

Hayes, John, ed. First & Second Corinthians. Baird, William. (Knox Preaching Guides Ser.). pap. 4.95 (ISBN 0-8042-3239-3). John Knox.

--John Fred Craddock. (Knox Preaching Guide Ser.). 1983. pap. 6.95 (ISBN 0-8042-3236-9). John Knox.

Hayes, John, ed. see Blevins, James L.

Hayes, John, ed. see Brueggemann, Walter.

Hayes, John, ed. see Culpepper, R. Alan.

Hayes, John, ed. see Martin, Ralph.

Hayes, John, ed. see Saunders, Ernest W.

Hayes, John, ed. see Talbert, Charles H.

Hayes, John, ed. see Ward, James.

Hayes, John H. An Introduction to Old Testament Study. LC 78-20993. 1979. pap. text ed. 14.50 (ISBN 0-687-01363-1). Abingdon.

--Introduction to the Bible. LC 76-105395. (Illus.). 556p. 1971. pap. 13.95 (ISBN 0-664-24883-7). Westminster.

--Understanding the Psalms. LC 75-22034. 128p. 1976. pap. 4.95 (ISBN 0-8170-0683-4). Judson.

Hayes, John H. & Holladay, Carl. Biblical Exegesis: A Beginner's Handbook. LC 82-17999. 132p. 1982. pap. 7.95 (ISBN 0-8042-0030-0). John Knox.

Hayes, John H. & Prussner, Frederick. Old Testament Theology: Its History & Development. LC 84-47798. 336p. 1984. pap. 15.95 (ISBN 0-8042-0146-3). John Knox.

Hayes, John H., jt. auth. see Miller, J. Maxwell.

Hayes, John H., ed. Old Testament Form Criticism. LC 72-97351. (Trinity University Monograph Series in Religion: Vol. 2). pap. 77.50 (ISBN 0-317-28182-8, 2022566). Bks Demand UMI.

Hayes, John H., ed. see Achtemeier, Elizabeth.

Hayes, John H., ed. see Bailey, Lloyd R.

Hayes, John H., ed. see Craddock, Fred B.

Hayes, John H., ed. see Johnson, Luke T.

Hayes, K. H. Stories of Great Muslims. 4.75 (ISBN 0-686-18389-4). Kazi Pubns.

Hayes, Norvel. From Heaven Come God's Weapons for the Church. 1979. pap. 0.75 (ISBN 0-89274-366-2). Harrison Hse.

--The Gift of the Word of Wisdom. 1979. pap. 0.75 (ISBN 0-89274-367-0). Harrison Hse.

--The Gift of Tongues & Interpretation. 1980. pap. 0.75 (ISBN 0-89274-374-3). Harrison Hse.

--The Gift of Working of Miracles. 1980. pap. 0.75 (ISBN 0-89274-371-9). Harrison Hse.

--God's Boot Camp. 30p. (Orig.). 1979. pap. 1.50 (ISBN 0-89274-277-1). Harrison Hse.

--God's Power Through the Laying On of Hands. 45p. 1982. pap. 2.50 (ISBN 0-89274-280-1). Harrison Hse.

--How to Live & Not Die. (Orig.). 1986. pap. 5.95 (ISBN 0-89274-395-6). Harrison Hse.

--How to Protect Your Faith. 70p. (Orig.). 1983. pap. 3.95 (ISBN 0-89274-279-8). Harrison Hse.

--Jesus Taught Me to Cast Out Devils. 90p. (Orig.). 1982. pap. 2.75 (ISBN 0-89274-272-0). Harrison Hse.

--Number One Way to Fight the Devil. 1978. pap. 0.75 (ISBN 0-89274-094-9, HH-094). Harrison Hse.

--The Seven Ways Jesus Heals. 142p. (Orig.). 1982. pap. 4.95 (ISBN 0-89274-235-6, HH-235). Harrison Hse.

--The Unopened Gift. cancelled (ISBN 0-89841-002-9). Zoe Pubns.

--Winds of God. 90p. (Orig.). 1985. pap. 4.95 (ISBN 0-89274-375-1). Harrison Hse.

--You Can Be a Soulwinner. 150p. (Orig.). 1983. pap. 4.95 (ISBN 0-89274-269-0). Harrison Hse.

--Your Faith Can Heal You. 80p. 1983. pap. 2.50 (ISBN 0-89274-273-9). Harrison Hse.

Hayes, Paul J. Meditations for Lent. 1985. pap. 1.95 (ISBN 0-8198-4719-4). Dghtrs St Paul.

Hayes, Rebecca S. Grant Me a Portion. 1987. pap. 4.50 (ISBN 0-8054-6585-5). Broadman.

Hayes, Richard E., jt. auth. see Evans, Gary T.

Hayes, Sarah. A Bad Start for Santa. (Illus.). 12.95 (ISBN 0-87113-093-9). Atlantic Monthly.

Hayes, Sue T. God Made Farm Animals. (Happy Day Bks.). (Illus.). 24p. 1984. 1.59 (ISBN 0-87239-735-1, 3705). Standard Pub.

Hayes, Theresa. Getting Your Act Together. LC 85-16548. 112p. 1986. pap. 4.95 (ISBN 0-87239-998-2, 3358). Standard Pub.

Hayes, Theresa, compiled by. God Is Everywhere: Fifteen Stories to Help Children Know God. (Illus.). 80p. 1986. 7.95 (ISBN 0-87403-097-8, 3617). Standard Pub.

--God Is On Your Side: Fifteen Stories to Help Young Children Trust God. (Illus.). 80p. 1986. 7.95 (ISBN 0-87403-096-X, 3616). Standard Pub.

Hayes, Wanda. A Child's First Book of Bible Stories. LC 83-664. (Illus.). 128p. 1983. text ed. 7.95 (ISBN 0-87239-659-2, 2949). Standard Pub.

--Jesus Makes Me Happy. (A Happy Day Book). (Illus.). 24p. 1979. 1.59 (3620). Standard Pub.

--My Book of Bible Stories. (Illus.). 1964. board cover 5.95 (ISBN 0-87239-240-6, 3047). Standard Pub.

--My Jesus Book. (Illus.). 32p. 1963. pap. 5.95 (ISBN 0-87239-239-2, 3046). Standard Pub.

--My Thank You Book. (Illus.). 32p. 1964. 5.95 (ISBN 0-87239-241-4, 3048). Standard Pub.

--Saying Thank You Makes Me Happy. (A Happy Day Book). (Illus.). 24p. 1979. 1.59 (ISBN 0-87239-353-4, 3623). Standard Pub.

Hayes, William C. Ostraka & Name Stones from the Tomb of Sen-Mut (No. 71) at Thebes: Metropolitan Museum of Art Publications in Reprint. LC 76-168406. (Illus.). 136p. 1972. Repr. of 1942 ed. 22.00 (ISBN 0-405-02239-5). Ayer Co Pubs.

Hayes, Zachary. The Hidden Center: Spirituality & Speculative Christology in St. Bonaventure. LC 80-84509. 240p. (Orig.). 1981. pap. 8.95 (ISBN 0-8091-2348-7). Paulist Pr.

--To Whom Shall We Go: Christ & the Mystery of Man. (Synthesis Ser). 96p. 1975. 1.25 (ISBN 0-8199-0702-2). Franciscan Herald.

--What Are They Saying about Creation? LC 80-80870. 128p. 1980. pap. 3.95 (ISBN 0-8091-2286-3). Paulist Pr.

--What Are They Saying about the End of the World? (WATSA Ser.). 80p. (Orig.). 1983. pap. 4.95 (ISBN 0-8091-2550-1). Paulist Pr.

Hayes, Zachary, tr. Saint Bonaventure's Disputed Questions on the Mystery of the Trinity. (Works of Saint Bonaventure Ser.). 1980. 11.00 (ISBN 0-686-28123-3). Franciscan Inst.

Hayes, Zachary, tr. see Ratzinger, Joseph & Lehmann, Karl.

Hayford, Jack. Daybreak. 112p. (Orig.). 1987. mass 2.95, (ISBN 0-8423-0524-6). Tyndale.

--Newborn. 96p. 1987. 2.95 (ISBN 0-8423-4677-5). Tyndale.

--Prayer Is Invading the Impossible. LC 77-71684. 1977. pap. 4.95 (ISBN 0-88270-218-1). Bridge Pub.

--Prayer Is Invading the Impossible. (Epiphany Bks.). 160p. 1983. pap. 2.50 (ISBN 0-345-30467-5). Ballantine.

--Prayerpath. 80p. (Orig.). 1987. mass 2.95, (ISBN 0-8423-4964-2). Tyndale.

--Spirit-Filled. 112p. (Orig.). 1987. mass 2.95, (ISBN 0-8423-6407-2). Tyndale.

--The Visitor. 128p. 1986. pap. 4.95 (ISBN 0-8423-7802-2). Tyndale.

--Water Baptism. 96p. (Orig.). cancelled (ISBN 0-8423-7814-6). Tyndale.

Hayford, Jack W. Daybreak: Walking Daily in Christ's Presence. LC 84-80749. (Orig.). 1984. pap. 2.95 (ISBN 0-916847-05-5). Living Way.

--Newborn: Alive in Christ, the Savior. (Orig.). 1984. pap. 2.95 (ISBN 0-916847-00-4). Living Way.

--La Oracion Invade Lo Imposible. Carrodeguas, Angel, ed. Oyola, Eliezer, tr. from Span. Orig. Title: Prayer Is Invading the Impossible. 160p. 1985. pap. text ed. 2.95 (ISBN 0-8297-1457-X). Life Pubs Intl.

--Rebuilding the Real You. 195p. (Orig.). 1986. pap. 7.95 (ISBN 0-8307-1156-2, 5418849). Regal.

--Spirit-Filled: Anointed by Christ the King. LC 84-80747. (Orig.). 1984. pap. 2.95 (ISBN 0-916847-04-7). Living Way.

--Stepping Up in Faith. LC 84-80748. (Orig.). 1984. pap. 2.95 (ISBN 0-916847-02-0). Living Way.

--Water Baptism: Sealed by Christ, the Lord. LC 84-80750. (Orig.). 1984. pap. 2.95 (ISBN 0-916847-01-2). Living Way.

Hayhoe, D. The Creation Psalms of David. 40p. pap. 2.95 (ISBN 0-88172-148-4). Believers Bkshelf.

Hayhurst, Emma L. I Will. 2nd ed. 1982. pap. 4.95 (ISBN 0-938736-09-4). Life Enrich.

Haykal, M. H. The Life of Muhammad. Faruqi, R. I., tr. LC 76-3060. 1976. 15.95 (ISBN 0-89259-002-5); pap. 12.95. Am Trust Pubns.

Hayley, Thomas T. Anatomy of Lango Religion & Groups. LC 74-100263. Repr. of 1947 ed. cancelled (ISBN 0-8371-2871-4, HLR&, Pub. by Negro U Pr). Greenwood.

Hayley, William. The Life of Milton. LC 76-26849. Repr. of 1796 ed. lib. bdg. 45.00 (ISBN 0-8414-4739-X). Folcroft.

--Life of Milton. LC 78-122485. 1970. Repr. of 1796 ed. 50.00x (ISBN 0-8201-1081-7). Schol Facsimiles.

Hayman, Robert W. Catholicism in Rhode Island & the Diocese of Providence, 1780-1886. LC 82-73128. 353p. 1982. 17.95 (ISBN 0-917012-55-0). RI Pubns Soc.

Hayner, Jerry. God's Best to You. LC 81-71257. 1982. pap. 5.95 (ISBN 0-8054-5192-7). Broadman.

--Yes, God Can. LC 84-4153. 1985. 6.95 (ISBN 0-8054-2258-7). Broadman.

Hayner, Jerry & Hayner, Karen. Marriage Can Be Meaningful. (Orig.). 1983. pap. 3.95 (ISBN 0-8054-2303-6). Broadman.

Hayner, Karen, jt. auth. see Hayner, Jerry.

Haynes, Aliene M. What after World War III. 1987. 11.95 (ISBN 0-533-06842-8). Vantage.

Haynes, Glenda, ed. see Martin, Bill.

Haynes, Jane B., ed. see Baba, Meher, et al.

Haynes-Klassen, Joanne. Learning to Live, Learning to Love: A Book about You, A Book about Everyone. (Illus.). 150p. 1984. pap. 7.95 (ISBN 0-915190-38-9). Jalmar Pr.

Hays, Brooks & Steely, John E. The Baptist Way of Life. rev ed. LC 81-11245. 220p. 1981. 14.95 (ISBN 0-86554-008-X, MUP-H13). Mercer Univ Pr.

Hays, Edward. The Ethiopian Tattoo Shop. LC 83-82276. (Illus.). 184p. (Orig.). 1983. pap. 7.95 (ISBN 0-939516-06-3). Forest Peace.

--Pray All Ways. LC 81-69329. (Illus.). 164p. (Orig.). 1981. pap. 7.95 (ISBN 0-939516-01-2). Forest Peace.

--Prayers for the Domestic Church: A Handbook for Worship in the Home. rev. ed. LC 82-72077. (Illus.). 216p. 1979. pap. 8.95 (ISBN 0-939516-02-0); pap. 10.95 spiral bound (ISBN 0-939516-08-X); leather 17.95 (ISBN 0-939516-09-8). Forest Peace.

--Prayers for the Servants of God. (Illus.). 144p. (Orig.). 1980. pap. 6.95 (ISBN 0-939516-03-9). Forest Peace.

--Secular Sanctity. rev. ed. LC 84-81954. (Illus.). 176p. 1984. pap. 7.95 (ISBN 0-939516-05-5). Forest Peace.

Hays, Henry B. Swayed Pines Song Book. x, 88p. 1981. wirebound 7.95 (ISBN 0-8146-1238-5). Liturgical Pr.

Hays, Richard B. The Faith of Jesus Christ. LC 82-10660. (SBL Dissertation Ser.). 316p. 1983. pap. 15.00 (ISBN 0-89130-589-0, 06 01 56). Scholars Pr GA.

Haystead, Wes. Teaching Your Child About God. LC 68-29315. 144p. 1981. text ed. 8.95 (ISBN 0-8307-0798-0, 5109406). Regal.

Haystead, Wes, jt. auth. see Brown, Lowell.

Haystead, Wesley. Creative Bible Learning for Early Childhood: Birth Through 5 Years. LC 77-77030. 192p. 1977. pap. 3.95 (ISBN 0-8307-0477-9, 9000100). Regal.

--Single Again. (Study & Grow Electives). 64p. 1985. pap. 3.95 (ISBN 0-8307-1042-6, 6102111). Regal.

Haystead, Wesley, ed. ICL Planbook--Early Childhood. 1978. pap. 1.65 (ISBN 0-8307-0670-4, 90-603-08). Regal.

Hayward, John. A Reporte of a Discourse Concerning Supreme Power in Affaires of Religion. LC 79-84116. (English Experience Ser.: No. 935). 64p. 1979. Repr. of 1606 ed. lib. bdg. 8.00 (ISBN 90-221-0935-6). Walter J Johnson.

Hayward, Robert. Divine Name & Presence: The Memra. LC 81-10928. (Publications of the Oxford Centre for Postgraduate Hebrew Study). 208p. 1981. 25.50x (ISBN 0-86598-067-5). Allanheld.

Haywood, Carolyn. Make a Joyful Noise! Bible Verses for Children. LC 84-2401. (Illus.). 96p. 1984. 11.95 (ISBN 0-664-32711-7). Westminster.

Haywood, H. L., ed. The Great Teachings of Masonry. rev. enl. ed. 200p. 1971. Repr. of 1921 ed. text ed. 8.75 (ISBN 0-88053-041-3, M-90). Macoy Pub.

--How to Become a Masonic Lodge Officer. 228p. 1983. Repr. of 1958 ed. soft cover 7.50 (ISBN 0-88053-028-6, M-77). Macoy Pub.

--The Newly Made Mason: What He & Every Mason Should Know about Masonry. 5th ed. (Illus.). 256p. 1978. Repr. of 1973 ed. text ed. 12.50 (ISBN 0-88053-030-8, M-80). Macoy Pub.

Haywood, Harryl. Christian Mysticism. 59.95 (ISBN 0-87968-862-9). Gordon Pr.

Hayyim, Hafetz, pseud. Ahavath Chesed: The Love of Kindness As Required by G-D. 2nd & rev. ed. Oschry, Leonard, tr. from Hebrew. Orig. Title: Ahavath Hesed. 1976. 9.95 (ISBN 0-87306-110-1). Feldheim.

Hazard, Harry W. see Setton, Kenneth M.

Hazard, Paul. European Thought in the Eighteenth Century: From Montesquieu to Lessing. 16.50 (ISBN 0-8446-2226-5). Peter Smith.

Hazel, John, jt. auth. see Grant, Michael.

Hazelden Foundation Staff. Food for Thought. 400p. (Orig.). 1985. pap. 5.95 (ISBN 0-86683-503-2, HarpR). Har-Row.

Hazelip, Harold. Discipleship. LC 77-89541. (Twentieth Century Sermons Ser.). 11.95 (ISBN 0-89112-309-1, Bibl Res Pr). Abilene Christ U.

--Happiness in the Home: Guidelines for Spouses & Parents. 120p. 1985. pap. 3.95 (ISBN 0-8010-4294-1). Baker Bk.

--Lord, Help Me When I'm Hurting. pap. 3.95 (ISBN 0-8010-4285-2). Baker Bk.

--Questions People Ask Ministers Most. 1986. pap. 3.95 (ISBN 0-8010-4302-6). Baker Bk.

Hazelip, Harold, jt. auth. see Baxter, Batsell B.

Hazeltine, Alice I. see Smith, Elva S.

Hazelton, Charles J. Pocket Concordance to the New Testament. 1984. leather flex 4.95 (ISBN 0-8407-5824-3). Nelson.

Hazelton, Roger. Graceful Courage: A Venture in Christian Humanism. LC 84-48706. 128p. 1985. pap. 4.95 (ISBN 0-8006-1850-5, 1-1850). Fortress.

--New Accounts in Contemporary Theology. LC 78-12237. 1979. Repr. of 1960 ed. lib. bdg. cancelled (ISBN 0-313-21181-7, HANA). Greenwood.

Hazlitt, William, tr. The Spirit of the Age or Contemporary Portaits. 271p. 1979. Repr. lib. bdg. 25.00 (ISBN 0-89987-353-7). Darby Bks.

Hazlitt, William C. Faiths & Folklore of the British Isles, 2 Vols. LC 64-18758. 1905. Set. 44.00 (ISBN 0-405-08604-0, Blom Pubns); 22.00 ea. Vol. 1 (ISBN 0-405-08605-9). Vol. 2 (ISBN 0-405-08606-7). Ayer Co Pubs.

Hazra, R. C. Studies in the Puranic Records on Hindu Rites & Customs. 2nd ed. 1975. 28.00 (ISBN 0-8426-0965-2). Orient Bk Dist.

Hazrat Inayat Khan. The Awakening of the Human Spirit. LC 82-80091. (The Collected Works of Hazyat Inayat Khan Ser.). 224p. (Orig.). 1982. pap. 8.95 (ISBN 0-930872-27-4, 1014P). Omega Pr NM.

Hazzard, David, ed. see Rosewell, Pamela.

Head, Constance. Jeremiah & the Fall of Jerusalem. (Arch Bks.). (Illus.). 24p. 1986. pap. 0.99 saddlestitched (ISBN 0-570-06201-2, 59-1424). Concordia.

--The Man Who Carried the Cross for Jesus. (Arch Bk.: No. 16). (Illus.). 1979. 0.99 (ISBN 0-570-06124-5, 59-1242). Concordia.

--The Story of Deborah. (Arch Bk Ser.: No. 15). (Illus.). 1978. 0.99 (ISBN 0-570-06116-4, 59-1234). Concordia.

Head, Diane. Come to the Waters. 96p. 1985. pap. 5.95 (ISBN 0-310-25941-X, 9586P). Zondervan.

Head, E. D., ed. see Scarborough, Lee R.

Head, Joseph & Cranston, S. L. Reincarnation: An East-West Anthology. LC 68-146. 1968. pap. 5.50 (ISBN 0-8356-0035-1, Quest). Theos Pub Hse.

--Reincarnation: the Phoenix Fire Mystery. 1977. 10.95 (ISBN 0-517-52893-2). Crown.

Head, William. Yenan: Colonel Peterkin's Dixie Mission to China. 1986. write for info. (ISBN 0-89712-175-9). Documentary Pubns.

Heading, John. Understanding Chronicles One & Two. pap. 7.95 (ISBN 0-937396-10-9). Walterick Pubs.

Headings, Mildred J. French Freemasonry under the Third Republic. LC 78-64206. (Johns Hopkins University. Studies in the Social Sciences. Sixty-Sixth Ser. 1948: 1). Repr. of 1949 ed. 26.00 (ISBN 0-404-61311-X). AMS Pr.

Headington, Bonnie J. Communication in the Counseling Relationship. LC 78-9026. 1979. cloth 16.50x (ISBN 0-910328-23-4); pap. 11.00x (ISBN 0-910328-24-2). Carroll Pr.

Headlam, Arthur C., jt. auth. see Sanday, William.

Headley, John M. Luther's View of Church History. 1963. 49.50x (ISBN 0-686-51413-0). Elliots Bks.

Headley, John M., ed. see More, St. Thomas.

Heagle, John. Suffering & Evil. (Guidelines for Contemporary Catholics Ser.). (Orig.). 1987. pap. 7.95 (ISBN 0-88347-212-0). Thomas More.

Heal, Felicity. Of Prelates & Princes: A Study of the Economic & Social Position of the Tudor Episcopate. LC 79-41791. (Illus.). 368p. 1980. 59.50 (ISBN 0-521-22950-2). Cambridge U Pr.

Heal, Felicity & O'Day, Rosemary. Church & Society in England: Henry VIII to James I. LC 76-51728. vi, 206p. 1977. 23.50 (ISBN 0-208-01649-X, Archon). Shoe String.

Heal, Felicity, jt. ed. see O'Day, Rosemary.

Healey, Estelle R., tr. see Von Duerckheim, Karlfried.

Healey, John, tr. see Augustine, Saint.

Healey, Joseph G. A Fifth Gospel: The Experience of Black Christian Values. LC 80-25033. (Illus.). 220p. (Orig.). 1981. pap. 3.98 (ISBN 0-88344-013-X). Orbis Bks.

Healey, Robert M. Jefferson on Religion in Public Education. LC 73-114422. xi, 294p. 1970. Repr. of 1962 ed. 27.50 (ISBN 0-208-00841-1, Archon). Shoe String.

Healy, E. M. Christian Art in Italy, Spain, Holland & Germany. (Illus.). 145p. 1986. 127.45 (ISBN 0-86650-193-2). Gloucester Art.

Healy, Sr. Emma T. De Reductione Artium Ad Theologiam. (Works of Saint Bonaventure Ser). (Translated). 1955. 4.50 (ISBN 0-686-11590-2). Franciscan Inst.

Healy, Kilian. The Assumption of Mary. (Mary Library Ser.). 1982. pap. 5.95 (ISBN 0-89453-288-X). M Glazier.

Healy, Mary E. Society & Social Change in the Writings of St. Thomas, Ward, Sumner, & Cooley. LC 75-156191. 159p. 1972. Repr. of 1948 ed. lib. bdg. 22.50x (ISBN 0-8371-6140-1, HESC). Greenwood.

Healy, Patrick J. The Valerian Persecution: A Study of the Relations Between Church & State in the Third Century A. D. LC 76-185943. xv, 285p. 1972. Repr. of 1905 ed. 21.00 (ISBN 0-8337-4169-1). B Franklin.

Heaney, John J. Psyche & Spirit. rev. ed. 1984. pap. 10.95 (ISBN 0-8091-2610-9). Paulist Pr.

Heap, Norman L. Abraham, Isaac, & Jacob, Servants & Prophets of God. 1987. 12.50 (ISBN 0-533-07272-7). Vantage.

Heard, Albert F. Russian Church & Russian Dissent. LC 70-127907. Repr. of 1887 ed. 24.50 (ISBN 0-404-03198-6). AMS Pr.

Heard, Gerald. A Quaker Mutation. 1983. pap. 2.50x (ISBN 0-87574-007-3, 007). Pendle Hill.

--Ten Questions on Prayer. LC 51-10133. (Orig.). 1951. pap. 2.50x (ISBN 0-87574-058-8, 058). Pendle Hill.

Heard, Gerry C. Mystical & Ethical Experience. LC 84-29569. viii, 82p. 1985. 8.50 (ISBN 0-86554-149-3, MUP/H140). Mercer Univ Pr.

Heard, William H. From Slavery to the Bishopric in the A. M. E. Church: An Autobiography. LC 69-18564. (American Negro: His History & Literature, Ser. No. 2). 1969. Repr. of 1924 ed. 10.00 (ISBN 0-405-01867-3). Ayer Co Pubs.

Hearn, Lafcadio. Gleanings in Buddha-Fields. LC 73-172539. Repr. of 1897 ed. 20.00 (ISBN 0-405-08609-1). Ayer Co Pubs.

--Gleanings in Buddha-Fields: Studies of Hand & Soul in the Far East. LC 72-146523. 1971. pap. 6.25 (ISBN 0-8048-0978-X). C E Tuttle.

--Glimpses of Unfamiliar Japan, 2 Vols. LC 70-101093. Repr. of 1894 ed. 32.50 (ISBN 0-404-03205-2). AMS Pr.

--In Ghostly Japan. LC 79-138068. (Illus.). (YA) 1971. pap. 5.25 (ISBN 0-8048-0965-8). C E Tuttle.

--Kokoro: Hints & Echoes of Japanese Inner Life. LC 79-184814. 1972. pap. 6.50 (ISBN 0-8048-1035-4). C E Tuttle.

--Kokoro: Hints & Echoes of Japanese Inner Life. Repr. of 1896 ed. lib. bdg. 22.50x (ISBN 0-8371-1633-3, HEKO). Greenwood.

Hearnshaw, F. J., ed. The Social & Political Ideas of Some Great Thinkers of the Renaissance & the Reformation. LC 85-7662. 216p. 1985. lib. bdg. 39.75x (ISBN 0-313-23862-6, HREN). Greenwood.

Hearnshaw, Fossey J., ed. Medieval Contributions to Modern Civilization. LC 66-25917. 1966. Repr. of 1921 ed. 18.00x (ISBN 0-8046-0198-4, Pub. by Kennikat). Assoc Faculty Pr.

Heath, Carl. Social & Religious Heretics in Five Centuries. LC 78-147622. (Library of War & Peace; Non-Resis. & Non-Vio.). 1972. lib. bdg. 46.00 (ISBN 0-8240-0397-7). Garland Pub.

Heath, Douglas. Why a Friends School. LC 75-81158. (Orig.). 1969. pap. 2.50x (ISBN 0-87574-164-9). Pendle Hill.

Heath, Douglas H. The Peculiar Mission of a Friends School. LC 79-84919. 1979. pap. 2.50x (ISBN 0-87574-225-4). Pendle Hill.

Heath, Lou. Daniel: Faithful Captive. (Biblearn Ser.). (Illus.). 1977. bds. 5.95 (ISBN 0-8054-4231-6, 4242-31). Broadman.

--Ed Taylor: Father of Migrant Missions. LC 81-70911. (Meet the Missionary Ser.). 1982. 5.50 (ISBN 0-8054-4278-2, 4242-78). Broadman.

Heath, Lou & Taylor, Beth. Reading My Bible in Fall. LC 85-30947. (Orig.). 1986. pap. 4.50 (ISBN 0-8054-4322-3). Broadman.

--Reading My Bible in Spring. (Orig.). 1987. pap. 4.50 (ISBN 0-8054-4320-7). Broadman.

--Reading My Bible in Summer. (Orig.). 1987. pap. 4.50 (ISBN 0-8054-4321-5). Broadman.

--Reading My Bible in Winter. LC 85-30940. (Orig.). 1986. pap. 4.50 (ISBN 0-8054-4323-1). Broadman.

Heath, Richard. Anabaptism, from Its Rise at Zwickau to Its Fall at Munster. LC 83-45615. Date not set. Repr. of 1895 ed. 28.00 (ISBN 0-404-19833-3). AMS Pr.

Heath, Robert G. Crux Imperatorum Philosophia: Imperial Horizons of the Cluniac Confraternitas, 964-1109. LC 76-56099. (Pittsburgh Theological Monographs: No. 13). 1977. pap. 10.00 (ISBN 0-915138-17-4). Pickwick.

Heath, Sidney. The Romance of Symbolism & Its Relation to Church Ornament & Architecture. LC 70-174054. (Illus.). 1976. Repr. of 1909 ed. 40.00x (ISBN 0-8103-4302-9). Gale.

Heath, Virginia S. Dramatic Elements in American Indian Ceremonials. (American History & Americana Ser., No. 47). 1970. pap. 22.95x (ISBN 0-8383-0093-6). Haskell.

Heathcote, A. W. From the Death of Solomon to the Captivity of Judah. (London Divinity Ser.). 140p. 1977. pap. 3.95 (ISBN 0-227-67462-6). Attic Pr.

--From the Exile to Herod the Great. (London Divinity Ser). 140p. 1964. 3.95 (ISBN 0-227-67658-0). Attic Pr.

Heaton, Charles H., ed. Hymnbook for Christian Worship. LC 69-14339. 1970. Red. 7.95x (ISBN 0-8272-8020-3). Blue. 7.95x (ISBN 0-8272-8021-1); Beige. 7.95x (ISBN 0-8272-8024-6); 19.50x (ISBN 0-8272-8023-8); 8.95x (ISBN 0-8272-8022-X); brown gift 8.50x (ISBN 0-8272-8027-0). CBP.

Heaton, E. W. Everyday Life in Old Testament Times. LC 76-29288. (Illus.). 1977. lib. rep. ed. 17.50H (ISBN 0-684-14836-6). Scribner.

--Solomon's New Men. LC 74-13412. (Illus.). 216p. 1975. 15.00x (ISBN 0-87663-714-4, Pica Pr). Universe.

Heaton, Eric W. Hebrew Kingdoms. (New Clarendon Bible Ser.). 1968. 10.95x (ISBN 0-19-836922-0). Oxford U Pr.

Heaton, Rose H. The Perfect Christmas. Repr. of 1932 ed. 20.00 (ISBN 0-686-20659-2). Lib Serv Inc.

Heavenrich, Elaine, jt. auth. see Greene, Roberta M.

Heavilin, Marilyn W. Roses in December: Finding Strength Within Grief. 1987. pap. 6.95. Heres Life.

Hebart, Friedemann. One in the Gospel. 1981. pap. 4.25 (ISBN 0-570-03830-8, 12-2796). Concordia.

Hebbel, Friedrich. Herod & Mariamne. Curts, Paul H., tr. LC 51-895. (North Carolina. University. Studies in the Germanic Languages & Literatures: No. 3). Repr. of 1950 ed. 27.00 (ISBN 0-404-50903-7). AMS Pr.

Hebbelthwaite, Margaret. Motherhood & God. 144p. 1984. pap. 5.95 (ISBN 0-225-66384-8, HarpR). Har-Row.

Hebblethwaite, Brian. Christian Ethics in the Modern Age. LC 81-13105. 144p. 1982. pap. 6.95 (ISBN 0-664-24395-9). Westminster.

--The Christian Hope. 248p. (Orig.). 1985. pap. 9.95 (ISBN 0-8028-0054-8). Eerdmans.

Hebblethwaite, Brian, jt. ed. see Hick, John.

Hebblethwaite, Brian L. The Problems of Theology. LC 79-41812. 176p. 1980. o. p. 29.95 (ISBN 0-521-23104-3); pap. 9.95 (ISBN 0-521-29811-3). Cambridge U Pr.

Hebblethwaite, Brian L., ed. The Philosophical Frontiers of Christian Theology: Essays Presented to D. M. Mackinnon. Sutherland, Stewart. LC 81-10132. (Illus.). 230p. 1982. 29.50 (ISBN 0-521-24012-3). Cambridge U Pr.

Hebblethwaite, Peter. In the Vatican. LC 86-7927. 214p. 1986. 16.95 (ISBN 0-917561-24-4). Adler & Adler.

--Pope John XXIII: Shepherd of the Modern World. LC 82-45484. (Illus.). 576p. 1985. 19.95 (ISBN 0-385-17298-2). Doubleday.

--Synod Extraordinary: An Evaluation of the Catholic Church on the 20th Anniversary of Vatican Council II. LC 85-27160. 144p. 1986. 15.95 (ISBN 0-385-23466-X). Doubleday.

Hebblethwaite, Peter, et al. The Vatican. LC 80-50854. (Illus.). 226p. 1980. 50.00 (ISBN 0-86565-002-0). Vendome.

Hebert, Albert, compiled by. A Prayerbook of Favorite Litanies: 116 Favorite Catholic Litanies & Responsory Prayers. LC 84-51818. 192p. 1985. pap. 7.50 (ISBN 0-89555-252-3). Tan Bks Pubs.

Hebert, Albert J. Priestly Celibacy: Recurrent Battle & Lasting Values. 198p. 1971. 6.00 (ISBN 0-912414-01-4). Lumen Christi.

Hebert, Clarence, tr. Jesus Reveals His Heart: Letters of St. Margaret Mary. 1980. 4.75 (ISBN 0-8198-3905-1); pap. 3.50 (ISBN 0-8198-3906-X). Dghtrs St Paul.

Hebert, Peter E., ed. Selections from the Latin Fathers. (College Classical Ser.). xvii, 186p. 1982. lib. bdg. 25.00x (ISBN 0-89241-357-3); pap. text ed. 12.50x (ISBN 0-89241-370-0). Caratzas.

Hebert, Yvonne C. Finding Peace in Pain. 108p. (Orig.). 1984. pap. text ed. 3.50 (ISBN 0-914544-53-5). Living Flame Pr.

Hebgin, D. Scholastica, tr. see St. Augustine.

Hebgin, Scholastica, tr. see Augustine, St.

Hebly, J. A. Protestants in Russia. Pott, John, tr. LC 76-149. pap. 48.00 (ISBN 0-317-08445-3, 2012741). Bks Demand UMI.

Hecht, Johanna, notes by. The Nativity. LC 81-65400. (Illus.). 1981. pop-up bk. 9.95 (ISBN 0-385-28713-5). Delacorte.

Hecht, Michael. Have You Ever Asked Yourself These Questions. LC 75-163738. 267p. 1971. 7.95 (ISBN 0-88400-034-6). Shengold.

Hecht, Neil S., jt. auth. see Quint, Emanuel.

Hecht, Neil S., jt. auth. see Quint, Emanuel B.

Hecht, Richard, jt. auth. see Smart, Ninian.

Hecht, Richard, jt. ed. see Smart, Ninian.

Hecht, Richard B., jt. ed. see Smart, Ninian.

Hecht, Shea & Clorfene, Chaim. Confessions of a Jewish Cultbuster. Crossen, Chaya, ed. 256p. 1985. 8.37 (ISBN 0-318-18531-8); pap. 5.97 (ISBN 0-318-18532-6). Tosefos.

Hechtle, Ranier, ed. see Reay, Lee.

Heck, H. J., ed. see Schuster, Ignatius.

Heck, Joel D. Make Disciples. 1984. pap. 6.50 (ISBN 0-570-03934-7, 12-2869). Concordia.

Heck, Klaus. Before You Cast the Second Stone. 1979. 7.95 (ISBN 0-915948-05-2); pap. 5.95 (ISBN 0-686-52664-3). Bks Distinction.

Heck, Timothy A. Revelation. (Standard Bible Study Workbooks Ser.). 64p. 1986. pap. text ed. 1.95 (ISBN 0-87403-193-1, 40213). Standard Pub.

Hecke, Karl-Heinz. Die Alttestamentlichen Perikopen der Reihen III-VI. (European University Studies Twenty-Three: Vol. 180). (Ger.). 203p. 1982. 24.20 (ISBN 3-8204-5759-3). P Lang Pubs.

Hecker, Julius F. Religion & Communism. LC 73-842. (Russian Studies: Perspectives on the Revolution Ser.). 302p. 1987. Repr. of 1934 ed. 26.75 (ISBN 0-88355-037-7). Hyperion Conn.

Heckewelder, John. Narrative of the Mission of the United Brethren Among the Delaware & Mohegan Indians. LC 79-146399. (First American Frontier Ser). 1971. Repr. of 1820 ed. 29.00 (ISBN 0-405-02852-0). Ayer Co Pubs.

Heckman, Shirley J. Visions of Peace. LC 83-16522. 75p. (Orig.). 1984. pap. 5.95 (ISBN 0-377-00140-6). Friend Pr.

Hector, Lee H. The Three Nephites: Substance & Significance of the Legend in Folklore. Dorson, Richard, ed. LC 77-70608. (International Folklore Ser.). 1977. Repr. of 1949 ed. lib. bdg. 14.00x (ISBN 0-405-10105-8). Ayer Co Pubs.

Hedberg, Thomas, jt. auth. see Caprio, Betsy.

Hedeman, Robert. Arnold, Heaven's Loudest Angel. 1982. 3.75 (ISBN 0-89536-549-9, 0103). CSS of Ohio.

Hedengren, Paul. In Defense of Faith: Assessing Arguments Against Latter-Day Saint Belief. 240p. (Orig.). 1985. pap. 14.95 (ISBN 0-915073-00-5). Bradford & Wilson.

Hedin, Sven A. Central Asia & Tibet Towards the Holy City of Lassa, 2 Vols. Bealby, J. T., tr. LC 68-55192. (Illus.). 1968. Repr. of 1903 ed. lib. bdg. 97.50x (ISBN 0-8371-3893-0, HECA). Greenwood.

Hedley, George P. The Superstitions of the Irreligious. LC 78-10274. 1979. Repr. of 1951 ed. lib. bdg. 22.50x (ISBN 0-313-20755-0, HESU). Greenwood.

Hedley, Leslie W. The Day Japan Bombed Pearl Harbor & Other Stories. 148p. 1984. pap. 7.95 (ISBN 0-933515-03-0). Exile Pr.

Hedlund, Mary F., tr. see Grollenberg, Luc H.

Hedrick, Dr. Charles W., Sr. & Hodgson, Robert, Jr. Nag Hammadi, Gnosticism & Early Christianity. 296p. 1986. pap. 14.95 (ISBN 0-913573-16-7). Hendrickson MA.

Heeg, Aloysius J. Jesus & I. pap. text ed. 1.00 (ISBN 0-8294-0214-4). Loyola.

Heeney, Brian. A Different Kind of Gentleman: Parish Clergy As Professional Men in Early & Mid-Victorian England. LC 76-17329. (Studies in British History & Culture: Vol. 5). (Illus.). xii, 169p. 1976. 21.50 (ISBN 0-208-01605-8, Archon). Shoe String.

Heer, Friedrick. Medieval World: Europe Eleven Hundred to Thirteen Fifty. 1964. pap. 5.95 (ISBN 0-451-62542-0, ME2165, Ment). NAL.

Heer, Nicholas L., tr. see Abd al-Rahman al Jami.

Heeren, Fatima, jt. auth. see Lemu, Aisha.

Heering, Gerrit J. Fall of Christianity. LC 77-147670. (Library of War & Peace; Relig. & Ethical Positions on War). 1973. lib. bdg. 46.00 (ISBN 0-8240-0428-0). Garland Pub.

Heesterman, J. C. Ancient Indian Royal Consecration: The Rajasuya Described According to the Yajus Texts & Annotated. (Disputationes Rheno-Trajectinae Ser: No. 2). (Orig.). 1957. pap. text ed. 25.60x (ISBN 90-2790-028-0). Mouton.

Hefele, Karl J. A History of the Councils of the Church from the Original Documents, 5 vols. Clark, William R., ed. & tr. from Ger. LC 79-39294. Repr. of 1896 ed. Set. 172.50 (ISBN 0-404-03260-5); 34.50 ea.; Vol. 1. (ISBN 0-404-03261-3); Vol. 2. (ISBN 0-404-03262-1); Vol. 3. (ISBN 0-404-03263-X); Vol. 4. (ISBN 0-404-03264-8); Vol. 5. (ISBN 0-404-03265-6). AMS Pr.

Hefener, Philip, jt. auth. see Benne, Robert.

Hefley, James & Hefley, Marti. By Their Blood. 1986. pap. 8.95 (ISBN 0-8010-4312-3). Baker Bk.

--By Their Blood: Christian Martyrs of the Twentieth Century. LC 78-6187. 1979. pap. 7.95 (ISBN 0-915134-24-1). Mott Media.

--China: Christian Martyrs of the Twentieth Century. LC 78-6187. 1978. pap. 2.25 (ISBN 0-915134-16-0). Mott Media.

--Prisoners of Hope. LC 76-28840. 1976. 6.95 (ISBN 0-87509-122-9); pap. 3.95 (ISBN 0-87509-123-7). Chr Pubns.

Hefley, James C. The Truth in Crisis: The Controversy in the Southern Baptist Convention. LC 86-70962. 208p. 1986. pap. 7.95 (ISBN 0-937969-00-1). Criterion Pubns.

--Way Back in the Hills. (Living Bks.). 352p. (Orig.). 1985. 3.95 (ISBN 0-8423-7821-9). Tyndale.

Hefley, James C., jt. auth. see Steinberg, Jeff.

Hefley, Marti. Assignment in the Philippines: Dramatic Accounts from Jared & Marilee Barker. (Orig.). 1984. pap. 7.95 (ISBN 0-8024-0265-8). Moody.

Hefley, Marti, jt. auth. see Dean, Dave.

Hefley, Marti, jt. auth. see Hefley, James.

Heflin, J. Boo. Nahum, Habakkuk, Zephaniah & Haggai. (Bible Study Commentary). 240p. (Orig.). 1986. pap. text ed. 7.95 (ISBN 0-310-27531-8, 18385P). Zondervan.

Heflin, James L., jt. auth. see Hall, Eugene E.

Hefling, Charles. Why Doctrines? LC 82-83553. 196p. (Orig.). 1984. pap. 8.00 (ISBN 0-936384-09-3). Cowley Pubns.

Hefling, Charles C., Jr. Jacob's Ladder: Theology & Spirituality in the Thought of Austin Farrer. LC 80-117760. xiii, 132p. (Orig.). 1979. pap. 5.00 (ISBN 0-936384-01-8). Cowley Pubns.

Hefner, Robert W. Hindu Javanese: Tengger Tradition & Islam. LC 85-3426. (Illus.). 300p. 1985. text ed. 36.00x (ISBN 0-691-09413-6). Princeton U Pr.

Heft, James. John XXII & Papal Taching Authority. (Texts & Studies in Religion: Vol. 27). 282p. 1986. lib. bdg. 49.95x (ISBN 0-88946-815-X). E Mellen.

Hegel, G. W. Early Theological Writings. Knox, T. M. & Kroner, R., trs. from Ger. (Works in Continental Philosophy Ser). 1971. pap. 12.95x (ISBN 0-8122-1022-0, Pa. Paperbacks). U of Pa Pr.

--Faith & Knowledge: The Reflective Philosophy of Subjectivity. Harris, H. S. & Cerf, Walter, eds. Harris, H. S. & Cerf, Walter., trs. from Ger. LC 76-10250. 1977. 39.50 (ISBN 0-87395-338-X). State U NY Pr.

--Hegel: Phenomenology of Spirit. Miller, A. V. & Findlay, J. N., trs. 1977. 34.95x (ISBN 0-19-824530-0); pap. 13.95 (ISBN 0-19-824597-1). Oxford U Pr.

--Hegel's System of Ethical Life & First Philosophy of Spirit. Harris, H. S. & Knox, T. M., eds. Harris, H. S. & Knox, T. M., trs. LC 79-11477. 1979. 39.50 (ISBN 0-87395-386-X). State U NY Pr.

--Lectures on the Philosophy of Religion. Hodgson, Peter, ed. Incl. Vol. 1. Introduction & the Concept of Religion. 1984. lib. bdg. 50.00x (ISBN 0-520-04676-5); Vol. 3. The Consumate Religion. 1985. lib. bdg. 45.00x (ISBN 0-520-05514-4); Vol. II. Determinate Religion. Hegel, G. W. Hodgson, Peter C., ed. & tr. 816p. 1987. text ed. 50.50 (ISBN 0-520-05513-6). LC 83-9132. 450p. U of Cal Pr.

--Philosophy of Right. Knox, T. M., tr. 1942. 37.50x (ISBN 0-19-824128-3); pap. 10.95x (ISBN 0-19-500276-8). Oxford U Pr.

--Three Essays, Seventeen Ninety-Three to Seventeen Ninety-Five: The Tubingen Essay, Berne Fragments, The Life of Jesus. Fuss, Peter & Dobbins, John, eds. LC 83-40599. 192p. 1984. text ed. 18.95x (ISBN 0-268-01854-5, 85-18540). U of Notre Dame Pr.

Hegel, Georg W. The Christian Religion. Lasson, Georg, ed. Hodgson, Peter C., tr. from Ger. LC 79-424. (American Academy of Religion, Texts & Translation Ser.: No. 2). 1979. pap. 10.25_o.s. (ISBN 0-89130-276-X, 010202). Scholars Pr GA.

--Lectures on the Philosophy of Religion, 3 vols. Speirs, E. B. & Sanderson, J. B., trs. 1968. Repr. of 1895 ed. Set. text ed. 70.00x (ISBN 0-7100-6080-7). Humanities.

--The Metaphysics of the Jewish, the Aegyptian & the Assyrian Spirit. (Illus.). 177p. 1981. 67.85 (ISBN 0-89266-280-8). Am Classical Coll Pr.

Hegele, Paul. When Messiah Comes. Sherer, Michael L., ed. (Orig.). 1986. pap. 6.25 (ISBN 0-89536-823-4, 6832). CSS of Ohio.

Hegener, Mark. Poverello: St. Francis of Assisi. pap. 2.00 (ISBN 0-8199-0358-2). Franciscan Herald.

Hegener, Mark, ed. see Van Moorselaar, Corinne.

Heggie, James. Baha'i References to Judaism, Christianity & Islam. 272p. 1986. 11.95. G Ronald Pub.

--Index of Quotations From the Baha'i Scared Writings. 824p. 39.50 (ISBN 0-85398-145-0). G Ronald Pub.

Hegre, T. A. Creative Faith. LC 80-17869. 96p. (Orig.). 1980. pap. 3.95 (ISBN 0-87123-020-8, 210020). Bethany Hse.

--Cross & Sanctification. LC 51-7866. Orig. Title: Three Aspects of the Cross. 288p. 1960. pap. 3.95 (ISBN 0-87123-067-4, 210067). Bethany Hse.

--How to Find Freedom from the Power of Sin. 96p. 1969. pap. 3.50 (ISBN 0-87123-217-0, 200217). Bethany Hse.

--Libre Para Vivir. 96p. 1964. 2.25 (ISBN 0-88113-020-6). Edit Betania.

--La Vida Que Nace de la Muerte. 272p. 1977. 2.95 (ISBN 0-88113-311-6). Edit Betania.

Hegstad & Munson. War of the Star Lords. 34p. 1983. pap. 2.50 (ISBN 0-8163-0517-X). Pacific Pr Pub Assn.

Heide, Della M. The Covenant Renewed. 176p. 1983. pap. 7.95 (ISBN 0-317-04516-4). Coleman Pub.

Heidegger, Martin. What Is a Thing? Barton, W. B. & Deutsch, Vera, trs. from Ger. 320p. 1985. pap. text ed. 8.75 (ISBN 0-8191-4545-9). U Pr of Amer.

Heidel, Alexander. Babylonian Genesis. 2nd ed. LC 51-822. 1963. 6.00x (ISBN 0-226-32399-4, P133, Phoen). U of Chicago Pr.

--Gilgamesh Epic & Old Testament Parallels. 2nd ed. LC 49-5734. 1963. 8.95 (ISBN 0-226-32398-6, P136, Phoen). U of Chicago Pr.

Heider, George C. The Cult of Molek: A Reassessment. (JSOT Supplement Ser.: No. 43). xiv, 446p. 1986. text ed. 28.50x (ISBN 1-85075-019-X, Pub. by JSOT Pr England); pap. text ed. 13.50x (ISBN 1-85075-018-1). Eisenbrauns.

Heider, John. The Tao of Leadership: Lao Tzu's Tao te Ching Adapted for a New Age. LC 84-19750. 184p. (Orig.). 1984. pap. 9.95 (ISBN 0-89334-079-0). Humanics Ltd.

Heidinger, James V., II, ed. Basic United Methodist Beliefs: (An Evangelical View) 128p. 1986. pap. 4.95 (ISBN 0-917851-01-3). Forum Script.

Heie, Harold & Wolfe, David L., eds. Reality of Christian Learning: Strategies for Faith-Discipline Integration. 448p. 1987. pap. 19.95 (ISBN 0-8028-0233-8). Eerdmans.

Heifetz, Hank. The Origin of the Young God: Kalidasa's Kumarasambhava. 1985. 30.00x (ISBN 0-520-05304-4). U of Cal Pr.

Heifetz, Harold, ed. Zen & Hasidism. LC 78-9073. 1978. 10.95 (ISBN 0-8356-0514-0). Theos Pub Hse.

Heifner, Fred. Isaiah: Messenger for God. (BibLearn Ser.). (Illus.). 1978. 5.95 (ISBN 0-8054-4243-X, 4242-43). Broadman.

Heiges, Donald R. The Christian's Calling. rev. ed. LC 84-47923. 112p. 1984. pap. 4.95 (ISBN 0-8006-1795-9). Fortress.

Heijke, Joseph. St. Augustine's Comments on Imago Dei. 3.00 (ISBN 0-686-23375-1). Classical Folia.

Heijkoop, H. J. Holy Spirit Is a Divine Person. 5.95 (ISBN 0-88172-084-4); pap. 4.95 (ISBN 0-88172-085-2). Believers Bkshelf.

Heijkoop, H. L. Beginning with Christ. 6.95 (ISBN 0-88172-081-X); pap. 4.95 (ISBN 0-88172-082-8). Believers Bkshelf.

--The Book of Ruth. 6.95 (ISBN 0-88172-086-0). Believers Bkshelf.

--Faith Healing & Speaking in Tongues. 40p. pap. 2.95 (ISBN 0-88172-083-6). Believers Bkshelf.

--Unto Christ. 47p. pap. 0.60 (ISBN 0-88172-087-9). Believers Bkshelf.

Heil, Ruth. My Child Within. LC 82-83901. 128p. 1983. pap. 5.95 (ISBN 0-89107-268-3). Good News.

Heilbut, Anthony. The Gospel Sound: Good News & Bad Times. rev. updated ed. LC 84-26122. (Illus.). 416p. 1985. pap. 9.95 (ISBN 0-87910-034-6). Limelight Edns.

Heiler, Anne M., ed. see Heiler, Friedrich.

Heiler, Friedrich. Die Frau in den Religionen der Menschheit. Heiler, Anne M., ed. (Theologische Bibliothek Toepelmann: Vol. 33). 1977. 15.20x (ISBN 3-11-006583-5). De Gruyter.

Heiligenkreuz. Austria (Cistercian Abbey) Urkunden Des Cisterciensег-Stiftes Heiligenkreuz Im Wiener Walde, 2 vols. 1856-1859. Vol. 11. pap. 23.00 (ISBN 0-384-22083-5); Vol. 16. pap. 62.00 (ISBN 0-685-27596-5). Johnson Repr.

Heillig, Roma J. Adolescent Suicidal Behavior: A Family Systems Model. Nathan, Peter E., ed. LC 83-3594. (Research in Clinical Psychology Ser.: No. 7). 170p. 1983. 37.95 (ISBN 0-8357-1390-3). Univ Microfilms.

Heilman, Samuel. Inside the Jewish Schools: A Study of the Cultural Setting for Jewish Education. 50p. 1984. pap. 2.50 (ISBN 0-87495-057-0). Am Jewish Comm.

Heilman, Samuel C. The People of the Book: Drama, Felloship, & Religion. LC 82-13369. x, 338p. 1987. pap. text ed. price not set (ISBN 0-226-32493-1). U of Chicago Pr.

--The People of the Book: Drama, Fellowship, & Religion. LC 82-13369. 264p. 1983. lib. bdg. 25.00x (ISBN 0-226-32492-3). U of Chicago Pr.

--Synagogue Life: A Study in Symbolic Interaction. LC 75-36403. 1976. 12.95x (ISBN 0-226-32488-5); pap. 9.95x (ISBN 0-226-32490-7, P824, Phoen). U of Chicago Pr.

Heim, Karl. Christian Faith & Natural Science. 10.25 (ISBN 0-8446-0690-1). Peter Smith.

Heim, Pamela. The Woman God Can Use. LC 85-73070. 176p. 1986. pap. 6.95 (ISBN 0-89636-190-X). Accent Bks.

Heim, Ralph D. Harmony of the Gospels. LC 47-2807. 228p. 1974. pap. 6.95 (ISBN 0-8006-1494-1, 1-1494). Fortress.

Heim, S. Mark. Is Christ the Only Way. 160p. 1984. pap. 7.95 (ISBN 0-317-18066-5). Judson.

Heiman, Carrie J. The Nine-Month Miracle. (Illus.). 144p. (Orig.). 1986. pap. 4.95 (ISBN 0-89243-250-0). Liguori Pubns.

Heiman, David, tr. see Cornier, Henri.

Heimbeck, Raeburne S. Theology & Meaning: A Critique of Metatheological Scepticism. LC 68-13146. 1969. 22.50x (ISBN 0-8047-0704-9). Stanford U Pr.

Heimert, Alan & Delbanco, Nicholas, eds. The Puritans in America: A Narrative Anthology. 456p. 1985. text ed. 25.00x (ISBN 0-674-74065-3); pap. text ed. 7.95x (ISBN 0-674-74066-1). Harvard U Pr.

Heimert, Alan E. & Miller, Perry, eds. Great Awakening: Documents Illustrating the Crisis & Its Consequences. LC 66-23537. (Orig.). 1967. pap. 14.47 scp (ISBN 0-672-60044-7, AHS34). Bobbs.

Heimmel, Jennifer P. God Is Our Mother: Julian of Norwich & the Medieval Image of Christian Feminine Divinity. Hogg, James, ed. (Elizabethan & Renaissance Studies). 111p. (Orig.). 1982. pap. 15.00 (ISBN 0-317-40145-9, Pub by Salzburg Studies). Longwood Pub Group.

Heimsath, Charles H. Indian Nationalism & Hindu Social Reform. LC 63-20660. pap. 98.30 (ISBN 0-317-08688-X, 2000888). Bks Demand UMI.

Hein, Lucille E. I Can Make My Own Prayers. LC 72-154026. (Illus.). 1971. 3.95 (ISBN 0-8170-0528-5). Judson.

--Thank You, God. (Illus.). 32p. 1981. pap. 3.50 (ISBN 0-8170-0912-4). Judson.

Hein, Marvin. The Ties That Bind: Moorings of a Life with God. LC 80-81705. 135p. (Orig.). 1980. pap. 5.95 (ISBN 0-937364-04-5). Kindred Pr.

Hein, Norvin. The Miracle Plays of Mathura. LC 75-99826. pap. 81.30 (ISBN 0-317-09863-2, 2022003). Bks Demand UMI.

Hein, Rolland. The Harmony Within: The Spiritual Vision of George MacDonald. LC 82-1488. pap. 45.80 (ISBN 0-317-30142-X, 2025325). Bks Demand UMI.

Hein, Rolland, ed. see MacDonald, George.

Hein, Virginia H. The British Followers of Theodor Herzl: English Zionist Leaders, 1896-1904. McNeill, William H. & Stansky, Peter, eds. (Modern European History Ser.). 325p. 1987. lib. bdg. 50.00 (ISBN 0-8240-7815-2). Garland Pub.

Heinberg, Richard. Memories & Visions of Paradise. (Illus.). 61p. (Orig.). 1985. pap. 4.95 (ISBN 0-932869-00-9). Emissaries Divine.

Heine, Heinrich. Jewish Stories & Hebrew Melodies. Sarna, Jonathan D., ed. Leyland, Charles G., tr. from Ger. LC 86-40567. (Masterworks of Modern Jewish Writing Ser.). (Illus.). 200p. 1987. text ed. 18.95 (ISBN 0-910129-68-1); pap. 8.95 (ISBN 0-910129-62-2). Wiener Pub Inc.

--Religion & Philosophy in Germany. Snodgrass, John, tr. from Ger. 210p. (Orig.). 1986. 29.50x (ISBN 0-88706-282-2); pap. 9.95 (ISBN 0-88706-283-0). State U NY Pr.

Heine, Helme. One Day in Paradise. LC 85-72492. (Illus.). 32p. 1986. 12.95 (ISBN 0-689-50394-6, McElderry Bk). Macmillan.

Heinecken, Martin J. We Believe & Teach. Rast, Harold W., ed. LC 80-16363. (A Lead Book). 128p. (Orig.). 1980. pap. 3.95 (ISBN 0-8006-1387-2, 1-1387). Fortress.

Heinegg, Peter, tr. see Beltz, Walter.

Heinegg, Peter, tr. see Schuller, Bruno.

Heineman, Benno. The Maggid of Dubno & His Parables. rev ed. 1978. 11.95 (ISBN 0-87306-156-X). Feldheim.

Heinemann, Joseph. Prayer in the Talmud: Forms & Patterns. (Studia Judaica: Vol. 9). 1977. 61.00 (ISBN 3-11-004289-4). De Gruyter.

Heinemann, Margot. Puritanism & Theatre: Thomas Middleton & Opposition Drama Under the Early Stuarts. LC 79-14991. (Past & Present Publications Ser.). 309p. 1982. 34.50 (ISBN 0-521-22602-3); pap. 13.95 (ISBN 0-521-27052-9). Cambridge U Pr.

Heinemann, Marlene E. Gender & Destiny: Women Writers & the Holocaust. LC 86-367. (Contributions in Women's Studies: No. 72). 158p. 1986. 27.95 (ISBN 0-313-24665-3, HGD/). Greenwood.

Heiner, Wolfgang. Jesus Is Different. 112p. 1983. pap. 4.50 (ISBN 0-85364-344-X, Pub. by Paternoster UK). Attic Pr.

Heinerman, John & Shupe, Anson. The Mormon Corporate Empire: The Eye-Opening Report on the Church & Its Political & Financial Agenda. LC 85-47527. 352p. 1986. 19.95 (ISBN 0-8070-0406-5). Beacon Pr.

Heintzen, Erich H. & Starr, Frank. Love Leaves Home. LC 72-94586. 1973. 3.50 (ISBN 0-570-03513-9, 14-2017). Concordia.

Heinze, Thomas F. Creation vs. Evolution Handbook. (Direction Books). 1973. pap. 3.50 (ISBN 0-8010-4002-7). Baker Bk.

Heinzmann, Josef. Faith is Friendship. 146p. 1983. pap. 6.95 (ISBN 0-8189-0451-8). Alba.

Heisberger, Jean M., ed. Arise Jerusalem: Parish Advent Program, Advent Family Handbook. LC 78-70425. 1978. pap. text ed. 1.25 (ISBN 0-8091-9179-2). Paulist Pr.

Heisenberg, Werner. Tradition in Science. 160p. (Orig.). 1983. pap. 10.95 (ISBN 0-8164-2488-8, HarpR). Har-Row.

Heisig, James W. Imago Dei: A Study of C. G. Jung's Psychology of Religion. LC 77-74405. 256p. 1978. 26.50 (ISBN 0-8387-2076-5). Bucknell U Pr.

Heisig, James W., tr. see Waldenfels, Hans.

Heisler, Hermann. Our Relationship to Those Who Have Died. 1976. pap. 2.50 (ISBN 0-916786-03-X). St George Bk Serv.

Heissig, Walther. The Religions of Mongolia. Samuel, Geoffrey, tr. from Ger. LC 80-146381. 1980. 31.00x (ISBN 0-520-03857-6). U of Cal Pr.

Heit, Edmund. The Soviets Are Coming. LC 80-18836. 160p. 1980. pap. 2.95 (ISBN 0-88243-585-X, 02-0585). Gospel Pub.

Heitzenrater, Richard, ed. Methodist Conference Minutes & Traveling Preachers: 1773-1794. LC 79-51893. Date not set. pap. 9.25 (ISBN 0-914960-18-0). Academy Bks.

Heitzenrater, Richard P. The Elusive Mr. Wesley: John Wesley His Own Biographer. LC 83-25882. 220p. 1984. pap. 9.75 (ISBN 0-687-11554-X); Set. pap. 19.50 (ISBN 0-687-11556-6). Abingdon.

Heitzenrater, Richard P., ed. Diary of an Oxford Methodist: Benjamin Ingham, 1733-34. xvi, 304p. 1985. 37.50 (ISBN 0-8223-0595-X). Duke.

Heitzenrather, Richard P. The Elusive Mr. Wesley, Vol. II. 224p. (Orig.). 1984. pap. 9.75 (ISBN 0-687-11555-8). Abingdon.

Hekman, Randall. Justice for the Unborn: Why We Have Legal Abortion & How We Can Stop It. 200p. (Orig.). 1984. pap. 5.95 (ISBN 0-89283-194-4). Servant.

Hekman, Susan J. Hermeneutics & the Sociology of Knowledge. LC 85-52311. 224p. 1986. text ed. 29.95x (ISBN 0-268-01083-8). U of Notre Dame Pr.

Helbron, Peter. Catholic Baptisms in Western Pennsylvania, 1799-1828: Father Peter Helbron's Greensburg Register. LC 84-73331. 123p. 1985. Repr. of 1915 ed. 12.50 (ISBN 0-8063-1113-4). Genealog Pub.

Helby, Hans. Eastbound Ecumenicism: A Collection of Essays on the World Council of Churches & Eastern Europe. LC 86-9137. 154p. (Orig.). 1986. lib. bdg. 24.50 (ISBN 0-8191-5400-8, Pub. by Interuniversity Inst for Missiological & Ecumenical Res); pap. text ed. 12.25 (ISBN 0-8191-5401-6). U Pr of Amer.

Held, Ronald G. Learning Together. LC 76-9515. 128p. 1976. pap. 1.25 (ISBN 0-88243-571-X, 02-0571). Gospel Pub.

Helena, M., tr. see Simma, Maria.

Helgeland, John & Daly, Robert J. Christians & the Military: The Early Experience. Burns, J. Patout, ed. LC 84-48718. 112p. 1985. pap. 5.95 (ISBN 0-8006-1836-X, 1-1836). Fortress.

Helgeson, Donald V. Handbook for Writing Technical Proposals That Win Contracts. LC 85-3549. 178p. 1985. pap. 24.95 (ISBN 0-13-379686-8). P-H.

Helick, R. Martin. The Complex Vision of Philo St. John. LC 75-27035. 1975. 10.00 (ISBN 0-912710-07-1). Regent Graphic Serv.

Heline, Corinne. The Blessed Virgin Mary: Her Life & Mission. (Illus.). 152p. 1986. pap. text ed. 8.95 (ISBN 0-933963-12-2). New Age Bible.

--Healing & Regeneration Through Color & Music. 96p. 1983. pap. 3.95 (ISBN 0-87516-512-5). DE Vorss.

--Mysteries of the Holy Grail. pap. 3.95 (ISBN 0-87613-015-5). New Age.

--Mystic Masonry & the Bible. pap. 1.00 (ISBN 0-87613-017-1). New Age.

--Mythology & the Bible. 1972. pap. 4.50 (ISBN 0-87613-018-X). New Age.

--Mythology & the Bible. 75p. pap. text ed. 4.50 (ISBN 0-933963-13-0). New Age Bible.

--New Age Bible Interpretation, Vol. 1. (Illus.). 496p. 1985. Repr. of 1935 ed. lib. bdg. 16.00 (ISBN 0-933963-01-7). New Age Bible.

--New Age Bible Interpretation, Vol. 2. (Illus.). 469p. Repr. lib. bdg. 16.00 (ISBN 0-933963-02-5). New Age Bible.

--New Age Bible Interpretation, Vol. 3. (Illus.). 516p. Repr. text ed. 16.00 (ISBN 0-87613-046-5). New Age Bible.

--New Age Bible Interpretation, Vol. 4. 144p. 1985. Repr. of 1935 ed. lib. bdg. 8.00 (ISBN 0-87613-089-9). New Age Bible.

--New Age Bible Interpretation, Vol. 5. 230p. Repr. lib. bdg. 11.00 (ISBN 0-933963-05-X). New Age Bible.

--New Age Bible Interpretation, Vol. 6. (Illus.). 255p. lib. bdg. 12.00 (ISBN 0-933963-06-8). New Age Bible.

--New Age Bible Interpretation, Vol. 7. (Illus.). 298p. lib. bdg. 14.00 (ISBN 0-933963-07-6). New Age Bible.

--New Testament, 3 Vols. Vol. 4. 8.00 (ISBN 0-87613-086-4); Vol. 5. 12.00 (ISBN 0-87613-082-1); Vol. 6. 12.00 (ISBN 0-87613-083-X). New Age.

--Occult Anatomy & the Bible. 1985. pap. 9.95 (ISBN 0-87613-093-7). New Age.

--Questions & Answers, Biblical. pap. 2.50 (ISBN 0-87613-026-0). New Age.

--The Sacred Science of Numbers. 140p. 1981. pap. 4.00 (ISBN 0-87516-442-0). De Vorss.

--Sacred Science of Numbers. 33p. pap. 4.00 (ISBN 0-87613-027-9). New Age.

--Star Gates. 7.95 (ISBN 0-933963-09-2). New Age.

--Twelve Labors of Hercules. (In the Zodiacal School of Life Ser.). pap. 2.50 (ISBN 0-87613-029-5). New Age.

Helldorfer, Martin C. Prayer: A Guide When Troubled. LC 85-13561. (Illus.). 88p. (Orig.). 1985. pap. 7.95 (ISBN 0-89571-024-2). Affirmation.

--The Work Trap. LC 80-52059. 96p. 1983. pap. 5.95 (ISBN 0-89571-017-X). Affirmation.

Helldorfer, Martin C. & Polcino, Anna. Relationships: Issues of Emotional Living in an Age of Stress for Clergy & Religious. Sammon, Sean D., ed. LC 83-2706. 144p. (Orig.). 1983. pap. 8.00 (ISBN 0-89571-015-3). Affirmation.

Helleberg, Marilyn M. Beyond T. M. A Practical Guide to the Lost Tradition of Christian Meditation. LC 80-82811. 144p. (Orig.). 1981. pap. 7.95 (ISBN 0-8091-2325-8). Paulist Pr.

--A Guide to Christian Meditation. 258p. 1985. pap. 9.95 large print ed. (ISBN 0-8027-2489-2). Walker & Co.

Heller, Agnes & Feher, Ferenc. Doomsday or Deterence? On the Antinuclear Issue. 192p. 1986. 35.00 (ISBN 0-87332-368-8); pap. 12.95 (ISBN 0-87332-369-6). M E Sharpe.

Heller, Alfred L. Your Body, His Temple: Reaching a Balanced Christian View of Diet & Physical Fitness. LC 81-1897. 192p. 1981. pap. 4.95 (ISBN 0-8407-5769-7). Nelson.

Heller, Celia. On the Edge of Destruction: Jews in Poland Between the Two World Wars. LC 76-22646. (Illus.). 1977. 36.00x (ISBN 0-231-03819-4). Columbia U Pr.

Heller, Celia S. On the Edge of Destruction: Jews of Poland Between the Two World Wars. LC 79-24645. 384p. 1980. pap. 8.95 (ISBN 0-8052-0651-5). Schocken.

Heller, David. The Children's God. LC 85-24581. (Illus.). 176p. 1986. 15.95 (ISBN 0-226-32635-7). U of Chicago Pr.

Heller, H. The Conquest of Poverty: The Calvinist Revolt in Sixteenth-Century France. (Studies in Medieval & Reformation Thought: No. 35). xiv, 281p. 1986. 40.00 (ISBN 90-04-07598-4, Pub. by E J Brill). Heinman.

Heller, James E. Our Share of Morning. LC 73-5262. 360p. 1974. Repr. of 1961 ed. lib. bdg. 22.50x (ISBN 0-8371-6874-0, BUOS). Greenwood.

Heller, John. The Report on the Shroud of Turin. 1984. pap. 8.95 (ISBN 0-395-36568-6). HM.

Heller, John H. Report on the Shroud of Turin. LC 83-127. 1983. 15.95 (ISBN 0-395-33967-7). HM.

Heller, Michael. The World & the Word: Between Science & Religion. Kisiel, Adam C., tr. from Polish. LC 86-61668. (Philosophy in Science Library: Vol. 1). 184p. 1987. pap. 14.95 (ISBN 0-88126-724-4). Pachart Pub Hse.
Heller, Nevin, ed. see Zwingli, Ulrich.
Heller, Rachelle, jt. auth. see Martin, Dianne.
Heller, Wendy. My Name Is Nabil. (Illus.). 48p. 1981. 5.95 (ISBN 0-933770-17-0). Kalimat.
Hellholm, David, ed. Apocalypticism in the Mediterranean World & the Near East: Proceedings of the International Colloquium. 889p. 1983. lib. bdg. 157.50x (ISBN 3-16-144460-4, Pub. by J C B Mohr BRD). Coronet Bks.
Hellman, Frances, tr. see Leroy-Beaulieu, Anatole.
Hellman, Peter, text by. The Auschwitz Album. 1987. 25.00 (ISBN 0-89604-085-2). Holocaust Pubns.
Hellmann, S., ed. see Gregorius, Saint.
Hellwig, Monika. The Christian Creeds. 112p. 1973. pap. 1.95 (ISBN 0-8278-9057-5, Pub. by Pflaum Pr). Peter Li.
--The Eucharist & the Hunger of the World. LC 76-18050. 100p. 1976. pap. 3.95 (ISBN 0-8091-1958-7). Paulist Pr.
--The Meaning of the Sacraments. 1.95 (ISBN 0-686-13702-7, Pub. by Pflaum Pr). Peter Li.
--Sign of Reconciliation & Conversion: The Sacrament of Penance for Our Times. (Message of the Sacraments Ser.: Vol. 4). 1982. 13.95 (ISBN 0-89453-394-0); pap. 8.95 (ISBN 0-89453-272-3). M Glazier.
--Tradition: The Catholic Story Today. 96p. (Orig.). 1974. pap. 2.95 (ISBN 0-8278-9060-5, Pub. by Pflaum Pr). Peter Li.
--What Are the Theologians Saying. (Orig.). 1970. pap. 2.95 (ISBN 0-8278-9051-6, Pub. by Pflaum Pr). Peter Li.
--Whose Experience Counts in Theological Reflection? LC 82-80331. (Pere Marquette Lecture Ser.). 112p. 1982. 7.95 (ISBN 0-87462-537-8). Marquette.
Hellwig, Monika K. Christian Women in a Troubled World: Madeleva Lecture 1984. 60p. (Orig.). 1985. 2.95 (ISBN 0-8091-2713-X). Paulist Pr.
--Jesus, the Compassion of God: New Perspectives on the Tradition of Christianity. 1983. 12.95 (ISBN 0-89453-365-7); pap. 7.95 (ISBN 0-89453-375-4). M Glazier.
--Understanding Catholicism. LC 81-80047. 200p. (Orig.). 1981. pap. 5.95 (ISBN 0-8091-2384-3). Paulist Pr.
--What Are They Saying about Death & Christian Hope? LC 78-61726. 1978. pap. 3.95 (ISBN 0-8091-2165-4). Paulist Pr.
Helm, Janet. Jesus Changes People. Duckert, Mary, ed. (New Vacation Venture Ser.). leader's guide 3.95; 1.95 (ISBN 0-664-24172-7); resource packet 11.95 (ISBN 0-664-24174-3); New Life Songbook. 0.95 (ISBN 0-664-24171-9). Westminster.
Helm, Mary. From Darkness to Light: The Story of Negro Progress. LC 76-88433. Repr. of 1909 ed. cancelled (ISBN 0-8371-1908-1, HED&, Pub. by Negro U Pr). Greenwood.
Helm, Paul. The Beginnings: Word & Spirit in Conversion. 133p. (Orig.). 1986. pap. 4.95 (ISBN 0-85151-470-7). Banner of Truth.
--Calvin & the Calvinists. 84p. (Orig.). 1982. pap. 5.95 (ISBN 0-85151-344-1). Banner of Truth.
--The Divine Revelation. LC 82-72325. (Foundations for Faith Ser.). 144p. (Orig.). 1982. pap. 8.95 (ISBN 0-89107-258-6, Crossway Bks). Good News.
Helm, Paul, ed. Divine Commands & Morality. (Readings in Philosophy Ser.). 1981. pap. 9.95x (ISBN 0-19-875049-8). Oxford U Pr.
Helm, Paul, ed. see Edwards, Jonathan.
Helman, Ethel. An Autumn Life: How a Surgeon Faced His Fatal Illness. 120p. (Orig.). 1986. pap. 6.95 (ISBN 0-571-13704-0). Faber & Faber.
Helmbold, F. Wilbur. Selma: The Gospel at Work. 1983. 12.50; pap. 8.50. Banner Pr AL.
Helmbold, F. Wilbur, ed. Seventy-Five Years, Central Park Baptist Church, Birmingham, Alabama, 1910-1985. (Illus., Orig.). 1985. 25.00 (ISBN 0-87121-447-4). Banner Pr AL.
Helming, Dennis M. Footprints in the Snow: A Pictorial Biography of the Founder of Opus Dei, Josemaria Escriva. (Illus.). 80p. (Orig.). 1986. pap. write for info. (ISBN 0-933932-50-2). Scepter Pubs.
Helminiak, Daniel A. Spiritual Development: An Interdisciplinary Study. 256p. 1987. 15.95 (ISBN 0-8294-0530-5). Loyola.
Helminiak, Daniel A., ed. The Same Jesus: A Contemporary Christology. 368p. 1986. 15.95 (ISBN 0-8294-0521-6). Loyola.
Helmold Priest Of Bosau. Chronicle of the Slavs. Tschan, Francis J., tr. 1967. lib. bdg. 29.00x (ISBN 0-374-98018-7, Octagon). Hippocrene Bks.
Helmreich, Ernst. The German Churches Under Hitler: Background, Struggle & Epilogue. LC 78-17737. 617p. 1978. 35.00x (ISBN 0-8143-1603-4). Wayne St U Pr.
Helmreich, Ernst, ed. Church & State in Europe. LC 78-68021. (Problems in Civilization Ser.). 1979. pap. 6.95x (ISBN 0-88273-405-9). Forum Pr IL.
Helmreich, Ernst C. Religion at Bowdoin College: A History. LC 81-71331. (Illus.). 1981. pap. 7.50 (ISBN 0-916606-03-1). Bowdoin Coll.
--Religious Education in German Schools: An Historical Approach. LC 59-11509. 1959. 22.50x (ISBN 0-674-75850-1). Harvard U Pr.
Helmreich, William B. The World of the Yeshiva: An Intimate Portrait of Orthodox Jewry. 405p. 1982. 19.95 (ISBN 0-02-914640-2). Free Pr.
--The Yeshiva in America. 384p. 1981. text ed. 19.95 (ISBN 0-02-914640-2, 914640). Free Pr.
Helmreich, William N. The World of the Yeshiva: An Intimate Portrait of Orthodox Jewry. LC 81-67440. 424p. 1986. pap. 14.95x (ISBN 0-300-03715-5). Yale U Pr.
Helms, Hal. Confessions of St. Augustine: Modern English Version. 304p. 1986. pap. 8.95 (ISBN 0-941478-55-6). Paraclete Pr.
Helms, Hal H., ed. see Lawrence.
Helms, Hal M. With the Lord Today, 4 vols. (Orig.). 1985. Set. 14.95 set (ISBN 0-941478-39-4). Paraclete Pr.
Helms, Hal M., ed. Saints Alive! the Book. (Orig.). 1985. pap. 9.95 (ISBN 0-941478-44-0). Paraclete Pr.
Helms, Hal M., ed. see Bunyan, John.
Helms, Hal M., ed. see Carver, Estelle C.
Helms, Hal M., ed. see De Salignac de la Mothe-Fenelon, Francoise.
Helms, Hal M., ed. see Fenelon, Archbishop.
Helms, Hal M., ed. see Thomas a Kempis.
Helmstadter, Richard J. & Phillips, Paul T., eds. Religion in Victorian Society: A Sourcebook of Documents. 484p. (Orig.). 1986. lib. bdg. 36.00 (ISBN 0-8191-4994-2); pap. text ed. 17.75 (ISBN 0-8191-4995-0). U Pr of Amer.
Helps, Arthur. The Life of las Casas: The Apostle of the Indies. 1976. lib. bdg. 75.00 (ISBN 0-8490-2165-0). Gordon Pr.
Helser, Albert D. Education of Primitive People. LC 75-97403. Repr. of 1934 ed. cancelled (ISBN 0-8371-2651-7, HPP&, Pub. by Negro U Pr). Greenwood.
Helten, William L. Van, ed. Die Altostniederfraenkischen Psalmenfragmente: Die Lipsius'schen Glossen & Die Altsuedmittelfraenkischen Psalmenfragmente. 222p. 1970. 30.00 (ISBN 0-384-22230-7). Johnson Repr.
Helwig, Terry. Forgive Me, Lord, I Goofed! (Orig.). 1986. pap. 3.25 (ISBN 0-8054-5035-1). Broadman.
Helwys, Thomas. Objections Answered by Way of Dialogue, Wherein Is Proved That No Man Ought to Be Persecuted for His Religion. LC 73-6139. (English Experience Ser.: No. 603). 80p. 1973. Repr. of 1615 ed. 6.00 (ISBN 90-221-0603-9). Walter J Johnson.
Helyot, P. Dictionnaires des Ordres Religieux ou Historie des Ordres Monastiques, Religieux et Militaires, 4 vols. Migne, J. P., ed. (Encyclopedie Theologique Ser.: Vols. 20-23). (Fr.). 2724p. Repr. of 1859 ed. lib. bdg. 347.50x (ISBN 0-89241-239-9). Caratzas.
Helzel, Florence B., jt. auth. see Levy, Jane.
Hembree, Ron. Fruits of the Spirit. (Direction Bks.). pap. 4.95 (ISBN 0-8010-4301-8). Baker Bk.
--Good Morning, Lord: Devotions for New Christians. (Good Morning, Lord Ser.). 96p. 1983. 4.95 (ISBN 0-8010-4271-2). Baker Bk.
--Good Morning, Lord: Devotions for Newlyweds. 128p. 1982. 4.95 (ISBN 0-8010-4262-3). Baker Bk.
--Good Morning, Lord: More Five Minute Devotions. (Good Morning, Lord Ser.). 64p. 1977. Repr. 3.95 (ISBN 0-8010-4178-3). Baker Bk.
--The Mark Buntain Story. LC 83-73187. 256p. 1984. pap. 3.95 (ISBN 0-87123-595-5, 200593). Bethany Hse.
--The Speck in Your Brother's Eye: How to Be a More Loving Christian. 192p. 1985. 9.95 (ISBN 0-8007-1426-1). Revell.
Hemenway, Joan E. Holding on... While Letting Go. (Looking Up Ser.). (Orig.). 1985. pap. 1.25 (ISBN 0-8298-0548-6). Pilgrim NY.
Hemer, C. J. The Letters to the Seven Churches of Asia in Their Local Setting. (JSoT Supplement Ser.: No. 11). 375p. 1986. text ed. 32.50x (ISBN 0-905774-95-7, Pub. by JSOT Pr England); pap. text ed. 14.95x (ISBN 0-905774-96-5). Eisenbrauns.
Hemesath, Caroline. From Slave to Priest. 1974. 6.95 (ISBN 0-8199-0468-6). Franciscan Herald.
Hemingway, Donald W. Utah & the Mormons. (Illus.). 1979. pap. 2.50 (ISBN 0-686-30193-5). D W Hemingway.
Hemingway, Donald W., ed. Utah & the Mormons. (Travel Ser.). (Illus.). 32p. 1983. pap. write for info. (ISBN 0-938440-47-0). Colourpicture.
Hemleben, Johannes. Rudolf Steiner: A Documentary Biography. Twyman, Leo, tr. (Illus.). 1975. (Pub by Henry Goulden, Ltd); pap. 10.95 (ISBN 0-904822-03-6). St George Bk Serv.
Hemmendinger, Judith. Survivors: Children of the Holocaust. Tr. of Les Enfants De Buchenwald. 200p. (Orig.). 1986. Repr. of 1984 ed. 15.95 (ISBN 0-915765-24-1). Natl Pr Inc.
Hemmenway, John. The Apostle of Peace: Memoir of William Ladd. LC 70-137544. 272p. 1972. Repr. of 1872 ed. lib. bdg. 20.95x (ISBN 0-89198-072-5). Ozer.
Hemming, James. Instead of God? A Pragmatic Reconsideration of Beliefs & Values. 244p. 1986. 19.95 (ISBN 0-7145-2835-8, Dist. by Kampmann). M Boyars Pubs.
Hemmingway, Donald W. Gospel Themes. 90p. 1982. 3.95 (ISBN 0-934126-25-9). Randall Bk Co.
--Gospel Themes II. 71p. 1983. 3.95 (ISBN 0-934126-40-2). Randall Bk Co.
Hemon, Michael, tr. see Von Daniken, Erich.
Hempel, Charles J. True Organization of the New Church. LC 40-30032. Repr. of 1848 ed. 31.50 (ISBN 0-404-08464-8). AMS Pr.
Hempton, David. Methodism & Politics in British Society, 1750-1850. LC 84-51419. 276p. 1984. 27.50x (ISBN 0-8047-1269-7). Stanford U Pr.
Hemrick, Eugene F., et al. Seminarians in Theology: A National Profile. 128p. 1986. pap. 8.95 (ISBN 1-55586-978-5). US Catholic.
Hendee, John. Ambassadors for Christ. (Ambassadors Training Program Ser.). 64p. (Orig.). 1984. pap. 2.95 trainer's manual (ISBN 0-87239-812-9, 3221); student book 2.50 (ISBN 0-87239-813-7, 3222). Standard Pub.
--Discipling New Christians with the Spiritual T. E. A. M. Veteran Season. (Spiritual T.E.A.M Ser.). 64p. 1986. pap. 2.95 wkbk. (ISBN 0-87403-153-2, 3246). Standard Pub.
--Discipling New Christians with the Spiritual T. E. A. M. Rookie Season. (Spiritual T.E.A.M. Ser.). 64p. 1986. pap. 2.95 wkbk. (ISBN 0-87403-152-4, 3245). Standard Pub.
--Discipling New Christians with the Spiritual T. E. A. M. Coach's Manual. (Spiritual T.E.A.M. Ser.). 136p. 1986. pap. 5.95 (ISBN 0-87403-151-6, 3244). Standard Pub.
--Peace Treaty with God. (Ambassadors Training Program Ser.). 16p. (Orig.). 1984. pap. 0.50 (ISBN 0-87239-814-5, 3223). Standard Pub.
Hendel, Charles W., ed. see Hume, David.
Hendel-Sebestyen, Giselle. The Sephardic Home: Ethnic Homogeneity & Cultural Traditions in a Total Institution. LC 83-45356. (Immigrant Communities & Ethnic Minorities in the United States & Canada Ser.). 1986. 67.50 (ISBN 0-404-19409-5). AMS Pr.
Henderlite, Rachel. Call to Faith. LC 55-5552. 224p. 1955. pap. 2.49 (ISBN 0-8042-3136-2). John Knox.
--Exploring the New Testament. (Orig.). 1946. pap. 5.95 (ISBN 0-8042-0240-0). John Knox.
--Exploring the Old Testament. (Orig.). 1945. pap. 5.95 (ISBN 0-8042-0120-X). John Knox.
Hendershot, Kathy. Obedience: The Road to Reality. 176p. (Orig.). 1982. pap. 3.50 (ISBN 0-911567-00-3). Christian Mini.
Henderson, Charles P., Jr. God & Science: The Death & Rebirth of Theism. LC 85-23091. 216p. 1986. pap. 10.95 (ISBN 0-8042-0668-6). John Knox.
Henderson, E. Harold. Now Abideth Faith. 120p. 1962. pap. 0.50 (ISBN 0-89114-149-9). Baptist Pub Hse.
--Roman Dogma vs. Bible Doctrine. 152p. 1964. pap. 1.00 (ISBN 0-89114-060-3). Baptist Pub Hse.
--Triumph of Trust: Habakkuk. (Illus.). 96p. (Orig.). 1980. pap. 2.00 (ISBN 0-89114-092-1); study guide 0.75 (ISBN 0-89114-138-3). Baptist Pub Hse.
Henderson, Florence, jt. auth. see Lewis, Shari.
Henderson, George. A Religious Foundation of Human Relations: Beyond Games. LC 76-62510. 1977. 15.95x (ISBN 0-8061-1398-7). U of Okla Pr.
Henderson, Henry F. Calvin in His Letters. 59.95 (ISBN 0-87968-810-6). Gordon Pr.
Henderson, John B. The Development & Decline of Chinese Cosmology. LC 84-4000. (Neo-Confucian Studies). 280p. 1984. 36.00 (ISBN 0-231-05772-5); pap. cancelled (ISBN 0-231-05773-3). Columbia U Pr.
Henderson, John L. John Strachan, Seventeen Hundred Seventy-Eight to Eighteen Hundred Sixty-Seven. LC 70-408188. (Canadian Biographical Studies: No. 1). pap. 30.50 (ISBN 0-317-09154-9, 2019176). Bks Demand UMI.
Henderson, Joseph L. Thresholds of Initiation. LC 67-24110. 1967. pap. 10.95 (ISBN 0-8195-6061-8). Wesleyan U Pr.
Henderson, Joseph L. see Watts, Alan W.
Henderson, Robert T. Beating the Church Going Blahs. LC 86-21338. 132p. 1986. pap. 5.95 (ISBN 0-87784-516-6). Inter Varsity.
--Joy to the World: An Introduction to Kingdom Evangelism. LC 80-14597. 207p. (Orig.). 1980. pap. 6.50 (ISBN 0-8042-2096-4). John Knox.
Hendley, Jesse M. The Fifth Horseman of the Apocalypse. LC 85-19795. 236p. (Orig.). 1985. pap. 10.95 (ISBN 0-8254-2849-1). Kregel.
Hendren, Bob. Chosen for Riches. LC 77-25775. (Journey Bks.). 1978. 3.50 (ISBN 0-8344-0096-0). Sweet.
--Life Without End. LC 80-54164. (Journey Adult Ser.). 144p. 1981. pap. 3.50 (ISBN 0-8344-0118-5). Sweet.
Hendren, Samuel R. Government & Religion of the Virginia Indians. LC 78-63845. (Johns Hopkins University. Studies in the Social Sciences. Thirteenth Ser. 1895: 11-12). Repr. of 1895 ed. 11.50 (ISBN 0-404-61102-8). AMS Pr.
Hendrick, Burton J. The Jews in America. Grob, Gerald, ed. LC 76-46081. (Anti-Movements in America). 1977. Repr. of 1923 ed. lib. bdg. 17.00x (ISBN 0-405-09954-1). Ayer Co Pubs.
Hendrick, Eddie. I Write for You. 48p. 1983. 5.95 (ISBN 0-686-82586-1). Todd & Honeywell.
Hendricks, Frances K., tr. see Latorre Cabal, Hugo.
Hendricks, Gay & Weinhold, Barry. Transpersonal Approaches to Counseling & Psychotherapy. 199p. 1982. pap. text ed. 12.95 (ISBN 0-89108-112-7). Love Pub Co.
Hendricks, Howard. Las Familias Conviven Mejor con Amor. 48p. 1979. 1.65 (ISBN 0-88113-095-8). Edit Betania.
Hendricks, Howard & Hendricks, Jeanne. Footprints: Walking Through the Passages of Life. LC 80-25868. (Illus.). 96p. 1981. pap. 5.95 (ISBN 0-930014-55-3). Multnomah.
Hendricks, Howard G. Heaven Help the Home! LC 73-78689. 143p. 1973. pap. 5.95 (ISBN 0-88207-240-4). Victor Bks.
--Say It with Love. LC 72-77011. 143p. 1972. pap. 5.95 (ISBN 0-88207-050-9). Victor Bks.
--Taking a Stand: What God Can Do Through Ordinary You. LC 83-8241. 1983. pap. 4.95 (ISBN 0-88070-025-4). Multnomah.
Hendricks, Jeanne, jt. auth. see Hendricks, Howard.
Hendricks, Rhoda A. Mythologies of the World: A Concise Encyclopedia. Shapiro, Max S., ed. (McGraw-Hill Paperbacks Ser.). 240p. 1981. pap. 5.95 (ISBN 0-07-056421-3). McGraw.
Hendricks, Rhoda A., tr. & intro. by. Classical Gods & Heroes: Myths As Told by the Ancient Authors. 1974. pap. 7.95 (ISBN 0-688-05279-7). Morrow.
Hendricks, Robert J. Bethel & Aurora. LC 75-134380. Repr. of 1933 ed. 26.50 (ISBN 0-404-08428-1). AMS Pr.
Hendricks, Tyler, jt. ed. see Flinn, Frank K.
Hendricks, William. Quien es Jesuscristo? Martinez, Jose L., tr. from Eng. (Bibloteca de Doctrina Cristiana Ser.). Tr. of Who is Jesus Christ? (Span.). 164p. 1986. pap. 5.95 (ISBN 0-311-09112-1). Casa Bautista.
Hendricks, William C. Good Morning, Lord: Devotions for Boys. (Good Morning Lord Ser.). 1974. 4.95 (ISBN 0-8010-4100-7). Baker Bk.
Hendricks, William C. & Den Bleyker, Merle. Object Lessons from Sports & Games. (Object Lessons Ser). 126p. 1975. pap. 3.95 (ISBN 0-8010-4134-1). Baker Bk.
--Object Lessons That Teach Bible Truths. (Object Lessons Ser.). 1977. pap. 3.95 (ISBN 0-8010-4172-4). Baker Bk.
Hendricks, William C. & Noord, Glenn Van. Bible Word Chain Puzzles. (Quiz & Puzzle Bks.). 96p. (Orig.). 1981. pap. 2.95 (ISBN 0-8010-4238-0). Baker Bk.
Hendricks, William C. & Vogel, Cora. Handbook of Christmas Programs. 1978. pap. 9.95 (ISBN 0-8010-4204-6). Baker Bk.
Hendricks, William L. A Theology for Aging. 1986. 10.95 (ISBN 0-8054-1712-5). Broadman.
--A Theology for Children. LC 80-65539. 1980. 10.95 (ISBN 0-8054-1711-7). Broadman.
--Who Is Jesus Christ? LC 83-71265. (Layman's Library of Christian Doctrine Ser.). 1985. 5.95 (ISBN 0-8054-1632-3). Broadman.
Hendricksen, W., tr. see Bavinck, Herman.
Hendrickson, Michael C., ed. The Role of the Church in Aging: Implications for Policy & Action. LC 85-17564. (Journal of Religion & Aging: Vol. 2, Nos. 1-2). 178p. 1986. text ed. 29.95 (ISBN 0-86656-482-9, B482); pap. text ed. 19.95 (ISBN 0-86656-483-7, B483). Haworth Pr.
Hendrickson, Paul. Seminary: A Search. 320p. 1987. pap. 6.95 (ISBN 0-671-63586-7). Summit Bks.
Hendrickx, Herman. The Infancy Narratives. (Commentary on Synoptic Gospels Ser.). 144p. 1984. pap. 9.95 (ISBN 0-225-66398-8, 8523, HarpR). Har-Row.

--The Passion Narratives. (Commentary on the Synoptic Gospels Ser.). 210p. 1984. pap. 9.95 (ISBN 0-225-66400-3, 8524, HarpR). Har-Row.
--The Resurrection Narratives. (Commentary on the Synoptic Gospels Ser.). 168p. 1984. pap. 9.95 (ISBN 0-225-66401-1, 8525, HarpR). Har-Row.
--The Sermon on the Mount. (Commentary on the Synoptic Gospels Ser.). 228p. 1984. pap. 9.95 (ISBN 0-225-66399-6, 8526, HarpR). Har-Row.
Hendriksen, William. Bible on the Life Hereafter. (Direction Books). 1971. pap. 6.95 (ISBN 0-8010-4022-1). Baker Bk.
--The Covenant of Grace. 1978. pap. 2.95 (ISBN 0-8010-4196-1). Baker Bk.
--Galatians & Ephesians. (New Testament Commentary Ser.). 290p. 1979. 18.95 (ISBN 0-8010-4211-9). Baker Bk.
--John. (New Testament Commentary Ser.). 1961. 24.95 (ISBN 0-8010-4051-5). Baker Bk.
--Luke. (New Testament Commentary Ser.). 1978. 24.95 (ISBN 0-8010-4191-0). Baker Bk.
--Mark. (New Testament Commentary Ser). 708p. 1975. 21.95 (ISBN 0-8010-4114-7). Baker Bk.
--Matthew. (New Testament Commentary Ser.). 1973. 24.95 (ISBN 0-8010-4066-3). Baker Bk.
--More Than Conquerors. Commeritive ed. 11.95 (ISBN 0-8010-4026-4). Baker Bk.
--NTC-Romans, 1 Vol. 1981. 19.95 (ISBN 0-8010-4265-8). Baker Bk.
--Philippians, Colossians, & Philemon. (New Testament Commentary). 243p. 1979. 17.95 (ISBN 0-8010-4212-7). Baker Bk.
--Survey of the Bible. rev. ed. LC 76-507. 515p. 1976. 17.95 (ISBN 0-8010-4288-7). Baker Bk.
--Thessalonians, Timothy & Titus. 404p. 1979. 21.95 (ISBN 0-8010-4213-5). Baker Bk.
Hendrix, John & Householder, Lloyd, eds. The Equipping of Disciples. LC 76-29803. 1977. bds. 9.95 (ISBN 0-8054-3218-3). Broadman.
Hendrix, John D. To Thessalonians with Love. LC 81-70974. (Orig.). 1983. pap. 6.50 (ISBN 0-8054-1312-X). Broadman.
Hendrix, Olan. Management for the Christian Leader. 1986. text ed. 8.95 (ISBN 0-8010-4313-1). Baker Bk.
Hendrix, Scott H. Luther & the Papacy: Stages in a Reformation Conflict. LC 80-2393. pap. 56.30 (2027874). Bks Demand UMI.
Hendry, George S. Theology of Nature. LC 79-27375. 258p. 1980. pap. 13.95 (ISBN 0-664-24305-3). Westminster.
Henel, Heinrich. Studien Zum Altenglischen Computus. 1934. pap. 8.00 (ISBN 0-384-22300-1). Johnson Repr.
Henery, Charles R., ed. Beyond the Horizon. 96p. (Orig.). 1986. pap. 4.30 (ISBN 0-88028-055-7). Forward Movement.
Heng Chau, jt. auth. see Heng Sure.
Hengel, Martin. Acts & the History of Earliest Christianity. LC 79-8893. 160p. 1980. 9.95 (ISBN 0-8006-0630-2, 1-630); pap. 7.50 (ISBN 0-8006-1876-9, 1-1876). Fortress.
--Between Jesus & Paul. LC 83-48003. 256p. 1983. pap. 14.95 (ISBN 0-8006-1720-7). Fortress.
--The Charismatic Leader & His Followers. LC 81-9708. 124p. 1981. 10.95 (ISBN 0-8245-0137-3). Crossroad NY.
--Crucifixion: In the Ancient World & the Folly of the Message of the Cross. Bowden, John, tr. from Ger. LC 77-78629. 118p. 1977. pap. 5.50 (ISBN 0-8006-1268-X, 1-1268). Fortress.
--Judaism & Hellenism: Studies in Their Encounter in Palestine During the Early Hellenistic Period, 2 Vols. pap. 160.00 (2027202). Bks Demand UMI.
--Property & Riches in the Early Church: Aspects of a Social History of Early Christianity. Bowden, John, tr. from Ger. LC 75-305658. pap. 26.00 (2026856). Bks Demand UMI.
--The Son of God: The Origin of Christology & the History of Jewish-Hellenistic Religion. Bowden, John, tr. from Ger. LC 75-37151. 112p. 1976. pap. 5.50 (ISBN 0-8006-1227-2, 1-1227). Fortress.
--Studies in the Gospel of Mark. Bowden, John, tr. LC 85-4508. 216p. 1985. pap. 12.95 (ISBN 0-8006-1881-5). Fortress.
Hengstenberg, E. W. Christology of the Old Testament. Arnold, T. K., tr. from Ger. LC 77-129739. (Kregel Reprint Library). 716p. 1988. pap. 16.95 (ISBN 0-8254-2812-2). Kregel.
--Commentary on the Gospel of John, 2 vols. 1980. Set. 34.95 (ISBN 0-86524-047-7, 4302). Klock & Klock.
Heng Sure & Heng Chau. News from True Cultivators, Vol. I. 128p. (Orig.). 1983. pap. 5.00 (ISBN 0-88139-016-X). Buddhist Text.
--News from True Cultivators, Vol. 2. 130p. (Orig.). 1983. pap. 5.00 (ISBN 0-88139-024-0). Buddhist Text.
--With One Heart Bowing to the City of Ten Thousand Buddhas, Vol. IV. (Illus.). 136p. (Orig.). 1980. pap. 4.00 (ISBN 0-917512-90-1). Buddhist Text.
--With One Heart Bowing to the City of Ten Thousand Buddhas, Vol. VI. (Illus.). 200p. (Orig.). 1981. pap. 6.00 (ISBN 0-917512-92-8). Buddhist Text.
--With One Heart Bowing to the City of Ten Thousand Buddhas, Vol. I. (Illus.). 180p. (Orig.). 1977. pap. 6.00 (ISBN 0-917512-21-9). Buddhist Text.
--With One Heart Bowing to the City of Ten Thousand Buddhas, Vol. II. (Illus.). 322p. (Orig.). 1979. pap. 7.00 (ISBN 0-917512-23-5). Buddhist Text.
--With One Heart Bowing to the City of Ten Thousand Buddhas, Vol. IX. 220p. (Orig.). 1983. pap. 7.50 (ISBN 0-88139-016-X). Buddhist Text.
Heng Sure, et al. Open Your Eyes. (Illus.). 347p. (Orig.). 1979. pap. 7.50 (ISBN 0-917512-32-4). Buddhist Text.
Heng Tao, Bhikshuni see Buddhist Text Translation Society Staff.
Heng Yin, et al. Songs for Awakening. (Illus.). 112p. (Orig.). 1979. pap. 8.00 (ISBN 0-917512-31-6). Buddhist Text.
Henig, Martin. Religion in Roman Britain. LC 84-6914. 256p. 1984. 29.95 (ISBN 0-312-67059-1). St Martin.
Hening, Mrs. E. F. History of the African Mission of the Protestant Episcopal Church in the United States. facsimile ed. LC 77-173608. (Black Heritage Library Collection). Repr. of 1849 ed. 20.75 (ISBN 0-8369-8900-7). Ayer Co Pubs.
Henisch, Bridget Ann. Fast & Feast: Food in Medieval Society. LC 76-15677. (Illus.). 1977. pap. 12.50x (ISBN 0-271-00424-X). Pa St U Pr.
Henke, Peter. Vor Dem Nichts. (Theologischo Bibliothek Toepelmann: Vol. 34). (Illus.). 1978. 26.80 (ISBN 3-11-007254-8). De Gruyter.
Henkel, Arthur, ed. Emblemata: Supplement der Erstausgabe. Schoene, Albrecht. (Ger.). 400p. 1976. 65.00 (ISBN 0-317-02568-6). Interbk Inc.
Henkelmann, Ervin F. & Carter, Stephen J. How to Develop a Team Ministry & Make It Work. 1985. pap. 8.95 (ISBN 0-570-03946-0, 12-2879). Concordia.
Henken, Elissa R. Traditions of the Welsh Saints. 200p. 1986. 37.50 (ISBN 0-85991-221-3, Pub. by Boydell & Brewer). Longwood Pub Group.
Henkes, Robert. The Crucifixion in American Painting. 1978. lib. bdg. 79.95 (ISBN 0-8490-1370-4). Gordon Pr.
Henle, Jane. Greek Myths: A Vase Painter's Notebook. LC 72-75639. (Illus.). 256p. 1973. 35.00x (ISBN 0-253-32635-4); pap. 7.95x (ISBN 0-253-32636-2). Ind U Pr.
Henley, Gurden. He Is Risen Indeed! 1986. 3.50 (ISBN 0-89536-795-5, 6813). CSS of Ohio.
--Joy to You & Me. Sherer, Michael L., ed. (Orig.). 1986. pap. 4.75 (ISBN 0-89536-832-3, 6846). CSS of Ohio.
Henley, W. E., ed. The Golden Ass of Apuleius. Aldington, William, tr. from Lat. 249p. 1981. Repr. of 1893 ed. lib. bdg. 50.00 (ISBN 0-89984-233-X). Century Bookbindery.
Henman, J. Robert. The Child As Quest: Method & Religious Education. LC 83-19877. 70p. (Orig.). 1984. pap. text ed. 6.75 (ISBN 0-8191-3633-6). U Pr of Amer.
Hennecke, Edgar. New Testament Apocrypha, 2 vols. Incl. Vol. 1. Gospels & Related Writings. 532p. 1963. 18.95 (ISBN 0-664-20385-X); Vol. 2. Writings Relating to the Apostles; Apocalypses & Related Subjects. LC 63-7492. 852p. 1966. 32.50 (ISBN 0-664-20680-8). Westminster.
Hennesey, James. American Catholics: A History of the Roman Catholic Community in the United States. 1981. pap. 10.95 (ISBN 0-19-503268-3). Oxford U Pr.
Hennesey, James J. American Catholics: A History of the Roman Catholic Community in the United States. 1981. 19.95x (ISBN 0-19-502946-1). Oxford U Pr.
Hennessey, Augustine. The Paschal Mystery: Core Grace in the Life of the Christian. (Synthesis Ser.). 37p. 1977. pap. 0.75 (ISBN 0-8199-0707-3). Franciscan Herald.
Hennessey, James. Catholics in the Promised Land of the Saints. LC 81-80935. (Pere Marquette Lecture Ser.). 100p. 1981. 7.95 (ISBN 0-87462-536-X). Marquette.
Hennig, David, compiled by. Good Stuff! (Good Stuff, Resources for Youth Leaders Ser.: Vol. 4). 160p. 1987. tchr's wkbk. 9.95 (ISBN 0-87403-216-4, 3416). Standard Pub.
Hennig, David, ed. Good Stuff, Vol. 2. 160p. 1986. wkbk. 9.95 (ISBN 0-87403-014-5, 3407). Standard Pub.
Henning, M., tr. see Avesta.
Henningsen, Gustav. The Witches' Advocate: Basque Witchcraft & the Spanish Inquisition, 1609-1614. LC 79-20340. (Basque Book Ser.). (Illus.). xxxii, 607p. 1980. 24.00 (ISBN 0-87417-056-7). U of Nev Pr.
Henningsen, Gustav & Tedeschi, John, eds. The Inquisition in Early Modern Europe: Studies on Sources & Methods. 254p. 1986. 27.50 (ISBN 0-87580-102-1). N Ill U Pr.
Henri, De Lubac. The Splendor of the Church. LC 86-82080. 382p. 1986. pap. 12.95 (ISBN 0-89870-120-1). Ignatius Pr.
Henrichsen, Walter. Apres le Sacrifice. Orig. Title: After the Sacrifice. (Fr.). 1986. write for info. (ISBN 0-8297-0524-4). Life Pubs Intl.
--Is It Any of God's Business? A Provocative Look at Faith in the Workplace. LC 86-63651. 204p. (Orig.). 1987. pap. price not set (ISBN 0-89109-138-6). NavPress.
Henrichsen, Walter A. After the Sacrifice. 1979. pap. 5.95 (ISBN 0-310-37711-0, 11231P). Zondervan.
--Disciples Are Made-Not Born. LC 74-79162. 160p. 1974. pap. 4.50 (ISBN 0-88207-706-6). Victor Bks.
--Entendamos. Cook, David A., tr. from Eng. Tr. of Understand. (Span.). 112p. 1979. pap. 2.95 (ISBN 0-89922-131-9). Edit Caribe.
--How to Disciple Your Children. 120p. 1981. pap. 4.95 (ISBN 0-88207-260-9). Victor Bks.
--A Layman's Guide to Interpreting the Bible. 112p. (Orig.). 1985. pap. 5.95 (ISBN 0-310-37681-5). Zondervan.
--A Layman's Guide to Studying the Bible. 144p. (Orig.). 1985. pap. 6.95 (ISBN 0-310-37631-9, 11236P). Zondervan.
Henrichsen, Walter A. & Jackson, Gayle. A Layman's Guide to Applying the Bible. 224p. (Orig.). 1985. pap. 7.95 (ISBN 0-310-37691-2, 11233P, Pub. by Lamplight); Set pack. pap. 19.95 (ISBN 0-310-37698-X, 11238P, Pub. by Lamplight). Zondervan.
Henry, Antonir Marie & LaBrosse, Olivier De, eds. Dictionnaire de la Foi Chretienne, 2 vols. (Fr.). 792p. 1968. pap. 47.50 (ISBN 0-686-56818-4, M-6596). French & Eur.
Henry, Avril. The Mirour of Mans Saluacioune: A Middle English Translation of Speculum Humanae Salvationis. LC 86-19364. (Middle Ages Ser.). (Illus.). 347p. 1987. text ed. 49.95x (ISBN 0-8122-8054-7). U of Pa Pr.
Henry, Caleb S. Moral & Philosophical Essays. LC 75-3178. Repr. of 1839 ed. 10.50 (ISBN 0-404-59181-7). AMS Pr.
Henry, Carl F. Christian Countermoves in a Decadent Culture. LC 86-5286. (Orig.). 1986. 9.95 (ISBN 0-88070-151-X). Multnomah.
--The Christian Mindset in a Secular Society. LC 83-25136. (Critical Concern Ser.). 1984. 9.95 (ISBN 0-88070-041-6); pap. 6.95. Multnomah.
--Christian Personal Ethics. (Twin Brooks Ser). 1977. pap. 12.95 (ISBN 0-8010-4165-1). Baker Bk.
--God, Revelation & Authority: God Who Speaks & Shows, Vols. 1 & 2. Incl. Vol. 1 (ISBN 0-87680-477-6, 80477); Vol. 2 (ISBN 0-87680-485-7, 80485). LC 76-15936. 1976. 22.95 ea. Word Bks.
--God, Revelation & Authority: God Who Speaks & Shows, Vols. 3, 4, 5 & 6. 1979. Vol. 3. 24.95 (ISBN 0-8499-0091-3); Vol. 4. 24.95 (ISBN 0-8499-0126-X); Vol. 5. 24.95 (ISBN 0-8499-0320-3); Vol. 6. 24.95 (ISBN 0-8499-0333-5). Word Bks.
Henry, Carl F., ed. Basic Christian Doctrines. (Twin Brooks Ser). pap. 8.95 (ISBN 0-8010-4033-7). Baker Bk.
--The Biblical Expositor. 1332p. 1986. Repr. text ed. 49.95 (ISBN 0-8010-0890-5). Baker Bk.
--Horizons of Science: Christian Scholars Speak Out. LC 77-7849. 1978. pap. 6.95xi (ISBN 0-06-063866-4, RD 240, HarpR). Har-Row.
Henry, Carl F. & Hancock, Robert L., eds. The Ministry of Development in Evangelical Perspective: A Symposium on the Social & Spiritual Mandate. LC 78-27821. 1979. pap. 4.95 (ISBN 0-87808-164-X). William Carey Lib.
Henry, Carl F., ed. see Holmes, Arthur F.
Henry, Carl F., et al. Conversations with Carl Henry: Christianity for Today. (Symposium Ser.: No. 18). 204p. 1986. lib. bdg. 49.95 (ISBN 0-88946-709-9). E Mellen.
Henry, D. P. Commentary on 'De Grammatico' The Historical-Logical Dimensions of a Dialogue of St. Anselm's. LC 73-86092. (Synthese Historical Library: No. 8). 200p. 1973. lib. bdg. 66.00 (ISBN 90-277-0382-5, Pub. by Reidel Holland). Kluwer Academic.
Henry, David P. The Early Development of the Hermeneutic of Karl Barth. (Dissertation Ser.: No. 5). ix, 215p. pap. 18.95 (ISBN 0-86554-130-2). NABPR.
--The Early Development of the Hermeneutic of Karl Barth As Evidenced by His Appropriation of Romans Chapter Five, Twelve to Twenty-One. ix, 275p. 1985. 18.95 (ISBN 0-86554-130-2, MUP/P16). Mercer Univ Pr.
Henry Duke Of Lancaster. Livre de Seyntz Medicines. Arnould, E. J., ed. 1967. Repr. of 1940 ed. 19.00 (ISBN 0-384-22400-8). Johnson Repr.
Henry, Ed. In Remembrance. 1978. pap. 1.50 (ISBN 0-89900-113-0). College Pr Pub.
Henry, Edward. Chant the Names of God. (Illus.). 260p. 1984. 20.00 (ISBN 0-916304-65-5). SDSU Press.
Henry, Frances. Victims & Neighbors: A Small Town in Nazi Germany Remembered. (Illus.). 216p. 1984. 27.95 (ISBN 0-89789-047-7); pap. 12.95 (ISBN 0-89789-048-5). Bergin & Garvey.
Henry, Francoise. Early Christian Irish Art. rev. ed. (Illus.). 128p. 1979. pap. 6.95 (ISBN 0-85342-462-4, Pub. by Mercier Pr Ireland). Irish Bks Media.
Henry, Granville C., Jr. Logos: Mathematics & Christian Theology. LC 74-25529. 361p. 1976. 25.00 (ISBN 0-8387-1653-9). Bucknell U Pr.
Henry, James. Prescriptions from the Beloved Physician. 108p. 1972. pap. 1.00 (ISBN 0-89114-055-7). Baptist Pub Hse.
Henry, Jim. Heartwarmers. LC 77-79094. 1977. 5.95 (ISBN 0-8054-5156-0). Broadman.
Henry, Kay V. Jesus Was a Helper. LC 86-17540. (Bible-&-Me Ser.). 1987. pap. 5.95 (ISBN 0-8054-4176-X). Broadman.
Henry, Mathew & Scott, Thomas. Matthew Henry Concise Commentary on the Whole Bible. (Affordable Ser.). 1024p. 13.95 (ISBN 0-8024-0417-0). Moody.
Henry, Matthew. A Commentary on the Whole Bible, 6 vols. 7100p. 89.95 (ISBN 0-8007-0196-8); reference lib. ed. 74.95 (ISBN 0-8007-0968-3). Revell.
--A Commentary on the Whole Bible, 6 vols, Vols. 1-6. (Reference Library Edition). 7152p. 1986. Repr. Set. text ed. 59.95 (ISBN 0-529-06371-9). World Bible.
--A Commentary on the Whole Bible, Vol. 1: Genesis to Deuteronomy. (Reference Library Edition). 912p. 1986. Repr. text ed. 10.95 (ISBN 0-529-06365-4). World Bible.
--A Commentary on the Whole Bible, Vol. 2: Joshua to Esther. (Reference Library Edition). 1160p. 1986. Repr. text ed. 10.95 (ISBN 0-529-06366-2). World Bible.
--A Commentary on the Whole Bible, Vol. 3: Job to Song of Solomon. (Reference Library Edition). 1112p. 1986. Repr. text ed. 10.95 (ISBN 0-529-06367-0). World Bible.
--A Commentary on the Whole Bible, Vol. 4: Isaiah to Malachi. (Reference Library Edition). 1520p. 1986. Repr. text ed. 10.95 (ISBN 0-529-06368-9). World Bible.
--A Commentary on the Whole Bible, Vol. 5: Matthew to John. (Reference Library Edition). 1248p. 1986. Repr. text ed. 10.95 (ISBN 0-529-06369-7). World Bible.
--A Commentary on the Whole Bible, Vol. 6: Acts to Revelation. (Reference Library Edition). 1200p. 1986. Repr. text ed. 10.95 (ISBN 0-529-06370-0). World Bible.
--Matthew Henry's Commentary in One Volume. Church, Leslie F., ed. 1966. 29.95 (ISBN 0-310-26010-8, 9802). Zondervan.
--Matthew Henry's Commentary on the Whole Bible, 6 vols. 7152p. Date not set. Set. 79.95 (ISBN 0-917006-21-6). Hendrickson MA.
--The Secret of Communion with God. LC 79-93431. (Shepherd Illustrated Classics Ser.). (Illus.). 144p. 1981. pap. 5.95 (ISBN 0-87983-220-7). Keats.
Henry, Matthew & Scott, Thomas. Commentary on the Holy Bible, 3 vols. 1979. 59.95 (ISBN 0-8407-5163-X). Nelson.
--Matthew Henry Concise Commentary on the Whole Bible. 25.95 (ISBN 0-8024-5190-X). Moody.
Henry, Matthew, ed. Matthew Henry's Commentary on the New Testament, 10 vols. 1983. 59.95 (ISBN 0-8010-4277-1). Baker Bk.
Henry, Matthew, et al. The Bethany Parallel Commentary on the New Testament. 1500p. 1983. 39.95 (ISBN 0-87123-474-2). Bethany Hse.
--The Bethany Parallel Commentary on the Old Testament. 1500p. 1985. 49.95 (ISBN 0-87123-617-6). Bethany Hse.
Henry, P. Plotin & l'Occident: Firmicus Maternus, Marius Victorinus, Saint Augustin, et Macrobe. (Classical Studies Ser.). (Fr.). Repr. of 1934 ed. lib. bdg. 39.50x (ISBN 0-697-00039-7). Irvington.
Henry, Patrick. New Directions in New Testament Study. LC 79-16267. 300p. 1979. 19.95 (ISBN 0-664-21376-6); pap. 10.95 (ISBN 0-664-24283-9). Westminster.
Henry, Patrick & Stransky, Thomas F. God on Our Minds. LC 81-70593. 176p. 1982. pap. 6.95 (ISBN 0-8006-1600-6, 1-1600). Fortress.
--God on Our Minds. LC 81-70593. 176p. 1982. pap. 6.95 (ISBN 0-8146-1249-0). Liturgical Pr.
Henry, Patrick, ed. Schools of Thought in the Christian Tradition. LC 84-47924. 208p. 1984. 19.95 (ISBN 0-8006-0730-9, 1-730). Fortress.

Henry, Paul. The Path to Transcendence: From Philosophy to Mysticism in Saint Augustine. Burch, Francis F., tr. (Pittsburgh Theological Monographs: No. 37). 1981. pap. 12.50 (ISBN 0-915138-49-2). Pickwick.

Henry, Paul, ed. see Plotinus.

Henry, Paul E. The Life & Times of John Calvin, 2 vols. Stebbing, Henry, tr. from Ger. LC 83-45613. Date not set. Repr. of 1851 ed. Set. 95.00 (ISBN 0-404-19831-7). AMS Pr.

Henry, Philip. Christ All in All. 7.95 (ISBN 0-685-88369-8). Reiner.

Henry, Stuart C. Unvanquished Puritan: A Portrait of Lyman Beecher. LC 85-30520. 299p. 1986. Repr. of 1973 ed. lib. bdg. 45.00x (ISBN 0-313-25097-9, HEUN). Greenwood.

Henry, Victor. La Magie dans L'Inde Antique: Paris, 1904. LC 78-74261. (Oriental Religions Ser.: Vol. 5). 325p. 1980. lib. bdg. 40.00 (ISBN 0-8240-3903-3). Garland Pub.

Henry Tall Bull & Weist, Tom. Cheyenne Legends of Creation. (Indian Culture Ser.). 1972. 1.95 (ISBN 0-89992-025-X). Coun India Ed.

Henry VII. Answere Made by the Kynges Hyghnes to the Petitions of the Rebelles in Yorkshire. LC 77-7417. (English Experience Ser.: No. 872). 1977. Repr. of 1536 ed. lib. bdg. 3.50 (ISBN 90-221-0872-4). Walter J Johnson.

Henry VIII. A Copy of the Letters Wherein Kyng Henry the Eyght Made Answere into a Certayn Letter of Martyn Luther. LC 72-204. (English Experience Ser.: No. 322). 100p. 1971. Repr. of 1528 ed. 14.00 (ISBN 90-221-0322-6). Walter J Johnson.

Henshaw, Paul & Weemhoff, Harold. Worship in Our Family. LC 81-52045. 84p. 1981. pap. 4.95x (ISBN 0-8358-0421-6). Upper Room.

Hensley, Dennis E. & Adkins, Rose A. Writing for Religious & Other Specialty Markets. (Orig.). 1987. pap. 8.95 (ISBN 0-8054-7911-2). Broadman.

Hensley, Dennis E. & Groen, Jim. One Young Billion: The Youth For Christ Story-the People, the Promise, & the Hope for Reaching... 224p. Date not set. 10.95 (ISBN 0-8407-5455-8). Nelson.

Hensley, J. Clark. Coping with Being Single Again. LC 78-52623. 1978. 7.95 (ISBN 0-8054-5420-9). Broadman.

Hensley, Jeffrey, ed. The Zero People. 310p. 1983. pap. 7.95 (ISBN 0-89283-126-X). Servant.

Henson, H. H. The Liberty of Prophesying: With Its Just Limits & Temper Considered with Reference to the Circumstances of the Modern Church. 1910. 39.50x (ISBN 0-686-51411-4). Elliots Bks.

Henson, Herbert H. Christian Morality, Natural, Developing, Final. LC 77-27189. (Gifford Lectures: 1935-36). Repr. of 1936 ed. 27.00 (ISBN 0-404-60494-3). AMS Pr.

--Puritanism in England. LC 70-185944. 294p. 1973. Repr. of 1912 ed. 23.50 (ISBN 0-8337-4177-2). B Franklin.

Henson, Josiah. Father Henson's Story of His Own Life. 212p. 1973. Repr. of 1855 ed. 16.95 (ISBN 0-87928-037-9). Corner Hse.

--Father Henson's Story of His Own Life. LC 70-99381. (Illus.). vii, 212p. 1972. Repr. of 1858 ed. lib. bdg. 12.50 (ISBN 0-8411-0052-7). Metro Bks.

--Father Henson's Story of His Own Life. (Illus.). 224p. 1986. pap. text ed. 6.95x (ISBN 0-8290-1902-2). Irvington.

Henson, Paul F. Teach the Word. 1972. 5.25 (ISBN 0-87148-826-4); pap. 4.25 (ISBN 0-87148-827-2). Pathway Pr.

Hentoff, Nat, ed. Black Anti-Semitism & Jewish Racism. LC 70-89955. 1970. pap. 3.75 (ISBN 0-8052-0280-3). Schocken.

Henze, Paul. The Plot to Kill the Pope. 224p. 1985. pap. 4.50 rack size (ISBN 0-684-18357-9). Scribner.

Hepburn, Daisy. Be It Ever So Humble. LC 83-24603. (Life with Spice Bible Study Ser.). 1984. 2.95 (ISBN 0-8307-0943-6, 6101805). Regal.

--Be Mine. LC 83-24618. (Life with Spice Bible Study Ser.). 1984. 2.95 (ISBN 0-8307-0944-4, 6101817). Regal.

--Color Me Christian. LC 83-24624. (Life with Spice Bible Study Ser.). 1984. 2.95 (ISBN 0-8307-0949-5, 6101867). Regal.

--Consider Christ. LC 83-24623. (Life with Spice Bible Study Ser.). 1984. 2.95 (ISBN 0-8307-0945-2, 6101829). Regal.

--Get Up & Go. LC 84-3362. (Life with Spice Bible Study Ser.). 64p. 1984. 2.95 (ISBN 0-8307-0946-0, 6101833). Regal.

--Get Up & Grow. LC 84-3361. (Life with Spice Bible Study Ser.). 64p. 1984. 2.95 (ISBN 0-8307-0942-8, 6101800). Regal.

--Lead, Follow or Get Out of the Way! LC 81-84568. (Orig.). 1982. pap. 4.95 (ISBN 0-8307-0822-7, 5416209); Resource Manual o.p. 5.95 (ISBN 0-8307-0872-3, 5202802). Regal.

--Life with Spice Resource Manual. 1984. 5.95 (ISBN 0-8307-0936-3, 5203006). Regal.

--Living Simply. LC 84-3360. (Life with Spice Bible Study Ser.). 1984. 2.95 (ISBN 0-8307-0947-9, 6101848). Regal.

--Look, You're a Leader. LC 85-19637. 284p. 1985. pap. write for info. (ISBN 0-8307-1098-1, 5418667); resource manual avail. (ISBN 0-8307-1074-4, 5203023). Regal.

--Never Underestimate the Power of God's Woman. LC 84-3337. (Life with Spice Bible Study Ser.). 1984. 2.95 (ISBN 0-8307-0948-7, 6101856). Regal.

Hepburn, Daisy & Klope, Joan B. How to Grow a Women's Minis-Tree. LC 86-11812. (Illus.). 140p. (Orig.). 1986. pap. 5.95 (ISBN 0-8307-1159-7, 5418863). Regal.

--How to Grow a Women's Minis-Tree. (Illus., Orig.). 1986. resource manual 7.95 (ISBN 0-8307-1055-8, 5203018). Regal.

Heper, Metin & Israeli, Raphael, eds. Islam & Politics in the Modern Middle East. LC 84-40042. 131p. 1984. 25.00 (ISBN 0-312-43742-0). St Martin.

Heppe, Heinrich. Reformed Dogmatics. Bizer, Ernst, ed. Thomson, G. T., tr. (Twin Brooks Ser.). 1978. pap. 19.95 (ISBN 0-8010-4207-0). Baker Bk.

Heppenstall, Margit S. Deborah. new ed. LC 67-19497. (Crown Ser.). 1977. pap. 4.95 (ISBN 0-8127-0169-0). Review & Herald.

Heppenstall, Rayner. Double Image: Mutations of Christian Mythology in the Works of Four French Catholic Writers of Today & Yesterday. LC 72-93063. 1969. Repr. of 1947 ed. 23.00 (ISBN 0-8046-0676-5, Pub. by Kennikat). Assoc Faculty Pr.

Heraclius. Here Begynneth the Boke Intituled Eracles & Also Godefrey of Boloyne. Caxton, William, tr. LC 73-6140. (English Experience Ser.: No. 604). 1973. Repr. of 1481 ed. 52.00 (ISBN 90-221-0604-7). Walter J Johnson.

Herberg, Will. Judaism & Modern Man. LC 59-12913. (Temple Bks). 1970. pap. text ed. 8.95x (ISBN 0-689-70232-9, T13). Atheneum.

--Protestant, Catholic, Jew: An Essay in American Religious Sociology. LC 83-9120. xvi, 310p. 1983. pap. 11.00x (ISBN 0-226-32734-5). U of Chicago Pr.

Herberg, Will, ed. Four Existentialist Theologians. LC 75-17472. 346p. 1975. Repr. of 1958 ed. lib. bdg. 29.75x (ISBN 0-8371-8303-0, HEFE). Greenwood.

Herberg, Will, ed. see Buber, Martin.

Herberholz, Don & Alexander, Kay. Developing Artistic & Perceptual Awareness: Art Practice in the Elementary Classroom. 5th. ed. 128p. 1985. pap. write for info. (ISBN 0-697-03221-3). Wm C Brown.

Herbert, A. S. The Book of the Prophet Isaiah. LC 74-16997. (Cambridge Bible Commentary on the New English Bible, Old Testament Ser.). (Illus.). 250p. 1975. Bks. 1-39. pap. 12.95 (ISBN 0-521-09766-5); Bks. 40-66. 27.95 (ISBN 0-521-20721-5); pap. 12.95 (ISBN 0-521-09933-1). Cambridge U Pr.

--The Book of the Prophet Isaiah, 1-39. LC 73-79495. (Cambridge Bible Commentary on the New English Bible Ser.: NEB Old Testament). 232p. 1973. pap. 10.95. Cambridge U Pr.

--Historical Catalogue of Printed Editions of the English Bible: 1525-1961. 589p. 1968. 40.00 (ISBN 0-686-87735-7). A Wofsy Fine Arts.

Herbert, A. S., ed. Historical Catalogue of Printed Editions of the English Bible 1525-1961. rev. ed. 1968. 12.75 (ISBN 0-564-00130-9, 17066, Pub. by United Bible). Am Bible.

Herbert, Frank. The God Makers. 1983. pap. 2.95 (ISBN 0-425-06388-7, Medallion). Berkley Pub.

Herbert, George. Bodleian Manuscript of George Herbert's Poems. LC 81-18454. 1984. 125.00x (ISBN 0-8201-1373-5). Schol Facsimiles.

--The Temple: Sacred Poems & Private Ejaculations. 6th ed. LC 72-5489. (Select Bibliographies Reprint Ser.). 1972. Repr. of 1882 ed. 18.00 (ISBN 0-8369-6915-4). Ayer Co Pubs.

Herbert, Janet. ABC's of Praise. (Sparkler Bks.). (Illus.). 32p. 1986. plastic comb bdg. 2.95 (ISBN 0-89191-926-0, 59261, Chariot Bks). Cook.

--Happy Birthday to You. 32p. 1986. 2.95 (50401, Chariot Bks). Cook.

--Hurray for Birthdays. (Sparklers Ser.). 1986. comb binding 2.95 (ISBN 1-55513-040-2, Chariot Bks). Cook.

--Love Is Kind. (Sparkler Bks.). (Illus.). 32p. 1986. plastic comb bndg. 2.95 (ISBN 0-89191-928-7, 59287, Chariot Bks). Cook.

Herbert, Jerry, ed. America, Christian or Secular? Readings in American Christian History. LC 84-11478. (Orig.). 1984. pap. 10.95 (ISBN 0-88070-067-X). Multnomah.

Herbert, R. T. Paradox & Identity in Theology. LC 78-20784. 221p. 1979. 24.50x (ISBN 0-8014-1222-6). Cornell U Pr.

Herbert, T. Walter, Jr. Moby Dick & Calvinism: A World Dismantled. 1977. 27.00x (ISBN 0-8135-0829-0). Rutgers U Pr.

Herbig, Reinhard, jt. auth. see Krauss, Friedrich.

Herbrandson, Dee. Shaker Herbs & Their Medicinal Uses. (Illus.). 28p. 1985. pap. 4.00. Shaker Her Soc.

Herbst, Winfrid. New Regulations on Indulgences. 47p. 1970. pap. 1.50 (ISBN 0-89555-103-9). TAN Bks Pubs.

Herbst, Wolfgang, jt. auth. see Jonsson, Carl O.

Herbster, Carl D., jt. auth. see Deuink, James W.

Herculano, Alexandre. History of the Origin & Establishment of the Inquisition in Portugal. Branner, John C., tr. LC 68-54274. (Stanford University. Stanford Studies in History, Economics, & Political Science: No. 1, Pt. 2). Repr. of 1926 ed. 20.00 (ISBN 0-404-50962-2). AMS Pr.

--History of the Origin & Establishment of the Inquisition in Portugal. rev. ed. 1971. 35.00x (ISBN 0-87068-153-2). Ktav.

Herdt, Gilbert H., ed. Rituals of Manhood: Male Initiation in Papua New Guinea. 392p. 1982. 38.50x (ISBN 0-520-04448-7); pap. 10.95 (ISBN 0-520-04454-1, CAL 564). U of Cal Pr.

Hereford, Philip, ed. see Bede the Venerable.

Herford, C. H. Dante & Milton. 1924. lib. bdg. 10.00 (ISBN 0-8414-5044-7). Folcroft.

Herford, Julius, jt. ed. see Decker, Harold A.

Herford, R. Travers. Christianity in Talmud & Midsrah. Repr. of 1903 ed. 16.95x (ISBN 0-87068-479-5). Ktav.

Herford, R. Travers, ed. The Ethics of the Talmud: Sayings of the Fathers. LC 62-13138. 1962. pap. 6.25 (ISBN 0-8052-0023-1). Schocken.

Herget, Winfried, ed. Studies in New England Puritanism. 240p. 1983. 28.95. P Lang Pubs.

Herhold, Robert M., ed. see Sittler, Joseph A.

Heritage Village Church & Missionary Fellowship, Inc. Staff. People That Love. Boulton, Roger H., ed. (Illus.). 128p. (Orig.). 1986. text ed. write for info. (ISBN 0-912275-05-7); pap. text ed. write for info. (ISBN 0-912275-06-5). PTL Enterprises.

Herlick, Stanford. What You Should Know about the Bible: A Practical Guide to Bible Basics. LC 85-82137. (Illus.). 255p. 1985. 12.50 (ISBN 0-9616026-0-0). FBF Pubns.

Herman, A. L. An Introduction to Buddhist Thought: A Philosophic History of Indian Buddhism. (Illus.). 480p. (Orig.). 1984. lib. bdg. 35.75 (ISBN 0-8191-3594-1); pap. text ed. 13.50 (ISBN 0-8191-3595-X). U Pr of Amer.

--The Problem of Evil & Indian Thought. 1976. 13.95 (ISBN 0-8426-0991-1). Orient Bk Dist.

Herman, Abbot. Blessed John, the Wonderworker. rev. ed. St. Herman of Alaska Brotherhood Staff, ed. (Illus.). 350p. 1987. pap. 15.00 (ISBN 0-938635-01-8). St Herman AK.

Herman, David V., tr. see Guttmann, Yitzhak J.

Herman, E. Creative Prayer. 1985. pap. 2.00 (ISBN 0-88028-049-2). Forward Movement.

--The Meaning & Value of Mysticism. 3rd facsimile ed. LC 72-164607. (Select Bibliographies Reprint Ser.). Repr. of 1922 ed. 22.00 (ISBN 0-8369-5891-8). Ayer Co Pubs.

--The Meaning & Value of Mysticism. 1977. lib. bdg. 59.95 (ISBN 0-8490-2216-9). Gordon Pr.

Herman, Edward S. & Brodhead, Frank. The Rise & Fall of the Bulgarian Connection. 270p. (Orig.). 1986. 19.95 (ISBN 0-940380-07-2); pap. text ed. 9.95 (ISBN 0-940380-06-4). Sheridan Square Pubns.

Herman, Stewart W. It's Your Souls We Want. LC 72-180406. Repr. of 1943 ed. 29.50 (ISBN 0-404-56130-6). AMS Pr.

Hermann, Dolores E. Preparing Your Own Chapel Talks for Children. 1987. pap. 3.95 (ISBN 0-570-04466-9). Concordia.

Hermansen, Janet. On the Crest of the Wave: Leader's Guide. LC 83-8616. 64p. 1985. pap. 3.95 (ISBN 0-8307-1010-8, 6101974). Regal.

Hermanson, Renee. Here or Nowhere. LC 83-51401. 128p. (Orig.). 1984. pap. 5.50 (ISBN 0-8358-0478-X). Upper Room.

--Raspberry Kingdom. LC 78-62985. 1978. pap. 4.50 (ISBN 0-8358-0374-0). Upper Room.

Hernandez, Anna M. The Lords Prayer. (Illus.). 32p. 1987. 6.95 (ISBN 0-89962-601-7). Todd & Honeywell.

Hernandez, Armida O. de Carrera see De Hernandez Carrera, Armida O.

Hernandez, David & Page, Carole G. La Familia del Cirujano. 272p. 1982. 3.50 (ISBN 0-88113-090-7). Edit Betania.

Herndon, Booton. The Seventh Day: The Story of the Seventh-Day Adventists. LC 78-11705. 1979. Repr. of 1960 ed. lib. bdg. 24.75x (ISBN 0-313-21054-3, HESD). Greenwood.

Herner, Russell A. Stonehenge: An Ancient Masonic Temple. rev., enl. ed. LC 83-63526. (Illus.). 160p. 1984. text ed. 15.95 (ISBN 0-88053-077-4). Macoy Pub.

Hero, Alfred O. American Religious Groups View Foreign Policy: Trends in Rank & File Opinion, 1937-1969. LC 72-81335. pap. 141.00 (ISBN 0-317-26767-1, 2023400). Bks Demand UMI.

Herold, A. Ferdinand. Life of Buddha: According to the Legend of Ancient India. LC 55-12748. 1954. pap. 6.95 (ISBN 0-8048-0382-X). C E Tuttle.

Herold, Sr. Duchesne. New Life: Preparation of Religious for Retirement. LC 73-76987. 168p. 1973. pap. 5.50 (ISBN 0-87125-007-1). Cath Health.

Heron, Alasdair I. A Century of Protestant Theology. LC 80-17409. 240p. 1980. pap. 9.95 (ISBN 0-664-24346-0). Westminster.

--The Holy Spirit. LC 82-24705. 224p. (Orig.). 1983. pap. 11.95 (ISBN 0-664-24439-4). Westminster.

--Table & Tradition. LC 83-14762. 206p. (Orig.). 1984. pap. 11.95 (ISBN 0-664-24516-1). Westminster.

Heron, Alasdair I., ed. The Westminster Confession in the Church Today: Church of Scotland Panel on Doctrine. 1982. 9.95x (ISBN 0-7152-0497-1). Outlook.

Heron, Michael, tr. see Von Daniken, Erich.

Heron-Allen, E., tr. A Fool of God: The Mystical Verse of Baba Tahir. 1979. 12.95 (ISBN 0-900860-70-7, Pub. by Octagon England). Ins Study Human.

Herr, Alan F. Elizabethan Sermon. LC 77-75996. 1969. Repr. of 1940 ed. lib. bdg. 16.50x (ISBN 0-374-93838-5, Octagon). Hippocrene Bks.

Herr, Dan. Start Digging! 1987. 9.95 (ISBN 0-88347-204-X). Thomas More.

Herr, Ethel. Bible Study for Busy Women. 160p. 1983. pap. 6.95 (ISBN 0-8024-0147-3). Moody.

--Chosen Women of the Bible. LC 75-36503. 96p. (Orig.). 1976. pap. 4.95 (ISBN 0-8024-1297-1). Moody.

--Growing up Is a Family Affair. LC 78-17581. 1978. pap. 5.95 (ISBN 0-8024-3359-6). Moody.

--An Introduction to Christian Writing. 315p. 1983. pap. 8.95 (ISBN 0-8423-1590-X). Tyndale.

Herr, Vincent V., et al. Screening Candidates for the Priesthood & Religious Life. (Illus.). 1964. 2.80 (ISBN 0-8294-0038-9). Loyola.

Herr, William A. Catholic Thinkers in the Clear: Giants of Catholic Thought from Augustine to Rahner. LC 85-118829. (Basics of Christian Thought Ser.). 276p. 1985. 15.95 (ISBN 0-88347-179-5). Thomas More.

--This Our Church: The People and Events That Shaped It. (Basics of Christian Thought Ser.). 1986. 17.95 (ISBN 0-88347-193-0). Thomas More.

Herrera, Robert A. Lamps of Fire. 168p. (Orig.). 1986. pap. 7.95 (ISBN 0-932506-40-2). St Bedes Pubns.

Herrick, Eduard F. Old Indian Temples, Idols & Worship. (Illus.). 154p. 1985. Repr. of 1882 ed. 91.45 (ISBN 0-89901-209-4). Found Class Reprints.

Herrick, Joy F. & Schraffenberger, Nancy. Something's Got to Help-& Yoga Can. LC 73-80177. (Illus.). 128p. 1974. 5.95 (ISBN 0-87131-126-7). M Evans.

Herrick, Samuel E. Some Heretics of Yesterday. LC 83-45614. Date not set. Repr. of 1885 ed. 37.50 (ISBN 0-404-19832-5). AMS Pr.

Herrigel, Eugen. Zen in the Art of Archery. 1971. pap. 3.95 (ISBN 0-394-71663-9, V663, Vin). Random.

Herrigel, Eugene. Method of Zen. Hull, R. F. & Watts, Alan, eds. LC 74-5120. 1974. pap. 2.95 (ISBN 0-394-71244-7, Vin). Random.

Herrigel, Gustie L. Zen in the Art of Flower Arrangement: An Introduction to the Spirit of the Japanese Art of Flower Arrangement. 1974. pap. 6.95 (ISBN 0-7100-7942-7). Methuen Inc.

Herring, Basil. Joseph Ibn Kaspi's Gevia' Kesef: A Study in Medieval Jewish Philosophical Bible Commentary. 1982. 35.00x (ISBN 0-87068-716-6). Ktav.

Herring, Basil F. Jewish Ethics & Halakhah for Our Time. 1984. 15.00 (ISBN 0-88125-044-9); pap. 9.95 (ISBN 0-88125-045-7). Ktav.

Herring, Clyde L. If God Talked Out Loud. LC 76-27479. (Illus.). 1977. pap. 5.50 (ISBN 0-8054-5325-3, 4253-25). Broadman.

--When God & I Talk. LC 80-70917. 1981. pap. 4.95 (ISBN 0-8054-5334-2, 4253-34). Broadman.

Herring, Ralph, et al. How to Understand the Bible. LC 74-75674. 1974. 8.95 (ISBN 0-8054-1127-5). Broadman.

Herring, Reuben. Your Family Worship Guidebook. LC 78-19976. 1978. 4.50 (ISBN 0-8054-5627-9). Broadman.

Herring, William. The Role of Music in the New Roman Liturgy. LC 75-14548. 1971. pap. 0.50 (ISBN 0-915866-01-3). Am Cath Pr.

Herrman, Irwin, jt. auth. see Hardie, Frank.

Herrmann, Robert A. Oneness, the Trinity & Logic. Wallace, Mary, ed. 112p. 1984. pap. 4.95 (ISBN 0-912315-80-6). Word Aflame.

Herrmann, Siegfried. A History of Israel in Old Testament Times. 2nd, rev. & enl. ed. Bowden, John, tr. from Ger. LC 81-43092. Tr. of Geschichte Israels in alttestamentlicher Zeit. 456p. 1981. pap. 16.95 (ISBN 0-8006-1499-2, 1-1499). Fortress.
--Israel in Egypt. LC 73-77371. (Studies in Biblical Theology, Second Ser.: No. 27). (Orig.). 1973. pap. text ed. 10.00x (ISBN 0-8401-3077-5). A R Allenson.
--Time & History. Belvins, James L., tr. LC 80-25323. (Biblical Encounter Ser.). 208p. (Orig.). 1981. pap. 9.95 (ISBN 0-687-42100-4). Abingdon.
Herron, George D. Between Caesar & Jesus. LC 75-324. (The Radical Tradition in America Ser). 278p. 1975. Repr. of 1899 ed. 23.10 (ISBN 0-88355-227-2). Hyperion Conn.
--Christian Society. 1969. Repr. of 1894 ed. 19.00 (ISBN 0-384-22640-X). Johnson Repr.
--Christian State: A Political Vision of Christ. (American Studies). 1969. Repr. of 1894 ed. 22.00 (ISBN 0-384-22650-7). Johnson Repr.
--Social Meanings of Religious Experiences. (American Studies Ser.). 1969. Repr. of 1896 ed. 18.00 (ISBN 0-384-22660-4). Johnson Repr.
Herron, Liz. Liz: A Life of Courage. LC 85-60126. 176p. (Orig.). 1986. pap. 4.95 (ISBN 0-89081-472-4, 4724). Harvest Hse.
Herrscher, Michele W. Forever Fit: Aerobic Dance & Exercise for the Latter-day Saint Woman. LC 85-13637. (Illus.). 120p. 1985. pap. 12.95 (ISBN 0-87747-768-X). Deseret Bk.
Herscher, Uri D., ed. The East European Jewish Experience in America: A Century of Memories, 1882-1982. LC 83-6416. (Monographs of the American Jewish Archives: No. 9). 192p. 1983. 15.75x (ISBN 0-87820-011-8). Ktav.
Hersey, Eileen V., tr. see Steiner, Rudolf.
Hersey, Herman. Faith for Today: Teacher's Guide. 1980. pap. 1.50 (ISBN 0-89265-067-2). Randall Hse.
--Preparation for Ordination. 1981. pap. 1.95 (ISBN 0-89265-069-9). Randall Hse.
Hersey, Jean. The Touch of the Earth. 396p. 1985. pap. 10.95 large print ed. (ISBN 0-8027-2481-7). Walker & Co.
Hershberger, Carol, jt. auth. see Kelley, Gail.
Hershberger, Guy F. War, Peace & Nonresistance. rev. ed. LC 53-7586. (Christian Peace Shelf Ser.). 375p. 1969. 15.95 (ISBN 0-8361-1449-3). Herald Pr.
Hershberger, Guy F., ed. The Recovery of the Anabaptist Vision: A Sixtieth Anniversary Tribute to Harold S. Bender. LC 57-10214. pap. 92.00 (ISBN 0-317-26605-5, 2025419). Bks Demand UMI.
Hershey, Terry. Beginning Again: Involvement Guide. 64p. 1986. cancelled (ISBN 0-8407-3084-5). Nelson.
--Beginning Again: Life after a Relationship Ends. 152p. 1986. pap. 7.95 (ISBN 0-8407-3075-6). Nelson.
--Intimacy: Where Do I Go To Find Love? 144p. 1984. text ed. 9.95 (ISBN 0-915929-06-6). Merit Bks.
--Young Adult Ministry. LC 86-3103. 276p. (Orig.). 1986. pap. 12.95 (ISBN 0-931529-08-5). Group Bks.
Hershey, Terry & McAfee, Lisa. Beginning Again. 64p. 1984. involvement guide 4.95 (ISBN 0-915929-11-2). Merit Bks.
--How to Start a Beginning Again Ministry. 64p. 1984. 4.95 (ISBN 0-915929-15-5). Merit Bks.
Hershman, Abraham M. see Maimonides, Moses.
Herskovits, Frances S., jt. auth. see Herskovits, Melville J.
Herskovits, Melville J. & Herskovits, Frances S. Outline of Dahomean Religious Belief. LC 34-5259. (American Anthro. Association Memoirs). 1933. 11.00 (ISBN 0-527-00540-1). Kraus Repr.
Hertel, J. The Panchatantra. lib. bdg. 79.95 (ISBN 0-87968-523-9). Krishna Pr.
Herter, Frederic P., et al, eds. Human & Ethical Issues in the Surgical Care of Patients with Life-Threatening Disease. 264p. 1986. 31.50x (ISBN 0-398-05194-1). C C Thomas.
Hertling, Ludwig. Communio: Church & Papacy in Early Christianity. Wicks, Jared, tr. from Ger. LC 75-38777. (Orig.). 1972. pap. 2.95 (ISBN 0-8294-0212-8). Loyola.
Hertz, J. H. Affirmations of Judaism. 338p. 1975. 9.95 (ISBN 0-900689-54-4). Soncino Pr.
--Penateuch & Haftorahs. 1067p. 1960. 25.00 (ISBN 0-900689-21-8). Soncino Pr.
Hertz, Joseph H. Authorized Daily Prayer Book. (Eng. & Hebrew.). 1948. 25.00x (ISBN 0-8197-0094-0). Bloch.
--Pirke Aboth: Sayings of the Fathers. 1945. pap. 3.95x (ISBN 0-87441-155-6). Behrman.
Hertz, Joseph H., ed. A Book of Jewish Thoughts. 1976. Repr. 8.95 (ISBN 0-8197-0252-8). Bloch.
Hertzberg, Arthur. Being Jewish in America: The Modern Experience. LC 78-54390. 320p. 1980. pap. 7.95 (ISBN 0-8052-0654-X). Schocken.
--The French Enlightenment & the Jews. LC 68-18996. pap. 108.00 (ISBN 0-317-26825-2, 2023485). Bks Demand UMI.
Hertzberg, Arthur, ed. Zionist Idea: A Historical Analysis & Reader. LC 77-90073. (Temple Books). 1969. pap. text ed. 7.95x (ISBN 0-689-70093-8, T4). Atheneum.
--Zionist Idea: A Historical Analysis & Reader. Repr. of 1959 ed. 23.50x (ISBN 0-8371-2565-0, HEZI). Greenwood.
Hertzberg, Hans. I & II Samuel: A Commentary. (The Old Testament Library Ser.). 22.95. Westminster.
Hertzberg, Hans W. First & Second Samuel, A Commentary. LC 65-10074. (Old Testament Library). 416p. 1965. 22.95 (ISBN 0-664-20541-0). Westminster.
Hertzler, Daniel, ed. Not by Might. LC 83-10831. 192p. (Orig.). 1983. pap. 9.95 (ISBN 0-8361-3342-0). Herald Pr.
Hertzler, Lois S. Prayers for the Newly Single. 32p. 1981. pap. 1.95 (ISBN 0-8170-0914-0). Judson.
Hertzog, Ed. Sex & Violence under God. LC 81-84292. 212p. 1982. 12.00 (ISBN 0-937894-02-8); pap. 7.00 (ISBN 0-937894-03-6). Life Arts.
Heruka, Tsang N. The Life of Marpa the Translator. Nalanda Translation Committee & Trungpa, Chogyam, trs. from Tibetan. LC 86-11837. 320p. 1986. pap. 12.95 (ISBN 0-87773-377-5). Shambhala Pubns.
Hervey, Thomas K. The Book of Christmas. 1977. lib. bdg. 59.95 (ISBN 0-8490-1530-8). Gordon Pr.
Herz, E. Emil. Before the Fury. LC 66-18484. 1967. 7.95 (ISBN 0-8022-0710-3). Philos Lib.
Herzberger, Radhika. An Essay in the Development of Fifth & Sixth Century Indian Thought. 1986. lib. bdg. 64.00 (ISBN 90-277-2250-1, Pub. by Reidel Holland). Kluwer Academic.
Herzl, Theodor. Diaries of Theodor Herzl. Lowenthal, ed. 16.50 (ISBN 0-8446-2247-8). Peter Smith.
Herzog, Frederick. Justice Church: The New Function of the Church in North American Christianity. LC 80-15091. 176p. (Orig.). 1980. pap. 6.95 (ISBN 0-88344-249-3). Orbis Bks.
Herzog, Isaac. Judaism-Law & Ethics. 227p. 1974. 9.95 (ISBN 0-900689-73-0). Soncino Pr.
--Main Institutions of Jewish Law, 2 Vols. Set. pap. 15.95x (ISBN 0-900689-14-5). Bloch.
--The Main Institutions of Jewish Law, 2 vols. 1939. Set. pap. 15.95 (ISBN 0-900689-14-5). Soncino Pr.
Herzog, Stephanie. Joy in the Classroom. Ray, Ann, ed. LC 82-4724. (Illus.). 224p. 1982. text ed. 7.95 (ISBN 0-916438-46-5). Univ of Trees.
Herzog, Yaacov. A People That Dwells Alone. Louvish, Misha, ed. 282p. 1975. 10.95 (ISBN 0-88482-895-6, Sanhedrin Pr). Hebrew Pub.
Herzog, Yaacov D. The Mishnah. 15.00x (ISBN 0-686-84235-9). Bloch.
Hes, Hindle S. Jewish Physicians in the Netherlands 1600-1940. 248p. 1980. pap. text ed. 14.50 (ISBN 0-317-51979-4, Pub. by Van Gorcum Holland). Longwood Pub Group.
Hesburgh, Theodore M. God & the World of Man. 2nd ed. 1960. 8.95x (ISBN 0-268-00112-X). U of Notre Dame Pr.
--Patterns for Educational Growth. 1958. 5.95x (ISBN 0-268-00202-9). U of Notre Dame Pr.
Hesch, John B. Clinical Pastoral Care for Hospitalized Children & Their Families. 224p. 1987. pap. 9.95 (ISBN 0-8091-2871-3). Paulist Pr.
--Prayer & Meditation for Middle School Kids. 144p. (Orig.). 1985. pap. 7.95 (ISBN 0-8091-2723-7). Paulist Pr.
Heschel, Abraham J. Between God & Man, an Interpretation of Judaism. 1965. pap. 8.95 (ISBN 0-02-914510-4). Free Pr.
--The Circle of Baal Shem Tov: Studies in Hasidism. Dresner, Samuel H., ed. 280p. 1985. 24.95 (ISBN 0-226-32960-7). U of Chicago Pr.
--The Earth Is the Lord's: The Inner World of the Jew in Eastern Europe. 109p. 1978. 8.95 (ISBN 0-374-14613-6); pap. 5.95. FS&G.
--God in Search of Man: A Philosophy of Judaism. 464p. 1976. pap. 10.95 (ISBN 0-374-51331-7). FS&G.
--God in Search of Man: Philosophy of Judaism. 437p. 1987. Repr. of 1955 ed. 30.00 (ISBN 0-87668-955-1). Aronson.
--I Asked for Wonder: A Spiritual Anthology. 128p. 1983. pap. 8.95 (ISBN 0-8245-0542-5). Crossroad NY.
--The Insecurity of Freedom: Essays on Human Existence. LC 66-16293. 320p. 1985. pap. 7.95 (ISBN 0-8052-0361-3). Schocken.
--Maimonides. Neugroschel, Joachim, tr. from Ger. 273p. 1982. 15.00 (ISBN 0-374-19874-8); pap. 7.25 (ISBN 0-374-51759-2). FS&G.
--Man Is Not Alone: A Philosophy of Religion. 320p. 1976. pap. 8.95 (ISBN 0-374-51328-7). FS&G.
--Man Is Not Alone: A Philosophy of Religion. LC 74-169258. 306p. 1972. Repr. of 1951 ed. lib. bdg. 25.50x (ISBN 0-374-93879-2, Octagon). Hippocrene Bks.
--Man's Quest for God: Studies in Prayer & Symbolism. LC 54-10371. (Hudson River Edition Ser.). 1981. 22.50x (ISBN 0-684-16829-4, ScribT). Scribner.
--Man's Quest for God: Studies in Prayer & Symbolism. LC 54-10371. 1954. 5.95 (ISBN 0-684-13582-5, ScribT). Scribner.
--Prophets, 2 vols. Vol. 1, 1969. pap. 6.95x (ISBN 0-06-131421-8, TB1421, Torch); Vol. 2, 1971. pap. 7.95x (ISBN 0-06-131557-5, TB1557, Torch). Har-Row.
--Quest for God: A Journey into Prayer & Symbolism. (Crossroad Paperback Ser.). 176p. 1982. pap. 7.95 (ISBN 0-8245-0436-4). Crossroad NY.
--The Sabbath. 118p. 1975. pap. 4.50 (ISBN 0-374-51267-1). FS&G.
--Theology of Ancient Judaism, 2 vols. (Hebrew.). 1973. Set. 14.95x (ISBN 0-685-32988-7). Bloch.
Heseltine, jt. auth. see Lewis, Wyndham.
Hesiod. Hesoid: Theogony, Works & Days. Athanassakis, Apostolos N., tr. LC 83-6143. 184p. 1983. 20.00x (ISBN 0-8018-2998-4); pap. 6.95x (ISBN 0-8018-2999-2). Johns Hopkins.
Heskes, Irene, jt. ed. see Holde, Artur.
Hesky, Olga. Painted Queen. 1962. 12.95 (ISBN 0-8392-1083-3). Astor-Honor.
Heslop. Diamonds in Daniel. pap. 2.95 (ISBN 0-686-12865-6). Schmul Pub Co.
Heslop, W. G. Gems from Genesis. LC 75-13661. (W. G. Heslop Bible Study Aids). 136p. 1975. pap. 4.50 (ISBN 0-8254-2825-4). Kregel.
--Heslop Bible Study Aids, 6 vols. 1979. Set. pap. 24.00 (ISBN 0-8254-2858-0). Kregel.
--Nuggets From Numbers. LC 75-13660. (W. G. Heslop Bible Study Aids). 192p. 1975. pap. 4.50 (ISBN 0-8254-2828-9). Kregel.
Heslop, William G. Diamonds From Daniel. LC 76-12082. (W. G. Heslop Bible Study Aids Ser.). 184p. 1976. pap. text ed. 4.50 (ISBN 0-8254-2833-5). Kregel.
--Pearls from the Prophet Ezekiel. LC 76-12081. (W. G. Heslop Bible Study Aids). 160p. 1976. pap. 4.50 (ISBN 0-8254-2832-7). Kregel.
--Rubies from Ruth. LC 76-12078. (W. G. Heslop Bible Study Aids Ser.). 116p. 1976. pap. 4.50 (ISBN 0-8254-2830-0). Kregel.
--Sermon Seeds from Psalms. LC 76-12080. (W. G. Heslop Bible Study Aids Ser.). 144p. 1976. pap. 4.50 (ISBN 0-8254-2831-9). Kregel.
Hess, Bartlett & Hess, Margaret. Never Say Old. 156p. 1984. pap. 5.95 (ISBN 0-89693-375-X). Victor Bks.
Hess, Edith & Blass, Jacqueline. Peter & Susie Find a Family. Tr. of Peter & Susi Finden eine Familie. (Illus.). 28p. 1985. Repr. of 1981 ed. 10.95 (ISBN 0-687-30848-8). Abingdon.
Hess, Karen, jt. auth. see Halverson, K.
Hess, Mahlon M. The Pilgrimage of Faith of Tanzania Mennonite Church, 1934-83. (Illus.). 176p. 1985. 5.00 (ISBN 0-9613368-2-X). E Mennonite Bd.
Hess, Margaret. Unconventional Women. 1981. pap. 5.95 (ISBN 0-88207-340-0). Victor Bks.
Hess, Margaret, jt. auth. see Hess, Bartlett.
Hess, Margaret L. The Triumph of Love. 96p. 1987. pap. 4.95 (ISBN 0-89693-247-8). Victor Bks.
Hess, Moses. Judische Schriften. Katz, Steven, ed. LC 79-7135. (Jewish Philosophy, Mysticism & History of Ideas Ser.). 1980. Repr. of 1905 ed. lib. bdg. 14.00x (ISBN 0-405-12261-6). Ayer Co Pubs.
Hess, Nancy B. By the Grace of God. 1979. 12.50 (ISBN 0-87813-207-4). Park View.
Hessel, Dieter, ed. see Kuhn, Margaret E.
Hessel, Dieter T. Social Ministry. LC 82-6960. 228p. 1982. pap. 10.95 (ISBN 0-664-24422-X). Westminster.
Hessel, Dieter T., ed. Energy Ethics: A Christian Response. (Orig.). 1979. pap. 4.25 (ISBN 0-377-00094-9). Friend Pr.
--For Creation's Sake: Preaching, Ecology, & Justice. LC 85-816. 144p. 1985. pap. 8.95 (ISBN 0-664-24637-0, A Geneva Press Publication). Westminster.
--Social Themes of the Christian Year: A Commentary on the Lectionary. LC 83-1504. 284p. (Orig.). 1983. pap. 10.95 (ISBN 0-664-24472-6, A Geneva Press Publication). Westminster.
Hessel, Dietert T. & Conner, John T., eds. Agricultural Mission of Churches & Land-Grant Universities: A Report of an Informal Consultation. 1979. pap. text ed. 8.50x (ISBN 0-8138-0920-7). Iowa St U Pr.
Hessel, Eugene A. The Religious Thought of Jose Rizal. rev. ed. 354p. (Orig.). 1984. pap. 12.25x (ISBN 0-318-01161-1, Pub. by New Day Philippines). Cellar.
Hesselgrave, David J. Communicating Christ Cross-Culturally. 1978. 12.95 (ISBN 0-310-36691-7, 11157P). Zondervan.
--Counseling Cross-Culturally. 1984. 14.95p (ISBN 0-8010-4282-8). Baker Bk.
--Planting Churches Cross-Culturally. 1980. pap. 12.95 (ISBN 0-8010-4219-4). Baker Bk.
Hesselgrave, David J., ed. Dynamic Religious Movements: Case Studies of Rapidly Growing Religious Movement Around the World. 1978. 9.95 (ISBN 0-8010-4130-9). Baker Bk.
Hession, Roy. Be Filled Now. 1968. pap. 1.50 (ISBN 0-87508-235-1). Chr Lit.
--Forgotten Factors. 1976. pap. 2.95 (ISBN 0-87508-234-3). Chr Lit.
--From Shadow to Substance. 1976. pap. 3.95 (ISBN 0-87508-260-2). Chr Lit.
--My Calvary Road. 1978. pap. 4.95 (ISBN 0-87508-262-9). Chr Lit.
--Not I but Christ. 1980. pap. 3.95 (ISBN 0-87508-198-3). Chr Lit.
--Our Nearest Kinsman. 1976. pap. 2.95 (ISBN 0-87508-229-7). Chr Lit.
--When I Saw Him. 1975. pap. 2.95 (ISBN 0-87508-239-4). Chr Lit.
Hestenes, Roberta. Building Christian Community Through Small Groups. pap. 69.95x incl. tapes (ISBN 0-9602638-5-3). Fuller Theol Soc.
--Using the Bible in Groups. LC 84-15291. 118p. (Orig.). 1985. pap. 6.95 (ISBN 0-664-24561-7). Westminster.
Hestenes, Roberta & Curley, Lois, eds. Women & the Ministries of Christ. pap. 6.95x (ISBN 0-9602638-2-9). Fuller Theol Soc.
Hester, Dennis, compiled by see Havner, Vance.
Hester, Glenn & Nygren, Bruce. Child of Rage. LC 81-9490. 192p. 1981. pap. 5.95 (ISBN 0-8407-5810-3). Nelson.
Hester, H. I. The Heart of Hebrew History. 1980. Repr. of 1949 ed. 12.95 (ISBN 0-8054-1217-4). Broadman.
--The Heart of the New Testament. 1980. Repr. of 1950 ed. 12.95 (ISBN 0-8054-1386-3). Broadman.
--Introduccion Al Estudio Del Nuevo Testamento. Benlliure, Felix, tr. from Eng. Tr. of The Heart of the New Testament. (Span.). 366p. 1980. pap. 7.95 (ISBN 0-311-04330-5). Casa Bautista.
Hester, Joseph P. & Killian, Don R. Cartoons for Thinking: Issues in Ethics & Values. (Illus.). 1984. 9.95 (ISBN 0-89824-007-7). Trillium Pr.
Hetata, Sherif, tr. see El Saadawi, Nawal.
Heth, William A. & Wenham, Gordon J. Jesus & Divorce: The Problem with the Evangelical Consensus. 288p. 1985. pap. 7.95 (ISBN 0-8407-5962-2). Nelson.
Hetherington, William M., ed. Lectures on the Revival of Religion by Ministers of the Church of Scotland. (Revival Library). xxvi, 444p. 1980. Repr. of 1840 ed. lib. bdg. 15.95 (ISBN 0-940033-15-1). R O Roberts.
Hettlinger, Richard. Sex Isn't That Simple: The New Sexuality on Campus. LC 73-17876. 256p. 1974. 6.95 (ISBN 0-8264-0155-4); pap. 3.95 (ISBN 0-8264-0156-2). Continuum.
Heubach, Paul. Living with Suffering. Coffen, Richard W., ed. (Better Living Ser.). 32p. (Orig.). 1986. pap. 1.25 (ISBN 0-8280-0322-X). Review & Herald.
Heufelder, Emmanuel. The Way to God According to the Rule of Saint Benedict. Eberle, Luke, tr. from Ger. (Cistercian Studies: No. 49). 1983. 25.95 (ISBN 0-87907-849-9); pap. 8.00 (ISBN 0-87907-949-5). Cistercian Pubns.
Heuman, Fred S. The Uses of Hebraisms in Recent Bible Translations. 154p. 1977. 9.95 (ISBN 0-8022-2190-4). Philos Lib.
Heurck, Jan van see Pieper, Josef & Raskop, Heinrich.
Heuscher, Julius E. A Psychiatric Study of Myths & Fairy Tales: Their Origins, Meaning & Usefulness. 2nd ed. (Illus.). 440p. 1974. 23.75x (ISBN 0-398-02851-6). C C Thomas.
Heusser, D-B & Heusser, Phyllis. Children As Partners in the Church. LC 85-9934. 64p. 1985. pap. 3.95 (ISBN 0-8170-1054-8). Judson.
Heusser, Phyllis, jt. auth. see Heusser, D-B.
Heuzinger, Lutz. Michelangelo. (Illus.). 96p. (Orig.). 1982. pap. 13.95 (ISBN 0-935748-43-1). Scala Books.
Heuzinger, Lutz & Mancinelli, Fabrizio. The Sistine Chapel. LC 84-50553. (Illus.). 96p. (Orig.). 1984. pap. 13.95 (ISBN 0-935748-58-X). Scala Books.
Hevener, Natalie K., ed. Dynamics of Human Rights in United States Foreign Policy. LC 79-66435. 375p. 1981. pap. 14.95x. Transaction Bks.
Hewat, Matthew L. Bantu Folk Lore. LC 77-129948. Repr. of 1906 ed. 22.50x (ISBN 0-8371-4992-4, HBF&, Pub. by Negro U Pr). Greenwood.
Hewetson, David & Miller, David. Christianity Made Simple: Belief, Vol. 1. LC 83-10866. 160p. 1983. pap. 4.95 (ISBN 0-87784-811-4). Inter-Varsity.
Hewett, John H. After Suicide. LC 79-24373. (Christian Care Bks.: Vol. 4). 118p. 1980. pap. 7.95 (ISBN 0-664-24296-0). Westminster.

Hewitt, J. F. History & Chronology of the Myth-Making Age. LC 76-27523. (Illus.). 1976. Repr. of 1901 ed. lib. bdg. 60.00 (ISBN 0-89341-036-5). Longwood Pub Group.

Hewitt, James. The Complete Yoga Book: Yoga of Breathing, Yoga of Postures, & Yoga of Meditation. LC 77-15934. (Illus., Orig.). 1978. pap. 11.95 (ISBN 0-8052-0592-6). Schocken.

Hewitt, Joe B. I Was Raised a Jehovah's Witness. LC 78-73255. 1979. pap. 3.95 (ISBN 0-89636-018-0). Accent Bks.

Hewitt, John N. Iroquoian Cosmology, 2 pts. in 1. LC 73-8095. Repr. of 1928 ed. 60.00 (ISBN 0-404-11202-1). AMS Pr.

Hexeltine, G. C., jt. auth. see Lewis, D. B.

Hexham, Irving & Poewe, Karla. Understanding Cults & New Religions. 192p. (Orig.). 1986. pap. 8.95 (ISBN 0-8028-0170-6). Eerdmans.

Hexham, Irving, ed. Texts on Zulu Religion: Traditional Zulu Ideas about God. (African Studies). 496p. 1987. text ed. 69.95 (ISBN 0-88946-181-3). E Mellen.

Hexter, Jack H. The Judaeo Christian Tradition. (Orig.). 1966. pap. text ed. 10.95 scp (ISBN 0-06-042815-5, HarpC). Har-Row.

--More's Utopia: The Biography of an Idea. LC 76-15177. (History of Ideas Ser.: No. 5). 1976. Repr. of 1952 ed. lib. bdg. 22.50x (ISBN 0-8371-8947-0, HEMU). Greenwood.

Heyd, David. Supererogation: Its Status in Ethical Theory. LC 81-15476. (Cambridge Studies in Philosophy). 180p. 1982. 37.50 (ISBN 0-521-23935-4). Cambridge U Pr.

Heyd, Thomas. Planning for Stewardship: Developing a Giving Program for Congregations. (Administration for Churches Ser.). 40p. (Orig.). 1980. pap. 3.95 (ISBN 0-8066-1782-9, 10-4992). Augsburg.

Heyd, Tom. Accounting Systems for Churches. (Administration Series for Churches). 64p. 1984. pap. 3.95 (ISBN 0-8066-2032-3, 10-0126). Augsburg.

Heyd, Uriel, ed. Studies in Islamic History & Civilization. (Scripta Hierosolymitana Ser.: Vol. 9). pap. 60.00 (ISBN 0-317-08597-2, 2051596). Bks Demand UMI.

Heyden, A. B. The Blessed Virgin Mary in Early Christian Latin Poetry. 59.95 (ISBN 0-87968-755-X). Gordon Pr.

Heyden, A. Van Der see Gafni, Shlomo S. & Van der Heyden, A.

Heyden, Doris & Villasenor, Luis F. The Great Temple & the Aztec Gods. (Illus.). 72p. 1984. pap. 4.50 (ISBN 968-7074-12-4). Ocelot Pr.

Heyden, Doris, tr. see Duran, Fr. Diego.

Heyder, Wolfgang & Mallwitz, Alfred. Das Kabirenheiligtum Bei Theben: Die Bauten Im Kabirenheiligtum Bei Theben, Vol. 2. (Illus.). 1978. 52.00 (ISBN 3-11-005754-9). De Gruyter.

Heydon, Christopher. A Defence of Iudiciall Astrologie: In Answer to a Treatise Lately Published by M. John Chamber. LC 77-7407. (English Experience Ser.: No. 873). 1977. Repr. of 1603 ed. lib. bdg. 58.00 (ISBN 90-221-0873-2). Walter J Johnson.

Heydt, Henry J. Comparison of World Religions. 1967. pap. 2.50 (ISBN 0-87508-241-6). Chr Lit.

Heyen, Franz J., ed. Germania Sacra: Die Bistuemer der Kirchenprovinz Trier: Das Erzbistum Trier, 1. das Stift St. Paulin Vor Trier. (Germania Sacra: Historisch-Statistische Beschreibung der Kirche Des Alten Reiches, N. F. 6). xiv, 855p. 1972. pap. 88.00 (ISBN 3-11-002273-7). De Gruyter.

Heyer, Friedrich. Die Kirche Aethiopiens: Eine Bestandsaufnahme. (Theologische Bibliothek Toepelmann 22). 360p. 1971. 32.25 (ISBN 3-11-001850-0). De Gruyter.

--Konfessionskunde. 1977. 39.20 (ISBN 3-11-006651-3). De Gruyter.

Heyer, Robert, ed. Enriching Your Marriage. 2.45 (ISBN 0-8091-2261-8). Paulist Pr.

--Nuclear Disarmament: Key Statements of Popes, Bishops, Councils & Churches. 1982. pap. 7.95 (ISBN 0-8091-2456-4). Paulist Pr.

Heylin, Peter. A Briefe & Moderate Answer to H. Burton. LC 76-57389. (English Experience Ser.: No. 806). 1977. Repr. of 1637 ed. lib. bdg. 22.00 (ISBN 90-221-0806-6). Walter J Johnson.

Heylyn, Peter. The History of the Sabbath, 2 pts. LC 75-26002. (English Expericne Ser.: No. 150). 272p. 1969. Repr. of 1636 ed. 49.00 (ISBN 90-221-0150-9). Walter J Johnson.

--Memorials of Bishop Waynflete, Founder of St. Mary Magdalen College, Oxford. Bloxam, John R., ed. 1851. 24.00 (ISBN 0-8337-0311-0). B Franklin.

Heymann, Frederick G. John Zizka & the Hussite Revolution. LC 71-77671. (Illus.). 1969. Repr. of 1955 ed. 17.50x (ISBN 0-8462-1344-3). Russell.

Heymann, Michael, intro. by. The Uganda Controversy: Minutes of the Zionist General Council, Vol. 1. 136p. 1970. casebound 12.95x (ISBN 0-87855-185-9). Transaction Bks.

Heynen, A. James, jt. auth. see Brinks, Herbert.

Heynen, Ralph. Christian Home. (Contemporary Discussion Ser.). (Orig.). 1974. pap. 1.25 (ISBN 0-8010-4109-0). Baker Bk.

--Creative Discussions on I Corinthians 13. (Contemporary Discussion Ser.). 96p. 1982. pap. 2.95 (ISBN 0-8010-4260-7). Baker Bk.

Heynen, William, tr. see Balke, William.

Heyward, Carter, ed. see Mud Flower Collective.

Heyward, Isabel C. The Redemption of God: A Theology of Mutual Relation. LC 81-43706. 266p. (Orig.). 1982. lib. bdg. 29.25 (ISBN 0-8191-2389-7); pap. text ed. 12.25 (ISBN 0-8191-2390-0). U Pr of Amer.

Heywood, Ellis. Il Moro: Ellis Heywood's Dialogue in Memory of Thomas More. Deakins, Roger L., tr. LC 75-184107. 176p. 1972. 12.50x (ISBN 0-674-58735-9). Harvard U Pr.

Heywood, William S., ed. see Ballou, Adin.

Hibbard, Caroline M. Charles I & the Popish Plot. LC 81-23075. ix, 342p. 1983. 30.00x (ISBN 0-8078-1520-9). U of NC Pr.

Hibbard, Howard. Michelangelo. LC 74-6576. (Icon Editions). (Illus.). 348p. 1975. 20.00i (ISBN 0-06-433323-X, HarpT); (HarpT). Har-Row.

Hibbert, Albert. Smith Wigglesworth: The Secret of His Power. 112p. 1982. pap. 4.95 (ISBN 0-89274-211-9, HH-211). Harrison Hse.

Hibbert, Giles, et al. John. LC 71-173033. (Scripture Discussion Commentary Ser.: Pt. 9). 256p. 1972. pap. text ed. 4.50 (ISBN 0-87946-008-3). ACTA Found.

Hibler, Lincoln A. Four Thousand Questions & Answers on the Old & New Testament, Vol. 1. 1986. 8.95 (ISBN 0-8062-2431-2). Carlton.

Hick, John. Classical & Contemporary Readings in the Philosophy of Religion. 2nd ed. LC 75-98092. (Philosophy Ser). 1969. text ed. write for info. (ISBN 0-13-135269-5). P-H.

--God Has Many Names. LC 82-1959. 140p. 1982. pap. 8.95 (ISBN 0-664-24419-X). Westminster.

--Philosophy of Religion. 3rd ed. 160p. 1983. pap. write for info. (ISBN 0-13-663906-2). P-H.

--Problems of Religious Pluralism. LC 85-2505. 144p. 1985. 19.95 (ISBN 0-312-65154-6). St Martin.

Hick, John & Askari, Hasan. The Experience of Religious Diversity. 242p. 1985. text ed. 39.95 (ISBN 0-566-05020-X). Gower Pub Co.

Hick, John, ed. The Myth of God Incarnate. LC 77-9965. 224p. 1978. pap. 7.95 (ISBN 0-664-24178-6). Westminster.

Hick, John & Hebblethwaite, Brian, eds. Christianity & Other Religions: Selected Readings. LC 80-2383. 256p. 1981. pap. 8.95 (ISBN 0-8006-1444-5, 1-1444). Fortress.

Hick, John H. Death & Eternal Life. LC 76-9965. 496p. 1980. pap. text ed. 11.95 (ISBN 0-06-063904-0, RD 332, HarpR). Har-Row.

--Evil & the God of Love. rev. ed. LC 76-62953. 1977. pap. 6.95 (ISBN 0-06-063902-4, RD219, HarpR). Har-Row.

--Existence of God. 305p. 1964. pap. 4.95 (ISBN 0-02-085450-1, Collier). Macmillan.

Hickes, George. Two Treatises on the Christian Priesthood, 3 Vols. (Library of Anglo-Catholic Theology: No. 9). Repr. of 1848 ed. Set. 87.50 (ISBN 0-404-52100-2). AMS Pr.

Hickey, Anne E. Women of the Roman Aristocracy As Christian Monastics. Miles, Margaret R., ed. LC 86-19242. (Studies in Religion: No. 1). 159p. 1986. 39.95 (ISBN 0-8357-1757-7). UMI Res Pr.

Hickey, Edward J. The Society for the Propagation of the Faith: Its Foundation, Organization & Success (1822-1922) LC 73-3557. (Catholic University of America. Studies in American Church History: No. 3). Repr. of 1922 ed. 25.00 (ISBN 0-404-57753-9). AMS Pr.

Hickey, John. Religion & the Northern Ireland Problem. LC 83-26612. 162p. 1984. 23.50x (ISBN 0-389-20448-X, 08012). B&N Imports.

Hickey, Marilyn. Divorce Is Not the Answer. LC 75-32006. 1979. pap. 4.95 (ISBN 0-89221-009-5). New Leaf.

--Fear Free Faith Filled. 176p. 1982. pap. 3.50 (ISBN 0-89274-259-3). Harrison Hse.

--God in You, to You, & for You. 199p. (Orig.). 1983. pap. text ed. 4.95 (ISBN 0-914307-13-4, Dist. by Harrison Hse) Word Faith.

--God's Covenant for Your Family. 140p. (Orig.). 1982. pap. 4.95 (ISBN 0-89274-245-3). Harrison Hse.

Hickey, Mary E., tr. from Fr. Novena of Confidence & Thanksgiving to the Sorrowful & Immaculate Heart of Mary. (Illus.). 20p. 1962. pap. 0.25 (ISBN 0-913382-21-3, 107-2). Prow Bks-Franciscan.

Hickey, Raymond. A Case for an Auxiliary Priesthood. LC 81-16950. 160p. (Orig.). 1982. pap. 1.99 (ISBN 0-88344-021-0). Orbis Bks.

Hickingbotham, Ian. Turn Around One Hundred Times. 1985. 21.00x (ISBN 0-7223-1917-7, Pub. by A H Stockwell England). State Mutual Bk.

Hickman, Bill. Brigham's Destroying Angel. facsimile ed. LC 74-165642. (Select Bibliographies Reprint Ser). Repr. of 1904 ed. 18.00 (ISBN 0-8369-5951-5). Ayer Co Pubs.

Hickman, Hoyt. A Primer for Church Worship. 112p. (Orig.). 1984. pap. 7.95 (ISBN 0-687-34033-0). Abingdon.

--Word & Table. 1983. pap. 3.95 (ISBN 0-687-46127-8). Abingdon.

Hickman, Hoyt L. United Methodist Altars: A Guide for the Local Church. 96p. 1984. pap. 6.95 (ISBN 0-687-42985-4). Abingdon.

Hickman, Hoyt L., et al, eds. Handbook of the Christian Year. 304p. (Orig.). 1986. pap. 16.95 (ISBN 0-687-16575-X). Abingdon.

Hickman, Martha H. Waiting & Loving: Thoughts Occasioned by the Illness & the Death of a Parent. LC 83-51399. 160p. (Orig.). 1984. pap. 5.95 (ISBN 0-8358-0483-6). Upper Room.

Hickman, Martha W. The Growing Season. LC 80-68983. 128p. (Orig.). 1980. pap. 4.50x (ISBN 0-8358-0411-9). Upper Room.

--When Our Church Building Burned Down. 48p. 1986. 9.95 (ISBN 0-687-45023-3). Abingdon.

Hickman, Martin. David Matthew Kennedy: Banker, Statesman, Churchman. 1987. 14.95 (ISBN 0-87579-093-3). Deseret Bk.

Hickman, Richard, ed. A Jehovah's Witness Finds the Truth. 115p. (Orig.). 1983. pap. 4.95 (ISBN 0-914605-00-3). Love Agape Min.

Hickok, Laurens P. Humanity Immortal: Or, Man Tried, Fallen & Redeemed. LC 75-3180. Repr. of 1872 ed. 25.00 (ISBN 0-404-59183-3). AMS Pr.

Hicks, Darryl E. God Comes to Nashville. LC 79-89583. 1979. pap. 3.50 (ISBN 0-89221-065-6). New Leaf.

Hicks, Florence J. Mary McLeod Bethune: Her Own Words of Inspiration. LC 75-18004. 96p. 1975. 4.95 (ISBN 0-912444-00-2). Gaus.

Hicks, George D. Berkeley. LC 68-15129. 1968. Repr. of 1932 ed. 9.00x (ISBN 0-8462-1235-8). Russell.

--The Philosophical Bases of Theism. LC 77-27142. (Hibbert Lectures: 1931). Repr. of 1937 ed. 31.00 (ISBN 0-404-60427-7). AMS Pr.

Hicks, Margaret. Christian Woman's Answer to Aging. 29p. (Orig.). 1986. pap. 0.75 (ISBN 0-89274-394-8). Harrison Hse.

Hicks, Olan, jt. auth. see Connally, Andrew M.

Hicks, Robert & Bewes, Richard. The Christian. (Understanding Bible Truth Ser.). (Orig.). 1981. pap. 0.95 (ISBN 0-89840-023-6). Heres Life.

--The Church. (Understanding Bible Truth Ser.). (Orig.). 1981. pap. 0.95 (ISBN 0-89840-018-X). Heres Life.

--God. (Understanding Bible Truth Ser.). (Orig.). 1981. pap. 0.95 (ISBN 0-89840-024-4). Heres Life.

--The Holy Spirit. (Understanding Bible Truth Ser.). (Orig.). 1981. pap. 0.95 (ISBN 0-89840-021-X). Heres Life.

--Jesus Christ. (Understanding Bible Truth Ser.). (Orig.). 1981. pap. 0.95 (ISBN 0-89840-026-0). Heres Life.

--The Last Things. (Understanding Bible Truth Ser.). (Orig.). 1981. pap. 1.50 (ISBN 0-89840-020-1). Heres Life.

--Man. (Understanding Bible Truth Ser.). (Orig.). 1981. pap. 0.95 (ISBN 0-89840-025-2). Heres Life.

--Salvation. (Understanding Bible Truth Ser.). (Orig.). 1981. pap. 0.95 (ISBN 0-89840-019-8). Heres Life.

Hicks, Robert F. The Gift of Faithfulness. Jenkins, Simon, ed. (The Gift of... Ser.). (Illus.). 24p. 1984. pap. 1.25 (ISBN 0-687-14700-X). Abingdon.

--The Gift of Gentleness. Jenkins, Simon, ed. (The Gift of... Ser.). (Illus.). 24p. 1984. pap. 1.25 (ISBN 0-687-14703-4). Abingdon.

--The Gift of Goodness. Jenkins, Simon, ed. (The Gift of... Ser.). (Illus.). 24p. 1984. pap. 1.25 (ISBN 0-687-14698-4). Abingdon.

--The Gift of Joy. Jenkins, Simon, ed. (The Gift of... Ser.). 24p. 1984. pap. 1.25 (ISBN 0-687-14704-2). Abingdon.

--The Gift of Love. Jenkins, Simon, ed. (The Gift of... Ser.). (Illus.). 24p. 1984. pap. 1.25 (ISBN 0-687-14705-0). Abingdon.

--The Gift of Patience. Jenkins, Simon, ed. (The Gift of... Ser.). (Illus.). 24p. 1984. pap. 1.25 (ISBN 0-687-14699-2). Abingdon.

--The Gift of Peace. Jenkins, Simon, ed. (The Gift of... Ser.). (Illus.). 24p. 1984. pap. 1.25 (ISBN 0-687-14701-8). Abingdon.

--The Gift of Self-Control. Jenkins, Simon, ed. (The Gift of... Ser.). (Illus.). 24p. 1984. pap. 1.25 (ISBN 0-687-14697-6). Abingdon.

Hicks, Robert H., ed. A Gift More Precious than Gold. (Illus.). 200p. 1985. Repr. 9.95 (ISBN 0-687-14691-7). Abingdon.

Hicks, Roy. Another Look at the Rapture. 120p. (Orig.). 1982. pap. 3.95 (ISBN 0-89274-246-1). Harrison Hse.

Hicks, Roy H. He Who Laughs...Lasts...& Lasts...& Lasts. (Orig.). 1976. pap. 2.95 (ISBN 0-89274-003-5). Harrison Hse.

--Power of Positive Resistance. 128p. 1983. pap. 2.95 (ISBN 0-89274-294-1). Harrison Hse.

--Praying Beyond God's Ability. 96p. 1977. 2.95 (ISBN 0-89274-052-3). Harrison Hse.

--Use It or Lose It: The Word of Faith. (Orig.). 1976. pap. 2.95 (ISBN 0-89274-002-7). Harrison Hse.

--Whatever Happened to Hope. 1978. mini book 0.75 (ISBN 0-89274-074-4). Harrison Hse.

Hieatt, A. Kent. Chaucer, Spenser, Milton: Mythopoeic Continuities & Transformations. (Illus.). 336p. 1975. 25.00x (ISBN 0-7735-0228-9). McGill-Queens U Pr.

Hiebel, Frederick. The Epistles of Paul & Rudolf Steiner's Philosophy of Freedom. 1979. pap. 4.95 (ISBN 0-916786-41-2). St George Bk Serv.

Hiebel, Friedrich. Novalis: German Poet, European Thinker, Christian Mystic. LC 54-62201. (North Carolina University Studies in the Germanic Languages & Literatures: No. 10). Repr. of 1953 ed. 27.00 (ISBN 0-404-50910-X). AMS Pr.

Hiebert, Clarence. The Holdeman People: The Church in Christ, Mennonite, 1869-1969. LC 72-94133. 1973. 17.95 (ISBN 0-87808-411-8). William Carey Lib.

Hiebert, Clarence, ed. Brothers in Deed to Brothers in Need. new ed. LC 74-76588. (Illus.). 486p. 1974. 29.95 (ISBN 0-87303-037-0). Faith & Life.

Hiebert, D. Edmond. The Epistle of James. LC 78-23925. 1979. 13.95 (ISBN 0-8024-2357-4). Moody.

--First Timothy. (Everyman's Bible Commentary Ser.). 1967. pap. 5.95 (ISBN 0-8024-2054-0). Moody.

--Second Timothy. (Everyman's Bible Commentary Ser). 1958. pap. 5.95 (ISBN 0-8024-2055-9). Moody.

--Titus & Philemon. (Everyman's Bible Commentary Ser.). 1957. pap. 5.95 (ISBN 0-8024-2056-7, MBP). Moody.

Hiebert, Edmond. Tito y Filemon: Comentario Biblico Portavoz. Orig. Title: Titus & Philemon (Everyman's Bible Commentary) (Span.). 136p. 1981. pap. 3.95 (ISBN 0-8254-1317-6). Kregel.

Hiebert, Paul G. Anthropological Insights for Missionaries. 280p. 1987. pap. 13.95 (ISBN 0-8010-4291-7). Baker Bk.

Hiebert, Waldo & Kopp, Herb. Deacons & Their Ministry. (Orig.). 1981. pap. 1.95 (ISBN 0-937364-02-9). Kindred Pr.

Hieronymus, Lynn. What the Bible Says about Worship. (What the Bible Says Ser.). 300p. 1984. 13.95 (ISBN 0-89900-097-5). College Pr Pub.

Hiers, Richard H. The Historical Jesus & the Kingdom of God: Present & Future in the Message & Ministry of Jesus. LC 73-2623. (University of Florida Humanities Monographs: No. 38). 1973. pap. 3.50 (ISBN 0-8130-0386-5). U Presses Fla.

--Kingdom of God in the Synoptic Tradition. LC 70-630982. (U of Fla. Humanities Monograph Ser.: No. 33). Repr. of 1970 ed. 29.00 (ISBN 0-8357-9821-6, 2015531). Bks Demand UMI.

Hiers, Richard H., ed. see Weiss, Johannes.

Hiesberger, Jean M., ed. Healing Family Hurts. LC 79-90991. (Paths of Life Ser.). 128p. (Orig.). 1979. pap. 2.95 (ISBN 0-8091-2266-9). Paulist Pr.

--Preparing for Marriage Handbook. LC 80-80386. (Paths of Life Ser.). 112p. 1980. 2.95 (ISBN 0-8091-2260-X). Paulist Pr.

--Young Adult Living Handbook. LC 79-92005. (Paths of Life Ser.). 126p. 1980. 2.95 (ISBN 0-8091-2259-6). Paulist Pr.

Hifler, Joyce S. Put Your Mind at Ease. 128p. (Orig.). 1983. pap. 7.75 (ISBN 0-687-34929-X). Abingdon.

Higby, Chester P. Religious Policy of the Bavarian Government During the Napoleonic Period. LC 19-12150. (Columbia University. Studies in the Social Sciences: No. 196). Repr. of 1919 ed. 36.00 (ISBN 0-404-51196-1). AMS Pr.

Higby, Roy C. A Man from the Past. 2nd ed. (Illus.). pap. 4.25 (ISBN 0-914692-02-X). Big Moose.

Higdon, Barbara M. Good News for Today. 1981. pap. 7.00 (ISBN 0-8309-0298-8). Herald Hse.

Higgens, Elford. Hebrew Idolatry & Superstition. 1971. Repr. of 1893 ed. 19.50x (ISBN 0-8046-1150-5, Pub. by Kennikat). Assoc Faculty Pr.

Higginbotham, Mary. With Each Passing Moment. pap. 1.25 (ISBN 0-686-12748-X). Grace Pub Co.

Higgins, A. J. The Son of Man in the Teaching of Jesus. LC 79-42824. (Society for New Testament Studies Monographs: No. 39). 186p. 1981. 32.50 (ISBN 0-521-22363-6). Cambridge U Pr.

Higgins, Daniel. The Challenge: Life of Dominic Savio. (Illus.). 1959. 4.25 (ISBN 0-89944-025-8). Don Bosco Multimedia.

Higgins, Edward J. Stewards of God. 1984. 3.25 (ISBN 0-86544-022-0). Salv Army Suppl South.

Higgins, Godfrey. Celtic Druids. 40.00 (ISBN 0-89314-412-6). Philos Res.

Higgins, John J. Thomas Merton on Prayer. 200p. 1975. pap. 3.95 (ISBN 0-385-02813-X, Im). Doubleday.

Higgins, Paul L. Pilgrimages: A Guide to the Holy Places of Europe for Today's Traveler. 146p. 1984. 12.95 (ISBN 0-13-676163-1); pap. 5.95 (ISBN 0-13-676155-0). P-H.

--Pilgrimages to Rome & Beyond: A Guide to the Holy Places of Southern Europe for Today's Traveler. (Illus.). 156p. 1985. 17.95 (ISBN 0-13-676073-2); pap. 7.95 (ISBN 0-13-676065-1). P-H.

Higginson, William J. Death Is, & Approaches to the Edge. (Xtras Ser.: No. 9). 48p. (Orig.). 1981. pap. 2.50 (ISBN 0-89120-019-3). From Here.

Higgs, D., jt. auth. see Callahan, W. J.

Highet, Gilbert, tr. see Jaeger, Werner.

Highfield, A. C. Book of Celestial Images: Angelic & Godform Images in Ritual Magic. LC 86-16209. 192p. 1986. lib. bdg. 19.95 (ISBN 0-8095-7004-1). Borgo Pr.

Hightower, J. A., Jr. El Cuidado Pastoral: Desde la Cuna Hasta la Tumba. Morales, Edgar, tr. from Eng. Tr. of Caring for Folks from Birth to Death. (Span.). 192p. (Orig.). 1986. pap. 5.75 (ISBN 0-311-11045-2). Casa Bautista.

Hightower, James E., Jr. Illustrating Paul's Letter to the Romans. LC 84-7074. 1984. pap. 5.95 (ISBN 0-8054-2251-X). Broadman.

--Voices from the Old Testament. LC 81-68611. (Orig.). 1983. pap. 3.95 (ISBN 0-8054-2245-5). Broadman.

Hightower, James E., Jr., ed. Caring for Folks from Birth to Death. LC 84-20005. 1985. pap. 6.95 (ISBN 0-8054-2415-6). Broadman.

Highwater, Jamake. Native Land: Sagas of the Indian Americas. 1986. 24.95 (ISBN 0-316-36087-2). Little.

Hilali, T., jt. auth. see Khan, M. M.

Hilarius, Saint Opera. Feder, A., ed. (Corpus Scriptorum Ecclesiasticorum Latinorum Ser: Vol. 65). 1916. 50.00 (ISBN 0-384-23110-1). Johnson Repr.

Hilary Of Poitiers, St. The Trinity. LC 67-28585. (Fathers of the Church Ser: Vol. 25). 555p. 1954. 34.95 (ISBN 0-8132-0025-3). Cath U Pr.

Hilberg, Raul. The Destruction of the European Jews, 3 vols. rev. ed. LC 84-18369. 1312p. 1985. Boxed Set. text ed. 159.50x (ISBN 0-8419-0832-X); pap. 14.95 student ed. (ISBN 0-8419-0910-5). Holmes & Meier.

Hilberg, Raul & Staron, Stanislaw, eds. The Warsaw Diary of Adam Czerniakow: Prelude to Doom. 480p. Repr. 14.00 (ISBN 0-686-95101-8). ADL.

Hilbert, Frances F. & Paul, G. Case Studies in Missions. 1987. pap. 7.95 (ISBN 0-8010-4308-5). Baker Bk.

Hilbert, Vi, ed. & tr. Haboo: Native American Stories from Puget Sound. LC 85-40397. (Illus.). 228p. 1985. pap. 9.95 (ISBN 0-295-96270-4). U of Wash Pr.

Hilburn, May S. One Hundred Short Prayers. 4th ed. 100p. 1983. pap. 3.50 softcover (ISBN 0-88053-313-7). Macoy Pub.

Hildebrand, Alice J. Von see Von Hildebrand, Alice J.

Hildebrand, Alice Von see Von Hildebrand, Alice.

Hildebrand, Alice Von see Von Hildebrand, Dietrich & Von Hildebrand, Alice.

Hildebrand, Dietrich von. Man & Woman. LC 65-25840. pap. 25.80 (ISBN 0-317-28166-6, 2022575). Bks Demand UMI.

Hildebrand, Dietrich Von see Von Hildebrand, Dietrich.

Hildebrand, Dietrich Von see Von Hildebrand, Dietrich & Von Hildebrand, Alice.

Hildebrand, Henry. In His Loving Service. Mattson, Lloyd, frwd. by. 226p. (Orig.). 1985. pap. 6.95 (ISBN 0-942684-08-7). Camp Guidepts.

Hildebrande, Dietrich von see Von Hildebrand, Dietrich.

Hildebrandt, Franz. Melanchthon: Alien or Ally. LC 46-3804. 1968. Repr. of 1946 ed. 16.00 (ISBN 0-527-40600-7). Kraus Repr.

Hildeburn, Charles R. Baptisms & Burials From the Records of Christ Church, Philadelphia, 1709-1760. LC 81-86323. 231p. 1982. Repr. of 1893 ed. 15.00 (ISBN 0-8063-0979-2). Genealog Pub.

Hildegard of Bingen. Hildegard of Bingen's Book of Divine Works with Music & Letters. Fox, Matthew, ed. 408p. (Orig.). 1987. pap. 14.95 (ISBN 0-939680-32-7). Bear & Co.

Hilderbrand, Dietrich Von see Von Hilderbrand, Dietrich.

Hilderbrandt, Franz, ed. see Wesley, John.

Hildreth, Dolly, et al. The Money God. (Indian Culture Ser.). 1972. 1.95 (ISBN 0-89992-031-4). Coun India Ed.

Hileman, Louis G. The Celebration of Holy Mass. 154p. 1976. pap. 2.95 (ISBN 0-912414-23-5). Lumen Christi.

Hilgeman, George A. El Programa del Espiritu Santo. 174p. 1982. pap. 4.50 (ISBN 0-89922-216-1). Edit Caribe.

Hilko, Michael P., tr. see Rodzianko, M.

Hill, jt. auth. see Clevenger.

Hill, jt. ed. see Clevenger.

Hill, Alice, jt. auth. see Narramore, Kathy.

Hill, Bert H. Temple of Zeus at Nemea. rev., suppl. ed. Williams, Charles, ed. LC 67-102135. (Illus.). 1966. portfolio 22.00x (ISBN 0-87661-921-9). Am Sch Athens.

Hill, Brennan. The Near-Death Experience: A Christian Approach. 66p. 1981. pap. 3.50 (ISBN 0-697-01756-7). Wm C Brown.

--Rediscovering the Sacraments: Approaches to the Sacrament. 126p. (Orig.). 1982. 3.95 (ISBN 0-8215-9882-1). Sadlier.

Hill, Brennan & Newland, Mary R., eds. Why Be a Catholic? 108p. (Orig.). 1979. pap. 2.00 (ISBN 0-697-01713-3). Wm C Brown.

Hill, C. R., Jr. Between Two Worlds: An Approach to Ministry. LC 76-4276. 1976. 3.50 (ISBN 0-89937-007-1). Ctr Res Soc Chg.

Hill, Canon D. Canterbury Cathedral. (The New Bell's Cathedral Guides Ser.). 1986. cancelled (ISBN 0-918678-13-7). Historical Times.

Hill, Carole E., ed. Symbols & Society: Essays on Belief Systems in Action. LC 74-21905. (Southern Anthropological Society Proceedings Ser: No. 9). 150p. 1975. pap. 6.50x (ISBN 0-8203-0371-2). U of Ga Pr.

Hill, Caroline M., ed. The World's Great Religious Poetry. LC 70-137058. 836p. 1973. Repr. of 1938 ed. lib. bdg. 47.50x (ISBN 0-8371-5521-5, HIRP). Greenwood.

Hill, Charles L., tr. see Melanchthon, Philip.

Hill, Charles L., tr. see Melanchthon, Philipp.

Hill, Christopher. The Collected Essays of Christopher Hill: Religion & Politics in Seventeenth-Century England, Vol. 2. LC 84-16446. 368p. 1986. lib. bdg. 27.50x (ISBN 0-87023-503-6). U of Mass Pr.

Hill, Dave. Boy Who Gave His Lunch Away. (Arch Bks: Set 4). 1967. laminated bdg. 0.99 (59-1138). Concordia.

--Most Wonderful King. (Arch Bks.: Set 5). (Illus.). 1968. laminated bdg. 0.99 (ISBN 0-570-06032-X, 59-1145). Concordia.

--Walls Came Tumbling Down. (Arch Bks.: Set 4). 1967. laminated bdg 0.99 (ISBN 0-570-06024-9, 59-1135). Concordia.

Hill, David. The Gospel of Matthew. rev. ed. (New Century Bible Commentary Ser.). 368p. 1981. pap. 8.95 (ISBN 0-8028-1886-2). Eerdmans.

--New Testament Prophecy. LC 79-16707. (New Foundations Theological Library). 260p. (Peter Toon & Ralph Martin series editors). 1980. 6.49 (ISBN 0-8042-3702-6). John Knox.

Hill, Dick. Death & Dying. 4.25 (ISBN 0-89137-532-5). Quality Pubns.

Hill, Donald, jt. auth. see Al-Hassan, Ahmed.

Hill, Donald E. God's Plan for the Local Church. 32p. 1982. pap. 2.49 (ISBN 0-88151-022-X). Lay Leadership.

--Pathway of Discipleship One Hundred One: Group Leader's Guide. 2nd rev. ed. 48p. 1983. 4.00 (ISBN 0-88151-028-9). Lay Leadership.

--Pathway of Discipleship One Hundred One: Home Study Guide. 2nd rev. ed. 56p. 1983. 8.00 (ISBN 0-88151-027-0). Lay Leadership.

--Pathway of Discipleship One Hundred One. 2nd rev. ed. (Pathway of Discipleship Ser.). 184p. 1983. pap. text ed. 15.00 (ISBN 0-88151-026-2). Lay Leadership.

Hill, Donald E., jt. auth. see Craig, James D.

Hill, Donald E., jt. ed. see Craig, James D.

Hill, Donna. Joseph Smith: The First Mormon. 552p. 1983. pap. 5.95 (ISBN 0-941214-16-8). Signature Bks.

Hill, Dorothy, jt. auth. see Benson, Peter L.

Hill, Edmund. Being Human. 304p. 1984. pap. 14.95 (ISBN 0-225-66358-9, AY8486, HarpR). Har-Row.

--The Mystery of God: St. Augustine on the Trinity. (Catholic Theology Ser.). 200p. pap. 14.95 (ISBN 0-225-66470-4, HarpR). Har-Row.

Hill, Elsie Isensce & Dudley, Cliff. Abused But Chosen. LC 83-61439. 144p. 1983. 4.95 (ISBN 0-89221-106-7). New Leaf.

Hill, G. L. The Best Birthday: A Christmas Entertainment for Children. 8.95 (ISBN 0-89190-404-2, Pub. by Am Repr). Amereon Ltd.

Hill, George H., jt. auth. see Brown, Edna M.

Hill, George H., jt. auth. see Davis, Lenwood.

Hill, Georgia, jt. auth. see Barnard, Laura B.

Hill, Glynn, jt. ed. see Simpson, Floyd.

Hill, Grace L. The Angel of His Presence. LC 83-51594. 96p. 1984. pap. 2.50 (ISBN 0-8423-0047-3). Tyndale.

Hill, Harold. Bible Answers for King's Kids. rev. ed. 224p. 1983. pap. 5.95 (ISBN 0-8007-5131-0, Power Bks). Revell.

--How to Flip Your Flab-Forever. LC 79-64912. 1979. pap. 2.95 (ISBN 0-88270-377-3). Bridge Pub.

--How to Live Like a King's Kid. LC 73-93002. 1974. pap. 2.95 pocket size (ISBN 0-88270-375-7). Bridge Pub.

Hill, Harold & Harrell, Irene. How to Be a Winner. LC 76-31676. 1976. (Pub. by Logos); pap. 2.95 (ISBN 0-88270-456-7). Bridge Pub.

--How to Live in High Victory. LC 77-80293. 1977. pap. 2.95 (ISBN 0-88270-421-4). Bridge Pub.

Hill, Harold & Harrell, Irene B. God's in Charge Here. 160p. (Orig.). 1982. pap. 6.95 (ISBN 0-8007-5078-0, Power Bks). Revell.

--How to Live the Bible Like a King's Kid. (Illus.). 128p. 1980. pap. 5.95 (ISBN 0-8007-5051-9, Power Bks). Revell.

Hill, Harold & Rogers, Liz. Power to Change: How to Stay Slim, Sober, & Smokeless. (Orig.). 1987. pap. 4.95 (ISBN 0-88270-625-X, P625-X). Bridge Pub.

Hill, Harold, et al. From Goo to You by Way of the Zoo. rev. ed. 224p. 1984. pap. 5.95 (ISBN 0-8007-5174-4, Power Bks). Revell.

--The Impossible Takes a Little Longer. 224p. 1985. pap. 6.95 (ISBN 0-8007-5192-2). Revell.

Hill, Henry B., tr. Political Testament of Cardinal Richelieu: The Significant Chapters & Supporting Selections. (Illus.). 148p. 1961. 15.00x (ISBN 0-299-02420-2); pap. 8.95x (ISBN 0-299-02424-5). U of Wis Pr.

Hill, Ida T. Medieval Humanist: Michael Akominatos. LC 73-3164. 48p. 1974. Repr. of 1923 ed. lib. bdg. 14.00 (ISBN 0-8337-3497-0). B Franklin.

Hill, J. Arthur. Emerson & His Philosophy. LC 72-192678. 1919. lib. bdg. 15.00 (ISBN 0-8414-0783-5). Folcroft.

Hill, J. R. John. (Bible Study Commentaries Ser.). 112p. 1980. pap. 4.95 (ISBN 0-87508-169-X). Chr Lit.

Hill, James H., tr. see Marcion Of Sinope.

Hill, John H. Dear God, Pourquoi? Why Did You Born Me in Texas. LC 84-91310. 167p. 1985. 10.95 (ISBN 0-533-06400-7). Vantage.

Hill, John H. & Hill, Laurita L. Peter Tudebode: Historia De Hierosolymitano Itinere. LC 74-78091. (Memoirs Ser.: Vol. 101). 1974. 6.50 (ISBN 0-87169-101-9). Am Philos.

Hill, John L. The Enlightened Society. LC 86-40403. 278p. (Orig.). 1987. pap. 7.95 (ISBN 0-8356-0615-5). Theos Pub Hse.

Hill, John S. John Milton: Poet, Priest & Prophet: A Study of Divine Vocation in Milton's Poetry & Prose. 233p. 1979. 24.50x (ISBN 0-8476-6124-5). Rowman.

Hill, Laurita L., jt. auth. see Hill, John H.

Hill, Leonard E. Your Work on the Pulpit Committee. LC 70-93916. 1970. pap. 3.25 (ISBN 0-8054-3502-6). Broadman.

Hill, Marvin S. & Rooker, C. Keith. The Kirtland Economy Revisited: A Market Critique of Sectarian Economics. LC 78-3848. (Studies in Mormon History: No. 3). (Illus.). 1977. pap. 4.95 (ISBN 0-8425-1230-6). Brigham.

Hill, Mary V. Angel Children: Those Who Die Before Accountability. LC 73-75397. (Illus.). 70p. (Orig.). 1973. pap. 5.50 (ISBN 0-88290-017-X). Horizon Utah.

Hill, Patricia R. The World Their Household: The American Women's Foreign Mission Movement & Cultural Transformation, 1870-1920. (Women & Culture Ser.). 300p. 1985. text ed. 19.50x (ISBN 0-472-10055-6). U of Mich Pr.

Hill, Richard A., ed. see Hatcher, John S.

Hill, Richard O. Training Evangelism Callers. 64p. (Orig.). 1986. Leader Guide. pap. 4.95 (ISBN 0-8066-2227-X, 23-1960); Caller Manual. pap. 3.50 (ISBN 0-8066-2228-8, 23-1961). Augsburg.

Hill, Robert. The Pathway to Prayer & Pietie. LC 74-28864. (English Experience Ser.: No. 744). 1975. Repr. of 1613 ed. 26.50 (ISBN 90-221-0744-2). Walter J Johnson.

Hill, Robert C., ed. see Smith, Hannah W.

Hill, Robert C., tr. see St. John Chrysostom.

Hill, Ruth L. Jeweled Sword. 1987. pap. 5.95 (ISBN 0-89081-565-8). Harvest Hse.

Hill, Samual S., Jr., intro. by see Eighmy, John L.

Hill, Samuel G., jt. auth. see Clevenger, Ernest, Jr.

Hill, Samuel S. The South & the North in American Religion. LC 80-234. (Mercer University Lamar Memorial Lecture Ser.: No. 23). 168p. 1980. 14.00x (ISBN 0-8203-0516-2). U of Ga Pr.

Hill, Samuel S. & Owen, Dennis E. The New Religious-Political Right in America. LC 81-20661. 160p. 1982. 10.95 (ISBN 0-687-27867-8). Abingdon.

Hill, Samuel S., jt. auth. see Mead, Frank S.

Hill, Samuel S., ed. Encyclopedia of Religion in the South. LC 84-8957. viii, 878p. 1984. 60.00 (ISBN 0-86554-117-5, MUP/H97). Mercer Univ Pr.

Hill, Thomas D. & Farrell, Robert T. The Anglo-Saxon Cross. (Yale Studies in English: Nos. 23 & 50). iv, 282p. 1976. Repr. of 1904 ed. 27.50 (ISBN 0-208-01555-8, Archon). Shoe String.

Hill, Tomas. Rios De Tinta: Historia y Ministerio De la Casa Bautista De Publicaciones. Smith, Josie, tr. from Eng. Orig. Title: Rivers of Ink. 64p. 1980. pap. 2.50 (ISBN 0-311-29009-4). Casa Bautista.

Hill, W. Speed, ed. see Hooker, Richard.

Hill, William. Organizing & Developing a Free Will Baptist Sunday School. (Sunday School Workers Training Course Ser.: No. 1). 1969. pap. 3.95 (ISBN 0-89265-002-8, Free Will Baptist Dept). Randall Hse.

Hill, William J. The Three-Personed God: The Trinity As a Mystery of Salvation. LC 81-18012. 354p. 1982. 37.95x (ISBN 0-8132-0560-3). Cath U Pr.

Hillal Dessouki, Ali E. see Dessouki, Ali E. Hillal.

Hillam, Ray C., ed. By the Hands of Wise Men: Essays on the U. S. Constitution. LC 79-13702. 1979. pap. text ed. 5.95 (ISBN 0-8425-1647-6). Brigham.

Hillebrandt, Alfred. Vedic Mythology, Vol. I. rev. 2nd ed. Sarma, Sreeramula R., tr. from Ger. Tr. of Vedische Mythologie. 472p. 1980. text ed. 22.00 (ISBN 0-89684-098-0, Pub. by Motilal Banarsidass India). Orient Bk Dist.

Hillel, jt. auth. see Silverman, Morris.

Hillen, Kathryn. Cooking up Dreams. 160p. 1987. pap. 9.95 (ISBN 0-310-34551-0). Zondervan.

Hillenbrand, Carole, tr. see Endress, Gerhard.

Hillenbrand, Robert. Islamic Architecture: Style, Function, & Form. (Illus.). 200p. 1986. 22.50x (ISBN 0-85224-391-X, Pub. by Edinburgh U Pr Scotland). Columbia U Pr.

Hiller, Joseph A. Albrecht Von Eyb, Medieval Moralist. LC 70-140027. (Catholic University Studies in German Ser.: No. 13). 1970. Repr. of 1939 ed. 25.00 (ISBN 0-404-50233-4). AMS Pr.

Hillerbrand, Hans J. Men & Ideas in the Sixteenth Century. 130p. 1984. pap. text ed. 7.95x (ISBN 0-88133-080-9). Waveland Pr.

--The World of the Reformation. (Twin Brooks Ser.). 229p. 1981. pap. 6.95 (ISBN 0-8010-4248-8). Baker Bk.

Hillerbrand, Hans J., ed. Protestant Reformation. (Documentary History of Western Civilization Ser). (Orig.). 1968. pap. 7.95x (ISBN 0-06-131342-4, TB 1342, Torch). Har-Row.

--The Reformation: A Narrative History Related by Contemporary Observers & Participants. (Twin Brooks Ser). (Illus.). 1978. pap. 11.95 (ISBN 0-8010-4185-6). Baker Bk.

Hillerbrand, Hans J. & Lehmann, Helmut T., eds. Luther's Works: Sermons II, Vol. 52. LC 55-9893. 416p. 1974. 19.95 (ISBN 0-8006-0352-4, 1-352). Fortress.

Hillers, Delbert R. Covenant: The History of a Biblical Idea. LC 69-13539. (Seminars in the History of Ideas Ser: No. 3). 206p. (Orig.). 1969. pap. 4.95x (ISBN 0-8018-1011-6). Johns Hopkins.

--Micah. LC 83-48002. (Hermenaia Ser.). 192p. 1983. 17.95 (ISBN 0-8006-6012-9, 20-6012). Fortress.

Hillers, Delbert R., tr. Lamentations. LC 70-176347. (Anchor Bible Ser: Vol. 7A). (Illus.). 168p. 1972. 14.00 (ISBN 0-385-00738-8, Anchor Pr). Doubleday.

Hillesum, Etty. An Interrupted Life: The Diaries of Etty Hillesum 1941-1943. Pomerans, Arno, tr. LC 83-47750. 226p. 1984. 13.45 (ISBN 0-394-53217-1). Pantheon.

--Letters from Westerbork. Pomerans, Arnold, tr. LC 86-42625. (Dutch.). 160p. 1986. 14.95 (ISBN 0-394-55350-0). Pantheon.

Hillgarth, J. N., ed. Christianity & Paganism, Three Hundred Fifty to Seven Hundred Fifty: The Conversion of Western Europe. rev. ed. LC 85-1154. (Middle Ages Ser.). 160p. 1986. lib. bdg. 25.00 (ISBN 0-8122-7993-X); pap. 10.95 (ISBN 0-8122-1213-4). U of Pa Pr.

Hilliard, Beverly Valenti see Hilliard, Dick & Valenti-Hilliard, Beverly.

Hilliard, Dick. The Lord Blesses Me. LC 78-61308. (Illus.). 1978. pap. 11.95 (ISBN 0-89390-005-2). Resource Pubns.

--My Heart Is Happy. LC 79-64822. 1979. pap. 4.95 (ISBN 0-89390-008-7). Resource Pubns.

Hilliard, Dick & Valenti-Hilliard, Beverly. Happenings. (Center Celebration Ser.). (Illus.). 60p. 1981. pap. text ed. 3.95 (ISBN 0-89390-033-8). Resource Pubns.

--Surprises. (Center Celebration Ser.). (Illus.). 60p. (Orig.). 1981. pap. text ed. 3.95 (ISBN 0-89390-031-1). Resource Pubns.

--Wonders. (Center Celebration Ser.). (Illus.). 60p. (Orig.). 1981. pap. text ed. 3.95 (ISBN 0-89390-032-X). Resource Pubns.

Hilliard, F. H. The Teacher & Religion. 191p. 1963. 7.95 (ISBN 0-227-67675-0). Attic Pr.

Hilliard, Francis. The Elements of Law-the Formative Years: Being a Comprehensive Summary of American Civil Jurisprudence. LC 78-37979. (American Law Ser.). 372p. 1972. Repr. of 1835 ed. 22.00 (ISBN 0-405-04022-9). Ayer Co Pubs.
Hilliard, Richard, jt. auth. see Valenti-Hilliard, Beverly.
Hillila, Bernhard, tr. see Kaukola, Olavi.
Hillis, Dick. Not Made for Quitting. 144p. 1973. pap. 2.95 (ISBN 0-87123-396-7, 200396, Dimension Bks). Bethany Hse.
Hillis, Don. Heaven is Out of This World. (Illus.). 47p. 1982. pap. 2.00 (ISBN 0-89323-032-4). Bible Memory.
Hillis, Don W. Evangelical Idolatry. (Illus.). 95p. (Orig.). 1983. pap. 2.75 (ISBN 0-89323-040-5). Bible Memory.
--John: Gospel of Light & Life. rev. & expanded ed. (Teach Yourself the Bible Ser.). Date not set. pap. 2.75 (ISBN 0-8024-4375-3). Moody.
--Stories of Love that Lasts. 80p. 1980. pap. 1.25 (ISBN 0-89323-015-4). Bible Memory.
Hillis, Newell D. Great Men As Prophets of a New Era. facs. ed. LC 68-16939. (Essay Index Reprint Ser). 1968. Repr. of 1922 ed. 15.00 (ISBN 0-8369-0541-5). Ayer Co Pubs.
--Great Men As Prophets of a New Era. 1922. Repr. 20.00 (ISBN 0-8274-2445-0). R West.
Hillman, James. Suicide & the Soul. LC 85-11901. (Dunquin Ser.: No. 8). 191p. 1964. pap. 12.00 (ISBN 0-88214-208-9). Spring Pubns.
Hillman, James, jt. auth. see Roscher, Wilhelm.
Hillman, James, ed. Spring 1982: An Annual of Archetypal Psychology & Jungian Thought. 316p. (Orig.). 1982. pap. 15.00 (ISBN 0-88214-017-5). Spring Pubns.
Hillman, James, ed. see Christou, Evangelos.
Hillman, Priscilla, illus. Merry-Mouse Book of Prayers & Graces. LC 82-45497. (Balloon Bks.). (Illus.). 32p. 1983. 4.95 (ISBN 0-385-18337-2). Doubleday.
Hillock, Wilfred M. Involved. LC 77-78102. (Anvil Ser.). 1977. pap. 8.95 (ISBN 0-8127-0140-2). Review & Herald.
Hillriegel, Caroleen, et al, eds. Alpha & Omega: Essays on the Trinity in Honor of James A. Nichols, Jr. 140p. (Orig.). 1980. pap. 4.50 (ISBN 0-913439-01-0). Henceforth.
Hills. Pastoral Theology. kivar 6.95 (ISBN 0-686-12899-0). Schmul Pub Co.
Hills, A. M. Fundamental Christian Theology. boards 29.95 (ISBN 0-686-27770-8). Schmul Pub Co.
--Holiness & Power for the Church & the Ministry. Dayton, Donald W., ed. (The Higher Christian Life Ser.). 386p. 1984. 50.00 (ISBN 0-8240-6422-4). Garland Pub.
--Pentacostal Light. 2.95 (ISBN 0-686-27775-9). Schmul Pub Co.
Hills, C., ed. The Secrets of Spirulina. LC 80-22087. 224p. 1980. 6.95 (ISBN 0-916438-38-4). Univ of Trees.
Hills, Christopher. The Christ Book: What Did He Really Say? Hills, Norah, ed. LC 80-5865. (Illus.). 224p. 1980. gift ed. 15.95; text ed. 10.95 (ISBN 0-916438-37-6). Univ of Trees.
--Christ-Yoga of Peace: Proposal for a World Peace Center. 156p. 1970. 4.00 (ISBN 0-916438-01-5). Univ of Trees.
--Into Meditation Now: A Course on Direct Enlightenment. LC 79-5124. (Illus.). 128p. 1979. pap. 5.95 (ISBN 0-916438-30-9). Univ of Trees.
--The Rise of the Phoenix: Universal Government by Nature's Laws. new ed. Ray, Ann & Rozman, Deborah, eds. LC 76-53176. (Illus.). 1024p. (Orig.). 1979. 24.95 (ISBN 0-916438-04-X). Univ of Trees.
--To the One I Love. Ray, Ann & Hills, Norah, eds. LC 84-11814. (Illus.). 256p. 1984. 14.95; pap. text ed. pns (ISBN 0-916438-51-1). Univ of Trees.
Hills, Desmond B. Light for My Life. Van Dolson, Bobbie J., ed. 384p. 1981. 7.95 (ISBN 0-8280-0041-7). Review & Herald.
Hills, Edward F. Believing Bible Study. 2nd ed. (Illus.). 258p. pap. 4.50 (ISBN 0-915923-01-7). Christian Res Pr.
--The King James Version Defended. 4th ed. (Illus.). 280p. 1984. pap. 8.95x (ISBN 0-915923-00-9). Christian Res Pr.
--Space Age Science. 2nd ed. (Illus.). 50p. pap. 1.50 (ISBN 0-915923-02-5). Christian Res Pr.
Hills, M. T. & Eisenhart, E. J., eds. Concise History of the English Bible. 7th ed. 1983. pap. 3.50x (ISBN 0-8267-0326-7, 16228, Pub. by United Bible). Am Bible.
Hills, Norah, ed. You Are a Rainbow. LC 79-13393. (Illus.). 128p. (Orig.). 1979. pap. 4.95 (ISBN 0-916438-25-2). Univ of Trees.
Hills, Norah, ed. see Hills, Christopher.
Hills, Tynette, jt. auth. see Ross, Floyd H.
Hilpinen, Risto, ed. New Studies in Deontic Logic: Norms, Actions & the Foundations of Ethics. 272p. 1981. 39.50 (ISBN 90-277-1278-6, Pub. by Reidel Holland). Kluwer Academic.
Hilprecht, Hermann V. Mathematical Metrological & Chronological Tablets from the Temple Library of Nippur. LC 8-33648. (University of Pennsylvania, Babylonian Expedition, Series A: Cuneiform Texts: Vol. 20, Pt. 1). pap. 33.80 (ISBN 0-317-28568-8, 2052019). Bks Demand UMI.
Hilsenrad, Zalman A. My Soul Thirsts Still. 1985. 13.95 (ISBN 0-87306-923-4). Feldheim.
Hilt, James. How to Have a Better Relationship with Anybody: A Biblical Approach. 1984. pap. 5.95 (ISBN 0-8024-1661-6). Moody.
--Melhor Relacionamento com. Orig. Title: How to Have a Better Relationship with Anybody. (Port.). 1986. write for info. (ISBN 0-8297-0542-2). Life Pubs Intl.
Hiltebeitel, Alf, tr. see Dumezil, Georges.
Hiltebeiten, Alf, tr. see Eliade, Mircea.
Hiltner, Seward. Pastoral Counseling. rev. ed. (Series AF). 1969. pap. 9.95 (ISBN 0-687-30317-6, Apex). Abingdon.
Hiltner, Seward, ed. Toward a Theology of Aging. LC 74-19593. (Special Issue of Pastoral Psychology). 83p. 1975. 16.95 (ISBN 0-87705-278-6); pap. 9.95 (ISBN 0-87705-287-5). Human Sci Pr.
Hilton, Bruce, et al, eds. Ethical Issues in Human Genetics: Genetic Counseling & the Use of Genetic Knowledge. LC 72-93443. 468p. 1973. 35.00x (ISBN 0-306-30715-4, Plenum Pr). Plenum Pub.
Hilton, J. Bells & Bellringing. 1977. 12.50x (ISBN 0-317-54264-8, Pub. by J Richardson UK). State Mutual Bk.
--Joseph Hatch, the Ulcombe Bellfounder. 1985. 11.25x (ISBN 0-317-54278-8, Pub. by J Richardson UK). State Mutual Bk.
Hilton, Walter. The Stairway of Perfection. LC 78-60288. 1979. pap. 4.95 (ISBN 0-385-14059-2, Im). Doubleday.
--Toward a Perfect Love: The Spiritual Counsel of Walter Hilton. Jeffrey, David L., ed. LC 85-15470. (Classics of Faith & Devotion Ser.). 1986. 10.95 (ISBN 0-88070-103-X); pap. 7.95 (ISBN 0-88070-176-5). Multnomah.
Hilty, Hiram. Toward Freedom for All: North Carolina Quakers & Slavery. 120p. 1984. pap. 9.95 (ISBN 0-913408-83-2). Friends United.
Hilu, Virginia, ed. Beloved Prophet: The Love Letters of Kahlil Gibran & Mary Haskell & Her Private Journal. 1972. 18.95 (ISBN 0-394-43298-3). Knopf.
Himalayan Institute. Chants from Eternity. (Illus.). 64p. 1977. plastic comb bdg. 4.95 (ISBN 0-89389-033-2). Himalayan Pubs.
--Meditation in Christianity. rev. ed. 130p. pap. 5.95 (ISBN 0-89389-085-5). Himalayan Pubs.
--The Theory & Practice of Meditation. 2nd ed. 150p. (Orig.). 1986. pap. 5.95 (ISBN 0-89389-075-8). Himalayan Pubs.
Himalayan International Institute. Inner Paths. 110p. pap. 3.95 (ISBN 0-89389-049-9). Himalayan Pubs.
--Therapeutic Value of Yoga. 108p. (Orig.). pap. 3.95 (ISBN 0-89389-054-5). Himalayan Pubs.
--The Yoga Way Cookbook: Natural Vegetarian Recipes. rev. ed. LC 80-81994. (Illus.). 249p. 1980. spiral bdg. 9.95 (ISBN 0-89389-067-7). Himalayan Pubs.
Himelick, Raymond, tr. Erasmus & the Seamless Coat of Jesus. LC 70-151515. 232p. 1971. 6.25 (ISBN 0-911198-29-6). Purdue U Pr.
Himelick, Raymond, tr. see Erasmus.
Himes, John A. A Study of Milton's Paradise Lost. LC 76-17888. 1976. lib. bdg. 42.00 (ISBN 0-8414-4841-8). Folcroft.
Himmel, Roger J. & Manoni, Mary H. The Big Easter Egg Hunt. LC 72-739482. (The Adventures of the Lollipop Dragon Ser.). (Illus.). 1978. pap. text ed. 25.95 (ISBN 0-89290-030-3). Soc for Visual.
Himmelfarb, Martha. Tours of Hell: An Apocalyptic Form in Jewish & Christian Literature. LC 83-23789. 256p. 1983. 23.00x (ISBN 0-8122-7882-8). U of Pa Pr.
--Tours of Hell: An Apocalyptic Form in Jewish & Christian Literature. LC 84-48729. 208p. 1985. pap. 12.95 (ISBN 0-8006-1845-9, 1-1845). Fortress.
Himmelfarb, Milton & Singer, David, eds. American Jewish Year Book, Vol 86. LC 99-4040. 516p. 1986. 25.95 (ISBN 0-8276-0269-3). Am Jewish Comm.
Hinchey, James F. & Corrado, Dennis, eds. Shepherds Speak: American Bishops Confront the Social & Moral Issues That Challenge Christians Today. 240p. (Orig.). 1986. pap. 11.95 (ISBN 0-8245-0737-1). Crossroad NY.
Hinchliff, Peter B. Holiness & Politics. LC 83-1749. pap. 55.80 (ISBN 0-317-30143-8, 2025326). Bks Demand UMI.
Hinckley, Gordon B. Be Thou an Example. LC 81-15109. 144p. 1981. 7.95 (ISBN 0-87747-899-6). Deseret Bk.
Hinckley, Lawrence. Bridge to a Better Life: An Introduction to New Thought. 1978. pap. 2.25 (ISBN 0-87516-255-X). De Vorss.
Hinckley, Ted C. Alaskan John G. Brady: Missionary, Businessman, Judge, & Governor, 1878-1918. LC 81-19030. (Illus.). 415p. 1982. 40.00x (ISBN 0-8142-0336-1). Ohio St U Pr.
Hind, Arthur M. Catalogue of Rembrandt's Etchings 2 Vols. in 1. 2nd ed. LC 67-27456. (Graphic Art Ser). 1967. Repr. of 1923 ed. lib. bdg. 65.00 (ISBN 0-306-70977-5). Da Capo.
Hind, Carolyn S. Whither Thou Goest. LC 85-51991. (Illus.). 192p. 1985. 12.50 (ISBN 0-936029-00-5). Western Bk Journ.
Hindery, Roderick. Comparative Ethics in Hindu & Buddhist Traditions. 1978. 18.95 (ISBN 0-89684-017-4, Pub. by Motilal Banarsidass India). Orient Bk Dist.
Hindman, Jane F. An Ordinary Saint, John Neumann. 1977. pap. 1.95 (ISBN 0-88479-004-5). Arena Lettres.
Hindman, Sandra. Text & Image in Fifteenth-Century Illustrated Dutch Bibles (1977) (Corpus Sacrae Scripturae Neerlandicae Medii Aevi Ser.: Miscellanea: Vol. 1). (Illus.). 35.00 (ISBN 90-04-04901-0). Heinman.
Hinds, John T see Gospel Advocate.
Hinds, Martin, jt. auth. see Crone, Patricia.
Hindson, Edward & Byrd, Walter. When the Road Gets Tough. 160p. 1986. 9.95 (ISBN 0-8007-1495-4). Revell.
Hindson, Edward E. The Philistines & the Old Testament. (Baker Studies in Biblical Archaeology). pap. 6.95 (ISBN 0-8010-4034-5). Baker Bk.
Hindson, Edward E., jt. ed. see Falwell, Jerry.
Hine, James R. The Springtime of Love & Marriage. (Family Life Ser.). 160p. 1985. pap. 6.95 (ISBN 0-317-38064-8). Judson.
Hine, Virginia H., jt. auth. see Gerlach, Luther P.
Hines, Eugene B. Asking the Hard Questions. LC 85-19528. 1986. pap. 4.95 (ISBN 0-8054-5013-0). Broadman.
--Living in the Presence of God. LC 84-24305. 1985. pap. 4.95 (ISBN 0-8054-5229-X). Broadman.
Hines, Theodore C., jt. auth. see Regazzi, John J.
Hingley, Ronald. Dostoevsky: His Life & Work. 1978. 5.95 (ISBN 0-684-15916-3, ScribT); encore ed. 5.95 (ISBN 0-684-17232-1). Scribner.
Hingora. The Prophecies of the Holy Quran. pap. 4.50 (ISBN 0-686-18509-9). Kazi Pubns.
Hingorani, A. T., ed. see Gandhi, Mohandas K.
Hinke, William J., ed. Life & Letters of the Rev. John Philip Boehm: Founder of the Reformed Church in Pennsylvania, 1683-1749. LC 71-38784. (Religion in America, Ser. 2). 572p. 1972. Repr. of 1916 ed. 35.00 (ISBN 0-405-04069-5). Ayer Co Pubs.
Hinke, William J., tr. see Weiser, Frederick S.
Hinkelammert, Franz. The Ideological Weapons of Death: A Theological Critique of Capitalism. Berryman, Phillip, tr. from Span. LC 86-2557. Tr. of Las Armas Ideologicas de la Muerte. 320p. (Orig.). 1986. pap. 17.95 (ISBN 0-88344-260-4). Orbis Bks.
Hinkle, Joseph & Cook, Melva. How to Minister to Families in Your Church. LC 77-82925. 1978. 8.50 (ISBN 0-8054-3224-8). Broadman.
Hinkle, Joseph W., et al. Oikos: A Practical Approach to Family Evangelism. LC 81-69328. 1982. pap. 4.95 (ISBN 0-8054-6234-1). Broadman.
Hinnebusch, Paul. Friendship in the Lord. LC 73-90411. 144p. 1974. pap. 2.75 (ISBN 0-87793-065-1). Ave Maria.
--The Mother of Jesus: Present with Us. LC 79-93231. 1980. pap. 5.95 (ISBN 0-913382-32-9, 101-27). Prow Bks-Franciscan.
Hinnells, John. Zoroastrianism & the Parsis. 1985. 13.00x (ISBN 0-7062-3973-3, Pub. by Ward Lock Educ Co Ltd). State Mutual Bk.
Hinnells, John, ed. see Boyce, Mary.
Hinnells, John R. Persian Mythology. LC 85-70554. (The Library of the World's Myths & Legends). (Illus.). 144p. 1985. 18.95 (ISBN 0-87226-017-8). P Bedrick Bks.
Hinnells, John R., ed. The Facts on File Dictionary of Religions. LC 83-20834. 560p. 1984. 24.95x (ISBN 0-87196-862-2). Facts On File.
--The Penguin Dictionary of Religions. (Reference Ser.). 464p. 1984. pap. 7.95 (ISBN 0-14-051106-7). Penguin.
Hinshaw, Cecil E. Nonviolent Resistance. 1983. pap. 2.50x (ISBN 0-87574-088-X, 088). Pendle Hill.
Hinshaw, David. Rufus Jones, Master Quaker. facsimile ed. LC 74-133522. (Select Bibliographies Reprint Ser.). Repr. of 1951 ed. 19.00 (ISBN 0-8369-5554-4). Ayer Co Pubs.
Hinson, E. Glenn. The Evangelization of the Roman Empire: Identity & Adaptability. LC 81-11266. viii, 332p. 1981. 22.00 (ISBN 0-86554-244-9, MUP-P36). Mercer Univ Pr.
--The Integrity of the Church. LC 77-82400. 1978. 8.95 (ISBN 0-8054-1616-1). Broadman.
Hinson, E. Glenn, jt. auth. see Garrett, James L., Jr.
Hinson, E. Glenn, ed. & tr. Understanding of the Church: Sources of Early Christian Thought. pap. 6.95 (ISBN 0-317-52518-2). Fortress.
Hinson, E. Glenn, ed. Understandings of the Church. LC 86-45227. (Sources of Early Christian Thought Ser.). 128p. 1986. pap. 7.95 (ISBN 0-8006-1415-1, 1-1415). Fortress.
Hinson, William H. A Place to Dig In. 1987. 10.95t (ISBN 0-687-31549-2). Abingdon.
--Solid Living in a Shattered World. 160p. 1985. 8.95 (ISBN 0-687-39048-6). Abingdon.
Hinten, Marvin D., ed. see Taylor, Jeremy.
Hinton, Keith. Growing Churches: Singapore Style. 1985. pap. 4.95 (ISBN 9971-972-24-7). OMF Bks.
Hinton, Pat C. Images of Peace. 96p. 1983. pap. 4.95 (ISBN 0-86683-748-5, HarpR). Har-Row.
--Prayer after Nine Rainy Days & Other Family Prayers. 1978. pap. 4.95 (ISBN 0-86683-626-8, HarpR). Har-Row.
Hintz, Debra T. Gathering Prayers. 80p. (Orig.). 1986. pap. 7.95 (ISBN 0-89622-296-9). Twenty-Third.
--Prayer Services for Parish Meetings. (Illus.). 96p. (Orig.). 1983. pap. 9.95 (ISBN 0-89622-170-9). Twenty-Third.
Hintz, Howard W. Quaker Influence in American Literature. Repr. of 1940 ed. lib. bdg. 18.75 (ISBN 0-8371-3945-7, HIGA). Greenwood.
Hintze, Barbara. Mary: Mother of Jesus. (BibLearn Ser.). (Illus.). 1977. bds. 5.95 (ISBN 0-8054-4232-4, 4242-32). Broadman.
Hiorns, F. R., jt. auth. see Gater, George H.
Hipple, John & Cimbolic, Peter. The Counselor & Suicidal Crisis: Diagnosis & Intervention. 136p. 1979. 16.25x (ISBN 0-398-03872-4). C C Thomas.
Hippolytus, Saint. Antichrist. 1979. pap. 2.95 (ISBN 0-686-26145-3). Eastern Orthodox.
Hirai, Tomio. Zen & the Mind: A Scientific Approach to Zen Practice. (Illus., Orig.). 1978. 10.50 (ISBN 0-87040-391-5). Japan Pubns USA.
--Zen Meditation & Psychotherapy. LC 85-81591. (Illus.). 160p. (Orig.). 1986. pap. 11.95 (ISBN 0-87040-666-3). Japan Pubns USA.
Hiral, Ange-Marie. The Revelations of Margaret of Cortona. (Spirit &Life Ser). 1952. 3.00 (ISBN 0-686-11562-7). Franciscan Inst.
Hirn, K. E. Monographie & Iconographie der Oedogoniaceen. (Illus.). 1960. pap. 95.00x (ISBN 3-7682-7056-4). Lubrecht & Cramer.
Hiroa, Te Rangi, jt. auth. see Buck, Peter.
Hirsch. Psalms, 2 vols. 1975. 26.95 (ISBN 0-87306-025-3). Feldheim.
Hirsch, David E. Rabbi Emil G. Hirsch: The Reform Advocate. LC 68-24717. 1968. pap. 3.00x (ISBN 0-87655-502-4). Collage Inc.
Hirsch, David E., ed. Theology of Emil G. Hirsch. 1977. pap. text ed. 12.50x (ISBN 0-87655-539-3). Collage Inc.
Hirsch, David H. & Aschkenasy, Nehama, eds. Biblical Patterns in Modern Literature. (Brown Judiac Studies: No. 77). 252p. 1985. o.s. 21.95 (ISBN 0-89130-813-X, 14 00 77); pap. 17.95 (ISBN 0-89130-814-8). Scholars Pr GA.
Hirsch, E. D., Jr. The Aims of Interpretation. LC 75-21269. 1978. pap. 7.00x (ISBN 0-226-34241-7, P767, Phoen). U of Chicago Pr.
Hirsch, Emanuel see Luther, Martin.
Hirsch, Emil G. My Religion. Levi, Gerson B., ed. Incl. The Crucifixion Viewed from a Jewish Standpoint (1908. LC 73-2207. (The Jewish People; History, Religion, Literature Ser.). Repr. of 1925 ed. 33.00 (ISBN 0-405-05271-5). Ayer Co Pubs.
Hirsch, Ernest A. Starting Over. 1977. 8.95 (ISBN 0-8158-0350-8). Chris Mass.
Hirsch, S. R. Collected Writings of Samson Raphael Hirsch, Vol. 2: The Jewish Year, Elul-Adar. (The Hirsch Heritage Ser.). 1985. 15.75 (ISBN 0-87306-951-X). Feldheim.
--Horeb, 1 vol. Set. 19.95x (ISBN 0-900689-40-4). Bloch.
--Judaism Eternal, 2 Vols. 1956. Set. 29.95 (ISBN 0-900689-70-6). Soncino Pr.
Hirsch, Sampson R. From the Wisdom of Mishle. Paritzky-Joshua, Karin, tr. 260p. 1976. pap. 7.95 (ISBN 0-87306-040-7). Feldheim.
Hirsch, Samson R. Chapters of the Fathers. Hirschler, Gertrude, tr. 1979. 5.95 (ISBN 0-87306-182-9). Feldheim.
--The Hirsch Siddur. Samson Raphael Hirsch Publication Society Staff, tr. from Ger. Tr. of Tefilot Yisrael. 1978. 16.95 (ISBN 0-87306-141-1); compact ed 9.95 (ISBN 0-87306-142-X). Feldheim.
--The Nineteen Letters of Ben Uziel. Paritzky, Karen, tr. from Ger. 6.95 (ISBN 0-87306-180-2). Feldheim.
--The Nineteen Letters of Ben Uziel on Judaism. Drachman, Bermard, tr. LC 69-131727. 1969. 4.95 (ISBN 0-87306-045-8). Feldheim.
Hirsch, Samuel. Die Religionsphilosophie der Juden. Katz, Steven, ed. LC 79-7136. (Jewish Philosophy, Mysticism & History of Ideas Ser.). 1980. Repr. of 1842 ed. lib. bdg. 74.50x (ISBN 0-405-12262-4). Ayer Co Pubs.

Hirsch, Somson R. Nineteen Letters of Ben Uziel: A Spiritual Presentation of the Principles of Judaism. Drachman, Bernard, tr. (Eng. & Ger., Heb). 27.50 (ISBN 0-87559-076-4). Shalom.

Hirsch, W. Rabbinic Psychology. LC 73-2208. (The Jewish People; History, Religion, Literature Ser.). Repr. of 1947 ed. 24.50 (ISBN 0-405-05272-3). Ayer Co Pubs.

Hirschfeld, Gerhard, ed. The Policies of Genocide: Jews & Soviet Prisoners of War in Nazi Germany. (Illus.). 176p. 1986. text ed. 24.95x (ISBN 0-04-943045-9); pap. text ed. 9.95x (ISBN 0-04-943046-7). Allen Unwin.

Hirschfield, Jerry. My Ego, Higher Self & I. 281p. (Orig.). 1986. pap. 11.95 (ISBN 0-87418-014-7, 151). Coleman Pub.

Hirschler, Gertrude, ed. see Zuker, Simon.

Hirschler, Gertrude, tr. from German. The Psalms: Translation & Commentary by Rabbi Samson Raphael Hirsch. (Compact Ser.). 1978. 16.95 (ISBN 0-87306-135-7). Feldheim.

Hirschler, Gertrude, tr. see Friedman, Alexander Z.

Hirschler, Gertrude, tr. see Hirsch, Samson R.

Hirschmann, Maria A. Are You Prepared? Hansi Shares How You Can Face the Future Without Fear. LC 79-90957. 64p. (Orig.). 1979. pap. 1.95 (ISBN 0-932878-06-7, HB-06). Hansi.

--I Am But a Child in Christ: A Basic Guide for Christian Living. LC 77-89331. (Bible Study & Sharing Ser.: No. 1). 192p. (Orig.). 1977. pap. 4.95 (ISBN 0-932878-00-8, HB-00). Hansi.

--I'll Never Walk Alone: Hansi's Journal. LC 73-81015. 170p. (Orig.). 1986. pap. 6.95 (ISBN 0-932878-08-3, HB-009). Hansi.

Hirschmann, Maria A. & Pershing, Betty. Follow Me: A Study of the Life of Christ. LC 79-84331. (Bible Study & Sharing Ser.: No. 2). 224p. (Orig.). 1979. pap. 4.95 (ISBN 0-932878-01-6, HB/01). Hansi.

--God's Word: A Living Rainbow. LC 63-1848. 167p. (Orig.). 1984. pap. 6.95 (ISBN 0-932878-07-5, HB-008). Hansi.

--Learn of Me: A Study of the Teachings of Christ. LC 79-90958. (Bible Study & Sharing Ser.: No. 3). 144p. (Orig.). 1980. pap. 4.95 (ISBN 0-932878-02-4, HB-02). Hansi.

Hirsh, Ethel S. Jewish Buildings & Cemeteries Guide to Visual Resources: International Holdings in Israel, Vol. I. 75p. 1982. pap. 10.00 (ISBN 0-943376-17-3). Magnes Mus.

Hirsh, Marilyn. The Hanukkah Story. LC 77-22183. (Illus.). 1977. pap. 4.95 (ISBN 0-88482-761-5, Bonim Bks). Hebrew Pub.

Hirshaut, Julien. Jewish Martyrs of Pawiak. LC 81-85301. 256p. 1982. 16.95 (ISBN 0-8052-5039-5); pap. 10.95 (ISBN 0-8052-5040-9). Holocaust Pubns.

Hirshaw, Cecil F. Apology for Perfection. LC 64-22766. (Orig.). 1964. pap. 2.50x (ISBN 0-87574-138-X). Pendle Hill.

Hirst, Edward W. Jesus & the Moralists. 1977. lib. bdg. 59.95 (ISBN 0-8490-2097-2). Gordon Pr.

Hirst, Margaret E. Quakers in Peace & War. LC 70-147671. (Library of War & Peace; Relig. & Ethical Positions on War Ser.). lib. bdg. 46.00 (ISBN 0-8240-0429-9). Garland Pub.

--The Quakers in Peace & War: An Account of Their Peace Principles & Practice. LC 73-137545. (Peace Movement in America Ser). 560p. 1972. Repr. of 1923 ed. lib. bdg. 32.95x (ISBN 0-89198-073-3). Ozer.

Hirst, Michael, ed. see Wilde, Johannes.

Hirst, Wolf Z. The Romantic Hero & His Biblical Sources. Hogg, James, ed. (Romantic Reassessment ser.). (Orig.). 1985. pap. 15.00 (ISBN 3-7052-0573-0, Pub. by Salzburg Studies). Longwood Pub Group.

Hirstein, Sandra, jt. auth. see Fearon, Mary.

Hirstein, Sandra J., jt. auth. see Fearon, Mary.

Hirstein, Sandra J., jt. auth. see Tully, Mary Jo.

Hirth, Mary, compiled by. The Stanley Marcus Collection of Christmas Books. (Illus., Orig.). 1968. pap. 6.00 (ISBN 0-87959-029-7). U of Tex H Ransom Ctr.

Hisamatsu, Shinichi. Zen & the Fine Arts. Tokiwa, Gishin, tr. LC 76-136562. (Illus.). 400p. 1982. pap. 24.95 (ISBN 0-87011-519-7). Kodansha.

Hiscox, Edward T. Hiscox Guide for Baptist Churches. 12.95 (ISBN 0-8170-0329-0). Judson.

--Hiscox Standard Baptist Manual. 1965. pap. 5.95 (ISBN 0-8170-0340-1). Judson.

--Principles & Practices for Baptist Churches. LC 80-8083. 598p. (Orig.). 1985. pap. 11.95 (ISBN 0-8254-2860-2). Kregel.

--Star Book for Ministers. rev. ed. 1967. 7.95 (ISBN 0-8170-0167-0). Judson.

Hiskett, Mervyn. The Sword of Truth: The Life & Times of the Shehu Usuman Dan Fodlo. (Illus.). 1973. pap. 3.00x (ISBN 0-19-501647-5). Oxford U Pr.

Hislop, Alexander. The Two Babylons. 9.95 (ISBN 0-87213-330-3). Loizeaux.

Hislop, D. H. Our Heritage in Public Worship. 354p. 1935. 12.95 (ISBN 0-567-02138-6, Pub. by T & T Clark Ltd UK). Fortress.

Hislop, John S. Conversations with Sathya Sai Baba. LC 79-51262. (Illus.). 1979. pap. 5.40 (ISBN 0-9600958-5-3). Birth Day.

--My Baba & I. LC 85-61733. 1985. pap. 6.30 (ISBN 0-9600958-8-8). Birth Day.

Historical Records Survey, WPA Staff. Inventory of the Roman Catholic Church Records of New Hampshire. 19p. 1985. pap. 3.50 (ISBN 0-935207-18-X). DanBury Hse Bks.

Hitchcock, Donald R. The Appeal of Adam to Lazarus in Hell. (Slavistic Printings & Reprintings Ser.: No. 302). 1979. text ed. 80.00x (ISBN 0-686-27016-9). Mouton.

Hitchcock, Elsie V. & Chambers, R. W., eds. Harpsfield's Life of More. (EETS OS Ser.: Vol. 186). Repr. of 1931 ed. 40.00 (ISBN 0-8115-3377-8). Kraus Repr.

Hitchcock, Ethan A. Swedenborg: A Hermetic Philosopher. 59.95 (ISBN 0-8490-1164-7). Gordon Pr.

Hitchcock, James. Catholicism & Modernity. 250p. 1983. pap. 8.95 (ISBN 0-89283-179-0). Servant.

--The New Enthusiasts: And What They Are Doing to the Catholic Church. 168p. 1982. pap. 9.95 (ISBN 0-88347-150-7). Thomas More.

--What Is Secular Humanism? Why Humanism Became Secular & How It Is Changing Our World. (Illus.). 158p. 1982. pap. 6.95 (ISBN 0-89283-163-4). Servant.

Hitchcock, John. Atoms, Snowflakes & God. LC 85-40842. (Illus.). 222p. 1986. pap. 6.75 (ISBN 0-8356-0604-X, Quest). Theos Pub Hse.

Hitchcock, Roswell D. Baker's Topical Bible. 768p. 1984. pap. 11.95 (ISBN 0-8010-4284-4). Baker Bk.

Hitchens, Robert J. Multiple Marriage: A Study of Polygamy in Light of the Bible. LC 86-72269. 160p. (Orig.). 1987. pap. 6.95 (ISBN 0-9617379-1-3). Doulos Pubs.

Hitchock, Helen. Helping Yourself with Numerology. LC 72-172406. (Illus.). 228p. 1972. pap. 5.95 (ISBN 0-13-386854-0, Reward). P-H.

Hite, Jordan, et al, eds. Religious Institutes, Secular Institutes, Societies of the Apostolic Life. (A Handbook on Canons Ser.: Nos. 573-746). 400p. 1985. pap. 22.50 (ISBN 0-8146-1403-5). Liturgical Pr.

Hite, Jordan F., et al. Readings, Cases, Materials in Canon Law: A Textbook for Ministerial Students. LC 79-24977. 370p. (Orig.). 1980. pap. text ed. 8.50 (ISBN 0-8146-1081-1). Liturgical Pr.

Hitt, Russell, ed. see Holman Company.

Hitt, Russell T. How Christians Grow. 1979. 12.95x (ISBN 0-19-502558-X). Oxford U Pr.

Hitti, Philip K. Islam: A Way of Life. 1971. pap. 7.50 (ISBN 0-89526-992-9). Regnery Bks.

--Islam & the West: A Historical Cultural Survey. LC 78-10793. (Anvil Ser.). 192p. 1979. pap. 7.50 (ISBN 0-88275-787-3). Krieger.

--Origins of the Druze People & Religion, with Extracts from Their Sacred Writings. LC 30-27674. (Columbia University. Oriental Studies: No. 28). Repr. of 1928 ed. 19.00 (ISBN 0-404-50518-X). AMS Pr.

Hitti, Philip K. see Ahmad Ibn Yahya, Al-Baladuri.

Hittleman, Richard. Yoga for Health. LC 82-90825. 256p. (Orig.). 1983. pap. 7.95 (ISBN 0-345-30852-2). Ballantine.

Hittorpius, Melchior. De Divinsis Catholicae Ecclesiae Officiis et Mysteriis. 796p. Repr. of 1610 ed. text ed. 207.00 (ISBN 0-576-99170-8, Pub. by Gregg Intl Pubs England). Gregg Intl.

Hitz, Donna. The Triangular Pattern of Life. LC 79-84851. 94p. 1980. 7.95 (ISBN 0-8022-2249-8). Philos Lib.

Hixon, Robert. Lawrie Tatum: Indian Agent. LC 81-81684. 28p. 1981. pap. 2.50x (ISBN 0-87574-238-6, 238). Pendle Hill.

Hjelm, Ingalill H., tr. see Geres, Paul.

Ho, Van H. Moving Meditation: Enlightenment of the Mind & Total Fitness. LC 79-88748. (Illus.). 214p. 1979. pap. 15.00 (ISBN 0-9602904-1-9). V H Ho.

Hoad, Harold. Grey Friars. 1979. 6.95 (ISBN 0-8199-0779-0). Franciscan Herald.

Hoag, John D. Islamic Architecture. LC 76-41805. (Masters of Art Ser.). (Illus.). 1977. 50.00 (ISBN 0-8109-1010-1). Abrams.

Hoagland, Donald. Rome & the Political Theory of History with Cogent Applications to the Rivalries Between the United States & Soviet Russia. (Illus.). 166p. 1985. 167.95 (ISBN 0-86722-103-8). Inst Econ Pol.

Hoagland, Victor. Prayers: For Daily & Occasional Use. pap. 1.45 (ISBN 0-8091-5158-8). Paulist Pr.

Hoard, Laurie. Standard Christmas Program Book, No. 46. 48p. 1985. pap. 1.95 (ISBN 0-87239-850-1, 8646). Standard Pub.

Hoard, Laurie, ed. Christmas Programs for Children. 48p. 1986. pap. 1.95 (ISBN 0-87239-940-0, 8601). Standard Pub.

--Christmas Programs for the Church, No. 19. 64p. 1986. pap. 2.95 (ISBN 0-87239-914-1, 8619). Standard Pub.

Hoard, Laurie, compiled by. Easter Programs for the Church, No. 8. 64p. (Orig.). 1984. pap. 2.95 (ISBN 0-87239-767-X, 8720). Standard Pub.

--Easter Programs for the Church, No. 9. 64p. 1985. pap. 2.95 (ISBN 0-87239-845-5, 8721). Standard Pub.

--Easter Programs for the Church, No. 10. 64p. 1986. pap. 2.95 (ISBN 0-87403-082-X, 8722). Standard Pub.

Hoard, Laurie, ed. Mother-Daughter-Father-Son Banquets & Programs, No. 7. 64p. (Orig.). 1984. pap. 2.95 (ISBN 0-87239-769-6, 8737). Standard Pub.

--Standard Easter Program Book, No. 35. 48p. (Orig.). 1984. pap. 1.95 (ISBN 0-87239-768-8, 8705). Standard Pub.

Hoard, Laurie, compiled by. Standard Easter Program Book, No. 36. 48p. 1985. pap. 1.95 (ISBN 0-87239-870-6, 8706). Standard Pub.

Hoard, Walter B., ed. Outstanding Black Sermons, Vol. 2. 1978. pap. 5.95 (ISBN 0-8170-0832-2). Judson.

Hoare, Frederick R. Eight Decisive Books of Antiquity. LC 73-99638. (Essay Index Reprint Ser). 1952. 19.50 (ISBN 0-8369-1414-7). Ayer Co Pubs.

Hoare, H. W. Our English Bible. 1925. 27.00 (ISBN 0-8274-3083-3). R West.

Hobart, John H. Can Quakerism Speak to the Times? 1983. pap. 2.50x (ISBN 0-87574-078-2, 078). Pendle Hill.

Hobart, Michael E. Science & Religion in the Thought of Nicolas Malebranche. LC 81-7419. x, 196p. 1982. 19.95x (ISBN 0-8078-1487-3). U of NC Pr.

Hobbie, F. Wellford. Easter. LC 84-18756. (Proclamation Three C Ser.). 64p. 1986. pap. 3.75 (ISBN 0-8006-4129-9, 1-4129). Fortress.

Hobbie, Francis W., jt. auth. see Keck, Leander E.

Hobbs & Paschall, eds. Teacher's Bible Commentary. LC 75-189505. 24.95 (ISBN 0-8054-1116-X). Broadman.

Hobbs, Carolyn. And He Loved Her. 185p. (Orig.). 1979. pap. 1.95 (ISBN 0-89084-113-6). Bob Jones Univ Pr.

Hobbs, Edward C., ed. Stubborn Faith: Papers on Old Testament & Related Subjects Presented to Honor William Andrew Irwin. LC 56-12567. 1956. 13.95x (ISBN 0-87074-079-2). SMU Press.

Hobbs, Herschel H. Fundamentals of Our Faith. LC 60-5200. (Orig.). 1960. pap. 6.95 (ISBN 0-8054-1702-8). Broadman.

--Hebrews. LC 81-65388. 1981. pap. 4.95 (ISBN 0-8054-1323-5). Broadman.

--John: A Study Guide Commentary. 96p. 1973. pap. 4.95 (ISBN 0-310-26113-9). Zondervan.

--A Layman's Handbook of Christian Doctrine. LC 74-78615. 1975. 5.75 (ISBN 0-8054-1927-6). Broadman.

--What Baptists Believe. LC 64-12411. 1963. bds. 4.25 (ISBN 0-8054-8101-X). Broadman.

Hobbs, Herschel H. & Mullins, E. Y. The Axioms of Religion. LC 78-50799. 1978. 8.50 (ISBN 0-8054-1707-9). Broadman.

Hobbs, James R. Pastor's Manual. 1940. 8.95 (ISBN 0-8054-2301-X). Broadman.

Hobbs, Ruth. The Christian Short Story. 10.95 (ISBN 0-686-32320-3). Rod & Staff.

Hobe, Phyllis. The Meaning of Christmas. LC 75-12627. 1982. Repr. of 1975 ed. 7.95 (ISBN 0-8054-5118-8). Broadman.

--The Meaning of Love. LC 76-23415. 1982. Repr. of 1976 ed. 7.95 (ISBN 0-8054-5119-6). Broadman.

--Your Personal Handbook of Prayer. LC 83-3475. 256p. 1983. 11.95 (ISBN 0-664-27007-7, A Bridgebooks Publication). Westminster.

--Your Personal Handbook of Prayer. LC 83-3475. 256p. 1987. 11.95 (A Bridgebooks Publication). Westminster.

Hobe, Phyllis, ed. The Wonder of Comfort. LC 82-8322. (Small Wonders Ser.). (Illus.). 108p. (Orig.). 1982. pap. 4.95 (ISBN 0-664-26003-9, A Bridgebooks Publication). Westminster.

--The Wonder of Love. LC 82-8376. (Small Wonders Ser.). (Illus.). 112p. 1982. pap. 4.95 (ISBN 0-664-26001-2, A Bridgebooks Publication). Westminster.

--The Wonder of Prayer. LC 82-8317. (Small Wonders Ser.). (Illus.). 112p. (Orig.). 1982. pap. 4.95 (ISBN 0-664-26002-0, A Bridgebooks Publication). Westminster.

Hobe, Phyllis L. When Love Isn't Easy. 192p. 1986. pap. 3.50 (ISBN 0-553-26055-3). Bantam.

Hobhouse, Stephen, ed. see Law, William.

Hobson, John. Hinduism & Its Relation to Christianity. 1977. lib. bdg. 59.95 (ISBN 0-8490-1951-6). Gordon Pr.

Hochbaum, Martin, jt. ed. see Levine, Naomi.

Hochhuth, Rolf. The Deputy. Winston, Richard & Winston, Clara, trs. from Ger. 1963. pap. 7.95 (ISBN 0-394-17125-X, B154, BC). Grove.

Hock, Goh E., jt. auth. see Pang, Chia S.

Hock, Ronald F. The Social Context of Paul's Ministry: Tentmaking & Apostleship. LC 79-7381. 112p. 1980. 8.95 (ISBN 0-8006-0577-2, 1-577). Fortress.

Hocken, Peter. Streams of Renewal. 288p. (Orig.). 1986. pap. 11.95 (ISBN 0-932085-03-2). Word Among Us.

Hocken, Peter, jt. auth. see Tugwell, Simon.

Hockett, Betty & Abbott, Grace. Life Changing Learning for Children: Resources That Work. (C. E. Ministries Ser.). 1977. pap. 3.50 (ISBN 0-89367-020-0). Light & Life.

Hocking, David. Are You Spirit-Filled? (Orig.). pap. 5.95 (ISBN 0-89081-493-7). Harvest Hse.

--Be a Leader People Follow. LC 78-67854. 192p. 1979. pap. 5.95 (ISBN 0-8307-0680-1, 5411718). Regal.

--Marrying Again: A Guide for Christians. 160p. 1983. 5.95 (ISBN 0-8007-5188-4, Power Bks). Revell.

--Pleasing God. 144p. 1985. pap. 5.95 (ISBN 0-89840-101-1). Heres Life.

Hocking, David L. How to Be Happy in Difficult Situations: Studies in Philippians. pap. 4.95 (ISBN 0-88469-027-X). BMH Bks.

--Pleasing God. LC 84-47802. 144p. 1984. Heres Life.

--Who Am I & What Difference Does It Make? LC 85-8810. (Living Theology Ser.). 1985. pap. 7.95 (ISBN 0-88070-102-1). Multnomah.

Hocking, W. E., et al. Church & the New World Mind: The Drake Lectures for 1944. facsimile ed. LC 68-57311. (Essay Index Reprint Ser). Repr. of 1944 ed. 18.00 (ISBN 0-8369-9698-4). Ayer Co Pubs.

Hocking, W. J. The Son of His Love. 6.25 (ISBN 0-88172-088-7). Believers Bkshelf.

Hocking, William E. Living Religions & a World Faith. LC 75-3187. (Hibbert Lectures Ser. 1938). Repr. of 1940 ed. 28.50 (ISBN 0-404-59189-2). AMS Pr.

--The Meaning of Immortality in Human Experience, Including Thoughts on Death & Life. rev. ed. 263p. 1973. Repr. of 1957 ed. lib. bdg. 27.50x (ISBN 0-8371-6621-7, HOMI). Greenwood.

Hockings, Paul, ed. Ancient Hindu Refugees: Badaga Social History 1550-1975. (Studies in Anthropology). 1980. text ed. 39.50x (ISBN 90-279-7798-4). Mouton.

Hocquard, Gaston. Les Meditations du Bienheureux de Guigues de Saint Romain: Cinquieme Prieur de Chartreuse (1109-1136) Hogg, James, ed. (Analecta Cartusiana Ser.: No. 112). 311p. (Orig.). 1984. pap. 25.00 (ISBN 0-317-42589-7, Pub. by Salzburg Studies). Longwood Pub Group.

Hocquard, Gaston, et al. Collectanea Cartusiensa, No. 1. Hogg, James, ed. (Analecta Cartusiana Ser.: No. 82-1). (Fr., Illus.). 1980. pap. 25.00 (ISBN 3-7052-0119-0, Pub. by Salzburg Studies). Longwood Pub Group.

Hodann, Max. History of Modern Morals. LC 72-9651. Repr. of 1937 ed. 47.50 (ISBN 0-404-57460-2). AMS Pr.

Hodder, John, jt. auth. see Davies, Tom.

Hodder, Sharon. The Ultimate Deception. 112p. 1982. pap. 4.95 (ISBN 0-89221-096-6). New Leaf.

Hodge, A. A. Confession of Faith. 1978. 13.95 (ISBN 0-85151-275-5). Banner of Truth.

--Evangelical Theology. 1976. pap. 6.95 (ISBN 0-85151-236-4). Banner of Truth.

--Outlines of Theology. 1983. 16.95 (ISBN 0-85151-160-0). Banner of Truth.

Hodge, A. A. & Warfield, B. B. Inspiration. 1979. pap. 2.95 (ISBN 0-8010-4222-4). Baker Bk.

Hodge, Archibald A. Life of Charles Hodge, Professor in the Theological Seminary, Princeton, New Jersey. LC 71-83425. (Religion in America, Ser. 1). 1969. Repr. of 1881 ed. 32.00 (ISBN 0-405-00250-5). Ayer Co Pubs.

Hodge, Charles. Commentary on the Epistle to the Ephesians. (Thornapple Commentaries Ser.). 1980. pap. 8.95 (ISBN 0-8010-4221-6). Baker Bk.

--Corinthians 1 & 2. (Geneva Commentaries Ser.). 1978. 15.95 (ISBN 0-85151-185-6). Banner of Truth.

--Essays & Reviews: New York, 1879. Kuklick, Bruce, ed. (American Religious Thought of the 18th & 19th Centuries Ser.). 633p. 1987. lib. bdg. 85.00 (ISBN 0-8240-6966-8). Garland Pub.

--Princeton Sermons. 1979. 13.95 (ISBN 0-85151-285-2). Banner of Truth.

--Romans. (Geneva Commentaries Ser.). 1975. 13.95 (ISBN 0-85151-213-5). Banner of Truth.

--Systematic Theology, 3 Vols. 1960. Set. 49.95 (ISBN 0-8028-8135-1). Eerdmans.

--Way of Life. 1978. pap. 4.95 (ISBN 0-85151-273-9). Banner of Truth.

Hodge, Charles B. Will God Run. LC 70-187827. (Illus.). 1965. 6.95 (ISBN 0-89112-053-X, Bibl Res Pr). Abilene Christ U.

Hodge, Charles B., Jr. Hodge Podge. LC 71-92047. 1969. 6.95 (ISBN 0-89112-051-3, Bibl Res Pr). Abilene Christ U.
--Onion Creek Philosophy. LC 79-87865. 1979. 6.95 (ISBN 0-89112-054-8, Bibl Res Pr). Abilene Christ U.
Hodge, Ian. Baptized Inflation: A Critique of "Christian" Keynesian. Date not set. price not set (ISBN 0-930462-13-0). Am Bur Eco Res.
Hodge, Peter, ed. see Massey, Michael.
Hodge, R. I., ed. see Milton, John.
Hodge, Susan W. The Elfreth Book of Letters. ltd. ed. (Illus.). 320p. (Orig.). 1985. text ed. 50.00 leather & Bucksam (ISBN 0-8122-7982-4); pap. 9.95 (ISBN 0-8122-1208-8). U of Pa Pr.
Hodges. Moses & the Ten Plagues. (Arch Bks.). 24p. (Orig.). 1985. pap. 0.99 (ISBN 0-570-06190-3, 59-1291). Concordia.
Hodges, Donald C. Socialist Humanism: The Outcome of Classical European Morality. LC 73-96983. 384p. 1974. 19.75 (ISBN 0-87527-042-5). Green.
Hodges, Doris. Healing Stones. 14th ed. pap. 3.95 (ISBN 0-686-12935-0). Hiawatha Bondurant.
Hodges, George. Saints & Heroes Since the Middle Ages. LC 75-107713. (Essay Index Reprint Ser.). 1912. 21.50 (ISBN 0-8369-1515-1). Ayer Co Pubs.
--Saints & Heroes to the End of the Middle Ages. facs. ed. LC 67-26749. (Essay Index Reprint Ser). 1911. 20.00 (ISBN 0-8369-0544-X). Ayer Co Pubs.
--Saints & Heroes to the End of the Middle Ages. facsimile ed. LC 67-26749. (Essay Index Reprint Ser.). (Illus.). 268p. 1982. Repr. of 1911 ed. lib. bdg. 19.00 (ISBN 0-8290-0526-9). Irvington.
Hodges, Graham R. Did Jesus Go to Church? And Fifty-One Other Children's Sermons. LC 81-20585. 128p. (Orig.). 1982. pap. 5.95 (ISBN 0-687-10762-8). Abingdon.
Hodges, H. A. God Beyond Knowledge. Hudson, W. D., ed. LC 77-22634. (Library of Philosophy & Religion Ser). 182p. 1979. text ed. 28.50x (ISBN 0-06-492922-1). B&N Imports.
Hodges, Melvin L. The Indigenous Church. rev. ed. 160p. 1976. pap. 2.95 (ISBN 0-88243-527-2, 02-0527). Gospel Pub.
--The Indigenous Church & the Missionary: A Sequel to the Indigenous Church. LC 77-14519. 1978. pap. 2.95 (ISBN 0-87808-151-8). William Carey Lib.
--A Theology of the Church & Its Mission: A Pentecostal Perspective. LC 76-20892. 1977. 6.95 (ISBN 0-88243-605-8, 02-0605); pap. 3.95 (ISBN 0-88243-607-4, 02-0607). Gospel Pub.
--When the Spirit Comes. (Charismatic Bks.). 46p. 1972. pap. 0.69 (ISBN 0-88243-919-7, 02-0919). Gospel Pub.
Hodges, Serena M. Look on the Fields. 202p. 1956. pap. 2.00 (ISBN 0-88243-540-X, 02-0540). Gospel Pub.
Hodges, Susan & Bryant, M. Darrol, eds. Exploring Unification Theology. LC 78-51957. 226p. 1978. write for info. E Mellen.
Hodges, Susan, jt. ed. see Bryant, Darrol.
Hodges, Susan, jt. ed. see Bryant, M. Darrol.
Hodges, Turner. Bible Story Library. 1963. 12.95 (ISBN 0-672-23099-2, Pub. by Audel). Macmillan.
Hodges, Zane C. El Evangelio Bajo Sito: Un Estudio Sobre la Fe y las Obras. Whitehouse, Thomas, tr. 128p. (Orig.). 1985. pap. 4.95 (ISBN 0-9607576-4-3). Redencion Viva.
--The Gospel under Siege: A Study on Faith & Works. 124p. (Orig.). 1981. pap. 4.95 (ISBN 0-9607576-0-0). Redencion Viva.
--Grace in Eclipse: A Study on Eternal Rewards. viii, 120p. (Orig.). 1985. pap. 4.95 (ISBN 0-9607576-3-5). Redencion Viva.
Hodges, Zane C., jt. ed. see Farstad, Arthur L.
Hodgson, Geraldine E. English Mystics. LC 73-13663. 1973. lib. bdg. 25.00 (ISBN 0-8414-4756-X). Folcroft.
--English Mystics. 1977. lib. bdg. 59.95 (ISBN 0-8490-1777-7). Gordon Pr.
--The Sanity of Mysticism. LC 76-11826. 1976. Repr. of 1926 ed. lib. bdg. 20.00 (ISBN 0-8414-4845-0). Folcroft.
Hodgson, James T. Memoir of the Rev. Francis Hodgson, B.D., Scholar, Poet, & Divine, 2 vols. LC 75-26864. 1975. Repr. of 1878 ed. lib. bdg. 75.00 (ISBN 0-8414-4804-3). Folcroft.
--Memoirs of the Rev. Francis Hodgson, 2 Vols. LC 76-169470. Repr. of 1878 ed. Set. 65.00 (ISBN 0-404-07374-3). Vol. 1 (ISBN 0-404-07375-1). Vol. 2 (ISBN 0-404-07376-X). AMS Pr.
Hodgson, Joan. Hullo Sun. (Illus.). 1972. 5.95 (ISBN 0-85487-019-9). De Vorss.
--Our Father. (Illus.). 1977. pap. 2.95 (ISBN 0-85487-040-7). De Vorss.
--A White Eagle Lodge Book of Health & Healing. 240p. 1983. text ed. 10.50 (ISBN 0-85487-063-6). De Vorss.
Hodgson, Leonard. Essays in Christian Philosophy. facs. ed. LC 69-17577. (Essay Index Reprint Ser). 1930. 14.00 (ISBN 0-8369-0079-0). Ayer Co Pubs.
Hodgson, Marshall G. The Order of Assassins. LC 78-63343. (The Crusades & Military Orders: Second Ser.). Repr. of 1955 ed. 46.50 (ISBN 0-404-17018-8). AMS Pr.
--Venture of Islam: Conscience & History in World Civilization, 3 vols. LC 73-87243. 1975. 30.00x ea.; Vol. 2. (ISBN 0-226-34680-3); Vol. 3. (ISBN 0-226-34681-1). U of Chicago Pr.
Hodgson, P. The Orcherd of Syon & the English Mystical Tradition. (Sir Israel Gollancz Memorial Lectures in Old English). 1964. pap. 2.25 (ISBN 0-85672-264-2, Pub. by British Acad). Longwood Pub Group.
Hodgson, Peter, ed. see Hegel, G. W.
Hodgson, Peter C. Children of Freedom: Black Liberation in Christian Perspective. LC 74-76930. pap. 24.00 (2027866). Bks Demand UMI.
Hodgson, Peter C. & King, Robert H., eds. Christian Theology: An Introduction to Its Traditions & Tasks. rev. & enl. 2nd ed. LC 84-48720. 432p. 1985. pap. 16.95 (ISBN 0-8006-1848-3, 1-1848). Fortress.
--Readings in Christian Theology. LC 84-48721. 432p. 1985. pap. 19.95 Kivar (ISBN 0-8006-1849-1, 1-1849). Fortress.
Hodgson, Peter C. see Hegel, G. W.
Hodgson, Peter C., tr. see Hegel, Georg W.
Hodgson, Phyllis, ed. The Cloud of Unknowing. (Analecta Cartusiana Ser.: No. 3). (Eng.). 234p. (Orig.). 1982. pap. 25.00 (ISBN 3-7052-0003-8, Pub by Salzburg Studies). Longwood Pub Group.
Hodgson, Robert, Jr., jt. auth. see Hedrick, Dr. Charles W., Sr.
Hodgson, Shadworth H. & Nathanson, Maurice. The Metaphysic of Experience, 4 vols. LC 78-66730. (Phenomenology Ser.). 858p. 1980. lib. bdg. 233.00 (ISBN 0-8240-9564-2). Garland Pub.
Hodkinson, Keith. Muslim Family Law: A Sourcebook. 401p. (Orig.). 1984. pap. 25.00 (ISBN 0-7099-1256-0, Pub. by Croom Helm Ltd). Methuen Inc.
Hodous, Lewis. Buddhism & Buddhists in China. LC 78-72440. Repr. of 1924 ed. 17.50 (ISBN 0-404-17306-3). AMS Pr.
Hodson. Basic Theosophy. 18.95 (ISBN 0-8356-7560-2). Theos Pub Hse.
--Concealed Wisdom in World Mythology. 13.50 (ISBN 0-8356-7556-4). Theos Pub Hse.
--Occult Powers in Nature & in Man. 5.50 (ISBN 0-8356-7085-6). Theos Pub Hse.
--Pathway of Perfection. 2.50 (ISBN 0-8356-7018-X). Theos Pub Hse.
--Through the Gateway of Death. 2.95 (ISBN 0-8356-7202-6). Theos Pub Hse.
Hodson, Geoffrey. The Christ Life from Nativity to Ascension. LC 75-4169. 540p. 1975. pap. 5.50 (ISBN 0-8356-0467-5, Quest). Theos Pub Hse.
--Clairvoyant Investigations. LC 84-40166. (Illus.). 160p. (Orig.). 1984. pap. 9.25 (ISBN 0-8356-0585-X). Theos Pub Hse.
--The Hidden Wisdom in the Holy Bible, Vol. 3. 1971. 7.95 (ISBN 0-8356-7493-2). Theos Pub Hse.
--The Hidden Wisdom in the Holy Bible, Vol. 4. LC 67-8724. 375p. (Orig.). 1981. pap. 5.95 (ISBN 0-8356-0548-5, Quest). Theos Pub Hse.
--Kingdom of the Gods. 7th ed. (Illus.). 1972. 15.95 (ISBN 0-8356-7081-3). Theos Pub Hse.
--Reincarnation, Fact or Fallacy. rev. ed. LC 67-4405. 1967. pap. 2.95 (ISBN 0-8356-0046-7, Quest). Theos Pub Hse.
--Seven Human Temperaments. 6th ed. 1977. 3.25 (ISBN 0-8356-7222-0). Theos Pub Hse.
Hoeckmann, Olaf. Dance in Hebrew Poetry. Adams, Doug, ed. 1987. pap. 3.00 (ISBN 0-941500-44-6). Sharing Co.
Hoedemaker, Libertus. The Theology of H. Richard Niebuhr. LC 78-139271. 1979. pap. 6.95 (ISBN 0-8298-0186-3). Pilgrim NY.
Hoefler, Richard C. At Noon on Friday. 1983. 3.50 (ISBN 0-89536-557-X, 0111). CSS of Ohio.
--Creative Preaching & Oral Writing. 1978. 7.95 (ISBN 0-89536-349-6, 0342). CSS of Ohio.
--Realize & Rejoice. 1981. 4.00 (ISBN 0-89536-468-9, 1803). CSS of Ohio.
--A Sign in the Straw. 128p. (Orig.). 1980. pap. text ed. 6.95 (ISBN 0-89536-465-4, 1969). CSS of Ohio.
--With Wings of Eagles. 1983. 5.35 (ISBN 0-89536-624-X, 2352). CSS of Ohio.
Hoehler, Richard S. Three Transcendentalists: Kant, Thoreau, & Contemporary. LC 71-185781. (Illus.). 432p. 1972. 10.00 (ISBN 0-930590-00-7). R S Hoehler.
Hoehn, Matthew, ed. Catholic Authors: Contemporary Biographical Sketches, 1930-1947. 800p. 1981. Repr. of 1947 ed. 75.00x (ISBN 0-8103-4314-2). Gale.
Hoehn, Richard A. Up from Apathy: A Study of Moral Awareness & Social Involvement. LC 83-7057. 179p. (Orig.). 1983. pap. 10.95 (ISBN 0-687-43114-X). Abingdon.
Hoehner, Harold W. Chronological Aspects of the Life of Christ. 1976. pap. text ed. 9.95 (ISBN 0-310-26211-9, 10841P). Zondervan.
--Herod Antipas: A Contemporary of Jesus Christ. new ed. 456p. 1980. pap. 11.95 (ISBN 0-310-42251-5, 10842P). Zondervan.
Hoekema, Anthony A. The Bible & the Future. 1979. 24.95 (ISBN 0-8028-3516-3). Eerdmans.
--The Christian Looks at Himself. 1975. pap. 5.95 (ISBN 0-8028-1595-2). Eerdmans.
--Christian Science. 1974. pap. 2.95 (ISBN 0-8028-1492-1). Eerdmans.
--Created in God's Image. 272p. 1986. 19.95 (ISBN 0-8028-3626-7). Eerdmans.
--The Four Major Cults. 1963. 24.95 (ISBN 0-8028-3117-6). Eerdmans.
--Jehovah's Witnesses. 1974. pap. 4.95 (ISBN 0-8028-1489-1). Eerdmans.
--Mormonism. 1974. pap. 2.95 (ISBN 0-8028-1491-3). Eerdmans.
--Seventh-Day Adventism. 1974. pap. 3.95 (ISBN 0-8028-1490-5). Eerdmans.
Hoekstra, Donald J. Adult Education in the Church. LC 85-17433. 109p. (Orig.). 1985. pap. 4.95 (ISBN 0-930265-14-9). CRC Pubns.
Hoeldtke, Clyde, jt. auth. see Richards, Lawrence O.
Hoeller, Stephen. The Gnostic Jung & the Seven Sermons to the Dead. LC 82-50220. 282p. (Orig.). 1982. 13.95 (ISBN 0-8356-0573-6). Theos Pub Hse.
Hoenig, jt. auth. see Litvin.
Hoenig, Sidney B. The Era of the Second Temple. LC 74-79271. Orig. Title: Korot Am Olam. 480p. 1974. 11.95 (ISBN 0-88400-009-5). Shengold.
Hoerber, Robert G. Reading the New Testament for Understanding. 192p. 1986. pap. 7.50 (ISBN 0-570-03988-6, 12-3016). Concordia.
Hoermann, Karl. Diccionario de Moral Cristiana. 2nd ed. (Span.). 704p. 1978. pap. 35.95 (ISBN 84-254-0966-7, S-50192). French & Eur.
--Diccionario De Moral Cristiana. 2nd ed. (Span.). 704p. 1978. 41.95 (ISBN 84-254-0967-5, S-50193). French & Eur.
Hoernle, R. F. Idealism, as a Philosophical Doctrine. 1979. Repr. of 1924 ed. lib. bdg. 25.00 (ISBN 0-8495-2281-1). Arden Lib.
Hoeven, James W. Van see Van Hoeven, James W.
Hoeven, Johan Van Der see Hart, Hendrik & Van Der Hoeven, Johan.
Hoever, H. Lives of the Saints. (Illus.). maroon cloth, colored edges 4.75 (ISBN 0-89942-870-3, 870/22). Catholic Bk Pub.
Hoff, B. J. Baby's First Days: Enrollment Certificate. (Certificate Booklets Ser.). (Illus.). 16p. 1982. pap. 0.95 self-cover (ISBN 0-87239-530-8, 1182). Standard Pub.
--Mists of Danger. LC 86-70567. 196p. 1986. pap. 6.95 (ISBN 0-89636-206-X). Accent Bks.
Hoff, Benjamin. The Tao of Pooh. (Illus.). 162p. 1982. 8.95 (ISBN 0-525-24124-8, 0869-260). Dutton.
Hoff, Paul. Le Pasteur & la Cure d'Ame. Tr. of The Pastor As a Counselor. (Fr.). 240p. 1986. pap. 4.10 (ISBN 0-8297-0692-5). Life Pubs Intl.
Hoffding, H. The Philosophy of Religion. 1977. lib. bdg. 59.95 (ISBN 0-8490-2435-8). Gordon Pr.
Hoffding, Harald. The Philosophy of Religion. facsimile ed. Meyer, B. E., tr. from Ger. LC 71-152987. (Select Bibliographies Reprint Ser). Repr. of 1906 ed. 24.50 (ISBN 0-8369-5739-3). Ayer Co Pubs.
Hoffecker, W. Andrew. Piety & the Princeton Theologians. (Orig.). 1981. pap. 5.95 (ISBN 0-8010-4253-4). Baker Bk.
--Piety & the Princeton Theologians: Archibald Alexander, Charles Hodge, & Benjamin Warfield. 1981. pap. 5.95 (ISBN 0-87552-280-7). Presby & Reformed.
Hoffecker, W. Andrew & Smith, Gary S., eds. Building a Christian World View, Vol. 1: God, Man, & Knowledge. 368p. Date not set. 14.95 (ISBN 0-87552-281-5). Presby & Reformed.
Hoffer, Eric. Before the Sabbath. LC 78-69626. 1979. 11.45i (ISBN 0-06-011914-4, HarpT). Har-Row.
--True Believer. 1966. pap. 3.95 (ISBN 0-06-080071-2, P71, PL). Har-Row.
Hoffman, Bengt, ed. The Theologia Germanica of Martin Luther. LC 80-50155. (Classics of Western Spirituality). 224p. 1980. 12.95 (ISBN 0-8091-0308-7); pap. 8.95 (ISBN 0-8091-2291-X). Paulist Pr.
Hoffman, Brunhilde. Die Aufhebung der Kartause Gaming. Hogg, James, ed. (Analecta Cartusiana Ser: No. 58). (Ger.). 120p. (Orig.). 1981. pap. 25.00 (ISBN 3-7052-0084-4, Pub. by Salzburg Studies). Longwood Pub Group.
Hoffman, Charles, tr. see Horowitz, Dan & Lissak, Moshe.
Hoffman, David. A Commentary on the Will & Testament of Abdu'l-Baha. 56p. pap. 2.95 (ISBN 0-85398-158-2). G Ronald Pub.
Hoffman, Diane, jt. auth. see Shinn, Duane.
Hoffman, Dominic. Beginnings in the Spiritual Life. 1976. 5.25 (ISBN 0-8198-0387-1); pap. text ed. 4.25 (ISBN 0-8198-0388-X). Dghtrs St Paul.
Hoffman, Dominic M. Living Divine Love: Transformation, the Goal of Christian Life. LC 82-11552. 200p. (Orig.). 1982. pap. 7.95 (ISBN 0-8189-0443-7). Alba.
--Maturing the Spirit. new ed. 1973. 5.00 (ISBN 0-8198-0257-3); pap. 4.00 (ISBN 0-8198-0258-1). Dghtrs St Paul.
Hoffman, Douglas, ed. see Total Environmental Action, Inc.
Hoffman, Douglas R., ed. see Adams, Jennifer A.
Hoffman, Edward. The Heavenly Ladder: A Jewish Guide to Inner Growth. LC 85-42779. 160p. (Orig.). 1986. pap. 8.95 (ISBN 0-06-064001-4, HarpR). Har-Row.
--The Way of Splendor: Jewish Mysticism & Modern Psychology. LC 81-50967. (Illus.). 224p. 1981. pap. 10.95 (ISBN 0-87773-210-8). Shambhala Pubns.
Hoffman, Edward, jt. auth. see Schachter, Zalman M.
Hoffman, Felix. The Story of Christmas. LC 75-6921. (Illus.). 32p. 1975. 6.95 (ISBN 0-689-50031-9, McElderry Bk). Macmillan.
Hoffman, Frederick J. Imagination's New Beginning: Theology & Modern Literature. LC 67-12121. (Ward-Phillips Lecture Ser.: No. 1). 1967. pap. 1.95x (ISBN 0-268-00329-7). U of Notre Dame Pr.
Hoffman, Gail. The Land & People of Israel. rev. ed. LC 77-37286. (Portraits of the Nations Ser.). (Illus.). 1972. PLB 11.89i (ISBN 0-397-31258-X, Lipp Jr Bks). HarpJ.
Hoffman, Hallock. Loyalty by Oath. 1983. pap. 2.50x (ISBN 0-87574-094-4, 094). Pendle Hill.
Hoffman, Joan, ed. see Gregorich, Barbara.
Hoffman, John C. Ethical Confrontation in Counseling. LC 78-11799. 1979. lib. bdg. 10.50x (ISBN 0-226-34785-0). U of Chicago Pr.
Hoffman, John S., jt. ed. see Peck, George.
Hoffman, Joy. With Wandering Steps & Slow. LC 81-18566. 140p. (Orig.). 1982. pap. 4.95 (ISBN 0-87784-804-1). Inter-Varsity.
Hoffman, Judy. Joseph & Me. 1979. pap. 5.95x (ISBN 0-87068-655-0). Ktav.
Hoffman, Lawrence. Beyond the Text: A Holistic Approach to Liturgy. (Jewish Literature & Culture Ser.). 1987. 35.00 (ISBN 0-253-31199-3). Ind U Pr.
Hoffman, Lawrence, ed. Gates of Understanding. LC 77-23488. 1977. pap. text ed. 4.95 (ISBN 0-8074-0009-2, 142689). UAHC.
--Gates of Understanding, Vol. 1. 1977. 5.95 (ISBN 0-916694-43-7). Central Conf.
Hoffman, Lawrence A. The Canonization of the Synagogue Service. LC 78-62972. (Studies in Judaism & Christianity in Antiquity: No. 4). 1979. text ed. 18.95 (ISBN 0-268-00727-6). U of Notre Dame Pr.
--The Canonization of the Synagogue Service. LC 78-62972. 245p. 1986. pap. 12.95 (ISBN 0-268-00756-X). U of Notre Dame Pr.
--The Land of Israel: Jewish Perspectives. LC 86-40241. (Studies in Judaism & Christianity in Antiquity: Vol. 6). 352p. 1986. text ed. 29.95x (ISBN 0-268-02180-5). U of Notre Dame Pr.
Hoffman, Manfred. Martin Luther & the Modern Mind: Freedom, Conscience, Toleration, Rights. LC 85-3054. (Toronto Studies in Theology: Vol. 22). 281p. 1985. 49.95x (ISBN 0-88946-766-8). E Mellen.
Hoffman, Marlin A. The Power of Prayer & Fasting. 2.50 (ISBN 0-89137-535-X). Quality Pubns.
Hoffman, Michael A., II. Blaspheming Against the Holy Peoples Holy Hoax. 1986. pap. 2.00 (ISBN 0-317-53014-3). Noontide.
--The Great Holocaust Trial. (Illus.). 95p. (Orig.). 1985. pap. 5.95 (ISBN 0-939484-22-6). Inst Hist Rev.
--The Great Holocaust Trial. (Illus.). 95p. 1986. pap. 5.95 (ISBN 0-317-53011-9). Noontide.
Hoffman, Oswald C. God's Joyful People: One in the Spirit. LC 72-96742. 104p. 1973. pap. 2.95 (ISBN 0-570-03152-4, 12-2537). Concordia.
--There Is Hope. 104p. 1985. 9.95 (ISBN 0-570-03979-7, 15-2184). Concordia.
Hoffman, Philip T. Church & Community in the Diocese of Lyon: 1500-1789. LC 83-23404. (Historical Publications Ser.: No. 132). 256p. 1984. text ed. 22.50x (ISBN 0-300-03141-6). Yale U Pr.
Hoffman, Ross. Tradition & Progress, & Other Historical Essays in Culture, Religion & Politics. LC 68-26213. 1968. Repr. of 1938 ed. 23.50x (ISBN 0-8046-0211-5, Pub by Kennikat). Assoc Faculty Pr.
Hoffman, Wayne. Letters to the Modern Church. LC 79-88401. 1979. pap. 3.75 (ISBN 0-933350-23-6). Morse Pr.

Hoffmann, David. The First Mishna & the Controversies of the Tannaim. Forchheimer, Paul, tr. from German. Incl. The Highest Court in the City of Sanctuary. LC 77-98683. 1977. 12.50 (ISBN 0-87203-072-5). Hermon.

Hoffmann, Hans W. Die Intention der Verkuendigung Jesajas. LC 74-80632. (Beiheft 136 zur Zeitschrift fuer die alttestamentliche Wissenschaft). 125p. 1974. 30.00 (ISBN 3-11-004672-5). De Gruyter.

Hoffmann, Helmut. The Religions of Tibet. LC 78-11420. (Illus.). 1979. Repr. of 1961 ed. lib. bdg. 24.75x (ISBN 0-313-21120-5, HORT). Greenwood.

Hoffmann, Manfred, tr. see Von Campenhausen, Hans.

Hoffmann, R. Joseph. Jesus Outside the Gospels. LC 84-42862. (The Skeptic's Bookshelf Ser.). 132p. 1984. 17.95 (ISBN 0-87975-263-7). Prometheus Bks.

--Marcion: On the Restitution of Christianity. LC 83-9008. (AAR Academy Ser.). 356p. 1984. 16.50 (ISBN 0-89130-638-2, 01 01 46). Scholars Pr GA.

Hoffmann, R. Joseph & Larue, Gerald. Jesus in History & Myth. 300p. 1986. 21.95 (ISBN 0-87975-332-3). Prometheus Bks.

Hoffmann, R. Joseph, ed. The Origins of Christianity: A Critical Introduction. 326p. (Orig.). 1985. pap. 15.95 (ISBN 0-87975-308-0). Prometheus Bks.

Hoffmann, Stanley. Duties Beyond Borders: On the Limits & Possibilities of Ethical International Politics. LC 81-2401. 288p. 1981. 22.00x (ISBN 0-8156-0167-0); pap. 10.95x (ISBN 0-8156-0168-9). Syracuse U Pr.

Hoffmeister, Gerhart. The Renaissance & Reformation in Germany: An Introduction. LC 77-5429. 1977. 25.00 (ISBN 0-8044-1391-6); pap. 9.95 (ISBN 0-8044-6272-0). Ungar.

Hoffs, Harry. God Giveth Strength. pap. 0.45 (ISBN 0-686-23472-3). Rose Pub MI.

Hofinger, Johannes. Art of Teaching Christian Doctrine. rev. ed. 1962. 14.95 (ISBN 0-268-00015-8). U of Notre Dame Pr.

--Pastoral Life in the Power of the Spirit. LC 81-1439. (Illus.). 215p. 1982. pap. 6.95 (ISBN 0-8189-0427-5). Alba.

--Prayer Services for the Christian Educator. 1983. 5.35 (ISBN 0-686-40164-6). Natl Cath Educ.

Hofler, Karl A., ed. Geschichtschreiber der Husitischen Bewegung in Bohmen, Vols. 2, 6, 7. (Ger). pap. 65.00 ea. vol. 2, 6; pap. 23.00 vol. 7 (ISBN 0-384-23810-6). Johnson Repr.

Hofman, David. George Townshend, A Life of. (Illus.). 448p. 23.50 (ISBN 0-85398-126-4); pap. 12.95 (ISBN 0-85398-127-2). G Ronald Pub.

--God & His Messengers. (Illus.). 1986. pap. 5.95 (ISBN 0-85398-049-7). G Ronald Pub.

Hogan, Bernice. The Church Is a Who. LC 78-24087. (Illus.). 1979. 9.95 (ISBN 0-8272-0442-6). CBP.

Hogan, Edmund. The Latin Lives of the Saints. LC 78-72684. (Royal Irish Academy. Todd Lecture Ser.: Vol. 5). Repr. of 1894 ed. 21.50 (ISBN 0-404-60565-6). AMS Pr.

Hogan, Griff, ed. The Church & Disabled Persons. 128p. 1983. pap. 8.95 (ISBN 0-87243-123-1). Templegate.

Hogan, Jan. Gladdys Makes Peace. (Illus.). 22p. 1985. 5.95 (ISBN 0-87178-313-4). Brethren.

Hogan, John G. Heralds of the King. LC 79-107714. (Essay Index Reprint Ser.). 1934. 17.00 (ISBN 0-8369-1516-X). Ayer Co Pubs.

Hogan, Richard M. & Levoir, John M. Covenant of Love: Pope John Paul II on Sexuality, Marriage & Family in the Modern World. LC 84-18666. 264p. 1985. 15.95 (ISBN 0-385-19540-0). Doubleday.

--Covenant of Love: Pope John Paul II on Sexuality, Marriage, & Family in the Modern World. LC 86-4395. 264p. 1986. pap. 7.95 (ISBN 0-385-23240-3, Im). Doubleday.

Hogarth, D. G. Kings of the Hittites. (British Academy, London, Schweich Lectures on Biblical Archaeology Ser.). pap. 19.00 (ISBN 0-8115-1266-5). Kraus Repr.

Hoge, Dean R. Commitment on Campus: Changes in Religion & Values Over Five Decades. LC 74-7236. (Illus.). 240p. 1974. 10.00 (ISBN 0-664-20706-5). Westminster.

Hoge, Dean R. & Roozen, David A., eds. Understanding Church Growth & Decline, 1950-78. LC 79-4166. (Illus.). 1979. pap. 9.95 (ISBN 0-8298-0358-0). Pilgrim NY.

Hoge, Dean R., et al. Converts, Dropouts, Returnees: A Study of Religious Change among Catholics. LC 81-15351. 200p. 1981. 14.95 (ISBN 0-8298-0483-8); pap. 7.95 (ISBN 0-8298-0487-0). Pilgrim NY.

--Research on Men's Vocations to the Priesthood & the Religious Life. 104p. 1984. pap. 6.50 (ISBN 1-55586-904-1). US Catholic.

Hogg, C. F. & Vine, W. E. Epistle to the Galatians. 360p. (Orig.). pap. cancelled (ISBN 0-8254-2858-0). Kregel.

--Epistle to the Thessalonians. (Orig.). pap. cancelled (ISBN 0-8254-2859-9). Kregel.

--Epistles of Paul the Apostle to the Thessalonians. 5.95 (ISBN 0-89315-040-1). Lambert Bk.

Hogg, Gayle, ed. see Maston, T. B.

Hogg, James. Adam of Witham De Quadripartito Exercitio Cellae. (Analecta Cartusiana Ser.: No. 98). (Orig.). 1986. pap. 25.00 (ISBN 3-7052-0169-7, Pub. by Salzburg Studies). Longwood Pub Group.

--L' Ancienne Chartreuse du Reposoir Aujoud'hui Carmel, et les Chartruses de la Savoie. (Analecta Cartusiana Ser.: No. 39-2). (Illus.). 110p. (Orig.). 1979. pap. 25.00 (ISBN 3-7052-0047-X, Pub by Salzburg Studies). Longwood Pub Group.

--L' Anciennne Chartreuse du Reposior, Aujourd'hui Carmel, et les Chartreusesde la Savoie, Introduction. (Analecta Cartusiana Ser.: No. 39-1). (Orig.). 1986. pap. 25.00 (ISBN 3-7052-0046-1, Pub by Salzburg Studies). Longwood Pub Group.

--As Cartuxas de Portugal. Hogg, James, ed. (Analecta Cartusiana Ser.: No. 69). Tr. of The Charterhouses of Portugal. (Ger. Span. & Port., Illus.). 145p. (Orig.). 1984. pap. 25.00 (ISBN 3-7052-0101-8, Pub. by Salsburg Studies). Longwood Pub Group.

--The Cartae of the Carthusian General Chapter of the Urbanist Observance During the Great Schism. (Analecta Cartusiana Ser.: No. 119). (Orig.). 1988. pap. 25.00 (ISBN 0-317-42562-5, Pub. by Salzburg Studies). Longwood Pub Group.

--La Cartuja De Aniago. (Analecta Cartusiana Ser.: No. 94/2). 204p. (Orig.). 1980. pap. 25.00 (ISBN 3-7052-0164-6, Pub. by Salzburg Studies). Longwood Pub Group.

--La Cartuja De Aniago: Introduction, Vol. 1. (Analecta Cartusiana: No. 94/1). 1987. pap. 25.00 (ISBN 3-7052-0163-8, Pub. by Salzburg Studies). Longwood Pub Group.

--La Cartuja de Aula Dei. Hogg, James, ed. (Analecta Cartusiana Ser.: No. 70). (Orig.). 1982. pap. 25.00 (ISBN 3-7052-0103-4, Pub. by Salzburg Studies). Longwood Pub Group.

--La Cartuja de la Conception. Hogg, James, ed. (Analecta Cartusiana Ser.). Tr. of The Charterhouse of the Conception. (Span.). 44p. (Orig.). 1980. pap. 25.00 (ISBN 3-7052-0105-0, Pub. by Salzburg Studies). Longwood Pub Group.

--La Cartuja de las Fuentes. Hogg, James, ed. (Anaalecta Cartusiana Ser.). Tr. of The Charterhouse of las Fuentes. (Ital., Illus.). 52p. (Orig.). 1980. pap. 25.00 (ISBN 3-7052-0104-2, Pub. by Salzburg Studies). Longwood Pub Group.

--La Cartuja de Miraflores. Hogg, James, ed. (Analecta Cartusiana Ser.: No. 79). Tr. of The Charterhouse of MiraFlores. (Span., Illus., Orig.). 1979. pap. 25.00 (ISBN 3-7052-0116-6, Pub. by Salzburg Studies). Longwood Pub Group.

--La Cartuja de Miraflores: Introduction, Vol. 1. Hogg, James, ed. (Analecta Cartusiana Ser.: No. 79). (Orig.). 1986. pap. 25.00 (ISBN 3-7052-0115-8, Pub. by Salzburg Studies). Longwood Pub Group.

--La Cartuja de Scala Dei: (The Charterhouse of Scala Dei) (Analecta Cartusiana Ser.: No. 41-3). (Span. & Eng., Illus.). 54p. (Orig.). 1980. pap. 25.00 (ISBN 3-7052-0051-8, Pub by Salzburg Studies). Longwood Pub Group.

--La Cartuja de Val de Cristo: (The Charterhouse of Val de Cristo) (Analecta Cartusiana Ser.: No. 41-5). (Span. & Eng., Illus.). 50p. (Orig.). 1979. pap. 25.00 (ISBN 3-7052-0053-4, Pub by Salzburg Studies). Longwood Pub Group.

--Las Cartujas de las Cuevas, Cazalla de la Sierra y Granada: (The Charterhouses of las Cuevas, Cazalla de la Sierra & Granada) (Analecta Cartuasiana Ser.: No. 47-3). (Span., Illus.). 110p. (Orig.). 1979. pap. 25.00 (ISBN 3-7052-0065-8, Pub by Salzburg Studies). Longwood Pub Group.

--Las Cartujas de Montalegre, Sant Pol de Maresme, Vallparadis, Ara Coeli y Via Coeli. (Analecta Cartusiana Ser.: No. 41-2). (Span., Illus.). 140p. (Orig.). 1983. pap. 25.00 (ISBN 3-7052-0050-X, Pub by Salzburg Studies). Longwood Pub Group.

--La Certosa Di Firenze. Hogg, James, ed. (Analecta Cartusiana Ser.: No. 66). Tr. of The Charterhouse of Florence. (Ital., Illus.). 110p. (Orig.). 1979. pap. 25.00 (ISBN 3-7052-0097-6, Pub. by Salzburg Studies). Longwood Pub Group.

--La Certosa di Serra San Bruno. (Analecta Cartusiana Ser.: No. 26-2). (Ital. & Eng., Illus.). 61p. (Orig.). 1980. pap. 25.00 (ISBN 3-7052-0027-5, Pub by Salzburg Studies). Longwood Pub Group.

--The Charterhouse of Padula: Introduction. Hogg, James, ed. (Analecta Cartusiana: No. 54). (Orig.). 1986. pap. 25.00 (ISBN 3-7052-0074-7, Pub. by Salzburg Studies). Longwood Pub Group.

--The Charterhouse of Pavia, 2 vols. Hogg, James, ed. (Analecta Cartusiana Ser.: No. 52). (Orig.). 1986. pap. 50.00 (ISBN 3-7052-0072-0, Pub. by Salzburg Studies). Longwood Pub Group.

--Les Charterhouses de Montrieux et XXX de la verne. Hogg, James, ed. (Analecta Cartusiana Ser.: No. 75). (Orig.). 1986. pap. 25.00 (ISBN 3-7052-0111-5, Pub. by Salzburg Studies). Longwood Pub Group.

--The Charterhouses of Aragon: Introduction, Vol. 1. (Analecta Carusiana Ser.: No. 70-1). (Orig.). 1986. pap. 25.00 (ISBN 3-7052-0102-6, Pub. by Salzburg Studies). Longwood Pub Group.

--The Charterhouses of Basel, Cologne, Konz (Trier) & Roermond. Hogg, James, ed. (Analecta Cartusiana Ser.: No. 62). (Orig.). 1986. pap. 25.00 (ISBN 3-7052-0090-9, Pub. by Salzburg Studies). Longwood Pub Group.

--The Charterhouses of Buxheim, Ittingen & la Valsainte. (Analecta Cartusiana Ser.: No. 38). (Illus.). 220p. (Orig.). 1977. pap. 25.00 (ISBN 3-7052-0045-3, Pub by Salzburg Studies). Longwood Pub Group.

--The Charterhouses of las Cuevas, Jerez de la Frontera, Cazalla & Granada: Introduction. (Analecta Cartusiana Ser.: No. 47-1). (Orig.). 1986. pap. 25.00 (ISBN 3-7052-0063-1, Pub by Salzburg Studies). Longwood Pub Group.

--The Charterhouses of Naples & Capri. Hogg, James, ed. (Analecta Cartusiana Ser.: No. 57-2). (Illus.). 175p. 1978. pap. 25.00 (ISBN 3-7052-0083-6, Pub. by Salzburg Studies). Longwood Pub Group.

--The Charterhouses of Padula, Parma, Ferrara & Bologna. Hogg, James, ed. (Analecta Cartusiana Ser.: No. 53). (Orig.). 1986. pap. 25.00 (ISBN 3-7052-0073-9, Pub. by Salzburg Studies). Longwood Pub Group.

--The Charterhouses of Seitz, Gairach, Freudenthal & Pletriach. Hogg, James, ed. (Analecta Cartusiana Ser.: No. 56). (Orig.). 1985. pap. 25.00 (ISBN 3-7052-0081-X, Pub. by Salzburg Studies). Longwood pub Group.

--The Charterhouses of the Carthusian Provinces of Catalonia. (Analecta Cartusiana Ser.: No. 41-1). (Orig.). 1986. pap. 25.00 (ISBN 3-7052-0049-6, Pub by Salzburg Studies). Longwood Pub Group.

--The Charterhouses of Tuscany, 3 vols. Hogg, James, ed. (Analecta Cartusiana Ser.: No. 60). (Orig.). 1986. pap. 25.00 (ISBN 3-7052-0088-7, Pub. by Salzburg Studies). Longwood Pub Group.

--The Charterhouses of Vedana & Schnals, With a Supplement on the Montelli & Venice. Hogg, James, ed. (Analecta Cartusiana Ser.: No. 50). (Orig.). 1985. pap. 25.00 (ISBN 3-7052-0070-4, Pub. by Salzburg Studies). Longwood Pub Group.

--The Charterhouses of Villeneuve Les Avignon, Mougeres, Toulouse & Ste-Croix-en-Jarez. Hogg, James, ed. (Analecta Cartusiana Ser.: No. 63). (Orig.). 1986. pap. 25.00 (ISBN 3-7052-0091-7, Pub. by Salzburg Studies). Longwood Pub Group.

--The Chaterhouse of Padula: Album. Hogg, James, ed. (Analecta Cartusiana Ser.: No. 54). (Illus.). 210p. (Orig.). 1978. pap. 25.00 (ISBN 3-7052-0075-5, Pub. by Salzburg Studies). Longwood Pub Group.

--The Chaterhouse of Rome. Hogg, James, ed. (Analecta Cartusiana Ser.: No. 78). (Illus.). 55p. (Orig.). 1984. pap. 25.00 (ISBN 3-7052-0114-X, Pub. by Salzburg Studies). Longwood Pub Group.

--The Chaterhouses of Naples & Capri Album, Vol. 1. Hogg, James, ed. (Analecta Cartusiana Ser.: No. 57-1). (Orig.). 1985. pap. 25.00 (ISBN 3-7052-0082-8, Pub. by Salzburg Studies). Longwood Pub Group.

--The Evolution of the Carthusian Statutes from the Consuetudines Guigonis to the Teria Compilatio, 2 Vols. (Analecta Cartusiana: No. 99). (Orig.). 1988. pap. 50.00 (ISBN 3-7052-0170-0, Pub. by Salzburg Studies). Longwood Pub Group.

--The Fyrst Boke of the Introduction of Knowledge by Andrew Borde, Vol. 2 Text. (Analecta Cartusiana Ser.: No. 92/2). 103p. (Orig.). 1979. pap. 25.00 (ISBN 3-7052-0161-1, Pub. by Salzburg Studies). Longwood Pub Group.

--The Fyrst Boke of the Introduction of Knowledge by Andrew Borde: Introduction, Vol. 1. (Analecta Cartusiana Ser.: No. 92/1). (Orig.). 1987. pap. 25.00 (ISBN 3-7052-0160-3, Pub. by Salzburg Studies). Longwood Pub Group.

--La Grande Chartreuse, et les Chartreuses de Portes Selignac et Pierre Chatel. (Analecta Cartusiana: No. 61). (Orig.). 1984. pap. 85.00 (ISBN 3-7052-0089-5, Pub. by Salzburg Studies). Longwood Pub Group.

--Gugleilmo di Saint-Thierry: La Lettera d'Oro. (Analecta Cartusiana Ser.: No. 37). 144p. (Orig.). 1977. pap. 25.00 (ISBN 3-7052-0044-5, Pub by Salzburg Studies). Longwood Pub Group.

--An Illustrated Yorkshire Carthusian Religious Miscellany, 2 Vols. (Analecta Cartusiana Ser.: No. 95/1-2). (Orig.). 1985. pap. 50.00 (ISBN 3-7052-0165-4, Pub. by Salzburg Studies). Longwood Pub Group.

--An Illustrated Yorkshire Carthusian Religious Miscellany, Vol. 3. (Analecta Cartusiana Ser.: No. 95/3). 140p. (Orig.). 1981. pap. 25.00 (ISBN 3-7052-0166-2, Pub. by Salzburg Studies). Longwood Pub Group.

--Die Kartauser und die Reformation: Internationaler Kongress Vom 24 bis 27 1983, 2 vols. (Analecta Cartusiana Ser.: No. 108). 320p. (Orig.). 1984. pap. 50.00 (ISBN 0-317-42576-5, Pub. by Salzburg Studies). Longwood Pub Group.

--The Latin Version of The Cloud of Unknowing. (Analecta Cartusiana Ser.: No. 120). (Orig.). 1988. pap. 25.00 (ISBN 0-317-42582-X, Pub. by Salzburg Studies). Longwood Pub Group.

--Leopold Brenner, Historia Cartusia Mauerancensis. (Analecta Cartusiana Ser.: No. 32). (Orig.). 1987. pap. 25.00 (ISBN 3-7052-0033-X, Pub by Salzburg Studies). Longwood Pub Group.

--Medieval Carthisian Costomaries, Pt. 2. (Analecta Carusiana Ser.: No. 2). (Orig.). 1986. pap. 25.00 (ISBN 3-7052-0002-X, Pub by Salzburg Studies). Longwood Pub Group.

--Mount Grace Charterhouse & Late English Medieval Spirituality: John Norton, Vol. 3. (Analecta Cartusiana Ser.: No. 64-3). (Orig.). 1987. pap. 25.00 (ISBN 3-7052-0094-1, Pub. by Salzburg Studies). Longwood Pub Group.

--Mount Grace Charterhouse & Late Medieval English Spirituality, Vol. 2. (Analecta Cartusiana Ser.: No. 64-2). 144p. (Orig.). 1978. pap. 25.00 (ISBN 3-7052-0093-3, Pub. by Salzburg Studies). Longwood Pub Group.

--Mount Grace Charterhouse & Late Medieval English Spirituality: Richard Methley, Vol. 1. (Analecta Cartusiana Ser.: No. 64-1). (Orig.). 1987. pap. 25.00 (ISBN 3-7052-0092-5, Pub. by Salzburg Studies). Longwood Pub Group.

--Passio XVIII Cartusianorum in Anglia Martyrum a Domo Maurito Chauncy: A Critical Study. (Analecta Cartusiana Ser.: No. 86). (Orig.). 1987. pap. 25.00 (ISBN 3-7052-0143-3, Pub. by Salzburg Studies). Longwood Pub Group.

--La Real Caruja de Jesus Nazareno de Valldemossa. (Analecta Cartusiana Ser.: No. 41-9). (Span., Illus.). 66p. (Orig.). 1983. pap. 25.00 (ISBN 3-7052-0057-7, Pub by Salzburg Studies). Longwood Pub Group.

--The Register of the Charterhouse of London: Land Rev. Misc Book 61 of the London Public Record Office. (Analecta Cartusiana Ser.: No. 89). (Orig.). 1987. 25.00 (ISBN 3-7052-0146-8, Pub. by Salzburg Studies). Longwood Pub Group.

--El Santo Rosario en la Cartuja. (Analecta Cartusiana Ser.: No. 103). 134p. (Orig.). 1983. pap. 25.00 (ISBN 0-317-42593-5, Pub. by Salzburg Studies). Longwood Pub Group.

--The Speculum Devotorum of an Anonymous Carhusian of Sheen: From the manuscripts Cambridge University Library (Gg. 1.6 & Foyle Vol.2) (Analecta Carusiana Ser.: No. 12). (Eng.). 173p. (Orig.). 1973. pap. 25.00 (ISBN 3-7052-0013-5, Pub by Salzburg Studies). Longwood Pub Group.

--The Speculum Devotorum of an Anonymous Carthusian of Sheen: Introduction. (Analceta Cartusiana Ser.: No. 11). (Orig.). 1985. pap. 25.00 (ISBN 3-7052-0012-7, Pub by Salzburg Studies). Longwood Pub Group.

--The 'Speculum Inclusorum' MS. British Library London Harley 2372: A Critical Edition, Vol. 1. (Analecta Cartusiana Ser.: No. 59-1). (Orig.). 1985. pap. 25.00 (ISBN 3-7052-0086-0, Pub. by Salzburg Studies). Longwood Pub Group.

--The 'Speculum Incusorum' MS. British Library London Harley 2372. (Analecta Cartusiana Ser.: No. 59-2). (Lat.). 139p. (Orig.). 1981. pap. 25.00 (ISBN 3-7052-0087-9, Pub. by Salzburg Studies). Longwood Pub Group.

--The Statuta Jancelini Twelve Twenty-Two & the De Reformatione of Prior Bernard Twelve Forty-Eight. (Analecta Cartusiana Ser.: No. 65-2). 162p. (Orig.). 1978. pap. 25.00 (ISBN 3-7052-0096-8, Pub. by Salzburg Studies). Longwood Pub Group.

--The 'Statuta Jancelini' Twelve Twenty-Two & The 'De Reformatione of Prior Bernard Twelve Forty-Eight: A Critical Edition, Vol. 1. (Analecta Cartusiana Ser.: No. 65-1). (Orig.). 1985. pap. 25.00 (ISBN 3-7052-0095-X, Pub. by Salzburg Studies). Longwood Pub Group.

--Trisulti: Art & Architecture. (Analecta Cartusiana Ser.: No. 74-2). (Orig.). 1984. pap. 25.00 (ISBN 3-7052-0110-7, Pub. by Salzburg Studies). Longwood Pub Group.

--Webster 'Reformed' A Study of Post-Restoration Versions of John Webster's Plays, 2 vols. (Jacobean Drama Studies). (Orig.). 1986. pap. 30.00 (ISBN 3-7052-0323-1, Pub. by Salzburg Studies). Longwood Pub Group.

--The Yorkshire Cistercian Heritage: Introduction. (Orig.). 1985. pap. 16.00 (ISBN 3-7052-0260-X, Pub. by Salzburg Studies). Longwood Pub Group.

--The Yorkshire Cistercian Heritage, Vol. 2: Rievaulx, Jervaulx, Byland. (Orig.). 1978. pap. 16.00 (ISBN 3-7052-0261-8, Pub. by Salzburg Studies). Longwood Pub Group.

--The Yorkshire Cistercian Heritage, Vol. 3: Fountains, Kirstall, Meaux. (Orig.). 1978. pap. 16.00 (ISBN 3-7052-0262-6, Pub. by Salzburg Studies). Longwood Pub Group.

Hogg, James & Brauer, Wilhelm. Collectanea Cartusiensia, No. 3. Hogg, James, ed. (Analecta Cartusiana Ser.: No. 82-3). (Lat. & Ger.). 120p. (Orig.). 1980. pap. 25.00 (ISBN 3-7052-0121-2, Pub. by Salzburg Studies). Longwood Pub Group.

Hogg, James & Ellis, Roger. The Contemplative Life in England: Carthusians, Bridgettines, Benedictines, 2 Vols. Hogg, James, ed. (Analecta Cartusiana Ser.: No. 68). (Orig.). 1985. pap. 50.00 (ISBN 3-7052-0100-X, Pub. by Salzburg Studies). Longwood Pub Group.

Hogg, James & Hogg, James. Collectanea Cartusiensia, No. 6. (Analecta Cartusiana Ser.: No. 82-6). (Orig.). 1985. pap. 25.00 (ISBN 3-7052-0124-7, Pub. by Salzburg Studies). Longwood Pub Group.

Hogg, James & Sargent, Michael. The Chartae Of The Carthusian General Chapter, Vol. 1. (Analecta Catusiana Ser.: No. 100/1). 186p. (Orig.). 1983. pap. 25.00 (ISBN 3-7052-0171-9, Pub. by Salzburg Studies). Longwood Pub Group.

--The Chartae of the Carthusian General Chapter, Vol. 2. (Analecta Cartusiana Ser.: No. 100/2). 229p. (Orig.). 1983. pap. 25.00 (ISBN 3-7052-0172-7, Pub. by Salzburg Studies). Longwood Pub Group.

--The Chartae of the Carthusian General Chapter, Vol. 3. (Analecta Cartusiana Ser.: No. 100/3). 209p. (Orig.). 1984. pap. 25.00 (ISBN 3-7052-0173-5, Pub. by Salzburg Studies). Longwood Pub Group.

--The Chartae of the Carthusian General Chapter, Vol. 4. (Analecta Cartusiana Ser.: No. 100/4). 241p. (Orig.). 1984. pap. 25.00 (ISBN 0-317-42565-X, Pub. by Salzburg Studies). Longwood Pub Group.

--The Chartae of the Carthusian General Chapter, Vol. 5. (Analecta Cartusiana Ser.: No. 100/5). 229p. (Orig.). 1985. pap. 25.00 (ISBN 0-317-42566-8, Pub. by Salzburg Studies). Longwood Pub Group.

--The Chartae of the Carthusian General Chapter, Vol. 6. (Analecta Cartusiana Ser.: No. 100/6). 1985. pap. 25.00 (ISBN 0-317-42567-6, Pub. by Salzburg Studies). Longwood Pub Group.

--The Chartae of the Carthusian General Chapter, Vol. 7. (Analecta Cartusiana Ser.: No. 100/7). (Orig.). 1985. pap. 25.00 (ISBN 0-317-42569-2, Pub. by Salzburg Studies). Longwood Pub Group.

--The Chartae of the Carthusian General Chapter, Vol. 8. (Analecta Cartusiana Ser.: No. 100/8). (Orig.). 1986. pap. 25.00 (ISBN 0-317-42570-6, Pub. by Salzburg Studies). Longwood Pub Group.

--The Chartae of the Carthusian General Chapter, Vol. 9. (Analecta Cartusiana Ser.: No. 100/9). (Orig.). 1987. pap. 25.00 (ISBN 0-317-42571-4, Pub. by Salzburg Studies). Longwood Pub Group.

Hogg, James, jt. auth. see Beltrutti, Giorgio.

Hogg, James, jt. auth. see Gomez, Ildefonso M.

Hogg, James, jt. auth. see Sargent, Michael.

Hogg, James, jt. auth. see Singh, Charu S.

Hogg, James, ed. Los Cartujos, Hoy: Una Vida Para la Vida de la Iglesia. (Analecta Cartusiana Ser.: No. 81). 110p. (Orig.). 1980. pap. 25.00 (ISBN 3-7052-0118-2, Pub. by Salzburg Studies). Longwood Pub Group.

--Collectanea Cartusiensia, No. 4. (Analecta Cartusiana Ser.: No. 82-4). (Orig.). 1985. pap. 25.00 (ISBN 3-7052-0122-0, Pub. by Salzburg Studies). Longwood Pub Group.

--Collectanea Cartusiensia, No. 5. (Analecta Cartusiana Ser.: No. 82-5). (Orig.). 1985. pap. 25.00 (ISBN 3-7052-0123-9, Pub. by Salzburg Studies). Longwood Pub Group.

--Collectanea Cartusiensia, No. 7. (Analecta Cartusiana Ser.: No. 82-7). (Orig.). 1986. pap. 25.00 (ISBN 3-7052-0125-5, Pub. by Salzburg Studies). Longwood Pub Group.

--Collectanea Cartusiensia, No. 8. (Analecta Cartusiana Ser.: No. 82-8). (Orig.). 1987. pap. 25.00 (ISBN 3-7052-0126-3, Pub. by Salzburg Studies). Longwood Pub Group.

--Collectanea Cartusiensia, No. 9. (Analecta Cartusiana Ser.: No. 82-9). (Orig.). 1987. pap. 25.00 (ISBN 3-7052-0127-1, Pub. by Salzburg Studies). Longwood Pub Group.

--La Cultura Artistica Nelle Certose Europee. (Analecta Cartusiana Ser.: No. 115). (Orig.). 1986. pap. 25.00 (ISBN 0-317-42572-2, Pub. by Salzburg Studies). Longwood Pub Group.

--Die Kartauser In Osterreich, Vol. 2. Wharton, Janet, tr. (Analecta Cartusiana Ser.: No. 83-2). (Ger. Ital. & Eng., Illus.). 308p. (Orig.). 1981. pap. 25.00 (ISBN 3-7052-0129-8, Pub. by Salzburg Studies). Longwood Pub Group.

--Kartauserliturgie. (Analecta Cartusiana Ser.: No. 116). (Orig.). 1987. pap. 25.00 (ISBN 3-7052-0196-4, Pub. by Salzburg Studies). Longwood Pub Group.

--Kartausermystik und Mystiker, Vol. 1. (Analecta Cartusiana Ser.: No. 55-1). 238p. (Orig.). 1981. pap. 25.00 (ISBN 0-317-40525-X, Pub. by Salzburg Studies). Longwood Pub Group.

--Kartausermystik und Mystiker, Vol. 2. (Analecta Cartusiana Ser.: No. 55-2). 226p. (Orig.). 1981. pap. 25.00 (ISBN 3-7052-0077-1, Pub. by Salzburg Studies). Longwood Pub Group.

--Kartausermystik und Mystiker, Vol. 3. (Analecta Cartusiana Ser.: No. 55-3). 198p. 1982. pap. 25.00 (ISBN 3-7052-0078-X, Pub. by Salzburg Studies). Longwood Pub Group.

--Kartausermystik und Mystiker, Vol. 4. (Analecta Cartusiana Ser.: No. 55-4). 172p. (Orig.). 1982. pap. 25.00 (ISBN 3-7052-0079-8, Pub. by Salzburg Studies). Longwood Pub Group.

--Kartausermystik und Mystiker, Vol. 5. (Analecta Cartusiana Ser.: No. 55-5). 103p. (Orig.). 1982. pap. 25.00 (ISBN 3-7052-0080-1, Pub. by Salzburg Studies). Longwood Pub Group.

--Kartauserregel und Kartauserleben: Internationaler Kongress Vom XX, 30 Mai bis 3 Juni 1984, Sift Heilgenkrezv, 3 vols. (Analecta Cartusiana Ser.: No. 113/1-3). 744p. (Orig.). 1984. pap. 85.00 (ISBN 0-317-42577-3, Pub. by Salzburg Studies). Longwood Pub Group.

--Kartauserschriftsteller. (Analecta Cartusiana Ser.: No. 117). (Orig.). 1988. pap. 25.00 (ISBN 0-317-42580-3, Pub. by Salzburg Studies). Longwood Pub Group.

Hogg, James, ed. & intro. by. Late Fifteenth Century Carthusian Rubrics for the Deacon & The Sacristan: (From the Ms. Valsainte 42-T.I.8) (Analecta Cartusiana Ser.: No. 4). (Lat. & Eng.). 169p. (Orig.). 1971. pap. 25.00 (ISBN 3-7052-0004-6, Pub. by Salzburg Studies). Longwood Pub Group.

Hogg, James, ed. Mauerbach und die Kartauser: Symposium Uber die Kartausegeschichte und - Spiritualitat 27, 28 May 1983. (Analecta Cartusiana Ser.: No. 110). 98p. (Orig.). 1984. pap. 25.00 (ISBN 0-317-42585-4, Pub. by Salzburg Studies). Longwood Pub Group.

--Mittelalterliche Caerimonialia der Kartauser, Pr. 1. (Analecta Cartusiana Ser.: No. 2). (Ger. & Lat.). 354p. 1971. pap. 25.00 (ISBN 3-7052-0001-1, Pub by Salzburg Studies). Longwood Pub Group.

--Spatmittelalterliche Geistliche Literatur in der Nationalsprache, Vol. 1. (Analecta Cartusiana Ser.: No. 106/1). 236p. (Orig.). 1983. pap. 25.00 (ISBN 0-317-42595-1, Pub. by Salzburg Studies). Longwood Pub Group.

--Spatmittelalterliche Geistliche Literatur in der Nationalsprache, Vol. 2. (Analecta Cartusiana Ser.: No. 106/2). 190p. (Orig.). 1984. pap. 25.00 (ISBN 0-317-42596-X, Pub. by Salzburg Studies). Longwood Pub Group.

--The Speculum Devotorum of an Anonymous Carhusian of Sheen: From the Manuscripts Cambridge University Library (Gg. I.6 & Foyle Vol.3, Pt. 2) (Analecta Carusiana Ser.: No. 13). (Eng.). 174p. (Orig.). 1974. pap. 25.00 (ISBN 3-7052-0014-3, Pub by Salzburg Studies). Longwood Pub Group.

--Spiritualitat Heute und Gestern, Vol. 1. (Analceta Cartusiana Ser.: No. 35). (Eng, Ger, & Fr.). 236p. (Orig.). 1982. pap. 25.00 (ISBN 3-7052-0037-2, Pub by Salzburg Studies). Longwood Pub Group.

--Spiritualitat Heute und Gestern, Vol. 3. (Analecta Cartusiana Ser.: No. 35). (Ital, Ger, & Eng.). 174p. (Orig.). 1983. pap. 25.00 (ISBN 3-7052-0039-9, Pub by Salzburg Studies). Longwood Pub Group.

--Spiritualitat Heute und Gestern, Vol. 4. (Analecta Cartusiana Ser.: No. 35). (Fr, Ital, Ger, & Eng., Illus.). 131p. (Orig.). 1984. pap. 25.00 (ISBN 3-7052-0040-2, Pub by Salzburg Studies). Longwood Pub Group.

--Spiritualitat Heute und Gestern, Vol. 5. (Analecta Cartusiana Ser.: No. 35). (Orig.). 1984. pap. 25.00 (ISBN 3-7052-0041-0, Pub by Salzburg Studies). Longwood Pub Group.

--Spiritualitiat Heute und Gestern, Vol. 2. (Analecta Cartusiana Ser.: No. 35). (Ger. & Eng.). 200p. (Orig.). 1983. pap. 25.00 (ISBN 3-7052-0038-0, Pub by Salzburg Studies). Longwood Pub Group.

Hogg, James, ed. see Arntz, Mary Luke.

Hogg, James, ed. see Atkins, Dorothy.

Hogg, James, ed. see Baier, Walter.

Hogg, James, ed. see Bastin, Dom P.

Hogg, James, ed. see Bauer, Erika.

Hogg, James, ed. see Beltrutti, Giorgio.

Hogg, James, ed. see Beltrutti, Giorgio & Hogg, James.

Hogg, James, ed. see Birch, David.

Hogg, James, ed. see Bodenstedt, Mary I.

Hogg, James, ed. see Boenig, Robert.

Hogg, James, ed. see Boyer, Raymond & Brisson, Marie.

Hogg, James, ed. see Brauer, Wilhelm.

Hogg, James, ed. see Chaix, Gerald.

Hogg, James, ed. see Chiarelli, Caterina.

Hogg, James, ed. see Conway, Charles A., Jr.

Hogg, James, ed. see Cornelius, Peter S.

Hogg, James, ed. see Courtade, Anthony E.

Hogg, James, ed. see Daly, John P.

Hogg, James, ed. see De Grauwe, Jan.

Hogg, James, ed. see Devaux, Augustin.

Hogg, James, ed. see Dupont, Dom P.

Hogg, James, ed. see Du Pont, Guigo.

Hogg, James, ed. see DuPont, Philippe.

Hogg, James, ed. see Englert, Robert W.

Hogg, James, ed. see Gfollner, Adelheid.

Hogg, James, ed. see Giacometti, Mario.

Hogg, James, ed. see Gilhodes, Abbe L.

Hogg, James, ed. see Gomez, Ildefonso.

Hogg, James, ed. see Gomez, Ildefonso M. & Hogg, James.

Hogg, James, ed. see Goreau, Eloise K.

Hogg, James, ed. see Griffin, Robert P.

Hogg, James, ed. see Hamilton, M. J.

Hogg, James, ed. see Hantschk, Rolanda.

Hogg, James, ed. see Harp, Richard L.

Hogg, James, ed. see Heimmel, Jennifer P.

Hogg, James, ed. see Hirst, Wolf Z.

Hogg, James, ed. see Hocquard, Gaston, et al.

Hogg, James, ed. see Hocquard, Gaston.

Hogg, James, ed. see Hoffman, Brunhilde.

Hogg, James, ed. see Hogg, James & Brauer, Wilhelm.

Hogg, James, ed. see Hogg, James & Ellis, Roger.

Hogg, James, ed. see Jelinek, Heienrich.

Hogg, James, ed. see Kempf, Nicolas.

Hogg, James, ed. see Kennedy, David G.

Hogg, James, ed. see Lees, Rosemary A.

Hogg, James, ed. see Legendre, Jaquelin.

Hogg, James, ed. see Leoncini, Giovanni.

Hogg, James, ed. see McCarthy, Adrian J.

Hogg, James, ed. see Macken, Raymond.

Hogg, James, ed. see Madigan, Mary F.

Hogg, James, ed. see Marks, Richard B.

Hogg, James, ed. see Mayer, Erwin.

Hogg, James, ed. see Mayr, Roswitha.

Hogg, James, ed. see Miller, Edmund.

Hogg, James, ed. see Moyes, Malcolm.

Hogg, James, ed. see O'Connell, Patrick F.

Hogg, James, ed. see Orban, A. P.

Hogg, James, ed. see Pasachoff, Naomi E.

Hogg, James, ed. see Pisani, Maria S.

Hogg, James, ed. see Reeves, Troy D.

Hogg, James, ed. see Rossman, Heribert.

Hogg, James, ed. see Rossmann, Heribert.

Hogg, James, ed. see Salter, Elizabeth.

Hogg, James, ed. see Sargent, Michael G.

Hogg, James, ed. see Savary, Louis M.

Hogg, James, ed. see Schwengel, Georgius.

Hogg, James, ed. see Sechi, Antonietta A.

Hogg, James, ed. see Shalvi, Alice.

Hogg, James, ed. see Stevenson, Warren.

Hogg, James, ed. see Stodder, Joseph H.

Hogg, James, ed. see Stohlker, Friedrich.

Hogg, James, ed. see Taitt, Peter S.

Hogg, James, ed. see Thomson, Ogilvie.

Hogg, James, ed. see Tromby, Benedetto.

Hogg, James, ed. see Tuma, George W.

Hogg, James, ed. see Weiser, David K.

Hogg, James, ed. see Whatmore, L. E.

Hogg, James, ed. see Wohrer, Franz K.

Hogg, James, et al. Die Kartauser In Osterreich, Vol. 1. Hogg, James, ed. (Analecta Cartusiana Ser.: No. 83-1). (Ger.). 236p. (Orig.). 1980. pap. 25.00 (ISBN 3-7052-0128-X, Pub. by Salzburg Studies). Longwood Pub Group.

Hoggard, Robert. Surveying the Scriptures. 1981. pap. 2.95 (ISBN 0-86544-013-1). Salv Army Suppl South.

Hogrefe, Pearl. The Sir Thomas More Circle: A Program of Ideas & Their Impact on Secular Drama. LC 59-10553. 366p. 1959. 29.95 (ISBN 0-252-72653-7). U of Ill Pr.

Hogrogian, Nonny, illus. The Pearl: Hymn of the Robe of Glory. LC 79-66092. (Illus.). 1979. 7.95 (ISBN 0-89756-002-7). Two Rivers.

Hogue, C. B. I Want My Church to Grow. LC 77-85280. 1977. 7.95 (ISBN 0-8054-6217-1). Broadman.

Hohensee, Donald W. Church Growth in Burundi. LC 76-54342. 1977. pap. 4.95 (ISBN 0-87808-316-2). William Carey Lib.

Hohensee, Herbert. The Augustinian Concept of Auctoritas. 3.00 (ISBN 0-686-23374-3). Classical Folia.

Hohenstein, Herbert E. Upper Room to Garden Tomb: Messages for Lent & Easter on the Passion Narrative in Mark. LC 84-21735. 80p. (Orig.). 1984. pap. 4.95 (ISBN 0-8066-2117-6, 10-6840). Augsburg.

Hohenstein, Mary, compiled by. Games. LC 80-23047. 298p. (Orig.). 1980. pap. 6.95 (ISBN 0-87123-191-3, 210191). Bethany Hse.

Hohlberg, L., ed. Meaning & Measurement of Moral Development. (Heinz Werner Lecture: No. 13). 1979. pap. 6.00 (ISBN 0-914206-18-4). Clark U Pr.

Hojeda, Diego de. Christiada: Introduction & Text. Corcoran, Sr. Mary H., ed. LC 35-9384. (Catholic University of America. Studies in Romance Languages & Literatures: No. 11). Repr. of 1935 ed. 49.50 (ISBN 0-404-50311-X). AMS Pr.

Holash, Lisa. Evangelization. 80p. 1984. pap. 3.50 (ISBN 0-697-01868-7). Wm C Brown.

Holbach, Paul H. D' see D'Holbach, Paul H.

Holbein, Hans. Images of the Old Testament. (Children's Books from the Past: Vol. 1). 100p. 1973. Repr. of 1549 ed. 32.65 (ISBN 3-261-01003-7). P Lang Pubs.

Holborn, H. A History of Modern Germany, 3 vols. 1982. Vol. 1, The Reformation. 47.50 (ISBN 0-691-05357-X); pap. 10.50 (ISBN 0-691-00795-0); Vol. 2, 1648-1840. 60.50 (ISBN 0-691-05358-8); pap. 11.50 (ISBN 0-691-00796-9); Vol. 3, 1840-1945. 79.00 (ISBN 0-691-05359-6); pap. 13.95 (ISBN 0-691-00797-7); Set. 155.00; Set. pap. 27.50. Princeton U Pr.

Holborn, Hajo. Ulrich Von Hutten & the German Reformation. Bainton, Roland H., tr. LC 77-25067. (Yale Historical Publications Studies: No. XI). (Illus.). 1978. Repr. of 1937 ed. lib. bdg. 22.50x (ISBN 0-313-20125-0, HOUV). Greenwood.

Holbrook, Becky T. Revised Handful of Ideas. 5.95 (ISBN 0-89137-611-9). Quality Pubns.

Holbrook, Clyde A. The Iconoclastic Deity: Biblical Images of God. 240p. 1984. 29.50 (ISBN 0-8387-5069-9). Bucknell U Pr.

Holbrook, Clyde A., ed. see Edwards, Jonathan.

Holbrook, David & Postan, Elizabeth, eds. The Apple Tree: Christmas Music from the Cambridge Hymnal. LC 76-12916. 1976. pap. 7.95 o. p. (ISBN 0-521-29116-X). Cambridge U Pr.

Holck, Frederick H., ed. Death & Eastern Thought: Understanding Death in Eastern Religions & Philosophies. LC 74-10650. pap. 49.10 (ISBN 0-8357-9004-5, 2015656). Bks Demand UMI.

Holck, Manfred, Jr. Annual Budgeting: Developing & Using an Annual Budget Effectively. 1977. pap. 3.95 (ISBN 0-8066-1549-4, 10-0360). Augsburg.

--Cash Management: Stewardship of the Church's Cash Resources. (Administration for Churches Ser.). 1978. pap. 3.95 (ISBN 0-8066-1650-4, 10-0972). Augsburg.

--Church Finance in a Complex Economy. 138p. (Orig.). 1983. pap. 6.95 (ISBN 0-687-08156-4). Abingdon.

--Clergy Desk Book. 288p. (Orig.). 1985. pap. 19.95 (ISBN 0-687-08656-6). Abingdon.

--Money & Your Church. LC 74-75979. (Illus.). 189p. 1974. 7.95 (ISBN 0-87983-080-8). Keats.

Holck, Manfred, Jr., compiled by. Dedication Services for Every Occasion. 96p. 1984. pap. 5.95 (ISBN 0-8170-1033-5). Judson.

Holcomb, Brent. Marriage & Death Notices from Southern Christian Advocate, 1837-1860, Vol. 1. 1979. 40.00 (ISBN 0-89308-111-6). Southern Hist Pr.

Holcomb, Brent H., ed. Journal of the Rev. Godfrey Drehr, Eighteen Nineteen to Eighteen Fifty-One. 104p. 1978. 15.00 (ISBN 0-89308-060-8). Southern Hist Pr.

Holdcraft, Paul E. Snappy Bulletin Bits. LC 72-109673. pap. 20.00 (ISBN 0-8357-9027-4, 2016076). Bks Demand UMI.

Holdcroft, Thomas L. The Holy Spirit: A Pentecostal Interpretation. LC 79-54991. (Illus.). 272p. 1979. Repr. 5.95 (ISBN 0-88243-554-X, 02-0554). Gospel Pub.

Holde, Artur & Heskes, Irene, eds. Jews in Music: From the Age of Enlightenment to the Mid-Twentieth Century. rev. ed. LC 74-83942. 364p. 1974. 10.00 (ISBN 0-8197-0372-9). Bloch.

Holden, Carol W., jt. auth. see Sweetser, Thomas P.

Holden, Erik, jt. auth. see Jefferson, Thomas.

Holden, Pat, ed. Women's Religious Experience. LC 82-24314. 218p. 1983. text ed. 28.50x (ISBN 0-389-20363-7, 07226). B&N Imports.

Holden, Vincent F. The Early Years of Isaac Thomas Hecker (1819-1844) LC 73-3583. (Catholic University of America. Studies in American Church History: No. 29). Repr. of 1939 ed. 29.00 (ISBN 0-404-57779-2). AMS Pr.

Holder, Philip. Captain Mahjong. 1976. pap. 2.40 (ISBN 0-85363-113-1). OMF Bks.

Holder, Ray. The Mississippi Methodists, Seventeen Ninety-Nine to Nineteen Eighty-Three: A Moral People "Born of Conviction". Date not set. 11.95 (ISBN 0-9612932-0-9); pap. 8.95 (ISBN 0-9612932-1-7). Maverick Prints.

Holderness, Ginny W. The Exuberant Years: A Guide for Junior High Leaders. LC 75-13458. 128p. 1976. pap. 7.95 (ISBN 0-8042-1225-2). John Knox.

--Youth Ministry: The New Team Approach. LC 80-82186. (Illus.). 160p. (Orig.). 1981. pap. 11.95 (ISBN 0-8042-1410-7). John Knox.

Holdren, Shirley. Why God Gave Me Pain. 128p. 1984. pap. 3.95 (ISBN 0-8294-0469-4). Loyola.

Hole, F. B. Assembly Principles. Daniel, R. P., ed. 40p. pap. 3.50 (ISBN 0-88172-141-7). Believers Bkshelf.

--Great Salvation. Daniel, R. P., ed. 72p. pap. 3.75 (ISBN 0-88172-142-5). Believers Bkshelf.

--Outlines of Truth. Daniel, R. P., ed. 73p. pap. 3.75 (ISBN 0-88172-143-3). Believers Bkshelf.

Hole, Helen G. Prayer: The Cornerstone. LC 62-19073. (Orig.). 1962. pap. 2.50x (ISBN 0-87574-123-1). Pendle Hill.

Holfelder, Hans H. Tentatio et Consolatio: Studien zu Bugenhagens Interpretatio in Librum Psalmorum. LC 73-80563. (Arbeiten Zur Kirchengeschichte, Vol. 46). (Ger.). 132p. 1974. 35.60 (ISBN 3-11-004327-0). De Gruyter.

Holifield, E. Brooks. The Gentlemen Theologians: American Theology in Southern Culture, 1795-1860. LC 78-59580. x, 262p. 1978. 23.00 (ISBN 0-8223-0414-7). Duke.

--Health & Medicine & the Methodist Tradition. 176p. 1986. 17.95x (ISBN 0-8245-0792-4). Crossroad NY.

--A History of Pastoral Care in America: From Salvation to Self-Realization. 416p. (Orig.). 1983. pap. 16.95 (ISBN 0-687-17249-7). Abingdon.

Holinger, Paul C. Pastoral Care for Severe Emotional Disorders: Principles of Diagnosis & Treatment. LC 83-18670. 145p. 1985. text ed. 24.95x (ISBN 0-8290-1509-4). Irvington.

Holl, jt. auth. see Autery.

Holl, Adolf. Jesus in Bad Company. 1978. pap. 1.65 (ISBN 0-380-00022-9, 19281, Discus). Avon.

Holladay, Carl, jt. auth. see Hayes, John H.

Holladay, Carl R. Fragments from Hellenistic Jewish Authors: Historians, Vol. I. LC 79-18090. (SBL Texts & Translations). 404p. 1983. pap. 16.50 (ISBN 0-89130-349-9, 06 02 20). Scholars Pr GA.

Holladay, William L. Architecture of Jeremiah, 1-20. 204p. 1976. 20.00 (ISBN 0-8387-1523-0). Bucknell U Pr.

--A Concise Hebrew & Aramaic Lexicon of the Old Testament. (Hebrew & Aramaic.). 1971. 27.95 (ISBN 0-8028-3413-2). Eerdmans.

--Isaiah: Scroll of a Prophetic Heritage. 270p. 1987. pap. 9.95 (ISBN 0-8298-0658-X). Pilgrim NY.

--Jeremiah One. LC 85-45498. (Hermeneia Ser.). 752p. 1986. 44.95 (ISBN 0-8006-6017-X, 20-6017). Fortress.

--Jeremiah: Spokesman Out of Time. LC 74-7052. 160p. 1974. pap. 5.95 (ISBN 0-8298-0283-5). Pilgrim NY.

Holland, Barron, compiled by. Popular Hinduism & Hindu Mythology: An Annotated Bibliography. LC 79-7188. 1979. lib. bdg. 45.00 (ISBN 0-313-21358-5, HPH/). Greenwood.

Holland, Caroline, tr. see Cavallini, Giuliana.

Holland, Clifton L. The Religious Dimension in Hispanic Los Angeles: A Protestant Case Study. LC 74-5123. 542p. (Orig.). 1974. pap. 10.95 (ISBN 0-87808-309-X). William Carey Lib.

Holland, Clifton L., ed. World Christianity: Central America & the Caribbean. LC 79-89819. 1981. pap. 15.00 (ISBN 0-912552-36-0). Missions Adv Res Comm Ctr.

Holland, Daniel W., et al. Using Nonbroadcast Video in the Church. 128p. 1980. pap. 5.95 (ISBN 0-8170-0895-0). Judson.

Holland, DeWitte T. The Preaching Tradition: A Brief History. LC 80-16339. (Abingdon Preacher's Library). 128p. (Orig.). 1980. pap. 6.95 (ISBN 0-687-33875-1). Abingdon.

Holland, G. A. A True Love Story. Date not set. 14.95 (ISBN 0-533-06799-5). Vantage.

Holland, H., tr. see Calvin, Jean.

Holland, Jeffrey R. However Long & Hard the Road. LC 85-12945. 144p. 1985. 8.95 (ISBN 0-87747-625-X). Deseret Bk.

Holland, John M., et al. Religion & Sexuality: Judaic-Christian Viewpoints in the U. S. A. LC 81-66867. (The Association of Sexologists Monographs: No. 1). 80p. 1981. pap. 5.95 (ISBN 0-939902-00-1). Assn Sexologists.

Holland, Larrimore D., ed. see Weiss, Johannes.

Holland, Leo. Images of God. LC 84-72318. (Illus.). 112p. (Orig.). 1985. pap. 4.95 (ISBN 0-87793-276-X). Ave Maria.

--Twice the Challenge: Athlete & Christian. LC 86-80387. 128p. (Orig.). 1986. pap. 4.95 (ISBN 0-89243-251-9). Liguori Pubns.

Holland, Mary G. The British Catholic Press & the Eductional Controversy, 1847-1865. McNeill, William H. & Stanksy, Peter, eds. (Modern European History Ser.). 400p. 1987. lib. bdg. 60.00 (ISBN 0-8240-7817-9). Garland Pub.

Holland, Muhtar, tr. Al Ghazali: On the Duties of Brotherhood. LC 76-8057. 96p. 1976. 10.00 (ISBN 0-87951-046-3); pap. 7.95 (ISBN 0-87951-083-8). Overlook Pr.

Holland, Muhtar, tr. see Al-Ghazali.

Holland, Muhtar, tr. see Taymiya, Ibn.

Holland Society of New York. Records of the Reformed Dutch Church of Albany, New York, 1683-1809. LC 78-54063. 922p. (Repr. of the 1904-1927 eds.). 1978. 38.50 (ISBN 0-8063-0808-7). Genealog Pub.

Holland, Thomas W. God & Jesus: Nothing More Than Four-Letter Words. 1987. 6.95 (ISBN 0-533-07206-9). Vantage.

Hollander, Lee M., tr. from Norse. The Poetic Edda. rev. ed. 375p. 1986. pap. 12.95 (ISBN 0-292-76499-5). U of Tex Pr.

Hollaway, Lee. David: Shepherd, Musician, & King. (BibLearn Ser.). (Illus.). 1977. bds. 5.95 (ISBN 0-8054-4230-8, 4242-30). Broadman.

--The Donald Orrs: Missionary Duet. LC 82-732666. (Meet the Missionary Ser.). 1983. 5.50 (ISBN 0-8054-4283-9, 4242-83). Broadman.

Hollenbach, David. Claims in Conflict: Retrieving & Renewing the Catholic Human Rights Tradition. LC 79-84239. (Woodstock Ser.: No. 4). (Orig.). 1979. pap. 7.95 (ISBN 0-8091-2197-2). Paulist Pr.

--Nuclear Ethics: A Christian Moral Argument. 112p. 1983. pap. 3.95 (ISBN 0-8091-2546-3). Paulist Pr.

Hollender, Betty. Bible Stories for Little Children, Bk. 1. rev. ed. (Illus.). 80p. (Orig.). 1985. pap. text ed. 6.00 (ISBN 0-8074-0309-1, 103100). UAHC.

Hollender, Betty R. Bible Stories for Little Children, Vol. 2. rev. ed. (Illus.). 80p. 1987. pap. text ed. 6.00 (ISBN 0-8074-0324-5). UAHC.

Holleran, Mary P. Church & State in Guatemala. LC 73-19956. 359p. 1974. Repr. of 1949 ed. lib. bdg. 23.00x (ISBN 0-374-93929-2, Octagon). Hippocrene Bks.

Hollerbach, Marion. Das Religionsgespraech Als Mittel Der Konfessionellen Und Politischen Auseinandersetzung Im Deutschland Des 16. Jahrhunderts. (European University Studies: No. 3, Vol. 165). (Ger.). 1982. 36.85 (ISBN 3-8204-7015-8). P Lang Pubs.

Hollerweger, jt. ed. see Berger.

Holley, Horace. Religion for Mankind. 248p. 1956. 12.95 (ISBN 0-87743-011-X); pap. 5.95 (ISBN 0-85398-000-4). G Ronald Pub.

Holley, Marietta. Samantha among the Brethren, By Josiah Allen's Wife. Gifford, Carolyn & Dayton, Donald, eds. (Women in American Protestan Religion 1800-1930 Ser.). 437p. 1987. lib. bdg. 60.00 (ISBN 0-8240-0664-X). Garland Pub.

Hollingdale, R. J., tr. see Nietzsche, Friedrich.

Hollinger, Dennis P. Individualism & Social Ethics: An Evangelical Syncretism. 284p. 1984. lib. bdg. 28.50 (ISBN 0-8191-3580-1); pap. text ed. 13.50 (ISBN 0-8191-3581-X). U Pr of Amer.

Hollinger, Robert, ed. Hermeneutics & Praxis. LC 85-40599. (Revisions Ser.: Vol. 6). 320p. 1985. text ed. 29.95x (ISBN 0-268-01080-3, 85-10802, Dist. by Har-Row); pap. text ed. 12.95x (ISBN 0-268-01081-1, 85-10810). U of Notre Dame Pr.

Hollings, G. S., ed. see Alcantara, S. Peter.

Hollings, Michael. Enfolded by Christ: An Encouragement to Pray. Orig. Title: Day by Day. 128p. 1976. pap. 2.95 (ISBN 0-914544-10-1). Living Flame Pr.

Hollings, Michael, ed. Daily Readings with St. Therese of Lisieux. 1987. pap. 4.95 (ISBN 0-87243-154-1). Templegate.

Hollingsworth, Gerelyn. Ex-Nuns: Women Who Have Left the Convent. LC 84-43207. 136p. 1985. lib. bdg. 16.95x (ISBN 0-89950-156-7). McFarland & Co.

Hollingsworth, T. R. Ezra of Galilee. 80p. (Orig.). 1987. pap. text ed. 6.95 (ISBN 0-9617668-0-8). Hollybridge Pubns.

Hollingworth, G. E. English Mystics. 1973. lib. bdg. 15.00 (ISBN 0-8414-5096-X). Folcroft.

Hollis, Christopher. The Mind of Chesterton. LC 76-130447. 1970. 14.95x (ISBN 0-87024-184-2). U of Miami Pr.

--Thomas More. 1934. Repr. 20.00 (ISBN 0-8274-3614-9). R West.

Hollis, Daniel W., III. A History of First Baptist Church, Jacksonville Alabama, 1836-1986. (Illus.). 241p. 1986. 10.00 (ISBN 0-9616158-0-X). First Bapt AL.

Hollis, Marcia & Hollis, Reginald. The Godswept Heart: Parables of Family Life. (Illus.). 96p. 1983. pap. 5.95 (ISBN 0-8164-2410-1, HarpR). Har-Row.

Hollis, Reginald, jt. auth. see Hollis, Marcia.

Holloway, Julia B. THe Pilgrim & the Book: A Study of Dante, Langland & Chaucer. (American University Studies IV- English Language & Literature: Vol. 42). 343p. 1987. text ed. 30.75 (ISBN 0-8204-0345-8). P Lang Pubs.

Holloway, Marcella. Should You Become a Sister? 1978. pap. 1.50 (ISBN 0-89243-073-7, 29553). Liguori Pubns.

Holloway, Maurice R. Introduction to Natural Theology. LC 59-6522. 1959. text ed. 19.95x (ISBN 0-89197-244-7). Irvington.

Holloway, Maurice R., jt. auth. see Klubertanz, George P.

Holloway, Richard. Beyond Belief: The Christian Encounter with God. LC 81-5438. pap. 43.50 (ISBN 0-317-19824-6, 2023217). Bks Demand UMI.

--The Killing. 77p. 1985. pap. 5.95 (ISBN 0-8192-1367-5). Morehouse.

--The Sidelong Glance: Politics, Conflict & the Church. LC 86-13473. 86p. 1986. pap. 6.95 (ISBN 0-936384-40-9). Cowley Pubns.

--Signs of Glory. 96p. 1983. pap. 5.95 (ISBN 0-8164-2412-8, HarpR). Har-Row.

Holloway, Richard, et al. The Anglican Tradition. Holloway, Richard, ed. LC 83-62541. 132p. (Orig.). 1984. pap. 6.95 (ISBN 0-8192-1338-1). Morehouse.

Hollway, Richard. Suffering, Sex & Other Paradoxes. 150p. 1985. 10.95 (ISBN 0-8192-1358-6). Morehouse.

Holly, David. A Complete Categorized Greek-English New Testament Vocabulary. (Eng. & Gr.). 141p. 1978. 9.50 (ISBN 0-85150-119-2). Attic Pr.

--A Complete Categorized Greek-English New Testament Vocabulary. (Gr. & Eng.). 1980. pap. 6.95 (ISBN 0-8010-4224-0). Baker Bk.

Holly, Donna. Jesus, Our Savior. (Illus.). 16p. (Orig.). 1984. pap. 0.60 (ISBN 0-87239-701-7, 2307). Standard Pub.

Holly, Henry H. Church Architecture. 1980. lib. bdg. 75.00 (ISBN 0-8490-3141-9). Gordon Pr.

Hollyer, Belinda. David & Goliath. LC 84-50452. (Bible Stories Ser.). (Illus.). 24p. 1984. 5.45 (ISBN 0-382-06940-4); PLB 6.96 (ISBN 0-382-06791-6). Silver.

--Jonah & the Great Fish. LC 84-50451. (Bible Stories Ser.). (Illus.). 24p. 1984. 5.45 (ISBN 0-382-06792-4); pap. 5.96 (ISBN 0-382-06941-2). Silver.

--Noah & the Ark. LC 84-50450. (Bible Stories Ser.). (Illus.). 24p. 1984. PLB 6.96 (ISBN 0-382-06793-2); pap. 5.45 (ISBN 0-382-06942-0). Silver.

Hollyer, Belinda, adapted by. Daniel in the Lions' Den. LC 84-50453. (Bible Stories Ser.). (Illus.). 24p. 1984. 6.96 (ISBN 0-382-06939-0); PLB 5.96 (ISBN 0-382-06939-0). Silver.

Holm, Marilyn F. Tell Me Why: A Guide to Children's Questions about Faith & Life. LC 85-7355. 144p. (Orig.). 1985. pap. 6.95 (ISBN 0-8066-2160-5, 10-6230). Augsburg.

Holm, Nils G., ed. Religious Ecstasy. (Scripta Instituti Donnerain Aboensis: No. XI). 306p. 1982. pap. text ed. 25.00x (ISBN 91-22-00574-9, Pub. by Almqvist & Wiksell Sweden). Humanities.

Holman Bible Publishers. The Holman Bible Atlas. Hooper, Jerry L., ed. (Illus.). 1978. pap. 6.95 (ISBN 0-87981-099-8). Holman Bible Pub.

--Holman Topical Concordance: An Index to the Bible Arranged by Subjects in Alphabetical Order. LC 73-7656. 288p. 1973. 8.95 (ISBN 0-87981-019-X). Holman Bible Pub.

Holman Company. Holman Bible Concordance. Hitt, Russell, ed. 1979. pap. 3.95 (ISBN 0-87981-093-9). Holman Bible Pub.

Holman, Vernon A. Painful Blessings. LC 85-8042. (Illus.). 45p. (Orig.). 1985. pap. write for info. (ISBN 0-933315-07-4). Taran House Pub.

Holmberg, Bengt. Paul & Power: The Structure of Authority in the Primitive Church Reflected in the Pauline Epistles. LC 79-8905. 240p. 1980. 3.00 (ISBN 0-8006-0634-5, 1-634). Fortress.

Holmberg, Kathleen. Our First Penance: Celebrating God's Forgiving Love. Fischer, Carl, ed. 1986. dupl. masterbk 9.95 (ISBN 0-89837-108-2). Peter Li.

Holmberg, Uno. Finno-Ugric, Siberian Mythology. (Mythology of All Races Ser: Vol. Iv). (Illus.). Repr. of 1932 ed. 30.00x (ISBN 0-8154-0116-7). Cooper Sq.

Holme. Myths of Greece & Rome. 288p. 1981. pap. 18.95 (ISBN 0-14-005643-2). Penguin.

Holme see Kerenyi, Carl.

Holme, Leonard R. Extinction of the Christian Churches in North Africa. 1969. 20.50 (ISBN 0-8337-1724-3). B Franklin.

Holmer, Paul L. Making Christian Sense. LC 83-27373. (Spirituality & the Christian Life Ser.: Vol. 3). 118p. (Orig.). 1984. pap. 7.95 (ISBN 0-664-24614-1). Westminster.

Holmes, Alice C., jt. auth. see Carl, Angela R.

Holmes, Arthur F. All Truth is God's Truth. LC 83-18411. 148p. 1983. pap. 4.95 (ISBN 0-87784-818-1). Inter-Varsity.

--Contours of a World View. Henry, Carl F., ed. (Studies in a Christian World View: Vol. 1). 256p. 1983. pap. 8.95 (ISBN 0-8028-1957-5). Eerdmans.

--The Idea of a Christian College. 1975. pap. 5.95 (ISBN 0-8028-1592-8). Eerdmans.

--The Idea of A Christian College. rev. ed. 104p. 1987. pap. 6.95 (ISBN 0-8028-0258-3). Eerdmans.

--War & Christian Ethics. LC 75-14602. pap. 13.95 (ISBN 0-8010-4170-8). Baker Bk.

Holmes, Arthur F., et al. The Making of a Christian Mind. LC 84-22476. 160p. (Orig.). 1984. pap. 6.95 (ISBN 0-87784-525-5). Inter-Varsity.

Holmes, C. Raymond. Sing a New Song! Worship Renewal for Adventists Today. LC 84-70077. xii, 190p. 1984. pap. 9.95 (ISBN 0-943872-88-X). Andrews Univ Pr.

--Stranger in My Home. LC 73-9253. (Crown Ser.). 128p. 1974. pap. 5.95 (ISBN 0-8127-0075-9). Review & Herald.

Holmes, Colin. Anti-Semitism in British Society Eighteen Seventy-Six to Nineteen Thirty-Nine. LC 78-21023. 328p. 1979. text ed. 49.50x (ISBN 0-8419-0459-6). Holmes & Meier.

Holmes, D. A. Towers with Three Bells or Less: Basingstoke. 1985. 11.25x (ISBN 0-317-54325-3, Pub. by J Richardson UK). State Mutual Bk.

Holmes, Dana. Your Faith Account. 48p. (Orig.). 1983. pap. 0.95 (ISBN 0-88144-019-1, CPS/019). Christian Pub.

Holmes, Deborah A. Survival Prayers for Young Mothers. 6.95 (ISBN 0-8042-2195-2). John Knox.

Holmes, Derek, ed. see Newman, John H.

Holmes, Derek J. The Papacy in the Modern World Nineteen Fourteen to Nineteen Seventy. LC 81-65110. 275p. 1981. 14.95 (ISBN 0-8245-0047-4). Crossroad NY.

Holmes, Derek J. & Bickers, Bernard W. A Short History of the Catholic Church. LC 83-63193. 315p. 1984. pap. 8.95 (ISBN 0-8091-2623-0). Paulist Pr.

Holmes, Edmond. The Creed of Buddha. LC 72-9918. 260p. 1973. Repr. of 1957 ed. lib. bdg. 22.50x (ISBN 0-8371-6606-3, HOCB). Greenwood.

Holmes, Elizabeth. Henry Vaughan & the Hermetic Philosophy. (English Literature Ser., No. 33). 1970. pap. 22.95x (ISBN 0-8383-0094-4). Haskell.

Holmes, Ernest. The Basic Ideas of Science of Mind. 96p. 1957. pap. 4.50 (ISBN 0-911336-23-0). Sci of Mind.

--Creative Ideas. Kinnear, Willis H., ed. 96p. 1964. pap. 4.50 (ISBN 0-911336-00-1). Sci of Mind.

--Creative Mind & Success. 1947. 10.95 (ISBN 0-396-02070-4). Dodd.

--Discover a Richer Life. Kinnear, Willis H., ed. 96p. 1961. pap. 4.50 (ISBN 0-911336-27-3). Sci of Mind.

--Effective Prayer. Kinnear, Willis H., ed. 52p. 1966. pap. 4.50 (ISBN 0-911336-02-8). Sci of Mind.

--Freedom from Stress. Kinnear, Willis H., ed. 96p. 1964. pap. 4.50 (ISBN 0-911336-30-3). Sci of Mind.

--Freedom to Live. Kinnear, Willis H., ed. 96p. 1969. pap. 4.50 (ISBN 0-911336-35-4). Sci of Mind.

--Give Us This Day. pap. 0.75 (ISBN 0-87516-144-8). De Vorss.

--How to Use the Science of Mind. 1950. 8.95 (ISBN 0-396-03212-5). Dodd.

--Journey into Life. Kinnear, Willis H., ed. 88p. 1967. pap. 5.50 (ISBN 0-911336-05-2). Sci of Mind.

--Keys to Wisdom. Kinnear, Willis H., ed. 96p. 1965. pap. 5.50 (ISBN 0-911336-06-0). Sci of Mind.

--Know Yourself! Kinnear, Willis H., ed. 96p. (Orig.). 1970. pap. 4.50 (ISBN 0-911336-36-2). Sci of Mind.

--The Larger Life. Kinnear, Willis H., ed. 84p. 1969. pap. 5.50 (ISBN 0-911336-07-9). Sci of Mind.

--Living Without Fear. Kinnear, Willis H., ed. 96p. 1962. pap. 4.50 (ISBN 0-911336-28-1). Sci of Mind.

--Observations. Kinnear, Willis H., ed. 64p. 1968. pap. 5.50 (ISBN 0-911336-12-5). Sci of Mind.

--Philosophy of Jesus. Kinnear, Willis, ed. 94p. 1973. pap. 4.50 (ISBN 0-911336-51-6). Sci of Mind.

--The Power of an Idea. Kinnear, Willis H., ed. 96p. 1965. pap. 4.50 (ISBN 0-911336-31-1). Sci of Mind.

--The Power of Belief. Kinnear, Willis H., ed. 96p. 1970. pap. 5.50 (ISBN 0-911336-13-3). Sci of Mind.

--Science of Mind. rev. & enl. ed. 17.95 (ISBN 0-396-02069-0). Dodd.

--Spiritual Awareness. Kinnear, Willis H., ed. 96p. 1972. pap. 5.50 (ISBN 0-911336-41-9). Sci of Mind.

--Spiritual Universe & You. Kinnear, Willis, ed. 96p. 1971. pap. 4.50 (ISBN 0-911336-37-0). Sci of Mind.

--Ten Ideas That Make a Difference. Kinnear, Willis H., ed. 96p. 1966. pap. 4.50 (ISBN 0-911336-32-X). Sci of Mind.

--Think Your Troubles Away. Kinnear, Willis H., ed. 96p. 1963. pap. 4.50 (ISBN 0-911336-29-X). Sci of Mind.

--This Thing Called Life. 1947. 8.95 (ISBN 0-396-02851-9). Dodd.

--Thoughts Are Things. Kinnear, Willis H., ed. 96p. 1967. pap. 4.50 (ISBN 0-911336-33-8). Sci of Mind.

--Words That Heal Today. 1948. 10.95 (ISBN 0-396-03093-9). Dodd.

Holmes, Ernest & Barker, Raymond C. Richer Living. 372p. 1973. pap. 9.50 (ISBN 0-911336-48-6). Sci of Mind.

Holmes, Ernest & Hornaday, William H. Help for Today. 256p. 1969. pap. 7.50 (ISBN 0-911336-03-6). Sci of Mind.

Holmes, Ernest & Kinnear, Willis. Practical Application of Science of Mind. 96p. 1958. pap. 4.50 (ISBN 0-911336-24-9). Sci of Mind.

Holmes, Ernest & Kinnear, Willis H. It Can Happen to You. 96p. 1959. pap. 4.50 (ISBN 0-911336-25-7). Sci of Mind.

Holmes, Ernest, et al. Light. Kinnear, Willis H., ed. 96p. 1971. pap. 5.50 (ISBN 0-911336-09-5). Sci of Mind.

Holmes, Fenwicke & McEathron, Margaret. Philip's Cousin Jesus: The Untold Story. LC 81-65247. 425p. 1982. pap. 9.95. Reading Hse.

Holmes, Fenwicke L. The Faith That Heals. 100p. 1986. pap. 6.00 (ISBN 0-89540-124-X, SB 124). Sun Pub.

Holmes, George. He Is Lord. LC 76-20891. (Radiant Life Ser.). 128p. 1977. pap. 2.50 (ISBN 0-88243-902-2, 02-0902); teacher's ed 3.95 (ISBN 0-88243-172-2, 32-0172). Gospel Pub.

--Toward an Effective Pulpit Ministry. LC 72-152056. 1971. 4.00 (ISBN 0-88243-610-4, 02-0610). Gospel Pub.

Holmes, J. Derek. More Roman Than Rome: English Catholicism in the Nineteenth Century. LC 77-92886. (Illus.). 278p. 1978. 21.95x (ISBN 0-915762-05-6). Patmos Pr.

--The Triumph of the Holy See: A Short History of the Papacy in the Nineteenth Century. LC 78-18616. (Illus.). viii, 306p. 1978. 21.95x (ISBN 0-915762-06-4). Patmos Pr.

Holmes, J. Derek, ed. see Newman, John H.

Holmes, John H. The Enduring Significance of Emerson's Divinity School Address. LC 73-9537. 1938. Repr. lib. bdg. 8.50 (ISBN 0-8414-2073-4). Folcroft.

--New Wars for Old. LC 71-147623. (Library of War & Peace; Non-Resis. & Non-Vio.). 1972. lib. bdg. 46.00 (ISBN 0-8240-0398-5). Garland Pub.

Holmes, Majorie. Three from Galilee. 240p. 1986. pap. 3.50 (ISBN 0-553-26166-5). Bantam.

Holmes, Marjorie. God & Vitamins. 368p. 1982. pap. 3.50 (ISBN 0-380-56994-9, 68536-1). Avon.

--God & Vitamins. LC 80-911. 360p. 1980. 10.95 (ISBN 0-385-15249-3, Galilee). Doubleday.

--Hold Me up a Little Longer, Lord. LC 76-42338. (Illus.). 1977. 9.95 (ISBN 0-385-12403-1). Doubleday.

--I've Got to Talk to Somebody. 144p. 1984. pap. 2.95 (ISBN 0-8007-8080-9, Spire Bks). Revell.

--I've Got to Talk to Somebody, God. 160p. 1985. pap. 3.50 (ISBN 0-553-26428-1). Bantam.

--I've Got to Talk to Somebody, God. LC 69-10938. 1969. 8.95 (ISBN 0-385-05209-X). Doubleday.

--I've Got to Talk to Somebody, God. 15th, anniversary ed. LC 84-28724. 144p. 1985. pap. 5.95 (ISBN 0-385-19751-9, Galilee). Doubleday.

--Lord, Let Me Love. 288p. 1981. pap. 3.95 (ISBN 0-553-25859-1). Bantam.

--Lord, Let Me Love: A Marjorie Holmes Treasury. LC 77-26516. 1978. 12.95 (ISBN 0-385-14093-2, Galilee). Doubleday.

--Nobody Else Will Listen. 1976. pap. 2.95 (ISBN 0-553-23457-9). Bantam.

--To Help You Through the Hurting. LC 81-43571. (Illus.). 160p. 1983. 9.95 (ISBN 0-385-17842-5). Doubleday.

--To Help You Through the Hurting. 176p. 1985. pap. 8.95 (ISBN 0-8027-2508-2). Walker & Co.

Holmes, Peter. Resistance & Compromise: The Political Thought of the Elizabethan Catholics. LC 81-17990. (Cambridge Studies in the History & Theory of Politics). 296p. 1982. 44.50 (ISBN 0-521-24343-2). Cambridge U Pr.

Holmes, Reed M. The Church in Israel. (Illus.). 1983. pap. 10.00 (ISBN 0-8309-0383-6). Herald Hse.

--The Patriarchs. LC 78-1895. 1978. pap. 7.00 (ISBN 0-8309-0205-8). Herald Hse.

Holmes, Reed M., jt. auth. see Booz, Gretchen.

Holmes, Robert M. Why Jesus Never Had Ulcers. 96p. (Orig.). 1986. pap. 6.95 (ISBN 0-687-45359-3). Abingdon.

Holmes, Roger W. The Idealism of Giovanni Gentile. LC 78-63683. (Studies in Fascism: Ideology & Practice). Repr. of 1937 ed. 29.50 (ISBN 0-404-16948-1). AMS Pr.

Holmes, Ronald. Witchcraft in History. 1977. pap. 5.95 (ISBN 0-8065-0575-3). Citadel Pr.

Holmes, Stewart W. & Horioka, Chimyo. Zen Art for Meditation. LC 73-78279. (Illus.). 1978. pap. 4.75 (ISBN 0-8048-1255-1). C E Tuttle.

Holmes, T. Scott. The Origin & Development of the Christian Church in Gaul During the First Six Centuries of the Christian Era. 1977. lib. bdg. 59.95 (ISBN 0-8490-2382-3). Gordon Pr.

Holmes, Theda. Holiness & Honor of Praise. LC 85-62801. 1986. pap. 3.50 (ISBN 0-88270-599-7). Bridge Pub.

Holmes, Thomas J. Cotton Mather: A Bibliography of His Works, 3 vols. 1395p. 1974. Repr. Set. 70.00x (ISBN 0-89020-000-9). Crofton Pub.

Holmes, Thomas S. Cotton Mather: A Bibliography of His Works. 1940. Set. 70.00 (ISBN 0-89020-000-9); Vol. 3. Brown Bk.

Holmes, Urban T. Praying with the Family of God: Leader Guide. 1980. pap. 3.95 (ISBN 0-03-049551-2, HarpR). Har-Row.

Holmes, Urban T., jt. auth. see Fiorenza, Elisabeth S.

Holmes, Urban T., jt. auth. see Terwilliger, Robert E.

Holmes, Urban T., III. A History of Christian Spirituality: An Analytical Introduction. 176p. 1981. pap. 6.95 (ISBN 0-8164-2343-1, HarpR). Har-Row.

--Ministry & Imagination. 288p. 1981. pap. 5.50 (ISBN 0-8164-2351-2, HarpR). Har-Row.

--Spirituality for Ministry. LC 81-47839. 244p. 1982. 14.45 (ISBN 0-06-064008-1, HarpR). Har-Row.

--Turning to Christ: A Theology of Renewal & Evangelization. 240p. (Orig.). 1981. pap. 8.95 (ISBN 0-8164-2289-3, HarpR). Har-Row.

--Young Children & the Eucharist. rev. ed. 128p. 1982. pap. 6.95 (ISBN 0-8164-2425-X, HarpR). Har-Row.

Holmes, Urban T., III & Westerhoff, John H. Christian Believing. (Church's Teaching Ser.: Vol. I). 144p. 1979. 5.95 (ISBN 0-8164-0418-6, HarpR); pap. 3.95 (ISBN 0-8164-2214-1); study guide 1.50 (ISBN 0-8164-2221-4). Har-Row.

Holmes, Urban T., III & Westerhoff, John H., III. The Church's Teaching Series, 9 Vols. 1979. Set. 45.45 (ISBN 0-8164-0453-4, HarpR); Set. pap. 24.95 (ISBN 0-8164-2271-0). Har-Row.

Holmes, Urban T., 3rd. What Is Anglicanism? LC 81-84715. 112p. (Orig.). 1982. pap. 5.95 (ISBN 0-8192-1295-4). Morehouse.

Holmgern, Frederick, ed. see Knight, George A.

Holmgren, Frederick. The God Who Cares: A Christian Looks at Judaism. LC 78-52445. (Orig.). 1979. pap. 1.95 (ISBN 0-8042-0588-4). John Knox.

Holmgren, Frederick & Knight, George A., eds. International Theological Commentary, 6 vols. Incl. Vol. 1. Joshua. Hamlin, E. J. 8.95. 1983. pap. write for info. Eerdmans.

Holmgren, Frederick, ed. see Hamlin, E. J.

Holmgren, Frederick, ed. see Knight, George A.

Holmgren, Fredrick C. Israel Alive Again: Ezra & Mehemiah. Knight, G. A., ed. (International Theological Commentary Ser.). 200p. (Orig.). 1987. pap. 9.95 (ISBN 0-8028-0259-1). Eerdmans.

Holroyd, Stuart. Emergence from Chaos. LC 73-167356. (Essay Index Reprint Ser.). Repr. of 1957 ed. 18.00 (ISBN 0-8369-2695-1). Ayer Co Pubs.

Holschbach, Corine. Relatives in Orbit. (Illus.). 64p. 1986. 7.95 (ISBN 0-89962-514-2). Todd & Honeywell.

Holscher, Uvo, jt. auth. see Nelson, Harold H.

Holst, Lawrence. Hospital Ministry. Marty, Martin E., intro. by. 256p. 1985. 19.95 (ISBN 0-8245-0697-9). Crossroad NY.

--Hospital Ministry. 256p. 1987. pap. 10.95 (ISBN 0-8245-0819-X). Crossroad NY.

Holt, Edwin B. The Concept of Consciousness. LC 73-2969. (Classics in Psychology Ser.). Repr. of 1914 ed. 23.50 (ISBN 0-405-05141-7). Ayer Co Pubs.

Holt, John C. Discipline: The Canonical Buddhism of the Vinayapataka. 1983. 16.00x (ISBN 0-8364-0951-5). South Asia Bks.

Holt, John D., ed. see Johnson, Rubellite K.

Holt, Lucius H. Elene of Cynewulf. LC 75-11897. (Yale Studies in English Ser: Vol. 21). 1904. lib. bdg. 12.50 (ISBN 0-8414-4851-5). Folcroft.

Holt, Lucius H., ed. The Elene of Cynewulf. 1904. 20.00 (ISBN 0-8274-2235-0). R West.

Holt, P. M., et al, eds. Cambridge History of Islam. Incl. Vol. 1A. Central Islamic Lands from Pre-Islamic Times to the First World War. 67.50 (ISBN 0-521-21946-9); pap. 29.95 (ISBN 0-521-29135-6); Vol. 1B. Central Islamic Lands Since 1918. 62.50 (ISBN 0-521-21947-7); pap. 24.95 (ISBN 0-521-29136-4); Vol. 2A. The Indian Subcontinent, Southeast Asia, Africa & the Muslim West. 64.50 (ISBN 0-521-21948-5); pap. 24.95 (ISBN 0-521-29137-2); Vol. 2B. Islamic Society & Civilization. 77.50 (ISBN 0-521-21949-3); pap. 32.95 (ISBN 0-521-29138-0). 1977-78. Set. 250.00 (ISBN 0-521-22310-5); Set. pap. 90.00 (ISBN 0-521-08755-4). Cambridge U Pr.

Holt, Pat. Gideon: God's Warrior. 32p. 1986. 7.95 (ISBN 0-687-14220-2). Abingdon.

--Mommy's Lesson. 32p. 1985. pap. 3.95 (ISBN 0-570-04131-7, 56-1545). Concordia.

Holtom, Daniel C. The Political Philosophy of Modern Shinto: A Study of the State Religion of Japan. LC 84-3072. (BCC Ser.). 338p. 1984. Repr. of 1922 ed. 37.50 (ISBN 0-404-15937-0). AMS Pr.

Holton, Susan & Jones, David L. Spirit Aflame: Luis Palau's Mission to London. 258p. 1985. 7.95 (ISBN 0-8010-4293-3). Baker Bk.

Holtz, Barry, ed. Back to the Sources: Reading the Classic Jewish Texts. (Illus.). 416p. 1984. 19.95 (ISBN 0-671-45467-6). Summit Bks.

Holtzclaw, Robert F. The Saints Go Marching In. rev. ed. LC 84-52751. (Illus.). 194p. (Orig.). 1984. write for info.; pap. 10.00 (ISBN 0-933144-00-8). Keeble Pr.

Holweck, Frederick G. Biographical Dictionary of the Saints. LC 68-30625. 1969. Repr. of 1924 ed. 75.00x (ISBN 0-8103-3158-6). Gale.

Holwerda, David E. John: A Study Guide. (Revelation Series for Adults). 1977. pap. text ed. 2.50 (ISBN 0-933140-06-1). CRC Pubns.

Holy Transfiguration Monastery, ed. The Life of St. Maximus the Confessor. Birchall, Christopher, tr. from Greek, & Russian. (Illus.). 73p. (Orig.). 1982. pap. 5.00 (ISBN 0-913026-52-2). St Nectarios.

Holy Transfiguration Monastery, ed. & tr. see Mother Martha.

Holy Transfiguration Monastery, tr. from Greek. The Lamentations: From the Matins of Holy & Great Saturday. 65p. (Orig.). 1981. pap. 4.95x (ISBN 0-913026-51-4). St Nectarios.

Holy Transfiguration Monastery Staff. The Elder Joseph of Optina. LC 82-81456. 312p. (Orig.). 1985. pap. 10.50x (ISBN 0-913026-53-0). St Nectarios.

--Prayers for Holy Communion. 120p. (Orig.). 1986. pap. 3.00x (ISBN 0-913026-60-3, Holy Transfiguration). St Nectarios.

--Selected Byzantine Hymns. 2nd ed. 120p. (Orig.). 1987. pap. 10.00x (ISBN 0-913026-59-X, Holy Transfiguration). St Nectarios.

Holz, Ron. Heralds of Victory. (Illus.). 256p. (Orig.). 1986. 8.00 (ISBN 0-89216-068-3); pap. 5.00 (ISBN 0-89216-065-9). Salvation Army.

Holzbauer, Beth. Love in Action. 1987. Instrs's., 128 pgs. pap. price not set (ISBN 0-87403-043-9, 39968); Student's, 112 pgs. pap. price not set (ISBN 0-87403-044-7, 39967). Standard Pub.

Holzman, Michael. Lukac's Road to God: The Early Criticism Against Its Pre-Marxist Background. (Current Continental Research Ser.: No. 208). 196p. (Orig.). 1985. lib. bdg. 25.00 (ISBN 0-8191-4719-2); pap. text ed. 11.25 (ISBN 0-8191-4720-6). U Pr of Amer.

Homan, Helen. By Post to the Apostles. facs. ed. LC 74-148219. (Biography Index Reprint Ser.). 1952. 20.00 (ISBN 0-8369-8066-2). Ayer Co Pubs.

--Letters to the Martyrs. facs. ed. LC 79-148220. (Biography Index Reprint Ser.). 1951. 20.00 (ISBN 0-8369-8067-0). Ayer Co Pubs.

Homan, Roger, compiled by. The Sociology of Religion: A Bibliographical Survey. LC 86-18471. (Bibliographies & Indexes in Religious Studies: No. 9). 309p. 1986. lib. bdg. 45.00 (ISBN 0-313-24710-2, HOS/). Greenwood.

Homan, Walter J. Children & Quakerism. LC 70-169387. (Family in America Ser). 180p. 1972. Repr. of 1939 ed. 14.00 (ISBN 0-405-03864-X). Ayer Co Pubs.

Homans, Peter. Theology After Freud: An Interpretive Inquiry. LC 76-84162. 1970. 29.50x (ISBN 0-672-51245-9); pap. text ed. 16.95x (ISBN 0-8290-1399-7). Irvington.

Homans, Peter, ed. Dialogue Between Theology & Psychology. LC 68-16698. (Essays in Divinity Ser: Vol. 3). 1968. 25.00x (ISBN 0-226-35110-6). U of Chicago Pr.

Homburg, Arthur. A New Wedding Service For You. 1985. 5.95 (ISBN 0-89536-731-9, 5815). CSS of Ohio.

Homer. Odysseus & the Giants. Richardson, I. M., adapted by. LC 83-14233. (Tales from the Odyssey Ser.). (Illus.). 32p. 1984. PLB 9.79 (ISBN 0-8167-0009-5); pap. text ed. 2.50 (ISBN 0-8167-0010-9). Troll Assocs.

Homer, F., jt. auth. see Curtiss, Harriete.

Homer, F., jt. auth. see Curtiss, Harriette.

Honan, Park. Matthew Arnold: A Life. LC 80-26131. (Illus.). 544p. 1981. 19.95 (ISBN 0-07-029697-9). McGraw.

Hone, William. Ancient Mysteries Described. LC 67-23905. (Illus.). 1969. Repr. of 1823 ed. 35.00x (ISBN 0-8103-3444-5). Gale.

--Ancient Mysteries Described. 59.95 (ISBN 0-8490-1426-3). Gordon Pr.

Honea, Charla, compiled by. Family Rituals. LC 81-52861. (Illus., Orig.). 1981. pap. 3.95x (ISBN 0-8358-0433-X). Upper Room.

Honer, Stanley M. & Hunt, Thomas C. Invitation to Philosophy: Issues & Options. 4th ed. 272p. 1981. pap. text ed. write for info. (ISBN 0-534-00997-2). Wadsworth Pub.

Honeycutt, Roy L., Jr. Layman's Bible Book Commentary: Leviticus, Numbers, Deuteronomy, Vol. 3. LC 78-73278. 1979. 5.95 (ISBN 0-8054-1173-9). Broadman.

Hong, Christopher C. To Whom the Land of Palestine Belongs. 1979. 6.50 (ISBN 0-682-49161-6). Exposition Pr FL.

Hong, Edna. Bright Valley of Love. LC 75-22723. 160p. 1985. pap. 3.95 (ISBN 0-8066-1700-4, 10-0911). Augsburg.

--The Downward Ascent. LC 78-66942. 1979. pap. 5.95 (ISBN 0-8066-1679-2, 10-1955). Augsburg.

--Forgiveness Is a Work As Well As a Grace. LC 84-6470. 128p. (Orig.). 1984. pap. 5.95 (ISBN 0-8066-2081-1, 10-2356). Augsburg.

--The Way of the Sacred Tree. LC 82-72643. 192p. 1983. pap. 10.95 (ISBN 0-8066-1949-X, 10-6958). Augsburg.

Hong, Edna H., ed. see Kierkegaard, Soren.

Hong, Edna H., tr. see Kierkegaard, Soren.

Hong, Edna H., tr. see Malantschuk, Gregor.

Hong, Howard V., ed. see Kierkegaard, Soren.

Hong, Howard V., tr. see Kierkegaard, Soren.

Hong, Howard V., tr. see Malantschuk, Gregor.

Honko, Lauro, ed. Science of Religion, Studies in Methodology. (Religion & Reason Ser.). 1979. text ed. 50.50x (ISBN 90-279-7854-9). Mouton.

Honnald, Annamarie. Divine Therapy: Pearls of Wisdom from the Bahai Writings. 1986. 14.95 (ISBN 0-85398-236-8); pap. 6.95 (ISBN 0-85398-237-6). G Ronald Pub.

Honnold, Annamarie. Vignettes from the Life of Abdu'l-Baha. (Illus.). 224p. pap. 8.95 (ISBN 0-85398-129-9). G Ronald Pub.

Honor, Leo L. Sennacherib's Invasion of Palestine. LC 26-20926. (Columbia University. Contributions to Oriental History & Philology: No. 12). Repr. of 1926 ed. 15.00 (ISBN 0-404-50542-2). AMS Pr.

Honors, Mildred O. One Thousand Bible Questions in Rhymes, Puzzles, Quizzes & Games. (Quiz & Puzzle Bks.). pap. 2.95 (ISBN 0-8010-4136-8). Baker Bk.

Hood, Abdul Latif Al. Islam: Religions of the World Ser. (Illus.). 48p. 1987. lib. bdg. 11.40 (ISBN 0-531-18063-8, Pub. by Bookwright Pr). Watts.

Hood, Christobel M. The Book of Robert Southwell: Priest, Poet, Prisoner. LC 72-13696. 1972. Repr. of 1926 ed. lib. bdg. 30.00 (ISBN 0-8414-1290-1). Folcroft.

Hood, Fred J. Reformed America: The Middle & Southern States, Seventeen Eighty-Three to Eighteen Thirty-Seven. LC 79-28834. 304p. 1980. 21.50 (ISBN 0-8173-0034-1). U of Ala Pr.

Hood, George. History of Music in New England, with Biographical Sketches of Reformers & Psalmists. (American Studies). 1970. Repr. of 1846 ed. 24.00 (ISBN 0-384-24140-9). Johnson Repr.

Hood, John C. Icelandic Church Saga. LC 79-8720. (Illus.). xii, 241p. 1981. Repr. of 1946 ed. lib. bdg. 27.50x (ISBN 0-313-22194-4, HOIC). Greenwood.

Hood, Robert E. Contemporary Political Orders & Christ: Karl Barth's Christology & Political Praxis. (Pittsburgh Theological Monographs, New Ser.: 14). (Orig.). 1985. pap. 19.90 (ISBN 0-915138-56-5). Pickwick.

Hoofien, Sigfried. Report of Mr. S. Hoofien to the Joint Distribution Committee of the American Funds for Jewish War Sufferers,New York. Davis, Moshe, ed. LC 77-70702. (America & the Holy Land Ser.). (Illus.). 1977. Repr. of 1918 ed. lib. bdg. 17.00x (ISBN 0-405-10254-2). Ayer Co Pubs.

Hooft, W. A. & Oldham, J. H. The Church & Its Function in Society. 1977. lib. bdg. 59.95 (ISBN 0-8490-1625-8). Gordon Pr.

Hook, jt. auth. see Hayes.

Hook, Diane F. The I Ching & You. 160p. 1985. pap. 8.95 (ISBN 0-7100-8042-5). Methuen Inc.

Hook, Frances, jt. auth. see Hook, Richard.

Hook, Frances, illus. Frances Hook Picture Book. Hayes, Wanda. (Illus.). 1963. 7.95 (ISBN 0-87239-243-0, 2868). Standard Pub.

Hook, John E. Van see Van Hook, John E.

Hook, Martha. Letter of Unity: A Woman's Workshop on Ephesians. (Woman's Workshop Ser.). 1987. Leader's Guide, 80p. pap. 4.95 (ISBN 0-310-26181-3); Student's Guide, 64p. pap. 3.95 (ISBN 0-310-26191-0). Zondervan.

--A Woman's Workshop on Faith. (A Woman's Workshop Ser.). 1977. leaders 3.95 (ISBN 0-310-26231-3, 11681P); students 2.95 (ISBN 0-310-26241-0, 11682P). Zondervan.

Hook, Richard & Hook, Frances. Jesus: El Amigo De los Ninos. Tr. of Jesus, the Friend of Children. (Illus.). 112p. 1981. 19.50 (ISBN 0-311-38552-4, Edit Mundo); pap. 14.95 (ISBN 0-311-38553-2). Casa Bautista.

Hook, Sidney. Religion in a Free Society. LC 67-11242. xii, 120p. 1967. 10.95x (ISBN 0-8032-0077-3). U of Nebr Pr.

Hooke, Beatrice E., tr. see Parrot, Andre.

Hooke, S. H. The Origins of Early Semitic Ritual. (British Academy, London, Schweich Lectures on Biblical Archeology Series, 1935). pap. 19.00 (ISBN 0-8115-1277-0). Kraus Repr.

Hooke, S. H., tr. see Lods, Adolphe.

Hooke, Samuel H. In the Beginning. LC 78-10638. (The Clarendon Bible Old Testament Ser.: Vol. VI). (Illus.). 1979. Repr. of 1947 ed. lib. bdg. 22.50x (ISBN 0-313-21014-4, HOIB). Greenwood.

--Middle Eastern Mythology. (Orig.). 1963. pap. 5.95 (ISBN 0-14-020546-2, Pelican). Penguin.

Hooker, Douglas. The Healthy Personality & the Christian Life. 1977. 10.95 (ISBN 0-8158-0351-6). Chris Mass.

Hooker, M. B., ed. Islam in South East Asia. 272p. 1983. text ed. 39.95x (ISBN 0-686-46644-6, Pub. by EJ Brill Holland). Humanities.

Hooker, Morna. A Preface to Paul. 1980. pap. 4.95 (ISBN 0-19-520188-4). Oxford U Pr.

--The Son of Man in Mark: A Study of the Background of the Term "Son of Man" & Its Use in St. Mark's Gospel. LC 67-4912. pap. 60.00 (ISBN 0-317-26028-6, 2023832). Bks Demand UMI.

Hooker, Morna D. The Son of Man in Mark. 1967. 12.50 (ISBN 0-7735-0049-9). McGill-Queens U Pr.

--Studying the New Testament. LC 82-70959. 224p. (Orig.). 1982. pap. 10.95 (ISBN 0-8066-1934-1, 10-6140). Augsburg.

Hooker, Richard. The Answer of Mr. R. Hooker, to a Supplication to the Privie Counsell. LC 76-57390. (English Experience Ser.: No. 807). 1977. Repr. of 1612 ed. lib. bdg. 5.00 (ISBN 90-221-0807-4). Walter J Johnson.

--Ecclesiastical Polity, Bk. 8. LC 77-170046. Repr. of 1931 ed. 24.00 (ISBN 0-404-03329-6). AMS Pr.

--Of the Lawes of Ecclesiasticall Politie, 2 pts. LC 76-171765. (English Experience Ser.: No. 390). 500p. 1971. Repr. of 1594 ed. 46.00 (ISBN 90-221-0390-0). Walter J Johnson.

--Of the Laws of Ecclesiastical Polity, Bks. VI-VIII. Stanwood, P. G., ed. LC 76-24883. (Folger Library Edition of the Works of Richard Hooker). 1980. text ed. 65.00x (ISBN 0-674-63210-9, Belknap). Harvard U Pr.

--Of the Laws of Ecclesiastical Polity: Preface & Books I-V, 2 vols. Hill, W. Speed, ed. (Folger Library Edition of the Works of Richard Hooker). 1977. Set. 85.00x (ISBN 0-674-63205-2, Belknap Pr). Harvard U Pr.

--Two Sermons Upon S. Judes Epistle. LC 70-26033. (English Experience Ser.: No. 195). 56p. 1969. Repr. of 1614 ed. 8.00 (ISBN 90-221-0195-9). Walter J Johnson.

--Works of That Learned & Judicious Divine Mr. Richard Hooker with an Account of His Life & Death by Isaac Walton, 3 vols. 7th ed. LC 76-125020. (Research & Source Works Ser.: No. 546). 1970. Repr. of 1888 ed. 103.00 (ISBN 0-8337-1731-6). B Franklin.

Hooker, Richard, jt. ed. see Booty, John E.

Hooker, Richard J., ed. see Woodmason, Charles.

Hooker, Thomas. Application of Redemption, by the Effectual Work of the Word, & the Spirit of Christ, for the Bringing Home of Lost Sinners to God. LC 70-141111. (Research Library of Colonial Americana). 1972. Repr. of 1657 ed. 37.50 (ISBN 0-405-03324-9). Ayer Co Pubs.

--Christian's Two Chief Lessons, Viz. Selfe Deniall, & Selfe Tryall. LC 74-14112. (Research Library of Colonial Americana). 1972. Repr. of 1640 ed. 34.50 (ISBN 0-405-03325-7). Ayer Co Pubs.

--Redemption: Three Sermons, 1637-1656. LC 56-9145. 1977. Repr. 30.00x (ISBN 0-8201-1234-8). Schol Facsimiles.

--The Soules Exaltation. LC 78-298. (American Puritan Writings Ser.: No. 18). Repr. of 1638 ed. 67.50 (ISBN 0-404-60818-3). AMS Pr.

--The Soules Humiliation. LC 78-293. (American Puritan Writings Ser.: No. 16). 232p. Repr. of 1640 ed. 67.50 (ISBN 0-404-60816-7). AMS Pr.

--The Soules Implantation. LC 78-297. (American Puritan Writings Ser.: No. 17). 328p. Repr. of 1640 ed. 57.50 (ISBN 0-404-60817-5). AMS Pr.

--The Soules Preparation for Christ: Or, a Treatise of Contrition. LC 78-291. (American Puritan Writings Ser.). (Illus.). 256p. 1981. Repr. of 1638 ed. 67.50 (ISBN 0-404-60815-9). AMS Pr.

--Survey of the Summe of Church-Discipline Wherein the Way of the Congregational Churches of Christ in New England Is Warranted & Cleared, by Scripture & Argument. LC 78-141113. (Research Library of Colonial Americana). 1971. Repr. of 1648 ed. 40.00 (ISBN 0-405-03326-5). Ayer Co Pubs.

Hooks, Margaret Anne. God Cares for Timothy. 1982. 6.95 (ISBN 0-686-36253-5). Rod & Staff.

Hoonacker, A. Van. Une Communaute Judeo-Arameenne a Elephantine en Egypte aux VI et V Siecles avant Jesus-Christ. (British Academy, London, Schweich Lectures on Biblical Archaeology Series, 1914). pap. 19.00 (ISBN 0-8115-1256-8). Kraus Repr.

Hooper, Jerry L., ed. see Holman Bible Publishers.

Hooper, John. The Early Writings of John Hooper. 1843. 51.00 (ISBN 0-384-24210-3). Johnson Repr.

--The Later Writings of Bishop Hooper. 1852. 55.00 (ISBN 0-384-24211-1). Johnson Repr.

Hooper, Sr. M. Rachel & Buytaert, Eligius M., eds. Petrus Thomae, O. F. M. Quodlibet. (Text Ser). 1957. 10.00 (ISBN 0-686-11556-2). Franciscan Inst.

Hooper, Robert E. A Call to Remember. 1978. pap. 5.00 (ISBN 0-89225-183-2). Gospel Advocate.

Hooper, Walter. Through Joy & Beyond: A Pictorial Biography of C. S. Lewis. LC 82-9884. 192p. 1982. 15.75 (ISBN 0-02-553670-2). Macmillan.

Hooper, Walter, jt. auth. see Green, Roger L.

Hooper, Walter, ed. see Lewis, C. S.

Hoose, Bernard, tr. see Fuchs, Josef.

Hooton, E. A., ed. see Reisner, G. A.

Hoover, Arlie J. Fallacies of Unbelief. LC 75-36313. (Way of Life Ser: No. 128). 94p. 1976. pap. 3.95 (ISBN 0-89112-128-5, Bibl Res Pr). Abilene Christ U.

--Ideas & Their Consequences. LC 76-3176. (Way of Life Ser: No. 129). 1976. pap. 3.95 (ISBN 0-89112-129-3, Bibl Res Pr). Abilene Christ U.

Hoover, Dwight W. Henry James, Sr. & the Religion of the Community. LC 68-57113. pap. 38.00 (ISBN 0-317-08994-3, 2012947). Bks Demand UMI.

Hoover, James. Mark. (Lifebuilder Bible Studies). 96p. (Orig.). 1985. pap. text ed. 2.95 (ISBN 0-8308-1004-8). Inter-Varsity.

Hoover, Janet, jt. auth. see Hanna, Barbara.

Hoover, Mab G. God Even Likes My Pantry: Devotions for Dieters. 128p. 1983. pap. 3.95 (ISBN 0-310-47012-9, 11269P). Zondervan.

--God Still Loves My Kitchen. 208p. (Orig.). 1981. pap. 3.95 (ISBN 0-310-35622-9, 11271P). Zondervan.

--God Still Loves My Kitchen Best: Devotions for the Homemaker. 206p. (Orig.). 1977. pap. 3.95 (ISBN 0-310-35612-1, 11270P). Zondervan.

--In My Upstairs Room. 96p. (Orig.). 1982. pap. 2.95 (ISBN 0-310-35632-6, 11272P). Zondervan.

--Lord, Please Zip Up My Armor. 112p. 1986. pap. 3.95 (ISBN 0-310-35642-3). Zondervan.

Hoover, Robert L. & Costello, Julia G., eds. Excavations at Mission San Antonio, 1976-1978. (Monographs: No. XXVI). (Illus.). 221p. 1985. pap. 16.00 (ISBN 0-917956-48-6). UCLA Arch.

Hoover, Stewart M. The Electronic Giant: A Critique of the Telecommunications Revolution from a Christian Perspective. LC 81-6083. pap. 42.80 (2029383). Bks Demand UMI.

Hoover, Thomas. The Zen Experience. (Illus., Orig.). 1980. pap. 5.95 (ISBN 0-452-25315-2, Z5315, Plume). NAL.

Hope, Alexander. Are You Thinking of Becoming a Catholic? (Illus.). 90p. 1974. 47.35 (ISBN 0-913314-39-0). Am Classical Coll Pr.

Hope, Marjorie & Young, James. South African Churches in a Revolutionary Situation. LC 81-9584. 288p. (Orig.). 1981. pap. 9.95 (ISBN 0-88344-466-6). Orbis Bks.

Hope, Richard O. Racial Strife in the U. S. Military: Toward the Elimination of Discrimination. LC 79-65932. 144p. 1979. 35.95 (ISBN 0-03-046146-4). Praeger.

Hope, Robert C. Legendary Lore of the Holy Wells of England. LC 68-21775. (Illus.). 1968. Repr. of 1893 ed. 35.00x (ISBN 0-8103-3445-3). Gale.

Hope-Moncrieff, Ascott R. Classic Myth & Legend. LC 77-85616. 1977. Repr. of 1912 ed. lib. bdg. 45.00 (ISBN 0-89341-317-8). Longwood Pub Group.

Hopewell, James F. Congregation: Stories & Structures. Wheeler, Barbara G., ed. LC 86-45914. 240p. 1987. pap. 14.95 (ISBN 0-8006-1956-0). Fortress.

Hopewell, James F., et al. Ministry & Mission: Theological Reflections for the Life of the Church. Taylor, Barbara B., ed. 192p. (Orig.). 1985. pap. 9.95x (ISBN 0-935311-00-9). Post Horn Pr.

Hopfe, Lewis M. Religions of the World. 4th ed. 522p. 1987. pap. write for info. (ISBN 0-02-356930-1). Macmillan.

Hopfl, Harro. The Christian Polity of John Calvin. (Cambridge Studies in the History & Theory of Politics). 320p. 1985. pap. 14.95 (ISBN 0-521-31638-3). Cambridge U Pr.

Hopkin, C. Edward, tr. see Ellul, Jacques.

Hopkins, C. & Baur, P. V. Christian Church at Dura-Europos. (Illus.). 1934. pap. 39.50x (ISBN 0-686-50041-5). Elliots Bks.

Hopkins, C. Edward, tr. see Ellul, Jacques.

Hopkins, C. Howard. John R. Mott, Eighteen Sixty-Five to Nineteen Fifty-Five: A Biography. LC 79-15069. 22.50 (ISBN 0-8028-3525-2). Eerdmans.

Hopkins, C. Howard, jt. auth. see White, Ronald C., Jr.

Hopkins, Charles H. The Rise of the Social Gospel in American Protestantism, 1865-1895. LC 75-41141. (BCL Ser.: Vol. II). 368p. Repr. of 1940 ed. 30.00 (ISBN 0-404-14771-2). AMS Pr.

Hopkins, David C. The Highlands of Canaan: Agricultural Life in the Early Iron Age. (The Social World of Biblical Antiquity Ser.). 315p. 1985. text ed. 29.95x (ISBN 0-907459-38-2, Pub. by Almond Pr England); pap. text ed. 15.95 (ISBN 0-907459-39-0). Eisenbrauns.

Hopkins, E. Washburn. Epic Mythology. rev. ed. LC 76-75358. 1968. Repr. of 1915 ed. 18.00 (ISBN 0-8196-0228-0). Biblo.

--Epic Mythology. 1974. Repr. 14.00 (ISBN 0-8426-0560-6). Orient Bk Dist.

Hopkins, Edward W. The Religions of India. LC 77-94585. 1979. Repr. of 1895 ed. lib. bdg. 65.00 (ISBN 0-89341-312-7). Longwood Pub Group.

Hopkins, Emma C. For unto Us a Child Is Born. pap. 1.00 (ISBN 0-87516-322-X). De Vorss.

--High Mysticism. 368p. 1974. pap. 8.95 (ISBN 0-87516-198-7). De Vorss.

--Scientific Christian Mental Practice. 1974. pap. 7.95 (ISBN 0-87516-199-5). De Vorss.

Hopkins, Jasper. Anselm of Canterbury: Vol. IV, Hermeneutical & Textual Problems in the Complete Treatises of St. Anselm. LC 74-19840. 202p. 1976. 49.95x (ISBN 0-88946-551-7). E Mellen.

--A Companion to the Study of St. Anselm. LC 72-79097. 278p. 1972. 13.95x (ISBN 0-8166-0657-9). U of Minn Pr.

--A Concise Introduction to the Philosophy of Nicholas of Cusa. 3rd ed. LC 85-72432. xii, 194p. 1986. text ed. 20.00x (ISBN 0-938060-32-5). Banning Pr.

--A New Interpretive Translation of St. Anselm's Monologion & Proslogion. LC 86-70086. xiv, 188p. Date not set. text ed. 25.00x (ISBN 0-938060-33-3); pap. text ed. 10.00x (ISBN 0-938060-34-1). Banning Pr.

--Nicholas of Cusa on God as Not-other: A Translation & an Appraisal of De Li Non Aliud. 2nd ed. LC 82-73976. ix, 179p. 1983. text ed. 20.00x (ISBN 0-938060-26-0). Banning Pr.

--Nicholas of Cusa on God as Not-other: A Translation & an Appraisal of De li non aliud. LC 78-22006. pap. 46.30 (ISBN 0-317-39689-7, 2055880). Bks Demand UMI.

--Nicholas of Cusa on Learned Ignorance: A Translation & an Appraisal of De Docta Ignorantia. 2nd ed. LC 80-82907. ix, 205p. 1985. text ed. 23.00x (ISBN 0-938060-30-9); pap. text ed. 10.00x (ISBN 0-938060-27-9). Banning Pr.

--Nicholas of Cusa's Debate with John Wenck: A Translation & an Appraisal of De Ignota Litteratura & Apologia Doctae Ignorantiae. 2nd ed. LC 80-82908. viii, 119p. 1984. text ed. 23.00x (ISBN 0-938060-31-7). Banning Pr.

Hopkins, Jasper, ed. Anselm of Canterbury, 4 vols. Richardson, Herbert, tr. from Lat. LC 74-19840. 1919. Set. 149.95x (ISBN 0-88946-977-6). E Mellen.

Hopkins, Jasper, ed. see Anselm Of Canterbury.

Hopkins, Jasper, tr. see Anselm Of Canterbury.

Hopkins, Jeffery, ed. see Rinbochay, Khetsun S.

Hopkins, Jeffrey. Emptiness Yoga. LC 86-6484. 504p. 1987. 35.00 (ISBN 0-937938-36-X); pap. 19.95 (ISBN 0-937938-31-9). Snow Lion.

--Meditation on Emptiness. Napper, Elizabeth, ed. (Wisdom Advanced Book: Blue Ser.). (Illus.). 700p. 1983. 35.00 (ISBN 0-86171-014-2, Pub. by Wisdom Pubns). Great Traditions.

--The Tantric Distinction. Klein, Anne C., ed. (A Wisdom Intermediate Book, White Ser.). 184p. (Orig.). 1984. pap. 8.95 (ISBN 0-86171-023-1, Wisdom Pubns). Great Traditions.

Hopkins, Jeffrey & Klein, Ann. Compassion in Tibetan Buddhism. 2nd ed. Napper, Elizabeth, ed. LC 80-85453. 263p. 1980. pap. 10.95 (ISBN 0-937938-04-1). Snow Lion.

Hopkins, Jeffrey, jt. auth. see Rinbochay, Lati.

Hopkins, Jeffrey, jt. auth. see Sopa, Geshe Lhundup.

Hopkins, Jeffrey, ed. see Fourteenth Dalai Lama His Holiness Tenzin Gyatso.

Hopkins, Jeffrey, tr. see Rinbochay, Lati, et al.

Hopkins, Lee B., ed. Good Morning to You, Valentine. LC 75-11650. (Illus.). 32p. 1976. 11.95 (ISBN 0-15-232134-9, HJ). HarBraceJ.

Hopkins, Mark. The Law of Love & Love As a Law: Or, Christian Ethics. 3rd ed. LC 75-3196. Repr. of 1871 ed. 42.50 (ISBN 0-404-59197-3). AMS Pr.

--Lectures on Moral Science. LC 75-3197. Repr. of 1862 ed. 37.50 (ISBN 0-404-59198-1). AMS Pr.

Hopkins, Paul A. What Next in Mission? LC 77-21776. 122p. 1977. pap. 3.95 (ISBN 0-664-24143-3). Westminster.

Hopkins, Quincie, ed. see Carlson, George A.

Hopkins, Quincie, ed. see Waldrum, Harold J.

Hopkins, Samuel. A Treatise on the Millennium. LC 70-38450. (Religion in America, Series 2). 162p. 1972. Repr. of 1793 ed. 14.00 (ISBN 0-405-04070-9). Ayer Co Pubs.

Hopkins, Vivian C. Spires of Forms: A Study of Emerson's Aesthetic Theory. LC 80-2537. Repr. of 1951 ed. 33.50 (ISBN 0-404-19263-7). AMS Pr.

Hopkinson, Arthur W. Mysticism: Old & New. LC 77-118528. 1971. Repr. of 1946 ed. 21.50x (ISBN 0-8046-1151-3, Pub. by Kennikat). Assoc Faculty Pr.

Hopkinson, Dorothy, jt. auth. see Hopkinson, Tom.

Hopkinson, Tom & Hopkinson, Dorothy. Much Silence: The Life & Work of Meher Baba. 3rd ed. LC 74-26821. 232p. 1982. pap. 4.95 (ISBN 0-913078-53-0, Pub. by Meher Foun Australia). Sheriar Pr.

Hopko, T., et al. God & Charity: Images of Eastern Orthodox Theology, Spirituality & Practice. Costa, Francis D., ed. LC 79-3027. (Pan-Am Books). 103p. (Orig.). 1979. pap. text ed. 3.95 (ISBN 0-916586-34-0). Holy Cross Orthodox.

Hopko, Thomas. All the Fulness of God: Essays on Orthodoxy, Ecumenism & Modern Society. LC 82-5454. 188p. (Orig.). 1982. pap. 7.95 (ISBN 0-913836-96-6). St Vladimirs.

--The Lenten Spring. LC 83-4278. 229p. 1983. pap. text ed. 5.95 (ISBN 0-88141-014-4). St Vladimirs.

--Winter Pascha. LC 84-27622. 1983. pap. text ed. 6.95 (ISBN 0-88141-025-X). St Vladimirs.

Hopko, Thomas, ed. see Ware, Kallistos & Barrois, Georges.

Hopler, Thom. A World of Difference: Following Christ Beyond Your Cultural Walls. LC 81-57818. 192p. (Orig.). 1981. pap. 7.95 (ISBN 0-87784-747-9); pap. 1.95 study guide (ISBN 0-87784-802-5). Inter-Varsity.

Hopp, Ken. Lawyer Looks at Judgement. (Anchor Ser.). 1984. 5.95 (ISBN 0-8163-0557-9). Pacific Pr Pub Assn.

Hopp, Kenneth H. Christianity Makes Sense. (Lifline Ser.). 80p. 1983. pap. 5.95 (ISBN 0-8163-0522-6). Pacific Pr Pub Assn.

Hoppe, Leslie. Being Poor: A Biblical Study. (Theology & Life Ser.). 240p. 1987. pap. 9.95 (ISBN 0-89453-620-6). M Glazier.

--Joshua, Judges, with Excursus on Charismatic Leadership in Israel. (Old Testament Message Ser.: Vol. 5). 1982. text ed. 12.95 (ISBN 0-89453-405-X); pap. 8.95 (ISBN 0-89453-240-5). M Glazier.

Hoppe, Leslie J. Deuteronomy. (Bible Commentary Ser.). 104p. 1985. pap. 2.95 (ISBN 0-8146-1374-8). Liturgical Pr.

--What Are They Saying about Biblical Archaeology? LC 83-63110. (WATSA Ser.). 1984. pap. 4.95 (ISBN 0-8091-2613-3). Paulist Pr.

Hopper, Carol. Daughter of the Sanctuary. 111p. (Orig.). 1984. pap. 3.95 (ISBN 0-88144-022-1, CPS023). Christian Pub.

Hopper, Jeffery. Understanding Modern Theology I: Cultural Revolutions & New World. LC 86-45210. 192p. 1986. 14.95 (ISBN 0-8006-1929-3). Fortress.

Hopper, Vincent F. & Lahey, Gerald B., eds. Medieval Mysteries, Moralities & Interludes. LC 61-18362. 1962. pap. text ed. 5.95 (ISBN 0-8120-0135-4). Barron.

Hopwood, P. G. The Religious Experience of the Primitive Church Proir to the Influence of Paul. 1977. lib. bdg. 59.95 (ISBN 0-8490-2512-5). Gordon Pr.

Hora, Thomas. Can Meditation Be Done? (Discoures in Metapsychiatry Ser.). 33p. 1984. pap. 4.00 (ISBN 0-913105-09-0). PAGL Pr.

--Commentaries on the Scriptures. 35p. 1987. pap. 4.00 (ISBN 0-913105-10-4). PAGL Pr.

--Dialogues in Metapsychiatry. LC 77-8268. 238p. 16.00x (ISBN 0-913105-16-3). PAGL Pr.

--Forgiveness. (Discourses in Metapsychiatry Ser.). 48p. 1983. pap. 4.00 (ISBN 0-913105-05-8). PAGL Pr.

--God in Phychiatry. (Discoures in Metapsychistry Ser.). 35p. 1984. pap. 4.00 (ISBN 0-913105-06-6). PAGL Pr.
--Healing Through Spiritual Understanding. (Discourses in Metapsychiatry Ser.). 48p. (Orig.). 1983. pap. 4.00 (ISBN 0-913105-02-3). PAGL Pr.
--A Hierarchy of Values. (Discourses in Metapsychiatry Ser.). 48p. (Orig.). 1983. pap. 4.00 (ISBN 0-913105-03-1). PAGL Pr.
--Right Usefulness. 35p. 1987. pap. 4.00 (ISBN 0-913105-12-0). PAGL Pr.
--The Soundless Music of Life. (Discourses in Metapsychiatry Ser.). 48p. 1983. pap. 3.95 (ISBN 0-913105-04-X). PAGL Pr.
--What God Wants. 35p. 1987. pap. 4.00 (ISBN 0-913105-11-2). PAGL Pr.
Horbury, W. & McNeil, B., eds. Suffering & Martyrdom in the New Testament. LC 80-40706. 240p. 1981. 49.50 (ISBN 0-521-23482-4). Cambridge U Pr.
Horcasitas, Fernando, tr. see Duran, Fr. Diego.
Horden, William. Experience & Faith. LC 82-72653. 160p. 1983. pap. 9.95 (ISBN 0-8066-1960-0, 10-2133). Augsburg.
Horder, W. G. Treasury of American Sacred Song. facs. ed. LC 74-76944. (Granger Index Reprint Ser). 1896. 18.00 (ISBN 0-8369-6019-X). Ayer Co Pubs.
Hordern, William. Introduction. (New Directions in Theology Today: Vol. 1). 168p. 1966. pap. 4.95 (ISBN 0-664-24706-7). Westminster.
--Living by Grace. LC 75-6548. 208p. 1975. pap. 7.95 (ISBN 0-664-24763-6). Westminster.
Hordern, William E. Layman's Guide to Protestant Theology. rev. ed. 1968. pap. 5.95 (ISBN 0-02-085470-6, Collier). Macmillan.
Hordern, William E., jt. auth. see Bruner, Frederick D.
Hore, Edward C. Missionary to Tanganyika: 1877-1888. Wolf, James B., ed. 200p. 1971. 28.50x (ISBN 0-7146-2605-8, F Cass Co). Biblio Dist.
Hore-Lacy, Ian. Creating Common Wealth. 103p. (Orig.). 1985. pap. 4.95 (ISBN 0-86760-024-1, Pub. by Albatross Bks). ANZ Religious Pubns.
Horey, Adrian. The Catholic Subjects of Elizabeth I. LC 78-312404. pap. 60.00 (ISBN 0-317-20042-9, 2023264). Bks Demand UMI.
Horgan, Edward R. The Shaker Holy Land: A Community Portrait. LC 81-20214. (Illus.). 272p. 1982. 15.95 (ISBN 0-916782-22-0). Harvard Common Pr.
Horgan, Paul. Memories of the Future. 216p. 1966. 4.95 (ISBN 0-374-20756-9). FS&G.
--Under the Sangre de Cristo. (Charlotte Ser.). 90p. 1985. 150.00x (ISBN 0-911292-00-4). Rydal.
Hori, Ichiro. Folk Religion in Japan: Continuity & Change. Kitagawa, Joseph M. & Miller, Alan L., eds. LC 67-30128. (Midway Reprint Ser.). xvi, 278p. 1983. pap. text ed. 15.00x (ISBN 0-226-35335-4). U of Chicago Pr.
Horigan, James E. Chance or Design? LC 79-83605. 242p. 1979. 13.95 (ISBN 0-8022-2238-2). Philos Lib.
Horioka, Chimyo, jt. auth. see Holmes, Stewart W.
Horkheimer, Max. Eclipse of Reason. LC 73-17887. 1973. pap. 12.95x (ISBN 0-8264-0009-4, Continuum). Continuum.
Horkheimer, Max & Adorno, Theodor W. Dialectic of Enlightenment. Cumming, John, tr. from Ger. LC 77-167870. 1975. pap. 9.95x (ISBN 0-8264-0093-0, Continuum). Continuum.
Hormann, Elizabeth. After the Adoption. 1987. 8.95. Revell.
Horn, Bill Van see Van Horn, Bill.
Horn, Dorothy D. Sing to Me of Heaven: A Study of Folk & Early American Materials in Three Old Harp Books. LC 74-99212. (Illus.). 1970. 10.00 (ISBN 0-8130-0293-1). U Presses Fla.
Horn, Dorothy D., et al, eds. see Swan, M. L.
Horn, Geoffrey, illus. Bible Studies for Children. Cavanaugh, Arthur. LC 79-27811. (Illus.). 336p. 1980. 12.95 (ISBN 0-02-554060-2). Macmillan.
Horn, Merritt C. The Call of the Spirit. 82p. (Orig.). 1984. pap. 5.95 (ISBN 0-932661-00-9). Archangel Pub.
Horn, Siegfried. Promise Deferred. Wheeler, Gerald, ed. 96p. 1987. pap. price not set (ISBN 0-8280-0380-7). Review & Herald.
Horn, Siegfried H., jt. auth. see Boraas, Roger S.
Hornaday, William H. & Ware, Harlan. Your Aladdin's Lamp. 288p. 1979. pap. 8.50 (ISBN 0-911336-75-3). Sci of Mind.
Hornaday, William H., jt. auth. see Holmes, Ernest.
Hornak, Angelo, jt. auth. see Keates, Jonathan.
Hornblower, Jane. Hieronymus of Cardia. (Classical & Philosophical Monographs). 1981. text ed. 52.00x (ISBN 0-19-814717-1). Oxford U Pr.
Hornbrook, John & Bakker, Dorothy F. The Miracle of Touching. Keith, Bill, ed. 160p. (Orig.). 1985. pap. 5.95 (ISBN 0-910311-28-5). Huntington Hse Inc.
Horne, Charles. Doctrine of Salvation. 1984. pap. 5.95 (ISBN 0-8024-0424-3). Moody.
Horne, Chevis F. Dynamic Preaching. LC 82-70871. (Orig.). 1983. pap. 6.95 (ISBN 0-8054-2110-6). Broadman.
--Preaching the Great Themes of the Bible. (Orig.). 1986. pap. 7.95 (ISBN 0-8054-2262-5). Broadman.
Horne, Herman H. Essentials of Leadership & Other Papers in Moral & Religious Education. LC 76-117808. (Essay Index Reprint Ser). 1931. 14.00 (ISBN 0-8369-1660-3). Ayer Co Pubs.
--Teaching Techniques of Jesus. LC 64-16634. 224p. 1971. pap. 5.95 (ISBN 0-8254-2804-1). Kregel.
Horne, James. The Moral Mystic. 144p. 1983. pap. text ed. 9.25x (ISBN 0-88920-149-8, Pub. by Wilfrid Lauries Canada). Humanities.
Horne, James R. Beyond Mysticism. 158p. 1978. pap. text ed. 9.25x (ISBN 0-919812-08-2, Pub. by Wilfred Laurier Canada). Humanities.
Horne, John C. van see Van Horne, John C.
Horner, I. B. Women under Primitive Buddhism. 1975. Repr. 12.50 (ISBN 0-8426-0955-5). Orient Bk Dist.
Horner, I. B., jt. auth. see Coomaraswamy, Ananda K.
Horner, Ralph C. From the Altar to the Upper Room. Dayton, Donald W., ed. (The Higher Christian Life Ser.). 301p. 1985. 40.00 (ISBN 0-8240-6423-2). Garland Pub.
Horner, Thomas M., tr. see Gunkel, Hermann.
Horner, Tom. Homosexuality & the Judeo-Christian Tradition: An Annotated Bibliography. LC 81-889. (ATLA Bibliography Ser.: No. 5). 141p. 1981. 16.50 (ISBN 0-8108-1412-9). Scarecrow.
--Jonathan Loved David: Homosexuality in Biblical Times. LC 77-15628. 164p. 1978. pap. 8.95 (ISBN 0-664-24185-9). Westminster.
--Sex in the Bible. LC 73-87676. 1974. 8.50 (ISBN 0-8048-1124-5). C E Tuttle.
Horniman, R. The Living Buddha. LC 78-72441. Repr. of 1903 ed. 33.00 (ISBN 0-404-17307-1). AMS Pr.
Horning, Mary E. Evidences of Romantic Treatment of Religious Elements in Late Eighteenth Century Minor Poetry, 1771-1800. LC 72-3719. (English Literature Ser., No. 33). 1972. Repr. of 1932 ed. lib. bdg. 29.95x (ISBN 0-8383-1542-9). Haskell.
Hornsby, Sarah. Who I Am in Jesus. (Illus.). 160p. 1986. 8.95 (ISBN 0-8007-9087-1). Revell.
Hornsby-Smith, Michael P. Roman Catholics in England: Studies in Social Structure Since the Second World War. (Illus.). 288p. 1987. 29.50 (ISBN 0-521-30313-3). Cambridge U Pr.
Hornung, Clarence P. Old-Fashioned Christmas in Illustration & Decoration. (Orig.). 1970. pap. 5.00 (ISBN 0-486-22367-1). Dover.
Hornung, Clarence P., ed. An Old-Fashioned Christmas in Illustration & Decoration. (Illus.). 15.75 (ISBN 0-8446-0147-0). Peter Smith.
Hornung, Erik & Baines, John, trs. from Ger. Conceptions of God in Ancient Eygpt: The One & the Many. LC 82-71602. (Illus.). 296p. 1982. 29.95x (ISBN 0-8014-1223-4). Cornell U Pr.
Hornus, Jean-Michel. It Is Not Lawful for Me to Fight. LC 79-26846. (Christian Peace Shelf Ser.). 376p. 1980. pap. 15.95 (ISBN 0-8361-1911-8). Herald Pr.
Horodezky, Samuel A. Religiose Stromungen Judentum: Mit besondered Berucksichtigung des Chassidismus. Katz, Steven, ed. LC 79-7137. (Jewish Philosophy, Mysticism & History of Ideas Ser.). 1980. Repr. of 1920 ed. lib. bdg. 23.00x (ISBN 0-405-12263-2). Ayer Co Pubs.
Horosz, William & Clements, Tad, eds. Religion & Human Purpose. 1987. lib. bdg. 64.50 (ISBN 90-247-3000-7, Pub. by Martinus Nijhoff Netherlands). Kluwer Academic.
Horowitz, Aharon. The Quarternary of Israel. LC 78-8855. 1979. 45.00 (ISBN 0-12-356170-1). Acad Pr.
Horowitz, Dan & Lissak, Moshe. Origins of the Israeli Polity: Palestine Under the Mandate. Hoffman, Charles, tr. LC 78-3175. (Illus.). 320p. 1979. lib. bdg. 24.00x (ISBN 0-226-35366-4). U of Chicago Pr.
Horowitz, David. Pastor Charles Taze Russell. LC 85-20511. 159p. 1986. 15.95 (ISBN 0-8022-2503-9); pap. 9.95 (ISBN 0-8022-2504-7). Philos Lib.
--State in the Making. Meltzer, Julian, tr. from Hebrew. LC 81-6649. viii, 349p. 1981. Repr. of 1953 ed. lib. bdg. 28.75x (ISBN 0-313-23011-0, HOSI). Greenwood.
Horowitz, Edward. How the Hebrew Language Grew. rev. ed. 1967. pap. 9.95x (ISBN 0-87068-066-8). Ktav.
Horowitz, Franklin E. Sievers' Law & the Evidence of the Rigveda. LC 73-81807. (Janua Linguarum, Ser. Practica: No. 216). 74p. (Orig.). 1974. pap. text ed. 18.00x (ISBN 90-2792-706-5). Mouton.
Horowitz, George. The Spirit of Jewish Law. LC 53-7535. 1979. Repr. of 1953 ed. text ed. 40.00x (ISBN 0-87632-167-8). Bloch.
Horowitz, Irving L. Philosophy, Science & the Sociology of Knowledge. LC 76-27756. 1976. Repr. of 1961 ed. lib. bdg. 22.50x (ISBN 0-8371-9051-7, HOPS). Greenwood.
Horowitz, Irving L., ed. Science, Sin & Scholarship: The Politics of Reverend Moon & the Unification Church. 312p. 1978. pap. 7.95x (ISBN 0-262-58042-X). MIT Pr.
Horowitz, Michael, ed. see Huxley, Aldous.
Horowitz, Tamar R., ed. Between Two Worlds: Children from the Soviet Union in Israel. LC 86-11071. 240p. (Orig.). 1986. lib. bdg. 26.00 (ISBN 0-8191-5454-7); pap. text ed. 12.75 (ISBN 0-8191-5455-5). U Pr of Amer.
Horrell, Benjamin C. Broken Chains. 1972. pap. 2.95 (ISBN 0-87148-106-5). Pathway Pr.
Horsch, James E., jt. auth. see Crockett, Richard H.
Horsch, James E., jt. ed. see Crockett, Richard H.
Horsch, John. Hutterian Brethren. 189p. 1931. 9.95x (ISBN 0-8361-1188-5). Herald Pr.
--Hutterian Brethren, 1528-1931. 190p. 1931. 7.00 (ISBN 0-317-47168-6). Plough.
--Mennonites in Europe. (Illus.). 414p. 1950. 12.95 (ISBN 0-8361-1395-0). Herald Pr.
--Principle of Non-Resistance As Held by the Mennonite Church. Bd. with Hutterian Brethren, Fifteen Twenty-Eight to Nineteen Thirty-One. Horsch, John. LC 74-147672. (Library of War & Peace; Relig. & Ethical Positions on War). lib. bdg. 46.00 (ISBN 0-8240-0430-2). Garland Pub.
Horsch, John, jt. auth. see Bender, Harold S.
Horsfield, Peter. Religious Television: The Experience in America. LC 83-11313. (Communication & Human Values Ser.). (Illus.). 192p. 1984. text ed. 15.00 (ISBN 0-582-28432-5). Longman.
Horsley, Richard A., jt. auth. see Hanson, John.
Horst, I. B. The Dutch Dissenters: A Critical Companion to Their History & Ideas with a Bibliographical Survey of Recent Research Pertaining to the Early Reformation in the Netherlands. (Kerhistorische Bijdragen Ser.: No. 13). vii, 233p. 1986. 39.25 (ISBN 90-04-07454-6, Pub. by E J Brill). Heinman.
Horst, Irvin B. A Bibliography of Menno Simons. 157p. 1962. 45.00x (ISBN 0-8361-1104-4). Herald Pr.
--The Radical Brethren. 216p. 1972. 30.00x (ISBN 0-8361-1193-1). Herald Pr.
Horst, John L., ed. Instructions to Beginners in the Christian Life. 121p. 1934. pap. 1.95 (ISBN 0-8361-1378-0). Herald Pr.
Horst, Samuel L. Mennonites in the Confederacy. LC 67-15991. 148p. 1967. 6.95 (ISBN 0-317-37856-2). Herald Pr.
--Mennonities in the Confederacy: A Study in Civil War Pacifism. LC 67-15991. (Illus.). 148p. 1967. 8.95x (ISBN 0-8361-1180-X). Herald Pr.
Horstman, C. Yorkshire Writers, Richard Rolle of Hampole, 2 vols. 1979. Repr. of 1895 ed. Set. lib. bdg. 400.00 (ISBN 0-8492-5264-4). R West.
Horstmann, C., ed. Prose Lives of Women Saints of Our Contrie of England. (EETS, OS Ser.: No.86). Repr. of 1886 ed. 45.00 (ISBN 0-527-00082-5). Kraus Repr.
Horstmann, C., ed. see Bradshaw, H.
Horstmann, Carl, ed. see Capgrave, John.
Horstmann, Rolf-Peter, et al, eds. Transcendental Arguments & Science. (Synthese Library: No. 133). 1979. lib. bdg. 34.00 (ISBN 90-277-0963-7, Pub. by Reidel Holland); pap. 16.00 (ISBN 90-277-0964-5). Kluwer Academic.
Hort, A. F., jt. auth. see Hort, F. J.
Hort, Erasmus. The Bible Book: Resources for Reading the New Testament. 172p. 1983. pap. 12.95x (ISBN 0-8245-0557-3). Crossroad NY.
Hort, F. J. & Hort, A. F. Expository & Exegetical Studies. 1980. 29.50 (ISBN 0-86524-021-3, 7103). Klock & Klock.
Hort, Greta. Piers Plowman & Contemporary Religious Thought. LC 72-193685. lib. bdg. 15.00 (ISBN 0-8414-5129-X). Folcroft.
--Piers Plowman & Contemporary Religious Thought. (Church Historical Society, London, New Ser.: No. 29). Repr. of 1938 ed. 40.00 (ISBN 0-8115-3153-8). Kraus Repr.
Hort, Greta, tr. see Buber, Martin.
Horton, jt. auth. see Byrd.
Horton, Douglas, tr. see Barth, Karl.
Horton, F. L. The Melchizedek Tradition. LC 75-32479. (Society for New Testament Studies Monographs: No. 30). 220p. 1976. 42.50 (ISBN 0-521-21014-3). Cambridge U Pr.
Horton, Harold. The Gifts of the Spirit. 208p. 1975. pap. 2.50 (ISBN 0-88243-504-3, 02-0504, Radiant Bks). Gospel Pub.
Horton, Isabelle. High Adventure: Life of Lucy Rider Meyer. Gifford, Carolyn & Dayton, Donald, eds. (Women in American Protestant Religion 1800-1930 Ser.). 359p. 1987. lib. bdg. 50.00 (ISBN 0-8240-0665-8). Garland Pub.
Horton, Marilee. Free to Stay Home. 177p. 1984. pap. text ed. 5.95 (ISBN 0-8499-3011-1, 3011-1). Word Bks.
Horton, Michael S. Mission Accomplished: What Today's Christian Must Know About God & Salvation. 192p. 1985. pap. 6.95 (ISBN 0-8407-5947-9). Nelson.
Horton, Robin, jt. auth. see Fortes, Meyer.
Horton, Stanley M. The Book of Acts: A Radiant Commentary on the New Testament. LC 80-65892. 304p. (Orig.). 1981. 10.95 (ISBN 0-88243-317-2, 02-0317). Gospel Pub.
--It's Getting Late. LC 74-33869. 1975. pap. 1.25 (ISBN 0-88243-570-1, 02-0570). Gospel Pub.
--Tongues & Prophecy. (Charismatic Bks.). 32p. 1972. pap. 0.69 (ISBN 0-88243-917-0, 02-0917). Gospel Pub.
--Welcome Back Jesus. 1975. pap. 1.25 (ISBN 0-88243-629-5, 02-0629). Gospel Pub.
Horton, Wade H. Evangel Sermons. LC 76-57860. 1977. pap. 3.95 (ISBN 0-87148-287-8). Pathway Pr.
--Glossolalia Phenomenon. 1966. 7.95 (ISBN 0-87148-351-3). Pathway Pr.
--Pentecost Yesterday & Today. 1972. 7.25 (ISBN 0-87148-676-8). Pathway Pr.
--Sound Scriptual Sermon Outlines, No. 2. 1974. 7.25 (ISBN 0-87148-769-1); pap. 6.25 (ISBN 0-87148-770-5). Pathway Pr.
--Sound Scriptural Outlines, No. 3. 1977. 7.25 (ISBN 0-87148-781-0); pap. 6.25 (ISBN 0-87148-780-2). Pathway Pr.
--Sound Scriptural Sermon Outlines, No. 4. 1979. 7.95 (ISBN 0-87148-783-7); pap. 6.95 (ISBN 0-87148-784-5). Pathway Pr.
--Sound Scriptural Sermon Outlines, No. 5. (YA) 1982. text ed. 7.95 (ISBN 0-87148-799-3); pap. 6.95 (ISBN 0-87148-800-0). Pathway Pr.
--Sound Scriptural Sermon Outlines, No. 6. 1984. text ed. 7.95 (ISBN 0-87148-806-X); pap. text ed. 6.95 (ISBN 0-87148-807-8). Pathway Pr.
--Trinitarian Concept of God. 1964. pap. 1.95 (ISBN 0-87148-833-7). Pathway Pr.
Horton, Walter M. Contemporary Continental Theology: An Interpretation for Anglo-Saxons. 1979. Repr. of 1938 ed. lib. bdg. 30.00 (ISBN 0-8482-4497-4). Norwood Edns.
--Realistic Theology. 207p. 1982. Repr. of 1934 ed. lib. bdg. 30.00 (ISBN 0-89760-362-1). Telegraph Bks.
Horvath, David G., ed. Papers of the American Home Missionary Society, 1816 (1826-1894) 1936: A Guide to the Microfilm Edition. 94p. 1975. pap. 50.00 (ISBN 0-88455-994-7). Microfilming Corp.
Horvath, Tibor. Faith under Scrutiny. LC 75-1179. 343p. 1975. pap. text ed. 5.95 (ISBN 0-8190-0073-6). Loyola.
--Sacrificial Interpretation of Jesus' Achievement in the New Testament. 1980. 9.95 (ISBN 0-8022-2240-4). Philos Lib.
Horwitz, Robert H. Moral Foundations of the American Republic. 2nd ed. LC 79-20387. 275p. 1982. 15.00x (ISBN 0-8139-0853-1). U Pr of Va.
Horwitz, Robert H., ed. The Moral Foundations of the American Republic. 3rd ed. LC 85-17772. (Kenyon Public Affairs Conference Center Ser.). xii, 347p. 1986. 25.00x (ISBN 0-8139-1081-1); pap. 5.95x (ISBN 0-8139-1082-X). U Pr of Va.
Horwitz, Tem, jt. ed. see Kimmelman, Susan.
Hosain, S. Who Was Muhammad? pap. 3.50 (ISBN 0-686-18418-1). Kazi Pubns.
Hosansky, Tamar, jt. auth. see Colao, Flora.
Hoshor, John. God in a Rolls Royce. facsimile ed. LC 70-170698. (Black Heritage Library Collection). Repr. of 1936 ed. 15.00 (ISBN 0-8369-8888-4). Ayer Co Pubs.
Hosier, Helen K. Living Cameos. 192p. (Orig.). 1984. pap. 8.95 (ISBN 0-8007-1398-2). Revell.
Hoskins, Charles L. Black Episcopalians in Georgia: Strife, Struggle & Salvation. (Illus.). 168p. 1980. 8.00 (ISBN 0-686-31304-6). St Matthew's.
Hoskyns, Edwyn C., tr. see Barth, Karl.
Hosmer, Rachel. Gender & God: Love & Desire in Christian Spirituality. LC 86-8980. 142p. (Orig.). 1986. pap. 7.95 (ISBN 0-936384-39-5). Cowley Pubns.
Hosmer, Rachel & Jones, Alan. Living in the Spirit. (Church's Teaching Ser.: Vol. 7). 272p. 1979. 5.95 (ISBN 0-8164-0424-0, HarpR); pap. 4.95 (ISBN 0-8164-2220-6); pap. text ed. 1.50 (ISBN 0-8164-2227-3). Har-Row.
Hosmer, William. Slavery & the Church. facs. ed. LC 78-133156. (Black Heritage Library Collection Ser). 1853. 14.25 (ISBN 0-8369-8711-X). Ayer Co Pubs.
--Slavery & the Church. LC 70-82465. Repr. of 1853 ed. 22.50 (ISBN 0-8371-1646-5, HOS&). Greenwood.
Hospers, John. Human Conduct: Problems of Ethics. 2nd ed. 481p. 1982. pap. text ed. 15.95 (ISBN 0-15-540094-0, HC). HarBraceJ.

Hospital, Clifford G. Breakthrough: Insights of the Great Religious Discoverers. LC 85-5135. 208p. (Orig.). 1985. pap. 9.95 (ISBN 0-88344-206-X). Orbis Bks.

Hossain, Seyyed F. The Sufis of Today. (Sufi Research Ser.). 1981. pap. 4.95 (ISBN 0-86304-007-1, Pub. by Octagon Pr England). Ins Study Human.

Hoste, D. E. If I Am to Lead. 1968. pap. 0.90 (ISBN 0-85363-068-2). OMF Bks.

Hoster, Helen K. To Love Again: Remarriage for the Christian. (Orig.). 1985. pap. 8.95 (ISBN 0-687-42187-X). Abingdon.

Hosteter, John A. The Amish. (Illus.). 40p. 1982. pap. 1.95 (ISBN 0-8361-3317-X). Herald Pr.

Hostetler, Beulah S. American Mennonites & Protestant Movements. (Studies in Anabaptist & Mennonnite History). 344p. 1987. 29.95x (ISBN 0-8361-1288-1). Herald Pr.

Hostetler, Harold, jt. auth. see Cho, Paul Y.

Hostetler, John A. Amish Life. 2nd ed. LC 82-83964. (Illus.). 48p. (Orig.). 1983. pap. 4.95 (ISBN 0-8361-3326-9). Herald Pr.

--Amish Society. rev., 3rd ed. LC 79-23823. 432p. 1980. pap. 9.95 (ISBN 0-8018-2334-X). Johns Hopkins.

--Hutterite Life. 2nd ed. LC 82-83962. (Illus., Orig.). 1983. pap. 4.95 (ISBN 0-8361-3329-3). Herald Pr.

--Hutterite Society. LC 74-6827. (Illus.). 420p. 1974. 30.00x (ISBN 0-8018-1584-3). Johns Hopkins.

--An Invitation to Faith. 40p. (Orig.). 1957. pap. 1.00 (ISBN 0-8361-1381-0). Herald Pr.

--Mennonite Life. 2nd ed. LC 82-83963. (Illus.). 48p. 1983. pap. 4.95 (ISBN 0-8361-1995-9). Herald Pr.

Hostetler, John A. & Huntington, Gertrude E. Children in Amish Society: Socialization & Community Education. LC 72-157454. (Case Studies in Education & Culture). 1971. pap. text ed. 9.95 (ISBN 0-03-077750-X, HoltC). HR&W.

--The Hutterites in North America. LC 79-19718. 141p. 1980. pap. text ed. 9.95 (ISBN 0-03-045391-7, HoltC). HR&W.

Hostetler, Lester & Yoder, Walter E., eds. Mennonite Hymnal. LC 69-18131. 1969. 7.50x (ISBN 0-87303-515-1). Faith & Life.

Hostetler, Marian. Journey to Jerusalem. LC 77-19347. (Illus.). 128p. 1978. pap. 3.95 (ISBN 0-8361-1848-0). Herald Pr.

Hostetler, Michael J. Introducing the Sermon: The Art of Compelling Beginnings. 96p. 1986. pap. 5.95 (ISBN 0-310-30741-4, 10570P). Zondervan.

Hostetler, Paul, jt. auth. see Sider, E. Morris.

Hostetter, B. David. Psalms & Prayers for Congregational Participation: Series A. 1983. 7.75 (ISBN 0-89536-639-8, 1633). CSS of Ohio.

--Psalms & Prayers for Congregational Participation: Series B (Common Consensus Lectionary) 1984. 7.75 (ISBN 0-89536-694-0, 4871). CSS of Ohio.

--Psalms & Prayers for Congregational Participation: Series C (Common Consensus Lectionary) 1985. 7.75 (ISBN 0-89536-770-X, 5865). CSS of Ohio.

Hotchkiss, Burt. Have Miracles, Will Travel. 96p. 1982. pap. 4.95 (ISBN 0-8187-0047-5). Harlo Pr.

Hotchkiss, Robert V. A Pseudo-Epiphanius Testimony Book. LC 74-15203. (Society of Biblical Literature. Texts & Translation-Early Christian Literature Ser.). 1974. pap. 8.95 (060204). Scholars Pr GA.

Hotema, Hilton. Cosmic Science of the Ancient Masters. 2nd ed. 32p. 1960. pap. 8.95 (ISBN 0-88697-031-8). Life Science.

--Kingdom of Heaven. 45p. 1960. pap. 8.95 (ISBN 0-88697-030-X). Life Science.

--Secret of Regeneration. Orig. Title: The Science of Human Regeneration (Postgraduate Orthopathy) (Illus.). 900p. 1963. pap. 59.95 (ISBN 0-88697-019-9). Life Science.

Ho Ting-Jui. A Comparative Study of Myths & Legends of Formosan Aborigines. (Asian Folklore & Social Life Monograph: No. 18). 1972. 17.00 (ISBN 0-89986-020-6). Oriental Bk Store.

Houck, Fannie L. Proverbs Puzzle. 48p. 1986. pap. 2.50 (ISBN 0-87403-048-X, 2692). Standard Pub.

Houck, John, jt. ed. see Williams, Oliver.

Houck, John M., jt. auth. see Williams, Oliver F.

Houck, John W. & Williams, Oliver F., eds. Co-Creation & Capitalism: John Paul II's Laborem Exercens. 318p. (Orig.). 1983. lib. bdg. 30.75 (ISBN 0-8191-3358-2); pap. text ed. 12.50 (ISBN 0-8191-3359-0). U Pr of Amer.

Hough, Edith L. Sicily: The Fabulous Island. (Illus.). 1949. 4.00 (ISBN 0-8338-0027-2). M Jones.

Hough, Joseph C., Jr. Black Power & White Protestants: A Christian Response to the New Negro Pluralism. 1968. 18.95x (ISBN 0-19-501178-3). Oxford U Pr.

Hough, Joseph C., Jr. & Cobb, John B., Jr. Christian Identity & Theological Education. (Studies in Religious & Theological Scholarship). 1985. pap. 11.95 (ISBN 0-89130-855-5, 00-08-01). Scholars Pr GA.

Hough, Lindy, jt. ed. see Grossinger, Richard.

Houghton, S. M. Sketches from Church History. Murray, Iain, ed. (Illus.). 256p. (Orig.). 1981. pap. 12.45 (ISBN 0-85151-317-4). Banner of Truth.

Houghton, Walter E., Jr. Formation of Thomas Fuller's Holy & Profane States. (Harvard Studies in English: Vol. 19). 1969. Repr. of 1938 ed. 23.00 (ISBN 0-384-24390-8). Johnson Repr.

Houk, Neil B. Church Bytes Nineteen Eighty-Six. 74p. (Orig.). 1987. pap. 7.95 (ISBN 0-9615086-5-5). Church Bytes.

--Church Bytes Software Guide: For Church Administration & Finances. 110p. (Orig.). 1986. pap. 10.95 (ISBN 0-9615086-3-9). Church Bytes.

--Church Bytes: 1985. 60p. (Orig.). 1986. pap. 5.95 (ISBN 0-9615086-1-2). Church Bytes.

--Pastor Goode & His Marvelous Micro. 59p. (Orig.). 1984. pap. 5.95 (ISBN 0-9615086-0-4). Church Bytes.

Houlbrooke, Ralph. Church Courts & the People During the English Reformation Fifteen Twenty to Fifteen Seventy. (Oxford Historical Monographs). 1979. 36.00x (ISBN 0-19-821876-1). Oxford U Pr.

Houlden. Ethics & the New Testament. 1977. pap. 6.95 (ISBN 0-19-519958-8). Oxford U Pr.

Houlden, J. L. The Johannine Epistles. LC 74-4634. (New Testament Commentary Ser.). 176p. 1974. 10.95 (ISBN 0-06-064020-0, HarpR). Har-Row.

Houlden, J. L., ed. Paul's Letters from Prison: Philippians, Colossians, Philemon & Ephesians. LC 77-24028. (Westminster Pelican Commentaries). 358p. 1978. 11.50 (ISBN 0-664-21347-2); pap. 6.95 (ISBN 0-664-24182-4). Westminster.

Houle, Peter J. The English Morality & Related Drama: A Bibliographical Survey. LC 70-38714. xviii, 195p. 1972. 26.00 (ISBN 0-208-01264-8, Archon). Shoe String.

Houlgate, Stephen. Hegel, Nietzsche & the Criticism of Metaphysics. 304p. 1987. 39.50 (ISBN 0-521-32255-3). Cambridge U Pr.

Houmes, Lola H. Sword Drill Games Can Be Fun. 48p. pap. 2.95 (ISBN 0-87403-126-5, 2778). Standard Pub.

Hourani, Albert. Europe & the Middle East. LC 78-59452. 1980. 33.00x (ISBN 0-520-03742-1). U of Cal Pr.

Hourani, G. F. On the Harmony of Religion & Philosophy. 128p. 1976. 25.00x (ISBN 0-317-39133-X, Pub. by Luzac & Co Ltd). State Mutual Bk.

--Reason & Tradition in Islamic Ethics. 282p. 1985. 39.50 (ISBN 0-521-26712-9). Cambridge U Pr.

Hourani, George F., ed. Essays on Islamic Philosophy & Science. LC 74-13493. 1974. 49.50 (ISBN 0-87395-224-3). State U Ny Pr.

House, ed. see Trotsky, Leon, et al.

House, H. Wayne. Chronological & Background Charts of the New Testament. 160p. (Orig.). 1981. pap. 10.95 spiral bdg. (ISBN 0-310-41641-8, 11149P). Zondervan.

House, H. Wayne, jt. auth. see Fowler, Richard A.

Householder, Lloyd, jt. ed. see Hendrix, John.

Houselander, Caryll. Lift up Your Hearts. 1979. pap. 2.25 (ISBN 0-88479-020-7). Arena Lettres.

--The Reed of God. 128p. 1978. pap. 3.95 (ISBN 0-88479-013-4). Arena Lettres.

Houser, Schuyler O., jt. ed. see McNeill, William H.

Housley, Norman. The Avignon Papacy & the Crusades, Thirteen Five to Thirteen Seventy-Eight. 450p. 1986. 55.00x (ISBN 0-19-821957-1). Oxford U Pr.

--The Italian Crusade: The Papal-Angevin Alliance & the Crusades Against Christian Lay Powers, 1254-1343. (Illus.). 1982. 47.50x (ISBN 0-19-821925-3). Oxford U Pr.

Houston, James, ed. see Pascal.

Houston, James M. Motifs of Spirituality. Date not set. pap. cancelled (ISBN 0-88070-106-4). Multnomah.

Houston, James M., ed. see Baxter, Richard.

Houston, James M., ed. see Bernard of Clairvaux & William of St. Thierry.

Houston, James M., ed. see Edwards, Jonathan.

Houston, James M., ed. see Owen, John.

Houston, James M., ed. see St. Teresa of Avila.

Houston, James M., ed. see Simeon, Charles.

Houston, James M., ed. see Wilberforce, William.

Houston, John P. Demonic Imagination: Style & Theme in French Romantic Poetry. LC 69-15051. xi, 177p. 20.00x (ISBN 0-8071-0306-3). La State U Pr.

Houston, Victor. One Step Between Death & Me. (Illus.). 68p. (Orig.). 1986. pap. 9.95 (ISBN 1-55630-019-0). Brentwood Comm.

Houtart, Francois. Aspects Sociologiques du Catholicisme Americain: Vie Urbaine et Institutions Religieuses. 30.00 (ISBN 0-405-10835-4, 11841). Ayer Co Pubs.

--Sociology & Pastoral Work. pap. 1.50 (ISBN 0-8199-0133-4, L38828). Franciscan Herald.

Houtepen, Anton. People of God: A Plea for the Church. Bowden, John, tr. from Dutch. Orig. Title: Mensen Van God. 224p. (Orig.). 1985. pap. 10.95 (ISBN 0-88344-402-X). Orbis Bks.

Houtsma, Roger V. Understanding the Feasts of the Lord, God's Time Clock for the Ages. 195p. (Orig.). 1986. pap. 6.95 (ISBN 0-9617623-0-6). World Outreach.

Hovannisian, R., ed. Ethics in Islam. (Giorgio Levi Della Vida Biennial Conference Ser.: Vol. 9). 150p. 1984. pap. 20.50x (ISBN 0-89003-182-7). Undena Pubns.

Hovannisian, Richard G. & Vryonis, Speros, Jr., eds. Islam's Understanding of Itself. LC 82-50987. (Giorgio Levi Della Vida Biennial Conference Ser.: Vol. 8). viii, 151p. 1983. pap. 18.50x (ISBN 0-89003-135-5). Undena Pubns.

Hovda, Robert, ed. see Mitchell, Henry, et al.

Hovda, Robert W. Strong, Loving & Wise: Presiding in Liturgy. 5th ed. (Illus.). 96p. 1983. pap. 5.95 (ISBN 0-8146-1253-9). Liturgical Pr.

Hovemeyer, Gretchen A., jt. ed. see Orange County Genealogical Committee Members.

Hovenden, Robert, ed. The Registers of the Walloon or Strangers' Church in Canterbury, 3 pts. (Huguenot Society of London Publications Ser.: Vol. 5). Repr. of 1891 ed. Set. 107.00 (ISBN 0-8115-1644-X). Kraus Repr.

Hovenkamp, Herbert. Science & Religion in America, 1800-1860. LC 78-53332. 1978. 26.00x (ISBN 0-8122-7748-1). U of Pa Pr.

Hover, Margot K. & Breidenbach, Monica E. Christian Family Almanac. 128p. (Orig.). 1980. pap. 9.95 (ISBN 0-697-01740-0). Wm C Brown.

Hoversten, Cheryl. Come September. 1984. 5.95 (ISBN 0-89536-961-3, 7512). CSS of Ohio.

Hovey, Alvah. Memoir of the Life & Times of the Reverend Isaac Backus. LC 73-148598. (Era of the American Revolution Ser.). 367p. 1972. Repr. of 1858 ed. lib. bdg. 47.50 (ISBN 0-306-70415-3). Da Capo.

How, Nehemiah. A Narrative of the Captivity of Nehemiah How. 59.95 (ISBN 0-8490-0708-9). Gordon Pr.

How, Samuel B. Slaveholding Not Sinful. facs. ed. LC 70-152922. (Black Heritage Library Collection Ser). 1855. 15.25 (ISBN 0-8369-8766-7). Ayer Co Pubs.

Howard, Alan. Sex in the Light of Reincarnation & Freedom. 1980. pap. 5.95 (ISBN 0-916786-48-X). St George Bk Serv.

--The Study of Anthroposophy As an Aspect of the Free Spiritual Life. 1985. pap. 2.00 (ISBN 0-916786-80-3). St George Bk Serv.

--Thinking about Knowing. 1985. pap. 5.95 (ISBN 0-916786-81-1). St George Bk Serv.

Howard, Alan, ed. see Steiner, Rudolf.

Howard, Barbara. The Journey of Forgiveness. 1986. pap. 7.50 (ISBN 0-8309-0463-8). Herald Hse.

Howard, Barbara, ed. Children: Of Such Is the Kingdom of God. LC 79-7102. 1979. pap. 8.00 (ISBN 0-8309-0243-0). Herald Hse.

Howard, Claud. Coleridge's Idealism. LC 72-191125. 1924. lib. bdg. 17.50 (ISBN 0-8414-5131-1). Folcroft.

Howard, Clifford. Sex & Religion. LC 72-9654. Repr. of 1925 ed. 34.50 (ISBN 0-404-57463-7). AMS Pr.

Howard, Dale A. Golden Ark of Covenant. (Illus.). 40p. 1987. pap. 5.00 (ISBN 0-940517-04-3). JCMC Louisiana.

--Scroll of Remembrance. (Illus.). 48p. 1987. pap. 5.00 (ISBN 0-940517-02-7). JCMC Louisiana.

--Tribulation Temple. (Illus.). 80p. 1987. pap. 5.00 (ISBN 0-940517-03-5). JCMC Louisiana.

Howard, David. Why World Evangelism. pap. 0.75 (ISBN 0-87784-141-1). Inter-Varsity.

Howard, David M. Moving Out: The Story of Student Initiative in World Missions. 80p. 1984. pap. 2.95 (ISBN 0-87784-565-4). Inter-Varsity.

--What Makes a Missionary. (Orig.). 1987. pap. 5.95 (ISBN 0-8024-5204-3). Moody.

Howard, David M., jt. auth. see Owen, Robert.

Howard, Diana. London Theatres & Music Halls, 1850-1950. 291p. 1986. text ed. 40.00x (ISBN 0-85365-471-9, L471-9). ALA.

Howard, Dick, ed. see Clancy, Bill.

Howard, Donald. Christians Grieve Too. 1980. pap. 1.45 (ISBN 0-85151-315-8). Banner of Truth.

Howard, Elsie. Basic Bible Survey. LC 82-19686. 96p. (Orig.). 1983. pap. 2.95 (ISBN 0-87239-572-3, 3210). Standard Pub.

Howard, Fred D. Layman's Bible Book Commentary: First, Second, Third John, Jude & Revelation, Vol. 24. LC 80-66807. 1982. 5.95 (ISBN 0-8054-1194-1). Broadman.

Howard, George. The Gospel of Matthew According to a Primitive Hebrew Text. 240p. 1987. 49.95 (ISBN 0-86554-250-3, MUP/H215). Mercer Univ Pr.

--Paul: Crisis in Galatia: A Study in Early Christian Theology. LC 77-84002. (Society for New Testament Studies Monographs: No. 35). pap. 31.50 (ISBN 0-317-29375-3, 2024478). Bks Demand UMI.

--The Teaching of Addai. LC 81-5802. (SBL Texts & Translations Ser.). 1981. pap. 13.50 (ISBN 0-89130-490-8, 060216). Scholars Pr GA.

--Think It Through. 48p. (Orig.). 1984. pap. 2.95 (ISBN 0-89109-163-7). NavPress.

Howard, I. K., tr. see Al-Din, Shaykh M.

Howard, I. K., tr. see Al-Mufid, Shaykh.

Howard, I. K., tr. see Kattani, Sulayman.

Howard, J. Grant. Balancing Life's Demands: A New Perpective on Priorities. LC 82-24581. 1983. pap. 6.95 (ISBN 0-88070-012-2); study guide 2.95 (ISBN 0-88070-033-5). Multnomah.

--Creativity in Preaching. Ruark, J., ed. (Craft of Preaching Ser.). 112p. 1987. pap. price not set (ISBN 0-310-26251-8). Zondervan.

--Trauma of Transparency: A Biblical Approach to Inter-Personal Communication. LC 79-87716. (Critical Concern Bks). 1979. pap. 6.95 (ISBN 0-686-86369-0); study guide 2.95 (ISBN 0-930014-74-X). Multnomah.

Howard, J. Grant, Jr. Knowing God's Will & Doing It! 116p. 1983. pap. 4.95 (ISBN 0-310-26281-X, 9986P). Zondervan.

Howard, John. Infernal Poetics: Poetic Structure in Blake's Lambeth Prophecies. LC 82-49319. (Illus.). 256p. 1984. 34.50 (ISBN 0-8386-3176-2). Fairleigh Dickinson.

Howard, Leon. Essays on Puritans & Puritanism. Barbour, James & Quirk, Thomas, eds. LC 85-28878. 221p. 1986. 19.95 (ISBN 0-8263-0877-5). U of NM Pr.

Howard, Leslie G. The Expansion of God. LC 81-4521. 464p. (Orig.). 1981. pap. 3.74 (ISBN 0-88344-121-7). Orbis Bks.

Howard, Maude L. Myriam & the Mystic Brotherhood. 370p. 1981. pap. 20.00 (ISBN 0-89540-105-3, SB-105). Sun Pub.

Howard, Mildred T. These Are My People. (Illus.). 152p. (Orig.). 1984. pap. 5.95 (ISBN 0-89084-242-6). Bob Jones Univ Pr.

Howard, Richard. Newness of Life. 300p. 1975. 5.95 (ISBN 0-8341-0353-2). Beacon Hill.

--Where on Earth Is God? 144p. 1983. pap. 3.95 (ISBN 0-8341-0823-2). Beacon Hill.

Howard, Richard, tr. see Barthes, Roland.

Howard, Richard, tr. see Cioran, E. M.

Howard, Richard E. So Who's Perfect? 140p. (Orig.). 1985. pap. 5.95 (ISBN 0-8341-1070-9). Beacon Hill.

Howard, Ted, jt. auth. see Rifkin, Jeremy.

Howard, Thomas. The Liturgy Explained. (Illus.). 48p. (Orig.). 1981. pap. 2.95 (ISBN 0-8192-1285-7). Morehouse.

Howard, Thomas, jt. auth. see Packer, J. I.

Howard, Vernon. There Is a Way Out. LC 75-11137. 173p. 1982. pap. 6.00 (ISBN 0-87516-472-2). De Vorss.

Howard, Virgil P. Pentecost 1. LC 84-18756. (Proclamation 3 A). 64p. 1987. pap. 3.75 (ISBN 0-8006-4122-1, 1-4122). Fortress.

Howard, Virginia. The Messenger. 1971. pap. 3.95 (ISBN 0-910122-31-8). Amherst Pr.

Howard, Wayne. Samavedic Chant. LC 76-49854. (Illus.). 1977. 50.00x (ISBN 0-300-01956-4). Yale U Pr.

--Veda Recitation in Varanasi. 1986. 42.00x (ISBN 0-8364-0872-1). South Asia Bks.

Howard, Wilbert F., jt. auth. see Moulton, James H.

Howard-Hill, T. H. Literary Concordances: A Complete Handbook for the Preparation of Manual & Computer Concordances. 1979. text ed. 18.00 (ISBN 0-08-023021-0). Pergamon.

Howe, Claude L., Jr. The Theology of William Newton Clarke: Doctoral Dissertation. Gaustad, Edwin S., ed. LC 79-52571. (The Baptist Tradition Ser.). 1980. lib. bdg. 14.00x (ISBN 0-405-12440-6). Ayer Co Pubs.

Howe, Daniel W. The Unitarian Conscience. LC 75-116737. 15.00 (ISBN 0-674-92121-6). Harvard U Pr.

Howe, Eber D. Mormonism Unvailed; or, a Faithful Account of That Singular Imposition & Delusion, from Its Rise to the Present Time. LC 72-2967. Repr. of 1834 ed. 32.50 (ISBN 0-404-10730-3). AMS Pr.

Howe, Eunice D. The Hospital of Santo Spirito & Pope Sixtus IV. LC 77-94698. (Outstanding Dissertations in the Fine Arts Ser.). (Illus.). 444p. 1978. lib. bdg. 52.00 (ISBN 0-8240-3230-6). Garland Pub.

Howe, Frederic R. Challenge & Response. 176p. 1985. pap. text ed. 7.95 (ISBN 0-310-45071-3, 12375P). Zondervan.

Howe, Irving. World of Our Fathers. LC 75-16342. (Illus.). 714p. 1976. 14.95 (ISBN 0-15-146353-0). HarBraceJ.

--World of Our Fathers. 560p. 1983. pap. 12.95 (ISBN 0-671-49252-7, Touchstone). S&S.

Howe, Irving, jt. auth. see Libo, Kenneth.

Howe, Irving, ed. Jewish-American Stories. 1977. pap. 4.95 (ISBN 0-451-62515-3, ME2302, Ment). NAL.

Howe, Irving & Greenberg, Eliezer, eds. Ashes out of Hope: Fiction by Soviet-Yiddish Writers. LC 76-49731. 1978. pap. 4.95 (ISBN 0-8052-0605-1). Schocken.

--A Treasury of Yiddish Stories. LC 54-9599. (Illus.). 630p. 1973. pap. 11.95 (ISBN 0-8052-0400-8). Schocken.

Howe, Jeffery W. The Symbolist Art of Fernand Khnoff. Foster, Stephen, ed. LC 82-4734. (Studies in the Fine Arts: The Avant Garde: No. 28). 274p. 1982. 44.95 (ISBN 0-8357-1317-2). UMI Res Pr.

Howe, Joanne. A Change of Habit. 117p. (Orig.). 1986. 9.95 (ISBN 0-89225-290-1); pap. 6.95 (ISBN 0-89225-292-8). Gospel Advocate.

Howe, John. Whole Works of John Howe, 6 Vols. Rogers, H., ed. LC 71-169450. Repr. of 1863 ed. Set. lib. bdg. 115.00 (ISBN 0-404-03360-1); lib. bdg. 20.00 ea. AMS Pr.

Howe, Mark D. The Garden & the Wilderness: Religion & Government in American Constitutional History. (Phoenix Bks.). pap. 47.50 (ISBN 0-317-08469-0, 2020085). Bks Demand UMI.

Howe, Reuel L. Herein Is Love. pap. 3.95 (ISBN 0-8170-0263-4). Judson.

--Miracle of Dialogue. 1963. pap. 6.95 (ISBN 0-86683-886-4, SP9, HarpR). Har-Row.

Howell, Alice O. Jungian Symbolism in Astrology. LC 86-40406. 238p. (Orig.). 1987. pap. 6.95 (ISBN 0-8356-0618-X). Theos Pub Hse.

Howell, Clinton T., ed. Better Than Gold. (Illus.). 200p. 1984. 12.95 (ISBN 0-8407-5388-8). Nelson.

--Lines to Live By. 200p. 1984. Repr. 12.95 (ISBN 0-8407-5389-6). Nelson.

--Seasons of Inspiration. 160p. 1984. Repr. 10.95 (ISBN 0-8407-5345-4). Nelson.

Howell, John C. Equality & Submission in Marriage. LC 78-67292. 1979. 8.50 (ISBN 0-8054-5632-5). Broadman.

--Senior Adult Family Life. LC 79-51139. 1979. pap. 4.95 large type (ISBN 0-8054-5423-3). Broadman.

Howell, Mary. Helping Ourselves: Families & the Human Network. LC 75-5291. 1975. pap. 6.95x (ISBN 0-8070-2759-6, BP551). Beacon Pr.

Howell, Patrick. Reducing the Storm to a Whisper: The Story of a Breakdown. 228p. 1985. 15.95 (ISBN 0-88347-183-3). Thomas More.

Howell, Roger, Jr. Puritans & Radicals in North England: Essays on the English Revolution. LC 84-10411. 226p. (Orig.). 1984. lib. bdg. 24.25 (ISBN 0-8191-4013-9); pap. text ed. 12.25 (ISBN 0-8191-4014-7). U Pr of Amer.

Howells, W. W. Hutterite Age Differences in Body Measurements. LC 78-115048. (Peabody Museum Papers: Vol. 57, No. 2). 1970. pap. 10.00x (ISBN 0-87365-168-5). Peabody Harvard.

Howells, William. The Heathens Primitive Man & His Religions. 302p. pap. text ed. 9.95 (ISBN 0-88133-240-2). Sheffield Wisc.

Howells, William D., et al. In After Days: Thoughts on Future Life. Kastenaum, Robert, ed. LC 76-19576. (Death & Dying Ser.). (Illus.). 1977. Repr. of 1910 ed. lib. bdg. 24.50x (ISBN 0-405-09574-0). Ayer Co Pubs.

Howes, Elizabeth, ed. see Pelgrin, Mark.

Howes, Elizabeth B. & Moon, Sheila. The Choicemaker. LC 76-54534. 1977. pap. 3.95 (ISBN 0-8356-0492-6, Quest). Theos Pub Hse.

Howes, Fred. This Is the Prophet Jesus. LC 82-72741. 276p. 1983. pap. 8.95 (ISBN 0-87516-497-8). De Vorss.

Howey, M. Oldfield. The Cat in the Mysteries of Religion & Magic. LC 81-51289. (Illus.). 254p. 1982. Repr. of 1930 ed. 12.50 (ISBN 0-8048-1360-4). C E Tuttle.

Howie, Carl G. Ezekiel, Daniel. LC 59-10454. (Layman's Bible Commentary, Vol. 13). 1961. pap. 4.95 (ISBN 0-8042-3073-0). John Knox.

Howie, John. Perspectives for Moral Decisions. LC 80-6102. 192p. 1981. lib. bdg. 25.00 (ISBN 0-8191-1375-1); pap. text ed. 11.25 (ISBN 0-8191-1376-X). U Pr of Amer.

Howie, John, ed. Ethical Principles for Social Policy. LC 82-5801. 176p. 1982. 16.95x (ISBN 0-8093-1063-5). S Ill U Pr.

Howington, Nolan P. A Royal Priesthood. LC 85-22376. 1986. pap. 4.95 (ISBN 0-8054-1622-6). Broadman.

--The Vigil of Prayer. (Orig.). 1987. pap. 4.95 (ISBN 0-8054-1505-X). Broadman.

Howitt, William. Colonization & Christianity: A Popular History of the Treatment of the Natives by the Europeans in All Their Colonies. LC 70-76856. Repr. of 1838 ed. 22.75x (ISBN 0-8371-1162-5, HOC&, Pub. by Negro U Pr). Greenwood.

Howkins, Christopher. Discovering Church Furniture. (Discovering Ser.: No. 69). (Illus.). 80p. 1983. pap. 3.50 (ISBN 0-85263-496-X, Pub. by Shire Pubns England). Seven Hills Bks.

Howlett, Duncan. The Critical Way in Religion. LC 80-7460. (Library of Liberal Religion). 360p. 1984. pap. 14.95 (ISBN 0-87975-266-1). Prometheus Bks.

Howlett, William J. Old St. Thomas' at Poplar Neck, Bardstown, Kentucky. (Illus.). 200p. 1971. pap. 3.25 (ISBN 0-913228-02-8). R J Liederbach.

Howorth, Henry H. Golden Days of the Early English Church from the Arrival of Theodore to the Death of Bede, 3 Vols. LC 79-153612. Repr. of 1917 ed. Set. 75.00 (ISBN 0-404-09470-8); 25.00 ea. Vol. 1 (ISBN 0-404-09471-6). Vol. 2 (ISBN 0-404-09472-4). Vol. 3 (ISBN 0-404-09473-2). AMS Pr.

Howson, J. S., jt. auth. see Conybeare, W. J.

Howson, Mark, tr. see Barthel, Manfred.

Hoyer, George W. The Lord Be with You. LC 77-85172. (Child of God Ser.: Vol. 1). 1977. pap. text ed. 4.95 (ISBN 0-915644-11-8). Clayton Pub Hse.

Hoyer, Jeff. Life-Changing Learning for Adults. (C. E. Ministries Ser.). 96p. (Orig.). 1984. pap. 3.50 (ISBN 0-89367-097-9). Light & Life.

Hoyer, Robert. He Calls Me by My Name: A Pre-Membership Course for Adults. LC 77-74385. 1977. pap. text ed. 4.75 (ISBN 0-915644-09-6). Clayton Pub Hse.

Hoyland, Geoffrey. The Use of Silence. 1983. pap. 2.50x (ISBN 0-87574-083-9, 083). Pendle Hill.

Hoyle, Fred. The Cosmogony of the Solar System. LC 78-21286. (Illus.). 168p. 1979. 17.95x (ISBN 0-89490-023-4). Enslow Pubs.

Hoyt, Charles A. Witchcraft. LC 80-24731. 160p. 1981. pap. 12.95 (ISBN 0-8093-1015-5). S Ill U Pr.

Hoyt, Herman A. Christ, God's Final Word to Man: An Exposition of the Epistle to the Hebrews. pap. 4.95 (ISBN 0-88469-009-1). BMH Bks.

--Commentary on Second Peter. 136p. 1983. pap. 4.95 (ISBN 0-88469-153-5). BMH Bks.

--The End Times. pap. 6.95 (ISBN 0-88469-077-6). BMH Bks.

--The First Christian Theology Studies in Romans. pap. 4.95 (ISBN 0-88469-038-5). BMH Bks.

--Is the United States in Prophecy? 1979. pap. 1.00 (ISBN 0-88469-040-7). BMH Bks.

--Studies in Revelation. pap. 5.95 (ISBN 0-88469-118-7). BMH Bks.

Hoyt, Herman A., et al. War: Four Christian Views. Clouse, Robert G., ed. 216p. (Orig.). 1981. pap. 5.95 (ISBN 0-88469-097-0). BMH Bks.

Hoyt, Olga. Witches. LC 68-13233. (Illus.). 1969. 11.70i (ISBN 0-200-71593-3, B91350, AbS-J). HarpJ.

Hoyt, Robert S. & Chodorow, Stanley. Europe in the Middle Ages. 3rd ed. (Illus.). 707p. 1976. text ed. 25.95 (ISBN 0-15-524712-3, HC). HarBraceJ.

Hoyt, Robert S., ed. Life & Thought in the Early Middle Ages. LC 67-15065. (Illus.). 1968. pap. 1.95 (ISBN 0-8166-0464-9, MP11). U of Minn Pr.

Hridayananda dasa Goswami Acaryadeva. Srimad-Bhagavatam: Eleventh Canto, Vol. 1. (Illus.). 450p. 1982. 12.95 (ISBN 0-89213-112-8); text ed. 9.95 (ISBN 0-686-98021-2). Bhaktivedanta.

Hromadka, Joseph, ed. see Pennsylvania University Bicentennial Conference.

Hruska, Eva J. The Alpha thru Omega Bible Survey. LC 85-90314. 1985. pap. 3.95 (ISBN 0-9614616-1-6); tchr's. ed 7.95 (ISBN 0-9614616-0-8). Eva Hruska.

Hsi, Chu. The Philosophy of Human Nature. 1976. lib. bdg. 59.95 (ISBN 0-8490-2432-3). Gordon Pr.

Hsia, R. Po-chia. Society & Religion in Munster. LC 83-14819. (Yale Historical Publications Ser.: No. 131). 320p. 1984. text ed. 27.50x (ISBN 0-300-03005-3). Yale U Pr.

Hsiang, Paul Stanislaus. The Catholic Missions in China During the Middle Ages: 1294-1368, No. 37. (Studies in Sacred Theology, Second Series). 57p. 1983. Repr. of 1949 ed. 12.00x (ISBN 0-939738-32-5). Zubal Inc.

Hsu, Dorothy. Mending. 1982. pap. 2.95 (ISBN 0-87508-263-7). Chr Lit.

Hsu, F. G., tr. see Chow Tun Yi.

Hsu, Francis L. Exorcising the Trouble Makers: Magic, Science, & Culture. LC 83-5522. (Contributions to the Study of Religion Ser.: No. 11). (Illus.). xvi, 164p. 1983. lib. bdg. 29.95 (ISBN 0-313-23780-8, HET/). Greenwood.

--Religion, Science & Human Crises. LC 73-7308. (Illus.). 142p. 1973. Repr. of 1952 ed. lib. bdg. 22.50x (ISBN 0-8371-6921-6, HSRS). Greenwood.

Hsu, Lily, tr. see Kaung, Stephen.

Hsun Tzu. Hsun Tzu: Basic Writings. Watson, Burton, tr. LC 63-20340. (Translations from Oriental Classics Ser.). (Orig.). 1963. pap. 10.00x (ISBN 0-231-08607-5). Columbia U Pr.

Htin Aung, U. Folk Elements in Burmese Buddhism. LC 77-29231. 1978. Repr. of 1962 ed. lib. bdg. 22.50x (ISBN 0-313-20275-3, HTFE). Greenwood.

Hu, Shih. The Development of the Logical Method in Ancient China. lib. bdg. 79.95 (ISBN 0-87968-524-7). Krishna Pr.

Hua, Ellen K. Meditations of the Masters. LC 76-47649. (Illus., Orig.). 1977. pap. 3.00 (ISBN 0-87407-203-4, FP-3). Thor.

--Wisdom from the East: Meditations, Reflections, Proverbs & Chants. LC 73-21886. (Illus.). 128p. (Orig.). 1974. pap. 3.00 (ISBN 0-87407-202-6, FP2). Thor.

Hua, Ellen K., adapted by. Kung Fu Meditations & Chinese Proverbial Wisdom. LC 73-7731. (Illus.). 1973. o. p. 3.95 (ISBN 0-87407-511-4); pap. 3.00 (ISBN 0-87407-200-X, FPI). Thor.

Hua, Ellen Kei see Hua, Ellen K.

Hua, Husan. Sutra of the Past Vows of Earthstore Bodhisattva: The Collected Lectures of Tripitaka Master Hsuan Hua. Ching, Heng, tr. from Chinese. (IASWR Ser.). 235p. 1974. 12.75 (ISBN 0-686-47598-4, S-10); pap. 6.75 (ISBN 0-915078-00-7, S-11). Inst Adv Stud Wld.

Hua, Tripitaka Master. Heart Sutra & Verses Without a Stand, With Prose Commentary. Buddhist Text Translation Society, tr. from Chinese. (Illus.). 160p. (Orig.). 1980. pap. 7.50 (ISBN 0-917512-27-8). Buddhist Text.

--The Shurangama Sutra, Vol. 7. Buddhist Text Translation Society, tr. from Chinese. (Illus.). 270p. (Orig.). 1982. pap. 8.50 (ISBN 0-917512-97-9). Buddhist Text.

Hua, Tripitaka Master, commentary by. Flower Adornment Sutra, Chapter 39: Entering the Dharma Realm Part VIII. Buddhist Text Translation Society, tr. from Chinese. 228p. (Orig.). 1984. pap. 8.50 (ISBN 0-88139-055-0). Buddhist Text.

Hua-Ching, jt. auth. see Ni Hua-Ching, Master.

Huang, Al C. Embrace Tiger, Return to Mountain: The Essence of T'ai Chi. LC 73-80134. (Illus.). 185p. 1973. 10.00 (ISBN 0-911226-12-5); pap. 6.50 (ISBN 0-911226-13-3). Real People.

Huang, Hsiu-Chi. Lu Hsiang-Shan: A 12th Century Chinese Idealist Philosopher. LC 75-39028. (China Studies: from Confucius to Mao Ser.). (Illus.). 116p. 1976. Repr. of 1944 ed. 18.15 (ISBN 0-88355-384-8). Hyperion-Conn.

Huang, Juh-Hua, tr. see Men-Ching, Cheng.

Huang Po. The Zen Teaching of Huang Po: On the Transmission of the Mind. Blofeld, John, tr. 1959. pap. 9.95 (ISBN 0-394-17217-5, E171, Ever). Grove.

Huang, Quentin K. Y. Pilgrim from a Red Land. 1981. 8.00 (ISBN 0-682-49669-3). Exposition Pr FL.

Huart, C., tr. see Aflaki.

Hubbard, Barbara M. Happy Birthday Planet Earth: The Instant of Co-Operation. (No. 1). (Illus.). 64p. (Orig.). 1986. pap. 6.00 perfect bdg. (ISBN 0-943734-08-8). Ocean Tree Bks.

Hubbard, Bede, ed. Companion on Life's Journey: A Book of Prayers & Readings. 260p. 1986. pap. 9.95 (ISBN 0-8146-1550-3). Liturgical Pr.

Hubbard, David. Beyond Futility. 2nd ed. Semarians, Beer-Shiba, tr. (Chinese.). 106p. 1982. pap. write for info (ISBN 0-941598-02-0). Living Spring Pubns.

Hubbard, David A. Pentecost One: Proclamation 3B. LC 84-18756. (Proclamation Ser.). 64p. 1985. pap. 3.75 (ISBN 0-8006-4106-X, 1-4106). Fortress.

--The Practice of Prayer. 91p. 1983. pap. 2.95 (ISBN 0-87784-393-7). Inter-Varsity.

--Unwrapping Your Spiritual Gifts. 160p. 1985. 9.95 (ISBN 0-8499-0478-1, 0478-1). Word Bks.

Hubbard, David A., jt. auth. see La Sor, W. S.

Hubbard, Elbert. Jesus Was an Anarchist. 1974. lib. bdg. 59.95 (ISBN 0-87700-304-1). Revisionist Pr.

Hubbard, Ethel D. Ann of Ava. LC 76-160921. (Biography Index Reprint Ser.). (Illus.). Repr. of 1941 ed. 17.25 (ISBN 0-8369-8084-0). Ayer Co Pubs.

Hubbard, L. Ron. Advanced Procedure & Axioms. 1951. 30.00 (ISBN 0-88404-021-6). Bridge Pubns Inc.

--Advanced Procedures & Axioms. 31.00 (ISBN 0-686-30782-8). Church Scient NY.

--All about Radiation. 20.00 (ISBN 0-686-30790-9). Church Scient NY.

--Axioms & Logics. 5.00 (ISBN 0-686-30793-3). Church Scient NY.

--Axioms & Logics. 1958. pap. 6.97 (ISBN 0-88404-066-6). Bridge Pubns Inc.

--Background & Ceremonies of the Church of Scientology. 40.00 (ISBN 0-686-30794-1). Church Scient NY.

--The Book Introducing the E-Meter. 8.75 (ISBN 0-686-30797-6). Church Scient NY.

--The Book of E-Meter Drills. 8.75 (ISBN 0-686-30796-8). Church Scient NY.

--Child Dianetics. 20.00 (ISBN 0-686-30781-X). Church Scient NY.

--Control & Mechanics of S. C. S. (Start, Change, Stop) 1951. pap. 9.67 (ISBN 0-88404-067-4). Bridge Pubns Inc.

--Control & the Mechanics of SCS. 8.75 (ISBN 0-686-30792-5). Church Scient NY.

--The Creation of Human Ability. 31.00 (ISBN 0-686-13922-4). Church Scient NY.

--The Creation of Human Ability: A Handbook for Scientologists. 292p. 1954. 36.44 (ISBN 0-88404-011-9). Bridge Pubns Inc.

--Dianetica: la Ciencia Moderna De Salud Mental. spanish ed. 1976. pap. 3.95 (ISBN 0-88404-086-0). Bridge Pubns Inc.

--Dianetics. 1977. pap. 2.00 (ISBN 0-685-76384-6). Church of Scient Info.

--Dianetics & Scientology Technical Dictionary. 50.00 (ISBN 0-686-30803-4). Church Scient NY.

--Dianetics & Scientology Technical Dictionary. 1975. 79.32 (ISBN 0-88404-037-2). Bridge Pubns Inc.

--Dianetics: Evolution of a Science. 20.00 (ISBN 0-686-30777-1). Church Scient NY.

--Dianetics Fifty-Five. 20.00 (ISBN 0-686-13920-8). Church Scient NY.

--Dianetics Fifty-Five. 168p. 1955. 36.44 (ISBN 0-88404-003-8). Bridge Pubns Inc.

--Dianetics: The Evolution of a Science. 110p. 1950. 21.44 (ISBN 0-88404-017-8). Bridge Pubns Inc.

--Dianetics: The Modern Science of Mental Health. 20.00 (ISBN 0-686-30776-3). Church Scient NY.

--Dianetics: The Modern Science of Mental Health. 483p. 1950. 32.16 (ISBN 0-88404-000-3). Bridge Pubns Inc.

--Dianetics, the Original Thesis. 20.00 (ISBN 0-686-13917-8). Church Scient NY.

--Dianetics: The Original Thesis. 157p. 1951. 21.44 (ISBN 0-88404-002-X). Bridge Pubns Inc.

--Dianetics Today. 76.00 (ISBN 0-686-30802-6). Church Scient NY.

--Dianetics Today. 1975. 120.04 (ISBN 0-88404-036-4). Bridge Pubns Inc.

--E-Meter Essentials. 8.75 (ISBN 0-686-30795-X). Church Scient NY.

--Fundamentals of Thought. 20.00 (ISBN 0-686-13919-4). Church Scient NY.

--Group Auditor's Handbook. 50.00 (ISBN 0-686-30787-9). Church Scient NY.

--Handbook for Preclears. 20.00 (ISBN 0-686-30783-6). Church Scient NY.

--Handbook for Preclears. (Illus.). 192p. 1951. 38.59 (ISBN 0-88404-016-X). Bridge Pubns Inc.

--Have You Lived Before This Life? 20.00 (ISBN 0-686-13921-6). Church Scient NY.

--Have You Lived Before This Life? A Study of Death & Evidence of Past Lives. 1978. 42.87 (ISBN 0-88404-055-0). Bridge Pubns Inc.

--How to Live Though an Executive: Communications Manual. 132p. 1953. 32.16 (ISBN 0-88404-010-0). Bridge Pubns Inc.

--How to Live Through an Executive. 20.00 (ISBN 0-686-30786-0). Church Scient NY.

--Hymn of Asia. 40.00 (ISBN 0-686-30801-8). Church Scient NY.

--Introduction to Scientology Ethics. 20.00 (ISBN 0-686-13916-X). Church Scient NY.

--Introduction to Scientology Ethics. 74p. 1968. 32.16 (ISBN 0-88404-015-1). Bridge Pubns Inc.

--The Management Series. (Vol. I). 100.00 (ISBN 0-686-30799-2). Church Scient NY.

--Mission into Time. 20.00 (ISBN 0-686-13923-2). Church Scient NY.

--Modern Management Technology Defined. 94.00 (ISBN 0-686-30806-9). Church Scient NY.

--Modern Management Technology Defined. 1977. text ed. 107.18 (ISBN 0-88404-040-2). Bridge Pubns Inc.

--Notes on the Lectures. 31.00 (ISBN 0-686-30778-X). Church Scient NY.

--Notes on the Lectures of L. Ron Hubbard. (Illus.). 160p. 1951. 36.44 (ISBN 0-88404-005-4). Bridge Pubns Inc.

--The Organization Executive Course. 840.00 (ISBN 0-686-30798-4). Church Scient NY.

--The Organization Executive Course: An Encyclopedia of Scientology Policy (1950-1951, 1953-1974, 7 vols. Incl. Vol. 0. Basic Staff Volume of the Organization Executive Course (ISBN 0-88404-025-9); Vol. 1. Hubbard Communications Office Division One of the Organization Executive Course (ISBN 0-88404-026-7); Vol. 2. Hubbard Communications Office Dissemination Division Two of the Organization Executive Course (ISBN 0-88404-027-5); Vol. 3. Treasury Division Three of the Organization Executive Course (ISBN 0-88404-028-3); Vol. 4. Technical Division Four of the Organization Executive Course (ISBN 0-88404-029-1); Vol. 5. Qualifications Division Five of the Organization Executive Course (ISBN 0-88404-030-5); Vol. 6. Distribution Division Six of the Organization Executive Course. 1971 (ISBN 0-88404-031-3); Vol. 7. Executive Division Seven: The Executive's Handbook of the Organization Executive Course (ISBN 0-88404-032-1). 1974. 836.00 set (ISBN 0-88404-033-X); 107.18 ea. Bridge Pubns Inc.

--The Phoenix Lectures. 31.00 (ISBN 0-686-13925-9). Church Scient NY.

--The Problems of Work. 20.00 (ISBN 0-686-30789-5). Church Scient NY.

--The Problems of Work: Scientology Applied to the Work-a-Day World. 106p. 1956. 21.44 (ISBN 0-88404-007-0). Bridge Pubns Inc.

--Research & Discovery Series, 8 vols. Set. write for info. (ISBN 0-686-30030-0); Vol. 1, June 1950. 100.00 (ISBN 0-686-30031-9); Vol. 2, July 1950. 100.00 (ISBN 0-686-30032-7); Vol. 3. 100.00; Vol. 4. 100.00. Church Scient NY.

--Science of Survival. 31.00 (ISBN 0-686-30779-8). Church Scient NY.

--Science of Survival: Prediction of Human Behavior. LC 51-5566. (Illus.). 550p. 1951. 47.16 (ISBN 0-88404-001-1). Bridge Pubns Inc.

--Scientology: A History of Man. 31.00 (ISBN 0-686-30784-4). Church Scient NY.

--Scientology: A History of Man. 1952. 13.00 (ISBN 0-88404-024-0). Bridge Pubns Inc.

--Scientology: A New Slant on Life. 20.00 (ISBN 0-686-13918-6). Church Scient NY.

--Scientology: A New Slant on Life. 160p. 1965. 21.44 (ISBN 0-88404-013-5). Bridge Pubns Inc.

--Scientology: Clear Procedure. 8.75 (ISBN 0-686-30791-7). Church Scient NY.

--Scientology: Clear Procedure Issue One. 1957. pap. 9.50 (ISBN 0-88404-069-0). Bridge Pubns Inc.

--Scientology Eight to Eight Thousand Eight. 152p. 1953. 32.16 (ISBN 0-88404-008-9). Bridge Pubns Inc.

--Scientology: Eight to Eights. 31.00 (ISBN 0-686-30785-2). Church Scient NY.

--Scientology Eight to Eighty: The Discovery & Increase of Life Energy in the Genus Homo Sapiens. 1952. 27.85 (ISBN 0-88404-020-8). Bridge Pubns Inc.

--Scientology: The Fundamentals of Thought. 20.00 (ISBN 0-686-30788-7). Church Scient NY.

--Scientology: The Fundamentals of Thought. 128p. 1956. 21.44 (ISBN 0-88404-018-6). Bridge Pubns Inc.

--Scientology Zero-Eight, the Book of Basics. 31.00 (ISBN 0-686-30808-5). Church Scient NY.

--Scientology Zero to Eight: The Book of Basics. 159p. 1950. 32.16 (ISBN 0-88404-009-7). Bridge Pubns Inc.

--Scientology: 8-8008. 31.00 (ISBN 0-686-13924-0). Church Scient NY.

--Self Analysis. 20.00 (ISBN 0-686-30780-1). Church Scient NY.

--Self Analysis. 254p. 1983. pap. 8.95 (ISBN 0-88404-109-3). Bridge Pubns Inc.

--The Volunteer Minister's Handbook. 76.00 (ISBN 0-686-30805-0). Church Scient NY.

--Volunteer Minister's Handbook. 1976. 124.33 (ISBN 0-88404-039-9). Bridge Pubns Inc.

--What Is Scientology? 50.00 (ISBN 0-686-30807-7). Church Scient NY.

Hubbard, L. Ron, jt. auth. see Church of Scientology Information Service Staff.

Hubbard, L. Ron, intro. by. Child Dianetics. 1951. 38.59 (ISBN 0-88404-022-4). Bridge Pubns Inc.

Hubbard, Mary Sue. Marriage Hats. 1970. pap. 12.87 (ISBN 0-88404-068-2). Bridge Pubns Inc.

Hubbard, Robert, ed. see Goldingay, John.

Hubbard, Stanley. Nietzche und Emerson. LC 80-2538. Repr. of 1958 ed. 25.50 (ISBN 0-404-19264-5). AMS Pr.

Hubbeling, H. G. Principles of Philosophy of Religion. (Philosophia Religionis Ser.: Vol. 25). 280p. 1987. pap. 22.95 (ISBN 90-232-2272-5, Pub. by Van Gorcum Holland). Longwood Pub Group.

Hubbuck, Rodney. Portsea Island Churches. 1969. 39.00x (ISBN 0-317-43678-3, Pub. by City of Portsmouth). State Mutual Bk.

Huber, Elaine C. Women & the Authority of Inspiration: A Reexamination of Two Prophetic Movements from a Contemporary Feminist Perspective. LC 85-15823. 262p. (Orig.). 1985. lib. bdg. 27.75 (ISBN 0-8191-4903-9); pap. text ed. 13.75 (ISBN 0-8191-4904-7). U Pr of Amer.

Huber, Evelyn M., jt. auth. see Blazier, Kenneth D.

Huber, Friedrich. Jahwe, Juda und die anderen Voelker beim Proheton Jesaja. (Beiheft 137 Zur Zeitschrift Fuer die Alttestamentliche Wissenschaft). (Ger.). 1976. 46.40 (ISBN 3-11-005729-8). De Gruyter.

Huber, Georges. My Angel Will Go Before You. Adams, Michael, tr. from Fr. Tr. of Mon Ange Marchera Devant Toi. 135p. 1983. pap. 9.95. Chr Classics.

Huber, J. William, et al. Fear: Issues of Emotional Living in an Age of Stress for Clergy & Religious. Kraus, Marie, ed. LC 86-3533. 141p. 1986. pap. 8.00 (ISBN 0-89571-028-5). Affirmation.

Huber, Jane P. A Singing Faith. LC 86-753277. 144p. (Orig.). 1987. pap. 7.95 (ISBN 0-664-24055-0); spiral bound 10.95 (ISBN 0-664-24056-9). Westminster.

Huber, Phillip C., jt. auth. see Gobbel, A. Roger.

Hubert, Henri & Mauss, Marcel. Sacrifice: Its Nature & Function. Halls, W. D., tr. LC 64-12260. 1964. pap. 11.00x (ISBN 0-226-35679-5). U of Chicago Pr.

Hubert, Marie L. Pascal's Unfinished Apology. LC 70-153272. 165p. 1973. Repr. of 1952 ed. 21.50 (ISBN 0-8046-1699-X, Pub. by Kennikat). Assoc Faculty Pr.

Hubert, Morton J. & La Monte, John L. Crusade of Richard Lion-Heart, by Ambroise. (Illus.). 1969. lib. bdg. 40.00x (ISBN 0-374-94009-6, Octagon). Hippocrene Bks.

Hubner, Hans. Law in Paul's Thought. Riches, John, ed. Greig, James, tr. 186p. 26.95 (ISBN 0-567-09313-1, Pub. by T & T Clark Ltd UK). Fortress.

Hubner, Pauline, jt. auth. see Stewart, Stan.

Huchede, P. History of Antichrist. 1976. pap. 2.00 (ISBN 0-89555-100-4). TAN Bks Pubs.

Huck, Albert. Synopsis of the First Three Gospels With the Addition of the Johannine Parallels. 1982. 22.50x (ISBN 0-8028-3568-6). Eerdmans.

Huck, Gabe. A Book of Family Prayer. 1979. 9.95 (ISBN 0-8164-0415-1, HarpR); pap. 9.95 (ISBN 0-8164-2486-1). Har-Row.

Huck, Gabe, jt. auth. see Jeep, Elizabeth M.

Huck, Gabe, ed. Simple Gifts, Vols. 1&2. 1974. pap. 6.50 (ISBN 0-918208-65-3). Liturgical Conf.

Huck, Gabe & Klenicki, Leon, eds. Spirituality & Prayer, Jewish & Christian Understandings (Stimulus Bk.) LC 82-62966. 200p. (Orig.). 1983. pap. 7.95 (ISBN 0-8091-2538-2). Paulist Pr.

Huck, Gabe & Sloyan, Virginia, eds. Parishes & Families: A Model for Christian Formation Through Liturgy. 1973. pap. 5.00 (ISBN 0-918208-11-4). Liturgical Conf.

Hucke, H. & Wagner, Johannes, eds. Church Worships. LC 66-17730. (Concilium Ser.: Vol. 12). 196p. 1966. 7.95 (ISBN 0-8091-0020-7). Paulist Pr.

Huckle, John. The Gospel According to St. John Vols. I, II & III, the New Testament for Spiritual Reading Vols. 7, 8, & 9. 1978. Vol. I. pap. 4.95 (ISBN 0-8245-0116-0); Vol. II. pap. 4.95 (ISBN 0-8245-0117-9); Vol. III. pap. 4.95 (ISBN 0-8245-0118-7). Crossroad NY.

Huckle, John & Visokay, Paul. The Gospel According to St. John, Vol. I. McKenzie, John L., ed. LC 81-605. (The New Testament for Spiritual Reading Ser.). 282p. 1981. 10.00; pap. 4.95. Crossroad NY.

Huddleston, Mary A., ed. Celibate Loving: Encounter in Three Dimensions. (Orig.). 1984. pap. 9.95 (ISBN 0-8091-2588-9). Paulist Pr.

Hudnut, Robert K. This People, This Parish. 192p. 1986. pap. 7.95 (ISBN 0-310-38241-6, 12329P). Zondervan.

Hudnut, William H., III & Keene, Judy. Minister-Mayor. LC 86-32512. 192p. 1987. 12.95 (ISBN 0-664-21321-9). Westminster.

Hudson, Anne, ed. see Wycliffe, John.

Hudson, David. Memoir of Jemima Wilkinson, a Preacheress of the 18th Century. LC 78-134417. Repr. of 1844 ed. 23.00 (ISBN 0-404-08475-3). AMS Pr.

Hudson, Jay T. New Discoveries into the Realm of Psychic Phenomena. (Illus.). 129p. 1983. 85.85 (ISBN 0-89920-065-6). Am Inst Psych.

Hudson, Julius. Go Ask God. 1981. 4.75 (ISBN 0-8062-1827-4). Carlton.

Hudson, Kenneth. Churchyards & Cemeteries. (Illus.). 48p. 1984. laminated boards 9.95 (ISBN 0-370-30543-4, Pub. by Bodley Head). Salem Hse Pubs.

Hudson, Paul, tr. see Tournier, Paul.

Hudson, R. Lofton. Como Mejorar Sus Relaciores Humanas. De Lerin, O. S. D., tr. 62p. 1984. Repr. of 1982 ed. 1.75 (ISBN 0-311-46037-2). Casa Bautista.

Hudson, Stephen D. Human Character & Morality: Reflections from the History of Ideas. 160p. 1986. 18.95 (ISBN 0-7102-0770-0, 07700). Methuen Inc.

Hudson, T. J. A New System of Mental Therapeutics & the Phenomena of Spiritism. (Illus.). 171p. 1986. 187.65 (ISBN 0-89920-138-5). Am Inst Psych.

Hudson, Thomas. A Scientific Demonstration of the Future Life. 1979. pap. 2.50 (ISBN 0-89083-464-4). Zebra.

Hudson, Thomson J. Physical Manifestations & Philosophy of Christ. 1978. pap. 4.50 deluxe (ISBN 0-87852-003-1). Inst Human Growth.

Hudson, Van D., ed. Choice Messages from Free Will Baptist Pulpits. 1976. pap. 2.50 (ISBN 0-89265-030-3). Randall Hse.

Hudson, W. D., ed. Is-Ought Question. LC 79-106390. (Controversies in Philosophy Ser). 1970. 12.95 (ISBN 0-312-43715-3). St Martin.

Hudson, W. D., ed. see Hodges, H. A.

Hudson, Winthrop. Religion in America: An Historical Account of the Development of American Religious Life. 4th ed. 512p. 1987. text ed. write for info. (ISBN 0-02-357280-9). Macmillan.

Hudson, Winthrop S. American Protestantism. LC 61-15936. (Chicago History of American Civilization Ser). 1961. pap. 4.95x (ISBN 0-226-35803-8, CHAC10). U of Chicago Pr.

--Baptist Convictions. pap. 1.50 (ISBN 0-8170-0295-2). Judson.

--Nationalism & Religion in America: Concepts of American Identity & Mission. 12.00 (ISBN 0-8446-0711-8). Peter Smith.

Hudson, Winthrop S., jt. auth. see Maring, Norman H.

Hudson, Winthrop S., ed. Walter Rauscenbusch: Selected Writings. (Sources of American Spirituality Ser.). 252p. 1985. text ed. 14.95 (ISBN 0-8091-0356-7). Paulist Pr.

Hueckstedt, Robert A. The Style of Bana: An Introduction to Sanskrit Prose Poetry. 228p. (Orig.). 1986. lib. bdg. 27.50 (ISBN 0-8191-4998-5); pap. text ed. 12.75 (ISBN 0-8191-4999-3). U Pr of Amer.

Hueffer, Hermann, tr. see Johannes Canaparius.

Huegel, F. J. Bone of His Bone. (Christian Classic Ser.). 96p. 1980. pap. 3.95 (ISBN 0-310-26321-2, 9955P). Zondervan.

--Enthroned Christian. 1967. pap. 2.95 (ISBN 0-87508-905-4). Chr Lit.

--Ministry of Intercession. LC 76-15861. (Orig.). 1971. pap. 2.95 (ISBN 0-87123-365-7, 200365). Bethany Hse.

--Secretos de la Oracion. Orig. Title: Secrets of Prayer. (Span.). 1984. pap. 3.25 (ISBN 0-8254-1323-0). Kregel.

Huelin, Gordon, ed. Old Catholics & Anglicans: 1931-81. (Illus.). 1983. text ed. 27.50x (ISBN 0-19-920129-3). Oxford U Pr.

Huels, J. M. The Faithful of Christ: The New Canon Law for the Laity. 1983. 5.50 (ISBN 0-8199-0873-8). Franciscan Herald.

Huels, John. One Table, Many Laws: Essays on Catholic Eucharistic Discipline. 112p. 1986. pap. 5.95 (ISBN 0-8146-1465-5). Liturgical Pr.

Huels, John M. The Pastoral Companion: A Canon Law Handbook for Catholic Ministry. LC 85-29316. 1986. 25.00 (ISBN 0-8199-0900-9); pap. 15.00. Franciscan Herald.

--The Pastoral Companion: A Canon Law Handbook for Pastoral Ministry. 1986. 25.00 (ISBN 0-8199-0900-9); pap. 15.00. Franciscan Herald.

Huelsman. Pray: Moderator's Manual: An Introduction to the Spiritual Life for Busy People. LC 76-2449. 168p. 1976. pap. 7.95 (ISBN 0-8091-1975-7). Paulist Pr.

Huelsman, Richard J. Intimacy with Jesus: An Introduction. LC 82-60587. 1983. pap. 5.95 (ISBN 0-8091-2492-0). Paulist Pr.

--Pray: An Introduction to the Spiritual Life for Busy People. LC 76-24449. (Participants Handbook). 136p. 1976. pap. 4.95 (ISBN 0-8091-1976-5). Paulist Pr.

Huemer, Iohnnes, ed. see Sedulius.

Huesman, John S. Isaiah, 2 pts. (Bible Ser.). Pt. 1. pap. 1.00 (ISBN 0-8091-5069-7); Pt. 2. pap. 1.00 (ISBN 0-8091-5070-0). Paulist Pr.

Huessy, Hans R., jt. auth. see Bryant, M. Darrol.

Huett, Lenora, jt. auth. see Richardson, Wally G.

Huey, F. B., Jr. Exodus. (Bible Study Commentary Ser.). 1977. pap. 4.95 (ISBN 0-310-36053-6, 11021P). Zondervan.

--Jeremiah: Bible Study Commentary. (Bible Study Commentary Ser.). 144p. (Orig.). 1981. pap. 4.95 (ISBN 0-310-36063-3, 11063P). Zondervan.

--Layman's Bible Book Commentary: Ezekiel, Daniel, Vol. 12. LC 81-66848. 1984. 5.95 (ISBN 0-8054-1182-8). Broadman.

--Numbers: Bible Study Commentary. (Bible Study Commentary Ser.). 144p. (Orig.). 1981. pap. 4.95 (ISBN 0-310-36073-0, 11064P). Zondervan.

Huey, F. B., Jr. & Corley, Bruce. A Student's Dictionary for Biblical & Theological Studies. 1986. pap. 6.96 (ISBN 0-310-45951-6, 12726P). Zondervan.

Huff, Joan. Celebrating Pentecost Through Dance. Adams, Doug, ed. (Orig.). 1986. pap. 3.00 (ISBN 0-941500-41-1). Sharing Co.

Huff, Sr. M. Cyria. The Sonnet-No Me Mueve, Mi Dios-Its Theme in Spanish Tradition. LC 73-94177. (Catholic University of America Studies in Romance Languages & Literatures Ser: No. 33). Repr. of 1948 ed. 20.00 (ISBN 0-404-50333-0). AMS Pr.

Huffard, Evertt W. Deciding to Grow. 1983. pap. 3.95 (ISBN 0-89137-540-6). Quality Pubns.

Huffman, Carolyn & Barrow, Lu Ann. Life Between the Questions. 80p. 1985. 8.95 (ISBN 0-8499-0446-3, 0446-3). Word Bks.

Huffman, John. Joshua (CC, Vol. 6. 320p. 1986. 18.95 (ISBN 0-8499-0411-0). Word Bks.

Huffman, Vicki. The Best of Times: Ecclesiastes 3: 1-8. LC 85-29087. 1986. pap. 5.95 (ISBN 0-8054-1234-4). Broadman.

Huffman, Walter. The Prayer of the Faithful: Understanding & Creatively Using the Prayer of the Church. 80p. (Orig.). 1986. pap. 5.95 (ISBN 0-8066-2230-X, 10-5079). Augsburg.

Huffmon, H. B., et al, eds. The Quest for the Kingdom of God: Essays in Honor of George E. Mendenhall. 1983. text ed. 20.00x (ISBN 0-931464-15-3). Eisenbrauns.

Hufford, David J. The Terror That Comes in the Night: An Experience Centered Study of Supernatural Assault Traditions. LC 82-40350. 352p. 1982. 27.50x (ISBN 0-8122-7851-8). U of Pa Pr.

Hufford, David J., jt. auth. see Foster, Genevieve.

Hufstader, Anselm. God's Time Is the Best Time. (Ways of Prayer Ser.: Vol. 11). 8.95 (ISBN 0-89453-386-X); pap. 4.95 (ISBN 0-89453-385-1). M Glazier.

Hufton, Richard A. Ephesians: The Mystery Within. 126p. (Orig.). 1984. pap. 3.50 (ISBN 0-933643-04-7). Grace World Outreach.

--Galatians: The Gospel of Freedom. LC 85-80103. 130p. (Orig.). 1985. pap. 4.00 (ISBN 0-933643-00-4). Grace World Outreach.

--James: Faith in Action. 146p. (Orig.). 1984. pap. 4.00 (ISBN 0-933643-03-9). Grace World Outreach.

--The Pastor's Handbook. 47p. (Orig.). 1984. pap. 3.00 (ISBN 0-933643-05-5). Grace World Outreach.

--Philippians: Our High Calling. LC 85-70134. 116p. (Orig.). 1985. pap. 4.00 (ISBN 0-933643-01-2). Grace World Outreach.

--Psalms: A Matchless Treasury. LC 84-82058. 106p. (Orig.). 1984. pap. 4.00 (ISBN 0-933643-02-0). Grace World Outreach.

Hufton, Richard A., jt. auth. see Tucker, Ronald D.

Hug, James E. Renew the Earth: A Guide to the Second Draft of the U. S. Bishops' Pastoral Letter on Catholic Social Teachings & the U. S. Economy. (Illus.). 32p. (Orig.). 1985. pap. text ed. 1.50 (ISBN 0-934255-02-4). Center Concern.

Hug, James E., ed. Tracing the Spirit: Communities, Social Action & Theological Reflection. LC 82-62419. (Woodstock Studies: No. 7). 288p. 1983. pap. 9.95 (ISBN 0-8091-2529-3). Paulist Pr.

Hugel, Friedrich Von. Essays & Addresses on the Philosophy of Religion. LC 72-9828. 308p. 1974. Repr. of 1921 ed. lib. bdg. 29.50x (ISBN 0-8371-6219-X, HUPR). Greenwood.

Huges, Robert D. Plays That'll Preach. LC 85-365. 1985. pap. 4.95 (ISBN 0-8054-6812-9). Broadman.

Huggenvik, Theodore. We Believe. 1950. pap. 3.95 (ISBN 0-8066-0151-5, 15-7102). Augsburg.

Huggett, Joyce. Approaching Easter. Reynolds, A., ed. 96p. 1987. pap. 6.95 (ISBN 0-7459-1120-X). Lion USA.

--Dating, Sex & Friendship. LC 85-19734. 204p. 1985. pap. 5.95 (ISBN 0-87784-406-2). Inter-Varsity.

--The Joy of Listening to God. LC 86-27689. 240p. (Orig.). 1987. pap. 6.95 (ISBN 0-87784-729-0). Inter-Varsity.

Huggins, Larry. Believer's Bible Companion. 32p. (Orig.). 1984. pap. 1.95 (ISBN 0-89274-314-X, HH-314). Harrison Hse.

--The Blood Speaks. 128p. 1982. pap. 3.95 (ISBN 0-89274-231-3, HH-231). Harrison Hse.

Huggins, Nathan I. Protestants Against Poverty: Boston's Charities, 1870-1900. (Contributions in American History: No. 9). 1970. lib. bdg. 29.95 (ISBN 0-8371-3307-6, HUP/). Greenwood.

Huggins, William H. & Entwisle, Doris R. Iconic Communication: An Annotated Bibliography. LC 73-8130. (Illus.). 184p. 1974. 18.50x (ISBN 0-8018-1528-2). Johns Hopkins.

Hughes. Dictionary of Islam. 45.00 (ISBN 0-686-18366-5). Kazi Pubns.

Hughes, Alfred C. Preparing for Church Ministry: A Practical Guide to Spiritual Formation. 6.95 (ISBN 0-87193-167-2). Dimension Bks.

Hughes, Amelia. Missions Studies: Australia. (Illus.). 32p. (Orig.). 1984. pap. 1.00 (ISBN 0-89114-117-0). Baptist Pub Hse.

--Missions Studies: Bolivia. 32p. (Orig.). 1982. pap. text ed. 1.00 (ISBN 0-89114-109-X). Baptist Pub Hse.

--Missions Studies: Japan. pap. 1.00 (ISBN 0-89114-113-8). Baptist Pub Hse.

Hughes, Andrew. Medieval Manuscripts for Mass & Office: A Guide to Their Organization & Terminology. 496p. 1981. 65.00x (ISBN 0-8020-5467-6). U of Toronto Pr.

Hughes, Barbara & Dwiggins, Gwen. God Loves Children. (God Loves...Coloring Book Ser.). (Illus.). 0.75 (ISBN 0-8091-6562-7). Paulist Pr.

--God Loves Colors. (God Loves...Coloring Book Ser.). (Illus.). 0.60 (ISBN 0-8091-6566-X). Paulist Pr.

--God Loves Fun. (God Loves...Coloring Book Ser.). (Illus.). 0.75t (ISBN 0-8091-6564-3). Paulist Pr.

--God Loves Love. (God Loves...Coloring Book Ser.). (Illus.). 0.60 (ISBN 0-8091-6565-1). Paulist Pr.

--God Loves Seasons. (God Loves...Coloring Book Ser.). (Illus.). 0.75t (ISBN 0-8091-6563-5). Paulist Pr.

Hughes, Blaine. Second Man: Monster, Myth, or Minister. 20p. 1976. pap. text ed. 0.95 (ISBN 0-89265-110-5). Randall Hse.

Hughes, Caroline A., jt. auth. see Westerhoff, John H., III.

Hughes, David. The Star of Bethlehem: An Astronomer's Confirmation. (Illus.). 1979. 14.95 (ISBN 0-8027-0644-4). Walker & Co.

Hughes, Dom A., compiled by. Liturgical Terms for Music Students: A Dictionary. LC 70-166236. 1972. Repr. of 1940 ed. 29.00x (ISBN 0-403-01363-1). Scholarly.

Hughes, Don. Free from Guilt & Condemnation. (Orig.). 1977. pap. 0.75 minibook (ISBN 0-89274-048-5, HH-048). Harrison Hse.

--Paul's Thorn. (Orig.). 1977. pap. 0.75 (ISBN 0-89274-047-7, HH-047). Harrison Hse.

Hughes, Emmet J. Church & the Liberal Society. 1961. pap. 1.95x (ISBN 0-268-00046-8). U of Notre Dame Pr.

Hughes, Eric, ed. Sri Aurobindo & the Mother on Collective Yoga. 75p. 1974. pap. 1.25 (ISBN 0-89071-000-7). Matagiri.

Hughes, G. Hebrews & Hermeneutics. LC 77-84806. (Society for New Testament Studies Monographs: No. 36). 1980. 32.50 (ISBN 0-521-21858-6). Cambridge U Pr.

Hughes, G. W. With Freedom Fired: The Story of Robert Robinson, Cambridge Nonconformist. 123p. 1955. Repr. 2.95 (ISBN 0-87921-018-4). Attic Pr.

Hughes, George R. Medinet Habu - Epigraphic Survey: The Temple Proper, Part Three, the Third Hypostyle Hall, All Rooms Accessible from It, with Friezes of Scenes from the Roof Terraces & Exterior Walls of the Temple. LC 30-22847. (Oriental Institute Pubns. Ser). 1964. 65.00x (ISBN 0-226-62196-0, OIP93). U of Chicago Pr.

--Medinet Habu - Epigraphic Survey: The Temple Proper, Part Two, the Re Chapel, the Mortuary Complex, & Adjacent Rooms with Miscellaneous Material from Pylons, the Forecourts & the First Hypostyle Hall, Vol. 6. LC 30-22847. (Oriental Institute Pubns. Ser). 1963. 65.00x (ISBN 0-226-62185-5, OIP84). U of Chicago Pr.

Hughes, Gerald & Travis, Stephen. Harper's Introduction to the Bible. LC 80-8607. (Illus.). 144p. (Orig.). 1981. pap. 11.95 (ISBN 0-06-064078-2, RD 350, HarpR). Har-Row.

Hughes, Gerard. Authority in Morals. 160p. (Orig.). 1984. pap. 6.95 (ISBN 0-87840-410-4). Georgetown U Pr.

Hughes, Gerard J., ed. The Philosophical Assessment of Theology: Essays in Honor of F. C. Copleston. (Orig.). 1987. pap. price not set (ISBN 0-87840-449-X). Georgetown U Pr.

Hughes, Glyn T. Williams Pantycelyn. (Writer of Wales Ser.). 180p. 1983. pap. text ed. 8.50x (ISBN 0-7083-0840-6, Pub. by U of Wales). Humanities.

Hughes, H. Stuart. Prisoners of Hope: The Silver Age of the Italian Jews, 1924-1974. 184p. 1983. text ed. 15.00x (ISBN 0-674-70727-3). Harvard U Pr.

Hughes, Hugh P. The Philanthropy of God: Described & Illustrated in a Series of Sermons. 1978. Repr. of 1892 ed. lib. bdg. 12.50 (ISBN 0-8482-4402-8). Norwood Edns.

Hughes, Jeff, ed. see Strahan, Loretta.

Hughes, John & Breckinridge, John. A Discussion: Is the Roman Catholic Religion Inimical to Civil or Religious Liberty? Is the Presbyterian Religion Inimical to Civil or Religious Liberty? LC 76-122167. (Civil Liberties in American History Ser). 1970. Repr. of 1836 ed. lib. bdg. 75.00 (ISBN 0-306-71979-7). Da Capo.

Hughes, John J. Homilies for the C Cycle: Proclaiming the Good News. LC 85-60893. 160p. 1985. text ed. 14.95 (ISBN 0-87973-724-7, 724). Our Sunday Visitor.

--Proclaiming the Good News: Homilies for the A Cycle. LC 82-62554. 156p. 1983. pap. 14.95 (ISBN 0-87973-722-0, 722). Our Sunday Visitor.

--Proclaiming the Good News: Homilies for the "B" Cycle. LC 84-60750. 156p. 1984. 14.95 (ISBN 0-87973-723-9, 723). Our Sunday Visitor.

--Proclaiming the Good News: Homilies for the "C" Cycle, No. 724. 1985. 14.95 (ISBN 0-87973-724-7). Our Sunday Visitor.

Hughes, Leonard V., Jr. St. George's Episcopal Church, Germantown, Tennessee: The First Twenty Years. Russell, James D., ed. LC 83-50804. (Illus.). 224p. 1984. 6.00 (ISBN 0-9613533-0-9). St Georges Episcopal.

Hughes, Patrick, tr. see Boff, Leonardo.

Hughes, Philip. Commentary on the Second Epistle to the Corinthians. (New International Commentary on the New Testament). 1962. 19.95 (ISBN 0-8028-2186-3). Eerdmans.

Hughes, Philip E. Christian Ethics in Secular Society: An Introduction to Christian Ethics. 240p. 1983. 13.95 (ISBN 0-8010-4267-4). Baker Bk.

--Commentary on the Epistle to the Hebrews. LC 82-90554. 1977. text ed. 18.95 (ISBN 0-8028-3495-7). Eerdmans.

--Confirmation in the Church Today. pap. 20.00 (ISBN 0-317-08439-9, 2012949). Bks Demand UMI.

--Lefevre: Pioneer of Ecclesiastical Renewal in France. 224p. (Orig.). 1984. pap. 15.95x (ISBN 0-8028-0015-7). Eerdmans.

Hughes, Philip E., ed. & intro. by. Faith & Works: Cranmer & Hooker on Justification. 128p. (Orig.). 1982. pap. 7.95 (ISBN 0-8192-1315-2). Morehouse.

Hughes, Philip E., tr. see Marcel, Pierre.

Hughes, Phillip E. Hope for a Despairing World. LC 77-89680. (Canterbury Bks.). pap. 2.95 (ISBN 0-8010-4159-7). Baker Bk.

Hughes, Phyllis, jt. auth. see Ely, Evelyn.

Hughes, R. Kent. Abba Father: The Lord's Pattern for Prayer. LC 85-72920. 128p. 1986. pap. 5.95 (ISBN 0-89107-377-9, Crossway Bks). Good News.

--Behold the Lamb. 180p. 1984. pap. 5.95 (ISBN 0-88207-623-X). Victor Bks.

--Behold the Man. LC 84-50144. 180p. 1984. pap. 5.95 (ISBN 0-89693-379-2). Victor Bks.

--Blessed Are the Born Again. 132p. 1986. pap. 4.95 (ISBN 0-89693-369-5). Victor Bks.

--Living on the Cutting Edge: Joshua & the Challenge of Spiritual Leadership. LC 86-72055. 176p. (Orig.). 1987. pap. 6.95 (ISBN 0-89107-414-7, Crossway Bks). Good News.

Hughes, R. Kent, jt. auth. see Muzzy, Ruth.

Hughes, Ray H. The Order of Future Events. 1970. pap. 3.50 (ISBN 0-87148-650-4). Pathway Pr.

--Pentecostal Preaching. LC 81-84606. 159p. (Orig.). 1981. pap. text ed. 5.95 (ISBN 0-87148-711-X). Pathway Pr.

Hughes, Ray H. & Woodard, Bernice Stout. Planning for Sunday School Progress. 5.25 (ISBN 0-87148-682-2). Pathway Pr.

Hughes, Ray H., ed. Distintivos de la Iglesia de Dios. (Span.). 116p. 1970. pap. 5.95 (ISBN 0-87148-256-8). Pathway Pr.

Hughes, Richard. Theology & the Cain Complex. LC 81-43698. 148p. (Orig.). 1982. lib. bdg. 24.75 (ISBN 0-8191-2357-9); pap. text ed. 9.50 (ISBN 0-8191-2358-7). U Pr of Amer.

Hughes, Richard & Serig, Joseph A., eds. Evangelism: The Ministry of the Church. 1981. pap. 12.00 (ISBN 0-8309-0304-6). Herald Hse.

Hughes, Richard E. The Lively Image: Four Myths in Literature. 1975. pap. text ed. 12.00 (ISBN 0-316-38034-2). Little.

Hughes, Robert. A Trumpet in Darkness: Preaching to Mourners. LC 85-47719. (Fortress Resources for Preaching Ser.). 112p. 1985. pap. 5.95 (ISBN 0-8006-1141-1). Fortress.

Hughes, Robert, jt. auth. see Vale, John.

Hughes, Robert B. First Corinthians. (Everyman's Bible Commentary Ser.). (Orig.). 1985. pap. 5.95 (ISBN 0-8024-0447-2). Moody.

--Second Corinthians. (Everyman's Bible Commentary Ser.). 1983. pap. 5.95 (ISBN 0-8024-0241-0). Moody.

Hughes, Selwyn. The Christian Counselor's Pocket Guide. rev. ed. LC 80-65443. 96p. 1985. pap. 3.50 (ISBN 0-87123-844-6, 200047). Bethany Hse.

--How to Live the Christian Life. 160p. (Orig.). 1982. pap. 6.95 (ISBN 0-8164-2395-4, HarpR). Har-Row.

--The Introvert's Guide to Spontaneous Witnessing. LC 83-22390. 192p. 1984. pap. 5.95 (ISBN 0-87123-428-9, 210428). Bethany Hse.

Hughes, Susan C., jt. auth. see Boskey, James B.

Hughes, Thomas A. Loyola & the Educational System of the Jesuits. 34.95 (ISBN 0-8490-0565-5). Gordon Pr.

--Loyola & the Educational System of the Jesuits. LC 83-45594. Date not set. Repr. of 1892 ed. 35.00 (ISBN 0-404-19887-2). AMS Pr.

--Loyola & the Educational Systems of the Jesuits. 1892. 39.00 (ISBN 0-403-00121-8). Scholarly.

Hughes, Thomas P. A Dictionary of Islam, 2 vols. 1980. Set. lib. bdg. 199.95 (ISBN 0-8490-3121-4). Gordon Pr.

--Dictionary of Islam. (Illus.). 750p. 1977. Repr. of 1885 ed. 48.00x (ISBN 0-89684-103-0, Pub. by Cosmo Pubns India). Orient Bk Dist.

--A Dictionary of Islam. 1976. Repr. 37.50x (ISBN 0-8364-0395-9). South Asia Bks.

--A Dictionary of Islam: A Cyclopedia of the Muhammadan Religion. (Reprints in History). (Illus.). 750p. lib. bdg. 34.00 (ISBN 0-697-00053-2). Irvington.

--Notes on Muhammadanism: Being Outlines of the Religious System of Islam. LC 74-83164. (Islam & MidEast Ser). 1976. Repr. of 1877 ed. 33.00 (ISBN 0-8420-1756-9). Scholarly Res Inc.

Hughey, John D. Religious Freedom in Spain: Its Ebb & Flow. facsimile ed. LC 77-119935. (Select Bibliographies Reprint Ser). Repr. of 1955 ed. 21.50 (ISBN 0-8369-5378-9). Ayer Co Pubs.

Hughey, Michael W. Civil Religion & Moral Order: Theoretical & Historical Dimensions. LC 82-15429. (Contributions in Sociology Ser.: No. 43). 256p. 1983. lib. bdg. 32.95 (ISBN 0-313-23522-8, HUR/). Greenwood.

Hugh-Jones, S. The Palm & the Pleiades. LC 78-5533. (Studies in Social Anthropology: No. 24). (Illus.). 1979. 37.50 (ISBN 0-521-21952-3). Cambridge U Pr.

Hughley, Ella J. The Truth about Black Biblical Hebrew Israelites (Jews) (Orig.). 1982. pap. 5.00 (ISBN 0-9605150-1-1). Hughley Pubns.

Hughley, Neal. Trends in Protestant Social Idealism. LC 74-167359. (Essay Index Reprint Ser.). Repr. of 1948 ed. 18.00 (ISBN 0-8369-2771-0). Ayer Co Pubs.

Hugh of St. Victor. Hugh of St. Victor: On the Sacraments of the Christian Faith. Deferrari, R. J., tr. (Eng.). 1976. Repr. of 1951 ed. 18.00x (ISBN 0-910956-32-4). Medieval Acad.

Hughston, Karen M., jt. auth. see Jensen, Larry C.

Hugh The Chantor. The History of the Church of York, Ten Sixty Six-Eleven Twenty Seven. Johnson, Charles, ed. (Oxford Medieval Texts Ser.). 1984. 22.00x (ISBN 0-19-822213-0). Oxford U Pr.

Hugo, John. St. Augustine on Nature, Sex & Marriage. 249p. 1969. pap. 8.95 (ISBN 0-933932-23-5). Scepter Pubs.

Huhm, Halla Pai. Kut: Korean Shamanist Rituals. 102p. 1980. 14.50x (ISBN 0-930878-18-3). Hollym Intl.

Hui-neng. The Sutra of Wei Lang. Wong Mou-lam, tr. from Chinese. LC 73-879. (China Studies: from Confucius to Mao Ser.). 128p. 1973. Repr. of 1944 ed. 15.75 (ISBN 0-88355-073-3). Hyperion Conn.

Hui Seng, commentary by. Brahma Net Sutra, Vol. 1. Buddhist Text Translation Society, tr. from Chinese. (Illus.). 312p. (Orig., Bilingual Text). 1981. pap. 10.00 (ISBN 0-917512-79-0). Buddhist Text.

Huizing, Peter & Walf, Knut, eds. Electing Our Own Bishops. (Concilium Ser.: Vol. 137). 128p. (Orig.). 1980. pap. 5.95 (ISBN 0-8164-2279-6, HarpR). Har-Row.

--The Revised Code of Canon Law: A Missed Opportunity, Vol. 147. (Concilium 1981). 128p. (Orig.). 1981. pap. 6.95 (ISBN 0-8164-2347-4, HarpR). Har-Row.

Huizinga, J. Waning of the Middle Ages. LC 54-4529. pap. 5.95 (ISBN 0-385-09288-1, A42, Anch). Doubleday.

Huizinga, Johan. Erasmus & the Age of Reformation: With a Selection from the Letters of Erasmus. LC 84-42547. (Illus.). 312p. 1984. text ed. 32.50x (ISBN 0-691-05421-5); pap. 8.95 (ISBN 0-691-00801-9). Princeton U Pr.

Hu Kuo-chen, Peter, tr. see Ricci, Matteo.

Hulbert, Terry C. World Missions Today. LC 78-68233. 96p. 1979. pap. text ed. 4.95 (ISBN 0-910566-16-X); Perfect bdg. instr's. guide 5.95 (ISBN 0-910566-28-3). Evang Tchr.

Hulings, Martha. Shaker Days Remembered. pap. 5.00 (ISBN 0-317-17252-2). Shaker Her Soc.

Hull, Bill. Jesus Christ, Disciplemaker. LC 84-70471. 216p. 1984. 5.95 (ISBN 0-89109-516-0). NavPress.

--Revitalizing the Church. 1986. pap. cancelled (ISBN 0-89109-539-X). NavPress.

--Right Thinking: Insights for Spiritual Growth. LC 84-63115. 144p. 1985. pap. 4.95 (ISBN 0-89109-531-4). NavPress.

Hull, J. Studies in Religion & Education. 292p. 1984. 29.00x (ISBN 0-905273-52-4, Falmer Pr); pap. 17.00x (ISBN 0-905273-51-6). Taylor & Francis.

Hull, Jerry. Beacon Small-Group Bible Studies, Luke: Good News for All of Us, Vol. 1. 72p. (Orig.). 1980. pap. 2.50 (ISBN 0-8341-0657-4). Beacon Hill.

Hull, John. Hellenistic Magic & the Synoptic Tradition. LC 73-77369. (Studies in Biblical Theology, 2nd Ser.: No. 28). 1974. pap. text ed. 12.00x (ISBN 0-8401-3078-3). A R Allenson.

Hull, John, ed. New Directions in Religious Education. 226p. 1982. text ed. 24.50x (ISBN 0-905273-31-1, Falmer Pr); pap. 15.00x (ISBN 0-905273-30-3). Taylor & Francis.

Hull, Karen. The Mommy Book: Advice to New Mothers from Those Who've Been There. 240p. 1986. pap. 8.95 (ISBN 0-310-32241-3). Zondervan.

Hull, R. F., ed. see Herrigel, Eugene.

Hull, R. F., tr. see Adler, Gerard, et al.

Hull, R. F., tr. see Neumann, Erich.

Hull, Shirley, jt. ed. see Wilson, Valerie.

Hull, Walter E. God - Isn't There Any Other Way!? 1983. 5.95 (ISBN 0-8062-2173-9). Carlton.

Hull, William E. The Christian Experience of Salvation. LC 84-20501. (Layman's Library of Christian Doctrine Ser.). 1987. 5.95 (ISBN 0-8054-1639-0). Broadman.

Hull, William I. William Penn. facsimile ed. LC 78-179525. (Select Bibliographies Reprint Ser). Repr. of 1937 ed. 32.00 (ISBN 0-8369-6654-6). Ayer Co Pubs.

Hullinger, Robert N., ed. Mormon Answer to Skepticism: Why Joseph Smith Wrote the Book of Mormon. LC 79-54055. 201p. (Orig.). 1980. pap. 14.95x (ISBN 0-915644-18-5). Clayton Pub Hse.

Hullum, Everett, jt. auth. see Loucks, Celeste.

Hullum, Everett, ed. see Furlow, Elaine.

Hulme, Dale, jt. auth. see Hulme, William.

Hulme, Edward M. The Renaissance, the Protestant Revolution & the Catholic Reformation in Continental Europe. LC 83-45662. Date not set. Repr. of 1915 ed. 62.50 (ISBN 0-404-19812-0). AMS Pr.

Hulme, F. E. History, Principles & Practice of Symbolism in Christian Art. 35.00 (ISBN 0-8490-0364-4). Gordon Pr.

Hulme, F. Edward. History, Principles, & Practice of Symbolism in Christian Art. LC 68-18027. 1969. Repr. of 1891 ed. 37.00x (ISBN 0-8103-3214-0). Gale.

Hulme, Kathryn. Undiscovered Country: In Search of Gurdjieff. 1972. pap. 4.95 (ISBN 0-316-38138-1, Pub. by Atlantic Monthly Pr). Little.

Hulme, William. Managing Stress in Ministry. LC 84-48221. 160p. 1985. 13.45 (ISBN 0-06-064077-4, HarpR). Har-Row.

Hulme, William & Hulme, Dale. Who Am I Lord... & Why Am I Here? LC 83-25175. 1984. pap. 4.95 (ISBN 0-570-03926-6, 12-2860). Concordia.

Hulme, William E. Building a Christian Marriage. LC 65-22192. 1968. pap. 5.95 (ISBN 0-8066-0813-7, 10-0940). Augsburg.

--Creative Loneliness. LC 76-27083. 112p. 1977. pap. 5.95 (ISBN 0-8066-1556-7, 10-1715). Augsburg.

--I Hate to Bother You, But: Clues for Youth on Personal Problems. rev. ed. Orig. Title: Face Your Life with Confidence. 1970. pap. 4.95 (ISBN 0-570-06617-4, 12-2327). Concordia.

--Mid-Life Crises. LC 80-11539. (Christian Care Bks.: Vol, 7). 118p. 1980. pap. 7.95 (ISBN 0-664-24324-X). Westminster.

--Pastoral Care & Counseling: Using the Unique Resources of the Christian Tradition. LC 80-67806. 160p. (Orig.). 1981. pap. 9.95 (ISBN 0-8066-1869-8, 10-4896). Augsburg.

--Vintage Years: Growing Older with Meaning & Hope. LC 85-26399. 120p. (Orig.). 1986. pap. 8.95 (ISBN 0-664-24684-2). Westminster.

--When Two Become One: Reflections for the Newly Married. LC 76-176481. 1974. pap. 5.95 (ISBN 0-8066-1438-2, 10-7061). Augsburg.

Hulme, William E., ed. see Jackson, Edgar N.

Hulme, William E., ed. see Keller, John E.

Hulme, William E., et al, eds. Pastors in Ministry: Guidelines for Seven Critical Issues. LC 85-1213. 176p. (Orig.). 1985. pap. 9.95 (ISBN 0-8066-2159-1, 10-4898). Augsburg.

Hulse, Erroll. Billy Graham: The Pastor's Dilemma. pap. 2.50 (ISBN 0-685-61833-1). Reiner.

Hulshizer, S. J. Obedience. 69p. pap. 3.95 (ISBN 0-88172-156-5). Believers Bkshelf.

Hulsmann, Carl. Awakening of Consciousness. (Illus.). 192p. 1982. 18.00 (ISBN 0-86164-151-5, Pub. by Momenta Publishing Ltd. U. K.). Hunter Hse.

Hultgren, Arland J. Christ & His Benefits: Christology & Redemption in the New Testament. LC 86-45917. 288p. 1987. text ed. 24.95 (ISBN 0-8006-0861-5). Fortress.

--Paul's Gospel & Mission: The Outlook from His Letter to the Romans. LC 85-4430. 176p. 1985. pap. 9.95 (ISBN 0-8006-1871-8). Fortress.

Hultgren, Arland J. & Aus, Roger. Augsburg Commentary on the New Testament: 1 Timothy 2 Timothy, Titus, 2 Thessalonians. LC 83-72126. (Augsburg Commentary New Testament Ser.). 224p. 1984. kivar 8.95 (ISBN 0-8066-8874-2, 10-9032). Augsburg.

Hultkrantz, Ake. Belief & Worship in Native North America. Vecsey, Christopher, ed. LC 81-18356. (Illus.). 358p. 1981. 30.00x (ISBN 0-8156-2248-1). Syracuse U Pr.

--The Religions of the American Indians. LC 73-90661. (Hermeneutics: Studies in the History of Religions). 1979. 20.95x (ISBN 0-520-02653-5); pap. 7.95 (ISBN 0-520-04239-5, CAL 463). U of Cal Pr.

--The Study of American Indian Religions. Vecsey, Christopher, ed. LC 82-10533. (The American Academy of Religion - Studies in Religion). 142p. 1983. 12.95 (ISBN 0-89130-587-4, 01 00 29). Scholars Pr GA.

Human, Johnnie. Finlay & Julia Graham: Missionary Partners. LC 86-4148. (Meet the Missionary Ser.). 1986. 5.50 (ISBN 0-8054-4327-4). Broadman.

--John the Baptist: Forerunner of Jesus. (BibLearn Ser.). (Illus.). 1978. 5.95 (ISBN 0-8054-4240-5, 4242-40). Broadman.

Humayun, Kabir. Science, Democracy, & Islam: And Other Essays. LC 80-2195. Repr. of 1955 ed. 20.00 (ISBN 0-404-18967-9). AMS Pr.

Humbertson, Jame E., ed. Evangelical Sunday School Lesson Commentary, 1982-1983. (YA) 1982. 3.65 (ISBN 0-87148-298-3). Pathway Pr.

Humbertson, James, ed. Evangelical S. S. Commentary, 1985-1986. text ed. 7.95 (ISBN 0-87148-312-2). Pathway Pr.

Humbertson, James E., ed. Evangelical Sunday School Lesson Commentary, 1976. 396p. 1976. 2.25 (ISBN 0-87148-281-9). Pathway Pr.

--Evangelical Sunday School Lesson Commentary 1980-1981. 448p. 3.50 (ISBN 0-87148-294-0). Pathway Pr.

--Evangelical Sunday School Lesson Commentary, 1981-1982. 448p. text ed. 3.65 (ISBN 0-87148-297-5). Pathway Pr.

--Evangelical Sunday School Lesson Commentary: 1983-1984. 1983. text ed. 7.95 (ISBN 0-87148-301-7). Pathway Pr.

--Evangelical Sunday School Lesson Commentary 1984-1985. 424p. 1984. 4.00 (ISBN 0-87148-302-5). Pathway Pr.

Humble, B. J., ed. see Kenya Mission Team.

Humble, Linda. Tell Me about God. LC 81-86703. (Happy Day Bks.). (Illus.). 24p. (Orig.). 1982. pap. 1.59 (ISBN 0-87239-544-8, 3590). Standard Pub.

Hume, Alexander. Hymns & Sacred Songs. Repr. of 1599 ed. 20.00 (ISBN 0-384-24880-2). Johnson Repr.

Hume, Basil. To Be a Pilgrim: A Spiritual Notebook. LC 84-47726. 240p. 1984. 13.45 (ISBN 0-06-064081-2, HarpR). Har-Row.

Hume, C. W. Status of Animals in the Christian Religion. 1980. 20.00x (ISBN 0-317-43856-5, Pub. by Univ Federation Animal). State Mutual Bk.

Hume, David. Dialogues Concerning Natural Religion. Smith, Norman K., ed. 1947. pap. 8.40 scp (ISBN 0-672-60404-3, LLA174). Bobbs.

--Dialogues Concerning Natural Religion. Popkin, Richard H., ed. LC 79-25349. 132p. 1980. lib. bdg. 15.00 (ISBN 0-915144-46-8); pap. text ed. 2.95 (ISBN 0-915144-45-X). Hackett Pub.

--Dialogues Concerning Natural Religion. Aiken, Henry D., ed. (Library of Classics Ser: No. 5). pap. text ed. 5.95x (ISBN 0-02-846180-0). Hafner.

--Dialogues Concerning Natural Religion: Text & Critical Essays. Pike, Nelson, ed. LC 77-132933. (Text & Critical Essays Ser). (Orig.). 1970. pap. write for info. (ISBN 0-02-358440-8, TC6). Macmillan.

--Enquiries Concerning Human Understanding & Concerning the Principles of Morals. 3rd ed. Nidditch, P. H., ed. 1975. pap. text ed. 10.95x (ISBN 0-19-824536-X). Oxford U Pr.

--Enquiry Concerning the Principles of Morals. 2nd ed. 200p. 1966. 15.95 (ISBN 0-87548-017-9); pap. 4.95 (ISBN 0-87548-018-7). Open Court.

--An Enquiry Concerning the Principles of Morals. Schneewind, J. B., ed. LC 82-11679. (HPC Philosophical Classics Ser.). 132p. 1983. lib. bdg. 15.00 (ISBN 0-915145-46-4); pap. text ed. 3.45 (ISBN 0-915145-45-6). Hackett Pub.

--Inquiry Concerning the Principles of Morals: With a Supplement, a Dialogue. Hendel, Charles W., ed. 1957. pap. 7.20 scp (ISBN 0-672-60236-9, LLA62). Bobbs.

--Moral & Political Philosophy. Aiken, Henry D., ed. (Library of Classics Ser.: No. 3). 1975. pap. text ed. 8.95x (ISBN 0-02-846170-3). Hafner.

--The Natural History of Religion. Root, H. E., ed. 1957. pap. 4.95x (ISBN 0-8047-0333-7). Stanford U Pr.

--The Natural History of Religion & Dialogues Concerning Natural Religion. Colver, A. Wayne & Price, Vladimir, eds. 1976. 49.95x (ISBN 0-19-824379-0). Oxford U Pr.

--Of Miracles. LC 85-11410. 60p. 1985. pap. 4.95 (ISBN 0-912050-72-1). Open Court.

--A Treatise of Human Nature, 2 vols. Green, T. H. & Grose, T. H., eds. 1025p. 1981. Repr. of 1898 ed. lib. bdg. 200.00 (ISBN 0-89987-377-4). Darby Bks.

Hume, Leslie, ed. see Schoenl, William J.

Hume, R. E., tr. from Sanskrit. Upanishas: The Thirteen Principal Upanishads. 2nd ed. 1931. pap. 16.95x (ISBN 0-19-561641-3). Oxford U Pr.

Hume, Robert E. The World's Living Religions. rev. ed. LC 58-12515. 335p. 1978. pap. text ed. write for info. (ISBN 0-02-358450-5, Pub. by). Macmillan.

Hume, Roberto E. Las Religiones Vivas. Beltroy, Manuel, tr. from Eng. Orig. Title: Living Religions of the World. (Span.). 320p. 1981. pap. 5.25 (ISBN 0-311-05758-6, Edit Mundo). Casa Bautista.

Humez, Jean M., ed. Gifts of Power: The Writings of Rebecca Jackson, Black Visionary, Shaker Eldress. LC 81-4684. (Illus.). 376p. 1981. lib. bdg. 22.50x (ISBN 0-87023-299-1); pap. 11.95 (ISBN 0-87023-565-6). U of Mass Pr.

Hummel, Anne, jt. auth. see Hummel, Charles.

Hummel, Charles. Becoming Free. pap. 0.75 (ISBN 0-87784-137-3). Inter-Varsity.

--Tyranny of the Urgent. pap. 0.75 (ISBN 0-87784-128-4). Inter-Varsity.

Hummel, Charles & Hummel, Anne. Genesis. (Lifebuilder Bible Studies). 96p. (Orig.). 1985. pap. text ed. 3.50 (ISBN 0-8308-1022-6). Inter-Varsity.

--I Corinthians: Problems & Solutions in a Growing Church. (Fisherman Bible Studyguide). 93p. 1981. saddle-stitched 2.95 (ISBN 0-87788-137-5). Shaw Pubs.

Hummel, Horace. The Word Becoming Flesh. 1979. 22.95 (ISBN 0-570-03273-3, 15-2718). Concordia.

Hummel, Leonard C. Time Is Running Out: It's Much Later Than You Think. 26p. (Orig.). 1986. pap. 1.95 (ISBN 0-940853-00-0). Power Word Pubns.

Humphrey. What Do You Communicate. 1985. pap. 4.50 (ISBN 0-89349-000-8). Gospel Advocate.

Humphrey, A. W. Robert Applegarth: Trade Unionist, Educationist, Reformer. Leventhal, F. M., ed. LC 83-48484. (The World of Labour - English Workers 1850-1890 Ser.). 328p. 1984. lib. bdg. 44.00 (ISBN 0-8240-5711-2). Garland Pub.

Humphrey, Hugh M. A Bibliography for the Gospel of Mark: 1954-1980. LC 81-18717. (Studies in the Bible & Early Christianity: Vol. 1). 176p. 1982. 49.95x (ISBN 0-88946-916-4). E Mellen.

Humphrey, J. Edward. Emil Brunner. Patterson, Bob E., ed. LC 75-36186. (Maker's of the Modern Theological Mind Ser.). 1976. 8.95 (ISBN 0-87680-453-9). Word Bks.

--Emil Brunner. 183p. 1984. pap. text ed. 8.95 (ISBN 0-8499-3006-5, 3006-5). Word Bks.

Humphrey, Nicholas, jt. ed. see Lifton, Robert J.

Humphrey, Rilda. Jesus Story & Color Book. (Illus.). 64p. (Orig.). 1982. pap. 2.95 (ISBN 0-87239-583-9, 2398). Standard Pub.

Humphrey, Ruth. Bible Story & Color Book. (Illus.). 64p. (Orig.). 1982. pap. 2.95 (ISBN 0-87239-582-0, 2397). Standard Pub.

Humphreys. Search Within. pap. 8.95 (ISBN 0-8356-5143-6). Theos Pub Hse.

Humphreys, Alice L. Heaven in My Hand. 5.95 (ISBN 0-8042-2352-1). John Knox.

Humphreys, Christmas. Buddhism. (Pelican Ser.). 256p. (Orig.). 1951. pap. 6.95 (ISBN 0-14-020228-5). Penguin.

--The Development of Buddhism in England. LC 78-72442. Repr. of 1937 ed. 17.50 (ISBN 0-404-17308-X). AMS Pr.

--Exploring Buddhism. LC 74-12206. 188p. (Orig.). 1975. pap. 2.50 (ISBN 0-8356-0454-3, Quest). Theos Pub Hse.

--Karma & Rebirth. 110p. 1983. pap. 5.75 (ISBN 0-8356-0306-7, Quest). Theos Pub Hse.

--A Popular Dictionary of Buddhism. 224p. 1984. pap. 8.95 (ISBN 0-7007-0184-2). Salem Hse Pubs.

--Western Approach to Zen. LC 72-76428. 212p. 1981. pap. 5.50 (ISBN 0-8356-0550-7, Quest). Theos Pub Hse.

--Zen: A Way of Life. LC 65-17332. 1971. pap. 7.70i (ISBN 0-316-38160-8). Little.

Humphreys, Christmas, ed. The Wisdom of Buddhism. 2nd, rev. ed. 280p. 1987. pap. text ed. 9.95 (ISBN 0-391-03464-2, Pub. by Humanities Press & Curzon Pr England). Humanities.

Humphreys, Christmas, ed. see Blavatsky, Helena P.

Humphreys, David. Historical Account of the Incorporated Society for the Propagation of the Gospel in Foreign Parts - to the Year 1728. LC 75-83426. (Religion in America, Ser. 1). 1969. Repr. of 1730 ed. 21.00 (ISBN 0-405-00251-3). Ayer Co Pubs.

Humphreys, Fisher. La Naturaleza de Dios. Canclini, Arnoldo, tr. from Eng. (Biblioteca de Doctrina Cristiana). Tr. of The Nature of God. (Span.). 144p. (Orig.). 1987. pap. 5.95 (ISBN 0-311-09114-8). Casa Bautista.

--The Nature of God. LC 84-20037. (Layman's Library of Christian Doctrine Ser.). 1985. 5.95 (ISBN 0-8054-1634-X). Broadman.

--Nineteenth Century Evangelical Theology. LC 83-71439. (Orig.). 1984. pap. 10.95 (ISBN 0-8054-6579-0). Broadman.

--Thinking about God. LC 74-81556. 228p. (Orig.). 1974. pap. 9.00 (ISBN 0-914520-00-8). Insight Pr.

Humphreys, Fisher & Tolbert, Malcolm. Speaking in Tongues. LC 73-86749. 94p. (Orig.). 1973. pap. 3.00 (ISBN 0-914520-05-9). Insight Pr.

Humphreys, Fisher & Wise, Philip. A Dictionary of Doctrinal Terms. LC 81-86635. (Orig.). 1983. pap. 4.95 (ISBN 0-8054-1141-0). Broadman.

Humphreys, S. C. & King, H., eds. Mortality & Immortality: The Anthropology & Archaeology of Death. LC 81-67910. (Research Seminars in Archaeology Ser.). 1982. 54.50 (ISBN 0-12-361550-X). Acad Pr.

Humphreys, W. Lee. Crisis & Story: Introduction to the Old Testament. LC 78-64594. (Illus.). 313p. 1979. text ed. 21.95 (ISBN 0-87484-437-1). Mayfield Pub.

--The Tragic Vision & the Hebrew Tradition. LC 85-47724. (Overtures to Biblical Theology Ser.). 176p. 1985. pap. 9.95 (ISBN 0-8006-1542-5). Fortress.

Humphries, Christmas. Concentration & Meditation. 343p. 1981. pap. 18.00 (ISBN 0-89540-068-5, SD-068). Sun Pub.

Humphries, Jefferson. The Puritan & the Cynic: Moralists & Theorists in French Letters. 144p. 1986. 15.95 (ISBN 0-19-504180-1). Oxford U Pr.

Hundert, Gershon D. & Bacon, Gershon C. The Jews in Poland & Russia: Bibliographical Essays. LC 83-49285. (The Modern Jewish Experience Ser.). 288p. 1985. 25.00x (ISBN 0-253-33158-7). Ind U Pr.

Huneke, Douglas K. The Moses of Rovno: The Stirring Story of Fritz Graeve, a German Christian Who Risked His Life to Lead Hundreds of Jews to Safety During the Holocaust. (Holocaust Studies). (Illus.). 236p. 1985. 17.95 (ISBN 0-396-08714-0). Dodd.

Hunger, H. Lexikon der Griechischen und Roemischen Mythologie. (Ger.). 452p. 1974. pap. 7.95 (ISBN 3-499-16178-8, M-7252). French & Eur.

Hungerford, Edward B. Shores of Darkness. 10.75 (ISBN 0-8446-2285-0). Peter Smith.

Hunsberger, Eydie M., jt. auth. see Loeffler, Chris.

Hunsinger, George, ed. Karl Barth & Radical Politics. LC 76-976. 236p. 1976. softcover 6.45 (ISBN 0-664-24797-0). Westminster.

Hunt, Arnold D. Christ & the World's Religious. 124p. (Orig.). 1970. pap. 8.45 (ISBN 0-85819-003-6, Pub. by JBCE). ANZ Religious Pubns.

Hunt, Arnold D. & Crotty, Robert B. Ethics of World Religions. (Illus.). 1978. lib. bdg. 11.95 (ISBN 0-912616-74-1); pap. 6.95 (ISBN 0-912616-73-3). Greenhaven.

Hunt, D., ed. see Law, William.

Hunt, Dave. Beyond Seduction. 1987. pap. 7.95 (ISBN 0-89081-558-5). Harvest Hse.

--The Cult Explosion. LC 80-80458. 240p. 1980. pap. 6.95 (ISBN 0-89081-241-1). Harvest Hse.

--Peace, Prosperity & the Coming Holocaust. LC 82-84069. 224p. 1983. pap. 6.95 (ISBN 0-89081-331-0). Harvest Hse.

Hunt, Dave & Kristian, Hans. The Secret Invasion. 224p. 1987. pap. 5.95 (ISBN 0-89081-560-7). Harvest Hse.

Hunt, Dave & McMahon, T. A. The Seduction of Christianity. LC 84-81211. 242p. 1985. pap. 7.95 (ISBN 0-89081-441-4, 4414). Harvest Hse.

Hunt, Dave, jt. auth. see Decker, Ed.

Hunt, Dave, jt. auth. see Maharaj, Rabindranath R.

Hunt, Don. What the Bible Says about the Unfolded Plan of God. LC 81-82988. (What the Bible Says Ser.). 500p. 1981. 13.95 (ISBN 0-89900-084-3). College Pr Pub.

Hunt, Donald. Pondering the Proverbs. (The Bible Study Textbook Ser.). (Illus.). 1974. 14.30 (ISBN 0-89900-018-5). College Pr Pub.

Hunt, E. Stephen, jt. ed. see Lefever, Ernest W.

Hunt, Earl G. A Bishop Speaks His Mind. 160p. 1987. 14.95 (ISBN 0-317-54253-2). Abingdon.

Hunt, Edward D. Holy Land Pilgramage in the Later Roman Empire, AD 312-460. 1982. 47.00x (ISBN 0-19-826438-0); pap. 13.50x (ISBN 0-19-826449-6). Oxford U Pr.

Hunt, Ernest E., III. Sermon Struggles: Four Methods of Sermon Preparation. 160p. (Orig.). 1982. pap. 8.95 (ISBN 0-8164-2375-X, HarpR). Har-Row.

Hunt, G. N. About the New English Bible. 1970. 1.25 (ISBN 0-521-07938-1). Cambridge U Pr.

Hunt, Garth. God Is Not Hiding. 1974. pap. 0.95 (ISBN 0-87509-087-7). Chr Pubns.

Hunt, George L. Secret Societies: Can a Christian Belong to Them & Still Honor Christ? pap. 1.50 (ISBN 0-87213-338-9). Loizeaux.

Hunt, George W. John Updike & the Three Great Secret Things: Sex, Religion & Art. LC 80-23796. pap. 60.50 (ISBN 0-317-20577-3, 2023218). Bks Demand UMI.

Hunt, Gladys. Family Secrets: What You Need to Know to Build a Strong Christian Family. 98p. 1985. pap. 3.95 (ISBN 0-89283-233-9, Pub. by Vine Books). Servant.

--The God Who Understands Me: The Sermon on the Mount. LC 75-181992. (Fisherman Bible Studyguide Ser.). 87p. 1971. saddle-stitched 2.95 (ISBN 0-87788-316-5). Shaw Pubs.

--Hebrews: From Shadows to Reality. (Fisherman Bible Studyguides). 79p. 1979. saddle stitch 2.95 (ISBN 0-87788-338-6). Shaw Pubs.

--Honey for a Child's Heart. 1969. pap. 5.95 (ISBN 0-310-26381-6, 9891P). Zondervan.

--John: Eyewitness. LC 70-158130. (Fisherman Bible Studyguide Ser.). 87p. 1971. pap. 2.95 saddle stitch (ISBN 0-87788-245-2). Shaw Pubs.

--Luke: A Daily Dialogue with God. (Personal Bible Studyguide Ser.). 192p. (Orig.). 1986. pap. 5.95 (ISBN 0-87788-510-9). Shaw Pubs.

--Relationships. (Fisherman Bible Studyguide Ser.). 64p. 1983. saddle stitched 2.95 (ISBN 0-87788-721-7). Shaw Pubs.

--Revelation: The Lamb Who Is the Lion. (Fisherman Bible Studyguide). 73p. 1973. saddle-stitched 2.95 (ISBN 0-87788-486-2). Shaw Pubs.

--Stories Jesus Told. (Fisherman Bible Studyguide Ser.). 96p. (Orig.). pap. 2.95 (ISBN 0-87788-791-8). Shaw Pubs.

--You Can Start a Bible Study Group: Making Friends, Changing Lives. rev. ed. (Resource for Fisherman Bible Studyguides). 96p. 1984. Repr. of 1971 ed. lib. bdg. 2.95 (ISBN 0-87788-974-0). Shaw Pubs.

Hunt, Ignatius. Genesis, 2 Bks. (Bible Ser.). Bk. 1. pap. 1.00 (ISBN 0-8091-5048-4); Bk. 2. pap. 1.00 (ISBN 0-8091-5049-2). Paulist Pr.

Hunt, Joan & Hunt, Richard. Growing Love in Christian Marriage: Couple's Manual. 1981. pap. 2.50 (ISBN 0-687-15931-8). Abingdon.

Hunt, Joan A. & Hunt, Richard A. Preparing for Christian Marriage: Couples. LC 81-1770. 96p. 1982. 6.95 (ISBN 0-687-33919-7). Abingdon.

Hunt, Joan A., jt. auth. see Hunt, Richard A.

Hunt, John. Irish Medieval Figure Sculpture 1200-1600: A Study of Irish Tombs with Notes on Costume & Armour, 2 vols. (Illus.). 550p. 1974. 75.00 (ISBN 0-85667-012-X). Sotheby Pubns.

--Pantheism & Christianity. LC 78-102573. 1970. Repr. of 1884 ed. 25.50 (ISBN 0-8046-0733-8, Pub. by Kennikat). Assoc Faculty Pr.

--Religious Thought in England from the Reformation to the End of the Last Century, 3 Vols. LC 72-153593. Repr. of 1873 ed. Set. 125.00 (ISBN 0-404-09480-5). AMS Pr.

--Religious Thought in England in the Nineteenth Century. 424p. Repr. of 1896 ed. text ed. 62.10x (ISBN 0-576-29211-7, Pub. by Gregg Intl Pubs England). Gregg Intl.

Hunt, Larry E. Frederick M. Smith: Saint as Reformer. LC 81-7213. 1982. Vol. 1. pap. 12.00 (ISBN 0-8309-0320-8); Vol. 2. 12.00 (ISBN 0-8309-0341-0). Herald Hse.

Hunt, Margaret & Jacob, Margaret, eds. Women & the Enlightenment. LC 84-590. (Women & History: No. 9). 93p. 1984. text ed. 24.95 (ISBN 0-86656-190-0). Haworth Pr.

Hunt, Marigold. A Life of Our Lord. 191p. 1959. 5.00 (ISBN 0-912414-25-1). Lumen Christi.

--St. Patrick's Summer. 273p. 1950. 6.00 (ISBN 0-912414-24-3). Lumen Christi.

Hunt, Noreen. Cluny under Saint Hugh, Ten Forty-Nine to Eleven Hundred Nine. 1st ed. LC 68-11411. pap. 60.00 (ISBN 0-317-29696-5, 2022064). Bks Demand UMI.

Hunt, Noreen, ed. Cluniac Monasticism in the Central Middle Ages. x, 248p. 1971. 25.00 (ISBN 0-208-01247-8, Archon). Shoe String.

Hunt, P. Bible Stories from the Old Testament. (Illus.). 4.98 (ISBN 0-517-43909-3). Outlet Bk Co.

Hunt, R. W. & Gibson, Margaret. The Schools & the Cloister: The Life & the Writings of Alexander Nequam, 1157-1217. 1984. 49.00x (ISBN 0-19-822398-6). Oxford U Pr.

Hunt, Richard, jt. auth. see Hunt, Joan.

Hunt, Richard A. & Hunt, Joan A. Called to Minister. LC 81-22796. (Into Our Third Century Ser.). (Orig.). 1982. pap. 3.95 (ISBN 0-687-04560-6). Abingdon.

Hunt, Richard A., jt. auth. see Hunt, Joan A.

Hunt, Richard A., jt. auth. see King, Morton B.

Hunt, Robert N. Calvin. LC 83-45617. Date not set. Repr. of 1933 ed. 37.50 (ISBN 0-404-19835-X). AMS Pr.

Hunt, Roland. The Seven Keys to Color Healing: Successful Treatment Through Color. LC 81-47849. (Library of Spiritual Wisdom). 128p. 1982. pap. 7.95 (ISBN 0-06-064080-4, CN 4028, HarpR). Har-Row.

Hunt, Ruth, jt. auth. see Linke, Maria Z.

Hunt, Sonja, jt. auth. see Wooten, Bill D.

Hunt, Sonjia, ed. Youth Leadership Resource Manual. 32p. (Orig.). 1981. pap. text ed. 1.75 (ISBN 0-87148-933-3, 817206). Pathway Pr.

--Youth Leadership Resource Manual, Vol. 2. 54p. (Orig.). 1982. pap. text ed. 2.00 (ISBN 0-87148-934-1). Pathway Pr.

Hunt, Sonjia L. Shaping Faith Through Involvement. 72p. (Orig.). 1981. pap. text ed. 2.50 (ISBN 0-87148-796-9). Pathway Pr.

Hunt, T. W. Music in Missions: Discipling Through Music. LC 86-28333. (Orig.). 1987. pap. 9.95 (ISBN 0-8054-6343-7). Broadman.

Hunt, Thomas C., jt. auth. see Honer, Stanley M.

Hunt, Thomas C. & Maxson, Marilyn M., eds. Religion & Morality in American Schooling. LC 81-40154. 297p. (Orig.). 1981. lib. bdg. 25.75 (ISBN 0-8191-1584-3); pap. text ed. 12.50 (ISBN 0-8191-1585-1). U Pr of Amer.

Hunt, Thomas C., et al. Religious Schools in America: A Selected Bibliography. LC 86-12118. (Reference Library of Social Science: Vol. 338). 416p. 1986. lib. bdg. 47.00 (ISBN 0-8240-8583-3). Garland Pub.

Hunt, William. English Church from Its Foundation to the Norman Conquest, 597-1066. LC 2-21442. (History of the English Church: No. 1). Repr. of 1899 ed. 29.50 (ISBN 0-404-50751-4). AMS Pr.

--The Puritan Moment: The Coming of Revolution in an English County. (Harvard Historical Studies: No. 102). (Illus.). 384p. 1983. text ed. 36.00x (ISBN 0-674-73903-5). Harvard U Pr.

--The Puritan Moment: The Coming of Revolution in an English County. (Harvard Historical Studies: No. 102). 384p. 1985. pap. text ed. 8.95x (ISBN 0-674-73904-3). Harvard U Pr.

Hunter, Adam M. The Teaching of Calvin: A Modern Interpretation. LC 83-45618. Date not set. Repr. of 1950 ed. 37.50 (ISBN 0-404-19836-8). AMS Pr.

Hunter, Archibald M. Galatians-Colossians. LC 59-10454. (Layman's Bible Commentary Ser.: Vol. 22). 1959. pap. 4.95 (ISBN 0-8042-3082-X). John Knox.

--Gospel According to John. (Cambridge Bible Commentary on the New English Bible, New Testament Ser.). (Orig.). 1965. pap. 11.95x (ISBN 0-521-09255-8). Cambridge U Pr.

--The Gospel According to St. Paul. rev. ed. LC 67-10511. Orig. Title: Interpreting Paul's Gospel. 126p. 1967. pap. 7.95 (ISBN 0-664-24742-3). Westminster.

--Interpreting the Parables. LC 61-5122. 126p. 1976. pap. 5.95 (ISBN 0-664-24746-6). Westminster.

--Introducing the New Testament. 3rd. rev. ed. LC 72-7110. 224p. 1973. pap. 7.95 (ISBN 0-664-24965-5). Westminster.

--The Parables Then & Now. LC 72-170113. 128p. 1972. pap. 5.95 (ISBN 0-664-24940-X). Westminster.

--A Pattern for Life: An Exposition of the Sermon on the Mount. rev. ed. LC 66-11517. 128p. 1966. pap. 5.95 (ISBN 0-664-24687-7). Westminster.

--Preaching the New Testament. LC 81-19482. pap. 39.00 (ISBN 0-317-30145-4, 2025328). Bks Demand UMI.

--The Work & Words of Jesus. rev. ed. LC 73-7559. 230p. 1973. pap. 8.95 (ISBN 0-664-24976-0). Westminster.

Hunter, Charles. Born Again, What Do You Mean? 1982. pap. 0.75 (ISBN 0-917726-48-0). Hunter Bks.

--Follow Me! 1975. pap. 4.95 (ISBN 0-917726-35-9). Hunter Bks.

--God's Conditions For Prosperity. rev. & enlarged ed. 1984. pap. 4.95 (ISBN 0-917726-41-3). Hunter Bks.

--God's Conditions for Prosperity: How to Earn the Rewards of Christian Living in Tough Times. 110p. 1984. 12.95 (ISBN 0-13-357285-4); pap. 5.95 (ISBN 0-13-357277-3). P-H.

Hunter, Charles & Hunter, Frances. Angels on Assignment. 1979. pap. 4.95 (ISBN 0-917726-33-2). Hunter Bks.

--Don't Limit God. 1976. pap. 4.95 (ISBN 0-917726-04-9). Hunter Bks.

--His Power Through You. 247p. (Orig.). 1986. pap. 4.95 (ISBN 0-917726-74-X). Hunter Bks.

--Impossible Miracles. 1976. pap. 4.95 (ISBN 0-917726-05-7). Hunter Bks.

--Nuggets of Truth. 1975. pap. 3.25 (ISBN 0-917726-01-4). Hunter Bks.

--Simple as A, B, C. 1982. pap. 0.75 (ISBN 0-917726-51-0). Hunter Bks.

--This Way Up. 1978. pap. 5.00 (ISBN 0-917726-23-5). Hunter Bks.

--The Two Sides of a Coin. 1973. pap. 3.95 (ISBN 0-917726-36-7). Hunter Bks.

--Why Should "I" Speak in Tongues. 1976. pap. 4.95 (ISBN 0-917726-02-2). Hunter Bks.

Hunter, Charles, jt. auth. see Hunter, Frances.

Hunter, Christine, jt. auth. see Aylward, Gladys.

Hunter, Emily. Como Ser Encantadora (Para Alumna) Mendoza De Mann, Wilma & Mariotti, F. A., trs. Orig. Title: Christian Charm Notebook. (Span., Illus.). 56p. 1984. pap. 2.50 teachers ed. (ISBN 0-311-46054-2); pap. 5.45 student ed., 100 pp. (ISBN 0-311-46055-0). Casa Bautista.

--Little Lips Shall Praise Thee. (Illus.). 96p. 1986. 11.95 (ISBN 0-89081-543-7). Harvest Hse.

Hunter, Emily & Hunter, Wayne. Man in Demand. Rev. ed. (Illus.). 1986. Repr. of 1975 ed. tchr's ed., 224 pp. 7.95 (ISBN 0-89081-511-9, 5119); student's wkbk. 80 pp 4.95 (ISBN 0-89081-510-0, 5100). Harvest Hse.

Hunter, Emily, jt. auth. see Hunter, Wayne.

Hunter, Frances. Come Alive. 1975. pap. 4.95 (ISBN 0-917726-34-0). Hunter Bks.

--A Confession a Day Keeps the Devil Away. 1980. pap. 4.95 (ISBN 0-917726-37-5). Hunter Bks.

--Devil, You Can't Steal What's Mine. 1982. pap. 0.75 (ISBN 0-917726-42-1). Hunter Bks.

--God Is Fabulous. 1978. pap. 3.25 (ISBN 0-87162-115-0). Hunter Bks.

--Hot Line to Heaven. 1978. pap. 3.25 (ISBN 0-87162-117-7). Hunter Bks.

--How to Talk to God Every Day of the Year: A Book of Devotions for Twelve Positive Months. 240p. 1984. 14.95 (ISBN 0-13-435248-3); pap. 6.95 (ISBN 0-13-435230-0). P-H.

--It's So Simple. 1978. pap. 3.25 (ISBN 0-87162-130-4). Hunter Bks.

--Let's Go Witnessing. 1978. pap. 3.25 (ISBN 0-685-90803-8). Hunter Bks.

--Possessing the Mind of Christ. 1984. pap. 4.95 (ISBN 0-917726-64-2). Hunter Bks.

--Praise the Lord Anyway. 1978. pap. 3.25 (ISBN 0-87162-131-2). Hunter Bks.

Hunter, Frances & Hunter, Charles. Since Jesus Passed By. 1973. pap. 3.95 (ISBN 0-917726-38-3). Hunter Bks.

Hunter, Frances, jt. auth. see Hunter, Charles.

Hunter, G. K. Paradise Lost. (Critical Library). 232p. 1980. text ed. 24.95x (ISBN 0-04-800004-3). Allen Unwin.

Hunter, George G., III. And Every Tongue Confess. LC 83-73224. 56p. (Orig.). 1983. pap. 4.50 (ISBN 0-88177-004-3, DR004B). Discipleship Res.

--To Spread the Power. 224p. 1987. pap. 9.95 (ISBN 0-687-42259-0). Abingdon.

Hunter, George G., III, jt. auth. see McGavran, Donald.

Hunter, George, 3rd. The Contagious Congregation: Frontiers in Evangelism & Church Growth. LC 78-12322. 1979. pap. 6.95 (ISBN 0-687-09490-9). Abingdon.

Hunter, Harold D. Spirit-Baptism: A Pentecostal Alternative. LC 83-10500. 322p. (Orig.). 1983. lib. bdg. 28.50 (ISBN 0-8191-3323-X); pap. text ed. 14.50 (ISBN 0-8191-3324-8). U Pr of Amer.

Hunter, Irene, ed. American Mystical Verse. LC 79-116407. (Granger Index Reprint Ser). 1925. 19.00 (ISBN 0-8369-6148-X). Ayer Co Pubs.

Hunter, J. H. Beside All Waters. 245p. 1964. 3.95 (ISBN 0-87509-050-8). Chr Pubns.

--Flame of Fire. 5.00 (ISBN 0-685-20860-5). Univ Place.

Hunter, James D. American Evangelicalism: Conservative Religion & the Quandary of Modernity. LC 82-317. 166p. 1983. 27.50x (ISBN 0-8135-0960-2); pap. 9.95x (ISBN 0-8135-0985-8). Rutgers U Pr.

--Evangelicalism: The Coming Generation. LC 86-16022. (Illus.). 320p. 1987. lib. bdg. 19.95 (ISBN 0-226-36082-2). U of Chicago Pr.

Hunter, Jane. The Gospel of Gentility: American Women Missionaries in Turn-of-the Century-China. LC 83-16668. 352p. 1984. 27.50x (ISBN 0-300-02878-4). Yale U Pr.

Hunter, JoAnn H. & Freund, John. Mirror of God's Love. 64p. 1984. pap. 2.50 (ISBN 0-916134-60-1). Pueblo Pub Co.

Hunter, John E. Jesus Speaks Today. LC 81-68042. 1982. pap. 4.25 (ISBN 0-8054-5184-6). Broadman.

Hunter, Joseph. Milton, A Sheaf of Gleanings. LC 76-26898. 1850. lib. bdg. 12.50 (ISBN 0-8414-4737-3). Folcroft.

Hunter, Joseph, ed. Ecclesiastical Documents. 1840. 19.00 (ISBN 0-384-24935-3). Johnson Repr.

Hunter, Kent R. Your Church Has Personality. Schaller, Lyle E., ed. (Creative Leadership Ser.). 129p. (Orig.). 1985. pap. 6.95 (ISBN 0-687-46875-2). Abingdon.

Hunter, Lea A. & Sienkiewicz, Magdalen. Learning Clubs for the Poor. LC 83-82024. (Orig.). 1984. pap. 4.95 (ISBN 0-8091-2602-8). Paulist Pr.

Hunter, Leona W. The Easter Bunny Book: A Celebration of the Easter Season. LC 85-23216. (Illus.). 96p. (Orig.). 1986. pap. 8.95 (ISBN 0-915590-84-0). Main Street.

Hunter, Robert G. Shakespeare & the Mystery of God's Judgments. LC 75-11449. 224p. 1976. 17.00x (ISBN 0-8203-0388-7). U of Ga Pr.

Hunter, Robert L. Helping When It Hurts: A Practical Guide to Helping Relationships. LC 85-47738. 80p. 1985. pap. 3.95 (ISBN 0-8006-1879-3, 1-1879). Fortress.

Hunter, Stanley A., ed. Music & Religion. LC 72-1615. Repr. of 1930 ed. 19.00 (ISBN 0-404-08316-1). AMS Pr.

Hunter, Victor L. & Johnson, Phillip. The Human Church in the Presence of Christ: The Congregation Rediscovered. xii, 180p. 1985. 15.50 (ISBN 0-86554-171-X, MUP-H161). Mercer Univ Pr.

Hunter, W. Bingham. The God Who Hears. LC 86-7268. 250p. (Orig.). 1986. pap. 6.95 (ISBN 0-87784-604-9). Inter-Varsity.

Hunter, Wayne & Hunter, Emily. Christian Charm Course. Rev. ed. 1986. Repr. of 1967 ed. tchr's ed., 112 pp. 7.95 (ISBN 0-89081-509-7, 5097); student's wkbk., 56 pp 4.95 (ISBN 0-89081-508-9, 5089). Harvest Hse.

--Como Ser un Joven Ideal (Para Alumno) Mariotti, Federico A., tr. Orig. Title: Man in Demand. (Span.). 1980. pap. 6.95 student ed., 80p. (ISBN 0-311-46074-7); pap. 8.75 teacher ed. 1981 (ISBN 0-311-46075-5). Casa Bautista.

Hunter, Wayne, jt. auth. see Hunter, Emily.

Hunter, William. Milton on the Nature of Man. LC 76-48905. 1946. lib. bdg. 12.50 (ISBN 0-8414-4908-2). Folcroft.

Hunter, William B., Jr., et al. Bright Essence: Studies in Milton's Theology. LC 74-161485. 1971. 14.95x (ISBN 0-87480-061-7). U of Utah Pr.

Hunter, Wm. Bridges. Milton on the Nature of Man. 1978. Repr. of 1946 ed. lib. bdg. 15.00 (ISBN 0-8492-1186-7). R West.

Hunting, Constance, ed. see Young, Douglas.

Hunting, Constance, ed. see Young, Muriel.

Hunting, Gardner. Working with God. 1934. 5.95 (ISBN 0-87159-174-X). Unity School.

Huntington, F. D. Hymns of the Ages, 3 vols. 1977. 300.00 (ISBN 0-8490-2031-X). Gordon Pr.

Huntington, Gertrude E., jt. auth. see Hostetler, John A.

Huntington, Helen, jt. auth. see Wetzler, Robert.

Huntington, R. & Metcalf, P. Celebrations of Death. LC 79-478. (Illus.). 1979. 39.50 (ISBN 0-521-22531-0); pap. 10.95x (ISBN 0-521-29540-8). Cambridge U Pr.

Huntington, Wm. The Kingdom of Heaven Taken by Prayer. pap. 2.50 (ISBN 0-686-48162-3). Reiner.

Huntley, Frank L. Bishop Joseph Hall & Protestant Meditation in Seventeenth-Century England: A Study, with Texts of the Art of Divine Meditation (1606) & Occasional Meditations (1633) (Medieval & Renaissance Texts & Studies: 1). (Illus.). 234p. (Orig.). 1981. 15.00 (ISBN 0-86698-000-8); pap. 9.00 (ISBN 0-86698-005-9). Medieval.

Huntly, Alyson, ed. see Canadian Christian Movement for Peace Staff, et al.

Huntly, Alyson, et al, eds. see Canadian Christian Movement for Peace Staff.

Hunton, Johnny. In Time of Need: Jesus. 35p. (Orig.). 1983. pap. 2.25 (ISBN 0-89323-041-3). Bible Memory.

Hunttmiller, Patrique. The First Twelve Meditations: On Black American Philosophy & Theology - A Study into the Meaning of Genesis & the African Concept of the Great Past & African Time Concepts As Spiritual & Two Dimensional. 150p. Date not set. pap. 6.95 (ISBN 0-318-20332-4). Scojtia Renee.

--A Zen Song: Twenty Meditations for the Black Martial Artist. 52p. 1986. pap. 5.95 (ISBN 0-9615560-3-X). Scojtia Renee.

Huold, Harry N. Twelve Who Followed: The Story of Jesus & His First Disciples. 128p. (Orig.). (YA) 1986. pap. 6.95 (ISBN 0-8066-2242-3, 10-6722). Augsburg.

Hupka, Robert. Michelangelo: Pieta. (Illus.). 96p. 1975. pap. 6.95 (ISBN 0-517-52414-7). Crown.

Huray, Peter Le see Le Huray, Peter, et al.

Hurd, J., jt. auth. see Richardson, P.

Hurd, Jerrie W. Our Sisters in the Bible. LC 83-50986. 168p. 1983. 8.95 (ISBN 0-87747-981-X). Deseret Bk.

--Our Sisters in the Latter-Day Scriptures. 1987. 10.95 (ISBN 0-87579-091-7). Deseret Bk.

Hurding, Roger F. Christian Care & Counseling: A Practical Guide. (Illus.). 128p. (Orig.). 1983. pap. 4.95 (ISBN 0-8192-1321-7). Morehouse.

--Restoring the Image: An Introduction to Christian Caring & Counselling. 128p. 1986. pap. 6.50 (ISBN 0-85364-268-0). Attic Pr.

Hure. Dictionnaire Universel de Philologie Sacree... Suivi du Dictionnaire de Lanque Sainte... par Louis de Wolzoque, 3 vols. in 4. Migne, J. P., ed. (Encyclopedie Theologique Ser.: Vols. 5-7). (Fr.). 2426p. Repr. of 1846 ed. lib. bdg. 309.50x (ISBN 0-89241-232-1). Caratzas.

Hureau, Jean. Mecca Today. (J. A. Editions: Today Ser.). (Illus.). 240p. 1980. 14.95 (ISBN 2-85258-214-7, Pub. by J. A. Editions France). Hippocrene Bks.

Hurgronje, Christian S. Mohammedanism: Lectures in Its Origin, Its Religious & Political Growth, & Its Present State. LC 79-2865. 184p. 1980. Repr. of 1916 ed. 18.00 (ISBN 0-8305-0038-3). Hyperion Conn.

Hurlbut, E. P., jt. auth. see Currell, R. G.

Hurlbut, Jesse L. Hurlbut's Story of the Bible. rev. ed. (Illus.). 15.95 (ISBN 0-310-26520-7, 6524). Zondervan.

--Story of the Christian Church. rev. ed. 192p. 1986. 11.95 (ISBN 0-310-26510-X, 6527). Zondervan.

Hurlbutt, Robert H., jt. auth. see Dewey, Robert E.

Hurley, Dermot, ed. Everyday Prayer Book with the Order of Mass. 208p. 1984. pap. 1.95 (ISBN 0-225-66273-6, HarpR). Har-Row.

Hurley, James B. Man & Woman in Biblical Perspective. 288p. (Orig.). 1981. pap. 9.95 (ISBN 0-310-42731-2, 10460P). Zondervan.

Hurley, Mark J. The Church & Science. 167p. 1982. 6.00 (ISBN 0-8198-1420-2, MS0125); pap. 5.00 (ISBN 0-8198-1421-0). Dghtrs St Paul.

Hurley, Patricia S. Religion & Medicine: A Medical Subject Analysis & Research Index with Bibliography. LC 83-71656. 148p. 1985. 34.50 (ISBN 0-88164-032-8); pap. 26.50 (ISBN 0-88164-033-6). ABBE Pubs Assn.

Hurlington, Vincent J. Great Art Madonnas Classed According to Their Significance As Types of Impressive Motherhood. (The Great Art Masters Library). (Illus.). 143p. 1981. 127.75 (ISBN 0-930582-97-7). Gloucester Art.

Hurll, E. M. The Life of Our Lord in Art. 59.95 (ISBN 0-8490-0534-5). Gordon Pr.

Hurll, Estelle M. Life of Our Lord in Art: With Some Account of the Artistic Treatment of the Life of St. John the Baptist. LC 76-89272. 1969. Repr. of 1898 ed. 31.00 (ISBN 0-8103-3137-3). Gale.

Hurnard, Hannah. God's Transmitters. 1975. pap. 2.95 (ISBN 0-8423-1085-1). Tyndale.

--Hearing Heart. 1975. pap. 2.95 (ISBN 0-8423-1405-9). Tyndale.

--Hind's Feet on High Places. 1979. pap. 3.95 (ISBN 0-8423-1429-6). Tyndale.

--Hurnard Gift Set, 8 vols. 1975. 26.50 (ISBN 0-8423-1547-0). Tyndale.

--Mountains of Spices. 1975. pap. 3.50 (ISBN 0-8423-4611-2). Tyndale.

--Walking Among the Unseen. 1977. pap. 3.50 (ISBN 0-8423-7805-7). Tyndale.

Huron, Rod. Christian Minister's Manual. (Illus.). 256p. (Orig.). 1984. skivertex 12.95 (ISBN 0-87239-753-X, 3028); sewn 19.95 (ISBN 0-87239-592-8, 3029). Standard Pub.

Hurry, J. B. Imhotep: The Egyptian God of Medicine. (Illus.). 120p. 1978. 12.50 (ISBN 0-89005-239-5). Ares.

Hurst, D. V. E Ele Concedeu Uns Para Mestres. (Portuguese Bks.). Tr. of And He Gave Teachers. 1979. 2.40 (ISBN 0-8297-0838-3). Life Pubs Intl.

Hurst, David. The Venerable Bede: Commentary on the Catholic Epistles. 1985. 24.95 (ISBN 0-317-18074-6); pap. 9.00 (ISBN 0-317-18075-4). Cistercian Pubns.

Hurst, George. An Outline of the History of Christian Literature. 1977. lib. bdg. 69.95 (ISBN 0-8490-2395-5). Gordon Pr.

Hurst, Jane. La Historia de las Ideas sobre el Aborto en la Iglesia Catolica: Una Relacion Desconocida. Boyd, Susan J. & Peterson, Jan, eds. Inda, Caridad, tr. from Eng. (Aborto de Buena Fe Ser.). (Span., Illus.). 31p. 1985. pap. 1.00 (ISBN 0-915365-11-1). Cath Free Choice.

--The History of Abortion in the Catholic Church. McKenna, Constance, ed. (Illus.). 31p. 1983. pap. 1.00 (ISBN 0-915365-04-9). Cath Free Choice.

Hurst, John F. Literature of Theology. LC 77-85625. 1977. Repr. of 1896 ed. lib. bdg. 50.00 (ISBN 0-89341-196-5). Longwood Pub Group.

Hurston, Zora N. The Sanctified Church. 107p. 1983. pap. 6.95 (ISBN 0-913666-44-0). Turtle Isl Foun.

Hurtado, Larry. Mark: A Good News Commentary. LC 82-48930. 288p. (Orig.). 1983. pap. 9.95 (ISBN 0-06-064085-5, RD/447, HarpR). Har-Row.

--Text-Critical Methodology & the Pre-Caesarean Text. 112p. (Orig.). 1981. pap. 15.00x (ISBN 0-8028-1872-2). Eerdmans.

Hurter, Hugo. Nomenclator Litterarius Theologiae Catholicae Theologo Sexhibens Aetate, Natione, Disciplins Distinctos, 5 Vols. in 6. 1903. Set. 294.00 (ISBN 0-8337-1772-3). B Franklin.

Hurtig, Judith W. Armored Gisant Before Fourteen Hundred. LC 78-74368. (Outstanding Dissertations in the Fine Arts, Fourth Ser.). 1979. lib. bdg. 63.00 (ISBN 0-8240-3956-4). Garland Pub.
Hurvitz, Leon & Shotaro, Lida, eds. Chinese Buddhism at Sixes & Sevens: A Study of the First Systematization of Buddhist Thought in China. 1987. 30.00 (ISBN 0-89581-906-6). Asian Human Pr.
Hurvitz, Leon, tr. from Chin & Sanskrit. Scripture of the Lotus Blossom of the Fine Dharma: The Lotus Sutra. LC 75-45381. 1976. pap. 16.00x (ISBN 0-231-03920-4). Columbia U Pr.
Hurvitz, Leon, tr. see Tsukamoto, Zenryi.
Hurwitz, Shimon. Being Jewish. rev. ed. 1979. pap. 5.95 (ISBN 0-87306-196-9). Feldheim.
Hurwitz, Simon. Responsa of Solomon Luria (Marharshal) Legal Decisions of the Famous Sixteenth-Century Sage. 2nd ed. LC 68-31710. 1969. 10.00 (ISBN 0-8197-0096-7). Bloch.
Hus, Jan. Mag. Johannis Hus Tractatus Responsiyus. LC 78-63201. (Heresies of the Early Christian & Medieval Era: Second Ser.). Repr. of 1927 ed. 34.50 (ISBN 0-404-16229-0). AMS Pr.
Husain, A. M. Tughluq Dynasty. (Illus.). 1976. Repr. of 1935 ed. 30.00x (ISBN 0-89684-461-7). Orient Bk Dist.
Husain, I. Dogmatic & Mystical Theology of Donne. LC 70-119088. (Studies in Philosophy, No. 40). 1970. Repr. of 1938 ed. lib. bdg. 39.95x (ISBN 0-8383-1084-2). Haskell.
Husain, Itra. Dogmatic & Mystical Theology of John Donne. LC 75-43972. 1938. lib. bdg. 17.50 (ISBN 0-8414-4747-0). Folcroft.
Husain, Itrat. Dogmatic & Mystical Theology of John Donne. Repr. of 1938 ed. lib. bdg. 22.50x (ISBN 0-8371-4243-1, HUJD). Greenwood.
Husain, S. A. Glorious Caliphate. 15.50 (ISBN 0-686-18626-5). Kazi Pubns.
Husaini. Ibn-Al-Arabi. pap. 1.75 (ISBN 0-686-18320-7). Kazi Pubns.
Husaini, S. A. The Pantheistic Monism of Ibn Al-Arabi. 1970. 9.30x (ISBN 0-87902-164-0). Orientalia.
Husayn, Sayyid S. The Early History of Islam. 360p. 1984. pap. 7.50 (ISBN 0-941724-25-5). Islamic Seminary.
Husayn at-Tabatabai, S. Muhammad. Al-Mizan: An Exegesis of the Qur'an, Vol. 4. Rizvi, S. Saeed, tr. from Arabic. LC 85-52243. 336p. (Orig.). 1985. pap. 30.00 (ISBN 0-940368-59-5). Tahrike Tarsile Quran.
--Al-Mizan: An Exegesis of the Qur'an, Vol. 5. Rizvi, S. Saeed, tr. from Arabic. LC 85-52243. 288p. (Orig.). 1985. pap. 30.00 (ISBN 0-940368-60-9). Tahrike Tarsile Quran.
Husayn at-Tabatabai, S. Muhammad & S. Saeed, Akhtar-Rizvi. Al-Mizan: An Exegesis of the Qur'an, Vol. 1. LC 85-52243. 366p. (Orig.). 1985. pap. 30.00 (ISBN 0-940368-57-9). Tahrike Tarsile Quran.
Husband, Thomas F. Emerson. A Lecture. LC 77-23227. 1977. Repr. of 1892 ed. lib. bdg. 8.50 (ISBN 0-8414-4947-3). Folcroft.
Husband, Timothy, jt. auth. see Caviness, Madeline E.
Huse, Scott M. Collapse of Evolution. 192p. 1986. pap. 7.95 (ISBN 0-8010-4310-7). Baker Bk.
Husemann, Friedrich, et al. The Anthroposophical Approach to Medicine, Vol. 1. (Illus.). 411p. 1983. 30.00 (ISBN 0-88010-031-1). Anthroposophic.
Husk, William A. Songs of the Nativity. LC 73-9861. (Folklore Ser). 32.50 (ISBN 0-88305-258-X). Norwood Edns.
Huskey, Hyrum H., Jr. Counseling Skills for Church Leadership. 1980. pap. 6.00 (ISBN 0-8309-0295-3). Herald Hse.
Hussain, Ahmed. The Philosophy of Faqirs. 126p. (Orig.). 1981. pap. 5.25 (ISBN 0-88004-006-8). Sunwise Turn.
Hussain, Asaf. Islamic Iran: Revolution & Counter-Revolution. LC 85-40078. 250p. 1985. 27.50 (ISBN 0-312-43745-5). St Martin.
--Islamic Movements in Egypt, Pakistan & Iran: An Annotated Bibliography. 182p. 1983. 36.00x (ISBN 0-7201-1648-1). Mansell.
Hussain, Asaf, et al, eds. Orientalism, Islam & Islamists. LC 84-72244. 300p. (Orig.). 1985. 17.50 (ISBN 0-915597-15-2); pap. 9.95 (ISBN 0-915597-09-8). Amana Bks.
Hussain, F. Wives of the Prophet. 9.50 (ISBN 0-686-18463-7). Kazi Pubns.
Hussain, Freeda, ed. Muslim Women: The Ideal & Contextual Realities. LC 83-11189. 240p. 1984. 22.50 (ISBN 0-312-55586-5). St Martin.
Hussain, J. M. The Occultation of the Twelfth Imam: A Historical Background. 221p. 1982. 35.00x (ISBN 0-317-39132-1, Pub. by Luzac & Co Ltd). State Mutual Bk.
Hussain, Jassim M. The Occulation of Imam: A Historical Background. 221p. 1986. lib. bdg. 30.00 (ISBN 0-7103-0158-8). Methuen Inc.
Hussain, M. Shamail Tirmidhi. 22.50 (ISBN 0-317-01594-X). Kazi Pubns.
Hussain, M. N. Islam vs. Socialism. pap. 6.50 (ISBN 0-686-18569-2). Kazi Pubns.
Hussain, S. A. Sayings of Muhammad, the Last Prophet. pap. 1.25 (ISBN 0-686-18340-1). Kazi Pubns.
Husserl. Cartesian Meditations. 1977. pap. 13.00 (ISBN 90-247-0068-X, Pub. by Martinus Nijhoff Netherlands). Kluwer Academic.
--Cartesianische Meditationen und Pariser Vortrage: Photomechanischer Nachdruck. (Husserliana Ser: No. 1). 1973. lib. bdg. 29.00 (ISBN 90-247-0214-3, Pub. by Martinus Nijhoff Netherlands). Kluwer Academic.
Husserl, Edmund. Crisis of European Sciences & Transcendental Phenomenology: An Introduction to Phenomenological Philosophy. Carr, David, tr. LC 77-82511. (Studies in Phenomenology & Existential Philosophy Ser). 1970. 28.95 (ISBN 0-8101-0255-2); pap. 11.95 (ISBN 0-8101-0458-X). Northwestern U Pr.
Hussey, J. M. The Orthodox Church in the Byzantine Empire. (History of the Christian Church Ser.). 320p. 1986. 59.00x (ISBN 0-19-826901-3). Oxford U Pr.
Hussey, J. M., tr. see Cabasilas, Nicholas.
Hussey, Maurice, adapted by. Chester Mystery Plays. 2nd ed. 1975. pap. 3.50x (ISBN 0-87830-572-6). Theatre Arts.
Hustad, Donald P. Jubilate!(Church Music in the Evangelical Tradition) LC 80-85185. 368p. 1981. 17.95 (ISBN 0-916642-17-8). Hope Pub.
Hustad, Donald P. & Shorney, George H, Jr. Dictionary-Handbook to Hymns for the Living Church. LC 77-75916. 1978. 14.95 (ISBN 0-916642-09-7). Hope Pub.
Huston, Sterling. Crusade Evangelism & the Local Church. 215p. 1984. pap. 5.95 (ISBN 0-89066-047-6). World Wide Pubs.
Hustvedt, Sigurd B., tr. see Munch, Peter A.
Hutch, Richard A. Emerson's Optics: Biographical Process & the Dawn of Religious Leadership. 380p. (Orig.). 1983. lib. bdg. 34.25 (ISBN 0-8191-3005-2); pap. text ed. 17.75 (ISBN 0-8191-3006-0). U Pr of Amer.
Hutches, G. E. Just Passing Through. LC 78-71390. (Stories That Win Ser.). 1979. pap. 1.25 (ISBN 0-8163-0320-7, 10617-9). Pacific Pr Pub Assn.
Hutcheson, Francis. Essay on the Nature & Conduct of the Passions & Affections, 1742. 3rd ed. LC 76-81361. (History of Psychology Ser.). 1969. Repr. of 1742 ed. 50.00x (ISBN 0-8201-1058-2). Schol Facsimiles.
--Inquiry into the Original of Our Ideas of Beauty & Virture. 4th ed. 1986. lib. bdg. 20.00X (ISBN 0-935005-22-6); pap. text ed. 12.50X (ISBN 0-935005-33-1). Ibis Pub VA.
Hutcheson, George. John. (Geneva Commentary Ser.). 448p. 1985. Repr. of 1657 ed. 17.95 (ISBN 0-85151-155-4). Banner of Truth.
Hutcheson, Richard G., Jr. Mainline Churches & the Evangelicals. LC 80-84648. 192p. (Orig.). 1981. pap. 9.95 (ISBN 0-8042-1502-2). John Knox.
Hutchings, Arthur. Church Music in the Nineteenth Century. (Studies in Church Music). 1977. Repr. of 1967 ed. lib. bdg. 22.50x (ISBN 0-8371-9695-7, HUCMN). Greenwood.
Hutchins, Barbara W., jt. auth. see Cheesman, Paul R.
Hutchins, Eileen. Observation-Thinking-the Senses. 1975. pap. 1.95 (ISBN 0-916786-13-7). St George Bk Serv.
Hutchins, Francis G. Young Krishna. LC 80-66834. (Illus.). 132p. 1980. 29.50 (ISBN 0-935100-01-6); pap. 14.00 (ISBN 0-935100-05-9). Amarta Pr.
Hutchins, John. Hutchins' Guide to Bible Reading. LC 83-102876. (Illus.). 608p. 1983. 25.00x (ISBN 0-938386-00-X). Button Gwin.
Hutchins, Robert M. Saint Thomas & the World State. (Aquinas Lecture). 1949. 7.95 (ISBN 0-87462-114-3). Marquette.
Hutchinson, Dorothy. From Where They Sit. 1983. pap. 2.50x (ISBN 0-87574-084-7, 084). Pendle Hill.
--Unless One Is Born Anew. LC 65-26994. (Orig.). 1965. pap. 2.50x (ISBN 0-87574-143-6, 143). Pendle Hill.
Hutchinson, Duane. Exon, Biography of a Governor. (Illus.). 243p. (Orig.). 1973. 5.95 (ISBN 0-934988-01-3); pap. 2.95 (ISBN 0-934988-02-1). Foun Bks.
--Pastor Pete. (Illus.). pap. write for info (ISBN 0-934988-05-6). Foun Bks.
Hutchinson, F. Milton & the English Mind. LC 74-7187. (Studies in Milton, No. 22). 1974. lib. bdg. 49.95x (ISBN 0-8383-1906-8). Haskell.
Hutchinson, F. E. Milton & the English Mind. LC 74-28171. 1946. Repr. lib. bdg. 17.50 (ISBN 0-8414-4897-3). Folcroft.
Hutchinson, Gloria. Jesus' Saving Questions. 118p. (Orig.). 1984. pap. text ed. 4.95 (ISBN 0-86716-028-4). St Anthony Mess Pr.
--Six Ways to Pray from Six Great Saints. (Illus.). 152p. 1982. pap. text ed. 4.95 (ISBN 0-86716-007-1). St Anthony Mess Pr.
Hutchinson, John. An Exposition of Paul's Epistle to the Philippians. 328p. 1985. smythe sewn 13.00 (ISBN 0-86524-190-2, 5003). Klock & Klock.
Hutchinson, John & O'Connor, David. York Minister. (The New Bell's Cathedral Guides Ser.). 1986. cancelled 24.95 (ISBN 0-918678-14-5). Historical Times.
Hutchinson, Roger. Works. 1842. 31.00 (ISBN 0-384-25120-X). Johnson Repr.
Hutchinson, Warner. The Oral Roberts Scrapbook. LC 78-58611. 1978. pap. 5.95 (ISBN 0-448-16259-8). Brown Bk.
Hutchinson, William R. Errand to the World: American Protestant Thought & Foreign Missions. 216p. 1987. lib. bdg. 24.95x (ISBN 0-226-36257-4). U of Chicago Pr.
Hutchison, John A. Living Options in World Philosophy. LC 76-46489. 323p. 1977. 16.00x (ISBN 0-8248-0455-4). UH Pr.
--Paths of Faith. 3rd ed. (Illus.). 608p. 1981. 31.95x (ISBN 0-07-031532-9). McGraw.
Hutchison, William G. The Oxford Movement: Being a Selection from the Tracts for the Times. (Victorian Age Ser). 1906. Repr. 20.00 (ISBN 0-8482-4421-4). Norwood Edns.
Hutchison, William R. The Modernist Impulse in American Protestantism. (Illus.). 384p. 1976. 22.50x (ISBN 0-674-58058-3). Harvard U Pr.
--The Modernist Impulse in American Protestantism. (Illus.). 1982. pap. 9.95x (ISBN 0-19-503084-2). Oxford U Pr.
Hutchison, William R., ed. American Protestant Thought in the Liberal Era. LC 84-19614. 252p. 1985. pap. text ed. 10.75 (ISBN 0-8191-4336-7). U Pr of Amer.
Hutson, Joan. Heal My Heart O Lord. LC 75-30493. 112p. 1976. pap. 2.95 (ISBN 0-87793-106-2). Ave Maria.
--Heaven & Earth. (Little Learner Ser.). 24p. 1985. 5.95 (ISBN 0-570-08952-2, 56-1544). Concordia.
--I Think...I Know: A Poster Book about God. (Illus.). 32p. (Orig.). 1979. pap. 1.95 (ISBN 0-87793-186-0). Ave Maria.
--The Lord's Prayer. LC 82-62736. (Happy Day Bks.). (Illus.). 24p. 1983. 1.59 (ISBN 0-87239-640-1, 3560). Standard Pub.
--Love Never Ever Ends. LC 82-6737. (Happy Day Bks.). (Illus.). 24p. 1983. 1.59 (ISBN 0-87239-641-X, 3561). Standard Pub.
Huttar, Leora W. Church Time for Preschoolers. LC 75-17368. 1975. spiral 6.95 (ISBN 0-916406-36-9). Accent Bks.
Huttenlocker, Keith. Becoming the Family of God: A Handbook for Developing Creative Relationships in the Church. 128p. 1986. pap. 6.95 (ISBN 0-310-75211-6). Zondervan.
--God, Can I Get to Know You. 1979. pap. 3.95 (ISBN 0-87162-211-4, D3810). Warner Pr.
Hutterian Brethren, ed. & tr. see Arnold, Eberhard.
Hutterian Brethren, ed. see Arnold, Heini.
Hutterian Brethren, ed. see Braitmichel, Kasper, et al.
Hutterian Society of Brothers, ed. & tr. Salz und Licht. (Ger.). 186p. 1982. pap. 4.95 (ISBN 3-87067-166-1, Pub. by Brendow-Verlag, West Germany). Plough.
Hutterian Society of Brothers, ed. see Arnold, Ebehard.
Hutterian Society of Brothers, ed. see Arnold, Eberhard.
Huttl, Willy. Antoninus Pius. LC 75-7326. (Roman History Ser.). (Ger.). 1975. Repr. 57.00x (ISBN 0-405-07089-6). Ayer Co Pubs.
Huttman, Maude A. Establishment of Christianity & the Proscription of Paganism. LC 15-703. (Columbia University. Studies in the Social Sciences: No. 147). Repr. of 1914 ed. 18.50 (ISBN 0-404-51147-3). AMS Pr.
Hutton, Edward. Catholicism & English Literature. LC 76-26671. 1942. lib. bdg. 30.00 (ISBN 0-8414-4926-0). Folcroft.
Hutton, Richard H. Aspect of Religious & Scientific Thought. 766p. Repr. of 1899 ed. text ed. 49.68x (ISBN 0-576-29209-5). Gregg Intl.
--Cardinal Newman. LC 75-30029. Repr. of 1891 ed. 21.00 (ISBN 0-404-14033-5). AMS Pr.
--Essays on Some of the Modern Guides to English Thought in Matters of Faith. LC 72-8580. (Essay Index Reprint Ser.). 1972. Repr. of 1887 ed. 23.50 (ISBN 0-8369-7319-4). Ayer Co Pubs.
Hutton, Ronald. The Restoration: A Political & Religious History of England & Wales 1658-1667. (Illus.). 379p. 1985. 29.95x (ISBN 0-19-822698-5). Oxford U Pr.
Hutton, Samuel W. Minister's Marriage Manual. 1968. 6.95 (ISBN 0-8010-4031-0). Baker Bk.
--Minister's Service Manual. 1964. 8.95 (ISBN 0-8010-4035-3). Baker Bk.
Hutton, W. H. John Bunyan. LC 77-24947. Repr. of 1927 ed. lib. bdg. 15.00 (ISBN 0-8414-4861-2). Folcroft.
--S. Thomas of Canterbury. 59.95 (ISBN 0-8490-0983-9). Gordon Pr.
Hutton, Warwick. Jonah & the Great Fish. LC 83-15477. (Illus.). 32p. 1984. 12.95 (ISBN 0-689-50283-4, McElderly Bk). Macmillan.
--Moses in the Bulrushes. LC 85-72261. (Illus.). 32p. 1986. 12.95 (ISBN 0-689-50393-8, McElderry Bk). Macmillan.
--Noah & the Great Flood. LC 77-3217. (Illus.). 32p. 1977. 8.95 (ISBN 0-689-50098-X, McElderry Bk). Macmillan.
Hutton, William H. English Church from the Accession of Charles First to the Death of Anne, 1625-1714. LC 4-4381. (History of the English Church Ser.: No. 6). Repr. of 1903 ed. 29.50 (ISBN 0-404-50756-5). AMS Pr.
Huxhold, Harry N. Bible Readings for Church Workers. LC 84-21574. 112p. (Orig.). 1984. pap. 3.95 (ISBN 0-8066-2132-X, 10-0684). Augsburg.
--Family Altar. rev. ed. 1964. 12.95 (ISBN 0-570-03071-4, 6-1085). Concordia.
--Followers of the Cross. LC 85-22823. 80p. (Orig.). 1985. pap. 4.95 (ISBN 0-8066-2184-2, 10-2346). Augsburg.
Huxhold, Harry N., ed. Adventures with God. LC 66-15551. 1966. pap. 7.95 (ISBN 0-570-03736-0, 12-2640). Concordia.
Huxley, Aldous. Doors of Perception. Bd. with Heaven & Hell. pap. 5.95 (ISBN 0-06-090007-5, CN7, PL). Har-Row.
--Doors of Perception. 1970. pap. 3.95 (ISBN 0-06-080171-9, P171, PL). Har-Row.
--Moksha: Writings on Psychedelics & the Visionary Experience (1931-1963) Horowitz, Michael & Palmer, Cynthia, eds. LC 81-21239. 300p. 1982. pap. 7.95 (ISBN 0-87477-208-7). J P Tarcher.
--Perennial Philosophy. 1970. pap. 7.95 (ISBN 0-06-090191-8, CN191, PL). Har-Row.
Huxley, Aldous L. Perennial Philosophy. LC 76-167362. (Essay Index Reprint Ser.). Repr. of 1945 ed. 25.50 (ISBN 0-8369-2773-7). Ayer Co Pubs.
Huxley, Dee, jt. auth. see Solomon, Charmaine.
Huxley, Julian, et al. Science & Religion. facs. ed. LC 75-84336. (Essay Index Reprint Ser). 1931. 14.25 (ISBN 0-8369-1106-7). Ayer Co Pubs.
Huxley, Julian S. Religion Without Revelation. LC 78-12065. 1979. Repr. of 1967 ed. lib. bdg. 24.75x (ISBN 0-313-21225-2, HURR). Greenwood.
Huxley, Julian S., ed. The New Systematics. LC 40-35139. 583p. 1940. Repr. 49.00 (ISBN 0-403-01786-6). Scholarly.
Huxley, Thomas H. Evolution & Ethics, & Other Essays. LC 70-8391. 334p. 1897. Repr. 49.00x (ISBN 0-403-00041-6). Scholarly.
--Science & Christian Tradition. 419p. 1981. Repr. of 1894 ed. lib. bdg. 45.00 (ISBN 0-89984-285-2). Century Bookbindery.
--Science & Hebrew Tradition: Essays. 1979. Repr. of 1894 ed. lib. bdg. 30.00 (ISBN 0-8495-2263-3). Arden Lib.
Huyck, Donna. With Death at My Back. (Uplook Ser.). pap. 0.99 (ISBN 0-8163-0427-0). Pacific Pr Pub Assn.
Huyck, Peter H. Scriptural Meditations for the Rosary. (Greeting Book Line Ser.). (Illus.). 48p. 1982. pap. 1.50 (ISBN 0-89622-157-1). Twenty-Third.
Huysmans, J. K. The Cathedral. 59.95 (ISBN 0-87968-815-7). Gordon Pr.
Huysmans, Joris K. The Cathedral. Paul, C. Kegan, ed. Bell, Clara, tr. from Fr. LC 77-10270. Repr. of 1922 ed. 32.50 (ISBN 0-404-16322-X). AMS Pr.
Hveberg, H. Norweigian of Gods & Giants. 4th ed. (Tanum of Norway Tokens Ser). 86p. pap. 12.75x (ISBN 82-518-0083-8, N430). Vanous.
Hyams, Joe. Zen in the Martial Arts. 144p. 1982. pap. 3.50 (ISBN 0-553-26078-2). Bantam.
Hyamson, Albert M. Palestine: A Policy. LC 75-6438. (The Rise of Jewish Nationalism & the Middle East Ser). 214p. 1975. Repr. of 1942 ed. 20.35 (ISBN 0-88355-325-2). Hyperion Conn.
Hyamson, Moses, jt. auth. see Maimondies.
Hyamson, Moses, tr. see Maimonides.
Hyatt, Christopher S. Undoing Yourself with Energized Meditation & Other Devices. LC 82-83293. 114p. 1982. pap. 6.95 (ISBN 0-941404-06-4). Falcon Pr Az.
Hyatt, Irwin T., Jr. Our Ordered Lives Confess. (American-East Asian Relations Ser.: No. 8). 1976. 20.00x (ISBN 0-674-64735-1). Harvard U Pr.
Hyatt, J. P. Commentary on Exodus. Clements, Ronald E., ed. (New Century Bible Commentary Ser.). 1980. pap. 8.95 (ISBN 0-8028-1844-7). Eerdmans.
--The Heritage of Biblical Faith. LC 64-13404. 1977. pap. 9.95 (ISBN 0-8272-1416-2). CBP.
Hybels, Bill. Caution: Christians under Construction. LC 77-93854. 144p. 1986. pap. 3.95 (ISBN 0-88207-759-7). Victor Bks.
--Christians in the Marketplace. 144p. 1982. pap. 5.95 (ISBN 0-88207-314-1). Victor Bks.
--Laws That Liberate. 132p. 1985. pap. 4.95 (ISBN 0-89693-394-6). Victor Bks.

Hybels, Lynne. Joy of Personal Worship. 156p. 1984. pap. 5.95 (ISBN 0-89693-373-3). Victor Bks.

Hyde, Clarence. Search the Scriptures. (Illus.). 112p. (Orig.). 1986. pap. 9.95 (ISBN 1-55630-014-X). Brentwood Comm.

Hyde, Clark. To Declare God's Forgiveness: Toward a Pastoral Theology of Reconciliation. LC 84-60626. 188p. (Orig.). 1984. pap. 8.95 (ISBN 0-8192-1348-9). Morehouse.

Hyde, Floy. Protestant Leadership Education Schools. LC 70-176892. (Columbia University. Teachers College. Contributions to Education: No. 965). Repr. of 1950 ed. 22.50 (ISBN 0-404-55965-4). AMS Pr.

Hyde, Gordon. The Gospel of the Here & Now. Wheeler, Gerald, ed. (Illus.). 128p. (Orig.). 1984. pap. 4.95 (ISBN 0-8280-0247-9). Review & Herald.

Hyde, Henry J. For Every Idle Silence: A Congressman Speaks Out. 140p. (Orig.). 1985. pap. 6.95 (ISBN 0-89283-282-7). Servant.

Hyde, Kathy. Teaching the Bible to Change Lives. LC 84-47801. 143p. (Orig.). 1984. pap. 6.95 (ISBN 0-89840-064-3). Heres Life.

Hyde, Orson. Speech of Elder Orson Hyde: 1845. 16p. (Orig.). 1986. pap. 1.95 (ISBN 0-942284-07-0). Restoration Re.

Hyde, Walter W. Greek Religion & Its Survivals. LC 63-10268. (Our Debt to Greece & Rome Ser). 1963. Repr. of 1930 ed. 18.50x (ISBN 0-8154-0117-5). Cooper Sq.

Hyder, O. Quentin. Shape Up. rev. & updated ed. (Illus.). 160p. 1984. pap. 4.95 (ISBN 0-8007-5158-2, Power Bks). Revell.

Hye-Am Choi, jt. auth. see Myo-Bong, Master.

Hye-Am Choi, ed. see Myo-Bong Master.

Hyers, Conrad. And God Created Laughter: The Bible As Divine Comedy. LC 86-46037. 132p. (Orig.). 1987. pap. 9.95 (ISBN 0-8042-1653-3). John Knox.

--The Comic Vision & the Christian Faith: A Celebration of Life & Laughter. LC 81-5221. 96p. (Orig.). 1981. pap. 8.95 (ISBN 0-8298-0440-4). Pilgrim NY.

--The Meaning of Creations. LC 84-47795. 212p. pap. 11.95 (ISBN 0-8042-0125-0). John Knox.

Hykes, Susan S. The Leading Edge of Now: The Living Love of God. 24p. (Orig.). 1982. pap. 3.00 (ISBN 0-9608894-0-X). S S Hykes.

Hyland, Anne M. Manual: School Library-Media Skills Test. 50p. 1986. pap. text ed. 5.00 (ISBN 0-87287-524-5). Libs Unl.

Hyland, Judy. In the Shadow of the Rising Sun. LC 84-12303. 128p. (Orig.). 1984. pap. 5.95 (ISBN 0-8066-2091-9, 10-3260). Augsburg.

Hylkema, G. W. & Tuuk, E. J. A First Book of Christian Doctrine. rev. ed. (YA) pap. 2.95 (ISBN 0-8028-8012-6). Eerdmans.

Hyma, Albert. Luther's Theological Development from Erfurt to Augsburg. LC 76-137247. Repr. of 1928 ed. 12.50 (ISBN 0-404-03479-9). AMS Pr.

Hyman, Arthur & Walsh, James J., eds. Philosophy in the Middle Ages: The Christian, Islamic & Jewish Traditions. 2nd ed. LC 82-23337. 816p. (Orig.). 1983. lib. bdg. 30.00 (ISBN 0-915145-81-2); pap. text ed. 15.00x (ISBN 0-915145-80-4). Hackett Pub.

Hyman, Arthur, jt. ed. see Lieberman, Saul.

Hyman, B. D. & Hyman, Jeremy. Narrow Is the Way. Golbitz, Pat, ed. LC 86-28588. 352p. 1987. 17.95 (ISBN 0-688-06345-4). Morrow.

Hyman, Frieda C. The Jewish Experience, Bk. 2. (Illus.). 1978. text ed. 6.95x (ISBN 0-8381-0192-5). United Syn Bk.

--The Jewish Experience: Book I. 1975. 5.25x (ISBN 0-8381-0191-7). United Syn Bk.

Hyman, Jeremy, jt. auth. see Hyman, B. D.

Hyman, Paula, jt. auth. see Brown, Charlotte.

Hyman, Paula E., jt. ed. see Cohen, Steven M.

Hyneman, Charles S., ed. Hymns Ancient & Modern for Use in the Services of the Church, with Accompanying Tunes. LC 74-24123. (Illus.). Repr. of 1909 ed. 150.00 (ISBN 0-404-12981-1). AMS Pr.

Hynes, Arleen. Passover Meal. LC 76-187207. 64p. 1972. pap. 2.50 (ISBN 0-8091-1653-7). Paulist Pr.

Hynes, Kathleen. Un Cuestionamiento Etico. Peterson, Jan & Isasi-Diaz, Ada M., eds. Toro, Olga L., tr. from Eng. Tr. of An Ethical Inquiry. (Span.). 16p. 1984. pap. 1.00 (ISBN 0-915365-01-4). Cath Free Choice.

--An Ethical Inquiry. McKenna, Constance & Johnson, Karen, eds. 16p. 1981. pap. 1.00 (ISBN 0-915365-07-3). Cath Free Choice.

Hynes, William J. Shirley Jackson Case & the Chicago School: The Socio-Historical Method. Richards, Kent, ed. LC 81-8973. (The Society of Biblical Literature Biblical Scholarship in North America Ser.). 1981. pap. text ed. 15.00 (ISBN 0-89130-510-6, 06-11-05). Scholars Pr GA.

Hynson, Leon O. To Reform the Nation: Theological Foundations of Wesley's Ethics. Chapman, Ben & Terpstra, Gerard, eds. 192p. (Orig.). 1984. pap. 7.95 (ISBN 0-310-75071-7, 17030P). Zondervan.

Hynson, Leon O., jt. ed. see Scott, Lane A.

I

Iacobucci, Albert A. In the Name of Jesus Christ. 129p. 1985. 10.95 (ISBN 0-533-06419-8). Vantage.

Iamblichus. On the Mysteries. Taylor, Thomas, tr. from Greek. LC 81-50200. (Secret Doctrine Reference Ser.). Tr. of Iamblichus on the Mysteries. 400p. 1984. Repr. of 1895 ed. 20.00 (ISBN 0-913510-51-3). Wizards.

Iannaci, Tina. For a Special Friend. (Greeting Book Line Ser.). 24p. (Orig.). 1986. pap. 1.50 (ISBN 0-89622-303-5). Twenty-Third.

Iannarelli, S. Joseph. The Third Testament of the Holy Bible. 1985. 5.95 (ISBN 0-533-06645-X). Vantage.

Ianucci, R. J. Treatment of the Capital Sins. LC 70-140024. (Catholic University Studies in German: No. 17). Repr. of 1942 ed. 21.00 (ISBN 0-404-50237-7). AMS Pr.

Iatesta, Robert. Fathers: A Fresh Start for the Christian Family. 238p. (Orig.). 1980. pap. 5.95 (ISBN 0-89283-083-2). Servant.

Ibish, Yusuf & Marculescu, Ileana, eds. Contemplation & Action in World Religions. LC 78-61504. (Rothko Chapel). 1979. pap. 4.95 (ISBN 0-295-95634-8). U of Wash Pr.

Iblacker, Reinhold, jt. ed. see Lange, Martin.

Ibn Al-Firkah & Ibrahim ibn Abd Al-Rahman. Palestine: Mohammedan Holy Land. Matthews, Charles, ed. LC 78-63568. (Yale Oriental Ser. Researches: No. 24). Repr. of 1949 ed. 34.50 (ISBN 0-404-60324-6). AMS Pr.

Ibn Al-Qalanisi. The Damascus Chronicle of the Crusades. Gibb, H. A., tr. LC 78-63342. (The Crusades & Military Orders: Second Ser.). Repr. of 1967 ed. 32.50 (ISBN 0-404-17019-6). AMS Pr.

Ibn'Arabi. Wisdom of the Prophets. Burckardt, Titus, tr. 1976. pap. write for info. (ISBN 0-685-67327-8). Weiser.

Ibn Ezra. Commentary of Ibn Ezra on Isaiah. Friedlander, Michael, tr. LC 66-15771. 1966. 15.00 (ISBN 0-87306-013-X). Feldheim.

Ibn-Gabirol, Solomon B. Improvement of the Moral Qualities: An Ethical Treatise of the Eleventh Century. Wise, Stephen S., ed. LC 2-8360. (Columbia University. Oriental Studies: No. 1). Repr. of 1902 ed. 17.25 (ISBN 0-404-50491-4). AMS Pr.

Ibn Isma'il, A. H. Ali see Ali ibn Isma'il, A. H., et al.

Ibrahim ibn Abd Al-Rahman, jt. auth. see Ibn Al-Firkah.

Ibuse, Masuji. Black Rain. 304p. 1985. pap. 3.95 (ISBN 0-553-24988-6). Bantam.

Icaza, Sr. Rosa M. Stylistic Relationship Between Poetry & Prose in the Cantico Espiritual of San Juan De la Cruz. LC 76-94191. (Catholic University of America Studies in Romance Languages & Literatures Ser: No. 54). 1969. Repr. of 1957 ed. 21.00 (ISBN 0-404-50354-3). AMS Pr.

Ice, Rhoderick. Thirteen Lessons on the Gospel of Mark. (Bible Student Study Guides Ser). 1977. pap. 2.95 (ISBN 0-89900-151-3). College Pr Pub.

Ichazo, Oscar. Between Metaphysics & Protoanalysis: A Theory for Analyzing the Human Psyche. Bleibtreu, John, ed. LC 82-70811. 120p. 1982. 15.95 (ISBN 0-916554-05-8); pap. 11.95 (ISBN 0-916554-06-6). Arica Inst Pr.

--Hypergnostic Questions & Concomitant Association for Discharging the Past. LC 86-70565. 90p. 1986. ring-binder 35.00 (ISBN 0-916554-13-9). Arica Inst Pr.

--Kinerhythm Meditation: A Multfaceted Concentration. (Illus.). 54p. 1978. pap. 12.95 (ISBN 0-916554-07-4). Arica Inst Pr.

Idahosa, Benson. Fire in His Bones. (Orig.). 1986. pap. 4.95 (ISBN 0-89274-429-4). Harrison Hse.

Ide, Arthur F. Calendar of Death: The Socio-Psychological Factors Influencing the Martyrdom of Thomas of Canterbury. LC 86-15455. (Medieval People: Vol. 2). (Illus.). viii, 157p. (Orig.). 1986. pap. 9.95 (ISBN 0-934667-02-0). Tangelwuld.

--Evangelical Terrorism: Censorship, Jerry Falwell, Pat Robertson & the Seamy Side of Christian Fundamentalism. LC 86-22013. xxxi, 195p. 1986. pap. 12.95 (ISBN 0-938659-01-4). Scholars Bks.

--God's Girls: Ordination of Women in the Early Christian & Agnostic Churches. (Illus.). 185p. (Orig.). 1986. pap. 8.95 (ISBN 0-934667-01-2). Tangelwuld.

--Gomorrah & the Rise of Homophobia. (Illus.). 114p. (Orig.). 1985. pap. 5.95 (ISBN 0-934659-01-X). Liberal Pr.

--Idol Worshippers in Twentieth Century America. (Illus.). 150p. (Orig.). 1984. pap. 10.95 (ISBN 0-930383-02-8). Monument Pr.

--Martyrdom of Women in the Early Christian Church. LC 85-14741. (Illus.). 100p. 1985. pap. 6.95 (ISBN 0-934667-00-4). Tangelwuld.

--Sex, Woman & Religion. (Illus.). xi, 212p. (Orig.). 1984. 14.95 (ISBN 0-930383-00-1). Monument Pr.

--Unholy Rollers: The Selling of Jesus. LC 85-19883. (Illus.). 120p. 1985. pap. 5.95 (ISBN 0-935175-01-6). Lib Arts Pr.

--Woman as Priest, Bishop & Laity in the Early Catholic Church to 440 A.D. 2nd ed. LC 81-13464. (Woman in History Ser.: Vol. 9B). (Illus.). viii, 125p. 1983. 20.95 (ISBN 0-86663-037-6); pap. 5.95 (ISBN 0-86663-038-4). Ide Hse.

Ideal Editors. Ideals Easter. 1985. pap. 3.50 (ISBN 0-8249-1041-9). Ideals.

Ideals Staff. Book of Christmas Carols. (Illus.). 24p. 1984. pap. 2.95 (ISBN 0-8249-8072-7). Ideals.

Idel, Moshe. The Mystical Experience in Abraham Abulafia. (SUNY Series in Judaica: Hermeneutics, Mysticism & Religion). 240p. 1987. text ed. 39.50x (ISBN 0-88706-552-X); pap. 12.95x (ISBN 0-88706-553-8). State U NY Pr.

Idelsohn, Abraham Z. Jewish Music in Its Historical Development. LC 80-24235. (Illus.). xi, 535p. 1981. Repr. of 1948 ed. lib. bdg. 35.00 (ISBN 0-313-22749-7, IDJM). Greenwood.

--Jewish Music: In Its Historical Development. LC 67-25236. 1967. pap. 12.50 (ISBN 0-8052-0165-3). Schocken.

Idle, Christopher. Stories of Our Favorite Hymns. (Illus.). 80p. 1980. 12.95 (ISBN 0-8028-3535-X). Eerdmans.

Idung Of Prufening. Cistercians & Cluniacs: The Case for Citeaux. O'Sullivan, Jeremiah F. & Leahey, Joseph, trs. LC 77-9289. 1977. 12.95 (ISBN 0-87907-633-X). Cistercian Pubns.

Idziak, Janine M. Divine Command Morality: Historical & Contemporary Readings. LC 79-91621. (Texts & Studies in Religion: Vol. 5). 348p. 1980. 49.95x (ISBN 0-88946-969-5). E Mellen.

Ife, Elaine & Sutton, Rosalind. Now You Can Read Stories from the Bible. (Illus.). 208p. 1984. 9.95 (ISBN 0-8407-5396-9). Nelson.

Ife, Elaine & Sutton, Rosalind, eds. The Birth of Jesus. (Now You Can Read Stories from the Bible Ser.). (Illus.). 24p. 1984. 2.50 (ISBN 0-8407-5393-4). Nelson.

--The Childhood of Jesus. (Now You Can Read Stories from the Bible Ser.). (Illus.). 24p. 1985. 2.50 (ISBN 0-8407-5394-2). Nelson.

--David & Goliath. (Now You Can Read Stories from the Bible Ser.). (Illus.). 24p. 1985. 2.50 (ISBN 0-8407-5392-6). Nelson.

--David & Jonathan. (Now You Can Read Stories from the Bible Ser.). (Illus.). 24p. 1985. 2.50 (ISBN 0-8407-5448-5). Nelson.

--Moses in the Bulrushes. (Now You Can Read Stories from the Bible Ser.). (Illus.). 24p. 1985. 2.50 (ISBN 0-8407-5481-7). Nelson.

--Noah & the Ark. (Now You Can Read Stories from the Bible Ser.). (Illus.). 24p. 1985. 2.50 (ISBN 0-8407-5390-X). Nelson.

--Samuel. (Now You Can Read Stories from the Bible Ser.). (Illus.). 24p. 1985. 2.50 (ISBN 0-8407-5449-3). Nelson.

--Stories Jesus Told. (Now You Can Read Stories from the Bible Ser.). (Illus.). 24p. 1984. 2.50 (ISBN 0-8407-5395-0). Nelson.

Ife, Elaine, jt. ed. see Sutton, Rosalind.

Igglesden, Charles. Those Superstitions. LC 73-12798. 1974. Repr. of 1932 ed. 40.00x (ISBN 0-8103-3621-9). Gale.

Igleheart, Glenn A. Church Members & Nontraditional Religious Groups. LC 85-4226. (Broadman Leadership Ser.). 1985. pap. 5.95 (ISBN 0-8054-6608-8). Broadman.

Ignacio Loyola. The Autobiography of St. Ignatius. lib. bdg. 59.95 (ISBN 0-87968-685-5). Gordon Pr.

Ignatius, May, tr. see Ratzinger, Joseph, et al.

Ignatius, Saint Epistles of St. Ignatius. Lightfoot, J. D., tr. pap. 1.25 (ISBN 0-686-25549-6). Eastern Orthodox.

--Spiritual Exercises of St. Ignatius of Loyola. Delmage, Lewis, tr. 1978. 4.00 (ISBN 0-8198-0557-2); pap. 2.25 (ISBN 0-8198-0558-0). Dghtrs St Paul.

Ignatius Of Loyola, St. The Constitutions of the Society of Jesus. Ganss, George E., tr. & commentary by. LC 72-108258. (Jesuit Primary Sources in English Translation Ser.: No. 1). 432p. 1970. pap. 12.00 smyth sewn (ISBN 0-912422-20-3). Inst Jesuit.

Ignatius of Loyola, Saint Letters of Saint Ignatius of Loyola. Young, William J., ed. LC 59-13459. 1959. 8.95 (ISBN 0-8294-0085-0). Loyola.

Ignoffo, Matthew. One Perfect Lover: A Story of the Resurrection. LC 86-60171. 200p. 1987. 14.95 (ISBN 0-89390-084-2). Resource Pubns.

Ihara, Graig K., jt. ed. see Runzo, Joseph.

Ihde, Don. Hermeneutic Phenomenology: The Philosophy of Paul Ricoeur. (Studies in Phenomenology & Existential Philosophy). 1971. 20.95 (ISBN 0-8101-0347-8); pap. 11.95 (ISBN 0-8101-0611-6). Northwestern U Pr.

Ihli, Sr. Jan. Liturgy of the Word for Children. LC 79-90003. 176p. 1979. pap. 9.95 (ISBN 0-8091-2176-X). Paulist Pr.

Iijima, Kanjitsu. Buddhist Yoga. (Illus.). 184p. 1975. pap. 8.95 (ISBN 0-87040-349-4). Japan Pubns USA.

Ijima, Kanjitsu. The Lotus Textbook. 62p. (Orig.). 1984. pap. 10.00 (ISBN 0-86627-010-8). Crises Res Pr.

Ikeda, Daisaku. Buddhism: The First Millennium. Watson, Burton, tr. LC 77-84915. 1978. 12.95x (ISBN 0-87011-321-6). Kodansha.

--Buddhism: The First Millennium. LC 82-80739. 172p. 1982. pap. 5.25 (ISBN 0-87011-534-0). Kodansha.

--The Flower of Chinese Buddhism. (Illus.). 216p. 1986. 19.95 (ISBN 0-8348-0208-2). Weatherhill.

--The Human Revolution, Vol. 5. (Illus.). 250p. 1984. 13.95 (ISBN 0-8348-0198-1). Weatherhill.

--The Living Buddha: An Interpretive Biography. LC 75-40446. (Illus.). 164p. 1975. 7.95 (ISBN 0-8348-0117-5). Weatherhill.

Ikeda, Diasaku & Wilson, Bryan. Human Values in a Changing World. 384p. (Orig.). 1987. 20.00 (ISBN 0-8184-0427-2). Lyle Stuart.

Ikeler, Bernard. Parenting Your Disabled Child. LC 86-9118. 138p. (Orig.). 1986. pap. 8.95 (ISBN 0-664-24044-5). Westminster.

Ikemoto, Takashi, jt. tr. see Stryk, Lucien.

Ikerman, Ruth C. A Heart-Trimmed Christmas: Christmas Inspiration for Your Heart & Home. 112p. (Orig.). 1984. pap. 7.95 (ISBN 0-687-16804-X). Abingdon.

Ikram, S. M. History of Muslim Civilization in India. 25.50 (ISBN 0-317-46089-7). Kazi Pubns.

Iles, Robert H. & Callison, William L. Selecting Computers for Ministry. LC 84-62333. (Illus.). 160p. (Orig.). 1985. pap. 13.95 (ISBN 0-932489-00-1). New Begin Co.

Illanes, Jose L. On the Theology of Work: Aspects of the Teaching of the Founder of Opus Dei. Adams, Michael, tr. from Span. Tr. of La Santification del Trabajo. 107p. (Orig.). 1983. pap. 3.95 (ISBN 0-906127-56-4). Scepter Pubs.

Illion, Theodore. Darkness over Tibet. 192p. 1983. pap. 6.95 (ISBN 0-912181-03-6). East School Pr.

--In Secret Tibet: In Disguise Amongst Lamas, Robbers & Wise Men. A Key to the Mysteries of Tibet. 190p. 1983. pap. 6.95 (ISBN 0-912181-01-X). East School Pr.

Ilon. The Supremacy of God. LC 80-66408. 1980. pap. 4.50 (ISBN 0-9600958-6-1). Birth Day.

Imam. Introduction to Islam: The First & Final Religion. abr. ed. 18p. (Orig.). 1983. pap. 1.50 (ISBN 0-916157-01-6). African Islam Miss Pubns.

Imam, S. M. Scenes from Indian Mythology. 2nd ed. 1975. pap. 1.50 (ISBN 0-89684-347-5). Orient Bk Dist.

Imam Alhaji Obaba Muhammadu. The African Islamic Mission. 38p. (Orig.). 1982. pap. 1.00 (ISBN 0-916157-04-0). African Islam Miss Pubns.

Imbonati, Carlo, jt. auth. see Bartolocci, Giulio.

Immerwahr, Sara A. Early Burials from the Agora Cemeteries. (Excavations of the Athenian Agora Picture Bks.: No. 13). (Illus.). 1973. pap. 3.00x (ISBN 0-87661-613-9). Am Sch Athens.

Impe, Jack Van see Van Impe, Jack.

Impe, Rexella Van see Van Impe, Rexella.

Inada, Kenneth K. Guide to Buddhist Philosophy. (Reference Books - Area Studies: Area Studies). 1985. lib. bdg. 45.00 (ISBN 0-8161-7899-2). G K Hall.

Inada, Kenneth K. & Jacobson, Nolan P. Buddhism & American Thinkers. 182p. 1983. 39.50 (ISBN 0-87395-753-9); pap. 14.95 (ISBN 0-87395-754-7). State U NY Pr.

Inada, Kenneth K., tr. see Matsuo, Hosaku.

Inayat, Taj, et al. The Crystal Chalice. rev. ed. (Illus.). 170p. Date not set. pap. price not set (1011P). Omega Pr NM.

Inayat Khan. The Development of Spiritual Healing. LC 85-22358. 112p. 1985. Repr. lib. bdg. 19.95x (ISBN 0-89370-582-9). Borgo Pr.

Inayat-Khan, F. Old Thinking, New Thinking. 2nd ed. 256p. 1985. cancelled. Hunter Hse.

Inayat Khan, Hazrat. Spiritual Dimensions of Psychology. LC 80-54830. (Collected Works of Hazrat Inayat Khan Ser.). 256p. (Orig.). 1981. 7.95 (ISBN 0-930872-24-X, 1012P). Omega Pr NM.

Inbar, Michael & Adler, Chaim. Ethnic Integration in Israel: A Comparative Study of Moroccan Brothers Who Settled in France & in Israel. LC 76-27933. (Illus.). 120p. 1977. lib. bdg. 16.95 (ISBN 0-87855-204-9). Transaction Bks.

Inch, Morris, jt. ed. see Youngblood, Ronald.

Inch, Morris A. Making the Good News Relevant: Keeping the Gospel Distinctive in Any Culture. 128p. 1986. pap. 8.95 (ISBN 0-8407-7540-7). Nelson.

--Saga of the Spirit. 12.95 (ISBN 0-8010-5037-5). Baker Bk.
Inch, Morris A. & Bullock, C. Hassell, eds. The Literature & Meaning of Scripture. 360p. 1981. 14.95 (ISBN 0-8010-5032-4). Baker Bk.
Inclusive-Language Lectionary Committee, Division of Education & Ministry, National Council of Churches of Christ in the U. S. A. An Inclusive-Language Lectionary: Readings for Year A. rev. & enl. ed. 292p. 1986. pap. 10.95 (ISBN 0-664-24051-8). Westminster.
Incognito, Magnus. Secret Doctrine of the Rosicrucians. 8.00 (ISBN 0-911662-30-8). Yoga.
Inda, Caridad, tr. see Hurst, Jane.
Indich, William M. Consciousness in Advaita Vedanta. 1980. 14.00x (ISBN 0-8364-0607-9). South Asia Bks.
Ineman, K., ed. see McCausland, Clare.
Inesse, Daniel, jt. auth. see Wright, Ezekiel.
Infield, Louis, tr. see Kant, Immanuel.
Information Ser. Scientology: A Religion Helping Others. (Illus.). 1978. pap. 4.00 (ISBN 0-915598-21-3). Church of Scient Info.
Information Service. The Spies Among Us: Agents Provocateurs. 1978. pap. 3.00 (ISBN 0-915598-19-1). Church of Scient Info.
Ingalls, Daniel H., ed. see Vedas.
Ingalls, Jeremiah. The Christian Harmony. (Earlier American Music Ser.: Vol. 22). 230p. 1981. Repr. of 1805 ed. lib. bdg. 29.50 (ISBN 0-306-79617-1). Da Capo.
Inge, W. R. The Religious Philosophy of Plotinus & Some Modern Philosophies of Religion. 1977. lib. bdg. 59.95 (ISBN 0-8490-2513-3). Gordon Pr.
--Science & Ultimate Truth. 1978. lib. bdg. 12.50 (ISBN 0-8495-2603-5). Arden Lib.
--Science & Ultimate Truth. LC 73-7513. 1926. Repr. lib. bdg. 8.50 (ISBN 0-8414-2109-9). Folcroft.
Inge, W. R., et al. Religion & Life: The Foundations of Personal Religion. facs. ed. LC 68-22940. (Essay Index Reprint Ser). 1923. 13.00 (ISBN 0-8369-0819-8). Ayer Co Pubs.
Inge, William R. Christian Ethics & Modern Problems. Repr. of 1930 ed. lib. bdg. 22.50x (ISBN 0-8371-3960-0, INCE). Greenwood.
--Church in the World. facs. ed. LC 68-57324. (Essay Index Reprint Ser). 1927. 17.00 (ISBN 0-8369-0080-4). Ayer Co Pubs.
--Faith & Its Psychology. LC 10-654. (Studies in Theology Ser.: No. 12). 1909. text ed. 8.50x (ISBN 0-8401-6012-7). A R Allenson.
--Mysticism in Religion. LC 76-15407. 1976. Repr. of 1948 ed. lib. bdg. 22.50x (ISBN 0-8371-8953-5, INMR). Greenwood.
--Philosophy of Plotinus: The Gifford Lectures at St. Andrews, 1917-1918, 2 Vols. 3rd ed. LC 68-8740. (Illus.). 1968. Repr. of 1929 ed. Set. lib. bdg. 67.50x (ISBN 0-8371-0113-1, INPP). Greenwood.
--The Platonic Tradition in English Religious Thought. LC 77-8095. 1977. Repr. of 1926 ed. lib. bdg. 15.00 (ISBN 0-8414-5055-2). Folcroft.
--Studies of English Mystics. facs. ed. LC 69-17578. (Essay Index Reprint Ser). 1906. 15.00 (ISBN 0-8369-0081-2). Ayer Co Pubs.
Inge, Williiam R. The Post Victorians. 1933. Repr. lib. bdg. 21.45 (ISBN 0-8414-5059-5). Folcroft.
Inger, Judith. Victory Dances: The Story of Fred Berk, a Modern Day Jewish Dancing Master. 225p. pap. 15.95 (ISBN 0-934682-11-9). Emmett.
Ingersoll, Robert. Some Reasons Why I Am a Freethinker. 38p. 1983. pap. 3.00 (ISBN 0-911826-67-X). Am Atheist.
--What Can You Believe in the Bible. 106p. 1987. 4.00. Am Atheist.
Ingersoll, Robert G. Atheist Truth vs. Religion's Ghosts. 57p. 1980. pap. 3.25 (ISBN 0-911826-03-3). Am Atheist.
--The Gods & Other Lectures. 69.95 (ISBN 0-87968-246-9). Gordon Pr.
--Some Mistakes of Moses. 270p. 1986. pap. 12.95 (ISBN 0-87975-361-7). Prometheus Bks.
--The Trial of C. B. Reynolds. 44p. (Orig.). 1986. pap. 3.00 (ISBN 0-910309-25-6). Am Atheist.
Ingham, John M. Mary, Michael, & Lucifer: Folk Catholicism in Central Mexico. (Latin American Monographs: No. 69). (Illus.). 228p. 1986. text ed. 25.00x (ISBN 0-292-75089-7). U of Tex Pr.
Ingham, Kenneth. Reformers in India, 1793-1833: An Account of the Work of Christian Missionaries on Behalf of Social Reform. LC 73-16425. xi, 150p. 1973. Repr. of 1956 ed. lib. bdg. 17.00x (ISBN 0-374-94112-2, Octagon). Hippocrene Bks.
Ingle, Clifford, ed. Children & Conversion. LC 79-113212. 160p. 1975. pap. 4.95 (ISBN 0-8054-2514-4). Broadman.
Ingle, E. Parish Institutions of Maryland, with Illustrations from Parish Records. 1973. pap. 9.00 (ISBN 0-384-25740-2). Johnson Repr.
Ingle, Edward. Parish Institutions of Maryland. LC 78-63736. (Johns Hopkins University. Studies in Social Sciences. First Ser. 1882-1883: 6). Repr. of 1883 ed. 11.50 (ISBN 0-404-61006-4). AMS Pr.
Ingle, H. Larry. Quakers in Conflict: The Hicksite Reformation. LC 86-1528. 330p. 1986. text ed. 29.95x (ISBN 0-87049-501-1). U of Tenn Pr.
Ingles, David. Worshipping the Father in Spirit & in Truth. 40p. (Orig.). 1986. wkbk. 4.95 (ISBN 0-914307-63-0). Word Faith.
Inglis, James. A Topical Dictionary of Bible Texts. (Paperback Reference Library). 528p. 1985. pap. 12.95 (ISBN 0-8010-5038-3). Baker Bk.
Ingoldsby, Mary F., tr. see Rosmini, Antonio.
Ingraham, F. & Anderson, Eric. Prince of the House of David. Orig. Title: Three Years in the Holy City. 363p. 1980. Repr. text ed. 15.95 (ISBN 0-89841-003-7). Zoe Pubns.
Ingraham, Sarah R. Walks of Usefulness: Or Reminiscenes of Mrs. Margaret Prior. Gifford, Carolyn & Dayton, Donald, eds. (Women in American Protestant Religion 1800-1930 Ser.). 324p. 1987. lib. bdg. 45.00 (ISBN 0-8240-0666-6). Garland Pub.
Ingram, J. K., ed. Imitation Christi. (EETS, ES Ser.: No. 63). Repr. of 1893 ed. 54.00 (ISBN 0-527-00268-2). Kraus Repr.
Ingram, Kristen. Quiet Time with God. 96p. 1984. pap. 3.95 (ISBN 0-8170-1026-2). Judson.
Ingram, Kristen J Being a Christian Friend. 112p. 1985. pap. 5.95 (ISBN 0-8170-1084-X). Judson.
--Bible Stories for the Church Year. Russell, Joseph P., ed. LC 83-20135. 184p. (Orig.). 1986. pap. 10.95 (ISBN 0-86683-537-7, HarpR). Har-Row.
--Family Worship Through the Year. 80p. 1984. pap. 5.95 (ISBN 0-8170-1052-1). Judson.
--With the Huckleberry Christ: A Spiritual Journey. 96p. (Orig.). 1985. pap. 5.95 (ISBN 0-86683-798-1, HarpR). Har-Row.
Ingram, Leonard, ed. see Puri, Ishwar C.
Ingram, Paul O. & Streng, Frederick J., eds. Buddhist-Christian Dialogue: Mutual Renewal & Transformation. LC 85-24528. 1986. pap. text ed. 10.00x (ISBN 0-8248-1050-3). UH Pr.
Ingram, T. Robert. New Liturgy, Old Heresy. LC 81-52116. (Orig.). 1981. pap. 4.50 (ISBN 0-686-75087-X). St Thomas.
--What's Wrong with Human Rights. LC 78-68732. (Orig.). 1979. pap. 3.50 (ISBN 0-686-24267-X). St Thomas.
--The World under God's Law. 5th ed. LC 62-16216. 1970. pap. text ed. 3.50 (ISBN 0-686-05040-1). St Thomas.
Ingram, William & Swain, Kathleen M., eds. Concordance to Milton's English Poetry. 1972. 135.00x (ISBN 0-19-811138-X). Oxford U Pr.
Ingram-Hill, Canon D. Canterbury Cathedral. (The New Bell Cathedral Guides Ser.). (Illus.). 192p. (Orig.). 1987. pap. 14.95 (ISBN 0-7135-2619-X, Pub. by Automobile Assn Brit). Salem Hse Pubs.
Ingrams, Richard. God's Apology. (Illus.). 192p. 1986. pap. 13.95 (ISBN 0-241-11746-1, Pub. by Hamish Hamilton England). David & Charles.
Ingulf, Abbot. Ingulph's Chronicle of the Abbey of Croyland. Riley, H. T., tr. LC 68-55553. (Bohn's Antiquarian Library Ser). Repr. of 1854 ed. 34.50 (ISBN 0-404-50018-8). AMS Pr.
Inkel, Simone, tr. see Thevenot, Xavier.
Inkpen, Mick, jt. auth. see Butterworth, Nick.
Inman, Thomas. Ancient, Pagan & Modern Christian Symbolism. LC 77-6998. Repr. of 1884 ed. lib. bdg. 25.00 (ISBN 0-89341-301-1). Longwood Pub Group.
--Ancient, Pagan & Modern Christian Symbolism. 147p. 1978. Repr. of 1884 ed. 15.95 (ISBN 0-87928-101-4). Corner Hse.
Inman, V. Kerry. Prophets of Doom in an Age of Optimism. (Orig.). 1981. pap. 4.95 (ISBN 0-934688-02-8). Great Comm Pubns.
Inmon, Marvin, jt. auth. see Wright, Norman.
Inmon, Marvin N., jt. auth. see Wright, H. Norman.
Innes, A. T. & Powell, F. J. The Trial of Christ. 287p. 1982. lib. bdg. 10.75 (ISBN 0-86524-138-4, 9513). Klock & Klock.
Innes, A. Taylor. John Knox. 1978. Repr. of 1896 ed. lib. bdg. 17.50 (ISBN 0-8414-5057-9). Folcroft.
Innes, Cosmo, ed. Registrum De Dunfermelyn. LC 70-164810. (Bannatyne Club, Edinburgh. Publications: No. 74). Repr. of 1842 ed. 55.00 (ISBN 0-404-52793-0). AMS Pr.
--Registrum Episcopatus Glasguensis, 2 Vols. LC 70-168151. (Maitland Club, Glasgow. Publications: No. 61). Repr. of 1843 ed. Set. 95.00 (ISBN 0-685-05956-1). AMS Pr.
Innes, Cosmo, ed. see Kelso Abbey.
Innes, Cosmo, ed. see Newbattle Abbey.
Innes, Cosmo, ed. see North Berwick Priory.
Innes, Cosmo, ed. see Paisley Abbey.
Innes, Cosmo, et al, eds. Origines Parochiales Scotiae, 2 Vols. in 3. LC 76-170804. (Bannatyne Club, Edinburgh. Publications: No. 97). Repr. of 1855 ed. 210.00 (ISBN 0-404-52850-3). AMS Pr.
Innes, Cosmo N., ed. see Scotland.
Innes, Dick. I Hate Witnessing. LC 84-27531. 1985. pap. 2.95 (ISBN 0-8307-1003-5, 5418403). Regal.
--I Hate Witnessing: A Handbook for Effective Christian Communication. LC 84-27531. 1985. pap. text ed. 2.95 (ISBN 0-8307-1003-5, 5418403). Vision Hse.
Innes, Kathleen E. The Bible As Literature. 255p. 1980. Repr. of 1930 ed. lib. bdg. 25.00 (ISBN 0-8492-1222-7). R West.
Innes, William C. Social Concern in Calvin's Geneva. (Pittsburgh Theological Monographs: New Series 7). 1983. pap. 22.50 (ISBN 0-915138-33-6). Pickwick.
Innis, Pauline, ed. Prayer & Power in the Capital: With Prayers of the Presidents. LC 82-156801. (Illus.). 120p. 1982. 10.00 (ISBN 0-941402-02-9). Devon Pub.
Innocent Third, Pope Register Innocenz' 3rd Uber Die Reichsfrage, 1198-1209. Tangl, Georgine, ed. 1923. 23.00 (ISBN 0-384-07885-0). Johnson Repr.
Inoue, T., jt. auth. see Genoud, C.
Inrig, Gary. A Call to Excellence. 132p. 1985. pap. 5.95 (ISBN 0-89693-523-X). Victor Bks.
--Life in His Body: Discovering Purpose, Form & Freedom in His Church. 182p. 1975. pap. 5.95 (ISBN 0-87788-500-1). Shaw Pubs.
--Quality Friendship. LC 81-38379. 192p. (Orig.). 1981. pap. 5.95 (ISBN 0-8024-2891-6). Moody.
Inrig, Gary, ed. Hearts of Iron, Feet of Clay. 1979. pap. 7.95 (ISBN 0-8024-3487-8). Moody.
Institut Des Etudes Augustiniennes, Paris. Fichier Augustinien, 4 vols. (Augustine Bibliography). 1972. Set. 355.00 (ISBN 0-8161-0947-8, Hall Library). G K Hall.
--Fichier Augustinien, First Supplement. 1981. lib. bdg. 125.00 (ISBN 0-8161-0365-8, Hall Library). G K Hall.
Institut Dominicain d'Etudes Orientales du Caire. Melanes: French-Arabic Text, Vol. 14. 1980. 30.00x (ISBN 0-86685-284-0). Intl Bk Ctr.
--Melanges: Tables Generales Tomes 1-13 (1954-1977) (Fr. & Arabic.). 1980. 10.00x (ISBN 0-86685-283-2). Intl Bk Ctr.
Institut fuer Neutestamentliche Textforschung, Muenster-Westf. & Aland, Kurt, eds. Vollstaendige Konkordanz zum griechischen Neuen Testament, 2 vols. viii, 96p. Vol. 1, 2 pts., 1983. 908.00 (ISBN 3-11-009698-6); Vol. 2, 1978. 105.00 (ISBN 3-11-007349-8). De Gruyter.
Institute for Palestine, Beirut, Lebanon Staff. Palestine & the Zionist Threat. Date not set. cancelled (ISBN 0-88728-190-7). Inst Palestine.
Institute for Religious & Social Studies. Hour of Insight. facsimile ed. MacIver, R. M., ed. LC 70-167366. (Essay Index Reprint Ser). Repr. of 1954 ed. 15.00 (ISBN 0-8369-2655-2). Ayer Co Pubs.
--Integrity & Compromise: Problems of Public & Private Conscience. facsimile ed. MacIver, R. M., ed. LC 76-167367. (Essay Index Reprints - Religion & Civilization Ser). Repr. of 1957 ed. 15.00 (ISBN 0-8369-2656-0). Ayer Co Pubs.
Institute of Contemporary Jewry of The Hebrew University of Jerusalem. Studies in Contemporary Jewry, Vol.I. (Illus.). 608p. 1984. 22.50X (ISBN 0-253-39511-9). Ind U Pr.
Institute of Oriental Studies. Chinese Tomb Pottery Figures: Catalogue of Exhibition Arranged by the Institute of Oriental Studies. 1953. pap. 22.50x (ISBN 0-317-44053-5, Pub. by Han-Shan Tang Ltd). State Mutual Bk.
Integral Yoga Institutes. Integral Yoga Hatha Booklet & Tape. 1979. 6.95 (ISBN 0-932040-23-3). Integral Yoga Pubns.
Inter-Lutheran Commission on Worship. Lutheran Book of Worship. 10.50 (ISBN 0-8006-3330-X). Bd of Pubn LCA.
Inter-Varsity Staff. Christ in You. pap. 0.75 (ISBN 0-87784-175-6). Inter Varsity.
--First Mornings with God. pap. 0.75 (ISBN 0-87784-134-9). Inter-Varsity.
--Grow Your Christian Life. pap. 5.95 (ISBN 0-87784-661-8). Inter-Varsity.
--Quiet Time. pap. 1.95 (ISBN 0-87784-250-7). Inter Varsity.
--Rough Edges of the Christian Life. pap. 2.50 (ISBN 0-87784-442-9). Inter-Varsity.
Intercollegiate Zionist Association of America. Kadimah. Davis, Moshe, ed. LC 77-70704. (America & the Holy Land Ser.). (Illus.). 1977. Repr. of 1918 ed. lib. bdg. 20.00x (ISBN 0-405-10255-0). Ayer Co Pubs.
Interdisciplinary Symposium. Contemplative Community. LC 70-184548. (Cistercian Studies: No. 21). 1972. 7.50 (ISBN 0-87907-821-9). Cistercian Pubns.
Interfaith Consultative Group, Board for Mission & Unity, Church of England. Towards a Theology for Inter-Faith Dialogue. (Lambeth Study Bks.). 56p. 1986. pap. 2.25 (ISBN 0-88028-058-1). Forward Movement.
International African Seminar - 3rd - Salisburg - Southern Rhodesia. African Systems of Thought. Fortes, Meyer & Dieterlen, Germaine, eds. 1965. 42.00x (ISBN 0-19-724158-1). Oxford U Pr.
International Center for University Teaching of Jewish Civilization Staff & Shimmoni, Gideon, eds. Contemporary Jewish Civilization. LC 85-40515. (Selected Course Outlines & Curriculum Resources Ser.). 250p. 1985. pap. text ed. 14.50x (ISBN 0-910129-28-2). Wiener Pub Inc.
International Center for University Teaching of Jewish Civilization Staff, et al, eds. Jewish Political Traditions. LC 85-40516. (Selected Course Outlines & Curriculum Resources from Leading Universities Ser.). 250p. 1985. pap. text ed. 14.50 (ISBN 0-910129-29-0). Wiener Pub Inc.
International Center for University Teaching of Jewish Civilization Staff & Verbit, Mervin, eds. World Register of University Teaching of Jewish Civilization. LC 85-40514. (Selected Syllabi in University Teaching of Jewish Civilization Ser.). 250p. 1985. pap. text ed. 14.50x (ISBN 0-910129-30-4). Wiener Pub Inc.
International Colloquium on Philosophy, Science, & Theology in the Middle Ages, 1st, Boston, Sept. 1973. Boston Studies in the Philosophy of Science, Vol. 26: The Cultural Context of Medieval Learning, Proceedings. Murdoch, J. E. & Sylla, E. D., eds. LC 75-24997. (Synthese Library: No. 76). 566p. 1975. 68.50 (ISBN 90-277-0560-7, Pub. by Reidel Holland); pap. 39.50 (ISBN 90-277-0587-9). Kluwer Academic.
International Colloquium on Philosophy, Science Theology in the Middle Ages, 1st, 1973. The Cultural Context of Medieval Learning: Proceedings, No.76. Murdock, John E. & Sylla, Edith D., eds. (Synthese Library: Boston Studies in the Philosophy of Science 26). ix, 540p. (Orig.). 1975. 68.50 (ISBN 90-277-0560-7, Pub. by Reidel Holland); pap. 39.50 (ISBN 90-277-0587-9, Pub. by Reidel Holland). Kluwer Academic.
International Commission of Jurists, Geneva. The Trial of Beyers Naude: Christian Witness & the Rule of Law. 1975. pap. 5.95 (ISBN 0-377-00057-4, Pub. by Search Pr England). Friend Pr.
International Commission on English in the Liturgy, tr. see Sacred Congregation for Divine Worship.
International Committee on English in the Liturgy, Confraternity of Christian Doctrine for the New American Bible, tr. see Catholic Church-Sacred Congregation of Divine Worship Staff.
International Committee on English in the Liturgy Confraternity of Christian Doctrine for the New American Bible, tr. see Catholic Church, Sacred Congregation for Divine Worship.
International Committee on English in the Liturgy Confraternity of Christian Doctrine for the New American Bible, tr. see Catholic Church, Sacred Congregation of Divine Worship Staff.
International Committee on English in the Liturgy, Confraternity of Christian Doctrine for the New American Bible, tr. see Catholic Church, Sacred Congregation of Divine Worship Staff.
International Committee on English in the Liturgy, tr. see Sacred Congregation for Divine Worship.
International Committee on English in the Liturgy. Documents on the Liturgy, 1963-1979: Conciliar, Papal & Curial Texts. O'Brien, Thomas C., ed. LC 82-83580. 1496p. 1983. text ed. 49.95 (ISBN 0-8146-1281-4). Liturgical Pr.
International Committee on English in the Liturgy, tr. Rite of Funerals. blue cloth 8.50 (ISBN 0-89942-350-7, 350/22). Catholic Bk Pub.
International Conference on the Unity of the Sciences, 2nd, Tokyo, Nov. 18-21, 1973. Modern Science & Moral Values: Proceedings. LC 75-306280. 608p. 1974. casebound smythesewn 20.00x (ISBN 0-89226-000-9, Pub. by ICF Pr). Paragon Hse.

International Congress on Biblical Studies, 6th, Oxford, 3-7 April,1978. Studia Biblica Nineteen Seventy-Eight, III: Papers on Paul & Other New Testament Authors. Livingstone, E. A., ed. (Journal for the Study of the New Testament, Supplement Ser.: No. 3). 468p. 1981. text ed. 37.50x (ISBN 0-905774-27-2, Pub. by JSOT Pr England). Eisenbrauns.
International Congress on Biblical Studies. Studia Biblica Nineteen Seventy-Eight II: Papers on the Gospels. Livingston, E. A., ed. (Journal for the Study of the New Testament Supplement Ser.: No. 2). 350p. 1980. text ed. 37.50x (ISBN 0-905774-22-1, Pub. by JSOT Pr England). Eisenbrauns.
International Missionary Council - Department of Social & Economic Research & Council. Modern Industry & the African. 2nd ed. Davis, J. Mearle, ed. LC 67-24749. 1961. Repr. of 1932 ed. 37.50x (ISBN 0-678-05042-2). Kelley.
International Partners in Prayer. Biblical References to Prayer. 15p. 1984. pap. 1.75 (ISBN 0-917593-03-0, Pub. by Intl Partners). Prosperity & Profits.
--Fasting: A Reference. 25p. Date not set. pap. text ed. 2.00 (ISBN 0-917593-07-3, Pub. by Intl Partners). Prosperity & Profits.
--Index to Prayer Books, Pamphlets, Etc. 50p. 1984. pap. 2.50 (ISBN 0-917593-01-4, Pub. by Intl Partners). Prosperity & Profits.
--Prayer Seminar-Workshop Workbook. 11p. 1984. pap. 2.50 (ISBN 0-917593-02-2, Pub. by Intl Partners). Prosperity & Profits.
International Partners in Prayer Staff. Prayer Movements: An International Directory. 20p. Date not set. pap. 3.00 (ISBN 0-917593-00-6, Pub. by Intl Partners). Prosperity & Profits.
International Partners in Prayers. International Partners in Prayer Triumpeting News: Packet of Past Issues. 6p. 1984. pap. 0.50 (ISBN 0-917593-04-9, Pub. by Intl Partners). Prosperity & Profits.
International Partners to Prayer. Starting a Prayer Bank: Deposits & Withdrawals. 1985. pap. text ed. 1.00 (ISBN 0-917593-09-X, Pub. by Intl Partners). Prosperity & Profits.
International Philosophy Year Conferences, Brockport. Contemporary Philosophic Thought: Proceedings, 4 vols. Kiefer, Howard E. & Munitz, Milton K., eds. Incl. Vol. 1. Language, Belief, & Metaphysics. LC 69-14643. 21.50x (ISBN 0-87395-151-4); Vol. 2. Mind, Science, & History. LC 69-14642. 49.50 (ISBN 0-87395-052-6); Vol. 3. Perspectives in Education, Religion, & the Arts. LC 69-14641. 33.50x (ISBN 0-87395-153-0); Vol. 4. Ethics & Social Justice. LC 69-14640. 49.50x (ISBN 0-87395-054-2). 1970. State U NY Pr.
Inwood, Brad. Ethics & Human Action in Early Stoicism. (Illus.). 1985. 32.00x (ISBN 0-19-824739-7). Oxford U Pr.
Ions, Veronica. Egyptian Mythology. rev. ed. LC 83-71478. (The Library of the World's Myths & Legends). (Illus.). 144p. 1983. 18.95 (ISBN 0-911745-07-6). P Bedrick Bks.
--Egyptian Mythology. (Library of the World's Myths & Legends). (Illus.). 144p. PLB 16.95 (ISBN 0-317-31011-9). Creative Ed.
Ioseliani, Platon. A Short History of the Georgian Church. 208p. 1983. pap. 6.00 (ISBN 0-317-30451-8). Holy Trinity.
Iparraguirre, Ignacio. Contemporary Trends in Studies on the Constitutions of the Society of Jesus: Annotated Bibliographical Orientations. Ganss, George E., ed. Meenan, Daniel F., tr. from Span. LC 74-77120. (Study Aids on Jesuit Topics Ser: No. 1). 96p. 1974. pap. 2.00 (ISBN 0-912422-10-6). Inst Jesuit.
Iqbal, A. Contemporary Muslim World: A Brief Note on Current Muslim World. 27.50 (ISBN 0-317-46090-0). Kazi Pubns.
--Culture of Islam. 1981. 16.50 (ISBN 0-686-97867-6). Kazi Pubns.
--Diplomacy in Islam. 14.95 (ISBN 0-686-18588-9). Kazi Pubns.
Iqbal, Afzal. Islamization of Pakistan. 1985. 15.00x (ISBN 0-8364-1493-4, Pub. by Idarah). South Asia Bks.
--The Life & Work of Muhammed Jalal-ud-Din Rumi. 1983. 29.95 (ISBN 0-86304-033-0, Pub. by Octagon England). Ins Study Human.
Iqbal, M. The Reconstruction of Religious Thoughts in Islam. 15.50 (ISBN 0-686-18482-3). Kazi Pubns.
Iqbal, Mohammad. Secrets of the Self. Nicholson, tr. (Orig.). 1979. pap. 3.95 (ISBN 0-89684-083-2, Pub. by Arnold Heinemann India). Orient Bk Dist.
Iqbal, Mohammed. Shikwa & Jawab-I-Shikwa (Answer) Iqbal's Dialogue with Allah. Singh, Krushwant, tr. from Urdu. 96p. (Orig.). 1981. pap. 7.95x (ISBN 0-19-561324-4). Oxford U Pr.
Iqbal, Muhammad. Way of the Muslim. (The Way Ser.). pap. 5.95 (ISBN 0-7175-0632-0). Dufour.
Iqbal, Sufi M. The Achievement of Love. Ahmad, Aftab, tr. from Arabic. 190p. 1987. pap. 9.95 (ISBN 0-915597-44-6). Amana Bks.
Irani, Adi K. Just to Love Him: Talks & Essays about Meher Baba. Berry, Steve & Booth, Peter, eds. LC 85-10709. 160p. (Orig.). 1985. pap. 8.95 (ISBN 0-913078-56-5). Sheriar Pr.
Irani, George E. The Papacy & the Middle East: The Role of the Holy See in the Arab-Israeli Conflict, 1962-1984. LC 85-41013. 224p. 1986. text ed. 22.95x (ISBN 0-268-01560-0). U of Notre Dame Pr.
Iremonger, Frederick A. William Temple, Archbishop of Canterbury: His Life & Letters. LC 83-45439. Repr. of 1948 ed. 62.50 (ISBN 0-404-20128-8). AMS Pr.
Irfani, Suroosh. Iran's Islamic Revolution: Popular Liberation or Religious Dictatorship? (Illus.). 278p. 1983. 29.50x (ISBN 0-86232-157-3, Pub. by Zed Pr England); pap. 10.75 (ISBN 0-86232-158-1). Humanities.
Iriarte, Lazaro. History of the Franciscan Order. 1983. 25.00 (ISBN 0-8199-0831-2). Franciscan Herald.
Irimie, Cornel & Focsa, Marcela. Romanian Icons Painted on Glass. (Illus.). 1971. 75.00 (ISBN 0-393-04309-6). Norton.
Irion, Clyde. Profit & Loss of Dying. 4.95 (ISBN 0-87516-030-1). De Vorss.
Irion, J. Everett. Interpreting the Revelation with Edgar Cayce. 440p. 1982. 19.95 (ISBN 0-87604-137-3). ARE Pr.
Irion, Paul E. The Funeral: Vestige or Value? Kastenaum, Robert, ed. LC 76-19578. (Death & Dying Ser.). 1977. Repr. lib. bdg. 22.00x (ISBN 0-405-09575-9). Ayer Co Pubs.
Irish Bishop's Pastoral. Human Life Is Sacred. 1977. pap. 1.50 (ISBN 0-8198-0416-9). Dghtrs St Paul.
Irish, Charles M. The Gospel Conspiracy Workbook. 40p. 1986. wkbk. 2.95 (ISBN 0-8192-1387-X). Morehouse.
Irish, Jerry A. The Religious Thought of H. Richard Niebuhr. LC 83-6202. pap. 32.30 (2027155). Bks Demand UMI.
Irland, Nancy. Baby Jesus' Birthday. (Cut & Color Bks.). (Illus.). 16p. (Orig.). 1982. pap. 0.95 (ISBN 0-87239-585-5, 2389). Standard Pub.
Irland, Nancy B. Little Talks with Jesus. Wheeler, Gerald, ed. 1985. 9.95 (ISBN 0-8280-0251-7). Review & Herald.
--No More Alphabet Soup. Van Dolson, Bobbie J., ed. LC 83-3303. (A Banner Bk.). 128p. (Orig.). 1984. pap. 5.95 (ISBN 0-8280-0165-0). Review & Herald.
Ironbiter, Suzanne. Devl. 125p. (Orig.). 1987. pap. 6.95 (ISBN 0-938999-02-8). Yuganta Pr.
Ironside, H. A. Acts. 13.95 (ISBN 0-87213-351-6). Loizeaux.
--Baptism. pap. 1.50 (ISBN 0-87213-345-1). Loizeaux.
--The Best of H. A. Ironside. (Best Ser.). 296p. (Orig.). 1981. pap. 4.95 (ISBN 0-8010-5033-2). Baker Bk.
--Complete Set of Commentaries, 22 vols. 244.90 (ISBN 0-87213-350-8). Loizeaux.
--The Continual Burnt Offering: Daily Meditations on the Word of God. 370p. 1981. pap. 4.95 (ISBN 0-87213-353-2). Loizeaux.
--Corinthians One. 12.95x (ISBN 0-87213-354-0). Loizeaux.
--Corinthians Two. 8.95 (ISBN 0-87213-355-9). Loizeaux.
--The Daily Sacrifice: Daily Meditations on the Word of God. 370p. 1982. pap. 4.95 (ISBN 0-87213-356-7). Loizeaux.
--Daniel the Prophet. with chart 9.95 (ISBN 0-87213-357-5); chart only 0.15. Loizeaux.
--Death & Afterwards. pap. 1.50 (ISBN 0-87213-346-X). Loizeaux.
--Doctor Ironside's Bible. (Illus.). pap. 4.25 (ISBN 0-87213-393-1). Loizeaux.
--Ephesians: Galatians. 11.95 (ISBN 0-87213-397-4). Loizeaux.
--Esther: Joshua, Ezra, Nehemiah. 11.95 (ISBN 0-87213-396-6). Loizeaux.
--Eternal Security of the Believer. pap. 1.50 (ISBN 0-87213-347-8). Loizeaux.
--Ezekiel. 9.95 (ISBN 0-87213-359-1). Loizeaux.
--Ezra: Joshua, Nehemiah & Esther. 11.95 (ISBN 0-87213-396-6). Loizeaux.
--Four Hundred Silent Years. pap. 3.50 (ISBN 0-87213-361-3). Loizeaux.
--Galatians & Ephesians. 11.95 (ISBN 0-87213-397-4). Loizeaux.
--Gospel of John. 16.95 (ISBN 0-87213-373-7). Loizeaux.
--Gospel of Luke. 14.95 (ISBN 0-87213-376-1). Loizeaux.
--Gospel of Mark. 8.95 (ISBN 0-87213-377-X). Loizeaux.
--Gospel of Matthew. 9.95 (ISBN 0-87213-378-8). Loizeaux.
--Hebrews, James, Peter. 9.95 (ISBN 0-87213-399-0). Loizeaux.
--Holy Spirit: Mission of, & Praying in. pap. 2.95 (ISBN 0-87213-366-4). Loizeaux.
--Holy Trinity. pap. 1.50 (ISBN 0-87213-348-6). Loizeaux.
--Isaiah. 9.95 (ISBN 0-87213-369-9). Loizeaux.
--James: Hebrews, Peter. 9.95 (ISBN 0-87213-399-0). Loizeaux.
--Jeremiah: Prophecy & Lamentations. 10.95 (ISBN 0-87213-371-0). Loizeaux.
--John & Jude, Epistles. 9.95 (ISBN 0-87213-372-9). Loizeaux.
--Joshua, Ezra, Nehemiah, Esther. 11.95 (ISBN 0-87213-396-6). Loizeaux.
--Jude: John. 9.95 (ISBN 0-87213-372-9). Loizeaux.
--Letters to a Roman Catholic Priest. pap. 1.25 (ISBN 0-87213-349-4). Loizeaux.
--Minor Prophets. 11.95 (ISBN 0-87213-379-6). Loizeaux.
--Not Wrath: But Rapture. pap. 1.50 (ISBN 0-87213-380-X). Loizeaux.
--Philemon: Timothy, Titus. 9.95 (ISBN 0-87213-391-5). Loizeaux.
--Philippians, Colossians, Thessalonians. 433p. 11.95 (ISBN 0-87213-398-2). Loizeaux.
--Proverbs, Song of Solomon. 12.95 (ISBN 0-87213-395-8). Loizeaux.
--Psalms, Studies on Book One. 8.95 (ISBN 0-87213-383-4). Loizeaux.
--Revelation. 9.95 (ISBN 0-87213-384-2). Loizeaux.
--Romans. 7.95 (ISBN 0-87213-386-9). Loizeaux.
--Sailing with Paul. pap. 1.35 (ISBN 0-87213-387-7). Loizeaux.
--Timothy, Titus & Philemon. 9.95 (ISBN 0-87213-391-5). Loizeaux.
--Wrongly Dividing the Word of Truth. pap. 1.25 (ISBN 0-87213-392-3). Loizeaux.
Ironside, H. A. & Ottman, F. Studies in Biblical Eschatology. 426p. 1983. lib. bdg. 16.00 Smythe Sewn (ISBN 0-86524-143-0, 9806). Klock & Klock.
Ironside, Harry. Notas Sobre el Cantar de los Cantares. Orig. Title: Song of Solomon. (Span.). 128p. Date not set. pap. 4.75 (ISBN 0-8254-1328-1). Kregel.
Ironside, Harry A. Full Assurance. 1937. pap. 3.95 (ISBN 0-8024-2896-7). Moody.
Irsch, Ed. As It Was Told: A Play for Christmas. 16p. (Orig.). 1980. pap. text ed. 3.75 (ISBN 0-89536-439-5, 0146). CSS of Ohio.
--The Undisturbed Soldier. 1983. 4.25 (ISBN 0-89536-602-9, 2105). CSS of Ohio.
Irvine, A. D., jt. ed. see Emilsen, William W.
Irvine, William C. Heresies Exposed. pap. 4.95 (ISBN 0-87213-401-6). Loizeaux.
Irving, J. B. Had You Been Born a Muslim. pap. 1.50 (ISBN 0-686-18471-8). Kazi Pubns.
Irving, Lynn. Pocketful of Puppets: Poems for Church School. Keller, Merily H., ed. (Puppetry in Education ser.). (Illus.). 48p. (Orig.). 1982. 11.50; pap. 7.50 (ISBN 0-931044-05-7). Renfro Studios.
Irving, Ronald E. The Christian Democratic Parties of Western Europe. LC 78-41082. pap. 90.00 (ISBN 0-317-42290-1, 2023267). Bks Demand UMI.
Irving, T. B. Religion & Social Responsibility. pap. 1.00 (ISBN 0-686-18445-9). Kazi Pubns.
--Tide of Islam. 7.95 (ISBN 0-686-83887-4). Kazi Pubns.
Irving, T. B., tr. The Qur'an: The First American Version. LC 84-72242. 500p. (Orig.). 1985. 17.50 (ISBN 0-915597-08-X). Amana Bks.
Irving, T. B., et al. The Quran: Basic Teachings. 278p. (Orig.). 1979. pap. 10.00 (ISBN 0-86037-021-6, Pub by Islamic Found UK). New Era Pubns MI.
Irving, Thomas B. The World of Islam. Orig. Title: The Tide of Islam. (Illus.). 200p. 1985. 17.50 (ISBN 0-915597-20-9); pap. 9.95 (ISBN 0-915597-18-7). Amana Bks.
Irving, Thomas B., ed. The Maya's Own Words: An Anthology Comprising Abridgements of the Popol-Vuh, Warrior of Rabinal, & Selections from the Memorial of Solola, the Book of Chilam Balam of Chumayel, & the Title of the Lords Of Totonicapan. LC 84-81822. (Illus.). 102p. (Orig.). 1985. pap. 12.00X (ISBN 0-911437-14-2). Labyrinthos.
Irving, Washington. Mahomet & His Successors, 2 Vols. 1983. Repr. of 1868 ed. lib. bdg. 200.00 set (ISBN 0-89987-405-3). Darby Bks.
--Old Christmas. LC 77-8465. (Illus.). 208p. 1977. Repr. of 1875 ed. 10.00 (ISBN 0-912882-30-1). Sleepy Hollow.
Irwin, C. H. The Every Day Bible Commentary. Orig. Title: Irwin's Bible Commentary. 582p. 1983. pap. 8.95 (ISBN 0-310-26531-2, 9906P). Zondervan.
Irwin, Elvin. O Plano de Deus para a Familia. Orig. Title: Living on God's Family Plan. (Port.). 1986. write for info. (ISBN 0-8297-0708-5). Life Pubs Intl.
Irwin, James B. More Than Earthlings. LC 83-70369. 1983. 6.95 (ISBN 0-8054-5255-9). Broadman.
Irwin, James B. & Unger, Monte. More Than an Ark on Ararat. LC 85-4157. 1985. 6.95 (ISBN 0-8054-5018-1). Broadman.
Irwin, James B., Jr. & Emerson, W. A. Un Astronauta y la Lumbrera de la Noche. 176p. 1981. Repr. of 1978 ed. 4.25 (ISBN 0-311-01066-0). Casa Bautista.
Irwin, Joyce, ed. Sacred Sound: Music in Religious Thought & Practice. LC 83-15390. (AAR Thematic Studies). 180p. 1984. 22.50 (ISBN 0-89130-655-2, 01 25 01). Scholars Pr GA.
Irwin, Joyce L. Womanhood in Radical Protestantism: 1525-1675. LC 79-66370. (Studies in Women & Religion: Vol. 1). xxx, 296p. 1979. 49.95x (ISBN 0-88946-547-9). E Mellen.
Irwin, Kay. Primer of Prayer Gesture. 43p. 1977. pap. 3.00 (ISBN 0-941500-21-7). Sharing Co.
Irwin, Kevin. Lent, a Guide to the Eucharist & Hours. (Liturgical Seasons Ser.). 300p. (Orig.). 1985. pap. 12.95 (ISBN 0-916134-68-7). Pueblo Pub Co.
Irwin, Kevin W. Advent Christmas: A Guide to the Eucharist & Hours. (Liturgical Seasons Ser.). 300p. (Orig.). 1986. pap. 12.95 (ISBN 0-916134-80-6). Pueblo Pub Co.
--Liturgy, Prayer & Spirituality. 1984. pap. 9.95 (ISBN 0-8091-2560-9). Paulist Pr.
--Sunday Worship. 1983. pap. 14.95 (ISBN 0-916134-52-0). Pueblo Pub Co.
Irwin, Paul B. The Care & Counseling of Youth in the Church. Clinebell, Howard J. & Stone, Howard W., eds. LC 74-26334. (Creative Pastoral Care & Counseling Ser.). 96p. 1975. pap. 4.50 (ISBN 0-8006-0552-7, 1-552). Fortress.
Irwin, William A., ed. see Smith, John M.
Isaac, Heirich. Five Polyphonic Masses. Cuyler, Louise, ed. LC 56-7145. pap. 38.50 (ISBN 0-317-09652-4, 2051077). Bks Demand UMI.
Isaac, Reid. Conversations with the Crucified. 128p. (Orig.). 1982. pap. 6.95 (ISBN 0-8164-2417-9, HarpR). Har-Row.
Isaac, Stephen. Songs from the House of Pilgrimage. LC 77-169595. 1971. 9.50 (ISBN 0-8283-1334-2). Christward.
--The Way of Discipleship to Christ. LC 76-57021. 1976. pap. 4.50 (ISBN 0-910378-12-6). Christward.
Isaacman, Clara & Grossman, Joan A. Clara's Story. LC 84-14339. 180p. 1984. 11.95 (ISBN 0-8276-0243-X). Jewish Pubns.
Isaac Of Stella. Isaac of Stella: Sermons on the Christian Year, Vol. 1. McCaffrey, Hugh, tr. LC 78-868. (Cistercian Fathers Ser.: No. 11). 1979. 15.95 (ISBN 0-87907-611-9). Cistercian Pubns.
Isaacs, A. Lionel. The Jews of Majorca. 1976. lib. bdg. 59.95 (ISBN 0-8490-2105-7). Gordon Pr.
Isaacs, Abram S. Stories from the Rabbis. LC 79-175868. Repr. of 1911 ed. 20.00 (ISBN 0-405-08661-X, Blom Pubns). Ayer Co Pubs.
Isaacs, David. Character Building: A Guide for Parents & Teachers. Tr. of La Educacion de las Virtudes Humanas. 268p. (Orig.). 1984. write for info. (ISBN 0-906127-68-8, Pub. by Four Courts Pr Ireland); pap. 8.95 (ISBN 0-906127-67-X, Pub. by Four Courts Pr Ireland). Scepter Pubs.
Isaacs, Leora, jt. auth. see Isaacs, Ron.
Isaacs, Ron & Isaacs, Leora. A Jewish Grandparents' Book of Memories. 100p. 1987. 20.00 (ISBN 0-87668-976-4). Aronson.
Isaacson, Cheryl. Yoga for All Ages. (Illus., Orig.). 1986. pap. 10.95 (ISBN 0-7225-1210-4). Thorsons Pubs.
Isaacson, Harold J., tr. The Throat of the Peacock: Japanese Senryu on Filial Devotion. (Bhaisajaguru Ser.). 1977. pap. 1.85 (ISBN 0-87830-557-2). Theatre Arts.
Isaac The Syrian. Mystical Writings of St. Isaac the Syrian. Wensinck, A. J., tr. from Syriac. 1977. pap. 6.95 (ISBN 0-686-19231-1). Eastern Orthodox.
Isabel, Damien. The Spiritual Director. (Synthesis Ser.). 1976. pap. 2.00 (ISBN 0-8199-0712-X). Franciscan Herald.
Isabel, Linda, jt. auth. see Debor, Jane.
Isacco, Enrico & Dallapiccola, Anna L., eds. Krishna: The Divine Lover. LC 82-83044. (Illus.). 224p. 1983. 75.00 (ISBN 0-87923-457-1). Godine.
Isasi-Diaz, Ada M., ed. see Hynes, Kathleen.
Isbell, Charles D. Corpus of the Aramaic Incantation Bowls. LC 75-15949. (Society of Biblical Literature. Dissertation Ser.: No. 17). pap. 40.70 (ISBN 0-317-10143-9, 2017519). Bks Demand UMI.
--Malachi: Bible Study Commentary. (Bible Study Commentary Ser.). 128p. (Orig.). 1980. pap. 4.95 (ISBN 0-310-41673-6, 9350P). Zondervan.
Isbell, Charles D., jt. auth. see Finley, Harvey E.
Isberner, Fred, et al. Sex Education in a Church Setting: The OCTOPUS Training Manual. 128p. (Orig.). 1986. pap. text ed. 8.95x (ISBN 0-8093-1315-4). S Ill U Pr.
Isham, Linda. On Behalf of Children. LC 74-17842. 48p. (Orig.). 1975. pap. 1.95 (ISBN 0-8170-0666-4). Judson.
Ishaq, I. The Life of Muhammad: A Translation of Ishaq's Sirat Rasul Allah. Guillaume, A., intro. by. 1979. pap. text ed. 24.95x (ISBN 0-19-636034-X). Oxford U Pr.

Ishee, John A. Design for Living: The Sermon on the Mount. 36p. 1982. pap. 3.50 (ISBN 0-939298-07-4). J M Prods.

--Everyman's Gospel: Studies in Romans. 34p. (Orig.). 1983. pap. 3.50 (ISBN 0-939298-19-8). J M Prods.

--God's Purpose-God's People: Studies in Ephesians. 36p. 1982. pap. 3.50 (ISBN 0-939298-03-1). J M Prods.

--God's Wisdom-God's Way: Studies in First Corinthians. 35p. (Orig.). 1983. pap. 3.50 (ISBN 0-939298-20-1). J M Prods.

--New Beginning: Studies in John's Gospel. 35p. (Orig.). 1982. pap. 3.50 (ISBN 0-939298-13-9, 139). J. M. Prods.

--What Every Person Should Know About God: Bible Study for New Christians. 36p. 1982. pap. 3.50 (ISBN 0-939298-05-8). J M Prods.

Isherwood, C., tr. see Bhagavad-Gita.

Isherwood, Christopher. Approach to Vedanta. 1970. pap. 3.95 (ISBN 0-87481-003-5). Vedanta Pr.

--My Guru & His Disciple. 352p. 1981. pap. 4.95 (ISBN 0-14-005837-0). Penguin.

--Ramakrishna & His Disciples. LC 65-17100. 384p. 1980. pap. 8.95 (ISBN 0-87481-037-X). Vedanta Pr.

Isherwood, Christopher, jt. auth. see Prabhavananda, Swami.

Isherwood, Christopher, ed. Vedanta for the Western World: A Symposium on Vedanta. LC 46-25052. 1945. pap. 7.95 (ISBN 0-87481-000-0). Vedanta Pr.

Isherwood, Christopher, jt. tr. see Prabhavananda, Swami.

Ishida, Hisatoyo. Esoteric Buddhist Painting: Japanese Arts Library, Vol. 15. LC 86-40437. (Japanese Arts Library). (Illus.). 210p. 1987. 29.95 (ISBN 0-87011-767-X). Kodansha.

Ishida, T., ed. Studies in the Period of David & Solomon & Other Essays: Papers Read at the International Symposium for Biblical Studies, 6-7 December 1979. LC 82-11183. 409p. 1982. text ed. 35.00x (ISBN 0-931464-16-1). Eisenbrauns.

Ishida, Tomoo. The Royal Dynasties in Ancient Israel. 1977. 45.25 (ISBN 3-1100-6519-3). De Gruyter.

Ishii, Yoneo. Sangha, State, & Society: Thai Buddhism in History. Hawkes, Peter, tr. from Japanese. (Monographs, Center for Southeast Asian Studies, Kyoto University). 224p. 1985. text ed. 25.00x (ISBN 0-8248-0993-9); pap. text ed. 16.00x (ISBN 0-8248-0994-7). UH Pr.

Isho, Anan. Stories of the Holy Fathers, 2 vols. Budge, E. A., tr. 1980. Set. lib. bdg. 125.00 (ISBN 0-8490-3195-8). Gordon Pr.

Isichei, Elizabeth. Entirely for God. (Cistercian Studies: No. 43). 132p. 1980. pap. 11.95 (ISBN 0-87907-943-6). Cistercian Pubns.

Isidorus. Isidors Geschichte der Gothen, Vandalen, Sueven, Nebst Ausuzegen Aus der Kirchengeschichte Des Beda Venerablis. pap. 8.00 (ISBN 0-384-25980-4). Johnson Repr.

Islam, Fida E. The Political Personality of Islam. 280p. 1985. pap. 6.95 (ISBN 0-940368-37-4). Tahrike Tarsile Quran.

Islam, K. M. Spectacle of Death. pap. 16.50 (ISBN 0-686-63915-4). Kazi Pubns.

Isler, Betty. Here I Am Again, Lord. (Continued Applied Christianity Ser.). 1983. pap. 4.95 (ISBN 0-570-03895-2, 12-2977). Concordia.

--I'm Still Here Lord! 1984. pap. 4.95 (ISBN 0-570-03938-X, 12-2873). Concordia.

--Thank You for My Grandchild. 1983. pap. 4.95 (ISBN 0-570-03915-0, 12-2850). Concordia.

--A Time for Every Purpose. 80p. (Orig.). 1986. pap. 4.95 (ISBN 0-570-03986-X, 12-3013). Concordia.

Ismael, Jacqueline S., jt. auth. see Ismael, Tareq Y.

Ismael, Tareq Y. & Ismael, Jacqueline S. Government & Politics in Islam. LC 85-2265. 177p. 1985. 27.50 (ISBN 0-312-34126-1). St Martin.

Isma'il, A. H. Ali Ibn see Ali ibn Isma'il, A. H., et al.

Ismail, V. Muhammad: The Last Prophet. 8.50 (ISBN 0-686-83579-4). Kazi Pubns.

Isoardi, Gian C. Don Bosco the Catechist. Cornell, Wallace L., tr. from Ital. 89p. 1981. pap. 4.75 (ISBN 0-89944-053-3). Don Bosco Multimedia.

Ison, Colleen. Goliath's Last Stand. LC 85-17315. 112p. 1986. pap. 4.95 (ISBN 0-87239-997-4, 3357). Standard Pub.

--Skits That Teach. (Illus.). 112p. 1985. pap. 4.95 (ISBN 0-87239-848-X, 3356). Standard Pub.

Israel Exploration Society, Jerusalem & Levine, Lee I., eds. Ancient Synagogues Revealed. LC 81-53031. (Illus.). 199p. 1982. 27.50x (ISBN 0-8143-1706-5). Wayne St U Pr.

Israel, Fred L., ed. Amish. LC 85-17516. (Let's Meet the Peoples of North America Ser.). (Illus.). 112p. 1986. lib. bdg. 15.95 (ISBN 0-87754-853-6). Chelsea Hse.

--Jews. (Let's Meet the Peoples of North America Ser.). (Illus.). 112p. 1987. lib. bdg. 15.95 (ISBN 0-87754-887-0). Chelsea Hse.

Israel, Jonathan L. European Jewry in the Age of Mercantilism, 1550-1750. 1985. 34.50x (ISBN 0-19-821928-8). Oxford U Pr.

Israel, Martin. Coming in Glory: Christ's Presence in the World Today. 128p. 1986. pap. 7.95 (ISBN 0-8245-0785-1). Crossroad NY.

--Discipline of Love. 128p. (Orig.). 1986. pap. 8.95 (ISBN 0-8245-0739-8). Crossroad NY.

--Healing As Sacrament: The Sanctification of the World. LC 84-72482. 116p. 1985. pap. 6.00 (ISBN 0-936384-23-9). Cowley Pubns.

--Living Alone. Kelsey, Morton T., intro. by. LC 82-72725. 144p. (Orig.). 1983. pap. 8.95 (ISBN 0-8245-0503-4). Crossroad NY.

--The Pain That Heals: The Place of Suffering in the Growth of the Person. (Crossroad Paperback Ser.). 192p. 1982. pap. 8.95 (ISBN 0-8245-0437-2). Crossroad NY.

--Smouldering Fire. 192p. 1986. pap. 8.95 (ISBN 0-8245-0728-2). Crossroad NY.

--Smouldering Fire: The Work of the Holy Spirit. LC 81-9794. 192p. 1981. 10.95 (ISBN 0-8245-0072-5). Crossroad NY.

Israel, Milton & Wagle, N. K., eds. Islamic Society & Culture: Essays in Honour of Professor Aziz Ahmad. 1983. 32.50x (ISBN 0-8364-1047-5, Pub. by Manohar India). South Asia Bks.

Israel Ministry. What Is a Jew? 1975. 30.00 (ISBN 0-379-13904-9). Oceana.

Israeli, Raphael. Muslims in China: A Study in Cultural Confrontation. (Scandinavian Institute of Asian Studies: No. 29). 272p. 1981. pap. text ed. 17.50x (ISBN 0-391-00718-1, Pub. by Curzon Pr UK). Humanities.

Israeli, Raphael, ed. The Crescent in the East: Islam in Asia Major. 240p. 1981. 30.00x (ISBN 0-7007-0143-5, Pub. by Curzon England). State Mutual Bk.

Israeli, Raphael, jt. ed. see Heper, Metin.

Israeli, Raphuel. Peace Is in the Eye of the Beholder. xxiv, 389p. 1985. text ed. 62.00 (ISBN 0-89925-077-7). Mouton.

Israelowitz, Oscar. Synagogues of New York City. 1983. 14.00 (ISBN 0-8446-5954-1). Peter Smith.

--Synagogues of New York City: A Pictorial Survey in 150 Photographs. (Illus.). 155p. (Orig.). pap. 6.00 (ISBN 0-486-24231-5). Dover.

Issac, Erich, jt. auth. see Jean, Rael.

Issawi, Charles. An Arab Philosophy of History: Selections from the Prolegomena of Ibn Khaldun of Tunis (1332-1406) LC 86-29199. xiv, 192p. 1986. 9.95 (ISBN 0-87850-056-1). Darwin Pr.

Istavridis, Vasil T. Orthodoxy & Anglicanism. LC 67-79982. 1966. 15.00x (ISBN 0-8401-1183-5). A R Allenson.

Itivuttaka. Sayings of Buddha: The Iti-Vuttaka. LC 9-4569. (Columbia University. Indo-Iranian Ser.: No. 5). Repr. of 1908 ed. 16.50 (ISBN 0-404-50475-2). AMS Pr.

Itrat-Husain. The Mystical Element in the Metaphysical Poets of the Seventeenth Century. LC 66-23522. 1948. 15.00 (ISBN 0-8196-0177-2). Biblo.

Ivanoff, N. K Tchemu Privodit Bezbozhije. Tr. of What are the Consequeces of Godlessness. 24p. 1983. pap. 1.50 (ISBN 0-317-29144-0). Holy Trinity.

Ivar, Asheim. Christ & Humanity. LC 73-10426. pap. 50.80 (2026913). Bks Demand UMI.

Iverson, Dick. The Holy Spirit Today. (Illus.). 1977. pap. 5.50 (ISBN 0-914936-24-7). Bible Temple.

Iverson, Dick & Grant, Ray. Team Ministry. (Illus.). 143p. 1984. pap. 8.95 (ISBN 0-914936-61-1). Bible Temple.

Iverson, Dick, jt. auth. see Elders of Bible Temple.

Iverson, Edie, et al. Bible Study Leadership Training. (Illus.). 53p. 1980. pap. 6.75 (ISBN 0-914936-46-8). Bible Temple.

Iverson, K. R., jt. auth. see Conner, Kevin J.

Iverson, Percy E. What Is Life All About. 1985. 10.95 (ISBN 0-533-06511-9). Vantage.

Iverson, Shari. Worship Leader's Guide. (Illus.). 40p. 1986. pap. 4.50 (ISBN 0-914936-97-2). Bible Temple.

Ives, Carolyn. Being OK. (Orig.). 1987. pap. 7.00 (ISBN 0-915541-19-X). Star Bks Inc.

Ives, Colta. Picturesque Ideas on the Flight into Egypt. LC 82-4405. (Illus.). 72p. 1982. Repr. 20.00 (ISBN 0-8076-1047-X). Braziller.

Ives, Howard C. Portals to Freedom. 256p. 1937. pap. 8.95 (ISBN 0-87743-013-6). G Ronald Pub.

Ives, J. Moss. Ark & the Dove: The Beginnings of Civil & Religious Liberties in America. LC 76-79200. (Illus.). 1969. Repr. of 1936 ed. 32.50x (ISBN 0-8154-0293-7). Cooper Sq.

Ives, Kenneth, ed. see Wood, Raquel & Banerji, Ranan.

Ives, Kenneth, et al. Black Quakers: Brief Biographies. (Studies in Quakerism: 12). (Illus.). 118p. (Orig.). 1986. pap. 8.00 (ISBN 0-89670-015-1). Progresiv Pub.

Ives, Kenneth H. Nurturing Spiritual Development: Stages, Structure, Style. (Studies in Quakerism: No. 8). 60p. (Orig.). 1982. pap. 4.00 (ISBN 0-89670-011-9). Progresiv Pub.

Ivimey, Joseph. John Milton: His Life & Times, Religious & Political Opinions. LC 72-190658. 1833. lib. bdg. 37.50 (ISBN 0-8414-5069-2). Folcroft.

Ivins, Dan. God's Surprising Goodness. 128p. 1984. pap. 4.95 (ISBN 0-8170-1044-0). Judson.

--Model for Christian Wholeness. LC 84-9436. 1985. pap. 4.25 (ISBN 0-8054-2252-8). Broadman.

Ivory, Thomas P., ed. see Archdiocese of Newark Staff.

Iyengar, B. K. The Concise Light on Yoga. LC 82-5473. (Illus.). 256p. 1982. pap. 7.95 spiral (ISBN 0-8052-0723-6). Schocken.

Iyengar, K. R. On the Mother: The Chronicle of a Manifestation & Ministry, 2 vols. 1979. pap. 45.00 (ISBN 0-89744-947-9). Auromere.

Iyengar, K. Srinivasa. The Epic Beautiful: An English Verse Rendering of the Sundara Kanda of the Ramayana of Valmiki. 1986. 12.50x (ISBN 0-8364-1545-0, Pub. by National Sahitya Akademi). South Asia Bks.

Iyengar, K. Srinivasa, ed. Asian Variations in Ramayana. 1986. 14.00x (ISBN 0-8364-1571-X, Pub. by National Sahitya Akademi). South Asia Bks.

Iyer, B. R. Rambles in Vedanta. 1974. Repr. 22.50 (ISBN 0-8426-0601-7). Orient Bk Dist.

Iyer, Pico. The Recovery of Innocence. (Illus.). 1984. 8.75 (ISBN 0-88695-019-8). Concord Grove.

Iyer, Raghavan. The Beacon Light. (Sangam Texts Ser.). 124p. 1984. pap. 8.75 (ISBN 0-88695-021-X). Concord Grove.

--The Moral & Political Thought of Mahatma Gandi. (Illus.). xviii, 478p. pap. 17.50 (ISBN 0-88695-002-3). Concord Grove.

--The Society of the Future. 84. 8.75 (ISBN 0-88695-018-X). Concord Grove.

Iyer, Raghavan, ed. Chants for Contemplation: Shikh Text. (Sacred Texts Ser.). Orig. Title: ADI Granth. 144p. (Orig.). 1984. pap. 8.75 (ISBN 0-88695-030-9). Concord Grove.

--The Jewel in the Lotus. 606p. (Orig.). 1983. pap. 19.75 (ISBN 0-88695-000-7). Concord Grove.

Iyer, Raghavan, ed. see Shankar, Bhavani.

Izard, Michel & Smith, Pierre, eds. Between Belief & Transgression: Structuralist Essays in Religion, History & Myth. Leavitt, John, tr. LC 81-16377. (Chicago Originals Ser.). (Illus.). 1982. lib. bdg. 20.00x (ISBN 0-226-38861-1). U of Chicago Pr.

Izetbegovic, Alija A. Islam Between East & West. LC 84-45552. 248p. (Orig.). 1984. pap. 12.00 (ISBN 0-89259-057-2). Am Trust Pubns.

Izutsu, Toshihiko. The Concept of Belief in Islamic Theology. LC 79-52553. (Islam Ser.). 1980. Repr. of 1965 ed. lib. bdg. 20.00x (ISBN 0-8369-9261-X). Ayer Co Pubs.

--God & Man in the Koran. LC 79-52554. (Islam Ser.). 1980. Repr. of 1964 ed. lib. bdg. 20.00x (ISBN 0-8369-9262-8). Ayer Co Pubs.

--The Interior & Exterior in Zen Buddhism. LC 84-5580. (Eranos Lectures Ser.: No. 1). 36p. (Orig.). 1984. pap. 7.00 (ISBN 0-88214-401-4). Spring Pubns.

--Sufism & Taoism: A Comparative Study of Key Philosophical Concepts. LC 84-78. 493p. 1984. text ed. 40.00x (ISBN 0-520-05264-1). U of Cal Pr.

Izutsu, Toshihiku, tr. see Sabzavari, Hadi Ibn Mahdi.

Izzidien, Mouel Y. Nisab Al Ihtisab. Quinlan, Hamid, ed. LC 82-70458. (Illus.). 230p. (Orig.). Date not set. pap. 5.00 (ISBN 0-89259-031-9). Am Trust Pubns.

Izzidien, Movel Y., tr. see Sabiq, Sayyed.

J

J. M. Armstrong Company. The Biographical Encyclopedia of Kentucky: Of the Dead & Living Men of the Ninteenth Century. 1978. Repr. of 1877 ed. 42.50 (ISBN 0-89308-193-0). Southern Hist Pr.

Jabay, Earl. The God-Players. LC 69-11637. 155p. 1970. pap. 5.95 (ISBN 0-310-26541-X, 9939P). Zondervan.

--Kingdom of Self. LC 73-89494. 1974. pap. 3.95 (ISBN 0-88270-062-6). Bridge Pub.

Jaberg, Gene & Wargo, Louis G., Jr. The Video Pencil: Cable Communications for Church & Community. LC 80-7951. 156p. 1980. lib. bdg. 24.00 (ISBN 0-8191-1085-X); pap. text ed. 9.75 (ISBN 0-8191-1086-8). U Pr of Amer.

Jablonski, Moineddin, ed. see Lewis, Samuel L.

Jablonski, Moineddin, ed. see Lewis, Samuel L. & Khan, Hazrat I.

Jabusch, Willard F. The Person in the Pulpit: Preaching as Caring. LC 79-28812. (Abingdon Preacher's Library). (Orig.). 1980. pap. 5.95 (ISBN 0-687-30784-8). Abingdon.

--Walk Where Jesus Walked: A Pilgrim's Guide with Prayer & Song. LC 86-71224. (Illus.). 200p. (Orig.). 1986. pap. 6.95 (ISBN 0-87793-339-1). Ave Maria.

Jack, Homer A., ed. see World Conference on Religion & Peace, 3rd Assembly.

Jack, James W. Daybreak in Livingstonia: The Story of the Livingstonia Mission, British Central Africa. rev. ed. LC 79-77204. (Illus.). Repr. of 1900 ed. cancelled (ISBN 0-8371-1308-3, JAL&, Pub. by Negro U Pr). Greenwood.

Jack, LaWant P. All Things in Their Time. pap. 5.95 (ISBN 0-89036-145-2). Hawkes Pub Inc.

Jack, S. Spiritual Reflections for the Recovering Alcoholic. LC 84-18590. (Illus.). 90p. 1985. pap. 5.95 (ISBN 0-8189-0477-1). Alba.

Jackins, Harvey. Is Death Necessary? 1970. pap. 0.50 (ISBN 0-911214-22-4). Rational Isl.

Jackman, Paul, ed. see Castelli, Jim, et al.

Jackman, Paul, ed. see Maguire, Marjorie R. & Maguire, Daniel C.

Jacks, Bob, et al. Your Home, a Lighthouse. LC 85-73824. 142p. (Orig.). 1986. pap. text ed. 4.95 (ISBN 0-934396-41-8). Churches Alive.

--Your Home: A Lighthouse. rev ed. LC 87-60179. 150p. 1987. pap. 5.95 (ISBN 0-89109-127-0). NavPress.

Jacks, Lawrence P. Religious Perplexities. 3rd ed. LC 77-27149. (Hibbert Lectures: 1922). Repr. of 1923 ed. 20.00 (ISBN 0-404-60421-8). AMS Pr.

Jackson, Abraham. The Pious Prentice, or, the Prentices Piety. LC 74-28866. (English Experience Ser.: No. 746). 1975. Repr. of 1640 ed. 7.00 (ISBN 90-221-0746-9). Walter J Johnson.

Jackson, Abraham V. Researches in Manichaeism with Special Reference to the Turfan Fragments. LC 32-9567. (Columbia University. Indo-Iranian Ser.: No. 13). Repr. of 1932 ed. 31.00 (ISBN 0-404-50483-3). AMS Pr.

--Zoroaster: Prophet of Ancient Iran. LC 98-2277. (Columbia University. Indo-Iranian Ser.: No. 14). Repr. of 1928 ed. 26.00 (ISBN 0-404-50484-1). AMS Pr.

--Zorostrian Studies: Iranian Religion & Various Monographs. LC 28-29344. (Columbia University. Indo-Iranian Ser.: No. 12). Repr. of 1928 ed. 27.50 (ISBN 0-404-50482-5). AMS Pr.

Jackson, Anne A. & Spears, Cleola I. Women in Ministry. (Illus.). 350p. (Orig.). pap. write for info. (ISBN 0-9605892-3-6). Dawn Ministries.

Jackson, Bernard S. & Jewish Law Association, International Congress Staff. Studies in Jewish Law I: The Touro Conference Volume. LC 84-1329. (SP Occasional Papers & Proceedings: No. 3). 1985. 26.75 (ISBN 0-89130-732-X, 15-00-01); pap. 17.75 (ISBN 0-89130-868-7). Scholars Pr GA.

Jackson, Bernard S., ed. Jewish Law Association Studies II: The Jerusalem Conference Volume. (Occasional Papers & Proceedings). 208p. 26.95 (ISBN 0-89130-950-0, 15-00-02); pap. 19.95 (ISBN 0-89130-951-9). Scholars Pr GA.

Jackson, Carl T. The Oriental Religious & American Thought: Nineteenth-Century Explorations. LC 80-25478. (Contributions in American Studies: No. 55). 296p. 1981. lib. bdg. 32.95 (ISBN 0-313-22491-9, JOR/). Greenwood.

Jackson, Carolyn, tr. see Garin, Eugenio.

Jackson, Catherine. The Christian's Secret of a Happy Life for Today. 224p. 1979. pap. 5.95 (ISBN 0-8007-5061-6, Power Bks). Revell.

Jackson, D. N. Baptist Doctrines & History. 1974. pap. 3.50 (ISBN 0-89114-003-4). Baptist Pub Hse.

Jackson, Dave. Dial 911: Peaceful Christians & Urban Violence. LC 81-2541. 160p. 1981. pap. 5.95 (ISBN 0-8361-1952-5). Herald Pr.

Jackson, Dave, jt. auth. see Brandt, Patricia.

Jackson, Dave, jt. auth. see Ferguson, Larry.

Jackson, David J., jt. auth. see Slaughter, James N., Jr.

Jackson, Edgar. Parish Counseling. LC 84-45066. 221p. 1983. 25.00x (ISBN 0-87668-672-2). Aronson.

Jackson, Edgar N. Group Counseling: Dynamic Possibilities for Small Groups. LC 73-91167. (Orig.). 1969. pap. 2.95 (ISBN 0-8298-0053-0). Pilgrim NY.

--The Role of Faith in the Process of Healing. 216p. 1982. pap. 9.95 (ISBN 0-86683-679-9, HarpR). Har-Row.

--When Someone Dies. Hulme, William E., ed. LC 76-154488. (Pocket Counsel Bks). 58p. (Orig.). 1971. pap. 2.50 (ISBN 0-8006-1103-9, 1-1103). Fortress.

--Your Health & You: How Awareness, Attitudes, & Faith Contribute to a Healthy Life. LC 86-22226. (Augsburg Religion & Medicine). 112p. (Orig.). 1986. pap. 5.95 (ISBN 0-8066-2221-0, 10-7426). Augsburg.

Jackson, Forrest W. Their Story-Our Story. LC 85-6623. 1985. pap. 4.95 (ISBN 0-8054-3618-9, 4236-18). Broadman.
Jackson, Forrest W., compiled by. Bible Studies for Special Occasions in Youth Ministry. LC 82-70109. 1982. pap. 4.95 (ISBN 0-8054-3617-0, 4236-17). Broadman.
Jackson, Francis, ed. Anthems for Choirs One: Fifty Anthems for Mixed Voices. 1973. pap. 8.75 (ISBN 0-19-353214-X). Oxford U Pr.
Jackson, Gayle, jt. auth. see Henrichsen, Walter A.
Jackson, George P. White & Negro Spirituals, Their Life Span & Kinship. (Music Reprint Ser.). (Illus.). xii, 349p. 1975. Repr. of 1944 ed. lib. bdg. 42.50 (ISBN 0-306-70667-9). Da Capo.
Jackson, George P., ed. Down-East Spirituals & Others: Three Hundred Songs Supplementary to the Author's "Spiritual Folk-Songs of Early America". LC 74-34317. (Music Reprint Ser.). (Illus.). 296p. 1975. Repr. of 1943 ed. lib. bdg. 35.00 (ISBN 0-306-70666-0). Da Capo.
--Spiritual Folk-Songs of Early America. 11.25 (ISBN 0-8446-2297-4). Peter Smith.
Jackson, Gordon E. Pastoral Care & Process Theology. LC 81-40159. 266p. (Orig.). 1981. lib. bdg. 29.75 (ISBN 0-8191-1710-2); pap. text ed. 12.75 (ISBN 0-8191-1711-0). U Pr of Amer.
Jackson, Gregory L. Prophetic Voice for the Kingdom. Paulson, Ross E., ed. LC 86-71907. (Augustana Historical Society Pub. Ser.: No. 35). 239p. 1986. text ed. 19.95 (ISBN 0-910184-35-6). Augustana.
Jackson, Holbrook. Dreamers of Dreams: The Rise & Fall of 19th Century Idealism. LC 78-15808. 1978. Repr. of 1948 ed. lib. bdg. 35.00 (ISBN 0-8414-5410-8). Folcroft.
Jackson, Howard. The Lion Becomes Man: The Gnostic Leontomorphic Creator & the Creator & the Platonic Tradition. (SBL Dissertation Ser.). 1985. 17.95 (ISBN 0-89130-872-5, 06-01-81); pap. 11.95 (ISBN 0-89130-873-3). Scholars Pr GA.
Jackson, Hulen. Sunshine Through the Shadows. 4.95 (ISBN 0-89315-283-8). Lambert Bk.
Jackson, Irene V., compiled by. Afro-American Religious Music: A Bibliography & a Catalogue of Gospel Music. LC 78-60527. (Illus.). 1979. lib. bdg. 35.00 (ISBN 0-313-20560-4, JGM/). Greenwood.
Jackson, J. B. Dictionary of Scripture Proper Names of the Old & New Testaments. 1909. pap. 3.95 (ISBN 0-87213-410-5). Loizeaux.
Jackson, Jared J. & Kessler, Martin, eds. Rhetorical Criticism: Essays in Honor of James Muilenburg. LC 74-22493. (Pittsburgh Theological Monographs: No. 1). 1974. pap. 9.50 (ISBN 0-915138-00-X). Pickwick.
Jackson, Jesse. Make a Joyful Noise unto the Lord: The Life of Mahalia Jackson, Queen of Gospel Singers. LC 72-7549. (Women of America Ser.). 1974. 12.70 (ISBN 0-690-43344-1, Crowell Jr Bks). HarpJ.
Jackson, Jewell N. The Agony of Grief. LC 85-52320. (Illus.). 96p. (Orig.). 1986. pap. 8.95 (ISBN 0-934955-02-6). Watercress Pr.
Jackson, John G. Christianity Before Christ. 238p. (Orig.). 1985. pap. 7.00 (ISBN 0-910309-20-5). Am Atheist.
Jackson, Kent, jt. auth. see Millett, Robert.
Jackson, Kent P. & Millet, Robert, eds. Studies in Scripture: The Gospels, Vol. 5. 1986. text ed. 15.95 (ISBN 0-87579-064-X). Deseret Bk.
Jackson, Neil E., Jr. Beyond All Expectations. (Orig.). 1987. pap. 6.95 (ISBN 0-8054-5044-0). Broadman.
--Motivational Ideas for Changing Lives. LC 81-68366. 1982. pap. 4.95 (ISBN 0-8054-5647-3). Broadman.
Jackson, Neta. Building Christian Relationships. 64p. 1984. pap. 3.95 (ISBN 0-87123-407-6); pap. 4.95 tchr's guide (ISBN 0-87123-429-7). Bethany Hse.
--A New Way to Live. LC 82-83392. 104p. 1983. pap. 4.95 (ISBN 0-8361-3323-4). Herald Pr.
Jackson, Paul, ed. Sharafuddin Maneri: The Hundred Letters. LC 79-56754. (Classics of Western Spirituality Ser.). 480p. 1980. 13.95 (ISBN 0-8091-0291-9); pap. 9.95 (ISBN 0-8091-2229-4). Paulist Pr.
Jackson, Paul R. The Doctrine & Administration of the Church. rev. ed. LC 68-28699. 1980. pap. 3.95 (ISBN 0-87227-072-6). Reg Baptist.
Jackson, Phil. Ready to Use Cartoons for Church Publications. 160p. 1987. pap. price not set (ISBN 0-8010-5221-1). Baker Bk.
Jackson, Richard H., ed. The Mormon Role in the Settlement of the West. LC 78-24728. (Charles Redd Monographs in Western History Ser.: No. 9). (Illus.). 1978. pap. 6.95 (ISBN 0-8425-1321-3, Dist. by Signature Bks). C Redd Ctr.
Jackson, Robert. John Donne's Christian Vocation. 1970. 19.95 (ISBN 0-8101-0289-7). Northwestern U Pr.
Jackson, Ron. The Seer: Joseph Smith. Orig. Title: Joseph Smith: the Seer. 1977. 5.95 (ISBN 0-89036-088-X). Hawkes Pub Inc.
Jackson, S. Trevena. Fanny Crosby's Story. (Christian Biography Ser.). 198p. 1981. pap. 3.95 (ISBN 0-8010-5127-4). Baker Bk.
Jackson, Samuel M. Huldrych Zwingli: The Reformer of German Switzerland. 2nd rev. ed. LC 75-170836. Repr. of 1901 ed. 24.50 (ISBN 0-404-03543-4). AMS Pr.
Jackson, Samuel M., ed. see Zwingli, Ulrich.
Jackson, Samuel T. Lincoln's Use of the Bible. LC 74-26790. 1974. Repr. of 1909 ed. lib. bdg. 17.00 (ISBN 0-8414-5329-2). Folcroft.
Jackson, Shirley. Witchcraft of Salem Village. (Landmark Ser.: No. 69). (Illus.). 1956. PLB 6.99 (ISBN 0-394-90369-2, BYR). Random.
Jackson, Sue B. Hooked on Prescription Drugs. Wallace, Mary H., ed. 112p. (Orig.). 1981. pap. 2.95 (ISBN 0-912315-33-4). Word Aflame.
Jackson, W. Barbara. Faith & Freedom: A Study of Western Society. LC 72-8239. 308p. 1974. Repr. of 1954 ed. lib. bdg. 22.50x (ISBN 0-8371-6542-3, JAFF). Greenwood.
Jackson, Wayne. The Bible Translation Controversy. (That You May Believe Ser.). 20p. (Orig.). 1985. pap. 1.50 (ISBN 0-932859-01-1). Apologetic Pr.
--Biblical Studies in the Light of Archaeology. 69p. (Orig.). 1982. pap. 2.50 (ISBN 0-932859-00-3). Apologetic Pr.
--Book of Job. pap. 5.50 (ISBN 0-89137-541-4). Quality Pubns.
--Fortify Your Faith. 74p. (Orig.). 1974. pap. text ed. 2.50 (ISBN 0-932859-09-7). Apologetic Pr.
--The Mythology of Modern Geology: A Refutation of Evolution's Most Influential Argument. 45p. (Orig.). 1980. pap. 1.95 (ISBN 0-932859-13-5). Apologetic Pr.
--A Study Guide to Greater Bible Knowledge. 156p. (Orig.). 1986. pap. 5.00 (ISBN 0-932859-12-7). Apologetic Pr.
Jackson, Wayne, jt. auth. see Thompson, Bert.
Jackson, William J. Sai Krishna Lila. LC 80-67137. 1980. pap. 4.50 (ISBN 0-9600958-7-X). Birth Day.
Jackson-Miller, Kathleen A., jt. auth. see Miller, William R.
Jacob, Ben Chayyim. Introduction to the Rabbinic Bible of 1525. rev. ed. (Library of Biblical Studies Ser). 1969. 39.50x (ISBN 0-87068-067-6). Ktav.
Jacob, Benno. Das Erste Buch der Tora Genesis. (Ger.). 1934. 100.00 (ISBN 0-87068-247-4). Ktav.
Jacob, E. F., jt. ed. see Crump, C. G.
Jacob, Henry. An Attestation of Many Learned, Godly, & Famous Divines...Justifying...That the Church Government Ought to Be Always with the Peoples Free Consent. LC 74-28868. (English Experience Ser.: No. 747). 1975. Repr. of 1613 ed. 16.00 (ISBN 90-221-0747-7). Walter J Johnson.
Jacob, Kenneth. Coins & Christianity. 9.50 (ISBN 0-900652-73-X). Numismatic Fine Arts.
Jacob, Margaret, jt. ed. see Hunt, Margaret.
Jacob, Norma. From One to Another. LC 59-8917. (Orig.). 1959. pap. 2.50x (ISBN 0-87574-102-9). Pendle Hill.
--Growing Old: A View from Within. LC 81-83072. 29p. 1981. 2.50x (ISBN 0-87574-239-4). Pendle Hill.
Jacob, P. L., pseud. Bibliographie et Iconographie De Tous les Ouvrages De Restif De la Bretonne. 1971. Repr. of 1875 ed. lib. bdg. 32.50 (ISBN 0-8337-1817-7). B Franklin.
Jacob, Walter. Christianity Through Jewish Eyes. 1974. pap. 9.95x (ISBN 0-685-56220-4). Ktav.
--The Second Book of the Bible: Exodus. 1983. 59.50x (ISBN 0-88125-028-7). Ktav.
Jacob, Walter, ed. American Reform Responsa. 561p. 1983. pap. text ed. 20.00 (ISBN 0-916694-83-6). Central Conf.
Jacobi, H. Gaina Sutras, 2 vols. lib. bdg. 200.00 (ISBN 0-87968-526-3). Krishna Pr.
Jacobi, Peter. The Messiah Book: The Life & Times of G. F. Handel's Greatest Hit. (Illus.). 169p. 1982. 10.95 (ISBN 0-312-53072-2). St Martin.
Jacobs, Barbara & Jacobs, Briant. Missions for Marrieds. LC 83-70189. 136p. 1983. 6.95 (ISBN 0-87747-953-4). Deseret Bk.
Jacobs, Betty J., jt. auth. see Jacobs, Sidney J.
Jacobs, Briant, jt. auth. see Jacobs, Barbara.
Jacobs, C. M., tr. see Luther, Martin.
Jacobs, Carrie, jt. auth. see Mason, Robert L.
Jacobs, Donald R. Pilgrimage in Mission. LC 83-306. 168p. 1983. pap. 6.50 (ISBN 0-8361-3324-2). Herald Pr.
Jacobs, Henry E. A History of the Evangelical Lutheran Church in the United States. LC 83-45644. Date not set. Repr. of 1893 ed. 54.50 (ISBN 0-404-19853-8). AMS Pr.
--Martin Luther, the Hero of the Reformation. LC 72-170838. Repr. of 1898 ed. 27.50 (ISBN 0-404-03544-2). AMS Pr.
Jacobs, J. Vernon & Wade, John W. Workbook on the Book of Acts. 112p. 1986. pap. 3.95 (ISBN 0-87403-095-1, 3346). Standard Pub.
Jacobs, James P. Rome, Judea & Christianity: The Crucifixion. 300p. 1987. pap. 7.95 (ISBN 0-9617280-0-0). James Pr Inc.
Jacobs, Jerry. The Moral Justification of Suicide. (Illus.). 148p. 1982. pap. 16.25x spiral bdg. (ISBN 0-398-04725-1). C C Thomas.
Jacobs, Joseph. Jesus as Others Saw Him: A Retrospect A.D. 54. LC 73-2211. (The Jewish People; History, Religion, Literature Ser.). Repr. of 1925 ed. 21.00 (ISBN 0-405-05275-8). Ayer Co Pubs.
--Jewish Ideals & Other Essays. LC 72-311. (Essay Index Reprint Ser.). Repr. of 1896 ed. 18.00 (ISBN 0-8369-2795-8). Ayer Co Pubs.
Jacobs, Joy. They Were Women Like Me: Women of the New Testament in Devotions for Today. 216p. 1985. 14.95 (ISBN 0-13-917048-0); pap. 7.95 (ISBN 0-13-917030-8). P-H.
--They Were Women, Too. LC 1-67319. 375p. 1981. pap. 8.95 (ISBN 0-87509-304-3). Chr Pubns.
Jacobs, Louis. The Book of Jewish Belief. 250p. (Orig.). 1984. pap. text ed. 7.95x (ISBN 0-87441-379-6). Behrman.
--The Book of Jewish Values. (The Limited Editions Reprints). 160p. 1984. pap. text ed. 6.95 (ISBN 0-940646-06-4, 83-21278). Rossel Bks.
--Chain of Tradition Series, 4 vols. Incl. Vol. 1. Jewish Law. LC 68-27329. pap. text ed. 5.95x (ISBN 0-87441-211-0); Vol. 2. Jewish Ethics, Philosophy & Mysticism. LC 71-80005. pap. text ed. 5.95x (ISBN 0-87441-212-9); Vol. 3. Jewish Thought Today. LC 73-116679. (Illus.). 1974. pap. text ed. 5.95x (ISBN 0-87441-213-7); Vol. 4. Hasidic Thought; Vol. 5. Jewish Biblical Exegesis. LC 78-1487. (Illus.). 1974. pap. Behrman.
--Hasidic Prayer. LC 72-86765. (Littman Library of Jewish Civilization). 1978. pap. 4.95 (ISBN 0-8052-0604-3). Schocken.
--Hasidic Prayer. (Littman Library of Jewish Civilization). 1972. 17.95x (ISBN 0-19-710024-4). Oxford U Pr.
--Jewish Ethics, Philosophy & Mysticism. LC 71-80005. (Chain of Tradition Ser.). 1969. pap. 5.95x (ISBN 0-87441-012-6). Behrman.
--Jewish Law. LC 68-27329. (Chain of Tradition Ser). 1968. pap. text ed. 5.95x (ISBN 0-87441-010-X). Behrman.
--Jewish Mystical Testimonies. LC 76-46644. 1977. pap. 8.95 (ISBN 0-8052-0585-3). Schocken.
--Jewish Theology. LC 73-17442. 384p. 1973. pap. 9.95x (ISBN 0-87441-248-X). Behrman.
--Jewish Thought Today. LC 73-116679. (Chain of Tradition Ser). (Illus.). 1970. pap. 5.95x (ISBN 0-87441-014-2). Behrman.
--Jewish Values. LC 75-103241. 10.95x (ISBN 0-87677-001-4). Hartmore.
--The Talmudic Argument: A Study in Talmudic Reasoning & Methodology. LC 84-4351. 240p. 1984. 44.50 (ISBN 0-521-26370-0). Cambridge U Pr.
--Teyku: The Unsolved Problem in the Babylonian Talmus. LC 80-70887. 312p. 1981. 20.00 (ISBN 0-8453-4501-X, Cornwall Bks). Assoc Univ Prs.
--Theology in the Responsa. (Littman Library of Jewish Civilization). 1975. 35.50x (ISBN 0-19-710022-8). Oxford U Pr.
--A Tree of Life: Diversity, Creativity, & Flexibility in Jewish Law. (Littman Library of Jewish Civilization). 32.50x (ISBN 0-19-710039-2). Oxford U Pr.
--Way of the Jews. (The Way Ser.). pap. 5.95 (ISBN 0-7175-0875-7). Dufour.
Jacobs, Louis, tr. see Cordovero, Moses.
Jacobs, Melville. Content & Style of an Oral Literature: Clackamas Chinook Myths & Tales. LC 58-5617. 1959. 17.50x (ISBN 0-226-38973-1). U of Chicago Pr.
Jacobs, Michael. Mythological Painting. LC 78-25563. (Mayflower Gallery Ser.). (Illus.). 1979. 12.50 (ISBN 0-8317-6282-9, Mayflower Bks); pap. 6.95 (ISBN 0-8317-6283-7). Smith Pubs.
Jacobs, Mildred Spires. Come unto Me. (Illus.). 56p. (Orig.). 1982. pap. 2.95 (ISBN 0-9609612-0-8). Enrich Enter.
Jacobs, Noah J., tr. see Schaeder, Grete.
Jacobs, Noah J., tr. see Tal, Uriel.
Jacobs, Ruth K. The Successful Children's Choir. 64p. 1984. pap. 5.00 (ISBN 0-912222-12-3). FitzSimons.
Jacobs, Sidney J. & Jacobs, Betty J. Clues about Jews for People Who Aren't. LC 85-90337. 128p. (Orig.). 1985. pap. 8.95 (ISBN 0-933647-00-X). Jacobs Ladder Pubns.
Jacobs, Steven L. Shirot Bialik: A New & Annotated Translation of Chaim Nachman Bialik's Epic Poems. (The Hebraica-Judaica Bookshelf Ser.). Date not set. price not set (ISBN 0-933771-03-7). Alpha Pub Co.
Jacobs, Sylvia M., ed. Black Americans & the Missionary Movement in Africa. LC 81-13230. (Contributions in Afro-American & African Studies: No. 66). (Illus.). xii, 255p. 1982. lib. bdg. 29.95 (ISBN 0-313-23280-6, JAA/). Greenwood.
Jacobsen, Liz, ed. see Friedman, Michael.
Jacobsen, Thorkild. The Treasures of Darkness: A History of Mesoptamian Religon. LC 75-27576. (Illus.). 1976. pap. 9.95x (ISBN 0-300-02291-3). Yale U Pr.
Jacobsen, Wayne. The Naked Church. 208p. (Orig.). 1987. pap. 6.95 (ISBN 0-89081-569-0). Harvest Hse.
Jacobson, Abraham, jt. ed. see Spiegelman, J. Marvin.
Jacobson, Betty. Blessed be God, Choral Instrumental Ensemble. pap. 20.00 (ISBN 0-317-09814-4, 2003553). Bks Demand UMI.
Jacobson, David C. Modern Midrash: The Retelling of Traditional Jewish Narratives by Twentieth-Century Hebrew Writers. (SUNY Series in Modern Jewish Literature & Culture). 208p. 1986. 34.50x (ISBN 0-88706-323-3); pap. 10.95x (ISBN 0-88706-325-X). State U NY Pr.
Jacobson, Dick & Naujoks, Bob. ABC for Christmas. 55p. (Orig.). Date not set. pap. 4.95 (ISBN 0-941988-04-X). K Q Assocs.
Jacobson, Howard. The Exagoge of Ezekiel. LC 82-4410. 240p. 1983. 49.50 (ISBN 0-521-24580-X). Cambridge U Pr.
Jacobson, James R. Soul Talk-How to Rejuvenate Your Life. Ashton, Sylvia, ed. LC 78-54160. 1979. 14.95 (ISBN 0-87949-107-8). Ashley Bks.
Jacobson, Jay. El Mormonismo Refutado. (Modern Doctrines Collection). 32p. 1984. Repr. of 1981 ed. 0.75 (ISBN 0-311-05030-1). Casa Bautista.
Jacobson, Lyle. Home & Church: Ministering to Youth. 32p. 1977. pap. 1.50 (ISBN 0-8307-0501-5, 977208). Regal.
Jacobson, Nolan P. Buddhism & the Contemporary World: Change & Self Correction. LC 82-5909. 203p. 1982. 18.95x (ISBN 0-8093-1052-X); pap. 9.95 (ISBN 0-8093-1071-6). S Ill U Pr.
--Buddhism: The Religion of Analysis. LC 66-71124. (Arcturus Books Paperbacks). 202p. 1970. pap. 7.95x (ISBN 0-8093-0463-5). S Ill U Pr.
--Understanding Buddhism. 224p. (Orig.). 1985. text ed. 19.95x (ISBN 0-8093-1224-7); pap. text ed. 10.95x (ISBN 0-8093-1225-5). S Ill U Pr.
Jacobson, Nolan P., jt. auth. see Inada, Kenneth K.
Jacobson, Pearl. I Can't Help Singing for Jesus Gives the Song. 192p. (Orig.). 1983. pap. 3.95 (ISBN 0-88144-010-8, CPS-010). Christian Pub.
Jacobson, W. Fragmentary Illustrations of the History of the Book of Common Prayer. 122p. Repr. of 1874 ed. text ed. 33.12x (ISBN 0-576-99146-5, Pub. by Gregg Intl Pubs England). Gregg Intl.
Jacobus, Lee A. Sudden Apprehension: Aspects of Knowledge in Paradise Lost. (Studies in English Literature: No. 94). 225p. 1976. text ed. 27.20x (ISBN 90-2793-253-0). Mouton.
Jacobus, Verheiden. The History of the Moderne Protestant Divines, Containing Their Parents, Countries, Education, with Register of Their Writings. Lupton, D., tr. from Latin. LC 79-84142. (English Experience Ser.: No. 959). 400p. 1979. Repr. of 1637 ed. lib. bdg. 28.00 (ISBN 90-221-0959-3). Walter J Johnson.
Jacobus De Vitriaco. Exempla, or Illustrative Stories from the Sermones Vulgares of Jacques De Vitry. Crane, Thomas F., ed. 1971. Repr. of 1890 ed. lib. bdg. 23.50 (ISBN 0-8337-0715-9). B Franklin.
Jacoby, George P. Catholic Child Care in Nineteenth Century New York: With a Correlated Summary of Public & Protestant Child Welfare. LC 74-1686. (Children & Youth Ser.: Vol. 10). 284p. 1974. Repr. of 1941 ed. 23.90x (ISBN 0-405-05963-9). Ayer Co Pubs.
Jacoby, Hilla & Jacoby, Max. The Jews: God's People. (Illus.). 224p. 1984. 49.95 (ISBN 0-310-42430-5, 18369). Zondervan.
Jacoby, Hilla & Jacoby, Max, photos by. The Land of Israel. (Illus.). 1978. 25.00f. Thames Hudson.
Jacoby, John E. Two Mystic Communities in America. LC 75-326. (The Radical Tradition in America Ser). 104p. 1975. Repr. of 1931 ed. 15.00 (ISBN 0-88355-230-2). Hyperion Conn.
Jacoby, Max, jt. auth. see Jacoby, Hilla.
Jacqueny, Mona G. The Golden Age Society & Other Studies. LC 77-87939. 183p. 1978. 12.00 (ISBN 0-8022-2219-6). Philos Lib.
Jacques, Reginald & Willcocks, David. Carols for Choirs: Fifty Christmas Carols, Bk. 1. (YA) 1961. 12.00 (ISBN 0-19-353221-2); pap. 7.00 (ISBN 0-19-353222-0). Oxford U Pr.

Jacques, Reginald, ed. Oxford S-A-B Carol Book: Forty Carols. (YA) 1960. limp linen 7.25x (ISBN 0-19-330514-3). Oxford U Pr.

Jacques, Xavier. List of New Testament Words Sharing Common Elements. (Scripta Pontificci Instituti Biblici: Vol. 119). 1969. pap. 13.00 (ISBN 88-7653-497-0). Loyola.

Jacquet, Constant H., Jr., ed. Yearbook of American & Canadian Church 1986. 304p. (Orig.). 1986. pap. 17.95 (ISBN 0-687-46641-5). Abingdon.

Jacquet, H. Constant, ed. Yearbook of American & Canadian Churches, 1987. 304p. 1987. pap. 18.95 (ISBN 0-687-46642-3). Abingdon.

Jaeger, Werner. Early Christianity & Greek Paideia. 160p. 1985. pap. text ed. 5.95x (ISBN 0-674-22052-8, Belknap Pr). Harvard U Pr.

--Humanism & Theology. (Aquinas Lecture). 1943. 7.95 (ISBN 0-87462-107-0). Marquette.

--Paideia: The Ideals of Greek Culture, 3 vols. Highet, Gilbert, tr. from Ger. Incl. Vol. 1. Archaic Greece; The Mind of Athens. 2nd ed. 1945 (ISBN 0-19-500399-3); Vol. 2. In Search of the Divine Center. 1943 (ISBN 0-19-500592-9); Vol. 3. The Conflict of Cultural Ideals in the Age of Plato. 1944 (ISBN 0-19-500593-7). 35.00x ea. Oxford U Pr.

Jaeger, Werner W. The Theology of the Early Greek Philosophers: The Gifford Lectures, 1936. Robinson, Edward S., tr. LC 79-9940. vi, 259p. 1980. Repr. of 1947 ed. lib. bdg. 55.00x (ISBN 0-313-21262-7, JATH). Greenwood.

Jaegher, Paul De see De Jaegher, Paul.

Jae Jah Noh. Do You See What I See? LC 77-5255. (Orig.). 1977. pap. 3.95 (ISBN 0-8356-0499-3, Quest). Theos Pub Hse.

Jaekle, Charles, jt. auth. see Clebsch, William.

Jafery, Askari, tr. see Talib, Ali B. Abi.

Jafery, Syded A., tr. see Talib, Ali-Ibne-Abu.

Jaffa, Harry V. Thomism & Aristotelianism: A Study of the Commentary by Thomas Aquinas on the Nicomachean Ethics. LC 78-21520. 1979. Repr. of 1952 ed. lib. bdg. 29.75x (ISBN 0-313-21149-3, JATA). Greenwood.

Jaffe, Eliezer D. Pleaders & Protesters: The Future of Citizens' Organizations in Israel. LC 80-68431. 40p. 1980. pap. 2.50 (ISBN 0-87495-028-7). Am Jewish Comm.

Jaffe, Hirshel, et al. Why Me? Why Anyone? 256p. 1986. 15.95 (ISBN 0-312-87803-6, Pub. by Marek). St Martin.

Jaffe, Leonard. The Pitzel Holiday Book. (Illus.). 1962. 7.95x (ISBN 0-87068-359-4). Ktav.

Jaffee, Martin. Mishnah's Theology of Tithing: A Study of Tractate Maaserot. Neusner, Jacob, ed. LC 80-29333. (Brown Judaic Studies). 1981. pap. text ed. 15.00 (ISBN 0-89130-459-2, 14-00-19). Scholars Pr GA.

Jafolla, Mary-Alice. Simple Truth. 90p. 1982. 5.95 (ISBN 0-87159-146-4). Unity School.

Jafolla, Mary-Alice, et al. Nourishing the Life Force. LC 82-51301. 200p. 1983. 6.95 (ISBN 0-87159-114-6). Unity School.

Jafolla, Richard. Soul Surgery: The Ultimate Self-Healing. LC 81-71018. 176p. (Orig.). 1982. pap. 5.95 (ISBN 0-87516-473-0). De Vorss.

Jagadananda, Swami, tr. see Shankara.

Jagadiswarananda, Swami, tr. Brhadaranyaka Upanishad. 2nd ed. (Sanskrit & Eng). 7.95 (ISBN 0-87481-415-4). Vedanta Pr.

--Devi-Mahatmyam (the Chandi) (Sanskrit & Eng). pap. 3.25 (ISBN 0-87481-426-X). Vedanta Pr.

Jager, Willigis. The Way to Contemplation: Encountering God Today. O'connell, Matthew J., tr. 1987. pap. 7.95. Paulist Pr.

Jagersma, Henk. A History of Israel from Alexander the Great to Bar Kochba. Kok, J. H., tr. LC 85-45497. 256p. 1986. pap. 12.95 (ISBN 0-8006-1890-4, 1-1890). Fortress.

--A History of Israel in the Old Testament Period. Bowden, John, tr. LC 82-48548. 320p. 1983. pap. 13.95 (ISBN 0-8006-1692-8). Fortress.

Jagger, Peter J. Clouded Witness: Initiation in the Church of England in the Mid-Victorian Period 1850-1875. (Pittsburgh Theological Monographs New Ser.: No. 1). vii, 221p. (Orig.). 1982. pap. 12.00 (ISBN 0-915138-51-4). Pickwick.

Jahner, Elaine A., ed. see Walker, James R.

Jahoda, Gustav. The Psychology of Superstition. LC 74-9667. 158p. 1974. Repr. 20.00x (ISBN 0-87668-185-2). Aronson.

Jahsmann, Allan H. Church Teaching Her Young. 1967. pap. text ed. 3.75 (ISBN 0-570-06330-2, 22-1287); teacher's guide 4.50 (ISBN 0-570-06331-0, 22-1289). Concordia.

--It's All about Jesus. LC 74-21233. (Illus.). 160p. 1975. pap. 5.95 (ISBN 0-570-03031-5, 6-1157). Concordia.

--My Favorite Bible Stories. LC 67-15957. 1967. 5.95 (ISBN 0-570-03415-9, 56-1064). Concordia.

Jahsmann, Allan H. & Simon, Martin P. Little Visits with God. 1957. 9.50 (ISBN 0-570-03016-1, 6-1055); pap. 6.95 (ISBN 0-570-03032-3, 6-1158). Concordia.

--More Little Visits with God. 1961. 9.50 (ISBN 0-570-03017-X, 6-1080); pap. 6.95 (ISBN 0-570-03033-1, 6-1159). Concordia.

Jahsmann, Allan H., jt. auth. see Gross, Arthur W.

Jaideva Singh. Vijnana Bhairava or Divine Consciousness. 1979. text ed. 14.00 (ISBN 0-89684-100-6, Pub. by Motilal Banarsidas India); pap. 9.95 (ISBN 0-89684-099-9). Orient Bk Dist.

Jaimini. The Mimamsa Sutras of Jaimini. Sandal, Mohan L., tr. LC 73-3820. (Sacred Books of the Hindus: No. 27). (Eng. & Sanskrit.). Repr. of 1925 ed. 79.50 (ISBN 0-404-57827-6). AMS Pr.

--The Purva-Mimamsa-Sutras of Jaimini. Jha, Ganganath, tr. & commentary by. LC 73-3797. (Sacred Books of the Hindus: No. 10). Repr. of 1916 ed. 55.00 (ISBN 0-404-57810-1). AMS Pr.

Jain, C. R. Confluence of Opposites or Scientific Comparative Study of Religions. 432p. 1975. Repr. 16.00 (Pub. by Messers Today & Tomorrows Printers & Publishers India). Scholarly Pubns.

--Gems of Islam: Lifting of the Veil, Pt. I. 196p. 1975. 6.00 (ISBN 0-88065-136-9, Pub. by Messers Today & Tomorrows Printers & Publishers India). Scholarly Pubns.

--Key of Knowledge: The Key to Unlock the Mysteries of Important Religions of the World. 1012p. 1975. 35.00 (ISBN 0-88065-137-7, Pub. by Messers Today & Tomorrows Printers & Publishers India). Scholarly Pubns.

Jain, J. Life in Ancient India as Depicted in Jaina Canon & Commentaries. 2nd ed. 1984. text ed. 34.00x. Coronet Bks.

Jain, Jyotindra, jt. auth. see Fischer, Eberhard.

Jain, Naresh K., ed. Muslims in India: A Biographical Dictionary, Vol. II. 1984. 40.00x (ISBN 0-8364-1150-1, Pub. by Manohar India). South Asia Bks.

Jain, Nirmal K. Sikh Religion & Philosophy. 1979. text ed. 12.50 (ISBN 0-89684-077-8, Pub. by Sterling New Delhi). Orient Bk Dist.

Jain, Pratibha. Gandhian Ideas, Social Movements & Creativity. 1986. 32.00x (ISBN 81-7033-007-6, Pub. by Rawat). South Asia Bks.

Jain, Sushila. Muslims & Modernization. 1986. 27.50x (ISBN 81-7033-009-2, Pub. by Rawat). South Asia Bks.

Jaini, J. L., ed. & intro. by see Umasvati.

Jaini, Jagmandar L. Outlines of Jainism. Thomas, F. W., ed. LC 78-14128. (Illus.). 1981. Repr. of 1940 ed. 21.00 (ISBN 0-88355-801-7). Hyperion Conn.

Jaini, Manak C. Life of Mahavira. 1986. 8.00X (ISBN 0-8364-1559-0, Pub. by Academic India). South Asia Bks.

Jaini, Padmanabh S. The Jaina Path of Purification. LC 77-73496. 1979. 35.95x (ISBN 0-520-03459-7). U of Cal Pr.

Jaini, Rai B., ed. & intro. by see Devendra Gani.

Jaini, Rai B., ed. see Devendra Gani.

Jaini, Rai B., ed. & tr. see Gunabhadra Acharya.

Jaini, Rai B., tr. & commentaries by see Kundakunda Acharya.

Jaki, Stanley L. The Keys of the Kingdom: A Tool's Witness to Truth. (Illus.). 1986. 9.95 (ISBN 0-8199-0898-3). Franciscan Herald.

--The Road of Science & the Ways to God. LC 77-21667. 1978. lib. bdg. 14.95x (ISBN 0-226-39144-2). U of Chicago Pr.

Jaki, Stanley L., tr. see Bruno, Giordano.

Jakim, Boris, tr. see Frank, S. L.

Jakobcic, Cathy. Prayer Room Counselor's Handbook. 47p. 1983. pap. 2.25 (ISBN 0-88144-015-9). Christian Pub.

Jakobovits, Immanuel. The Timely & the Timeless: Jews, Judaism & Society in a Storm-Tossed Decade. 432p. 1977. 25.00x (ISBN 0-85303-189-4, Pub. by Vallentine Mitchell England). Biblio Dist.

Jakubec, Jan. Johannes Amos Comenius. LC 70-135811. (Eastern Europe Collection Ser). 1970. Repr. of 1928 ed. 12.00 (ISBN 0-405-02753-2). Ayer Co Pubs.

Jakubowsky, Frank. The Psychological Patterns of Jesus Christ. 342p. (Orig.). 1982. pap. 14.95 (ISBN 0-932588-02-6). Jakubowsky.

Jalal, Ayesha. The Sole Spokesman: Jinnah, the Muslim League & the Demand for Pakistan. (South Asian Studies: No. 31). (Illus.). 336p. 1985. 49.50 (ISBN 0-521-24462-5). Cambridge U Pr.

Jalbani, G. N., tr. see Shah Waliullah.

Jamal, Hafiz, ed. Key Concepts in Sufi Understanding. (Sufi Research Ser.). 47p. 1980. pap. 4.95 (ISBN 0-86304-006-3, Pub. by Octagon Pr England). Ins Study Human.

Jamart, Francois. Complete Spiritual Doctrine of St. Therese of Lisieux. Van De Putte, Walter, tr. LC 61-8203. 1977. pap. 6.95 (ISBN 0-8189-0347-3). Alba.

Jameelah, M. Islam & Modernism. pap. 10.50 (ISBN 0-686-18574-9). Kazi Pubns.

--Islam & Orientalism. pap. 6.50 (ISBN 0-686-18573-0). Kazi Pubns.

--Islam in Theory & Practice. pap. 14.50 (ISBN 0-686-18501-3). Kazi Pubns.

--Islam vs, Ahl-al-Kitab, Past & Present. pap. 15.95 (ISBN 0-686-18570-6). Kazi Pubns.

--Islam vs the West. pap. 1.75 (ISBN 0-686-18568-4). Kazi Pubns.

James, Allix B. Calling a Pastor to a Baptist Church. rev. ed. Jones, Amos, Jr., ed. 50p. (Orig.). 1983. pap. 4.95 (ISBN 0-910683-00-X). Sunday School.

James, Bruno S., tr. see Bernard de Clairvaux, Saint.

James, Charles F. Documentary History of the Struggle for Religious Liberty in Virginia. LC 70-121101. (Civil Liberties in American History Ser). 1971. Repr. of 1900 ed. lib. bdg. 37.50 (ISBN 0-306-71977-0). Da Capo.

James, E., tr. & illus. Gregory of Tours-Life of the Fathers. (Translated Texts for Historians-Latin Ser.: No. I). (Illus.). 174p. 1985. pap. text ed. 15.00x (ISBN 0-85323-115-X, Pub. by Liverpool U Pr). Humanities.

James, Edgar C. Epistles of Peter. (Teach Yourself the Bible Ser.). 1964. pap. 2.75 (ISBN 0-8024-2355-8). Moody.

--Second Corinthians: Keys to Triumphant Living. (Teach Yourself the Bible Ser.). 1964. pap. 2.75 (ISBN 0-8024-7680-5). Moody.

James, Edward, jt. auth. see Morris, Peter M.

James, Edwin O. The Beginnings of Religion: An Introductory & Scientific Study. 159p. 1973. Repr. of 1950 ed. lib. bdg. 22.50x (ISBN 0-8371-6706-X, JABE). Greenwood.

--Christian Myth & Ritual: A Historical Study. 11.25 (ISBN 0-8446-2307-5). Peter Smith.

James, Fannie B. Truth & Health. 1970. 8.95 (ISBN 0-686-24356-0). Divine Sci Fed.

James, Fannie B., compiled by. Divine Science: Its Principle & Practice. 1957. pap. 7.50 (ISBN 0-686-24361-7). Divine Sci Fed.

James, Francis G. North Country Bishop: A Biography of William Nicolson. 1956. 59.50x (ISBN 0-686-51425-4). Elliots Bks.

James, G. Ingli, ed. see Blake, William.

James, Gene G., ed. The Family & the Unification Church. LC 83-80638. (Conference Ser.: No. 17). 1983. 14.95 (ISBN 0-932894-19-4, Pub. by New Era Bks); pap. text ed. 10.95 (ISBN 0-932894-17-8). Paragon Hse.

--The Family & the Unification Church. LC 83-80638. 269p. (Orig.). 1983. 15.95; pap. 11.95. Rose Sharon Pr.

James, George W. The Old Franciscan Missions of California. LC 77-91532. 1977. Repr. of 1913 ed. lib. bdg. 25.00 (ISBN 0-89341-321-6). Longwood Pub Group.

James, H. J. The Consolation of Philosophy of Boethius. 1897. 25.00 (ISBN 0-8274-2093-5). R West.

James, Henry. Society, the Redeemed Form of Man, & the Earnest of God's Omnipotence in Human Nature: Affirmed in Letters to a Friend. 1971. Repr. of 1879 ed. 35.00 (ISBN 0-384-26735-1). Johnson Repr.

James, Henry, Sr. Christianity the Logic of Creation. LC 72-921. (The Selected Works of Henry James, Sr.: Vol. 1). 272p. 1983. Repr. of 1875 ed. 30.00 (ISBN 0-404-10081-3); Set, 10 vols. 295.00. AMS Pr.

--The Church of Christ Not An Ecclesiasticism: A Letter to a Sectarian. LC 72-922. (The Selected Works of Henry James Sr.: Vol. 2). 80p. Repr. of 1854 ed. 17.00 (ISBN 0-404-10082-1). AMS Pr.

--Lectures & Miscellanies. LC 72-923. (The Selected Works of Henry James, Sr.: Vol. 3). 456p. 1983. Repr. of 1852 ed. 42.50 (ISBN 0-404-10083-X). AMS Pr.

--Moralism & Christianity: Or Man's Experience & Destiny in Three Lectures. LC 72-917. (The Selected Works of Henry James, Sr.: Vol. 4). 192p. 1983. Repr. of 1850 ed. 28.50 (ISBN 0-404-10084-8). AMS Pr.

--Morality & the Perfect Life. LC 72-918. (The Selected Works of Henry James, Sr.: Vol. 5). 88p. 1983. Repr. of 1906 ed. 18.00 (ISBN 0-404-10085-6). AMS Pr.

--The Nature of Evil: Considered in a Letter to the Rev. Edward Beecher, D.D. LC 72-920. (The Selected Works of Henry James, Sr.: Vol. 6). 352p. 1983. Repr. of 1855 ed. 37.50 (ISBN 0-404-10086-4). AMS Pr.

--The Secret of Swedenborg: Being an Elucidation of His Doctrine of the Divine Humanity. LC 72-914. (The Selected Works of Henry James, Sr.: Vol. 7). 264p. 1983. Repr. of 1869 ed. 30.00 (ISBN 0-404-10087-2). AMS Pr.

--Substance & Shadow: Or, Morality & Religion in Their Relation to Life, an Essay upon the Physics of Creation. LC 72-915. (The Selected Works of Henry James, Sr.: Vol. 8). 552p. 1983. Repr. of 1863 ed. 49.50 (ISBN 0-404-10088-0). AMS Pr.

--Tracts for the New Times: No. 1 Letter to a Swedenborgian. LC 72-916. (The Selected Works of Henry James, Sr.: Vol. 9). 1983. Repr. of 1847 ed. 24.50 (ISBN 0-404-10089-9). AMS Pr.

James, J. Courtenay. Hebrew & English: Some Likenesses, Psychic & Linguistic. Repr. of 1920 ed. lib. bdg. 20.00 (ISBN 0-8495-2723-6). Arden Lib.

James, Janet W., ed. Women in American Religion. LC 79-5261. 288p. 1980. 32.00x (ISBN 0-8122-7780-5); pap. 13.50x (ISBN 0-8122-1104-9). U of Pa Pr.

James, Joseph. The Way of Mysticism. 256p. 1981. pap. 14.50 (ISBN 0-89540-086-3, SB-086). Sun Pub.

--The Way of Mysticism: An Anthology. 1977. lib. bdg. 59.95 (ISBN 0-8490-2810-8). Gordon Pr.

James, M. R., ed. Apocrypha Anecdota. (Texts & Studies Ser.: No. 1, Vol. 2, Pt. 3). pap. 19.00 (ISBN 0-8115-1686-5). Kraus Repr.

--Apocrypha Anecdota: Second Series. (Texts & Studies Ser.: No. 1, Vol. 5, Pt. 1). pap. 19.00 (ISBN 0-8115-1696-2). Kraus Repr.

--The Testament of Abraham. (Texts & Studies: No. 1, Vol. 2, Pt. 2). pap. 19.00 (ISBN 0-8115-1685-7). Kraus Repr.

James, Sydney V. People among Peoples: Quaker Benevolence in Eighteenth Century America. LC 62-20248. (Center for the Study of the History of Liberty in America Ser). 1963. 27.50x (ISBN 0-674-66050-1). Harvard U Pr.

James, William. Essays in Religion & Morality. LC 81-7040. (Illus.). 376p. text ed. 25.00x (ISBN 0-674-26735-4). Harvard U Pr.

--Varieties of Religious Experience. LC 37-27013. 1936. 6.95 (ISBN 0-394-60463-6). Modern Lib.

--Varieties of Religious Experience. pap. 4.50 (ISBN 0-451-62486-6, ME2069, Ment). NAL.

--The Varieties of Religious Experience. (The Works of William James). (Illus.). 728p. 1985. text ed. 45.00x (ISBN 0-674-93225-0). Harvard U Pr.

--The Varieties of Religious Experience: A Study in Human Nature. Marty, Martin, ed. (Penguin American Library). 1982. pap. 4.95 (ISBN 0-14-039034-0). Penguin.

--Varieties of Religious Experiences. 1961. pap. 3.95 (ISBN 0-02-085960-0, Collier). Macmillan.

--The Will to Believe & Human Immortality. pap. 5.95 (ISBN 0-486-20291-7). Dover.

--Will to Believe & Other Essays in Popular Philosophy & Human Immortality. 15.75 (ISBN 0-8446-2313-X). Peter Smith.

James, Wilma. Gardening with Biblical Plants. LC 83-2290. (Illus.). 272p. 1983. 24.95x (ISBN 0-8304-1009-0). Nelson-Hall.

James First King Of England. Daemonologie, in Forme of a Dialogue. (English Experience Ser.: No. 94). 1969. Repr. of 1597 ed. 13.00 (ISBN 90-221-0094-4). Walter J Johnson.

Jameson, Anna B. The History of Our Lord As Exemplified in Works of Art; with That of His Type; St. John the Baptist; & Other Persons of the Old & New Testament, 2 vols. LC 92-167006. (Illus.). 1976. Repr. of 1890 ed. Set. 70.00x (ISBN 0-8103-4304-5). Gale.

--Legends of the Madonna, As Represented in the Fine Arts. LC 70-89273. (Tower Bks.). (Illus.). lxxvi, 344p. 1972. Repr. of 1890 ed. 42.00x (ISBN 0-8103-3114-4). Gale.

--Legends of the Monastic Orders As Represented in the Fine Arts. LC 75-41154. 1976. Repr. of 1866 ed. 29.50 (ISBN 0-404-14767-4). AMS Pr.

--Sacred & Legendary Art, 2 Vols. LC 71-124594. Repr. of 1896 ed. 18.50 (ISBN 0-404-03551-5). AMS Pr.

Jameson, Kenneth P. & Wilber, Charles K., eds. Religious Values & Development. (Illus.). 154p. 1981. 44.00 (ISBN 0-08-026107-8). Pergamon.

Jameson, Russell P. Montesquieu et l'Esclavage: Etude Sur les Origines De l'Opinion Antiesclavage En France Au Dix-Huitieme Siecle. LC 72-171409. (Research & Source Works Ser.: No. 859). (Fr.). 371p. (Philosophy & Religious History Monographs, No. 81). 1972. Repr. of 1911 ed. lib. bdg. 23.50 (ISBN 0-8337-4185-3). B Franklin.

Jamieson, et al. Unabridged Bible Commentary, 3 vols. 1974. 75.00 (ISBN 0-8028-8033-9). Eerdmans.

Jamison, A. Leland, ed. Tradition & Change in Jewish Experience: B.G. Rudolph Lectures in Judaic Studies. 1978. pap. 5.95x (ISBN 0-8156-8097-X). Syracuse U Pr.

Jamison, Kaleel. The Nibble Theory & the Kernel of Power. LC 83-63112. 74p. (Orig.). 1984. 4.95 (ISBN 0-8091-2621-4); pap. 3.95 (ISBN 0-8091-2621-4). Paulist Pr.

Jamison-Peterson, Vicki. El Shaddai. 191p. 1983. pap. 4.95 (ISBN 0-88144-055-8). Christian Pub.

--How You Can Have Joy. 130p. 1976. pap. 2.95 (ISBN 0-88144-054-X). Christian Pub.

Jamspal, Lozang, et al. Nagarjuna's Letter to King Gautamiputra. 1978. 9.95 (ISBN 0-89684-022-0, Pub. by Motilal Banarsidass India). Orient Bk Dist.

Janda, J. Julian: A Play Based on the Life of Julian of Norwich. 112p. (Orig.). 1984. pap. 6.95 (ISBN 0-8164-2632-5, 6464, HarpR). Har-Row.

--The Legend of the Holy Child of Atocha. (Illus.). 48p. (Orig.). 1986. pap. 2.95 (ISBN 0-8091-6559-7). Paulist Pr.

Jane, M., tr. see Tauler, John.

Janelle, Pierre. Robert Southwell the Writer. LC 72-162495. 347p. 1971. Repr. of 1935 ed. 12.00x (ISBN 0-911858-18-0). Appel.

Janelle, Pierre, ed. see Gardiner, Stephen.

Jang, A. Notes on Islam. pap. 1.50 (ISBN 0-686-18487-4). Kazi Pubns.

Janice, Brewi, jt. auth. see Brennan, Anne.

Janney, Samuel M. The Life of William Penn: With Selections from His Correspondence & Autobiography. facsimile ed. LC 74-130555. (Select Bibliographies Reprint Ser.). Repr. of 1851 ed. 24.00 (ISBN 0-8369-5528-5). Ayer Co Pubs.

Janovy, John, Jr. Back in Keith County. LC 83-17003. (Illus.). x, 179p. 1983. pap. 5.95 (ISBN 0-8032-7560-9, BB 875, Bison). U of Nebr Pr.

Janowitz, Morris. Judaism of the Next Generation. pap. 2.00 (ISBN 0-686-15805-9). Rostrum Bks.

Janowitz, Morris B., jt. auth. see Bettelheim, Bruno.

Janowsky, Oscar I. Jews & Minority Rights, 1898-1919. LC 33-31678. (Columbia University. Studies in the Social Sciences: No. 384). Repr. of 1933 ed. 24.50 (ISBN 0-404-51384-0). AMS Pr.

Janowsky, Oscar I., ed. American Jew. facs. ed. LC 76-142647. (Essay Index Reprint Ser). 1942. 18.00 (ISBN 0-8369-2166-6). Ayer Co Pubs.

Jansen, G. H. Zionism, Israel & Asian Nationalism. 347p. 1971. 6.00 (ISBN 0-88728-112-5); pap. 3.00 (ISBN 0-88728-113-3). Inst Palestine.

Jansen, Harris. The Making of a Sunday School. 128p. 1972. pap. 1.95 (ISBN 0-88243-737-2, 02-0737). Gospel Pub.

Jansen, J. F. Calvin's "Doctrine of the Work of Christ". 120p. 1956. 10.00 (ISBN 0-227-67425-1). Attic Pr.

Jansen, J. Gerald, et al, eds. Job: A Bible Commentary for Teaching & Preaching. LC 84-48512. (Interpretation Ser.). 288p. 1985. 18.95 (ISBN 0-8042-3114-1). John Knox.

Jansen, John F. The Resurrection of Jesus Christ in New Testament Theology. LC 80-231. 188p. 1980. pap. 9.95 (ISBN 0-664-24309-6). Westminster.

Janss, Edmund W. Making the Second Half the Best Half. LC 83-15779. 192p. (Orig.). 1984. pap. 4.95 (ISBN 0-87123-404-1, 210404). Bethany Hse.

Janssen, Al, jt. auth. see Kole, Andre.

Janssen, Al, jt. auth. see Thornton, Andre.

Janssen, Al, jt. auth. see Winters, Ted.

Janssen, Johannes. History of the German People at the Close of the Middle Ages, 17 Vols. LC 67-104463. Repr. of 1925 ed. Set. 637.50 (ISBN 0-404-03570-1); 37.50 ea. AMS Pr.

Jansson, Fred O., et al, trs. see Anderson, Glenn P.

Jantzen, Grace. God's World, God's Body. LC 84-3697. 186p. (Orig.). 1984. pap. 10.95 (ISBN 0-664-24619-2). Westminster.

Jantzen, Hans. High Gothic. LC 83-43099. (Illus.). 196p. 1984. 25.00x (ISBN 0-691-04026-5); pap. 7.95x (ISBN 0-691-00372-6). Princeton U Pr.

Janz, Denis. Luther & Late Medieval Thomism: A Study in Theological Anthropology. 191p. 1984. text ed. 25.00x (ISBN 0-88920-132-3). Humanities.

Janz, Denis, ed. Three Reformation Catechisms: Catholic, Anabaptist, Lutheran. LC 82-20799. (Texts & Studies in Religion: Vol. 13). viii, 224p. 1982. 49.95x (ISBN 0-88946-800-1). E Mellen.

Janzen, John G. Studies in the Text of Jeremiah. LC 73-81265. (Harvard Semitic Monographs: Vol. 6). pap. 64.00 (ISBN 0-317-09145-X, 2021591). Bks Demand UMI.

Janzen, John M. Lemba, Sixteen Fifty to Nineteen Thirty: A Drum of Affliction in Africa & the New World. 1982. lib. bdg. 91.00 (ISBN 0-8240-9306-2). Garland Pub.

Janzen, Waldemar. By Faith Abraham & Sarah: Genesis 12-25. Shelly, Maynard, ed. LC 86-83035. (Faith & Life Bible Studies). 70p. (Orig.). 1987. pap. 4.95 (ISBN 0-87303-108-3). Faith & Life.

--Mourning Cry & Woe Oracle. (Beiheft 125 zur Zeitschrift fuer die alttestamentliche Wissenschaft). 120p. 1972. 27.50x (ISBN 3-11-003848-X). De Gruyter.

--Still in the Image: Essays in Biblical Theology & Anthrpology. LC 82-83886. (Institute of Mennonite Studies: No.6). 226p. (Orig.). 1982. pap. 10.95 (ISBN 0-87303-076-1). Faith & Life.

Janzen, Waldemar, tr. see Wolff, Hans W., Jr.

Janzow, F. Samuel. Getting into Luther's Large Catechism. 1979. pap. 4.25 (ISBN 0-570-03783-2, 12-2737). Concordia.

Japananda, K. Yoga, You, Your New Life. (Illus.). 208p. pap. 5.95 spiral bdg. (ISBN 0-9613099-0-3). Temple Kriya Yoga.

Japikse, Carl, jt. auth. see Leichtman, Robert R.

Jaques, Faith. The Christmas Party: A Model Book. (Illus.). 6p. 1986. 8.95 (ISBN 0-399-21393-7, Philomel). Putnam Pub Group.

Jarc, Jerry A. Development & Public Relations for the Catholic School. 65p. 1986. 6.60 (ISBN 0-318-20562-9). Natl Cath Educ.

Jarc, Jerry A., jt. auth. see Stuhr, Robert L.

Jardine, N. The Fortunes of Inquiry. (Clarendon Library of Logic & Philosophy). 204p. 36.00 (ISBN 0-19-824929-2). Oxford U Pr.

Jardine, Samuel. Anchor of the Soul. 1978. pap. 1.95 (ISBN 0-937396-05-2). Walterick Pubs.

Jarnagin, Roy C. Christianity & the Narrow Way. 128p. 1982. 7.50 (ISBN 0-682-49832-7). Exposition Pr FL.

Jarow, Rick. In Search of the Sacred. LC 86-40122. (Illus.). 242p. (Orig.). 1986. pap. 6.95 (ISBN 0-8356-0613-9). Theos Pub Hse.

Jarrard, Dan. The Calling. Wheeler, Gerald, ed. 96p. 1987. pap. price not set (ISBN 0-8280-0382-3). Review & Herald.

Jarrat, Kristin, tr. see Colombo, Furio.

Jarrell, Howard R. International Yoga Bibliography, 1950 to 1980. LC 81-13518. 231p. 1981. 17.50 (ISBN 0-8108-1472-2). Scarecrow.

Jarrett, Bede. No Abiding City. 1.95 (ISBN 0-87243-012-X). Templegate.

Jarrett, Emmett. God's Body. LC 75-8967. 32p. 1975. pap. 1.50 (ISBN 0-914610-05-8). Hanging Loose.

Jarrett, R. H. It Works. 31st ed. 1976. pap. 1.00 (ISBN 0-87516-323-8). De Vorss.

Jarrett, Richard B. Gods Rainbowed Week. (Orig.). 1982. pap. text ed. 5.00 (ISBN 0-9606884-1-2). Jarrett.

--July Fourth Is Every Day! To Serve, Is to Be Served! (Orig.). 1981. pap. text ed. write for info. Jarrett.

Jarrett-Kerr, Martin. Studies in Literature & Belief. facsimile ed. LC 74-134101. (Essay Index Reprint Ser). Repr. of 1954 ed. 18.00 (ISBN 0-8369-1978-5). Ayer Co Pubs.

Jarvis, F. Washington. Prophets, Poets, Priests, & Kings: The Old Testament Story. 288p. 1975. pap. 6.95 (ISBN 0-8164-2089-0, HarpR). Har-Row.

Jasper, David. The New Testament & the Literary Imagination. 128p. 1987. text ed. 19.95 (ISBN 0-391-03482-0). Humanities.

Jasper, David, ed. Images of Belief in Literature. LC 83-40170. 195p. 1984. 22.50 (ISBN 0-312-40920-6). St Martin.

--The Interpretation of Belief: Coleridge, Schleiermacher & Romanticism. LC 85-26204. 192p. 1986. 25.00x (ISBN 0-312-42401-9). St Martin.

Jasper, R. C. & Cuming, G. J., eds. Prayers of the Eucharist: Early & Reformed. 2nd ed. 1980. 17.95x (ISBN 0-19-520140-X); pap. 5.95 (ISBN 0-19-520141-8). Oxford U Pr.

Jasper, Ronald, et al. Everyday Prayer. 1978. pap. 5.95 (ISBN 0-916134-34-2). Pueblo Pub Co.

Jasper, Tony. Jesus & the Christian in a Pop Culture. 224p. 1984. 29.00x (ISBN 0-947728-02-3, Pub. by R Royce Ltd Publ England). State Mutual Bk.

Jaspers, Karl. Die Geistige Situation der Zeit. (Sammlung Goeschen: No. 1000). 1979. 7.80x (ISBN 3-11007-878-3). De Gruyter.

--Man in the Modern Age. LC 75-41155. Repr. of 1933 ed. 28.50 (ISBN 0-404-14558-2). AMS Pr.

--Plato & Augustine: Taken from Vol. 1 of the Great Philosophers. Manheim, Karl, tr. LC 67-38117. Orig. Title: Great Philosophers, Vol. 1 (Pt. 2) 1966. pap. 4.95 (ISBN 0-15-672035-3, Harv). HarBraceJ.

--Socrates, Buddha, Confucius & Jesus: Taken from Vol. 1 of the Great Philosophers. Manheim, Ralph, tr. 1966. pap. 3.95 (ISBN 0-15-683580-0, Harv). HarBraceJ.

--Spinoza. Arendt, Hannah, ed. Manheim, Ralph, tr. from Ger. LC 74-4336. (From the Great Philosophers Ser.). 120p. 1974. pap. 2.95 (ISBN 0-15-684730-2, Harv). HarBraceJ.

Jasson, Wilbur A. Beyond Evolution. LC 84-52700. (Illus.). 141p. 1986. 14.95 (ISBN 0-9614464-0-4); pap. 8.95 (ISBN 0-9614464-1-2). Sarasota Sci.

Jastrow, Joseph. The Psychology of Conviction: A Study of Beliefs & Attitudes. 1979. Repr. of 1918 ed. lib. bdg. 40.00 (ISBN 0-8495-2744-9). Arden Lib.

Jastrow, Marcus. Hebrew-Aramaic-English Dictionary, a Dictionary of Talmud Babli & Talmud Yerushalmi Targum & Midrash, 2 Vols. (Hebrew, Aramaic & Eng.). 75.00 (ISBN 0-87559-019-5). Shalom.

Jastrow, Morris. Aspects of Religious Belief & Practice in Babylonia & Assyria. LC 68-56503. Repr. of 1911 ed. 25.00 (ISBN 0-405-08667-9, Blom Pubns). Ayer Co Pubs.

--A Gentle Cynic: Being a Translation of the Book of Koheleth Commonly Known As Ecclesiastes Stripped of Later Additions also Its Origin, Growth & Interpretation. 255p. 1985. Repr. of 1919 ed. 50.00 (ISBN 0-8495-2810-0). Arden Lib.

--A Gentle Cynic: Translation of the Book of Koheleth Commonly Known As Ecclesiastes Stripped of Later Additions Also Its Origins, Growth, & Interpretation. 1978. Repr. of 1919 ed. lib. bdg. 35.00 (ISBN 0-8495-2733-3). Arden Lib.

--Zionism & the Future of Palestine. (The Rise of Jewish Nationalism & the Middle East Ser.). 159p. 1975. Repr. of 1919 ed. 18.15 (ISBN 0-88355-326-0). Hyperion Conn.

Jastrow, Morris, Jr. The Book of Job. 1920. 40.00 (ISBN 0-8274-1953-8). R West.

--A Gentle Cynic. 242p. 1980. Repr. of 1919 ed. lib. bdg. 35.00 (ISBN 0-89984-258-5). Century Bookbindery.

--The Study of Religion. Clebsch, William A., ed. LC 81-9184. (Classics & Reprints Series of the American Academy of Religion & Scholars Press). 1981. text ed. 10.95 (ISBN 0-89130-519-X, 01-05-01). Scholars Pr GA.

Jastrow, Robert. God & the Astronomers. (Illus.). 1978. 9.95 (ISBN 0-393-85000-5). Norton.

--Two Faces of Reality. Date not set. 14.95 (ISBN 0-393-02400-8). Norton.

Jathanna, Origen V. The Decisiveness of the Christ-Event & the Universality of Christianity in a World of Religious Plurality. (IC-Studies in the Intercultural History of Christianity: Vol. 29). 583p. 1982. pap. 51.60 (ISBN 3-261-04974-X). P Lang Pubs.

Jauncey, J. H. La Ciencia Retorna a Dios. Swenson, Ana M., tr. Moore, J. N. Tr. of Science Returns to God. (Span.). 110p. 1981. pap. 2.35 (ISBN 0-311-05004-2). Casa Bautista.

Jaussi, Laureen & Chaston, Gloria. Genealogical Records of Utah. LC 73-87713. 336p. 1974. 5.95 (ISBN 0-87747-507-5). Deseret Bk.

Javad, Nurbakhsh. Jesus in the Eyes of the Sufis. Graham, Terry, et al, trs. 1983. pap. 6.00 (ISBN 0-317-07015-0). KhaniQahi-Nimatullahi-Sufi.

--Spiritual Poverty in Sufism. Lewishon, Leonard, tr. 1984. pap. 6.00x (ISBN 0-933546-11-4). KhaniQahi-Nimatullahi-Sufi.

Javane, Faith & Bunker, Dusty. Numerology & the Divine Triangle. (Illus.). 1979. pap. 13.95 (ISBN 0-914918-10-9). Para Res.

Javernick, Ellen. Celebrate the Christian Family. (Celebrate Ser.). (Illus.). 144p. 1987. pap. 9.95 (ISBN 0-86653-391-5, SS844). Good Apple.

Jaworski, Leon & Schneider, Dick. Encrucijadas. 1982. 3.95 (ISBN 0-88113-082-6). Edit Betania.

Jay, Carroll E. Gretchen, I Am. 1979. pap. 2.25 (ISBN 0-380-42820-2, 42820-2). Avon.

Jay, E. G. Son of Man, Son of God. 1965. 4.95c (ISBN 0-7735-0029-4). McGill-Queens U Pr.

Jay, Elisabeth. The Evangelical & Oxford Movements. LC 82-9605. (Cambridge English Prose Texts Ser.). 232p. 1983. 34.50 (ISBN 0-521-24403-X); pap. 13.95 (ISBN 0-521-28669-7). Cambridge U Pr.

--Faith & Doubt in Victorian Britain. (Context & Commentary Ser.). (Illus.). 152p. 1986. text ed. 29.95 (ISBN 0-333-37658-7, Pub. by Macmillan Pubs UK); pap. text ed. 9.95 (ISBN 0-333-37659-5). Humanities.

--The Religion of the Heart: Anglican Evangelicalism & the Nineteenth-Century Novel. 1979. 49.00x (ISBN 0-19-812092-3). Oxford U Pr.

Jay, Eric G. The Church: Its Changing Image Through Twenty Centuries. LC 79-92070. 1980. 12.95 (ISBN 0-8042-0877-8). John Knox.

--The Church: Its Changing Image Through Twenty Centuries. LC 79-92070. pap. 120.50 (2027153). Bks Demand UMI.

Jay, Lynn & Jay, Steve. A Glimpse into Reality. LC 81-71020. 144p. (Orig.). 1982. pap. 5.25 (ISBN 0-87516-475-7). De Vorss.

Jay, Ruth J. Learning from God's Animals. (Illus.). 36p. (Orig.). 1981. pap. 3.25 (ISBN 0-934998-04-3). Bethel Pub.

--Learning from God's Birds. (Illus.). 34p. (Orig.). 1981. pap. 3.25 (ISBN 0-934998-05-1). Bethel Pub.

--Learning from God's Wonderful Wildwood. (Learning From...Ser.). (Illus.). 36p. 1982. pap. 3.25 (ISBN 0-934998-13-2). Bethel Pub.

Jay, Steve, jt. auth. see Jay, Lynn.

Jayakar, Pupul. Krishnamurti: A Biography. LC 85-45739. (Illus.). 525p. 1986. 22.95 (ISBN 0-06-250401-0, HarpR). Har-Row.

Jayaswal, Sita R., jt. auth. see Dowsett, Norman.

Jayatilleke, K. Early Buddhist Theory of Knowledge. 1981. 22.00x (ISBN 0-8364-0795-4, Pub. by Motilal Banarsidass). South Asia Bks.

Jayatilleke, K. N. The Message of the Buddha. Smart, Ninian, ed. LC 75-15431. 1975. 12.95 (ISBN 0-02-916350-1). Free Pr.

Jayatilleke, K. N., jt. auth. see Malalasekera, George P.

Jayne, Allen. The Religious & Moral Wisdom of Thomas Jefferson: An Anthology. 1984. 12.95 (ISBN 0-533-05800-7). Vantage.

Jayne, Sears R. John Colet & Marsilio Ficino. LC 80-17262. (Illus.). 172p. 1980. Repr. of 1963 ed. lib. bdg. 24.75x (ISBN 0-313-22606-7, JACF). Greenwood.

Jayne, Walter A. The Healing Gods of Ancient Civilizations. LC 75-23728. Repr. of 1925 ed. 49.00 (ISBN 0-404-13286-3). AMS Pr.

Jazayery, Mohammad A., ed. see Kasravi, Ahmad.

Jean, Rael & Issac, Erich. The Coercive Utopians. (Christian Activist Ser.). 1985. pap. 7.95 (ISBN 0-89526-815-9). Regnery Bks.

Jean-Mesmy, Claude. Conscience & Confession. Malachy, Carroll, tr. LC 65-22643. 239p. 1965. 4.95 (ISBN 0-8199-0013-3, L38877). Franciscan Herald.

Jeanne D'Arc, Saint. Proces De Condamnation et De Rehabilitation De Jeanne D'Arc, 5 Vols. Quicherat, Jules, ed. 1841-1849. Set. 230.00 (ISBN 0-384-27070-0); Set. pap. 200.00 (ISBN 0-384-27071-9). Johnson Repr.

Jeanroy, A. & Vignaux, A., eds. Voyage Au Purgatoire De Saint Patrice, Visions De Tindale & De Saint Paul. Repr. of 1903 ed. 21.00 (ISBN 0-384-64950-5). Johnson Repr.

Jebb, Eleanor & Jebb, Reginald. Testimony to Hilaire Belloc. 1956. 25.00 (ISBN 0-8274-3587-8). R West.

Jebb, Philip. Widowed. LC 83-11160. 1984. pap. 3.95 (ISBN 0-932506-30-5). St Bedes Pubns.

Jebb, Philip, intro. by. By Death Parted: The Stories of Six Widows. 1986. pap. 5.95 (ISBN 0-932506-45-3). St Bedes Pubns.

Jebb, Reginald, jt. auth. see Jebb, Eleanor.

Jebb, Richard C. Erasmus. (Select Bibliographies Reprint Ser). 1890. 12.00 (ISBN 0-8369-5289-8). Ayer Co Pubs.

Jech, Carl. Shadows & Symbols. 1985. 6.25 (ISBN 0-89536-751-3, 5857). CSS of Ohio.

Jedin, Hubert & Dolan, John, eds. Reformation & Counter-Reformation. 1980. 59.50x (ISBN 0-686-95526-9). Crossroad NY.

Jedin, Hubert & Dolan, John P., eds. The Church Between Revolution & Restoration. (History of the Church: Vol. 7). 1980. 59.50x (ISBN 0-8245-0004-0). Crossroad NY.

--The Church in the Age of Absolutism & Enlightenment. (History of the Church: Vol. 6). 1981. 59.50x (ISBN 0-8245-0010-5). Crossroad NY.

--The Church in the Age of Feudalism. (History of the Church: Vol. 3). 1980. 59.50x (ISBN 0-8245-0316-3). Crossroad NY.

--The Church in the Age of Liberalism. (History of the Church: Vol. 8). 1981. 59.50x (ISBN 0-8245-0011-3). Crossroad NY.

--The Church in the Industrial Age. (History of the Church: Vol. 9). 1981. 59.50x (ISBN 0-8245-0012-1). Crossroad NY.

--The Church in the Modern Age. (History of the Church: Vol. 10). 1980. 59.50x (ISBN 0-8245-0013-X). Crossroad NY.

--From the Apostolic Community to Constantine. (History of the Church: Vol. 1). 1980. 59.50x (ISBN 0-8245-0314-7). Crossroad NY.

--From the High Middle Ages to the Eve of the Reformation. (History of the Church: Vol. 4). 1980. 59.50x (ISBN 0-8245-0317-1). Crossroad NY.

--The Imperial Church from Constantine to the Early Middle Ages. (History of the Church: Vol. 2). 1980. 59.50x (ISBN 0-8245-0315-5). Crossroad NY.

Jeep, Elizabeth M. & Huck, Gabe. Celebrate Summer! Guidebook for Families & Congregations, 2 vols. 1973. 5.95 (ISBN 0-918208-98-X). Liturgical Conf.

Jeeves, Malcolm A., et al. Free to Be Different. American ed. LC 84-10525. Repr. of 1985 ed. 40.80 (2027547). Bks Demand UMI.

Jefferson. Minister As Shepherd. (Orig.). 1970. pap. 3.25 (ISBN 0-87508-290-4). Chr Lit.

Jefferson, Patti, jt. auth. see Bussard, Paula J.

Jefferson, Thomas. American Christian Bible. LC 82-80548. 128p. 1982. pap. 5.00 (ISBN 0-914752-14-6). Sovereign Pr.

--The Life & Morals of Jesus of Nazareth. LC 76-17582. 1976. Repr. of 1904 ed. lib. bdg. 30.00 (ISBN 0-8414-5323-3). Folcroft.

--The Life & Morals of Jesus of Nazareth. 82p. 1983. Repr. of 1904 ed. lib. bdg. 25.00 (ISBN 0-8492-5611-9). R West.

--Thomas Jefferson's Life of Jesus. 1976. 2.95 (ISBN 0-87243-056-1). Templegate.

Jefferson, Thomas & Holden, Erik. An American Christian Bible. 128p. 1986. pap. 5.00 (ISBN 0-317-53278-2). Noontide.

Jeffery, Arthur. The Qur'an As Scripture. LC 80-1924. Repr. of 1952 ed. 18.00 (ISBN 0-404-18970-9). AMS Pr.

Jeffery, Arthur, ed. Materials for the History of the Text of the Qur'an. LC 79-180350. Repr. of 1937 ed. 57.50 (ISBN 0-404-56282-5). AMS Pr.

Jeffrey, David L. The Early English Lyric & Franciscan Spirituality. LC 74-78478. (Illus.). xvi, 306p. 1975. 24.50x (ISBN 0-8032-0845-6). U of Nebr Pr.

Jeffrey, David L., ed. A Burning & a Shining Light: English Spirituality in the Age of Wesley. 512p. (Orig.). 1987. pap. 16.95 (ISBN 0-8028-0234-6). Eerdmans.

Jeffrey, David L., ed. see Hilton, Walter.

Jegen, Carol F. Mary According to Women. LC 84-82550. 163p. (Orig.). 1985. pap. 7.95 (ISBN 0-934134-31-6, Leaven Pr). Sheed & Ward MO.

Jegen, Mary E. How You Can Be a Peacemaker. 128p. 1985. pap. 2.95 (ISBN 0-89243-231-4). Liguori Pubns.

Jehan, L. F. Dictionnaire de Philosophie Catholique, 3 vols. Migne, J. P., ed. (Troisieme et Derniere Encyclopedie Theologique Ser.: Vols. 48-50). (Fr.). 2047p. Repr. of 1864 ed. lib. bdg. 260.00x (ISBN 0-89241-321-2). Caratzas.

--Dictionnaire des Controverses Historiques. Migne, J. P., ed. (Troisieme et Derniere Encyclopedie Theologique Ser.: Vol. 66). (Fr.). 698p. Repr. of 1866 ed. lib. bdg. 90.00x (ISBN 0-89241-329-8). Caratzas.

--Dictionnaire des Origines du Christianisme. Migne, J. P., ed. (Troisieme et Derniere Encyclopedie Theologique Ser.: Vol. 15). (Fr.). 630p. Repr. of 1856 ed. lib. bdg. 81.00x (ISBN 0-89241-298-4). Caratzas.

Jehle, Paul. Go Ye Therefore & Teach: Operation Manual for Christian Day School. 300p. 1982. tchr's. ed. 10.00 (ISBN 0-942516-01-X). Plymouth Rock Found.

Jelinek, Heienrich. Die Kartause Gaming. Hogg, James, ed. (Analecta Cartusiana Ser.: No. 58-2). (Ger., Illus.). 175p. 1981. pap. 25.00 (ISBN 3-7052-0085-2, Pub. by Salzburg Studies). Longwood Pub Group.

Jellicoe, Sidney. The Septuagint & Modern Study. 1978. Repr. of 1968 ed. 12.50x (ISBN 0-931464-00-5). Eisenbrauns.

Jellinek, Adolph. Beitrage zur Geschichte der Kabbala. Katz, Steven, ed. LC 79-7138. (Jewish Philosophy, Mysticism, & History of Ideas Ser.). 1980. Repr. of 1852 ed. lib. bdg. 16.00x (ISBN 0-405-12264-0). Ayer Co Pubs.

Jenkins, jt. auth. see Mauck.

Jenkins, Barbara, jt. auth. see Jenkins, Peter.

Jenkins, Claude. Bishop Barlow's Consecration & Archbishop Parker's Register: With Some New Documents. (Church Historical Society London New Ser.: No. 17). Repr. of 1935 ed. 20.00 (ISBN 0-8115-3140-6). Kraus Repr.

--The Monastic Chronicler & the Early School of St. Albans: A Lecture. LC 74-19113. 1974. Repr. of 1922 ed. lib. bdg. 20.00 (ISBN 0-8414-5320-9). Folcroft.

--Sir Thomas More. 1935. Repr. 20.00 (ISBN 0-8274-3431-6). R West.

Jenkins, David. Teaching Children with Confidence. 48p. 1983. pap. 3.95 (ISBN 0-910566-39-9); seminar planbook 3.95 (ISBN 0-910566-40-2). Evang Tchr.

Jenkins, G. H. Literature, Religion & Society in Wales: 1660-1730. (Studies in Welsh History: Vol. 2). 357p. 1980. text ed. 32.50x (ISBN 0-7083-0669-1, Pub. by U of Wales). Humanities.

Jenkins, J. J. Understanding Locke. 192p. 1983. 15.00x (ISBN 0-85224-449-5, Pub. by Edinburgh U Pr Scotland). Columbia U Pr.

Jenkins, Janet, jt. auth. see Mauck, Diane.

Jenkins, Jerry, jt. auth. see Tippit, Sammy.

Jenkins, Jerry, jt. auth. see Williams, Pat.

Jenkins, Jerry B., jt. auth. see Flood, Robert G.

Jenkins, Joe. The Theologic Principle of Universalism: A Way of Life. (Orig.). 1984. pap. 4.00 (ISBN 0-916801-00-4). Inst Univ.

Jenkins, M. F., tr. see Voltaire.

Jenkins, Peggy. Climbing the Rainbow. 92p. pap. 5.95 (ISBN 0-942494-48-2). Coleman Pub.

Jenkins, Peter & Jenkins, Barbara. The Road Unseen. (General Ser.). 406p. 1986. lib. bdg. 18.95 (ISBN 0-317-46368-3, Large Print Bks). G K Hall.

Jenkins, Phil, tr. see Berselli, Costante & Gharib, Georges.

Jenkins, R. B. Henry Smith: England's Silver-Tongued Preacher. LC 83-878. vi, 131p. 1983. 10.95 (ISBN 0-86554-077-2, H64). Mercer Univ Pr.

Jenkins, R. J., ed. & tr. Nicholas I, Patriarch of Constantinople: Letters. LC 74-28930. (Dumbarton Oaks Texts: Vol. 2). 668p. 1973. 45.00x (ISBN 0-88402-039-8). Dumbarton Oaks.

Jenkins, Simon. Kick-Starting the Bible. (Illus.). 160p. 1987. pap. 5.95 (ISBN 0-7459-1004-1). Lion USA.

Jenkins, Simon, jt. auth. see Watson, David.

Jenkins, Simon, ed. see Hicks, Robert F.

Jenkins, Simon, ed. see Parker, T. H.

Jenkins, Ulysses D. Ancient African Religion & the African American Church. LC 78-65794. (Illus.). 1978. 12.95 (ISBN 0-933184-00-X); pap. 6.95 (ISBN 0-933184-01-8). Flame Intl.

Jenks, Tudor. In the Days of Milton. LC 76-170812. Repr. of 1905 ed. 19.45 (ISBN 0-404-03559-0). AMS Pr.

Jenni, Ernst. Diccionario Teologico Manual del Antiguo Testamento, 2 vols. (Span.). 642p. 1978. Set. 75.00 (S-50105). French & Eur.

Jennings, A. Day the Little Children Came. (Arch Bks.). 1984. pap. 0.99 (ISBN 0-570-06092-3, 59-1210). Concordia.

Jennings, Don. A Spiritual Almanac: Guidelines for Better Living Each Month of the Year. 240p. 1984. pap. 5.95 (ISBN 0-13-834748-4). P-H.

Jennings, F. C. Isaiah. rev. ed. LC 55-41748. 1935. 14.95 (ISBN 0-87213-420-2). Loizeaux.

--Judges & Ruth. 9.95 (ISBN 0-88172-152-2). Believers Bkshelf.

--Meditations on Ecclesiastes. 143p. 5.95 (ISBN 0-88172-090-9). Believers Bkshelf.

Jennings, Hargrave. The Rosicrucians: Their Rites & Mysteries. 4th ed. LC 75-36845. (Occult Ser.). (Illus.). 1976. Repr. of 1907 ed. 36.50x (ISBN 0-405-07957-5). Ayer Co Pubs.

Jennings, J. G. Vedantic Buddhism of Buddha. 1974. Repr. 28.00 (ISBN 0-8426-0683-1). Orient Bk Dist.

Jennings, Kathryn. Beginning Special Religious Education Programs. (Special Education Newsletter Ser.: Vol. 2). 1980. 4.80 (ISBN 0-686-40038-0). Natl Cath Educ.

Jennings, Shirley. God Is Always Near. Sherer, Michael L., ed. (Orig.). 1987. pap. 5.95 (ISBN 0-89536-857-9, 7816). CSS of Ohio.

Jennings, T. The Bells of Haslemere Parish Church, Surrey. 1985. 11.25x (ISBN 0-317-54272-9, Pub. by J Richardson UK). State Mutual Bk.

--A History of Staffordshire Bells. 1985. 22.50x (ISBN 0-317-54277-X, Pub. by J Richardson UK). State Mutual Bk.

Jennings, Theodore W. Introduction to Theology: An Invitation to Reflection upon the Christian Mythos. LC 76-7867. pap. 48.00 (2027873). Bks Demand UMI.

--Life As Worship: Prayer & Praise in Jesus' Name. LC 82-7283. pap. 37.80 (ISBN 0-317-30146-2, 2025329). Bks Demand UMI.

Jennings, Theodore W., Jr. Beyond Theism: A Grammar of God-Language. 1985. 29.95x (ISBN 0-19-503613-1). Oxford U Pr.

Jennings, Theodore W., Jr., ed. Vocation of the Theologian. LC 84-48722. 160p. 1985. pap. 7.95 (ISBN 0-8006-1838-6, 1-1838). Fortress.

Jennings, Sr. Vivian. Valiant Woman: At the Heart of Reconciliation. LC 74-6037. 128p. 1974. 3.95 (ISBN 0-8189-0291-4). Alba.

Jensen, Adolf E. Beschneidung und Reifezeremonien Bei Naturvoelkern. 1933. 19.00 (ISBN 0-384-27160-X). Johnson Repr.

--Myth & Cult Among Primitive Peoples. LC 63-20909. 1963. 10.00x (ISBN 0-226-39823-4). U of Chicago Pr.

Jensen, Adolf E. & Bolle, Kees W., eds. Myth, Mensch & Umwelt. LC 77-79134. (Mythology Ser.). (Ger., Illus.). 1978. Repr. of 1950 ed. lib. bdg. 36.50x (ISBN 0-405-10544-4). Ayer Co Pubs.

Jensen, Andrew, jt. auth. see Jensen, Mary.

Jensen, De Lamar. Reformation Europe: Age of Reform & Revolution. 480p. 1981. pap. text ed. 12.95 (ISBN 0-669-03626-9). Heath.

Jensen, DeLamar. Diplomacy & Dogmatism: Bernardino de Mendoza & the French Catholic League. LC 63-20769. (Illus.). 1964. 22.50x (ISBN 0-674-20800-5). Harvard U Pr.

Jensen, Irving. Disfrute Su Biblia. Orig. Title: Enjoy Your Bible. (Span.). 1981. pap. 3.50 (ISBN 0-8254-1350-8). Kregel.

--Haggai, Zechariah & Malachi. (Bible Self Study Guide Ser.). 1976. pap. 3.25 (ISBN 0-8024-1037-5). Moody.

--Irving Jensen's Do-It-Yourself Bible Study: Mark. (Irving Jensen's Do-It-Yourself Bible Study Ser.). 118p. (Orig.). 1983. wkbk 5.95 (ISBN 0-89840-035-X). Heres Life.

--The Layman's Bible Study Notebook. parallel new testament ed. LC 77-93518. (King James & New International Version Ser.). (Orig.). 1978. pap. 26.95 (ISBN 0-89081-116-4). Harvest Hse.

--Romans. (Irving Jensen's Do-It Yourself Bible Study). 114p. (Orig.). 1983. pap. 5.95 wkbk. (ISBN 0-89840-036-8). Heres Life.

--Second Corinthians. (Bible Self-Study Ser). (Illus.). 108p. 1972. pap. 3.25 (ISBN 0-8024-1047-2). Moody.

Jensen, Irving L. Acts. (Bible Self-Study Ser). 1970. pap. 3.25 (ISBN 0-8024-1044-8). Moody.

--Acts: An Inductive Study. 256p. 1973. pap. 7.95 (ISBN 0-8024-0138-4). Moody.

--Colossians & Philemon. (Bible Self-Study Ser.). 80p. 1973. pap. 3.25 (ISBN 0-8024-1052-9). Moody.

--Ecclesiastes & the Song of Solomon. (Bible Self Study Guide Ser.). 1974. pap. 3.25 (ISBN 0-8024-1021-9). Moody.

--Enjoy Your Bible. 1969. pap. 5.95 (ISBN 0-8024-2347-7). Moody.

--Ephesians. (Bible Self-Study Ser.). 1973. pap. 3.25 (ISBN 0-8024-1049-9). Moody.

--Exodus. (Bible Self-Study Ser.). 1970. pap. 3.25 (ISBN 0-8024-1002-2). Moody.

--Ezekiel & Daniel. (Bible Self Study Ser.). 1970. pap. 2.95 (ISBN 0-8024-1026-X). Moody.

--Ezra, Nehemiah & Esther. (Bible Self-Study Ser.). 1970. pap. 3.25 (ISBN 0-8024-1015-4). Moody.

--First & Second Peter. (Bible Self-Study Ser.). 1971. pap. 3.25 (ISBN 0-8024-1060-X). Moody.

--First & Second Samuel. (Bible Self-Study Ser.). 1970. pap. 3.25 (ISBN 0-8024-1009-X). Moody.

--First & Second Thessalonians. (Bible Self-Study Ser.). 112p. 1974. pap. 3.25 (ISBN 0-8024-1053-7). Moody.

--First & Second Timothy & Titus. (Bible Self-Study Ser.). 1973. pap. 3.25 (ISBN 0-8024-1054-5). Moody.

--First Corinthians. (Bible Self-Study). 98p. 1972. pap. 3.25 (ISBN 0-8024-1046-4). Moody.

--Galatians. (Bible Self Study Ser). 1973. pap. 3.25 (ISBN 0-8024-1048-0). Moody.

--Genesis. (Bible Self-Study Ser.). 1967. pap. 3.25 (ISBN 0-8024-1001-4). Moody.

--Hebrews. (Bible Self-Study Ser.). 1970. pap. 3.25 (ISBN 0-8024-1058-8). Moody.

--Hebrews & the Pastoral Epistles. (Irving Jensen's Do-It-Yourself Bible Study Ser.). 139p. (Orig.). 1985. wkbk. 5.95 (ISBN 0-89840-077-5). Heres Life.

--How to Profit from Bible Reading. (Orig.). 1985. pap. 5.95 (ISBN 0-8024-0460-X). Moody.

--Independent Bible Study. LC 68-12114. 1972. pap. 6.95 (ISBN 0-8024-4050-9). Moody.

--Isaiah & Jeremiah. rev. ed. (Bible Self-Study Ser.). (Illus., Orig.). 1968. pap. 3.25 (ISBN 0-8024-1023-5). Moody.

--James. (Bible Self-Study Ser). (Illus.). 1972. pap. 3.25 (ISBN 0-8024-1059-6). Moody.

--Jensen's Survey of the New Testament. 608p. 1981. text ed. 19.95 (ISBN 0-8024-4308-7). Moody.

--Jensen's Survey of the Old Testament. 1978. text ed. 19.95 (ISBN 0-8024-4307-9). Moody.

--Jeremiah & Lamentations. (Everyman' Bible Commentary Ser.). (Orig.). 1966. pap. 5.95 (ISBN 0-8024-2024-9). Moody.

--Jeremias y Lamentaciones (Commentario Biblico Portavoz) Orig. Title: Jeremiah & Lamentations (Everyman's Bible Commentary) (Span.). 142p. 1979. pap. 3.95 (ISBN 0-8254-1352-4). Kregel.

--Job. (Bible Self Study Guide Ser.). 1975. pap. 3.25 (ISBN 0-8024-1018-9). Moody.

--John. (Bible Self-Study Guide). 1970. pap. 3.25 (ISBN 0-8024-1043-X). Moody.

--John. (Irving Jensen's Do-It-Yourself Bible Study Ser.). 160p. (Orig.). 1983. wkbk. 5.95 (ISBN 0-89840-051-1). Heres Life.

--Joshua. rev. ed. (Bible Self-Study Ser). (Illus.). 80p. 1967. pap. 3.25 (ISBN 0-8024-1006-5). Moody.

--Joshua: Rest-Land Won. (Everyman's Bible Commentary Ser.). (Orig.). 1966. pap. 5.95 (ISBN 0-8024-2006-0). Moody.

--Josue: La Tierra de Reposo, Conquistada (Comentario Biblico Portavoz) Orig. Title: Joshua: Rest-Land Won (Everyman's Bible Commentary) (Span.). 118p. 1980. pap. 3.50 (ISBN 0-8254-1353-2). Kregel.

--Judges & Ruth. rev. ed. (Bible Self-Study Ser). (Illus.). 96p. 1967. pap. 3.25 (ISBN 0-8024-1007-3). Moody.

--Leviticus. (Bible Self Study Ser.). 1970. pap. 3.25 (ISBN 0-8024-1003-0). Moody.

--Luke. (Bible Self Study Ser.). 1970. pap. 3.25 (ISBN 0-8024-1042-1). Moody.

--Mark. (Bible Self-Study Ser.). (Illus.). 1972. pap. 3.25 (ISBN 0-8024-1041-3). Moody.

--Matthew. (Bible Self Study Ser.). 1974. pap. 3.25 (ISBN 0-8024-1040-5). Moody.

--Minor Prophets of Israel. (Bible Self-Study Guides Ser.). 112p. (Orig.). 1975. pap. 3.25 (ISBN 0-8024-1028-6). Moody.

--Minor Prophets of Judah. (Bible Self-Study Guide Ser.). 112p. 1976. pap. 3.25 (ISBN 0-8024-1029-4). Moody.

--Numbers & Deuteronomy. (Bible Self Study Ser.). 1970. pap. 3.25 (ISBN 0-8024-1004-9). Moody.

--Numbers: Journey to God's Rest-Land. (Everyman's Bible Commentary Ser.). 1968. pap. 5.95 (ISBN 0-8024-2004-4). Moody.

--Numeros: Viaje a la Tierra de Reposo (Comentario Biblico Portavoz) Orig. Title: Numbers(Everyman's Bible Commentary) (Span.). 112p. 1980. pap. 3.50 (ISBN 0-8254-1355-9). Kregel.

--Philippians. (Bible Self-Study Ser.). 80p. 1973. pap. 3.25 (ISBN 0-8024-1051-0). Moody.

--Proverbs. (Bible Self-Study Guide Ser.). (Illus.). 96p. 1976. pap. 3.25 (ISBN 0-8024-1020-0). Moody.

--Psalms. (Bible Self-Study Guides). 1968. pap. 3.25 (ISBN 0-8024-1019-7). Moody.

--Revelation. (Bible Self-Study Ser.). 124p. (Orig.). 1971. pap. 3.25 (ISBN 0-8024-1066-9). Moody.

--Revelation. (Irving Jensen's Do-It-Yourself Bible Study Ser.). 110p. (Orig.). 1985. wkbk. 5.95 (ISBN 0-89840-081-3). Heres Life.

--Romans. (Bible Self-Study Ser.). 1970. pap. 3.25 (ISBN 0-8024-1045-6). Moody.

Jensen, Irving L., ed. First Kings & Chronicles. (Bible Self-Study Ser.). (Illus.). 1968. pap. 3.25 (ISBN 0-8024-1011-1). Moody.

--Second Kings with Chronicles. rev. ed. (Bible Self-Study Ser.). (Illus., Orig.). 1968. pap. 3.25 (ISBN 0-8024-1012-X). Moody.

Jensen, Irving R. Life of Christ. (Bible Self Study Ser.). pap. 3.25 (ISBN 0-8024-1067-7). Moody.

Jensen, Joseph. God's Word to Israel: An Introduction to the Old Testament. 400p. 1982. pap. 9.95 (ISBN 0-89453-289-8). M Glazier.

--Isaiah One to Thirty-Nine. (Old Testament Message Ser.: Vol. 8). 1984. 15.95 (ISBN 0-89453-408-4); pap. 10.95 (ISBN 0-89453-243-X). M Glazier.

--The Use of Tora by Isaiah: His Debate with the Wisdom Tradition. LC 73-83134. (Catholic Biblical Quarterly Monographs: No. 3). 3.00 (ISBN 0-915170-02-7). Catholic Biblical.

Jensen, Larry C. & Hughston, Karen M. Responsibility & Morality: Helping Children Become Responsible & Morally Mature. LC 79-10727. (Illus.). 1979. pap. 7.95x (ISBN 0-8425-1679-4). Brigham.

Jensen, Larry C., jt. auth. see Boyce, William D.

Jensen, Margaret. First We Have Coffee. LC 83-48412. 144p. (Orig.). 1983. pap. 5.95 (ISBN 0-89840-050-3). Heres Life.

--Lena. LC 84-62381. 150p. (Orig.). 1985. pap. text ed. 9.95 (ISBN 0-89840-074-0). Heres Life.

Jensen, Mary & Jensen, Andrew. Making Your Marriage Work. LC 85-7528. 144p. 1985. pap. 6.95 (ISBN 0-8066-2124-9, 10-4265). Augsburg.

Jensen, Mary E. Bible Women Speak to Us Today. LC 83-70507. 128p. (Orig.). 1983. pap. 5.95 (ISBN 0-8066-2013-7, 10-0708). Augsburg.

--Women of the Bible Tell Their Stories. LC 78-52193. 1978. pap. 6.95 (ISBN 0-8066-1663-6, 10-7235). Augsburg.

Jensen, Richard. The Crucified Ruler. (Orig.). 1987. pap. price not set (ISBN 0-89536-870-6, 7856). CSS of Ohio.

Jensen, Richard A. Telling the Story: Variety & Imagination in Preaching. LC 79-54113. 190p. (Orig.). 1979. pap. 9.95 (ISBN 0-8066-1766-7, 10-6232). Augsburg.

--Touched by the Spirit: One Man's Struggle to Understand His Experience of the Holy Spirit. LC 75-2838. 160p. 1975. pap. 7.95 (ISBN 0-8066-1484-6, 10-6675). Augsburg.

Jensen, Ronald A. How to Succeed the Biblical Way. 1981. pap. 4.95 (ISBN 0-8423-1541-1). Tyndale.

Jensen, Vi. Blessed Is the Woman. Silvey, James L., ed. 95p. (Orig.). 1983. pap. 3.50 (ISBN 0-89114-116-2). Baptist Pub Hse.

Jensh, Barbara L., ed. see Miyoshi, Sekiya.

Jenson, Andrew. Church Chronology: A Record of Important Events Pertaining to the History of the Church of Jesus Christ of the Latter-Day Saints (Mormons, 2 vols. 1980. lib. bdg. 200.00 (ISBN 0-8490-3139-7). Gordon Pr.

Jenson, Irving L. Epistles of John & Jude. (Bible Self-Study Ser.). 128p. (Orig.). 1971. pap. 3.25 (ISBN 0-8024-1062-6). Moody.

Jenson, Robert W. The Triune Identity: God According to the Gospel. LC 81-43091. 1982. 16.95 (ISBN 0-8006-0672-8). Fortress.

--The Triune Identity: God According to the Gospel. LC 81-43091. pap. 51.80 (2029621). Bks Demand UMI.

Jenson, Robert W., jt. auth. see Gritsch, Eric W.

Jenson, Robert W., jt. ed. see Braaten, Carl E.

Jenson, Ron & Stevens, Jim. Dynamics of Church Growth. 280p. 1981. pap. 8.95 (ISBN 0-8010-5161-4). Baker Bk.

Jenson, Ronald, jt. auth. see Reeves, R. Daniel.

Jenyns, Soame. A Free Enquiry into the Nature & Origin of Evil. 2nd ed. Wellek, Rene, ed. LC 75-11226. (British Philosophers & Theologians of the 17th & 18th Centuries: Vol. 28). 1976. Repr. of 1757 ed. lib. bdg. 51.00 (ISBN 0-8240-1780-3). Garland Pub.

Jeppesen, Knud & Otzen, Benedikt, eds. The Productions of Time: Tradition History in the Old Testament Scholarship. 169p. 1984. 24.95x (ISBN 0-907459-36-6, Pub. by Almond Pr England); pap. text ed. 10.95x (ISBN 0-907459-37-4). Eisenbrauns.

Jepsen, Dee. Women, the Challenge & the Call: An Agenda for Christian Women in Today's World. (Christian Essentials Ser.). 48p. (Orig.). 1987. pap. 1.95 (ISBN 0-89283-323-8). Servant.

Jepson, J. W. Don't Blame It All on Adam. 144p. 1984. pap. 4.95 (ISBN 0-87123-437-8, 210437). Bethany Hse.

--What You Should Know about the Holy Spirit. LC 85-81719. 160p. 1986. pap. 3.95 (ISBN 0-88243-639-2, 02-0639). Gospel Pub.

Jepson, Sarah. Solo. LC 72-131443. 1970. pap. 1.95 (ISBN 0-88419-134-6). Creation Hse.

Jerde, Rebecca. Fabric Applique for Worship: Patterns & Guide for Sewing Banners, Vestments, & Paraments. LC 83-133006. 80p. 1983. pap. 8.95 (ISBN 0-8066-1965-1, 10-2153). Augsburg.

Jeremiah, David. Abraham: Twenty-Six Daily Bible Studies. (Steps to Higher Ground Ser.). 1982. pap. 1.95 (ISBN 0-86508-201-4). BCM Intl Inc.

--John I, II, III: Twenty-Six Daily Bible Studies. (Steps to Higher Ground Ser.). 1983. pap. 1.95 (ISBN 0-86508-206-5). BCM Intl Inc.

--Malachi: Twenty-Six Daily Bible Studies. (Steps to Higher Ground Ser.). 1983. pap. 1.95 (ISBN 0-86508-207-3). BCM Intl Inc.

--Overcoming Loneliness. LC 83-48411. 143p. 1983. pap. 5.95 (ISBN 0-89840-049-X). Heres Life.

--Philippians: Twenty-Six Daily Bible Studies. (Steps to Higher Ground Ser.). 1983. pap. 1.95 (ISBN 0-86508-208-1). BCM Intl Inc.

--Wisdom of God. 1986. pap. 5.95 (ISBN 0-8010-5220-3). Baker Bk.

Jeremiah, James T. God's Answers to Our Anxieties. (Direction Bks.). 1979. pap. 1.95 (ISBN 0-8010-5083-9). Baker Bk.

Jeremias, Joachim. The Central Message of the New Testament. LC 81-66890. pap. 23.80 (2027865). Bks Demand UMI.

--The Eucharistic Words of Jesus. Perrin, Norman, tr. from Ger. LC 77-78633. 280p. 1977. pap. 12.95 (ISBN 0-8006-1319-8, 1-1319). Fortress.

--Jerusalem in the Time of Jesus: An Investigation into Economic & Social Conditions During the New Testament Period. Cave, F. H. & Cave, C. H., trs. from Ger. LC 77-81530. 434p. 1975. pap. 7.95 (ISBN 0-8006-1136-5, 1-1136). Fortress.

--The Lord's Prayer. Reumann, John, ed. & tr. from Ger. LC 64-11859. (Facet Bks.). 56p. 1964. pap. 2.50 (ISBN 0-8006-3008-4, 1-3008). Fortress.

--New Testament Theology. LC 70-143936. lib. rep. ed. 30.00x (ISBN 0-684-15157-X, ScribT). Scribner.

--The Parables of Jesus. 2nd ed. LC 63-22114. (Illus.). 248p. 1972. pap. text ed. 8.95 (ISBN 0-02-360510-3, Pub. by Scribner). Macmillan.

--The Prayers of Jesus. Bowden, John, et al, trs. from Ger. LC 77-10427. 132p. 1978. pap. 4.95 (ISBN 0-8006-1322-8, 1-1322). Fortress.

--Sermon on the Mount. Reumann, John, ed. Perrin, Norman, tr. from Ger. LC 63-17882. (Facet Bks.). (Orig.). 1963. pap. 2.50 (ISBN 0-8006-3002-5, 1-3002). Fortress.

Jeremy, David. Business & Religion in Britain, Vol. 5. (Business and History Ser.). 220p. 1987. text ed. 60.00 (ISBN 0-566-05096-X). Gower Pub Co.

Jerman, William E., tr. see Lange, Martin & Iblacker, Reinhold.

Jerman, William E., tr. see Tonna, Benjamin.

Jernigan. Salvation, Entire Sanctification. pap. 1.95 (ISBN 0-686-12907-5). Schmul Pub Co.

Jernigan, Wade. The Unsealed Book: An Amillennial View of Revelation. 1975. pap. 3.50 (ISBN 0-89265-028-1). Randall Hse.

Jerome. Life of Saint Hilarion. 1976. 1.95 (ISBN 0-686-15462-2). Eastern Orthodox.

Jerome, St. Dogmatic & Polemical Works. (Fathers of the Church Ser: Vol. 53). 405p. 1965. 21.95x (ISBN 0-8132-0053-9). Cath U Pr.

--Homilies, Nos. 1-59. LC 64-13360. (Fathers of the Church Ser: Vol. 48). 430p. 1964. 23.95x (ISBN 0-8132-0048-2). Cath U Pr.

--Homilies, Nos. 60-96. LC 64-13360. (Fathers of the Church Ser: Vol. 57). 295p. 1966. 15.95x (ISBN 0-8132-0057-1). Cath U Pr.

Jerome, Saint Letters of Saint Jerome, Vol. 1. Quasten & Burqhardt, eds. (Ancient Christian Writers Ser: Vol. 33). 1963. 11.95 (ISBN 0-8091-0087-8). Paulist Pr.

--Vitas Patrum: The Lyff of the Olde Auncyent Fathers Hermytes. Caxton, W., tr. LC 77-7409. (English Experience Ser.: No. 874). 1977. Repr. of 1495 ed. lib. bdg. 99.00 (ISBN 90-221-0874-0). Walter J Johnson.

Jerrold, Blanchard. The Chronicles of the Crutch. 1979. Repr. of 1860 ed. lib. bdg. 40.00 (ISBN 0-8482-1394-7). Norwood Edns.

Jerrold, Douglas. Future of Freedom: Notes on Christianity & Politics. facs. ed. LC 68-20311. (Essay Index Reprint Ser). 1938. 18.00 (ISBN 0-8369-0570-9). Ayer Co Pubs.

Jersild, Paul T. Invitation to Faith: Christian Belief Today. LC 77-84097. 1978. pap. 9.95 (ISBN 0-8066-1623-7, 10-3395). Augsburg.

Jersild, Paul T. & Johnson, Dale A. Moral Issues & Christian Responses. 3rd ed. 1983. pap. text ed. 25.95 (ISBN 0-03-062464-9). HR&W.

Jerusalem Ideological Conference Hebrew University. Proceedings, World Zionist Organization. Repr. of 1959 ed. lib. bdg. 23.00x (ISBN 0-8371-4120-6, WOZO). Greenwood.

Jervell, Jacob. Jesus in the Gospel of John. Cleven, Harry T., tr. LC 84-14547. 96p. (Orig.). 1984. pap. 5.95 (ISBN 0-8066-2089-7, 10-3516). Augsburg.

--Luke & the People of God: A New Look at Luke-Acts. LC 72-78565. 208p. 1979. pap. 10.95 (ISBN 0-8066-1730-6, 10-4136). Augsburg.

--The Unknown Paul: Essays on Luke-Acts & Early Christian History. LC 84-24605. 192p. (Orig.). 1984. pap. 10.95 (ISBN 0-8066-2119-2, 10-6815). Augsburg.

Jeschke, Marlin. Believers Baptism for Children of the Church. LC 82-23406. 160p. (Orig.). 1983. pap. 7.95 (ISBN 0-8361-3318-8). Herald Pr.

--Discipling the Brother. rev. ed. LC 72-2052. 190p. 1979. pap. 2.95 (ISBN 0-8361-1897-9). Herald Pr.

Jeske, John C. Daniel. (People's Bible Ser.). 1985. pap. 6.50 (ISBN 0-8100-0197-7, 15N0407); study guide, 32p 1.50 (ISBN 0-938272-52-7). Northwest Pub.

Jeske, Patrick J. Bring out the Best in Your Child. 1987. pap. 4.95. Pelican.

Jeske, Richard L. Revelation for Today: Images of Hope. LC 82-16079. 144p. 1983. pap. 6.95 (ISBN 0-8006-1693-6). Fortress.

--Understanding & Teaching the Bible. Rast, Harold W., ed. LC 80-69756. (A Lead Book). 128p. (Orig.). 1981. pap. 3.95 (ISBN 0-8006-1601-4, 1-1601). Fortress.

Jeske, Richard L. & Barr, Browne. Holy Week. Achtemeier, Elizabeth, et al, eds. LC 79-7377. (Proclamation 2: Aids for Interpreting the Lessons of the Church Year, Ser. A). 64p. (Orig.). 1980. pap. 3.75 (ISBN 0-8006-4094-2, 1-4094). Fortress.

Jessen, Joel. The Physical, the Mental, the Spiritual. 185p. 1978. pap. 10.00 (ISBN 0-942958-05-5). Kappeler Inst Pub.

Jessey, Cornelia. The Prayer of Cosa: Praying in the Way of Francis of Assisi. (Orig.). 1985. pap. 5.95 (ISBN 0-86683-936-4, AY8512, HarpR). Har-Row.

Jessie, Karen. O. T. Books of the Bible. 48p. (Orig.). (YA) 1983. 1.95 (ISBN 0-87239-674-6, 2774). Standard Pub.

Jessop, Augustus. Wise Words & Quaint Counsels of Thomas Fuller: Selected & Arranged with a Short Sketch of the Author's Life. 1979. Repr. of 1892 ed. lib. bdg. 45.00 (ISBN 0-8492-5602-X). R West.

Jessop, T. E., ed. see Berkeley, George.

Jessop, Thomas E. Bibliography of George Berkeley. LC 68-56592. (Bibliography & Reference Ser: No. 234). 1968. Repr. of 1934 ed. 14.50 (ISBN 0-8337-1840-1). B Franklin.

Jessopp, A., ed. see Norwich England Diocese.

Jessopp, Augustus. The Coming of the Friars & Other Historic Essays. facsimile ed. (Select Bibliographies Reprint Ser). Repr. of 1892 ed. 21.00 (ISBN 0-8369-6696-1). Ayer Co Pubs.

--John Donne: Sometime Dean of St. Paul's AD 1621-1631. LC 71-39284. (English Biography Ser. 31). 238p. 1972. Repr. of 1897 ed. lib. bdg. 49.95x (ISBN 0-8383-1395-7). Haskell.

--Studies by a Recluse in Cloister, Town & Country. 3rd ed. 1969. Repr. of 1883 ed. lib. bdg. 20.50 (ISBN 0-8337-1841-X). B Franklin.

Jesudasan, Ignatius. A Gandhian Theology of Liberation. LC 83-19486. 192p. (Orig.). 1984. pap. 10.95 (ISBN 0-88344-154-3). Orbis Bks.

Jesuit Missionaries. China. (Illus.). 216p. 150.00 (ISBN 0-8478-5402-7). Rizzoli Intl.

Jesuit Philosophical Association Of The Eastern States. Phases of American Culture. facs. ed. LC 69-17579. (Essay Index Reprint Ser). 1942. 14.00 (ISBN 0-8369-0021-9). Ayer Co Pubs.

Jesus, Gonzalo de see De Jesus, Gonzalo.

Jesus d' Elbee, Jean du Couer de see Couer de Jesus d' Elbee, Jean du.

Jeter, Hugh P. By His Stripes: The Doctrine of Divine Healing. LC 76-20893. 224p. 1977. pap. 4.95 (ISBN 0-88243-521-3, 02-0521). Gospel Pub.

Jeter, Jeremiah B. Recollections of a Long Life. Gaustad, Edwin S., ed. LC 79-52595. (The Baptist Tradition Ser.). 1980. Repr. of 1891 ed. lib. bdg. 24.00x (ISBN 0-405-12462-7). Ayer Co Pubs.

Jettmar, Karl. The Religions of the Hindukush, Vol. 1: The Religion of the Kafirs: The Pre-Islamic Heritage of Afghan Nuristan. Nayyar, Adam, tr. from Ger. (Illus.). 184p. 1986. text ed. 35.00 (ISBN 0-85668-163-6, Pub. by Aris & Phillips UK). Humanities.

--The Religions of the Hindukush Volume III: The Religions of the Chitralis. Nayyar, Adam, tr. from Ger. (Central Asian Studies). 1989. pap. text ed. 45.00 (ISBN 0-85668-368-X, Pub. by Aris & Phillips UK). Humanities.

--The Religions of the Hindukush Volume II: The Religion of the Dards. Nayyar, Adam, tr. from Ger. (Central Asian Studies). 200p. 1987. text ed. 45.00 (ISBN 0-85668-291-8, Pub. by Aris & Phillips UK). Humanities.

Jevons, Frank B. Comparative Religion. LC 76-57969. 1977. Repr. of 1913 ed. lib. bdg. 15.00 (ISBN 0-8414-5326-8). Folcroft.

Jewel, John. An Apologie or Answer in Defence of the Church of England. Bacon, Ann, tr. LC 72-38204. (English Experience Ser.: No. 470). 140p. 1972. Repr. of 1562 ed. 20.00 (ISBN 90-221-0470-2). Walter J Johnson.

--An Apology of the Church of England. Booty, John E., ed. (Paperbacks Ser). 1978. pap. 7.90x (ISBN 0-918016-63-0). Folger Bks.

--Works, 4 Vols. 1845-1850. Set. 204.00 (ISBN 0-384-27217-7). Johnson Repr.

Jewett, Dick. Say Uncle. (Quest Ser.). 32p. 1982. pap. 0.99 (ISBN 0-8163-0489-0). Pacific Pr Pub Assn.

Jewett, Edward H. Diabolology: The Person & Kingdom of Satan. 1977. lib. bdg. 59.95 (ISBN 0-8490-1715-7). Gordon Pr.

Jewett, Paul K. Baptist Catechism. pap. 0.85x (ISBN 0-9602638-4-5). Fuller Theol Soc.

--Election & Predestination. 184p. (Orig.). 1985. pap. 8.95 (ISBN 0-8028-0090-4). Eerdmans.

--The Ordination of Women. LC 80-15644. 160p. (Orig.). 1980. pap. 5.95 (ISBN 0-8028-1850-1). Eerdmans.

Jewett, Richard M. Orientation for New Adventists. (Waymark Ser.). 1978. pap. 2.95 (ISBN 0-8127-0184-4). Review & Herald.

Jewett, Robert. The Captain America Complex. LC 82-73362. 220p. (Orig.). 1984. pap. 4.95 (ISBN 0-939680-15-7). Bear & Co.

--Christian Tolerance: Paul's Message to the Modern Church. LC 82-13480. (Biblical Perspectives on Current Issues Ser.). 168p. 1982. pap. 9.95 (ISBN 0-664-24444-0). Westminster.

--A Chronology of Paul's Life. LC 78-54553. 176p. 1979. 14.95 (ISBN 0-8006-0522-5, 1-522). Fortress.

--Jesus Against the Rapture: Seven Unexpected Prophecies. LC 78-31759. 148p. 1979. pap. 5.95 (ISBN 0-664-24253-7). Westminster.

--Letter to Pilgrims. LC 80-28102. 244p. (Orig.). 1981. pap. 7.95 (ISBN 0-8298-0425-0). Pilgrim NY.

--Semeia Thirty, Christology & Exegesis: New Approaches. (SBL-Semeia Ser.). 1985. pap. 9.95 (ISBN 0-317-38906-8, 06-20-30). Scholars Pr Ga.

--The Thessalonian Correspondence: Pauline Rhetoric & Millenarian Piety. LC 86-45204. (Foundations & Facets Ser.). 256p. 1986. text ed. 17.95 (ISBN 0-8006-2111-5, 1-2111). Fortress.

Jewett, Robert, jt. ed. see Groh, Dennis E.

Jewish Frontier (Periodical) Anthology, Nineteen Thirty-Four to Nineteen Forty-Four. facsimile ed. LC 76-167370. (Essay Index Reprint Ser). Repr. of 1945 ed. 31.00 (ISBN 0-8369-2459-2). Ayer Co Pubs.

Jewish Law Association, International Congress Staff, jt. auth. see Jackson, Bernard S.

Jewish Peace Fellowship, ed. The Jewish Tradition of Peace. 1984. lib. bdg. 79.95 (ISBN 0-87700-626-1). Revisionist Pr.

--Judaism & Peacemaking. 1984. lib. bdg. 79.95 (ISBN 0-87700-627-X). Revisionist Pr.

--Martin Buber & the Covenant of Peace. 1984. lib. bdg. 79.95 (ISBN 0-87700-629-6). Revisionist Pr.

--Roots of Jewish Nonviolence. 1984. lib. bdg. 79.95 (ISBN 0-87700-628-8). Revisionist Pr.

Jewish Reconstructionist Foundation. The New Haggadah. 3rd rev. ed. Kaplan, Mordecai M., et al, eds. LC 77-16803. (Illus.). 1978. pap. text ed. 3.95x (ISBN 0-87441-304-4). Behrman.

Jezernik, Maksimiljan. Frederick Baraga: A Portrait of the First Bishop of Marquette Based on the Archives of the Congregatio De Propaganda Fide. LC 68-16856. 155p. 1968. 8.00 (ISBN 0-686-28380-5); pap. 6.00 (ISBN 0-686-28381-3). Studia Slovenica.

Jha, Akhileshwar. The Imprisoned Mind: Guru Shisya Tradition in Indian Culture. 1980. 18.50x (ISBN 0-8364-0665-6, Pub. by Ambika India). South Asia Bks.

Jha, Ganganath, tr. & commentary by see Jaimini.

Jha, Ganganath, tr. see Shantaraksita.

Jha, Ganganatha. The Prabhakara School of Purva Mimamsa. 2nd, rev. ed. 1978. 12.50 (ISBN 0-89684-016-6, Pub. by Motilal Banarsidass India). Orient Bk Dist.

Jha, Makhan, ed. Dimensions of Pilgrimage: An Anthropoligical Appraisal (Based on the Transactions of a World Symposium of Pilgrimage) (Illus.). xvi, 180p. 1986. text ed. 45.00x (ISBN 81-210-0007-6, Pub. by Inter India Pubns N Delhi). Apt Bks.

Jhunjhuniwala, Shyam S., ed. see Sri Aurobindo.

Jhunjhunwala, Shyam S., ed. see Aurobindo, Sri.

Ji, Brachmachari S., ed. see Devendra Gani.

Jick, Leon A. The Americanization of the Synagogue, 1820-1870. LC 75-18213. (Illus.). 260p. 1976. 25.00x (ISBN 0-87451-119-4). U Pr of New Eng.

--The Teaching of Judaica in American Universities: Proceedings. 1970. 10.00x (ISBN 0-87068-127-3). Ktav.

Jicks, John M. & Morton, Bruce L. Woman's Role in the Church. pap. 2.95 (ISBN 0-89315-362-1). Lambert Bk.

Jiede, E. A. Living God's Word. 1947. pap. 2.25 (ISBN 0-570-03505-8, 14-1262). Concordia.

Jiggetts, Robert C., Jr. Beyond Circumstances. (Illus.). 96p. (Orig.). 1986. pap. 9.95 (ISBN 1-55630-016-6). Brentwood Comm.

Jim & Reapsome, Martha. Discipleship: The Growing Christians Lifestyle. (Fisherman Bible Studyguide). 64p. 1984. pap. 2.95 (ISBN 0-87788-175-8). Shaw Pubs.

Jim, Strange De see De Jim, Strange.

Jinapriya, Ginige. Buddhist Education in Ceylon, & Other Essays. LC 78-72901. Repr. of 1931 ed. 18.50 (ISBN 0-404-17313-6). AMS Pr.

Jinarajadasa. K. H. Letters to C. W. Leadbeater. 5.95 (ISBN 0-8356-7552-1). Theos Pub Hse.

--Letters From the Masters of the Wisdom. (Series 1). 3.50 (ISBN 0-8356-7135-6). Theos Pub Hse.

--Letters From the Masters of Wisdom. (Series 2). 3.50 (ISBN 0-8356-7311-1). Theos Pub Hse.

Jinarajadasa, C. Seven Veils over Consciousness. 2.50 (ISBN 0-8356-7231-X). Theos Pub Hse.

Jinarajadasa, Curuppumullage. The Reign of Law (Buddhist Essays) LC 78-72902. Repr. of 1923 ed. 22.50 (ISBN 0-404-17314-4). AMS Pr.

Jindel, Rajendra. Culture of a Sacred Town: Sociological Study of Nathdwara. 233p. 1986. 12.00X (ISBN 0-8364-1672-4, Pub. by Popular Prakashan). South Asia Bks.

Jivananda, Bhagavan. This Is It: It's How You Live It Now, the Endless Meditation. (Orig.). pap. cancelled (ISBN 0-941404-27-7). Falcon Pr AZ.

Jividen, Jimmy. Miracles: From God or Men. 288p. 1987. 9.95 (ISBN 0-915547-93-7). Abilene Christ U.

Jiyu-Kennett, Roshi & MacPhillamy, Daizui. The Book of Life. (Illus.). 1979. pap. 9.95 (ISBN 0-930066-04-9). Shasta Abbey.

Jnanadev. Jnaneshwari. Bhagwat, Ramachandra K., tr. (Illus.). 1979. 36.00 (ISBN 0-89744-188-5). Auromere.

Jnanatmananda, Swami. Invitation to Holy Company. Dey, J. N., tr. from Bengali. (Illus.). 1979. pap. 2.95 (ISBN 0-87481-491-X). Vedanta Pr.

Joachim Pillai, C. A. The Apostolic Interpretation of History: A Commentary on Acts 13: 16-41. 1980. 9.00 (ISBN 0-682-49404-6, University). Exposition Pr FL.

--Early Missionary Preaching: A Study of Luke's Report in Acts 13. 1979. 8.00 (ISBN 0-682-49403-8, University). Exposition Pr FL.

Joad, Cyril E. The Present & Future of Religion. LC 77-109756. 310p. 1974. Repr. of 1930 ed. lib. bdg. 22.50x (ISBN 0-8371-4246-6, JOPF). Greenwood.

Joannes, Damascenus. On Holy Images. Allies, Mary H., tr. from Greek. 1977. pap. 2.95 (ISBN 0-686-19232-X). Eastern Orthodox.

Job, John. Watchman in Babylon: A Study Guide to Ezekiel. 112p. (Orig.). pap. 4.95 (ISBN 0-85364-339-3). Attic Pr.

Job, Reuben & Shawchuck, Norman. A Guide to Prayer for Ministers & Other Servants. LC 83-80409. 400p. (Orig.). 1983. pap. 21.95 bible bdg. (ISBN 0-8358-0460-7). Upper Room.

Job, Rueben P. & Shawchuck, Norman. A Guide to Prayer. 432p. 1987. pap. 11.95 (ISBN 0-8358-0559-X). Upper Room.

Jobe, Bobbie C. Striving for Holiness. 2.70 (ISBN 0-89137-423-X). Quality Pubns.

Jobe, Bobbie J. God Opens the Doors. (Orig.). 1987. pap. 5.95 (ISBN 0-8054-5041-6). Broadman.

Jobes, Gertrude. Dictionary of Mythology, Folklore & Symbols, 3 Vols. LC 61-860. 1759p. 1961. Vols. 1 & 2. 70.00 (ISBN 0-8108-0034-9); Vol. 3 index, 482 pgs. 35.00 (ISBN 0-8108-1697-0). Scarecrow.

Jobling, David. THe Sense of Biblical Narrative II: Stuctural Analyses in the Hebrew Bible. (JSOT Supplement Ser.: No. 39). 120p. 1986. text ed. 21.00x (ISBN 1-85075-010-6, Pub. by JSOT Pr England); pap. text ed. 8.95x (ISBN 1-85075-011-4, Pub. by JSOT Pr England). Eisenbrauns.

Jocelin De Brakelond. Chronica Jocelini De Brakelonda. LC 17-17164. (Camden Society, London. Publications, First Series: No. 13). Repr. of 1840 ed. 19.00 (ISBN 0-404-50113-3). AMS Pr.

Jocelin De Brakelonda. Chronica Jocelini De Brakelonda, De Rebus Gestis Samsonis. 1840. 19.00 (ISBN 0-384-27530-3). Johnson Repr.

Jocelyn, Beredene. Citizens of the Cosmos: Life's Unfolding from Conception Through Death to Rebirth. (Freedeeds Library). (Illus.). 198p. 1983. Repr. of 1981 ed. 14.00 (ISBN 0-89345-040-5, Freedeeds Bks). Garber Comm.

Jocelyn, Beredene, jt. auth. see Jocelyn, John.

Jocelyn, John & Jocelyn, Beredene. Beneficent Rule of Destiny. 1983. pap. 1.50 (ISBN 0-916786-73-0). St George Bk Serv.

Jochai, Simeon B. In the Beginning. (Sacred Text Ser.). (Illus.). vii, 88p. 1983. pap. 8.75 (ISBN 0-88695-008-2). Concord Grove.

Jochim, Christian. Chinese Religions: A Cultural Perspective. (Illus.). 224p. 1986. pap. text ed. 17.00 (ISBN 0-13-132994-4). P-H.

Jocz, Jakob. The Jewish People & Jesus Christ. 1979. pap. 7.95 (ISBN 0-8010-5085-5). Baker Bk.

--The Jewish People & Jesus Christ After Auschwitz. 172p. (Orig.). 1981. pap. 9.95 (ISBN 0-8010-5123-1). Baker Bk.

Joel, David H. Religionsphilosophie des Sohar und Ihr Verhaltnis zur Allgemeinen Judischen Theologie. Katz, Steven, ed. LC 79-7139. (Jewish Philosophy, Mysticism & History of Ideas Ser.). 1980. Repr. of 1923 ed. lib. bdg. 34.50x (ISBN 0-405-12265-9). Ayer Co Pubs.

Joel, Manuel. Beitrage zur Geschichte der Philosophie. Katz, Steven, ed. LC 79-7140. (Jewish Philosophy, Mysticism & History of Ideas Ser.). 1980. Repr. of 1876 ed. lib. bdg. 51.50x (ISBN 0-405-12266-7). Ayer Co Pubs.

Joffe, Judah, tr. see Sachs, Abraham S.

Jogn, Norman de see De Jong, Norman.

Johani, Maneh al see Yakan, Fathi.

Johann, Robert O. Pragmatic Meaning of God. (Aquinas Lecture). 1966. 7.95 (ISBN 0-87462-131-3). Marquette.

Johann, Robert O., ed. Freedom & Value. LC 76-13969. xii, 186p. 1976. pap. 9.00 (ISBN 0-8232-1011-1). Fordham.

Johannes Canaparius. Das Leben Des Bischofs Adalbert Von Prag. Hueffer, Hermann, tr. xiv, 54p. (Ger.). pap. 8.00 (ISBN 0-384-31946-7). Johnson Repr.

Johannesen, S. K., jt. ed. see Bettis, Joseph.

Johannesen, Stanley, jt. ed. see Bettis, Joseph.

Johanson, E. Jane, jt. auth. see Napoleone, Mary A.

Johanson, Gregory J., ed. Feed My Sheep: Sermons on Contemporary Issues in Pastoral Care. 6.95. Paulist Pr.

--Pastoral Care Issues in the Pulpit. 1984. 7.50 (ISBN 0-89536-621-5, 1630). CSS of Ohio.

Johansson, Anders B., jt. auth. see Cratch, Stephen C.

Johansson, B. Religion & Superstition in the Plays of Ben Johnson & Thomas Middleton. (Essays & Studies on English Language & Literature: Vol. 7). pap. 28.00 (ISBN 0-8115-0205-8). Kraus Repr.

Johansson, Calvin M. Music & Ministry: A Biblical Counterpoint. 152p. 1984. pap. 6.95 (ISBN 0-913573-07-8). Hendrickson MA.

Johansson, Lilian M., ed. see Cratch, Stephen C. & Johansson, Anders B.

Johansson, Rune. The Dynamic Psychology of Early Buddhism. (Scandinavian Institute of Asian Studies Monographs: No. 37). (Illus.). 1979. pap. text ed. 15.00x (ISBN 0-7007-0114-1). Humanities.

Johansson, Rune E. Pali Buddhist Texts. 160p. 1982. 30.00x (ISBN 0-7007-0063-3, Pub. by Curzon England). State Mutual Bk.

--Pali Buddhist Texts Explained to the Beginner. 1981. pap. 12.00 (ISBN 0-8364-0329-0, Pub. by Curzon Pr). South Asia Bks.

Johari, Harish. Chakras: Energy Centers of Transformation. (Illus.). 192p. 1987. pap. 14.95 (ISBN 0-89281-054-8). Inner Tradit.

--Tools for Tantra. (Illus.). 192p. 1986. pap. 14.95 (ISBN 0-89281-055-6, Inner Traditions). Inner Tradit.

John & Carr, Adrienne. The Pilgrimage Project: Leader's Guide. 64p. (Orig.). 1987. pap. 4.95 (ISBN 0-8358-0550-6). Upper Room.

John, Catherine R., rev. by see Attwater, Donald.

John, Da F. Do You Know What Anything Is? LC 84-70215. 1984. pap. 8.95 (ISBN 0-913922-87-0). Dawn Horse Pr.

--Enlightenment & the Transformation of Man. LC 83-72730. 1983. pap. 7.95 (ISBN 0-913922-83-8). Dawn Horse Pr.

--God Is Not a Gentleman & I Am That One. LC 83-73178. 1983. 6.95 (ISBN 0-913922-85-4). Dawn Horse Pr.

--The Great Way of Wisdom: An Anthology of Written Teaching of Da Free John. Feuerstein, Georg, ed. 1984. pap. 3.95 (ISBN 0-913922-88-9). Dawn Horse Pr.

John, Da Free. The Dreaded Gom-Boo: Or the Imaginary Desease That Religion Seeks to Cure. LC 83-70401. 400p. (Orig.). 1983. pap. 9.95 (ISBN 0-913922-74-9). Dawn Horse Pr.

--The Fire Gospel. 224p. (Orig.). 1982. pap. 8.95 (ISBN 0-913922-73-0). Dawn Horse Pr.

--The Liberator, Eleutherios. (Illus.). 114p. 1982. 12.95 (ISBN 0-913922-66-8); pap. 6.95 (ISBN 0-913922-67-6). Dawn Horse Pr.

--Nirvanasara. 280p. (Orig.). 1982. pap. 9.95 (ISBN 0-913922-65-X). Dawn Horse Pr.

--The Yoga of Consideration & the Way That I Teach. (Orig.). 1982. pap. 3.95 (ISBN 0-913922-63-3). Dawn Horse Pr.

John, Erwin E. Key to a Successful Church Library. rev. ed. LC 58-13940. (Orig.). 1967. pap. 5.95 (ISBN 0-8066-0711-4, 10-3684). Augsburg.

John, Michael, tr. see Casalis, George.

John, Robin, tr. see Bermann, Richard A.

John, Sally, jt. auth. see John, Tommy.

John, Tommy & John, Sally. The Sally & Tommy John Story. 288p. 1985. pap. 3.50 (ISBN 0-425-07304-1). Berkley Pub.

John Chrysostom, St. Homilies on St. John 1-47. LC 57-1545. (Fathers of the Church Ser: Vol. 33). 485p. 1957. 25.95x (ISBN 0-8132-0033-4). Cath U Pr.

--Homilies, 48-88. LC 57-1545. (Fathers of the Church Ser.: Vol. 41). 485p. 1960. 29.95x (ISBN 0-8132-0041-5). Cath U Pr.

John Damascene, Saint Barlaam & Iosaph. (Loeb Classical Library: No. 34). 13.95x (ISBN 0-674-99038-2). Harvard U Pr.

Johnes, Thomas, tr. see De Lion, Gwoffrey, et al.

Johnian, Mona. Renewing Your Mind. (Orig.). 1986. pap. text ed. 3.95 (ISBN 0-88368-182-X). Whitaker Hse.

John Lame Deer & Erdoes, Richard. Lame Deer Seeker of Visions: The Life of a Sioux Medicine Man. 288p. 1976. pap. 3.95 (ISBN 0-671-45586-9, 80391). WSP.

John Of Damascus, St. Selected Works. LC 56-792. (Fathers of the Church Ser: Vol. 37). 426p. 1958. 23.95x (ISBN 0-8132-0037-7). Cath U Pr.

--Veneration of Icons. pap. 0.50 (ISBN 0-686-05666-3). Eastern Orthodox.

John of Ford. John of Ford: Sermons on the Final Verses of the Song of Songs, Vol. 6. Beckett, Wendy M., tr. from Latin. (Cistercian Fathers Ser.: No. 46). 26.95 (ISBN 0-87907-646-1). Cistercian Pubns.

--John of Ford: Sermons on the Final Verses of the Song of Songs, Vol. 7. Beckett, Wendy M., tr. from Latin. (Cistercian Fathers Ser.: No. 47). 1985. 26.95 (ISBN 0-87907-647-X). Cistercian Pubns.

--Sermons on the Final Verses of the Song of Songs, Vol. 1. (Cistercian Fathers Ser.: No. 29). 14.95 (ISBN 0-87907-629-1). Cistercian Pubns.

--Sermons on the Final Verses of the Song of Songs, Vol. 2. Beckett, Wendy M., tr. from Latin. (Cistercian Fathers Ser.: No. 39). 1982. 21.95 (ISBN 0-87907-639-9). Cistercian Pubns.

--Sermons on the Final Verses of the Song of Songs, Vol. 4. (Cistercian Fathers Ser.: No. 44). 24.95 (ISBN 0-87907-644-5). Cistercian Pubns.

--Sermons on the Final Verses of the Song of Songs, Vol. 5. (Cistercian Fathers Ser.: No. 45). 24.95 (ISBN 0-87907-645-3). Cistercian Pubns.

--Sermons on the Final Verses of the Song of Songs, Vol. 6. 24.95 (ISBN 0-87907-646-1). Cistercian Pubns.

--Sermons on the Final Verses of the Song of Songs, Vol. 7. 24.95. Cistercian Pubns.

John Of Landsburg. A Letter of Jesus Christ. Griffiths, John, ed. LC 81-126. (The Spiritual Classics Ser.). 176p. 1981. 9.95 (ISBN 0-8245-0080-6). Crossroad NY.

John of Salisbury. The Metalogicon of John of Salisbury: A Twelfth-Century Defense of Verbal & Logical Arts of the Trivium. McGarry, Daniel D., tr. from Latin. LC 82-2989. xxvii, 305p. 1982. Repr. of 1955 ed. lib. bdg. 39.75x (ISBN 0-313-23539-2, JOME). Greenwood.

John of Smolensk. Iisus Khristos Pred Sudom Sovemjennogo Razuma. Tr. of Jesus Christ Before the Judgement of Contemporaty Intellect. 16p. pap. 1.00 (ISBN 0-317-28988-8). Holy Trinity.

John of the Cross. Dark Night of the Soul. Zimmerman, Benedict, tr. 246p. 1974. pap. 10.95 (ISBN 0-227-67807-9). Attic Pr.

John Paul, II. A Year with Mary. Buono, Anthony M., tr. from Italian. 320p. (Orig.). 1986. pap. 6.00 (ISBN 0-89942-370-1, 370/22). Catholic Bk Pub.

John Paul II. A Commentary on "Catechesi Trandendae: The New Chsrter for Religious Education in Our Time. LC 80-26792. 243p. 1980. 4.50 (ISBN 0-8199-0815-0). Franciscan Herald.

--Pope John Paul II: Pilgrim of Peace. 1987. 25.00 (ISBN 0-517-56423-8, Harmony). Crown.

John Paul II, Pope Day by Day With Pope John Paul II. 1982. pap. 6.95 (ISBN 0-8091-2458-0). Paulist Pr.

--Faith According to St. John of the Cross. Aumann, Jordan, tr. LC 80-82265. Orig. Title: Doctrina de Fide apud S. Joannem a Cruce. 276p. (Orig.). 1981. pap. 13.95 (ISBN 0-89870-010-8). Ignatius Pr.

--Healing & Hope. 266p. 1982. 5.00 (ISBN 0-8198-3317-7, EP0545); pap. 3.50 (ISBN 0-8198-3318-5). Dghtrs St Paul.

--Pilgrimage of Peace: John Paul II in Ireland & the United States. (Illus.). 175p. 1980. 17.50 (ISBN 0-374-23307-1); pap. 9.95 (ISBN 0-374-51578-6). FS&G.

--Prayers of John Paul II. McDonald, John F., ed. LC 82-72495. 108p. 1982. pap. 6.95 (ISBN 0-8245-0537-9). Crossroad NY.

--Redeemer of Man. 103p. (Orig.). 1979. pap. 3.95 (ISBN 1-55586-003-6). US Catholic.

--Sources of Renewal: The Fulfillment of Vatican II. LC 79-1780. 448p. 1980. 15.00 (ISBN 0-06-064188-6, HarpR). Har-Row.

John-Roger. Baraka: Movement of Spiritual Inner Awareness. 1978. pap. 5.00 (ISBN 0-914829-01-7). Baraka Bk.

--The Buddha Consiousness. LC 76-17344. 1976. pap. 5.00 (ISBN 0-914829-03-3). Baraka Bk.

--The Christ Within. LC 77-70405. 1976. pap. 5.00 (ISBN 0-914829-04-1). Baraka Bk.

--The Consciousness of Soul. LC 77-81388. 1977. pap. 5.00 (ISBN 0-914829-05-X). Baraka Bk.

--Disciples of Christ. 1976. pap. 5.00 (ISBN 0-914829-07-6). Baraka Bk.

--Dynamics of the Lower Self. LC 77-70406. 1976. pap. 5.00 (ISBN 0-914829-10-6). Baraka Bk.

--Inner Worlds of Meditation. LC 76-56625. pap. 5.00 (ISBN 0-914829-11-4). Baraka Bk.

--Journey of the Soul. LC 77-81387. 1977. pap. 5.00 (ISBN 0-914829-12-2). Baraka Bk.

--Possessions, Projections & Entities. 1976. pap. 5.00 (ISBN 0-914829-17-3). Baraka Bk.

--Sex, Spirit & You. LC 77-81389. 1977. pap. 5.00 (ISBN 0-914829-18-1). Baraka Bk.

--The Spiritual Family. 1976. pap. text ed. 5.00 (ISBN 0-914829-21-1, 978-5). Baraka Bk.

Johns, Alger F. A Short Grammar of Biblical Aramaic. rev. ed. (Andrews University Monographs, Studies in Religion: Vol. 1). xii, 108p. 1972. pap. text ed. 7.95 (ISBN 0-943872-01-4). Andrews Univ Pr.

Johns, C. H. The Relations Between the Laws of Babylonia & the Laws of the Hebrew Peoples. (British Academy, London, Schweich Lectures on Biblical Archaeology Series, 1912). pap. 19.00 (ISBN 0-8115-1254-1). Kraus Repr.

Johns, Cheryl B. Finding Eternal Treasures. (International Correspondence Program Ser.). (Orig.). 1985. pap. text ed. 6.95 (ISBN 0-87148-340-8). Pathway Pr.

Johns, Roger D. Man in the World: The Political Theology of Johannes Baptist Metz. LC 76-26491. (American Academy of Religion. Dissertation Ser.). 1976. pap. 9.95 (ISBN 0-89130-079-1, 010116). Scholars Pr GA.

Johnsen, Henry. People of the Way: Biblical Ecumenism. 5.95 (ISBN 0-685-00743-X). Reiner.

John Smith the Platonist. The Excellency & Nobleness of the True Religion. 1984. pap. 4.95 (ISBN 0-916411-35-4, Pub by Alexandrian Pr). Holmes Pub.

Johnson, A. Wetherell. Created for Commitment. 1982. 12.95 (ISBN 0-8423-0484-3). Tyndale.

Johnson, Alan. Romans, Vol. 1. rev. ed. (Everyman's Bible Commentary Ser.). 1984. pap. 5.95 (ISBN 0-8024-0446-4). Moody.

Johnson, Alan F. Revelation: Bible Study Commentary. (Bible Study Commentary Ser.). 1986. pap. 7.95 (ISBN 0-310-45173-6, 12386P). Zondervan.

--Romans: The Freedom Letter, Vol. 2. rev. ed. (Everyman's Bible Commentary Ser.). Date not set. pap. 5.95 (ISBN 0-8024-2079-6). Moody.

Johnson, Alan F., jt. ed. see Gundry, Stanley N.

Johnson, Albert. Best Church Plays: A Bibliography of Religious Drama. 11.25 (ISBN 0-8446-2328-8). Peter Smith.

Johnson, Alfred M. A Bibliography of Semiological & Structural Studies of Religion. LC 79-110955. 1979. 10.00 (ISBN 0-931222-10-9). Pitts Theolog.

Johnson, Alfred M., Jr., ed. & tr. The New Testament & Structuralism: A Collection of Essays. LC 76-25447. (Pittsburgh Theological Monographs: No. 11). 1976. pap. text ed. 11.50 (ISBN 0-915138-13-1). Pickwick.

--Structuralism & Biblical Hermeneutics. LC 79-9411. (Pittsburgh Theological Monographs: No. 22). 1979. pap. 12.95 (ISBN 0-915138-18-2). Pickwick.

Johnson, Alfred M., Jr., tr. see Barthes, R., et al.

Johnson, Alfred M., Jr., tr. see Bowman, John.

Johnson, Alfred M., Jr., tr. see Marin, Louis.

Johnson, Alvin D. Celebrating Your Church Anniversary. LC 68-28077. 1968. pap. 3.95 (ISBN 0-8170-0408-4). Judson.

--The Work of the Usher. (Orig.). pap. 3.95 (ISBN 0-8170-0356-8). Judson.

Johnson, Alvin W. The Legal Status of Church-State Relationships in the United States with Special Reference to the Public Schools. ix, 332p. 1982. Repr. of 1934 ed. lib. bdg. 30.00x (ISBN 0-8377-0739-0). Rothman.

Johnson, Alvin W. & Yost, Frank H. Separation of Church & State in the United States. 279p. Repr. of 1948 ed. lib. bdg. 22.50x (ISBN 0-8371-2436-0, JOCS). Greenwood.

Johnson, Ann. Miryam of Nazareth: Woman of Strength & Wisdom. LC 84-71347. 128p. (Orig.). 1984. pap. 4.95 (ISBN 0-87793-321-9). Ave Maria.

Johnson, Ann D. The Value of Determination: The Story of Helen Keller. 2nd ed. LC 76-54762. (Valuetales Ser). (Illus.). 1976. 7.95 (ISBN 0-916392-07-4, Dist. by Oak Tree Pubns.). Value Comm.

Johnson, B. C. The Atheist Debater's Handbook. LC 81-80487. (Skeptics Bookshelf Ser.). 134p. 1981. 14.95 (ISBN 0-87975-152-5); pap. 8.95 (ISBN 0-87975-210-6). Prometheus Bks.

Johnson, B. W. & DeWelt, Don. The Gospel of Mark. LC 76-1069. (The Bible Study Textbook Ser.). (Illus.). 1965. 15.90 (ISBN 0-89900-033-9). College Pr Pub.

Johnson, B. W., ed. People's New Testament with Notes, 1 vol. 1971. 14.95 (ISBN 0-89225-141-7). Gospel Advocate.

Johnson, Barbara. Where Does a Mother Go to Resign? LC 79-12686. 160p. 1979. pap. 4.95 (ISBN 0-87123-606-0, 210606). Bethany Hse.

Johnson, Barbara M. Pilgrim on a Bicycle. LC 81-68637. 144p. 1982. write for info. (ISBN 0-86693-001-9). B M Johnson.

Johnson, Barry L. Visit of the Tomten. LC 81-70361. pap. 4.95x (ISBN 0-8358-0439-9). Upper Room.

Johnson, Ben. Blueprint for Sainthood: A Study of the Series C Epistles for Lent. 1980. 4.25 (ISBN 0-89536-416-6, 0234). CSS of Ohio.

Johnson, Ben C. An Evangelism Primer: Practical Principles for Congregations. LC 82-49021. 120p. 1983. pap. 5.95 (ISBN 0-8042-2039-5). John Knox.

--Rethinking Evangelism: A Theological Approach. LC 86-26787. 142p. (Orig.). 1987. pap. 9.95 (ISBN 0-664-24060-7). Westminster.

Johnson, Bev. Drama in the Church: Planning & Staging Dramatic Productions. 80p. 1983. pap. 8.95 (ISBN 0-8066-2027-7, 10-1976). Augsburg.

Johnson, Buford. Seasonal Subjects. 1981. pap. 3.95 (ISBN 0-934942-25-0). White Wing Pub.

Johnson, C. Phillip. Will a Man Rob God? 1981. pap. 3.00 (ISBN 0-933184-29-8). Flame Intl.

Johnson, Carl G. Special Occasion Sermon Outlines. (Pocket Pulpit Library). 112p. 1980. pap. 3.50 (ISBN 0-8010-5126-6). Baker Bk.

Johnson, Carlton. Overcome Any Problem. (Out Ser.). 1985. pap. 1.25 (ISBN 0-8163-0580-3). Pacific Pr Pub Assn.

Johnson, Charles, ed. see Hugh The Chantor.

Johnson, Charles, tr. from Lat. see Sottovagina, Hugh.

Johnson, Charles A. The Frontier Camp Meeting: Religion's Harvest Time. LC 55-8783. (Illus.). xiv, 325p. 1985. 21.95x (ISBN 0-87074-201-9). SMU Press.

Johnson, Christopher J. & McGee, Marsha G., eds. Encounters with Eternity. LC 85-17045. (Paperback Ser.). 352p. 1986. 19.95 (ISBN 0-8022-2493-8); pap. 12.95 (ISBN 0-8022-2508-X). Philos Lib.

Johnson, Connie. Living Our Visions of Peace. (Illus.). 35p. (Orig.). 1984. pap. 4.95 (ISBN 0-377-00141-4). Friend Pr.

Johnson County Historical Society Staff. A History of Johnson County Churches. Morgan, John, ed. 176p. 1986. 20.00 (ISBN 0-916369-06-4). Magnolia Pr.

Johnson, D., jt. ed. see Capper, W. M.

Johnson, Dale A., jt. auth. see Jersild, Paul T.

Johnson, Dale A., ed. Women in English Religion, Seventeen Hundred thru Nineteen Twenty-Five. LC 83-12124. (Studies in Women & Religion: Vol. 10). 368p. 1984. 49.95x (ISBN 0-88946-539-8). E Mellen.

Johnson, Daniel. Building with Buses. pap. 2.95 (ISBN 0-8010-5059-6). Baker Bk.

Johnson, Daniel L. Starting Right, Staying Strong: A Guide to Effective Ministry. LC 82-22383. 108p. (Orig.). 1983. pap. 5.95 (ISBN 0-8298-0648-2). Pilgrim NY.

Johnson, David L. A Reasoned Look at Asian Religions. 150p. 1985. pap. 5.95 (ISBN 0-87123-798-9, 210798). Bethany Hse.

Johnson, David M., ed. Justice & Peace Education: Models for College & University Faculty. LC 85-25808. 256p. (Orig.). 1986. pap. 16.95 (ISBN 0-88344-247-7). Orbis Bks.

Johnson, David W. Arches: The Story Behind the Scenery. LC 85-80445. (Illus.). 48p. (Orig.). 1985. pap. 4.50 (ISBN 0-88714-002-5). KC Pubns.

Johnson, Dennis C. A Liturgical Narrative on the Service for the Day. 1984. 3.50 (ISBN 0-89536-657-6, 1268). CSS of Ohio.

Johnson, Douglas W. The Care & Feeding of Volunteers. LC 78-8295. (Creative Leadership Ser.). 1978. pap. 7.25 (ISBN 0-687-04669-6). Abingdon.

--The Challenge of Single Adult Ministry. 112p. 1982. pap. 5.95 (ISBN 0-8170-0939-6). Judson.

--Computer Ethics: A Guide for the New Age. 128p. (Orig.). 1984. pap. 6.95 (ISBN 0-87178-155-7). Brethren.

--Growing up Christian in the Twenty-First Century. 128p. 1984. pap. 4.95 (ISBN 0-8170-1048-3). Judson.

--Let's Be Realistic about Your Church Budget. 112p. 1984. pap. 3.95 (ISBN 0-8170-1025-4). Judson.

--Ministry with Young Couples: A Pastor's Planbook. 128p. (Orig.). 1985. pap. 6.95 (ISBN 0-687-27043-X). Abingdon.

--The Tithe: Challenge or Legalism. 128p. 1984. pap. 5.95 (ISBN 0-687-42127-6). Abingdon.

Johnson, Douglas W., et al. Churches & Church Membership in the United States, 1971. LC 73-94224. 256p. 1974. pap. 15.00x (ISBN 0-914422-01-4). Glenmary Res Ctr.

Johnson, E. H., ed. & tr. see Asvaghosa.

Johnson, Edwin C. In Search of God in the Sexual Underworld: A Mystical Journey. LC 83-943. 224p. 1983. 13.95 (ISBN 0-688-01478-X). Morrow.

--The Myth of the Great Secret: A Search for Spiritual Meaning in the Face of Emptiness. 1982. 10.50 (ISBN 0-688-00781-3). Morrow.

Johnson, Elliot. The Point After: Advice from God's Athletes. 128p. 1987. pap. 5.95 (ISBN 0-310-26171-6, 12416P). Zondervan.

Johnson, Elsie. Man Who Freed Slaves: Wilberforce. (Stories of Faith, Fame Ser.). (YA) 1975. pap. 2.95 (ISBN 0-87508-615-2). Chr Lit.

Johnson, Emily C. Dean Bond of Swarthmore, a Quaker Humanist. 25.00 (ISBN 0-932062-92-X). Sharon Hill.

Johnson, Emmett V. Work of the Pastoral Relations Committee. 128p. 1983. pap. 4.95 (ISBN 0-8170-0984-1). Judson.

Johnson, Eric W. An Introduction to Jesus of Nazareth. (Illus.). 512p. (Orig.). 1981. pap. 11.95x (ISBN 0-88334-146-8). Ind Sch Pr.

Johnson, Eugene J. S. Andrea in Mantua: The Building. LC 74-30085. (Illus.). 220p. 1975. 42.50x (ISBN 0-271-01186-6). Pa St U Pr.

Johnson, Euteline. Young People's Medicine. 32p. 1986. 5.95 (ISBN 0-89962-522-3). Todd & Honeywell.

Johnson, F. Ernest, ed. American Education & Religion. LC 68-26192. (Essay & General Literature Index Reprint Ser). 1969. Repr. of 1952 ed. 21.50x (ISBN 0-8046-0220-4, Pub. by Kennikat). Assoc Faculty Pr.

--Religion & the World Order. LC 68-26189. (Essay & General Literature Index Reprint Ser). 1969. Repr. of 1944 ed. 22.50x (ISBN 0-8046-0221-2, Pub. by Kennikat). Assoc Faculty Pr.

Johnson, F. Roy. North Carolina Indian Legends & Myths. (Illus.). 112p. 1981. 8.50 (ISBN 0-930230-43-4). Johnson NC.

--Witches & Demons in History & Folklore. (Illus.). 1978. Repr. 9.50 (ISBN 0-930230-31-0). Johnson NC.

Johnson, Francis, jt. auth. see Ainsworth, Henry.

Johnson, Gary. Catholic Church Story: Leader's Guide. 1978. tchr's ed 2.95 (ISBN 0-89243-092-3). Liguori Pubns.

--The Illustrated Catechism: Leader's Guide. (Illus.). 96p. 1981. pap. 4.95 (ISBN 0-89243-150-4). Liguori Pubns.

Johnson, Gary L. Come Songbook. 1980. pap. 2.50 (ISBN 0-87123-777-6, 280777). Bethany Hse.

--Reminded of His Goodness Songbook. 32p. 1981. pap. 2.50 (ISBN 0-87123-779-2, 280779). Bethany Hse.

--Son Songs for Christian Folk, 2 vols. Incl. Vol. I. pap. 1.25 (ISBN 0-87123-509-9, 280509); Vol. II. pap. 1.50 (ISBN 0-87123-532-3, 280532). 1975. pap. Bethany Hse.

--Thanks Songbook. 32p. 1980. pap. 2.50 (ISBN 0-87123-776-8, 280776). Bethany Hse.

Johnson, George. Christmas Ornaments, Lights & Decorations. (Illus.). 320p. 1986. 19.95 (ISBN 0-317-52660-X). Collector Bks.

Johnson, George, et al. The Story of the Church. LC 80-51329. 521p. 1980. pap. 12.50 (ISBN 0-89555-156-X). Tan Bks Pubs.

Johnson, Gordon G. & Putman, Bob. Our Church. LC 83-82990. (Foundation Ser.). (Illus.). 147p. (Orig.). 1984. pap. 2.95 (ISBN 0-935797-06-8). Harvest IL.

Johnson, Gustaf F. Hearts Aflame. 1970. 4.50 (ISBN 0-910452-06-7). Covenant.

Johnson, Guye. Treasury of Great Hymns: And Their Stories. 382p. (Orig.). 1986. pap. 9.95 (ISBN 0-89084-249-3). Bob Jones Univ Pr.

Johnson, H. Eugene. The Christian Church Plea. LC 75-12012. (New Life Bks). 96p. 1975. pap. 2.95 (ISBN 0-87239-053-5, 40028). Standard Pub.

Johnson, Harold J. The Medieval Tradition of Natural Law. LC 86-31126. (Studies in Medieval Culture: No. 22). Date not set. price not set (ISBN 0-918720-81-8). Medieval Inst.

Johnson, Harry. Humanity of the Saviour. 1962. 8.50x (ISBN 0-8401-1248-3). A R Allenson.

Johnson, Harry M., ed. Religious Change & Continuity: Sociological Perspectives. LC 79-83574. (Jossey-Bass Social & Behavioral Science Ser.). pap. 94.80 (2027756). Bks Demand UMI.

Johnson, Henry C., Jr. The Public School & Moral Education. LC 80-20768. (The Education of the Public & the Public School Ser.). 96p. (Orig.). 1981. pap. 5.95 (ISBN 0-8298-0420-X). Pilgrim NY.

Johnson, Hubert R. Who Then Is Paul? Chevy Chase Manuscripts Staff, ed. LC 80-1406. 272p. 1981. lib. bdg. 28.25 (ISBN 0-8191-1364-6); pap. text ed. 10.00 (ISBN 0-8191-1365-4). U Pr of Amer.

Johnson, Irene. Prophecy Foretold-Fulfilled: Puzzle Book. (Illus.). 48p. 1983. pap. 2.50 (ISBN 0-87239-590-1, 2788). Standard Pub.

Johnson, Irene L. The Apostle Peter & His Writing. 48p. (Orig.). 1983. pap. 2.50 (ISBN 0-87239-672-X, 2772). Standard Pub.

Johnson, J. R., jt. ed. see Johnson, James Weldon.

Johnson, James T., ed. The Bible & American Law, Politics, & Political Rhetoric. LC 83-16327. (Bible in American Culture Ser.: No. 4). 216p. 1985. 14.95 (ISBN 0-8006-0614-0, 1-614). Fortress.

--The Bible in American Law, Politics, & Political Rhetoric. LC 83-16327. (The Bible in American Culture Ser.). 1984. pap. 15.95 (ISBN 0-89130-652-8, 06 12 04). Scholars Pr GA.

Johnson, James Weldon. God's Trombones. (Poets Ser). 1976. pap. 4.95 (ISBN 0-14-042217-X). Penguin.

Johnson, James Weldon & Johnson, J. R., eds. The Books of American Negro Spirituals, 2 vols. in one. LC 77-23414. 1977. Repr. of 1926 ed. text ed. 11.95 (ISBN 0-306-80074-8). Da Capo.

Johnson, Jan. Mary Bethune & Her Somedays. (Stories About Christian Heroes Ser.). (Illus.). 1979. pap. 1.95 (ISBN 0-03-049421-4, HarpR). Har-Row.

Johnson, Joe, compiled by. A Field of Diamonds. LC 73-87067. 12.95 (ISBN 0-8054-5133-1). Broadman.

Johnson, John. Collection of the Laws & Canons of the Church of England: Theological Works, 4 Vols. LC 72-1032. (Library of Anglo-Catholic Theology: No. 10). Repr. of 1851 ed. Set. 115.00 (ISBN 0-404-52110-X). AMS Pr.

Johnson, John R. Liturgy for the Free Church. LC 86-18782. 176p. 1986. lib. bdg. 19.95x (ISBN 0-89370-527-6). Borgo Pr.

Johnson, John S. The Rosary in Action. 1977. pap. 5.00 (ISBN 0-89555-023-7). TAN Bks Pubs.

Johnson, Joseph A., Jr. The Soul of the Black Preacher. LC 70-162411. 176p. 1971. 4.95 (ISBN 0-8298-0193-6). Pilgrim NY.

Johnson, Karen, ed. see Hynes, Kathleen.

Johnson, Keith. Life's Priorities. LC 79-63739. 1979. pap. 3.95 (ISBN 0-89841-000-2). Zoe Pubns.

Johnson, Kenneth M. Church Ushers: Embodiment of the Gospel. LC 81-21022. 64p. (Orig.). 1982. pap. 3.95 (ISBN 0-8298-0493-5). Pilgrim NY.

Johnson, Kent L. Called to Teach: Ideas & Encouragement for Teachers in the Church. LC 83-72127. 128p. (Orig.). 1984. pap. 5.95 (ISBN 0-8066-2071-4, 10-0964). Augsburg.

--Paul the Teacher: A Resource for Teachers in the Church. LC 86-17384. 128p. (Orig.). 1986. pap. 6.95 (ISBN 0-8066-2226-1, 10-4905). Augsburg.

Johnson, L. C. Chapel Messages. 1982. pap. 5.95 (ISBN 0-89265-081-8). Randall Hse.

Johnson, L. D. Images of Eternity. LC 84-4987. 1984. pap. 3.75 (ISBN 0-8054-5342-3). Broadman.

--Layman's Bible Book Commentary: Proverbs, Ecclesiastes, Song of Solomon, Vol. 9. LC 80-66543. 1982. 5.95 (ISBN 0-8054-1179-8). Broadman.

--The Morning after Death. LC 77-99255. 1978. 7.50 (ISBN 0-8054-2412-1). Broadman.

Johnson, L. T. The Serving Church. 2nd ed. LC 83-80609. (Enabling Ser.). (Illus.). 104p. (Orig.). 1984. pap. 5.95 (ISBN 0-935797-01-7). Harvest IL.

Johnson, L. T. & Buchanan, Edward A. The Teaching Church. 2nd ed. (Enabling Ser.). (Illus.). 95p. (Orig.). 1984. pap. 5.95 (ISBN 0-935797-00-9). Harvest IL.

Johnson, Lawrence. The Word & Eucharist Handbook. LC 86-60896. 150p. (Orig.). 1985. pap. text ed. 9.95 (ISBN 0-89390-067-2). Resource Pubns.

Johnson, Lawrence, ed. Called to Prayer: Liturgical Spirituality Today. 96p. 1986. pap. 4.95 (ISBN 0-8146-1488-4). Liturgical Pr.

--The Church Gives Thanks & Remembers. 88p. 1984. pap. 4.95 (ISBN 0-8146-1355-1). Liturgical Pr.

Johnson, Lawrence, ed. see Duffy, Regis, et al.

Johnson, Lawrence J. The Mystery of Faith: The Ministers of Music. 128p. (Orig.). 1983. pap. 5.95 (ISBN 0-9602378-9-5). Pastoral Pr.

Johnson, Lin. The Growing Season. 96p. 1987. pap. 4.95 (ISBN 0-89693-009-2). Victor Bks.

Johnson, Lissa H. Something to Live For. 1986. 5.95 (ISBN 0-8007-5228-7). Revell.

Johnson, Lois. Just a Minute, Lord: Prayers for Girls. LC 73-78265. (Illus.). 96p. (Orig.). 1973. pap. 3.95 (ISBN 0-8066-1329-7, 10-3605). Augsburg.

Johnson, Lois W. Come as You Are. LC 82-70951. 112p. (Orig.). 1982. pap. 3.95 (ISBN 0-8066-1926-0, 10-1517). Augsburg.

--Either Way, I Win: A Guide for Growth in the Power of Prayer. LC 79-50078. 1979. pap. 4.95 (ISBN 0-8066-1706-3, 10-2040). Augsburg.

--Falling Apart or Coming Together: How You Can Experience the Faithfulness of God. LC 83-72112. 128p. (Orig.). 1984. pap. 5.95 (ISBN 0-8066-2056-0, 10-2208). Augsburg.

--Gift in My Arms: Thoughts for New Mothers. LC 77-72448. 1977. pap. 5.95 (ISBN 0-8066-1586-9, 10-2549). Augsburg.

--Songs for Silent Moments: Prayers for Daily Living. LC 79-54115. 128p. (Orig.). 1980. pap. 4.95 (ISBN 0-8066-1765-9, 10-5851). Augsburg.

--You're My Best Friend, Lord. LC 76-3866. 96p. (Orig.). 1976. pap. 3.95 (ISBN 0-8066-1541-9, 10-7490). Augsburg.

Johnson, Luke T. Decision Making in the Church: A Biblical Model. LC 82-17675. 112p. 1983. pap. 6.95 (ISBN 0-8006-1694-4). Fortress.

--First & Second Timothy, Titus. Hayes, John H., ed. LC 86-45403. (Preaching Guides). 132p. (Orig.). 1987. pap. 7.95 (ISBN 0-8042-3242-3). John Knox.

--The Literary Function of Possession in Luke-Acts. LC 77-21055. (Society of Biblical Literature. Dissertation Ser.: No. 39). 1985. pap. 11.25 (ISBN 0-89130-200-X, 060139). Scholars Pr GA.

--Luke Acts: A Story of Prophet & People. LC 81-4520. 65p. 1.75 (ISBN 0-8199-0524-0). Franciscan Herald.

--Sharing Possessions: Mandate & Symbol of Faith. Brueggemann, Walter & Donahue, John R., eds. LC 80-2390. (Overtures to Biblical Theology Ser.: No. 9). 176p. (Orig.). 1981. pap. 8.95 (ISBN 0-8006-1534-4, 1-1534). Fortress.

--Some Hard Blessings: Meditations on the Beatitudes in Matthew. LC 81-69108. 96p. 1981. pap. 3.95 (ISBN 0-89505-058-7, 21053). Argus Comm.

--The Writings of the New Testament: An Interpretation. LC 85-16202. 640p. 1986. 34.95 (ISBN 0-8006-0886-0, 1-886); pap. 18.95 (ISBN 0-8006-1886-6, 1-1886). Fortress.

Johnson, Martin C. The Churchyard Carvers' Art. 104p. 1986. 30.00x (ISBN 0-947939-00-8, Pub. by Elmcrest UK). State Mutual Bk.

Johnson, Marvin L. Signs of the Times. 1983. 6.95 (ISBN 0-8062-2021-X). Carlton.

Johnson, Mary H. Where Our Lives Touch. 35p. (Orig.). 1985. pap. 3.00 (ISBN 0-914631-00-4). Questpr.

Johnson, Maxwell E. Beginnings: Preparing for Your Child's Baptism. (Pass Along Ser.). 32p. (Orig.). 1986. pap. 2.95 (ISBN 0-933350-47-3). Morse Pr.

Johnson, Mayme H. A Treasury of Tennessee Churches. (Illus.). 160p. 1986. 29.95 (ISBN 0-939298-60-0, 600). J M Prods.

Johnson, Merle A. Sermons for Christians Seasons. LC 75-44210. Repr. of 1976 ed. 21.10 (ISBN 0-8357-9026-6, 2016406). Bks Demand UMI.

Johnson, Michael J. Prometheus Reborn. LC 76-52144. 1977. 7.95 (ISBN 0-87212-073-2). Libra.

Johnson, Nels. Islam & the Politics of Meaning in Palestinian Nationalism. 111p. 1983. 21.95x (ISBN 0-7103-0021-2). Methuen Inc.

Johnson, Pamela F., illus. The Miracle of the Loaves & Fishes. (Golden Bible Stories Ser.). (Illus.). 32p. 1986. 3.95 (ISBN 0-307-11622-0, Pub. by Golden Bks). Western Pub.

Johnson, Paul. A History of Christianity. LC 76-9002. 560p. 1976. pap. 11.95 (ISBN 0-689-70591-3, 252). Atheneum.

--A History of the Jews. LC 85-42575. 480p. 1987. 24.50i (ISBN 0-06-015698-8, HarpT). Har-Row.

--Pope John Paul II & the Catholic Restoration. 224p. 1982. 11.95 (ISBN 0-312-63032-8). St Martin.

Johnson, Paul, et al. Unsecular America. Neuhaus, Richard J., ed. (The Encounter Ser.). 176p. (Orig.). 1986. pap. 8.95 (ISBN 0-8028-0202-8). Eerdmans.

Johnson, Paul G. Grace: God's Work Ethic. 144p. 1985. pap. 6.95 (ISBN 0-8170-1070-X). Judson.

Johnson, Paul R. Gays & Fundamentalism. (Illus.). 56p. (Orig.). 1983. pap. 2.95 (ISBN 0-910097-02-X). Paul R Johnson.

--Gays & the Bible. (Illus.). 52p. (Orig.). 1983. pap. 2.95 (ISBN 0-910097-00-3). Paul R Johnson.

--Gays & the Church. (Illus.). 48p. (Orig.). 1983. pap. 2.95 (ISBN 0-910097-04-6). Paul R Johnson.

Johnson, Penelope. Prayer, Patronage, & Power: The Abbey of la Trinite, Vendome, 1032-1187. (Illus.). 224p. 1981. 30.00x (ISBN 0-8147-4162-2). NYU Pr.

Johnson, Philip E. And More Celebrating the Seasons with Children. 120p. (Orig.). 1986. pap. 6.95 (ISBN 0-8298-0735-7). Pilgrim NY.

--Celebrating the Seasons with Children. 112p. (Orig.). 1984. pap. 6.95 (ISBN 0-8298-0723-3). Pilgrim NY.

--More Celebrating the Seasons with Children. 112p. 1985. pap. 7.95 (ISBN 0-8298-0731-4). Pilgrim NY.

Johnson, Phillip, jt. auth. see Hunter, Victor L.

Johnson, Phyllis & Cazelles, Brigitte. Le Vain Siecle Guerpir: A Literary Approach to Sainthood through Old French Hagiography of the Twelfth Century. (Studies in the Romance Languages & Literatures: No.205). 320p. 1979. pap. 19.50x (ISBN 0-8078-9205-X). U of NC Pr.

Johnson, R., et al. Critical Issues in Modern Religion. 1973. pap. write for info. (ISBN 0-13-193979-3). P-H.

Johnson, R. K. Builder of Bridges: The Biography of Dr. Bob Jones, Sr. (Illus.). 383p. 1982. pap. 5.95 (ISBN 0-89084-157-8). Bob Jones Univ Pr.

--Fortress of Faith. 3rd ed. (Illus.). 456p. 1984. pap. 7.95 (ISBN 0-89084-252-3). Bob Jones Univ Pr.

Johnson, Rex. Communication: Key to Your Parents. LC 78-61874. 1978. pap. 3.95 (ISBN 0-89081-157-1). Harvest Hse.

Johnson, Rex, jt. auth. see Wright, H. Norman.

Johnson, Rex, jt. auth. see Wright, Norman.

Johnson, Robert C. The Meaning of Christ. LC 58-6120. (Layman's Theological Library). 96p. 1958. pap. 3.45 (ISBN 0-664-24009-7). Westminster.

Johnson, Roger A., ed. Views from the Pews: Christian Beliefs & Attitudes. LC 82-18237. 272p. 1983. pap. 15.95 (ISBN 0-8006-1695-2, 1-1695). Fortress.

Johnson, Roger A., et al. Psychohistory & Religion: The Case of Young Man Luther. LC 76-7870. pap. 51.50 (2026895). Bks Demand UMI.

Johnson, Ronald C., et al, eds. Conscience, Contract, & Social Reality: Theory & Research in Behavioral Science. LC 77-166108. 1972. 39.50x (ISBN 0-8290-0382-7); pap. text ed. 19.95x (ISBN 0-8290-0381-9). Irvington.

Johnson, Rose & Ratzlaff, Don. As Angels of Light. LC 80-82926. (Illus.). 160p. (Orig.). 1980. pap. 4.95 (ISBN 0-937364-00-2). Kindred Pr.

Johnson, Rubellite K. Kumulipo: The Hawaiian Hymn of Creation. Holt, John D., ed. (Illus.). 1981. text ed. 19.95 (ISBN 0-914916-53-X); leather 100.00 (ISBN 0-914916-59-9). Topgallant.

Johnson, Ruby E. From the Heart of a Mother. LC 82-8218. 1982. pap. 3.95 (ISBN 0-8024-5090-3). Moody.

Johnson, Ruth I. Devotions for Early Teens, 4 vols. 1960-74. Vol. 1. pap. 2.95 (ISBN 0-8024-2181-4); Vol. 3. pap. 2.95 (ISBN 0-8024-2183-0). Moody.

Johnson, S. Lawrence. The Cross-Eyed Bear & Other Children's Sermons. LC 79-24765. (Orig.). 1980. pap. 6.50 (ISBN 0-687-09980-3). Abingdon.

Johnson, S. Lewis. The Old Testament in the New: An Argument for Biblical Inspiration. (Contemporary Evangelical Perspectives Ser.). 128p. (Orig.). 1980. pap. 4.95 (ISBN 0-310-41851-8, 18244P). Zondervan.

Johnson, Samuel. Doctor Johnson's Prayers. LC 76-25954. 1976. Repr. of 1947 ed. lib. bdg. 17.50 (ISBN 0-8414-8580-1). Folcroft.

--Dr. Johnson's Prayers. Trueblood, Elton, ed. 88p. 1980. pap. 2.50 (ISBN 0-932970-17-6). Prinit Pr.

--Johnson: Selected Writings. Cruttwell, Patrick, ed. 1982. pap. 6.95 (ISBN 0-14-043033-4). Penguin.

--Oriental Religions & Their Relation to Universal Religion. 999p. Repr. of 1877 ed. text ed. 42.50x (ISBN 0-89644-558-5, Pub. by Chineses Matl Ctr). Coronet Bks.

--Sermons: The Yale Edition of the Works of Samuel Johnson, Vol. 14. Hagstrum, Jean H. & Gray, James, eds. LC 57-918. (Illus.). 1978. 42.00x (ISBN 0-300-02104-6). Yale U Pr.

Johnson, Samuel, jt. auth. see Browne, T.

Johnson, Sarah B. Hadji in Syria: Three Years in Jerusalem. Davis, Moshe, ed. LC 77-70708. (America & the Holy Land Ser.). (Illus.). 1977. Repr. of 1858 ed. lib. bdg. 26.50x (ISBN 0-405-10258-5). Ayer Co Pubs.

Johnson, Sherman E. The Year of the Lord's Favor: Preaching the Three-Year Lectionary. 300p. 1983. pap. 13.95 (ISBN 0-8164-2359-8, HarpR). Har-Row.

Johnson, Spencer. The Value of Dedication: The Story of Albert Schweitzer. LC 79-21805. (Value Tales Ser.). (Illus.). 1979. 7.95 (ISBN 0-916392-44-9, Dist. by Oak Tree Pubns.). Value Comm.

--The Value of Honesty: The Story of Confucius. LC 78-4351. (ValueTales Ser.). (Illus.). 1979. 7.95 (ISBN 0-916392-36-8, Dist. by Oak Tree Pubns). Value Comm.

Johnson, Sylvia A. Mosses. LC 83-17488. (Lerner Natural Science Bks.). (Illus.). 48p. 1983. PLB 12.95 (ISBN 0-8225-1482-6). Lerner Pubns.

Johnson, T. H., jt. auth. see Miller, Perry.

Johnson, Bro. Theodore E. Hands to Work & Hearts to God. 2nd ed. LC 72-78927. 64p. (Orig.). 1983. pap. 4.95 (ISBN 0-915836-08-4). Shaker Pr ME.

Johnson, Bro. Theodore E., frwd. by. A Concise Statement of the Principles of the Only True Church According to the Gospel of the Present Appearance of Christ...with a Letter from James Whittaker. facsimile ed. (Mother's Work Ser.: No. 2). 14p. 1963. pap. 1.75 (ISBN 0-915836-07-6). Shaker Pr ME.

Johnson, Thomas C. The Life of Robert Lewis Dabney. 1977. 16.95 (ISBN 0-85151-253-4). Banner of Truth.

Johnson, Thomas H. Printed Writings of Jonathan Edwards 1703-1758: A Bibliography. 1970. Repr. of 1940 ed. text ed. 21.50 (ISBN 0-8337-1854-1). B Franklin.

Johnson, Thomas H., jt. auth. see Faust, Clarence H.

Johnson, Thomas H., jt. ed. see Miller, Perry.

Johnson, Tom. Your Healing Is Today. 5th ed. 64p. 1986. pap. 4.95 (ISBN 0-941992-07-1). Los Arboles Pub.

Johnson, Una, et al. Krishna Reddy: A Retrospective. (Illus.). 78p. (Orig.). 1981. pap. 10.00 (ISBN 0-89062-138-1, Pub by Bronx Museum Arts). Pub Ctr Cult Res.

Johnson, Vera & Wommack, Thomas. The Secrets of Numbers. large type ed. LC 81-70270. 272p. 1982. pap. 12.50 (ISBN 0-87728-541-1). Weiser.

Johnson, W. B. see Calvin, John.

Johnson, Wallace R. A History of Christianity in Belize 1776-1838. (Illus.). 300p. (Orig.). 1985. lib. bdg. 26.00 (ISBN 0-8191-4552-1); pap. text ed. 13.50 (ISBN 0-8191-4553-X). U Pr of Amer.

Johnson, Walton J. Worship & Freedom: A Black American Church in Zambia. LC 77-22388. 190p. 1978. text ed. 34.50x (ISBN 0-8419-0315-8, Africana). Holmes & Meier.

Johnson, Wayne G. Theological Method in Luther & Tillich: Law-Gospel & Correlation. LC 80-5691. 204p. 1982. lib. bdg. 27.50 (ISBN 0-8191-1895-8); pap. text ed. 12.50 (ISBN 0-8191-1896-6). U Pr of Amer.

Johnson, Willard. Riding the Ox Home: A History of Meditation from Shamanism to Science. LC 86-47752. (Illus.). 262p. 1987. pap. 8.95 (ISBN 0-8070-1305-6, BP-735). Beacon Pr.

Johnson, Willard, Jr. Poetry & Speculation of the Rg Veda. LC 80-14040. (Hermaneutics: Studies in the History of Religions). 175p. 1980. 25.95x (ISBN 0-520-02560-1). U of Cal Pr.

Johnson, Willard L., jt. auth. see Robinson, Richard H.

Johnson, William A. Africa's Mountain Valley; or, the Church in Regent's Town, West Africa. LC 72-3995. (Black Heritage Library Collection Ser.). Repr. of 1856 ed. 18.75 (ISBN 0-8369-9098-6). Ayer Co Pubs.

Johnson, William J. Abraham Lincoln the Christian. (Great American Christian Ser.). (Illus.). 1976. pap. 3.95 (ISBN 0-915134-13-6). Mott Media.

Johnson, William R. The Pastor & the Personal Computer: Information Management for Ministers. 224p. (Orig.). 1985. pap. 10.50 (ISBN 0-687-30134-3). Abingdon.

--Selecting the Church Computer. 160p. (Orig.). 1984. pap. 8.95 (ISBN 0-687-37135-X). Abingdon.

Johnson, Wingate M. The Years after Fifty. 14.00 (ISBN 0-405-18502-2). Ayer Co Pubs.

Johnsson, Noelene. Today with My Father. Wheeler, Gerald, ed. (Illus.). 384p. 1984. 7.95 (ISBN 0-8280-0240-1). Review & Herald.

Johnsson, William. Religion in Overalls. LC 77-22464. (Anvil Ser.). 1977. pap. 8.95 (ISBN 0-8127-0143-7). Review & Herald.

Johnsson, William G. Blessed Assurance. Coffen, Richard W., ed. 144p. (Orig.). 1985. pap. 5.95 (ISBN 0-8280-0313-0). Review & Herald.

--Clean: The Meaning of Christian Baptism. LC 80-15681. (Horizon Ser.). 96p. 1980. pap. 5.95 (ISBN 0-8127-0293-X). Review & Herald.

--Hebrews. LC 79-92068. (Knox Preaching Guides Ser.). 98p. (Orig., John Hayes series editor). 1980. pap. 4.95. John Knox.

--In Absolute Confidence. LC 79-1387. (Anvil Ser.). 1979. pap. 8.95 (ISBN 0-8127-0225-5). Review & Herald.

--Why I'm a Seventh-Day Adventist. Coffen, Richard W., ed. (Better Living Ser.). 32p. (Orig.). 1986. pap. 1.25 (ISBN 0-8280-0352-1). Review & Herald.

Johnston, A. J. Religion in Life at Louisbourg, 1713-1758. 288p. 1984. 30.00x (ISBN 0-7735-0427-3). McGill-Queens U pr.

Johnston, Charles & Giles, Lionel, trs. Selections from the Upanishads & The Tao Te King. 142p. 1951. Repr. of 1897 ed. 3.00 (ISBN 0-938998-15-3). Cunningham Pr.

--Selections from the Upanishads & the Tao Te King. 142p. 1951. 3.00 (ISBN 0-938998-15-3). Theosophy.

Johnston, Charles, tr. see Patanjali.

Johnston, Dorothy G. & Abbas, Kathleen. Church Time for Children. LC 80-67855. 120p. (Orig.). 1981. 10.95 (ISBN 0-89636-056-3). Accent Bks.

Johnston, E. H. Early Samkhya. 1974. Repr. 5.95 (ISBN 0-8426-0684-X). Orient Bk Dist.

Johnston, E. R. Buddhacarita: Acts of Buddha. 1978. Repr. 26.00 (ISBN 0-8426-0474-X). Orient Bk Dist.

Johnston, Francis. Fatima: The Great Sign. 152p. 1980. 4.95 (ISBN 0-911988-37-8). AMI Pr.

--Fatima: The Great Sign. LC 80-54423. 1980. Repr. of 1979 ed. 5.00 (ISBN 0-89555-163-2). Tan Bks Pubs.

--The Wonder of Guadalupe. LC 81-53041. 143p. 1981. pap. 4.50 (ISBN 0-89555-168-3). TAN Bks Pubs.

Johnston, Geoffrey. Of God & Maxim Guns: Presbyterianism in Nigeria, 1846-1966, Vol. 8. 270p. 1987. pap. 17.50 (ISBN 0-88920-180-3, Pub. by Wilfrid Laurier Canada). Humanities.

Johnston, George A. Development of Berkeley's Philosophy. LC 65-17903. 1965. Repr. of 1923 ed. 10.00x (ISBN 0-8462-0686-2). Russell.

Johnston, James. Missionary Landscapes in the Dark Continent. LC 72-3911. (Black Heritage Library Collection Ser.). Repr. of 1892 ed. 16.00 (ISBN 0-8369-9100-1). Ayer Co Pubs.

Johnston, Jon. Christian Excellence. 1985. 9.95 (ISBN 0-8010-5215-7); pap. 6.95 (ISBN 0-8010-5195-9). Baker Bk.

Johnston, Jon & Sullivan, Bill M., eds. The Smaller Church in a Super Church Era. 152p. 1983. pap. 5.95 (ISBN 0-8341-0895-X). Beacon Hill.

Johnston, Leonard & Smith, Michael. Psalms & Wisdom. Bright, Laurence, ed. LC 71-173033. (Scripture Discussion Commentary Ser.: Pt. 6). 256p. 1972. pap. text ed. 4.50. ACTA Found.

Johnston, Lyle. The Dubuque District - A History: The United Methodist Church. (Illus.). 128p. (Orig.). 1979. pap. 2.95 (ISBN 0-9616365-1-3). Grt Plains Emporium.

--The Mason City District - A History: The United Methodist Church. (Illus.). 109p. (Orig.). 1984. pap. 6.50 (ISBN 0-9616365-2-1). Grt Plains Emporium.

--The Ottumwa District - A History: The United Methodist Church. (Illus.). 118p. (Orig.). 1986. pap. 6.50 (ISBN 0-9616365-3-X). Grt Plains Emporium.

--The Sioux City District - A History: The United Methodist Church. (Illus.). 90p. (Orig.). 1978. pap. 1.95 (ISBN 0-9616365-0-5). Grt Plains Emporium.

Johnston, Maury. Gays Under Grace: A Gay Christian's Response to the Moral Majority. LC 82-51217. 250p. 1983. 15.95 (ISBN 0-938232-20-7). Winston-Derek.

Johnston, O. R. Who Needs the Family? LC 80-7780. 152p. (Orig.). 1980. pap. 5.95 (ISBN 0-87784-588-3). Inter-Varsity.

Johnston, O. R., tr. see Luther, Martin.

Johnston, Patricia C. The Minnesota Christmas Book. LC 85-90344. (Illus.). 96p. 1985. text ed. 27.50 (ISBN 0-942934-08-3). Johnston Pub.

Johnston, Reginald F. Confucianism & Modern China. LC 79-2830. (Illus.). 272p. 1986. Repr. of 1934 ed. 24.50 (ISBN 0-8305-0007-3). Hyperion Conn.

Johnston, Robert. Psalms for God's People. LC 82-5344. (Bible Commentary for Laymen Ser.). 160p. 1982. pap. 3.50 (ISBN 0-8307-0820-0, S362105). Regal.

Johnston, Robert G. The Scriptures: Sacred Fact or Pious Fiction? 1970. pap. 2.25 (ISBN 0-8100-0024-5, 12-0337). Northwest Pub.

Johnston, Robert K. The Christian at Play. LC 83-16552. Repr. of 1983 ed. 43.50 (2027548). Bks Demand UMI.

--Evangelicals at an Impasse: Biblical Authority in Practice. pap. 3.99 (ISBN 0-8042-2038-7). John Knox.

Johnston, Robert K., ed. The Use of the Bible in Theology. LC 84-48513. 1985. pap. 11.95 (ISBN 0-8042-0530-2). John Knox.

Johnston, Russ & Rank, Maureen. Dynamic Praying for Exciting Results. 1982. pap. 3.95 (ISBN 0-8423-0611-0); pap. 2.95 leader's guide (ISBN 0-8423-0612-9). Tyndale.

Johnston, William. Christian Mysticism Today. LC 83-48418. 192p. 1984. 12.45i (ISBN 0-06-064202-5, HarpR). Har-Row.

--Christian Zen: A Way of Meditation. 2nd ed. LC 80-8430. (Illus.). 144p. 1981. pap. 6.95 (ISBN 0-06-064198-3, RD 343, HarpR). Har-Row.

--The Inner Eye of Love: Mysticism & Religion. LC 78-4428. 1978. pap. 6.95 (ISBN 0-06-064195-9, RD-349, HarpR). Har-Row.

--The Mirror Mind: Spirituality & Transformation. LC 80-8350. 192p. 1981. 10.45 (ISBN 0-06-064197-5, HarpR). Har-Row.

--The Mirror Mind: Spirituality & Transformation. LC 80-8350. 192p. 1984. pap. 6.95 (ISBN 0-06-064206-8, RD 516, HarpR). Har-Row.

--The Mysticism of the Cloud of Unknowing: A Modern Interpretation. LC 74-30738. (Religious Experience Ser.: Vol. 8). pap. 74.30 (2052172). Bks Demand UMI.

--Silent Music: The Science of Meditation. LC 73-18688. 1979. pap. 7.95 (ISBN 0-06-064196-7, RD 293, HarpR). Har-Row.

--Still Point: Reflections on Zen & Christian Mysticism. LC 75-95713. 1986. pap. 9.00 (ISBN 0-8232-0861-3). Fordham.

Johnston, William, ed. The Cloud of Unknowing & the Book of Privy Counselling. LC 73-79737. 200p. 1973. pap. 3.50 (ISBN 0-385-03097-5, Im). Doubleday.

Johnstone, Hilda. Oliver Cromwell & His Times. 92p. 1981. Repr. lib. bdg. 20.00 (ISBN 0-89987-430-4). Darby Bks.

Johnstone, Parker L. A Book for Unitarians. LC 76-21519. 1977. cloth 7.95 (ISBN 0-917802-02-0). Theoscience Found.

--Is God a Separate Being? LC 76-706635. 1977. cloth 7.95 (ISBN 0-917802-01-2). Theoscience Found.

--Life, Death & Hereafter. LC 76-21518. 1976. cloth 7.95 (ISBN 0-917802-00-4). Theoscience Found.

--Origin of the Universe, Life, Then Religion. 235p. 7.95 (ISBN 0-917802-20-9). Theoscience Found.

--Pantheism Is Heresy. 208p. 1982. cloth 7.95 (ISBN 0-917802-05-5). Theoscience Found.

--Quandary of Life, Science & Religion. LC 82-83297. 212p. 1982. cloth 7.95 (ISBN 0-917802-04-7). Theoscience Found.

--A Religious Science Book. 212p. 1984. 7.95 (ISBN 0-917802-13-6). Theoscience Found.

--Russia's New Religion. 208p. 1984. 7.95 (ISBN 0-917802-11-X). Theoscience Found.

--Who, or What, Is God? 212p. 1984. 7.95 (ISBN 0-917802-12-8). Theoscience Found.

Johnstone, Patrick. Operation World: A Day-to-Day Guide to Praying for the World. 4th ed. 502p. Date not set. pap. 5.95 (ISBN 0-87808-211-5). William Carey Lib.

Johnstone, Robert. James. (Geneva Commentaries Ser.). 1977. 15.95 (ISBN 0-85151-257-7). Banner of Truth.

--Lectures on the Epistle of James. 1977. 16.50 (ISBN 0-86524-111-2, 5901). Klock & Klock.

Johnstone, Robert, ed. Samuel Butler on the Resurrection. 64p. Date not set. 9.95 (ISBN 0-901072-59-1). Dufour.

Johnstone, Ronald L. Religion in Society: A Sociology of Religion. 2nd ed. (Illus.). 320p. 1983. text ed. write for info. (ISBN 0-13-773077-2). P-H.

Johnstone, W. A., tr. see Fohrer, Georg, et al.

Joiner, E. Earl. A Christian Considers Divorce & Remarriage. LC 81-70411. 1983. pap. 5.95 (ISBN 0-8054-5427-6). Broadman.

Joinville, jt. auth. see De Villehardouin, Geoffroi.

Joinville, Jean De see De Joinville, Jean.

Joinville, Jean De see De Villehardouin, Geoffrey & De Joinville, Jean.

Jolly, J. The Institutes of Vishnu. lib. bdg. 79.95 (ISBN 0-87968-528-X). Krishna Pr.

Jolly, Julius, ed. The Institutes of Vishnu. (Sacred Bks. of the East: Vol. 7). 15.00 (ISBN 0-89581-517-6). Asian Human Pr.

Jolly, Stephen, tr. see Langer, Jiri.

Joly, Edward Le. Mother Teresa: A Biography. LC 84-48238. (Illus.). 352p. 1985. 16.30 (ISBN 0-06-065217-9, HarpR). Har-Row.

Joly, Henri. Saint Ignatius of Loyola. LC 70-170821. Repr. of 1899 ed. 21.00 (ISBN 0-404-03597-3). AMS Pr.

Jonas, Hans. Gnostic Religion. 1958. pap. 10.95x (ISBN 0-8070-5799-1, BP259). Beacon Pr.

--Gnostic Religion: The Message of the Alien God & the Beginnings of Christianity. 2nd, rev. ed. 18.00 (ISBN 0-8446-2339-3). Peter Smith.

--The Imperative of Responsibility: In Search of an Ethics for the Technological Age. LC 83-18249. xii, 256p. 1985. lib. bdg. 25.00x (ISBN 0-226-40596-6); pap. 10.95 (ISBN 0-226-40597-4). U of Chicago Pr.

Jonassen, Christen T. Value Systems & Personality in a Western Civilization: Norwegians in Europe & America. LC 83-11391. 400p. 1984. 25.00x (ISBN 0-8142-0347-7). Ohio St U Pr.

Jones, Aaron I. Conquering the Night Season. LC 84-17515. 1985. pap. 4.95 (ISBN 0-8054-2255-2). Broadman.

Jones, Aaron Isaiah. God's Promises to Preachers. LC 81-67128. 1982. 5.50 (ISBN 0-8054-2240-4). Broadman.

Jones, Alan. Exploring Spiritual Direction. 160p. 1982. (HarpR); pap. 7.95 (ISBN 0-8164-2483-7). Har-Row.

--Soul Making: The Desert Way of Spirituality. LC 84-48222. 192p. 1985. 14.45 (ISBN 0-06-064182-7, HarpR). Har-Row.

Jones, Alan, jt. auth. see Hosmer, Rachel.

Jones, Alan H. Independence of Exegesis: The Study of Christianity in the Work of Alfred Loisy, Charles Guignebert. & Maurice Goguel. 313p. 1983. lib. bdg. 75.00x (ISBN 3-16-144451-5, Pub. by J C B Mohr BRD). Coronet Bks.

Jones, Alan W. Journey into Christ. 1977. pap. 6.95 (ISBN 0-8164-0338-4, HarpR). Har-Row.

Jones, Alex. Seven Mansions of Color. LC 82-73248. (Illus.). 152p. 1983. pap. 7.95 (ISBN 0-87516-500-1). De Vorss.

Jones, Alfred. Jones' Dictionary of Old Testament Proper Names: Keyed to Strong's Numbering System. rev. ed. Archer, Gleason L., Jr., ed. & frwd. by. LC 86-3001. 400p. 1988. Repr. of 1856 ed. 24.95 (ISBN 0-8254-2961-7). Kregel.

Jones, Allen H. Essenes: The Elect of Israel & the Priests of Artemis. (Illus.). 146p. (Orig.). 1985. lib. bdg. 23.50 (ISBN 0-8191-4744-3); pap. text ed. 9.50 (ISBN 0-8191-4745-1). U Pr of Amer.

Jones, Amos, Jr. Paul's Message of Freedom: What Does It Mean to the Black Church? 256p. 1984. 12.95 (ISBN 0-8170-0840-3). Judson.

Jones, Amos, Jr., ed. see Haney, William R.

Jones, Amos, Jr., ed. see James, Allix B.

Jones, Amos, Jr., ed. see Matthews, William R., Sr.

Jones, Amos, Jr., ed. see Oglesby, Enoch H.

Jones, Arthur. Illustrated Dictionary of World Religions. pap. 20.00 (ISBN 0-08-024176-X). Pergamon.

Jones, Arthur E., jt. auth. see Francuch, Peter D.

Jones, Barry, tr. from Rus. Zionism: Enemy of Peace & Social Progress Issue, No. 3. 220p. 1984. 13.75x (ISBN 0-317-53829-2, Pub. by Collets (UK)). State Mutual Bk.

Jones, Beneth P. Beauty & the Best: A Handbook of Christian Loveliness. (Illus.). 164p. (Orig.). 1980. pap. 3.95 (ISBN 0-89084-123-3). Bob Jones Univ Pr.

--More Sunshine on the Soapsuds. 110p. (Orig.). 1983. pap. 2.95 (ISBN 0-89084-192-6). Bob Jones Univ Pr.

--Ribbing Him Rightly. (Orig.). 1987. pap. write for info. (ISBN 0-89084-381-3). Bob Jones Univ Pr.

--Sunshine on the Soapsuds. 86p. (Orig.). 1977. pap. 2.95 (ISBN 0-89084-054-7). Bob Jones Univ Pr.

Jones, Bill. Free Will Baptist Missions, Missionaries, & Their Message. (Way of Life Ser.). 1972. pap. 1.50 (ISBN 0-89265-008-7, Free Will Baptist Dept); tchr's guide 3.95 (ISBN 0-89265-007-9). Randall Hse.

Jones, Bob. All Fulness Dwells. 152p. 1971. 4.95 (ISBN 0-89084-002-4). Bob Jones Univ Pr.

--Cornbread & Caviar. (Illus.). 236p. 1985. 12.95 (ISBN 0-89084-305-8); pap. 8.95 (ISBN 0-89084-306-6). Bob Jones Univ Pr.

--How to Improve Your Preaching. 2nd ed. 151p. 1964. pap. 3.95 (ISBN 0-89084-141-1). Bob Jones Univ Pr.

--Prologue: A Drama of John Hus. (Illus.). 85p. 1968. pap. 3.95 (ISBN 0-89084-195-0). Bob Jones Univ Pr.

Jones, Bob, ed. Rhyme & Reason. (Illus.). 222p. (Orig.). 1981. pap. 9.95 (ISBN 0-89084-142-X). Bob Jones Univ Pr.

Jones, Bob, III. Biblical Answers to Bothersome Questions. 71p. (Orig.). 1981. pap. 2.00 (ISBN 0-89084-150-0). Bob Jones Univ Pr.

--A Sermon a Day Keeps the Devil Away. 208p. (Orig.). 1980. pap. 2.95 (ISBN 0-89084-114-4). Bob Jones Univ Pr.

Jones, Bob, Sr. Bob Jones' Sermons. (Illus.). 148p. 1983. pap. 3.95 (ISBN 0-89084-232-9). Bob Jones Univ Pr.

--Comments on Here & Hereafter. Haight, Grace W., ed. 189p. 1942. 3.95 (ISBN 0-89084-006-7). Bob Jones Univ Pr.

--My Friends. (Illus.). 131p. 1983. pap. 3.95 (ISBN 0-89084-230-2). Bob Jones Univ Pr.

--Things I Have Learned: Chapel Talks. 224p. 1944. pap. 3.95 (ISBN 0-89084-022-9). Bob Jones Univ Pr.

Jones, Bob, Sr., et al. Heritage of Faith. 183p. (Orig.). 1973. pap. 3.95 (ISBN 0-89084-009-1). Bob Jones Univ Pr.

Jones, Bonnie S., jt. auth. see Langford, Thomas A., III.

Jones, Bridgette A., jt. ed. see Cheney, C. R.

Jones, Bruce, ed. Becoming Makers of Peace. 1987. pap. 7.00 (ISBN 0-8309-0476-X). Herald Hse.

Jones, C. C. Religious Instruction of the Negroes in the United States. 1842. 23.00 (ISBN 0-527-46700-6). Kraus Repr.

Jones, Carolyn A. From Hope to Faith. 134p. 1979. 9.50 (ISBN 0-87881-075-7). Mojave Bks.

Jones, Charles C. Religious Instruction of the Negroes in the United States. facs. ed. LC 70-149869. (Black Heritage Library Collection). 1842. 16.50 (ISBN 0-8369-8718-7). Ayer Co Pubs.

--Religious Instruction of the Negroes in the United States. LC 73-82466. Repr. of 1842 ed. 22.50x (ISBN 0-8371-1645-7, JOI&). Greenwood.

Jones, Charles E. Guide to the Study of the Holiness Movement. LC 74-659. (ATLA Bibliography Ser.: No. 1). 946p. 1974. 57.50 (ISBN 0-8108-0703-3). Scarecrow.

--A Guide to the Study of the Pentecostal Movement, 2 Vols, Vol. 1. Pts. 1 & 2; Vol. 2 pts 3 &4; index. LC 82-10794. (ATLA Bibliography Ser.: No. 6). 1249p. 1983. Set. 82.50 (ISBN 0-8108-1583-4). Scarecrow.

--Perfectionist Persuasion: The Holiness Movement & American Methodism, 1867-1936. LC 74-13766. (ATLA Monograph: No. 5). (Illus.). 262p. 1974. 22.50 (ISBN 0-8108-0747-5). Scarecrow.

Jones, Charles W. Saint Nicholas of Myra, Bari & Manhattan: Biography of a Legend. LC 77-51487. 1978. lib. bdg. 36.00x (ISBN 0-226-40699-7). U of Chicago Pr.

Jones, Cheslyn, et al, eds. The Study of Liturgy. 1978. 27.00x (ISBN 0-19-520075-6); pap. 13.95x (ISBN 0-19-520076-4). Oxford U Pr.

Jones, Chris. Lord, I Want to Tell You Something: Prayers for Boys. LC 73-78266. (Illus.). 96p. (Orig.). 1973. pap. 3.95 (ISBN 0-8066-1330-0, 10-4100). Augsburg.

--What Do I Do Now Lord? LC 76-3860. 96p. (Orig.). 1976. pap. 3.95 (ISBN 0-8066-1539-7, 10-7044). Augsburg.

--Y Ahora, Que Hago, Senor? Cabeza, Susana, tr. from Eng. Tr. of What Do I Do Now, Lord? (Span.). 107p. 1978. pap. 2.75 (ISBN 0-89922-123-8). Edit Caribe.

Jones, Cliff. Winning Through Integrity. 160p. 1985. 9.95 (ISBN 0-687-45604-5). Abingdon.

Jones, Clifford M. New Testament Illustrations. (Cambridge Bible Commentary on the New English Bible, New Testament Ser.). 27.95 (ISBN 0-521-05446-X); pap. 12.95x (ISBN 0-521-09376-7, 376). Cambridge U Pr.

--Old Testament Illustrations. LC 76-142131. (Cambridge Bible Commentary on the New English Bible, Old Testament Ser.). (Illus.). 1971. 29.95 (ISBN 0-521-08007-X); pap. 12.95 (ISBN 0-521-09646-4). Cambridge U Pr.

Jones, D. Faulkner. The English Spirit. 2nd ed. 235p. 1982. 13.95 (ISBN 0-85440-388-4, Pub. by Steinerbooks); pap. 9.95 (ISBN 0-85440-389-2). Anthroposophic.

Jones, D. Gareth. Brave New People: Ethical Issues at the Commencement of Life. LC 85-4582. 232p. 1985. pap. 8.95 (ISBN 0-8028-0070-X). Eerdmans.

Jones, Dale. Youth Ministries Ideas III. 1986. pap. 6.00 (ISBN 0-8309-0470-0). Herald Hse.

Jones, David L., jt. auth. see Holton, Susan.

Jones, Dennis M. And Then There Was Peace. (Orig.). 1987. pap. 3.00 (ISBN 0-941992-08-X). Los Arboles Pub.

Jones, Donald G. The Sectional Crisis & Northern Methodism: A Study in Piety, Political Ethics & Civil Religion. LC 78-9978. 349p. 1979. lib. bdg. 22.50 (ISBN 0-8108-1175-8). Scarecrow.

Jones, Donald G., ed. Business, Religion & Ethics: Inquiry & Encounter. LC 82-14479. 288p. 1982. 25.00 (ISBN 0-89946-164-6); pap. text ed. 12.95 (ISBN 0-89946-166-2). Oelgeschlager.

Jones, E. S., et al. Christian Message for the World Today. facs. ed. LC 77-152163. (Essay Index Reprint Ser). 1934. 17.00 (ISBN 0-8369-2184-4). Ayer Co Pubs.

Jones, E. Stanley. Abundant Living. (Festival Bks.). 1976. pap. 4.25 (ISBN 0-687-00689-9). Abingdon.

--Christ at the Round Table. 328p. 1981. Repr. of 1928 ed. lib. bdg. 30.00 (ISBN 0-89984-267-4). Century Bookbindery.

--The Christ of the Mount. (Festival Ser.). 336p. 1981. pap. 2.45 (ISBN 0-687-06925-4). Abingdon.

--Christian Maturity. (Festival Bks.). 1980. pap. 2.25 (ISBN 0-687-07453-3). Abingdon.

--Cristo y el Comunismo. Gattinoni, C. T., tr. from Eng. Orig. Title: Christ's Alternative to Communism. (Span.). 96p. 1981. pap. 2.10 (ISBN 0-311-05040-9, Edit Mundo). Casa Bautista.

--Divine Yes. 1976. pap. 1.50 (ISBN 0-89129-154-7). Jove Pubns.

--Ghandi: Portrayal of a Friend. 192p. 1983. pap. 3.25 (ISBN 0-687-13999-6). Abingdon.

--Growing Spiritually. (Festival Books). 1978. pap. 3.25 (ISBN 0-687-15968-7). Abingdon.

--In Christ. (Festival Bks.). 1980. pap. 2.25 (ISBN 0-687-18786-9). Abingdon.

--A Song of Ascents: A Spiritual Autobiography. LC 68-17451. (Festival Bks). 1979. pap. 2.25 (ISBN 0-687-39100-8). Abingdon.

--Victory Through Surrender: Self-Realization Through Self-Surrender. (Festival Ser.). 128p. 1980. pap. 1.50 (ISBN 0-687-43750-4). Abingdon.

--The Way: Three Hundred Sixty-Four Adventures in Daily Living. 368p. (Orig.). 1984. pap. 4.35 (ISBN 0-687-44099-8). Abingdon.

--The Way to Power & Poise. (Festival Bks). 1978. pap. 2.25 (ISBN 0-687-44190-0). Abingdon.

--The Word Became Flesh. (Festival Bks). 1979. pap. 3.25 (ISBN 0-687-46128-6). Abingdon.

Jones, Edgar D. American Preachers of Today: Intimate Appraisals of Thirty-Two Leaders. facsimile ed. LC 76-156667. (Essay Index Reprint Ser). Repr. of 1933 ed. 19.00 (ISBN 0-8369-2279-4). Ayer Co Pubs.

--Lincoln & the Preachers. (Biography Index Reprint Ser). 1948. 21.00 (ISBN 0-8369-8018-2). Ayer Co Pubs.

--Royalty of the Pulpit. LC 79-134105. (Essay Index Reprint Ser). 1951. 27.50 (ISBN 0-8369-1979-3). Ayer Co Pubs.

Jones, Elizabeth B. Let the Children Come. 112p. 1980. pap. 2.95 (ISBN 0-8010-5102-9). Baker Bk.

Jones, Ernest. Geoffrey of Monmouth. LC 73-20320. 1944. Repr. lib. bdg. 20.00 (ISBN 0-8414-5283-0). Folcroft.

Jones, Ezra E. Strategies for New Churches. LC 75-36731. 1979. pap. 7.95 (ISBN 0-06-064184-3, RD 276, HarpR). Har-Row.

Jones, Ezra E., jt. auth. see Anderson, James D.

Jones, F. A. Famous Hymns & Their Authors. 59.95 (ISBN 0-8490-0154-4). Gordon Pr.

Jones, Franklin, ed. The Spiritual Instructions of Saint Seraphim of Sarov. LC 73-89308. 1973. pap. 3.95 (ISBN 0-913922-05-6). Dawn Horse Pr.

Jones, Fraymond, Jr. & Kashaf Abdul Haq. Self Interpretation of All Religions. 80p. 1983. 8.95 (ISBN 0-89962-293-3). Todd & Honeywell.

Jones, G. Curtis. One Thousand Illustrations for Preaching & Teaching. 1986. pap. 9.95 (ISBN 0-8054-2249-8). Broadman.

--We Knew His Power: Nine Whose Lives Were Touched by Jesus. LC 75-44181. pap. 24.40 (ISBN 0-8357-9031-2, 2016419). Bks Demand UMI.

Jones, G. E. Twenty-Six New Testament Lessons. 111p. 1978. pap. 2.00 (ISBN 0-89114-080-8). Baptist Pub Hse.

Jones, G. H. First Kings. (New Century Bible Commentary Ser.). 384p. 1984. pap. 8.95 (ISBN 0-8028-0019-X). Eerdmans.

--Second Kings. (New Century Bible Commentary Ser.). 352p. 1984. pap. 8.95 (ISBN 0-8028-0040-8). Eerdmans.

Jones, Gary. Patience Never Fails. 45p. 1985. pap. 0.95 (ISBN 0-88144-048-5). Christian Pub.

Jones, Geraint V. Christology & Myth in the New Testament. LC 56-4228. 1956. A R Allenson.

Jones, Girault M. That Reminds Me. (Illus.). xiv, 211p. (Orig.). 1984. pap. write for info. (ISBN 0-918769-08-6). Univ South.

Jones, Gladys V. The Flowering Tree. 316p. 1984. pap. 8.95 (ISBN 0-87516-527-3). De Vorss.

Jones, Gwyn. Three Poetical Prayer-Makers of the Island of Britain. (Warton Lectures on English Peotry). 9p. 1981. pap. 3.00 (ISBN 0-85672-356-8, Pub. by British Acad). Longwood Pub Group.

Jones, Helen H. Over the Mormon Trail. LC 63-9706. (Frontiers of America Ser.). (Illus.). 128p. 1980. PLB 10.60 (ISBN 0-516-03354-9). Childrens.

Jones, Henry. A Faith That Enquires. LC 77-27211. (Gifford Lectures: 1920-21). Repr. of 1922 ed. 20.00 (ISBN 0-404-60466-8). AMS Pr.

Jones, Howard A. Hooked on Horses: Bits of This & That about People & Horses after 21 Years in the Racing Game. (Illus.). 144p. 1982. 12.50 (ISBN 0-682-49792-4, Banner). Exposition Pr FL.

Jones, Idris W. The Superintendent Plans His Work. 1956. pap. 4.95 (ISBN 0-8170-0172-7). Judson.

Jones, Ilion T. Principles & Practice of Preaching. LC 56-7761. 1974. pap. 7.75 (ISBN 0-687-34061-6). Abingdon.

Jones, J. Estill. Hechos: Colaborando en la Mision de Cristo. Canclini, Arnoldo, tr. from Eng. (Estudios Biblicos Basicos Ser.). Orig. Title: Acts: Working Together in Christ's Mission. 157p. 1981. pap. 2.50 (ISBN 0-311-04339-9). Casa Bautista.

Jones, James A. Counseling Principles for Christian Leaders. 5.95 (ISBN 0-89137-534-1). Quality Pubns.

--I Never Thought It Would Be This Way. 5.50 (ISBN 0-89137-533-3). Quality Pubns.

Jones, James A., III. Conversations with Children. LC 85-40201. (Illus.). 96p. 1985. 7.95 (ISBN 0-938232-72-X). Winston-Derek.

Jones, James W. The Redemption of Matter: Towards the Rapprochment of Science & Religion. 154p. (Orig.). 1984. lib. bdg. 23.00 (ISBN 0-8191-3675-1); pap. text ed. 9.25 (ISBN 0-8191-3676-X). U Pr of Amer.

--The Texture of Knowledge: An Essay on Religion & Science. LC 80-69036. 112p. 1981. lib. bdg. 23.00 (ISBN 0-8191-1360-3); pap. text ed. 8.50 (ISBN 0-8191-1361-1). U Pr of Amer.

Jones, Jean G. Time Out for Grief: A Practical Guide to Passing Through Grief to Happiness. LC 81-85051. 228p. 1982. pap. 4.50 (ISBN 0-87973-654-2, 654). Our Sunday Visitor.

Jones, Jeffrey D. Youth Ministry: Making & Shaping Disciples. 96p. 1986. pap. 5.95 (ISBN 0-8170-1091-2). Judson.

Jones, Jeffrey D. & Potts, Kenneth C. Organizing a Youth Ministry to Fit Your Needs. 64p. 1983. pap. 3.95 (ISBN 0-8170-1004-1). Judson.

Jones, Jenkin L. The Agricultural Social Gospel in America: The Gospel of the Farm. Graham, Thomas E., ed. & intro. by. (Studies in American Religion: Vol. 19). 349p. 1986. lib. bdg. 59.95x (ISBN 0-88946-663-7). E Mellen.

Jones, John D. The Apostles of Christ. 268p. 1982. lib. bdg. 10.00 Smythe Sewn (ISBN 0-86524-139-2, 8403). Klock & Klock.

--Exposition of First Corinthians Thirteen. 253p. 1982. lib. bdg. 9.50 Smythe Sewn (ISBN 0-86524-144-9, 4603). Klock & Klock.

Jones, John D. & Griesbach, Marc F. Just War Theory in the Nuclear Age. LC 85-6092. 236p. (Orig.). 1985. lib. bdg. 25.50 (ISBN 0-8191-4659-5); pap. text ed. 10.75 (ISBN 0-8191-4660-9). U Pr of Amer.

Jones, John D., tr. Pseudo-Dionysius Aeropagite: The Divine Names & Mystical Theology. (Mediaeval Philosophical Texts in Translation: No. 21). 320p. 24.95 (ISBN 0-87462-221-2). Marquette.

Jones, John E. Reconciliation. 164p. 1984. 8.95 (ISBN 0-87123-438-6); pap. 4.95 (ISBN 0-87123-862-4). Bethany Hse.

Jones, John G. Methodism in Mississippi, 2 Vols. in 1. 25.00 (ISBN 0-87511-592-6). Claitors.

Jones, Joseph. Poems & Hymn Tunes As Songs: Metrical Partners. 84p. 1983. with 2 audio cassettes 24.50, (ISBN 0-88432-119-3, S1560). J Norton Pubs.

Jones, Judie. Succeeding as a Woman in Music Leadership. LC 83-7249. 202p. (Orig.). 1983. pap. text ed. 8.95 perfect binding (ISBN 0-912801-00-X). Creat Arts Dev.

Jones, Judie, jt. auth. see Urfer, Pamela.

Jones, Julie. Houses for the Hereafter: Funerary Temples from Guerrero, Mexico. (Illus.). 32p. 1987. pap. 10.00 (ISBN 0-9617356-1-9). Metro Mus Art.

Jones, K. R. The New Government: Prophecies for Today. 1984. 16.95 (ISBN 0-533-05993-3). Vantage.

Jones, Katherine, ed. see Freud, Sigmund.

Jones, Kathy. Acting for God. (Helping Hand Ser.). 48p. (YA) 1984. wkbk. 4.95 (ISBN 0-86653-236-6). Good Apple.

--Celebrate Christmas. (Celebrate Ser.). (Illus.). 144p. 1985. wkbk. 9.95 (ISBN 0-86653-279-X). Good Apple.

Jones, Kenneth, ed. Sickness & Sectarianism: Exploratory Studies in Medical & Religious Sectarianism. 517p. 1985. text ed. 28.95x (ISBN 0-566-00662-6). Gower Pub Co.

Jones, Kenneth E. Commitment to Holiness. 1985. pap. 5.95 (ISBN 0-87162-413-3, D1350). Warner Pr.

--The Word of God. 1980. pap. 3.95 (ISBN 0-87162-224-6, D9205). Warner Pr.

Jones, Kenneth R. The Winner's Circle: Triumph of Jesus Christ. 1987. 16.95 (ISBN 0-533-07092-9). Vantage.

Jones, Kenneth W. Arya Dharm: Hindu Consciousness in Nineteenth-Century Punjab. LC 74-27290. 350p. 1976. 41.95x (ISBN 0-520-02919-4). U of Cal Pr.

Jones, L. W., ed. Classical & Mediaeval Studies in Honor of Edward Kennard Rand, Presented upon the Completion of His Fortieth Year of Teaching. facs. ed. LC 68-57312. (Essay Index Reprint Ser). 1938. 21.50 (ISBN 0-8369-0312-9). Ayer Co Pubs.

Jones, Larry. Practice to Win. 1982. pap. 4.95 (ISBN 0-8423-4887-5). Tyndale.

Jones, Major J. Christian Ethics for Black Theology. LC 74-8680. pap. cancelled (ISBN 0-317-30065-2, 2020267). Bks Demand UMI.

--The Color of God: The Concept of God in Afro-American Religious Thought. 160p. 1987. 24.95 (ISBN 0-86554-274-0, H237); pap. 14.95 (ISBN 0-86554-276-7). Mercer Univ Pr.

Jones, Margaret J. The World in My Mirror. LC 79-17730. 1979. 8.75 (ISBN 0-687-46270-3). Abingdon.

Jones, Margaret W. The Christmas Invitation. Easson, Roger R., ed. LC 85-2035. (A Child's Christmas in Memphis Ser.: Vol. 3). (Illus.). 48p. 1985. 9.95 (ISBN 0-918518-42-3). St Luke TN.

Jones, Mary A. Favorite Bible Stories & Verses. 112p. 1986. 9.95 (ISBN 0-02-689034-8). Macmillan.

--Favorite Stories of Jesus. LC 81-50278. (Rand McNally "Favorite" Ser.). (Illus.). 112p. 1981. 9.95 (ISBN 0-02-689035-6). Macmillan.

Jones, Mary H. Quaker Poets Past & Present. LC 75-7414. 32p. (Orig.). 1975. pap. 2.50x (ISBN 0-87574-202-5). Pendle Hill.

Jones, Michael J. The Defences of the Upper Roman Enclosure. (Archaeology of Lincoln Ser.: Vol. 7). 62p. 1980. pap. text ed. 25.00x (ISBN 0-906780-00-4, Pub. by Coun Brit Archaeology). Humanities.

Jones, Nathan. Sharing the Old, Old Story: Educational Ministry in the Black Community. LC 81-86046. (Illus.). 104p. (Orig.). 1982. pap. 8.95 (ISBN 0-88489-144-5). St Mary's.

Jones, Peter R. The Teachings of the Parables. LC 78-654367. 1982. 13.95 (ISBN 0-8054-1371-5). Broadman.

Jones, Philipa. Selected Garlands. 160p. 1986. pap. 30.00x (ISBN 0-947939-02-4, Pub. by Elmcrest UK). State Mutual Bk.

Jones, R. H. About Bells & Bell Ringing. 1985. 11.25x (ISBN 0-317-54257-5, Pub. by J Richardson Uk). State Mutual Bk.

Jones, R. Tudur. The Great Reformation. LC 85-23930. 272p. 1986. pap. 9.95 (ISBN 0-87784-606-5). Inter-Varsity.

Jones, R. Wayne. Using Spiritual Gifts. LC 83-70642. 1985. pap. 4.95 (ISBN 0-8054-6940-0). Broadman.

Jones, Ralph H. Charles Albert Tindley: Prince of Preachers. 192p. 1982. pap. 8.95 (ISBN 0-687-06325-6). Abingdon.

Jones, Richard H. Science & Mysticism: A Comparative Study of Western Natural Science, Theravada Buddhism, & Advaita Vedanta. LC 84-46098. 272p. 1986. 35.00x (ISBN 0-8387-5093-1, Pub. by Bucknell U Pr). Assoc Univ Prs.

Jones, Robert. Limited to Everyone: An Invitation to Christian Faith. 144p. (Orig.). 1982. pap. 7.95 (ISBN 0-8164-2381-4, HarpR). Har-Row.

Jones, Rufus M. The Faith & Practice of the Quakers. 181p. 1980. pap. 3.95 (ISBN 0-913408-57-3). Friends United.

--The Journal of George Fox. 576p. 1976. pap. 8.50 (ISBN 0-913408-24-7). Friends United.

--The Later Periods of Quakerism, 2 vols. LC 74-109758. 1921. Repr. Set. lib. bdg. 95.00x (ISBN 0-8371-4248-2, JOQU). Greenwood.

--Mysticism in Robert Browning. 1924. Repr. 15.00 (ISBN 0-8274-2784-0). R West.

--New Studies in Mystical Religion. 69.95 (ISBN 0-87968-102-0). Gordon Pr.

--Rethinking Quaker Principles. 1983. pap. 2.50x (ISBN 0-87574-008-1, 008). Pendle Hill.

--Social Law in the Spirtual World. (Studies in Human & Divine Inter-Relationship Ser.). 1978. Repr. of 1904 ed. lib. bdg. 25.00 (ISBN 0-8495-2731-7). Arden Lib.

--Spiritual Reformers of the Sixteenth & Seventeenth Centuries. 1959. 11.25 (ISBN 0-8446-0161-6). Peter Smith.

--Thou Dost Open up My Life. LC 63-11819. (Orig.). 1963. pap. 2.50x (ISBN 0-87574-127-4). Pendle Hill.

Jones, Russel A. Guidebook for Victorious Christian Living. 192p. 1983. pap. 5.95 (ISBN 0-8170-1001-7). Judson.

Jones, Russell B. Gold from Golgotha. (Orig.). 1978. pap. 1.50 (ISBN 0-89228-024-7). Impact Bks MO.

Jones, Russell G. Our God. LC 81-66135. 1981. pap. 4.95 (ISBN 0-89636-069-5). Accent Bks.

Jones, Samuel M. The New Right: A Plea for Fair Play Through a More Just Social Order. LC 75-327. (The Radical Tradition in America Ser.). (Illus.). 479p. 1975. Repr. of 1899 ed. 32.45 (ISBN 0-88355-231-0). Hyperion Conn.

Jones, Shirley. Don't Give Me That Stuff about the Birds & the Bees. LC 82-24610. (Outreach Ser.). 32p. 1983. pap. 0.99 (ISBN 0-8163-0518-8). Pacific Pr Pub Assn.

Jones, Shirley M. The Coming of Yahweh. (Illus.). 600p. 1985. 17.50 (ISBN 0-9615111-0-9). Sandbird Pub.

Jones, Stanley F., tr. see Luedemann, Gerd.

Jones, Stanton L., ed. Psychology & the Christian Faith: An Introductory Reader. 1986. pap. 11.95 (ISBN 0-8010-5217-3). Baker Bk.

Jones, Stephen D. Transforming Discipleship in the Inclusive Church. 160p. 1984. pap. 6.95 (ISBN 0-8170-1049-1). Judson.

Jones, Stephen D., jt. auth. see Hargrove, Barbara.

Jones, Terry L. & Nixon, David L. Venom in My Veins: The Terry Jones Story. 88p. (Orig.). 1985. pap. 3.95 (ISBN 0-8341-1078-4). Beacon Hill.

Jones, Thelma H. The Road to San Luis Rey. LC 73-87882. (Illus.). 1974. text ed. 5.00 (ISBN 0-912472-18-9). Miller Bks.

Jones, Thomas W., ed. see Bedell, William.

Jones, Vera R. Stories of Jesus. 1983. 6.95 (ISBN 0-8062-2242-5). Carlton.

Jones, Violet R. Woman in Islam: A Manual with Special Reference to Conditions in India. LC 79-2942. (Illus.). 455p. 1980. Repr. of 1941 ed. 31.50 (ISBN 0-8305-0107-X). Hyperion Conn.

Jones, W. Paul. The Province Beyond the River: The Diary of a Protestant at a Trappist Monastery. 160p. (Orig.). 1986. pap. 6.95 (ISBN 0-8358-0546-8). Upper Room.

Jones, William. The History of the Christian Church, or Jones' Church History, 2 vols. 1983. Repr. of 1826 ed. 42.50 set (ISBN 0-317-01250-9). Church History.

--The History of the Waldenses, 2 vols. 2nd enl. ed. LC 78-63186. (Heresies of the Early Christian & Medieval Era: Second Ser.). Repr. of 1816 ed. 125.00 set (ISBN 0-404-16080-8). AMS Pr.

Jones, William R., jt. ed. see Bruce, Calvin E.

Jong, Benjamin R. De see De Jong, Benjamin R.

Jong, Erica. Witches. (Illus.). 1982. pap. 12.50 (ISBN 0-452-25357-8, Z5357, Plume). NAL.

Jong, J. W. De. Buddhist Studies. Schopen, Gregory, ed. 1980. 35.00 (ISBN 0-89581-002-6). Asian Human Pr.

Jong, James de see De Jong, James.

Jong, Norman De see De Jong, Norman.

Jong, Norman de see De Jong, Norman.

Jonge, Joanne E. De see De Jonge, Joanne E.

Jonge, Marinus De see De Jonge, Marinus.

Jongen, H. Look-the Madonna Is Weeping. pap. 3.00 (ISBN 0-910984-12-3). Montfort Pubns.

Jonsson, Carl O. & Herbst, Wolfgang. The "Sign" of the Last Days--When? LC 86-72140. (Illus.). 288p. 1987. pap. 7.95 (ISBN 0-914675-09-5). Comment Pr.

Jooharigian, Robert B. God & Natural Evil. 85p. (Orig.). 1985. pap. 6.95x (ISBN 0-932269-30-3). Wyndham Hall.

Joranson, Philip N. & Butigan, Ken, eds. Cry of the Environment: Rebuilding the Christian Creation Tradition. LC 84-72254. (Illus.). 476p. (Orig.). 1984. pap. 14.95 (ISBN 0-939680-17-3). Bear & Co.

Jordac, George. The Voice of Human Justice. Haq, M. Fazal, tr. 508p. 1984. 25.00 (ISBN 0-941724-24-7). Islamic Seminary.

Jordan, A. T., tr. see Tazbir, Janusz.

Jordan, Bernice. Footsteps to God: Six Basic Bible Truth Lessons. (Illus.). 1970. pap. text ed. 6.50 (ISBN 0-86508-025-9). BCM Intl Inc.

--Guia de la Ensenanza Efectiva. Tr. of Guidebook to Better Teaching. (Span.). 1976. pap. text ed. 5.95 (ISBN 0-86508-420-3). BCM Intl Inc.

--Guidebook to Better Teaching. 126p. 1980. pap. text ed. 5.95 (ISBN 0-86508-090-9). BCM Intl Inc.

Jordan, Bernice C. Acts: 14 Lessons, Vol. 1. (Footsteps of Faith Ser.). 1954. pap. text ed. 2.50 (ISBN 0-86508-039-9); figure text 11.45 (ISBN 0-86508-040-2). BCM Intl Inc.

--Acts: 15 Lessons, Vol. 2. (Footsteps of Faith Ser.). 1954. pap. text ed. 2.50 (ISBN 0-86508-041-0); figure text 11.45 (ISBN 0-86508-042-9). BCM Intl Inc.

--El Almacen de Dios: Exodo, 16 Lecciones, Vol. 2. (Pasos De Fe Ser.). (Span.). pap. text ed. 2.50 tchrs'. manual (ISBN 0-86508-403-3); figuras 8.95 (ISBN 0-86508-404-1). BCM Intl Inc.

--En las Huellas de los Heroes: 14 Lecciones, Tomo 4. (Pasos De Fe Ser.). (Span.). pap. text ed. 2.50 (ISBN 0-86508-407-6); figuras 8.95 (ISBN 0-86508-408-4). BCM Intl Inc.

--Los Evangelios-Para que vino Jesus? 14 Lecciones, Tomo 2. (Pasos De Fe Ser.). (Span.). pap. text ed. 2.50 (ISBN 0-86508-411-4); figuras 8.95 (ISBN 0-86508-412-2). BCM Intl Inc.

--Los Evangelios-Quien es Jesus? 14 Lecciones, Tomo 1. (Pasos De Fe Ser.). (Span.). pap. text ed. 2.50 (ISBN 0-86508-409-2); figuras 8.95 (ISBN 0-86508-410-6). BCM Intl Inc.

--Fighting Giants: Joshua-Solomon 14 Lessons, Vol. 3. (Footsteps of Faith Ser.). 1957. pap. text ed. 2.50 (ISBN 0-86508-031-3); figures text 11.45 (ISBN 0-86508-032-1). BCM Intl Inc.

--Genesis: Fifteen Lessons, Vol. 1. (Footsteps of Faith Ser.). 1960. pap. text ed. 2.50 (ISBN 0-86508-027-5); figures text 11.45 (ISBN 0-86508-028-3). BCM Intl Inc.

--Genesis: Quinze Lecciones, Tomo 1. (Pasos De Fe Ser.). (Span.). pap. text ed. 2.50 (ISBN 0-86508-401-7); figuras 8.95 (ISBN 0-86508-402-5). BCM Intl Inc.

--Los Gigantes en Canaan: 14 Lecciones, Tomo 3. (Pasos de Fe Ser.). (Span.). pap. text ed. 2.50 (ISBN 0-86508-405-X); figuras 8.95 (ISBN 0-86508-406-8). BCM Intl Inc.

--God's Storehouse: Exodus 16 Lessons, Vol. 2. (Footsteps of Faith Ser.). (Illus.). 1961. pap. text ed. 2.50 (ISBN 0-86508-029-1); 11.45 (ISBN 0-86508-030-5). BCM Intl Inc.

--Gospels: 14 Lessons, Vol. 1. (Footsteps of Faith Ser.). 1955. pap. text ed. 2.50 (ISBN 0-86508-035-6); figures text 11.45 (ISBN 0-86508-036-4). BCM Intl Inc.

--Gospels: 14 Lessons, Vol. 2. (Footsteps of Faith Ser.). 1956. pap. text ed. 2.50 (ISBN 0-86508-037-2); figures text 11.45 (ISBN 0-86508-038-0). BCM Intl Inc.

--Los Hechos Epistolas-El Mar De la Vida: 14 Lecciones. (Pasos De Fe Ser.). (Span.). pap. text ed. 2.50 (ISBN 0-86508-415-7); figuras 8.95 (ISBN 0-86508-416-5). BCM Intl Inc.

--Los Hechos Epistolas-Vosotros sois Edificio de Dios: 14 Lecciones, Tomo 1. (Pasos De Fe Ser.). (Span.). pap. text ed. 2.50 (ISBN 0-86508-413-0); figuras 8.95 (ISBN 0-86508-414-9). BCM Intl Inc.

Jordan, Clarence. Cotton Patch Version of Hebrews & the General Epistles. LC 73-14856. (Cotton Patch Translations of the Bible Ser.). 1973. pap. 4.95 (ISBN 0-8329-1879-2, Assn Pr). New Century.

--Cotton Patch Version of Luke & Acts. LC 69-18840. 1969. pap. 4.95 (ISBN 0-8329-1173-9, Assn Pr). New Century.

--Cotton Patch Version of Matthew & John. LC 83-61334. 1970. pap. 4.95 (ISBN 0-8329-1062-7, Assn Pr). New Century.

--Cotton Patch Version of Paul's Epistles. LC 68-11487. 1968. pap. 4.95 (ISBN 0-8329-1041-4, Assn Pr). New Century.

--Sermon on the Mount. 1970. pap. 4.95 (ISBN 0-8170-0501-3). Judson.

Jordan, George J. The Inner History of the Great Schism of the West, 1378-1417; a Problem in Church Unity. LC 72-80392. 216p. 1972. Repr. of 1930 ed. lib. bdg. 19.50 (ISBN 0-8337-4193-4). B Franklin.

Jordan, James B. Judges: God's War Against Humanism. (Trinity Biblical Commentary Ser.). xxi, 333p. 1985. 14.95 (ISBN 0-939404-10-9). Geneva Ministr.

--Sabbath Breaking & the Death Penalty: A Theological Investigation. LC 86-80679. 109p. (Orig.). 1986. pap. 9.95 (ISBN 0-939404-13-3). Geneva Ministr.

--The Sociology of the Church: Essays in Reconstruction. LC 86-80571. 320p. (Orig.). 1986. pap. 12.95 (ISBN 0-939404-12-5). Geneva Ministr.

Jordan, James B., ed. The Reconstruction of the Church. LC 86-80570. (Christianity & Civilization Ser.: No. 4). xiv, 338p. (Orig.). 1986. pap. 12.95 (ISBN 0-939404-11-7). Geneva Ministr.

Jordan, Jeanne. Marry Me, Marybeth. Woolsey, Raymond, ed. 96p. 1987. pap. price not set (ISBN 0-8280-0379-3). Review & Herald.

Jordan, Jerry M. Another Brown Bag. LC 80-36849. (Illus.). 1980. pap. 6.95 (ISBN 0-8298-0406-4). Pilgrim NY.

--The Brown Bag: A Bag Full of Sermons for Children. LC 77-16813. (Illus.). 117p. 1981. pap. 6.95 (ISBN 0-8298-0411-0). Pilgrim NY.

--One More Brown Bag. (Illus.). 128p. 1983. pap. 6.95 (ISBN 0-8298-0645-8). Pilgrim NY.

Jordan, Joseph A. We Can Make It...Together. (Illus.). 64p. 1984. 5.50 (ISBN 0-682-40157-9). Exposition Pr FL.

Jordan, Lawrence W. Christian Psychiatry. 112p. 1984. pap. 8.95 (ISBN 0-8059-2910-X). Dorrance.

Jordan, Lewis G. Up the Ladder in Foreign Missions. Gausted, Edwin S., ed. LC 79-52596. (The Baptist Tradition Ser.). (Illus.). 1980. Repr. of 1901 ed. lib. bdg. 27.50x (ISBN 0-405-12463-5). Ayer Co Pubs.

Jordan, Louis H. Comparative Religion: Its Genesis & Growth. Kitagawa, Joseph M., ed. (SP-Reprints & Translations Ser.). 1986. pap. 19.50 (ISBN 1-55540-014-0, 00 07 11). Scholars Pr GA.

Jordan, Mickey & Harrell, Irene B. Let Yesterday Go. LC 84-51995. 285p. 1984. pap. 6.00 (ISBN 0-915541-01-7). Star Bks Inc.

Jordan, Phillip D. The Evangelical Alliance for the United States of America, 1847-1900: Ecumenism, Identity & the Religion of the Republic. LC 82-24953. (Studies in American Religion: Vol. 7). 288p. 1983. 49.95x (ISBN 0-88946-650-5). E Mellen.

Jordan, Robert L. Black Theology Exposed. LC 81-90503. (Illus.). 92p. 1983. 8.95 (ISBN 0-533-05215-7). Vantage.

Jordan, Theodus J. The Contributions of Black Theology to Contemporary Thought. 1987. 7.95 (ISBN 0-533-06711-1). Vantage.

Jordan, W. K. The Development of Religious Toleration in England, 4 vols. Incl. Vol. 1. From the Beginning of the English Reformation to the Death of Queen Elizabeth (ISBN 0-8446-1251-0); Vol. 2. From the Accession of James One to the Convention of the Long Parliament; Vol. 3. From the Convention of the Long Parliament to the Restoration (ISBN 0-8446-1253-7); Vol. 4. Attainment of the Theory & Accommodations in Thought & Institutions (ISBN 0-8446-1254-5). 1932. 16.50 ea. Peter Smith.

Jordan, William C. Louis the IX: The Challenge of the Crusade. LC 79-83996. (Illus.). 1979. 37.00 (ISBN 0-691-05285-9). Princeton U Pr.

Jordan of Saxony. Jordan of Saxony: On the Beginnings of the Order of Preachers. Tugwell, Simon, ed. & tr. (Dominican Sources: New Editions in English). 35p. 1982. pap. 4.00 (ISBN 0-9511202-0-4). Parable.

Jorden, Paul J. & Adair, James R. Surgeon on Safari. (Living Bks.). 192p. (Orig.). 1985. pap. 3.95 (ISBN 0-8423-6686-5). Tyndale.

Jordon, Mark D. Ordering Wisdom: The Hierarchy of Philosophical Discourses in Aquinas. LC 86-40335. (Publications in Medieval Studies: No. 24). 448p. 1986. text ed. 35.00 (ISBN 0-268-01500-7). U of Notre Dame Pr.

Jorgensen, Hans, ed. Vicitrakarnika-Vadanoddhrta: A Collection of Buddhistic Legends. LC 78-70134. Repr. of 1931 ed. 34.50 (ISBN 0-404-17404-3). AMS Pr.

Jorgensen, Johannes. Saint Francis of Assisi. pap. 4.95 (ISBN 0-385-02875-X, D22, Im). Doubleday.

Jorgensen, Joseph G. The Sun Dance Religion: Power for the Powerless. LC 70-182089. 1972. pap. 12.50x (ISBN 0-226-41085-4). U of Chicago Pr.

--The Sun Dance Religion: Power for the Powerless. LC 70-182089. (Illus.). xii, 360p. 1986. pap. 14.95 (ISBN 0-226-41086-2). U of Chicago Pr.

Jorgenson, Dale A. Christianity & Humanism. LC 83-70878. 115p. (Orig.). 1983. pap. 2.95 (ISBN 0-89900-149-1). College Pr Pub.

Jorns, Auguste. Quakers As Pioneers in Social Work. LC 68-8232. 1969. Repr. of 1931 ed. 26.50x (ISBN 0-8046-0244-1, Pub. by Kennikat). Assoc Faculty Pr.

--Quakers As Pioneers in Social Work. Brown, Thomas K., tr. LC 69-14934. (Criminology, Law Enforcement, & Social Problems Ser.: No. 27). 1969. Repr. of 1931 ed. 8.50x (ISBN 0-87585-027-8). Patterson Smith.

Jorstad, Erling. Being Religious in America: The Deepening Crises over Public Faith. LC 86-3360. 128p. (Orig.). 1986. pap. 6.95 (ISBN 0-8066-2222-9, 10-0585). Augsburg.

--Evangelicals in the White House: The Cultural Maturation of Born-Again Christianity, 1960-1981. LC 81-9674. (Studies in American Religion: Vol. 4). 171p. 1981. 39.95x (ISBN 0-88946-982-2). E Mellen.

--The New Christian Right, Nineteen Eighty-One to Nineteen Eighty-Eight: Prospects for the Next Presidential Election. LC 87-1636. (Studies in American Religion: Vol. 25). 280p. 1987. lib. bdg. 49.95 (ISBN 0-88946-669-6). E Mellen.

--The Politics of Moralism: The New Christian Right in American Life. LC 81-65641. 128p. (Orig.). 1981. pap. 6.95 (ISBN 0-8066-1877-9, 10-5011). Augsburg.

Joseph Breuer Foundation, ed. Collected Writings of Samson Raphael Hirsch, Vol. III: Jewish Symbolism. (The Hirsch Heritage Ser.). Tr. of Gessamelte Schriften. 260p. 1984. 15.75 (ISBN 0-87306-924-2). Feldheim.

Joseph Brever Foundation, ed. Collected Writings of Samson Raphael Hirsch, Vol. I: The Jewish Year, Nissan-Av. (The Hirsch Heritage). Tr. of Gessamelte Schriften. 391p. 1984. 15.75 (ISBN 0-87306-364-3). Feldheim.

Joseph, Curt M. Crossroads. (Orig.). 1987. pap. 4.75 (ISBN 0-89536-843-9, 7802). CSS of Ohio.

Joseph, Howard, et al, eds. Truth & Compassion: Essays on Judaism & Religion in Memory of Rabbi Dr. Solomon Frank, Vol. 12. 217p. 1983. pap. text ed. 13.95x (ISBN 0-919812-17-1, Pub. by Wilfrid Laurier Canada). Humanities.

Joseph, John. Muslim-Christian Relations & Inter-Christian Rivalries in the Middle East: The Case of the Jacobites in an Age of Transition. LC 82-870. 320p. 1983. 49.50x (ISBN 0-87395-600-1); pap. 19.95 (ISBN 0-87395-601-X). State U NY Pr.

Joseph, John B. The Nestorians & Their Muslim Neighbors, A Study of Western Influence on Their Relations. LC 61-7417. (Princeton Studies on the Near East). pap. 74.30 (ISBN 0-317-08465-8, 2000553). Bks Demand UMI.

Joseph, Keith, ed. see Sailes, Samuel.

Joseph, Lillian. God's Gift. 112p. (Orig.). 1985. pap. 5.95 (ISBN 0-916829-10-3). Apollo Bks.

Joseph, O. L. The Influence of the English Bible Upon the English Language & Upon English & American Literature. 59.95 (ISBN 0-8490-0409-8). Gordon Pr.

Joseph, Samuel. History of the Baron DeHirsch Fund: The Americanization of the Jewish Immigrant. LC 76-52987. (Illus.). Repr. of 1935 ed. lib. bdg. 32.50x (ISBN 0-678-01151-6). Kelley.

--Jewish Immigration to the United States from 1881 to 1910. LC 14-15042. (Columbia University. Studies in the Social Sciences: No. 145). Repr. of 1914 ed. 7.50 (ISBN 0-404-51145-7). AMS Pr.

--Jewish Immigration to the United States from 1881 to 1910. LC 69-18781. (American Immigration Collection Ser., No. 1). (Illus.). 1969. Repr. of 1914 ed. 10.00 (ISBN 0-405-00529-6). Ayer Co Pubs.

Joseph Cardinal Ratzinger. Seeking God's Face. 1982. 6.95 (ISBN 0-317-46880-4). Franciscan Herald.

Josephson, E., ed. see M, Nectario.

Josephson, Elmer A. God's Key to Health & Happiness. 224p. 1976. pap. 6.95 (ISBN 0-8007-5018-7, Power Bks). Revell.

Josephson, Emanuel. The Unheeded Teachings of Jesus Christ or Christ Rejected: The Strangest Story Never Told. LC 59-15870. (Blacked-Out History Ser.). (Illus.). 96p. 1959. 3.50 (ISBN 0-686-32441-2); pap. 3.00 (ISBN 0-686-32442-0). A-albionic Res.

Josephson, Emanuel M. Unheeded Teachings of Christ or Christ Rejected. 1979. write for info. (ISBN 0-685-96472-8). Revisionist Pr.

--Unheeded Teachings of Jesus: Christ Rejected. (Illus.). 50.00 (ISBN 0-685-07976-7). Chedney.

Josephson, J. M., tr. see Steiner, Rudolf.

Josephus. Works of Josephus, 9 vols. Warmington, E. H., ed. Incl. Vol. 1. Life; Against Apion (ISBN 0-674-99205-9); Vols 2-3. Jewish War. Vol. 2, Bks 1-3. (ISBN 0-674-99223-7); Vol. 3, Bks. 4-7, Index To Vols. 2 & 3. (ISBN 0-674-99232-6); Vols 4-9. Antiquities. Vol. 4, Bks 1-4. (ISBN 0-674-99267-9); Vol. 5, Bks 5-8. (ISBN 0-674-99310-1); Vol. 6, Bks 9-11. (ISBN 0-674-99360-8); Vol. 7, Bks 12-14. (ISBN 0-674-99402-7); Vol. 8, Bks 15-17. (ISBN 0-674-99451-5); Vol. 9, Bks 18-20, General Index. (ISBN 0-674-99477-9). (Loeb Classical Library: No. 186, 203, 210, 242, 281, 326, 365, 410, 433). 13.95x ea. Harvard U Pr.

Josephus, Flavius. Complete Works of Josephus, 4 vols. 39.95 set (ISBN 0-8010-5056-1). Baker Bk.

--Complete Works of Josephus. Whiston, William, tr. LC 60-15405. 840p. (Orig.). 1974. 18.95 (ISBN 0-8254-2951-X); kivar 14.95 (ISBN 0-8254-2952-8). Kregel.

--Great Roman-Jewish War: A.D. 66-70. Whiston, tr. 11.25 (ISBN 0-8446-0729-0). Peter Smith.

--Hegesippi Qui Dicitur Historiae, Libri 5. Ussani, V., ed. (Corpus Scriptorum Ecclesiasticorum Latinorum Ser: Vol. 66). 1932. 31.00 (ISBN 0-384-27880-9). Johnson Repr.

--The Jewish War. Smallwood, E. Mary, ed. Wiliiamson, G. A., tr. (Classics Ser.). 512p. (Orig.). 1984. pap. 6.95 (ISBN 0-14-044420-3). Penguin.

Joshi, K. S. Yoga in Daily Life. 163p. 1971. pap. 2.00 (ISBN 0-88253-044-5). Ind-US Inc.

--Yogic Pranayama: Breathing for Long, Long Life. 180p. 1983. pap. 9.00 (ISBN 0-86578-222-9). Ind-US Inc.

Joshi, Lal M. Studies in the Buddhistic Culture of India (During the 7th & 8th Centuries A.D.) 1977. text ed. 35.00x (ISBN 0-8426-1056-1). Verry.

Joshi, Lalman. Studies in the Buddhistic Culture of India. 2nd rev. ed. 1977. 28.00 (ISBN 0-89684-325-4, Pub. by Motilal Banarsidass India). Orient Bk Dist.

Joshi, N. P. Iconography of Balarama. 1979. 16.50x (ISBN 0-8364-0538-2). South Asia Bks.

Joshi, V. C., ed. Sri Aurobindo: An Interpretation. 1973. 7.50 (ISBN 0-686-20308-9). Intl Bk Dist.

Josipovic, Zoran, jt. auth. see Blackstone, Judith.

Jospe, Raphael & Wagner, Stanley M. Great Schisms in Jewish History. 1980. 25.00x (ISBN 0-87068-784-0). Ktav.

Jossua, Jean-Pierre, jt. auth. see Geffre, Claude.

Jossua, Jean-Pierre, jt. ed. see Geffre, Claude.

Jossua, Jean-pierre, jt. ed. see Geffre, Claude.

Jossua, Jean-Pierre, jt. ed. see Geffre, Claude.

Jostes, Franz, ed. Meister Eckhart und seine Juenger: Ungedruckte Texte zur Geschichte der deutschen Mystik. (Deutsche Neudrucke Texte des Mittelalters Ser.). (Ger.). 216p. 1972. 17.40 (ISBN 3-11-004356-4). De Gruyter.

Jou, Tsung H. The Tao of Meditation: Way to Enlightenment. (Illus.). 186p. 1983. 15.00 (ISBN 0-8048-1465-1, Pub. by Tai Chi Foun). C E Tuttle.

Joudry, Patricia. Spirit River to Angels' Roost: Religions I Have Loved & Left. LC 76-22996. 1977. 12.95 (ISBN 0-912766-46-8). Tundra Bks.

Jouffroy, A. Dictionnaire des Erreurs Sociales. Migne, J. P., ed. (Nouvelle Encyclopedie Theologique Ser.: Vol. 19). (Fr.). 664p. Repr. of 1852 ed. lib. bdg. 84.50x (ISBN 0-89241-266-6). Caratzas.

Jouhanneaud, P. Dictionnaire d'Anecdotes Chretiennes. Migne, J. P., ed. (Nouvelle Encyclopedie Theologique Ser.: Vol. 10). (Fr.). 610p. Repr. of 1857 ed. lib. bdg. 78.00x (ISBN 0-89241-260-7). Caratzas.

--Dictionnaire Dogmatique, Historique, Ascetique et Pratique, des Indulgences des Confreries et Associations Catholiques. Migne, J. P., ed. (Nouvelle Encyclopedie Theologique Ser.: Vol. 27). (Fr.). 686p. Repr. of 1852 ed. lib. bdg. 87.50x (ISBN 0-89241-270-4). Caratzas.

Jouve, E. G. Dictionnaire d'Esthetique Chretienne ou Theorie du Beau dans l'Art Chretien. Migne, J. P., ed. (Troisieme et Derniere Encyclopedie Theologique Ser.: Vol. 17). (Fr.). 646p. Repr. of 1856 ed. lib. bdg. 82.50x (ISBN 0-89241-300-X). Caratzas.

Jovah. The Lord's Hidden Message in Money. 1986. 5.75 (ISBN 0-8062-2404-5). Carlton.

Jowers, Lawrence V. Places & Visions Shared: The Collected Poems of Lawrence V. Jowers. Westburg, John E., ed. 64p. pap. 10.00 (ISBN 0-87423-032-2). Westburg.

Jowett, Benjamin. Theological Essays of the Later Benjamin Jowett. 1906. 20.00 (ISBN 0-932062-91-1). Sharon Hill.

Jowett, Benjamin, ed. see Pattison, Mark.

Jowett, Garth S., ed. see Adler, Mortimer J.

Jowett, John H. Best of John Henry Jowett. Kennedy, Gerald, ed. LC 79-179729. (Biography Index Reprint Ser.). Repr. of 1948 ed. 16.00 (ISBN 0-8369-8097-2). Ayer Co Pubs.

Joy, A. F. We Are the Shakers. Orig. Title: The Queen of the Shakers. (Illus.). 130p. (Orig.). 1985. pap. 5.00 (ISBN 0-934703-00-0). Saturscent Pubns.

--We Are the Shakers. rev., & abr. ed. (Illus.). 130p. 1985. pap. 5.50 (ISBN 0-318-18279-3). A F Joy.

Joy, Charles R., ed. Harper's Topical Concordance. LC 62-11129. 640p. 1976. pap. 10.95 (ISBN 0-06-064229-7, RD 132, HarpR). Har-Row.

Joy, Donald. Bonding: Relationships in the Image of God. LC 84-27121. 192p. 1985. 9.95 (ISBN 0-8499-0440-4, 0440-4). Word Bks.

--Lovers: Whatever Happened to Eden? 220p. 1987. 12.95 (ISBN 0-8499-0541-9). Word Bks.

--Rebonding: Preventing & Restoring Damaged Relationships. 192p. 1986. 11.95 (ISBN 0-8499-0519-2, 0519-2). Word Bks.

Joy, Donald M. Meaningful Learning in the Church. 1969. 3.25 (ISBN 0-89367-019-7). Light & Life.

Joy, Donald M., ed. Moral Development Foundations: Judeo-Christian Alternatives to Piaget-Kohlberg. 240p. (Orig.). 1983. pap. 13.95 (ISBN 0-687-27177-0). Abingdon.

Joyce, George H. Principles of Natural Theology. LC 79-170829. Repr. of 1923 ed. 37.45 (ISBN 0-404-03609-0). AMS Pr.

Joyce, Jon L. And This Will Be a Sign. (Orig.). 1980. pap. 2.95 (ISBN 0-937172-05-7). JLJ Pubs.

--Easter Plays. (Orig.). 1983. pap. 2.95 (ISBN 0-937172-48-0). JLJ Pubs.

--Evangelists Speak. (Orig.). 1983. pap. 2.95 (ISBN 0-937172-50-2). JLJ Pubs.

--For My Sins, He Died. (Orig.). 1981. pap. 3.25 (ISBN 0-937172-20-0). JLJ Pubs.

--Glory of the Only Son. (Orig.). 1982. pap. 4.95 (ISBN 0-937172-43-X). JLJ Pubs.

--How to Use Chancel Drama Effectively. (Orig.). 1980. pap. 2.25 (ISBN 0-937172-00-6). JLJ Pubs.

--Jesus on Our Hands. (Orig.). 1983. pap. 4.95 (ISBN 0-937172-57-X). JLJ Pubs.

--Luther Had a Wife. (Orig.). 1985. pap. 2.95 (ISBN 0-937172-60-X). JLJ Pubs.

--Perspectives on the Cross. (Orig.). 1982. pap. 3.25 (ISBN 0-937172-33-2). JLJ Pubs.

--Profiles of Our Heritage. (Orig.). 1983. pap. 3.00 (ISBN 0-937172-51-0). JLJ Pubs.

--The Seven Deadly Sins. 1973. pap. 3.50 (ISBN 0-89536-210-4, 1912). CSS of Ohio.

--Stories We Love, Vol. 2. (Orig.). 1983. pap. 14.95 (ISBN 0-937172-52-9). JLJ Pubs.

--When the Angels Go Away. (Orig.). 1980. pap. 3.95 (ISBN 0-937172-14-6). JLJ Pubs.

--Who Are You? (Orig.). 1985. pap. 2.95 (ISBN 0-937172-61-8). JLJ Pubs.

Joyce, Julian J. Translation. 1979. 9.95 (ISBN 0-89962-010-8). Todd & Honeywell.

Joyce, Paul. Divine Initiative & Human Response in Ezekiel. (JSOT Supplement Ser.: No. 51). 200p. 1987. text ed. 30.00x (ISBN 1-85075-041-6, Pub. by JSOT Pr England); pap. text ed. 14.95x (ISBN 1-85075-042-4, Pub. by JSOT Pr England). Eisenbrauns.

Joyce, Robert. Thoughts to Ponder. 1980. 6.00 (ISBN 0-8198-7305-5); pap. 5.00 (ISBN 0-8198-7306-3). Dghtrs St Paul.

Jozwiak, William G. Meetings with the Master. LC 84-91374. 118p. 1985. 10.00 (ISBN 0-533-06459-7). Vantage.

Judaeus, see Ehrmann, Naftali H.

Judah, jt. tr. see Maimonides, Moses.

Judah, J. Stillson. Hare Krishna & the Counterculture. LC 74-8209. (Contemporary Religious Movements Ser.). pap. 80.00 (ISBN 0-317-07867-4, 2007717). Bks Demand UMI.

Judd, Judy, ed. Prayers & Reading for Worship. 1987. pap. 12.50 (ISBN 0-8309-0478-6). Herald Hse.

Judd, Kathy R. & Kalnitz, Joanne. World Shakers. 224p. 1986. pap. text ed. 13.95 (ISBN 0-03-006503-8, HoltC). HR&W.

Judd, Mary T. Love & Lifestyles. LC 80-54285. (Illus.). 200p. (Orig.). 1981. pap. text ed. 6.80x (ISBN 0-88489-132-1); teacher's guide 9.00x (ISBN 0-88489-134-8). St Mary's.

Judd, Peter & Lindgren, Bruce. An Introduction to the Saints Church. LC 75-35763. 1976. 14.00 (ISBN 0-8309-0154-X). Herald Hse.

Judd, Peter A. The Sacraments. LC 78-12776. 1978. pap. 7.00 (ISBN 0-8309-0225-2). Herald Hse.

--The Worshiping Community. 177p. 1984. pap. text ed. 9.00 (ISBN 0-8309-0403-4). Herald Hse.

Judd, Peter A. & Cole, Clifford A. Distinctives: Yesterday & Today. 168p. 1983. pap. 10.50 (ISBN 0-8309-0378-X). Herald Hse.

Judd, Wayne. Breaking up. (Uplook Ser.). 1978. pap. 0.99 (ISBN 0-8163-0194-8, 12466). Pacific Pr Pub Assn.

--Healing: Faith or Fraud. (Uplook Ser.). 1978. pap. 0.99 (ISBN 0-8163-0199-9, 08303-0). Pacific Pr Pub Assn.

--Kissing, Hugging, &... LC 79-20362. (Nugget Ser.). 1979. pap. 0.79 (ISBN 0-8127-0249-2). Review & Herald.

Judge, W. Q. Hit the Mark. (Sangam Texts Ser.). 126p. 1986. pap. 8.75 (ISBN 0-88695-024-4). Concord Grove.

--Notes on the Bhagavad-Gita. 69.95 (ISBN 0-8490-0739-9). Gordon Pr.

--The Ocean of Theosophy. 69.95 (ISBN 0-8490-0752-6). Gordon Pr.

--Yoga Aphorisms. 59.95 (ISBN 0-8490-1343-7). Gordon Pr.

Judge, William Q. Letters That Have Helped Me. Niemand, Jasper, ed. & intro. by. (Illus.). x, 300p. 1946. 6.00 (ISBN 0-938998-08-0). Theosophy.

--The Ocean of Theosophy. LC 73-78147. 1973. 6.00 (ISBN 0-911500-25-1); pap. 3.50 (ISBN 0-911500-26-X). Theos U Pr.

--The Ocean of Theosophy. (Illus.). 153p. 1915. Repr. of 1893 ed. 5.00 (ISBN 0-938998-07-2). Theosophy.

--El Oceano de la Teosofia. Polanco, Bermudez Y., tr. from Eng. Tr. of The Ocean of Theosophy. (Span.). 128p. 1983. pap. 3.75 (ISBN 0-938998-28-5). Theosophy.

--Theosophical Articles: Articles by Wm. Q. Judge Reprinted from Nineteenth-Century Theosophical Periodicals, 2 vols. 1276p. 1980. Set. 25.00 (ISBN 0-938998-20-X). Theosophy.

Judge, William Q. & Crosbie, Robert. Notes on the Bhagavad-Gita. 237p. 1918. Repr. 4.00 (ISBN 0-938998-10-2). Theosophy.

Judge, William Q., ed. Bhagavad-Gita: Recension with Essays. LC 70-92964. 1977. 6.00 (ISBN 0-911500-27-8); pap. 3.50 (ISBN 0-911500-28-6). Theos U Pr.

Judge, William Q., tr. from Sanskrit. & intro. by. The Bhagavad-Gita: The Book of Devotion Dialogue Between Krishna, Lord of Devotion, & Arjuna, Prince of India. xviii, 133p. 1930. Repr. of 1891 ed. 3.50 (ISBN 0-938998-09-9). Theosophy.

Judge, William Q., tr. & pref. by. The Yoga Aphorisms of Patanjali. xxi, 74p. 1930. Repr. of 1889 ed. 3.00 (ISBN 0-938998-11-0). Theosophy.

Juel, Donald. Luke-Acts: The Promise of History. LC 82-25845. 136p. 1983. pap. 8.95 (ISBN 0-8042-0321-0). John Knox.

--Messiah & Temple: The Trial of Jesus in the Gospel of Mark. LC 76-46397. (Society of Biblical Literature. Dissertation Ser.: No. 31). Repr. of 1977 ed. 43.60 (ISBN 0-8357-9578-0, 2017527). Bks Demand UMI.

Juel, Donald, et al. An Introduction to New Testament Literature. LC 77-18036. (Illus.). 1978. 16.50 (ISBN 0-687-01360-7); pap. 10.95 (ISBN 0-687-01361-5). Abingdon.

Juel, Donald H. Living a Biblical Faith. LC 82-8652. (Library of Living Faith: Vol. 6). 118p. 1982. pap. 5.95 (ISBN 0-664-24429-7). Westminster.

Juel, Donald H. & Buttrick, David. Pentecost 2. Achtemeier, Elizabeth, et al, eds. LC 79-7377. (Proclamation 2: Aids for Interpreting the Lessons of the Church Year, Ser. C). 64p. 1980. pap. 3.75 (ISBN 0-8006-4083-7, 1-4083). Fortress.

Juelicher, A., et al, eds. Itala: Das Neue Testament in Altlateinischer Ueberlieferung, Vol. 3. 2nd ed. viii, 282p. 1976. 162.25x (ISBN 3-11-002255-9). De Gruyter.

--Itala: Das Neue Testament in Altlateinischer Ueberlieferung, Vols. 1-2 & 4. Incl. Vol. 1. Matthaeus-Evangelium. rev. 2nd ed. viii, 160p. 1972. 84.00 (ISBN 3-11-002256-7); Vol. 2. Marcus-Evangelium. x, 230p. 1970. 76.00 (ISBN 3-11-001244-8); Vol. 4. Johannes-Evangelium. x, 230p. 1963. 96.00x (ISBN 3-11-001243-X). (Ger.). De Gruyter.

Juergensmeyer, Mark & Barrier, Gerald, eds. Sikh Studies: Comparative Perspectives of a Changing Tradition. 1980. 16.00 (ISBN 0-89581-100-6). Asian Human Pr.

Juhnke, James C. A People of Mission: A History of General Conference Mennonite Overseas Missions. LC 78-74809. 1979. pap. 5.95 (ISBN 0-87303-019-2). Faith & Life.

--A People of Two Kingdoms. new ed. LC 74-84697. (Mennonite Historical Ser.). (Illus.). 221p. 1975. 7.95 (ISBN 0-87303-662-X). Faith & Life.

Jukes, Andrew. Four Views of Christ. LC 82-7800. 128p. 1982. pap. 5.95 (ISBN 0-8254-2953-6). Kregel.

--The Law of the Offerings. LC 68-19198. 220p. 1976. pap. 6.95 (ISBN 0-8254-2957-9). Kregel.

--Names of God in Holy Scripture. LC 67-28843. 1976. pap. 7.95 (ISBN 0-8254-2958-7). Kregel.

--The Restitution of All Things. 194p. 1976. pap. text ed. 4.00 (ISBN 0-910424-65-9). Concordant.

Juknialis, Joseph J. When God Began in the Middle. (Illus.). 80p. (Orig.). 1981. pap. text ed. 7.95 (ISBN 0-89390-027-3). Resource Pubns.

Jules-Rosette, Bennetta. African Apostles: Ritual & Conversion in the Church of John Maranke. LC 75-8437. (Symbol, Myth & Ritual Ser.). (Illus.). 352p. 1975. 34.50x (ISBN 0-8014-0846-6). Cornell U Pr.

Jules-Rosette, Bennetta, ed. The New Religions of Africa. LC 78-16925. (Modern Sociology Ser.). (Illus.). 1979. 34.50x (ISBN 0-89391-014-7). Ablex Pub.

Julian, Helen. Key to Abundant Living. 1977. tchr's manual 2.00 (ISBN 0-87509-099-0); student manual 1.25 (ISBN 0-87509-100-8). Chr Pubns.

Julian, J., ed. A Dictionary of Hymnology: Origin & History of Christian Hymns, 4 vols. 1977. Set. lib. bdg. 600.00 (ISBN 0-8490-1719-X). Gordon Pr.

Julian, John. Dictionary of Hymnology, 2 vols. LC 83-8373. 1786p. 1985. Repr. of 1907 ed. 120.00 (ISBN 0-8254-2960-9). Kregel.

Julian Shrine Members Staff, tr. see Julian of Norwich.

Julian of Norwich. Daily Readings with Julian of Norwich, 2 vols. LLewelyn, Robert, ed. (Daily Reading Ser.). 1986. pap. 4.95 ea. Vol. 1 (ISBN 0-87243-142-8). Vol. 2 (ISBN 0-87243-143-6). Templegate.

--Enfolded in Love: Daily Readings with Julian of Norwich. Julian Shrine Members Staff, tr. 96p. (Orig.). 1981. pap. 4.95 (ISBN 0-8164-2318-0, HarpR). Har-Row.

--Revelations of Divine Love. Roberts, Roger L., ed. LC 82-80471. (Treasures from the Spiritual Classics Ser.). 64p. 1982. pap. 2.95 (ISBN 0-8192-1308-X). Morehouse.

Julien, Tom. Handbook for Young Christians. 1976. pap. 1.00 (ISBN 0-88469-037-7). BMH Bks.

--Inherited Wealth: Studies in Ephesians. pap. 4.95 (ISBN 0-88469-034-2). BMH Bks.

--Spiritual Greatness: Studies in Exodus. (Orig.). 1979. pap. 4.95 (ISBN 0-88469-121-7). BMH Bks.

Jump, John D. Matthew Arnold. LC 76-7983. 1955. lib. bdg. 20.00 (ISBN 0-8414-5348-9). Folcroft.

Junankar, N. S. Gautama: The Nyaya Philosophy. 1979. 34.00x (ISBN 0-89684-002-6). South Asia Bks.

Junankar, N. S., tr. see Gautama.

Jung. Men of the Spirit. cancelled (ISBN 0-685-48594-3). Feldheim.

Jung, C. G. Psychology & Western Religion. LC 84-42548. (Bollingen Ser.). (Illus.). 312p. (Orig.). 1984. pap. 8.95x (ISBN 0-691-01862-6). Princeton U Pr.

Jung, Carl G. Psychology & Religion. (Terry Lecture Ser.). 1938. pap. 5.95 (ISBN 0-300-00137-1, Y14). Yale U Pr.

Jung, Carl G. & Kerenyi, Carl. Essays on a Science of Mythology: The Myths of the Divine Child & The Mysteries of Eleusis. rev. ed. (Bollingen Ser.: Vol. 22). 1963. pap. 6.95 (ISBN 0-691-01756-5). Princeton U Pr.

Jung, Emma & Von Franz, Marie-Louise. The Grail Legend. 452p. (Orig.). 1986. 27.50 (ISBN 0-938434-07-1); pap. 14.95 (ISBN 0-938434-08-X). Sigo Pr.

Jung, Leo. Fallen Angels in Jewish & Christian & Mohammedan Literature. 1926. 25.00x (ISBN 0-87068-236-9). Ktav.

--Heirloom: Sermons, Lectures & Studies. 1961. 7.50 (ISBN 0-87306-107-1). Feldheim.

--The Jewish Library. Incl. Vol. 1. Faith. 9.50x (ISBN 0-685-23058-9); Vol. 2. Folk. 9.50x (ISBN 0-685-23059-7); Vol. 3. Women. 9.50x (ISBN 0-685-23060-0); Vol. 4. Judaism in a Changing World. 9.50x (ISBN 0-685-23061-9); Vol. 5. Panorama of Judaism: Part 1. 9.50x (ISBN 0-685-23062-7); Vol. 6. Panorama of Judaism: Part 2. 9.50x (ISBN 0-685-23063-5). Bloch.

--Judaism in a Changing World. 273p. 1971. 9.50 (ISBN 0-900689-08-0). Soncino Pr.

--Love & Life. LC 79-87873. 84p. 1979. 7.50 (ISBN 0-8022-2355-9). Philos Lib.

--The Path of a Pioneer: The Autobiography of Rabbi Leo Jung. 408p. 1980. 9.50 (ISBN 0-900689-51-X). Soncino Pr.

--The Rhythm of Life. 742p. 32.50 (ISBN 0-87559-145-0). Shalom.

--Sages & Saints. (The Jewish Library: Vol. X). 1987. pap. 20.00. Ktav.

--Woman. 239p. 1970. 9.50 (ISBN 0-900689-07-2). Soncino Pr.

Jung, Leo & Levine, Aaron. Business Ethics in Jewish Law. LC 86-22889. Date not set. 27.50x (ISBN 0-88482-918-9). Hebrew Pub.

Jung, Leo, ed. Faith. 212p. 1968. 8.50 (ISBN 0-900689-01-3). Soncino Pr.

--Panorama of Judaism, 2 pts. 1974. Pt. 1, 275 pp. 9.50 (ISBN 0-900689-48-X); Pt. 2, 243 pp. 9.50 (ISBN 0-900689-49-8). Soncino Pr.

Jung, Loyle S. Identity & Community: A Social Introduction to Religion. LC 79-87753. pap. 51.00 (2027156). Bks Demand UMI.

Jung, N. An Approach to the Study of the Quran. pap. 4.75 (ISBN 0-686-18520-X). Kazi Pubns.

--An Approach to the Study of the Qur'an. 1970. 4.75x (ISBN 0-87902-168-3). Orientalia.

Jung, Nizamat. An Approach to the Study of the Qur'an. 84p. (Orig.). 1981. pap. 4.50 (ISBN 0-88004-002-5). Sunwise Turn.

Jung, Wolfgang. Liturgisches Woerterbuch. (Ger.). 1964. leatherette 13.50 (ISBN 3-87537-023-6, M-7544, Pub. by Merseburger Berlin). French & Eur.

Jungel, Eberhard. La Doctrina de la Trinidad. Canclini, Arnoldo, tr. from Eng. Tr. of The Doctrine of the Trinity. (Span.). 152p. 1980. pap. 4.50 (ISBN 0-89922-153-X). Edit Caribe.

--God As the Mystery of the World: On the Foundation of the Theology of the Crucified One in the Dispute Between Theism & Atheism. Guder, Darrell L., tr. (Ger.). 428p. 1983. 20.95 (ISBN 0-8028-3586-4). Eerdmans.

--Karl Barth, a Theological Legacy. Paul, Garrett E., tr. LC 86-7793. 96p. (Orig.). 1986. pap. 13.95 (ISBN 0-664-24031-3). Westminster.

Jungerman, Joan. Share Your Bread. rev. ed. 1.25 (ISBN 0-8091-9313-2). Paulist Pr.

--Spiritual Growth: I Am the Way, the Truth, & the Life. rev. ed. 1.17 (ISBN 0-8091-9314-0). Paulist Pr.

Jung-Inglesis, E. M. Saint Peter's. (Illus.). 64p. (Orig.). 1980. pap. 12.50 (ISBN 0-935748-15-6). Scala Books.

Jungkuntz, Richard see Luther, Martin.

Jungkuntz, Theodore R. Confirmation & the Charismata. LC 83-10450. 126p. (Orig.). 1983. lib. bdg. 24.00 (ISBN 0-8191-3344-2); pap. text ed. 8.75 (ISBN 0-8191-3345-0). U Pr of Amer.

--Formulators of the Formula of Concord. 1977. pap. 8.50 (ISBN 0-570-03740-9, 12-2644). Concordia.

Jungmann, Josef. Christian Prayer Through the Centuries. LC 78-61729. Orig. Title: Christliches Beten. 176p. 1978. pap. 3.95 (ISBN 0-8091-2167-0). Paulist Pr.

Jungmann, Josef A. Early Liturgy, to the Time of Gregory the Great. Brunner, Francis A., tr. (Liturgical Studies: No. 7). 1959. 10.95 (ISBN 0-268-00083-2). U of Notre Dame Pr.

Jungmann, Joseph A. The Mass of the Roman Rite: Its Origins and Development, 2 vols. Brunner, Francis A., tr. from German. 1050p. 1986. pap. 39.95 (ISBN 0-87061-129-1). Chr Classics.

Jurjevich, Ratibor-Ray. The Contemporary Faces of Satan. 437p. 1985. 21.95 (ISBN 0-930711-00-9); pap. 14.95 (ISBN 0-317-19630-8). Ichthys Bks.

Jurji, Edward J. The Middle East, Its Religion & Culture. LC 72-9809. 159p. 1973. Repr. of 1956 ed. lib. bdg. 22.50x (ISBN 0-8371-6597-0, JUME). Greenwood.

Jurkowitz, Carolyn, jt. auth. see Brent, Daniel.

Jurries, Ginger & Mulder, Karen. Fun Ideas for Family Devotions (with Activity Pages) LC 81-50347. (Illus.). 176p. (Orig.). 1981. pap. 6.50 (ISBN 0-87239-415-8, 2968). Standard Pub.

Juster, Daniel. Jewishness & Jesus. 1977. pap. 0.75 (ISBN 0-87784-163-2). Inter-Varsity.
Juster, Daniel C. Growing to Maturity: A Messianic Jewish Guide. 2nd ed. (Illus.). 278p. (Orig.). 1985. pap. 7.00 (ISBN 0-9614555-0-0). Union Messianic Jew Pub.
Justice, William G., Jr. When Your Patient Dies. LC 83-15064. 60p. 1983. pap. 7.50 (ISBN 0-87125-091-8). Cath Health.
Justice, William M. Our Visited Planet. 1978. pap. 4.95 (ISBN 0-918626-03-X). Word Serv.
Justin Martyr, St. Complete Writings. (Fathers of the Church Ser.: Vol. 6). 486p. 1948. 34.95 (ISBN 0-8132-0006-7). Cath U Pr.
Justus, Adalu. Dear Mommy, Please Don't Kill Me. 14p. 1986. pap. 2.50 (ISBN 0-937109-01-0). Silo Pubs.
Justus, Adalu & Marlin, Ira J. My Son, My Mother: Indestructible Chain of Love. LC 86-3884. 200p. (Orig.). 1986. pap. 7.95 (ISBN 0-937109-00-2). Silo Pubs.
Juvenaly, Archimandrite, ed. Khristijanskaja Zhizn' po Dobrotoljubiju: Izbrannija Mjesta iz Tborenji Svjatikh Otsoff i Utchitjeljej Tserkvi. Tr. of Christian Life by the Philokalia; Selected Passages from the Writings of the Holy Fathers. (Rus.). 216p. (Orig.). 1972. 13.00x (ISBN 0-88465-031-6); pap. 8.00x (ISBN 0-88465-032-4). Holy Trinity.
Juvenaly, Arcimndrite, ed. Khristianskaya Zhizn' po Dobrotolijubiju. Tr. of Christian Life According to the Philokalia. 216p. 13.00 (ISBN 0-317-28893-8); pap. 8.00 (ISBN 0-317-28894-6). Holy Trinity.
Juvencus, C. Vettius. Evangeliorum Libri Quattuor. (Corpus Scriptorum Ecclesiasticorum Latinorum Ser: Vol. 24). 1891. 30.00 (ISBN 0-384-28270-9). Johnson Repr.
Juynboll, G. H. Muslim Tradition: Studies in Chronology, Provenance & Authorship of Early Hadith. LC 82-19778. (Cambridge Studies in Islamic Civilization). 264p. 1983. 62.50 (ISBN 0-521-25382-9). Cambridge U Pr.
Jyoti, Swami A. In Light of Wisdom. 2nd ed. LC 84-50889. 74p. 1984. handbound 13.00 (ISBN 0-933572-05-0). Truth Consciousness.
Jyoti, Swami Amar. Retreat into Eternity: An Upanishad-Book of Aphorisms. LC 80-54236. (Illus.). 128p. (Orig.). 1981. pap. 12.95 (ISBN 0-933572-03-4). Truth Consciousness.
--Spirit of Himalaya: The Story of a Truth Seeker. LC 78-73995. (Illus.). 1979. 7.95 (ISBN 0-933572-00-X). Truth Consciousness.
Jyotir Maya Nanda. Vedanta in Brief. (Orig.). 1978. pap. 3.99 (ISBN 0-934664-37-4). Yoga Res Foun.
Jyotir Maya Nanda, Swami. Applied Yoga. (Illus.). 1971. 6.99 (ISBN 0-934664-01-3). Yoga Res Foun.
--Concentration & Meditation. (Illus.). 1971. 6.99 (ISBN 0-934664-03-X). Yoga Res Foun.
--Death & Reincarnation. (Illus.). 1970. 6.99 (ISBN 0-934664-04-8). Yoga Res Foun.
--Jnana Yoga (Yoga Secrets of Wisdom) (Illus.). 1974. pap. 1.99 (ISBN 0-934664-05-6). Yoga Res Foun.
--Mantra, Kirtana, Yantra & Tantra. (Illus.). 1974. pap. 3.99 (ISBN 0-934664-06-4). Yoga Res Foun.
--Mysticism of Hindu Gods & Goddesses. (Illus.). 1974. pap. 3.99 (ISBN 0-934664-08-0). Yoga Res Foun.
--Raja Yoga (The Study of the Mind) (Illus.). 1970. 5.99 (ISBN 0-934664-09-9). Yoga Res Foun.
--Yoga Can Change Your Life. (Illus.). 1975. pap. 4.99 (ISBN 0-934664-14-5). Yoga Res Foun.
--Yoga Guide. (Illus.). 1972. pap. 2.99 (ISBN 0-934664-16-1). Yoga Res Foun.
--Yoga in Practice. (Illus.). 1974. pap. 0.99 (ISBN 0-934664-18-8). Yoga Res Foun.
--Yoga Mystic Stories & Parables. (Illus.). 1974. pap. 3.99 (ISBN 0-934664-24-2). Yoga Res Foun.
--Yoga of Perfection (Srimad Bhagavad Gita) (Illus.). 1973. pap. 3.99 (ISBN 0-934664-25-0). Yoga Res Foun.
--Yoga of Sex-Sublimation, Truth & Non-Violence. (Illus.). 1974. pap. 3.99 (ISBN 0-934664-26-9). Yoga Res Foun.
--Yoga Secrets of Psychic Powers. (Illus.). 1974. pap. 4.99 (ISBN 0-934664-28-5). Yoga Res Foun.
Jyotirmayananda, Swami. Yoga Vasistha, Vol. III. 304p. (Orig.). 1986. pap. 4.99 (ISBN 0-934664-33-1). Yoga Res Foun.

K

Kaaikaula, Becky. The Innkeeper's Wife. (Illus.). 12p. (Orig.). 1983. write for info. (ISBN 0-914599-00-3). Kaaikaula.
Kaam, Adrian V. Formative Spirituality: Fundamental Formation, Vol. I. LC 82-22079. (Formative Spirituality Ser.). 320p. 1983. 24.50x (ISBN 0-8245-0544-1). Crossroad NY.
Kaam, Adrian van. Transcendent Self. 5.95 (ISBN 0-87193-180-X). Dimension Bks.
Kaam, Adrian van & Muto, Susan. Am I Living A Spiritual Life? 4.95 (ISBN 0-87193-173-7). Dimension Bks.
--Practicing the Prayer of Presence. 7.95 (ISBN 0-87193-174-5). Dimension Bks.
Kaam, Adrian Van, jt. auth. see Muto, Susan A.
Kaam, Adrian van see Van Kaam, Adrian.
Kaam, Adrian van see Van Kaam, Adrian & Muto, Susan.
Kaam, Adrian van see Van Kaam, Adrian, et al.
Kaasa, Harris & Rosholt, Malcolm, trs. Pioneer Churchman: The Narrative & Journal of J. W. C. Dietrichson, 1844-1850. Nelson, Clifford, ed. 265p. 1973. 9.00 (ISBN 0-87732-053-5). Norwegian-Am Hist Assn.
Kaasa, Harris, tr. see Nelson, E. Clifford.
Kabakoff, Jacob. Jewish Book Annual, Vol. 35. 1977. 10.00 (ISBN 0-914820-05-2). JWB.
--Jewish Book Annual, Vol. 37. 1979. 12.00 (ISBN 0-914820-07-9). JWB.
--Jewish Book Annual, Vol. 41. 1983. 17.50 (ISBN 0-914820-12-5). JWB.
--Jewish Book Annual, Vol. 42. 18.00 (ISBN 0-914820-13-3). JWB.
--Jewish Book Annual, Vol. 43. 1985. 18.00 (ISBN 0-914820-14-1). JWB.
Kabakoff, Jacob, ed. Jewish Book Annual, Vol. 36. 1978. 10.00 (ISBN 0-914820-06-0). JWB.
--Jewish Book Annual, Vol. 38. 1980. 15.00 (ISBN 0-914820-33-8). JWB.
--Jewish Book Annual, Vol. 39. 1981. 15.00 (ISBN 0-914820-34-6). JWB.
--Jewish Book Annual, Vol. 40. 1982. 17.50 (ISBN 0-914820-10-9). JWB.
Kabat, Carl, tr. see Comblin, Jose.
Kabell, Margaret. Prophet of the Pacific. (Stories of Faith, Fame Ser.). (YA) 1976. pap. 2.95 (ISBN 0-87508-619-5). Chr Lit.
Kabir. Ocean of Love: Anurag Sagar of Kabir. Perkins, Rusell, ed. Bagga, Raaj K. & Singh, Pratap, trs. LC 82-50369. (Illus.). 252p. (Orig.). 1982. pap. 15.00 (ISBN 0-89142-039-8). Sant Bani Ash.
Kac, Arthur W. Messianic Hope. pap. 4.95 (ISBN 0-8010-5362-5). Baker Bk.
--Spiritual Dilemma of the Jewish People. 5.95 (ISBN 0-8010-5456-7). Baker Bk.
Kachelman, John L. Studies in Jonah. pap. 5.50 (ISBN 0-89137-319-5). Quality Pubns.
Kackelman, John, Jr. Studies in Colossiani. 1986. pap. 5.50 (ISBN 0-89137-562-7). Quality Pubns.
--Studies in Judges. 1986. pap. 5.95 (ISBN 0-89137-564-3). Quality Pubns.
Kadden, Barbara B., jt. auth. see Loeb, Sorel G.
Kadel, Thomas E., ed. Growth in Ministry. LC 79-8902. 176p. 1980. pap. 6.95 (ISBN 0-8006-1383-X, 1-1383). Fortress.
Kadel, William H. Prayers for Every Need. pap. 4.95 (ISBN 0-8042-2496-X). John Knox.
Kadloubovsky, Palmer, tr. see Chariton, Igumen.
Kadloubowsky, E. Early Fathers from the Philokalia. Palmer, G. E., tr. 454p. 1954. 18.95 (ISBN 0-571-03794-1). Faber & Faber.
--Writings from the Philokalia. Palmer, G. E., tr. (Illus.). 420p. 1951. 18.95 (ISBN 0-571-07062-0). Faber & Faber.
Kadowaki, J. K. Zen & the Bible: A Priest's Experience. (Orig.). 1980. pap. 8.95 (ISBN 0-7100-0402-8). Methuen Inc.
Kadushin, Max. A Conceptual Approach to the Mekilta. 11.95x (ISBN 0-87334-014-0). Ktav.
--Rabbinic Mind. 3rd ed. LC 75-189016. 1972. 12.50 (ISBN 0-8197-0007-X). Bloch.
--Worship & Ethics: A Study in Rabbinic Judaism. LC 63-10586. 350p. 1975. pap. 8.95x (ISBN 0-8197-0011-8). Bloch.
--Worship & Ethics: A Study in Rabbinic Judaism. LC 77-18849. 1978. Repr. of 1964 ed. lib. bdg. cancelled (ISBN 0-313-20217-6, KAWE). Greenwood.
Kaemke, Ernst, tr. see Niemoller, Martin.
Kaemlein, Wilma, ed. see Painter, Muriel T.
Kaeser, Clifford. Beyond Authority: How to Play to Win by the New Ethics. LC 82-4020. 143p. 1984. pap. 9.95 (ISBN 0-87949-222-8). Ashley Bks.
Kafra. The Illuminated Haggadah. (Illus.). 27.50 (ISBN 0-87306-078-4). Feldheim.
Kagan, Berl. Hebrew Subscription Lists. 50.00x (ISBN 0-87068-282-2, Pub. by Jewish Theol. Seminary). Ktav.
Kaganoff, Nathan M., ed. Guide to America-Holy Land Studies: Vol. 1, American Presence. LC 79-8575. (Illus.). 1980. lib. bdg. 22.00x (ISBN 0-405-12755-3). Ayer Co Pubs.
--Solidarity & Kinship: Essays on American Zionism. (Illus.). 1980. 5.00 (ISBN 0-911934-14-6). Am Jewish Hist Soc.
Kaganoff, Nathan M. & Urofsky, Melvin I., eds. Turn to the South: Essays on Southern Jewry. LC 78-9306. 205p. 1979. 10.95x (ISBN 0-8139-0742-X). U Pr of Va.
Kaganovich, Moshe. Jewish Partisans of Eastern Europe. 340p. 1985. 15.95 (ISBN 0-8052-5053-0); pap. 11.95 (ISBN 0-8052-5054-9). Schocken.
Kaganovoch, Moshe. Jewish Partisans of Eastern Europe. 1984. 17.95 (ISBN 0-89604-048-8); pap. 13.95 (ISBN 0-89604-049-6). Holocaust Pubns.
Kagawa, Toyohiko. Meditations. LC 78-12761. 1979. Repr. of 1950 ed. lib. bdg. 22.50x (ISBN 0-313-21180-9, KAMD). Greenwood.
Kageler, Len. Short Stops with the Lord. 104p. 1984. 5.95 (ISBN 0-87509-348-5). Chr Pubns.
Kageler, Len & Dale, Daryl. Discipleship for High School Teens. 76p. 1984. wkbk. 5.25 (ISBN 0-87509-351-5). Chr Pubns.
Kageyama, Akiko. Journey to Bethlehem. 26p. 1983. 7.95 (ISBN 0-8170-1012-2). Judson.
Kahan, Arcadius. Essays in Jewish Social & Economic History. Weiss, Roger, ed. LC 86-1427. xx, 208p. 1986. lib. bdg. 27.50x (ISBN 0-226-42240-2). U of Chicago Pr.
Kahana, K. Case for Jewish Civil Law in the Jewish State. 6.25x (ISBN 0-685-01037-6). Bloch.
--The Case for Jewish Civil Law in the Jewish State. 120p. 1960. 6.50. Soncino Pr.
Kahana, Kalman. Daughter of Israel: Laws of Family Purity. Oschry, Leonard, tr. 6.95 (ISBN 0-87306-092-X). Feldheim.
Kahana, S. Z. Legends of Zion. 256p. 1986. pap. 9.95 (ISBN 0-943688-63-9). Res Ctr Kabbalah.
Kahane, Henry & Kahane, Renee. The Krater & the Grail: Hermetic Sources of the Parzival. LC 84-16179. 216p. 1965. 31.00 (ISBN 0-252-01196-1). U of Ill Pr.
Kahane, Meir. Uncomfortable Questions for Comfortable Jews. 288p. 1987. 18.00 (ISBN 0-8184-0438-8). Lyle Stuart.
--Why Be Jewish? Intermarriage, Assimilation, & Alienation. LC 77-8774. 264p. 1982. pap. 7.95 (ISBN 0-8128-6129-9). Stein & Day.
Kahane, Renee, jt. auth. see Kahane, Henry.
Kahawai Collective Staff, ed. Not Mixing up Buddhism: Essays on Women & Buddhist Practice. 1987. 10.00 (ISBN 0-934834-71-7). White Pine.
Kahn, Ada P. Diabetes Control & the Kosher Diet. LC 84-51535. 180p. 1985. pap. 9.95x (ISBN 0-930121-00-7). Wordscope Inc.
Kahn, Leon. Les Juifs de Paris Pendant la Revolution. (Research & Source Works Ser.: No. 198). 1968. Repr. of 1899 ed. 30.50 (ISBN 0-8337-1892-4). B Franklin.
Kahn, Lothar, ed. God: What People Have Said about Him. 320p. 1980. 9.95 (ISBN 0-8246-0251-X). Jonathan David.
Kahn, Paul, ed. Proceedings of the Association of Orthodox Jewish Scientists, Vol. 7. 240p. 1984. pap. 9.95. Hermon.
Kahoe, Richard D., jt. auth. see Meadow, Mary J.
Kaihong. The Cult Phenomenon: Its Recognition, Evaluation & Control. 100p. (Orig.). 1987. pap. text ed. 19.00. Kaihong.
Kail, Owen C. Buddist Cave Temples of India. (Illus.). xi, 138p. 1981. text ed. 25.00x (ISBN 0-86590-043-4, Pub. by Taraporevala India). Apt Bks.
Kainz, Howard P. Ethica Dialectica. x, 145p. 1980. lib. bdg. 34.00 (ISBN 90-247-2078-8, Pub. by Martinus Nijhoff Netherlands). Kluwer Academic.
--Hegel's Phenomenology, Part II: The Evolution of Ethical & Religious Consciousness to the Absolute Standpoint. LC 82-22444. xii, 211p. 1983. text ed. 23.95x (ISBN 0-8214-0677-9); pap. 12.95x (ISBN 0-8214-0738-4). Ohio U Pr.
--Wittenberg, Revisited: A Polymorphous Critique of Religion & Theology. LC 81-40729. 236p. (Orig.). 1982. lib. bdg. 27.50 (ISBN 0-8191-1949-0); pap. text ed. 12.50 (ISBN 0-8191-1950-4). U Pr of Amer.
Kaiser, Bill. Gospel of Jesus & Paul. 152p. (Orig.). 1985. pap. text ed. 5.95 (ISBN 0-914307-37-1). Word Faith.
--No Other Gospel. 153p. (Orig.). 1984. pap. 6.95 (ISBN 0-914307-16-9, Dist. by Harrison Hse). Word Faith.
--Who in the World in Christ Are You? 231p. (Orig.). 1983. pap. text ed. 5.50 (ISBN 0-914307-12-6, Dist. by Harrison Hse). Word Faith.
--Who Is Christ. 152p. (Orig.). 1983. pap. text ed. 4.95 (ISBN 0-914307-01-0, Dist. by Harrison Hse). Word Faith.
Kaiser, Christopher B. The Doctrine of God. LC 82-72324. (Foundations for Faith Ser.). 160p. 1982. pap. 8.95 (ISBN 0-89107-259-4, Crossway Bks). Good News.
Kaiser, Edgar P. How to Respond to the Latter Day Saints. (The Response Ser.). 1977. 1.95 (ISBN 0-570-07680-3, 12-2669). Concordia.
Kaiser, Eldor & Symmank, Leo. A New Start in Youth Ministry. 1980. pap. 4.95 (ISBN 0-570-03805-7, 12-2914). Concordia.
Kaiser, Grace. Dr. Frau. LC 86-81059. 168p. 1986. 14.95 (ISBN 0-934672-34-2). Good Bks PA.
Kaiser, Judith B. Quick-Line Stories for Young Children. 1975. spiral bdg. 3.95 (ISBN 0-916406-12-1). Accent Bks.
Kaiser, Otto. Isaiah, One to Twelve, A Commentary. 2nd ed. LC 82-23785. (The Old Testament Library Ser.). 288p. 1983. 19.95 (ISBN 0-664-21827-X). Westminster.
--Isaiah Thirteen to Thirty-Nine, A Commentary. LC 73-21949. (Old Testament Library). 432p. 1974. 19.95 (ISBN 0-664-20984-X). Westminster.
Kaiser, Robert B. The Politics of Sex & Religion: A Case History in the Development of Doctrine, 1962-1984. LC 84-82552. 200p. (Orig.). 1985. pap. 10.95 (ISBN 0-934134-16-2, Leaven Pr). Sheed & Ward MO.
Kaiser, Walter. Malachi: God's Unchanging Love. 1984. pap. 6.95 (ISBN 0-8010-5464-8). Baker Bk.
Kaiser, Walter C. The Uses of the Old Testament in the New. 1985. 13.95 (ISBN 0-8024-9085-9). Moody.
Kaiser, Walter C., Jr. Classical Evangelical Essays in Old Testament Interpretation. 1972. pap. 9.95 (ISBN 0-8010-5314-5). Baker Bk.
--Ecclesiastes: Total Life. (Everyman's Bible Commentary Ser.). 1979. pap. 5.95 (ISBN 0-8024-2022-2). Moody.
--Old Testament in Contemporary Preaching. 1973. pap. 6.95 (ISBN 0-8010-5331-5). Baker Bk.
--Quality Living. rev. ed. (MP Electives Ser.). 1986. pap. text ed. 3.95 (ISBN 0-8024-7069-6); tchr's ed. 4.95 (ISBN 0-8024-7070-X). Moody.
--Quest for Renewal: Personal Revival in the Old Testament. (Orig.). 1986. pap. 6.95 (ISBN 0-8024-7050-5). Moody.
--Toward an Exegetical Theology. LC 80-68986. 224p. 1981. 11.95 (ISBN 0-8010-5425-7). Baker Bk.
--Toward an Old Testament Theology. 1978. 16.95 (ISBN 0-310-37100-7, 12320). Zondervan.
--Toward Old Testament Ethics. 1986. 16.95 (ISBN 0-310-37110-4, 12321). Zondervan.
Kaiser, Walter C., Jr., jt. ed. see Youngblood, Ronald.
Kakar, Sudhir. The Inner World: A Psycho-Analytic Study of Childhood & Society in India. 2nd ed. (Illus.). 1981. pap. text ed. 8.95x (ISBN 0-19-561508-5). Oxford U Pr.
--Shamans, Mystics, & Doctors: A Psychological Inquiry into India & Its Healing Traditions. LC 83-70654. 324p. 1983. pap. 10.95x (ISBN 0-8070-2903-3, BP 660). Beacon Pr.
Kakhun. Lives of Eminent Korean Monks: The Haedong Kosung Chon. Lee, Peter H., tr. LC 69-18037. (Harvard-Yenching Institute Studies: No. 25). 1969. pap. text ed. 7.00x (ISBN 0-674-53662-2). Harvard U Pr.
Kakimoto, Kozo. God, You Are Always With Us. 28p. 9.95 (ISBN 0-687-15303-4). Abingdon.
Kakonis, Tom E. & Scally, John, eds. We Have but Faith. LC 74-20434. 152p. 1975. 6.95 (ISBN 0-88498-023-5). Brevet Pr.
Kalabadhi, Muhammed. The Doctrine of the Sufis. Arberry, Arthur J., tr. from Arabic. LC 75-41003. Repr. of 1935 ed. 18.00 (ISBN 0-404-14637-6). AMS Pr.
Kalas, Ellsworth. Our First Song: Evangelism in the Hymns of Charles Wesley. LC 84-70133. 64p. (Orig.). 1984. pap. 2.95 (ISBN 0-88177-010-8, DRO10B). Discipleship Res.
Kalas, J. Ellsworth. A Pilgrimage. Sherer, Michael L., ed. (Orig.). 1987. pap. 3.95 (ISBN 0-89536-845-5, 7804). CSS of Ohio.
Kalberer, Augustine. Lives of the Saints. (Illus.). 380p. 1976. 18.50 (ISBN 0-8199-0539-9). Franciscan Herald.
Kalberer, Jan, jt. auth. see Krall, Jack.
Kalchuri, Bhau. Let's Go to Meherabad. 120p. 1981. 10.95 (ISBN 0-940700-12-3); pap. 5.95 (ISBN 0-940700-11-5). Meher Baba Info.
--Meher Roshani. 144p. (Orig.). Date not set. pap. 10.00 (ISBN 0-932947-06-9). Manifestation.
Kalderon, Albert E. Abraham Galante: A Biography. (Illus.). 124p. 1983. 10.00 (ISBN 0-87203-111-X). Hermon.
Kale, M. R., ed. see Kalidasa.
Kalechofsky, Roberta. The Sixth Day of Creation: A Discourse on Post Biblical, Post Modern Thought. (Illus.). 24p. 1986. 10.00 (ISBN 0-916288-20-X). Micah Pubns.
Kalechofsky, Roberta, ed. South African Jewish Voices. LC 81-83903. (Echad 2: a Global Anthology Ser.). 280p. 1982. pap. text ed. 10.00 (ISBN 0-916288-10-2). Micah Pubns.

Kaler, Patrick. You & The Bibles: Tough Questions & Straight Answers. 64p. (Orig.). 1985. pap. 1.95 (ISBN 0-89243-240-3). Liguori Pubns.

Kalidasa. Kumarasambhava. Kale, M. R., ed. 1986. Repr. 17.50 (ISBN 81-208-0160-1, Pub. by Motilal Banarsidass). South Asia Bks.

Kalin, Everett R., tr. see Soelle, Dorothee.

Kalin, Everett R., tr. see Stuhlmacher, Peter.

Kalir, Joseph. Introduction to Judaism. LC 79-6758. 170p. 1980. text ed. 25.00 (ISBN 0-8191-0948-7); pap. text ed. 10.75 (ISBN 0-8191-0949-5). U Pr of Amer.

Kalisch, Isidor. The Sepher Yezirah. 1984. write for info (ISBN 0-686-21219-3). Heptangle.

Kalisch, Isidor, tr. see Munk, S.

Kalisch, Shoshana & Meister, Barbara. Yes, We Sang! Songs of the Ghettos & Concentration Camps. LC 84-48172. (Illus.). 160p. 1985. 22.45 (ISBN 0-06-015448-9, HarpT). Har-Row.

Kallas, James. Revelation: God & Satan in the Apocalypse. LC 73-78268. 128p. 1973. pap. 6.95 (ISBN 0-8066-1332-7, 10-5490). Augsburg.

--Story of Paul. LC 66-19206. (Orig.). 1966. pap. 6.95 (ISBN 0-8066-0608-8, 10-6055). Augsburg.

Kallen, Horace M. Frontiers of Hope. Davis, Moshe, ed. LC 77-70711. (America & the Holy Land Ser.). 1977. Repr. of 1929 ed. lib. bdg. 37.50x (ISBN 0-405-10260-7). Ayer Co Pubs.

--Judaism at Bay: Essays Toward the Adjustment of Judaism to Modernity. LC 74-38451. (Religion in America, Ser. 2). 268p. 1972. Repr. of 1932 ed. 20.00 (ISBN 0-405-04071-7). Ayer Co Pubs.

Kallstad, T. Psychological Studies on Religious Man. 252p. 1978. pap. text ed. 22.00x (ISBN 91-554-0801-X, Pub. by Almqvist & Wiksell). Coronet Bks.

Kalnitz, Joanne, jt. auth. see Judd, Kathy R.

Kalokyris, Constantine D. The Essence of Orthodox Inconography. Chamberas, Peter A., tr. from Greek. (Illus.). 129p. 1971. pap. 9.95 (ISBN 0-917651-12-X). Holy Cross Orthodox.

Kalomiros, Alexander. Against False Union. 2nd ed. Gabriel, George, tr. from Greek. (Illus., Orig.). 1979. pap. 2.50x (ISBN 0-913026-20-4). St Nectarios.

Kalsbeek, L. Contours of a Christian Philosophy. 1975. pap. 9.95x (ISBN 0-88906-000-2). Wedge Pub.

Kaltenmark, Max. Lao-Tzu & Taoism. Greaves, Roger, tr. LC 69-13179. 1969. 15.00x (ISBN 0-8047-0688-3); pap. 5.95 (ISBN 0-8047-0689-1, SP96). Stanford U Pr.

Kalu, Ogbu. Divided People of God. LC 74-81853. 1978. 13.95x (ISBN 0-88357-048-3); pap. 4.95 (ISBN 0-88357-070-X). NOK Pubs.

Kalupahana, David J. Buddhist Philosophy: A Historical Analysis. LC 75-20040. 210p. 1976. (Eastwest Ctr); pap. 4.95x (ISBN 0-8248-0392-2). UH Pr.

--Nagarjuna: The Philosophy of the Middle Way. (Buddhist Studies). 488p. 1986. 49.50x (ISBN 0-88706-148-6); pap. 19.95 (ISBN 0-88706-149-4). State U NY Pr.

--A Path of Righteousness: Dhammapada-An Introductory Essay, Together with the Pali Text, English Translation with Commentary. LC 86-9088. (Eng. & Pali.). 234p. (Orig.). 1986. lib. bdg. 24.75 (ISBN 0-8191-5365-6); pap. text ed. 12.50 (ISBN 0-8191-5366-4). U Pr of Amer.

--The Principles of Buddhist Psychology. (Buddhist Studies). 256p. 1987. 39.50 (ISBN 0-88706-404-3); pap. 12.95 (ISBN 0-88706-403-5). State U NY Pr.

Kalupahana, David J. & Kalupahana, Indrani. The Way of Siddhartha: A Life of the Buddha. 242p. 1987. pap. text ed. 11.75 (ISBN 0-8191-6066-0). U Pr of Amer.

Kalupahana, Indrani, jt. auth. see Kalupahana, David J.

Kalu Rinpoche. The Dharma: That Benefits All Beings Impartially Like the Light of the Sun & Moon. 256p. (Orig.). 1986. 34.50x (ISBN 0-88706-156-7); pap. 10.95x (ISBN 0-88706-157-5). State U NY Pr.

Kalus, Ludvik. Catalogue of Islamic Seals & Talismans in the Ashmolean Museum. 1985. 45.00x (Pub. by Ashmolean Museum). State Mutual Bk.

Kalven, Bruce, et al. Value Development: A Practical Guide. 1982. pap. 10.00 (ISBN 0-8091-2445-9); learning summaries 2.50 (ISBN 0-8091-2520-X); time diary 3.00 (ISBN 0-8091-2519-6). Paulist Pr.

Kamal, A. A. Everyday Fight, 2 vols. Set. pap. 18.00 (ISBN 0-686-63899-9). Kazi Pubns.

Kambylis, Athanasios, ed. Symeon Neos Theologos, Hymnen Einleitung und kritischer Text. (Supplementa Byzantina, Vol. 3). 1976. 234.00x (ISBN 3-11-004888-4). De Gruyter.

Kameeta, Zephania. Why, O Lord? Psalms & Sermons from Namibia. LC 86-45211. 80p. 1987. pap. 3.95 (ISBN 0-8006-1923-4, 1-1923). Fortress.

Kamen, Henry. Inquisition & Society in Spain in the Sixteenth & Seventeenth Centuries. LC 85-10804. (Illus.). 320p. 1985. 27.50x (ISBN 0-253-33015-7); pap. 10.95x (ISBN 0-253-22775-5). Ind U Pr.

Kamen, Martin D. Radiant Science, Dark Politics: A Memoir of the Nuclear Age. 1987. pap. 8.95 (ISBN 0-520-05897-6). U of Cal Pr.

Kamen, Robert M. Growing up Hasidic: Education & Socialization in the Bobover Hasidic Community. LC 83-45358. (Immigrant Communities & Ethnic Minorities in the United States & Canada Ser.). 1985. 30.00 (ISBN 0-404-19411-7). AMS Pr.

Kamhi, D. J. Modern Hebrew: An Introductory Course. (OUP for the School of Oriental & African Studies Ser.). 1982. 15.95x (ISBN 0-19-713594-3). Oxford U Pr.

Kamil, A. Abd-Al-Qadir. Islam & the Race Question. 65p. (Orig.). 1970. pap. 5.00 (ISBN 92-3-100833-1, U342, UNESCO). Bernan-Unipub.

Kamil, Jill. The Ancient Egyptians: How They Lived & Worked. LC 76-42175. 1977. 12.95 (ISBN 0-8023-1267-5). Dufour.

Kamin, Philip. Paul Young. (Illus.). 32p. 1985. pap. 4.95 (ISBN 0-88188-411-1, 00183876, Robus Bks). H Leonard Pub Corp.

Kaminetsky, Joseph & Gross, Alexander. The Founder of Torah Umesorah. pap. 1.00 (ISBN 0-914131-21-4, E-23). Torah Umesorah.

Kaminetsky, Joseph, ed. see Finkel, Nosson.

Kamiya, Artie & Kamiya, Elizabeth. Mobiles, Banners & Chariots. (Helping Hand Ser.). (Illus.). 48p. (YA) 1984. wkbk 4.95 (ISBN 0-86653-184-X). Good Apple.

Kamiya, Elizabeth, jt. auth. see Kamiya, Artie.

Kamm, Adrian van see Van Kamm, Adrian & Muto, Susan A.

Kammer, Charles L., 3rd. The Kingdom Revisited: An Essay on Christian Social Ethics. LC 81-40045. 188p. (Orig.). 1981. lib. bdg. 26.00 (ISBN 0-8191-1737-4); pap. text ed. 12.50 (ISBN 0-8191-1738-2). U Pr of Amer.

Kampe, Norbert, jt. ed. see Strauss, Herbert A.

Kampelman, Max M. Jewish Power: Myth or Reality. 21p. 1.50 (ISBN 0-686-74974-X). ADL.

Kamper, Karl G. & Carson, Karen M. A Call to Awaken, Vol. I. 269p. 1986. text ed. 15.00 (ISBN 0-9616739-1-5). Atonement Ent.

Kampf, Avram. Contemporary Synagogue Art: Developments in the United States, 1945-1965. LC 65-25292. (Illus.). 1976. 15.00 (ISBN 0-8074-0085-8, 382630). UAHC.

--Jewish Experience in the Art of the Twentieth-Century. (Illus.). 240p. 1984. 49.50 (ISBN 0-89789-039-6). Bergin & Garvey.

Kamstra, Doug. The Get-Away Book. (Good Things for Youth Leaders Ser.). 1984. pap. 5.95 (ISBN 0-8010-5459-1). Baker Bk.

Kamstra, Douglas, compiled by. Good Times Game Book: Good Things for Youth Leaders. 1981. pap. 5.95 (ISBN 0-8010-7705-2). Baker Bk.

Kanaar, Barbara. A Child's Story of Jesus. (Happy Day Bks.). (Illus.). 24p. 1986. 1.59 (ISBN 0-87403-023-4, 3483). Standard Pub.

Kanada. The Vaisesika Sutras of Kanada, with the Commentary of Sankara & Extracts from the Gloss of Jayanarayana. Sinha, Nandalal, tr. & intro. by. Incl. Notes from the Commentary of Chandrakanta. LC 73-3791. (Sacred Books of the Hindus: No. 6). Repr. of 1911 ed. 42.50 (ISBN 0-404-57806-3). AMS Pr.

Kanal, S. The Philosophy of Religion. 480p. 1984. text ed. 45.00x (ISBN 0-86590-272-0, Sterling Pubs India). Apt Bks.

Kanda, Christine G. Shinzo: Hachiman Imagery & Its Development. (Harvard East Asian Monographs: No. 119). 1985. text ed. 30.00x (ISBN 0-674-80650-6, Pub. by Coun East Asian Stud). Harvard U Pr.

Kane, Aletheia, tr. from Fr. Complete Works of Elizabeth of the Trinity: Major Spiritual Writings, Vol. 1. LC 84-3748. Tr. of J'ai Trouve Dieu, Oeuvres Completes. (Illus.). 208p. (Orig.). 1984. pap. 6.95x (ISBN 0-935216-01-4). ICS Pubns.

Kane, Franzita, jt. ed. see Burrell, David B.

Kane, G. Stanley. Anselm's Doctrine of Freedom & The Will. LC 81-16939. (Texts & Studies in Religion, Vol. 10). 240p. 1982. 49.95x (ISBN 0-88946-914-8). E Mellen.

Kane, Herbert T. Christian Missions in Biblical Perspective. 14.95 (ISBN 0-8010-5370-6). Baker Bk.

Kane, Israel. In Quest of the Truth: A Survey of Medieval Jewish Thought. LC 84-90191. 77p. 1985. 8.95 (ISBN 0-533-06243-8). Vantage.

Kane, J. Herbert. The Christian World Mission: Today & Tomorrow. 240p. 1981. 13.95 (ISBN 0-8010-5426-5). Baker Bk.

--A Concise History of the Christian World Mission. 2nd ed. 1978. 7.95 (ISBN 0-8010-5395-1). Baker Bk.

--Global View of Christian Missions. 1971. 19.95 (ISBN 0-8010-5308-0). Baker Bk.

--Life & Work on the Mission Field. LC 80-65010. 1980. 16.95 (ISBN 0-8010-5406-0). Baker Bk.

--The Making of a Missionary. 160p. 1975. pap. 5.95 (ISBN 0-8010-5481-8). Baker Bk.

--Understanding Christian Missions. 16.95 (ISBN 0-8010-5344-7). Baker Bk.

--Wanted: World Christians. 204p. 1986. pap. 9.95 (ISBN 0-8010-5474-5). Baker Bk.

Kane, John F. Pluralism & Truth in Religion. Dietrich, Wendell, ed. LC 80-20659. (American Academy of Religion Dissertation Ser.). 1981. 13.95 (ISBN 0-89130-413-4, 01-01-33); pap. 9.95 (ISBN 0-89130-414-2). Scholars Pr GA.

Kane, P. V., ed. see Banabhatta.

Kane, R. Free Will & Values. (Series in Philosophy). 328p. 1985. 44.50 (ISBN 0-88706-101-X); pap. 18.95 (ISBN 0-88706-102-8). State U NY Pr.

Kane, T. A., ed. see Kelley, Kathleen, et al.

Kane, Thomas A. Happy Are You Who Affirm. LC 80-26834. (Illus.). 184p. 1980. pap. 5.00 (ISBN 0-89571-010-2). Affirmation.

--The Healing Touch of Affirmation. LC 76-151154. 126p. 1976. pap. 4.95 (ISBN 0-89571-001-3). Affirmation.

Kane, Thomas S. Journey of the Heart. LC 81-5278. 1981. pap. 4.95 (ISBN 0-932506-13-5). St Bedes Pubns.

Kanfield, William L. Heaven Is Not That Far Away. LC 85-91401. 88p. 1986. 8.95 (ISBN 0-533-06917-3). Vantage.

Kang, C. H. & Nelson, Ethel. The Discovery of Genesis. 1979. pap. 4.95 (ISBN 0-570-03792-1, 12-2755). Concordia.

Kangle, R. P. The Kautiliya Arthasastra, 3 pts. 1986. Repr. of 1965 ed. Set. 75.00 (Pub. by Motilal Banarsidass). Pt. 1 (ISBN 81-208-0039-7). Pt. 2. 36.00 (ISBN 81-208-0040-0); Pt. 3. 46.00 (ISBN 81-208-0024-9). South Asia Bks.

Kaniel, Michael. Timeless Judaism for Our Time. 1985. pap. 2.95 (ISBN 0-87306-944-7). Feldheim.

Kanitkar, V. P. Hinduism. (Religions of the World Ser.). (Illus.). 48p. 1986. PLB 10.90 (ISBN 0-531-18068-9, Pub. by Bookwright). Watts.

Kann, Robert A. A Study in Austrian Intellectual History from Late Baroque to Romanticism. LC 73-16356. 367p. 1973. Repr. lib. bdg. 27.50x (ISBN 0-374-94504-7, Octagon). Hippocrene Bks.

Kannengiesser, Charles, ed. Early Christian Spirituality. Bright, Pamela, tr. from Lat. & Gr. LC 86-45226. (Sources of Early Christian Thought). 144p. 1986. pap. 7.95 (ISBN 0-8006-1416-X). Fortress.

Kanof, Abram, intro. by. Ceremonial Art in the Judaic Tradition. LC 75-126321. (Illus.). 92p. 1975. pap. 3.00 (ISBN 0-88259-078-2). NCMA.

Kant, Immanuel. Critique of Pure Reason. 480p. 1986. Repr. of 1900 ed. lib. bdg. 75.00 (ISBN 0-8495-3103-9). Arden Lib.

--The Doctrine of Virtue: Metaphysic of Morals, Pt. II. (Works in Contin. Philos. Ser.). 1971. 10.95x (ISBN 0-8122-1025-5). U of Pa Pr.

--Foundations of the Metaphysics of Morals. Beck, Lewis W., tr. Bd. with What Is Enlightenment. LC 59-11679. 1959. pap. 4.79 scp (ISBN 0-672-60312-8, LLA113). Bobbs.

--Foundations of the Metaphysics of Morals: Text & Critical Essays. Wolff, Robert P., ed. LC 68-9841. (Text & Critical Essays Ser.). 1969. pap. 10.28 scp (ISBN 0-672-61114-7, TC1). Bobbs.

--Fundamental Principles of the Metaphysic of Ethics. Manthey-Zorn, Otto, tr. (Century Philosophy Ser.). 1966. pap. text ed. 7.95x (ISBN 0-89197-185-8). Irvington.

--Fundamental Principles of the Metaphysics of Morals. Abbott, Thomas K., tr. 1949. pap. 4.24 scp (ISBN 0-672-60177-X, LLA16). Bobbs.

--Grounding for the Metaphysics of Morals. Ellington, James W., tr. from Ger. LC 80-28839. (HPC Philosophical Classics Ser.). 80p. 1981. lib. bdg. 16.50 (ISBN 0-915145-01-4); pap. text ed. 3.45 (ISBN 0-915145-00-6). Hackett Pub.

--Groundwork of the Metaphysics of Morals. Paton, H. J., tr. Orig. Title: Moral Law. pap. 6.95x (ISBN 0-06-131159-6, TB1159, Torch). Har-Row.

--Kant's Cosmogony. Hastie, W., ed. 1971. Repr. 25.00 (ISBN 0-384-28575-9). Johnson Repr.

--Lectures on Ethics. Infield, Louis, tr. from Ger. LC 80-22092. 272p. 1980. pap. text ed. 6.95 (ISBN 0-915144-26-3). Hackett Pub.

--Lectures on Ethics. 11.25 (ISBN 0-8446-2348-2). Peter Smith.

--Lectures on Philosophical Theology. Wood, Allen W. & Clark, Gertrude M., trs. from Ger. LC 78-58034. 192p. 1986. pap. text ed. 7.95x (ISBN 0-8014-9379-X). Cornell U Pr.

--Metaphysical Elements of Justice: Part I of the Metaphysics of Morals. Ladd, John, tr. (Orig.). 1965. pap. 7.20 scp (ISBN 0-672-60250-4, LLA72). Bobbs.

--Metaphysical Knowledge & Transcendental Problems. (Illus.). 167p. 1985. Repr. 89.55 (ISBN 0-89901-200-0). Found Class Reprints.

--Perpetual Peace. Beck, Lewis W., tr. LC 57-3588. 1957. pap. 3.56 scp (ISBN 0-672-60227-X, LLA54). Bobbs.

--Perpetual Peace. 59.95 (ISBN 0-8490-0815-8). Gordon Pr.

--The Reconstruction in Schematic Representations of Kant's Psychological Theory of God. (Illus.). 110p. 1983. 87.45x (ISBN 0-89266-430-4). Am Classical Coll Pr.

--Religion Within Limits or Reason Alone. pap. 8.95x (ISBN 0-06-130067-5, TB67, Torch). Har-Row.

Kanter, Shamai. Rabban Gamaliel II: The Legal Traditions. LC 80-12229. (Brown Judaic Studies: No. 8). 15.00x (ISBN 0-89130-403-7, 14 00 08); pap. 10.50x (ISBN 0-89130-404-5). Scholars Pr GA.

Kantiotes, Angoustinos N. On the Divine Liturgy: Orthodox Homilies, Vol. 2. Gerostergios, Asterios, tr. (Illus.). 285p. 1986. 14.95 (ISBN 0-914744-73-9). Inst Byzantine.

Kantiotes, Augoustinos N., tr. see Gerostergios, Asterios.

Kantonen, T. A. To Live Is Christ. 1978. pap. 4.50 (ISBN 0-89536-306-2, 2028). CSS of Ohio.

Kantonen, T. A., tr. see Siirala, Aarne.

Kantor, Alfred. The Book of Alfred Kantor: An Artist's Journal of the Holocaust. (Illus.). 224p. 1987. 25.00x (ISBN 0-8052-4029-2); pap. 16.95x (ISBN 0-8052-0825-9). Schocken.

Kantor, Marvin, ed. Medieval Slavic Lives of Saints & Princes. (Michigan Slavic Translations: No. 5). 1983. 15.00 (ISBN 0-930042-44-1). Mich Slavic Pubns.

Kantor, Mattis. Chassidic Insights: A Guide for the Entangled. pap. 6.95x (ISBN 0-87068-679-8). Ktav.

Kantowicz, Edward. Corporation Sole: Cardinal Mundelein & Chicago Catholicism. LC 82-13420. (Notre Dame Studies in American Catholicism). 320p. 1983. text ed. 19.95 (ISBN 0-268-00738-1); pap. text ed. 9.95 (ISBN 0-268-00739-X). U of Notre Dame Pr.

Kantzer, Kenneth, jt. auth. see Nicholls, Bruce.

Kao, Charles C. Psychological & Religious Development: Maturity & Maturation. LC 80-5852. 382p. (Orig.). 1981. lib. bdg. 30.00 (ISBN 0-8191-1759-5); pap. text ed. 15.25 (ISBN 0-8191-1760-9). U Pr of Amer.

Kao, James. Chinese Divination. pap. 26.80 (ISBN 0-317-26229-7, 2055584). Bks Demand UMI.

Kapferer, Bruce. A Celebration of Demons: Exorcism & the Aesthetics of Healing in Sri Lanka. LC 81-48677. (Midland Bks: No. 304). (Illus.). 312p. 1983. 32.50x (ISBN 0-253-31326-0); pap. 18.50x (ISBN 0-253-20304-X). Ind U Pr.

Kapilla, Cleo & Simons, Eleanor. The Joy of Christmas: A Manual for Holiday Survival. LC 83-90104. 96p. (Orig.). 1983. pap. 7.95 (ISBN 0-686-88978-9). K & S.

Kapilla, Cleo, et al. Joy of Christmas. 96p. 1983. pap. 7.95 (ISBN 0-9611466-0-5). Wimmer Bks.

Kaplan, Aryeh. Ethics of the Talmud. 2nd ed. 336p. 1981. pap. 2.95 (ISBN 0-940118-31-9). Maznaim.

--The Handbook of Jewish Thought. 307p. 13.95 (ISBN 0-940118-27-0). Maznaim.

--Jewish Meditation: A Practical Guide. LC 84-23589. 174p. 1985. 17.95 (ISBN 0-8052-4006-3); pap. 9.95 (ISBN 0-8052-0781-3). Schocken.

--The Laws of Chanukah. 124p. pap. 5.45 (ISBN 0-940118-28-9). Maznaim.

--The Light Beyond: Adventure in Hassidic Thought. 384p. 1981. 15.95 (ISBN 0-940118-33-5). Maznaim.

--Meditation & Kabbalah. LC 81-70150. 368p. (Orig.). 1985. pap. 12.50 (ISBN 0-87728-616-7). Weiser.

--Meditation & the Bible. reprinting ed. 1978. pap. 9.95 (ISBN 0-87728-617-5). Weiser.

--The Story of Tisha B'Av. 160p. (Orig.). 1981. pap. 2.95 (ISBN 0-940118-32-7). Maznaim.

Kaplan, Aryeh, intro. by. see Magriso, Yitzchak.

Kaplan, Aryeh, tr. The Book of Esther. 268p. 8.95 (ISBN 0-686-27543-8); pap. 6.45 (ISBN 0-940118-21-1). Maznaim.

Kaplan, Aryeh, tr. & intro. by. The MeAm Lo'ez Haggadah. 216p. pap. 6.45 (ISBN 0-940118-24-6). Maznaim.

Kaplan, Aryeh, tr. The Passover Haggadah. (MeAm Lo'ez Ser.). 288p. sephardic 11.95 (ISBN 0-940118-23-8). Maznaim.

Kaplan, Aryeh, tr. see Culi, Yaakov.

Kaplan, Aryeh, tr. see Luzatto, Moshe C.

Kaplan, Aryeh, tr. see Nachman of Breslov.

Kaplan, Aryeh, tr. see Nachman of Breslov & Nathan of Breslov.

Kaplan, Ayreh, tr. see Nachman of Breslov.

Kaplan, Benjamin. Jew & His Family. LC 67-21376. 1967. 25.00x (ISBN 0-8071-0545-7). La State U Pr.

Kaplan, David & Kaplan, Marcia. Smiles. (Inspirational Ser.). (Illus.). 100p. 1982. pap. 4.95 (ISBN 0-939944-05-7). M & L Sales.

Kaplan, David & Phillips, Marcia. Cheers. (Inspirational Ser.). (Illus.). 96p. 1981. pap. 4.95 (ISBN 0-939944-04-9). M & L Sales.

Kaplan, Jonathan, ed. International Bibliography of Jewish History & Thought. 483p. 1984. lib. bdg. 41.00 (ISBN 3-598-07503-0). K G Saur.

Kaplan, Lawrence, tr. see Soloveitchik, Joseph B.

Kaplan, Louis E. Gates of Mercy. LC 79-64616. (Orig.). 1979. pap. 3.75 (ISBN 0-87203-085-7). Hermon.

Kaplan, Marcia, jt. auth. see Kaplan, David.

Kaplan, Marion. The Jewish Feminist Movement in Germany: The Campaigns of the Judischer Frauenbund, 1904-1938. LC 78-67567. (Contributions in Women's Studies: No. 8). (Illus.). lib. bdg. 29.95 (ISBN 0-313-20736-4, KGJ/). Greenwood.

Kaplan, Mordecai M. Dynamic Judaism: The Essential Writings of Mordecai M. Kaplan. Goldsmith, Emanuel S. & Scult, Mel, eds. LC 85-2391. 256p. (Orig.). 1985. text ed. 22.00x (ISBN 0-8052-3997-9); pap. 12.95 (ISBN 0-8052-0786-4). Schocken.

--Future of the American Jew. LC 67-31309. 571p. 1981. pap. 13.95 (ISBN 0-935457-13-5). Reconstructionist Pr.

--Greater Judaism in the Making. LC 59-15683. 565p. 1967. pap. 12.95 (ISBN 0-935457-14-3). Reconstructionist Pr.

--Judaism As a Civilization: Toward a Reconstruction of American-Jewish Life. LC 81-6057. 601p. 1981. 25.00 (ISBN 0-8276-0193-X, 474); pap. 12.95 (ISBN 0-8276-0194-8, 480). Jewish Pubns.

--Judaism Without Supernaturalism. LC 58-10056. 254p. 1958. pap. 6.50 (ISBN 0-935457-18-6). Reconstructionist Pr.

--The Meaning of God in Modern Jewish Religion. 1975. pap. 10.95 (ISBN 0-935457-19-4). Reconstructionist Pr.

--Questions Jews Ask. Rev ed. LC 56-8577. 532p. 1956. pap. 10.50 (ISBN 0-935457-21-6). Reconstructionist Pr.

--The Religion of Ethical Nationhood. 1970. pap. 11.50 (ISBN 0-935457-22-4). Reconstructionist Pr.

Kaplan, Mordecai M. & Cohen, Arthur A. If Not Now, When? LC 72-95901. 134p. 1973. 7.95 (ISBN 0-935457-15-1). Reconstructionist Pr.

Kaplan, Mordecai M. & Kohn, Eugene, eds. Sabbath Prayerbook. LC 57-9678. 573p. 1979. 11.50 (ISBN 0-935457-32-1). Reconstructionist Pr.

Kaplan, Mordecai M., et al, eds. High Holiday Prayerbook: Rosh Hashanah, Vol. 1. 360p. 1948. 9.00 (ISBN 0-935457-29-1). Reconstructionist Pr.

--High Holiday Prayerbook: Yom Kippur, Vol. 2. 597p. 1948. 13.00 (ISBN 0-935457-30-5). Reconstructionist Pr.

--The Faith of America. LC 51-14109. 328p. 1951. pap. 4.95 (ISBN 0-935457-33-X). Reconstructionist Pr.

Kaplan, Mordecai M., et al, eds. see Jewish Reconstructionist Foundation.

Kaplan, Morton A. Justice, Human Nature, & Political Obligation. LC 76-8145. 1976. 18.95 (ISBN 0-02-916890-2). Free Pr.

Kaplan, N. & Katsanos, T. Origins of American Transcendentalism. 1975. pap. 11.95x (ISBN 0-8084-0415-6). New Coll U Pr.

Kaplan, Nathaniel, jt. auth. see Katsaros, Thomas.

Kaplan, Paul H. The Rise of the Black Magus in Western Art. Seidel, Linda, ed. LC 85-8461. (Studies in the Fine Arts: Iconography: No. 10). 344p. 1985. 49.95 (ISBN 0-8357-1667-8). UMI Res Pr.

Kaplan, Steven K. & Schoeneberg, Lynn A. New Approaches in Pastoral Counseling. 1987. text ed. 19.95 (ISBN 0-8290-1806-9). Irvington.

Kaplan, Steven L., ed. Understanding Popular Culture: Europe from the Middle Ages to the Nineteenth Century. LC 84-1001. (New Babylon, Studies in the Social Sciences: No. 40). viii, 311p. 1984. 64.75x (ISBN 3-11-009600-5). Mouton.

Kaplan, Sylvia R., jt. auth. see Levi, Shonie B.

Kaplan, Usher, ed. see Klein, A. M.

Kapleau, Philip. The Three Pillars of Zen: Teaching, Practice, Enlightenment. LC 78-22794. (Illus.). 1980. pap. 9.95 (ISBN 0-385-14786-4, Anch). Doubleday.

--Zen: Dawn in the West. LC 78-22794. (Illus.). 1980. pap. 5.95 (ISBN 0-385-14274-9, Anch). Doubleday.

Kapleau, Roshi P. To Cherish All Life: A Buddhist View of Animal Slaughter & Meat Eating. LC 81-51149. (Illus., Orig.). 1981. pap. text ed. 4.25 (ISBN 0-940306-00-X). Zen Ctr.

Kaploon, Uri, ed. see Zevin, Shlomo Y.

Kaploun, Uri, tr. see Zevin, Schlomo Y.

Kaploun, Uri, tr. see Zevin, Shlomo Y.

Kapoor, Jagdish C. Bhagavad-Gita: An International Bibliography of Imprints, 1785-1979. LC 82-24253. 425p. 1983. lib. bdg. 66.00 (ISBN 0-8240-9266-X). Garland Pub.

Kapp, Ardeth G. I Walk by Faith. 1987. 9.95 (ISBN 0-87579-072-0). Deseret Bk.

Kappeler, Max. The Christ Idea. LC 79-868476. 30p. 1975. pap. 3.50 (ISBN 0-85241-079-4). Kappeler Inst Pub.

--Compendium for the Study of Christian Science: No. 1, Introduction. 28p. 1951. pap. 3.50 (ISBN 0-85241-055-7). Kappeler Inst Pub.

--Compendium for the Study of Christian Science: No. 10, Love. 23p. 1953. pap. 3.50 (ISBN 0-85241-064-6). Kappeler Inst Pub.

--Compendium for the Study of Christian Science: No. 2, The Seven Days of Creation. 24p. 1951. pap. 3.50 (ISBN 0-85241-056-5). Kappeler Inst Pub.

--Compendium for the Study of Christian Science: No. 3, The Commandments, the Beatitudes, the Lord's Prayer. 29p. 1951. pap. 3.50 (ISBN 0-85241-057-3). Kappeler Inst Pub.

--Compendium for the Study of Christian Science: No. 4, Mind. 35p. 1951. pap. 3.50 (ISBN 0-85241-058-1). Kappeler Inst Pub.

--Compendium for the Study of Christian Science: No. 5, Spirit. 28p. 1951. pap. 3.50 (ISBN 0-85241-059-X). Kappeler Inst Pub.

--Compendium for the Study of Christian Science: No. 6, Soul. 23p. 1952. pap. 3.50 (ISBN 0-85241-060-3). Kappeler Inst Pub.

--Compendium for the Study of Christian Science: No. 7, Principle. 25p. 1952. pap. 3.50 (ISBN 0-85241-061-1). Kappeler Inst Pub.

--Compendium for the Study of Christian Science: No. 8, Life. 23p. 1952. pap. 3.50 (ISBN 0-85241-062-X). Kappeler Inst Pub.

--Compendium for the Study of Christian Science: No. 9, Truth. 20p. 1953. pap. 3.50 (ISBN 0-85241-063-8). Kappeler Inst Pub.

--The Development of the Christian Science Idea & Practice. LC 73-178890. 78p. 1970. pap. 6.50 (ISBN 0-85241-092-1). Kappeler Inst Pub.

--The Epistles in the Light of Christian Science. LC 72-200094. 253p. 1962. 14.00 (ISBN 0-85241-042-5). Kappeler Inst Pub.

--Epitomes for the Structural Interpretation of the Christian Science Textbook. LC 82-82377. 120p. 1982. write for info. (ISBN 0-942958-06-3). Kappeler Inst Pub.

--Exodus. LC 82-80905. (Bible in the Light of Christian Science Ser.: Vol. II). 90p. (Orig.). 1982. pap. 6.00 (ISBN 0-942958-01-2). Kappeler Inst Pub.

--First & Second Samuel. Larson, Rory, tr. from Ger. LC 82-80904. (The Bible in the Light of Christian Science Ser.: Vol. IV). Orig. Title: Die Wissenschaft der Bibel. Tr. of Das Buch 1 und 2 Samuel. 200p. 1985. 12.00 (ISBN 0-942958-10-1). Kappeler Inst Pub.

--The Four Levels of Spiritual Consciousness. LC 72-883567. 198p. 1970. 14.00 (ISBN 0-85241-091-3). Kappeler Inst Pub.

--Introduction to the Science of Christian Science. LC 79-313991. 169p. 1978. 12.00 (ISBN 0-85241-099-9). Kappeler Inst Pub.

--Joshua, Judges. Larson, Rory, tr. from Ger. LC 82-80904. (The Bible in the Light of Christian Science Ser.: Vol. 3). Orig. Title: Die Wissenschaft der Bibel, Das Buch Josua und Das Buch der Richter. 210p. (Orig.). 1983. pap. 12.00 (ISBN 0-942958-07-1). Kappeler Inst Pub.

--Metaphysics & Science in Christian Science. (Orig.). 1985. pap. 3.50 (ISBN 0-942958-11-X). Kappeler Inst Pub.

--The Minor Prophets in the Light of Christian Science. LC 64-36062. 214p. 1962. 14.00 (ISBN 0-85241-041-7). Kappeler Inst Pub.

--The Seven Synonyms for God. Lee, Kathleen, tr. from Ger. LC 83-83266. Tr. of Die sieben Synonyme fur Gott. 400p. 35.00 (ISBN 0-942958-09-8). Kappeler Inst Pub.

--The Spiritual Breakthrough to the Next Millennium. LC 85-82058. 75p. 1986. pap. 7.00 (ISBN 0-942958-12-8). Kappeler Inst Pub.

--The Spiritual Principle of Prayer. 26p. 1969. pap. 3.50 (ISBN 0-85241-077-8). Kappeler Inst Pub.

--The Structure of the Christian Science Textbook: Our Way of Life. LC 58-26857. 206p. 1954. 14.00 (ISBN 0-85241-071-9). Kappeler Inst Pub.

--Why Study Christian Science as a Science? 30p. 1973. pap. 3.50 (ISBN 0-85241-040-9). Kappeler Inst Pub.

Kappen, Sebastian. Jesus & Freedom. LC 76-25927. 186p. (Orig.). 1977. 4.48 (ISBN 0-88344-232-9). Orbis Bks.

Kapsner, Oliver L., ed. A Benedictine Bibliography: An Author-Subject Union List. LC 81-20790. 832p. 1982. first suppl. 22.50 (ISBN 0-8146-1258-X). Liturgical Pr.

Kapstein, Israel J., jt. tr. see Braude, William G.

Kapstein, M., jt. auth. see Aziz, Barbara N.

Kapur, Rajiv A. Sikh Separatism: The Politics of Faith. 240p. 1986. text ed. 29.95x (ISBN 0-04-320179-2). Allen Unwin.

Kar, Bijayananda. Indian Philosophy: An Analytical Study. 1986. 17.00x (ISBN 0-317-44233-3, Pub. by Ajanta). South Asia Bks.

Karagulla, Shafica. Breakthrough to Creativity. 12.95 (ISBN 0-87516-034-4). De Vorss.

Karaka, Dosabhai F. History of the Parsis, 2 vols. LC 74-21259. Repr. of 1884 ed. Set. 70.00 (ISBN 0-404-12812-2). AMS Pr.

Karandikar, Maheshwar A. Islam in India's Transition to Modernity. 1972. lib. bdg. 35.00 (ISBN 0-8371-2337-2, KAI/). Greenwood.

Karant-Nunn, Susan C. Luther's Pastors: The Reformation in the Ernestine Countryside. LC 79-51539. (Transactions Ser.: Vol. 69, Pt. 8). 1979. 8.00 (ISBN 0-87169-698-3). Am Philos.

--Zwickau in Transition, Fifteen-Hundred to Fifteen Forty-Seven: The Reformation as an Agent of Change. 1987. 29.50x (ISBN 0-8142-0421-X). Ohio St U Pr.

Karas, Joza. Music in Terezin Nineteen Forty-One to Nineteen Forty Five. LC 84-24411. (Illus.). 212p. 1985. 16.95x (ISBN 0-918728-34-7). Pendragon NY.

Karay, Diane. All the Seasons of Mercy. LC 86-18948. 156p. (Orig.). 1987. pap. 7.95 (ISBN 0-664-24067-4). Westminster.

Karff, Samuel E. Agada: The Language of Jewish Faith. 15.00x (ISBN 0-87820-114-9). Ktav.

Karim, A. Beauty & Wisdom of the Holy Quran. 4.95 (ISBN 0-686-18519-6). Kazi Pubns.

Karim, F. Heroes of Islam. Incl. Bk. 1. Muhammad; Bk. 2. Abu Bakr; Bk. 3. Umar; Bk. 4. Othman; Bk. 5. Ali; Bk. 6. Khalid Bin Walid; Bk. 7. Mohammad Bin Qasim; Bk. 8. Mahmood of Ghazni; Bk. 9. Mohyuddin; Bk. 10. Sultan Tipu; Bk. 11. Aisha the Truthful; Bk. 12. Hussain the Martyr; Bk. 13. Some Companions of the Prophet-I; Bk. 14. Some Companions of the Prophet-II; Bk. 15. Some Companions of the Prophet-III. pap. 37.50 complete set (ISBN 0-686-18393-2); pap. 2.50 ea bk. Kazi Pubns.

Kariuki, Joseph. The Possibility of Universal Moral Judgement in Existential Ethics: A Critical Analysis of the Phenomenology of Moral Experience According to Jean-Paul Sartre. (European University Studies: Series 20, Philosophy: Vol. 87). 363p. 1981. 37.95 (ISBN 3-261-04962-6). P Lang Pubs.

Karlinsky, Isaiah & Karlinsky, Ruth. My First Book of Mitzvos. (Illus.). 1986. 7.95 (ISBN 0-87306-388-0). Feldheim.

Karlinsky, Ruth, jt. auth. see Karlinsky, Isaiah.

Karnow, G., tr. see Wolff, Otto.

Karo, Joseph Ben Ephraim. The Traditional Jewish Law of Sale: Shulhan Arukh Hoshen Mishpat, Chapters 189-240. Passamaneck, Stephen M., tr. LC 83-4287. (Hebrew Union College Monographs No. 9). 1983. 20.00x (ISBN 0-87820-408-3). Hebrew Union Coll Pr.

Karo, Nancy & Mickelson, Alvera. La Aventura de Morir. Flores, Jose, tr. from Eng. LC 77-15812. Tr. of Adventure in Dying. (Span.). 197p. 1977. pap. 4.50 (ISBN 0-89922-098-3). Edit Caribe.

Karotempel, Sebastian. Albizuri Among the Lyngams: A Brief History of the Catholic Mission Among the Lyngams on North East India. 1986. 17.50x (ISBN 0-8364-1569-8, Pub. by KL Mukhopadhyay). South Asia Bks.

Karp, Abraham J. Haven & Home: A History of the Jews in America. LC 84-5530. 416p. 1985. 24.95 (ISBN 0-8052-3920-0). Schocken.

Karp, Abraham. J. Haven & Home: A History of the Jews in America. 416p. 1986. pap. 9.95 (ISBN 0-8052-0817-8). Schocken.

Karp, Abraham J. The Jewish Way of Life & Thought. 1981. pap. 9.95x (ISBN 0-87068-717-4). Ktav.

--To Give Life: The UJA in the Shaping of the American Jewish Community. LC 80-16487. 224p. 1980. 12.95 (ISBN 0-8052-3751-8). Schocken.

Karp, Abraham J., intro. by. Beginnings: Early American Judaica a Collection of Ten Publications in Facsimile, Illustrative of the Religious, Communal, Cultural & Political Life of American Jewry, 1761-1845. LC 75-23405. (Illus.). 1975. 20.00 (ISBN 0-8276-0076-3, 376). Jewish Pubns.

Karp, Deborah. Heroes of American Jewish History. 1972. pap. 6.95x (ISBN 0-87068-394-2). Ktav.

--Heroes of American Jewish History. Effron, Benjamin, ed. 155p. pap. 6.95 (ISBN 0-686-95130-1). ADL.

--Heroes of Jewish Thought. (Illus.). 1965. pap. 6.95x (ISBN 0-87068-538-4). Ktav.

--Heroes of Modern Jewish Thought. (Illus.). 1966. pap. 6.95x (ISBN 0-87068-539-2). Ktav.

Karpeles, Gustav. Jewish Literature & Other Essays. facsimile ed. LC 78-37159. (Essay Index Reprint Ser). Repr. of 1895 ed. 22.00 (ISBN 0-8369-2512-2). Ayer Co Pubs.

Karris, Robert. Following Jesus: A Guide to the Gospels. (Biblical Ser.). 1973. pap. 1.25 (ISBN 0-8199-0514-3). Franciscan Herald.

--The Gospel of St. Luke. (Read & Pray Ser.). 1974. 1.75 (ISBN 0-8199-0626-3). Franciscan Herald.

Karris, Robert, ed. see Schenke, Ludger.

Karris, Robert, ed. see Weiser, Alfons.

Karris, Robert J. Luke, Artist & Theologian. LC 84-61030. 144p. (Orig.). 1985. pap. 7.95 (ISBN 0-8091-2651-6). Paulist Pr.

--Pastoral Epistles. (New Testament Message Ser.: Vol. 17). 9.95 (ISBN 0-89453-205-7); pap. 5.95 (ISBN 0-89453-140-9). M Glazier.

Karris, Robert J., jt. auth. see Getty, Mary A.

Karris, Robert J., jt. auth. see Havener, Ivan.

Karris, Robert J., jt. auth. see Kurz, William S.

Karris, Robert J., jt. auth. see Pilch, John J.

Karris, Robert J., ed. Collegeville Bible Commentary Series, 11 Vols. 1983. Set. pap. 28.00. Liturgical Pr.

Karris, Robert J., ed. see Endres, John C.

Karris, Robert J., ed. see Flanagan, Neal M.

Karris, Robert J., ed. see Harrington, Daniel J.

Karris, Robert J., ed. see Kodell, Jerome.

Karris, Robert J., ed. see MacRae, George W.

Karris, Robert J., ed. see Neyrey, Jerome H.

Karris, Robert J., ed. see Perkins, Pheme.

Karris, Robert J., ed. see Van Linden, Philip.

Karris, Robert J., tr. see Lohse, Eduard.

Karssen, Gien. Getting the Most Out of Being Single. rev. ed. LC 82-62240. 192p. 1983. pap. 3.95 (ISBN 0-89109-505-5). NavPress.

--Her Name Is Woman, 2 bks. LC 77-81187. Bk. 1, 1975. pap. 5.95 (ISBN 0-89109-420-2); Bk. 2, 1977. pap. 5.95 (ISBN 0-89109-424-5). NavPress.

--The Man Who Was Different. 1987. price not set (ISBN 0-89109-136-X). NavPress.

Karsten, Dennis. Are You Well, Why Not? 96p. (Orig.). 1983. pap. 2.95 (ISBN 0-88144-011-6). Christian Pub.

Karta, Neturei. Judaism & Zionism: Principles & Definitions. 1980. lib. bdg. 59.95 (ISBN 0-87700-305-X). Revisionist Pr.

Karuna Jemal, Sophia. The Story of Joy. (Illus.). 1978. pap. 3.00 (ISBN 0-932286-00-3). Suratao.

Karve, Iravati. Yuganta: The End of an Epoch. 1974. lib. bdg. 4.50x (ISBN 0-8364-0482-3). South Asia Bks.

Kasawara, Kenju. The Dharma-Samgraha, an Ancient Collection of Buddhist Technical Terms. Muller, F. Max & Wenzel, H., eds. LC 78-72425. Repr. of 1885 ed. 17.50 (ISBN 0-404-17286-5). AMS Pr.

Kaschmitter, William A. About Happiness. 100p. 1983. pap. 5.00 (ISBN 0-912414-34-0). Lumen Christi.

--The Spirituality of the Catholic Church. 980p. 1982. 20.00 (ISBN 0-912414-33-2). Lumen Christi.

Kasdorf, Hans. Christian Conversion in Context. LC 80-12871. 208p. 1980. pap. 9.95 (ISBN 0-8361-1926-6). Herald Pr.

Kasemann, Ernst. Commentary on Romans. Bromiley, Geoffrey W., tr. 1978. 25.95 (ISBN 0-8028-3499-X). Eerdmans.

--Jesus Means Freedom. Clarke, Frank, tr. from Ger. LC 75-94357. 168p. (Orig.). 1972. pap. 6.50 (ISBN 0-8006-1235-3, 1-1235). Fortress.

--Perspectives on Paul. LC 79-157540. pap. 45.80 (2029296). Bks Demand UMI.

--The Testament of Jesus: A Study of the Gospel of John in the Light of Chapter 17. LC 78-104781. 96p. (Orig.). 1978. pap. 3.95 (ISBN 0-8006-1399-6, 1-1399). Fortress.

--The Wandering People of God: An Investigation of the Letter to the Hebrews. Harrisville, Roy A., tr. LC 84-20523. 272p. (Orig.). 1984. 21.95 (ISBN 0-8066-2121-4, 10-6940). Augsburg.

Kasemann, Ernst, et al. Distinctive Protestant & Catholic Themes Reconsidered. Funk, Robert W. & Ebeling, Gerhard, eds. 1967. lib. bdg. 17.50x (ISBN 0-88307-161-4). Gannon.

Kashaf Abdul Haq, jt. auth. see Jones, Fraymond, Jr.

Kashap, S. Paul. Spinoza & Moral Freedom. (SUNY Series in Philosophy). 130p. 1987. text ed. 32.50x (ISBN 0-88706-529-5); pap. 10.95x. State U NY Pr.

Kashap, S. Paul, ed. Studies in Spinoza: Critical & Interpretative Essays. LC 71-174459. 360p. 1973. pap. 10.95x (ISBN 0-520-02590-3, CAMPUS 109). U of Cal Pr.

Kasher, Aryek. The Jews in Hellenistic & Roman Egypt: The Struggle for Equal Rights. 442p. 1985. lib. bdg. 90.00x (ISBN 3-16-144829-4, Pub. by J C B Mohr BRD). Coronet Bks.

Kasher, M. M. Encyclopedia of Biblical Interpretation, 9 vols. Set. 35.00 ea. (ISBN 0-87068-315-2). Ktav.

Kasher, Menachem M. Israel Passover Haggadah. LC 64-17316. (Illus.). 1983. Repr. of 1964 ed. 15.00 (ISBN 0-88400-018-4). Shengold.

Kashima, Tetsuden. Buddhism in America: The Social Organization of an Ethnic Religious Institution. LC 76-57837. (Contributions in Sociology: No. 26). (Illus.). 1977. lib. bdg. 29.95 (ISBN 0-8371-9534-9, KSO/). Greenwood.

Kashinath. The Scientific Vedanta. LC 73-900893. 129p. 1974. 7.50x (ISBN 0-89684-451-X). Orient Bk Dist.

Kashyap, Lalitesh, jt. auth. see Dash, Bhagwan.

Kaspar, Walter. God of Jesus Christ. rev. ed. 450p. 1986. text ed. 14.95 (ISBN 0-8245-0777-0). Crossroad NY.

Kasper, Walter. Faith & the Future. LC 82-12720. 192p. 1982. 12.95 (ISBN 0-8245-0504-2). Crossroad NY.

--God of Jesus Christ. 1984. 24.50x (ISBN 0-8245-0629-4). Crossroad NY.

--God's Time for Mankind. 93p. 1983. 8.00 (ISBN 0-8199-0812-6). Franciscan Herald.

--Introduction to Christian Faith. Smith, David, tr. from Ger. LC 80-82808. 224p. 1981. pap. 4.95 (ISBN 0-8091-2324-X). Paulist Pr.

--Jesus the Christ. LC 76-20021. 294p. 1977. pap. 9.95 (ISBN 0-8091-2081-X). Paulist Pr.

--Theology of Christian Marriage. LC 81-5444. 112p. 1983. pap. 7.95 (ISBN 0-8245-0559-X). Crossroad NY.

Kasravi, Ahmad. On Religion: Shi'ism & on Islam, Bk. 1. Jazayery, Mohammad A., ed. Ghanoonparvar, M. R., tr. from Persian. 180p. Date not set. lib. bdg. write for info. (ISBN 0-939214-39-3); pap. text ed. write for info. (ISBN 0-939214-42-3). Mazda Pubs.

Kassis, Hanna E. A Concordance of the Qur'an. LC 82-40100. 1400p. 1984. 95.00x (ISBN 0-520-04327-8). U of Cal Pr.

Kaste, Omar, tr. see Harupa, Gisela & Nold, Liselotte.

Kasten, Lloyd & Anderson, Jean. Concordance to the Celestina. 1977. 12.50 (ISBN 0-87535-124-7). Hispanic Soc.

Kastenaum, Robert, ed. see Frazer, James G.

Kastenaum, Robert, ed. see Howells, William D., et al.

Kastenaum, Robert, ed. see Irion, Paul E.

Kastenaum, Robert, ed. see Landsberg, Paul-Louis.

Kastenaum, Robert, ed. see Walker, George A.

Kastenbaum, Robert, ed. Death As a Speculative Theme in Religious, Scientific, & Social Thought: An Original Anthology. LC 76-19566. (Death & Dying Ser.). 1977. Repr. of 1976 ed. lib. bdg. 29.00x (ISBN 0-405-09562-7). Ayer Co Pubs.

--Return to Life: Two Imaginings of the Lazarus Theme. an original anthology ed. LC 76-19587. (Death & Dying Ser.). 1977. Repr. of 1976 ed. lib. bdg. 19.00x (ISBN 0-405-09582-1). Ayer Co Pubs.

Kastenbaum, Robert, ed. see Abrahamsson, Hans.

Kastenbaum, Robert, ed. see Austin, Mary.

Kastenbaum, Robert, ed. see Barth, Karl.

Kastenbaum, Robert, ed. see Carrington, Hereward.

Kastenbaum, Robert, jt. ed. see Comper, Frances M. M.

Kastenbaum, Robert, ed. see Fechner, Gustav T.

Kastenbaum, Robert, ed. see Fulton, Robert.

Kastenbaum, Robert, ed. see Gorer, Geoffrey.

Kastenbaum, Robert, ed. see Gruman, Gerald J.

Kastenbaum, Robert, ed. see Taylor, Jeremy.

Kastenbaum, Robert, ed. see Warthin, Alfred S.

Kastenbaum, Robert, ed. see Whyte, Florence.

Kastenbaum, Robert, ed. see Zandee, Jan.

Kasulis, T. P. Zen Action-Zen Person. LC 80-27858. 192p. 1985. pap. text ed. 7.95x (ISBN 0-8248-1023-6). UH Pr.

Kasulis, Thomas P., ed. see Yuasa, Yasuo.

Kasuya, Masahiro. The Beginning of the World. LC 81-3582. (Illus.). 1982. 8.95g (ISBN 0-687-02765-9). Abingdon.

Katchen, Aaron L. Christian Hebraists & Dutch Rabbis: Seventeenth Century Apologetics & the Study of Maimonides' Mishneh Torah. (Harvard Judaic Texts & Studies: No. 3). 430p. 1985. text ed. 28.00x (ISBN 0-674-12865-6). Harvard U Ctr Jewish.

Katenkamp, Jane B. Respecting Life: An Activity Guide. (Illus.). 144p. (Orig.). 1985. pap. 14.95 (ISBN 1-55586-964-5). US Catholic.

Kater, John. Another Letter of John to James. (Illus.). 64p. (Orig.). 1982. pap. 3.95 (ISBN 0-8164-2376-8, HarpR). Har-Row.

--Christians on the Right: The Moral Majority in Perspective. 176p. (Orig.). 1982. pap. 8.95 (ISBN 0-8164-2379-2, HarpR). Har-Row.

--The Letter of John to James. (Illus.). 64p. (Orig.). 1981. pap. 3.95 (ISBN 0-8164-2344-X, HarpR). Har-Row.

Kato, Bunno, et al, trs. The Threefold Lotus Sutra. LC 74-23158. Orig. Title: Hokke Sambu-Kyo. 404p. 1975. 19.75 (ISBN 0-8348-0105-1); pap. 10.95 (ISBN 0-8348-0106-X). Weatherhill.

Katoppo, Marianne. Compassionate & Free: An Asian Woman's Theology. (Illus.). 96p. (Orig.). 1980. pap. 4.95 (ISBN 0-88344-085-7). Orbis Bks.

Katsanos, T., jt. auth. see Kaplan, N.

Katsaros, Thomas & Kaplan, Nathaniel. The Western Mystical Tradition: An Intellectual History of Western Civilization, Vol. 1. 1969. 15.95x (ISBN 0-8084-0316-8); pap. 11.95x (ISBN 0-8084-0317-6). New Coll U Pr.

Katsh, A. I. The Biblical Heritage of American Democracy. pap. 9.95x (ISBN 0-87068-488-4). Ktav.

Katsh, Abraham I. Judaism in Islam: Biblical & Talmudic Background of the Koran & Its Commentaries. 3rd ed. LC 80-50001. 1980. pap. 9.75 (ISBN 0-87203-086-5). Hermon.

Katsh, Abraham I., ed. Bar Mitzvah Illustrated. 8th ed. LC 76-23713. (Illus.). 1976. 18.95 (ISBN 0-88400-048-6). Shengold.

Katsujo, Terayama, jt. auth. see Sogen, Omori.

Kattani, Sulayman. Imam Ali: Source of Light, Wisdom & Might. Howard, I. K., tr. 148p. Date not set. text ed. 25.00 (ISBN 0-7103-0153-7). Methuen Inc.

Katter, Reuben L. History of Creation & Origin of the Species: A Scientific Theological Viewpoint (How the Universe Came into Being) 3rd ed. 480p. 1984. 16.95 (ISBN 0-911806-01-6, C13374); pap. 11.95 (ISBN 0-911806-00-8). Theotes.

--Jesus Christ: The Divine Executive; Architect of the Universe (Why the Universe Was Created) 400p. 1986. 18.95. Theotes.

--A Paradisical Universe for Man: Man's Preparation for Sharing. 2nd ed. 200p. 1984. pap. 5.95 (ISBN 0-911806-03-2). Theotes.

Katterjohn, Arthur & Fackler, Mark. Lord, When? LC 76-16284. 1976. pap. 1.50 (ISBN 0-88419-003-X). Creation Hse.

Katz, Eliezer. A Classified Concordance, 4 vols. Incl. Vol. 1. The Torah. 415p. 1964. 30.00x (ISBN 0-8197-0382-6); Vol. 2. The Early Prophets. 702p. 1967. 30.00x (ISBN 0-8197-0383-4); Vol. 3. The Later Prophets. 683p. 1970. 30.00x (ISBN 0-8197-0384-2). Bloch.

--Classified Concordance: To the Bible & Its Various Subjects, Vol. 4. (Hebrew & Eng.). 1000p. 1974. 40.00x (ISBN 0-8197-0385-0). Bloch.

Katz, Ernst. About Your Relation to Rudolf Steiner. (Illus.). 64p. (Orig.). 1986. pap. 6.95 (ISBN 0-9613745-0-0, 86-1955). E Katz.

Katz, Esther & Ringelheim, Joan M. Women Surviving: The Holocaust-Proceedings of the Conference. (Occasional Papers: No. 1). 100p. (Orig.). 1983. pap. write for info. (ISBN 0-913865-00-1). Inst Res Hist.

Katz, Esther, jt. ed. see Ringelheim, Joan.

Katz, Jacob. Exclusiveness & Tolerance. 208p. 1983. pap. 7.95x (ISBN 0-87441-365-6). Behrman.

--Exclusiveness & Tolerance: Studies in Jewish-Gentile Relations in Medieval & Modern Times. LC 80-12181. (Scripta Judaica: No. III). xv, 200p. 1980. Repr. of 1961 ed. lib. bdg. 24.75x (ISBN 0-313-22387-4, KAEX). Greenwood.

--From Prejudice to Destruction: Anti-Semitism, 1700-1933. LC 80-14404. 398p. 1980. 27.50x (ISBN 0-674-32505-2). Harvard U Pr.

--From Prejudice to Destruction: Anti-Semitism, 1700-1933. 400p. 1982. pap. 7.95 (ISBN 0-674-32507-9). Harvard U Pr.

--Jewish Emancipation & Self-Emancipation. 179p. 1986. 14.95 (ISBN 0-8276-0261-8). Jewish Pubns.

--Jews & Freemasons in Europe, 1723-1939. Oschry, Leonard, tr. from Heb. LC 71-115475. 1970. 22.50x (ISBN 0-674-47480-5). Harvard U Pr.

--Out of the Ghetto: The Social Background of Jewish Emancipation, 1770-1870. LC 72-86386. 1973. 18.50x (ISBN 0-674-64775-0). Harvard U Pr.

--The Traditional Jewish Family in Historical Perspective. 1983. pap. 1.00 (ISBN 0-87495-048-1). Am Jewish Comm.

Katz, Jacob, ed. Toward Modernity: The European Jewish Model. 246p. (Orig.). 1986. 24.95 (ISBN 0-88738-092-1). Transaction Bks.

Katz, Lilian G. & Ward, Evangeline H. Ethical Behavior in Early Childhood Education. LC 78-57538. 26p. 1978. pap. text ed. 2.00 (ISBN 0-912674-61-X, NAEYC #112). Natl Assn Child Ed.

Katz, Menke. A Chair for Elijah. LC 85-61563. (Illus.). 104p. 1985. 9.95 (ISBN 0-912292-78-4); pap. 6.95 (ISBN 0-912292-77-6). The Smith.

Katz, Milton S. Ban the Bomb: A History of SANE, the Committee for a SANE Nuclear Policy, 1957-1985. LC 85-24824. (Contributions in Political Science Ser.: No. 147). (Illus.). 230p. 1986. lib. bdg. 35.00 (ISBN 0-313-24167-8, KBB/). Greenwood.

Katz, Mordecai. Protection of the Weak in the Talmud. LC 26-5707. (Columbia University. Oriental Studies: No. 24). Repr. of 1925 ed. 12.50 (ISBN 0-404-50514-7). AMS Pr.

Katz, Mordechai. Lilmod Ulelamade: From the Teachings of Our Sages on Judges. (Rothman Foundation Ser.). 1986. 8.95 (ISBN 0-87306-207-8); pap. 6.95 (ISBN 0-87306-928-5). Feldheim.

--Lilmod Ulelamade on Joshua. (Rothman Foundation Ser.). 1984. 8.95 (ISBN 0-87306-925-0); pap. 6.95 (ISBN 0-87306-926-9). Feldheim.

--Lishmor Velaasos: Guide to Basic Principles of Jewish Law & Their Applications in Theory & Practice. (Rothman Foundation Ser.). 159p. 1981. 8.95 (ISBN 0-87306-974-9); pap. 6.95 (ISBN 0-317-42416-5). Feldheim.

--Menucha Vesimcha. (Rothman Foundation Ser.). 1982. 7.95 (ISBN 0-87306-977-3); pap. 5.95 (ISBN 0-317-42411-4). Feldheim.

Katz, Nathan, ed. Buddhist & Western Psychology. LC 82-12325. 300p. (Orig.). 1983. pap. 15.00 (ISBN 0-87773-758-4, Prajna). Shambhala Pubns.

Katz, Neil, jt. auth. see Lawyer, John.

Katz, Peter. The Text of the Septuagint: Its Corruptions & Their Emendation. Gooding, D. W., ed. LC 74-161292. pap. 110.00 (ISBN 0-317-28405-3, 2022451). Bks Demand UMI.

Katz, Robert L. Pastoral Care & the Jewish Tradition: Empathic Process & Religious Counseling. LC 84-47925. (Theology & Pastoral Care Ser.). 128p. 1984. pap. 7.95 (ISBN 0-8006-1731-2). Fortress.

Katz, Ruth. Pumpkin Personalities. (Illus.). 1979. 5.95 (ISBN 0-8027-6364-2); PLB 5.85 (ISBN 0-8027-6365-0). Walker & Co.

Katz, S. Jews in the Visigothic & Frankish Kingdoms of Spain & Gaul. (Mediaeval Academy of America Publications). 1937. 21.00 (ISBN 0-527-01697-7). Kraus Repr.

Katz, Stephen, ed. see Meisl, Josef.

Katz, Steven, ed. Jewish Neo-Platonism: Selected Essays. An Original Anthology. LC 79-7178. (Jewish Philosophy, Mysticism & History of Ideas Ser.). 1980. lib. bdg. 48.50x (ISBN 0-405-12236-5). Ayer Co Pubs.

--Maimonides: Selected Essays, Original Anthology. LC 79-7176. (Jewish Philosophy, Mysticism & the History of Ideas Ser.). 1980. lib. bdg. 51.50x (ISBN 0-405-12234-9). Ayer Co Pubs.

--Medieval Jewish Philosophy: Original Anthology. LC 79-7177. (Jewish Philosophy, Mysticism & the History of Ideas Ser.). (Ger., Eng., Ital, Fr. Span.). 1980. lib. bdg. 44.00x (ISBN 0-405-12235-7). Ayer Co Pubs.

--Saadiah Gaon: Selected Essays: An Original Anthology. LC 79-7171. (Jewish Philosophy, Mysticism & History of Ideas Ser.). 1980. lib. bdg. 34.50x (ISBN 0-405-12230-6). Ayer Co Pubs.

--Selected Writings of Julius Guttmann: An Original Anthology. LC 79-7175. (Jewish Philosophy, Mysticism & History of Ideas Ser.). 1980. lib. bdg. 34.50x (ISBN 0-405-12232-2). Ayer Co Pubs.

--Studies by Samuel Horodezky: An Original Anthology. LC 79-51391. (Jewish Philosophy, Mysticism & History of Ideas Ser.). 1980. lib. bdg. 17.00x (ISBN 0-405-12233-0). Ayer Co Pubs.

Katz, Steven, ed. see Abrahams, Israel.

Katz, Steven, ed. see Alexander Kohut Memorial Foundation Staff.

Katz, Steven, ed. see Bacher, Wilhelm.

Katz, Steven, ed. see Berliner, Abraham.

Katz, Steven, ed. see Brann, M. & Elbogen, I.

Katz, Steven, ed. see Brann, M. & Rosenthal, F.

Katz, Steven, jt. ed. see Cohen, Boaz.

Katz, Steven, ed. see Cohen, Hermann.

Katz, Steven, ed. see Eppenstein, Simon, et al.

Katz, Steven, jt. ed. see Finkelstein, Louis.

Katz, Steven, ed. see Formstecher, Salomon.

Katz, Steven, ed. see Fraenckelscher, Stiftung.

Katz, Steven, ed. see Geiger, Abraham.

Katz, Steven, ed. see Gesellschaft zur Forderung der Wissenschaft des Judentums.

Katz, Steven, ed. see Gudemann, Moritz.

Katz, Steven, ed. see Guttmann, Jacob.

Katz, Steven, ed. see Hess, Moses.

Katz, Steven, ed. see Hirsch, Samuel.

Katz, Steven, ed. see Horodezky, Samuel A.

Katz, Steven, ed. see Jellinek, Adolph.

Katz, Steven, ed. see Joel, David H.

Katz, Steven, ed. see Joel, Manuel.

Katz, Steven, ed. see Kaufmann, David.

Katz, Steven, ed. see Kayserling, Meyer.

Katz, Steven, jt. ed. see Krauss, Samuel.

Katz, Steven, ed. see Munk, Salomon.

Katz, Steven, ed. see Neumark, David.

Katz, Steven, ed. see Philipson, David, et al.

Katz, Steven, jt. ed. see Rosenthal, Erwin I.

Katz, Steven, ed. see Sachs, Michael.

Katz, Steven, ed. see Steinheim, Salomon L.

Katz, Steven, ed. see Steinschneider, Moritz.

Katz, Steven, jt. ed. see Zeithlin, William.

Katz, Steven, et al, eds. Judaica Festschrift zu Hermann Cohens Siebzigstem Geburtstage. LC 79-7156. (Jewish Philosophy, Mysticism & History of Ideas Ser.). 1980. Repr. of 1912 ed. lib. bdg. 60.00x (ISBN 0-405-12246-2). Ayer Co Pubs.

Katz, Steven T. The Jewish Philosophers. LC 75-7590. (Illus.). 300p. 1975. 10.95x (ISBN 0-8197-0387-7); pap. 8.95x (ISBN 0-8197-0010-X). Bloch.

--Mysticism & Philosophical Analysis. 1978. 19.95x (ISBN 0-19-520010-1); pap. 8.95x (ISBN 0-19-520011-X). Oxford U Pr.

--Mysticism & Religious Traditions. 1983. 19.95x (ISBN 0-19-503313-2, 739); pap. 9.95 (ISBN 0-19-503314-0, GB). Oxford U Pr.

--Post-Holocaust Dialogues: Critcal Studies in Modern Jewish Thought. 416p. 1983. 45.00x (ISBN 0-8147-4583-0). NYU Pr.

--Post-Holocaust Dialogues: Critical Studies in Modern Jewish Thought. 1985. pap. 15.00 (ISBN 0-8147-4587-3). NYU Pr.

Katz, Steven T., ed. Collected Papers of Jacob Guttmann: An Original Anthology. LC 79-7172. (Jewish Philosophy, Mysticism & History of Ideas Ser.). 1980. lib. bdg. 40.00x (ISBN 0-405-12231-4). Ayer Co Pubs.

--Jewish Philosophy, Mysticism & History of Ideas Series, 50 bks. (Illus.). 1980. Set. lib. bdg. 2389.00x (ISBN 0-405-12229-2). Ayer Co Pubs.

Katz, William L., jt. auth. see Halliburton, Warren J.

Katz, Yoseph. She'erit Yoseph. Siev, Asher, ed. LC 83-50567. 350p. 1984. 15.00 (ISBN 0-87203-116-0). Hermon.

Katzburg, Nathaniel. Hungary & the Jews: Policy & Legislation 1920-1943. 299p. cancelled (ISBN 965-226-020-7). Hermon.

Katzenellenbogen, Adolf. Sculptural Programs of Chartres Cathedral. (Illus.). 1964. pap. 6.95x (ISBN 0-393-00233-0, Norton Lib). Norton.

Katzenellenbogen, Adolf E. The Sculptural Programs of Chartres Cathedral: Christ, Mary, Ecclesia. LC 59-14894. pap. 57.50 (ISBN 0-317-10764-X, 2007368). Bks Demand UMI.

Kauffeld, Eugene P. Divine Footprints. 1983. pap. 9.95 (ISBN 0-8100-0148-9, 15N0382). Northwest Pub.

Kauffman, Christmas Carol. Light from Heaven. 1965. pap. 5.95 (ISBN 0-8024-3814-8). Moody.

Kauffman, Donald T. Ask & It Shall Be Given. 48p. 1986. 6.95 (ISBN 0-8378-5095-9). Gibson.

--Baker's Concise Dictionary of Religion. (Paperback Reference Library). 446p. 1985. pap. 11.95 (ISBN 0-8010-5467-2). Baker Bk.

Kauffman, Donald T., compiled by. Baker's Pocket Treasury of Religious Verse. (Direction Bks.). 384p. 1980. pap. 4.95 (ISBN 0-8010-5417-6). Baker Bk.

Kauffman, Elizabeth J., jt. auth. see Kauffman, Nancy J.

Kauffman, Friedrich. Northern Mythology. LC 76-5464. 1976. Repr. of 1903 ed. lib. bdg. 17.50 (ISBN 0-8414-5524-4). Folcroft.

Kauffman, J. H. & Harder, Leland. Anabaptists: Four Centuries Later. LC 74-30347. 400p. 1975. 14.95x (ISBN 0-8361-1136-2); pap. 6.95 o. p. (ISBN 0-8361-1137-0). Herald Pr.

Kauffman, Karen, compiled by. With Faith All Things Are Possible. (Illus.). 1983. 8.00 (ISBN 0-8378-1802-8). Gibson.

Kauffman, Milo. Personal Work. 1940. pap. 2.00 (ISBN 0-87813-951-6). Christian Light.

--Stewards of God. LC 74-13130. 264p. 1975. 9.95 (ISBN 0-8361-1747-6). Herald Pr.

Kauffman, Nancy J. & Kauffman, Elizabeth J. Heavy Bread. LC 73-75087. (Pivot Family Reader Ser). 192p. (Orig.). 1973. pap. 1.25 (ISBN 0-87983-030-1). Keats.

Kauffman, Richard A. Big Questions. (Illus.). 128p. 1984. pap. 2.95 (ISBN 0-8361-3353-6). Herald Pr.

--Pilgrimage in Mission: Leader's Guide. 60p. 1983. pap. 4.95x (ISBN 0-8361-1260-1). Herald Pr.

Kauffman, Suzanne. God Comforts His People: Activity Book. (Story Bible Ser.). (Illus.). 84p. (Orig.). 1986. pap. 3.00 (ISBN 0-8361-3411-7). Herald Pr.

--God Gives the Land Activity Book. (Story Bible Ser.: Bk. 3). 64p. 1984. pap. 3.00 (ISBN 0-8361-3359-5). Herald Pr.

Kauffmann, Friedrich. Northern Mythology. 1978. Repr. of 1903 ed. lib. bdg. 15.00 (ISBN 0-8495-3022-9). Arden Lib.

--Northern Mythology. 106p. 1980. Repr. of 1903 ed. lib. bdg. 15.00 (ISBN 0-89987-450-9). Darby Bks.

Kauffmann, Joel. The Weight. LC 79-27262. 176p. 1980. pap. 5.95 (ISBN 0-8361-3335-8). Herald Pr.

Kaufman, Arnold S., ed. see Edwards, Jonathan.

Kaufman, Daniel. Doctrines of the Bible. 639p. 1928. 12.95 (ISBN 0-8361-1358-6). Herald Pr.

Kaufman, Donald D. What Belongs to Caeser? LC 70-109939. 128p. 1969. pap. 5.95 (ISBN 0-8361-1621-6). Herald Pr.

Kaufman, Gordon D. An Essay on Theological Method. LC 75-31656. (American Academy of Religion. Studies in Religion: No. 11). 1975. pap. 10.25 (010011). Scholars Pr GA.

--God the Problem. LC 70-174543. 1972. 17.50x (ISBN 0-674-35525-3); pap. 8.95x (ISBN 0-674-35526-1). Harvard U Pr.

--Nonresistance & Responsibility, & Other Mennonite Essays. (Institute of Mennonite Studies: No. 5). 1979. pap. 7.95 (ISBN 0-87303-024-9). Faith & Life.

--Relativism, Knowledge, & Faith. LC 59-11620. pap. 38.80 (2026778). Bks Demand UMI.

--The Theological Imagination: Constructing the Concept of God. LC 81-12960. 310p. 1981. pap. 13.95 (ISBN 0-664-24393-2). Westminster.

--Theology for a Nuclear Age. 78p. 1985. 12.95 (ISBN 0-664-21400-2); pap. 8.95 (ISBN 0-664-24628-1). Westminster.

Kaufman, Milo. The Way of True Riches. LC 79-83505. (Mennonite Faith Ser: No. 6). 64p. 1979. pap. 1.50 (ISBN 0-8361-1885-5). Herald Pr.

Kaufman, Peter I. Augustinian Piety & Catholic Reform: Augustine, Colet, & Erasmus. LC 82-12491. 161p. 1982. text ed. 9.45 (ISBN 0-86554-047-0, MUP-H46). Mercer Univ Pr.

--The Polytyque Churche: Religion & Early Tudor Political Culture. 208p. 1986. 24.95 (ISBN 0-86554-211-2, MUP-H191). Mercer Univ Pr.

Kaufman, Walter, tr. see Buber, Martin, et al.

Kaufman, Walter, tr. see Nietzsche, Friedrich.

Kaufman, William E. Contemporary Jewish Philosophies. 290p. 1986. pap. text ed. 12.25 (ISBN 0-8191-5092-4). U Pr of Amer.

--Journeys: An Introductory Guide to Jewish Mysticism. LC 80-69017. 1980. 12.50 (ISBN 0-8197-0482-2); pap. 7.95 (ISBN 0-686-77548-1). Bloch.

Kaufmann, David. George Eliot & Judaism. LC 75-130251. (English Literature Ser., No. 33). 1970. Repr. of 1888 ed. lib. bdg. 27.95x (ISBN 0-8383-1141-5). Haskell.

--Gesammelte Schriften, 3 vols. Katz, Steven, ed. LC 79-7143. (Jewish Philosophy, Mysticism & the History of Ideas Ser.). (Ger.). 1980. Repr. of 1915 ed. Set. lib. bdg. 120.00x (ISBN 0-405-12268-3); lib. bdg. 40.00x ea. Vol. 1 (ISBN 0-405-12269-1). Vol. 2 (ISBN 0-405-12270-5). Vol. 3 (ISBN 0-405-12271-3). Ayer Co Pubs.

--Die Sinne: Beitrage Zur Geschichte der Physiologie und Psychologie Im Ittelalter Aus Hebraischen und Arabisch En Quellen. Katz, Steven, ed. LC 79-7141. (Jewish Philosophy, Mysticism & History of Ideas Ser.). 1980. Repr. of 1884 ed. lib. bdg. 17.00x (ISBN 0-405-12267-5). Ayer Co Pubs.

--Studien uber Salomon Ibn Gabirol. Katz, Steven, ed. LC 79-7144. (Jewish Philosophy, Mysticism & the History of Ideas Ser.). (Ger. & Hebrew.). 1980. Repr. of 1899 ed. lib. bdg. 14.00x (ISBN 0-405-12272-1). Ayer Co Pubs.

Kaufmann, Helen L. From Jehovah to Jazz: Music in America from Psalmody to the Present Day. facs. ed. LC 68-54352. (Essay Index Reprint Ser). 1968. Repr. of 1937 ed. 20.00 (ISBN 0-8369-0585-7). Ayer Co Pubs.

Kaufmann, M. Charles Kingsley: Christian Social Reformer. LC 77-20677. 1892. Repr. 30.00 (ISBN 0-8492-1416-5). R West.

--Charles Kingsley: Christian Socialist & Social Reformer. 1978. Repr. of 1892 ed. lib. bdg. 25.00 (ISBN 0-8495-3010-5). Arden Lib.

Kaufmann, Ronald G. Armadeus Prophecy & Teaching in the New Ages, Bk. 2. 155p. (Orig.). 1987. pap. 12.95 (ISBN 0-940539-02-0). Heridonius.

Kaufmann, Walter. Critique of Religion & Philosophy. 1979. pap. 13.50x (ISBN 0-691-02001-9). Princeton U Pr.

--Existentialism, Religion & Death. 1976. pap. 4.95 (ISBN 0-452-00648-1, F648, Mer). NAL.

--Tibetan Buddhist Chant: Musical Notations & Interpretations of a Song Book by the Bkah Brgyud Pa & Sa Skya Pa Sects. Norbu, Thubten Jigme, tr. LC 72-85606. (Humanities Ser.: No. 70). 578p. 1975. 25.00x (ISBN 0-253-36017-X). Ind U Pr.

Kaufmann, Yehezkel. Religion of Israel. Greenberg, Moshe, tr. LC 60-5466. 1960. 36.00x (ISBN 0-226-42728-5). U of Chicago Pr.

--The Religion of Israel: From Its Beginnings to the Babylonian Exile. Greenberg, Moshe, tr. LC 60-5466. 304p. 1972. pap. 10.95 (ISBN 0-8052-0364-8). Schocken.

Kaukola, Olavi. The Riches of Prayer. Hillila, Bernhardt, tr. LC 85-47716. 80p. 1986. pap. 3.95 (ISBN 0-8006-1861-0). Fortress.

Kaung, Stephen. Discipled to Christ. Fader, Herbert L., ed. 1976. pap. 2.25 (ISBN 0-935008-17-9). Christian Fellow Pubs.

--Discipled to Christ. Hsu, Lily, tr. from Eng. (Chinese.). 1984. pap. write for info. (ISBN 0-941598-13-6). Living Spring Pubns.

--Songs of Degrees. Fader, Herbert L., ed. 1970. 4.00 (ISBN 0-935008-32-2); pap. 2.75 (ISBN 0-935008-33-0). Christian Fellow Pubs.

--The Splendor of His Way. Hsu, Lily, tr. from Eng. (Chinese.). 1984. pap. write for info. (ISBN 0-941598-14-4). Living Spring Pubns.

--The Splendor of His Ways. Fader, Herbert L., ed. 1974. 5.00 (ISBN 0-935008-42-X); pap. 3.25 (ISBN 0-935008-43-8). Christian Fellow Pubs.

Kaung, Stephen, tr. see Nee, Watchman.

Kaung, Stephen, tr. from Chines see Nee, Watchman.

Kaung, Stephen, tr. see Nee, Watchman.

Kaung, Stephen, tr. see Watchman, Nee.

Kaung, Stephen, tr. see Watchman Nee.

Kauper, Paul G. Religion & the Constitution. LC 64-7898. (Edward Douglass White Lectures). 1964. pap. 6.95x (ISBN 0-8071-0114-1). La State U Pr.

--Religion & the Constitution. LC 64-7898. pap. 36.80 (ISBN 0-317-29869-0, 2051881). Bks Demand UMI.

Kaur, Amarjit, et al. The Punjab Story. 1985. 12.50x (ISBN 0-8364-1319-9, Pub. by Roli Books). South Asia Bks.

Kaur, Jitender. The Politics of Sikhs. 280p. 1986. 24.00x (ISBN 0-8364-1795-X, Pub. by Manohar India). South Asia Bks.

Kaur, Madanjit. The Golden Temple, Past & Present. 1985. 17.50x (ISBN 0-8364-1325-3, Pub. by Nank Dev Univ India). South Asia Bks.

Kaushik, R. P. Light of Exploration. LC 76-39622. 1977. pap. 5.95 (ISBN 0-918038-00-6). Journey Pubns.

Kautsky, Karl. Communism in Central Europe in the Time of the Reformation. Mulliken, J. L. & Mulliken, E. G., trs. LC 66-22631. 1966. Repr. of 1897 ed. 29.50x (ISBN 0-678-00193-6). Kelley.

--Foundations of Christianity. Hartmann, Jacob W., tr. from Ger. LC 72-81774. 512p. 1972. pap. 15.00 (ISBN 0-85345-262-8, PB-2628). Monthly Rev.

--Foundations of Christianity. Hartmann, Jacob W., tr. from Ger. LC 72-81774. Repr. of 1972 ed. 120.00 (ISBN 0-8357-9441-5, 2016442). Bks Demand UMI.

Kautzsch, E., ed. see Gesunius, William.

Kauz, Herman. T'ai Chi Handbook: Exercise, Meditation, Self-Defense. LC 73-10552. (Illus.). 192p. 1974. pap. 9.95 (ISBN 0-385-09370-5, Dolp). Doubleday.

Kavanagh, Aidan. On Liturgical Theology. 216p. (Orig.). 1984. pap. 9.95 (ISBN 0-916134-67-9). Pueblo Pub Co.

--The Shape of Baptism: The Rite of Christian Initiation. (Studies in the Reformed Rites of the Catholic Church: Vol. 1). 1978. pap. 9.95 (ISBN 0-916134-36-9). Pueblo Pub Co.

Kavanagh, Aidan, jt. auth. see Tiede, David L.

Kavanagh, Aidan, ed. see Mitchell, Nathan.

Kavanagh, P. J., ed. see Chesterton, G. K.

Kavanagh, Peter. Irish Mythology: A Dictionary. (Illus.). 150p. (Hand Set & Printed). 100.00 (ISBN 0-914612-00-X). Kavanagh.

--Savage Rock: Inniskeen, the History of a Parish. LC 78-58360. 1978. 20.00. Kavanagh.

Kavanaugh, Aidan. Elements of Rite. LC 84-158728. 110p. (Orig.). 1982. pap. 7.95 (ISBN 0-916134-54-7). Pueblo Pub CO.

Kavanaugh, James. Search: A Guide for Those Who Dare Ask of Life Everything Good & Beautiful. LC 85-42781. 224p. 1985. 14.95 (ISBN 0-06-250448-7, HarpR). Har-Row.

Kavanaugh, John, ed. Quaker Approach to Contemporary Problems. Repr. of 1953 ed. lib. bdg. 22.50x (ISBN 0-8371-4432-9, KAGA). Greenwood.

Kavanaugh, John F. Following Christ in a Consumer Society: The Spirituality of Cultural Resistance. LC 81-38359. 192p. (Orig.). 1981. pap. 6.95 (ISBN 0-88344-090-3). Orbis Bks.

Kavanaugh, Kieran & Rodrigues, Otilio, trs. from Span. Teresa of Avila: The Interior Castle. LC 79-66484. (Classics of Western Spirituality Ser.). 256p. 1979. 12.95 (ISBN 0-8091-0303-6); pap. 9.95 (ISBN 0-8091-2254-5). Paulist Pr.

Kavanaugh, Kieran & Rodriguez, Otilio, trs. from Span. The Collected Works of St. John of the Cross. 2nd ed. LC 78-65789. 1979. 14.95x (ISBN 0-9600876-5-6); pap. 8.95x (ISBN 0-9600876-7-2). ICS Pubns.

Kavanaugh, Kieran & Rodriguez, Otilio, trs. The Collected Works of St. Teresa of Avila, Vol. 2. LC 75-31305. 560p. 1980. pap. 6.95x (ISBN 0-9600876-6-4). ICS Pubns.

Kavanaugh, Kieran & Rodriguez, Otilio, trs. from Span. The Collected Works of St. Teresa of Avila, Vol. 3. LC 75-31305. (Illus.). 504p. (Orig.). 1985. pap. 7.95x (ISBN 0-935216-06-5). ICS Pubns.

Kavanaugh, Kieran & Rodriquez, Otillo, trs. from Span. The Collected Works of St. Teresa of Avila, Vol. 1. Incl. The Book of Her Life, Spiritual Testimonies, Soliloquies. LC 75-31305. 416p. (Orig.). 1976. 6.95x (ISBN 0-9600876-2-1). ICS Pubns.

Kavanaugh, Kiernan, ed. & intro. by. John of the Cross: Selected Writings. (Classics of Western Spirituality Ser.: No. 53). 1987. 16.95 (ISBN 0-8091-0384-2); pap. 12.95 (ISBN 0-8091-2839-X). Paulist Pr.

Kaveeshwar, G. W. The Ethics of Gita. 1971. 8.50 (ISBN 0-89684-203-7). Orient Bk Dist.

Kaviratna, Harischandra, tr. Dhammapada, Wisdom of the Buddha. LC 80-52031. 1980. 12.50 (ISBN 0-911500-39-1); pap. 7.50 (ISBN 0-911500-40-5). Theos U Pr.

Kawamura, Leslie, jt. ed. see Coward, Harold.

Kawamura, Leslie S. Bodhisattva Doctrine. 306p. 1981. pap. text ed. 11.95x (ISBN 0-919812-12-0, Pub. by Wilfrid Laurier Canada). Humanities.

Kawamura, Leslie S. & Scott, Keith, eds. Buddhist Thought & Asian Civilization: Essays in Honor of Herbert V. Genther on His Sixtieth Birthday. LC 77-71194. 1977. 25.00 (ISBN 0-913546-51-8). Dharma Pub.

Kawamura, Leslie S., tr. see Lama Mi-phan.

Kawamura, Leslie S., tr. see Ye-Shes Rgyal-Mtshan.

Kawashima, Yasuhide. Puritan Justice & the Indian: White Man's Law in Massachusetts, 1630-1763. (Illus.). xii, 258p. 1984. 35.00x (ISBN 0-8195-5068-X). Wesleyan U Pr.

Kawiak, Matthew, jt. auth. see Sullivan, Susan.

Kay, Donald, jt. ed. see Burke, John J., Jr.

Kay, Jeffrey A. Theological Aesthetics: Theology. (European University Studies: Ser. 23, Vol. 60). 115p. 1976. pap. 12.90 (ISBN 3-261-01893-3). P Lang Pubs.

Kaye, Bruce N. The Thought Structure of Romans with Special Reference to Chapter Six. 203p. (Orig.). 1979. pap. 5.95 (ISBN 0-931016-03-7). Schola Pr TX.

Kaye, Buddy, jt. auth. see Mandino, Og.

Kaye, Evelyn. The Hole in the Sheet. 224p. 1987. 14.95 (ISBN 0-8184-0437-X). Lyle Stuart.

Kaye, G. R. Hindu Astronomy: Ancient Science of the Hindus. 134p. 1981. text ed. 42.00x. Coronet Bks.

Kaye, J. Patrick. Call Me Monsignor. LC 74-78032. (Illus.). 1974. pap. 5.00 (ISBN 0-87423-008-X). Westburg.

Kaye-Smith, Sheila. Quartet in Heaven. facs. ed. LC 75-136649. (Biography Index Reprint Ser.). 1952. 18.00 (ISBN 0-8369-8044-1). Ayer Co Pubs.

Kaylor, Earl C. Out of the Wilderness: The Brethren & Two Centuries of Life in Central Pennsylvania. (Illus.). 384p. 1981. 12.50 (ISBN 0-8453-4716-0, Cornwall Bks). Assoc Univ Prs.

Kayne, Joseph D. Pencils & Sticks: Scripture Word-Searches for LDS Families. 32p. (Orig.). 1983. pap. 3.95 (ISBN 0-88290-218-0). Horizon Utah.

Kayser, Rudolf. The Saints of Qumran: Stories & Essays on Jewish Themes. Zohn, Harry, ed. LC 76-20273. 188p. 1977. 18.00 (ISBN 0-8386-2024-8). Fairleigh Dickinson.

Kayserling, Meyer. Biblioteca Espanola-Portugeza-Judaica. rev. ed. 1971. 35.00x (ISBN 0-87068-146-X). Ktav.

--Judischen Frauen in der Geschichte, Literatur und Kunst. Katz, Steven, ed. (Jewish Philosophy, Mysticism & the History of Ideas Ser.). 1980. Repr. of 1879 ed. lib. bdg. 21.50x (ISBN 0-405-12273-X). Ayer Co Pubs.

Kaystal, Phyllis. Sai Baba the Ultimate Experience. (Illus.). 277p. (Orig.). 1985. pap. 7.95. Aura Bks.

Kazantzakis, Nikos. Buddha. Friar, Kimon & Dallas-Damis, Athena, trs. from Greek. LC 81-71164. 172p. (Orig.). 1983. pap. 11.95 (ISBN 0-932238-14-9, Pub. by Avant Bks.). Slawson Comm.

--The Last Temptation of Christ. 1966. Translation 1971. pap. 9.95 (ISBN 0-671-21170-6, Touchstone Bks). S&S.

--Saint Francis. 1963. Translation 1971. pap. 9.95 (ISBN 0-671-21247-8, Touchstone Bks). S&S.

Kazee, Buell H. Faith is the Victory. 1983. pap. 4.95 (ISBN 0-8423-0844-X). Tyndale.

Kazemi, Hassan. Ten Signs of Faith. Graves, Helen, ed. LC 85-51959. 154p. 1986. 8.95 (ISBN 1-55523-012-1). Winston-Derek.

Kazi, A. K., tr. see Shahrastani, Muhammad B.

Kazi, M. Adhan over Anatolia. pap. 7.95. Am Trust Pubns.

Kazin, Alfred. New York Jew. LC 77-20359. 1978. 12.95 (ISBN 0-394-49567-5). Knopf.

Kazis, Richard & Grossman, Richard L. Fear at Work: Job Blackmail, Labor & the Environment. LC 82-9829. 306p. (Orig.). 1982. pap. 10.95 (ISBN 0-8298-0600-8). Pilgrim NY.

Keach, Benjamin. Exposition of the Parables. LC 73-85297. (Kregel Reprint Library). 918p. 1988. 29.95 (ISBN 0-8254-3016-X). Kregel.

--Preaching from the Types & Metaphors of the Bible. LC 78-165059. (Kregel Reprint Library). 1038p. 1975. 31.95 (ISBN 0-8254-3008-9). Kregel.

Kealey, Robert J. Everyday Issues Related to Justice & Other Gospel Values. 80p. 1984. 4.80 (ISBN 0-318-17779-X). Natl Cath Educ.

Kealy, Sean. Mark's Gospel: A History of Its Interpretation. LC 81-84384. 144p. (Orig.). 1982. pap. 8.95 (ISBN 0-8091-2417-3). Paulist Pr.

Keane, Bil. At Home with the Family Circus. LC 72-11667. (Illus.). 64p. (Orig.). 1973. pap. 1.00 (ISBN 0-8170-0598-6). Judson.

Keane, Philip. Sexual Morality: A Catholic Perspective. LC 77-83536. 252p. 1978. pap. 8.95 (ISBN 0-8091-2070-4). Paulist Pr.

Keane, Philip S. Christian Ethics & Imagination. 224p. (Orig.). 1984. pap. 9.95 (ISBN 0-8091-2647-8). Paulist Pr.

Kearney, Lawrence. Kingdom Come. 64p. 1980. 15.00x (ISBN 0-8195-2098-5); pap. 7.95 (ISBN 0-8195-1098-X). Wesleyan U Pr.

Kearns, Patrick, tr. see Suarez, Federico.

Kearns, Thomas F. The Art of the Mystic: The Master Course in Spiritual & Psychic Development. Paterson, Kathy, ed. (Illus.). 160p. (Orig.). 1986. pap. 9.95 (ISBN 0-935251-00-6). Manchurch.

Keary, Charles F. Outlines of Primitive Belief among the Indo-European Races. LC 77-85620. 1977. Repr. of 1882 ed. lib. bdg. 50.00 (ISBN 0-89341-305-4). Longwood Pub Group.

Keates, Jonathan & Hornak, Angelo. Canterbury Cathedral. (Illus.). pap. 13.95 (ISBN 0-935748-17-2). Scala Books.

Keating, Charles J. Dealing with Difficult People. LC 83-82018. 224p. 1984. pap. 7.95 (ISBN 0-8091-2596-X). Paulist Pr.

--The Gentle Touch. (Illus.). 112p. (Orig.). 1985. pap. 5.95 (ISBN 0-89622-217-9). Twenty-Third.

--The Heart of the Christian Message. school ed. flexible bdg 1.50 (ISBN 0-89942-246-2, 246-05-SD). Catholic Bk Pub.

--Infant Baptism & the Christian Community. LC 76-25620. (Illus.). 1977. pap. 2.95 (ISBN 0-89622-022-2). Twenty-Third.

--The Leadership Book. rev. ed. LC 77-99300. 144p. 1982. pap. 4.95 (ISBN 0-8091-2504-8). Paulist Pr.

Keating, Dr. Charles J. Who We Are Is How We Pray: Matching Personality & Spirituality. 144p. (Orig.). 1987. 13.95 (ISBN 0-89622-292-6); pap. 7.95 (ISBN 0-89622-321-3). Twenty-Third.

Keating, J. F. Agape & the Eucharist in the Early Church: Studies in the History of Christian Love Feasts. LC 71-79511. Repr. of 1901 ed. 27.50 (ISBN 0-404-03640-6). AMS Pr.

Keating, John. Strength Under Control: Meekness & Zeal in the Christian Life. (Living As a Christian Ser.). 152p. (Orig.). 1981. pap. 3.50 (ISBN 0-89283-104-9). Servant.

Keating, Thomas. Crisis of Faith. LC 79-13036. 1979. pap. 4.00 (ISBN 0-932506-05-4). St Bedes Pubns.

--The Heart of the World: An Introduction to Contemplative Christianity. 96p. 1981. 8.95 (ISBN 0-8245-0014-8). Crossroad NY.

Keating, Thomas, et al. Finding Grace at the Center. rev. ed. LC 78-10514. 1979. 2.50 (ISBN 0-932506-20-8); pap. 2.50 (ISBN 0-932506-00-3). St Bedes Pubns.

Keatinge, M. W. The Great Didactic of John Amos Comenius. (Educational Ser.). 1896. Repr. 40.00 (ISBN 0-8482-4764-7). Norwood Edns.

Keatinge, M. W., ed. The Great Didactic of John Maos Comenius. 316p. 1981. Repr. of 1907 ed. lib. bdg. 50.00 (ISBN 0-89984-304-2). Century Bookbindery.

Keble, John. The Christian Year: Thoughts in Verse for the Sundays & Holidays Throughout the Year. LC 70-167019. (Illus.). 291p. 1975. Repr. of 1896 ed. 43.00x (ISBN 0-8103-4095-X). Gale.

--Concordance to the Christian Year. 1871. 28.00 (ISBN 0-384-28985-1). Johnson Repr.

Keck, Leander. New Testament Experience of Faith. 2nd ed. LC 76-46491. 160p. 1985. pap. 6.95 (ISBN 0-8272-2508-3). CBP.

Keck, Leander, et al. Pauline Letters. 160p. (Orig.). 1984. pap. 9.50 (ISBN 0-687-30494-6). Abingdon.

Keck, Leander E. The Bible in the Pulpit: The Renewal of Biblical Preaching. LC 77-12015. 1978. pap. 8.95 (ISBN 0-687-03160-5). Abingdon.

--A Future for the Historical Jesus: The Place of Jesus in Preaching & Theology. LC 81-43081. pap. 70.80 (2029605). Bks Demand UMI.

--Paul & His Letters. Krodel, Gerhard, ed. LC 78-54554. (Proclamation Commentaries, The New Testament Witnesses for Preaching). 144p. 1979. pap. 4.95 (ISBN 0-8006-0587-X, 1-587). Fortress.

Keck, Leander E. & Hobbie, Francis W. Pentecost One. LC 79-7377. (Proclamation 2: Aids for Interpreting the Lessons of the Church Year, Series B). 64p. 1982. pap. 3.75 (ISBN 0-8006-4089-6, 1-4089). Fortress.

Keck, Leander E. & Martyn, J. Louis, eds. Studies in Luke-Acts. LC 79-8886. 324p. 1980. pap. 9.95 (ISBN 0-8006-1379-1, 1-1379). Fortress.

Keck, Saundria. God Made Me. LC 86-17572. (Bible & Me Ser.). 1987. 5.95 (ISBN 0-8054-4173-5). Broadman.

Kedar, Benjamin Z. Crusade & Mission. LC 84-3403. (Illus.). 256p. 1984. text ed. 26.50x (ISBN 0-691-05424-X). Princeton U Pr.

Keddie, Hikke R. An Islamic Response to Imperialism: Political & Religious Writings of Sayyid Jamal ad-Din "al-Afghani". LC 68-13224. (California Library Reprint Ser. Near Eastern Center, UCLA: No. 119). 224p. 1983. 35.00x (ISBN 0-520-04766-4); pap. 7.95 (ISBN 0-520-04774-5, CAL 586). U of Cal Pr.

Keddie, Nikki, jt. ed. see Beck, Lois.

Keddie, Nikki R. Religion & Politics in Iran: Shi'ism from Quiestism to Revolution. LC 82-17351. 288p. 1983. text ed. 28.50x (ISBN 0-300-02874-1). Yale U Pr.

--Religion & Rebellion in Iran: The Iranian Tobacco Protest of 1891-1892. 163p. 1966. 27.50x (ISBN 0-7146-1971-X, F Cass Co). Biblio Dist.

Keddie, Nikki R., jt. auth. see Cole, Juan R.

Keddie, Nikki R., ed. Religion & Politics in Iran: Shi'ism from Quietism to Revolution. LC 82-17351. 288p. 1984. pap. 9.95x (ISBN 0-300-03245-5, Y-504). Yale U Pr.

--Scholars, Saints & Sufis: Muslim Religious Institutions Since 1500. LC 77-153546. (Near Eastern Center, UCLA). 350p. 1972. pap. 9.95x (ISBN 0-520-03644-1, CAMPUS 210). U of Cal Pr.

--Scholars, Saints & Sufis: Muslim Religious Institutions since 1500. 1983. 14.50 (ISBN 0-8446-5970-3). Peter Smith.

Kedourie, Elie. Afghani & Abduh: Essay on Religious Unbelief & Political Activism in Modern Islam. 97p. 1966. 28.50x (ISBN 0-7146-1989-2, F Cass Co). Biblio Dist.

--The Crossman Confessions & Other Essays in Politics, History & Religion. 255p. 1985. 30.00x (ISBN 0-7201-1712-7). Mansell.

Kedourie, Elie & Haim, Sylvia G., eds. Palestine & Israel in the Nineteenth & Twentieth Centuries. (Illus.). 286p. 1982. 39.50x (ISBN 0-7146-3121-3, F Cass Co). Biblio Dist.

--Towards a Modern Iran: Studies in Thought, Politics & Society. 262p. 1980. 29.50x (ISBN 0-7146-3145-0, F Cass Co). Biblio Dist.

--Zionism & Arabism in Palestine & Israel. 266p. 1982. text ed. 37.50x (ISBN 0-7146-3169-8, F Cass Co). Biblio Dist.

Kee, Howard, ed. see Rhyne, C. Thomas.

Kee, Howard C. Christian Origins in Sociological Perspective: Methods & Resources. LC 79-26668. 204p. 1980. soft cover 9.95 (ISBN 0-664-24307-X). Westminster.

--Community of the New Age: Studies in Mark's Gospel. LC 83-17416. xii, 225p. 1983. 16.95 (ISBN 0-86554-100-0, MUP/H92). Mercer Univ Pr.

--Jesus in History: An Approach to the Study of the Gospels. 2nd ed. LC 77-75349. 312p. 1977. pap. text ed. 13.95 (ISBN 0-15-547382-4, HC). HarBraceJ.

--Medicine, Miracle & Magic in New Testament Times. (Society for New Testament Studies Monographs: No. 55). 200p. 1986. 29.95 (ISBN 0-521-32309-6). Cambridge U Pr.

--Miracle in the Early Christian World: A Study in Sociohistorical Method. LC 83-40004. 304p. 1983. 30.00x (ISBN 0-300-03008-8); pap. 9.95 (ISBN 0-300-03632-9, Y-570). Yale U Pr.

--The New Testament in Context: Sources & Documents. (Illus.). 256p. 1984. pap. text ed. 20.33 (ISBN 0-13-615774-2). P-H.

--The Origins of Christianity: Sources & Documents. LC 73-4830. 320p. 1973. P-H.

--Understanding the New Testament. 4th ed. (Illus.). 464p. 1983. text ed. 33.00 (ISBN 0-13-936591-5). P-H.

Kee, Howard C. & Gomes, Peter J. Pentecost One. Achtemeier, Elizabeth, et al, eds. LC 79-7377. (Proclamation 2: Aids for Interpreting the Lessons of the Church Year, Ser. C). 64p. 1980. pap. 3.75 (ISBN 0-8006-4081-0, 1-4081). Fortress.

Kee, Howard C., ed. see Meyer, Marvin W.

Kee, Howard C., tr. see Kuemmel, Werner G.

Keeble, Marshall. From Muleback to Super Jet with the Gospel. 2.50 (ISBN 0-89225-091-7). Gospel Advocate.

Keeble, N. H. Richard Baxter: Puritan Man of Letters. 1982. 45.00x (ISBN 0-19-811716-7). Oxford U Pr.

Keech, L. Is There a Difference Between a Khazar Jew & a Palestinian Jew? 1982. lib. bdg. 59.95 (ISBN 0-87700-335-1). Revisionist Pr.

Keefauver, Larry. Friends & Faith: How to Use Friendship Evangelism In Youth Ministry. LC 86-7577. 156p. (Orig.). 1986. pap. 9.95 (ISBN 0-931529-10-7). Group Bks.

Keefauver, Larry, jt. auth. see Stone, J. David.

Keefer, Luke, Jr. Everything Necessary: God's Provisions for the Holy Life. 1984. Teacher ed. 64p. 3.95 (ISBN 0-916035-11-5); Student ed. 160p. 4.95 (ISBN 0-916035-12-3). Evangel Indiana.

Keefer, Sarah L. The Old English Metrical Psalter: An Annotated Set of Collation Lists with the Psalter Glosses. LC 79-7920. (Garland Reference Library of the Humanities). 200p. 1979. lib. bdg. 36.00 (ISBN 0-8240-9538-3). Garland Pub.

Keegan, G. Kearnie. Your Next Big Step. LC 60-9533. 1960. gift ed. 8.95 (ISBN 0-8054-5317-2, 4253-17). Broadman.

Keegan, Terence. A Commentary on the Gospel of Mark. LC 81-82332. 224p. (Orig.). 1981. pap. 7.95 (ISBN 0-8091-2359-2). Paulist Pr.

Keegan, Terence J. Interpreting the Bible: A Popular Introduction to Biblical Hermeneutics. 224p. (Orig.). 1986. pap. 8.95 (ISBN 0-8091-2747-4). Paulist Pr.

Keel, Othmar. The Symbolism of the Biblical World Ancient Near Eastern Iconography & the Book of Psalms. (Illus.). 1978. 39.50x (ISBN 0-8245-0376-7). Crossroad NY.

Keeler, Laura. Geoffrey of Monmouth & the Late Latin Chroniclers. LC 74-5455. 1946. Repr. lib. bdg. 27.50 (ISBN 0-8414-5493-0). Folcroft.

Keeler, Sr. Mary J. Catholic Literary France from Verlaine to the Present Time. LC 76-90649. (Essay Index Reprint Ser). 1938. 19.00 (ISBN 0-8369-1219-5). Ayer Co Pubs.

Keeler, Ronald F. Bible Games & Activities. (Game & Party Bks.). Orig. Title: The Bible Game Book. 96p. 1982. pap. 2.95 (ISBN 0-8010-5436-2). Baker Bk.

Keeley, Robin, ed. Christianity in Today's World: An Eerdmans Handbook. (Illus.). 384p. 1985. 29.95 (ISBN 0-8028-3618-6). Eerdmans.

Keeling, William. Liturgiae Britannicae. 498p. Repr. of 1851 ed. text ed. 74.52x (ISBN 0-576-99718-8, Pub. by Gregg Intl Pubs England). Gregg Intl.

Keely, R., ed. see Watson, David & Jenkins, Simon.

Keely, Robin. Eerdmans' Handbook to Christian Belief. (Illus.). 480p. 1982. 24.95 (ISBN 0-8028-3577-5). Eerdmans.

Keen, Benjamin, tr. see Lafaye, Jacques.

Keen, Maurice. Pelican History of Medieval Europe. 1969. pap. 5.95 (ISBN 0-14-021085-7, Pelican). Penguin.

Keen, Sam. Gabriel Marcel. LC 67-11288. (Makers of Contemporary Theology Ser). pap. 15.00 (ISBN 0-8357-9258-7, 2015434). Bks Demand UMI.

Keenan, Desmond J. The Catholic Church in Nineteenth-Century Ireland: A Sociological Study. LC 83-11941. 300p. 1984. 29.50X (ISBN 0-389-20426-9, 07312). B&N Imports.

Keene, Donald, tr. Essays in Idleness: The Tsurezuregusa of Kenko. LC 67-23566. (Records of Civilization Sources & Studies & Translations of the Oriental Classics Ser.). (Illus.). 213p. 1967. pap. 12.50x (ISBN 0-231-08308-4). Columbia U Pr.

Keene, Judy, jt. auth. see Hudnut, William H., III.

Keene, Laurence C. Offering Meditations & Prayers. Lambert, Herbert, ed. LC 84-266. 64p. (Orig.). 1984. pap. 4.95 (ISBN 0-8272-2706-X). CBP.

Keene, Michael. Looking into Being a Muslim. (Looking into World Religions Ser.). (Illus.). 64p. 1987. 16.95 (ISBN 0-7134-4667-6, Pub. by Batsford England). David & Charles.

Keene, Michael & Wood, Angela. Looking into Being Jewish. (Looking into World Religions Ser.). (Illus.). 64p. 1987. 16.95 (ISBN 0-7134-4668-4, Pub. by Batsford England). David & Charles.

Keene, Milton H. Patterns for Mature Living. LC 76-27093. Repr. of 1976 ed. 21.30 (ISBN 0-8357-9019-3, 2016389). Bks Demand UMI.

Keep, David. St. Boniface & His World. (Illus.). 64p. 1979. pap. 4.50 (ISBN 0-85364-276-1). Attic Pr.

Keese, Dayton. Re-Evaluation of the Eldership. pap. 2.50 (ISBN 0-89137-552-X). Quality Pubns.

Keesecker, William F., ed. & selected by. A Calvin Reader: Reflections on Living. LC 85-15237. 144p. 1985. pap. 9.95 (ISBN 0-664-24667-2). Westminster.

Keet, Cuthbert C. Study of the Psalms of Ascents: A Critical & Exegetical Commentary Upon Psalms 120-134. (Illus.). 200p. 1969. 9.50 (ISBN 0-7051-0041-3). Attic Pr.

Kegley, Charles W., ed. Reinhold Niebuhr: His Religious, Social & Political Thought. rev. ed. LC 82-22531. 448p. (Orig.). 1984. pap. 11.95 (ISBN 0-8298-0616-4). Pilgrim NY.

--The Theology of Paul Tillich. rev. ed. LC 82-301. 432p. 1982. pap. 10.95 (ISBN 0-8298-0499-4). Pilgrim NY.

Kehl, Medard, ed. see Von Balthasar, Hans U.

Kehle, Mary. You're Nearly There: Christian Sex Education for Ten-to-Teens. LC 73-85963. (Illus.). 80p. 1973. pap. 2.50 (ISBN 0-87788-969-4). Shaw Pubs.

Keidel, Levi. Caught in the Crossfire. LC 79-10910. 256p. 1979. pap. 7.95 (ISBN 0-8361-1888-X). Herald Pr.

Keifer, Howard & Munitz, Milton, eds. Perspectives in Education, Religion, & the Arts. LC 69-14641. Repr. of 1970 ed. 82.70 (ISBN 0-8357-9596-9, 2010111). Bks Demand UMI.

Keifer, Ralph. Blessed & Broken: An Exploration of the Contemporary Experience of God in Eucharistic Celebration. (Message of the Sacraments Ser.: Vol. 3). 1982. 12.95 (ISBN 0-89453-393-2); pap. 8.95 (ISBN 0-89453-267-7). M Glazier.

Keifer, Ralph A. Liturgy Against Itself. 128p. (Orig.). 1986. pap. 7.95 (ISBN 0-06-254480-2, HarpR). Har-Row.

Keightley, Thomas. An Account of the Life, Opinions, & Writings of John Milton. LC 73-11332. 1855. Repr. lib. bdg. 49.50 (ISBN 0-8414-2222-2). Folcroft.

--Classical Mythology: The Myths of Ancient Greece & Italy. xviii, 507p. 1976. 25.00 (ISBN 0-89005-189-5). Ares.

Keijiro, Marui. Survey of Taiwanese Religions in 1919, 2 vols. (Asian Folklore & Social Life Monograph: Nos. 56-57). (Japanese.). 428p. 1974. 25.00 (ISBN 0-89986-053-2). Oriental Bk Store.

Keil, Carl F. & Delitzsch, Franz. Old Testament Commentaries, 10 vols. Incl. Vol. 1. Pentateuch (ISBN 0-8028-8035-5); Vol. 2. Joshua - Second Samuel (ISBN 0-8028-8036-3); Vol. 3. First Kings - Esther (ISBN 0-8028-8037-1); Vol. 4. Job (ISBN 0-8028-8038-X); Vol. 5. Psalms (ISBN 0-8028-8039-8); Vol. 6. Proverbs - Song of Solomon (ISBN 0-8028-8040-1); Vol. 7. Isaiah (ISBN 0-8028-8041-X); Vol. 8. Jeremiah-Lamentations (ISBN 0-8028-8042-8); Vol. 9. Ezekiel-Daniel (ISBN 0-8028-8043-6); Vol. 10. Minor Prophets (ISBN 0-8028-8044-4). 1971. Repr. Set. 225.00 (ISBN 0-8028-8034-7); 22.50 ea. Eerdmans.

Keiling, Hanns P., compiled by. The Formation of the United Church of Christ (U. S. A.) Battles, Ford L., ed. LC 79-25049. (Bibliographia Tripotamopolitana: No.2). 1970. 7.00x (ISBN 0-931222-01-X). Pitts Theolog.

Keim, Curtis A. & Brown, Howard. Missions in Africa: Relevant or Relic? A Conference. (African Humanities Ser.). 89p. (Orig.). 1980. pap. text ed. 5.00 (ISBN 0-941934-30-6). Indiana Africa.

Keiningham, C. W. Outlines for Evangelistic Preaching. 80p. 1984. pap. 2.95 (ISBN 0-8010-5461-3). Baker Bk.

--Sermon Outlines for Funerals. (Sermon Outline Ser.). (Orig.). 1981. pap. 2.50 (ISBN 0-8010-5427-3). Baker Bk.

--Year 'Round Sermon Outlines. (Pulpit Library). 96p. 1987. pap. price not set (ISBN 0-8010-5483-4). Baker Bk.

Keiser, Clarence E. Selected Temple Documents of the Ur Dynasty. LC 78-63533. (Yale Oriental Series: Babylonian Texts: No. 4). (Illus.). 240p. Repr. of 1919 ed. 42.50 (ISBN 0-404-60254-1). AMS Pr.

Keiser, Jacqueline L., jt. auth. see Keiser, Thomas W.

Keiser, Thomas W. & Keiser, Jacqueline L. The Anatomy of Illusion: Religious Cults & Destructive Persuasion. (Illus.). 160p. 1987. 25.25 (ISBN 0-398-05295-6). C C Thomas.

Keith, A. B. Buddhist Philosophy in India & Ceylon. lib. bdg. 90.00 (ISBN 0-87968-181-0). Krishna Pr.

--The Religion & Philosophy of the Veda & Upanishads, 2 vols. 1976. Repr. Set. 42.00 (ISBN 0-89684-304-1). Orient Bk Dist.

--The Veda of the Black Yajus School: Taittiriya Sanhita, 2 vols. 1967. Repr. Set. 42.00 (ISBN 0-89684-334-3). Orient Bk Dist.

Keith, A. Berriedale. Indian Mythology & Iranian Mythology. Bd. with Carnoy, Albert J. LC 63-19091. (Mythology of All Races Ser.: Vol. 6). (Illus.). Repr. of 1932 ed. 30.00x (ISBN 0-8154-0126-4). Cooper Sq.

Keith, Alexander. Christian Evidences: Fulfilled Bible Prophecy. 456p. 1984. Repr. smythe sewn 20.00 (ISBN 0-86524-181-3, 9807). Klock & Klock.

Keith, Arthur, ed. Rigveda Brahmanas. lib. bdg. 100.00 (ISBN 0-87968-440-2). Krishna Pr.

Keith, Arthur B. Indian Logic & Atomism: An Exposition of the Nyaya & Vaicesika Systems. lib. bdg. 79.95 (ISBN 0-87968-529-8). Krishna Pr.

--The Karma-Mimamsa. LC 78-72451. Repr. of 1921 ed. 27.00 (ISBN 0-404-17318-7). AMS Pr.

--The Religion & Philosophy of the Veda & Upanishads, 2 vols. LC 71-109969. Repr. of 1925 ed. lib. bdg. 34.00x (ISBN 0-8371-4475-2, KEVU). Greenwood.

Keith, Bill, ed. see Hornbrook, John & Bakker, Dorothy F.

Keith, Bill, ed. see Pratney, Winkie.

Keith, Bill, ed. see Rawlings, Meridel.

Keith, Gerald, ed. see Dickson, Albert A.

Keith, M. R. How I Found Out About Heaven. 1970. 4.95 (ISBN 0-910122-23-7). Amherst Pr.

--So You're Going to Heaven. 1965. 4.95 (ISBN 0-910122-22-9). Amherst Pr.

Keitzell, Von F. see Von Keitzell, F.

Kelber, Werner H. Mark's Story of Jesus. LC 78-14668. 96p. 1979. pap. 4.50 (ISBN 0-8006-1355-4, 1-1355). Fortress.

--The Oral & the Written Gospel: The Hermeneutics of Speaking & Writing in the Synoptic Tradition, Mark, Paul, & Q. LC 82-7450. 272p. 1983. 23.95 (ISBN 0-8006-0689-2, 1-689). Fortress.

Kelderman, Duane. The Gentle Whisper. 1985. 6.25 (ISBN 0-89536-752-1, 5858). CSS of Ohio.

--When a Good God Lets Bad Things Happen. 1983. 3.25 (ISBN 0-89536-583-9, 2333). CSS of Ohio.

Kelfer, Russell. Self-Control. (Living Studies). 240p. 1985. pap. 5.95 (ISBN 0-8423-5859-5); leader's guide 2.95 (ISBN 0-8423-5860-9). Tyndale.

Kellenberger, J. The Cognitivity of Religion: Three Perspectives. LC 84-27999. 1985. 20.00x (ISBN 0-520-05383-4). U of Cal Pr.

Keller, A. G., ed. see Sumner, William G.

Keller, Charles R. The Second Great Awakening in Connecticut. LC 68-26923. ix, 275p. 1968. Repr. of 1942 ed. 25.00 (ISBN 0-208-00662-1, Archon). Shoe String.

Keller, Clifton & Appel, Jeanette. Science Activities for Christian Children. rev. ed. 112p. 1986. pap. 5.50 (ISBN 0-930192-15-X). Gazelle Pubns.

Keller, Ernst & Keller, Marie-Luise. Miracles In Dispute: A Continuing Debate. 256p. pap. 8.95 (ISBN 0-317-31482-3, 30-1012-259). Fortress.

Keller, Frank R. Preparation for Covenant Life. LC 79-53522. 1979. pap. 4.95x (ISBN 0-87303-018-4). Faith & Life.

Keller, Helen. My Religion. LC 74-11654. 1972. pap. 2.95 (ISBN 0-87785-103-4); Span. ed. leatherette o.s.i. 5.00 (ISBN 0-87785-114-X). Swedenborg.

--My Religion: Large Print Edition. LC 74-11645. 1979. 4.75 (ISBN 0-87785-158-1). Swedenborg.

Keller, James G. & Berger, Meyer. Men of Maryknoll. LC 78-142650. (Essay Index Reprint Ser.). Repr. of 1943 ed. 18.00 (ISBN 0-8369-2775-3). Ayer Co Pubs.

Keller, John E. Drinking Problem. Hulme, William E., ed. LC 75-133036. (Pocket Counsel Bks.). 56p. 1971. pap. 2.50 (ISBN 0-8006-0155-6, 1-155). Fortress.

--Let Go, Let God. LC 85-11048. 128p. 1985. pap. 6.95 (ISBN 0-8066-2162-1, 10-3815). Augsburg.

--Ministering to Alcoholics. rev. ed. LC 66-22560. 1966. pap. 8.95 (ISBN 0-8066-0922-2, 10-4439). Augsburg.

Keller, John E. & Kinkade, Richard P. Iconography in Medieval Spanish Literature. LC 83-2478. (Illus.). 160p. 1984. 50.00x (ISBN 0-8131-1449-7). U Pr of Ky.

Keller, Marie-Luise, jt. auth. see Keller, Ernst.

Keller, Merily H., ed. see Irving, Lynn.

Keller, Paul F. Studies in Lutheran Doctrine. LC 60-15574. (YA) 1959. pap. 5.50 (ISBN 0-570-03517-1, 14-1265); correction & profile chart 0.40 (ISBN 0-570-03526-0, 14-1267); tests 0.45 (ISBN 0-570-03525-2, 14-1266). Concordia.

Keller, Phillip. Elijah: Prophet of Power. 160p. 1980. 8.95 (ISBN 0-8499-0266-5). Word Bks.

--A Gardener Looks at the Fruits of the Spirit. 1983. 6.95 (ISBN 0-8499-2958-X). Word Bks.

--A Layman Looks at the Love of God. 122p. 1984. pap. 7.95 (ISBN 0-87123-618-4). Bethany Hse.

--A Layman Looks at the Love of God. (Orig.). 1982. pap. 4.95 (210314). Bethany Hse.

--Master's Hands: Understanding the Parable of the Potter & the Clay. (Christian Essentials Ser.). 48p. (Orig.). 1985. cat. not set. pap. 1.95 (ISBN 0-89283-330-0, Pub. by Vine Books). Servant.

--Salt for Society. 1986. 5.95 (ISBN 0-8499-3059-6). Word Bks.

--A Shepard's Look at Psalm 23. 1976. 8.95 (ISBN 0-310-26790-0, 6780); large print 6.95 (ISBN 0-310-26797-8, 12553L). Zondervan.

--A Shepherd Looks at Psalm 23. (Illus.). 160p. 1987. padded gift ed. 19.95 (ISBN 0-310-35670-9). Zondervan.

--A Shepherd Looks at the Good Shepherd & His Sheep. 1979. 9.95 (ISBN 0-310-26800-1, 6784); large print kivar 7.95 (ISBN 0-310-26807-9, 12568L). Zondervan.

--La Vida en el Redil. Vargas, Carlos A., tr. from Eng. LC 76-14500. Tr. of A Shepherd Looks at Psalm Twenty-Three. (Span.). 141p. 1976. pap. 3.50 (ISBN 0-89922-073-8). Edit Caribe.

--Wonder O' the Wind. 1986. 7.95 (ISBN 0-8499-3061-8). Word Bks.

Keller, Phillip, tr. Meditacoes De Um Leigo. (Portugese Bks.). Tr. of A Layman Looks at the Lord's Prayer. (Port.). 1979. 1.60 (ISBN 0-8297-0788-3). Life Pubs Intl.

Keller, Rosemary S., jt. ed. see Ruether, Rosemary R.

Keller, Rosemary S., jt. ed. see Thomas, Hilah F.

Keller, W. Phillip. As a Tree Grows: Reflections on Growing in the Image of Christ. 96p. 1985. pap. 2.95 (ISBN 0-89283-248-7, Pub. by Vine Bks). Servant.

--A Child's Look at the Twenty-Third Psalm. LC 80-976. (Illus.). 96p. 1981. 8.95 (ISBN 0-385-15456-9, Galilee). Doubleday.

--A Child's Look at the Twenty-Third Psalm. LC 84-13718. (Illus.). 96p. 1985. pap. 5.95 (ISBN 0-385-15457-7, Galilee). Doubleday.

--David I: The Time of Saul's Tyranny. 256p. 1985. 10.95 (ISBN 0-8499-0470-6, 0470-6). Word Bks.

--David II: The Shepherd King. 224p. 1986. 11.95 (ISBN 0-8499-0559-1). Word Bks.

--A Layman Looks at the Lamb of God. LC 82-4568. 122p. (Orig.). 1982. 7.95 (ISBN 0-87123-313-4, 230314); pap. 3.95 (ISBN 0-87123-314-2, 210314). Bethany Hse.

--A Layman Looks at the Lord's Prayer. 160p. 1976. pap. 5.95 (ISBN 0-8024-4644-2). Moody.

--A Layman Looks at the Lord's Prayer. (Moody Press Electives Ser.). 1985. pap. text ed. 3.95 (ISBN 0-8024-0699-8); leader's guide 2.50 (ISBN 0-8024-0701-3). Moody.

--Lessons from a Sheepdog. 1983. 8.95 (ISBN 0-8499-0335-1). Word Bks.

--Mighty Man of Valor. 128p. 1979. pap. 4.95 (ISBN 0-8007-5072-1, Power Bks). Revell.

--Rabboni. 256p. 1980. pap. 6.95 (ISBN 0-8007-5053-5, Power Bks). Revell.

--Salt for Society. 160p. 1981. 8.95 (ISBN 0-8499-0290-8). Word Bks.

--Sea Edge. 120p. 1985. 9.95 (ISBN 0-8499-0457-9, 0457-9). Word Bks.

--Walking with God. 160p. 1980. pap. 5.95 (ISBN 0-8007-5187-6). Revell.

--Wonder O' the Wind. 1982. 9.95 (ISBN 0-8499-0337-8). Word Bks.

Keller, Werner. The Bible As History. (Illus.). 544p. 1974. pap. 4.95 (ISBN 0-553-25438-3). Bantam.

--The Bible As History. 2nd, rev. ed. Rehork, Joachim, ed. Neil, William & Rasmussen, B. H., trs. from Ger. LC 80-22218. Orig. Title: Und Die Bibel Hat Docht Recht. (Illus.). 448p. 1981. 14.95 (ISBN 0-688-03724-0). Morrow.

Keller-Grimm, M., ed. see Grimm, George.

Kellerman, Eli. Jewish Ceremonial: A Guide to Jewish Prayer & Ritual. 69p. 1983. pap. 9.95 (ISBN 965-220-038-7, Carta Pub Isreal). Hippocrene Bks.

Kellermann, Joseph L. Reconciliation with God & Family. 16p. 1981. pap. 0.95 (ISBN 0-89486-146-8). Hazelden.

Kellett, Ernest E. Short History of Religions. facsimile ed. LC 71-156671. (Essay Index Reprint Ser). Repr. of 1934 ed. 30.00 (ISBN 0-8369-2281-6). Ayer Co Pubs.

Kellett, Ernst E. Story of Myths. (Folklore & Society Ser). 1969. Repr. of 1927 ed. 20.00 (ISBN 0-384-29025-6). Johnson Repr.

Kelley, Bennet. Catholic Faith Today. green, flexible bdg. 3.00 (ISBN 0-89942-243-8, 243-04). Catholic Bk Pub.

Kelley, Dean M. Government Intervention in Religious Affairs, No. II. 200p. (Orig.). 1986. pap. 11.95 (ISBN 0-8298-0564-8). Pilgrim NY.

--Government Intervention in Religious Affairs, No. 1. LC 82-355. 224p. (Orig.). 1982. 17.95 (ISBN 0-8298-0602-4); pap. 9.95 (ISBN 0-8298-0434-X). Pilgrim NY.

Kelley, Emily. Christmas around the World. (On My Own Bks.). (Illus.). 48p. 1986. lib. bdg. 8.95 (ISBN 0-87614-249-8). Carolrhoda Bks.

Kelley, Francis D., pref. by. Media & Catechetics Today: Towards the Year 2000. 24p. 1980. 3.60 (ISBN 0-686-29243-X). Natl Cath Educ.

Kelley, Francis E., jt. ed. see Etzkorn, Girard J.

Kelley, Gail. Traditionally Yours. LC 86-43230. 100p. (Orig.). 1987. pap. text ed. 7.95 (ISBN 0-89390-103-2). Resource Pubns.

Kelley, Gail & Hershberger, Carol. Come Mime with Me: Ten Liturgical Dramas for Children. LC 86-62621. 100p. 1987. 11.95 (ISBN 0-89390-089-3). Resource Pubns.

Kelley, Kathleen, et al. Happiness: Issues of Emotional Living in an Age of Stress for Clergy & Religious. Kane, T. A., ed. LC 82-1733. 128p. (Orig.). 1982. pap. 5.00 (ISBN 0-89571-014-5). Affirmation.

Kelley, Kathleen E., ed. see Agudo, Philomena, et al.

Kelley, P. J. So High the Price. LC 68-28104. (St. Paul Editions). 1968. 3.00 (ISBN 0-8198-0148-8). Dghtrs St Paul.

Kelley, Page H. Layman's Bible Book Commentary: Micah, Nahum, Habbakuk, Zephaniah, Haggai, Zechariah, Malachi, Vol. 14. LC 83-26288. 1984. 5.95 (ISBN 0-8054-1184-4). Broadman.

Kelley, Walter R. Clergy Say the Dardnest Things: Or How to Speak "Clergy-ese". (Illus.). 200p. (Orig.). 1987. pap. text ed. write for info. (ISBN 0-937071-01-3). Pyramid Designs Pr.

Kelling, Furn F. Prayer Is... (Illus.). 1979. 5.95 (ISBN 0-8054-4256-1, 4242-56). Broadman.

Kelling, Hans-Wilhelm. The Idolatry of Poetic Genius in German Goethe Criticism. (European University Studies: Series 1, German Language & Literature: Vol. 27). 200p. 1970. pap. 9.80 (ISBN 3-261-00026-0). P Lang Pubs.

Kellner, Menachem. Dogma in Medieval Jewish Thought: From Maimonides to Abravanel. (Littman Library of Jewish Civilization). 350p. 1987. 45.00 (ISBN 0-19-710044-9). Oxford U Pr.

Kellner, Menachem M., ed. Contemporary Jewish Ethics. new ed. (Sanhedrin Jewish Studies). 1978. (Sanhedrin Pr); pap. 11.95x (ISBN 0-88482-920-0, Sanhedrin Pr). Hebrew Pub.

Kellock, Harold. Parson Weems of the Cherry-Tree. LC 75-107137. 1971. Repr. of 1928 ed. 35.00x (ISBN 0-8103-3785-1). Gale.

Kellogg, Alice M. Christmas Entertainments. facs. ed. LC 72-139764. (Granger Index Reprint Ser). 1897. 15.00 (ISBN 0-8369-6218-4). Ayer Co Pubs.

Kellogg, Alice M., ed. How to Celebrate Thanksgiving & Christmas. facs. ed. LC 76-139765. (Granger Index Reprint Ser). 1897. 15.00 (ISBN 0-8369-6219-2). Ayer Co Pubs.

Kellogg, Mrs. Dennis. He Lifted Me. 1966. pap. 3.95 (ISBN 0-88027-046-2). Firm Foun Pub.

Kellogg, Gene. The Vital Tradition: The Catholic Novel in a Period of Convergence. LC 74-108375. 1970. 8.35 (ISBN 0-8294-0192-X). Loyola.

Kellogg, Hallie A. Woman of God. 1962. pap. 3.95 (ISBN 0-88027-051-9). Firm Foun Pub.

Kellogg, Jean. Dark Prophets of Hope. LC 75-5697. 1975. pap. 5.95 (ISBN 0-8294-0243-8). Loyola.

Kellogg, Samuel H. The Book of Leviticus. 1978. 21.00 (ISBN 0-86524-132-5, 0301). Klock & Klock.

Kelly, Armandine. Stories for Seasonal Festivals. LC 86-62627. 100p. (Orig.). 1987. pap. 7.95 (ISBN 0-89390-096-6). Resource Pubns.

Kelly, Balmer H. Ezra-Job. LC 59-10454. (Layman's Bible Commentary, Vol. 8). 1962. 4.95 (ISBN 0-8042-3008-0); pap. 3.95 (ISBN 0-8042-3068-4). John Knox.

Kelly, Balmer H., et al, eds. see Foreman, Kenneth J., et al.

Kelly, Caleb G. French Protestantism, Fifteen Fifty-Nine to Fifteen Sixty-Two. LC 78-63967. (Johns Hopkins University. Studies in the Social Sciences, 1918: No. 36 4). Repr. of 1918 ed. 24.50 (ISBN 0-404-61213-X). AMS Pr.

--French Protestantism, Fifteen Fifty-Nine to Fifteen Sixty-Two. LC 83-45621. Date not set. Repr. of 1918 ed. 24.50 (ISBN 0-404-19839-2). AMS Pr.

Kelly, Clifton M. & Wantz, Sherman P. Train up a Child. LC 82-84318. 110p. (Orig.). 1983. pap. 4.95. Highlands Pub.

Kelly, Clint, jt. auth. see Hampsch, John H.

Kelly, David F. The Emergence of Roman Catholic Medical Ethics in North America: An Historical-Methodological-Bibliographical Study. LC 79-66372. (Texts & Studies in Religion: Vol. 3). xi, 534p. 1982. Repr. 79.95x (ISBN 0-88946-877-X). E Mellen.

Kelly, Eamon. Bless Me Father. 1977. pap. 6.95 (ISBN 0-85342-489-6, Pub. by Mercier Pr Ireland). Irish Bks Media.

Kelly, Elin M., ed. Elizabeth Seton: Selected Writings, Vol. 5. (Sources of American Spirituality Ser.). 384p. 1986. 16.95 (ISBN 0-8091-0382-6). Paulist Pr.

Kelly, Ellin M., ed. Numerous Choirs: A Chronicle of Elizabeth Bayley Seton & Her Spiritual Daughters, Volume 1: the Seton Years 1774-1821. LC 81-80304. (Illus.). x, 296p. 1981. 15.00 (ISBN 0-9605784-0-4). Mater Dei Provincialate.

Kelly, Eugene, jt. ed. see Navia, Luis E.

Kelly, Faye L. Prayer in Sixteenth Century England. LC 66-64090. (U of Fla. Humanities Monographs: No. 22). 1966. pap. 3.50 (ISBN 0-8130-0127-7). U Presses Fla.

Kelly, Geffrey B. Liberating Faith: Bonhoeffer's Message for Today. LC 84-15863. 208p. (Orig.). 1984. pap. 11.95 (ISBN 0-8066-2092-7, 10-3832). Augsburg.

Kelly, Geffrey B. & Godsey, John D., eds. Ethical Responsibility: Bonhoeffer's Legacy to the Churches. LC 81-18823. (Toronto Studies in Theology: Vol. 6). 352p. 1982. 59.95x (ISBN 0-88946-960-1). E Mellen.

Kelly, George. Sacrament of Penance & Reconciliation. (Synthesis Ser). 96p. 1976. 0.75 (ISBN 0-8199-0701-4). Franciscan Herald.

Kelly, George, ed. Human Sexuality in Our Time. 1979. 5.95 (ISBN 0-8198-0610-2); pap. 4.95 (ISBN 0-8198-0611-0). Dghtrs St Paul.

--The Sacrament of Penance in Our Time. 1976. 4.00 (ISBN 0-8198-0455-X). Dghtrs St Paul.

Kelly, George A. Catechetical Instruction & the Catholic Faithful. 226p. 1982. 5.95 (ISBN 0-8198-1418-0, RA0015); pap. 4.95 (ISBN 0-8198-1419-9). Dghtrs St Paul.

--The Catholic Church & the American Poor. LC 75-16293. 202p. 1976. 5.95 (ISBN 0-8189-0321-X). Alba.

--The Church's Problem with Bible Scholars. LC 85-1507. 60p. 1985. 2.50 (ISBN 0-8199-0929-7). Franciscan Herald.

--The Crisis of Authority: John Paul II & the American Bishops. LC 81-52143. 116p. 1982. 10.95 (ISBN 0-89526-666-0). Regnery Bks.

--The Political Struggle of Active Homosexuals to Gain Social Acceptance. 106p. 1975. pap. 1.50 (ISBN 0-8199-0365-5). Franciscan Herald.

--Sacrament of the Eucharist in Our Time. 1978. 3.75 (ISBN 0-8198-0553-X); pap. 2.25 (ISBN 0-8198-0554-8). Dghtrs St Paul.

--An Uncertain Church: The New Catholic Problem. (Synthesis Ser.). 1977. pap. 1.25 (ISBN 0-8199-0705-7). Franciscan Herald.

Kelly, George A., ed. Catholic Ministries in Our Times. 1981. 4.00 (ISBN 0-8198-1400-8); pap. 3.00 (ISBN 0-8198-1401-6). Dghtrs St Paul.

--The Teaching Church in Our Time. 1978. 6.00 (ISBN 0-8198-0523-8); pap. 4.50 (ISBN 0-8198-0524-6). Dghtrs St Paul.

Kelly, Henry A. Canon Law & the Archpriest of Hita. LC 82-12403. (Medieval & Renaissance Texts & Studies: Vol. 27). 204p. 1984. 16.00 (ISBN 0-86698-058-X). Medieval & Renaissance NY.

--The Devil at Baptism: Ritual, Theology, & Drama. LC 85-404. 304p. 1985. text ed. 29.95x (ISBN 0-8014-1806-2). Cornell U Pr.

--Divine Providence in the England of Shakespeare's Histories. LC 75-111485. 1970. 22.50x (ISBN 0-674-21292-4). Harvard U Pr.

--The Matrimonial Trials of Henry VIII. LC 75-7483. xiv, 334p. 1976. 27.50x (ISBN 0-8047-0895-9). Stanford U Pr.

Kelly, J. N. A Commentary on the Epistles of Peter & Jude. (Thornapple Commentaries). 397p. 1981. pap. 9.95 (ISBN 0-8010-5430-3). Baker Bk.

--A Commentary on the Pastoral Epistles. (Thornapple Commentaries Ser.). 272p. 1981. pap. 7.95 (ISBN 0-8010-5428-1). Baker Bk.

--Early Christian Creeds. 3rd ed. 446p. 1981. text ed. 16.95 (ISBN 0-582-49219-X). Longman.

--Early Christian Doctrines. rev. ed. LC 58-12933. 1978. pap. 10.95xi (ISBN 0-06-064334-X, RD 233, HarpR). Har-Row.

--The Oxford Dictionary of Popes. LC 85-15599. 450p. 1986. 24.95 (ISBN 0-19-213964-9). Oxford U Pr.

Kelly, Joan B., jt. auth. see Wallerstein, Judith S.

Kelly, Kelly B. Bread for the Eating. 121p. (Orig.). 1982. pap. 3.50 (ISBN 0-914544-39-X). Living Flame Pr.

Kelly, Kent. Abortion-the American Holocaust. LC 81-65240. (Illus.). 149p. (Orig.). 1981. pap. 2.95 (ISBN 0-9604138-1-2). Calvary Pr.

--Inside the Tuplic Contoversy: Calvinism Rebuked & Revisited. LC 86-70927. (Illus.). 264p. 1986. 9.95 (ISBN 0-9604138-4-7). Calvary Pr.

--State of North Carolina vs Christian Liberty. 112p. (Orig.). 1978. pap. 2.95 (ISBN 0-9604138-3-9). Calvary Pr.

Kelly, Kent, et al. The Separation of Church & Freedom: A War Manual for Christian Soldiers. LC 80-80341. (Illus.). 308p. 1980. 7.95 (ISBN 0-9604138-0-4). Calvary Pr.

Kelly, Kevin T. Divorce & Second Marriage: Facing the Challenge. 112p. 1983. pap. 6.95 (ISBN 0-8164-2471-3, HarpR). Har-Row.

Kelly, Margaret, ed. Justice & Health Care: Christian Perspectives. LC 84-9459. 1985. pap. 16.50 (ISBN 0-87125-097-7). Cath Health.

Kelly, Sr. Marie, tr. see De Aspurz-Iriarte, Lazaro.

Kelly, Marjorie, ed. Islam: The Religious & Political Life of a World Community. LC 84-13307. 336p. 1984. 42.95 (ISBN 0-275-91204-3); pap. 16.95 (ISBN 0-03-001087-X); study guide 9.95 (ISBN 0-03-001084-5). Praeger.

--Islam: The Religious & Political Life of a World Community. LC 84-13307. 325p. 1984. 39.95; pap. 16.95. Foreign Policy.

Kelly, Mary G. Catholic Immigrant Colonization Projects in the United States, 1815-1860. LC 74-145485. (The American Immigration Library). x, 290p. 1971. Repr. of 1939 ed. lib. bdg. 17.95x (ISBN 0-89198-016-4). Ozer.

Kelly, Peter. Roman Catholicism. 1985. 13.00x (ISBN 0-7062-3601-7, Pub. by Ward Lock Educ Co Ltd). State Mutual Bk.

Kelly, Robert. The Alchemist to Mercury. 230p. 1981. 30.00 (ISBN 0-913028-82-7); pap. 7.95 (ISBN 0-686-69476-7). North Atlantic.

--How Do I Make Up My Mind, Lord? LC 82-70948. (Young Readers Ser.). (Orig.). 1982. pap. 3.95 (ISBN 0-8066-1923-6, 10-3168). Augsburg.

Kelly, Thomas. Reality of the Spiritual World. LC 76-9644. (Orig.). 1942. pap. 2.50x (ISBN 0-87574-021-9). Pendle Hill.

Kelly, Thomas R. A Testament of Devotion. 1941. 12.45 (ISBN 0-06-064370-6, HarpR). Har-Row.

Kelly, W. Christ Tempted & Sympathizing. 3.95 (ISBN 0-88172-091-7). Believers Bkshelf.

--Collections of Selected Pamphlets. pap. text ed. 6.95 (ISBN 0-88172-093-3). Believers Bkshelf.

--Epistle to the Hebrews. 272p. pap. 8.50 (ISBN 0-88172-155-7). Believers Bkshelf.

--Exposition of the Epistles of John. 6.25 (ISBN 0-88172-100-X). Believers Bkshelf.

--Exposition of the Gospel of Luke. 6.25 (ISBN 0-88172-102-6). Believers Bkshelf.

--Exposition of the Gospel of Mark. 5.50 (ISBN 0-88172-103-4). Believers Bkshelf.

--Isaac. 135p. pap. 4.95 (ISBN 0-88172-144-1). Believers Bkshelf.

--Lectures on the Church of God. 7.50 (ISBN 0-88172-092-5). Believers Bkshelf.

--Lectures on the Doctrine of the Holy Spirit. 7.95 (ISBN 0-88172-095-X). Believers Bkshelf.

--Lectures on the Epistle of Jude. 6.95 (ISBN 0-88172-101-8). Believers Bkshelf.

--Lectures on the Gospel of Matthew. 6.95 (ISBN 0-88172-104-2). Believers Bkshelf.

--Notes on First Corinthians. 8.50 (ISBN 0-88172-094-1). Believers Bkshelf.

--Notes on Romans. 8.50 (ISBN 0-88172-107-7). Believers Bkshelf.

--Preaching to the Spirits in Prison. pap. 4.75 (ISBN 0-88172-105-0). Believers Bkshelf.

--Revelation Expounded. 5.95 (ISBN 0-88172-106-9). Believers Bkshelf.

--Titus & Philemon. 6.50 (ISBN 0-88172-110-7). Believers Bkshelf.

Kelly, William. The Acts, Catholic Epistles & Revelation. (Introductory Lecture Ser.). 580p. 6.95 (ISBN 0-88172-096-8). Believers Bkshelf.

--An Exposition of the Book of Isaiah. 1979. 15.25 (ISBN 0-86524-003-5, 2301). Klock & Klock.

--The Gospel of Luke. 1981. 18.50 (ISBN 0-86524-046-9, 4201). Klock & Klock.

--The Gospels. (Introductory Lecture Ser.). 567p. 6.95 (ISBN 0-88172-097-6). Believers Bkshelf.

--The Pauline Epistles. (Introductory Lecture Ser.). 551p. 6.95 (ISBN 0-88172-098-4). Believers Bkshelf.

--The Pentateuch. (Introductory Lecture Ser.). 524p. 6.95 (ISBN 0-88172-099-2). Believers Bkshelf.

--The Second Coming. 375p. 6.25 (ISBN 0-88172-108-5). Believers Bkshelf.

Kelly, William J. Karl Rahner, S. J., Theology & Discovery: Essays in Honor of Karl Rahner, S. J. 320p. 24.95 (ISBN 0-87462-521-1). Marquette.

Kelm, Paul. Christianity Is All Talk. Fischer, William, ed. (Bible Class Course for Young Adults Ser.: Student's Guide). (Illus.). 44p. 1984. pap. text ed. 2.95 (ISBN 0-938272-16-0). Wels Board.

--Christianity Is All Talk. Fischer, William, ed. (Bible Class Course for Young Adults Ser.: Leader's Guide). 64p. 1984. pap. text ed. 2.95 (ISBN 0-938272-17-9). Wels Board.

Kelman, John. Prophets of Yesterday & Their Message for Today. facs. ed. LC 74-152181. (Essay Index Reprint Ser). 1924. 17.00 (ISBN 0-8369-2193-3). Ayer Co Pubs.

--Road: A Study of John Bunyan's Pilgrim's Progress, 2 Vols. LC 77-113339. 1970. Repr. of 1912 ed. Set. 50.00x (ISBN 0-8046-1025-8, Pub. by Kennikat). Assoc Faculty Pr.

Kelman, Stuart. Prayer Transparencies. 32p. (Orig.). 1982. 29.95x (ISBN 0-686-81835-0). Arbit.

Kelman, Victoria, ed. see Anderson, Joseph.

Kelsey, David H. Uses of Scripture in Recent Theology. LC 74-26344. 240p. 1975. pap. 7.95 (ISBN 0-8006-1374-0, 1-1374). Fortress.

Kelsey, Morton. The Age of Miracles. LC 78-74095. 80p. 1979. pap. 2.45 (ISBN 0-87793-169-0). Ave Maria.

--The Christian & the Supernatural. LC 76-3865. 160p. (Orig.). 1976. pap. 8.95 (ISBN 0-8066-1525-7, 10-1100). Augsburg.

--Christianity As Psychology: The Healing Power of the Christian Message. LC 85-22864. 114p. (Orig.). 1986. pap. 7.95 (ISBN 0-8066-2194-X, 10-1184). Augsburg.

--Christopsychology. 177p. 1984. pap. 9.95 (ISBN 0-8245-0630-8). Crossroad NY.

--Discernment: A Study in Ecstasy & Evil. LC 78-58958. 168p. 1978. pap. 7.95 (ISBN 0-8091-2157-3). Paulist Pr.

--Encounter with God: A Theology of Christian Experience. 48p. 1972. pap. 8.95 (ISBN 0-87123-123-9, 210123); study guide 1.25 (ISBN 0-87123-506-4, 210506). Bethany Hse.

--Healing & Christianity. LC 72-78065. 1976. pap. 10.95 (ISBN 0-06-064381-1, RD 161, HarpR). Har-Row.

--Myth, History & Faith: The Re-Mythologizing of Christianity. LC 73-94216. 192p. 1974. pap. 5.95 (ISBN 0-8091-1827-0). Paulist Pr.

--Prophetic Ministry. 224p. 1984. pap. 9.95 (ISBN 0-8245-0631-6). Crossroad NY.

--Tongue Speaking: The History & Meaning of the Charismatic Experience. 256p. 1981. pap. 8.95 (ISBN 0-8245-0073-3). Crossroad NY.

Kelsey, Morton, intro. by see Bakken, Kenneth.

Kelsey, Morton T. Adventure Inward: Christian Growth Through Personal Journal Writing. LC 80-65551. 224p. (Orig.). 1980. pap. 9.95 (ISBN 0-8066-1796-9, 10-0166). Augsburg.

--Can Christians Be Educated? Burgess, Harold W., ed. LC 77-3691. 154p. (Orig.). 1977. pap. 8.95 (ISBN 0-89135-008-X). Religious Educ.

--Caring: How Can We Love One Another? LC 80-84659. 198p. (Orig.). 1981. pap. 8.95 (ISBN 0-8091-2366-5). Paulist Pr.

--Companions on the Inner Way: The Art of Spiritual Guidance. LC 82-23541. 250p. 1983. 17.50 (ISBN 0-8245-0585-9); pap. 9.95 (ISBN 0-8245-0560-3). Crossroad NY.

--The Cross: Meditations on the Last Seven Words of Christ. LC 80-82086. 128p. 1980. pap. 3.95 (ISBN 0-8091-2337-1). Paulist Pr.

--The Other Side of Silence: A Guide to Christian Meditation. LC 76-9365. 314p. 1976. pap. 9.95 (ISBN 0-8091-1956-0). Paulist Pr.

--Prophetic Ministry: The Psychology & Spirituality of Pastoral Care. 258p. 1982. 12.95 (ISBN 0-8245-0441-0). Crossroad NY.

--Resurrection: Release from Oppression. LC 84-62150. 201p. 1985. pap. 8.95 (ISBN 0-8091-2673-7). Paulist Pr.

--Transcend: A Guide to the Spiritual Quest. 240p. (Orig.). 1981. pap. 9.95 (ISBN 0-8245-0015-6). Crossroad NY.

Kelsey, Morton T., intro. by see Israel, Martin.

Kelsey, Rayner W., ed. see Cazenove, Theophile.

Kelso Abbey. Liber S. Marie De Calchou, Registrum Abbacie Tironensis De Kelso, 1113-1567, 2 Vols. Innes, Cosmo, ed. LC 71-171552. Repr. of 1846 ed. 75.00 (ISBN 0-404-52805-8). AMS Pr.

Kelso, Alexander. Matthew Arnold. 1978. lib. bdg. 10.00 (ISBN 0-8492-1444-0). R West.

Kelso, James L. & Baramki, Dimitri. Excavations at New Testament Jericho & Khirbet en-Nitla. (Annual of the American Schools of Oriental Research: Vols. 29 & 30). 60p. 1955. text ed. 10.00x (ISBN 0-89757-030-8, Am Sch Orient Res). Eisenbrauns.

Kelty, Matthew, jt. auth. see Paulsell, William.

Kemelman, Y. A Guide to the Jewish Dietary Laws. 3rd ed. 1971. pap. 2.50x (ISBN 0-685-40445-5); pap. 13.00 (ISBN 0-231-05147-6). Bloch.

Kemeseye, Johannes De see De Kemeseye, Johannes.

Kemmer, Alfons. The Creed in the Gospels. Schnaus, Urban, tr. 144p. (Orig.). 1986. pap. 7.95 (ISBN 0-8091-2830-6). Paulist Pr.

Kemp, Brian. Church Monuments. (Shire Album Ser.: No. 149). (Illus., Orig.). 1985. pap. 3.50 (ISBN 0-85263-768-3, Pub. by Shire Pubns England). Seven Hills Bks.

--English Church Monuments. 240p. 1980. 45.00 (ISBN 0-7134-1735-8, Pub. by Batsford England). David & Charles.

Kemp, Charles F. The Caring Pastor: An Introduction to Pastoral Counseling in the Local Church. LC 85-3994. (Orig.). 1985. pap. 9.95 (ISBN 0-687-35548-6). Abingdon.

--Reflections: Fifty Years of Pastoral Ministry. (Orig.). pap. 9.95 (ISBN 0-937689-04-1). Chisum Pub.

--Reflections: 50 Years of Pastoral Ministry. 150p. (Orig.). 1986. pap. 9.95 (ISBN 0-318-20075-9). Chisum Pub.

Kemp, Eric W. Canonization & Authority in the Western Church. LC 78-63467. Repr. of 1948 ed. 20.00 (ISBN 0-404-16397-1). AMS Pr.

--Canonization & Authority in the Western Church. LC 78-20474. 1980. Repr. of 1948 ed. 20.35 (ISBN 0-88355-852-1). Hyperion Conn.

--Counsel & Consent. LC 62-3455. (Bampton Lectures). 1961. 15.00x (ISBN 0-8401-1317-X). A R Allenson.

Kemp, Raymond. A Journey in Faith. pap. 5.95 (ISBN 0-8215-9329-3). Sadlier.

Kemp, Russell A. Live Youthfully Now. LC 69-93890. 1969. 5.95 (ISBN 0-87159-232-0). Unity School.

Kemp, William W. Support of Schools in Colonial New York by the Society for the Propagation of the Gospel in Foreign Parts. LC 78-176933. (Columbia University. Teachers College. Contributions to Education: No. 56). Repr. of 1913 ed. 22.50 (ISBN 0-404-55056-8). AMS Pr.

--Support of Schools in Colonial New York by the Society for the Propagation of the Gospel in Foreign Parts. LC 72-89192. (American Education: Its Men, Institutions, & Ideas, Ser. 1). 1969. Repr. of 1913 ed. 12.00 (ISBN 0-405-01430-9). Ayer Co Pubs.

Kempe, Janice. Listening to God: Lessons from Everyday Places. (Orig.). 1985. pap. 2.95 (ISBN 0-310-34822-6, 12748P). Zondervan.

Kempe, Margery, et al. The Cell of Self Knowledge: Seven Early English Mystical Treatises. Griffiths, John, ed. LC 81-126. (The Spiritual Classics Ser.). 128p. 1981. 8.95 (ISBN 0-8245-0082-2). Crossroad NY.

Kemper, Deane A. Effective Preaching: A Manual for Students & Pastors. LC 84-20880. 142p. (Orig.). 1985. pap. 10.95 (ISBN 0-664-24595-1). Westminster.

Kemper, Frederick. The Christmas Cycle. 1982. 6.95 (ISBN 0-570-03842-1, 12-2945). Concordia.

--Kirigami. 1979. pap. 4.95 (ISBN 0-570-03782-4, 12-2736). Concordia.

Kemper, Frederick & Bass, George M. You Are My Beloved Sermon Book. 1980. pap. 6.95 (ISBN 0-570-03821-9, 12-2761). Concordia.

Kemper, Frederick W. The Lamb. LC 12-2983. (Christian Education & the Church Ser.). 1983. pap. 5.95 (ISBN 0-570-03901-0). Concordia.

--Variety for Worship: Resources for Festival Worship Liturgies. 1984. pap. 7.95 (ISBN 0-570-03936-3, 12-2871). Concordia.

Kemper, R. W. The Pentecost Cycle. LC 12-2965. 1982. pap. 7.95 (ISBN 0-570-03872-3). Concordia.

Kemper, Robert G. Beginning a New Pastorate. LC 77-18055. (Creative Leadership Ser.). 1978. pap. 6.95 (ISBN 0-687-02750-0). Abingdon.

--Kind Words for Our Kind of Faith. 144p. (Orig.). 1986. pap. 8.95 (ISBN 0-8298-0738-1). Pilgrim NY.

--What Every Church Member Should Know about Clergy. 180p. 1985. pap. 7.95 (ISBN 0-8298-0728-4). Pilgrim NY.

Kempf, Charles. Revival & Local Church Evangelism. (Orig.). 1987. pap. price not set (ISBN 0-89084-369-4). Bob Jones Univ Pr.

Kempf, Nicolas. Tractatus de Mystica Theologia, Vol. 2. Hogg, James, ed. (Analecta Cartusiana Ser.: No. 9). (Lat. & Fr.). 574p. (Orig.). 1973. pap. 50.00 (ISBN 3-7052-0010-0, Pub by Salzburg Studies). Longwood Pub Group.

Kempfer, Lester L. The Salem Light Guard. LC 73-76068. (Illus.). 128p. 1973. 5.95 (ISBN 0-686-04916-0); pap. 3.95 (ISBN 0-686-04917-9). L Kempfer.

Kempff, D. Christianity & Scholarship. Date not set. pap. 12.50x cancelled (ISBN 0-86990-687-9). Radix Bks.

Kempis, Thomas a. The Imitation of Christ. 217p. 1986. 16.95 (ISBN 0-88029-078-1, Pub. by Dorset). Hippocrene Bks.

Kemp-Welch, A., tr. see De Coinci, Gautier.

Kendall, Guy. Charles Kingsley & His Ideas. LC 72-6679. (English Biography Ser., No. 31). 195p. 1972. Repr. of 1937 ed. lib. bdg. 39.95x (ISBN 0-8383-1639-5). Haskell.

Kendall, Joan. The Story of Samuel. (Very First Bible Stories Ser.). 1984. 1.59 (ISBN 0-87162-271-8, D8500). Warner Pr.

Kendall, Laurel & Dix, Griffin, eds. Religion & Ritual in Korean Society. LC 86-82390. (Korea Research Monograph Ser.: No. 12). xii, 240p. 1987. pap. 15.00x. IEAS.

Kendall, R. T. Once Saved, Always Saved. (Orig.). 1985. pap. 3.95 (ISBN 0-8024-6064-X). Moody.

--Stand up & Be Counted: Calling for Public Confession of Faith. 128p. (Orig.). 1985. pap. 5.95 (ISBN 0-310-38351-X, 9281P). Zondervan.

--Tithing: A Call to Serious, Biblical Giving. 128p. 1983. pap. 4.95 (ISBN 0-310-38331-5, 9279P). Zondervan.

Kendall, Ritchie D. The Drama of Dissent: The Radical Poetics of Nonconformity, 1380-1590. LC 86-1289. (Studies in Religion). 286p. 1986. 27.50x (ISBN 0-8078-1700-7). U of NC Pr.

Kendrick, Ben. A World of Treasure. LC 82-332. 1981. pap. 4.95 (ISBN 0-87227-081-5). Reg Baptist.

Kendrick, Bv. Ben. Battle for Yanga. LC 80-20643. 127p. 1980. pap. 3.95 (ISBN 0-87227-074-2). Reg Baptist.

Kendrick, Dolores. Now is the Thing to Praise. LC 83-82774. 116p. 1984. pap. 7.00 perf. bnd. (ISBN 0-916418-54-5). Lotus.

Kendrick, Graham. Learning to Worship As a Way of Life. 214p. 1985. pap. 4.95 (ISBN 0-87123-863-2, 210863). Bethany Hse.

Kendrick, Lionel. Scriptures to Success. 99p. 1983. 3.95 (ISBN 0-934126-42-9). Randall Bk Co.

Kendrick, Rosalyn. Does God Have a Body? 1979. pap. 4.95 (ISBN 0-8192-1257-1). Morehouse.

--In the Steps of Jesus. 128p. 1985. pap. 8.95 (ISBN 0-7175-1309-2). Dufour.

Kendrick, Thomas D. Druids. (Illus.). 227p. 1966. Repr. of 1927 ed. 32.50x (ISBN 0-7146-1485-8, BHA-01485, F Cass Co). Biblio Dist.

Kendrick, V. Ben. Buried Alive for Christ & Other Missionary Stories. LC 78-14984. 1978. pap. 3.95 (ISBN 0-87227-061-0). Reg Baptist.

Kendzierski, Lotti H., tr. see St. Thomas Aquinas.

Kenik, Helen A. Design for Kingship: The Deuteronomistic Narrative Technique in 1 Kings 3: 4-15. LC 82-21054. (SBL Dissertation Ser.). 258p. 1983. pap. 13.50 (ISBN 0-89130-605-6, 06 01 69). Scholars Pr GA.

Kenna. Man's Judgement Call-the Irrevocable Master Contract. Date not set. price not set. Port Love Intl.

Kennan, Elizabeth T., jt. tr. see Anderson, John D.

Kennard, Edward A., jt. auth. see Earle, Edwin.

Kennard, Joseph S. Friar in Fiction, Sincerity in Art, & Other Essays. facs. ed. LC 68-20313. (Essay Index Reprint Ser). 1923. 20.00 (ISBN 0-8369-0588-1). Ayer Co Pubs.

Kenneally, Christy. Strings & Things: Poems & Other Messages for Children. (Orig.). 1984. pap. 3.50 (ISBN 0-8091-6555-4). Paulist Pr.

Kennedy, Alex. The Buddhist Vision. (Illus.). 216p. (Orig.). 1987. pap. 8.95 (ISBN 0-87728-620-5). Weiser.

Kennedy, Barbara L., tr. see Weinstein, Frida S.

Kennedy, C. W., tr. Cynewulf's Poems. 11.25 (ISBN 0-8446-1143-3). Peter Smith.

Kennedy, Charles W. Early English Christian Poetry. 1977. lib. bdg. 59.95 (ISBN 0-8490-1739-4). Gordon Pr.

Kennedy, Charles W., tr. Early English Christian Poetry. 1963. pap. 5.95 (ISBN 0-19-500246-6). Oxford U Pr.

Kennedy, D. James. Knowing the Whole Truth: Basic Christianity & What It Means in Your Life. 192p. 1985. 11.95 (ISBN 0-8007-1407-5). Revell.

--Learning to Live with the People You Love. 200p. (Orig.). 1987. pap. text ed. 3.95 (ISBN 0-88368-190-0). Whitaker Hse.

--Truths That Transform. 160p. 1974. power bks. 5.95 (ISBN 0-8007-5148-5). Revell.

--Why I Believe. 1980. 6.95 (ISBN 0-8499-2943-1). Word Bks.

Kennedy, D. James & Moore, T. M. Chain Reaction: Changing the World from Where You Are. LC 85-6458. 160p. 1985. 9.95 (ISBN 0-8499-0486-2, 0486-2). Word Bks.

Kennedy, David G. Catholicism & the Mysticisms of the East. LC 86-62211. viii, 70p. (Orig.). 1986. pap. 4.95x (ISBN 0-934995-01-X). OLW Editions.

--The Incarnation & Hilton's Spirituality. LC 85-62297. x, 312p. (Orig.). 1986. pap. 12.95x (ISBN 0-934995-00-1). OLW Editions.

--Incarnational Element in Hiltons Spirituality. Hogg, James, ed. (Elizabethan & Renaissance Studies). 312p. (Orig.). 1982. pap. 15.00 (ISBN 0-317-40146-7, Pub by Salzburg Studies). Longwood Pub Group.

Kennedy, Eugene. Loneliness & Everyday Problems. LC 82-45971. 160p. 1983. pap. 3.95 (ISBN 0-385-18797-1, Im). Doubleday.

--Now & Future Church. LC 83-20574. 216p. 1985. pap. 7.95 (ISBN 0-385-23236-5, Im). Doubleday.

--The Now & Future Church: The Psychology of Being an American Catholic. LC 83-20574. 216p. 1984. 13.95 (ISBN 0-385-19040-9). Doubleday.

Kennedy, Eugene C. The Joy of Being Human: Reflections for Every Day of the Year. 360p. 1976. pap. 5.95 (ISBN 0-385-00943-7, Im). Doubleday.

--The Pain of Being Human. LC 73-83645. 280p. 1974. pap. 4.95 (ISBN 0-385-06888-3, Im). Doubleday.

--A Sense of Life, a Sense of Sin. 200p. 1976. pap. 3.50 (ISBN 0-385-12070-2, Im). Doubleday.

Kennedy, George A. New Testament Interpretation Through Rhetorical Criticism. LC 83-23577. x, 171p. 1984. 14.00x (ISBN 0-8078-1601-9); pap. 6.95 (ISBN 0-8078-4120-X). U of NC Pr.

Kennedy, Gerald, ed. see Jowett, John H.

Kennedy, H. A. St. Paul & the Mystery Religions. 1977. lib. bdg. 59.95 (ISBN 0-8490-2561-3). Gordon Pr.

Kennedy, H. E., et al, trs. see Masaryk, Tomas G.

Kennedy, Harry A. Theology of the Epistles. LC 20-15157. (Studies in Theology: No. 13). 1919. 6.00x (ISBN 0-8401-6013-5). A R Allenson.

Kennedy, Hugh. The Early Abbasid Caliphate: A Political History. 238p. 1981. 28.50x (ISBN 0-389-20018-2, 06791). B&N Imports.

Kennedy, J. M. The Pater Calendar. LC 73-606. 1973. lib. bdg. 12.50 (ISBN 0-8414-1531-5). Folcroft.

Kennedy, James, Jr. Library Research Guide to Religion & Theology: Illustrated Search Strategy & Sources. 2nd Rev. ed. LC 73-90317. (Library Research Guides Ser.: No. 1). 1984. 19.50 (ISBN 0-87650-185-4); pap. 12.50 (ISBN 0-87650-184-6). Pierian.

Kennedy, James W. Holy Island. 2nd ed. 144p. 1984. pap. 1.70 (ISBN 0-88028-028-X). Forward Movement.

Kennedy, John W. Torch of the Testimony. (Orig.). 1983. pap. 6.95 (ISBN 0-940232-12-X). Christian Bks.

Kennedy, Margaretta. Considering Marriage? 12p. 1982. pap. 0.15 (ISBN 0-686-36261-6). Faith Pub Hse.

Kennedy, Moorhead. The Ayatollah in the Cathedral: Reflections of a Hostage. 241p. 1986. 17.95 (ISBN 0-8090-2765-8). Hill & Wang.

Kennedy, Nell. Dream Your Way to Success. LC 79-93290. 1980. pap. 4.95 (ISBN 0-88270-407-9). Bridge Pub.

--Worthy Vessels: Clay in the Hands of the Master. 160p. (Orig.). 1984. 8.95 (ISBN 0-310-47100-1, 11287). Zondervan.

Kennedy, Richard. Basic Training. 100p. 1987. three-ring binder 12.95 (ISBN 0-89265-104-0). Randall Hse.

--International Dictionary of Religion. LC 83-27209. (Illus.). 1984. 24.50x (ISBN 0-8245-0632-4). Crossroad NY.

--International Dictionary of Religion. 256p. 1986. pap. 12.95 (ISBN 0-8245-0733-9). Crossroad NY.

--Now That You're Saved. 1977. pap. 0.95 (ISBN 0-89265-046-X). Randall Hse.

Kennedy, Roger. American Churches. (Illus.). 296p. 1982. 50.00 (ISBN 0-8245-0539-5). Crossroad NY.

Kennedy, Stanislaus. Who Should Care: The Development of Kilkenny Social Services. (Turoe Press Ser.). 228p. pap. 12.95 (ISBN 0-905223-26-8, Dist. by Scribner). M Boyars Pubs.

Kennedy, Timothy, jt. auth. see Twombly, Gerald.

Kennedy, William J. Jacopo Sannazaro & the Uses of Pastoral. LC 83-40011. 248p. 1983. pap. 22.50x (ISBN 0-87451-268-9). U Pr of New Eng.

Kennedy, William S. Clues to Emerson's Mystic Verse. (Studies in Emerson, No. 12). 1970. pap. 39.95x (ISBN 0-8383-0048-0). Haskell.

Kennel, Leroy. Mennonites: Who & Why. LC 63-17081. 32p. 1966. pap. 1.00 (ISBN 0-8361-1396-9). Herald Pr.

Kenner, Dru A. My Friend Consider. LC 84-51459. 100p. (Orig.). 1985. pap. 4.95 (ISBN 0-930551-00-1). Vistara Pubns.

Kennett, R. H. Ancient Hebrew Social Life & Custom As Indicated in Law, Narrative & Metaphor. (British Academy, London, Schweich Lectures on Biblical Archaeology Series, 1931). pap. 19.00 (ISBN 0-8115-1273-8). Kraus Repr.

--The Composition of the Book of Isaiah in the Light of History & Archaeology. (British Academy, London, Schweich Lectures on Biblical Archaeology Series, 1909). pap. 19.00 (ISBN 0-8115-1251-7). Kraus Repr.

Kenney, Betty Jo. The Missionary Family. LC 83-6572. (Mission Candidate Aids Ser.). 120p. 1983. pap. 5.95 (ISBN 0-87808-193-3). William Carey Lib.

Kenney, Edward H. A Confucian Notebook. LC 79-2828. 89p. 1986. Repr. of 1950 ed. 15.00 (ISBN 0-8305-0008-1). Hyperion Conn.

Kenney, Scott G. & Smith, Hyrum, III. From Prophet to Son. LC 81-15173. 132p. 1981. 6.95 (ISBN 0-87747-885-6). Deseret Bk.

Kenny, A. J., ed. see Prior, Arthur N.

Kenny, Anthony. Aquinas. (Past Masters Ser.). 1980. pap. 4.95 (ISBN 0-19-287500-0). Oxford U Pr.

--Faith & Reason. LC 82-22187. (Bampton Lectures in America Ser.). 100p. 1983. 21.50 (ISBN 0-231-05488-2). Columbia U Pr.

--The Five Ways: St. Thomas Aquinas' Proofs of God's Existence. LC 80-10416. 140p. 1980. pap. text ed. 4.95 (ISBN 0-268-00952-X). U of Notre Dame Pr.

--Freewill & Responsibility: Four Lectures. 1978. 15.00x (ISBN 0-7100-8998-8). Methuen Inc.

--The God of the Philosophers. 1979. 26.00x (ISBN 0-19-824594-7). Oxford U Pr.

--A Stylometric Study of the New Testament. 160p. 1986. text ed. 38.00 (ISBN 0-19-826178-0). Oxford U Pr.

--Thomas More. (Past Master Ser.). 1983. text ed. 13.95x (ISBN 0-19-287574-4); pap. 4.95 (ISBN 0-19-287573-6). Oxford U Pr.

--Wyclif. (Past Masters Ser.). 1985. 13.95x (ISBN 0-19-287647-3); pap. 4.95 (ISBN 0-19-287646-5). Oxford U Pr.

Kenny, Bernadette. Children's Liturgies: Seventy-Four Eucharistic Liturgies, Prayer Services & Penance Services Designed for Primary, Middle & Junior High Children. LC 77-74582. 176p. 1977. pap. 9.95 (ISBN 0-8091-2030-5). Paulist Pr.

Kenny, J. Frank & Poling, Tommy H. The Hare Krishna Character Type: A Study of the Sensate Personality. (Studies in Religion & Society: No. 15). 202p. 1986. 49.95 (ISBN 0-88946-859-1). E Mellen.

Kenny, James & Kenny, Mary. When Your Marriage Goes Stale. LC 79-51277. (When Bks). (Illus.). 1979. pap. 2.45 (ISBN 0-87029-150-5, 20236-6). Abbey.

Kenny, James & Spicer, Stephen. Caring for Your Aging Parent. 152p. 1984. pap. 5.95 (ISBN 0-86716-037-3). St Anthony Mess Pr.

Kenny, John. Now That You Are a Catholic. rev. & enl. ed. LC 73-80417. 108p. (Orig.). 1986. pap. 3.95 (ISBN 0-8091-1743-6). Paulist Pr.

Kenny, John P. The Supernatural. new ed. LC 72-3575. 165p. 1972. 4.95 (ISBN 0-8189-0251-5). Alba.

Kenny, Mary, jt. auth. see Kenny, James.

Kenny, Michael. Romance of the Floridas. LC 70-120573. (Illus.). Repr. of 1934 ed. 15.00 (ISBN 0-404-03656-2). AMS Pr.

Kenny, Vincent. Herman Melville's "Clarel". A Spiritual Autobiography. LC 73-3074. xvi, 272p. 1973. 26.00 (ISBN 0-208-01226-5, Archon). Shoe String.

Kenseth, Arnold & Unsworth, Richard P. Prayers for Worship Leaders. LC 77-15249. 132p. (Orig.). 1978. pap. 5.95 (ISBN 0-8006-1331-7, 1-1331). Fortress.

Kenslea, Timothy, jt. auth. see Caffrey, Stephanie.

Kenslea, Timothy, jt. ed. see Caffrey, Stephanie.

Kent, Charles. The Egyptian Background of Hebrew History. (Illus.). 133p. 1982. Repr. of 1908 ed. 73.45 (ISBN 0-89901-068-7). Found Class Reprints.

Kent, Charles F. Biblical Geography & History. 296p. 1981. Repr. of 1911 ed. lib. bdg. 30.00 (ISBN 0-89760-431-8). Telegraph Bks.

--The Messages of Israel's Lawgivers. Sanders, Frank K., ed. 386p. 1981. Repr. of 1916 ed. lib. bdg. 25.00 (ISBN 0-89760-430-X). Telegraph Bks.

--The Origin & Permanent Value of the Old Testament. 270p. 1981. Repr. of 1906 ed. lib. bdg. 30.00 (ISBN 0-89760-429-6). Telegraph Bks.

Kent, Dan G. Lamentations. (Bible Study Commentary Ser.). 80p. 1983. pap. 3.95 (ISBN 0-310-44011-4, 12482P). Zondervan.

--Layman's Bible Book Commentary: Joshua, Judges, Ruth, Vol. 4. LC 79-51136. 1980. 5.95 (ISBN 0-8054-1174-7). Broadman.

Kent, Homer A., Jr. Ephesians, the Glory of the Church. pap. 5.95 (ISBN 0-88469-078-4). BMH Bks.

--Epistle to the Hebrews. 1972. pap. 8.95 (ISBN 0-8010-5458-3). Baker Bk.

--The Epistle to the Hebrews. pap. 11.95 (ISBN 0-88469-069-5). BMH Bks.

--Faith That Works. 1986. pap. 7.95 (ISBN 0-88469-180-2). BMH Bks.

--Faith That Works: Studies in the Epistle of James. 1986. pap. 7.95 (ISBN 0-8010-5476-1). Baker Bk.

--The Freedom of God's Sons: Studies in Galatians. (Illus.). pap. 5.95 (ISBN 0-88469-058-X). BMH Bks.

--A Heart Opened Wide: Studies in II Corinthians. (New Testament Studies). 176p. (Orig.). 1982. pap. 4.95 (ISBN 0-8010-5438-9). Baker Bk.

--A Heart Opened Wide: Studies in II Corinthians. 176p. (Orig.). 1982. pap. 4.95 (ISBN 0-88469-152-7). BMH Bks.

--Jerusalem to Rome: Studies in Acts. (Illus.). pap. 5.95 (ISBN 0-88469-056-3). BMH Bks.

--Jerusalem to Rome: Studies in the Book of Acts. (New Testament Studies Ser.). pap. 5.95 (ISBN 0-8010-5313-7). Baker Bk.

--Light in the Darkness. (New Testament Studies Ser.). 1974. pap. 5.95 (ISBN 0-8010-5343-9). Baker Bk.

--Light in the Darkness: Studies in the Gospel of John. (Illus.). pap. 5.95 (ISBN 0-88469-055-5). BMH Bks.

--Pastoral Epistles. 320p. 1982. pap. 10.95 (ISBN 0-88469-075-X). BMH Bks.

--Treasures of Wisdom: Studies in Colossians & Philemon. pap. 5.95 (ISBN 0-88469-062-8). BMH Bks.

Kent, Homer A., Sr. Conquering Frontiers: A History of the Brethren Church. 8.95 (ISBN 0-88469-018-0); pap. 6.95 (ISBN 0-88469-017-2). BMH Bks.

--The Pastor & His Work. pap. 8.95 (ISBN 0-88469-079-2). BMH Bks.

Kent, Homer, Jr. Efesios: La Gloria de la Iglesia (Comentario Biblico Portavoz) Orig. Title: Ephesians: The Glory of the Church (Everyman's Bible Commentary) (Span.). 144p. 1981. pap. 3.95 (ISBN 0-8254-1405-9). Kregel.

--Ephesians: The Glory of the Church. (Everyman's Bible Commentary Ser.). 1971. pap. 5.95 (ISBN 0-8024-2049-4). Moody.

--Pastoral Epistles. rev. ed. 1958. 10.95 (ISBN 0-8024-6357-6). Moody.

Kent, Howard. Yoga for the Disabled: A Practical Self-Help Guide to a Happier Healthier Life. (Illus.). 160p. 1985. pap. 7.95 (ISBN 0-7225-0902-2). Thorsons Pubs.

Kent, John H. The End of the Line? The Development of Christian Theology in the Last Two Centuries. LC 82-7263. 144p. 1982. pap. 6.95 (ISBN 0-8006-1652-9, 1-1652). Fortress.

Kent, K. V., tr. see Falco, Giorgio.

Kent, Maxwell. A Comparative Analysis of the Italians & the Jews: The Two People Who Contributed the Most to the Civilization of Mankind with Strange & Unexpected Conclusions. (Illus.). 1977. 117.25 (ISBN 0-89266-056-2). Am Classical Coll Pr.

Kent, Peter. The Pope & the Duce. 1981. 26.00 (ISBN 0-312-63024-7). St Martin.

Kenworthy, Leonard. Living in a Larger World: The Life of Murray S. Kenworthy. (Illus.). 120p. (Orig.). 1987. pap. 8.95 (ISBN 0-913408-93-X). Friends United.

Kenworthy, Leonard S. Quakerism: A Study Guide on the Religious Society of Friends. LC 81-80656. 224p. 1981. pap. 5.00 (ISBN 0-932970-21-4). Prinit Pr.

Kenworthy, Leonard S., ed. Friends Face the World: Some Continuing & Current Quaker Concerns. 220p. 1987. pap. 6.95 (ISBN 0-913408-97-2). Friends United.

Kenya Mission Team. Church Planting, Watering & Increasing in Kenya. Humble, B. J., ed. (Illus.). 130p. 1981. pap. 2.95 (ISBN 0-88027-002-0). Firm Foun Pub.

Kenyon, Don J. The Double Mind. 95p. 1981. pap. 2.25 (ISBN 0-87509-288-8). Chr Pubns.

--Romans, 2 vols. Incl. Vol. 1. Triumph of Truth. pap. text ed. 4.95 (ISBN 0-87509-147-4); leader's guide 2.95 (ISBN 0-87509-265-9); student's manual 1.00 (ISBN 0-87509-262-4); Vol 2. Glory of Grace. pap. text ed. 4.95 (ISBN 0-87509-148-2); leader's guide 2.95 (ISBN 0-87509-266-7); student's manual 1.00 (ISBN 0-87509-263-2). 1978. pap. Chr Pubns.

Kenyon, F. G. Recent Developments in the Textual Criticism of the Greek Bible. (British Academy of London Ser.). pap. 19.00 (ISBN 0-8115-1274-6). Kraus Repr.

--The Text of the Greek Bible. 3rd, rev. ed. 1975. 40.50 (ISBN 0-7156-0641-7, Pub. by Duckworth London); pap. 13.50 (ISBN 0-7156-0652-2). Longwood Pub Group.

Kenyon, Frederic G. The Bible & Modern Scholarship. LC 78-9892. 1979. Repr. of 1948 ed. lib. bdg. 22.50x (ISBN 0-313-21009-8, KEBI). Greenwood.

Kenyon, Dame Kathleen. The Bible & Recent Archaeology. LC 78-4089. (Illus.). 1979. pap. 8.95 (ISBN 0-8042-0010-6). John Knox.

Kenyon, Kathleen M. Archaeology in the Holy Land. 4th ed. (Illus.). 1979. 10.95x (ISBN 0-393-01285-9). Norton.

Kenyon, Mel & Christophus, Mike. Burned to Life. LC 76-1060. (Illus.). 1976. pap. 2.95 (ISBN 0-87123-044-5, 200044). Bethany Hse.

Kenyon, Ruth. The Catholic Faith & the Industrial Order. 1980. lib. bdg. 59.95 (ISBN 0-8490-3129-X). Gordon Pr.

Keogh, Dermot F. The Vatican, the Bishops & Irish Politics: Church & State in Ireland, 1919-1939. (Illus.). 318p. 1986. 39.50 (ISBN 0-521-30129-7). Cambridge U Pr.

Keough, G. Arthur. Infinitely Happy. LC 78-21952. (Horizon Ser.). 1978. pap. 5.95 (ISBN 0-8127-0213-1). Review & Herald.

--Our Church Today: What It Is & Can Be. (Horizon Ser.). 160p. 1980. pap. 5.95 (ISBN 0-8127-0300-6). Review & Herald.

Kepelino. Kepelino's Traditions of Hawaii. Beckwith, Martha W., ed. (BMB). Repr. of 1932 ed. 25.00 (ISBN 0-527-02201-2). Kraus Repr.

Kepes, Joanne L. Church History. 1981. 9.95 (ISBN 0-89837-070-1, Pub. by Pflaum Pr). Peter Li.

--God's Wonderful World & Me. 1982. 9.95 (ISBN 0-89837-086-8, Pub. by Pflaum Pr). Peter Li.

--I Believe: The Creed. 1981. 9.95 (ISBN 0-89837-067-1, Pub. by Pflaum Pr). Peter Li.

--Jesus & His Parables. 1982. 9.95 (ISBN 0-89837-087-6, Pub. by Pflaum Pr). Peter Li.

--Life in Bible Times & Places. 1982. 9.95 (Pub. by Pflaum Pr). Peter Li.

--Our Father. 1982. 9.95 (ISBN 0-89837-060-4, Pub. by Pflaum Pr). Peter Li.

--The Rosary. 1982. 9.95 (ISBN 0-89837-061-2, Pub. by Pflaum Pr). Peter Li.

Kephala, Euphrosyne. The Church of the Greek People. LC 77-87528. Repr. of 1930 ed. 14.50 (ISBN 0-404-16594-X). AMS Pr.

Kepler, Thomas S. Journey with the Saints. facs. ed. LC 70-148223. (Biography Index Reprint Ser.). 1951. 17.00 (ISBN 0-8369-8070-0). Ayer Co Pubs.

Keppel, L., tr. see Menendez, Josefa.

Kepple, Robert J. Reference Works for Theological Research: An Annotated Selective Bibliographical Guide. 2nd ed. LC 81-40350. 298p. 1981. lib. bdg. 29.00 (ISBN 0-8191-1679-3); pap. text ed. 13.75 (ISBN 0-8191-1680-7). U Pr of Amer.

Ker, Ian, ed. see Newman, John H.

Ker, Ian, ed. & intro. by see Newman, John H.

Ker, J. M., jt. ed. see Sharpe, K. J.

Kerbs, John G. Answers to Your People Problems. LC 68-25949. (Harvest Ser.). 1978. pap. 4.95 (ISBN 0-8163-0192-1, 01634-5). Pacific Pr Pub Assn.

Keren, Nili, jt. auth. see Bauer, Yehuda.

Kerenyi, C. The Gods of the Greeks. (Illus.). 1980. pap. 9.95 (ISBN 0-500-27048-1). Thames Hudson.

--Prometheus: Archetypal Image of Human Existence. 1963. 50.00 (ISBN 0-8274-3210-0). R West.

Kerenyi, Carl. Archetypal Images in Greek Religion, 5 vols. Manheim, R., tr. Incl. Vol. 1. Prometheus: Archetypal Image of Human Existence. 1963; Vol. 2. Dionysos: Archetypal Image of Industructible Life. 1975; Vol. 3. Asklepios: Archetypal Image of the Physician's Existence. 1959. 37.00x (ISBN 0-691-09703-8); Vol. 4. Eleusis: Archetypal Image of Mother & Daughter. 1967; Vol. 5. Zeus & Hera-Archetypal Image of Father, Husband & Wife. Holme, tr. 1975. (Bollingen Ser.: Vol. 65). Princeton U Pr.

Kerenyi, Carl, jt. auth. see Jung, Carl G.

Kerenyi, Karl. Athene. Stein, Murray, tr. from Ger. (Dunquin Ser.: No. 9). 106p. (Orig.). 1978. pap. 7.50 (ISBN 0-88214-209-7). Spring Pubns.

--Goddesses of Sun & Moon: Circe, Aphrodite, Medea, Niobe. Stein, Murray, tr. from Ger. (Dunquin Ser.: No. 11). 84p. 1979. pap. 7.50 (ISBN 0-88214-211-9). Spring Pubns.

--Hermes-Guide of Souls: The Mythologem of the Masculine Source of Life. Stein, Murray, tr. LC 85-18263. (Dunquin Ser.: No. 7). 104p. 1986. pap. 8.50 (ISBN 0-88214-207-0). Spring Pubns.

Kerenyi, Karoly. The Religion of the Greeks & Romans. LC 72-9823. (Illus.). 303p. 1973. Repr. of 1962 ed. lib. bdg. 24.75x (ISBN 0-8371-6605-5, KERG). Greenwood.

Keresztes, Paul. Constantine: A Great Christian Monarch & Apostle. (London Studies in Classical Philology Ser.). 218p. 1981. pap. text ed. 28.50x (ISBN 90-70265-03-6, Pub. by Gieben Holland). Humanities.

Kerl, Mary A. Where Are You, Lord? LC 82-70949. (Young Readers Ser.). 112p. (Orig.). 1982. pap. 3.95 (ISBN 0-8066-1924-4, 10-7069). Augsburg.

Kermode, Frank, ed. see Kolakowski, Leszek.

Kern, Alma. You Are Special. (Illus.). 144p. (Orig.). 1985. pap. 5.00 (ISBN 0-9614955-0-2, 2050). Lutheran Womens.

Kern, H. Manual of Indian Buddhism. 1974. Repr. 6.95 (ISBN 0-8426-0674-2). Orient Bk Dist.

--The Saddharma-Pundarika or the Lotus of the Good Law. (Sacred Bks. of the East: Vol. 21). 15.00 (ISBN 0-89581-524-9). Asian Human Pr.

Kern, H., tr. The Saddharma-Pundarika: Lotus of True Law. lib. bdg. 79.95 (ISBN 0-87968-530-1). Krishna Pr.

Kern, Herbert. How to Respond to Jehovah's Witnesses. (The Response Ser.). 1977. 1.95 (ISBN 0-570-07679-X, 12-2664). Concordia.

Kern, Louis J. An Ordered Love: Sex Roles & Sexuality in Victorian Utopias--the Shakers, the Mormons, & the Oneida Community. LC 80-10763. xv, 430p. 1981. 27.00x (ISBN 0-8078-1443-1); pap. 9.95x (ISBN 0-8078-4074-2). U of NC Pr.

Kern, Mary M. Be a Better Parent. LC 79-9098. 160p. 1979. pap. 6.95 (ISBN 0-664-24271-5). Westminster.

Kern, Walter. New Liturgy & Old Devotions. LC 78-73623. (Illus., Orig.). 1979. pap. 3.50 (ISBN 0-8189-1151-4, 151, Pub. by Alba Bks). Alba.

--Pastoral Ministry with Disabled Persons. LC 84-24619. 248p. 1985. pap. 6.95 (ISBN 0-8189-0472-0). Alba.

--Updated Devotion to the Sacred Heart. LC 75-9277. (Illus.). 192p. 1975. pap. 2.95 (ISBN 0-8189-1124-7, Pub. by Alba Bks). Alba.

Kerr, Donal A. Peel, Priests & Politics: Sir Robert Peel's Administration & the Roman Catholic Church in Ireland, 1841-1846. (Oxford Historical Monographs). 400p. 1982. pap. 15.95x (ISBN 0-19-822932-1). Oxford U Pr.

Kerr, Fergus. Theology after Wittgenstein. 224p. 1986. text ed. 45.00 (ISBN 0-631-14688-1). Basil Blackwell.

Kerr, Horace L. How to Minister to Senior Adults in Your Church. LC 77-80944. 1980. 8.50 (ISBN 0-8054-3222-1). Broadman.

Kerr, Howard. Mediums, & Spirit Rappers, & Roaring Radicals: Spiritualism in American Literature, 1850-1900. LC 78-170964. pap. 67.80 (ISBN 0-317-41918-8, 2025919). Bks Demand UMI.

Kerr, Hugh. Protestantism. LC 76-16065. (World Religions Ser.). 1979. pap. text ed. 6.95 (ISBN 0-8120-0665-8). Barron.

Kerr, Hugh T., ed. Readings in Christian Thought. LC 66-14992. 1966. 25.95 (ISBN 0-687-35549-4). Abingdon.

--Sons of the Prophets: Leaders in Protestantism from Princeton Seminary. 1963. 26.50x (ISBN 0-691-07136-5). Princeton U Pr.

Kerr, Hugh T. & Mulder, John M., eds. Conversions. 288p. 1983. 12.95 (ISBN 0-8028-3587-2). Eerdmans.

Kerr, Hugh T. & Mulder, John T., eds. Conversions. 384p. 1985. pap. 7.95 (ISBN 0-8028-0016-5). Eerdmans.

Kerr, Hugh T., Jr., ed. Compend of Luther's Theology. LC 43-16154. 276p. 1966. Westminster.

--Compend of the Institutes of the Christian Religion by John Calvin. 240p. 1964. pap. 8.95 (ISBN 0-664-24557-9). Westminster.

Kerr, James L. Wilfred Grenfell, His Life & Work. LC 73-21177. 1977. lib. bdg. 22.50x (ISBN 0-8371-6068-5, KEWG). Greenwood.

Kerr, John H. Harmony of the Gospels. 236p. 10.95 (ISBN 0-8007-0131-3). Revell.

Kerr, Malcolm H., ed. An Islamic Tradition & Its Problems. LC 80-53523. (Giorgio Levi Della Vida Conference: Vol. 7). 140p. (Orig.). 1983. pap. 18.50x (ISBN 0-89003-069-3). Undena Pubns.

Kerrigan, Anthony & Nozick, Martin, eds. Selected Works of Miguel de Unamuno, Vol. 5: The Agony of Christianity & Essays on Faith. LC 67-22341. (Bollingen Ser.: Vol. 85). 313p. 1974. 34.00x (ISBN 0-691-09933-2). Princeton U Pr.

Kerrigan, William. The Prophetic Milton. LC 74-6118. Repr. of 1974 ed. 74.30 (ISBN 0-8357-9813-5, 2016964). Bks Demand UMI.

Kershaw, Beulah S. Scared Woman: True Expose, Vol. I. (Illus.). 44p. (Orig.). 1981. pap. 3.00x (ISBN 0-911870-03-2). Beulah.

Kershaw, Jack. Christ's Mass. LC 74-28633. 1975. 9.95 (ISBN 0-87695-178-7). Aurora Pubs.

Kershner, Frederick D. Pioneers of Christian Thought. facs. ed. LC 68-57327. (Essay Index Reprint Ser). 1930. 20.00 (ISBN 0-8369-0594-6). Ayer Co Pubs.

Kersten, Dorothy B. Classifying Church or Synagogue Library Materials. LC 77-16476. (Guide Ser.: No. 7). 1977. pap. 3.95x (ISBN 0-915324-13-X); pap. 3.00 members. CSLA.

--Subject Headings for Church or Synagogue Libraries. rev. ed. LC 78-818. (Guide Ser.: No. 8). 1984. pap. 4.95 (ISBN 0-915324-14-8); pap. 3.95 members. CSLA.

Kersten, John C. Bible Meditations for Every Day: A Guide to Living the Year in the Spirit of the Scriptures. flexible bdg. 4.95 (ISBN 0-89942-277-2, 277/04). Catholic Bk Pub.

--Understanding Hebrew Literature: A Guide to a Better Understanding of the Bible As a Source Book for the Humanities. 2.25 (ISBN 0-89942-145-8, 145/04). Catholic Bk Pub.

Kersten, Lawrence K. The Lutheran Ethic: The Impact of Religion on Laymen & Clergy. LC 71-102200. 310p. 1970. 25.00x (ISBN 0-8143-1416-3). Wayne St U Pr.

Kersten, Phyllis N. & Williams, E. Louise. Talented, Tired, Beautiful Feet: A Bible Study for Women. 64p. (Orig.). 1985. pap. 2.95 (ISBN 0-570-03967-3, 12-3002). Concordia.

Kertlege, Karl. The Epistles to the Romans. McKenzie, John L., ed. LC 81-605. (The New Testament for Spiritual Reading Ser.). 144p. 1981. pap. 4.95 (ISBN 0-8245-0121-7). Crossroad NY.

Kertzer, Morris N. What Is a Jew. rev. ed. LC 73-77280. 217p. 1973. Repr. of 1953 ed. 8.95x (ISBN 0-8197-0299-4). Bloch.

--What Is a Jew? 4th ed. 1978. pap. 4.95 (ISBN 0-02-086350-0, Collier). Macmillan.

Keshavadas, Satguru S. Cosmic Hymns & Prayers. (Illus.). 174p. (Orig.). 1982. pap. text ed. 10.00 (ISBN 0-942508-13-0). Vishwa.

--Cosmic Meditations. (Illus.). 22p. (Orig.). 1974. pap. 1.99 (ISBN 0-942508-08-4). Vishwa.

--Cosmic Shakti Kundalini: The Universal Mother. LC 76-11347. (Illus.). 112p. (Orig.). 1976. pap. 3.50 (ISBN 0-942508-04-1). Vishwa.

--Essence of Bhagavad Gita & Bible. LC 80-50446. (Illus.). 303p. 1982. pap. 30.00 (ISBN 0-942508-00-9); pap. 15.00 (ISBN 0-942508-01-7). Vishwa.

--Garland of Prayers. (Illus.). 30p. (Orig.). 1975. pap. 1.99 (ISBN 0-942508-03-3). Vishwa.

--Gayatri: The Highest Meditation. LC 78-69857. (Illus.). 164p. 1978. 6.50 (ISBN 0-533-03188-5). Vishwa.

--Healing Techniques of the Holy East. LC 80-50447. (Illus.). 116p. (Orig.). 1980. pap. 3.95 (ISBN 0-931290-30-9). Vishwa.

--Liberation from Karma & Rebirth. (Illus.). 164p. (Orig.). 1970. pap. 3.50 (ISBN 0-942508-02-5). Vishwa.

--Life & Teaching of Satguru Sant Keshavadas. LC 77-81277. (Illus.). 150p. (Orig.). 1977. pap. 3.50 (ISBN 0-942508-12-2). Vishwa.

--The Purpose of Life. LC 78-50754. (Illus.). 112p. 1978. 5.95 (ISBN 0-533-03147-8). Vishwa.

--Ramayana at a Glance. (Illus.). 184p. (Orig.). 1978. pap. 3.50 (ISBN 0-942508-11-4). Vishwa.

--Sadguru Speaks. (Illus.). 96p. (Orig.). 1975. pap. 3.50 (ISBN 0-942508-06-8). Vishwa.

--Saints of India. 100p. (Orig.). 1975. pap. 3.50 (ISBN 0-942508-05-X). Vishwa.

--Self-Realization. (Illus.). 131p. (Orig.). 1976. pap. 3.50 (ISBN 0-942508-11-4). Vishwa.
--Stories & Parables. (Illus.). 100p. 1979. 6.50 (ISBN 0-533-03818-9). Vishwa.
--This Is Wisdom. (Illus.) 96p. (Orig.). 1975. pap. 3.50 (ISBN 0-942508-07-6). Vishwa.
Kesich, Lydia W., jt. auth. see Kesich, Veselin.
Kesich, Veselin. The First Day of the New Creation: The Resurrection & the Christian Faith. LC 81-21516. 206p. 1982. pap. 7.95 (ISBN 0-913836-78-8). St Vladimirs.
--The Passion of Christ. 84p. pap. 1.95 (ISBN 0-913836-80-X). St Vladimirs.
Kesich, Veselin & Kesich, Lydia W. Treasures of the Holy Land: A Visit to the Places of Christian Origins. LC 85-18403. (Illus., Orig.). 1985. pap. 6.95 (ISBN 0-88141-045-4). St Vladimirs.
Kesler, Jay. Family Forum. 1984. 12.95 (ISBN 0-88207-820-8). Victor Bks.
Kesler, Jay, ed. Parents & Teenagers. 696p. 1984. pap. 16.95 (ISBN 0-88207-817-8). Victor Bks.
Kesler, Jay, et al, eds. Parents & Children. 640p. 1986. 16.95 (ISBN 0-89693-809-3). Victor Bks.
Kessell, John L. Mission of Sorrows: Jesuit Guevari & the Pimas, 1691-1767. LC 79-101098. pap. 60.00 (ISBN 0-317-28586-6, 2055248). Bks Demand UMI.
--The Missions of New Mexico Since 1776. LC 79-4934. (Illus.). 320p. 1980. 45.00x (ISBN 0-8263-0514-8). U of NM Pr.
Kessler, Christel. The Carved Masonry Domes of Mediaeval Cairo. 1976. pap. 15.00x (ISBN 0-686-19945-6). Intl Learn Syst.
Kessler, David. The Falashas. (Illus.). 205p. 1985. pap. 7.95 (ISBN 0-8052-0791-0). Schocken.
Kessler, Herbert L. The Illustrated Bibles from Tours. LC 76-45902. (Studies in Manuscript Illumination: No. 7). (Illus.). 236p. 1977. 61.00 (ISBN 0-691-03923-2). Princeton U Pr.
Kessler, Martin, jt. ed. see Jackson, Jared J.
Kessner, Thomas. The Golden Door: Italian & Jewish Immigrant Mobility in New York City, 1880-1915. 1977. text ed. 22.50x (ISBN 0-19-502116-9); pap. 8.95x (ISBN 0-19-502161-4). Oxford U Pr.
Ketcham, Charles B. A Theology of Encounter: The Ontological Ground for a New Christology. LC 77-21905. 1978. 22.50x (ISBN 0-271-00520-3). Pa St U Pr.
Ketcherside, C. Clergy System. pap. 0.50 (ISBN 0-686-64390-9). Reiner.
Ketcherside, Carl. Which Church. pap. 0.50 (ISBN 0-686-70363-4). Reiner.
Ketcherside, W. Carl. A Clean Church. 165p. 1987. pap. 3.95 (ISBN 0-938855-17-4). Gospel Themes Pr.
Kettani, M. Ali. Muslim Minorities in the World Today. 267p. 1986. 56.00x (ISBN 0-7201-1802-6). Mansell.
--Muslim Minorities in the World Today. 267p. 1986. 56.00 (ISBN 0-7201-1802-6). Wilson.
Ketterman, Grace H. The Complete Book of Baby & Child Care. rev. & updated ed. 560p. 1981. 18.95 (ISBN 0-8007-1421-0); pap. 8.95 (ISBN 0-8007-1515-2). Revell.
Kettinger, Leroy. Youth as Learners. (C. E. Ministries Ser.). 96p. 1983. pap. 3.50 (ISBN 0-89367-086-3). Light & Life.
Kettler, Wilfried. Das Juengste Gericht Philologische Studien zu den Eschatologie Vorstellungen in den Alt-und Fruehmittel-Hochdeutschen Denkmaelern. (Quellen und Forschungen Zur Sprach-und Kulturgeschichte der Germanischen Voelker: Vol.70). 1977. 38.80x (ISBN 3-11-007345-5). De Gruyter.
Kettlewell, S. Thomas A'Kempis, 2 vols. 1882. 85.00 set (ISBN 0-8274-3599-1). R West.
Kettner, Elmer. Training for Leadership in the Church. 1.95 (ISBN 0-933350-09-0). Morse Pr.
Keuls, E. The Water Carriers in Hades: A Study of Catharsis Through Toil in Classical Antiquity. (Illus.). 179p. 1974. pap. text ed. 48.50 (Pub. by A. M. Hakkert). Coronet Bks.
Kevan, Ernest F. The Grace of Law. 9.95 (ISBN 0-8010-5373-0). Baker Bk.
Kevane, Eugene. The Lord of History. 1980. 4.00 (ISBN 0-8198-0636-6); pap. 3.00 (ISBN 0-8198-0637-4). Dghtrs St Paul.
Kevane, Eugene, ed. Teaching the Catholic Faith Today. (Resources for Catechetical Teachers). 352p. 1982. 12.00 (ISBN 0-8198-7319-5, EP1048); pap. 10.00 (ISBN 0-8198-7320-9). Dghtrs St Paul.
Kew, Clifton E. & Kew, Clinton J. Therapist Responds. LC 79-171467. 1972. 6.95 (ISBN 0-8022-2070-3). Philos Lib.
Kew, Clinton J., jt. auth. see Kew, Clifton E.
Key, Ellen S. Rahel Varnagen. LC 75-7680. (Pioneers of the Woman's Movement: an International Perspective Ser.). (Illus.). xix, 312p. 1976. Repr. of 1913 ed. 23.10 (ISBN 0-88355-351-1). Hyperion Conn.
Key, Jeanette. Sanctification & the Christian. 1979. pap. 2.95 (ISBN 0-88027-049-7). Firm Foun Pub.
Keydell, Rudolfus, ed. see Agathias.
Keyes, Charles F. Thailand: Buddhist Kingdom As Modern Nation State. (Profiles-Nations of Contemporary Asia Ser.). 240p. 1987. 32.50 (ISBN 0-86531-138-2). Westview.
Keyes, Charles F. & Daniel, E. Valentine. Karma: An Anthropological Inquiry. LC 81-19719. 328p. 1983. text ed. 33.00x (ISBN 0-520-04429-0). U of Cal Pr.
Keyes, Dick. Beyond Identity: Finding Your Self in the Image & Character of God. 264p. (Orig.). 1984. pap. 7.95 (ISBN 0-89283-137-5). Servant.
Keyes, Elizabeth & Chivington, Paul K. What's Eating You? (Illus.). 1978. pap. 4.50 (ISBN 0-87516-263-0). De Vorss.
Keyes, Frances P. Three Ways of Love. 1975. 6.00 (ISBN 0-8198-0477-0); pap. 5.00 (ISBN 0-8198-0478-9). Dghtrs St Paul.
Keyes, G. L. Christian Faith & the Interpretation of History: A Study of St. Augustine's Philosophy of History. LC 66-10314. xiv, 206p. 1966. 17.50x (ISBN 0-8032-0091-9). U of Nebr Pr.
Keyes, Ken, Jr. Handbook to Higher Consciousness. 5th ed. LC 73-83071. 240p. 1975. pap. 4.95 (ISBN 0-9600688-8-0). Living Love.
Keyes, Ken, Jr. & Burkan, Bruce. How to Make Your Life Work. 1976. pap. 3.95 (ISBN 0-346-12226-0). Cornerstone.
Keyes, Nelson B. El Fascinante Mundo de la Biblia. Orig. Title: Story of the Bible World. (Span., Illus.). 216p. 1980. 20.95 (ISBN 0-311-03664-3, Edit Mundo); pap. 16.95 (ISBN 0-311-03665-1, Edit Mundo). Casa Bautista.
Keyes, Paul T. Pastoral Presence & the Diocesan Priest. LC 78-22009. 142p. 1978. pap. 4.95 (ISBN 0-89571-004-8). Affirmation.
Keyes, Sharrel. Luke: Following Jesus. (Fisherman Bible Studyguide Ser.). 96p. 1983. pap. 2.95 saddlestitched (ISBN 0-87788-511-7). Shaw Pubs.
--Working Out Together: Keeping Your Group in Shape. (Fisherman Bible Studyguides). 64p. (Orig.). 1985. pap. 1.00 (ISBN 0-87788-263-0). Shaw Pubs.
Keyes, Sharrel, jt. auth. see Fromer, Margaret.
Keynes, Geoffrey, ed. see Milton, John.
Keys, A. C., jt. tr. see Blaiklock, E. M.
Keyser, Barbara, jt. auth. see Keyser, Les.
Keyser, L. D., ed. Un Sistema de Evidencias Christianas. (Span.). 172p. pap. 4.95 (ISBN 0-87148-885-X). Pathway Pr.
Keyser, Les & Keyser, Barbara. Hollywood & the Catholic Church: The Image of Roman Catholicism in American Movies. LC 84-12556. 294p. 1984. 12.95 (ISBN 0-8294-0468-6). Loyola.
Keysor, Charles W. Our Methodist Heritage. LC 84-80824. 174p. pap. 3.95 (ISBN 0-917851-00-5). Good News KY.
Keyt, George, tr. Song of Love. Orig. Title: Gita Govinda. 123p. 1969. pap. 2.00 (ISBN 0-88253-048-8). Ind-US Inc.
Khadduri, Majid. Law of War & Peace in Islam: A Study of Moslem International Law. LC 76-147599. (Library of War & Peace; International Law). lib. bdg. 42.00 (ISBN 0-8240-0360-8). Garland Pub.
Khadduri, Majid, intro. by. & tr. The Islamic Law of Nations: Shaybani's Siyar. 366p. 1966. 34.50x (ISBN 0-8018-0334-9). Johns Hopkins.
Khairallah, Shereen, jt. auth. see Dodd, Erica C.
Khalid, Anas. The Search for Truth. Abdal-aziz, Aliyah F., ed. LC 86-51061. 56p. 1986. pap. 5.00 (ISBN 0-9617422-0-8). A Khalid.
Khalidi, Tarif. Classical Arab Islam: The Culture & Heritage of the Golden Age. LC 84-70416. 158p. 1985. 16.95 (ISBN 0-87850-047-2). Darwin Pr.
Khalidi, Walid, ed. From Haven to Conquest: Readings in Zionism & the Palestine Problem until 1948. 2nd ed. LC 85-237727. (Antholgy Ser. (Mu'assasat Al Dirasatal-Filastiniyah): No. 2). 914p. 1987. text ed. 29.95 (ISBN 0-88728-155-9); pap. 17.50 (ISBN 0-88728-156-7). Inst Palestine.
--Zionist Congress Resolutions, 1897-1972. Date not set. text ed. price not set (ISBN 0-88728-164-8). Inst Palestine.
Khalifa, R. A. Koran, Hadith, & Islam. 90p. (Orig.). 1983. 6.00 (ISBN 0-934894-35-3). Islamic Prods.
Khalifa, Rashad. The Computer Speaks: God's Message to the World. (Illus.). 250p. (Orig.). 1981. 9.50 (ISBN 0-934894-38-8). Islamic Prods.
--Koran: The Final Scripture. 600p. (Orig.). 1981. 13.30 (ISBN 0-934894-19-1). Islamic Prods.
Khalifa, Saida M. The Fifth Pillar: The Story of a Pilgrimage to Mecca & Medina. 1977. 7.50 (ISBN 0-682-48772-4). Exposition Pr FL.
Khalilzad, Zalmay, jt. auth. see Benard, Cheryl.
Khalsa, D. K., ed. The New Consciousness Sourcebook: Spiritual Community Guide, No. 6. 6th ed. 256p. 1985. pap. 8.95 (ISBN 0-89509-055-4). Arcline Pubns.
Khalsa, Harbhajan S. Yoga for the Eighties: Kundalini Yoga. LC 85-11680. 1985. Repr. lib. bdg. 19.95x (ISBN 0-89370-879-8). Borgo Pr.
Khan, Ali-Kuli, tr. see Abul-Fadl, Mirza.
Khan, Emir A., jt. auth. see Abbas, H.
Khan, Gazanfar A. & Sparroy, Wilfred. With the Pilgrims to Mecca: The Great Pilgrimage of A.H. 1319, A.D. 1902. LC 77-876447. Repr. of 1905 ed. 24.50 (ISBN 0-404-16417-X). AMS Pr.
Khan, Hazrat I. The Inner Life: An Introduction to Sufism. (Orient Paperbacks Ser.). 1980. pap. 3.25 (ISBN 0-86578-082-X). Ind-US Inc.
--Mastery Through Accomplishment: Developing Inner Strength for Life's Challenges. rev. ed. LC 79-101639. (Collected Works of Hazrat Inayat Khan Ser.). 336p. 1985. pap. 11.95 (ISBN 0-930872-07-X). Omega Pr NM.
--Nature Meditations. LC 80-50829. (Collected Works of Hazrat Inayat Khan Ser.). (Illus.). 128p. (Orig.). 1980. pap. 6.95 (ISBN 0-930872-12-6). Omega Pr NM.
--The Soul Whence & Whither. LC 77-15697. (The Collected Works of Hazrat Inayat Khan Ser.). 190p. 1977. 7.95 (ISBN 0-930872-00-2). Omega Pr NM.
--The Unity of Religious Ideals. (The Collected Works of Hazrat Inayat Khan Ser.). 264p. 1979. 9.95 (ISBN 0-930872-09-6); pap. 6.95 (ISBN 0-930872-10-X). Omega Pr NM.
Khan, Hazrat I., jt. auth. see Lewis, Samuel L.
Khan, Inayat. The Art of Personality. (Sufi Message of Hazrat Inayat Khan Ser.: Vol. 3). 256p. 1979. 14.95 (ISBN 90-6077-570-8, Pub. by Servire BV Netherlands). Hunter Hse.
--The Bowl of Saki. rev., 4th ed. LC 78-65653. 128p. (Orig.). 1979. pap. 4.95 (ISBN 0-900217-12-X, Pub. by Sufi Pub Co England). Hunter Hse.
--The Development of Spiritual Healing. 3rd ed. LC 78-65080. 112p. pap. 4.95 (ISBN 0-900217-15-4, Pub. by Sufi Pub Co England). Hunter Hse.
--Healing & the Mind World. (Sufi Message of Hazrat Inayat Khan Ser.: Vol. 4). 288p. 1979. 14.95 (ISBN 90-6077-952-5, Pub. by Servire BV Netherlands). Hunter Hse.
--In an Eastern Rose Garden. (Sufi Message of Hazrat Inayat Khan Ser.: Vol. 7). 256p. 1979. 14.95 (ISBN 90-6325-096-7, Pub. by Servire BV Netherlands). Hunter Hse.
--The Inner Life. (Sufi Message of Hazrat Inayat Khan Ser.: Vol. 1). 256p. 1979. 14.95 (ISBN 90-6325-094-0, Pub. by Servire BV Netherlands). Hunter Hse.
--The Mysticism of Sound. (Sufi Message of Hazrat Inayat Khan Ser.: Vol. 2). 262p. 1979. 14.95 (ISBN 90-6077-569-4, Pub. by Servire BV Netherlands). Hunter Hse.
--The Path of Initiation. (Sufi Message of Hazrat Inayat Khan Ser.: Vol. 10). 270p. 1979. 14.95 (ISBN 90-6325-098-3, Pub. by Servire BV Netherlands). Hunter Hse.
--Philosophy, Psychology & Mysticism. (Sufi Message of Hazrat Inayat Khan Ser.: Vol. 11). 256p. 1979. 14.95 (ISBN 90-6325-099-1, Pub. by Servire BV Netherlands). Hunter Hse.
--Sacred Readings: The Gathas. (Sufi Message of Hazrat Inayat Khan Ser.: Vol. 13). 304p. 1982. 14.95 (ISBN 90-6325-021-5, Pub. by Servire BV Netherlands). Hunter Hse.
--Spiritual Liberty. (Sufi Message of Hazrat Inayat Khan Ser.: Vol. 5). 256p. 1979. 14.95 (ISBN 90-6325-095-9, Pub. by Servire BV Netherlands). Hunter Hse.
--The Unity of Religious Ideals. (Sufi Message of Hazrat Inayat Khan Ser.: Vol. 9). 280p. 1979. 14.95 (ISBN 90-6325-097-5, Pub. by Servire BV Netherlands). Hunter Hse.
Khan, K. The Secrets of Anal-Haqq. 1981. 12.50 (ISBN 0-686-97864-1). Kazi Pubns.
Khan, M. K. The Science of Spirituality. 135p. 1983. text ed. 15.00x (ISBN 0-86590-164-3). Apt Bks.
Khan, M. M. The Noble Qur'an, Arabic-English: A Summarized Version of At-Tabari, Al-Qurtubi & Ibn Kathir with comments from Sahih Al-Bukhari, Vol I. 49.00 (ISBN 0-317-46109-5). Kazi Pubns.
--Pages in the Life of a Sufi. 1979. 14.95 (ISBN 11-1910-334-7, Pub. by Sufi Pub Co England). Hunter Hse.
Khan, M. M. & Hilali, T. Noble Quran, Vol. 1. 1986. 49.95 (ISBN 0-317-43012-2). Kazi Pubns.
Khan, M. Y. God, Soul & Universe in Science & Islam. 1969. 3.50 (ISBN 0-87902-170-5). Orientalia.
Khan, M. Z. & Saleem, M. Umar the Great (Al-Farqu, 2 vols. 1970. Vol. 1. 12.50x (ISBN 0-87902-196-9); Vol. 2. 12.50x (ISBN 0-685-33011-7). Orientalia.
Khan, Muhammad S. Islamic Medicine. (Illus.). 102p. Date not set. lib. bdg. 24.95 (ISBN 0-7102-0329-2). Methuen Inc.
Khan, Muhammad Z. Muhammad: Seal of the Prophets. 400p. 1980. pap. 10.50 (ISBN 0-7100-0610-1). Methuen Inc.
Khan, Muhammed Z., tr. The Quran: Arabic Text with English Translation. 736p. 1981. 40.00x (ISBN 0-7007-0148-6, Pub. by Curzon England). State Mutual Bk.
Khan, Pir V. The Message in Our Time: The Life & Teachings of the Sufi Master, Hazrat Inayat Khan. LC 78-4751. (Illus.). 1979. 15.45 (ISBN 0-06-064237-8, HarpR). Har-Row.
Khan, S. A. Essays on the Life of Muhammad. 1968. 27.00x (ISBN 0-87902-172-1). Orientalia.
Khan, Syed A. Sir Sayyid Ahmad Khan's History of Bijnor Rebellion. Malik, Hafeez, tr. 1983. 13.50x (ISBN 0-8364-1080-7, Pub. by Idarah). South Asia Bks.
Khanum, Munirih. Munirih Khanum: Memoirs & Letters. Smith, Sammireh A., tr. (Persian., Illus.). 1987. 7.95 (ISBN 0-933770-51-0). Kalimat.
Khare, R. S. The Changing Brahmans: Association & Elites among the Kanya-Kybjas of North India. LC 72-128711. (Illus.). 1970. text ed. 21.00x (ISBN 0-226-43433-8). U of Chicago Pr.
Khomeini, Imam. Islam & Revolution: Writings & Declarations. Algar, Hamid, tr. 460p. 1986. pap. 19.95 (ISBN 0-7103-0098-0, Kegan Paul). Methuen Inc.
--Practical Laws of Islam. LC 83-50077. 1983. pap. 9.00 (ISBN 0-940368-25-0). Tahrike Tarsile Quran.
Khomiakov, Aleksiei S. L' Eglise Latine et le Protestantisme, Au Point De Vue De l'Eglise d'Orient. LC 80-2362. Repr. of 1872 ed. 49.00 (ISBN 0-404-18908-3). AMS Pr.
Khomiakov, Alexei S. The Church Is One. (Illus.). 1980. pap. 1.25x (ISBN 0-913026-23-9). St Nectarios.
Khosla, G. S. Bhai Vir Singh. 1984. 15.00x (ISBN 0-8364-1230-3, Pub. by Heritage India). South Asia Bks.
Khrapovitsky, Antony. Confession. Birchall, Christopher, tr. from Rus. LC 74-29537. 100p. (Orig.). 1975. pap. 3.00 (ISBN 0-88465-005-7). Holy Trinity.
--Moral Idea of the Main Dogmas of the Faith. Novakshonoff, Varlaam & Puhalo, Lazar, trs. from Rus. 170p. (Orig.). 1984. pap. text ed. 8.00 (ISBN 0-911523-01-4). Synaxis Pr.
--Moral Idea of the Main Dogmas of the Faith. Novakshonoff, V. & Puhalo, L., trs. from Rus. 96p. (Orig.). 1986. pap. 7.50. Synaxis Pr.
Khumayni, Ruh A. Islam & Revolution: Writings & Declarations of Imam Khomeini. Algar, Hamid, tr. LC 80-24032. 480p. 1981. 24.95 (ISBN 0-933782-04-7); pap. 11.95 (ISBN 0-933782-03-9). Mizan Pr.
Khurana, G. British Histography on the Sikh Power in the Punjab. 159p. 1985. 35.00x (ISBN 0-7201-1767-4). Mansell.
--British Historiography on the Sikh Power in Punjab. 174p. 1985. 20.95x (ISBN 0-317-39858-X, Pub. by Allied Pubs India). Asia Bk Corp.
--British Historiography on the Sikh Power in Punjab. 1985. 14.50x (ISBN 0-8364-1504-3, Pub. by Allied India). South Asia Bks.
Khurshid, Salman. At Home in India. x, 226p. 1987. text ed. 27.95 (ISBN 0-7069-3197-1, Pub. by Vikas India). Advent NY.
Kiavantash, Venus, tr. see Shariati, Ali.
Kibbey, Ann. The Interpretation of Material Shapes in Puritanism: A Study of Rhetoric, Prejudice & Violence. (Cambridge Studies in American Literature & Culture). (Illus.). 256p. 1986. 27.95 (ISBN 0-521-26509-6). Cambridge U Pr.
Kibildis, Ralph. Turning Road. 112p. (Orig.). 1981. 2.95 (ISBN 0-914544-34-9). Living Flame Pr.
Kidd, Beresford J. The Churches of Eastern Christendom from Four Hundred Fifty-One A.D. to the Present Time, 2 vols. 1980. Set. lib. bdg. 195.00 (ISBN 0-8490-3196-6). Gordon Pr.
--The Counter-Reformation, Fifteen Fifty to Sixteen Hundred. LC 79-8713. 270p. 1980. Repr. of 1933 ed. lib. bdg. 24.75x (ISBN 0-313-22193-6, KICR). Greenwood.
--A History of the Church to A.D. 461, 3 vols. LC 75-41165. Repr. of 1922 ed. Set. 135.00 (ISBN 0-404-15010-1). AMS Pr.
Kidd, Beresford J., ed. Documents Illustrative of the Continental Reformation. LC 83-45663. Date not set. Repr. of 1911 ed. 64.50 (ISBN 0-404-19813-9). AMS Pr.
Kidd, James W., jt. auth. see Kidd, Sunnie D.
Kidd, James W., ed. Philosophy, Psychology & Spirituality. LC 83-80836. 87p. (Orig.). 1984. pap. text ed. 9.95 (ISBN 0-910727-05-8). Golden Phoenix.
Kidd, Sunnie D. & Kidd, James W. Brother Jerry's Stories: Hearing the Inspirations of the Holy Spirit. 34p. (Orig.). 1982. pap. text ed. 3.50 (ISBN 0-910727-00-7). Golden Phoenix.
--The Dynamic Aspects of Inspiration. 38p. (Orig.). 1982. pap. text ed. 3.50 (ISBN 0-910727-02-3). Golden Phoenix.

Kidder, Danuiel P. Mormonism & the Mormons. 59.95 (ISBN 0-8490-0674-0). Gordon Pr.

Kidner, D. Psalms One - Seventy-Two. LC 75-23852. 1973. 12.95 (ISBN 0-87784-868-8); pap. 6.95 (ISBN 0-87784-264-7). Inter-Varsity.

Kidner, Derek. Ezra & Nehemiah. Wiseman, D. J., ed. (Tyndale Old Testament Commentaries Ser.). 1979. text ed. 12.95 (ISBN 0-87784-962-5); pap. 6.95 (ISBN 0-87784-261-2). Inter-Varsity.

--The Message of Ecclesiastes. LC 76-21460. (Bible Speaks Today Ser.). 1976. pap. 5.95 (ISBN 0-87784-286-8). Inter-Varsity.

--The Message of Hosea. Motyer, J. A. & Stott, John R., eds. (Bible Speaks Today Ser.). 132p. (Orig.). 1982. text ed. 5.95 (ISBN 0-87784-290-6). Inter-Varsity.

--The Wisdom of Proverbs, Job & Ecclesiastes. LC 85-11826. 176p. 1985. pap. 5.95 (ISBN 0-87784-405-4). Inter-Varsity.

Kidner, F. Derek. Genesis. LC 75-23851. (Tyndale Old Testament Commentary). 1968. 12.95 (ISBN 0-87784-881-5); pap. 6.95 (ISBN 0-87784-251-5). Inter-Varsity.

--Proverbs. LC 75-23850. (Tyndale Old Testament Commentary Ser.). 12.95 (ISBN 0-87784-861-0); pap. 6.95 (ISBN 0-87784-266-3). Inter-Varsity.

Kidwai, Mohammad A., tr. see Nadawi, Abul H.

Kidwell, R. J. & DeWelt, Don. Ecclesiastes; Song of Solomon. LC 78-301088. (The Bible Study Textbook Ser.). 1977. 14.30 (ISBN 0-89900-019-3). College Pr Pub.

Kieckhefer, Richard. European Witch Trials: Their Foundations in Popular & Learned Culture, 1300-1500. 1976. 34.00x (ISBN 0-520-02967-4). U of Cal Pr.

--Unquiet Souls: Fourteenth-Century Saints & Their Religious Milieu. LC 84-210. 248p. 1984. lib. bdg. 24.95x (ISBN 0-226-43509-1). U of Chicago Pr.

--Unquiet Souls: Fourteenth Century Saints & Their Religious Milieu. LC 84-210. (Illus.). viii, 238p. 1987. pap. 10.95 (ISBN 0-226-43510-5). U of Chicago Pr.

Kiefer, Howard E. & Munitz, Milton K., eds. Ethics & Social Justice. (Contemporary Philosophic Thought: Vol. 4). 1970. 49.50 (ISBN 0-87395-054-2). State U NY Pr.

Kiefer, Howard E., ed. see International Philosophy Year Conferences, Brockport.

Kiefer, Velma B. Stories to Tell in Children's Church. (Paperback Program Ser.). Orig. Title: Please Tell Me a Story. 1976. pap. 5.95 (ISBN 0-8010-5371-4). Baker Bk.

Kieffer, Gene. Kundalini for the New Age. 288p. (Orig.). 1987. pap. 7.95 (ISBN 0-553-34433-1). Bantam.

Kiemel, Ann. Hi, I'm Ann. (Direction Bks). pap. 2.50 (ISBN 0-8010-5346-3). Baker Bk.

--I Love the Word Impossible. 1978. pock. pap 3.50 (ISBN 0-8423-1578-0). Tyndale.

--I'm Out to Change My World. 128p. 1983. pap. 4.95 (ISBN 0-310-70141-4, 14034P). Zondervan.

--It's Incredible. 1977. pap. 2.50 (ISBN 0-8423-1818-6). Tyndale.

Kiemen, Mathias, et al, eds. United States Documents in the Propaganda Fide Archives, Vol. 10. 1984. 40.00 (ISBN 0-88382-211-3). AAFH.

Kiene, Paul F. The Tabernacle of God in the Wilderness of Sinai. 1977. 19.95 (ISBN 0-310-36200-8, 11066). Zondervan.

Kiener, Ronald C., jt. ed. see Dan, Joseph.

Kieninger, Richard. Spiritual Seekers' Guidebook: And Hidden Threats to Mental & Spiritual Freedom. 1986. 12.95 (ISBN 0-9600308-6-7). Stelle.

Kierkegaard, Soren. Attack upon "Christendom". Lowrie, Walter, tr. 1944. pap. 8.50x (ISBN 0-691-01950-9). Princeton U Pr.

--Christian Discourses. Lowrie, W., tr. 1971. pap. 10.50x (ISBN 0-691-01973-8). Princeton U Pr.

--Concluding Unscientific Postscript. Swenson, D. F. & Lowrie, W., trs. (American-Scandinavian Foundation). 1941. pap. 10.50x (ISBN 0-691-01960-6). Princeton U Pr.

--Diary of Soren Kierkegaard. Rohde, Peter P., ed. 1971. pap. 2.75 (ISBN 0-8065-0251-7). Citadel Pr.

--Either-Or, 2 Vols. Lowrie, W., tr. 1944. Vol 1. pap. 7.95 (ISBN 0-691-01976-2); Vol. 2. pap. 7.95x (ISBN 0-691-01977-0). Princeton U Pr.

--Fear & Trembling-Repetition, 2 vols. in 1. Hong, Howard V. & Hong, Edna H., eds. Hong, Howard V. & Hong, Edna H., trs. LC 82-9006. (Kierkegaard's Writings Ser.: No. VI). 420p. 1983. 37.00 (ISBN 0-691-07237-X); pap. 7.95 (ISBN 0-691-02026-4). Princeton U Pr.

--For Self-Examination & Judge for Yourself. (American-Scandinavian Foundation Ser.). 1944. pap. 8.50x (ISBN 0-691-01952-5). Princeton U Pr.

--Philosophical Fragments, or a Fragment of Philosophy-Johannes Climacus, or De Omnibus Dubitandum Est, 2 bks. in 1 vol. Hong, Howard V. & Hong, Edna H., eds. LC 85-3420. (No. VII). 386p. 1985. text ed. 35.00x (ISBN 0-691-07273-6); pap. 7.95x (ISBN 0-691-02036-1). Princeton U Pr.

--Present Age. Dru, Alexander, ed. & tr. pap. 5.95x (ISBN 0-06-130094-2, TB94, Torch). Har-Row.

--Purity of Heart. Steere, Douglas, tr. pap. 7.95x (ISBN 0-06-130004-7, TB4, Torch). Har-Row.

--The Sickness Unto Death: A Christian Psychological Exposition for Upbuilding & Awakening. Hong, Howard V. & Hong, Edna H., trs. LC 79-3218. (Kierkegaard's Writings Ser.: Vol. XIX). 216p. 1980. 27.50x (ISBN 0-691-07247-7); pap. 9.50x (ISBN 0-691-02028-0). Princeton U Pr.

--Training in Christianity. Lowrie, Walter, tr. (American-Scandinavian Foundation Ser.). 1944. 31.00x (ISBN 0-691-07140-3); pap. 7.95x (ISBN 0-691-01959-2). Princeton U Pr.

--Works of Love: Some Christian Reflections in the Form of Discourse. pap. 7.95x (ISBN 0-06-130122-1, TB122, Torch). Har-Row.

--Works of Love: Some Christian Reflections in the Form of Discourses. Long, tr. LC 64-7445. 1962. 17.75 (ISBN 0-8446-2373-3). Peter Smith.

Kierman, Frank A., Jr., tr. see Maspero, Henri.

Kiesling, Christopher. Celibacy, Prayer & Friendship: A Making-Sense-Out-of-Life Approach. LC 77-25084. 1978. pap. 7.95 (ISBN 0-8189-0365-1). Alba.

Kiessling, Elmer C. Early Sermons of Luther & Their Relation to the Pre-Reformation Sermon. LC 75-171064. Repr. of 1935 ed. 21.50 (ISBN 0-404-03669-4). AMS Pr.

Kiessling, Nicolas. The Incubus in English Literature: Provenance & Progeny. (Illus.). 1977. pap. 12.95 (ISBN 0-87422-006-8). Wash St U Pr.

Kietzel, F. Von see Von Kietzel, F.

Kightly, Charles. A Traveller's Guide to Places of Worship. 1986. 14.95 (ISBN 0-918678-18-8). Historical Times.

Kik, J. M. Eschatology of Victory. 1971. pap. 8.95 (ISBN 0-87552-313-7). Presby & Reformed.

Kikawada, Isaac M. & Quinn, Arthur. Before Abraham Was: A Provocative Challenge to the Documentary Hypothesis. 144p. 1985. pap. 10.95 (ISBN 0-687-02602-4). Abingdon.

Kikkert, Lois. Prayers for the Seasons. 1.50 (ISBN 0-8091-9306-X). Paulist Pr.

--Prayers to a God of Surprises. 1.50 (ISBN 0-8091-9327-2). Paulist Pr.

Kilar, Jacqueline, ed. see De Paul, Vincent.

Kilby, Clyde S., ed. A Mind Awake: An Anthology of C. S. Lewis. LC 80-14133. 256p. 1980. pap. 3.95 (ISBN 0-15-659772-1, Harv). HarBraceJ.

Kiley, Mark. Colossians as Pseudepigraphy. (Biblical Seminar Ser.: No. 4). 240p. 1986. pap. text ed. 11.95x (ISBN 1-85075-024-6, Pub. by JSOT Pr England). Eisenbrauns.

Kilgallen, John J. First Corinthians: An Introduction & Study Guide. (Illus.). 128p. (Orig.). 1987. pap. 5.95 (ISBN 0-8091-2847-0). Paulist Pr.

Kilgo, Edith F. Handbook for Christian Homemakers. 200p. (Orig.). 1982. pap. 5.95 (ISBN 0-8010-5439-7). Baker Bk.

--Money Management: Dollars & Sense for Christian Homemakers. 200p. 1980. pap. 5.95 (ISBN 0-8010-5422-2). Baker Bk.

Kilian, Sabbas. Theological Models for the Parish. LC 76-42986. 1977. 5.95 (ISBN 0-8189-0337-6). Alba.

Kilinski, Kenneth & Wolfert, Jerry. Organization & Leadership in the Local Church. 14.95 (ISBN 0-310-26810-9, 18132). Zondervan.

Killen, John, ed. The Irish Christmas Book. (Illus.). 132p. (Orig.). 1986. pap. 8.95 (ISBN 0-85640-345-8, Pub. by Blackstaff Pr). Longwood Pub Group.

Killen, Shelly, ed. see Kim, Chi-ha.

Killgallon, James, et al. Life in Christ. rev. ed. LC 76-26451. 1976. pap. 2.25 (ISBN 0-914070-08-8). ACTA Found.

Killgallon, James J. Becoming Catholic, Even If You Happen to Be One. LC 79-89875. 1980. pap. 4.50 (ISBN 0-914070-13-4). ACTA Found.

Killgallon, James J., et al. La Vida en Cristo. Pascual, Manuel, tr. from Eng. LC 76-26451. 1978. pap. 2.25 (ISBN 0-914070-12-6). ACTA Found.

Killian, Don R., jt. auth. see Hester, Joseph P.

Killinger, John. Christ & the Seasons of Marriage. LC 86-17411. 1987. 7.95 (ISBN 0-8054-5666-X). Broadman.

--The Cup & the Waterfall: The Adventure of Living in the Present Moment. LC 82-61421. 1983. pap. 4.95 (ISBN 0-8091-2515-3). Paulist Pr.

--A Devotional Guide to the Gospels: Three Hundred Sixty-Six Meditations. 588p. 1984. Repr. 14.95 (ISBN 0-8499-3008-1, 3008-1). Word Bks.

--The Fragile Presence: Transcendence in Modern Literature. LC 72-91520. pap. 44.00 (2026902). Bks Demand UMI.

--Fundamentals of Preaching. LC 84-47926. 224p. 1985. pap. 9.95 (ISBN 0-8006-1796-7, 1-1796). Fortress.

--Sea Breezes: Thoughts of God from a Summer Beach. 96p. (Orig.). 1985. pap. 6.95 (ISBN 0-687-37088-4). Abingdon.

--Steeple People & the World: Planning for Mission Through the Church. (Orig.). 1977. pap. 2.50 (ISBN 0-377-00059-0). Friend Pr.

--The Tender Shepherd. 208p. (Orig.). 1985. pap. 9.95 (ISBN 0-687-41242-0). Abingdon.

Killinger, John, ed. Experimental Preaching. LC 72-8419. Repr. of 1973 ed. 33.30 (ISBN 0-8357-9006-1, 2009067). Bks Demand UMI.

Killinger, Margaret, ed. see Painter, Desmond & Shepard, John.

Killingray, Margaret. Constantine. Yapp, Malcolm, et al, eds. (World History Ser.). (Illus.). 32p. 1980. lib. bdg. 6.95 (ISBN 0-89908-040-5); pap. text ed. 2.45 (ISBN 0-89908-015-4). Greenhaven.

Killingray, Margaret, ed. see Duckworth, John, et al.

Killingray, Margaret, ed. see Yapp, Malcolm.

Kilmer, Aline M. Hunting a Hair Shirt: And Other Spiritual Adventures. LC 76-39123. (Essay Index Reprint Ser.). Repr. of 1923 ed. 14.00 (ISBN 0-8369-2697-8). Ayer Co Pubs.

Kilmister, C. A., ed. see Neill, Stephen, et al.

Kilpack, Gilbert. Ninth Hour. 1983. pap. 2.50x (ISBN 0-87574-063-4, 063). Pendle Hill.

Kilpack, Gilbert, jt. auth. see Robinson, Forbes.

Kilpatrick, Anna G., jt. auth. see Kilpatrick, Jack F.

Kilpatrick, G. D. The Eucharist in Bible & Lithurgy: The Moorhouse Lectures 1975. LC 83-14315. 130p. 1984. 32.50 (ISBN 0-521-24675-X). Cambridge U Pr.

Kilpatrick, G. D., jt. auth. see Barns, J. W.

Kilpatrick, Gilbert. Our Hearts Are Restless. 1983. pap. 2.50x (ISBN 0-87574-032-4, 032). Pendle Hill.

Kilpatrick, Jack F. & Kilpatrick, Anna G. Run Toward the Nightland: Magic of the Oklahoma Cherokees. LC 67-19814. (Illus.). 1967. pap. 9.95 (ISBN 0-87074-084-9). SMU Press.

Kilpatrick, Paula & Dudley, Cliff. The Ninth Floor. LC 81-80942. 128p. 1981. pap. 4.95 (ISBN 0-89221-085-0). New Leaf.

Kilpatrick, T. B. The Redemption of Man. (Short Course Ser.). 200p. 1940. 6.95 (ISBN 0-567-08320-9, Pub. by T & T Clark Ltd UK). Fortress.

Kilpatrick, William K. Psychological Seduction: The Failure of Modern Psychology. LC 83-12151. 228p. 1983. pap. 5.95 (ISBN 0-8407-5843-X). Nelson.

Kilvert, Francis. Kilvert's Diary 1870-1879. LC 86-80573. 288p. 1986. 24.95 (ISBN 0-87923-637-X). Godine.

Kim, Ashida. Secrets of the Ninja. (Illus.). 168p. 1981. 16.95 (ISBN 0-87364-234-1). Paladin Pr.

Kim, Chang S. & Kim, Maria. The Art of Zen Sword: The History of Shim Gum Do, Pt. I. LC 85-5973. (Illus.). 144p. 1985. 19.95 (ISBN 0-9614427-0-0). Am Buddhist Shim Do.

Kim, Chi-ha. The Gold-Crowned Jesus & Other Writings. Kim, Chong Sun & Killen, Shelly, eds. LC 77-17522. pap. 44.50 (ISBN 0-317-26644-6, 2025119). Bks Demand UMI.

Kim, Chong Sun, ed. see Kim, Chi-ha.

Kim, Esther A. If I Perish. 1979. pap. 3.95 (ISBN 0-8024-4003-7). Moody.

Kim, Hee-Jin. Dogen Kigen - Mystical Realist. LC 74-33725. (Association for Asian Studies Monograph: No. 29). 384p. 1975. pap. 8.95x (ISBN 0-8165-0513-6). U of Ariz Pr.

Kim, Maria, jt. auth. see Kim, Chang S.

Kim, Seyoon. The Origin of Paul's Gospel. 2nd., rev., enl. ed. 426p. (Orig.). 1984. pap. 52.00x (ISBN 3-16-144836-7, Pub. by J C B Mohr BRD). Coronet Bks.

--The Son of Man As the Son of God. 128p. (Orig.). 1985. pap. 12.95x (ISBN 0-8028-0056-4). Eerdmans.

Kim, Yong C. Oriental Thought: An Introduction to the Philosophical & Religious Thought of Asia. (Quality Paperback Ser.: No. 365). 144p. 1981. pap. 4.95 (ISBN 0-8226-0365-9). Littlefield.

Kim, Yong Choon. Oriental Thought: An Introduction to the Philosophical & Religious Thought of Asia. LC 80-39672. 144p. 1981. Repr. of 1973 ed. 11.50x (ISBN 0-8476-6972-6). Rowman.

Kim, Young O. An Introduction to Theology. LC 82-84722. 190p. 1983. pap. 8.95 (ISBN 0-318-11687-1). Rose Sharon Pr.

--The Types of Modern Theology. LC 83-80105. 296p. 1983. pap. 11.95 (ISBN 0-910621-32-2). Rose Sharon Pr.

--Unification Theology. LC 80-52872. 294p. 1980. pap. 8.95 (ISBN 0-318-11689-8). Rose Sharon Pr.

--Unification Theology & Christian Thought. LC 74-32590. 302p. 1976. pap. 6.95 (ISBN 0-318-11688-X). Rose Sharon Pr.

--World Religions, Vol. 1. LC 76-23739. 275p. 1982. pap. 8.95 (ISBN 0-318-11690-1). Rose Sharon Pr.

--World Religions, Vol. 2. LC 76-23739. 413p. 1982. pap. 10.95 (ISBN 0-318-11691-X). Rose Sharon Pr.

--World Religions I: Near & Middle Eastern Religions. 2nd, rev. ed. 275p. 1982. pap. 5.75 (ISBN 0-910621-36-5). HSA Pubns.

--World Religions II: India's Religious Quest & the Faiths of the Far East. 2nd rev. ed. 415p. 1982. pap. 7.75 (ISBN 0-910621-37-3). HSA Pubns.

Kim, Young Oon. An Introduction to Theology. LC 82-94722. 190p. (Orig.). 1983. pap. 7.50 (ISBN 0-910621-25-X). HSA Pubns.

Kim, Dr. Young Oon. Unification Theology & Christian Thought. pap. 4.00 (ISBN 0-686-13407-9). Unification Church.

Kimar Daso, Satyendra see Das Satyendra Kimar.

Kimball, Edward A. Lectures & Articles on Christian Science. (Illus.). 1976. 12.50 (ISBN 0-911588-01-9); pap. 8.00; leatherette 18.00. N S Wait.

Kimball, Edward L., jt. auth. see Miner, Caroline E.

Kimball, Gayle. The Religious Ideas of Harriet Beecher Stowe: Her Gospel of Womanhood. LC 82-80377. (Studies in Women & Religion: Vol. 8). 216p. 1982. 49.95x (ISBN 0-88946-544-4). E Mellen.

Kimball, Robert C., ed. see Tillich, Paul.

Kimball, Spencer W. Faith Precedes the Miracle. 9.95 (ISBN 0-87747-490-7). Deseret Bk.

--Marriage. LC 78-4132. (Illus.). 1978. 5.95 (ISBN 0-87747-675-6). Deseret Bk.

--My Beloved Sisters. LC 79-3620. 1979. 5.95 (ISBN 0-87747-798-1). Deseret Bk.

--President Kimball Speaks Out. LC 81-68861. 103p. 1981. 5.95 (ISBN 0-87747-881-3). Deseret Bk.

Kimball, Spencer W., et al. Prayer. LC 77-15521. 1977. 8.95 (ISBN 0-87747-657-8). Deseret Bk.

--Prayer. 1977. pap. 1.95 (ISBN 0-87747-739-6). Deseret Bk.

--Priesthood. LC 81-5394. 170p. 1981. 8.95 (ISBN 0-87747-859-7). Deseret Bk.

--Woman. LC 79-64908. 1979. 8.95 (ISBN 0-87747-758-2). Deseret Bk.

Kimball, Spencer W., et al, eds. Faith. LC 83-72343. 119p. 1983. 8.95 (ISBN 0-87747-980-1). Deseret Bk.

Kimball, Stanley B. Discovering Mormon Trails. LC 79-53092. (Illus.). 1979. pap. 4.95 (ISBN 0-87747-756-6). Deseret Bk.

--Heber C. Kimball: Mormon Patriarch & Pioneer. LC 80-21923. (Illus.). 345p. 1981. pap. 13.50 (ISBN 0-252-01299-2). U of Ill Pr.

Kimball, Stanley B., ed. see Clayton, William.

Kimball, William. Book of Books. LC 86-71101. 160p. (Orig.). 1986. pap. 6.95 (ISBN 0-89900-211-0). College Pr Pub.

--What the Bible Says about the Great Tribulation. LC 83-71918. (What the Bible Says Ser.). (Illus.). 291p. 1983. 13.95 (ISBN 0-89900-093-2). College Pr pub.

Kimball, William R. Rapture: A Question of Timing. 200p. (Orig.). pap. 5.95 (ISBN 0-89900-205-6). College Pr Pub.

--The Rapture: A Question of Timing. 1985. pap. 6.95 (ISBN 0-8010-5468-0). Baker Bk.

--What the Bible Says about the Great Tribulation. 304p. 1985. pap. 7.95 (ISBN 0-8010-5466-4). Baker Bk.

Kimber, Rita, tr. see Soelle, Dorothee.

Kimber, Rita, tr. see Solle, Dorothee.

Kimber, Robert, tr. see Soelle, Dorothee.

Kimber, Robert, tr. see Solle, Dorothee.

Kimbrough, M. The Joy & Adventure of Growing Younger. LC 12-2969. 1983. pap. 4.95 (ISBN 0-570-03876-6). Concordia.

Kimbrough, S., Jr. Lost in Wonder: Charles Wesley - The Meaning of His Hymns Today. 176p. (Orig.). 1987. pap. 6.95 (ISBN 0-8358-0558-1). Upper Room.

Kimchi, David B. Commentary of David Kimchi on Isaiah. Finkelstein, Louis, ed. LC 27-4417. (Columbia University. Oriental Studies: No. 19). Repr. of 1926 ed. 24.50 (ISBN 0-404-50509-0). AMS Pr.

--Commentary of Rabbi David Kimchi on Hosea. Cohen, Harry, ed. LC 30-27876. (Columbia University. Oriental Studies: No. 20). Repr. of 1929 ed. 17.00 (ISBN 0-404-50510-4). AMS Pr.

Kimmel, Jo. Steps to Prayer Power. (Festival Bks.). 1976. pap. 5.95 (ISBN 0-687-39339-6). Abingdon.

Kimmelman, Susan & Horwitz, Tem, eds. T'ai Chi Ch'uan: The Technique of Power. LC 76-41613. (Illus.). 1980. pap. 9.95 (ISBN 0-914090-24-0). Chicago Review.

Kimmens, A. C., ed. The Stowe Psalter. LC 78-23622. (Toronto Old English Ser.). 1979. 47.50x (ISBN 0-8020-2201-4). U of Toronto Pr.

Kimmering, Barach. Zionism & the Economy. 170p. 1983. 18.95 (ISBN 0-87073-775-9); pap. 11.25 (ISBN 0-87073-784-8). Schenkman Bks Inc.

Kimmerle, Heinz, ed. see Schleiermacher, Friedrich.

Kimmerling, Baruch. Zionism & Territory: The Socio-Territorial Dimensions of Zionist Politics. LC 83-102. (Illus.). xii, 288p. 1983. pap. 12.50x (ISBN 0-87725-151-7). U of Cal Intl St.

Kimpel, Ben. Moral Philosophies in Shakespeare's Plays. (Studies in Art & Religious Interpretation). 262p. 1987. text ed. 49.95 (ISBN 0-88946-558-4). E Mellen.

--A Philosophy of the Religions of Ancient Greeks & Israelites. LC 83-6512. 362p. (Orig.). 1983. lib. bdg. 30.00 (ISBN 0-8191-3225-X); pap. text ed. 15.50 (ISBN 0-8191-3226-8). U Pr of Amer.

Kimura, Ryukan. A Historical Study of the Terms Hinayana & Mahayana & the Origin of Mahayana Buddhism. LC 78-72455. Repr. of 1927 ed. 26.50 (ISBN 0-404-17324-1). AMS Pr.

Kimura, Yuriko. Christmas Present from a Friend. (Illus.). 28p. 1985. Repr. 10.95 (ISBN 0-687-07817-2). Abingdon.

Kinard, J. Spencer. A Time for Reflection. 1986. text ed. 9.95 (ISBN 0-87579-049-6). Deseret Bk.

Kinard, Malvina & Crisler, Janet. Loaves & Fishes: Foods from Bible Times. LC 75-19544. (Illus.). 224p. 1975. pap. 4.95 (ISBN 0-87983-173-1). Keats.

Kinast, Robert L. Caring for Society. 168p. 1985. pap. 9.95 (ISBN 0-88347-197-3). Thomas More.

--When a Person Dies: Pastoral Theology in Death Experiences. LC 84-11431. 160p. (Orig.). 1984. pap. 9.95 (ISBN 0-8245-0657-X). Crossroad NY.

Kincevicious, Joseph B. Russia's Attitude Towards Union with Rome: 9th-16th Centuries. 208p. 1983. Repr. of 1927 ed. 24.95x (ISBN 0-939738-10-4). Zubal Inc.

Kincheloe, Samuel C. Research Memorandum on Religion in the Depression. LC 71-162843. (Studies in the Social Aspects of the Depression). 1971. Repr. of 1937 ed. 17.00 (ISBN 0-405-00846-5). Ayer Co Pubs.

Kinder, A. Gordon. Spanish Protestants & Reformers in the Sixteenth Century: A Bibliography. (Research Bibliographies & Checklists Ser.: No. 39). 108p. (Orig.). 1983. pap. 11.95 (ISBN 0-7293-0146-X, Pub. by Grant & Cutler). Longwood Pub Group.

Kindersley, David. Eric Gill: Further Thoughts by an Apprentice. (Illus.). 60p. 1982. pap. 14.00 (ISBN 0-913720-35-6). Beil.

King. No Church Is an Island: Study Guide. 1980. pap. 1.00 (ISBN 0-8298-0389-0). Pilgrim NY.

King, Archdale A. Rites of Eastern Christendom, 2 Vols. LC 70-142246. Repr. of 1948 ed. Set. 125.00 (ISBN 0-404-03677-5). Vol. 1 (ISBN 0-404-03678-3). Vol. 2 (ISBN 0-404-03679-1). AMS Pr.

King, Barbara. Do I Need a Flood? 3.00 (ISBN 0-317-46971-1). CSA Pr.

--What Is a Flood? 61p. 1981. pap. 3.00 (ISBN 0-317-20874-8). CSA Pr.

--What Is a Miracle? 61p. 1981. pap. 3.00 (ISBN 0-317-20876-4). CSA Pr.

King, C. W. The Gnostics & Their Remains. LC 73-76092. (Secret Doctrine Reference Ser.). (Illus.). 500p. 1982. Repr. of 1887 ed. 21.00 (ISBN 0-913510-34-3). Wizards.

King, Christine E. The Nazi State & the New Religions: Five Case Studies in Non-conformity. LC 82-20910. (Studies in Religion & Society: Vol. 4). 332p. 1982. 59.95x (ISBN 0-88946-865-6). E Mellen.

King, David S. No Church Is an Island. LC 79-27113. (Orig.). 1980. pap. 5.95 (ISBN 0-8298-0385-8). Pilgrim NY.

King, Edwin J. The Grand Priory of the Order of the Hospital of St. John of Jerusalem in England: A Short History. LC 76-29826. Repr. of 1924 ed. 28.00 (ISBN 0-404-15420-4). AMS Pr.

King, Eldress E. A Shaker's Viewpoint. Facsimile ed. 4p. 1957. pap. 0.25 (ISBN 0-937942-15-4). Shaker Mus.

King, Francis. Sexuality, Magic & Perversion. (Illus.). 1972. 6.95 (ISBN 0-8065-0289-4). Citadel Pr.

King, George D. Lessons on the Holy Spirit. (Orig.). 1987. pap. 6.95 (ISBN 0-8054-1153-4). Broadman.

King, Georgiana G., ed. see Street, George E.

King, Georgianna G. The Way of St. James, 3 vols. LC 78-63469. Repr. of 1920 ed. Set. 140.00 (ISBN 0-404-17160-5). AMS Pr.

King, Guy H. Belief That Behaves. 1971. pap. 3.95 (ISBN 0-87508-271-8). Chr Lit.

--Crossing the Border (Colossians) 1957. pap. 3.95 (ISBN 0-87508-274-2). Chr Lit.

--Fellowship. 1972. pap. 3.95 (ISBN 0-87508-279-3). Chr Lit.

--Leader Led. 1971. pap. 3.95 (ISBN 0-87508-283-1). Chr Lit.

--To My Son (II Timothy) 1972. pap. 3.95 (ISBN 0-87508-287-4). Chr Lit.

King, H., jt. ed. see Humphreys, S. C.

King, Henry. A Sermon Preached at Pauls Crosse Touching the Supposed Apostasie of J. King, Late Bishop of London. LC 76-57392. (English Experience Ser.: No. 809). 1977. Repr. of 1621 ed. lib. bdg. 9.50 (ISBN 90-221-0809-0). Walter J Johnson.

King, J. Norman. Experiencing God All Ways & Every Day. 160p. (Orig.). 1982. pap. 7.95 (ISBN 0-86683-632-2, HarpR). Har-Row.

--The God of Forgiveness & Healing in the Theology of Karl Rahner. LC 81-40932. 100p. (Orig.). 1982. lib. bdg. 24.00 (ISBN 0-8191-2237-8); pap. text ed. 8.25 (ISBN 0-8191-2238-6). U Pr of Amer.

King, James M. Facing the Twentieth Century. Grob, Gerald, ed. LC 76-46085. (Anti-Movements in America Ser.). (Illus.). 1977. Repr. of 1899 ed. lib. bdg. 54.00x (ISBN 0-405-09958-4). Ayer Co Pubs.

King, John G. Rites & Ceremonies of the Greek Church in Russia. LC 73-126673. Repr. of 1772 ed. 34.50 (ISBN 0-404-03692-9). AMS Pr.

King, Joseph H. Christ: God's Love Gift. 3.50 (ISBN 0-911866-84-1). Advocate.

--From Passover to Pentecost. pap. 3.95 (ISBN 0-911866-57-4). Advocate.

King, Ken, ed. see Kruschwitz & Roberts.

King, Ken, ed. see Pojman, Louis P.

King, L. L., intro. by see Simpson, A. B.

King, L. W. Legends of Babylon & Egypt in Relation to Hebrew Tradition. 59.95 (ISBN 0-8490-0504-3). Gordon Pr.

King, Leonard W. Babylonian Religion & Mythology. LC 73-18854. (Illus.). Repr. of 1899 ed. 18.45 (ISBN 0-404-11352-4). AMS Pr.

--Babylonian Religion & Mythology. LC 77-94592. 1978. Repr. of 1899 ed. lib. bdg. 25.00 (ISBN 0-89341-311-9). Longwood Pub Group.

--Legends of Babylonia & Egypt in Relation to the Hebrew Tradition. LC 77-94593. 1979. Repr. of 1918 ed. lib. bdg. 20.00 (ISBN 0-89341-310-0). Longwood Pub Group.

King, Marie G., ed. Foxe's Book of Martyrs. 50p. pap. 3.95 (ISBN 0-317-06922-5, 06742-3). Jove Pubns.

King, Martin Luther, Jr. Strength to Love. LC 80-2374. 160p. 1981. pap. 4.95 (ISBN 0-8006-1441-0, 1-1441). Fortress.

--Strength to Love. 208p. 1985. pap. 11.95 (ISBN 0-8027-2472-8). Walker & Co.

King, Mike. The Mike King Story. LC 85-81940. (Illus.). 176p. (Orig.). 1985. 15.95 (ISBN 0-934672-33-4). Good Bks PA.

--The Mike King Story. LC 85-81940. (Illus.). pap. 5.95 (ISBN 0-934672-42-3). Good Bks PA.

King, Morton B. & Hunt, Richard A. Measuring Religious Dimensions: Studies of Congregational Involvement. (Studies in Social Science: No. 1). 1972. pap. 5.95x (ISBN 0-87074-174-8). SMU Press.

King, Neil. Mystery & Morality. (Drama Ser.). pap. 8.95 (ISBN 0-7175-1231-2). Dufour.

King, Noel Q. African Cosmos: An Introduction to Religion in Africa. 1985. pap. text ed. write for info (ISBN 0-534-05334-3). Wadsworth Pub.

King, Pat & Botz, Myrna. Triumph Through Temptation. (Basic Bible Study). 64p. 1978. 2.95 (ISBN 0-932305-35-0, 521012). Aglow Pubns.

King, Pat & Wood, George. The Beatitudes-Expressing the Character of Jesus. (Bible Study Enrichment Ser.). 64p. 1985. pap. 2.95 (ISBN 0-930756-92-4). Aglow Pubns.

King, Pat, jt. auth. see Lance, Fran.

King, Paul G. & Woodyard, David O. The Journey Toward Freedom. (Illus.). 248p. 1982. 28.50 (ISBN 0-8386-3115-0). Fairleigh Dickinson.

King, Peter. Cistercian Finances in the Fourteenth Century. 24.95 (ISBN 0-87907-885-5). Cistercian Pubns.

King, Philip J. Judges. (Bible Ser.). pap. 1.00 (ISBN 0-8091-5077-8). Paulist Pr.

King, Rachel H. Omission of the Holy Spirit from Reinhold Niebuhr's Theology. LC 64-13324. 209p. 1964. 6.95 (ISBN 0-8022-0865-7). Philos Lib.

King, Robert H., jt. ed. see Hodgson, Peter C.

King, S. Temple of Your Being. 1985. Book & Cassette Pack. 27.50x (ISBN 0-317-54328-8, Pub. by J Richardson UK). State Mutual Bk.

King, Serge. Imagineering for Health. LC 80-53949. 211p. (Orig.). 1981. pap. 6.95 (ISBN 0-8356-0546-9, Quest). Theos Pub Hse.

King, Stephen S. Gods Master Plan. 85p. 1985. pap. 3.95 (ISBN 0-317-52285-X). Christian Pub.

King, Thomas M. Sartre & the Sacred. LC 73-87304. xii, 196p. 1974. 17.00x (ISBN 0-226-43612-8). U of Chicago Pr.

--Teilhard's Mysticism of Knowing. 192p. 1981. 14.95 (ISBN 0-8164-0491-7, HarpR). Har-Row.

King, Thomas M. & Salmon, James F., eds. Teilhard & the Unity of Knowledge. LC 82-60590. 1983. pap. 6.95 (ISBN 0-8091-2491-2). Paulist Pr.

King, U. R. Bible Mystery Word Puzzle. 64p. 1986. pap. text ed. 3.00 (ISBN 0-935545-02-6). Land & Land.

King, Ursula. Towards a New Mysticism: Teilhard de Chardin & Eastern Religions. 320p. 1980. (HarpR); pap. 8.95 (ISBN 0-8164-2327-X). Har-Row.

King, Ursula, ed. Women in the World Religions, Past & Present. (God Ser.). 256p. (Orig.). 1987. 22.95 (ISBN 0-913757-32-2, Pub. by New Era Bks.); pap. 12.95 (ISBN 0-913757-33-0, Pub. by New Era Bks). Paragon Hse.

King, William. An Essay on the Origin of Evil. Bd. with Dissertations Concerning the Fundamental Principle & Immediate Criterion of Virtue. LC 75-11228. (British Philosophers & Theologians of the 17th & 18th Centuries Ser.). 391p. 1978. lib. bdg. 51.00 (ISBN 0-8240-1782-X). Garland Pub.

--Historical Account of Heathen Gods & Heroes Necessary for the Understanding of Ancient Poets. LC 64-18550. (Centaur Classics Ser.). (Illus.). 290p. 1965. 15.00x (ISBN 0-8093-0150-4). S Ill U Pr.

King, Winston. Death Was His Koan: The Samurai Zen of Suzuki Shosan. 1986. 40.00 (ISBN 0-89581-998-8). Asian Human Pr.

King, Winston L. In the Hope of Nibbana: The Ethics of Theravada Buddhism. LC 62-9575. 308p. 1964. 22.95 (ISBN 0-87548-230-9); pap. 9.95 (ISBN 0-87548-231-7). Open Court.

--Theravada Meditation: The Buddhist Transformation of Yoga. LC 79-25856. 192p. 1980. 22.75x (ISBN 0-271-00254-9). Pa St U Pr.

Kingdon, R. M. Geneva & the Consolidation of the French Protestant Movement, 1564-1572: A Contribution to the History of Congregationalism, Presbyterianism, & Calvinist Resistance Theory. 244p. (Orig.). 1967. pap. text ed. 27.50x (Pub. by Droz Switzerland). Coronet Bks.

King-Farlow, J. & Christensen, W. N. Faith & the Life at Reason. LC 72-83376. 253p. 1973. lib. bdg. 36.00 (ISBN 90-277-0275-6, Pub. by Reidel Holland). Kluwer Academic.

King-Farlow, John, ed. The Challenge of Religion Today: Essays on the Philosophy of Religion. LC 76-13492. 1976. pap. text ed. 6.95 (ISBN 0-88202-157-5). Watson Pub Intl.

Kinghorn, Kenneth C. Christ Can Make You Fully Human. LC 79-10855. 1979. pap. 4.35 (ISBN 0-687-06930-0). Abingdon.

--Discovering Your Spiritual Gifts: A Personal Inventory Method. 1981. pap. 2.95 (ISBN 0-310-75061-X, 17029P). Zondervan.

--Dynamic Discipleship. 160p. 1975. pap. 4.95 (ISBN 0-8010-5357-9). Baker Bk.

--Fresh Wind of the Spirit. 128p. 1986. pap. 6.95 (ISBN 0-310-75221-3, 17033P). Zondervan.

--Gifts of the Spirit. LC 75-22268. 128p. 1976. pap. 5.95 (ISBN 0-687-14695-X). Abingdon.

Kings, John, ed. see Wilson, Bob.

Kingsbury, Jack D. The Christology of Mark's Gospel. LC 83-5576. 224p. 1983. 19.95 (ISBN 0-8006-0706-6, 1-706). Fortress.

--Jesus Christ in Matthew, Mark, & Luke. Krodel, Gerhard, ed. LC 80-69755. (Proclamation Commentaries Ser.: The New Testament Witnesses for Preaching). 144p. (Orig.). 1981. pap. 4.95 (ISBN 0-8006-0596-9, 1-596). Fortress.

--Matthew. 2nd, enl. & rev. ed. LC 84-45212. (Proclamation Commentaries Ser.). 144p. 1986. pap. 6.95 (ISBN 0-8006-0597-7). Fortress.

--Matthew As Story. LC 85-16204. 160p. 1986. pap. 9.95 (ISBN 0-8006-1891-2). Fortress.

--The Parables of Jesus in Matthew 13. LC 76-40850. 1976. pap. text ed. 12.95 (ISBN 0-915644-08-8). Clayton Pub Hse.

Kingsbury, Jack D. & Pennington, Chester. Lent. Achtemeier, Elizabeth, et al, eds. LC 79-7377. (Proclamation 2: Aids for Interpreting the Lessons of the Church Year, Ser. A). 64p. (Orig.). 1980. pap. 3.75 (ISBN 0-8006-4093-4, 1-4093). Fortress.

Kingsford, Anna & Maitland, Edward. Clothed with the Sun. 248p. Date not set. pap. 14.00 (ISBN 0-89540-132-0, SB 132). Sun Pub.

Kingsford, C. L. Collectanea Franciscana II. 169p. Repr. of 1922 ed. text ed. 33.12x (ISBN 0-576-99210-0, Pub. by Gregg Intl Pubs England). Gregg Intl.

Kingsford, Charles L., jt. auth. see Archer, Thomas A.

Kingsley, Charles. Charles Kingsley: His Letters & Memories of His Life, 2 Vols. LC 74-148803. (Illus.). Repr. of 1877 ed. Set. 37.50 (ISBN 0-404-08869-4); deluxe ed. 19.00 ea. Vol. 1 (ISBN 0-404-08870-8). Vol. 2 (ISBN 0-404-08871-6). AMS Pr.

--The Heroes. (Facsimilie Classics Ser.). (Illus.). 224p. 1980. 8.95 (ISBN 0-8317-4448-0, Mayflower Bks). Smith Pubs.

--The Heroes of Greek Fairy Tales for My Children. 1889. Repr. lib. bdg. 15.00 (ISBN 0-8414-5578-3). Folcroft.

--The Heroes; or, Greek Fairy Tales. Repr. of 1882 ed. 20.00 (ISBN 0-686-20097-7). Quality Lib.

Kingsley, Rose G. The Order of St. John of Jerusalem: Past & Present. LC 76-29842. Repr. of 1918 ed. 27.50 (ISBN 0-404-15422-0). AMS Pr.

Kingsmill, Hugh. Matthew Arnold. 1973. Repr. of 1928 ed. 40.00 (ISBN 0-8274-0720-3). R West.

--The Progress of a Biographer. 1973. lib. bdg. 25.00 (ISBN 0-8414-5588-0). Folcroft.

Kingston, Frederick T. French Existentialism, a Christian Critique. LC 61-925. pap. 59.30 (ISBN 0-317-08761-4, 2014272). Bks Demand UMI.

Kingston, Robert. See & Share Stories about Jesus, 4 bks. Orig. Title: Bible Stories. (Illus.). 40p. Repr. Set. 7.95 (ISBN 0-687-37132-5). Abingdon.

Kington-Oliphant, Thomas L. Rome & Reform, 2 Vols. LC 76-118541. 1971. Repr. of 1902 ed. Set. 47.50x (ISBN 0-8046-1165-3, Pub. by Kennikat). Assoc Faculty Pr.

Kinigsberg, David. Modern Man & An Old-Fashioned God. 1985. 7.95 (ISBN 0-533-06659-X). Vantage.

Kinkade, Richard P., jt. auth. see Keller, John E.

Kinkead, Thomas L. An Explanation of the Baltimore Catechism. LC 78-74571. (Baltimore Catechism Ser.: No. 4). 1978. pap. text ed. 8.50 (ISBN 0-89555-085-7). TAN Bks Pubs.

Kinlaw, Dennis F. Preaching in the Spirit. 1985. pap. 6.95 (ISBN 0-310-75091-1, 17036P). Zondervan.

--We Have the Mind of Christ. 128p. Date not set. pap. text ed. 5.95 (ISBN 0-310-75231-0). Zondervan.

Kinlock, Tom F. Pioneers of Religious Education. facs. ed. LC 69-18929. (Essay Index Reprint Ser). 1939. 14.00 (ISBN 0-8369-0045-6). Ayer Co Pubs.

Kinnaird, Judith, ed. see Ward, Harvey.

Kinnaman, Gary D. And Signs Shall Follow. 1987. pap. 6.95 (Chosen Bks). Revell.

Kinnara Inc. Pilgrimage. (Illus., Orig.). 1977. pap. 4.95 (ISBN 0-89346-011-7). Heian Intl.

Kinnear, Angus. A Table in the Wilderness. 1978. pap. 4.95 (ISBN 0-8423-6900-7). Tyndale.

Kinnear, Willis. Thirty Day Mental Diet. 144p. 1965. pap. 7.95 (ISBN 0-911336-20-6). Sci of Mind.

Kinnear, Willis, jt. auth. see Holmes, Ernest.

Kinnear, Willis, ed. see Holmes, Ernest.

Kinnear, Willis H., jt. auth. see Holmes, Ernest.

Kinnear, Willis H., ed. Spiritual Healing. 110p. (Orig.). 1973. pap. 4.95 (ISBN 0-911336-50-8). Sci of Mind.

Kinnear, Willis H., ed. see Holmes, Ernest.

Kinnear, Willis H., ed. see Holmes, Ernest, et al.

Kinnear, Willis H., ed. see Holmes, Ernest.

Kinneavy, James L. Greek Rhetorical Origins of Christian Faith. 256p. 1986. 29.95x (ISBN 0-19-503735-9). Oxford U Pr.

Kinneer, Jack. How to Grow in Christ. 1981. pap. 2.95 (ISBN 0-87552-284-X). Presby & Reformed.

Kinnier-Wilson, J. V. & Vanstiphout, Herman. The Rebel Lands: An Investigation into the Origins of Early Mesopotamian Mythology. LC 77-1272. (Oriental Publications Ser.: No. 29). (Illus.). 1979. 39.00 (ISBN 0-521-21469-6). Cambridge U Pr.

Kinns, Samuel. Graven in the Rock or the Historical Accuracy of the Bible. LC 77-85611. 1977. Repr. of 1891 ed. lib. bdg. 65.00 (ISBN 0-89341-319-4). Longwood Pub Group.

Kinsella, Nivard. Unprofitable Servants: Conferences on Humility. 1981. 5.95 (ISBN 0-317-46888-X). Franciscan Herald.

Kinsler, F. Ross, ed. Ministry by the People: Theological Education by Extension. 348p. (Orig.). 1983. pap. 12.95 (ISBN 0-88344-334-1). Orbis Bks.

Kinsley, David. Hindu Goddesses: Visions of the Divine Feminine in the Hindu Religious Tradition. LC 84-28000. (Hermeneutics: Studies in the History of Religions). 1985. 35.00x (ISBN 0-520-05393-1). U of Cal Pr.

--Hinduism: A Cultural Perspective. (Illus.). 200p. 1982. 17.00 (ISBN 0-13-388975-0). P-H.

Kinsley, David R. The Divine Player: A Study of Krishna Lila. 1978. 17.95 (ISBN 0-89684-019-0, Pub. by Motilal Barnarsidass India). Orient Bk Dist.

--The Divine Player: A Study of Krishna Lila. 1979. 22.00x (ISBN 0-89684-019-0). South Asia Bks.

--The Sword & the Flute-Kali & Krsna: Dark Visions of the Terrible & the Sublime in Hindu Mythology. LC 73-91669. (Hermeneutics: Studies in the History of Religions). 175p. 1975. pap. 10.95x (ISBN 0-520-03510-0). U of Cal Pr.

Kinzer, Mark. Living with a Clear Conscience: A Christian Strategy for Overcoming Guilt & Self-Condemnation. (Living As a Christian Ser.). 160p. 1982. pap. 3.50 (ISBN 0-89283-115-4). Servant.

--Self-Image of a Christian: Humility & Self-Esteem. (Living As a Christian Ser.). 106p. (Orig.). 1980. pap. 2.95 (ISBN 0-89283-088-3). Servant.

--Taming the Tongue: Why Christians Should Care about What They Say. (Living as a Christian Ser.). 1982. pap. 2.95 (ISBN 0-89283-165-0). Servant.

Kinzer, Mark, jt. auth. see Ghezzi, Bert.

Kinzie, Frederick E. & Kinzie, Vera D. Strength Through Struggle. Stewart, James, ed. & intro. by. LC 86-1645. (Illus.). 350p. (Orig.). 1986. pap. 6.95 (ISBN 0-912315-98-9). Word Aflame.

Kinzie, Vera D., jt. auth. see Kinzie, Frederick E.

Kipp, Maxine. Living Life to the Fullest. LC 79-52997. (Radiant Life Ser.). 160p. 1980. pap. 2.95 (ISBN 0-88243-896-4, 02-0896); teacher's ed 3.95 (ISBN 0-88243-187-0, 32-0187). Gospel Pub.

Kipp, Rita S. & Rodgers, Susan, eds. Indonesian Religions in Transition. LC 86-30742. 304p. 1987. 29.95x (ISBN 0-8165-1020-2). U of Ariz Pr.

Kippax, J. R. Churchyard Literature. 59.95 (ISBN 0-87968-870-X). Gordon Pr.

Kippax, John R. Churchyard Literature: A Choice Collection of American Epitaphs. 213p. 1978. Repr. of 1876 ed. 16.95 (ISBN 0-87928-087-5). Corner Hse.

Kippenberg, Hans G. Garizim und Synagoge: Traditionsgeschichtliche Untersuchungen zur samaritanischen Religion der aramaeischen Periode. (Religionsgeschichtliche Versuche und Vorarbeiten, 30). (Ger). 1971. 43.20x (ISBN 3-11-001864-0). De Gruyter.

Kippenberg, Hans G., ed. Struggles of Gods. LC 84-11501. (Religion & Reason Ser.: No. 31). vii, 296p. 1984. 34.95 (ISBN 90-279-3460-6). Mouton.

Kipper, Lenore & Bogot, Howard. Alef-Bet of Jewish Values: Code Words of Jewish Life. (Illus.). 64p. 1985. pap. text ed. 6.00 (ISBN 0-8074-0267-2, 101087). UAHC.

Kiraly, Bela K., ed. Tolerance & Movements of Religious Dissent in Eastern Europe. (East European Monographs: No. 13). 227p. 1976. 20.00x (ISBN 0-914710-06-0). East Eur Quarterly.

Kirban, Diane, jt. auth. see Kirban, Doreen.

Kirban, Doreen & Kirban, Diane. Stranger in Tomorrow's Land. 1970. 4.95 (ISBN 0-912582-40-5). Kirban.

Kirban, Salem. Charts on Prophecy. 1982. pap. 14.92 (ISBN 0-912582-39-1). Kirban.

--Christian Science. LC 75-124142. (Illus.). 1974. pap. 4.95 (ISBN 0-912582-11-1). Kirban.

--Church Promotion Handbook. 1963. 10.00 (ISBN 0-912582-38-3). Kirban.

--The Day Israel Dies! (Illus.). 1975. pap. 2.95 (ISBN 0-912582-21-9). Kirban.

--Guide to Survival. 1979. pap. 6.95 (ISBN 0-912582-24-3). Kirban.

--How to Be Sure of Crowns in Heaven. 1980. pap. 5.95 (ISBN 0-912582-34-0). Kirban.

--Jehovah's Witnesses. (Illus.). 1972. pap. 4.95 (ISBN 0-912582-03-0). Kirban.

--Mormonism. (Illus.). 1971. pap. 4.95 (ISBN 0-912582-13-8). Kirban.

--One Thousand. (Illus.). 1973. pap. 2.95 (ISBN 0-912582-09-X). Kirban.

--Plain Truth About the Plain Truth. (Illus.). 1972. pap. 4.95 (ISBN 0-912582-12-X). Kirban.

--Questions Frequently Asked Me on Prophecy. (Illus.). 1981. pap. 4.95 (ISBN 0-912582-01-4). Kirban.

--Satan's Angels Exposed. 1980. pap. 5.95 (ISBN 0-912582-32-4). Kirban.

--Satan's Music Exposed. 1980. pap. 5.95 (ISBN 0-912582-35-9). Kirban.

--Six Hundred Sixty-Six: Pictoral Format. 1980. pap. 4.95 (ISBN 0-912582-33-2). Kirban.

--Your Last Goodbye. LC 70-87000. (Illus.). 1969. pap. 5.95 (ISBN 0-912582-06-5). Kirban.

Kirban, Salem & Cohen, Gary. Revelation Visualized. 1971. pap. 14.95 (ISBN 0-912582-08-1). Kirban.

Kirban, Salem, jt. auth. see Cohen, Gary.

Kirby, John & Thompson, William M., eds. Voegelin & the Theologian: Ten Studies in Interpretation. LC 82-22914. (Toronto Studies in Theology: Vol. 10). 392p. 1983. 59.95x (ISBN 0-88946-751-X). E Mellen.

Kirby, John C. Ephesians, Baptism & Pentecost: An Inquiry into the Structure & Purpose of the Epistle to the Ephesians. 1968. 12.50x (ISBN 0-7735-0051-0). McGill-Queens U Pr.

Kirby, Leo. Should You Become a Brother? 1979. pap. 1.95 (ISBN 0-89243-102-4). Liguori Pubns.

Kirby, Peadar. Is Irish Catholicism Dying? 93p. 1984. pap. 5.95 (ISBN 0-87061-112-7). Chr Classics.

Kirby, Philippa. Christmas Wrappings. LC 86-5617. (Illus.). 72p. 1986. 4.95 (ISBN 1-55584-009-4). Weidenfeld.

Kirby, Scott. Dating: Guidelines from the Bible. 1979. pap. 2.95 (ISBN 0-8010-5400-1). Baker Bk.

Kirby, Wallace. If Only... 1985. 6.25 (ISBN 0-89536-753-X, 5859). CSS of Ohio.

Kirby, Wallace H. Programs & Promises: Reflections on the Beatitudes. 1980. 3.50 (ISBN 0-89536-414-X, 1640). CSS of Ohio.

--Sounds of the Passion. 1984. 4.25 (ISBN 0-89536-647-9, 1944). CSS of Ohio.

Kirchner, Hubert. Luther & the Peasants' War. LC 73-171507. (Facet Books-Historical Ser.: No. 22). pap. 20.00 (2027181). Bks Demand UMI.

Kirk, Albert & Obach, Robert E. Commentary on the Gospel of Matthew. LC 78-65715. 300p. 1978. pap. 8.95 (ISBN 0-8091-2173-5). Paulist Pr.

Kirk, Albert, jt. auth. see Obach, Robert E.

Kirk, G. S. Myth: Its Meaning & Functions in Ancient & Other Cultures. LC 72-628267. (Sather Classical Lectures: No. 40). 1970. pap. 8.95x (ISBN 0-520-02389-7, CAMPUS 94). U of Cal Pr.

--The Nature of Greek Myths. LC 74-21683. 336p. 1975. 27.95 (ISBN 0-87951-031-5). Overlook Pr.

--Nature of Greek Myths. 1975. pap. 5.95 (ISBN 0-14-021783-5, Pelican). Penguin.

Kirk, Hazel J., jt. auth. see Clokey, Joseph W.

Kirk, J. Andrew. Good News of the Kingdom Coming. LC 84-19293. 164p. 1985. pap. 5.95 (ISBN 0-87784-938-2). Inter-Varsity.

--Liberation Theology: An Evangelical View from the Third World. LC 79-5212. (New Foundations Theological Library). 246p. (Peter Toon & Ralph Martin series editor). 1980. 12.95 (ISBN 0-8042-3704-2). John Knox.

--Theology & the Third World Church. LC 83-8560. (Outreach & Identity: Evangelical Theological Monographs). 64p. (Orig.). 1983. pap. 2.95 (ISBN 0-87784-892-0). Inter-Varsity.

Kirk, James G. When We Gather: A Book of Prayers for Worship, Year A. LC 83-14221. (Illus.). 142p. 1983. pap. 8.95 (ISBN 0-664-24505-6, A Geneva Press Publication). Westminster.

--When We Gather: A Book of Prayers for Worship, Year B. LC 83-14221. (Illus.). 144p. 1984. pap. 8.95 (ISBN 0-664-24553-6). Geneva Pr.

--When We Gather: A Book of Prayers for Worship, Year C. LC 83-14221. (Illus.). 142p. 1985. pap. 8.95 (ISBN 0-664-24652-4, A Geneva Press Publication). Westminster.

Kirk, Jerry. The Mind Polluters. 224p. 1985. pap. 6.95 (ISBN 0-8407-5965-7). Nelson.

Kirk, John. Biographies of English Catholics in the Eighteenth Century. xvi, 293p. 1985. Repr. of 1901 ed. lib. bdg. 39.00 (ISBN 0-932051-45-6, Pub. by Am Repr Serv). Am Biog Serv.

Kirk, Joseph E. Death, Resurrection, Immortality. 111p. 1977. 4.00 (ISBN 0-910424-66-7); pap. 3.00 (ISBN 0-910424-67-5). Concordant.

Kirk, Kenneth E. The Vision of God: The Christian Doctrine of the Summum Bonum. abr. ed. Dunstan, G. R., ed. 223p. 1977. Repr. of 1934 ed. 13.95 (ISBN 0-227-67830-3). Attic Pr.

Kirk, Margaret. God Was a Stranger. 1980. pap. 2.75 (ISBN 0-85363-130-1). OMF Bks.

Kirk, Martha A. Mexican & Native American Dances in Christian Worship & Education. Adams, Doug, ed. (Orig.). 1981. pap. 3.00 (ISBN 0-941500-22-5). Sharing Co.

Kirk, Pat, jt. auth. see Brown, Alice.

Kirk, Russell. The Assault on Religion. LC 86-656. 126p. 1986. lib. bdg. 19.00 (ISBN 0-8191-5294-3, Pub. by Ctr for Judical Studies); pap. text ed. 8.25 (ISBN 0-8191-5295-1). U Pr of Amer.

Kirk, T. & Rawlinson, G. Studies in the Books of Kings. 556p. 1983. lib. bdg. 20.75 Smythe Sewn (ISBN 0-86524-155-4, 1301). Klock & Klock.

Kirk, Thomas. Jonah: His Life & Mission. 344p. 1983. lib. bdg. 12.95 (ISBN 0-86524-166-X, 3202). Klock & Klock.

--The Life of Joseph. 319p. 1985. smythe sewn 12.75 (ISBN 0-86524-193-7, 8408). Klock & Klock.

Kirkari, Abu B., tr. see Nabi, Malik B.

Kirkbride, Alec. From the Wings: Amman Memoirs, 1947-1951. 194p. 1976. 28.50x (ISBN 0-7146-3061-6, F Cass Co). Biblio Dist.

Kirkconnell, Watson. Celestial Cycles: The Theme of Paradise Lost in World Literature with Translations of the Major Analogues. LC 67-30308. 701p. 1967. Repr. of 1952 ed. 47.50x (ISBN 0-87752-058-5). Gordian.

Kirkland, Margie. A Grateful Heart. LC 84-9398. 1984. pap. 3.95 (ISBN 0-8054-5012-2). Broadman.

Kirkley, Robert G. By God, You Can Do It. 1985. 9.95 (ISBN 0-345-32266-5, Pub. by Ballantine Epiphany). Ballantine.

Kirkpatrick, A. F. Psalms. (Thornapple Commentaries Ser.). 964p. 1982. pap. 19.95 (ISBN 0-8010-5453-2). Baker Bk.

Kirkpatrick, Charles. Cow in the Clinic & Other Missionary Stories from Around the World. 1977. pap. 4.95 (ISBN 0-89367-016-2). Light & Life.

Kirkpatrick, Frank G., jt. auth. see Nolan, Richard T.

Kirkpatrick, Jean. Fear & Worry: Our Common Enemies. 14p. 1982. pap. 1.50 (ISBN 0-686-19760-7). WFS.

--The Nature of Guilt. 16p. 1983. pap. 1.50 (ISBN 0-318-19524-0). WFS.

Kirkpatrick, John E. Timothy Flint: Pioneer, Missionary, Author, Editor, 1780-1840. LC 68-56780. (Research & Source Works Ser: No. 267). 1968. Repr. of 1911 ed. 21.50 (ISBN 0-8337-1930-0). B Franklin.

Kirkpatrick, R. Dante's Paradiso & the Limitations of Modern Criticism. LC 77-80839. 1978. 39.50 (ISBN 0-521-21785-7). Cambridge U Pr.

Kirkup, James, tr. see Dumitriu, Petru.

Kirkwood, G. M. Short Guide to Classical Mythology. 1960. pap. text ed. 10.95 (ISBN 0-03-008865-8, HoltC). H Holt & Co.

Kirsch, A. Thomas. Feasting & Social Oscillation: A Working Paper on Religion & Society in Upland Southeast Asia. 57p. 1973. 5.00 (ISBN 0-87727-092-9, DP 92). Cornell SE Asia.

--Feasting & Social Oscillation: A Working Paper on Religion & Society in Upland Southeast Asia. LC 74-168308. (Cornell University, Southeast Asia Program, Data Paper: No. 92). pap. 20.00 (ISBN 0-317-29889-5, 2021843). Bks Demand UMI.

Kirsch, Felix M., ed. Classics: Their History & Present Status in Education: A Symposium of Essays. facs. ed. LC 68-22104. (Essay Index Reprint Ser). 1928. 20.00 (ISBN 0-8369-0600-4). Ayer Co Pubs.

Kirsch, George B. Jeremy Belknap: A Biography. 25.00 (ISBN 0-405-14112-2). Ayer Co Pubs.

Kirsch, Johann P. Heilige Caecilia in der Roemischen Kirche Des Altertums. 1910. pap. 8.00 (ISBN 0-384-29610-6). Johnson Repr.

--Roemischen Titelkirchen Im Altertum. 1918. 19.00 (ISBN 0-384-29614-9). Johnson Repr.

Kirsch, Paul J. We Christians & Jews. 160p. pap. 3.95 (ISBN 0-686-95187-5). ADL.

--We Christians & Jews. LC 74-26332. pap. 40.00 (2026838). Bks Demand UMI.

Kirsch, Thomas. Feasting & Social Oscillation: A Working Paper on Religion & Society in Upland Southeast Asia, No. 92. 67p. 1984. 5.00 (ISBN 0-317-11683-5). Cornell SE Asia.

Kirschenbaum, Aaron. Self-Incrimination in Jewish Law. 1970. 8.00x (ISBN 0-8381-3111-5). United Syn Bk.

Kirschner, Robert S., ed. Rabbinic Responsa of the Holocaust Era. LC 84-23509. 204p. 1985. 17.95 (ISBN 0-8052-3978-2). Schocken.

Kirshenblatt-Gimblett, B., jt. auth. see Dobroczcki, L.

Kirshenblatt-Gimblett, Barbara, jt. auth. see Dobroszycki, Lucjan.

Kirshner, Julius, jt. ed. see Boyer, John W.

Kirt, T., jt. auth. see Deane, W. J.

Kirtanananda Bhaktipada. Christ & Krishna: The Path of Pure Devotion. LC 85-73024. 182p. 1986. 10.95 (ISBN 0-317-43353-9); pap. 6.95 (ISBN 0-317-43354-7). Bhaktipada Bks.

Kirvan, John. Our Heritage Is the Lord. new ed. 1980. 5.95 (ISBN 0-03-047661-5, HarpR). Har-Row.

Kirvan, John J., ed. Infallibility Debate. LC 76-168745. Repr. of 1971 ed. 40.00 (ISBN 0-8357-9485-7, 2013529). Bks Demand UMI.

Kirwan, J. R., ed. see Danielou, Jean.

Kirwan, Willia. Biblical Concepts for Christian Counseling: A Case for Integrating Psychology & Theology. 240p. (Orig.). 1984. pap. 9.95 (ISBN 0-8010-5454-0). Baker Bk.

Kirwen, Michael C., ed. A Model Four Semester Syllabus for Transcultural Theology Overseas. LC 86-8618. 224p. 1986. 49.95 (ISBN 0-88946-047-7). E Mellen.

Kisare. Kisare, A Mennonite of Kiseru: An Autobiography As Told to Joseph C. Shenk. Shenk, Joseph C., as told to. (Illus.). 194p. 1984. 5.00 (ISBN 0-9613368-1-1). E Mennonite Bd.

Kisch, Frederick H. Palestine Diary. LC 73-180354. Repr. of 1938 ed. 31.45 (ISBN 0-404-56286-8). AMS Pr.

Kiser, Wayne. Getting More Out of Church. 168p. 1986. pap. 5.95 (ISBN 0-89693-530-2). Victor Bks.

Kishpaugh, Charles R. & Finnell, Kathy B. A Fork in the Road: Young Adult Decisions. 72p. (Orig.). 1986. pap. 3.75 (ISBN 0-88177-042-6, DR042B). Discipleship Res.

Kishta, Leila. ABC Rhymes for Young Muslims. Quinlan, Hamid, ed. LC 83-70183. (Illus.). 32p. 1983. pap. 3.00 (ISBN 0-89259-044-0). Am Trust Pubns.

Kisiel, Adam C., tr. see Heller, Michael.

Kissinger, Warren S. The Lives of Jesus: A History & Bibliography. LC 83-48284. 200p. 1985. lib. bdg. 39.00 (ISBN 0-8240-9035-7). Garland Pub.

--The Parables of Jesus: A History of Interpretation & Bibliography. LC 78-23271. (American Theological Library Association (ATLA) Bibliography Ser.: No. 4). 463p. 1979. lib. bdg. 30.00 (ISBN 0-8108-1186-3). Scarecrow.

--Sermon on the Mount: A History of Interpretation & Bibliography. LC 75-29031. (ATLA Bibliography Ser.: No. 3). 309p. 1975. 22.50 (ISBN 0-8108-0843-9). Scarecrow.

Kistemaker, Simon. The Gospels in Current Study. rev. ed. 192p. 1980. pap. 7.95 (ISBN 0-8010-5316-1). Baker Bk.

--The Parables of Jesus. 264p. 1980. 11.95 (ISBN 0-8010-5462-1). Baker Bk.

Kistemaker, Simon J. Exposition of the Epistles of James & John. 1986. 18.95 (ISBN 0-8010-5469-9). Baker Bk.

--Expositions of the Epistles of Peter & Jude: New Testament Commentary. 1987. text ed. 19.95 (ISBN 0-8010-5484-2). Baker Bk.

--Hebrews. 350p. 1984. 18.95 (ISBN 0-8010-5460-5). Baker Bk.

Kistler, Charles E., tr. see Brokering, Herbert F.

Kistler, Don. The Father & Sons Shall Be One, Vol. 1. 141p. (Orig.). 1978. pap. 3.50x (ISBN 0-940532-01-8). AOG.

Kistler, Don, ed. The Arithmetic of God, Vol. 1. 187p. (Orig.). 1976. pap. 3.95x (ISBN 0-940532-00-X). AOG.

--God's Numbers in Creation, Vol. 1. 1986. pap. 4.95 (ISBN 0-940532-03-4). AOG.

Kistler, Robert. Adventists & Labor Unions in the U. S. Wheeler, Gerald, ed. LC 83-13664. (Illus.). 127p. (Orig.). 1984. pap. 9.95 (ISBN 0-8280-0221-5). Review & Herald.

Kistler, Robert C. Marriage, Divorce, And... Woolsey, Raymond H., ed. 160p. (Orig.). 1987. 10.95 (ISBN 0-8280-0367-X). Review & Herald.

Kistler, Robert C., jt. auth. see Crider, Charles C.

Kitagawa, Joseph, jt. auth. see Eliade, Mircea.

Kitagawa, Joseph, jt. ed. see Eliade, Mircea.

Kitagawa, Joseph M. Religion in Japanese History. LC 65-23669. 475p. 1966. 35.00x (ISBN 0-231-02834-2). Columbia U Pr.

--Religions of the East. enl. ed. LC 60-7742. 352p. 1968. pap. 7.95 (ISBN 0-664-24837-3). Westminster.

Kitagawa, Joseph M., jt. auth. see Wach, Joachim.

Kitagawa, Joseph M., ed. American Refugee Policy: Ethical & Religious Reflections. 192p. (Orig.). 1985. pap. 9.95 (ISBN 0-86683-955-0, AY8541, HarpR). Har-Row.

--The History of Religions: Retrospect & Prospect. 192p. 1985. 19.95x (ISBN 0-02-916490-7). Macmillan.

Kitagawa, Joseph M., ed. see Hori, Ichiro.

Kitagawa, Joseph M., ed. see Jordan, Louis H.

Kitagawa, Joseph M., ed. see Wach, Joachim.

Kitaro, Nishida. Last Writings: Nothingness & the Religious Worldview. Dilworth, David A., tr. 176p. 1987. text ed. 18.00x (ISBN 0-8248-1040-6). UH Pr.

Kitay, P. M. Radicalism & Conservatism Toward Conventional Religion: A Psychological Study Based on a Group of Jewish College Students. LC 72-176953. (Columbia University. Teachers College. Contributions to Education: No. 919). Repr. of 1947 ed. 22.50 (ISBN 0-404-55919-0). AMS Pr.

Kitcher, Philip. Abusing Science: The Case Against Creationism. (Illus.). 224p. 1982. 22.50x (ISBN 0-262-11085-7); pap. 7.95 (ISBN 0-262-61037-X). MIT Pr.

Kite, Florence, tr. see Lachmund, Margarethe.

Kite, Roger. Evil & Suffering. 1985. 19.00x (ISBN 0-7062-3911-3, Pub. by Ward Lock Educ Co Ltd). State Mutual Bk.

--What Do We Mean Religion? 1985. 19.00x (ISBN 0-7062-3906-7, Pub. by Ward Lock Educ Co Ltd). State Mutual Bk.

Kitov, A. E. The Jew & His Home. 14th ed. Bulman, Nathan, tr. LC 63-17660. 233p. 1976. 12.50 (ISBN 0-88400-004-4). Shengold.

Kitov, Eliyahu. The Book of Our Heritage, 3 vols. Bulman, Nathan, tr. from Hebrew. Orig. Title: Sefer HaToda'ah. 1978. 32.50 (ISBN 0-87306-151-9); slipcased ed. 33.95 (ISBN 0-87306-157-8). Feldheim.

Kittel, Bonnie, tr. see Kittel, Bonnie P.

Kittel, Bonnie P. The Hymns of Qumran: Translation & Commentary. Kittel, Bonnie, tr. LC 80-11616. 1981. pap. 13.50 (ISBN 0-89130-397-9, 06 01 50). Scholars Pr GA.

Kittel, Gerhard & Friedrich, Gerhard, eds. Theological Dictionary of the New Testament, 10 vols. Incl. Vol. 1. 1964. 29.95 (ISBN 0-8028-2243-6); Vol. 2. 1965. 29.95 (ISBN 0-8028-2244-4); Vol. 3. 1966. 29.95 (ISBN 0-8028-2245-2); Vol. 4. 1967. 29.95 (ISBN 0-8028-2246-0); Vol. 5. 1968. 29.95 (ISBN 0-8028-2247-9); Vol. 6. 1969. 29.95 (ISBN 0-8028-2248-7); Vol. 7. 1970. 29.95 (ISBN 0-8028-2249-5); Vol. 8. 1972. 29.95 (ISBN 0-8028-2250-9); Vol. 9. 1973. 29.95 (ISBN 0-8028-2322-X); Vol; Vol. 10. 1976. 29.95 (ISBN 0-8028-2323-8); Vol. 10. 1976. 29.95 (ISBN 0-8028-2323-8). Set. 299.50 (ISBN 0-8028-2324-6). Eerdmans.

--Theological Dictionary of the New Testament. abridged ed. Bromiley, Geoffrey, tr. from Ger. 1300p. 1985. pap. 49.95 cloth (ISBN 0-8028-2404-8). Eerdmans.

Kittel, Helmuth. Evangelische Religionspaedagogik. (Ger). 1970. 23.20x (ISBN 3-11-002654-6). De Gruyter.

Kittel, Muriel, tr. see Cipolla, Carlo M.

Kittel, Rudolf. Great Men & Movements in Israel. rev. ed. LC 66-29121. (Library of Biblical Studies). 1968. 20.00x (ISBN 0-87068-071-4). Ktav.

Kittelson, James M. Luther the Reformer: The Story of the Man & His Career. LC 86-17266. (Illus.). 320p. 1986. text ed. 24.95 (ISBN 0-8066-2240-7, 10-4148). Augsburg.

Kittlaus, Paul & Leas, Speed. Church Fights: Managing Conflict in the Local Church. LC 73-6790. 184p. 1973. pap. 9.95 (ISBN 0-664-24974-4). Westminster.

Kittlaus, Paul, jt. auth. see Leas, Speed.

Kittler, Glenn D., jt. auth. see Wade, Marion E.

Kitto, John. Kitto's Daily Bible Illustrations, 2 vols. LC 80-8069. 1934p. 1982. 64.95 (ISBN 0-8254-3025-9). Kregel.

Kittrie, Nicholas N. F., jt. ed. see Alexander, Yonah.

Kitts, Eustace J. Pope John the Twenty-Third & Master John Hus of Bohemia. LC 77-84726. Repr. of 1910 ed. 47.00 (ISBN 0-404-16127-8). AMS Pr.

Kitzinger, Ernst & Senior, Elizabeth. Portraits of Christ. (Illus.). 62p. 1983. Repr. of 1940 ed. lib. bdg. 25.00 (ISBN 0-89987-459-2). Darby Bks.

Kitzinger, Sheila. Giving Birth: The Parents' Emotions in Childbirth. LC 77-2518. (Orig.). 1978. pap. 4.95 (ISBN 0-8052-0573-X). Schocken.

Kiyota, Minoru. Mahayana Buddhist Meditation: Theory & Practice. 327p. 1978. text ed. 17.50x (ISBN 0-8248-0556-9). UH Pr.

--Shingon Buddhism. LC 77-27894. 1978. text ed. 9.95x (ISBN 0-914910-09-4); pap. 7.95x (ISBN 0-914910-10-8). Buddhist Bks.

Kiyota, Minoru, et al, eds. Japanese Buddhism: Its Tradition, New Religions & Interaction with Christianity. 1987. 24.50 (ISBN 0-914910-76-0). Buddhist Bks.

Kizer, Kathryn W. The Harley Shields: Alaskan Missionaries. LC 84-5821. (Meet the Missioanry Ser.). 1984. 5.50 (ISBN 0-8054-4285-5, 4242-85). Broadman.

Klaaren, Eugene M. Religious Origins of Modern Science: Belief in Creation in Seventeenth-Century Thought. LC 85-17804. 256p. 1985. pap. text ed. 12.75 (ISBN 0-8191-4922-5). U Pr of Amer.

Klaassen, Walter. Anabaptism in Outline: Selected Primary Sources. 424p. 1981. pap. 12.95 (ISBN 0-8361-1241-5). Herald Pr.

--Selecciones Teologias Anabautista. Snyder, C. Arnoldo, tr. from Eng. LC 85-81079. (Span.). 280p. (Orig.). 1985. pap. 4.50 (ISBN 0-8361-1281-4). Herald Pr.

Klaassen, Walter, jt. ed. see Klassen, William.

Klah, Hasteen. Navajo Creation Myth: The Story of Emergence. LC 76-43762. (Museum of Navajo Ceremonial Art. Religion Ser.: Vol. 1). Repr. of 1942 ed. 24.50 (ISBN 0-404-15615-0). AMS Pr.

Klaiber, Jeffrey L. Religion & Revolution in Peru, 1824-1976. LC 76-51616. 1977. text ed. 22.95x (ISBN 0-268-01599-6). U of Notre Dame Pr.

Klaiman, M. H., tr. Singing the Glory of Lord Krishna Baru Candidasa's Srikrsnakirtana: Baru Candidasa's Srikrsnakirtana. LC 84-3905. (SP AAR Classics in Religious Studies). 1984. 28.75 (ISBN 0-89130-736-2, 01 05 05); pap. 20.75 (ISBN 0-89130-737-0). Scholars Pr GA.

Klaits, Joseph. Servants of Satan: The Age of the Witch Hunts. LC 84-48252. (Illus.). 224p. 1987. 24.95X (ISBN 0-253-35182-0); pap. 7.95 (ISBN 0-253-20422-4). Ind U Pr.

Klann, Norman H., jt. auth. see Martin, Walter.

Klaperman, Gilbert & Klaperman, Libby. The Story of the Jewish People, 4 vols. Incl. Vol. 1. From Creation to the Second Temple. pap. text ed. 4.50x (ISBN 0-87441-207-2); Vol. 2. From the Building of the Second Temple Through the Age of the Rabbis. pap. text ed. 4.50x (ISBN 0-87441-208-0); Vol. 3. From the Golden Age in Spain Through the European Emancipation. pap. text ed. 5.50x (ISBN 0-87441-209-9); Vol. 4. From the Settlement of America Through Israel Today. pap. text ed. 5.50x (ISBN 0-87441-210-2). LC 56-12175. (Illus.). 1974. pap. Behrman.

Klaperman, Libby, jt. auth. see Klaperman, Gilbert.

Klarmann, Andrew F. Gregorian Chant, a Textbook for Seminaries, Novitiates, & Secondary Schools. (Illus.). ix, 148p. Repr. of 1945 ed. lib. bdg. 22.50x (ISBN 0-8371-9019-3, KLGC). Greenwood.

Klarsfeld, Serge. The Children of Izieu: A Human Tragedy. (Illus.). 128p. 1985. pap. 9.95 (ISBN 0-8109-2307-6). Abrams.

Klassen, A. J., jt. ed. see Springer, Nelson.

Klassen, James R. Jimshoes in Vietman. LC 86-9801. (Illus.). 400p. (Orig.). 1986. pap. 14.95 (ISBN 0-8361-3412-5). Herald Pr.

Klassen, Peter. The Reformation. LC 79-54030. (Problems in Civilization Ser.). (Orig.). 1980. pap. text ed. 6.95x (ISBN 0-88273-408-3). Forum Pr IL.

Klassen, Randolph J. Reaching Out in Love. 144p. (Orig.). 1981. pap. 5.95 (ISBN 0-910452-47-4). Covenant.

Klassen, William. Love of Enemies: The Way to Peace. LC 84-47927. (Overtures to Biblical Theology Ser.). 176p. 1984. pap. 8.95 (ISBN 0-8006-1539-5). Fortress.

Klassen, William, ed. The New Way of Jesus. LC 80-65049. 158p. 1980. pap. 7.95 (ISBN 0-87303-038-9). Faith & Life.

Klassen, William & Klaassen, Walter, eds. The Writings of Pilgrim Marpeck. LC 77-87419. (Classics of the Radical Reformation Ser.: No. 2). (Illus.). 608p. 1978. 24.95x (ISBN 0-8361-1205-9). Herald Pr.

Klauder, Francis, ed. see Archenti, Augustine & Petrini, Arnold.

Klauder, Francis J. The Wonder of the Real: A Sketch in Basic Philosophy. rev., enlarged ed. LC 72-94706. (Illus.). 116p. 1973. 9.95 (ISBN 0-8158-0300-1). Chris Mass.

Klaus, Robert J. The Pope, the Protestants, & the Irish: Papal Aggression & Anti-Catholicism in Mid-Nineteenth Century England. McNeill, William H. & Stansky, Peter, eds. (Modern European History Ser.). 400p. 1987. lib. bdg. 60.00 (ISBN 0-8240-7820-9). Garland Pub.

Klause, John. The Unfortunate Fall: Theodicy & the Moral Imagination of Andrew Marvell. LC 83-13521. x, 208p. 1984. 22.50 (ISBN 0-208-02026-8, Archon Bks). Shoe String.

Klauser, Theodor. A Short History of the Western Liturgy. 2nd ed. Halliburton, John, tr. from Ger. 1979. pap. text ed. 10.95x (ISBN 0-19-213223-7). Oxford U Pr.

Klausmeier, Robert. Elementary Teacher Survival Kit. 80p. 1986. tchr's ed 9.95 (ISBN 0-89191-363-7). Cook.

--Preschool Teacher Survival Kit. 80p. 1986. tchr's ed 9.95 (ISBN 0-89191-362-9). Cook.

--Teen Teacher Survival Kit. 80p. 1986. tchr's ed 9.95 (ISBN 0-89191-364-5). Cook.

Klausner, Abraham J. Weddings: A Guide to All Religious & Interfaith Marriage Services. LC 86-7892. (Life-Cycle Bookshelf Ser.). (Orig.). 1986. pap. 11.90 (ISBN 0-933771-00-2). Alpha Pub Co.

Klausner, Joseph. From Jesus to Paul. Stinespring, William, tr. from Hebrew. 1978. 15.95x (ISBN 0-932232-03-5); pap. 12.95 (ISBN 0-932232-04-3). Menorah Pub.

--Jesus of Nazareth: His Life, Times & Teaching. Danby, Herbert, tr. from Hebrew. 1978. 15.95x (ISBN 0-932232-01-9); pap. 12.95 (ISBN 0-932232-02-7). Menorah Pub.

Klaven, Janet & Buckley, Mary I., eds. Women's Spirit Bonding. 320p. (Orig.). 1984. pap. 12.95 (ISBN 0-8298-0707-1). Pilgrim NY.

Klawiter, Randolph J., tr. see Dyorak, Max.

Klay, Grace Vander see Vander Klay, Grace.

Klay, Robin K. Counting the Cost: The Economics of Christian Stewardship. 176p. (Orig.). 1986. pap. 9.95 (ISBN 0-8028-0171-4). Eerdmans.

Kleba, Gerald J. The People Parish: A Model of Church Where People Flourish. LC 86-82035. 136p. (Orig.). 1986. pap. 4.95 (ISBN 0-87793-346-4). Ave Maria.

Kleeblatt, Norman, jt. auth. see Mann, Vivian B.

Kleen, Tyra De see De Kleen, Tyra.

Kleiber, Kenneth & Lemire, Deacon H. Deacons: Permanent or Passing? 70p. 1982. 6.95 (ISBN 0-911519-02-5). Richelieu Court.

Klein, A. M. Beyond Sambation: Selected Essays & Editorials, 1928-1955. Steinberg, M. W. & Kaplan, Usher, eds. (The Collected Works of A. M. Klein). 1982. 35.00 (ISBN 0-8020-5566-4). U of Toronto Pr.

Klein, Aaron, tr. see Ashtor, Eliyahu.

Klein, Ann, jt. auth. see Hopkins, Jeffrey.

Klein, Anne. Knowledge & Liberation. LC 86-1784. 283p. (Orig.). 1986. 27.50 (ISBN 0-937938-24-6); pap. 15.95 (ISBN 0-937938-23-8). Snow Lion.

Klein, Anne, ed. see Rinbochay, Khetsun S.

Klein, Anne C., ed. see Hopkins, Jeffrey.

Klein, Arthur J. Intolerance in the Reign of Elizabeth, Queen of England. LC 67-27614. 1968. Repr. of 1917 ed. 26.50x (ISBN 0-8046-0249-2, Pub. by Kennikat). Assoc Faculty Pr.

Klein, Carol M. We Went to Gabon. 1974. pap. 2.95 (ISBN 0-87509-151-2). Chr Pubns.

Klein, Chuck. So You Want Solutions. 1979. pap. 4.95 (ISBN 0-8423-6161-8). Tyndale.

--So You Want to Get into the Race. 1980. concordance study guide 4.95 (ISBN 0-8423-6082-4). Tyndale.

--So You Want to Lead Students. 96p. 1982. pap. 4.95 leader's guide (ISBN 0-8423-6084-0). Tyndale.

--So You Want to Set the Pace. 96p. 1982. pap. 4.95 (ISBN 0-8423-6083-2). Tyndale.

Klein, David G., jt. auth. see Grupper, David.

Klein, Dennis B. Jewish Origins of the Psychoanalytic Movement: With a New Preface. 224p. 1985. pap. 8.95 (ISBN 0-226-43960-7). U of Chicago Pr.

Klein, Earl. Jewish Prayer: Concepts & Customs. LC 85-23944. (The Hebraica-Judaica Bookshelf Ser.). (Orig.). 1986. 17.95 (ISBN 0-933771-01-0). Alpha Pub Co.

Klein, F. A. The Religion of Islam. 248p. 1985. text ed. 17.95x (ISBN 0-7007-0010-2, Pub. by Curzon Pr England); pap. text ed. 8.95 (ISBN 0-7007-0190-7). Apt Bks.

--Religion of Islam. 241p. 1978. Repr. of 1906 ed. 16.50 (ISBN 0-89684-153-7). Orient Bk Dist.

--The Religion of Islam. 8.95x (ISBN 0-317-20253-7). Intl Bk Ctr.

--The Religion of Islam. 248p. 1985. pap. text ed. 12.50x (ISBN 0-7007-0190-7, Pub by Curzon Pr UK). Humanities.

Klein, Gerda W. Promise of a New Spring: The Holocaust & Renewal. (Illus.). 64p. 1981. 10.95 (ISBN 0-940646-50-1); pap. 5.95 (ISBN 0-940646-51-X). Rossel Bks.

Klein, Herbert A. The Peoples of Israel: Fifty-Seven Centuries of Presence. rev. & enl. ed. Simon, Joseph, ed. Orig. Title: Israel - Land of the Jews. (Illus.). 240p. 1986. Repr. of 1972 ed. 23.50 (ISBN 0-934710-13-9). J Simon.

--Temple Beyond Time: Mount Moriah - From Solomon's Temple to Christian & Islamic Shrines. rev. ed. Simon, Joseph, ed. (Illus.). 192p. 1986. Repr. of 1970 ed. 27.50 (ISBN 0-934710-14-7). J Simon.

Klein, Hyman see Maimonides, Moses.

Klein, Hyman, tr. see Maimonides, Moses.

Klein, I. A Guide to Jewish Religious Practice. (Moreshet Ser: No. 6). 20.00x (ISBN 0-87334-004-3, Pub. by Jewish Theol Seminary). Ktav.

Klein, Isaac. Responsa & Halakhic Studies. 15.00x. Ktav.

--Spiritual Legacies: Holiday Sermons. 15.00x (ISBN 0-87068-276-8). Ktav.

Klein, Isaac, ed. see Maimonides, Moses.

Klein, Isaac see Maimonides, Moses.

Klein, Jacob. Royal Hymns of Shulgi, King of Ur: Man's Quest for Immortal Fame. LC 81-65929. (Transactions Ser.: Vol. 71, Pt. 7.). 1981. 6.00 (ISBN 0-87169-717-3). Am Philos.

Klein, Jean. Ease of Being. 2nd ed. xiii, 110p. 1986. pap. 8.50 (ISBN 0-89386-015-8). Acorn NC.

Klein, Jenny M., tr. see Ashtor, Eliyahu.

Klein, Judith W. Jewish Identity & Self-Esteem: Healing Wounds Through Ethnotherapy. 64p. 1980. 2.75. Am Jewish Comm.

Klein, Martin A. Islam & Imperialism in Senegal: Sine-Saloum, 1847-1914. 1968. 25.00x (ISBN 0-8047-0621-2). Stanford U Pr.

Klein, Nancy I. Heritage of Faith: Two Pioneers of Judaism in America. 16.95 (ISBN 0-88125-119-4). Ktav.

Klein, Ralph W. Israel in Exile: A Theological Interpretation. Brueggemann, Walter & Donahue, John R., trs. LC 79-7382. (Overtures to Biblical Theology Ser.). 180p. (Orig.). 1979. pap. 8.95 (ISBN 0-8006-1532-8, 1-1532). Fortress.

--Textual Criticism of the Old Testament: The Septuagint After Qumran. Tucker, Gene M., ed. LC 74-80420. (Guides to Biblical Scholarship: Old Testament Ser.). 96p. (Orig.). 1974. pap. 3.95 (ISBN 0-8006-1087-3, 1-1087). Fortress.

Klein, Sydney T. The Way of Attainment. 220p. 1981. pap. 13.00 (ISBN 0-89540-106-1, SB-106). Sun Pub.

Klein, Theodore M., jt. ed. see Aycock, Wendell M.

Klein, W. C., tr. see Ali ibn Isma'il, A. H., et al.

Klein, Walter C. Johann Conrad Beissel: Mystic & Martinet 1690-1768. LC 74-187453. (The American Utopian Adventure Ser.). 218p. 1973. Repr. of 1942 ed. lib. bdg. 22.50x (ISBN 0-87991-012-7). Porcupine Pr.

Kleinbard, Gitel. Oh, Zalmy! Or, the Tale of the Porcelain Pony, Bk. 1. (Oh, Zalmy Ser.). (Illus.). 1976. 4.95 (ISBN 0-917274-04-0); pap. 2.95 (ISBN 0-917274-01-6). Mah Tov Pubns.

Kleiner, Diana E. Roman Group Portraiture: The Funerary Reliefs of the Late Republic & Early Empire. LC 76-23634. (Outstanding Dissertations in the Fine Arts - 2nd Series - Ancient). (Illus.). 1977. Repr. lib. bdg. 76.00 (ISBN 0-8240-2703-5). Garland Pub.

Kleiner, Sighard. Serving God First. 1985. 14.95 (ISBN 0-87907-883-9). Cistercian Pubns.

Kleinig, John. Ethical Issues in Psychosurgery. (Studies in Applied Philosophy: No. 1). (Illus.). 176p. 1985. text ed. 19.95x (ISBN 0-04-170032-5); pap. text ed. 7.95x (ISBN 0-04-170033-3). Allen Unwin.

Kleinman, Isador. Bach a Bisl: Laugh a Little. 1985. pap. 5.95 (ISBN 0-910818-61-4). Judaica Pr.

Kleinman, Sherryl. Equals Before God: Seminarians as Humanistic Professionals. LC 83-24208. 160p. 1984. lib. bdg. 15.00x (ISBN 0-226-43999-2). U of Chicago Pr.

Kleinsasser, Jacob, et al. For the Sake of Divine Truth: 1974 Visit of Four Brothers to Central Europe. LC 74-23787. 1974. pap. 1.20 (ISBN 0-87486-146-2). Plough.

Kleinz, John P. The "Who's Who" of Heaven: Saints for All Seasons. 220p. (Orig.). 1987. pap. 12.95 (ISBN 0-87061-136-4). Chr Classics.

Kleist, James A., tr. see Quasten & Plumpe.

Klejment, Anne. The Berrigans: A Bibliography of Published Works by Daniel, Philip, & Elizabeth Berrigan. LC 78-68214. (Garland Reference Library of Humanities: No. 154). 1979. lib. bdg. 36.00 (ISBN 0-8240-9788-2). Garland Pub.

Klem, Herbert V. Oral Communication of the Scripture: Insights from African Oral Art. LC 81-10052. (Applied Cultural Anthropology Ser.). (Illus.). 280p. (Orig.). 1982. pap. text ed. 9.95x (ISBN 0-87808-332-4). William Carey Lib.

Klemke. Studies in the Philosophy of Kierkegaard. 1976. pap. 16.00 (ISBN 90-247-1852-X, Pub. by Martinus Nijhoff Netherlands). Kluwer Academic.

Klemke, E. D., intro. by. Humanism vs Theism. 154p. 1982. pap. 8.50x (ISBN 0-8138-0916-9). Iowa St U Pr.

Klemm, David E., ed. Hermeneutical Inquiry, Vol. I: The Interpretations of Texts. (American Academy of Religion, Studies in Religion). 299p. 1986. 22.95 (ISBN 1-55540-032-9, 01-00-43); pap. 16.95 (ISBN 1-55540-033-7). Scholars Pr GA.

--Hermeneutical Inquiry, Vol. II: The Interpretation of Existence. (American Academy of Religion, Studies in Religion). 409p. 1986. 26.95 (ISBN 1-55540-034-5, 01-00-44); pap. 19.95 (ISBN 1-55540-035-3). Scholars Pr GA.

Klemp, Harold. Book of ECK Parables, Vol. 1. (Illus.). 265p. (Orig.). 1986. pap. 8.95 (ISBN 0-88155-046-9). IWP Pub.

Klemperer, Klemens Von see Von Klemperer, Klemens.

Klenck, Robert H. Words Fitly Spoken: Reflections & Prayers. LC 79-13449. 1979. 10.95 (ISBN 0-934878-35-8, 07764-1, Dist. by W.W. Norton). Dembner Bks.

Klenicki, Leon & Wigoder, Geoffrey, eds. A Dictionary of the Jewish-Christian Dialogue. (Stimulus Book, Studies in Judaism & Christianity). (Orig.). 1984. pap. 7.95 (ISBN 0-8091-2590-0). Paulist Pr.

Klenicki, Leon, jt. ed. see Croner, Helga.

Klenicki, Leon, jt. ed. see Huck, Gabe.

Klepfisz, Heszel. Culture of Compassion: The Spirit of Polish Jewry from Hasidism to the Holocaust. LC 83-13626. 265p. 1983. 25.00x (ISBN 0-88125-037-6). Ktav.

Klepper, Robert F. Methodist Hymnal Concordance. LC 86-29811. 800p. 1987. 62.50 (ISBN 0-8108-1968-6). Scarecrow.

Kleps, Arthur J. Boo Hoo Bible: The Neo-American Church Catechism & Handbook. rev. ed. LC 73-29356. Orig. Title: Neo-American Church Catechism. (Illus.). 218p. 1971. pap. 5.00 (ISBN 0-9600388-1-7). Neo-Am Church.

Klewin, Jean & Klewin, Thomas. When the Man You Love Is an Alcoholic. LC 79-51276. (When Bks). (Illus.). 1979. pap. 2.45 (ISBN 0-87029-149-1, 20232-5). Abbey.

Klewin, Thomas, jt. auth. see Klewin, Jean.

Klibanov, A. I. History of Religious Sectarianism in Russia (1860s-1917) Dunn, Stephen P., ed. LC 81-12180. (Illus.). 380p. 1982. 54.00 (ISBN 0-08-026794-7). Pergamon.

Klieman, Aaron. Zionist Evidence Before the Peel Commission, 1933-1937. Sachar, Howard M., ed. (The Rise of Israel Ser.). 320p. 1987. lib. bdg. 65.00 (ISBN 0-8240-4921-7). Garland Pub.

Klien, B. D. see Maimonides, Moses.

Klien, James H. Thunder in the Valley: The Massabielle Saga. (Illus.). 92p. 4.00 (ISBN 0-8198-7316-0, MA0135); pap. 3.00 (ISBN 0-8198-7317-9). Dghtrs St Paul.

Kliever, Lonnie. H. Richard Niebuhr. LC 77-92452. (Makers of the Modern Theological Mind Ser.). 1978. 8.95 (ISBN 0-8499-0078-6, 0078-6). Word Bks.

Kliever, Lonnie D. The Shattered Spectrum: A Survey of Contemporary Theology. LC 80-82184. 276p. (Orig.). 1981. pap. 10.95 (ISBN 0-8042-0707-0). John Knox.

Kliewer, Evelyn. Laughter Lives Here. LC 81-70476. 1982. pap. 4.95 (ISBN 0-8054-5203-6). Broadman.

--Please, God, Help Me Get Well in Your Spare Time. LC 79-17683. 128p. 1979. pap. 3.95 (ISBN 0-87123-027-5, 210027). Bethany Hse.

Kliewer, Marilyn P. Have the Mind of Christ. LC 85-81041. (Faith & Life Bible Studies). 90p. 1985. pap. 4.95 (ISBN 0-87303-104-0). Faith & Life.

Kligman, Gail. Calus: Symbolic Transformation in Romanian Ritual. LC 80-21372. (Chicago Originals Ser.). (Illus.). 240p. 1981. lib. bdg. 14.00x (ISBN 0-226-44221-7). U of Chicago Pr.

Klim, Mary K. Bible Studies for Senior Citizens. 91p. 1986. pap. 5.95x (ISBN 0-932910-59-9). Potentials Development.

Klima, Otakar. Mazdak: Geschichte einer sozialen Bewegung im sassanidischen Persien. Finley, Moses, ed. LC 79-4986. (Ancient Economic History Ser.). (Ger.). 1980. Repr. of 1957 ed. lib. bdg. 27.50x (ISBN 0-405-12371-X). Ayer Co Pubs.

Klimkeit, H. M., tr. see Mensching, G.

Klin, George, tr. see Lehrmann, Charles C.

Kline, Donald L. One Flesh. 1985. 4.95 (ISBN 0-89536-730-0, 5814). CSS of Ohio.

Kline, George L. Religious & Anti-Religious Thought in Russia. LC 68-54484. (The Weil Lectures). Repr. of 1968 ed. 47.30 (ISBN 0-317-09813-6, 2020097). Bks Demand UMI.

Kline, Leslie L. The Sayings of Jesus in the Pseudo-Clementine Homilies. LC 75-1645. (Society of Biblical Literature. Dissertation Ser.: No. 14). Repr. of 1975 ed. 52.00 (ISBN 0-8357-9579-9, 2017517). Bks Demand UMI.

Klinger, Harry E. One Day in the Life of Christ. 96p. 1987. 6.95 (ISBN 0-8059-3042-6). Dorrance.

Klingner, Erich. Luther und der Deutsche Volksaberglaube. 18.00 (ISBN 0-384-29830-3); pap. 13.00 (ISBN 0-685-02277-3). Johnson Repr.

Klinsing, P. David, et al. Is There Life after High School. LC 79-53677. 116p. 1979. pap. 2.50 (ISBN 0-87509-264-0). Chr Pubns.

Klock, Christoph, jt. auth. see Spira, Andreas.

Klocker, Harry R., ed. Thomism & Modern Thought. LC 62-9414. 1962. 32.50x (ISBN 0-89197-451-2). Irvington.

Kloetzli, Walter. The Church & the Urban Challenge. LC 61-14757. pap. 23.80 (2027195). Bks Demand UMI.

Klong-chen rab-byams pa. Looking Deeper. Guenther, Herbert V., tr. from Tibetan. (Illus.). 64p. (Orig.). 1984. pap. 3.50 (ISBN 0-931454-09-3). Timeless Bks.

Kloos, Carola. Yhwh's Combat with the Sea: A Canaanite Tradition in the Religion of Ancient Israel. 243p. 1986. pap. 35.75 (ISBN 90-04-08096-1, Pub. by E J Brill). Heinman.

Klope, Joan B., jt. auth. see Hepburn, Daisy.

Kloppenberg, Bonaventure. Temptations for the Theology of Liberation. (Synthesis Ser.). 1974. 0.75 (ISBN 0-8199-0362-0). Franciscan Herald.

Kloppenborg, John S. The Formation of Q: Trajectories in Ancient Wisdom Collections. LC 86-45225. 416p. 1987. 39.95 (ISBN 0-8006-3101-3). Fortress.

Kloppenburg, Bonaventure. Ecclesiology of Vatican II. 1974. 6.95 (ISBN 0-8199-0484-8). Franciscan Herald.

--Pastoral Practice & the Paranormal. Smith, David, tr. from Span. 1979. 8.95 (ISBN 0-685-92509-9). Franciscan Herald.

--The People's Church. 1978. 8.95 (ISBN 0-8199-0692-1). Franciscan Herald.

Kloss, Jethro. Back to Eden. authorized ed. LC 81-82411. 702p. 1984. pap. 9.95. World Wide OR.

--Back to Eden: Authorized Kloss Family Edition. rev. ed. (Illus.). 724p. 1985. pap. 3.50 (ISBN 0-940676-00-1). Back to Eden.

Klostermaier, K. Mythologies & Philosophies of Salvation in the Theistic Traditions of India. (Editions SR Ser.: No. 5). 549p. 1984. pap. text ed. 23.95x (ISBN 0-88920-158-7, Pub. by Wilfrid Laurier Canada). Humanities.

Klotz, J. A Christian View of Abortion. (Contemporary Theology Ser.). 1973. 3.95 (ISBN 0-570-06721-9, 12RT2560). Concordia.

Klotz, John. Studies in Creation: A General Introduction to the Creation-Evolution Debate. 224p. (Orig.). 1985. pap. 9.95 (ISBN 0-570-03969-X, 12-3004). Concordia.

Klotz, John W. Genes, Genesis & Evolution. rev. ed. 1970. pap. 17.95 (ISBN 0-570-03212-1, 12-2637). Concordia.

Klotz, Saadi, ed. see Lewis, Samuel L.

Klotz, Saadi, ed. see Lewis, Samuel L. & Khan, Hazrat I.

Kluback, William, jt. tr. see Duran, Manuel.

Klubertanz, George P. St. Thomas Aquinas on Analogy: A Textual Analysis & Systematic Synthesis. LC 60-9602. (Jesuit Studies). pap. 81.80 (ISBN 0-317-09004-6, 2000813). Bks Demand UMI.

Klubertanz, George P. & Holloway, Maurice R. Being & God: Introduction to the Philosophy of Being & to Natural Theology. LC 63-15359. 1963. 39.50x (ISBN 0-89197-045-2); pap. text ed. 19.95x (ISBN 0-89197-674-4). Irvington.

Kluckhohn, Clyde. Navaho Witchcraft. 1962. pap. 8.95x (ISBN 0-8070-4697-3, BP243). Beacon Pr.

Kluckhohn, Clyde & Wyman, L. C. Introduction to Navaho Chant Practice. LC 42-2722. (HU PMP Ser.). 1940. 21.00 (ISBN 0-527-00552-5). Kraus Repr.

Kluckhohn, Clyde, jt. auth. see Wyman, L. C.

Klug, Eugene F. Getting into the Formula of Concord. 1977. pap. 3.75 (ISBN 0-570-03742-5, 12-2646). Concordia.

Klug, Lyn. Bible Readings for Women. LC 85-7508. 112p. 1985. pap. 3.95 (ISBN 0-8066-2163-X, 10-0687). Augsburg.

--I Know I Can Trust You, Lord: Prayers for Girls. LC 83-70503. (Young Readers Ser.). 80p. 1983. pap. 3.95 (ISBN 0-8066-2009-9, 10-3192). Augsburg.

Klug, Lyn, jt. auth. see Klug, Ron.

Klug, Lyn, jt. ed. see Klug, Ron.

Klug, Ron. Bible Readings on Prayer. LC 85-28979. 112p. (Orig.). 1986. pap. 3.95 (ISBN 0-8066-2189-3, 10-0690). Augsburg.

--Growing in Joy: God's Way to Increase Joy in All of Life. LC 82-72637. 128p. 1983. pap. 5.95 (ISBN 0-8066-1943-0, 10-2902). Augsburg.

--Job: God's Answer to Suffering. (Fisherman Bible Studyguide Ser.). 61p. 1982. saddle-stitched 2.95 (ISBN 0-87788-430-7). Shaw Pubs.

--Lord I've Been Thinking: Prayer Thoughts for High School Boys. LC 78-52183. 1978. pap. 3.95 (ISBN 0-8066-1657-1, 10-4105). Augsburg.

--Mark: A Daily Dialogue with God. (Personal Bible Studyguide Ser.). 156p. 1984. pap. 5.95 (ISBN 0-87788-539-7). Shaw Pubs.

--Philippians: Living Joyfully. (Young Fisherman Bible Studyguide Ser.). (Illus.). 64p. 1983. tchr's ed. 4.95 (ISBN 0-87788-682-2); saddle-stitched student's ed. 2.95 (ISBN 0-87788-681-4). Shaw Pubs.

--The Real Questions: Searching the Psalms for Answers. (Young Fisherman Bible Studyguide Ser.). 64p. 1984. saddle-stitched tchr's. ed. 4.95 (ISBN 0-87788-702-0); saddle-stitched student ed. 2.95 (ISBN 0-87788-701-2). Shaw Pubs.

--You Promised, Lord: Prayers for Boys. LC 83-70502. (Young Readers Ser.). 80p. (Orig.). 1983. pap. 3.95 (ISBN 0-8066-2008-0, 10-7417). Augsburg.

Klug, Ron & Klug, Lyn. Bible Reading for Parents. LC 81-52277. (Bible Readings Ser.). 112p. (Orig.). 1982. pap. 3.95 (ISBN 0-8066-1909-0, 10-0679). Augsburg.

--Family Prayers. LC 79-50081. 1979. pap. 4.95 (ISBN 0-8066-1708-X, 10-2258). Augsburg.

--Jesus Comes: the Story of Jesus' Birth for Children. LC 86-81808. (Illus.). 32p. (Orig.). 1986. pap. 4.95 saddlestitch (ISBN 0-8066-2234-2, 10-3497). Augsburg.

--Jesus Lives. LC 82-72848. 32p. (Orig.). 1983. pap. 3.95 (ISBN 0-8066-1952-X, 10-3527). Augsburg.

--Thank You, God: Prayers for Young Children. LC 80-67800. 32p. (Orig.). 1980. pap. 3.95 (ISBN 0-8066-1862-0, 10-6243). Augsburg.

Klug, Ron, jt. auth. see Vaughn, Joe.

Klug, Ron & Klug, Lyn, eds. The Christian Family Bedtime Reading Book. LC 82-70952. 128p. pap. 10.95 (ISBN 0-8066-1927-9, 10-1112). Augsburg.

Klug, Ron, et al. Jesus Loves: Stories about Jesus for Children. LC 86-81807. (Illus.). 32p. (Orig.). 1986. pap. 4.95 saddlestitch (ISBN 0-8066-2235-0, 10-3526). Augsburg.

Klug, Ronald. Following Christ: Prayers from Imitation of Christ. LC 80-25260. (Illus.). 63p. 1981. pap. 3.95 (ISBN 0-570-03826-X, 12-2791). Concordia.

--How to Keep a Spiritual Journal. LC 82-14383. 144p. 1982. pap. 4.95 (ISBN 0-8407-5815-4). Nelson.

--My Prayer Journal. LC 12-2964. 1982. pap. 3.95 (ISBN 0-570-03871-5). Concordia.

Klus, Ronald. John the Baptist. (Arch Book Ser.: No. 21). 1984. pap. 0.99 (ISBN 0-570-06189-X, 59-1290). Concordia.

Klusmeyer, Joann. What about Me? (Illus.). 1987. 3.95 (ISBN 0-570-03641-0). Concordia.

Kluxen, Kurt, jt. ed. see Birke, Adolf M.

Kluyme, Robert Van see Walsingham, Thomas.

Kluyve, Robert A. Van see Walsingham, Thomae.

Klyver, F. H. Supervision of Student-Teachers in Religious Education. LC 79-176952. (Columbia University. Teachers College. Contributions to Education: No. 198). Repr. of 1925 ed. 22.50 (ISBN 0-404-55198-X). AMS Pr.

Knapp, C. Samuel the Prophet. 6.95 (ISBN 0-88172-113-1). Believers Bkshelf.

Knapp, Christopher. Kings of Judah & Israel. Rev. ed. 1982. pap. 5.95 (ISBN 0-87213-461-X). Loizeaux.

Knapp, Doug, et al. Thunder in the Valley. (Orig.). 1986. pap. 6.95 (ISBN 0-8054-6342-9). Broadman.

Knapp, Elsie M. Horary Art & It's Synthesis. 1974. 5.00x (ISBN 0-686-17210-8). Sandollar Pr.

Knapp, John, II. My Book of Bible Rhymes. (Illus.). 1987. 11.95. Cook.

Knapp, Sr. Justina. Christian Symbols & How to Use Them. LC 74-8172. (Illus.). 164p. 1975. Repr. of 1935 ed. 43.00x (ISBN 0-8103-4050-X). Gale.

Knapp, P. The Style of John Wyclif's English Sermons. 1977. 16.00x (ISBN 90-279-3156-9). Mouton.

Knappen, Marshall M. Tudor Puritanism: A Chapter in the History of Idealism. LC 39-10082. 1965. pap. 3.45x (ISBN 0-226-44627-1, P194, Phoen). U of Chicago Pr.

Knappen, Marshall M., ed. see Rogers, Richard & Ward, Samuel.

Knappert, J., jt. ed. see Rippin, A.

Knappert, Jan. Myths & Legends of the Swahili. (African Writers Ser.). 1970. pap. text ed. 5.00x (ISBN 0-435-90075-7). Heinemann Ed.

Knapton, Ernest J. Lady of the Holy Alliance: The Life of Julie De Krudener. LC 39-14081. Repr. of 1939 ed. 22.45 (ISBN 0-404-03732-1). AMS Pr.

Knauft, Bruce M. Good Company & Violence: Sorcery & Social Action in a Lowland New Guinea Society. LC 85-967. (Studies in Melanasian Anthropology). 1985. 40.00x (ISBN 0-520-05530-6). U of Cal Pr.

Knecht, F. J. Child's Bible History. Schumacher, Philip, tr. (Illus.). 1973. pap. 2.00 (ISBN 0-89555-005-9). TAN Bks Pubs.

Knechtle, Cliffe. Give Me an Answer. LC 86-10549. 132p. (Orig.). 1986. pap. 5.95 (ISBN 0-87784-569-7). Inter-Varsity.

Knee, Stuart E. The Concept of Zionist Dissent in the American Mind 1917-1941. 1979. 14.95 (ISBN 0-8315-0177-4). Speller.

Knelman, F. H. Reagan, God & the Bomb. 350p. 1985. 19.95 (ISBN 0-87975-310-2). Prometheus Bks.

Kniazev, V. V. Zhizn' dlja vsjekh i smert' za vsjekh. Tr. of Life is for All & Death is for All. 1971. pap. 1.00 (ISBN 0-317-30338-4). Holy Trinity.

Knibb, M. A., jt. auth. see Coggins, R. J.

Knibb, M. A., ed. The Ethiopic Book of Enoch, 2 vols. 1978. 84.00x set (ISBN 0-19-826163-2). Oxford U Pr.

Knickerbocker, Charles, ed. see Cuffee, James W.

Knierim, Rolf, ed. see Long, Burke O.

Knierim, Rolf, et al, eds. see Collins, John J.

Knight, A. R. & Schroeder, Gordon H. New Life. rev. ed. 1971. pap. 1.50 (ISBN 0-8170-0120-4); pap. 1.00 spanish ed. (ISBN 0-8170-0696-6). Judson.

Knight, Carol B. Passing the Torch. LC 81-82491. 130p. (Orig.). 1985. pap. 7.95 (ISBN 0-913299-16-2). Stillpoint.

Knight, Cecil B. Keeping the Sunday School Alive. 1959. 5.25 (ISBN 0-87148-475-7). Pathway Pr.

--Pentecostal Worship. 1974. pap. 3.95 (ISBN 0-87148-684-9). Pathway Pr.

Knight, David. Confession Can Change Your Life. (Illus.). 64p. (Orig.). 1985. pap. text ed. 2.50 (ISBN 0-86716-041-1). St Anthony Mess Pr.

--The Good News about Sex. 312p. (Orig.). 1980. pap. 4.95 (ISBN 0-912228-57-1). St Anthony Mess Pr.

--His Way: An Everyday Plan for Following Jesus. 1977. pap. 3.50 (ISBN 0-912228-39-3). St Anthony Mess Pr.

--Lift Your Eyes to the Mountain. 8.95 (ISBN 0-87193-137-0); pap. 6.95 (ISBN 0-87193-190-7). Dimension Bks.

--To Follow His Way: A Parish Renewal Program. 112p. (Orig.). 1980. pap. 3.95 (ISBN 0-912228-70-9). St Anthony Mess Pr.

Knight, David M. Chastity: Who Lives It. LC 85-19516. 32p. (Orig.). 1985. pap. 3.95 (ISBN 0-915488-10-8, BV4647.C5K57). Clarity Pub.

--Living the Sacraments: A Call to Conversion. LC 85-60888. 140p. (Orig.). 1985. pap. 6.50 (ISBN 0-87973-815-4, 815). Our Sunday Visitor.

--Make Me A Sabbath of Your Heart. 6.95 (ISBN 0-87193-191-5). Dimension Bks.

--Meditations for Priests. 1978. write for info. (ISBN 0-915488-05-1). Clarity Pub.

--Saving Presence: The Ministry & Mystery of the Church. 1983. 6.95 (ISBN 0-87193-205-9). Dimension Bks.

Knight, Douglas, jt. ed. see Tucker, Gene.

Knight, Douglas A. Rediscovering the Traditions of Israel. LC 75-6868. (Society of Biblical Literature. Dissertation Ser.: No. 9). pap. 86.50 (ISBN 0-317-07884-4, 2017515). Bks Demand UMI.

Knight, Douglas A., jt. auth. see Tucker, Gene M.

Knight, Douglas A. & Tucker, Gene M., eds. The Hebrew Bible & Its Modern Interpreters. LC 83-49216. (The Bible & Its Modern Interpreters Ser.). 496p. 1984. 24.95 (ISBN 0-8006-0721-X, 1-721). Fortress.

Knight, Frank H. & Merriam, Thornton W. The Economic Order & Religion. LC 78-31760. 1979. Repr. of 1945 ed. lib. bdg. 24.75x (ISBN 0-313-20970-7, KNEO). Greenwood.

Knight, G. A., ed. see Holmgren, Fredrick C.

Knight, G. Wilson. Chariot of Wrath: The Message of John Milton to Democracy at War. LC 72-196540. 1942. lib. bdg. 20.00 (ISBN 0-8414-5589-9). Folcroft.

--Christ & Nietzsche. 1948. lib. bdg. 17.50 (ISBN 0-8414-5590-2). Folcroft.

--Christ & Nietzsche: An Essay in Poetic Wisdom. 1982. 17.00 (ISBN 0-8495-3135-7). Arden Lib.

--The Christian Renaissance: With Interpretations of Dante, Shakespeare & Goethe & New Discussions of Oscar Wilde & the Gospel of Thomas. LC 81-40252. 366p. 1982. lib. bdg. 32.00 (ISBN 0-8191-1913-X); pap. text ed. 16.50 (ISBN 0-8191-1914-8). U Pr of Amer.

--Myth & Miracle: An Essay on the Mystic Symbolism of Shakespeare. 59.95 (ISBN 0-8490-0699-6). Gordon Pr.

--Myth & Miracle: Essay on the Mystic Symbolism of Shakespeare. 1978. Repr. of 1929 ed. lib. bdg. 17.50 (ISBN 0-8495-3014-8). Arden Lib.

Knight, Gareth. Practical Guide to Qabalistic Symbolism. 1978. 22.50 (ISBN 0-87728-397-4). Weiser.

Knight, George & Edwards, James R., eds. The Layman's Overview of the Bible. 224p. 1987. pap. text ed. 8.95 (ISBN 0-8407-3109-4). Nelson.

Knight, George A. The International Theological Commentary on Isaiah 40-55. Holmgren, Frederick, ed. (The International Theological Commentary Ser.). 208p. (Orig.). 1983. pap. 9.95 (ISBN 0-8028-1039-X). Eerdmans.

--Isaiah Fifty-Six to Sixty-Six. Holmgern, Frederick, ed. (International Theological Commentary Ser.). 148p. (Orig.). 1985. pap. 5.95 (ISBN 0-8028-0021-1). Eerdmans.

--Leviticus. LC 81-3007. (Daily Study Bible-Old Testament Ser.). 182p. 1981. 12.95 (ISBN 0-664-21802-4); pap. 6.95 (ISBN 0-664-24569-2). Westminster.

--Psalms: Nos. 1-72, Vol. 1. LC 82-20134. (Daily Study Bible Old Testament Ser.). 350p. 1982. 12.95 (ISBN 0-664-21805-9); pap. 7.95 (ISBN 0-664-24572-2). Westminster.

--Psalms: Nos. 73-150, Vol. 2. LC 82-20134. (Daily Study Bible Old Testament Ser.). 384p. 1983. 15.95 (ISBN 0-664-21808-3); pap. 8.95 (ISBN 0-664-24575-7). Westminster.

Knight, George A., ed. see Anderson, R. A.

Knight, George A., ed. see Hamlin, E. J.

Knight, George A., jt. ed. see Holmgren, Frederick.

Knight, George R. Myths in Adventism Education. Wheeler, Gerald, ed. 1985. 16.95 (ISBN 0-8280-0277-0). Review & Herald.

--Philosophy & Education: An Introduction in Christian Perspective. LC 81-117900. (Illus.). xii, 244p. 1980. pap. text ed. 10.95 (ISBN 0-943872-79-0). Andrews Univ Pr.

Knight, George R., ed. Early Adventist Educators. LC 83-71043. (Illus.). xvi, 250p. 1983. 12.95 (ISBN 0-943872-60-X). Andrews Univ Pr.

Knight, George W. Chariot of Wrath. 1978. Repr. of 1942 ed. lib. bdg. 25.00 (ISBN 0-8495-3012-1). Arden Lib.

--Church Bulletin Bits 3. 128p. 1987. pap. 4.95 (ISBN 0-8010-5479-6). Baker Bk.

--Clip Art Features for Church Newsletters. 1984. pap. 4.50 (ISBN 0-8010-5465-6). Baker Bk.

--Clip-Art Features for Church Newsletters, No. 2. (Illus.). 96p. 1986. pap. 4.95 (ISBN 0-8010-5471-0). Baker Bk.

--Wedding Ceremony Idea Book. 96p. 1982. pap. 7.95 (ISBN 0-939298-01-5). J M Prods.

Knight, George W., compiled By. Church Bulletin Bits, No. 2. 144p. (Orig.). 1980. pap. 4.50 (ISBN 0-8010-5424-9). Baker Bk.

--Clip-Art Sentence Sermons for Church Publications. 96p. 1986. pap. 3.95 (ISBN 0-8010-5475-3). Baker Bk.

--Instant Cartoons for Church Newsletters, No. 1. 4.95 (ISBN 0-8010-5451-6). Baker Bk.

--Instant Cartoons for Church Newsletters, No. 2. (Illus.). 112p. 1984. pap. 4.95 (ISBN 0-8010-5457-5). Baker Bk.

--Instant Cartoons for Church Newsletters, No. 3. 1986. pap. 4.95 (ISBN 0-8010-5473-7). Baker Bk.

Knight, George W. & Edwards, James R., eds. The Layman's Overview of the Bible. 1987. 14.95 (ISBN 0-8407-7560-1). Nelson.

Knight, George W., III. The Faithful Sayings in the Pastoral Letters. (Baker Biblical Monographs). 1979. pap. 6.95 (ISBN 0-8010-5402-8). Baker Bk.

Knight, Harold, tr. see Brunner, Heinrich E.

Knight, Harold, tr. see Diem, Hermann.

Knight, Harold, tr. see Quistorp, Heinrich.

Knight, Harold, tr. see Schoeps, Hans J.

Knight, Hilary. Christmas Nutshell Library, 4 bks. Incl. Angels & Berries & Candy Canes (ISBN 0-06-023200-5); Christmas Stocking Story (ISBN 0-06-023205-6); Firefly in a Fir Tree (ISBN 0-06-023190-4); The Night Before Christmas. LC 63-18904. 1963. Set. 9.70 (ISBN 0-06-023165-3). HarpJ.

Knight, John A. Beacon Bible Expositions: Philippians, Colossians, Philemon. Greathouse, William H., ed. 320p. 1985. 8.95 (ISBN 0-8341-0320-6). Beacon Hill.

Knight, Margaret. Morals Without Religion. 124p. 1981. 25.00x (ISBN 0-686-97044-6, Pub. by Dobson Bks England). State Mutual Bk.

Knight, R. Gaveston. Miracles Among You. 100p. 1985. 13.50x (ISBN 0-85088-379-2, Pub. by Gomer Pr). State Mutual Bk.

Knight, Richard. History of the General or Six Principle in Europe & America. Gaustad, Edwin S., ed. LC 79-52597. (The Baptist Tradition Ser.). 1980. Repr. of 1827 ed. lib. bdg. 30.50x (ISBN 0-405-12464-3). Ayer Co Pubs.

Knight, Richard P. Ancient Art & Mythology. (The Most Meaningful Classics in World Culture Ser.). 1979. Repr. of 1876 ed. 69.75 (ISBN 0-89266-189-5). Am Classical Coll Pr.

--The Interpretation of Ancient, Strange Mythological Symbols. (Illus.). 137p. 1983. 147.75 (ISBN 0-89901-125-X). Found Class Reprints.

--Worship of Priapus. LC 73-76829. (Illus.). 300p. 1974. Repr. of 1786 ed. 25.00 (ISBN 0-8216-0207-1). Univ Bks.

Knight, Stephen. The Brotherhood: The Secret World of the Freemasons. LC 84-45208. 336p. 1984. 17.95 (ISBN 0-8128-2994-8). Stein & Day.

Knight, Walker & Touchton, Ken. Seven Beginnings. LC 75-44496. (Human Torch Ser.: 2nd). (Illus.). 1976. 5.95 (ISBN 0-937170-17-8). Home Mission.

Knight, Walter B. Knight's Master Book of New Illustrations. 1956. pap. 13.95 (ISBN 0-8028-1699-1). Eerdmans.

Knight, Walter W. How to Publish a Church Newsletter. LC 83-70372. (Orig.). 1983. pap. 6.95 (ISBN 0-8054-3108-X). Broadman.

Knight, William, ed. The Poets on Christmas. Repr. of 1907 ed. lib. bdg. 25.00 (ISBN 0-8495-3016-4). Arden Lib.

Knights of Malta. The Rule Statutes & Customs of the Hospitallers, 1099-1310. LC 78-63347. (The Crusades & Military Orders: Second Ser.). 272p. Repr. of 1934 ed. 29.00 (ISBN 0-404-16246-0). AMS Pr.

Kniker, Charles R. Teaching about Religion in the Public Schools. LC 84-62994. (Fastback Ser.: No. 224). 50p. (Orig.). 1985. pap. 0.90 (ISBN 0-87367-224-0). Phi Delta Kappa.

Knipping, John B. Iconography of the Counter Reformation in the Netherlands: Heaven on Earth, 2 vols. LC 73-85234. (Illus.). 539p. 1974. Set. text ed. 195.00x (Pub. by B De Graaf Netherlands). Coronet Bks.

Kniseley, S. Philip. Masses of Francesco Soriano: A Style-Critical Study. LC 67-22198. (University of Florida Humanities Monographs: No. 26). (Illus.). 1967. pap. 3.50 (ISBN 0-8130-0131-5). U Presses Fla.

Kniss, Lloy A. Practical Pointers for Training Your Child. 1975. pap. 2.75 (ISBN 0-87813-509-X). Christian Light.

Knitter, Paul F. No Other Name? A Critical Survey of Christian Attitudes Toward the World Religions. LC 84-16491. 304p. (Orig.). 1985. pap. 14.95 (ISBN 0-88344-347-3). Orbis Bks.

Knobel, Peter, ed. Gates of the Seasons: A Guide to the Jewish Year. 200p. 1983. pap. text ed. 9.95 (ISBN 0-916694-92-5). Central Conf.

Knoch, A. E. All in All. rev. ed. 222p. 1978. pap. text ed. 4.00 (ISBN 0-910424-74-8). Concordant.

--Concordant Commentary on the New Testament. rev. ed. 407p. 1968. 10.00 (ISBN 0-910424-48-9). Concordant.

--Concordant Studies in the Book of Daniel. rev. ed. 464p. 1968. 7.00 (ISBN 0-910424-52-7). Concordant.

--Concordant Studies in the Book of Daniel. rev. ed. 1968. pap. 4.00 (ISBN 0-910424-53-5). Concordant.

--The Mystery of the Gospel. 297p. 1976. pap. text ed. 4.00 (ISBN 0-910424-55-1). Concordant.

--The Problem of Evil & the Judgments of God. 351p. 1976. pap. text ed. 4.00 (ISBN 0-910424-59-4). Concordant.

Knoch, A E., compiled by. Concordant Greek Text. rev. ed. 735p. 1975. leather bdg. o.p. 25.00 (ISBN 0-910424-32-2); 12.00 (ISBN 0-910424-31-4). Concordant.

Knoch, A. E., compiled by. Concordant Literal New Testament. 624p. 1978. pap. text ed. 5.00 (ISBN 0-910424-09-8). Concordant.

--Concordant Literal New Testament with Keyword Concordance. 992p. 1983. text ed. 15.00 (ISBN 0-910424-14-4). Concordant.

Knoch, Adolph E. Spirit, Spirits & Spirituality. 157p. 1977. pap. text ed. 3.00 (ISBN 0-910424-69-1). Concordant.

Knoche, Grace F., ed. see De Purucker, G.

Knoche, Grace F., ed. see Ryan, Charles J.

Knoche, Keith. Beyond Knoche's Law. Phillips, ed. (Redwood Ser.). 96p. 1983. pap. 4.95 (ISBN 0-8163-0488-2). Pacific Pr Pub Assn.

--Knoche Writes Again. (Friendship Ser.). 64p. 1983. pap. 4.95 (ISBN 0-8163-0508-0). Pacific Pr Pub Assn.

--Side Trips. (FRD Ser.). 1985. pap. 4.95 (ISBN 0-8163-0596-X). Pacific Pr Pub Assn.

Knoche, Philip B. Has God Given You up? (Uplook Ser). 1970. pap. 0.99 (ISBN 0-8163-0257-X, 08165-3). Pacific Pr Pub Assn.

Knoche, Vikki. Parish the Thought. 1984. pap. 4.95 (ISBN 0-8163-0560-9). Pacific Pr Pub Assn.

Knoop, Anna, tr. see Meslier, Jean.

Knopp, Anna, tr. see Meslier, Jean.

Knopp, Josephine Z. The Trial of Judaism in Contemporary Jewish Writing. LC 74-18319. 164p. 1975. 15.95 (ISBN 0-252-00386-1). U of Ill Pr.

Knopp, Robert, ed. see Von Le Fort, Gertrud.

Knorozov, Yuri V. & Proskouriakoff, Tatiana, eds. Selected Chapters from the Writings of the Maya Indians. Coe, Sophie, tr. LC 70-38502. (Harvard University. Peabody Museum of Archaeology & Ethnology. Russian Translation Ser.: No. 4). Repr. of 1967 ed. 28.00 (ISBN 0-404-52647-0). AMS Pr.

Knorr, Dandi. The Blessing Is in the Doing. LC 83-70643. (Orig.). 1983. pap. 4.95 (ISBN 0-8054-6001-2). Broadman.

Knorr, Dandi D. A Spiritual Handbook for Women. 192p. 1984. 13.95 (ISBN 0-13-834796-4, Spec); pap. 6.95 (ISBN 0-13-834788-3). P-H.

--When the Answer Is No. 1985. pap. 4.95 (ISBN 0-8054-5801-8). Broadman.

Knott, John R., Jr. Milton's Pastoral Vision: An Approach to "Paradise Lost". LC 79-145576. 1971. text ed. 15.00x (ISBN 0-226-44846-0). U of Chicago Pr.

Knott, Kim. My Sweet Lord: The Hare Krishna Movement. 112p. 1986. pap. 11.95. Newcastle Pub.

--My Sweet Lord: The Hare Krishna Movement. LC 86-18810. 176p. 1986. lib. bdg. 19.95x (ISBN 0-8095-7023-8). Borgo Pr.

Knott, Ron. Trophies of Heaven. Wallace, Mary, ed. LC 86-26649. 160p. 1986. pap. 5.95 (ISBN 0-932581-06-4). Word Aflame.

Knowles, Andrew. The Crossroad Children's Bible. (Illus.). 448p. 1981. 12.95 (ISBN 0-8245-0138-1); pap. 7.95 (ISBN 0-8245-0473-9). Crossroad NY.

Knowles, David. Monastic Order in England. 2nd ed. 1963. 89.50 (ISBN 0-521-05479-6). Cambridge U Pr.

--Religious Orders in England. Incl. Vol. 1. The Old Orders. 1948. 57.50 (ISBN 0-521-05480-X); Vol. 2. End of the Middle Ages. 1955. 67.50 (ISBN 0-521-05481-8); pap. 22.95 (ISBN 0-521-29567-X); Vol. 3. The Tudor Age. Knowles, David. 1979. 72.50 (ISBN 0-521-05482-6); pap. 24.95 (ISBN 0-521-29568-8). Cambridge U Pr.

--Thomas Becket. LC 77-143785. 1971. 15.00x (ISBN 0-8047-0766-9). Stanford U Pr.

Knowles, David & Hadcock, R. Neville. Medieval Religious Houses, England & Wales. LC 72-181783. pap. 147.00 (ISBN 0-317-08419-4, 2016312). Bks Demand UMI.

Knowles, David & Obolensky, Dimitri. Christian Centuries, Vol. 2: Middle Ages. LC 63-22123. 628p. 1969. 22.95 (ISBN 0-8091-0276-5). Paulist Pr.

Knowles, David, ed. see St. Augustine.

Knowles, M. D. Archbishop Thomas Beckett: A Character Study. (Raleigh Lectures on History). 1970. pap. 2.25 (ISBN 0-85672-313-4, Pub. by British Acad). Longwood Pub Group.

Knowles, Richard T. Human Development & Human Possibility: Erikson in the Light of Heidegger. LC 85-20498. (Illus.). 224p. (Orig.). 1986. lib. bdg. 26.00 (ISBN 0-8191-4992-6); pap. text ed. 12.25 (ISBN 0-8191-4993-4). U Pr of Amer.

Knowles, Richard T. & McLean, George F., eds. Psychological Foundations of Moral Education & Character Development: An Integrated Theory of Moral Development. 374p. (Orig.). 1986. lib. bdg. 26.75 (ISBN 0-8191-5406-7, Pub. by The Council for Research in Values & Philosophy); pap. 14.50 (ISBN 0-8191-5407-5, Pub by The Council for Research in Values & Philosophy). U Pr of Amer.

Knowles, Victor. Thirteen Lessons in I & II Peter. (Bible Study Guide Ser.). 105p. (Orig.). pap. 2.95 (ISBN 0-89900-175-0). College Pr Pub.

--What the Bible Says about Angels & Demons. LC 86-71104. (What the Bible Says Ser.). 405p. 1986. 13.95 (ISBN 0-89900-252-8). College Pr Pub.

Knowles, Victoria, jt. auth. see Bunker, Dusty.

Knowlson, Thomas S. Origins of Popular Superstitions & Customs. LC 68-30946. 1968. Repr. of 1910 ed. 36.00x (ISBN 0-8103-3357-0). Gale.

Knowlton, Charles. Fruits of Philosophy. 58p. 1980. pap. 4.00 (ISBN 0-911826-16-5). Am Atheist.

Knowlton, Charles & Owen, Robert D. Birth Control & Morality in Nineteenth Century America: Two Discussions. (Family in America Ser.). 1972. cancelled (ISBN 0-405-03883-6, 13318). Ayer Co Pubs.

Knox, David B. The Lord's Supper from Wycliffe to Crammer. 75p. 1986. pap. 6.25 (ISBN 0-85364-379-2, Pub. by Paternoster UK). Attic Pr.

Knox, Edmund A. John Bunyan in Relation to His Times. 1928. lib. bdg. 12.50 (ISBN 0-8414-5598-8). Folcroft.

Knox, George W. The Development of Religion in Japan. LC 78-72456. Repr. of 1907 ed. 27.00 (ISBN 0-404-17325-X). AMS Pr.

Knox, Ian P. Above or Within? The Supernatural in Religious Education. LC 76-55589. 164p. (Orig.). 1977. pap. 10.95 (ISBN 0-89135-006-3). Religious Educ.

Knox, John. Chapters in a Life of Paul. rev., 2nd ed. Hare, Douglas R., ed. 192p. 1987. 29.95 (ISBN 0-86554-266-X, MUP/H227/P32); pap. 14.95 (ISBN 0-86554-281-3). Mercer Univ Pr.

--Humanity & Divinity of Christ. (Orig.). pap. 9.95 (ISBN 0-521-09414-3). Cambridge U Pr.

--Marcion & the New Testament. LC 78-63168. (Heresies of the Early Christian & Medieval Era: Second Ser.). Repr. of 1942 ed. 31.00 (ISBN 0-404-16183-9). AMS Pr.

--Works of John Knox, 6 Vols. Laing, David, ed. LC 67-35016. Repr. of 1864 ed. Set. 345.00 (ISBN 0-404-52880-5). AMS Pr.

Knox, Lloyd H., ed. A Faith to Grow by. 1977. pap. 2.95 (ISBN 0-89367-009-X). Light & Life.

Knox, Robert B. James Ussher, Archbishop of Armagh: 1581-1656. 205p. 1968. text ed. 17.50x (ISBN 0-7083-0061-8, Pub. by U of Wales). Humanities.

Knox, Ronald. The Pastoral Sermons. 1960. 12.50 (ISBN 0-8199-0823-1). Franciscan Herald.

Knox, Ronald A. Enthusiasm. 630p. 1983. pap. 14.95 (ISBN 0-87061-080-5). Chr Classics.

Knox, T. M., jt. auth. see Fordyce, C. J.

Knox, T. M., ed. see Hegel, G. W.

Knox, T. M., tr. see Hegel, G. W.

Knox, W. L. Some Hellenistic Elements in Primitive Christianity. (British Academy, London, Schweich Lectures on Biblical Archaeology Series, 1942). pap. 19.00 (ISBN 0-8115-1284-3). Kraus Repr.

Knox, Wilfred L. The Catholic Movement in the Church of England. 1979. Repr. of 1923 ed. lib. bdg. 30.00 (ISBN 0-8495-3029-6). Arden Lib.

--The Catholic Movement in the Church of England. 1925. 15.00 (ISBN 0-8414-5599-6). Folcroft.

Knudsen, Harald. Gottesbeweise im Deutschen Idealismus: Die modaltheoretische Begruendung des Absoluten, dargestellt an Kant, Hegel und Weisse. (Theologische Bibliothek Toepelmann 23). vi, 280p. 1972. 31.60x (ISBN 3-11-003787-4). De Gruyter.

Knudsen, Johannes. The Formation of the Lutheran Church in America. LC 77-15235. pap. 31.50 (2026956). Bks Demand UMI.

Knudsen, Johannes, ed. N. F. S. Grundtvig: Selected Writings. LC 76-7873. 192p. 1976. pap. 1.50 (ISBN 0-8006-1238-8, 1-1238). Fortress.

Knudsen, Raymond B. Developing Dynamic Stewardship: Fifteen Sermons on Commitment & Giving. LC 78-7846. 1978. pap. 5.50 (ISBN 0-687-10500-5). Abingdon.

--Models for Ministry: Creative Administration in the Local Church. (Orig.). 1978. pap. 5.95 (ISBN 0-377-00082-5). Friend Pr.

--New Models for Financing the Local Church. 2nd ed. 157p. 1985. pap. 8.95 (ISBN 0-8192-1369-1). Morehouse.

--Stewardship Enlistment & Commitment. 130p. 1985. pap. 8.95 (ISBN 0-8192-1371-3). Morehouse.

Knudson, Albert C. Philosophy of Personalism: A Study in the Metaphysics of Religion. LC 27-21477. 1968. Repr. of 1927 ed. 26.00 (ISBN 0-527-51600-7). Kraus Repr.

Knutson, Gerhard. Ministry to Inactives: A Manual for Establishing a Listening Witness to Inactive Members. 40p. (Orig.). 1983. pap. 3.95 (ISBN 0-8066-1729-2, 10-4443). Augsburg.

Koberlein, Jean. A Spiritual Encounter with the Holy One. LC 84-8938. (Mellen Lives Ser.: Vol. 2). 200p. 1984. pap. 9.95x (ISBN 0-88946-012-4). E Mellen.

Kobler, Franz. Letters of Jews Through the Ages, Vol. 2. 1978. pap. 7.95 (ISBN 0-85222-213-0, East & West Lib). Hebrew Pub.

Kobler, Franz, ed. Letters of Jews Through the Ages, Vol. 1. 1978. pap. 7.95 (ISBN 0-85222-212-2, East & West Lib). Hebrew Pub.

Kobler, John F. Vatican II & Phenomenology. 1986. lib. bdg. 37.50 (ISBN 90-247-3193-3, Pub. by Martinus Nijhoff Netherlands). Kluwer-Academic.

Koblik, Steven. The Stones Cry Out: Sweden's Response to Persecution of the Jews 1933-1945. 1987. 20.95 (ISBN 0-89604-118-2); pap. 13.95 (ISBN 0-89604-119-0). Holocaust Pubns.

Kobobel, Janet. The Family Covenant: Leaders Manual. 35p. 1984. tchr's ed. 10.95 (ISBN 0-89191-892-2). Cook.

Kobobel, Janet, ed. see Bush, Barbara.

Kobobel, Janet, ed. see Fromer, Margaret & Fromer, Paul.

Kobobel, Janet, ed. see Richards, Larry.

Kocache, R., tr. The Journey of the Soul: The Story of Hai bin Yaqzan. 1982. 11.95 (ISBN 0-900860-90-1, Pub. by Octagon Pr England). Ins Study Human.

Koch, Carl, jt. auth. see Pluth, Alphonsus.

Koch, Dietrich-Alex. Die Bedeutung der Wundererzaehlungen fuer die Christologie des Markusevangeliums. (Beiheft 42 zur Zeitschrift fuer die neutestamentliche Wissenschaft Ser.). 217p. 1975. 44.40x (ISBN 3-11-004783-7). De Gruyter.

Koch, Klaus. The Book of Books: The Growth of the Bible. LC 69-12299. 192p. 1969. pap. 2.65 (ISBN 0-664-24840-3). Westminster.

--Growth of the Biblical Tradition. 1968. lib. bdg. 24.50x (ISBN 0-684-14524-3, ScribT). Scribner.

--The Prophets, Volume One. Kohl, Margaret, tr. from Ger. LC 79-8894. 224p. 1982. pap. 10.95 (ISBN 0-8006-1648-0, 1-1648). Vol. 1, The Assyrian Age. Fortress.

--The Prophets, Volume Two: The Babylonian & Persian Period. LC 79-8894. 224p. 1984. pap. 10.95 (ISBN 0-8006-1756-8, 1-1756). Fortress.

Koch, Kurt E. The Coming One. LC 72-85597. 96p. 1974. pap. 2.95 (ISBN 0-8254-3011-9). Kregel.

--Darkness or Light. 80p. 1981. pap. 2.95 (ISBN 0-8254-3048-8). Kregel.

--God among the Zulus. 336p. 1981. pap. 4.95 (ISBN 0-8254-3046-1). Kregel.

--Revival Fires in Canada. LC 72-93352. 96p. 1975. pap. 2.95 (ISBN 0-8254-3015-1). Kregel.

--World Without Chance. LC 72-85598. 96p. 1974. pap. 2.95 (ISBN 0-8254-3012-7). Kregel.

Koch, Sr. M. Pierre. Analysis of the Long Prayers in Old French Literature with Special Reference to the Biblical Creed Narrative Prayers. LC 70-94168. (Catholic University of America Studies in Romance Languages & Literatures Ser: No. 19). Repr. of 1940 ed. 24.00 (ISBN 0-404-50319-5). AMS Pr.

Koch, Martha & Koch, Roy. My Personal Pentecost. LC 77-79229. 296p. 1977. pap. 4.95 (ISBN 0-8361-1816-2). Herald Pr.

Koch, R. Riddle of Genesis. pap. 0.75 (ISBN 0-8199-0395-7). Franciscan Herald.

Koch, Ron. Goodbye, Grandpa. LC 74-14183. 96p. 1975. pap. 4.95 (ISBN 0-8066-1465-X, 10-2816). Augsburg.

Koch, Roy, jt. auth. see Koch, Martha.

Kochan, Lionel. The Jew & His History. (Scholars Press Reprints & Translations: No. 1). 1985. pap. 8.25 (ISBN 0-89130-821-0, 00 07 06). Scholars Pr GA.

Kochan, Lionel, ed. The Jews in Soviet Russia Since 1917. 3rd ed. (Illus.). 1978. pap. 9.95 (ISBN 0-19-281199-1). Oxford U Pr.

Kochan, Miriam, tr. see Poliakov, Leon.

Kocher, Paul. Alabado, a Story of Old California. 1978. 6.95 (ISBN 0-8199-0689-1). Franciscan Herald.

Kock, Ernst A. Benedictus, Saint: Abbot of Monte Cassino. (EETS, OS Ser.: No. 120). (Three Middle-English Versions of the Rule of St. Benet). Repr. of 1902 ed. 50.00 (ISBN 0-527-00118-X). Kraus Repr.

Kodell, Jerome. The Catholic Bible Study Handbook: A Popular Introduction to Studying Scripture. 266p. (Orig.). 1985. pap. 7.95 (ISBN 0-89283-185-5). Servant.

--The Gospel According to Luke, No. 3. Karris, Robert J., ed. LC 82-20350. (Collegeville Bible Commentary Ser.). (Illus.). 128p. 1983. pap. 2.95 (ISBN 0-8146-1303-9). Liturgical Pr.

--Lamentations, Haggai, Zechariah, Second Zechariah, Malachi, Obadiah, Joel, Baruch. (Old Testament Ser.: Vol. 14). 1982. 12.95 (ISBN 0-89453-414-9); pap. 8.95 (ISBN 0-89453-248-0). M Glazier.

Kodjak, Andreij. A Structural Analysis of the Sermon on the Mount. (Religion & Reasons Ser.: No. 34). (Illus.). x, 234p. 1986. lib. bdg. 54.50x (ISBN 0-89925-159-5). Mouton.

Koeblitz, Roy E. The Psalms: A New Version. LC 85-63357. 208p. 1986. 12.95 (ISBN 0-936187-11-5). Palm Pub Co.

Koebner, Richard, ed. Studies in Classics & Jewish Hellenism. (Scripts Hierosolymitana Ser.: Vol. 1). pap. 39.00 (ISBN 0-317-28711-7, 2051594). Bks Demand UMI.

Koehler, Alfred W. Light from Above. 1960. 3.95 (ISBN 0-570-03506-6, 14-1260). Concordia.

Koehler, George E. Visiting Two-by-Two: Visitor's Guide. LC 86-70579. 72p. (Orig.). 1986. 2.95 (ISBN 0-88177-034-5, DR034B). Discipleship Res.

Koehler, J. The Epistle of Paul to the Galatians. Sauer, E. E., tr. 1957. 2.95 (ISBN 0-8100-0038-5, 15N0315). Northwest Pub.

Koehler, Ludwig & Baumgartner, Walter. Lexicon in Veteris Testamenti Libros: Hebrew-Aramaic Lexicon, Incl. Supplement. (Hebrew & Aramaic.). 1951-53. 49.50x (ISBN 0-8028-2176-6). Eerdmans.

Koehler, Lugmilla. Svjatoj Ioann (Pommer) Arkiepiskop Rihskij i Latvijskij. Tr. of St. John (Pommer) Archbishop of Riga & Latvia. (Illus.). 72p. 1985. pap. 3.00 (ISBN 0-317-29224-2). Holy Trinity.

Koehler, Walter J. Counseling & Confession. 1982. pap. 7.50 (ISBN 0-570-03849-9, 12-2804). Concordia.

Koehn, Ilse. Mischling, Second Degree: My Childhood in Nazi Germany. LC 77-6189. 240p. 1977. 13.00 (ISBN 0-688-80110-2); PLB 12.88 (ISBN 0-688-84110-4). Greenwillow.

Koenen, Ludwig, ed. see Alexander of Lycopolis.

Koenig, F. Are You Really... Formed? pap. 0.60 (ISBN 0-88172-111-5). Believers Bkshelf.

Koenig, John. Charismata: God's Gift for God's People. LC 77-12700. (Biblical Perspectives on Current Issues). 214p. 1978. softcover 5.95 (ISBN 0-664-24176-X). Westminster.

--Jews & Christians in Dialogue: New Testament Foundations. LC 79-17583. 188p. 1979. pap. 8.95 (ISBN 0-664-24280-4). Westminster.

--New Testament Hospitality: Partnership with Strangers As Promise & Mission. LC 85-47725. (Overtures to Biblical Theology Ser.). 176p. 1985. pap. 9.95 (ISBN 0-8006-1543-3, 1-1543). Fortress.

--Stories to Learn by. (Illus.). 5.00 (ISBN 0-8198-0333-2); pap. 4.00 (ISBN 0-8198-0334-0). Dghtrs St Paul.

Koenig, Norma E. Ventures in Leisure-Time Christian Education. (Orig.). 1979. pap. 4.15 (ISBN 0-687-43670-2). Abingdon.

Koenig, Thomas R., ed. An Introduction to Ethics: A Philosophical Orientation. 187p. 1974. pap. text ed. 8.95x (ISBN 0-8422-0444-X). Irvington.

Koenig, William J., jt. auth. see Trager, Frank N.

Koepke, Fred T. How to Be Sure of Immortality. 1985. 6.95 (ISBN 0-533-06491-0). Vantage.

Koeppel, Josephine, tr. from Ger. Edith Stein: Life in a Jewish Family. LC 84-25164. (Illus.). 576p. (Orig.). 1986. pap. 10.95x (ISBN 0-935216-04-9). ICS Pubns.

Koerbel, Pam. Abortion's Second Victim. 204p. 1986. pap. 6.95 (ISBN 0-89693-177-3). Victor Bks.

Koerber, Hildegard Von see Lorber, Jakob.

Koers, Shirley. The Eyes Are Sunlight: A Journey Through Grief. LC 86-82036. 200p. (Orig.). 1986. pap. 4.95 (ISBN 0-87793-345-6). Ave Maria.

Koester, Camilla. Into This Land: Centennial History of the Cleveland Poor Clare Monastery of the Blessed Sacrament. LC 80-83390. (Illus.). 274p. 1981. 8.95 (ISBN 0-934906-28-9). R J Liederbach.

Koester, Helmut. Introduction to the New Testament. 1982. Vol. 1: History, Culture, & Religion of the Hellenistic Age. 24.95 (ISBN 0-89925-198-6); Vol. 2: History & Literature of Early Christianity. 22.95 (ISBN 0-89925-199-4). De Gruyter.

Koester, Helmut, jt. auth. see Robinson, James M.

Koester, Helmut, ed. see Dibelius, Martin.

Koester, Helmut, ed. see Dibelius, Martin & Conzelmann, Hans.

Koester, Helmut, ed. see Lohse, Eduard.

Koestler, Arthur. The God That Failed. Crossman, Richard H., ed. LC 81-85867. 1982. pap. 7.50 (ISBN 0-89526-867-1). Regnery Bks.

Koffarnus, Richard. Why Believe? LC 80-53673. 96p. (Orig.). 1981. pap. 2.25 (ISBN 0-87239-425-5, 40090). Standard Pub.

Koffarnus, Richard, et al. Good Stuff, No. 3. (Illus.). 160p. 1986. wkbk. 9.95 (ISBN 0-87403-066-8, 3411). Standard Pub.

Koghbatsi, Yeznik. Refutation of the Sects. Samuelian, Thomas J., ed. (Armenian Church Classics Ser.). (Illus.). 1986. pap. write for info (ISBN 0-934728-13-5). D O A C.

Kogon, Eugen, et al, eds. Zyklon B: Nazi Mass Murder by Poison Gas. 1987. 19.95 (ISBN 0-89604-110-7); pap. 13.95 (ISBN 0-89604-111-5). Holocaust Pubns.

Kogos, Fred. One Thousand One Yiddish Proverbs. 1970. 5.95 (ISBN 0-8065-0013-1). Citadel Pr.

--One Thousand One Yiddish Proverbs. 160p. 1974. pap. 3.95 (ISBN 0-8065-0455-2). Citadel Pr.

Kohanski, Alexander. Martin Buber's Philosophy of Interhuman Relation. LC 80-70626. 300p. 1981. 28.50 (ISBN 0-8386-3085-5). Fairleigh Dickinson.

Kohl, H., tr. see Otto Bishop of Freising.

Kohl, Horst, tr. see Otto, Von St. Blasien.

Kohl, Margaret, tr. see Koch, Klaus.

Kohl, Margaret, tr. see Marxsen, Willi.

Kohl, Margaret, tr. see Moltmann, Jurgen.

Kohl, Margaret, tr. see Soelle, Dorothee.

Kohl, Margaret, tr. see Von Der Osten-Sacken, Peter.

Kohl, Margaret, tr. see Wolf, Hans W.

Kohl, Margaret, tr. see Wolff, Hans W.

Kohl, Rachel & Rodda, Dorothy. Church & Synagogue Library Resources. 4th ed. LC 75-1178. 1984. pap. 3.95x (ISBN 0-915324-08-3); pap. 3.00 members. CSLA.

Kohlberg, Lawrence, jt. auth. see Colby, Anne.

Kohlenberger, John, III. NIV Interlinear Hebrew-English Old Testament: Isaiah-Malachi, Vol. 4. 640p. 1985. 24.95 (ISBN 0-310-44210-9, 6283). Zondervan.

Kohlenberger, John P., jt. auth. see Goodrick, Edward W.

Kohlenberger, John R. All about Bibles. (Illus.). 76p. 1985. pap. 0.95 (ISBN 0-19-526951-9). Oxford U Pr.

Kohlenberger, John R., III. Books about the Book: A Guide to Biblical Reference Works. 272p. 1986. pap. 10.95 (ISBN 0-310-39341-8). Zondervan.

--Jonah-Nahum. (Everyman's Bible Commentary Ser.). (Orig.). 1984. pap. 5.95 (ISBN 0-8024-0352-2). Moody.

--The NIV Interlinear Hebrew-English Old Testament. 544p. 1980. Vol. 1. 24.95 (ISBN 0-310-38880-5, 6280); Vol. 2. 24.95 (ISBN 0-310-38890-2, 6281); Vol. 3. 24.95 (ISBN 0-310-44200-1, 6282). Zondervan.

--The NIV Interlinear Hebrew-English Old Testament: Genesis-Malachi, 4 vols. 1985. Set. text ed. 95.80 (ISBN 0-310-38948-8, 6284). Zondervan.

--Read Through the Bible in a Year. (Orig.). 1986. pap. 1.95 (ISBN 0-8024-7168-4). Moody.

--Words about the Word: A Guide to Choosing & Using Your Bible. 176p. 1986. pap. 9.95 (ISBN 0-310-39361-2, 6287P). Zondervan.

Kohlenberger, John R., III, jt. auth. see Goodrick, Edward W.

Kohler, Christine. Help Me: I'm Lost. (Growing up Christian Ser.). 24p. (Orig.). 1985. pap. 3.95 (ISBN 0-570-04115-5, 56-1526). Concordia.

--I Help the Handicapped. (Growing Up Christian Ser.). 24p. (Orig.). 1985. pap. 3.95 (ISBN 0-570-04114-7, 56-1525). Concordia.

--Jesus Makes Me Well. (Growing up Christian Ser.). (Illus.). 24p. (Orig.). 1985. pap. 3.95 (ISBN 0-570-04113-9, 56-1524). Concordia.

Kohler, Kaufmann. Heaven & Hell in Comparative Religion. 1923. 25.00 (ISBN 0-8414-5601-1). Folcroft.

--The Origins of the Synagogue & the Church. Enelow, H. G., ed. LC 73-2213. (The Jewish People; History, Religion, Literature Ser.). Repr. of 1929 ed. 24.50 (ISBN 0-405-05277-4). Ayer Co Pubs.

Kohler, Mary C. Young People Learning to Care: Making a Difference through Youth Participation. 160p. 1983. pap. 7.95 (ISBN 0-8164-2429-2, HarpR). Har-Row.

Kohler, Walther. Zwingli und Luther, Ihr Streit uber das Abendmahl nach Seinen Politischen und Religiosen Beziehung En. (Ger). 61.00 (ISBN 0-384-30019-7); pap. 55.00 (ISBN 0-384-30018-9). Johnson Repr.

Kohli, S. S. Critical Study of Adigranth. 1976. Repr. 12.50 (ISBN 0-89684-038-7). Orient Bk Dist.

Kohmescher, Matthew F. Catholicism Today: A Survey of Catholic Belief & Practice. LC 80-82085. 216p. (Orig.). 1980. pap. 4.95 (ISBN 0-8091-2335-5). Paulist Pr.

--Good Morality Is Like Good Cooking... & Other Suggestions for Right Living. 112p. (Orig.). 1987. pap. 4.95 (ISBN 0-8091-2856-X). Paulist Pr.

Kohn, Eugene. Good to Be a Jew. LC 59-13350. 180p. 1959. pap. 8.95 (ISBN 0-935457-23-2). Reconstructionist Pr.

--Religious Humanism. LC 53-10661. 154p. 1953. pap. 8.95 (ISBN 0-935457-24-0). Reconstructionist Pr.

Kohn, Eugene, ed. Festival Prayerbook. LC 57-13301. 547p. 1958. 10.00 (ISBN 0-935457-28-3). Reconstructionist Pr.

Kohn, Eugene, jt. ed. see Eisenstein, Ira.

Kohn, Eugene, jt. ed. see Kaplan, Mordecai M.

Kohn, Gary J. The Jewish Experience: A Guide to Manuscript Sources in the Library of Congress. (Monographs of the American Jewish Archives). 250p. 1986. text ed. write for info. (ISBN 0-87820-014-2, Pub. by Am Jewish Archives). Ktav.

Kohn, Moshe, tr. see Friedling, Sheila.

Kohn, Nahum & Roiter, Howard. A Voice from the Forest. LC 80-81685. (Illus.). 256p. (Orig.). 1985. 16.95 (ISBN 0-89604-020-8); pap. 10.95 (ISBN 0-89604-021-6). Holocaust Pubns.

--A Voice from the Forest: Memoirs of a Jewish Partisan. (Illus.). 288p. pap. 5.95 (ISBN 0-686-95099-2). ADL.

Kohn, Richard. The Church in a Democracy. McKenna, Constance, ed. (Illus.). 23p. 1981. pap. 1.00 (ISBN 0-915365-03-0). Cath Free Choice.

Kohn, Zwi H. Ginzei Droshos V'rayons, Treasures of Ideas & Thoughts: Sermons in Yiddish Language for All Holidays, Memorials, Eulogies, Installations, & for All Other Occasions. 416p. 27.50 (ISBN 0-87559-149-3). Shalom.

Kohner, Hanna, et al. Hanna & Walter. 224p. 1985. pap. 3.50 (ISBN 0-445-20109-6, Popular Lib). Warner Bks.

Kohut, George A., ed. A Hebrew Anthology: A Collection of Poems & Dramas Inspired by the Old Testament & Post Biblical Tradition Gathered from Writings of English Poets, from the Elizabethan Period & Earlier to the Present Day, 2 vols. 1399p. Repr. of 1913 ed. Set. lib. bdg. 250.00 (ISBN 0-918377-86-2). Russell Pr.

Koilparampil, George. Caste in the Catholic Community in Kerala. 289p. 1986. 14.50X (Pub. by Macmillan India). South Asia Bks.

Kok, J. H., tr. see Jagersma, Henk.

Kokosalakis, N. Ethnic Identity & Religion: Tradition & Change in Liverpool Jewry. LC 82-13609. (Illus.). 276p. 1983. lib. bdg. 29.75 (ISBN 0-8191-2732-9); pap. text ed. 13.25 (ISBN 0-8191-2733-7). U Pr of Amer.

Kolakowski, Leszek. Religion. LC 81-85135. 1982. 22.50x (ISBN 0-19-520372-0). Oxford U Pr.

--Religion: If There Is No God.. On God, the Devil, Sin & Other Worries of the So-Called Philosophy of Religion. Kermode, Frank, ed. 1982. pap. 7.95 (ISBN 0-19-520429-8). Oxford U Pr.

Kolatch, A. J. The Jewish Book of Why's. 1985. gift set 28.95 (ISBN 0-8246-0314-1). Jonathan David.

--The Second Jewish Book of Why. LC 84-21477. 432p. 1985. 13.95 (ISBN 0-8246-0305-2). Jonathan David.

Kolatch, Alfred J. Family Seder. rev. ed. LC 67-17778. (Illus.). 1972. pap. 3.95 (ISBN 0-8246-0132-7). Jonathan David.

--Fun-In-Learning about Passover. LC 74-175489. (Illus.). 1972. pap. 3.95 (ISBN 0-8246-0133-5). Jonathan David.

--The Jewish Book of Why. 1981. 12.95 (ISBN 0-8246-0256-0). Jonathan David.

--Sermons for the Seventies. LC 75-164518. 1971. 7.95x (ISBN 0-8246-0122-X). Jonathan David.

--Who's Who in the Talmud. rev. ed. LC 64-24891. 228p. 1981. Repr. 9.95 (ISBN 0-8246-0263-3). Jonathan David.

Kolatch, Jonathan, tr. see Ben-Gurion, David.

Kolb, David. The Critique of Pure Modernity: Hegel, Heidegger, & After. LC 85-24510. 334p. 1987. lib. bdg. 25.00 (ISBN 0-226-45031-7). U of Chicago Pr.

Kolb, Erwin. A Prayer Primer. 1982. pap. 4.25 (ISBN 0-570-03843-X, 12-2946). Concordia.

Kolb, Erwin J. Witness Primer. 128p. (Orig.). 1986. pap. 4.95 (ISBN 0-570-04441-3). Concordia.

Kolb, R. & Lumpp, D. Martin Luther: Companion of the Contemporary Christian. LC 12-2959. 1982. pap. 9.95 (ISBN 0-570-03866-9). Concordia.

Kolb, Robert. Andreae & the Formula of Concord. 1977. pap. 8.50 (ISBN 0-570-03741-7, 12-2645). Concordia.

--For All the Saints: Changing Perceptions of Martyrdom & Sainthood in the Lutheran Reformation. (Illus.). 192p. 1987. 29.95 (ISBN 0-86554-270-8, H233). Mercer Univ Pr.

Kolb, Robert A. Speaking the Gospel Today: A Theology for Evangelism. 1984. 16.95 (ISBN 0-570-04205-4, 15-2173). Concordia.

Kolbrek, Loyal. The Day God Made It Rain. (Arch Books Series Fourteen). 1977. pap. 0.99 (ISBN 0-570-06108-3, 59-1226). Concordia.

--Paul Believes in Jesus. (Illus.). 24p. 1987. pap. 00.99 (ISBN 0-570-09008-3, 59-1436). Concordia.

Kolbrek, Loyal & Larsen, Chris. Samson's Secret. (Arch Bks.: Set 8). (Orig.). 1970. pap. 0.99 (ISBN 0-570-06052-4, 59-1168). Concordia.

Kolden, Marc. Called by the Gospel: An Introduction ot the Christian Faith. LC 82-72651. 112p. 1983. pap. 5.95 (ISBN 0-8066-1958-9, 10-0967). Augsburg.

Kole, Andre & Janssen, Al. Miracles or Magic? rev. ed. 1987. pap. 5.95 (ISBN 0-89081-579-8). Harvest Hse.

Kolenda, Konstantin. Philosophy in Literature: Metaphysical Darkness & Ethical Light. LC 81-7979. 250p. 1982. 28.75x (ISBN 0-389-20224-X). B&N Imports.

--Religion Without God. LC 76-19349. (Skeptic's Bookshelf Ser.). 125p. 1976. 13.95 (ISBN 0-87975-066-9). Prometheus Bks.

Kolig, Erich. Silent Revolution: The Effects of Modernization on Australian Aboriginal Religion. LC 81-6430. (Illus.). 224p. 1981. text ed. 27.50 (ISBN 0-89727-020-7). ISHI PA.

Kolitz, Zvi. Survival for What. LC 70-75761. 234p. 1969. 10.00 (ISBN 0-8022-2272-2). Philos Lib.

Kolk, Justin Vander see Vander Kolk, Justin.

Koll, Elsie. The Golden Thread: Diary of Mrs. Elsie Koll, Missionary to China. Scales, John L., ed. (Illus.). 180p. (Orig.). 1982. pap. 4.95 (ISBN 0-942504-00-3). Overcomer Pr.

Kollar, Nathan R. Songs of Suffering. 160p. (Orig.). 1982. pap. 7.95 (ISBN 0-86683-672-1, HarpR). Har-Row.

Kollar, Nathan R., ed. Options in Roman Catholicism: An Introduction. LC 82-21823. 224p. (Orig.). 1983. lib. bdg. 27.00 (ISBN 0-8191-2958-5); pap. text ed. 12.50 (ISBN 0-8191-2959-3). U Pr of Amer.

Koller, Carmeline. Walk in Love. 10.50 (ISBN 0-8199-0843-6). Franciscan Herald.

Koller, Charles W. Expository Preaching Without Notes Plus Sermons Preached Without Notes. 1962. 10.95 (ISBN 0-8010-5301-3). Baker Bk.

--Sermon Starters for Fifty-Two Sundays. 160p. (Orig.). 1982. pap. 6.95 (ISBN 0-8010-5440-0). Baker Bk.

Kollstedt, Paula L. Surviving the Crisis of Motherhood: Strategies for Caring for Your Child & Yourself. (Illus.). 117p. 1981. pap. 3.50 (ISBN 0-912228-91-1). St Anthony Mess Pr.

Kolmer, Elizabeth. Religious Women in the United States: A Survey of the Literature from 1950 to 1983. (Consecrated Life Studies Ser.: Vol. 4). 1984. pap. 6.95 (ISBN 0-89453-445-9). M Glazier.

Kolnai, Aurel. Ethics, Value, & Reality: Selected Papers of Aurel Kolnai. LC 77-83145. 280p. 1978. 25.00 (ISBN 0-915144-39-5); pap. text ed. 15.00 cancelled (ISBN 0-915144-40-9). Hackett Pub.

Kolsti, Arthur H. The Lion Roars. 1985. 4.95 (ISBN 0-89536-720-3, 5804). CSS of Ohio.

Kolstoe, John E. Consultation: A Universal Lamp of Guidance. 208p. 1985. 13.95 (ISBN 0-85398-186-8); pap. 7.95 (ISBN 0-85398-187-6). G Ronald Pub.

Kolten, Diana Van see Van Kolken, Diana.

Koltun, Elizabeth, ed. The Jewish Woman: New Perspectives. LC 75-35445. 320p. 1976. pap. 7.95 (ISBN 0-8052-0532-2). Schocken.

Koltuv, Barbara B. The Book of Lilith. (Illus.). 142p. (Orig.). 1986. pap. 9.95 (ISBN 0-89254-014-1). Nicolas-Hays.

Kolve, V. A. Play Called Corpus Christi. LC 66-15301. 1966. 27.50x (ISBN 0-8047-0277-2); pap. 8.95 (ISBN 0-8047-0278-0, SP126). Stanford U Pr.

Komensky, John A. Labyrinth of the World & the Paradise of the Heart. LC 73-135812. (Eastern Europe Collection Ser). 1970. Repr. of 1901 ed. 22.00 (ISBN 0-405-02754-0). Ayer Co Pubs.

Kommers, Donald P. & Loescher, Gilburt D., eds. Human Rights & American Foreign Policy. LC 78-62966. 1979. pap. text ed. 9.95 (ISBN 0-268-01075-7). U of Notre Dame Pr.

Kon, Abraham. Prayer. 12.95x (ISBN 0-900689-05-6). Bloch.

--Prayer. 277p. 1971. 9.95 (ISBN 0-900689-05-6). Soncino Pr.

Kongtrul, Jamgon. The Torch of Certainty. Hanson, Judith, tr. from Tibetan. LC 86-11835. 184p. 1986. pap. 12.95 (ISBN 0-87773-380-5). Shambhala Pubns.

Konieczny, Stanley, ed. The Hands & Feet of Christ. 1987. pap. 1.50 (ISBN 0-8189-0515-8). Alba.

Konig. Diccionario De las Religiones. (Span.). 816p. 1977. 37.50 (ISBN 84-254-0358-8, S-50201). French & Eur.

Konig, Adrio. Here Am I! A Christian Reflection on God. LC 82-11377. pap. 62.00 (ISBN 0-317-30148-9, 2025331). Bks Demand UMI.

Konig, David T. Law & Society in Puritan Massachusetts: Essex County, 1629-1692. xxi, 215p. 1981. pap. 9.95x (ISBN 0-8078-4081-5). U of NC Pr.

Konig, Karl. Brothers & Sisters. 96p. 1984. pap. 7.95 (ISBN 0-88010-112-1). Anthroposophic.

Koning, Frederick. Diccionario de Demonologia. 3rd ed. (Span.). 1978. pap. 2.95 (ISBN 0-686-57362-5, S-50155). French & Eur.

Konkel, Wilbur. Living Hymn Stories. 128p. 1982. pap. 3.95 (ISBN 0-87123-317-7, 210317). Bethany Hse.

Konopka, Coles, et al. Function of Rebellion: Is Youth Creating New Family Values? LC 66-17843. 1968. pap. 2.85 (ISBN 0-686-25738-3). Jewish Bd Family.

Konrady, Marlene. The Jesse Tree: A Cutout Book. (The Learning Connections Ser.). 48p. (Orig.). 1984. pap. 8.95 (ISBN 0-86683-830-9, 8439, HarpR). Har-Row.

Konstant, David. Treasured Catholic Prayers & Devotions. 1987. pap. 4.95 (ISBN 0-89622-312-4). Twenty-Third.

Kontoglou, Photios. Byzantine Sacred Art. 2nd, rev. & enl. ed. Cavarnos, Constantine, compiled by. & tr. from Gr. LC 83-81152. (Illus.). 171p. 1985. 10.50 (ISBN 0-914744-60-7); pap. 7.95 (ISBN 0-914744-61-5). Inst Byzantine.

Kontsevich, I. M. Optina Pustin' i jeja vremja. Tr. of Optina Hermitage & It's Time. (Illus.). 604p. 1970. 25.00 (ISBN 0-317-29246-3); pap. 20.00 (ISBN 0-317-29247-1). Holy Trinity.

Konvitz, Milton R. Judaism & the American Idea. LC 78-58028. 265p. 1978. 19.50x (ISBN 0-8014-1181-5). Cornell U Pr.

Koop, Allen V. American Evangelical Missionaries in France, 1945-1975. (Illus.). 220p. (Orig.). 1986. lib. bdg. 27.00 (ISBN 0-8191-5204-8); pap. text ed. 13.50 (ISBN 0-8191-5205-6). U Pr of Amer.

Koop, C. E. To Live or Die: Facing Decisions at the End of Life. (Christian Essentials Ser.). 48p. 1987. pap. 1.95 (ISBN 0-89283-322-X). Servant.

Koop, C. Everett. The Right to Live: the Right to Die. 1980. pap. 3.95 (ISBN 0-8423-5594-4). Tyndale.

Koop, C. Everett & Schaeffer, Francis A. Whatever Happened to the Human Race? LC 83-70955. 168p. 1983. pap. 7.95 (ISBN 0-89107-291-8, Crossway Bks). Good News.

Koopman, LeRoy. Scriptural Worship Aids. (Illus.). 1978. pap. 2.95 (ISBN 0-8010-5392-7). Baker Bk.

--Seasonal Sermon Outlines. (Sermon Outlines Ser.). 1979. pap. 2.50 (ISBN 0-8010-5405-2). Baker Bk.

--Twenty-Six Vital Issues. (Contemporary Discussion Ser.). 1978. pap. 2.45 (ISBN 0-8010-5398-6). Baker Bk.

Kopas, Jane, ed. Interpreting Tradition: The Art of Theological Reflection. (College Theology Society - Annual Publications Ser.). 1984. pap. 11.95 (ISBN 0-89130-621-8, 34 10 83). Scholars Pr GA.

Kopecek, Thomas A. A History of Neo-Arianism. LC 79-89557. (Patristic Monograph: No. 8). 1979. pap. 14.00 (ISBN 0-915646-07-2). Phila Patristic.

Kopeck. In the Shadow of the Flames: Six Lectures on the Holocaust. LC 82-72377. (Witness to the Holocaust Ser.: No. 4). 86p. 1982. 6.75. Witness Holocaust.

Kopf, Carl H. Windows on Life. facs. ed. LC 70-76908. (Essay Index Reprint Ser). 1941. 17.50 (ISBN 0-8369-1041-9). Ayer Co Pubs.

Kopin, Rita. The Lively Jewish Classroom: Games & Activities for Learning. (Illus.). 132p. 1980. pap. text ed. 8.75 (ISBN 0-86705-014-4). AIRE.

Koplik, William & Brady, Joan. Celebrating Forgiveness. LC 81-51994. 96p. 1981. pap. 9.95 (ISBN 0-89622-137-7). Twenty-Third.

Kopp, Herb, jt. auth. see Hiebert, Waldo.

Kopp, Richard L., jt. auth. see Fraser, Theodore P.

Kopp, Ruth & Sorenson, Stephen. When Someone You Love Is Dying: A Handbook for Counselors & Those Who Care. 2nd ed. 240p. 1985. pap. 8.95 (ISBN 0-310-41601-9, 11165P). Zondervan.

Kopp, Sheldon. The Way Out Is the Way In. 224p. Date not set. 13.95 (ISBN 0-87477-413-6). J P Tarcher.

Koppejan, Helene. Strange Parallel: Zebulun a Tribe of Israel. Rev. ed. LC 83-73689. (Illus.). 96p. 1984. pap. 4.00 (ISBN 0-934666-13-X). Artisan Sales.

Kopper, Philip, ed. & intro. by. A Christmas Testament. LC 82-5843. (Illus.). 144p. 1982. slipcased 25.00 (ISBN 0-941434-23-0). Stewart Tabori & Chang.

Koppman, Lionel & Postol, Bernard. Guess Who's Jewish in American History. 336p. 1986. pap. 7.95 (ISBN 0-933503-55-5). Shapolsky Pubs.

Koppman, Lionel, jt. auth. see Postal, Bernard.

Koralek, Jenny, tr. see Zuber, Rene.

Korczak, Janusz. Ghetto Diary. LC 77-91911. (Illus.). 192p. 1978. 16.95 (ISBN 0-89604-004-6); pap. 10.95 (ISBN 0-317-06362-6). Holocaust Pubns.

Korem, Danny & Meier, Paul. The Fakers: Exploding the Myths of the Supernatural. LC 80-23180. (Illus.). 1981. pap. 4.95 (ISBN 0-8010-5435-4). Baker Bk.

Koren, H. J., jt. auth. see Luijpen, William A.

Koren, Henry J. To the Ends of the Earth: A General History of the Congregation of the Holy Ghost. 656p. 1982. text ed. 18.50x (ISBN 0-8207-0157-2). Duquesne.

Koren, Nathan, ed. Jewish Physicians: A Biographical Index. 275p. 1973. 25.00 (ISBN 0-87855-184-0). Transaction Bks.

Korfker, Dena. Good Morning, Lord: Devotions for Children. (Good Morning Lord Ser.). 1973. 4.95 (ISBN 0-8010-5328-5). Baker Bk.

Kormos, Zsofia, tr. see Lukacs, Lajos.

Korn, Bertram. A Bicentennial Festschrift for Jacob Rader Marcus. 35.00x (ISBN 0-87068-457-4). Ktav.

Korn, Bertram W. American Jewry: The Formative Years. (Texts & Studies). (Hebrew.). 1971. 10.00 (ISBN 0-911934-04-9). Am Jewish Hist Soc.

Korn, Daniel, jt. auth. see Rietcheck, Robert.

Korn, Frank J. Country of the Spirit: Vatican City. (Illus.). 139p. 1982. pap. 7.00 (ISBN 0-8198-1415-6, MS0214). Dghtrs St Paul.

--From Peter to John Paul II. LC 80-65721. 300p. (Orig.). 1980. pap. 5.50 (ISBN 0-8189-1161-1, 161, Pub. by Alba Bks). Alba.

Korn, Yitshak. Jews at the Crossroads. LC 81-86479. 208p. 1983. 12.95 (ISBN 0-8453-4754-3, Cornwall Bks). Assoc Univ Prs.

Kornberg, Jacques, ed. At the Crossroads: Essays on Ahad Ha'am. (Modern Jewish History Ser.). 242p. 1983. 44.50 (ISBN 0-87395-738-5); pap. 14.95 (ISBN 0-87395-739-3). State U NY Pr.

Kornfield, Jack & Breiter, Paul. A Still Forest Pool. LC 85-40411. (Illus.). 225p. (Orig.). 1985. pap. 6.50 (ISBN 0-8356-0597-3, Quest). Theos Pub Hse.

Kors, Alan C. & Peters, Edward, eds. Witchcraft in Europe, 1100-1700: A Documentary History. LC 71-170267. (Illus.). 1972. pap. 13.95x (ISBN 0-8122-1063-8, Pa Paperbks). U of Pa pr.

Kort, Ann & Morschauer, Scott, eds. Biblical & Related Studies Related to Samuel Iwry. xvii, 274p. 1985. text ed. 25.00x (ISBN 0-931464-23-4). Eisenbrauns.

Kort, Kees De, illus. What the Bible Tells Us: A Series for Young Children. Incl. Jesus Is Born (ISBN 0-8066-1576-1, 10-3520); Jesus at the Wedding (ISBN 0-8066-1577-X, 10-3490); The Good Samaritan (ISBN 0-8066-1578-8, 10-2815); Jesus Is Alive (ISBN 0-8066-1579-6, 10-3518). (Illus.). 1977. pap. 2.95 ea. Augsburg.

Kort, Wesley A. Moral Fiber: Character & Belief in Recent American Fiction. LC 81-71389. 160p. 1982. pap. 1.00 (ISBN 0-8006-1624-3, 1-1624). Fortress.

--Narrative Elements & Religious Meanings. LC 75-15257. pap. 32.00 (2026873). Bks Demand UMI.

Kortals, Richard, jt. auth. see Foust, Paul.

Kortelling, Jacomina. Mysticism in Blake & Wordsworth. LC 68-2111. (Studies in Poetry, No. 38). 1969. Repr. of 1928 ed. lib. bdg. 39.95x (ISBN 0-8383-0577-6). Haskell.

Kortenhoeven, Helen, tr. see Oosterhouse, Kenneth, et al.

Korth, Bob, ed. Baptism. (Discipleship Booklets Ser.). (Illus., Orig.). 1984. pap. 0.95 (ISBN 0-87239-787-4, 1151). Standard Pub.

--Membership. (Discipleship Booklets Ser.). (Illus.). 1984. 0.95 (ISBN 0-87239-788-2, 1152). Standard Pub.

Korth, Bob, compiled by. Object Talks for Special Days. (Illus.). 48p. (Orig.). 1984. pap. 2.95 (ISBN 0-87239-723-8, 2859). Standard Pub.

--Object Talks on Christian Living. (Illus.). 48p. (Orig.). 1984. pap. 2.95 (ISBN 0-87239-724-6, 2860). Standard Pub.

--Object Talks on the Teachings of Jesus. (Illus.). 48p. (Orig.). 1984. pap. 2.95 (ISBN 0-87239-722-X, 2858). Standard Pub.

Korth, Bob, ed. see Matthews, Velda & Beard, Ray.

Korth, Robert, ed. Communion Meditations & Prayers. LC 81-16668. 128p. (Orig.). 1982. pap. 4.95 (ISBN 0-87239-483-2, 3032). Standard Pub.

Korth, Robert E., compiled by. Special Ministries for Caring Churches. 128p. 1986. pap. 5.95 (ISBN 0-87403-145-1, 3183). Standard Pub.

Korth, Russ & Wormser, Ron, Jr. Going up! rev. ed. 82p. 1980. pap. text ed. 5.00 (ISBN 0-934396-26-4). Churches Alive.

Korty, Margaret B. Audio-Visual Materials in the Church Library: How to Select, Catalog, Process, Store, Circulate & Promote. LC 77-74780. (Illus.). 102p. 1977. spiral bdg. 4.95 (ISBN 0-9603060-0-5). Church Lib.

--Bible Bits & Relevant Rhymes. LC 84-71870. 117p. 1984. spiral binding 5.95 (ISBN 0-9603060-1-3). Church Lib.

--God's Mundane World in Risible Rhyme. LC 86-72990. (Illus.). 135p. 1986. 6.95 (ISBN 0-9603060-2-1). Church Lib.

Kosicki, George W. The Good News of Suffering. LC 81-13644. 87p. (Orig.). 1981. pap. 1.95 (ISBN 0-8146-1240-7). Liturgical Pr.

Kosicki, George W. & Farrell, Gerald J. The Spirit & the Bride Say, "Come!". Mary's Role in the New Pentecost. 112p. pap. 3.95 (ISBN 0-911988-41-6). AMI Pr.

Koski, Marnie. Personal Talks with Jesus. (Orig.). 1979. pap. 4.95 (ISBN 0-917200-25-X). ESPress.

Kosovsky, Binyamin. Concordance of the Sifrei. 75.00x (ISBN 0-685-56222-0, Pub. by Jewish Theol Seminary). Ktav.

--Otzar Leshon Ha-Tannaim-Sifra-Tarat Kohanim, 4 vols. 1967. Set. 75.00x (ISBN 0-685-31426-X, Pub. by Jewish Theol Seminary). Ktav.

--Otzar Leshon Ho-Tannaim-Mekilta d'rabi Ishmael, 4 vols. 1965. Set. 75.00x (ISBN 0-685-31425-1, Pub. by Jewish Theol Seminary). Ktav.

Koss, Stephen. Nonconformity in Modern British Politics. LC 75-8646. 272p. 1975. 26.00 (ISBN 0-208-01553-1, Archon). Shoe String.

Kostelanetz, Richard. Reincarnations. 1981. pap. 5.00 (ISBN 0-686-84602-8); signed 50.00 (ISBN 0-686-84603-6). Future Pr.

Kostlin, Julius. Life of Luther. 1883. Repr. 50.00 (ISBN 0-8274-2894-4). R West.

Kostovski, Ilya. Goethe & Dostoyevsky: Two Devils, Two Geniuses, a Study of the Demonic in Their Work. 1974. lib. bdg. 69.95 (ISBN 0-87700-215-0). Revisionist Pr.

Kotb, Sayed. Social Justice in Islam. LC 75-96205. 1969. Repr. of 1953 ed. lib. bdg. 20.00x (ISBN 0-374-94617-5, Octagon). Hippocrene Bks.

Koteskey, Ronald L. General Psychology for Christian Counselors. 308p. (Orig.). 1983. pap. 11.95 (ISBN 0-687-14044-7). Abingdon.

--Understanding Adolescence. 168p. 1987. pap. 5.95 (ISBN 0-89693-249-4). Victor Bks.

Kotler, Yair. Heil Kahane: The Life of a Fanatic Whose Influence is Growing. Levin, Ed, tr. from Hebrew. LC 86-1035. 212p. 1986. 17.95 (ISBN 0-915361-35-3, 09712-9, Dist. by Watts). Adama Pubs Inc.

Kotrba, Danella G. God's Helper. (Come Unto Me Ser.: Year 2, Bk. 1). 32p. 1980. pap. 1.65 (ISBN 0-8127-0211-5). Review & Herald.

Kotre, John N. The Best of Times, the Worst of Times: Andrew Greeley & American Catholicism, 1950-1975. LC 78-14224. 256p. 1978. 21.95x (ISBN 0-88229-380-X). Nelson-Hall.

Kottak, Conrad, ed. see Brown, Diana D.

Kotter, Bonnie. Thank God for the Crumbs. Wheeler, Gerald, ed. (Banner Bks.). 96p. (Orig.). 1986. pap. 6.50 (ISBN 0-8280-0315-7). Review & Herald.

Kotter, P. Bonifatius, ed. Die Schriften des Johannes von Damaskos, Vol. 3: Contra imaginum columniatores orationes tres. (Patristische Texte und Studien: Vol. 17). (Ger. & Lat.). xvi, 224p. 1975. 51.20x (ISBN 3-11-005971-1). De Gruyter.

Kottmeyer, William A., et al. Greek & Roman Myths. 1962. pap. 7.96 (ISBN 0-07-033738-1). McGraw.

Kotwal, Firoze M. & Boyd, James W. A Guide to the Zoroastrian Religion: A Nineteenth-Century Catechism with Modern Commentary. LC 82-3236. (Harvard University - Center for the Study of World Religions Ser.). 1982. 18.75 (ISBN 0-89130-573-4, 03-00-03); pap. 12.50 (ISBN 0-89130-574-2). Scholars Pr GA.

Kotwal, Firoze M. & Boyd, James W., eds. Erbadistan ud Nirangistan: Facsimile Edition of the Manuscript TD. (Harvard Iranian Ser.: No. 3). 152p. 1981. text ed. 16.00x (ISBN 0-674-26040-6). Harvard U Pr.

Koulomzin, Sophie. Our Church & Our Children. LC 75-20215. 158p. 1975. pap. 6.95 (ISBN 0-913836-25-7). St Vladimirs.

Koung, Stephen, tr. see Nee, Watchman.

Kourdakov, Sergei. Persecutor. (Illus.). 256p. 1974. pap. 3.50 (ISBN 0-8007-8177-5, Spire Bks). Revell.

Koushiafes, Nicholas J. God. LC 81-90329. (Illus.). 300p. 1982. 25.00 (ISBN 0-9607228-0-7). Gods Universe.

Kousser, J. Morgan & McPherson, James M. Region, Race & Reconstruction: Essays in Honor of C. Vann Woodward. 1982. 25.00x (ISBN 0-19-503075-3). Oxford U Pr.

Kovach, Francis J., jt. auth. see Shahan, Robert W.

Kovach, Francis J. & Shahan, Robert W., eds. Albert the Great: Commemorative Essays. LC 79-6713. 250p. 1980. 16.95x (ISBN 0-8061-1666-8). U of Okla Pr.

Kovacs, Brian W., jt. ed. see Perdue, Leo G.

Kovalevsky, Pierre. St. Sergius & Russian Spirituality. LC 76-13018. (Illus.). 190p. 1976. 7.95 (ISBN 0-913836-24-9). St Vladimirs.

Kovats, Alexandra. Prayer: A Discovery of Life. (Nazareth Bks). 128p. 1983. pap. 4.95 (ISBN 0-86683-714-0, AY8361, HarpR). Har-Row.

Kowalczyk, John. An Orthodox View on Abortion. pap. 1.95 (ISBN 0-686-27070-3). Light&Life Pub Co MN.

Kowalski, Isaac. Anthology on Armed Jewish Resistance 1939-1945, Vol. 1. (Illus.). 648p. 1984. Repr. 30.00x. Jewish Com Pub.

--Anthology on Armed Jewish Resistance 1939-1945, Vol. 2. 648p. 1985. Repr. 30.00x (ISBN 0-317-46999-1). Jewish Com Pub.

--Anthology on Armed Jewish Resistance 1939-1945, Vol. 3. 648p. 1986. Repr. 30.00x (ISBN 0-317-47002-7). Jewish Com Pub.

Kowles, Richard V. Genetics, Society, & Decisions. 1985. Repr. text ed. write for info. (ISBN 0-673-18678-4). Scott F.

Kownacki, Mary L. & Clark, Carol. Let Peace Begin With Me: Teacher Manual. 1983. pap. 2.95 (ISBN 0-89622-185-7). Twenty-Third.

Kownacki, Mary L., jt. auth. see Chittister, Joan.

Kownacki, Mary Lou & Clark, Carol. Let Peace Begin With Me: Peace Book. 1983. pap. 1.00 (ISBN 0-89622-186-5). Twenty-Third.

Koyama, Kosuke. Fifty Meditations. LC 77-7026. (Illus.). 191p. (Orig.). 1979. pap. 6.95 (ISBN 0-88344-134-9). Orbis Bks.

--Mount Fuji & Mount Sinai: A Critique of Idols. LC 84-16556. Orig. Title: Mount Fui & Mount Sinai - A Pilgramage in Theology. 288p. (Orig.). 1985. pap. 12.95 (ISBN 0-88344-353-8). Orbis Bks.

--No Handle on the Cross: An Asian Meditation on the Crucified Mind. LC 76-23160. pap. 32.00 (ISBN 0-317-26647-0, 2025120). Bks Demand UMI.

--Three Mile an Hour God. LC 79-24785. 160p. (Orig.). 1980. pap. 3.48 (ISBN 0-88344-473-9). Orbis Bks.

--Waterbuffalo Theology. LC 74-80980. (Illus.). 250p. (Orig.). 1974. pap. 7.95 (ISBN 0-88344-702-9). Orbis Bks.

Koyre, Alexandre. Essai Sur l'Idee De Dieu et les Preuves de Son Existence Chez Descartes. Doney, Willis, ed. (The Philosophy of Descartes Ser.). (Fr.). 250p. 1987. lib. bdg. 40.00 (ISBN 0-8240-4665-X). Garland Pub.

--Philosophie De Jacob Boehme. 1929. 32.00 (ISBN 0-8337-1953-X). B Franklin.

Kozodoy, Neal, ed. see Chazan, Robert.

Kozodoy, Neil, ed. see Rossel, Seymour.

Kozodoy, Ruth. The Book of Jewish Holidays. Rossel, Seymour, ed. (Illus.). 192p. (Orig.). 1981. pap. text ed. 5.95x (ISBN 0-87441-334-6); tchr's. guide with duplicating masters by Moshe Ben-Aharon 3.25x (ISBN 0-87441-367-2). Behrman.

Kozodoy, Ruth, jt. auth. see Simms, Laura.

Krabill, Russell. Beginning the Christian Life. 1958. pap. 2.95 (ISBN 0-8361-1312-8); (leader's guide) 4.95 (ISBN 0-8361-1313-6). Herald Pr.

Kraeling, C. H. The Synagogue. rev ed. 1979. 100.00x (ISBN 0-87068-331-4). Ktav.

Kraeling, Carl H. Anthropos & Son of Man. LC 27-23162. (Columbia University. Oriental Studies: No. 25). Repr. of 1927 ed. 18.50 (ISBN 0-404-50515-5). AMS Pr.

--The Christian Building: Final Report VIII, Part II. LC 43-2669. 32.50 (ISBN 0-685-71744-5). J J Augustin.

Kraeling, Emil G. Aram & Israel Or, Aramaeans in Syria & Mesopotamia. LC 18-9797. (Columbia University. Oriental Studies: No. 13). Repr. of 1918 ed. 17.00 (ISBN 0-404-50503-1). AMS Pr.

Kraeling, Emil G., jt. auth. see Bewer, Julius A.

Kraemer, Bonita. Rules Mean Happiness. (Come Unto Me Ser.). 1979. pap. 1.65 (ISBN 0-8127-0254-9). Review & Herald.

Kraemer, Joel L., ed. Jerusalem: Problems & Prospects. LC 80-19418. 256p. 1980. 38.95 (ISBN 0-03-057733-0); pap. 17.95 (ISBN 0-03-057734-9). Praeger.

Kraemer, Paul E. Awakening from the American Dream: The Human Rights Movement in the U. S. Assessed During a Crucial Decade, 1960-1970. LC 73-78045. (Studies in Religion & Society Ser.). 1973. pap. 8.95x (ISBN 0-913348-09-0). Ctr Sci Study.

Kraft, Charles H. Christianity in Culture. LC 78-13736. 463p. (Orig.). 1979. 14.95 (ISBN 0-88344-075-X). Orbis Bks.

--Communicating the Gospel God's Way. LC 80-53945. 60p. 1980. pap. 2.95x (ISBN 0-87808-742-7). William Carey Lib.

Kraft, Charles H. & Wisley, Thomas N., eds. Readings in Dynamic Indigeneity. LC 79-24160. (Applied Cultural Anthropology Ser). 1979. pap. 12.95x (ISBN 0-87808-739-7). William Carey Lib.

Kraft, Marguerite G. Worldview & Communication of the Gospel. LC 78-10196. (Illus.). 1978. pap. 7.95 (ISBN 0-87808-324-3). William Carey Lib.

Kraft, R. Wayne. Reason to Hope: A Synthesis of Teilhard de Chardin's Vision & Systems Thinking. (Systems Inquiry Ser.). 292p. 1983. pap. 12.95x (ISBN 0-914105-14-0). Intersystems Pubns.

Kraft, Robert A. Septuagintal Lexicography. LC 75-15894. (Society of Biblical Literature. Septuagint & Cognate Studies). 1975. pap. 9.95 (ISBN 0-89130-008-2, 060401). Scholars Pr GA.

--The Testament of Job. LC 74-15201. (Society of Biblical Literature. Text & Translation-Psuedepigrapha Ser.: No. 5). pap. 17.70 (ISBN 0-8357-9580-2, 2017530). Bks Demand UMI.

Kraft, Robert A. & Purintun, Ann-Elizabeth. Paraleipomena Jeremiou. LC 72-88436. (Society of Biblical Literature. Texts & Translation-Psuedepigrapha Ser.). 49p. 1972. pap. 8.95 (ISBN 0-89130-169-0, 06 02 01). Scholars Pr GA.

Kraft, Robert A., ed. see Bauer, Walter.

Kraft, Robert A., jt. ed. see Nickelsburg, George W.

Kraft, Robert A., et al, eds. Early Judaism & Its Modern Interpreters. (SBL Bible & Its Modern Interpreters Ser.). 1986. 24.95 (ISBN 0-89130-669-2, 06-14-02); pap. 19.95 (ISBN 0-89130-884-9). Scholars Pr GA.

Kraft, William F. Achieving Promises: A Spiritual Guide for the Transitions of Life. LC 81-10496. 132p. 1981. pap. 6.95 (ISBN 0-664-24384-3). Westminster.

Krahn, Cornelius, ed. see Smith, C. Henry.

Krahn, John & Foster, Betty J. Ministry Ideabank III. (Orig.). 1987. pap. price not set (ISBN 0-89536-895-1, 7881). CSS of Ohio.

--Ministry Ideabank No. 2. 1986. 7.50 (ISBN 0-89536-801-3, 6819). CSS of Ohio.

Krahn, John H. Reaching the Inactive Member. 1982. 5.25 (ISBN 0-89536-570-7, 1815). CSS of Ohio.

--Seasonings for Sermons, Vol. 3. 1983. 4.50 (ISBN 0-89536-585-5, 1922). CSS of Ohio.

Krahn, John H. & Foster, Betty J. Ministry Ideabank. 136p. (Orig.). 1981. pap. text ed. 6.75 (ISBN 0-89536-488-3, 1314). CSS of Ohio.

Krailsheimer, A. J. Rance & the Trappist Legacy. 16.95 (ISBN 0-87907-886-3); pap. 6.95. Cistercian Pubns.

Krailsheimer, A. J., ed. The Letters of Armand Jean de Rance Abbot & Reformer of La Trappe, 2 vols. Vol. I. 25.00; Vol. II. 25.00. Cistercian Pubns.

Krailsheimer, A. J., tr. see Pascal, Blaise.

Kraines, Oscar. The Impossible Dilemma: Who Is a Jew in the State of Israel? 1976. 8.95x (ISBN 0-8197-0392-3). Bloch.

Krakovsky, Levi. Kabbalah: The Light of Redemption. 1970. 14.95 (ISBN 0-943688-06-X); pap. 11.95 (ISBN 0-943688-32-9). Res Ctr Kabbalah.

--The Omnipotent Light Revealed: Wisdom of the Kabbalah. 4.00 (ISBN 0-686-13335-8). Yesod Pubs.

Krakowski, Shmuel. The War of the Doomed: Jewish Armed Resistance in Poland, 1942-1944. LC 83-18537. 340p. 1984. text ed. 44.50x (ISBN 0-8419-0851-6). Holmes & Meier.

Krakowski, Shmuel, jt. ed. see Gutman, Yisrael.

Kralik, A. F. Jesus: Fact, Fable or Myth. 1985. 6.50 (ISBN 0-8062-2480-0). Carlton.

Kraljevic, Sveosar. Apparitions of Our Lady at Medugorje: An Historical Account with Interviews. Scanlan, Michael, ed. LC 84-5983. 217p. 1984. 9.50 (ISBN 0-8199-0878-9). Franciscan Herald.

Krall, Jack & Kalberer, Jan. Upside Down & Inside Out: A Study Experience in Christian Clowning. 120p. 1987. cancelled (ISBN 0-317-46796-4). Resource Pubns.

Kramer, Fred, tr. see Chemnitz, Martin.

Kramer, Heinrich & Sprenger, James. The Malleus Maleficarum: The Witches Hammer of Heinrich Kramer & James Sprenger. Summers, Montague, tr. 15.50 (ISBN 0-8446-0169-1). Peter Smith.

Kramer, Herman B. The Book of Destiny. LC 75-13556. (Illus.). 1975. pap. 12.50 (ISBN 0-89555-046-6). TAN Bks Pubs.

Kramer, Janice. Princess & the Baby. (Arch Bks: Set 6). 1969. laminated bdg 0.99 (ISBN 0-570-06043-5, 59-1158). Concordia.

Kramer, Janice & Mathews. Good Samaritan. LC 63-23369. (Arch Bks: Set 1). (Illus.). 1964. laminated bdg 0.99 (ISBN 0-570-06000-1, 59-1102). Concordia.

Kramer, Joel. The Passionate Mind. 122p. 1983. pap. 7.95 (ISBN 0-938190-12-1). North Atlantic.

Kramer, Joel J. Humanism in the Renaissance of Islam: The Cultural Revival During the Buyid Age. ix, 329p. 1986. 54.50 (ISBN 90-04-07259-4, Pub. by E J Brill). Heinman.

Kramer, Kenneth. World Scriptures: An Introduction to Comparative Religion. LC 85-62933. 304p. 1986. pap. 12.95 (ISBN 0-8091-2781-4). Paulist Pr.

Kramer, Martin. Islam Assembled: The Advent of the Muslim Congresses. LC 84-21407. 280p. 1985. 30.00x (ISBN 0-231-05994-9). Columbia U Pr.

Kramer, Milton, ed. Shi'ism, Resistance & Revolution. 350p. 1986. 39.85 (ISBN 0-8133-0453-9). Westview.

Kramer, Ralph M. & Schild, Philip, eds. The Bay Area Jewish Forum Hagadah. rev. ed. (Illus.). 69p. 1985. 13.95 (ISBN 0-917883-00-4). Benmir Bks.

Kramer, Robert A. The Colors of Christmas. (Orig.). 1980. pap. 1.75 (ISBN 0-937172-07-3). JLJ Pubs.

Kramer, Samuel N. Sumerian Mythology. (Illus.). 1972. pap. 10.95x (ISBN 0-8122-1047-6, Pa Paperbks). U of Pa Pr.

Kramer, Samuel Noah, ed. Mythologies of the Ancient World. LC 60-13538. 1961. pap. 6.95 (ISBN 0-385-09567-8, A229, Anch). Doubleday.

Kramer, Victor A. Thomas Merton. (United States Authors Ser.: No. 462). 1984. lib. bdg. 17.95 (ISBN 0-8057-7402-5, Twayne). G K Hall.

Kramer, William. Here & Hereafter. 1978. pap. 4.95 (ISBN 0-8100-0053-9, 15-0365). Northwest Pub.

Kramer, William A. God's People. LC 75-16790. 1975. lib. bdg. 7.25 (ISBN 0-8100-0010-5, 06N552). Northwest Pub.

--Living for Christ. rev. ed. LC 72-96585. 1973. 3.25 (ISBN 0-570-03157-5, 12-2542). Concordia.

--Teenagers Pray. LC 55-12193. 1956. 4.50 (ISBN 0-570-03018-8, 6-1054). Concordia.

Kramer-Lampher, A. H. Baby Born in a Stable. LC 65-15145. (Arch Bks.: Set. 2). 1965. pap. 0.99 (ISBN 0-570-06013-3, 59-1118). Concordia.

Kramers, J. H., jt. ed. see Gibb, H. A.

Kramrisch, Stella. The Hindu Temple, 2 vols. 1980. Repr. Set. 65.00x (ISBN 0-8364-0411-4). South Asia Bks.

--Hindu Temple, 2 vols. 1986. Repr. 60.00 (ISBN 81-208-0222-5, Pub. by Motilal Banarsidass). South Asia Bks.

--The Presence of Siva. LC 80-8558. (Illus.). 550p. 1981. 50.00x (ISBN 0-691-03964-X); pap. 18.95x (ISBN 0-691-10115-9). Princeton U Pr.

Kranich, Ernst M. Planetary Influences Upon Plants: Cosmological Botany. 184p. (Orig.). pap. 12.50 (ISBN 0-938250-20-5). Anthroposophic.

Kranidas, Thomas, ed. New Essays on Paradise Lost. LC 72-82463. 1969. pap. 4.95x (ISBN 0-520-01902-4, CAMPUS51). U of Cal Pr.

Kranzler, George. Face of Faith. 1972. 15.00x (ISBN 0-685-38401-2). Ktav.

Krapp, George P., ed. The Paris Psalter & Meters of Boethius. LC 33-2302. 239p. 1932. 30.00 (ISBN 0-231-08769-1). Columbia U Pr.

--The Vercelli Book. LC 32-10861. 152p. 1932. 27.50 (ISBN 0-231-08766-7). Columbia U Pr.

Krapp, Philip, tr. see Dumezil, Georges.

Krappe, Alexandre H. Mythologie universelle: Universal Mythology. Bolle, Kees W., ed. LC 77-79135. (Mythology Ser.). 1978. Repr. of 1930 ed. lib. bdg. 36.50x (ISBN 0-405-10545-2). Ayer Co Pubs.

Krasovec, Bernice. A Legend of Saint Nicholas. (Illus.). 48p. 1985. 5.95 (ISBN 0-89962-467-7). Todd & Honeywell.

Krass, Alfred C. Evangelizing Neopagan North America. LC 81-23768. (Mennonite Missionary Study Ser.: No. 9). 256p. (Orig.). 1982. pap. 9.95 (ISBN 0-8361-1989-4). Herald Pr.

Krastel, Joseph, jt. auth. see Hamroque, John.

Kratzig, Guillermo, tr. see Haney, David.

Kratzig, Guillermo, tr. see Neighbour, Ralph.

Kratzmann, Gregory & Simpson, James, eds. Medieval English Religious & Ethical Literature. 224p. 1986. 37.50 (ISBN 0-85991-220-5, Pub. by Boydell & Brewer). Longwood Pub Group.

Kraus, C. Norman. The Authentic Witness. LC 78-24012. 200p. 1981. pap. 5.95 (ISBN 0-8361-1959-2). Herald Pr.

Kraus, C. Norman, ed. Evangelicalism & Anabaptism. LC 79-12663. 192p. 1979. pap. 5.95 (ISBN 0-8361-1892-8). Herald Pr.

Kraus, Dorothy & Kraus, Henry. The Hidden World of the Misericords. LC 75-10869. (Illus.). 192p. 1975. 20.00 (ISBN 0-8076-0804-1). Braziller.

Kraus, Elizabeth M. The Metaphysics of Experience: A Companion to Whitehead's "Process & Reality". LC 78-70564. xiv, 190p. 1979. 22.50 (ISBN 0-8232-1038-3); pap. 9.00 (ISBN 0-8232-1039-1). Fordham.

Kraus, George. A Guide to a Year's Reading in Luther's Works. (Continued Applied Christianity Ser.). 1983. pap. 2.50 (ISBN 0-570-03902-9, 12-2984). Concordia.

--The Pastor at Prayer. LC 6-1188. (Continued Applied Christianity Ser.). 1983. 15.95 (ISBN 0-570-03073-0, 6-1188). Concordia.

Kraus, Hans J. Theology of the Psalms. Crim, Keith, tr. from Ger. LC 86-17267. 240p. 1986. 24.95 (ISBN 0-8066-2225-3, 10-6292). Augsburg.

Kraus, Henry. Gold Was the Mortar: The Economics of Cathedral Building. (Illus.). 1979. 37.95x (ISBN 0-7100-8728-4). Methuen Inc.

Kraus, Henry, jt. auth. see Kraus, Dorothy.

Kraus, Marie, ed. see Huber, J. William, et al.

Kraus, Norman C. Missions, Evangelism, & Church Growth. LC 80-10922. (Mennonite Central Committee Story Ser.). 176p. 1980. pap. 6.95 (ISBN 0-8361-1925-8). Herald Pr.

Kraus, Richard. Recreation Leadership Today. 1985. text ed. write for info. (ISBN 0-673-18140-5); instr's. manual & test items incl. Scott F.

Krause, G. & Mueller, G., eds. Theologische Realeuzyklopaedic, 25 vols. (Ger.). write for info. De Gruyter.

Krause, Johann U. Bible Illustration. (Printed Sources of Western Art Ser.). (Ger., Illus.). 50p. 1981. pap. 35.00 slipcase (ISBN 0-915346-54-0). A Wofsy Fine Arts.

Krause, Paul M. Planning a Christian Wedding. 1963. pap. 0.95 (ISBN 0-570-03504-X, 14-2010). Concordia.

Krausen, Edgard. Germania Sacra, New Series II: Bistuemer der Kirchenprovinz Salzburg. 1977. 62.40x (ISBN 3-11-006826-5). De Gruyter.

Krauss, Friedrich. Die Tempel von Paestum, 2 pts. (Denkmaeler Antiker Architektur, Vol. 9, Pt. 1, Fascicule 1). (Ger., Illus.). 97p. 1978. Repr. of 1959 ed. 70.0000169042x (ISBN 3-110022-37-0). De Gruyter.

Krauss, Friedrich & Herbig, Reinhard. Der Korinthisch-dorische Tempel am Forum von Paestum. (Denkmaeler antiker Architektur, Vol. 7). (Ger., Illus.). xii, 82p. 1978. Repr. of 1939 ed. 79.20x (ISBN 3-11-004991-0). De Gruyter.

Krauss, Johann U. Baroque Cartouches for Designers & Artists. (Pictorial Archive Ser). (Illus.). 1970. pap. 6.50 (ISBN 0-486-22222-5). Dover.

Krauss, Samuel. Talmudische Archaologie, 3 vols. Finley, Moses, ed. LC 79-4988. (Ancient Economic History). (Ger., Illus.). 1980. Repr. of 1912 ed. Set. lib. bdg. 172.00x (ISBN 0-405-12373-6); lib. bdg. 57.50x ea. Vol. 1 (ISBN 0-405-12374-4). Vol. 2 (ISBN 0-405-12375-2). Vol. 3 (ISBN 0-405-12376-0). Ayer Co Pubs.

Krauss, Samuel & Katz, Steven, eds. Festschrift Adolf Schwarz zum Siebzigsten Geburtstage. LC 79-7162. (Jewish Philosophy, Mysticism & History of Ideas Ser.). (Illus.). 1980. Repr. of 1917 ed. lib. bdg. 57.50x (ISBN 0-405-12275-6). Ayer Co Pubs.

Kraut, Benny. From Reform Judaism to Ethical Culture: The Religious Evolution of Felix Adler. LC 79-14441. (Monographs: No. 5). 285p. 1979. 16.50x (ISBN 0-87820-404-0). Ktav.

Krautheimer, Richard. The Rome of Alexander VII, 1655-1667. LC 84-26553. (Illus.). 214p. 1987. 34.50 (ISBN 0-691-04032-X); pap. 12.95 (ISBN 0-691-00277-0). Princeton U Pr.

Kravette, Steve. Complete Meditation. (Illus.). 320p. (Orig.). 1982. pap. 10.95 (ISBN 0-914918-28-1). Para Res.

Kravitz, David. Who's Who in Greek & Roman Mythology. 256p. 1977. (C N Potter Bks); pap. 5.95 (ISBN 0-517-52747-2). Crown.

Kraybill, Donald B. Ethnic Education: The Impact of Mennonite Schooling. LC 77-81022. 1977. soft bdg. 11.95 (ISBN 0-88247-480-4). R & E Pubs.

--The Upside-Down Kingdom. LC 78-9435. (Christian Peace Shelf Ser.). 328p. 1978. pap. 6.95 (ISBN 0-8361-1860-X). Herald Pr.

Kraybill, Donald B. & Good, Phyllis P. Perils of Professionalism. LC 82-3052. 240p. (Orig.). 1982. pap. 9.95 (ISBN 0-8361-1997-5). Herald Pr.

Kraybill, Ronald S. Repairing the Breach: Ministering in Community Conflict. LC 82-80586. 95p. 1982. pap. 3.95 (ISBN 0-8361-3302-1). Herald Pr.

Krebs, Manfred. Quellen zur Geschichte der Taufer, Band IV. 61.00 (ISBN 0-384-30425-7); pap. 55.00 (ISBN 0-384-30424-9). Johnson Repr.

Krebs, Manfred & Rott, H. G., eds. Elsass Eins, Stadt Strassburg: 1522-32. (Tauferakten Kommission Ser., Vol. 7). 599p. (Ger). 1959. 35.00x (ISBN 0-8361-1167-2). Herald Pr.

--Elsass Zwei, Stadt Strassburg: 1533-35. (Tauferakten Kommission Ser., Vol. 8). 555p. (Ger). 1959. 35.00x (ISBN 0-8361-1168-0). Herald Pr.

Krebs, Richard. Alone Again. LC 77-84085. 1978. pap. 5.95 (ISBN 0-8066-1611-3, 10-0240). Augsburg.

Krebs, Robert G. Why We're Here. 1987. 7.95 (ISBN 0-533-07098-8). Vantage.

Kreckel, Marga. Communicative Acts & Shared Knowledge in Natural Discourse. LC 81-66392. 1981. 68.00 (ISBN 0-12-426180-9). Acad Pr.

Kreeft, Peter. Best Things in Life. LC 84-6697. 160p. (Orig.). 1984. pap. 6.95 (ISBN 0-87784-922-6). Inter-Varsity.

--For Heaven's Sake. 192p. 1986. 12.95 (ISBN 0-8407-5494-9). Nelson.

--Making Sense Out of Suffering. 160p. (Orig.). 1986. pap. 6.95 (ISBN 0-89283-219-3). Servant.

--Prayer: The Great Conversation-Straight Answers to Tough Questions about Prayer. 164p. (Orig.). 1985. pap. 6.95 (ISBN 0-89283-218-5). Servant.

--Socrates Meets Jesus. 180p. (Orig.). 1987. pap. 5.95 (ISBN 0-87784-999-4). Inter-Varsity.

--Yes or No? Straight Answers to Tough Questions about Christianity. 168p. (Orig.). 1984. 5.95 (ISBN 0-89283-217-7). Servant.

Kreeft, Peter J. Between Heaven & Hell. LC 82-8975. 144p. (Orig.). 1982. pap. 5.95 (ISBN 0-87784-389-9). Inter-Varsity.

--Everything You Ever Wanted to Know About Heaven-But Never Dreamed of Asking. LC 82-47747. 160p. (Orig.). 1982. pap. 7.95 (ISBN 0-06-064777-9, RD/413, HarpR). Har-Row.

--Heaven: The Heart's Deepest Longing. LC 80-7747. 160p. 1980. 10.00 (ISBN 0-06-064776-0, HarpR). Har-Row.

--Love Is Stronger Than Death. LC 78-15839. 1979. 8.95 (ISBN 0-06-064774-4, HarpR). Har-Row.

Kreider, Alan. English Chantries: The Road to Dissolution. LC 78-12453. (Harvard Historical Studies: No. 97). 1979. 22.50x (ISBN 0-674-25560-7). Harvard U Pr.

--The Ethics of Social Holiness: A Way of Living for God's Global Nation. 1987. 14.95 (ISBN 0-310-38390-0). Zondervan.

--Journey Towards Holiness. LC 86-22838. 304p. (Orig.). 1987. pap. 9.95 (ISBN 0-8361-3423-0). Herald Pr.

Kreider, Carl. The Christian Entrepreneur. LC 80-16836. (Conrad Grebel Lectures Ser.). 214p. 1980. pap. 8.95 (ISBN 0-8361-1936-3). Herald Pr.

Kreider, Harry J. Lutheranism in Colonial New York. LC 78-38452. (Religion in America, Ser. 2). 184p. 1972. Repr. of 1942 ed. 13.00 (ISBN 0-405-04072-5). Ayer Co Pubs.

Krein, Linda. Bible Crosswords. (Bible Baffler Ser.). 48p. 1986. wkbk. 4.95 (ISBN 0-86653-366-4). Good Apple.

Kreipe, Christian E. Milton's Samson Agonistes. LC 76-10958. (Ger.). 1926. lib. bdg. 20.00 (ISBN 0-8414-5458-2). Folcroft.

--Milton's Samson Agonistes. 59.95 (ISBN 0-8490-0638-4). Gordon Pr.

Kreis, Bernadine & Pattie, Alice. Up from Grief: Patterns of Recovery. 160p. 1982. pap. 5.95 (ISBN 0-8164-2364-4, AY7442, HarpR). Har-Row.

Kreis, Bernardine & Pattie, Alice. Up from Grief. 292p. 1984. pap. 9.95 large print ed. (ISBN 0-8027-2486-8). Walker & Co.

Kreissman, Bernard, ed. see Scott, Sir Walter.

Kreitzman, Sue. Comfort Food: Ninety-Five Recipes to Nourish the Soul As Well As the Body. 96p. 1985. pap. 6.95 (ISBN 0-517-55939-0, Harmony). Crown.

Kremen, Kathryn R. The Imagination of the Resurrection: The Poetic Continuity of a Religious Motif in Donne, Blake, & Yeats. LC 71-168812. (Illus.). 344p. 1972. 26.50 (ISBN 0-8387-7940-9). Bucknell U Pr.

Kremers, Edward. Christ the Healer. 24p. 1911. pap. 0.95 (ISBN 0-317-40411-3). Open Court.

Kreml, Patricia B. Slim for Him. LC 78-53422. 1978. pap. 4.95 (ISBN 0-88270-300-5). Bridge Pub.

Krempa, S. Joseph. Daily Homilies, 3 Vols. Incl. Vol. 1. Ordinary Time (Year One) 242p. 1985 (ISBN 0-8189-0480-1); Vol. 2. Ordinary Time (Year Two) 253p. 1985 (ISBN 0-8189-0481-X); Vol. 3. Seasonal & Sanctoral Cycle: Advent, Christmas, Lent & Easter & all Obligatory Memorials. 217p. 1985 (ISBN 0-8189-0479-8). 1985. pap. 7.50 ea.; Set. pap. 19.95 (ISBN 0-8189-0483-6). Alba.

Kremsdorf, Deborah L., jt. ed. see Spiegel, Marcia C.

Kren, George M. & Rappoport, Leon H. Holocaust & the Crisis of Human Behavior. LC 79-23781. 200p. 1980. text ed. 29.50x (ISBN 0-8419-0544-4). Holmes & Meier.

Krencker, Daniel & Zschietzschmann, Willy. Roemische Tempel in Syrien: Nach Aufnahmen und Untersuchungen von Mitgliedern der Deutschen Baalbekexpedition, 1901-1904, 2 pts. (Denkmaeler antiker Architektur, Vol. 5). (Ger., Illus.). 298p. 1978. Repr. of 1938 ed. Pt. 1. 132.00x (ISBN 3-11-004989-9); Pt. 2. 84.00 (ISBN 3-11-004990-2). De Gruyter.

Krentz, Edgar. Easter. LC 84-18756. (Proclamation 3, Ser. B). 64p. 1985. pap. 3.75 (ISBN 0-8006-4105-1, 1-4105). Fortress.

--The Historical-Critical Method. LC 74-26345. (Guides to Biblical Scholarship: Old Testament Ser.). 96p. 1975. pap. 4.50 (ISBN 0-8006-0460-1, 1-460). Fortress.

Krentz, Edgar & Vogel, Arthur A. Easter. Achtemeier, Elizabeth, et al, eds. LC 79-7377. (Proclamation 2: Aids for Interpreting the Lessons of the Church Year, Ser. C). 64p. 1980. pap. 3.75 (ISBN 0-8006-4080-2, 1-4080). Fortress.

Krentz, Edgar, ed. see Hahn, Ferdinand.

Krentz, Edgar, et al, eds. Augsburg Commentary on the New Testament: Galatians, Philippians, Philemon. LC 85-11116. 256p. (Orig.). 1985. kivar 9.95 (ISBN 0-8066-2166-4, 10-9028). Augsburg.

Kress, Robert. The Church: Communion, Sacrament, Communication. 288p. (Orig.). 1985. pap. 9.95 (ISBN 0-8091-2663-X). Paulist Pr.

--The Difference Jesus Makes. (Synthesis Ser.). 1981. 1.25 (ISBN 0-8199-0372-8). Franciscan Herald.

--A Rahner Handbook. LC 81-85333. 118p. 1982. pap. 10.95 (ISBN 0-8042-0652-X). John Knox.

Kretschmar, Freda. Hundestammvater und Kerberos, 2 vols. Repr. of 1938 ed. Set. 37.00 (ISBN 0-384-30430-3). Johnson Repr.

Kretz, Thomas. North American Psalms. LC 81-69454. 166p. 1981. pap. 4.95 (ISBN 0-933402-24-4). Charisma Pr.

Kretzmann, Norman, ed. Paul of Venice, Logica Magna, Pt. I, Fasc. I. 344p. 1979. 52.50 (ISBN 0-85672-690-7, Pub. by British Acad). Longwood Pub Group.

Kretzmann, Norman, ed. see Paul Of Venice.

Kretzmann, Norman, tr. see William Of Ockham.

Kretzmann, Paul E. Popular Commentary of the Bible, 4 Vols. 2 Pts. Set. 70.95 (ISBN 0-570-06735-9, 15-1201). Concordia.

Kretzschmar, Louise. The Voice of Black Theology in South Africa. 136p. 1986. pap. 10.95 (ISBN 0-86975-269-3, Pub. by Ravan Pr). Ohio U Pr.

Kreuziger, Frederick A. Church & Catechism: The Baltimore Catechism Revisited. xiii, 126p. 1986. pap. 8.95 (ISBN 0-9616430-0-5). Reflex Bks.

Krey, A. C. The First Crusade: Accounts of Eye-Witnesses & Participants. 11.75 (ISBN 0-8446-1272-3). Peter Smith.

Krey, A. C., jt. auth. see Sellery, G. C.

Krey, Peter C. Lo! the Bridegroom. LC 66-20393. 1966. 3.95 (ISBN 0-686-05043-6). St Thomas.

Krick, L., tr. see Makrakis, Apostolos.

Krimsky, Joseph. Pilgrimage & Service. Davis, Moshe, ed. LC 77-70712. (America & the Holy Land Ser.). 1977. Repr. of 1919 ed. lib. bdg. 17.00x (ISBN 0-405-10261-5). Ayer Co Pubs.

Kring, Walter D. Henry Whitney Bellows. 1979. pap. 7.95 (ISBN 0-933840-03-9). Unitarian Univ.

--Liberals Among the Orthodox: Unitarian Beginnings in New York City, 1819-1839. LC 73-21275. (Illus.). 1974. 14.95x (ISBN 0-8070-1662-4). Beacon Pr.

Krinsky, Carol H. Synagogues of Europe: Architecture, History, Meaning. (Architectural History Foundation Ser.). 470p. 1987. pap. 25.00 (ISBN 0-262-61048-5). MIT Pr.

Kripalu Center for Holistic Health Staff. The Best of Kripalu Yoga Quest: Handbook for Total Living. LC 82-84671. 101p. (Orig.). 1983. pap. 4.95 (ISBN 0-940258-08-0). Kripalu Pubns.

Kripalvanandaji, Shri. A Pilgrimage of Love, Book I. LC 81-82015. 86p. (Orig.). 1981. pap. 4.50 (ISBN 0-940258-02-1). Kripalu Pubns.

Kripalvanandji, Shri. The Passion of Christ. LC 83-80214. 51p. 1983. pap. 4.50 (ISBN 0-940258-09-9). Kripalu Pubns.

--Pilgrimage of Love: Premyatra, Bk. III. LC 81-82015. (Illus.). 136p. (Orig.). 1984. pap. 5.50 (ISBN 0-940258-12-9). Kripalu Pubns.

Kripalvandji, Swami Shri. Pilgrimage of Love, Book II. LC 81-82015. 416p. (Orig.). 1982. pap. 7.50 (ISBN 0-940258-05-6). Kripalu Pubns.

Kripke, Dorothy K. Lets Talk about the Jewish Holidays. 1982. pap. 5.95 (ISBN 0-8246-0267-6). Jonathan David.

Kripke, Dorothy K. & Levin, Meyer. God & the Story of Judaism. LC 62-17078. (Jewish Heritage Ser: Vol. 1). 1962. 5.95x (ISBN 0-87441-000-2). Behrman.

Krippner, Stanley & Villoldo, Alberto. The Realms of Healing. LC 75-7858. 320p. (Orig.). 1986. pap. 9.95 (ISBN 0-89087-474-3). Celestial Arts.

Krippner, Stanley, jt. auth. see Viloldo, Alberto.

Krishna, Gopi. Kundalini: The Evolutionary Energy in Man. LC 73-75656. 252p. 1971. pap. 8.95 (ISBN 0-87773-043-1). Shambhala Pubns.

Krishna, Gopi see Gopi Krishna.

Krishna, Nanditha. The Art & Iconography of Vishnu-Narayana. (Illus.). xiv, 122p. 1981. text ed. 45.00x (ISBN 0-86590-025-6, Pub. by Taraporevala India). Apt Bks.

Krishna, Swami P., ed. see Rajneesh, Bhagwan S.

Krishna Murthy, C. Saiva Art & Architecture in South India. 1985. 48.00x (ISBN 0-8364-1417-9, Pub. by Sundeep). South Asia Bks.

Krishnamurti. Krishnamurti's Journal. Lutyens, Mary, ed. LC 81-48210. 1982. pap. 5.95 (ISBN 0-06-064841-4, RD-396, HarpR). Har-Row.

Krishnamurti, J. Early Writings of Krishnamurti, 2 Vols. 1974. lib. bdg. 250.00 (ISBN 0-87968-533-6). Krishna Pr.

--Education & the Signficance of Life. LC 53-10971. 128p. 1981. pap. 6.95 (ISBN 0-06-064876-7, RD 356, HarpR). Har-Row.

--Exploration into Insight. LC 79-6651. 192p. (Orig.). 1980. pap. 7.95 (ISBN 0-06-064811-2, RD 326, HarpR). Har-Row.

--Talks & Dialogues of J. Krishnamurti. 1976. pap. 4.95 (ISBN 0-380-01573-0, Discus). Avon.

--The Wholeness of Life. LC 78-19495. 256p. 1981. pap. 8.95 (ISBN 0-06-064868-6, RD362, HarpR). Har-Row.

Krishnamurti, J. see Alcyone, pseud.

Krishnamurti, Jiddu. Commentaries on Living, 3 Bks. 3 ser ed. Rajagopal, D., ed. (Ser. 1, LC 67-8405; Ser. 2, LC 67-8407; Ser. 3, LC 67-8416). 1967. Ser. 1. pap. 4.75 (ISBN 0-8356-0390-3, Quest); Ser. 2. pap. 5.50 (ISBN 0-8356-0415-2); Ser. 3. pap. 5.50 (ISBN 0-8356-0402-0). Theos Pub Hse.

--Think on These Things. 1970. pap. 4.95 (ISBN 0-06-080192-1, P192, PL). Har-Row.

--You Are the World. 160p. 1973. pap. 4.95 (ISBN 0-06-080303-7, P303, PL). Har-Row.

Krishnamurti, U. G., jt. auth. see Bobroff, Alvin.

Krishnananda & Bhagyalakshmi, S., eds. Facets of Spirituality: Dialogues & Discourses of Swami Krishnananda. 1986. 22.00X (ISBN 81-208-0087-7, Pub. by Motilal Banarsidass). South Asia Bks.

Krishna Prasad. Religious Freedom under Indian Constitution. 1976. 9.00x (ISBN 0-88386-839-3). South Asia Bks.

Krishna Prem, Sri. The Yoga of the Kathopanishad. 1983. Repr. 15.00x (ISBN 0-318-20321-9, Pub. by New Order Bk Co India). Humanities.

Krishna Sastri, H. South Indian Images of Gods & Goddesses. 308p. 1986. Repr. 37.50X (ISBN 0-8364-1710-0, Pub. by Chanakya India). South Asia Bks.

Krishna Sri, Prem. The Yoga of the Bhagavat Gita. 1982. Repr. 15.00x (ISBN 0-318-20320-0, Pub. by New Order Bk Co India). Humanities.

Kristeller, Paul O. Renaissance Thought: The Classic, Scholastic & Humanistic Strains. 15.50 (ISBN 0-8446-2405-5). Peter Smith.

Kristeva, Julia. Tales of Love. Roudiez, Leon S., tr. from Fr. LC 86-28311. 448p. 1987. text ed. 30.00 (ISBN 0-231-06024-6). Columbia U Pr.

Kristian, Hans, jt. auth. see Hunt, Dave.

Kriyananda, Goswami. Beginner's Guide to Meditation. 104p. (Orig.). pap. text ed. 3.95 (ISBN 0-317-43470-5). Temple Kriya Yoga.

--The Bhagavad Gita: The Song of God. 2nd ed. (Illus.). 137p. pap. text ed. 5.95 (ISBN 0-9613099-3-8). Temple Kriya Yoga.

--The Spiritual Science of Kriya Yoga. 2nd ed. (Illus.). pap. text ed. 16.95 (ISBN 0-9613099-1-1). Temple Kriya Yoga.

Kriyananda, Swami. How to Spiritualize your Marriage. 2nd, enl. ed. 136p. 1982. pap. 6.95 (ISBN 0-916124-21-5). Dawn Pubns CA.

--The Path: Autobiography of a Western Yogi. LC 77-72787. (Illus.). 640p. 1977. 15.00 (ISBN 0-916124-11-8); pap. 4.95 (ISBN 0-916124-12-6). Dawn Pubns CA.

--The Shortened Path: Autobiography of a Western Yogi. abr. ed. 240p. 1980. pap. 6.95 (ISBN 0-916124-19-3). Dawn Pubns CA.

--Yoga Postures for Higher Awareness. 2nd, enl. ed. (Illus.). 140p. 1971. pap. 8.95 (ISBN 0-916124-25-8). Dawn Pubns CA.

Krodel, ed. & tr. from Ger. Luther's Works: Letters II, Vol. 49. LC 55-9893. 480p. 1972. 19.95 (ISBN 0-8006-0349-4, 1-349). Fortress.

Krodel, Gerhard. Acts. LC 80-2395. (Proclamation Commentaries: the New Testament Witnesses for Preaching). 128p. (Orig.). 1981. pap. 5.95 (ISBN 0-8006-0585-3, 1-585). Fortress.

Krodel, Gerhard, ed. see Achtemeier, Paul J.

Krodel, Gerhard, ed. see Bauer, Walter.

Krodel, Gerhard, ed. see Danker, Frederick W.

Krodel, Gerhard, ed. see Fiorenza, Elisabeth S. & Holmes, Urban T.

Krodel, Gerhard, ed. see Fuller, Reginald H., et al.

Krodel, Gerhard, ed. see Keck, Leander E.

Krodel, Gerhard, ed. see Kingsbury, Jack D.

Krodel, Gerhard, ed. see Smith, D. Moody.

Krodel, Gerhard A. Augsburg Commentary on the New Testament: Acts. LC 86-10796. 500p. (Orig.). 1986. pap. 19.95 (ISBN 0-8066-8884-X, 10-9046). Augsburg.

Krodel, Gottfried G. & Lehman, Helmut T., eds. Luther's Works: Letters I, Vol. 48. LC 55-9893. 1963. 19.95 (ISBN 0-8006-0348-6). Fortress.

Krodel, Gottfried G. & Lehmann, Helmut T., eds. Luther's Works: Letters III, Vol. 50. LC 74-76934. 416p. 1975. 19.95 (ISBN 0-8006-0350-8, 1-350). Fortress.

Kroeber, Alfred L. Yurok Myths. LC 75-3772. 460p. 1976. 31.00x (ISBN 0-520-02977-1); pap. 6.95 (ISBN 0-520-03639-5, CAL 386). U of Cal Pr.

Kroeber, Alfred L. & Gifford, E. W. Karok Myths. Buzaljko, Grace, ed. LC 78-66022. 450p. 1980. 31.00 (ISBN 0-520-03870-3). U of Cal Pr.

Kroeger, Karl & Crawford, Richard, eds. The Complete Works of William Billings, Vol. III: The Psalm-Singer's Amusement, the Suffolk Harmony, & Independent Publications. (Illus.). 456p. 1986. text ed. 50.00x (ISBN 0-8139-1130-3, Pub. by American Musicological Society-Colonial Society MA). U Pr of Va.

Krokosz, B., tr. see Buhlmann, Walbert.

Krol, John C. Church: Life Giving Union with Christ. 1978. 5.50 (ISBN 0-8198-0525-4); pap. 5.95 (ISBN 0-8198-0526-2). Dghtrs St Paul.

--God-the Cornerstone of Our Life. 1978. 5.50 (ISBN 0-8198-0531-9); pap. 3.95 (ISBN 0-8198-0532-7). Dghtrs St Paul.

Krol, Cardinal John. To Insure Peace Acknowledge God. 1978. 5.50 (ISBN 0-8198-0561-0); pap. 3.95 (ISBN 0-8198-0562-9). Dghtrs St Paul.

Krolick, Sanford. Recollective Resolve: A Phenomenological Understanding of Time & Myth. 160p. 1987. 24.95 (ISBN 0-86554-248-1, MUP H-214). Mercer Univ Pr.

Krolikowski, Walter, ed. Faith & Justice. 174p. 1982. pap. text ed. 6.95 (ISBN 0-8294-0397-3). Loyola.

Kroll, Una. Flesh of My Flesh. 112p. 1975. pap. 6.50 (ISBN 0-232-51336-8). Attic Pr.

Kroll, Woodrow. Bible Country. 1982. 22.95 (ISBN 0-89636-060-1). Accent Bks.

Kroll, Woodrow M. Early in the Morning. 128p. 1986. 4.95 (ISBN 0-87213-474-1). Loizeaux.

--Prescription for Preaching. 1980. 11.95 (ISBN 0-8010-5409-5). Baker Bk.

--Psalms: The Poetry of Palestine. 464p. (Orig.). 1987. lib. bdg. 37.50 (ISBN 0-8191-5750-3); pap. text ed. 24.75 (ISBN 0-8191-5751-1). U Pr of Amer.

Krom, N. J., ed. The Life of Buddha on the Stupa of Barabudur, According to the Lalitavistara-Text. LC 78-72460. Repr. of 1926 ed. 30.00 (ISBN 0-404-17328-4). AMS Pr.

Kromminga, Carl. Bringing God's News to Neighbors. 1976. pap. 4.50 (ISBN 0-87552-314-5). Presby & Reformed.

Kroner, R., tr. see Hegel, G. W.

Kroner, Richard. Culture & Faith. LC 51-7837. pap. 73.50 (ISBN 0-317-09283-9, 2016993). Bks Demand UMI.

--The Primacy of Faith. LC 77-27184. (Gifford Lectures: 1939-40). Repr. of 1943 ed. 26.25 (ISBN 0-404-60497-8). AMS Pr.

Kropf, Richard W. Evil & Evolution. LC 81-72041. 224p. 1983. 27.50 (ISBN 0-8386-3157-6). Fairleigh Dickinson.

--Teilhard, Scripture, & Revelation: Teilhard de Chardin's Reinterpretation of Pauline Themes. LC 73-20907. 352p. 1980. 29.50 (ISBN 0-8386-1481-7). Fairleigh Dickinson.

Krosnicki, Thomas A. Ancient Patterns in Modern Prayer. LC 74-172790. (Catholic University of America. Studies in Christian Antiquity Ser.). pap. 79.30 (2029516). Bks Demand UMI.

Kroy, M. The Conscience: A Structural Theory. 244p. 1974. text ed. 49.00x (ISBN 0-7065-1462-9, Pub. by Keter Pub Jerusalem). Coronet Bks.

Kruckman, Herbert L. Joey Meets His People. 44p. 1940. 2.95 (ISBN 0-88482-732-1). Hebrew Pub.

Krueger, David A., jt. ed. see Grelle, Bruce.

Krueger, Gustav. History of Early Christian Literature in the First Three Centuries. Gillet, Charles R., tr. from Ger. 1969. 26.00 (ISBN 0-8337-1963-7). B Franklin.

Krueger, John R. An Analysis of the Names of Mormonism. 1979. pap. 3.00x (ISBN 0-911706-21-6). Selbstverlag.

Krueger, John R., ed. see Pozdneyev, Aleksei M.

Krueger, Kenneth W., ed. The History of the Evangelical United Brethren Church. LC 79-14738. (Illus.). 1979. 17.95 (ISBN 0-687-17206-3). Abingdon.

Krueger, P., jt. auth. see Assfalg, Julius.

Kruger, Mollee. Daughters of Chutzpah: Humorous Verse on the Jewish Woman. LC 82-71394. (Illus.). 112p. (Orig.). 1983. pap. 5.00 (ISBN 0-9602036-7-2). Biblio NY.

--More Unholy Writ: Jewish Verses & Vices. 100p. 1973. pap. 2.25 (ISBN 0-913184-02-0). Maryben Bks.

Kruis, John G. Quick Scripture Reference for Counseling. 80p. 1987. pap. price not set (ISBN 0-8010-5488-5). Baker Bk.

Kruk, Herman. Togbukh Fun Vilner Geto. Bernstein, Mordecai W., ed. LC 62-56072. (Yivo Institute for Jewish Research, Memoirs Ser.: No. 1). (Yiddish., Illus.). 620p. 1961. 10.00 (ISBN 0-914512-29-3). Yivo Inst.

Krumbine, Miles H., ed. The Process of Religion: Essays in Honor of Dean Shailer Mathews. facsimile ed. LC 71-38776. (Essay Index Reprint Ser). Repr. of 1933 ed. 18.00 (ISBN 0-8369-2667-6). Ayer Co Pubs.

Krumm, John M. Why Choose the Episcopal Church? 160p. 1974. pap. 1.35 (ISBN 0-88028-030-1). Forward Movement.

Krummacher, Frederick W. David, King of Israel. 548p. 1983. lib. bdg. 20.50 (ISBN 0-86524-142-2, 8404). Klock & Klock.

Krumpelmann, John T., tr. see Von Schiller, Friedrich.

Krumroy, Jeri. Grief Is Not Forever. 128p. (Orig.). 1985. pap. 6.95 (ISBN 0-87178-326-6). Brethren.

Krupp, Nate. Bible Studies for Christian Discipleship. 2nd ed. 1979. Repr. 1.45 (ISBN 0-89221-052-4). New Leaf.

--Bible Studies for New Christians. 2nd ed. 1979. Repr. 1.45 (ISBN 0-89221-053-2). New Leaf.

--Bible Studies for Soul Winners. 1979. Repr. 1.45 (ISBN 0-89221-054-0). New Leaf.

--You Can Be a Soul Winner, Here's How! LC 78-64961. 176p. 1978. pap. 3.95 (ISBN 0-89221-050-8). New Leaf.

Krupp, R. A. Saint John Chrysostom: A Scripture Index. LC 84-21028. 270p. 1985. lib. bdg. 27.50 (ISBN 0-8191-4380-4). U Pr of Amer.

Kruschwitz & Roberts. Virtues: Contemporary Essay of Moral Character. King, Ken, ed. (Orig.). 1986. write for info. (ISBN 0-534-06720-4). Wadsworth Pub.

Krusentierna, Sten von see Von Krusenstierna, Sten.

Krutch, Joseph W., et al. Wildlife's Christmas Treasury. Rifkin, Natalie S., ed. LC 76-12388. (Illus.). 160p. 1976. 11.95 (ISBN 0-912186-22-4). Natl Wildlife.

Krutza, William J. Facing Yourself in the Bible: Studies in Human Personalities from the Bible. (Contemporary Discussion Ser.). 128p. 1976. pap. 1.25 (ISBN 0-8010-5369-2). Baker Bk.

--Graduate's Guide to Success. 96p. 1976. 4.95 (ISBN 0-8010-5374-9). Baker Bk.

--Leader's Guide to Facing the Issues, No. 3 & 4. (Contemporary Discussion Ser.). pap. 1.95 (ISBN 0-8010-5387-0). Baker Bk.

--One Hundred One Ways to Enrich Your Marriage. 144p. 1982. pap. 4.95 (ISBN 0-8010-5452-4). Baker Bk.

--Prayer: The Vital Link. 96p. 1983. pap. 3.95 (ISBN 0-8170-0986-8). Judson.

--Reaching Out for Life's Best. (Contemporary Discussion Ser.). 96p. (Orig.). 1982. pap. 2.95 (ISBN 0-8010-5444-3). Baker Bk.

--The Second Coming Bible Study Guide, No. 2. (Contemporary Discussion Ser.). (Orig.). 1973. pap. 0.95 (ISBN 0-8010-5330-7). Baker Bk.

--Twenty-Five Keys to a Happy Marriage. (Contempo Ser). pap. 1.75 (ISBN 0-8010-5447-8). Baker Bk.

Krutza, William J. & Dicicco, Philip P. Facing the Issues, No. 1. (Contemporary Discussion Ser.). 1969. pap. 3.50 (ISBN 0-8010-5325-0). Baker Bk.

--Facing the Issues, No. 2. (Contemporary Discussion Ser.). pap. 3.50 (ISBN 0-8010-5326-9). Baker Bk.

--Facing the Issues, No. 3. (Contemporary Discussion Ser.). (Orig.). 1970. pap. 3.50 (ISBN 0-8010-5300-5). Baker Bk.

--Facing the Issues, No. 4. (Contemporary Discussion Ser.). (Orig.). 1971. pap. 3.50 (ISBN 0-8010-5310-2). Baker Bk.

--Facing Your Nation. (Contemporary Discussion Ser.). 1975. pap. 1.95 (ISBN 0-8010-5372-2). Baker Bk.

--Youth Face Today's Issues 2. (Contemporary Discussion Ser.). pap. 3.50 (ISBN 0-8010-5311-0). Baker Bk.

Krutza, William J., jt. auth. see Wood, George O.

Krutza, Willlam J. Let's All Pray Together. 128p. 1984. pap. 3.95 (ISBN 0-8170-1024-6). Judson.

Kselman, Thomas A. Miracles & Prophecies in Nineteenth-Century France. (Illus.). 312p. 1983. 30.00 (ISBN 0-8135-0963-7). Rutgers U Pr.

Kuasten, J. & Plumpe, J., eds. St. Augustine, Faith, Hope & Charity. Arand, Louis A., tr. LC 78-62450. (Ancient Christian Writers Ser.: No. 3). 165p. 1947. 10.95 (ISBN 0-8091-0045-2). Paulist Pr.

Kubie, Nora B. Jews of Israel: History & Sources. Silberman, Mark, ed. LC 75-18510. (Illus.). 128p. (Orig.). 1975. pap. text ed. 3.95x (ISBN 0-87441-246-3). Behrman.

Kubler-Ross, Elisabeth. Working It Through. (Illus.). 176p. 1987. pap. 5.95 (ISBN 0-02-022000-6, Collier). Macmillan.

Kubo, Sakae. A Beginner's New Testament Greek Grammar. LC 79-64247. 1979. pap. text ed. 11.00 (ISBN 0-8191-0761-1). U Pr of Amer.

--The Open Rapture. (Flame Ser.). 1978. pap. 0.99 (ISBN 0-8127-0170-4). Review & Herald.

--A Reader's Greek-English Lexicon of the New Testament & a Beginner's Guide for the Translation of New Testament Greek. (Andrews University Monographs, Studies in Religion: Vol. IV). x, 327p. 1975. text ed. 14.95 (ISBN 0-943872-04-9). Andrews Univ Pr.

--A Reader's Greek-English Lexicon of the New Testament & Benjamin's Guide. 1975. text ed. 15.95 (ISBN 0-310-26920-2, 6269). Zondervan.

--Theology & Ethics of Sex. (Horizon Ser.). 1980. pap. 5.95 (ISBN 0-8127-0288-3). Review & Herald.

Kubo, Sakae & Specht, Walter. So Many Versions? rev. enlarged ed. 320p. 1983. pap. 9.95 (ISBN 0-310-45691-6, 12458P). Zondervan.

Kucharek, Casimir. The Byzantine Slav Liturgy of St. John Chrysostom, Its Origin & Evolution. LC 74-147735. (Illus.). 840p. 1971. 18.75 (ISBN 0-911726-06-3, BSL). Alleluia Pr.

--Our Faith. Vinck, Jose D., ed. LC 82-73784. 350p. 1983. 17.75 (ISBN 0-911726-43-8). Alleluia Pr.

--The Sacramental Mysteries: A Byzantine Approach. 416p. 1976. 15.75 (ISBN 0-911726-17-9); pap. 12.75 laminated (ISBN 0-911726-25-X). Alleluia Pr.

Kucharek, Wilma S., jt. auth. see Drobena, Thomas J.

Kuck, Glen. Help My Faith Grow, Lord! (Continued Applied Christianity Ser.). 1983. pap. 4.95 (ISBN 0-570-03894-4, 12-2976). Concordia.

Kuczynski, Barbara, tr. see Block, Martin.

Kuehl, Gerald, ed. see Olson, Stuart A.

Kuehnelt-Leddihn, Erik von see Von Kuehnelt-Leddihn, Erik.

Kuemmel, Werner G. Introduction to the New Testament. rev. ed. Kee, Howard C., tr. from Ger. LC 74-26804. 624p. 1975. 16.95 (ISBN 0-687-19575-6). Abingdon.

Kuenen, Abraham. National Religions & Universal Religions. LC 77-27169. (Hibbert Lectures Ser.: 1882). Repr. of 1882 ed. 34.00 (ISBN 0-404-60403-X). AMS Pr.

Kuenning, Larry. Exiles in Babylon. LC 77-85708. 1978. pap. 2.25 (ISBN 0-930682-00-9). Friends Truth.

Kugel, James L. The Idea of Biblical Poetry: Parallelism & Its History. LC 80-25227. August 1983, 351p. pap. 10.95 (ISBN 0-300-03101-7, Y-470). Yale U Pr.

Kugel, James L. & Greer, Rowan A. Early Biblical Interpretation. LC 85-26397. (Library of Early Christianity: Vol. 3). 214p. 1986. 16.95 (ISBN 0-664-21907-1). Westminster.

Kugelman, Richard. James & Jude. (New Testament Message Ser.: Vol. 19). 10.95 (ISBN 0-89453-207-3); pap. 5.95 (ISBN 0-89453-142-5). M Glazier.

Kugelmann, Robert. The Windows of Soul. LC 81-70032. 220p. 1983. 24.50 (ISBN 0-8387-5035-4). Bucknell U Pr.

Kugelmass, Jack & Boyarin, Jonathan. From a Ruined Garden: The Memorial Books of Polish Jewry. (Illus.). 309p. 1985. pap. 8.95 (ISBN 0-8052-0789-9). Schocken.

Kuhatschek, Jack. Galatians: Why Christ Accepts Us. (LifeBuilder Bible Studies). (Orig.). 1986. pap. 2.95 (ISBN 0-8308-1011-0). Inter-Varsity.

--Romans: The Gift of Righteousness. (Lifebuilder Bible Studies). 96p. (Orig.). 1986. pap. 2.95 (ISBN 0-8308-1008-0). Inter-Varsity.

Kuhatschek, Jack, jt. auth. see Nyquist, James F.

Kuhlewind, Georg. Becoming Aware of the Logos. LC 85-23126. 195p. (Orig.). 1985. pap. 9.95 (ISBN 0-89281-071-8, Lindisfarne Pr). Inner Tradit.

--Forgiving. St. Goar, Maria, tr. from Ger. Miller, John, ed. (Illus.). 24p. (Orig.). 1985. pap. 3.50 (ISBN 0-932776-09-4). Adonis Pr.

--Stages of Consciousness: Meditations on the Boundaries of the Soul. St. Goar, Maria, tr. from Ger. 144p. (Orig.). 1985. pap. 8.95 (ISBN 0-89281-065-3, Lindisfarne Pr). Inner Tradit.

Kuhlman, Kathryn. Glimpse into Glory. Buckingham, Jamie, compiled by. LC 79-90558. 1979. pap. 3.50 pocket size (ISBN 0-88270-393-5). Bridge Pub.

--I Believe in Miracles. 1975. pap. 2.25 (ISBN 0-515-05858-0). Jove Pubns.

--Nothing Is Impossible with God. (Orig.). 1976. pap. 1.75 (ISBN 0-89129-084-2). Jove Pubns.

Kuhmerker, Lisa, et al, eds. Evaluating Moral Development. LC 80-68348. (Orig.). 1980. 9.95 (ISBN 0-915744-24-4); pap. 6.95 (ISBN 0-915744-21-X). Character Res.

Kuhn, Alvin B. Rebirth for Christianity. LC 76-104032. 1970. 6.50 (ISBN 0-8356-0015-7). Theos Pub Hse.

--The Red Sea Is Your Blood. 66p. 1976. pap. 5.95 (ISBN 0-88697-007-5). Life Science.

Kuhn, Barbara. The Whole Lay Ministry Catalog. (Orig.). 1979. pap. 8.95 (ISBN 0-8164-2187-0, HarpR). Har-Row.

Kuhn, Heinz. Der Gemeinschaftagedanke Bei Chesterton. pap. 10.00 (ISBN 0-384-30680-2). Johnson Repr.

Kuhn, Isobel. By Searching. 1959. pap. 3.95 (ISBN 0-8024-0053-1). Moody.

--In the Arena. 1960. pap. 3.95 (ISBN 9971-972-19-0). OMF Bks.

--Nests Above the Abyss. pap. 3.95 (ISBN 9971-83-817-6). OMF Bks.

--Second-Mile People. 1982. pap. 3.50 (ISBN 0-85363-145-X). OMF Bks.

--Stones of Fire. 1951. pap. 3.95 (ISBN 9971-972-00-X). OMF Bks.

Kuhn, Margaret E. Maggie Kuhn on Aging. Hessel, Dieter, ed. LC 77-24294. 140p. 1977. pap. 3.95 (ISBN 0-664-24146-8). Westminster.

Kuhn, Wilfried. Das Prinzipieproblem in der Philosophie des Thomas von Aquin. (Bochum Studies in Philosophy Ser.: No. 1). 531p. 1982. 40.00x (ISBN 90-6032-227-4, Pub by B R Gruener Amsterdam). Benjamins North Am.

Kuhne, Gary W. The Change Factor: The Risks & the Joys. 128p. 1986. pap. 5.95 (ISBN 0-310-27251-3, 12316). Zondervan.

--La Dinamica de Adiestrar Discipulos. 160p. 1980. 2.95 (ISBN 0-88113-040-0). Edit Betania.

--The Dynamics of Discipleship Training. 1977. pap. 5.95 (ISBN 0-310-26961-X, 12311P). Zondervan.

--The Dynamics of Personal Follow-up. 192p. 1976. pap. 5.95 (ISBN 0-310-26951-2, 12310P). Zondervan.

Kuhner, Hans. Dictionnaire des Papes. (Fr.). pap. 6.95 (ISBN 0-686-56856-7, M-6634). French & Eur.

Kuhns, Dennis R. Women in the Church. LC 78-53968. 80p. (Orig.). 1978. pap. 2.95 (ISBN 0-8361-1852-9). Herald Pr.

Kuiper, B. K. The Church in History. pap. 12.95x (ISBN 0-8028-1777-7); tchrs.' manual 6.95x (ISBN 0-8028-1314-3). Eerdmans.

Kuiper, R. B. The Bible Tells Us So: Twelve Short Chapters on Major Themes of the Bible. 1978. pap. 3.45 (ISBN 0-85151-001-9). Banner of Truth.

--God Centered Evangelism. 1978. pap. 5.45 (ISBN 0-85151-110-4). Banner of Truth.

Kuist, Howard T. Jeremiah, Lamentations. LC 59-10454. (Layman's Bible Commentary Ser: Vol. 12). 1960. pap. 4.95 (ISBN 0-8042-3072-2). John Knox.

Kuitert, H. M. Everything Is Politics but Politics Is Not Everything. Bowden, John, tr. from Dutch. 208p. (Orig.). 1986. pap. 8.95 (ISBN 0-8028-0235-4). Eerdmans.

Kujath, Mentor, ed. see Gedde, Palmer.

Kujath, Mentor, ed. see Lauterbach, William.

Kuklick, Bruce. Churchmen & Philosophers: From Jonathan Edwards to John Dewey. LC 84-19579. 352p. 1985. 30.00 (ISBN 0-300-03269-2). Yale U Pr.

--Jonathan Edwards Jr. Works, 2 vols. (American Religious Thought of the 18th & 19th Centuries Ser.). 1114p. 1987. Set. lib. bdg. 145.00 (ISBN 0-8240-6953-6). Garland Pub.

--Nathaniel Emmons: Works, 6 vols. (American Religious Thought of the 18th & 19th Centuries Ser.). 4935p. 1987. Set. lib. bdg. 620.00 (ISBN 0-8240-6952-8). Garland Pub.

--Samuel Hopkins Works, 3 vols. (American Religious Thought of the 18th & 19th Centuries Ser.). 1838p. 1987. Set. lib. bdg. 240.00 (ISBN 0-8240-6951-X). Garland Pub.

Kuklick, Bruce, ed. The Unitarian Controversy, 1819-1823, 2 vols. (American Religious Thought of the 18th & 19th Centuries Ser.). 857p. 1987. Set. lib. bdg. 120.00 (ISBN 0-8240-6958-7). Garland Pub.

Kuklick, Bruce, ed. see Boardman, George N.

Kuklick, Bruce, ed. see Bushnell, Horace.

Kuklick, Bruce, ed. see Fisher, George P.

Kuklick, Bruce, ed. see Foster, Frank H.

Kuklick, Bruce, ed. see Hodge, Charles.

Kuklick, Bruce, ed. see Nevin, John W.

Kuklick, Bruce, ed. see Park, Edwards A.

Kuklick, Bruce, ed. see Pope, Earl.

Kuklick, Bruce, ed. see Schaff, Philip.

Kuklick, Bruce, ed. see Smith, Henry B.

Kuklick, Bruce, ed. see Smith, Hilary S.

Kuklick, Bruce, ed. see Taylor, Nathaniel W.

Kuklick, Bruce, ed. see Wayland, John T.

Kukoff, Lydia. Choosing Judaism. (Orig.). 1981. 10.00 (ISBN 0-8074-0151-X); pap. 5.95 (ISBN 0-8074-0150-1). UAHC.

--Choosing Judaism. 152p. (Orig.). 1983. pap. 5.95 (ISBN 0-686-88518-X, Pub. by UAHC Israel). Hippocrene Bks.

Kulka, Erich. Escape from Auschwitz. (Illus.). 192p. (Orig.). 1986. 27.95 (ISBN 0-89789-088-4); pap. 12.95 (ISBN 0-89789-089-2). Bergin & Garvey.

Kulp, Kim. Yes. 144p. (Orig.). 1987. pap. 5.95 (ISBN 0-937947-03-2). Publius Pub.

Kulp, Mary A. No Longer Strangers: A Biogrpahy of H. Stover Kulp. LC 68-4439. pap. 47.00 (ISBN 0-317-28389-8, 2022413). Bks Demand UMI.

Kumarappa, B., ed. see Gandhi, M. K.

Kumarappa, Bharatan. Realism & Illusionism in Hinduism. xvi, 356p. 1986. Repr. text ed. 40.00x (ISBN 81-7047-012-9, Pub. by Mayur Pubns India). Apt Bks.

Kummer, Irene. Blaise Pascal: Das Heil Im Widerspruch. 1978. 56.80x (ISBN 3-11-007253-X). De Gruyter.

Kunath, Anne & Riegert, Lillian. Prayers & Inspiration for Senior Children of God. 1979. pap. 1.75. De Vorss.

Kundakunda Acharya. Building of the Cosmos; Or, Panchastikayasara (the Five Cosmic Constituents) Chakravartinayanan, A., ed. LC 73-3837. (No. 3). Repr. of 1920 ed. 25.00 (ISBN 0-404-57703-2). AMS Pr.

--Niyamsara (the Perfect Law) Sain, Uggar, tr. & intro. by. LC 73-3844. (Sacred Books of the Jainas: No. 9). Repr. of 1931 ed. 18.00 (ISBN 0-404-57709-1). AMS Pr.

--Samayasara (the Soul Essence) Jaini, Rai B., tr. & commentaries by. LC 73-3843. (Sacred Books of the Jainas: No. 8). Repr. of 1930 ed. 25.00 (ISBN 0-404-57708-3). AMS Pr.

Kung, Hans. The Church. 600p. 1976. pap. 6.95 (ISBN 0-385-11367-6, Im). Doubleday.

--The Church-Maintained in Truth: A Theological Meditation. LC 81-69569. 88p. 1982. pap. 2.95 (ISBN 0-394-70816-4, Vin). Random.

--Do We Know the Others? LC 66-20895. (Concilium Ser.: Vol. 14). 196p. 1966. 7.95 (ISBN 0-8091-0033-9). Paulist Pr.

--Does God Exist? An Answer for Today. LC 81-40072. 864p. 1981. pap. 10.95 (ISBN 0-394-74737-2, Vin). Random.

--Eternal Life: Life after Death as a Medical, Philosophical, & Theological Problem. Quinn, Edward, tr. LC 82-45112. 271p. 1984. 15.95 (ISBN 0-385-18207-4). Doubleday.

--Eternal Life: Life after Death As a Medical, Philosophical, & Theological Program. LC 82-45112. 288p. 1985. 9.95 (ISBN 0-385-19910-4, Im). Doubleday.

--Freud & the Problem of God. Quinn, Edward, tr. LC 78-25581. (Terry Lecture Ser.). 136p. 1980. 19.50 (ISBN 0-300-02350-2, Y-237); pap. 5.95 (ISBN 0-300-02597-1). Yale U Pr.

--The Incarnation of God. 660p. 1987. 34.50 (ISBN 0-8245-0793-2). Crossroad NY.

--Infallible? An Inquiry. LC 82-45641. 288p. 1983. pap. 10.95 (ISBN 0-385-18483-2). Doubleday.

--Justification: The Doctrine of Karl Barth & a Catholic Reflection. LC 80-26001. 378p. 1981. pap. 14.95 (ISBN 0-664-24364-9). Westminster.

--Structures of the Church. LC 82-4706. 350p. 1982. pap. 12.95 (ISBN 0-8245-0508-5). Crossroad NY.

Kung, Hans, ed. Apostolic Succession. LC 68-25948. (Concilium Ser.: Vol. 34). 196p. 1968. 7.95 (ISBN 0-8091-0003-7). Paulist Pr.

Kung, Hans & Moltman, Jurgen, eds. Christianity Among World Religions. (Concilium Nineteen Eighty-Six Ser.). 120p. 1986. pap. 6.95 (ISBN 0-567-30063-3, Pub. by T & T Clark Ltd UK). Fortress.

--Who Has the Say in the Church, Vol. 148. (Concilium 1981). 128p. (Orig.). 1981. pap. 6.95 (ISBN 0-8164-2348-2, HarpR). Har-Row.

Kung, Hans & Moltmann, Jurgen, eds. Conflicting Ways of Interpreting the Bible. (Concilium Ser.: Vol. 138). 128p. (Orig.). 1980. pap. 5.95 (ISBN 0-8164-2280-X, HarpR). Har-Row.

--Conflicting Ways of Interpreting the Bible, Concilium 138. (New Concilium 1980). 128p. 1981. pap. 5.95 (ISBN 0-8245-4771-3, HarpR). Har-Row.

--Mary in the Churches. (Concilium 1983: Vol. 168). 128p. (Orig.). 1983. pap. 6.95 (ISBN 0-8164-2448-9, HarpR). Har-Row.

Kung, Hans & Schillebeeckx, Edward, eds. Concilium: Religion in the Eighties. (Concilium Ser.: Vols. 131-140). 128p. (Orig.). 1980. pap. 53.55 (ISBN 0-8164-2283-4, HarpR). Har-Row.

--Concilium: Religion in the Eighties. (Concilium Ser.: Vols. 151-160). 128p. (Orig.). 1982. pap. 62.55 (ISBN 0-8164-2392-X, HarpR). Har-Row.

Kuniholm, Whitney. Amos: Israel on Trial. (Fisherman Bible Studyguide). 67p. 1981. saddle stitch 2.95 (ISBN 0-87788-043-3). Shaw Pubs.

--First & Second Thessalonians, First & Second Timothy, Titus, Philemon: A Daily Dialogue. (Personal Bible Studyguide Ser.). 120p. (Orig.). 1986. pap. 5.95 (ISBN 0-87788-809-4). Shaw Pubs.

--Galatians, Ephesians, Philippians, & Colossians: A Daily Dialogue with God. (Personal Bible Studyguide Ser.). 144p. 1983. pap. 5.95 (ISBN 0-87788-292-4). Shaw Pubs.

--John: A Daily Dialogue with God. (Personal Bible Studyguide Ser.). 155p. 1982. pap. 4.95 (ISBN 0-87788-431-5). Shaw Pubs.

Kunjavihari, Vasu. Lord Buddha & His Doctrine. LC 78-72458. Repr. of 1927 ed. 39.50 (ISBN 0-404-17326-8). AMS Pr.

Kunst, H. Evangelisches Staatslexikon. 2nd rev. ed. (Ger.). 1975. 125.00 (ISBN 3-7831-0463-7, M-7373, Pub. by Kreuz Vlg.). French & Eur.

Kuntz, Arnold G. Serving God Always. 1966. pap. text ed. 2.75 (ISBN 0-570-06645-X, 22-2014); pap. 5.85 manual (ISBN 0-570-06646-8, 22-2015). Concordia.

Kuntz, J. Kenneth. The People of Ancient Israel: An Introduction to the Old Testament Literature, History & Thought. (Illus.). 1974. pap. text ed. 21.95 scp (ISBN 0-06-043822-3, HarpC). Har-Row.

Kuntz, Marion L., jt. auth. see Kuntz, Paul G.

Kuntz, Paul G. & Kuntz, Marion L. Jacob's Ladder & the Tree of Life: Concepts of Hierarchy & the Great Chain of Being. (American University Studies V-Philosophy: Vol. 14). 444p. 1987. text ed. 40.00 (ISBN 0-8204-0233-8). P Lang Pubs.

Kuntzleman, Charles T. The Well Family Book. 256p. 1985. 13.95 (ISBN 0-89840-092-9). Heres Life.

Kunz, Dora, compiled by. Spiritual Aspects of the Healing Art. LC 85-40410. 294p. (Orig.). 1985. pap. 6.50 (ISBN 0-8356-0601-5, Quest). Theos Pub Hse.

Kunz, George. The Curious Lore of Precious Stones. (Illus.). 14.50 (ISBN 0-8446-0173-X). Peter Smith.

Kunz, George F. Curious Lore of Precious Stones. 1970. pap. 7.95 (ISBN 0-486-22227-6). Dover.

Kunz, Marilyn. Patterns for Living with God. pap. 2.95 (ISBN 0-87784-409-7). Inter-Varsity.

Kunz, Marilyn & Schell, Catherine. Acts. (Neighborhood Bible Study Ser.). 1972. pap. 2.95 (ISBN 0-8423-0030-9). Tyndale.

--Amos (Neighborhood Bible Study) 1978. pap. 2.50 (ISBN 0-8423-0067-8). Tyndale.

--Celebrate. (Neighborhood Bible Studies). 48p. (Orig.). 1984. pap. 2.95 (ISBN 0-8423-0218-2). Tyndale.

--Choose Life. (Neighborhood Bible Studies). 1973. pap. 2.50 (ISBN 0-8423-0460-6). Tyndale.

--Corinthians One. (Neighborhood Bible Studies Ser.). 1974. pap. 2.50 (ISBN 0-8423-0441-X). Tyndale.

--Courage to Cope. (Neighborhood Bible Studies). 48p. (Orig.). 1984. pap. 2.50 (ISBN 0-8423-0446-0). Tyndale.

--Efesios y Filemon. Orozco, Julio, tr. from Eng. LC 77-83811. (Encuentros Biblicos Ser.). Tr. of Ephesians & Philemon. (Span.). 55p. 1977. pap. 1.25 (ISBN 0-89922-095-9). Edit Caribe.

--Ephesians & Philemon. (Neighborhood Bible Studies). 1973. pap. 2.95 (ISBN 0-8423-0695-1). Tyndale.

--Four Men of God, Neighborhood Bible Study. 1972. pap. 2.95 (ISBN 0-8423-0900-4). Tyndale.

--Genesis. 1981. pap. 2.95 (ISBN 0-8423-0995-0). Tyndale.

--Hebrews. (Neighborhood Bible Study). 1971. pap. 2.95 (ISBN 0-8423-1410-5). Tyndale.

--How to Start a Neighborhood Bible Study. (Neighborhood Bible Studies). 1970. pap. 2.00 (ISBN 0-8423-1540-3). Tyndale.

--How to Start a Neighborhood Bible Study. incl. cassette 8.95 (ISBN 0-8423-1533-0). Tyndale.

--John, Book One. 1978. pap. 2.95 (ISBN 0-8423-1895-X). Tyndale.

--John, Book Two. 1979. pap. 2.95 (ISBN 0-8423-1896-8). Tyndale.

--John, One, & James: Neighborhood Bible Study. 1978. pap. 2.95 (ISBN 0-8423-1930-1). Tyndale.

--Luke. (Neighborhood Bible Studies). 1973. pap. 2.95 (ISBN 0-8423-3880-2). Tyndale.

--Mark, Neighborhood Bible Study. 1970. pap. 2.95 (ISBN 0-8423-4101-3). Tyndale.

--Matthew Book One. 1980. pap. 2.50 (ISBN 0-8423-4188-9). Tyndale.

--Matthew Book Two. 1980. pap. 2.95 (ISBN 0-8423-4189-7). Tyndale.

--Peter, One & Two. (Neighbnorhood Bible Studies). 1973. pap. 2.95 (ISBN 0-8423-4820-4). Tyndale.

--Philippians & Colossians. (Neighborhood Bible Studies). 1974. pap. 2.95 (ISBN 0-8423-4825-5). Tyndale.

--Prophets of Hope. (Neighborhood Bible Studies). 48p. (Orig.). 1984. pap. 2.50 (ISBN 0-8423-4908-1). Tyndale.

--Psalms & Proverbs, Neighborhood Bible Study. 1971. pap. 2.95 (ISBN 0-8423-4991-X). Tyndale.
--Romans, Neighborhood Bible Study. 1970. pap. 2.95 (ISBN 0-8423-5701-7). Tyndale.
--Set Free. 1982. pap. 2.95 (ISBN 0-8423-5867-6). Tyndale.
--They Met Jesus, Neighborhood Bible Study. 1971. pap. 2.95 (ISBN 0-8423-7080-3). Tyndale.
Kunz, Phillip R., jt. auth. see Dyer, William G.
Kunze, Michael. Highroad to the Stake: A Tale of Witchcraft. Yuill, William, tr. LC 86-11230. (Illus.). 440p. 1987. 24.95 (ISBN 0-226-46211-0). U of Chicago Pr.
Kup, Karl. Christmas Story in Medieval & Renaissance Manuscripts from the Spencer Collection, the New York Public Library. LC 70-98680. (Illus.). 128p. 1969. pap. 10.00 (ISBN 0-87104-053-0). NY Pub Lib.
Kupfer, Grace H. Legends of Greece & Rome. 1911. 20.00 (ISBN 0-686-20105-1). Quality Lib.
Kupferle, Mary. God Will See You Through. 1983. 5.95 (ISBN 0-87159-043-3). Unity School.
Kupferle, Mary L. God Never Fails. 141p. 1983. pap. 4.95 (ISBN 0-87516-513-3). De Vorss.
--The Light Will Dawn. LC 77-91310. 1978. 5.95 (ISBN 0-87159-087-5). Unity School.
Kupperman, Robert H., jt. auth. see Brzezinski, Zbigniew.
Kuppuswamy, B. Elements of Ancient Indian Psychology. 305p. 1986. text ed. 30.00x (ISBN 0-7069-2620-X, Pub. by Vikas India); pap. text ed. 10.95x (ISBN 0-7069-2620-X, Pub. by Vikas India). Advent NY.
Kur'An. Here Begynneth a Lytell Treatyse of the Turkes Lawe Called Alcaron. LC 77-7411. (English Experience Ser.: No. 876). 1977. Repr. of 1519 ed. lib. bdg. 3.50 (ISBN 90-221-0876-7). Walter J Johnson.
Kuran, Aptullah. Mosque in Early Ottoman Architecture. LC 68-16701. (Publications of the Center for Middle Eastern Studies Ser). (Illus.). 1968. 25.00x (ISBN 0-226-46293-5). U of Chicago Pr.
Kurath, Gertrude P. Dance & Song Rituals of Six Nations Reserve, Ontario. (Illus.). 205p. 1968. pap. text ed. 5.50x (ISBN 0-660-02066-1, 56320-0, Pub. by Natl Mus Canada). U of Chicago Pr.
--Iroquois Music & Dance: Ceremonial Arts of Two Seneca Longhouses. Repr. of 1964 ed. 39.00x (ISBN 0-403-03618-6). Scholarly.
Kurdi, Abdulrahman A. The Islamic State: A Study Based on the Qur'an & Sunnah. 147p. 1984. 33.00x (ISBN 0-7201-1725-9). Mansell.
Kurelek, William. A Northern Nativity. (Illus.). 1976. 14.95 (ISBN 0-88776-071-6); pap. 5.95 (ISBN 0-88776-071-6). Tundra Bks.
Kurfees, M. C. Instrumental Music in Worship. 10.95 (ISBN 0-89225-106-9). Gospel Advocate.
Kurl, Shreeprakash, tr. The Devotional Poems of Mirabai. (Writers Workshop Saffronbird Ser.). 87p. 1975. 15.00 (ISBN 0-88253-722-9); pap. 6.75 (ISBN 0-89253-539-3). Ind-US Inc.
Kurland, Philip B. Church & State: The Supreme Court & the First Amendment. 1975. pap. 5.95x (ISBN 0-226-46402-4). U of Chicago Pr.
Kurt, Rudolph. Historical Fundamentals & the Study of Religions. 180p. 1985. 17.95x (ISBN 0-02-927190-8). Macmillan.
Kurth, Edwin W. Catechetical Helps. 1981. pap. text ed. 4.95 (ISBN 0-570-03507-4, 14-1261). Concordia.
Kurth, Erwin, et al. Growing in Christ: Catechism. (Illus.). 1953. text ed. 4.85 (ISBN 0-570-01517-0, 22-1097); wkbk. 1.95 (ISBN 0-570-01518-9, 22-1100). Concordia.
Kurth, Godefried J. Saint Clotilda. Crawford, M. V., tr. LC 72-171634. Repr. of 1906 ed. 7.00 (ISBN 0-404-03788-7). AMS Pr.
Kurtz, Ernest. Shame & Guilt: Characteristics of the Dependency Cycle. 68p. 4.95 (ISBN 0-89486-132-8, 1940A). Hazelden.
Kurtz, J. H. Sacrificial Worship of the Old Testament. Martin, James, tr. (Twin Brooks Ser.). 454p. 1980. pap. 8.95 (ISBN 0-8010-5419-2). Baker Bk.
Kurtz, John H. Sacrificial Worship of the Old Testament. 1979. 16.50 (ISBN 0-86524-012-4, 8703). Klock & Klock.
Kurtz, L. P. The Dance of Death & the Macabre Spirit in European Literature. 79.95 (ISBN 0-87968-188-8). Gordon Pr.
Kurtz, Lester R. The Politics of Heresy: The Modernist Crisis in Roman Catholicism. LC 85-1179. 256p. 1986. text ed. 32.50x (ISBN 0-520-05537-3). U of Cal Pr.
Kurtz, Muriel T. Prepare Our Hearts: Advent & Christmas Traditions for Families. 144p. (Orig.). 1986. pap. 6.95 spiral bdg. (ISBN 0-8358-0544-1). Upper Room.
Kurtz, Paul. In Defense of Secular Humanism. LC 83-62188. 273p. 1983. 18.95 (ISBN 0-87975-221-1); pap. 11.95 (ISBN 0-87975-228-9). Prometheus Bks.
--A Secular Humanist Declaration. 40p. 1981. pap. 2.95 (ISBN 0-87975-149-5). Prometheus Bks.
--The Transcendental Temptation: A Critique of Religion & the Paranormal. 450p. 1986. 18.95 (ISBN 0-87975-362-5). Prometheus Bks.
Kurtz, Paul, ed. Humanist Manifestos One & Two. 32p. 1973. pap. 2.95 (ISBN 0-87975-031-6). Prometheus Bks.
--Moral Problems in Contemporary Society: Essays in Humanistic Ethics. 2nd ed. 301p. 1973. pap. 10.95 (ISBN 0-87975-022-7). Prometheus Bks.
Kurtz, Seymour. Jewish America. LC 84-10065. (Illus.). 250p. 1985. 29.95 (ISBN 0-07-035655-6). McGraw.
Kurtzman, Jeffrey. Essays on the Monteverdi Mass & Vespers of 1610. LC 78-66039. (Rice University Studies: Vol. 64, No.4). (Illus.). 182p. 1979. pap. 10.00x (ISBN 0-89263-238-0). Rice Univ.
Kury, Zaher P. From a Gun to a Flower. (Illus.). 352p. (Orig.). 1985. pap. 13.50 (ISBN 0-9615041-0-2). Unity Pr.
--From a Gun to a Flower: Messages Through the Mediumship of Zaher P. Kury. (Illus.). 192p. 1984. 10.00 (ISBN 0-682-40160-9). Exposition Pr FL.
Kurz, Albert L. Disciple-Maker Workbook. 1981. pap. 10.95 (ISBN 0-8024-2217-9). Moody.
Kurz, Harry, tr. see La Boetie, Etienne.
Kurz, Otto, jt. auth. see Buchtal, Hugo.
Kurz, Ron. Step into Heaven, Here & Now: The Acrobatics of Soul. 48p. (Orig.). 1986. pap. 4.95 (ISBN 0-939829-00-2). R Kurz.
Kurz, William S. & Karris, Robert J. The Acts of the Apostles, No. 5. LC 82-20872. (Collegeville Bible Commentary Ser.). (Illus.). 112p. 1983. pap. 2.95 (ISBN 0-8146-1305-5). Liturgical Pr.
Kurzband, Toby, jt. auth. see Levin, Meyer.
Kurzinger, Josef. The Acts of the Apostles, Vol. I. McKenzie, John L., ed. LC 81-605. (The New Testament for Spiritual Reading Ser.). 227p. 1981. pap. 4.95 (ISBN 0-8245-0119-5). Crossroad NY.
--The Acts of the Apostles, Vol. II. McKenzie, John L., ed. LC 81-605. (The New Testament for Spiritual Reading Ser.). 227p. 1981. pap. 4.95 (ISBN 0-8245-0120-9). Crossroad NY.
Kurzweil, Arthur & Strauss, Ruby. My Generations: A Course in Jewish Family History. (Illus.). 128p. 1984. pap. 6.50x (ISBN 0-87441-383-4). Behrman.
Kurzweil, Arthur, jt. auth. see Strassfeld, Sharon.
Kurzweil, Zvi. The Modern Impulse of Traditional Judaism. LC 84-28892. 156p. 1985. 12.95 (ISBN 0-88125-068-6). Ktav.
Kusakratha dasa, tr. see Goswami, Srila Hridayananda dasa.
Kuschel, Harlyn J. A Study Guide for Philippians-Colossians & Philemon. Fischer, William E., ed. (Study Guide for People's Bible Ser.). 48p. (Orig.). 1987. pap. text ed. 1.50 (ISBN 0-938272-57-8). Wels Board.
Kuse, James A., ed. see Wiersum, Beverly.
Kushner, Arlene. The Ethiopian Jews: Photographs & Letters. 1986. pap. 9.95 (ISBN 0-933503-47-4). Shapolsky Pubs.
--Falasha No More: An Ethiopian Jewish Child Comes Home. (Illus.). 58p. 1986. 9.95 (ISBN 0-933503-43-1). Shapolsky Pubs.
Kushner, Arlene, jt. auth. see Auraham, Samuel.
Kushner, Eva, tr. see Mehl, Roger.
Kushner, Harold. Commanded to Live. LC 73-91738. 1973. 10.95x (ISBN 0-87677-154-1). Hartmore.
Kushner, Harold S. When Bad Things Happen to Good People. LC 81-40411. 160p. 1981. 11.95 (ISBN 0-8052-3773-9). Schocken.
--When Bad Things Happen to Good People. (General Ser.). 1982. lib. bdg. 13.95 (ISBN 0-8161-3465-0, Large Print Bks). G K Hall.
--When Children Ask about God. LC 76-9140. 1976. pap. 4.95 (ISBN 0-8052-0549-7). Schocken.
Kushner, Lawrence. The Book of Miracles: A Young Person's Guide to Jewish Spirituality. 96p. (Orig.). (YA) 1987. pap. text ed. 8.95 (ISBN 0-8074-0323-7). UAHC.
--Honey from The Rock: Ten Gates of Jewish Mysticism. LC 77-7832. 160p. 1983. pap. 7.95 (ISBN 0-06-064904-6, RD/442, HarpR). Har-Row.
--The River of Light: Spirituality, Judaism, & the Evolution of Consciousness. LC 80-7738. 192p. (Orig.). 1981. pap. 7.95 (ISBN 0-06-064902-X, RD 370, HarpR). Har-Row.
--The River of Light: Spirituality, Judaism, & the Evolution of Consciousness. LC 80-7738. 192p. 1981. 12.95 (ISBN 0-940646-00-5). Rossel Bks.
Kuske, David P. Catechism Handbook. 228p. 1982. three ring binder 19.95 (ISBN 0-938272-12-8). WELS Board.
--Luther's Catechism. (Illus.). 383p. 1982. text ed. 7.50 (ISBN 0-938272-11-X); pap. 2.50 catechism aid bklet. (ISBN 0-938272-13-6). WELS Board.
--A Study Guide for Paul's Letters to the Thessalonians. 41p. (Orig.). 1984. pap. 1.50 (ISBN 0-938272-51-9). WELS Board.
--Thessalonians. (People's Bible Ser.). 1984. pap. 4.95 (ISBN 0-8100-0193-4, 15N0406). Northwest Pub.
Kuspit, Donald, ed. see Mathews, Patricia.
Kustanowitz, Shulamit & Foont, Ronnie. A First Haggadah. LC 98-11598. (Illus.). 64p. 1980. 6.95 (ISBN 0-88482-766-6). Hebrew Pub.
Kutler, Sandy, ed. see Omaha Section National Council of Jewish Women.
Kutsche, Paul. A Guide to Cherokee Documents in the Northeastern United States. LC 85-11798. (Native American Bibliography Ser.: No. 7). 541p. 1986. 75.00 (ISBN 0-8108-1827-2). Scarecrow.
Kutscher, Austin H. & Kutscher, M. L., eds. Bibliography of Books on Death, Bereavement, Loss & Grief, Supplement, 1935-1971. 170p. 1970. pap. 9.95 (ISBN 0-930194-79-9). Ctr Thanatology.
Kutscher, M. L., jt. ed. see Kutscher, Austin H.
Kutscher, Martin L., et al, eds. A Comprehensive Bibliography of the Thanatology Literature. LC 75-5627. 285p. 1976. 14.00 (ISBN 0-8422-7274-7). Irvington.
Kutscher, Raphael. Oh Angry Sea (a-ab-ba hu-luh-ha) The History of a Sumerian Congregational Lament. LC 74-77343. (Near Eastern Researches Ser.: No. 6). (Illus.). 208p. 1975. 24.50x (ISBN 0-300-01579-8). Yale U Pr.
Kuykendall, Carol. Learning to Let Go. 160p. (Orig.). 1985. pap. 6.95 (ISBN 0-310-33621-X, 12763P). Zondervan.
Kuykendall, Carolyn. Babies of the Bible. (Happy Day Bks.). (Illus.). 24p. 1986. 1.59 (ISBN 0-87403-021-8, 3481). Standard Pub.
Kuykendall, John W. Southern Enterprize: The Work of National Evangelical Societies in the Antebellum South. LC 81-23723. (Contributions to the Study of Religion Ser.: No. 7). xv, 188p. 1982. lib. bdg. 29.95 (ISBN 0-313-23212-1, KSE/). Greenwood.
Kuykendall, John W., jt. auth. see Lingle, Walter L.
Kuykendall, John W., ed. see Old, Hughes O.
Kuykendall, John W., ed. see Wallace, Alston M., Jr.
Kuyper, Abraham. Lectures on Calvinism. pap. 3.95 (ISBN 0-8028-1607-X). Eerdmans.
--Principles of Sacred Theology. DeVries, J. Hendrick, tr. from Dutch. (Twin Brooks Ser.). 712p. 1980. pap. 12.95 (ISBN 0-8010-5420-6). Baker Bk.
--Women of the New Testament. pap. 4.95 (ISBN 0-310-36751-4, 9996P). Zondervan.
--Women of the Old Testament. pap. 5.95 (ISBN 0-310-36761-1, 9997P). Zondervan.
Kuyper, Neal A. No Matter What, We Still Love You. (Illus.). 40p. (Orig.). 1985. pap. 2.95 (ISBN 0-933350-48-1). Morse Pr.
Kuyvenhoven, Andrew. Partnership, A Study of the Covenant. 80p. 1983. pap. 2.50 (ISBN 0-933140-89-4). CRC Pubns.
--Romans: A Study Guide. (Revelation Series for Adults). 1976. pap. text ed. 2.50 (ISBN 0-933140-04-5). CRC Pubns.
Kuzma, Kay. Filling Your Loving Cup. Rev. ed. LC 83-60606. 1983. pap. 5.95 (ISBN 0-910529-02-7). Parent Scene.
--Living with God's Kids. LC 83-61552. 1983. pap. 5.95 (ISBN 0-910529-03-5). Parent Scene.
Kuzniewski, Anthony. Faith & Fatherland. 183p. 1980. text ed. 16.95 (ISBN 0-268-00948-1). U of Notre Dame Pr.
Kvamme, Rodney A. Miracles Today. 96p. (Orig.). 1986. pap. 4.95 (ISBN 0-570-04439-1). Concordia.
Kvanvig, Jonathan L. The Possibility of an All-Knowing God. LC 86-6465. 224p. 1986. 27.50 (ISBN 0-312-63195-2). St Martin.
Kverndal, Roald. Seamen's Missions: Their Origins & Early Growth. LC 85-25508. (Illus.). 936p. 1987. text ed. 29.95x (ISBN 0-87808-440-1, WCL440-1); pap. text ed. cancelled (ISBN 0-87808-439-8, WCL439-8). William Carey Lib.
Kvindlog, Norma, jt. auth. see Anderson, Esther.
Kwak, Chung H., ed. Principle of Creation. (Home Study Course Ser.). 60p. 1980. pap. 4.00. HSA Pubns.
--Resurrection (Five) (Home Study Course Ser.). 40p. (Orig.). 1980. pap. 4.00 (ISBN 0-910621-14-4). HSA Pubns.
--The Second Advent (6) (Home Study Course Ser.). 50p. (Orig.). 1980. pap. 4.00 (ISBN 0-910621-15-2). HSA Pubns.
Kwak, Chung Hwan, ed. The Fall of Man (2) (Home Study Course Ser.). 60p. (Orig.). 1980. pap. 4.00 (ISBN 0-910621-11-X). HSA Pubns.
--Home Study Course, 6 vols. (Orig.). Date not set. Set. 24.95 (ISBN 0-910621-09-8). HSA Pubns.
--The Mission of The Messiah (Three) (Home Study Course Ser.). 40p. (Orig.). 1980. pap. 4.00 (ISBN 0-910621-12-8). HSA Pubns.
Kwak, Chung Hwan Rev., ed. Consummation of Human History (4) (Home Study Course Ser.). 40p. 1980. pap. 4.00 (ISBN 0-910621-13-6). HSA Pubns.
Kwatera, Michael. The Liturgical Ministry of the Deacon. (Ministry Ser.). 96p. 1985. pap. 1.95 (ISBN 0-8146-1386-1). Liturgical Pr.
--The Ministry of Communion. (Illus.). 48p. 1983. pap. text ed. 1.25 (ISBN 0-8146-1292-X). Liturgical Pr.
--The Ministry of Servers. (Illus.). 48p. (Orig.). 1982. pap. 1.25 (ISBN 0-8146-1300-4). Liturgical Pr.
Kwatera, Michael & Reinhart, Dietrich. Prayers at Meals. 48p. 1983. pap. 0.50 (ISBN 0-8146-1318-7). Liturgical Pr.
Kwiatkowski, Diana, ed. The Poet Pope. 67p. 1981. 9.50 (ISBN 0-933906-16-1); pap. 4.50 (ISBN 0-933906-15-3). Gusto Pr.
Kwok, D. W. Scientism in Chinese Thought, Nineteen Hundred to Nineteen Fifty. LC 73-162297. 231p. 1972. Repr. of 1965 ed. 18.00 (ISBN 0-8196-0275-2). Biblo.
Kyani, A. S. Islam & Muslims in Red Regimes. pap. 4.50 (ISBN 0-686-18575-7). Kazi Pubns.
Kydd, Dr. Ronald A. Charismatic Gifts in the Early Church. 172p. 1984. pap. 4.95 (ISBN 0-913573-09-4). Hendrickson MA.
Kyes, Robert L., ed. The Old Low Franconian Psalms & Glosses. LC 69-15843. pap. 42.50 (ISBN 0-317-09363-0, 2051048). Bks Demand UMI.
Kyker, Rex, compiled by. I Am Born Again. (Undenominational Christianity Ser.: Vol. 2). 94p. (Orig.). 1983. pap. 2.95 (ISBN 0-88027-110-8). Firm Foun Pub.
Kyker, Rex, compiled by see Lemmons, Reuel & Bannister, John.
Kyker, Rex P. Sermons for Today, No. 1. LC 80-50106. 196p. 1980. 11.95 (ISBN 0-89112-401-2, Bibl Res Pr). Abilene Christ U.
Kyle, John E., compiled by. The Unfinished Task. LC 84-11727. 1984. pap. 6.95 (ISBN 0-8307-0983-5, 5418342). Regal.
Kyle, Louisa V. Country Woman's Christmas. LC 83-81553. (Illus.). 80p. 1984. 10.95 (ISBN 0-938694-12-X). JCP Corp VA.
Kyle, Melvin G. Excavating Kirjath-Sepher's Ten Cities. 19.00 (ISBN 0-405-10262-3, 14452). Ayer Co Pubs.
--Explorations at Sodom: Story of Ancient Sodom in the Light of Modern Research. Davis, Moshe, ed. LC 77-70715. (America & the Holy Land Ser.). (Illus.). 1977. Repr. of 1928 ed. lib. bdg. 12.00x (ISBN 0-405-10304-2). Ayer Co Pubs.
Kylin, Helen. When Silence Becomes Singing. LC 84-61827. 32p. (Orig.). 1985. pap. 2.50x (ISBN 0-87574-258-0). Pendle Hill.
Kyngeston, Richard. Expeditions to Prussia & the Holy Land Made by Henry Earl of Derby. Smith, L. T., ed. 1965. Repr. of 1894 ed. 27.00 (ISBN 0-384-30775-2). Johnson Repr.
Kysar, Robert. Augsburg Commentary on the New Testament- John. LC 85-26736. (Augsburg Commentaries on the New Testament Ser.). 336p. (Orig.). 1986. kivar 14.95 (ISBN 0-8066-8860-2, 10-9018). Augsburg.
--Augsburg Commentary on the New Testament: 1, 2, 3 John. LC 86-17416. 176p. (Orig.). 1986. pap. 9.95 Kivar (ISBN 0-8066-8862-9, 10-9044). Augsburg.
--The Fourth Evangelist & His Gospel: An Examination of Contemporary Scholarship. LC 75-22711. 320p. (Orig.). 1975. pap. 11.95 (ISBN 0-8066-1504-4, 10-2365). Augsburg.
--John, the Maverick Gospel. LC 76-12393. (Biblical Foundations Ser.). 1976. pap. 7.95 (ISBN 0-8042-0302-4). John Knox.
--John's Story of Jesus. LC 83-16537. 96p. 1984. pap. 4.50 (ISBN 0-8006-1775-4, 1-1775). Fortress.

L

Labacqz, Karen. Professional Ethics: Power & Paradox. 192p. (Orig.). 1985. pap. 11.95 (ISBN 0-687-34325-9). Abingdon.
Labadie, Laurance. Humanism & Morality. (Men & Movements in the History & Philosophy of Anarchism Ser.). 1979. lib. bdg. 59.95 (ISBN 0-685-96397-7). Revisionist Pr.
--Jesus As an Anarchist. (Men & Movements in the History & Philosophy of Anarchism Ser.). 1979. lib. bdg. 59.95 (ISBN 0-685-96404-3). Revisionist Pr.
Labarge, Margaret W. Court, Church & Castle. (Illus.). 112p. 1972. pap. 3.25 (ISBN 0-88884-431-X, 56310-3, Pub. by Natl Mus Canada). U of Chicago Pr.
LaBarre, Weston. The Peyote Cult. 4th ed. LC 75-19425. (Illus.). xix, 296p. 1975. 27.50 (ISBN 0-208-01456-X, Archon). Shoe String.

Labbe, Dolores E. Jim Crow Comes to Church: The Establishment of Segregated Catholic Parishes in South Louisiana. 14.00 (ISBN 0-405-10838-9, 11845). Ayer Co Pubs.
LaBerge, Agnes N. What God Hath Wrought. Dayton, Donald W., ed. (The Higher Christian Life Ser.). 127p. 1985. 20.00 (ISBN 0-8240-6425-9). Garland Pub.
Laberthonniere. Etudes sur Descartes, 2 tomes. Set. 29.90 (ISBN 0-685-34226-3). French & Eur.
Labib, Muhammad. The Seven Martyrs of Hurmuzak. Momen, Moojan, tr. & frwd. by. (Illus.). 80p. 9.95 (ISBN 0-85398-105-1); pap. 4.95 (ISBN 0-85398-104-3). G Ronald Pub.
La Boetie, Etienne. The Politics of Obedience: The Discourse of Voluntary Servitude. Kurz, Harry, tr. from Fr. Tr. of De la Servitude Volontaire. 88p. 1975. 19.95 (ISBN 0-919618-58-8, Dist. by U of Toronto Pr); pap. 9.95 (ISBN 0-919618-57-X, Dist. by U of Toronto Pr). Black Rose Bks.
La Boetie, Etienne de, jt. auth. see Montaigne, Michel de.
Labovitz, Annette & Labovitz, Eugene. Time for My Soul: A Treasury of Jewish Stories for Our Holy Days. LC 86-32243. 400p. 1987. 30.00 (ISBN 0-87668-954-3). Aronson.
Labovitz, Eugene, jt. auth. see Labovitz, Annette.
Labovitz, Sherman. Attitudes Toward Blacks among Jews: Historical Antecedents & Current Concerns. LC 75-5365. 1975. soft bdg. 12.00 (ISBN 0-88247-358-1). R & E Pubs.
Labrie, Ross. The Art of Thomas Merton. LC 79-1341. 188p. 1979. pap. 9.95x (ISBN 0-912646-55-1). Tex Christian.
Labriolle, Pierre C. Les Sources de l'Histoire du Montanisme. LC 80-13175. (Heresies of the Early Christian & Medieval Era: Second Ser.). Repr. of 1913 ed. 42.00 (ISBN 0-404-16184-7). AMS Pr.
LaBrosse, Olivier De, jt. ed. see Henry, Antonir Marie.
LaBud, Verona, jt. auth. see Coleman, Bernard.
Labunka, Miroslav & Rudnytzky, Leonid, eds. The Ukrainian Catholic Church: 1945-1975. LC 76-26753. 1976. 7.50 (ISBN 0-686-28475-5). St Sophia Religious.
Lace, O. Jessie. Understanding the New Testament. (Cambridge Bible Commentary on the New English Bible, New Testament Ser.). 16.95 (ISBN 0-521-04205-4); pap. 9.95 (ISBN 0-521-09281-7). Cambridge U Pr.
Lace, O. Jessie, ed. Understanding the Old Testament. LC 75-178282. (Cambridge Bible Commmentary on the New English Bible, Old Testament Ser.). (Illus.). 200p. 1972. 18.95 (ISBN 0-521-08415-6); pap. 9.95 (ISBN 0-521-09691-X). Cambridge U Pr.
Lacey, D. R. de see De Lacey, D. R.
Lacey, Paul. Quakers & the Use of Power. LC 81-85558. (Pendle Hill Pamphlets Ser.). 32p. (Orig.). 1982. pap. 2.50x (ISBN 0-87574-241-6, 241). Pendle Hill.
Lacey, Paul A. Leading & Being Led. LC 85-63379. (Orig.). 1985. pap. 2.50 (ISBN 0-87574-264-5). Pendle Hill.
Lacey, Thomas A. The Reformation & the People. LC 83-45583. Date not set. Repr. of 1929 ed. 22.00 (ISBN 0-404-19901-1). AMS Pr.
Lacey, Thomas A., ed. The King's Book, or a Necessary Doctrine & Erudition for Any Christian Man, 1543. (Church Historical Society, London, N.S. Ser.: No. 10). Repr. of 1932 ed. 40.00 (ISBN 0-8115-3134-1). Kraus Repr.
LaChance, Paul, tr. see Flood, David & Matura, Thadee.
Lachance, Paul, tr. see Leclerc, Eloi.
Lachance, Paul, tr. see Matura, Thaddee.
Lachance, Paul, tr. see Vorreux, Damien.
Lachmund, Margarethe. With Thine Adversary in the Way: A Quaker Witness for Reconciliation. Kite, Florence, tr. LC 79-91957. (Orig.). pap. 2.50x (ISBN 0-87574-228-9). Pendle Hill.
Lachs, John, ed. Animal Faith & Spiritual Life: Previously Unpublished & Uncollected Writings by George Santayana with Critical Essays on His Thought. LC 67-20665. (Century Philosophy Ser.). 1967. 39.50x (ISBN 0-89197-607-8). Irvington.
Lachs, Samuel T. Rabbinic Commentary on the New Testament: The Gospels of Matthew, Mark & Luke. 600p. 1987. 39.50 (ISBN 0-88125-089-9); pap. 19.95. Ktav.
Lackener, Bede K. The Eleventh-Century Background of Citeaux. LC 70-152484. (Cistercian Studies: No. 8). xxii, 305p. 1972. 7.50 (ISBN 0-87907-808-1). Cistercian Pubns.
Lackey, Donald L. Faith, the Ultimate Power. LC 81-52786. 144p. (Orig.). 1981. pap. 4.95x (ISBN 0-941116-00-X, 711A). Univ Pubns.
Lackner, Bede K., ed. Stephen of Sawley: Treatises. O'Sullivan, Jeremiah F., tr. 1984. 24.95 (ISBN 0-87907-636-4). Cistercian Pubns.
Lacocque, Andre & Lacocque, Pierre. Jonah Complex. LC 80-84649. 1981. pap. 8.95 (ISBN 0-8042-0092-0). John Knox.
Lacocque, Pierre, jt. auth. see Lacocque, Andre.
Lacomara, Aelred, ed. The Language of the Cross. 1977. 5.95 (ISBN 0-8199-0617-4). Franciscan Herald.
Lacordaire, Henry D. Henri Dominique Lacordaire: Essay on the Re-establishment in France of the Order of Preachers. Tugwell, Simon, ed. (Dominican Sources). 70p. 1983. pap. 4.00 (ISBN 0-9511202-1-2). Parable.
Lacoste, Auguste. Henri Arnaud und die Waldenser. (Basler und Berner Studien zur historischen und systematischen: Vol. 47). 213p. 1982. 20.00 (ISBN 3-261-04890-5). P Lang Pubs.
La Crawford, Richard see Crawford, Richard L.
Lacroix & De Djunkovskoy, E. Dictionnaire des Missions Catholiques, 2 vols. Migne, J. P., ed. (Troisieme et Derniere Encyclopedie Theologique Ser.: Vols. 59-60). (Fr.). 1545p. Repr. of 1864 ed. lib. bdg. 197.50x (ISBN 0-89241-325-5). Caratzas.
Lacroix, Paul see Jacob, P. L., pseud.
LaCroix, W. L. Meaning & Reason in Ethics. rev. ed. LC 79-52963. 1979. pap. text ed. 8.75 (ISBN 0-8191-0786-7). U Pr of Amer.
Lactantius. Divine Institutes, Bks. 1-7. LC 64-18669. (Fathers of the Church Ser: Vol. 49). 495p. 1964. 29.95x (ISBN 0-8132-0049-0). Cath U Pr.
--Minor Works. (Fathers of the Church Ser: Vol. 54). 1965. 15.95x (ISBN 0-8132-0054-7). Cath U Pr.
Lactantius, Lucius C. Opera Omnia: 1890-97, 4 pts. (Corpus Scriptorum Ecclesiasticorum Latinorum Ser: Vols. 19, 2 Pts.). 1890-97. Set Pts. 1 & 2. Vol 19. pap. 50.00 (ISBN 0-384-30865-1); Pts. 1 & 2 Vol 27. pap. 44.00 ea. Johnson Repr.
Lacue, Juan J., tr. see Francisco, C. T.
Lacueva, Francisco. Mi Camino de Damasco. Orig. Title: My Way from Damascus. (Span.). 112p. 1982. pap. 2.75 (ISBN 0-8254-1426-1). Kregel.
LaCugna, Catherine M. The Theological Methodology of Hans Kung. LC 81-16654. (American Academy of Religion Academy Ser.). 1982. 12.95 (ISBN 0-89130-546-7, 01 01 39). Scholars Pr GA.
Lacuria, Paul F. Les Harmonies De L'etre Exprimees Par les Nombres. LC 75-36848. (Occult Ser.). (Fr.). 1976. Repr. of 1899 ed. 55.00x (ISBN 0-405-07964-8). Ayer Co Pubs.
Lacy, C. Rosary Novenas. 1974. pap. 1.00 (ISBN 0-02-645810-1). Macmillan.
Lacy, Donald C. Healing Echoes: Values for Christian Unity. Sherer, Michael L., ed. (Orig.). 1986. pap. 6.25 (ISBN 0-89536-826-9, 6835). CSS of Ohio.
--Methodist Mass. 1984. 2.95 (ISBN 0-89536-977-X, 7533). CSS of Ohio.
Lacy, G. H. Introduccion a la Teologia Sistematica. (Span.). 417p. 1983. pap. 6.95 (ISBN 0-311-09032-X). Casa Bautista.
Lad, Vasant. Ayurveda, the Science of Self-Healing: A Practical Guide. Elliot, Malinda & Slavitz, Harriet, eds. LC 83-80620. (Illus.). 176p. (Orig.). 1984. text ed. 37.95 (ISBN 0-914955-01-2); pap. text ed. 9.95 (ISBN 0-914955-00-4). Lotus Light.
Ladany, L. The Catholic Church in China. LC 87-23. (Perspectives on Freedom Ser.: No. 7). (Orig.). 1987. pap. 5.00 (ISBN 0-932088-12-0). Freedom Hse.
Ladd, G., ed. see Lotze, H.
Ladd, George E. El Apocalipsis de Juan: Un Comentario. Canclini, Arnoldo, tr. from Eng. LC 78-50625. Tr. of A Commentary on the Revelation of John. (Span.). 269p. (Orig.). pap. 6.95 (ISBN 0-89922-111-4). Edit Caribe.
--Blessed Hope. 1956. pap. 6.95 (ISBN 0-8028-1111-6). Eerdmans.
--Commentary on the Book of Revelation of John. 1971. pap. 8.95 (ISBN 0-8028-1684-3). Eerdmans.
--Creo en la Resurreccion de Jesus. Blanch, Miguel, tr. from Eng. LC 77-79934. (Serie Creo). Tr. of I Believe in the Resurrection of Jesus. (Span.). 204p. 1977. pap. 5.95 (ISBN 0-89922-091-6). Edit Caribe.
--L' Evangile du Royaume. Cosson, Annie L., ed. Martin, Marie-Therese, tr. Tr. of The Gospel of the Kingdom. (Fr.). 192p. 1985. pap. text ed. 2.25 (ISBN 0-8297-1012-4). Life Pubs Intl.
--Gospel of the Kingdom. 1959. pap. 4.95 (ISBN 0-8028-1280-5). Eerdmans.
--I Believe in the Resurrection. (I Believe). 160p. 1975. pap. 5.95 (ISBN 0-8028-1611-8). Eerdmans.
--The Last Things. 1978. pap. 3.95 (ISBN 0-8028-1727-0). Eerdmans.
--New Testament & Criticism. 1966. pap. 6.95 (ISBN 0-8028-1680-0). Eerdmans.
--The Presence of the Future: The Eschatology of Biblical Realism. 1973. pap. 7.95 (ISBN 0-8028-1531-6). Eerdmans.
--A Theology of the New Testament. 1974. 24.95 (ISBN 0-8028-3443-4). Eerdmans.
Ladd, George T. Knowledge, Life & Reality: An Essay in Systemic Philosophy. LC 75-3221. Repr. of 1909 ed. 37.50 (ISBN 0-404-59217-1). AMS Pr.
--Philosophy of Conduct: A Treatise of the Facts, Principles, & Ideals of Ethics. LC 75-3222. Repr. of 1902 ed. 46.50 (ISBN 0-404-59218-X). AMS Pr.
--The Philosophy of Religion, 2 vols. LC 75-3225. 1976. Repr. of 1905 ed. 82.50 set (ISBN 0-404-59221-X). AMS Pr.
Ladd, John, tr. see Kant, Immanuel.
Ladendecker, Dianne. Holidays & Holy Days. 36p. 1986. pap. text ed. 6.95 (ISBN 0-8497-4854-2, C8630). Kjos.
Ladies Home Journal & Christian Science Monitor. America's Twelve Great Women Leaders During the Past Hundred Years As Chosen by the Women of America. facs. ed. LC 74-90600. (Essay Index Reprint Ser). 1933. 14.00 (ISBN 0-8369-1202-0). Ayer Co Pubs.
Ladies Of The Mission. Old Brewery & the New Mission House at the Five Points. LC 72-112563. (Rise of Urban America). (Illus.). 1970. Repr. of 1854 ed. 26.50 (ISBN 0-405-02461-4). Ayer Co Pubs.
Lady Queenborough. Judaism. 1982. lib. bdg. 55.95 (ISBN 0-87700-410-2). Revisionist Pr.
Laemmlen, Ann, jt. auth. see Owen, Jackie.
Laetsch, Theodore. Jeremiah. pap. 13.95 (ISBN 0-570-03218-0, 15-2003). Concordia.
--Minor Prophets. 1956. 16.95 (ISBN 0-570-03249-0, 15-1719). Concordia.
Laeuchli, Samuel. Power & Sexuality: The Emergence of Canon Law at the Synod of Elvira. LC 72-83671. 143p. 1972. 9.95 (ISBN 0-87722-015-8). Temple U Pr.
La Farge, Grant. Faith in God & Full Speed Ahead: Fe en Dios y Adelante. LC 84-23948. (Illus.). 160p. (Orig.). 1985. pap. 14.95 (ISBN 0-86534-050-1). Sunstone Pr.
LaFargue, J. Michael. Language & Gnosis: Form & Meaning in the Acts of Thomas Chapters 1-10. LC 84-45191. (Harvard Dissertations in Religion Ser.). 288p. 1984. pap. 14.95 (ISBN 0-8006-7016-7, 1-7016). Fortress.
Lafaye, Jacques. Quetzalcoatl & Guadalupe: The Formation of Mexican National Consciousness, 1531-1813. Keen, Benjamin, tr. from Fr. LC 75-20889. 1976. lib. bdg. 26.00x (ISBN 0-226-46794-5). U of Chicago Pr.
Laffey, Alice. The First & Second Books of Chronicles. (Bible Commentary Ser.). 96p. 1985. pap. 2.95 (ISBN 0-8146-1417-5). Liturgical Pr.
--The First & Second Kings. (Bible Commentary Ser.). 112p. 1985. pap. text ed. 2.95 (ISBN 0-8146-1416-7). Liturgical Pr.
Laffoucriere. Le Destin De la Pensee et, la Mort De Dieu, Selon Heidegger. (Phaenomenologica Ser: No. 24). 1968. lib. bdg. 29.00 (ISBN 90-247-0255-0, Pub. by Martinus Nijhoff Netherlands). Kluwer Academic.
Lafleur, Laurence J., tr. see Descartes, Rene.
LaFleur, William R. The Karma of Words: Buddhism & the Literary Arts in Medieval Japan. LC 82-45909. 232p. 1983. text ed. 30.00x (ISBN 0-520-04600-5); pap. 9.95 (ISBN 0-520-05622-1, CAL764). U of Cal Pr.
LaFleur, William R., ed. Dogen Studies. LC 85-16427. (Studies in East Asian Buddhism Ser.: No. 2). 288p. 1985. pap. text ed. 19.00x (ISBN 0-8248-1011-2). UH Pr.
La Follette, Marcel see Follette, Marcel la.
LaFontaine, Charles V. & Stone, Glenn C., eds. Exploring the Faith We Share. LC 79-92856. 144p. 1980. pap. 3.50 (ISBN 0-8091-2301-0). Paulist Pr.
Lafuma, Louis, jt. auth. see Pascal, Blaise.
Lagerkvist, Par. Barabbas. Blair, Alain, tr. (YA) 1955. pap. 2.95 (ISBN 0-394-70134-8, Vin). Random.
La Gorce, Pierre F. Histoire Religieuse de la Revolution francaise, 5 Vols. LC 71-88239. (Fr). Repr. of 1923 ed. Set. 235.50 (ISBN 0-404-03810-7); 47.00 ea. Vol. 1 (ISBN 0-404-03811-5). Vol. 2 (ISBN 0-404-03812-3). Vol. 3 (ISBN 0-404-03813-1). Vol. 4 (ISBN 0-404-03814-X). Vol. 5 (ISBN 0-404-03815-8). AMS Pr.
Lagorio, Valerie M., jt. auth. see Bradley, Ritamary.
LaHaye, Berverly & LaHaye, Tim. La Familia Sujeta al Espiritu. 208p. 1980. 3.75 (ISBN 0-88113-085-0). Edit Betania.
La Haye, Beverly. I Am a Woman by God's Design. 160p. 1980. pap. 5.95 (ISBN 0-8007-5100-0, Power Bks); study guide o.p. 3.95 (ISBN 0-8007-1294-3). Revell.
LaHaye, Beverly. La Mujer Sujeta al Espiritu. 208p. 1978. 3.25 (ISBN 0-88113-210-1). Edit Betania.
--The Restless Woman. 176p. 1984. pap. 5.95 (ISBN 0-310-27091-X, 18337P). Zondervan.
--The Spirit-Controlled Woman. LC 76-5562. 1976. pap. 4.95 (ISBN 0-89081-020-6, 0206). Harvest Hse.
LaHaye, Beverly, jt. auth. see LaHaye, Tim.
LaHaye, Tim. The Battle for the Family. (Illus.). 256p. 1981. power ed. 6.95 (ISBN 0-8007-5117-5). Revell.
--The Battle for the Mind. 224p. 1980. pap. 6.95 (ISBN 0-8007-5043-8, Power Bks). Revell.
--Beginning of the End. 1981. pap. 3.50 mass market (ISBN 0-8423-0114-3). Tyndale.
--The Coming Peace in the Middle East. 208p. 1984. pap. 6.95 (ISBN 0-310-27031-6, 18341P). Zondervan.
--Como Estudiar la Biblia por Si Mismo. 192p. 1977. 3.75 (ISBN 0-88113-042-7); 3.75 (ISBN 0-88113-033-8). Edit Betania.
--How to Be Happy Though Married. 1968. pap. 5.95 (ISBN 0-8423-1501-2). Tyndale.
--How to Be Happy Though Married. (Living Book Ser.). 1979. 3.50 (ISBN 0-8423-1499-7). Tyndale.
--How to Manage Pressure: Before Pressure Manages You. 240p. 1983. pap. 6.95 (ISBN 0-310-27081-2, 18336P). Zondervan.
--How to Study the Bible for Yourself. LC 76-5568. 1976. pap. 4.95 (ISBN 0-89081-021-4, 0214). Harvest Hse.
--How to Win Over Depression. 224p. 1974. pap. text ed. 6.95 (ISBN 0-310-26981-4, 18072P); pap. 3.95 (ISBN 0-310-26982-2, 18082P). Zondervan.
--Life in the Afterlife. Tyndale.
--Revelation-Illustrated & Made Plain. rev. ed. 456p. 1975. 7.95 (ISBN 0-310-26991-1, 18073P). Zondervan.
--Six Keys to a Happy Marriage. 1978. pap. 1.95 (ISBN 0-8423-5895-1). Tyndale.
--Ten Steps to Victory over Depression. 1974. pap. 1.50 (ISBN 0-310-27002-2, 18074P). Zondervan.
--Transformed Temperaments. 1971. pap. 5.95 (ISBN 0-8423-7306-3). Tyndale.
--El Varon y Su Temperamento. 217p. 1978. 3.95 (ISBN 0-88113-340-X). Edit Betania.
--Your Temperament: Discover Its Potential. 400p. 1984. 12.95 (ISBN 0-8423-8752-8). Tyndale.
--Your Temperament: Discover Its Potential. (Living Bk). 400p. 1987. pap. cancelled (ISBN 0-8423-8757-9). Tyndale.
LaHaye, Tim & LaHaye, Beverly. The Act of Marriage: The Beauty of Married Love. 1976. pap. 8.95 (ISBN 0-310-27061-8, 18077P); pap. 3.95 (ISBN 0-310-27062-6, 18083P). Zondervan.
--Spirit-Controlled Family Living. 224p. pap. 6.95 (ISBN 0-8007-5026-8, Power Bks). Revell.
LaHaye, Tim, jt. auth. see LaHaye, Berverly.
Lahey, Gerald B., jt. ed. see Hopper, Vincent F.
Lahiri, P. C. Concept of Riti & Guna in Sanskrit Poetics in Their Historical Development. xvi, 310p. 1974. 12.00x (ISBN 0-8364-0393-2). South Asia Bks.
Laidlaw, John. Studies in the Miracles of Our Lord. 390p. 1984. lib. bdg. 14.75 (ISBN 0-86524-168-6, 9518). Klock & Klock.
--Studies in the Parables of Our Lord. 352p. 1984. 13.25 (ISBN 0-86524-183-X, 9521). Klock & Klock.
Laidlaw, R. A., jt. auth. see Edman, V. E.
Laidlaw, Robert A. The Reason Why. 48p. 1975. pap. 1.95 (ISBN 0-310-27112-6, 18243P). Zondervan.
Laifer, Miryam. Edmond Jabes: Un Judaisme Apres Dieu. (American University Studies II: Romance Languages & Literature: Vol. 39). 165p. 1986. pap. 33.70 (ISBN 0-8204-0283-4). P Lang Pubs.
Laing, Alastair, ed. see Saalman, Howard.
Laing, David, ed. Original Letters Relating to the Ecclesiastical Affairs of Scotland, 2 Vols. LC 73-171637. (Bannatyne Club, Edinburgh. Publications: No. 92). Repr. of 1852 ed. 95.00 (ISBN 0-404-52833-3). AMS Pr.
--Registrum Cartarum Ecclesie Sancti Egidii De Edinburgh. LC 76-174803. (Bannatyne Club, Edinburgh. Publications: No. 105). Repr. of 1859 ed. 47.50 (ISBN 0-404-52860-0). AMS Pr.
--Registrum Domus De Soltre. LC 77-171638. (Bannatyne Club, Edinburgh. Publications: No. 109). Repr. of 1861 ed. 42.50 (ISBN 0-404-52863-5). AMS Pr.
Laing, David, ed. see Knox, John.
Laing, Gordon. Survivals of Roman Religion. LC 63-10280. (Our Debt to Greece & Rome Ser). 257p. 1963. Repr. of 1930 ed. 25.00x (ISBN 0-8154-0130-2). Cooper Sq.
Laing, Joseph & McClung, Grant. Effective Communications Instructor's Manual. 1977. pap. 5.25 (ISBN 0-87148-289-4). Pathway Pr.
Laird, Carobeth. Encounter with an Angry God. 1977. pap. 2.25 (ISBN 0-345-28464-X). Ballantine.
Laird, John. Enquiry into Moral Notions. LC 76-114045. Repr. of 1936 ed. 22.50 (ISBN 0-404-03802-6). AMS Pr.
--The Idea of the Soul. 1979. Repr. lib. bdg. 25.00 (ISBN 0-8495-3333-3). Arden Lib.
--Idea of the Soul. LC 76-107811. (Select Bibliographies Reprint Ser). 1924. 18.00 (ISBN 0-8369-5207-3). Ayer Co Pubs.

--Knowledge, Belief & Opinion. LC 72-6560. 515p. 1972. Repr. of 1930 ed. 37.50 (ISBN 0-208-01215-X, Archon). Shoe String.
--Mind & Deity. LC 70-114424. 322p. 1970. Repr. of 1941 ed. 32.50 (ISBN 0-208-00937-X, Archon). Shoe String.
--Theism & Cosmology. facs. ed. LC 74-84317. (Essay Index Reprint Ser). 1942. 21.50 (ISBN 0-8369-1147-4). Ayer Co Pubs.
Laird, M. A., ed. Bishop Heber in Northern India: Selections from Heber's Journal. LC 70-123673. (European Understanding of India Ser). (Illus.). 1971. 39.50 (ISBN 0-521-07873-3). Cambridge U Pr.
Laird-Brown, May, tr. see Steiner, Rudolf.
Lairdon, Roberts, ed. I Saw Heaven. 31p. 1983. pap. 2.00 (ISBN 0-915693-00-3). Christian Pub.
Laistner, Max L. Intellectual Heritage of the Early Middle Ages. 1966. lib. bdg. 24.00x (ISBN 0-88254-852-2, Octagon). Hippocrene Bks.
Laitin, David D. Hegemony & Culture: Politics & Religious Change among the Yoruba. (Illus.). xiv, 252p. 1986. 30.00 (ISBN 0-226-46789-9); pap. 13.95 (ISBN 0-226-46790-2). U of Chicago Pr.
Laity, Edward. Priesthood, Old & New. 1980. 2.25 (ISBN 0-86544-012-3). Salv Army Suppl South.
--Tabernacle Types & Teaching. 1980. pap. 2.95 (ISBN 0-86544-011-5). Salv Army Suppl South.
Lake, Alice. Our Own Years. 244p. 1982. pap. 8.95 (ISBN 0-86683-667-5, HarpR). Har-Row.
Lake, Frank. Clinical Theology. 256p. 1987. 18.95 (ISBN 0-8245-0821-1). Crossroad NY.
Lake, H. S., tr. see Van Eeden, Frederik.
Lake, John G. Adventures in God. 131p. 1981. pap. 4.95 (ISBN 0-89274-206-2). Harrison Hse.
Lake, John G., jt. auth. see Reidt, Wilford H.
Lake, K. Codex One of the Gospels & Its Allies. (Texts & Studies Ser.: No. 1, Vol. 7, Pt. 3). pap. 19.00 (ISBN 0-8115-1705-5). Kraus Repr.
Lake, Kirsopp & New, Silva, eds. Six Collations of New Testament Manuscripts. (Harvard Theol Studies). 1932. 24.00 (ISBN 0-527-01017-0). Kraus Repr.
Lake, Peter. Moderate Puritans & the Elizabethan Church. LC 81-17052. 345p. 1982. 57.50 (ISBN 0-521-24010-7). Cambridge U Pr.
Lake, Russell W. Thank God for Prayer. LC 83-50397. 293p. 1983. 5.95 (ISBN 0-87159-159-6). Unity School.
Lakey, George. Non-Violent Action: How it Works. 1983. pap. 2.50x (ISBN 0-87574-129-0, 129). Pendle Hill.
Lakhani, M. P. Spiritualism & Mysticism. x, 119p. 1984. text ed. 20.00x (ISBN 0-86590-381-6, Pub. by Inter Pubns N Delhi). Apt Bks.
Lakshmi Narasu, Pokala. The Essence of Buddhism. 3rd rev. & enl. ed. LC 78-72459. Repr. of 1948 ed. 32.50 (ISBN 0-404-17327-6). AMS Pr.
Lal, Basant K. Contemporary Indian Philosophy. xxi, 345p. 1986. 15.00 (ISBN 81-208-0260-8, Pub. by Motilal Banarsidass). South Asia Bks.
Lal, Hazra Kanai. Royal Patronage of Buddhism in Ancient India. 1984. text ed. 55.00x (ISBN 0-86590-167-8). Apt Bks.
Lal, P. An Annotated Mahabharata Bibliography. 31p. 1973. 10.00 (ISBN 0-88253-306-1). Ind-US Inc.
--The Mahabharata. 352p. 1980. (Pub. by Vikas India); pap. 14.50 (ISBN 0-686-77530-9). Advent NY.
Lal, P., tr. from Sanskrit. The Avyakta Upanisad. 25p. 1973. 8.00 (ISBN 0-88253-272-3). Ind-US Inc.
--The Brhadaranyaka Upanisad. (Saffronbird Bk.). (Eng.). 117p. 1975. pap. text ed. 6.75 (ISBN 0-88253-828-4). Ind-US Inc.
Lalitananda, Swami. Yoga in Life. (Illus.). 1972. pap. 2.99 - (ISBN 0-934664-17-X). Yoga Res Foun.
--Yoga Mystic Songs for Meditation, 6 Vols. 1975. pap. 2.99 ea. (ISBN 0-934664-19-6). Yoga Res Foun.
Lalitananda, Swami, ed. Yoga Quotations from the Wisdom of Swami Jyotir Maya Nanda. (Illus.). 1974. pap. 3.99 (ISBN 0-934664-27-7). Yoga Res Foun.
Lalive D'Epinay, Christian. Religion, Dynamique Sociale et Dependance: Les Mouvements Protestants En Argentine et Au Chili. (Interaction Ser: L'homme et Son Environnementsocial, No. 4). (Fr., Illus.). 368p. 1976. pap. text ed. 36.40x (ISBN 90-2797-922-7). Mouton.
Lalljee, Yousuf N. Know Your Islam. LC 81-51707. 256p. 1981. pap. 7.00 (ISBN 0-940368-02-1). Tahrike Tarsile Quran.
Lalo, Laurent. David & Goliath. LC 83-24975. (Illus.). 24p. 1985. 4.95 (ISBN 0-88070-044-0). Multnomah.
--Jesus & John the Baptist. LC 83-25075. (Illus.). 24p. 1985. 4.95 (ISBN 0-88070-045-9). Multnomah.
--Peter & the First Christians. LC 84-42946. (Illus.). 24p. 1985. 4.95 (ISBN 0-88070-084-X). Multnomah.
Lalwani, K. C. Dasavaikalika Sutra. 1973. 8.95 (ISBN 0-89684-192-8). Orient Bk Dist.
--Sramana Bhagavan Mahavira: Life & Doctrine. LC 75-904150. 1975. 10.00x (ISBN 0-88386-533-5). South Asia Bks.
Lalwani, K. C., tr. Jaina Stories. 1985. 15.00x (ISBN 0-317-31633-8, Pub. by Arthat Prakashon). South Asia Bks.
Lam, Nora & Harrell, Irene B. China Cry. LC 79-63932. 120p. (Orig.). 1984. pap. 5.95 (ISBN 0-89221-110-5). New Leaf.
Lama Mipham. Clear Light: The Distinction Between Appearance & Reality. 1980. write for info. Dharma Pub.
Lama Mi-phan. Golden Zephyr. Kawamura, Leslie S., tr. from Tibetan. LC 75-5259. (Tibetan Translation Ser.: Vol.4). (Illus.). 192p. (Orig.). 1975. 12.95 (ISBN 0-913546-22-4); pap. 6.95 (ISBN 0-913546-21-6). Dharma Pub.
Lamartine, Alphonse de. A Pilgrimage to the Holy Land. LC 78-14368. 1978. Repr. of 1838 ed. 75.00x (ISBN 0-8201-1323-9). Schol Facsimiles.
Lamb, Bob. The Blood of Jesus: A Foundation for Faith. 1983. pap. 1.95 (ISBN 0-910709-07-6). PTL Repro.
--The Lord's Supper: More Than a Ritual. 1983. pap. 2.95 (ISBN 0-910709-08-4). PTL Repro.
--Speaking Blood: Speaking Faith. 1983. pap. 2.95 (ISBN 0-910709-09-2). PTL Repro.
Lamb, George, tr. see Gelin, Albert.
Lamb, Harold. The Crusades: Iron Men & Saints. 368p. 1983. Repr. of 1930 ed. lib. bdg. 36.50 (ISBN 0-89987-527-0). Darby Bks.
Lamb, John W. Saint Wulstan, Prelate & Patriot: A Study of His Life & Times. (Church Historical Society, London, New Ser.: No. 16). Repr. of 1933 ed. 40.00 (ISBN 0-8115-3139-2). Kraus Repr.
Lamb, M. L., tr. see St. Thomas Aquinas.
Lamb, Matthew L. History, Method, & Theology: A Dialectical Comparison of Wilhelm Dilthey's Critique of Historical Reason & Bernard Lonergan's Meta-Methodology. LC 78-18707. 1978. pap. 19.95_o.s. (ISBN 0-89130-238-7, 01-01-25). Scholars Pr GA.
--Solidarity with Victims: Toward a Theology of Social Transformation. LC 81-22145. 176p. 1982. 12.95 (ISBN 0-8245-0471-2). Crossroad NY.
Lamb, Shirley. Washing & Dressing Prayers with Jesus. 1983. pap. 1.50 (ISBN 0-910709-41-6). PTL Repro.
Lambe, John. A Briefe Description of the Notorious Life of J. Lambe. LC 76-57394. (English Experience Ser.: No. 811). 1977. Repr. of 1628 ed. lib. bdg. 3.50 (ISBN 90-221-0811-2). Walter J Johnson.
Lambek, Michael. Human Spirits: A Cultural Account of Trance in Mayotte. LC 81-1842. (Cambridge Studies in Cultural Systems). (Illus.). 272p. 1981. 39.50 (ISBN 0-521-23844-7); pap. 17.95 (ISBN 0-521-28255-1). Cambridge U Pr.
Lambek, Ruth. A Passion for the Divine. 1979. pap. 4.95 (ISBN 0-87516-289-4). De Vorss.
Lambert, Byron C. The Rise of the Anti-Mission Baptists: Sources & Leaders, 1800-1840. Gaustad, Edwin S., ed. LC 79-52573. (The Baptist Tradition Ser.). 1980. lib. bdg. 39.00x (ISBN 0-405-12441-4). Ayer Co Pubs.
Lambert, Eleanor R. In the Palm of His Hand: 1838 to 1984. LC 85-9036. (Illus.). 200p. 1985. 14.98 (ISBN 0-935304-92-4). August Hse.
Lambert, Gussie. Bulletin Builders. 3.95 (ISBN 0-89315-024-X). Lambert Bk.
--Facts from Acts. 1.50 (ISBN 0-89315-056-8). Lambert Bk.
--One Thousand Questions on Genesis. 2.50 (ISBN 0-89315-188-2). Lambert Bk.
Lambert, Herbert, ed. see Adams, Harry B.
Lambert, Herbert, ed. see Bayer, Charles H.
Lambert, Herbert, ed. see Bennett, Gordon C.
Lambert, Herbert, ed. see Boring, W. Eugene.
Lambert, Herbert, ed. see Brame, Grace A.
Lambert, Herbert, ed. see Christensen, James L.
Lambert, Herbert, ed. see Cleverly, D. W.
Lambert, Herbert, ed. see Cope, Lamar.
Lambert, Herbert, ed. see Farnsworth, Kenneth C.
Lambert, Herbert, ed. see Harrison, Russell F.
Lambert, Herbert, ed. see Hateley, B. J.
Lambert, Herbert, ed. see Keene, Laurence C.
Lambert, Herbert, ed. see Langford, Alec J.
Lambert, Herbert, ed. see Linn, Jan G.
Lambert, Herbert, ed. see McCall, Donald D.
Lambert, Herbert, ed. see McClelland, W. Robert.
Lambert, Herbert, ed. see Merrell, James L.
Lambert, Herbert, ed. see Miller, Roger F.
Lambert, Herbert, ed. see Morgan, Peter.
Lambert, Herbert, ed. see Nottingham, William J.
Lambert, Herbert, ed. see O'Brien, Marian M.
Lambert, Herbert, ed. see Patrick, Mary.
Lambert, Herbert, ed. see Pendleton, Winston K.
Lambert, Herbert, ed. see Purcell, William.
Lambert, Herbert, ed. see Ryan, James M.
Lambert, Herbert, ed. see Sampson, Tom S.
Lambert, Herbert, ed. see Smith, W. Alan.
Lambert, Herbert, ed. see Straughn, Harold.
Lambert, Herbert, ed. see Tremmel, William C.
Lambert, J. H. History of Siloam Missionary Baptist Church. pap. 2.50x (ISBN 0-686-12399-9). Church History.
Lambert, James F. Luther's Hymns. LC 83-45646. Date not set. Repr. of 1917 ed. 34.50 (ISBN 0-404-19855-4). AMS Pr.
Lambert, Jean C. The Human Action of Forgiving: A Critical Application of the Metaphysics of Alfred North Whitehead. (Illus.). 300p. (Orig.). 1985. lib. bdg. 26.00 (ISBN 0-8191-4596-3); pap. text ed. 14.50 (ISBN 0-8191-4597-1). U Pr of Amer.
Lambert, Malcolm. Medieval Heresy: Popular Movements from Bogomil to Hus. LC 76-49949. 446p. 1977. 54.50x (ISBN 0-8419-0298-4). Holmes & Meier.
Lambert, O. C. Catholicism Against Itself, Vol. 1. 11.95 (ISBN 0-89315-005-3). Lambert Bk.
--Catholicism Against Itself, Vol. 1. abr. ed. 1963. pap. 1.50 (ISBN 0-89315-012-6). Lambert Bk.
--Catholicism Against Itself, Vol. 2. 11.95 (ISBN 0-89315-006-1). Lambert Bk.
--Russellism Unveiled. 1940. pap. 3.50 (ISBN 0-88027-090-X). Firm Foun Pub.
Lambert, Regina. Every Woman Has a Ministry. LC 79-84321. (Illus.). 1979. pap. 2.95 (ISBN 0-89221-062-1). New Leaf.
Lambert, Richard D., ed. see Shur, Irene G. & Littell, Franklin H.
Lambert, W. A., tr. see Luther, Martin.
Lamberti, Marjorie. Jewish Activism in Imperial Germany: The Struggle for Civil Equality. LC 77-17325. (Yale Historical Publications: No. 119). 1978. 27.50x (ISBN 0-300-02163-1). Yale U Pr.
Lamberton, Robert. Homer the Theologian: Neoplatonist Allegorical Rading & the Growth of the Epic Tradition. LC 85-1184. (Transformation of the Classical Heritage Ser.: No. 9). 375p. 1986. text ed. 40.00x (ISBN 0-520-05437-7). U of Cal Pr.
--Homer the Theologian: Neoplatonist Allegorical Reading & the Growth of the Epic Tradition, Vol. 10. Date not set. price not set. Oxford U Pr.
Lambin, H. R., jt. auth. see Massion, J. C.
Lambin, Thomas O. An Introduction to Biblical Hebrew. 345p. 1971. text ed. write for info. (ISBN 0-02-367250-1, Pub. by Scribner). Macmillan.
Lambrecht, Jan. Once More Astonished: The Parables of Jesus Christ. 262p. 1981. pap. 9.95 (ISBN 0-8245-0093-8). Crossroad NY.
--The Sermon on the Mount: Proclamation & Exhortation. (Good News Studies: Vol. 14). 1985. pap. 12.95 (ISBN 0-89453-467-X). M Glazier.
Lambrides, Daniel H., jt. auth. see Crunlan, Stephen A.
Lamdon, Michele. How to Live with Jesus - Leader's Guide. 64p. 1981. pap. 4.95 (ISBN 0-89243-148-2). Liguori Pubns.
Lamech. Chronicon Ephratense: A History of the Community of Seventh Day Baptists at Ephrata, Lancaster County, Pennsylvania. Hark, J. Max, tr. LC 77-185946. (Research & Source Works Ser). 288p. 1972. Repr. of 1880 ed. lib. bdg. 22.50 (ISBN 0-8337-1993-9). B Franklin.
Lamera, Stephen. James Alberione: A Marvel for Our Times. (Illus.). 1977. 4.00 (ISBN 0-8198-0428-2); pap. 3.00 (ISBN 0-8198-0429-0). Dghtrs St Paul.
--Maggiorino. 1976. pap. 1.75 (ISBN 0-8198-0437-1). Dghtrs St Paul.
Lamigueiro, Fernando, ed. see Miranda, Juan C.
Lamm. The Royal Reach. 11.95 (ISBN 0-87306-133-0). Feldheim.
Lamm, Maurice. Jewish Way in Death & Mourning. rev. ed. LC 69-11684. 1972. pap. 7.95 (ISBN 0-8246-0126-2). Jonathan David.
Lamm, Norman. Faith & Doubt. 1986. 11.95x (ISBN 0-87068-138-9). Ktav.
--A Hedge of Roses: Jewish Insights into Marriage. LC 66-19539. 1977. pap. 2.95 (ISBN 0-87306-095-4). Feldheim.
--Supplement for the Days of Remembrance & Thanksgiving. 1973. 0.85x (ISBN 0-87306-079-2). Feldheim.
--Torah Lishmah: The Study of Torah for Its Own Sake in the Work of Rabbi Hayyim of Volozhin & His Contemporaries. 1987. 25.00 (ISBN 0-88125-117-8); pap. 16.95 (ISBN 0-88125-133-X). Ktav.
Lamm, Norman, ed. Treasury of Tradition. Wurzburger, Walter S. 462p. 1967. 9.95 (ISBN 0-88482-434-9). Hebrew Pub.
Lammens, Henri. Islam: Beliefs & Institutions. 1976. lib. bdg. 59.95 (ISBN 0-8490-2080-8). Gordon Pr.
--Islam: Beliefs & Institutions. Ross, E. Denison, tr. from Fr. 265p. Repr. of 1929 ed. text ed. 23.50x. Coronet Bks.
Lammers, Stephen E. & Verhey, Allen, eds. On Moral Medicine: Theological Perspectives in Medical Ethics. 680p. 1987. 35.00 (ISBN 0-8028-3629-1). Eerdmans.
Lammerts, Walter E. Why Not Creation? (Illus.). 388p. (Orig.). 1970. pap. 6.95 (ISBN 0-8010-5528-8). Creation Research.
Lamont, Corliss. Humanist Funeral Service. 3rd ed. LC 77-76001. 48p. 1977. pap. 6.95 (ISBN 0-87975-090-1). Prometheus Bks.
--Illusion of Immortality. 4th ed. LC 65-25140. 1965. pap. 6.95 (ISBN 0-8044-6377-8). Ungar.
--The Philosophy of Humanism. 6th ed. LC 81-70127. 340p. 1982. 15.95 (ISBN 0-8044-5997-5); pap. 9.95 (ISBN 0-8044-6379-4). Ungar.
--Philosophy of Humanism. 5th ed. LC 65-16612. 10.50 (ISBN 0-8044-5595-3); pap. 10.95 (ISBN 0-8044-6378-6). Ungar.
Lamont, S. Religion Inc. 1986. 49.75X (ISBN 0-245-54334-1, Pub. by Harrap Ltd England). State Mutual Bk.
Lamont, William D. Introduction to Green's Moral Philosophy. LC 78-20478. 1980. Repr. of 1934 ed. 21.45 (ISBN 0-88355-855-6). Hyperion Conn.
La Monte, John L., jt. auth. see Hubert, Morton J.
LaMotte, Victor S., jt. auth. see Magno, Joseph A.
Lampert, E. The Apocalypse of History: Problems of Providence & Human Destiny. 1948. 34.50x (ISBN 0-317-07646-9). Elliots Bks.
Lampkin, Bill. Palm Leaves, Peanuts, & Sixty-One Other Children's Sermons. LC 81-3497. 112p. 1981. pap. 6.50 (ISBN 0-687-30000-2). Abingdon.
Lamport, F. J. Lessing & the Drama. 1981. text ed. 39.00x (ISBN 0-19-815767-3). Oxford U Pr.
Lampson, Adelene. An Open Book to Padre Pio. 160p. 1986. 11.95 (ISBN 0-89962-554-1). Todd & Honeywell.
Lamsa, G. M., jt. auth. see Emhardt, William C.
Lamsa, George. Idioms in the Bible Explained & a Key to the Original Gospels. LC 85-42782. 128p. 1985. pap. 8.95 (ISBN 0-06-064927-5, HarpR). Har-Row.
Lamsa, George M. And the Scroll Opened. LC 67-23820. (Illus.). 1978. pap. 3.50 (ISBN 0-87516-274-6). De Vorss.
--Gospel Light: An Indispensable Guide to the Teachings of Jesus & the Customs of His Time. LC 86-45020. 416p. 1986. pap. 12.95 (ISBN 0-06-064928-3, HarpR). Har-Row.
--Old Testament Light. LC 84-48774. 1008p. 1985. 34.95 (ISBN 0-06-064924-0, HarpR); pap. 19.95 (ISBN 0-06-064925-9, HarpR). Har-Row.
Lamsa, George M., tr. Holy Bible. 29.45 (ISBN 0-317-52395-3, HarpR); pap. 19.95 (ISBN 0-317-52396-1, RD 423). Har-Row.
--Holy Bible: From the Ancient Eastern Text. 1248p. 1986. 29.95 (ISBN 0-06-064922-4, HarpR); pap. 19.95 (ISBN 0-06-064923-2, HarpR). Har-Row.
Lamson, David R. Two Years Experience Among the Shakers. LC 71-134418. Repr. of 1848 ed. 19.00 (ISBN 0-404-08477-X). AMS Pr.
Lamson, Theresa, jt. auth. see Aranza, Jacob.
Lamy, Lucie. Egyptian Mysteries: New Light on Ancient Spiritual Knowledge. Purce, Jill, ed. LC 81-66806. (The Illustrated Library of Sacred Imagination Ser.). (Illus.). 96p. 1981. pap. 9.95 (ISBN 0-8245-0055-5). Crossroad NY.
Lancashire, Douglas, tr. see Ricci, Matteo.
Lancaster, F. Matthew. Hang Tough. 24p. 1985. pap. 3.95 (ISBN 0-8091-2696-6). Paulist Pr.
Lancaster, Helen. Aging. 1980. pap. 4.50 (ISBN 0-8309-0290-2). Herald Hse.
Lancaster, John. The Spirit-Filled Church. LC 75-22584. 112p. 1975. pap. 1.25 (ISBN 0-88243-601-5, 02-0601, Radiant Bks). Gospel Pub.
Lancaster, Lewis, jt. ed. see Conze, Edward.
Lancaster, Lewis R., ed. The Korean Buddhist Canon: A Descriptive Catalogue. LC 75-40662. (Center for Korean Studies, UC Berkeley). 1980. 60.00x (ISBN 0-520-03159-8). U of Cal Pr.
Lancaster, Reid. Rejoice & Sing. 1984. pap. 2.95 (ISBN 0-8344-0126-6). Sweet.
Lance, Fran & King, Pat. Tell Your Secret. 128p. 1986. pap. 5.95 (ISBN 0-89221-142-3). New Leaf.
Lance, H. Darrell. The Old Testament & the Archaeologist. Tucker, Gene M., ed. LC 80-2387. (Guides to Biblical Scholarship: Old Testament Ser.). 112p. (Orig.). 1981. pap. 4.50 (ISBN 0-8006-0467-9, 1-467). Fortress.
Lancer, Bob. Inner Freedom Through Qabala. (Illus.). 134p. (Orig.). 1986. pap. 6.95 (ISBN 0-917913-02-7). Limitless Light.
Lanciani, Rodolfo. Pagan & Christian Rome. LC 67-23856. (Illus.). 1968. Repr. of 1892 ed. 27.50 (ISBN 0-405-08728-4, Blom Pubns). Ayer Co Pubs.
Lanckton, Alice K. Bar Mitzvah Mother's Manual. (Illus.). 304p. 1986. pap. 6.95 (ISBN 0-87052-283-3). Hippocrene Bks.

Land, Gary, ed. Adventism in America. 304p. (Orig.). 1986. pap. 14.95 (ISBN 0-8028-0237-0). Eerdmans.
Land, Philip, ed. Theology Meets Progress: Human Implications of Development. 1971. pap. 6.50 (ISBN 0-8294-0326-4, Pub. by Gregorian U Pr). Loyola.
Land, Sipke van der. Stories from the Bible-Newly Retold. LC 79-10049. pap. 51.30 (ISBN 0-317-39654-4, 2023224). Bks Demand UMI.
Landa, Gertrude see Aunt Naomi, pseud.
Landa, Myer J. Jew in Drama. LC 68-26290. 1968. Repr. of 1926 ed. 23.00x (ISBN 0-8046-0257-3, Pub. by Kennikat). Assoc Faculty Pr.
Landa, Robin. Religious Art: A Workbook for Artists & Designers. 272p. 1985. 29.95 (ISBN 0-13-773037-3); pap. 16.95 (ISBN 0-13-773029-2). P-H.
Landau, Elliott D. & Egan, M. Winston. Guiding Your Child: A 60-Point Checklist for Parents. LC 78-70361. 48p. 1978. pap. 3.95 (ISBN 0-88290-103-6). Horizon Utah.
Landau, Jacob M. The Hejaz Railway & the Muslim Pilgrimage: A Case of Ottoman Political Progaganda. LC 78-12918. pap. 73.80 (2027676). Bks Demand UMI.
Landau, Ron. The Book of Jewish Lists. LC 81-40500. 192p. 1982. 14.95 (ISBN 0-8128-2839-9). Stein & Day.
Landaw, Jonathan. Prince Siddhartha. (Illus.). 144p. 1984. 15.95 (ISBN 0-318-04415-3, Wisdom Pubns). Great Traditions.
--The Story of Buddha. (Illus.). 1979. 7.50 (ISBN 0-89744-140-0). Auromere.
Landaw, Jonathan, ed. see Gyatso, Geshe K.
Landaw, Jonathan, ed. see Yeshe, Lama & Rinpoche, Zopa.
Landaw, Jonathan, ed. see Yeshe, Lama T.
Lande, Nathaniel & Slade, Afton. Stages: Understanding How You Make Your Moral Decisions. LC 78-195000. 1979. 10.00 (ISBN 0-06-250510-6, HarpR). Har-Row.
Landersdorfer, Simon K., ed. Der Bael Tatpauopoos und Die Kerube Des Ezechiel. pap. 8.00 (ISBN 0-384-31200-4). Johnson Repr.
Landes, George M. A Student's Vocabulary of Biblical Hebrew. 56p. (Orig.). 1961. pap. text ed. write for info. (ISBN 0-02-367410-5, Pub. by Scribner). Macmillan.
Landes, Paula F. Augustine on Romans: Propositions From the Epistle to the Romans & Unfinished Commentary on the Epistle to the Romans. LC 82-10259. (Society of Biblical Literature, Texts & Translations Ser.). 124p. 1982. pap. 12.75 (ISBN 0-89130-583-1, 06-02-23). Scholars Pr GA.
Landgraf, Arthur. Commentarius Cantabrigiensis in Epistolas Pauli e Schola Petri Abaelardi, 3 vols. Incl. Vol. 1. In Epistolam Ad Romanos. 223p. 1937. 17.95 (ISBN 0-268-00133-2); Vol. 2. In Epistolam Ad Corinthios Iam et Iiam, Ad Galatas et Ad Ephesios. 1223p. 1960. 17.95 (ISBN 0-268-00134-0); Vol. 3. In Epistolam ad Philippenses, ad Colossenses, ad Thessalonicenses Primam et Secundam, ed Timotheam Primam et Secundam, ad Titum et Philemonem. 447p. 1944. 17.95 (ISBN 0-268-00132-4). (Mediaeval Studies Ser.: No. 2). U of Notre Dame Pr.
Landis, Benson Y. Outline of the Bible: Book by Book. (Orig.). 1963. pap. 5.95 (ISBN 0-06-463263-6, EH 263, B&N Bks). Har-Row.
Landis, Mary M. Health for the Glory of God. 1976. write for info. (ISBN 0-686-15484-3); tchr's. ed. avail. (ISBN 0-686-15485-1). Rod & Staff.
Landis, Paul M. Purity in the Christian Home. 1978. 0.95 (ISBN 0-686-25260-8). Rod & Staff.
Landman, L., ed. Messianism in the Talmudic Era. 59.50x (ISBN 0-87068-445-0). Ktav.
Landman, Leo. Rabbi Joseph H. Lookstein Memorial Volume. 1979. 35.00x (ISBN 0-87068-705-0). Ktav.
Landon, Harold R., ed. Reinhold Niebuhr: A Prophetic Voice in Our Time. (Essay Index Reprint Ser.). Repr. of 1962 ed. 11.00 (ISBN 0-518-10150-9). Ayer Co Pubs.
Landorf, Joyce. His Stubborn Love. pap. 2.95 (ISBN 0-310-27122-3, 9991P). Zondervan.
--I Came to Love You Late. 192p. 1981. pap. 3.50 (ISBN 0-8007-8411-1, Spire Bks). Revell.
--Irregular People. 1982. 9.95 (ISBN 0-8499-0291-6). Word Bks.
--Joseph. 1985. pap. 7.95 (ISBN 0-8007-5197-3, Power Bks.). Revell.
--Let's Have a Banquet: Or will One Dollar & thirtysix cents be Enough. 1968. pap. 4.95 (ISBN 0-310-27131-2, 9994P). Zondervan.
--Mourning Song. 192p. 1974. 10.95 (ISBN 0-8007-0680-3). Revell.
--The Richest Lady in Town. 1979. pap. 2.95 (ISBN 0-310-27142-8, 10123P). Zondervan.
--Silent September. 1984. pap. 10.00 (ISBN 0-317-14051-5). Word Bks.
--Tough & Tender. rev. ed. 160p. 1981. 9.95 (ISBN 0-8007-1283-8). Revell.
Landow, George. William Holman Hunt & Typological Symbolism. LC 77-91017. 1979. 42.00x (ISBN 0-300-02196-8). Yale U Pr.
Landregan, Steve. Reflections on Deacon Spirituality. (Orig.). Date not set. pap. price not set (ISBN 1-55586-150-4). US Catholic.
Landrum, Eli, Jr. More Than Symbol. LC 81-86669. (Orig.). 1983. pap. 3.95 (ISBN 0-8054-2304-4). Broadman.
Landsberg, Paul-Louis. The Experience of Death: The Moral Problem of Suicide. Kastenaum, Robert, ed. LC 76-19579. (Death & Dying Ser.). 1977. Repr. of 1953 ed. lib. bdg. 19.00x (ISBN 0-405-09576-7). Ayer Co Pubs.
Landsberger, Henry A., ed. Church & Social Change in Latin America. LC 77-85355. 1970. 21.95x (ISBN 0-268-00356-4). U of Notre Dame Pr.
Landsman, Michael. Doubling Your Ability Through God. 58p. 1982. pap. 2.25 (ISBN 0-89274-266-6). Harrison Hse.
--Supportive Ministries. 1981. pap. 1.95 (ISBN 0-89274-181-3). Harrison Hse.
Landsman, Michael, jt. auth. see Harrison, Doyle.
Landstrom, Elsie H. Friends, Let Us Pray. LC 79-146679. (Orig.). 1970. pap. 2.50x (ISBN 0-87574-174-6, 174). Pendle Hill.
Landtman, Gunnar. Origin of the Inequality of the Social Classes. LC 68-56332. (Illus.). 1968. Repr. of 1938 ed. lib. bdg. 22.50x (ISBN 0-8371-0522-6, LASC). Greenwood.
Landy, Francis. Paradoxes of Paradise: Identity & Difference in the Song of Songs. (Bible & Literature Ser.: No. 7). 1983. text ed. 29.95x (ISBN 0-907459-16-1, Pub. by Almond Pr England); pap. text ed. 16.95x (ISBN 0-907459-17-X, Pub. by Almond Pr England). Eisenbrauns.
Lane, A. C. Bible Truths. pap. 0.50 (ISBN 0-88243-696-1, 02-0696). Gospel Pub.
Lane, Belden C. Storytelling: Study Guide, The Enchantment of Theology Cassette Tapes. LC 86-6079. 24p. (Orig.). 1982. pap. 2.50 (ISBN 0-8272-3419-8, 10S2113). CBP.
Lane, Christel. Christian Religion in the Soviet Union: A Sociological Study. LC 77-801. 1978. 49.50 (ISBN 0-87395-327-4). State U NY Pr.
--The Rites of Rulers: Ritual in Industrial Society-the Soviet Case. LC 80-41747. (Illus.). 338p. 1981. 57.50 (ISBN 0-521-22608-2); pap. 18.95 (ISBN 0-521-28347-7). Cambridge U Pr.
Lane, David C. The Making of a Spiritual Movement: The Untold Story of Paul Twitchell & Eckankar. (Understanding Cults & Spiritual Movements Ser.: No. 1). (Illus.). 154p. (Orig.). 1983. pap. 9.95 (ISBN 0-9611124-0-9). Del Mar Pr.
Lane, Denis. God's Powerful Weapon. 1977. pap. 1.25 (ISBN 9971-972-21-2). OMF Bks.
--Keeping Body & Soul Together. 1982. pap. 2.25 (ISBN 0-85363-144-1). OMF Bks.
--When God Guides. 1984. pap. 3.95 (ISBN 9971-972-16-6). OMF Bks.
Lane, Dermont A. The Reality of Jesus. LC 77-70635. (Exploration Book Ser.). 180p. 1977. pap. 6.95 (ISBN 0-8091-2020-8). Paulist Pr.
Lane, Dermot, ed. Religious Education & the Future. 240p. (Orig.). 1987. pap. 9.95 (ISBN 0-8091-2877-2). Paulist Pr.
Lane, Dermot A. The Experience of God: An Invitation to Do Theology. LC 81-80873. 96p. (Orig.). 1981. pap. 4.95 (ISBN 0-8091-2394-0). Paulist Pr.
--Foundations for Social Theology: Praxis, Process & Salvation. (Orig.). 1984. pap. 7.95 (ISBN 0-8091-2622-2). Paulist Pr.
Lane, Francis E. American Charities & the Child of the Immigant: Study of Typical Child Caring Institutions New York & Massachusetts-1845-1880, Vol. 6. LC 74-1691. (Children & Youth Ser.). 188p. 1974. Repr. of 1932 ed. 18.00x (ISBN 0-405-05967-1). Ayer Co Pubs.
Lane, G. W. Doctrine of the New Testament in Ten Great Subjects. 127p. 1964. pap. 1.95 (ISBN 0-87148-250-9). Pathway Pr.
Lane, George A. Chicago Churches & Synagogues. iv, 236p. 1981. 25.00 (ISBN 0-8294-0373-6). Loyola.
--Christian Spirituality. 88p. 1984. pap. 3.95 (ISBN 0-8294-0450-3). Loyola.
Lane, Helen, tr. see Friedlander, Saul.
Lane, J., jt. auth. see Miller, Madeleine S.
Lane, Laura B. Praise the Lord with Psalms: Metrical Paraphrases of Selected Psalms. 1986. 5.95 (ISBN 0-533-06823-1). Vantage.
Lane, Tony. Harper's Concise Book of Christian Faith. LC 84-47728. (Illus.). 224p. (Orig.). 1984. pap. 9.95 (ISBN 0-06-064921-6, RD 523, HarpR). Har-Row.
Lane, Virginia. Little Lamb & the Good Shepherd. (Illus.). 48p. 1983. 6.95 (ISBN 0-89274-254-2). Harrison Hse.
Lane, W. Ben, ed. see Fogle, Jeanne S.
Lane, W. Benson, ed. see Fogle, Jeanne S.
Lane, William L. Call to Commitment: Responding to the Message of Hebrews. LC 85-15597. 192p. 1985. pap. 8.95 (ISBN 0-8407-5948-7). Nelson.
--Commentary on the Gospel of Mark. (New International Commentary on the New Testament). 1973. 18.95 (ISBN 0-8028-2340-8). Eerdmans.
--Highlights of the Bible: New Testament. LC 80-50543. 160p. 1980. pap. 3.50 (ISBN 0-8307-0676-3, S343118). Regal.
Lane, William L., et al. The New Testament Speaks. 1969. 16.95 (ISBN 0-06-064917-8, HarpR). Har Row.
Lane-Poole, S. Medieval India under Mohammedan Rule: A. D. 712-1764, 2 Vols. in 1. LC 52-33515. Repr. of 1951 ed. 29.00 (ISBN 0-527-54300-4). Kraus Repr.
Laney, J. Carl. Baker's Concise Bible Atlas. (Illus.). 192p. (Orig.). 1987. pap. 10.95 (ISBN 0-8010-5638-1). Baker Bk.
--The Divorce Myth. LC 81-7690. 152p. 1981. 8.95 (ISBN 0-87123-144-1, 230144). Bethany Hse.
--The Divorce Myth. pap. 5.95 (ISBN 0-87123-892-6, 210892). Bethany Hse.
--Ezra, Nehemiah. (Everyman's Bible Commentary Ser.). (Orig.). 1982. pap. 5.95 (ISBN 0-8024-2014-1). Moody.
--First & Second Samuel. (Everyman's Bible Commentary Ser.). 1982. pap. 5.95 (ISBN 0-8024-2010-9). Moody.
--A Guide to Church Discipline. 160p. 1985. 8.95 (ISBN 0-87123-834-9, 230834). Bethany Hse.
--Zechariah. (Everyman's Bible Commentary Ser.). (Orig.). 1984. pap. 5.95 (ISBN 0-8024-0445-6). Moody.
Laney, Lily. Thoughts from Heaven. 128p. 1986. 8.95 (ISBN 0-89962-542-8). Todd & Honeywell.
Lang, Andrew. Custom & Myth. 2nd rev. ed. LC 68-59267. Repr. of 1885 ed. 11.00 (ISBN 0-404-03817-4). AMS Pr.
--Custom & Myth. (Illus.). 1977. Repr. of 1885 ed. 14.95x (ISBN 0-85409-969-7). Charles River Bks.
--Magic & Religion. 59.95 (ISBN 0-8490-0576-0). Gordon Pr.
--Magic & Religion. Repr. of 1901 ed. lib. bdg. 22.50x (ISBN 0-8371-0933-7, LAMR). Greenwood.
--Modern Mythology. LC 68-54279. Repr. of 1897 ed. 16.75 (ISBN 0-404-03852-2). AMS Pr.
--Myth, Ritual & Religion, 2 Vols in 1. LC 68-54280. Repr. of 1906 ed. 35.00 (ISBN 0-404-03868-9). AMS Pr.
--Secret of the Totem. LC 70-115094. 1970. Repr. of 1905 ed. 16.75 (ISBN 0-404-03866-2). AMS Pr.
Lang, Bernhard. Monotheism & the Prophetic Minority: An Essay in Biblical History & Sociology. (Social World of Biblical Antiquity: No. 1). 191p. 1983. text ed. 22.95x (ISBN 0-907459-30-7, Pub. by Almond Pr England); pap. text ed. 10.95x (ISBN 0-907459-31-5). Eisenbrauns.
--Wisdom & the Book of Proverbs. 192p. 1985. pap. 10.95 (ISBN 0-8298-0568-0). Pilgrim NY.
Lang, Bernhard, ed. Anthropological Approaches to the Old Testament. LC 84-48723. (Issues in Religion & Theology Ser.). 176p. 1985. pap. 7.95 (ISBN 0-8006-1771-1, 1-1771). Fortress.
Lang, David M., ed. Lives & Legends of the Georgian Saints. 179p. 1976. pap. 4.95 (ISBN 0-913836-29-X). St Vladimirs.
Lang, Edgar A. Ludwig Tieck's Early Concept of Catholic Clergy & Church. LC 74-140044. (Catholic University Studies in German Ser.: No. 8). Repr. of 1936 ed. 28.00 (ISBN 0-404-50228-8). AMS Pr.
Lang, J. David. Devotion for Every Day. (Illus.). pap. cancelled (ISBN 0-87239-230-9, 2099). Standard Pub.
--Your Phone's Ringing! (Illus.). 64p. 1985. pap. 2.50 (ISBN 0-87239-897-8, 2827). Standard Pub.
--Your Phone's Ringing, No. 2. (Illus.). 64p. 1985. pap. 2.50 (ISBN 0-87239-898-6, 2828). Standard Pub.
Lang, John M. Studies in the Book of Judges. 473p. 1983. Repr. lib. bdg. 17.75 Smythe Sewn (ISBN 0-86524-151-1, 0603). Klock & Klock.
Lang, Joseph R., jt. ed. see Motte, Mary.
Lang, Jovian. Dictionary of the Liturgy. 1986. 8.00 (ISBN 0-89942-273-X). Catholic BK Pub.
Lang, June & Carl, Angela. Twenty-Six Children's Church Programs: Getting to Know Jesus. (Illus.). 112p. 1983. pap. 7.95 (ISBN 0-87239-608-8, 3378). Standard Pub.
Lang, Martin A. Acquiring Our Image of God: The Emotional Basis for Religious Education. LC 82-62968. 160p. (Orig.). 1983. pap. 6.95 (ISBN 0-8091-2537-4). Paulist Pr.
Lang, Paul H. Church Ushering. rev. ed. 1957. pap. 1.25 (ISBN 0-570-03522-8, 14-1141). Concordia.
--What an Altar Guild Should Know. 1964. ring bdg. 5.95 (ISBN 0-570-03501-5, 14-1528). Concordia.
Langdon, Arthur G. Old Cornish Crosses. 1977. lib. bdg. 134.95 (ISBN 0-8490-2367-X). Gordon Pr.
Langdon, Larry, ed. The Words of Jesus on Peace. LC 84-28866. (Illus.). 72p. 1985. pap. 3.95 (ISBN 0-943726-02-6). Langdon Pubns.
Langdon, Rohen. Lighthouse of Langdon: Presenting 20th Century Jehovah to Doomsday Man. 207p. 1980. 9.00 (ISBN 0-682-49637-5). Exposition Pr FL.
Langdon, Stephen H. Babylonian Menologies & the Semitic Calendars. LC 78-72744. (Ancient Mesopotamian Texts & Studies). Repr. of 1935 ed. 21.50 (ISBN 0-404-18192-9). AMS Pr.
--Semitic Mythology. LC 63-19090. (Mythology of All Races Ser.: Vol. 5). (Illus.). Repr. of 1932 ed. 30.00x (ISBN 0-8154-0133-7). Cooper Sq.
--Tammuz & Ishtar. LC 78-72750. (Ancient Mesopotamian Texts & Studies). Repr. of 1914 ed. 34.50 (ISBN 0-404-18193-7). AMS Pr.
Lange, A. H. Catechetical Review. pap. 0.55 (ISBN 0-570-03520-1, 14-1102). Concordia.
Lange, John, ed. see Lewis, Clarence I.
Lange, Martin & Iblacker, Reinhold, eds. Witnesses of Hope: The Persecution of Christians in Latin America. Jerman, William E., tr. from Ger. LC 81-38378. Orig. Title: Christenverfolgung in SudAmerica: Zeugen du Hoffnung. Tr. of Christenverfalgung in Sudamerica: Zeugen der Hoffreung. 176p. (Orig.). 1981. pap. 6.95 (ISBN 0-88344-759-2). Orbis Bks.
Lange, N. R. De see De Lange, N. R.
Lange, Nicholas de. Atlas of the Jewish World. (Cultiral Atlas Ser.). (Illus.). 240p. 1984. 35.00 (ISBN 0-87196-043-5). Facts on File.
Lange, Nicholas de see De Lange, Nicholas.
Langer, Fritz. Intellektualmythologie: Betrachtungen Uber das Wesen das Mythus und Die Mythologische Methode. Bolle, Kees W., ed. LC 77-79136. (Mythology Ser.). (Ger.). 1978. Repr. of 1916 ed. lib. bdg. 21.00x (ISBN 0-405-10546-0). Ayer Co Pubs.
Langer, Jiri. Nine Gates to the Chassidic Mysteries. new ed. Rossel, Seymour, ed. Jolly, Stephen, tr. from Czech, Fr. LC 76-5859. (Jewish Legacy Ser.). 266p. 1976. pap. text ed. 4.95x (ISBN 0-87441-241-2). Behrman.
Langer, Maryn. The Book of Esther. 224p. 1987. pap. 5.95 (ISBN 0-310-47841-3). Zondervan.
Langer, Susanne K. Mind: An Essay on Human Feeling. Incl. Vol. I. Mind. (Illus.). 512p. 1967. 34.50x (ISBN 0-8018-0360-8); pap. 11.95 (ISBN 0-8018-1150-3); Vol. II. 412p. 1973. 28.50x (ISBN 0-8018-1428-6); pap. 9.95 (ISBN 0-8018-1607-6); Vol. III. 264p. Set of 3 vols. 26.50 (ISBN 0-8018-2756-6); pap. 8.95 (ISBN 0-8018-2511-3); pap. 28.85x (ISBN 0-8018-2555-5). LC 66-26686. Johns Hopkins.
Langer, Susanne K., tr. see Cassirer, Ernst.
Langford, Alec J. Invitations to Communion. Lambert, Herbert, ed. LC 86-6116. 112p. (Orig.). 1986. pap. 7.95 (ISBN 0-8272-1607-6). CBP.
Langford, Anne. Meditation for Little People. LC 75-46191. (Illus.). 40p. 1976. pap. 3.00 (ISBN 0-87516-211-8). De Vorss.
Langford, Jerome J. Galileo, Science & the Church. rev. ed. 1971. pap. 7.95x (ISBN 0-472-06173-9, 173, AA). U of Mich Pr.
Langford, Thomas. Prayer & the Common Life. LC 83-51396. 96p. (Orig.). 1984. pap. 3.95 (ISBN 0-8358-0473-9). Upper Room.
Langford, Thomas A. Christian Wholeness. LC 78-58011. 1979. pap. 3.50x (ISBN 0-8358-0383-X). Upper Room.
--Harvest of the Spirit. LC 81-50602. 64p. 1981. pap. 3.50x (ISBN 0-8358-0428-3). Upper Room.
--Practical Divinity: Theology in the Wesleyan Tradition. 304p. (Orig.). 1983. pap. 9.95 (ISBN 0-687-33326-1). Abingdon.
--Wesleyan Theology: A Sourcebook. 326p. 1984. lib. bdg. 24.95 (ISBN 0-939464-40-3); pap. 14.95 (ISBN 0-939464-41-1). Labyrinth Pr.
Langford, Thomas A., jt. ed. see Abernethy, George L.
Langford, Thomas A., III & Jones, Bonnie S. The Worship Handbook: A Practical Guide to Reform & Renewal. LC 84-70648. 88p. (Orig.). 1984. pap. 5.95 (ISBN 0-88177-011-6, DRO11B). Discipleship Res.
Langley, Florence. With Prayer & Psalm: The History of Wilmot, New Hampshire Churches. LC 81-5116. 80p. 1981. 7.95x (ISBN 0-914016-77-6). Phoenix Pub.
Langley, G. H. Sri Aurobindo. 59.95 (ISBN 0-8490-1119-1). Gordon Pr.
Langley, Myrtle. Religions. (Book of Beliefs Ser.). 1981. 9.95 (ISBN 0-89191-478-1, 54783). Cook.
Langley, Myrtle, et al. A Book of Beliefs. Alexander, P., ed. 192p. 1987. pap. 12.95 (ISBN 0-85648-504-7). Lion USA.
Langley, Noel, ed. see Swain, Jasper.

Langness, L. L. & Frank, Gelya F. Lives: An Anthropological Approach to Biography. Edgerton, R. B., ed. LC 81-15460. (Chandler & Sharp Publications in Anthropology Ser.). 232p. (Orig.). 1981. pap. 9.95x (ISBN 0-88316-542-2). Chandler & Sharp.

Lango, John. Whitehead's Ontology. LC 78-171184. 1972. 34.50x (ISBN 0-87395-093-3). State U NY Pr.

Langre, Jacques De see De Langre, Jacques.

Langsam, Aviva. Nichtov M'aleph V'ad Tav: Spirit Duplicating Primer. text ed. 15.00 (ISBN 0-915152-03-7, A05). Torah Umesorah.

Langsam, Avivia. M'aleph V'ad Tav: Spirit Duplicating Primer. text ed. 15.00 (ISBN 0-915152-02-9, A04). Torah Umesorah.

Langstaff, John & Langstaff, Nancy, eds. The Christmas Revels Songbook. LC 85-70140. (Illus.). 128p. 1985. cancelled (ISBN 0-87923-586-1); pap. 14.95 (ISBN 0-87923-591-8). Godine.

Langstaff, Nancy, jt. ed. see Langstaff, John.

Langston, A. Leon, ed. see Leavitt, Guy P.

Langston, Douglas C. God's Willing Knowledge: The Influence of Scotus' Analysis of Omniscience. LC 85-31956. 151p. 1986. 18.95x (ISBN 0-271-00429-0). PA St U Pr.

Langton, Edward. Satan, A Portrait: A Study of the Character of Satan Through All the Ages. LC 74-2434. 1973. lib. bdg. 35.00 (ISBN 0-8414-5716-6). Folcroft.

--Satan, a Portrait: A Study of the Character of Satan Through All the Ages. 1976. lib. bdg. 59.95 (ISBN 0-8490-2568-0). Gordon Pr.

Langton, H. H., tr. see Sagard-Theodat, Gabriel.

Lanham, Jan, jt. auth. see Paul, Cecil.

Lanier, Jean. Paraphrases for Pilgrims. 1977. pap. 1.75 (ISBN 0-89192-187-7). Interbk Inc.

Lanier, Roy H., Jr. Cross Questions Scripture Answers. pap. 1.75 (ISBN 0-89137-618-6). Quality Pubns.

Lanier, Roy, Sr. Outlines of Bible History. 2.50 (ISBN 0-89315-189-0). Lambert Bk.

--The Timeless Trinity. pap. 9.95 (ISBN 0-89137-551-1). Quality Pubns.

Lanman, Charles. Beginnings of Hindu Pantheism. 35.00 (ISBN 0-87968-719-3). Gordon Pr.

Lannan, Paul A. & Spaniol, LeRoy J. Getting Unstuck: Moving on after Divorce. (Orig.). 1984. pap. 5.95 (ISBN 0-8091-2580-3). Paulist Pr.

Lannie, Vincent. Public Money & Parochial Education: Bishop Hughes, Governor Seward & the New York School Controversy. 294p. (Pub. by Press of Case Western University). 1968. 16.95 (ISBN 0-268-00565-6). U of Notre Dame Pr.

Lanning, John T. Spanish Missions of Georgia. (Illus.). 1971. Repr. of 1935 ed. 39.00 (ISBN 0-403-00803-4). Scholarly.

Lannoy, Richard. Speaking Tree: A Study of Indian Culture & Society. 1971. 32.50x (ISBN 0-19-501469-3). Oxford U Pr.

Lanot, Marra P. Passion & Compassion: Mga Tula Sa Ingles at Pilipino. 153p. 1981. pap. 6.50x (ISBN 0-686-32581-8, Pub. by New Day Phillipines). Cellar.

Lans, J. M. van Der see Van Belzen, J. A. & Van Der Lans, J. M.

Lansbury, George. My Pilgrimage for Peace. Bd. with Peace Through Economic Cooperation. Lansbury, George. LC 70-147723. (Library of War & Peace; Peace Leaders: Biographies & Memoirs). 1972. lib. bdg. 46.00 (ISBN 0-8240-0251-2). Garland Pub.

Lansdowne, Zachary F. The Chakras & Esoteric Healing. LC 84-51108. 1986. pap. 8.95 (ISBN 0-87728-584-5). Weiser.

Lanslots, D. I. The Primitive Church. LC 79-67862. 295p. 1980. pap. 5.50 (ISBN 0-89555-134-9). TAN Bks Pubs.

Lanstrom, Edith. Christian Parent Burnout. LC 12-2979. (Continued Applied Christianity Ser.). 1983. pap. 2.95 (ISBN 0-570-03897-9). Concordia.

Lantero, Erminie H. Feminine Aspects of Divinity. LC 73-84214. 36p. (Orig.). 1973. pap. 2.50x (ISBN 0-87574-191-6). Pendle Hill.

Lantry, Eileen. Good People Get Burned Too. (Life Ser.). 1984. pap. 4.95 (ISBN 0-8163-0549-8). Pacific Pr Pub Assn.

Lantry, Eileen E. Dark Night, Brilliant Star. (Daybreak Ser.). 112p. 1981. pap. 2.89 (ISBN 0-8163-0397-5). Pacific Pr Pub Assn.

--He Chose to Listen. (Trailblazer Ser.). 85p. 1983. pap. 4.95 (ISBN 0-8163-0485-8). Pacific Pr Pub Assn.

Lanz, Kerry J. The Complete Server. (Illus.). 1978. 1.95 (ISBN 0-8192-1245-8). Morehouse.

Lanzone, R. V. Dizionario Di Mitologia Egizia, 3 vols. (Ital.). 1312p. 1974. 400.00x (ISBN 90-272-0931-6, 0932-4, 0933-2). Benjamins North Am.

--Dizzionario Di Mitologia Egizia, Vol. 4. xv, 205p. 1975. Repr. of 1881 ed. 80.00x (ISBN 90-272-0934-0). Benjamins North Am.

Laor, Eran. Maps of the Holy Land: Cartobibliography of Printed Maps, 1475-1900. LC 86-15298. 224p. 1986. 77.50 (ISBN 0-8451-1705-X). A R Liss.

Lao Tse. Tao. Mackintosh, Charles H., tr. 1971. pap. 3.25 (ISBN 0-8356-0426-8, Quest). Theos Pub Hse.

Lao Tsu. Tao Te Ching. Gia-Fu Feng, ed. English, Jane, tr. 1972. pap. 10.95 (ISBN 0-394-71833-X, V-833, Vin). Random.

Lao Tze. Treatise on Response & Retribution. Carus, Paul & Suzuki, D. T., trs. from Chin. LC 6-28775. (Illus.). 139p. 1973. pap. 2.95 (ISBN 0-87548-244-9). Open Court.

Lapati, Americo D. A High School Curriculum for Leadership. 1961. 14.95x (ISBN 0-8084-0375-3). New Coll U Pr.

La Perchia, Alex. A Spiritual Guide to Eternal Life. LC 77-75258. 89p. 1977. 6.95 (ISBN 0-8022-2203-X). Philos Lib.

Lapide, Cornelius A. The Personality of St. Paul. 1959. 3.50 (ISBN 0-8198-5802-1); pap. 2.25 (ISBN 0-8198-5803-X). Dghtrs St Paul.

Lapide, Pinchas. Hebrew in the Church. 208p. (Orig.). 1985. 24.95x (ISBN 0-8028-3615-1). Eerdmans.

--The Resurrection of Jesus: A Jewish Perspective. Linss, Wilhelm C., tr. LC 83-70514. 160p. (Orig.). 1983. pap. 8.95 (ISBN 0-8066-2020-X, 10-5485). Augsburg.

--The Sermon on the Mount: Utopia or Program for Action? Swindler, Arlene, tr. from Ger. Tr. of DieBergpre digt-Utopie oder Program? 160p. (Orig.). 1986. pap. 9.95 (ISBN 0-88344-248-5, 85-29810). Orbis Bks.

Lapide, Pinchas & Luz, Ulrich. Jesus in Two Perspectives. LC 85-15760. Tr. of Der Jude Jesus. 176p. 1985. pap. 8.95 (ISBN 0-8066-2171-0, 10-3517). Augsburg.

Lapide, Pinchas & Stuhlmacher, Peter. Paul: Rabbi & Apostle. Denef, Lawrence W., tr. LC 84-23482. 80p. (Orig.). 1984. pap. 5.95 (ISBN 0-8066-2122-2, 10-4903). Augsburg.

Lapidus, Ira M. Contemporary Islamic Movements in Historical Perspective. LC 83-82308. (Policy Papers in International Affairs: No. 18). viii, 76p. 1983. pap. 4.95x (ISBN 0-87725-518-0). U of Cal Intl St.

Lapierre, Dominique, jt. auth. see Collins, Larry.

LaPlace, Jean. An Experience of Life in the Spirit. Mooney, John R., tr. 220p. 1977. 6.95 (ISBN 0-8199-0594-1). Franciscan Herald.

--Preparing for Spiritual Direction. 196p. 1975. 6.95 (ISBN 0-8199-0558-5). Franciscan Herald.

Lapomarda, Vincent A. The Jesuit Heritage in New England. LC 76-42896. (Illus., Orig.). 1977. 8.00x (ISBN 0-9606294-0-8). Jesuits Holy Cross.

Lapon, Lenny. Mass Murderers in White Coats: Psychiatric Genocide in Nazi Germany & the United States. (Orig.). 1986. pap. 9.00 (ISBN 0-9614961-9-3). Psych Genocide Res.

LaPorte, Jean. The Role of Women in Early Christianity. LC 82-8281. (Studies in Women & Religion: Vol. 7). 196p. 1982. 39.95x (ISBN 0-88946-545-2). E Mellen.

La Porte, Linda M., jt. auth. see Meitler, Neal D.

Lapp, Elizabeth. Journal of Tears. 1984. 2.95 (ISBN 0-87813-522-7). Christian Light.

Lapp, Hannah B. To Belize with Love. LC 86-70999. 380p. (Orig.). (YA) 1986. pap. 14.95 (ISBN 0-931494-94-X). Brunswick Pub.

Lapp, John A. The Mennonite Church in India: Eighteen Ninety-Seven to Nineteen Sixty-Two. LC 75-186445. 248p. 1972. 12.95 (ISBN 0-8361-1122-2). Herald Pr.

Lapp, Nancy L., ed. The Tale of the Tell: Archaeological Studies by Paul W. Lapp. LC 75-5861. (Pittsburgh Theological Monographs: No. 5). 1975. pap. text ed. 9.25 (ISBN 0-915138-05-0). Pickwick.

Lapp, Rhonda S. Devotionals for Nurses. (Ultra Bks.). 4.95 (ISBN 0-8010-5539-3). Baker Bk.

Lappe, Marc & Morison, Robert S., eds. Ethical & Scientific Issues Posed by Human Uses of Molecular Genetics, Vol. 265. (Annals of the New York Academy of Sciences). 208p. 1976. 26.00x (ISBN 0-89072-019-3). NY Acad Sci.

Lappin, Peter. Conquistador. LC 69-19398. 1970. 6.95 (ISBN 0-89944-040-1). Don Bosco Multimedia.

--Dominic Savio: Teenage Saint. LC 54-11044. 1982. 2.75 (ISBN 0-89944-034-7, D Bosco Pubns); pap. 1.25 (ISBN 0-89944-033-9). Don Bosco Multimedia.

--The Falcon & the Dove: The Story of Laura Vicuna. (Illus.). 180p. (YA) 1985. pap. 4.95 (ISBN 0-89944-067-3). Don Bosco Multimedia.

--General Mickey. (Orig.). 1977. pap. 2.95 (ISBN 0-89944-029-0). Don Bosco Multimedia.

--Halfway to Heaven. LC 80-68485. 265p. (Orig.). 1980. pap. 6.95 (ISBN 0-89944-052-5). Don Bosco Multimedia.

--Stories of Don Bosco. 2nd ed. LC 78-72525. (Illus.). 1979. pap. 2.95 (ISBN 0-89944-036-3). Don Bosco Multimedia.

--Sunshine in the Shadows. LC 79-57184. 218p. 1980. pap. 6.95 (ISBN 0-89944-042-8). Don Bosco Multimedia.

--The Wine in the Chalice. (Orig.). 1972. pap. 3.25 (ISBN 0-89944-031-2). Don Bosco Multimedia.

Lapple, Alfred. A Concise History of the Catholic Church. (Orig.). 1985. pap. 4.95 (ISBN 0-8091-9567-4). Paulist Pr.

Lapsanski, Duane. Evangelical Perfection: An Historical Examination of the Concept in the Early Franciscan Sources. (Theology Ser.). 1977. 15.00 (ISBN 0-686-27933-6). Franciscan Inst.

Lapsanski, Duane V. The First Franciscans & the Gospel. 1976. 6.95 (ISBN 0-8199-0568-2). Franciscan Herald.

Laqueur, Thomas W. Religion & Respectability: Sunday Schools & English Working Class Culture, 1780-1850. LC 74-29728. 1976. 38.50x (ISBN 0-300-01859-2). Yale U Pr.

Laqueur, Walter. A History of Zionism. LC 75-36491. (Illus.). 1976. pap. 12.95 (ISBN 0-8052-0523-3). Schocken.

Laqueur, Walter & Rubin, Barry, eds. The Human Rights Reader. (Orig.). 1979. pap. 9.95 (ISBN 0-452-00853-0, F661, Mer). NAL.

--The Human Rights Reader. 384p. 1979. 29.95 (ISBN 0-87722-170-7). Temple U Pr.

Laracy, Hugh. Marists & Melanesians: A History of Catholic Missions in the Solomon Islands. 222p. 1976. text ed. 15.00x (ISBN 0-8248-0361-2). UH Pr.

Larcher, F. R., tr. see St. Thomas Aquinas.

Larcher, Fabian R., tr. see St. Thomas Aquinas.

Larimore, John. The Creator of This World & the Universe. LC 74-54161. 1979. 13.95 (ISBN 0-87949-115-9). Ashley Bks.

Lariviere, Richard W. The Divyatattva of Raghunandana Bhattacarya: Ordeals in Classical Hindu Law. 1982. 22.00x (ISBN 0-8364-0854-3, Pub. by Manohar India). South Asia Bks.

Larkin, Emmet. The Historical Dimensions of Irish Catholicism. LC 76-6350. (Irish Americans Ser.). 1976. 20.00 (ISBN 0-405-09344-6). Ayer Co Pubs.

--The Historical Dimensions of Irish Catholicism. LC 83-23175. 139p. 1984. pap. 9.95x (ISBN 0-8132-0594-8). Cath U Pr.

--The Making of the Roman Catholic Church in Ireland, 1850-1860. LC 79-19560. xxiv, 520p. 1980. 32.50x (ISBN 0-8078-1419-9). U of NC Pr.

--The Roman Catholic Church in Ireland & the Fall of Parnell, 1888-1891. LC 78-22056. xxi, 316p. 1979. 30.00x (ISBN 0-8078-1352-4). U of NC Pr.

Larkin, Emmet J. The Roman Catholic Church & the Creation of the Modern Irish State, 1878-1886. LC 75-7169. (American Philosophical Society Memoirs Ser.: Vol. 108). pap. 109.00 (ISBN 0-317-29437-7, 2024293). Bks Demand UMI.

Larkin, Ernest. Silent Presence. 4.95 (ISBN 0-87193-172-9). Dimension Bks.

Larkin, Ernest & Broccolo, Gerald T., eds. The Priest & Sacred Scripture. cancelled (ISBN 0-686-18989-2, V-226). US Catholic.

Larkin, Ernest E. Christ Within Us. 1984. pap. 6.95 (ISBN 0-87193-215-6). Dimension Bks.

Larkin, Ernest E. & Broccolo, Gerald T., eds. Spiritual Renewal of the American Priesthood. 1973. pap. 2.75 (ISBN 1-55586-230-6, V-230). US Catholic.

Larkin, Francis. Enthronement of the Sacred Heart. 1978. 6.95 (ISBN 0-8198-0529-7); pap. 4.95 (ISBN 0-8198-0530-0). Dghtrs St Paul.

--Understanding the Heart. rev. ed. LC 80-81066. 127p. 1980. pap. 5.95 (ISBN 0-89870-007-8). Ignatius Pr.

Larking, Lambert B., ed. Proceedings Principally in the County of Kent, in Connection with the Parliaments Called in 1640, & Especially with the Committee of Religion Appointed in That Year. (Camden Society, London. Publications, First Series: No. 80a). Repr. of 1862 ed. 37.00 (ISBN 0-404-50180-X). Ams Pr.

--Proceedings, Principally in the County of Kent, in Connection with the Parliaments Called in 1640. Repr. of 1862 ed. 37.00 (ISBN 0-384-31380-9). Johnson Repr.

Larking, Lambert B., ed. see Philippus De Thame.

Larlham, Hattie. Dear Children. LC 82-25842. 152p. 1983. 9.95 (ISBN 0-8361-3325-0). Herald Pr.

Larned, E. D. Church Records of Killingly, Connecticut. 56p. 1984. pap. 5.95 (ISBN 0-912606-22-3). Hunterdon Hse.

Larner, Christina. Enemies of God: The Witch-Hunt in Scotland. LC 81-47605. 256p. 1981. text ed. 25.00x (ISBN 0-8018-2699-3). Johns Hopkins.

--Witchcraft & Religion: The Politics of Popular Belief. 256p. 1984. 29.95x (ISBN 0-631-13447-6). Basil Blackwell.

--Witchcraft & Religion: The Politics of Popular Belief. Macfarlane, Alan, ed. 184p. 1986. pap. text ed. 12.95x (ISBN 0-631-14779-9). Basil Blackwell.

LaRondelle, Hans K. The Israel of God in Prophecy: Principles of Prophetic Interpretation. LC 82-74358. (Andrews University Monographs, Studies in Religion: Vol.13). viv, 226p. 1983. 14.95 (ISBN 0-943872-13-8); pap. 8.50 (ISBN 0-943872-14-6). Andrews Univ Pr.

--Perfection & Perfectionism: A Dogmatic-Ethical Study of Biblical Perfection & Phenomenal Perfectionism. (Andrews University Monographs, Studies in Religion: Vol. III). vii, 364p. pap. 9.95 (ISBN 0-943872-02-2). Andrews Univ Pr.

Larose, Paul. Working with Children & the Liturgy. LC 81-14984. (Illus.). 95p. 1982. pap. 2.95 (ISBN 0-8189-0428-3). Alba.

Larousse. Larousse Dictionnaire des Proverbs, Sentences et Maximes. 37.50 (ISBN 0-317-45655-5). French & Eur.

Larrabee, James, ed. Religion, BL-BX. LC 85-6863. (LC Cumulative Classification Ser.). 1000p. 1985. loose-leaf set 105.00 (ISBN 0-933949-11-1); vol. 1 0.00 (ISBN 0-933949-12-X); vol. 2 0.00 (ISBN 0-933949-13-8); fiche set 0.00 (ISBN 0-933949-15-4); fiche vol. 1 0.00 (ISBN 0-933949-16-2); fiche vol. 2 0.00 (ISBN 0-933949-17-0). Livia Pr.

Larranaga, Ignacio & Diercksmeier, John. Sensing Your Hidden Presence: Toward Intimacy With God. LC 87-5232. 264p. 1987. pap. 7.95 (ISBN 0-385-24021-X, Im). Doubleday.

Larrick, Nancy. Tambourines! Tambourines to Glory! Prayers & Poems. LC 81-23158. (Illus.). 122p. 1982. 8.95 (ISBN 0-664-32689-7). Westminster.

Larsen, Chris, jt. auth. see Kolbrek, Loyal.

Larsen, Dale. Hebrews, James, 1 & 2 Peter, Jude: A Daily Dialogue with God. (Personal Bible Studyguide Ser.). 144p. 1984. pap. 5.95 (ISBN 0-87788-339-4). Shaw Pubs.

Larsen, Dale & Larsen, Sandy. Getting to Know God. (Carpenter Studyguide). 80p. 1985. memb. ed. 1.95 (ISBN 0-87788-317-3); leader ed. 2.95 (ISBN 0-87788-318-1). Shaw Pubs.

Larsen, Dale, jt. auth. see Larsen, Sandy.

Larsen, Earnest. Whatever Happened to Good Old Plastic Jesus? 144p. 1978. pap. 3.95 (ISBN 0-697-01696-X). Wm C Brown.

Larsen, John A. When a Member of the Family Needs Counseling. LC 79-51274. (When Bk.). (Illus.). 1979. pap. 2.45 (ISBN 0-87029-147-5, 20234-1). Abbey.

Larsen, John M. Between Us Friends. LC 83-61454. 1983. pap. 7.95 (ISBN 0-89390-050-8). Resource Pubns.

Larsen, Norma C. His Everlasting Love, Vol. 2. LC 81-80956. 150p. 1981. 7.95 (ISBN 0-88290-182-6, 1062). Horizon Utah.

--His Everlasting Love: Stories of the Father's Help to His Children. LC 77-79752. 173p. 1977. 8.95 (ISBN 0-88290-083-8). Horizon Utah.

Larsen, Paul E. The Mission of a Covenant. 1985. pap. 6.95 (ISBN 0-910452-61-X). Covenant.

--Wise up & Live. 2nd ed. LC 73-86222. 256p. pap. 3.50 (ISBN 0-8307-0453-1, S274124). Regal.

Larsen, Sandy. Choosing: Which Way Do I Go? (Bible Discovery Guide for Campers Ser.). 32p. 1985. pap. 1.50 camper (ISBN 0-87788-115-4); pap. 3.50 counselor (ISBN 0-87788-116-2). Shaw Pubs.

--Everybody Needs the Body. 1984. pap. 3.95 (ISBN 0-88207-594-2). Victor Bks.

--Eye Opening Bible Studies. (Bible Discovery Guide for Campers Ser.). 32p. 1986. pap. 1.95 (ISBN 0-87788-247-9). Shaw Pubs.

--For Real People Only. 96p. 1986. pap. 1.95 student bk. (ISBN 0-89693-516-9); tchr's. ed. 11.95 (ISBN 0-89693-513-2). Victor Bks.

--Forgiving: Lightening Your Load. (Bible Discovery Guide). 32p. 1985. pap. 1.50 campers (ISBN 0-87788-279-7); pap. 3.50 counselor (ISBN 0-87788-280-0). Shaw Pubs.

--Joseph: Non Stop Faith. (Young Fisherman Bible Studyguides). 64p. (Orig.). 1987. pap. 4.95 tchr's. ed. (ISBN 0-87788-438-2); pap. 2.95 student ed. (ISBN 0-87788-437-4). Shaw Pubs.

--Running the Race: Keeping the Faith. (Young Fisherman Bible Studyguide Ser.). 64p. (Orig.). 1986. pap. 2.95 (ISBN 0-87788-740-3); tchr's. ed. 4.95 (ISBN 0-87788-741-1). Shaw Pubs.

--Standing Strong: Notes from Joseph's Journal. (Bible Discovery Guides for Teen Campers Ser.). (Illus.). 32p. (Orig.). (YA) 1986. pap. 1.50 camper (ISBN 0-87788-784-5); pap. 1.50 counselor (ISBN 0-87788-785-3). Shaw Pubs.

--Sticking Together: Friendships for Life. (Bible Discovery Guides for Teen Campers Ser.). 32p. (Orig.). (YA) 1987. pap. 1.50 camper (ISBN 0-87788-787-X); pap. 1.50 counselor (ISBN 0-87788-788-8). Shaw Pubs.

--Things. 144p. 1984. pap. 3.95 (ISBN 0-88207-109-2). Victor Bks.

Larsen, Sandy & Larsen, Dale. Choices: Picking Your Way Through the Ethical Jungle. (Young Fisherman Bible Studyguide). (Illus.). 61p. (Orig.). (YA) 1983. saddle-stitched student ed. 2.95 (ISBN 0-87788-113-8); tchr's. ed. 4.95 (ISBN 0-87788-114-6). Shaw Pubs.

--Forgiveness: No Guilt, No Grudges. (Young Fisherman Bible Studyguides). (Illus.). 80p. 1984. pap. 2.95 student ed. (ISBN 0-87788-277-0); tchr's. ed. 4.95 (ISBN 0-87788-278-9). Shaw Pubs.

--Galatians: Free at Last. (Young Fisherman Bible Studyguide Ser.). (Illus.). 73p. 1982. saddle-stitched student ed. 2.95 (ISBN 0-87788-293-2); tchr's ed. 4.95 (ISBN 0-87788-294-0). Shaw Pubs.

Larsen, Sandy, jt. auth. see Dale.

Larsen, Sandy, jt. auth. see Larsen, Dale.

Larson. No Longer Strangers. 145p. 1985. pap. 5.95 (ISBN 0-8499-3020-0, 3020-0). Word Bks.

Larson, Bart, jt. auth. see McDowell, Josh.

Larson, Betsy. Kidstories: Seasonal & Topical Sermons for Children. (Paperback Program Ser.). 128p. 1980. pap. 2.95 (ISBN 0-8010-5598-9). Baker Bk.

Larson, Bob. Larson's Book of Cults. 1982. 9.95 (ISBN 0-8423-2104-7). Tyndale.

Larson, Bruce. The Communicator's Commentary-Luke, Vol. 3. Ogilvie, Lloyd J., ed. (The Communicator's Commentaries Ser.). 1984. 18.95 (ISBN 0-8499-0156-1). Word Bks.

--My Creator, My Friend. 192p. 1986. 10.95 (ISBN 0-8499-0458-7). Word Bks.

Larson, Christian D. Leave It to God. pap. 1.00 (ISBN 0-87516-191-X). De Vorss.

Larson, Clinton F. & Revill, Joseph N. Illustrated Stories of the Book of Mormon, 16 vols. (Illus.). write for info 0.00 (ISBN 0-911712-38-0). Promised Land.

Larson, Don & Larson, Joanie. Bought & Paid For. 1977. 5.95 (ISBN 0-89221-038-9); pap. 2.95 (ISBN 0-89221-051-6). New Leaf.

Larson, Doris, jt. auth. see Larson, Roland.

Larson, E. Richard & McDonald, Laughlin. The Rights of Racial Minorities. 1979. pap. 1.95 (ISBN 0-380-75077-5, 75077-5, Discus). Avon.

Larson, Edward J. Trial & Error: The American Controversy over Creation & Evolution. LC 85-7144. 232p. 1985. 17.95 (ISBN 0-19-503666-2). Oxford U Pr.

Larson, Gary N., ed. see Unger, Merrill F.

Larson, Gerald J. & Bhattacharya, Ram Shankar, eds. Samkhya: A Dualist Tradition in Indian Philosophy. LC 85-43199. (Encyclopedia of Indian Philosophies: Vol. 4). 800p. 1987. 75.00x (ISBN 0-691-07301-5). Princeton U Pr.

Larson, Gustave O. Prelude to the Kingdom: Mormon Desert Conquest, a Chapter in American Cooperative Experience. LC 78-5694. 1978. Repr. of 1947 ed. lib. bdg. 25.75x (ISBN 0-313-20452-7, LAPK). Greenwood.

Larson, Jim. Caring Enough to Hear & Be Heard: Leader's Guide. LC 82-403. (Caring Enough Ser.). 1984. pap. 3.95 (ISBN 0-8307-0994-0, 6101948). Regal.

--Growing a Healthy Family. LC 85-28657. 128p. (Orig.). 1986. pap. 6.95 (ISBN 0-8066-2193-1, 10-2901). Augsburg.

--Rights, Wrongs, & In-Betweens: Guiding Our Children to Christian Maturity. LC 83-72121. 144p. (Orig.). 1984. pap. 6.95 (ISBN 0-8066-2065-X, 10-5518). Augsburg.

--Teaching Christian Values in the Family. (Illus.). 48p. 1982. pap. text ed. 29.95 (ISBN 0-89191-649-0). Cook.

--Walking in God's Light. LC 84-9963. 1984. pap. 3.95 (ISBN 0-8307-0953-3, S181216). Regal.

--When Enough Is Enough. LC 84-11644. (Caring Enough Ser.). 64p. 1985. pap. 3.95 (ISBN 0-8307-0987-8, 6101872). Regal.

Larson, Jim & Feldmeth, Joanne. Your Spiritual Gifts Can Help Your Church Grow. 64p. 1985. pap. 3.95 (ISBN 0-8307-1008-6, 6101951). Regal.

Larson, Joanie, jt. auth. see Larson, Don.

Larson, John. A Church Guide for Strengthening Families: Strategies, Models, Programs, & Resources. LC 86-7965. 128p. (Orig.). 1986. pap. 8.95 (ISBN 0-8066-2217-2, 10-1320). Augsburg.

Larson, Martin. New Thought: The Revolt Against Orthodoxy. 352p. cancelled (ISBN 0-8159-6317-3). Devin.

Larson, Martin A. The Essence-Christian Faith. 273p. 10.95 (ISBN 0-318-19483-X). Truth Seeker.

--The Essene-Christian Faith. LC 79-83606. 297p. 1980. 10.95 (ISBN 0-8022-2241-2). Philos Lib.

--The Essene Christian Faith. 273p. 1986. 12.00 (ISBN 0-317-53276-6). Noontide.

--The Essene-Christian Faith. 273p. 10.95. Truth Seeker.

--Modernity of Milton. LC 76-23120. 1927. lib. bdg. 7.95 (ISBN 0-8414-5800-6). Folcroft.

--Modernity of Milton: A Theological & Philosophical Interpretation. LC 76-124764. Repr. of 1927 ed. 18.75 (ISBN 0-404-03880-8). AMS Pr.

--New Thought or a Modern Religious Approach: The Philosophy of Health, Happiness & Prosperity. LC 84-7637. 475p. 1985. 19.95 (ISBN 0-8022-2464-4). Philos Lib.

--New Thought Religion. 2nd., rev. ed. LC 86-16947. 390p. 1987. 16.95 (ISBN 0-8022-2525-X); pap. 9.95 (ISBN 0-8022-2527-6). Philos Lib.

--The Story of Christian Origins. LC 76-40842. 1977. 12.50 (ISBN 0-88331-090-2). J J Binns.

Larson, Mobby. Prayers of a Christian Educator. (Greeting Book Line Ser.). 32p. (Orig.). 1985. pap. 1.50 (ISBN 0-89622-277-2). Twenty-Third.

--Prayers of a New Mother. (Greeting Book Line Ser.). 48p. (Orig.). 1985. pap. 1.50 (ISBN 0-89622-230-6). Twenty Third.

Larson, Muriel. Joy Every Morning. (Quiet Time Books). 1979. pap. 3.50 (ISBN 0-8024-4396-6). Moody.

--Living by Faith: A Study of Romans. 60p. 1984. pap. 2.95 (ISBN 0-930756-80-0, 521016). Aglow Pubns.

--Praise Every Day. 135p. 1984. 10.95 (ISBN 0-910311-11-0). Huntington Hse Inc.

--Ways Women Can Witness. LC 84-5006. 1984. pap. 5.95 (ISBN 0-8054-5250-8). Broadman.

Larson, Nora E. The Alphabet of God. LC 81-66071. (Illus.). 56p. (Orig.). 1981. pap. 4.00 (ISBN 0-87516-450-1). De Vorss.

--As a Little Child. LC 81-66072. (Illus.). 56p. (Orig.). 1981. pap. 4.00 (ISBN 0-87516-451-X). De Vorss.

Larson, Ray. A Season of Singleness. LC 83-81762. 128p. (Orig.). 1984. 2.50 (ISBN 0-88243-584-1, 02-0584). Gospel Pub.

Larson, Robert C., jt. auth. see Engstrom, Ted.

Larson, Robert C., jt. auth. see Engstrom, Ted W.

Larson, Robert L. Bible Stories Reader. 1985. 8.95 (ISBN 0-533-06749-9). Vantage.

Larson, Roland & Larson, Doris. Values & Faith: Value Clarifying Exercises for Family & Church Groups. (Illus.). 260p. 1976. pap. 6.95 (ISBN 0-86683-673-X, HarpR). Har-Row.

Larson, Rory, tr. see Kappeler, Max.

Lart, Charles E. see Peet, Henry.

Larue, Gerald. Sex & the Bible. LC 83-60201. 212p. 1983. 19.95 (ISBN 0-87975-206-8); pap. 11.95 (ISBN 0-87975-229-7). Prometheus Bks.

Larue, Gerald, jt. auth. see Hoffmann, R. Joseph.

Larue, Gerald A. Euthanasia & Religion: A Survey of the Attitudes of World Religions to the Right-to-Die. LC 84-62806. 155p. 1985. pap. 10.00 (ISBN 0-394-62078-X). Hemlock Soc.

La Rue, Pierre De see De La Rue, Pierre.

LaRuffa, Anthony L. San Cipriano: Life in a Puerto Rican Community. LC 73-136765. (Library of Anthropology Ser.). (Illus.). 166p. 1971. 44.00 (ISBN 0-677-03470-9). Gordon & Breach.

Larus, Joel. Culture & Political-Military Behavior: The Hindus in Pre-Modern India. 1980. 16.50x (ISBN 0-8364-0038-0). South Asia Bks.

La Saussaye, P. Chantepie De see De La Saussaye, P. Chantepie.

Lasch, Christopher. Haven in a Heartless World: The Family Besieged. LC 77-75246. 1979. pap. 7.95x (ISBN 0-465-02884-5, TB-5047). Basic.

Lash, Jamie S. Roots & Fruits. Date not set. pap. 3.00 (ISBN 0-915775-04-2). Love Song Mess Assn.

Lash, Jamie S., jt. auth. see Lash, Neil A.

Lash, Neil A. & Lash, Jamie S. A Jewish Wedding. (Jewish Jewels Ser.: Vol. 2). (Illus.). 24p. 1985. pap. 1.50 (ISBN 0-915775-03-4). Love Song Mess Assn.

--Looking for Leaven. (Jewish Jewels: Vol. 1). (Illus.). 21p. (Orig.). 1985. pap. 1.50 (ISBN 0-915775-02-6). Love Song Mess Assn.

Lash, Nicholas. A Matter of Hope: A Theologian's Reflections on the Thought of Karl Marx. LC 82-1980. 312p. 1982. text ed. 19.95 (ISBN 0-268-01352-7). U of Notre Dame Pr.

--A Matter of Hope: A Theologian's Reflections on the Thought of Karl Marx. LC 82-1980. 312p. 1984. pap. text ed. 9.95 (ISBN 0-268-01360-8, 85-13608). U of Notre Dame Pr.

--Voices of Authority. LC 76-29603. viii, 119p. 1976. pap. 3.95x (ISBN 0-915762-03-X). Patmos Pr.

Lash, Nicholas, jt. auth. see Tracy, David.

Lashbrook, Marilyn. A Champion Is... (I'm Growing Up Ser.). (Illus.). 32p. 1986. casebound 3.95 (ISBN 0-87403-121-4, 3601). Standard Pub.

Lasher, George W., ed. Baptist Ministerial Directory. 1987. 45.00. Banner Pr Al.

Lask, I. M., tr. see Agnon, S. Y.

Lask, I. M., tr. see Gorion, Micha J. bin & Gorion, Emanuel bin.

Laska, Vera, ed. Women in the Resistance & in the Holocaust: The Voices of Eyewitnesses. LC 82-12018. (Contributions in Women Studies: No. 37). xv, 330p. 1983. lib. bdg. 29.95 (ISBN 0-313-23457-4, LWH/). Greenwood.

Lasker, D. J. Jewish Philosophical Polemics Against Christianity in the Middle Ages. 25.00x (ISBN 0-87068-498-1). Ktav.

Lasker, Daniel J. Jewish Philosophical Polemics Against Christianity in the Middle Ages. 320p. 15.00 (ISBN 0-686-95177-8). ADL.

Laski, Harold J. Authority in the Modern State. LC 68-21685. 398p. 1968. Repr. of 1919 ed. 35.00 (ISBN 0-208-00460-2, Archon). Shoe String.

--Faith, Reason & Civilization: An Essay in Historical Analysis. facsimile ed. LC 74-167375. (Essay Index Reprint Ser). Repr. of 1944 ed. 15.00 (ISBN 0-8369-2662-5). Ayer Co Pubs.

--Studies in the Problem of Sovereignty. 1968. Repr. 29.50x (ISBN 0-86527-191-7). Fertig.

Laski, Marghanita. Ecstasy: A Study of Some Secular & Religious Experiences. LC 68-55635. (Illus.). 1968. Repr. of 1962 ed. bds. 27.50x (ISBN 0-8371-0529-3, LAEC). Greenwood.

Lasley, Don & Lasley, Kay. Scripture Handbook on Business & Finance. 1985. pap. 6.95 (ISBN 0-89274-317-4). Harrison Hse.

Lasley, Kay, jt. auth. see Lasley, Don.

Lasne, Sophie & Gaultier, Andre P. A Dictionary of Superstitions. LC 84-11717. 304p. 1984. 20.95 (ISBN 0-13-210881-X); pap. 10.95 (ISBN 0-13-210873-9). P-H.

La Sor, W. S. & Hubbard, David A. Old Testament Survey: The Message, Form, & Background of the Old Testament. 698p. 1982. 24.95 (ISBN 0-8028-3556-2). Eerdmans.

LaSor, William S. The Dead Sea Scrolls & the New Testament. 280p. 1972. pap. 5.95 (ISBN 0-8028-1114-0). Eerdmans.

--Handbook of Biblical Hebrew, 3 vols. Set. 14.95x (ISBN 0-8028-2379-3). Eerdmans.

--Handbook of New Testament Greek: An Inductive Approach Based on the Greek Text of Acts, 2 vols. 1973. pap. text ed. 24.95 (ISBN 0-8028-2341-6). Eerdmans.

--The Truth about Armageddon. 240p. 1987. pap. 6.95 (ISBN 0-8010-5637-3). Baker Bk.

Lass, Abraham H., et al. The Facts on File Dictionary of Classical, Biblical, & Literary Allusions. 240p. 1987. 18.95 (ISBN 0-8160-1267-9). Facts on File.

Lassalle, H. M. Enomiya: Zen Meditation for Christians. Maraldo, John C., tr. 187p. 1974. 16.95 (ISBN 0-87548-151-5). Open Court.

Lasserre, Jean. War & the Gospel. Coburn, O., tr. 248p. 1962. 9.95 (ISBN 0-227-67635-1). Attic Pr.

--War & the Gospel. (Christian Peace Shelf Ser.). 243p. 1962. 12.95 (ISBN 0-8361-1475-2). Herald Pr.

Lassiter, Perry. Once Saved...Always Saved. new ed. LC 74-15289. 98p. 1975. pap. 3.75 (ISBN 0-8054-1931-4). Broadman.

Lasson, Georg, ed. see Hegel, Georg W.

Laster, James, compiled by. Catalogue of Choral Music Arranged in Biblical Order. LC 82-16745. 269p. 1983. 27.50 (ISBN 0-8108-1592-3). Scarecrow.

Laster, James H., compiled by. Catalogue of Vocal Solos & Duets Arranged in Biblical Order. LC 84-14187. 212p. 1984. 17.50 (ISBN 0-8108-1748-9). Scarecrow.

LaSuer, Donald F. & Sells, L. Ray. Bonds of Belonging: Pathways to Discipleship for Church Members. LC 86-72150. 88p. (Orig.). 1986. pap. 5.95 (ISBN 0-88177-038-8, DR038B). Discipleship Res.

Las Vergnas, Raymond. Chesterton, Belloc, Baring. LC 73-4884. 1938. lib. bdg. 27.00 (ISBN 0-8414-2268-0). Folcroft.

Laszlo, Ervin & Wilbur, James B., eds. Human Values & Natural Science. (Current Topics of Contemporary Thought Ser.: Vol. 4). 310p. 1970. 63.95 (ISBN 0-677-13960-8). Gordon & Breach.

Lategan, Bernard C. & Vorster, Willem S. Text & Reality: Aspects of Reference in Biblical Texts. LC 85-47735. 144p. 1985. pap. 9.95 (ISBN 0-8006-1514-X). Fortress.

--Text & Reality: Aspects of Reference in Biblical Texts. 14.95 (ISBN 0-89130-822-9, 06 06 14); pap. 9.95 (ISBN 0-89130-823-7). Scholars Pr GA.

Lateiner, Donald & Stephens, Susan, eds. Selected Papers of Lionel Pearson. LC 83-16485. (Homage Ser.). 282p. 1983. 14.95 (ISBN 0-89130-646-3, 00 16 04). Scholars Pr GA.

Latham, Joy. Living & Learning with Nursery Children. (Teaching Helps Ser.). 128p. 1976. pap. 2.95 (ISBN 0-8010-5562-8). Baker Bk.

Latham, Judy. Women in the Bible: Helpful Friends. (BibLearn Ser.). (Illus.). 1979. 5.95 (ISBN 0-8054-4248-0, 4242-48). Broadman.

Latham, Robert, ed. Catalogue of the Pepys Library at Magdalene College Cambridge: Volume 5, Part 2: Modern Manuscripts, Vol. V - Pt. 2. 302p. 1981. 135.00x (ISBN 0-8476-7050-3). Rowman.

Latham, Robert O. Trail Maker (David Livingstone) 1973. pap. 2.95 (ISBN 0-87508-626-8). Chr Lit.

Latham, William I. The Last Outpost of Texas: A History of First Baptist Church, El Paso, Texas--The First Fifty Years. 1987. 20.00 (ISBN 0-930208-21-8). Mangan Bks.

Lathem, Judy. Hattie Gardner: Determined Adventurer. LC 81-70909. (Meet the Missionary Ser.). 1982. 5.50 (ISBN 0-8054-4280-4, 4242-80). Broadman.

Lathrop, Gordon, tr. see Wegman, Herman A.

Latif, S. A. The Mind Al-Quran Builds. 200p. 1983. 9.95 (ISBN 0-935782-16-8). Kazi Pubns.

Latimer, Hugh. Selected Sermons of Hugh Latimer. Chester, Allan G., ed. (Documents Ser). 1978. 16.00x (ISBN 0-918016-43-6). Folger Bks.

--Sermons. LC 76-172301. Repr. of 1906 ed. 23.50 (ISBN 0-404-03886-7). AMS Pr.

--Sermons. 379p. 1985. Repr. of 1984 ed. lib. bdg. 35.00 (ISBN 0-8482-4878-3). Norwood Edns.

--Seven Sermons Before Edward VI, Fifteen Forty-Nine. Arber, Edward, ed. 1985. pap. 17.50. Saifer.

--Works of Hugh Latimer, Sometime Bishop of Worcester, Martyr, 1555, 2 Vols. Repr. of 1845 ed. Set. 80.00 (ISBN 0-384-31480-5). Johnson Repr.

Latimer, James. Foundations of the Christian Missions in the British, French & Spanish West Indies. 1984. 10.95 (ISBN 0-533-05875-9). Vantage.

Latner, Helen. The Book of Modern Jewish Etiquette: A Guide To Contemporary Manners & Religious Customs. LC 86-45124. 400p. 1986. pap. 9.95 (ISBN 0-06-097054-5, PL-7054, PL). Har-Row.

--Your Jewish Wedding. LC 83-45567. (Illus.). 224p. 1985. pap. 4.95 (ISBN 0-385-18873-0). Doubleday.

Latorre Cabal, Hugo. The Revolution of the Latin American Church. Hendricks, Frances K. & Berler, Beatrice, trs. from Span. LC 77-9117. 1978. 14.95x (ISBN 0-8061-1449-5). U of Okla Pr.

Latour, Anny. The Jewish Resistance In France. LC 80-84246. (Illus.). 287p. 1981. 16.95 (ISBN 0-89604-025-9); pap. 10.95 (ISBN 0-89604-026-7). Holocaust Pubns.

--The Jewish Resistance in France, Nineteen Forty to Nineteen Forty-Four. (Illus.). 1981. 14.95 (ISBN 0-8052-5025-5, Pub. by Holocaust Library); pap. 8.95 (ISBN 0-8052-5024-7). Schocken.

Latourelle, Rene. Man & His Problems. O'Connell, Matthew, tr. LC 82-24334. (Fr.). 395p. (Orig.). 1983. pap. 9.95 (ISBN 0-8189-0450-X). Alba.

--Theology of Revelation. LC 65-15734. 1966. pap. 12.95 (ISBN 0-8189-0143-8). Alba.

Latourelle, Rene & O'Collins, Gerald, eds. Problems & Perspectives of Fundamental Theology. 416p. 1982. pap. 12.95 (ISBN 0-8091-2466-1). Paulist Pr.

Latourette, Jane & Mathews. Daniel in the Lions' Den. (Arch Bks.: Set 3). 1966. laminated bdg. 0.99 (ISBN 0-570-06018-4, 59-1127). Concordia.

Latourette, Jane & Wind, Betty. Jon & the Little Lost Lamb. LC 65-15145. (Arch Bks: Set 2). 1965. pap. 0.99 (ISBN 0-570-06008-7, 59-1106). Concordia.

Latourette, Kenneth, ed. Gospel, the Church & the World. LC 76-134107. (Essay Index Reprint Ser). 1946. 18.00 (ISBN 0-8369-1972-6). Ayer Co Pubs.

Latourette, Kenneth S. Christianity in a Revolutionary Age, 5 vols. 1973. Repr. of 1958 ed. Set. lib. bdg. 160.50x (ISBN 0-8371-5700-5, LACH). Greenwood.

--Christianity Through the Ages. (Orig.). pap. 8.95 (ISBN 0-06-065011-7, CB1, HarpR). Har-Row.

--Christianity Through the Ages. 16.75 (ISBN 0-8446-2434-9). Peter Smith.

--Historia del Cristianismo, Tomo II. Quarles, Jaime C. & Quarles, Lemuel C., trs. (Desde el Siglo XVI Hasta el Siglo XX). Orig. Title: A History of the Expansion of Christianity. 968p. 1983. pap. 17.95 (ISBN 0-311-15012-8). Casa Bautista.

--Historia del Cristianismo, Tomo I. Quarles, Jaime C. & Quarles, Lemuel C., trs. from Eng. (Illus.). 819p. 1984. pap. 17.95 (ISBN 0-311-15010-1). Casa Bautista.

--History of Christian Missions in China. LC 66-24721. 1967. Repr. of 1929 ed. 22.50x (ISBN 0-8462-0992-6). Russell.

--A History of Christianity. rev. ed. Incl. Vol. 1. Beginnings to 1500. 758p. pap. 11.00 (ISBN 0-06-064952-6, RD-93); Vol. 2. Reformation to the Present. 922p. pap. 13.95 (ISBN 0-06-064953-4, RD-94). LC 74-25692. 1975. pap. (HarpR). Har-Row.
--A History of Christianity, 2 vols. Date not set. Vol. I. 13.95 (ISBN 0-317-52393-7, RD 93, HarpR); Vol. II. 13.95 (ISBN 0-317-52394-5, RD 94, HarpR). Har-Row.
Lattimore, Richard, tr. The Four Gospels & the Revelation. 288p. 1981. pap. 3.95 (ISBN 0-671-50441-X). WSP.
Lattimore, Richmond, tr. from Greek. Acts & Letters of the Apostles. 287p. 1982. 16.50 (ISBN 0-374-10082-9). FS&G.
--The Four Gospels & the Revelation. 320p. 1979. 14.95 (ISBN 0-374-15801-0). FS&G.
Lau, D. C., tr. see Confucius.
Lau, Dicksen T. The New Religion & Relativity. LC 83-62038. 138p. (Orig.). 1983. pap. 5.95 (ISBN 0-9612000-0-6). Magnolia Bks.
Lau, Robert J. Old Babylonian Temple Records. (Columbia University. Oriental Studies: No. 3). Repr. of 1906 ed. 15.50 (ISBN 0-404-50493-0). AMS Pr.
Laub, Morris. Last Barrier to Freedom: Internment of Jewish Holocaust Survivors on Cyprus 1946-1949. LC 84-82475. (Illus., Orig.). 1985. pap. 8.95 (ISBN 0-943376-25-4). Magnes Mus.
Laubach, Frank, jt. auth. see Brother Lawrence.
Laubach, John H. School Prayers. 1969. 9.00 (ISBN 0-8183-0206-2). Pub Aff Pr.
Laube, Clifford J. Their Music Is Mary. 3.50 (ISBN 0-910984-11-5). Montfort Pubns.
Laubin, Gladys, jt. auth. see Laubin, Reginald.
Laubin, Reginald & Laubin, Gladys. Indian Dances of North America: Their Importance to Indian Life. LC 75-40962. (The Civilization of the American Indian Ser: No.141). 1979. 32.50 (ISBN 0-8061-1319-7). U of Okla Pr.
Lauckner, Edie. Signs of Celebration. 1978. 3.50 (ISBN 0-570-03770-0, 12-2706). Concordia.
Laud, William. Articles Exhibited in Parliament Against William, Archbishop of Canterbury. LC 72-212. (English Experience Ser.: No. 333). 16p. 1971. Repr. of 1640 ed. 7.00 (ISBN 90-221-0333-1). Walter J Johnson.
--A Speech Delivered in the Starr-Chamber, at the Censure of J. Bastwick. LC 79-171771. (English Experience Ser.: No. 396). 92p. 1971. Repr. of 1637 ed. 14.00 (ISBN 90-221-0396-X). Walter J Johnson.
--The Works of the Most Reverend Father in God, William Laud, D. D, 3 vols. LC 74-5373. (Library of Anglo-Catholic Theology: No. 11). Repr. of 1860 ed. Set. 350.00 (ISBN 0-404-52120-7). AMS Pr.
Lauder, Robert E. Becoming a Christian Person. 140p. (Orig.). 1985. pap. 5.95 (ISBN 0-914544-58-6). Living Flame Pr.
--Loneliness Is for Loving. LC 77-94033. (Illus.). 144p. 1978. pap. 2.95 (ISBN 0-87793-147-X). Ave Maria.
--The Love Explosion: Human Experience & the Christian Mystery. 128p. (Orig.). 1979. pap. 2.95 (ISBN 0-914544-22-5). Living Flame Pr.
--The Priest as a Person: A Philosophy of Priestly Existence. LC 81-3665. 144p. (Orig.). 1981. pap. 5.00 (ISBN 0-89571-013-7). Affirmation.
Lauer, Eugene & Mlecko, Joel. A Christian Understanding of the Human Person: Basic Readings. LC 81-8434. 160p. (Orig.). 1982. pap. 7.95 (ISBN 0-8091-2433-5). Paulist Pr.
Lauer, Eugene F. Sunday Morning Insights. 252p. 1984. pap. 8.95 (ISBN 0-8146-1361-6). Liturgical Pr.
Lauer, Paul E. Church & State in New England. LC 78-63809. (Johns Hopkins University. Studies in the Social Sciences. Tenth Ser. 1892: 2-3). Repr. of 1892 ed. 11.50 (ISBN 0-404-61072-2). AMS Pr.
Lauer, Quentin. Hegel's Concept of God. 432p. 1982. 44.50 (ISBN 0-87395-597-8); pap. 16.95 (ISBN 0-87395-598-6). State U NY Pr.
--The Triumph of Subjectivity: An Introduction to Transcendental Phenomenology. 2nd ed. LC 58-12363. xxiv, 182p. 1978. 20.00 (ISBN 0-8232-0336-0); pap. 9.00 (ISBN 0-8232-0337-9). Fordham.
Lauer, Robert H. Temporal Man: The Meaning & Uses of Social Time. LC 81-11917. 192p. 1981. 34.95 (ISBN 0-03-059719-6). Praeger.
Lauersdorf, Richard E. A Study Guide for Hebrews. Fischer, William E., ed. (Study Guide for People's Bible Ser.). 48p. (Orig.). 1986. pap. 1.50 (ISBN 0-938272-56-X). WELS Board.
Laufer, Berthold. Jade: A Study in Chinese Archaeology & Religion. LC 74-81085. (Illus.). 480p. 1975. pap. 6.95 (ISBN 0-486-23123-2). Dover.
--Jade: A Study in Chinese Archaeology & Religion. (Field Museum of Natural History). (Illus.). 1912. 41.00 (ISBN 0-527-01870-8). Kraus Repr.
--Jade: A Study in Chinese Archaeology & Religion. (Illus.). 15.25 (ISBN 0-8446-5214-8). Peter Smith.
Laufer, William, jt. ed. see Day, James M.
Laugher, Charles T. Thomas Bray's Grand Design: Libraries of the Church of England in America, 1695-1785. LC 73-16332. (ACRL Publications in Librarianship Ser.: No. 35). pap. 31.30 (ISBN 0-317-29444-X, 2024224). Bks Demand UMI.
Laughlin, J., jt. ed. see Hayes, Albert.
Laughlin, Paul A. Lectionary Worship Aids B: Series II. (Orig.). 1987. pap. price not set (ISBN 0-89536-886-2, 7872). CSS of Ohio.
Laughlin, Sceva B., ed. Beyond Dilemmas. LC 79-86035. (Essay & General Literature Index Reprint Ser). 1969. Repr. of 1937 ed. 25.50x (ISBN 0-8046-0567-X, Pub. by Kennikat). Assoc Faculty Pr.
Laun, Hellmut. How I Met God: An Unusual Conversion. Smith, David, tr. 163p. 1983. 10.50 (ISBN 0-8199-0871-1). Franciscan Herald.
Launius, Roger D. The Kirtland Temple: A Historical Narrative. 1986. pap. 12.50 (ISBN 0-8309-0449-2). Herald Hse.
--Zion's Camp: Expedition to Missouri, 1834. 1984. pap. 14.00 (ISBN 0-8309-0385-2). Herald Hse.
Laurance, John D. Priest as Type of Christ: The Leader of the Eucharist in Salvation History According to Cyprian of Carthage. LC 84-47539. (American University Studies VII (Theology & Religion): Vol. 5). 245p. (Orig.). 1984. 37.25 (ISBN 0-8204-0117-X). P Lang Pubs.
Laurello, Bartholomew J. Ministering to the Aging. LC 79-90992. (Paths of Life Ser.). 96p. (Orig.). 1979. pap. 2.95 (ISBN 0-8091-2268-5). Paulist Pr.
Laurence, Margaret. The Christmas Birthday Story. LC 79-27159. (Illus.). 32p. 1980. PLB 6.99 (ISBN 0-394-94361-9). Knopf.
Laurence, Richard. The Book of Enoch the Prophet. 2nd ed. Laurence, Richard, tr. from Old Ethiopic. LC 72-95273. (Secret Doctrine Reference Ser). 220p. 1972. Repr. of 1883 ed. 11.00 (ISBN 0-913510-01-7). Wizards.
Laurence, Theoder. The Miracle Power of Believing. 1976. (Parker). P-H.
Laurens Van, De Post see Van Der Post, Laurens.
Laurentin, Rene. Miracles in El Paso. (Illus.). 135p. 1982. pap. 6.95 (ISBN 0-89283-150-2). Servant.
--The Truth of Christmas Beyond the Myths: The Gospel of the Infancy of Christ. (Studies in Scripture: Vol. III). 1986. pap. 29.95 (ISBN 0-932506-34-8). St Bedes Pubns.
Laurentin, Rene & Rupcic, Ljudevit. Is the Virgin Mary Appearing at Medjugorje? Martin, Francis, tr. from Fr. (Illus.). 170p. 1984. 12.95 (ISBN 0-932085-02-4); pap. 6.95 (ISBN 0-932085-00-8). Word Among Us.
Laures, John. Catholic Church in Japan: A Short History. Repr. of 1954 ed. lib. bdg. 22.50x (ISBN 0-8371-2974-5, LACC). Greenwood.
Laurie, Greg. God's Design for Christian Dating. 2nd ed. LC 82-83836. 96p. (YA) 1983. pap. 2.25 (ISBN 0-89081-373-6). Harvest Hse.
--Spiritual Survival in the Last Days. LC 82-81919. Orig. Title: Occupy Till I Come. 144p. (Orig.). 1985. pap. 3.95. Harvest Hse.
Laurie, Sanders, et al. Centering: Your Guide to Inner Growth. 299p. 1983. 6.95 (ISBN 0-89281-050-5, Destiny Bks). Inner Tradit.
Laurie, Simon S. John Amos Comenius, Bishop of the Moravians, His Life & Educational Works. LC 72-10020. (Illus.). 272p. 1973. Repr. of 1893 ed. 21.00 (ISBN 0-8337-2028-7). B Franklin.
Laurin, Robert B. The Layman's Introduction to the Old Testament. 1970. pap. 4.95 (ISBN 0-8170-0451-3). Judson.
Laurin, Roy L. Acts of the Apostles: Life in Action. LC 85-8158. 408p. 1985. pap. 11.95 (ISBN 0-8254-3127-1). Kregel.
--Colossians. 192p. 1987. pap. 9.95 (ISBN 0-8254-3135-2). Kregel.
--First Corinthians. Orig. Title: First Corinthians: Where Life Matures. 336p. 1987. pap. 10.95 (ISBN 0-8254-3132-8). Kregel.
--First John. LC 86-27394. Orig. Title: Epistle of John: Life at its Best. 200p. 1987. pap. 8.95 (ISBN 0-8254-3136-0). Kregel.
--Philippians. 208p. 1987. pap. 8.95 (ISBN 0-8254-3134-4). Kregel.
--Romans. Orig. Title: Romans: Where Life Begins. 540p. 1988. Repr. of 1955 ed. 12.95 (ISBN 0-8254-3130-1). Kregel.
--Second Corinthians: Where Life Endures. LC 85-8154. 248p. 1985. pap. 9.95 (ISBN 0-8254-3129-8). Kregel.
Lautensach, Hermann. Das Mormoneniand Als Beispiel Eines Sozialgeographischen Raumes. Repr. of 1953 ed. 20.00 (ISBN 0-384-31640-9). Johnson Repr.
Lauterbach, Jacob Z. Rabbinic Essays. LC 52-18170. pap. 146.50 (ISBN 0-317-42031-3, 2025693). Bks Demand UMI.
Lauterbach, Jacob Z., intro. by. & tr. from Heb. Mekilta De-Rabbi Ishmael, 3 vols. LC 75-40823. (JPS Library of Jewish Classics). 808p. 1976. pap. 19.95 (ISBN 0-8276-0078-X, 382). Jewish Pubns.
Lauterbach, William. The Crucial Hours. 1977. pap. 5.95 (ISBN 0-8100-0050-4, 15-0358). Northwest Pub.
--Es Will Abend Werden. Kujath, Mentor, ed. 1978. pap. 2.25 (ISBN 0-8100-0101-2, 26-0511). Northwest Pub.
Lauterbach, William A. Heaven Bound. LC 74-34277. 128p. 1974. pap. 5.50 (ISBN 0-570-03028-5, 6-1156). Concordia.
--Prayers for the Sickroom. 1953. 1.10 (ISBN 0-570-03524-4, 14-1236). Concordia.
--When Shadows Fall. 1945. pap. 0.85 (ISBN 0-570-03537-6, 14-1573). Concordia.
Laux, Dorothy. John: Beloved Apostle. (BibLearn Ser.). (Illus.). 1977. bds. 5.95 (ISBN 0-8054-4234-0, 4242-34). Broadman.
La Valle, Maria T., tr. see Brenneman, Helen G.
LaValle, Maria T., tr. see Robertson, Jenny.
La Valle, Maria T., et al, trs. see Grant, Wilson W.
LaValle, Teresa, tr. see Ralph, Margaret.
La Vallee Poussin, Louis de. The Way to Nirvana: Six Lectures on Ancient Buddhism As a Discipline of Salvation. LC 77-27154. (Hibbert Lectures Ser.: 1916). Repr. of 1917 ed. 24.50 (ISBN 0-404-60417-X). AMS Pr.
La Vallee Poussin, Louis De see La Vallee Poussin, Louis de.
Lavan, Spencer. Unitarians & India. 1984. pap. 5.95 (ISBN 0-933840-23-3). Unitarian Univ.
Lavasik, Lawrence. Mary My Hope. rev. ed. (Illus., LargeType). blue bdg., colored edges 4.95 (ISBN 0-89942-365-5, 365/00). Catholic Bk Pub.
Laveille, E. Life of Father De Smet, S. J. Eighteen Hundred One to Eighteen Seventy-Three. Lindsay, Marian, tr. (Loyola Request Reprint Ser.). 398p. 1981. Repr. of 1915 ed. 8.95 (ISBN 0-8294-0372-8). Loyola.
LaVelle, Steven. Just Passing Through. (Illus.). 32p. (Orig.). 1980. pap. 1.50 (ISBN 0-87516-402-1). De Vorss.
Lavender, Abraham D., ed. A Coat of Many Colors: Jewish Subcommunities in the United States. LC 77-71865. (Contributions in Family Studies: No. 1). 1977. lib. bdg. 29.95 (ISBN 0-8371-9539-X, LCM/). Greenwood.
Lavender, John A. Marriage at Its Best. LC 82-71375. 160p. (Orig.). 1982. pap. 4.95 (ISBN 0-89636-091-1). Accent Bks.
Lavender, Lucille. They Cry, Too. 176p. 1986. pap. 6.95 (ISBN 0-310-41651-5, 9970P). Zondervan.
Laverdiere & Casgrain, eds. Le Journal des Jesuites. (French-Canadian Civilization Ser.). (Fr.). Repr. of 1871 ed. lib. bdg. 46.00x (ISBN 0-697-00050-8). Irvington.
LaVerdiere, Eugene. Acts of the Apostles. LC 79-1395. (The Read & Pray Ser.). 98p. 1979. 1.75 (ISBN 0-8199-0632-8). Franciscan Herald.
--Luke. (New Testament Message Ser.: Vol. 5). 15.95 (ISBN 0-89453-193-X); pap. 10.95 (ISBN 0-89453-128-X). M Glazier.
--The New Testament in the Life of the Church. LC 80-67403. 192p. (Orig.). 1980. pap. 4.95 (ISBN 0-87793-213-1). Ave Maria.
--When We Pray: Meditation on the Lord's Prayer. LC 82-73512. 176p. 1983. pap. 4.95 (ISBN 0-87793-263-8). Ave Maria.
LaVey, Anton S. The Satanic Rituals. 1972. pap. 4.50 (ISBN 0-380-01392-4). Avon.
LaVigne, Ruth A. Special Messenger. 1978. 3.50 (ISBN 0-8198-0555-6); pap. 2.50 (ISBN 0-8198-0556-4). Dghtrs St Paul.
Lavin, Irving & Plummer, John, eds. Studies in Late Medieval & Renaissance Painting in Honor of Millard Meiss. LC 75-27118. 550p. 1978. 200.00x set (ISBN 0-8147-4963-1); Vol. I (ISBN 0-8147-5001-X); Vol. II (ISBN 0-8147-4978-X). NYU Pr.
Lavin, Ron. You Can't Start a Car with a Cross. 1984. 5.95 (ISBN 0-89536-648-7, 2507). CSS of Ohio.
Lavin, Ronald J. You Can Grow in a Small Group. 144p. 1976. pap. 5.75 (ISBN 0-89536-273-2, 2500). CSS of Ohio.
LaViolette, Wesley. The New Gita. (Illus.). 1973. pap. 4.95 (ISBN 0-87516-172-3). De Vorss.
--Wings Unfolding. LC 70-140225. 1971. 4.95 (ISBN 0-87516-040-9). De Vorss.
Lavoie, Claire, tr. see Salmon, Pierre.
LaVon Kincaid, J., Sr., ed. Thanks Giving: Stewardship Sermons out of the Ethnic Minority Experience. LC 83-73266. 88p. 1984. pap. text ed. 6.95 (ISBN 0-88177-007-8, DR007B). Discipleship Res.
Lavroff, S. Yako s Nami Bog. Tr. of For God is with Us. 73p. 1980. pap. 3.00 (ISBN 0-317-29142-4). Holy Trinity.
Law, Bimala C. The Buddhist Conception of Spirits. 2nd rev. & enl. ed. LC 78-72462. Repr. of 1936 ed. 21.50 (ISBN 0-404-17334-9). AMS Pr.
--History of Buddha's Religion. (Bibliotheca Indo-Buddhica Ser.: No. 29). 174p. 1986. Repr. of 1952 ed. 24.00 (ISBN 81-7030-011-8, Pub. by SRI SATGURU Pubns India). Orient Bk Dist.
Law, Bimala C., ed. Buddhistic Studies. LC 78-72463. Repr. of 1931 ed. 74.50 (ISBN 0-404-17335-7). AMS Pr.
--Geography of Early Buddhism. LC 78-72464. Repr. of 1932 ed. 21.00 (ISBN 0-404-17336-5). AMS Pr.
--A Study of the Mahavastu. LC 78-72469. Repr. of 1930 ed. 26.50 (ISBN 0-404-17339-X). AMS Pr.
Law, Edmund. An Enquiry into the Ideas of Space & Time. Wellek, Rene, ed. LC 75-11230. (British Philosophers & Theologians of the 17th & 18th Century: Vol. 31). 1976. Repr. of 1734 ed. lib. bdg. 51.00 (ISBN 0-8240-1783-8). Garland Pub.
Law, Helen H. Bibliography of Greek Myth in English Poetry. LC 77-9519. 1955. lib. bdg. 15.00 (ISBN 0-8414-5827-8). Folcroft.
Law, Helen M., et al, trs. see De Paul, Vincent.
Law, Jerry L. The Fruits of Repentance. (Orig.). 1985. pap. 3.95 (ISBN 0-930875-00-1). Seed Life Pubns.
Law, Peter. Portrait of My Father: The Wonder of Knowing God. LC 85-15458. (Living Theology Ser.). 1985. pap. 7.95 (ISBN 0-88070-107-2). Multnomah.
Law, R., jt. auth. see Blaikie, W. G.
Law, Robert. Tests of Life. 3rd ed. (Thornapple Commentary Ser.). 1978. pap. 11.95 (ISBN 0-8010-5501-6). Baker Bk.
Law, Sylvia, jt. auth. see Dorsen, Norman.
Law, Terry. The Power of Praise & Worship. (Illus.). 256p. (Orig.). 1985. pap. 6.95 (ISBN 0-932081-01-0). Victory Hse.
--Your Spiritual Weapons. (Illus.). 48p. 1985. pap. 1.95 (ISBN 0-932081-00-2). Victory Hse.
--Your Spiritual Weapons & How to Use Them. (Orig.). 1983. pap. write for info. (ISBN 0-88144-028-0, CPS028). Christian Pub.
Law, Thomas G., ed. The Archpriest Controversy, 2 Vols. Repr. of 1898 ed. 54.00 (ISBN 0-384-31730-8). Johnson Repr.
Law, William. Freedom from a Self-Centered Life. Murray, Andrew, ed. LC 77-71426. 144p. 1977. pap. 3.50 (ISBN 0-87123-104-2, 200104). Bethany Hse.
--The Power of the Spirit. Murray, Andrew, ed. LC 76-57110. (Classics of Devotions Ser). 224p. 1977. pap. 4.95 (ISBN 0-87123-463-7, 200463). Bethany Hse.
--Power of the Spirit. Hunt, D., ed. 1971. pap. 2.95 (ISBN 0-87508-247-5). Chr Lit.
--A Serious Call to a Devout & Holy Life. 1967. Repr. of 1906 ed. 12.95x (ISBN 0-460-00091-8, Evman). Biblio Dist.
--A Serious Call to a Devout & Holy Life. Meister, John, et al, eds. LC 55-5330. 156p. 1968. pap. 6.95 (ISBN 0-664-24833-0). Westminster.
--A Serious Call to a Devout & Holy Life. LC 82-80470. (Treasures from the Spiritual Classics Ser.). 64p. 1982. pap. 2.95 (ISBN 0-8192-1306-3). Morehouse.
--A Serious Call to Holy Living. Abriged by ed. 96p. 1985. pap. 3.95 (ISBN 0-8423-5861-7). Tyndale.
--Spirit of Prayer & Spirit of Love. Spencer, Sydney, ed. 301p. 1969. 17.50 (ISBN 0-227-67720-X). Attic Pr.
--Wholly for God. Murray, Andrew, ed. LC 76-6622. 336p. 1976. pap. 4.95 (ISBN 0-87123-602-8, 200602). Bethany Hse.
--William Law & Eighteenth-Century Quakerism. Hobhouse, Stephen, ed. LC 77-175870. (Illus.). Repr. of 1927 ed. 24.50 (ISBN 0-405-08736-5). Ayer Co Pubs.
--William Law: Christian Perfection. Rev. ed. 96p. 1986. pap. 4.95 (ISBN 0-8423-0259-X). Tyndale.
--William Law: Selections on the Interior Life. Morrison, Mary, ed. LC 62-15272. (Orig.). 1962. pap. 2.50x (ISBN 0-87574-120-7). Pendle Hill.
Lawhead, Alice, jt. auth. see Lawhead, Steve.
Lawhead, Stephen R. In the Hall of the Dragon King, Bk. I. LC 82-71942. (Dragon King Trilogy Ser.). 348p. 1982. pap. 8.95 (ISBN 0-89107-257-8, Crossway Bks). Good News.
--Turn Back the Night: A Christian Response to Popular Culture. LC 84-72005. 192p. (Orig.). 1985. pap. 6.95 (ISBN 0-89107-340-X, Crossway Bks). Good News.
Lawhead, Steve & Lawhead, Alice. Judge for Yourself. 160p. 1985. pap. 3.95 (ISBN 0-88207-597-7). Victor Bks.
Lawhead, Wendell H., jt. auth. see Farnsworth, Kirk E.
Lawler, Edwina. David Friedrich Strauss & His Critics: The Life of Jesus Debate in Early Nineteenth-Century German Journals. (American University Studies VII - Theology & Religion: Vol. 16). 170p. 1986. text ed. 21.95 (ISBN 0-8204-0290-7). P Lang Pubs.

Lawler, Michael. Secular Marriage, Christian Sacrament. 192p. (Orig.). 1985. pap. text ed. 8.95 (ISBN 0-89622-273-X). Twenty-Third.

Lawler, Michael G. Raid on the Inarticulate: An Invitation to Adult Religion. LC 80-1438. 168p. 1980. pap. text ed. 9.50 (ISBN 0-8191-1186-4). U Pr of Amer.

Lawler, Philip F. How Bishops Decide: An American Catholic Case Study. 45p. (Orig.). pap. 4.00 (ISBN 0-89633-101-6). Ethics & Public Policy.

Lawler, Ronald. Light from Light: What Catholics Believe about Jesus. 240p. (Orig.). 1987. pap. 7.50 (ISBN 0-87973-547-3, 547). Our Sunday Visitor.

Lawler, Ronald, et al. Catholic Sexual Ethics. LC 84-62225. 360p. (Orig.). 1985. pap. text ed. 7.95 (ISBN 0-87973-805-7, 805). Our Sunday Visitor.

--Teaching of Christ. 2nd ed. LC 75-34852. 640p. 1983. pap. 9.95 (ISBN 0-87973-850-2, 850). Our Sunday Visitor.

Lawler, Ronald, et al, eds. The Catholic Catechism. 200p. (Orig.). 1986. pap. 6.50 (ISBN 0-87973-802-2, 802). Our Sunday Visitor.

Lawler, T. C., jt. ed. see Burghardt, W. J.

Lawler, Thomas, tr. see Augustine, St.

Lawler, Thomas C. & Burghart, Johannes, eds. The Octavius of Marcus Minucius Felix. Clarke, G. W., tr. from Latin. (Ancient Christian Writers Ser.: Vol. 39). 1974. 14.95 (ISBN 0-8091-0189-0). Paulist Pr.

Lawless, Agnes & Goodboy, Eadie. The Word: God's Manual for Maturity. (Bible Study Enrichment Ser.). 64p. (Orig.). 1980. pap. 2.95 (ISBN 0-930756-59-2, 522004). Aglow Pubns.

Lawless, Richard M. When Love Unites the Church. LC 81-72000. (When Bks.). 88p. (Orig.). 1982. pap. 2.45 (ISBN 0-87029-181-5, 20273-9). Abbey.

Lawlor, Deborah, tr. see Schwaller de Lubicz, R. A.

Lawlor, Deborah, tr. see Schwaller De Lubicz, R. A.

Lawlor, Deborah, tr. from Fr. & see Schwaller de Lubicz, R. A.

Lawlor, George. Almah: Virgin or Young Woman? LC 73-76072. 1973. pap. 1.50 (ISBN 0-87227-036-X). Reg Baptist.

Lawlor, Hugh J. The Reformation & the Irish Episcopate. 2nd ed. (Church Historical Society, London, Ser.: No. 11). Repr. of 1932 ed. 20.00 (ISBN 0-8115-3135-X). Kraus Repr.

Lawlor, Richard V. Answers to Your Questions. 1980. 5.00 (ISBN 0-8198-0700-1); pap. 4.00 (ISBN 0-8198-0701-X). Dghtrs St Paul.

Lawlor, Robert. Sacred Geometry: Philosophy & Practice. Purce, Jill, ed. LC 81-67703. (The Illustrated Library of Sacred Imagination Ser.). (Illus.). 96p. 1982. pap. 9.95 (ISBN 0-8245-0067-9). Crossroad NY.

Lawlor, Robert, tr. see Schwaller de Lubicz, R. A.

Lawlor, Robert, tr. see Schwaller De Lubicz, R. A.

Lawne, Christopher. Brownisme Turned the In-Side Out-Ward. LC 76-6282. (English Experience Ser: No. 74). 40p. 1968. Repr. of 1613 ed. 7.00 (ISBN 90-221-0074-X). Walter J Johnson.

Lawrence. The English Church & the Papacy in the Middle Ages. LC 65-12529. 265p. 1984. pap. 10.00 (ISBN 0-8232-0646-7). Fordham.

--Practicando la Presencia de Dios. LC 82-50949. Tr. of The Practice of the Presence of God. (Span.). 72p. (Orig.). 1983. pap. 1.35 (ISBN 0-8358-0456-9). Upper Room.

--Practice of the Presence of God. 128p. 1981. pap. 6.95 (ISBN 0-87243-129-0). Templegate.

--The Practice of the Presence of God. Helms, Hal H., ed. LC 84-61019. (Living Library Ser.). 161p. (Orig.). 1984. pap. 5.95 (ISBN 0-941478-29-7). Paraclete Pr.

Lawrence, Anthony. The Psalm Locator. 2nd ed. (Orig.). 1985. pap. 10.95 (ISBN 0-89390-063-X). Resource Pubns.

Lawrence, Bette. Mike: A Mother's Prayers. LC 84-21247. 64p. 1985. pap. 2.95 (ISBN 0-8006-1857-2, 1-1857). Fortress.

Lawrence, Brother. The Practice of the Presence of God. Blaiklock, E. M., tr. 96p. 1982. pap. 4.95 (ISBN 0-8407-5803-0). Nelson.

--The Practice of the Presence of God. 96p. 1982. pap. 3.50 (ISBN 0-88368-105-6). Whitaker Hse.

Lawrence, Brother Of The Resurrection see Delaney, John J.

Lawrence, C. H. Medieval Monasticism: Forms of Religious Life, Western Europe in the Middle Ages. 288p. 1984. pap. text ed. 12.95 (ISBN 0-582-49186-X). Longman.

Lawrence, Carl. The Church in China. 176p. (Orig.). 1985. pap. 5.95 (ISBN 0-87123-815-2). Bethany Hse.

Lawrence, D. H. Fantasia & Psychoanalysis & the Unconscious. 1978. pap. 6.95 (ISBN 0-14-003303-3). Penguin.

Lawrence, David H. Saint Mawr. Bd. with The Man Who Died. 1959. pap. 3.95 (ISBN 0-394-70071-6, Vin). Random.

Lawrence, Emeric. Believe the Good News: Daily Meditations on the Lenten Masses. LC 82-97. 144p. 1982. pap. 5.75 (ISBN 0-8146-1256-3). Liturgical Pr.

--Jesus Present & Coming: Daily Meditations on the Advent & Christmas Masses. LC 82-20380. 128p. 1982. pap. 7.95 (ISBN 0-8146-1284-9). Liturgical Pr.

--Risen & with You Always: Daily Meditations for the Easter Season Masses. 140p. 1986. pap. 5.95 (ISBN 0-8146-1448-5). Liturgical Pr.

Lawrence, Emeric A. The Ministry of Believers. 24p. (Orig.). 1982. pap. text ed. 1.25 (ISBN 0-8146-1276-8). Liturgical Pr.

Lawrence, Fred, ed. The Beginning & the Beyond: Papers from the Gadamer & Voegelin Conferences. LC 84-13940. (Boston College-Supplements to Lonergan Workshop Ser.). 1984. pap. 13.50 (ISBN 0-89130-772-9, 19 20 04). Scholars Pr GA.

Lawrence, Fred, tr. see Von Balthasar, Hans U.

Lawrence, Gene H. Right Human Relations: The Only Way to World Peace. 110p. 1980. pap. 3.00 (ISBN 0-682-49627-8). Exposition Pr FL.

Lawrence, Henry W. The Not Quite Puritans: Some Genial Follies & Peculiar Frailities of Our Revered New England Ancestors. (Illus.). 1975. Repr. of 1928 ed. 40.00x (ISBN 0-8103-3993-5). Gale.

Lawrence, Howard W., jt. ed. see Biebel, David B.

Lawrence, Irene. Linguistics & Theology: The Significance of Noam Chomsky for Theological Construction. LC 80-24210. (ATLA Monograph: No. 16). 214p. 1980. 17.50 (ISBN 0-8108-1347-5). Scarecrow.

Lawrence, J., jt. auth. see Crabb, Jr.

Lawrence, Jane. Easter Joy. 1983. 0.50 (ISBN 0-89536-594-4, 0501). CSS of Ohio.

Lawrence, John. The Hammer & the Cross. LC 86-4025. 208p. 1986. text ed. 15.00x (ISBN 0-87663-470-6). Universe.

--Life's Choices: Discovering the Consequences of Sowing & Reaping. LC 82-3438. 120p. 1982. pap. 5.95 (ISBN 0-930014-85-5). Multnomah.

Lawrence, Joy & Ferguson, John. A Musician's Guide to Church Music. LC 80-27567. 280p. 1981. 16.95 (ISBN 0-8298-0424-2). Pilgrim NY.

Lawrence, Kenneth, ed. Classic Themes of Disciples Theology: Rethinking the Traditional Affirmations of the Christian Church (Disciples of Christ) LC 85-50712. 150p. 1986. text ed. 20.00x (ISBN 0-87565-024-4). Tex Christian.

Lawrence, M. Therese. Toward a New Christendom. LC 81-84244. (Illus.). 80p. 1982. pap. 5.95 write for info. (ISBN 0-938034-05-7). PAL Pr.

Lawrence, Patricia, jt. auth. see Amyx, D. A.

Lawrence, Richard, tr. The Book of Enoch. LC 80-65736. 96p. 1980. pap. 4.00 (ISBN 0-934666-06-7). Artisan Sales.

Lawrence, Roy. Christian Healing Rediscovered. LC 80-7470. 128p. (Orig.). 1980. pap. 3.95 (ISBN 0-87784-621-9). Inter-Varsity.

Lawrence, Theodor. The Parker Lifetime Treasury of Mystic & Occult Powers. 1982. pap. 4.95 (ISBN 0-13-650747-6, Reward). P-H.

Lawry, Antje, tr. see Balthasar, Hans Urs Von.

Laws, Sophie. The Epistle of James. LC 80-8349. (Harper's New Testament Commentaries Ser.). 288p. 1981. 16.00 (ISBN 0-06-064918-6, HarpR). Har-Row.

Lawson, Brian C. Life, Death, Eternity & the Secret of the Universe. (Illus.). 1979. 47.45 (ISBN 0-89266-207-7). Am Classical Coll Pr.

Lawson, E. L. Galatians-Ephesians. (Standard Bible Studies). (Illus.). 288p. 1987. pap. price not set (ISBN 0-87403-169-9, 40109). Standard Pub.

Lawson, E. Leroy. Matthew. (Standard Bible Studies). 352p. 1986. pap. 9.95 (ISBN 0-87403-161-3, 40101). Standard Pub.

Lawson, E. Leroy, jt. auth. see Yamamori, Tetsunao.

Lawson, George. Exposition of Proverbs, 2 vols. in 1. LC 80-8070. (Kregel Timeless Classics Ser.). 904p. 1981. 27.50 (ISBN 0-8254-3123-9). Kregel.

Lawson, James G. Deeper Experiences of Famous Christians. 1981. pap. 2.95 (ISBN 0-87162-069-3, D3349). Warner Pr.

--The World's Best Religious Quotations. 1979. Repr. lib. bdg. 35.00 (ISBN 0-8492-1610-9). R West.

Lawson, James G., compiled by. The Best-Loved Religious Poems. 256p. 1981. 9.95 (ISBN 0-8007-0019-8). Revell.

Lawson, John. Introduction to Christian Doctrine. Burgess, Harold, ed. 1980. pap. 9.95 (ISBN 0-310-75021-0). Zondervan.

--Introduction to Christian Doctrine. 1986. 14.95 (ISBN 0-310-75020-2). Zondervan.

Lawson, LeRoy. Cracking the Code. LC 76-57045. 1977. pap. 2.25 (ISBN 0-87239-125-6, 40042). Standard Pub.

--The Family of God: The Meaning of Church Membership. LC 80-53497. 64p. (Orig.). 1981. pap. 1.50 (ISBN 0-87239-432-8, 39970). Standard Pub.

--God's Word A. D. LC 83-348. 112p. (Orig.). 1984. pap. 2.95 (ISBN 0-87239-668-1, 41022). Standard Pub.

--The Lord of Parables: Instructor Edition. LC 83-12640. 128p. (Orig.). 1984. pap. 2.95 (ISBN 0-87239-706-8, 39980); pap. 2.50 student edition (ISBN 0-87239-707-6, 39981). Standard Pub.

--Lord of Promises. LC 82-17034. 112p. 1983. pap. 2.50 (ISBN 0-87239-611-8, 39988). Standard Pub.

--The New Testament Church Then & Now. LC 81-50631. 160p. (Orig.). 1981. pap. 3.95 (ISBN 0-87239-443-3, 88585). Standard Pub.

--The New Testament Church Then & Now Workbook. 48p. 1983. pap. 1.75 (ISBN 0-87239-609-6, 88586). Standard Pub.

--Where Do You Grow from Here? 128p. 1985. pap. 2.95 (ISBN 0-87239-967-2, 41034). Standard Pub.

Lawson, McEwan. Master John Milton of the Citie of London. LC 72-10632. 1973. Repr. lib. bdg. 12.50 (ISBN 0-8414-0725-8). Folcroft.

Lawson, Thomas E. Religions of Africa. LC 84-47729. (Religious Traditions of the World Ser.). (Illus.). 128p. (Orig.). 1984. pap. 6.95 (ISBN 0-06-065211-X, HarpR). Har-Row.

Lawton, Clive. I Am a Jew. Sloan, Frank, ed. LC 85-50167. (My Heritage Ser.). 32p. 1985. PLB 9.40 (ISBN 0-531-10019-7). Watts.

Lawton, Florrie A. God Loves Me. LC 85-24342. (Bible & Me Ser.). (Illus.). 1986. 5.95 (ISBN 0-8054-4163-8). Broadman.

Lawton, George. Within the Rock of Ages: Life & Work of Augustus Moretague Toplady. 249p. 1983. 25.00 (ISBN 0-227-67836-2). Attic Pr.

Lawton, George, jt. auth. see Schneider, Herbert.

Lawyer, John & Katz, Neil. Communication Skills for Ministry. 176p. 1983. pap. text ed. 17.95 (ISBN 0-8403-2987-3, 40371201). Kendall-Hunt.

Lay, Benjamin. All Slave-Keepers That Keep the Innocent in Bondage, Apostates Pretending to Lay Claim to the Pure & Holy Christian Religion. LC 72-82203. (Anti-Slavery Crusade in America Ser). 1969. Repr. of 1737 ed. 12.00 (ISBN 0-405-00642-X). Ayer Co Pubs.

Lay Commission on Catholic Social Teaching & the U. S. Economy. Toward the Future: Catholic Social Thought & the U. S. Economy, a Lay Letter. 120p. 1985. pap. text ed. 4.75 (ISBN 0-8191-4860-1). U Pr of Amer.

Laycock, Steven W. & Hart, James G., eds. Essays in Phenomenological Theology. 204p. (Orig.). 1986. 44.50x (ISBN 0-88706-164-8); pap. 14.95x (ISBN 0-88706-165-6). State U NY Pr.

Layish, Ahron. Women & Islamic Law in a Non-Muslim State. 369p. 1975. 19.95. Transaction Bks.

Layman, Emma M. Buddhism in America. LC 76-4566. (Illus.). 364p. 1976. pap. 13.95x (ISBN 0-88229-436-9). Nelson-Hall.

Laymon, Charles M., ed. Interpreter's One-Volume Commentary on the Bible. (Illus.). 1971. 24.95 (ISBN 0-687-19299-4); thumb indexed 28.95 (ISBN 0-687-19300-1). Abingdon.

Layne, James N. Old Testament Study Simplified. new ed. LC 77-23715. 1978. pap. 3.95 (ISBN 0-87148-656-3). Pathway Pr.

Layton, Bentley. The Gnostic Scriptures: A New Translation with Annotations. LC 85-25234. (Illus.). 800p. 1987. 35.00 (ISBN 0-385-17447-0). Doubleday.

Layton, Karen & Layton, Ron. Bible Word Fun. (Bible Baffler Ser.). 48p. 1986. wkbk. 4.95 (ISBN 0-86653-367-2). Good Apple.

Layton, Marilyn S., jt. auth. see Handlin, Mimi.

Layton, Ron, jt. auth. see Layton, Karen.

Laz, Medard. Spiritual Guidance for the Separated & Divorced. 64p. 1982. pap. 1.95 (ISBN 0-89243-158-X). Liguori Pubns.

Lazare, Bernard. Anti-Semitism: Its History & Causes. 1982. lib. bdg. 59.95 (ISBN 0-87700-426-9). Revisionist Pr.

Lazarer, V. N. Novgorodian Icon-Painting. (Illus.). 40.00 (ISBN 0-912729-00-7). Newbury Bks.

Lazareth, William H., ed. see Bonino, Jose M.

Lazaroff, Allan. The Theology of Abraham Bibago: A Defense of the Divine Will, Knowledge, & Providence in Fifteenth-Century Spanish-Jewish Philosophy. LC 77-10611. (Judaic Studies Ser.). 192p. 1981. text ed. 17.50 (ISBN 0-8173-6906-6). U of Ala Pr.

Lazarre, Jane. The Mother Knot. LC 85-47944. 210p. 1986. pap. 8.95 (ISBN 0-8070-6725-3, BP710). Beacon Pr.

Lazarus, Josephine. Spirit of Judaism. facsimile ed. LC 77-38031. (Essay Index Reprint Ser). Repr. of 1895 ed. 16.00 (ISBN 0-8369-2602-1). Ayer Co Pubs.

Lazarus, M. & Winter, Jakob. Die Ethnik des Judenthums, 2 vols. LC 79-7146. (Jewish Philosophy, Mysticism & History of Ideas Ser.). 1980. Repr. of 1911 ed. Set. lib. bdg. 80.00x (ISBN 0-405-12276-4). Ayer Co Pubs.

Lazear, Robert. Maestro de Dolores. (Span., Illus.). 342p. (Orig.). 1979. pap. 4.50 (ISBN 0-89922-138-6). Edit Caribe.

La Zebnik, Edith. Such a Life. 1979. pap. 2.50 (ISBN 0-671-82282-9). PB.

Lazzarin, Piero, jt. auth. see Lubich, Gino.

Lea, Charlene A. Emancipation, Assimilation & Stereotype: The Image of the Jew in German & Austrian Drama (1800-1850) (Modern German Studies: Vol. 2). viii, 171p. (Orig.). 1978. pap. 18.00x (ISBN 3-416-01420-0, Pub. by Bouvier Verlag W Germany). Benjamins North Am.

Lea, F. A. The Wild Knight of Battersea: G. K. Chesterton. 1973. Repr. of 1945 ed. 25.00 (ISBN 0-8274-0321-6). R West.

Lea, Henry. Moriscos of Spain, Their Conversion & Expulsion. LC 68-26358. (Studies in Spanish Literature, No. 36). 1969. Repr. of 1901 ed. lib. bdg. 51.95x (ISBN 0-8383-0266-1). Haskell.

Lea, Henry C. Chapters from the Religious History of Spain Connected with the Inquisition. LC 68-56760. (Research & Source Work Ser.: No. 245). 1967. Repr. of 1890 ed. 26.00 (ISBN 0-8337-2035-X). B Franklin.

--History of Auricular Confession & Indulgences in the Latin Church, 3 Vols. LC 68-19287. 1968. Repr. of 1896 ed. lib. bdg. 67.25x (ISBN 0-8371-0140-9, LEHC). Greenwood.

--History of the Inquisition of Spain, 4 Vols. LC 72-181943. Repr. of 1907 ed. Set. 145.00 (ISBN 0-404-03920-0). Vol. 1 (ISBN 0-404-03921-9). Vol. 2 (ISBN 0-404-03922-7). Vol. 3 (ISBN 0-404-03923-5). Vol. 4 (ISBN 0-404-03924-3). AMS Pr.

--Moriscos of Spain. LC 68-56783. 1968. Repr. of 1901 ed. 20.50 (ISBN 0-8337-4218-3). B Franklin.

--Moriscos of Spain: Their Conversion & Expulsion. 1968. Repr. of 1901 ed. lib. bdg. 23.50x (ISBN 0-8371-0141-7, LEMS). Greenwood.

Lea, L. J., ed. Compendium of the Scriptures. 1951. pap. 10.00 (ISBN 0-8309-0253-8). Herald Hse.

Lea, Thomas D., jt. auth. see Vaughan, Curtis.

Leach, ed. Funk & Wagnalls Standard Dictionary of Folklore, Mythology & Legend. LC 72-78268. (Funk & W Bk.). 23.00i (ISBN 0-308-40090-9). T Y Crowell.

Leach, Arthur F., ed. see Southwell Cathedral.

Leach, Ben. Groaning Up. (Uplook Ser.). 32p. 1982. pap. 0.99 (ISBN 0-8163-0513-7). Pacific Pr Pub Assn.

--I Can't Turn Off My Happy. (Uplook Ser.). 32p. 1982. pap. 0.79 (ISBN 0-8163-0515-3). Pacific Pr Pub Assn.

--Riding High. (Uplook Ser.). 32p. 1982. pap. 0.79 (ISBN 0-8163-0514-5). Pacific Pr Pub Assn.

--Worry Free Worry. (Uplook Ser.). 32p. 1982. pap. 0.99 (ISBN 0-8163-0516-1). Pacific Pr Pub Assn.

Leach, David A. Genesis: The Book of Beginnings. 96p. 1984. pap. 4.95 (ISBN 0-8170-1047-5). Judson.

Leach, Edmund & Aycock, Alan. Structuralist Interpretations of Biblical Myth. LC 82-25263. (Illus.). 176p. 1983. 34.50 (ISBN 0-521-25491-4); pap. 11.95 (ISBN 0-521-27492-3). Cambridge U Pr.

Leach, Edmund, ed. Structural Study of Myth & Totenism. (Orig.). 1968. pap. 12.95 (ISBN 0-422-72530-7, NO.2287, Pub by Tavistock England). Methuen Inc.

Leach, Edmund R. Dialectic in Practical Religion. (Cambridge Papers in Social Anthropology: No. 5). 34.50 (ISBN 0-521-05525-3). Cambridge U Pr.

Leach, Maria & Fried, Jerome, eds. Funk & Wagnall's Standard Dictionary of Folklore, Mythology, & Legends. 1984. pap. 29.95 (ISBN 0-06-250511-4, HarpR). Har-Row.

Leach, Maureen, jt. auth. see Schreck, Nancy.

Leach, Robert J. Women Ministers: A Quaker Contribution. Blattenberger, Ruth, ed. LC 79-84922. 1979. pap. 2.50x (ISBN 0-87574-227-0). Pendle Hill.

Leach, Robert J., ed. see Penington, Isaac.

Leach, Vickie, tr. see Bonino, Jose M.

Leach, Virgil. Attitudes I. 1979. pap. 4.25 (ISBN 0-89137-803-0). Quality Pubns.

--Attitudes II. 1981. pap. 4.25 (ISBN 0-89137-804-9). Quality Pubns.

--Get Behind Me Satan. 1977. 8.75 (ISBN 0-89137-521-X); pap. 5.95 (ISBN 0-89137-520-1). Quality Pubns.

Leadbeater. Devachanic Plane. 5.50 (ISBN 0-8356-7075-9). Theos Pub Hse.

--Invisible Helpers. 6.95 (ISBN 0-8356-7160-7). Theos Pub Hse.

--Life after Death. 4.50 (ISBN 0-8356-7148-8). Theos Pub Hse.

--Monad. 3.00 (ISBN 0-8356-7646-3). Theos Pub Hse.

--Outline of Theosophy. 2.95 (ISBN 0-8356-7185-2). Theos Pub Hse.

--Science of the Sacraments. 18.95 (ISBN 0-8356-7126-7). Theos Pub Hse.

--Textbook of Theosophy. 6.95 (ISBN 0-8356-7110-0). Theos Pub Hse.

Leadbeater & Besant. Talks on the Path of Occultism, Vol. 1: At the Feet of the Master. 9.50 (ISBN 0-8356-7047-3). Theos Pub Hse.

--Talks on the Path of Occultism, Vol. 3: Light on the Path. 7.95 (ISBN 0-8356-7068-6). Theos Pub Hse.

Leadbeater, jt. auth. see Beasant.

Leadbeater, jt. auth. see Besant.

Leadbeater, C. W. The Soul & Its Vestures. 24p. 1983. pap. 1.50 (ISBN 0-918980-12-7). St Alban Pr.

Leadbeater, Charles W. Astral Plane. 1973. 5.95 (ISBN 0-8356-7093-7). Theos Pub Hse.

--Chakras. 10th ed. 1973. 7.95 (ISBN 0-8356-7016-3). Theos Pub Hse.

--The Chakras. LC 73-147976. (Illus.). 148p. 1972. pap. 5.75 (ISBN 0-8356-0422-5, Quest). Theos Pub Hse.

--Man, Visible & Invisible. 9.95 (ISBN 0-8356-7388-X). Theos Pub Hse.

Leadbeater, Charles W., jt. auth. see Besant, Annie.

Leaders of the Christian Church Staff & Teegarden, Kenneth L. Seeking God's Peace in a Nuclear Age. Osborn, Ronald, ed. LC 85-7836. 96p. (Orig.). 1985. pap. 2.50 (ISBN 0-8272-3422-8). CBP.

Leaf, Hayim, jt. ed. see Ben-Asher, Naomi.

Leaf, Walter, tr. see Solovyoff, Vsevolod S.

Leahey, Grace E., jt. auth. see Leahey, Thomas H.

Leahey, Joseph, tr. see Idung Of Prufening.

Leahey, Thomas H. & Leahey, Grace E. Psychology's Occult Doubles: Psychology & the Problem of Pseudoscience. LC 82-24635. 296p. 1983. lib. bdg. 25.95x (ISBN 0-88229-717-1). Nelson-Hall.

Leahy, John A. Eagle's Chase: The Agony of Success. LC 85-21644. (Illus.). 192p. 1986. 13.95 (ISBN 0-88280-114-7). ETC Pubns.

Leaman, Oliver. An Introduction to Medieval Islamic Philosophy. 224p. 1985. 34.50 (ISBN 0-521-24707-1); pap. 12.95 (ISBN 0-521-28911-4). Cambridge U Pr.

Leaney, Alfred R. Letters of Peter & Jude. (Cambridge Bible Commentary on the New English Bible, New Testament Ser.). (Orig.). 16.95 (ISBN 0-521-04216-X); pap. 8.95x (ISBN 0-521-09403-8). Cambridge U Pr.

Lear, Floyd S., jt. ed. see Drew, Katherine F.

Learsi, Rufus. The Jew in America: A History. rev. ed. 1972. 11.95x (ISBN 0-87068-177-X). Ktav.

Leary, James. Hear O Israel. 1980. pap. 3.95 (ISBN 0-88479-029-0). Arena Lettres.

Leary, James F. Hear, O Israel: A Guide to the Old Testament. 144p. 1986. pap. 4.95 (ISBN 0-88479-029-0). Chr Classics.

--A Light to the Nations: A Guide to the New Testament. 144p. 1986. pap. 4.95 (ISBN 0-88479-036-3). Chr Classics.

Leary, John, jt. auth. see Boisen, Anton T.

Leary, Lewis. The Book-Peddling Parson: An Account of the Life & Works of Mason Locke Weems. (Illus.). 1984. 15.95 (ISBN 0-912697-09-1). Algonquin Bks.

Leary, Michael. Christ & the Catechist: The Spiritual Life of the Christian Teacher. LC 86-83017. 128p. 1987. pap. 6.95 (ISBN 0-89870-139-2). Ignatius Pr.

Leary, Norma. Christmas on Trial. (Orig.). 1983. pap. 2.95 (ISBN 0-937172-56-1). JLJ Pubs.

--Good Friday Unchanged. (Orig.). 1982. pap. 3.75 (ISBN 0-937172-34-0). JLJ Pubs.

--Portraits of Customs & Carols. 1983. pap. 2.95 (ISBN 0-937172-54-5). JLJ Pubs.

--Voices of Christmas. (Orig.). 1983. pap. 3.25 (ISBN 0-937172-55-3). JLJ Pubs.

Leary, Timothy & Metzner, Ralph. The Psychedelic Experience: A Manual Based on the Tibetan Book of the Dead. 1976. pap. 4.95 (ISBN 0-8065-0552-4). Citadel Pr.

Leary, William. Hidden Bible. 1955. 19.95 (ISBN 0-910140-07-3). C & R Anthony.

Leas, Speed & Kittlaus, Paul. The Pastoral Counselor in Social Action. Clinebell, Howard J. & Stone, Howard W., eds. LC 80-8059. (Creative Pastoral Care & Counseling Ser.). 96p. (Orig.). 1981. pap. 4.50 (ISBN 0-8006-0565-9, 1-565). Fortress.

Leas, Speed, jt. auth. see Kittlaus, Paul.

Leas, Speed B. Leadership & Conflict. (Creative Leadership Ser.). 128p. (Orig.). 1982. pap. 7.50 (ISBN 0-687-21264-2). Abingdon.

--Time Management. LC 78-8628. (Creative Leadership Ser.). 1978. pap. 5.95 (ISBN 0-687-42120-9). Abingdon.

Leask, Harold G. Irish Churches & Monastic Buildings, 3 Vols. Vol. I: First Phases & Romanesque, 173p. 16.95 (ISBN 0-85221-016-7); Vol. II: Gothic to A.D. 1400, 162p. 16.95 (ISBN 0-85221-011-6). Dufour.

Leathem, Diana. They Built on Rock: The Story of the Celtic Christian Church. 1977. lib. bdg. 59.95 (ISBN 0-8490-2743-8). Gordon Pr.

Leatherbarrow, J. Stanley. The Lancashire Elizabethan Recusants. Repr. of 1947 ed. 24.00 (ISBN 0-384-31910-6). Johnson Repr.

Leatherbarrow, William J. Feodor Dostoevsky. (World Authors Ser.). 15.95 (ISBN 0-8057-6480-1, Twayne). G K Hall.

Leavell, Landrum P. Angels, Angels, Angels. LC 73-75627. 96p. 1973. pap. 5.95 (ISBN 0-8054-2222-6). Broadman.

--Sermons for Celebrating. LC 77-90220. 1978. pap. 3.75 (ISBN 0-8054-2231-5). Broadman.

Leavell, Landrum P. & Bryson, Harold. Evangelism: Christ's Imperative Commission. rev. ed. LC 78-59983. 1979. 10.95 (ISBN 0-8054-2534-9). Broadman.

Leavenworth, Lynn J., jt. auth. see Carter, Velma T.

Leaver, Robin A. Luther on Justification. LC 74-11781. 1975. pap. 4.75 (ISBN 0-570-03188-5, 12-2590). Concordia.

--Music in the Service of the Church: The Funeral Sermon for Heinrich Schuetz. 68p. (Orig.). 1985. pap. 6.75 (ISBN 0-570-01331-3, 99-1261). Concordia.

Leaver, Robin A., ed. see Stiller, Gunther.

Leavey, John P., Jr., tr. see Derrida, Jacques.

Leavitt, Guy P. Superintend with Success. rev. ed. Langston, A. Leon, ed. LC 79-66658. (Illus.). 144p. 1980. pap. 7.95 (ISBN 0-87239-377-1, 3203). Standard Pub.

Leavitt, John, tr. see Izard, Michel & Smith, Pierre.

Lebacqz, Karen. Genetics, Ethics & Parenthood. 128p. (Orig.). 1983. pap. 7.95 (ISBN 0-8298-0671-7). Pilgrim NY.

--Six Theories of Justice: Perspectives from Philosophical & Theological Ethics. LC 86-26457. 144p. (Orig.). 1986. pap. 9.95 (ISBN 0-8066-2245-8, 10-5820). Augsburg.

Lebar, Lois & Berg, Miguel. Llamados a Ensenar. Blanch, Jose M., tr. from Eng. LC 77-5183. (Span., Illus.). 160p. 1970. pap. 3.95 (ISBN 0-89922-006-1). Edit Caribe.

LeBar, Mary E. The Best Family of All. 32p. 1977. pap. 3.95 (ISBN 0-88207-251-X). Victor Bks.

Le Blanc, Andre, illus. Great Adventures from the Bible. (Illus.). 200p. (Orig.). 1984. pap. 3.95 (ISBN 0-89191-848-5). Cook.

Le Blanc, Sr. M. Francis. Cause of Our Joy. 1981. 4.00 (ISBN 0-8198-0391-X); pap. 3.00 (ISBN 0-8198-1414-8). Dghtrs St Paul.

Lebra, William P. Okinawan Religion: Belief, Ritual, & Social Structure. 256p. 1985. pap. text ed. 8.95x (ISBN 0-87022-450-6). Uh Pr.

Le Bras, Gabriel. Etudes De Sociologie Religieuse: Studies in Religious Sociology, 2 vols. in one. LC 74-25763. (European Sociology Ser.). 824p. 1975. Repr. 59.50x (ISBN 0-405-06517-5). Ayer Co Pubs.

Lebreton, Jules & Zeiller, Jacques. History of the Primitive Church. 80.00 (ISBN 0-8490-0361-X). Gordon Pr.

Lebuffe, Francis P. Friends Aren't Kept Waiting. 1975. pap. 1.75 (ISBN 0-88479-000-2). Arena Lettres.

--More of My Changeless Friend. 1977. pap. 1.95 (ISBN 0-88479-007-X). Arena Lettres.

Lebzelter, Gisela C. Political Anti-Semitism in England 1918-1939. LC 78-16795. 222p. 1979. text ed. 49.50x (ISBN 0-8419-0426-X). Holmes & Meier.

Lecanu, A. F. Dictionnaire des Propheties et des Miracles, 2 vols. Migne, J. P., ed. (Nouvelle Encyclopedie Theologique Ser.: Vols. 24-25). (Fr.). 1246p. Repr. of 1852 ed. lib. bdg. 159.00x (ISBN 0-89241-268-2). Caratzas.

Lecaro, Giacomo. John Twenty Third: Simpleton or Saint. 1968. 3.50 (ISBN 0-8199-0055-9, L38351). Franciscan Herald.

Lechford, Thomas. Plain Dealing: Or News from New England. 1969. Repr. of 1867 ed. 19.00 (ISBN 0-384-31985-8). Johnson Repr.

Lechler, Gotthard V. John Wycliffe & His English Precursors. LC 78-63197. (Heresies of the Early Christian & Medieval Era: Second Ser.). Repr. of 1884 ed. 49.50 (ISBN 0-404-16235-5). AMS Pr.

Leckey, Dolores R. Laity Stirring the Church: Prophetic Questions. LC 86-45213. (Laity Exchange Ser.). 128p. pap. 6.95 (ISBN 0-8006-1659-6, 1-1659). Fortress.

--The Ordinary Way: A Family Spirituality. (Crossroad Paperback Ser.). 192p. 1982. pap. 7.95 (ISBN 0-8245-0442-9). Crossroad NY.

Leckey, Dolores R., ed. Journeying Together: Proceedings of Three Regional Convocations on Shared Responsibility in America. 48p. 1986. pap. 4.95 (ISBN 1-55586-975-0). US Catholic.

Leclerc, Eloi. People of God in the Night. Lachance, Paul & Schwartz, Paul, trs. (Tau Ser.). 1979. 5.95 (ISBN 0-8199-0768-5). Franciscan Herald.

Leclerc, Ivor. Whitehead's Metaphysics: An Introductory Exposition. LC 86-4027. 248p. 1986. pap. text ed. 11.00 (ISBN 0-8191-4852-0). U Pr of Amer.

Le Clercq, Chretien. First Establishment of the Faith in New France, 2 Vols. LC 77-172312. Repr. of 1881 ed. Set. 67.50 (ISBN 0-404-03914-6). Vol. 1 (ISBN 0-404-03915-4). Vol. 2 (ISBN 0-404-03916-2). AMS Pr.

--New Relation of Gaspesia: With the Customs & Religion of the Gaspesian Indian. Ganong, William F., ed. LC 68-28600. 1968. Repr. of 1910 ed. lib. bdg. 33.75x (ISBN 0-8371-5044-2, LERG). Greenwood.

Leclercq, Dom H. & Marron, Henri. Dictionnaire d'Archeologie Chretienne et de Liturgie, 28 vols. (Fr.). 1903. Set. 1995.00 (ISBN 0-686-57001-4, M-6342). French & Eur.

Leclercq, Jacques. This Day Is Ours. Livingstone, Dinah, tr. from Fr. LC 80-50314. Orig. Title: Le Jour de L'Homme. 128p. (Orig.). 1980. pap. 1.74 (ISBN 0-88344-504-2). Orbis Bks.

Leclercq, Jean. Love of Learning & Desire for God: A Study of Monastic Culture. 3rd ed. LC 60-53004. x, 282p. 1985. pap. 10.00 (ISBN 0-8232-0407-3). Fordham.

--Monks on Marriage: A Twelfth-Century View. 144p. 1982. 10.95 (ISBN 0-8164-0507-7, HarpR). Har-Row.

Leclercq, Jean, intro. by. Thomas Merton on St. Bernard. (Cistercian Studies: No. 9). 1980. 13.95 (ISBN 0-87907-809-X); pap. 4.95 (ISBN 0-87907-909-6). Cistercian Pubns.

LeClercq, Jean, et al. A History of Christian Spirituality, 3 vols. 1982. Set. pap. 45.00 slip-cased (ISBN 0-8164-2369-5, HarpR). Har-Row.

--The Spirituality of the Middle Ages. (A History of Christian Spirituality Ser.: Vol. 2). 616p. 1982. pap. 14.95 (ISBN 0-8164-2373-3, HarpR). Har-Row.

--St. Bede: A Tribute. LC 85-8214. (Word & Spirit Ser.: Vol. VII). 1985. pap. 7.00. St Bedes Pubns.

Le Conte, Joseph. Evolution: Its Nature Its Evidences, - Its Relation to Religious Thought. 2nd ed. 1897. 29.00 (ISBN 0-527-55700-5). Kraus Repr.

--Religion & Science. LC 75-3239. Repr. of 1874 ed. 21.50 (ISBN 0-404-59231-7). AMS Pr.

LeCours, Zoe S. Exit Here Please: Puzzles, Games & Mazes about the Book of Exodus. (Illus.). 64p. (Orig.). 1986. pap. 4.95 (ISBN 0-934661-01-4, 7078). Lions Head Pr.

--To Begin with Puzzles, Games & Mazes about the Book of Genesis. (Illus.). 48p. (Orig.). 1985. pap. 4.49 (ISBN 0-934661-00-6, 7077). Lions Head Pr.

Lecourt, Nancy. Rainbow. (Books I Can Read). 32p. 1980. pap. 1.95 (ISBN 0-8127-0290-5). Review & Herald.

LeCroy, Anne K. & Hatchett, Marion J. The Altar Guild Handbook. 108p. (Orig.). 1986. pap. 4.95 (ISBN 0-86683-784-1, HarpR). Har-Row.

Lectorium Rosicrucianum, ed. see De Petri, Catharose.

Lectorium Rosicrucianum, tr. see Van Rijckenborgh, Jan.

Lectorium Rosicrucianum Staff, tr. see De Petri, Catharose.

Leder, Arnold. Catalysts of Change: Marxist versus Muslim in a Turkish Community. LC 76-29323. (Middle East Monograph: No. 1). 70p. 1976. pap. text ed. 3.95x (ISBN 0-292-71042-9, Pub. by Ctr Mid East Stud). U of Tex Pr.

Lederach, Paul M. Teaching in the Congregation. LC 79-83594. (Mennonite Faith Ser: No. 7). 1979. pap. 1.50 (ISBN 0-8361-1886-3). Herald Pr.

--A Third Way. LC 80-26280. 152p. 1980. pap. 6.95 (ISBN 0-8361-1934-7). Herald Pr.

Lederer, William J. A Happy Book of Christmas Stories. (Illus.). 1984. 7.95 (ISBN 0-393-01414-2). Norton.

Ledger, Philip, ed. Anthems for Choirs Three: Twenty-Four Anthems for Sopranos & Altos, Three or More Parts. 1973. pap. text ed. 8.75x (ISBN 0-19-353242-5). Oxford U Pr.

--Anthems for Choirs Two: Twenty-Four Anthems for Sopranos & Altos, Unison & Two-Part. 1973. pap. text ed. 8.75x (ISBN 0-19-353240-9). Oxford U Pr.

Ledkovsky, Boris. Great Vespers. (Music Ser.). 218p. 1976. pap. 10.00 (ISBN 0-913836-26-5). St Vladimirs.

Ledwith, Miceal, tr. from Lat. Propositions on the Dignity & Rights of the Human Person. (International Theological Commission Ser.). 28p. (Orig.). 1986. pap. 1.95 (ISBN 1-55586-997-1). US Catholic.

Lee, Albert. Henry Ford & the Jews. LC 79-3694. 252p. 1980. 12.95 (ISBN 0-8128-2701-5). Stein & Day.

Lee, Amy. Throbbing Drums: The Story of James H. Robinson. (Orig.). 1968. pap. 0.95 (ISBN 0-377-84141-2). Friend Pr.

Lee, Anthony A. The Scottish Visitors: A Story about 'Abdu'l-Baha in Britain. (Stories About 'Abdu'l-Baha Ser.). (Illus.). 24p. (Orig.). 1981. pap. 2.50 (ISBN 0-933770-05-7). Kalimat.

--The Unfriendly Governor. (Stories About 'Abdu'l-Baha Ser.). (Illus.). 24p. 1980. pap. 2.50 (ISBN 0-933770-02-2). Kalimat.

Lee, Anthony A., ed. Circle of Unity: Baha'i Approaches to Current Social Issues. 268p. (Orig.). 1984. pap. 9.95 (ISBN 0-933770-28-6). Kalimat.

Lee, Anthony A., jt. ed. see Smith, Peter.

Lee, Atkinson. Groundwork of the Philosophy of Religion. LC 46-19011. (Studies in Theology Ser: No. 48). 1946. text ed. 6.00x (ISBN 0-8401-6048-8). A R Allenson.

Lee, Betsy. Mother Teresa: Caring for All God's Children. LC 80-20286. (Taking Part Ser.). (Illus.). 48p. 1981. PLB 8.95 (ISBN 0-87518-205-4). Dillon.

Lee, Bruce. Tao of Jeet Kune Do. LC 75-13803. (Series 401). (Illus.). 1975. pap. 12.50 (ISBN 0-89750-048-2). Ohara Pubns.

Lee, Charles. Divine Wisdom & Awareness of a Spiritual & True Religious Life. 1986. 6.95 (ISBN 0-533-06748-0). Vantage.

Lee, Clay F. Jesus Never Said Everyone Was Lovable. 112p. 1987. pap. 6.95 (ISBN 0-687-19980-8). Abingdon.

Lee, Daniel & Frost, Joseph H. Ten Years in Oregon. LC 72-9457. (The Far Western Frontier Ser.). (Illus.). 348p. 1973. Repr. of 1844 ed. 24.50 (ISBN 0-405-04985-4). Ayer Co Pubs.

Lee, Don Y. An Outline of Confucianism. LC 85-80477. 113p. 1984. 29.50x (ISBN 0-939758-10-5). Eastern Pr.

Lee, Dorothy. Valuing the Self: What We Can Learn from Other Cultures. (Illus.). 1986. pap. text ed. 6.95x (ISBN 0-88133-229-1). Waveland Pr.

Lee, Douglas. T'ai Chi Ch'uan the Philosophy of Yin & Yang & Its Applications. Lucas, Charles, ed. LC 76-6249. (Ser. 317). (Illus.). 1976. pap. text ed. 6.95 (ISBN 0-89750-044-X). Ohara Pubns.

Lee, Elizabeth M. He Wears Orchids & Other Latin American Stories. LC 76-117327. (Biography Index Reprint Ser). 1951. 19.00 (ISBN 0-8369-8019-0). Ayer Co Pubs.

Lee, Eva. Motivate with Bulletin Boards, No. 2. (Illus.). 48p. 1985. pap. 2.95 (ISBN 0-87239-919-2, 3289). Standard Pub.

Lee, Francis G. Wall of Controversy. 1986. lib. bdg. 6.50 (ISBN 0-89874-828-3). Krieger.

Lee, Frank. Bedtime Stories of the Saints, Bk. 2. 64p. (Orig.). 1980. pap. 1.95 (ISBN 0-89243-126-1). Liguori Pubns.

Lee, Frederick G. A Glossary of Liturgical & Ecclesiastical Terms. LC 76-174069. (Tower Bks.). (Illus.). xl, 452p. 1972. Repr. of 1877 ed. 44.00x (ISBN 0-8103-3949-8). Gale.

Lee, G. Avery. Elijah: Yahweh Is My God. (Orig.). 1987. pap. 5.50 (ISBN 0-8054-1539-4). Broadman.

--The Glorious Company. LC 86-2601. (Orig.). 1986. pap. 3.25 (ISBN 0-8054-1536-X). Broadman.

Lee, Harris W. Theology of Administration: A Bibical Basis for Organizing the Congregation. LC 81-147067. 40p. 1981. pap. 3.95 (ISBN 0-8066-1875-2, 10-6290). Augsburg.

Lee, Helen. This Is My Home, Lord. 128p. 1983. pap. 4.95 (ISBN 0-86683-683-7, HarpR). Har-Row.

Lee, J. A. A Lexical Study of the Septuagint Version of the Pentateuch. LC 82-5460. (Septuagint & Cognate Studies). 186p. 1983. pap. 12.50 (ISBN 0-89130-576-9, 06 04 14). Scholars Pr GA.

Lee, James M. The Content of Religious Instruction: A Social Science Approach. LC 84-18255. 815p. (Orig.). 1985. pap. 14.95 (ISBN 0-89135-050-0). Religious Educ.

--The Flow of Religious Instruction: A Social-Science Approach. LC 74-29824. (Illus.). 379p. (Orig.). 1975. pap. 14.95 (ISBN 0-89135-003-9). Religious Educ.

Lee, James M., ed. Catholic Education in the Western World. 1967. 17.95x (ISBN 0-268-00030-1). U of Notre Dame Pr.

--The Religious Education We Need: Toward the Renewal of Christian Education. LC 76-55587. 174p. (Orig.). 1977. pap. 7.95 (ISBN 0-89135-005-5). Religious Educ.

--The Spirituality of the Religious Educator. 209p. (Orig.). 1985. pap. 12.95 (ISBN 0-89135-045-4). Religious Educ.

Lee, James Michael. The Shape of Religious Instruction: A Social-Science Approach. LC 74-29823. 330p. (Orig.). 1971. lib. bdg. 16.95 (ISBN 0-89135-000-4); pap. 14.95 (ISBN 0-89135-002-0). Religious Educ.

Lee, Jesse & Thrift, Minton. Memoir of the Reverend Jesse Lee, with Extracts from His Journals. LC 72-83428. (Religion in America, Ser. 1). 1969. Repr. of 1823 ed. 19.00 (ISBN 0-405-00253-X). Ayer Co Pubs.
Lee, Jung Y. Death & Beyond in the Eastern Perspective. new ed. LC 73-85065. 112p. 1974. 24.50x (ISBN 0-677-05010-0). Gordon & Breach.
--Korean Shamanistic Rituals. (Religion & Society Ser.: No. 12). 250p. 1980. 39.50 (ISBN 90-279-3378-2). Mouton.
--The Theology of Change: A Christian Concept of God in an Eastern Perspective. LC 78-16745. 155p. (Orig.). 1979. pap. 5.95 (ISBN 0-88344-492-5). Orbis Bks.
Lee, Kathleen, tr. see Kappeler, Max.
Lee, Kwan-Jo. Search for Nirvana. (Illus.). 124p. 1984. 24.00 (ISBN 0-8048-1417-1, Pub. by Seoul Intl Publishing House). C E Tuttle.
Lee, Laurel. To Comfort You. Phillips, Cheryl M. & Harvey, Bonnie C., eds. (Illus.). 32p. (Orig.). 1984. pap. 0.98 (ISBN 0-937420-11-5). Stirrup Assoc.
Lee, Linda, compiled by. Meditate Upon These Things. 2nd ed. (Illus.). 160p. 1981. pap. 5.00 (ISBN 0-87516-463-3). De Vorss.
Lee, Luther. Autobiography of the Rev. Luther Lee. Dayton, Donald W., ed. (The Higher Christian Life Ser.). 345p. 1985. 45.00 (ISBN 0-8240-6426-7). Garland Pub.
--Slavery Examined in the Light of the Bible. LC 76-92434. 185p. 1855. Repr. 39.00x (ISBN 0-403-00166-8). Scholarly.
Lee, Mark & Grant, James M. This Family Business. LC 82-73873. 150p. 1984. pap. 6.45 (ISBN 0-87509-328-0); pap. 2.95 (ISBN 0-87509-356-6). Chr Pubns.
Lee, Mark W. How to Have a Good Marriage. LC 78-56794. 1981. pap. 5.95 (ISBN 0-915684-89-6). Chr Pubns.
--Who Am I & What Am I Doing Here. 1986. pap. 5.95 (ISBN 0-8010-5643-8). Baker Bk.
Lee, Maurice. James Stewart, Earl of Moray: A Political Study of the Reformation in Scotland. LC 73-104251. 1971. Repr. of 1953 ed. lib. bdg. 22.50x (ISBN 0-8371-3975-9, LEJS). Greenwood.
Lee, Paul. My Heart a Hiding Place. 1986. pap. 7.95 (ISBN 0-87508-316-1). Chr Lit.
Lee, Peter, et al. Food for Life. LC 77-27693. 1978. pap. 3.95 (ISBN 0-87784-489-5). Inter-Varsity.
Lee, Peter H., tr. see Kakhun.
Lee, Philip J., Jr. Against the Protestant Gnostics. 288p. 1987. 18.95 (ISBN 0-19-504067-8). Oxford U Pr.
Lee, Rebecca, ed. see Nauman, Eileen.
Lee, Robert. The Outlined Bible. 1986. pap. 7.95 (ISBN 0-310-44821-2, 10465P). Zondervan.
Lee, Ronald R. Clergy & Clients: The Practice of Pastoral Psychotherapy. 1980. 10.95 (ISBN 0-8164-0115-2, HarpR). Har-Row.
Lee, Sang H. Explaining Unificatiion Thought. LC 80-54858. 356p. pap. 10.95 (ISBN 0-9606480-0-3). Rose Sharon Pr.
--Explaining Unification Thought. LC 80-54858. 356p. (Orig.). 1981. pap. 9.95 (ISBN 0-9606480-0-3). HSA Pubns.
Lee, Sharon. Christmas Handbook, No. 3. 112p. 1985. 7.95 (ISBN 0-87239-913-3, 3043). Standard Pub.
--Grandfather Clock & Other Finger Plays, Word Rhythms, & Action Rhymes. (Illus.). 64p. 1984. pap. 5.95 (ISBN 0-86683-834-1, HarpR). Har-Row.
--Joyous Days: A Collection of Advent & Christmas Activities. (The Learning Connections Ser.). 96p. (Orig.). 1984. pap. 7.95 (ISBN 0-86683-833-3, 8443, HarpR). Har-Row.
--When the Time Had Fully Come: Christmas Service for Church Schools. 32p. (Orig.). 1984. pap. 0.90 ea. (ISBN 0-8066-2101-X, 23-3010). Augsburg.
Lee, Stephen. Grace: Living on the Friendship of God. (Orig.). 1987. pap. 3.25 (ISBN 0-8054-5437-3). Broadman.
Lee, Thomas R. Studies in the form of Sirach 44-50. (Dissertation Ser.). 284p. 1986. 17.95 (ISBN 0-89130-834-2, 06-01-75); pap. 13.95 (ISBN 0-89130-835-0). Scholars Pr GA.
Lee, Umphrey. Historical Backgrounds of Early Methodist Enthusiasm. LC 31-18047. (Columbia University. Studies in the Social Sciences: No. 339). Repr. of 1931 ed. 17.50 (ISBN 0-404-51339-5). AMS Pr.
Leech, Bryan J. Lift My Spirits, Lord: Prayers of a Struggling Christian. LC 84-9351. 128p. (Orig.). 1984. pap. 5.95 (ISBN 0-8066-2090-0, 10-3850). Augsburg.
Leech, Bryan J., jt. ed. see Bock, Fred.
Leech, Jane K., jt. auth. see Brown, Marion M.
Leech, Kenneth. Experiencing God: Theology as Spirituality. LC 84-48237. 352p. 1985. 20.45 (ISBN 0-06-065226-8, HarpR). Har-Row.
--Soul Friend: The Practice of Christian Spirituality. LC 79-2994. 272p. 1980. 14.45 (ISBN 0-06-065225-X, HarpR). Har-Row.
--True Prayer: An Invitation to Christian Spirituality. LC 80-8358. 208p. 1981. 12.00 (ISBN 0-06-065227-6, HarpR). Har-Row.
--True Prayer: An Invitation to Christian Spirituality. LC 80-8358. 208p. 1986. pap. 7.95 (ISBN 0-06-065232-2, HarpR). Har-Row.
Leeder, S. H. Modern Sons of the Pharaohs. LC 73-6288. (The Middle East Ser.). Repr. of 1918 ed. 29.00 (ISBN 0-405-05346-0). Ayer Co Pubs.
Leedy, Kay. Life Never Ends. 141p. pap. 7.95 (ISBN 0-942494-41-5). Coleman Pub.
Leek, Sybil. The Complete Art of Witchcraft. (Illus.). 208p. 1973. pap. 2.95 (ISBN 0-451-12714-5, AE2714, Sig). NAL.
Leemhuis, F., et al. The Arabic Text of the Apocalypse of Baruch: Edited & Translated With a Parallel Translation of the Syriac Text. viii, 154p. 1986. 32.25 (ISBN 90-04-07608-5, Pub. by E J Brill). Heinman.
Leeming, David A. Flights: Readings in Magic, Mysticism, Fantasy & Myth. 388p. (Orig.). 1974. pap. text ed. 11.95 (ISBN 0-15-527556-9, HC). HarBraceJ.
--Mythology: The Voyage of the Hero. 2nd ed. (Illus.). 370p. 1980. pap. text ed. 14.50 scp (ISBN 0-06-043942-4, HarpC); instr's manual avail. (ISBN 0-06-363950-5). Har-Row.
Leen, Edward. Progress Through Mental Prayer. 1978. pap. 2.45 (ISBN 0-88479-012-6). Arena Lettres.
Leen, Jason. The Death of the Prophet. LC 79-18719. (Illus.). 1979. 11.95 (ISBN 0-87961-094-8); pap. 5.95 (ISBN 0-87961-093-X). Naturegraph.
Leenhardt, Franz J., jt. auth. see Cullmann, Oscar.
Leenhardt, Maurice. Do Kamo: La Personne et le Mythe Dans le Monde Melanesien. Bolle, Kees W., ed. LC 77-79137. (Mythology Ser.). (Fr.). 1978. Repr. of 1971 ed. lib. bdg. 24.50x (ISBN 0-405-10547-9). Ayer Co Pubs.
Leeper, John H. The Brothers of the Sled & Other Faith-Building Stories. (Orig.). 1985. pap. 4.95 (ISBN 0-8024-0622-X). Moody.
--The Riddle of the Outlaw Bear & Other Faith-Building Stories. (Illus.). 1984. pap. 4.95 (ISBN 0-8024-7352-0). Moody.
Leer, E. Fleseman-Van see Flesseman-Van Leer, E.
Lees, Rosemary A. The Negative Language of the Dionysian School of Mystical Theology: An Approach to the Cloud of Unknowing, 2 vols. Hogg, James, ed. (Analecta Cartusiana Ser.: No. 107). 549p. (Orig.). 1983. pap. 50.00 (ISBN 0-317-42591-9, Pub. by Salzburg Studies). Longwood Pub Group.
Lees, W. C. Second Thoughts on Missions. 1965. pap. 0.95 (ISBN 0-87508-908-9). Chr Lit.
Leese, A. Bolshevism Is Jewish. 1982. lib. bdg. 59.95 (ISBN 0-87700-409-9). Revisionist Pr.
--The Jewish War of Survival. 1982. lib. bdg. 59.95 (ISBN 0-87700-347-5). Revisionist Pr.
Leeser, Isaac. The Holy Scriptures Holy Bible Commentary. 32.50 (ISBN 0-317-30499-2). Shalom.
Leeuw, Gerardus Van Der see Van Der Leeuw, Gerardus.
Leeuw, J. J. Van Der see Van Der Leeuw, J. J.
Leeuwen, Mary S. van see Van Leeuwen, Mary S.
Le Fanu, Thomas P., ed. Registers of the French Non-Conformist Churches of Lucy Lane & Peter Street, Dublin. Bd. with History of the Walloon & Huguenot Church at Canterbury. Cross, F. W. Repr. of 1898 ed; Pt. 3. Registers of the French Church. Colyer-Fergusson, T. C., ed. Repr. of 1906 ed. (Hugenot Society of London Publication Ser.: Vols. 14-16). Repr. of 1901 ed. 135.00 (ISBN 0-8115-1649-0). Kraus Repr.
Le Fanu, Thomas P. see Peet, Henry.
LeFeber, Larry. Building a Young Adult Ministry. 1980. pap. 5.95 (ISBN 0-8170-0848-9). Judson.
Lefebure, Marcus, ed. Conversation on Counseling Between a Doctor & a Priest. 2nd ed. 128p. pap. 6.95 (ISBN 0-317-31445-9) (ISBN 0-317-31446-7). Fortress.
--Conversations on Counselling. 126p. 1985. pap. 10.95 (ISBN 0-567-29120-0, Pub. by T&T Clark Ltd UK). Fortress.
--Human Experience & the Art of Counselling. 160p. 1985. pap. 9.95 (ISBN 0-567-29121-9, Pub. by T&T Clark Ltd UK). Fortress.
Lefebvre, Dom G. God Present. 1979. pap. 3.95 (ISBN 0-03-053436-4, HarpR). Har-Row.
Lefebvre, G., ed. Inscriptiones Graecae Aegypti, No. 5: Christian Inscriptions. xlii, 173p. 1978. 30.00 (ISBN 0-89005-248-4). Ares.
LeFebvre, George, jt. auth. see Bloom, Anthony.
Lefever, Ernest W. Amsterdam to Nairobi: The World Council of Churches & the Third World. LC 79-2607. 126p. 1979. 10.00 (ISBN 0-89633-025-7); pap. 6.00 (ISBN 0-89633-024-9). Ethics & Public Policy.
--Amsterdam to Nairobi: The World Council of Churches & the Third World. 128p. 1985. pap. text ed. 7.50 (ISBN 0-8191-4484-3). U Pr of Amer.
Lefever, Ernest W. & Hunt, E. Stephen, eds. The Apocalyptic Premise: Nuclear Arms Debated. LC 82-18315. 429p. 1982. 22.00 (ISBN 0-89633-062-1); pap. 14.00 (ISBN 0-89633-063-X). Ethics & Public Policy.
LeFever, Marlene & Weyna, Kathy. Creative Kid Books, No. 1. 1984. pap. 1.95 (ISBN 0-89191-935-X, 59352). Cook.
--Creative Kid Books, No. 2. 1984. pap. 1.95 (ISBN 0-89191-936-8, 59360). Cook.
LeFever, Marlene D. Creative Teaching Methods. 320p. 1985. pap. 14.95 (ISBN 0-89191-760-8). Cook.
LeFever, Marlene D., jt. auth. see Richards, Lawrence O.
LeFevre, Carol & LeFevre, Perry, eds. Aging & the Human Spirit: A Reader in Religion & Gerontology. 2nd ed. LC 84-72932. 367p. 1985. text ed. 24.95x (ISBN 0-913552-27-5); pap. text ed. 12.95x (ISBN 0-913552-28-3). Exploration Pr.
LeFevre, G. L. Favorite Bible Stories. (Bible Quiz 'N Tattletotals Ser.). 16p. (Orig.). 1982. pap. 0.98 (ISBN 0-87239-578-2, 2805). Standard Pub.
--Parables & Miracles of Jesus. (Bible Quiz 'N Tattletotals Ser.). 16p. (Orig.). 1982. pap. 0.98 (ISBN 0-87239-580-4, 2807). Standard Pub.
--Stories from Acts. (Bible Quiz 'N Tattletotals Ser.). 16p. (Orig.). 1982. pap. 0.98 (ISBN 0-87239-581-2, 2808). Standard Pub.
LeFevre, Greg L. Life of Jesus. (Bible Quiz 'N Tattletotals Ser.). 16p. (Orig.). 1982. pap. 0.98 (ISBN 0-87239-579-0, 2806). Standard Pub.
Lefevre, Jacques. Le Nouveau Testament, 2 Vols. 1970. Repr. of 1523 ed. 135.00 (ISBN 0-384-32082-1). Johnson Repr.
LeFevre, Perry. Radical Prayer: Contemporary Interpretations. LC 82-72097. 100p. 1982. text ed. 13.95x (ISBN 0-913552-18-6); pap. text ed. 5.95x (ISBN 0-913552-19-4). Exploration Pr.
--Understandings of Man. LC 66-10432. 186p. 1966. pap. 6.95 (ISBN 0-664-24678-8). Westminster.
--Understandings of Prayer. LC 81-11622. 212p. 1981. pap. 10.95 (ISBN 0-664-24382-7). Westminster.
LeFevre, Perry & Schroeder, W. Widick, eds. Pastoral Care & Liberation Praxis: Studies in Personal & Social Transformation. (Studies in Ministry & Parish Life). 112p. 1986. text ed. 18.95x (ISBN 0-913552-31-3); pap. text ed. 8.95x (ISBN 0-913552-32-1). Exploration Pr.
--Spiritual Nurture & Congregational Development. (Studies in Ministry & Parish Life). 186p. 1984. text ed. 19.95x (ISBN 0-913552-20-8); pap. text ed. 8.95x (ISBN 0-913552-23-2). Exploration Pr.
LeFevre, Perry, jt. ed. see LeFevre, Carol.
LeFevre, Perry, ed. see Williams, Daniel D.
LeFevre, Perry D., ed. Conflict in a Voluntary Association: A Case Study of a Classic Suburban Church Fight. LC 75-12388. (Studies in Ministry & Parish Life). 1975. 13.95x (ISBN 0-913552-03-8); pap. 6.95x (ISBN 0-913552-09-7). Exploration Pr.
--Prayers of Kierkegaard. LC 56-11000. (Midway Reprint Ser.). 1956. pap. 14.00x (ISBN 0-226-47059-8). U of Chicago Pr.
Leffler, John C. Go into the City: Sermons for a Strenuous Age. LC 85-23366. 288p. 1986. 15.95 (ISBN 0-88089-014-2). Madrona Pubs.
Lefkowitz, Mary R. Women in Greek Myth. LC 86-7146. 164p. 1986. text ed. 22.50x (ISBN 0-8018-3367-1). Johns Hopkins.
Le Fort, Gertrud von see Von Le Fort, Gertrud.
Lefort, Rafael. The Teachers of Gurdjieff. LC 66-68145. 157p. (Orig.). 1975. pap. 6.95 (ISBN 0-87728-283-8). Weiser.
Lefroy, William. Church Leaders in Primitive Times. 1977. lib. bdg. 69.95 (ISBN 0-8490-1628-2). Gordon Pr.
Leftwich, Joseph, ed. An Anthology of Modern Yiddish Literature. LC 74-82386. (Anthology Ser: No. 1). 346p. 1974. pap. text ed. 13.60x (ISBN 90-2793-496-7). Mouton.
Leftwich, Joseph & Chertoff, Mordecai S., eds. Why Do the Jews Need a Land of Their Own? LC 83-45297. 242p. 1984. 19.95 (ISBN 0-8453-4774-8, Cornwall Bks). Assoc Univ Prs.
Leftwich, Joseph, tr. see Lehmann, Marcus.
Leftwich, Joseph, tr. see Schachnowitz, Selig.
Le Gai Eaton, Charles. Islam & the Destiny of Man. (Islam Ser.). 256p. 1985. 44.50x (ISBN 0-88706-161-3); pap. 14.95 (ISBN 0-88706-163-X). State U NY Pr.
Legendre, Jaquelin. La Chartruese de Lugne des Origines au Debut 14e Siecle 1172-1332. Hogg, James, ed. (Analecta Cartusiana Ser.: No. 27). (Fr., Illus.). 204p. (Orig.). 1975. pap. 25.00 (ISBN 3-7052-0028-3, Pub by Salzburg Studies). Longwood Pub Group.
Leger, Sr. Mary C. The Catholic Indian Missions in Maine (1611-1820) LC 73-3563. (Catholic University of America. Studies in American Church History: No. 8). Repr. of 1929 ed. 26.00 (ISBN 0-404-57758-X). AMS Pr.
Legere, Thomas E. Thoughts on the Run: Glimpses of Wholistic Spirituality. 144p. 1983. pap. 7.95 (ISBN 0-86683-698-5, HarpR). Har-Row.
Legeza, Laszlo. Tao Magic: The Secret Language of Diagrams & Calligraphy. LC 86-51463. (Illus.). 167p. 1987. pap. 10.95 (ISBN 0-500-27062-7). Thames Hudson.
Legeza, Laszlo, jt. auth. see Rawson, Philip.
Legge, Francis. Forerunners & Rivals of Christianity, 2 vols. in 1. 19.00 (ISBN 0-8446-1280-4). Peter Smith.
Legge, J., tr. Texts of Taoism: The Sacred Books of China, 2 Vols. (Sacred Books of the East Ser). 28.50 set (ISBN 0-8446-3059-4). Peter Smith.
Legge, James. I Ching: Book of Changes. 449p. 1983. pap. 7.95 (ISBN 0-8065-0458-7). Citadel Pr.
--The Religions of China. LC 78-2685. 1979. Repr. of 1880 ed. lib. bdg. 45.00 (ISBN 0-8495-3313-9). Arden Lib.
--The Religions of China. LC 76-28535. 1976. Repr. of 1880 ed. lib. bdg. 40.00 (ISBN 0-8414-5809-X). Folcroft.
--The Sacred Books of China, 6 vols. 600.00. Krishna Pr.
--The Sacred Books of China. (Sacred Bks. of the East: Vols. 3, 16, 27, 28, 39, 40). 6 vols. 90.00 (ISBN 0-686-97476-X); 15.00 ea. Asian Human Pr.
Legge, James, ed. see Confucius.
Legge, James, tr. The Ch'un Ts'ew with the Tso Chuen, 4 vols, Vol. 4. (Chinese Classics Ser.). (Chinese & Eng.). 1983. Repr. of 1893 ed. 25.00x (ISBN 0-89986-356-6); 95.00x (ISBN 0-89986-352-3). Oriental Bk Store.
--I Ching. 1969. pap. 4.95 (ISBN 0-553-26002-2). Bantam.
--The Sho King, or the Book of Historical Documents, 4 vols, Vol. 2. (Chinese Classics Ser.). (Chinese & Eng.). 1983. Repr. of 1893 ed. 25.00x (ISBN 0-89986-354-X); Set. 95.00x (ISBN 0-89986-352-3). Oriental Bk Store.
--The Texts of Taoism, 2 vols. Muller, F. Max, ed. 396p. 1891. Vol. 1. pap. 6.95 (ISBN 0-486-20990-3); Vol. 2. pap. 6.95 (ISBN 0-486-20991-1). Dover.
Legge, James, tr. see Mencius.
Leggett, Gary. Letters to Timothy. LC 80-82830. (Radiant Life Ser.). 128p. (Orig.). 1981. 2.50 (ISBN 0-88243-877-8, 02-0877); teacher's ed. 3.95 (ISBN 0-88243-189-7, 32-0189). Gospel Pub.
Leggett, Marshall. Introduction to the Restoration Ideal. 240p. 1986. pap. text ed. 7.95 (ISBN 0-87403-067-6, 3175). Standard Pub.
--Workbook for the Restoration Ideal. 96p. 1986. pap. 2.95 wkbk. (ISBN 0-87403-068-4, 3176). Standard Pub.
Leggett, Trevor. The Chapter of the Self. (Illus.). 1978. 12.95 (ISBN 0-7100-8702-0). Methuen Inc.
--Encounters in Yoga & Zen. 1982. pap. 9.95 (ISBN 0-7100-9241-5). Methuen Inc.
--Second Zen Reader. Sakade, Florence, ed. (Illus.). 192p. (Orig.). 1987. pap. 7.95 (ISBN 0-8048-1525-9). C E Tuttle.
--Shankara on the Yoga Sutras. (Vol. 1). 140p. 1981. 30.00 (ISBN 0-7100-0826-0). Methuen Inc.
--The Warrior Koans: Early Zen in Japan. 256p. 1985. pap. 8.95 (Ark Paperbks). Methuen Inc.
--Zen & the Ways. Sakade, Florence, ed. (Illus.). 258p. (Orig.). 1987. pap. 9.95 (ISBN 0-8048-1524-0). C E Tuttle.
Leggett, Trevor P. First Zen Reader. LC 60-12739. (Illus.). 1960. pap. 6.95 (ISBN 0-8048-0180-0). C E Tuttle.
Le Goff, Jacques. The Birth of Purgatory. Goldhammer, Arthur, tr. from Fr. LC 83-1108. (Illus.). 448p. 1984. 25.00 (ISBN 0-226-47082-2). U of Chicago Pr.
LeGoff, Jacques. The Birth of Purgatory. Goldhammer, Arthur, tr. LC 83-1108. (Illus.). x, 430p. 1986. pap. 13.95 (ISBN 0-226-47083-0). U of Chicago Pr.
Le Goff, Jacques. Heresies et Societes Dans L'europe Pre-Industrielle 11e-18e Siecles: Communications et Debats Du Colloque De Royaumont. (Civilisations et Societes: No. 10). 1968. pap. 28.40x (ISBN 90-2796-079-8). Mouton.
LeGrande, William. Christian Persecution & Genocide. 1982. lib. bdg. 59.95 (ISBN 0-87700-392-0). Revisionist Pr.
Le Grand Richards. A Marvelous Work & a Wonder. 424p. 14.00 (ISBN 0-87747-686-1); pap. 2.95 (ISBN 0-87747-614-4). Deseret Bk.
Legum, Colin & Shaked, Haim, eds. Arab Relations in the Middle East: The Road to Realignment. LC 78-20888. (Middle Affairs Ser.: No. 1). 104p. 1978. pap. text ed. 12.50x (ISBN 0-8419-0447-2). Holmes & Meier.
Lehman, Carolyn. God's Wonderful World: Thirteen Pupil Activities, Bk. 1. (God's Wonderful World Ser.). (Illus.). 32p. 1985. wkbk 1.50 (ISBN 0-87239-837-4, 3317). Standard Pub.

--God's Wonderful World: Thirteen Pupil Activities, Bk. 2. (God's Wonderful World Ser.). (Illus.). 32p. 1985. 1.50 (ISBN 0-87239-838-2, 3318). Standard Pub.

--God's Wonderful World: Twenty Six Lessons for Primary Church. (Children's Church Ser.). (Illus.). 144p. 1985. wkbk 8.95 (ISBN 0-87239-839-0, 3316). Standard Pub.

--Twenty-Six Complete Programs for Children's Church: Traveling with Bible People. (Children's Church Ser.). 144p. 1986. tchr's ed. 8.95 (ISBN 0-87403-060-9, 3324). Standard Pub.

Lehman, Edward C., Jr. English Church Members' Responses to Women Clergy: A Sociological Analysis. LC 86-28547. (Studies in Religion & Society). 224p. 1987. text ed. 49.95 (ISBN 0-88946-858-3). E Mellen.

--Women Clergy: Breaking Through Gender Barriers. 300p. 1985. 24.95 (ISBN 0-88738-071-9). Transaction Bks.

Lehman, Elsie. God's Wisdom & Power Activity Book. (Story Bible Ser.). 80p. 1985. pap. 3.00 (ISBN 0-8361-3391-9). Herald Pr.

Lehman, Elsie E. God Sends His Son Activity Book. (Bible Story Ser.: Bk. 8). 80p. (Orig.). 1987. pap. 3.00 (ISBN 0-8361-3429-X). Herald Pr.

Lehman, Emil. Israel: Idea & Reality. (Illus.). 3.95x (ISBN 0-8381-0205-0, 10-205). United Syn Bk.

Lehman, Gaylord L. Sunday Words for a Monday World. 75p. (Orig.). Date not set. pap. price not set (ISBN 0-938828-03-7). Falls Tar.

Lehman, Harold D. In Praise of Leisure. LC 74-16399. 200p. 1974. 6.95 (ISBN 0-8361-1752-2); leader's guide o.p. 1.75 (ISBN 0-8361-1750-6). Herald Pr.

Lehman, Helmut H., jt. ed. see Bergendoff, Conrad.

Lehman, Helmut T., jt. ed. see Krodel, Gottfried G.

Lehman, Helmut T., jt. ed. see Lehman, Martin E.

Lehman, Helmut T., jt. ed. see Sherman, Franklin.

Lehman, Helmut T., jt. ed. see Wiencke, Gustav K.

Lehman, Israel O., tr. see Auerbach, Elias.

Lehman, James H. The Old Brethren. LC 76-20274. (Illus.). 1976. pap. 2.45 (ISBN 0-87178-650-8). Brethren.

--Thank God for New Churches! Church Planting: Source of New Life. 108p. (Orig.). 1984. pap. 6.95 (ISBN 0-87178-840-3). Brethren.

Lehman, Louis P. How to Find & Develop Effective Illustrations. LC 75-12109. 102p. 1985. pap. 4.95 (ISBN 0-8254-3133-6). Kregel.

Lehman, Martin E. & Lehman, Helmut T., eds. Luther's Works: Word & Sacrament IV, Vol. 38. LC 55-9893. 1971. 19.95 (ISBN 0-8006-0338-9, 1-338). Fortress.

Lehmann, jt. ed. see Wentz, Abdel R.

Lehmann, Arnold O. Lehmann's Little Dictionary of Liturgical Terms. 1980. 3.75 (ISBN 0-8100-0127-6, 15N0371). Northwest Pub.

Lehmann, Arthur C. & Myers, James E. Magic, Witchcraft, & Religion. (Illus.). 416p. 1985. pap. text ed. 22.95 (ISBN 0-87484-685-4). Mayfield Pub.

Lehmann, Helmut T. & Atkinson, James, eds. Luther's Works: The Christian in Society I, Vol. 44. LC 55-9893. 1966. 19.95 (ISBN 0-8006-0344-3, 1-344). Fortress.

Lehmann, Helmut T. & Doberstein, John W., eds. Luther's Works: Sermons I, Vol. 51. Doberstein, John W., tr. LC 55-9893. 1959. 19.95 (ISBN 0-8006-0351-6, 1-353). Fortress.

Lehmann, Helmut T. & Gritsch, Eric W., eds. Luther's Works: Church & Ministry III, Vol. 41. LC 55-9893. 1966. 19.95 (ISBN 0-8006-0341-9, 1-341). Fortress.

Lehmann, Helmut T., jt. ed. see Bachmann, Theodore.

Lehmann, Helmut T., jt. ed. see Brandt, Walter I.

Lehmann, Helmut T., jt. ed. see Dietrich, Martin O.

Lehmann, Helmut T., jt. ed. see Fischer, Robert H.

Lehmann, Helmut T., jt. ed. see Forell, George W.

Lehmann, Helmut T., jt. ed. see Grimm, Harold J.

Lehmann, Helmut T., jt. ed. see Gritsch, Eric W.

Lehmann, Helmut T., jt. ed. see Hillerbrand, Hans J.

Lehmann, Helmut T., jt. ed. see Krodel, Gottfried G.

Lehmann, Helmut T., jt. ed. see Leupold, Ulrich S.

Lehmann, Helmut T., jt. ed. see Schultz, Robert C.

Lehmann, Helmut T., jt. ed. see Spitz, Lewis W.

Lehmann, Helmut T., jt. ed. see Tappert, Theodore G.

Lehmann, Helmut T., jt. ed. see Watson, Philip S.

Lehmann, Karl, jt. auth. see Ratzinger, Joseph.

Lehmann, L. H. Out of the Labyrinth. 252p. 1983. pap. 6.95 (ISBN 0-937958-13-1). Chick Pubns.

Lehmann, Marcus. Akiba. Leftwich, Joseph, tr. 7.95 (ISBN 0-87306-120-9). Feldheim.

--Just in Time: A Novel about Medieval Jewish Community. 1982. pap. 6.95 (ISBN 0-87306-257-4). Feldheim.

--Royal Resident. 1981. 6.95 (ISBN 0-686-76251-7). Feldheim.

Lehmann, Paul L. Ethics in a Christian Context. LC 78-31749. 1979. Repr. of 1963 ed. lib. bdg. 27.50x (ISBN 0-313-20971-5, LEEC). Greenwood.

--Ethics in a Christian Context. LC 63-11545. 1976. pap. 4.95x (ISBN 0-06-065231-4, RD 192, HarpR). Har-Row.

Lehn, Cornelia. God Keeps His Promise: A Bible Story Book for Young Children. LC 76-90377. (Illus.). 1970. 11.95x (ISBN 0-87303-291-8). Faith & Life.

--Peace Be with You. LC 80-70190. (Illus.). 126p. 1981. 12.95 (ISBN 0-87303-061-3). Faith & Life.

Lehner, Ernst & Lehner, Johanna. Picture Book of Devils, Demons, & Witchcraft. LC 72-137002. 1972. pap. 6.50 (ISBN 0-486-22751-0). Dover.

--Picture Book of Devils, Demons & Witchcraft. (Illus.). 15.50 (ISBN 0-8446-5830-8). Peter Smith.

Lehner, Johanna, jt. auth. see Lehner, Ernst.

Lehner, Mark. The Egyptian Heritage: Based on the Edgar Cayce Readings. 136p. 1974. pap. 5.95 (ISBN 0-87604-071-7). ARE Pr.

Lehodey, Dom V. The Ways of Mental Prayer. 408p. 1982. pap. 8.00 (ISBN 0-89555-178-0). TAN Bks Pubs.

Lehrer, Keith, ed. Freedom & Determinism. 204p. 1976. pap. text ed. 7.95x (ISBN 0-391-00537-5). Humanities.

Lehrer, Stanley, jt. auth. see Ehrensperger, Harold A.

Lehrer, Stanley, jt. ed. see Brickman, William W.

Lehrman, S. M. The Jewish Design for Living. LC 76-24242. 1976. 11.95 (ISBN 0-88400-003-6). Shengold.

Lehrmann, Charles C. Jewish Influences on European Thought. Klin, George & Carpenter, Victor, trs. LC 72-3264. 323p. 1976. 27.50 (ISBN 0-8386-7908-0). Fairleigh Dickinson.

Lehrs, Ernst. Spiritual Science, Electricity & Michael Faraday. 30p. 1975. pap. 3.00 (ISBN 0-85440-296-9, Pub. by Steinerbooks). Anthroposophic.

Le Huray, Peter, ed. The Treasury of English Church Music 1545-1650. 250p. 1982. 47.50 (ISBN 0-521-24889-2); pap. 19.95 (ISBN 0-521-28405-8). Cambridge U Pr.

Le Huray, Peter, et al. Anthems for Men's Voices, 2 vols. Incl. Vol. 1. Altos, Tenors & Basses. 11.50x (ISBN 0-19-353234-4); Vol. 2. Tenors & Basses. 11.50x (ISBN 0-19-353235-2). 1965. Oxford U Pr.

Leibniz, Gottfried W. & Parkinson, G. H. Leibniz Philosophical Writings. Morris, Mary, tr. from Ger. (Rowman & Littlefield University Library). 270p. 1973. 13.50x (ISBN 0-87471-659-4). Rowman.

Leibowitz. Studies in the Shemoth, 2 vols. 1976. 17.50 (ISBN 0-685-71930-8). Feldheim.

Leibowitz, A. H. Chochmas Hamussar. (Annual Fryer Memorial Lectures Ser.). 1.00 (ISBN 0-914131-11-7, I37). Torah Umesorah.

Leibrecht, Walter. Religion & Culture: Essays in Honor of Paul Tillich. facsimile ed. LC 78-167376. (Essay Index Reprint Ser). Repr. of 1959 ed. 24.50 (ISBN 0-8369-2558-0). Ayer Co Pubs.

Leichner, J. Joy Joy, the Mass: Our Family Celebration. (Illus.). 1978. pap. 2.75 (ISBN 0-87973-350-0). Our Sunday Visitor.

Leichner, Jeannine T. Making Things Right: The Sacrament of Reconciliation. (Illus.). 62p. (Orig.). 1980. pap. 3.50 (ISBN 0-87973-351-9, 351). Our Sunday Visitor.

Leichtman, Robert R. Cheiro Returns. (From Heaven to Earth Ser.). (Illus.). 80p. (Orig.). 1979. pap. 3.50 (ISBN 0-89804-053-1). Ariel OH.

--Churchill Returns. LC 81-66847. (From Heaven to Earth Ser.). (Illus.). 96p. (Orig.). 1981. pap. 3.50 (ISBN 0-89804-065-5). Ariel OH.

--Edgar Cayce Returns. (From Heaven to Earth Ser.). (Illus.). 112p. (Orig.). 1978. pap. 3.50 (ISBN 0-89804-052-3). Ariel OH.

--H. P. Blatavsky Returns. (From Heaven to Earth Ser.). (Illus.). 95p. (Orig.). 1980. pap. 3.50 (ISBN 0-89804-059-0). Ariel OH.

--Yogananda Returns. (From Heaven to Earth Ser.). 104p. (Orig.). 1981. pap. 3.50 (ISBN 0-89804-066-3). Ariel OH.

Leichtman, Robert R. & Japikse, Carl. Active Meditation: The Western Tradition. LC 82-72785. 512p. 1983. 24.50 (ISBN 0-89804-040-X). Ariel OH.

--The Art of Living, Vol. IV. LC 83-703086. (Illus.). 280p. (Orig.). 1984. pap. 6.95 (ISBN 0-89804-035-3). Ariel OH.

--Books of Light. (Illus.). 160p. (Orig.). 1986. pap. 3.95 (ISBN 0-89804-049-3). Ariel OH.

--Life of Spirit, Vol. I. (Illus.). 216p. (Orig.). 1986. pap. 7.95 (ISBN 0-89804-132-5). Ariel OH.

--Life of Spirit Series. (Orig.). 1982. pap. 2.25 ea. Ariel OH.

Leiden, Carl. The Conflict of Traditionalism & Modernism in the Muslim Middle East: A Symposium. LC 68-59178. pap. 40.50 (ISBN 0-317-08447-X, 2000823). Bks Demand UMI.

Leigh, Dub. A Zen Approach to Bodytherapy: From Rolf to Feldenfrais to Tanouye Roshi. 1987. pap. 10.95x (ISBN 0-8248-1099-6, Pub. by Inst Zen Studies). UH Pr.

Leigh, Ronald W. Direct Bible Discovery. LC 81-67203. 1982. pap. 7.95 (ISBN 0-8054-1139-9). Broadman.

--Effective Christian Ministry. 256p. 1984. pap. 6.95 (ISBN 0-8423-0733-8); leader's guide 2.95 (ISBN 0-8423-0734-6). Tyndale.

Leigh, Vanora. Mother Teresa. LC 85-72245. (Great Lives Ser.). 32p. 1986. lib. bdg. 10.40 (ISBN 0-531-18033-6, Pub. by Bookwright Pr). Watts.

Leigh-Bennett, Ernest. Handbook of Early Christian Fathers. 59.95 (ISBN 0-8490-0276-1). Gordon Pr.

--Handbook of the Early Church Fathers. 1980. lib. bdg. 75.00 (ISBN 0-8490-3107-9). Gordon Pr.

Leighton, Audrey O. Fingerplay Friends. 128p. 1984. pap. 5.95 (ISBN 0-8170-1051-3). Judson.

Leighton, Robert. Commentary on First Peter. LC 74-165058. 512p. 16.95 (ISBN 0-8254-3103-4). Kregel.

Leighton, Walter L. French Philosophers-New England Transcendentalism. LC 68-19289. 1968. Repr. of 1908 ed. lib. bdg. 22.50x (ISBN 0-8371-0143-3, LEPT). Greenwood.

Leih, Virginia. Portrait of a Fulfilled Woman. 1979. pap. 4.95 (ISBN 0-8423-4860-3). Tyndale.

Leih, Virginia K. Enjoy! 124p. 1983. pap. 3.95 (ISBN 0-8341-0814-3). Beacon Hill.

Leikind, Miriam, et al. Index to Jewish Periodicals. Per Volume. 80.00 (ISBN 0-686-75688-6). IJP.

Leiman, Harold I. Koheleth. 1978. 8.95 (ISBN 0-87306-143-8); pap. 2.95. Feldheim.

Lein, Laura & O'Donnell, Lydia. Children. LC 84-7543. (Choices: Guides for Today's Woman Ser.: Vol. 9). 120p. 1984. pap. 6.95 (ISBN 0-664-24550-1). Westminster.

Leipsiger, Michael, tr. see Porto, Humberto & Schlesinger, Hugo.

Leiser, Burton M. Liberty, Justice, & Morals: Contemporary Value Conflicts. 2nd ed. (Illus.). 1979. text ed. write for info. (ISBN 0-02-369510-2). Macmillan.

Leiser, Joseph. American Judaism: The Religion & Religious Institutions of the Jewish People in the United States. LC 78-26230. 1979. Repr. of 1925 ed. lib. bdg. 22.50x (ISBN 0-313-20879-4, LEAJ). Greenwood.

Leitch, James W., tr. see Conzelmann, Hans.

Leitch, James W., tr. see Ebeling, Gerhard.

Leites, Edmund. The Puritan Conscience & Modern Sexuality. LC 85-20198. 208p. 1986. 17.50 (ISBN 0-300-03490-3). Yale U Pr.

Leith, John A., ed. see Calvin, John.

Leith, John H. The Church, a Believing Fellowship. LC 80-82192. 192p. 1981. pap. 3.95 (ISBN 0-8042-0518-3). John Knox.

--Introduction to the Reformed Tradition: A Way of Being the Christian Community. rev. ed. LC 81-5968. (Illus.). 253p. 1981. pap. 10.95 (ISBN 0-8042-0479-9). John Knox.

Leith, John H., ed. Creeds of the Churches: A Reader in Christian Doctrine from the Bible to the Present. 3rd ed. LC 82-48029. 1982. pap. 10.95 (ISBN 0-8042-0526-4). John Knox.

Leith, John H., ed. see Old, Hughes O.

Leith, John H., ed. see Wallace, Alston M., Jr.

Leiva, Erasmo, tr. see Muggeridge, Malcolm, et al.

Leiva, Erasmo, tr. see Von Balthasar, Hans Urs.

Leiva-Merikakis, Erasmo, tr. see Von Balthasar, Hans U.

Leiva-Merikakis, Erasmo, tr. see Von Balthasar, Hans Urs.

Leiva-Merikakis, Erasmo, tr. see Von Speyr, Adrienne.

Lejbowicz, Agnes. Omraam Mikhael Aivanhov: Master of the Great Universal White Brotherhood. (Testimonials Ser.). 115p. (Orig.). 1982. pap. 4.95 (ISBN 2-85566-191-9, Pub. by Prosveta France). Prosveta USA.

Lejeune, Abbe P. An Introduction to the Mystical Life. 1977. lib. bdg. 59.95 (ISBN 0-8490-2070-0). Gordon Pr.

Lejeune, R. Christoph Blumhardt & His Message. LC 63-15816. 1963. 7.00 (ISBN 0-87486-200-0). Plough.

Le Joly, Edward. Servant of Love: Mother Teresa & Her Missionaries of Charity. LC 77-15874. (Illus.). 1978. 4.95 (ISBN 0-06-065215-2, HarpR). Har-Row.

Lekai, Louis J. The Cistercians: Ideals & Reality. LC 77-3692. (Illus.). 534p. 1977. 28.50x (ISBN 0-87338-201-3). Kent St. U Pr.

--Nicolas Cotheret's Annals of Citeaux, Outlined from the Original French. (Cistercian Studies Ser.: 57). 1983. pap. 13.95 (ISBN 0-87907-857-X). Cistercian Pubns.

Lekatsos, Anthony, tr. see Makrakis, Apostolos.

Lekeux, Martial. The Art of Prayer. Oligny, Paul J., tr. LC 59-14706. pap. 78.50 (ISBN 0-317-28176-3, 2022570). Bks Demand UMI.

--Short Cut to Divine Love. LC 61-11203. 332p. 1961. pap. 2.50 (ISBN 0-8199-0131-8, L38796). Franciscan Herald.

Lelama, Homero. Diccionario de Mitologia. (Span.). 364p. 1974. 44.95 (ISBN 0-686-56670-X, S-33075). French & Eur.

Leland, Charles G. Fusang or the Discovery of America by Chinese Buddhist Priests. 212p. 1981. pap. 12.00 (ISBN 0-89540-094-4, SB-094). Sun Pub.

--The Gypsies. LC 75-3460. Repr. of 1882 ed. 27.00 (ISBN 0-404-16891-4). AMS Pr.

--The Mystic Will. 1976. Repr. of 1907 ed. 6.00 (ISBN 0-911662-58-8). Yoga.

Leland, Dorothy, ed. Husserl, Heidegger, Sartre, Merleau-Ponty: Phenomenology & the Problem of Intentionality. 640p. (Orig.). 1987. lib. bdg. 35.00 (ISBN 0-87220-005-1); pap. text ed. 19.50 (ISBN 0-87220-004-3). Hackett Pub.

Lelen, J. M. Pray the Rosary. (Illus., Purse-Size). blue bdg. 0.60 (ISBN 0-89942-040-0, 40/05). Catholic Bk Pub.

Lelia, Mary. Leading the Little Ones to Mary. pap. 1.00 (ISBN 0-910984-13-1). Montfort Pubns.

Leliaert, Richard M., jt. ed. see Gower, Joseph F.

Lella, Alexander A. Di see Hartman, Louis F. & Di Lella, Alexander A.

Lelly, Charles. The Beautiful Way of Life. 1980. 4.95 (ISBN 0-87159-010-7). Unity School.

Lely, James A. Virgo. (Sun Signs Ser.). (Illus.). 1978. pap. 3.95 (ISBN 0-89812-076-4). Creative Ed.

LeMahieu, D. L. The Mind of William Paley: A Philosopher & His Age. LC 75-22547. xiv, 215p. 1976. 18.50x (ISBN 0-8032-0865-0). U of Nebr Pr.

LeMaire, H. Paul. Personal Decisions. LC 81-43668. 220p. (Orig.). 1982. lib. bdg. 28.25 (ISBN 0-8191-2329-3); pap. text ed. 11.75 (ISBN 0-8191-2330-7). U Pr of Amer.

LeMaitre, Solange. Ramakrishna & the Vitality of Hinduism. Markmann, Charles L., tr. from Fr. LC 68-54059. (The Overlook Spiritual Masters Ser.). (Illus.). 244p. 1986. pap. 9.95 (ISBN 0-87951-241-5). Overlook Pr.

Leman, Kevin. Parenthood Without Hassles-Well, Almost. LC 78-656211. 144p. 1982. pap. 2.95 (ISBN 0-89081-304-3). Harvest Hse.

--Sex Begins in the Kitchen. LC 80-54004. 1983. pap. 5.95 (ISBN 0-8307-1190-2, 5419017). Regal.

--Smart Girls Don't & Guys Don't Either. LC 82-7686. 1982. 8.95 (ISBN 0-8307-0824-3, 5419026). Regal.

Lemche, Niels P. Ancient Israel: A New History of Israelite Society. (The Biblical Seminar Ser.: No. 5). 250p. 1987. pap. text ed. 9.50x (ISBN 1-85075-017-3, Pub. by JSOT Pr England). Eisenbrauns.

Lemelman, Martin. My Jewish Home: Sinchah Ba'ambatyah - Fun in the Bathtub. (Illus.). 10p. 1987. polyvinyl 3.95 (ISBN 0-8074-0327-X). UAHC.

Lemesurier, Peter. The Great Pyramid Decoded. (YA) 1984. pap. 4.95 (ISBN 0-380-43034-7, 43034-7). Avon.

Lemieux, Joanne H. Diet Signs: Follow Your Horoscope to a Slimmer You. LC 82-16251. 1982. pap. 6.95 (ISBN 0-87491-491-4). Acropolis.

Lemire, Deacon H., jt. auth. see Kleiber, Kenneth.

Lemius, J. B. Catechism of Modernism. LC 81-52536. 160p. 1981. pap. 3.00 (ISBN 0-89555-167-5). TAN Bks Pubs.

Lemke, Steve. Joy in Christ: Studies in Philippians. 36p. 1981. pap. 3.50 (ISBN 0-939298-10-4). J M Prods.

--Living Hope: Studies in I Peter. 35p. (Orig.). 1982. pap. 3.50 (ISBN 0-939298-12-0, 120). J M Prods.

Lemmon, Sarah M. Parson Pettigrew of the "Old Church". 1744-1807. (James Sprunt Studies in History & Political Science: No. 52). vii, 168p. 1971. pap. 5.00x (ISBN 0-8078-5052-7). U of NC Pr.

Lemmons, Reuel. The King & His Kingdom. Thomas, J. D., ed. LC 68-59307. (Twentieth Century Sermons Ser). 1968. 11.95 (ISBN 0-89112-301-6, Bibl Res Pr). Abilene Christ U.

Lemmons, Reuel & Bannister, John. Unto Us a Child is Born. Kyker, Rex, compiled by. 126p. (Orig.). 1982. pap. 2.95 (ISBN 0-88027-109-4). Firm Foun Pub.

Lemmons, Reuel, ed. The Majestic Hymnal, No. 2. 1959. 2.75x (ISBN 0-88027-056-X). Firm Foun Pub.

Lemon, tr. see Gonzales, F. Jose.

Lemon, Patricia H., ed. see Lutz, Kathryn.

Lemon, Robert. God's People & Church Government. 64p. (Orig.). 1983. pap. 2.25 (ISBN 0-89274-282-8). Harrison Hse.

Lemons, Frank W. In Remembrance of Me. 1975. 4.95 (ISBN 0-87148-430-7); pap. 3.95 (ISBN 0-87148-431-5). Pathway Pr.

--Looking Beyond. 78p. 1969. 3.95 (ISBN 0-87148-506-0); pap. 2.95 (ISBN 0-87148-507-9). Pathway Pr.

--Our Pentecostal Heritage. 174p. 1963. pap. 4.95 (ISBN 0-87148-653-9). Pathway Pr.

--Perennial Pentecost. 1971. pap. 2.95 (ISBN 0-87148-679-2). Pathway Pr.

--Profiles of Faith. 1971. pap. 2.95 (ISBN 0-87148-683-0). Pathway Pr.

Lemons, Paul G. A Message for the Human Race. 1984. 15.95 (ISBN 0-533-06058-3). Vantage.

Lemoyne, G. B., et al. The Biographical Memoirs of Saint John Bosco, 14 vols. Borgatello, Diego, tr. from Ital. Incl. Vol. I. lib. bdg. 14.95 (ISBN 0-89944-001-0); Vol. II. lib. bdg. 15.95 (ISBN 0-89944-002-9); Vol. III. lib. bdg. 16.95 (ISBN 0-89944-003-7); Vol. IV. lib. bdg. 19.95 (ISBN 0-89944-004-5); Vol. V. lib. bdg. 21.95 (ISBN 0-89944-005-3); Vol. VI. lib. bdg. 22.95 (ISBN 0-89944-006-1); Vol. VII. lib. bdg. 18.95 (ISBN 0-89944-007-X); Vol. VIII. lib. bdg. 15.95 (ISBN 0-89944-008-8); Vol. IX. lib. bdg. 16.95 (ISBN 0-89944-009-6); Vol. X. lib. bdg. 20.95 (ISBN 0-89944-010-X); Vol. XI. lib. bdg. 18.95 (ISBN 0-89944-011-8); Vol. XII. lib. bdg. 17.95 (ISBN 0-89944-012-6); Vol. XIII. Rev. ed. 1983. lib. bdg. 24.95 (ISBN 0-89944-013-4). LC 65-3104. Orig. Title: Memorie Biografiche di Don Giovanni Bosco. 1981. Set. lib. bdg. write for info. (ISBN 0-89944-000-2). Don Bosco Multimedia.

Lemu, Aisha & Heeren, Fatima. Women in Islam. 51p. (Orig.). 1978. pap. 3.50 (ISBN 0-86037-004-6, Pub. by Islamic Found UK). New Era Pubns MI.

Le Nain De Tillemont, Louis S. Vie De Saint Louis, Roi De France, 6 Vols. 255.00 (ISBN 0-384-32195-X); pap. 220.00 (ISBN 0-384-32196-8). Johnson Repr.

Lenardon, Robert J., jt. auth. see Morford, Mark P.

L'Engle, Madeleine. And It Was Good: Reflections on Beginnings. LC 83-8518. 219p. 1983. 11.95 (ISBN 0-87788-046-8). Shaw Pubs.

--A Circle of Quiet. (The Crosswicks Journal Trilogy). 246p. 1977. pap. 7.95 (ISBN 0-8164-2260-5, HarpR); Three Volume Set. 19.95 (ISBN 0-8164-2617-1). Har-Row.

--The Irrational Season. (The Crosswicks Journal Trilogy). 224p. 1977. 12.95 (ISBN 0-8164-0324-4, HarpR); pap. 7.95 (ISBN 0-8164-2261-3); Three Volume Set 19.95 (ISBN 0-8164-2617-1). Har-Row.

--The Irrational Season. 430p. 1985. pap. 13.95 large print ed. (ISBN 0-8027-2476-0). Walker & Co.

--The Love Letters. (Epiphany Ser.). 384p. 1983. pap. 2.95 (ISBN 0-345-30617-1). Ballantine.

--The Other Side of the Sun. (Epiphany Bks.). 352p. (Orig.). 1983. pap. 3.50 (ISBN 0-345-30616-3). Ballantine.

--Prayers for Sunday. (Illus.). 1974. pap. 1.95 (ISBN 0-8192-1153-2). Morehouse.

--A Stone for a Pillow: Journeys with Jacob. (Wheaton Literary Ser.). 240p. (Orig.). 1986. 11.95 (ISBN 0-87788-789-6); pap. cancelled. Shaw Pubs.

--Trailing Clouds of Glory: Spiritual Values in Children's Books. 144p. 1985. 12.95 (ISBN 0-664-32721-4). Westminster.

--Walking on Water: Reflections on Faith & Art. LC 80-21066. (Wheaton Literary Ser.). 198p. 1980. 10.95 (ISBN 0-87788-918-X); pap. 6.95 (ISBN 0-87788-919-8). Shaw Pubs.

Lenin, V. I. Against Dogmatism & Sectarianism. 215p. 1978. 4.95 (ISBN 0-8285-0066-5, Pub. by Progress Pubs USSR). Imported Pubns.

--Lenin on the Jewish Question. Lumer, Hyman, ed. LC 74-6278. (Eng.). 156p. 1974. 7.50 (ISBN 0-7178-0398-8); pap. 2.75 (ISBN 0-7178-0399-6). Intl Pubs Co.

--Marx-Engels-Marxism. 176p. 1977. pap. 1.40 (ISBN 0-8285-2194-8, Pub. by Progress Pubs USSR). Imported Pubns.

Lenin, Vladimir I. Acerca De la Religion. (Span.). 81p. 1976. pap. 1.45 (ISBN 0-8285-1359-7, Pub. by Progress Pubs USSR). Imported Pubns.

Lenker, J. M., tr. see Luther, Martin.

Lenker, John N., ed. see Luther, Martin.

Lenn, Dorothy, tr. see Steiner, Rudolf.

Lenn, Dorothy, et al, trs. see Steiner, Rudolf.

Lenning, Larry G. Blessing in Mosque & Mission. LC 80-25110. 176p. (Orig.). 1981. pap. 5.95 (ISBN 0-87808-433-9). William Carey Lib.

LeNoir, C. P. Dictionnaire des Droits et de la Raison. Migne, J. P., ed. (Troisieme et Derniere Encyclopedie Theologique Ser.: Vol. 57). (Fr.). 952p. Repr. of 1860 ed. lib. bdg. 120.00x (ISBN 0-89241-323-9). Caratzas.

--Dictionnaire des Harmonies de la Raison et de la Foi. Migne, J. P., ed. (Troisieme et Derniere Encyclopedie Theologique Ser.: Vol. 19). (Fr.). 876p. Repr. of 1856 ed. lib. bdg. 110.50x (ISBN 0-89241-302-6). Caratzas.

Lensch, Rodney. My Personal Pentecost. 60p. (C :g.). 1972. pap. 1.25 (ISBN 0-89228-025-5). Impact Bks MO.

Lense, Esther. Light Triumphant. 1978. pap. 3.25 (ISBN 0-89536-301-1, 1253). CSS of Ohio.

Lenski, Gerhard E. The Religious Factor: A Sociological Study of Religion's Impact on Politics, Economics, & Family Life. LC 77-1275. 1977. Repr. of 1961 ed. lib. bdg. 27.50x (ISBN 0-8371-9506-3, LERF). Greenwood.

Lenski, Lois. Sing for Peace. 16p. 1985. pap. 1.50 (ISBN 0-8361-3396-X). Herald Pr.

Lenski, R. C. Interpretation of St. John's Gospel. 1936. 22.95 (ISBN 0-8066-9000-3, 10-3364). Augsburg.

--Interpretation of St. John's Revelation. 1935. 21.95 (ISBN 0-8066-9001-1, 10-3372). Augsburg.

--Interpretation of St. Luke's Gospel. 1934. 22.95 (ISBN 0-8066-9002-X, 10-3363). Augsburg.

--Interpretation of St. Mark's Gospel. 1946. 21.95 (ISBN 0-8066-9003-8, 0-3362). Augsburg.

--Interpretation of St. Matthew's Gospel. 1933. 22.95 (ISBN 0-8066-9004-6, 10-3361). Augsburg.

Lenski, Richard C. Interpretation of Acts. 1934. 22.95 (ISBN 0-8066-9009-7, 10-3365). Augsburg.

--Interpretation of Colossians, Thessalonians First & Second, Timothy First & Second, Titus, & Philemon. 1937. 21.95 (ISBN 0-8066-9006-2, 10-3369). Augsburg.

--Interpretation of First & Second Corinthians. 1935. 22.95 (ISBN 0-8066-9008-9, 10-3367). Augsburg.

--Interpretation of First & Second Peter, First, Second & Third John, Jude. 1938. 21.95 (ISBN 0-8066-9011-9, 10-3371). Augsburg.

--Interpretation of Galatians, Ephesians, & Philippians. 1937. 21.95 (ISBN 0-8066-9007-0, 10-3368). Augsburg.

--Interpretation of Hebrews & James. 1938. 21.95 (ISBN 0-8066-9010-0, 10-3370). Augsburg.

--Interpretation of Romans. 1936. 21.95 (ISBN 0-8066-9005-4, 10-3366). Augsburg.

--Interpretation of the New Testament, 12 Vols. 1933-46. Set. 235.00 (ISBN 0-8066-9012-7, 10-3360). Augsburg.

Lenta, Clementine. What Can I Do for Christ? 5.50 (ISBN 0-910984-17-4). Montfort Pubns.

Lentfoehr, Sr. Therese. Words & Silence: On the Poetry of Thomas Merton. LC 78-21475. 1979. 12.50 (ISBN 0-8112-0712-9); pap. 4.95 (ISBN 0-8112-0713-7, NDP472). New Directions.

Lenz, Frederick. Lifetimes: True Accounts of Reincarnation. 224p. 1986. pap. 2.95 (ISBN 0-449-20908-3, Crest). Fawcett.

Lenz, Friedel. Celebrating the Festivals with Children. Tr. of Mit Kindren Feste feiern. 20p. (Orig.). 1986. pap. 3.95 (ISBN 0-88010-151-2). Anthroposophic.

Lenzkes, Susan. A Silver Pen for Cloudy Days. 144p. 1987. pap. 7.95 (ISBN 0-310-43671-0). Zondervan.

--When the Handwriting on the Wall Is in Brown Crayon. 1986. pap. 4.95 (ISBN 0-310-43631-1, 6891P). Zondervan.

Leo, Alan. Saturn: The Reaper. LC 75-16450. 1975. pap. 3.95 (ISBN 0-87728-019-3). Weiser.

Leo Baeck Institute Staff. Leo Baeck Institute Yearbook XXXI. 1987. 35.00 (ISBN 0-436-25545-6, Pub. by Secker & Warburg UK). David & Charles.

Leo, Pope The Practice of Humility. O'Connor, John F., tr. 1976. lib. bdg. 59.95 (ISBN 0-8490-2462-5). Gordon Pr.

--The Practice of Humility. O'Conor, John F., tr. 1980. lib. bdg. 59.95 (ISBN 0-8490-3177-X). Gordon Pr.

Leon, Abram. Jewish Question: A Marxist Interpretation. LC 76-108721. 1971. 23.00 (ISBN 0-87348-133-X); pap. 7.95 (ISBN 0-87348-134-8). Path Pr NY.

Leon, Daniel De see De Leon, Daniel.

Leon, De Poncins see De Poncins, Leon.

Leon, Jorge A. Cada Muchacho Necesita un Modelo Vivo. (Span.). 96p. 1983. pap. 4.75 (ISBN 0-311-46087-9). Casa Bautista.

--Psicologia Pastoral de la Iglesia. LC 77-43121. (Span.). 192p. (Orig.). pap. 5.95 (ISBN 0-89922-113-0). Edit Caribe.

--Psicologia Pastoral para Todos los Cristianos. LC 76-43121. (Span.). 181p. (Orig.). 1976. pap. 5.95 (ISBN 0-89922-020-7). Edit Caribe.

Leon, Judene. Bible Games for Teams & Groups. (Illus.). 64p. 1984. pap. 6.95 (ISBN 0-86683-832-5, HarpR). Har-Row.

Leon, Mariette, tr. see Grousset, Rene.

Leonard, Bill J. Early American Christianity. LC 83-71489. 1984. pap. 10.95 (ISBN 0-8054-6578-2). Broadman.

--The Nature of the Church. (Orig.). 1986. 5.95 (ISBN 0-8054-1642-0). Broadman.

Leonard, Ellen. George Tyrrell & the Catholic Tradition. 208p. 1982. pap. 9.95 (ISBN 0-8091-2424-6). Paulist Pr.

Leonard, Harry, ed. J. N. Andrews: The Man & the Mission. xii, 355p. (Orig.). 1985. pap. 11.95 (ISBN 0-943872-91-X). Andrews Univ Pr.

Leonard, Henrietta see McIlvain, James W.

Leonard, Joe, Jr. Planning Family Ministry: A Guide for the Teaching Church. 64p. 1982. pap. 3.95 (ISBN 0-8170-0971-X). Judson.

Leonard, Joe, Jr., ed. Church Family Gatherings. 1978. pap. 6.95 (ISBN 0-8170-0809-8). Judson.

Leonard, Larry & McCormick, Jack, eds. Youth Program Hour Idea Book. 156p. 1985. pap. 6.95 (ISBN 0-8341-0949-2). Beacon Hill.

Leonard, Leah W. Jewish Cookery. (International Cook Book Ser.). 512p. 1949. 10.95 (ISBN 0-517-09758-3). Crown.

Leonard of Taize. Belonging. 172p. 1985. pap. 7.95 (ISBN 0-8298-0565-6). Pilgrim NY.

Leonard of Taize, Brother. Listening to People of Hope. 180p. 1985. pap. 6.95 (ISBN 0-8298-0544-3). Pilgrim NY.

Leoncini, Giovanni. La Certosa Di Firenze: Nei Suoi Rapporti con L'Architettura Certosina. Hogg, James, ed. (Analecta Cartusiana Ser.: No. 71). (Ital., Illus.). 231p. (Orig.). 1979. pap. 25.00q (ISBN 3-7052-0106-9, Pub. by Salzburg Studies). Longwood Pub Group.

Leon-Dufour, Xavier. Dictionary of the New Testament. LC 79-3004. 464p. 1983. pap. 12.95 (ISBN 0-06-065242-X, RD-486, HarpR). Har-Row.

--Dictionnaire du Nouveau Testament. (Fr.). 1975. 29.95 (ISBN 0-686-57011-1, M-6352). French & Eur.

--Life & Death in the New Testament. 1986. 18.45 (ISBN 0-317-52379-1, HarpR). Har-Row.

--Sharing the Eucharistic Bread: The Witness of the New Testament. 368p. (Orig.). 1987. pap. 12.95 (ISBN 0-8091-2865-9). Paulist Pr.

Leone, Bruno, jt. ed. see Bender, David L.

Leone, Bruno, et al, eds. Death-Dying, 1985 Annual. (Opposing Viewpoints SOURCES Ser.). 115p. 1985. pap. text ed. 9.95 (ISBN 0-89908-511-3). Greenhaven.

--Death-Dying. (Opposing Viewpoints SOURCES Ser.). 375p. 1984. text ed. 39.95 (ISBN 0-89908-515-6). Greenhaven.

Leone, Mark P. Roots of Modern Mormonism. LC 78-25965. 1979. 17.50x (ISBN 0-674-77970-3). Harvard U Pr.

Leone, Mark P., jt. ed. see Zaretsky, Irving I.

Leon-Portilla, Miguel. Broken Spears: The Aztec Account of the Conquest of Mexico. (Illus.). 1962. pap. 7.95x (ISBN 0-8070-5499-2, BP230). Beacon Pr.

Leon-Portilla, Miguel, ed. Native Mesoamerican Spirituality. Anderson, Arthur J. & Dibble, Charles E., trs. LC 80-80821. (Classics of Western Spirituality Ser.). 320p. 1980. 13.95 (ISBN 0-8091-0293-5); pap. 9.95 (ISBN 0-8091-2231-6). Paulist Pr.

Leopold, Simon R. Spiritual Aspects of Indian Music. 1985. 22.50x (ISBN 0-8364-1258-3, Pub. by Sundeep). South Asia Bks.

Leo The Great, St. Selected Letters. LC 63-18826. (Fathers of the Church Ser: Vol. 34). 312p. 1957. 15.95x (ISBN 0-8132-0034-2). Cath U Pr.

Le Page, William, ed. see Baba, Meher.

Le Peau, Andrew T. Paths of Leadership. LC 82-23221. 132p. (Orig.). 1983. pap. 3.95 (ISBN 0-87784-806-8). Inter-Varsity.

Le Peau, Andrew T. & Le Peau, Phyllis J. Ephesians. (Lifefuilder Bible Studies). 60p. (Orig.). 1985. pap. text ed. 2.95 (ISBN 0-8308-1012-9). Inter-Varsity.

LePeau, Andrew T. & LePeau, Phyllis J. Faith That Works: Eleven Studies in James. 72p. (Orig.). 1980. pap. 2.25 (ISBN 0-87784-365-1). Inter Varsity.

--James: Faith That Works. (LifeGuide Bible Studies). 64p. (Orig.). 1987. pap. 2.95. Inter-Varsity.

Le Peau, Andrew T., jt. auth. see Le Peau, Phyllis J.

Le Peau, Phyllis J. & Le Peau, Andrew T. One Plus One Equals One. 96p. (Orig.). 1981. pap. 3.95 (ISBN 0-87784-803-3). Inter-Varsity.

LePeau, Phyllis J., jt. auth. see LePeau, Andrew T.

Le Peau, Phyllis J., jt. auth. see Le Peau, Andrew T.

LePeau, Phyllis J., jt. auth. see LePeau, Andrew T.

Lepicier, A. M. Unseen World: Catholic Theology & Spiritualism. 69.95 (ISBN 0-8490-1251-1). Gordon Pr.

Le Plongeon, Augustus. Sacred Mysteries among the Mayas & the Quiches. LC 73-76094. (Secret Doctrine Reference Ser). (Illus.). 200p. 1985. Repr. of 1886 ed. 12.00 (ISBN 0-913510-02-5). Wizards.

Lepon, Shoshana. The Ten Tests of Abraham. (Bible Series for Young Children). (Illus.). 32p. (Orig.). 1986. 7.95 (ISBN 0-317-52412-7); pap. 5.95 (ISBN 0-910818-67-3). Judaica Pr.

Leppard, Lois G. Mandie & the Abandoned Mine. (Mandie Ser.). 144p. (Orig.). 1987. pap. 2.95 (ISBN 0-87123-932-9). Bethany Hse.

Le Prevost, A., ed. see Ordericus, Vitalis.

Lerin, A., jt. auth. see Sloan, W. H.

Lerin, Alfredo, compiled by. Quinientas Ilustraciones. (Span.). 324p. 1984. pap. 5.95 (ISBN 0-311-42037-0). Casa Bautista.

Lerin, Alfredo, tr. see Summers, Ray.

Lerin, Olivia de see Crane, J. D.

Lerin, Olivia S. de see De Lerin, Olivia S.

Lerin, Olivia Y Alfredo, tr. see Brown, Raymond B.

Lerner, Arthur. Words for All Seasons. (Illus.). 104p. (Orig.). 1983. pap. 6.95 (ISBN 0-938292-06-4). Being Bks.

Lerner, Carol. A Biblical Garden. (Illus.). 1982. 13.50 (ISBN 0-688-01071-7). Morrow.

Lerner, Robert E. The Powers of Prophecy: The Cedar of Lebanon Vision from the Mongol Onslaught to the Dawn of the Enlightenment. LC 82-4824. 256p. 1983. text ed. 38.50x (ISBN 0-520-04461-4). U of Cal Pr.

Le Roy. Evangelismo en Accion. Pierson, Carlos C., tr. 144p. 1979. 4.95 (ISBN 0-311-13831-4). Casa Bautista.

Le Roy, Alexander. Religion of the Primitives. Thompson, Newton, tr. LC 72-78769. Repr. of 1922 ed. cancelled (ISBN 0-8371-1400-4). Greenwood.

LeRoy, Douglas. Basic Bible Study. LC 78-65822. 72p. (Orig.). 1978. pap. text ed. 1.25 (ISBN 0-87148-699-7). Pathway Pr.

--I Didn't Know That. 1973. pap. 3.95 (ISBN 0-87148-425-0). Pathway Pr.

--We Believe. (Illus.). 56p. 1975. pap. 3.95 (ISBN 0-87148-906-6). Pathway Pr.

LeRoy, Ford. Design for Teaching & Training: A Self-Study Guide to Lesson Planning. LC 77-87249. (Illus.). 1978. pap. 12.95 (ISBN 0-8054-3422-4). Broadman.

Leroy-Beaulieu, Anatole. Israel among the Nations: A Study of the Jews & Antisemitism. facsimile ed. Hellman, Frances, tr. from Fr. LC 74-27996. (Modern Jewish Experience Ser.). (Eng.). 1975. Repr. of 1904 ed. 32.00x (ISBN 0-405-06723-2). Ayer Co Pubs.

Le Sage, Wilfred. Vision of Renewal. (Orig.). 1967. 4.00 (ISBN 0-8198-0169-0); pap. 3.00 (ISBN 0-8198-0170-4). Dghtrs St Paul.

Le Saux, Henri. The Eyes of Light. 1983. 12.95 (ISBN 0-87193-202-4). Dimension Bks.

Lesbaupin, Ivo. Blessed Are the Persecuted: Christian Life in the Roman Empire, A.D. 64-313. Barr, Robert R., tr. from Port. Tr. of A Bem-Aventuranca da Persecucion & La Bienaventuranza de la Persecution. 112p. (Orig.). 1987. 16.95 (ISBN 0-88344-562-X); pap. 7.95 (ISBN 0-88344-561-1). Orbis Bks.

Leschnitzer, Adolf. The Magic Background of Modern Anti-Semitism. LC 55-6501. x, 236p. (Orig.). pap. text ed. 12.95 (ISBN 0-8236-8134-3). Intl Univs Pr.

Lescoe, Francis J. Existentialism: With or Without God. LC 74-1427. 1976. pap. 10.95 (ISBN 0-8189-0340-6). Alba.

Lescohier, Don D. Knights of St. Crispin, Eighteen Sixty-Seven to Eighteen Seventy-Four. LC 77-89748. (American Labor from Conspiracy to Collective Bargaining, Ser. 2). 101p. 1969. Repr. of 1910 ed. 14.00 (ISBN 0-405-02136-4). Ayer Co Pubs.

LeShan, Lawrence. How to Meditate: A Guide to Self-Discovery. 176p. 1986. pap. 3.95 (ISBN 0-553-24453-1). Bantam.

Lesick, Lawrence T. The Lane Rebels: Evangelicalism & Antislavery in Antebellum America. LC 80-24123. (Studies in Evangelicalism: No. 2). 287p. 1980. 21.00 (ISBN 0-8108-1372-6). Scarecrow.

Lesker, G. A., ed. Three Late Medieval Morality Plays: Mankind, Everyman & Mundis et Infans. (New Mermaids Ser.). 1984. pap. text ed. 6.95x (ISBN 0-393-90054-1). Norton.

Lesko, Leonard H. Index of the Spells on Egyptian Middle Kingdom Coffins & Related Documents. LC 79-66500. (Orig.). 1979. pap. text ed. 6.00x (ISBN 0-930548-02-7). B C Scribe.

Leskov, Nikolai. The Jews in Russia. Schefski, Harold K., ed. & tr. from Rus. 143p. 1986. 21.00 (ISBN 0-940670-29-1). Kingston Pr.

Leslau, Wolf, tr. Falasha Anthology. (Judaica Ser.: No. 6). (Illus.). 1951. 26.00x (ISBN 0-300-00681-0). Yale U Pr.

Leslie, Donald D. The Survival of the Chinese Jews: The Jewish Community of Kaifeng. (Illus.). 270p. 1973. text ed. 59.95 (ISBN 90-040-3413-7). Humanities.
Leslie, Robert C. Jesus As Counselor. (Festival Ser.). 144p. 1982. pap. 4.50 (ISBN 0-687-19930-1). Abingdon.
Leslie, Robert C., jt. auth. see Wuellner, Wilhelm H.
Leslie, Shane. Studies in Sublime Failure. LC 70-117817. (Essay Index Reprint Ser). 1932. 20.00 (ISBN 0-8369-1670-0). Ayer Co Pubs.
Lesnoff-Caravaglia, Gari, ed. Values, Ethics & Aging, Vol. 4. (Frontiers in Aging Ser.). 196p. 1985. 29.95 (ISBN 0-89885-162-9). Human Sci Pr.
Le Sourd, Howard M. The University Work of the United Lutheran Church in America: A Study of the Work Among Lutheran Students at Non-Lutheran Institutions. LC 70-176990. (Columbia University. Teachers College. Contributions to Education: No. 377). Repr. of 1929 ed. 17.50 (ISBN 0-404-55377-X). AMS Pr.
LeSourd, Leonard, jt. auth. see Marshall, Catherine.
Le Sourd, Leonard, jt. auth. see Marshall, Catherine.
LeSourd, Leonard, ed. see Marshall, Catherine.
Lessa, William A. & Vogt, Evon Z. Reader in Comparative Religion: An Anthropological Approach. 4th ed. 1979. pap. text ed. 27.50 scp (ISBN 0-06-043991-2, HarpC). Har-Row.
Lesse, N., tr. see Erasmus, Desiderius.
Lesse, Nicholas, tr. see Melanchthon, Philipp.
Lesser, Alexander. Pawnee Ghost Dance Hand Game. LC 79-82340. (Columbia Univ. Contributions to Anthropology Ser.: Vol. 16). 1969. Repr. of 1933 ed. 37.00 (ISBN 0-404-50566-X). AMS Pr.
Lesser, Allen. Israel's Impact, Nineteen Hundred Fifty to Fifty-One: A Personal Record. LC 84-12013. (Orig.). 1984. lib. bdg. 28.00 (ISBN 0-8191-4125-9); pap. text ed. 15.50 (ISBN 0-8191-4126-7). U Pr of Amer.
Lesser, Isaac. The Pentateuch-Haftaroth & Sabeth Prayers: Hebrew with English. 22.50 (ISBN 0-317-00457-3). Shalom.
Lessin, Roy. Como Disciplinar a Tus Hijos. 96p. 1982. 2.25 (ISBN 0-88113-032-X). Edit Betania.
--How to Be Parents of Happy Obedient Children. 1978. 8.95 (ISBN 0-89728-003-2, 702120); pap. 4.95 (ISBN 0-686-67298-4). Omega Pubns OR.
--Spanking: Why? When? How? LC 79-54028. 96p. 1979. pap. 2.95 (ISBN 0-87123-494-7, 200494). Bethany Hse.
Lessing, F. D. & Wayman, Alex. Introduction to the Buddhist Tantric System. 1978. 21.00 (ISBN 0-89684-037-9, Pub. by Motilal Banarsidass India). Orient Bk Dist.
Lessing, F. D., jt. auth. see Wayman, Alex.
Lessing, Gotthold. Lessing's Theological Writings: Selections in Translation. Chadwick, Henry, tr. 1957. pap. 3.25x (ISBN 0-8047-0335-3). Stanford U Pr.
Lessmann, Heinrich. Aufgaben und Ziele der Vergleichenden Mythenforschung: Tasks & Goals of Comparative Mythology. Bolle, Kees W., ed. LC 77-79138. (Mythology Ser.). (Ger.). 1978. Repr. of 1908 ed. lib. bdg. 17.00x (ISBN 0-405-10548-7). Ayer Co Pubs.
Lestarjette, Steve, jt. auth. see Golden, Jerry.
Lestarjette, Steve, jt. auth. see Palandro, Michael.
Lester. Look to the East. 8.95x (ISBN 0-685-22017-6). Wehman.
Lester, Andrew D. Coping with Your Anger: A Christian Guide. LC 82-24730. 114p. 1983. pap. 6.95 (ISBN 0-664-24471-8). Westminster.
--It Hurts So Bad, Lord! LC 75-42860. 1976. 5.95 (ISBN 0-8054-5238-9). Broadman.
--Pastoral Care with Children in Crisis. LC 84-21901. 144p. (Orig.). 1985. pap. 9.95 (ISBN 0-664-24598-6). Westminster.
Lester, Andrew D. & Lester, Judith L. Understanding Aging Parents. LC 80-17832. (Christian Care Bks.: Vol. 8). 120p. 1980. pap. 7.95 (ISBN 0-664-24329-0). Westminster.
Lester, Andrew D., jt. ed. see Borchert, Gerald L.
Lester, Judith L., jt. auth. see Lester, Andrew D.
Lester, Ralph P. Look to the East. 8.50 (ISBN 0-685-19484-1). Powner.
Lester, Robert C. Theravada Buddhism in Southeast Asia. LC 71-185154. 1973. 7.95 (ISBN 0-472-06184-4). U of Mich Pr.
L'Estrange, Francis L. Random Talks with the Living Christ. 107p. 1986. 30.00X (ISBN 0-7223-2038-8, Pub. by A H Stockwell England). State Mutual Bk.
Le Strange, Guy, tr. Palestine under the Moslems. LC 70-180356. Repr. of 1890 ed. 47.50 (ISBN 0-404-56288-4). AMS Pr.
L'Estrange, Hamon. Alliance of Divine Offices. LC 71-172316. (Library of Anglo-Catholic Theology: No. 12). Repr. of 1846 ed. 27.50 (ISBN 0-404-52104-5). AMS Pr.
LeSueur, Stephen C. The Eighteen Thirty-Eight Mormon War in Missouri. LC 86-16090. 736p. 1987. text ed. 24.00 (ISBN 0-8262-0626-3, 83-36349). U of Mo Pr.
Letch, Ralph A. Myths of the Atonement. 1985. 20.00x (ISBN 0-7223-1657-7, Pub. by A H Stockwell England). State Mutual Bk.
Letgers, Lyman H., ed. Western Society after the Holocaust. (Replica Editon Ser.). 200p. 1984. 20.00x (ISBN 0-86531-985-5). Westview.
Lethaby, William. Architecture, Mysticism & Myth. LC 74-25316. (Illus.). 280p. 1975. 10.00 (ISBN 0-8076-0783-5). Braziller.
Lethaby, William R. Mediaeval Art: From the Peace of the Church to the Eve of the Renaissance, 312-1350. facsimile ed. LC 70-157345. (Select Bibliographies Reprint Ser). Repr. of 1904 ed. 33.00 (ISBN 0-8369-5806-3). Ayer Co Pubs.
--Westminster Abbey Re-Examined. LC 69-13244. (Illus.). Repr. of 1925 ed. 27.50 (ISBN 0-405-08744-6, Pub. by Blom). Ayer Co Pubs.
Lethbridge, T. C. The Legend of the Sons of God: A Fantasy. (Illus.). 126p. 1983. pap. 5.95 (ISBN 0-7100-9500-7). Methuen Inc.
Letis, Theodore P. Martin Luther & Charismatic Ecumenism. (Orig.). 1979. pap. 1.95 (ISBN 0-936592-00-1). Reformation Res.
LeTourneau, Richard H. Laws of Success for Christians: There's Only One-Way to Success Both for Today & Forever. LC 85-91034. (LeTourneau One-Way Ser.: Vol. 7). 130p. (Orig.). 1985. pap. 5.95 (ISBN 0-935899-03-0). LeTourneau Pr.
Le Tourneau, Roger. L'Islam Contemporain. LC 80-1922. Repr. of 1950 ed. 24.50 (ISBN 0-404-18975-X). AMS Pr.
Letteris, Meir H., ed. & tr. Megillat Esther: The Story of Esther. 1979. pap. 0.95 (ISBN 0-88482-583-3). Hebrew Pub.
Lettsom, William N. The Nibelungenlied. LC 77-13811. 1977. lib. bdg. 45.00 (ISBN 0-8414-5830-8). Folcroft.
Leu, Barbara De see Walters, Julie & De Leu, Barbara.
Leuba, J. H. The Belief in God & Immortality, a Psychological, Anthropological & Statistical Study. LC 17-54. Repr. of 1916 ed. 29.00 (ISBN 0-527-56600-4). Kraus Repr.
Leuba, James H. The Psychological Origin & the Nature of Religion. LC 78-1577. 17.00 (ISBN 0-8414-5837-5). Folcroft.
--The Psychological Origin & the Nature of Religion. 94p. 1980. Repr. of 1909 ed. lib. bdg. 17.50 (ISBN 0-8482-1622-9). Norwood Edns.
Leuchter, Sara, ed. Guide to Wisconsin Survivors of the Holocaust: A Documentary Project of the Wisconsin Jewish Archives. 192p. 1983. pap. 12.50 (ISBN 0-87020-216-2). State Hist Soc Wis.
Leupold, Herbert C. Exposition of Daniel. 1969. 13.95 (ISBN 0-8010-5531-8). Baker Bk.
--Exposition of Ecclesiastes. 1966. 12.95 (ISBN 0-8010-5505-9). Baker Bk.
--Exposition of Genesis, 2 Vols. Vol. 1. 15.95 (ISBN 0-8010-5549-0); Vol. 2. 15.95 (ISBN 0-8010-5522-9). Baker Bk.
--Exposition of Isaiah, 1 vol. ed. 1977. 22.95 (ISBN 0-8010-5577-6). Baker Bk.
--Exposition of Psalms. 1970. 24.95 (ISBN 0-8010-5521-0). Baker Bk.
--Exposition of Zechariah. 1965. 9.95 (ISBN 0-8010-5512-1). Baker Bk.
Leupold, Ulrich S. & Lehmann, Helmut T., eds. Luther's Works: Liturgy & Hymns, Vol. 53. LC 55-9893. 1965. 19.95 (ISBN 0-8006-0353-2, 1-353). Fortress.
Leuser, David V. How to Send Healing Energy: Diccionari Enciclopedic D'abast Universal, 8 vols. (Catalan.). 3500p. 1974. Set. 300.00 (ISBN 84-345-3560-2, S-50517). French & Eur.
Leutenegger, Benedict, tr. Life of Fray Antonio Margil De Jesus. (Illus.). 1967. 10.00 (ISBN 0-88382-254-7). AAFH.
Leuven, J. V. Prehistoric Religion in Greece. (Illus.). 280p. 1987. lib. bdg. 72.00 (Pub. by A. M. Hakkert). Coronet Bks.
Leveen, J. Catalogue of the Hebrew & Samaritan Manuscripts in the British Museum: Introduction, Indexes, etc, Pt. 4. 224p. 1977. Repr. of 1935 ed. 22.50 (ISBN 0-7141-0619-4, Pub. by British Lib). Longwood Pub Group.
--The Hebrew Bible in Art. (British Academy, London, Schweich Lectures on Biblical Archaeology Series, 1939). pap. 28.00 (ISBN 0-8115-1281-9). Kraus Repr.
Levenson, Dode B., et al. Jewish Trivia. LC 84-63112. (Illus.). 195p. (Orig.). 1985. pap. 7.95 (ISBN 0-9611268-7-6). Quinlan Pr.
Levenson, Jon D. Sinai & Zion: An Entry into the Jewish Bible. 240p. (Orig.). 1985. 16.95 (ISBN 0-86683-961-5, AY8551, HarpR). Har-Row.
--Theology of the Program of Restoration of Ezekiel Forty to Forty-Eight. LC 76-3769. (Harvard Semitic Museum, Monographs). 1976. 9.00 (ISBN 0-89130-105-4, 040010). Scholars Pr GA.
Levenson, Jon D., jt. ed. see Halpern, Baruch.
Levenston, Edward A. & Sivan, Reuven. The New Bantam-Megiddo Hebrew Dictionary. (Hebrew.). 1975. pap. 4.95 (ISBN 0-553-26387-0). Bantam.
Levenston, Edward A., jt. auth. see Sivan, Reuven.
Leventhal, F. M., ed. see Humphrey, A. W.
Lever, Thomas. Sermons. 143p. pap. 15.00 (ISBN 0-87556-200-0). Saifer.
Leverenz, David. The Language of Puritan Feeling: An Exploration in Literature, Psychology, & Social History. 1980. 32.00x (ISBN 0-8135-0882-7). Rutgers U Pr.
Levering, Ralph, jt. auth. see Levinson, Henry S.
Le Verrier, Jean, jt. auth. see Bontier, Pierre.
Levertoff, Paul, jt. tr. see Simon, Maurice.
Levertov, Denise, jt. tr. see Dimock, Edward C., Jr.
Levesque, George H. Social Credit & Catholicism. 1979. lib. bdg. 39.95 (ISBN 0-8490-3006-4). Gordon Pr.
Levey, Samson H. The Messiah: An Aramoic Interpretation. 1974. 20.00x (ISBN 0-87820-402-4, Pub. by Anti-Defamation League). Ktav.
Levi. The Aquarian Gospel of Jesus Christ. 1972. 7.95 (ISBN 0-87516-041-7); pap. 6.95 (ISBN 0-87516-168-5). De Vorss.
--Jewish Chrononomy. 12.95 (ISBN 0-87306-213-2). Feldheim.
--Vistas from Mount Moriah. 6.95 (ISBN 0-87306-983-8). Feldheim.
Levi, Eliphas. The Mysteries of the Qabalah, or the Occult Agreement of the Two Testaments. (Studies in Hermetic Tradition Ser.: Vol. 2). (Illus.). 1974. pap. 12.95 (ISBN 0-85030-274-9). Weiser.
Levi, Gerson B., ed. see Hirsch, Emil G.
Levi, Ken, ed. Violence & Religious Commitment: Implications of Jim Jones's People's Temple Movement. LC 81-83147. (Illus.). 224p. 1982. 24.50x (ISBN 0-271-00296-4). Pa St U Pr.
Levi, Miriam. Effective Jewish Parenting. 1986. 10.95 (ISBN 0-87306-405-4). Feldheim.
Levi, Primo. The Reawakening. 224p. 1987. 4.95 (ISBN 0-02-022370-6, Collier). Macmillan.
Levi, Shonie B. & Kaplan, Sylvia R. Guide for the Jewish Homemaker. 2nd ed. LC 59-12039. (Illus.). 1965. pap. 6.95 (ISBN 0-8052-0087-8). Schocken.
Levi, Yaakov, jt. auth. see Radday, Yehuda.
Leviant, Curt. Masterpieces of Hebrew Literature: A Treasury of Two Thousand Years of Jewish Creativity. 1969. pap. 14.95x (ISBN 0-87068-079-X). Ktav.
Levick. Breakfast of Champions. 1986. pap. 5.95 (ISBN 0-89225-284-7). Gospel Advocate.
Levieux, Eleanor, tr. see Duby, Georges.
Levieux, Eleanor, tr. see Memmi, Albert.
Levin, Arthur, tr. see Lvov-Rogachevsky, V.
Levin, Beatrice. Indian Myths from the Southeast. (Indian Culture Ser.). 1974. 1.95 (ISBN 0-89992-071-3). Coun India Ed.
Levin, David. Cotton Mather: The Young Life of the Lord's Remembrancer, 1663-1703. LC 78-2355. (Illus.). 1978. 25.00x (ISBN 0-674-17507-7). Harvard U Pr.
--Did the Mathers Disagree about the Salem Witchcraft Trials? Proceedings of the American Antiquarian Society. 19p. 1985. pap. 3.95 (ISBN 0-912296-77-1, Dist. by U Pr of Va). Am Antiquarian.
Levin, David, ed. see Mather, Cotton.
Levin, Dov. Fighting Back: Lithuanian Jewry's Armed Resistance to the Nazis. 325p. 1985. text ed. 49.50x (ISBN 0-8419-0831-1). Holmes & Meier.
Levin, Ed, tr. see Kotler, Yair.
Levin, Meyer. Beginnings in Jewish Philosophy. LC 76-116677. (Jewish Heritage Ser). (Illus.). 192p. 1971. text ed. 5.95x (ISBN 0-87441-063-0). Behrman.
--Classic Hassidic Tales. (Illus.). 10.00 (ISBN 0-8446-5216-4). Peter Smith.
--Eva: A Novel of the Holocaust. LC 79-14440. 1979. pap. text ed. 5.95x (ISBN 0-87441-283-8). Behrman.
--Israel Haggadah. rev. ed. LC 70-99933. (Illus.). 1977. pap. 5.95 (ISBN 0-8109-2040-9). Abrams.
Levin, Meyer & Kurzband, Toby. Story of the Jewish Way of Life. LC 59-13487. (Jewish Heritage Ser: Vol. 3). 1959. 5.95x (ISBN 0-87441-003-7). Behrman.
--Story of the Synagogue. LC 57-13093. (Jewish Heritage Ser: Vol. 2). 1957. pap. 5.95x (ISBN 0-87441-006-1). Behrman.
Levin, Meyer, jt. auth. see Kripke, Dorothy K.
Levin, Michael G. Journey to Tradition: The Odyssey of a Born-Again Jew. 129p. 1986. 14.95 (ISBN 0-88125-093-7). Ktav.
Levin, Nora. The Holocaust: The Destruction of European Jewry, 1933-1945. LC 67-23676. (Illus.). 784p. 1973. pap. 12.95 (ISBN 0-8052-0376-1). Schocken.
--Jewish Socialist Movements, Eighteen Seventy-One to Nineteen Seventeen: While Messiah Tarried. (Littman Library of Jewish Civilization). (Illus.). 566p. 1978. 32.00x (ISBN 0-19-710029-5). Oxford U Pr.
--The Jews in the Soviet Union: A History from 1917 to the Present, 2 vols. (Illus.). 864p. 1987. Set. text ed. 75.00 (ISBN 0-8147-5018-4); Vol. 1 (432p.) text ed. 45.00 (ISBN 0-8147-5034-6); Vol. 2 (432p.) text ed. 45.00 (ISBN 0-8147-5035-4). NYU Pr.
Levin, S. Jesus Alias Christ. LC 71-81814. 1969. 6.95 (ISBN 0-8022-2293-5). Philos Lib.
Levin, S. I. & Boyden, Edward A. Kosher Code of the Orthodox Jew. LC 76-76170. (Illus.). 264p. 1983. pap. 9.75 (ISBN 0-87203-011-3). Hermon.
Levin, Samuel R. The Semantics of Metaphor. LC 77-4550. pap. 44.00 (ISBN 0-317-41827-0, 2025626). Bks Demand UMI.
Levin, Shmarya. Youth in Revolt. facsimile ed. Samuel, Maurice, tr. LC 74-27998. (Modern Jewish Experience Ser.). (Eng.). 1975. Repr. of 1930 ed. 24.50x (ISBN 0-405-06725-9). Ayer Co Pubs.
Levine, Aaron. Free Enterprise & Jewish Law: Aspects of Jewish Business Ethics. 1979. 20.00 (ISBN 0-87068-702-6). Ktav.
Levine, Aaron, jt. auth. see Jung, Leo.
Levine, Daniel H., ed. Churches & Politics in Latin America. LC 79-23827. (Sage Focus Editions: Vol. 14). 288p. 1980. 29.00 (ISBN 0-8039-1298-6); pap. 14.95 (ISBN 0-8039-1299-4). Sage.
--Religion & Political Conflict in Latin America. LC 85-24525. xiii, 266p. 1986. 24.95x (ISBN 0-8078-1689-2); pap. 9.95x (ISBN 0-8078-4150-1). U of NC Pr.
Levine, David, tr. see Nathanael Ibn Al-Fayyumi.
Levine, Etan. The Aramaic Version of Jonah. 2nd ed. LC 76-27614. 1979. pap. 12.75 (ISBN 0-87203-068-7). Hermon.
--The Aramaic Version of Lamentations. LC 76-276212. 203p. 1981. pap. 14.75 (ISBN 0-87203-065-2). Hermon.
--The Aramaic Version of Qohelet. new ed. 1979. pap. 14.75 (ISBN 0-87203-087-3). Hermon.
Levine, Etan, ed. Diaspora. LC 82-6723. 350p. 1983. 20.00 (ISBN 0-87668-601-3). Aronson.
--Diaspora: Exile & the Contemporary Jewish Condition. 363p. 1986. 18.95 (ISBN 0-933503-50-4). Shapolsky Pubs.
Levine, Faye. Solomon & Sheba. 240p. 1986. pap. 9.95 (ISBN 0-312-74283-5). St Martin.
Levine, Howard. Life Choices: Confronting the Life & Death Decisions Created by Modern Medicine. 304p. 1986. 16.95 (ISBN 0-671-55385-2). S&S.
Levine, Israel. Faithful Rebels. LC 76-118533. 1971. Repr. of 1936 ed. 22.00x (ISBN 0-8046-1156-4, Pub. by Kennikat). Assoc Faculty Pr.
Levine, Jonathan, jt. auth. see Greenberg, Sidney.
Levine, Jonathan D., jt. auth. see Greenberg, Sidney.
Levine, Lee I., ed. The Jerusalem Cathedra: Studies in the History, Archaeology, Geography, & Ethnography of the Land of Israel, Vol. 1. (Illus.). 362p. 1982. 35.00x (ISBN 0-8143-1691-3). Wayne St U Pr.
--The Jerusalem Cathedra: Studies in the History, Archaeology, Geography & Ehthnography of the Land of Israel, Vol. 2. 355p. 1983. 35.00x (ISBN 0-8143-1715-4). Wayne St U Pr.
--The Synagogue in Late Antiquity: A Centennial Publication of the Jewish Theological Seminary of America. xiv, 223p. 1986. 26.95 (ISBN 0-89757-510-5, Dist. by Eisenbrauns); pap. 15.95 (ISBN 0-89757-509-1). Am Sch Orient Res.
Levine, Lee I., jt. ed. see Israel Exploration Society, Jerusalem.
Levine, Mark & Rachlis, Eugene, eds. The Complete Book of Bible Quotations. pap. 12.95 (ISBN 0-671-49864-9). PB.
Levine, Mark S. Canonical Analysis & Factor Comparison. LC 77-75941. (University Papers: Quantitative Applications in the Social Sciences, No. 6). 62p. 1977. 6.00 (ISBN 0-8039-0655-2). Sage.
Levine, Maurice. Psychiatry & Ethics. LC 72-18354. 384p. 1972. 12.50 (ISBN 0-8076-0642-1). Braziller.
Levine, Naomi & Hochbaum, Martin, eds. Poor Jews: An American Awakening. LC 73-85097. 206p. 1974. 19.95 (ISBN 0-87855-073-9); pap. 8.95x (ISBN 0-87855-570-6). Transaction Bks.
Levine, Samuel. You Take Jesus, I'll Take God. LC 80-82731. 134p. (Orig.). 1980. pap. 4.95 (ISBN 0-9604754-1-9); pap. 4.95 (ISBN 0-9604754-1-9). Hamoroh Pr.
Levine, Shlomo D. The Singular Problems of the Single Jewish Parent. 39p. (Orig.). 1981. pap. text ed. 1.25 (ISBN 0-8381-2115-2). United Synagogue.
Levine, Stephen. Just This Much: Healing Into Life & Death. 288p. 1987. 16.95 (ISBN 0-385-23371-X, Anch); pap. 8.95 (ISBN 0-385-23372-8, Anch). Doubleday.
--Meetings at the Edge: Conversations with the Grieving & the Dying, the Healing & the Healed. LC 82-45931. 264p. 1984. pap. 7.95 (ISBN 0-385-18786-6, Anchor Pr). Doubleday.

Levinger, Elma E. Beautiful Garden & Other Bible Tales. (Illus.). 5.95 (ISBN 0-8197-0253-6). Bloch.
--Great Jews Since Bible Times. (Illus.). 2.50x (ISBN 0-87441-053-3). Behrman.
Levinger, Jacob S., tr. see Breuer, Isaac.
Levinsky, Sara A. A Bridge of Dreams: The Story of Paramananda, a Modern Mystic. LC 83-82698. (Illus.). 632p. (Orig.). 1984. pap. 12.95 (ISBN 0-89281-063-7, Lindisfarne Pr). Inner Tradit.
Levinson, Frederick. The Gospel at Infant Baptism. pap. 4.95x (ISBN 0-7152-0443-2). Outlook.
Levinson, Hanna, jt. auth. see Reif, Joseph A.
Levinson, Henry S. Science, Metaphysics, & the Chance of Salvation: An Interpretation of the Thought of William James. LC 78-7383. 1978. pap. 9.95 (ISBN 0-89130-234-4, 01-01-24). Scholars Pr GA.
Levinson, Henry S. & Levering, Ralph. The Religious Investigations of William James. LC 80-26109. (Studies in Religion). xii, 316p. 1981. 27.50x (ISBN 0-8078-1468-7). U of NC Pr.
Levison, N. The Jewish Background of Christianity: 586 B.C. to A.D. 1. 1977. lib. bdg. 59.95 (ISBN 0-8490-2100-6). Gordon Pr.
Levi-Strauss, Claude. From Honey to Ashes. (Science of Mythology Ser.). 1980. Repr. of 1973 ed. lib. bdg. 34.50x (ISBN 0-374-94952-2, Octagon). Hippocrene Bks.
--From Honey to Ashes: Introduction to a Science of Mythology, Vol. 2. Weightman, John & Weightman, Doreen, trs. LC 82-15965. 512p. 1973. pap. 13.00x (ISBN 0-226-47489-5). U of Chicago Pr.
--Myth & Meaning. LC 78-25833. 1979. pap. 3.95 (ISBN 0-8052-0622-1). Schocken.
--The Raw & the Cooked. (Science of Mythology Ser.). 1979. Repr. of 1970 ed. lib. bdg. 29.00x (ISBN 0-374-94953-0, Octagon). Hippocrene Bks.
--The Raw & the Cooked: Introduction to a Science of Mythology, Vol. 1. Weightman, John & Weightman, Doreen, trs. LC 82-15895. (Illus.). xiv, 388p. 1969. pap. 11.00x (ISBN 0-226-47487-9). U of Chicago Pr.
--Totemism. (Orig.). 1963. pap. 7.95x (ISBN 0-8070-4671-X, BP157). Beacon Pr.
Levita, Elijah. Massoreth Ha Massoreth. rev. ed. LC 67-11894. (Library of Biblical Studies). 1969. 39.50x (ISBN 0-87068-081-1). Ktav.
Leviticus. Sefer Ha'hinnuch: The Book of Education, Vols. 2 & 3. 1985. 29.95 (ISBN 0-87306-145-4). Feldheim.
Levitt, Annette S., jt. ed. see Bertholf, Robert J.
Levitt, Joy, jt. auth. see Davis, Nancy.
Levitt, Zola. Creation: A Scientist's Choice. 1981. pap. 4.95 (ISBN 0-89051-074-1). Master Bks.
--An Israeli Love Story. LC 77-27611. 1977. pap. 3.95 (ISBN 0-8024-4181-5). Moody.
Levitt, Zola & McCall, Tom. Raptured. LC 75-15481. 1975. pap. 4.95 (ISBN 0-89081-014-1). Harvest Hse.
Levitt, Zola, jt. auth. see Fix, Janet.
Levitt, Zola, jt. auth. see McCall, Thomas S.
Levitt, Zola, jt. auth. see McCall, Thomas.
Levitt, Zola, jt. auth. see McCall, Thomas S.
Levitt, Zola, jt. auth. see Martin, Norma.
Levitt, Zola, jt. auth. see Weldon, John.
Levkov, Ilya. Bitburg & Beyond. 1986. 14.95 (ISBN 0-933503-52-0). Shapolsky Pubs.
Levner, J. B., tr. see Snowman, Joel.
Levoir, John M., jt. auth. see Hogan, Richard M.
Levtzion, Nehemia, ed. Conversion to Islam. LC 77-26771. 265p. 1979. text ed. 39.50x (ISBN 0-8419-0343-3). Holmes & Meier.
Levy, B. B. Targun Neophyti One: A Textual Study: Introduction, Genesis, Exodus. LC 86-11117. (Studies in Judaism). 470p. (Orig.). 1986. lib. bdg. 36.50 (ISBN 0-8191-5464-4, Pub. by Studies in Judaism); pap. text ed. 21.75 (ISBN 0-8191-5465-2). U Pr of Amer.
Levy, B. H. Savannah's Old Jewish Community Cemeteries. LC 83-1045. vii, 118p. 1983. 10.95 (ISBN 0-86554-076-4, H68). Mercer Univ Pr.
Levy, D. A., et al. Zen Concrete & Etc. (Illus.). 100p. 1987. pap. 10.00 (ISBN 0-941160-04-1). Ghost Pony Pr.
Levy, Harold. Hebrew for All. 260p. 1976. Repr. of 1970 ed. 15.00x (ISBN 0-85303-191-6, Pub. by Vallentine Mitchell England). Biblio Dist.
Levy, Harriet L. Nine-Twenty O'Farrell Street. facsimile ed. LC 74-29501. (Modern Jewish Experience Ser.). (Illus.). 1975. Repr. of 1947 ed. 23.50x (ISBN 0-405-06728-3). Ayer Co Pubs.
Levy, Howard S., tr. from Chinese. China's Dirtiest Trickster: Folklore About Hsu Wen-ch'ang (1521-1593) (Sino-Japanese Folklore Translations Ser.: No. 1). (Illus.). 68p. 1974. 15.00 (ISBN 0-686-05428-8). Oriental BK Store.
Levy, Howard S. & Yang, F. S., trs. Chinese Monks & Nuns in a Sea of Sins: Short Stories. 1971. 15.00 (ISBN 0-686-01016-7). Oriental Bk Store.
Levy, Jane & Helzel, Florence B. The Jewish Illustrated Book. LC 86-80427. (Illus.). 150p. (Orig.). 1986. pap. 16.00 (ISBN 0-943376-33-5). Magnes Mus.
Levy, Leonard. Blasphemy in Massachusetts: Freedom of Conscience & the Abner Kneeland Case. LC 70-16634. 592p. 1973. lib. bdg. 65.00 (ISBN 0-306-70221-5). Da Capo.
Levy, Leonard W. The Establishment Clause: Religion & the First Amendment. LC 86-5417. 1986. 16.95 (ISBN 0-02-918750-8). Macmillan.
Levy, Maurice, jt. auth. see Cournand, Andre.
Levy, Max. Der Sabbaath in England. Repr. of 1933 ed. 24.00 (ISBN 0-384-32425-8). Johnson Repr.
Levy, Oscar, ed. see Count Gobineau, Arthur.
Levy, Oscar, ed. see Gobineau, Arthur.
Levy, Raphael. The Astrological Works of Abraham Ibn Ezra: A Literary & Linguistic Study. (Johns Hopkins University Studies in Romance Literatures & Languages: Vol. 8). 172p. Repr. of 1927 ed. 16.00 (ISBN 0-384-32427-4). Johnson Repr.
Levy, Reuben. A Baghdad Chronicle. LC 77-10580. (Studies in Islamic History: No. 17). (Illus.). 1978. Repr. of 1929 ed. lib. bdg. 27.50x (ISBN 0-87991-466-1). Porcupine Pr.
--Social Structure of Islam. 1957. 70.00 (ISBN 0-521-05544-X). Cambridge U Pr.
Levy, Rosalie. Heavenly Friends: A Saint for Each Day. 7.00 (ISBN 0-8198-0638-2); pap. 6.00 (ISBN 0-8198-0639-0). Dghtrs St Paul.
Levy, Rosalie M. Joseph, the Just Man. 4.00 (ISBN 0-8198-3901-9); pap. 3.00 (ISBN 0-8198-3902-7). Dghtrs St Paul.
--The Man in Chains, St. Paul. 1951. 4.00 (ISBN 0-8198-4704-6); pap. 3.00 (ISBN 0-8198-4705-4). Dghtrs St Paul.
--What Think You of Christ. 1962. 1.50 (ISBN 0-8198-0172-0). Dghtrs St Paul.
Levy, Zelev. Between Yafeth & Shem: On the Relationship Between Jewish & General Philosophy. (American University Studies V-Philosophy: Vol. 21). 262p. 1986. text ed. 23.50 (ISBN 0-8204-0373-3). P Lang Pubs.
Levy-Bruel, Lucien. Primitive Mythology: The Mythic World of the Australian & Papuan Natives. Elliott, Brian, tr. LC 82-17332. 332p. 1984. text ed. 32.50 (ISBN 0-7022-1667-4). U of Queensland Pr.
Levy-Bruhl, J. Primitives & the Supernatural. LC 73-4358. (Studies in Comparative Literature, No. 35). 1972. Repr. of 1935 ed. lib. bdg. 58.95x (ISBN 0-8383-1589-5). Haskell.
Lew, Dayan. Humanity of Jewish Law. 198p. 1986. 11.95 (ISBN 0-900689-87-0). Soncino Pr.
Lew, Meyer S., ed. see Marmorstein, Arthur.
Lewak, Richard W., jt. auth. see Nelson, Gerald E.
Lewalski, Barbara K. Protestant Poetics & the Seventeenth Century Religious Lyric. LC 78-70305. (Illus.). 536p. 1984. 47.50x (ISBN 0-691-06395-8); pap. 14.50x (ISBN 0-691-01415-9). Princeton U Pr.
Lewanski, Robert T. & Zuraw, Robert A. Health Force. 2nd, rev. ed. (Illus.). 252p. 1982. 14.95 (ISBN 0-9608030-0-9). Taoist Pubs.
Lewellen, Christine. I Am What I Am for God Whosoever Will. 1987. 8.95 (ISBN 0-533-07150-X). Vantage.
Lewin, Isaac. Towards International Guarantees for Religious Liberty. LC 81-52086. 128p. 7.95 (ISBN 0-88400-078-8). Shengold.
Lewis, Allan P. Living in Harmony: Through Kahuna Wisdom. LC 84-25244. (Illus.). 192p. (Orig.). 1985. pap. 10.95 (ISBN 0-915563-01-0). Homana Pubns.
Lewis, Anthony, jt. ed. see Fortune, Nigel.
Lewis, Arthur. Judges & Ruth. (Everyman's Bible Commentary Ser.). 1979. pap. 5.95 (ISBN 0-8024-2007-9). Moody.
Lewis, Arthur, jt. auth. see Darrow, Clarence.
Lewis, Arthur H. Dark Side of the Millennium: The Problem of Evil in Revelation 20: 1-10. 96p. (Orig.). 1980. pap. 3.95 (ISBN 0-8010-5596-2). Baker Bk.
--Jueces y Rut (Comentario Biblico Portavoz) Orig. Title: Judges & Ruth (Everyman's Bible Commentary) (Span.). 128p. 1982. pap. 3.50 (ISBN 0-8254-1434-2). Kregel.
Lewis, Arthur M., jt. auth. see Darrow, Clarence S.
Lewis, B., et al, eds. Encyclopedia of Islam, 4 vols. Incl. Vol. 1. A-B: Fasc. 1-22. Gibb, H. A., et al, eds. 1960. text ed. 185.75x (ISBN 90-040-0530-7); Vol. 2. C-G: Fasc. 23-40. Lewis, B., et al, eds. 1965; Vol. 3. H-Iram: Fasc. 41-60. 1969. text ed. 226.25x (ISBN 90-040-3275-4); Vols. 4 & 5. I-Ram &K-Ha: Fasc. 61-78. 1978. text ed. 275.50. Humanities.
Lewis, Bernard. The Assassins: A Radical Sect in Islam. 1987. pap. 8.95 (ISBN 0-19-520550-2). Oxford U Pr.
--The Jews of Islam. LC 84-42575. (Illus.). 259p. 1984. 42.50x (ISBN 0-691-05419-3). Princeton U Pr.
--The Jews of Islam. 280p. 1987. pap. 8.95 (ISBN 0-691-00807-8). Princeton U Pr.
--The Muslim Discovery of Europe. (Illus.). 352p. 1982. 19.95 (ISBN 0-393-01529-7). Norton.
--The Origins of Isma'ilism: A Study of the Historical Background of the Fatimid Caliphate. LC 74-180357. Repr. of 1940 ed. 22.50 (ISBN 0-404-56289-2). AMS Pr.
Lewis, Bernard, jt. ed. see Braude, Benjamin.
Lewis, Bernard, ed. see Goldziher, Ignaz.
Lewis, C. S. The Business of Heaven: Daily Readings from C. S. Lewis. 1984. pap. 7.95 (ISBN 0-15-614863-3, Harv). HarBraceJ.
--Christian Reflections. 1974. pap. 4.95 (ISBN 0-8028-1430-1). Eerdmans.
--God in the Dock. Hooper, Walter, ed. 1970. pap. 8.95 (ISBN 0-8028-1456-5). Eerdmans.
--The Grand Miracle. (Epiphany Ser.). 176p. 1983. pap. 2.95 (ISBN 0-345-30539-6). Ballantine.
--A Grief Observed. 160p. 1976. pap. 3.50 (ISBN 0-553-25614-9). Bantam.
--A Grief Observed. 64p. (Orig.). 1966. pap. 3.95 (ISBN 0-571-06624-0). Faber & Faber.
--Grief Observed. 1963. 6.95 (ISBN 0-8164-0137-3, HarpR). Har-Row.
--A Grief Observed. 120p. 1985. pap. 5.95 large print ed. (ISBN 0-8027-2470-1). Walker & Co.
--The Joyful Christian: One Hundred Readings from the Works of C. S. Lewis. LC 77-21685. 1977. 11.95 (ISBN 0-02-570900-3). Macmillan.
--The Joyful Christian: 127 Readings. 256p. 1984. 5.95 (ISBN 0-02-086930-4, Collier). Macmillan.
--Letters to Malcolm: Chiefly on Prayer. LC 64-11536. 124p. 1973. pap. 3.95 (ISBN 0-15-650880-X, Harv). HarBraceJ.
--Literary Impact of the Authorized Version. Reumann, John, ed. LC 63-17883. (Facet Bks). 48p. (Orig.). 1963. pap. 2.50 (ISBN 0-8006-3003-3, 1-3003). Fortress.
--Mere Christianity. 1964. 10.95 (ISBN 0-02-570610-1); pap. 3.95 (ISBN 0-02-086830-8). Macmillan.
--Mere Christianity. (Illus.). 211p. 1981. 12.95 (ISBN 0-02-570590-3). Macmillan.
--Mere Christianity. 1978. pap. 3.95 (Collier). Macmillan.
--Mere Christianity. (Christian Library). 1985. Repr. 6.95 (ISBN 0-916441-18-0). Barbour & Co.
--Mere Christianity. 180p. 1986. pap. 4.95 (ISBN 0-02-086940-1, Collier). Macmillan.
--Miracles. 1978. pap. 3.95 (ISBN 0-02-086760-3, Collier). Macmillan.
--Pilgrim's Regress. 224p. 1981. pap. 3.50 (ISBN 0-553-26063-4). Bantam.
--The Pilgrim's Regress: An Allegorical Apology for Christianity, Reason, & Romanticism. LC 82-101595. pap. 55.30 (ISBN 0-317-30149-7, 2025332). Bks Demand UMI.
--The Problem of Pain. 1978. pap. 3.95 (ISBN 0-02-086850-2, Collier). Macmillan.
--El Problema del Dolor. Vilela, Ernesto S., tr. from Eng. LC 77-16715. Tr. of The Problem of Pain. (Span.). 156p. 1977. pap. 3.95 (ISBN 0-89922-097-5). Edit Caribe.
--Reflections on the Psalms. LC 58-10910. 1964. pap. 3.95 (ISBN 0-15-676248-X, Harv). HarBraceJ.
--Reflections on the Psalms. 224p. 1985. pap. 9.95 (ISBN 0-8027-2512-0). Walker & Co.
--The Screwtape Letters. Bd. with Screwtape Proposes a Toast. 1964-67. 9.95 (ISBN 0-02-571240-3). Macmillan.
--The Screwtape Letters. (Illus.). 144p. 1978. pap. 2.95 (ISBN 0-8007-8336-0, Spire Bks); pap. 4.95 (ISBN 0-8007-5014-4, Power Bks). Revell.
--The Seeing Eye & Other Selected Essays from Christian Reflections. 256p. 1986. pap. 3.50 (ISBN 0-345-32866-3). Ballantine.
--Six by Lewis, 6 vols. 1978. pap. 18.95 (ISBN 0-02-086770-0, Collier). Macmillan.
--Spirits in Bondage: A Cycle of Lyrics. 1984. pap. 3.95 (ISBN 0-15-684748-5, Harv). HarBraceJ.
--Surprised by Joy: The Shape of My Early Life. LC 56-5329. 248p. 1956. 12.95 (ISBN 0-15-187011-X). HarBraceJ.
--Surprised by Joy: The Shape of My Early Life. LC 56-5329. 1966. pap. 4.95 (ISBN 0-15-687011-8, Harv). HarBraceJ.
--The Visionary Christian: One Hundred Thirty-One Readings from C. S. Lewis, Selected & Edited by Chad Walsh. 256p. 1981. 10.95 (ISBN 0-02-570540-7). Macmillan.
Lewis, C. S., ed. see MacDonald, George.
Lewis, C. S., et al. Christian Childhoods: An Anthology of Personal Memories. Van Oss, Celia, ed. 270p. 1986. 15.95 (ISBN 0-8245-0695-2); pap. cancelled (ISBN 0-8245-0696-0). Crossroad NY.
Lewis, Clarence I. Values & Imperatives: Studies in Ethics. Lange, John, ed. LC 69-13181. 1969. 17.50x (ISBN 0-8047-0687-5). Stanford U Pr.
Lewis, Clive S. Preface to Paradise Lost. 1942. pap. 7.95x (ISBN 0-19-500345-4). Oxford U Pr.
Lewis, D. B. & Hexeltine, G. C. A Christmas Book. 1977. Repr. of 1928 ed. lib. bdg. 10.00 (ISBN 0-8495-3204-3). Arden Lib.
Lewis, David, tr. see Lochman, Jan M.
Lewis, David A. Dark Angels of Light. LC 84-61915. 100p. (Orig.). 1985. pap. 5.95 (ISBN 0-89221-117-2). New Leaf.
Lewis, Dio. Chastity: Our Secret Sins. LC 73-20634. (Sex, Marriage & Society). 324p. 1974. Repr. of 1874 ed. 24.50x (ISBN 0-405-05809-8). Ayer Co Pubs.
Lewis, Douglas. The Late Baroque Churches of Venice. LC 78-94704. (Outstanding Dissertations in the Fine Arts Ser.). 1979. lib. bdg. 63.00 (ISBN 0-8240-3236-5). Garland Pub.
Lewis, Douglass. Resolving Church Conflicts: A Case Study Approach for Local Congregations. LC 80-8347. 192p. (Orig.). 1981. pap. 7.95 (ISBN 0-06-065244-6, RD 342, HarpR). Har-Row.
Lewis, E. R. Life & Teaching of Jesus Christ: According to the Synoptic Gospels. (London Divinity Ser.). 170p. 1977. pap. 3.95 (ISBN 0-227-67519-3). Attic Pr.
Lewis, E. Ridley. Acts of the Apostles & the Letters of St. Paul. (London Divinity Ser.). 160p. 1964. Repr. of 1960 ed. 3.95 (ISBN 0-227-67401-4). Attic Pr.
--Johannine Writings & Other Epistles. (London Divinity Ser). 144p. 1961. 3.95 (ISBN 0-227-67663-7). Attic Pr.
Lewis, Ernest. Light for the Journey: Living the Ten Commandments. 1985. 10.95. Word Bks.
Lewis, Gladys S. On Earth As It Is... LC 83-70006. (Orig.). 1983. pap. 6.50 (ISBN 0-8054-6332-1). Broadman.
Lewis, Gordon. Bible, Christian & Latter Day Saints. pap. 1.25 (ISBN 0-8010-5567-9). Baker Bk.
--Bible, Christian & Seventh Day Adventists. pap. 1.25 (ISBN 0-8010-5573-3). Baker Bk.
--Bible, Christians & Jehovah's Witnesses. pap. 1.25 (ISBN 0-8010-5568-7). Baker Bk.
--Bible, the Christian & Jehovah's Witnesses. 1966. pap. 1.25 (ISBN 0-87552-324-2). Presby & Reformed.
--Bible, the Christian & Latter Day Saints. 1966. pap. 1.25 (ISBN 0-87552-325-0). Presby & Reformed.
--Bible, the Christian & Seventh Day Adventists. 1966. pap. 1.25 (ISBN 0-87552-326-9). Presby & Reformed.
--Confronting the Cults. pap. 6.50 (ISBN 0-8010-5560-1). Baker Bk.
Lewis, Gordon R. Confronting the Cults. 1966. pap. 6.50 (ISBN 0-87552-323-4). Presby & Reformed.
--Decide for Yourself: A Theological Workbook. LC 71-116046. (Orig.). 1970. pap. 7.95 (ISBN 0-87784-633-2). Inter-Varsity.
Lewis, Gordon R. & Demarest, Bruce A. Integrative Theology: Knowing Ultimate Reality; The Living God, Vol. 1. 352p. 1986. 16.95 (ISBN 0-310-39230-6). Zondervan.
Lewis, Gordon R. & Demarest, Bruce, eds. Challenges to Inerrancy: A Theological Response. 458p. (Orig.). 1984. pap. 13.95 (ISBN 0-8024-0237-2). Moody.
Lewis, Gregg, jt. auth. see Lewis, Margie M.
Lewis, Gregg, jt. auth. see Lewis, Ralph L.
Lewis, Gregg, jt. auth. see Tirabassi, Becky.
Lewis, H. Bell Ringing Minimus Three & Four Bell Methods. 1985. 18.75x (ISBN 0-317-54263-X, Pub. by J Richardson UK). State Mutual Bk.
Lewis, H. Spencer. Las Mansiones del Alma. 16th ed. AMORC Staff, tr. from Eng. (Span., Illus.). 235p. 1981. pap. 7.00 (ISBN 0-912057-67-X, GS-511). AMORC.
--Mansions of the Soul. 19th ed. LC 30-34218. 1981. 11.95 (ISBN 0-912057-07-6, G-511). AMORC.
--Manual Rosacruz. 8th ed. AMORC Staff, tr. from Eng. (Span., Illus.). 268p. (Orig.). 1981. pap. 8.00 (ISBN 0-912057-60-2, GS-508). AMORC.
--The Mystical Life of Jesus. 25th ed. LC 54-20988. 1982. 11.95 (ISBN 0-912057-06-8, G-503). AMORC.
--Mystical Life of Jesus. LC 54-20988. (Illus.). 320p. 1986. pap. 9.95 (ISBN 0-912057-46-7, G-658). AMORC.
--Preguntas y Respuestas Rosacruces: Con la historia completa de la Orden. 8th ed. AMORC Staff, tr. from Eng. (Span., Illus.). 231p. 1982. pap. 8.00 (ISBN 0-912057-61-0, GS-501). AMORC.
--Principios Rosacruces para el Hogar y los Negocios. 4th ed. AMORC Staff, tr. from Eng. (Span.). 210p. (Orig.). 1980. pap. 8.00 (ISBN 0-912057-76-9, GS-502). AMORC.
--La Profecia Simbolica de la Gran Piramide. 4th ed. AMORC Staff, tr. from Eng. (Span., Illus.). 167p. (Orig.). 1982. pap. 7.00 (ISBN 0-912057-70-X, GS-514). AMORC.
--Rosicrucian Manual. 28th ed. LC 78-104932. (Illus.). 214p. 1987. 8.95 (ISBN 0-912057-39-4, G-508). AMORC.

--Rosicrucian Principles for the Home & Business. 21st ed. LC 54-21694. 241p. 1981. 11.95 (ISBN 0-912057-04-1, G-502). AMORC.
--Rosicrucian Questions & Answers with Complete History. 16th ed. LC 65-14964. 358p. 1984. 12.50 (ISBN 0-912057-37-8, G-501). AMORC.
--The Secret Doctrines of Jesus. 19th ed. LC 37-22922. 237p. 1981. 10.95 (ISBN 0-912057-14-9, G-504). AMORC.
--Self Mastery & Fate with the Cycles of Life. 33rd ed. LC 55-16785. 253p. 1982. 11.95 (ISBN 0-912057-05-X, G-507). AMORC.
--Self Mastery & Fate with the Cycles of Life. LC 55-16785. (Illus.). 253p. 1986. pap. 8.95 (ISBN 0-912057-45-9, G-657). AMORC.
--Symbolic Prophecy of the Great Pyramid. 16th ed. LC 37-3808. 192p. 1982. 8.95 (ISBN 0-912057-13-0, G-514). AMORC.
--A Thousand Years of Yesterday. 22nd ed. LC 20-9068. 156p. 1982. 8.95 (ISBN 0-912057-01-7, G-506). AMORC.
--La Vida Mistica de Jesus. 14th ed. AMORC Staff, tr. from Eng. (Span., Illus.). 234p. (Orig.). 1981. pap. 8.00 (ISBN 0-912057-63-7, GS 503). AMORC.
Lewis, I. M. Religion in Context: Cults & Charisma. (Essays in Social Anthropology Ser.). (Illus.). 160p. 1986. 37.50 (ISBN 0-521-30616-7); pap. 9.95 (ISBN 0-521-31596-4). Cambridge U Pr.
Lewis, I. M., ed. Islam in Tropical Africa. 2nd ed. LC 79-3292. 324p. 1980. 25.00x (ISBN 0-253-14956-8); pap. 10.95x (ISBN 0-253-28514-3). Ind U Pr.
Lewis, Jack. The Archaeology & Bible. LC 75-20804. (Way of Life Ser: No. 113). 112p. 1975. pap. 3.95 (ISBN 0-89112-113-7, Bibl Res Pr). Abilene Christ U.
--Leadership Questions Confronting the Church. 1985. pap. 5.95 (ISBN 0-89225-275-8). Gospel Advocate.
Lewis, Jack P. Minor Prophets. 1966. pap. 3.95 (ISBN 0-8010-5509-1). Baker Bk.
Lewis, James C. The Key to Spiritual Growth. 128p. 1985. 5.95 (ISBN 0-87159-004-2). Unity School.
Lewis, James K. Religious Life of Fugitive Slaves & Rise of the Coloured Baptist Churches, 1820-1865, in What Is Now Ontario. Gaustad, Edwin S., ed. LC 79-52574. (The Baptist Tradition Ser.). 1980. lib. bdg. 21.00x (ISBN 0-405-12442-2). Ayer Co Pubs.
Lewis, Jim. Biblical Favorites. LC 85-50948. 134p. (Orig.). 1985. pap. 7.95 (ISBN 0-942482-08-5). Unity Church Denver.
--Finding the Treasure Within You. LC 81-70339. 128p. 1982. pap. 4.75 (ISBN 0-87516-469-2). De Vorss.
--The Great Commitment. LC 81-71542. 120p. (Orig.). 1982. pap. 7.50 (ISBN 0-942482-03-4). Unity Church Denver.
--Mystical Teachings of Christianity. 150p. 1980. pap. 7.95 (ISBN 0-942482-01-8). Unity Church Denver.
--Positive Thoughts for Successful Living. LC 80-50277. 138p. (Orig.). 1979. pap. 7.95 (ISBN 0-942482-00-X). Unity Church Denver.
--Reincarnation & Translation. 31p. (Orig.). 1981. pap. 3.00 (ISBN 0-942482-02-6). Unity Church Denver.
--Spiritual Gospel. LC 82-51231. 145p. (Orig.). 1982. pap. 8.95 (ISBN 0-942482-05-0). Unity Church Denver.
--The Ten Commandments: Then & Now. LC 84-50912. 95p. (Orig.). 1984. pap. 5.95 (ISBN 0-942482-07-7). Unity Church Denver.
--The Upward Path. LC 82-60277. 150p. (Orig.). 1982. pap. 7.95 (ISBN 0-942482-04-2). Unity Church Denver.
Lewis, Joe O. Layman's Bible Book Commentary: First & Second Samuel & First Chronicles, Vol. 5. LC 79-54796. 1981. 5.95 (ISBN 0-8054-1175-5). Broadman.
Lewis, John. The History of the Life & Sufferings of the Revered & Learned John Wiclif, D. D. LC 74-178543. Repr. of 1820 ed. 39.50 (ISBN 0-404-56625-1). AMS Pr.
--Religions of the World Made Simple. rev. ed. (Made Simple Ser.). 1958. pap. 4.95 (ISBN 0-385-02276-X). Doubleday.
Lewis, John, et al, eds. Christianity & the Social Revolution. facsimile ed. LC 79-37892. (Select Bibliographies Reprint Ser). Repr. of 1935 ed. 25.00 (ISBN 0-8369-6729-1). Ayer Co Pubs.
Lewis, John M. Revelation, Inspiration, Scripture. LC 83-71822. (Layman's Library of Christian Doctrine Ser.). 1985. 5.95 (ISBN 0-8054-1633-1). Broadman.
Lewis, John M. & Deiros, Pablo A. La Revelacion e Inspiracion de las Escrituras. (Biblioteca de Doctrina Cristiana). (Span.). 162p. 1986. pap. 5.95 (ISBN 0-311-09113-X). Casa Bautista.
Lewis, Joseph. American Atheist Heritage. O'Hair, Madalyn M., ed. (Illus.). 55p. 1981. pap. 4.00 (ISBN 0-911826-28-9). Am Atheist.
--Atheism & Other Addresses. LC 72-161333. (Atheist Viewpoint Ser). (Illus.). 510p. 1972. Repr. of 1960 ed. 32.00 (ISBN 0-405-03800-3). Ayer Co Pubs.
--The Ten Commandments. 644p. cancelled (ISBN 0-911826-36-X). Am Atheist.
Lewis, Karen. From Arapesh to Zuni: A Book of Bibleless Peoples. (Illus.). 31p. 1986. pap. text ed. 4.95 (ISBN 0-938978-07-1). Wycliffe Bible.
Lewis, Kay O. The Christian Wedding Handbook. 192p. 1981. 10.95 (ISBN 0-8007-1259-5). Revell.
Lewis, Lionel S. St. Joseph of Arimathea at Glastonbury. (Illus.). 212p. 1983. pap. 8.95 (ISBN 0-227-67868-0). Attic Pr.
Lewis, Margie M. & Lewis, Gregg. The Hurting Parent. 160p. (Orig.). 1980. pap. 5.95 (ISBN 0-310-41731-7, 11222P). Zondervan.
Lewis, Martha W. The Official Priests of Rome under the Julio-Claudians: A Study of the Nobility from 44 B. C. to 68 A. D. LC 56-2111. (American Academy in Rome. Papers & Monographs: Vol. 16). pap. 48.00 (2026730). Bks Demand UMI.
Lewis, Paul. Forty Ways to Teach Your Child Values. 224p. 1985. pap. 6.95 (ISBN 0-8423-0920-9). Tyndale.
Lewis, Paul, jt. auth. see McDowell, Josh.
Lewis, Ralph. Mental Alchemy. 3rd ed. LC 79-66799. 270p. 1984. 11.95 (ISBN 0-912057-38-6, G-639). AMORC.
Lewis, Ralph, ed. The Immortalized Words of the Past. LC 85-63539. 300p. (Orig.). 1986. pap. 9.95 (ISBN 0-912057-42-4, G-654). AMORC.
Lewis, Ralph L. Inductive Preaching: Activities Guidbook. 32p. 1983. pap. 3.95 (ISBN 0-9608180-2-2). Asbury Theological.
--Persuasive Preaching Today. 276p. 1982. Repr. of 1979 ed. 6.95 (ISBN 0-9608180-0-6). Asbury Theological.
Lewis, Ralph L. & Lewis, Gregg. Inductive Preaching: Helping People Listen. LC 83-70321. 224p. 1983. pap. 6.95 (ISBN 0-89107-287-X, Crossway Bks). Good News.
Lewis, Ralph M. Behold the Sign. 12th ed. LC 44-30695. 1981. 7.95 (ISBN 0-912057-16-5, G521). AMORC.
--Cosmic Mission Fulfilled. 3rd ed. LC 66-25243. 364p. 1978. 12.50 (ISBN 0-912057-22-X, G-631). AMORC.
--Mision Cosmica Cumplida. 4th ed. AMORC Staff, tr. from Eng. (Span., Illus.). 403p. (Orig.). 1981. pap. 7.00 (ISBN 0-912057-73-4, GS-631). AMORC.
--A Traves del Ojo de la Mente. AMORC Staff, tr. from Eng. (Span.). 290p. (Orig.). 1983. pap. 8.00 (ISBN 0-912057-84-X, GS-646). AMORC.
Lewis, Ralph M., ed. The Universe of Numbers. LC 83-51126. 209p. (Orig.). 1984. pap. 7.95 (ISBN 0-912057-11-4, G-649). AMORC.
Lewis, Roger. Color & the Edgar Cayce Readings. 48p. 1973. pap. 3.50 (ISBN 0-87604-068-7). Are Pr.
Lewis, Ron S., jt. auth. see Chaney, Charles L.
Lewis, Samuel L. Introduction to Spiritual Brotherhood: Science, Mysticism & the New Age. Klotz, Saadi, ed. (Bismillah Bks.: No. 3). (Illus.). 112p. (Orig.). 1981. pap. 4.50 (ISBN 0-915424-07-X). Sufi Islamia-Prophecy.
--The Jerusalem Trilogy. Meyer, Wali A., et al, eds. (Illus.). 336p. (Orig.). 1975. pap. 5.95 (ISBN 0-915424-03-7, Prophecy Pressworks). Sufi Islamia-Prophecy.
--The Rejected Avatar. (Illus.). 24p. (Orig.). 1968. pap. 1.25 saddlestitched (ISBN 0-915424-00-2, Prophecy Pressworks). Sufi Islamia-Prophecy.
--Siva! Siva! Cresent & Heart: Selected Poetry of Murshid Samuel L. Lewis. (Bismillah Bks.: No. 1). (Illus.). 112p. (Orig.). 1980. pap. 3.50 (ISBN 0-915424-04-5). Sufi Islamia-Prophecy.
--Spiritual Dance & Walk: An Introduction from the Work of Murshid Samuel L. Lewis. 2nd, rev. ed. Jablonski, Moineddin, ed. (Illus.). 64p. (Orig.). 1978. pap. 4.50 (ISBN 0-915424-05-3, Prophecy Pressworks). Sufi Islamia-Prophecy.
Lewis, Samuel L. & Khan, Hazrat I. The Bowl of Saki Commentary. Jablonski, Moineddin & Klotz, Saadi, eds. 180p. (Orig.). 1981. pap. 18.00 (ISBN 0-915424-08-8). Sufi Islamia-Prophecy.
Lewis, Sergeant. John Wycliffe: Last of the Schoolmen & First of the Reformers. 1978. Repr. of 1892 ed. lib. bdg. 25.00 (ISBN 0-8492-8060-5). R West.
Lewis, Shari. One-Minute Bible Stories: Old Testament. LC 86-2011. (Illus.). 48p. 1986. 6.95 (ISBN 0-385-19565-6); PLB 6.95 (ISBN 0-385-19566-4). Doubleday.
Lewis, Shari & Henderson, Florence. One-Minute Bible Stories: New Testament. LC 86-6401. (Illus.). 48p. 1986. 6.95 (ISBN 0-385-23286-1); PLB 6.95 (ISBN 0-385-23287-X). Doubleday.
Lewis, Spencer H. Mansions of the Soul. LC 30-34218. 338p. 1986. pap. 9.95 (ISBN 0-912057-43-2, G-655). AMORC.
Lewis, Tommy & Harrell, Irene B. Isn't It Amazin'? A Book about the Love of God. 184p. (Orig.). 1983. pap. 6.00 (ISBN 0-915541-00-9). Star Bks Inc.
Lewis, V. H. The Church Winning Souls. 83p. 1983. pap. 2.95 (ISBN 0-8341-0893-3). Beacon Hill.
Lewis, W. H., ed. The Letters of C. S. Lewis. LC 74-13416. (Illus.). 308p. 1975. pap. 5.95 (ISBN 0-15-650870-2, Harv). HarBraceJ.
Lewis, Warren, ed. Towards a Global Congress of the World's Religions. LC 79-56121. 63p. 1979. pap. 2.95 (ISBN 0-932894-03-8). Rose Sharon Pr.
--Towards a Global Congress of the Worlds's Religions. LC 78-73771. 1978. write for info. (ISBN 0-932894-01-1). Rose Sharon Pr.
--Towards a Global Congress of World's Religions. LC 80-53764. 79p. 1980. pap. 3.25 (ISBN 0-932894-07-0). Rose Sharon Pr.
Lewis, Wyndham. The Caliph's Design. (Illus.). 188p. (Orig.). 1986. 20.00 (ISBN 0-87685-665-2); pap. 9.50 (ISBN 0-87685-664-4); deluxe ed. 30.00 (ISBN 0-87685-666-0). Black Sparrow.
--The Jews, Are They Human? LC 72-82188. 1972. Repr. of 1939 ed. lib. bdg. 75.00 (ISBN 0-87968-008-3). Gordon Pr.
Lewis, Wyndham & Heseltine. A Christmas Book: An Anthology for Moderns. 1977. Repr. of 1928 ed. 30.00 (ISBN 0-89984-217-8). Century Bookbindery.
Lewisehn, Leonard, tr. see Nurbakhsh, Javad.
Lewishon, Leonard, tr. see Javad, Nurbakhsh.
Lewisohn, Leonard, tr. see Nurbakhsh, Javad.
Lewisohn, Leonard, tr. see Nurbakhsh, Dr. Javad.
Lewisohn, Leonard, tr. see Nurbakhsh, Jawad.
Lewisohn, Ludwig. Israel. LC 76-138122. 1971. Repr. of 1925 ed. lib. bdg. 22.50x (ISBN 0-8371-5698-X, LEIS). Greenwood.
--Permanent Horizon. LC 73-117818. (Essay Index Reprint Ser). 1934. 19.00 (ISBN 0-8369-1811-8). Ayer Co Pubs.
Lewisohn, Ludwig, tr. see Buber, Martin.
Lewit, Jane & Epstein, Ellen R. The Bar-Bat Mitzvah Planbook. LC 81-48459. (Illus.). 176p. 1982. 18.95 (ISBN 0-8128-2861-5). Stein & Day.
Lewittes, M. Religious Foundations of the Jewish State: The Concept & Practice of Jewish Statehood from Biblical Times to the Modern State of Israel. 25.00x (ISBN 0-87068-433-7). Ktav.
Lewittes, Mendell. Principles & Development of Jewish Law. 200p. Date not set. 19.95x (ISBN 0-8197-0512-8); pap. 10.95x (ISBN 0-8197-0506-3). Bloch.
Lewittes, Mendell see Maimonides, Moses.
Lewittes, Mordecai. Easy Hebrew (Iurit Kallah) 5.95 (ISBN 0-88482-682-1). Hebrew Pub.
--Heroes of Jewish History: From Abraham to Moses, Vol. 1. 255p. 1952. pap. 6.95x (ISBN 0-88482-626-0). Hebrew Pub.
--Highlights of Jewish History: From Dan to Ramban, Vol. 3. 303p. 1955. pap. 6.95x (ISBN 0-88482-628-7). Hebrew Pub.
--Highlights of Jewish History: From Joshua to Jeremiah, Vol. 2. 288p. 1953. pap. 6.95x (ISBN 0-88482-627-9). Hebrew Pub.
--Highlights of Jewish History: From Middle Ages to Modern Times, Vol. 4. 319p. 1957. 6.95x (ISBN 0-88482-629-5). Hebrew Pub.
Lewittes, Mordecai, jt. auth. see Blumberg, Harry.
Lewy, Hans, et al, eds. Three Jewish Philosophers: Philo, Saadya, Gaon, Jehuda, Halevi. LC 60-9081. 1969. pap. text ed. 7.95x (ISBN 0-689-70126-8, T6). Atheneum.
Lexau, Henry. A Treasury of Catholic Digest: Favorite Stories of Fifty Years, 1936-1986. LC 86-81597. 598p. 1986. 24.95 (ISBN 0-89870-115-5). Ignatius Pr.
Ley, Henry G., jt. ed. see Davies, Walford.
Leyburn, John. Soldier of the Cross. 2nd ed. 339p. 1986. Repr. of 1851 ed. lib. bdg. 27.50 (ISBN 0-89941-509-1). W S Hein.
Leyland, Charles G., tr. see Heine, Heinrich.
Leymarie, Jean, intro. by. The Jerusalem Windows of Marc Chagall. LC 62-18146. (Illus.). 120p. 1975. 15.00 (ISBN 0-8076-0423-2); pap. 9.95 (ISBN 0-8076-0807-6). Braziller.
Leypoldt, Martha M. Learning Is Change. LC 70-144082. 1971. pap. 4.95 (ISBN 0-8170-0526-9). Judson.
Leyser, Henrietta. Hermits & the New Monasticism: A Study of Religious Communities in Western Europe, 1000-1150. LC 83-40611. 131p. 1984. 25.00 (ISBN 0-312-36999-9). St Martin.
Lhalungpa, Lobsang P., tr. see Takpo Tashi Namgyal.
L'Heureux, Conrad E. In & Out of Paradise: The Book of Genesis From Adam & Eve to the Tower of Babel. LC 82-62415. 128p. 1983. pap. 3.95 (ISBN 0-8091-2530-7). Paulist Pr.
--Life Journey & the Old Testament: An Experiential Approach to the Bible & Personal Transformations. 184p. 1986. pap. 8.95 (ISBN 0-8091-2828-4). Paulist Pr.
--Rank among the Canaanite Gods: El, Baal, & the Raphaim. LC 79-15582. (Harvard Semitic Monographs: No. 21). 1979. 10.50 (ISBN 0-89130-326-X, 040021). Scholars Pr GA.
L'Heureux, Mother Aloysius G. Mystical Vocabulary of Venerable Mere Marie De L'Incarnation & Its Problems. LC 72-94190. (Catholic University of America Studies in Romance Languages & Literatures Ser: No. 53). (Fr.). Repr. of 1956 ed. 24.00 (ISBN 0-404-50353-5). AMS Pr.
Li, Shao-ch'Ang. Popular Buddhism in China. lib. bdg. 79.95 (ISBN 0-87968-539-5). Krishna Pr.
Liang Chi-Chao. History of Chinese Political Thought. LC 70-100526. Repr. of 1930 ed. 17.50 (ISBN 0-404-03985-5). AMS Pr.
Liang, T. T. T'ai Chi Ch'uan for Health & Self-Defense: Philosophy & Practice. 1977. pap. 5.95 (ISBN 0-394-72461-5, Vin). Random.
Liao, David. The Unresponsive: Resistant or Neglected? The Hakka Chinese in Taiwan Illustrate the Homogeneous Unit Principle. LC 73-175494. 1979. pap. 5.95 (ISBN 0-87808-735-4). William Carey Lib.
Lias, Edward J., jt. auth. see Perry, Lloyd M.
Lias, John J. First Epistle of John. 1982. lib. bdg. 15.75 (ISBN 0-86524-092-2, 6201). Klock & Klock.
Libanio, J. B. Spiritual Discernment & Politics: Guidelines for Religious Communities. Morrow, Theodore, tr. from Port. LC 82-2257. Orig. Title: Discernment E politica. 144p. (Orig.). 1982. pap. 1.74 (ISBN 0-88344-463-1). Orbis Bks.
Libby, Larry, jt. auth. see McMinn, Gordon.
Liber de Duobus Principiis. Un Traite Neo-Manicheen du XIIIe siecle. LC 78-63185. (Heresies of the Early Christian & Medieval Era: Second Ser.). 1979. Repr. of 1939 ed. 32.00 (ISBN 0-404-16224-X). AMS Pr.
Liberles, Robert. Religious Conflict in Social Context: The Resurgence of Orthodox Judaism in Frankfurt Am Main, 1838-1877. LC 84-27981. (Contributions to the Study of Religion Ser.: No. 13). xvi, 297p. 1985. lib. bdg. 29.95 (ISBN 0-313-24806-0, LRX/). Greenwood.
Liberman, David. The Eternal Torah: A Commentary upon the Books of Joshua-Judges-Smauel One, Samuel Two, Pt. 2. 360p. 1983. 20.00 (ISBN 0-9609840-1-1). Twin Pines Pr.
Libersat, Henry, jt. auth. see McKenna, Briege.
Liberty, Gene. The Meaning of Life. (Orig.). 1975. pap. text ed. 8.67 (ISBN 0-87720-010-6). AMSCO Sch.
Libo, Kenneth & Howe, Irving. We Lived There Too: A Documentary History of Pioneer Jews & the Westward Movement of America, 1630-1930. LC 84-11787. (Illus.). 352p. 1984. 24.95 (ISBN 0-312-85866-3, Pub. by Marek). St Martin.
--We Lived There Too: In Their Own Words & Pictures-Pioneer Jews & the Westward Movement of America 1630-1930. (Illus.). 352p. 1985. pap. 13.95 (ISBN 0-312-85867-1, Pub. by Marek). St Martin.
Licht, Jacob. Storytelling in the Bible. 154p. 1978. text ed. 18.50x (ISBN 965-223-301-3, Pub. by Magnes Pr Israel). Humanities.
--Storytelling in the Bible. 2nd ed. 156p. 1986. Repr. of 1978 ed. text ed. 22.50 (ISBN 965-223-542-3, Pub. by Magnes Pr Israel). Humanities.
Lichten, Frances. Fraktur: The Illuminated Manuscripts of the Pennsylvania Dutch. 1958. wrappers 1.00 (ISBN 0-911132-10-4). Phila Free Lib.
Lichtenstadter, Ilse. Islam & the Modern Age. 228p. 1958. text ed. 29.00x (ISBN 0-8290-0179-4). Irvington.
Lichtfield, Hugh. Preaching the Christmas Story. LC 83-71689. 1984. pap. 5.50 (ISBN 0-8054-2101-7). Broadman.
Lickley, W. A. Malachi: Lessons for Today. pap. 3.95 (ISBN 0-88172-114-X). Believers Bkshelf.
Liddell, Eric. Disciplines of the Christian Life. 160p. (Orig.). 1985. pap. 6.95 (ISBN 0-687-10810-1). Abingdon.
Lidden, H. P. & Orr, J. The Birth of Christ. 1980. 15.25 (ISBN 0-86524-058-2, 9502). Klock & Klock.
Liddon, Henry P. The Divinity of Our Lord. 1978. 20.50 (ISBN 0-86524-130-9, 9801). Klock & Klock.
--The First Epistle to Timothy. 1978. 6.00 (ISBN 0-86524-109-0, 5401). Klock & Klock.
Liddy, Richard. In Gods Gentle Arms. 1979. pap. 2.95 (ISBN 0-88479-022-3). Arena Lettres.
Liderbach, Daniel. The Theology of Grace & the American Mind: A Representation of Catholic Doctrine. LC 83-22154. (Toronto Studies in Theology: Vol. 15). 170p. 1983. lib. bdg. 39.95x (ISBN 0-88946-761-7). E Mellen.
Lidgett, John S. The Biblical Doctrine of the Atonement. 522p. 1983. 19.50 (ISBN 0-86524-145-7, 8801). Klock & Klock.
Lidiard, Victoria. Christianity: Faith, Love & Healing. LC 84-90145. 80p. 1985. 5.95 (ISBN 0-533-06204-7). Vantage.

Lidin, Olof. The Life of Ogyu Sorai: A Tokugawa Philosopher. (Scandinavian Institute of Asian Studies Monograph Ser.: No. 19). 250p. 1982. pap. text ed. 18.95x (ISBN 0-7007-0068-4, Pub. by Curzon Pr England). Apt Bks.

Lidmus, Susan B. Church Family Ministry: Changing Loneliness to Fellowship in the Church. 1985. pap. 6.95 (ISBN 0-570-03945-2, 12-2878). Concordia.

Lieb, Michael. The Dialectics of Creation: Patterns of Birth & Regeneration in "Paradise Lost". LC 71-76047. 272p. 1970. 17.50x (ISBN 0-87023-049-2). U of Mass Pr.

Liebelt, Gerita G. From Dilemma to Delight. Coffen, Richard W., ed. 96p. (Orig.). 1986. pap. 6.95 (ISBN 0-8280-0298-3). Review & Herald.

Lieberman, Chaim. The Grave Concern. LC 68-58650. 202p. 1968. 10.00 (ISBN 0-88400-016-8). Shengold.

Lieberman, David. The Eternal Torah: A Commentary Integrating All the Prophets into the Books of Kings, Bk. 3. 600p. 1986. 25.00x (ISBN 0-9609840-2-X). Twin Pines Pr.

--The Eternal Torah: A Commentary upon Torah Pentateuch Consolidating the Scholarship Throughout Hebrew Literature, Pt. 1. 570p. 1986. Repr. of 1979 ed. 25.00 (ISBN 0-9609840-0-3). Twin Pines Pr.

Lieberman, Donald. Heroes of Hanukkah. 1980. 8.95x (ISBN 0-87068-866-9). Ktav.

Lieberman, Leo, ed. Classics of Jewish Literature. Beringause, Arthur. LC 86-8124. 432p. 1986. 24.95 (ISBN 0-8022-2092-4). Philos Lib.

Lieberman, Saul. Alexander Marx Jubilee Volume, 2 vols. 1950. 35.00x (ISBN 0-685-31434-0, Pub. by Jewish Theol Seminary). KTAV.

--Siphre Zutta. 1968. 10.00x (ISBN 0-685-31431-6, Pub. by Jewish Theol Seminary). Ktav.

--Texts & Studies. 1973. 35.00x (ISBN 0-87068-210-5). Ktav.

--The Tosefta, 5 Vols. 25.00x ea. (ISBN 0-685-31430-8, Pub. by Jewish Theol Seminary). KTAV.

Lieberman, Saul & Hyman, Arthur, eds. Salo Wittmayer Baron Jubilee Volume: On the Occasion of His Eightieth Birthday, 3 vols. new ed. LC 74-82633. 1533p. 1975. 112.00x set (ISBN 0-685-51945-7); Vol. 1. (ISBN 0-231-03911-5); Vol. 2. (ISBN 0-231-03912-3); Vol. 3. (ISBN 0-231-03913-1). Columbia U Pr.

Liebermann, Jeremiah, ed. see Garvy, John W., Jr.

Liebersat, Henry. Caught in the Middle. 176p. (Orig.). 1987. pap. 8.95 (ISBN 0-8245-0822-X). Crossroad NY.

Liebersohn, Harry. Religion & Industrial Society: The Protestant Social Congress in Wilhelmine Germany. LC 86-71421. (Transaction Ser.: Vol. 76, Pt. 6). 1986. 15.00 (ISBN 0-87169-766-1). Am Philos.

Liebert, Arthur. Mythus und Kultur: Myth & Culture. Bolle, Kees W., ed. (Mythology Ser.). (Ger.). 1978. Repr. of 1925 ed. lib. bdg. 17.00x (ISBN 0-405-10549-5). Ayer Co Pubs.

Liebert, Gosta. Iconographic Dictionary of the Indian Religions: Hinduism, Buddhism, Jainism. (Illus.). 377p. 1986. Repr. lib. bdg. 75.00 (ISBN 81-7030-098-3, Pub. by Sri Satguru Pubns India). Orient Bk Dist.

Liebeschuetz, J. H. Continuity & Change in Roman Religion. 1979. text ed. 65.00x (ISBN 0-19-814822-4). Oxford U Pr.

Liebman, Charles S. & Don-Yehiya, Eliezer. Civil Religion in Israel: Traditional Judaism & Political Culture in the Jewish State. LC 82-17427. 270p. 1983. 27.50x (ISBN 0-520-04817-2). U of Cal Pr.

--Religion & Politics in Israel. LC 83-48172. (Jewish Political & Social Studies Ser.). 160p. 1984. 17.50x (ISBN 0-253-34497-2). Ind U pr.

Liebman, Robert C. & Wuthnow, Robert. The New Christian Right: Mobilization & Legitimation. (Social Institutions & Social Change Ser.). 1983. lib. bdg. 26.95x (ISBN 0-202-30307-1); pap. text ed. 9.95 (ISBN 0-202-30308-X). De Gruyter Aldine.

Liebman, Seymour B. The Inquisitors & the Jews in the New World: Summaries of Procesos 1500-1810, & Bibliographical Guide. LC 72-85110. 160p. 1973. 12.95x (ISBN 0-87024-245-8). U of Miami Pr.

--Jews in New Spain: Faith, Flame & the Inquisition. LC 70-91213. (Illus.). 1970. 19.95x (ISBN 0-87024-129-X). U of Miami Pr.

--New World Jewry, Fourteen Ninety-Three to Eighteen Twenty-Five: Requiem for the Forgotten. 25.00x (ISBN 0-87068-277-6). Ktav.

Liederbach, Clarence A. America's Thousand Bishops: From 1513 to 1974, from Abramowicz to Zuroweste. LC 73-94081. 80p. 1974. pap. 3.50 (ISBN 0-913228-09-5). R J Liederbach.

--Canada's Bishops: Sixteen Fifty-Eight to Nineteen Seventy-Five. LC 73-94082. 1976. pap. 2.95 (ISBN 0-913228-10-9). R J Liederbach.

--Mexico's Bishops: From Fifteen Twenty-eight to Nineteen Seventy-six from Abad to Zumarraga. LC 76-29279. 80p. 1977. pap. 2.95 (ISBN 0-913228-18-4). R J Liederbach.

Lief, Nina R. The First Year of Life: A Curriculum for Parenting Information. 362p. 21.95 (ISBN 0-686-86720-3). Sadlier.

Liefeld, Walter L. New Testament Exposition: From Text to Sermon. 176p. 1984. 11.95 (ISBN 0-310-45910-9, 12607P). Zondervan.

Liem, Ann. Jacob Boehme: Insights into the Challenge of Evil. LC 77-79823. 32p. (Orig.). 1977. pap. 2.50x (ISBN 0-87574-214-9). Pendle Hill.

Lienhard, Joseph T. Ministry. (Message of the Fathers of the Church Ser.: Vol. 8). 15.00 (ISBN 0-89453-348-7); pap. 7.95 (ISBN 0-89453-320-7). M Glazier.

Lienhard, M. The Origins & Characteristics of Anabaptism. (International Archives of the History of Ideas Ser: No. 87). 1977. lib. bdg. 53.00 (ISBN 90-247-1896-1, Pub. by Martinus Nijhoff Netherlands). Kluwer Academic.

Lienhard, Marc. Luther: Witness to Jesus Christ: Stages & Themes of the Reformer's Christology. Robertson, Edwin H., tr. LC 81-52285. 432p. 1982. text ed. 24.95 (ISBN 0-8066-1917-1, 10-4149). Augsburg.

Lienhardt, Godfrey. Divinity & Experience: The Religion of the Dinka. 1961. 45.00x (ISBN 0-19-823119-9). Oxford U Pr.

Lierde, Peter C. Van see Van Lierde, Peter C.

Lietzmann, Hans. Geschichte der Alten Kirche, 4 vols. in 1. 1220p. 1975. Repr. 79.20x (ISBN 3-11-004625-3). De Gruyter.

Lieu, Judith. The Second & Third Epistles of John. 280p. 1987. 19.95 (ISBN 0-567-09443-X, Pub. by T & T Clark Ltd UK). Fortress.

Lieu, Samuel N. Manichaeism in the Later Roman Empire & Medieval China. LC 84-26093. 240p. 1985. 54.00 (ISBN 0-7190-1088-8, Pub. by Manchester Univ Pr). Longwood Pub Group.

Lievano, Franscisco, tr. see Bennett, Dennis & Bennett, Rita.

Lievano, M. Francisco, tr. see Cho, Paul Y. & Manzano, R. Whitney.

Lievano, M. Francisco, tr. see Foster, Richard.

Lievano, M. Francisco, tr. see Ogilvie, Lloyd J.

Liffring-Zug, Joan, ed. & illus. see McDonald, Julie J.

Liffring-Zug, Joan, et al, eds. see McDonald, Julie J.

Lifton, Robert J. The Future of Immortality: And Other Essays for a Nuclear Age. LC 86-47763. 368p. 1987. 21.95 (ISBN 0-465-02597-8). Basic.

--The Nazi Doctors: Medical Killing & the Psychology of Genocide. LC 85-73874. 576p. 1986. 19.95 (ISBN 0-465-04904-4). Basic.

Lifton, Robert J. & Humphrey, Nicholas, eds. In a Dark Time. LC 84-10816. 154p. (Orig.). 1984. 15.00 (ISBN 0-674-44538-4); pap. 5.95 (ISBN 0-674-44539-2). Harvard U Pr.

Ligeti, L., ed. Tibetan & Buddhist Studies Commemorating the Two Hundreth Anniversary of the Birth of Alexander Csoma de Koros, 2 vols. (Bibliotheca Orientalis Hungarica: No. 29). 827p. 1984. Set. text ed. 115.00x (ISBN 963-05-3573-4, Pub. by Akademiai Kiado Hungary). Vol. 1 (ISBN 963-05-3902-0). Vol. 2 (ISBN 963-05-3903-9). Humanities.

Ligeti, Louis. Proceedings of the Cosma de Koros Memorial Symposium. 586p. 1978. 142.50x (ISBN 0-569-08468-7, Pub. by Collets (UK)). State Mutual Bk.

--Tibetan & Buddhist Studies Commemorating the 200th Anniversary of the Birth of Alexander Csoma de Koros, 2 vols. 388p. 1984. 350.00x (ISBN 0-569-08826-7, Pub. by Collets (UK)). State Mutual Bk.

Light, Mary. God: Incidences or Divine Providence. 1975. pap. 1.00 (ISBN 0-910924-69-4). Macalester.

--God's Guidance at Dawn. pap. 1.00 (ISBN 0-910924-68-6). Macalester.

--Joy of the Lord. pap. 0.50 (ISBN 0-910924-67-8). Macalester.

--Rays of Light. pap. 1.00 (ISBN 0-910924-59-7). Macalester.

--Rejoice & Be Exceeding Glad. pap. 1.00 (ISBN 0-910924-60-0). Macalester.

--Signs & Wonders. 1968. pap. 1.00 (ISBN 0-910924-66-X). Macalester.

Lightfoot, J. B. Apostolic Fathers. (Twin Brooks Ser). pap. 7.95 (ISBN 0-8010-5514-8). Baker Bk.

--Biblical Essays. (Canterbury Books Ser.). 1979. pap. 8.95 (ISBN 0-8010-5586-5). Baker Bk.

--The Christian Ministry. LC 83-62042. 120p. 1983. pap. 8.95 (ISBN 0-8192-1331-4). Morehouse.

--Commentaries on Galatians, Philippians, Colossians & Philemon, 3 vols. 1208p. 1981. 39.95 (ISBN 0-913573-02-7). Hendrickson MA.

--Notes on Epistles of Saint Paul. Harmer, J. R., ed. (Thornapple Commentaries Ser.). 345p. 1980. pap. 8.95 (ISBN 0-8010-5602-0). Baker Bk.

Lightfoot, J. B., ed. The Apostolic Fathers. (Twin Brooks Ser.). 584p. 1984. pap. 15.95 (ISBN 0-8010-5627-6). Baker Bk.

Lightfoot, J. B., ed. see Mansel, Henry L.

Lightfoot, J. D., tr. see Ignatius, Saint.

Lightfoot, Neil R. How We Got the Bible. 1962. 7.95 (ISBN 0-8010-5502-4). Baker Bk.

--How We Got the Bible. rev. ed. (Way of Life Ser.). 95p. 1986. pap. 3.95. Abilene Christ U.

--How We Got the Bible. rev. ed. 1987. price not set (ISBN 0-8010-5644-6). Baker Bk.

--Jesus Christ Today. LC 76-42590. 360p. 1976. pap. 8.95 (ISBN 0-8010-5604-7). Baker Bk.

--Parables of Jesus, 2 vols. (Way of Life Ser.). 1986. pap. 3.95 ea. Vol. 1, 95p; Vol. 2, 95p. Abilene Christ U.

--The Role of Women: New Testament Perspectives. (Orig.). 1978. pap. 2.95 (ISBN 0-931118-00-X). Student Assn.

Lightley, John W. Jewish Sects & Parties in the Time of Jesus. 1980. lib. bdg. 75.00 (ISBN 0-8490-3150-8). Gordon Pr.

Lightman, Bernard. The Origins of Agnosticism: Victorian Unbelief & the Limits of Knowledge. LC 86-46288. 272p. 1987. text ed. 29.50x (ISBN 0-8018-3375-2). Johns Hopkins.

Lightman, Bernard V., jt. auth. see Eisen, Sydney.

Lightman, Sidney, ed. The Jewish Travel Guide, 1986. (Illus.). 296p. (Orig.). 1986. pap. 9.25 (ISBN 0-317-39976-4, Pub. by Jewish Chronicle Pubns England). Hermon.

Lightner, Robert P. The Death Christ Died. LC 67-30992. 1975. pap. 3.25 (ISBN 0-87227-012-2). Reg Baptist.

--Evangelical Theology. 1984. 15.95 (ISBN 0-8010-5628-4). Baker Bk.

--Heaven for Those Who Can't Believe. LC 76-50303. 1977. pap. 1.95 (ISBN 0-87227-035-1). Reg Baptist.

--James: Apostle of Practical Christianity. LC 81-70775. (The Chosen Messengers Ser.). 128p. (Orig.). 1982. pap. text ed. 3.50 (ISBN 0-89636-079-2). Accent Bks.

--Neoevangelicalism Today. LC 78-11426. (Illus.). 1979. pap. 3.95 (ISBN 0-87227-067-X). Reg Baptist.

--Speaking in Tongues & Divine Healing. LC 65-5805. 1978. pap. 1.95 (ISBN 0-87227-059-9). Reg Baptist.

Lighton, Merle. Addict to Yearning: Inspirational Philosophy & Religion. 1952. 5.00 (ISBN 0-910892-00-8, 910892). Lighton Pubns.

Lightstone, Jack N. The Commerce of the Sacred. LC 83-20180. (Brown Judaic Ser.). 234p. 1984. pap. 18.75 (ISBN 0-89130-664-1, 14 00 59). Scholars Pr GA.

Ligon, Ernest M. Christian Social Potential: Junior High Unit. (A Research Curriculum for Character Education Ser.). 1978. lesson bk. 2.00 (ISBN 0-915744-12-0); junior high unit plan 0.75 (ISBN 0-915744-14-7); junior high home assignment sheets 0.75 (ISBN 0-915744-13-9). Character Res.

--Psychology of Christian Personality. LC 35-22951. 1975. 7.00 (ISBN 0-915744-00-7); pap. 4.00 (ISBN 0-915744-01-5). Character Res.

Ligon, Ernest M. & Character Research Project Staff. Vicarious Sacrifice. Incl. Junior High Unit-Lesson Book. 2.00 (ISBN 0-915744-15-5); Junior High Unit-PLAN. 0.75 (ISBN 0-915744-17-1); Junior High Unit-Home Assignment Sheets. 0.75 (ISBN 0-915744-16-3). (Research Curriculum for Character Education Ser.). (Illus.). 1979. Character Res.

Liguori, Alfonso M. & Redemptorists. The Mission-Book of the Congregation of the Most Holy Redeemer. 38.50 (ISBN 0-405-10843-5, 11848). Ayer Co Pubs.

Liguori, Alphonse. The Blessed Virgin Mary: Excerpt from the Glories of Mary. 96p. 1974. pap. 3.00 (ISBN 0-89555-177-2). TAN Bks Pubs.

Liguori, Alphonse De see De Liguori, Alphonse.

Liguori, Alphonsus. Praying to God As a Friend. 48p. 1987. pap. text ed. 1.50 (ISBN 0-89243-264-0). Liguori Pubns.

--Preparation for Death. abr. ed. 1982. pap. 5.00 (ISBN 0-89555-174-8). TAN Bks Pubs.

--To Love Christ Jesus. 96p. 1987. pap. 2.95 (ISBN 0-89243-262-4). Liguori Pubns.

Liguori, Alphonsus de. Sermons of St. Alphonsus Liguori for All the Sundays of the Year. LC 82-50894. 408p. 1982. pap. 10.00 (ISBN 0-89555-193-4). TAN Bks Pubs.

Liguori, St. Alphonsus. How to Face Death Without Fear. 1976. pap. 1.95 (ISBN 0-89243-029-X, 28376). Liguori Pubns.

--Love Is Prayer - Prayer Is Love. LC 72-97592. 1973. pap. 2.95 (ISBN 0-89243-047-8, 41500). Liguori Pubns.

Lijegren, Sten. Studies in Milton. LC 67-30816. (Studies in Milton, No. 22). 1969. Repr. of 1918 ed. lib. bdg. 75.00x (ISBN 0-8383-0718-3). Haskell.

Likoudis, James & Whitehead, K. D. The Pope, the Council, & the Mass. 1981. 13.95 (ISBN 0-8158-0400-8). Chris Mass.

Lilienthal, Alfred M. The Zionist Connection II. 1983. pap. 10.95 (ISBN 0-949667-33-1). Concord Bks.

--The Zionist Connection II: What Price Peace? Rev. ed. LC 82-61135. 904p. 1982. 11.95 (ISBN 0-686-43256-8); pap. 9.95. North American Inc.

Li Lin-Tsan. Studies in Mo-So Tribal Stories. (Asian Folklore & Social Life Monograph: No. 3). (Chinese.). 1970. 17.00 (ISBN 0-89986-006-0). Oriental Bk Store.

Lilipaly, Hendrik Th. Experiences with God & His Messengers: The Key to God's Kingdom. 1980. 6.00 (ISBN 0-682-49506-9). Exposition Pr FL.

Liljegren, Sten B. Studies in Milton. 1918. lib. bdg. 20.00 (ISBN 0-8414-5707-7). Folcroft.

Lilker, Shalom. Kibbutz Judaism: A New Tradition in the Making. LC 80-70886. (Norwood Editions, Kibbutz, Cooperative Societies, & Alternative Social Policy Bk.: Vol. 7). 240p. 1982. 14.95 (ISBN 0-8453-4740-3, Cornwall Bks). Assoc Univ Prs.

--Kibbutz Judaism: A New Tradition in the Making. (Kibbutz, Cooperative Society, & Alternative Social Policy Ser.: Vol. 7). 264p. 1982. lib. bdg. 19.50 (ISBN 0-8482-4876-7). Norwood Edns.

Lillevold, Joani, jt. auth. see Thompson, Paul M.

Lilley, Alfred L. Modernism: A Record & Review. LC 75-102575. 1970. Repr. of 1908 ed. 25.00x (ISBN 0-8046-0735-4, Pub. by Kennikat). Assoc Faculty Pr.

Lillich, Meredith, et al, eds. Studies in Cistercian Art & Architecture, I. (Cistercian Studies: No. 66). (Illus., Orig.). 1982. pap. 12.95 (ISBN 0-87907-866-9). Cistercian Pubns.

Lillich, Meredith P. The Stained Glass of Saint-Pere de Chartres. LC 77-13926. (Illus.). 1978. 50.00x (ISBN 0-8195-5023-X). Wesleyan U Pr.

Lillich, Meredith P., ed. Studies in Cistercian Art & Architecture, II. (Cistercian Studies: No. 69). (Illus.). pap. 14.95 (ISBN 0-87907-869-3). Cistercian Pubns.

--Studies in Cistercian Art & Architecture, III. (Cistercian Studies: No. 89). (Orig.). 1987. pap. write for info. (ISBN 0-87907-889-8). Cistercian Pubns.

Lillie, Arthur. Buddha & Buddhism. LC 76-100573. 1975. 11.25x (ISBN 0-89684-372-6). Orient Bk Dist.

--The Influence of Buddhism on Primitive Christianity. LC 78-70094. 1980. Repr. of 1893 ed. 58.75 (ISBN 0-404-17343-8). AMS Pr.

Lillie, John. Lectures on the First & Second Epistles of Peter. 1978. 19.75 (ISBN 0-86524-116-3, 7102). Klock & Klock.

Lilly, Sr. Catherine M., ed. see Ramm, Charles A.

Lilly, Fred. Word Gifts: Keys to Charismatic Power. 100p. (Orig.). 1984. pap. 2.95 (ISBN 0-89283-182-0). Servant.

Lilly, Fred, jt. auth. see Bertolucci, John.

Lilly, Fred, jt. auth. see Osburn, Charlie.

Lilly, Gene. God Is Calling His People to Forgiveness. 1977. pap. 3.95 (ISBN 0-917726-15-4). Hunter Bks.

Lilly, W. S., ed. A Newman Anthology. 356p. 1981. 25.00x (ISBN 0-234-77060-0, Pub. by Dobson Bks England). State Mutual Bk.

Lilly, W. S., ed. see Newman, Cardinal John H.

Lima, Tiago. Dios, Tu y la Escuela. Diaz, Alfredo, tr. (Dios, Tu y La Vida). 32p. (Orig.). 1974. pap. 0.95 (ISBN 0-311-46200-6). Casa Bautista.

Limardo, Miguel. Luces Encendidas Para Cada Dia. 376p. 1983. Repr. of 1981 ed. 5.50 (ISBN 0-311-40038-8). Casa Bautista.

Limb, Akio. Because of Jesus. Thomas, J. D., ed. (Twentieth Century Sermons Ser). 1972. 11.95 (ISBN 0-89112-307-5, Bibl Res Pr). Abilene Christ U.

Limbert, Paul M. Denominational Policies in the Support & Supervision of Higher Education. LC 75-176994. (Columbia University. Teachers College. Contributions to Education: No. 378). Repr. of 1929 ed. 22.50 (ISBN 0-404-55378-8). AMS Pr.

Limburg, James. Old Stories for a New Time. LC 82-49019. 127p. 1983. pap. 8.95 (ISBN 0-8042-0148-X). John Knox.

--The Prophets & the Powerless. LC 76-12397. 1976. pap. 6.95 (ISBN 0-8042-0156-0). John Knox.

--Psalms for Sojourners. LC 86-2621. (Illus.). 112p. (Orig.). 1986. pap. 5.95 (ISBN 0-8066-2206-7, 10-5306). Augsburg.

Lin, Paul J. A Translation of Lao Tzu's "Tao Te Ching" & Wang Pi's "Commentary.". (Michigan Monographs in Chinese Studies: No. 30). 232p. (Orig.). 1977. pap. 8.50 (ISBN 0-89264-030-8). U of Mich Ctr Chinese.

Lin, Robert H. The Taiping Revolution: A Failure of Two Missions. 1979. pap. text ed. 10.75 (ISBN 0-8191-0734-4). U Pr of Amer.

Linam, Gail. Celebrate Christmas. 1982. pap. 2.95 (ISBN 0-8054-9305-0, 4293-05). Broadman.
--Celebrate Easter. LC 84-12692. 1985. pap. 2.95 (ISBN 0-8054-9306-9). Broadman.
--God's People: A Book of Children's Sermons. LC 85-25736. (Orig.). 1986. pap. 4.95 (ISBN 0-8054-4928-0). Broadman.
--God's Spring Gifts. (Illus., Orig.). 1980. pap. 3.25 (ISBN 0-8054-4157-3, 4142-57). Broadman.
--God's Winter Gifts. (Illus.). 1980. pap. 3.25 (ISBN 0-8054-4158-1, 4142-58). Broadman.
Linant De Bellefonds, Y. Traite De Droit Musulman Compare: Filiation - Incapacites - Liberalites Entre Vifs, Tome 3. (Recherches Mediterraneennes: No. 9). 1973. pap. 34.40x (ISBN 90-2797-199-4). Mouton.
Lincoln, Andrew T. Paradise Now & Not Yet. LC 80-41024. (Society for the New Testament Studies Monographs: No. 43). 240p. 1981. 44.50 (ISBN 0-521-22944-8). Cambridge U Pr.
Lincoln, Bruce. Priests, Warriors & Cattle: A Study in the Ecology of Religions. LC 78-68826. (Hermeneutics: Studies in the History of Religions Ser.). 240p. 1981. 37.95x (ISBN 0-520-03880-0). U of Cal Pr.
Lincoln, Bruce, ed. Religion, Rebellion, Revolution: An Interdisciplinary & Cross-Cultural Collection of Essays. LC 85-1992. 312p. 1985. 27.50 (ISBN 0-312-67061-3). St Martin.
Lincoln, C. Eric. Race, Religion, & the Continuing American Dilemma. 304p. 1984. 17.95 (ISBN 0-8090-8016-8). Hill & Wang.
Lincoln, C. Eric, jt. auth. see Frazier, E. Franklin.
Lincoln, Eric. Race, Religion, & the Continuing American Dilemma. (American Century Ser.). 304p. 1985. 17.95 (ISBN 0-8090-8016-8). FS&G.
Lincoln, Victoria. Teresa: A Woman; A Biography of Teresa of Avila. Rivers, Elias & De Nicolas, Antonio T., eds. LC 84-8561. (Series in Cultural Perspectives). 440p. 1984. 44.50x (ISBN 0-87395-936-1); pap. 16.95 (ISBN 0-87395-937-X). State U NY Pr.
Lincoln, William C. Personal Bible Study. LC 75-2345. 160p. 1975. pap. 4.95 (ISBN 0-87123-458-0, 210458). Bethany Hse.
Lind, Frank. How to Understand the Tarot. (Paths to Inner Power Ser). 1971. pap. 3.50 (ISBN 0-87728-098-3). Weiser.
Lind, Millard. Respuesta a La Guerra. Orig. Title: Answer to War. 188p. 1963. pap. 1.50x (ISBN 0-8361-1149-4). Herald Pr.
Lind, Millard C. Yahweh Is a Warrior. LC 80-16038. (Christian Peace Shelf Ser.). 240p. 1980. pap. 11.95x (ISBN 0-8361-1233-4). Herald Pr.
Lind, Miriam S. No Crying He Makes. LC 78-181580. 96p. 1972. pap. 1.50 (ISBN 0-8361-1321-7). Herald Pr.
Lindars, B. & Smalley, S. S. Christ & Spirit in the New Testament. LC 72-91367. 300p. 1974. 72.50 (ISBN 0-521-20148-9). Cambridge U Pr.
Lindars, Barnabas. Jesus, Son of Man. 256p. (Orig.). 1984. pap. 9.95 (ISBN 0-8028-0022-X). Eerdmans.
Lindbeck, George A. The Nature of Doctrine: Religion & Theology in a Postliberal Age. LC 83-27332. 142p. 1984. 16.95 (ISBN 0-664-21829-6); pap. 9.95 (ISBN 0-664-24618-4). Westminster.
Lindberg, Carter. The Third Reformation: Charismatic Movements & the Lutheran Tradition. LC 83-11371. x, 346p. 1983. 24.95 (ISBN 0-86554-075-6, MUP/H83). Mercer Univ Pr.
Lindberg, Carter, ed. Piety, Politics, & Ethics: Reformation Studies in Honor of George Wolfgang Forell. (Sixteenth Century Essays & Studies: Vol. III). (Illus.). 200p. 1984. smythe sewn 25.00x (ISBN 0-940474-03-4). Sixteenth Cent.
Lindberg, Conrad. The Middle English Bible: Prefatory Epistles of St. Jerome. 172p. 1978. text ed. 19.50x. Oxford U Pr.
--The Middle English Bible: The Book of Baruch. 174p. 1986. 45.00 (ISBN 82-00-06057-8); pap. 23.00x. Oxford U Pr.
Lindberg, David C., ed. John Pecham: Tractatus De Perspectiva. (Text Ser). 1972. 13.00 (ISBN 0-686-11561-9). Franciscan Inst.
Lindberg, Duane R. Men of the Cloth & the Social-Cultural Fabric of the Norwegian Ethnic Community in North Dakota. Cordasco, Francesco, ed. LC 80-877. (American Ethnic Groups Ser.). 1981. lib. bdg. 38.00x (ISBN 0-405-13438-X). Ayer Co Pubs.
Lindblom, J. Prophecy in Ancient Israel. LC 63-907. 480p. 1962. 17.95 (ISBN 0-8006-0916-6, 1-916). Fortress.
Lindblom, Johannes. Prophecy in Ancient Israel. LC 63-907. pap. 120.00 (2029298). Bks Demand UMI.
Lindemann, Andreas, jt. auth. see Conzelmann, Hans.
Lindemann, Emil R. Jesus' Revelation of What Is True. Wegener, Wilfried W., ed. 154p. (Orig.). 1983. pap. text ed. 4.00 (ISBN 0-9612192-0-3). E R Lindemann.
Linden, Franz. Sozialismus und Religion. Repr. of 1932 ed. 16.00 (ISBN 0-384-32740-0). Johnson Repr.
Linden, Ian. Emirs & Evangelicals. 1986. 29.50x (ISBN 0-7146-3146-9, BHA-03146, F Cass Co). Biblio Dist.
Linden, Ian & Linden, Jane. Catholics, Peasants & Chewa Resistance in Nyasaland, 1889-1939. 1974. 38.50x (ISBN 0-520-02500-8). U of Cal Pr.
--Church & Revolution in Rwanda. LC 76-58329. 295p. 1977. text ed. 39.50x (ISBN 0-8419-0305-0, Africana). Holmes & Meier.
Linden, Ingemar. The Last Trump. (IC-Studies in the Intercultural History of Christianity: Vol. 17). 372p. 1978. pap. 34.10 (ISBN 3-261-02370-8). P Lang Pubs.
Linden, Jane, jt. auth. see Linden, Ian.
Linden, Nico ter see Ter Linden, Nico.
Linden, Philip Van. The Gospel of Mark. 1976. 1.75 (ISBN 0-8199-0630-1). Franciscan Herald.
--Knowing Christ Through Mark's Gospel. 1977. pap. 1.25 (ISBN 0-8199-0727-8). Franciscan Herald.
Lindenbaum, Peter. Changing Landscapes: Anti-Pastoral Sentiment in the English Renaissance. LC 85-24546. 264p. 1986. 27.50x (ISBN 0-8203-0835-8). U of GA Pr.
Lindenberger, James M. The Aramaic Proverbs of Ahiqar. LC 82-18000. (Near Eastern Studies). 384p. 1983. text ed. 38.00x (ISBN 0-8018-2797-3). Johns Hopkins.
Linderman, Frank B. Pretty-shield: Medicine Woman of the Crows. LC 72-3273. (Illus.). 256p. 1974. pap. 6.95 (ISBN 0-8032-5791-0, BB 580, Bison). U of Nebr Pr.
Lindey, A., jt. auth. see Ernst, M. L.
Lindgren. Teaching Bible Truths with Single Objects. 1979. 3.50 (ISBN 0-88207-036-3). Victor Bks.
Lindgren, Alvin J. Foundations for Purposeful Church Administration. LC 65-16459. 1965. 13.95 (ISBN 0-687-13339-4). Abingdon.
Lindgren, Alvin J. & Shawchuck, Norman. Let My People Go: Empowering Laity for Ministry. LC 80-16035. 144p. (Orig.). 1982. pap. 7.95 (ISBN 0-687-21377-0). Abingdon.
Lindgren, Alvin J., jt. auth. see Shawchuck, Norman.
Lindgren, Bruce, jt. auth. see Judd, Peter.
Lindhardt, Jan. Martin Luther: Knowledge and Mediation in the Renaissance. (Texts and Studies in Religion: Vol. 29). 270p. lib. bdg. 49.95 (ISBN 0-88946-817-6). E Mellen.
Lindl, Ernest. Das Priester und Beamtentum der Altbabylonischen Kontrakte. Repr. of 1913 ed. 37.00 (ISBN 0-384-32780-X). Johnson Repr.
Lindner, Eileen W., et al. When Churches Mind the Children: A Study of Day Care in Local Parishes. LC 83-22545. 192p. (Orig.). 1983. pap. 10.00 (ISBN 0-931114-23-3). High-Scope.
Lindo, E. H., tr. see Ben-Israel, Manasseh.
Lindo, Elias H. History of the Jews of Spain & Portugal. LC 71-112055. (Research & Source Works Ser: No. 4). (Illus.). 1970. Repr. of 1848 ed. 32.50 (ISBN 0-8337-2109-7). B Franklin.
Lindow, John. Myths & Legends of the Vikings. (Illus.). 1980. pap. 2.95 (ISBN 0-88388-071-7). Bellerophon Bks.
--Scandinavian Mythology: An Annotated Bibliography. LC 82-49170. (Folklore Ser.). 200p. 1986. lib. bdg. 25.00 (ISBN 0-8240-9173-6). Garland Pub.
Lindsay. My Diary Secrets by Mrs. Lindsay. 3.95 (ISBN 0-89985-021-9). Christ Nations.
Lindsay, Alexander D. Religion, Science, & Society in the Modern World. facsimile ed. LC 70-37847. (Essay Index Reprint Ser). Repr. of 1943 ed. 12.00 (ISBN 0-8369-2604-8). Ayer Co Pubs.
Lindsay, Gordon. Abraham, Friend of God. (Old Testament Ser.). 1.25 (ISBN 0-89985-126-6). Christ Nations.
--Acts in Action, 5 vols. (Book of Acts Ser.). 1.25 ea. Christ Nations.
--Acts in Action, Christs Great Commission. (Acts in Action Ser.: Vol. 1). pap. 1.25 (ISBN 0-89985-962-3). Christ Nations.
--Amazing Discoveries in the Words of Jesus. 4.50 (ISBN 0-89985-112-6). Christ Nations.
--America, Russia, & the Antichrist, Vol. 4. (Daniel Ser.). 0.95 (ISBN 0-89985-051-0). Christ Nations.
--The Antichrist & His Forerunner. (End of the Age Ser.: Vol. 2). 1.25 (ISBN 0-89985-068-5). Christ Nations.
--The Antichrist's Rise to Power. (End of the Age Ser.: Vol. 3). 1.25 (ISBN 0-89985-069-3). Christ Nations.
--Apostles, Prophets & Governments. 1.50 (ISBN 0-89985-121-5). Christ Nations.
--Armageddon. (Revelation Ser.). 1.25 (ISBN 0-89985-047-2). Christ Nations.
--The Art of Successful Praying. (School of Prayer Ser.). 1.25 (ISBN 0-89985-079-0). Christ Nations.
--The Beast from the Bottomless Pit. (Revelation Ser.). 1.25 (ISBN 0-89985-043-X). Christ Nations.
--Bible Days Are Here Again. pap. 4.00 (ISBN 0-89985-194-0). Christ Nations.
--The Bible Is a Scientific Book. 1.50 (ISBN 0-89985-117-7). Christ Nations.
--The Bible Secret of Divine Health. (Divine Healing & Health Ser.). 1.25 (ISBN 0-89985-023-5). Christ Nations.
--Charismatic Ministry. 3.25 (ISBN 0-89985-122-3). Christ Nations.
--Christ the Great Physician. (Divine Healing & Health Ser.). 1.25 (ISBN 0-89985-024-3). Christ Nations.
--A Citizen of Two Worlds. 1.50 (ISBN 0-89985-000-6). Christ Nations.
--The Creation. (Old Testament Ser.). 1.25 (ISBN 0-89985-123-1). Christ Nations.
--David Comes into the Kingdom. (Old Testament Ser.). 1.25 (ISBN 0-89985-142-8). Christ Nations.
--David Reaping the Whirlwind. (Old Testament Ser.). 1.25 (ISBN 0-89985-143-6). Christ Nations.
--Death & Resurrection of Christ. (Life of Christ Ser.: Vol. 3). (Span.). 1.50 (ISBN 0-89985-983-6). Christ Nations.
--Death & the Hereafter. (Sorcery & Spirit World Ser.). 1.25 (ISBN 0-89985-096-0). Christ Nations.
--The Death Cheaters. (Sorcery & Spirit World Ser.). 1.25 (ISBN 0-89985-081-2). Christ Nations.
--The Decline & Fall of Israel & Judah. (Old Testament Ser.). 1.25 (ISBN 0-89985-153-3). Christ Nations.
--Did Politics Influence Jesus? 86p. (Orig.). 1982. pap. 2.50 (ISBN 0-89985-113-4, 1002). Christ Nations.
--Difficult Questions About the Bible Answered. 1.25 (ISBN 0-89985-114-2). Christ Nations.
--The Early Life of David. (Old Testament Ser.). 1.25 (ISBN 0-89985-141-X). Christ Nations.
--Elijah: The Man Who Did Not Die. (Old Testament Ser.). 1.25 (ISBN 0-89985-149-5). Christ Nations.
--Elijah: The Whirlwind Prophet. (Old Testament Ser.). 1.25 (ISBN 0-89985-148-7). Christ Nations.
--Elisha-Prophet of the Supernatural. (Old Testament Ser.). 1.25 (ISBN 0-89985-151-7). Christ Nations.
--Elisha-The Man Who Received the Double Portion. (Old Testament Ser.). 1.25 (ISBN 0-89985-150-9). Christ Nations.
--Enoch & Noah, Patriarchs of the Deluge. (Old Testament Ser.). 1.25 (ISBN 0-89985-125-8). Christ Nations.
--Evolution-The Incredible Hoax. 1.50 (ISBN 0-89985-115-0). Christ Nations.
--Ezra & Nehemiah & the Return from Babylon. (Old Testament Ser.). 1.25 (ISBN 0-89985-154-1). Christ Nations.
--False Christs, False Prophets. (Prophecy Ser.). 1.95 (ISBN 0-89985-054-5). Christ Nations.
--Fire over the Holy Land. 1.25 (ISBN 0-89985-185-1). Christ Nations.
--The Forgotten Miracles of the Bible. (Miracles in the Bible Ser.: Vol. 6). 0.95 (ISBN 0-89985-183-5). Christ Nations.
--Forty Signs of the Soon Coming of Christ. (Prophecy Ser.). 1.95 (ISBN 0-89985-055-3). Christ Nations.
--Four Hundred & Fifty-Year Judgment Cycles. (Miracles in the Bible Ser.: Vol. 5). 0.95 (ISBN 0-89985-182-7). Christ Nations.
--The Four Hundred Silent Years. (Old Testament Ser.). 1.25 (ISBN 0-89985-158-4). Christ Nations.
--Gideon & the Early Judges. (Old Testament Ser.). 1.25 (ISBN 0-89985-135-5). Christ Nations.
--Gifts of the Spirit, 4 vols. 2.50 ea. Vol. 1 (ISBN 0-89985-195-9). Vol. 2 (ISBN 0-89985-196-7). Vol. 3 (ISBN 0-89985-197-5). Vol. 4 (ISBN 0-89985-199-1). Christ Nations.
--God's Master Key to Prosperity. 1.95 (ISBN 0-89985-001-4). Christ Nations.
--God's Plan of the Ages. (Prophecy Ser.). 5.00 (ISBN 0-89985-056-1). Christ Nations.
--God's Twentieth Century Barnabas: The Gordon Lindsay Story. Christ for the Nations, ed. 284p. (Orig.). 1982. pap. 3.95 (ISBN 0-89985-002-2, 104). Christ Nations.
--The Great Day of the Lord. (Revelation Ser.). 1.25 (ISBN 0-89985-037-5). Christ Nations.
--The Great Judgment Throne & the Seven Seals. (Revelation Ser.). 1.25 (ISBN 0-89985-036-7). Christ Nations.
--The Great Tribulation. (End of the Age Ser.: Vol. 4). 1.50 (ISBN 0-89985-070-7). Christ Nations.
--The Great Trumpets & the Vial Judgments. (End of the Age Ser.: Vol. 6). 1.25 (ISBN 0-89985-072-3). Christ Nations.
--The Great White Throne. (End of the Age Ser.: Vol. 9). 1.25 (ISBN 0-89985-075-8). Christ Nations.
--Hades-Abode of the Unrighteous Dead. (Sorcery & Spirit World Ser.). 1.25 (ISBN 0-89985-082-0). Christ Nations.
--The House the Lord Built. 1.00 (ISBN 0-89985-015-4). Christ Nations.
--How to Be Enriched by Giving. 1.75 (ISBN 0-89985-012-X). Christ Nations.
--How to Find the Perfect Will of God. 1.25 (ISBN 0-89985-003-0). Christ Nations.
--How You Can Be Healed. (Divine Healing & Health Ser.). 1.25 (ISBN 0-89985-026-X). Christ Nations.
--How You Can Have Divine Health. (Divine Healing & Health Ser.). 1.25 (ISBN 0-89985-027-8). Christ Nations.
--Increase Your Prayer Power Tenfold. (School of Prayer Ser.). 1.25 (ISBN 0-89985-080-4). Christ Nations.
--Isaac & Rebekah. (Old Testament Ser.). 1.25 (ISBN 0-89985-127-4). Christ Nations.
--Isaiah & Jeremiah. (Old Testament Ser.). 1.25 (ISBN 0-89985-155-X). Christ Nations.
--Israel, the False Prophet & the Two Witnesses, Vol. 5. (End of the Age Ser.). 1.25 (ISBN 0-89985-071-5). Christ Nations.
--Israel's Forty-Eight Signs of Christ Return. 2.25 (ISBN 0-89985-186-X). Christ Nations.
--It's Sooner Than You Think. (Prophecy Ser.). 1.25 (ISBN 0-89985-057-X). Christ Nations.
--Jacob & His Son, Joseph. (Old Testament Ser.). 1.25 (ISBN 0-89985-129-0). Christ Nations.
--Jacob, The Supplanter Who Became a Prince with God. (Old Testament Ser.). 1.25 (ISBN 0-89985-128-2). Christ Nations.
--Jephthah & Samson. (Old Testament Ser.). 1.25 (ISBN 0-89985-136-3). Christ Nations.
--John Alexander Dowie: A Life of Tragedies & Triumphs. 1980. 4.95 (ISBN 0-89985-985-2). Christ Nations.
--John G. Lake: Apostle to Africa. 1.75 (ISBN 0-89985-011-1). Christ Nations.
--John G. Lake: Sermons on Dominion over Demons, Disease, & Death. (Divine Healing & Health Ser.). 3.50 (ISBN 0-89985-028-6). Christ Nations.
--Joseph & His Brethren. (Old Testament Ser.). 1.25 (ISBN 0-89985-130-4). Christ Nations.
--Joshua, Conqueror of Canaan. (Old Testament Ser.). 1.25 (ISBN 0-89985-134-7). Christ Nations.
--The Judgment Seat of Christ, Vol. 7. (End of the Age Ser.). 1.25 (ISBN 0-89985-073-1). Christ Nations.
--The Key to Israel's Future-The Forgotten Covenant. 1.95 (ISBN 0-89985-191-6). Christ Nations.
--The Last Days of David & His Contemporaries. (Old Testament Ser.). 1.25 (ISBN 0-89985-144-4). Christ Nations.
--Life after Death. (Sorcery & Spirit World Ser.). 3.00 (ISBN 0-89985-083-9). Christ Nations.
--Life & Teachings of Christ, Vol. 1. (Life of Christ & Parable Ser.). 238p. (Orig.). 1980. pap. 5.00 (ISBN 0-89985-967-4, 4101). Christ Nations.
--Life & Teachings of Christ, Vol. 2. (Life of Christ & Parable Ser.). 244p. (Orig.). 1980. pap. 5.00 (ISBN 0-89985-968-2). Christ Nations.
--Life & Teachings of Christ, Vol. 3. (Life of Christ & Parable Ser.). 288p. 1980. pap. 5.75 (ISBN 0-89985-969-0). Christ Nations.
--Lot & Lots Wife. (Old Testament Ser.: Vol. 4). pap. 1.25 (ISBN 0-89985-958-5). Christ Nations.
--Maria Woodworth Etter: Her Life & Ministry. 2.50 (ISBN 0-89985-022-7). Christ Nations.
--Men Who Change the World, 7 vols. 0.95 ea. Christ Nations.
--Messiah Witness-Israel's Destiny & Coming Deliverer. 0.95 (ISBN 0-89985-187-8). Christ Nations.
--The Millennium. (Revelation Ser.). 1.25 (ISBN 0-89985-048-0). Christ Nations.
--Ministry of Angels. 1.25 (ISBN 0-89985-018-9). Christ Nations.
--Ministry of Casting Out Demons, Vol. 7. (Sorcery & Spirit World Ser.). 1.25 (ISBN 0-89985-090-1). Christ Nations.
--The Minor Prophets: Hosea, Joel, Amos, Obadiah, Jonah, Micah. (Old Testament Ser.). 1.25 (ISBN 0-89985-156-8). Christ Nations.
--The Minor Prophets: Nahum, Habakkuk, Zephaniah, Haggai. Zechariah, Malachi. (Old Testament Ser.). 1.25 (ISBN 0-89985-157-6). Christ Nations.
--The Miracle of Israel. 1.95 (ISBN 0-89985-188-6). Christ Nations.
--Miracles of Christ, 2 parts, Vols. 2 & 3. (Miracles in the Bible Ser.). 0.95 ea. Vol. 2 (ISBN 0-89985-960-7). Vol. 3 (ISBN 0-89985-960-7). Christ Nations.
--The Miracles of Divine Discipline, Vol. 7. (Miracles in the Bible Ser.). 0.95 (ISBN 0-89985-184-3). Christ Nations.

--Miracles of the Apostles, Vol. 4. (Miracles in the Bible Ser.). 0.95 (ISBN 0-89985-181-9). Christ Nations.
--Moses & His Contemporaries. (Old Testament Ser.). 1.25 (ISBN 0-89985-133-9). Christ Nations.
--Moses & the Church in the Wilderness. (Old Testament Ser.). 1.25 (ISBN 0-89985-132-0). Christ Nations.
--Moses, The Deliverer. (Old Testament Ser.). 1.25 (ISBN 0-89985-131-2). Christ Nations.
--Moses the Lawgiver. (Old Testament Ser.: Vol. 10). pap. 1.25 (ISBN 0-89985-959-3). Christ Nations.
--Mystery of Jeane Dixon. (Sorcery & Spirit World Ser.). 0.95 (ISBN 0-89985-084-7). Christ Nations.
--The New Heavens & the New Earth. (Revelation Ser.). 1.25 (ISBN 0-89985-049-9). Christ Nations.
--The New John G. Lake Sermons. 1982. 1.75 (ISBN 0-686-79435-4). Christ Nations.
--Old Testament Healings. (Miracles in the Bible Ser.: Vol. 1). 0.95 (ISBN 0-89985-179-7). Christ Nations.
--One Body, One Spirit, One Lord. pap. 3.95 (ISBN 0-89985-991-7). Christ Nations.
--The One Hundred Forty-Four Thousand on Mt. Zion & the First-Fruits. (Revelation Ser.). 1.25 (ISBN 0-89985-044-8). Christ Nations.
--One in Every Other Family. 1.00 (ISBN 0-89985-016-2). Christ Nations.
--Origin of Demons & the Orders, Vol. 5. (Sorcery & Spirit World Ser.). 0.95 (ISBN 0-89985-088-X). Christ Nations.
--Out of the Dark Valley. 1.25 (ISBN 0-89985-019-7). Christ Nations.
--Parables of Christ, Vol. 1. (Span.). 1.50 (ISBN 0-89985-980-1). Christ Nations.
--Paradise-Abode of the Righteous Dead. (Sorcery & Spirit World Ser.). 1.25 (ISBN 0-89985-085-5). Christ Nations.
--Paul & Silas Evangelize Greece. (Acts in Action Ser.: Vol. 4). pap. 1.25 (ISBN 0-89985-965-8). Christ Nations.
--Paul Before the Sanhedrin. (Acts in Action Ser.: Vol. 5). pap. 1.25 (ISBN 0-89985-966-6). Christ Nations.
--Peter Escapes From Prison. (Acts in Action Ser.: Vol. 3). pap. 1.25 (ISBN 0-89985-964-X). Christ Nations.
--Prayer & Fasting. (School of Prayer Ser.). 1.75 (ISBN 0-89985-076-6). Christ Nations.
--Prayer That Moves Mountains. (School of Prayer Ser.). 2.50 (ISBN 0-89985-078-2). Christ Nations.
--Praying to Change the World, 2 vols. (School of Prayer Ser.). 2.95 ea. Vol. 1 (ISBN 0-89985-956-9). Vol. 2 (ISBN 0-89985-957-7). Christ Nations.
--Prophecies of Daniel. (Daniel Ser.). 4.00 (ISBN 0-89985-052-9). Christ Nations.
--The Rapture. (Prophecy Ser.). 1.50 (ISBN 0-89985-063-4). Christ Nations.
--The Rapture & the Second Coming of Christ. (Revelation Ser.). 1.25 (ISBN 0-89985-041-3). Christ Nations.
--The Real Reason Why Christians Are Sick. (Divine Healing & Health Ser.). 3.50 (ISBN 0-89985-029-4). Christ Nations.
--Red China in Prophecy. (Prophecy Ser.). 2.25 (ISBN 0-89985-059-6). Christ Nations.
--The Revolution & After. (Old Testament Ser.). 1.25 (ISBN 0-89985-152-5). Christ Nations.
--The Rise of the Antichrist. (Revelation Ser.). 1.25 (ISBN 0-89985-042-1). Christ Nations.
--Ruth, The Gleaner, & the Boy Samuel. (Old Testament Ser.). 1.25 (ISBN 0-89985-137-1). Christ Nations.
--Samuel, the Prophet. (Old Testament Ser.). 1.25 (ISBN 0-89985-138-X). Christ Nations.
--Satan, Fallen Angels & Demons. (Satan Ser.: Vol. 2). pap. 1.25 (ISBN 0-89985-954-2). Christ Nations.
--Satan, Rebellion & Fall, 3 vols. (Sorcery & Spirit World Ser.: Vol. 3). 1.25 ea. (ISBN 0-89985-953-4). Christ Nations.
--Satan's Demon Manifestations & Delusions. (Satan Ser.: Vol. 3). pap. 1.25 (ISBN 0-89985-955-0). Christ Nations.
--Saul & Jonathan. (Old Testament Ser.). 1.25 (ISBN 0-89985-140-1). Christ Nations.
--Saul, Israel's First King. (Old Testament Ser.). 1.25 (ISBN 0-89985-139-8). Christ Nations.
--The Scarlet Sin, Vol. 4. (Sorcery & Spirit World Ser.). 3.00 (ISBN 0-89985-087-1). Christ Nations.
--Scenes Beyond the Grave. (Sorcery & Spirit World Ser.). 2.95 (ISBN 0-89985-091-X). Christ Nations.
--The Second Coming of Christ. (Prophecy Ser.). 0.95 (ISBN 0-89985-061-8). Christ Nations.
--The Sermons of John Alexander Dowie. (Champion of the Faith Ser.). 2.50 (ISBN 0-89985-193-2). Christ Nations.
--The Seven Churches of Prophecy, 2 vols. (Revelation Ser.). 1.25 ea. Vol. 1 (ISBN 0-89985-977-1). Vol. 2 (ISBN 0-89985-978-X). Christ Nations.
--Seven Keys to Triumphant Christian Living. 1.25 (ISBN 0-89985-006-5). Christ Nations.
--The Seventh Day. 1.25 (ISBN 0-89985-116-9). Christ Nations.
--Should Christians Attend Movies? 0.95 (ISBN 0-89985-007-3). Christ Nations.
--Signs of the Coming of the Antichrist. (End of the Age Ser.: Vol. 1). 1.25 (ISBN 0-89985-067-7). Christ Nations.
--Signs of the Times in the Heavens. (Prophecy Ser.). 1.25 (ISBN 0-89985-062-6). Christ Nations.
--Solomon & Rehoboam. (Old Testament Ser.). 1.25 (ISBN 0-89985-145-2). Christ Nations.
--Spiritual Hunger. 2.50 (ISBN 0-89985-020-0). Christ Nations.
--Stephen's Defense & Martyrdom. (Acts in Action Ser.: Vol. 2). pap. 1.25 (ISBN 0-89985-963-1). Christ Nations.
--The Story of Adam & Eve. (Old Testament Ser.). 1.25 (ISBN 0-89985-124-X). Christ Nations.
--The Sun-Clothed Woman & the Manchild. (Revelation Ser.). 1.25 (ISBN 0-89985-040-5). Christ Nations.
--They Saw It Happen. 1.50 (ISBN 0-89985-010-3). Christ Nations.
--Thirty Bible Reasons Why Christ Heals Today. (Divine Healing & Health Ser.). 1.25 (ISBN 0-89985-031-6). Christ Nations.
--Those Amazing Prophecies That Prove the Bible. (Prophecy Ser.). 1.25 (ISBN 0-89985-053-7). Christ Nations.
--A Thousand Years of Peace. (End of the Age Ser.: Vol. 8). 1.25 (ISBN 0-89985-074-X). Christ Nations.
--The Tribulation Temple. (Revelation Ser.). 1.25 (ISBN 0-89985-038-3). Christ Nations.
--Twenty-Five Objections to Divine Healing & the Bible Answers. (Divine Healing & Health Ser.). 1.25 (ISBN 0-89985-030-8). Christ Nations.
--Twenty-One Things Shortly to Come to Pass in Israel. 1.25 (ISBN 0-89985-192-4). Christ Nations.
--Twenty-Two Questions Most Frequently Asked by the Unsaved. 1.50 (ISBN 0-89985-118-5). Christ Nations.
--The Two Babylons. (Revelation Ser.). 1.25 (ISBN 0-89985-046-4). Christ Nations.
--The Two Witnesses. (Revelation Ser.). 1.25 (ISBN 0-89985-039-1). Christ Nations.
--The Vial Judgments, or, The Seven Last Plagues. (Revelation Ser.). 1.25 (ISBN 0-89985-045-6). Christ Nations.
--Visitation: Key to Church Growth. 1.25 (ISBN 0-89985-119-3). Christ Nations.
--What About Jehovah's Witnesses? 1.25 (ISBN 0-89985-017-0). Christ Nations.
--Why Do the Righteous Suffer? (Divine Healing & Health Ser.). 1.50 (ISBN 0-89985-032-4). Christ Nations.
--Why Do They Do It? 1.00 (ISBN 0-89985-120-7). Christ Nations.
--Why Some Are Not Healed. (Divine Healing & Health Ser.). 1.25 (ISBN 0-89985-033-2). Christ Nations.
--Will Christians Go Through the Great Tribulation? (Prophecy Ser.). 1.50 (ISBN 0-89985-065-0). Christ Nations.
--Will the Antichrist Come Out of Russia? (Prophecy Ser.). 1.25 (ISBN 0-89985-066-9). Christ Nations.
--Within the Gates. (Sorcery & Spirit World Ser.). 1.75 (ISBN 0-89985-095-2). Christ Nations.
--The World Two Thousand A.D. (Prophecy Ser.). 2.50 (ISBN 0-89985-064-2). Christ Nations.
Lindsay, Gordon & Autry, Jarry. Israel: Prophetic Signs. 72p. (Orig.). 1982. Repr. of 1968 ed. 2.95 (ISBN 0-89985-189-4). Christ Nations.
Lindsay, Jack. John Bunyan: Maker of Myths. LC 77-85138. 1969. Repr. of 1937 ed. 25.00x (ISBN 0-678-00523-0). Kelley.
--John Bunyan: Maker of Myths. LC 73-86039. 1969. Repr. of 1937 ed. 23.00x (ISBN 0-8046-0623-4, Pub. by Kennikat). Assoc Faculty Pr.
Lindsay, Marian, tr. see Laveille, E.
Lindsay, Thomas. History of the Reformation. (Illus.). 648p. 1908. 16.95 (ISBN 0-567-07212-6, Pub. by T & T Clark Ltd UK). Fortress.
Lindsay, Thomas M. Acts II. (Handbooks for Bible Classes & Private Students Ser.). 168p. 1885. 8.95 (ISBN 0-567-08117-6, Pub. by T & T Clark Ltd UK). Fortress.
--A History of the Reformation, 2 vols. facsimile ed. LC 72-37893. (Select Bibliographies Reprint Ser). Repr. of 1907 ed. Set. 54.00 (ISBN 0-8369-6730-5). Ayer Co Pubs.
--A History of the Reformation, 2 vols. LC 83-45664. Date not set. Repr. of 1904 ed. Set. 105.00 (ISBN 0-404-19814-7). AMS Pr.
--Luther & the Germany Reformation. facsimile ed. LC 71-133524. (Select Bibliographies Reprint Ser.). Repr. of 1900 ed. 18.00 (ISBN 0-8369-5556-0). Ayer Co Pubs.
--The Reformation. Whyte, A. & Moffatt, J., eds. (Handbooks for Bible Classes & Private Students Ser.). 228p. 1889. pap. 6.95 (ISBN 0-686-70864-4, Pub. by T & T Clark Ltd UK). Fortress.
Lindsell, Harold. The Armageddon Spectre. LC 84-72012. 142p. (Orig.). 1984. pap. 5.95 (ISBN 0-89107-329-9, Crossway Bks). Good News.
--Free Enterprise: A Judeo-Christian Defense. 1982. pap. 6.95 (ISBN 0-8423-0922-5). Tyndale.
Lindsell, Harold & Woodbridge, Charles J. A Handbook of Christian Truth. 352p. 1972. Repr. 13.95 (ISBN 0-8007-0129-1). Revell.
Lindsey, F. Duane. The Servant Songs: A Study in Isaiah. 1985. pap. 7.95 (ISBN 0-8024-4093-2). Moody.
Lindsey, Hal. Combat Faith. 256p. (Orig.). 1986. pap. 7.95 (ISBN 0-553-34342-4). Bantam.
--La Liberacion del Planeta Tierra. Tr. of The Liberation of Planet Earth. (Span.). 192p. 1982. pap. 3.95 (ISBN 0-311-13023-2). Casa Bautista.
--The Liberation of Planet Earth. 256p. 1976. pap. 3.95 (ISBN 0-553-25307-7). Bantam.
--The Promise. 208p. 1984. pap. 5.95 (ISBN 0-89081-424-4). Harvest Hse.
--A Prophetical Walk Through the Holy Land. LC 83-80121. 200p. 1983. text ed. 29.95 (ISBN 0-89081-381-7). Harvest Hse.
--The Rapture: Truth or Consequences. 224p. (Orig.). 1985. pap. 3.95 (ISBN 0-553-26692-6). Bantam.
--Satan Is Alive & Well on Planet Earth. 256p. 1985. pap. 3.95 (ISBN 0-553-24406-X). Bantam.
--There's a New World Coming. 320p. 1975. pap. 3.95 (ISBN 0-553-24555-4). Bantam.
--There's a New World Coming. LC 73-87773. 308p. 1973. text ed. 2.95 (ISBN 0-88449-001-7, A324292). Vision Hse.
--There's a New World Coming: An In-Depth Analysis of the Book of Revelation. updated ed. 288p. 1984. pap. 6.95 (ISBN 0-89081-440-6). Harvest Hse.
Lindsey, Hal & Carlson, C. C. The Late Great Planet Earth. 192p. 1980. pap. 3.50 (ISBN 0-553-23958-9). Bantam.
--Late Great Planet Earth. 1976. pap. 3.95 mass market (ISBN 0-310-27772-8, 18093P); pap. 5.95 (ISBN 0-310-27771-X, 18089P); study guide o.p. 0.75 (ISBN 0-310-27773-6). Zondervan.
--Satan Is Alive & Well on Planet Earth. 256p. (Orig.). 1974. pap. 4.95 (ISBN 0-310-27792-2, 18195P00687079X). Zondervan.
Lindskoog, Kathryn. A Partir del Eden. Orozco, Julio, tr. from Eng. LC 77-73843. Tr. of Up from Eden. (Span.). 144p. 1977. pap. 3.50 (ISBN 0-89922-092-4). Edit Caribe.
--A Child's Garden of Christian Verses. LC 83-9534. 160p. 1983. 6.95 (ISBN 0-8307-0890-1, 5110603). Regal.
--Mere Christian. 264p. Date not set. pap. 9.95 (ISBN 0-87788-543-5). Shaw Pubs.
Lindskoog, Kathryn, ed. Around the Year with C. S. Lewis & His Friends. 384p. 1986. 12.95 (ISBN 0-8378-5126-2). Gibson.
Lindsley, James Elliott. This Planted Vine: A Narrative History of the Episcopal Diocese of New York. LC 84-47588. (Illus.). 320p. 1984. 24.50 (ISBN 0-06-015347-4, HarpT). Harper Row.
Lindstrom, Harold. Wesley & Sanctification. LC 83-17025. 256p. (Orig.). 1984. 8.95 (ISBN 0-310-75011-3, 17025P). Zondervan.
Lindt, Gillian, ed. Religion in America. LC 75-54571. (Great Contemporary Issues Ser.). 1977. lib. bdg. 35.00x (ISBN 0-405-09865-0). Ayer Co Pubs.
Lindtner, Christian, tr. from Sanskrit, Chinese, Tibetan. Master of Wisdom: Writings of the Buddhist Master Nagarjuna. (Tibetan Translation Ser.). 420p. 1987. 28.00 (ISBN 0-89800-139-0). Dharma Pub.
Lindvall, Ella. Miracles by the Sea. (People of the Bible Ser.). (Illus.). 1984. 4.95 (ISBN 0-8024-0397-2). Moody.
Lindvall, Ella K. The Bible Illustrated for Little Children. (Illus.). 1985. text ed. 11.95 (ISBN 0-8024-0596-7). Moody.
--Jesus Begins His Work. (People of the Bible Ser.). (Illus.). 1983. 4.95 (ISBN 0-8024-0394-8). Moody.
--Jonah & the Great Fish. 2nd ed. (People of the Bible Ser.). (Illus.). 1984. 4.95 (ISBN 0-8024-0398-0). Moody.
--Joseph & His Brothers. (People of the Bible Ser.). (Illus.). 1983. 4.95 (ISBN 0-8024-0395-6). Moody.
--Joseph & the King. 2nd ed. (People of the Bible Ser.). (Illus.). 1984. 4.95 (ISBN 0-8024-0400-6). Moody.
--The Lost Son & Other Stories. (People of the Bible Ser.). (Illus.). 1984. 4.95 (ISBN 0-8024-0399-9). Moody.
--Noah & His Ark. (People of the Bible Ser.). 4.95 (ISBN 0-8024-0396-4). Moody.
--Read-Aloud Bible Stories, Vol. 1. LC 82-2114. 160p. 1982. 16.95 (ISBN 0-8024-7163-3). Moody.
--Read-Aloud Bible Stories, Vol. 2. (Illus.). 1985. text ed. 16.95 (ISBN 0-8024-7164-1). Moody.
Line, Francis & Line, Helen. Our Road to Prayer. 1974. pap. 1.25x (ISBN 0-8358-0305-8). Upper Room.
Line, Francis R. & Line, Helen E. Man with a Song. 1978. 8.95 (ISBN 0-8199-0756-1). Franciscan Herald.
Line, Helen, jt. auth. see Line, Francis.
Line, Helen E., jt. auth. see Line, Francis R.
Lineberry, John. That We May Have Fellowship: Studies in First John. 112p. 1986. pap. 4.95 (ISBN 0-87227-115-3). Reg Baptist.
Linedecker, Clifford. God, the Unknown & the Country Music Singer. (Illus.). 200p. 1987. 17.95x (ISBN 0-938294-50-4); pap. 9.95x (ISBN 0-938294-51-2). Global Comm.
Lineman, Rose & Popelka, Jan. The Compendium of Astrology. 1984. pap. 14.95 (ISBN 0-914918-43-5). Para Res.
Linenthal, Edward T. Changing Images of the Warrior Hero in America: A History of Popular Symbolism. LC 82-22885. (Studies in American Religion: Vol. 6). 296p. 1983. 49.95 (ISBN 0-88946-921-0). E Mellen.
Lines, Kathleen, ed. Faber Book of Greek Legends. 268p. 1973. 13.95 (ISBN 0-571-09830-4). Faber & Faber.
Lines, Timothy A. Systemic Religious Education. LC 86-20383. 264p. (Orig.). 1987. pap. 14.95 (ISBN 0-89135-057-8). Religious Educ.
Linford, Marilyne. Is Anyone Out There Building Mother's Self Esteem? 1986. text ed. 8.95 (ISBN 0-87579-048-8). Deseret Bk.
Linforth, Ivan M. The Arts of Orpheus. LC 72-9296. (The Philosophy of Plato & Aristotle Ser.). Repr. of 1941 ed. 24.50 (ISBN 0-405-04847-5). Ayer Co Pubs.
Ling, T. O. A Dictionary of Buddhism. LC 72-37231. 244p. 1972. 7.95 (ISBN 0-684-12763-6, ScribT). Scribner.
Ling, Trevor. Buddha, Marx & God: Some Aspects of Religion in the Modern World. 2nd ed. 1979. 26.00 (ISBN 0-312-10679-3). St Martin.
--Buddhism, Imperialism & War. (Illus.). 1979. text ed. 13.95x (ISBN 0-04-294105-9). Allen Unwin.
--Buddhist Revival in India: Aspects of the Sociology of Buddhism. LC 79-20167. 1980. 26.00 (ISBN 0-312-10681-5). St Martin.
--Buddism. 1985. 13.00x (ISBN 0-7062-3594-0, Pub. by Ward Lock Educ Co Ltd). State Mutual Bk.
--A Dictionary of Buddhism. 1985. 15.00x (ISBN 0-8364-1436-5, Pub. by KP Bagchi India). South Asia Bks.
--Karl Marx & Religion: In Europe & India. LC 79-55947. 168p. 1980. text ed. 28.50x (ISBN 0-06-494294-5). B&N Imports.
Ling, Trevor, ed. The Buddha's Philosophy of Man: Early Indian Buddhist Dialogues. 229p. 1981. pap. 5.95x (ISBN 0-460-01247-9, Evman). Biblio Dist.
Lingard, John. History & Antiquities of the Anglo-Saxon Church, 2 vols. LC 77-6976. 1977. Repr. of 1845 ed. lib. bdg. 70.00 (ISBN 0-89341-212-0). Longwood Pub Group.
Lingle, Walter L. & Kuykendall, John W. Presbyterians, Their History & Beliefs. LC 77-15750. 1978. pap. 5.95 (ISBN 0-8042-0985-5). John Knox.
Lings, Martin. Ancient Beliefs & Modern Superstitions. (Unwin Paperbacks). 1980. pap. 4.50 (ISBN 0-04-200034-3). Allen Unwin.
--Muhammad. LC 83-49. 349p. 1983. 24.95 (ISBN 0-89281-046-7). Inner Tradit.
--A Sufi Saint of the Twentieth Century: Shaikh Ahmad al-'Alawi, His Spiritual Heritage & Legacy. (Near Eastern Center, UCLA Ser.). (Illus.). 242p. 1972. 30.00x (ISBN 0-520-02174-6); pap. 4.95 (ISBN 0-520-02486-9). U of Cal Pr.
Link, Eugene P. Labor-Religion Prophet: The Times & Life of Harry F. Ward. (Academy of Independent Scholars Retrospections Ser.). 270p. 1984. 22.00x (ISBN 0-86531-621-X). Westview.
Link, Henry C. The Return to Religion. LC 77-17291. 1977. Repr. of 1937 ed. lib. bdg. 16.50 (ISBN 0-8414-5846-4). Folcroft.
Link, Julie, ed. Kneeling Christian. 112p. 1986. pap. 5.95 (ISBN 0-310-33491-8, 6659P, Clarion Class). Zondervan.
Link, Julie, ed. see More, Hannah.
Link, Julie, ed. see Unknown Christian.
Link, Julie, ed. see Wirt, Sherwood E.
Link, Julie A., ed. see Evans, W. Glyn.
Link, Margaret S., retold by. The Pollen Path: A Collection of Navajo Myths. LC 56-7272. (Illus.). 1956. 17.50x (ISBN 0-8047-0473-2). Stanford U Pr.
Link, Mark. Breakway: Twenty-Eight Steps to a More Reflective Life. LC 67553. 144p. 1980. pap. 3.25 (ISBN 0-89505-050-1). Argus Comm.

--The Seventh Trumpet. LC 78-53943. 1978. 7.95 (ISBN 0-89505-014-5). Argus Comm.
--These Stones Will Shout: A New Voice for the Old Testament. LC 82-74383. (Illus.). 300p. 1983. pap. 7.95x (ISBN 0-89505-117-6). Argus Comm.
--You: Prayer for Beginners & Those Who Have Forgotten How. LC 76-41584. 1976. pap. 2.95 (ISBN 0-913592-78-1). Argus Comm.
Linke, Maria Z & Hunt, Ruth. East Wind. 1978. pap. 2.50 (ISBN 0-310-27852-X). Zondervan.
Linkh, Richard M. American Catholicism & European Immigrants (1900-1924) LC 74-79914. vii, 200p. 1974. pap. 9.95x (ISBN 0-913256-17-X). Ctr Migration.
Link-Salinger, Ruth. Jewish Law in Our Time. 183p. 22.50x (ISBN 0-8197-0486-5); pap. 12.95x (ISBN 0-8197-0487-3). Bloch.
Linksman, Ricki, jt. auth. see Scotti, Juliet.
Linley, Eliza, jt. ed. see Welch, Marni.
Linn, D., jt. auth. see Linn, Matthew L.
Linn, Dennis & Linn, Matthew. Healing Life's Hurts: Healing Memories Through the Five Stages of Forgiveness. LC 77-14794. 324p. 1978. pap. 5.95 (ISBN 0-8091-2059-3). Paulist Pr.
Linn, Dennis, jt. ed. see Linn, Matthew.
Linn, Dennis, et al. At Peace with the Unborn: A Book for Healing. 1.50 (ISBN 0-8091-5187-1). Paulist Pr.
--Healing the Greatest Hurt: Healing Grief & the Family Tree. LC 85-60407. 258p. (Orig.). 1985. pap. 5.95 (ISBN 0-8091-2714-8). Paulist Pr.
Linn, Dennis, jt. auth. see Linn, Matthew.
Linn, Dennis M., et al. Praying with One Another for Healing. 1984. pap. 4.95 (ISBN 0-8091-2619-2). Paulist Pr.
Linn, Elbridge B. That They May All Be One. 1969. 4.50 (ISBN 0-88027-020-9). Firm Foun Pub.
Linn, Jan G. Christians Must Choose. Lambert, Herbert, ed. LC 85-3731. (Orig.). 1985. pap. 7.95 (ISBN 0-8272-0448-5). CBP.
Linn, Sr. Mary J., et al. Healing the Dying. LC 79-53111. 128p. 1979. pap. 3.95 (ISBN 0-8091-2212-X). Paulist Pr.
Linn, Matthew & Linn, Dennis. Prayer Course for Healing Life's Hurts: Book. 128p. 1983. pap. 5.95 (ISBN 0-8091-2522-6). Paulist Pr.
Linn, Matthew, jt. auth. see Linn, Dennis.
Linn, Matthew & Linn, Dennis, eds. Deliverance Prayer: Experiential, Psychological & Theological Approaches. LC 81-82334. 256p. (Orig.). 1981. pap. 6.95 (ISBN 0-8091-2385-1). Paulist Pr.
Linn, Matthew L. & Linn, D. Healing of Memories: Prayers & Confession-Steps to Inner Healing. LC 74-17697. 112p. (Orig.). 1974. pap. 3.95 (ISBN 0-8091-1854-8). Paulist Pr.
Linn, W. A., et al. The Mormons & Mormonism, 15 vols. 1973. lib. bdg. 50.00 (ISBN 0-8490-0675-9). Gordon Pr.
Linss, Wilhelm C., tr. see Bultmann, Rudolf.
Linss, Wilhelm C., tr. see Lapide, Pinchas.
Linssen, Robert. Living Zen. Abrahams-Curiel, Diana, tr. 1960. pap. 3.95 (ISBN 0-394-17391-0, E578, Ever). Grove.
Lint, J. G. De see De Lint, J. G.
Linthorst, Ann T. A Gift of Love: Marriage As A Spiritual Journey. 166p. 1985. pap. 9.95 (ISBN 0-913105-17-1). PAGL Pr.
--Gift of Love: Marriage As a Spiritual Journey. 9.95 (ISBN 0-8091-0299-4). Paulist Pr.
--Thus Saith the Lord: Giddyap: Metapsychiatric Commentaries on Human Experience & Spiritual Growth. 106p. (Orig.). 1986. pap. 11.00 (ISBN 0-913105-18-X). PAGL Pr.
Linthorst, Jan & Rubadeau, Joan. Handbook for Building a Beautiful Homelife. 1987. pap. 12.00 (ISBN 0-913105-20-1). PAGL Pr.
Linton, Sydney, tr. see Sjogren, Per-Olof.
Linville, Barbara. God Made the One & Only Me. LC 76-8737. (Illus.). 1976. pap. text ed. 3.95 (ISBN 0-916406-28-8). Accent Bks.
Linvingstone, Dinah, tr. see Bloom, Anthony & LeFebvre, George.
Linzer, Norman. The Jewish Family: Authority & Tradition in Modern Perspectives. 217p. 1984. 34.95 (ISBN 0-89885-149-1); pap. 14.95 (ISBN 0-89885-191-2). Human Sci Pr.
Linzey, Stanford E. Why I Believe in the Baptism with the Holy Spirit. 1962. pap. 0.75 (ISBN 0-88243-764-X, 02-0764). Gospel Pub.
Lion The Printer. Seven Days a Week. (Illus.). 1977. spiral 2.00 (ISBN 0-914080-62-8). Shulsinger Sales.
Lipman, Ed. No Capital Crime. 1975. pap. 2.00x (ISBN 0-915016-04-4). Second Coming.
Lipman, Kennard, ed. see Norbu, Namkhai.
Lipman, Kennard, tr. see Manjusrimitra.
Lipman, Matthew. Mark. LC 80-80849. (Philosophy for Children Ser.). 86p. 1980. pap. 8.00 (ISBN 0-916834-13-1, TX 752-903). First Mntn Foun.
Lipman, Zev, illus. Baruch Ata Befi Hataf: Illustrated Prayers & Blessings for Young Children. (Illus.). 4.95 (ISBN 0-685-84974-0). Feldheim.
Lipner, Julius J. The Face of Truth: A Study of Meaning & Metaphysics in the Vedantic Theology of Ramanuja. 224p. 1986. 44.50x (ISBN 0-88706-038-2); pap. 18.95x (ISBN 0-88706-039-0). State U NY Pr.
Lippard, George, jt. auth. see Clymer, R. Swinburne.
Lippman, Thomas W. Islam: Politics & Religion in the Muslim World. (Headline Series 258). (Illus.). 64p. 1982. pap. 4.00 (ISBN 0-87124-075-0). Foreign Policy.
--Understanding Islam: An Introduction to the Moslem World. LC 81-85142. 208p. 1982. pap. 3.50 (ISBN 0-451-62501-3, ME2079, Ment). NAL.
Lipps, Gottlob F. Mythenbildung und Erkenntnis: Eine Abhandlung Uber Die Grundlagen der Philosophie. Bolle, Kees W., ed. LC 77-79141. (Mythology Ser.). 1978. lib. bdg. 27.50x (ISBN 0-405-10550-9). Ayer Co Pubs.
Lippy, Charles H. Bibliography of Religion in the South. LC 85-13575. xvi, 498p. 1985. text ed. 49.95 (ISBN 0-86554-161-2, MUP-H151). Mercer Univ Pr.
--Seasonable Revolutionary: The Mind of Charles Chauncy. LC 81-9560. 176p. 1981. text ed. 19.95x (ISBN 0-88229-625-6). Nelson-Hall.
Lippy, Charles H., ed. Religious Periodicals of the United States: Academic & Scholarly Journals. LC 85-9861. (Historical Guides to the World's Periodicals & Newspapers Ser.). 626p. 1986. lib. bdg. 65.00 (ISBN 0-313-23420-5, LRP/). Greenwood.
Lipscomb, David see Gospel Advocate.
Lipshitz, Abe. The Commentary of Abraham Ibn Ezra on Hosea. 190p. 1987. 19.95 (ISBN 0-87203-127-6). Hermon.
Lipshitz, Devora, jt. auth. see Anderson, Joseph.
Lipski, Alexander. Thomas Merton & Asia: His Quest for Utopia. (Cistercian Studies: No. 74). 1983. 17.95 (ISBN 0-87907-874-X); pap. 7.95 (ISBN 0-87907-974-6). Cistercian Pubns.
Lipsky, Abram. John Wesley: A Portrait. LC 76-155619. Repr. of 1928 ed. 20.50 (ISBN 0-404-03994-4). AMS Pr.
Lipsky, Louis. Thirty Years of American Zionism, Vol.1. Davis, Moshe, ed. LC 77-70718. (America & the Holy Land Ser.). 1977. Repr. of 1927 ed. lib. bdg. 26.50x (ISBN 0-405-10263-1). Ayer Co Pubs.
Lipson, Dorothy Ann. Freemasonry in Federalist Connecticut, 1789-1835. 1977. 40.00 (ISBN 0-691-04646-8). Princeton U Pr.
Lipson, Eric-Peter. Passover Haggadah: A Messianic Celebration. LC 85-82168. (Illus.). 128p. 1986. 10.95 (ISBN 0-9616148-0-3). JFJ Pub.
Lipson, Ruth. Modeh Ani Means Thank You. (Illus.). 1986. 5.95 (ISBN 0-317-42732-6). Feldheim.
Lipstadt, Deborah. Beyond Belief: The American Press & the Coming of the Holocaust. 336p. 19.95 (ISBN 0-02-919160-2). Free Pr.
Lipstadt, Deborah E. The Zionist Career of Louis Lipsky, 1900-1921. 35.00 (ISBN 0-405-14086-X). Ayer Co Pubs.
Liptak, David Q. Biblical Advent Homilies. 68p. (Orig.). 1986. pap. 8.95 (ISBN 0-941850-15-3). Sunday Pubns.
--Biblical-Catechetical Homilies for Sundays & Holy Days (A, B & C) Based on the Lectionary & Reflecting the Syllabus of the Pastoral Homiletic Plan. LC 79-27895. 370p. (Orig.). 1980. pap. 10.95 (ISBN 0-8189-0400-3). Alba.
--Biblical Lenten Homilies for Preaching & Meditation. rev. & exp. ed. pap. 11.95 (ISBN 0-941850-05-6). Sunday Pubns.
--The New Code & the Sacraments. 140p. 1983. pap. 7.95 (ISBN 0-941850-12-9). Sunday Pubns.
--Preaching the Saints As Models. 1983. pap. 8.95 (ISBN 0-941850-10-2). Sunday Pubns.
--Questions about Your Faith, Bk. IV. pap. 3.95 (ISBN 0-941850-09-9). Sunday Pubns.
--Sacramental & Occasional Homilies. LC 80-29287. 96p. (Orig.). 1981. pap. 5.95 (ISBN 0-8189-0408-9). Alba.
Liptak, David Q. & Sheridan, Philip A. The New Code: Laity & Deacons. 128p. (Orig.). 1986. pap. 7.95 (ISBN 0-941850-20-X). Sunday Pubns.
Liptak, Dolores. European Immigrants & the Catholic Church in Connecticut: 1870-1920. 1987. 17.50 (ISBN 0-913256-79-X); pap. text ed. 12.95 (ISBN 0-913256-80-3). Ctr Migration.
Liptzin, Sol. Biblical Themes in World Literature. LC 84-19457. 316p. 1985. 20.00 (ISBN 0-88125-063-5). Ktav.
Lischer, Richard. Marx & Teilhard: Two Ways to the New Humanity. LC 79-4438. 192p. (Orig.). 1979. pap. 3.48 (ISBN 0-88344-303-1). Orbis Bks.
--Speaking of Jesus: Finding the Words for Witness. LC 81-70556. 144p. 1982. pap. 6.95 (ISBN 0-8006-1631-6, 1-1631). Fortress.
--A Theology of Preaching: The Dynamics of the Gospel. LC 81-1470. (Abingdon Preacher's Library). (Orig.). 1981. pap. 6.95 (ISBN 0-687-41570-5). Abingdon.
Liscner, Richard, ed. Theories of Preaching: Selected Readings in the Nomiletical Tradition. 384p. 1987. pap. 30.00 (ISBN 0-939464-46-2); pap. 15.95 (ISBN 0-939464-45-4). Labyrinth Pr.
Liscombe, Rhodri W. The Church Architecture of Robert Mills. (Illus.). 160p. 1985. 30.00 (ISBN 0-89308-542-1). Southern Hist Pr.
Lisiero, Dario. People Ideology-People Theology: New Perspectives on Religious Dogma. 226p. 1980. 10.95 (ISBN 0-682-49664-2, Banner). Exposition Pr FL.
Liskofsky, Sidney. U. N. Declaration on the Elimination of Religious Intolerance & Discrimination. 20p. 1982. pap. 2.00 (ISBN 0-87495-041-4). Am Jewish Comm.
Lisney, M. I., tr. see Makrakis, Apostolos.
Lissak, Moshe, jt. auth. see Horowitz, Dan.
Lister, Louis & Lister, Rebecca. The Religious School Board: A Manual. 1978. pap. 5.00 (ISBN 0-8074-0014-9, 243870). UAHC.
Lister, Louis, jt. auth. see Lister, Rebecca.
Lister, Rebecca & Lister, Louis. The Smaller Religious School: A Manual. 1977. pap. text ed. 5.00 (ISBN 0-685-88426-0, 241850). UAHC.
Lister, Rebecca, jt. auth. see Lister, Louis.
Litchfield, Hugh. Preaching the Easter Story. (Orig.). 1987. pap. 5.95 (ISBN 0-8054-2117-3). Broadman.
Litfin, Duane. Public Speaking: A Handbook for Christians. LC 81-65993. 400p. (Orig.). 1981. pap. 13.95 (ISBN 0-8010-5605-5). Baker Bk.
Litfin, Duane & Robinson, Haddon, eds. Recent Homiletical Thought: A Bibliography, 1966-1979. LC 82-72135. 296p. 1983. 16.95 (ISBN 0-8010-5613-6). Baker Bk.
Litherland, Janet. Youth Ministry from Start to Finish. Zapel, Arthur L., ed. LC 85-62467. (Illus.). 115p. (Orig.). 1985. pap. 7.95 (ISBN 0-916260-35-6, B-193). Meriwether Pub.
Litman, Jacob. The Economic Role of Jews in Medieval Poland: The Contribution of Yitzhak Schipper. (Illus.). 320p. (Orig.). 1985. lib. bdg. 29.50 (ISBN 0-8191-4244-1); pap. text ed. 15.25 (ISBN 0-8191-4245-X). U Pr of Amer.
Litt, D., jt. auth. see Arya, Usharbudh.
Litt, D., jt. auth. see Harris, Errol E.
Littauer, Florence. After Every Wedding Comes a Marriage. LC 81-80023. 208p. (Orig.). 1981. pap. 5.95 (ISBN 0-89081-289-6). Harvest Hse.
--Christian Leader's & Speaker's Seminars. 100p. 1983. incl. lab manual & 12 cassettes 89.95 (ISBN 0-89081-369-8). Harvest Hse.
--How to Get along with Difficult People. LC 83-83371. 1984. pap. 4.95 (ISBN 0-89081-429-5). Harvest Hse.
--Personality Plus. (Illus.). 192p. 1982. 5.95 (Power Ed.); pap. 9.95 (ISBN 0-8007-1323-0). Revell.
--Pursuit of Happiness. LC 80-85333. 1981. pap. 4.95 (ISBN 0-89081-284-5). Harvest Hse.
Littaur, Fred. National Directory of Christian Artists. LC 85-80487. 256p. (Orig.). 1985. pap. 9.95 (ISBN 0-89081-490-2). Harvest Hse.
Littell, Franklin H. The Crucifixion of the Jews. (Reprints of Scholarly Excellence: No. 12). 160p. 1986. Repr. of 1975 ed. 10.95 (ISBN 0-86554-227-9). Mercer Univ Pr.
--Macmillan Atlas History of Christianity. LC 75-22113. (Illus.). 176p. 1976. 24.95 (ISBN 0-02-573140-8, 57314). Macmillan.
--A Pilgrim's Interfaith Guide to the Holy Land. (Illus.). 84p. 1982. 7.95 (ISBN 9-65220-030-1, Carta Pub Israel). Hippocrene Bks.
Littell, Franklin H., jt. auth. see Shur, Irene G.
Littell, Marcia S., ed. Liturgies on the Holocaust: An Interfaith Anthology. LC 86-23507. 208p. 1986. lib. bdg. 39.95x (ISBN 0-88946-030-2). E Mellen.
Litthauer, Florence. It Takes so Little to Be above Average. 192p. 1983. pap. 4.95 (ISBN 0-89081-376-0). Harvest Hse.
Little, A. G. Introduction of the Observant Friars into England. 1925. pap. 2.25 (ISBN 0-85672-686-9, Pub. by British Acad). Longwood Pub Group.
--Some Recently Discovered Franciscan Documents & Their Relation to the Second Life by Celano & the "Speculum Perfections". 1926. pap. 2.25 (ISBN 0-85672-691-5, Pub. by British Acad). Longwood Pub Group.
Little, A. G., et al. Collectanea Franciscana I. 170p. 1914. text ed. 41.40x (ISBN 0-576-99205-4, Pub. by Gregg Intl Pubs England). Gregg Intl.
Little, B., tr. see Sheehan, Thomas.
Little, Bryan. Abbeys & Priories of England & Wales. LC 79-213. (Illus.). 216p. 1979. text ed. 34.50x (ISBN 0-8419-0485-5). Holmes & Meier.
Little, Charles. Ten Thousand Illustrations from the Bible. pap. 15.95 (ISBN 0-8010-5606-3). Baker Bk.
Little, David. Religion, Order, & Law: A Study in Pre-Revolutionary England. LC 84-2611. 270p. 1984. pap. text ed. 11.00x (ISBN 0-226-48546-3). U of Chicago Pr.
--Tabernacle in the Wilderness. pap. 1.50 (ISBN 0-87213-520-9). Loizeaux.
Little, Geraldine C. Contrasts in Keening: Ireland. LC 82-60038. 50p. (Orig.). 1982. pap. 3.50 (ISBN 0-943710-00-6). Silver App Pr.
Little, Gilbert. Como Vencer Tension Nerviosa. Orig. Title: Nervous Christians. 128p. (Span). 1987. pap. 3.25 (ISBN 0-8254-1443-1). Kregel.
Little, Henry. YHWH: Tetragrammaton. LC 84-90091. 177p. 1985. 12.95 (ISBN 0-533-06173-3). Vantage.
Little, J. M. The Gospel in the Last Days. LC 84-90258. 143p. 1985. 10.95 (ISBN 0-533-06299-3). Vantage.
Little, L. Gilbert. Nervous Christians. 1956. pap. 3.95 (ISBN 0-8024-5878-5). Moody.
Little, Lawrence C. Wider Horizons in Christian Adult Education. LC 62-14381. pap. 87.00 (ISBN 0-8357-9763-5, 2017871). Bks Demand UMI.
Little, Lester K. Religious Poverty & the Profit Economy in Medieval Europe. LC 78-58630. 278p. (Orig.). 1983. pap. 10.95x (ISBN 0-8014-9247-5). Cornell U Pr.
Little, Mark. Handbook for Advanced Souls: Eternal Reminders for the Present Moment. (Illus.). 136p. 1984. 6.95 (ISBN 0-9613783-0-1). M A Little.
Little, Paul. Affirming the Will of God. pap. 0.75 (ISBN 0-87784-139-X). Inter-Varsity.
--Know What You Believe. 192p. 1985. pap. 2.95 (ISBN 0-89693-526-4). Victor Bks.
Little, Paul E. The Answer to Life. LC 86-72378. Orig. Title: Faith is for People. 96p. 1987. pap. 4.95 (ISBN 0-89107-429-5, Crossway Bks). Good News.
--Como Compartir Su Fe. 144p. 1985. pap. 3.95 (ISBN 0-311-13025-9). Casa Bautista.
--How to Give Away Your Faith. LC 66-20710. 1966. pap. 5.95 (ISBN 0-87784-553-0). Inter-Varsity.
--Know Why You Believe. rev. ed. LC 68-8267. 1968. pap. 5.95 (ISBN 0-87784-529-8). Inter-Varsity.
--Know Why You Believe. 160p. 1984. pap. 2.95 (ISBN 0-89693-717-8). Victor Bks.
Little, Sara. To Set One's Heart: Belief & Teaching in the Church. LC 82-49020. 160p. 1983. pap. 8.95 (ISBN 0-8042-1442-5). John Knox.
Littledale, Richard F. Offices from the Service Books of the Holy Eastern Church. LC 77-133819. 1970. Repr. of 1863 ed. 24.50 (ISBN 0-404-03996-0). AMS Pr.
Littlefield, Mark G., ed. Biblia Romanceada I.I.8: The Thirteenth-Century Spanish Bible Contained in Escorial MS. I. I. 8. (Dialect Ser.: No. 4). (Illus.). xiv, 334p. 1983. inc. 10 microfiches 35.00x (ISBN 0-942260-34-1). Hispanic Seminary.
Littlehales, H., ed. The Prymer, or Lay Folks Prayer Book, Pts. 1 & 2. (EETS, OS Ser.: No. 109). Repr. of 1897 ed. Set. 18.00 (ISBN 0-527-00108-2). Kraus Repr.
--St. Mary at Hill Church: The Medieval Records of a London City Church A.D. 1420-1559, Pts. 1 & 2. (EETS, OS Ser.: Nos. 125, 128). Repr. of 1905 ed. Set. 77.00 (ISBN 0-527-00121-X). Kraus Repr.
Littlejohn, Ronnie. Exploring Christian Theology. 542p. (Orig.). 1985. lib. bdg. 37.25 (ISBN 0-8191-4459-2); pap. text ed. 19.75 (ISBN 0-8191-4460-6). U Pr of Amer.
Littlepage, Loyd. How to Make Your Dreams Come True. (Illus.). 32p. 1981. pap. 4.50 (ISBN 0-911336-85-0). Sci of Mind.
Littleton, Mark. A Place to Stand: When Life Throws You Off Balance. (Christian Living Ser.). 1986. pap. 6.95 (ISBN 0-88070-141-2). Multnomah.
Liturgical Committee of the Christian Reformed Church. Service Book: Heidelberg Catechism, Pt. No. 5. 64p. (Orig.). 1981. pap. text ed. 2.25 (ISBN 0-933140-35-5). CRC Pubns.
--Service Book: Liturgical Forms for Baptism & the Lord's Supper, Pt. No. 1. 30p. (Orig.). 1981. pap. text ed. 1.50 (ISBN 0-933140-31-2). CRC Pubns.
--Service Book: Liturgical Forms (Non-Sacramental, Pt. No. 2. 30p. (Orig.). 1981. pap. text ed. 1.50 (ISBN 0-933140-32-0). CRC Pubns.
--Service Book: Prayers & Responsive Readings of the Law, Pt. No. 4. 37p. (Orig.). 1981. pap. text ed. 1.50 (ISBN 0-933140-34-7). CRC Pubns.
--Service Book: Service of Word & Sacrament, Pt. No. 3. 64p. (Orig.). 1981. pap. text ed. 1.95 (ISBN 0-933140-33-9). CRC Pubns.
Liturgical Prayer Magazine. Prayers of the Faithful. Fehren, Henry, ed. 1977. pap. 11.50 (ISBN 0-916134-29-6). Pueblo Pub Co.
Litvak, Stuart. Seeking Wisdom: The Sufi Path. LC 82-60163. 128p. (Orig.). 1984. pap. 6.95 (ISBN 0-87728-543-8). Weiser.

Litvak, Stuart & Burba, Nora. In the World but Not of It: A Guide to More Spirituality in Your Life. 156p. 1984. pap. 5.95 (ISBN 0-13-453994-X). P-H.

Litvin & Hoenig. Jewish Identity. 13.95 (ISBN 0-87306-096-2). Feldheim.

Litvin, Baruch & Litvin, Jeanne. The Sanctity of the Synagogue. 1987. 19.95 (ISBN 0-88125-113-5). KTAV.

Litvin, Jeanne, jt. auth. see Litvin, Baruch.

Liu, Da. Taoist Health Exercise Book. 3rd ed. (Illus.). 172p. 1983. pap. 5.95 (ISBN 0-399-50745-0, Perigee). Putnam Pub Group.

Liu, James T. Ou-yang Hsiu: An Eleventh-Century Neo-Confucianist. 1967. 18.50x (ISBN 0-8047-0262-4). Stanford U Pr.

Liu, Shih S., tr. see Chen, Liu F.

Liu, Tai. Puritan London: A Study of Religion & Society in the City Parishes. LC 85-40534. 256p. 1986. 38.50x (ISBN 0-87413-283-5, Pub. by U Delaware Pr). Assoc Univ Prs.

Liu, Wu-Chi. A Short History of Confucian Philosophy. LC 78-20480. 1983. Repr. of 1955 ed. 20.50 (ISBN 0-88355-857-2). Hyperion Conn.

Liu Da. T'ai Chi Ch'uan & I Ching: A Choreography of Body & Mind. LC 79-183640. 1987. pap. 5.95 (ISBN 0-06-091309-6, PL-1309, PL). Har-Row.

Liu I-ming, jt. auth. see Chang Po-tuan.

Liu Kwang-Ching, ed. American Missionaries in China: Papers from Harvard Seminars. LC 66-31226. (East Asian Monographs Ser.: No. 21). 1966. pap. 11.00x (ISBN 0-674-02600-4). Harvard U Pr.

Liu Wu-Chi. Confucius, His Life & Time. LC 73-138159. 189p. 1972. Repr. of 1955 ed. lib. bdg. 22.50x (ISBN 0-8371-5616-5, LICO). Greenwood.

Livadeas, Themistocles & Charitos, Minas. The Real Truth Concerning Apostolos Makrakis. Orthodox Christian Educational Society, ed. Cummings, Denver, tr. from Hellenic. 230p. (Orig.). 1952. pap. 4.50x (ISBN 0-938366-30-0). Orthodox Chr.

Livermore, Penny. Called to His Supper: The Biblical Eucharist. 2.95 (ISBN 0-89453-089-5). M Glazier.

Living Spring Publications Staff, tr. see Foster, Harry.

Livingood, J., et al, eds. Christmas I Remember Best. (Illus., Orig.). write for info. (ISBN 0-910901-00-7); pap. 5.95 (ISBN 0-910901-01-5). Deseret News.

Livingston, David. Missionary Travels & Researches in South Africa. LC 5-15250. 1971. Repr. of 1857 ed. 62.00 (ISBN 0-384-32983-7). Johnson Repr.

Livingston, E. A., ed. see International Congress on Biblical Studies.

Livingston, G. Herbert. The Pentateuch in Its Cultural Environment. pap. 12.95 (ISBN 0-8010-5630-6). Baker Bk.

Livingston, J. B. Love Yourself. 2.70 (ISBN 0-89137-421-3). Quality Pubns.

Livingston, Mrs. J. B. Today's Victorious Woman, Vol. 2. pap. 4.00 (ISBN 0-89137-427-2). Quality Pubns.

Livingston, James. The Ethics of Belief. LC 74-18616. (American Academy of Religion. Studies in Religion). 1974. pap. 7.50 (ISBN 0-88420-121-X, 010009). Scholars Pr GA.

Livingston, James C. Anatomy of the Sacred: An Introduction to Religion. 734p. 1987. text ed. write for info. (ISBN 0-02-371370-4). Macmillan.

--Matthew Arnold & Christianity: His Religious Prose Writings. 250p. 1986. text ed. 17.95x (ISBN 0-87249-462-4). U of SC Pr.

--Modern Christian Thought: From the Enlightenment to Vatican Two. 1971. text ed. write for info. (ISBN 0-02-371420-4). Macmillan.

Livingston, James C., ed. see Arnold, Matthew.

Livingstone, Alasdair. Mystical & Mythological Explanatory Works of Assyrian & Babylonian Scholars. 280p. 1986. 55.00x (ISBN 0-19-815462-3). Oxford U Pr.

Livingstone, David. Missionary Travels & Researches in South Africa. LC 72-5439. (Select Bibliographies Reprint Ser.). 1972. Repr. of 1857 ed. 52.00 (ISBN 0-8369-6918-9). Ayer Co Pubs.

Livingstone, David N. Darwin's Forgotten Defenders: The Encounter Between Evangelical Theology & Evolutionary Thought. 144p. (Orig.). 1987. pap. 9.95 (ISBN 0-8028-0260-5). Eerdmans.

Livingstone, Dinah, tr. see Beyerlin, Walter.

Livingstone, Dinah, tr. see Leclercq, Jacques.

Livingstone, Dinah, tr. see Voillaume, Rene.

Livingstone, E. A., ed. see International Congress on Biblical Studies, 6th, Oxford, 3-7 April,1978.

Livingstone, Elizabeth A., jt. auth. see Cross, F. L.

Livingstone, W. P. Mary Slessor of Calabar. LC 83-9286. 352p. 1984. 7.95 (ISBN 0-310-27451-6, 9286P, Clarion class). Zondervan.

--Mary Slessor of Calabar. (Heroes of the Faith Ser.). 1986. Repr. 6.95 (ISBN 0-916441-49-0). Barbour & Co.

Lizardos, Georgia, jt. tr. see Papadopulos, Leonidas J.

Llerena, Mario, ed. see Wilson, William P. & Slattery, Kathryn.

Llewellyn Publications Staff. The Truth about Witchcraft. Galde, Phyllis, ed. (Educational Guide Ser.). 32p. 1987. pap. 2.00 (ISBN 0-87542-357-4). Llewellyn Pubns.

Llewellyn Staff. The Truth about Astral Projection. Weschcke, Carl L., ed. (Educational Guide Ser.). 32p. (Orig.). 1983. pap. 2.00 (ISBN 0-87542-350-7, L-350). Llewellyn Pubns.

Llewelyn, Robert. All Shall Be Well: The Spirituality of Julian of Norwich for Today. 160p. 1985. pap. 7.95 (ISBN 0-8091-2668-0). Paulist Pr.

--A Doorway to Silence: The Contemplative Use of the Rosary. 96p. (Orig.). 1987. pap. 5.95 (ISBN 0-8091-2900-0). Paulist Pr.

--Love Bade Me Welcome. 96p. (Orig.). 1985. pap. 5.95 (ISBN 0-8091-2715-6). Paulist Pr.

Llewelyn, Robert, ed. Daily Readings from the Cloud of Unknowing. (Daily Readings Ser.). 1986. pap. 4.95 (ISBN 0-87243-149-5). Templegate.

--Julian: Woman of Our Day. 1987. pap. 6.95 (ISBN 0-89622-334-5). Twenty-Third.

Llewelyn, Robert & Moss, Edward, eds. Daily Readings with William Law. 1987. pap. 4.95 (ISBN 0-87243-153-3). Templegate.

Llewelyn, Robert, ed. see Brother Lawrence.

LLewelyn, Robert, ed. see De Caussode, Jean Pierre.

LLewelyn, Robert, ed. see Julian of Norwich.

LLewelyn, Robert, ed. see St. Francis de Sales.

Llewelyn, Robert, ed. see St. John of the Cross.

LLewelyn, Robert, ed. see St. Teresa of Avila.

LLosa, Mario V. see Vargas, Mario.

Lloyd, jt. auth. see Rawson.

Lloyd, Alfred H. Dynamic Idealism. LC 75-3243. Repr. of 1898 ed. 17.00 (ISBN 0-404-59233-3). AMS Pr.

Lloyd, Arnold. Quaker Social History: Sixteen Sixty-Nine to Seventeen Thirty-Eight. LC 79-4398. 1979. Repr. of 1950 ed. lib. bdg. 22.50x (ISBN 0-313-20943-X, LLQU). Greenwood.

Lloyd, Arthur. The Creed of Half Japan: Historical Sketches of Japanese Buddhism. LC 78-70095. Repr. of 1912 ed. 40.50 (ISBN 0-404-17344-6). AMS Pr.

Lloyd, Frederick E., ed. Lloyd's Church Musicians Directory. LC 72-1733. Repr. of 1910 ed. 14.75 (ISBN 0-404-08319-6). AMS Pr.

Lloyd, Helen Y. The Awakening Soul. 1984. 10.95 (ISBN 0-8062-2346-4). Carlton.

Lloyd, J. A. Fyodor Dostoevsky. 1978. Repr. of 1946 ed. lib. bdg. 25.00 (ISBN 0-8495-3228-0). Arden Lib.

--Fyodor Dostoevsky. LC 78-164532. 1971. Repr. of 1947 ed. 24.50x (ISBN 0-8154-0401-8). Cooper Sq.

--Fyodor Dostyevsky. 1973. lib. bdg. 20.00 (ISBN 0-8414-5871-5). Folcroft.

Lloyd, J. P. Message of an Indian Relic: Seattle's Own Totem Pole. facs. ed. (Shorey Indian Ser.). (Illus.). 29p. pap. 1.95 (ISBN 0-8466-4006-6, 16). Shorey.

Lloyd, Janet, tr. see Aries, Philippe.

LLoyd, Janet, tr. see Gernet, Jacques.

Lloyd, Marjorie L. If I Had a Bigger Drum. (Harvest Ser.). 1981. pap. 4.50 (ISBN 0-8163-0399-1). Pacific Pr Pub Assn.

--Why the Cookie Crumbles. (Outreach Ser.). pap. 1.25 (ISBN 0-8163-0400-9). Pacific Pr Pub Assn.

Lloyd, Rawson. Stories Jesus Told. (Children's Picture Bible Ser.). 1982. 7.95 (ISBN 0-86020-516-9, Usborne-Hayes); PLB 12.96 (ISBN 0-88110-097-8); pap. 4.95 (ISBN 0-86020-521-5). EDC.

Lloyd, Roger B. Golden Middle Age. LC 75-90654. (Essay Index Reprint Ser). 1939. 18.00 (ISBN 0-8369-1208-X). Ayer Co Pubs.

--Revolutionary Religion: Christianity, Fascism, & Communism. LC 78-63686. (Studies in Fascism: Ideology & Practice). Repr. of 1938 ed. 24.50 (ISBN 0-404-16903-1). AMS Pr.

Lloyd-Jones, D. M. El Sermon del Monte, Vol. 1. 1978. 4.75 (ISBN 0-85151-414-6). Banner of Truth.

Lloyd-Jones, D. Martin. Romans: The Final Perseverance of the Saints (8: 17-39) 458p. 1976. text ed. 15.95 (ISBN 0-310-27930-5, 10592). Zondervan.

Lloyd-Jones, D. Martyn. Authority. 94p. pap. 3.45x (ISBN 0-85151-386-7). Banner of Truth.

--Christian Soldier. 12.95 (ISBN 0-8010-5583-0). Baker Bk.

--Christian Unity: An Exposition of Ephesians 4: 1-16. 280p. 1981. 12.95 (ISBN 0-8010-5607-1). Baker Bk.

--The Christian Warfare: An Exposition of Ephesians 6: 10-13. 1977. Repr. of 1976 ed. 12.95 (ISBN 0-8010-5574-1). Baker Bk.

--Darkness & Light: An Exposition of Ephesians 4 17-5 17. 408p. 1983. Repr. of 1965 ed. 12.95 (ISBN 0-8010-5617-9). Baker Bk.

--Evangelistic Sermons. 294p. (Orig.). 1983. pap. 9.45 (ISBN 0-85151-362-X). Banner of Truth.

--Faith on Trial: Studies in Psalm 73. 128p. 1982. pap. 4.50 (ISBN 0-8010-5618-7). Baker Bk.

--First Book of Daily Readings. 1970. pap. 6.95 (ISBN 0-8028-1354-2). Eerdmans.

--From Fear to Faith: Studies in the Book of Habakkuk. (Summit Bks.). 80p. 1982. pap. 2.95 (ISBN 0-8010-5620-9). Baker Bk.

--God's Ultimate Purpose. (Illus.). 12.95 (ISBN 0-8010-5591-1). Baker Bk.

--God's Way of Reconciliation: Studies in Ephesians II. 1972. 12.95 (ISBN 0-8010-5519-9). Baker Bk.

--II Peter. 15.95 (ISBN 0-85151-379-4). Banner of Truth.

--Life in the Spirit: In Marriage, Home & Work. 372p. 1975. Repr. 12.95 (ISBN 0-8010-5550-4). Baker Bk.

--Lloyd-Jones Expositions of Ephesians, 8 Vols. 1983. 95.00 (ISBN 0-8010-5623-3). Baker Bk.

--The Plight of Man & the Power of God. (Summit Bks.). 96p. 1982. pap. 2.95 (ISBN 0-8010-5621-7). Baker Bk.

--Preaching & Preachers. 325p. 1972. 15.95 (ISBN 0-310-27870-8, 10573). Zondervan.

--Revival. LC 86-72057. 320p. (Orig.). 1987. pap. 9.95 (ISBN 0-89107-415-5, Crossway Bks). Good News.

--Romans- The Gospel of God: An Exposition of Chapter 1. 416p. 1986. 16.95 (ISBN 0-310-27950-X, 10571). Zondervan.

--Romans: Assurance, Vol. 2. 272p. 1972. 14.95 (ISBN 0-310-27890-2, 10542). Zondervan.

--Romans: Atonement & Justification; an Exposition of Chapters 3: 20 - 4: 35, Vol. 1. 13.95 (ISBN 0-310-27880-5, 10561). Zondervan.

--Romans Five: Sons of God - Chapter 8: 17 - 39. 448p. 1975. 15.95 (ISBN 0-310-27920-8, 10592). Zondervan.

--Romans: The Law-Chapter 7: 1 to 8: 4. 368p. 1974. 14.95 (ISBN 0-310-27910-0, 10574); Six-volume Set. text ed. 87.70 (ISBN 0-310-27948-8, 10575). Zondervan.

--Romans: The New Man, Vol. 3. 1973. text ed. 14.95 (ISBN 0-310-27900-3, 10534). Zondervan.

--Spiritual Depression: Its Causes & Cure. 1965. pap. 5.95 (ISBN 0-8028-1387-9). Eerdmans.

--Studies in the Sermon on the Mount. 1984. 12.95 (ISBN 0-8028-0036-X). Eerdmans.

--Unsearchable Riches of Christ. 1980. 12.95 (ISBN 0-8010-5597-0). Baker Bk.

Lloyd-Jones, Hugh. The Justice of Zeus. 2nd ed. (Sather Classical Lectures: No. 41). 290p. 1983. pap. 8.95 (ISBN 0-520-04688-9). U of Cal Pr.

Lloyd-Jones, Martyn. The Cross. 192p. 1986. pap. 6.95 (ISBN 0-89107-382-5, Crossway Bks). Good News.

--The Sovereign Spirit: Discerning His Gifts. 160p. 1986. pap. 7.95 (ISBN 0-87788-697-0). Shaw Pubs.

Lloyd-Jones, Martyn, ed. Joy Unspeakable: Power & Renewal in the Holy Spirit. 284p. 1985. pap. 7.95 (ISBN 0-87788-441-2). Shaw Pubs.

Lloyd-Jones, Martyn D. De la Angoisse a la Foi. Tr. of From Fear to Faith. (Fr.). 1986. pap. 1.70 (ISBN 0-8297-0694-1). Life Pubs Intl.

Loader, Bill. What Does It Mean? 64p. (Orig.). 1985. pap. 6.95 (ISBN 0-85819-472-4, Pub. by JBCE). ANZ Religious Pubns.

Loader, J. A. Ecclesiastes. Van Der Woude, A. S., ed. Vriend, John, tr. from Dutch. (Text & Interpretation Commentary Ser.). 120p. (Orig.). 1986. pap. 6.95 (ISBN 0-8028-0102-1). Eerdmans.

Loader, Jamer A. Polar Structures in the Book of Qohelet. (Beihefte aur Zeitschrift fuer die alttestamentliche Wissenschaft). 150p. 1979. text ed. 32.75x (ISBN 3-11-007636-5). De Gruyter.

Loades, Ann see Eaton, Jeffrey C.

Loades, David M., ed. The End of Strife. 233p. 1984. 17.95 (ISBN 0-567-09347-6, PUb. by T&T Clark Ltd UK). Fortress.

Loane, Marcus. Grace & the Gentiles. 149p. (Orig.). 1981. pap. text ed. 6.45 (ISBN 0-85151-327-1). Banner of Truth.

Loane, Marcus L. Godliness & Contentment: Studies in the Three Pastoral Epistles. (Canterbury Bks.). 128p. (Orig.). 1982. pap. 5.95 (ISBN 0-8010-5619-5). Baker Bk.

--Makers of Puritan History. (Canterbury Bks). Orig. Title: Pioneers of Religious Freedom. 240p. 1980. pap. 6.95 (ISBN 0-8010-5593-8). Baker Bk.

--They Overcame: An Exposition of the First Three Chapters of Revelation. (Canterbury Books). 144p. 1981. pap. 3.95 (ISBN 0-8010-5609-8). Baker Bk.

Lobo, George V. A Guide to Christian Living: A New Compendium of Moral Theology. 420p. 1984. pap. 16.95 (ISBN 0-87061-092-9). Chr Classics.

Lo Bue, F., ed. The Turin Fragments of Tyconius' Commentary on Revelation. (Texts & Studies, N. S.: Vol. 7). Repr. of 1963 ed. 28.00 (ISBN 0-8115-1720-9). Kraus Repr.

Lochhaas, Philip H. How to Respond to Islam. 1981. pap. 1.95 (ISBN 0-570-07687-0, 12-2788). Concordia.

Lochman, Jan M. Encountering Marx: Bonds & Barriers between Christians & Marxists. Robertson, Edwin H., tr. LC 76-55827. pap. 39.00 (2026917). Bks Demand UMI.

--The Faith We Confess: An Ecumenical Dogmatics. Lewis, David, tr. LC 83-48908. 288p. 1984. 19.95 (ISBN 0-8006-0723-6, 1-723). Fortress.

--Signposts to Freedom: The Ten Commandments of Christian Ethics. Lewis, David, tr. LC 81-52283. 192p. (Orig.). 1982. pap. 10.95 (ISBN 0-8066-1915-5, 10-5767). Augsburg.

Lochner, Dorthy M. America's Aged. 0.50 (ISBN 0-911802-52-5). Free Church Pubns.

LoCigno, Joseph P., jt. ed. see Marcoux, Paul.

Lock, Walter. A Critical & Exegetical Commentary on The Pastoral Epistles. Driver, Samuel R., et al, eds. (International Critical Commentary Ser.). 212p. 1928. 22.95 (ISBN 0-567-05033-5, Pub. by T & T Clark Ltd UK). Fortress.

--John Keble. 1977. Repr. of 1895 ed. lib. bdg. 20.00 (ISBN 0-8495-3221-3). Arden Lib.

--John Keble. 1895. Repr. 20.00 (ISBN 0-8274-2626-7). R West.

Lockaby, George W. Sermon Outlines on Christian Living. LC 81-68536. 1981. pap. 2.95 (ISBN 0-8054-2244-7). Broadman.

--Sermon Outlines on the Person & Work of Christ. LC 80-67916. 1981. pap. 2.95 (ISBN 0-8054-2238-2). Broadman.

Locke, Don, jt. auth. see Weinreich-Haste, Helen.

Locke, Frederick W. Quest for the Holy Grail. LC 70-181948. (Stanford University. Stanford Studies in Language & Literature: No. 21). Repr. of 1960 ed. 22.50 (ISBN 0-404-51831-1). AMS Pr.

Locke, Hubert G., ed. The Barmen Confession: Papers from the Seattle Assembly. LC 86-23874. (Toronto Studies in Theology: Vol. 26). 370p. 1987. 59.95x (ISBN 0-88946-770-6). E Mellen.

--The Church Confronts the Nazis: Barmen Then & Now. (Toronto Studies in Theology: Vol. 16). 248p. 1984. 49.95x (ISBN 0-88946-762-5). E Mellen.

Locke, Hubert G., ed. see Niemoller, Martin.

Locke, John. A Paraphrase & Notes on the Epistles of St. Paul, 2 vols. (The Clarendon edition of the Works of John Locke). (Illus.). 800p. 1986. Set. 125.00x (ISBN 0-19-824801-6). Oxford U Pr.

--Reasonableness of Christianity & a Discourse of Miracles. Ramsey, I. T., ed. 1958. pap. 6.95x (ISBN 0-8047-0341-8). Stanford U Pr.

Locke, Raymond F. The Book of the Navajo. 3rd ed. pap. 4.95 (ISBN 0-87687-400-6, Pub. by Mankind Pub). Borden.

Lockerbie, D. Bruce. Asking Questions: A Classroom Model for Teaching the Bible. Zimmerman, Diane, ed. LC 80-18198. (Orig.). 1980. pap. text ed. 5.95 (ISBN 0-915134-75-6). Mott Media.

--The Cosmic Center: The Supremacy of Christ in a Secular Wasteland. LC 85-18741. (Critical Concern Bks.). 1986. Repr. of 1977 ed. 11.95 (ISBN 0-88070-132-3). Multnomah.

Lockerbie, D. Bruce, frwd. by see Gaebelein, Frank E.

Lockerbie, Jeanette. A Cup of Sugar, Neighbor. (Quiet Time Bks.). 128p. 1974. pap. 3.50 (ISBN 0-8024-1681-0). Moody.

--Forgive, Forget & Be Free. rev. ed. 160p. 1984. pap. 5.95 (ISBN 0-89840-068-6). Heres Life.

--More Salt in My Kitchen. LC 80-12357. (Quiet Time Bks.). 1980. pap. 3.50 (ISBN 0-8024-5668-5). Moody.

--A Plate of Hot Toast. (Quiet Time Bks.). 128p. (Orig.). 1971. pap. 3.50 (ISBN 0-8024-6625-7). Moody.

--The Quiet Moment: Devotions for the Golden Years. LC 82-7344. (Illus.). 96p. (Orig.). 1982. pap. 4.95 (ISBN 0-87239-606-1, 3009). Standard Pub.

--Time Out for Coffee. (Quiet Time Bks.). 1978. pap. 3.50 (ISBN 0-8024-8759-9). Moody.

--Twenty-Four Women's Programs: Please Pass the Fruit. 96p. (Orig.). 1986. pap. 4.95 (ISBN 0-87403-226-1, 2979). Standard Pub.

Lockerbie, Jeanette, jt. auth. see Graham, Franklinn.

Lockerbie, Jeanette W. Salt in My Kitchen. (Quiet Time Books). 1967. pap. 3.50 (ISBN 0-8024-7500-0). Moody.

Lockerbie, Jeannie. By Ones & By Twos: Single & Double Missionaries. LC 83-7272. (Mission Candidate Aids Ser.). 96p. 1983. pap. 4.95 (ISBN 0-87808-194-1). William Carey Lib.

Lockhart, Earl G., compiled by. My Vocation, by Eminent Americans; or, What Eminent Americans Think of Their Callings. LC 72-5602. (Essay Index Reprint Ser.). 1972. Repr. of 1938 ed. 32.00 (ISBN 0-8369-2997-7). Ayer Co Pubs.

Lockman, Vic. Biblical Economics in Comics. (Illus.). 112p. (Orig.). 1985. pap. 6.00 (ISBN 0-936175-00-1). V Lockman.

--The Catechism for Young Children with Cartoon, Bk. 1. (Illus., Orig.). 1984. pap. 1.00 (ISBN 0-936175-01-X); pap. text ed. 1.00 (ISBN 0-936175-03-6). V Lockman.

--God's Law for Modern Man: God's Law or Chaos. (Illus.). 150p. (Orig.). Date not set. pap. 9.95 (ISBN 0-936175-05-2). V Lockman.

Lockward, George, tr. see Elwood, Roger.

Lockwood, Laura E. Lexicon to the English Poetical Works of John Milton. LC 68-56596. (Bibliography & Reference Ser: No. 323). 1968. Repr. of 1907 ed. 32.00 (ISBN 0-8337-2132-1). B Franklin.

Lockwood, Loni, tr. see Steiner, Rudolf.

Lockwood, Samuel, tr. see Steiner, Rudolf.

Lockyer, Herbert. The All Series, Bks. 1-14. Incl. Bk. 1. All the Apostles of the Bible. 15.95 (ISBN 0-310-28010-9, 10052); Bk. 2. All the Books & Chapters of the Bible; Bk. 3. All the Doctrines of the Bible. 15.95 (ISBN 0-310-28050-8, 10082); Bk. 4. All the Children of the Bible; Bk. 5. All the Holy Days & Holidays; Bk. 6. All the Kings & Queens of the Bible; Bk. 7. All the Men of the Bible. 15.95 (ISBN 0-310-28080-X, 10054); Bk. 8. All the Women of the Bible. 14.95 (ISBN 0-310-28150-4, 10038); Bk. 9. All the Miracles of the Bible. 16.95 (ISBN 0-310-28100-8, 10066); Bk. 10. All the Parables of the Bible. 15.95 (ISBN 0-310-28110-5, 10075); Bk. 11. All the Prayers of the Bible. 15.95 (ISBN 0-310-28120-2, 10041); Bk. 12. All the Promises of the Bible. 16.95 (ISBN 0-310-28130-X, 10074); Bk. 13. All the Trades & Occupations of the Bible; Bk. 14. All the Messianic Prophecies of the Bible. 19.95 (ISBN 0-310-28090-7, 10076). Zondervan.

--All the Divine Names & Titles in the Bible. 352p. 1975. 15.95 (ISBN 0-310-28040-0, 10077). Zondervan.

--Everything Jesus Taught. LC 83-48431. 576p. 1984. pap. 6.95 (ISBN 0-06-065259-4, RD 503, HarpR). Har-Row.

--The Holy Spirit of God. 240p. (Orig.). 1983. pap. 5.50 (ISBN 0-687-17323-X). Abingdon.

--Love Is Better Than Wine. LC 80-84903. 1981. pap. 3.95 (ISBN 0-89221-083-4). New Leaf.

--Retratos del Salvador. Tr. of Portraits of the Savior. (Span.). 192p. 1986. pap. 3.50 (ISBN 0-8297-0741-7). Life Pubs Intl.

--Sins of Saints. LC 75-108378. 1970. pap. 5.95 (ISBN 0-87213-532-2). Loizeaux.

Lockyer, Herbert, ed. Light to Live By (Wedding Edition) 384p. 1981. graduation ed. 9.95 (ISBN 0-310-28230-6, 10145); pap. 9.95 all-occasion ed. (ISBN 0-310-28211-X, 10124P). Zondervan.

Lockyer, Herbert, ed. see Thomas, David.

Lockyer, Herbert, Sr., ed. Nelson's Illustrated Bible Dictionary. 1088p. 1986. 26.95 (ISBN 0-8407-4955-4). Nelson.

Locock, K. B., ed. see De Deguilleville, Guillaume.

Loder, James E. The Transforming Moment: Understanding Convictional Experiences. LC 80-8354. 256p. 1981. 15.45 (ISBN 0-06-065276-4, HarpR). Har-Row.

Loder, Ted. Guerrillas of Grace: Prayers for the Battle. 2nd ed. LC 84-26096. (Illus.). 133p. (Orig.). 1984. pap. 9.95 (ISBN 0-931055-04-0). LuraMedia.

--No One But Us: Personal Reflections on Public Sanctuary. LC 86-7516. 224p. (Orig.). 1986. pap. 9.95 (ISBN 0-931055-09-1). LuraMedia.

--Sand in the Cloud: Voices of Old Testament Witnesses. Broucek, Marcia, ed. 180p. (Orig.). 1987. pap. 9.95 (ISBN 0-931055-42-3). LuraMedia.

Lodge, Ann, ed. Creation Sings. 1980. pap. 1.25 (ISBN 0-664-10091-0). Westminster.

Lodge, David, ed. see Eliot, George.

Lodge, Richard. Richelieu. LC 77-112812. 1970. Repr. of 1896 ed. 23.00x (ISBN 0-8046-1079-7, Pub. by Kennikat). Assoc Faculty Pr.

Lodo, Venerable L. Bardo Teachings: The Way of Death & Rebirth. Clark, Nancy & Parke, Caroline M., eds. LC 82-21372. (Illus.). 76p. 1982. pap. text ed. 5.95 (ISBN 0-910165-00-9). KDK Pubns.

Lodo, Venerable Larma. The Quintessence of the Animate & Inanimate: A Discourse on the Holy Dharma. Clark, Nancy & Parke, Caroline, eds. LC 85-2290. (Illus.). 238p. 1985. pap. 11.95 (ISBN 0-910165-01-7). KDK Pubns.

Lods, Adolphe. Israel, from Its Beginning to the Middle of the Eighth Century. Hooke, S. H., tr. LC 75-41180. 1948. 34.75 (ISBN 0-404-14569-8). AMS PR.

--Prophets & the Rise of Judaism. Hooke, S. H., tr. LC 77-109772. (Illus.). 1971. Repr. of 1937 ed. lib. bdg. 25.75x (ISBN 0-8371-4262-8, LOPR). Greenwood.

Loeb, Edwin M. Blood Sacrifice Complex. LC 24-4020. (Amer Archaeology Association Memoirs Ser.). 1924. pap. 15.00 (ISBN 0-527-00529-0). Kraus Repr.

Loeb, L., ed. Outcaste: Jewish Life in Southern Iran. (Library of Anthropology). 354p. 1977. 42.95 (ISBN 0-677-04530-1). Gordon & Breach.

Loeb, Sorel G. & Kadden, Barbara B. Jewish History - Moments & Methods: An Activity Source Book for Teachers. LC 82-71283. (Illus.). 150p. (Orig.). 1982. pap. text ed. 10.00 (ISBN 0-86705-008-X). AIRE.

--Teaching Torah: A Treasury of Activities & Insights. LC 84-70318. 300p. 1984. pap. text ed. 15.00 (ISBN 0-86705-013-6). AIRE.

Loeffler, Chris & Hunsberger, Eydie M. Eydie Mae: How I Conquered Cancer Naturally. pap. 2.95 (ISBN 0-932638-01-5). Prod Hse.

Loeks, Mary F. The Glorious Names of God. 1986. pap. 3.95 (ISBN 0-8010-5629-2). Baker Bk.

--Good Morning, Lord: Devotions for Young Mothers. (Good Morning, Lord Ser.). 1977. 4.95 (ISBN 0-8010-5566-0). Baker Bk.

--Mom's Quiet Corner. (Comtempo Ser.). 1977. pap. 1.25 (ISBN 0-8010-5576-8). Baker Bk.

Loeks, Mary Foxwell. Object Lessons for Children's Worship. (Object Lesson Ser). 1979. pap. 3.50 (ISBN 0-8010-5584-9). Baker Bk.

Loer, Barbara. Das Absolute & die Wirklichkeit in Schellings Philosophie: Mit der Erstedition einer Handschrift aus dem Berliner Schelling-Nachlass. LC 73-93164. (Quellen & Studien zur Philosophie, Vol. 7). (Illus.). viii, 288p. 1974. 53.20x (ISBN 3-11-004329-7). De Gruyter.

Loeschen, John R. The Divine Community: Trinity, Church, & Ethics in Reformation Theologies. (Sixteenth Century Essays & Studies Ser.: Vol. I). 238p. 1981. 25.00x (ISBN 0-940474-01-8). Sixteenth Cent.

Loescher, Frank S. The Protestant Church & the Negro, a Pattern of Segregation. LC 76-135601. 159p. 1972. Repr. of 1948 ed. text ed. cancelled (ISBN 0-8371-5193-7, LPC&, Pub. by Negro U Pr). Greenwood.

Loescher, Gilburt D., jt. ed. see Kommers, Donald P.

Loetscher, Lefferts A. A Brief History of the Presbyterians: With a New Chapter by George Laird Hunt. 4th ed. LC 83-21652. 224p. 1984. pap. 4.95 (ISBN 0-664-24622-2). Westminster.

--Facing the Enlightenment & Pietism: Archibald Alexander & the Founding of Princeton Theological Seminary. LC 82-11995. (Contributions to the Study of Religion Ser.: No. 8). x, 303p. 1983. lib. bdg. 35.00 (ISBN 0-313-23677-1, LOE/). Greenwood.

Loew, M. R. Mission to the Poorest. 184p. 1984. pap. 7.95 (ISBN 0-7220-5524-2). Chr Classics.

Loewe, H., jt. ed. see Montefiore, C. G.

Loewe, Michael. Chinese Ideas of Life & Death. 240p. 1982. China Stands Up - see attached. text ed. 25.00x (ISBN 0-04-180001-X). Allen Unwin.

--Ways to Paradise: The Chinese Quest for Immortality. (Illus.). 1979. text ed. 34.00x (ISBN 0-04-181025-2). Allen Unwin.

Loewen, Harry. Goethe's Response to Protestantism. (Canadian Studies in German Language & Literature: Vol. 7). 168p. 1972. pap. 19.60. P Lang Pubs.

Loewen, Howard J., ed. One Lord, One Church, One Hope, & One God. (Text-Reader Ser.: No. 2). 369p. 1985. pap. text ed. 12.00x (ISBN 0-936273-08-9). Inst Mennonite.

Loewen, Jacob A. Culture & Human Values: Christian Intervention in Anthropological Perspective. Smalley, William A., ed. LC 75-12653. (Applied Cultural Anthropology Ser.). 443p. (Orig.). 1975. pap. 10.95x (ISBN 0-87808-722-2). William Carey Lib.

Loewenberg, Robert J. An American Idol: Emerson & the "Jewish Idea". LC 84-7206. 148p. (Orig.). 1984. lib. bdg. 20.75 (ISBN 0-8191-3955-6); pap. text ed. 9.25 (ISBN 0-8191-3956-4). U Pr of Amer.

Loewenich, Walter von see Von Loewenich, Walter.

Loewenich, Walther von. Martin Luther: The Man & His Work. Denef, Lawrence W., tr. from Ger. LC 83-70513. Tr. of Martin Luther: Der Mann und das Werk. 448p. 1986. text ed. 19.95 (ISBN 0-8066-2019-6, 10-4296). Augsburg.

Loewenich, Walther Von see Von Loewenich, Walther.

Lofgren, Mikal. Wheat: Humor & Wisdom of J. Golden Kimball. LC 80-81556. 95p. 1980. 6.50 (ISBN 0-936718-04-8). Moth Hse.

Lofland, John. Doomsday Cult: A Study of Conversion, Proselytization, & Maintenance of Faith. enl. ed. LC 77-23028. 1981. 29.00 (ISBN 0-8290-1111-0); pap. text ed. 12.95x (ISBN 0-8290-0095-X). Irvington.

Lofstedt, Bengt M. & Packard, David W. A Concordance to the Sermons of Bishop Zeno of Verona. (APA Philological Monographs). 1974. 37.00 (ISBN 0-89130-715-X, 40-00-32). Scholars Pr GA.

Lofthouse, William F. Israel after the Exile: Sixth & Fifth Centuries B. C. LC 78-10629. (Illus.). 1979. Repr. of 1928 ed. lib. bdg. 24.75x (ISBN 0-313-21008-X, LOIS). Greenwood.

Lofton, Fred C. Teach Us To Pray: The Disciples Request Cast Anew. 96p. 1983. pap. 4.00 (ISBN 0-89191-751-9). Prog Bapt Pub.

Logan, A. H. & Wedderburn, A. J., eds. New Testament & Gnosis. 272p. 1983. 22.95 (ISBN 0-567-09344-1, Pub. by T&T Clark Ltd UK). Fortress.

Logan, H. M. The Dialect of the "Life of Saint Katherine". A Linguistic Study of the Phonology & Inflections. (Janua Linguarum Ser. Practica: No. 130). 1973. pap. text ed. 34.40x (ISBN 0-686-22600-3). Mouton.

Logan, Natale, ed. The Catholic Periodical & Literature Index. Incl. Vol. 2 1934-38. 50.00 (ISBN 0-87507-010-8); Vol. 4. 1943-48. 50.00 (ISBN 0-87507-011-6); Vol. 10. 1959-60. 30.00 (ISBN 0-87507-012-4); Vol. 11. 1961-62; Vol. 12. 1963-64. 40.00 (ISBN 0-87507-014-0); Vol. 14. 1967-68. 40.00 (ISBN 0-87507-015-9); Vol. 15. 1969-70. 45.00 (ISBN 0-87507-016-7); Vol. 16. 1971-72. 60.00 (ISBN 0-87507-017-5); Vol. 17. 1973-1974. 55.00 (ISBN 0-87507-018-3); Vol. 18. 60.00 (ISBN 0-87507-019-1, 1975-1976); Vol. 19. 70.00 (ISBN 0-87507-020-5, 1977-1978); Vol. 21. 90.00 (ISBN 0-87507-025-6, 1981-1982). LC 70-649588. Orig. Title: The Catholic Periodical Index & The Guide to Catholic Literature. Cath Lib Assn.

Logan, Samuel T., Jr., ed. The Preacher & Preaching: Reviving the Art in the Twentieth Century. 480p. 1986. 16.95 (ISBN 0-87552-294-7). Presby & Reformed.

Loge, Marc, tr. see Steinilber-Oberlin, Emile.

Logeman, H., ed. Benedictus, Saint, Abbot of Monte Cassino: The Rule of S. Benet. (EETS, OS Ser.: No. 90). Repr. of 1888 ed. 18.00 (ISBN 0-527-00089-2). Kraus Repr.

Logsdon, S. Franklin. Lingering at Calvary. 157p. (Orig.). 1981. pap. 3.95 (ISBN 0-89323-025-1). Bible Memory.

Loh, ed. A Festival of Asian Christmas Music: Christmas Music from Hongkong, India, Indonesia, Malaysia, Philippines & Taiwan. (Asian Inst. for Liturgy & Music Anthems Ser: No. 2). 68p. (Orig.). 1984. pap. 8.50x (ISBN 971-10-0228-0, Pub. by New Day Philippines). Cellar.

Loh, I. & Nida, E. A. Translator's Handbook on Paul's Letter to the Philippians. LC 82-17585. (Helps for Translators Ser.). 167p. 1977. 3.30x (ISBN 0-8267-0144-2, 08528, Pub. by United Bible). Am Bible.

Lohan, Maria, jt. ed. see Lohan, Robert.

Lohan, Robert & Lohan, Maria, eds. A New Christmas Treasury: With More Stories for Reading Aloud. LC 54-12862. 14.50 (ISBN 0-8044-2536-1, Pub. by Stephen Daye Pr). Ungar.

Lohfink, Gerhard. The Bible, Now I Get It: A Form Criticism Handbook. LC 78-1209. (Illus.). 1979. pap. 7.95 (ISBN 0-385-13432-0). Doubleday.

--The Conversion of Saint Paul: Narrative & History in Acts. Malina, Bruce J., ed. & tr. 156p. 1976. 5.95 (ISBN 0-8199-0572-0). Franciscan Herald.

--Jesus & Community: The Social Dimension of Christian Faith. Galvin, John P., tr. LC 84-47928. 224p. 1984. pap. 9.95 (ISBN 0-8006-1802-5). Fortress.

--Jesus & Community: The Social Dimension of Christian Faith. 224p. 1985. pap. 9.95 (ISBN 0-8091-2661-3). Paulist Pr.

--The Last Day of Jesus. Attanasio, Salvator, tr. from Ger. LC 83-73026. Tr. of De Letzte Tag Jesu. 80p. 1984. pap. 2.95 (ISBN 0-87793-312-X). Ave Maria.

--The Work of God Goes On. LC 86-45202. (The Bible for Christian Life Ser.). 80p. 1987. pap. 4.95 (ISBN 0-8006-2026-7). Fortress.

Lohfink, Norbert. Great Themes from the Old Testament. 1981. 10.95 (ISBN 0-8199-0801-0). Franciscan Herald.

Lohkamp, Nicholas. Living the Good News: An Introduction to Moral Theology. 170p. (Orig.). 1982. pap. text ed. 4.50 (ISBN 0-86716-016-0). St Anthony Mess Pr.

Lohmeyer, Ernst. Lord of the Temple: A Study of the Relation Between Cult & Gospel. LC 62-18409. 1961. text ed. 8.50x (ISBN 0-8401-1423-0). A R Allenson.

Lohne, Alf. Adventists in Russia. Woolsey, Raymond H., ed. 160p. (Orig.). 1987. pap. 9.95 (ISBN 0-8280-0373-4). Review & Herald.

Lohr, Andrew. Talks on Mystic Christianity. Challgren, Patricia & Crater, Mildred, eds. LC 84-90346. (Illus.). 152p. (Orig.). 1984. pap. 6.50 (ISBN 0-9613401-0-X). Fiery Water.

Lohse, Bernhard. Martin Luther: An Introduction to His Life & Work. Schultz, Robert C., tr. from Ger. LC 85-45496. 304p. 1986. 26.95 (ISBN 0-8006-0764-3, 1-764); pap. 16.95 (ISBN 0-8006-1964-1, 1-1964). Fortress.

--A Short History of Christian Doctrine: From the First Century to the Present. rev American ed. Stoeffer, F. Ernest, tr. from Ger. LC 66-21732. 320p. 1978. pap. 9.95 (ISBN 0-8006-1341-4, 1-1341). Fortress.

Lohse, Eduard. Colossians & Philemon. Koester, Helmut, ed. Poehlman, William R. & Karris, Robert J., trs. from Ger. LC 76-157550. (Hermeneia: A Critical & Historical Commentary on the Bible Ser). 256p. 1971. 22.95 (ISBN 0-8006-6001-3, 20-6001). Fortress.

--The First Christians: Their Beginnings, Writings, & Beliefs. LC 82-7454. 128p. (Orig.). 1983. pap. 6.95 (ISBN 0-8006-1646-4, 1-1646). Fortress.

Lohse, Edward. The Formation of the New Testament. Boring, M. Eugene, tr. LC 80-27032. 256p. (Orig.). 1981. pap. 9.95 (ISBN 0-687-13294-0). Abingdon.

--The New Testament Environment. Steely, John E., tr. from Ger. LC 75-43618. 320p. 1976. pap. 10.95 (ISBN 0-687-27944-5). Abingdon.

Loisy, Alfred F. My Duel with the Vatican: The Autobiography of a Catholic Modernist. Boynton, Richard W., tr. 1968. Repr. of 1924 ed. lib. bdg. 22.50 (ISBN 0-8371-0148-4, LODV). Greenwood.

Lojnikov, Paul. Seven Years Conversing with Spirits. 1987. 6.95 (ISBN 0-533-07213-1). Vantage.

Lokhande, Ajit. Tukarama, His Person & His Religion: A Relio-Historical, Phenomenological & Typological Enquiry. (European University Studies: Series 20, Philosophy: Vol. 22). 210p. 1976. 23.50 (ISBN 3-261-02009-1). P Lang Pubs.

Lomatuway'ma, Michael, jt. auth. see Geertz, Armin W.

Lomatuway'ma, Michael, jt. auth. see Malotki, Ekkehart.

Lomax, Louis E. When the Word Is Given... A Report on Elijah Muhammad, Malcolm X, & the Black Muslim World. LC 78-14002. (Illus.). 1979. Repr. of 1964 ed. lib. bdg. 22.50x (ISBN 0-313-21002-0, LOWW). Greenwood.

Lombardo, Edith F., jt. auth. see Lombardo, Victor S.

Lombardo, Victor S. & Lombardo, Edith F. Kids Grieve Too! (Illus.). 88p. 1986. 17.75x (ISBN 0-398-05275-1). C C Thomas.

Lomperis, Timothy. Hindu Influence on Greek Philosophy. 1985. 9.00x (ISBN 0-8364-1311-3). South Asia Bks.

Lonchyna, Taras, jt. auth. see Zinkewych, Osyp.

London County Council. The Parishes of Christ Church & All Saints & the Liberties of Norton Folgate & the Old Artillery Ground. LC 74-6547. (London County Council. Survey of London: No. 27). Repr. of 1957 ed. 74.50 (ISBN 0-404-51677-7). AMS Pr.

--Survey of London: The Parish of St. Mary Lambeth. Pt. 2, Southern Area. LC 74-6546. Repr. of 1956 ed. 74.50 (ISBN 0-404-51676-9). AMS Pr.

London, Hannah. Miniatures & Silhouttes of Early American Jews. (Illus.). 199p. 25.00 (ISBN 0-686-47008-7). Apollo.

London, Hannah R. Miniatures & Silhouettes of Early American Jews. LC 78-87797. (Illus.). 1969. Repr. 16.50 (ISBN 0-8048-0657-8). C E Tuttle.

--Portraits of Jews by Gilbert Stuart & Other Early American Artists. LC 69-19613. (Illus.). 1969. Repr. 13.75 (ISBN 0-8048-0459-1). C E Tuttle.

London Missionary Society. London Missionary Society's Report of the Proceedings Against the Late Rev. J. Smith of Demerara, Who Was Tried Under Martial Law & Condemned to Death, on a Charge of Aiding & Assisting in a Rebellion of Negro Slaves. LC 78-79809. Repr. of 1824 ed. 22.50x (ISBN 0-8371-1506-X, LMS&, Pub. by Negro U Pr). Greenwood.

London. St. Bartholomew's Priory. The Book of the Foundation of St. Bartholomew's Church in London. (EETS, OS Ser.: No. 163). 1923. pap. 12.00 (ISBN 0-527-00160-0). Kraus Repr.

London - St. Paul'S Cathedral. Documents Illustrating the History of St. Paul's Cathedral. Simpson, W. S., ed. 1880. 27.00 (ISBN 0-384-55530-6). Johnson Repr.

London-St. Paul'S Cathedral. Domesday of Saint Paul of the Year Twelve Twenty-Two. Repr. of 1858 ed. 37.00 (ISBN 0-384-33475-X). Johnson Repr.

London - St. Paul'S Cathedral. Visitations of Churches Belonging to St. Paul's Cathedral in 1297 & 1458. Repr. of 1895 ed. 27.00 (ISBN 0-384-33490-3). Johnson Repr.

London Times. The Bible Today: Historical, Social, & Literary Aspects of the Old & New Testaments. LC 78-6130. 1978. Repr. of 1955 ed. lib. bdg. cancelled (ISBN 0-313-20449-7, TIBT). Greenwood.

Lonergan, Bernard. Method in Theology. LC 78-181008. 1979. pap. 11.50 (ISBN 0-8164-2204-4, HarpR). Har-Row.

Lonergan, Bernard J. A Second Collection. LC 74-14798. 314p. 1975. 12.00 (ISBN 0-664-20721-9). Westminster.

Lonergan, Bernard J. F. Understanding & Being: An Introduction & Companion to Insight. Morelli, Elizabeth A. & Morelli, Mark D., eds. (Toronto Studies in Theology: Vol. 5). xii, 368p. 1980. 59.95x (ISBN 0-88946-909-1). E Mellen.

Long, tr. see Kierkegaard, Soren.

Long, Burke O. I Kings, with an Introduction to Historical Literature, 24 Vols, Vol. 9. Knierim, Rolf & Tucker, Gene, eds. (The Forms of the Old Testament Literature Ser.). 288p. (Orig.). 1984. pap. 20.95 (ISBN 0-8028-1920-6). Eerdmans.

--The Problem of Etiological Narrative in the Old Testament. (Beiheft 108 zur Zeitschrift fuer die alttestamentliche Wissenschaft). 1968. 15.50x (ISBN 3-11-005590-2). De Gruyter.

Long, Burke O., ed. Images of Man & God: Old Testament Short Stories in Literary Focus. (Bible & Literature Ser.: No. 1). 128p. 1981. text ed. 19.95x (ISBN 0-907459-00-5, Pub. by Almond Pr England); pap. text ed. 6.95x (ISBN 0-907459-01-3). Eisenbrauns.

Long, Charles H. Alpha: The Myths of Creation. LC 82-21532. (AAR-SP Classics in Religious Studies). 320p. 1982. Repr. of 1963 ed. 13.50x (ISBN 0-89130-604-8, 01-05-04). Scholars Pr GA.

--Significations: Signs, Symbols & Images in the Interpretation of Religion. LC 85-45495. 208p. 1986. pap. 12.95 (ISBN 0-8006-1892-0, 1-1892). Fortress.

--Vancouver Voices. 144p. (Orig.). 1983. pap. 1.40 (ISBN 0-88028-026-3). Forward Movement.

Long, Charles H., ed. Anglican Cycle of Prayer, Nineteen Eighty-Seven. (Partners in Prayer Ser.). (Illus.). 128p. (Orig.). 1986. pap. 1.75 (ISBN 0-88028-053-0). Forward Movement.

Long, Charles H., ed. see Allen, Roland.

Long, David. The Hajj Today: A Survey of the Contemporary Pilgrimage to Makkah. (Illus.). 1979. 34.50 (ISBN 0-87395-382-7). State U NY Pr.

Long, E. B. The Saints & the Union: Utah Territory During the Civil War. LC 80-16775. (Illus.). 292p. 1981. 22.50 (ISBN 0-252-00821-9). U of Ill Pr.

Long, Edward L., Jr. Peace Thinking in a Warring World. LC 83-14675. 118p. 1983. pap. 6.95 (ISBN 0-664-24503-X). Westminster.

--A Survey of Christian Ethics. 1967. pap. 12.95x (ISBN 0-19-503242-X). Oxford U Pr.

--A Survey of Recent Christian Ethics. 1982. pap. 8.95x (ISBN 0-19-503160-1). Oxford U Pr.

Long, Edward S. An E. T. Christmas: Two Nativity Dramas. 1985. 3.25 (ISBN 0-89536-763-7, 5870). CSS of Ohio.

--Go Forth into the World. 1983. 3.10 (ISBN 0-89536-604-5, 0732). CSS of Ohio.

--Two Nativity Dramas. 1984. 4.75 (ISBN 0-89536-697-5, 4874). CSS of Ohio.

Long, Eugene T. Existence, Being & God: An Introduction to the Philosophical Theology of John Mcquarrie. LC 84-16566. 144p. 1985. 17.95 (ISBN 0-913729-02-7); pap. 10.95 (ISBN 0-913729-08-6). Paragon Hse.

Long, Eugene T., jt. ed. see Clarke, Bowman.

Long, Eugene Thomas, ed. God, Secularization, and History: Essays in Memory of Ronald Gregor Smith. LC 73-15712. (Illus.). xiv, 164p. 1974. 21.95x (ISBN 0-87249-293-1). U of SC Pr.

Long, Haniel. Notes for a New Mythology: Pittsburgh Memoranda, 2 Vols. in 1. 1971. Repr. of 1926 ed. 27.00 (ISBN 0-384-33540-3). Johnson Repr.

Long, Huey B. Adult Education in Church & Synagogue. LC 73-13292. (Ocassional Paper Ser.: No. 37). 1973. pap. 2.50 (ISBN 0-87060-061-3, OCP 37). Syracuse U Cont Ed.

Long, J. B., ed. Judaism & the Christian Seminary Curriculum. 166p. pap. 2.95 (ISBN 0-686-95180-8). ADL.

Long, J. Bruce, jt. ed. see Clothey, Fred.

Long, James. What Is Man? Leader's Guide. Chao, Lorna Y., tr. (Basic Doctrine Ser.). 1986. pap. write for info. (ISBN 0-941598-36-5). Living Spring Pubns.

Long, James A. Expanding Horizons. LC 65-24093. 1965. pap. 3.50 (ISBN 0-911500-75-8). Theos U Pr.

Long, Jim, ed. How Could God Let This Happen. (Campus Life Bks). 160p. 1986. pap. 5.95 (ISBN 0-8423-1377-X). Tyndale.

Long, Marvin R. God's Works Through Elvis. 1979. 4.00 (ISBN 0-682-49294-9). Exposition Pr FL.

Long, Max F. What Jesus Taught in Secret. (Illus.). 144p. 1983. pap. 5.95 (ISBN 0-87516-510-9). De Vorss.

Long, Mildred. Listen to the Silence. (Orig.). 1970. pap. 2.50 (ISBN 0-87516-049-2). De Vorss.

Long, Theodore E., jt. ed. see Hadden, Jeffrey K.

Long, Thomas. Shepherds & Bathrobes. (Orig.). 1987. pap. price not set (ISBN 0-89536-869-2, 7855). CSS of Ohio.

Long, Tic, ed. Resource Directory for Youth Workers, 1985. 128p. (Orig.). 1985. pap. 8.95 (ISBN 0-687-36167-2). Abingdon.

Long, Valentine. Angels in Religion & Art. LC 77-117712. 1971. pap. 2.95 (ISBN 0-8199-0430-9). Franciscan Herald.

--The Mother of God. 1977. 7.95 (ISBN 0-8199-0619-0). Franciscan Herald.

Longacre, Doris. More-with-Less Cookbook. LC 75-23563. 320p. 1976. pap. 9.95 (ISBN 0-8361-1786-7). Herald Pr.

Longacre, Robert E., ed. OPTAT: Occasional Papers in Translation & Textlinguistics, Studies in Translation, Discourse Analysis, & Related Areas of Biblical Research. 88p. (Orig.). 1986. pap. 5.00 (ISBN 0-88312-668-0). Summer Inst Ling.

Longenecker, Richard N. The Christology of Early Jewish Christianity. (Twin Brooks Ser.). 178p. 1981. pap. 8.95 (ISBN 0-8010-5610-1). Baker Bk.

--Ministry & Message of Paul. (Contemporary Evangelical Perspective Ser). 1971. kivar 6.95 (ISBN 0-310-28341-8, 12234P). Zondervan.

--New Testament Social Ethics for Today. 128p. (Orig.). 1984. pap. 5.95 (ISBN 0-8028-1992-3). Eerdmans.

Longenecker, Richard N., jt. auth. see Tenney, Merrill C.

Longford, Lord. Pope John Paul II: An Authorized Biography. LC 82-8001. (Illus.). 208p. 1982. 20.50 (ISBN 0-688-01393-7). Morrow.

Longley, Edna, jt. ed. see Dawe, Gerald.

Longmire, Linda, jt. ed. see Cernic, David.

Longstaff, R. W., jt. ed. see Orchard, D. B.

Longstaff, Thomas R. Evidence of Conflation in Mark? A Study in the Synoptic Problem. LC 76-40001. (Society of Biblical Literature. Dissertation Ser.: No. 28). (Illus.). 1977. pap. 9.95 (ISBN 0-89130-086-4, 060128). Scholars Pr GA.

Longstaff, Thomas R. W., jt. auth. see Tyson, Joseph B.

Longstreet, Stephen. More Drawings of Rembrandt. (Master Draughtsman Ser). 48p. treasure trove bdg. 10.95x (ISBN 0-87505-054-9); pap. 4.95 (ISBN 0-87505-207-X). Borden.

Longstreet, Stephen, ed. see Van Rijn Rembrandt, Hermansz.

Longsworth, Robert M. Cornish Ordinalia: Religion & Dramaturgy. LC 67-22869. 1967. 12.50x (ISBN 0-674-17200-0). Harvard U Pr.

Lonigan, Paul R. Early Irish Church: From the Beginnings to the Two Doves. 2nd ed. (Illus.). 100p. 1986. pap. 15.99x (ISBN 0-9614753-1-5). Celt Heritage Pr.

Lonning, Per. The Dilemma of Contemporary Theology Prefigured in Luther, Pascal, Kierkegaard, Nietzsche. LC 78-16470. 1978. Repr. of 1962 ed. lib. bdg. cancelled (ISBN 0-313-20596-5, LODC). Greenwood.

Loofs, Richard. Nestorius & His Place in the History of the Christian Doctrine. LC 75-1225. 1975. Repr. of 1914 ed. 18.50 (ISBN 0-8337-4903-X). B Franklin.

Loomis, Darlene. Growing Together with Guys, Gals & Animal Pals. (Illus., Orig.). 1977. pap. 2.00 (ISBN 0-686-36276-4). Drain Enterprise.

--He Touched Me. (Illus.). 62p. (Orig.). 1977. pap. 3.00 (ISBN 0-686-36275-6). Drain Enterprise.

--Joint Heirs in Christ. (Illus., Orig.). 1977. pap. 2.00 (ISBN 0-686-36277-2). Drain Enterprise.

--On Fire for God. (Illus.). 53p. (Orig.). 1976. 2.00 (ISBN 0-686-36274-8). Drain Enterprise.

--Those Who Won't & Those Who Will. (Illus.). 12p. (Orig.). 1977. pap. 1.00 (ISBN 0-686-36278-0). Drain Enterprise.

Loomis, Evarts G. & Paulson, Sig. Healing for Everyone. 2nd, rev. ed. LC 74-345. (Illus., Orig.). 1979. pap. 5.95 (ISBN 0-87516-377-7). De Vorss.

Loomis, Farnsworth W. God Within. (Illus.). 1968. 5.95 (ISBN 0-8079-0122-9). October.

Loomis, Louis R., jt. ed. see Shotwell, James T.

Loomis, Louise R., tr. Book of the Popes. 1965. lib. bdg. 19.50x (ISBN 0-374-95093-8, Octagon). Hippocrene Bks.

Loomis, Roger S. Celtic Myth & Arthurian Romance. LC 67-31638. (Arthurian Legend & Literature Ser., No. 1). 1969. Repr. of 1927 ed. lib. bdg. 75.00x (ISBN 0-8383-0586-5). Haskell.

Loomis, Roger S. & Wells, Henry W., eds. Representative Medieval & Tudor Plays. LC 77-111109. (Play Anthology Reprint Ser). 1942. 22.50 (ISBN 0-8369-8202-9). Ayer Co Pubs.

Loomis, Samuel L. Modern Cities & Their Religious Problems. LC 73-112558. (Rise of Urban America). 1970. Repr. of 1887 ed. 23.50 (ISBN 0-405-02464-9). Ayer Co Pubs.

Loori, John D., jt. auth. see Maezumi, Hakuyu T.

Loos, Amandus W., ed. Religious Faith & World Culture. LC 71-128270. (Essay Index Reprint Ser). 1951. 20.00 (ISBN 0-8369-1976-9). Ayer Co Pubs.

Loos, Amandus W., tr. see Brunner, Emil.

Looy, H. van der see Van der Looy, H.

Lopatto, Paul. Religion & the Presidential Election. LC 84-26281. (American Political Parties & Elections Ser.). 192p. 1985. 34.95 (ISBN 0-03-001474-3, C0138). Praeger.

Lopeshinskaya, Elena. Martyr Bishop Confessors under Communism. (Rus.). pap. 5.00 (ISBN 0-686-05413-X). Eastern Orthodox.

Lopez, Albert C., tr. see Ray, C. A.

Lopez, Alberto, tr. see Edge, Findley B.

Lopez, Barry H. Desert Notes: Reflections in the Eye of a Raven. LC 76-6099. (Illus.). 96p. 1976. 6.95 (ISBN 0-8362-0661-4). Andrews McMeel Parker.

--Giving Birth to Thunder, Sleeping with His Daughter: Coyote Builds North America. LC 77-17395. 1978. 8.95 (ISBN 0-8362-0726-2). Andrews McMeel Parker.

Lopez, Donald S, Jr. A Study of Svatantrika. 490p. (Orig.). 1987. lib. bdg. 35.00 (ISBN 0-937938-20-3); pap. 19.95 (ISBN 0-937938-19-X). Snow Lion.

Lopez, Donald S., Jr. & Rockefeller, Stephen C., eds. The Christ & the Bodhisattva. (Buddhist Studies). 304p. (Orig.). 1987. 44.50X (ISBN 0-88706-401-9); pap. 14.95X (ISBN 0-88706-402-7). State U NY Pr.

L'Orange, H. P. Studies on the Iconography of Cosmic Kingship in the Ancient World. (Illus.). 206p. 1982. Repr. of 1953 ed. lib. bdg. 50.00X (ISBN 0-89241-150-3). Caratzas.

Lorbeer, Floyd I. Philosophy of Light: An Introductory Treatise. 259p. 1981. pap. 15.00 (ISBN 0-89540-102-9, SB-102). Sun Pub.

Lorber, Jakob. The Dream of Zorel. Ozols, Violet, tr. from Ger. 124p. 1985. pap. cancelled (ISBN 0-934616-17-5). Valkyrie Pub Hse.

--The Lord's Sermons. Ozols, Violet & Von Koerber, Hildegard, trs. from Ger. LC 80-50280. (Jakob Lorber Ser.). 278p. 1981. 15.95 (ISBN 0-934616-06-X). Valkyrie Pub Hse.

--The Three Days Scene at the Temple in Jerusalem. 2nd ed. Nordewin, Dr. & Von Koerber, Hildegard, trs. from Ger. LC 82-83492. 128p. 1982. pap. 6.00 (ISBN 0-934616-10-8). Valkyrie Pub Hse.

Lorch, Netanel. One Long War. 1976. 8.00 (ISBN 0-685-82597-3). Herzl Pr.

Lord, Daniel A. Played by Ear. LC 56-7099. (Illus.). 1956. 11.95 (ISBN 0-8294-0049-4). Loyola.

Lord, Eileen, jt. auth. see Lord, Luther.

Lord, F. Townley. Acts of the Apostles (Missionary Message of the New Testament) 119p. 1946. 2.95 (ISBN 0-87921-003-6). Attic Pr.

Lord, J. Raymond, tr. see Conzelmann, Hans.

Lord, James H. The Jews in India & the Far East. LC 70-97292. 1976. Repr. of 1907 ed. lib. bdg. 22.50x (ISBN 0-8371-2615-0, LOJI). Greenwood.

Lord, Luther & Lord, Eileen. How to Communicate in Sobriety. LC 77-94793. (Illus.). 120p. (Orig.). 1978. pap. 5.95 (ISBN 0-89486-046-1). Hazelden.

Loredano, Giovanni. Life of Adam. LC 67-26617. 1967. Repr. of 1659 ed. 25.00x (ISBN 0-8201-1031-0). Schol Facsimiles.

Lore-Kelly, Christin. Caring Community: A Design for Ministry. 1984. 12.95 (ISBN 0-8294-0423-6). Loyola.

Loren, Mary E. Leader's Guide: Meeting the Forgiving Jesus. 48p. 1985. pap. 2.95 (ISBN 0-89243-225-X). Liguori Pubns.

Lorenz, Ed B. Jesus: A Biography. (Illus.). 1977. 4.95 (ISBN 0-89328-011-9). Lorenz Pr.

Lorenzo. The Relaxation Sensation: The Number One Success Factor in Life. (Illus.). 128p. (Orig.). 1981. pap. 9.95 (ISBN 0-941122-00-X). Prema Bks.

Loret, Pierre. The Story of the Mass: From the Last Supper to the Present Day. LC 82-83984. 144p. 1983. pap. 3.50 (ISBN 0-89243-171-7). Liguori Pubns.

Lorimer, David. Survival: Body, Mind & Death in the Light of Psychic Experience. 288p. (Orig.). 1984. pap. 12.95 (ISBN 0-7102-0003-X). Methuen Inc.

Loring, Marion. A Christian View of Economics. 80p. 1983. 5.50 (ISBN 0-682-49903-X). Exposition Pr FL.

Lorit, Sergius C. Everybody's Pope: The Life of John 23rd. LC 67-15775. 1966. pap. 2.95 (ISBN 0-911782-06-0). New City.

Lorit, Sergius C. & Grimaldi, Nuzzo. Focolare: After Thirty Years: Insights into the Life of the Focolare Movement. LC 76-18456. (Illus.). 268p. 1976. pap. 4.50 (ISBN 0-911782-27-3). New City.

Lorr, Regina E. & Crary, Robert W. The Path of Light. LC 83-71354. 180p. (Orig.). 1983. pap. 7.95 (ISBN 0-87516-520-6). De Vorss.

Lorrance, Arleen. Musings for Meditation. LC 76-14783. (Illus.). 180p. (Orig.). 1976. pap. 4.50 (ISBN 0-916192-03-2). L P Pubns.

--Why Me? How to Heal What's Hurting You. LC 77-88151. 186p. 1982. 6.95 (ISBN 0-916192-19-9). L P Pubns.

Lorusso, Julia & Glick, Joel. Stratagems. 108p. (Orig.). 1985. pap. 7.95 (ISBN 0-914732-15-3). Bro Life Inc.

Loser, Werner, ed. see Von Balthasar, Hans U.

Loserth, Johann. Wiclif & Hus. Evans, M. J., tr. LC 78-63198. (Heresies of the Early Christian & Medieval Era: Second Ser.). 1979. Repr. of 1884 ed. 48.00 (ISBN 0-404-16236-3). AMS Pr.

Lossing, Benson T. Visiting the Shakers in 1857: Harper's New Monthly Magazine. Facsimile ed. (Illus.). 14p. 1975. pap. 2.50 (ISBN 0-937942-14-6). Shaker Mus.

Lossing, Larry D., ed. see Pope John Center Staff.

Lossky, Vladimir. In the Image & Likeness of God. LC 76-383878. 232p. 1974. pap. 9.95 (ISBN 0-913836-13-3). St Vladimirs.

--Mystical Theology of the Eastern Church. 252p. 1973. Repr. of 1957 ed. 17.95 (ISBN 0-227-67536-3). Attic Pr.

--The Mystical Theology of the Eastern Church. LC 76-25448. Orig. Title: Essai sur la theologie mystique de L'eglise d'orient. 252p. 1976. pap. 8.95 (ISBN 0-913836-31-1). St Vladimirs.

--Orthodox Theology: An Introduction. LC 78-1853. 137p. 1978. pap. 5.95 (ISBN 0-913836-43-5). St Vladimirs.

--The Vision of God. 139p. 1963. 7.95 (ISBN 0-913836-19-2). St Vladimirs.

Lossky, Vladimir & Ouspensky, Leonid. The Meaning of Icons. 1981. pap. 52.50x (ISBN 0-913836-77-X, Pub. by Mowbrays Pub Div). State Mutual Bk.

Losty, Jeremiah P. Krishna: A Hindu Vision of God. (Illus.). 52p. (Orig.). 1980. pap. 3.75 (ISBN 0-904654-51-6, Pub. by British Lib). Longwood Pub Group.

Loth, Bernard & Michel, Albert. Dictionnaire de Theologie Catholique, Tables Generales: De Raison a Stolz, 3 vols. (Fr.). 256p. 1970. Set. 295.00 (ISBN 0-686-57021-9, M-6379). French & Eur.

Loth, Paul E. Teaching Adults with Confidence. 48p. 1984. pap. 3.95 (ISBN 0-910566-43-7); seminar planbook 3.95 (ISBN 0-910566-44-5). Evang Tchr.

Lothrop, Gloria, ed. see Mengarini, Gregory.

Loti, Pierre. Jerusalem. 15.00 (ISBN 0-8482-4859-7). Norwood Edns.

Lotstra, H. Abortion: The Catholic Debate in America. 340p. 1985. 39.50x (ISBN 0-8290-0728-8). Irvington.

Lott, Eric. Vedantic Approaches to God. LC 78-17886. (Library of Philosophy & Religion Ser.). 214p. 1980. text ed. 28.50x (ISBN 0-06-494365-8). B&N Imports.

Lottman, Herbert. Albert Camus: A Biography. LC 80-68394. (Illus.). 753p. 1981. pap. 8.95 (ISBN 0-8076-0998-6). Braziller.

Lotz, Adolf. Sklaverei, Staatskirche und Freikirche. pap. 10.00 (ISBN 0-384-33770-8). Johnson Repr.

Lotz, Elsa, jt. auth. see Hartshorne, Hugh.

Lotz, Philip H., ed. Founders of Christian Movements. LC 71-111843. (Essay Index Reprint Ser). 1941. 17.00 (ISBN 0-8369-1672-7). Ayer Co Pubs.

Lotze, H. Outlines of the Philosophy of Religion: Dictated Portions of the Lectures of Hermann Lotze. Ladd, G., ed. LC 11-24754. Repr. of 1885 ed. 20.00 (ISBN 0-527-58550-5). Kraus Repr.

Louapre, Albert C., jt. ed. see Campion, Donald R.

Loucks, Celeste & Hullum, Everett. American Montage. Furlow, Elaine S., ed. (Human Touch Ser.: No. 3). (Illus.). 1976. 6.95 (ISBN 0-686-16312-5); lib. bdg. 6.95 (ISBN 0-937170-10-0). Home Mission.

Loucks, Celeste, et al. And a Cast of Thousands. Furlow, Elaine S., ed. (The Human Touch Photo-Text Ser.). (Illus.). 1978. 6.95 (ISBN 0-937170-11-9). Home Mission.

Loud, G. A. Church & Society in the Norman Principality of Capua, 1058-1197. (Historical Monographs). (Illus.). 1985. 42.00x (ISBN 0-19-822931-3). Oxford U Pr.

Loud, Grover C. Evangelized America. facsimile ed. LC 70-169770. (Select Bibliographies Reprint Ser). Repr. of 1928 ed. 27.50 (ISBN 0-8369-5990-6). Ayer Co Pubs.

Loudy, Adlai. God's Eonian Purpose. text ed. 7.00 (ISBN 0-910424-56-X). Concordant.

Loudy, Aldai. The Gospel of Our Salvation. 122p. 1973. text ed. 4.00 (ISBN 0-910424-60-8). Concordant.
Louf, Andre. The Cistercian Way. (Cistercian Studies: No. 76). pap. 7.95 (ISBN 0-87907-976-2). Cistercian Pubns.
Loughborough, J. N. The Great Second Advent Movement: Its Rise & Progress. LC 71-38453. (Religion in America, Ser. 2). 502p. 1972. Repr. of 1905 ed. 32.00 (ISBN 0-405-04073-3). Ayer Co Pubs.
Louie, Kamm. Critiques of Confucius in Contemporary China. LC 80-214. 210p. 1980. 27.50 (ISBN 0-312-17645-7). St Martin.
Louis. True Devotion to Mary. Fathers of the Company of Mary, ed. LC 85-50571. 215p. 1985. pap. 5.00 (ISBN 0-89555-279-5). Tan Bks Pubs.
Louis C.O. Newman's Vision of Faith. LC 86-81425. 210p. 1986. pap. 10.95 (ISBN 0-89870-113-9). Ignatius Pr.
Louis, Kenneth R. Literary Interpretations of Biblical Narratives 11. LC 74-12400. 320p. (Orig.). 1982. pap. 10.95 (ISBN 0-687-22132-3). Abingdon.
Louis, Montfort de see Louis.
Louise, Mary see Mary Louise, Sr.
Louis Of Granada. Summa of the Christian Life, 3 vols. Aumann, Jordan, tr. from Sp. LC 79-65716. 1979. Set. pap. 24.00 (ISBN 0-89555-121-7). Vol. 1 (ISBN 0-89555-118-7). Vol. 2 (ISBN 0-89555-119-5). Vol. 3 (ISBN 0-89555-120-9). TAN Bks Pubs.
Loukashevitch, Claudia. Sejatel. Tr. of The Sower. (Illus.). 462p. 1966. 20.00 (ISBN 0-317-30416-X); pap. 15.00 (ISBN 0-317-30417-8). Holy Trinity.
Loukes, Harold. Friends & Their Children: A Study in Quaker Education. LC 79-12928. 1979. Repr. of 1958 ed. lib. bdg. 22.50x (ISBN 0-313-21150-7, LOFT). Greenwood.
--Readiness for Religion. LC 63-11818. (Orig.). 1963. pap. 2.50x (ISBN 0-87574-126-6). Pendle Hill.
Lounibos, John, jt. ed. see Smith, Robert C.
Lourie, Iven, pref. by see Gold, E. J.
Louth, Andrew. Discerning the Mystery: An Essay on the Nature of Theology. 1983. text ed. 32.00x (ISBN 0-19-826657-X). Oxford U Pr.
--The Origins of the Christian Mystical Tradition: From Plato to Denys. 1981. pap. text ed. 9.95x (ISBN 0-19-826668-5). Oxford U Pr.
Louth, Andrew, et al, trs. see Von Balthasar, Hans U.
Louvish, Misha, ed. see Herzog, Yaacov.
Louw, Eric. The Jewish Problem in South Africa. 1982. lib. bdg. 59.95 (ISBN 0-87700-342-4). Revisionist Pr.
Louw, J. P. Semantics of New Testament Greek. LC 81-67308. (Semeia Studies). 176p. 1982. pap. 12.95 (ISBN 0-8006-1511-5). Fortress.
--Semantics of New Testament Greek. (Semeia Studies). pap. 12.95 (ISBN 0-89130-693-5, 06 06 11). Scholars Pr GA.
Lovasik, Lawerence G. Concise Church History: St. Joseph Edition. (Orig.). 1986. pap. 5.95 (ISBN 0-89942-262-4). Catholic BK Pub.
Lovasik, Lawrence. Jesus, Joy of the Suffering. 3.00 (ISBN 0-8198-0641-2); pap. 2.00 (ISBN 0-8198-0642-0). Dghtrs St Paul.
--Meditations on the Rosary. LC 82-72204. (Living Meditation & Prayerbook Ser.). (Illus.). 270p. (Orig.). 1985. pap. text ed. 5.00 (ISBN 0-932406-09-2). AFC.
--Saint Joseph New American Catechism. (Illus.). flexible bdg. 3.00 (ISBN 0-89942-253-5, 253/05). Catholic Bk Pub.
Lovasik, Lawrence G. The Angels: God's Messengers & Our Helpers. (Saint Joseph Picture Bks.). (Illus.). flexible bdg. 0.95 (ISBN 0-89942-281-0, 281). Catholic Bk Pub.
--Clean Love in Courtship. 1974. pap. 1.50 (ISBN 0-89555-095-4). TAN Bks Pubs.
--God Loves Us All. (Saint Joseph Picture Bks.). (Illus.). flexible bdg. 0.95 (ISBN 0-89942-282-9, 282). Catholic Bk Pub.
--Good St. Joseph. (Saint Joseph Picture Bks.). (Illus.). flexible bdg. 0.95 (ISBN 0-89942-283-7, 283). Catholic Bk Pub.
--The Holy Rosary. (Saint Joseph Picture Bks.). (Illus.). flexible bdg. 0.95 (ISBN 0-89942-284-5, 284). Catholic Bk Pub.
--I Believe in God: The Apostles' Creed. (Saint Joseph Picture Bks.). (Illus.). flexible bdg. 0.95 (ISBN 0-89942-276-4, 276). Catholic Bk Pub.
--The Lord Jesus. (Illus.). hard bd 3.95 (ISBN 0-89942-419-8, 419/22). Catholic Bk Pub.
--Mary My Mother. rev. ed. (Saint Joseph Picture Bks). (Illus., LargeType). flexible bdg. 0.95 (ISBN 0-89942-280-2, 280). Catholic Bk Pub.
--The Miracles of Jesus. (Saint Joseph Picture Bks.). flexible dg. 0.95 (ISBN 0-89942-279-9, 279). Catholic Bk Pub.
--My Picture Missal. (Saint Joseph Picture Bks.). (Illus.). flexible bdg. 0.95 (ISBN 0-89942-275-6, 275). Catholic Bk Pub.
--Picture Book of Saints. (Illus.). 4.95 (ISBN 0-89942-235-7, 235-22). Catholic Bk Pub.
--The Seven Sacraments. (Saint Joseph Picture Bks.). (Illus.). flexible bdg 0.95 (ISBN 0-89942-278-0, 278). Catholic Bk Pub.
--The Ten Commandments. (Saint Joseph Picture Bks.). (Illus.). flexible bdg. 0.95 (ISBN 0-89942-287-X, 287). Catholic Bk Pub.
--What Catholics Believe. (Illus.). 1977. pap. 2.50 (ISBN 0-89555-027-X). TAN Bks Pubs.
Lovato, Carol N. Brother Mathias: Founder of the Little Brothers of the Good Shepherd. LC 86-62454. 288p. 1987. pap. 8.95 (ISBN 0-87973-485-X, 485). Our Sunday Visitor.
Love, Bessie & Newey, Paul. Water, 4 bks. Incl. Bk. 1. Source of Life; Bk. 2. Destroyer; Bk. 3. Sustainer; Bk. 4. Transformer. (Illus., Orig.). 1974. Set. pap. 3.50x (ISBN 0-8192-4041-9); leaders guide 2.50x (ISBN 0-8192-4042-7). Morehouse.
Love, Julian P. First John-Revelation. LC 59-10454. (Layman's Bible Commentary, Vol. 25). pap. 4.95 (ISBN 0-8042-3085-4). John Knox.
Love, Vicky. Childless Is Not Less. 144p. (Orig.). 1984. pap. 5.95 (ISBN 0-87123-449-1). Bethany Hse.
Lovejoy, Arthur O. Revolt Against Dualism. 2nd ed. (Paul Carus Lecture Ser.). 420p. 1960. 21.95 (ISBN 0-87548-106-X); pap. 8.95 (ISBN 0-87548-107-8). Open Court.
Lovejoy, David S. Religious Enthusiasm in the New World: Heresy to Revolution. 336p. 1985. text ed. 25.00x (ISBN 0-674-75864-1). Harvard U Pr.
Lovejoy, Joseph C. & Lovejoy, Owen. Memoir of the Rev. Elijah P. Lovejoy. facsimile ed. LC 72-117882. (Select Bibliographies Reprint Ser). Repr. of 1838 ed. 21.00 (ISBN 0-8369-5335-5). Ayer Co Pubs.
Lovejoy, Owen, jt. auth. see Lovejoy, Joseph C.
Lovekin, A. Adams, jt. auth. see Malony, H. Newton.
Lovelace, Austin C. The Organist & Hymn Playing. rev. ed. LC 81-80265. (Illus.). 61p. 1981. pap. 5.95 (ISBN 0-916642-16-X). Hope Pub.
Lovelace, Austin C. & Rice, William C. Music & Worship in the Church. rev. ed. LC 76-13524. pap. 64.00 (ISBN 0-317-09866-7, 2020266). Bks Demand UMI.
Lovelace, Glen. Zenzen: A Book of Illustrated Koans. (Illus.). 1978. pap. 4.00 (ISBN 0-87516-279-7). De Vorss.
Lovelace, Lawrence. The Theory of Sin & the Problem of the Damnation of Man. (Illus.). 137p. 1987. 97.75 (ISBN 0-89920-145-8). Am Inst Psych.
Lovelace, Richard. Dynamics of Spiritual Life. LC 78-24757. 1979. pap. 11.95 (ISBN 0-87784-626-X). Inter-Varsity.
Lovelace, Richard F. Renewal As a Way of Life. LC 85-10029. 216p. 1985. pap. 7.95 (ISBN 0-87784-594-8). Inter-Varsity.
Lovelady, Janet, ed. see Drew, Naomi.
Loveland, Anne C. Southern Evangelicals & the Social Order, 1800-1860. LC 80-11200. 354p. 1980. 32.50x (ISBN 0-8071-0690-9); pap. 9.95x (ISBN 0-8071-0783-2). La State U Pr.
Lovelich, Henry. The History of the Holy Grail, Pts. 1-5. Furnivall, F. J., ed. (EETS, ES Ser.: Nos. 20, 24, 28, 30, 95). Repr. of 1875 ed. Pts. I & II. 45.00 (ISBN 0-527-00234-8); Pts. 3-5, 1877 - 1905. 29.00 (ISBN 0-527-00235-6). Kraus Repr.
Lovell, John, Jr. Black Song: The Forge & the Flame. (Illus.). 704p. 1986. pap. 12.95 (ISBN 0-913729-53-1). Paragon Hse.
Lovell, Percy & Marcham, William, eds. Parish of St. Pancras, Pt. 2. LC 70-37855. (London County Council. Survey of London: No. 19). Repr. of 1938 ed. 74.50 (ISBN 0-404-51669-6). AMS Pr.
Lovett, C. S. C. S. Lovett: Maranatha Man. (Illus.). 1978. pap. 5.95 (ISBN 0-938148-02-8). Personal Christianity.
--Census Manual. 1961. pap. 1.00 (ISBN 0-938148-18-4). Personal Christianity.
--Dealing with the Devil. 1967. pap. 5.45 (ISBN 0-938148-05-2). Personal Christianity.
--Death: Graduation to Glory. 1974. pap. 4.25 (ISBN 0-938148-20-6). Personal Christianity.
--Does God Condemn Those Who Never Hear the Gospel? 1963. pap. 2.95 (ISBN 0-938148-19-2). Personal Christianity.
--Dynamic Truths for the Spirit-Filled Life. 1973. pap. 5.95 (ISBN 0-938148-13-3). Personal Christianity.
--Jesus Is Coming-Get Ready Christian. 1969. pap. 4.25 (ISBN 0-938148-04-4). Personal Christianity.
--Jesus Wants You Well. 1973. pap. 6.45 (ISBN 0-938148-29-X). Personal Christianity.
--Jogging with Jesus. (Illus.). 1978. pap. 3.95 (ISBN 0-938148-34-6). Personal Christianity.
--Latest Word on the Last Days. (Illus., Orig.). 1980. pap. 6.95 (ISBN 0-938148-00-1). Personal Christianity.
--Lovett's Lights on Acts. 1972. pap. 6.95 (ISBN 0-938148-28-1). Personal Christianity.
--Lovett's Lights on Galatians, Ephesians, Philippians, Colossians, 1 & 2 Thessalonians. 1970. pap. 5.95 (ISBN 0-938148-25-7). Personal Christianity.
--Lovett's Lights on John. 1970. pap. 6.45 (ISBN 0-938148-24-9). Personal Christianity.
--Lovett's Lights on Romans. 1975. pap. 6.95 (ISBN 0-938148-30-3). Personal Christianity.
--Lovett's Lights on the Sermon on the Mount. 176p. (Orig.). 1985. pap. 5.45 (ISBN 0-938148-40-0). Personal Christianity.
--The One Hundred Percent Christian. 1970. pap. 4.25 (ISBN 0-938148-07-9). Personal Christianity.
--Operation Manhunt Made Easy. 1961. 2.95 (ISBN 0-938148-17-6). Personal Christianity.
--Soul-Winning Classes Made Easy. 1962. pap. 2.95 tchr's. guide (ISBN 0-938148-12-5). Personal Christianity.
--Soul-Winning Made Easy. 1978. pap. 4.25 (ISBN 0-938148-10-9). Personal Christianity.
--Teach Dynamic Truths. 1973. pap. 5.95 tchr's. guide (ISBN 0-938148-14-1). Personal Christianity.
--Teach Them About Satan. 1970. pap. 5.45 tchr's guide (ISBN 0-938148-26-5). Personal Christianity.
--Teach Witnessing. 1966. pap. 5.95 tchr's. guide (ISBN 0-938148-09-5). Personal Christianity.
--The Thrill of Faith. 1960. pap. 2.95 (ISBN 0-938148-21-4). Personal Christianity.
--Unequally Yoked Wives. 1968. pap. 5.45 (ISBN 0-938148-22-2). Personal Christianity.
--Visitation Made Easy. 1959. pap. 2.95 (ISBN 0-938148-15-X). Personal Christianity.
--What to Do When Your Friends Reject Christ. 1966. pap. 4.25 (ISBN 0-938148-06-0). Personal Christianity.
--What's a Parent to Do? 1971. pap. 6.45 (ISBN 0-938148-27-3). Personal Christianity.
--Witnessing Made Easy. 1964. pap. 5.95 (ISBN 0-938148-01-X). Personal Christianity.
Lovette, Roger. A Faith of Our Own. LC 75-27086. 144p. 1976. 6.95 (ISBN 0-8298-0299-1). Pilgrim NY.
--Questions Jesus Raised. LC 85-15137. 1986. 4.95 (ISBN 0-8054-2259-5). Broadman.
Lovik, Craig J. The Exodus. (Arch Bks.). (Illus.). 24p. 1987. pap. 0.99 (ISBN 0-570-09001-6, 59-1429). Concordia.
Lovin, Robin W. Christian Faith & Public Choices: The Social Ethics of Barth, Brunner, & Bonhoeffer. LC 83-48922. 192p. 1984. pap. 10.95 (ISBN 0-8006-1777-0, 1-1777). Fortress.
Loving, Jerome. Emerson, Whitman, & the American Muse. LC 82-1868. xii, 220p. 1982. 22.00 (ISBN 0-8078-1523-3). U of NC Pr.
Lovinger, Robert J. Working with Religious Issues in Therapy. LC 84-6198. 328p. 1984. 30.00x (ISBN 0-87668-727-3). Aronson.
Lovorn, Janie, jt. auth. see Lovorn, Tom.
Lovorn, Tom & Lovorn, Janie. Building a Caring Church. 104p. 1986. pap. 8.95 (ISBN 0-89693-150-1). Victor Bks.
Low, Albert. The Iron Cow of Zen. LC 85-40413. 226p. (Orig.). 1985. pap. 6.50 (ISBN 0-8356-0598-1, Quest). Theos Pub Hse.
--Zen & Creative Management. 272p. 1982. pap. 3.50 (ISBN 0-86721-083-4). Jove Pubns.
Low, Alfred D. Jews in the Eyes of the Germans: From the Enlightenment to Imperial Germany. LC 79-334. (Illus.). 528p. 1979. 19.95 (ISBN 0-915980-86-X). ISHI PA.
Low, Alice. The Macmillan Book of Greek Gods & Heroes. LC 85-7170. (Illus.). 192p. 1985. 15.95 (ISBN 0-02-761390-9). Macmillan.
Low, Anthony. The Blaze of Noon: A Reading of "Samson Agonistes". LC 74-1484. 236p. 1974. 28.00x (ISBN 0-231-03842-9). Columbia U Pr.
Low, Leopold. Beitrage zur Judischen Alterthumskunde, 2 vols. 922p. Date not set. Repr. text ed. 149.04x (ISBN 0-576-80127-5, Pub. by Gregg Intl Pubs England). Gregg Intl.
Lowance, Mason I, Jr. The Language of Canaan: Metaphor & Symbol in New England from the Puritans to the Transcendentalists. LC 79-21179. 1980. 22.50x (ISBN 0-674-50949-8). Harvard U Pr.
Lowde, James. Disclosure Concerning the Nature of Man, 1694. LC 75-11233. (British Philosophers & Theologians in the 17th & 18th Century Ser.). 271p. 1979. lib. bdg. 51.00 (ISBN 0-8240-1786-2). Garland Pub.
Lowden, John. Illuminated Prophet Books: A Study of Byzantine Manuscripts of the Major & Minor Prophets. LC 86-43164. 250p. 1987. 49.75x (ISBN 0-271-00604-8). Pa St U Pr.
Lowe, Cylvia Archer. Words of Wisdom from the Masters. 2nd ed. 120p. 1981. pap. 6.95 (ISBN 0-9606080-0-1). Book Dept.
Lowe, Victor. Alfred North Whitehead: The Man & His Work, Vol. 1: 1861-1910. LC 84-15467. 392p. 1985. 27.50 (ISBN 0-8018-2488-5). Johns Hopkins.
Lowe, Walter. Evil & the Unconscious. LC 82-19147. (AAR Studies in Religion Ser.). 142p. 1983. 16.50 (ISBN 0-89130-600-5, 01 00 30). Scholars Pr GA.
Lowell, James R. Among My Books. LC 75-126666. 1970. 11.50 (ISBN 0-404-04039-X). AMS Pr.
Lowell, Percival. Occult Japan. 59.95 (ISBN 0-8490-0750-X). Gordon Pr.
Lowenthal, ed. see Herzl, Theodor.
Lowenthal, Marvin, tr. see Gluckel.
Lowery, Claire. Christian Spirituality for the Eighties. 96p. 1983. pap. 4.50 (ISBN 0-697-01940-3). Wm C Brown.
Lowery, Daniel. Following Christ: A Handbook of Catholic Moral Teaching. LC 82-84373. 160p. 1983. pap. 3.50 (ISBN 0-89243-173-3). Liguori Pubns.
Lowery, Daniel L. A Basic Catholic Dictionary. LC 85-80600. (Orig.). 1986. pap. 3.95 (ISBN 0-89243-241-1). Liguori Pubns.
--Catholic Beliefs, Laws, Practices: Twenty-Six Questions & Answers. 64p. 1984. pap. 1.50 (ISBN 0-89243-213-6). Liguori Pubns.
--Day by Day Through Advent: Reflections, Prayers, Practices. 80p. 1984. pap. 1.95 (ISBN 0-89243-216-0). Liguori Pubns.
--Day by Day Through Lent: Reflections, Prayers, Practices. 160p. 1983. pap. 3.95 (ISBN 0-89243-194-6). Liguori Pubns.
--Growth Through Virtue. 64p. 1984. pap. 1.50 (ISBN 0-89243-222-5). Liguori Pubns.
--The Parables of Jesus: Twenty Stories with a Message. 64p. 1987. pap. 1.95 (ISBN 0-89243-266-7). Liguori Pubns.
Lowery, Fred. Whistling in the Dark: The Story of Fred Lowery, the Blind Whistler. McDowell, John, as told to. LC 83-4085. (Illus.). 416p. 1983. 15.95 (ISBN 0-88289-298-3). Pelican.
Lowery, T. L., ed. El Don del Espiritu Santo. (Span.). 80p. 1978. pap. 2.25 (ISBN 0-87148-307-6). Pathway Pr.
Lowie, Robert H. Myths & Traditions of the Crow Indians. LC 74-7981. Repr. of 1918 ed. 24.00 (ISBN 0-404-11872-0). AMS Pr.
--Primitive Religion. new ed. LC 75-114373. 1970. pap. 5.95 (ISBN 0-87140-209-2). Liveright.
--The Religion of the Crow Indians. LC 74-7986. Repr. of 1922 ed. 15.00 (ISBN 0-404-11876-3). AMS Pr.
Lowith, Karl. Meaning in History: The Theological Implications of the Philosophy of History. LC 57-7900. 1957. pap. 7.50x (ISBN 0-226-49555-8, P16, Phoen). U of Chicago Pr.
Lown, Albert J. Portraits of Faith. 155p. (Orig.). 1981. pap. 3.95 (ISBN 0-8341-0695-7). Beacon Hill.
Lownethal, Rudolph. The Religious Periodical Press in China, 2 vols. (Illus.). 300p. Repr. of 1940 ed. Set. text ed. 45.50x (ISBN 0-89644-569-0, Pub. by Chinese Matl Ctr). Coronet Bks.
Lownsbery, Eloise. Saints & Rebels. facsimile ed. LC 72-156682. (Essay Index Reprint Ser). Repr. of 1937 ed. 22.00 (ISBN 0-8369-2322-7). Ayer Co Pubs.
Lowrey, Mark D. Ecumenism: Striving for Unity amid Diversity. 272p. (Orig.). 1985. pap. text ed. 9.95 (ISBN 0-89622-274-8). Twenty-Third.
Lowrie, Donald A. Rebellious Prophet: A Life of Nicolai Berdgaev. LC 73-11867. (Illus.). 310p. 1974. Repr. of 1960 ed. lib. bdg. 35.00x (ISBN 0-8371-7095-8, LORP). Greenwood.
Lowrie, Harold. The Salient Characteristics of Ancient Christian Architecture. (Illus.). 142p. 1982. Repr. of 1880 ed. 84.55 (ISBN 0-89901-053-9). Found Class Reprints.
Lowrie, W., tr. see Kierkegaard, Soren.
Lowrie, Walter. Kierkegaard, 2 vols. Set. 28.50 (ISBN 0-8446-0778-9). Peter Smith.
--Short Life of Kierkegaard. 1942. pap. 9.50x (ISBN 0-691-01957-6). Princeton U Pr.
Lowrie, Walter, tr. see Kierkegaard, Soren.
Lowry, Charles W. The First Theologians. 200p. (Orig.). 1986. pap. 7.95 (ISBN 0-89526-804-3). Regnery Bks.
--To Pray or Not to Pray: A Handbook for Study of Recent Supreme Court Decisions & American Church-State Doctrine. 1969. enlarged ed. 6.00 (ISBN 0-87419-013-4, U Pr of Wash). Larlin Corp.
--To Pray or Not to Pray: A Handbook for Study of Recent Supreme Court Decisions & American Church-State Doctrine. (Special bicentennial facsimile of enlarged ed). 1978. 7.00 (ISBN 0-685-88420-1, U Pr of Wash). Larlin Corp.
--William Temple: An Archbishop for All Seasons. LC 81-43869. 170p. (Orig.). 1982. lib. bdg. 22.25 (ISBN 0-8191-2355-2); pap. text ed. 7.75 (ISBN 0-8191-2356-0). U Pr of Amer.
Lowry, Eugene. The Homiletical Plot: The Sermon As Narrative Art Form. LC 79-92074. 100p. (Orig.). 1980. pap. 6.95 (ISBN 0-8042-1652-5). John Knox.
Lowry, Eugene L. Doing Time in the Pulpit. 112p. (Orig.). pap. 6.95 (ISBN 0-687-11034-3). Abingdon.
Lowry, James W. In the Whale's Belly & Other Martyr Stories. (Illus.). (YA) 1981. 4.70 (ISBN 0-87813-513-8). Christian Light.

--North America Is the Lord's. (Christian Day School Ser.). 1980. 17.05x (ISBN 0-87813-916-8). Christian Light.

Lowry, Mark. The Temple of Divine Truth. 1986. 6.95 (ISBN 0-8062-2423-1). Carlton.

Lowry, Shirley. Familiar Mysteries: The Truth in Myth. LC 80-27792. (Illus.). 1981. 25.00x (ISBN 0-19-502925-9). Oxford U Pr.

Loyola College, Pastoral & Counseling Faculty. Pastoral Counseling. (Illus.). 352p. 1982. 29.67 (ISBN 0-13-652867-8). P-H.

Lozano, John M. Life As Parable: Reinterpreting the Religious Life. 208p. (Orig.). 1986. pap. 8.95 (ISBN 0-8091-2825-X). Paulist Pr.

Lubac, Henri De. The Motherhood of the Church. Englund, Sr. Sergia, tr. from Fr. LC 81-83857. Tr. of Les Eglises particulieres & La maternite de l'eglise. 363p. (Orig.). 1983. pap. 12.95 (ISBN 0-89870-014-0). Ignatius Pr.

Lubac, Henri de see De Lubac, Henri.

Lubac, Henry de see De Lubac, Henry.

Lubeck, Paul M. Islam & Urban Labor in Northern Nigeria: The Making of a Muslim Working Class. (African Studies Ser.: No. 52). (Illus.). 368p. Date not set. 49.50 (ISBN 0-521-30942-5). Cambridge U Pr.

Lubetski, Edith & Lubetski, Meir. Building a Judaica Library Collection: A/Resource Guide. 185p. 1983. lib. bdg. 30.00 (ISBN 0-87287-375-7). Libs Unl.

Lubetski, Meir, jt. auth. see Lubetski, Edith.

Lubheid, Colm. John Climacus, The Ladder of Divine Ascent. (The Classics of Western Spirituality). 224p. pap. 12.95 (ISBN 0-8091-0312-5); pap. 9.95 (ISBN 0-8091-2330-4). Paulist Pr.

Lubich, Chiara. The Eucharist. LC 77-82230. 93p. 1977. pap. 2.50 (ISBN 0-911782-30-3). New City.

--Jesus in the Midst: Spiritual Writings. LC 76-18455. 80p. 1976. pap. 2.95 (ISBN 0-911782-26-5). New City.

--Journey: Spiritual Insights. Moran, Hugh & Hartnett, William, trs. from Ital. 158p. 1984. pap. 4.95 (ISBN 0-911782-51-6). New City.

--May They All Be One. Tr. of Tutti Siano Uno. 96p. (Orig.). 1983. pap. 3.95 (ISBN 0-911782-46-X). New City.

--May They All Be One: Origins & Life of the Focolare Movement. LC 71-77438. 1977. pap. 2.50 cancelled (ISBN 0-911782-28-1). New City.

--Meditations. LC 74-79452. 148p. 1974. pap. 4.95 (ISBN 0-911782-20-6). New City.

--Our Yes to God. Moran, Hugh J., tr. from Ital. LC 81-82064. 112p. (Orig.). 1981. pap. 3.95 (ISBN 0-911782-38-9). New City.

--Servants of All. Moran, Hugh, tr. from It. LC 78-59470. 176p. 1978. pap. 3.50 (ISBN 0-911782-05-2). New City.

--Stars & Tears. LC 85-72399. 153p. 1986. pap. 5.25 (ISBN 0-911782-54-0). New City.

--Unity & Jesus Forsaken. LC 85-72397. 105p. 1985. pap. 4.95 (ISBN 0-911782-53-2). New City.

--When Did We See You Lord? Moran, Hugh, tr. from Ital. LC 79-88680. Tr. of Gesu Nel Fratello. 134p. 1979. pap. 3.50 (ISBN 0-911782-34-6). New City.

--When Our Love Is Charity. LC 72-85632. 82p. 1972. pap. 2.95 (ISBN 0-911782-02-8). New City.

Lubich, Gino & Lazzarin, Piero. Joan Antida Thouret: When God Was the Voice of the Poor. Brody, Joel, tr. from Ital. LC 84-62540. 1985. pap. 5.95 (ISBN 0-911782-47-8). New City.

Lubicz, Isha S. De see De Lubicz, Isha S.

Lubicz, R. A. Schwaller De see Schwaller De Lubicz, R. A.

Lubke, Wilhelm. Ecclesiastical Art in Germany During the Middle Ages. Wheatley, L. A., tr. from Ger. LC 78-16244. 1978. Repr. of 1877 ed. lib. bdg. 35.00 (ISBN 0-89341-359-3). Longwood Pub Group.

Lucado, Max. No Wonder They Call Him the Savior: Chronicles of the Cross. LC 85-31026. 1986. 6.95 (ISBN 0-88070-133-1). Multnomah.

--On the Anvil. 128p. 1985. pap. 4.95 (ISBN 0-8423-4738-0). Tyndale.

Lucas, Angela. Women in the Middle Ages: Religion, Marriage & Letters. LC 82-42578. 215p. 1984. 11.95 (ISBN 0-312-88744-2). St Martin.

Lucas, Charles, ed. see Lee, Douglas.

Lucas, Claudia, tr. see Renirkens, Clement.

Lucas, DeWitt B. God Tells the World. 1964. pap. 2.50 (ISBN 0-910140-08-1). C & R Anthony.

--Secret Bible Prophecies. 1965. pap. 2.50 (ISBN 0-910140-10-3). C & R Anthony.

--Visions of the New Life. 1963. pap. 2.50 (ISBN 0-910140-11-1). C & R Anthony.

Lucas, E. V. At the Shrine of St. Charles. 1934. Repr. 25.00 (ISBN 0-8274-1898-1). R West.

Lucas, George R. Two Views of Freedom in Process & Thought. LC 79-12287. (American Academy of Religion, Dissertation Ser.: No. 28). 1979. 14.00 (ISBN 0-89130-285-9, 010128); pap. 9.95 (ISBN 0-89130-304-9). Scholars Pr GA.

Lucas, Henry S. The Renaissance & the Reformation. LC 83-45665. Date not set. Repr. of 1934 ed. 67.50 (ISBN 0-404-19815-5). AMS Pr.

Lucas, J. R. Weeping in Ramah. LC 85-70477. 250p. (Orig.). 1985. pap. 7.95 (ISBN 0-89107-357-4, Crossway Bks). Good News.

Lucas, Jerri McCann see McCann Lucas, Jerri.

Lucas, Marc, tr. see Renirkens, Clement.

Lucas, Paul R. Valley of Discord: Church & Society along the Connecticut River, 1636-1725. LC 75-22520. (Illus.). 288p. 1976. 25.00x (ISBN 0-87451-121-6). U Pr of New Eng.

Lucas, R. J. The Message of Colossians & Philemon. Motyer, J. A. & Stott, J. R., eds. LC 79-3635. (The Bible Speaks Today Ser.). 1980. pap. 6.95 (ISBN 0-87784-284-1). Inter-Varsity.

Lucas, Sidney. The Quaker Message. 1983. pap. 2.50x (ISBN 0-87574-040-5, 040). Pendle Hill.

Luccock, Halford E. American Mirror: Social, Ethical & Religious Aspects of American Literature, 1930-1940. LC 75-156806. 300p. 1971. Repr. of 1940 ed. lib. bdg. 28.50x (ISBN 0-8154-0385-2). Cooper Sq.

--Contemporary American Literature & Religion. LC 73-111471. 1970. Repr. of 1934 ed. 20.50 (ISBN 0-404-00607-8). AMS Pr.

--Contemporary American Literature & Religion. 300p. 1980. Repr. of 1934 ed. lib. bdg. 30.00 (ISBN 0-89984-324-7). Century Bookbindery.

--Enter the Crocus. Hartman, Charles S., ed. LC 79-22592. 1980. 3.50 (ISBN 0-8298-0386-6). Pilgrim NY.

--A Sprig of Holly. new ed. Hartman, Charles S., ed. & intro. by. LC 78-17096. 64p. 1978. text ed. 3.50 (ISBN 0-8298-0354-8). Pilgrim NY.

Luccock, Halford E. & Rauschenbusch, Walter. Living a Thousand Lives. LC 82-9091. 80p. (Orig.). 1982. pap. 5.95 (ISBN 0-8298-0622-9). Pilgrim NY.

Luce, Gordon H. Old Burma-Early Pagan, 3 Vols. 1969. 120.00 set (ISBN 0-686-92654-4). J J Augustin.

Luce, Simeon, ed. Chronique Du Mont-Saint-Michel 1343-1468, 2 Vols. 1879-83. Set. 67.00 (ISBN 0-384-09010-9); Set. pap. 55.00 (ISBN 0-384-09011-7). Johnson Repr.

Lucey, William L. Catholic Church in Maine. (Illus.). 372p. 1957. 7.50x (ISBN 0-686-00233-4). O'Brien.

Luchs, Allison. Cestello: A Cistercian Church of the Florentine Renaissance. LC 76-23642. (Outstanding Dissertations in the Fine Arts - 2nd Series - 15th Century). (Illus.). 1977. Repr. lib. bdg. 76.00 (ISBN 0-8240-2706-X). Garland Pub.

Lucifer of Cagliari. Opvuscula. (Corpus Scriptorum Ecclesiasticorum Latinorum Ser: Vol. 14). (Lat). pap. 40.00 (ISBN 0-384-34090-3). Johnson Repr.

Luck, G. C. The Bible Book by Book: An Introduction to Bible Synthesis. 1955. pap. text ed. 3.95 (ISBN 0-8024-0045-0). Moody.

Luckert, Karl W. Coyoteway: A Navajo Holyway Healing Ceremonial. LC 78-10358. 243p. 1979. pap. 13.95 (ISBN 0-8165-0655-8). U of Ariz Pr.

--A Navajo Bringing-Home Ceremony: The Claus Chee Sonny Version of Deerway Ajilee. LC 78-59701. (Illus.). 14p. 1978. pap. 14.95x (ISBN 0-89734-027-2). Mus Northern Ariz.

--Olmec Religion: A Key to Middle America & Beyond. LC 75-12869. (The Civilization of the American Indian: Vol. 137). (Illus.). 200p. 1976. 14.95x (ISBN 0-8061-1298-0). U of Okla Pr.

Luckert, Karl W., ed. see Haile, Berard.

Lucy, Margaret. Shakespeare & the Supernatural. LC 70-144653. Repr. of 1906 ed. 6.50 (ISBN 0-404-04065-9). AMS Pr.

--Shakespeare & the Supernatural. LC 73-16087. 1906. lib. bdg. 15.00 (ISBN 0-8414-5699-2). Folcroft.

Lucy, Reda, pseud. The Lord's Prayer for Children. (Illus.). 24p. (Orig.). 1981. pap. 2.25 (ISBN 0-87516-437-4). De Vorss.

Luder, Hope E. Women & Quakerism. LC 74-82914. 36p. (Orig.). 1974. pap. 2.50x (ISBN 0-87574-196-7). Pendle Hill.

Ludlow, Dan. A Companion to Your Study of the Book of Mormon. LC 76-27139. 1976. 9.95 (ISBN 0-87747-610-1). Deseret Bk.

Ludlow, Daniel H. A Companion to Your Study of the Doctrine & Covenants, 2 vols. LC 78-64752. 1978. Set. 17.95 (ISBN 0-87747-722-1). Deseret Bk.

--Companion to Your Study of the New Testament: The Four Gospels. 454p. 1982. 9.95 (ISBN 0-87747-945-3). Deseret Bk.

--A Companion to Your Study of the Old Testament. LC 80-28088. 437p. 1981. 9.95 (ISBN 0-87747-853-8). Deseret Bk.

--Marking the Scriptures. 105p. (Orig.). 1980. pap. 4.95 (ISBN 0-87747-815-5). Deseret Bk.

Ludlow England Parish. Churchwardens' Accounts of the Town of Ludlow in Shropshire from 1540 to the End of the Reign of Queen Elizabeth. Repr. of 1869 ed. 19.00 (ISBN 0-384-34130-6). Johnson Repr.

Ludlow, Fitz H. Heart of the Continent. LC 74-134396. (Illus.). Repr. 35.45 (ISBN 0-404-08438-9). AMS Pr.

Ludlow, James M. The Age of the Crusades. 1977. lib. bdg. 59.95 (ISBN 0-8490-1405-0). Gordon Pr.

Ludlow, John M. Woman's Work in the Church. LC 75-33300. 1976. Repr. of 1866 ed. 14.95 (ISBN 0-89201-007-X). Zenger Pub.

Ludlow, Victor L. Isaiah: Prophet, Poet, & Seer. LC 82-1444. (Illus.). 578p. 1982. 13.95 (ISBN 0-87747-884-8). Deseret Bk.

--Unlocking the Old Testament. LC 81-68266. (Illus.). 239p. 1981. 8.95 (ISBN 0-87747-873-2). Deseret Bk.

Ludlow, William L. What It Means to Be a Christian. 1986. 7.95 (ISBN 0-8158-0434-2). Chris Mass.

Ludolphy, Ingetraut. From Luther to Fifteen Eighty: A Pictorial Account. (Illus.). 1977. 15.95 (ISBN 0-570-03264-4, 15-2710). Concordia.

Ludwig, Charles. Francis Asbury. 1984. pap. 6.95 (ISBN 0-88062-024-2). Mott Media.

--He Freed Britains Slaves. LC 77-9521. 208p. 1977. 7.95 (ISBN 0-8361-1822-7). Herald Pr.

--Ludwig's Handbook of New Testament Cities & Rulers. LC 83-71619. 244p. (Orig.). 1983. pap. 6.95 (ISBN 0-89636-111-X). Accent Bks.

--Ludwig's Handbook of Old Testament Rulers & Cities. LC 84-70426. 244p. (Orig.). 1984. pap. 6.95 (ISBN 0-89636-130-6). Accent Bks.

Ludwig, David. The Spirit of Your Marriage. LC 79-50088. 1979. pap. 6.95 (ISBN 0-8066-1721-7, 10-5890). Augsburg.

Ludwig, David J. In Good Spirits. LC 82-70944. (Orig.). 1982. pap. 6.95 (ISBN 0-8066-1919-8, 10-3208). Augsburg.

Ludwig, Glenn E. Building an Effective Youth Ministry. LC 79-12282. (Creative Leadership Ser.). 1979. pap. 6.95 (ISBN 0-687-03992-4). Abingdon.

Ludwig, Martin. Religion und Sittlichkeit Bei Luther Bis Zum Sermon Von Den Guten Werken 1520. (Ger). 34.00 (ISBN 0-384-34151-9); pap. 28.00 (ISBN 0-384-34150-0). Johnson Repr.

Ludwig, Nancy. Christmas Puppets Plays & Art Project Puppets. (Stick-Out-Your-Neck Ser.). (Illus.). 32p. 1983. pap. 1.98 (ISBN 0-88724-045-3, CD-8021). Carson-Dellos.

Ludwigson, Raymond. A Survey of Bible Prophecy. (Contemporary Evangelical Perspective Ser.). Orig. Title: Outlines to Bible Eschatology. 192p. 1973. Repr. 6.95 (ISBN 0-310-28421-X, 10100P). Zondervan.

Luebering, Carol. The Forgiving Family: First Steps to Reconciliation. 84p. (Orig.). 1983. pap. text ed. 2.50 (ISBN 0-86716-027-6). St Anthony Mess Pr.

--To Comfort All Who Mourn: A Parish Handbook for Ministry to the Grieving. (Illus.). 96p. 1985. pap. 4.95 (ISBN 0-86716-045-4). St Anthony Mess Pr.

--What Do You Ask for Your Child. 64p. (Orig.). 1980. pap. 1.35 (ISBN 0-912228-64-4). St Anthony Mess Pr.

--Your Child's Confirmation: Reflections for Parents on the Sacrament of Christian Identity. 1987. pap. 1.95. St Anthony Mess Pr.

Luebering, Carol & Schmitz, Robert E. Nothing to Fear: Unleashing the Power of the Resurrection. (Illus.). 104p. 1985. pap. text ed. 4.50 (ISBN 0-86716-047-0). St Anthony Mess Pr.

Luecke, Jane-Marie. Measuring Old English Rhythm: An Application of the Principles of Gregorian Chant Rhythm to the Meter of Beowolf. LC 66-25869. (Literary Monographs: Vol. 9). 168p. 1978. 25.00x (ISBN 0-299-07510-9). U of Wis Pr.

Luecke, Janemarie. The Rape of the Sabine Women. 1978. 5.95 (ISBN 0-87482-097-9). Wake-Brook.

Luedemann, Gerd. Paul, Apostle to the Gentiles: Studies in Chronology. Jones, Stanley F., tr. from Ger. LC 83-48919. 320p. 1984. 29.95 (ISBN 0-8006-0714-7, 1-714). Fortress.

Lueders, Edward. The Clam Lake Papers. (Festival Ser.). 160p. 1982. pap. 3.25 (ISBN 0-687-08580-2). Abingdon.

Lueker, Erwin. Companion Dictionary of the Bible. 192p. 1985. pap. 5.95 (ISBN 0-570-03947-9, 12-2880). Concordia.

Lueker, Erwin, tr. see Mildenberger, Friedrich.

Luel, Steven & Marcus, Paul. Psychoanalytic Reflections on the Holocaust: Selected Essays. 1985. 25.00 (ISBN 0-88125-041-4). Ktav.

Lufburrow, Bill. Illustrations Without Sermons. 128p. (Orig.). 1985. pap. 7.95 (ISBN 0-687-18677-3). Abingdon.

Luft, Eric, ed. & tr. Hegel, Hinrichs & Schleiermacher on Feeling & Reason in Religion: The Texts of Their 1821-22 Debate. LC 87-5550. (Studies in German Thought & History: Volume 3). 544p. 1987. lib. bdg. 79.95 (ISBN 0-88946-352-2). E Mellen.

Lugenbeel, Barbara. Your Spiritual Growth Handbook. LC 84-61016. 164p. (Orig.). 1984. pap. 5.95 (ISBN 0-8192-1352-7). Morehouse.

Lught, Henry Vander see Vander Lught, Henry.

Lugt, Herbert Vander see Vander Lugt, Herbert.

Luhmann, Niklas. Religious Dogmatics & the Evolution of Societies. Beyer, Peter, tr. LC 84-8976. (Studies in Religion & Society: Vol. 9). 192p. 1984. 49.95x (ISBN 0-88946-866-4). E Mellen.

Luibheid, Colm. Eusebius of Caesarea & the Arian Crisis. 136p. 1981. 22.50x (ISBN 0-7165-2277-2, BBA 03636, Pub. by Irish Academic Pr Ireland). Biblio Dist.

Luibheid, Colm, tr. see Cassian, John.

Luijpen, William A. & Koren, H. J. Religion & Atheism. 200p. 1982. pap. 10.95 (ISBN 0-391-02801-4). Humanities.

Luk, Charles. Secrets of Chinese Meditation. (Illus.). 1969. pap. 6.95 (ISBN 0-87728-066-5). Weiser.

--Taoist Yoga. 1970. pap. 6.95 (ISBN 0-87728-067-3). Weiser.

--The Transmission of the Mind Outside the Teaching. LC 75-15055. 1976. pap. 2.95 (ISBN 0-394-17888-2, E666, Ever). Grove.

Lukacher, Ned. Primal Scenes: Literature, Philosophy, Psychoanalysis. LC 85-25513. 366p. 1986. text ed. 24.95x (ISBN 0-8014-1886-0). Cornell U Pr.

Lukacs, Lajos. The Vatican & Hungary 1846-1878: Reports & Correspondence on Hungary of the Apostolic Nuncios in Vienna. Kormos, Zsofia, tr. 795p. 1981. text ed. 65.00x (ISBN 963-05-2446-5, Pub. by Akademiai Kiado UK). Humanities.

Lukas, Elisabeth. Meaning in Suffering: Comfort in Crisis Through Logotherapy. Fabry, Joseph, tr. from Ger. Tr. of Auch Dein Leiden hat Sinn. 160p. (Orig.). 1986. pap. 7.95 (ISBN 0-917867-05-X). Inst Logo.

Luke, Helen. The Inner Story: Myth & Symbol in the Bible & Literature. 112p. 1982. 8.95 (ISBN 0-8245-0443-7). Crossroad NY.

--The Voice Within: Love & Virtue in the Age of the Spirit. 128p. 1984. pap. 7.95 (ISBN 0-8245-0659-6). Crossroad NY.

--Woman, Earth & Spirit: The Feminine in Symbol & Myth. 144p. 1981. 9.95 (ISBN 0-8245-0018-0). Crossroad NY.

Luke, Helen M. Life of the Spirit in Women: A Jungian Approach. 1983. pap. 2.50x (ISBN 0-87574-230-0, 230). Pendle Hill.

Luker, Kristin. Abortion & the Politics of Motherhood. LC 83-47849. (California Series on Social Choice & Political Economy). 350p. 1984. 25.00x (ISBN 0-520-04314-6); pap. 7.95 (ISBN 0-520-05597-7, CAL759). U of Cal Pr.

Luker, Ralph. A Southern Tradition in Theology & Social Criticism, 1830-1930: The Religious Liberalism & Social Conservatism of James Warley Miles, William Porcher Dubose & Edgar Gardner Murphy. LC 84-8954. (Studies in American Religion: Vol. 11). 476p. 1984. 69.95x (ISBN 0-88946-655-6). E Mellen.

Luke the Physician. I, Luke. LC 81-80713. (Illus.). 120p. 1981. pap. 3.25 (ISBN 0-87973-665-8, 665). Our Sunday Visitor.

--On Trial: Being a Summary of Eyewitness Reports Concerning the Early Church. LC 82-60668. (Illus.). 120p. 1982. pap. 3.25 (ISBN 0-87973-648-8, 648). Our Sunday Visitor.

Lull, David J. The Spirit in Galatia: Paul's Interpretation of Pneuma As Divine Power. LC 79-26094. (Society of Biblical Literature Dissertation Ser.: No. 49). 15.95 (ISBN 0-89130-367-7, 06-01-49); pap. 10.95 (ISBN 0-89130-368-5). Scholars Pr GA.

Lull, Ramon, pseud. The Art of Contemplation. Peers, Allison, tr. 1976. lib. bdg. 69.95 (ISBN 0-8490-1451-4). Gordon Pr.

Lully, Raymond see Lull, Ramon, pseud.

Lum, A. Advanced Tai Chi. 11.95x (ISBN 0-685-63740-9). Wehman.

Lum, A. C. Combat Tai Chi. 11.95x (ISBN 0-685-63750-6). Wehman.

Lum, Ada. A Hitchhiker's Guide to Missions. LC 84-19149. 144p. 1984. pap. 5.95 (ISBN 0-87784-328-7). Inter-Varsity.

--How to Begin an Evangelistic Bible Study. pap. 2.50 (ISBN 0-87784-317-1). Inter-Varsity.

--Jesus the Life Changer. 40p. 1978. pap. 2.25 (ISBN 0-87784-316-3). Inter-Varsity.

Lum, Dyer D. The Mormon Question in Its Economic Aspects. 1973. lib. bdg. 59.95 (ISBN 0-8490-0672-4). Gordon Pr.

Lumby, F. R., ed. Be Domes Daege (Bede's de Die Judicii) (EETS OS Ser.: Vol. 65). Repr. of 1876 ed. 15.00 (ISBN 0-8115-3419-7). Kraus Repr.

Lumby, J. R., ed. Bernardus de Cura Rei Familiaris: Early Scottish Prophecies, Etc. (EETS OS Ser.: Vol. 42). pap. 15.00 (ISBN 0-8115-3351-4). Kraus Repr.

Lumby, Joseph R. Ratis Raving, & Other Moral & Religious Pieces. (EETS, OS Ser.: No. 43). Repr. of 1870 ed. 12.00 (ISBN 0-527-00038-8). Kraus Repr.

Lumer, Hyman, ed. see Lenin, V. I.

Lumiansky, R. M. & Mills, David. The Chester Mystery Cycle: Essays & Documents. LC 82-1838. viii, 339p. 1983. 40.00x (ISBN 0-8078-1522-5); essay "Music in the Cycle" by Richard Rastall incl. U of NC Pr.

Lumiansky, Robert, jt. ed. see Mills, David.

Lummis, Charles F. My Friend Will. 1972. 3.50 (ISBN 0-87516-161-8). De Vorss.

Lumpkin, William L. Baptist Confessions of Faith. (Illus.). 1959. 17.95 (ISBN 0-8170-0016-X). Judson.

Lumpkin, William L. & Butterfield, Lyman. Colonial Baptists & Southern Revivals: An Original Anthology. Gaustad, Edwin S., ed. LC 79-52585. (The Baptist Tradition Ser.). 1980. lib. bdg. 25.50x (ISBN 0-405-12452-X). Ayer Co Pubs.

Lumpp, D., jt. auth. see Kolb, R.

Lumpuy, Luis B., tr. see Robertson, John M.

Luna, Luis E. Vegetalismo: Shamanism among the Mestizo Population of the Peruvian Amazon. (Stockholm Studies in Comparative Religion). (Illus.). 202p. (Orig.). 1986. pap. text ed. 20.00x. Coronet Bks.

Luna, Roger M., tr. see Desramaut, Francis.

Lund, Candida, ed. If I Were Pope. 1987. 11.95 (ISBN 0-88347-187-6). Thomas More.

--In Joy & in Sorrow. Large type ed. 164p. 1984. 12.95 (ISBN 0-88347-167-1). Thomas More.

Lund, Carol A. A Journey with Jesus. (Illus.). 214p. (Orig.). 1982. pap. 4.95x (ISBN 0-9608418-0-6). MasterSon Pub.

Lund, Gene J., tr. see Fagerberg, Holsten.

Lund, Lynn S. Songs of Eternal Faith: Artistic Piano Arrangements of Best-Loved Hymns. LC 81-80954. 56p. (Orig.). 1982. pap. 5.95 (ISBN 0-88290-184-2, 2901). Horizon Utah.

--Songs of Inspiration: Artistic Piano Arrangements of New Latter-day Saint Hymns. 40p. 1986. pap. text ed. 7.95 (ISBN 0-88290-276-8). Horizon Utah.

Lund, Shirley & Foster, Julia A. Variant Versions of Targumic Traditions Within Codex Neofiti 1. LC 77-5389. (Society of Biblical Literature. Aramaic Studies). 1977. pap. 10.50 (ISBN 0-89130-137-2, 061302). Scholars Pr GA.

Lund, T. W. Matthew Arnold: The Message & Meaning of a Life. LC 76-28474. 1888. lib. bdg. 8.50 (ISBN 0-8414-5807-3). Folcroft.

Lunday, Berneice. Unblessed. LC 78-15244. (Orion Ser). 1979. pap. 3.50 (ISBN 0-8127-0200-X). Review & Herald.

Lundbom, Jack R. Jeremiah: A Study in Ancient Hebrew Rhetoric. LC 75-15732. (Society of Biblical Literature. Dissertation Ser.: No. 18). Repr. of 1975 ed. 39.80 (ISBN 0-8357-9574-8, 2017520). Bks Demand UMI.

Lunde, Alfred E. Christian Education Thru Music. LC 78-51509. (Evangelical Leadership Preparation Ser.). 80p. 1978. pap. 3.95 (ISBN 0-910566-83-6). Evang Tchr.

Lunde, Norman. You Unlimited. LC 65-23608. 1985. pap. 5.95 (ISBN 0-87516-249-5). De Vorss.

Lundeen, Joel W., ed. Luther's Works-Index. LC 86-45197. 512p. 1986. 24.95 (ISBN 0-8006-0355-9). Fortress.

--Luther's Works: Index. through 12/31/86 19.95 (ISBN 0-317-52515-8, 1-355). Fortress.

Lundeen, Lyman T. Risk & Retoric in Religion: Whitehead's Theory of language. LC 71-171501. pap. 72.00 (202868). Bks Demand UMI.

Lundin, Roger & Noll, Mark, eds. Voices from the Heart: Four Centuries of American Piety. 416p. 1987. 19.95 (ISBN 0-8028-3633-X). Eerdmans.

Lundquist, Carl, et al. Proclaim the Good News: Essays in Honor of Gordon G. Johnson. Magnuson, Norris, ed. LC 86-80862. 244p. (Orig.). 1986. pap. 4.95 (ISBN 0-935797-24-6). Harvest IL.

Lundquist, Carl H. Silent Issues of the Church. 156p. 1985. pap. 5.95 (ISBN 0-89693-721-6). Victor Bks.

Lundstrom, Lowell. Certain Hope for Uncertain Times. Orig. Title: What's Coming Next? 368p. 1984. pap. text ed. 5.95 (ISBN 0-88368-152-8). Whitaker Hse.

--Heaven's Answer for the Home. rev. ed. 142p. 1985. pap. 3.50 (ISBN 0-938220-16-0). Whitaker Hse.

--How You Can Pray with Power & Get Results. 272p. 1984. pap. text ed. 3.50 (ISBN 0-88368-151-X). Whitaker Hse.

Lundy, John P. Monumental Christianity: The Art & Symbolism of the Primitive Church. 1977. lib. bdg. 59.95 (ISBN 0-8490-2278-9). Gordon Pr.

Lundy, Richard A. You Can Say That Again: Cultivating New Life in Time-Worn Christian Sayings. LC 80-67556. 72p. 1980. pap. 2.95 (ISBN 0-89505-051-X). Argus Comm.

Lungu, N., et al. A Guide to the Music of the Eastern Orthodox Church. Apostola, Nicholas K., tr. from Rumanian. Orig. Title: Gramatica Muzicii Psaltice. (Illus.). 180p. (Orig.). 1984. pap. 15.00 (ISBN 0-917651-00-6). Holy Cross Orthodox.

Lunn, Arnold H. The Revolt Against Reason. LC 72-108396. xiv, 273p. Repr. of 1951 ed. lib. bdg. 22.50x (ISBN 0-8371-3819-1, LURA). Greenwood.

--Roman Converts. facs. ed. LC 67-22102. (Essay Index Reprint Ser). 1923. 18.00 (ISBN 0-8369-0636-5). Ayer Co Pubs.

Lunn, David. The English Benedictines, Fifteen Forty to Sixteen Eighty-Eight: From Reformation to Revolution. (Illus.). 282p. 1980. 28.50x (ISBN 0-06-494411-5). B&N Imports.

Lunt, Horace G. Old Church Slavonic Grammar. rev. ed. (Slavistic Printings & Reprintings Ser: No. 3). 1974. text ed. 54.00x (ISBN 90-2793-362-6). Mouton.

Lunt, Horace G., jt. ed. see Altbauer, Mosha.

Lunt, W. E. Financial Relations of the Papacy with England to 1327. 1967. Repr. of 1939 ed. 20.00X (ISBN 0-910956-13-8). Medieval Acad.

--Financial Relations of the Papacy with England, 1327-1534. 1962. 25.00X (ISBN 0-910956-48-0). Medieval Acad.

Luoma, William. God So Loved the World. 1986. pap. 3.95 (6806). CSS of Ohio.

Luomala, K. Oceanic, American Indian, & African Myths of Snaring the Sun. (BMB Ser.). Repr. of 1940 ed. 11.00 (ISBN 0-527-02276-4). Kraus Repr.

Lupinin, Nickolas B. Religious Revolt in the Seventeenth Century: The Schism of the Russian Church. 220p. 1984. 24.00 (ISBN 0-940670-12-7). Kingston Pr.

Lupton, D., tr. see Jacobus, Verheiden.

Lupton, Joseph H. Life of John Colet. 1887. 20.50 (ISBN 0-8337-4243-4). B Franklin.

Lupul, M. R. The Roman Catholic Church & the North-West School Question: A Study in Church-State Relations in Western Canada, 1875-1905. LC 73-89844. 1974. 27.50x (ISBN 0-8020-5301-7). U of Toronto Pr.

Luria. Gates of Reincarnation. (Hebrew.). 200p. 1985. pap. 9.95 (ISBN 0-943688-49-3). Res Ctr Kabbalah.

--Kitve Ari: Hebrew Text, 17 vols. 1985. 340.00 set (ISBN 0-943688-16-7); 25.00 ea. Res Ctr Kabbalah.

Luria, Gina, ed. see Hamilton, Elizabeth.

Lurker, Manfred. The Gods & Symbols of Ancient Egypt: An Illustrated Dictionary. Clayton, Peter A., rev. by. (Illus.). 144p. 1980. 19.95 (ISBN 0-500-11018-2, Quest). Thames Hudson.

--Gods & Symbols of Ancient Egypt: An Illustrated Dictionary. Clayton, Peter A., rev. by. (Illus.). 142p. 1984. pap. 9.95f (ISBN 0-500-27253-0). Thames Hudson.

--Woerterbuch Biblischer Bilder und Symbole. (Ger.). 1973. 25.00 (ISBN 3-466-20158-6, M-7046). French & Eur.

Luscombe, D. E., ed. see Abelard, Peter.

Lusk, David T. Within the Halls of Pilate. 4.50 (ISBN 0-89137-538-4). Quality Pubns.

Lussier, Ernest. Adore the Lord: Adoration Viewed Through the Old Testament. LC 78-20783. 1979. 6.95 (ISBN 0-8189-0380-5). Alba.

--Christ's Farewell Discourse. LC 79-19798. 90p. (Orig.). 1980. pap. 3.95 (ISBN 0-8189-0394-5). Alba.

--The Eucharist: The Bread of Life. LC 77-3035. 248p. 1979. pap. 3.95 (ISBN 0-8189-0349-X). Alba.

--Jesus Christ Is Lord: Adoration Viewed Through the New Testament. LC 79-15581. 1980. 7.95 (ISBN 0-8189-0382-1). Alba.

Lustiger, Jean-Marie. Dare to Believe: Addresses, Sermons, Interviews, 1981-1984. Marana, Nelly, tr. 260p. 1986. 14.95 (ISBN 0-8245-0778-9). Crossroad NY.

Luther, Martin. Basic Luther. 1984. pap. 14.95 (ISBN 0-87243-131-2). Templegate.

--The Bondage of the Will. Packer, J. I. & Johnston, O. R., trs. from Ger. 323p. 1973. Repr. of 1957 ed. cancelled 15.95 (ISBN 0-227-67417-0). Attic Pr.

--Bondage of the Will. Cole, Henry, tr. (Summit Books). 1976. pap. 6.95 (ISBN 0-8010-5570-9). Baker Bk.

--Bondage of the Will. Packer, J. I. & Johnston, O. R., trs. 322p. 1970. 13.95 (ISBN 0-8007-0028-7). Revell.

--The Chiefe & Prycypall Articles of the Christian Faythe. LC 72-6080. (English Experience Ser.: No. 84). 248p. 1969. Repr. of 1548 ed. 21.00 (ISBN 90-221-0084-7). Walter J Johnson.

--Christian Liberty. Grimm, Harold J., ed. Lambert, W. A., tr. from Ger. 1943. pap. 1.50 (ISBN 0-8006-0182-3, 1-182). Fortress.

--Commentary on First and Second Peter & Jude. LC 82-4652. 320p. 1982. 12.95 (ISBN 0-8254-3125-5). Kregel.

--Commentary on Galatians. LC 78-59151. (Kregel Reprint Library). Orig. Title: A Commentary on St. Paul's Epistle to the Galatians. 408p. 1979. 14.95 (ISBN 0-8254-3121-2). Kregel.

--Commentary on the Epistle to the Galatians. Watson, P. S., tr. from Ger. 573p. 1978. Repr. of 1972 ed. 15.95 (ISBN 0-227-67437-5). Attic Pr.

--Day by Day We Magnify Thee. LC 82-2481. 448p. 1982. pap. 10.95 (ISBN 0-8006-1637-5, 1-1637). Fortress.

--Devotions & Prayers of Martin Luther: 52 One-Page Meditations & Prayers on the Psalms. 1978. pap. 2.95 (ISBN 0-8010-5582-2). Baker Bk.

--The Large Catechism of Martin Luther. Fischer, Robert H., tr. from Ger. LC 61-3802. 112p. 1959. 4.95 (ISBN 0-8006-0885-2, 1-885). Fortress.

--Luther's Large Catechism. Lenker, J. M., tr. 1967. flexible bdg. 6.95 (ISBN 0-8066-0720-3, 10-4211). Augsburg.

--Luther's Ninety-Five Theses. Jacobs, C. M., tr. 1957. pap. 0.95 (ISBN 0-8006-1265-5, 1-1265). Fortress.

--Luthers Werke, 4 vols. (Ger.). 1920p. 1982. Set. pap. 67.50 (ISBN 3-11-008942-4). De Gruyter.

--Luthers Werke in Auswahl, 8 vols. Clemen, Otto, ed. Incl. Vol. 1. Schriften von 1517 bis 1520. 6th rev. ed. (Illus.). xxxii, 512p. 1966. 20.00x (ISBN 3-11-003152-3); Vol. 2. Schriften von 1520 bis 1524. 6th rev. ed. vi, 464p. 1967. 20.00x (ISBN 3-11-003153-1); Vol. 3. Schriften von 1524 bis 1528. 6th rev. ed. vi, 516p. 1966. 20.00x (ISBN 3-11-003154-X); Vol. 4. Schriften von 1529 bis 1545. 6th rev. ed. vi, 428p. 1967. 20.00x (ISBN 3-11-003151-5); Vol. 5. Der Junge Luther. 3rd rev. ed. Vogelsang, Erich, ed. xi, 434p. 1963. 22.10 (ISBN 3-11-005609-7); Vol. 6. Luthers Briefe. 3rd rev. ed. Rueckert, Hanns, ed. xv, 451p. 1966. 22.10x (ISBN 3-11-005610-0); Vol. 7. Predigten. 3rd ed. Hirsch, Emanuel, ed. xii, 420p. 1962. 22.10x (ISBN 3-11-005611-9); Vol. 8. Tischreden. 3rd ed. Clemen, Otto, ed. x, 387p. 1962. 22.10 (ISBN 3-11-005612-7). De Gruyter.

--Luther's Works, Vol. 12 Psalms. LC 55-9893. 1955. 15.95 (ISBN 0-570-06412-0, 15-1754). Concordia.

--Luther's Works, Vol. 14 Selected Psalms 3. LC 55-9893. 1958. 14.95 (ISBN 0-570-06414-7, 15-1756). Concordia.

--Luther's Works, Vol. 17. Bouman, Herbert J., tr. LC 55-9893. 1972. 16.95 (ISBN 0-570-06417-1, 15-1759). Concordia.

--Luther's Works, Vol. 28. LC 55-9893. 1973. 15.95 (ISBN 0-570-06428-7, 15-1770). Concordia.

--Luther's Works: Catholic Epistles, Vol. 30. Pelikan, Jaroslav, ed. LC 55-9893. 1967. 14.95 (ISBN 0-570-06430-9, 15-1772). Concordia.

--Luther's Works: Lectures on Galatians, Vols. 26 & 27. Incl. Vol. 26. Pelikan, Jaroslav, ed. 1962; Vol. 27. Pelikan, Jaroslav, ed. Jungkuntz, Richard, tr. 1963. 16.95 (ISBN 0-570-06427-9, 15-1769). LC 55-9893. 16.95 (ISBN 0-570-06426-0, 15-1768). Concordia.

--Luther's Works: Lectures on Romans Glosses & Scholia, Vol. 25. LC 55-9893. (Luther's Works). 1972. 17.95 (ISBN 0-570-06425-2, 15-1767). Concordia.

--Luther's Works: Selected Psalms 2, Vol. 13. Pelikan, Jaroslav, ed. LC 55-9893. 1956. 16.95 (ISBN 0-570-06413-9, 15-1755). Concordia.

--Martin Luther: Selections from His Writings. Dillenberger, John, ed. LC 61-9503. pap. 7.95 (ISBN 0-385-09876-6, Anch). Doubleday.

--Romans. Mueller, J. Theodore, tr. LC 76-12077. Orig. Title: Commentary on the Epistle to the Romans. 1976. kivar 8.95 (ISBN 0-8254-3119-0). Kregel.

--Sermons of Martin Luther: On the New Testament, 8 vols. Lenker, John N., ed. 1983. Repr. of 1904 ed. 95.00 (ISBN 0-8010-5626-8). Baker Bk.

--Small Catechism in Contemporary English. LC 15-6732. 1963. pap. 8.25 (ISBN 0-8066-0324-0, 15-6732). Augsburg.

--Three Treatises. rev. ed. LC 73-114753. 320p. 1970. pap. 4.95 (ISBN 0-8006-1639-1, 1-1639). Fortress.

--Von Christlicher Religion und Christlicher Bildung. (Classics in German Literature & Philosophy Ser). (Ger). 1968. Repr. of 1883 ed. 18.00 (ISBN 0-384-34280-9). Johnson Repr.

Lutheran Church in America Task Group for Long-Range Planning. Theology: An Assessment of Current Trends Report. LC 68-557557. pap. 43.50 (2026880). Bks Demand UMI.

Lutheran Historical Conference Staff, jt. auth. see Concordia Historical Institute Staff.

Lutkin, Peter C. Music in the Church. LC 72-135722. Repr. of 1910 ed. 21.45 (ISBN 0-404-04069-1). AMS Pr.

Lutske, Harvey. The Book of Jewish Customs. LC 86-2362. 300p. 1986. 25.00 (ISBN 0-87668-916-0). Aronson.

Luttikhuizen, Gerard P. The Revelation of Elchasai: Investigations into the Evidence for a Mesopotamian Jewish Apocalypse of the Second Century & Its Reception by Judeo-Christian Propagandists. 263p. 1985. lib. bdg. 60.00x (ISBN 3-16-144935-5, Pub. by J C B Mohr BRD). Coronet Bks.

Luttrell, Susan E. Love Was Born at Christmas. (Orig.). 1981. pap. 3.25 (ISBN 0-89536-483-2, 1234). CSS of Ohio.

Lutyens, Mary. Krishnamurti: The Years of Fulfillment. 248p. 1983. 15.50 (ISBN 0-374-18224-8). FS&G.

Lutyens, Mary, ed. see Krishnamurti.

Lutz, Charles P. Abounding in Hope: A Family of Faith at Work through the Lutheran World Federation. LC 85-1216. 144p. (Orig.). 1985. pap. 5.95 (ISBN 0-8066-2158-3, 10-0123). Augsburg.

--Farming the Lord's Land: Christian Perspectives on American Agriculture. LC 80-80285. 208p. (Orig.). 1980. pap. 8.95 (ISBN 0-8066-1785-3, 10-2264). Augsburg.

Lutz, Charles P. & Folk, Jerry L. Peaceways: Sixteen Christian Perspectives on Security in a Nuclear Age. LC 83-70500. 224p. (Orig.). 1983. pap. 10.95 (ISBN 0-8066-2006-4, 10-4904). Augsburg.

Lutz, Charles P., ed. Church Roots: Stories of Nine Immigrant Groups That Became the American Lutheran Church. LC 85-1217. 208p. (Orig.). 1985. pap. 9.95 (ISBN 0-8066-2156-7, 10-1366). Augsburg.

--God, Goods & the Common Good: Eleven Perspectives on Economic Justice in Dialog with the Roman Catholic Bishops' Pastoral Letter. 160p. (Orig.). 1987. pap. 9.95 (ISBN 0-8066-2286-5, 10-2563). Augsburg.

Lutz, Howard T., ed. & tr. see Fogelklou, Emilia.

Lutz, Jesse G. & El-Shakhs, Salah S. Tradition & Modernity: The Role of Traditionalism in the Modernization Process. LC 81-43464. 234p. 1982. lib. bdg. 29.00 (ISBN 0-8191-2326-9). U Pr of Amer.

Lutz, Kathryn. God Wants Us to Listen. Lemon, Patricia H., ed. (Christian Storybooks Ser.). 1986. pap. 5.95 (ISBN 0-939697-03-3). Graded Pr.

--God's Gift of Touch. Lemon, Patricia H., ed. (Christian Storybooks Ser.). 24p. (Orig.). 1986. pap. 5.95 packaged with audio cass. (ISBN 0-939697-02-5). Graded Pr.

--The Smells in God's World. Lemon, Patricia H., ed. (Christian Storybooks). 24p. (Orig.). 1986. pap. 5.95 packaged with audio cassette (ISBN 0-939697-01-7); audio cassette incl. Graded Pr.

Lutz, Lorry. Destined for Royalty: A Brahmin Priest's Search for Truth. LC 85-22681. 152p. (Orig.). 1986. pap. 5.95 (ISBN 0-87808-202-6, WCL202-6). William Carey Lib.

Lutz, Norma J. Good-Bye Beedee. LC 85-12826. (Marcia Stallings Ser.). 128p. 1986. pap. 2.95 (ISBN 0-89191-738-1, 57380, Chariot Bks). Cook.

Lutze, Lothar. Hindu Writings in Post-Colonial India. 1985. 27.00x (ISBN 0-8364-1422-5, Pub. by Manohar India). South Asia Bks.

Lutzer. Living with Your Passion. 1983. 5.95 (ISBN 0-686-46315-3). Victor Bks.

Lutzer, Erwin. Failure: The Back Door to Success. LC 75-16177. 1977. pap. 3.50 (ISBN 0-8024-2516-X). Moody.

--Managing Your Emotions. 180p. 1983. pap. 5.95 (ISBN 0-88207-386-9). Victor Bks.

Lutzer, Erwin & Van Stone, Doris. Dorie: The Girl Nobody Loved. 1981. pap. 5.95 (ISBN 0-8024-2275-6). Moody.

Lutzer, Erwin, jt. auth. see Orr, Bill.

Lutzer, Erwin W. Exploding the Myths That Could Destroy America. (Orig.). 1986. pap. 6.95 (ISBN 0-8024-5692-8). Moody.

--How to Say No to a Stubborn Habit. LC 79-64039. 143p. 1979. pap. 5.95 (ISBN 0-88207-787-2). Victor Bks.

--The Necessity of Ethical Absolutes: (CFUC) 112p. (Orig.). 1981. pap. 6.95 (ISBN 0-310-35791-8, 12659P). Zondervan.

Lutzer, Erwin W., ed. How in This World Can I Be Holy? (Moody Press Electives Ser.). 1985. pap. text ed. 3.95 (ISBN 0-8024-0730-7); leader's guide 2.50 (ISBN 0-8024-0731-5). Moody.

Lutzow, Franz. The Life & Times of Master John Hus. LC 77-84728. (Illus.). Repr. of 1909 ed. 40.00 (ISBN 0-404-16128-6). AMS Pr.

Lutzweiler, D. Who Are "The Jews" Today? 1984. lib. bdg. 79.95 (ISBN 0-87700-568-0). Revisionist Pr.

Lurie, Donald A., tr. see Berdiaer, Nicolaii.

Luz, Ulrich, jt. auth. see Lapide, Pinchas.

Luzac & Co. Ltd. Staff, ed. see De Boulainvilliers, H.

Luzatto, Moshe C. Derech HaShem: The Way of G-D. Kaplan, Aryeh, tr. from Hebrew. 1978. 12.95 (ISBN 0-87306-136-5); pap. 9.95. Feldheim.

Luzer, Erwin W. When a Good Man Falls. 132p. 1985. pap. 4.95 (ISBN 0-89693-361-X). Victor Bks.

Luzwick, Dierdre. The Surrealist's Bible. LC 75-44001. (Illus.). 128p. 1976. 10.00 (ISBN 0-8246-0206-4). Jonathan David.

Luzzato. The Path of the Just-Mesilath Yesharim. 1982. 10.95 (ISBN 0-87306-114-4); pap. 7.95 (ISBN 0-87306-115-2). Feldheim.

Luzzatto, Mosche Chaim. Daat Tevnoth: The Knowing Heart. Silverstein, Shraga, tr. from Hebrew. (Torah Classics Library). 357p. 1982. 12.95 (ISBN 0-87306-194-2); pap. 9.95 (ISBN 0-87306-345-7). Feldheim.

Luzzatto, Moses. General Principles of Kabbalah. 288p. 1970. 13.75 (ISBN 0-943688-07-8); pap. 11.95 (ISBN 0-943688-31-0). Res Ctr Kabbalah.

Lvov-Rogachevsky, V. A History of Russian Jewish Literature: Including Russian Literature & the Jews. Levin, Arthur, tr. from Rus. 1979. 15.00 (ISBN 0-88233-271-6); pap. 5.50 (ISBN 0-88233-272-4). Ardis Pubs.

Lyall, Alfred C. Asiatic Studies: Religious & Social, 2 vols. 826p. Repr. of 1882 ed. Set. text ed. 57.50x. Coronet Bks.

--Studies in Literature & History. facs. ed. LC 68-29227. (Essay Index Reprint Ser). 1968. Repr. of 1915 ed. 21.50 (ISBN 0-8369-0637-3). Ayer Co Pubs.

Lyall, Francis. Of Presbyters & Kings: Church & State in the Law of Scotland. 220p. 1980. 20.00 (ISBN 0-08-025715-1). Pergamon.

--Slaves, Citizens, Sons: Legal Metaphors in the Epistles. 320p. 1984. pap. 9.95 (ISBN 0-310-45191-4, 12452P). Zondervan.

Lyall, Leslie. Three of China's Mighty Men. pap. 3.95 (ISBN 0-340-25561-7). OMF Bks.

Lyall, Leslie T. God Reigns in China. 1985. pap. 4.50 (ISBN 0-340-36199-9). OMF Bks.

--A Passion for the Impossible. 1965. pap. 2.40 (ISBN 0-85363-115-8). OMF Bks.

Lybrand, R. E., Jr. Holy Communion Is... Sherer, Michael L., ed. (Orig.). 1987. pap. 6.50 (ISBN 0-89536-853-6, 7812). CSS of Ohio.

--Home Is a Four-Letter Word. 1985. 5.95 (ISBN 0-89536-719-X, 5803). CSS of Ohio.

Lydekker, John W. Faithful Mohawks. LC 68-18362. (Empire State Historical Publications Ser.: No. 50). (Illus.). 1968. Repr. of 1938 ed. 27.50 (ISBN 0-87198-050-9). Friedman.

--The Life & Letters of Charles Inglis: His Ministry in America & Consecration As First Colonial Bishop from 1759 to 1787. (Church Historical Society London N. S. Ser.: No. 20). Repr. of 1936 ed. 50.00 (ISBN 0-8115-3144-9). Kraus Repr.

Lydgate, John. Here Endeth the Book of the Lyf of Our Lady. LC 73-38207. (English Experience Ser.: No. 473). 192p. 1972. Repr. of 1484 ed. 63.00 (ISBN 90-221-0473-7). Walter J Johnson.

Lyke, James P. What We Have Seen & Heard: A Pastoral Letter on Evangelization from the Black Bishops of the United States. 40p. (Orig.). 1984. pap. text ed. 1.95 (ISBN 0-86716-040-3). St Anthony Mess Pr.

Lyles, Jean C. A Practical Vision of Christian Unity. LC 81-15032. (Into Our Third Century Ser.). 96p. (Orig.). 1982. pap. 3.95 (ISBN 0-687-33330-X). Abingdon.

Lyman, Darius, Jr. Leaven for Doughfaces: Parables Touching Slavery. facs. ed. LC 78-146266. (Black Heritage Library Collection Ser). 1856. 18.00 (ISBN 0-8369-8741-1). Ayer Co Pubs.

Lyman, Darryl. Great Jews in Music. 500p. 1986. 24.95 (ISBN 0-8246-0315-X). Jonathan David.

Lyman, Frederick C. Posture of Contemplation. LC 68-54973. 123p. 1969. 5.00 (ISBN 0-8022-2258-7). Philos Lib.

Lyman, Mary E. Death & the Christian Answer. 1983. pap. 2.50x (ISBN 0-87574-107-X, 107). Pendle Hill.

Lyman, Stanford M., jt. auth. see Vidich, Arthur J.

Lynall, Leonard D., tr. see Confucius.

Lynch, Frederick H. Christian in Wartime. LC 71-147674. (Library of War & Peace; Relig. & Ethical Positions on War). 1972. lib. bdg. 46.00 (ISBN 0-8240-0431-0). Garland Pub.

Lynch, John E. The Theory of Knowledge of Vital Du Four. (Philosophy Ser). 1972. 17.00 (ISBN 0-686-11546-5). Franciscan Inst.

Lynch, John W. Bernadette: The Only Witness. 5.00 (ISBN 0-8198-1104-1); pap. 4.00 (ISBN 0-8198-1105-X). Dghtrs St Paul.

--A Woman Wrapped in Silence. 288p. 1976. pap. 4.95 (ISBN 0-8091-1905-6). Paulist Pr.

Lynch, Joseph H. Simoniacal Entry into Religious Life, 1000 to 1260: A Social, Economic, & Legal Study. LC 76-22670. (Illus.). 286p. 1976. 15.00x (ISBN 0-8142-0222-5). Ohio St U Pr.

Lynch, Kilian F. The Sacrament of Confirmation in the Early - Middle Scholastic Period: Texts, Vol. 1. (Theology Ser). 1957. 17.00 (ISBN 0-686-11589-9). Franciscan Inst.

Lynch, Kilian F., ed. John de la Rochelle: Eleven Marian Sermons. (Text Ser). 1961. 7.00 (ISBN 0-686-11557-0). Franciscan Inst.

Lynch, Patrick, tr. see Ott, Ludwig.

Lynch, Richard. Health & Spiritual Healing. 140p. Date not set. pap. 8.00 (ISBN 0-89540-146-0, SB-146). Sun Pub.

--Know Thyself. 1967. 5.95 (ISBN 0-87159-077-8). Unity School.

Lynch, Stanley G. A Bird's Eye View of the Dispensation of Time. 1986. 7.00 (ISBN 0-8062-2433-9). Carlton.

Lynch, William F. Christ & Apollo: The Dimensions of the Literary Imagination. 224p. 1975. pap. 5.95x (ISBN 0-268-00712-8). U of Notre Dame Pr.

--Christ & Prometheus: A New Image of the Secular. LC 70-122046. 1970. 14.95 (ISBN 0-268-00431-5); pap. 4.95 (ISBN 0-268-00480-3). U of Notre Dame Pr.

Lynchard, Danny. Sure to Endure. 43p. 1983. pap. 1.95 (ISBN 0-88144-043-4). Christian Pub.

Lynchburg College Faculty Staff, ed. Faith & Morals. LC 81-71948. (Classical Selections on Great Issues, Symposium Readings Ser.: Vol. 4). 472p. 1982. lib. bdg. 24.00 (ISBN 0-8191-2301-3); pap. text ed. 9.25 (ISBN 0-8191-2302-1). U Pr of Amer.

Lynche, Richard see Batman, Stephen.

Lynd, Helen M., jt. auth. see Lynd, Robert S.

Lynd, Robert S. & Lynd, Helen M. Middletown. 550p. 1959. pap. 8.95 (ISBN 0-15-659550-8, Harv). HarBraceJ.

--Middletown in Transition: A Study in Cultural Conflicts. LC 37-27243. 604p. 1982. pap. 9.95 (ISBN 0-15-659551-6, Harv). HarBraceJ.

Lynd, Sylvia. The Christmas Omnibus. 1932. lib. bdg. 15.00 (ISBN 0-8414-5634-8). Folcroft.

Lyngheim, Linda, et al. Father Junipero Serra, the Traveling Missionary. LC 85-82131. (Illus.). 64p. 1986. 12.95 (ISBN 0-915369-01-X). Langtry Pubns.

Lynn, Claire. B-I-B-L-E That's the Book for Me! (A Doctrinal Series for Children: Bk. 1). (Illus.). 18p. (Orig.). 1981. pap. 1.50 (ISBN 0-89323-013-8). Bible Memory.

--Esther, Queen of Persia. 63p. 1981. pap. 1.50 (ISBN 0-89323-019-7). Bible Memory.

--No Crib for a Bed. (Doctrinal Ser.: Bk. 2). (Illus., Orig.). 1983. pap. 1.95 (ISBN 0-89323-029-4). Bible Memory.

Lynn, Claire, jt. auth. see Ellis, Joyce.

Lynn, Holly. Disease: The Cause & Cure. 32p. pap. 3.00 (ISBN 0-942494-67-9). Coleman Pub.

Lynn, John A. Will the Real You Please Remain Standing! 191p. 1981. pap. 2.95 (ISBN 0-910068-38-0). Am Christian.

--Will the Real You Please Stand Up! 113p. 1980. pap. 2.95 (ISBN 0-910068-28-3). Am Christian.

Lynn, Robert W. & Wright, Elliott. The Big Little School: Two Hundred Years of Sunday School. 178p. 1980. pap. 7.75 (ISBN 0-687-03523-6). Abingdon.

Lyon, Audley B. Growing Life: Devotionals for the Young in Christ. LC 77-82056. 1970. pap. 5.95 (ISBN 0-930014-07-3). Multnomah.

Lyon, Bryce, ed. High Middle Ages, One Thousand to Thirteen Hundred. LC 64-21207. (Orig.). 1964. pap. text ed. 13.95 (ISBN 0-02-919480-6). Free Pr.

Lyon, David. Karl Marx: A Christian Assessment of His Life & Thought. LC 81-8268. 192p. (Orig.). 1981. pap. 5.95 (ISBN 0-87784-879-3). Inter-Varsity.

--Sociology & the Human Image. LC 83-22644. 220p. 1983. pap. 9.95 (ISBN 0-87784-843-2). Inter-Varsity.

--The Steeple's Shadow: On the Myths & Realities of Secularization. 176p. (Orig.). 1987. pap. 9.95 (ISBN 0-8028-0261-3). Eerdmans.

Lyon, James. Urania: A Choice Collection of Psalm-Tunes, Anthems & Hymns. LC 69-11667. (Music Reprint Ser.). 198p. 1974. Repr. of 1761 ed. lib. bdg. 37.50 (ISBN 0-306-71198-2). Da Capo.

Lyon, Jene, ed. see Walker, Mary J.

Lyon, K. Brynolf. Toward a Practical Theology of Aging. LC 85-47720. (Theology & Pastoral Care Ser.). 128p. 1986. pap. 7.95 (ISBN 0-8006-1735-5). Fortress.

Lyon, Lawrence A. Choral Settings for Six LDS Hymns. 56p. (Orig.). 1975. pap. 4.95 (ISBN 0-87747-605-5). Deseret Bk.

Lyon, Nancy. The Mystery of Stonehenge. LC 77-10044. (Great Unsolved Mysteries). (Illus.). 1977. PLB 14.65 (ISBN 0-8172-1049-0). Raintree Pubs.

--The Mystery of Stonehenge. LC 77-10044. (Great Unsolved Mysteries Ser.). (Illus.). 48p. 1983. pap. 9.27 (ISBN 0-8172-2164-6). Raintree Pubs.

Lyon, Roy B. Bosquejos Utiles para Laicos. (Span., Illus.). 96p. 1985. pap. 1.95 (ISBN 0-311-42401-5). Casa Bautista.

Lyon, William. A Pew for One, Please. LC 76-41976. 1977. 6.95 (ISBN 0-8164-0374-0, HarpR). Har-Row.

Lyonnet, Stanislas & Sabarin, Leopold. Sin Redemption & Sacrifice: A Biblical & Patristic Study. (Analecta Biblica: Vol. 48). (Eng.). 1971. pap. 22.00 (ISBN 88-7653-048-7, Biblical Inst. Press). Loyola.

Lyons, Arthur, jt. auth. see Gauchat, Dorothy.

Lyons, Bob E. Kingdom of Priests. LC 77-92990. 160p. 1984. pap. text ed. 5.95 (ISBN 0-87148-478-1). Pathway Pr.

--Single Truth. 1982. text ed. 5.25 (ISBN 0-87148-801-9); pap. 4.25 (ISBN 0-87148-802-7); instr's. manual 6.95 (ISBN 0-87148-804-3). Pathway Pr.

Lyons, Elizabeth & Peters, Heather. Buddhism: History & Diversity of a Great Tradition. (Illus.). 64p. 1985. pap. 8.95 (ISBN 0-934718-76-8). Univ Mus of U PA.

--Buddhism: History & Diversity of a Great Tradition. LC 85-28817. (University of Pennsylvaina Museum Ser.). (Illus.). 64p. 1985. pap. 12.95 (ISBN 0-317-46953-3). U of Pa Pr.

Lyons, George. Pauline Autobiography: Toward a New Understanding. (Society of Biblical Literature Dissertation Ser.). 1985. 23.50 (ISBN 0-89130-730-3, 06-01-73); pap. 15.50 (ISBN 0-89130-765-6). Scholars Pr GA.

Lyons, H. P. Praying Our Prayers. 1976. 4.95 (ISBN 0-8199-0598-4). Franciscan Herald.

Lyons, Harold D. The Final Prophet. Graves, Helen, ed. LC 86-40282. 288p. 1987. 12.95 (ISBN 1-55523-037-7). Winston-Derek.

Lyons, J. A. The Cosmic Christ in Origen & Teilhard de Chardin. Wiles, Maurice, ed. (Theological Monographs). 1982. 34.95x (ISBN 0-19-826721-5). Oxford U Pr.

Lyons, James R., ed. The Intellectual Legacy of Paul Tillich. LC 68-63714. (Slaughter Foundation Lectures: 1966). pap. 29.80 (2027636). Bks Demand UMI.

Lyons, Jeanne M., tr. see Casalis, George.

Lyons, John D. & Nichols, Stephen G., Jr., eds. Mimesis: From Mirror to Method, Augustine to Descartes. LC 82-40340. (Illus.). 287p. 1982. 25.00x (ISBN 0-87451-244-1). U Pr of New Eng.

Lyons, L. Bible in Everyday Speech. 1986. cancelled (ISBN 0-442-25325-7). Van Nos Reinhold.

Lyons, Leonard, jt. ed. see Donnelly, John.

Lyons, Sr. Letitia M. Francis Norbet Blanchet & the Founding of the Oregon Missions (1838-1848) LC 73-3585. (Catholic University of America. Studies in American Church History: No. 31). Repr. of 1940 ed. 28.00 (ISBN 0-404-57781-4). AMS Pr.

Lyons, Mark. The Good Parishioner. 1983. 4.50 (ISBN 0-8199-0830-4). Franciscan Herald.

Lysaght, Moira. Father Theobald Matthew: Apostle of Temperance. 48p. 1984. 3.00 (ISBN 0-912414-42-1). Lumen Christi.

Lysebeth, Andre Van see Van Lysebeth, Andre.

Lysne, Mary E. Bible Activity Fun for Kids. 24p. 1983. pap. 1.50 (ISBN 0-87239-693-2, 2363). Standard Pub.

--Bible Learning Fun for Kids. 24p. 1983. pap. 1.50 (ISBN 0-87239-694-0, 2364). Standard Pub.

Lythgoe, Dennis, et al. You're a Mormon Now: A Handbook for New Members of the Church of Jesus Christ of Latter-day Saints. 75p. (Orig.). 1983. pap. 6.95 (ISBN 0-913420-37-9). Olympus Pub Co.

Lythgoe, Dennis L. A Marriage of Equals. 160p. 1985. 8.95 (ISBN 0-87747-700-0). Deseret Bk.

--The Sensitive Leader. 1986. text ed. 9.95 (ISBN 0-87579-061-5). Deseret Bk.

Lytle, Guy F., ed. Reform & Authority in the Medieval & Reformation Church. LC 79-17380. pap. 87.80 (2029496). Bks Demand UMI.

Lyttle, David. Studies in Religion in Early American Literature: Edwards, Poe, Channing, Emerson, Some Minor Transcendentalists, Hawthorne & Thoreau. 262p. (Orig.). 1984. lib. bdg. 28.50 (ISBN 0-8191-3499-6). U Pr of Amer.

M

M, pseud. The Condensed Gospel of Sri Ramakrishna. 1979. pap. 4.95 (ISBN 0-87481-489-8). Vedanta Pr.

M. Lord God of Truth Within. 1976. Repr. of 1940 ed. 12.00 (ISBN 0-911662-56-1). Yoga.

M, Nectario. Juan Colon, Alias Cristobal Colon, Alias Christopher Columbus, Was a Spanish Jew. Josephson, E., ed. 1985. lib. bdg. 79.95 (ISBN 0-87700-867-1). Revisionist Pr.

Ma Prem Maneesha, ed. see Rajneesh, Bhagwan Shree.

Maalouf, Amin. The Crusades Through Arab Eyes. 312p. 1985. 16.95 (ISBN 0-8052-4004-7). Schocken.

--The Crusades Through Arab Eyes. LC 85-8367. 312p. 1987. pap. 8.95 (ISBN 0-8052-0833-X). Schocken.

Maarsingh, B. Numbers. Van der Woude, A. S., ed. Vriend, John, tr. from Dutch. (Text & Interpretation Commentary Ser.). 128p. (Orig.). 1987. pap. 6.95 (ISBN 0-8028-0104-8). Eerdmans.

Maas, E. van der see McGrath, Allister E.

Maas, E. van der see Douglas, J. D. & Van der Maas, E.

Maas, Henry, tr. see Goldmann, Lucien.

Maas, Robin. The Church Bible Study Handbook. 208p. (Orig.). 1982. pap. 11.95 (ISBN 0-687-08146-7). Abingdon.

Maassen, Pierce. Heavenly Comfort. pap. 0.45 (ISBN 0-686-23473-1). Rose Pub MI.

--Motherhood. pap. 0.45 (ISBN 0-686-23476-6). Rose Pub MI.

Maatman, Russell. The Bible, Natural Science, & Evolution. (Orig.). 1980. pap. 4.95 (ISBN 0-932914-03-9). Dordt Coll Pr.

--The Unity in Creation. 143p. (Orig.). 1978. pap. 4.95 (ISBN 0-932914-00-4). Dordt Coll Pr.

Mabee, Charles. Reimagining America: A Theological Critique of the American Mythos & Biblical Hermeneutics. LC 84-27335. xvi, 156p. 1985. 13.95 (ISBN 0-86554-148-5, MUP/H139). Mercer Univ Pr.

Mabee, Charles, ed. see Mercer, Calvin R.

Mabie, C. W. Behold I Show You a Mystery. LC 80-82229. 150p. (Orig.). 1980. pap. 4.95 (ISBN 0-9601416-5-0). J C Print.

Mabie, Hamilton W. Myths That Every Child Should Know. Repr. of 1905 ed. 20.00 (ISBN 0-89987-175-5). Darby Bks.

Mabie, Hamilton W., ed. Myths Every Child Should Know: A Selection of the Classic Myths of All Times for Young People. (Illus.). 351p. 1986. Repr. of 1914 ed. lib. bdg. 40.00 (ISBN 0-8482-5040-0). Norwood Edns.

McAdoo, Henry R. The Unity of Anglicanism: Catholic & Reformed. 48p. 1983. pap. 4.95 (ISBN 0-8192-1324-1). Morehouse.

McAfee, Cleland B. The Greatest English Classic. LC 77-18104. 1977. Repr. of 1912 ed. lib. bdg. 30.00 (ISBN 0-8414-6231-3). Folcroft.

McAfee, Lisa, jt. auth. see Hershey, Terry.

McAfee, Lisa, jt. auth. see Smoke, Jim.

McAfee, Lisa, jt. auth. see Timmons, Tim.

McAfee, Ward. A History of the World's Great Religions. 240p. (Orig.). 1983. lib. bdg. 27.00 (ISBN 0-8191-3394-9); pap. text ed. 12.25 (ISBN 0-8191-3395-7). U Pr of Amer.

McAleer, J. Phillip. The Romanesque Church Facade in Britain. LC 83-48699. (Theses from the Courtauld Institute of Art Ser.). (Illus.). 785p. 1984. lib. bdg. 80.00 (ISBN 0-8240-5979-4). Garland Pub.

Macalister, Robert A. A Century of Excavation in Palestine. Davis, Moshe, ed. LC 77-70720. (America & the Holy Land Ser.). (Illus.). 1977. Repr. of 1925 ed. lib. bdg. 32.00x (ISBN 0-405-10265-8). Ayer Co Pubs.

McAlister, Walter E, compiled By. Listen to the King: Meditations Just from the Scriptures. (Direction Bks.). 96p. (Orig.). 1980. pap. 2.95 (ISBN 0-8010-6104-0). Baker Bk.

McAllaster, Elva. When a Father Is Hard to Honor. 126p. (Orig.). 1984. pap. 6.95 (ISBN 0-87178-930-2). Brethren.

McAllester, David P. Peyote Music. pap. 19.00 (ISBN 0-384-36490-X). Johnson Repr.

McAllister, Dawson & Webster, Dan. El Discipulado Del Joven una Guia de Estudio. (Span.). 80p. 1986. pap. 4.50 (ISBN 0-311-12324-4, Edit Mundo). Casa Bautista.

McAllister, Lester G. & Tucker, William E. Journey in Faith: A History of the Christian Church. LC 75-11738. 512p. 1975. 14.95 (ISBN 0-8272-1703-X). CBP.

McAllister, Robert J. Living the Vows. Date not set. 19.45 (ISBN 0-317-52397-X, HarpR). Har-Row.

McAlpine, Campbell. Alone with God: A Manual of Biblical Meditation. 1981. pap. 5.95 (ISBN 0-87123-000-3, 210000). Bethany Hse.

McAlpine, Thomas H. Sleep, Divine & Human, in the Old Testament. (JSOT Supplement Ser.: No. 38). 232p. 1986. text ed. 32.50x (ISBN 0-317-46791-3, Pub. by JSOT Pr England); pap. text ed. 14.95x (ISBN 0-317-46792-1). Eisenbrauns.

Macann, Christopher, tr. see Theunissen, Michael.

Macarius, Saint Fifty Spiritual Homilies. 1974. Repr. of 1921 ed. 17.50 (ISBN 0-686-10200-2). Eastern Orthodox.

Macarius, Staretz. Russian Letters of Direction. LC 75-1064. 115p. 1975. pap. 4.95 (ISBN 0-913836-23-0). St Vladimirs.

McArthur, Erna, tr. see Steiner, Rudolf.

McArthur, Harvey K. Understanding the Sermon on the Mount. LC 78-16404. 1978. Repr. of 1960 ed. lib. bdg. 22.50 (ISBN 0-313-20569-8, MCUS). Greenwood.

MacArthur, John. The Charismatics. 1980. pap. 6.95 (ISBN 0-310-28491-0, 12645P). Zondervan.

--The Family. 1982. pap. 5.95 (ISBN 0-8024-2524-0). Moody.

--Giving God's Way. 1978. pap. 3.95 (ISBN 0-8423-1034-7). Tyndale.

--Hebrews. (The MacArthur New Testament Commentary Ser.). (Orig.). 14.95 (ISBN 0-8024-0753-6). Moody.

MacArthur, John F., Jr. Ephesians. 1986. 14.95 (ISBN 0-88469-171-3). BMH Bks.

--Hebrews. 1983. 14.95 (ISBN 0-88469-155-1). BMH Bks.

--Keys to Spiritual Growth. 132p. 1976. pap. 5.95 (ISBN 0-8007-5013-6, Power Bks). Revell.

--Liberated for Life a Christian Declaration of Indepence. LC 75-23511. 1984. pap. 4.95 (ISBN 0-8307-0931-2, 5418165). Regal.

--Matthew One-Seven. 1985. 14.95 (ISBN 0-88469-168-3). BMH Bks.

--Take God's Word for It. LC 79-91704. 160p. 1980. pap. 2.50 (ISBN 0-8307-0674-7, S341107). Regal.

--Why Believe the Bible. LC 79-91704. 160p. 1980. 5.95 (ISBN 0-8307-0750-6, 5413818). Regal.

MacArthur, John J. Liberty in Christ. (John MacArthur's Bible Studies). (Orig.). 1986. pap. 3.50 (ISBN 0-8024-5094-6). Moody.

MacArthur, John, Jr. Abiding in Christ. (John MacArthur's Bible Studies). (Orig.). 1986. pap. 3.50 (ISBN 0-8024-5128-4). Moody.

--Acting on the Good News. (John MacArthur's Bible Studies). (Orig.). 1987. pap. 3.95 (ISBN 0-8024-5348-1). Moody.

--The Anatomy of a Church. 2nd ed. (John MacArthur's Bible Studies). 1986. pap. 3.95 (ISBN 0-8024-5132-2). Moody.

--Assurance of Victory. (John MacArthur's Bible Studies). (Orig.). 1986. pap. 3.50 (ISBN 0-8024-5130-6). Moody.

--The Believers Armor. (John MacArthur's Bible Studies). 1986. pap. 4.95 (ISBN 0-8024-5092-X). Moody.

--Christ Displays His Glory: Matthew Sixteen Verse Twenty Four to Seventeen Verses Thirteen. (John MacArthur Bible Studies Ser.). 1987. pap. 3.50 (ISBN 0-8024-5317-1). Moody.

--The Christian & Government. (John MacArthur's Bible Studies). (Orig.). 1986. pap. 3.50 (ISBN 0-8024-5095-4). Moody.

--Comfort for Troubled Hearts. (John MacArthur's Bible Studies). (Orig.). 1986. pap. 3.95 (ISBN 0-8024-5342-2). Moody.

--Condemned & Crucified. (John MacArthur's Bible Studies). (Orig.). 1987. pap. 3.95 (ISBN 0-8024-5349-X). Moody.

--Confession of Sin. (John MacArthur's Bible Studies). 1986. pap. 3.50 (ISBN 0-8024-5093-8). Moody.

--The Consequences of Sin. (John MacArthur's Bible Studies). 1985. pap. 3.50 (ISBN 0-8024-5109-8). Moody.

--The Disciples' Prayer. (John MacArthur's Bible Studies). (Orig.). 1986. pap. 4.95 (ISBN 0-8024-5129-2). Moody.

--Empowered to Serve: Acts one Verses one to two Verses Thirteen. (John Mac Arthur Bible Studies Ser.). 1987. pap. 3.95 (ISBN 0-8024-5314-7). Moody.

--Entering God's Rest: Hebrew Three Through Four. (John MacArthur Bible Studies). 1987. pap. 3.50 (ISBN 0-8024-5316-3). Moody.

--Ephesians. (MacArthur New Testament Commentary Ser.). 1986. text ed. 14.95 (ISBN 0-8024-2358-2). Moody.

--Exposing False Spiritual Leaders. (John MacArthur's Bible Studies). (Orig.). 1986. pap. 3.95 (ISBN 0-8024-5345-7). Moody.

--First Corinthians. 1984. 14.95 (ISBN 0-88469-161-6). BMH Bks.

--First Corinthians: MacArthur New Testament Commentary. 1984. 14.95 (ISBN 0-8024-0754-4). Moody.

--Found God's Will. 1977. pap. 1.95 (ISBN 0-88207-503-9). Victor Bks.

--Freedom from Sin: Romans Six Through Seven. (John MacArthur Bible Studies Ser.). 1987. pap. 4.50 (ISBN 0-8024-5309-0). Moody.

--God's High Calling for Women: First Timothy Two Verses Nine through Fifteen. (John MacArthur Bible Studies Ser.). 1987. pap. 3.50 (ISBN 0-8024-5308-2). Moody.

--God's Plan for Giving. (John MacArthur's Bible Studies). 1985. pap. 3.50 (ISBN 0-8024-5107-1). Moody.

--Guidelines for Singleness & Marriage. (John MacArthur's Bible Studies). (Orig.). 1986. pap. 3.95 (ISBN 0-8024-5343-0). Moody.

--How to Study the Bible. (John MacArthur's Bible Studies). 1985. pap. 3.50 (ISBN 0-8024-5105-5). Moody.

--Jesus' Pattern of Prayer. LC 81-3947. 200p. 1981. 5.95 (ISBN 0-8024-4962-X). Moody.

--Jesus Silences His Critics: Mattew Twenty-Two Verses Fifteen Through Forty-Six. (John MacArthur Bible Studies Ser.). 1987. pap. 3.50 (ISBN 0-8024-5313-9). Moody.

--Justification by Faith. (John MacArthur's Bible Studies). 1985. pap. 4.95 (ISBN 0-8024-5120-9). Moody.

--Kingdom Living Here & Now. LC 79-25326. 1980. pap. 5.95 (ISBN 0-8024-4562-4). Moody.

--The Last Will Be First. (John MacArthur's Bible Studies). (Orig.). 1987. pap. 3.95 (ISBN 0-8024-5347-3). Moody.

--The Legacy of Jesus. pap. 5.95 (ISBN 0-8024-8524-3). Moody.

--Living in the Spirit: Ephesians Five Eighteen Through Twenty. (John MacArthur Bible Studies Ser.). 1987. pap. 3.95 (ISBN 0-8024-5315-5). Moody.

--The Lord's Supper: Mattew Twenty-six Vs Seventeen to Thirty, Corinthians Eleven Seventeen Through Thirty-four. (John MacArthur Bible Studies). 1987. pap. 3.50 (ISBN 0-8024-5310-4). Moody.

--Love Not the World. (John MacArthur's Bible Studies). (Orig.). 1986. pap. 3.50 (ISBN 0-8024-5098-9). Moody.

--Love's Humility. (John MacArthur's Bible Studies). (Orig.). 1986. pap. 3.95 (ISBN 0-8024-5097-0). Moody.

--Marks of a True Believer: First John Two Vs Eighteen Through Four Twenty-One. (John MacArthur Bible Studies Ser.). 1987. pap. 3.95 (ISBN 0-8024-5312-0). Moody.

--The Master's Men. (John MacArthur's Bible Studies). 1985. pap. text ed. 3.50 (ISBN 0-8024-5106-3). Moody.

--Matthew Eight-Fifteen. (MacArthur New Testament Commentary Ser.). 1986. text ed. 14.95 (ISBN 0-8024-0763-3). Moody.

--Matthew 1-7. (MacArthur New Testament Commentary Ser.). 1985. text ed. 14.95 (ISBN 0-8024-0755-2). Moody.

--Matthew 8-15. 1986. 14.95 (ISBN 0-88469-172-1). BMH Bks.

--On Divorce. (John MacArthur's Bible Studies). 1985. pap. 3.50 (ISBN 0-8024-5111-X). Moody.

--Overcoming Materialism. (John MacArthur's Bible Studies). (Orig.). 1986. pap. 3.50 (ISBN 0-8024-5099-7). Moody.

--The Parables of the Kingdom. (John MacArthur's Bible Studies). (Orig.). 1985. pap. 3.50 (ISBN 0-8024-5112-8). Moody.

--Paul on Trial. (John MacArthur's Bible Studies). (Orig.). 1986. pap. 3.95 (ISBN 0-8024-5131-4). Moody.

--Paul's Perilous Journey. (John MacArthur's Bible Studies). (Orig.). 1987. pap. 3.50 (ISBN 0-8024-5350-3). Moody.

--Perfect Love. (John MacArthur's Bible Studies). 1985. pap. 3.50 (ISBN 0-8024-5110-1). Moody.

--The Resurrection & the Life. (John MacArthur's Bible Studies). 1986. pap. 3.50 (ISBN 0-8024-5091-1). Moody.

--Signs of Christ's Return: Matthew Twenty-Four Through Twenty-Five. (John MacArthur Bible Studies Ser.). 1987. pap. 5.95 (ISBN 0-8024-5311-2). Moody.

--Spiritual Gifts. (John MacArthur's Bible Studies). 1985. pap. 5.95 (ISBN 0-8024-5121-7). Moody.

--The Superiority of Christ. (John MacArthur's Bible Studies). (Orig.). 1986. pap. 3.95 (ISBN 0-8024-5344-9). Moody.

--The Supernatural Power of Jesus. (John MacArthur's Bible Studies). 1985. pap. 3.50 (ISBN 0-8024-5113-6). Moody.

--The Tragedy of Rejecting Salvation. (John MacArthur's Bible Studies). (Orig.). 1986. pap. 3.50 (ISBN 0-8024-5346-5). Moody.

--True Worship. (John MacArthur's Bible Studies). 1985. pap. 3.50 (ISBN 0-8024-5108-X). Moody.

--The Ultimate Priority. 1983. pap. 5.50 (ISBN 0-8024-0186-4). Moody.

--Unity in Action: Romans Fourteen vs One Through Fifteen-Thirteen. (John MacArthur Bible Studies Ser.). 1987. pap. 3.95 (ISBN 0-8024-5307-4). Moody.

--Why I Trust the Bible. 120p. 1983. pap. 4.95 (ISBN 0-88207-389-3). Victor Bks.

--The Wrath of God. (John MacArthur's Bible Studies). (Orig.). 1986. pap. 3.50 (ISBN 0-8024-5096-2). Moody.

--Your Completeness in Christ. (John MacArthur's Bible Studies). 1985. pap. 3.50 (ISBN 0-8024-5114-4). Moody.

--Your Family. rev. & expanded ed. (Moody Press Electives Ser.). 1983. pap. 3.95 (ISBN 0-8024-0257-7). Moody.

MacArthur, Rod, jt. ed. see Dawson, Samuel G.

McArthur, Tom. Yoga & the Bhagavad-Gita. 128p. 1986. pap. 11.95 (ISBN 0-85030-479-2). Newcastle Pub.

--Yoga & the Bhagavad-Gita. 1986. Repr. lib. bdg. 19.95x (ISBN 0-8095-7037-8). Borgo Pr.

Macartney, C. A., tr. see Shestov, Lev.

Macartney, Clarence E. The Chosen Twelve Plus One. LC 80-17881. (Illus.). 124p. 1980. 39.95 (ISBN 0-930014-43-X); ltd. ed. 200.00 (ISBN 0-930014-52-9); portfolio 24.95. Multnomah.

--Great Women of the Bible. (Macartney Bible Characters Library). (Orig.). 1974. pap. 5.95 (ISBN 0-8010-5961-5). Baker Bk.

--Six Kings of the American Pulpit. facsimile ed. LC 75-152192. (Essay Index Reprint Ser). Repr. of 1942 ed. 16.00 (ISBN 0-8369-2323-5). Ayer Co Pubs.

--Woman of Tekoah & Other Sermons on Bible Characters. (Macartney Bible Characters Library). 1977. pap. 2.95 (ISBN 0-8010-6020-6). Baker Bk.

Macaulay, David. Cathedral. (Illus.). 1981. pap. 6.95 (ISBN 0-395-31668-5); prepack of 10 59.50 (ISBN 0-395-31766-5). HM.

Macaulay, J. C. Behold Your King. LC 81-22580. 256p. 1982. pap. 9.95 (ISBN 0-8024-2417-1). Moody.

Macaulay, Ranald & Barrs, Jerram. Being Human: The Nature of Spiritual Experience. LC 77-11365. 1978. pap. 6.95 (ISBN 0-87784-796-7). Inter-Varsity.

Macaulay, Rose. Milton. LC 74-7050. (Studies in Milton, No. 22). 1974. lib. bdg. 75.00x (ISBN 0-8383-1911-4). Haskell.

Macaulay, Susan S. For the Children's Sake: Foundations of Education for Home & School. LC 83-72043. 192p. 1984. pap. 6.95 (ISBN 0-89107-290-X, Crossway Bks). Good News.

McAuley, Marilyn. Let's Count. (Peek & Find Bks.). (Illus.). 28p. 1984. board book 3.95 (ISBN 0-89191-879-5, 58792). Cook.

--My Bible Says. (Peek & Find Bks.). (Illus.). 28p. 1984. board book 3.95 (ISBN 0-89191-877-9, 58776). Cook.

--What Did God Make? (Peek & Find Bks.). (Illus.). 28p. 1984. board book 3.95 (ISBN 0-89191-878-7, 58784). Cook.

McAuley, Marilyn, jt. auth. see Gray, Alice.

Macauley, Richard M. The Medieval Philosophers from St. Augustine to St. Anselm. (Illus.). 196p. 1984. 88.85 (ISBN 0-89266-483-5). Am Classical Coll Pr.

Mcauliffe, Max A. The Sikh Religion, 6 vols. in 3. 1963. text ed. 100.00. Coronet Bks.

McAvoy, Thomas T. Catholic Church in Indiana, Seventeen Eighty-Nine to Eighteen Thirty-Four. LC 41-6425. (Columbia University. Studies in the Social Sciences: No. 471). Repr. of 1940 ed. 20.00 (ISBN 0-404-51471-5). AMS Pr.

McAvoy, Thomas T., ed. Roman Catholicism & the American Way of Life. LC 72-13177. (Essay Index Reprint Ser.). Repr. of 1960 ed. 14.75 (ISBN 0-8369-8167-7). Ayer Co Pubs.

McBain, Alexander. Celtic Mythology & Religion. LC 76-1877. 1976. Repr. of 1917 ed. lib. bdg. 28.50 (ISBN 0-8414-6043-4). Folcroft.

McBain, Robert A., jt. auth. see Stravinskas, Peter M.

Macbeath, Alexander. Experiments in Living: A Study of the Nature & Foundation of Ethics or Morals in the Light of Recent Work in Social Anthropology. LC 77-27180. (Gifford Lectures: 1948-49). Repr. of 1952 ed. 28.00 (ISBN 0-404-60503-6). AMS Pr.

McBee, Alice F. From Utopia to Florence: The Story of a Transcendentalist Community in Northampton, Massachusetts, 1830-1852. LC 74-31281. (American Utopian Adventure Ser). (Illus.). ix, 93p. 1975. Repr. of 1947 ed. lib. bdg. 17.50x (ISBN 0-87991-027-5). Porcupine Pr.

McBeth, H. Leon. The Baptist Heritage: Four Centuries of Baptist Witness. (Orig.). 1987. 24.95 (ISBN 0-8054-6569-3). Broadman.

--English Baptist Literature on Religious Liberty to Sixteen Eighty Nine: Doctoral Dissertation. Gaustad, Edwin S., ed. LC 79-52575. (The Baptist Tradition Ser.). 1980. lib. bdg. 39.00x (ISBN 0-405-12443-0). Ayer Co Pubs.

McBeth, Leon. Hombres Claves En las Misiones. Orig. Title: Men Who Made Missions. 128p. 1980. pap. 3.75 (ISBN 0-311-01070-9). Casa Bautista.

--Strange New Religions. LC 76-47780. 1977. pap. 4.25 (ISBN 0-8054-1806-7). Broadman.

--Women in Baptist Life. LC 78-54245. 1979. 7.95 (ISBN 0-8054-6925-7). Broadman.

McBeth, Leon H. History of Baptists. LC 81-68736. 1983. cancelled 17.95 (ISBN 0-8054-6569-3). Broadman.

Macbeth, Norman, tr. see Poppelbaum, Hermann.

Macbeth, Norman, tr. see Steiner, Rudolf.

McBirnie, William S. How to Motivate Your Child Toward Success. 1979. pap. 3.95 (ISBN 0-8423-1528-4). Tyndale.

--The Search for the Twelve Apostles. 1979. pap. 4.50 (ISBN 0-8423-5839-0). Tyndale.

Macbride, A. S. Speculative Masonry Its Mission, Its Evolution & Its Landmarks. 264p. 1971. Repr. of 1924 ed. text ed. 6.00 (ISBN 0-88053-040-5, M-89). Macoy Pub.

McBride, Alfred. The Gospel of the Holy Spirit. 1975. pap. 1.50 (ISBN 0-88479-951-4). Arena Lettres.

--Interviewing & Supporting the Catholic Educator. 1983. 3.35 (ISBN 0-318-00784-3). Natl Cath Educ.

--The Kingdom & the Glory. 1977. pap. 1.75 (ISBN 0-88479-003-7). Arena Lettres.

--Saints Are People: Church History Through the Saints. 144p. (Orig.). 1981. pap. 4.50 (ISBN 0-697-01785-0). Wm C Brown.

--Year of the Lord: Reflections on the Sunday Readings. 240p. cycle A 6.95 (ISBN 0-697-01847-4); cycle B 6.95 (ISBN 0-697-01848-2); cycle C 6.95 (ISBN 0-697-01849-0). Wm C Brown.

McBride, Alfred & Praem, O. The Christian Formation of Catholic Educators. 32p. 1981. 3.00 (ISBN 0-686-39896-3); member 2.25. Natl Cath Educ.

--The Pre-Service Formation of Teachers for Catholic Schools. 24p. 1982. 2.40 (ISBN 0-686-39890-4). Natl Cath Educ.

--The Story of the Church: Peak Moments from Pentecost to the Year 2000. (Illus.). 168p. 1984. pap. text ed. 7.95 (ISBN 0-86716-029-2). St Anthony Mess Pr.

McBride, Dean, ed. see Wolff, Hans W., Jr.

McBride, Esther B. Open Church: History of an Idea. LC 83-91256. (Illus.). 112p. 1983. pap. 10.50 (ISBN 0-9613017-0-8). Esther McBride.

McBride, L. R. Kahuna: Versatile Mystics of Old Hawaii. pap. 4.25 (ISBN 0-912180-18-8). Petroglyph.

--Pele, Volcano Goddess of Hawaii. (Illus.). 1968. pap. 3.25 (ISBN 0-912180-11-0). Petroglyph.

McBride, Neal. Equipping Adults Through Bible Study. 32p. 1977. pap. 1.50 (ISBN 0-8307-0505-8, 9970118). Regal.

McBride, Neal F. Teacher! A Christlike Model in Students. (Complete Teacher Training Meeting Ser.). 48p. 1986. 9.95 (ISBN 0-89191-313-0). Cook.

McBride, Richard, et al. Love & Creation. pap. text ed. 2.16 (ISBN 0-317-39314-6); 3.99 (ISBN 0-8215-5842-0); Parent Guidebook 1.98 (ISBN 0-317-39315-4). Sadlier.

McBrien, Richard P. Caesar's Coin: Religion & Politics in America. 320p. 1987. 19.95 (ISBN 0-02-919720-1). Macmillan.

--Catholicism, 2 vols. 1368p. 1980. Set. 45.00 (ISBN 0-03-056907-9, HarpR). Har-Row.

--Catholicism Study Edition. 1312p. (Orig.). 1981. pap. 24.50 (ISBN 0-86683-601-2, HarpR). Har-Row.

McCabe, John, jt. auth. see Harrison, G. B.

McCabe, Joseph. A Candid History of the Jesuits. 1977. lib. bdg. 59.95 (ISBN 0-8490-1567-7). Gordon Pr.

--The Church Defies Modern Life. 31p. pap. cancelled (ISBN 0-911826-75-0). Am Atheist.

--The Church, the Enemy of the Workers. 32p. 1942. cancelled (ISBN 0-911826-74-2). Am Atheist.

--Crises in the History of the Papacy. 1977. lib. bdg. 59.95 (ISBN 0-8490-1684-3). Gordon Pr.

--History of Free Masonry. 31p. pap. cancelled (ISBN 0-911826-73-4). Am Atheist.

--History's Greatest Liars. 176p. (YA) 1985. pap. 5.00. Am Atheist.

--Is the Position of Atheism Growing Stronger. 30p. pap. cancelled (ISBN 0-911826-85-8). Am Atheist.

--The Logic & Virtue of Atheism. 58p. 1980. saddle stitched 3.00 (ISBN 0-911826-13-0). Am Atheist.

--Peter Abelard. facsimile ed. LC 74-148889. (Select Bibliographies Reprint Ser). Repr. of 1901 ed. 22.00 (ISBN 0-8369-5655-9). Ayer Co Pubs.

--Peter Abelard (1079-1142) LC 72-85102. ix, 402p. 1972. Repr. of 1901 ed. lib. bdg. 23.50 (ISBN 0-8337-4244-2). B Franklin.

--The Pope & the Italian Jackal. 31p. pap. cancelled (ISBN 0-911826-88-2). Am Atheist.

--The Pope Helps Hitler to World Power. 30p. pap. cancelled (ISBN 0-911826-87-4). Am Atheist.

--Rationalist Encyclopaedia: A Book of Reference on Religion, Philosophy, Ethics, & Science. LC 79-164054. 1971. Repr. of 1948 ed. 51.00x (ISBN 0-8103-3754-1). Gale.

McCabe, Joseph, tr. see Drews, Arthur.

McCabe, Joseph E. Handel's Messiah: A Devotional Commentary. LC 77-25860. 120p. 1978. pap. 5.95 (ISBN 0-664-24192-1). Westminster.

McCabe, Kendall K. The Path of the Phoenix. Sherer, Michael L., ed. (Orig.). 1986. pap. 7.25 (ISBN 0-89536-818-8, 6827). CSS of Ohio.

McCabe, Richard A. Joseph Hall: A Study in Satire & Meditation. (Illus.). 1982. 72.00x (ISBN 0-19-812807-X). Oxford U Pr.

McCabe, William H. An Introduction to the Jesuit Theater: A Posthumous Work. Oldani, Louis J., intro. by. LC 83-81114. (Series III-Original Studies, Composed in English: No. 6). xxiv, 338p. 1983. pap. 19.00 smyth sewn (ISBN 0-912422-62-9). Inst Jesuit.

McCaffrey, Hugh, tr. see Isaac Of Stella.

MacCaffrey, I., ed. see Milton, John.

MacCaffrey, Isabel G. Paradise Lost As Myth. LC 59-9282. 1959. 15.00x (ISBN 0-674-65450-1). Harvard U Pr.

MacCaffrey, James. History of the Catholic Church from the Renaissaince to the French Revolution, 2 vols. facsimile ed. LC 75-130558. (Select Bibliographies Reprint Ser.). Repr. of 1915 ed. Set. 53.00 (ISBN 0-8369-5531-5); Vol. 1. 26.50 (ISBN 0-8369-9984-3); Vol. 2. 26.50 (ISBN 0-8369-9985-1). Ayer Co Pubs.
--History of the Catholic Church: From the Renaissance to the French Revolution, Vol. II. facsimile ed. LC 75-130558. 470p. Repr. of 1915 ed. lib. bdg. 25.50 (ISBN 0-8290-0464-5). Irvington.
--History of the Catholic Church: From the Renaissance to the French Revolution, Vol. I. facsimile ed. LC 75-130558. 419p. Repr. of 1915 ed. lib. bdg. 25.50 (ISBN 0-8290-0463-7). Irvington.
McCaffrey, James. Thirsting for God in Scripture. 96p. 1984. pap. 2.95 (ISBN 0-914544-55-1). Living Flame Pr.
McCalden, David. Exiles from History. (Illus.). 40p. (Orig.). 1982. pap. 5.00 (ISBN 0-910607-00-1). Truth Missions.
McCalden, David, ed. see Carter, Nicholas.
McCall, Clark B. Putting up with Your Put Downs. (Uplook Ser.). 1978. pap. 0.79 (ISBN 0-8163-0093-3, 16970-6). Pacific Pr Pub Assn.
--Taking Dreams Off Hold. (Out Ser.). 1984. pap. 1.25 (ISBN 0-8163-0551-X). Pacific Pr Pub Assn.
--Tiptoeing Through the Minefield. (Outreach Ser.). 32p. 1982. pap. 1.25 (ISBN 0-8163-0460-2). Pacific Pr Pub Assn.
McCall, Donald D. In God's Hand: Meditations for the Sick & Their Families. Lambert, Herbert, ed. LC 84-1744. 64p. 1984. pap. 4.95 (ISBN 0-8272-1606-8). CBP.
McCall, Emmanuel L. Black Church Life-Styles. LC 86-17591. 1986. pap. 5.95 (ISBN 0-8054-5665-1). Broadman.
McCall, Thoma S. & Levitt, Zola. The Coming Russian Invasion of Israel, Updated. 96p. 1987. pap. 4.95 (ISBN 0-8024-1624-1). Moody.
McCall, Thomas & Levitt, Zola. El Anticristo y el Santuario. Orig. Title: Satan in the Sanctuary. (Span.). 128p. 1983. pap. 3.25 (ISBN 0-8254-1474-1). Kregel.
McCall, Thomas S. & Levitt, Zola. The Coming Russian Invasion of Israel. 96p. 1976. pap. 4.95 (ISBN 0-8024-1607-1). Moody.
McCall, Tom, jt. auth. see Levitt, Zola.
McCall, Yvonne H. The Story of Jacob, Rachel & Leah. (Arch Bks.). (Illus.). 24p. 1986. pap. 0.99 saddlestitched (ISBN 0-570-06205-5, 59-1428). Concordia.
Maccallum, Hugh R., ed. see Woodhouse, A. S.
McCan, Robert L. World Economy & World Hunger: The Response of the Churches. 119p. 1982. 16.00 (ISBN 0-89093-497-5); pap. 5.00. U Pubns Amer.
MacCana, Proinsias. Celtic Mythology. LC 84-45597. (The Library of the World's Myths & Legends). (Illus.). 144p. 1985. 18.95 (ISBN 0-87226-002-X). P Bedrick Bks.
McCane, Bryon R. & VanLoon, Preston C. Building a Faith to Live By: Programs for Youth (Foundation for Discipleship) 128p. 1987. pap. 9.95 (ISBN 0-8170-1107-2). Judson.
McCann, A. M. The Portraits of Septimus Severus, A.D. 193-211. 222p. 1968. 48.00x (ISBN 0-271-00452-5). Pa St U Pr.
McCann, Dennis P. Christian Realism & Liberation Theology: Practical Theologies in Creative Conflict. LC 80-23163. 256p. (Orig.). 1981. pap. 9.95 (ISBN 0-88344-086-5). Orbis Bks.
McCann, Dennis P. & Strain, Charles R. Polity & Praxis: A Program for American Practical Theology. 176p. 1985. 15.95 (ISBN 0-86683-986-0, AY8571, HarpR). Har-Row.
McCann, Dom J., tr. see Adam, Karl.
McCann, Edna. The Heritage Book, 1985. (Illus.). 192p. 1984. 5.95 (ISBN 0-02-582880-0). Macmillan.
McCann, Michael D. Hebrews. (Standard Bible Study Workbooks). 64p. 1986. pap. text ed. 1.95 (ISBN 0-87403-191-5, 40211). Standard Pub.
McCann, Mike. Galatians-Ephesians. (Standard Bible Study Workbooks Ser.). 80p. 1987. wkbk. 1.95 (ISBN 0-87403-189-3, 40209). Standard Pub.
McCann Lucas, Jerri. Christianity: A Growing Experience. pap. 4.95 (ISBN 0-89137-429-9). Quality Pubns.
McCant, Jerry. Teens & Self Esteem: Helping Christian Youth Discover Their Worth. 152p. (Orig.). 1985. pap. 5.95 (ISBN 0-8341-1055-5). Beacon Hill.
McCants, Sr. Dorothea O., ed. They Came to Louisiana: Letters of a Catholic Mission, 1854-1882. LC 72-96258. (Illus.). Repr. of 1970 ed. 72.80 (ISBN 0-8357-9392-3, 2020997). Bks Demand UMI.
McCardle, Arthur W. Friedrich Schiller & Swabian Pietism. (American University Studies I-Germanic Languages & Literature: Vol. 36). 236p. 1986. text ed. 40.65 (ISBN 0-8204-0196-X). P Lang Pubs.
McCarroll, Tolbert. Guiding God's Children: A Foundation for Spiritual Growth in the Home. 240p. (Orig.). 1983. pap. 9.95 (ISBN 0-8091-2547-1). Paulist Pr.
--Notes from the Song of Life. rev. ed. LC 77-7135. (Illus.). 144p. (Orig.). 1986. pap. 6.95. Celestial Arts.
--Notes from the Song of Life: Spiritual Reflections. LC 77-7135. (Illus.). 1977. pap. 6.95 (ISBN 0-89087-200-7). Celestial Arts.
--A Way of the Cross. LC 84-61025. 128p. (Orig.). 1985. pap. 4.95 (ISBN 0-8091-2653-2). Paulist Pr.
McCarter, P. Kyle, Jr. Samuel One: Volume Eight, a New Translation with Introduction & Commentary. LC 79-7201. (Anchor Bible Ser.). 1980. 20.00 (ISBN 0-385-06760-7). Doubleday.
--Textual Criticism: Recovering the Text of the Hebrew Bible. LC 86-4388. (Guides to Biblical Scholarship, Old Testament Ser.). 96p. 1986. pap. 4.95 (ISBN 0-8006-0471-7, 1-471). Fortress.
McCarter, P. Kyle, Jr., ed. Samuel II. LC 81-43919. (Anchor Bible Ser.: No. 9). (Illus.). 576p. 1984. 18.00 (ISBN 0-385-06808-5, Anchor Pr). Doubleday.
McCarthy, Adrian J. Studies in the English Mystics: Book to a Mother, No. 1. Hogg, James, ed. (Elizabethan & Renaissance Studies). 275p. (Orig.). 1981. pap. 15.00 (ISBN 3-7052-0742-3, Pub. by Salzburg Studies). Longwood Pub Group.
McCarthy, Caritas. The Spirituality of Cornelia Connelly: In God, For God, With God. LC 86-21718. (Studies in Women & Religion Ser.). 280p. 1986. text ed. 49.95 (ISBN 0-88946-530-4). E Mellen.
McCarthy, Charles, jt. auth. see McCarthy, Estelle.
McCarthy, David. Devotions from a Stamp Album. 104p. 1983. pap. 4.95 (ISBN 0-8010-6156-3). Baker Bk.
McCarthy, David S. Memo to a Weary Sunday School Teacher. LC 77-92877. 1978. pap. 3.95 (ISBN 0-8170-0807-1). Judson.
--Our Constant Companion. 96p. 1984. pap. 2.95 (ISBN 0-8170-1019-X). Judson.
--Practical Guide for the Christian Writer. 112p. 1983. pap. 5.95 (ISBN 0-8170-0979-5). Judson.
--That Unforgettable Encounter. 108p. (Orig.). 1983. pap. 2.95 (ISBN 0-8341-0834-8). Beacon Hill.
Mac Carthy, Denis Florence. Love the Greatest Enchantment: The Sorceries of Sin, the Devotion of the Cross. 1861. 50.00 (ISBN 0-8274-3002-7). R West.
McCarthy, Donald G. & Bayer, Edward J. A Handbook on Critical Life Issues. 230p. (Orig.). 1982. pap. 9.95 (ISBN 0-935372-10-5). Pope John Ctr.
McCarthy, Donald G., ed. The Family Today & Tomorrow: The Church Addresses Her Future. 291p. 1985. pap. 17.95 (ISBN 0-935372-17-2). Pope John Ctr.
McCarthy, Donald G. & Bayer, Edward J., eds. A Handbook on Critical Sexual Issues. 240p. (Orig.). 1983. pap. 9.95 (ISBN 0-935372-11-3). Pope John Ctr.
McCarthy, Doran C. The Inner Heart of Ministry. LC 85-15152. (Orig.). 1985. pap. 3.25 (ISBN 0-8054-6942-7). Broadman.
McCarthy, Estelle & McCarthy, Charles. The Power Picture. (Orig.). 1973. pap. 1.95 (ISBN 0-377-03031-7). Friend Pr.
McCarthy, Flor. And the Master Answered. LC 84-72678. (Illus.). 96p. (Orig.). 1985. pap. 4.95 (ISBN 0-87793-279-4). Ave Maria.
McCarthy, Gerald. The Ethics of Belief Debate. (AAR Studies in Religion). 1986. 20.95 (ISBN 0-89130-892-X, 01-00-41); pap. 15.95 (ISBN 0-89130-893-8). Scholars Pr GA.
McCarthy, John F. In Defense of Human Life. 71p. 1970. pap. 1.50 (ISBN 0-912414-02-2). Lumen Christi.
McCarthy, John P. Hilaire Belloc: Edwardian Radical. LC 78-5635. (Illus.). 1979. 8.00 (ISBN 0-913966-43-6, Liberty Pr); pap. 3.00 (ISBN 0-913966-44-4). Liberty Fund.
McCarthy, Joseph M., ed. see Fenwick, Benedict J.
McCarthy, Martha M. A Delicate Balance: Church, State & the Schools. LC 83-60797. 184p. 1983. pap. 6.00 (ISBN 0-87367-427-8). Phi Delta Kappa.
McCarthy, Mary. Memories of a Catholic Girlhood. LC 57-8842. 245p. 1972. pap. 5.95 (ISBN 0-15-658650-9, Harv). HarBraceJ.
McCarthy, Mary F., tr. see Pieper, Josef.
McCarthy, Mary F., tr. see Ratzinger, Joseph C.
McCarthy, Mary F., tr. see Von Balthasar, Hans Urs.
McCarthy, Mary F., tr. see Von Speyr, Adrienne.
McCarthy, Scott. Creation Liturgy. LC 86-43232. 150p. (Orig.). 1987. pap. 10.95 (ISBN 0-89390-105-9). Resource Pubns.
McCarthy, Vincent A. Quest for a Philosophical Jesus: Christianity & Philosophy in Rousseau, Kant, Hegel, & Schelling. xv, 240p. 1986. 28.95 (ISBN 0-86554-210-4, MUP-H190). Mercer Univ Pr.
McCarthy, William. Bible, Church & God. 2nd ed. LC 70-169211. (Atheist Viewpoint Ser). (Illus.). 736p. 1972. Repr. of 1946 ed. 41.00 (ISBN 0-405-03805-4). Ayer Co Pubs.
McCartney, Eugene S., ed. see Campbell, Oscar J., et al.
McCartney, Hazel S. Saga of Seven Sisters. 1985. 12.00 (ISBN 0-533-06270-5). Vantage.
McCartney, James J. Unborn Persons: Pope John Paul II & the Abortion Debate. (American University Studies VII-Theology & Religion: Vol. 21). 176p. 1987. text ed. 16.75 (ISBN 0-8204-0349-0). P Lang Pubs.
McCarty, C. Barry. A Parliamentary Guide for Church Leaders. 1987. pap. 6.95 (ISBN 0-8054-3116-0). Broadman.
McCarty, Doran C. Working with People. (Orig.). 1987. pap. 5.95 (ISBN 0-8054-3241-8). Broadman.
McCarty, Michele. Becoming. 1983. pap. 6.95 (ISBN 0-697-01856-3); program manual 10.00 (ISBN 0-697-01857-1); Journal 3.25 (ISBN 0-697-01869-5). Wm C Brown.
--Believing. (Fullness of Life Ser.). 160p. 1980. pap. text ed. 6.95 (ISBN 0-697-01753-2); tchr's manual 8.00 (ISBN 0-697-01754-0). Wm C Brown.
--Belonging. (Fullness of Life Ser.). (YA) 1985. pap. text ed. 7.95 (ISBN 0-697-02068-1); tchr's. ed. 10.00 (ISBN 0-697-02069-X); wkbk. 3.25 (ISBN 0-697-02070-3). Wm C Brown.
--Relating. (Fullness of Life Ser.). 128p. (Orig.). 1979. pap. text ed. 5.50 (ISBN 0-697-01710-9); tchr's manual 8.00 (ISBN 0-697-01711-7). Wm C Brown.
McCaskey, John P. Christmas in Song, Sketch & Story: Nearly Three Hundred Christmas Songs, Hymns & Carols. 1980. lib. bdg. 67.95 (ISBN 0-8490-3175-3). Gordon Pr.
McCasland. Free to Choose. 1983. 3.95 (ISBN 0-88207-593-4). Victor Bks.
McCaughney, J. D. Diversity & Unity in the New Testament Picture of Christ. (Lectures in Biblical Studies: No. III). 1969. pap. 2.00x (ISBN 0-85564-016-2, Pub. by U of W Austral Pr). Intl Spec Bk.
McCauley, George. The Unfinished Image. 462p. (Orig.). 1983. pap. 10.95 (ISBN 0-8215-9903-8). Sadlier.
McCausland, Clare. An Element of Love. Mobium Corporation & Ineman, K., eds. (Illus.). 140p. (Orig.). 1981. pap. 10.00 (ISBN 0-9607400-0-7). Children's Memorial.
McCaw, Mabel N. What God Can Do. LC 81-70865. 1982. 5.95 (ISBN 0-8054-4290-1, 4242-90). Broadman.
McCay, Gracie R. & Sargent, Virginia A., eds. Children Together, Vol. 3. 128p. 1985. pap. 9.95 (ISBN 0-8170-1078-5). Judson.
McChesney, Stewart R. Let the Children Come. LC 81-67995. 1982. pap. 4.25 (ISBN 0-8054-4925-6). Broadman.
M'Cheyne, R. M. Sermons of R. M. M'Cheyne. 1985. pap. 4.95 (ISBN 0-85151-165-1). Banner of Truth.
M'Cheyne, Robert M. Bethany. 1974. pap. 1.65 (ISBN 0-685-52814-6). Reiner.
McClain, Alva J. Bible Truths. 1981. pap. 1.25 (ISBN 0-88469-013-X). BMH Bks.
--Daniel's Prophecy of the Seventy Weeks. pap. 3.95 (ISBN 0-88469-076-8). BMH Bks.
--Daniel's Prophecy of the Seventy Weeks. pap. 3.95 (ISBN 0-310-29011-2, 10177P). Zondervan.
--Freemasonry & Christianity. 1979. pap. 1.00 (ISBN 0-88469-012-1). BMH Bks.
--The Greatness of the Kingdom. 11.95 (ISBN 0-88469-011-3). BMH Bks.
--The Inspiration of the Bible. 1980. pap. 1.00 (ISBN 0-88469-115-2). BMH Bks.
--The Jewish Problem. 1979. pap. 1.00 (ISBN 0-88469-014-8). BMH Bks.
--Law & Grace. pap. 1.75 (ISBN 0-88469-001-6). BMH Bks.
--The "Problems" of Verbal Inspiration. 1968. pap. write for info. (ISBN 0-88469-116-0). BMH Bks.
--Romans Outlined & Summarized. 1979. pap. 1.95 (ISBN 0-88469-015-6). BMH Bks.
--Romans, the Gospel of God's Grace. 11.95 (ISBN 0-88469-080-6). BMH Bks.
--Romans: The Gospel of God's Grace. 1979. 11.95 (ISBN 0-8024-7373-3). BMH Bks.
McClain, Ernest G. Meditations Through the Quran: Tonal Images in an Oral Culture. LC 81-82124. (Illus.). 166p. 1981. 12.95 (ISBN 0-89254-009-5). Nicolas-Hays.
McClain, S. C. Highlights in Church History. 9th ed. (Illus.). 66p. 1983. pap. 2.95 (ISBN 0-912315-06-7). Word Aflame.
McClain, William B. Black People in the Methodist Church: Whither Thou Goest? 160p. (Orig.). 1986. pap. 8.95 (ISBN 0-687-03588-0). Abingdon.
McClanahan, John H. Man As Sinner. LC 84-20036. (Layman's Library of Christian Doctrine Ser.). 1987. 5.95 (ISBN 0-8054-1637-4). Broadman.
McClean, Adam. The Triple Goddess: An Exploration of the Archetypal Feminine. 1987. pap. 10.00. Phanes Pr.
--The Western Mandala: A Survey of the Mandala in the Western Esoteric Tradition. (Illus.). 1987. pap. 10.00. Phanes Pr.
McClean, Charles, ed. The Conduct of the Services. (Illus.). 138p. 1975. pap. 6.50 (ISBN 0-915644-04-5). Clayton Pub Hse.
McCleary, Paul & Wogaman, J. Philip. Quality of Life in a Global Society. (Orig.). 1978. pap. 2.50 (ISBN 0-377-00070-1). Friend Pr.
McClellan, Albert, compiled by. Meet Southern Baptists. LC 78-52960. (Illus.). 1978. pap. 7.95 (ISBN 0-8054-6534-0). Broadman.
McClellan, Robert W. & Usher, Carolyn E. Claiming a Frontier: Ministry & Older People. LC 77-85413. 1977. 10.00x (ISBN 0-88474-040-4, 05741-X). Lexington Bks.
McClellan, Thomas L. Science of Mind Hymnal. 9.50 (ISBN 0-87516-343-2). De Vorss.
McClelland, Bryan L., ed. Fruit of the Vine. LC 85-72071. (Illus.). 392p. (Orig.). 1985. pap. 5.95 (ISBN 0-913342-50-5). Barclay Pr.
McClelland, David C., ed. Education for Values. 220p. 1982. 29.50x (ISBN 0-8290-0090-9). Irvington.
McClelland, Kate M. The Mouth of Witnesses: Biblical Exegesis & the Dead Sea Scrolls. LC 76-48407. 1978. 10.00 (ISBN 0-916620-09-3). Portals Pr.
McClelland, W. Robert. Chance to Dance: Risking a Spiritually Mature Life. Lambert, Herbert, ed. LC 85-18987. 128p. (Orig.). 1986. pap. 8.95 (ISBN 0-8272-0449-3). CBP.
McClelland, W. Robertt. God Our Loving Enemy. LC 81-12680. 160p. 1982. pap. 7.75 (ISBN 0-687-15220-8). Abingdon.
McClendon, Charles B. The Imperial Abbey of Farfa. LC 86-3466. 336p. 1987. text ed. 35.00 (ISBN 0-300-03333-8). Yale U Pr.
McClendon, James W., Jr. Biography as Theology: How Life Stories Can Remake Today's Theology. LC 74-9715. 224p. 1974. pap. 7.75 (ISBN 0-687-03539-2). Abingdon.
--Ethics: Systematic Theology. 400p. 1986. 22.95 (ISBN 0-687-12015-2). Abingdon.
--Understanding Religious Convictions. LC 74-34519. 256p. 1975. text ed. 16.95x (ISBN 0-268-01903-7); pap. 7.95x (ISBN 0-268-01904-5). U of Notre Dame Pr.
McClendon, James W., Jr., jt. ed. see Steuer, Alexel D.
McClintock, James. Mormon Settlement in Arizona. LC 78-134397. Repr. of 1921 ed. 27.00 (ISBN 0-404-08439-7). AMS Pr.
McClintock, James H. Mormon Settlement in Arizona. LC 85-8458. (Illus.). 384p. 1985. pap. 9.95 (ISBN 0-8165-0953-0). U of Ariz Pr.
McClintock, John & Strong, James. Cyclopaedia of Biblical, Theological, & Ecclesiastical Literature: Cyclopaedia of Biblical Literature, Vol. 1-10. 250.00 (ISBN 0-405-00020-0, 11917). Ayer Co Pubs.
--Cyclopedia of Biblical, Theological, & Ecclesiastical Literature, 12 vols. 12400p. 1981. text ed. 395.00 (ISBN 0-8010-6123-7). Baker Bk.
McClintock, Walter. The Old North Trail; or, Life, Legends & Religion of the Blackfeet Indians. LC 68-13651. (Illus.). xxvii, 539p. 1968. pap. 11.50 (ISBN 0-8032-5130-0, BB 379, Bison). U of Nebr Pr.
McCloskey, Michael. The Formative Years of the Missionary College of Santa Cruz of Queretaro: 1683-1733. (Monograph Ser.). 1955. 10.00 (ISBN 0-88382-051-X). AAFH.
McCloskey, Pat. When You Are Angry with God. 1987. pap. 4.95. Paulist Pr.
McCloy, Shelby T. Gibbon's Antagonism to Christianity. 1933. 23.50 (ISBN 0-8337-2311-1). B Franklin.
McCluney, Roalla. Outwit the Devil. 160p. (Orig.). 1987. pap. 6.95 (ISBN 0-89896-296-X, Linolean). Larksdale.
McClung, Grant, jt. auth. see Laing, Joseph.
M'Clure, David & Parish, Elijah. Memoirs of the Rev. Eleazar Wheelock, D. D. LC 75-38454. (Religion in America, Ser. 2). 338p. 1972. Repr. of 1811 ed. 22.00 (ISBN 0-405-04074-1). Ayer Co Pubs.
McClure, Kevin. The Evidence for Visions of the Virgin Mary. (Illus.). 158p. (Orig.). 1984. pap. 5.95 (ISBN 0-85030-351-6, Pub. by Aquarian Pr England). Sterling.
McCluskey, Neil S., ed. Catholic University: A Modern Appraisal. LC 70-85353. 1970. 22.95 (ISBN 0-268-00355-6). U of Notre Dame Pr.
Maccoby, Hyam. The Mythmaker: Paul & the Invention of Christianity. LC 85-45680. 256p. 1986. 17.45 (ISBN 0-06-015582-5, HARPT). Har-Row.

--Revolution in Judaea: Jesus & the Jewish Resistance. LC 80-16752. 256p. 1980. 9.95 (ISBN 0-8008-6784-X). Taplinger.

--The Sacred Executioner: Human Sacrifice & the Legacy of Guilt. LC 82-80492. (Illus.). 208p. 1983. 19.95 (ISBN 0-500-01281-4). Thames Hudson.

Maccoby, Hyman. Judaism on Trial: Jewish-Christian Disputations in the Middle Ages. (Littman Library of Jewish Civilization). 246p. 1982. 34.00x (ISBN 0-19-710046-5). Oxford U Pr.

MacCollam, Joel A. The Way of Victor Paul Wierwille. 32p. 1978. pap. 0.75 (ISBN 0-87784-162-4). Inter-Varsity.

McCollister. The Christian Catalogue. LC 77-29136. Date not set. 12.50 (ISBN 0-8246-0226-9). Jonathan David.

McCollister, John C. The Christian Book of Why. 340p. 1983. 11.95 (ISBN 0-8246-0297-8). Jonathan David.

--The Christian Book of Why. 360p. 1986. pap. 7.95 (ISBN 0-8246-0317-6). Jonathan David.

McCollough, Charles. Heads of Heaven, Feet of Clay: Ideas & Stories for Adult Faith Education. 192p. (Orig.). 1983. pap. 11.95 (ISBN 0-8298-0693-8). Pilgrim NY.

McComas, Henry C. Psychology of Religious Sects. LC 70-172763. Repr. of 1912 ed. 20.00 (ISBN 0-404-04107-8). AMS Pr.

McComb, S. The Making of the English Bible. 59.95 (ISBN 0-8490-0578-7). Gordon Pr.

McComish, William A. The Epigones: A Study of the Theology of the Synod of Dort, with Special Reference to Giovanni Diodati. (Princeton Theological Monograph Ser.: No. 13). (Orig.). 1987. pap. price not set (ISBN 0-915138-62-X). Pickwick.

McConkey, Dale. Goal Setting: A Guide to Achieving the Church's Mission. (Administration for Churches Ser.). 1978. pap. 3.95 (ISBN 0-8066-1651-2, 10-2558). Augsburg.

McConkey, James H. El Triple Secreto Del Espiritu Santo. Agostini, Beatrice, tr. from Eng. Orig. Title: The Three Fold Secret of the Holy Spirit. (Span.). 112p. 1980. pap. 1.95 (ISBN 0-311-09090-7). Casa Bautista.

McConkie, Bruce R. The Millennial Messiah. LC 81-19599. 726p. 1982. 17.95 (ISBN 0-87747-896-1). Deseret Bk.

--The Mortal Messiah: From Bethlehem to Calvary, 4 vols, Bk. 1. LC 79-19606. 536p. 1979. 16.95 (ISBN 0-87747-784-1). Deseret Bk.

--The Mortal Messiah: From Bethlehem to Calvary, Bk. 2. LC 79-19606. 424p. 1980. 16.95 (ISBN 0-87747-803-1). Deseret Bk.

--The Mortal Messiah, from Bethlehem to Calvary, Bk. 3. LC 79-19606. 486p. 1980. 14.95 (ISBN 0-87747-825-2). Deseret Bk.

--The Mortal Messiah: From Bethlehem to Calvary, Bk. 4. LC 79-19606. (The Mortal Messiah Ser.). 447p. 1981. 14.95 (ISBN 0-87747-856-2). Deseret Bk.

--A New Witness for the Articles of Faith. LC 85-12888. 735p. 1985. 17.95 (ISBN 0-87747-872-4). Deseret Bk.

--The Promised Messiah. LC 78-3478. 1978. 17.95 (ISBN 0-87747-702-7). Deseret Bk.

McConkie, Joseph F. Seeking the Spirit. LC 78-13372. 122p. 1985. pap. 4.95 (ISBN 0-87747-818-X). Deseret Bk.

--Spirit of Revelation. LC 84-1705. 144p. 1984. 6.95 (ISBN 0-87747-990-9). Deseret Bk.

McConnachie, John. Barthian Theology. LC 72-2493. (Select Bibliography Reprint Ser). 1972. Repr. of 1933 ed. 19.00 (ISBN 0-8369-6861-1). Ayer Co Pubs.

McConnaughey, Bayard & McConnaughey, Evelyn. Pacific Coast. Elliott, Charles, ed. LC 84-48673. (The Audubon Society Nature Guides Ser.). (Illus.). 633p. 1985. pap. 14.95 (ISBN 0-394-73130-1). Knopf.

McConnaughey, Evelyn, jt. auth. see McConnaughey, Bayard.

McConnell, Cecil. Conozcamos Nuestro Himnario. 144p. 1980. pap. 3.75 (ISBN 0-311-32432-0). Casa Bautista.

McConnell, Cecil & McConnell, Mary. Objetos Que Ensenan de Dios. (Span.). 96p. 1986. pap. 3.50 (ISBN 0-311-44007-X). Casa Bautista.

McConnell, Francis J., ed. see National Study Conference of the Churches on a Just & Durable Peace 1st Ohio Wesleyan University 1942.

McConnell, Frank, ed. The Bible & Narrative Tradition. 168p. 1986. 16.95x (ISBN 0-19-503698-0). Oxford U Pr.

McConnell, Mary, jt. auth. see McConnell, Cecil.

McConnell, S. D. The Evolution of Immortality. 1978. Repr. of 1901 ed. lib. bdg. 25.00 (ISBN 0-8495-3508-5). Arden Lib.

McConnell, Theodore, jt. ed. see Atkins, Stanley.

McConnell, Theodore A. Finding a Pastor: The Search Committee Handbook. 72p. (Orig.). 1985. pap. 4.95 (ISBN 0-86683-493-1, HarpR). Har-Row.

McConnell, William T. The Gift of Time. LC 83-120. 132p. (Orig.). 1983. pap. 3.95 (ISBN 0-87784-838-6). Inter-Varsity.

McConville, J. G. Ezra, Nehemiah, & Esther. LC 84-25825. (The Daily Study Bible-Old Testament Ser.). 210p. 1985. 14.95 (ISBN 0-664-21814-8); pap. 7.95 (ISBN 0-664-24583-8). Westminster.

--First & Second Chronicles. LC 84-2371. (Daily Study Bible-Old Testament Ser.). 280p. 1984. 14.95 (ISBN 0-664-21811-3); pap. 7.95 (ISBN 0-664-24578-1). Westminster.

--Law & Theology in Deuteronomy. (JSOT Supplement Ser.: No. 33). 200p. 1985. text ed. 28.50x (ISBN 0-905774-78-7, Pub. by JSOT Pr England); pap. text ed. 13.50x (ISBN 0-905774-79-5, Pub. by JSOT Pr England). Eisenbrauns.

McCool, Gerald, ed. Rahner Reader. (Orig.). 1975. pap. 10.95 (ISBN 0-8245-0370-8). Crossroad NY.

McCord, David. The King Is Coming. 112p. (Orig.). 1984. pap. 2.95 (ISBN 0-87239-670-3, 41026). Standard Pub.

--Let Us Give. 64p. 1986. pap. 2.95 (ISBN 0-87403-098-6, 3024). Standard Pub.

--Let Us Pray. 64p. 1986. pap. 2.95 (ISBN 0-87403-099-4, 3025). Standard Pub.

--Let Us Remember. 64p. 1986. pap. 2.95 (ISBN 0-87403-071-4, 3023). Standard Pub.

--A Loser, a Winner, & a Wise-Guy: Saul, David & Solomon. LC 79-67438. 96p. 1980. pap. 2.25 (ISBN 0-87239-380-1, 40084). Standard Pub.

McCord, Hugo. From Heaven or from Men. 1970. pap. 2.75 (ISBN 0-88027-033-0). Firm Foun Pub.

MacCormac, Earl R. Metaphor & Myth in Science & Religion. LC 75-23941. pap. 46.80 (2052207). Bks Demand UMI.

McCormack, Ellen. Cuomo vs. O'Connor: Did a Catholic Politician Make an Anti-Catholic Appeal? LC 85-71482. 100p. (Orig.). 1985. pap. 5.95 (ISBN 0-934117-00-4). Dolores Pr.

MacCormack, Sabine. Art & Ceremony in Late Antiquity. (The Transformation of the Classical Heritage Ser.: Vol. 1). (Illus.). 450p. 1981. 45.00x (ISBN 0-520-03779-0). U of Cal Pr.

McCormack, Thomas J., tr. see Cumont, Franz.

McCormick, Jack, jt. ed. see Leonard, Larry.

McCormick, Joe & McKenney, Tom. Holy Spirit Baptism. (Illus.). 23p. (Orig.). 1982. pap. 2.95 (ISBN 0-934527-02-4). Words Living Minis.

McCormick, John F. Saint Thomas & the Life of Learning. (Aquinas Lecture). 1937. 7.95 (ISBN 0-87462-101-1). Marquette.

McCormick, Malachi. Yiddish Proverbs: A Collection. (Proverbs of the World Ser.). (Illus.). 60p. (Orig.). 1982. pap. text ed. 12.50 (ISBN 0-943984-02-5). Stone St Pr.

McCormick, Richard, jt. auth. see Curran, Charles E.

McCormick, Richard A. Ambiguity in Moral Choice. (Pere Marquette Theology Lectures). 1977. pap. 7.95 (ISBN 0-87462-505-X). Marquette.

--Health & Medicine in the Roman Catholic Tradition: Tradition in Transition. 176p. 1984. 15.95x (ISBN 0-8245-0661-8). Crossroad NY.

--Notes on Moral Theology. LC 80-5682. 902p. 1981. lib. bdg. 33.00 (ISBN 0-8191-1439-1); pap. text ed. 17.75 (ISBN 0-8191-1440-5). U Pr of Amer.

McCormick, Richard A., jt. auth. see Curran, Charles E.

McCormick, Richard A. & Curran, Charles, eds. Readings in Moral Theology, No. 5: Official Catholic Social Teaching. 400p. (Orig.). 1986. pap. 9.95 (ISBN 0-8091-2738-5). Paulist Pr.

McCormick, Richard A. & Ramsey, Paul, eds. Doing Evil to Achieve Good: Moral Choice in Conflict Situations. LC 78-11316. 1978. 11.95 (ISBN 0-8294-0285-3). Loyola.

--Doing Evil to Achieve Good: Moral Choice in Conflict Situations. 274p. 1985. pap. text ed. 11.75 (ISBN 0-8191-4586-6). U Pr of Amer.

McCormick, Richard A., jt. ed. see Curran, Charles E.

McCormick, Richard J. Notes on Moral Theology: Nineteen Eighty-One Through Nineteen Eighty-Four. 242p. 1985. lib. bdg. 22.00 (ISBN 0-8191-4351-0); pap. text ed. 9.25 (ISBN 0-8191-4352-9). U Pr of Amer.

McCormick, Thomas & Fish, Sharon. Meditation: A Practical Guide to a Spiritual Discipline. 132p. (Orig.). 1983. pap. 3.95 (ISBN 0-87784-844-0). Inter-Varsity.

McCosh, James. Our Moral Nature. LC 75-3260. Repr. of 1892 ed. 18.00 (ISBN 0-404-59247-3). AMS Pr.

--The Supernatural in Relation to the Natural. LC 75-3267. Repr. of 1862 ed. 38.00 (ISBN 0-404-59255-4). AMS Pr.

McCown, Donald E. & Haines, Richard C. Nippur One: Temple of Enlil, Scribal Quarter & Soundings. LC 66-17104. (Illus.). 1967. 10.00 (ISBN 0-226-55688-3, OIP78). U of Chicago Pr.

McCown, Joe. Availability: Gabriel Marcel & the Phenomenology of Human Openness. LC 77-22358. (American Academy of Religion. Studies in Religion: No. 14). 1978. pap. 9.95 (ISBN 0-89130-144-5, 010014). Scholars Pr GA.

McCown, Wayne & Massey, James, eds. God's Word for Today. (Wesleyan Theological Perspectives Ser.: Vol. II). 1982. 14.95 (ISBN 0-87162-257-2, D4851). Warner Pr.

McCoy, Adam D. Holy Cross: A Century of Anglican Monasticism. 1987. 29.95. Morehouse.

McCoy, Charles S. & McCoy, Marjorie C. The Transforming Cross. LC 77-10884. Repr. of 1977 ed. 27.80 (ISBN 0-8357-9030-4, 2016417). Bks Demand UMI.

McCoy, Isaac. History of Baptist Indian Missions. LC 19-11605. 1970. Repr. of 1840 ed. 36.00 (ISBN 0-384-36590-6). Johnson Repr.

McCoy, James C. Jesuit Relations of Canada, 1632-1673: A Bibliography. LC 76-153038. (Illus.). xv, 346p. 1972. Repr. of 1937 ed. lib. bdg. 23.50 (ISBN 0-8337-2314-6). B Franklin.

McCoy, L. M., tr. see Alves, Rubem.

McCoy, Marjorie C., jt. auth. see McCoy, Charles S.

McCracken, J. Politics & Christianity in Malawi 1875-1940. LC 76-27905. (Cambridge Commonwealth Ser.). (Illus.). 1977. 49.50 (ISBN 0-521-21444-0). Cambridge U Pr.

McCrank, Lawrence J., compiled by. Mt. Angel Abbey: A Centennial History of the Benedictine Community & Its Library, 1882-1982. LC 83-10536. 176p. 1983. pap. 15.00 (ISBN 0-8420-2212-0). Scholarly Res Inc.

McCray, Walter A. Black Folks & Christian Liberty: Black, Christian, & Free to Be Cultural & Social. LC 78-71258. (Black Light Fellowship Ser.). 1978. pap. 9.95 (ISBN 0-933176-01-5). Black Light Fellow.

--Black Spirituality. 150p. (Orig.). pap. write for info. (ISBN 0-933176-04-X). Black Light Fellow.

--Discipling the Children of Black America: A Discussion of Christian Black Education for Black Youth. 50p. (Orig.). pap. write for info. (ISBN 0-933176-02-3). Black Light Fellow.

--How to Stick Together During Times of Tension: Directives for Christian Black Unity. LC 83-70288. 170p. (Orig.). 1983. 11.95 (ISBN 0-933176-04-X); pap. 7.50 (ISBN 0-933176-03-1). Black Light Fellow.

--Who Says? A Black Perspective on the Authority of New Testament Exegesis Highlighting the Foundation for Its Interpretations & Applications. Bentley, William H., ed. 75p. (Orig.). pap. write for info. (ISBN 0-933176-35-X). Black Light Fellow.

McCreary, W. Burgess. One Thousand Bible Drill Questions. 1980. pap. 1.75 (ISBN 0-87162-263-7, WP#D5899). Warner Pr.

MacCregor, Geddes, ed. Immortality & Human Destiny. 256p. 21.95 (ISBN 0-913757-45-4); pap. 12.95 (ISBN 0-913757-46-2). Paragon Hse.

McCrie, Thomas. The Early Years of John Calvin: A Fragment, 1509-1536. LC 83-45622. Date not set. Repr. of 1880 ed. 28.00 (ISBN 0-404-19840-6). AMS Pr.

--History of the Progress & Suppression of the Reformation in Spain in the Sixteenth Century. LC 79-127433. Repr. of 1829 ed. 30.00 (ISBN 0-404-04117-5). AMS Pr.

--History of the Progress & Suppression of the Reformation in Italy. LC 72-1006. Repr. of 1856 ed. 22.45 (ISBN 0-404-04118-3). AMS Pr.

--Life of John Knox. LC 83-45584. (Illus.). Date not set. Repr. of 1898 ed. 57.50 (ISBN 0-404-19902-X). AMS Pr.

McCrossan, T. J. Bodily Healing & the Atonement. 1982. pap. 3.50 (ISBN 0-89276-505-4). Hagin Ministries.

McCrossen, Vincent A. The Two Loves. LC 78-61110. 383p. 1979. 13.95 (ISBN 0-8022-2237-4). Philos Lib.

McCue, James F., jt. auth. see Forell, George W.

MacCulloch, Diarmaid. Suffolk & the Tudors: Politics & Religion in an English County 1500-1600. (Illus.). 360p. 1987. text ed. 66.00 (ISBN 0-19-822914-3). Oxford U Pr.

MacCulloch, J. Arnott. Medieval Faith & Fable. 1978. Repr. of 1932 ed. lib. bdg. 47.50 (ISBN 0-8492-1662-1). R West.

MacCulloch, John A. The Celtic & Scandinavian Religions. LC 72-11739. 180p. 1973. Repr. of 1948 ed. lib. bdg. 22.50x (ISBN 0-8371-6705-1, MCSR). Greenwood.

--Celtic Mythology & Slavic Mythology. Bd. with Machal, Jan. LC 63-19088. (Mythology of All Races Ser.: Vol. 3). (Illus.). 477p. Repr. of 1964 ed. 30.00x (ISBN 0-8154-0142-6). Cooper Sq.

--Eddic Mythology. LC 63-19087. (Mythology of All Races Ser.: Vol. 2). (Illus.). Repr. of 1932 ed. 30.00x (ISBN 0-8154-0143-4). Cooper Sq.

--The Religion of the Ancient Celts. LC 77-4127. 1977. lib. bdg. 52.50 (ISBN 0-8414-5998-3). Folcroft.

McCulloh, Gerald O. Ministerial Education in the American Methodist Movement. LC 80-69028. (An Informed Ministry Ser.: 200 Years of American Methodist Thought). 342p. (Orig.). 1980. pap. 3.95 (ISBN 0-938162-00-4). United Meth Educ.

McCullough, Mamie. I Can, You Can Too! 224p. 1986. 14.95 (ISBN 0-8407-3068-3). Nelson.

McCullough, W. Stewart. The History & Literature of Palestinian Jews from Cyrus to Herod 550 BC-4 BC. LC 74-80889. 1975. 25.00x (ISBN 0-8020-5317-3); pap. 9.50 (ISBN 0-8020-6324-1). U of Toronto Pr.

--A Short History of Syriac Christianity to the Rise of Islam. LC 80-29297. (Scholars Press Polebridge Bks.). 1981. 21.95 (ISBN 0-89130-454-1, 00-03-04). Scholars Pr GA.

McCullough, William W., Jr. John McCullough: Pioneer Presbyterian Missionary in Texas. (Illus.). 9.50 (ISBN 0-8363-0055-6). Jenkins.

Macculluch, John A. The Harrowing of Hell: A Comparative Study of an Early Christian Doctrine. LC 79-8113. 1983. Repr. of 1930 ed. 33.50 (ISBN 0-404-18426-X). AMS Pr.

McCullum, James R., tr. see Abailard, Pierre.

McCumber, W. E. The Good News: Mark. 184p. 1982. pap. 4.95 (ISBN 0-8341-0699-X). Beacon Hill.

--Holy God-Holy People. 124p. 1982. pap. 3.95 (ISBN 0-8341-0779-1). Beacon Hill.

--The Widening Circle: Sermons in Acts. 80p. (Orig.). 1983. pap. 2.95 (ISBN 0-8341-0838-0). Beacon Hill.

McCumber, William. Take a Bible Break. 115p. 1986. pap. 3.95 (ISBN 0-8341-1080-6). Beacon Hill.

McCumber, William E., et al. Beacon Bible Expositions: Vol. 1, Matthew. (Beacon Bible Expositions Ser.). 1975. 8.95 (ISBN 0-8341-0312-5). Beacon Hill.

McCune, George. Blessings of Temple Marriage. 1974. pap. 4.95 (ISBN 0-89036-040-5). Hawkes Pub Inc.

McCune, Marjorie W., ed. see Colloquium on Myth in Literature, Bucknell & Susquehanna Universities, Mar. 21-2, 1974, et al.

McCurley, Foster R. Ancient Myths & Biblical Faith. LC 82-48589. 208p. 1983. pap. 12.95 (ISBN 0-8006-1696-0, 1-1696). Fortress.

--Genesis, Exodus, Leviticus, Numbers. LC 78-14670. (Proclamation Commentaries: the Old Testament Witness for Preaching). 128p. 1979. pap. 4.95 (ISBN 0-8006-0593-4, 1-593). Fortress.

McCurley, Foster R., ed. see Anderson, Bernhard W.

McCurley, Foster R., ed. see Mays, James L.

McCurley, Foster R., ed. see Rast, Walter E.

McCurley, Foster R., Jr. Proclaiming the Promise: Christian Preaching from the Old Testament. LC 74-76921. 176p. (Orig.). 1974. pap. 5.75 (ISBN 0-8006-1083-0, 1-1083). Fortress.

McCurry, Don M., ed. The Gospel & Islam: A Compendium. abr. ed. 269p. 1979. pap. 6.95 (ISBN 0-912552-26-3). Missions Adv Res Com Ctr.

--World Christianity: Middle East. LC 79-87790. 156p. 1979. pap. text ed. 12.00 (ISBN 0-912552-27-1). Missions Adv Res Com Ctr.

McCusker, Honor C. John Bale: Dramatist & Antiquary. facsimile ed. LC 79-148890. (Select Bibliographies Reprint Ser). Repr. of 1942 ed. 17.00 (ISBN 0-8369-5678-8). Ayer Co Pubs.

Mc Cutchan, Robert G. Hymn Tune Names: Their Sources & Significance. Repr. of 1957 ed. 39.00x (ISBN 0-403-03608-9). Scholarly.

McCutcheon, W. J. Essays in American Theology: The Life & Thought of Harris Franklin Rall. LC 72-190198. 350p. 1972. 15.00 (ISBN 0-8022-2085-1). Philos Lib.

McDaniel, Audrey. Greatest of These Is Love. LC 64-23538. (Illus.). 1972. 6.95 (ISBN 0-8378-1713-7). Gibson.

--Hope for Every Heart. LC 85-29110. 1986. 5.50 (ISBN 0-8054-5031-9). Broadman.

McDaniel, Elsiebeth, jt. auth. see Gangel, Elizabeth.

McDaniel, Elsiebeth, et al. Adventures in Creative Teaching. 96p. 1986. pap. 6.95 (ISBN 0-89693-557-4). Victor Bks.

McDaniel, Timothy R. The Creational Theory of Man & of the Universe. (Illus.). 141p. 1980. deluxe ed. 88.85 (ISBN 0-89266-242-5). Am Classical Coll Pr.

McDannell, Colleen. The Christian Home in Victorian America, 1840-1900. LC 85-42947. (Religion in North America Ser.). (Illus.). 224p. 1986. 25.00x (ISBN 0-253-31376-7). Ind U Pr.

McDargh, John. Psychoanalytic Object Relations Theory & the Study of Religion: On Faith & the Imaging of God. 296p. 1983. lib. bdg. 28.50 (ISBN 0-8191-3510-0); pap. text ed. 12.75 (ISBN 0-8191-3511-9). U Pr of Amer.

McDermott, A. C., ed. An Eleventh-Century Buddhist Logic of 'Exists' Ratnakirti's Ksanabhangasiddih Vyatirekatmika. (Foundations of Language Supplementary Ser: No. 11). 88p. 1969. 18.50 (ISBN 90-277-0081-8, Pub. by Reidel Holland). Kluwer Academic.
McDermott, Brian O. What Are They Saying about the Grace of Christ? (WATSA Ser.). 1984. pap. 4.95 (ISBN 0-8091-2584-6). Paulist Pr.
McDermott, F. William Penn, Thomas Gray & an Account of the Historical Associations of Stoke Poges. 1973. Repr. of 1930 ed. lib. bdg. 25.00 (ISBN 0-8414-6026-4). Folcroft.
McDermott, Gerald. Daughter of Earth: A Roman Myth. LC 82-23585. (Illus.). 32p. 1984. 15.00 (ISBN 0-385-29294-5). Delacorte.
--Sun Flight. LC 79-5067. (Illus.). 40p. 1980. 10.95 (ISBN 0-02-765610-1, Four Winds). Macmillan.
McDermott, John M., tr. see Ratzinger, Joseph.
McDermott, Robert A., ed. The Essential Rudolf Steiner. LC 82-48934. 320p. 1983. pap. 10.95 (ISBN 0-06-065345-0, RD-399, HarpR). Har-Row.
--Focus on Buddhism. LC 81-8084. (Focus on Hinduism & Buddhism Ser.). 160p. 1981. text ed. 14.50 (ISBN 0-89012-020-X); pap. 7.95 (ISBN 0-89012-021-8). Anima Pubns.
--Focus on Hinduism: Audio Visual Resources for Teaching Religion. 2nd, enl. ed. Morgan, Kenneth W. & Smith, Daniel. LC 81-8085. (Focus on Hinduism & Buddhism Ser.). 160p. 1981. text ed. 14.50 (ISBN 0-89012-018-8); pap. text ed. 7.95 (ISBN 0-89012-019-6). Anima Pubns.
McDermott, Robert A., et al. Six Pillars: Introduction to the Major Works of Sri Aurobindo. McDermott, Robert A., ed. LC 74-77411. 300p. 1974. pap. 5.95 (ISBN 0-89012-001-3). Anima Pubns.
McDermott, William C. see Peters, Edward.
McDill, Wayne. Making Friends for Christ. LC 79-55290. 1980. pap. 4.95 (ISBN 0-8054-6224-4). Broadman.
McDonagh, E. Social Ethics & the Christian: Towards Freedom in Communion. 96p. 1979. pap. 8.00 (ISBN 0-7190-0739-9, Pub. by Manchester Univ Pr). Longwood Pub Group.
McDonagh, Edna. Church & Politics: From Theology to a Case History of Zimbabwe. LC 80-53070. 200p. 1980. text ed. 14.95 (ISBN 0-268-00734-9); pap. text ed. 5.95 (ISBN 0-268-00736-5). U of Notre Dame Pr.
--Doing the Truth: The Quest for Moral Theology. LC 79-63361. 223p. 1980. pap. text ed. 6.95 (ISBN 0-268-00845-0). U of Notre Dame Pr.
--Doing the Truth: The Quest for Moral Theology. LC 79-63361. 1979. text ed. 14.95x (ISBN 0-268-00844-2). U of Notre Dame Pr.
McDonagh, Enda. Between Chaos & New Creation: Doing Theology at the Fringe. 1987. pap. 12.95. M Glazier.
McDonagh, Francis, tr. see Pannenberg, Wolfhart.
McDonagh, Francis, tr. see Theissen, Gerd.
McDonagh, Francis, et al. Prophets Two. LC 71-173033. (Scripture Discussion Commentary Ser.: Pt. 4). 184p. 1972. pap. text ed. 4.50 (ISBN 0-87946-003-2). ACTA Found.
McDonagh, John M. Christian Psychology: Toward a New Synthesis. 144p. 1982. 9.95 (ISBN 0-8245-0449-6). Crossroad NY.
Macdonald, Alexander, ed. Reports on the State of Certain Parishes in Scotland. LC 79-175588. (Maitland Club, Glasgow. Publications: No. 34). Repr. of 1835 ed. 24.50 (ISBN 0-404-53003-6). AMS Pr.
Macdonald, Allan J. Berengar & the Reform of the Sacramental System. 444p. 1977. Repr. of 1930 ed. lib. bdg. 30.00 (ISBN 0-915172-25-9). Richwood Pub.
--Hildebrand: A Life of Gregory the Seventh. (Great Medieval Churchmen Ser.). 254p. 1977. Repr. of 1932 ed. lib. bdg. 17.50x (ISBN 0-915172-26-7). Richwood Pub.
--Trade, Politics & Christianity in Africa & the East. LC 77-89007. Repr. of 1916 ed. lib. bdg. cancelled (ISBN 0-8371-1755-0, MAT&, Pub. by Negro U Pr). Greenwood.
McDonald, C. L. In the Likeness of God or, of Moses, of Pride & of Thorns. 1986. 10.95 (ISBN 0-533-07031-7). Vantage.
MacDonald, Charles. Church & World in the Plan of God: Aspects of History & Eschatology in the Thought of Pere Yves Congar. (Regensburger Studien zur Theologie: Vol. 27). 178p. 1981. 22.75 (ISBN 3-8204-5945-6). P Lang Pubs.
McDonald, Cleveland. Creating a Successful Christian Marriage. LC 74-20202. 1975. 14.95 (ISBN 0-8010-5957-7). Baker Bk.
--Creating a Successful Christian Marriage. LC 74-20202. 1975. 10.95 (ISBN 0-87227-038-6). Reg Baptist.
MacDonald, D. B. Development of Muslim Jurisprudence & Constitutional Theory. 1964. 29.00 (ISBN 0-87902-173-X). Orientalia.
MacDonald, Dennis R. The Legend & the Apostle: The Battle for Paul in Story & Canon. LC 82-21953. 144p. (Orig.). 1983. pap. 9.95 (ISBN 0-664-24464-5). Westminster.
--There Is No Male & Female: The Fate of a Dominical Saying in Paul & Gnosticism. LC 86-45200. (Harvard Dissertations in Religion Ser.). 160p. 1987. pap. 14.95 (ISBN 0-8006-7076-0, 1-7076). Fortress.
MacDonald, Donald. Biblical Doctrine of Creation & the Fall: Genesis 1-3. 502p. 1984. lib. bdg. 18.95 (ISBN 0-86524-165-1, 0104). Klock & Klock.
McDonald, Donald. Catholics in Conversation: Seventeen Interviews with Leading American Catholics. LC 78-5695. 1978. Repr. of 1960 ed. lib. bdg. cancelled (ISBN 0-313-20486-1, MCCC). Greenwood.
Macdonald, Duff. Africana, or, the Heart of Heathen Africa, 2 Vols. LC 70-82058. (Illus.). Repr. of 1882 ed. 14.50x (ISBN 0-8371-1523-X, MAA&, Pub. by Negro U Pr). Greenwood.
Macdonald, Duncan B. Aspects of Islam. facsimile ed. LC 77-179530. (Select Bibliographies Reprint Ser). Repr. of 1911 ed. 25.50 (ISBN 0-8369-6659-7). Ayer Co Pubs.
--Development of Muslim Theology, Jurisprudence & Constitutional Theory. LC 65-18818. 1965. Repr. of 1903 ed. 14.00 (ISBN 0-89684-381-5). Orient Bk Dist.
--Hebrew Philosophical Genius. LC 65-18819. 1965. Repr. of 1936 ed. 7.50x (ISBN 0-8462-0688-9). Russell.
--Religious Attitude & Life in Islam. LC 70-121277. Repr. of 1909 ed. 20.50 (ISBN 0-404-04125-6). AMS Pr.
Macdonald, Fergus. The Catholic Church & the Secret Societies in the United States. LC 46-8049. (Monograph Ser.: No. 22). 1946. 12.50x (ISBN 0-930060-04-0). US Cath Hist.
Macdonald, Frederick. Bishop Stirling of the Falklands. 1976. lib. bdg. 59.95 (ISBN 0-8490-1509-X). Gordon Pr.
MacDonald, Gail. High Call, High Privilege. 1981. pap. 6.95 (ISBN 0-8423-1424-5). Tyndale.
MacDonald, Gail & MacDonald, Gordon. If Those Who Reach Could Touch. 128p. 1985. Repr. of 1984 ed. 5.95 (ISBN 0-8007-5201-5, Power Bks). Revell.
MacDonald, Gail, jt. auth. see MacDonald, Gordon.
MacDonald, George. The Boyhood of Ranald Bannerman. Hamilton, Dan, ed. 168p. 1987. pap. 3.95 (ISBN 0-89693-748-8). Victor Bks.
--Creation in Christ: Unspoken Sermons. Hein, Rolland, ed. LC 76-11282. (Wheaton Literary Ser.). 342p. 1976. pap. 8.95 (ISBN 0-87788-860-4). Shaw Pubs.
--Diary of an Old Soul. LC 65-12143. 132p. 1965. pap. 6.95 (ISBN 0-8066-1503-6, 10-1895). Augsburg.
--The Genius of Willie MacMichael. Hamilton, Dan, ed. 168p. 1987. pap. 3.95 (ISBN 0-89693-750-X). Victor Bks.
--George MacDonald: An Anthology. Lewis, C. S., ed. 192p. 1986. pap. 6.95 (ISBN 0-02-022640-3, Collier). Macmillan.
--Getting to Know Jesus. LC 79-93430. (Shepherd Illustrated Classics Ser.). 208p. (Orig.). 1980. pap. 5.95 (ISBN 0-87983-219-3). Keats.
--Getting to Know Jesus. 160p. 1987. pap. 2.95 (ISBN 0-345-34307-7, Pub. by Ballantine Epiphany). Ballantine.
--Heather & Snow. Hamilton, Dan, ed. 288p. 1987. pap. 5.95 (ISBN 0-89693-760-7). Victor Bks.
--Life Essential: The Hope of the Gospel. 2nd ed. Hein, Rolland, ed. LC 74-16732. (Wheaton Literary Ser.). 102p. 1978. pap. 4.95 (ISBN 0-87788-499-4). Shaw Pubs.
--The Miracles of Our Lord. Hein, Rolland, ed. LC 79-22261. (Wheaton Literary Ser.). 166p. 1980. pap. 6.95 (ISBN 0-87788-547-8). Shaw Pubs.
--The Musician's Quest. Phillips, Michael, ed. 272p. 1984. pap. 5.95 (ISBN 0-87123-444-0, 210444). Bethany Hse.
--On Tangled Paths. Hamilton, Dan, ed. 288p. 1987. pap. 5.95 (ISBN 0-89693-791-7). Victor Bks.
--The Wanderings of Clare Skymer. Hamilton, Dan, ed. 168p. 1987. pap. 3.95 (ISBN 0-89693-757-7). Victor Bks.
MacDonald, Gordon. The Effective Father. 1977. pap. 6.95 (ISBN 0-8423-0680-3). Tyndale.
--Magnificent Marriage. 1976. pap. 3.50 1980 (ISBN 0-8423-3891-8). Tyndale.
--Restoring Your Spiritual Passion. 192p. 1986. 12.95 (ISBN 0-8407-9069-4). Oliver-Nelson.
MacDonald, Gordon & MacDonald, Gail. Affirmation & Rebuke. (PathFinder Pamphlets Ser.). 32p. (Orig.). 1986. pap. 1.95 (ISBN 0-87784-219-1). Inter-Varsity.
MacDonald, Gordon, jt. auth. see MacDonald, Gail.
Macdonald, Greville. George MacDonald & His Wife. Repr. of 1924 ed. 50.00 (ISBN 0-384-34777-0, E240). Johnson Repr.
McDonald, H. D. The Atonement of the Death of Christ. 352p. 1985. pap. 19.95 (ISBN 0-8010-6194-6). Baker Bk.
--The Christian View of Man. LC 81-65471. (Foundations for Faith Ser.). 160p. 1981. pap. 8.95 (ISBN 0-89107-217-9, Crossway Bks). Good News.
--Forgiveness & Atonement. 1984. 5.95p (ISBN 0-8010-6165-2). Baker Bk.
--The God Who Responds. 200p. (Orig.). 1986. pap. 5.95 (ISBN 0-87123-840-3, 210840). Bethany Hse.
--Theories of Revelation. 1979. pap. 10.95 (ISBN 0-8010-6081-8). Baker Bk.
McDonald, Henry. The Ethics of Comparative Religion. LC 84-17370. 102p. (Orig.). 1985. lib. bdg. 19.75 (ISBN 0-8191-4304-9); pap. text ed. 7.75 (ISBN 0-8191-4305-7). U Pr of Amer.
McDonald, Hope. Descubramos Como Orar. Coleman, F. G., tr. from Eng. Tr. of Discovering How to Pray. (Span.). 128p. 1982. pap. 3.20 (ISBN 0-311-40040-X). Casa Bautista.
MacDonald, Hope. Discovering How to Pray. 160p. 1976. pap. 2.95 (ISBN 0-310-28512-7, 10050P). Zondervan.
--When Angels Appear. 128p. (Orig.). 1982. pap. 4.95 (ISBN 0-310-28531-3, 10047P). Zondervan.
McDonald, J. H. Kerygma & Didache: The Articulation & Structure of the Earliest Christian Message. LC 77-95446. (Society for New Testament Studies Monograph: No. 37). 1980. 29.95 (ISBN 0-521-22055-6). Cambridge U Pr.
MacDonald, James. Religion & Myth. LC 74-82059. Repr. of 1893 ed. 22.50x (ISBN 0-8371-1550-7, MAR&, Pub. by Negro U Pr). Greenwood.
MacDonald, James M. Ecclesiastes. 1982. lib. bdg. 15.50 (ISBN 0-86524-091-4, 2101). Klock & Klock.
--The Life & Writings of St. John of the Cross. 1977. lib. bdg. 59.95 (ISBN 0-8490-2164-2). Gordon Pr.
Macdonald, John. Samaritan Chronicle No. 2 (or, Sepher Ha-Yamim) from Joshua to Nebuchadnezzar. (Beiheft 107 zur Zeitschrift fuer die alttestamentliche Wissenschaft). 1969. 34.80 (ISBN 3-11-002582-5). De Gruyter.
McDonald, John F., ed. see John Paul II, Pope.
McDonald, Julie J. A Diary of Personal Prayer. Liffring-Zug, Joan, ed. & illus. (Illus.). 96p. (Orig.). 1986. pap. 9.95. Penfield.
--Good Graces: Table Prayers. Liffring-Zug, Joan, et al, eds. (Illus.). 64p. (Orig.). 1986. pap. 7.95. Penfield.
McDonald, Kathleen. How to Meditate: A Practical Guide. Courtin, Robina, ed. (A Wisdom Basic Book, Orange Ser.). 200p. (Orig.). 1984. pap. 9.95 (ISBN 0-86171-009-6, Wisdom Pubns). Great Traditions.
McDonald, Laughlin, jt. auth. see Larson, E. Richard.
Macdonald, Mary, jt. auth. see Davidson, Graeme J.
McDonald, Mary R. Little Stories About God. (Illus.). 1964. 5.50 (ISBN 0-8198-0080-5). pap. 4.50 (ISBN 0-8198-0081-3). Dghtrs St Paul.
McDonald, Perry & Odell, William. Laws of Christian Living: The Commandments. 170p. (Orig.). 1986. pap. 6.95 (ISBN 0-87973-593-7, 593). Our Sunday Visitor.
McDonald, Peter C. Grieving: A Healing Process. 24p. (Orig.). 1985. pap. 0.95 (ISBN 0-89486-318-5). Hazelden.
MacDonald, Timothy I. The Ecclesiology of Yves Congar: Foundational Themes. LC 83-19882. 346p. (Orig.). 1984. lib. bdg. 28.75 (ISBN 0-8191-3644-1); pap. text ed. 14.75 (ISBN 0-8191-3645-X). U Pr of Amer.
McDonald, V. M., ed. see Al-Tabari.
McDonald, V. M., tr. see Al-Tabari.
MacDonald, W. G. Prison & Pastoral Letters. 96p. 1967. pap. 0.75 (ISBN 0-88243-792-5, 02-0792). Gospel Pub.
McDonald, W. H. Creation Tales from the Salish. (Indian Culture Ser.). 1973. 1.95 (ISBN 0-89992-061-6). Coun India Ed.
McDonald, W. J. see Calvin, John.
MacDonald, William. Acts: Studies in Dynamic Christianity. 5.95 (ISBN 0-937396-01-X). Walterick Pubs.
--Christ Loved the Church. pap. 2.95 (ISBN 0-937396-09-5). Walterick Pubs.
--Cual Es la Diferencia? Orig. Title: What Is the Difference? (Span.). 112p. 1981. pap. 2.75 (ISBN 0-8254-1450-4). Kregel.
--Early Christian & Byzantine Architecture. LC 62-7531. (Great Ages of World Architecture Ser). 128p. 1963. 7.95 (ISBN 0-8076-0176-4); pap. 7.95 (ISBN 0-8076-0338-4). Braziller.
--Enjoying the Proverbs. 1982. pap. 4.00 (ISBN 0-937396-23-0). Walterick Pubs.
--Enjoying the Psalms, 2 vols. 1977. pap. 7.00 ea. Vol. 1 (ISBN 0-937396-34-6). Vol. 2 (ISBN 0-937396-35-4). Walterick Pubs.
--God's Answers to Man's Questions. pap. 1.95 (ISBN 0-937396-16-8). Walterick Pubs.
--Grace of God. pap. 1.95 (ISBN 0-937396-18-4). Walterick Pubs.
--Here's the Difference. pap. 2.95 (ISBN 0-937396-55-9). Walterick Pubs.
--Let Me Introduce You to the Bible. 1980. pap. 2.50 (ISBN 0-937396-22-2). Walterick Pubs.
--Letter to Titus. pap. 2.50 (ISBN 0-937396-46-X). Walterick Pubs.
McDonald, William. Letters to the Thessalonians. rev. ed. 1982. pap. 3.50 (ISBN 0-937396-43-5). Walterick Pubs.
MacDonald, William. Listen, My Son. Rev. ed. pap. 3.00 (ISBN 0-937396-23-0). Walterick Pubs.
--Lord, Break Me. pap. 1.75 (ISBN 0-937396-24-9). Walterick Pubs.
--Old Testament Digest: Vol. 3, Job-Malachi. 1981. pap. 7.50 (ISBN 0-937396-29-X). Walterick Pubs.
--Romans: Justification by Faith. (Orig.). 1981. pap. 5.95 (ISBN 0-937396-36-2). Walterick Pubs.
--There's a Way Back to God. 1986. pap. 2.25 (ISBN 0-937396-42-7). Walterick Pubs.
--Thessalonians. 5.00 (ISBN 0-686-27147-5); pap. 3.95 (ISBN 0-937396-43-5). Walterick Pubs.
--Think of Your Future. pap. 1.95 (ISBN 0-937396-44-3). Walterick Pubs.
--True Discipleship. expanded ed. pap. 3.25 (ISBN 0-937396-50-8). Walterick Pubs.
--True Discipleship. pap. 2.50 (ISBN 0-937396-49-4). Walterick Pubs.
MacDonald, William & Hamel, Mike. Old Testament Digest: Gen-Deut, Vol. 1. 1981. pap. 7.50 (ISBN 0-937396-59-1). Walterick Pubs.
--Old Testament Digest: Vol. 2, Joshua - Esther. 1982. pap. 8.50 (ISBN 0-937396-61-3). Walterick Pubs.
McDonald, William & Searless, John E. The Life of the Rev. John S. Inskip. Dayton, Donald W., ed. (The Higher Christian Life Ser.). 374p. 1985. 45.00 (ISBN 0-8240-6424-0). Garland Pub.
MacDonald, William C. Glossolalia in the New Testament. 22p. 1964. pap. 1.50 (ISBN 0-88243-508-6, 02-0508). Gospel Pub.
McDonald, William J. The General Council: Special Studies in Doctrinal & Historical Background. LC 62-20329. pap. 48.00 (ISBN 0-317-07854-2, 2005223). Bks Demand UMI.
McDonald, William J., ed. The General Council: Special Studies in Doctrinal & Historical Background. LC 78-10099. 1979. Repr. of 1962 ed. lib. bdg. cancelled (ISBN 0-313-20753-4, MCGC). Greenwood.
MacDonald-Bayne, Murdo. Divine Healing of Mind & Body. 215p. 1983. pap. 8.75 (ISBN 0-85243-035-3). Ariel OH.
--Life Everlasting. 165p. 1981. pap. 9.50 (ISBN 0-85243-365-4). Ariel OH.
Macdonell, A. A. Vedic Mythology. 1974. Repr. 15.50 (ISBN 0-8426-0674-2). Orient Bk Dist.
Macdonell, Arthur A. India's Past: A Survey of Her Literatures, Religions, Languages & Antiquities. LC 78-20481. 1979. Repr. of 1927 ed. text ed. 29.00 (ISBN 0-88355-858-0). Hyperion Conn.
--Vedic Mythology. 69.95 (ISBN 0-87968-153-5). Gordon Pr.
MacDonell, Robert W. Belle Harris Bennett, Her Life Work. Gifford, Carolyn D. & Dayton, Donald, eds. (Women in American Protestant Religion 1800-1930 Ser.). 297p. 1987. lib. bdg. 40.00 (ISBN 0-8240-0669-0). Garland Pub.
McDonnell, John J. The World Council of Churches & the Catholic Church. (Toronto Studies in Theology: Vol. 21). 479p. 1985. lib. bdg. 49.95x (ISBN 0-88946-765-X). E Mellen.
McDonnell, Kilian. John Calvin, the Church, & the Eucharist. LC 65-17149. pap. 105.00 (ISBN 0-317-08461-5, 2010572). Bks Demand UMI.
--Presence, Power, Praise: Documents on Charismatic Renewal: National Documents, Vol. 2. LC 79-26080. 568p. 1980. 20.00 (ISBN 0-8146-1189-3). Liturgical Pr.
McDonnell, Kilian, ed. Presence, Power, Praise; Documents on Charismatic Renewal: International Documents, Vol. 3. LC 79-26080. 306p. 1980. 15.00 (ISBN 0-8146-1065-X). Liturgical Pr.
--Presence, Power, Praise: Documents on Charismatic Renewal: National Documents, Vol. 1. LC 79-26080. 696p. 1980. 20.00 (ISBN 0-8146-1066-8). Liturgical Pr.
McDonnell, Rea. Prayer Pilgrimage Through Scripture. LC 83-82025. (Orig.). 1984. pap. 6.95 (ISBN 0-8091-2601-X). Paulist Pr.
--Prayer Pilgrimage with Paul. 112p. 1986. pap. 4.95 (ISBN 0-8091-2746-6). Paulist Pr.
McDonnell, Thomas P. Saints in Due Season. LC 83-60742. 196p. (Orig.). 1983. pap. 5.95 (ISBN 0-87973-623-2, 623). Our Sunday Visitor.
McDonnell, Thomas P., ed. A Thomas Merton Reader. LC 74-29. 600p. 1974. pap. 6.50 (ISBN 0-385-03292-7, Im). Doubleday.

--Through the Year with Thomas Merton: Daily Meditations. LC 85-11827. (Illus.). 240p. 1985. pap. 7.95 (ISBN 0-385-23234-9, Im). Doubleday.
McDonough, Reginald. Keys to Effective Motivation. LC 77-26532. 1979. pap. 4.25 (ISBN 0-8054-3226-4). Broadman.
McDonough, Reginald M. Working with Volunteer Leaders in the Church. LC 75-16579. 140p. 1976. pap. 6.50 (ISBN 0-8054-3214-0). Broadman.
McDonough, S. Muslim Ethics & Modernity. (Comparative Ethics Ser.: No. 1). 126p. 1984. pap. 11.95x (ISBN 0-88920-162-5, Pub. by Wilfrid Laurier Canada). Humanities.
McDonough, Sheila. The Authority of the Past. LC 76-141690. (American Academy of Religion. Studies in Religion). 46p. pap. 8.95 (ISBN 0-89130-153-4, 010001). Scholars Pr GA.
MacDougall, Hamilton C. Early New England Psalmody: An Historical Appreciation, 1620-1820. LC 79-87398. (Music Reprint Ser.). 1969. Repr. of 1940 ed. lib. bdg. 29.50 (ISBN 0-306-71542-2). Da Capo.
MacDougall, John. Land or Religion? The Sardar & Kherwar Movements in Bihar, 1858-1895. 1986. 27.00x (ISBN 0-8364-1591-4, Pub. by Manohar India). South Asia Bks.
MacDougall, Mary K. Happiness Now. 178p. 1971. 5.95 (ISBN 0-87159-053-0). Unity School.
MacDougall, Mary-Katherine. Dear Friend, I Love You. 176p. (Orig.). 1986. pap. 9.95 (ISBN 0-87707-226-4). Now Comns.
McDougall, William. Religion & the Sciences of Life: With Other Essays on Allied Topics. LC 70-39108. (Essay Index Reprint Ser.). Repr. of 1934 ed. 20.00 (ISBN 0-8369-2700-1). Ayer Co Pubs.
McDow, Jane. Golden Thoughts for Children. (Illus.). 48p. (Orig.). 1986. pap. write for info. (ISBN 0-9616464-0-3). Candy Apple Pub.
Macdowall, M. W., tr. see Franzos, Karl E.
McDowell, Catherine, ed. Letters from the Ursuline 1852-1853. LC 77-85460. 1978. boxed 20.00 (ISBN 0-911536-69-8); 18.00. Trinity U Pr.
McDowell, Gordon. Jesus Christ Returns by 1988? LC 83-90836. 66p. 1984. 5.95 (ISBN 0-533-05838-4). Vantage.
McDowell, John, as told to see Lowery, Fred.
McDowell, John P. The Social Gospel in the South: The Woman's Home Mission Movement in the Methodist Episcopal Church, South, 1886-1939. LC 82-15292. 167p. 1982. text ed. 20.00x (ISBN 0-8071-1022-1). La State U Pr.
McDowell, Josh. Bien Plus Qu'un Charpentier. Cosson, Annie, ed. Flammanc, Solveng, tr. Orig. Title: More Than a Carpenter. 128p. 1982. pap. 1.75 (ISBN 0-8297-1248-8). Life Pubs Intl.
--Building Your Self-Image. (Living Bks.). Orig. Title: His Image...My Image. 192p. 1986. Repr. 3.95 (ISBN 0-8423-1395-8). Tyndale.
--Evidence That Demands a Verdict. rev. ed. LC 78-75041. 1979. pap. 7.95 (ISBN 0-918956-46-3). Campus Crusade.
--Guide to Understanding Your Bible. LC 82-73526. 221p. 1982. pap. 6.95 (ISBN 0-86605-087-6). Here's Life.
--His Image...My Image: Biblical Principles for Improving Your Self Image. 180p. 1985. pap. 6.95 (ISBN 0-89840-103-8). Heres Life.
--More Evidence That Demands a Verdict. rev. ed. 425p. 1981. pap. 7.95 (ISBN 0-918956-73-0). Campus Crusade.
--More Than a Carpenter. 1980. pap. 2.95 (ISBN 0-8423-4552-3). Tyndale.
--The Resurrection Factor. 180p. (Orig.). 1981. (ISBN 0-918956-71-4, Dist. by Here's Life Publishers Inc.); pap. 6.95 (ISBN 0-918956-72-2). Campus Crusade.
--The Secret of Loving. 200p. 1985. 11.95 (ISBN 0-86605-157-0). Campus Crusade.
--The Secret of Loving. (Living Bks.). 240p. Repr. 3.95 (ISBN 0-8423-5845-5). Tyndale.
--What I Wish My Parents Knew about Sexuality. 1987. pap. 6.95. Heres Life.
McDowell, Josh & Bellis, Dale. Evidence for Joy. 192p. 1986. pap. 3.50 (ISBN 0-553-26153-3). Bantam.
--Evidence Growth Guide, Vol. 1: Explaining Misconceptions about Christianity. (Truth Alive Ser.). 80p. (Orig.). 1981. 4.95 (ISBN 0-86605-018-3). Campus Crusade.
--Evidence Growth Guide, Vol. 2: Uniqueness of the Bible. 80p. (Orig.). 1981. 4.95 (ISBN 0-86605-019-1). Campus Crusade.
--Evidence Growth Guide, Vol. 3: Trustworthiness of the Bible. (Truth Alive Ser.: Pt. III). 120p. (Orig.). 1983. pap. 4.95 (ISBN 0-86605-020-5). Campus Crusade.
McDowell, Josh & Gilchrist, John. The Islam Debate. (Orig.). 1983. pap. 6.95 (ISBN 0-86605-104-X). Campus Crusade.
McDowell, Josh & Larson, Bart. Jesus: A Biblical Defense of His Deity. 144p. (Orig.). 1983. pap. 5.95. Campus Crusade.
McDowell, Josh & Lewis, Paul. Givers, Takers & Other Kinds of Lovers. 1981. pap. 2.95 (ISBN 0-8423-1031-2). Tyndale.
McDowell, Josh & Stewart, Don. Answers: Living Book Ser. 256p. (Orig.). 1986. 3.95 (ISBN 0-8423-0021-X). Tyndale.
--Answers to Tough Questions. 190p. (Orig.). 1980. pap. 6.95 (ISBN 0-918956-65-X). Campus Crusade.
--Answers to Tough Questions Skeptics Ask About the Christian Faith. LC 80-67432. 190p. 1980. pap. 6.95 (ISBN 0-918956-65-X, 402776). Campus Crusade.
--The Creation. LC 83-72898. (Family Handbook of Christian Knowledge Ser.). 178p. 1983. 18.95 (ISBN 0-86605-118-X). Campus Crusade.
--Handbook of Today's Religions. 512p. 1983. 18.95 (ISBN 0-86605-121-X). Campus Crusade.
--Reasons. LC 80-67432. (Answers to Tough Questions Ser.: Vol.II). 160p. (Orig.). 1981. pap. 6.95 (ISBN 0-918956-98-6). Campus Crusade.
--Reasons. (Living Bks.). 256p. 1986. 3.95 (ISBN 0-8423-5287-2). Tyndale.
--Understanding Non-Christian Religions. LC 81-86543. (Handbook of Today's Religion Ser.). 208p. 1982. pap. 6.95 (ISBN 0-86605-092-2, 402834). Heres Life.
--Understanding Secular Religions. 140p. 1982. pap. 6.95 (ISBN 0-86605-093-0). Here's Life.
--Understanding the Cults. LC 81-81850. (Handbook of Today's Religion Ser.). 199p. 1982. pap. 6.95 (ISBN 0-86605-090-6, 402826). Heres Life.
McDowell, Mary. Hello, Tomorrow. LC 76-27935. 1977. 5.95 (ISBN 0-87212-069-4). Libra.
MacDuff, John R. The Footsteps of St. Peter. 648p. 1982. lib. bdg. 24.25 Smythe Sewn (ISBN 0-86524-149-X, 8406). Klock & Klock.
Mace, A. C., jt. auth. see Carter, Howard.
Mace, Arthur C. & Winlock, Herbert E. The Tomb of Senebtisi at Lisht: Metropolitan Museum of Art Egyptian Expedition Publications, Vol. 1. LC 73-168408. (Metropolitan Museum of Art Publications in Reprint). (Illus.). 228p. 1972. Repr. of 1916 ed. 32.00 (ISBN 0-405-02241-7). Ayer Co Pubs.
Mace, Aurelia G. The Aletheia: Spirit of Truth. 2nd ed. LC 72-2989. Repr. of 1907 ed. 17.50 (ISBN 0-404-10751-6). AMS Pr.
Mace, David & Mace, Vera. How to Have a Happy Marriage. 1983. pap. 3.95 (ISBN 0-687-17831-2, Festival). Abingdon.
--In the Presence of God: Readings for Christian Marriage. LC 84-26928. 116p. 1985. 8.95 (ISBN 0-664-21261-1). Westminster.
--Letters to a Retired Couple. 160p. 1984. pap. 6.95 (ISBN 0-8170-1005-X). Judson.
--Marriage Enrichment in the Church. LC 76-49710. 1977. pap. 4.50 o. p. (ISBN 0-8054-5621-X). Broadman.
--The Sacred Fire Christian Marriage Through the Ages. 1986. 16.95 (ISBN 0-687-36712-3). Abingdon.
Mace, David R. Christian Response to the Sexual Revolution. (Orig.). 1970. pap. 7.75 (ISBN 0-687-07570-X). Abingdon.
--Getting Ready for Marriage. 128p. 1985. pap. 5.95 (ISBN 0-687-14136-2). Abingdon.
--Success in Marriage. (Festival Ser.). 160p. 1980. pap. 3.95 (ISBN 0-687-40555-6). Abingdon.
--Whom God Hath Joined. rev. ed. LC 73-8871. 96p. 1984. pap. 6.95 (ISBN 0-664-24510-2). Westminster.
Mace, David R., ed. Modern Marriage & the Clergy. LC 74-19593. (Special Issues of Pastoral Psychology). 84p. 1978. 9.95 (ISBN 0-87705-368-5). Human Sci Pr.
Mace, Vera, jt. auth. see Mace, David.
McEachern, Alton H. Dramatic Monologue Preaching. LC 82-82953. 1984. pap. 4.50 (ISBN 0-8054-2111-4). Broadman.
--From the Mountain. LC 82-82948. (Orig.). 1983. pap. 4.95 (ISBN 0-8054-1529-7). Broadman.
--Here at Thy Table Lord. LC 77-1024. 1978. pap. 4.50 (ISBN 0-8054-2310-9). Broadman.
--Layman's Bible Book Commentary: Psalms Vol. 8. LC 79-56593. 1981. 5.95 (ISBN 0-8054-1178-X). Broadman.
--The Lord's Presence. LC 85-29055. 1986. pap. 4.95 (ISBN 0-8054-2314-1). Broadman.
--Set Apart for Service. LC 79-5114. 1980. 7.50 (ISBN 0-8054-2537-3). Broadman.
McEachern, James E., jt. auth. see Glass, Bill.
McEathron, Margaret, jt. auth. see Holmes, Fenwicke.
Macek, Josef. The Hussite Movement in Bohemia. Fried, Vilem & Milner, Ian, trs. LC 78-63207. (Heresies of the Early Christian & Medieval Era: Second Ser.). Repr. of 1958 ed. 39.50 (ISBN 0-404-16237-1). AMS Pr.
McEleney, Neil J. First Book of Maccabees. (Bible Ser.: No. 22). (Orig.). 1974. pap. 1.00 (ISBN 0-8091-5166-9). Paulist Pr.
--The Growth of the Gospels. LC 79-90141. 96p. (Orig.). 1979. pap. 4.95 (ISBN 0-8091-2243-X). Paulist Pr.
--Law Given Through Moses. (Bible Ser.). pap. 0.50 (ISBN 0-8091-5079-4). Paulist Pr.
--Melody of Israel. (Bible Ser.). pap. 1.00 (ISBN 0-8091-5089-1). Paulist Pr.
--Oracle of the Lord. (Bible Ser.: No. 24). (Orig.). 1974. pap. 1.00 (ISBN 0-8091-5174-X). Paulist Pr.
--Second Book of Maccabees. (Bible Ser.: Vol. 23). (Orig.). 1974. pap. 1.00 (ISBN 0-8091-5167-7). Paulist Pr.
McElhaney, Dolly, jt. auth. see Adams, Carl.
McEllhenney, John G. Proclaiming Grace & Freedom: The Story of United Methodism in America. (Orig.). 1982. pap. 7.95 (ISBN 0-687-34323-2). Abingdon.
McElligott, Arlene F. & McElligott, Joseph P. The Catholic Elementary School Extension Program. 33p. 1986. 5.30 (ISBN 0-318-20576-9). Natl Cath Educ.
McElligott, Joseph P., jt. auth. see McElligott, Arlene F.
McElrath, Ruth G., tr. see McElrath, William N.
McElrath, William E. Judges & Kings: God's Chosen Leaders. (Illus.). 1979. 5.95 (ISBN 0-8054-4249-9, 4242-49). Broadman.
McElrath, William N. Bible Dictionary for Young Readers. LC 65-15604. (Illus.). 1965. 9.95 (ISBN 0-8054-4404-1, 4244-04). Broadman.
--Bible Guidebook. LC 72-79174. 144p. 1972. 9.95 (ISBN 0-8054-4410-6, 4244-10). Broadman.
--Bold Bearers of His Name. 1987. 12.95 (ISBN 0-8054-4339-8). Broadman.
--Mi Primer Diccionario Biblico. McElrath, Ruth G., tr. from Eng. (Span., Illus.). 128p. 1985. pap. 2.95 (ISBN 0-311-03656-2). Casa Bautista.
--Mi Primer Diccionario Biblico. (Span.). 122p. 1978. pap. 4.95 (S-37577). French & Eur.
--Oz & Mary Quick: Taiwan Teammates. LC 84-2962. (Meet the Missionary Ser.). 1984. pap. 5.50 (ISBN 0-8054-4287-1, 4242-87). Broadman.
McElroy. Jesus Forgives Peter. (Arch Bks.). 24p. (Orig.). 1985. pap. 0.99 (ISBN 0-570-06192-X, 59-1293). Concordia.
McElvaney, William K. Good News Is Bad News Is Good News. LC 79-22032. 132p. (Orig.). 1980. pap. 5.95 (ISBN 0-88344-157-8). Orbis Bks.
--The People of God in Ministry. LC 80-26077. 176p. (Orig.). 1981. pap. 7.75 (ISBN 0-687-30660-4). Abingdon.
McElveen, Floyd. The Mormon Illusion. rev. ed. LC 76-57036. 1980. pap. text ed. 3.95 (ISBN 0-8307-0735-2, 5017807). Regal.
McElwain, Hugh T. Theology of Limits & the Limits of Theology: Reflections on Language, Environment & Death. LC 83-1331. 190p. (Orig.). 1983. lib. bdg. 26.00 (ISBN 0-8191-3093-1); pap. text ed. 11.50 (ISBN 0-8191-3094-X). U Pr of Amer.
MacEoin, Denis. Studies in Babi & Baha'i History, Vol. 5: A Survey of Sources for Early Babi History & Doctorine. 1987. 19.95 (ISBN 0-933770-63-4). Kalimat.
MacEoin, Denis & Al-Shahi, Ahmed, eds. Islam in the Modern World. LC 83-8992. 148p. 1983. 22.50 (ISBN 0-317-13515-5). St Martin.
MacEoin, Gary. Memoirs & Memories. 308p. (Orig.). 1986. pap. 9.95 (ISBN 0-89622-317-5). Twenty-Third.
McEvenne, Sean E. Narrative Style of the Priestly Writer. (Analecta Biblica: Vol. 50). 1971. pap. 17.00 (ISBN 88-7653-050-9). Loyola.
McEvoy, Helena M. Concordance to Progress & Poverty. 729p. 1959. 1.00 (ISBN 0-911312-11-0). Schalkenbach.
McEvoy, James. The Philosophy of Robert Grosseteste. 450p. 1986. pap. 19.95x (ISBN 0-19-824939-X). Oxford U Pr.
McEwan, Elaine. How to Raise a Young Reader. 1987. pap. 5.95. Cook.
McEwen, June H. The Gift of Simplicity. LC 84-6327. 1984. pap. 3.75 (ISBN 0-8054-5914-6). Broadman.
Macey, Samuel L. Clocks & the Cosmos: Time in Western Life & Thought. LC 79-18891. (Illus.). 256p. 1980. 25.00 (ISBN 0-208-01773-9, Archon). Shoe String.
McFadden, Charles. Christianity Confronts Communism. 1983. 15.00 (ISBN 0-8199-0841-X). Franciscan Herald.
McFadden, Elizabeth S. God's Beloved Rebel. (Daybreak Ser.). 1982. pap. 4.95 (ISBN 0-8163-0442-4). Pacific Pr Pub Assn.
McFadden, Jim. The Fear Factor. (Living As a Christian Ser.). (Orig.). 1983. pap. 3.95 (ISBN 0-89283-159-6). Servant.
McFadden, John, tr. see Erdozain, Placido.
McFadden, Thomas M., ed. Liberation, Revolution & Freedom-Theological Perspectives: Proceedings of the College Theology Society. 222p. 1984. pap. text ed. 13.00 (ISBN 0-8191-4021-X). U Pr of Amer.
McFague, Sallie. Metaphorical Theology: Models of God in Religious Language. LC 82-7246. 240p. 1982. pap. 11.95 (ISBN 0-8006-1687-1, 1-1687). Fortress.
--Speaking in Parables: A Study in Metaphor & Theology. LC 74-26338. 192p. 1975. pap. 5.95 (ISBN 0-8006-1097-0, 1-1097). Fortress.
McFarlan, Dr. Donald M. Concise Bible Dictionary. 2nd ed. 208p. 1986. pap. 3.95 (ISBN 0-89622-301-9). Twenty-Third.
Macfarlan, Duncan. The Revivals of the Eighteenth Century, Particulary at Cambuslang: With Three Sermons by the Rev. George Whitefield. (Revival Library). (Illus.). 263p. 1980. Repr. of 1847 ed. lib. bdg. 12.95 (ISBN 0-940033-14-3). R O Roberts.
MacFarland, Charles S. The New Church & the New Germany: A Study of Church & State. LC 78-63691. (Studies in Fascism: Ideology & Practice). 224p. Repr. of 1934 ed. 28.00 (ISBN 0-404-16953-8). AMS Pr.
McFarland, Dorothy T. Flannery O'Connor. LC 74-78443. (Literature and Life Ser.). 141p. 1976. 14.95x (ISBN 0-8044-2609-0). Ungar.
McFarland, H. Neill. Daruma: The Founder of Zen in Japanese Art & Popular Culture. LC 87-45214. (Illus.). 120p. 1987. 22.50 (ISBN 0-87011-817-X). Kodansha.
--Rush Hour of the Gods. 1967. 11.95x (ISBN 0-02-583200-X). Macmillan.
McFarland, Ken. Christian Atheist. (Uplook Ser.). 16p. 1982. pap. 0.99 (ISBN 0-8163-0500-5). Pacific Pr Pub Assn.
McFarland, Ken, ed. see Sheldon, Jean.
McFarland, Ken, ed. see Winn, Dick.
McFarland, Kenneth. Gospel Showdown. (Outreach Ser.). 32p. 1981. pap. 1.25 (ISBN 0-8163-0435-1). Pacific Pr Pub Assn.
McFarland, Thomas. Coleridge & the Pantheist Tradition. 1969. 48.00x (ISBN 0-19-811664-0). Oxford U Pr.
Macfarlane, Alan. The Family Life of Ralph Josselin: An Essay in Historical Anthropology. (Illus.). 1977. pap. 7.95 (ISBN 0-393-00849-5, Norton Lib). Norton.
Macfarlane, Alan, ed. see Larner, Christina.
MacFarlane, Gwyn. Howard Florey: The Making of a Great Scientist. (Illus.). 1979. 23.95x (ISBN 0-19-858161-0). Oxford U Pr.
MacFarlane, Katherine N. Isidore of Seville on the Pagan Gods, Vol. 70, Pt. 3. 1980. 6.00 (ISBN 0-87169-703-3). Am Philos.
MacGaffey, Wyatt. Modern Kongo Prophets: Religion in a Plural Society. LC 82-48554. (African Systems of Thought: Midland Bks: No. 307). (Illus.). 304p. 1983. 22.50x (ISBN 0-253-33865-4); pap. 15.00X (ISBN 0-253-20307-4, MB 307). Ind U Pr.
--Religion & Society in Central Africa: The BaKongo of Lower Zaire. LC 85-31805. (Illus.). xii, 296p. 1986. lib. bdg. 45.00x (ISBN 0-226-50029-2); pap. text ed. 16.95 (ISBN 0-226-50030-6). U of Chicago Pr.
McGann, Dairmuid. The Journeying Self: The Gospel of Mark through a Jungian Perspective. 144p. (Orig.). 1985. pap. 7.95 (ISBN 0-8091-2662-1). Paulist Pr.
McGarry, Daniel D. Medieval History & Civilization. (Illus.). 896p. 1976. text ed. write for info. (ISBN 0-02-379100-4). Macmillan.
McGarry, Daniel D., tr. see John of Salisbury.
McGaughey, C. E. The Hope of the World. Thomas, J. D., ed. LC 74-180791. (Twentieth Century Sermons Ser). 1971. 11.95 (ISBN 0-89112-306-7, Bibl Res Pr). Abilene Christ U.
McGavran, Donald. The Bridges of God. rev. ed. 1981. pap. 5.95 (ISBN 0-377-45071-5). Friend Pr.
--Understanding Church Growth. rev. ed. 488p. (Orig.). 1980. pap. 12.95 (ISBN 0-8028-1849-8). Eerdmans.
McGavran, Donald & Arn, Winfield. Back to Basics in Church Growth. 1981. pap. 5.95 (ISBN 0-8423-0116-X). Tyndale.
McGavran, Donald & Hunter, George G., III. Church Growth: Strategies That Work. LC 79-26962. (Creative Leadership Ser.). (Orig.). 1980. pap. 6.95 (ISBN 0-687-08160-2). Abingdon.
McGavran, Donald A. Church Growth & Group Conversion. new ed. LC 73-80163. 128p. 1973. pap. 3.95 (ISBN 0-87808-712-5). William Carey Lib.
--Ethnic Realities & the Church: Lessons from India. LC 78-11517. (Illus.). 1979. pap. 8.95 (ISBN 0-87808-168-2). William Carey Lib.
--How Churches Grow. (Orig.). 1965. pap. 6.95 (ISBN 0-377-40011-4). Friend Pr.
--Momentous Decisions in Missions Today. 1984. pap. 11.95 (ISBN 0-8010-6176-8). Baker Bk.
McGavran, Donald A. & Arn, Winfield C. How to Grow a Church. LC 73-80207. 192p. (Orig.). 1973. pap. 6.95 (ISBN 0-8307-0238-5, 5406706). Regal.
--Ten Steps for Church Growth. LC 76-62950. 1977. pap. 6.95 (ISBN 0-06-065352-3, RD 215, HarpR). Har-Row.
McGavran, Donald A., jt. auth. see Glasser, Arthur F.

McGavran, Donald A., ed. Church Growth Bulletin: Second Consolidated Volume (Sept. 1969 -July 1975) LC 77-5192. 1977. pap. 7.95x (ISBN 0-87808-702-8). William Carey Lib.

McGaw, Francis. John Hyde. 64p. 1986. pap. 3.50. Bethany Hse.

McGaw, Francis A. Praying Hyde. 80p. 1970. pap. 2.95 (ISBN 0-87123-454-8, 200454). Bethany Hse.

McGaw, Martha M. Sixty Ways to Let Yourself Grow. 64p. 1984. pap. 1.50 (ISBN 0-89243-211-X). Liguori Pubns.

McGeachy, Pat. Beyond the Facts, Acts. (Orig.). 1973. pap. 1.95 (ISBN 0-377-03051-1). Friend Pr.

McGee, Cecil. Dramatic Programs for Christmas. LC 74-93917. 1970. pap. 4.95 (ISBN 0-8054-7507-9). Broadman.

McGee, Gary B. This Gospel...Shall Be Preached: A History & Theology of Assemblies of God Foreign Missions to 1959. LC 86-80015. 288p. (Orig.). 1986. pap. 8.95 (ISBN 0-88243-511-6, 02-0511). Gospel Pub.

McGee, J. Vernon. Esther: The Romance of Providence. LC 81-22362. 140p. 1982. pap. 4.95 (ISBN 0-8407-5796-4). Nelson.

McGee, Marsha G., jt. ed. see Johnson, Christopher J.

McGeehan, Jude J. Ministry to the Sick & Dying. (Synthesis Ser.). 1981. 1.75 (ISBN 0-8199-0836-3). Franciscan Herald.

McGiffert, A. C. Protestant Thought Before Kant. 11.25 (ISBN 0-8446-0204-3). Peter Smith.

McGiffert, Arhtur C. Jonathan Edwards. LC 75-3134. (Philosophy of American Ser.). Repr. of 1932 ed. 28.00 (ISBN 0-404-59143-4). AMS Pr.

McGiffert, Arthur C. Martin Luther, the Man & His Work. LC 83-45647. Date not set. Repr. of 1911 ed. 42.50 (ISBN 0-404-19856-2). AMS Pr.

McGiffert, Arthur C., Jr. Public Prayers. LC 83-83269. (Studies in Ministry & Parish Life). 44p. 1984. pap. 2.50x (ISBN 0-913552-24-0). Exploration Pr.

McGiffert, Michael, ed. God's Plot: The Paradoxes of Puritan Piety, Being the Autobiography & Journal of Thomas Shepard. LC 71-181364. (Commonwealth Ser.: Vol. 1). (Illus.). 264p. 1972. 20.00x (ISBN 0-87023-100-6). U of Mass Pr.

McGill, Arthur. Death & Life: An American Theology. Wilson, Charles A. & Anderson, Per M., eds. LC 86-45215. 112p. 1987. pap. 7.95 (ISBN 0-8006-1927-7, 1-1927). Fortress.

McGill, Arthur C. Suffering: A Test of Theological Method. LC 82-6934. 130p. 1982. pap. 7.95 (ISBN 0-664-24448-3). Westminster.

McGill, Ormond. Hypnotism & Mysticism of India. 2nd ed. (Illus.). 208p. 1979. Repr. of 1977 ed. text ed. 12.50 (ISBN 0-930298-01-2). Westwood Pub Co.

McGinlay, Hugh, ed. The Year of Luke. 96p. (Orig.). 1982. pap. 8.95 (Pub. by JBCE). ANZ Religious Pubns.

--The Year of Mark. 86p. (Orig.). 1984. text ed. 8.95 (ISBN 0-85819-477-5, Pub. by JBCE). ANZ Religious Pubns.

--The Year of Matthew. 94p. (Orig.). 1983. pap. 8.95 (ISBN 0-85819-454-6, Pub. by JBCE). ANZ Religious Pubns.

McGinley, Phyllis. Saint Watching. (The Crossroad Paperback Ser.). 256p. 1982. pap. 6.95 (ISBN 0-8245-0450-X). Crossroad NY.

McGinn, Bernard. The Calabrian Abbott: Jaochim of Fiore in the History of Thought. 320p. 1985. 17.95 (ISBN 0-02-919550-0). Macmillan.

--The Golden Chain: A Study in the Theological Anthropology of Isaac of Stella. LC 70-152487. (Cistercian Studies: No. 15). 280p. 1972. 7.50 (ISBN 0-87907-815-4). Cistercian Pubns.

--Visions of the End: Apocalyptic Traditions in the Middle Ages. LC 79-4303. (Records of Civilization XCVI). 1979. 38.00 (ISBN 0-231-04594-8). Columbia U Pr.

McGinn, Bernard & Meyendorf, John. Christian Spirituality. (World Spirituality Ser.). 1985. 49.50x (ISBN 0-8245-0681-2). Crossroad NY.

McGinn, Bernard, ed. Three Treatises on Man: A Cistercian Anthropology. LC 77-184906. (Cistercian Fathers Ser.: No. 24). 1977. 13.95 (ISBN 0-87907-024-2). Cistercian Pubns.

McGinn, Bernard, tr. Apocalyptic Spirituality. LC 79-90834. (Classics of Western Spirituality Ser.). 352p. 1979. 13.95 (ISBN 0-8091-0305-2); pap. 7.95 (ISBN 0-8091-2242-1). Paulist Pr.

McGinn, Bernard, et al. Meister Eckhart: Teacher & Preacher. (Classics of Western Spirituality Ser.: Vol. 52). 448p. 1986. 15.95 (ISBN 0-8091-0377-X); pap. 12.95 (ISBN 0-8091-2827-6). Paulist Pr.

McGinnis, Alan L. La Amistad Factor Decisivo. Orig. Title: The Friendship Factor. (Span.). 204p. 1986. pap. 5.95 (ISBN 0-311-46093-3, Edit Mundo). Casa Bautista.

McGinnis, Carol, jt. auth. see Bristol, Goldie.

McGinnis, James. Solidarity with the People of Nicaragua. LC 84-27202. (Illus.). 192p. (Orig.). 1985. pap. 7.95 (ISBN 0-88344-448-8). Orbis Bks.

McGinnis, James, jt. auth. see McGinnis, Kathleen.

McGinnis, James B. Bread & Justice: Toward a New International Economic Order. LC 79-90224. 372p. 1979. tchrs. ed. 6.95 (ISBN 0-8091-9536-4). Paulist Pr.

McGinnis, Kathleen & McGinnis, James. Parenting for Peace & Justice. LC 81-3917. 143p. (Orig.). 1981. pap. 7.95 (ISBN 0-88344-376-7). Orbis Bks.

McGinniss, Alan L. The Friendship Factor: How to Get Closer to the People You Care for. LC 79-50076. 1979. 12.95 (ISBN 0-8066-1710-1, 10-2410); pap. 3.95 (ISBN 0-8066-1711-X, 10-2411). Augsburg.

McGinnity, Gerard. Christmen: Experience of Priesthood Today. 94p. 1986. pap. 7.95 (ISBN 0-87061-124-0). Chr Classics.

McGinty, John. How to Raise the Level of Giving in Your Church. LC 78-12994. (P.A.C.E. Ser.). 1979. pap. 4.95 (ISBN 0-8272-1418-9). CBP.

McGinty, Martha E., tr. see Foucher De Chartres.

McGinty, Park. Interpretation & Dionysos: Method in the Study of a God. (Religon & Reason Ser.: No. 16). 1978. 37.50x (ISBN 90-279-7844-1). Mouton.

McGloin, Joseph T. How to Get More Out of the Mass. LC 74-80938. 1974. pap. 3.50 (ISBN 0-89243-011-7, 41230). Liguori Pubns.

--The Way I See Him: A Writer's Look at Jesus. LC 86-8030. 212p. (Orig.). 1986. pap. 6.95 (ISBN 0-8189-0498-4). Alba.

McGoldrick, J. E. Luther's English Connection. 1979. pap. 7.50 (ISBN 0-8100-0070-9, 15-0368). Northwest Pub.

MacGorman, J. W. The Gifts of the Spirit. LC 75-55191. 1980. pap. 3.95 (ISBN 0-8054-1385-5). Broadman.

--The Layman's Bible Commentary: Romans, I Corinthians, Vol. 20. LC 79-51501. 1980. 5.95 (ISBN 0-8054-1190-9). Broadman.

McGovern, Arthur. Marxism: An American Christian Perspective. LC 79-27257. 352p. (Orig.). 1980. pap. 12.95 (ISBN 0-88344-301-5). Orbis Bks.

McGovern, James. To Give the Love of Christ. LC 77-14832. (Emmaus Book). 128p. 1978. pap. 2.95 (ISBN 0-8091-2076-3). Paulist Pr.

McGovern, Patrick E. Late Bronze Palestinian Pendants: Innovation in a Cosmopolitian Age. (JSOT-ASOR Monographs: No. 1). (Illus.). xx, 184p. 1985. text ed. 35.00x (ISBN 0-905774-90-6, Pub. by JSOT Pr England). Eisenbrauns.

McGovern, William M. Introduction to Mahayana Buddhism. LC 70-149665. Repr. of 1922 ed. 17.00 (ISBN 0-404-04129-9). AMS Pr.

--A Manual of Buddhist Philosophy. LC 78-70097. Repr. of 1923 ed. 27.50 (ISBN 0-404-17346-2). AMS Pr.

McGowan, Chris. In the Beginning: A Scientist Shows Why the Creationists Are Wrong. LC 83-62997. (Illus.). 208p. 1984. pap. 12.95 (ISBN 0-87975-240-8). Prometheus Bks.

McGowan, John P. Pierre d'Ailly & the Council of Constance. 110p. 1984. Repr. of 1936 ed. 22.00x (ISBN 0-939738-34-1). Zubal Inc.

McGowen, Charles H. In Six Days. 108p. 1986. pap. 3.95 (ISBN 0-936369-03-5). Son-Rise Pubns.

McGrath, Alister E. The Intellectual Origins of the European Reformation. 272p. 1987. text ed. 39.95 (ISBN 0-631-15144-3). Basil Blackwell.

--Iustitia Dei: A History of the Doctrine of Justification. 250p. 1986. 39.50 (ISBN 0-521-30887-9). Cambridge U Pr.

--Iustitia Dei: A History of the Doctrine of Justification, Vol. II--From the Reformation to the Present Day. 272p. 1986. 39.50 (ISBN 0-521-32274-X). Cambridge U Pr.

--Luther's Theology of the Cross: Martin Luther on Justification 1509-1519. 224p. 1985. 34.95x (ISBN 0-631-13855-2). Basil Blackwell.

--The Making of Modern German Christology: From the Enlightenment to Pannenberg. 240p. 1986. text ed. 34.95x (ISBN 0-631-14512-5). Basil Blackwell.

McGrath, Allister E. Understanding Jesus: Who Jesus Christ Is & Why He Matters. Van der Maas, E., ed. (Orig.). 1987. Repr. write for info. (ISBN 0-310-29810-5). Zondervan.

McGrath, William. The Anabaptists: Neither Catholics nor Protestants. pap. 1.25 (ISBN 0-686-32317-3). Rod & Staff.

McGravie, Anne. The Boyhood of Pope John XXIII. (Stories about Christian Heroes Ser.). (Illus.). 1979. pap. 1.95 (ISBN 0-03-049446-X, HarpR). Har-Row.

McGraw, Woody. Marriage According to God's Word: How to Succeed at Marriage. LC 83-9121. 86p. (Orig.). 1983. pap. 2.95 (ISBN 0-913309-00-1). Trinity House.

MacGregor, G. H. & Purdy, A. C. Jew & Greek: Tutors Unto Christ. 59.95 (ISBN 0-8490-0444-6). Gordon Pr.

MacGregor, Geddes. Angels: Ministers of Grace. (Illus.). 256p. 1987. 18.95 (ISBN 0-913729-42-6). Paragon Hse.

--Apostles Extraordinary: A Celebration of Saints & Sinners. (Illus.). 168p. (Orig.). 1986. pap. 8.95 (ISBN 0-89407-065-7). Strawberry Hill.

--The Bible in the Making. LC 82-17499. 318p. 1983. pap. 14.50 (ISBN 0-8191-2810-4). U Pr of Amer.

--The Christening of Karma. LC 83-40234. 200p. (Orig.). 1984. pap. 6.95 (ISBN 0-8356-0581-7, Quest). Theos Pub Hse.

--Gnosis. LC 78-64908. 1979. pap. 10.75 (ISBN 0-8356-0522-1). Theos Pub Hse.

--The Gospels As a Mandala of Wisdom. 224p. (Orig.). 1982. pap. 6.50 (ISBN 0-8356-0554-X, Quest). Theos Pub Hse.

--He Who Lets Us Be. 194p. 1987. pap. 8.95 (ISBN 0-913729-61-2). Paragon Hse.

--The Nicene Creed, Illumined by Modern Thought. LC 80-19348. pap. 40.80 (ISBN 0-317-20013-5, 2023220). Bks Demand UMI.

--Reincarnation As a Christian Hope. LC 81-8013. (Library of Philosophy & Religion). 174p. 1982. 28.50x (ISBN 0-389-20220-7). B&N Imports.

--Reincarnation in Christianity. LC 77-20925. (Orig.). 1978. 9.75 (ISBN 0-8356-0504-3). Theos Pub Hse.

McGregor, Horace C., tr. see Cicero.

McGregor, J. F. Radical Religion in the English Revolution. Reay, B., ed. 219p. 1984. 34.95x (ISBN 0-19-873044-6); pap. 14.95x (ISBN 0-19-873045-4). Oxford U Pr.

McGregor, Jeffrey P., jt. auth. see Barnett, Donald L.

McGregor, Leslie J. The Greek Text of Ezekiel: An Examination of it's Homogeneity. (SBL & SCS Ser.). 1985. 18.25 (ISBN 0-89130-902-0, 06-0418); pap. 13.95 (ISBN 0-89130-903-9). Scholars Pr GA.

MacGregor, Malcolm & Baldwin, Stanley C. Your Money Matters. LC 75-56123. 176p. 1977. pap. 4.95 (ISBN 0-87123-662-1, 210662). Bethany Hse.

MacGregor, Malcolm B. The Sources & Literature of Scottish Church History. LC 76-1125. 260p. 1977. Repr. of 1934 ed. lib. bdg. 20.00x (ISBN 0-915172-10-0). Richwood Pub.

McGucken, William J. The Catholic Way in Education. (Request Reprint). 1962. 3.00 (ISBN 0-8294-0052-4). Loyola.

McGuckin, John A. The Transfiguration of Christ in Scripture & Tradition. LC 86-23892. (Studies in Bible & Early Christianity: Vol. 9). 333p. 1987. 59.95 (ISBN 0-88946-609-2). E Mellen.

McGuckin, Paul, tr. see St. Symeon.

McGuiness, Thomas. Family Renewal in the Home. LC 83-63006. 83p. (Orig.). 1984. pap. text ed. 4.95 (ISBN 0-911905-17-0). Past & Mat Rene Ctr.

--Pilgrimage of the Heart. LC 83-63477. 74p. (Orig.). 1984. pap. text ed. 2.95 (ISBN 0-911905-19-7). Past & Mat Rene Ctr.

McGuinness, Frank. Observe the Sons of Ulster Marching Towards the Somme. (Orig.). 1986. pap. 8.95 (ISBN 0-571-14611-2). Faber & Faber.

McGuire. Religion: The Social Context. 2nd ed. Fullerton, Sheryl, ed. 1986. pap. text ed. write for info. (ISBN 0-534-07242-9). Wadsworth Pub.

McGuire, Brian P. The Cistercians in Denmark: Their Attitudes, Roles, & Functions in Medieval Society. (Cistercian Studies: No. 35). 1982. 35.00 (ISBN 0-87907-835-9). Cistercian Pubns.

McGuire, Meredith B. Pentecostal Catholics: Power, Charisma, & Order in a Religious Movement. 270p. 1982. 29.95 (ISBN 0-87722-235-5). Temple U Pr.

McGuire, Michael A. Father McGuire's New, Modern Catechism Know, Love, & Serve: The Holy Father, Our God-Given Supreme Teacher. LC 73-158919. (Know, Love, & Serve Catechisms Ser.). (Illus.). 222p. 1973. pap. 11.00 (ISBN 0-913382-43-4, 103-5). Prow Bks-Franciscan.

--Father McGuire's New, Modern Catechism Know, Love, & Serve, Bk. 1. LC 73-158919. (Know, Love & Serve Catechisms). (Illus.). 58p. 1971. pap. 5.25 (ISBN 0-913382-39-6, 103-1). Prow Bks-Franciscan.

--Father McGuire's New, Modern Catechism Know, Love, & Serve: Preparing for First Holy Communion, BK. 2. LC 73-158919. (Know, Love, & Serve Catechisms Ser.). (Illus.). 90p. 1971. pap. 6.50 (ISBN 0-913382-40-X, 103-2). Prow Bks-Franciscan.

--Father McGuire's New, Modern Catechism Know, Love, & Serve, Bk. 3. LC 73-158919. (Know, Love, & Serve Catechisms Ser.). (Illus.). 175p. 1972. pap. 9.50 (ISBN 0-913382-41-8, 103-3). Prow Bks-Franciscan.

--Father McGuire's New, Modern Catechism Know, Love, & Serve, Bk. 4. LC 73-158919. (Know, Love, & Serve Catechisms Ser.). (Illus.). 192p. 1973. pap. 10.00 (ISBN 0-913382-42-6, 103-4). Prow Bks-Franciscan.

McGuire, Michael A. & Mangieri, Rose M. Know, Love & Serve: General Principles & the Christo-Centric Method. (Know, Love & Serve Cathechism Ser.). 30p. (Orig.). 1973. pap. 2.50 (ISBN 0-913382-44-2). Prow Bks-Franciscan.

Mach, Rudolph. Catalogue of Arabic Manuscripts (Yahuda Section) in the Garrett Collection, Princeton University Library. LC 75-2999. (Illus.). 1976. 160.00x (ISBN 0-691-03908-9). Princeton U Pr.

Macha, Karel. Glaube und Vernunft: Eight Hundred Sixty-Three to Eighteen Hundred. 350p. 1987. lib. bdg. 50.00 (ISBN 3-598-20130-3). K G Saur.

Machado, Mary K. How to Plan Children's Liturgies. LC 86-60892. (Orig.). 1985. pap. 9.95 (ISBN 0-89390-074-5). Resource Pubns.

MacHaffie, Barbara J. Her Story: Women in Christian Tradition. LC 85-45494. 192p. 1986. pap. 9.95 (ISBN 0-8006-1893-9). Fortress.

MacHaffie, Ingeborg S. To Teachers with Love. Nielsen, Margaret, ed. (Illus.). 90p. (Orig.). 1986. pap. 5.95 perfect bdg. (ISBN 0-9609374-2-0). Skribent.

Machairas, Leontios. Recital Concerning the Sweet Land of Cyprus, 2 vols. Dawkins, R. M., ed. LC 78-63351. (The Crusades & Military Orders: Second Ser.). Repr. of 1932 ed. Set. 92.50 (ISBN 0-404-17030-7). AMS Pr.

Machal, Jan see MacCulloch, John A.

MacHaster, Eve B. God Comforts His People. LC 95-835. (Story Bible Ser: No. 7). (Illus.). 176p. (Orig.). 1985. pap. 5.95 (ISBN 0-8361-3393-5). Herald Pr.

Machem, J. Gresham. The New Testament: An Introduction to Its History & Literature. 1976. 11.95 (ISBN 0-85151-240-2). Banner of Truth.

Machen, J. Gresham. The Christian View of Man. pap. 6.95 (ISBN 0-85151-112-0). Banner of Truth.

--Christianity & Liberalism. 1923. pap. 6.95 (ISBN 0-8028-1121-3). Eerdmans.

--Education, Christianity & the State. Robbins, John W., ed. & intro. by. (Trinity Papers: No. 19). 150p. (Orig.). 1987. pap. 5.95 (ISBN 0-940931-19-2). Trinity Found.

--New Testament Greek for Beginners. 1923. text ed. write for info. (ISBN 0-02-373480-9). Macmillan.

--Virgin Birth of Christ. 427p. 1958. Repr. of 1930 ed. 13.95 (ISBN 0-227-67630-0). Attic Pr.

--Virgin Birth of Christ. (Twin Brooks Ser). 1967. pap. 10.95 (ISBN 0-8010-5885-6). Baker Bk.

McHenry, Robert, ed. Contexts: Absalom & Achitophel. LC 84-24160. (Contexts Ser.: No. 3). (Illus.). xiv, 296p. 1986. lib. bdg. 29.50 (ISBN 0-208-01845-X, Archon Bks). Shoe String.

Machiavelli, Niccolo. Machiavelli's Thoughts on the Management of Men. (Illus.). 119p. 1982. 107.50 (ISBN 0-89266-364-2). Am Classical Coll Pr.

Machin, G. I. Politics & the Churches in Great Britain, 1832-1868. 1977. 57.00x (ISBN 0-19-826436-4). Oxford U Pr.

Machlachlan, Lewis. God Face to Face. 160p. 1968. pap. 2.95 (ISBN 0-227-67728-5). Attic Pr.

Machlis, Gary E., ed. Interpretive Views: Opinions on Evaluating Interpretation. LC 86-61991. (Illus., Orig.). 1986. pap. 9.95 (ISBN 0-940091-15-1). Natl Parks & Cons.

Machlowitz Klein, Aaron, tr. see Ashtor, Eliyahu.

McHuch, P. Meditating the Sunday Gospels. 1976. 5.95 (ISBN 0-8198-0443-6); pap. 4.95 (ISBN 0-8198-0444-4). Dghtrs St Paul.

McHugh, Dorothea H. A Personal Pathway to Prayer. LC 85-51408. 104p. 1985. 6.95 (ISBN 0-938232-90-8, Dist. by Baker & Taylor). Winston-Derek.

McIlvain, James W. Early Presbyterianism in Maryland. Bd. with The Study of History in Germany & France. Fredericq, Paul. Leonard, Henrietta, tr. from Fr.. (Johns Hopkins University Studies in Historical & Political Science, 8: No. 5,6). Repr. of 1890 ed. 15.00 (ISBN 0-384-16755-1). Johnson Repr.

McIlwaine, H. R. The Struggle of Protestant Dissenters for Religious Toleration in Virginia. pap. 9.00 (ISBN 0-384-34893-9). Johnson Repr.

McIlwaine, Henry R. The Struggle of Protestant Dissenters for Religious Toleration in Virginia. LC 78-63830. (Johns Hopkins University. Studies in the Social Sciences. Twelfth Ser. 1894: 4). Repr. of 1894 ed. 11.50 (ISBN 0-404-61090-0). AMS Pr.

McIndoo, Ethel. Freeda Harris: Woman of Prayer. LC 84-2978. (Meet the Missionary Ser.). 1984. 5.50 (ISBN 0-8054-4286-3, 4242-86). Broadman.

McInerny, Ralph. Being & Predication: Thomistic Interpretations. (Studies in Philosophy & the History of Philosophy: Vol. 16). 1986. 36.95 (ISBN 0-8132-0612-X). Cath U Pr.
--Ethica Thomistica: The Moral Philosophy of Thomas Aquinas. LC 78-62029. 129p. 1982. pap. 7.95 (ISBN 0-8132-0561-1). Cath U Pr.
--Miracles: A Catholic View. LC 86-61141. 153p. (Orig.). 1986. pap. 6.95 (ISBN 0-87973-540-6). Our Sunday Visitor.
--Rhyme & Reason: St. Thomas & Modes of Discourse. LC 81-80234. (Aquinas Lecture Ser.). 84p. 1981. 7.95 (ISBN 0-87462-148-8). Marquette.
--St. Thomas Aquinas. LC 81-16293. 197p. 1982. pap. text ed. 5.95 (ISBN 0-268-01707-7). U of Notre Dame Pr.
McInerny, Ralph M. History of Western Philosophy: Philosophy from St. Augustine to Ockham. LC 63-20526. 1970. 12.00x (ISBN 0-268-00417-X). U of Notre Dame Pr.
McInerny, Ralph M., ed. New Themes in Christian Philosophy. LC 68-20439. 1968. 17.95 (ISBN 0-8290-1654-6); pap. text ed. 9.50x (ISBN 0-8290-1606-6). Irvington.
--New Themes in Christian Philosophy. LC 68-20439. 1968. 19.95 (ISBN 0-268-00192-8). U of Notre Dame Pr.
--Thomism in an Age of Renewal. 1968. pap. 5.95x (ISBN 0-268-00276-2). U of Notre Dame Pr.
McInnes, Celia. An English Christmas: The Traditions, the Observances, the Festivities. LC 86-7553. (Illus.). 104p. 1986. 14.95 (ISBN 0-8050-0043-7). H Holt & Co.
MacInnis, Donald, jt. auth. see Martin, Mary L.
McIntire, C. T. England Against the Papacy: 1858-1861. LC 82-9405. (Illus.). 280p. 1983. 44.50 (ISBN 0-521-24237-1). Cambridge U Pr.
McIntire, C. T., ed. The Legacy of Herman Dooyeweerd: Reflections on Critical Philosophy in the Christian Tradition. (Illus.). 198p. (Orig.). 1986. lib. bdg. 25.25 (ISBN 0-8191-5033-9, Pub. by Inst Christ Stud); pap. text ed. 12.00 (ISBN 0-8191-5034-7). U Pr of Amer.
McIntire, Roger. Losing Control of Your Teenager: Ten Rules for Raising an Adult While Keeping a Friend. 290p. 1985. pap. 15.00x (ISBN 0-87425-017-X). Human Res Dev Pr.
McIntire, Russell. Live Your Faith! LC 78-25579. 167p. 1979. 6.95 (ISBN 0-88289-217-7). Pelican.
Macintosh, A. A. Isaiah XXI: A Palimpsest. LC 79-41375. 160p. 1980. 34.50 (ISBN 0-521-22943-X). Cambridge U Pr.
McIntosh, Carol P. & Cole, Carole O. What Price Zion? LC 82-23567. 126p. 1983. 6.95 (ISBN 0-87747-927-5). Deseret Bk.
Macintosh, Douglas C. Theology As an Empirical Science. Gaustad, Edwin S., ed. LC 79-52601. (The Baptist Tradition Ser.). 1980. Repr. of 1919 ed. lib. bdg. 23.00x (ISBN 0-405-12466-X). Ayer Co Pubs.
McIntosh, Duncan. The Everyday Evangelist. 64p. 1984. pap. 2.95 (ISBN 0-8170-1042-4). Judson.
McIntosh, Duncan & Rusbuldt, Richard E. Planning Growth in Your Church. 224p. 1983. pap. 16.95 (ISBN 0-8170-1007-6). Judson.
McIntosh, Hugh. Is Christ Infallible & the Bible True? 1981. lib. bdg. 27.00 (ISBN 0-86524-076-0, 8603). Klock & Klock.
McIntosk & Twyman, trs. The Archko Volume. LC 74-33199. 248p. 1975. 9.95 (ISBN 0-87983-067-0). Keats.
MacIntyre, Alasdair. Marxism & Christianity. LC 83-40600. 143p. 1984. pap. text ed. 6.95 (ISBN 0-268-01358-6, 85-13590). U of Notre Dame Pr.
MacIntyre, Alasdair & Ricoeur, Paul. The Religious Significance of Atheism. LC 68-28398. (Bampton Lectures in America Ser.: No. 18). 98p. 1969. 20.00 (ISBN 0-231-03139-4). Columbia U Pr.
--The Religious Significance of Atheism. LC 68-28398. (Bampton Lectures in America: No. 18). 98p. 1986. pap. 10.00 (ISBN 0-231-06367-9). Columbia U Pr.
MacIntyre, Alasdair, jt. ed. see Hauerwas, Stanley.
M'Intyre, David M. Hidden Life of Prayer. 96p. 1962. pap. 2.50 (ISBN 0-87123-214-6, 200214). Bethany Hse.
McIntyre, Marie. Ears to Hear: Hearts to Praise. (Greeting Book Line Ser.). (Illus.). 48p. (Orig.). 1985. pap. 1.50 (ISBN 0-89622-210-1). Twenty-Third.
--Eucharist: Our Communal Celebration. LC 76-25620. (Illus., Orig.). 1978. pap. 2.95 (ISBN 0-89622-077-X). Twenty-Third.
--Female & Catholic: A Journal of Mind & Heart. 80p. (Orig.). 1986. pap. 3.95 (ISBN 0-89622-307-8). Twenty-Third.
--Little Things Mean a Lot: Minute Meditations. (Greeting Book Line Ser.). (Illus.). 48p. 1982. pap. 1.50 (ISBN 0-89622-155-5). Twenty-Third.
--Meditations on the Mass. (Greeting Book Line Ser.). 48p. 1983. pap. 1.50 (ISBN 0-89622-201-2). Twenty-Third.
McIntyre, Michael, et al. Peaceworld. (Illus., Orig.). 1976. pap. 2.50 (ISBN 0-377-00054-X). Friend Pr.
McIntyre, William. Christ's Cabinet. rev. ed. 143p. 1982. Repr. of 1937 ed. 3.95 (ISBN 0-86544-017-4). Salv Army Suppl South.
MacIver, Kenneth & Thomson, William. An Old New England Christmas. (Illus.). 47p. (Orig.). 1980. pap. 3.00 (ISBN 0-88448-019-4). Harpswell Pr.
MacIver, R. M., ed. Great Moral Dilemmas. (Religion & Civilization Ser). 189p. 1964. Repr. of 1956 ed. 21.50x (ISBN 0-8154-0145-0). Cooper Sq.
MacIver, R. M., ed. see Institute for Religious & Social Studies.
Mack, Burton L. A Myth of Innocence: Mark & Christian Origins. LC 86-45906. (Foundations and Facets Ser.). 448p. 1987. text ed. 9.95 (ISBN 0-8006-2113-1). Fortress.
--Wisdom & the Hebrew Epic: Ben Sira's Hymn in Praise of the Fathers. LC 85-8564. (Chicago Studies in the History of Judaism). xiv, 264p. 1986. lib. bdg. 25.00x (ISBN 0-226-50049-7). U of Chicago Pr.
Mack, Grace C. My Special Book of Jewish Celebrations. (Illus.). 36p. (Orig.). 1984. pap. 8.95 (ISBN 0-9602338-4-9). Rockdale Ridge.
Mack, Jane, ed. see Meier, Paul.
Mack, Wayne. Homework Manual for Biblical Counseling: Family & Marital Problems, Vol. 2. 1980. pap. 3.95 (ISBN 0-87552-357-9). Presby & Reformed.
--Homework Manual for Biblical Counseling: Personal & Interpersonal Problems, Vol. 1. 1979. pap. 5.50 (ISBN 0-87552-356-0). Presby & Reformed.
--How to Pray Effectively. (Christian Growth Ser.). 1977. pap. 2.95 (ISBN 0-87552-331-5). Presby & Reformed.
Mackail, John W. Bentley's Milton. LC 73-7628. 1973. lib. bdg. 15.00 (ISBN 0-8414-2343-1). Folcroft.
--Studies in Humanism. facs. ed. LC 73-84322. (Essay Index Reprint Ser). 1938. 17.75 (ISBN 0-8369-1092-3). Ayer Co Pubs.
McKane, William. Jeremiah: Chapters 1-25, Vol. 1. Cranfield, Charles E. & Emerton, John A., eds. (International Critical Commentary Ser.). 784p. 1986. 39.95 (ISBN 0-567-05042-4, Pub. by T & T Clark Ltd UK). Fortress.
--Proverbs: A New Approach. LC 75-108185. (Old Testament Library). 692p. 1970. Westminster.
McKarns, James. Go Tell Everyone: A Commentary on the Sunday Readings - Cycles A-B & C. LC 85-20036. 279p. 1985. 9.95 (ISBN 0-8189-0488-7). Alba.
--Seldom-Told Bible Tales. 1985. 4.95 (ISBN 0-89536-738-6, 5821). CSS of Ohio.
Mackay, A. M. A. M. Mackay: Pioneer Missionary of the Church of the Missionary Society of Uganda. (Illus.). 485p. 1970. Repr. of 1890 ed. 35.00x (ISBN 0-7146-1874-8, F Cass Co). Biblio Dist.
McKay, Bobbie. The Unabridged Woman. LC 79-14297. (Orig.). 1979. pap. 5.95 (ISBN 0-8298-0369-6). Pilgrim NY.
McKay, David & Crawford, Richard. William Billings of Boston: Eighteenth-Century Composer. LC 74-2971. (Illus.). 320p. 1975. 37.00x (ISBN 0-691-09118-8). Princeton U Pr.
MacKay, Donald M. Human Science & Human Dignity. LC 79-2383. 1979. pap. 3.50 (ISBN 0-87784-461-5). Inter-Varsity.
Mackay, H. G. Story of Your Bible. 1985. pap. 2.95 (ISBN 0-937396-65-6). Walterick Pubs.
Mackay, Harold. How to Study Your Bible. Date not set. pap. 2.95 (ISBN 0-937396-68-0). Walterick Pubs.
Mackay, Henry F. Followers in the Way. LC 71-93359. (Essay Index Reprint Ser). 1934. 17.00 (ISBN 0-8369-1304-3). Ayer Co Pubs.
McKay, John. Religion in Judah under the Assyrians. LC 72-97460. (Studies in Biblical Theology, 2nd Ser.: No. 26). 1973. pap. text ed. 10.00x (ISBN 0-8401-3076-7). A R Allenson.
Mackay, Kris. No Greater Love. LC 81-22123. 99p. 1982. 6.95 (ISBN 0-87747-906-2). Deseret Bk.
McKay, William J., jt. auth. see Haugh, Kenneth.
McKay, William P., jt. auth. see Barna, George.
McKean, Sr. M. Faith. Interplay of Realistic & Flamboyant Art Elements in the French Mysteres. LC 74-94196. (Catholic University of America Studies in Romance Languages & Literatures Ser: No. 60). Repr. of 1959 ed. 23.00 (ISBN 0-404-50360-8). AMS Pr.
McKeating, H., tr. see Simon, Marcal.
McKeating, Henry. Studying the Old Testament. LC 82-70960. 224p. (Orig.). 1982. pap. 10.95 (ISBN 0-8066-1935-X, 10-6141). Augsburg.
McKeating, Henry, ed. The Books of Amos, Hosea, Micah. (Cambridge Bible Commentary on the New English Bible, Old Testament Ser.). (Illus.). 1971. 22.95 (ISBN 0-521-08133-5); pap. 10.95 (ISBN 0-521-09647-2). Cambridge U Pr.
McKee, Arnold F. Economics & the Christian Mind. 1987. 10.95 (ISBN 0-533-07175-5). Vantage.
McKee, David & Woo, Nancy E. Ecclesiastes in A. S. L. - Chapter Three, Verses 1-4: Written in Sutton Sign Writing. text ed. 3.00x. Ctr Sutton Movement.
McKee, David R. Simon Tyssot de Patot & the Seventeenth-Century Background of Critical Deism. (Johns Hopkins University Studies in Romance Literatures & Languages: Vol. 40). 105p. pap. 14.00 (ISBN 0-384-34885-8). Johnson Repr.
McKee, John. The Enemy Within the Gate. LC 74-80023. 1974. 10.00 (ISBN 0-912414-16-2). Lumen Christi.
--A Martyr Bishop: The Life of St. Oliver Plunkett. 181p. 1975. 7.95 (ISBN 0-912414-21-9). Lumen Christi.
McKee, William. How to Reach Out to Inactive Catholics: A Practical Parish Program. 40p. 1982. pap. 6.95 (ISBN 0-89243-155-5). Liguori Pubns.
MacKeeby, Margaret. Is Jesus Coming in a Flying Saucer? 1984. 8.95 (ISBN 0-533-05998-4). Vantage.
McKeever, James. Become Like Jesus. 408p. 1984. write for info. (ISBN 0-86694-101-0); pap. 9.95 (ISBN 0-86694-100-2). Omega Pubns OR.
--Victory Bible Reading Plan. 1984. 1.00 (ISBN 0-86694-102-9). Omega Pubns OR.
--Victory in Prayer. 32p. (Orig.). 1985. pap. 1.00 (ISBN 0-86694-103-7). Omega Pubns OR.
McKeever, Jim. Almighty & the Dollar Workbook. 1980. 23.95. Omega Pubns OR.
--Christians Will Go Through the Tribulation. LC 78-55091. (Illus.). 1978. 10.95 (ISBN 0-931608-01-5); pap. 5.95 (ISBN 0-931608-02-3). Omega Pubns OR.
--Coming Climax of History. 1983. 6.95 (ISBN 0-86694-099-5). Omega Pubns OR.
--The Coming Climax of History. 324p. 1983. 15.95 (ISBN 0-86694-098-7). Omega Pubns OR.
--Financial Guidance. 400p. 1980. 10.95 (ISBN 0-931608-09-0); pap. 7.95 (ISBN 0-931608-10-4). Omega Pubns OR.
--How You Can Know the Will of God. 24p. 1982. 1.00 (ISBN 0-86694-095-2). Omega Pubns OR.
--Knowledge of Good & Evil. 1981. 1.00 (ISBN 0-86694-084-7). Omega Pubns OR.
--Only One Word. 1979. 1.00 (ISBN 0-86694-011-1). Omega Pubns OR.
--Revelation for Layman. 1980. 10.95 (ISBN 0-931608-07-4); pap. 5.95 (ISBN 0-931608-08-2). Omega Pubns OR.
--Why Were You Created. 1980. 1.00 (ISBN 0-86694-083-9). Omega Pubns OR.
McKellar, Shona. The Beginning of the Rainbow. LC 81-7954. (Illus.). 1982. 8.95g (ISBN 0-687-02770-5). Abingdon.
MacKemzie, Joy & Bledsoe, Shirley. The Bible Book of Lists. 128p. 1984. pap. 5.95 (ISBN 0-310-70321-2, 14035P). Zondervan.
Macken, Raymond. Denys the Carthusian: Commentator on Boethius's De Consolatione Philosophiae. Hogg, James, ed. (Analecta Cartusiana Ser.: No. 118). 94p. (Orig.). 1984. pap. 25.00 (ISBN 0-317-42573-0, Pub. by Salzburg Studies). Longwood Pub Group.
McKendrick, Melveena. Ferdinand & Isabella. LC 68-14974. (Horizon Caravel Bks.). 1544p. (YA) 1968. PLB 15.89 (ISBN 0-06-024165-9). HarpJ.
McKenna, Briege & Libersat, Henry. Miracles Do Happen. 170p. (Orig.). 1987. pap. 4.95 (ISBN 0-89283-316-5). Servant.
McKenna, Constance, ed. I Support You But I Can't Sign My Name. 20p. 1982. pap. 1.00 (ISBN 0-915365-06-5). Cath Free Choice.
McKenna, Constance, ed. see Ellingston, Jenefer.
McKenna, Constance, ed. see Hurst, Jane.
McKenna, Constance, ed. see Hynes, Kathleen.
McKenna, Constance, ed. see Kohn, Richard.
McKenna, Constance, et al, eds. My Conscience Speaks. (Illus.). 48p. 1981. pap. 1.00 (ISBN 0-915365-05-7). Cath Free Choice.
McKenna, David. Job (CC) 320p. 1986. 18.95 (ISBN 0-317-43277-X). Word Bks.
--Job (CC, Vol. 12. 320p. 1986. 18.95 (ISBN 0-8499-0418-8). Word Bks.
--Megatruth: The Church in the Age of Information. 1987. 12.95. Heres Life.
--The Whisper of His Grace: A Fresh Look at Suffering Through the Eyes of Job & Jesus. 192p. 1987. 12.95 (ISBN 0-8499-0560-5). Word Bks.
McKenna, David L. The Communicator's Commentary-Mark, Vol. 2. Ogilvie, Lloyd, ed. (The Communicator's Commentaries Ser.). 1982. 18.95 (ISBN 0-8499-0155-3). Word Bks.
--Contemporary Issues for Evangelical Christians. (Contemporary Discussion Ser). 1978. pap. 1.95 (ISBN 0-8010-6053-2). Baker Bk.
McKenna, Edward J. The Ministry of Musicians. 40p. (Orig.). 1983. pap. 1.25 (ISBN 0-8146-1295-4). Liturgical Pr.
McKenna, Gail T. Through the Year with the DRE: A Seasonal Guide for Christian Educators. 128p. (Orig.). 1987. pap. 7.95 (ISBN 0-8091-2860-8). Paulist Pr.
McKenna, Marian. Concise History of Catholicism. (Quality Paperback: No. 143). 285p. 1962. pap. 2.95 (ISBN 0-8226-0143-5). Littlefield.
McKenna, Megan & Ducote, Darryl. Beginnings of the Church. LC 78-71533. (Followers of the Way Ser.: Vol. 6). 1980. 22.50 (ISBN 0-8091-9547-X); cassette 7.50 (ISBN 0-8091-7671-8). Paulist Pr.
--Jesus Living the Father's Values. LC 78-71530. (Followers of the Way Ser.: Vol. 3). 1979. 22.50 (ISBN 0-8091-9544-5); cassette 7.50 (ISBN 0-8091-7668-8). Paulist Pr.
--New Testament Understanding of Jesus. LC 78-71529. (Followers of the Way Ser.: Vol. 2). 1979. 22.50 (ISBN 0-8091-9543-7); cassette 7.50 (ISBN 0-8091-7667-X). Paulist Pr.
--Old Testament Journeys in Faith. LC 78-71528. (Followers of the Way Ser.: Vol. 1). 1979. 22.50 (ISBN 0-8091-9542-9); 7.50 (ISBN 0-8091-7666-1). Paulist Pr.
--Sacraments, Liturgy & Prayer. LC 78-71531. (Followers of the Way Ser.: Vol. 5). 221p. 1979. 22.50 (ISBN 0-8091-9546-1); cassette 7.50 (ISBN 0-8091-7670-X). Paulist Pr.
--The Spirit in the Church. LC 78-71531. (Followers of the Way Ser.: Vol. 4). 1979. 22.50 (ISBN 0-8091-9545-3); cassette 7.50 (ISBN 0-8091-7669-6). Paulist Pr.
MacKenna, Richard. God for Nothing. 186p. 1986. 12.95 (ISBN 0-285-62623-X, Pub. Souvenir Pr Ltd UK). Intl Spec Bk.
Mackenna, Stephen, tr. see Turnbull, Grace R.
McKenney, Tom, jt. auth. see McCormick, Joe.
McKenney, Tom C. Come & Live. LC 84-242781. (Illus.). 167p. 1982. pap. 5.95 (ISBN 0-934527-01-6). Words Living Minis.
--Come & Live. LC 84-242781. (Illus.). 167p. (Orig.). 1981. pap. 3.95 (ISBN 0-934527-00-8). Words Living Minis.
--Live Free. LC 84-91415. (Illus.). 317p. 1985. 9.95 (ISBN 0-934527-04-0). Words Living Minis.
MacKenthun, Carole & Dwyer, Paulinus. Faith. (Fruit of the Spirit Ser.). (Illus.). 48p. 1986. wkbk. 4.95 (ISBN 0-86653-361-3). Good Apple.
--Gentleness. (Fruit of the Spirit Ser.). 48p. 1987. pap. 5.95 (ISBN 0-86653-395-8, SS879). Good Apple.
--Goodness. (Fruit of the Spirit Ser.). (Illus.). 48p. 1986. wkbk. 4.95 (ISBN 0-86653-363-X). Good Apple.
--Joy. (Fruit of the Spirit Ser.). (Illus.). 48p. 1986. wkbk. 4.95 (ISBN 0-86653-360-5). Good Apple.
--Kindness. (Fruit of the Spirit Ser.). (Illus.). 48p. 1987. pap. 5.95 (ISBN 0-86653-379-6, SS880). Good Apple.
--Love. (Fruit of the Spirit Ser.). (Illus.). 48p. Date not set. wkbk. 4.95 (ISBN 0-86653-359-1). Good Apple.
--Patience. (Fruit of the Spirit Ser.). (Illus.). 48p. Date not set. wkbk. 4.95 (ISBN 0-86653-364-8). Good Apple.
--Peace. (Fruit of the Spirit Ser.). (Illus.). 48p. 1986. wkbk. 4.95 (ISBN 0-86653-365-6). Good Apple.
--Self-Control. (Fruit of the Spirit Ser.). (Illus.). 48p. 1987. pap. 5.95 (ISBN 0-86653-396-6, SS878). Good Apple.
McKenzie, A. Dean. Russian Icons in the Santa Barbara Museum of Art. LC 82-62426. (Illus.). 54p. (Orig.). 1982. pap. 8.25 (ISBN 0-89951-049-3). Santa Barb Mus Art.
Mackenzie, Agnes M. The Scotland of Queen Mary & the Religious Wars, 1513-1638. LC 75-41506. (Illus.). 404p. 1976. Repr. of 1957 ed. lib. bdg. 24.00x (ISBN 0-8371-8704-4, MASQ). Greenwood.
Mackenzie, Campbell, tr. see Bonnechose, Emile de.
MacKenzie, Charles S. Pascal's Anguish & Joy. LC 73-77404. 272p. 1973. 12.95 (ISBN 0-8022-2117-3). Philos Lib.
Mackenzie, Compton. Catholicism & Scotland. LC 75-118486. 1971. Repr. of 1936 ed. 23.50x (ISBN 0-8046-1235-8, Pub. by Kennikat). Assoc Faculty Pr.
Mackenzie, D. Myths of Pre-Columbian America. 75.00 (ISBN 0-8490-0701-1). Gordon Pr.
McKenzie, David. Wolfhart Pannenberg & Religious Philosophy. LC 80-8171. 169p. 1980. lib. bdg. 25.00 (ISBN 0-8191-1314-X); pap. text ed. 11.25 (ISBN 0-8191-1315-8). U Pr of Amer.

Mackenzie, Donald. Indian Myth & Legend. LC 77-85615. 1978. Repr. of 1913 ed. lib. bdg. 50.00 (ISBN 0-89341-316-X). Longwood Pub Group.

Mackenzie, Donald A. Buddhism in Pre-Christian Britain. 1977. lib. bdg. 59.95 (ISBN 0-8490-1558-8). Gordon Pr.

--Egyptian Myth & Legend. LC 76-27520. (Illus.). 1976. Repr. of 1907 ed. lib. bdg. 40.00 (ISBN 0-89341-033-0). Longwood Pub Group.

--Egyptian Myth & Legend. 454p. 1984. pap. cancelled (ISBN 0-89341-487-5). Longwood Pub Group.

--Migration of Symbols & Their Relations to Beliefs & Customs. LC 68-18029. 1968. Repr. of 1926 ed. 34.00x (ISBN 0-8103-3074-1). Gale.

McKenzie, Donald A. More Notices from Methodist Papers 1830-1857. 424p. 1986. lib. bdg. 22.00 (ISBN 0-912606-29-0). Hunterdon Hse.

MacKenzie, Donald A. Myths of Babylonia & Assyria. LC 77-94601. 1978. Repr. of 1915 ed. lib. bdg. 60.00 (ISBN 0-89341-315-1). Longwood Pub Group.

--The Myths of China & Japan. LC 77-6878. 1977. Repr. of 1923 ed. lib. bdg. 45.00 (ISBN 0-89341-149-3). Longwood Pub Group.

--Myths of Crete & Pre-Hellenic Europe. LC 76-27522. (Illus.). 1976. Repr. of 1918 ed. lib. bdg. 45.00 (ISBN 0-89341-035-7). Longwood Pub Group.

--Myths of Pre-Columbian America. LC 77-94602. 1978. Repr. of 1923 ed. lib. bdg. 40.00 (ISBN 0-89341-314-3). Longwood Pub Group.

--Otfrid Von Weissenburg: Narrator or Commentator. (Stanford University. Stanford Studies in Language & Literature: Vol. 6, Pt. 3). Repr. of 1946 ed. 18.00 (ISBN 0-404-51812-5). AMS Pr.

--Teutonic Myth & Legend. LC 77-91530. 1978. Repr. of 1912 ed. lib. bdg. 50.00 (ISBN 0-89341-313-5). Longwood Pub Group.

McKenzie, E. C. Mac's Giant Book of Quips & Quotes. 1983. pap. 12.95 (ISBN 0-8010-6164-4). Baker Bk.

--Quips & Quotes for Church Bulletins. (Direction Bks). 1978. pap. 2.95 (ISBN 0-8010-6059-1). Baker Bk.

McKenzie, George J., tr. see Calvez, Jean Y.

McKenzie, J. L., ed. New Testament for Spiritual Reading, 25 vols. Incl. Vol. 1. Gospel According to St. Matthew, Pt. 1 (ISBN 0-8245-0334-1); Vol. 2. Gospel According to St. Matthew, Pt. 2 (ISBN 0-8245-0335-X) (ISBN 0-8245-0111-X); Vol. 3. Gospel According to St. Mark, Pt. 1 (ISBN 0-8245-0336-8) (ISBN 0-8245-0112-8); Vol. 4. Gospel According to St. Mark, Pt. 2 (ISBN 0-8245-0337-6) (ISBN 0-8245-0113-6); Vol. 5. Gospel According to St. Luke, Pt. 1 (ISBN 0-8245-0338-4) (ISBN 0-8245-0114-4); Vol. 6. Gospel According to St. Luke, Pt. 2 (ISBN 0-8245-0339-2) (ISBN 0-8245-0115-2); Vol. 7. Gospel According to St. John, Pt. 1 (ISBN 0-8245-0340-6) (ISBN 0-8245-0116-0); Vol. 8. Gospel According to St. John, Pt. 2 (ISBN 0-8164-1079-8) (ISBN 0-8245-0117-9); Vol. 9. Gospel According to St. John, Pt. 3 (ISBN 0-8245-0342-2) (ISBN 0-8245-0118-7); Vol. 10. Acts of the Apostles, Pt. 1 (ISBN 0-8245-0343-0) (ISBN 0-8245-0119-5); Vol. 11. Acts of the Apostles, Pt. 2 (ISBN 0-8245-0344-9) (ISBN 0-8245-0120-9); Vol. 12. **Epistle to the Romans (ISBN 0-8245-0345-7) (ISBN 0-8245-0121-7); Vol. 13. First Epistle to the Corinthians (ISBN 0-8245-0346-5) (ISBN 0-8245-0122-5); Vol. 14. Second Epistle to the Corinthians (ISBN 0-8245-0347-3) (ISBN 0-8245-0123-3); Vol. 15. Epistle to the Galatians (ISBN 0-8245-0348-1) (ISBN 0-8245-0124-1); Vol. 16. Epistle to the Ephesians (ISBN 0-8245-0349-X) (ISBN 0-8245-0125-X); Vol. 17. Epistle to the Philippians. Epistle to the Colossians (ISBN 0-8164-1088-7) (ISBN 0-8245-0126-8); Vol. 18. First Epistle to the Thessalonians. Second Epistle to the Thessalonians (ISBN 0-8245-0352-X) (ISBN 0-8245-0127-6); Vol. 19. First Epistle to Timothy. Second Epistle to Timothy (ISBN 0-8245-0353-8) (ISBN 0-8245-0128-4); Vol. 20. Epistle to Titus. Epistle to Philemon (ISBN 0-8245-0354-6) (ISBN 0-8245-0129-2); Vol. 21. Epistle to the Hebrews. Epistle to James (ISBN 0-8245-0355-4) (ISBN 0-8245-0130-6); Vol. 22. First Epistle to Peter. Second Epistle to Peter (ISBN 0-8245-0356-2) (ISBN 0-8245-0131-4); Vol. 23. Epistle to Jude. Three Epistles of John (ISBN 0-8245-0357-0) (ISBN 0-8245-0132-2); Vol. 24. The Revelation of St. John, Pt. 1 (ISBN 0-8245-0358-9) (ISBN 0-8245-0133-0); Vol. 25. The Revelation of St. John, Pt. 2 (ISBN 0-8245-0359-7) (ISBN 0-8245-0134-9). 10.00 ea.; Set. 123.75 (ISBN 0-8245-0135-7); pap. 4.95 ea. Crossroad NY.**

Mackenzie, John. Dictionary of Bible. 1967. pap. 14.95 (ISBN 0-02-087720-X, Collier). Macmillan.

--Dictionary of Bible. 1965. 29.95 (ISBN 0-02-583470-3). Macmillan.

McKenzie, John G. Nervous Disorders & Religion: A Study of Souls in the Making. LC 79-8719. 183p. 1981. Repr. of 1951 ed. lib. bdg. 22.50x (ISBN 0-313-22192-8, MCND). Greenwood.

McKenzie, John L. The Civilization of Christianity. 1986. pap. 9.95 (ISBN 0-88347-208-2). Thomas More.

--Mastering the Meaning of the Bible. 140p. 1986. 4.95 (ISBN 0-87193-252-0). Dimension Bks.

--The New Testament Without Illusion. (The Crossroad Paperback Ser.). 256p. 1982. pap. 6.95 (ISBN 0-8245-0451-8). Crossroad NY.

--Source: What the Bible Says about the Problems of Contemporary Life. (Basics of Christian Thought Ser.). 228p. 1984. 14.95 (ISBN 0-88347-172-8). Thomas More.

--A Theology of the Old Testament. LC 86-9230. 336p. 1986. pap. text ed. 12.00 (ISBN 0-8191-5354-0). U Pr of Amer.

McKenzie, John L., ed. Isaiah Two. LC 68-10565. (Anchor Bible Ser.: Vol. 20). 1968. 14.00 (ISBN 0-385-05390-8, Anchor Pr). Doubleday.

McKenzie, John L., ed. see Blank, Josef.

McKenzie, John L., ed. see Gnilka, Joachim & Mussner, Franz.

McKenzie, John L., ed. see Huckle, John & Visokay, Paul.

McKenzie, John L., ed. see Kertlege, Karl.

McKenzie, John L., ed. see Kurzinger, Josef.

McKenzie, John L., ed. see Reuss, Josef.

McKenzie, John L., ed. see Schick, Eduard.

McKenzie, John L., ed. see Schierse, F. J.

McKenzie, John L., ed. see Schnackenburg, Rudolf.

McKenzie, John L., ed. see Schnakenburg, Rudolf.

McKenzie, John L., ed. see Schneider, Gerhard.

McKenzie, John L., ed. see Schurmann, Heinz, et al.

McKenzie, John L., ed. see Stoger, Alois.

McKenzie, John L., ed. see Thusing, Wilhelm, et al.

McKenzie, John L., ed. see Trilling, Wolfgang.

McKenzie, John L., ed. see Walter, Eugen.

McKenzie, John L., ed. see Zerwick, Max.

McKenzie, John T., ed. see Schwank, Bernedikt.

MacKenzie, Joy. The Big Book of Bible Crafts & Projects. (Illus.). 212p. (Orig.). 1981. pap. 12.95 (ISBN 0-310-70151-1, 14019P). Zondervan.

MacKenzie, Joy & Bledsoe, Shirley. A Big Book of Bible Games & Puzzles. 192p. 1982. pap. 9.95 (ISBN 0-310-70271-2, 14029P). Zondervan.

McKenzie, Leon. The Religious Education of Adults. LC 81-19926. 256p. 1982. pap. 12.95 (ISBN 0-89135-031-4). Religious Educ.

Mackenzie, R. see Calvin, John.

MacKenzie, R. A. Faith & History in the Old Testament. LC 63-10585. 1963. 8.95 (ISBN 0-8166-0297-2). U of Minn Pr.

--Sirach. (Old Testament Message Ser.: Vol. 19). 12.95 (ISBN 0-89453-419-X); pap. 8.95 (ISBN 0-89453-253-7). M Glazier.

Mackenzie, Robert. John Brown of Haddington. 1964. pap. 2.95 (ISBN 0-85151-113-9). Banner of Truth.

McKenzie, Steven L. The Chronicler's Use of the Deuteronomistic History. (Harvard Semitic Monograph Ser.: No. 33). 1985. 16.50 (ISBN 0-89130-828-8, 04 00 33). Scholars Pr GA.

McKenzie, Venetia. Creative Self-Communication. 1978. pap. 1.25 (ISBN 0-87516-254-1). De Vorss.

MacKenzie, W. Roy. English Moralities from the Point of View of Allegory. LC 68-54172. (Studies in Drama, No. 39). 1969. Repr. of 1914 ed. lib. bdg. 49.95x (ISBN 0-8383-0592-X). Haskell.

Mackenzie, William R. English Moralities from the Point of View of Allegory. LC 66-29466. 278p. 1966. Repr. of 1914 ed. 25.00x (ISBN 0-87752-066-6). Gordian.

--The English Moralities from the Point of View of Allegory. (Harvard Studies in English). Repr. of 1914 ed. 23.00 (ISBN 0-384-34880-7). Johnson Repr.

McKeon, Richard, ed. see Abailard, P.

McKernan, Llewellyn. More Songs of Gladness (Suppl.) (Arch Bks.). (Illus.). 24p. 1987. pap. 0.99 (ISBN 0-570-09004-0, 59-1432). Concordia.

Mackes, Shy. The Overcoming Power. LC 82-73708. 1983. pap. text ed. 5.00 (ISBN 0-932050-17-4). New Puritan.

--Seven Steps to God's Healing Power. pap. 0.95 (ISBN 0-910924-28-7). Macalester.

Mackey, A. G. Symbolism of Freemansonry. 12.00x (ISBN 0-685-22122-9). Wehman.

Mackey, Albert G. Jurisprudence of Freemasonry. 12.00 (ISBN 0-685-19480-9). Powner.

--Mackey's Jurisprudence of Freemasonry. 1985. Repr. 12.75 (ISBN 0-88053-026-X). Macoy Pub.

--Symbolism of Freemasonry. 12.00 (ISBN 0-685-19504-X). Powner.

Mackey, Bertha. A Saloon Keeper's Daughter Saved. 15p. 1982. pap. 0.15 (ISBN 0-686-36264-0); pap. 0.25 2 copies (ISBN 0-686-37285-9). Faith Pub HSe.

Mackey, Henry B., tr. see De Sales, Saint Francoise.

Mackey, James. The Religious Imagination. 256p. 1986. 17.50x (ISBN 0-85224-512-2, Pub. by Edinburgh U Pr Scotland). Columbia U Pr.

Mackey, James P. Jesus, the Man & the Myth. LC 78-61627. 320p. 1979. pap. 10.95 (ISBN 0-8091-2169-7). Paulist Pr.

--The Problems of Religious Faith. 344p. 1975. 12.95 (ISBN 0-8199-0454-6). Franciscan Herald.

McKibben, Jorge F., tr. see Davis, Guillermo H.

McKibbens, Thomas R., Jr. The Forgotten Heritage: A Lineage of Great Baptist Preaching. (Orig.). 1986. 27.95 (ISBN 0-86554-179-5, MUP-H169); pap. 18.95 (ISBN 0-86554-186-8, MUP-P18). Mercer Univ Pr.

McKibbens, Thomas R., Jr. & Smith, Kenneth. The Life & Work of Morgan Edwards: First Baptist Historian in the United States. Gaustad, Edwin S., ed. LC 79-5269. (The Baptist Tradition Ser.). 1980. lib. bdg. 23.00x (ISBN 0-405-12438-4). Ayer Co Pubs.

McKibben-Stockwell. Nuevo Lexico Griego Espanol. (Span.). 316p. 1985. pap. 6.95 (ISBN 0-311-42072-9, Edit Mundo). Casa Bautista.

Mackie, George M. Bible Manners & Customs. (Illus.). 176p. 1956. (Power Bks); pap. 6.95 (ISBN 0-8007-5179-5). Revell.

--Bible Manners & Customs. LC 84-230883. (Illus.). 192p. 1984. 6.95 (ISBN 0-8007-5179-5, Power Bks.). Revell.

Mackie, J. D. Cavalier & Puritan. 1930. Repr. 10.00 (ISBN 0-8482-5082-6). Norwood Edns.

Mackie, J. L. Ethics: Inventing Right & Wrong. 1977. pap. 6.95 (ISBN 0-14-021957-9, Pelican). Penguin.

--The Miracle of Theism. 1982. text ed. 32.50x (ISBN 0-19-824665-X); pap. text ed. 10.95x (ISBN 0-19-824682-X). Oxford U Pr.

MacKillop, James. Fionn Mac Cumhaill: Celtic Myth in English Literature. LC 85-22116. (Irish Studies). 256p. (Orig.). 1986. pap. text ed. 35.00x (ISBN 0-8156-2344-5); pap. 15.00x (ISBN 0-8156-2353-4). Syracuse U Pr.

McKim, Donald, jt. auth. see Rogers, Jack.

McKim, Donald K. Readings in Calvin's Theology. 304p. (Orig.). 1984. pap. 15.95 (ISBN 0-8010-6150-4). Baker Bk.

--What Christians Believe about the Bible. 183p. 1985. pap. 8.95 (ISBN 0-8407-5968-1). Nelson.

McKim, Donald K., ed. The Authoritative Word: Essays on the Nature of Scripture. 270p. 1983. pap. 10.95 (ISBN 0-8028-1948-6). Eerdmans.

--A Guide to Contemporary Hermeneutics: Major Trends in Biblical Interpretation. 312p. (Orig.). 1986. pap. 14.95 (ISBN 0-8028-0094-7). Eerdmans.

--How Karl Barth Changed My Mind. 216p. (Orig.). 1986. pap. 9.95 (ISBN 0-8028-0099-8). Eerdmans.

Mackin, Theodore. Divorce & Remarriage. (Marriage in the Catholic Church Ser.: Vol. II). 688p. (Orig.). 1984. pap. 19.95 (ISBN 0-8091-2585-4). Paulist Pr.

--What is Marriage: Marriage in the Catholic Church. LC 81-84386. (Marriage in the Catholic Church Ser.: Vol. 1). 384p. (Orig.). 1982. pap. 11.95 (ISBN 0-8091-2442-4). Paulist Pr.

McKinlay, A. P., ed. Arator: The Codices. 1942. 8.00x (ISBN 0-910956-18-9). Medieval Acad.

McKinley, E. H. Somebody's Brother: A History of the Salvation Army Men's Social Service Department 1891-1985. LC 86-8604. (Studies in American Religion Ser.: Vol. 21). 264p. 1986. 9.95 (ISBN 0-88946-665-3). E Mellen.

McKinley, Edward H. Marching to Glory. 290p. pap. 4.95 (ISBN 0-86544-039-5). Salv Army Suppl South.

McKinley, John. Group Development Through Participation Training: A Trainers Resource for Team Building. LC 78-71870. 162p. (Orig.). 1980. pap. text ed. 9.95 (ISBN 0-8091-2247-2); participant's bk. 2.50 (ISBN 0-8091-2299-5). Paulist Pr.

McKinnell, James. Now about Peace. (Orig.). 1971. pap. 1.50 (ISBN 0-87178-935-3). Brethren.

McKinney, et al. A Through the Bible Reading Program. (Illus.). 112p. (Orig.). 1983. pap. 3.95 (ISBN 0-87239-647-9, 3076). Standard Pub.

McKinney, Charles, jt. auth. see Carter, Stephen.

McKinney, Charles, jt. auth. see Carter, Stephen J.

McKinney, Donald. Living with Joy. LC 76-8203. Repr. of 1976 ed. 24.00 (ISBN 0-8357-9014-2, 2016375). Bks Demand UMI.

McKinney, Joseph C. Living in the Power of Pentecost. 112p. (Orig.). 1987. pap. 4.95 (ISBN 0-89283-311-4). Servant.

McKinney, Ken, tr. see Bovon, Francois.

McKinney, Lois. Writing for Theological Education by Extension. 64p. (Prog. Bk.). 1975. 1.95x (ISBN 0-87808-905-5). William Carey Lib.

McKinney, Richard I. Religion in Higher Education among Negroes. LC 75-38785. (Religion in America, Ser. 2). 186p. 1972. Repr. of 1945 ed. 15.00 (ISBN 0-405-04075-X). Ayer Co Pubs.

--Religion in Higher Education among Negroes. 1945. 13.50x (ISBN 0-686-51299-5). Elliots Bks.

McKinney, Richard W., ed. Creation, Christ & Culture. 336p. 19.95 (ISBN 0-567-01019-8, Pub. by T & T Clark Ltd UK). Fortress.

McKinney, Samuel B., jt. auth. see Massey, Floyd, Jr.

McKinney, Wiliam, jt. auth. see Roozen, David A.

McKinney, William, jt. auth. see Roof, Wade C.

Mackinnon, Donald. Enjoying the Harvest: Reflections for Your Mature Years. 48p. 1983. pap. 1.50 (ISBN 0-89243-196-2). Liguori Pubns.

Mackinnon, James. Calvin & the Reformation. LC 83-45648. Date not set. Repr. of 1936 ed. 37.50 (ISBN 0-404-19841-4). AMS Pr.

--Luther & the Reformation, 4 vols. LC 83-45648. Date not set. Repr. of 1925 ed. Set. 157.50 (ISBN 0-404-19857-0). AMS Pr.

McKinnon, James W. Music in Early Christian Literature. (Cambridge Readings in the Literature of Music Ser.). 300p. Date not set. price not set (ISBN 0-521-30497-0). Cambridge U Pr.

McKinsey, Elizabeth R. The Western Experiment: New England Transcendentalists in the Ohio Valley. LC 72-83467. (Essays in History & Literature Ser.). 80p. 1973. pap. 4.95x (ISBN 0-674-95040-2). Harvard U Pr.

Mackintosh, C. H. Genesis to Deuteronomy: Notes on the Pentateuch, 6 vols. in 1. LC 72-75082. 928p. 1972. 19.95 (ISBN 0-87213-617-5). Loizeaux.

--The Mackintosh Treasury: Miscellaneous Writings of C. H. Mackintosh. rev. ed. LC 75-44323. 1976. 6 vols. in 1 19.95 (ISBN 0-87213-609-4). Loizeaux.

--Short Papers on Scriptural Subjects, 2 vols. Set. 15.95 (ISBN 0-88172-115-8). Believers Bkshelf.

Mackintosh, Carlos H. La Oracion y los Cultos de Oracion. 2nd ed. Daniel, Roger P., ed. Bautista, Sara, tr. from Eng. (La Serie Diamante). Tr. of Prayer & the Prayer Meeting. (Span., Illus.). 40p. 1982. pap. 0.85 (ISBN 0-942504-08-9). Overcomer Pr.

--El Perdon de los Pecados. 2nd ed. Bennett, Gordon H., ed. Bautista, Sara, tr. from Eng. (La Serie Diamante). Tr. of The Forgiveness of Sins. (Span.). 36p. 1982. pap. 0.85 (ISBN 0-942504-02-X). Overcomer Pr.

Mackintosh, Charles H., tr. see Lao Tse.

Mackintosh, H. R. The Doctrine of the Person of Jesus Christ. 560p. 1913. pap. 15.95 (ISBN 0-567-27218-4, Pub. by T&T Clark Ltd UK). Fortress.

MacKintosh, H. R., jt. auth. see Caldecott, Alfred.

MacKintosh, H. R., ed. see Schleiermacher, Friedrich.

Mackintosh, Sam. Passover Seder for Christian Families. 32p. 1984. pap. 2.95 (ISBN 0-89390-057-5). Resource Pubns.

McKinty, Neil. In the Stillness Dancing: The Life of Father John Main. 192p. 1987. 14.95 (ISBN 0-8245-0799-1). Crossroad NY.

McKissack, Fredrick & McKissack, Patricia. Look What You've Done Now Moses! (Early Readers Ser.). (Illus.). 1984. 4.95 (ISBN 0-89191-839-6); pap. 2.95 (ISBN 0-89191-812-4). Cook.

McKissack, Fredrick, jt. auth. see McKissack, Patricia.

McKissack, Patricia. Michael Jackson, Superstar. LC 84-12170. (Today's Superstars Ser.). 96p. 1984. lib. bdg. 13.25 (ISBN 0-516-04380-3); pap. 4.50 (ISBN 0-516-44380-1). Childrens.

McKissack, Patricia & McKissack, Fredrick. When Do You Talk To God? Prayers for Small Children. LC 86-71903. (Illus.). 32p. (Orig.). 1986. pap. 4.95 (ISBN 0-8066-2239-3, 10-7078). Augsburg.

McKissack, Patricia, jt. auth. see McKissack, Fredrick.

McKissack, Patricia A. Lights Out, Christopher. LC 84-71375. (Christopher Bks.). (Illus.). 32p. (Orig.). 1984. pap. 3.95 (ISBN 0-8066-2110-9, 10-3870). Augsburg.

McKissack, Patricia C. It's the Truth, Christopher. LC 84-71376. (Christopher Bks.). (Illus.). 32p. (Orig.). 1984. pap. 3.95 (ISBN 0-8066-2111-7, 10-3457). Augsburg.

McKivigan, John R. The War Against Proslavery Religion: Abolitionism & the Northern Churches, 1830-1865. LC 83-45933. 328p. 1984. 32.50x (ISBN 0-8014-1589-6). Cornell U Pr.

McKnight, Edgar V. The Bible & the Reader: An Introduction to Literary Criticism. LC 85-4603. 176p. 1985. pap. 8.95 (ISBN 0-8006-1872-6). Fortress.
--What Is Form Criticism. Via, Dan O., Jr., ed. LC 71-81526. (Guides to Biblical Scholarship: New Testament Ser.). 96p. (Orig.). 1969. pap. 4.50 (ISBN 0-8006-0180-7, 1-180). Fortress.
McKnight, Floyd, tr. see Steiner, Rudolf.
McKnight, George H. Saint Nicholas: His Legend & His Role in the Christmas Celebration & Other Popular Customs. (Illus.). 153p. 1974. Repr. of 1917 ed. 15.95 (ISBN 0-87928-051-4). Corner Hse.
Macknight, James. Macknight on the Epistles. 784p. 1984. Repr. of 1966 ed. 24.95 (ISBN 0-8010-6031-1). Baker Bk.
McKnight, Mid. Vestibules of Heaven. 1982. pap. 3.95 (ISBN 0-89225-219-7). Gospel Advocate.
Mackowski, Richard M. Jerusalem: City of Jesus: An Exploration of the Traditions, Writings, & Remains of the Holy City from the Time of Christ. LC 79-28093. pap. 57.80 (ISBN 0-317-30152-7, 2025334). Bks Demand UMI.
McKuen, Rod. The Carols of Christmas. 1971. 3.95 (ISBN 0-394-47420-1). Random.
McLachlan, Elizabeth P. The Scriptorium of Bury St. Edmunds in the Twelfth Century. LC 83-48695. (Theses from the Courtauld Institute of Art Ser.). (Illus.). 515p. 1984. lib. bdg. 60.00 (ISBN 0-8240-5983-2). Garland Pub.
McLachlan, Herbert. The Religious Opinions of Milton, Locke & Newton. LC 74-20740. 1974. Repr. of 1941 ed. lib. bdg. 35.00 (ISBN 0-8414-5930-4). Folcroft.
--Religious Opinions of Milton, Locke & Newton. LC 74-173539. 1972. Repr. of 1941 ed. 12.00x (ISBN 0-8462-1623-X). Russell.
MacLachlan, Lewis. Commonsense about Prayer. 141p. 1965. pap. 2.95 (ISBN 0-227-67653-X). Attic Pr.
--How to Pray for Healing. 112p. 1977. pap. 2.95 (ISBN 0-227-67486-3). Attic Pr.
--Intelligent Prayer. 104p. 1965. pap. 3.50 (ISBN 0-227-67496-0). Attic Pr.
MacLagan, E. The Jesuits & the Great Mogul. LC 71-159212. 1971. Repr. of 1932 ed. lib. bdg. 26.00x (ISBN 0-374-95248-5, Octagon). Hippocrene Bks.
Maclagan, E., ed. see Blake, William.
MacLagan, E. R. & Russell, A. G., eds. The Prophetic Books of William Blake: Jerusalem. 1979. Repr. of 1904 ed. lib. bdg. 35.00 (ISBN 0-8495-3510-7). Arden Lib.
Maclaren, Alexander. Best of Alexander Maclaren. Atkins, Gaius G., ed. LC 74-179733. (Biography Index Reprint Ser). Repr. of 1949 ed. 14.00 (ISBN 0-8369-8101-4). Ayer Co Pubs.
--Expositions of Holy Scripture, 17 vols. 12830p. 1975. Repr. Set. 295.00 (ISBN 0-8010-5967-4). Baker Bk.
--Victory in Failure. LC 79-88309. (Shepherd Illustrated Classics Ser.). 208p. (Orig.). 1980. pap. 5.95 (ISBN 0-87983-212-6). Keats.
Maclaren, Alexander, et al. Communion Meditations & Outlines. (Pocket Pulpit Library). 1979. pap. 4.50 (ISBN 0-8010-6199-7). Baker Bk.
McLarney, James J. The Theism of Edgar Sheffied Brightman. LC 75-3089. Repr. of 1936 ed. 11.50 (ISBN 0-404-59087-X). AMS Pr.
MacLarsen, Alexander. The Psalms, 3 Vols. 1981. smythe sewn 45.00 (ISBN 0-86524-038-8, 1902). Klock & Klock.
McLaughlin. Commentary on Acts. kivar 5.95 (ISBN 0-686-12858-3). Schmul Pub Co.
--Commentary on Luke. kivar 5.95 (ISBN 0-686-12859-1). Schmul Pub Co.
--Commentary on Mark. kivar 5.95 (ISBN 0-686-12860-5). Schmul Pub Co.
--Commentary on Matthew. kivar 5.95 (ISBN 0-686-12861-3). Schmul Pub Co.
--Commentary on Romans. kivar 5.95 (ISBN 0-686-12862-1). Schmul Pub Co.
--Commentary on St. John. kivar 5.95 (ISBN 0-686-12863-X). Schmul Pub Co.
McLaughlin, Eleanor, jt. auth. see Raether, Rosemary.
McLaughlin, Elizabeth T. Ruskin & Gandhi. LC 72-3260. 202p. 1974. 20.00 (ISBN 0-8387-1086-7). Bucknell U Pr.
McLaughlin, Mary M. Intellectual Freedom & Its Limitations in the University of Paris in the Thirteenth & Fourteenth Centuries. Metzger, Walter P., ed. LC 76-55187. (The Academic Profession Ser.). 1977. Repr. lib. bdg. 34.50x (ISBN 0-405-10018-3). Ayer Co Pubs.
McLaughlin, Mary M., tr. see Weston, Jessie L.
McLaughlin, Raymond W. Ethics of Persuasive Preaching. 1978. 9.95 (ISBN 0-8010-6051-6). Baker Bk.
McLean, A. & Easton, J. W. Penuel; or Face to Face with God. Dayton, Donald W., ed. (The Higher Christian Life Ser.). 483p. 1985. 60.00 (ISBN 0-8240-6427-5). Garland Pub.
MacLean, Angus. The Wind in Both Ears. 2nd ed. 1987. pap. write for info. (ISBN 0-933840-30-6, Skinner Hse Bks). Unitarian Univ.
Maclean, Angus H. The Idea of God in Protestant Religious Education. LC 75-177033. (Columbia University. Teachers College. Contributions to Education: No. 410). Repr. of 1930 ed. 22.50 (ISBN 0-404-55410-5). AMS Pr.
Maclean, Dorothy. To Hear the Angels Sing. 217p. (Orig.). 1983. pap. text ed. 7.00 (ISBN 0-936878-01-0). Lorian Pr.
McLean, Edward B. Roman Catholicism & the Right to Work. 186p. (Orig.). 1986. lib. bdg. 25.50 (ISBN 0-8191-5009-6); pap. text ed. 11.25 (ISBN 0-8191-5010-X). U Pr of Amer.
McLean, George F., ed. Ethical Wisdom East &-or West. LC 78-106891. (Proceedings of the American Catholic Philosophical Association: Vol. 51). 1977. pap. 15.00 (ISBN 0-918090-11-3). Am Cath Philo.
--The Existence of God. LC 73-161203. (Proceedings of the American Catholic Philosophical Association: Vol. 46). 1972. pap. 15.00 (ISBN 0-918090-06-7). Am Cath Philo.
--Freedom. LC 77-153528. (Proceedings of the American Catholic Philosophical Association: Vol. 50). 1976. pap. 15.00 (ISBN 0-918090-10-5). Am Cath Philo.
--The Human Person. LC 80-66375. (Proceedings: Vol. 53). 1979. pap. 15.00 (ISBN 0-918090-13-X). Am Cath Philo.
--Immateriality. LC 79-88689. (Proceedings: Vol. 52). 1978. pap. 15.00 (ISBN 0-918090-12-1). Am Cath Philo.
--Myth & Philosophy. LC 72-184483. (Proceedings of the American Catholic Philosophical Association: Vol. 45). 1971. pap. 15.00 (ISBN 0-918090-05-9). Am Cath Philo.
--Scholasticism in the Modern World. (Proceedings of the American Catholic Philosophical Association: Vol. 40). 1966. pap. 15.00 (ISBN 0-918090-00-8). Am Cath Philo.
--Thomas & Bonaventure: A Septicentenary Commemoration. LC 75-319639. (Proceedings of the American Catholic Philosophical Association: Vol. 48). 1974. pap. 15.00 (ISBN 0-918090-08-3). Am Cath Philo.
--Truth & the Historicity of Man. (Proceedings of the American Catholic Philosophical Association: Vol. 43). 1969. pap. 15.00 (ISBN 0-918090-03-2). Am Cath Philo.
McLean, George F. & Dougherty, Jude P., eds. Philosophy & Christian Theology. (Proceedings of the American Catholic Philosophical Association: Vol. 44). 1970. pap. 15.00 (ISBN 0-918090-04-0). Am Cath Philo.
McLean, George F. & Ellrod, Frederick E., eds. Act & Agent: Philosophical Foundations for Moral Education & Character Development. LC 86-1619. 412p. (Orig.). 1986. lib. bdg. 34.75 (ISBN 0-8191-5281-1, Pub. by Council for Research in Values & Philosophy); pap. text ed. 17.50 (ISBN 0-8191-5282-X). U Pr of Amer.
McLean, George F., jt. ed. see Knowles, Richard T.
McLean, Gordon. Danger at Your Door. LC 83-70954. 183p. 1984. pap. 5.95 (ISBN 0-89107-296-9). Good News.
MacLean, John P. Bibliography of Shaker Literature, with an Introductory Study of the Writings & Publications Pertaining to Ohio Believers. 1970. Repr. of 1905 ed. 18.50 (ISBN 0-8337-2173-9). B Franklin.
McLean, Stuart. Humanity in the Thought of Karl Barth. 240p. 1981. 20.95 (ISBN 0-567-09304-2, Pub. by T&T Clark Ltd UK). Fortress.
Maclear, George F. Apostles of Mediaeval Europe. LC 72-624. (Essay Index Reprint Ser.). Repr. of 1869 ed. 21.50 (ISBN 0-8369-2803-2). Ayer Co Pubs.
McLeish, Barry, jt. auth. see Rust, Brian.
McLeish, James. Faithful Witness. LC 85-4300. 276p. (Orig.). 1985. pap. 6.95 (ISBN 0-87784-531-X). Inter-Varsity.
McLellan, Vern. Proverbs For People. LC 82-83841. (Illus.). 1983. pap. 3.25 (ISBN 0-89081-326-4). Harvest Hse.
McLelland, Joseph. Trabajo y Justicia. 128p. 1983. Repr. of 1978 ed. 2.50 (ISBN 0-311-46060-7). Casa Bautista.
McLelland, Joseph C. The Visible Words of God: An Exposition of the Sacramental Theology of Peter Martry Vermigli A.D. 1500-1562. LC 58-9551. 1957. text ed. 17.50x (ISBN 0-8401-1515-6). A R Allenson.
McLelland, Joseph C., ed. Peter Martyr Vermigli & Italian Reform. 155p. 1980. text ed. 17.95x (ISBN 0-88920-092-0, Pub. by Wilfrid Laurier Canada). Humanities.
McLemore, Clinton W. Good Guys Finish First: Success Strategies from the Book of Proverbs for Business Men & Women. LC 83-14708. 142p. 1983. pap. 7.95 (ISBN 0-664-26004-7, A Bridgebooks Publication). Westminster.
--Honest Christianity. LC 84-10450. 116p. (Orig.). 1984. pap. 7.95 (ISBN 0-664-26009-8, Pub. by Bridgebooks). Westminster.
Maclennan, David A. He Restoreth. (Contempo Ser.). pap. 0.95 (ISBN 0-8010-6093-1). Baker Bk.
Macleod, David I. Building Character in the American Boy: The Boy Scouts, YMCA, & Their Forerunners, 1870-1920. LC 83-47763. 464p. 1983. text ed. 27.50x (ISBN 0-299-09400-6). U of Wis Pr.
Macleod, Donald. Know the Way, Keep the Truth, Win the Life. (Orig.). 1987. pap. price not set (ISBN 0-89536-872-2, 7858). CSS of Ohio.
--Princeton Pulpit Prayers. 112p. (Orig.). 1987. prayerbook 9.95 (ISBN 0-941850-21-8). Sunday Pubns.
MacLeod, Gavin, et al. Back on Course. (Illus.). 1987. 12.95 (ISBN 0-8007-1533-0). Revell.
McLeod, H. Religion & the Working Class in Nineteenth Century Britain. (Studies in Economic & Social History). 72p. 1984. pap. text ed. 7.95x (ISBN 0-333-28115-2, Pub. by Macmillan UK). Humanities.
McLeod, H. W., ed. Sikhism. (Textual Sources for the Study of Religion). 224p. 1987. pap. 11.75 (ISBN 0-389-20718-7). B&N Imports.
McLeod, Hugh. Religion & the People of Western Europe, 1789-1970. (Oxford Paperbacks University Ser.). 1981. 17.95x (ISBN 0-19-215832-5); pap. 8.95x (ISBN 0-19-289101-4). Oxford U Pr.
MacLeod, Marian B. Dancing Through Pentecost: Dance Language for Worship from Pentecost to Thanksgiving. Adams, Doug, ed. (Orig.). 1981. pap. 3.00 (ISBN 0-941500-23-3). Sharing Co.
McLeod, Thomas E. The Work of the Church Treasurer. 80p. 1981. pap. 6.95 (ISBN 0-8170-0908-6). Judson.
McLeod, W. H. The Evolution of the Sikh Community: Five Essays. 1976. 22.00x (ISBN 0-19-826529-8). Oxford U Pr.
--Way of the Sikh. (The Way Ser.). pap. 5.95 (ISBN 0-7175-0731-9). Dufour.
McLeod, W. H., ed. Sikhism. LC 84-410. (Textual Sources for the Study of Religion Ser.). 208p. 1984. 23.50x (ISBN 0-389-20479-X, 08041). B&N Imports.
McLoughlin, Emmett. American Culture & Catholic Schools. 288p. 1973. pap. 2.75 (ISBN 0-8065-0356-4). Citadel Pr.
--Crime & Immorality in the Catholic Church. LC 62-7778. 1962. 4.95 (ISBN 0-910294-19-4). Brown Bk.
--Famous Ex-Priests. LC 68-18759. 1968. 4.95 (ISBN 0-8184-0030-7). Lyle Stuart.
--Letters to an Ex-Priest. 1965. 4.95 (ISBN 0-8184-0050-1). Lyle Stuart.
McLoughlin, William G. American Evangelicals, 1800-1900: An Anthology. 12.00 (ISBN 0-8446-0793-2). Peter Smith.
--Cherokees & Missionaries, 1789-1839. LC 83-11759. 375p. 1984. 35.00x (ISBN 0-300-03075-4). Yale U Pr.
--New England Dissent, 1630-1833: The Baptists & the Separation of Church & State, 2 vols. LC 70-131464. (Center for the Study of the History of Liberty in America Ser). (Illus.). 1971. Set. 80.00x (ISBN 0-674-61175-6). Harvard U Pr.
--Revivals, Awakening, & Reform: An Essay on Religion & Social Change in America, 1607 to 1977. LC 77-27830. xvi, 240p. 1980. pap. 9.00x (ISBN 0-226-56092-9, P891, Phoen). U of Chicago Pr.
McLoughlin, William G., jt. auth. see Clarke, John.
McLoughlin, William G., ed. see Backus, Isaac.
McMahon, Edwin M., jt. auth. see Campbell, Peter A.
McMahon, T. A., jt. auth. see Hunt, Dave.
McMahon, Thomas F., et al. Ethics on a Catholic University Campus. Barry, James D., ed. 1981. pap. 5.95 (ISBN 0-8294-0369-8). Loyola.
McMakin, Jacqueline & Nary, Rhoda. Doorways to Christian Growth. 300p. 1984. pap. 9.95 (ISBN 0-86683-818-X, HarpR). Har-Row.
McManners, John. The French Revolution & the Church. LC 82-15532. x, 161p. 1982. Repr. of 1969 ed. lib. bdg. 22.50x (ISBN 0-313-23074-9, MCFR). Greenwood.
McManus, Jane. Early Baptist Church West of the Mississippi: Calvary at Bayou Chicot; A History & Transcript of the Early Records. 1986. 30.00. Banner Pr AL.
McManus, Jim. The Healing Power of the Sacraments. LC 83-83397. 112p. (Orig.). 1984. pap. 3.95 (ISBN 0-87793-313-8). Ave Maria.
Macmanus, Sheila. The Adoption Book. (Orig.). 1984. pap. 4.95 (ISBN 0-8091-2578-1). Paulist Pr.
Macmaster, Eve. God Gives the Land. LC 83-182. (Story Bible Ser.: Vol. 3). (Illus.). 168p. (Orig.). 1983. pap. 5.95 (ISBN 0-8361-3332-3). Herald Pr.
--God Rescues His People: Stories of God & His People: Exodus, Leviticus, Numbers & Deuteronomy. LC 82-2849. (Story Bible Ser.: No. 2). (Illus.). 176p. (Orig.). 1982. pap. 5.95 (ISBN 0-8361-1994-0). Herald Pr.
--God's Chosen King. LC 83-12736. (Story Bible Ser.: Vol. 4). (Illus.). 190p. (Orig.). 1983. pap. 5.95 (ISBN 0-8361-3344-7). Herald Pr.
--God's Family. LC 81-6551. (Story Bible Ser.: No. 1). (Illus.). 168p. 1981. pap. 5.95 (ISBN 0-8361-1964-9). Herald Pr.
McMaster, Eve. God's Wisdom & Power. LC 84-8974. (Story Bible Ser.: No. 5). (Illus.). 168p. (Orig.). 1984. pap. 5.95 (ISBN 0-8361-3362-5). Herald Pr.
MacMaster, Eve B. God Builds His Church. (Story Bible Ser.: No. 10). (Illus.). 184p. (Orig.). 1987. pap. 5.95 (ISBN 0-8361-3446-X). Herald Pr.
--God Sends His Son. LC 86-18342. (Story Bible Ser.: Bk. 8). (Illus.). 160p. (Orig.). 1986. pap. 5.95 (ISBN 0-8361-3420-6). Herald Pr.
--God's Suffering Servant. LC 86-19526. (Story Bible Ser.: Bk. 9). (Illus.). 120p. (Orig.). 1987. pap. 5.95 (ISBN 0-8361-3422-2). Herald Pr.
MacMaster, Richard K. Land, Piety & Peoplehood. LC 84-15790. (Mennonite Experience in America Ser.: Vol. 1). 344p. (Orig.). 1984. pap. 12.00x (ISBN 0-8361-1261-X). Herald Pr.
MacMaster, Richard K., et al. Conscience in Crisis. LC 78-27530. (Studies in Anabapitst & Mennonite History: No. 20). 528p. 1979. 19.95x (ISBN 0-8361-1213-X). Herald Pr.
McMenamin, Robert W. Clergy Malpractice. LC 86-81075. 209p. 1986. lib. bdg. 27.50 (ISBN 0-89941-483-4). W S Hein.
McMichael, Betty. The Church Librarian's Handbook. 288p. 1984. pap. 9.95 (ISBN 0-8010-6166-0). Baker Bk.
McMillan, E. W. The Minister's Spiritual Life. 1959. 4.50 (ISBN 0-88027-009-8). Firm Foun Pub.
MacMillan, J. A. Authority of the Believer. 96p. 1981. pap. 2.25 (ISBN 0-87509-152-0). Chr Pubns.
MacMillan, John A. Encounter with Darkness. LC 80-67656. 116p. 2.25 (ISBN 0-87509-287-X). Chr Pubns.
McMillan, Mary. Baby Jesus. (Color, Cut & Paste Ser.). 48p. 1986. wkbk. 4.95 (ISBN 0-86653-369-9). Good Apple.
--God's ABC Zoo. 48p. 1987. pap. 5.95 (ISBN 0-86653-405-9, SS1802). Good Apple.
--King David. (Color, Cut & Paste Ser.). (Illus.). 48p. 1987. pap. 5.95 (ISBN 0-86653-392-3). Good Apple.
Macmillan, Mona, ed. see Milingo, Emmanuel.
McMillan, Richard C. Religion in the Public Schools: An Introduction. LC 84-9147. x, 301p. 1984. 21.95 (ISBN 0-86554-093-4, H85). Mercer Univ Pr.
McMillan, Richard C., ed. Education, Religion, & the Supreme Court. LC 78-74196. (Special Studies: No. 6). iv, 129p. 1979. pap. 8.95 (ISBN 0-932180-05-1). NABPR.
McMillan, Richard C., et al. Euthanasia & the Newborn: Conflicts Regarding Saving Lives. LC 86-33835. (Philosophy & Medicine Ser.: Vol. 24). 1987. 39.50 (ISBN 9-02-772299-4). Kluwer Academic.
McMillan, Robert M. Faith Without Fantasy. LC 80-66541. 1981. 4.50 (ISBN 0-8054-5285-0). Broadman.
M'Millan, Samuel, ed. see Boston, Thomas.
McMillan, William. The Worship of the Scottish Reformed Church, 1550-1638: The Hastie Lectures in the University of Glasgow, 1930. LC 83-45585. Date not set. Repr. of 1931 ed. 35.00 (ISBN 0-404-19903-8). AMS Pr.
McMillen, S. I. None of These Diseases. 160p. 1963. pap. 2.95 (ISBN 0-8007-8030-2, Spire Bks). Revell.
--None of These Diseases. rev. ed. Stern, David E., ed. 192p. 1984. pap. write for info. (ISBN 0-8007-5233-3). Revell.
McMillin, John & Glenn, Jim. Twelve Minutes over Fatima. 1986. 10.95 (ISBN 0-533-06492-9). Vantage.
McMinn, Don. Entering His Presence. LC 86-70743. 1986. pap. 5.95 (ISBN 0-88270-608-X). Bridge Pub.
McMinn, Gordon & Libby, Larry. Choosing to Be Close: Fill Your Life with the Rewards of Relationships. LC 84-3297. 1984. pap. 5.95 (ISBN 0-88070-053-X). Multnomah.
--Taking Charge: The Dynamics of Personal Decision-Making & Self-Management. LC 80-65061. 192p. (Orig.). 1980. pap. 4.95 (ISBN 0-89636-043-1). Accent Bks.
McMinn, Tom. The Caudills: Courageous Missionaries. LC 81-70474. (Meet the Missionary Ser.). 1982. 5.50 (ISBN 0-8054-4277-4, 4242-77). Broadman.
--Prophets: Preachers for God. (BibLearn Ser.). (Illus.). 1979. 5.95 (ISBN 0-8054-4250-2, 4242-50). Broadman.
McMlelland, David C. Psychoanalysis & Religious Mysticism. 1983. pap. 2.50x (ISBN 0-87574-104-5, 104). Pendle Hill.
McMullen, Eleanor & Sonnenfeld, Jean. Go-Groups: Gearing up for Reaching Out. (Orig.). 1977. pap. 2.50 (ISBN 0-377-00060-4). Friend Pr.

MacMullen, Ramsay. Christianizing the Roman Empire: A.D. 100-400. LC 84-3694. 200p. 1984. 22.50x (ISBN 0-300-03216-1); pap. 7.95 (ISBN 0-300-03642-6, Y-571). Yale U Pr.
--Paganism in the Roman Empire. LC 80-54222. 384p. 1981. 30.00x (ISBN 0-300-02655-2); pap. text ed. 8.95x (ISBN 0-300-02984-5). Yale U Pr.
McMullin, Ernan, ed. Evolution & Creation. LC 84-40818. (University of Notre Dame Studies in the Philosophy of Religion: Vol. 4). 307p. 1987. pap. 12.95 (ISBN 0-268-00918-X). U of Notre Dame Pr.
McMullin, Neil. Buddhism & the State in Sixteenth Century Japan. LC 84-42572. (Illus.). 408p. 1984. 45.00x (ISBN 0-691-07291-4). Princeton U Pr.
MacMunn, George. The Religions & Hidden Cults of India. (Illus.). xii, 244p. 1983. text ed. 30.00x (ISBN 0-86590-107-4). Apt Bks.
MacMurray, John. Self As Agent. 1978. pap. text ed. 5.95x (ISBN 0-391-02043-9). Humanities.
--The Structure of Religious Experience. LC 73-122406. xi, 77p. 1971. Repr. of 1936 ed. 15.00 (ISBN 0-208-00958-2, Archon). Shoe String.
Macmurray, John, ed. Some Makers of the Modern Spirit: A Symposium. facs. ed. LC 68-22926. (Essay Index Reprint Ser). Repr. of 1933 ed. 16.25 (ISBN 0-8369-0658-6). Ayer Co Pubs.
McMurrin, Sterling M. The Philosophical Foundations of Mormon Theology. 1959. pap. 4.95 (ISBN 0-87480-169-9). U of Utah Pr.
--Religion, Reason, & Truth: Historical Essays in the Philosophy of Religion. 1982. 24.95 (ISBN 0-87480-203-2). U of Utah Pr.
--The Theological Foundations of the Mormon Religion. LC 65-26131. 1965. pap. 9.95 (ISBN 0-87480-051-X). U of Utah Pr.
McMurrin, Sterling M., ed. The Tanner Lectures on Human Values, Vol. IV: 1983. 300p. 1983. 20.00x (ISBN 0-87480-216-4). U of Utah Pr.
--The Tanner Lectures on Human Values, Vol. VII: Nineteen Eighty-Six. 288p. 1986. 20.00x (ISBN 0-87480-259-8). U of Utah Pr.
McMurtrey, Martin, ed. see Von Le Fort, Gertrud.
McNab, J. Strathearn, tr. see Frey, Arthur.
MacNair, Donald J. The Challenge of the Eldership: A Handbook for the Elders of the Church. (Orig.). 1984. pap. text ed. 1.95 (ISBN 0-934688-12-5). Great Comm Pubns.
--The Living Church: A Guide for Revitalization. (Illus.). 167p. (Orig.). 1980. pap. 4.95 (ISBN 0-934688-00-1). Great Comm Pubns.
McNally, Dennis. Sacred Space: An Aesthetic for the Liturgical Environment. 215p. (Orig.). 1985. pap. 8.95x (ISBN 0-932269-45-1). Wyndham Hall.
McNally, Michael J. Catholicism in South Florida, 1868-1968. LC 84-7389. 334p. (Orig.). 1984. pap. 13.95 (ISBN 0-8130-0788-7). U Presses Fla.
McNally, Robert. The Bible in the Early Middle Ages. (Reprints & Translations Ser.). 1986. pap. 9.95 (ISBN 0-89130-912-8, 00-07-14). Scholars Pr GA.
McNally, Thomas & Storey, William. Day by Day: The Notre Dame Prayerbook for Students. (Illus.). 208p. 1975. pap. 2.95 (ISBN 0-87793-100-3). Ave Maria.
McNally, Thomas & Storey, William G., eds. Lord Hear Our Prayer. LC 78-67423. (Illus.). 1978. 5.95 (ISBN 0-87793-163-1). Ave Maria.
McNamara, James. The Power of Compassion. 1984. pap. 4.95 (ISBN 0-8091-2567-6). Paulist Pr.
McNamara, Jo Ann. A New Song: Celibate Women in the First Three Christian Centuries. LC 83-10852. (Women & History Ser.: Nos. 6 & 7). 154p. 1983. text ed. 29.95 (ISBN 0-86656-249-4, B249). Haworth Pr.
--A New Song: Celibate Women in the First Three Christian Centuries. LC 85-8505. 154p. 1985. pap. 8.95 (ISBN 0-918393-17-5). Harrington Pk.
McNamara, Kevin. Sacrament of Salvation. 1981. 9.50 (ISBN 0-8199-0806-1). Franciscan Herald.
McNamara, Martin. Intertestamental Literature. (Old Testament Message Ser.: Vol. 23). 16.95 (ISBN 0-89453-423-8); pap. 12.95 (ISBN 0-89453-256-1). M Glazier.
--Palestinian Judaism & the New Testament. (Good News Studies: Vol. 4). 1983. pap. 12.95 (ISBN 0-89453-274-X). M Glazier.
--Targum & Testament: Aramaic Paraphrases of the Hebrew Bible: a Light on the New Testament. 226p. 1972. 17.50x (ISBN 0-7165-0619-X, BBA 02203, Pub. by Irish Academic Pr Ireland). Biblio Dist.
MacNamara, Vincent. Faith & Ethics. 216p. (Orig.). 1985. 17.95 (ISBN 0-87840-426-0); pap. 10.95 (ISBN 0-87840-414-7). Georgetown U Pr.
McNamara, William. Art of Being Human. pap. 3.50 (ISBN 0-385-08323-8, E45, Im). Doubleday.
--The Catholic Church on the Northern Indiana Frontier, 1789-1844. LC 73-3567. (Catholic University of America. Studies in American Church History: No. 12). Repr. of 1931 ed. 19.00 (ISBN 0-404-57762-8). AMS Pr.
--Christian Mysticism: Psychotheology. LC 80-13139. 173p. 1981. 9.50 (ISBN 0-8199-0793-6). Franciscan Herald.
--Earthy Mysticism: Contemplation & the Life of Passionate Presence. LC 82-33554. 128p. 1983. pap. 6.95 (ISBN 0-8245-0562-X). Crossroad NY.
McNamee, Fantan, ed. see Steeman, T.
McNamee, Fintan, ed. Helping Disturbed Religious. O'Doherty, E. F. (Symthesis Ser.). pap. 0.75 (ISBN 0-8199-0393-0, L38268). Franciscan Herald.
--Psychology of the Catholic Intellectual. (Synthesis Ser.). 1967. pap. 0.75 (ISBN 0-8199-0241-1, L38669). Franciscan Herald.
McNaspy, C. J. Lost Cities of Paraguay: The Art & Architecture of the Jesuit Reductions. 1982. 24.95 (ISBN 0-8294-0396-5). Loyola.
McNaught, Brian R. A Disturbed Peace: Selected Writings of an Irish Catholic Homosexual. LC 81-67627. 125p. (Orig.). 1981. pap. 5.95 (ISBN 0-940680-00-9). Dignity Inc.
McNaught, Rosemond L., compiled by. Christmas Selections: For Readings & Recitations. facsimile ed. LC 74-38601. (Granger Index Reprint Ser.). Repr. of 1906 ed. 12.00 (ISBN 0-8369-6333-4). Ayer Co Pubs.
MacNaughton, Robin. Robin MacNaughton's Sun Sign Personality Guide. 1978. pap. 4.50 (ISBN 0-553-25747-1). Bantam.
McNaughton, William, ed. Taoist Vision. LC 70-143183. (Illus.). 1971. 7.95 (ISBN 0-472-09174-3). U of Mich Pr.
Macnauhten, William H. Principles of Muhammadan Law. 140p. (Orig.). 1981. pap. 6.50 (ISBN 0-88004-010-6). Sunwise Turn.
McNeal, Henry von see Van McNeal, Henry.
McNeal, Patricia F. The American Catholic Peace Movement, 1928-1972. 32.00 (ISBN 0-405-10840-0, 11820). Ayer Co Pubs.
McNeely, Kenneth. What Do We Really Know about God? LC 86-91364. 1987. 12.00 (ISBN 0-87212-201-8). Libra.
McNeely, Richard I. First & Second Kings. (Everyman's Bible Commentary Ser.). 1978. pap. 5.95 (ISBN 0-8024-2011-7). Moody.
McNeer, May & Ward, Lynd. John Wesley. 1957. pap. 3.95 (ISBN 0-687-20430-5). Abingdon.
McNeil. How Things Began. (Books of the World). 1975. 8.95 (ISBN 0-86020-027-2, Usborne-Hayes); PLB 12.96 (ISBN 0-88110-114-1); pap. 5.95 (ISBN 0-86020-199-6). EDC.
McNeil, B., jt. ed. see Horbury, W.
McNeil, Brian, tr. see Fuchs, Josef.
McNeil, Jesse Jai. Minister's Service Book. 212p. 1982. 7.95 (ISBN 0-8028-3580-5). Eerdmans.
MacNeil, John. The Spirit-Filled Life. (Moody Classics Ser.). 1984. pap. 3.50 (ISBN 0-8024-0493-6). Moody.
McNeil, John T. On God & Political Duty: Calvin. 1956. pap. text ed. write for info. (ISBN 0-02-379760-6). Macmillan.
McNeil, Margaret C. Come Sing with Me. 1971. pap. 2.95 (ISBN 0-8170-0535-8); bk. & record o.p. 5.95 (ISBN 0-685-01111-9). Judson.
McNeil, William H., ed. see Gunnin, Gerry C.
McNeilage, Alastair, ed. see Rawlinson, Ian.
McNeile, A. H. Gospel According to St. Matthew. (Thornapple Commentaries Ser.). 484p. 1980. pap. 8.95 (ISBN 0-8010-6099-0). Baker Bk.
McNeill, Don, et al. Compassion: A Reflection on the Christian Life. LC 83-45045. (Illus.). 160p. 1983. pap. 6.95 (ISBN 0-385-18957-5, Im). Doubleday.
McNeill, J. T. The History & Character of Calvinism. 1954. pap. 12.95 (ISBN 0-19-500743-3). Oxford U Pr.
McNeill, John T. Books of Faith & Power. facs. ed. LC 75-134112. (Essay Index Reprint Ser). 1947. 18.00 (ISBN 0-8369-1996-3). Ayer Co Pubs.
McNeill, John T. & Gamer, Helena M. Medieval Handbooks of Penance. 1965. lib. bdg. 40.00x (ISBN 0-374-95548-4, Octagon). Hippocrene Bks.
McNeill, John T., ed. Calvin: Institutes of the Christian Religion, 2 vols. LC 60-5379. (Library of Christian Classics). 1812p. 1960. Set. 34.95 (ISBN 0-664-22028-2). Westminster.
McNeill, Willaim H., ed. see Donovan, Robert K.
McNeill, William H. & Houser, Schuyler O., eds. Medieval Europe. (Oxford Readings in World History Ser: Vol. 8). 1971. pap. 7.95x (ISBN 0-19-501312-3). Oxford U Pr.
McNeill, William H. & Waldman, Marilyn Robinson, eds. The Islamic World. LC 83-18246. xviii, 468p. 1984. pap. 15.00x (ISBN 0-226-56155-0). U of Chicago Pr.
McNeill, William H., ed. see Cohen, Paul M.
McNeill, William H., ed. see Franklin, R. W.
McNeill, William H., ed. see Hein, Virginia H.
McNeill, William H., ed. see Holland, Mary G.
McNeill, William H., ed. see Klaus, Robert J.
McNeill, William H., ed. see Nurser, John.
McNichols, Donald. Portrait of a Quaker. LC 80-66654. (Illus.). 180p. 1980. 12.50 (ISBN 0-913342-24-6). Barclay Pr.
McNiff, William J. Heaven on Earth: A Planned Mormon Society. LC 72-8632. Repr. of 1940 ed. 14.00 (ISBN 0-404-11007-X). AMS Pr.
--Heaven on Earth: A Planned Mormon Society. LC 72-187474. (The American Utopian Adventure Ser.). 262p. 1973. Repr. of 1940 ed. lib. bdg. 27.50x (ISBN 0-87991-001-1). Porcupine Pr.
McNulty, Arthur F. Co-Creators with God. 88p. (Orig.). 1985. pap. 4.95 (ISBN 0-934134-29-4, Leaven Pr). Sheed & Ward MO.
McNulty, Frank J. Preaching Better. 1985. pap. 8.95 (ISBN 0-8091-2682-6). Paulist Pr.
McNulty, James F. Words of Power. LC 83-2514. 226p. (Orig.). 1983. pap. 8.95 (ISBN 0-8189-0442-9). Alba.
McNulty, Kenneth K., Sr. Street or Pulpit? The Witness of Activist Monsignor Charles Owen Rice of Pittsburgh. (The Answers Ser.). 288p. (Orig.). 1985. pap. 9.95 (ISBN 0-935025-00-6). Data & Res Tech.
McNulty, P. A., tr. see Cabasilas, Nicholas.
MacNutt, F. A. Bartolome de las Casas. 59.95 (ISBN 0-87968-708-8). Gordon Pr.
MacNutt, Francis. Healing. LC 74-81446. (Illus.). 336p. 1974. pap. 4.95 (ISBN 0-87793-074-0). Ave Maria.
--Healing. 320p. 1986. pap. 4.50 (ISBN 0-553-25993-8). Bantam.
--The Power to Heal. LC 77-77845. 256p. 1977. pap. 3.95 (ISBN 0-87793-133-X). Ave Maria.
--The Prayer That Heals. LC 80-69770. 120p. (Orig.). 1981. pap. 2.95 (ISBN 0-87793-219-0). Ave Maria.
--Praying for Your Unborn Child. (Illus.). 144p. 1987. 12.95 (ISBN 0-385-23281-0). Doubleday.
MacNutt, Francis A. Bartholomew De Las Casas: His Life, His Apostolate, & His Writings. LC 70-172712. Repr. of 1909 ed. 32.45 (ISBN 0-404-07146-5). AMS Pr.
Macoy, Robert. Christmas, Easter, Ascension & Burial Services for Knights Templar. rev. ed. 112p. 1978. pap. 4.00 (ISBN 0-88053-011-1). Macoy Pub.
--Worshipful Master's Assistant. rev/ ed. 302p. 1980. Repr. s.p. hardcover 11.95 (ISBN 0-88053-008-1). Macoy Pub.
Macphail, Andrew. Essays in Puritanism: Jonathan Edwards, John Winthrop, Margaret Fuller, Walt Whitman, John Wesley. LC 68-26205. 1969. Repr. of 1905 ed. 22.50x (ISBN 0-8046-0286-7, Pub. by Kennikat). Assoc Faculty Pr.
McPhee, Arthur G. Friendship Evangelism: The Caring Way to Share Your Faith. 1979. pap. 4.95 (ISBN 0-310-37311-5, 11262P). Zondervan.
--Have a Great Day Every Day. LC 84-565. 160p. 1984. pap. 6.50 (ISBN 0-8361-3352-8). Herald Pr.
McPhee, John, ed. Manual para la Familia Catolica Hispana de Hoy. Diaz, Olimpia, tr. (Span.). 1980. pap. 1.50 (ISBN 0-89243-123-7, 51900). Liguori Pubns.
--Tu Fe. Diaz, Olimpia, tr. (Span.). (YA) 1980. pap. 1.95 (ISBN 0-89243-124-5, 48290). Liguori Pubns.
McPhee, John, ed. see Norquist, Marilyn.
McPherson, Aimee S. This Is That: Personal Experiences, Sermons & Writings. Dayton, Daonald W., ed. (The Higher Christian Life Ser.). 685p. 1985. 85.00 (ISBN 0-8240-6428-3). Garland Pub.
Macpherson, Ann, et al. Prophets One. Bright, Laurence, ed. LC 71-173033. (Scripture Discussion Commentary Ser.: Pt. 2). 214p. 1971. pap. text ed. 4.50 (ISBN 0-87946-001-6). ACTA Found.
Macpherson, Duncan, et al. Paul One. Bright, Laurence, ed. LC 71-173033. (Scripture Discussion Ser.: Pt. 10). 224p. 1972. pap. text ed. 4.50 (ISBN 0-87946-009-1). ACTA Found.
--Luke. LC 71-173033. (Scripture Discussion Commentary Ser.: Pt. 8). 192p. 1971. pap. text ed. 4.50 (ISBN 0-87946-007-5). ACTA Found.
Macpherson, Ian. God's Plan for This Planet. LC 76-51001. 96p. 1977. pap. 1.25 (ISBN 0-88243-517-5, 02-0517, Radiant Bks). Gospel Pub.
--Sermon Outlines from Pulpit Masters. (Pulpit Library). 224p. 1984. pap. 4.95 (ISBN 0-8010-6180-6). Baker Bk.
McPherson, James M., jt. auth. see Kousser, J. Morgan.
McPherson, John. The Westminster Confession of Faith. (Handbooks for Bible Classes & Private Students). 182p. 1882. pap. 6.95 (ISBN 0-567-28143-4, Pub. by T & T Clark Ltd Uk). Fortress.
McPherson, Joseph M. Primitive Beliefs in the North-East of Scotland. Dorson, Richard M., ed. LC 77-70605. (International Folklore Ser.). 1977. Repr. of 1929 ed. lib. bdg. 24.50x (ISBN 0-405-10109-0). Ayer Co Pubs.
McPherson, Joseph W. The Moulids of Egypt: Egyptian Saints-Days. LC 77-87654. Repr. of 1941 ed. 28.50 (ISBN 0-404-16408-0). AMS Pr.
MacPherson, Malcolm C. The Blood of His Servants: The True Story of One Man's Search for His Family's Friend & Executioner. LC 83-40089. (Illus.). 310p. 1984. 16.95 (ISBN 0-8129-1098-2). Times Bks.
MacPhillamy, Daizui, jt. auth. see Jiyu-Kennett, Roshi.
McPolin, James. John. (New Testament Message Ser.: Vol. 6). 244p. 1979. 14.95 (ISBN 0-89453-194-8); pap. 9.95 (ISBN 0-89453-129-8). M Glazier.
McQuaid, Elwood. The Outpouring: Jesus in the Feasts of Israel. (Orig.). 1986. pap. 5.95 (ISBN 0-8024-6101-8). Moody.
Macquarrie, John. An Existentialist Theology: A Comparison of Heidegger & Bultmann. LC 79-4604. 1979. Repr. of 1955 ed. lib. bdg. 22.50x (ISBN 0-313-20795-X, MAAE). Greenwood.
--Faith of People of God. 191p. 1972. pap. text ed. write for info. (ISBN 0-02-374520-7, Pub. by Scribner). Macmillan.
--The Faith of the People of God: A Lay Theology. LC 72-1224. 188p. 1973. pap. 7.95 (ISBN 0-684-13060-2, ScribT). Scribner.
--God-Talk: An Examination of the Language & Logic of Theology. 1979. pap. 7.95 (ISBN 0-8164-2205-2, HarpR). Har-Row.
--The Humility of God. LC 77-18707. 96p. 1978. pap. 4.65 (ISBN 0-664-24200-6). Westminster.
--In Search of Humanity. rev. ed. 286p. 1985. pap. 11.95 (ISBN 0-8245-0708-8). Crossroad NY.
--In Search of Humanity: A Theological & Philosophical Approach. LC 82-22077. 288p. 1983. 16.95 (ISBN 0-8245-0564-6). Crossroad NY.
--Martin Heidegger. LC 68-11970. (Makers of Contemporary Theology Ser). 1968. pap. 3.95 (ISBN 0-8042-0659-7). John Knox.
--Mystery & Truth. (Pere Marquette Theology Lectures). 1970. 6.95 (ISBN 0-87462-518-1). Marquette.
--Principles of Christian Theology. 2nd ed. LC 76-23182. 544p. 1977. pap. text ed. write for info. (ISBN 0-02-374510-X, Pub. by Scribner). Macmillan.
--Theology, Church & Ministry. 224p. 1986. 16.95 (ISBN 0-8245-0787-8). Crossroad NY.
--Twentieth Century Religious Thought. LC 81-9349. 1981. pap. text ed. 18.95x (ISBN 0-684-17334-4). Scribner.
--Twentieth Century Religious Thought. 1983. 19.95 (ISBN 0-684-17333-6). Scribner.
Macquarrie, John, ed. Dictionary of Christian Ethics. LC 67-17412. 378p. 1967. 18.95 (ISBN 0-664-20646-8). Westminster.
Macquarrie, John, jt. ed. see Childress, James F.
McQuay, Earl. John-Apostle of Love. LC 81-70774. (Chosen Messenger Ser.). 128p. (Orig.). 1982. pap. text ed. 3.50 (ISBN 0-89636-080-6). Accent Bks.
McQuilkin, Robertson. The Great Omission. 96p. 1984. pap. 4.95 (ISBN 0-8010-6167-9). Baker Bk.
--Understanding & Applying the Bible. (Orig.). 1983. pap. 8.95 (ISBN 0-8024-0457-X). Moody.
MacRae, George W. Faith in the Word: The Fourth Gospel. (Biblical Booklets Ser.). 1975. pap. 1.25 (ISBN 0-8199-0515-1). Franciscan Herald.
--Hebrews. Karris, Robert J., ed. (Collegeville Bible Commentary Ser.: No. 10). 64p. 1983. pap. 2.95 (ISBN 0-8146-1310-1). Liturgical Pr.
--Invitation to John: A Commentary on the Gospel of John with Complete Text from the Jerusalem Bible. LC 77-91559. 1978. pap. 3.95 (ISBN 0-385-12212-8, Im). Doubleday.
MacRae, George W. & Price, Charles P. Easter. LC 79-7377. 64p. 1982. pap. 3.75 (ISBN 0-8006-4087-X, 1-4087). Fortress.
MacRae, George W., ed. see Conzelmann, Hans.
McRae, John R. The Northern School of & the Formation of Early Ch'an Buddhism. LC 86-4062. (Studies in East Asian Buddhism: No. 3). 456p. 1987. 40.00x (ISBN 0-8248-1056-2). UH Pr.
McRae, Shirley W. Glow Ree Bee (11 Traditional Black Spiritual Arrangements) Bennett, Michael D., ed. 28p. (Orig.). 1982. pap. text ed. 5.95 (ISBN 0-934017-02-6). Memphis Musicraft.
McRae, William. The Dynamics of Spiritual Gifts. 144p. 1983. pap. 4.95 (ISBN 0-310-29091-0). Zondervan.
McRae, William J. The Dynamics of Spiritual Gifts. 160p. 1976. pap. 2.95 (ISBN 0-310-29092-9). Zondervan.

--Preparing for Your Marriage. 160p. (Orig.). 1980. pap. 5.95 (ISBN 0-310-42761-4, 9366P). Zondervan.

MacRal, George W., jt. ed. see Nickelsburg, George W.

Macray, W. D., ed. Charters & Documents Illustrating the History of the Cathedral: City & Diocese of Salisbury in the 12th & 13th Centuries. (Rolls Ser.: No. 97). Repr. of 1891 ed. 44.00 (ISBN 0-8115-1176-6). Kraus Repr.

McReynolds, Janet. Something Supernatural. 103p. 1986. pap. 3.95 (ISBN 0-88144-038-8). Christian Pub.

Macris, George P. The Orthodox Church & the Ecumenical Movement During the Period 1920-1969. (Illus.). 196p. (Orig.). 1986. pap. 12.50 (ISBN 0-913026-74-3). St Nectarios.

McRoberts, Darlene. Family Fare: Christian Activities for Every Season of the Year. LC 81-65642. (Illus.). 80p. (Orig.). 1981. pap. 5.95 (ISBN 0-8066-1878-7, 10-2247). Augsburg.

--Second Marriage: The Promise & the Challenge. LC 77-84087. 1978. pap. 6.95 (ISBN 0-8066-1612-1, 10-5635). Augsburg.

McShane, Joseph M. Sufficiently Radical: Catholicism, Progressivism, & the Bishops Program of 1919. 1986. 38.95 (ISBN 0-8132-0631-6). Cath U Pr.

McShane, Philip. Music That is Soundless: An Introduction to God for the Graduate. 1977. pap. text ed. 9.25 (ISBN 0-8191-0236-9). U Pr of Amer.

--The Shaping of the Foundations: Being at Home in the Transcendental Method. 12.25 (ISBN 0-8191-0209-1). U Pr of Amer.

McSorley, Joseph. Isaac Hecker & His Friends. 314p. 1972. pap. 1.45 (ISBN 0-8091-1605-7). Paulist Pr.

McSorley, Richard. New Testament Basis of Peacemaking. LC 84-25121. 160p. 1985. pap. 7.95 (ISBN 0-8361-3383-8). Herald Pr.

MacStravic, Robin S. Marketing Religious Health Care. 140p. (Orig.). 1987. pap. 24.00 (ISBN 0-87125-121-3). Cath Health.

McSwain, Larry L. & Treadwell, William C., Jr. Conflict Ministry in the Church. LC 80-67781. 1981. pap. 7.95 (ISBN 0-8054-2540-3). Broadman.

McSweeney, William. Roman Catholicism: The Search for Relevance. 1980. 25.00 (ISBN 0-312-68969-1). St Martin.

McTaggart, John. Human Immortality & Pre-Existence. Repr. of 1916 ed. 23.00 (ISBN 0-527-59950-6). Kraus Repr.

--Some Dogmas of Religion. LC 7-7484. 1968. Repr. of 1906 ed. 23.00 (ISBN 0-527-60000-8). Kraus Repr.

McTaggart, John M. Studies in Hegelian Cosmology. 2nd ed. 1986. lib. bdg. 25.00x (ISBN 0-935005-59-5); pap. text ed. 13.00x (ISBN 0-935005-60-9). Ibis Pub VA.

McTavish, John B., ed. see Barth, Karl.

Macuch, Rudolf. Grammatik des Samaritanischen Hebraeisch. (Studia Samaritana 1). (Ger). 1969. 110.00x (ISBN 3-11-000133-0). De Gruyter.

--Handbook of Classical & Modern Mandaic. 1965. 129.00x (ISBN 3-11-000261-2). De Gruyter.

--Zur Sprache und Literatur der Mandaer: Mit Beitraegen von Kurt Rudolph & Eric Segelberg. 1976. 76.00x (ISBN 3-11-004838-8). De Gruyter.

Maculiffe, Max A. Sikh Religion, 6 vols. 1270p. 200.00X set (ISBN 0-317-52153-5, Pub. by S Chand India). State Mutual Bk.

MacVeagh, Lincoln, ed. Poetry from the Bible. 180p. 1981. Repr. of 1925 ed. lib. bdg. 30.00 (ISBN 0-8495-3531-X). Arden Lib.

McVeigh, Malcolm. God in Africa. 1982. 20.00 (ISBN 0-686-96557-4). Branden Pub Co.

McVeigh, Shaun, jt. auth. see Spence, Keith.

McWhirter, David. Millenial Harbinger - Index. LC 81-65031. (Millenial Harbinger Ser.). 776p. 1981. 19.95 (ISBN 0-89900-228-5). College Pr Pub.

McWhirter, David, jt. auth. see Gulledge, Dennis.

McWhorter, Jane. Caterpillars or Butterflies. (Illus.). 1977. pap. 4.95 (ISBN 0-89137-410-8). Quality Pubns.

--Let This Cup Pass. (Illus.). 1979. pap. 4.95 (ISBN 0-89137-414-0). Quality Pubns.

--Meet My Friend David. 4.95 (ISBN 0-89137-420-5). Quality Pubns.

McWilliam, H. O. Muhammad & the World of Islam. Reeves, Marjorie, ed. (Then & There Ser.). (Illus.). 96p. (Orig.). 1977. pap. text ed. 4.75 (ISBN 0-582-20537-9). Longman.

McWilliams, Anne W. Cuando Triunfa la Fe. Martinez, Jose L., tr. from Eng. Orig. Title: Champion of Faith: David Gomez. 152p. 1983. pap. 5.95 (ISBN 0-311-01071-7). Casa Bautista.

McWilliams, Carey. A Mask for Privilege: Anti-Semitism in America. LC 78-26197. 1979. Repr. of 1948 ed. lib. bdg. 24.75x (ISBN 0-313-20880-8, MCMP). Greenwood.

McWilliams, Donald A. Myth of Evolution. LC 73-88018. 1973. 3.95x (ISBN 0-916434-08-7). Plycon Pr.

McWilliams, Warren. Free in Christ. LC 84-2812. 1984. pap. 3.75 (ISBN 0-8054-1609-9). Broadman.

--The Passion of God: Divine Suffering in Contemporary Protestant Theology. 208p. 1985. text ed. 16.50 (ISBN 0-86554-158-2, MUP H148). Mercer Univ Pr.

--When You Walk Through the Fire. (Orig.). 1986. pap. 7.95 (ISBN 0-8054-1621-8). Broadman.

Macy, Gary. The Theologies of the Eucharist in the Early Scholastic Period. (Illus.). 1984. 32.00x (ISBN 0-19-826669-3). Oxford U Pr.

Macy, Joanna. Dharma & Development. rev. ed. LC 85-256. (KP Monograph: No. 2). 119p. 1985. pap. 8.75 (ISBN 0-931816-53-X). Kumarian Pr.

Madaule, Jacques, jt. ed. see Cattaui, Georges.

Madauss, Martyria. Jesus: A Portrait of Love. 1972. 6.50 (ISBN 3-87209-603-6). Evang Sisterhood Mary.

--The Shield of Faith. 1974. gift edition 0.95 (ISBN 3-87209-659-1). Evang Sisterhood Mary.

Madden, D. H. Chapter of Mediaeval History. LC 74-91048. 1969. Repr. of 1924 ed. 26.50x (ISBN 0-8046-0658-7, Pub. by Kennikat). Assoc Faculty Pr.

Madden, Edward H. & Hamilton, James E. Freedom & Grace: The Life of Asa Mahan. LC 82-5724. (Studies in Evangelicalism: No. 3). 287p. 1982. 19.00 (ISBN 0-8108-1555-9). Scarecrow.

Madden, Frederic W. History of Jewish Coinage & of Money in the Old & New Testaments. LC 66-26486. (Library of Biblical Studies). (Illus.). 1968. 39.50x (ISBN 0-87068-082-X). Ktav.

Madden, Mary B., jt. auth. see Madden, Myron C.

Madden, Sr. Mary. The Pagan Divinities & Their Worship As Depicted in the Work of St. Augustine. 59.95 (ISBN 0-8490-0796-8). Gordon Pr.

Madden, Myron C. Claim Your Heritage. LC 84-7315. (Potentials: Guides for Productive Living Ser.: Vol. 8). 116p. 1984. pap. 7.95 (ISBN 0-664-24531-5). Westminster.

Madden, Myron C. & Madden, Mary B. For Grandparents: Wonders & Worries. LC 80-12778. (Christian Care Bks.: Vol, 9). 118p. 1980. pap. 7.95 (ISBN 0-664-24325-8). Westminster.

Maddoux, Marlin. America Betrayed. Orig. Title: Humanism Exposed. 157p. 1984. pap. 5.95 (ISBN 0-910311-18-8). Huntington Hse Inc.

Maddox, J. L. The Medicine Man: A Sociological Study of the Character & Evolution of Shamanism. 1977. lib. bdg. 59.95 (ISBN 0-8490-2219-3). Gordon Pr.

Maddox, John L. The Medicine Man: A Sociological Study of the Character & Evolution of Shamanism. LC 75-23737. Repr. of 1923 ed. 45.00 (ISBN 0-404-13294-4). AMS Pr.

Maddox, Linda C., jt. auth. see Maddox, Robert L.

Maddox, Randy L. Toward an Ecumenical Fundamental Theology. LC 84-13838. (American Academy of Religion Studies in Religion). 1984. 13.50 (ISBN 0-89130-771-0, 01 01 47). Scholars Pr GA.

Maddox, Robert. Purpose of Luke-Acts. Riches, John, ed. 220p. 1982. 26.95 (ISBN 0-567-09312-3, Pub. by T&T Clark Ltd UK). Fortress.

Maddox, Robert, tr. see Hahn, Ferdinand.

Maddox, Robert L. & Maddox, Linda C. Get off My Back. (Orig.). 1987. pap. 5.95 (ISBN 0-8054-5344-X). Broadman.

Maddox, Robert L., Jr. Layman's Bible Book Commentary: Acts, Vol. 19. LC 78-67926. 1979. 5.95 (ISBN 0-8054-1189-5). Broadman.

Maddux, Bob. Fantasy Explosion. Beckwith, Mary, ed. LC 86-21938. 168p. (Orig.). pap. 5.95 (ISBN 0-8307-1163-5, 5418886). Regal.

Madeley, Hulon M. The Other Revelation for Christians. (Illus.). 48p. 1985. 7.95 (ISBN 0-89962-434-0). Todd & Honeywell.

Madeline, Sr. Within the Castle. 1983. 9.50 (ISBN 0-8199-0820-7). Franciscan Herald.

Mader, Andreas E. Altchristliche Basiliken und Lokaltraditionen in Sudjudaa. pap. 19.00 (ISBN 0-384-35000-3). Johnson Repr.

Ma Deva Sarito, ed. see Rajneesh, Bhagwan S.

Ma Deva Sarito, ed. see Rajneesh, Bhagwan Shree.

Madhava, K. G. Religions in Coastal Karnataka: 1500-1763. (Illus.). 206p. 1985. text ed. 37.50x (ISBN 0-86590-585-1, Inter India Pubns Delhi). Apt Bks.

Madhavananda, tr. The Brihadaranyaka Upanishad: With the Commentary of Shankaracharya. LC 83-45479. 1935. 78.50 (ISBN 0-404-20271-3, PK3521). AMS Pr.

Madhavananda, tr. from Sanskrit. Uddhava Gita or Last Message of Sri Krishna. 425p. pap. 9.50 (ISBN 0-87481-211-9). Vedanta Pr.

Madhavananda, Swami, tr. Brhadaranyaka Upanishad. (Sanskrit & Eng.). 1965. 14.00 (ISBN 0-87481-063-9). Vedanta Pr.

--Minor Upanishads. pap. 2.00 (ISBN 0-87481-061-2). Vedanta Pr.

Madhavananda, Swami, tr. see Adhvarindra, Dharmaraja.

Madhavananda, Swami, tr. see Shankara.

Madhava-Vidyaranya. Sankara-Dig-Vijaya: The Traditional Life of Sri Sankaracharya. Tapasyananda, Swami, tr. 1979. pap. 6.95 (ISBN 0-87481-484-7). Vedanta Pr.

Madhok, Balraj. Punjab Problem: The Muslim Connection. 1985. 14.00x (ISBN 0-8364-1519-1, Pub. by Vision). South Asia Bks.

Ma Dhyan Yogini, ed. see Zorba the Buddha Rajneesh Restaurants & Staff.

Madigan, Mary F. The Passio Domini Theme in the Works of Richard Rolle: His Personal Contribution in Its Religeous Cultural, & Literary Context. Hogg, James, ed. (Elizabethan & Renaissance Studies). 347p. (Orig.). 1978. pap. 15.00 (ISBN 3-7052-0723-7, Pub. by Salzburg Studies). Longwood Pub Group.

Madison, Leslie. Abraham's Test of Faith. 158p. (Orig.). 1982. pap. 3.50 (ISBN 0-89323-031-6). Bible Memory.

--Redemption of Ruth. 96p. (Orig.). 1982. pap. 2.50 (ISBN 0-89323-038-3). Bible Memory.

Madsen, Albert A., jt. auth. see Curtis, Edward L.

Madsen, Brigham D., ed. A Forty-Niner in Utah with the Stansbury Exploration of Great Salt Lake: Letters & Journal of John Hudson, 1848-50. 227p. 1981. 22.50 (ISBN 0-941214-39-7). Signature Bks.

Madsen, Brigham D., ed. see Roberts, B. H.

Madsen, Claudia, jt. auth. see Madsen, William.

Madsen, Erik C. Youth Ministry & Wilderness Camping. 160p. 1982. pap. 7.95 (ISBN 0-8170-0962-0). Judson.

Madsen, Keith. Fallen Images: Experiencing Divorce in the Ministry. 128p. 1985. pap. 5.95 (ISBN 0-8170-1076-9). Judson.

Madsen, Norman P. Bible Readers Tool Box. LC 86-24523. 168p. (Orig.). 1987. pap. 7.95 (ISBN 0-8272-0214-8). CBP.

--Lord, Teach Us to Live. LC 84-62161. 112p. 1985. pap. 4.95 (ISBN 0-87973-718-2, 718). Our Sunday Visitor.

--Lord, Teach Us to Pray. LC 83-61890. 96p. (Orig.). 1983. pap. 3.95 (ISBN 0-87973-611-9, 611). Our Sunday Visitor.

--St. Paul: The Apostle & His Letters. LC 85-62816. 165p. (Orig.). 1986. pap. 6.95 (ISBN 0-87973-589-9, 598). Our Sunday Visitor.

Madsen, William & Madsen, Claudia. A Guide to Mexican Witchcraft. (Illus.). 96p. 1977. pap. 4.50 (ISBN 0-912434-10-4). Ocelot Pr.

Maduro, Otto. Religion & Social Conflicts. Barr, Robert R., tr. from Span. LC 82-3439. Orig. Title: Religion y Lucha de Clase. 192p. (Orig.). 1982. pap. 8.95 (ISBN 0-88344-428-3). Orbis Bks.

Madvig, Donald, tr. see Schweizer, Eduard.

Madyapa, Swami Anand, ed. see Rajneesh, Bhagwan Shree.

Maecha, Alberto, ed. see Bourgeois, Jean-Francois.

Maeder, Gary & Williams, Don. The Christian Life: Issues & Answers. LC 76-29258. 208p. 1977. pap. 3.50 (ISBN 0-8307-0470-1, 5404606). Regal.

Maelzer, G., ed. Bibliographie zur Geschichte des Pietismus, Vol. 1, Die Werke Der Wuerttembergischen Pietisten des 17. Und 18. Jahrhunderts. 415p. 1972. 41.60 (ISBN 3-11-002219-2). De Gruyter.

Maestri, William. Bioethics: A Parish Resource. LC 81-40822. 64p. (Orig.). 1982. lib. bdg. 22.00 (ISBN 0-8191-2171-1); pap. text ed. 7.75 (ISBN 0-8191-2172-X). U Pr of Amer.

--Choose Life & Not Death: A Primer on Abortion, Euthanasia, & Suicide. LC 85-28687. 9.95 (ISBN 0-8189-0490-9). Alba.

Maestri, William, ed. Mary: Model of Justice: Reflections on the Magnificat. LC 86-22304. 87p. (Orig.). 1987. pap. 4.95 (ISBN 0-8189-0511-5). Alba.

Maestri, William F. A Time for Peace: Biblical Meditations for Advent. LC 83-22399. 94p. 1983. pap. 4.95 (ISBN 0-8189-0463-1). Alba.

--What Do You Seek? LC 85-60887. 170p. (Orig.). 1985. pap. 6.95 (ISBN 0-87973-803-0, 803). Our Sunday Visitor.

--A Word in Season. LC 84-11026. 153p. (Orig.). 1983. pap. 6.95 (ISBN 0-8189-0459-3). Alba.

Maezumi, Hakuyu T. & Glassman, Bernard T. The Hazy Moon of Enlightenment: On Zen Practice III. LC 77-81974. (Zen Writings Ser.: Vol. Four). (Illus.). 1978. pap. 5.95 (ISBN 0-916820-05-X). Center Pubns.

Maezumi, Hakuyu T. & Loori, John D. The Way of Everyday Life. LC 78-8309. (Illus.). 1978. 17.50 (ISBN 0-916820-17-3); pap. 9.95 (ISBN 0-916820-06-8). Center Pubns.

Maezumi, Hakuyu T. & Glassman, Bernard T., eds. On Zen Practice: Foundations of Practice. LC 76-9463. (Zen Writings Ser.: Vol. 1). (Illus.). 1976. pap. 5.00 (ISBN 0-916820-02-5). Center Pubns.

Magagna, Anna M., illus. First Prayers. LC 82-60742. (Illus.). 64p. 1983. 8.95 (ISBN 0-02-762120-0). Macmillan.

Magdamo, Patricia L., jt. auth. see Elwood, Douglas J.

Magee, William K. Bards & Saints. LC 76-8220. 1976. Repr. of 1906 ed. lib. bdg. 17.50 (ISBN 0-8414-3976-1). Folcroft.

Magers, Mary A. Bible Moments with Motions. Zapel, Arthur L., ed. Zapel, Michelle, tr. (Illus.). 53p. (Orig.). 1984. pap. 3.95 (ISBN 0-916260-27-5). Meriwether Pub.

--Holy Horoscopes...for Those under the Sign of the Cross. LC 85-50451. 112p. 1985. 6.95 (ISBN 0-938232-74-6). Winston-Derek.

Maggioni, Sr. M. Julie. Pensees of Pascal: A Study in Baroque Style. LC 79-94181. (Catholic University of America Studies in Romance Languages & Literature Ser: No. 39). Repr. of 1950 ed. 25.00 (ISBN 0-404-50339-X). AMS Pr.

Maghsoud Sadegh-ibn-Mohammad Angha, jt. auth. see Molana-al-Moazam Hazrat Shah.

Magie, Allan. Pets, People, Plagues. LC 79-19321. (Better Living Ser.). 1979. pap. 0.99 (ISBN 0-8127-0233-6). Review & Herald.

Magie, D., tr. see Warmington, E. H.

Magilton, J. R. The Church of St. Helen on the Walls, Aldwark, York. (Archaeology of York Ser.: Vol. 10). 64p. 1980. pap. text ed. 15.00x (ISBN 0-900312-98-X, Pub. by Coun Brit Archaeology). Humanities.

Magilton, J. R., jt. auth. see Dawes, Jean D.

Magistretti, Marco. Beroldus, Sive Ecclesiae Ambrosianae Mediolanensis Calendarium Et Ordines Saec XII. 294p. 1894. Repr. of 1894 ed. text ed. 66.24x (ISBN 0-576-99706-4, Pub. by Gregg Intl Pubs England). Gregg Intl.

Magliola, Robert R. Derrida on the Mend. LC 82-62779. 256p. 1984. 18.00 (ISBN 0-911198-69-5). Purdue U Pr.

Maglione, Harry, jt. ed. see Emmens, Carol A.

Magnani, Duane & Barrett, Arthur. The Watchtower Files. 340p. (Orig.). 1985. pap. 6.95 (ISBN 0-87123-816-0, 210816). Bethany Hse.

Magnes, J. L., jt. ed. see Buber, Martin.

Magnes, Judah L. & Buber, Martin. Arab-Jewish Unity: Testimony Before the Anglo-American Inquiry for the Ihud (Union) LC 75-7678. (The Rise of Jewish Nationalism & the Middle East Ser). 96p. 1975. Repr. of 1947 ed. 15.00 (ISBN 0-88355-348-1). Hyperion Conn.

Magness, Lee. Sense & Absence. (Semeia Studies). 1986. text ed. 14.95 (ISBN 1-55540-006-X, 06-06-15); pap. 10.95 (ISBN 1-55540-007-8). Scholars Pr GA.

Magnet, Charles E. Puppet Dialogues. LC 78-53323. 1978. spiral bdg. 4.95 (ISBN 0-916406-99-7). Accent Bks.

Magno, Joseph A. & LaMotte, Victor S. The Christian, the Atheist, & Freedom. LC 74-165170. 99p. 1975. 7.95 (ISBN 0-913750-08-5). Precedent Pub.

Magnus, Bernd. Nietzsche's Existential Imperative. LC 77-9864. (Studies in Phenomenology & Existential Philosophy Ser.). 256p. 1978. 20.00x (ISBN 0-253-34062-4). Ind U Pr.

Magnuson, Norris, ed. see Lundquist, Carl, et al.

Magnuson, Torgil. Rome in the Age of Bernini, Vol. II: From the Election of Innocent X to the Death of Innocent XI. Adler, Nancy, tr. from Swedish. (Illus.). 420p. 1986. 39.95 (ISBN 0-391-03448-0, Pub. by Humanities Press & Almgrist & Wiksell). Humanities.

Magnusson, M. eirikr. Thomas Saga Erkibyskups: A Life of Archbishop Thomas Becket, in Icelandic, with English Translation, Notes & Glossary, 2 vols. (Rolls Ser.: No. 65). Repr. of 1883 ed. Set. 120.00 (ISBN 0-8115-1133-2). Kraus Repr.

Magonet, Jonathan. Form & Meaning: Studies in Literary Techniques in the Book of Jonah. (Bible & Literature Ser.: No. 8). vi, 184p. 1983. pap. text ed. 10.95x (ISBN 0-907459-25-0, Pub. by Almond Pr England). Eisenbrauns.

Magriso, Yitzchak. Avoth. Barocas, David N., tr. Kaplan, Aryeh, intro. by. & 400p. 15.95 (ISBN 0-940118-22-X). Maznaim.

Magubane, Peter. Soweto: The Fruit of Fear. 1986. pap. 14.95 (ISBN 0-8028-0248-6). Eerdmans.

Maguire, Daniel. The New Subversives: Anti-Americanism of the Religious Right. 160p. 1982. 9.95 (ISBN 0-8264-0189-9). Continuum.

Maguire, Daniel C. The Moral Choice. 1979. pap. 12.95 (ISBN 0-86683-771-X, AY8112, HarpR). Har-Row.

--The Moral Revolution. 224p. (Orig.). 1986. pap. 12.95 (ISBN 0-06-254539-6, HarpR). Har-Row.

--The Moral Revolution: A Christian Humanist Vision. LC 85-51826. 224p. pap. 12.95 (ISBN 0-86683-520-2, RD 572, HarpR). Har-Row.

--A New American Justice: A Moral Proposal for the Reconciliation of Personal Freedom & Social Justice. 218p. 1982. pap. 9.95 (ISBN 0-86683-636-5, HarpR). Har-Row.

--Reflections of a Catholic Theologian on Visiting an Abortion Clinic. 11p. pap. 1.50 (ISBN 0-915365-10-3). Cath Free Choice.

Maguire, Daniel C., jt. auth. see Maguire, Marjorie R.

Maguire, Marjorie R. & Maguire, Daniel C. Abortion: A Guide to Making Ethical Choices. Jackman, Paul & Mooney, Anne S., eds. 44p. 1983. pap. 3.00 (ISBN 0-915365-00-6). Cath Free Choice.

Mahadevan, T. M. Superimposition in Advaita Vedanta. 80p. 1985. text ed. 20.00x (ISBN 0-86590-570-3, Pub. by Sterling Pubs India). Apt Bks.

--Upanisads: The Selections from 108 Upanisads. Mahadevan, T. M., tr. from Sanskrit. 240p. (Orig.). 1975. pap. 3.20 (ISBN 0-88253-985-X). Ind-US Inc.

Mahadevan, T. M., ed. Spiritual Perspectives: Essays in Mysticism & Metaphysics. 303p. 1975. lib. bdg. 12.00 (ISBN 0-89253-021-9). Ind-US Inc.

Mahadevan, T. M., tr. see Anantendra-Yati.

Mahaffy, John P. Descartes. facs. ed. LC 71-94277. (Select Bibliographies Reprint Ser.). 1902. 19.00 (ISBN 0-8369-5051-8). Ayer Co Pubs.

Mahalingam, N., ed. see Sekkizhaar.

Mahan, Asa. Autobiography - Intellectual, Moral & Spiritual. LC 75-3269. Repr. of 1882 ed. 30.00 (ISBN 0-404-59257-0). AMS Pr.

--Out of Darkness into Light. Dayton, Donald W., ed. (The Higher Christian Life Ser.). 366p. 1985. 45.00 (ISBN 0-8240-6429-1). Garland Pub.

--The Science of Natural Theology. LC 75-3273. Repr. of 1867 ed. 27.50 (ISBN 0-404-59261-9). AMS Pr.

Mahan, Brian see Richesin, L. Dale.

Mahan, Henry T. Galatians. 1983. pap. 1.50 (ISBN 0-686-40819-5). Pilgrim Pubns.

Mahan, Wayne W. Tillich's System. LC 73-91170. 1974. 10.00 (ISBN 0-911536-52-3). Trinity U Pr.

Mahany, Patricia. Animals in the Ark. (My Shape Bk.). (Illus.). 12p. 1984. 2.95 (ISBN 0-87239-781-5, 2721). Standard Pub.

--Baby Moses in a Basket. (Happy Day Bible Stories Bks.). (Illus.). 24p. 1984. 1.59 (ISBN 0-87239-761-0, 3721). Standard Pub.

--Bible Story Favorites. (My Shape Bk.). (Illus.). 1984. 2.95 (ISBN 0-87239-782-3, 2722). Standard Pub.

--God's Rainbow of Colors. (My Shape Bk.). (Illus.). 12p. 1984. 2.95 (ISBN 0-87239-783-1, 2723). Standard Pub.

--I Love Jesus. (My Shape Bk.). (Illus.). 12p. 1984. 2.95 (ISBN 0-87239-785-8, 2725). Standard Pub.

--My Baby Jesus Book. (My Surprise Book Ser.). (Illus.). 12p. 1984. 4.95 (ISBN 0-87239-800-5, 2732). Standard Pub.

--Stories Jesus Told. (Coloring Bks.). (Illus.). 16p. (Orig.). 1982. pap. 0.89 (ISBN 0-87239-601-0, 2390). Standard Pub.

Mahany, Patricia, ed. Bible Animals. (Classroom Activity Bks.). (Illus., Orig.). 1984. pap. 2.95 (ISBN 0-87239-715-7, 2445). Standard Pub.

--Bible Babies. (Classroom Activity Bks.). (Illus.). 48p. (Orig.). 1984. pap. 2.95 (ISBN 0-87239-716-5, 2446). Standard Pub.

--Bible Children. (Classroom Activity Bks.). (Illus.). 48p. (Orig.). 1984. pap. 2.95 (ISBN 0-87239-717-3, 2447). Standard Pub.

--Bible Verses in Action. (Stick-On Activity & Coloring Bks.). (Illus.). 16p. 1983. pap. 1.50 (ISBN 0-87239-686-X, 2366). Standard Pub.

--Favorite Bible Stories. (Classroom Activity Bks.). (Illus.). 48p. (Orig.). 1984. pap. 2.95 (ISBN 0-87239-718-1, 2448). Standard Pub.

Mahany, Patricia, compiled by. Friends of God. (Story & Color Bks.). (Illus.). 64p. (Orig.). 1984. pap. 2.95 (ISBN 0-87239-795-5, 2371). Standard Pub.

--God Can Do Anything-Bible Miracles. (Story & Color Bks.). (Illus.). 64p. (Orig.). 1984. pap. 2.95 (ISBN 0-87239-796-3, 2372). Standard Pub.

Mahany, Patricia, ed. God Made Kids Classroom Coloring Book. (Classroom Activities Bks.). (Illus.). 96p. (Orig.). 1982. pap. 2.95 (ISBN 0-87239-500-6, 2331). Standard Pub.

Mahany, Patricia, compiled by. Good News. (Story & Color Bks.). (Illus.). 64p. (Orig.). 1984. pap. 2.95 (ISBN 0-87239-797-1, 2373). Standard Pub.

Mahany, Patricia, ed. Jesus' Helpers Classroom Dot-to-Dot Book. (Classroom Activity Bks.). (Illus.). 96p. pap. 2.95 (ISBN 0-87239-503-0, 2334). Standard Pub.

--Jesus is Born. (Classroom Activity Bks.). (Illus.). 48p. (Orig.). 1984. pap. 2.95 (ISBN 0-87239-719-X, 2449). Standard Pub.

Mahany, Patricia, compiled by. Through the Bible with ABC's. (Story & Color Bks.). (Illus.). 64p. (Orig.). 1984. pap. 2.95 (ISBN 0-87239-798-X, 2374). Standard Pub.

Mahany, Patricia, ed. see Phillips, Cara L.

Mahany, Patricia S. Bible Who Am I? (Stick-On Activity & Coloring Bks.). (Illus.). 16p. 1983. pap. 1.50 (ISBN 0-87239-687-8, 2367). Standard Pub.

--Clint's "Be Cheerful" Day. (Happy Day Bks.). (Illus.). 24p. 1984. 1.59 (ISBN 0-87239-731-9, 3701). Standard Pub.

--Hurry Up, Noah. (Happy Day Bks.). (Illus.). 24p. 1986. 1.59 (ISBN 0-87403-028-5, 3488). Standard Pub.

Mahaprajna, Yuvacharya. Mysteries of Mind. 225p. 1982. 11.00 (ISBN 0-88065-223-3, Pub. by Messers Today & Tomorrow Printers & Publishers). Scholarly Pubns.

Maharaj, Rabindranath R. & Hunt, Dave. Death of a Guru. Rev. ed. LC 84-81212. 208p. 1986. pap. 5.95 (ISBN 0-89081-434-1). Harvest Hse.

Maharaja Yogiraja, ed. see Maitriya.

Maharshi, Ramana. The Spiritual Teaching of Ramana Maharshi. (Clear Light Ser). 112p. (Orig.). 1972. pap. 7.95 (ISBN 0-87773-024-5). Shambhala Pubns.

Mahasattva, Swami Devageet, ed. see Rajneesh, Bhagwan Shree.

Mahasattva, Swami Krishna, ed. see Rajneesh, Bhagwan S.

Mahasattva, Swami Krishna, ed. see Rajneesh, Bhagwan Shree.

Mahasattva, Swami Satya, ed. see Rajneesh, Bhagwan Shree.

Mahasattva Swami Krishna Prem, ed. see Bhagwan Shree Rajneesh.

Mahayogi, B. V., ed. see Sridhara, Swami B.

Mahecha, Alberto, ed. see Pollock, Algernon J.

Mahedy, William, jt. auth. see Carstens, Christopher.

Mahedy, William P., jt. auth. see Carstens, Christopher.

Mahendra Nath Gupta, see M, pseud.

Maher, Michael. Genesis. (Old Testament Message Ser.: Vol. 2). 1982. 15.95 (ISBN 0-89453-402-5); pap. 9.95 (ISBN 0-89453-237-5). M Glazier.

Maher, Robert W. Science, History & the Shroud of Turin. 1986. 8.95 (ISBN 0-533-06641-7). Vantage.

Maheshwar, ed. see Aurobindo, Sri.

Mahesh Yogi Maharishi, tr. Maharishi Mahesh Yogi on the Bhagavad-Gita. (Orig.). 1969. pap. 8.95 (ISBN 0-14-002913-3). Penguin.

Mahfuz, Nagib. God's World: An Anthology of Short Stories. Abadir, Akef & Allen, Roger, trs. LC 73-79201. (Studies in Middle Eastern Literatures: No. 2). 1973. pap. 12.00x student ed. (ISBN 0-88297-031-3). Bibliotheca.

Mahin, Mark. The New Scientific Case for God's Existence. LC 84-62349. 137p. (Orig.). 1985. pap. 8.95 (ISBN 0-931959-01-2). Mindlifter Pr.

--Sixty-Two Arguments That Justify a Bold New Creed. LC 85-71756. 225p. (Orig.). 1986. 17.95 (ISBN 0-931959-03-9); pap. 9.95 (ISBN 0-931959-04-7). Mindlifter Pr.

Mahler, Raphael. Hasidism & the Jewish Enlightenment: Their Confrontation in Galicia & Poland in the First Half of the Nineteenth Century. Orenstein, Eugene, et al, trs. from Yiddish & Hebrew. 432p. 1985. 29.95 (ISBN 0-8276-0233-2). Jewish Pubns.

Mahmoudi, Jalil. A Concordance to the Hidden Words of Baha'u'llah. LC 80-21346. (Orig.). 1980. pap. 2.95 (ISBN 0-87743-148-5, 368-052). Baha'i.

--The Story As Told. rev. ed. LC 79-65925. (Illus.). 80p. (Orig.). 1980. pap. 4.95 (ISBN 0-933770-10-3). Kalimat.

Mahmud Shabistari. The Secret Garden. 1969. 10.95 (ISBN 0-900860-38-3). Ins Study Human.

Mahoney, Edward P., ed. Philosophy & Humanism: Renaissance Essays in Honor of Paul Oskar Kristeller. LC 75-42285. 624p. 1976. 65.00 (ISBN 0-231-03904-2). Columbia U Pr.

Mahoney, James. Journey into Fullness. LC 73-91615. pap. 5.95 (ISBN 0-8054-5221-4). Broadman.

Mahoney, John. Bioethics & Belief. 128p. 1984. pap. 8.95 (ISBN 0-7220-1319-1). Chr Classics.

--The Making of Moral Theology: A Study of the Roman Catholic Tradition. 1987. 55.00. Oxford U Pr.

--Seeking the Spirit. 11.95 (ISBN 0-87193-187-7). Dimension Bks.

Mahoney, John F., tr. see Benoit, Hubert.

Mahoney, Robert. Two Disciples at the Tomb. (Theologie und Wirklichkeit: Vol. 6). 344p. 1974. pap. 29.75 (ISBN 3-261-00943-8). P Lang Pubs.

Mahony, Roger. The Bible in the Life of the Catholic Church. 32p. (Orig.). 1983. pap. 0.50 (ISBN 0-8146-1317-9). Liturgical Pr.

Mahr, Adolph R. Christian Art in Ancient Ireland, 2 vols. in 1. LC 75-11058. 1977. Repr. of 1932 ed. lib. bdg. 50.00 (ISBN 0-87817-173-8). Hacker.

Mah Talat Etemad Moghadam. From the Prophet to the Great Sufi Mir Ghotbeddin Mohammad. Peyravan, Abdosalam & Shahrivar, Mitra, trs. from Farsi. 231p. (Orig.). 1982. pap. 12.50 (ISBN 0-317-01145-6). M T O Shahmag.

Maida, Adam J. & Carfardi, Nicholas P. Church Property, Church Finances, & Church-Related Corporations: A Canon Law Handbook. LC 83-20946. 1984. 28.00 (ISBN 0-87125-090-X). Cath Health.

Maidat, Rita. The Twins Visit Israel. (Shayna & Keppi Ser.). (Illus.). 1978. pap. 2.00 (ISBN 0-914080-72-5). Shulsinger Sales.

Maidens, Melinda, ed. Religion, Morality & "the New Right". 224p. 1982. 24.95x (ISBN 0-87196-639-5). Facts on File.

Maier, D. J. E. Priests & Power: The Case of the Dente Shrine in Nineteenth-Century Ghana. LC 82-48582. (Illus.). 272p. 1983. 22.50X (ISBN 0-253-34602-9). Ind U Pr.

Maier, Gerhard. End of the Historical Critical Method. 1977. pap. 6.25 (ISBN 0-570-03752-2, 12-2656). Concordia.

Maier, Hans. Revolution & Church: The Early History of Christian Democracy, 1789-1901. Schossberger, Emily M., tr. LC 68-27577. 1969. 7.95 (ISBN 0-268-00319-X). U of Notre Dame Pr.

Maier, Johann. Geschichte der Juedischen Religion: Von der Zeit Alexanders des Grossen bis zur Aufklaerung. Mit einem Ausblick auf das 19.-20. Jahrhundert. LC 72-77437. (Ger.). xx, 641p. 1972. 29.60x (ISBN 3-11-002448-9). De Gruyter.

--The Temple Scroll: An Introduction, Translation & Commentary. (No. 34). xii, 147p. 1985. text ed. 28.50x (ISBN 1-85075-003-3, Pub. by JSOT Pr England); pap. text ed. 13.50x (ISBN 1-85075-004-1). Eisenbrauns.

Maier, Michael. Laws of the Fraternity of the Rosie Crosse (Themis Aurea) 12.50 (ISBN 0-89314-402-9). Philos Res.

Maier, Paul A. Caspar Schwenckfeld on the Person & Work of Christ. 115p. 1959. write for info. Concordia Schl Grad Studies.

Maier, Paul L. The Best of Walter A. Maier. 1980. pap. 7.95 (ISBN 0-570-03823-5, 12-2786). Concordia.

--First Christians: Pentecost & the Spread of Christianity. LC 75-36751. (Illus.). 160p. 1976. 11.00 (ISBN 0-06-065399-X, HarpR). Har-Row.

--First Christmas, First Easter, First Christians, 3 Bks. (Illus.). 128p. 1982. Boxed Set. pap. 11.00 ea. (ISBN 0-06-065395-7, RD 381, HarpR). Har-Row.

--First Christmas: The True & Unfamiliar Story in Words & Pictures. LC 76-163162. (Illus.). 1971. 10.45i (ISBN 0-06-065396-5, HarpR). Har-Row.

--The Flames of Rome. (Living Bks.). 640p. 1987. pap. 4.95 (ISBN 0-8423-0903-9). Tyndale.

--A Man Spoke, a World Listened. 1980. pap. 8.95 (ISBN 0-570-03822-7, 12-2762). Concordia.

--Pontius Pilate. 1981. pap. 3.95 (ISBN 0-8423-4852-2). Tyndale.

Maier, Walter A. The Book of Nahum. (Thornapple Commentaries). 392p. 1980. pap. 6.95 (ISBN 0-8010-6098-2). Baker Bk.

Maier, Walter A., III. Aserah: Extrabiblical Evidence. (Harvard Semitic Monographs). 274p. 1987. 21.95 (ISBN 1-55540-046-9, 04-00-37). Scholars Pr GA.

Maillard, Benjamin de see De Maillard, Benjamin.

Mails, Thomas E. Fool's Crow. 1980. pap. 3.50 (ISBN 0-380-52175-X, 52175-X, Discus). Avon.

Maimes, Steven L., ed. see Carlebach, Shlomo.

Maimon, Solomon. An Autobiography. Hadas, Moses, ed. 124p. 1985. pap. 4.95 (ISBN 0-8052-0150-5). Schocken.

Maimondies & Hyamson, Moses. Book of Adoration. (Mishneh Torah Ser.). 330p. 1981. 11.95 (ISBN 0-87306-086-5). Feldheim.

Maimonides. Book of Knowledge. Hyamson, Moses, tr. from Herbrew. (Mishneh Torah Ser.). 1981. 13.95 (ISBN 0-87306-085-7). Feldheim.

--Commandments, 2 Vols. Set. 35.00x (ISBN 0-685-01042-2); pap. 25.00. Bloch.

--Ethical Writings of Maimonides. (Philosophy & Religion Ser.). 182p. (Orig.). 1983. pap. 4.50 (ISBN 0-486-24522-5). Dover.

Maimonides, Moses. The Book of Women: The Code of Maimonides, Bk. 4. Klein, Isaac, ed. LC 49-9495. (Judaica Ser.: No. 19). 592p. 1972. 50.00x (ISBN 0-300-01438-4). Yale U Pr.

--Code of Maimonides, Bk. 3, Treatise 8, Sanctification Of The New Moon. Gandz, Solomon, tr. (Judaica Ser: No. 11). 1956. 23.50x (ISBN 0-300-00476-1). Yale U Pr.

--The Code of Maimonides, Bks. 5-6 & 8-14. Incl. Bk. 5. The Book of Holiness. Rabinowitz, Louis I. & Grossman, Philip, trs. xxxiv, 429p. 1965. 50.00x (ISBN 0-300-00846-5); Bk. 6. The Book of Asseverations. Klien, B. D., tr. 273p. 1962. 30.00x (ISBN 0-300-00633-0); Bk. 8. The Book of Temple Service. Lewittes, Mendell, tr. (Illus.). xxvii, 525p. 1957. 55.00x (ISBN 0-300-00717-5); Bk. 9. The Book of Offerings. Danby, Herbert, tr. xxi, 236p. 1950. 27.50x (ISBN 0-300-00398-6); Bk. 10. The Book of Cleanness. Danby, Herbert, tr. (Illus.). xiv, 645p. 1954. 60.00x (ISBN 0-300-00397-8); Bk. 11. The Book of Torts. Klein, Hyman, tr. xvii, 299p. 1954. 35.00x (ISBN 0-300-00632-2); Bk. 12. The Book of Acquisition. Klein, Isaac, tr. xv, 335p. 1951. 40.00x (ISBN 0-300-00631-4); Bk. 13. The Book of Civil Laws. Rabinowitz, Jacob J., tr. xxiv, 345p. 1949. 45.00 (ISBN 0-300-00845-7); Bk. 14. The Book of Judges. Hershman, Abraham M., tr. xxv, 335p. 1949. 40.00x (ISBN 0-300-00548-2). (Judaica Ser.). Yale U Pr.

--Code of Maimonides - Book Three: The Book of Seasons. Gandz, Solomon & Klein, Hyman, trs. (Judaica Ser: No. 14). 1961. 60.00x (ISBN 0-300-00475-3). Yale U Pr.

--Commentary to Mishnah Aboth. David, Arthur, tr. LC 68-27871. 1968. 9.95x (ISBN 0-8197-0154-8). Bloch.

--Guide for the Perplexed. Friedlander, M., tr. 1904. pap. 6.95 (ISBN 0-486-20351-4). Dover.

--Guide for the Perplexed. 2nd ed. 16.00 (ISBN 0-8446-2512-4). Peter Smith.

--Guide for the Perplexed: Morah Nevochim. (Heb, & Eng). 37.50 (ISBN 0-87559-079-9). Shalom.

--Guide of the Perplexed, 2 vols. Pines, Shlomo, tr. LC 62-18113. 1963. 25.00x ea.; Vol. 1. (ISBN 0-226-50232-5). Vol. 2 (ISBN 0-226-50233-3). U of Chicago Pr.

--The Guide of the Perplexed. Pines, Shlomo, tr. LC 62-18113. 1974. Vol. 1. pap. 15.95 (ISBN 0-226-50230-9, P609, Phoen); Vol. 2. pap. 15.95 (ISBN 0-226-50231-7, P610). U of Chicago Pr.

--Mishneh Torah. Abr. ed. Birnbaum, Philip, tr. (Eng. & Hebrew.). 755p. 1944. 19.50 (ISBN 0-88482-437-3). Hebrew Pub.

--Mishneh Torah. Abr. ed. Birnbaum, Philip, tr. 344p. 1944. pap. 9.95 (ISBN 0-317-26820-1). Hebrew Pub.

--The Reason of the Laws of Moses. Townley, James, ed. LC 78-97294. 451p. 1975. Repr. of 1827 ed. lib. bdg. 22.50x (ISBN 0-8371-2618-5, MARL). Greenwood.

Maimonides, Moses & Twersky, Isadore. Introduction to the Code of Maimonides (Mishneh Torah) LC 79-10347. (Yale Judaica Ser.: No. XXII). 1980. 50.00x (ISBN 0-300-02319-7); pap. 11.95x (ISBN 0-300-02846-6). Yale U Pr.

Maimonides, Moses & Judah, trs. Fathers According to Rabbi Nathan Goldin. (Judaica Ser.: No. 10). 1955. 26.50x (ISBN 0-300-00497-4). Yale U Pr.

Maimonides, Obadyah. The Treatise of the Pool. Fenton, Paul, tr. 1981. 19.95 (ISBN 0-900860-87-1, Pub. by Octagon Pr England). Ins Study Human.

Maimonodes, Moses. Guide of the Perplexed. abr. ed. Guttman, Julius W., ed. Rabin, Chaim, tr. 1978. pap. text ed. 5.95 (ISBN 0-85222-208-4, East & West Lib). Hebrew Pub.

Main, John. Letters from the Heart: Christian Monasticism & the Renewal of Community. 1982. pap. 6.95 (ISBN 0-8245-0444-5). Crossroad NY.

--Moment of Christ: The Path of Meditation. 144p. 1984. 10.95 (ISBN 0-8245-0679-0); pap. 7.95 (ISBN 0-8245-0660-X). Crossroad NY.

--Present Christ. 128p. (Orig.). 1986. pap. 7.95 (ISBN 0-8245-0740-1). Crossroad NY.

--Word into Silence. LC 80-84660. 96p. 1981. pap. 4.95 (ISBN 0-8091-2369-X). Paulist Pr.

Mainelli, Helen K. Numbers. (Bible Commentary Ser.). 136p. 1985. pap. 2.50 (ISBN 0-8146-1373-X). Liturgical Pr.

Maines, Clark. The Western Portal of Saint-Loup-De-Naud. LC 78-74373. (Fine Arts Dissertations, Fourth Ser.). (Illus.). 511p. 1979. lib. bdg. 53.00 (ISBN 0-8240-3960-2). Garland Pub.

Mainhood, Beth. Reaching Your World. 118p. 1986. pap. 4.95 (ISBN 0-89109-537-3). NavPress.

Mainkar, T. G. The Making of the Vedanta. 1980. 14.00x (ISBN 0-8364-0623-0, Pub. by Ajanta). South Asia Bks.

Mainprize, Donald. Happy Anniversary. (Contempo Ser). 1975. pap. 0.95 (ISBN 0-8010-5971-2). Baker Bk.

Mains, David. A Closer Walk with God. (Chapel Talks Ser.). 64p. 0.95 (ISBN 0-89191-264-9, 52647). Cook.

--Getting to Know the Holy Spirit. (Chapel Talks Ser.). 64p. 0.95 (ISBN 0-89191-262-2, 52621). Cook.
--Making Church More Enjoyable. (Chapel Talks Ser.). 64p. 0.95 (ISBN 0-89191-256-8, 52563). Cook.
--Making Scripture Yours. (Chapel Talks Ser.). 64p. 0.95 (ISBN 0-89191-272-X, 52720). Cook.
--Praying More Effectively. (Chapel Talks Ser.). 64p. 1.75 (ISBN 0-89191-261-4, 52613). Cook.
--Psalms That Touch Us Where We Live. (Chapel Talks Ser.). 64p. 0.95 (ISBN 0-89191-265-7, 52654). Cook.
Mains, David & Mains, Karen. The God Hunt: A Discovery Book for Men & Women. 1984. spiral wkbk. 4.95 (ISBN 0-89191-813-2, 58131). Cook.
--Our Favorite Verse. LC 86-73188. (My Favorite Verse Ser.). 24p. 1987. pap. 4.95 (ISBN 0-89636-232-9). Accent Bks.
Mains, David, jt. auth. see Mains, Karen.
Mains, David, jt. auth. see Mains, Karen B.
Mains, David R. The Rise of the Religion of Anti-Christism. Markham, Judith, ed. 1985. 9.95 (ISBN 0-310-34830-7, Pub. by Zondervan Bks). Zondervan.
--The Truth about the Lie. 128p. 1987. pap. 4.95 (ISBN 0-310-34831-5). Zondervan.
Mains, Karen. Karen! Karen! 1980. 6.95 (ISBN 0-8423-2026-1). Tyndale.
--Making Sunday Special. 192p. 1987. 12.95 (ISBN 0-8499-0612-1). Word Bks.
Mains, Karen & Mains, David. The God Hunt: A Discovery Book for Boys & Girls. LC 84-14204. (Illus.). 1984. Spiral 3.95 (ISBN 0-89191-886-8, 58867). Cook.
--Parenting Us: How God Does It. 96p. 1986. pap. 3.50 (ISBN 0-87788-669-5). Shaw Pubs.
Mains, Karen, jt. auth. see Mains, David.
Mains, Karen B. Open Heart-Open Home. LC 76-1554. 224p. 1976. 5.95 (ISBN 0-89191-111-1). Cook.
--Open Heart-Open Home. 1980. pap. 2.95 (ISBN 0-451-14183-0, AE2641, Sig). NAL.
Mains, Karen B. & Mains, David. Tales of the Kingdom. (Illus.). 96p. 1983. 12.95 (ISBN 0-89191-560-5). Cook.
Maio, Eugene, tr. see Pearson, D'Orsay W.
Mairet, Philip. Christian Essays in Psychiatry. 1957. 7.95 (ISBN 0-8022-1038-4). Philos Lib.
Mairet, Philip, tr. see Wendel, Francois.
Maisel, David, tr. see Neher, Andre.
Maisel, David, et al, trs. see Ye'or, Bat.
Maistre, Joseph M. De, tr. Letters on the Spanish Inquisition. LC 77-24949. 1977. Repr. of 1843 ed. 35.00x (ISBN 0-8201-1293-3). Schol Facsimiles.
Maitland, David J. Aging: A Time for New Learning. LC 86-46038. 192p. (Orig.). 1987. pap. 9.95 (ISBN 0-8042-1107-8). John Knox.
--Looking Both Ways: A Theology for Midlife. 240p. 1985. pap. 10.95 (ISBN 0-8042-1127-2). John Knox.
Maitland, Edward, jt. auth. see Kingsford, Anna.
Maitland, Frederic W. Roman Canon Law in the Church of England. 1969. Repr. of 1898 ed. 21.00 (ISBN 0-8337-2186-0). B Franklin.
Maitland, S. R. Dark Ages: Essays Illustrating the State of Religion & Literature in the Ninth, Tenth, Eleventh & Twelfth Centuries, 2 vols. LC 68-8242. 1969. Repr. of 1889 ed. 40.00 (ISBN 0-8046-0297-2, Pub. by Kennikat). Assoc Faculty Pr.
Maitland, Sara. A Map of the New Country: Women & Christianity. LC 82-13142. 218p. 1983. pap. 8.95 (ISBN 0-7100-9301-2). Methuen Inc.
Maitland, Sara see Garcia, Jo.
Maitra, H. Hinduism: The World Ideal. 34.95 (ISBN 0-8490-0302-4). Gordon Pr.
Maitreya, Aryasanga. Uttaratantra, or Ratnagotravibhaga: Sublime Science of the Great Vehicle to Salvation. Obermiller, E., tr. from Tibetan. 225p. 1984. Repr. of 1931 ed. lib. bdg. 22.50x (ISBN 0-88181-001-0). Canon Pubns.
Maitreya, Sthiramati. Madhyantavibhagatika: An Analysis of the Middle Path & the Extremes. Friedman, David L., tr. from Sanskrit. 154p. 1984. Repr. of 1937 ed. lib. bdg. 19.50x (ISBN 0-88181-004-5). Canon Pubns.
Maitriya. The Buddha Mimansa. Maharaja Yogiraja, ed. LC 78-70098. Repr. of 1925 ed. 23.50 (ISBN 0-404-17347-0). AMS Pr.
Major, Henry D. Civilization & Religious Values. LC 77-27137. (Hibbert Lectures: 1946). Repr. of 1948 ed. 20.00 (ISBN 0-404-60431-5). AMS Pr.
Major, J. Russell. Age of the Renaissance & Reformation: A Short History. LC 73-107245. (Orig.). 1970. pap. text ed. 5.50i (ISBN 0-397-47195-5). Har-Row.
Major, Richard H., ed. see Bontier, Pierre & Le Verrier, Jean.
Major, Wilfred, jt. auth. see O'Brien, Joan.
Majors, William R. Editorial Wild Oats: Edward Ward Carmack & Tennessee Politics. LC 84-10870. xx, 194p. 1984. 17.50 (ISBN 0-86554-133-7, MUP/H124). Mercer Univ Pr.
Majumdar, R. C. Kambuja-Desa; or, an Ancient Hindu Colony in Cambodia. LC 80-18307. 178p. 1980. Repr. of 1944 ed. text ed. 19.95 (ISBN 0-915980-28-2). ISHI PA.
Majumdar, Sachindra K. Yoga for Physical & Mental Fitness. LC 68-31613. (Illus.). 1968. 7.95 (ISBN 0-87396-013-0); pap. 3.95 (ISBN 0-87396-014-9). Stravon.
Majundar, Sachindra Kumar. Introduction to Yoga. 1977. pap. 4.95 (ISBN 0-8065-0542-7). Citadel Pr.
Makarem, Sami N., ed. see Firas, Shihab.
Makari, Victor E. Ibn Taymiyyah's Ethics: The Social Factor. LC 81-1019. (American Academy of Religion Academy Ser.). pap. write for info. (ISBN 0-89130-477-0). Scholars Pr GA.
--Ibn Taymiyyah's Ethics: The Social Factor. LC 81-1019. (AAR Academy Ser.). 246p. 1983. 17.95 (ISBN 0-89130-476-2, 01 01 34). Scholars Pr GA.
Makarim, Sami N. Druze Faith. LC 73-19819. 1974. 25.00x (ISBN 0-88206-003-1). Caravan Bks.
Makay, D. Bruce, compiled by. A Comprehensive Index to Biblical Archaeologist, Vol. 36-45. 225p. 1986. pap. 11.95 (ISBN 0-89757-008-1, Dist. by Eisenbrauns). Am Sch Orient Res.
Makdisi, G. Censure of Speculative Theology. 156p. 1962. 40.00x (ISBN 0-317-39046-5, Pub. by Luzac & Co Ltd). State Mutual Bk.
Maki, Lillian. Education, Human Nature & Peace: A Scientific Look at Religion. rev. ed. 192p. 1985. 8.50 (ISBN 0-9617372-0-4). Maryatta Co.
Makky, Ghazy A. Mecca, the Pilgrimage City: A Study of Pilgrim Accomodation. (Illus.). 95p. 1978. 28.00 (ISBN 0-85664-591-5, Pub. by Croom Helm Ltd). Methuen Inc.
Makolin, Jewell. Katie & Luther Speak. 1985. 4.95 (ISBN 0-89536-943-5, 7558). CSS of Ohio.
Makower, Felix. The Constitutional History & the Constitutions of the Church of England. LC 61-2869. (Research & Source Works Ser.). Tr. of Die Verfassung der Kirche Von England. 556p. 1972. Repr. of 1895 ed. lib. bdg. 32.00 (ISBN 0-8337-2195-X). B Franklin.
Makrakis, Apostolos. The Bible & the World & Triluminal Science. Orthodox Christian Educational Society, ed. Cummings, Denver, tr. from Hellenic. 531p. 1950. 10.00x (ISBN 0-938366-18-1). Orthodox Chr.
--Catechesis of the Orthodox Church. rev. ed. Orthodox Christian Educational Society, ed. 239p. 1969. pap. text ed. 5.00x (ISBN 0-938366-14-9). Orthodox Chr.
--The City of Zion-The Human Society in Christ, i.e., the Church Built Upon a Rock. Orthodox Christian Educational Society, ed. Cummings, Denver, tr. from Hellenic. 109p. 1958. pap. 4.00x (ISBN 0-938366-16-5). Orthodox Chr.
--Commentary on the Psalms of David. Orthodox Christian Educational Society, ed. Cummings, Denver, tr. from Hellenic. 990p. 1950. 16.00x (ISBN 0-938366-19-X). Orthodox Chr.
--Concerning Our Duties to God. Orthodox Christian Educational Society, ed. 170p. 1958. pap. text ed. 4.50x (ISBN 0-938366-13-0). Orthodox Chr.
--Divine & Sacred Catechism. Orthodox Christian Educational Society, ed. 224p. 1946. 5.50x (ISBN 0-938366-15-7). Orthodox Chr.
--The Foundation of Philosophy-a Refutation of Skepticism, the True Jesus Christ, the Science of God & Man; the God of the Christians. Orthodox Christian Educational Society, ed. Lekatsos, Anthony & Cummings, Denver, trs. from Fr. 395p. 1955. 7.50x (ISBN 0-938366-07-6). Orthodox Chr.
--Freemasonry Known by the Masonic Diploma. Cummings, Denver, tr. 135p. (Orig.). 1956. pap. 4.50 (ISBN 0-938366-42-4). Orthodox Chr.
--Hellenism & the Unfinished Revolution. Orthodox Christian Educational Society, ed. Stephanou, Archimandrite E., tr. from Hellenic. 191p. (Orig.). 1968. pap. 5.00x (ISBN 0-938366-26-2). Orthodox Chr.
--The Holy Orthodox Church. Orthodox Christian Educational Society, ed. Lisney, M. I. & Krick, L., trs. from Hellenic. 298p. (Orig.). 1980. pap. 7.95x (ISBN 0-938366-34-3). Orthodox Chr.
--The Human Nature of Christ: Growth & Perfection. Orthodox Christian Educational Society, ed. Cummings, D., tr. from Hellenic. 52p. (Orig.). 1965. pap. 1.00x (ISBN 0-938366-28-9). Orthodox Chr.
--The Innovations of the Roman Church. 82p. (Orig.). 1966. pap. 3.75x (ISBN 0-938366-39-4). Orthodox Chr.
--Interpretation of the Book of Revelation. Orthodox Christian Educational Society, ed. Alexander, A. G., tr. from Hellenic. 564p. 1972. 11.00x (ISBN 0-938366-12-2). Orthodox Chr.
--Interpretation of the Entire New Testament (Revelation Not Incl), 2 vols. Orthodox Christian Educational Society, ed. Alexander, Albert G., tr. from Hellenic. 2052p. (Vol. 1, 1127 pp.;vol. 2, 925 pp.). 1949. Set. 28.00x (ISBN 0-938366-08-4). Orthodox Chr.
--The Interpretation of the Gospel Law. Orthodox Christian Educational Society, ed. Cummings, Denver, tr. from Hellenic. 453p. 1955. 9.00x (ISBN 0-938366-10-6). Orthodox Chr.
--Kyriakodromion (Sunday Sermonary) Orthodox Christian Educational Society, ed. Cummings, D., tr. from Hellenic. 637p. 1951. 12.00x (ISBN 0-938366-20-3). Orthodox Chr.
--Memoir of the Nature of the Church of Christ. Orthodox Christian Educational Society, ed. Cummings, Denver, tr. from Hellenic. 175p. 1947. 4.75x (ISBN 0-938366-21-1). Orthodox Chr.
--The Orthodox Approach to Philosophy. Orthodox Christian Educational Society, ed. Cummings, Denver, tr. from Hellenic. (The Logos & Holy Spirit in the Unity of Christian Thought Ser.: Vol. 1). 82p. 1977. pap. 3.25x (ISBN 0-938366-06-8). Orthodox Chr.
--Orthodox Christian Meditations (Spiritual Discourses for the Orthodox Christians) Orthodox Christian Educational Society, ed. Cummings, Denver, tr. from Hellenic. 143p. (Orig.). 1965. pap. 3.50x (ISBN 0-938366-22-X). Orthodox Chr.
--The Orthodox Definition of Political Science. Orthodox Christian Educational Society, ed. Cummings, Denver, tr. from Hellenic. 163p. 1968. pap. 4.00x (ISBN 0-938366-31-9). Orthodox Chr.
--An Orthodox-Protestant Debate. Cummings, Denver, tr. 101p. 1949. pap. 3.25x (ISBN 0-938366-37-8). Orthodox Chr.
--The Paramount Doctrines of Orthodoxy-the Tricompositeness of Man, Apology of A. Makrakis & the Trial of A. Makrakis. Orthodox Christian Educational Society, ed. Cummings, Denver, tr. from Hellenic. 904p. 1954. 15.00x (ISBN 0-938366-17-3). Orthodox Chr.
--Philosophy: An Orthodox Christian Understanding. Orthodox Christian Educational Society, ed. Cummings, Denver, tr. from Hellenic. (The Logos & Holy Spirit in the Unity of Christian Thought Ser.: Vol. 5). 279p. 1977. pap. 5.50x (ISBN 0-938366-02-5). Orthodox Chr.
--The Political Philosophy of the Orthodox Church. Orthodox Christian Educational Society, ed. Cummings, Denver, tr. from Hellenic. Orig. Title: The Orthodox Definition of Political Science. 163p. (Orig.). 1965. pap. 4.00x (ISBN 0-938366-11-4). Orthodox Chr.
--Psychology: An Orthodox Christian Perspective. Orthodox Christian Educational Society, ed. Cummings, Denver, tr. from Hellenic. (The Logos & Holy Spirit in the Unity of Christian Thought Ser.: Vol. 2). 151p. 1977. pap. 4.25x (ISBN 0-938366-05-X). Orthodox Chr.
--A Revelation of Treasure Hid--Concerning Freedom, Concerning the Motherland, Concerning Justice, Apostolical Canons Respecting Baptism. Orthodox Christian Educational Society, ed. Cummings, Denver, tr. from Hellenic. 80p. (Orig.). 1952. pap. 2.00x (ISBN 0-938366-23-8). Orthodox Chr.
--A Scriptural Refutation of the Pope's Primacy. Cummings, Denver, tr. from Hellenic. 171p. (Orig.). 1952. pap. 3.75x (ISBN 0-938366-40-8). Orthodox Chr.
--Theology: An Orthodox Standpoint. Orthodox Christian Educational Society, ed. Cummings, Denver, tr. from Hellenic. (The Logos & Holy Spirit in the Unity of Christian Thought Ser.: Vol. 4). 216p. 1977. pap. 5.00x (ISBN 0-938366-03-3). Orthodox Chr.
--Three Great Friday Sermons & Other Theological Discourses. Orthodox Christian Educational Society, ed. Cummings, Denver, tr. from Hellenic. 107p. (Orig.). 1952. pap. 3.00x (ISBN 0-938366-48-3). Orthodox Chr.
--The Two Contrariant Schools, Concerning the Establishment of a Christian University. Orthodox Christian Educational Society, ed. Cummings, Denver, tr. from Hellenic. 87p. (Orig.). 1949. pap. 2.75x (ISBN 0-938366-27-0). Orthodox Chr.
Makrakis, Apostolos, jt. auth. see Stratman, Chrysostomos H.
Makris, Kallistos. The God-Inspired Orthodox Julian Calendar VS. the False Gregorian Papal Calendar. Vlesmas, Jerry, tr. from Hellenic. 118p. (Orig.). 1971. pap. 3.25x (ISBN 0-938366-36-X). Orthodox Chr.
Malachuck, Daniel. Stained Glass Religion: Who Needs It. 100p. pap. 4.95 (ISBN 0-89221-127-X, Pub. by SonLife). New Leaf.
Malachy, Carroll, tr. see Jean-Mesmy, Claude.
Malachy, Yona. American Fundamentalism & Israel: The Relation of Fundamentalist Churches to Zionism & the State of Israel. 178p. 1978. pap. text ed. 10.50x (Pub. by Magnes Pr Israel). Humanities.
Malagoda, Kirsiri. Buddhism in Sinhalese Society, 1750-1900: A Study of Religious Revival & Change. LC 74-22966. 1976. 42.00x (ISBN 0-520-02873-2). U of Cal Pr.
Malalasekera, George P. & Jayatilleke, K. N. Buddhism & the Race Question. LC 77-18853. (The Race Question in Modern Thought). 1978. Repr. of 1958 ed. lib. bdg. 22.50x (ISBN 0-313-20208-7, MABU). Greenwood.
Malament, Barbara C., ed. After the Reformation: Essays in Honor of J. H. Hexter. LC 79-5254. 256p. 1980. 36.95x (ISBN 0-8122-7774-0). U of Pa Pr.
Malandra, William W. An Introduction to Ancient Iranian Religion: Readings from the "Avesta" & "Achaemenid" Inscriptions. (Minnesota Publications in the Humanities Ser.: No. 2). 201p. 1983. 29.50 (ISBN 0-8166-1114-9); pap. 14.95x (ISBN 0-8166-1115-7). U of Minn Pr.
Malantschuk, Gregor. Kierkegaard's Thought. Hong, Howard V. & Hong, Edna H., trs. from Dan. LC 77-155000. (Eng.). 400p. 1972. 38.50 (ISBN 0-691-07166-7, 317); pap. 10.00 (ISBN 0-691-01982-7). Princeton U Pr.
Malatesta, Edward J., ed. see Ricci, Matteo.
Malbim, Meir. Turnabout. Weinbach, Mendel, tr. 1976. 5.95 (ISBN 0-87306-030-X). Feldheim.
Malbin, Michael J. Religion & Politics: The Intentions of the Authors of the First Amendment. 40p. 1978. pap. 3.25 (ISBN 0-8447-3302-4). Am Enterprise.
Malbon, Elizabeth S. Narrative Space & Mythic Meaning in Mark. 208p. (Orig.). 1986. 24.95 (ISBN 0-06-254540-X, HarpR). Har-Row.
Malcolm. Sketch of the Sikhs. 202p. 1986. Repr. of 1812 ed. 20.00X (ISBN 0-8364-1755-0, PUb. by Abhinav India). South Asia Bks.
Malcolm, Kari T. Building Your Family to Last. 180p. (Orig.). 1987. pap. 6.95 (ISBN 0-87784-984-6). Inter-Varsity.
Malcolm X. Autobiography of Malcolm X. 1977. pap. 2.75 (ISBN 0-345-29420-3). Ballantine.
Malcomson, William L. How to Survive in the Ministry. 88p. 1982. pap. 4.95 (ISBN 0-8170-0964-7). Judson.
Maldonado, Luis & Power, David, eds. Symbol & Art in Worship. (Concilium Ser.: Vol. 132). 128p. (Orig.). 1980. pap. 5.95 (ISBN 0-8164-2274-5, HarpR). Har-Row.
Male, Emile. The Gothic Image: Religious Art in France of the Thirteenth Century. Nussey, Dora, tr. from Fr. (Icon Editions). (Illus.). 440p. 1973. pap. 10.95 (ISBN 0-06-430032-3, IN-32, HarpT). Har-Row.
--Religious Art from the Twelfth to the Eighteenth Century. LC 82-47903. (Illus.). 256p. 1982. 31.50x (ISBN 0-691-04000-1); pap. 10.50x (ISBN 0-691-00347-5). Princeton U Pr.
--Religious Art in France: The Late Middle Ages: A Study of Medieval Iconography & Its Sources. Bober, Harry, ed. Mathews, Marthiel, tr. (Bollingen Ser. XC: No. 3). 600p. 1987. text ed. 85.00x (ISBN 0-691-09914-6). Princeton U Pr.
--Religious Art in France: The Twelfth Century. LC 72-14029. (Bollingen Ser.: No. 90). 1978. 73.50x (ISBN 0-691-09912-X). Princeton U Pr.
Malefijt, Anne M. Religion & Culture: An Introduction to Anthropology of Religion. 1968. text ed. write for info. (ISBN 0-02-374920-2). Macmillan.
Malefijt, Anne X. De Waal see Malefijt, Anne M.
Malehor, Harold A. Over Two Hundred Ways to Improve Your Sunday School. 1982. pap. 5.95 (ISBN 0-570-03857-X, 12-2811). Concordia.
Malfitano, Gilbert J. The Seven Steps on How to Become a Mystic & Enjoy the Most Exhilirating Pleasure Available to Man on This Earth. (Illus.). 1979. deluxe ed. 47.50 (ISBN 0-930582-37-3). Gloucester Art.
Malgo, Wim. Biblical Counseling. 4.95 (ISBN 0-937422-18-5). Midnight Call.
--Called to Pray. 3.95 (ISBN 0-937422-19-3). Midnight Call.
--Depression & Its Remedy. 1980. 2.95 (ISBN 0-937422-03-7). Midnight Call.
--Fifty Questions Most Frequently Asked about the Second Coming. 3.95 (ISBN 0-937422-04-5). Midnight Call.
--How to Walk with God. 1980. 1.95 (ISBN 0-937422-02-9). Midnight Call.
--In the Beginning Was the End. pap. 4.95 (ISBN 0-937422-33-9). Midnight Call.
--Israel Shall Do Valiantly. 3.95 (ISBN 0-937422-05-3). Midnight Call.
--Israel's God Does Not Lie. 4.95 (ISBN 0-937422-06-1). Midnight Call.
--Jerusalem: Focal Point of the World. 3.95 (ISBN 0-937422-08-8). Midnight Call.

--One Thousand Years Peace...A Utopia? 3.95 (ISBN 0-937422-11-8). Midnight Call.
--Prayer & Revival. 4.95 (ISBN 0-937422-12-6). Midnight Call.
--The Rapture & Its Mystery. pap. 1.95 (ISBN 0-937422-13-4). Midnight Call.
--Russia's Last Invasion. 1980. 3.95 (ISBN 0-937422-01-0). Midnight Call.
--Seven Signs of a Born Again Person. 1.45 (ISBN 0-937422-14-2). Midnight Call.
--Shadows of Armageddon. 4.95 (ISBN 0-937422-15-0). Midnight Call.
--The Sword of the Lord. pap. 2.95 (ISBN 0-937422-24-X). Midnight Call.
--There Shall Be Signs from 1948 to 1982. 1980. 2.95 (ISBN 0-937422-00-2). Midnight Call.
--Twentieth Century Handwriting on the Wall. 4.95 (ISBN 0-686-12823-0). Midnight Call.

Malherbe, Abraham. Paul & the Thessalonians: The Philosophic Tradition of Pastoral Care. LC 86-45918. 144p. 1987. 8.95 (ISBN 0-8006-0863-1, 1-863). Fortress.

Malherbe, Abraham, tr. Gregory of Nyssa: The Life of Moses. LC 78-56352. (Classics of Western Spirituality Ser.). (Illus.). 224p. 1978. 12.95 (ISBN 0-8091-0239-0); pap. 7.95 (ISBN 0-8091-2112-3). Paulist Pr.

Malherbe, Abraham J. Moral Exhortation, a Greco-Roman Sourcebook. LC 86-5499. (Library of Early Christianity: Vol. 4). 180p. 1986. 18.95 (ISBN 0-664-21908-X). Westminster.
--Social Aspects of Early Christianity. 2nd, rev. ed. LC 83-5602. 144p. 1983. pap. 7.95 (ISBN 0-8006-1748-7, 1-1748). Fortress.

Malhotra, S. S. Gangaotri & Gaumukh: A Trek to the Holy Source. 1984. 12.50x (ISBN 0-8364-1175-7, Pub. by Allied India). South Asia Bks.

Malik, Charles. The Two Tasks. 37p. 1980. pap. 1.95 (ISBN 0-89107-212-8, Crossway Bks). Good News.

Malik, Charles, ed. God & Man in Contemporary Christian Thought. 1970. 16.95x (ISBN 0-8156-6016-2, Am U Beirut). Syracuse U Pr.
--God & Man in Contemporary Islamic Thought. 1972. 16.95x (ISBN 0-8156-6035-9, Am U Beirut). Syracuse U Pr.

Malik, Fida H. Wives of the Prophet. 185p. (Orig.). 1981. pap. 5.75 (ISBN 0-686-31657-6) (ISBN 0-88004-005-X). Sunwise Turn.

Malik, Hafeez, tr. see Khan, Syed A.

Malik, Imam & Din, M. R. Muwata. 25.50 (ISBN 0-686-83588-3). Kazi Pubns.

Malik, S. C., ed. see Saraswati, Baidyanath.

Malina, Bruce J. Christian Origins & Cultural Anthropology: Practical Models for Biblical Interpretation. 288p. 1985. pap. 24.95 (ISBN 0-8042-0241-9). John Knox.
--The New Testament World: Insights from Cultural Anthropology. LC 80-84650. (Illus.). 169p. 1981. pap. 10.95 (ISBN 0-8042-0423-3). John Knox.

Malina, Bruce J., ed. & tr. see Lohfink, Gerhard.

Malino, Frances. The Sephardic Jews of Bordeaux: Assimilation & Emancipation in Revolutionary & Napoleonic France. LC 77-22659. (Judaic Studies: Vol. 7). 200p. 1978. 15.75 (ISBN 0-8173-6903-1). U of Ala Pr.

Malino, Frances & Albert, Phyllis C., eds. Essays in Modern Jewish History: A Tribute to Ben Halpern. LC 80-70585. 500p. 1981. 27.50 (ISBN 0-8386-3095-2). Fairleigh Dickinson.

Malinowski, Bronislaw. The Foundations of Faith & Morals. LC 74-20949. 1974. Repr. of 1936 ed. lib. bdg. 20.50 (ISBN 0-8414-5965-7). Folcroft.
--Myth in Primitive Psychology. LC 79-152394. 94p. 1972. Repr. of 1926 ed. text ed. 22.50x (ISBN 0-8371-5954-7, MMP&, Pub. by Negro U Pr). Greenwood.

Malinski, Mieczyslaw. Faith to Move Mountains: Reflections on the Gospels of the Lectionary (A, B, C,) LC 82-61194. 144p. 1982. 5.95 (ISBN 0-8245-0509-3). Crossroad NY.
--Our Daily Bread. 142p. 1979. 7.95 (ISBN 0-8245-0363-5). Crossroad NY.

Maliszewski, Joan M., et al. Economic Justice for All: Study Guide, the American Bishops' Pastoral on Social Teaching & the U. S. Economy. 48p. (Orig.). 1987. pap. 1.95 (ISBN 0-8091-5201-0). Paulist Pr.

Malkani, Ghanshamdas R. Philosophy of the Self. 15.00 (ISBN 0-384-35112-3); pap. 10.00 (ISBN 0-685-13549-7). Johnson Repr.

Malkin, Esther, tr. see Goldstein, Charles.

Mall, E. Jane. Abingdon Manual of Installation Services. 80p. (Orig.). 1983. pap. 4.95 (ISBN 0-687-00367-9). Abingdon.
--A Mother's Gifts: A Book of Praise & Inspiration. LC 75-33082. pap. 15.00 (ISBN 0-8357-9017-7, 2016382). Bks Demand UMI.

Mall, E. Jane, jt. auth. see Powers, Betty.

Mallard, William. The Reflection of Theology in Literature: A Case Study in Theology & Culture. LC 76-14036. (Trinity University Monograph Series in Religion). 271p. 1977. 10.00 (ISBN 0-911536-64-7). Trinity U Pr.

Malley, B., tr. see Pradera, Victor.

Mallik, G. N. Philosophy of Vaisnava Religion. 59.95 (ISBN 0-8490-0829-8). Gordon Pr.

Mallis, W. Way of the Wind. (YA) 1971. pap. 1.50 (ISBN 0-87508-326-9). Chr Lit.

Mallison, John. Building Small Groups in the Christian Community. (Abridged Small Group Ser.). (Illus.). 238p. (Orig.). 1978. pap. 7.95 (ISBN 0-909202-05-2, Pub. by Renewal Pubns). ANZ Religious Pubns.
--Creative Ideas for Small Group in the Christian Community. (Abridged Small Group Ser.). 250p. (Orig.). 1978. pap. 7.95 (ISBN 0-909202-06-0, Pub. by Renewal Pubns). ANZ Religious Pubns.

Mallison, John, ed. Youth Outreach & Evangelism: Youth Work Guides Ser. (Illus.). 104p. (Orig.). 1975. pap. 5.95 (ISBN 0-85819-108-3, Pub. by JBCE). ANZ Religious Pubns.

Mallock, W. H. Studies in Contemporary Superstition. 1973. Repr. of 1895 ed. 25.00 (ISBN 0-8274-1566-4). R West.

Mallock, William H. Studies of Contemporary Superstition. LC 72-333. (Essay Index Reprint Ser.). Repr. of 1895 ed. 20.00 (ISBN 0-8369-2804-0). Ayer Co Pubs.

Mallone, George, et al. Those Controversial Gifts. LC 83-8. 168p. (Orig.). 1983. pap. 5.95 (ISBN 0-87784-823-8). Inter-Varsity.

Mallory, James D. & Baldwin, Stanley C. The Kink & I: A Psychiatrist's Guide to Untwisted Living. LC 73-78688. 224p. 1973. pap. 5.95 (ISBN 0-88207-237-4). Victor Bks.

Mallory, Marilyn M. Christian Mysticism Transcending Techniques: A Theological Reflection on the Empirical Testing of the Teaching of St. John of the Cross. 320p. 1977. pap. text ed. 28.00 (ISBN 90-232-1535-4, Pub. by Van Gorcum Holland). Longwood Pub Group.

Mallough, Don. Living by Faith: How an Active Faith Can Change Your Life. LC 77-91484. 128p. 1978. pap. 1.50 (ISBN 0-88243-552-3, 02-0552). Gospel Pub.

Mallow, Vernon. The Demonic: A Selected Theological Study: An Examination into the Theology of Edwin Lewis, Karl Barth, & Paul Tillich. LC 83-1143. 192p. (Orig.). 1983. lib. bdg. 26.00 (ISBN 0-8191-3069-9); pap. text ed. 11.50 (ISBN 0-8191-3070-2). U Pr of Amer.

Malloy, Edward A. Homosexuality & the Christian Way of Life. LC 81-40385. 382p. (Orig.). 1981. lib. bdg. 32.50 (ISBN 0-8191-1794-3); pap. text ed. 14.75 (ISBN 0-8191-1795-1). U Pr of Amer.

Malloy, Joseph L., ed. Catechism for Inquirers. 4th ed. 1984. pap. 2.50 (ISBN 0-8091-5012-3). Paulist Pr.

Malloy, Michael P. Civil Authority in Medieval Philosophy: Lombard, Aquinas & Bonaventure. LC 85-3210. 240p. (Orig.). 1985. lib. bdg. 26.25 (ISBN 0-8191-4582-3); pap. text ed. 12.25 (ISBN 0-8191-4583-1). U Pr of Amer.

Mallwitz, Alfred, jt. auth. see Heyder, Wolfgang.

Malmgreen, Gail, ed. Religion in the Lives of English Women, 1760-1930. LC 86-45172. 224p. 1986. 29.95x (ISBN 0-253-34973-7). Ind U Pr.

Malmin, Ken. New Testament Survey. 1975. 4.25 (ISBN 0-914936-22-0). Bible Temple.
--Old Testament Survey. 1974. 4.25 (ISBN 0-914936-21-2). Bible Temple.

Malmin, Ken P., jt. auth. see Conner, Kevin J.

Malmin, Kenneth P. Bible Research. rev. ed. (Illus.). 149p. 1979. Repr. of 1976 ed. notebk. 11.95 (ISBN 0-914936-33-6). Bible Temple.

Malone, David M. The Church Cannot Ordain Women to the Priesthood. 1978. 0.75 (ISBN 0-8199-0724-3). Franciscan Herald.

Malone, Dumas. Saints in Action. facs. ed. LC 70-142664. (Essay Index Reprint Ser). 1939. 15.00 (ISBN 0-8369-2062-7). Ayer Co Pubs.

Malone, J. W. A New Testament Study Guide. kivar 4.95 (ISBN 0-686-12848-6). Schmul Pub Co.

Malone, Mary T. Step-by-Step: A Cathechetical Handbook for the RCIA. 1986. pap. 19.95 (ISBN 0-697-02204-8). Wm C Brown.
--Who Is My Mother? 144p. 1984. pap. 6.95 (ISBN 0-697-02019-3). Wm C Brown.
--Women Christian: New Vision. 176p. 1985. pap. 6.95 (ISBN 0-697-02064-9). Wm C Brown.

Malone, Richard & Connery, John, eds. Contemporary Perspectives on Christian Marriage. 1984. 19.95 (ISBN 0-8294-0472-4). Loyola.

Malone, Sylvester L. Dr. Edward McGlynn. 17.00 (ISBN 0-405-10841-9, 11847). Ayer Co Pubs.

Malone, Tom. Rejoicing with Creation. pap. 6.95 (ISBN 0-8042-1420-4). John Knox.

Malone, Willie. Your New Beginning: Step Two. 64p. (Orig.). 1983. pap. 2.50 (ISBN 0-88144-008-6). Christian Pub.

Maloney, Clarence, ed. The Evil Eye. LC 76-16861. (Illus.). 334p. 1976. 30.00 (ISBN 0-231-04006-7); pap. 14.50. Columbia U Pr.

Maloney, Dennis, jt. ed. see Eppsteiner, Fred.

Maloney, Elliott C. Semitic Interference in Marcan Syntax. LC 80-13016. (Society of Biblical Literature Dissertation Ser.: No. 51). pap. 15.00 (ISBN 0-89130-406-1, 06-01-51). Scholars Pr GA.

Maloney, George. The Breath of the Mystic. 8.95 (ISBN 0-87193-058-7). Dimension Bks.
--Centering on the Lord Jesus: The Whole Person at Prayer. (Ways of Prayer Ser.: Vol. 3). 1982. 8.95 (ISBN 0-89453-427-0). M Glazier.
--Inscape: God at the Heart of the Matter. 1978. pap. 4.95 (ISBN 0-87193-095-1). Dimension Bks.
--Invaded by God: Mysticism & the Indwelling Trinity. 1979. 5.95 (ISBN 0-87193-107-9). Dimension Bks.
--Inward Stillness. 6.95 (ISBN 0-87193-062-5). Dimension Bks.
--Jesus, Set Me Free! Inner Freedom Through Contemplation. 4.95 (ISBN 0-87193-096-X). Dimension Bks.
--Listen, Prophets! 5.95 (ISBN 0-87193-059-5). Dimension Bks.
--Mary, the Womb of God. 6.95 (ISBN 0-87193-057-9). Dimension Bks.
--Nesting in the Rock. 6.95 (ISBN 0-87193-002-1). Dimension Bks.

Maloney, George, ed. God's Exploding Love. LC 86-28802. 164p. (Orig.). 1987. pap. 7.95 (ISBN 0-8189-0514-X). Alba.

Maloney, George A. Alone with the Alone. LC 81-70021. (Illus.). 208p. (Orig.). 1982. pap. 4.95 (ISBN 0-87793-243-3). Ave Maria.
--Broken but Loved: Healing Through Christ's Power. LC 81-1802. 126p. (Orig.). 1981. pap. 6.95 (ISBN 0-8189-0411-9). Alba.
--Called to Intimacy. LC 83-3782. 164p. 1983. pap. 6.95 (ISBN 0-8189-0452-6). Alba.
--The Everlasting Now. LC 79-57550. 224p. (Orig.). 1980. pap. 3.95 (ISBN 0-87793-201-8). Ave Maria.
--Indwelling Presence. 112p. (Orig.). 1985. pap. 4.50 (ISBN 0-914544-62-4). Living Flame Pr.
--Journey into Contemplation. 144p. (Orig.). 1983. pap. 3.95 (ISBN 0-914544-51-9). Living Flame Pr.
--Manna in the Desert. 120p. (Orig.). 1984. pap. 5.95 (ISBN 0-914544-54-3). Living Flame Pr.
--Prayer of the Heart. LC 80-69095. 208p. (Orig.). 1981. pap. 3.95 (ISBN 0-87793-216-6). Ave Maria.
--The Returning Sun: Hope for a Broken World. 63p. (Orig.). 1982. pap. 2.50 (ISBN 0-914544-42-X). Living Flame Pr.
--The Silence of Surrendering Love: Body, Soul, Spirit Integration. LC 85-28636. 189p. 1986. pap. 7.95 (ISBN 0-8189-0494-1). Alba.
--Singers of the New Song: A Mystical Interpretation of the Song of Songs. LC 85-71639. 176p. (Orig.). 1985. pap. 4.95 (ISBN 0-87793-292-1). Ave Maria.
--Who Do You Say You Are? Christ's Love for Us. (Orig.). 1986. pap. 4.95 (ISBN 0-914544-64-0). Living Flame Pr.

Maloney, George A., ed. The First Day of Eternity: Resurrection Now. 128p. 1982. 8.95 (ISBN 0-8245-0445-3). Crossroad NY.

Maloney, George A., jt. auth. see Gallagher, Charles A.

Maloney, George S. A Theology of Uncreated Energies of God. (Pere Marquette Lecture Ser.). 1978. 7.95 (ISBN 0-87462-516-5). Marquette.

Maloney, L., tr. see Buhler, Walther.

Malony, H. Newton. Church Organization Development: Perspectives & Resources. LC 86-81285. (Orig.). 1986. pap. 10.00 (ISBN 0-9609928-2-0). Integ Pr.
--Clergy Malpractice. Needham, Thomas L. & Southaud, Samuel, eds. LC 85-31466. 192p. (Orig.). 1986. pap. 12.95 (ISBN 0-664-24591-9). Westminster.
--Integration Musings: Thoughts on Being A Christian Professional. LC 86-81512. (Orig.). 1986. pap. 12.95 (ISBN 0-9609928-3-9). Integ Pr.
--Wholeness & Holiness: Readings in the Psychology, Theology of Mental Health. 304p. (Orig.). 1983. pap. 12.95 (ISBN 0-8010-6147-4). Baker Bk.

Malony, H. Newton & Lovekin, A. Adams. Glossolalia: Behavioral Science Perspectives on Speaking in Tongues. 320p. 1985. 29.95x (ISBN 0-19-503569-0). Oxford U Pr.

Malony, H. Newton, jt. auth. see Sanders, Randolph K.

Malony, H. Newton, ed. Is There a Shrink in the Lord's House? How Psychologists Can Help the Church. LC 86-81513. (Orig.). 1986. pap. 12.00 (ISBN 0-9609928-4-7). Integ Pr.

Malony, H. Newton, jt. ed. see Rosik, Christopher H.

Malotki, Ekkehart & Lomatuway'ma, Michael. Maasaw: Profile of a Hopi God. LC 87-163. (American Tribal Religions Ser.: Vol. 11). (Illus.). vi, 432p. 1987. 24.95x (ISBN 0-8032-3118-0); pap. 14.95x (ISBN 0-8032-8148-X, Bison). U of Nebr Pr.
--Stories of Maasaw, a Hopi God. LC 87-164. (American Tribal Religions Ser.: Vol. 10). (Illus.). vi, 388p. 1987. 23.95x (ISBN 0-8032-3117-2); pap. 13.95x (ISBN 0-8032-8147-1). U of Nebr Pr.

Malphurs, J. G. My Hand in His. 1961. 5.00 (ISBN 0-88027-012-8). Firm Foun Pub.

Malraux, André. Metamorphose des Dieux: L'Intemporel. (Illus.). 424p. 1976. 125.00 (ISBN 0-686-56329-8). French & Eur.

Malsch, Sara A. The Image of Martin Luther in the Writings of Novalis & Friedrich Schlegel: The Speculative Vision of History & Religion. (European University Studies: Series 1, German Language & Literature: Vol. 103). 165p. 1974. pap. 18.25 (ISBN 3-261-01453-9). P Lang Pubs.

Malter, Henry, tr. & The Treatise Ta'anit of the Babylonian Talmud. LC 78-1171. (JPS Library of Jewish Classics). 528p. 1978. 6.50 (ISBN 0-8276-0108-5, 422). Jewish Pubns.

Malterner, Virginia M. Circles. (Illus.). 1977. tchrs'. manual 5.25x (ISBN 0-8192-4079-6); wkbk. 3.95x (ISBN 0-8192-4080-X); take-home cards packet 2.50x (ISBN 0-8192-4081-8). Morehouse.

Maltwood, K. E. A Guide to Glastonbury's Temple of the Stars. 128p. 1983. pap. 11.95 (ISBN 0-227-67867-2, Pub. by J Clarke UK). Attic Pr.

Maltz, B. My Glimpse of Eternity. 128p. 3.50 (ISBN 0-8007-8363-8, Spire Bks). Revell.

Maluf, Leonard, tr. see Feuillet, Andre.

Maly, Eugene H. Romans. (New Testament Message Ser.: Vol. 9). 160p. 1980. 12.95 (ISBN 0-89453-197-2); pap. 7.95 (ISBN 0-89453-132-8). M Glazier.
--Wisdom. (Bible Ser.). pap. 1.00 (ISBN 0-8091-5156-1). Paulist Pr.
--The Word Alive: Reflections & Commentaries on the Sunday Readings Cycles A, B, & C. LC 81-20571. (Illus.). 322p. 1982. pap. 12.95 (ISBN 0-8189-0416-X). Alba.

Malyala, P. Vishnu Sahasranamam. (Illus.). 18p. (Orig.). 1986. pap. text ed. 5.00 (ISBN 0-938924-28-1). Sri Shirdi Sai.

Malyala, Panduranga. Sri Sarasvati Puja: Goddess of Knowledge & Education. (Illus.). 28p. 1982. 2.00 (ISBN 0-938924-10-9). Sri Shirdi Sai.
--Yagna (The Eternal Energy) (Illus.). 36p. (Orig.). 1984. pap. text ed. 4.00x (ISBN 0-938924-23-0). Sri Shirdi Sai.

Malyala, Panduranga R. Aum: (Amen) Do, ed. (Illus.). 24p. (Orig.). 1983. pap. 2.00 (ISBN 0-938924-12-5). Sri Shirdi Sai.
--Bhagavadgeeta-Bible-Khuran (Krishna-Jesus Mohammad) Date not set. 3.99 (ISBN 0-938924-04-4). Sri Shirdi Sai.
--Interrelationship Between Atom-Body-Universe (Anda-Pinda-Brah Manda) Date not set. 1.99 (ISBN 0-938924-08-7). Sri Shirdi Sai.
--New Clear Energy: Rudra Abhisekam. (Illus.). 120p. 1983. 5.00 (ISBN 0-938924-11-7). Sri Shirdi Sai.
--Sri Ganesh Puja (Worship of God of Obstacles) (Illus.). 56p. 1982. 2.00 (ISBN 0-938924-03-6). Sri Shirdi Sai.
--Temples & Idol Worship. Date not set. 4.99 (ISBN 0-938924-02-8). Sri Shirdi Sai.
--Upanayanam (Thread Marriage) (Illus.). 20p. 1983. pap. text ed. 2.00 (ISBN 0-938924-15-X). Sri Shirdi Sai.
--Why Cow Protection? Date not set. 1.99 (ISBN 0-938924-01-X). Sri Shirdi Sai.

Malyala, Pandurangarao. Daily Prayers. (Illus., Orig.). 1984. pap. 2.00 (ISBN 0-938924-24-9). Sri Shirdi Sai.

Maly-Schlatter, Florence. Puritan Element in Victorian Fiction. LC 72-195449. 1940. lib. bdg. 20.00 (ISBN 0-8414-5974-6). Folcroft.

Malz, Betty. Prayers That Are Answered. 1981. pap. 3.50 (ISBN 0-451-14948-3, Sig). NAL.
--Super Natural Living. 1983. pap. 2.50 (ISBN 0-451-12517-7, Sig). NAL.

Mamertus, Claudianus. Opera. Engelbrecht, A., ed. (Corpus Scriptorum Ecclesiasticorum Latinorum Ser: Vol. 11). 1885. 50.00 (ISBN 0-384-09245-4). Johnson Repr.

Man, Martha L., jt. ed. see Chase, Barbara H.

Manahan, Nancy, jt. auth. see Curb, Rosemary.

Manahan, Nancy, jt. ed. see Curb, Rosemary.

Manchester, Frederick, jt. tr. see Prabhavananda, Swami.

Man Chong Fung, tr. Be Perfect. 2nd ed. (Chinese.). 160p. 1982. pap. write for info (ISBN 0-941598-03-9). Living Spring Pubns.

Mancinelli, Fabrizio. Catacombs & Basilicas: The Early Christians in Rome. (Illus.). 65p. (Orig.). 1981. pap. 12.50 (ISBN 0-935748-13-X). Scala Books.

Mancinelli, Fabrizio, jt. auth. see Heuzinger, Lutz.

Mancusi-Ungaro, Harold R., Jr. Michelangelo: The Bruges Madonna & the Piccolomini Altar. LC 70-151582. (College Ser.: No. 11). (Illus.). Repr. of 1971 ed. 45.60 (ISBN 0-8357-9387-7, 2013192). Bks Demand UMI.

Mancuso, Laurence. Liturgical Music: Dogmatica & Other Selections, Vol. II. (New Skete). 107p. (Orig.). 1978. pap. 15.00 (ISBN 0-9607924-2-2). Monks of New Skete.
--Liturgical Music: Selection for Vespers, Matins, & Liturgy, Vol. I. (New Skete). 172p. (Orig.). 1975. 18.00x (ISBN 0-9607924-0-6); pap. 15.00x (ISBN 0-9607924-1-4). Monks of New Skete.
--A Prayerbook. (New Skete). (Illus.). 720p. 1976. 35.00x (ISBN 0-9607924-3-0). Monks of New Skete.
Mancuso, Laurence, tr. from Slavonic & Gr. A Service Book. (New Skete). (Illus.). 214p. 1978. 20.00x (ISBN 0-9607924-4-9). Monks of New Skete.
Manda, Swami Jyotir. Yoga Stories & Parables. (Illus.). 1976. pap. 3.99 (ISBN 0-934664-41-2). Yoga Res Foun.
Mandalesvara dasa, ed. see Das Goswami, Satsvarupa.
Mandel, Neville. The Arabs & Zionism Before World War One. LC 73-78545. 1977. pap. 4.95 (ISBN 0-520-03940-8, CAL 430). U of Cal Pr.
Mandel, Oscar, tr. see Tieck, Ludwig.
Mandelbaum. Orah V'Simchoh. cancelled (ISBN 0-87306-117-9). Feldheim.
Mandelbaum, Allen, ed. see Yeshurun, Avoth.
Mandelbaum, Bernard. Choose Life. 1972. pap. 5.95 (ISBN 0-8197-0006-1). Bloch.
--Wisdom of Solomon Schechter. 1963. pap. 2.50 (ISBN 0-8381-3103-4). United Syn Bk.
Mandelbaum, Hugo. Jewish Life in Village Communities of Southern Germany. (Illus.). 96p. 1986. 6.95 (ISBN 0-87306-382-1). Feldheim.
Mandelbaum, Irving J. A History of the Mishnaic Law of Agriculture: Kilayim. Neusner, Jacob, ed. LC 81-1462. (Brown Judaic Studies Ser.: No. 26). 1981. pap. text ed. 18.00 (ISBN 0-89130-465-7, 14 00 26). Scholars Pr GA.
Mandelbaum, Maurice. The Phenomenology of Moral Experience. 336p. 1969. pap. 8.95x (ISBN 0-8018-1095-7). Johns Hopkins.
Mandelker, Ira L. Religion, Society, & Utopia in Nineteenth-Century America. LC 84-47. 200p. 1984. lib. bdg. 22.00x (ISBN 0-87023-436-6). U of Mass Pr.
Mandelkern, Nicholas, ed. see Bamberger, David.
Mandelkern, S. Heichal Hakodesh Concordance to the Old Testament, 1 vol. 95.00 (ISBN 0-87559-163-9). Shalom.
Mandevile. Good Samaritan. (Ladybird Ser.). 1979. 2.50 (ISBN 0-87508-837-6). Chr Lit.
Mandeville. Lost Sheep. (Ladybird Ser.). 1979. pap. 2.50 (ISBN 0-87508-849-X). Chr Lit.
Mandeville, Bernard. Enquiry into the Origin of Honour & the Usefullness of Christianity in War. 240p. 1971. Repr. of 1732 ed. 32.50x (ISBN 0-7146-2314-8, F Cass Co). Biblio Dist.
--Free Thoughts on Religion, the Church, & National Happiness. LC 77-17171. 1981. Repr. of 1720 ed. lib. bdg. 60.00x (ISBN 0-8201-1300-X). Schol Facsimiles.
Mandeville, Sylvia. Amigos de Dios. Gutierrez, Edna L., tr. from Eng. (Serie Apunta Con Tu Dedo). 24p. 1980. pap. 9.95 (ISBN 0-311-38532-X, Edit Mundo). Casa Bautista.
Mandeville, Sylvia & Pierson, Lance. Conoce a Jesus. Gutierrez, Edna L., tr. from Eng. (Pointing Out Bk.). 24p. 1980. pap. 9.95 (ISBN 0-311-38531-1, Edit Mundo). Casa Bautista.
Mandeville, Sylvia, ed. see Hassall, Phillip.
Mandino, Og. The God Memorandum. new ed. LC 80-81145. 112p. 1980. 6.95 (ISBN 0-8119-0337-0). Fell.
--The Greatest Gift in the World. LC 76-43508. (Illus.). 128p. 1976. 8.95 (ISBN 0-8119-0274-9). Fell.
--The Greatest Miracle in the World. 1977. pap. 3.50 (ISBN 0-553-25914-8). Bantam.
--The Greatest Salesman in the World. 128p. 1974. pap. 3.50 (ISBN 0-553-26880-5). Bantam.
--The Greatest Secret in the World. 1978. pap. 3.50 (ISBN 0-553-26545-8). Bantam.
Mandino, Og & Kaye, Buddy. Gift of Acabar. 1979. pap. 3.50 (ISBN 0-553-26084-7). Bantam.
Mandlebaum, Bernard. Live with Meaning. 1980. pap. 7.95 (ISBN 0-87677-182-7). Hartmore.
Maneesha, Ma P., ed. see Rajneesh, Bhagwan S.
Maneesha, Ma Prem, ed. see Rajneesh, Bhagwan S.
Maneesha, Ma Prem, ed. see Rajneesh, Bhagwan Shree.
Maneesha, ma Prem, ed. see Rajneesh, Bhagwan Shree.
Maneesha, Ma Prem, ed. see Rajneesh, Bhagwan Shree.
Maner, Robert E. Making the Small Church Grow. 101p. 1982. pap. 2.95 (ISBN 0-8341-0741-4). Beacon Hill.
Maney, Thomas. Basic Communities: A Practical Guide for Renewing Neighborhood Churches. 96p. (Orig.). 1984. pap. 5.95 (ISBN 0-86683-857-0, 8411, HarpR). Har-Row.
Manfra, Jo Ann, jt. auth. see Shannon, Thomas.
Mangan, Celine. Can We Still Call God "Father"? A Woman Looks at the Lord's Prayer Today. (Ways of Prayer Ser.: Vol. 12). 110p. 1984. pap. 4.95 (ISBN 0-89453-384-3). M Glazier.
--One-Two Chronicles, Ezra, Nehemiah. (Old Testament Message Ser.: Vol. 13). 1982. 12.95 (ISBN 0-89453-413-0); pap. 7.95 (ISBN 0-89453-247-2). M Glazier.
Mangan, John J. Life, Character & Influence of Desiderius Erasmus of Rotterdam, 2 Vols. LC 73-147113. Repr. of 1927 ed. 78.50 (ISBN 0-404-04178-7). AMS Pr.
Mangham, Evelyn. Great Missionaries in a Great Work. Schroeder, E. H., ed. (Illus.). 85p. 1970. pap. 1.75 (ISBN 0-87509-091-5). Chr Pubns.
Mangieri, Rose M. My Companion to Know, Love, & Serve. LC 73-158919. (Know, Love, & Serve Catechisms Ser.). (Illus.). 85p. (Orig.). 1977. pap. 5.50 (ISBN 0-913382-45-0, 103-7). Prow Bks-Franciscan.
Mangieri, Rose M., jt. auth. see McGuire, Michael A.
Mango, Cyril, tr. The Homilies of Photius, Patriarch of Constantinople. (Dumbarton Oaks Studies: Vol. 3). 327p. (LC A58-6068). 1958. 20.00x (ISBN 0-88402-003-7). Dumbarton Oaks.
Manhattan, Avro. Catholic Imperialism & World Freedom. LC 73-161336. (Atheist Viewpoint Ser). 528p. 1972. Repr. of 1952 ed. 29.00 (ISBN 0-405-03810-0). Ayer Co Pubs.
--The Vacation Moscow Washington Alliance. 352p. (Orig.). pap. 7.95 (ISBN 0-937958-12-3). Chick Pubns.
--The Vatican Billions. 304p. (Orig.). 1983. pap. 7.50 (ISBN 0-937958-16-6). Chick Pubns.
Manheim, Karl, tr. see Jaspers, Karl.
Manheim, R., tr. see Corbin, Henry.
Manheim, R., tr. see Kerenyi, Carl.
Manheim, Ralph, tr. see Cassirer, Ernst.
Manheim, Ralph, tr. see Jaspers, Karl.
Manibhai, ed. see Aurobindo, Sri.
Maniscalco, Joe. Bible Hero Stories. LC 74-28725. (Illus.). 144p. 1975. 6.95 (ISBN 0-87239-036-5, 2746). Standard Pub.
--Eight Laws of Health. 1985. pap. 3.95 (ISBN 0-8163-0568-4). Pacific Pr Pub Assn.
--Joseph. LC 74-28725. (Bible Hero Stories). (Illus.). 48p. (Orig.). 1975. pap. 2.00 (ISBN 0-87239-332-1, 2737). Standard Pub.
Manjusrimitra. Primordial Experience: An Introduction to Dzog-chen Meditation. Lipman, Kennard & Norbu, Namkhai, trs. from Tibetan. LC 86-11842. Tr. of Rdo La Gser Zhun. 140p. 1986. pap. 11.95 (ISBN 0-87773-372-4). Shambhala Pubns.
Mankin, Jim. Prescription for Troubled Hearts. 1984. pap. 5.95 (ISBN 0-89225-273-1). Gospel Advocate.
Manley, Gregory, jt. auth. see Crotty, Robert.
Manley, Stephen L. Journey into Wholeness. 96p. (Orig.). 1983. pap. 2.95 (ISBN 0-8341-0832-1). Beacon Hill.
Manley-Casimir, Michael, jt. ed. see Cochrane, Donald B.
Manly, John M. Specimens of the Pre-Shakespearean Drama, 2 Vols. LC 67-18432. 1897. 20.00 (ISBN 0-8196-0200-0). Biblo.
Mann, C. S. Mark: A New Translation with Introduction & Commentary, Vol. 27. LC 85-4433. (Illus.). 744p. 1986. 20.00 (ISBN 0-385-03253-6, Anchor). Doubleday.
Mann, C. S., jt. ed. see Albright, William F.
Mann, C. Stephen. Man for All Time. LC 75-161567. 1971. pap. 2.50 (ISBN 0-8192-1127-3). Morehouse.
--The Message Delivered. 128p. (Orig.). 1973. pap. 2.50 (ISBN 0-8192-1143-5). Morehouse.
Mann, Denese B. The Woman in Judaism. 1979. pap. 5.50 (ISBN 0-9603348-0-7). Jonathan Pubns.
Mann, George A. Recovery of Reality: Overcoming Chemical Dependency. LC 78-19496. (Illus.). 1979. 14.45 (ISBN 0-06-250560-2, HarpR). Har-Row.
Mann, Gertrude, jt. auth. see Rabinsky, Leatrice.
Mann, Jacob. The Bible As Read & Preached in the Old Synagogue, Vol. 1. rev. ed. (Library of Biblical Studies). 1970. 59.50x (ISBN 0-87068-083-8). Ktav.
--The Responsa of the Babylonian Geonim As a Source of Jewish History. LC 73-2215. (The Jewish People; History, Religion, Literature Ser.). Repr. of 1921 ed. 23.50 (ISBN 0-405-05279-0). Ayer Co Pubs.
--Texts & Studies in Jewish History & Literature, 2 Vols. rev. ed. 1970. Set. 99.50x (ISBN 0-87068-085-4). Ktav.
Mann, John, ed. see Rudrananda, Swami.
Mann, Leonard. Life-Size Living. Sherer, Michael L., ed. (Orig.). 1986. pap. 6.25 (ISBN 0-89536-820-X, 6829). CSS of Ohio.
--Where Two or Three Are Gathered. 1986. 6.25 (ISBN 0-89536-791-2, 6809). CSS of Ohio.
Mann, Leonard W. Stars for Your Sky. 1982. pap. 4.95 (ISBN 0-89536-520-0, 1901). CSS of Ohio.
Mann, Lester. On the Trail of Process. 592p. 1979. 46.00 (ISBN 0-8089-1137-6, 792678). Grune.
Mann, Richard D. The Light of Consciousness: Explorations in Transpersonal Psychology. 208p. 1984. 39.50 (ISBN 0-87395-905-1); pap. 10.95 trade disc. (ISBN 0-87395-906-X). State U NY Pr.
Mann, Stella T. Beyond the Darkness. 1972. pap. 2.95 (ISBN 0-87516-054-9). De Vorss.
--Change Your Life Through Prayer. 1971. pap. 3.95 (ISBN 0-87516-053-0). De Vorss.
--How to Live in the Circle of Prayer & Make Your Dreams Come True. (Illus.). 180p. 1975. pap. 4.95 (ISBN 0-87516-206-1). De Vorss.
Mann, Thomas. Joseph & His Brothers. (YA) 1948. 35.00 (ISBN 0-394-43132-4). Knopf.
Mann, Victor. He Remembered to Say "Thank You". (Arch Bks: No. 13). (Illus.). 32p. 1976. pap. 0.99 (ISBN 0-570-06103-2, 59-1221). Concordia.
Mann, Vivian B. & Kleeblatt, Norman. Treasures of the Jewish Museum. LC 85-28913. (Illus.). 216p. 1986. text ed. 35.00x (ISBN 0-87663-493-5); pap. 19.95 (ISBN 0-87663-890-6). Universe.
Mann, Vivian B. & Tucker, Gordon, eds. The Seminar on Jewish Art: Proceedings. 37p. (Orig.). 1985. pap. 6.00 (ISBN 0-87334-029-9). Jewish Sem.
Mann, Warner. The Healing Power of Inversion Thinking from Soul to Body. LC 85-91344. (Metaphysics for Everyone Ser.: No. 1). (Illus.). 250p. (Orig.). 1986. 14.95 (ISBN 0-9615973-0-5); pap. 9.95 (ISBN 0-9615973-1-3). Cos Sci Orange.
Mann, William E. Sect, Cult & Church in Alberta. rev. ed. LC 56-2838. 1972. 20.00x (ISBN 0-8020-5036-0). U of Toronto Pr.
Mannan, M. A. The Frontiers of Islamic Economics. 1985. 15.00x (ISBN 0-8364-1505-1, Pub. by Idarah). South Asia Bks.
Manney, James & Blattner, John. Death in the Nursery: The Secret Crime of Infanticide. 224p. (Orig.). 1984. pap. 6.95 (ISBN 0-89283-192-8). Servant.
Mannhardt, Wilhelm. Mythologische Forschungen Aus Dem Nachlasse, 2 vols. in 1. Bolle, Kees W., ed. LC 77-79142. (Mythology Ser.). (Ger.). 1978. Repr. of 1868 ed. lib. bdg. 38.50x (ISBN 0-405-10551-7). Ayer Co Pubs.
Manni, Alvin. Take & Read: Gems from the Bible. 280p. (Orig.). 1981. pap. 7.50 (ISBN 0-89944-054-1). Don Bosco Multimedia.
Manni, Alvin S. Brother Peter Ferraris. (Illus.). 1974. pap. 4.95 (ISBN 0-89944-027-4). Don Bosco Multimedia.
Manning, A. J. Helping Yourself with White Witchcraft. 1972. 9.95 (ISBN 0-13-386565-7, Reward); pap. 4.95 (ISBN 0-13-386573-8). P-H.
Manning, Al G. The Miraculous Laws of Universal Dynamics. 1964. pap. 5.95 (ISBN 0-317-46046-3). Pan Ishtar.
--Moon Lore & Moon Magic. 1980. 14.95 (ISBN 0-13-600668-X). Pan Ishtar.
Manning, Bernard L. Making of Modern English Religion. LC 70-161528. 1929. text ed. 6.00x (ISBN 0-8401-1558-X). A R Allenson.
Manning, Brennan. The Gentle Revolutionaries. 5.95 (ISBN 0-87193-012-9). Dimension Bks.
--The Parable of Willie Juan. 1985. 2.95 (ISBN 0-87193-162-1). Dimension Bks.
--Prophets & Lovers: In Search of the Holy Spirit. 1985. 4.95 (ISBN 0-87193-013-7). Dimension Bks.
--Stranger to Self-Hatred. 6.95 (ISBN 0-87193-156-7). Dimension Bks.
--The Wisdom of Accepted Tenderness. casebound 5.95 (ISBN 0-87193-110-9); pap. 4.95. Dimension Bks.
Manning, Doug. Comforting Those Who Grieve: A Guide for Helping Others. LC 84-48226. 112p. 1985. 10.45 (ISBN 0-06-065418-X, HarpR). Har-Row.
Manning, Joseph F. The Miracle of Agape Love. 160p. 1977. pap. 2.95 (ISBN 0-88368-079-3). Whitaker Hse.
Manning, Leonard F. The Law of Church-State Relations in a Nutshell. LC 80-22991. (Nutshell Ser.). 305p. 1981. pap. text ed. 10.95 (ISBN 0-8299-2113-3). West Pub.
Manning, Michael. Pardon My Lenten Smile: Daily Homily-Meditation Themes for the Weekdays of Lent. 90p. 1976. pap. 5.95 (ISBN 0-8189-0325-2). Alba.
Manning, Robert, jt. ed. see Cowper, J. M.
Manning, Warren F., ed. see Domingo De Guzman, Saint.
Manning, William O. & Vinton, Jean, eds. Harmfully Involved: Updated for the Eighties. 168p. (Orig.). 1978. pap. 10.95 (ISBN 0-89486-056-9). Hazelden.
Manns, Peter. Martin Luther: An Illustrated Biography. LC 83-1083. (Illus.). 128p. 1983. 14.95 (ISBN 0-8245-0563-8). Crossroad NY.
Manns, Peter & Meyer, Harding, eds. Luther's Ecumenical Significance: An Interconfessional Consultation. LC 83-48001. 336p. 1983. pap. 24.95 (ISBN 0-8006-1747-9, 1-1747). Fortress.
Manoni, Mary H., jt. auth. see Himmel, Roger J.
Manrique, Angel. Annales Cistercienses, 4 vols. 3196p. Date not set. Repr. of 1659 ed. text ed. 662.40x (ISBN 0-576-72863-2, Pub. by Gregg Intl Pubs England). Gregg Intl.
Manross, William W. Episcopal Church in the United States, 1800-1840: A Study in Church Life. LC 38-38020. (Columbia University. Studies in the Social Sciences: No. 441). Repr. of 1938 ed. 21.00 (ISBN 0-404-51441-3). AMS Pr.
Manschreck, Clyde L. A History of Christianity in the World: From Persecution to Uncertainty. 2nd ed. (Illus.). 352p. 1985. text ed. 28.67 (ISBN 0-13-389354-5). P-H.
--Melanchthon: The Quiet Reformer. LC 73-21263. (Illus.). 350p. 1975. Repr. of 1958 ed. lib. bdg. 27.25x (ISBN 0-8371-6131-2, MAMQ). Greenwood.
Manschreck, Clyde L., ed. A History of Christianity: Volume II, Readings in the History of the Church from the Reformation to the Present. 576p. 1981. pap. 23.95 (ISBN 0-8010-6124-5). Baker Bk.
Manschreck, Clyde L. & Zikmund, Barbara B., eds. The American Religious Experiment: Piety & Practicality. LC 76-7199. (Studies in Ministry & Parish Life). 128p. 1976. 13.95x (ISBN 0-913552-06-2); pap. 6.95x (ISBN 0-913552-07-0). Exploration Pr.
Manschreck, Clyde L., ed. & tr. see Melanchthon, Philip.
Mansel, H. L. The Limits of Religious Thought. 5th ed. 1986. Repr. of 1870 ed. lib. bdg. 25.00X (ISBN 0-935005-46-3). Ibis Pub VA.
Mansel, Henry L. The Gnostic Heresies of the First & Second Centuries. Lightfoot, J. B., ed. LC 78-63170. (Heresies of the Early Christian & Medieval Era: Second Ser.). Repr. of 1875 ed. 42.00 (ISBN 0-404-16185-5). AMS Pr.
--Limits of Religious Thought Examined. LC 72-172840. Repr. of 1859 ed. 25.00 (ISBN 0-404-04182-5). AMS Pr.
Manser, Nancy. Older People Have Choices: Information for Decisions about Health, Home, & Money. 32p. (Orig.). 1984. pap. 3.95 (ISBN 0-8066-2098-6, 10-4741). Augsburg.
Mansfield, Bruce. Phoenix of His Age: Interpretations of Erasmus, Fifteen Fifty to Seventeen Fifty. LC 79-14960. (Erasmus Studies). (Illus.). 1979. 30.00x (ISBN 0-8020-5457-9). U of Toronto Pr.
Manske, Ron. A Polish Love Story. LC 79-84322. (Illus.). 1979. pap. 2.50 (ISBN 0-89221-060-5). New Leaf.
Manson, T. W. A Companion to the Bible. Rowley, H. H., ed. 592p. 1963. 19.95x (ISBN 0-567-02197-1, Pub. by T & T Clark Ltd UK). Fortress.
Manson, William. Jesus & the Christian. 236p. 1967. 14.00 (ISBN 0-227-67723-4). Attic Pr.
Mansoor, Menahem. Biblical Hebrew Step by Step: A Significant Breakthrough for Learning Biblical Hebrew. 1978. pap. 12.95 (ISBN 0-8010-6041-9); cassette 7.95 (ISBN 0-8010-6074-5). Baker Bk.
--Biblical Hebrew Step by Step II: Readings from the Book of Genesis. 230p. (Orig.). 1984. pap. 13.95 (ISBN 0-8010-6151-2); cassette 7.95 (ISBN 0-8010-6198-9). Baker Bk.
--The Dead Sea Scrolls. 2nd ed. 300p. 1983. pap. 8.95 (ISBN 0-8010-6152-0). Baker Bk.
--Key to Biblical Hebrew Step by Step, No. 1. pap. 7.95 (ISBN 0-8010-6100-8). Baker Bk.
--Modern Hebrew Literature Reader for Advanced Students, 2 vols. 1971. Vol. 1. 14.95x; Vol. 2. 16.95x (ISBN 0-685-27921-9). Ktav.
Mansoor, Menahem, et al, trs. see Pakuda, Bahya I.
Mansoor, Menham. Key to the Biblical Hebrew, No. 2. 7.95 (ISBN 0-8010-6182-2). Baker Bk.
Manspeaker, Nancy. Jonathan Edwards, Seventeen Fifty-Six to Nineteen Seventy-Eight: Bibliographical Synopses. LC 81-9491. (Studies in American Religion: Vol. 3). (Illus.). xviii, 278p. 1981. 49.95x (ISBN 0-88946-907-5). E Mellen.
Mansukhana, Gobind Sigh. Maharaja Ranjit Singh. (Illus.). 1982. 6.25 (ISBN 0-89744-247-4). Auromere.
Mansur, Ina. A New England Church: Its First Hundred Years. LC 74-76868. (Illus.). 256p. 1974. 10.95 (ISBN 0-87027-139-3); pap. 5.95 (ISBN 0-87027-140-7). Cumberland Pr.
Manteau-Bonamy, H. M. Immaculate Conception & the Holy Spirit: The Marian Teachings of Father Kolbe. Geiger, Bernard M., ed. Arnandez, Richard, tr. from Fr. LC 77-93104. Tr. of Doctrine mariale du Pere Kolbe, Esprit-Saint et Conception Immaculee. (Illus.). 1977. pap. 4.00 (ISBN 0-913382-00-0, 101-20). Prow Bks-Franciscan.
Mantel, Herman & Mantel, Hugo. Mantel's Folks Redner: Mantel's Sermons & Address in Yiddish Language for All Jewish Holidays & Many Other Occasions. 320p. 27.50 (ISBN 0-87559-148-5). Shalom.
Mantel, Hugo, jt. auth. see Mantel, Herman.

Manternach, Janaan & Pfeifer, Carl J. Creative Catechist. (Illus.). 144p. (Orig.). 1983. pap. text ed. 6.95 (ISBN 0-89622-169-5). Twenty-Third.
--Living Water: Prayers of Our Heritage. LC 78-58965. (Illus.). 128p. 1978. pap. 3.95 (ISBN 0-8091-2128-X). Paulist Pr.
Manteuffel, Gregory, jt. auth. see Chernin, Dennis K.
Mantey, J. R., jt. auth. see Dana, H. E.
Mantey, R., jt. auth. see Dana, H. E.
Manthey, F. Die Sprachphilosophie Des Hl, Thomas Von Aquin. (Philosophy Reprints Ser.). (Ger.). Repr. of 1937 ed. lib. bdg. 45.00x (ISBN 0-697-00042-7). Irvington.
Manthey-Zorn, Otto, tr. see Kant, Immanuel.
Mantle, Alexander. The Sex Tenets of the Catholic Church & the Ultimate Destinies of Man. 1979. 41.75 (ISBN 0-89266-146-1). Am Classical Coll Pr.
Mantle, J. Gregory. Better Things from Above. 1971. pap. 3.00 (ISBN 0-87509-051-6). Chr Pubns.
--Beyond Humiliation. LC 75-6163. 256p. 1975. pap. 4.95 (ISBN 0-87123-040-2). Bethany Hse.
Manton, J. D. Introduction to Theological German. 1973. pap. 4.95 (ISBN 0-8028-1514-6). Eerdmans.
Manton, Joseph. Straws from the Crib. (Orig.). 1964. 5.95 (ISBN 0-8198-0150-X); pap. 4.95 (ISBN 0-8198-0151-8). Dghtrs St Paul.
--A View from the Steeple. LC 85-60519. 180p. (Orig.). 1985. pap. 7.95 (ISBN 0-87973-591-0, 591). Our Sunday Visitor.
Manton, Joseph E. Pennies from a Poor Box. 1962. 6.50 (ISBN 0-8198-0119-4). Dghtrs St Paul.
Manton, Thomas. Exposition of the Epistle of Jude. 375p. 14.00 (ISBN 0-86524-172-4, 6501). Klock & Klock.
--James. 1983. 15.95 (ISBN 0-85151-074-4). Banner of Truth.
Mantzaridis, Georgios I. The Deification of Man. Sherrard, Liadain, tr. from Gr. 136p. (Orig.). 1984. pap. text ed. 7.95 (ISBN 0-88141-027-6). St Vladimirs.
Manuel, David. Like a Mighty River. LC 77-90948. (Illus.). 220p. 1977. 5.95 (ISBN 0-932260-02-0). Rock Harbor.
Manuel, David & Marshall, Peter. In God They Trusted. 60p. (Orig.). 1983. pap. 6.95 (ISBN 0-919463-07-X). Paraclete Pr.
Manuel, David, jt. auth. see Marshall, Peter.
Manuel, David, jt. auth. see Wilkerson, Don.
Manuel, Frank E. The Changing of the Gods. LC 82-40475. 216p. 1983. 20.00x (ISBN 0-87451-254-9). U Pr of New Eng.
Manuel, M. Seventeenth Century Critics & Biographers of Milton. LC 77-23430. 1962. lib. bdg. 19.50 (ISBN 0-8414-6184-8). Folcroft.
Manwaring, Randle. From Controversy to Co-Existence: Evangelicals in the Church of England, 1914-1980. 240p. 1985. 34.50 (ISBN 0-521-30380-X). Cambridge U Pr.
Manzano, R. Whitney, jt. auth. see Cho, Paul Y.
Ma'Oz, Moshe, ed. Studies on Palestine During the Ottoman Period. 582p. 1975. text ed. 40.00x (Pub. by Magnes Pr Israel). Humanities.
Ma P. Karima, ed. see Rajneesh, Bhagwan S.
Maple. Superstition, Are You Superstitious? pap. 2.00 (ISBN 0-87980-245-6). Wilshire.
Mapou, May. Love Is Forever. 1984. 4.95 (ISBN 0-8062-2196-8). Carlton.
Mappen, Marc. Witches & Historians: Interpretations of Salem. LC 78-2579. (American Problem Studies). 126p. 1980. pap. 6.50 (ISBN 0-88275-653-2). Krieger.
Mappes, T. A. & Zembathy, J. S. Social Ethics: Morality & Social Policy. 3rd ed. 528p. 1987. 22.95 (ISBN 0-07-040125-X). McGraw.
Ma Prem Apa, ed. see Rajneesh, Bhagwan Shree.
Ma Prema Veena, ed. see Rajneesh, Bhagwan S.
Ma Prem Maneesha, ed. see Rajneesh, Bhagwan Shree.
Ma Prem Rajo, ed. see Rajneesh, Bhagwan Shree.
Mapson, J. Wendell, Jr. The Ministry of Music in the Black Church. 1984. pap. 5.95 (ISBN 0-8170-1057-2). Judson.
Maquarrie, John. In Search of Deity. 288p. 14.95 (ISBN 0-8245-0682-0). Crossroad NY.
--Twentieth Century Religion Thought: The Frontiers of Philosophy & Theology, 1900-1980. rev. ed. 429p. 1981. pap. text ed. write for info. (ISBN 0-02-374500-2, Pub. by Scribner). Macmillan.
Mara. The Middle Sphere. LC 81-67349. (Earth Song Ser.). (Illus.). 57p. (Orig.). 1981. pap. 4.95 (ISBN 0-9605170-1-4). Earth-Song.
--Tracings. LC 80-67934. (Earth Song Ser.). 84p. 1980. pap. 4.95 (ISBN 0-9605170-0-6). Earth-Song.
Marable, Manning. Blackwater: Essays on Black & Southern History. 1978. 12.00 (ISBN 0-89421-028-9). Challenge Pr.
Maraldo, John C., tr. see Dumoulin, Heinrich.
Maraldo, John C., tr. see Lassalle, H. M.
Marana, Nelly, tr. see Lustiger, Jean-Marie.
Maranell, Gary M. Responses to Religion: Studies in the Social Psychology of Religious Belief. LC 73-19860. (Illus.). xviii, 314p. 1974. 25.00x (ISBN 0-7006-0114-7). U Pr of KS.
Marans, Nelly, ed. see Varillon, Francois.
Marans, Nelly, tr. see Auboyer, Jeannine.
Marar, K. Narayana, tr. see Siddheswarananda, Swami.
Maras, Raymond J. Innocent XI, Pope of Christian Unity. (The Church & the World Ser.). xiv, 356p. 1984. 42.85x (ISBN 0-317-52635-9); lib. bdg. 42.85x. Cross Cultural Pubns.
Marathe, M. P., et al, eds. Studies in Jainism. 267p. 1986. pap. 9.50X (ISBN 0-8364-1665-1, Pub. by Abhinav India). South Asia Bks.
Marbeck, John see Buck, P. C. & Fellowes, E. H.
Marbury, Edward. Obadiah & Habakkuk. 1979. 23.95 (ISBN 0-86524-007-8, 7003). Klock & Klock.
MARC, ed. Directory: North American Protestant Schools & Professors of Mission. 220p. pap. 6.60 (ISBN 0-912552-37-9). Missions Adv Res Com Ctr.
Marcel, Gabriel. Being & Having: An Existentialist Diary. 11.25 (ISBN 0-8446-2528-0). Peter Smith.
--Creative Fidelity. (The New Crossroad Paperback Ser.). 304p. 1982. pap. 9.95 (ISBN 0-8245-0446-1). Crossroad NY.
--Mystery of Being, Vol. I: Reflection & Mystery. 238p. 1984. pap. text ed. 8.50 (ISBN 0-8191-3310-8). U Pr of Amer.
--Mystery of Being, Vol. II: Faith & Reality. 198p. 1984. pap. text ed. 7.75 (ISBN 0-8191-3311-6). U Pr of Amer.
Marcel, George, ed. see Moorman, John R.
Marcel, Pierre. The Biblical Doctrine of Infant Baptism. Hughes, Philip E., tr. from Fr. 256p. 1983. pap. 11.95 (ISBN 0-227-67855-9, Pub. by J Clarke UK). Attic Pr.
Marcel, Pierre Ch. Relevance of Preaching. (Notable Books on Preaching). 1977. pap. 2.95 (ISBN 0-8010-6037-0). Baker Bk.
Marcel, Raymond, et al. Builders & Humanists: The Renaissance Popes As Patrons of the Arts. (Illus.). 1966. pap. 8.00 (ISBN 0-914412-20-5). Inst for the Arts.
Marcello, Cristoforo. De Authoritate Summi Pontificis. 304p. Repr. of 1521 ed. text ed. 66.24x (ISBN 0-576-99483-9, Pub. by Gregg Intl Pubs England). Gregg Intl.
March, A. C. A Glossary of Buddhist Terms. 99p. 1986. Repr. of 1937 ed. lib. bdg. 10.50 (ISBN 81-7030-025-8, Pub. by Sri Satguru Pubns India). Orient Bk Dist.
March, Daniel. Night Scenes in the Bible. LC-77-189204. 348p. 1977. 12.95 (ISBN 0-8254-3211-1). Kregel.
March, W. Eugene, ed. Texts & Testaments: Critical Essays on the Bible & Early Church Fathers. LC 79-92585. 321p. 1980. 15.00 (ISBN 0-911536-80-9). Trinity U Pr.
Marc'hadour, Germain. The Bible in the Works of Thomas More, 2 vols. 1098p. 1969. Set. text ed. 127.50x (Pub. by B De Graaf Netherlands). Coronet Bks.
Marcham, William, jt. ed. see Lovell, Percy.
Marchand, Cecilia. Once upon a Rainbow. (Illus.). 128p. 1986. 8.95 (ISBN 0-89962-558-4). Todd & Honeywell.
Marchand, Roger. Meeting Jesus in Holy Communion. 32p. 1984. pap. 1.75 (ISBN 0-89243-202-0). Liguori Pubns.
Marchand, Roger, ed. see Thevenot, Xavier.
Marchant, David. Understanding Shmittah. 1987. 10.95. Feldheim.
Marchant, James. Anthology of Jesus. Wiersbe, Warren W., ed. LC 80-25038. 382p. 1981. Repr. of 1926 ed. 11.95 (ISBN 0-8254-4015-7). Kregel.
--The Reunion of Christendom: A Survey of Present Position. 329p. 1980. Repr. of 1929 ed. lib. bdg. 30.00 (ISBN 0-8495-3771-1). Arden Lib.
Marchbanks, John B. Great Doctrines Relating to Salvation. LC 73-123612. 1970. pap. 2.95 (ISBN 0-87213-640-X). Loizeaux.
--Your Little One Is in Heaven. pap. 1.95 (ISBN 0-87213-642-6). Loizeaux.
Marchi, Attilio de see De Marchi, Attilio.
Marchi, John Di see Di Marchi, John.
Marciano, Teresa & Sussman, Marvin B., eds. Families & the Prospect of Nuclear Attack-Holocaust. LC 86-18320. (Marriage & Family Review Ser.: Vol. 10, No. 2). 1986. pap. 22.95 (ISBN 0-86656-374-1). Haworth Pr.
Marcion Of Sinope. The Gospel of the Lord. Hill, James H., tr. LC 78-63171. (Heresies of the Early Christian & Medieval Era: Second Ser.). Repr. of 1891 ed. 19.50 (ISBN 0-404-16186-3). AMS Pr.
Marco, Tony, jt. auth. see Mayson, Barry.
Marcotte, Armand, jt. auth. see Druffel, Ann.
Marcoux, Marcene. Cursillo: Anatomy of a Movement: The Experience of Spiritual Renewal. 299p. 1982. 16.95x (ISBN 0-931186-00-5). Lambeth Pr.
Marcoux, Paul & LoCigno, Joseph P., eds. Reading, Preaching & Celebrating the Word. pap. 9.95 (ISBN 0-941850-00-5). Sunday Pubns.
Marculescu, Ileana, jt. ed. see Ibish, Yusuf.
Marcus, Audrey F. & Zwerin, Raymond A. Shabbat Can Be. Syme, Daniel B., ed. (Illus.). 1979. pap. text ed. 7.95 (ISBN 0-8074-0023-8, 102560); tchrs'. guide 3.00 (ISBN 0-8074-0024-6, 208025). UAHC.
Marcus, Audrey F., jt. auth. see Zwerin, Raymond A.
Marcus, Audrey F. & Zwerin, Raymond A., eds. The Jewish Principals Handbook. LC 83-70198. 525p. 1983. text ed. 45.00 (ISBN 0-86705-035-7); pap. text ed. 39.95 (ISBN 0-86705-010-1). AIRE.
Marcus, David. Jephthah & His Vow. 80p. 1986. 25.00 (ISBN 0-89672-136-1); pap. 15.00 (ISBN 0-89672-135-3). Tex Tech Univ Pr.
Marcus, J. R., ed. Jews & the American Revolution: A Bicentennial Documentary. 7.50x (ISBN 0-87068-875-8). Ktav.
Marcus, J. R. & Bilgray, A., eds. Index to Jewish Festschriften. Repr. of 1937 ed. 29.00 (ISBN 0-527-61300-2). Kraus Repr.
Marcus, Jacob R. The American Jewish Woman: A Documentary History. 1981. 35.00x (ISBN 0-87068-752-2). Ktav.
--An Index to Articles on American Jewish History. 1971. 20.00x (ISBN 0-87068-139-7). Ktav.
--An Index to the Picture Collection of the American Jewish Archives. 7.50 (ISBN 0-87820-005-3). Ktav.
--An Introduction to Early American Jewish History. (Texts & Studies). (Hebrew.). 1971. 10.00 (ISBN 0-911934-09-X). Am Jewish Hist Soc.
--Israel Jacobson: The Founder of the Reform Movement in Judaism. 12.50x (ISBN 0-87820-000-2, Pub. by Hebrew Union). Ktav.
--Jew in the Medieval World: A Source Book: 315-1791. LC 60-8666. (Temple Books). 1969. pap. text ed. 10.95x (ISBN 0-689-70133-0, T7). Atheneum.
--The Jew in the Medieval World: A Source Book, 315-1791. LC 71-97295. 504p. 1975. Repr. of 1938 ed. lib. bdg. 22.50x (ISBN 0-8371-2619-3, MAJM). Greenwood.
--Jewish Americana. 1954. 7.50x (ISBN 0-87068-799-9, Pub. by Hebrew Union). Ktav.
--The Rise & Destiny of the German Jew. rev. ed. 1971. 15.00x (ISBN 0-87068-148-6). Ktav.
--Studies in American Jewish History. 1969. 15.00x (ISBN 0-87820-003-7, Pub. by Hebrew Union). Ktav.
Marcus, Jacob R. & Peck, Abraham J. The American Rabbinate: A Century of Continuity & Change 1883-1983. 300p. 1985. text ed. 20.00x (ISBN 0-88125-076-7). Ktav.
Marcus, Jacob R., ed. The American Jewish Woman: 1654-1980. 1981. 15.00x (ISBN 0-87068-579-1). Ktav.
Marcus, Jacob R. & Peck, Abraham J., eds. Studies in the American Jewish Experience II: Contributions from the Fellowship Programs of the American Jewish Archives. 228p. (Orig.). 1984. lib. bdg. 25.25 (ISBN 0-8191-3714-6); pap. text ed. 12.25 (ISBN 0-8191-3715-4). U Pr of Amer.
Marcus, Joel. The Mystery of the Kingdom of God. (Dissertation Ser.). 270p. 1986. 17.95 (ISBN 0-89130-983-7, 06-01-90); pap. 12.95 (ISBN 0-89130-984-5). Scholars Pr GA.
Marcus, Joseph. Social & Political History of the Jews in Poland, 1919-1939. LC 82-22420. (New Babylon, Studies in the Social Sciences: No. 37). xviii, 569p. 1983. 88.50x (ISBN 90-279-3239-5). Mouton.
Marcus, Leah S. The Politics of Mirth: Jonson, Herrick, Milton, Marvell, & the Defense of Old Holiday Pastimes. LC 86-7133. (Illus.). 328p. 1986. lib. bdg. 29.00x (ISBN 0-226-50451-4). U of Chicago Pr.
Marcus, Paul, jt. auth. see Luel, Steven.
Marcus, Ralph. Law in the Apocrypha. LC 29-9822. (Columbia University. Oriental Studies: No. 26). Repr. of 1927 ed. 15.00 (ISBN 0-404-50516-3). AMS Pr.
Marcus, Russell, commentary by. Forms of Man: The Buddhist Vision of Thawan Duchanee. (Illus.). 1974. pap. 15.00 (ISBN 0-8048-1234-9). C E Tuttle.
Marcus, Sharon, ed. see Muhaiyaddeen, Bawa.
Marcus, Sophia. The Potato Man. Wheeler, Gerald, ed. (Banner Ser.). 128p. (Orig.). 1986. pap. 6.50 (ISBN 0-8280-0309-2). Review & Herald.
Marcuse, Herbert. From Luther to Popper: Studies in Critical Philosophy. 236p. 1984. pap. 7.95 (ISBN 0-8052-7196-1, Pub. by NLB England). Schocken.
Marcuse, Ludwig. Soldier of the Church: The Life of Ignatius Loyola. LC 70-172842. Repr. of 1939 ed. 23.00 (ISBN 0-404-04187-6). AMS Pr.
Mardi, N. Hussein, tr. see Ziad, Kumail I.
Mare, W. Harold. Archaeology of the Jerusalem Area. 1986. 19.95 (ISBN 0-8010-6126-1). Baker Bk.
--Mastering New Testament Greek. 1979. 14.95 (ISBN 0-8010-6064-8). Baker Bk.
Mare, Walter De La see De la Mare, Walter.
Marechal, Joseph. Studies in the Psychology of the Mystics. LC 65-1694. 1964. lib. bdg. 12.95x (ISBN 0-87343-044-1). Magi Bks.
Marechal, Paul. Dancing Madly Backwards: A Journey into God. (The Crossroad Paperback Ser.). 128p. 1982. pap. 5.95 (ISBN 0-8245-0408-9). Crossroad NY.
Maredsous, Monks of. Guide to the Bible. 2.25 (ISBN 0-87243-016-2). Templegate.
Marenbon, John. Early Medieval Philosophy Four Eighty to Eleven Fifty: An Introduction. 224p. 1983. 19.95x (ISBN 0-7100-9405-1). Methuen Inc.
Marenco, Ethne K. The Transformation of Sikh Society. 1974. pap. 16.95 (ISBN 0-913244-08-2). Hapi Pr.
Ma Renu, ed. see Dass, B. Hari.
Marett, Humphrey see Chamier, Adrian C.
Marett, R. R. Faith, Hope & Charity in Primitive Religion. LC 72-80150. Repr. of 1932 ed. 22.00 (ISBN 0-405-08780-2, Pub. by Blom). Ayer Co Pubs.
Marett, Robert R. Faith, Hope & Charity in Primitive Religion. LC 77-27193. (Gifford Lectures: 1931-32). Repr. of 1932 ed. 15.00 (ISBN 0-404-60487-0). AMS Pr.
--Sacraments of Simple Folk. LC 77-27192. (Gifford Lectures: 1932-33). Repr. of 1933 ed. 28.00 (ISBN 0-404-60488-9). AMS Pr.
--The Threshold of Religion. LC 76-44755. Repr. of 1900 ed. 26.50 (ISBN 0-404-15950-8). AMS Pr.
Margalith, Aaron M., jt. auth. see Adler, Cyrus.
Margenau, Henry. The Miracle of Existence. 143p. 1987. pap. 9.95 (ISBN 0-87773-407-0). Shambhala Pubns.
--Thomas & the Physics of Nineteen Fifty-Eight: A Confrontation. (Aquinas Lecture). 1958. 7.95 (ISBN 0-87462-123-2). Marquette.
Margerie, Bertrand De see De Margerie, Bertrand.
Margerie, Bertrand de see De Margerie, Bertrand.
Marglin, Frederique A. Wives of the God-King: The Rituals of the Devadasis of Puri. (Illus.). 1985. 29.95x (ISBN 0-19-561731-2). Oxford U Pr.
Margolin, Jean-Claude. Neuf Annees De Bibliographie Erasmienne (1962-1970) 1977. 85.00x (ISBN 0-8020-2276-6). U of Toronto Pr.
Margolin, Malcolm, ed. see Martin, Carol O.
Margoliouth, D. S. The Relations Between Arabs & Israelis Prior to the Rise of Islam. (British Academy, London, Schweich Lectures on Biblical Archaeology Series, 1921). pap. 19.00 (ISBN 0-8115-1263-0). Kraus Repr.
Margoliouth, D. S., tr. see Miskawayh, et al.
Margoliouth, David S. The Early Development of Mohammedanism. LC 77-27156. (Hibbert Lectures: 1913). Repr. of 1914 ed. 22.50 (ISBN 0-404-60415-3). AMS Pr.
--Mohammed & the Rise of Islam. LC 73-14455. Repr. of 1905 ed. 30.00 (ISBN 0-404-58273-7). AMS Pr.
--Mohammed & the Rise of Islam. LC 73-38361. (Select Bibliographies Reprint Ser.). Repr. of 1905 ed. 34.00 (ISBN 0-8369-6778-X). Ayer Co Pubs.
Margoliouth, G. Catalogue of the Hebrew & Samaritan Manuscripts in the British Museum, Pt. 3. 620p. 1965. Repr. of 1909 ed. 15.00 (ISBN 0-7141-0645-3, Pub. by British Lib). Longwood Pub Group.
Margoliovth, D. S., tr. see Mez, Adam.
Margolis, Isidor & Markowitz, Sidney L. Jewish Holidays & Festivals. (Orig.). 1962. pap. 3.95 (ISBN 0-8065-0285-1). Citadel Pr.
Margolis, Max L. & Marx, Alexander. History of the Jewish People. LC 70-90074. (Temple Books). 1969. pap. text ed. 10.95x (ISBN 0-689-70134-9, T8). Atheneum.
Margolis, Otto S. Grief & the Meaning of the Funeral. 15.50 (ISBN 0-405-12501-1). Ayer Co Pubs.
Margolis, Otto S. & Cherico, Daniel J. Thanatology Abstracts 1979. 15.00 (ISBN 0-405-14222-6, 19702). Ayer Co Pubs.
Margoliuth, D. S., tr. see Zaydan, Jirji.
Margoliuth, David S. Mohammed. LC 79-2875. 151p. 1981. Repr. of 1939 ed. 23.00 (ISBN 0-8305-0044-8). Hyperion Conn.
Margot, J. C., tr. see Nida, Eugene A.
Marharishi Mahesh Yogi. Transcendental Meditation. 320p. 1973. pap. 4.95 (ISBN 0-451-14081-8, Sig). NAL.
Marheine, Allen H. You Belong. LC 79-21954. (Orig.). 1980. pap. 2.95 (ISBN 0-8298-0380-7). Pilgrim NY.
Maria, Richard De see De Maria, Richard.
Mariah, Paul. For the Vietnamese Buddhists. Man-Root.
Marie, Patricia. Night Cries. 1981. 4.75 (ISBN 0-8062-1794-4). Carlton.

Mariechild, Diane. Crystal Visions: Nine Meditations for Personal & Planetary Peace. (Feminist Ser.). (Illus.). 128p. (Orig.). 1985. 15.95 (ISBN 0-89594-183-X); pap. 6.95 (ISBN 0-89594-182-1). Crossing Pr.

Marien, Bert. Bibliografica Critica Degli Studi Plotiniani: Con rassegna della loro recensioni. Cilento, V., ed. (Classical Studies Ser.). (Ital.). Repr. of 1949 ed. lib. bdg. 47.00x (ISBN 0-697-00043-5). Irvington.

Marien, Matthaeus. Iconum Biblicarum. (Illus.). 320p. 1981. Repr. of 1630 ed. 34.95 (ISBN 0-939688-06-9). Directed Media.

Marietta, Jack D. The Reformation of American Quakerism, 1748-1783. LC 83-23502. 352p. 1984. 28.95 (ISBN 0-8122-7922-0). U of Pa Pr.

Marilla, E. L. The Central Problem of Paradise Lost: The Fall of Man. (Essays & Studies on English Language & Literature: Vol. 15). pap. 15.00 (ISBN 0-8115-0213-9). Kraus Repr.

Marilla, Esmond L. Central Problem of Paradise Lost. 1953. lib. bdg. 12.00 (ISBN 0-8414-6200-3). Folcroft.

Marin, Javier J., tr. see Barclay, William.

Marin, Louis. The Semiotics of the Passion Narratives. Johnson, Alfred M., Jr., tr. (Pittsburgh Theological Monographs: No. 25). 1980. 12.95 (ISBN 0-915138-23-9). Pickwick.

Marinbach, Bernard. Galveston: Ellis Island of the West. (Modern Jewish History Ser.). 384p. 1983. 49.50x (ISBN 0-87395-700-8); pap. 17.95 (ISBN 0-87395-701-6). State U NY Pr.

Marinelli, Anthony J. Yahweh & Son: A Teenager's Guide to the Bible. 160p. (Orig.). 1986. pap. 7.95 (ISBN 0-8091-9568-2). Paulist Pr.

Maring, Norman H. & Hudson, Winthrop S. Baptist Manual of Polity & Practice. 10.95 (ISBN 0-8170-0299-5). Judson.

--Short Baptist Manual of Polity & Practice. 1965. pap. 4.95 (ISBN 0-8170-0338-X). Judson.

Marini, Stephen A. Radical Sects of Revolutionary New England. LC 81-6913. 224p. 1982. text ed. 16.50x (ISBN 0-674-74625-2). Harvard U Pr.

Marino, Joseph S., ed. Biblical Themes in Religious Education. LC 83-16124. 294p. (Orig.). 1983. pap. 14.95 (ISBN 0-89135-038-1). Religious Educ.

Mariological Society of America. Tampa, Fla. Convention, 1986. Marian Studies: Proceedings, Vol. 37. 1987. 10.00. Mariological Soc.

Mariological Society of America. Washington, D.C. Convention, 1984. Marian Studies: Proceedings, Vol. 35. 190p. 10.00 (ISBN 0-318-17634-3). Mariological Soc.

Marion-Wild, E. C. The Prologue of the Gospel of St. John: Esoteric Studies. Roboz, Helga & Roboz, Steven, trs. from Ger. 19p. 1984. pap. 3.75 (ISBN 0-919924-22-0). Anthroposophic.

Mariotti, F. A., tr. see Hunter, Emily.

Mariotti, Federico A., tr. see Hunter, Wayne & Hunter, Emily.

Marique, J. M., ed. Leaders of Iberian Christianity. 5.00 (ISBN 0-686-23369-7). Classical Folia.

Marique, Pierre J. Philosophy of Christian Education. Repr. of 1939 ed. lib. bdg. 22.50x (ISBN 0-8371-4271-7, MAED). Greenwood.

Maris, Ronald, jt. ed. see Battin, Margaret P.

Marison, Fiscar, tr. The Passion of Our Lord. 302p. 1980. pap. 4.50 (ISBN 0-911988-38-6). AMI Pr.

Marison, Fiscar, tr. see Agreda, Mary.

Maritain, Jacques. Approaches to God. O'Reilly, Peter, tr. from Fr. LC 78-16555. 1978. Repr. of 1954 ed. lib. bdg. 32.50x (ISBN 0-313-20606-6, MATG). Greenwood.

--Art & Scholasticism & the Frontiers of Poetry. Evans, Joseph W., tr. from Fr. LC 74-13601. 240p. 1974. pap. 6.95x (ISBN 0-268-00557-5). U of Notre Dame Pr.

--A Christian Looks at the Jewish Question. LC 73-2216. (The Jewish People; History, Religion, Literature Ser.). Repr. of 1939 ed. 17.00 (ISBN 0-405-05280-4). Ayer Co Pubs.

--Christianity & Democracy. Anson, Doris C., tr. from Fr. LC 72-6765. (Essay Index Reprint Ser). 1972. Repr. of 1944 ed. 15.00 (ISBN 0-8369-7243-0). Ayer Co Pubs.

--Christianity & Democracy. Bd. with Rights of Man & Natural Law. LC 83-80191. 1986. pap. write for info. (ISBN 0-89870-030-2). Ignatius Pr.

--Christianity & Democracy & The Rights of Man & Natural Law. LC 83-80191. 200p. 1986. pap. 12.95 (ISBN 0-89870-030-2). Ignatius Pr.

--De la Grace et de l'Humanite de Jesus. 2nd ed. 156p. 1967. 8.95 (ISBN 0-686-56347-6). French & Eur.

--De l'Eglise du Christ. 430p. 1970. 15.95 (ISBN 0-686-56348-4). French & Eur.

--Dieu et la Permission du Mal. 3rd ed. 116p. 1963. 8.95 (ISBN 0-686-56349-2). French & Eur.

--Distinguer Pour Unir: Les Degres du Savoir. 8th ed. 946p. 1959. 32.50 (ISBN 0-686-56350-6). French & Eur.

--Freedom & the Modern World. O'Sullivan, Richard, tr. LC 77-150414. 231p. 1971. Repr. of 1936 ed. 15.00x (ISBN 0-87752-147-6). Gordian.

--L' Homme et l'Etat. 2nd ed. 212p. 1965. 12.95 (ISBN 0-686-56353-0). French & Eur.

--The Living Thoughts of Saint Paul. 135p. 1983. Repr. of 1942 ed. lib. bdg. 20.00 (ISBN 0-8495-3946-3). Arden Lib.

--Man & the State. LC 51-555. 1956. pap. 4.45x (ISBN 0-226-50552-9, P5, Phoen). U of Chicago Pr.

--Le Mystere d'Israel. 260p. 1965. 9.95 (ISBN 0-686-56358-1). French & Eur.

--Notebooks. Evans, Joseph W., tr. from Fr. LC 83-26743. Tr. of Carnet de Notes. (Illus.). 320p. 1984. 12.95x (ISBN 0-87343-050-6). Magi Bks.

--On the Church of Christ: The Person of the Church & Her Personnel. Evans, Joseph W., tr. from Fr. LC 73-11559. Orig. Title: De l'Eglise Du Christ. (Eng. & Fr.). 352p. 1973. text ed. 24.95 (ISBN 0-268-00519-2); pap. text ed. 8.95x (ISBN 0-268-00525-7). U of Notre Dame Pr.

--Le Payson de Garonne: Un Vieux Laic s'Interroge a propos du Temps Present. 19.95 (ISBN 0-685-34274-3). French & Eur.

--Ransoming the Time. Binsse, Harry L., tr. LC 70-165665. 322p. 1972. Repr. of 1941 ed. 25.00x (ISBN 0-87752-153-0). Gordian.

--Religion et Culture. 176p. 1968. 3.95 (ISBN 0-686-56366-2). French & Eur.

--Rights of Man & Natural Law. LC 74-150416. 120p. 1971. Repr. of 1943 ed. 17.50x (ISBN 0-87752-146-8). Gordian.

--Saint Thomas & the Problem of Evil. (Aquinas Lecture). 1942. 7.95 (ISBN 0-87462-106-2). Marquette.

--Scholasticism & Politics. LC 72-353. (Essay Index Reprint Ser.). Repr. of 1940 ed. 15.00 (ISBN 0-8369-2805-9). Ayer Co Pubs.

--Theonas. facs. ed. LC 74-84325. (Essay Index Reprint Ser). 1933. 17.25 (ISBN 0-8369-1095-8). Ayer Co Pubs.

--The Things That Are Not Caesar's. Scanlan, J. F., tr. 227p. 1983. Repr. of 1930 ed. lib. bdg. 40.00 (ISBN 0-89760-589-6). Telegraph Bks.

--Three Reformers: Luther-Descartes-Rousseau. Repr. of 1950 ed. lib. bdg. 22.50x (ISBN 0-8371-2825-0, MATR). Greenwood.

--True Humanism. Adamson, M. R., tr. LC 71-114888. (Select Bibliographies Reprint Ser). 1938. 22.00 (ISBN 0-8369-5292-8). Ayer Co Pubs.

--True Humanism. 3rd ed. Adamson, Margot, tr. Repr. of 1941 ed. lib. bdg. 35.00x (ISBN 0-8371-2902-8, MAHU). Greenwood.

Maritain, Jacques, ed. see Pennsylvania University Bicentennial Conference.

Maritain, Jacques, et al. Wisdom: A Manifesto. 1965. pap. 1.00x (ISBN 0-87343-015-8). Magi Bks.

Maritain, Raissa. Raissa's Journal. LC 72-95648. 1974. 12.95x (ISBN 0-87343-041-7). Magi Bks.

Marjani, Fathollah, tr. see Shariati, Ali.

Marjorie, Palmer. God Saves Noah. (My Bible Story Reader Ser.: Vol. 2). (Illus., Orig.). 1983. pap. 1.95 (ISBN 0-8024-0192-9). Moody.

Mark-Age. How to Do All Things: Your Use of Divine Power. LC 72-121118. 144p. 1970. pap. 5.00 (ISBN 0-912322-01-2). Mark-Age.

--One Thousand Keys to the Truth: Spiritual Guidelines for Latter Days & Second Coming. LC 75-40976. 156p. 1976. pap. 5.00 (ISBN 0-912322-51-9). Mark-Age.

Mark, Emanuel, ed. A Composite Portrait of Israel. LC 80-40889. 1981. 55.50 (ISBN 0-12-476450-9). Acad Pr.

Markby, William. An Introduction to Hindu & Mohammedan Law. LC 78-58189. 1978. Repr. of 1906 ed. lib. bdg. 25.00 (ISBN 0-89341-509-X). Longwood Pub Group.

Markell, David. Expanded Ministry to Youth: Program Guidelines. (C. E. Ministries Ser.). 1977. pap. 3.50 (ISBN 0-89367-021-9). Light & Life.

Markell, Jan. Gone the Golden Dream. LC 79-16718. 176p. 1979. pap. 4.95 (ISBN 0-87123-049-6, 210049). Bethany Hse.

Markens, Isaac. The Hebrews in America: A Series of Historical & Biographical Sketches. facsimile ed. LC 74-29504. (Modern Jewish Experiences). 1975. Repr. of 1888 ed. 30.00x (ISBN 0-405-06731-3). Ayer Co Pubs.

Markham, Clements, ed. The Guanches of Tenerife, the Holy Image of Our Lady of Candelaria, with the Spanish Conquest & Settlement, by the Friar Alonsc de Espinosa. (Hakluyt Society Ser.: No. 2, Vol. 21). (Illus.). Repr. of 1907 ed. 25.00 (ISBN 0-8115-0341-0). Kraus Repr.

Markham, Clements R., ed. & tr. Narratives of the Rites & Laws of the Yncas. (Hakluyt Society First Ser.: No. 48). (Illus.). 1964. Repr. of 1873 ed. 26.50 (ISBN 0-8337-2232-8). B Franklin.

Markham, Judith, ed. see Mains, David R.

Markish, Shimon. Erasmus & the Jews. Olcott, Anthony, tr. from Rus. LC 85-16454. 1986. lib. bdg. 25.00x (ISBN 0-226-50590-1). U of Chicago Pr.

Markmann, Charles L., tr. see LeMaitre, Solange.

Mark Of Ephesus, Saint Encyclical Letter of St. Mark of Ephesus. pap. 0.50 (ISBN 0-686-16366-4). Eastern Orthodox.

Markowitz, Endel. The Encyclopedia Yiddishanica. LC 79-89973. (Illus.). 450p. 1980. 19.95 (ISBN 0-933910-02-9); pap. write for info. (ISBN 0-933910-04-5). Haymark.

Markowitz, Marvin D. Cross & Sword: The Political Role of Christian Missions in the Belgian Congo, 1908-1960. LC 75-170209. (Publications Ser.: No. 114). 1973. 13.50x (ISBN 0-8179-1141-3). Hoover Inst Pr.

Markowitz, Sidney L. What You Should Know about Jewish Religion, History, Ethics, & Culture. 226p. 1973. pap. 5.95 (ISBN 0-8065-0028-X). Citadel Pr.

Markowitz, Sidney L., jt. auth. see Margolis, Isidor.

Markquart, Edward F. Quest for Better Preaching: Resources for Renewal in the Pulpit. LC 85-13500. 240p. (Orig.). 1985. pap. 10.95 (ISBN 0-8066-2170-2, 10-5349). Augsburg.

Marks, Alfred. I've Taken a Page in the Bible. 208p. 1987. 14.95 (ISBN 0-86051-348-3). Parkwest Pubns.

Marks, Cara G. A Handbook of Hebrew Calligraphy: The ABC's of the Alef-Bet. (Illus.). 128p. 1983. cancelled (ISBN 0-89961-010-2); pap. cancelled (ISBN 0-89961-011-0). SBS Pub.

Marks, Ethel M., jt. auth. see Marks, Stanley J.

Marks, John, tr. see Von Rad, Gerhard.

Marks, Paul F. Bibliography of Literature Concerning Yemenite-Jewish Music. LC 72-90431. (Detroit Studies in Music Bibliography Ser.: No. 27). 1973. pap. 2.00 (ISBN 0-911772-57-X). Info Coord.

Marks, Richard B. The Medieval Manuscript Library of the Charterhouse of St. Barbara in Cologne, Vols. 1 & 2. Hogg, James, ed. (Analecta Cartusiana Ser.: Nos. 21 & 22). (Illus.). 473p. (Orig.). 1974. Set. pap. 50.00 (ISBN 3-7052-0022-4, Pub by Salzburg Studies). Longwood Pub Group.

Marks, Stanley J. The Two Christs; Or, the Decline & Fall of Christianity. 1983. pap. 14.95 (ISBN 0-938780-03-4). Bur Intl Aff.

Marks, Stanley J. & Marks, Ethel M. Judaism Looks at Christianity: 7 BC-1985 C. E. 1985. pap. 19.95; 24.95. Bur Intl Aff.

Marks, Thomas J. Bible Study Puzzle Book. 1981. pap. 2.95 saddlewire (ISBN 0-8054-9106-6). Broadman.

--More Bible Study Puzzles. (Orig.). 1983. pap. 2.95 (ISBN 0-8054-9108-2). Broadman.

Markun, Leo. Mrs. Grundy: A History of Four Centuries of Morals Intended to Illuminate Present Problems in Great Britain & the United States. 1930. 69.00 (ISBN 0-403-00130-7). Scholarly.

Markus, R. A. Saeculum: History & Society in the Theology of St Augustine. LC 71-87136. 1970. 54.50 (ISBN 0-521-07621-8). Cambridge U Pr.

Marlette, Doug. Preacher: The Wit & Wisdom of Reverend Will B. Dunn. 128p. 1984. pap. 4.95 (ISBN 0-8407-5895-2). Nelson.

Marlin, G., et al, eds. The Quotable Chesterton. LC 86-80788. 391p. 1986. 24.95 (ISBN 0-89870-102-3); pap. 16.95 (ISBN 0-89870-122-8). Ignatius Pr.

Marlin, George, ed. see Chesterton, G. K.

Marlin, Ira J., jt. auth. see Justus, Adalu.

Marlowe, Monroe & Reed, Bobbie. Creative Bible Learning for Adults. LC 77-76206. (International Center for Learning Handbooks). 192p. 1977. pap. 3.95 (ISBN 0-8307-0480-9, 9900152). Regal.

Marmorstein, A. Studies in Jewish Theology. 376p. Repr. of 1950 ed. text ed. 49.68x (ISBN 0-576-80153-4, Pub. by Gregg Intl Pubs England). Gregg Intl.

Marmorstein, Arthur. Studies in Jewish Theology: The Arthur Marmorstein Memorial Volume. Rabbinowitz, Joseph & Lew, Meyer S., eds. LC 76-39174. (Essay Index Reprint Ser.). Repr. of 1950 ed. 21.00 (ISBN 0-8369-2702-8). Ayer Co Pubs.

Marmorstein, Emil. The Murder of Jacob De Haan by the Zionists: A Martyr's Message. 1980. lib. bdg. 59.95 (ISBN 0-686-68747-7). Revisionist Pr.

Marmura, Michael E., ed. Islamic Theology & Philosophy: Studies in Honor of George F. Hourani. 344p. 1983. 49.50 (ISBN 0-87395-746-6); pap. 18.95 (ISBN 0-87395-747-4). State U NY Pr.

Marney, Carlyle. The Carpenter's Son. 96p. 1984. pap. 6.95 (ISBN 0-913029-02-5). Stevens Bk Pr.

--The Crucible of Redemption. 64p. 1984. pap. text ed. 5.95 (ISBN 0-913029-04-1). Stevens Bk Pr.

--Priests to Each Other. 125p. 1985. pap. 6.95 (ISBN 0-913029-06-8). Stevens Bk Pr.

Marnham, Patrick. Lourdes: A Modern Pilgrimage. LC 82-45299. 272p. 1982. pap. 4.95 (ISBN 0-385-18252-X, Im). Doubleday.

Marolles, Michel de. Tableaux Du Temple Des Muses, Repr. Of 1655 Ed. Bd. with Iconologia or Moral Problems. Ripa, Cesare. Repr. of 1709 ed. LC 75-27876. (Renaissance & the Gods Ser.: Vol. 31). (Illus.). 1976. lib. bdg. 80.00 (ISBN 0-8240-2080-4). Garland Pub.

Marongiu, Pietro & Newman, Graeme. Vengeance: The Fight Against Injustice. 176p. 1987. 27.50. Rowman.

Marquardt, H. Michael. A Tanner Bibliography. 32p. pap. 3.00 (ISBN 0-942284-08-9). Restoration Re.

Marquardt, Mervin A. The Temptation of Jesus. (Arch Bks.). (Illus.). 24p. 1986. pap. 0.99 saddlestitched (ISBN 0-570-06204-7, 59-1427). Concordia.

Marquart, Kurt E. Anatomy of an Explosion: A Theological Analysis of the Missouri Synod Conflict. 1978. pap. 3.95 (ISBN 0-8010-6049-4). Baker Bk.

Marquart, Kurt E., et al, eds. A Lively Legacy: Essays in Honor of Robert Preus. 224p. (Orig.). 1985. 13.95 (ISBN 0-9615927-0-2); pap. 11.95 (ISBN 0-9615927-1-0). Concordia Theo Sem.

Marquart, M. Jesus' Second Family. (Arch Book Series Fourteen). 1977. pap. 0.99 (ISBN 0-570-06111-3, 59-1229). Concordia.

Marquez, Angelina, tr. see Tully, Mary J.

Marquis, Anthony J. A Lifetime. 48p. 1986. 5.95 (ISBN 0-89962-521-5). Todd & Honeywell.

Marra, William A. Happiness & Christian Hope: A Phenomenological Analysis. 1979. 8.95 (ISBN 0-8199-0770-7). Franciscan Herald.

Marrin, Albert. The Last Crusade: The Church of England in the First World War. LC 72-97471. xv, 303p. 1973. 19.75 (ISBN 0-8223-0298-5). Duke.

Marriott, jt. auth. see Rachlin.

Marriott, Alice. The Ten Grandmothers. LC 45-1584. (The Civilization of the American Indians Ser.: Vol. 26). 306p. 1985. pap. 9.95 (ISBN 0-8061-1825-3). U of Okla Pr.

Marriott, Alice & Rachlin, Carol K. American Indian Mythology. 258p. (YA) 1972. pap. 3.50 (ISBN 0-451-62327-4, ME2327, Ment). NAL.

Marron, Henri, jt. auth. see Leclercq, Dom H.

Marrou, Henri, jt. auth. see Danielou, Jean.

Marrow, Stanley B. Paul, His Letters & Theology: An Introduction to Paul's Epistles. 288p. (Orig.). 1986. pap. 9.95 (ISBN 0-8091-2744-X). Paulist Pr.

--The Words of Jesus in Our Gospel. LC 79-52105. 160p. 1979. pap. 5.95 (ISBN 0-8091-2215-4). Paulist Pr.

Marrs, Texe W. Rush to Armageddon. (Living Bk.). 128p. (Orig.). 1987. 3.95 (ISBN 0-8423-5796-3). Tyndale.

Marrus, Michael R. & Paxton, Robert O. Vichy France & the Jews. LC 82-16869. 432p. (Orig.). 1983. pap. 12.95 (ISBN 0-8052-0741-4). Schocken.

Marryat, Florence. There Is No Death. 69.95 (ISBN 0-8490-1192-2). Gordon Pr.

Mars, Louis B. Crisis of Possession in Voodoo. Collins, Kathleen, tr. LC 76-51943. 1977. 10.00 (ISBN 0-918408-07-5); pap. 4.95 (ISBN 0-918408-00-8). Reed & Cannon.

Marsan, Jules. Pastorale Dramatique en France a la Fin du Seizieme & Au Commencement du Dix-Septieme Siecle. LC 79-159703. (Research & Source Works Ser.: No. 745). (Illus.). 1971. Repr. of 1905 ed. lib. bdg. 32.50 (ISBN 0-8337-4254-X). B Franklin.

Marsden, George, ed. Evangelicalism & Modern America. 212p. (Orig.). 1984. pap. 8.95 (ISBN 0-8028-1993-1). Eerdmans.

Marsden, George M. Fundamentalism & American Culture: The Shaping of Twentieth-Century Evangelicalism, 1870-1925. 1980. pap. 9.95 (ISBN 0-19-503083-4). Oxford U Pr.

Marsden, Joshua. The Narrative of a Mission to Nova Scotia, New Brunswick & the Somers Islands. Repr. of 1816 ed. 25.00 (ISBN 0-384-35430-0). Johnson Repr.

Marsden, Norman, ed. A Jewish Life under the Tsars: The Autobiography of Chaim Aronson, 1825-1888, Vol. 3. LC 81-10963. (Publications of the Oxford Centre for Postgraduate Hebrew Study). 368p. 1983. 23.95 (ISBN 0-86598-066-7). Allanheld.

Marsden, Victor E., ed. & tr. see Nilus.

Marsden, Victor E., tr. from Russian. The Protocols of the Meetings of the Learned Elders of Zion. 1978. pap. 4.00x (ISBN 0-911038-42-6). Noontide.

Marsella, Elena M. Quest for Eden. LC 66-16172. 275p. 1966. 8.95 (ISBN 0-8022-1063-5). Philos Lib.

Marsh, C. R. Share Your Faith with a Muslim. LC 75-15883. 1975. pap. 4.50 (ISBN 0-8024-7900-6). Moody.

Marsh, Carole. The Fortune Cookie Christmas. (Illus.). 50p. (Orig.). 1986. pap. 9.95 (ISBN 0-935326-53-7). Gallopade Pub Group.

Marsh, Clifton E. From Black Muslims to Muslims: The Transition from Separatism to Islam, 1930-1980. LC 84-5611. 159p. 1984. 16.50 (ISBN 0-8108-1705-5). Scarecrow.

Marsh, F. E. Devotional Bible Studies. LC 79-2548. 304p. 1980. 10.95 (ISBN 0-8254-3230-8). Kregel.

--Discipler's Manual. new ed. LC 79-2550. 412p. 1980. 12.95 (ISBN 0-8254-3231-6). Kregel.

--Emblems of the Holy Spirit. LC 63-11465. 268p. 1974. pap. 9.95 (ISBN 0-8254-3222-7). Kregel.

--Five Hundred Bible Study Outlines. LC 79-2549. 382p. 1985. pap. 10.95 (ISBN 0-8254-3248-0). Kregel.

--Illustrated Bible Study Outlines. LC 79-125116. 268p. 1979. pap. 8.95 (ISBN 0-8254-3245-6). Kregel.

--Living God's Way. LC 80-8073. 230p. (Reprint of The Spiritual Life). 1981. pap. 7.95 (ISBN 0-8254-3233-2). Kregel.

--One Thousand Bible Study Outlines. LC 75-125115. 1970. pap. 12.95 (ISBN 0-8254-3247-2). Kregel.

--Practical Truths from First Thessalonians. LC 86-2742. Orig. Title: Flashes from the Lighthouse of Truth. 272p. 1986. Repr. 12.95 (ISBN 0-8254-3234-0). Kregel.

--Why Did Christ Die? LC 85-18093. Orig. Title: The Greatest Theme in the World. 204p. 1985. pap. 6.95 (ISBN 0-8254-3249-9). Kregel.

Marsh, Frank L. Life, Man & Time. 2nd ed. LC 66-21121. (Illus.). (YA) 1967. 8.95 (ISBN 0-911080-15-5). Outdoor Pict.

Marsh, Fredda. Putting It All Together in a Puppet Ministry. LC 77-91674. 144p. 1978. pap. text ed. 6.95 (ISBN 0-88243-578-7, 02-0578). Gospel Pub.

Marsh, J. B. Story of the Jubilee Singers with Their Songs. rev. ed. LC 72-165509. (Illus.). Repr. of 1880 ed. 14.00 (ISBN 0-404-04189-2). AMS Pr.

--Story of the Jubilee Singers, with Their Songs. rev. ed. LC 79-78583. (Illus.). Repr. of 1881 ed. 22.50x (ISBN 0-8371-1424-1, MAJ&, Pub. by Negro U Pr). Greenwood.

Marsh, Jack. You Can Help the Alcoholic: A Christian Plan for Intervention. LC 82-74499. 88p. (Orig.). 1983. pap. 2.95 (ISBN 0-87793-270-0). Ave Maria.

Marsh, John. Confronting Jesus. LC 84-60895. 112p. (Orig.). 1984. pap. 3.50 (ISBN 0-89109-518-7). NavPress.

--The Gospel of Saint John: Commentaries. (Orig.). 1968. pap. 8.95 (ISBN 0-14-020491-1, Pelican). Penguin.

Marsh, John F. Papers Connected with the Affairs of Milton & His Family. LC 74-22180. 1974. Repr. of 1851 ed. lib. bdg. 15.00 (ISBN 0-8414-5959-2). Folcroft.

Marsh, Marilyn, jt. auth. see Ricks, Chip.

Marsh, Michael. A Matter of Personal Survival. LC 84-40514. (Illus.). 209p. (Orig.). 1985. pap. 7.50 (ISBN 0-8356-0596-5). Theos Pub Hse.

--Philosophy of the Inner Light. LC 76-50674. (Orig.). 1976. pap. 2.50x (ISBN 0-87574-209-2). Pendle-Hill.

--Reaching Toward God. LC 81-81683. 27p. 1981. pap. 2.50x (ISBN 0-87574-237-8, 237). Pendle Hill.

Marsh, Spencer. Beginnings: A Portrayal of the Creation. LC 81-18920. (Illus.). 72p. 1982. 16.95 (ISBN 0-930014-82-0); pap. 9.95 (ISBN 0-930014-81-2). Multnomah.

Marsh, Thomas A. Gift of Community: Baptism & Confirmation. (Message of the Sacraments Ser.: Vol. 2). 13.95 (ISBN 0-89453-392-4); pap. 9.95 (ISBN 0-89453-228-6). M Glazier.

Marshal, Walter G. Through America: Nine Months in the United States. LC 73-13143. (Foreign Travelers in America, 1810-1935 Ser.). (Illus.). 490p. 1974. Repr. 32.00x (ISBN 0-405-05466-1). Ayer Co Pubs.

Marshall, Alejandro & Bennett, Gordon H. La Salvacion y las Dudas de Algunas Personas. 2nd ed. Bautista, Sara, tr. from Span. (La Serie Diamante). Tr. of God's Way of Salvation. (Eng., Illus.). 36p. 1982. pap. 0.85 (ISBN 0-942504-01-1). Overcomer Pr.

Marshall, Alfred. Interlinear Greek-English New Testament. 27.95 (ISBN 0-310-20380-5, 6254, Pub. by Bagster). Zondervan.

--The NASB Interlinear Greek-English New Testament. 1056p. 1984. text ed. 27.95 (ISBN 0-310-45240-6, 12394). Zondervan.

--New Testament Greek Primer. 176p. (Orig.). 1981. leather edition 49.95 (ISBN 0-310-20540-9, 6246). Zondervan.

--NIV Interliear Greek-English New Testament. 1976. 21.95 (ISBN 0-310-28680-8). Zondervan.

--RSV Interlinear Greek, New Testament. 24.95 (ISBN 0-310-20410-0, 10108). Zondervan.

Marshall, Catherine. Adventures in Prayer. 1980. pap. 2.25 (ISBN 0-345-27210-2). Ballantine.

--Adventures in Prayer. (Illus.). 120p. 1976. pap. 2.95 (ISBN 0-8007-8269-0, Spire Bks). Revell.

--Algo Mas. 171p. 1981. 4.75 (ISBN 0-88113-001-X). Edit Betania.

--Aventuras en la Oracion. 192p. 1976. 2.95 (ISBN 0-88113-005-2). Edit Betania.

--El Ayudador. 208p. 1980. 3.25 (ISBN 0-88113-009-5). Edit Betania.

--Catherine Marshall's Story Bible. (Illus.). 216p. 1984. pap. 10.95 (ISBN 0-8245-0596-4). Crossroad NY.

--Catherine Marshall's Story Bible. 200p. 1985. pap. 9.95 (ISBN 0-380-69961-3). Avon.

--A Closer Walk. LeSourd, Leonard, ed. 256p. 1986. 12.95 (ISBN 0-8007-9065-0). Revell.

--A Closer Walk: Spirtual Discoveries from Her Journal. LeSourd, Leonard, ed. 1985. 12.95 (ISBN 0-317-46132-X). Revell.

--Friends with God. (Illus.). 1972. pap. 1.95 (ISBN 0-380-01199-9, 52803-7). Avon.

--God Loves You. 1973. pap. 0.95 (ISBN 0-380-01221-9, 14712). Avon.

--The Helper. 1979. pap. 3.95 (ISBN 0-380-45583-8). Avon.

--Man Called Peter. 1971. pap. 4.50 (ISBN 0-380-00894-7). Avon.

--Meeting God at Every Turn. 224p. 1985. pap. 3.50 (ISBN 0-553-23977-5). Bantam.

--Something More. 1976. pap. 3.50 (ISBN 0-380-00601-4, 60104-4). Avon.

--Something More. 276p. 1976. pap. 3.50 (ISBN 0-8007-8266-6, Spire Bks). Revell.

--To Live Again. 1976. pap. 3.95 (ISBN 0-380-01586-2). Avon.

Marshall, Catherine & LeSourd, Leonard. Mi Diario Personal de Oracion. 416p. 1981. 4.95 (ISBN 0-88113-306-X). Edit Betania.

Marshall, Catherine & Le Sourd, Leonard. My Personal Prayer Diary. (Epiphany Bks.). 1983. pap. 3.95 (ISBN 0-345-30612-0). Ballantine.

Marshall, George. Facing Death & Grief. LC 80-84402. (Library of Liberal Religion Ser.). 200p. 1981. 18.95 (ISBN 0-87975-140-1); pap. 11.95 (ISBN 0-87975-169-X). Prometheus Bks.

Marshall, Gordon. In Search of the Spirit of Capitalism: An Essay on Max Weber's Protestant Ethic Thesis. LC 81-18053. 233p. 1982. 26.50x (ISBN 0-231-05498-X); pap. 13.00x (ISBN 0-231-05499-8). Columbia U Pr.

--Presbyteries & Profits: Calvinism & the Development of Capitalism in Scotland, 1560 - 1707. 1980. 54.00x (ISBN 0-19-827246-4). Oxford U Pr.

Marshall, Helen L. Bright Laughter-Warm Tears: Inspirational Thoughts for Mothers. 64p. 1985. pap. 3.95 (ISBN 0-8010-6195-4). Baker Bk.

--Inspirational Resources for Women's Groups. 64p. 1985. pap. 3.95 (ISBN 0-8010-6196-2). Baker Bk.

--Quiet Power: Words of Faith, Hope, & Love. 64p. 1985. pap. 3.95 (ISBN 0-8010-6197-0). Baker Bk.

Marshall, I. Howard. Acts of the Apostles. (Tyndale New Testament Commentaries Ser.). (Orig.). 1980. pap. 7.95 (ISBN 0-8028-1423-9). Eerdmans.

--Biblical Inspiration. 128p. 1983. pap. 5.95 (ISBN 0-8028-1959-1). Eerdmans.

--First & Second Thessalonians. (New Century Bible Commentary Ser.). 240p. 1983. pap. 6.95 (ISBN 0-8028-1946-X). Eerdmans.

--The Gospel of Luke. (New International Greek Testament Commentary Ser.). 1978. 35.00 (ISBN 0-8028-3512-0). Eerdmans.

--I Believe in the Historical Jesus. (I Believe Ser). 1977. pap. 4.95 (ISBN 0-8028-1691-6). Eerdmans.

--Kept by the Power of God. LC 74-23996. 288p. 1975. pap. 8.95 (ISBN 0-87123-304-5, 210304). Bethany Hse.

--Last Supper & Lord's Supper. (Orig.). 1981. pap. 6.95 (ISBN 0-8028-1854-4). Eerdmans.

--Luke: Historian & Theologian. (Contemporary Evangelical Perspective Ser). 1971. kivar 7.95 (ISBN 0-310-28761-8, 10105P). Zondervan.

--The New International Commentary on the New Testament: The Epistles of John. 1978. 14.95 (ISBN 0-8028-2189-8). Eerdmans.

Marshall, I. Howard, ed. see Runia, Klaus.

Marshall, James W. Presbyterian Churches in Alabama 1811-1936: Sketches of Churches, Outposts, & Preaching Points in the Synod of Alabama, Pt. I: Abbeville-Butler, & Megargel. Foreman, Kenneth J., Jr., ed. (Illus.). 519p. (Orig.). 1985. 29.95 (ISBN 0-935883-01-0); pap. 14.95 (ISBN 0-935883-00-2); With computer-readable disk. 69.95 (ISBN 0-935883-02-9). Cooling Spring.

Marshall, John. The Buddhist Art of Gandhara. (Illus.). 1981. Repr. of 1960 ed. text ed. 30.00x. Coronet Bks.

Marshall, John F. By the Light of His Lamp. (Spirit & Life Ser). 1967. 2.00 (ISBN 0-686-11574-0). Franciscan Inst.

--Conferences on the Our Father. (Spirit & Life Ser). 1967. 2.00 (ISBN 0-686-11573-2). Franciscan Inst.

--In the Shadow of His Cross. (Spirit & Life Ser). 1969. 2.00 (ISBN 0-686-11577-5). Franciscan Inst.

--The Long Way Home, the Short Way of Love. (Spirit & Life Ser). 1968. 3.50 (ISBN 0-686-11575-9). Franciscan Inst.

--Sharing God's Love. LC 81-11794. 108p. 1981. pap. 5.95 (ISBN 0-8146-1068-4). Liturgical Pr.

Marshall, Lillian. Stepping Stones: Meditations in a Garden. (Illus.). 64p. 1984. 4.95 (ISBN 0-88088-506-8). Peter Pauper.

Marshall, Lyn. Everyday Yoga. LC 83-24177. (Illus.). 96p. (Orig.). 1984. pap. 6.95 (ISBN 0-8069-7864-3). Sterling.

Marshall, Madeleine F. & Todd, Janet M. English Congregational Hymns in the Eighteenth Century. LC 82-40176. 192p. 1982. 16.00x (ISBN 0-8131-1470-5). U Pr of Ky.

Marshall, Martha. What Child Is This? 1982. text ed. 4.95 (Sonflower Bks). SP Pubns.

--What Child Is This? LC 82-7239. (Illus.). 1982. lib. bdg. 6.95 (ISBN 0-89693-204-4). Dandelion Hse.

Marshall, Mary. Portraiture of Shakerism. LC 70-134420. Repr. of 1822 ed. 28.45 (ISBN 0-404-08461-3). AMS Pr.

Marshall, Mary R. It's Tuesday Night Again: Planning This Week's Program for Youth Group & Clubs. (Australian Youth Leadership Ser.). (Illus.). 56p. (Orig.). 1983. pap. 6.95 (ISBN 0-85819-416-3, Pub. by JBCE). ANZ Religious Pubns.

--Looking Ahead: Planning the Year's Program for Youth Groups & Clubs. (Australian Youth Leadership Ser.). 32p. (Orig.). 1983. pap. 4.95 (ISBN 0-85819-417-1, Pub. by JBCE). ANZ Religious Pubns.

Marshall, Mary R., jt. auth. see Baker, Pat.

Marshall, Michael. The Restless Heart: The Life & Influence of St. Augustine. (Illus.). 192p. 1987. 19.95 (ISBN 0-8028-3632-1). Eerdmans.

Marshall, Michael E. The Anglican Church Today & Tomorrow. LC 83-62718. 176p. (Orig.). 1984. pap. 7.95 (ISBN 0-8192-1341-1). Morehouse.

--Christian Orthodoxy Revisited. 137p. (Orig.). pap. 6.95 (ISBN 0-8192-1363-2). Morehouse.

--The Gospel Conspiracy in the Episcopal Church. (Orig.). 1986. pap. 6.95 (ISBN 0-8192-1386-1). Morehouse.

--Renewal in Worship. rev. ed. 120p. 1985. pap. 6.95 (ISBN 0-8192-1374-8). Morehouse.

Marshall, Nathaniel. Penitential Discipline of the Primitive Church. LC 74-172846. (Library of Anglo-Catholic Theology: No. 13). Repr. of 1844 ed. 27.50 (ISBN 0-404-52105-3). AMS Pr.

Marshall, Peter & Manuel, David. From Sea to Shining Sea. 448p. 1985. 14.95 (ISBN 0-8007-1451-2). Revell.

--The Light & the Glory. 352p. 1977. 14.95 (ISBN 0-8007-0886-5); pap. 7.95 (ISBN 0-8007-5054-3, Power Bks). Revell.

--The Light & the Glory Study Guide. 1981. pap. 5.95 (ISBN 0-8007-1279-X); photo enrichment pack o.p. 12.50. Revell.

Marshall, Peter, jt. auth. see Manuel, David.

Marshall, Peter J. The British Discovery of Hinduism in the 18th Century. 318p. 1970. text ed. 32.00x. Coronet Bks.

Marshall, Richard H., Jr., et al, eds. Aspects of Religion in the Soviet Union, 1917-1967. LC 70-115874. 1971. 35.00x (ISBN 0-226-50700-9). U of Chicago Pr.

Marshall, Sharon. Justin: Heaven's Baby. 128p. (Orig.). 1983. pap. 3.95 (ISBN 0-8341-0833-X). Beacon Hill.

Marshall, William, tr. see Constantine I.

Marstin, Ronald. Beyond Our Tribal Gods: The Maturing of Faith. LC 79-4354. 160p. (Orig.). 1979. pap. 5.95 (ISBN 0-88344-030-X). Orbis Bks.

Marston, E. Thomas Ken & Izaak Walton: A Sketch of Their Lives & Family Connection. 1908. Repr. 35.00 (ISBN 0-8274-3613-0). R West.

Marston, George W. Tongues Then & Now. 1983. pap. 2.95 (ISBN 0-87552-288-2). Presby & Reformed.

Marston, Leslie R. From Age to Age a Living Witness. 1960. 10.95 (ISBN 0-685-14209-4). Light & Life.

--He Lived on Our Street. 1979. pap. 4.95 (ISBN 0-89367-042-1). Light & Life.

Marston, Paul, jt. auth. see Forster, Roger.

Marston, V. Paul, jt. auth. see Forster, Roger T.

Marteilhe, Jean. The Memoirs of a Protestant Condemned to the Galleys of France for His Religion, 2 Vols. Goldsmith, Oliver, tr. 290p. 1983. Repr. of 1895 ed. Set. lib. bdg. 75.00 (ISBN 0-8495-2138-6). Arden Lib.

Martell, Dwane K. The Enigma of God & Man's Proclivity to Evil. (Institute for Religious Research Library). (Illus.). 77p. 1983. 47.75 (ISBN 0-89920-049-4). Am Inst Psych.

--The Nature of the Soul & Its Ultimate Goals. (Science of Man Library). (Illus.). 109p. 1983. 47.25 (ISBN 0-89920-048-6). Am Inst Psych.

Martello, Leo L. Witchcraft: The Old Religion. 1987. pap. 6.95 (ISBN 0-8065-1028-5). Citadel Pr.

Marten, Elizabeth H., jt. auth. see Crosby, Nina E.

Martene, Edmond & Durand, Ursin. Voyage Litteraire de Deux Benedictins de la Congregation de Saint-Maur, 2 vols. 1042p. Repr. of 1717 ed. text ed. 207.00x (ISBN 0-576-99707-2, Pub. by Gregg Intl Pubs England). Gregg Intl.

Martens, Elmer A. God's Design: A Focus on Old Testament Theology. pap. 10.95 (ISBN 0-8010-6209-8). Baker Bk.

--Jeremiah. LC 86-9958. (A Believers Church Bible Commentary Ser.). 328p. (Orig.). 1986. pap. 17.95 (ISBN 0-8361-3405-2). Herald Pr.

Martens, Larry. Life with Promise: Marriage as a Covenant Venture. LC 82-81266. 76p. (Orig.). 1982. pap. 4.95 (ISBN 0-937364-03-7). Kindred Pr.

Marthaler, Berard L. An Official Commentary for Sharing the Light of Faith. 119p. 1981. pap. 7.50 (ISBN 1-55586-694-8). US Catholic.

Marti, Fritz. Religion, Reason & Man. LC 74-9353. 127p. 1974. 7.50 (ISBN 0-87527-141-3). Green.

Marti, Oscar A. Economic Causes of the Reformation in England. LC 83-45586. Date not set. Repr. of 1929 ed. 32.50 (ISBN 0-404-19904-6). AMS Pr.

Martimort, A. G. The Church at Prayer: The Liturgy & Time, Vol. 4. 304p. 1986. pap. 14.95 (ISBN 0-8146-1366-7). Liturgical Pr.

Martimort, A. G., ed. The Church at Prayer: Part One-The Liturgy. 264p. 1969. text ed. 17.50x (ISBN 0-7165-0511-8, Pub. by Irish Academic Pr Ireland). Biblio Dist.

--The Church at Prayer Part Two: The Eucharist. (Illus.). 250p. 1972. 17.50x (ISBN 0-7165-1107-X, BBA 01006, Pub. by Irish Academic Pr Ireland). Biblio Dist.

Martimort, A. G., et al. The Church at Prayer: The Eucharist, Vol. 2. Martimort, A. G., ed. O'Connell, Matthew, tr. from Fr. Orig. Title: L'Eglise en Priere: L'eucharistie. 286p. 1986. pap. 14.95 (ISBN 0-8146-1364-0). Liturgical Pr.

--Principles of the Liturgy. Martimort, A. G., ed. O'Connell, Matthew J., tr. (The Church at Prayer: Vol. 1). 300p. 1987. pap. 14.95 (ISBN 0-8146-1363-2). Liturgical Pr.

Martin. But for the Grace of God.... (Orig.). 1984. pap. 1.00 (ISBN 0-914733-02-8). Desert Min.

Martin, A. L. Henry III & the Jesuit Politicians. 264p. (Orig.). 1973. pap. text ed. 48.50x (Pub. by Droz Switzerland). Coronet Bks.

Martin, A. N. Living the Christian Life. 32p. 1986. pap. 1.00 (ISBN 0-85151-493-6). Banner of Truth.

Martin, Albert N. Practical Implications of Calvinism. 1979. pap. 1.00 (ISBN 0-85151-296-8). Banner of Truth.

Martin, Alfred. Isaiah: The Salvation of Jehovah. (Everyman's Bible Commentary Ser.). 1967. pap. 5.95 (ISBN 0-8024-2023-0). Moody.

--Isaias: La Salvacion del Senor (Comentario Biblico Portavoz) Orig. Title: Isaiah: The Salvation of Jehovah (Everyman's Bible Commentary) (Span.). 112p. 1979. pap. 3.50 (ISBN 0-8254-1455-5). Kregel.

Martin, Alfred & Martin, John A. Isaiah: The Glory of the Messiah. (Orig.). 1983. pap. 9.95 (ISBN 0-8024-0168-6). Moody.

Martin, Aquinata. The Catholic Church on the Nebraska Frontier: 1854-1885. LC 73-3580. (Catholic University of America. Studies in American Church History: No. 26). Repr. of 1937 ed. 26.00 (ISBN 0-404-57776-8). AMS Pr.

Martin, B. G. Muslim Brotherhoods in 19th Century Africa. LC 75-35451. (African Studies Ser.: No. 18). 1977. 44.50 (ISBN 0-521-21062-3). Cambridge U Pr.

Martin, Bernard. The Existentialist Theology of Paul Tillich. 1963. 14.95x (ISBN 0-8084-0399-0); pap. 10.95x (ISBN 0-8084-0400-8). New Coll U Pr.

Martin, Bernard, jt. auth. see Silver, Daniel J.

Martin, Bernard, ed. Movements & Issues in American Judaism: An Analysis & Sourcebook of Developments Since 1945. LC 77-87971. 1978. lib. bdg. 35.00 (ISBN 0-313-20044-0, MCJ/). Greenwood.

Martin, Bernard, tr. see Shestov, Lev.

Martin, Bill. Fit for the King. Haynes, Glenda, ed. (Illus.). 384p. (Orig.). (YA) pap. 11.50 (ISBN 0-89114-154-5). Baptist Pub Hse.

Martin, Mrs. Bill. My Special Place. 136p. 1980. pap. 5.95 (ISBN 0-89114-111-1). Baptist Pub Hse.

Martin, Brian W. John Henry Newman: His Life & Work. (Illus.). 1982. 22.50x (ISBN 0-19-520387-9). Oxford U Pr.

--John Keble: Priest, Professor & Poet. 191p. 1976. 25.00 (ISBN 0-85664-381-5, Pub. by Croom Helm Ltd). Methuen Inc.

Martin, Carol O. Exploring the California Missions: Activity Cards. Margolin, Malcolm, ed. (Illus.). 94p. (Orig.). 1984. pap. 7.95 (ISBN 0-318-18397-8). Bay Area CA.
Martin, Catherine. Building Christian Community. 1.17 (ISBN 0-8091-9311-6). Paulist Pr.
Martin, Catherine, jt. auth. see Martin, John B.
Martin, D., tr. see Oberman, H. A.
Martin, Dan. Human Touch. Rutledge, Don, tr. (Illus.). 1979. 6.95 (ISBN 0-937170-03-8). Home Mission.
Martin, David. Breaking of Image: The Sociology of Christian Theory & Practice. 1980. 26.00 (ISBN 0-312-09522-8). St Martin.
--The Dilemmas of Contemporary Religion. LC 78-17704. 1978. 20.00x (ISBN 0-312-21055-8). St Martin.
Martin, David & Mullen, Peter, eds. Strange Gifts: A Guide to Charismatic Renewal. 208p. 1984. 24.95x (ISBN 0-631-13357-7); pap. 9.95x (ISBN 0-631-13592-8). Basil Blackwell.
Martin, David, et al, eds. Sociology & Theology. 170p. 1980. 26.00x (ISBN 0-312-74007-7). St Martin.
Martin, Dianne & Heller, Rachelle. Bible BASIC: Advanced. (Illus.). 64p. 1986. 5.95 (ISBN 0-87403-052-8, 3192). Standard Pub.
Martin, Dorothy. Faith at Work. (Peggy Ser.: No. 9). 1985. pap. 3.50 (ISBN 0-8024-8309-7). Moody.
--The Story of Billy McCarrell. 160p. (Orig.). 1983. pap. 3.95 (ISBN 0-8024-0519-3). Moody.
Martin, Dorothy, jt. auth. see Smith, G. Barnett.
Martin, E. Osborn. The Gods of India: A Brief Description of Their History, Character, & Worship. LC 77-87621. 1977. Repr. of 1914 ed. lib. bdg. 40.00 (ISBN 0-89341-302-X). Longwood Pub Group.
Martin, Edward A. Psychology of Funeral Service. 6th ed. text ed. 12.50 (ISBN 0-686-20530-8). E A Martin.
Martin, Edward J. A History of the Iconoclastic Controversy. (Church Historical Society London N. S. Ser.: No. 2). Repr. of 1930 ed. 55.00 (ISBN 0-8115-3126-0). Kraus Repr.
--The Trial of the Templars. LC 76-29845. Repr. of 1928 ed. 24.50 (ISBN 0-404-15424-7). AMS Pr.
Martin, Elva. Seek Ye First. 1973. pap. 1.65 (ISBN 0-915374-32-3, 32-3). Rapids Christian.
Martin, Everett D. Liberty. 307p. 1981. Repr. of 1930 ed. lib. bdg. 20.00 (ISBN 0-8495-3828-9). Arden Lib.
Martin, F. David. Art & the Religious Experience: The Language of the Sacred. LC 75-161508. (Illus.). 288p. 1972. 27.50 (ISBN 0-8387-7935-2). Bucknell U Pr.
Martin, Fay C. Availing Prayer. 120p. pap. 1.00 (ISBN 0-686-29098-4). Faith Pub Hse.
Martin, Florence. Observing National Holidays & Church Festivals: A Weekday Church School Unit in Christian Citizenship Series for Grades Three & Four. LC 76-174077. 1971. Repr. of 1940 ed. 44.00x (ISBN 0-8103-3804-1). Gale.
Martin, Francis, tr. see Bavarel, Michel.
Martin, Francis, tr. see Laurentin, Rene & Rupcic, Ljudevit.
Martin, George. Reading Scripture As the Word of God. Rev. ed. 200p. 1982. pap. 4.95 (ISBN 0-89283-152-9). Servant.
--To Pray As Jesus. 1978. pap. 2.50 (ISBN 0-89283-054-9). Servant.
Martin, George V. Are There a Beginning & an End to Man's Existence? 1983. 8.95 (ISBN 0-533-05562-8). Vantage.
Martin, Gib, jt. auth. see Richards, Lawrence.
Martin, Grant. Counseling in Cases of Family Violence & Abuse. 192p. 1987. 12.95 (ISBN 0-8499-0587-7). Word Bks.
--Please Don't Hurt Me. 180p. 1987. pap. 6.95 (ISBN 0-89693-743-7). Victor Bks.
--Transformed by Thorns. 156p. 1985. pap. 5.95 (ISBN 0-89693-397-0). Victor Bks.
Martin, Hugh. The Abiding Presence. LC 83-11337. 256p. 1984. 5.95 (ISBN 0-310-28921-1, 11337P, Clarion Class). Zondervan.
--Great Christian Books. facsimile ed. LC 71-142666. (Essay Index Reprint Ser). Repr. of 1945 ed. 13.00 (ISBN 0-8369-2242-5). Ayer Co Pubs.
--Jonah. (Geneva Series Commentaries). 1978. 12.95 (ISBN 0-85151-115-5). Banner of Truth.
--Shadow of Calvary. 1983. pap. 5.95 (ISBN 0-85151-373-5). Banner of Truth.
--Simon Peter. 1984. pap. 5.45 (ISBN 0-85151-427-8). Banner of Truth.
Martin, Hugh, ed. Christian Social Reformers of the Nineteenth Century. facsimile ed. LC 70-107725. (Essay Index Reprint Ser.). 1927. 18.00 (ISBN 0-8369-1526-7). Ayer Co Pubs.
Martin, Hugh, ed. see Bernard de Clairvaux, St.
Martin, Ilse, tr. see Wust, Klaus.
Martin, Ira J. Glossolalia, the Gift of Tongues. 75p. 1970. pap. 2.25 (ISBN 0-87148-352-1). Pathway Pr.
Martin, J. D. The Book of Judges. LC 74-31797. (Cambridge Bible Commentary on the New English Bible, Old Testament Ser.). (Illus.). 272p. 1975. 24.95 (ISBN 0-521-08639-6); pap. 10.95x (ISBN 0-521-09768-1). Cambridge U Pr.
Martin, James, tr. see Kurtz, J. H.
Martin, James, tr. see Weippert, Manfred.
Martin, James A. Empirical Philosophies of Religion. LC 78-111850. (Essay Index Reprint Ser.). 1945. 17.00 (ISBN 0-8369-1618-2). Ayer Co Pubs.
Martin, James D. & Davies, Phillip R. A Word in Season: Essays in Honour of William McKane. (JSOT Supplement Ser.: No. 42). 225p. 1986. text ed. 30.00x (ISBN 1-85075-016-5, Pub. by JSOT Pr England); pap. text ed. 15.95x (ISBN 1-85075-047-5). Eisenbrauns.
Martin, James D., jt. auth. see Hatcher, William.
Martin, James D., tr. see Von Rad, Gerhard.
Martin, Jerry N. The Faith of Little Waddle Duck: Love Conquers Fear. 1985. 5.95 (ISBN 0-8062-2483-5). Carlton.
Martin, John A., jt. auth. see Martin, Alfred.
Martin, John B. & Martin, Catherine. Works of Mercy. 1.17 (ISBN 0-8091-9337-X). Paulist Pr.
Martin, John D. Living Together on God's Earth. (Christian Day School Ser.). 1974. 12.95x (ISBN 0-87813-915-X); tchr's. guide 19.65x (ISBN 0-87813-910-9). Christian Light.
Martin, John D. & Showalter, Lester E. Perspectives of Truth in Literature. (Christian Day School Ser.). 1982. 15.05 (ISBN 0-87813-921-4); tchr's. guide 10.95x (ISBN 0-87813-922-2). Christian Light.
Martin, John R. Divorce & Remarriage: A Perspective for Counseling. LC 73-18038. 144p. 1974. pap. 6.95 (ISBN 0-8361-1328-4). Herald Pr.
--Keys to Successful Bible Study. LC 81-6459. 184p. 1981. pap. 6.95 (ISBN 0-8361-1963-0). Herald Pr.
--Portrait of John Milton at Princeton. LC 61-14263. (Illus.). 42p. 1961. 7.50 (ISBN 0-87811-006-2). Princeton Lib.
--Ventures in Discipleship. LC 84-19140. 304p. (Orig.). 1984. pap. 12.95 (ISBN 0-8361-3378-1). Herald Pr.
Martin, Joy R., jt. auth. see Handford, Elizabeth R.
Martin, Kate E., tr. see Zahan, Dominique.
Martin, Kay A., jt. auth. see Buchanan, Annette M.
Martin, L. C. Thomas Warton & the Early Poems of Milton. LC 77-9907. 1934. lib. bdg. 9.50 (ISBN 0-8414-6096-5). Folcroft.
Martin, LaJoyce. Happiness Is... Heaven Made Marriages. Wallace, Mary H., ed. LC 85-22522. (Illus.). 313p. (Orig.). 1985. pap. 6.95 (ISBN 0-912315-86-5). Word Aflame.
Martin, Laurence. Discover Life. LC 75-18373. 80p. 1975. pap. 1.95 (ISBN 0-8361-1779-4). Herald Pr.
Martin, Lawrence M., tr. see Zahan, Dominique.
Martin, Loren D. Isaiah: An Ensign to the Nations. LC 81-92840. (Isaiah Ser.: Vol. 1). (Illus.). 180p. 1982. 9.95 (ISBN 0-9608244-0-5); Set of Multivolumes. write for info. (ISBN 0-9608244-2-1). Valiant Pubns.
Martin, Luis. Intellectual Conquest of Peru: The Jesuit College of San Pablo, 1568-1767. LC 67-26159. (Orig.). 1968. 25.00 (ISBN 0-8232-0785-4). Fordham.
Martin, Luther H. & Goss, James, eds. Essays on Jung & the Study of Religion. LC 85-17865. 214p. (Orig.). 1986. lib. bdg. 29.50 (ISBN 0-8191-4923-3); pap. text ed. 12.75 (ISBN 0-8191-4924-1). U Pr of Amer.
Martin, Malachi. Hostage to the Devil: The Possession of Exorcism of Five Living Americans. LC 86-46207. 488p. 1987. pap. 8.95 (ISBN 0-06-097103-7, PL 7103, PL). Har-Row.
--The Jesuits: Revolt of Angels. 704p. 1987. 19.95 (ISBN 0-671-54505-1, Linden Pr). S&S.
--There Is Still Love. 224p. 1984. 12.95 (ISBN 0-02-580440-5). Macmillan.
--Vatican. LC 85-42645. 672p. 1986. 18.45 (ISBN 0-06-015478-0, HarpT). Har-Row.
Martin, Marcia O. The Christmas Book. (Illus.). 64p. 1985. 15.95 (ISBN 0-88363-585-2). H L Levin.
Martin, Marie-Louise. Kimbangu: An African Prophet & His Church. Moore, D. M., tr. LC 75-45371. pap. 55.50 (ISBN 0-317-08451-8, 2012735). Bks Demand UMI.
Martin, Marie-Therese, tr. see Ladd, George E.
Martin, Marty E. Health Medicine & Faith Traditions: An Inquiry into Religion & Medicine. Vaux, Kenneth L., ed. LC 81-71383. pap. 90.50 (2026975). Bks Demand UMI.
Martin, Mary L. & MacInnis, Donald. Values & Religion in China Today: A Teaching Workbook & Lesson Series. 141p. (Orig.). 1985. pap. 12.95 (ISBN 0-88344-527-1). Orbis Bks.
Martin, Maurice. Identity & Faith. LC 81-82655. (Focal Pamphlet Ser.). 104p. (Orig.). 1981. pap. 3.95 (ISBN 0-8361-1979-7). Herald Pr.
Martin, Nancy. Christianity. (Religions of the World Ser.). (Illus.). 48p. 1986. PLB 10.90 (ISBN 0-531-18064-6, Pub. by Bookwright). Watts.
Martin, Norma & Levitt, Zola. Divorce, a Christian Dilemma. LC 76-45939. 168p. 1977. pap. 1.95 (ISBN 0-8361-1808-1). Herald Pr.
Martin, Paul. Family Fare. 79p. 1976. pap. 1.25 (ISBN 0-8341-0403-2). Beacon Hill.
--Good Morning, Lord: Devotions for Teens. (Good Morning Lord Ser.). 1962. 4.95 (ISBN 0-8010-5879-1). Baker Bk.
--Good Morning, Lord: Devotions for Young People. (Good Morning, Lord Ser.). 1974. 4.95 (ISBN 0-8010-5958-5). Baker Bk.
--Good Morning, Lord: More Devotions for Teens. (Good Morning Lord Ser.). 1973. 4.95 (ISBN 0-8010-5915-1). Baker Bk.
--Good Night, Lord. 64p. 1974. 1.95 (ISBN 0-8341-0241-2). Beacon Hill.
Martin, Peter, jt. ed. see Toon, Peter.
Martin, R. A. Syntactical & Critical Concordance to the Greek Text of Baruch & the Epistle of Jeremiah. (Computer Bible Ser.: Vol. XII). (Gr.). 1977. pap. 15.00 (ISBN 0-935106-09-X). Biblical Res Assocs.
Martin, R. A., jt. auth. see Elliott, John H.
Martin, Ralph. A Crisis of Truth: The Attack on Faith, Morality & Mission in the Catholic Church. 245p. 1983. pap. 6.95 (ISBN 0-89283-146-4). Servant.
--Fire on the Earth. 1975. pap. 2.95 (ISBN 0-89283-021-2). Servant.
--Hungry for God: Practical Help in Personal Prayer. LC 74-4830. 168p. 1974. pap. 6.50 (ISBN 0-385-09534-1). Doubleday.
--Husbands, Wives, Parents, Children. rev. ed. 1983. pap. 6.95 (ISBN 0-89283-149-9). Servant.
--Mark. Hayes, John, ed. LC 81-82350. (Knox Preaching Guides). 96p. 1981. pap. 4.95 (ISBN 0-8042-3234-2). John Knox.
--The Return of the Lord. 118p. (Orig.). 1983. pap. 4.95 (ISBN 0-89283-145-6). Servant.
--Why Be a Christian. 48p. (Orig.). 1987. pap. 1.95 (ISBN 0-89283-336-X). Servant.
Martin, Ralph & Toon, Peter, eds. Reconciliation: A Study of Paul's Theology. LC 80-16340. (New Foundations Theological Library). 272p. 1981. 12.95 (ISBN 0-8042-3709-3); pap. 11.95 (ISBN 0-8042-3729-8). John Knox.
Martin, Ralph, ed. see Avis, Paul D.
Martin, Ralph, ed. see Carson, D. A.
Martin, Ralph P. Colossians & Philemon. rev. ed. (New Century Bible Commentary Ser.). 192p. 1981. pap. 5.95 (ISBN 0-8028-1908-7). Eerdmans.
--Colossians: The Church's Lord & the Christian's Liberty. 192p. 1972. 8.95 (ISBN 0-85364-125-0). Attic Pr.
--Commentary on Philippians. (New Century Bible Commentary Ser.). 192p. 1980. pap. 6.95 (ISBN 0-8028-1840-4). Eerdmans.
--Epistle of Paul to the Philippians. (Tyndale Bible Commentaries). 1960. pap. 4.95 (ISBN 0-8028-1410-7). Eerdmans.
--Mark: Evangelist & Theologian. (Contemporary Evangelical Perspective Ser.). 249p. 1973. kivar 7.95 (ISBN 0-310-28801-0). Zondervan.
--New Testament Books for Pastor & Teacher. LC 83-21654. 152p. (Orig.). 1984. pap. 8.95 (ISBN 0-664-24511-0). Westminster.
--New Testament Foundations: A Guide for Christian Students, Vol. 2. 1986. pap. 9.95 (ISBN 0-8028-0076-9). Eerdmans.
--Second Corinthians, Vol. 40, WBC. 380p. 1985. 25.95 (ISBN 0-8499-0239-8, 0239-8). Word Bks.
--The Spirit & the Congregation: Studies in I Corinthians 12-15. 160p. (Orig.). 1984. 11.95 (ISBN 0-8028-3608-9). Eerdmans.
--Worship in the Early Church. rev. ed. 144p. 1975. pap. 7.95 (ISBN 0-8028-1613-4). Eerdmans.
--The Worship of God: Some Theological, Pastoral & Practical Reflections. 237p. (Orig.). 1982. pap. 10.95 (ISBN 0-8028-1934-6). Eerdmans.
Martin, Raymond. An Introduction to New Testament Greek. 1980. text ed. 7.50x (ISBN 0-915948-07-9). Bks Distinction.
Martin, Richard C. Islam: A Cultural Perspective. (Illus.). 192p. 1982. pap. text ed. 17.00 (ISBN 0-13-506345-0). P-H.
Martin, Richard C., ed. Approaches to Islam in Reglious Studies. LC 85-1099. 1985. 18.95x (ISBN 0-8165-0868-2). U of Ariz Pr.
Martin, Richard M. Events, Reference, & Logical Form. LC 77-24685. pap. 67.80 (2029492). Bks Demand UMI.
Martin, Richie, ed. Judgment in the Gate. LC 86-70285. (Orig.). 1986. pap. 6.95 (ISBN 0-89107-396-5, Crossway Bks). Good News.
Martin, Robert J. Wise Words to the Graduate. (Contempo Ser.). 1978. pap. 1.50 (ISBN 0-8010-6043-5). Baker Bk.
Martin, Roger A. John J. Zubly: Colonial Georgia Minister. 25.00 (ISBN 0-405-14095-9). Ayer Co Pubs.
Martin, Roger H. Evangelicals United: Ecumenical Stirrings in Pre-Victorian Britain, 1795-1830. LC 82-10784. (Studies in Evangelicalism: No. 4). 244p. 1983. 19.00 (ISBN 0-8108-1586-9). Scarecrow.
Martin, Sara H. Frente Al Cancer, Un Gigante a Mi Lado. (Span.). 96p. 1985. pap. 4.50 (ISBN 0-311-46101-8). Casa Bautista.
Martin, Sydney. Beacon Bible Expositions, Vol. 10: Thessalonians, Timothy, Titus. Greathouse, William M & Taylor, Willard H., eds. 1978. 8.95 (ISBN 0-8341-0321-4). Beacon Hill.
--Living with Fire. 120p. (Orig.). 1983. pap. 3.95 (ISBN 0-8341-0845-3). Beacon Hill.
Martin, T. E. Beacon Bible Expositions, Vol. 12: John, Jude, Revelation. Greathouse, M., ed. 230p. 1983. 8.95 (ISBN 0-8341-0809-7). Beacon Hill.
Martin, Thomas M. Christian Family Values. 128p. 1984. pap. 7.95 (ISBN 0-8091-2579-X). Paulist Pr.
--Images & the Imageless: A Study in Religious Consciousness & Film. LC 79-57611. 200p. 1981. 18.50 (ISBN 0-8387-5005-2). Bucknell U Pr.
Martin, W. W. Manual of Ecclesiastical Architecture. 1977. lib. bdg. 75.00 (ISBN 0-8490-2206-1). Gordon Pr.
Martin, Walter. Christian Science. 32p. 1957. pap. 2.95 (ISBN 0-87123-064-X, 210064). Bethany Hse.
--Essential Christianity. 1985. pap. 4.95 (ISBN 0-8307-1029-9, 5418458). Regal.
--Herbert W. Armstrong. 32p. 1969. pap. 2.95 (ISBN 0-87123-213-8, 210213). Bethany Hse.
--Jehovah's Witnesses. 64p. 1969. pap. 2.95 (ISBN 0-87123-270-7, 210270). Bethany Hse.
--The Kingdom of the Cults. rev. ed. 450p. 1985. 14.95 (ISBN 0-87123-796-2, 230796). Bethany Hse.
--The Maze of Mormonism. LC 78-66067. (Orig.). 1979. pap. 6.95 (ISBN 0-88449-017-3, A424365). Vision Hse.
--Mormonism. 32p. 1968. pap. 2.95 (ISBN 0-87123-367-3, 210367). Bethany Hse.
--Mormonismo. 48p. 1982. 1.95 (ISBN 0-88113-208-X). Edit Betania.
--The New Cults. LC 80-52210. (Orig.). 1980. pap. 8.95 (ISBN 0-88449-016-5, A424378). Vision Hse.
--Los Testigos de Jehova. 80p. 1982. 2.25 (ISBN 0-88113-285-3). Edit Betania.
Martin, Walter & Klann, Norman H. Jehovah of the Watchtower. 192p. 1981. pap. 5.95 (ISBN 0-87123-267-7, 210267). Bethany Hse.
Martin, Walter, jt. auth. see Moody, Dwight L.
Martin, Walter R. Walter Martin's Cults Reference Bible. LC 81-52881. 1248p. 1981. 19.99 (ISBN 0-88449-075-0, VH301). Vision Hse.
Martin, Wayne W., tr. The Gospel of Mark: A Translation for Children. LC 84-50838. 112p. (Orig.). 1984. pap. 9.95 (ISBN 0-8358-0493-3). Upper Room.
Martin, William C. Christians in Conflict. LC 72-88018. (Studies in Religion & Society Ser.). 1972. 14.95x (ISBN 0-913348-01-5); pap. 8.95x (ISBN 0-913348-10-4). Ctr Sci Study.
Martin, William J. The Church in Mission: Sunday School Staff Training Text for 1987. LC 86-80022. 128p. (Orig.). 1986. pap. 2.50 (ISBN 0-88243-803-4, 02-0803). Gospel Pub.
Martin-Achard, R. & Re'emi, P. The International Theological Commentary on Amos & Lamentations. (The International Theological Commentary Ser.). 160p. (Orig.). 1983. pap. 8.95 (ISBN 0-8028-1040-3). Eerdmans.
Martindale, C. C. What Are Saints? Fourteen Studies in Sanctity. 1982. pap. 3.95 (ISBN 0-89453-270-7). M Glazier.
Martindale, Charles. John Milton & the Transformation of Ancient Epic. LC 86-3408. 254p. 1986. 28.50x (ISBN 0-389-20624-5). B&N Imports.
Martindale, Cyril C. What Are Saints: Fifteen Chapters in Sanctity. facs. ed. LC 68-16954. (Essay Index Reprint Ser). 1932. 13.75 (ISBN 0-8369-0681-0). Ayer Co Pubs.
Martindale, Don, ed. see Weber, Max.
Martin-Doisy, F. Dictionnaire d'Economic Charitable, 4 vols. Migne, J. P., ed. (Troisieme et Derniere Encyclopedie Theologique Ser.: Vols. 5-8). (Fr.). 3616p. Repr. of 1857 ed. lib. bdg. 456.00x (ISBN 0-89241-292-5). Caratzas.
Martineau, Harriet. Autobiography. 962p. Repr. of 1877 ed. text ed. 62.10x (ISBN 0-576-02159-8). Gregg Intl.
Martineau, James. A Study of Spinoza. 3rd facsimile ed. LC 78-152994. (Select Bibliographies Reprint Ser). Repr. of 1895 ed. 23.50 (ISBN 0-8369-5746-6). Ayer Co Pubs.
Martinet, Jan. Hasidic Legends: A Suite by H. N. Werkman. (Eng. & Dutch., Illus.). 80p. (Orig.). 1985. 175.00x (ISBN 90-6243-048-1, Pub. by Boumas Boekhuis Netherlands). Benjamins North Am.

Martinez, Jose. Novios: Conversemos Sobre Cosas Que Apenas Se Hablan. (Span.). 80p. 1986. pap. 2.95 (ISBN 0-311-46104-2). Casa Bautista.
Martinez, Jose & Trenchard, Ernesto. Escogidos en Cristo. Tr. of Chosen in Christ. (Span.). 320p. 1987. pap. 9.95 (ISBN 0-8254-1737-6). Kregel.
Martinez, Jose L. Cuando el Dinero Causa Problemas. (Serie de la Familia). (Span.). 96p. 1986. pap. 3.50 (ISBN 0-311-46265-0). Casa Bautista.
Martinez, Jose L., ed. see Neighbour, Ralph.
Martinez, Jose L., tr. see Hendricks, William.
Martinez, Jose L., tr. see McWilliams, Anne W.
Martinez, Jose L., tr. see Neighbour, Ralph W., Jr.
Martinez, Jose Luis, ed. see Haney, David.
Martinez, Luis M. The Sanctifier. 1981. 7.50 (ISBN 0-8198-6803-5); pap. 6.00 (ISBN 0-8198-6804-3). Dghtrs St Paul.
Martinez, Raul, tr. see Sizemore, Denver.
Martinez, Violeta S. de see Stowell, Gordon.
Martinez Dalmau, Eduardo. Study on the Synoptic Gospels. 1964. 5.95 (ISBN 0-8315-0013-1). Speller.
Martinez De Toledo, Alfonso. Little Sermons on Sin: The Archpriest of Talavera. Byrd, Leslie, tr. 1977. pap. 2.85 (ISBN 0-520-03281-0, CAL 346). U of Cal Pr.
Martin-Marrero, Vernetta. The Gospel Church Choir Organizer. 150p. 1984. 3 ring hard storage binder 29.95 (ISBN 0-9613430-0-1). Martin-Marrero.
Martland, T. R. Religion As Art. LC 80-27104. (Series in Philosophy). 265p. 1981. 49.50x (ISBN 0-87395-520-X); pap. 16.95 (ISBN 0-87395-521-8). State U NY Pr.
Martone, Thomas. The Iconography of the Conversion of Saint Paul. Freedberg, S. J., ed. (Outstanding Dissertations in Fine Arts Ser.). (Illus.). 325p. 1985. Repr. of 1978 ed. 45.00 (ISBN 0-8240-6882-3). Garland Pub.
Martos, Joseph. The Catholic Sacraments. (Message of the Sacraments Ser.: Vol 1). 13.95 (ISBN 0-89453-391-6); pap. 9.95 (ISBN 0-89453-227-8). M Glazier.
--Doors to the Sacred: A Historical Introduction to Sacraments in the Catholic Church. LC 82-45148. 552p. 1982. pap. 10.95 (ISBN 0-385-18180-9, Im). Doubleday.
Marty, Martin. Health & Medicine in the Lutheran Tradition. 192p. 1983. 16.95x (ISBN 0-8245-0613-8). Crossroad NY.
--An Invitation to American Catholic History. (Basics of Christian Thought Ser.). 1986. 14.95 (ISBN 0-88347-189-2). Thomas More.
Marty, Martin, ed. see James, William.
Marty, Martin E. Baptism. LC 77-78635. 1977. pap. 3.95 (ISBN 0-8006-1317-1, 1-1317). Fortress.
--Being Good & Doing Good. LC 84-47929. (Lead Bks.). 128p. 1984. pap. 4.95 (ISBN 0-8006-1603-0). Fortress.
--Christian Churches in the United States, 1800-1983. (Illus.). 126p. 1984. 12.95 (ISBN 0-86683-172-X, 1412, HarpR). Har-Row.
--Christianity in the New World: From 1500 to 1800. LC 82-83845. (Illustrated History of the Church Ser.). (Illus.). 127p. 1984. 12.95 (ISBN 0-86683-173-8, 1411, HarpR). Har-Row.
--A Cry of Absence: Reflections for the Winter of the Heart. LC 82-48416. (Illus.). 176p. 1983. 12.45 (ISBN 0-06-065434-1, HarpR). Har-Row.
--Friendship. LC 80-69243. 180p. 1980. pap. 4.50 (ISBN 0-89505-053-6). Argus Comm.
--The Lord's Supper. LC 79-6550. 80p. (Orig.). 1980. pap. 3.50 (ISBN 0-8006-1386-4, 1-1386). Fortress.
--Modern American Religion, Vol. 1: The Irony of It All, 1893-1919. LC 86-16524. (Illus.). 398p. 1986. 24.95 (ISBN 0-226-50893-5). U of Chicago Pr.
--The New Shape of American Religion. LC 78-1576. 1978. Repr. of 1959 ed. lib. bdg. 22.50x (ISBN 0-313-20353-9, MANE). Greenwood.
--Pilgrims in Their Own Land. 512p. 1985. pap. 7.95 (ISBN 0-14-008268-9). Penguin.
--Pilgrims in Their Own Land: Five Hundred Years of Religion in America. (Illus.). 416p. 1984. 25.00 (ISBN 0-316-54867-7). Little.
--Protestantism in the United States: Righteous Empire. 2nd ed. 320p. 1986. text ed. write for info. (ISBN 0-02-376500-3). Macmillan.
--The Public Church: Mainline-Evangelical-Catholic. 192p. 1981. 10.95 (ISBN 0-8245-0019-9). Crossroad NY.
--Religion & Republic: The American Circumstance. LC 86-47755. 320p. 1987. 25.00 (ISBN 0-8070-1206-8). Beacon Pr.
--Religious Crises in Modern America. LC 81-80740. (Charles Edmondson Historical Lectures Ser.). 40p. (Orig.). 1981. pap. 4.50 (ISBN 0-918954-26-6). Baylor Univ Pr.
--A Short History of Christianity. LC 80-8042. 384p. 1980. pap. 9.95 (ISBN 0-8006-1427-5, 1-1427). Fortress.
--The Word: People Participating in Preaching. LC 83-16611. 112p. 1984. pap. 3.95 (ISBN 0-8006-1778-9, 1-1778). Fortress.
Marty, Martin E., jt. auth. see Chittister, Joan D.
Marty, Martin E. & Peerman, Dean G., eds. A Handbook of Christian Theologians. 736p. (Orig.). 1984. pap. 13.50 (ISBN 0-687-16563-6). Abingdon.
Marty, Martin E., intro. by see Holst, Lawrence.
Marty, Martin E., et al. The Religious Press in America. LC 72-6844. 184p. 1973. Repr. of 1963 ed. lib. bdg. 22.50x (ISBN 0-8371-6500-8, MARP). Greenwood.
Marty, Myron A. Lutherans & Roman Catholicism: The Changing Conflict, 1917-1963. 1968. 14.95 (ISBN 0-268-00162-6). U of Notre Dame Pr.
Martyn, Carlos. Life & Times of John Milton. LC 76-39970. 1976. Repr. of 1866 ed. lib. bdg. 37.50 (ISBN 0-8414-6009-4). Folcroft.
Martyn, J. Louis. The Gospel of John in Christian History. LC 78-70821. 160p. 1979. pap. 5.95 (ISBN 0-8091-2170-0). Paulist Pr.
Martyn, J. Louis, jt. ed. see Keck, Leander E.
Martz, Louis L. John Donne in Meditation: The Anniversaries. LC 70-99172. (English Literature Ser., No. 33). 1970. Repr. of 1947 ed. lib. bdg. 39.95x (ISBN 0-8383-0335-8). Haskell.
Martz, Louis L., tr. see More, St. Thomas.
Marucchi, Orazio. Christian Epigraphy. Willis, J. Armine, tr. from It. LC 74-82057. 472p. 1975. 20.00 (ISBN 0-89005-070-8). Ares.
Marvel, Thomas S. & Moreno, Maria L. La Arquitectura de los Templos Parroquiales de Puerto Rico - Architecture of Parish Churches in Puerto Rico. bilingual ed. LC 81-10291. (Illus.). 1984. pap. 10.00 (ISBN 0-8477-2114-0). U of PR Pr.
Marvick, Elizabeth W. The Young Richelieu: A Psychoanalytic Approach to Leadership. LC 82-24754. (Orig.). 1983. 32.00x (ISBN 0-226-50904-4); pap. 14.00x (ISBN 0-226-50905-2). U of Chicago Pr.
Marvin, Abijah P. The Life & Times of Cotton Mather. LC 72-1979. (American Biography Ser., No. 32). 1972. Repr. of 1892 ed. lib. bdg. 59.95x (ISBN 0-8383-1454-6). Haskell.
Marwick, Lawrence. Biblical & Judaic Acronyms. 39.00x (ISBN 0-87068-438-8). Ktav.
Marwick, Max, ed. Witchcraft & Sorcery. 494p. 1987. pap. 6.95 (ISBN 0-14-022678-8, Pelican). Penguin.
Marx, A. Studies in Jewish History & Booklore. 472p. 1944. text ed. 49.68x (ISBN 0-576-80136-4, Pub. by Gregg Intl Pubs England). Gregg Intl.
Marx, Alexander. Essays in Jewish Biography. (Brown Classics in Judaica Ser.). 322p. 1986. pap. text ed. 14.25 (ISBN 0-8191-5022-3). U Pr of Amer.
Marx, Alexander, jt. auth. see Margolis, Max L.
Marx, Herbert L., ed. Religions in America. (Reference Shelf Ser.). 1977. 8.00 (ISBN 0-8242-0608-8). Wilson.
Marx, Karl & Engels, Friedrich. On Religion. LC 82-17032. (Classics in Religious Studies). 384p. 1982. Repr. of 1964 ed. 10.50x (ISBN 0-89130-599-8, 01 05 03). Scholars Pr GA.
Marx, Victor. Catholicism, Judaism & the Effort at World Domination. (Illus.). 1980. 65.00 (ISBN 0-89266-216-6). Am Classical Coll Pr.
Marxhausen, Evelyn. The Man Who Slept Through a Sermon. (Arch Bk.: No. 16). (Illus.). 1979. 0.99 (ISBN 0-570-06128-8, 59-1246). Concordia.
--Simeon & the Baby Jesus. (Arch Bks.). (Illus.). 24p. 1986. pap. 0.99 saddlestitched (ISBN 0-570-06202-0, 59-1425). Concordia.
--When God Laid Down the Law. LC 59-1259. (Arch Bk.). 1981. pap. 0.99 (ISBN 0-570-06142-3). Concordia.
Marxist-Leninist Party, USA. Zionism Is Racism in the Service of Imperialism. National Executive Committee of the MLP, USA, ed. (Illus.). 112p. (Orig.). 1983. pap. 1.00 (ISBN 0-86714-025-9). Marxist-Leninist.
Marxsen, Willi. The Beginnings of Christology: Together with the Lord's Supper As a Christological Problem. LC 79-7384. pap. 31.80 (2029295). Bks Demand UMI.
--Introduction to the New Testament: An Approach to Its Problems. Buswell, G., tr. from Ger. LC 68-15419. 304p. 1968. pap. 8.50 (ISBN 0-8006-1181-0, 1-1181). Fortress.
--Resurrection of Jesus of Nazareth. Kohl, Margaret, tr. from Ger. LC 76-120083. 192p. (Orig.). 1970. pap. 4.95 (ISBN 0-8006-0001-0, 1-1). Fortress.
Mary. You Are God. 1955. pap. 4.95 (ISBN 0-87516-057-3). De Vorss.
Mary da Bergamo, Cajetan. Humility of Heart. Vaughan, Herbert C., tr. 240p. 1978. pap. 4.50 (ISBN 0-89555-067-9). Tan Bks Pubs.
Mary Francis, Sr. Right to Be Merry. LC 73-6850. 1973. pap. 6.50 (ISBN 0-8199-0506-2). Franciscan Herald.
Mary Louise, Sr., ed. Over the Bent World. LC 73-105031. (Essay Index Reprint Ser). 1939. 40.00 (ISBN 0-8369-1676-X). Ayer Co Pubs.
Marzik, Thomas D., jt. ed. see Miller, Randall M.
Masani, Rustom P. Folklore of Wells. LC 77-11936. 1977. Repr. lib. bdg. 32.00 (ISBN 0-8414-6216-X). Folcroft.
Masaryk, Thomas G. Masaryk on Thought & Life. LC 78-135840. (Eastern Europe Collection Ser.). 1970. Repr. of 1938 ed. 16.00 (ISBN 0-405-02782-6). Ayer Co Pubs.
--Modern Man & Religion. facsimile ed. LC 74-107816. (Select Bibliographies Reprint Ser). 1938. 24.50 (ISBN 0-8369-5216-2). Ayer Co Pubs.
Masaryk, Tomas G. Modern Man & Religion. Kennedy, H. E., et al, trs. LC 78-109783. viii, 320p. Repr. of 1938 ed. lib. bdg. 22.50x (ISBN 0-8371-4273-3, MAMR). Greenwood.
Ma Satya Bharti, ed. see Rajneesh, Bhagwan Shree.
Mascall, E. L. The Triune God: An Ecumenical Study. (Princeton Theological Monograph: No. 10). 1986. pap. 12.90 (ISBN 0-915138-96-4). Pickwick.
Mascall, Eric L. Importance of Being Human. LC 74-12849. 118p. 1974. Repr. of 1958 ed. lib. bdg. 22.50 (ISBN 0-8371-7761-8, MABH). Greenwood.
Mascarenhas, Ives, tr. see Suarez, Federico.
Maschke, Ruby. Bible People Story-N-Puzzle Book. 48p. (Orig.). 1983. pap. 2.50 (ISBN 0-87239-673-8, 2773). Standard Pub.
--Children's Bible Stories Puzzle Book. 48p. 1986. pap. 2.50 (ISBN 0-87403-046-3, 2690). Standard Pub.
--Disciples of Christ Story-N-Puzzle Book. 48p. (Orig.). 1983. pap. 2.50 (ISBN 0-87239-675-4, 2775). Standard Pub.
--Life of Christ Story-N-Puzzle Book. 48p. (Orig.). 1981. pap. 2.50 (ISBN 0-87239-449-2, 2839). Standard Pub.
--Promises of Jesus from the Bibles: Puzzle Book. (Illus.). 48p. 1983. pap. 2.50 (ISBN 0-87239-591-X, 2789). Standard Pub.
Masefield, John. Letters to Margaret Bridges. Stanford, Donald, ed. 123p. 1984. 18.50 (ISBN 0-85635-477-5). Carcanet.
--Shakespeare & Spiritual Life. LC 77-1449. 1973. lib. bdg. 10.00 (ISBN 0-8414-2315-6). Folcroft.
Masefield, Peter. Divine Revelation in Pali Buddhism. 216p. 1986. 27.95 (ISBN 0-04-294132-6). Allen Unwin.
Maseroni, Robert S. Be Fruitful, No. 9. 1983. 0.80 (ISBN 0-89536-633-9, 0237). CSS of Ohio.
--Being Gifted, No. 1. 1983. 0.80 (ISBN 0-89536-616-9, 0228). CSS of Ohio.
--The Church Will Grow by These. 1983. 5.55 (ISBN 0-317-04044-8, 0060). CSS of Ohio.
--The Gift of Aid, No. 6. 1983. 0.80 (ISBN 0-89536-630-4, 0738). CSS of Ohio.
--The Gift of Encouragement, No. 4. 1983. 0.80 (ISBN 0-89536-628-2, 0736). CSS of Ohio.
--The Gift of Giving, No. 5. 1983. 0.80 (ISBN 0-89536-629-0, 0737). CSS of Ohio.
--The Gift of Mercy, No. 7. 1983. 0.80 (ISBN 0-89536-631-2, 0739). CSS of Ohio.
--The Gift of Ministry & Service, No. 2. 1983. 0.80 (ISBN 0-89536-626-6, 0734). CSS of Ohio.
--The Gift of Prophecy, No. 8. 1983. 0.80 (ISBN 0-89536-632-0, 0740). CSS of Ohio.
--The Gift of Teaching, No. 3. 1983. 0.80 (ISBN 0-89536-627-4, 0735). CSS of Ohio.
Masi, Michael. Boethius & the Liberal Arts: A Collection of Essays. (Utah Studies in Literature & Linguistics: Vol. 18). 220p. 1982. pap. 27.35 (ISBN 3-261-04722-4). P Lang Pubs.
Maskell, William. Ancient Liturgy of the Church of England. 3rd ed. LC 71-172848. Repr. of 1882 ed. 29.50 (ISBN 0-404-04196-5). AMS Pr.
--The Ancient Liturgy of the Church of England. 1977. lib. bdg. 59.95 (ISBN 0-8490-1425-5). Gordon Pr.
--Monumenta Ritualia Ecclestiae Anglicanae, 3 vols. 1710p. 1882. text ed. 186.30x (ISBN 0-576-99784-6, Pub. by Gregg Intl Pub England). Gregg Intl.
Mas-Latrie, L. des see Des Mas-Latrie, L.
Maslin, Simeon J., ed. Shaarei Mitzvah: Gates of Mitzvah. (Illus.). 1979. 9.95 (ISBN 0-916694-37-2); pap. 7.95 (ISBN 0-916694-53-4). Central Conf.
Maslow, Abraham H. Religions, Values, & Peak-Experiences. 1976. pap. 4.95 (ISBN 0-14-004262-8). Penguin.
--Religions: Values & Peak Experiences. 1983. 13.25 (ISBN 0-8446-6070-1). Peter Smith.
Mason, H. Lee. Sermon Outlines for Evangelism. (Sermon Outline Ser.). (Orig.). 1981. pap. 2.50 (ISBN 0-8010-6120-2). Baker Bk.
Mason, H. Lowell. Hymn-Tunes of Lowell Mason. LC 74-24144. Repr. of 1944 ed. 15.00 (ISBN 0-404-13035-6). AMS Pr.
Mason, Henry M., tr. see Anjou, Lars A.
Mason, Herbert, tr. see Massignon, Louis.
Mason, J. W. Shinto, 2 vols. 200.00 (ISBN 0-8490-1050-0). Gordon Pr.
Mason, John P. Island of the Blest: Islam in a Libyan Oasis Community. LC 77-620016. (Papers in International Studies: Africa Ser.: No. 31). (Illus.). 1977. pap. 10.00x (ISBN 0-89680-063-6, Ohio U Ctr Intl). Ohio U Pr.
Mason, Lowell. Musical Letters from Abroad. 2nd ed. LC 67-13035. (Music Ser). 1967. Repr. of 1854 ed. lib. bdg. 37.50 (ISBN 0-306-70940-6). Da Capo.
Mason, Lowell, ed. The Boston Handel & Haydn Society Collection of Church Music. LC 77-171078. (Earlier American Music Ser.: Vol. 15). 324p. 1973. Repr. of 1822 ed. lib. bdg. 37.50 (ISBN 0-306-77315-5). Da Capo.
Mason, Sr. M. Elizabeth. Active Life & Contemplative Life: A Study of the Concepts from Plato to the Present. Ganss, George E., ed. 1961. pap. 5.95 (ISBN 0-87462-418-5). Marquette.
Mason, Mike. The Mystery of Marriage: As Iron Sharpens Iron. LC 85-3048. 190p. 1985. 10.95 (ISBN 0-88070-097-1). Multnomah.
Mason, Philip P. Directory of Jewish Archival Institutions. LC 75-15504. 72p. 1975. pap. text ed. 7.95x (ISBN 0-8143-1547-X). Wayne St U Pr.
Mason, Robert L. & Jacobs, Carrie. How to Choose the Wrong Marriage Partner & Live Unhappily Ever After. LC 78-52452. 1979. pap. 2.99 (ISBN 0-8042-2093-X). John Knox.
Mason, Robert L., et al. The Clergyman & the Psychiatrist: When to Refer. LC 77-22597. 248p. 1978. 20.95x (ISBN 0-88229-260-9). Nelson-Hall.
Mason, Rosalie. Beginners' Guide to Family Preparedness. LC 77-79750. (Illus.). 160p. 1977. pap. 6.95 (ISBN 0-88290-082-X). Horizon Utah.
Mason, Thomas. Serving God & Mammon: William Juxon, 1582-1663. LC 83-40507. (Illus.). 208p. 1985. 29.50 (ISBN 0-87413-251-7). U Delaware Pr.
Maspero, Henri. Taoism & Chinese Religion. Kierman, Frank A., Jr., tr. from Fr. LC 80-13444. Orig. Title: Le Taoisme et les religions Chinoises. 656p. 1981. lib. bdg. 40.00x (ISBN 0-87023-308-4). U of Mass Pr.
Mass, Adriaan V. see Van Lutsenburg Maas, Adriaan.
Massabki, Charles. Christ: Liberation of the World Today. Mescall, Sr. Eloise T., tr. from Fr. LC 78-12998. 1979. pap. 6.95 (ISBN 0-8189-0374-0). Alba.
Masset, Evelyn. To Live Each Day Is to Meditate. (Illus.). 42p. 1982. pap. 5.00. Coleman Pub.
Massey, Barbara. Virginia Wingo: Teacher & Friend. LC 82-73665. (Meet the Missionary Ser.). 1983. 5.50 (ISBN 0-8054-4282-0, 4242-82). Broadman.
Massey, C. C. Thoughts of a Modern Mystic. 59.95 (ISBN 0-8490-1209-0). Gordon Pr.
Massey, C. C., tr. see Du Prel, Carl.
Massey, Craig. Adjust or Self-Destruct. LC 77-4088. pap. 3.50 (ISBN 0-8024-0136-8). Moody.
--Ajustarse o Autodestruirse. Orig. Title: Adjust or Self-Destruct. (Span.). 144p. 1983. pap. 3.50 (ISBN 0-8254-1470-9). Kregel.
Massey, Floyd, Jr. & McKinney, Samuel B. Church Administration in the Black Perspective. LC 76-9804. 176p. 1976. pap. 7.95 (ISBN 0-8170-0710-5). Judson.
Massey, Gerald. Gnostic & Historic Christianity. 1985. pap. 5.95 (ISBN 0-916411-51-6). Sure Fire.
Massey, James, jt. ed. see McCown, Wayne.
Massey, James A., ed. see Gleason, Elisabeth G.
Massey, James A., ed. see Schleiermacher, Friedrich.
Massey, James A., tr. see Feuerbach, Ludwig.
Massey, James E. Concerning Christian Unity. 1979. 3.95 (ISBN 0-87162-219-X, D3070). Warner Pr.
--Designing the Sermon: Order & Movement in Preaching. LC 80-17920. (Abingdon Preacher's Library). 128p. (Orig.). 1980. pap. 6.95 (ISBN 0-687-10490-4). Abingdon.
--Spiritual Disciplines: Growth Through the Practice of Prayer, Fasting, Dialogue, & Worship. rev. ed. Allison, Joseph D., ed. 112p. 1985. pap. 4.95 (ISBN 0-310-37151-1, 12410P). Zondervan.
Massey, Marilyn C. Christ Unmasked: The Meaning of "The Life of Jesus" in German Politics. LC 82-8547. (Studies in Religion Ser.). xi, 182p. 1983. 23.00x (ISBN 0-8078-1524-1). U of NC Pr.
Massey, Marilyn C., ed. In Defense of My "Life of Jesus" Against the Hegelians by David Friedrich Strauss. LC 83-10644. 112p. 1983. 17.50 (ISBN 0-208-02017-9, Archon Bks). Shoe String.
Massey, Michael. Roman Religion. Hodge, Peter, ed. (Aspects of Roman Life Ser.). 48p. (Orig.). 1979. pap. text ed. 4.40 (ISBN 0-582-21573-0). Longman.

Massey, William. Remarks upon Milton's Paradise Lost. LC 77-4961. 1751. lib. bdg. 30.00 (ISBN 0-8414-6194-5). Folcroft.

Massi, Jeri. Derwood, Inc. (English Skills for Christian Schools Ser.). 288p. (Orig.). 1986. pap. 5.95 (ISBN 0-89084-323-6). Bob Jones Univ Pr.

Massie, Robert. His Image... My Image: Leader's Guide. 86p. 1986. pap. 1.95 (ISBN 0-86605-159-7). Campus Crusade.

Massignon, Louis. The Passion of Al-Hallaj: Mystic & Martyr of Islam, 4 vols. Mason, Herbert, tr. from Fr. LC 80-11085. (Bollingen Ser.: No. XCVIII). 2010p. 1983. Set. 145.00x (ISBN 0-691-09910-3); 24.50x (ISBN 0-691-10203-1). Princeton U Pr.

Massion, J. C. & Lambin, H. R. Questions of Christians: Mark's Response, Vol. 1. LC 80-68045. 1980. pap. 2.75 (ISBN 0-914070-16-9). ACTA Found.

Masson, David. Life of John Milton: Narrated in Connection with the Political, Literary & Ecclesiastical History of His Time, 7 vols. Set. 117.25 (ISBN 0-8446-1303-7); 16.75 ea. Peter Smith.

--Three Devils: Luther's, Milton's & Goethe's. LC 72-193946. 1874. lib. bdg. 20.00 (ISBN 0-8414-6495-2). Folcroft.

Masson, J. Moussaieff. The Oceanic Feeling: The Origins of Religious Sentiment in Ancient India. (Studies of Classical India: No. 3). 228p. 1980. lib. bdg. 34.00 (ISBN 90-277-1050-3, Pub. by Reidel Holland). Kluwer Academic.

Masson, Robert, ed. The Pedagogy of God's Image: Essays on Symbol & the Religious Imagination. 214p. 1986. lib. bdg. 23.00 (ISBN 0-8191-5721-X, Pub. by College Theology Society); pap. text ed. 13.00 (ISBN 0-8191-5619-1, Pub. by College Theology Society). U Pr of Amer.

Massy, Robert. You Are What You Breathe: The Negative Ion Story. 32p. 1980. 1.50 (ISBN 0-916438-41-4, Dist. by New Era Pr). Univ of Trees.

Mast, Coleen K. Love & Life: A Christian Sexual Morality Guide for Teens Teacher's Guide. 150p. 1986. pap. 10.95 (ISBN 0-89870-108-2). Ignatius Pr.

Mast, Coleen K., et al. Love & Life: A Christian Sexual Morality Guide for Teens. 118p. 1986. pap. 7.95 (ISBN 0-89870-106-6). Ignatius Pr.

--Love & Life: A Christian Sexual Morality Guide for Teens Parents' Guide. LC 86-80604. 48p. 1986. pap. 5.95 (ISBN 0-89870-107-4). Ignatius Pr.

Mast, Russel. Preach the Word. LC 68-28782. 1968. pap. 1.25 (ISBN 0-87303-680-8). Faith & Life.

Master Hua, Tripitaka. Great Compassion Dharma Transmission Verses of the 42 Hands & Eyes. Buddhist Text Translation Society, tr. from Chinese. (Illus.). 100p. (Orig.). 1983. pap. 16.00 (ISBN 0-88139-002-X). Buddhist Text.

--Listen to Yourself: Think Everything Over, Vol. II. Buddhist Text Translation Society, tr. from Chinese. 172p. 1983. pap. 7.00 (ISBN 0-88139-010-0). Buddhist Text.

--Records of High Sanghans, Vol. I. Buddhist Text Translation Society, tr. from Chinese. 160p. (Orig.). 1983. pap. 7.00 (ISBN 0-88139-012-7). Buddhist Text.

--The Shurangama Mantra: A Commentary, Vol. III. Buddhist Text Translation Society, tr. from Chinese. (Illus.). 156p. (Orig.). 1982. pap. 6.50 (ISBN 0-917512-36-7). Buddhist Text.

--Water Mirror Reflecting Heaven. Buddhist Text Translation Society, tr. from Chinese. (Illus.). 82p. (Orig.). 1982. pap. 4.00 (ISBN 0-88139-501-3). Buddhist Text.

Master Hua, Tripitaka, commentary by. Dharma Flower Sutra, Vol. IV. Buddhist Text Translation Society, tr. from Chinese. (Illus.). 371p. (Orig.). 1980. pap. 9.00 (ISBN 0-917512-62-6). Buddhist Text.

--Dharma Flower Sutra, Vol. VII. Buddhist Text Translation Society, tr. from Chinese. (Illus.). 250p. (Orig.). 1980. pap. 8.50 (ISBN 0-917512-93-6). Buddhist Text.

--Dharma Flower Sutra, Vol. VIII. Buddhist Text Translation Society, tr. from Chinese. (Illus.). 160p. (Orig.). 1980. pap. 8.00 (ISBN 0-917512-71-5). Buddhist Text.

--Flower Adornment (Avatamsaka) Sutra: Chapter 26, The Ten Grounds, Pt. One. Buddhist Text Translation Society, tr. from Chinese. (Illus.). 234p. (Orig.). 1980. pap. 7.00 (ISBN 0-917512-87-1). Buddhist Text.

--Flower Adornment Sutra, Chapter 39: Entering the Dharma Realm., Part I. Buddhist Text Translation Society, tr. from Chinese. (Illus.). 284p. (Orig.). 1980. pap. 8.50 (ISBN 0-917512-68-5). Buddhist Text.

--Flower Adornment Sutra, Chapter 39: Entering the Dharma Realm, Part II. Buddhist Text Translation Society, tr. from Chinese. (Illus.). 312p. (Orig.). 1980. pap. 8.50 (ISBN 0-917512-70-7). Buddhist Text.

--Shurangama Sutra, Vol. 3. Buddhist Text Translation Society, tr. from Chinese. (Illus.). 240p. (Orig.). 1980. pap. 8.50 (ISBN 0-917512-94-4). Buddhist Text.

--Shurangama Sutra, Vol. 4. Buddhist Text Translation Society, tr. from Chinese. (Illus.). 285p. (Orig.). 1980. pap. 8.50 (ISBN 0-917512-90-1). Buddhist Text.

--Shurangama Sutra, Vol. 5. Buddhist Text Translation Society, tr. from Chinese. (Illus.). 250p. (Orig.). 1980. pap. 8.50 (ISBN 0-917512-91-X). Buddhist Text.

Master Hua, Tripitaka, commentary by see National Master Ch'ing Liang.

Master Hua, Tripitaka, commentary by see Vasubhandu, Bodhisattva.

Master Hua, Triptaka. Herein Lies the Treasure-Trove, Vol. 1. Buddhist Text Translation Society, tr. from Chinese. (Illus.). 160p. (Orig.). 1983. pap. 6.50 (ISBN 0-88139-001-1). Buddhist Text.

Masterman, J. Howard. The Age of Milton. 1906. Repr. lib. bdg. 15.00 (ISBN 0-8414-6453-7). Folcroft.

Master Ni. The Footsteps of the Mystical Child. 180p. 1986. pap. text ed. 9.50 (ISBN 0-937064-11-4). SEBT.

Masters, Edgar L. The Blood of Prophets. 59.95 (ISBN 0-87968-761-4). Gordon Pr.

Masters, Peter, ed. Remember the Prisoners: Current Accounts of Believers in Russia. pap. 6.95 (ISBN 0-8024-7388-1). Moody.

Masters, R. E. Eros & Evil: The Sexual Psychopathology of Witchcraft. LC 79-8114. Repr. of 1962 ed. 36.50 (ISBN 0-404-18427-8). AMS Pr.

Masters, Roy. The Satin Principle. LC 78-78158. 1978. pap. 6.50 (ISBN 0-933900-05-8). Foun Human Under.

--Sex, Sin & Salvation. LC 77-78040. 267p. 1977. pap. 6.50 (ISBN 0-933900-06-6). Foun Human Under.

Maston, T. B. Biblical Ethics -- A Survey: A Guide to the Ethical Message of the Scriptures from Genesis Through Revelation. LC 82-6470. 320p. 1982. 13.95 (ISBN 0-86554-051-9, MUP-H32). Mercer Univ Pr.

--Como Vivir en el Mundo de Hoy. Adams, Bob, tr. from Eng. Tr. of A World in Travail. (Span.). 224p. Date not set. pap. price not set (ISBN 0-311-46084-4). Casa Bautista.

--Consejos a la Juventud. Duffer, H. F., Jr., tr. Orig. Title: Advice to Youth. (Span.). 60p. 1985. pap. 1.55 (ISBN 0-311-46005-4). Casa Bautista.

--The Ethic of the Christian Life. Hogg, Gayle, ed. (Religious Education Ser.). 152p. 1982. kivar 10.75 (ISBN 0-311-72605-4). Casa Bautista.

--Etica de la Vida Cristiana Sus Principios Basicos. Ureta, Floreal, tr. from English. (Span.). 200p. 1981. pap. 6.50 (ISBN 0-311-46076-3). Casa Bautista.

--To Walk As He Walked. LC 85-17173. 1985. pap. 5.95 (ISBN 0-8054-5024-6). Broadman.

--Treasures from the Holy Scripture. (Orig.). 1987. pap. 3.25 (ISBN 0-8054-5043-2). Broadman.

--Why Live the Christian Life? LC 79-55292. 1980. pap. 5.95 (ISBN 0-8054-6121-3). Broadman.

Maston, T. B. & Tillman, William A. The Bible & Family Relations. LC 81-67196. 1983. 8.95 (ISBN 0-8054-6124-8). Broadman.

Mastrantonis, George. Augsburg & Constantinople: The Correspondence Between Patriarch Jeremiah II & the Tubingen Theologians. 424p. 1981. 22.95 (ISBN 0-916586-81-2); pap. 14.95 (ISBN 0-916586-82-0). Hellenic Coll Pr.

Masuda, Jiryo, tr. see Vasu-Mitra.

Mas'Ud Ibn Umar Al-Taftazani. A Commentary on the Creed of Islam. LC 79-52565. (Islam Ser.). 1980. Repr. of 1950 ed. lib. bdg. 18.00x (ISBN 0-8369-9268-7). Ayer Co Pubs.

Masunaga, Reiho, tr. see Dogen.

Masunaga, Shizuto & Brown, Stephen. Zen Imagery Exercises: Meridian Exercises for Wholesome Living. LC 86-80220. (Illus.). 192p. (Orig.). 1986. pap. 13.95 (ISBN 0-87040-669-8). Japan Pubns USA.

Mata, Sri Daya. Only Love. LC 75-44633. (Illus.). 295p. 1976. 6.50 (ISBN 0-87612-215-2). Self Realization.

Mataragnon, Rita H., jt. ed. see Bryant, M. Darrol.

Mataragnon, Rita H., jt. ed. see Ferre, Frederick P.

Matarasso, P. M., tr. Quest of the Holy Grail. (Classics Ser.). 304p. 1969. pap. 4.95 (ISBN 0-14-044220-0). Penguin.

Matczak, S. A., ed. & intro. by see Smith, William A.

Matczak, Sebastian A. Karl Barth on God: Our Knowledge of the Divine Existence. LC 62-15994. 358p. 1962. 7.25 (ISBN 0-912116-06-4). Learned Pubns.

--Le Probleme de Dieu dans la Pensee de Karl Barth. (Philosophical Questions Ser.: No. 1). 1968. pap. 19.50 (ISBN 0-912116-00-5). Learned Pubns.

Matczak, Sebastian A., ed. God in Contemporary Thought. LC 75-31391. 1119p. 1977. 55.00 (ISBN 0-910621-25-X). Rose Sharon Pr.

--God in Contemporary Thought: A Philosophical Perspective. LC 75-31391. (Philosophical Questions Ser.: No. 10). 1977. 65.00x (ISBN 0-912116-12-9). Learned Pubns.

Matczak, Sebastian A., intro. by see Mitros, Joseph F.

Matek, Ord. The Bible Through Stamps. LC 73-23126. 240p. 1974. 7.50x (ISBN 0-87068-397-7). Ktav.

Matenko, Percy. Ludwig Tieck & America. LC 54-62860. (North Carolina University. Studies in the Germanic Languages & Literatures: No. 12). Repr. of 1954 ed. 27.00 (ISBN 0-404-50912-6). AMS Pr.

Matera, Frank. The Kingship of Jesus: Composition & Theology in Mark Fifteen. LC 82-708. (SBL Dissertation Ser.). 1982. pap. 12.75 (ISBN 0-89130-564-5, 060166). Scholars Pr GA.

Matera, Frank J. Passion Narratives & Gospel Theologies: Interpreting the Synoptics Through Their Passion Stories. 320p. 1986. pap. 12.95 (ISBN 0-8091-2775-X). Paulist Pr.

--What Are They Saying about Mark? 1987. pap. 5.95. Paulist Pr.

Materne, Yves, ed. Indian Awakening in Latin America. 1980. pap. 5.95 (ISBN 0-377-00097-3). Friend Pr.

Matheison, Moira, ed. Consulting the American Catholic Laity: A Decade of Dialogue. 40p. (Orig.). 1986. pap. 2.95 (ISBN 1-55586-999-8). US Catholic.

Matheny, Ruth A. Scripture Stories for Today. 1983. 9.95 (ISBN 0-89837-089-2, Pub. by Pflaum Pr). Peter Li.

Mather, Cotton. Bonifacius: An Essay Upon the Good. Levin, David, ed. LC 66-14448. pap. 53.80 (2014654). Bks Demand UMI.

--Bonifacius: An Essay...to Do Good. LC 67-18712. 1967. Repr. of 1710 ed. 35.00x (ISBN 0-8201-1032-9). Schol Facsimiles.

--Christian Philosopher: A Collection of the Best Discoveries in Nature, with Religious Improvements. LC 68-29082. 1968. Repr. of 1721 ed. 45.00x (ISBN 0-8201-1033-7). Schol Facsimiles.

--Day of Humiliation: Times of Affliction & Disaster. LC 68-24211. 1970. 55.00x (ISBN 0-8201-1067-1). Schol Facsimiles.

--Great Works of Christ in America, 2 vols. 1979. Set. 44.95 (ISBN 0-85151-280-1). Banner of Truth.

--Magnalia Christi Americana, Bks. I & II In 1 vol. Murdock, Kenneth B., ed. (The John Harvard Library). 512p. 1976. text ed. 35.00x (ISBN 0-674-54155-3, Belknap Pr). Harvard U Pr.

--Magnalia Christi Americana, or the Ecclesiastical History of New-England from the Year 1620, Unto the Year 1698, 7 Bks. LC 74-141092. (Research Library of Colonial Americana). (Illus.). 1971. Repr. of 1702 ed. Set. 58.00 (ISBN 0-405-03297-8). Ayer Co Pubs.

--Magnalia Christi Americana: Or the Ecclesiastical History of New England. Cunningham, Raymond J., ed. LC 75-12340. (Milestones of Thought Ser). 1971. pap. 5.95x (ISBN 0-8044-6478-2). Ungar.

--Manuductio Administerium, Directions for a Candidate of the Ministry. LC 75-41190. Repr. of 1938 ed. 17.25 (ISBN 0-404-14685-6). AMS Pr.

--Ornaments for the Daughters of Zion. LC 78-8588. 1978. 35.00x (ISBN 0-8201-1311-5). Schol Facsimiles.

--Paterna: The Autobiography of Cotton Mather. Bosco, Ronald A., ed. LC 76-10595. (Center for Editions of American Authors). 504p. 1976. lib. bdg. 75.00x (ISBN 0-8201-1273-9). Schol Facsimiles.

--Ratio Disciplinae Fratrum Novanglorum: A Faithful Account of the Discipline Professed & Practised, in the Churches of New-England. LC 71-141114. (Research Library of Colonial Americana). 1971. Repr. of 1726 ed. 23.50 (ISBN 0-405-03327-3). Ayer Co Pubs.

--Selected Letters of Cotton Mather. Silverman, Kenneth, ed. LC 78-142338. pap. 118.00 (ISBN 0-317-29860-7, 2019565). Bks Demand UMI.

--The Wonders of the Invisible World. large type ed. pap. 6.95 (ISBN 0-910122-46-6). Amherst Pr.

Mather, Eleanore P. Anna Brinton: A Study in Quaker Character. LC 74-152086. (Illus., Orig.). 1971. pap. 2.50x (ISBN 0-87574-176-2). Pendle Hill.

--Barclay in Brief. 1983. pap. 2.50x (ISBN 0-87574-028-6, 028). Pendle Hill.

--Edward Hicks, Primitive Quaker. LC 75-110287. (Illus., Orig.). 1970. pap. 2.50x (ISBN 0-87574-170-3, 170). Pendle Hill.

--Pendle Hill: A Quaker Experiment in Education & Community. new ed. 128p. 1980. 7.00 (ISBN 0-87574-954-2). Pendle-Hill.

Mather, Eleanore P. & Miller, Dorothy C. Edward Hicks: His Peaceable Kingdoms & Other Paintings. LC 81-71405. (Illus.). 224p. 1983. 40.00 (ISBN 0-87413-208-8). U Delaware Pr.

Mather, Eleanore P., ed. see Fogelklou-Norlind, Emilia.

Mather, Eleanore P., ed. see Murphy, Carol.

Mather, Eleanore P., ed. see Robinson, Jo Ann.

Mather, Herbert. Becoming a Giving Church. LC 85-72879. 64p. (Orig.). 1985. pap. 3.50 (ISBN 0-88177-023-X, DR023B). Discipleship Res.

Mather, Increase. Departing Glory: Eight Jeremiads of Increase Mather. LC 86-31349. 1987. 50.00x (ISBN 0-8201-1415-4). Schol Facsimiles.

Mather, Increase & Stoddard, Solomon. Increase Mather Vs. Solomon Stoddard: Two Puritan Tracts. LC 72-141117. (Research Library of Colonial Americana). 1971. Repr. of 1700 ed. 17.00 (ISBN 0-405-03328-1). Ayer Co Pubs.

Mather, Richard. Church Covenant: Two Tracts. LC 75-141115. (Research Library of Colonial Americana). 1972. Repr. of 1643 ed. 23.50 (ISBN 0-405-03329-X). Ayer Co Pubs.

Mather, Samuel. The Figures or Types of the Old Testament. 1969. Repr. of 1705 ed. 34.00 (ISBN 0-384-35880-2). Johnson Repr.

Mathers, S. L. The Kabbalah Unveiled. LC 71-16504. 373p. (Orig.). 1983. pap. 12.50 (ISBN 0-87728-557-8). Weiser.

Mathers, S. L., tr. The Kabbala Unveiled: Books of the Zohar. lib. bdg. 100.00 (ISBN 0-87968-124-1). Krishna Pr.

Matheson, D. M. & Burckhardt, T. An Introduction to Sufi Doctrine. 1971. pap. 4.75x (ISBN 0-87902-175-6). Orientalia.

Matheson, D. M., tr. see Schuon, Frithjof.

Matheson, George. Portraits of Bible Men. LC 86-7428. (First Series (Adam to Job)). Orig. Title: Representative Men of the Bible. 384p. 1986. pap. 8.95 (ISBN 0-8254-3251-0). Kregel.

--Portraits of Bible Men. LC 86-27221. (Ishmael to David, Second Ser.). 368p. 1987. pap. 8.95 (ISBN 0-8254-3252-9). Kregel.

--Portraits of Bible Women. LC 86-7429. Orig. Title: Representative Women of the Bible (Eve to Mary Magdalene) 304p. 1986. pap. 7.95 (ISBN 0-8254-3250-2). Kregel.

--Voices of the Spirit. (Direction Bks). 1979. pap. 3.45 (ISBN 0-8010-6078-8). Baker Bk.

Matheson, Peter, ed. The Third Reich & the Christian Churches. 128p. Date not set. pap. 8.25 (ISBN 0-567-29105-7, Pub. by T & T Clark Ltd UK). Fortress.

Mathew, Arnold H., tr. Old Catholic Missal & Ritual. LC 73-84708. Repr. of 1909 ed. 27.45 (ISBN 0-404-01949-8). AMS Pr.

Mathew, David. Catholicism in England, Fifteen Thirty-Five to Nineteen Thirty-Five. 1977. lib. bdg. 59.95 (ISBN 0-8490-1587-1). Gordon Pr.

Mathews, jt. auth. see Elmer, Irene.

Mathews, jt. auth. see Kramer, Janice.

Mathews, jt. auth. see Latourette, Jane.

Mathews, jt. auth. see Warren, Mary P.

Mathews, Basil. A Life of Jesus. (Illus.). 1979. Repr. of 1931 ed. lib. bdg. 25.00 (ISBN 0-8495-3817-3). Arden Lib.

Mathews, Basil J., ed. East & West: Conflict or Cooperation. facs. ed. LC 67-26764. (Essay Index Reprint Ser). 1936. 14.25 (ISBN 0-8369-0694-2). Ayer Co Pubs.

Mathews, Donald G. Religion in the Old South. LC 77-587. 1979. pap. 11.00x (ISBN 0-226-51002-6, P819, Phoen). U of Chicago Pr.

--Slavery & Methodism: A Chapter in American Morality, 1780-1845. LC 78-13249. 1978. Repr. of 1965 ed. lib. bdg. 27.75 (ISBN 0-313-21045-4, MASAM). Greenwood.

Mathews, Godfrey W. Chester Mystery Plays. LC 77-4728. 1925. lib. bdg. 15.00 (ISBN 0-8414-6159-7). Folcroft.

Mathews, K. A., jt. auth. see Freedman, D. N.

Mathews, Marthiel, tr. see Male, Emile.

Mathews, Patricia. Aurier's Symbolist Art Criticism & Theory. Kuspit, Donald, ed. LC 85-20944. (Studies in the Fine Arts: Criticism: No. 18). 130p. 1986. 49.95 (ISBN 0-8357-1686-4). UMI Res Pr.

Mathews, R. Arthur. Born for Battle. 3rd ed. 1980. pap. 2.95 (ISBN 0-85363-143-3). OMF Bks.

Mathews, Shailer. Faith of Modernism. LC 71-108117. Repr. of 1924 ed. 17.50 (ISBN 0-404-04266-X). AMS Pr.

--Select Medieval Documents & Other Material Illustrative in the History of Church & Empire, 754 A.D.-1254 A.D. LC 70-178566. (Lat.). Repr. of 1900 ed. 21.00 (ISBN 0-404-56628-6). AMS Pr.

--The Spiritual Interpretation of History. 1977. lib. bdg. 59.95 (ISBN 0-8490-2661-X). Gordon Pr.

Mathews, Shailer & Smith, Gerald B., eds. Dictionary of Religion & Ethics. LC 70-145713. 1971. Repr. of 1921 ed. 51.00x (ISBN 0-8103-3196-9). Gale.

Mathews, Shailer, et al. Contributions of Science to Religion. LC 79-117822. (Essay Index Reprint Ser). 1924. 27.50 (ISBN 0-8369-1763-4). Ayer Co Pubs.

Mathews, Thomas, jt. ed. see Garsoian, Nina.

Mathews, Thomas F. The Byzantine Churches of Istanbul: A Photographic Survey. LC 75-27173. (Illus.). 425p. 1976. 60.00x (ISBN 0-271-01210-2). Pa St U Pr.

--Early Churches of Constantinople: Architecture & Liturgy. LC 78-111972. (Illus.). 1971. 29.95x (ISBN 0-271-00108-9). Pa St U Pr.

Mathias, Robert. Journey of God's People. 1982. pap. 4.95 (ISBN 0-89536-528-6, 1016). CSS of Ohio.

Mathias, Willis D. Ideas of God & Conduct. LC 71-177059. (Columbia University. Teachers College. Contributions to Education: No. 874). Repr. of 1943 ed. 22.50 (ISBN 0-404-55874-7). AMS Pr.

Mathis, Laura. The Road to Wholeness. 240p. 1986. pap. 6.95 (ISBN 0-8423-5674-6). Tyndale.

Mathis, Marcian & Bonner, Dismas, eds. Pastoral Companion. 14th ed. 1976. 17.50 (ISBN 0-8199-0084-2, L38625). Franciscan Herald.

Mathis, Mary E. A Scriptural Treasury of Eternal Life. 1981. pap. 0.40 (ISBN 0-570-08357-5, 12-2937). Concordia.

--A Scriptural Treasury of Forgiveness. 1981. pap. 0.40 (12-2935). Concordia.

--A Scriptural Treasury of Guidance. 1981. pap. 0.40 (ISBN 0-570-08350-8, 12-2930). Concordia.

--A Scriptural Treasury of Hope. LC 12-2931. 1981. pap. 0.40 (ISBN 0-570-08351-6). Concordia.

--A Scriptural Treasury of Joy. 1981. pap. 0.40 (ISBN 0-570-08353-2, 12-2933). Concordia.

--A Scriptural Treasury of Love. 1981. pap. 0.40 (ISBN 0-570-08356-7, 12-2936). Concordia.

--A Scriptural Treasury of Peace. 1981. pap. 0.40 (ISBN 0-570-08352-4, 12-2932). Concordia.

Mathis, Terry R. Against John Hick: An Examination of His Philosophy of Religion. 148p. (Orig.). 1985. lib. bdg. 22.00 (ISBN 0-8191-4512-2); pap. text ed. 9.25 (ISBN 0-8191-4513-0). U Pr of Amer.

Mathisen, Robert R., ed. The Role of Religion in American Life: An Interpretive Historical Anthology. LC 80-6246. 420p. (Orig.). 1982. pap. text ed. 14.75 (ISBN 0-8191-2514-8). U Pr of Amer.

Mathson, Patricia. Creative Learning Activities for Religious Education: A Catalog of Teaching Ideas for Church, School, & Home. (Illus.). 192p. 1984. pap. 8.95 (ISBN 0-13-189838-8). P-H.

Mathur, A. P. Radhasoami Faith: A Historical Study. 1974. 9.00 (ISBN 0-686-20296-1). Intl Bk Dist.

Mathur, J. S., ed. see Pyarelal, et al.

Matic, Marko. Juergen Moltmanns Theologie in Auseinandersetzung mit Ernst Bloch. (European University Studies Ser.: No. 23, Vol. 209). (Ger.). 428p. 1983. 41.05 (ISBN 3-8204-7741-1). P Lang Pubs.

Matilal, jt. ed. see Evans.

Matilal, Bimal K. Language & Reality: An Introduction to Indian Philosophical Studies. 450p. 1986. 31.00X (ISBN 0-317-53529-3, Pub. by Motilal Banarsidass). South Asia Bks.

--Logic, Language & Reality: An Introduction to Indian Philosophical Studies. 447p. 1985. 29.50 (ISBN 81-208-0008-7, Pub. by Motilal Banarsidass India). Orient Bk Dist.

--Perception & Inference: An Essay on Classical Indian Theories of Knowledge. 350p. 1986. 65.00x (ISBN 0-19-824625-0). Oxford U Pr.

Matini, Aldo, ed. The Gold Seals of the Vatican: Secret Archives. (Illus.). 288p. 150.00 (ISBN 0-8478-5404-3). Rizzoli Intl.

Matlack, Lucius C. History of American Slavery & Methodism from 1780 to 1849. facs. ed. LC 77-138342. (Black Heritage Library Collection Ser.). 1849. 19.75 (ISBN 0-8369-8734-9). Ayer Co Pubs.

Matonti, Charles. Celebrate with Song. LC 81-71237. (Illus.). 144p. (Orig.). 1982. pap. 3.95 (ISBN 0-87793-245-X). Ave Maria.

Matranga, Frances. Good Times Bible Activities. 24p. 1983. pap. 1.50 (ISBN 0-87239-692-4, 2362). Standard Pub.

--Happy Time Bible Activities. 24p. 1983. pap. 1.50 (ISBN 0-87239-691-6, 2361). Standard Pub.

--My Book of Prayers. (Happy Day Bks.). (Illus.). 24p. 1985. 1.59 (ISBN 0-87239-877-3, 3677). Standard Pub.

Matranga, Frances C. One Step at a Time. (Illus.). 1987. pap. 3.95 (ISBN 0-570-03642-9). Concordia.

--The Perfect Friend. 80p. (Orig.). 1985. pap. 3.95 (ISBN 0-570-04112-0, 56-1523). Concordia.

Matrisciana, Caryl. Gods of the New Age. (Orig.). 1985. pap. 6.95 (ISBN 0-89081-445-7). Harvest Hse.

Matrisian, Hugo. The Physiology of the Soul. (Illus.). 129p. 1980. deluxe ed. 49.75 (ISBN 0-89266-261-1). Am Classical Coll Pr.

Matson, Wallace I., jt. auth. see Warren, Thomas B.

Matsunaga, Alicia. Buddhist Philosophy of Assimilation. LC 68-57058. (Illus.). 1969. 29.50 (ISBN 0-8048-0730-2). C E Tuttle.

Matsunaga, Alicia & Matsunaga, Daigan. Foundation of Japanese Buddhism: The Mass Movement, Vol. 2. LC 74-83654. 1976. 16.95x (ISBN 0-914910-27-2); pap. 9.50 (ISBN 0-914910-28-0). Buddhist Bks.

Matsunaga, Alicia, jt. auth. see Matsunaga, Daigan.

Matsunaga, Daigan & Matsunaga, Alicia. Foundation of Japanese Buddhism: The Aristocratic Age, Vol. I. LC 74-83654. 1974. 14.95x (ISBN 0-914910-25-6); pap. 8.50x (ISBN 0-914910-26-4). Buddhist Bks.

Matsunaga, Daigan, jt. auth. see Matsunaga, Alicia.

Matsunami, Kodo. Introducing Buddhism. LC 75-28970. (Illus.). 304p. 1976. pap. 7.50 (ISBN 0-8048-1192-X). C E Tuttle.

Matsuo, Hosaku. The Logic of Unity: The Discovery of Zero & Emptiness in Prajanaparamita Thought. Inada, Kenneth K., tr. (Buddhist studies). 144p. 1987. 29.50 (ISBN 0-88706-391-8); pap. 9.95 (ISBN 0-88706-392-6). State U NY Pr.

Matsuura, Kaichi. Study of Donne's Imagery: A Revelation of His Outlook on the World & His Vision of a Christian Monarchy. LC 72-7223. Repr. of 1953 ed. lib. bdg. 25.00 (ISBN 0-8414-0270-1). Folcroft.

Matt, Daniel. The Book of Mirrors: Sefer Mar'ot ha-Zove'ot. LC 81-9308. (Brown Judiac Studies Ser.). 1982. pap. 22.50 (ISBN 0-89130-525-4, 14-00-30). Scholars Pr GA.

Matt, Daniel C. Zohar, The Book of Enlightment. (The Classics of Western Spirituality). 320p. 1982. 12.95 (ISBN 0-8091-0320-6); pap. 9.95 (ISBN 0-8091-2387-8). Paulist pr.

Mattfeld, Victor. Georg Rhaw's Publications for Vespers. (Wissenschaftliche Abhandlungen-Musicological Studies: Vol. 11). 361p. 1967. lib. bdg. 30.00 (ISBN 0-912024-81-X). Inst Mediaeval Mus.

Matthes, Joachim, et al, eds. The Annual Review of the Social Sciences of Religion, Vol. 3, 1979. 1979. pap. text ed. 26.00x (ISBN 0-686-27015-0). Mouton.

--The Annual Review of the Social Sciences of Religion, Vol. 1. 1977. pap. 23.20x (ISBN 90-279-7794-1). Mouton.

Matthew, David. Catholicism in England: The Portraits of a Minority, Its Culture & Tradition. 295p. 1984. Repr. of 1948 ed. lib. bdg. 45.00 (ISBN 0-89984-946-6). Century Bookbindery.

Matthew, Donald. The Norman Monasteries & Their English Possessions. LC 78-26293. (Oxford Historical Ser.). 1979. Repr. of 1962 ed. lib. bdg. 24.75x (ISBN 0-313-20847-6, MANM). Greenwood.

Matthew of Aquasparta. Knowledge & Deceit in the Intellectual Life of Man. (Illus.). 87p. 1984. pap. 23.75 (ISBN 0-89266-491-6). Am Classical Coll Pr.

Matthews, Anna M. God Answers Prayers. 96p. 1981. 8.95 (ISBN 0-89962-215-1). Todd & Honeywell.

Matthews, Boris, tr. from Ger. Herder Symbol Dictionary. LC 85-30872. Tr. of Herder Lexikon: Symbole. (Illus.). 222p. 1986. vinyl 14.95 (ISBN 0-933029-03-9). Chiron Pubns.

Matthews, Bruce. Craving & Salvation: A Study in Buddhist Soteriology. (SR Supplements). 138p. 1984. pap. text ed. 9.25x (ISBN 0-88920-147-1). Humanities.

Matthews, Caitlin. Goddess. (Art & Imagination Ser.). (Illus.). 1983. pap. cancelled (ISBN 0-500-81031-1). Thames-Hudson.

--Mabon & the Mysteries of Britain. 256p. 1987. pap. 11.95 (ISBN 1-85063-052-6, 30526, Ark Paperbks). Methuen Inc.

Matthews, Carole. Through the Bible with Preschoolers. 144p. 1985. 8.95 (ISBN 0-87239-945-1, 3330). Standard Pub.

Matthews, Charles, ed. see Ibn Al-Firkah & Ibrahim ibn Abd Al-Rahman.

Matthews, Edward M. A Means of Grace. 58p. 1946. pap. 1.50 (ISBN 0-935461-08-6). St Alban Pr CA.

Matthews, Elwood. A Maturing Ministry. 1981. pap. 3.50 (ISBN 0-934942-22-6). White Wing Pub.

Matthews, English J. Nature Is Lord. 80p. 1986. 7.95 (ISBN 0-89962-511-8). Todd & Honeywell.

Matthews, John. At the Table of the Grail: Magic & the Use of Imagination. 224p. (Orig.). 1984. pap. 10.95 (ISBN 0-7100-9938-X). Methuen Inc.

--The Grail: Quest for the Eternal. Purce, Jill, ed. LC 81-66807. (The Illustrated Library of Sacred Imagination). (Illus.). 110p. 1981. pap. 9.95 (ISBN 0-8245-0035-0). Crossroad NY.

Matthews, Margery I., et al. Churches of Foster: A History of Religious Life in Rural Rhode Island. (Illus.). 169p. (Orig.). 1978. pap. 5.00 (ISBN 0-917012-20-8). N Foster Baptist.

Matthews, Mary. Jacob & the Star. 1986. pap. 7.95 (ISBN 0-8192-1384-5). Morehouse.

Matthews, Narvella. Man Heal Thyself. Graves, Helen, ed. LC 85-51970. 65p. 1986. 6.95 (ISBN 1-55523-004-0). Winston-Derek.

Matthews, R. Arthur. Nascido para a Batalha. Orig. Title: Born for Battle. (Port.). 1986. write for info. (ISBN 0-8297-1606-8). Life Pubs Intl.

Matthews, Reginald L. Missionary Administration in the Local Church. 1972. 3.95 (ISBN 0-87227-002-5); pap. 2.95 (ISBN 0-87227-011-4). Reg Baptist.

Matthews, Robert. The Human Adventure. 1980. pap. 5.95 (ISBN 0-89536-426-3, 0834). CSS of Ohio.

Matthews, Robert J. A Plainer Translation: Joseph Smith's Translation of the Bible, a History & Commentary. LC 75-5937. 1975. 15.95 (ISBN 0-8425-1411-2). Brigham.

Matthews, Ronald. English Messiahs: Studies of Six English Religious Pretenders, 1656-1927. LC 76-172553. Repr. of 1936 ed. 12.75 (ISBN 0-405-18187-6, Pub. by Blom). Ayer Co Pubs.

Matthews, S. Church: Learning about God's People. LC 56-1396. (Concept Books Series Four). 1983. pap. 3.95 (ISBN 0-570-08525-X). Concordia.

Matthews, V. J. St. Philip Neri. LC 84-50406. 120p. 1984. pap. 3.00 (ISBN 0-89555-237-X). TAN Bks Pubs.

Matthews, Velda. Bible Places. (Illus.). 1985. 1.95 (ISBN 0-87239-254-6, 2782). Standard Pub.

Matthews, Velda & Beard, Ray. Basic Bible Dictionary. Korth, Bob, ed. (Illus.). 128p. (Orig.). 1984. pap. 7.95 (ISBN 0-87239-720-3, 2770). Standard Pub.

Matthews, W. R., ed. Christian Faith: Essays in Explanation & Defence. facsimile ed. LC 73-152162. (Essay Index Reprint Ser). Repr. of 1936 ed. 21.50 (ISBN 0-8369-2348-0). Ayer Co Pubs.

Matthews, Washington. The Night Chant: A Navaho Ceremony. LC 74-7991. Repr. of 1902 ed. 70.00 (ISBN 0-404-11880-1). AMS Pr.

Matthews, William R., Sr. Background Information for New Testament Students. Jones, Amos, Jr., ed. 250p. (Orig.). 1985. pap. cancelled (ISBN 0-910683-05-0). Sunday School.

Matthew the Poor. Communion of Love. LC 84-10561. 234p. (Orig.). 1984. pap. text ed. 8.95 (ISBN 0-88141-036-5). St Vladimirs.

Matthiessen, Peter. Nine-Headed Dragon River. 1987. pap. 9.95 (ISBN 0-87773-401-1). Shambhala Pubns.

--Nine-Headed Dragon River: Zen Journals 1969-1982. LC 85-27918. (Dragons Ser.). 288p. 1987. pap. 9.95 (ISBN 0-87773-401-1). Shambhala Pubns.

Mattill, A. J., Jr. Luke & the Last Things. 1979. pap. 8.95 (ISBN 0-915948-03-6). Bks Distinction.

Mattingly, Harold. Christianity in the Roman Empire. 1967. pap. 4.95x (ISBN 0-393-00397-3, Norton Lib). Norton.

Mattingly, M. R. The Catholic Church on the Kentucky Frontier: 1785-1812. LC 73-3579. (Catholic University of America. Studies in American Church History: No. 25). Repr. of 1936 ed. 29.00 (ISBN 0-404-57775-X). AMS Pr.

Mattison, H. Impending Crisis of Eighteen Sixty: The Present Connection of the Methodist Episcopal Church with Slavery. facs. ed. LC 75-149870. (Black Heritage Library Collection Ser). 1858. 14.25 (ISBN 0-8369-8750-0). Ayer Co Pubs.

Mattison, Judith. Beginnings: For the Newly Married. LC 79-54114. 96p. 1980. 6.95 (ISBN 0-8066-1753-5, 10-0573). Augsburg.

--Divorce-The Pain & the Healing: Personal Mediations When Marriage Ends. LC 85-11140. 96p. (Orig.). 1985. pap. 5.95 (ISBN 0-8066-2128-1, 10-1905). Augsburg.

--Prayers from a Mother's Heart. LC 74-14177. (Illus.). 96p. (Orig.). 1975. pap. 5.95 (ISBN 0-8066-1460-9, 10-5095). Augsburg.

--Who Will Listen to Me? Prayer Thoughts for High School Girls. LC 77-72450. (Illus.). 1977. pap. 3.95 (ISBN 0-8066-1596-6, 10-7085). Augsburg.

Mattox, Beverly. Help! I'm a Woman! LC 77-21631. 1977. pap. 1.95 (ISBN 0-87227-053-X). Reg Baptist.

Mattox, Robert. The Christian Employee. LC 77-20588. 1978. pap. 4.95 (ISBN 0-88270-263-7). Bridge Pub.

Matts, Abraham, tr. see Sperling, Abraham I.

Mattson, Lloyd. Build Your Church Through Camping. 48p. (Orig.). 1984. pap. 1.95 (ISBN 0-942684-06-0). Camp Guidepts.

--The Camp Couselor. (Illus.). 192p. 1984. pap. 3.95 (ISBN 0-942684-02-8). Camp Guidepts.

Mattson, Lloyd & Graendorf, Werner. Introduction to Christian Camping. Rev. ed. (Illus.). pap. 7.95 (ISBN 0-942684-07-9). Camp Guidepts.

Mattson, Lloyd, ed. God's Good Earth. (Illus.). 224p. (Orig.). 1985. pap. 25.00 (ISBN 0-942684-09-5). Camp Guidepts.

Mattson, Lloyd, frwd. by see Hildebrand, Henry.

Matty, Thomas. Peace & Conscience Formation. (Faith & Justice Issues Ser.). (Illus.). 68p. (Orig.). 1983. tchr's ed. 14.95 (ISBN 0-88489-147-X). St Mary's.

Matura, Thaddee. The Crisis of Religious Life. Lachance, Paul & Schwartz, Paul, trs. 1973. 4.95 (ISBN 0-8199-0453-8). Franciscan Herald.

--The Gospel Life of Francis of Assisi Today. 1980. 6.95 (ISBN 0-317-46873-1). Franciscan Herald.

--Gospel Radicalism: A Study of the Hard Sayings of Jesus. Despot, Maggi & Lachance, Paul, trs. from Fr. LC 83-6249. Orig. Title: Le Radicalisme Evangelique Aux Sources de la vie Chretienne. 208p. (Orig.). 1984. pap. 8.95 (ISBN 0-88344-182-9). Orbis Bks.

Matura, Thadee, jt. auth. see Flood, David.

Matus, Thomas. Yoga & the Jesus Prayer Tradition: An Experiment in Faith. 200p. (Orig.). 1984. pap. 8.95 (ISBN 0-8091-2638-9). Paulist Pr.

Matussek, Paul, jt. auth. see Egenter, Richard.

Matzat, Don. Inner Healing: Deliverance or Deception? 224p. (Orig.). 1987. pap. 6.95 (ISBN 0-89081-584-4). Harvest Hse.

--Inner Healing: Deliverance or Deception. 1987. pap. 5.95. Har-Row.

Matzner-Bekerman, Shoshana. The Jewish Child: Halakhic Perspectives. LC 83-19950. 314p. 1984. 20.00x (ISBN 0-88125-017-1); pap. 11.95 (ISBN 0-88125-024-4). Ktav.

Matzulewitsch, Leonid. Byzantinische Antike: Studien auf Grund der Silbergefaesse der Ermitage. (Archaeologische Mitteilungen aus Russischen Sammlungen, Vol. 2). (Ger., Illus.). xi, 150p. 1974. Repr. of 1929 ed. 216.00 (ISBN 3-1100-2245-1). De Gruyter.

Maubrey, Pierre. L' Expression de la Passion Interieure dans le Style de Bernanos Romancier. LC 70-94195. (Catholic University of America Studies in Romance Languages & Literatures Ser: No. 59). (Fr). Repr. of 1959 ed. 25.00 (ISBN 0-404-50359-4). AMS Pr.

Mauck & Jenkins. Teaching Primaries Workbook. pap. 2.95 (ISBN 0-89137-432-9). Quality Pubns.

Mauck, Diane & Jenkins, Janet. Teaching Primaries. 4.50 (ISBN 0-89137-610-0); write for info. wkbk. (ISBN 0-89137-612-7). Quality Pubns.

Mauck, Sue I., jt. auth. see Clapp, Steve.

Mauck, Sue I., jt. auth. see Schriner, Chris.

Maudadi, A. A. Tafhimul - Quran: Urdu Translation & Commentary. 95.00 (ISBN 0-686-18523-4). Kazi Pubns.

Maududi, A. Islamic Law & Constitution. 1969. pap. 14.95 (ISBN 0-87902-176-4). Orientalia.

Maududi, A. A. Ethical Viewpoint of Islam. pap. 1.00 (ISBN 0-686-18492-0). Kazi Pubns.

--Fundamentals of Islam. 12.50 (ISBN 0-686-18489-0). Kazi Pubns.

--Islamic Way of Life. pap. 3.50 (ISBN 0-686-18496-3). Kazi Pubns.

--The Meaning of the Quran, 12 vols. 10.50 ea. Kazi Pubns.

--Political Theory of Islam. pap. 1.00 (ISBN 0-686-18547-1). Kazi Pubns.

--Process of Islamic Revolution. pap. 1.50 (ISBN 0-686-18546-3). Kazi Pubns.

--Purdah & the Status of Women in Islam. pap. 9.50 (ISBN 0-686-18464-5). Kazi Pubns.

--Questions of Dress. pap. 1.50 (ISBN 0-686-63910-3). Kazi Pubns.

--The Religion of Truth. pap. 1.00 (ISBN 0-686-18537-4). Kazi Pubns.

--The Road to Salvation. pap. 1.00 (ISBN 0-686-18583-8). Kazi Pubns.

--Towards Understanding Islam. pap. 5.50 (ISBN 0-686-18479-3). Kazi Pubns.

Maududi, Abul A. Human Rights in Islam. 39p. (Orig.). 1981. pap. 1.95 (ISBN 0-9503954-9-8, Pub. by Islamic Found UK). New Era Pubns MI.

--Towards Understanding Islam. Ahmad, Khurshid, tr. from Urdu. 116p. (Orig.). pap. 5.95x (ISBN 0-86037-053-4, Pub. by Islamic Found UK). New Era Pubns MI.

Maududi, S. A. Towards Understanding Islam. 5.50x (ISBN 0-87902-065-2). Orientalia.

Maughan, Joyce B. Talks for Tots. LC 85-70993. 171p. 1985. 8.95 (ISBN 0-87747-804-X). Deseret Bk.

Maughon, Martha. Why Am I Crying? 1983. pap. 5.95 (ISBN 0-310-37671-8, 11221P). Zondervan.

Maugis, Edquard. Histoire du Parlement De Paris De l'Avenememt Des Rois Valois a la Mort D'Henri Quatre, 3 Vols. 1967. Repr. of 1913 ed. 92.50 (ISBN 0-8337-2304-9). B Franklin.

Maulana-Muhammad-Ali. Religion of Islam. 1978. 42.50x (ISBN 0-89684-447-1). Orient Bk Dist.

Maultsby, Maxie C., Jr. Help Yourself to Happiness. LC 75-15057. 1975. pap. 9.95 (ISBN 0-917476-06-9). Inst Rational-Emotive.
Maung Tin, tr. see Buddhaghosa.
Maurana, Humberto R. & Varela, Francisco. The Tree of Knowledge: The Biological Roots of Human Understanding. Crossen, Kendra, ed. LC 86-29698. (Illus.). 215p. 1987. 19.95 (ISBN 0-87773-373-2); pap. 12.95 (ISBN 0-87773-403-8). Shambhala Pubns.
Maurer, Armand A. St. Thomas & Historicity. LC 79-84278. (Aquinas Lecture Ser.). 1979. 7.95 (ISBN 0-87462-144-5). Marquette.
Maurer, Herrymon. The Power of Truth. 1983. pap. 2.50x (ISBN 0-87574-053-7, 053). Pendle Hill.
Maurer, Herrymon, ed. Pendle Hill Reader. facsimile ed. LC 74-142668. (Essay Index Reprint Ser). Repr. of 1950 ed. 18.00 (ISBN 0-8369-2415-0). Ayer Co Pubs.
Maurer, Herrymon, tr. see Tzu, Lao.
Maurer, Walter. Pinnacles of India's Past: Selections from the Rgveda. LC 85-30784. (University of Pennsylvania Studies on South Asia: No. 2). 350p. 1986. 44.00x (ISBN 0-915027-62-3); pap. 20.00x (ISBN 0-915027-83-6). Benjamins North Am.
Maurer, Wilhelm. Historical Commentary on the Augsburg Confession. Anderson, H. George, tr. from Ger. LC 86-45214. Tr. of Historischer Kommentar zur Confessio Augustana. 464p. 1986. 24.95 (ISBN 0-8006-0781-3). Fortress.
Mauriac, Francois. Anguish & Joy of the Christian Life. (Orig.). pap. 1.25x (ISBN 0-268-00005-0). U of Notre Dame Pr.
--Sainte Marguerite de Cortone. pap. 5.95 (ISBN 0-685-34304-9). French & Eur.
--Souffrances et Bonheur du Chretien. pap. 7.50 (ISBN 0-685-34305-7). French & Eur.
Maurice, Frederick D. Christmas Day & Other Sermons. 410p. 1982. Repr. of 1892 ed. lib. bdg. 50.00 (ISBN 0-89987-595-5). Darby Bks.
--The Gospel of the Kingdom of Heaven. 416p. 1977. Repr. of 1864 ed. 12.50 (ISBN 0-87921-037-0). Attic Pr.
--The Prayer Book & the Lord's Prayer. 416p. 1977. Repr. of 1880 ed. 12.50 (ISBN 0-87921-038-9). Attic Pr.
--Theological Essays. 436p. (Orig.). Date not set. pap. write for info. (ISBN 0-87921-048-6). Attic Pr.
--Toward the Recovery of Unity. Porter, John F. & Wolf, William J., eds. LC 64-12942. 1964. text ed. 10.00x (ISBN 0-8401-1596-2). A R Allenson.
--What Is Revelation? LC 76-173061. Repr. of 1859 ed. 37.50 (ISBN 0-404-04276-7). AMS Pr.
Maurice, J. F. D. The Life of Frederick Denison Maurice, Chiefly Told in His Own Letters. 1294p. Repr. of 1884 ed. text ed. 99.36x (ISBN 0-576-02191-1). Gregg Intl.
Maurice, Thomas. The History of Hindostan. Feldman, Burton & Richardson, Robert D., eds. LC 78-60888. (Myth & Romanticism Ser.). 1984. lib. bdg. 240.00 (ISBN 0-8240-3566-6). Garland Pub.
Mauro, Philip. Baptism: A Bible Defense of Believer's Immersion. pap. 2.95 (ISBN 0-685-88367-1). Reiner.
--Evolution. pap. 2.25 (ISBN 0-685-88374-4). Reiner.
--Gospel of the Kingdom. 6.95 (ISBN 0-685-19829-4). Reiner.
--The Last Call to the Godly Remnant. pap. 1.75 (ISBN 0-685-88381-7). Reiner.
--Life in the Word. pap. 1.25 (ISBN 0-87509-101-6). Chr Pubns.
--More Than a Prophet: On John the Baptist. pap. 1.50 (ISBN 0-685-36794-0). Reiner.
--Seventy Weeks & the Great Tribulation. 285p. 1975. pap. 5.95 (ISBN 0-685-53619-X). Reiner.
--Speaking in Tongues. 1978. pap. 0.50 (ISBN 0-685-36793-2). Reiner.
--Things Which Soon Must Come to Pass: Commentary on Revelation. 1984. Repr. 14.95 (ISBN 0-317-11813-7). Reiner.
--The World & Its God. 95p. 1981. pap. 2.95 (ISBN 0-89084-151-9). Bob Jones Univ Pr.
Mauro, Phillip. God's Pilgrims. 192p. 1969. pap. 3.00 (ISBN 0-87509-090-7). Chr Pubns.
Mauss, Armand L., jt. ed. see Bush, Lester E.
Mauss, Marcel, jt. auth. see Hubert, Henri.
Mavalankar, Damodar K. The Service of Humanity. (Sangam Texts). 132p. 1986. pap. 8.75 (ISBN 0-88695-025-2). Concord Grove.
Maves, Mary C., jt. auth. see Maves, Paul B.
Maves, Paul B. Faith for the Older Years: Making the Most of Life's Second Half. LC 85-13466. 192p. (Orig.). 1986. pap. 9.95 (ISBN 0-8066-2195-8, 10-2181). Augsburg.
Maves, Paul B. & Maves, Mary C. Finding Your Way Through the Bible. (Orig.). 1971. pap. 3.50 (ISBN 0-687-13049-2). Abingdon.
Mavrodes, George I. Belief in God: A Study in the Epistemology of Religion. LC 81-40788. 128p. 1981. pap. text ed. 7.50 (ISBN 0-8191-1816-8). U Pr of Amer.
Mawdsley, R. & Permuth, S. Legal Problems of Religious & Private Schools. 1983. 9.95 (ISBN 0-318-02068-8). NOLPE.
Mawdudi, Sayyid A. Towards Understanding Islam. Ahmad, Khurshid, tr. from Urdu. Tr. of Risala-e-Diniyat. 179p. (Orig.). 1980. pap. 5.95 (ISBN 0-939830-22-1, Pub. by IIFSO Kuwait). New Era Pubns MI.
Mawhinney, Brian & Wells, Ronald. Conflict & Christianity in Northern Ireland. LC 75-8948. (Illus.). pap. 31.50 (ISBN 0-317-09250-2, 2012891). Bks Demand UMI.
Max Mueller, F. Keshub Chunder Sen. rev. ed. Mookerjee, Nanda, ed. 1976. 6.00x (ISBN 0-88386-862-8). South Asia Bks.
Maxon, Gayle, ed. see Carlson, George A.
Maxon, Gayle, ed. see Waldrum, Harold J.
Maxson, Charles H. The Great Awakening in the Middle Colonies. 12.00 (ISBN 0-8446-1306-1). Peter Smith.
Maxson, J. Robin, jt. auth. see Friesen, Garry.
Maxson, Marilyn M., jt. ed. see Hunt, Thomas C.
Maxwell, C. Mervyn. God Cares, Vol. 1. 1981. pap. 9.95 (ISBN 0-8163-0390-8). Pacific Pr Pub Assn.
Maxwell, Cassandre. Legacy for My Loved Ones. 1984. 12.95 (ISBN 0-317-13919-3). Revell.
Maxwell, Charles H. Adventures of Gabriel in His Search for God. 1933. Repr. 12.50 (ISBN 0-8274-1821-3). R West.
--Adventures of the White Girl in Her Search for God. LC 74-20648. 1974. Repr. of 1933 ed. lib. bdg. 25.00 (ISBN 0-8414-5951-7). Folcroft.
Maxwell, Geraldine Boldt. Royal Matron's Treasury of Addresses & Ceremonies, No. 2. 1975. pap. 2.00 29 selections (ISBN 0-88053-320-X). Macoy Pub.
Maxwell, Jack M. Worship & Reformed Theology: The Liturgical Lessons of Mercersburg. LC 75-45492. (Pittsburgh Theological Monographs: No. 10). 1976. pap. 12.00 (ISBN 0-915138-12-3). Pickwick.
Maxwell, John. Think on These Things. 128p. 1979. pap. 2.95 (ISBN 0-8341-0600-0). Beacon Hill.
--Your Attitude: Key to Success. 156p. 1985. pap. 5.95 (ISBN 0-89840-102-X). Heres Life.
Maxwell, L. E. Born Crucified. (Moody Classic Ser.). 1984. pap. 3.95 (ISBN 0-8024-0038-8). Moody.
--Women in Ministry. 156p. 1987. pap. 6.95 (ISBN 0-89693-337-7). Victor Bks.
Maxwell, Mary. Human Evolution: A Philosophical Anthropology. 288p. 1984. 38.00x (ISBN 0-231-05946-9, King's Crown Paperbacks); pap. 18.00x (ISBN 0-231-05947-7). Columbia U Pr.
Maxwell, May. An Early Pilgrimage. 45p. pap. 2.95 (ISBN 0-85398-004-7). G Ronald Pub.
Maxwell, Mervyn. Tell It to the World. LC 76-6619. 1976. 6.95 (ISBN 0-8163-0217-0, 20077-4). Pacific Pr Pub Assn.
Maxwell, Neal A. All These Things Shall Give Thee Experience. LC 79-26282. 144p. 1979. 7.95 (ISBN 0-87747-796-5). Deseret Bk.
--Even As I Am. 128p. 1982. 8.95 (ISBN 0-87747-943-7). Deseret Bk.
--Notwithstanding My Weakness. LC 81-65352. 129p. 1981. 6.95 (ISBN 0-87747-855-4). Deseret Bk.
--Plain & Precious Things. LC 83-72478. 103p. 1983. 6.95 (ISBN 0-87747-979-8). Deseret Bk.
--We Talk of Christ, We Rejoice in Christ. LC 84-71873. 180p. 8.95 (ISBN 0-87747-762-0). Deseret Bk.
--We Will Prove Them Herewith. LC 82-1532. 132p. 1982. 6.95 (ISBN 0-87747-912-7). Deseret Bk.
Maxwell, Patricia. How to Become a Christian & Stay One. LC 79-4603. (Waymark Ser.). 1979. pap. 2.50 (ISBN 0-8127-0221-2). Review & Herald.
--Soldier for Jesus. (Trailblazers Ser.). 1981. pap. 5.95 (ISBN 0-8163-0374-6). Pacific Pr Pub Assn.
Maxym, Lucy, ed. & tr. see Vorobyev, Nicolai.
May, G. Lacey. English Religious Verse. 1937. lib. bdg. 8.50 (ISBN 0-8414-6604-1). Folcroft.
May, Gerald. Pilgrimage Home. LC 78-61720. 196p. 1979. pap. 6.95 (ISBN 0-8091-2143-3). Paulist Pr.
--Simply Sane: The Spirituality of Mental Health. (The Crossroad Paperback Ser.). 144p. 1982. pap. 8.95 (ISBN 0-8245-0448-8). Crossroad NY.
May, Gerald G. Care of Mind-Care of Spirit: Psychiatric Dimensions of Spiritual Direction. LC 81-47840. 128p. 1982. 14.45 (ISBN 0-06-065533-X, HarpR). Har-Row.
--Will & Spirit: A Comtemplative Psychology. LC 82-47751. 384p. 1982. 24.45 (ISBN 0-686-98141-3, HarpR). Har-Row.
May, Gerhard. Schoepfung aus dem Nichts: Die Entstehung der Lehre von der Creatio Ex Nihilo. (Arbeiten zur Kirchengeschichte: Vol. 48). 1978. 34.40 (ISBN 3-11-007204-1). De Gruyter.
May, Henry F. Ideas, Faiths, & Feelings: Essays on American Intellectual & Religious History, 1952-1982. 1983. 25.00x (ISBN 0-19-503235-7); pap. 9.95 (ISBN 0-19-503236-5). Oxford U Pr.
May, Herbert G., ed. Oxford Bible Atlas. 3rd. ed. 1985. 18.95 (ISBN 0-19-143452-3); pap. 10.95x (ISBN 0-19-143451-5). Oxford U Pr.
May, J. Lewis. Cardinal Newman. 1945. Repr. lib. bdg. 20.00 (ISBN 0-8414-6605-X). Folcroft.
--An English Treasury of Religious Prose. 1977. Repr. of 1932 ed. 15.00 (ISBN 0-89984-062-0). Century Bookbindery.
May, John R., ed. The Bent World: Essays on Religion & Culture. LC 81-5801. (College Theology Society Annual Publications Ser.). 215p. 1979. 18.00 (ISBN 0-89130-503-3, 34 10 79). Scholars Pr GA.
--The Bent World: Essays on Religion & Culture. 224p. (Orig.). 1986. pap. 23.00 (ISBN 0-8191-5614-0, Pub. by College Theology Society). U Pr of Amer.
May, John R. & Bird, Michael, eds. Religion in Film. LC 81-23983. (Illus.). 232p. 1982. text ed. 17.95x (ISBN 0-87049-352-3); pap. text ed. 8.95x (ISBN 0-87049-368-X). U of Tenn Pr.
May, Leland C. Good Morning, Lord: Meditations for College Students. (Good Morning Lord Ser.). 64p. (Orig.). 1981. 4.95 (ISBN 0-8010-6116-4). Baker Bk.
May, Lynn, ed. Encyclopedia of Southern Baptists, Vol. IV. LC 81-66989. 1982. 19.95 (ISBN 0-8054-6556-1). Broadman.
--Encyclopedia of Southern Baptists: Index to Vols. I-IV. 1982. pap. 1.75 (ISBN 0-8054-6562-6). Broadman.
May, William & Harvey, John. On Understanding Human Sexuality. (Synthesis Ser). 1978. pap. 1.50 (ISBN 0-8199-0720-0). Franciscan Herald.
May, William E. Human Existence, Medicine, & Ethics. LC 77-8149. 43p. 1977. 5.25 (ISBN 0-8199-0677-8). Franciscan Herald.
--The Nature & Meaning of Chastity. (Synthesis Ser.). 1977. pap. 1.75 (ISBN 0-8199-0710-3). Franciscan Herald.
--Sex, Love & Procreation: Synthesis Ser. 1976. pap. 0.75 (ISBN 0-8199-0711-1). Franciscan Herald.
--Sex, Marriage & Chastity: Reflections of a Catholic Layman, Spouse & Parent. 1981. 6.95 (ISBN 0-8199-0821-5). Franciscan Herald.
--The Unity of the Moral & Spiritual Life. (Synthesis Ser). 1978. pap. 0.75 (ISBN 0-8199-0745-6). Franciscan Herald.
May, William E., ed. Principles of Catholic Moral Life. LC 80-10969. 456p. 1981. 10.50 (ISBN 0-8199-0793-6). Franciscan Herald.
May, William F. The Physician's Covenant: Images of the Healer in Medical Ethics. LC 83-16992. 204p. 1983. pap. 10.95 (ISBN 0-664-24497-1). Westminster.
Maybaum, Ignay. Trialogue Between Jew, Christian & Muslim. (Littman Library of Jewish Civilization). 192p. 1973. 18.50x (ISBN 0-19-710032-5). Oxford U Pr.
Maycock, A. L. Nicholas Ferrar of Little Gidding. LC 80-16684. pap. 63.50 (ISBN 0-8357-9131-9, 2019345). Bks Demand UMI.
--The Papacy. 1928. 10.00 (ISBN 0-8414-6607-6). Folcroft.
Mayer, Egon. Becoming Jewish. 40p. (Orig.). Date not set. pap. price not set. Am Jewish Comm.
--Children of Intermarriage: A Study in Pattern of Identification & Family Life. LC 83-82077. 56p. 1983. pap. 2.50 (ISBN 0-87495-055-4). Am Jewish Comm.
--From Suburb to Shtetl: The Jews of Boro Park. (Illus.). 196p. 1979. 29.95 (ISBN 0-87722-161-8). Temple U Pr.
--Love & Tradition: Marriage Between Jews & Christians. 312p. 1985. (full discount avail.) 17.95 (ISBN 0-306-42043-0, Plenum Pr). Plenum Pub.
--Love & Tradition: Marriage Between Jews & Christians. LC 86-24823. 312p. 1987. pap. 8.95 (ISBN 0-8052-0828-3). Schocken.
Mayer, Egon & Sheingold, Carl. Intermarriage & the Jewish Future. LC 79-63378. 46p. 1980. pap. 2.00 (ISBN 0-87495-031-7). Am Jewish Comm.
Mayer, Erwin. Die Geschichte der Kartause Seitz. Hogg, James, ed. (Analecta Cartusiana Ser.: No. 104). 116p. (Orig.). 1983. pap. 25.00 (ISBN 0-317-42574-9, Pub. by Salzburg Studies). Longwood Pub Group.
Mayer, Fred S. Why Two Worlds: Relation of Physical to Spiritual Realities. LC 78-134425. Repr. of 1934 ed. 21.00 (ISBN 0-404-08465-6). AMS Pr.
Mayer, Gladys. Behind the Veils of Death & Sleep. 1973. lib. bdg. 79.95 (ISBN 0-87968-541-7). Krishna Pr.
Mayer, Hans E. The Crusades. Gillingham, John, tr. from Ger. (Illus.). 1972. pap. text ed. 12.95x (ISBN 0-19-873016-0). Oxford U Pr.
Mayer, Harry, ed. Modern Reader's Book of Psalms. (Black & Gold Lib). 1968. 6.95 (ISBN 0-87140-879-1, Co-Pub with Tudor). Liveright.
Mayer, J. P., ed. see Cortes, Juan D. & Schramm, Edmund.
Mayer, John E. Jewish-Gentile Courtships: An Exploratory Study of a Social Process. LC 80-16130. x, 240p. 1980. Repr. of 1961 ed. lib. bdg. 24.75x (ISBN 0-313-22465-X, MAJG). Greenwood.
Mayer, Milton, jt. auth. see Boulding, Kenneth E.
Mayer, Mordecai. Israel's Wisdom in Modern Life: Essays & Interpretations of Religious & Cultural Problems Based on the Talmudic & Midrashic Literature. 32.50 (ISBN 0-87559-147-7). Shalom.
Mayer, Robert T., tr. Bernard of Clairvaux: The Irishman. LC 78-768. (Cistercian Fathers Ser.). 1978. 7.95 (ISBN 0-685-87078-2); pap. 4.00 (ISBN 0-87907-910-X). Cistercian Pubns.
Mayers, Marvin. Christianity Confronts Culture. (Contemporary Evangelical Perspectives Ser.). 10.95 (ISBN 0-310-28891-6, 10230P). Zondervan.
Mayers, Marvin K., jt. auth. see Grunlan, Stephen A.
Mayers, Ronald B. Evangelical Perspectives: Toward a Biblical Balance. LC 86-28966. 204p. (Orig.). 1987. lib. bdg. 24.50 (ISBN 0-8191-6062-8); pap. text ed. 12.75 (ISBN 0-8191-6063-6). U Pr of Amer.
--Religious Ministry in a Transcendentless Culture. LC 79-3424. 1980. pap. text ed. 10.75 (ISBN 0-8191-0889-8). U Pr of Amer.
Mayers, Ronald B., jt. auth. see Bancroft, Emery.
Mayers, Ronald B., pref. by see Bancroft, Emery.
Mayers, W. E. The Chinese Reader's Manual: A Handbook of Biographical, Historical, Mythological, & General Literary Reference. 70.00 (ISBN 0-87968-855-6). Gordon Pr.
Mayer-Skumanz, Lene. The Story of Brother Francis. Bomer, Hildegard, tr. from Ger. LC 83-71779. (Illus.). 48p. (Orig.). 1983. pap. 6.95 (ISBN 0-87793-307-3). Ave Maria.
Mayerson, Phil. Classic Mythology in Literature, Art, & Music. 1971. text ed. write for info. (ISBN 0-673-15690-7). Scott F.
Mayes, A. D. Deuteronomy. (New Century Bible Ser.). 352p. 1979. 15.95 (ISBN 0-551-00804-0). Attic Pr.
--Deuteronomy. Clements, Ronald E., ed. (New Century Bible Commentary Ser.). (Orig.). 1981. pap. 9.95 (ISBN 0-8028-1882-X). Eerdmans.
--Judges. (Old Testament Guides Ser.). 98p. 1985. pap. text ed. 3.95x (ISBN 0-905774-58-2, Pub. by JSOT Pr England). Eisenbrauns.
Mayes, Andrew D. Israel in the Period of the Judges. (Studies in Biblical Theology, Second Ser.: No. 29). 1974. pap. text ed. 10.00x (ISBN 0-8401-3079-1). A R Allenson.
Mayes, Charles W. A Look at the Modern Healing Movement. 1979. pap. write for info. (ISBN 0-88469-113-6). BMH Bks.
Mayfair, Norman P. The Religious Practices of Primitive Peoples. (Illus.). 139p. 1980. deluxe ed. 67.75 (ISBN 0-89266-241-7). Am Classical Coll.
Mayhall, Carole. From the Heart of a Woman. LC 76-24066. 108p. 1976. pap. 3.95 (ISBN 0-89109-421-0). NavPress.
--Lord, Teach Me Wisdom. LC 78-78013. 180p. 1979. pap. 5.95 (ISBN 0-89109-432-6). NavPress.
--Words That Hurt, Words That Heal. 112p. 1986. hdbk. 8.95 (ISBN 0-89109-543-8). NavPress.
--Words That Hurt, Words That Heal. 112p. Date not set. pap. 3.95 (ISBN 0-89109-178-5). NavPress.
Mayhall, Carole, jt. auth. see Mayhall, Jack.
Mayhall, Jack. Discipleship: The Price & the Prize. 156p. 1984. pap. 5.95 (ISBN 0-88207-110-6). Victor Bks.
Mayhall, Jack & Mayhall, Carole. Marriage Takes More Than Love. LC 77-85736. 240p. 1978. pap. 5.95 (ISBN 0-89109-426-1). NavPress.
Mayhew, Eugene J., ed. Shalom: Essays in Honor of Dr. Charles H. Shaw. 23198. 1983. pap. 11.95 (ISBN 0-912407-01-8). William Tyndale Col Pr.
Mayhew, Henry. Mormons: Or, Latter Day Saints. LC 71-134398. Repr. of 1852 ed. 24.75 (ISBN 0-404-08440-0). AMS Pr.
Mayhew, Jonathan. Observations on the Charter & Conduct of the Society for the Propagation of the Gospel in Foreign Parts; Designed to Show Their Non-Conformity to Each Other. LC 72-38456. (Religion in America, Ser. 2). 180p. 1972. Repr. of 1763 ed. 15.00 (ISBN 0-405-04077-6). Ayer Co Pubs.
--Sermons. LC 76-83429. (Religion in America, Ser. 1). 1969. Repr. of 1749 ed. 19.00 (ISBN 0-405-00254-8). Ayer Co Pubs.
Mayhue, Richard. Divine Healing Today. 1983. pap. 6.95 (ISBN 0-8024-0453-7). Moody.

--Divine Healing Today. 1983. pap. 6.96 (ISBN 0-88469-154-3). BMH Bks.
--How to Interpret the Bible for Yourself. (Moody Press Electives Ser.). (Orig.). 1986. pap. text ed. 3.95 (ISBN 0-8024-0732-3); leader's guide 4.95 (ISBN 0-8024-0733-1). Moody.
--Snatched Before the Storm! 1980. pap. 1.00 (ISBN 0-88469-124-1). BMH Bks.
Mayhue, Richard L. How to Interpret the Bible for Yourself. 1986. pap. 3.95 (ISBN 0-88469-178-0). BMH Bks.
Maynard, Morlee. Happy Times with People. LC 85-25555. (Bible & Me Ser.). 1986. 5.95 (ISBN 0-8054-4165-4). Broadman.
Maynard, Theodore. The Humanist As Hero: The Life of Sir Thomas More. 1971. Repr. of 1947 ed. 14.75x (ISBN 0-02-849040-1). Hafner.
--Pillars of the Church. LC 76-136763. (Essay Index Reprint Ser). 1945. 19.00 (ISBN 0-8369-1940-8). Ayer Co Pubs.
Maynard-Reid, Pedrito U. Poverty & Wealth in James. LC 86-23506. 128p. (Orig.). 1987. pap. 8.95 (ISBN 0-88344-417-8). Orbis Bks.
Mayne, Zachary. Two Dissertations Concerning Sense, & the Immagination, with an Essay on Consciousness. Wellek, Rene, ed. LC 75-11234. (British Philosophers & Theologians of the 17th & 18th Centuries: Vol. 35). 1976. Repr. of 1728 ed. lib. bdg. 51.00 (ISBN 0-8240-1787-0). Garland Pub.
Mayo, Allen. Contract at Mount Horeb. LC 75-13402. (Illus.). 1977. 10.95 (ISBN 0-918268-01-X). Tex-Mex.
Mayo, Bernard. The Philosophy of Right & Wrong. 176p. 1986. 22.95 (ISBN 0-7102-0851-0, 08510); pap. 12.95 (ISBN 0-7102-0859-6, 08596). Methuen Inc.
Mayo, DeBarra. Runners' World Yoga, Bk. II. 180p. (Orig.). 1983. pap. 9.95 (ISBN 0-89037-274-8). Anderson World.
Mayo, Janet. A History of Ecclesiastical Dress. (Illus.). 196p. 1984. text ed. 39.50x (ISBN 0-8419-0983-0). Holmes & Meier.
Mayo, Mary A. A Christian Guide to Sexual Counseling: Recovering the Mystery & the Reality of "One Flesh". 288p. 1987. 16.95 (ISBN 0-310-35990-2). Zondervan.
--Parents' Guide to Sex Education. 208p. pap. 6.95 (ISBN 0-310-44581-7, 11357P). Zondervan.
Mayo, S. M. The Relevance of the Old Testament for the Christian Faith: Biblical Theology & Interpretive Methodology. 220p. (Orig.). 1982. lib. bdg. 27.75 (ISBN 0-8191-2656-X); pap. text ed. 12.50 (ISBN 0-8191-2657-8). U Pr of Amer.
Ma Yoga Sudha, ed. see Rajneesh, Bhagwan Shree.
Mayor, Joseph B. The Epistle of Saint James. 1977. 20.25 (ISBN 0-86524-971-7, 5902). Klock & Klock.
Mayr, Marlene, ed. Modern Masters of Religious Education. LC 82-25009. 323p. (Orig.). 1983. pap. 14.95 (ISBN 0-89135-033-0). Religious Educ.
Mayr, Roswitha. The Concept of Love in Sidney & Spenser. Hogg, James, ed. (Elizabethan & Renaissance Studies). 124p. (Orig.). 1978. pap. 15.00 (ISBN 0-317-40126-2, Pub. by Salzburg Studies). Longwood Pub Group.
Mays, Benjamin E. Negro's God As Reflected in His Literature. LC 69-16578. (Illus.). Repr. of 1938 ed. 24.75x (ISBN 0-8371-1139-0, MAG&, Pub. by Negro U Pr). Greenwood.
Mays, Benjamin E. & Nicholson, Joseph W. Negro's Church. LC 70-83430. (Religion in America, Ser. 1). 1969. Repr. of 1933 ed. 25.50 (ISBN 0-405-00255-6). Ayer Co Pubs.
Mays, James L. Amos: A Commentary. LC 79-76885. (Old Testament Library). 176p. 1969. 15.95 (ISBN 0-664-20863-0). Westminster.
--Ezekiel, Second Isaiah. McCurley, Foster R., ed. LC 77-15239. (Proclamation Commentaries, The Old Testament Witnesses for Preaching). 96p. (Orig.). 1978. pap. 4.95 (ISBN 0-8006-0592-6, 1-592). Fortress.
--Hosea: A Commentary. LC 75-79618. (Old Testament Library). 202p. 1969. 15.95 (ISBN 0-664-20871-1). Westminster.
--Leviticus, Numbers. LC 59-10454. (Layman's Bible Commentary Ser: Vol. 4). 1963. pap. 4.95 (ISBN 0-8042-3064-1). John Knox.
--Micah: A Commentary. LC 76-2599. (Old Testament Library). 180p. 1976. 15.95 (ISBN 0-664-20817-7). Westminster.
Mays, James L., ed. Interpreting the Gospels. LC 80-8057. pap. 79.30 (2027872). Bks Demand UMI.
Mays, James L. & Achtemeier, Paul J., eds. Interpreting the Prophets. LC 86-45223. 336p. 1987. pap. 16.95 (ISBN 0-8006-1932-3). Fortress.
Mays, James L., ed. see Achtemeier, Paul J.
Mays, James L., ed. see Best, Ernest.
Mays, James L., ed. see Craddock, Fred.
Mays, James L., ed. see Towner, W. Sibley.
Mays, James L., ed. see Williamson, Lamar, Jr.
Mays, Lois B. History of Folkston, Ga. Methodist Church. 37p. 1984. 3.25 (ISBN 0-9601606-1-2). Okefenokee Pr.
Mayshack, John L. One Hundred & Seventy-Five Sermon Outlines. (Sermon Outline Ser.). 1979. pap. 2.50 (ISBN 0-8010-6085-0). Baker Bk.
Mayson, Barry & Marco, Tony. Fallen Angel: Hell's Angel to Heaven's Saint. LC 81-43539. (Illus.). 312p. 1982. 15.95 (ISBN 0-385-17934-0); pap. write for info. (ISBN 0-385-19626-1). Doubleday.
Mazar, Benjamin & Avi-Yonah, Michael. Illustrated World of the Bible Library, 5 vols. Incl. Vol. 1. The Laws. 40.00 (ISBN 0-8088-1167-3); Vol. 2. The Early Prophets. 40.00 (ISBN 0-8088-1168-1); Vol. 3. The Late Prophets. 40.00 (ISBN 0-8088-1169-X); Vol. 4. The Writings. 40.00 (ISBN 0-8088-1170-3); Vol. 5. The New Testament. Avi-Yonah, Michael. 40.00 (ISBN 0-8088-1171-1). 1961. Vols. 1-4. old testament ed. 160.00 (ISBN 0-8088-1080-4); Vols. 1-5. new testament ed. 200.00 (ISBN 0-8088-1081-2). Davey.
Mazat, Alberta. That Friday in Eden. (Redwood Ser.). 1981. pap. 4.95 (ISBN 0-8163-0401-7). Pacific Pr Pub Assn.
Mazeroni, Robert S. Spiritual First Aid from A to Z. 176p. (Orig.). 1987. pap. 2.95 (ISBN 0-345-33824-3, Pub. by Ballantine Epiphany). Ballantine.
Mazow, Julia W., ed. The Woman Who Lost Her Names: Selected Writings by American Jewish Women. LC 79-2986. 240p. 1981. pap. text ed. 10.00 (ISBN 0-06-250567-X, CN 4017, HarpR). Har-Row.
Mazza, Enrico. The Eucharistic Prayers of the Roman Catholic Church. O'Connell, Matthew J., tr. from Ital. 380p. (Orig.). 1986. pap. 19.50 (ISBN 0-916134-78-4). Pueblo Pub Co.
Mazza, Valentino Del see Del Mazza, Valentino.
Mazzini, Giuseppe. The Morality & the Immorality of the Human Race. (Illus.). 144p. Repr. of 1862 ed. 127.45 (ISBN 0-89901-115-2). Found Class Reprints.
Mazziotta, Richard. Jesus In the Gospels: Old Stories Told Anew. LC 86-70132. 200p. (Orig.). 1986. pap. 5.95 (ISBN 0-87793-336-7). Ave Maria.
--We Pray to the Lord: General Intercessions Based on the Scriptural Readings for Sundays & Holy Days. LC 84-71135. 208p. (Orig.). 1984. pap. 9.95 (ISBN 0-87793-323-5). Ave Maria.
Mbiti, John S. African Religions & Philosophy. xiv, 290p. (Orig.). 1969. pap. text ed. 13.50x (ISBN 0-435-89589-3). Heinemann Ed.
--Afrikanische Religion und Weltanschauung. Feuser, W. F., tr. from Eng. (Ger.). xvi, 375p. 1974. 19.20 (ISBN 3-11-002498-5). De Gruyter.
--Introduction to African Religion. (Orig.). 1975. pap. text ed. 10.00x (ISBN 0-435-94001-5). Heinemann Ed.
Meacham, Standish. Lord Bishop: The Life of Samuel Wilberforce, 1805-1873. LC 70-102669. 1970. 20.00x (ISBN 0-674-53913-3). Harvard U Pr.
Mead, Daniel L. & Allen, Darrel J. Ministry by Objectives. LC 78-59182. (Evangelical Leadership Preparation Ser.). 80p. 1978. pap. 3.95 (ISBN 0-910566-84-4). Evang Tchr.
Mead, Frank S. Ten Decisive Battles of Christianity. LC 72-117823. (Essay Index Reprint Ser). 1937. 15.00 (ISBN 0-8369-1812-6). Ayer Co Pubs.
Mead, Frank S. & Hill, Samuel S. Handbook of Denominations in the United States. 8th ed. 400p. 1985. text ed. 10.95 (ISBN 0-687-16571-7). Abingdon.
Mead, Frank S., ed. The Encyclopedia of Religious Quotations. 540p. 1985. 16.95 (ISBN 0-8007-1410-5). Revell.
Mead, G. R. Five Years of Theosophy: Mystical, Philosophical, Theosophical, Historical & Scientific Essay. LC 75-36850. (Occult Ser.). 1976. Repr. of 1894 ed. 30.00x (ISBN 0-405-07966-4). Ayer Co Pubs.
--Fragments of a Faith Forgotten. 2nd ed. 633p. 1906. pap. 43.95 (ISBN 0-88697-011-3). Life Science.
--Pistis Sophia: A Gnostic Gospel, Vol. 21. 3rd ed. LC 83-83170. (Spiritual Science Library). 408p. 1984. Repr. of 1921 ed. lib. bdg. 25.00 (ISBN 0-89345-041-3, Spiritual Sci Lib). Garber Comm.
--Plotinus. 1983. pap. 5.95 (ISBN 0-916411-01-X, Pub. by Alexandrian Pr). Holmes Pub.
--World-Mystery: Four Comparative Studies in General Theosophy. 201p. 1987. pap. text ed. 15.95 (ISBN 0-915032-73-2). Natl Poster Foun.
Mead, G. R., ed. & intro. by see Blavatsky, Helena P.
Mead, G. R. S. Simon Magus. 1978. Repr. of 1892 ed. 10.00 (ISBN 0-89005-258-1). Ares.
Mead, G. R. S., tr. see Trismegistos, Hermes.
Mead, George R. The Hymn of Jesus. 78p. 1973. pap. 1.00 (ISBN 0-8356-0432-2, Quest). Theos Pub Hse.
Mead, James J. & Balch, Glenn M., Jr. Child Abuse & the Church: A New Mission. (Illus.). 160p. 1987. pap. 9.95 (ISBN 0-937359-10-6). HDL Pubs.
Mead, Jude C. St. Paul of the Cross: A Source-Workbook in Paulacrucian Studies. 560p. 1983. pap. 12.95 (ISBN 0-89944-070-3). Don Bosco Multimedia.
Mead, Margaret & Metraux, Rhoda. An Interview with Santa Claus. (Illus.). 1978. 4.95 (ISBN 0-8027-0620-7). Walker & Co.
Mead, Sidney. The Old Religion in the Brave New World: Reflections on the Relation Between Christendom & the Republic. LC 76-24588. (Jefferson Memorial Lectures). 1977. 16.95x (ISBN 0-520-03322-1). U of Cal Pr.
Mead, Sidney E. History & Identity. LC 78-26543. (American Academy of Religion. Studies in Religion: No. 19). 1979. 14.00 (ISBN 0-89130-274-3, 010019); pap. 9.95 (ISBN 0-89130-297-2). Scholars Pr GA.
--Lively Experiment: The Shaping of Christianity in America. 1963. pap. 6.95xi (ISBN 0-06-065545-3, RD-194, HarpR). Har-Row.
--Love & Learning. Doyle, Mary L., ed. 1978. lib. bdg. 12.95x (ISBN 0-914914-13-8); pap. 5.00 (ISBN 0-914914-12-X). New Horizons.
Meade, F. H., et al. Religions of the World. 97p. 1985. 32.00x (ISBN 0-7157-2355-3, Pub by Holmes McDougall Ltd). State Mutual Bk.
Meade, William. Old Churches, Ministers & Families of Virginia, 2 vols. Bd. with Digested Index & Genealogical Guide. Wise, Jennings C. Repr. of 1910 ed. LC 65-28854. 1100p. 1978. Repr. of 1857 ed. Set. 50.00 (ISBN 0-8063-0238-0). Genealog Pub.
Meader, Robert F., compiled by. Catalogue of the Emma B. King Library of the Shaker Museum. (Illus.). 63p. 1970. pap. write for info. (ISBN 0-937942-00-6). Shaker Mus.
Meador, Prentice A., Jr. Sermons for Today. LC 80-70788. 1981. 11.95 (ISBN 0-89112-402-0, Bibl Res Pr). Abilene Christ U.
--Who Rules Your Life? LC 79-64089. (Journey Bks.). 1979. pap. 3.50 (ISBN 0-8344-0107-X). Sweet.
Meador, Prentice A., Jr., jt. auth. see Pack, Frank.
Meadow, Mary J. Other People. LC 84-2315. (Choices; Guides for Today's Woman: Vol. 6). 120p. (Orig.). 1984. pap. 6.95 (ISBN 0-664-24544-7). Westminster.
Meadow, Mary J. & Kahoe, Richard D. Psychology of Religion: Religion in Individual Lives. 488p. 1984. text ed. 22.50 scp (ISBN 0-06-044411-8, HarpC). Har-Row.
Meadowcourt, Richard. Milton's Paradise Regained: Two Eighteenth-Century Critiques, 2 vols. in 1. Wittreich, Joseph A., Jr., ed. LC 76-161937. 1971. Repr. of 1732 ed. 50.00x (ISBN 0-8201-1087-6). Schol Facsimiles.
Meadows, Della A. Good Morning in the Dawn, Dear Son. 200p. 1985. 11.95 (ISBN 0-8059-2952-5). Dorrance.
Meadows, Denis. A Saint & a Half. 1963. 5.00 (ISBN 0-8159-6803-5). Devin.
--A Short History of the Catholic Church. 1959. 12.95 (ISBN 0-8159-6813-2). Devin.
Meagher, James L. How Christ Said the First Mass or the Lord's Last Supper. LC 82-74246. 438p. 1985. pap. 12.00 (ISBN 0-89555-207-8). Tan Bks Pubs.
Meagher, John C. Clumsy Construction in Mark's Gospel: A Critique of Form & Redaktionsgeschichte. LC 79-66373. (Toronto Studies in Theology: Vol. 3). xii, 178p. 1979. 39.95x (ISBN 0-88946-876-1). E Mellen.
--Five Gospels: An Account of How the Good News Came to Be. 324p. 1983. 24.50 (ISBN 0-86683-731-0, HarpR); pap. 11.95 (ISBN 0-86683-691-8). Har-Row.
Meagher, Paul K., et al. The Encyclopedic Dictionary of Religion, 3 vols. LC 78-62029. 3815p. 1979. 69.95 (ISBN 0-9602572-3-3). Cath U Pr.
Meagher, Robert. An Introduction to Augustine. LC 77-99085. 1978. 30.00x (ISBN 0-8147-5423-6). NYU Pr.
Mealy, Norman & Rock, Judith. Music, Dance & Religion: The Performing Arts in Worship. (Illus.). 192p. 1985. 15.95 (ISBN 0-13-607219-4); pap. 8.95 (ISBN 0-13-607201-1). P-H.
Means, Frank K. All Nations in God's Purpose: A Study Guide. LC 83-21073. 1984. pap. 4.25 (ISBN 0-8054-6334-8). Broadman.
Means, James. A Tearful Celebration: Courage in Crisis. LC 85-343. 1985. pap. 5.95 (ISBN 0-88070-078-5). Multnomah.
Mearns, James. Early Latin Hymnaries. 127p. Repr. of 1913 ed. lib. bdg. 38.50X (Pub. by G Olms BRD). Coronet Bks.
Mears, tr. Tao Teh King. 5.25 (ISBN 0-8356-5123-1). Theos Pub Hse.
Mears, Henrietta C. What the Bible is All About. Rev. ed. 642p. 1987. pap. 9.95 (ISBN 0-8423-7902-9). Tyndale.
--What the New Testament Is All About. 288p. pap. 3.95 (ISBN 0-8307-0525-2, 5015618). Regal.
--What the Old Testament Is All About. LC 76-51196. (Illus.). 1977. pap. 3.50 (ISBN 0-8307-0466-3, S111128). Regal.
Mears, Henrietta C., et al. What the Bible Is All About. rev. ed. Youngblood, Ronald & Tenney, Merrill C., eds. LC 83-4333. 1982. 13.95 (ISBN 0-8307-0902-9, 5110704); pap. 9.95 (ISBN 0-8307-0862-6, 5417202). Regal.
Mebust, J. Leland, jt. auth. see Achtemeier, Paul J.
Mecenseffy, Grete. Osterreichische Tauferakten One. (Tauferakten Kommision Ser., Vol. 11). 402p. (Ger). 1964. 15.00x (ISBN 0-8361-1171-0). Herald Pr.
--Osterreichische Tauferakten Two. (Tauferakten Kommission Ser.). 544p. 1973. 40.00x (ISBN 0-8361-1192-3). Herald Pr.
--Tauferaktenband Osterreich III. (TAK Ser.: Vol. XIV). (Ger.). 795p. 1982. 105.00 (ISBN 0-8361-1265-2). Herald Pr.
Mecham, J. Lloyd. Church & State in Latin America: A History of Politico-Ecclesiastical Relations. rev. ed. xi, 465p. 1969. pap. 7.95x (ISBN 0-8078-4042-4). U of NC Pr.
Mechie, Stewart. The Church & Scottish Social Development, 1780-1870. LC 75-3740. 181p. 1975. Repr. of 1960 ed. lib. bdg. 22.50x (ISBN 0-8371-8060-0, MECS). Greenwood.
Mechling, Jay, ed. Church, State & Public Policy. 1979. 12.25 (ISBN 0-8447-2159-X); pap. 5.25 (ISBN 0-8447-2160-3). Am Enterprise.
Mechoulan, Henry & Nahon, Gerard, eds. Menasseh ben Israel: The Hope of Israel. (Litman Library of Jewish Civilzation). (Illus.). 224p. 37.00 (ISBN 0-19-710054-6). Oxford U Pr.
Meconis, Charles. With Clumsy Grace: The American Catholic Left, 1961-1975. 1979. 9.95 (ISBN 0-8264-0175-9). Continuum.
Medeires, Humberto C. Whatever God Wants. 690p. 1984. 6.95 (ISBN 0-8198-8208-9); pap. 5.95 (ISBN 0-8198-8209-7). Dghtrs St Paul.
Medeiros, Huberto C. Thy Kingdom Come. 1980. 3.00 (ISBN 0-8198-7307-1); pap. 1.95 (ISBN 0-8198-7308-X). Dghtrs St Paul.
Medhurst, Kenneth N. The Church & Labour in Colombia. LC 82-62254. 320p. 1984. 46.00 (ISBN 0-7190-0969-3, Pub. by Manchester Univ Pr). Longwood Pub Group.
Medhurst, W. H. China: Its State & Prospects with Special Reference to the Spread of the Gospel. LC 72-79833. (The China Library Ser.). 1972. Repr. of 1842 ed. 42.00 (ISBN 0-8420-1379-2). Scholarly Res Inc.
Media Institute Staff, ed. see Corry, John.
Medlin, W. K. & Patrinelis, C. G. Renaissance Influences & Religious Reforms in Russia: Western & Post-Byzantine Impacts on Culture & Education, (16th-17th Centuries) 184p. (Orig.). 1970. pap. text ed. 22.00x (Pub. by Droz Switzerland). Coronet Bks.
Medlin, William K. Moscow & East Rome: A Political Study of the Relation of Church & State in Muscovite Russia. LC 79-2913. 252p. 1980. Repr. of 1952 ed. 23.00 (ISBN 0-8305-0082-0). Hyperion Conn.
Medoff, Rafael. The Deafening Silence: American Jewish Leaders & the Holocaust, 1933-1945. 1986. 14.95 (ISBN 0-933503-63-6). Shapolsky Pubs.
Medvedev, Anthony. The Young Elder: From Ambrose of Milkova. 70p. 1974. pap. 3.00 (ISBN 0-317-30442-9). Holy Trinity.
Meed, Steven, tr. see Meed, Vladka.
Meed, Vladka. On Both Sides of the Wall. Meed, Steven, tr. LC 78-71300. (Illus.). 304p. 1979. 16.95 (ISBN 0-89604-012-7); pap. 10.95 (ISBN 0-89604-013-5). Holocaust Pubns.
Meehan, Francis X., ed. A Contemporary Social Spirituality. LC 82-2253. 133p. (Orig.). 1982. pap. 6.95 (ISBN 0-88344-022-9). Orbis Bks.
Meek, George W. After We Die, What Then? LC 79-90909. (Life's Energy Fields Ser.: Vol. 3). (Illus., Orig.). 1980. 8.95 (ISBN 0-935436-00-6). Metascience.
--After We Die, What Then? rev. ed. LC 79-909. (Illus.). 216p. 1987. pap. 8.95 (ISBN 0-89804-099-X). Ariel OH.
Meek, George W., ed. Healers & the Healing Process. LC 77-5251. (Illus., Orig.). 1977. pap. 6.75 (ISBN 0-8356-0498-5, Quest). Theos Pub Hse.
Meek, Theophile J. Hebrew Origins. 1960. 11.25 (ISBN 0-8446-2572-8). Peter Smith.
Meeking, Basil, jt. ed. see Stott, John R.
Meekins, Inez P. Meekins' Ceremonies. 48p. 1981. soft cover 3.00 (ISBN 0-88053-326-9). Macoy Pub.
--Old Dominion Addresses & Ceremonies. 70p. 1975. Repr. of 1972 ed. softcover 1.00 (ISBN 0-88053-312-9, S-417). Macoy Pub.
Meeks, John, tr. see Bockemuhl, Jochen, et al.
Meeks, M. Douglas, ed. The Future of the Methodist Theological Traditions. 224p. 1985. pap. 9.95 (ISBN 0-687-13868-X). Abingdon.
Meeks, M. Douglas, tr. see Moltmann, Jurgen.
Meeks, Wayne, ed. see St. Paul.

Meeks, Wayne A. The First Urban Christians: The Social World of the Apostle Paul. LC 82-8447. (Illus.). 296p. 1982. 30.00x (ISBN 0-300-02876-8). Yale U Pr.
--The First Urban Christians: The Social World of the Apostle Paul. LC 82-8447. 312p. 1984. pap. 9.95 (ISBN 0-300-03244-7, Y-503). Yale U Pr.
--The Moral World of the First Christians. LC 86-5504. (Library of Early Christianity: Vol. 6). 180p. 1986. 18.95 (ISBN 0-664-21910-1). Westminster.
Meeks, Wayne A. & Wilken, Robert L. Jews & Christians in Antioch in the First Four Centuries of the Common Era. LC 78-3760. 1978. pap. 9.95 (ISBN 0-89130-229-8, 06-03-13). Scholars Pr GA.
Meeks, Wayne A., ed. Library of Early Christianity. 200p. 1987. 18.95. Westminster.
Meeks, Wayne A., ed. see Aune, David E.
Meeks, Wayne A., ed. see Cohen, Shaye J.
Meenan, Daniel F., tr. see Iparraguirre, Ignacio.
Meer, Charles Vander see Vander Meer, Charles.
Meer, Frederik Van Der see Van Der Meer, Frederik.
Meer, Haye Van Der see Van Der Meer, Haye S.
Meersman, Achilles. The Franciscans in the Indonesian Archipelago, 1300-1775. 1967. pap. 49.50x (ISBN 0-317-27470-8). Elliots Bks.
Mees, A. Choirs & Choral Music. LC 68-25296. (Studies in Music, No. 42). 1969. Repr. of 1901 ed. lib. bdg. 49.95x (ISBN 0-8383-0308-0). Haskell.
Mees, Arthur. Choirs & Choral Music. Repr. of 1901 ed. lib. bdg. 22.50 (ISBN 0-8371-1967-7, MECM). Greenwood.
Mees, L. F. Blessed by Illness. 248p. (Orig.). 1983. pap. 10.95 (ISBN 0-88010-054-0). Anthroposophic.
Meeter, Merle. Country of the Risen King: Anthology of Christian Poetry. LC 77-87993. 1978. 12.95 (ISBN 0-8010-6042-7). Baker Bk.
Meeter, Merle, et al. English Workbook for Christian Students. 1980. pap. 5.95x (ISBN 0-89051-066-0); tchr.'s guide 2.95x (ISBN 0-686-85807-7). Master Bks.
Megathlin, Earle. Why Doesn't God Do What We Tell Him? 192p. 1984. pap. 10.95 (ISBN 0-8059-2929-0). Dorrance.
Mehden, Fred R. Von Der see Von der Mehden, Fred R.
Mehden, Fred Von Der see Von Der Mehden, Fred.
Mehdi, M. T. Peace in Palestine. LC 75-43266. 1976. pap. 8.00 (ISBN 0-911026-08-8). New World Press NY.
Mehdi, M. T., ed. Palestine & the Bible. LC 71-114557. 1971. pap. 4.00 (ISBN 0-911026-06-1). New World Press NY.
Mehew, Karen, jt. auth. see Mehew, Randall.
Mehew, Randall & Mehew, Karen. Gospel Basics Busy Book. 150p. 1980. 4.95 (ISBN 0-934126-11-9). Randall Bk Co.
Mehl, Duane. At Peace with Failure. LC 83-721141. 128p. (Orig.). 1984. pap. 5.95 (ISBN 0-8066-2058-7, 10-0472). Augsburg.
--No More for the Road: One Man's Journey from Chemical Dependency to Freedom. LC 75-22721. 144p. 1976. pap. 7.95 (ISBN 0-8066-1515-X, 10-4665). Augsburg.
--You & the Alcoholic in Your Home. LC 78-66947. 1979. pap. 6.95 (ISBN 0-8066-1697-0, 10-7408). Augsburg.
Mehl, Roger. Condition of the Christian Philosopher. Kushner, Eva, tr. 221p. 1963. 9.95 (ISBN 0-227-67654-8). Attic Pr.
--Imagenes Del Hombre. Benlliure, Felix, tr. from Fr. Orig. Title: Images Del'homme. 64p. 1980. pap. 1.35 (ISBN 0-311-05051-4). Casa Bautista.
Mehlman, Israel. Genozot Sefarim: Bibliographical Essays. 10.00 (ISBN 0-405-12617-4). Ayer Co Pubs.
Mehlman, Jeffrey, tr. see Bredin, Jean-Denis.
Mehta. Creative Silence. 4.75 (ISBN 0-8356-7224-7). Theos Pub Hse.
--Yoga: The Art of Integration. 15.95 (ISBN 0-8356-7513-0). Theos Pub Hse.
Mehta, Hansa. Prince of Ayodhya. (Nehru Library for Children). (Illus.). 1979. pap. 2.00 (ISBN 0-89744-178-8). Auromere.
Mehta, J L. India & the West: The Problem of Understanding-Selected Essays of J.L. Mehta. (Studies in World Religions: No. 4). 1985. 20.75 (ISBN 0-89130-826-1, 03 00 04); pap. 13.75 (ISBN 0-89130-827-X). Scholars Pr GA.
Mehta, Rohit. Eternal Light. 1961. 8.95 (ISBN 0-8356-7004-X). Theos Pub Hse.
--Science of Meditation. 1978. 11.95 (ISBN 0-89684-007-7, Pub. by Motilal Banarsidass India). Orient Bk Dist.
Mehta, Rustam J. Masterpieces of Indian Temples. LC 75-901641. (Illus.). 110p. 1974. 22.00x (ISBN 0-89684-433-1). Orient Bk Dist.
Mehta, Ved. Vedi. (Illus.). 1982. 18.95x (ISBN 0-19-503005-2). Oxford U Pr.
Meiburg, Albert L. Sound Body Sound Mind. LC 84-10356. (Potentials: Guides for Productive Living Ser.: Vol. 9). 112p. 1984. pap. 7.95 (ISBN 0-664-24532-3). Westminster.
Meier, Arnold. Alttestamentliche Namengebung in England. pap. 9.00 (ISBN 0-685-13337-0). Johnson Repr.
Meier, C. A. The Psychology of C. G. Jung. Rolfe, Eugene, tr. (The Unconscious in Its Empirical Manifestations Ser.: Vol. I). (Illus.). 256p. 1985. 25.50 (ISBN 0-938434-10-1). Sigo Pr.
Meier, Gerhard. Die Assyrische Beschwoerungssamlung Maalu. LC 78-72751. (Ancient Mesopotamian Texts & Studies). Repr. of 1937 ed. 22.50 (ISBN 0-404-18194-5). AMS Pr.
Meier, John, jt. auth. see Brown, Raymond E.
Meier, John P. Matthew. (New Testament Message Ser.: Vol. 3). 15.95 (ISBN 0-89453-191-3); pap. 12.95 (ISBN 0-89453-126-3). M Glazier.
--The Vision of Matthew: Christ, Church & Morality in the First Gospel. LC 78-70820. 1979. pap. 8.95 (ISBN 0-8091-2171-9). Paulist Pr.
Meier, John P. & Gordon, Edmund F. Matthew: An Access Guide for Scripture Study. 174p. 1983. pap. 4.20 (ISBN 0-8215-5932-X); manual 3.45 (ISBN 0-8215-5935-4). Sadlier.
Meier, Levi, ed. Jewish Values in Bioethics. 195p. 1986. text ed. 26.95 (ISBN 0-89885-299-4). Human Sci Pr.
Meier, Paul. Meditating for Success. Mack, Jane, ed. 25p. (Orig.). 1985. pap. 2.95 (ISBN 0-8010-6207-1). Baker Bk.
Meier, Paul & Meier, Richard. Family Foundations. 96p. (Orig.). 1981. 8.95 (ISBN 0-8010-6117-2). Baker Bk.
Meier, Paul, jt. auth. see Korem, Danny.
Meier, Paul D. Christian Child Rearing & Personality Development. 1977. pap. 6.95 (ISBN 0-8010-6016-8). Baker Bk.
--You Can Avoid Divorce. (Christian Counseling Aids Ser). 1978. pap. 1.50 (ISBN 0-8010-6052-4). Baker Bk.
Meier, Paul D. & Burnett, Linda. Unwanted Generation. 1981. 7.95 (ISBN 0-8010-6101-6). Baker Bk.
Meier, Paul D., et al. Introduction to Psychology & Counseling: Christian Perspectives & Applications. LC 82-70462. 432p. 1982. 21.95 (ISBN 0-8010-6128-8). Baker Bk.
Meier, Richard, jt. auth. see Meier, Paul.
Meigs, Anna S. Food, Sex & Pollution: A New Guinea Religion. 195p. 1984. text ed. 22.50 (ISBN 0-8135-0968-8). Rutgers U Pr.
Meigs, Peveril. Dominican Mission Frontier of Lower California. pap. 25.00 (ISBN 0-384-38005-0). Johnson Repr.
Meilach, M. D. From Order to Omega. pap. 0.95 (ISBN 0-8199-0038-9, L38249). Franciscan Herald.
Meilach, Michael, ed. There Shall Be One Christ. (Spirit and Life Ser). 1968. 2.50 (ISBN 0-686-11576-7). Franciscan Inst.
Meilach, Michael, ed. see Hale, Robert.
Meilach, Michael D. Primacy of Christ. 1964. 4.95 (ISBN 0-8199-0087-7, L38655). Franciscan Herald.
Meilaender, Gilbert C. Friendship: A Study in Theological Ethics. LC 81-50459. 118p. 1981. text ed. 10.95 (ISBN 0-268-00956-2). U of Notre Dame Pr.
--The Theory & Practice of Virtue. LC 83-40598. 202p. 1985. pap. text ed. 8.95 (ISBN 0-268-01858-8, 85-18581). U of Notre Dame Pr.
Meinardus, Otto. The Holy Family in Egypt: In the Steps of the Tradition. 1987. pap. 10.00 (ISBN 977-424-129-0, Pub. by Am Univ Cairo Pr). Columbia U Pr.
Meinardus, Otto F. St. John of Patmos & the Seven Churches of the Apocalypse. LC 78-51245. (In the Footsteps of the Saints Ser.). (Illus.). 160p. 1979. 17.50 (ISBN 0-89241-070-1); pap. 6.95 (ISBN 0-89241-043-4). Caratzas.
--St. Paul in Ephesus & the Cities of Galatia & Cyprus. LC 78-51246. (In the Footsteps of the Saints Ser.). (Illus.). 160p. 1979. 17.50 (ISBN 0-89241-071-X); pap. 6.95 (ISBN 0-89241-044-2). Caratzas.
--St. Paul in Greece. LC 78-51244. (In the Footsteps of the Saints Ser.). 160p. 1979. 17.50 (ISBN 0-89241-072-8); pap. 6.95 (ISBN 0-89241-045-0). Caratzas.
--St. Paul's Last Journey. LC 78-51247. (In the Footsteps of the Saints Ser.). (Illus.). 160p. 1979. 17.50 (ISBN 0-686-85764-X); pap. 6.95 (ISBN 0-89241-073-6). Caratzas.
Meir Bar-Am. The Fateful Mission. 180p. 1986. 9.95 (ISBN 0-87306-420-8); pap. 6.95 (ISBN 0-87306-421-6). Feldheim.
Meirill Library Staff. Name Index to the Library of Congress Collection of Mormon Diaries. (Western Text Society Ser.: Vol. 1, No. 2). 391p. (Orig.). 1971. pap. 12.95 (ISBN 0-87421-045-3). Utah St U Pr.
Meiring, Bernard J. Educational Aspects of the Legislation of the Councils of Baltimore, 1829-1884. 25.50 (ISBN 0-405-10844-3, 11821). Ayer Co Pubs.
Meisel, Anthony C. & Del Mastro, M. L., trs. The Rule of St. Benedict. LC 74-33611. 120p. 1975. pap. 2.95 (ISBN 0-385-00948-8, Im). Doubleday.
Meiseles, Meir. Judaism, Thought & Legend. Schonfeld-Brand, Rebecca & Newman, Aryeh, trs. from Hebrew. 1978. pap. 9.95 (ISBN 0-87306-140-3). Feldheim.
Meiselman, M. Jewish Woman in Jewish Law. (Library of Jewish Law & Ethics: Vol. 6). 9.95x (ISBN 0-87068-329-2). Ktav.
Meisl, Josef. Haskalah: Geschichte der Aufklarungsbewegung unter den Juden in Russland. Katz, Stephen, ed. LC 79-7147. (Jewish Philosophy, Mysticism & History of Ideas Ser.). 1980. Repr. of 1919 ed. lib. bdg. 21.00x (ISBN 0-405-12277-2). Ayer Co Pubs.
Meislin, Bernard. Jewish Law in American Trials & Tribunals. 25.00x (ISBN 0-87068-288-1). Ktav.
Meiss, Millard. Giotto & Assisi. (Illus.). 12.50 (ISBN 0-912158-42-5). Hennessey.
--Giotto & Assisi. LC 60-9443. (Walter W. S. Cook Alumni Lecture Ser.: 1959). pap. 20.00 (ISBN 0-317-09361-4, 2050841). Bks Demand UMI.
--Painting in Florence & Siena after the Black Death: The Arts, Religion & Society in the Mid-Fourteenth-Century. 1976. 37.00x (ISBN 0-691-03919-4); pap. 9.95x (ISBN 0-691-00312-2). Princeton U Pr.
Meiss, Millard, jt. auth. see Tintori, Leonetto.
Meissner, W. W. Life & Faith: Psychoanalytic Perspectives on Religious Experience. 302p. 1987. 19.95 (ISBN 0-87840-429-5); pap. 11.95. Georgetown U Pr.
--Psychoanalysis & Religious Experience. 1984. 27.50 (ISBN 0-317-13715-8). Yale U Pr.
--Psychoanalysis & Religious Experience. LC 83-51296. 272p. 1986. pap. 9.95x (ISBN 0-300-03751-1, Y-599). Yale U Pr.
Meister, Barbara, jt. auth. see Kalisch, Shoshana.
Meister, Charles W. The Year of the Lord: A. D. 1844. LC 82-23976. 264p. 1983. lib. bdg. 18.95x (ISBN 0-89950-037-4). McFarland & Co.
Meister, John, et al, eds. see Law, William.
Meister, Michael W. Discourses on Siva. LC 83-12529. (Illus.). 568p. 1985. 75.00 (ISBN 0-8122-7909-3). U of Pa Pr.
Meister, Michael W., ed. Encyclopedia of Indian Temple Architecture: South India, Lower Dravidadesa, 300 B.C.-A.D. 1326, 2 pts, Vol. 1. LC 82-50173. (Illus.). 736p. 1982. Set. 84.00x (ISBN 0-8122-7840-2). U of Pa Pr.
Meister, Michael W. & Dhaky, M. A., eds. Encyclopedia of Indian Temple Architecture, Vol. 1, Part II: South India: Upper Dravidadesa. (Illus.). 736p. 1982. Set. text ed. 84.00x. U of Pa Pr.
Meitler, Neal D. & La Porte, Linda M. Standard Accounting System for Lutheran Congregations. 1981. 4.95 (ISBN 0-8100-0129-2, 21N2001). Northwest Pub.
Mekhilta, Munich. Early Hebrew Manuscripts in Facsimile, Vol. 7. Edelmann, Martin & Schmelzer, Menahem, eds. 220p. 1980. 450.00x (ISBN 0-8018-2464-8); pap. 410.00x (ISBN 0-8018-2465-6). Johns Hopkins.
Mekler, Eva, jt. auth. see Schulman, Michael.
Melanchthon. The Confessyon of the Fayth of the Germaynes in the Councell, 2 pts. LC 76-57351. (English Experience Ser.: No. 771). 1977. Repr. of 1536 ed. Set. lib. bdg. 39.00 (ISBN 90-221-0771-X). Walter J Johnson.
Melanchthon, Philip. The Loci Communes of Philip Melanchthon. Hill, Charles L., tr. LC 83-45649. Date not set. Repr. of 1944 ed. 32.50 (ISBN 0-404-19858-9). AMS Pr.
--Melanchthon on Christian Doctrine: Loci Communes 1555. Manschreck, Clyde L., ed. & tr. (Twin Brooks Ser.). 414p. 1982. pap. 11.95 (ISBN 0-8010-6143-1). Baker Bk.
--A Very Godly Defense, Defending the Marriage of Priests. Beuchame, L., tr. LC 76-25643. (English Experience Ser.: No. 199). 1969. Repr. of 1541 ed. 8.00 (ISBN 90-221-0199-1). Walter J Johnson.
Melanchthon, Philipp. The Justification of Man by Faith Only. Lesse, Nicholas, tr. LC 79-84123. (English Experience Ser.: No. 942). 204p. 1979. Repr. of 1548 ed. lib. bdg. 15.00 (ISBN 90-221-0942-9). Walter J Johnson.
--Opera Quae Supersunt Omnia, 28 Vols. (Corpus Reformatorum). Repr. of 1860 ed. Set. 1650.00 (ISBN 0-384-38050-6); 60.00 ea. Johnson Repr.
--Selected Writings. Flack, Elmer E. & Satre, Lowell J., eds. Hill, Charles L., tr. LC 78-5175. 1978. Repr. of 1962 ed. lib. bdg. cancelled (ISBN 0-313-20384-9, MESW). Greenwood.
Meland, Bernard E. Faith & Culture. (Arcturus Books Paperbacks). 176p. 1972. lib. bdg. 7.00x (ISBN 0-8093-0591-7); pap. 2.45x (ISBN 0-8093-0571-2). S Ill U Pr.
--Fallible Forms & Symbols: Discourses on Method in a Theology of Culture. LC 76-7868. pap. 56.50 (2026957). Bks Demand UMI.
--Future of Empirical Theology. Braver, J. C., ed. LC 78-83980. (Essays in Divinty Ser: Vol. 7). 1969. 20.00x (ISBN 0-226-51955-4). U of Chicago Pr.
--Realities of Faith. 1962. pap. 2.25x (ISBN 0-912182-03-2). Seminary Co-Op.
--Reawakening of Christian Faith. facsimile ed. LC 72-142670. (Essay Index Reprint Ser). Repr. of 1949 ed. 15.00 (ISBN 0-8369-2663-3). Ayer Co Pubs.
Meland, Bernard E., jt. auth. see Wieman, Henry N.
Melander, Ingrid. Middle English Metrical Paraphrase on the Old Testament. 116p. (Orig.). 1971. pap. text ed. 30.00x. Coronet Bks.
Melang, Karen. Jesus: The Servant. (Concept Ser.). (Illus.). 24p. (Orig.). 1986. pap. 3.95 saddlestitched (ISBN 0-570-08532-2, 56-1559). Concordia.
Melcer, Donald. Self Development Through Meditative Practice. 1983. pap. 2.95 (ISBN 0-916786-70-6). St George Bk Serv.
Melcher, Marguerite F. Shaker Adventure. 319p. 1986. pap. 9.95 (ISBN 0-937942-08-1). Shaker Mus.
Melden, A. I. Ethical Theories: A Book of Readings with Revisions. 2nd ed. 1967. text ed. write for info. (ISBN 0-13-290122-6). P-H.
Melden, A. I., ed. Essays in Moral Philosophy. LC 58-10483. 288p. 1966. 15.00x (ISBN 0-295-73774-3); pap. 4.95x (ISBN 0-295-74049-3, WP20). U of Wash Pr.
Melia, Pius. The Origin, Persecutions, & Doctrines of the Waldenses from Documents: Many Now for the First Time Collected & Edited. LC 77-84716. Repr. of 1870 ed. 27.50 (ISBN 0-404-16122-7). AMS Pr.
Melito. On Pascha & Fragments. Hall, Stuart G., ed. (Oxford Early Christian Texts). 1979. text ed. 34.95x (ISBN 0-19-826811-4). Oxford U Pr.
Melitz, Jacques, ed. see Viner, Jacob.
Mella, Dorothee I. Stone Power II: The Legendary & Practical Use of Gems & Stones. Orig. Title: Stone Power, The Legendary & Practical Use of Gems & Stones. (Illus.). 164p. (Orig.). 1986. pap. 11.95 (ISBN 0-914732-18-8). Bro Life Inc.
Mella, Orlando. Religion & Politics in Chile: An Analysis of Religious Models. (Illus.). 202p. (Orig.). 1986. pap. text ed. 22.00x. Coronet Bks.
Mellen, Francis, jt. auth. see Warren, Sukanya.
Mellen, Philip. Gerhart Hauptman: Religious Syncretism & Eastern Religions. (American University Studies I: Vol. 24). 284p. (Orig.). 1983. pap. text ed. 30.55 (ISBN 0-8204-0060-2). P Lang Pubs.
Mellinger, Martha. Little Ones Praise. 1981. 4.35 (ISBN 0-87813-518-9). Christian Light.
Mellinkoff, Ruth. The Horned Moses in Medieval Art & Thought. LC 77-85450. (California Studies in the History of Art: No. XIV). (Illus.). 1970. 40.00x (ISBN 0-520-01705-6). U of Cal Pr.
Mellis, Charles J. Committed Communities: Fresh Streams for World Missions. LC 76-53548. 1976. pap. 5.95 (ISBN 0-87808-426-6). William Carey Lib.
Mello, Anthony De see De Mello, Anthony.
Mello, Anthony de see De Mello, Anthony.
Mellone, Sydney H. The Dawn of Modern Thought: Descartes, Spinoza, Leibniz, with Introductory Note by W. D. Ross. LC 72-85001. 124p. 1973. Repr. of 1930 ed. 10.00x (ISBN 0-8462-1686-8). Russell.
--Western Christian Thought in the Middle Ages. 1977. lib. bdg. 59.95 (ISBN 0-8490-2816-7). Gordon Pr.
Mellor, Allec. Dictionnaire de la Franc-Maconnerie et des Francs-Macons. (Fr.). 400p. 1971. 27.50 (ISBN 0-686-57043-X, M-6403). French & Eur.
Mellor, E. B., ed. The Making of the Old Testament. (Cambridge Bible Commentary on the New English Bible, Old Testament Ser.). (Illus.). 226p. 1972. 22.95 (ISBN 0-521-08184-X); pap. 10.95 (ISBN 0-521-09673-1). Cambridge U Pr.
Mellows, Mary. A Lamp for Orchid. 126p. 1986. pap. 22.00X (ISBN 0-7223-1987-8, Pub. by A H Stockwell England). State Mutual Bk.
Melnick. Old Testament. (Book Note). 1985. pap. 2.50 (ISBN 0-8120-3531-3). Barron.
Melnick, Ralph. From Polemics to Apologetics: Jewish-Christian Rapprochment in 17th Century Amsterdam. 104p. 1981. pap. text ed. 8.75 (ISBN 90-232-1792-6, Pub. by Van Gorcum Holland). Longwood Pub Group.
Melnikov, F. E. Otkuda Proizoshla Vijera v Boga. Tr. of Where did Faith in God Come from? 48p. 1938. pap. 2.00 (ISBN 0-317-29132-7). Holy Trinity.

Melrose, Andrea LaSonde, ed. Nine Visions: A Book of Fantasies. 192p. 1983. pap. 8.95 (ISBN 0-8164-2490-X, HarpR). Har-Row.

Melton, Gordon J., jt. auth. see Enroth, Ronald M.

Melton, J. G, ed. see Bjorling, Joel.

Melton, J. Gordon. Biographical Dictionary of American Cult & Sect Leaders. LC 83-48226. (Library of Social Sciences). 534p. 1986. lib. bdg. 39.95 (ISBN 0-8240-9037-3). Garland Pub.

Melton, J. Gordon & Moore, Robert L. The Cult Experience: Responding to the New Religious Pluralism. LC 82-16136. 160p. (Orig.). 1982. pap. 8.95 (ISBN 0-8298-0619-9). Pilgrim NY.

Melton, J. Gordon, jt. auth. see Pruter, Karl.

Melton, J. Gordon, ed. Encyclopedia of American Religions. 2nd ed. 1200p. 1986. 165.00x (ISBN 0-8103-2133-5). Gale.

Melton, J. Gordon, ed. see Pritchett, W. Douglas.

Melton, James G. & Geisendorfer, James V. A Directory of Religious Bodies in the United States. (Reference Library of the Humanities: Vol. 91). (LC 76-052700). 1977. lib. bdg. 40.00 (ISBN 0-8240-9882-X). Garland Pub.

Meltzer, Julian, tr. see Horowitz, David.

Meltzer, Milton. The Human Rights Book. LC 79-13017. 272p. 1979. 11.95 (ISBN 0-374-33514-1). FS&G.

--The Jews in America: A Picture Album. LC 84-14344. (Illus.). 1985. 12.95 (ISBN 0-8276-0246-4). Jewish Pubns.

--Never to Forget: The Jews of the Holocaust. 192p. 1977. pap. 3.25 (ISBN 0-440-96070-3, LFL); tchr's. guide by Max Nadel 0.50. Dell.

--Never to Forget: The Jews of the Holocaust. LC 75-25409. (YA) 1976. PLB 13.89 (ISBN 0-06-024175-6). HarpJ.

--World of Our Fathers: The Jews of Eastern Europe. LC 74-14755. (Illus.). 256p. 1974. 11.95 (ISBN 0-374-38530-0). FS&G.

Melugin, Roy F. Formation of Isaiah 40-55. (Beiheft 141 Zur Zeitschrift fuer die Altestamentliche Wissenschaft). 1976. text ed. 42.00 (ISBN 3-11-005820-0). De Gruyter.

Melville, Annabelle M. Elizabeth Bayley Seton. 1976. pap. 2.25 (ISBN 0-515-09682-2). Jove Pubns.

--Elizabeth Bayley Seton. 1976. lib. bdg. 25.00x (ISBN 0-684-14735-1, ScribT). Scribner.

Melville, Cuthbert. The Rolling Files: A Study of the Bible. 1980. 7.95 (ISBN 0-682-48165-3). Exposition Pr FL.

Melville, James. Diary. LC 70-172723. (Bannatyne Club, Edinburgh. Publications: No. 34). Repr. of 1829 ed. 32.50 (ISBN 0-404-52740-X). AMS Pr.

--The Wages of Zen. 224p. 1985. pap. 2.95 (ISBN 0-449-20838-9, Crest). Fawcett.

Melville, Leinani. Children of the Rainbow: The Religions, Legends & Gods of Pre-Christian Hawaii. LC 69-17715. (Illus.). 1969. pap. 5.95 (ISBN 0-8356-0002-5, Quest). Theos Pub Hse.

Melvin, Billy A. Free Will Baptist Minister's Manual. 1974. ringbinder 8.95 (ISBN 0-89265-024-9). Randall Hse.

Melzer, Sara E. Discourses of the Fall: A Study of Pascal's Pensees. LC 85-24519. 128p. 1986. text ed. 22.95x (ISBN 0-520-05540-3). U of Cal Pr.

Members of Community at Taize, France, ed. Praise God: Common Prayer at Taize. LC 76-47437. 1977. 16.95x (ISBN 0-19-519915-4). Oxford U Pr.

Memmi, Albert. Jews & Arabs. Levieux, Eleanor, tr. from Fr. LC 75-10697. (Eng.). 224p. 1975. 9.95 (ISBN 0-87955-327-8); pap. 7.95 (ISBN 0-87955-328-6). O'Hara.

Memon, Muhammed U. Ibn Taimaya's Struggle Against Popular Religion with an Annotated Translation of His Kitab Iqtida Assirat Al Mustaquin Mukhalafat Ashab Al-Jahim. (Religion & Society: No. 1). 1976. text ed. 59.00x (ISBN 90-2797-591-4). Mouton.

Memorial Society Association of Canada see Continental Assocation of Funeral & Memorial Societies, Inc.

Menard, Eusebe. At All Times, in Every Age. 1977. 4.95 (ISBN 0-8199-0663-8). Franciscan Herald.

Men-Ching, Cheng. Lao-Tzu: My Words Are Very Easy to Understand. 2nd ed. Gibbs, Tam & Huang, Juh-Hua, trs. (Eng. & Chinese.). 256p. 1981. pap. 8.95 (ISBN 0-913028-91-6). North Atlantic.

Mencius. Works of Mencius. Legge, James, tr. 15.75 (ISBN 0-8446-0331-7). Peter Smith.

Menczer, Bela, ed. Catholic Political Thought: 1789-1848. 1962. pap. 5.95x (ISBN 0-268-00031-X). U of Notre Dame Pr.

Mendelkern, Solomon. Concordance of the Bible. (Hebrew & Lat.). 1985. Repr. of 1896 ed. 25.00 (ISBN 0-685-81426-2). Feldheim.

Mendelsohn, Ezra. The Jews of East Central Europe between the World Wars. LC 81-48676. (Illus.). 320p. 1983. 27.50x (ISBN 0-253-33160-9). Ind U Pr.

--Zionism in Poland: The Formative Years, 1915-1926. LC 81-10301. 416p. 1982. text ed. 42.00x (ISBN 0-300-02448-7). Yale U Pr.

Mendelsohn, J. The Final Solution in the Extermination Camps & the Aftermath. LC 81-80320. (The Holocaust Ser.). 250p. 1982. lib. bdg. 61.00 (ISBN 0-8240-4886-5). Garland Pub.

--The Judicial System & the Jews in Nazi Germany. LC 81-80321. (The Holocaust Ser.). 245p. 1982. lib. bdg. 61.00 (ISBN 0-8240-4887-3). Garland Pub.

--Relief & Rescue of Jews from Nazi Oppression, 1943-1945. LC 81-80322. (The Holocaust Ser.). 264p. 1982. lib. bdg. 61.00 (ISBN 0-8240-4888-1). Garland Pub.

--Relief in Hungary & the Failure of the Joel Brand Mission. LC 81-80323. (The Holocaust Ser.). 256p. 1982. lib. bdg. 61.00 (ISBN 0-8240-4889-X). Garland Pub.

--Rescue to Switzerland: The Mussy & Saly Mayer Affair. LC 81-80324. (The Holocaust Ser.). 280p. 1982. lib. bdg. 61.00 (ISBN 0-8240-4890-3). Garland Pub.

--The Wannsee Protocol & a 1944 Report on Auschwitz by the Office of Strategic Services. LC 81-80319. (The Holocaust Ser.). 264p. 1982. lib. bdg. 61.00 (ISBN 0-8240-4885-7). Garland Pub.

Mendelsohn, Jack. Channing: The Reluctant Radical. 2nd ed. 1986. pap. 10.95 (ISBN 0-933840-28-4, Skinner Hse Bks). Unitarian Univ.

--God, Allah & Ju Ju: Religion in Africa Today. LC 78-5872. 1978. Repr. of 1962 ed. lib. bdg. cancelled (ISBN 0-313-20483-7, MEGA). Greenwood.

Mendelsohn, John. Deportation of the Jews to the East: Settin, 1940 to Hungary 1944. LC 81-80316. (The Holocaust Ser.). 256p. 1982. lib. bdg. 61.00 (ISBN 0-8240-4882-2). Garland Pub.

--The Einsatzgruppen or Murder Commandos. LC 81-80318. (The Holocaust Ser.). 256p. 1982. lib. bdg. 61.00 (ISBN 0-8240-4884-9). Garland Pub.

--Jewish Emigration: The SS St. Louis Affair & Other Cases. LC 81-80315. (The Holocaust Ser.: Vol. 7). 274p. 1982. lib. bdg. 61.00 (ISBN 0-8240-4881-4). Garland Pub.

--Jewish Emigration 1938-1940: Rublee & Intergovernmental Committee. LC 81-80314. (The Holocaust Ser.). 250p. 1982. lib. bdg. 61.00 (ISBN 0-8240-4880-6). Garland Pub.

--Medical Experiments on Jewish Inmates of Concentration Camps. LC 81-80317. (The Holocaust Ser.). 282p. 1982. lib. bdg. 61.00 (ISBN 0-8240-4883-0). Garland Pub.

--Propaganda & Aryanization, 1938-1944. LC 81-80312. (The Holocaust Ser.). 255p. 1982. lib. bdg. 61.00 (ISBN 0-8240-4878-4). Garland Pub.

--Punishing the Perpetrators of the Holocaust: The Ohlendorf & Von Weizsaecker Cases. LC 81-80326. (The Holocaust Ser.). 310p. 1982. lib. bdg. 61.00 (ISBN 0-8240-4892-X). Garland Pub.

Mendelsohn, John & Detwiler, Donald S. Jewish Emigration from 1933 to the Evian Conference of 1938. LC 81-80313. (The Holocaust Ser.). 260p. 1982. lib. bdg. 61.00 (ISBN 0-8240-4879-2). Garland Pub.

Mendelsohn, Samuel. The Criminal Jurisprudence of the Jews. (Studies in Jewish Jurisprudence: Vol. 6). 280p. 1986. 19.50 (ISBN 0-87203-122-5). Hermon.

Mendelson, E. Michael. Sangha & State in Burma: A Study of Monastic Sectarianism & Leadership. Ferguson, John P., ed. LC 75-13398. (Illus.). 416p. 1975. 42.50x (ISBN 0-8014-0875-X). Cornell U Pr.

Mendelssohn, Kurt. The Riddle of Pyramids. (Illus.). 1986. 24.95f (ISBN 0-500-05015-5); pap. 12.95f (ISBN 0-500-27388-X). Thames Hudson.

Mendelssohn, Moses. Jerusalem: Or on Religious Power & Judaism. Altmann, Alexander, intro. by. Arkush, Allan, tr. LC 83-40015. 262p. 1983. 20.00x (ISBN 0-87451-263-8); pap. 10.00x (ISBN 0-87451-264-6). U Pr of New Eng.

Mendelssohn, S. Judaic or Semitic Legends & Customs Amongst South African Natives. 1976. lib. bdg. 59.95 (ISBN 0-8490-2111-1). Gordon Pr.

Mendelssohn, Sidney. The Jews of Africa, Especially in the 16th & 17th Centuries. 59.95 (ISBN 0-8490-0446-2). Gordon Pr.

--The Jews of Asia: Especially in the Sixteenth & Seventeenth Centuries. LC 77-87612. (Illus.). 256p. Repr. of 1920 ed. 29.50 (ISBN 0-404-16436-6). AMS Pr.

Mendenhall, George E. The Tenth Generation: The Origins of the Biblical Tradition. 266p. 1973. 25.00x (ISBN 0-8018-1267-4); pap. 8.95x (ISBN 0-8018-1654-8). Johns Hopkins.

Mendes, Reva. Words for the Quiet Moments. 35p. 1973. pap. 1.00 (ISBN 0-87516-185-5). De Vorss.

Mendes-Flohr, Paul, jt. ed. see Cohen, Arthur A.

Mendes-Flor, Paul, ed. see Buber, Martin.

Mendl, Wolf. The Study of War As a Contribution to Peace. (Orig.). 1983. pap. 2.50x (ISBN 0-87574-247-5, 247). Pendle Hill.

Mendoza, Celia, tr. see Edge, Findley B.

Mendoza De Mann, Wilma, tr. see Hunter, Emily.

Menedez, Josefa, et al. Words of Love. LC 84-51596. 95p. (Orig.). 1985. pap. 3.00 (ISBN 0-89555-244-2). Tan Bks Pubs.

Menendez, Albert J. Christmas in the White House. LC 83-3629. (Illus.). 128p. 1983. 11.95 (ISBN 0-664-21392-8). Westminster.

--Church-State Relations: An Annotated Bibliography. LC 75-24894. (Reference Library of Social Science: Vol. 24). 125p. 1976. lib. bdg. 25.00 (ISBN 0-8240-9956-7). Garland Pub.

--Religious Conflict in America: A Bibliography. LC 84-48078. (Reference Library of Social Science). 500p. 1984. lib. bdg. 20.00 (ISBN 0-8240-8904-9). Garland Pub.

--School Prayer & Other Religious Issues in American Public Education: A Bibliography. LC 84-48756. (Reference Library of Social Science). 178p. 1985. lib. bdg. 20.00 (ISBN 0-8240-8775-5). Garland Pub.

Menendez, Josefa. Christ's Appeal for Love. Keppel, L., tr. from Span. 1975. pap. 4.00 (ISBN 0-89555-013-X). TAN Bks Pubs.

--I Wait for You: Jesus' Lament Over Man's Indifference (Excerpts from the Way of Divine Love) 32p. (Orig.). 1985. pap. 0.50 (ISBN 0-89555-285-X). Tan Bks Pubs.

--The Way of Divine Love. LC 79-112493. 504p. 1972. pap. 12.00 (ISBN 0-89555-030-X). TAN Bks Pubs.

--The Way of Divine Love. 506p. 1981. pap. 5.00 (ISBN 0-89555-276-0). TAN Bks Pubs.

Mengarini, Gregory. Recollections of the Flathead Mission. Lothrop, Gloria, ed. LC 74-27573. (Illus.). 1977. 16.95 (ISBN 0-87062-111-4). A H Clark.

Menger, Matt. Valley of Mekong. 1970. 4.95 (ISBN 0-685-79412-1); pap. 3.95 (ISBN 0-685-79413-X). Guild Bks.

Menger, Matt J. In the Valley of the Mekong. LC 79-115966. 1970. pap. 3.95 (ISBN 0-686-18632-X). Oblate.

Menges, Matthew C. The Concept of Univocity Regarding the Predication of God & Creature According to William Ockham. (Philosophy Ser). 1952. 8.00 (ISBN 0-686-11539-2). Franciscan Inst.

Mengle, Kathy. Tools for Healing: Working Toward Harmony & Balance. LC 84-72359. (Illus.). 172p. (Orig.). 1985. pap. 9.95 (ISBN 0-87516-548-6). De Vorss.

Menken, John, ed. The Tent of Meeting Texts. (Illus.). 134p. (Orig.). 1985. pap. 8.00 (ISBN 0-9615531-0-3). Tent Meeting.

Menking, Stanley J. Helping Laity Help Others. LC 83-26061. (The Pastor's Handbook Ser.: Vol. 2). 114p. (Orig.). 1984. pap. 7.95 (ISBN 0-664-24615-X). Westminster.

Menninger, Karl. Whatever Became of Sin? 1973. (Hawthorn); pap. 9.50 (ISBN 0-8015-8554-6, 0922-280, Hawthorn). Dutton.

Mennonite Church. Mennonite Confession of Faith. LC 63-22593. 32p. (Orig.). 1963. pap. 0.95 (ISBN 0-8361-1314-4). Herald Pr.

Mennonite Church General Conference, Board of Christian Service Staff. Church, the State & the Offender. 1963. pap. 0.50 (ISBN 0-87303-200-4). Faith & Life.

Mensching, G. Structures & Patterns of Religion. Sharma, V. S. & Klimkeit, H. M., trs. 1976. 21.00 (ISBN 0-8426-0958-X). Orient Bk Dist.

Mensendiek, C. William. A Dream Incarnate. (Illus.). 136p. 1987. text ed. 12.95 (ISBN 0-8298-0715-2). Pilgrim NY.

--Not Without Struggle. (Illus.). 236p. 1986. 16.95 (ISBN 0-8298-0586-9). Pilgrim NY.

Mensendiek, Mark. Grace to You. 20p. (Orig.). 1985. pap. 0.75 (ISBN 0-933643-22-5). Grace World Outreach.

--Soulwinning: A Way of Life. LC 86-80315. 64p. (Orig.). 1986. pap. 3.50 (ISBN 0-933643-28-4). Grace World Outreach.

Mensing, Raymond C. Toleration & Parliament, Sixteen Sixty to Seventeen Nineteen. LC 79-63260. 1979. pap. text ed. 10.75 (ISBN 0-8191-0723-9). U Pr of Amer.

Mention, Leon. Documents Relatifs aux Rapports du Clerge avec la Royaute de 1682 a 1789, 2 vols. in 1. (Fr.). 461p. Repr. of 1893 ed. lib. bdg. 67.50x. Coronet Bks.

Menuhin, Moshe. The Decadence of Judaism in Our Time. 1981. lib. bdg. 59.95 (ISBN 0-686-73181-6). Revisionist Pr.

Menzel, Theophil, tr. see Andrae, Tor.

Menzies, A., ed. see Baur, Ferdinand C.

Menzies, Lucy, jt. ed. see Barkway, Lunsden.

Menzies, William W. Anointed to Serve: The Story of the Assemblies of God. LC 77-146707. (Illus.). 440p. 1971. 12.95 (ISBN 0-88243-465-9, 02-0465). Gospel Pub.

--Philippians: The Joyful Life. LC 81-80302. (Radiant Life Ser.). 128p. (Orig.). 1981. pap. 2.50 (ISBN 0-88243-880-8, 02-0880); tchr's ed. 3.95 (ISBN 0-88243-191-9, 32-0191). Gospel Pub.

--Understanding the Times of Christ. 128p. 1969. 1.50 (ISBN 0-88243-622-8, 02-0622). Gospel Pub.

Mercer, Calvin R. Norman Perrin's Interpretation of the New Testament. Mabee, Charles, ed. (Studies in American Biblical Hermeneutics). 192p. 1986. 19.95 (ISBN 0-86554-219-8, MUP-H197). Mercer Univ Pr.

Mercer, Ethel. A Child of the King. (Illus.). 80p. 1987. 8.95 (ISBN 0-89962-586-X). Todd & Honeywell.

Mercer, Henry C. The Bible in Iron. 3rd ed. (Illus.). 356p. 1961. pap. 15.00 (ISBN 0-910302-01-4). Bucks Co Hist.

Merchant, Joan de & Gallagher, Merchant. A Closer Look at the Sacraments: A Study Guide for Catholic Adults. pap. 6.95 (ISBN 0-937997-00-5). Hi Time Pub.

Merchant, M. V. Qur'anic Laws. 1971. 8.50x (ISBN 0-87902-177-2). Orientalia.

Merchant, Robert. Trust. (Literacy Volunteers of America Readers Ser.). 32p. (Orig.). 1983. pap. 1.95 (ISBN 0-8428-9618-X). Cambridge Bk.

Merchant, William M. Creed & Drama: An Essay in Religious Drama. LC 66-23222. pap. 31.80 (2027867). Bks Demand UMI.

Mercier, Desire. Selected Writings by Cardinal Mercier. (Illus.). 128p. 1984. 57.85 (ISBN 0-89901-136-5). Found Class Reprints.

Mercier, Jacques. Ethiopian Magic Scrolls. Molinaro, Ursule, tr. from Fr. LC 78-9330. (Illus.). 1979. 24.95 (ISBN 0-8076-0896-3); pap. 12.95 (ISBN 0-8076-0897-1). Braziller.

Meredith, Char, jt. auth. see Oraker, James.

Meredith, Don. Becoming One. LC 79-12691. 1979. pap. 5.95 (ISBN 0-8407-5688-7). Nelson.

--Who Says Get Married? How to Be Happy & Single. LC 81-16949. 176p. 1981. pap. 4.95 (ISBN 0-8407-5741-7). Nelson.

Meredith, Howard & Milan, Virginia E. A Cherokee Vision of Eloh' Proctor, Wesley, tr. (Eng. & Cherokee.). 37p. 1981. pap. 8.00x (ISBN 0-940392-04-6); write for info. Indian U Pr OK.

Meredith, Howard & Smith, Adeline. A Cherokee Prayerbook. (Eng. & Cherokee.). 44p. 1981. pap. 1.50x (ISBN 0-940392-02-X). Indian U Pr OK.

Meredith, J. M. Meredith's Second Book of Bible Lists. LC 83-3807. 192p. (Orig.). 1983. pap. 5.95 (ISBN 0-87123-319-3, 210319). Bethany Hse.

Meredith, Joel L. Meredith's Book of Bible Lists. LC 80-14486. 288p. (Orig.). 1980. text ed. 10.95 (ISBN 0-87123-022-4, 230022); pap. 6.95 (ISBN 0-87123-023-2, 210023). Bethany Hse.

Meredith, Maurice. Studies in Proverbs. pap. 2.50 (ISBN 0-89315-261-7). Lambert Bk.

Meredith, Peter & Tailby, John, eds. The Staging of Religious Drama in Europe in the Middle Ages. Sleeman, Margaret & Ferrari, Raffaella, trs. (Early Drama, Art & Music Ser.). (Illus.). 301p. 1983. 24.95x (ISBN 0-918720-23-0). Medieval Inst.

--The Staging of Religious Drama in Europe in the Middle Ages. Sleeman, Margaret & Ferrari, Raffaella, trs. (Early Drama, Art & Music Ser.). (Illus.). 301p. 1983. pap. 14.95x (ISBN 0-918720-24-9). Medieval Inst.

Meredith, Robert, jt. auth. see Smith, E. Brooks.

Meresco, Donald. New Light on the Rapture. LC 80-67028. (Orig.). 1980. pap. 6.95 (ISBN 0-937078-00-X). Bible Light.

Mergal, Angel M., jt. ed. see Williams, George H.

Meritt, Herbert D., ed. Old English Prudentius Glosses at Boulogne-Sur-Mer. LC 58-7843. (Stanford University. Stanford Studies in Language & Literature: No. 16). Repr. of 1959 ed. 24.00 (ISBN 0-404-51826-5). AMS Pr.

Merk, Federick & Merk, Lois B. Manifest Destiny & Mission in American History: A Reinterpretation. LC 82-25146. ix, 265p. 1983. Repr. lib. bdg. 35.00x (ISBN 0-313-23844-8, MERM). Greenwood.

Merk, Lois B., jt. auth. see Merk, Federick.

Merkl, Peter H., ed. Religion & Politics in the Modern World. Smart, Ninian. 296p. 1983. 37.50 (ISBN 0-8147-5389-2); pap. 12.50 (ISBN 0-8147-5393-0). NYU Pr.

Merkle, John C. Abraham Joshua Heschel: Exploring His Life & Thought. 184p. 1985. 17.95x (ISBN 0-02-920970-6). Macmillan.

Merkx, Gilbert, jt. ed. see Elkin, Judith L.

Merleau-Ponty, Jacques & Morando, Bruno. The Rebirth of Cosmology. LC 82-60404. (Illus.). xvi, 302p. 1982. pap. text ed. 9.95x (ISBN 0-8214-0606-X). Ohio U Pr.

Merle d'Aubigne, Jean H. History of the Reformation of the Sixteenth Century, 5 vols. White, H., tr. LC 83-45666. Date not set. Repr. of 1872 ed. Set. 225.00 (ISBN 0-404-19816-3). AMS Pr.

Merle d'Augbine, Jean H. History of the Reformation in Europe in the Time of Calvin, 8 vols. Cates, W. L., tr. LC 83-45624. Date not set. Repr. of 1873 ed. Set. 395.00 (ISBN 0-404-19842-2). AMS Pr.

Merlin, Lester. Courage for a Cross: Six Stories About Growing up Christian in the U. S. S. R. 1987. pap. 3.95. Friend Pr.

Merrell, James L. Finding Faith in the Headlines. Lambert, Herbert, ed. LC 85-481. (Orig.). 1985. pap. 7.95 (ISBN 0-8272-1012-4). CBP.

Merrell, JoAnn. Bible Stories for Family Devotions. (Illus.). 80p. 1982. pap. 4.95 (ISBN 0-87123-196-4, 210196). Bethany Hse.

Merrell, Karen D. Baptism. 24p. pap. 4.95 (ISBN 0-87747-559-8). Deseret Bk.

--Joseph Smith. 24p. 4.95 (ISBN 0-87747-561-X). Deseret Bk.

--Prayer. 23p. 4.95 (ISBN 0-87747-562-8). Deseret Bk.

--Tithing. 22p. pap. 4.95 (ISBN 0-87747-560-1). Deseret Bk.

Merriam, Thornton W., jt. auth. see Knight, Frank H.

Merrick, J. L., tr. see Balquir, Allama Muhammad Al-Majlisi.

Merrick, James, tr. see Al-Majilisi, Muhammad B.

Merrienboer, Edward van see Van Merrienboer, Edward, et al.

Merrifield, Fred, ed. Modern Religious Verse & Prose: An Anthology. LC 79-51964. (Granger Poetry Library). 1980. Repr. of 1925 ed. 32.50x (ISBN 0-89609-186-4). Roth Pub Inc.

Merrifield, William R., ed. see Powlison, Paul S.

Merril, Dean. Teaching for Life-Response. (Complete Teacher Training Meeting Ser.). 48p. 1986. 9.95 (ISBN 0-89191-316-5). Cook.

Merrill, Abbey R. Day Dawns in Fire: America's Quest for Meaning. LC 75-36439. pap. 32.00. Bks Demand UMI.

Merrill, Arthur L. & Overholt, Thomas W., eds. Scripture in History & Theology: Essays in Honor of J. Coert Rylaarsdam. LC 77-12106. (Pittsburgh Theological Monographs: No. 17). 1977. pap. 10.00 (ISBN 0-915138-32-8). Pickwick.

Merrill, Dean. Another Chance: How God Overrides Our Big Mistakes. 160p. (Orig.). 1981. pap. 4.95 (ISBN 0-310-35331-9, 11325P). Zondervan.

--Clergy Couples in Crisis. (Leadership Library). 216p. 1985. 9.95 (ISBN 0-917463-06-4). Chr Today.

Merrill, Dean, ed. Fresh Ideas for Discipleship & Nurture. Shelley, Marshall. (Fresh Ideas Ser.). 190p. 1984. pap. 6.95 (ISBN 0-917463-02-1). Chr Today.

Merrill, Dean & Shelley, Marshall, eds. Fresh Ideas for Preaching, Worship & Evangelism. (Fresh Ideas Ser.). 155p. 1984. pap. 6.95 (ISBN 0-917463-00-5). Chr Today.

Merrill, Eugene. Historical Survey of Old Testament. 1966. pap. 7.95 (ISBN 0-934532-16-8). Presby & Reformed.

Merrill, Eugene H. Historical Survey of the Old Testament. pap. 7.95 (ISBN 0-8010-5884-8). Baker Bk.

Merrill, Mary L., et al. A Light Unto My Path. (Illus.). 185p. 1981. Repr. of 1982 ed. 10.00 (ISBN 0-686-33180-X). Pathway Pubns.

Merrill, R. Dale. The Church Business Meeting. LC 68-28075. 1968. pap. 2.95 (ISBN 0-8170-0409-2). Judson.

Merrill, Selah. Ancient Jerusalem. Davis, Moshe, ed. LC 77-70724. (America & the Holy Land Ser.). (Illus.). 1977. Repr. of 1908 ed. lib. bdg. 40.00x (ISBN 0-405-10267-4). Ayer Co Pubs.

Merrill, Thomas F. Epic God-Talk: Paradise Lost & the Grammar of Religious Language. LC 85-29385. 140p. 1986. lib. bdg. 18.95x (ISBN 0-89950-194-X). McFarland & Co.

--Willian Perkins 1558-1602, English Puritanist--His Pioneer Works on Casuistry: Discourse on Conscience & the Whole Treatise of Cases of Conscience. xx, 242p. 1966. text ed. 28.50x (Pub. by B De Graaf Netherlands). Coronet Bks.

Merrill, Vic. Can You Hear Me God? 96p. 1981. 6.00 (ISBN 0-682-49740-1). Exposition Pr FL.

Merritt, Jeanna. Bread Cast upon the Waters. 25p. (Orig.). 1985. pap. 1.25 (ISBN 0-89265-092-3). Randall Hse.

Merritt, Robert E. & Corey, Arthur. Christian Science & Liberty. LC 70-132847. 1970. 5.50 (ISBN 0-87516-060-3). De Vorss.

Merryweather, F. Somner. Bibliomania in the Middle Ages. rev. ed. Copinger, H. B., ed. LC 72-83748. Repr. of 1933 ed. 22.00 (ISBN 0-405-08787-X, Pub. by Blom). Ayer Co Pubs.

Mersch, E. The Whole Christ. 638p. 1981. 39.00x (ISBN 0-234-77051-1, Pub. by Dobson Bks England). State Mutual Bk.

Merton, Robert K., ed. see Birnbaum, Norman.

Merton, Robert K., ed. see Fleck, Ludwig.

Merton, Robert K., ed. see Goode, Erich.

Merton, Robert K., ed. see Hammond, Phillip E.

Merton, Robert K., ed. see Yinger, Milton J.

Merton, Thomas. The Asian Journal of Thomas Merton. Stone, Naomi B., et al, eds. LC 71-103370. (Illus.). 448p. 1973. pap. 8.95 (ISBN 0-8112-0570-3, NDP394). New Directions.

--Bread in the Wilderness. LC 82-23864. 180p. 1986. pap. 5.95 (ISBN 0-8006-1912-9, 1-1912). Fortress.

--The Climate of Monastic Prayer. (Cistercian Studies: No. 1). 154p. 1973. Repr. of 1969 ed. 7.95 (ISBN 0-87907-801-4). Cistercian Pubns.

--Contemplation in a World of Action. 400p. 1973. pap. 5.50 (ISBN 0-385-02550-5, Im). Doubleday.

--Contemplative Prayer. 1971. pap. 3.50 (ISBN 0-385-09219-9, Im). Doubleday.

--Disputed Questions. 297p. 1960. 12.50 (ISBN 0-374-14061-8). FS&G.

--Faith & Violence: Christian Teaching & Christian Practice. 1968. pap. 6.95 (ISBN 0-268-00094-8). U of Notre Dame Pr.

--The Hidden Ground of Love: Letter on Religious Experience & Social Concerns. Shannon, William H., ed. 1986. pap. 14.95 (ISBN 0-374-51963-3). FS&G.

--The Hidden Ground of Love: Letters on Religious Experience & Social Concern. Shannon, William H., ed. LC 84-26045. 684p. 1985. 27.95 (ISBN 0-374-16995-0). FS&G.

--Last of the Fathers: Saint Bernard of Clairvaux & the Encyclical Letter, Doctor Mellifluus. Repr. of 1954 ed. lib. bdg. 22.50x (ISBN 0-8371-4434-5, MELF). Greenwood.

--The Last of the Fathers: Saint Bernard of Clairvaux & the Encyclical Letter, Doctor Mellifluus. LC 81-4105. 128p. 1981. pap. 4.95 (ISBN 0-15-649438-8, Harv). HarBraceJ.

--Life & Holiness. 1964. pap. 2.95 (ISBN 0-385-06277-X, D183, Im). Doubleday.

--The Living Bread. 157p. 1956. 12.95 (ISBN 0-374-14613-6); pap. 7.95 (ISBN 0-374-51520-4). FS&G.

--The Monastic Journey. Hart, Patrick, ed. LC 77-27714. 1978. pap. 4.50 (ISBN 0-385-14094-0, Im). Doubleday.

--Mystics & Zen Masters. 303p. 1986. pap. 8.95 (ISBN 0-374-52001-1). FS&G.

--The New Man. 256p. 1962. pap. 6.95 (ISBN 0-374-51444-5). FS&G.

--The New Man. 1983. 13.50 (ISBN 0-8446-5987-8). Peter Smith.

--New Seeds of Contemplation. rev. ed. LC 61-17869. 1972. pap. 5.50 (ISBN 0-8112-0099-X, NDP337). New Directions.

--No Man Is an Island. LC 78-7108. 264p. 1978. pap. 5.95 (ISBN 0-15-665962-X, Harv). HarBraceJ.

--No Man Is an Island. 264p. 1983. Repr. of 1955 ed. lib. bdg. 21.00 (ISBN 0-88254-872-7, Octagon). Hippocrene Bks.

--Opening the Bible. LC 85-24722. 96p. 1986. pap. 4.95 (ISBN 0-8006-1910-2). Fortress.

--Seasons of Celebration. 1983. 13.50 (ISBN 0-8446-5990-8). Peter Smith.

--The Secular Journal. 1983. 16.00 (ISBN 0-8446-5985-1). Peter Smith.

--Seeds of Contemplation. LC 78-10255. 1979. Repr. of 1949 ed. lib. bdg. 27.50x (ISBN 0-313-20756-9, MESC). Greenwood.

--Seeds of Destruction. 1983. 14.00 (ISBN 0-8446-5988-6). Peter Smith.

--The Seven Storey Mountain. LC 78-7109. 429p. 1978. pap. 7.95 (ISBN 0-15-680679-7, Harv). HarBraceJ.

--The Seven Storey Mountain. 1978. Repr. lib. bdg. 32.00x (ISBN 0-88254-843-3, Octagon). Hippocrene Bks.

--The Seven Storey Mountain. LC 85-6375. 784p. 1985. pap. 19.95 (ISBN 0-8027-2497-3). Walker & Co.

--The Sign of Jonas. LC 79-10283. 362p. 1979. pap. 6.95 (ISBN 0-15-682529-5, Harv). HarBraceJ.

--The Sign of Jonas. 362p. 1983. Repr. of 1953 ed. lib. bdg. 30.00 (ISBN 0-88254-871-9, Octagon). Hippocrene Bks.

--The Silent Life. 178p. 1975. pap. 6.95 (ISBN 0-374-51281-7). FS&G.

--The Silent Life. 1983. 12.75 (ISBN 0-8446-5986-X). Peter Smith.

--Thoughts in Solitude. 124p. 1976. pap. 4.25 (ISBN 0-374-51325-2). FS&G.

--Thoughts in Solitude. 1983. 14.50 (ISBN 0-8446-5989-4). Peter Smith.

--The Waters of Siloe. LC 79-10372. 377p. 1979. pap. 6.95 (ISBN 0-15-694954-7, Harv). HarBraceJ.

--Way of Chuang Tzu. LC 65-27556. (Illus.). 1969. pap. 4.95 (ISBN 0-8112-0103-1, NDP276). New Directions.

--What Is Contemplation? 80p. 1981. pap. 4.95 (ISBN 0-87243-103-7). Templegate.

--Wisdom of the Desert. LC 59-15021. 1970. 6.50 (ISBN 0-8112-0313-1); pap. 3.95 (ISBN 0-8112-0102-3, NDP295). New Directions.

--Zen & the Birds of Appetite. LC 68-25546. 1968. 6.50 (ISBN 0-8112-0314-X); pap. 4.95 (ISBN 0-8112-0104-X, NDP261). New Directions.

Merwick, Donna. Boston Priests, Eighteen Forty-Eight to Nineteen Ten: A Study in Social & Intellectual Change. LC 72-79309. 288p. 1973. 17.50x (ISBN 0-674-07975-2). Harvard U Pr.

Mescall, Sr. Eloise T., tr. see Massabki, Charles.

Meschler, Maurice. Life of St. Aloysius Gonzaga: Patron of Christian Youth. LC 84-52294. 344p. 1985. pap. 7.00 (ISBN 0-89555-275-2). Tan Bks Pubs.

Meschter, W. Kyrel. Twentieth-Century Schwenkfelders: A Narrative History. 1984. pap. write for info (ISBN 0-935980-03-2). Schwenkfelder Lib.

Meserve, Harry C. The Practical Meditator. LC 80-15631. 137p. 1981. 19.95 (ISBN 0-87705-506-8); professional 16.95. Human Sci Pr.

Meshack, B. A. Is the Baptist Church Relevant to the Black Community. LC 75-38304. 1976. perfect bdg. softcover 9.95 (ISBN 0-88247-385-9). R & E Pubs.

Meshorer, Ya'akov. Coins of the Ancient World. Currier, Richard L., ed. LC 72-10795. (The Lerner Archaeology Ser.: Digging up the Past). (Illus.). 96p. 1975. PLB 8.95 (ISBN 0-8225-0835-4). Lerner Pubns.

Mesle, C. Robert. Fire in My Bones: Reflection on Faith. 1984. pap. 14.00 (ISBN 0-8309-0387-9). Herald Hse.

Meslier, Jean. Superstition in All Ages. Knoop, Anna, tr. from Fr. LC 77-161337. (Atheist Viewpoint Ser). (Illus.). 346p. 1972. Repr. of 1890 ed. 23.50 (ISBN 0-405-03795-3). Ayer Co Pubs.

--Superstition in All Ages. Knopp, Anna, tr. 346p. 1974. pap. 13.95 (ISBN 0-88697-008-3). Life Science.

Meslier, Jean, jt. auth. see D'Holbach, Paul H.

Messbarger, Paul R. Fiction with a Parochial Purpose: Social Uses of American Catholic Literarture, 1884-1900. 1971. 11.95 (ISBN 0-87270-017-8). U of Notre Dame Pr.

Messenger, E. C., tr. see Guiraud, Jean.

Messenger, Ruth E. Ethical Teachings in the Latin Hymns of Medieval England. LC 30-20975. (Columbia University. Studies in the Social Sciences: No. 321). Repr. of 1930 ed. 18.50 (ISBN 0-404-51321-2). AMS Pr.

Messer, Dollas. Operation Discipleship, Level II. 1986. wkbk 12.95 (ISBN 0-317-40165-3). Pathway Pr.

--Operation Discipleship: Being in Christ. 138p. 1984. pap. text ed. 5.95 student manual (ISBN 0-87148-659-8). Pathway Pr.

--Operation Discipleship: Being in Christ. 70p. (Orig.). 1984. pap. text ed. 5.95 tchr's guide (ISBN 0-87148-660-1). Pathway Pr.

Messer, Donald E. Christian Ethics & Political Action. 176p. 1984. 8.95 (ISBN 0-8170-1018-1). Judson.

Messerli, Carlos R., jt. auth. see Pfatteicher, Philip H.

Messick, William L., jt. auth. see Chaney, Earlyne.

Messing, Simon D. The Story of the Falashas: "Black Jews" of Ethiopia. (Illus.). 134p. 1982. pap. 7.50 (ISBN 0-9615946-9-1). Messing Pub.

Messiter, Arthur. History of the Choir & Music of Trinity Church. LC 72-137317. Repr. of 1906 ed. 21.45 (ISBN 0-404-04313-5). AMS Pr.

Messori, Vittorio. Faith's Answer: The Mystery of Jesus. Brown, Eugene, ed. Whitehead, Kenneth, tr. from Ital. LC 86-13509. Tr. of Ipotesi su Jesu. 312p. (Orig.). 1986. lib. bdg. 16.95 (ISBN 0-89944-083-5); pap. 12.95 (ISBN 0-89944-084-3). Don Bosco Multimedia.

Messori, Vittorio, jt. auth. see Ratzinger, Joseph.

Mestinsek, Erma & Mestinsek, Minnie G. Discoveries of the Hidden Things of God. 64p. 1980. 12.50 (ISBN 0-682-49635-9). Exposition Pr FL.

Mestinsek, Minnie G., jt. auth. see Mestinsek, Erma.

Mestwerdt, Paul. Die Anfaenge Des Erasmus: Humanismus und Devotio Moderna. 34.00 (ISBN 0-384-38351-3); pap. 28.00 (ISBN 0-384-38350-5). Johnson Repr.

Metaxa, George, tr. see Steiner, Rudolf.

Metcalf, Barbara D. Islamic Revival in British India: Deoband, 1860-1900. LC 81-47934. (Illus.). 400p. 1982. 31.50 (ISBN 0-691-05343-X). Princeton U Pr.

Metcalf, Barbara D., ed. Moral Conduct & Authority: The Place of Adab in Sout h Asian Islam. LC 83-1361. 350p. 1984. text ed. 40.00x (ISBN 0-520-04660-9). U of Cal Pr.

Metcalf, Frank J. American Psalmody. 2nd ed. LC 68-13274. (Music Reprint Ser.). (Illus.). 1968. Repr. of 1917 ed. lib. bdg. 19.50 (ISBN 0-306-71132-X). Da Capo.

Metcalf, P., jt. auth. see Huntington, R.

Metcalf, Peter. A Borneo Journey into Death: Berawan Eschatology from Its Rituals. LC 82-8460. (Symbol & Culture Ser.). (Illus.). 304p. 1982. 26.00x (ISBN 0-8122-7849-6). U of Pa Pr.

Metcalf, Priscilla, jt. auth. see Pevsner, Nikolaus.

Metcalf, Robert, jt. auth. see Rose, Tom.

Metcalfe, Edna, compiled by. The Trees of Christmas. LC 79-12288. (Illus.). 1979. pap. 8.75 (ISBN 0-687-42591-3). Abingdon.

Metcalfe, J. C. Angry Prophet. 1970. pap. 2.25 (ISBN 0-87508-909-7). Chr Lit.

--Bible & Counselling. 1966. pap. 2.95 (ISBN 0-87508-911-9). Chr Lit.

--Bible & the Call of God. 1970. pap. 1.95 (ISBN 0-87508-910-0). Chr Lit.

--Bible & the Human Mind. pap. 2.95 (ISBN 0-87508-913-5). Chr Lit.

--Bible & the Spirit Filled Life. 1970. pap. 3.25 (ISBN 0-87508-912-7). Chr Lit.

--God the Spirit. 1972. pap. 1.50 (ISBN 0-87508-917-8). Chr Lit.

--Great Deliverance. 1970. pap. 2.25 (ISBN 0-87508-916-X). Chr Lit.

--Great Enemy. 1970. pap. 2.95 (ISBN 0-87508-914-3). Chr Lit.

--Jesus Christ Our Lord. 1970. pap. 2.25 (ISBN 0-87508-919-4). Chr Lit.

--Spirit of Calvary. 1970. pap. 3.25 (ISBN 0-87508-921-6). Chr Lit.

--There Must Be Heresies. 1963. pap. 2.25 (ISBN 0-87508-922-4). Chr Lit.

--To Be a Christian. 1966. pap. 2.25 (ISBN 0-87508-923-2). Chr Lit.

Metcalfe, W. M., ed. Legends of the Saints, in the Scottish Dialect of the Fourteenth Century, 3 Vols. 1896. Set. 140.00 (ISBN 0-384-32090-2). Johnson Repr.

Metford, J. C. A Dictionary of Christian Lore & Legend. LC 82-50815. (Illus.). 272p. 1983. 24.95f (ISBN 0-500-11020-4). Thames Hudson.

Metheny, Burton R. How to Develop the Power of Transcendental Experience. (Illus.). 139p. 1980. 59.45 (ISBN 0-89920-014-1). Am Inst Psych.

Methorst-Kuiper, A. J. Krishnamurti: A Biography. 1974. lib. bdg. 79.95 (ISBN 0-87968-545-X). Krishna Pr.

Meton, J. Gordon, ed. see Bjorling, Joel.

Metraux, Alfred. Myths of the Toba & Pilaga Indians of the Gran Chaco. LC 46-4565. (Amer. Folklore Society Memoirs Ser.). Repr. of 1946 ed. 15.00 (ISBN 0-527-01092-8). Kraus Repr.

--Voodoo in Haiti. LC 77-185327. (Illus.). 1972. pap. 8.95 (ISBN 0-8052-0341-9). Schocken.

Metraux, Rhoda, jt. auth. see Mead, Margaret.

Metropolitan Emilianos Timiadis. The Nicene Creed: Our Common Faith. LC 82-71826. 128p. (Orig.). 1983. pap. 7.95 (ISBN 0-8006-1653-7, 1-1653). Fortress.

Metropolitan Innocent of Moscow Staff. Ukazanije Puti v Tsarstvije Nebsnoje. Tr. of Indication of the Way Kingdom of Heaven. 59p. pap. 2.00 (ISBN 0-317-28978-0). Holy Trinity.

Metropolitan Panteleimon. Pravoslavije i Inoslavnija Khristijanskija Ispovjedanija. Tr. of Orthodoxy & Other Christian Faiths. 1950. pap. 0.55 (ISBN 0-317-30259-0). Holy Trinity.

Metropolitan Philaret Of Moscow. Catechism of the Orthodox Church. 1901. pap. 2.95 (ISBN 0-686-00252-0). Eastern Orthodox.

--Comparison of the Differences in the Doctrines of Faith Between the Eastern & Western Churches. Pinkerton, Robert, tr. from Rus. 1974. pap. 1.25 (ISBN 0-686-10206-1). Eastern Orthodox.

Metropolitan Philip Saliba & Allen, Joseph J. Out of the Depths Have I Cried: Thoughts on Incarnational Theology in the Eastern Christian Experience. LC 79-18611. (Illus., Orig.). 1979. pap. 4.95 (ISBN 0-916586-32-4). Holy Cross Orthodox.

Metropolitan Stefan Yavorsky. Dogmat o Svjatejshej Evkharistii. Tr. of The Dogma of the Holy Eucharist. 32p. pap. 1.00 (ISBN 0-317-28973-X). Holy Trinity.

Metropolitan Anthony Khrapovitsky. The Christian Faith & War. (Orig.). 1973. pap. 0.50 (ISBN 0-317-30278-7). Holy Trinity.

Metropolitan Innocent of Moscow. Indication of the Way Into the Kingdom of Heaven. 48p. (Orig.). 1981. pap. 2.00 (ISBN 0-317-30275-2). Holy Trinity.

Metropolitan Philaret Drozdov. Prostrannij Khristijanskij Katekhisis. Tr. of The Complete Christian Catechism. 170p. pap. text ed. 6.00 (ISBN 0-317-29305-2). Holy Trinity.

Metropulous, Lyman. The Illustrated Book of the Great Ancient Temples. (The Masterpieces of World Architecture Library). (Illus.). 141p. 1983. 112.50 (ISBN 0-86650-042-1). Gloucester Art.

Mette, Norbert, jt. ed. see Exeler, Adolf.

Mette, Norbert, jt. ed. see Greinacher, Norbert.

Metten, Patricia. The Power of Creativity. LC 81-50863. (Power Tales Ser.). pap. write for info. (ISBN 0-911712-89-5). Promised Land.

Metter, Bert. Bar Mitzvah, Bat Mitzvah: How Jewish Boys & Girls Come of Age. LC 83-23230. (Illus.). 64p. (Orig.). 1984. PLB 10.95 (ISBN 0-89919-149-5, Clarion); pap. 4.95 (ISBN 0-89919-292-0). HM.

Metts, Walley. Faith Brokers: Professional Christians & Their Un-Godly Gains. 1986. pap. 5.95 (ISBN 0-937931-00-4). Global TN.

Metts, Wallis C. Your Faith on Trial. 180p. (Orig.). 1979. pap. 3.95 (ISBN 0-89084-112-8). Bob Jones Univ Pr.

Metz, Donald. Studies in Biblical Holiness. 284p. 1971. 10.95 (ISBN 0-8341-0117-3). Beacon Hill.

Metz, Johann B. Emergent Church. 160p. 1986. pap. 9.95 (ISBN 0-8245-0729-0). Crossroad NY.

--The Emergent Church: The Future of Christianity in a Post-Bourgeois World. 160p. 1981. 10.95 (ISBN 0-8245-0036-9). Crossroad NY.

--Faith in History & Society: Toward a Practical Fundamental Theology. 1979. 12.95 (ISBN 0-8245-0305-8). Crossroad NY.

Metz, Johann B., jt. auth. see Rahner, Karl.

Metz, Johann B., jt. ed. see Schillebeeckx, Edward.

Metz, Johannes B. Faith & the World of Politics. LC 68-31786. (Concilium Ser.: Vol. 36). 191p. 7.95 (ISBN 0-8091-0046-0). Paulist Pr.

--Poverty of Spirit. LC 68-31045. 56p. 1968. 2.95 (ISBN 0-8091-1924-2). Paulist Pr.

--Theology of the World. 1969. pap. 3.95 (ISBN 0-8245-0396-1). Crossroad NY.

Metz, Johannes B. & Moltmann, Jurgen. Meditations on the Passion. LC 78-70823. 48p. 1979. pap. 2.50 (ISBN 0-8091-2184-0). Paulist Pr.

Metz, Johannes B., jt. auth. see Schillebeeckx, Edward.

Metz, Johannes B., ed. Evolving World & Theology. LC 67-25695. (Concilium Ser.: Vol. 26). 91p. 1967. 7.95 (ISBN 0-8091-0042-8). Paulist Pr.

--Is God Dead? LC 66-25679. (Concilium Ser.: Vol. 16). 189p. 7.95 (ISBN 0-8091-0078-9). Paulist Pr.

Metz, Johannes-Baptist & Schillebeeckx, Edward, eds. The Teaching Authority of the Believers. (Concilium Ser.). 128p. 1985. pap. 6.95 (Pub. by T & T Clark Ltd UK). Fortress.

Metz, Johannes-Baptist, jt. ed. see Schillebeeckx, Edward.

Metz, Kenneth & Trokan, John. Pre-Marital Assessment Skills Training Program Leader Guide. 144p. 1986. pap. 12.95 (ISBN 0-8091-2809-8). Paulist Pr.

--Pre-Marital Assessment Skills Training Program: Team Couple Workbook. 96p. 1986. pap. 9.95 (ISBN 0-8091-2810-1). Paulist Pr.

Metz, Rene & Schlick, Jean, eds. Informal Groups in the Church: Papers of the Second Cerdic Colloquium, Strasbourg, May 13-15, 1971. O'Connell, Matthew J., tr. LC 75-25591. (Pittsburgh Theological Monographs: No. 7). 1975. pap. 5.25 (ISBN 0-915138-08-5). Pickwick.

Metz, Rene, ed. see Cerdic Colloquium Staff.

Metz, Warren. Change of Face & Pace. LC 82-90982. 1983. 8.95 (ISBN 0-87212-165-8). Libra.

Metzger, Bruce. The Early Versions of the New Testament. 1977. 24.95x (ISBN 0-19-826170-5). Oxford U Pr.

Metzger, Bruce M. Lexical Aids for Students of New Testament Greek. 3rd ed. LC 70-73197. 1969. pap. 4.95x (ISBN 0-8401-1618-7). A R Allenson.

--Manuscripts of the Greek Bible: An Introduction to Paleography. (Illus.). 1981. 19.95x (ISBN 0-19-502924-0). Oxford U Pr.

--The New Testament: Its Background, Growth & Content. enl. ed. 310p. 1965. 16.50 (ISBN 0-687-27914-3). Abingdon.

--Text of the New Testament: Its Transmission, Corruption, & Restoration. 2nd ed. 1968. 13.95x (ISBN 0-19-500391-8). Oxford U Pr.

Metzger, Bruce M., ed. Oxford Annotated Apocrypha: Revised Standard Version. 1977. text ed. write for info. Oxford U Pr.

Metzger, Bruce M., compiled by. Oxford Concise Concordance to the Revised Standard of the Holy Bible. 1962. 7.95 (ISBN 0-19-528388-0). Oxford U Pr.

Metzger, Bruce M., ed. A Textual Commentary on the Greek New Testament. 776p. 1975. 5.45x (ISBN 3-438-06010-8, 08515, Pub. by United Bible). Am Bible.

Metzger, Charles R. The Silent River: A Pastoral Elegy in the Form of a Recollection of Arctic Adventure. (Illus.). xi, 161p. (Orig.). 1984. pap. 7.95x (ISBN 0-9613094-0-7). Omega LA.

Metzger, Walter P., ed. see McLaughlin, Mary M.

Metzger, Will. Tell the Truth. 2nd ed. LC 83-25304. 187p. (Orig.). 1981. pap. 6.95 (ISBN 0-87784-934-X). Inter Varsity.

Metzler, James F. From Saigon to Shalom. LC 84-9313. (Mennonite Missionary Study Ser.: No. 11). 144p. (Orig.). 1985. pap. 7.95 (ISBN 0-8361-3379-X). Herald Pr.

Metzner, Ralph, jt. auth. see Leary, Timothy.

Meuser, Fred W. Luther the Preacher. LC 83-72107. 80p. 1983. pap. 5.95 (ISBN 0-8066-2051-X, 10-4147). Augsburg.

Meuss, A. R., tr. see Eggstein, Kurt.

Meuss, Anna R., tr. see Steiner, Rudolf.

Mew, James. Traditional Aspects of Hell. LC 73-140321. 1971. Repr. of 1903 ed. 48.00x (ISBN 0-8103-3693-6). Gale.

Mews, Stuart, ed. Religion & National Identity. (Studies in Church History: Vol. 18). 500p. 1982. 45.00x (ISBN 0-631-18060-5). Basil Blackwell.

Meyendorf, John, jt. auth. see McGinn, Bernard.

Meyendorff, et al. The Primacy of Peter. 134p. 1963. 7.95 (ISBN 0-913836-20-6). St Vladimirs.

Meyendorff, Elizabeth, tr. see Ouspensky, Leonid.

Meyendorff, John. The Byzantine Legacy in the Orthodox Church. LC 82-797. 268p. (Orig.). 1982. pap. 8.95 (ISBN 0-913836-90-7). St Vladimirs.

--Byzantine Theology: Historical Trends & Doctrinal Themes. 2nd, rev. ed. LC 72-94167. viii, 243p. 1983. pap. 9.00 (ISBN 0-8232-0967-9). Fordham.

--Christ in Eastern Christian Thought. LC 75-31977. Orig. Title: Le Christ Dans la Theologie Byzantine. 248p. 1975. pap. 10.95 (ISBN 0-913836-27-3). St Vladimirs.

--Gregory Palamas, The Triads. (The Classics of Western Spirituality Ser.). 192p. 12.95 (ISBN 0-8091-0328-1); pap. 7.95 (ISBN 0-8091-2447-5). Paulist Pr.

--Living Tradition. LC 78-2031. 202p. 1978. pap. 7.95 (ISBN 0-913836-48-6). St Vladimirs.

--Marriage: An Orthodox Perspective. LC 75-14241. 144p. 1975. pap. 5.95 (ISBN 0-913836-05-2). St Vladimirs.

--The Orthodox Church: Its Past & Its Role in the World Today. LC 81-4978. 258p. 1981. pap. 8.95 (ISBN 0-913836-81-8). St Vladimirs.

--St. Gregory Palamas & Orthodox Spirituality. (Illus.). 184p. pap. 7.95 (ISBN 0-913836-11-7). St Vladimirs.

--A Study of Gregory Palamas. LC 65-56528. 245p. 1964. 12.95 (ISBN 0-913836-14-1). St Vladimirs.

--Vvedenie v Sviatootecheskoe Bogoslovia. rev. ed. Volokhonsky, Larisa, tr. from Eng. LC 85-61006. (Rus.). 359p. 1985. pap. 16.00 (ISBN 0-934927-00-6). RBR.

Meyendorff, Paul, tr. see St. Germanus of Constantinople.

Meyer, B. E., tr. see Hoffding, Harald.

Meyer, Ben F. & Sanders, E. P., eds. Jewish & Christian Self-Definition, Vol. 3: Self-Definition in the Greco-Roman World. LC 79-7390. 320p. 1983. 24.95 (ISBN 0-8006-0690-6, 1-690). Fortress.

Meyer, Carl S., ed. Moving Frontiers. 524p. 1986. pap. 12.95 (ISBN 0-570-04461-8). Concordia.

Meyer, Carolyn. Christmas Crafts. LC 74-2608. (Illus.). 160p. 1974. 11.70i (ISBN 0-06-024197-7). HarpJ.

Meyer, Donald. The Positive Thinkers: Religion As Pop Psychology from Mary Baker Eddy to Oral Roberts. 1980. 15.95 (ISBN 0-394-51029-1); pap. 5.95 (ISBN 0-394-73899-3). Pantheon.

Meyer, Donald H. The Instructed Conscience: The Shaping of the American National Ethic. LC 76-175512. (Illus.). 1972. 18.95x (ISBN 0-8122-7651-5); pap. 9.95x (ISBN 0-8122-1066-2). U of Pa Pr.

Meyer, F. B. Abraham. 1968. pap. 4.50 (ISBN 0-87508-340-4). Chr Lit.

--The Best of F. B. Meyer. 176p. 1984. pap. 5.95 (ISBN 0-8010-6179-2). Baker Bk.

--The Blessed Life. 1979. pap. 0.95 (ISBN 0-87509-052-4). Chr Pubns.

--Choice Notes on Joshua to Second Kings. LC 84-27869. (F. B. Meyer Memorial Library). 224p. 1985. pap. text ed. 8.95 (ISBN 0-8254-3241-3). Kregel.

--Choice Notes on the Psalms. LC 84-17109. (F. B. Meyer Memorial Library). 192p. 1984. pap. text ed. 7.95 (ISBN 0-8254-3242-1). Kregel.

--Christ in Isaiah. 1970. pap. 3.95 (ISBN 0-87508-341-2). Chr Lit.

--David. 1970. pap. 4.50 (ISBN 0-87508-342-0). Chr Lit.

--Devotional Commentary on Exodus. LC 78-9530. 476p. 1978. pap. 12.95 (ISBN 0-8254-3244-8). Kregel.

--Devotional Commentary on Philippians. LC 78-59146. 1978. pap. 7.95 (ISBN 0-8254-3227-8). Kregel.

--Elijah. 1972. pap. 4.50 (ISBN 0-87508-343-9). Chr Lit.

--Ephesians. 1968. pap. 4.50 (ISBN 0-87508-344-7). Chr Lit.

--Zacaras-el Profeta Esperanza: Zacarias-El Probeta de Esperanza. Orig. Title: The Prophet of Hope - Zechariah. (Span.). 1986. write for info. (ISBN 0-8297-0895-2). Life Pubs Intl.

--F. B. Meyer Bible Commentary. 1979. cloth 15.95 (ISBN 0-8423-4250-8). Tyndale.

--The Gift of Suffering. LC 79-93432. (Shepherd Illustrated Classics Ser.). (Illus.). 208p. (Orig.). 1980. pap. 5.95 (ISBN 0-87983-211-8). Keats.

--Gospel of John. 1970. pap. 6.95 (ISBN 0-87508-346-3). Chr Lit.

--Great Men of the Bible, 2 vols. 1986. Set. pap. 20.90 (ISBN 0-310-44288-5, 12362P). Zondervan.

--Great Thoughts from the Upper Room. 160p. 1983. pap. 5.95 (ISBN 0-310-44601-5, 12364P, Clarion Class). Zondervan.

--Great Verses of the Bible. 1984. gift ed. 6.95 (ISBN 0-915720-82-5). Brownlow Pub Co.

--Great Verses Through the Bible. 144p. 1982. pap. 13.95 (ISBN 0-310-29131-3, 10212P). Zondervan.

--Inherit the Kingdom. 168p. 1985. pap. 5.95 (ISBN 0-89693-396-2). Victor Bks.

--Israel. 1972. pap. 4.50 (ISBN 0-87508-347-1). Chr Lit.

--Jeremiah. 1972. pap. 4.50 (ISBN 0-87508-355-2). Chr Lit.

--John the Baptist. 1975. pap. 4.50 (ISBN 0-87508-345-5). Chr Lit.

--Joseph. 1975. pap. 4.50 (ISBN 0-87508-356-0). Chr Lit.

--Joshua. 1977. pap. 4.50 (ISBN 0-87508-357-9). Chr Lit.

--Moses. 1972. pap. 4.50 (ISBN 0-87508-354-4). Chr Lit.

--New Testament Men of Faith. LC 79-66338. 1979. pap. 4.95 (ISBN 0-89107-171-7). Good News.

--Old Testament Men of Faith. 1979. pap. 5.95 (ISBN 0-89107-170-9). Good News.

--Paul. 1968. pap. 4.50 (ISBN 0-87508-348-X). Chr Lit.

--Peter. 1968. pap. 4.50 (ISBN 0-87508-349-8). Chr Lit.

--O Profeta da Esperanca. Orig. Title: The Prophet of Hope. (Port.). 1986. write for info. (ISBN 0-8297-1607-6). Life Pubs Intl.

--Prophet of Hope. 157p. 1983. pap. 3.95 (ISBN 0-317-43398-9). Chr Lit.

--Samuel. 1978. pap. 4.50 (ISBN 0-87508-339-0). Chr Lit.

--Saved & Kept. 1970. pap. 4.50 (ISBN 0-87508-350-1). Chr Lit.

--The Secret of Guidance. LC 77-93177. 96p. 1978. pap. 2.95 (ISBN 0-87123-501-3, 200501). Bethany Hse.

--The Secret of Guidance. Taniguchi, Ruth, tr. from Eng. (Chinese.). 1984. pap. write for info. (ISBN 0-941598-07-1). Living Spring Pubns.

--Shepherd Psalm. 1972. pap. 2.95 (ISBN 0-87508-351-X). Chr Lit.

--Some Secrets of Christian Living. Allison, Joseph D., ed. 144p. (Orig.). 1985. pap. 4.95 (ISBN 0-310-38721-3, 17076P). Zondervan.

--Way into the Holiest. 1968. pap. 4.50 (ISBN 0-87508-353-6). Chr Lit.

Meyer, F. B. & Cumbers, Frank. Great Men of the Bible, Vol. 1. 384p. (Orig.). 1981. pap. 10.95 (ISBN 0-310-44271-0, 12360P). Zondervan.

--Great Men of the Bible, Vol. 2. 320p. 1982. pap. 10.95 (ISBN 0-310-44281-8, 12361P). Zondervan.

Meyer, F. B., et al. Funeral Sermons & Outlines. (Pulpit Library). 1984. pap. 3.50 (ISBN 0-8010-5873-2). Baker Bk.

Meyer, Frederick A. Life Is a Trust. (Religious Ser.). 95p. 1986. 8.95 (ISBN 0-935087-09-5). Wright Pub Co.

Meyer, Frederick B. The Shepherd Psalm. (Large Print Christian Classics Ser.). (Illus.). 1984. large print 9.95 (ISBN 0-87983-361-0). Keats.

Meyer, Harding, jt. ed. see Manns, Peter.

Meyer, Heinrich A. New Testament Commentary, 11 vols. 7050p. 250.00 (ISBN 0-913573-04-3). Hendrickson MA.

Meyer, Isidore S., ed. American Jew in the Civil War. Repr. of 1962 ed. 11.00 (ISBN 0-527-03218-2). Kraus Repr.

Meyer, James. Social Ideals of St. Francis. 2.75 (ISBN 0-8199-0296-9, L38825). Franciscan Herald.

--Words of St. Francis. Rev. ed. 1982. 6.00 (ISBN 0-8199-0833-9). Franciscan Herald.

Meyer, John C. Christian Beliefs & Teachings. LC 81-40353. 116p. (Orig.). 1981. lib. bdg. 23.50 (ISBN 0-8191-1757-9); pap. text ed. 9.50 (ISBN 0-8191-1758-7). U Pr of Amer.

Meyer, John P. Ministers of Christ. 1963. 6.95 (ISBN 0-8100-0042-3, 15N0328). Northwest Pub.

Meyer, John S. Outlines for Christmas Sermons. (Sermon Outline Ser.). 48p. 1980. pap. 2.95 (ISBN 0-8010-6107-5). Baker Bk.

Meyer, Kathleen A. God Sends the Seasons. LC 81-80712. (Illus.). 32p. 1981. 7.50 (ISBN 0-87973-668-2, 668). Our Sunday Visitor.

Meyer, Lawrence. Israel Now: Portrait of a Troubled Land. 1982. 16.95 (ISBN 0-385-28475-6). Delacorte.

Meyer, Lester. The Message of Exodus. LC 83-70519. 176p. (Orig.). 1983. pap. 8.95 (ISBN 0-8066-2025-0, 10-4347). Augsburg.

Meyer, Levin. Classic Hassidic Tales. 300p. 1985. 16.95 (ISBN 0-88029-035-8, Pub. by Dorset Pr). Hippocrene Bks.

Meyer, Marvin, ed. The Ancient Mysteries: A Sourcebook. LC 86-45022. (Illus.). 256p. (Orig.). 1986. 24.95 (ISBN 0-06-065577-1, HarpR); pap. 14.95 (ISBN 0-06-065576-3). Har-Row.

Meyer, Marvin W. The Letter of Peter to Philip. Kee, Howard C., ed. LC 80-28612. (Society of Biblical Literature Dissertation Ser.). 1981. pap. text ed. 13.50 (ISBN 0-89130-463-0, 06-01-53). Scholars Pr GA.

--Who Do People Say I Am? The Interpretation of Jesus in the New Testament Gospels. LC 82-24229. pap. 23.80 (ISBN 0-317-30155-1, 2025337). Bks Demand UMI.

Meyer, Marvin W., tr. The Secret Teachings of Jesus: Four Gnostic Gospels. LC 84-42528. 224p. 1984. 15.45 (ISBN 0-394-52959-6). Random.

Meyer, Michael A. The Origins of the Modern Jew: Jewish Identity & European Culture in Germany, 1749-1824. LC 67-12384. (Waynebooks Ser: No. 32). 250p. 1972. o. p. 9.95x (ISBN 0-8143-1315-9); pap. 7.95x (ISBN 0-8143-1470-8). Wayne St U Pr.

Meyer, Michael A., ed. Ideas of Jewish History. LC 73-19960. (Library of Jewish Studies). 384p. 1974. 15.95x (ISBN 0-87441-202-1). Behrman.

Meyer, Michael R. Handbook for the Humanistic Astrologer. LC 73-83657. 456p. 1974. pap. 8.95 (ISBN 0-385-05729-6, Anch). Doubleday.

Meyer, Nathan M. From Now to Eternity: Sermons from Revelation. pap. 6.00 (ISBN 0-88469-035-0). BMH Bks.

--The Land of Miracles. (Illus.). pap. 2.00 (ISBN 0-88469-021-0). BMH Bks.

--Noah's Ark, Pitched & Parked. pap. 4.00 (ISBN 0-88469-039-3). BMH Bks.

Meyer, Peter. Jews in the Soviet Satellites. LC 79-97297. 1971. Repr. of 1953 ed. lib. bdg. 45.00x (ISBN 0-8371-2621-5, MEJS). Greenwood.

Meyer, Richard M. Altgermanische Religionsgeschichte: History of Ancient Germanic Religion. Bolle, Kees W., ed. LC 77-79143. (Mythology Ser.). (Ger.). 1978. Repr. of 1910 ed. lib. bdg. 49.50x (ISBN 0-405-10552-5). Ayer Co Pubs.

Meyer, Robert T., ed. Palladius: Dialogue on the Life of St. John Chrysostom. (ACW Ser.: No. 45). 1985. text ed. 16.95 (ISBN 0-8091-0358-3). Paulist Pr.

Meyer, Samuel. The Deacon & the Jewess: Adventures in Heresy. LC 80-84734. 208p. 1982. 10.00 (ISBN 0-8022-2379-6). Philos Lib.

Meyer, Wali A., et al, eds. see Lewis, Samuel L.

Meyering, Robert A. Genesis One-Eleven. (Five-on-One Ser.). 96p. (Orig.). 1986. pap. text ed. 3.95 (ISBN 0-930265-16-5); tchr's. guide 7.95 (ISBN 0-930265-17-3). CRC Pubns.

Meyer-Plath & Schneider, A. M. Die Landmauer von Konstantinopel, Part 2: Aufnahme, Beschreibung und Geschichte. (Denkmaeler antiker Architektur, Vol. 8). (Ger., Illus.). x, 170p. 1978. Repr. of 1943 ed. 120.00 (ISBN 3-11-004992-9). De Gruyter.

Meyers, Carol L. The Tabernacle Menorah: A Synthetic Study of a Symbol from the Biblical Cult. LC 76-17105. (Amerian Schools of Oriental Research, Dissertation Ser.: Vol. 2). 243p. 1976. (Am Sch Orient Res); pap. text ed. 6.00x (ISBN 0-89757-101-0). Eisenbrauns.

Meyers, Carol L. & O'Connor, M., eds. The Word of the Lord Shall Go Forth: Essays in Honor of David Noel Freedman in Celebration of His Sixtieth Birthday. (American Schools of Oriental Research, Special Volume Ser.: No. 1). 1983. text ed. 35.00x (ISBN 0-931464-19-6). Eisenbrauns.

Meyers, Craig, jt. auth. see Schroeder, Frederick.

Meyers, John, ed. see Bartleman, Frank.

Meyers, Mary A. A New World Jerusalem: The Swedenborgian Experience in Community Construction. LC 82-11997. (Contributions in American Studies: No. 65). (Illus.). xiii, 217p. 1983. lib. bdg. 29.95 (ISBN 0-313-23602-X, MNJ/). Greenwood.

Meynell, Hugo A. The Intelligible Universe: A Cosmological Argument. LC 81-19065. 164p. 1982. 28.50x (ISBN 0-389-20253-3, 07057). B&N Imports.

--The Theology of Bernard Lonergan. (Studies in Religion). 1986. text ed. 15.95 (ISBN 1-55540-015-9, 01-00-42); pap. 11.95 (ISBN 1-55540-016-7). Scholars Pr GA.

Meyners, Robert & Wooster, Claire. Solomon's Sword: Clarifying Values in the Church. LC 77-9391. Repr. of 1977 ed. 27.40 (ISBN 0-8357-9028-2, 2016408). Bks Demand UMI.

Meyrinck, Gustav. Clockmaker. (Orig.). 1987. pap. 3.00. Rosycross Pr.

Meyrink, Gustav. Some Taoist Alchemical Legends. 1986. pap. 3.95 (ISBN 0-916411-52-4, Pub. by Alchemical Pr). Holmes Pub.

Meyzlisch, Saul, ed. A Child's Passover Haggadah. (Illus.). 76p. 1987. 9.95 (ISBN 0-915361-70-1, Dist. by Watts). Adama Pubs Inc.

Mez, Adam. The Renaissance of Islam. Bukhsl, Salahuddin K & Margoliovth, D. S., trs. LC 70-180361. Repr. of 1937 ed. 27.00 (ISBN 0-404-56293-0). AMS Pr.

Mezezers, Valdis. The Herrnhuterian Pietism in the Baltic. (Illus.). 160p. 1975. 8.95 (ISBN 0-8158-0322-2); pap. 6.95 (ISBN 0-8158-0413-X). Chris Mass.

Mezzatesta, Michael. The Art of Gianlorenzo Bernini: Selected Sculpture. LC 82-81080. (Illus.). 63p. (Orig.). 1982. pap. 8.50 (ISBN 0-912804-05-X). Kimbell Art.

Micah Publications Editors, et al. Haggadah for the Liberated Lamb. LC 84-43165. (Illus.). 96p. (Orig.). 1985. pap. 8.95 (ISBN 0-916288-19-6). Micah Pubns.

Miceli, Vincent. The Antichrist. 14.95 (ISBN 0-8158-0395-8). Chris Mass.

Miceli, Vincent P. Women Priests & Other Fantasies. LC 80-66294. 1985. 19.95 (ISBN 0-8158-0423-7). Chris Mass.

Michael, Aloysius. Radhakrishna on Hindu Moral Life & Action. 1979. 17.50x (ISBN 0-8364-0334-7). South Asia Bks.

Michael, Arnold. Blessed among Women. 1985. pap. 8.95 (ISBN 0-87613-091-0). New Age.

--Brothers of the Grape. LC 76-142525. 1972. pap. 6.95 (ISBN 0-87516-149-9). De Vorss.

Michael, Chester P. Scripture Themes & Texts for Meditation & Study. 1981. pap. 2.00. Open Door Inc.

Michael, Chester P. & Norrisey, Marie C. Arise: A Christian Psychology of Love. 162p. (Orig.). 1981. pap. 3.95 (ISBN 0-940136-00-7). Open Door Inc.

--Prayer & Temperament: Different Prayer Forms for Different Personality Types. 192p. (Orig.). 1984. pap. 5.95 (ISBN 0-940136-01-5). Open Door Inc.

Michael, Franz & Chang, Chung-Li. The Taiping Rebellion: Documents & Comments. Incl. Vol. 2. 756p (ISBN 0-295-73959-2); Vol. 3. 1107p (ISBN 0-295-73958-4). LC 66-13538. (Publications on Asia of the Institute for Foreign & Area Studies: No. 14, Pt. 2). 1971. 35.00x ea. U of Wash Pr.

--The Taiping Rebellion: History, Vol. 1. (Publications on Asia of the Institute for Foreign & Area Studies: No. 14, Pt. 1). 256p. 1966. pap. 8.95x (ISBN 0-295-95244-X). U of Wash Pr.

Michael, ed. see Schneider, D. Douglas.

Michaelle. Yoga & Prayer. Cumming, Diane, tr. pap. 6.50 (ISBN 0-87061-059-7). Chr Classics.

Michaels, J. Ramsey. John: A Good News Commentary. LC 83-47729. (The Good News Commentary Ser.). 288p. (Orig.). 1983. pap. 9.95 (ISBN 0-06-065575-5, RD-462, HarpR). Har-Row.

--Servant & Son: Jesus in Parable & Gospel. LC 80-84651. 322p. 1982. pap. 9.95 (ISBN 0-8042-0409-8). John Knox.

Michaels, Larry. Bible Object Talks for Children. (Illus.). 48p. (Orig.). 1982. pap. 2.95 (ISBN 0-87239-532-4, 2888). Standard Pub.

--Easy Bible Object Talks. (Illus.). 48p. 1985. pap. 2.95 (ISBN 0-87239-846-3, 2886). Standard Pub.

Michaels, Louis. The Words of Jesus: Arranged for Meditation. 1977. 6.95 (ISBN 0-87243-071-5). Templegate.

Michaelsen, Robert S. The American Search for Soul. LC 74-82005. (Rockwell Lecture Ser.). 132p. 1975. 15.95x (ISBN 0-8071-0097-8). La State U Pr.

Michaelsen, Robert S. & Roof, Wade C. Liberal Protestantism. 200p. (Orig.). 1986. pap. 11.95 (ISBN 0-8298-0584-2). Pilgrim NY.

Michaelson, S., jt. auth. see Morton, A. Q.

Michaelson, Sidney, jt. auth. see Morton, A. Q.

Michalson, G. E. The Historical Dimensions of Rational Faith: The Role of History in Kant's Religious Thought. 1977. 12.25 (ISBN 0-8191-0308-X). U Pr of Amer.

Michalson, Gordon E., Jr. Lessing's "Ugly Ditch". A Study of Theology & History. LC 84-42991. 224p. 1985. 22.50x (ISBN 0-271-00385-5). Pa St U Pr.

Michaud, E. Guillaume de Champeaux et les Ecoles de Paris. 2nd ed. (Medieval Studies Reprint Ser.). (Fr.). Repr. of 1867 ed. lib. bdg. 45.00x (ISBN 0-697-00011-7). Irvington.

Michaud, Joseph F. Bibliotheque des croisades, 4 vols. LC 76-29846. (Fr.). Repr. of 1829 ed. Set. 149.50 (ISBN 0-404-15450-6). AMS Pr.

--History of the Crusades, 3 Vols. Robson, W., tr. LC 72-172729. Repr. of 1852 ed. 110.00 (ISBN 0-404-04320-8). AMS Pr.

Michaud, Regis. Emerson, the Enraptured Yankee. Boas, George, tr. LC 74-5374. Repr. of 1930 ed. 30.00 (ISBN 0-404-11538-1). AMS Pr.

Michel, Albert, jt. auth. see Loth, Bernard.

Michel, Charles, jt. auth. see Waters, Ethel.

Michel, Emile. Rembrandt, 2 vols. 200.00 (ISBN 0-8490-0943-X). Gordon Pr.

Michel, Thomas F., tr. see Taymiyah, Ibn.

Michelet, Jules. Joan of Arc. Guerard, Albert, tr. 1957. pap. 6.95 (ISBN 0-472-06122-4, 122, AA). U of Mich Pr.

--Satanism & Witchcraft. 352p. 1983. pap. 5.95 (ISBN 0-8065-0059-X, 89). Citadel Pr.

Michell, George, ed. Architecture of the Islamic World: Its History & Social Meaning. LC 84-50341. (Illus.). 1984. 40.00f (ISBN 0-500-34076-5). Thames Hudson.

--Brick Temples of Bengal: From the Archives of David McCutchion. LC 82-3872. (Illus.). 450p. 1983. 90.00x (ISBN 0-691-04010-9). Princeton U Pr.

Michelson, Frida. Rumbuli. Goodman, Wolf, tr. from Rus. 224p. 1981. 16.95 (ISBN 0-89604-029-1); pap. 10.95 (ISBN 0-89604-030-5). Holocaust Pubns.

Michelson, Truman. Notes on the Buffalo-Head Dance of the Bear Gens of the Fox Indians. Repr. of 1928 ed. 29.00x (ISBN 0-403-03668-2). Scholarly.

Michie, Donald & Rhoads, David. Mark As Story: An Introduction to the Narrative of a Gospel. LC 81-43084. 176p. 1982. pap. 8.95 (ISBN 0-8006-1614-6). Fortress.

Michman-Melkman, Joseph, jt. ed. see Ramras-Rauch, Gila.

Michno, Dennis G. A Manual for Acolytes: The Duties of the Server at Liturgigal Celebrations. LC 80-81096. (Illus., Orig.). 1981. pap. 4.95 (ISBN 0-8192-1272-5). Morehouse.

--A Priest's Handbook: The Ceremonies of the Church. LC 81-84716. (Illus.). 304p. 1983. 32.50 (ISBN 0-8192-1300-4). Morehouse.

Mick, Lawrence E. To Live As We Worship. 100p. (Orig.). 1984. pap. 4.95 (ISBN 0-8146-1327-6). Liturgical Pr.

--Understanding the Mass Today. 20p. 1985. pap. 0.30 (ISBN 0-8146-1390-X). Liturgical Pr.

Mickaharic, Draja. Spiritual Cleansing. pap. 5.95 (ISBN 0-942272-09-9). Original Pubns.

Mickelsen, A. Berkeley. Interpreting the Bible. 1963. 20.95 (ISBN 0-8028-3192-3). Eerdmans.

Mickelsen, A. Berkeley & Mickelsen, Alvera M. Understanding Scripture. 2nd ed. LC 81-52231. (Better Bible Study Ser.). 1982. pap. 3.50 (ISBN 0-8307-0795-6, 5017302). Regal.

Mickelsen, Alvera. Women, Authority & the Bible. LC 86-7158. 252p. (Orig.). 1986. pap. 9.95 (ISBN 0-87784-608-1). Inter-Varsity.

Mickelsen, Alvera & Mickelsen, Berkley. Family Bible Encyclopedia, 2 vols. Incl. Volume I (A-K (ISBN 0-89191-100-6); Volume II (L-Z (ISBN 0-89191-127-8). LC 78-55384. (Illus.). 1978. 9.95 ea.; Set. 12.95 (ISBN 0-89191-201-0). Cook.

Mickelsen, Alvera M., jt. auth. see Mickelsen, A. Berkeley.

Mickelsen, Berkley, jt. auth. see Mickelsen, Alvera.

Mickelson, Alvera, jt. auth. see Karo, Nancy.

Mickelson, Einar H. God Can. (Illus.). 301p. 1966. 2.50 (ISBN 0-87509-086-9). Chr Pubns.

Mickey, Paul. Essentials of Wesleyan Theology: A Contemporary Affirmation. 160p. 1980. pap. 5.95 (ISBN 0-310-39151-2, 9312P). Zondervan.

Mickey, Paul & Proctor, William. Tough Marriage. Golbitz, Pat, ed. 256p. 1986. 14.95 (ISBN 0-688-05038-7). Morrow.

Micklem, Nathaniel. Prayers & Praises. 1982. pap. 3.95x (ISBN 0-7152-0541-2). Outlook.

--The Theology of Politics. 10.75 (ISBN 0-8369-7119-1, 7953). Ayer Co Pubs.

Mickler, Michael J. The Unification Church in America: Sects & Cults in America. LC 83-48225. (Bibliographical Guides Ser.). 130p. 1986. lib. bdg. 19.00 (ISBN 0-8240-9040-3). Garland Pub.

Micks, Marianne H. Epiphany. LC 84-18756. (Proclamation 3A Ser.). 64p. 1986. pap. 3.75 (ISBN 0-8006-4118-3). Fortress.

--Future Present: The Phenomenon of Christian Worship. LC 75-103844. 1970. pap. 6.95 (ISBN 0-8164-2109-9, HarpR). Har-Row.

--Introduction to Theology. rev. ed. 160p. 1983. pap. 9.95 (ISBN 0-8164-2465-9, HarpR). Har-Row.

--The Joy of Worship. LC 81-19667. (Library of Living Faith: Vol, 1). 120p. 1982. pap. 5.95 (ISBN 0-664-24402-5). Westminster.

--Our Search for Identity: Humanity in the Image of God. LC 81-70592. 176p. 1982. pap. 1.00 (ISBN 0-8006-1627-8). Fortress.

Micks, Marianne H. & Ridenhour, Thomas E. Lent. Achtemeier, Elizabeth, et al, eds. LC 79-7377. (Proclamation 2: Aids for Interpreting the Lessons of the Church Year Ser. C). 64p. 1979. pap. 3.75 (ISBN 0-8006-4082-9, 1-4082). Fortress.

Middlebrook, J. D. & Summers, Larry. The Church & Family. LC 80-66326. 128p. 1980. pap. 1.95 (ISBN 0-88243-482-9, 02-0482). Gospel Pub.

Middlekauff, Robert. The Mathers: Three Generations of Puritan Intellectuals, 1596-1728. LC 79-140912. 1971. pap. 7.95 (ISBN 0-19-502115-0). Oxford U Pr.

Middleton, Christopher. The Historie of Heaven. LC 76-57400. (English Experience Ser.: No. 816). 1977. Repr. of 1596 ed. lib. bdg. 5.00 (ISBN 90-221-0777-9). Walter J Johnson.

Middleton, Conyers. A Free Enquiry into the Miraculous Powers, Which Are Supposed to Have Subsisted in the Christian Church. Wellek, Rene, ed. LC 75-11235. (British Philosophers & Theologians of the 17th & 18th Centuries: Vol. 36). 1976. Repr. of 1749 ed. lib. bdg. 51.00 (ISBN 0-8240-1788-9). Garland Pub.

Middleton, J. Richard, jt. auth. see Walsh, Brian J.

Middleton, John. Lugbara Religion: Ritual & Authority among an East African People. LC 60-51074. pap. 71.00 (ISBN 0-317-28622-6, 2055387). Bks Demand UMI.

--Lugbara Religion: Ritual & Authority among East African People. LC 86-21889. (Illus.). 294p. 1987. pap. 14.95x (ISBN 0-87474-667-1). Smithsonian.

Middleton, John, jt. auth. see Beattie, John.

Middleton, John, ed. Gods & Rituals: Readings in Religious Beliefs & Practices. LC 75-44032. (Texas Press Sourcebooks in Anthropology Ser.: No. 6). 480p. 1976. pap. 11.50x (ISBN 0-292-72708-9). U of Tex Pr.

--Myth & Cosmos: Readings in Mythology & Symbolism. LC 75-43817. (Texas Press Sourcebooks in Anthropology: No. 5). 382p. 1976. pap. 9.95x (ISBN 0-292-75030-7). U of Tex Pr.

Midelfort, H. C. Erik, ed. see Moeller, Bernd.

Midelfort, H. Erik. Witch Hunting in Southwestern Germany, 1562-1684: The Social & Intellectual Foundations. LC 75-183891. 320p. 1972. 26.50x (ISBN 0-8047-0805-3). Stanford U Pr.

Midgett, Andre, ed. Faces. (Campus Life Bks.). (Illus.). 160p. (Orig.). 1987. pap. 5.95 (ISBN 0-8423-0826-1). Tyndale.

Midgley, Mary. Evolution As a Religion: Strange Hopes & Stranger Fears. 192p. 1986. text ed. 33.00 (ISBN 0-416-39650-X, 9512); pap. text ed. 12.95 (ISBN 0-416-39660-7, 9513). Methuen Inc.

--Heart & Mind: Varieties of Moral Experience. 1981. 20.00x (ISBN 0-312-36588-8). St Martin.

--Wickedness. 232p. 1986. pap. 8.95 (ISBN 0-7448-0053-6, 0053W). Methuen Inc.

Midlam, Don S. Flight of the Lucky Lady. (Illus.). 1954. 8.95 (ISBN 0-8323-0091-8). Binford-Metropolitan.

Midmer, Roy. English Mediaeval Monasteries, 1066-1540. LC 79-53097. 394p. 1980. 27.00x (ISBN 0-8203-0488-3). U of Ga Pr.

Midwood, Bart. The Nativity. 56p. 1982. 9.95 (ISBN 0-9607118-0-5). Bel Esprit.

Mieder, Wolfgang. International Bibliography of Explanatory Essays on Individual Proverbs & Proverbial Expressions: German Language & Literature. (European University Studies Ser.: No.1, Vol. 191). 146p. 1977. pap. 18.25 (ISBN 3-261-02932-3). P Lang Pubs.

--The P-H Encyclopedia of World Proverbs. LC 85-12345. 582p. 1986. 34.95 (ISBN 0-13-695586-X). P-H.

Miel, Jan. Pascal & Theology. LC 75-93822. 216p. 1970. 19.50x (ISBN 0-8018-1101-5). Johns Hopkins.

Mielziner, Moses. Introduction to the Talmud. 4th ed. LC 68-29908. 1969. 17.95 (ISBN 0-8197-0156-4); pap. 12.95 (ISBN 0-8197-0015-0). Bloch.

Mier, C. A., tr. see Fischer, Bernhard.

Mier, G. F., tr. see Fischer, Bernhard.

Mieth, Dietmar & Pohier, Jacques, eds. Christian Ethics & Economics: The North South Conflict, Concilium 140. (New Concilium 1980). 128p. 1980. pap. 5.95 (ISBN 0-8164-2282-6, HarpR). Har-Row.

--The Ethics of Liberation: The Liberation of Liberation, Vol. 172. (Concilium Ser.). 128p. 1984. pap. 6.95 (ISBN 0-567-30052-8, Pub. by T & T Clark Ltd UK). Fortress.

Mieth, Dietmar, jt. ed. see Pohier, Jacques.

Miethe, Terry. A Christian's Guide to Faith & Reason. 192p. (Orig.). 1987. pap. 5.95 (ISBN 0-87123-677-X). Bethany Hse.

--The New Christian's Guide to Following Jesus. 144p. 1984. pap. 4.95 (ISBN 0-87123-439-4, 210439). Bethany Hse.

Miethe, Terry L. & Bourke, Vernon J., eds. Thomistic Bibliography, 1940-1978. LC 80-1195. xxii, 318p. 1980. lib. bdg. 45.00 (ISBN 0-313-21991-5, MTH/). Greenwood.

Mifsud, Alfred. Knights Hospitallers of the Venerable Tongue of England in Malta. LC 78-63348. (The Crusades & Military Orders: Second Ser.). (Illus.). Repr. of 1914 ed. 34.50 (ISBN 0-404-17009-9). AMS Pr.

Migas, Abraham I. Kevod Elohim. 27.50 (ISBN 0-405-12616-6). Ayer Co Pubs.

Migliore, Daniel L. Called to Freedom: Liberation Theology & the Future of Christian Doctrine. LC 79-21879. 128p. 1980. pap. 5.95 (ISBN 0-664-24289-8). Westminster.

--The Power of God. LC 82-20037. (Library of Living Faith Ser.: Vol. 8). 116p. (Orig.). 1983. pap. 5.95 (ISBN 0-664-24454-8). Westminster.

Mignani, Rigo & Di Cesare, Mario A. A Concordance to Juan Ruiz's Libro De Buen Amor. 328p. 16.00 (ISBN 0-87395-322-3, Pub. by SUNY Pr). Medieval & Renaissance NY.

Mignani, Rigo, et al, eds. Concordance To Juan Ruiz Libro De Buen Amor. LC 76-46390. 328p. 1977. 55.50 (ISBN 0-87395-322-3). State U NY Pr.

Migne, J. P., ed. Dictionnaire de Mystique Chretienne. (Troisieme et Derniere Encyclopedie Theologique Ser.: Vol. 35). (Fr.). 784p. Date not set. Repr. of 1858 ed. lib. bdg. 99.50x (ISBN 0-89241-314-X). Caratzas.

--Dictionnaire de Mythologie. (Troisieme et Derniere Encyclopedie Theologique Ser.: Vol. 10). (Fr.). 760p. Repr. of 1855 ed. lib. bdg. 96.50x (ISBN 0-89241-294-1). Caratzas.

--Dictionnaires des Preuves de la Divinite de Jesus Christ. (Troisieme et Derniere Encyclopedie Theologique Ser.: Vol. 37). (Fr.). 516p. Repr. of 1858 ed. lib. bdg. 66.50x (ISBN 0-89241-316-6). Caratzas.

--Encyclopedie Theologique, 168 vols. in 171. (Fr., Illus.). 119060p. Repr. of 1873 ed. Set. lib. bdg. 14,177.48 (ISBN 0-89241-230-5). Caratzas.

--Nouvelle Encyclopedie Theologique (Second Series, 52 vols. in 53. 37237p. Repr. of 1862 ed. lib. bdg. 4695.75x (ISBN 0-89241-202-X). Caratzas.

--Origines et Raison De la Liturgie Catholique En Forme De Dictionnaire... Suivies De la Liturgie Armenienne Traduite En Francais. Avedichian, Gabriel & Pascal, E., trs. (Encyclopedie Theologique Ser.: Vol. 8). (Fr.). 652p. Repr. of 1883 ed. lib. bdg. 83.00x (ISBN 0-89241-233-X). Caratzas.

--Troisieme et Derniere Encyclopedie Theologique (Third Series, 66 vols. (Fr.). 47232p. Repr. of 1873 ed. lib. bdg. 5716.75x (ISBN 0-89241-203-8). Caratzas.

Migne, J. P., ed. see Andre.

Migne, J. P., ed. see Belouino, P.

Migne, J. P., ed. see Benoist De Matougues, L.

Migne, J. P., ed. see Bergier, N. S.

Migne, J. P., ed. see Berton, C.

Migne, J. P., ed. see Bertrand, F. M.

Migne, J. P., ed. see Boissonet, V. D.

Migne, J. P., ed. see Bourasse, J. J.

Migne, J. P., ed. see Brunet, G.

Migne, J. P., ed. see Calmet, A.

Migne, J. P., ed. see Cheve, C. F.

Migne, J. P., ed. see Constant, A. L.

Migne, J. P., ed. see D'Ault-Dumesnil, G. E.

Migne, J. P., ed. see Defeller, F. X. & Perennes, F.

Migne, J. P., ed. see De Grandmaison, C.

Migne, J. P., ed. see De Montrond, M.

Migne, J. P., ed. see De Sivry, L.

Migne, J. P., ed. see Des Mas-Latrie, L.

Migne, J. P., ed. see D'Ortigue, J. L.

Migne, J. P., ed. see Douhet, J.

Migne, J. P., ed. see Gainet, J. C.

Migne, J. P., ed. see Grosse, E.

Migne, J. P., ed. see Guenebault, L. J.

Migne, J. P., ed. see Guerin, L. F.

Migne, J. P., ed. see Helyot, P.

Migne, J. P., ed. see Hure.

Migne, J. P., ed. see Jehan, L. F.

Migne, J. P., ed. see Jouffroy, A.

Migne, J. P., ed. see Jouhanneaud, P.

Migne, J. P., ed. see Jouve, E. G.

Migne, J. P., ed. see Lacroix & De Djunkovskoy, E.

Migne, J. P., ed. see Lecanu, A. F.

Migne, J. P., ed. see LeNoir, C. P.

Migne, J. P., ed. see Martin-Doisy, F.

Migne, J. P., ed. see Morin, F.

Migne, J. P., ed. see Nadal, J. C.

Migne, J. P., ed. see Peltier, A. C.

Migne, J. P., ed. see Perennes, F.

Migne, J. P., ed. see Perennes, F M.

Migne, J. P., ed. see Petin, L. M.

Migne, J. P., ed. see Pierrot.

Migne, J. P., ed. see Pinard, C.

Migne, J. P., ed. see Pluquet, F. A.

Migne, J. P., ed. see Pontas, J.

Migne, J. P., ed. see Poujol, F. A.

Migne, J. P., ed. see Poussin, J. C. & Garnier, J. C.

Migne, J. P., ed. see Prompsault, J. H.

Migne, J. P., ed. see Quantin, M.

Migne, J. P., ed. see Saulcy, L. F.

Migne, J. P., ed. see Sevestre, A.

Migne, J. P., ed. see Thomassin, L.

Migne, J. P., ed. see Vallee, L.

Migne, Jacques P. Patrologiae Cursus Completus. Incl. Patrologia Latina, 221 vols. pap. write for info.; Patrologia Graeco Latina, 162 vols. pap. write for info.. 1965-71. pap. Adlers Foreign Bks.

Mignon, Charles W., ed. see Taylor, Edward.

Miguens, M. Mary, Servant of the Lord. 1978. 3.75 (ISBN 0-8198-0538-6); pap. 2.25 (ISBN 0-8198-0539-4). Dghtrs St Paul.
Miguens, Manuel. Gospels for Sundays & Feasts: Cycle A. 1981. 7.50 (ISBN 0-8198-3015-1); pap. 6.00 (ISBN 0-8198-3016-X). Dghtrs St Paul.
--Gospels for Sundays & Feasts: Cycle C. 1980. 7.50 (ISBN 0-8198-3000-3); pap. 6.00 (ISBN 0-8198-3001-1). Dghtrs St Paul.
Miguez-Bonino, Jose, ed. Faces of Jesus: Latin American Christologies. Barr, Robert R., tr. from Span. LC 83-19375. Tr. of Jesus ni Vencido ni Monarca Celestial. 192p. 1984. pap. 10.95 (ISBN 0-88344-129-2). Orbis Bks.
Mihalich, Joseph C. Existentialism & Thomism. (Orig.). pap. 0.95 (ISBN 0-685-19401-9, 77, WL). Citadel Pr.
--Existentialism & Thomism. (Quality Paperback: No. 170). 91p. 1969. pap. 3.95 (ISBN 0-8226-0170-2). Littlefield.
Mihaly, E. A Song to Creation: A Dialogue with a Text. (Jewish Perspectives Ser.: Vol. 1). 7.50x (ISBN 0-87820-500-4, HUC Pr). Ktav.
Mihaly, Eugene. A Song to Creation: A Dialogue with a Text. LC 75-35761. pap. 27.00 (ISBN 0-317-42034-8, 2025694). Bks Demand UMI.
Mikalson, Jon D. Athenian Popular Religion. LC 82-25616. x, 142p. 1983. 16.00x (ISBN 0-8078-1563-2). U of NC Pr.
--Athenian Popular Religion. LC 82-25616. xi, 142p. 1987. pap. text ed. 8.95x (ISBN 0-8078-4194-3). U of NC Pr.
Mikhail, Kyriakos. Copts & Moslems under British Control. LC 70-118537. 1971. Repr. of 1911 ed. 24.00x (ISBN 0-8046-1160-2, Pub. by Kennikat). Assoc Faculty Pr.
Mikhail, Mona N. Images of Arab Women: Fact & Fiction. LC 78-19969. 137p. (Orig.). 1978. 20.00 (ISBN 0-89410-023-8); pap. 10.00 (ISBN 0-89410-024-6). Three Continents.
Mikhailovsky, V. Uchenije o Pravoslavnom Bogosluzhenii. Tr. of Teachings of the Orthodox Divine Services. 146p. pap. text ed. 6.00 (ISBN 0-317-30287-6). Holy Trinity.
Mikkelsen, M. A. The Bishop Hill Colony, a Religious Communistic Settlement in Henry County, Illinois. pap. 9.00 (ISBN 0-384-38850-7). Johnson Repr.
--The Bishop Hill Colony: A Religious, Communistic Settlement in Henry County, Illinois. LC 72-187466. (The American Utopian Adventure Ser.). 1973. Repr. of 1892 ed. lib. bdg. 19.50x (ISBN 0-87991-014-3). Porcupine Pr.
Milam, Edward E., jt. auth. see Sellers, James H.
Milan, Virginia E., jt. auth. see Meredith, Howard.
Milash, Nikodim. Das Kirchenrecht der Morgenlandischen Kirche. 2nd ed. LC 80-2360. Repr. of 1905 ed. 83.00 (ISBN 0-404-18910-5). AMS Pr.
Milavec, Aaron. A Pilgrim Experiences the World's Religions: Discovering the Human Faces of the Hidden God. (Mellen Lives Ser.: Vol. 1). 96p. 1984. pap. 9.95x (ISBN 0-88946-010-8). E Mellen.
--To Empower as Jesus Did: Acquiring Spiritual Power through Apprenticeship. LC 82-6466. (Toronto Studies in Theology: Vol. 9). 358p. 1982. 59.95x (ISBN 0-88946-966-0). E Mellen.
Milburn, B. A. Curious Cases: A Collection of American & English Decisions Selected for Their Readability. (Illus.). xvi, 441p. 1985. Repr. of 1902 ed. lib. bdg. 37.50x (ISBN 0-8377-0819-2). Rothman.
Milburn, Joyce. Helping Your Children Love Each Other. LC 83-15505. 160p. (Orig.). 1983. pap. 4.95 (ISBN 0-87123-307-X, 210307). Bethany Hse.
Milburn, Robert L. Early Christian Interpretations of History. LC 79-21671. 1980. Repr. of 1954 ed. lib. bdg. 22.50x (ISBN 0-313-22157-X, MIEA). Greenwood.
Mild, Frieda H. The Potter's Clay. 160p. 1984. 10.50 (ISBN 0-89962-356-5). Todd & Honeywell.
Mildenberger, Friedrich. Theology of the Lutheran Confessions. Lueker, Erwin, tr. LC 85-47727. 272p. 1986. 19.95 (ISBN 0-8006-0749-X). Fortress.
--Theorie der Theologie: Enzyklopaedie als Methodenlehre. (Ger.). 164p. 1972. 12.95 (ISBN 3-7668-0384-0, M-7094). French & Eur.
Miles, A. Marie. Bible: Chain of Truth. 168p. pap. 1.25 (ISBN 0-686-29101-8). Faith Pub Hse.
Miles, Clement A. Christmas Customs & Traditions: Their History & Significance. LC 76-9183. (Illus.). 1976. pap. 6.50 (ISBN 0-486-23354-5). Dover.
--Christmas Customs & Traditions: Their History & Significance. (Illus.). 15.50 (ISBN 0-8446-5484-1). Peter Smith.
--Christmas in Ritual & Tradition, Christian & Pagan. LC 68-54858. 1968. Repr. of 1912 ed. 37.00x (ISBN 0-8103-3354-6). Gale.
--Christmas in Ritual & Tradition: Christian & Pagan. 1977. lib. bdg. 59.95 (ISBN 0-8490-1618-5). Gordon Pr.
Miles, Delos. Church Growth - A Mighty River. LC 80-67352. 1981. pap. 6.50 (ISBN 0-8054-6227-9). Broadman.
--Evangelism & Social Involvement. LC 86-2660. 1986. 9.95 (ISBN 0-8054-6248-1). Broadman.
--How Jesus Won Persons. LC 82-70049. 1982. pap. 5.95 (ISBN 0-8054-6236-8). Broadman.
--Introduction to Evangelism. LC 82-73078. 1983. 19.95 (ISBN 0-8054-6239-2). Broadman.
--Master Principles of Evangelism. LC 81-66291. 1982. pap. 3.95 (ISBN 0-8054-6232-5). Broadman.
--Overcoming Barriers to Witnessing. LC 83-70641. (Orig.). 1984. pap. 5.50 (ISBN 0-8054-6245-7). Broadman.
Miles, E., jt. auth. see Wesner, Maralene.
Miles, Eustace. Life after Life: The Theory of Reincarnation. 180p. 1985. pap. 10.00 (ISBN 0-89540-126-6, SB-126). Sun Pub.
Miles, Herbert J. Sexual Happiness in Marriage. 2nd rev. ed. 208p. 1982. pap. 3.95 (ISBN 0-310-29222-0). Zondervan.
Miles, Judith. Journal from an Obscure Place. LC 78-60279. 144p. 1978. pap. 3.95 (ISBN 0-87123-273-1, 200273). Bethany Hse.
Miles, Leland. John Colet & the Platonic Tradition. LC 60-16716. 258p. 1961. 11.95 (ISBN 0-87548-005-5); pap. 6.95 (ISBN 0-87548-006-3). Open Court.
Miles, Margaret R. Augustine on the Body. LC 79-14226. (American Academy of Religion, Dissertation Ser.: No. 31). 1979. 14.00 (ISBN 0-89130-288-3, 010131); pap. 9.95 (ISBN 0-89130-289-1). Scholars Pr GA.
--Fullness of Life: Historical Foundations for a New Asceticism. LC 81-11535. 186p. 1981. pap. 11.95 (ISBN 0-664-24389-4). Westminster.
--Image As Insight: Visual Understanding in Western Christianity & Secular Culture. LC 85-47528. (Illus.). 304p. 1985. 24.95 (ISBN 0-8070-1006-5). Beacon Pr.
--Image As Insight: Visual Understanding in Western Christianity & Secular Culture. LC 85-47528. (Illus.). 200p. 1987. pap. 12.95 (ISBN 0-8070-1007-3, BP 743). Beacon Pr.
Miles, Margaret R., ed. see Hickey, Anne E.
Miles, Margaret R., ed. see Rumsey, Peter L.
Miles, Margaret R., ed. see Wilkins, Walter J.
Miles, Mary L. Daily Look at Jesus, No. 1-2. (Pre-Teen Books Ser.). 1970. No. 2. Moody.
Miles, Michael. Love Is Always. LC 86-2378. 320p. 1986. 17.95 (ISBN 0-688-06218-0). Morrow.
Miles, Robert W. That Frenchman, John Calvin. LC 83-45625. Date not set. Repr. of 1939 ed. 29.00 (ISBN 0-404-19843-0). AMS Pr.
Milet, Jean. God or Christ: The Excesses of Christocentricity. LC 81-5566. 288p. 1981. 14.95 (ISBN 0-8245-0104-7). Crossroad NY.
Milik, J. T., jt. auth. see De Vaux, R.
Milikin. Testing Tongues by the Word. pap. 3.50 (ISBN 0-8054-1918-7). Broadman.
Milingo, Emmanuel. The World in Between: Christian Healing & the Struggle for Spiritual Survival. Macmillan, Mona, ed. 144p. (Orig.). 1985. pap. 5.95 (ISBN 0-88344-354-6). Orbis Bks.
Mill, Anna J. Medieval Plays in Scotland. LC 68-56497. 1969. Repr. of 1927 ed. 24.50 (ISBN 0-405-08789-6, Pub. by Blom). Ayer Co Pubs.
Mill, John S. Essays on Ethics, Religion & Society. Robson, J. M., ed. (Collected Works of John Stuart Hill Ser.: Vol. 10). pap. 160.00 (ISBN 0-317-41695-2, 2055827). Bks Demand UMI.
--Three Essays on Religion. LC 76-130995. Repr. of 1874 ed. 23.45 (ISBN 0-404-04325-9). AMS Pr.
--Three Essays on Religion. Repr. of 1874 ed. lib. bdg. 37.50x (ISBN 0-8371-1986-3, MIER). Greenwood.
Millais, John E. The Parables of Our Lord & Savior Jesus Christ. 7.75 (ISBN 0-8446-5225-3). Peter Smith.
Millar, John F. A Complete Life of Christ. LC 85-51584. (Illus.). 180p. (Orig.). 1986. 15.95 (ISBN 0-934943-04-4); pap. 8.95 (ISBN 0-934943-01-X). Thirteen Colonies Pr.
Millar, William R. Isaiah Twenty-Four to Twenty-Seven & the Origin of Apocalyptic. LC 76-3561. (Harvard Semetic Museum Ser.). 1976. pap. 11.95 (ISBN 0-89130-102-X, 04-00-11). Scholars Pr GA.
Millard, A. R. The Bible B. C. What Can Archaeology Prove? 1982. pap. 1.75 (ISBN 0-87552-291-2). Presby & Reformed.
Millard, A. R., jt. ed. see Wiseman, D. J.
Millard, Alan. First Kings, Second Chronicles. (Bible Study Commentaries Ser.). 126p. 1985. pap. 4.95 (ISBN 0-317-43372-5). Chr Lit.
Millard, Amos D. Learning from the Apostles. 128p. 1971. pap. 1.25 (ISBN 0-88243-537-X, 02-0537). Gospel Pub.
Mille, Carol E. Which Translation Do You Prefer. 1975. pap. 1.00 (ISBN 0-915374-52-8, 52-8). Rapids Christian.
Millen, Nina. Children's Festivals from Many Lands. 1964. pap. 4.95 (ISBN 0-377-44501-0). Friend Pr.
--Children's Games from Many Lands. 1965. pap. 5.95 (ISBN 0-377-45011-1). Friend Pr.
Miller. Devotional Dramas for Christmas. LC 72-79175. 1.95 (ISBN 0-8054-7510-9). Broadman.
--Sabbath Shiurim. 1979. Vol. I. 12.00 (ISBN 0-87306-993-5); Vol. II. 12.00 (ISBN 0-686-67019-1). Feldheim.
Miller, A. V., tr. see Hegel, G. W.
Miller, Adam W. Introduction to the New Testament. rev. ed. 1984. pap. 1.50 (ISBN 0-87162-141-X, D2403). Warner Pr.
--Introduction to the Old Testament. 1981. pap. 1.75 (ISBN 0-87162-193-2, D2401). Warner Pr.
Miller, Alan L., ed. see Hori, Ichiro.
Miller, Alan W. God of Daniel S: In Search of the American Jew. (Brown Classics in Judaica Ser.). 260p. 1986. pap. text ed. 13.25 (ISBN 0-8191-5047-9). U Pr of Amer.
Miller, Alberta P. Dorcas Sews for Others. (Arch Book Ser.: No. 21). pap. 0.99 (59-1285). Concordia.
Miller, Alexander. Faith & Learning: Christian Faith & Higher Education in Twentieth Century America. LC 77-23142. 1977. Repr. of 1960 ed. lib. bdg. 22.50x (ISBN 0-8371-9458-X, MIFL). Greenwood.
Miller, Allen O. & Osterhaven, M. Eugene, trs. Heidelberg Catechism. LC 62-20891. 1963. pap. 2.25 (ISBN 0-8298-0060-3). Pilgrim NY.
Miller, Alvin. Weird Eschatology: An Alternative View of the Second Coming. LC 86-80018. (Illus.). 52p. (Orig.). 1986. pap. 3.00 (ISBN 0-9616435-0-1). Last Things.
Miller, Arthur. The Obedience Experiments: A Case Study of Controversy in Social Science. LC 85-25723. 305p. 1986. 35.00 (ISBN 0-275-92012-7, C2012). Praeger.
Miller, Barbara & Conn, Charles P. Kathy. (Illus.). 160p. 1981. pap. 2.75 (ISBN 0-8007-8415-4, Spire Bks). Revell.
--El Milagro de Kathy. 144p. 1982. 2.75 (ISBN 0-88113-170-9). Edit Betania.
Miller, Barbara S., ed. Exploring India's Sacred Art: Selected Writings of Stella Kramrisch. LC 82-60302. (Illus., Orig.). 1983. 57.95x (ISBN 0-8122-7856-9); pap. 21.00x (ISBN 0-8122-1134-0). U of Pa Pr.
Miller, Barbara S., ed. see Archer, William G.
Miller, Barbara S., tr. The Bhagavad-Gita: Krishna's Counsel in Time of War. LC 86-13725. (Illus.). 176p. 1986. 20.00x (ISBN 0-231-06468-3). Columbia U Pr.
Miller, Basil. Charles Finney. 144p. 1983. pap. 2.95 (ISBN 0-88113-034-6). Edit Betania.
--Charles G. Finney. 144p. 1969. pap. 3.50 (ISBN 0-87123-061-5, 200061). Bethany Hse.
--George Mueller: Man of Faith. 160p. 1972. pap. 3.50 (ISBN 0-87123-182-4, 200182). Bethany Hse.
--John Wesley. 144p. 1969. pap. 3.50 (ISBN 0-87123-272-3, 200272). Bethany Hse.
--Mary Slessor. 144p. 1985. pap. 3.50 (ISBN 0-87123-849-7, 200849). Bethany Hse.
--William Carey. 154p. 1985. pap. 3.50 (ISBN 0-87123-850-0, 200850). Bethany Hse.
Miller, Basil, compiled by. Beautiful Poems on Jesus. facs. ed. LC 68-58826. (Granger Index Reprint Ser). 1948. 17.00 (ISBN 0-8369-6029-7). Ayer Co Pubs.
Miller, Benjamin, jt. auth. see Hartstein, Jacob I.
Miller, Betty. The Amish in Switzerland & Other European Countries. 1978. pap. 1.50 (ISBN 0-685-46025-8). O R Miller.
Miller, Betty, jt. auth. see Thomas, Virginia.
Miller, C. J. Evangelism & Your Church. 1980. pap. 2.95 (ISBN 0-87552-290-4). Presby & Reformed.
Miller, C. John. Outgrowing the Ingrown Church. 176p. 1986. pap. 7.95 (ISBN 0-310-28411-2). Zondervan.
--Repentance & Twentieth Century Man. (Orig.). 1980. pap. 2.95 (ISBN 0-87508-334-X). Chr Lit.
Miller, C. Leslie. All about Angels. LC 73-82096. 144p. (Orig.). 1973. pap. 3.50 (ISBN 0-8307-0467-1, 5010500). Regal.
Miller, Calvin. Becoming: Yourself in the Making. 1987. 10.95 (ISBN 0-8007-1522-5). Revell.
--The Finale. LC 78-70810. (Illus.). 1979. pap. 5.95 (ISBN 0-87784-627-8). Inter-Varsity.
--A Hunger for Meaning. 2nd ed. LC 83-26490. 180p. 1984. pap. 4.95 (ISBN 0-87784-830-0). Inter-Varsity.
--If This Be Love: The Journey of Two People Toward Each Other in Christian Love & Marriage. LC 83-48433. 112p. 1984. 11.45 (ISBN 0-06-065755-3, HarpR). Har-Row.
--Once upon a Tree. 1978. pap. 3.95 (ISBN 0-8010-6050-8). Baker Bk.
--The Philippian Fragment. LC 82-15. (Illus.). 175p. 1982. pap. 5.95 (ISBN 0-87784-805-X). Inter-Varsity.
--The Table of Inwardness. LC 84-9134. 132p. (Orig.). 1984. pap. 4.95 (ISBN 0-87784-832-7). Inter-Varsity.
--The Taste of Joy: Recovering the Lost Glow of Discipleship. LC 83-7839. Orig. Title: The Illusive Thing Called Joy. 144p. 1983. pap. 4.95 (ISBN 0-87784-831-9). Inter-Varsity.
Miller, Carol E. Disciples of Jesus, Beginner-Primary Teacher. 1984. pap. 1.75 (ISBN 0-915374-47-1). Rapids Christian.
--Teaching Toddlers. 1971. pap. 1.95 (ISBN 0-915374-22-6, 22-6). Rapids Christian.
--The Ten Commandments: Youth & Adult Student. 1971. pap. 0.85 (ISBN 0-915374-45-5). Rapids Christian.
Miller, Char, ed. Missions & Missionaries in the Pacific. LC 85-5074. (Symposium Ser.: Vol. 14). 136p. 1985. 19.95x (ISBN 0-88946-705-6). E Mellen.
Miller, Charles E. Making Holy the Day: A Commentary in the Liturgy of the Hours. red flexible bdg. 0.95 (ISBN 0-89942-410-4, 410/04). Catholic Bk Pub.
--Opening the Treasures: A Book of Daily Homily Meditations. LC 81-19095. (Illus.). 557p. 1982. pap. 16.95 (ISBN 0-8189-0424-0). Alba.
Miller, Charles E., et al. The Word Made Flesh: Homilies for the Sundays of the Three Cycles. LC 83-8819. 353p. 1983. pap. 14.95 (ISBN 0-8189-0436-4). Alba.
Miller, Clarence, tr. see More, St. Thomas.
Miller, Clarence H., intro. by see Erasmus, Desiderius.
Miller, Clarence H., ed. see More, Thomas.
Miller, Clarence H., et al, eds. see More, St. Thomas.
Miller, David, jt. auth. see Hewetson, David.
Miller, David H. Ghost Dance. LC 85-5876. (Illus.). xviii, 318p. 1985. 23.95x (ISBN 0-8032-3099-0); pap. 8.95 (ISBN 0-8032-8130-7, BB 943, Bison). U of Nebr Pr.
Miller, David L. Christs: Meditations on Archetypal Images in Christian Theology. 200p. 1981. 12.95x (ISBN 0-8164-0492-5, HarpR). Har-Row.
--The New Polytheism. 2nd, rev. ed. 148p. 1981. pap. 9.50 (ISBN 0-88214-314-X). Spring Pubns.
--Three Faces of God: Traces of the Trinity in Literature & Life. LC 85-45493. 176p. 1986. pap. 11.95 (ISBN 0-8006-1895-5, 1-1895). Fortress.
Miller, David W. Church, State & Nation in Ireland, 1898-1921. LC 72-95453. 1973. 49.95x (ISBN 0-8229-1108-6). U of Pittsburgh Pr.
Miller, Donald E. The Gospel & Mother Goose. 112p. (Orig.). 1987. pap. 6.95 (ISBN 0-87178-320-7). Brethren.
--The Wing-Footed Wanderer: Conscience & Transcendence. LC 77-1503. Repr. of 1977 ed. 45.60 (ISBN 0-8357-9032-0, 2016421). Bks Demand UMI.
Miller, Donald E., jt. auth. see Poling, James N.
Miller, Donald E., jt. auth. see Seymour, Jack L.
Miller, Donald G. Luke. LC 59-10454. (Layman's Bible Commentary Ser.: Vol. 18). 1959. pap. 4.95 (ISBN 0-8042-3078-1). John Knox.
--Nature & Mission of the Church. LC 57-9443. (Orig.). 1957. pap. 5.95 (ISBN 0-8042-3208-3). John Knox.
Miller, Donald G., ed. The Hermeneutical Quest: Essays in Honor of James Luther Mays on His Sixty-Fifth Birthday. (Princeton Theological Monograph Ser.: No. 4). 1986. pap. 27.95 (ISBN 0-915138-86-7). Pickwick.
Miller, Donald G, tr. see Bovon, Francois & Rouiller, Gregoire.
Miller, Donald G., et al. P. T. Forsyth: The Man, the Preacher's Theologian & Prophet for the Twentieth Century. (Pittsburgh Theological Monograph Ser.: No. 36). 1981. pap. 18.00 (ISBN 0-915138-48-4). Pickwick.
Miller, Dorothy C., jt. auth. see Mather, Eleanore P.
Miller, E. C., Jr. Toward a Fuller Vision: Orthodoxy & the Anglican Experience. LC 84-61015. 188p. (Orig.). 1984. pap. 7.95 (ISBN 0-8192-1351-9). Morehouse.
Miller, Ed L. God & Reason: A Historical Approach to Philosophical Theology. 224p. 1972. pap. text ed. write for info. (ISBN 0-02-381270-2). Macmillan.
Miller, Edmund. Drudgerie Divine: The Rhetoric of God & Man in George Herbert. Hogg, James, ed. (Elizabethan & Renaissance Studies). 250p. (Orig.). 1979. pap. 15.00 (ISBN 0-317-40130-0, Pub by Salzburg Studies). Longwood Pub Group.
Miller, Emmeline S. My Redeemer Lives. 1982. 4.35 (ISBN 0-89536-529-4, 1315). CSS of Ohio.
Miller, Ernest A. Let Your Light So Shine. 218p. (Orig.). 1981. pap. 7.50 (ISBN 0-89216-046-2). Salvation Army.
Miller, Graham. Treasury of His Promises. 386p. (Orig.). 1986. pap. 12.95 (ISBN 0-85151-472-3). Banner of Truth.

Miller, Gwendolyn. Let's Be Friends. 64p. 1971. pap. 1.50 (ISBN 0-87178-933-7). Brethren.
Miller, Harriet P. Pioneer Colored Christians. facsimile ed. LC 73-37313. (Black Heritage Library Collection). Repr. of 1911 ed. 13.50 (ISBN 0-8369-8950-3). Ayer Co Pubs.
Miller, Herb. Building a Meaningful Life with the Carpenter's Twenty Megatruths. 108p. (Orig.). 1968. pap. write for info. (ISBN 0-937462-03-9). Net Pr.
--How to Build a Magnetic Church. 128p. 1987. pap. 7.95 (ISBN 0-687-17762-6). Abingdon.
Miller, Herbert. Evangelism's open Secrets. 2nd ed. LC 77-23468. 112p. 1985. pap. 6.95 (ISBN 0-8272-0805-7). CBP.
--Fishing on the Asphalt. LC 83-10006. 208p. (Orig.). 1983. pap. 8.95 (ISBN 0-8272-1011-6). CBP.
--Tools for Active Christians. LC 79-14795. (P.A.C.E. Ser.). (Orig.). 1979. pap. 6.95 (ISBN 0-8272-3624-7). CBP.
Miller, Herbert S. Christian Worker's Manual. pap. 4.00 (ISBN 0-87509-065-6). Chr Pubns.
Miller, Hulda C. The Creche & the Cross. (Illus.). 73p. (Orig.). 1977. pap. 2.00 (ISBN 0-89216-014-4). Salvation Army.
Miller, Irving. Israel: The Eternal Idea. 1955. 19.50x (ISBN 0-686-50046-6). Elliots Bks.
Miller, J. Popery & Politics in England, 1660-1688. LC 73-79306. (Illus.). 278p. 1973. 44.50 (ISBN 0-521-20236-1). Cambridge U Pr.
Miller, J. Allen. Christian Doctrine: Lectures & Sermons. 1946. 2.50x (ISBN 0-934970-01-7). Brethren Ohio.
Miller, J. Hillis. The Disappearance of God: Five Nineteenth Century Writers. 392p. 1976. text ed. 22.50x (ISBN 0-674-21101-4, Belknap Pr). Harvard U Pr.
Miller, J. Lane, jt. auth. see Miller, Madeleine S.
Miller, J. M. & Tucker, G. M. The Book of Joshua. (Cambridge Bible Commentary on the New English Bible, Old Testament Ser.). (Illus.). 218p. 1974. 22.95 (ISBN 0-521-08616-7); pap. 9.95 (ISBN 0-521-09777-0). Cambridge U Pr.
Miller, J. Maxwell. Introducing the Holy Land. LC 82-14424. x, 189p. 1982. 13.95 (ISBN 0-86554-034-9, MUP-H38). Mercer Univ Pr.
--The Old Testament & the Historian. Tucker, Gene M., ed. LC 75-10881. (Guides to Biblical Scholarship: Old Testament Ser.). 96p. 1976. pap. 4.50 (ISBN 0-8006-0461-X, 1-461). Fortress.
Miller, J. Maxwell & Hayes, John H. A History of Ancient Israel & Judah. LC 85-11468. (Illus.). 524p. 1986. 27.95 (ISBN 0-664-21262-X). Westminster.
Miller, J. Q., jt. auth. see Hartshorne, Hugh.
Miller, J. R. The Building of Character. rev. ed. Zodhiates, Joan, ed. 1975. pap. 3.95 (ISBN 0-89957-516-1). AMG Pubs.
--Come Ye Apart. 4.95 (ISBN 0-317-12209-6). AMG Pubs.
--Dying to Live. rev. ed. Zodhiates, Joan, ed. LC 79-51337. Orig. Title: Making the Most of Life. (Illus.). 147p. 1980. pap. 3.95 (ISBN 0-89957-045-3). AMG Pubs.
--Learning to Love. Zodhiates, Joan, ed. Orig. Title: The Lesson of Love. 1977. pap. 3.95 (ISBN 0-89957-521-8). AMG Pubs.
--The Master's Blesseds: The Sermon on the Mount. pap. 1.50 (ISBN 0-685-88384-1). Reiner.
--Words of Comfort. (Illus.). 1976. 5.95 (ISBN 0-89957-518-8); pap. 2.95 (ISBN 0-89957-517-X). AMG Pubs.
Miller, Jack, ed. Jews in Soviet Culture. 325p. 1983. 24.95 (ISBN 0-87855-495-5). Transaction Bks.
Miller, Jack S. The Healing Power of Grief. 125p. 1985. pap. 7.95 (ISBN 0-914373-02-1). Wieser & Wieser.
Miller, James. Measures of Wisdom: The Cosmic Dance in Classical & Christian Antiquity. 672p. 1986. 60.00 (ISBN 0-8020-2553-6). U of Toronto Pr.
Miller, Jeanine. The Vision of Cosmic Order in the Vedas. 320p. 1985. 39.95x (ISBN 0-7102-0369-1). Methuen Inc.
Miller, John, ed. see Kuhlewind, Georg.
Miller, John F. The Art of Parenting in a Changing Society. 1979. 8.95 (ISBN 0-8199-0761-8). Franciscan Herald.
Miller, John W. Christian Way. new ed. LC 78-76622. (Christian Peace Shelf Ser.). 104p. 1969. pap. 2.95 (ISBN 0-8361-1605-4). Herald Pr.
--Step by Step Through the Parables. LC 81-80046. 176p. (Orig.). 1981. pap. 7.95 (ISBN 0-8091-2379-7). Paulist Pr.
Miller, Jolonda. You Can Become Whole Again: A Guide to Healing for Christians in Grief. LC 80-84652. 1981. pap. 6.50 (ISBN 0-8042-1156-6). John Knox.
Miller, Judy. Cups Running Over. 1973. cancelled 5.95 (ISBN 0-88027-096-9). Firm Foun Pub.
--Cups Running Over. 1985. pap. 5.95 (ISBN 0-89225-278-2). Gospel Advocate.
--Seasons of the Heart. 1984. pap. 5.95 (ISBN 0-89225-272-3). Gospel Advocate.
Miller, Keith. The Dream. 128p. 1985. 8.95 (ISBN 0-8499-0462-5, 0462-5). Word Bks.
--Habitation of Dragons. LC 72-123009. 1983. 6.95 (ISBN 0-8499-2973-3). Word Bks.
--A Second Touch. LC 67-31340. 1982. 7.95 (ISBN 0-8499-0338-6, 80036). Word Bks.
Miller, Ken. What the Mormons Believe: An Introduction to the Doctrines of the Church of Jesus Christ of Latter-Day Saints. LC 81-80958. 248p. 1981. 9.95 (ISBN 0-88290-177-X, 1040). Horizon Utah.
Miller, Kenneth R. & Wilson, Mary E. The Church That Cares. LC 85-14786. 96p. 1985. pap. 6.95 (ISBN 0-8170-1087-4). Judson.
Miller, Kevin. Our Heroes: Four Complete Meetings for Junior High Youth Groups. (The Best of Young Teen Action Ser.). 32p. 1985. pap. 4.95 (ISBN 0-89191-380-7). Cook.
Miller, Kevin, ed. Faith Questions: Seeking God's Answers to Our Toughest Questions. (Senior High Pacesetter Ser.). 64p. 1986. pap. 7.95 (ISBN 0-89191-329-7). Cook.
--Friends: Becoming a Friend Finder & Keeper. (Senior High Pacesetter Ser.). 64p. 1986. pap. 7.95 (ISBN 0-89191-343-2). Cook.
--Help: Coping with Crisis. (Senior High Pacesetter Ser.). 64p. 1986. pap. 7.95 (ISBN 0-89191-282-7). Cook.
--How Big Is God? Discovering Our Creator's Love & Power. (Senior High Pacesetter Ser.). 64p. 1986. pap. 7.95 (ISBN 0-89191-328-9). Cook.
--Inside the Church: Finding Your Place Within God's Family. (Senior High Pacesetter Ser.). 64p. 1986. pap. 7.95 (ISBN 0-89191-325-4). Cook.
--Life Choices: Tackling the Biggest Decisions You'll Ever Make. (Senior High Pacesetter Ser.). 64p. 1986. pap. 7.95 (ISBN 0-89191-327-0). Cook.
Miller, Levi. Our People: The Amish & Mennonites of Ohio. LC 82-84405. (Illus.). 56p. (Orig.). 1983. pap. 2.50 (ISBN 0-8361-3331-5). Herald Pr.
Miller, Lula, jt. auth. see Yoder, Elmina.
Miller, Madeleine S. & Lane, J. Harper's Bible Dictionary. rev. ed. 1973. 18.95i (ISBN 0-06-065673-5, HarpR). Har-Row.
--Harper's Bible Dictionary. Rev. ed. 1974. 22.07 (ISBN 0-06-065674-3, HarpR); indexed 21.95i. Har-Row.
Miller, Madeleine S. & Miller, J. Lane. Harper's Encyclopedia of Bible Life. Bennet, Boyce M., Jr. & Scott, David H., eds. LC 78-4752. (Illus.). 416p. 1983. pap. 10.95 (ISBN 0-06-065677-8, RD-436, HarpR). Har-Row.
Miller, Marge, ed. see Burke, Pratricia A, et al.
Miller, Marge, ed. see Carl, Angela R. & Holmes, Alice C.
Miller, Marge, jt. ed. see Tester, Sylvia R.
Miller, Mary E., jt. auth. see Scheke, Linda.
Miller, Max B. & Drew, Louise C., eds. Sing of Life & Faith. LC 68-22233. (Illus.). 1969. 5.95 (ISBN 0-8298-0123-5). Pilgrim NY.
Miller, Michael. What Are They Saying about Papal Primacy? (WATSA Ser.). 128p. 1983. pap. 4.95 (ISBN 0-8091-2501-3). Paulist Pr.
Miller, Mitchell H., Jr. Plato's "Parmenides". The "Conversion" of the Soul. LC 85-43301. 264p. 1986. 30.00x (ISBN 0-691-07303-1). Princeton U PR.
Miller, Molly. The Saints of Gwynedd. (Studies in Celtic History). 132p. 1979. 21.50x (ISBN 0-8476-6186-5). Rowman.
Miller, Nick, jt. ed. see Stott, John.
Miller, Page P. A Claim to New Roles. LC 85-2249. (ATLA Monograph Ser.: No. 22). 253p. 1985. 17.50 (ISBN 0-8108-1809-4). Scarecrow.
Miller, Patrick D. Sin & Judgment in the Prophets. LC 81-8950. (SBL Monograph Ser.). 1982. 19.50 (ISBN 0-89130-514-9, 06-00-27); pap. 16.00 (ISBN 0-89130-515-7). Scholars Pr GA.
Miller, Patrick D. & Roberts, J. J. M. The Hand of the Lord: A Reassessment of the "Ark Narrative" of Samuel. LC 76-48737. (The Johns Hopkins Near Eastern Studies). pap. 24.40 (ISBN 0-317-26633-0, 2010959). Bks Demand UMI.
Miller, Patrick D., ed. see Craddock, Fred.
Miller, Patrick D., ed. see Towner, W. Sibley.
Miller, Patrick D., Jr. Interpreting the Psalms. LC 85-16258. 176p. 1986. pap. 10.95 (ISBN 0-8006-1896-3). Fortress.
--Pentecost 2. LC 84-18756. (Proclamation 3 A). 64p. 1987. pap. 3.75 (ISBN 0-8006-4123-X). Fortress.
Miller, Patrick D., Jr. & Roberts, J. J. The Hand of the Lord: A Reassessment of the "Ark Narrative" of 1 Samuel. LC 76-48737. (Near Eastern Studies). 128p. 1977. 12.50x (ISBN 0-8018-1920-2). Johns Hopkins.
Miller, Paul M. Leading the Family of God. LC 81-2267. 215p. 1981. pap. 8.95 (ISBN 0-8361-1950-9). Herald Pr.
--Peer Counseling in the Church. LC 78-9299. 168p. 1978. pap. 7.95 (ISBN 0-8361-1854-5). Herald Pr.
--Servant of God's Servants: The Work of a Christian Minister. LC 63-15499. (The Conrad Grebel Lectures: 1963). pap. 59.00 (ISBN 0-317-26613-6, 2025423). Bks Demand UMI.
Miller, Perry. American Puritans: Their Prose & Poetry. 1959. 21.75 (ISBN 0-8446-2596-5). Peter Smith.
--Jonathan Edwards. LC 72-7877. (American Men of Letters Ser.). (Illus.). 348p. 1973. Repr. of 1949 ed. lib. bdg. 25.00x (ISBN 0-8371-6551-2, MIJE). Greenwood.
--Jonathan Edwards. LC 81-4496. (New England Writers Ser.). 384p. 1981. pap. text ed. 11.95x (ISBN 0-87023-328-9). U of Mass Pr.
Miller, Perry & Johnson, T. H. Puritans: A Sourcebook of Their Writings, 2 Vols. Set. 38.50 (ISBN 0-8446-2593-0). Vol. 2. Peter Smith.
Miller, Perry, ed. American Transcendentalists: Their Prose & Poetry. 17.25 (ISBN 0-8446-2595-7). Peter Smith.
Miller, Perry & Johnson, Thomas H., eds. Puritans: A Sourcebook of Their Writings, 2 vols. (Orig.). Vol. 1. pap. 8.95x (ISBN 0-06-131093-X, TB1093, Torch); Vol. 2. pap. 8.95x (ISBN 0-06-131094-8, TB1094, Torch). Har-Row.
Miller, Perry, ed. see Edwards, Jonathan.
Miller, Perry, jt. ed. see Heimert, Alan E.
Miller, Perry, ed. see Wise, John.
Miller, Perry, et al. Religion & Freedom of Thought. facs. ed. LC 78-128296. (Essay Index Reprint Ser). 1954. 10.00 (ISBN 0-8369-2199-2). Ayer Co Pubs.
Miller, Perry G. Errand into the Wilderness. LC 56-11285. 1956. 15.00x (ISBN 0-674-26151-8, Belknap Pr); pap. 6.95x (ISBN 0-674-26155-0). Harvard U Pr.
--Nature's Nation. LC 67-17316. 1967. 20.00x (ISBN 0-674-60550-0, Belknap Pr). Harvard U Pr.
Miller, Perry G., ed. Transcendentalists: An Anthology. LC 50-7360. 1950. pap. 9.95x (ISBN 0-674-90333-1). Harvard U Pr.
Miller, Randall M., jt. auth. see Wakelyn, Jon L.
Miller, Randall M. & Marzik, Thomas D., eds. Immigrants & Religion in Urban America. LC 76-62866. 208p. 1977. 32.95 (ISBN 0-87722-093-X); pap. 9.95 (ISBN 0-87722-146-4). Temple U Pr.
Miller, Randolph C. Live until You Die. LC 73-8657. 144p. 1973. 5.95 (ISBN 0-8298-0253-3). Pilgrim NY.
--Living with Anxiety. LC 75-168525. 190p. 1971. 5.95 (ISBN 0-8298-0206-1). Pilgrim NY.
--The Theory of Christian Education Practice: How Theology Affects Christian Education. LC 80-15886. 312p. (Orig.). 1980. pap. 12.95 (ISBN 0-89135-049-7). Religious Educ.
Miller, Randolph C., ed. Church & Organized Movements. facs. ed. LC 76-134115. (Essay Index Reprint Ser). 1946. 18.00 (ISBN 0-8369-1998-X). Ayer Co Pubs.
Miller, Robert J., ed. Religious Ferment in Asia. LC 73-11401. xii, 196p. 1974. 22.50x (ISBN 0-7006-0111-2). U Pr of KS.
Miller, Robert M. American Protestantism & Social Issues, 1919-1939. LC 77-22031. 1977. Repr. of 1958 ed. lib. bdg. 26.75x (ISBN 0-8371-9777-5, MIAM). Greenwood.
--Harry Emerson Fosdick: Preacher, Pastor, Prophet. LC 84-7168. (Illus.). 608p. 1985. 34.50x (ISBN 0-19-503512-7). Oxford U Pr.
--How Shall They Hear Without a Preacher: The Life of Ernest Fremont Tittle. LC 74-149031. xii, 524p. 1971. 35.00 (ISBN 0-8078-1173-4). U of NC Pr.
Miller, Robert T. & Flowers, Ronald B., eds. Toward Benevolent Neutrality: Church, State, & the Supreme Court. rev. ed. LC 82-81902. xi, 726p. 1982. 32.50x (ISBN 0-918954-28-2). Baylor Univ Pr.
--Toward Benevolent Neutrality: Church, State, & the Supreme Court. 3rd ed. LC 86-72072. 612p. 1987. 36.00x (ISBN 0-918954-44-4). Baylor Univ Pr.
Miller, Roger F. What Can I Say? Lambert, Herbert, ed. 96p. (Orig.). 1987. pap. 4.95 (ISBN 0-8272-4220-4). CBP.
Miller, Roland. Mapilla Muslims of Kerala: A Study of Islamic Trends. LC 76-901758. 1976. 14.00x (ISBN 0-88386-080-5). South Asia Bks.
Miller, Ronald H. The Holy Eucharist: Study Guide. 1977. pap. 2.95x (ISBN 0-8192-4075-3). Morehouse.
Miller, Russell. The Larger Hope, Vol. 1. 25.00 (ISBN 0-933840-00-4). Unitarian Univ.
--Larger Hope, Vol. 2. 1986. 25.00 (ISBN 0-933840-25-X). Unitarian Univ.
Miller, Samuel H. Religion in a Technical Age. LC 68-17628. 1968. 8.95x (ISBN 0-674-75650-9). Harvard U Pr.
--What Child Is This? Readings & Prayers for Advent-Christmas. LC 82-5084. (Illus.). 64p. (Orig.). 1982. pap. 3.50 (ISBN 0-8006-1638-3, 1-1638). Fortress.
Miller, Samuel H. & Wright, G. Ernest, eds. Ecumenical Dialogue at Harvard, the Roman Catholic-Protestant Colloquium. LC 64-19583. 1964. 25.00x (ISBN 0-674-23700-5, Belknap Pr). Harvard U Pr.
Miller, Sarah H. Devotional Dramas for a Mission Witness. 1967. pap. 1.95 (ISBN 0-8054-9716-1). Broadman.
Miller, Sarah W. Bible Dramas for Older Boys & Girls. LC 75-95409. 1970. pap. 4.95 (ISBN 0-8054-7506-0). Broadman.
--Christmas Drama for Youth. LC 76-20255. 96p. (Orig.). 1976. pap. 4.50 (ISBN 0-8054-7511-7). Broadman.
--Devotional Dramas for Easter. (Orig.). 1967. pap. 1.95 (ISBN 0-8054-9715-3). Broadman.
--Devotional Dramas for the Christian Life. (Orig.). 1968. pap. 1.95 (ISBN 0-8054-9717-X). Broadman.
--I Saw Him. (Orig.). 1964. pap. 1.95 (ISBN 0-8054-9708-0). Broadman.
--A Variety Book of Puppet Scripts. LC 78-57276. 1978. pap. 4.50 (ISBN 0-8054-7515-X). Broadman.
Miller, Sheila. Ian & the Gigantic Leafy Obstacle. 1983. pap. 1.50 (ISBN 9971-83-790-0). OMF Bks.
Miller, Stephen M. Beacon Small-Group Bible Studies, II Corinthians, Galatians: Reckless Freedom, Responsible Living. Wolf, Earl C., ed. 96p. (Orig.). 1985. pap. 2.50 (ISBN 0-8341-0957-3). Beacon Hill.
Miller, T., ed. The Old English Version of Bede's Ecclesiastical History, Pt. II, No. 1. (EETS OS Ser.: Vol. 110). Repr. of 1898 ed. 21.00 (ISBN 0-8115-3368-9). Kraus Repr.
Miller, T. Franklin. Life & Teachings of Jesus. rev. ed. 1971. pap. 1.95 (ISBN 0-87162-114-2, D5200). Warner Pr.
Miller, Ted, ed. The Story. 400p. 1986. 4.95 (ISBN 0-8423-6677-6). Tyndale.
Miller, W. M. & Dinda, R. J., trs. Luther's Works, Vol. 20. LC 55-9893. 300p. 1973. 14.95 (ISBN 0-570-06420-1, 15-1762). Concordia.
Miller, William. Essays on the Latin Orient. LC 78-63360. (The Crusades & Military Orders: Second Ser.). Repr. of 1921 ed. 54.50 (ISBN 0-404-17024-2). AMS Pr.
--The Latins in the Levant: A History of Frankish Greece. LC 75-41193. Repr. of 1908 ed. 57.50 (ISBN 0-404-14689-9). AMS Pr.
Miller, William A. Conversations. LC 80-54283. 96p. 1980. pap. 3.50 (ISBN 0-934104-04-2). Woodland.
--The Joy of Feeling Good: Eight Keys to a Happy & Abundant Life. LC 86-20574. 192p. (Orig.). (YA) 1986. pap. 4.50 (ISBN 0-8066-2236-9, 10-3601). Augsburg.
--Make Friends with Your Shadow: How to Accept & Use Positively the Negative Side of Your Personality. LC 80-67793. 144p. (Orig.). 1981. pap. 6.95 (ISBN 0-8066-1855-8, 10-4238). Augsburg.
--Prayers at Midpoint: Conversations with God for Those in Life's Second Half. LC 83-72110. 96p. 1984. pap. 5.95 (ISBN 0-8066-2054-4, 10-5081). Augsburg.
--When Going to Pieces Holds You Together. LC 76-3853. 128p. (Orig.). 1976. pap. 6.95 (ISBN 0-8066-1543-5, 10-7063). Augsburg.
--Why Do Christians Break Down? LC 73-78260. 1973. pap. 6.95 (ISBN 0-8066-1325-4, 10-7140). Augsburg.
--You Count-You Really Do! LC 76-27078. 1976. pap. 5.95 (ISBN 0-8066-1569-9, 10-7420). Augsburg.
Miller, William D. All Is Grace: The Spirituality of Dorothy Day. LC 86-1228. 216p. 1987. 14.95 (ISBN 0-385-23429-5). Doubleday.
--Dorothy Day: A Biography. LC 81-47428. (Illus.). 1984. pap. 10.95 (ISBN 0-06-065749-9, RD 501, HarpR). Har-Row.
Miller, William L. The First Liberty: Religion & the American Republic. LC 85-40342. 416p. 1986. 24.95 (ISBN 0-394-53476-X). Knopf.
Miller, William L. & Cureton, Charles T., eds. Supreme Court Decisions on Church & State. 570p. 1986. pap. 11.95x (ISBN 0-935005-08-0). Ibis Pub VA.
Miller, William M. The Baha'i Faith: Its History & Teachings. LC 74-8745. (Illus.). 464p. 1984. pap. 10.95 (ISBN 0-87808-137-2). William Carey Lib.
--A Christian Response to Islam. 1976. pap. 4.95 (ISBN 0-87552-335-8). Presby & Reformed.
Miller, William R. Living As if: How Positive Faith Can Change Your Life. LC 84-13001. 132p. (Orig.). 1985. pap. 7.95 (ISBN 0-664-24635-4). Westminster.
Miller, William R. & Jackson-Miller, Kathleen A. Practical Psychology for Pastors. (Illus.). 400p. 1985. 30.95 (ISBN 0-13-692807-2). P-H.
Miller, William T. Mysterious Encounters at Mamre & Jabbok. (Brown Judaic Studies: No. 50). 252p. 1985. 24.95 (ISBN 0-89130-816-4, 14 00 50); pap. 18.25 (ISBN 0-89130-817-2). Scholars Pr GA.

Miller, Yisroel. In Search of the Jewish Woman. 149p. 1984. 8.95 (ISBN 0-87306-358-9); pap. 6.95 (ISBN 0-87306-359-7). Feldheim.

Millet, Robert. Perfected Millenial Kingdom. 1974. pap. 2.00 (ISBN 0-89036-034-0). Hawkes Pub Inc.

Millet, Robert, jt. ed. see Jackson, Kent P.

Millet, Robert L., ed. Studies in Scripture, Vol. Six: Acts to Revelation. 1987. 15.95 (ISBN 0-87579-084-4). Deseret Bk.

Millett, Robert & Jackson, Kent. Studies in Scripture: The Old Testament, Vol. III. 345p. 1985. 13.95 (ISBN 0-934126-81-X). Randall Bk Co.

Millgram, Abraham E. Jewish Worship. LC 77-151316. (Illus.). 1971. 15.95 (ISBN 0-8276-0003-8, 179). Jewish Pubns.

Millgram, Abraham E., ed. Sabbath: The Day of Delight. (Illus.). 495p. 1944. 12.95 (ISBN 0-8276-0157-3, 247). Jewish Pubns.

Millheim, John E. Let Rome Speak for Herself. LC 82-16616. 1982. pap. 3.95. Reg Baptist.

Milligan, G., jt. auth. see Moulton, J. H.

Milligan, George. St. Paul's Epistle to the Thessalonians. 144p. 1980. 12.95 (ISBN 0-8007-1098-3). Revell.

--St. Paul's Epistles to the Thessalonians. 1980. 12.00 (ISBN 0-86524-022-1, 7104). Klock & Klock.

Milligan, George, jt. auth. see Moulton, James H.

Milligan, Robert see Gospel Advocate.

Milligan, William. The Ascension & Heavenly Priesthood of Our Lord. 416p. 1977. Repr. of 1894 ed. 12.50 (ISBN 0-87921-034-6). Attic Pr.

--The Ascension of Christ. 1980. 15.00 (ISBN 0-86524-061-2, 9505). Klock & Klock.

Millikan, Robert A. Evolution in Science & Religion. 1979. Repr. of 1929 ed. lib. bdg. 17.50 (ISBN 0-8495-3846-7). Arden Lib.

--Evolution in Science & Religion. 1935. 15.50x (ISBN 0-686-51381-9). Elliots Bks.

--Evolution in Science & Religion. LC 72-85283. 104p. 1973. Repr. of 1927 ed. 21.50x (ISBN 0-8046-1702-3, Pub. by Kennikat). Assoc Faculty Pr.

Millington, Ada, jt. auth. see Bershadsky, Luba.

Mills, Brenda. My Bible Story Picture Book. (Illus.). 128p. 1982. text ed. 12.95 (ISBN 0-89081-319-1). Harvest Hse.

Mills, C. A., ed. see Capgrave, John.

Mills, David. Overcoming Religion. 1980. pap. 3.95 (ISBN 0-8065-0742-X). Citadel Pr.

Mills, David, jt. auth. see Lumiansky, R. M.

Mills, David & Lumiansky, Robert, eds. The Chester Mystery Cycle: Commentary & Apparatus, Vol. II. (Early English Text Society Supplementary Ser.: No. 8). 1985. 34.50x (ISBN 0-19-722408-3). Oxford U Pr.

Mills, Dick. The Four Loves. (Orig.). 1983. pap. 0.75 minibook (HH-287). Harrison Hse.

--He Spoke & I Was Strengthened. 1973. pap. 2.95 (ISBN 0-88368-026-2). Whitaker Hse.

--How to Have a Happy Marriage. 91p. (Orig.). 1985. pap. 2.95 (ISBN 0-89274-381-6). Harrison Hse.

--Quick Reference Scripture Handbook. 50p. (Orig.). 1984. pap. 1.95 (ISBN 0-89274-323-9). Harrison Hse.

--Word in Season, Vol. 1. (Orig.). 1986. pap. 6.95 (ISBN 0-89274-418-9). Harrison Hse.

Mills, Dorothy. Renaissance & Reformation Times. LC 83-45667. Date not set. Repr. of 1939 ed. 55.00 (ISBN 0-404-19817-1). AMS Pr.

Mills, Frederick V., Sr. Bishops by Ballot: An Eighteenth-Century Ecclesiastical Revolution. 1978. 19.95x (ISBN 0-19-502411-7). Oxford U Pr.

Mills, George. The People of the Saints. (Illus.). 1967. 5.00 (ISBN 0-916537-30-7, Taylor Museum). CO Springs Fine Arts.

Mills, Joann. Making It. 1986. pap. 4.95 (ISBN 0-89137-439-6). Quality Pubns.

Mills, John. Three Months' Residence at Nablus: And an Account of the Modern Samaritans. LC 77-87610. Repr. of 1864 ed. 25.50 (ISBN 0-404-16434-X). AMS Pr.

Mills, Joy. One Hundred Years of Theosophy. 245p. (Orig.). 1987. pap. 9.95 (ISBN 0-8356-0235-4). Theos Pub Hse.

Mills, Joy, ed. H. P. Blavatsky: The Key to Theosophy, an Abridgement. LC 75-18176. pap. 4.50 (ISBN 0-8356-0427-6, Quest). Theos Pub Hse.

Mills, Kenneth G. The New Land! Conscious Experience Beyond Horizons. (Illus.). 77p. 1978. pap. 4.95 (ISBN 0-919842-01-1). Sun-Scape Pubns.

Mills, L. H., jt. auth. see Darmesteter, James.

Mills, L. H., jt. tr. see Darmesteter, J.

Mills, Lawrence H. Avesta Eschatology: Compared with the Books of Daniel & Revelations. LC 74-24644. Repr. of 1908 ed. 14.00 (ISBN 0-404-12816-5). AMS Pr.

--Dictionary of the Gathic Language. LC 74-21253. (Gaelic.). Repr. of 1913 ed. 57.50 (ISBN 0-404-12804-1). AMS Pr.

--Our Own Religion in Ancient Persia. LC 74-21262. Repr. of 1913 ed. 45.00 (ISBN 0-404-12811-4). AMS Pr.

--Zarathushtra, Philo, the Achaemenids & Israel. LC 74-21261. Repr. of 1906 ed. 34.50 (ISBN 0-404-12815-7). AMS Pr.

Mills, Lawrence H., ed. A Study of the Five Zarathustrian (Zorastrian) Gathas, 4 pts. in 1 vol, Pts. I-IV. LC 74-21252. Repr. of 1894 ed. 74.50 (ISBN 0-404-12803-3). AMS Pr.

Mills, Liston M. Pastoral Theologian of the Year: Seward Hiltner; Special Issue PP 29, No. 1. LC 80-82467. 112p. 1980. pap. 12.95 (ISBN 0-89885-068-1). Human Sci Pr.

Mills, Michael. Dirty Hands, Pure Hearts. 1985. 4.50 (ISBN 0-89536-724-6, 5808). CSS of Ohio.

Mills, Richard C. Workbook on the Four Gospels. (Illus.). 128p. (Orig.). 1948. pap. 3.95 (ISBN 0-87239-327-5, 3347). Standard Pub.

Mills, W. Douglas. A Daily Lectionary: Scripture Readings for Every Day Based on the New Common Lectionary. 144p. (Orig.). 1986. pap. 6.95 (ISBN 0-8358-0517-4). Upper Room.

Mills, Watson E. Charismatic Religion in Modern Research: A Bibliography. Scholer, David M., ed. LC 85-127327. (National Association of Baptist Professors of Religion Bibliographic Ser.: No. 1). viii, 178p. 1985. text ed. 14.50 (ISBN 0-86554-143-4, MUP/M010). Mercer Univ Pr.

--Glossolalia: A Bibliography. LC 85-8987. (Studies in the Bible & Early Christianity: Vol. 6). 144p. 1985. 39.95x (ISBN 0-88946-605-X). E Mellen.

--Index of Reviews of New Testament Books Between 1900-1950. repr. ed. LC 77-72827. (Special Studies: No. 2). viii, 69p. 1984. pap. 3.50 (ISBN 0-932180-01-9). NABPR.

--A Theological-Exegetical Approach to Glossolalia. 192p. (Orig.). 1985. lib. bdg. 25.00 (ISBN 0-8191-4526-2); pap. text ed. 10.75 (ISBN 0-8191-4527-0). U Pr of Amer.

Mills, Watson E., ed. Speaking in Tongues: A Guide to Research on Glossolalia. 552p. (Orig.). 1986. pap. 24.95 (ISBN 0-8028-0183-8). Eerdmans.

Milman, Henry H. History of Christianity from the Birth of Christ to the Abolition of Paganism in the Roman Empire, 3 Vols. new & rev. ed. LC 78-172733. Repr. of 1863 ed. Set. 125.00 (ISBN 0-404-04350-X). AMS Pr.

--History of Latin Christianity, 9 Vols. LC 71-172734. Repr. of 1887 ed. Set. lib. bdg. 145.00 (ISBN 0-404-04360-7). AMS Pr.

Milne, Bruce. Know the Truth. LC 82-4711. 288p. 1982. pap. 9.95 (ISBN 0-87784-392-9). Inter-Varsity.

--We Belong Together. LC 78-13882. 1979. pap. 2.95 (ISBN 0-87784-455-0). Inter-Varsity.

Milne, Hugh. Bhagwan: The God That Failed. (Illus.). 320p. 1987. pap. 10.95 (ISBN 0-312-00106-1, Pub. by Thomas Dunne Bks). St Martin.

Milner, Clyde A., II. With Good Intentions: Quaker Work among the Pawnees, Otos, & Omahas in the 1870's. LC 81-16238. (Illus.). xvi, 246p. 1982. 21.50x (ISBN 0-8032-3066-4). U of Nebr Pr.

Milner, Clyde A., II & O'Neil, Floyd A., eds. Churchmen & the Western Indians, 1820-1920. LC 85-40477. (Illus.). 272p. 1985. 19.95 (ISBN 0-8061-1950-0). U of Okla Pr.

Milner, Ian, tr. see Macek, Josef.

Milner, Max, ed. Entretiens Sur L'homme et le Diable. (Decades Du Centre Culturel International De Cerisy-la Salle, Nouvelle Ser.: No. 1). 1965. pap. 14.00x (ISBN 90-2796-012-7). Mouton.

Milner, Sonia. Sonia: Survival in War & Peace. LC 83-50758. 1983. pap. 4.95 (ISBN 0-88400-102-4). Shengold.

Milner, Wanda. How to Use Your Bible. (Illus.). 24p. (Orig.). 1983. pap. 2.95 (ISBN 0-87239-690-8, 3200). Standard Pub.

Milosh, Joseph E. The Scale of Perfection & the English Mystical Tradition. LC 66-22857. pap. 56.50 (ISBN 0-317-07863-1, 2010975). Bks Demand UMI.

Milosz, Czeslaw. Hymn O Perle: Hymn to the Pearl. (Michigan Slavic Materials Ser.: No. 21). 1982. 10.00 (ISBN 0-930042-45-X). Mich Slavic Pubns.

Milroy, M. E., ed. Church Lace: Being Eight Ecclesiastical Patterns in Pillow Lace. (Illus.). 121p. 1981. Repr. of 1920 ed. 42.00x (ISBN 0-8103-3014-8). Gale.

Milson, Menahem, tr. from Arabic. A Sufi Rule for Novices. LC 74-27750. (Middle Eastern Studies: No. 17). 112p. 1975. text ed. 8.95x (ISBN 0-674-85400-4); pap. 3.50 (ISBN 0-674-85403-9). Harvard U Pr.

Milson, S. F. F. W. Maitland. (Master-Mind Lectures (Henriette Hertz Trust)). 1980. pap. 3.75 (ISBN 0-85672-241-3, Pub. by British Acad). Longwood Pub Group.

Milton, John. Catalogue of an Exhibition Commemorative of the Tercentenary of the Birth of John Milton. Repr. of 1909 ed. lib. bdg. 20.00 (ISBN 0-8414-6620-3). Folcroft.

--Complete Poetry of John Milton. Shawcross, John T., ed. LC 72-150934. 1971. pap. 8.95 (ISBN 0-385-02351-0, Anch). Doubleday.

--Milton's "Paradise Lost.". new ed. Bentley, Richard, ed. LC 74-5237. Repr. of 1732 ed. 67.50 (ISBN 0-404-11537-3). AMS Pr.

--Milton's Paradise Lost, 3 Vols. Verity, A. W., ed. LC 72-4906. 1921. lib. bdg. 120.00 (ISBN 0-8414-0012-1). Folcroft.

--On the Morning of Christ's Nativity: Milton's Hymn with Illustrations by William Blake. Keynes, Geoffrey, ed. LC 77-22296. (Illus.). Repr. of 1923 ed. lib. bdg. 12.50 (ISBN 0-8414-9917-9). Folcroft.

--Paradise Lost. Elledge, Scott, ed. (Critical Editions Ser). 546p. 1975. 19.95 (ISBN 0-393-04406-8); pap. 8.95x (ISBN 0-393-09230-5). Norton.

--Paradise Lost. (Modern Critical Interpretations--Seventeenth & Eighteenth Century British Literature Ser.). 1987. 19.95 (ISBN 0-87754-421-2). Chelsea Hse.

--Paradise Lost, Bks. 3 & 4. Potter, L. J. & Broadbent, J., eds. LC 75-36681. (Milton for Schools & Colleges Ser.). 200p. 1976. pap. 8.95x (ISBN 0-521-21150-6). Cambridge U Pr.

--Paradise Lost, Bks. 5 & 6. Hodge, R. I. & MacCaffrey, I., eds. LC 75-8314. (Milton for Schools & Colleges Ser). (Illus.). 176p. 1975. pap. text ed. 8.95 (ISBN 0-521-20796-7). Cambridge U Pr.

--Paradise Lost, Bks. 7 & 8. Aers, D. & Radzinowicz, Mary Ann, eds. LC 77-181884. (Milton for Schools & Colleges Ser.). 200p. 1974. pap. text ed. 8.95 (ISBN 0-521-20457-7). Cambridge U Pr.

--Paradise Lost, Bks. 9 & 10. Evans, J. M., ed. LC 72-87438. (Milton for Schools & Colleges). 208p. 1973. 8.95 set (ISBN 0-521-20067-9). Cambridge U Pr.

--Paradise Regained, A Poem, in Four Books. LC 73-9863. Repr. of 1795 ed. lib. bdg. 50.00 (ISBN 0-8414-5950-9). Folcroft.

--Portraits, Prints & Writings of John Milton. LC 73-15855. 1908. lib. bdg. 17.50 (ISBN 0-8414-6060-4). Folcroft.

--Samson Agonistes. Prince, F. T., ed. 1957. pap. 7.95x (ISBN 0-19-831910-X). Oxford U Pr.

Milton, John & Potter, G. R. Zwingli. LC 75-46136. (Illus.). 1977. 59.50 (ISBN 0-521-20939-0). Cambridge U Pr.

Milton, Sybil & Friedlander, Henry, eds. The Simon Wiesenthal Center Annual, Vol. 3. 1986. lib. bdg. 35.00 (ISBN 0-527-96490-5). Kraus Intl.

Milton, Sybil, et al, eds. Simon Wiesenthal Center Annual, Vol. 2. 1985. lib. bdg. 30.00 (ISBN 0-527-96489-1). Kraus Intl.

Milward, Peter. Biblical Influences in Shakespeare's Great Tragedies. 1987. 20.00 (ISBN 0-253-31198-5). Ind U Pr.

--Religious Controversies of the Elizabethan Age: A Survey of Printed Sources. LC 77-80038. xvi, 202p. 1977. 21.00x (ISBN 0-8032-0923-1). U of Nebr Pr.

Milward, Peter, ed. Shakespeare's Religious Background. 312p. 1985. Repr. of 1973 ed. 8.95 (ISBN 0-8294-0508-9). Loyola.

Mims, Edwin. Great Writers As Interpreters of Religion. facsimile ed. LC 70-134116. (Essay Index Reprint Ser). Repr. of 1945 ed. 17.00 (ISBN 0-8369-1988-2). Ayer Co Pubs.

Minar, Edwin L., Jr., tr. see Burkert, Walter.

Minear, Mark. Richmond Eighteen Eighty-Seven: A Quaker Drama Unfolds. 150p. 1987. pap. 5.95 (ISBN 0-913408-98-0). Friends United.

Minear, Paul S. Images of the Church in the New Testament. LC 60-11331. 294p. 1970. pap. 9.95 (ISBN 0-664-24903-5). Westminster.

--John: The Martyr's Gospel. 192p. (Orig.). 1985. pap. 8.95 (ISBN 0-8298-0718-7). Pilgrim NY.

--Mark. LC 59-10454. (Layman's Bible Commentary, Vol. 17). 1962. pap. 4.95 (ISBN 0-8042-3077-3). John Knox.

--Matthew: The Teacher's Gospel. LC 82-10178. 160p. (Orig.). 1982. pap. 7.95 (ISBN 0-8298-0617-2). Pilgrim NY.

--New Testament Apocalyptic. LC 81-4721. (Interpreting Biblical Texts Ser.). 160p. (Orig.). 1981. pap. 8.95 (ISBN 0-687-27890-2). Abingdon.

Minear, Paul S. & Adams, Harry B. Pentecost 2. Achtemeier, Elizabeth, et al, eds. LC 79-7377. (Proclamation 2: Aids for Interpreting the Lessons of the Church Year, Ser. A). 64p. (Orig.). 1981. pap. 3.75 (ISBN 0-8006-4097-7, 1-4097). Fortress.

Miner, Caroline E. & Kimball, Edward L. Camilla. LC 80-69723. (Illus.). 1980. 8.95 (ISBN 0-87747-845-7). Deseret Bk.

Miner, Earl, ed. Literary Uses of Typology from the Late Middle Ages to the Present. LC 76-45904. 1977. 47.50 (ISBN 0-691-06327-3). Princeton U Pr.

Miner, Ernest. Living Thoughts. (Book of Inspirational Thoughts Ser.). 84p. 1985. 7.95 (ISBN 0-935087-00-1). Wright Pub Co.

Miner, Malcolm. Healing Is for Real. pap. 4.95 (ISBN 0-8192-1132-X). Morehouse.

Miner, Ron. Come Sit with Me: Sermons for Children. LC 81-10650. (Illus.). 96p. (Orig.). 1981. pap. 5.95 (ISBN 0-8298-0469-2). Pilgrim NY.

Miner, Ron, jt. auth. see Benjamin, Don-Paul.

Miners, Scott. A Spiritual Approach to Male-Female Relations. LC 83-40326. 220p. (Orig.). 1984. pap. 6.50 (ISBN 0-8356-0583-3, Quest). Theos Pub Hse.

Minet, William & Waller, William C., eds. Registers of the Church Known As La Patente in Spittlefields from 1689-1785. Bd. with Register of Baptisms in the Dutch Church at Colchester from 1645-1728. Moens, William J., ed. Repr. of 1905 ed; Pt. 2. Registers of the French Church. Moens, W. J., ed. Repr. of 1899 ed. (Hugenot Society of London Publications Ser.: Vols. 11-13). Repr. of 1898 ed. 135.00 (ISBN 0-8115-1648-2). Kraus Repr.

Minet, William see Chamier, Adrian C.

Ming Dao, Wong see Dao, Wong Ming.

Mings, Lonnie C. The Pure Land. (Orig.). 1979. pap. 4.95 (ISBN 0-8024-5989-7). Moody.

Ming-Shih, Y. T'ai Chi Ch'uan. 6.95x (ISBN 0-685-63782-4). Wehman.

Minichen, Sam. From God Through Me to You. 58p. 1984. 3.95 (ISBN 0-89697-188-0). Intl Univ Pr.

Minihan, Michael A., tr. see Mochulsky, Konstantin.

Minirth, Frank B. & Skipper, States. One Hundred Ways to Live a Happy & Successful Life. (Direction Bks.). 1979. pap. 4.95 (ISBN 0-8010-6213-6). Baker Bk.

Minirth, Frank B., et al. Beating the Clock: A Guide to Maturing Successfully. (Life Enrichment Ser.). 1986. pap. 3.95 (ISBN 0-8010-6205-5). Baker Bk.

Minkin, Jacob. The Teachings of Maimonides. 450p. 1987. Repr. of 1957 ed. 35.00 (ISBN 0-87668-953-5). Aronson.

Minnery, Tom, ed. Pornography: A Human Tragedy. 350p. 1986. pap. 14.95 (ISBN 0-8423-4947-2). Tyndale.

Minnich, Nelson H., ed. Studies in Catholic History. 1985. 35.00 (ISBN 0-89453-530-7). M Glazier.

Mino, Yutaka, ed. see Art Institute of Chicago.

Minor, Robert. Bhagavad Gita: An Exegetical Commentary. 1982. 38.00x (ISBN 0-8364-0817-9); text ed. 18.50x (ISBN 0-8364-0862-4). South Asia Bks.

Minor, Robert N. Radhakrishnan: A Religious Biography. 178p. 1987. text ed. 34.50x (ISBN 0-88706-554-6); pap. 10.95x (ISBN 0-88706-555-4). State U NY Pr.

--Sri Aurobindo: The Perfect & the Good. 1978. 15.00x (ISBN 0-8364-0033-X). South Asia Bks.

Minor, Robert N., ed. Modern Indian Interpreters of the Bhagavadgita. (Religious Studies Ser.). 288p. (Orig.). 1986. 44.50x (ISBN 0-88706-297-0); pap. 14.95x (ISBN 0-88706-298-9). State U NY Pr.

Minors, R. A., ed. see Bede the Venerable.

Mintz, Alan. Hurban: Responses to Catastrophe in Hebrew Literature. LC 83-23979. 288p. 1984. 27.50x (ISBN 0-231-05634-6). Columbia U Pr.

Mintz, Jerome R. Legends of the Hasidim: An Introduction to Hasidic Culture & Oral Tradition in the New World. LC 68-16707. 504p. 1974. pap. 14.95 (ISBN 0-226-53103-1, P612, Phoen). U of Chicago Pr.

Minucius Felix, M. Octavius. pap. 31.00 (ISBN 0-384-39070-6). Johnson Repr.

Minus, Paul M., Jr. The Catholic Rediscovery of Protestantism: A History of Ecumenical Pioneering. LC 75-44804. 276p. 1976. pap. 6.95 (ISBN 0-8091-1944-7). Paulist Pr.

Minus, Paul M., Jr., jt. auth. see Freudenberger, C. Dean.

Minz, Karl-Heinz. Pleroma Trinitatis: Die Trinitaetstheologie bei Matthias Joseph Scheeben. (Disputationes Theologicae Ser.: Vol. 10). 404p. 1982. 40.55 (ISBN 3-8204-6182-5). P Lang Pubs.

Mi-pham, Lama. Calm & Clear. LC 73-79058. (Tibetan Translation Ser., Vol. 1). (Illus.). 128p. 1973. pap. 6.95 (ISBN 0-913546-02-X). Dharma Pub.

Mirabai & Nandy, Pritish. Krishna: Devotional Songs of Mirabai. 68p. (Orig.). 1982. pap. text ed. O.P. (ISBN 0-7069-1495-3, Pub. by Vikas India); text ed. 5.25x (ISBN 0-7069-1494-5). Advent NY.

Mir Ahmad Ali, tr. Koran. LC 83-80220. 440p. Date not set. pap. 4.95 (ISBN 0-940368-36-6). Tahrike Tarsile Quran.

Miranda, Jose. Communism in the Bible. Barr, Robert R., tr. from Span. LC 81-16936. Orig. Title: Comunismo En la Biblia. 96p. (Orig.). 1982. pap. 6.95 (ISBN 0-88344-014-8). Orbis Bks.

Miranda, Jose P. Being & the Messiah: The Message of St. John. Eagleson, John, tr. from Span. LC 77-5388. Orig. Title: El Ser y el Mesias. 253p. (Orig.). 1977. 8.95x (ISBN 0-88344-027-X). Orbis Bks.

--Marx Against the Marxists: The Christian Humanism of Karl Marx. Drury, John, tr. from Span. LC 80-14415. Orig. Title: El Christianismo de Marx. 336p. (Orig.). 1980. pap. 12.95 (ISBN 0-88344-322-8). Orbis Bks.

--Marx & the Bible: A Critique of the Philosophy of Oppression. Eagleson, John, tr. from Span. LC 73-89053. Orig. Title: Marx y la Biblia: Critica a la filosofia de la oppresion. Tr. of Marx y la Biblia. 360p. (Orig.). 1974. pap. 8.95x (ISBN 0-88344-307-4). Orbis Bks.

Miranda, Juan C. Church Growth Manual. Lamigueiro, Fernando, ed. Orig. Title: Manual De Iglecrecimiento. 192p. 1985. pap. 4.50 (ISBN 0-8297-0707-7). Life Pubs Intl.

Mirandola, Giovanni Pico Della see Pico Della Mirandola, Giovanni.

Mirandola, Giovanni Pico Della see Pico della Mirandola, Giovanni.

Miravalle, Mark I. The Message of Medjugorje: The Marian Message to the Modern World. LC 86-1588. 168p. 1986. lib. bdg. 23.75 (ISBN 0-8191-5288-9); pap. 9.75 (ISBN 0-8191-5289-7). U Pr of Amer.

Mirchandani, Jyoti, jt. auth. see Vaswani, J. P.

Miri, Sujata. Religion & Society of North-East India. 128p. 1980. text ed. 13.95x (ISBN 0-7069-1136-9, Pub. by Vikas India). Advent NY.

Mirikitani, Janice, et al, eds. Time to Greez! Incantations from the Third World. LC 75-355. (Illus.). 224p. (Orig.). 1975. pap. 4.95 (ISBN 0-912078-44-8). Volcano Pr.

Miron, Dan. Sholem Aleykhem: Person, Persona, Presence. LC 73-161969. (Uriel Weinreich Memorial Lecture Ser.: No.1). 45p. 1972. pap. 2.00 (ISBN 0-914512-02-1). Yivo Inst.

Mirsky, Jeannette. Houses of God. LC 76-1536. 1976. pap. 25.00x (ISBN 0-226-53184-8, P690, Phoen). U of Chicago Pr.

Mirsky, Norman B. Unorthodox Judaism. LC 78-8683. 227p. 1978. 17.50 (ISBN 0-8142-0283-7). Ohio St U Pr.

Mirus, Jeffrey. The Divine Courtship: A History of Our Salvation. 183p. 1977. 7.95 (ISBN 0-931888-13-1). Christendom Pubns.

Mir Valiuddin. Love of God. LC 85-27481. 216p. 1985. Repr. lib. bdg. 19.95x (ISBN 0-89370-577-2). Borgo Pr.

Miscall, Peter D. A Reading of I Samuel. (Literary Bible Ser.). 256p. 1985. cancelled (ISBN 0-8245-0662-6). Crossroad NY.

--The Workings of Old Testament Narrative. LC 82-48570. (Semeia Studies). 160p. 1983. pap. 8.95 (ISBN 0-8006-1512-3). Fortress.

--The Workings of Old Testament Narrative. LC 82-5993. (SBL Semeia Studies). 158p. 1983. pap. 8.95 (ISBN 0-89130-584-X, 06-06-12). Scholars Pr GA.

Mische, Patricia M. Star Wars & the State of Our Souls: Deciding the Future of Planet Earth. 122p. (Orig.). 1985. pap. 4.95 (ISBN 0-86683-450-8, HarpR). Har-Row.

Mischke, Bernard C. & Mischke, Fritz. Pray Today's Gospel: Reflections on the Day's Good News. LC 80-14186. 358p. (Orig.). 1980. pap. 9.95 (ISBN 0-8189-0403-8). Alba.

Mischke, Fritz, jt. auth. see Mischke, Bernard C.

Miscitelli, Peter. Savonarola, Protestantism & the Church of Rome, 2 vols. (Illus.). 247p. 1985. Set. 187.50 (ISBN 0-89901-230-2). Found Class Reprints.

Mishan, E. J. Making the World Safe for Pornography. LC 73-83001. 262p. 1973. 1.95 (ISBN 0-912050-41-1, Library Pr). Open Court.

Mishr, R. P. Hinduism: The Faith of the Future. 131p. 1981. 15.95x (ISBN 0-940500-17-5, Pub. by S S Pubs India). Asia Bk Corp.

--Hinduism: The Faith of the Future. 131p. 1981. text ed. 15.00x (ISBN 0-391-02515-5). Humanities.

Mishra, K. C. The Cult of Jagannatha. 2nd, Rev. ed. 1985. 28.50x (ISBN 0-317-17545-9, Pub. by Mukhopadhyaya India). South Asia Bks.

Mishra, V. B. From the Vedas to the Manu-Samhita: A Cultural Study. 160p. 1982. text ed. 19.95x (ISBN 0-391-02705-0). Humanities.

Miskawayh, et al. The Eclipse of the Abbasid Caliphate, 7 vols. Amedroz, H. F. & Margoliouth, D. S., trs. from Arabic. Repr. of 1920 ed. lib. bdg. 500.00. Caratzas.

Misra, G. S. Development of Buddhist Ethics. 1984. text ed. 14.00x. Coronet Bks.

Misrahi, R. Le Desir et la Reflexion Dans la Philosophie De Spinoza. (Publications Gramma Ser.). 382p. 1972. pap. 30.25x (ISBN 0-677-50815-8). Gordon & Breach.

Missionary Research Library. New York Dictionary Catalog of the Missionary Research Library, 17 vols. 1968. Set. 1680.00 (ISBN 0-8161-0778-5, Hall Library). G K Hall.

Mistry, Freny. Nietzsche & Buddhism. (Monographien und Texte zur Nietzsche-Forschung, Vol. 6). 211p. 1981. 43.25 (ISBN 3-11-008305-1). De Gruyter.

Mistry, Jim. Letters from the Mandali of Avatar Meher Baba, Vol. 2. LC 83-142831. 176p. (Orig.). 1983. pap. 7.95 (ISBN 0-913078-46-8). Sheriar Pr.

Mistry, Jim, compiled by. Letters from the Mandali of Avatar Meher Baba, Vol 1. LC 83-142831. 152p. (Orig.). 1981. pap. 6.75 (ISBN 0-913078-42-5). Sheriar Pr.

Misyn, Richard, tr. see Rolle, Richard.

Mitcham, Carl & Grote, Jim, eds. Theology & Technology: Essays in Christian Analysis & Exegesis. LC 84-2183. 534p. (Orig.). 1984. lib. bdg. 36.00 (ISBN 0-8191-3808-8); pap. text ed. 20.50 (ISBN 0-8191-3809-6). U Pr of Amer.

Mitchel, Fordyce, ed. see Brady, Thomas A.

Mitchel, Larry A. A Student's Vocabulary for Biblical Hebrew & Aramaic. 128p. 1984. pap. 5.95 (ISBN 0-310-45461-1, 11607P). Zondervan.

Mitchell, Allan. Victors & Vanquished: The German Influences on Army & Church in France after 1870. LC 83-25917. xiv, 169p. 1984. 32.00x (ISBN 0-8078-1603-5). U of NC Pr.

Mitchell, Basil. The Justification of Religious Belief. (Orig.). 1981. pap. 7.95x (ISBN 0-19-520124-8). Oxford U Pr.

--Morality: Religious & Secular. 176p. 1986. pap. 10.95x (ISBN 0-19-824928-4). Oxford U Pr.

--Morality-Religious & Secular: The Dilemma of the Traditional Conscience. 1980. 29.95x (ISBN 0-19-824537-8). Oxford U Pr.

Mitchell, Basil, ed. Philosophy of Religion. (Oxford Readings in Philosophy Ser). (Orig.). 1971. pap. text ed. 9.95x (ISBN 0-19-875018-8). Oxford U Pr.

Mitchell, Bonner. Rome in the High Renaissance: The Age of Leo X. LC 72-9277. (Centers of Civilization Ser.: Vol. 33). 1973. 11.95x (ISBN 0-8061-1052-X). U of Okla Pr.

Mitchell, Carlton T., ed. see Moltmann, Jurgen, et al.

Mitchell, Carnell C., Jr. Speaking in Church Made Simple. 1985. pap. 3.95 (ISBN 0-8054-3431-3). Broadman.

Mitchell, Cathy, jt. auth. see Mitchell, David.

Mitchell, Curtis C. Praying Jesus' Way. 160p. 1977. 10.95 (ISBN 0-8007-0843-1). Revell.

Mitchell, David & Mitchell, Cathy. Light on Synanon. 1982. pap. 7.50 (ISBN 0-87223-761-3, Wideview Bks). Putnam Pub Group.

Mitchell, Edward, jt. auth. see Davies, Benjamin.

Mitchell, Edward C., ed. see Furst, Gesenius.

Mitchell, Ella P., ed. Those Preachin' Women. 128p. 1985. pap. 7.95 (ISBN 0-8170-1073-4). Judson.

Mitchell, H. G., et al. A Critical & Exegetical Commentary on Haggai, Zechariah, Malachi & Jonah. (International Critical Commentary Ser.). 544p. 1912. 24.95 (ISBN 0-567-05020-3, Pub. by T & T Clark Ltd UK). Fortress.

Mitchell, Henry, et al. This Far by Faith: American Black Worship & Its African Roots. Hovda, Robert, ed. LC 77-89744. 1977. pap. 7.95 (ISBN 0-918208-05-X). Liturgical Conf.

Mitchell, Henry H. Black Preaching. LC 78-19508. 1979. pap. 8.95xi (ISBN 0-06-065761-8, RD297, HarpR). Har-Row.

Mitchell, Hubert. Putting Your Faith on the Line. (Orig.). 1981. pap. 5.95 (ISBN 0-89840-027-9). Heres Life.

Mitchell, Joan. God's Plan for Us. 1984. 4.95 (ISBN 0-89837-092-2, Pub. by Pflaum Press). Peter Li.

--Me, Believing. (Infinity Ser.: No. 8). 1972. text ed. 2.50 (ISBN 0-03-004061-2, 241, HarpR). Har-Row.

--Our God Gives Life. 1984. 9.95 (ISBN 0-89837-098-1, Pub. by Pflaum Press). Peter Li.

--We Gather, Remember, & Eat. 1986. tchr's. ed. 2.00 (ISBN 0-89837-110-4); wkbk. 5.25 (ISBN 0-89837-109-0). Peter Li.

Mitchell, Joan & O'Neill, Irene. Beatitudes for Today. Fisher, Carl, ed. (Illus.). 1985. dupl. masterbook 9.95 (ISBN 0-89837-102-3, Pub. by Pflaum Pr). Peter Li.

--Making Moral Choices. Fisher, Carl, ed. (Illus.). 1985. Dupl. Masterbook 9.95 (ISBN 0-89837-103-1, Pub. by Pflaum Pr). Peter Li.

Mitchell, Joan & Sherlock, Therese. Celebrating the Gospel. Fisher, Carl, ed. (Illus.). 1985. dupl. masterbook 9.95 (ISBN 0-89837-105-8, Pub. by Pflaum Pr). Peter Li.

Mitchell, John. The Earth Spirit: Its Ways, Shrines & Mysteries. 1976. pap. 5.95 (ISBN 0-380-01154-9, 26880). Avon.

Mitchell, John G. An Everlasting Love: A Devotional Commentary on the Gospel of John. LC 82-22285. 1982. 13.95 (ISBN 0-88070-005-X). Multnomah.

--Fellowship: A Devotional Study of the Epistles of John. LC 84-193801. (Orig.). 1974. pap. text ed. 6.95 (ISBN 0-930014-06-5). Multnomah.

Mitchell, Julia P. Saint Jean De Crevecoeur. LC 71-181959. Repr. of 1916 ed. 20.00 (ISBN 0-404-04347-X). AMS Pr.

Mitchell, Kenneth R. & Anderson, Herbert. All Our Losses, All Our Griefs: Resources for Pastoral Care. LC 83-19851. 180p. (Orig.). 1983. pap. 8.95 (ISBN 0-664-24493-9). Westminster.

Mitchell, Kenneth R., tr. see Faber, Heije.

Mitchell, Kenneth R., tr. see Ter Linden, Nico.

Mitchell, Kurt. Poor Ralph. (Illus.). 32p. 1982. 8.95 (ISBN 0-89107-273-X, Crossway Bks). Good News.

Mitchell, Leonel L. Praying Shapes Believing: A Theological Commentary on the Book of Common Prayer. 220p. 1985. 17.95 (ISBN 0-86683-494-X, HarpR). Har-Row.

--The Way We Pray. 96p. (Orig.). 1984. pap. 1.35 (ISBN 0-88028-039-5). Forward Movement.

Mitchell, Marcia. Spiritually Single. LC 83-15754. 112p. 1984. pap. 3.95 (ISBN 0-87123-591-9, 210591). Bethany Hse.

Mitchell, Nathan. Cult & Controversy: The Worship of the Eucharist Outside Mass. Kavanagh, Aidan, ed. (Studies in the Reformed Rites of the Catholic Church: Vol. IV). 460p. (Orig.). 1982. pap. 14.95 (ISBN 0-916134-50-4). Pueblo Pub Co.

--Mission & Ministry: History & Theology in the Sacrament of Order. (Message of the Sacraments Ser.: Vol. 6). 1982. text ed. 16.95 (ISBN 0-89453-396-7); pap. 12.95 (ISBN 0-89453-292-8). M Glazier.

Mitchell, P. M., tr. see Gronbech, Vilhelm.

Mitchell, Phyllis. How to Study the Bible. (Workbook Ser.). (Illus.). 95p. 1982. pap. 4.95 (ISBN 0-930756-67-3, 581003). Aglow Pubns.

--With Christ in Heavenly Realms: A Study of Ephesians. (Enrichment Bible Studies). 60p. 1986. pap. 2.95 (ISBN 0-932305-22-9, 522007). Aglow Pubns.

Mitchell, Ralph. Einstein & Christ: A New Approach to the Defence of Christian Religion. (Theology & Science at the Frontiers of Knowledge Ser.: Vol. 5). 256p. 1986. 21.95 (ISBN 0-7073-0453-9, Pub. by Scot Acad Pr). Longwood Pub Group.

Mitchell, Robert. Abraham, Sarah & the Promised Son. (Arch Book Ser.: No. 21). 1984. pap. 0.99 (59-1284). Concordia.

Mitchell, Robert B. Heritage & Horizons: A History of the Open Bible Standard Churches. LC 81-18884. (Illus., Orig.). 1982. 6.95 (ISBN 0-9608160-0-3); pap. 4.95 (ISBN 0-9608160-1-1). Open Bible.

Mitchell, Robert H. Ministry & Music. LC 77-20815. 164p. 1978. pap. 8.95 (ISBN 0-664-24186-7). Westminster.

Mitchell, Rod. Bridge Building. 261p. (Orig.). 1981. pap. 21.95 (ISBN 0-85819-357-4, Pub. by JBCE). ANZ Religious Pubns.

Mitchell, Roy. The Exile of the Soul. Davenport, John L., ed. LC 83-62528. 338p. 1984. 18.95 (ISBN 0-87975-232-7); pap. 9.95 (ISBN 0-87975-233-5). Prometheus Bks.

Mitchell, Sandi. Why Christians Should Be the Healthiest People in the World. 300p. (Orig.). 1987. pap. 9.95 (ISBN 0-9617419-1-0). But It Really Works Bks.

Mitchell, Stephen, tr. & intro. by. The Book of Job. 176p. 1987. 22.50 (ISBN 0-86547-286-6); pap. 12.50 (ISBN 0-86547-270-X). N Point Pr.

Mitchell, T. Crichton. Great Holiness Classics: The Wesley Century, Vol. 2. 504p. 1984. 21.95 (ISBN 0-8341-0910-7). Beacon Hill.

Mitchell, Thomas A. Hedonism & Eudonism in Aquinas. 1983. 2.00 (ISBN 0-686-45793-5). Franciscan Herald.

Mitchell, W. J. Iconology: Image, Text, Ideology. LC 85-1177. x, 226p. 1986. 20.00 (ISBN 0-226-53228-3). U of Chicago Pr.

Mitchell, William E. Mishpokhe: A Study of New York City Jewish Family Clubs. (New Babylon Studies in the Social Sciences Ser.: No. 30). (Illus.). 1978. 20.50x (ISBN 90-279-7695-3). Mouton.

Mitgang, Herbert. The Man Who Rode the Tiger: The Life of Judge Samuel Seabury. (Illus.). 1979. pap. 5.95 (ISBN 0-393-00922-X). Norton.

Mitman, John L. Premarital Counseling: A Manual for Clergy & Counselors. 128p. (Orig.). 1984. pap. 6.95 (ISBN 0-86683-879-1, 7874, HarpR). Har-Row.

Mitra. Buddhist Monuments. 1971. 42.50 (ISBN 0-89684-490-0). Orient Bk Dist.

Mitra, Kana. Catholicism - Hinduism: Vedantic Investigation of Raimundo Panikkar's Attempt at Bridge Building. 186p. (Orig.). 1987. lib. bdg. 23.00 (ISBN 0-8191-6157-8); pap. text ed. 11.75 (ISBN 0-8191-6158-6). U Pr of Amer.

Mitropolsky, S. Kratkaja Grammatika Tserkovno-Slavjanskago Jazika. Tr. of A Concise Grammer of the Church-Slavonic Language. 92p. 1980. pap. 5.00 (ISBN 0-317-30307-4). Holy Trinity.

Mitros, Joseph F. Religions: A Select, Classified Bibliography. Matczak, Sebastian A., intro. by. LC 77-183042. (Philosophical Questions Ser.: No. 8). 350p. 1973. 45.00x (ISBN 0-912116-08-0). Learned Pubns.

Mitrovic, George. Atlan Revisited: The War of the Gods. LC 84-90082. 156p. 1985. 11.95 (ISBN 0-533-06152-0). Vantage.

Mittarelli, J. H. & Costadoni, A. Annales Camaldulenses Osb, 9 Vols. 6787p. 1773. text ed. 745.20x (ISBN 0-576-72247-2, Pub. by Gregg Intl Pubs England). Gregg Intl.

Mittelstaadt, Claudio O. The Essence of the Catholic Approach to Education. (Illus.). 134p. 1982. 59.15 (ISBN 0-89266-356-1). Am Classical Coll Pr.

Mitton, C. Leslie. Ephesians. Black, Matthew, ed. (New Century Bible Commentary Ser.). 256p. 1981. pap. 6.95 (ISBN 0-8028-1907-9). Eerdmans.

Mittring, Karl E., tr. see Ridderbos, N. H.

Mitxhell, Arthur, tr. see Bergson, Henri.

Mitzner, D. T., et al. Constitutional Problems in Church-State Relations: A Symposium. LC 75-155825. (Symposia on Law & Society Ser). 1971. Repr. of 1966 ed. lib. bdg. 19.50 (ISBN 0-306-70131-6). Da Capo.

Miura, Isshu & Sasaki, Ruth F. The Zen Koan. LC 65-19104. (Illus.). 156p. 1966. pap. 7.95 (ISBN 0-15-699981-1, Harv). HarBraceJ.

Mixon, Jerry W. Off the Main Road. LC 85-19065. 1985. 5.95 (ISBN 0-8054-5015-7). Broadman.

Miyamoto, Kazuo, ed. One Man's Journey. 120p. (Orig.). 1981. pap. 6.95 (ISBN 0-938474-02-2). Buddhist Study.

Miyamoto, Shoson. The Buddhist Philosophy of the Middle Way. 1983. cancelled 9.95x (ISBN 0-914910-07-8). Buddhist Bks.

Miyazaki, Kojiro, tr. see Niwano, Nikkyo.

Miyoshi, Sekiya. Jonah & the Big Fish. LC 81-3635. 1982. 8.95g (ISBN 0-687-20541-7). Abingdon.

--Oldest Story in the World. Jensh, Barbara L., ed. LC 69-18145. (Illus.). 5.95 (ISBN 0-8170-0436-X). Judson.

Miyuki, Mokusen, jt. auth. see Spiegelman, J. Marvin.

Mize, Jean. Night of Anguish: Morning of Hope. LC 79-88497. 1979. pap. 2.95 (ISBN 0-87123-398-3, 200398). Bethany Hse.

Mize, Terry. More Than Conquerors. rev ed. 224p. 1981. pap. text ed. 3.95 (ISBN 0-89274-200-3, HH-200). Harrison Hse.

Mizruchi, Ephraim H. Regulating Society: Beguines, Bohemians, & Other Marginals. LC 82-48161. xvi, 208p. 1987. pap. 10.95 (ISBN 0-226-53284-4). U of Chicago Pr.

Mizuki, John. The Growth of Japanese Churches in Brazil. LC 78-5415. (Illus.). 1978. pap. 8.95 (ISBN 0-87808-323-5). William Carey Lib.

Mjorud, Herbert. What's Baptism All about? LC 77-80413. 1978. pap. 2.95 (ISBN 0-88419-173-7). Creation Hse.

Mlecko, Joel, jt. auth. see Lauer, Eugene.

Mlodozeniec, Juventyn. I Knew St. Maximilian. 116p. 1982. pap. 2.95 (ISBN 0-911988-48-3). AMI Pr.

Mlotek, Chane & Gottlieb, Malke, eds. Yontefdike Teg. (Songbook for the Holidays Ser.). (Illus.). 105p. pap. 6.00 (ISBN 0-318-20363-4). Workmen's Circle.

Mlotek, Eleanor G. Mir Trogn Agezang Yiddish Songbook. 239p. 1977. pap. 8.50. Workmen's Circle.

Mlotek, Eleanor G. & Gottlieb, Malke. We Are Here: Songs of the Holocaust in Yiddish & Singable English Translation. 104p. 1983. 10.00 (ISBN 0-686-40805-5). Workmen's Circle.

Moak, Helen, tr. see Fortini, Arnaldo.

Moakley, Gertrude. Tarot Cards Painted by Bonifacio Bembo for the Visconti-Sforza Family. (Illus.). 124p. 1966. 15.00 (ISBN 0-87104-175-8). NY Pub Lib.

Moberg, David A. The Church As a Social Institution. 600p. 1984. pap. 18.95 (ISBN 0-8010-6168-7). Baker Bk.

Moberg, David O. Wholistic Christianity: An Appeal for a Dynamic, Balanced Faith. 228p. 1985. 11.95 (ISBN 0-87178-931-0). Brethren.

Moberly, Elizabeth. Homosexuality: A New Christian Ethic. 64p. 1983. pap. 6.95 (ISBN 0-227-67850-8, Pub. by J Clarke UK). Attic Pr.

Moberly, R. W. At the Mountain of God: Story & Theology in Exodus 32-34. (Journal for the Study of the Old Testament Monograph Ser.: No. 22). 258p. 1983. text ed. 22.50x (ISBN 0-905774-44-2, Pub. by JSOT Pr England); pap. text ed. 14.95x (ISBN 0-905774-45-0, Pub. by JSOT Pr England). Eisenbrauns.

Mobium Corporation, ed. see McCausland, Clare.

Mobley, Mona. Joyful Hospitality. pap. 4.95 (ISBN 0-89137-431-0). Quality Pubns.

Mocatta, Moses, tr. see Troki, Isaac.

Mochulsky, Konstantin. Dostoevsky: His Life & Work. Minihan, Michael A., tr. 1967. pap. 14.50x (ISBN 0-691-01299-7). Princeton U Pr.

Mock, Dorothy. Thank You, God, for Water. (Happy Day Bks.). (Illus.). 24p. 1985. 1.59 (ISBN 0-87239-880-3, 3680). Standard Pub.

Mocko, George. Good God, Where in the World Are You? (Orig.). 1987. pap. price not set (ISBN 0-89536-878-1, 7864). CSS of Ohio.

Mocko, George P. Lord, Empower Us! Sherer, Michael L., ed. (Orig.). 1987. pap. 2.75 (ISBN 0-89536-851-X, 7810). CSS of Ohio.

Mode, P. G. The Frontier Spirit in American Christianity. 1977. lib. bdg. 59.95 (ISBN 0-8490-1870-6). Gordon Pr.

Mode, Peter G. Source Book & Bibliographical Guide to American Church History. 1964. Repr. of 1921 ed. 17.50x (ISBN 0-910324-06-9). Canner.

Modesto, Ruby & Mount, Guy. Not for Innocent Ears: Spiritual Traditions of a Desert Cahuilla Medicine Woman. rev. ed. (Illus.). 128p. 1986. pap. 7.95 (ISBN 0-9604462-0-6). Sweetlight.

Modoc Press, Inc., Staff. Guide to Schools & Departments of Religion & Seminaries in the U. S. & Canada. 736p. 1986. reference 90.00x (ISBN 0-02-921650-8). Macmillan.

Modras, Ronald. Jesus of Nazareth: A Life Worth Living. (Nazareth Bks). 128p. 1983. pap. 4.95 (ISBN 0-86683-713-2, HarpR). Har-Row.

Modras, Ronald E. Paul Tillich's Theology of the Church: A Catholic Appraisal. LC 76-6082. 326p. 1976. 25.95x (ISBN 0-8143-1552-6). Wayne St U Pr.

Moe, Daniel. Basic Choral Concepts. 31p. 1972. pap. 4.00 (ISBN 0-8066-1216-9, 11-9080). Augsburg.

--Problems in Conducting. rev. ed. 1968. pap. 4.50 (ISBN 0-8066-0834-X, 11-9369). Augsburg.

Moe, Dean L. Christian Symbols Handbook: Commentary & Patterns for Traditional & Contemporary Symbols. 96p. (Orig.). 1985. pap. 9.95 (ISBN 0-8066-2153-2, 10-1180). Augsburg.

Moe, Terry A. Inklings of Grace. 64p. 1981. pap. 3.95 (ISBN 0-8170-0941-8). Judson.

Moeckel, Fred. None But a Child May Enter: Poetry. 80p. 1982. pap. 4.95 (ISBN 0-910452-49-0). Covenant.

Moehs, Teta E., tr. The Gospel of Jesus Christ According to Mistress Ava. (Senda de Estudios & Ensayos Ser.). (Ger. & Eng., Illus.). 176p. (Orig.). 1986. pap. 12.95 (ISBN 0-918454-53-0). Senda Nueva.

Moeller, Bernd. Imperial Cities & the Reformation. Midelfort, H. C. Erik & Edwards, Mark U., Jr., eds. 128p. (Orig.). 1982. pap. text ed. 5.95x (ISBN 0-939464-04-7). Labyrinth Pr.

Moeller, Charles. Man & Salvation in Literature. Quinn, Charles U., tr. LC 77-122048. Orig. Title: L' Homme Moderne Devant le Salut. 208p. 1973. 11.95 (ISBN 0-268-00351-3); pap. 6.95x (ISBN 0-268-00489-7). U of Notre Dame Pr.

Moens, W. J. see Minet, William & Waller, William C.

Moens, William J. The Walloons & Their Church at Norwich: Their History & Registers, 1565-1832, 2 pts. in 1 vol. (Hugenot Society of London Publications Ser.: Vol. 1). Repr. of 1887 ed. 30.00 (ISBN 0-8115-1642-3). Kraus Repr.

Moens, William J. see Minet, William & Waller, William C.

Moffat, Robert. Missionary Labours & Scenes in Southern Africa. (Landmarks in Anthropology Ser). (Illus.). 1969. Repr. of 1842 ed. 32.00 (ISBN 0-384-39470-1). Johnson Repr.

Moffatt, J., ed. see Fairweather, William.

Moffatt, J., ed. see Lindsay, Thomas M.

Moffatt, J., ed. see Reith, George.

Moffatt, J., ed. see Stalker, James.

Moffatt, James. The Approach to the New Testament. LC 77-27150. (Hibbert Lectures: 1921). Repr. of 1921 ed. 28.00 (ISBN 0-404-60420-X). AMS Pr.

--The Bible in Scots Literature. LC 73-14835. 1924. Repr. lib. bdg. 35.00 (ISBN 0-8414-6048-5). Folcroft.

--A Critical & Exegetical Commentary on the Epistle to the Hebrews. Driver, Samuel R. & Plummer, Alfred, eds. LC 24-21703. (International Critical Commentary Ser.). 336p. 1924. 22.95 (ISBN 0-567-05034-3, Pub. by T & T Clark Ltd UK). Fortress.

--Grace in the New Testament. 419p. 1981. Repr. of 1931 ed. lib. bdg. 45.00 (ISBN 0-89984-339-5). Century Bookbindery.

--An Introduction to the Literature of the New Testament. 704p. 1981. 19.95 (ISBN 0-567-07213-4, Pub. by T & T Clark Ltd UK). Fortress.

--An Introduction to the Literature of the New Testament. 630p. 1983. Repr. of 1911 ed. lib. bdg. 75.00 (ISBN 0-89984-820-6). Century Bookbindery.

Moffatt, James, ed. see Harnack, Adolf.

Moffatt, James, tr. see Harnack, Adolf.

Moffet, Ruth. DU'A, on Wings of Prayer. rev. ed. Brown, Keven, ed. 96p. 1984. 11.95 (ISBN 0-87961-142-1); pap. 5.95 (ISBN 0-87961-143-X). Naturegraph.

Moffitt, John. The Road to Now. LC 82-4650. 176p. 1982. pap. 7.95 (ISBN 0-8245-0514-X). Crossroad NY.

Moffitt, John, ed. New Charter for Monasticism. 1970. 17.95x (ISBN 0-268-00433-1). U of Notre Dame Pr.

Moffitt, Oleta S. Arranging Flowers for the Church. rev. ed. 1977. pap. 1.95 (ISBN 0-8006-1837-8, 1-1837). Fortress.

Mohaghegh, Mehdi, tr. see Sabzavari, Hadi Ibn Mahdi.

Mohamed. The Philosophical Essence of Islam. (The Essential Library of the Great Philosophies). (Illus.). 143p. 1985. 117.50 (ISBN 0-317-19583-2). Am Inst Psych.

Mohammed, O. Averroes' Doctrine of Immorality: A Matter of Controversy. (Editions Ser.: No. 6). 232p. 1984. pap. text ed. 11.95x (ISBN 0-88920-178-1, Wilfrid Laurier Canada). Humanities.

Mohan, Robert P. Eternal Answers for an Anxious Age. LC 85-60518. 140p. (Orig.). 1985. pap. 6.95 (ISBN 0-87973-592-9, 592). Our Sunday Visitor.

Mohapatra, A. R. Philosophy of Religion: An Approach to World Religions. 208p. 1986. text ed. 27.50x (ISBN 81-207-0110-0, Pub. by Sterling Pubs India). Apt Bks.

Mohler, James A. Dimensions of Faith. LC 69-13120. (Orig.). 1969. pap. 2.80 (ISBN 0-8294-0100-8). Loyola.

--Heresy of Monasticism. LC 76-148683. 1971. 5.95 (ISBN 0-8189-0183-7). Alba.

--The Origin & Evolution of the Priesthood. 137p. 1976. pap. 3.95 (ISBN 0-8189-0342-2). Alba.

--School of Jesus. new ed. LC 72-11835. 280p. 1973. 5.95 (ISBN 0-8189-0262-0). Alba.

Moholy, Noel, jt. auth. see DeNevi, Don.

Mohr, David & Schwartz, Faye. From Birth to Death. 1983. 2.50 (ISBN 0-89536-599-5, 0604). CSS of Ohio.

Mohr, David, jt. auth. see Schwartz, Faye.

Mohr, Victor. The Advent of Christ. 116p. 1985. pap. cancelled (ISBN 0-934616-16-7). Valkyrie Pub Hse.

--A Spiritual View of Life. Ozols, Violet, tr. from Ger. 364p. 1985. pap. cancelled (ISBN 0-934616-15-9). Valkyrie Pub Hse.

Mohrlang, Roger. Matthew & Paul: A Comparison of Ethical Perspectives. LC 83-10147. (Society for New Testament Studies Monograph: No. 48). 220p. 1984. 37.50 (ISBN 0-521-25093-5). Cambridge U Pr.

Moinuddin, Hasan. The Charter of the Islamic Conference: The Legal & Economic Framework. LC 86-802. 256p. 1986. 59.00x (ISBN 0-19-825524-1). Oxford U Pr.

Moinuddin, Shaykh. The Book of Sufi Healing. (Illus.). 256p. (Orig.). 1985. pap. 12.95 (ISBN 0-89281-043-2). Inner Tradit.

Moir, John S. A History of Biblical Studies in Canada: A Sense of Proportion. LC 82-5979. (Society of Biblical Literature: Biblical Scholarship in North America Ser.). 132p. 1982. pap. 17.95 (ISBN 0-89130-581-5, 06 11 07). Scholars Pr GA.

Moiser, Jeremy, tr. see Carretto, Carlo.

Moiser, Jeremy, tr. see Delumeau, Jean.

Moiser, Jeremy, tr. see Rahner, Karl.

Moiser, Jeremy, tr. see Voillaume, Rene.

Moiseyev, Ivan V. A Russian Martyr. 0.95 (ISBN 0-89985-107-X). Christ Nations.

Moissac France Benedictine Abbey. Hymnarius Moissiancensis. 1888. 60.00 (ISBN 0-384-39520-1). Johnson Repr.

Mojica, Fray Jose G. I, a Sinner. 1962. 5.95 (ISBN 0-685-10968-2, L38305). Franciscan Herald.

Mojica Sandoz, Luis. La Meditacion Segun la Mas Antigua Tradicion Budista. (Coleccion Uprex; Serie Manuales: No. 54). (Span., Illus.). 1979. pap. text ed. 1.85 (ISBN 0-8477-0054-2). U of PR Pr.

Mojumder, Atindra, tr. from Bengali. The Caryapadas: Tantric Poems of the Eighty-Four Mahasiddhas (Siddhacaryas) 2nd rev. ed. 225p. 1980. text ed. 13.95x (ISBN 0-935548-03-3). Santarasa Pubns.

Mojzes, Paul & Foster, Durwood, eds. Society & Original Sin: Ecumenical Essays on the Impact of the Fall. LC 84-25406. (Interreligious Explorations Ser.). 216p. (Orig.). 1985. pap. 11.95 (ISBN 0-913757-15-2, Pub. by New Era Bks). Paragon Hse.

Mokashi, D. B. Palkhi: An Indian Pilgrimage. Engblom, Philip C., tr. 160p. 1987. 34.50x (ISBN 0-88706-461-2); pap. 10.95x (ISBN 0-88706-462-0). State U NY Pr.

Mol, Hans. The Faith Of Australians. (Studies In Society: No. 25). 220p. 1985. text ed. 27.50x (ISBN 0-86861-628-1); pap. text ed. 12.50x (ISBN 0-86861-636-2). Allen Unwin.

--Meaning & Place: An Introduction to the Social Scientific Study of Religion. (Orig.). 1983. pap. 6.95 (ISBN 0-8298-0638-5). Pilgrim NY.

Mol, Hans, ed. Identity & Religion: International Cross-Cultural Approaches. LC 77-93700. (Sage Studies in International Sociology: Vol. 16). 246p. 1978. 28.00 (ISBN 0-8039-9890-2). Sage.

Mol, Hans, ed. & intro. by. Western Religion: A Country by Country Sociological Inquiry. (Religion & Reason Ser.: No. 2). (Illus.). 642p. 1972. text ed. 59.00x (ISBN 90-2797-004-1). Mouton.

Mol, Hans J. Indentity & the Sacred. LC 76-27153. 1977. 22.50 (ISBN 0-02-921600-1). Free Pr.

Molan, Chris, illus. The First Easter: Retold by Catherine Storr. (People of the Bible Ser.). (Illus.). 32p. 1984. 10.65 (ISBN 0-8172-1987-0, Raintree Childrens Books Belitha Press Ltd. - London). Raintree Pubs.

--Joseph the Dream Teller: Retold by Catererine Storr. (People of the Bible Ser.). (Illus.). 32p. 1984. 10.65 (ISBN 0-8172-1989-7, Raintree Children's Books Belitha Press Ltd. - London). Raintree Pubs.

Molana-al-Moazam Hazrat Shah & Maghsoud Sadegh-ibn-Mohammad Angha. Al Rasa'El. 146p. (Orig.). 1986. lib. bdg. 22.50 (ISBN 0-8191-5331-1); pap. text ed. 10.25 (ISBN 0-8191-5332-X). U Pr of Amer.

--The Mystery of Humanity: Tranquilty & Survival. 74p. (Orig.). 1986. lib. bdg. 19.75 (ISBN 0-8191-5329-X); pap. text ed. 8.75 (ISBN 0-8191-5330-3). U Pr of Amer.

Moldstad, Joslyn W. Few Minutes with Jesus. 1984. pap. 5.95 (ISBN 0-8100-0189-6, 06N0565). Northwest Pub.

Mole, John W. The ABC Catechism: Ordinary Sundays & Solemnities, Vol. II. LC 81-15227. 278p. 1983. 9.50 (ISBN 0-8199-0863-0). Franciscan Herald.

--The A.B.C. Catechism, Vol. 1: Advent to Pentecost. 262p. 1980. 9.50 (ISBN 0-8199-0814-2). Franciscan Herald.

Mole, Robert L. Thai Values & Behavior Patterns. LC 71-130419. (Illus.). 1971. 4.75 (ISBN 0-8048-0947-X). C E Tuttle.

Mole, Winifred A. So Dear to Me. 1985. 11.95 (ISBN 0-533-06486-4). Vantage.

Molina, S. P., tr. see Dobbins, G. S.

Molina, Sara P., tr. see Edge, Findley B.

Molinari, Paolo. Julian of Norwich. LC 74-13160. 1974. Repr. of 1958 ed. lib. bdg. 32.50 (ISBN 0-8414-6168-6). Folcroft.

Molinaro, Ursule, tr. see Mercier, Jacques.

Moline, Mary. The Eagle & the Butterfly. (Illus.). 57p. (Orig.). 1986. pap. 8.00 (ISBN 0-913444-10-3). Rumbleseat.

Molinier, Charles. Inquisition Dans le Midi De la France Au Treizieme et Au Quatorzieme Seicle: Etude Sur les Sources De Son Histoire. 1965. Repr. of 1880 ed. 32.00 (ISBN 0-8337-2421-5). B Franklin.

Molinos, Michael. The Spiritual Guide. Edwards, Gene, ed. 110p. pap. 5.95 (ISBN 0-940232-08-1). Christian Bks.

Moll, Albert. Hypnotism. (Hypnosis & Altered States of Consciousness Ser.). 626p. 1982. Repr. of 1902 ed. lib. bdg. 49.50 (ISBN 0-306-76079-7). Da Capo.

Moll, H., jt. auth. see Cummings, J. T.

Moll, Hans G., jt. auth. see Cumming, James T.

Molland, Einar. Church Life in Norway: 1800-1950. Harris, Kaasa, tr. LC 78-2711. 1978. Repr. of 1957 ed. lib. bdg. 22.50 (ISBN 0-313-20342-3, MOCL). Greenwood.

Mollat, G., ed. see Bernardus Guidonis.

Mollencott, Virginia R. Godding: Human Responsibility & the Bible. 144p. 1987. 12.95 (ISBN 0-8245-0824-6). Crossroad NY.

--Women of Faith in Dialogue. 144p. (Orig.). 1987. pap. 9.95 (ISBN 0-8245-0823-8). Crossroad NY.

Mollenhauer, Peter, ed. see Steiner, Rudolf.

Mollenhauer, Peter, tr. see Steiner, Rudolf.

Mollenkott, Virginia. Godding: The Bible & Human Responsibility. 1987. 12.95. Crossroad NY.

Mollenkott, Virginia R. The Divine Feminine: The Biblical Imagery of God As Female. 128p. 1984. pap. 8.95 (ISBN 0-8245-0669-3). Crossroad NY.

--Women, Men, & the Bible. LC 76-40446. 1977. pap. 8.95 (ISBN 0-687-45970-2) (ISBN 0-687-81914-8). Abingdon.

Mollenkott, Virginia R., jt. auth. see Scanzoni, Letha.

Molnar, Paul J. Quotes & Notes to Share. Goebel, Patrice, ed. (Orig.). 1982. pap. 4.95 (ISBN 0-938736-06-X). Life Enrich.

Molnar, Thomas. Christian Humanism, a Critique of the Secular City & Its Ideology. 1978. 7.95 (ISBN 0-8199-0694-8). Franciscan Herald.

--Dialogues & Ideologues. 1977. Repr. of 1964 ed. 6.95 (ISBN 0-8199-0679-4). Franciscan Herald.

--The Pagan Temptation. 208p. (Orig.). 1987. pap. 11.95 (ISBN 0-8028-0262-1). Eerdmans.

--Politics & the State: The Catholic View. 1980. 7.50 (ISBN 0-317-46875-8). Franciscan Herald.

--Theist & Atheist: A Typology of Non-Belief. 1979. text ed. 30.00x (ISBN 90-279-7788-7). Mouton.

Moloney, ed. see Corsini, Eugenio.

Moloney, F. J. Disciples & Prophets. 240p. 1981. 12.95 (ISBN 0-8245-0049-0). Crossroad NY.

Moloney, Francis J. A Life of Promise: Poverty, Chastity & Obedience. (Consecrated Life Studies Ser.: Vol. 1). 1983. 8.95 (ISBN 0-89453-370-3). M Glazier.

--The Living Voice of the Gospel: The Gospels Today. 1987. pap. 10.95. Paulist Pr.

--Woman: First among the Faithful. LC 85-73197. 128p. 1986. pap. 4.95 (ISBN 0-87793-333-2). Ave Maria.

Moloney, Raymond. Our Eucharistic Prayers in Worship, Preaching & Study. (Theology & Life Ser.: Vol. 14). 1985. pap. 8.95 (ISBN 0-89453-531-5). M Glazier.

Moloney, Thomas. Westminster, Whitehall, & the Vatican: The Role of Cardinal Hinsley, 1935-43. LC 85-19381. (Illus.). 263p. 1985. text ed. 24.95x (ISBN 0-268-01938-X, Pub. by Burns & Oates London). U of Notre Dame Pr.

Molony, J. N. Roman Mould of the Australian Catholic Church. 1969. 17.50x (ISBN 0-522-83934-7, Pub by Melbourne U Pr). Intl Spec Bk.

Molow, Doree, jt. auth. see Molow, Paul.

Molow, Paul & Molow, Doree. Beyond the Visible: The Triumph Over Yourself...Life & Emotions. 192p. 1981. 10.00 (ISBN 0-682-49739-8). Exposition Pr FL.

Moltman, Jurgen. God in Creation: A New Theology of Creation & the Spirit of God. LC 85-42785. 384p. 1985. 25.45 (ISBN 0-06-065899-1, HarpR). Har-Row.

Moltman, Jurgen, jt. ed. see Kung, Hans.

Moltmann, Juergen. The Church in the Power of the Spirit. LC 76-62932. 1977. 21.45 (ISBN 0-06-065905-X, HarpR). Har-Row.

Moltmann, Jurgen. The Crucified God. LC 73-18694. 352p. 1974. 18.45 (ISBN 0-06-065901-7, HarpR). Har-Row.

--Experiences of God. Kohl, Margaret, tr. from Ger. LC 80-8046. 96p. 1980. pap. 4.25 (ISBN 0-8006-1406-2, 1-1406). Fortress.

--Man Christian Anthropology in the Conflicts of the Present. LC 73-88350. pap. 34.00 (2026872). Bks Demand UMI.

--On Human Dignity: Political Theology & Ethics. Meeks, M. Douglas, tr. from Ger. LC 83-48913. 240p. 1984. 15.95 (ISBN 0-8006-0715-5, 1-715). Fortress.

--The Theology of Hope. LC 67-21550. 1976. pap. 10.00x (ISBN 0-06-065900-9, RD127, HarpR). Har-Row.

--The Trinity & the Kingdom. LC 80-8352. 320p. 1981. 19.45 (ISBN 0-06-065906-8, HarpR). Har-Row.

Moltmann, Jurgen, jt. auth. see Metz, Johannes B.

Moltmann, Jurgen, jt. auth. see Moltmann-Wendel, Elisabeth.

Moltmann, Jurgen, jt. ed. see Kung, Hans.

Moltmann, Jurgen, et al. Communities of Faith & Radical Discipleship. Mitchell, Carlton T. & Bryan, McLeod G., eds. (Luce Program on Religion & the Social Crisis Ser.). x, 130p. 1986. 16.95 (ISBN 0-86554-216-3). Mercer Univ Pr.

--Religion & Political Society. LC 73-18424. (Symposium Ser.: Vol. 1). xi, 209p. 1976. Repr. of 1974 ed. 19.95x (ISBN 0-88946-953-9). E Mellen.

Moltmann-Wendel, Elisabeth. A Land Flowing with Milk & Honey: Perspectives on Feminist Theology. 224p. 1986. 14.95 (ISBN 0-8245-0791-6). Crossroad NY.

--The Women Around Jesus. LC 82-72478. 160p. 1982. pap. 7.95 (ISBN 0-8245-0535-2). Crossroad NY.

Moltmann-Wendel, Elisabeth & Moltmann, Jurgen. Humanity in God. (Illus.). 160p. 1983. pap. 8.95 (ISBN 0-8298-0670-9). Pilgrim NY.

Moltmann-Wendel, Elizabeth. Liberty, Equality, Sisterhood: On the Emancipation of Women in Church & Society. Gritsch, Ruth, tr. LC 77-15240. pap. 23.80 (2026919). Bks Demand UMI.

Molton, Warren L. Friends, Partners, & Lovers. 1979. pap. 6.95 (ISBN 0-8170-0815-2). Judson.

Momen, Moojan. An Introduction to Shi'i Islam. LC 85-40438. 480p. 1987. pap. 15.95x (ISBN 0-300-03531-4). Yale U Pr.

--An Introduction to Shi'i Islam: The History & Doctrines of Twelver Shi'ism. LC 85-40438. (Illus.). 397p. 1985. 25.00x (ISBN 0-300-03499-7). Yale U Pr.

--Selections from the Writings of E. G. Browne on the Babi & Baha'i Religions. 528p. 1987. 29.50 (ISBN 0-85398-246-5); pap. 16.95 (ISBN 0-85398-247-3). G Ronald Pub.

Momen, Moojan, ed. The Babi & Baha'i Religions Eighteen Forty-Four to Nineteen Forty-Four: Some Contemporary Western Accounts. (Illus.). 608p. 29.50 (ISBN 0-85398-102-7). G Ronald Pub.

--Studies in Babi & Baha'i History, Vol. 1. (Illus.). 1983. text ed. 19.95 (ISBN 0-933770-16-2). Kalimat.

Momen, Moojan, jt. ed. see Cole, Juan R.

Momen, Moojan, tr. & frwd. by see Labib, Muhammad.

Mommsen, A. Athenae Christianae. (Illus.). 177p. 1977. 12.50 (ISBN 0-89005-216-6). Ares.

Monaco, Frank. They Dwell in Monasteries. (Illus.). 80p. (Orig.). 1982. pap. 7.95 (ISBN 0-8164-2409-8, HarpR). Har-Row.

Monaco, Vincent, tr. see Francesconi, Mario.

Monahan, Arthur P. John of Paris on Royal & Papal Power: A Translation with Introduction of the de Postestate Regia et Papali of John of Paris. LC 73-16302. (Records of Civilation Ser). 197p. 1974. 27.50x (ISBN 0-231-03690-6). Columbia U Pr.

Monasterio, Xavier O. To Be Human: An Introductory Experiment in Philosophy. 256p. (Orig.). 1985. pap. 7.95 (ISBN 0-8091-2704-0). Paulist Pr.

Monastier, Antoine. A History of the Vaudois Church from Its Origin & of the Vaudois of Piedmont to the Present Day. LC 80-24096. (Heresies of the Early Christian & Medieval Era: Second Ser.). Repr. of 1849 ed. 45.00 (ISBN 0-404-16554-0). AMS Pr.

Moncure, Jane B. The Gift of Christmas. 1985. 5.95 (ISBN 0-89565-083-5, R4914). Standard Pub.

--Growing Strong Inside. LC 85-10341. (A New Values Ser.). (Illus.). 32p. 1985. PLB 7.45 (ISBN 0-89565-333-8). Childs World.

--Honesty. LC 80-39571. (Values to Live by Ser.). (Illus.). 32p. 1981. PLB 10.35 (ISBN 0-516-06523-8). Childrens.

--How Beautiful God's Gifts. Buerger, Jane, ed. LC 80-15434. (Illus.). 32p. 1980. 5.95 (ISBN 0-89565-172-6, 4923). Standard Pub.

--I Learn to Read about Jesus: Primer. rev. ed. (Basic Bible Readers Ser.). 128p. 1983. text ed. 7.95 (ISBN 0-87239-660-6, 2950). Standard Pub.

--Joy. LC 82-1145. (What Does the Bible Say? Ser.). (Illus.). 32p. 1982. PLB 5.95 (ISBN 0-89565-222-6, 4940, Pub. by Childs World). Standard Pub.

--Joy. (Values to Live by Ser.). 1982. 10.35 (ISBN 0-516-06527-0). Childrens.

--Kindness. LC 80-15286. (What Does the Bible Say? Ser.). (Illus.). 32p. 1980. PLB 5.95 (ISBN 0-89565-167-X). Childs World.

--Love. rev. ed. LC 80-27479. (What Is It? Ser.). (Illus.). 32p. 1981. PLB 7.45 (ISBN 0-89565-205-6). Childs World.

--Our Christmas Book. rev. ed. LC 85-29132. (Special-Day Bks.). (Illus.). 32p. 1986. lib. bdg. 7.45 (ISBN 0-89565-341-9). Childs World.

Mondini, A. G. Africa or Death. (Illus.). 1964. 5.00 (ISBN 0-8198-0007-4). Dghtrs St Paul.

Money, Royce. Building Stronger Families. LC 83-51300. 156p. 1984. pap. 5.95 (ISBN 0-88207-244-7). Victor Bks.

--Ministering to Families. 300p. 1987. pap. 10.95 (ISBN 0-915547-92-9). Abilene Christ U.

Money-Kryle, R., tr. see Roheim, Geza.

Money-Kyrle, Roger E. Meaning of Sacrifice. Repr. of 1930 ed. 17.00 (ISBN 0-384-39690-9). Johnson Repr.

Monfalcone, Wesley R. Coping with Abuse in the Family. LC 80-15125. (Christian Care Bks.: Vol. 10). 120p. 1980. pap. 7.95 (ISBN 0-664-24326-6). Westminster.

Monfasani, John, ed. Collectanea Trapezuntiana: Texts, Documents & Bibliographies of George of Trebizond. LC 83-19366. (Medieval & Renaissance Texts & Studies: Vol. 25). 896p. 1984. 60.00 (ISBN 0-86698-060-1). Medieval & Renaissance NY.

Monges, tr. see Steiner, Rudolf.

Monges, Henry B., tr. see Steiner, Rudolf.

Monges, Maud B., tr. see Steiner, Rudolf.

Monheim, Gabriel. The Bible, Jesus & the Jews. LC 79-89891. 199p. 1980. 12.95 (ISBN 0-8022-2356-7). Philos Lib.

Monier-Williams. Buddhism, in Its Connection with Brahmanism & Hinduism, & in Contrast with Christianity. 2nd ed. LC 78-70101. Repr. of 1890 ed. 57.50 (ISBN 0-404-17349-7). AMS Pr.

Monier-Williams, M. Hinduism: Non-Christian Religious Systems. lib. bdg. 79.95 (ISBN 0-87968-546-8). Krishna Pr.

--Indian Epic Poetry: An Analysis of Ramayana. lib. bdg. 79.95 (ISBN 0-87968-547-6). Krishna Pr.

Monier-Williams, Monier. Indian Wisdom. 575p. 1978. Repr. of 1893 ed. 21.00x (ISBN 0-89684-105-7, Pub. by Cosmo Pubns India). Orient Bk Dist.

Monk, Maria & Grob, Gerald. Awful Disclosures by Marcia Monk of the Hotel Dieu Nunnery of Montrial. LC 76-46089. (Anti-Movements in America Ser.). 1977. lib. bdg. 29.00 (ISBN 0-405-09962-2). Ayer Co Pubs.

Monk of New Clairvaux. Don't You Belong to Me? LC 79-88985. 180p. 1979. pap. 7.95 (ISBN 0-8091-2217-0). Paulist Pr.

Monk of the Eastern Church. Orthodox Spirituality: An Outline of the Orthodox Ascetical & Mystical Tradition. 111p. 1978. pap. 4.95 (ISBN 0-913836-51-6). St Vladimirs.

Monk, Robert, et al. Exploring Religious Meaning. 2nd ed. (Illus.). 1980. text ed. write for info. (ISBN 0-13-297515-7). P-H.

Monk, Robert C. & Stamey, Joseph. Exploring Christianity: An Introduction. (Illus.). 256p. 1984. text ed. write for info. (ISBN 0-13-296385-X). P-H.

Monk, Robert C., et al. Exploring Religious Meaning. 3rd ed. Affleck, Bert & Yamori, Tetsuano, eds. (Illus.). 416p. 1987. pap. text ed. write for info. (ISBN 0-13-297524-6). P-H.

Monkers, Peter R. Ministry with the Divorced. 128p. 1985. pap. text ed. 7.95 (ISBN 0-8298-0566-4). Pilgrim NY.

Monks of New Skete. Monastic Typicon. 49p. (Orig.). 1980. pap. 10.00 (ISBN 0-9607924-6-5). Monks of New Skete.

--Transfiguration of Christ. Reverend Laurence Mancuso, tr. (Liturgical Music Series I: Great Feasts: Vol. 1). 40p. (Orig.). 1986. pap. text ed. 12.00 (ISBN 0-935129-02-2). Monks of New Skete.

Monks of New Skete, tr. from Ancient Languages. The Psalter. 286p. 1984. 39.50x (ISBN 0-9607924-5-7). Monks of New Skete.

Monks of New Skete, tr. from Ger., Church Slavonic. Troparia & Kondakia. 452p. 1984. 49.50x (ISBN 0-9607924-7-3). Monks of New Skete.

Monks of New Skete Staff. Birth of the Theotokos. (Liturgical Music Series I: Great Feasts: Vol. 3). 25p. 1986. pap. text ed. 10.00 (ISBN 0-935129-04-9). Monks of New Skete.

--Dormition of the Theotokos. Reverend Laurence Mancuso, tr. (Liturgical Music Series I: Great Feasts: Vol. 2). 40p. (Orig.). 1986. pap. text ed. 12.00 (ISBN 0-935129-03-0). Monks of New Skete.

--Entry of the Theotokos. Reverend Laurence Mancuso, tr. from Gr. & Church Slavonic. (Liturgical Music Series I: Great Feasts: Vol. 5). 40p. 1986. pap. text ed. 12.00 (ISBN 0-935129-06-5). Monks of New Skete.

--Exaltation of the Holy Cross. Reverend Laurence Mancuso, tr. from Gr. & Church Slavonic. (Liturgical Music Series I: Great Feasts: Vol. 4). 60p. 1986. pap. text ed. 15.00 (ISBN 0-935129-05-7). Monks of New Skete.

--Great & Holy Pascha. Reverend Laurence Mancuso, tr. from Gr. & Church Slavonic. (Liturgical Music Series I: Great Feasts: Vol. 6). 60p. (Orig.). 1986. pap. text ed. 15.00 (ISBN 0-935129-07-3). Monks of New Skete.

Monks of Solesmes. The Human Body. 1960. 6.50 (ISBN 0-8198-3309-6). Dghtrs St Paul.

Monks of Solesmes, ed. Education. 1960. 8.50 (ISBN 0-8198-2300-7). Dghtrs St Paul.

--The Holy Rosary. 1980. 5.50 (ISBN 0-686-74345-8). Dghtrs St Paul.

--Liturgy: One Hundred Sixty-Nine Pronouncements from Benedict Fourteenth to John Twenty-Third. 5.00 (ISBN 0-8198-0083-X). Dghtrs St Paul.

--Matrimony: One Hundred & Thirty-Eight Pronouncements from Benedict Fourteenth to John Twenty-Third. 5.50 (ISBN 0-8198-0098-8); pap. 4.50 (ISBN 0-8198-0099-6). Dghtrs St Paul.

--Our Lady: Eight Hundred & Sixty-Eight Pronouncements from Benedict Fourteenth to John Twenty-Third. 5.50 (ISBN 0-8198-0111-9). Dghtrs St Paul.

--Woman in the Modern World: Six Hundred & Thirty-Seven Pronouncements from Leo Thirteenth to Pius Twelfth. 4.00 (ISBN 0-8198-0178-X). Dghtrs St Paul.

Monks Of Solesmes, ed. see Pope Pius Twelfth.

Monks of the Ramakrishna Order. Meditation. Bhavyananda, Swami, ed. 1977. pap. 8.50 (ISBN 0-7025-0019-4). Vedanta Pr.

Monna, M. C. The Gathas of Zarathustra: A Reconstruction of the Text. 1978. pap. text ed. 35.00x (ISBN 90-6203-582-5). Humanities.

Monod, Albert. De Pascal a Chateaubriand: Les Defenseurs Francais de Christianisme de 1670 a 1802. LC 70-170954. (Philosophy Monographs Ser: No. 78). 1916. 32.50 (ISBN 0-8337-4283-3). B Franklin.

Monro, Margaret T. Book of Unlikely Saints. LC 77-107727. (Essay Index Reprint Ser.). 1943. 19.00 (ISBN 0-8369-1528-3). Ayer Co Pubs.

Monroe, Elvira. A Guide to Places of Worship in & Around San Francisco. 186p. (Orig.). 1984. pap. 6.95 (ISBN 0-933174-24-1). Wide World-Tetra.

Monroe, Will S. Comenius & the Beginnings of Educational Reform. LC 78-135824. (Eastern Europe Collection Ser). 1970. Repr. of 1900 ed. 13.50 (ISBN 0-405-02765-6). Ayer Co Pubs.

Monsell, Helen A. Her Own Way: The Story of Lottie Moon. LC 82-71443. 1982. pap. 4.50 (ISBN 0-8054-4319-3, 4243-19). Broadman.

Monser, Harold E. & Robertson, A. T. Topical Index & Digest of the Bible. (Paperback Reference Library). 688p. 1983. pap. 14.95 (ISBN 0-8010-6160-1). Baker Bk.

Monsma, Hester. Devotions for Graduates. 25p. 1984. pap. 1.50 (ISBN 0-8010-2939-2). Baker Bk.

--Devotions for Lifting Your Heart. 30p. 1984. pap. 1.25 (ISBN 0-8010-2940-6). Baker Bk.

--Devotions for Men. 30p. 1984. pap. 1.25 (ISBN 0-8010-2941-4). Baker Bk.

--Devotions for Mothers. 30p. 1984. pap. 1.25 (ISBN 0-8010-2942-2). Baker Bk.

--Devotions for Those God Loves. 30p. 1984. pap. 1.25 (ISBN 0-8010-2943-0). Baker Bk.

--Devotions for Those Who Sorrow. 30p. 1984. pap. 1.25 (ISBN 0-8010-2944-9). Baker Bk.

Monsma, Hester, compiled by. Devotions for Boys & Girls. (Devotions for Daily Living Ser.). 30p. 1982. pap. 1.50 (ISBN 0-8010-2924-4). Baker Bk.

--Devotions for Those Who Are Recovering. (Devotions for Daily Living Ser.). 30p. 1982. pap. 1.25 (ISBN 0-8010-2919-8). Baker Bk.

--Devotions for Today's Teens. (Devotions for Daily Living Ser.). 30p. 1982. pap. 1.25 (ISBN 0-8010-2923-6). Baker Bk.

--One Step at a Time. 86p. 1984. 5.95 (ISBN 0-8010-6177-6). Baker Bk.

Monsma, Stephen, et al. Responsible Technology: A Christian Perspective. 248p. (Orig.). 1986. pap. 12.95 (ISBN 0-8028-0175-7). Eerdmans.

Monson, Rela G. Jewish Campus Life: A Survey of Student Attitudes Toward Marriage & Family. LC 84-70026. 52p. 1984. pap. 3.00 (ISBN 0-87495-060-0). Am Jewish Comm.

Monson, Rela G., jt. auth. see Crawford, Albert G.

Monson, Thomas S. Be Your Best Self. LC 79-54782. 1979. 7.95 (ISBN 0-87747-787-6). Deseret Bk.

--Conference Classics. 59p. 1981. 4.95 (ISBN 0-87747-880-5). Deseret Bk.

--Conference Classics, Vol. 2. 63p. 1983. 5.95 (ISBN 0-87747-957-7). Deseret Bk.

--Conference Classics, Vol. 3. 64p. 5.95 (ISBN 0-87747-989-5). Deseret Bk.

--Pathway to Perfection. LC 73-886344. 328p. 1973. 6.95 (ISBN 0-87747-511-3). Deseret Bk.

Monstrelet, Enguerrand De see De Monstrelet, Enguerrend.

Montagu, Ashley. Coming into Being among the Australian Aborigines. LC 75-41195. (Illus.). Repr. of 1937 ed. 27.45 (ISBN 0-404-14573-6). AMS Pr.

Montagu, Ashley, ed. Science & Creationism. LC 82-14173. 434p. 1984. 24.95 (ISBN 0-19-503252-7); pap. 11.95x (ISBN 0-19-503253-5). Oxford U Pr.

Montagu, Henry. Contemplatio Mortis et Immortalitatis. LC 72-218. (English Experience Ser.: No. 337). 148p. 1971. Repr. of 1631 ed. 11.50 (ISBN 90-221-0337-4). Walter J Johnson.

Montagu, Richard. Appello Caesarem: A Just Appeale from Two Unjust Informers. LC 75-38210. (English Experience Ser.: No. 475). 348p. 1972. Repr. of 1625 ed. 49.00 (ISBN 90-221-0475-3). Walter J Johnson.

--A Gagg for the New Gospell? No: A New Gagg for an Old Goose. LC 74-28872. (English Experience Ser.: No. 751). 1975. Repr. of 1624 ed. 26.00 (ISBN 90-221-0751-5). Walter J Johnson.

Montague, E. R. Takes from the Talmud, 1906. 1977. 22.50 (ISBN 0-686-19672-4). Mill Bks.

Montague, George T. Books of Judith & Esther. (Pamphlet Bible Ser.: Vol. 21). (Orig.). 1973. pap. 1.00 (ISBN 0-8091-5173-1). Paulist Pr.

--Books of Ruth & Tobit. (Pamphlet Bible Ser.: Vol. 20). (Orig.). 1974. pap. 1.00 (ISBN 0-8091-5172-3). Paulist Pr.

--Building Christ's Body: The Dynamics of Christian Living According to St. Paul. 1976. 5.50 (ISBN 0-8199-0573-9). Franciscan Herald.

--The Holy Spirit: Growth of Biblical Tradition. LC 76-4691. 384p. 1976. pap. 10.95 (ISBN 0-8091-1950-1). Paulist Pr.

--Mark: Good News for Hard Times. 200p. (Orig.). 1981. pap. 6.95 (ISBN 0-89283-096-4). Servant.

--The Spirit & His Gifts. LC 74-77425. 72p. (Orig.). 1974. pap. 1.95 (ISBN 0-8091-1829-7, Deus). Paulist Pr.

Montague, H. Patrick. The Saints & Martyrs of Ireland: Feast Days Calendar. (Illus.). 138p. Date not set. 15.95 (ISBN 0-86140-106-9); pap. 5.95 (ISBN 0-86140-107-7). Dufour.

Montague, William P. Belief Unbound. LC 72-109630. (Select Bibliographies Reprint Ser). 1930. 15.00 (ISBN 0-8369-5239-1). Ayer Co Pubs.

--Beiief Unbound. 1930. 13.50x (ISBN 0-686-83485-2). Elliots Bks.

Montaigne, Michel de & La Boetie, Etienne de. Discours de la Servitude Volontaire ou le Contr'un. 90p. 1947. 12.50 (ISBN 0-686-54775-6). French & Eur.

--Les Essais, 4 vols. 1974. Set. 500.00 (ISBN 0-686-54776-4). French & Eur.

Montalembert, Charles, pseud. The Monks of the West from St. Benedict to St. Bernard, 6 vols. LC 3-11386. Repr. of 1896 ed. Set. 195.00 (ISBN 0-404-04410-7). Vol. 1 (ISBN 0-404-04411-5). Vol. 2 (ISBN 0-404-04412-3). Vol. 3 (ISBN 0-404-04413-1). Vol. 4 (ISBN 0-404-04414-X). Vol. 5 (ISBN 0-404-04415-8). Vol. 6 (ISBN 0-404-04416-6). AMS Pr.

Montane, Vincent. Earthquakes & Endtimes. (Orig.). pap. cancelled (ISBN 0-88070-155-2). Multnomah.

Montapert, Alfred A. Pray to Win! A Blueprint for Success. LC 86-73037. 235p. 1986. perfect bdg. 4.95 (ISBN 0-9603174-4-9). Bks of Value.

--Pray to Win: A Blueprint for Success. pap. 4.95 (ISBN 0-9603174-4-9, Pub. by Bks of Value). Borden.

Montefiore, C. G. Ancient Jewish & Greek Consolation. LC 75-184052. 86p. 1973. text ed. 7.95 (ISBN 0-87677-045-6). Hartmore.

Montefiore, C. G. & Loewe, H., eds. A Rabbinic Anthology. LC 73-91340. 1970. pap. 16.95 (ISBN 0-8052-0442-3). Schocken.

Montefiore, Claude G. Judaism & St. Paul. LC 73-2222. (The Jewish People; History, Religion, Literature Ser.). Repr. of 1914 ed. 23.50 (ISBN 0-405-05284-7). Ayer Co Pubs.

--Some Elements of the Religious Teaching of Jesus According to the Synoptic Gospels. LC 73-2223. (The Jewish People; History, Religion, Literature Ser.). Repr. of 1910 ed. 17.00 (ISBN 0-405-05285-5). Ayer Co Pubs.

Montefiore, Claude J. Lectures on the Origin & Growth of Religion as Illustrated by the Religion of the Ancient Hebrews. 3rd ed. LC 77-27162. (Hibbert Lectures: 1892). Repr. of 1892 ed. 46.50 (ISBN 0-404-60410-2). AMS Pr.

Montefiore, Hugh, jt. auth. see Turner, Henry E.

Monteil, Vincent. Black Islam: Africa's Rising Religion. 464p. cancelled (ISBN 0-86356-114-4, Pub. by Zed Pr England); pap. cancelled (ISBN 0-86356-024-5, Pub. by Zed Pr England). Humanities.

Montell, William L. Ghosts along the Cumberland: Deathlore in the Kentucky Foothills. LC 74-32241. (Illus.). 272p. 1975. 22.50x (ISBN 0-87049-165-2). U of Tenn Pr.

Montenat, C. & Plateaux, L. How to Read Creation & Evolution. 144p. 1985. pap. 10.95 (ISBN 0-8245-0721-5). Crossroad NY.

Monter, William. Ritual, Myth & Magic in Early Modern Europe. LC 83-43136. (Illus.). viii, 184p. 1984. cloth 24.95x (ISBN 0-8214-0762-7). Ohio U Pr.

Montero, Lidia D., tr. see Goetz, Joan.

Montessori, Mario, jt. auth. see Bennett, J. G.

Montfort, Louis De see De Montfort, Louis.

Montfort, St. Louis Marie De see De Montfort, St. Louis Marie.

Montgomery, Carrie J. The Life & the Teaching of Carrie Judd Montgomery. Dayton, Donald W., ed. (The Higher Christian Life Ser.). 420p. 1985. 50.00 (ISBN 0-8240-6430-5). Garland Pub.

Montgomery, Charles, ed. The Handbook for the Ultimate Church Musician. Montgomery, Jane. 1985. pap. 3.95 (ISBN 0-916043-04-5). Light Hearted Pub Co.

Montgomery, Helen B. Western Women in Eastern Lands: An Outline Study of Fifty Years of Women's Work in Foreign Missions. Gifford, Carolyn & Dayton, Donald, eds. (Women's American Protestant Religion 1800-1930 Ser.). 286p. 1987. lib. bdg. 40.00 (ISBN 0-8240-0670-4). Garland Pub.

Montgomery, Herb & Montgomery, Mary. Beyond Sorrow: Reflections on Death & Grief. rev. ed. 32p. 1985. pap. 6.95 (ISBN 0-86683-461-3, HarpR). Har-Row.

--The Christian Pattern Book: Dozens of Creative Activities for Children. (Illus.). 64p. 1984. wkbk. 5.95 (ISBN 0-86683-831-7, HarpR). Har-Row.

--The Joy of the Psalms. (Illus.). 64p. (Orig.). 1982. pap. 7.95 (ISBN 0-86683-631-4, HarpR). Har-Row.

Montgomery, Herb, jt. auth. see Delbene, Ron.

Montgomery, Herb, jt. auth. see DelBene, Ron.

Montgomery, Herb, jt. auth. see Montgomery, Mary.

Montgomery, James. Isaiah, 2 vols. 2.50 ea. (ISBN 0-686-73329-0); Vol. 1. (ISBN 0-89315-125-4); Vol. 2. (ISBN 0-89315-126-2). Lambert Bk.

Montgomery, James A. Arabia & the Bible. rev. ed. (Library of Biblical Studies). 1969. 25.00x (ISBN 0-87068-090-0). Ktav.

--A Critical & Exegetical Commentary on Kings I & II. Driver, Samuel R., et al, eds. LC 52-8522. (International Critical Commentary Ser.). 624p. 1951. 24.95 (ISBN 0-567-05006-8, Pub. by T & T Clark Ltd UK). Fortress.

--A Critical & Exegetical Commentary on Daniel. Driver, Samuel R. & Plummer, Alfred, eds. LC 27-14200. (International Critical Commentary Ser.). 520p. 1926. 24.95 (ISBN 0-567-05017-3, Pub. by T & T Clark Ltd UK). Fortress.

Montgomery, James A. & Harris, Zellig S. The Ras Shamra Mythological Texts. LC 36-2726. (American Philosophical Society. Philadelphia. Memoirs: Vol. 4). pap. 34.80 (ISBN 0-317-09878-0, 2000354). Bks Demand UMI.

Montgomery, James A., ed. History of Yaballaha III. 1967. lib. bdg. 14.00x (ISBN 0-374-95814-9, Octagon). Hippocrene Bks.

Montgomery, Jane see Montgomery, Charles.

Montgomery, John, tr. see Muston, Alexis.

Montgomery, John W. Crisis in Lutheran Theology, 2 vols. in one. 1973. pap. 8.95 (ISBN 0-87123-050-X, 210050). Bethany Hse.

--Damned Through the Church. 96p. 1970. 2.95 (ISBN 0-87123-090-9, 200090). Bethany Hse.

--Demon Possession. LC 75-19313. 1976. pap. 9.95 (ISBN 0-87123-102-6, 210102). Bethany Hse.

--History & Christianity. 128p. 1986. pap. 3.95 (ISBN 0-87123-890-X, 210890). Bethany Hse.

--How Do We Know There Is a God? LC 73-16882. 96p. 1973. pap. 3.50 (ISBN 0-87123-221-9, 200221). Bethany Hse.

--Human Rights & Human Dignity: An Apologetic for the Transcendent Perspective. 192p. 1986. pap. 10.95 (ISBN 0-310-28571-2, 18392P). Zondervan.

--In Defense of Martin Luther. (Illus.). 1970. 2.50 (ISBN 0-8100-0026-1, 12N0339). Northwest Pub.

--Law Above the Law. LC 75-31395. 168p. 1975. pap. 3.95 (ISBN 0-87123-329-0, 200329). Bethany Hse.

--Quest for Noah's Ark. LC 74-21993. (Illus.). 384p. 1972. pap. 4.95 (ISBN 0-87123-477-7, 200477). Bethany Hse.

--The Shape of the Past. LC 75-26651. 400p. 1975. pap. 9.95 (ISBN 0-87123-535-8, 210535). Bethany Hse.

--Slaughter of the Innocents. LC 81-65469. (Orig.). 1981. pap. 4.95 (ISBN 0-89107-216-0, Crossway Bks). Good News.

--Where Is History Going? LC 69-11659. 256p. 1969. 7.95 (ISBN 0-87123-640-0, 210640). Bethany Hse.

Montgomery, John W., jt. auth. see Fletcher, Joseph.

Montgomery, John W., ed. & intro. by. Christianity for the Tough-Minded. LC 73-4842. 304p. 1973. kivar 9.95 (ISBN 0-87123-076-3, 210079). Bethany Hse.

Montgomery, John W., ed. God's Inerrant Word. pap. 8.95 (ISBN 0-87123-292-8, 210292). Bethany Hse.

--Myth, Allegory, & Gospel. LC 74-1358. Orig. Title: Names & Titles of Christ. 160p. 1974. pap. 5.95 (ISBN 0-87123-358-4, 210358). Bethany Hse.

Montgomery, Mary. Home Is Where the Start Is: Ideas to Help Families Grow in Love & Faith. 132p. (Orig.). 1985. pap. 6.95 (ISBN 0-86683-868-6, HarpR). Har-Row.

Montgomery, Mary & Montgomery, Herb. Christmas Is Coming. 40p. (Orig.). 1983. pap. text ed. 1.50 (ISBN 0-89622-197-0). Twenty-Third.

--Easter Is Coming: Lenten Celebrations for the Family. (Illus.). 120p. (Orig.). 1982. pap. 7.95 (ISBN 0-86683-609-8, HarpR). Har-Row.

--The Jesus Story. 1974. pupil pack 5.55 (ISBN 0-03-012951-6, 125, HarpR); tchr's. manual 8.95 (ISBN 0-03-012956-7, 126). Har-Row.

--Live This Gift: A Program for Confirmation Preparation. 1975. student guide 3.25 (ISBN 0-03-014266-0, 127, HarpR); parent guide 1.95 (ISBN 0-03-014271-7, 128); tchr's. guide 4.35 (ISBN 0-03-014276-8, 129). Har-Row.

--Together at the Lord's Supper: Preparation for Holy Communion. (Illus.). 1977. pap. text ed. 3.25 (ISBN 0-03-021291-X, 141, HarpR); parent bk. 2.25 (ISBN 0-03-021286-3, 192); leader's guide 4.95 (ISBN 0-03-021296-0, 193). Har-Row.

Montgomery, Mary, jt. auth. see Montgomery, Herb.

Montgomery, Michael S., compiled by. American Puritan Studies: An Annotated Bibliography of Dissertations, 1882-1981. LC 84-6553. (Bibliographies & Indexes in American History Ser.: No. 1). xxii, 419p. 1984. lib. bdg. 49.95 (ISBN 0-313-24237-2, MON/). Greenwood.

Montgomery, R. G., et al. Franciscan Awatovi: The Excavation & Conjectural Reconstruction of a Seventeenth Century Spanish Mission. (Harvard University Peabody Museum of Archaeology & Ethnology Papers). 1949. 24.00 (ISBN 0-527-01292-0). Kraus Repr.

Montgomery, Ruth. Ruth Montgomery: Herald of the New Age. LC 85-25424. 288p. 1986. 16.95 (ISBN 0-385-23311-6, Dolp). Doubleday.

--A Search for the Truth. 256p. (Orig.). 1986. pap. 3.50 (ISBN 0-449-21085-5, Crest). Fawcett.

Montgomery, Shirley E. A Growth Guide for Ministers' Wives. LC 83-71066. 1984. pap. 6.95 (ISBN 0-8054-2708-2). Broadman.

Montgomery, W. St. Augustine: Aspects of His Life & Thought. 1977. lib. bdg. 34.95 (ISBN 0-8490-2556-7). Gordon Pr.

Montgomery, W., tr. see Pfleiderer, Otto.

Montgomery, William, jt. auth. see Gibb, John.

Monti, Joseph E. Who Do You Say That I Am? LC 83-82023. (Orig.). 1984. pap. 4.95 (ISBN 0-8091-2598-6). Paulist Pr.

Monticone, Ronald C. The Catholic Church in Communist Poland, 1945-1985: Forty Years of Church-State Relations. (East European Monographs: No. 205). 256p. 1986. 25.00 (ISBN 0-88033-102-X). East Eur Quarterly.

Montieth, Bill. Wild Bill. 164p. (Orig.). 1984. pap. 5.95 (ISBN 0-89274-324-7). Harrison Hse.

Montinari, Mazzino, ed. see Nietzsche, Friedrich.

Montmorency, J. E. De see De Montmorency, J. E.

Monto Hikkei Kai. The Jodoshinshu Book. (Illus.). 92p. 1973. pap. 2.50 (ISBN 0-685-65547-4). Nembutsu Pr.

Montrond, M. de see De Montrond, M.

Montstuart, John W. The Theory of the Physical Spirit & the Nature of God. (Illus.). 129p. 1987. 98.85 (ISBN 0-89266-591-2). Am Classical Coll Pr.

Moo, Douglas. James. Tasker, R. V., ed. (Tyndale New Testament Commentary Ser.). 176p. (Orig.). 1987. pap. 4.95 (ISBN 0-8028-0079-3). Eerdmans.

Moo, Douglas J. The Old Testament in the Gospel Passion Narratives. xii, 468p. 1983. text ed. 29.95x (ISBN 0-907459-28-5, Pub. by Almond Pr England); pap. text ed. 17.95x (ISBN 0-907459-29-3). Eisenbrauns.

Moodie, T. Dunbar. The Rise of Afrikanerdom: Power, Apartheid, & the Afrikaner Civil Religion. LC 72-85512. (Perspectives on Southern Africa Ser). 1975. pap. 5.95 (ISBN 0-520-03943-2, CAL 433). U of Cal Pr.

Moody. Religion of Soldier & Sailor. LC 45-3352. 1945. 8.50x (ISBN 0-674-75750-5). Harvard U Pr.

Moody, D. L. Heaven: How to Get There. 112p. 1982. pap. text ed. 3.50 (ISBN 0-88368-115-3). Whitaker Hse.

--Prevailing Prayer. pap. 3.50 (ISBN 0-8024-6814-4). Moody.

--Thoughts for the Quiet Hour. pap. 3.50 (ISBN 0-8024-8729-7). Moody.

--Way to God. pap. 3.95 (ISBN 0-8024-9231-2). Moody.

--The Way to God. 160p. 1983. pap. text ed. 3.50 (ISBN 0-88368-131-5). Whitaker Hse.

Moody, Dale. The Word of Truth. 624p. 1981. 24.95 (ISBN 0-8028-3533-3). Eerdmans.

Moody, Dwight L. El Camino Hacia Dios. Orig. Title: The Way to God. (Span.). 128p. 1983. pap. 3.25 (ISBN 0-8254-1490-3). Kregel.

--Doscientas Anecdotas e Ilustraciones. Orig. Title: Two Hundred Anecdotes & Illustrations. (Span.). 1983. pap. 3.25 (ISBN 0-8254-1491-1). Kregel.

Moody, Dwight L. & Martin, Walter. Secret Power. rev. ed. 1987. pap. 7.95 (ISBN 0-8307-1219-4). Regal.

Moody, Dwight L. & Turnbull, Ralph G., eds. The Best of Dwight L. Moody. (Best Ser.). 1979. pap. 6.95 (ISBN 0-8010-6216-0). Baker Bk.

Moody, J. B. My Church. 325p. 1974. Repr. of 1890 ed. 8.50 (ISBN 0-87921-030-3). Attic Pr.

Moody, John. John Henry Newman. 1946. Repr. 20.00 (ISBN 0-8482-5070-2). Norwood Edns.

Moody, Larry, jt. auth. see Boa, Kenneth.

Moody Press Editors. What Christians Believe. 1951. pap. 3.50 (ISBN 0-8024-9378-5). Moody.

Moody Press Staff, ed. see Nave, Orville.

Moody, Timothy E. Devotional Talks on Christian Commitment. (Devotional Resources for Adults Ser.). 96p. 1986. 4.95 (ISBN 0-8010-6203-9). Baker Bk.

Moody, W. R. The Life of Dwight L. Moody. (Heroes of the Faith Ser.). 508p. 1985. Repr. of 1900 ed. 6.95 (ISBN 0-916441-15-6). Barbour & Co.

Mookenthottam, Antony. Indian Theological Tendencies. (IC-Studies in the Intercultural History of Christianity: Vol. 21). 320p. 1979. pap. 34.80 (ISBN 3-261-04613-9). P Lang Pubs.

Mookerjee, Nanda, ed. Sri Ramakrishna in the Eyes of Brahma & Christian Admirers. LC 76-904430. 1976. 6.50x (ISBN 0-88386-791-5). South Asia Bks.

--Sri Sarada Devi: Consort of Sri Ramakrishna. 1978. 6.00x (ISBN 0-8364-0173-5). South Asia Bks.

Mookerjee, Nanda, ed. see Max Mueller, F.

Mookerjee, S. Buddhist Philosophy of Universal Flux. 1975. Repr. 20.00 (ISBN 0-8426-0852-4). Orient Bk Dist.

Mookerjee, Satkari. The Jaina Philosophy of Non-Absolutism. 1978. 15.00 (ISBN 0-89684-021-2, Pub. by Motilal Banarsidass India). Orient Bk Dist.

--The Jaina Philosophy of Non-Absolutism. 2nd ed. 24.00x (ISBN 0-89684-021-2). South Asia Bks.

Moon, Cyris H. A Korean Minjung Theology: An Old Testament Perspective. 96p. (Orig.). 1986. pap. 7.95 (ISBN 0-88344-250-7). Orbis Bks.

Moon, Ralph, ed. see Tarthang Tulku.

Moon, Sheila, jt. auth. see Howes, Elizabeth B.

Moon, Sheila, ed. see Pelgrin, Mark.

Moon, Sun M. The Divine Principle. 2nd rev. ed. 536p. 1973. 10.95 (ISBN 0-910621-05-5). HSA Pubns.

--The Divine Principle. 2nd rev. ed. 536p. 1973. pap. 7.95 (ISBN 0-910621-04-7). HSA Pubns.

--The Divine Principle. 5th rev. ed. 536p. 1977. pap. 5.95 (ISBN 0-910621-03-9). HSA Pubns.

--Home Church. LC 82-88432. (Illus.). 474p. 1983. 14.95 (ISBN 0-318-03061-6); pap. 11.95 (ISBN 0-910621-21-7). HSA Pubns.

--Science & Absolute Values: Ten Addresses by Sun Myung Moon. (Illus.). 139p. 1982. casebound 9.95 (ISBN 0-89226-023-8, Pub. by ICF Pr); pap. 5.95 (ISBN 0-89226-019-X). Paragon Hse.

--The Way of God's Will. 418p. (Orig.). Date not set. pap. 6.95 (ISBN 0-910621-31-4). HSA Pubns.

--The Way of Tradition I. 326p. (Orig.). Date not set. pap. 6.95 (ISBN 0-910621-22-5). HSA Pubns.

--Way of Tradition II. 295p. Date not set. pap. 6.95 (ISBN 0-910621-23-3). HSA Pubns.

--The Way of Tradition III. 541p. Date not set. pap. 6.95 (ISBN 0-910621-24-1). HSA Pubns.

--The Way of Tradition IV. 462p. 1980. pap. 8.00 (ISBN 0-910621-35-7). HSA Pubns.

Moon, Sun Myung. Christianity in Crisis. pap. 3.00 (ISBN 0-686-13410-9). HSA Pubns.

Moon, Warren G., ed. Ancient Greek Art & Iconography. LC 83-47765. (Illus.). 368p. 1983. 50.00 (ISBN 0-299-09250-X). U of Wis Pr.

Mooney, Anne S., ed. see Maguire, Marjorie R. & Maguire, Daniel C.

Mooney, Christopher F. Inequality & the American Conscience: Justice Through the Judicial System. (Woodstock Studies). 144p. 1983. pap. 6.95 (ISBN 0-8091-2500-5). Paulist Pr.

--Public Virtue: Law & the Social Character of Religion. LC 85-41014. 192p. 1986. text ed. 22.95x (ISBN 0-268-01561-9). U of Notre Dame Pr.

Mooney, Christopher F., ed. Presence & Absence of God. LC 68-8748. 1969. 20.00 (ISBN 0-8232-0810-9). Fordham.

Mooney, James. Ghost-Dance Religion & the Sioux Outbreak of 1890. Wallace, Anthony F., ed. LC 64-24971. (Orig.). 1965. pap. 14.00 (ISBN 0-226-53517-7, P176, Phoen). U of Chicago Pr.

--Ghost Dance Religion: Shakers of Puget Sound - Extracts. facsimile ed. (Shorey Indian Ser.). 21p. pap. 3.50 (ISBN 0-8466-0003-X, S3). Shorey.

--Myths of the Cherokee. LC 16-5534. (Landmarks in Anthropology Ser). Repr. of 1900 ed. 37.00 (ISBN 0-384-39920-7). Johnson Repr.

--Myths of the Cherokee. LC 70-108513. (American Indian History Sers). 1970. Repr. of 1900 ed. 89.00 (ISBN 0-403-00221-4). Scholarly.

--Myths of the Cherokee & Sacred Formulas of the Cherokees. LC 72-188151. (Illus.). 1982. 20.00 (ISBN 0-918450-05-5); pap. 14.00x (ISBN 0-918450-22-5). C Elder.

Mooney, John R., tr. see LaPlace, Jean.

Mooney, Lucindi F. Storming Eastern Temples. LC 76-4903. 1976. 9.75x (ISBN 0-8356-0482-9). Theos Pub Hse.

Mooney, Patrick. A Gift of Love: Remembering the Old Anew. (Greeting Book Line Ser.). 48p. (Orig.). 1983. pap. 1.50 (ISBN 0-89622-168-7). Twenty-Third.

Mooney, Tom. The Early History of a Purpose Machine. 1976. 5.95 (ISBN 0-9601240-1-2); pap. 2.95 (ISBN 0-9601240-2-0). Mooney.

Moor, Edward. Hindu Pantheon. 45.00 (ISBN 0-89314-409-6). Philos Res.

--The Hindu Pantheon. Feldman, Burton & Richardson, Robert D., eds. LC 78-60887. (Myth & Romanticism Ser.). 1984. lib. bdg. 80.00 (ISBN 0-8240-3567-4). Garland Pub.

Moor, Mary-Margaret, ed. I Come As a Brother: Bartholomew. 192p. 1986. pap. 10.95 (ISBN 0-9614010-1-X). High Mesa Pr.

Moore, tr. see Steiner, Rudolf.

Moore, C. R. & Moore, K. W. Prophecy Library. 957p. 1972. spiral bdg 19.80 (ISBN 0-914674-01-3). Freelandia.

Moore, Carey A. Daniel, Esther, & Jeremiah: The Additions. LC 76-42376. (Anchor Bible Ser.: Vol. 44). (Illus.). 1977. 16.00 (ISBN 0-385-04702-9, Anchor Pr). Doubleday.

--Judith. LC 83-11694. (Anchor Bible Ser.: Vol. 40). (Illus.). 312p. 1985. 14.00 (ISBN 0-385-14424-5). Doubleday.

--Studies in the Book of Esther. 1982. 59.50x (ISBN 0-87068-718-2). Ktav.

Moore, Carey A., ed. Esther. LC 75-140615. (Anchor Bible Ser.: Vol. 7B). 14.00 (ISBN 0-385-00472-9, Anchor Pr). Doubleday.

Moore, Charles. The Exercise of Church Leadership. 1976. pap. 2.75 (ISBN 0-88027-032-2). Firm Foun Pub.

--Functioning Leadership in the Church. 1973. pap. 2.75 (ISBN 0-88027-034-9). Firm Foun Pub.

--Life-There's More to It Than Meets the Eye. 1983. 5.95 (ISBN 0-8062-2110-0). Carlton.

Moore, Charles A., ed. see Takakusu, J.

Moore, Charles H. The Mediaeval Church Architecture of England. facsimile ed. LC 74-37900. (Select Bibliographies Reprint Ser). Repr. of 1912 ed. 29.00 (ISBN 0-8369-6738-0). Ayer Co Pubs.

Moore, Charles L. Incense & Iconoclasm. 343p. 1980. Repr. of 1915 ed. lib. bdg. 30.00 (ISBN 0-89987-573-4). Century Bookbindery.

Moore, Christopher W. The Mediation Process: Practical Strategies for Resolving Conflicts. LC 85-23675. (Social & Behavioral Science Ser.). 1986. text ed. 24.95x (ISBN 0-87589-673-1). Jossey Bass.

Moore, Clare, ed. The Visual Dimension: Aspects of Jewish Art. (Publications of the Oxford Centre for Postgraduate Hebrew Study Ser.: Vol. 5). (Illus.). 320p. 1987. text ed. 40.00x (ISBN 0-86598-081-0, Rowman & Littlefield). Rowman.

Moore, Clement C. The Night Before Christmas. (Pictureback Book & Cassette Library Ser.). (Illus.). 32p. 1985. pap. 4.95 incl. cassette (ISBN 0-394-87658-X). Random.

Moore, Clifford H. Ancient Beliefs in the Immortality of the Soul. LC 63-10283. (Our Debt to Greece & Rome Ser.). 183p. 1963. Repr. of 1930 ed. 20.00x (ISBN 0-8154-0154-X). Cooper Sq.

Moore, D. M., tr. see Martin, Marie-Louise.

Moore, Deborah D. B'nai B'rith & the Challenge of Ethnic Leadership. LC 81-906. (Modern Jewish History Ser.). 292p. 1981. 18.95x (ISBN 0-87395-480-7). State U NY Pr.

Moore, Donald. A Daily Guide to a Better Marriage. 32p. 1984. pap. 0.75 (ISBN 0-88144-021-3). Christian Pub.

--Improving Your Christian Personality. 61p. 1984. pap. 2.25 (ISBN 0-88144-037-X). Christian Pub.

Moore, Dorothy, jt. auth. see Moore, Raymond.

Moore, E. A. The Early Church in the Middle East. 55p. 1985. 19.00x (ISBN 0-317-39058-9, Pub. by Luzac & Co Ltd). State Mutual Bk.

Moore, E. Hamilton. English Miracle Plays & Moralities. LC 77-100517. Repr. of 1907 ed. 17.25 (ISBN 0-404-00598-5). AMS Pr.

Moore, Edward. Studies in Dante, First Series: Scriptures & Classical Authors in Dante. LC 68-57627. (Illus.). 1969. Repr. of 1896 ed. lib. bdg. 22.50x (ISBN 0-8371-0909-4, MODF). Greenwood.

--Studies in Dante, Second Series: Miscellaneous Essays. LC 68-57628. (Illus.). 1969. Repr. of 1899 ed. lib. bdg. 22.50x (ISBN 0-8371-0908-6, MOSD). Greenwood.

--Studies in Dante, Third Series: Miscellaneous Essays. LC 68-57629. (Illus.). 1969. Repr. of 1903 ed. lib. bdg. 22.50x (ISBN 0-8371-0917-5, MODT). Greenwood.

Moore, Emily. Fifty-Two Sundays of Worship for Children, Bk. 2. 1972. 6.95 (ISBN 0-8341-0253-6). Beacon Hill.

Moore, F. C. T. The Psychological Basis of Morality: An Essay on Value & Desire. LC 77-22632. (Library of Philosophy & Religion Ser). 106p. 1978. text ed. 28.50x (ISBN 0-06-494933-8). B&N Imports.

Moore, Florence. To Know the Unknown. 1984. 5.75 (ISBN 0-8062-2340-5). Carlton.

Moore, Gary. The Gift of God. Wallace, Mary H., ed. 96p. (Orig.). 1981. pap. 3.50 (ISBN 0-912315-37-7). Word Aflame.

Moore, Gary W., jt. ed. see Moore, Hastings.

Moore, George. Hail & Farewell: Ave, Salve, Vale. Cave, Richard, ed. 1985. pap. 16.95 (ISBN 0-8132-0602-2). Cath U Pr.

--Radical Love for a Broken World. 175p. (Orig.). 1987. pap. price not set (ISBN 0-89109-139-4). NavPress.

Moore, George E. Ethics. 1967. pap. 5.95x (ISBN 0-19-500354-3). Oxford U Pr.

--Principia Ethica. 1959. 37.50 (ISBN 0-521-05753-1); pap. 12.95 (ISBN 0-521-09114-4). Cambridge U Pr.

Moore, George F. The Birth & Growth of Religion. LC 23-13669. (Morse Lectures Ser.). 1923. text ed. 10.00x (ISBN 0-8401-1643-8). A R Allenson.

--A Critical & Exegetical Commentary on Judges. Driver, Samuel R., et al, eds. LC 25-19368. (International Critical Commentary Ser.). 528p. 1895. 24.95 (ISBN 0-567-05004-1, Pub. by T & T Clark Ltd UK). Fortress.

--History of Religions, 2 vols. 19.95 ea. (Pub. by T & T Clark Ltd UK). Vol. 1, 1914, 654 pgs (ISBN 0-567-07202-9). Vol. 2, 1920, 568 pgs (ISBN 0-567-07203-7). Fortress.

Moore, Gwendolyn, tr. see Paris, Ginette.

Moore, Harvey D. & Moore, Patsie S. The Mysterious Marvelous Snowflake. LC 80-20996. 128p. (Orig.). 1981. pap. 5.50 (ISBN 0-687-27640-3). Abingdon.

Moore, Hastings & Moore, Gary W., eds. The Neighborhood of IS, Approaches to the Inner Solitude, A Thematic Anthology: Plotinus, Dionysius the Areopagite, The Cloud of Unknowing, The Book of Privy Counseling, Meister Eckhart. 108p. (Orig.). 1984. pap. text ed. 9.50 (ISBN 0-8191-3972-6). U Pr of Amer.

Moore, J. N. see Jauncey, J. H.

Moore, J. R. The Post Darwinian Controversies. LC 77-94372. 1979. 57.50 (ISBN 0-521-21989-2); pap. 24.95 (ISBN 0-521-28517-8). Cambridge U Pr.

Moore, J. Staunton. The Annals & History of Henrico Parish, Diocese of Virginia, & St. John's P. E. Church. LC 78-72949. (Illus.). 578p. 1979. Repr. of 1904 ed. 25.00 (ISBN 0-8063-0829-X). Genealog Pub.

Moore, James T. Indian & Jesuit: A Seventeenth Century Encounter. 1982. 12.95 (ISBN 0-8294-0395-7). Loyola.

Moore, Jared S. Rifts in the Universe: A Study of the Historic Dichotomies & Modalities of Being. 1927. 29.50x (ISBN 0-686-51303-7). Elliots Bks.

Moore, John & Neff, Kenneth. New Testament Blueprint for the Church. 1985. pap. 7.95 (ISBN 0-8024-5901-3). Moody.

Moore, John A. Anabaptist Portraits. LC 84-12769. 256p. (Orig.). 1984. pap. 9.95 (ISBN 0-8361-3361-7). Herald Pr.

--Write for the Religion Market. LC 80-25607. 128p. 1981. 9.95 (ISBN 0-88280-084-1). ETC Pubns.

Moore, John N. How to Teach Origins. 1987. pap. 14.95 (ISBN 0-8010-6219-5). Baker Bk.

--Questions & Answers on Creation-Evolution. 128p. 1976. pap. 3.95 (ISBN 0-8010-5997-6). Baker Bk.

--Should Evolution Be Taught? 1977. pap. 1.00 (ISBN 0-89051-043-1). Master Bks.

Moore, John N., ed. see Bliss, Richard.

Moore, John Travers. Story of Silent Night. LC 65-19252. 1965. 5.95 (ISBN 0-570-03430-2, 56-1056). Concordia.

Moore, Joseph. Choice: Confirmation Journal. 96p. 1986. pap. text ed. 3.50 (ISBN 0-8091-9569-0). Paulist Pr.

--Fastened on God: A Practical Catechtical Program for Teenagers. 88p. (Orig.). 1984. pap. 4.95 (ISBN 0-8091-9566-6). Paulist Pr.

--Monday Morning Jesus. 96p. (Orig.). 1984. pap. 3.95 (ISBN 0-8091-2591-9). Paulist Pr.

Moore, Joseph, jt. auth. see Emswiler, James P.

Moore, Joy H. Ted Studebaker: A Man Who Loved Peace. LC 86-19419. (Illus.). 40p. (Orig.). 1987. pap. 9.95 (ISBN 0-8361-3427-3). Herald Pr.

Moore, K. R. Saying of Buddha. 159p. 1982. 15.95x. Coronet Bks.

Moore, K. W., jt. auth. see Moore, C. R.

Moore, Kenneth. Those of the Street: The Catholic-Jews of Mallorca. LC 76-636. 1979. pap. text ed. 7.95x (ISBN 0-268-01836-7). U of Notre Dame Pr.

Moore, Lazarus. Sacred Tradition in the Orthodox Church. 1984. pap. 2.95 (ISBN 0-937032-34-4). Light&Life Pub Co MN.

Moore, M. H. Sketches of the Pioneers of Methodism in North Carolina & Virginia. 314p. 1977. Repr. of 1884 ed. 8.95 (ISBN 0-87921-039-7). Attic Pr.

Moore, Marcia & Douglas, Mark. Reincarnation, Key to Immortality. LC 67-19603. 1968. 10.00 (ISBN 0-912240-02-4). Arcane Pubns.

--Yoga, Science of the Self. rev. ed. LC 67-19602. (Illus.). 1979. 10.00 (ISBN 0-912240-01-6). Arcane Pubns.

Moore, Martin. Boston Revival, Eighteen Forty-Two: A Brief History of the Evangelical Churches of Boston, Together with a More Particular Account of the Revival of 1842. (Revival Library). (Illus.). 148p. 1980. Repr. of 1842 ed. lib. bdg. 9.95. R O Roberts.

Moore, Marvin. How to Handle Guilt. (Better Living Ser.). 1977. pap. 0.99 (ISBN 0-8127-0158-5). Review & Herald.

--Sacrifice. LC 78-21712. (Flame Ser.). 1979. pap. 0.99 (ISBN 0-8127-0214-X). Review & Herald.

--When Religion Doesn't Work. Coffen, Richard W., ed. (Better Living Ser.). 32p. (Orig.). 1986. pap. 1.25 (ISBN 0-8280-0314-9). Review & herald.

--Where Is Bobby Now? (Flame Ser.). 1976. pap. 0.99 (ISBN 0-8127-0106-2). Review & Herald.

Moore, Marvin L. Witnesses Through Trial. LC 78-24294. (Orion Ser). 1979. pap. 3.50 (ISBN 0-8127-0216-6). Review & Herald.

Moore, Mary E. Education for Continuity & Change: A New Model for Christian Religious Education. 224p. (Orig.). 1983. pap. 10.95 (ISBN 0-687-11523-X). Abingdon.

Moore, Sr. Mary E. And I Married the Son of a King. 185p. 1979. pap. 6.95 (ISBN 0-8059-2868-7). Dorrance.

Moore, Oscar. Preachers: You Asked for It. pap. 2.00 (ISBN 0-911866-79-5). Advocate.

Moore, P. The Arts & Practices of Christianity. 96p. 1985. 20.00x (ISBN 0-7062-4125-8, Pub. by Ward Lock Educ Co Ltd). State Mutual Bk.

Moore, Patsie S., jt. auth. see Moore, Harvey D.

Moore, Philip S. & Dulong, Marthe. Sententiae Petri Pictaviensis 1. (Mediaeval Studies Ser.: No. 7). (Lat). 1943. 21.95 (ISBN 0-268-00250-9). U of Notre Dame Pr.

Moore, Philip S., jt. ed. see Corbett, James A.

Moore, R. I. The Origins of European Dissent. 338p. 1985. pap. 12.95x (ISBN 0-631-14404-8). Basil Blackwell.

Moore, R. I., ed. The Birth of Popular Heresy. LC 75-32934. (Documents of Medieval History Ser.). 176p. 1976. 25.00 (ISBN 0-312-08190-1). St Martin.

Moore, R. Laurence. In Search of White Crows: Spiritualism, Parapsychology, & American Culture. LC 76-50720. 1977. 22.50x (ISBN 0-19-502259-9). Oxford U Pr.

--Religious Outsiders & the Making of Americans. 288p. 1986. text ed. 24.95x (ISBN 0-19-503663-8). Oxford U Pr.

Moore, Ralph & Beach, Dan. Let Go of the Ring. (Religion Ser.). (Illus.). 150p. (Orig.). 1983. pap. 4.95 (ISBN 0-941018-10-5). Martin Pr CA.

Moore, Raymond & Moore, Dorothy. Home-Grown Kids. 253p. 1984. pap. text ed. 7.95 (ISBN 0-8499-3007-3, 3007-3). Word Bks.

--Homespun Schools. 1982. 9.95 (ISBN 0-8499-0326-2). Word Bks.

Moore, Rebecca. The Jonestown Letters Correspondence of the Moore Family. LC 86-18192. (Studies in American Religion Ser.: Vol. 23). (Illus.). 398p. 1986. lib. bdg. 59.95 (ISBN 0-88946-667-X). E Mellen.

Moore, Robert, jt. ed. see Stein, Murray.

Moore, Robert L. John Wesley & Authority: A Psychological Perspective. LC 79-13709. (American Academy of Religion. Dissertation Ser.: No. 29). 1979. 14.00 (ISBN 0-89130-290-5, 010129); pap. 9.95 (ISBN 0-89130-291-3). Scholars Pr GA.

Moore, Robert L., jt. auth. see Melton, J. Gordon.

Moore, Robert L., ed. Sources of Vitality in American Church Life. LC 78-71065. (Studies in Ministry & Parish Life). 1978. text ed. 13.95x (ISBN 0-913552-14-3). Exploration Pr.

Moore, Robert L. & Reynolds, Frank E., eds. Anthropology & the Study of Religion. LC 83-71781. (Studies in Religion & Society). 230p. 1984. text ed. 24.95x (ISBN 0-913348-20-1); pap. text ed. 11.95 (ISBN 0-913348-21-X). Ctr Sci Study.

Moore, Ruth N. The Sorrel Horse. LC 82-3136. 144p. (Orig.). 1982. pap. 3.95 (ISBN 0-8361-3303-X). Herald Pr.

Moore, Sally F. & Myerhoff, Barbara G., eds. Secular Ritual: A Working Definition of Ritual. 306p. 1977. text ed. 32.00 (ISBN 90-232-1457-9, Pub. by Van Gorcum Holland). Longwood Pub Group.

Moore, Sebastian. The Crucified Jesus Is No Stranger. 1977. (HarpR); pap. 5.95 (ISBN 0-86683-891-0). Har-Row.

--The Fire & the Rose Are One. 176p. 1980. 9.95 (ISBN 0-8164-0468-2, HarpR). Har-Row.

--The Inner Loneliness. LC 82-14862. 125p. 1982. 9.95 (ISBN 0-8245-0515-8). Crossroad NY.

--Inner Loneliness. 1984. pap. 6.95 (ISBN 0-8245-0619-7). Crossroad NY.

Moore, T. M. Making God's Good News Known. (Orig.). 1985. pap. text ed. 4.95 (ISBN 0-934688-18-4); pap. text ed. 3.95 leader's guide (ISBN 0-934688-19-2). Great Comm Pubns.

Moore, T. M., jt. auth. see Kennedy, D. James.

Moore, T. V. Haggai, Malachi, & Zechariah. (Banner of Truth Geneva Series Commentaries). 1979. 13.95 (ISBN 0-85151-288-7). Banner of Truth.

--The Last Days of Jesus. 212p. (Orig.). 1981. pap. 4.95 (ISBN 0-85151-321-2). Banner of Truth.

Moore, Wayland B. New Testament Follow-Up. (Orig.). 1963. pap. 3.95 (ISBN 0-8028-1136-1). Eerdmans.

Moore, Winfred. Faith for the Second Mile. LC 86-9535. 1986. 8.95 (ISBN 0-8054-5726-7). Broadman.

Moorehead, Bob. Free at Last. LC 86-71102. 88p. (Orig.). 1986. pap. 3.95 (ISBN 0-89900-212-9). College Pr Pub.

Moorehouse, Henry, et al. The Prodigal. (Moody Classics Ser.). 1984. pap. 3.50 (ISBN 0-8024-0494-4). Moody.

Moorey, P. R. Archaeology, Artefacts & the Bible: The Bible Lands in Ancient Times. (Ancient Ser.). (Illus.). 71p. (Orig.). 1969. pap. 4.50x (ISBN 0-900090-00-6, Pub. by Ashmolean Museum). State Mutual Bk.

Moorhead, James H. American Apocalypse: Yankee Protestants & the Civil War, 1860-1869. LC 77-14360. 1978. 32.00x (ISBN 0-300-02152-6). Yale U Pr.

Moorman, Jere. All Things Are Possible: Humorous Interpretations of Scripture. 96p. (Orig.). 1983. pap. 3.00 (ISBN 0-915561-00-X). Crane Pubns CA.

Moorman, John R. Church Life in England in the Thirteenth Century. LC 76-29401. Repr. of 1945 ed. 32.50 (ISBN 0-404-15352-6). AMS Pr.

--A History of the Church in England. 3rd rev ed. 485p. 1973. 19.95 (ISBN 0-8192-1282-2). Morehouse.

--Medieval Franciscan Houses. Marcel, George, ed. (History Ser.: No. 4). 1983. 40.00 (ISBN 0-318-00515-8). Franciscan Inst.

Moorman, John R. H. St. Francis of Assisi. 1986. 4.95 (ISBN 0-8199-0904-1). Franciscan Herald.

Moormann, Phillip G. The Christian Home Study Handbook 1986. (Illus.). 170p. 1985. pap. 24.95 (ISBN 0-9614323-0-6). G Whitefield Pub.

Moorselaar, Corinne Van see Van Moorselaar, Corinne.

Moosa, Matti. The Maronites in History. 350p. 1986. text ed. 35.00x (ISBN 0-8156-2365-8). Syracuse U Pr.

Mooth, Verla A. Completeness in Christ. 144p. 1984. pap. 5.95 (ISBN 0-8059-2954-1). Dorrance.

--The Spirit-Filled Life. 1978. 6.00 (ISBN 0-682-49113-6). Exposition Pr FL.

Moots, Philip R. & Gaffney, Edward M. Church & Campus: Legal Issues in Religiously Affiliated Higher Education. LC 79-14002. 1979. pap. text ed. 7.95 (ISBN 0-268-00732-2). U of Notre Dame Pr.

Mooyaart, B. M., tr. see Frank, Anne.

Mor, Barbara, jt. auth. see Sjoo, Monica.

Mora, Abdias A., tr. see Copeland, E. L.

Moraczewski, Albert S. & Showalter, J. Stuart. Determination of Death: Theological, Medical, Ethical & Legal Issues. LC 82-1127. 32p. (Orig.). 1982. pap. 3.00 (ISBN 0-87125-072-1). Cath Health.

Moraczewski, Albert S., jt. auth. see Atkinson, Gary M.

Morag, Shelomo. Vocalised Talmudic Manuscripts in the Cambridge Genizah Collections: Taylor-Schnechter Old Series, Vol. 1. (Cambridge University Library Genizan Ser.: No. 4). 60p. Date not set. Vol. I: Taylor-Schechter Old Series. price not set (ISBN 0-521-26863-X). Cambridge U Pr.

Morales, Edgar, tr. see Hightower, J. A., Jr.

Morales, Francisco. Ethnic & Social Background of the Franciscan Friars in Seventeenth Century Mexico. (Monograph Ser.). 1973. 20.00 (ISBN 0-88382-060-9). AAFH.

Morales, Francisco, ed. Franciscan Presence in the Americas. (Misc. Ser.). 1984. 40.00 (ISBN 0-88382-258-X). AAFH.

Morales, Phyllis S. Fray Angelico Chavez: A Bibliography of His Published Writings (1925-1978) LC 77-73462. 1980. 15.00 (ISBN 0-89016-035-X). Lightning Tree.

Moran, Bob. A Closer Look at Catholicism: A Guide for Protestants. 192p. 1986. 12.95 (ISBN 0-8499-0514-1, 0514-1). Word Bks.

Moran, Gabriel. Interplay: A Theory of Religion & Education. LC 80-53203. 125p. (Orig.). 1981. pap. 8.95 (ISBN 0-88489-125-9). St Mary's.

--Religious Education Development. (Images for the Future). 204p. 1983. pap. 12.95 (ISBN 0-86683-692-6, AY8272, HarpR). Har-Row.

--Theology of Revelation. 1968. pap. 5.95 (ISBN 0-8164-2567-1, HarpR). Har-Row.

Moran, Hugh, ed. Words to Live by: Chiara Lubich & Christians from All over the World. Dauphinais, Raymond & Moran, Hugh, trs. from Fr. & Ital. LC 80-82419. 157p. 1980. pap. 4.50 (ISBN 0-911782-08-7). New City.

Moran, Hugh, tr. see Lubich, Chiara.

Moran, Hugh, tr. see Moran, Hugh.

Moran, Hugh J., tr. see Foresi, Pascal.

Moran, Hugh J., tr. see Lubich, Chiara.

Moran, John. Joy in a Roman Jail. 208p. (Orig.). 1984. pap. 6.25 (ISBN 0-934998-17-5). Bethel Pub.

Moran, John C., et al, eds. The Romanist, No. 4-5. 1981. 10.00 (ISBN 0-318-20641-2). F M Crawford.

--The Romanist, No. 6-8. 1984. 10.00 (ISBN 0-318-20642-0). F M Crawford.

Moran, Mary Y. Angela Gods Magnet. (Illus.). 48p. 1987. 5.95 (ISBN 0-89962-583-5). Todd & Honeywell.

Moran, Pam. Christian Job Hunter. 224p. (Orig.). 1984. pap. 7.95 (ISBN 0-89283-178-2). Servant.

Moran, Patrick R. Day by Day with the Saints. 214p. (Orig.). 1985. pap. 7.95 (ISBN 0-87973-714-X, 714). Our Sunday Visitor.

Moran, Patrick R., ed. Day by Day with Mary. LC 83-60101. 204p. 1983. pap. 6.95 (ISBN 0-87973-613-5, 613). Our Sunday Visitor.

--Day by Day: With My Daily Visitor. LC 79-92536. 200p. (Orig.). 1980. pap. 5.95 (ISBN 0-87973-530-9, 530). Our Sunday Visitor.

Moran, Peter. Easy Essays. 1977. pap. 6.95 (ISBN 0-8199-0681-6). Franciscan Herald.

Morando, Bruno, jt. auth. see Merleau-Ponty, Jacques.

Morano, Roy W. The Protestant Challenge to Corporate America: Issues of Social Responsibility. Farmer, Richard, ed. LC 84-8514. (Research for Business Decisions Ser.: No. 69). 256p. 1984. 44.95 (ISBN 0-8357-1592-2). UMI Res Pr.

Morantte, M. P. God Is in the Heart: Poetical & Symbolical Essays. (Illus.). 78p. (Orig.). 1982. pap. 4.75 (ISBN 971-10-0040-7, Pub. by New Day Philippines). Cellar.

Moravec, Marilyn, et al. Push Me Gently, Lord. LC 85-80100. 186p. (Orig.). 1985. pap. 4.95 (ISBN 0-935797-21-1). Harvest IL.

Mordell, Albert. Dante & Other Waning Classics. LC 68-8219. 1969. Repr. of 1915 ed. 18.50x (ISBN 0-8046-0322-7, Pub. by Kennikat). Assoc Faculty Pr.

Mordell, Klein, ed. Passover. 128p. pap. 4.50 (ISBN 0-686-95142-5). ADL.

Morduch, Anna. Sovereign Adventure: The Grail of Mankind. 196p. 1970. 11.95 (ISBN 0-227-67754-4). Attic Pr.

More, Hannah. The Spirit of Prayer: From the Works of Hannah More. Link, Julie, ed. 144p. 1986. pap. 5.95 (ISBN 0-310-43641-9, 10272, Clarion Class). Zondervan.

More, Henry. A Collection of Several Philosophical Writings, 2 vols. 2nd ed. Wellek, Rene, ed. LC 75-11238. (British Philosophers & Theologians of the 17th & 18th Centuries Ser.). 839p. 1978. Set. lib. bdg. 101.00 (ISBN 0-8240-1790-0). Garland Pub.

More, P. E. Religion of Plato. (Greek Tradition: Vol. 1). Repr. of 1921 ed. 22.00 (ISBN 0-527-64950-3). Kraus Repr.

More, Paul E. On Being Human. 1978. Repr. of 1936 ed. lib. bdg. 25.00 (ISBN 0-8414-2308-3). Folcroft.

More, Thomas. Answer to a Poisoned Book. Foley, Stepehn & Miller, Clarence H., eds. LC 63-7949. (Complete Works of St. Thomas More Ser.: Vol. II). 544p. 1985. text ed. 60.00 (ISBN 0-300-03129-7). Yale U Pr.

--The Apolyge of Syr Thomas More. LC 72-221. (English Experience Ser.: No. 228). 1970. Repr. of 1533 ed. 42.00 (ISBN 90-221-0228-9). Walter J Johnson.

--A Book for All Seasons. Reynolds, E. E., ed. 1978. 8.95 (ISBN 0-87243-079-0). Templegate.

--A Fruteful & Pleasaunt Worke of the Beste State of a Publyque Weale & the Newe Yle Called Utopia. Robynson, R., tr. LC 75-26096. (English Experience Ser.: No. 108). 1969. Repr. of 1551 ed. 21.00 (ISBN 90-221-0108-8). Walter J Johnson.

--Sir Thomas More: Selected Letters. LC 61-14944. (The Yale Edition of the Works of St. Thomas More: Modernized Ser.). pap. 74.00 (ISBN 0-317-28285-9, 2022022). Bks Demand UMI.

--The Supplycacyon of Soulys: Agaynst the Supplycacyon of Beggars. LC 72-220. (English Experience Ser.: No. 353). 88p. 1971. Repr. of 1529 ed. 14.00 (ISBN 90-221-0353-6). Walter J Johnson.

More, Thomas, jt. auth. see Benson, Robert H.

More, Thomas, jt. auth. see Chesterton, G. K.

More, St. Thomas. The Confutation of Tyndale's Answer, 3 pts. Schuster, Louis A., et al, eds. LC 63-7949. (Complete Works of St. Thomas More Ser.: No. 8). 1836p. 1973. Set. 155.00x (ISBN 0-300-01302-7). Yale U Pr.

--A Dialogue of Comfort Against Tribulation. (The Complete Works of St. Thomas More Ser.: No. 12). 1976. 77.00x (ISBN 0-300-01609-3). Yale U Pr.

--Responsio Ad Lutherum, 2 Vols. Headley, John M., ed. LC 63-7949. (Complete Works of St. Thomas More Ser.: No. 5). 1969. Set. 85.00x (ISBN 0-300-01123-7). Yale U Pr.

--St. Thomas More: Vol. 3, Pt. 2-Latin Poems. Miller, Clarence H., et al, eds. LC 63-7949. (Yale Edition of the Complete Works of St. Thomas More). 800p. 1984. text ed. 62.00x (ISBN 0-300-02591-2). Yale U Pr.

--Thomas More's Prayer Book: A Facsimile Reproduction of the Annotated Pages. Martz, Louis L. & Sylvester, Richard S., trs. LC 69-15454. (Elizabethan Club Ser.: No. 4). (Lat. & Eng., Illus.). 1969. 26.00x (ISBN 0-300-00179-7). Yale U Pr.

--The Tower Works: Devotional Writings. Haupt, Garry E., ed. Miller, Clarence, tr. from Lat. LC 78-16995. (Selected Works of St. Thomas More). (Illus.). 368p. 1980. text ed. 42.00x (ISBN 0-300-02265-4). Yale U Pr.

More, St. Thomas, et al, eds. A Dialogue Concerning Heresies: Complete Works of St. Thomas More, Vol. 6, Pts. 1 & 2. LC 63-7949. (Illus.). 910p. 1981. Set. text ed. 87.00x (ISBN 0-300-02211-5). Yale U Pr.

More, Sir Thomas. A Dyaloge of Syr T. More...Wherein Be Treatyd Dyvers Maters, As of the Veneration & Worshyp of Ymagys. LC 74-28873. (English Experience Ser.: No. 752). 1975. Repr. of 1529 ed. 26.50 (ISBN 90-221-0752-3). Walter J Johnson.

Moreau, Celestin. Bibliographie Des Mazarinades, 3 Vols. Set. 113.00 (ISBN 0-384-40060-4); Set. pap. 95.00 (ISBN 0-384-40061-2). Johnson Repr.

Moreau, Celestin, ed. Choix de Mazarinades, 2 Vols. 1853. Set. 102.00 (ISBN 0-384-40103-1); Set. pap. 90.00 (ISBN 0-685-13377-X). Johnson Repr.

Moreau, Jacques. Die Christenverfolgung im roemischen Reich. 2nd ed. 119p. 1971. 9.00 (ISBN 3-1100-2456-X). De Gruyter.

Moreau, Jules L., tr. see Boman, Thorleif.

Moreen, Vera B. Iranian Jewry's Hour of Peril & Heroism. (A Study of the American Academy for Jewish Research). 247p. 1987. text ed. 25.00 (ISBN 0-231-06578-7). Columbia U Pr.

Morehouse, Joyce M., jt. auth. see Gamblin, Eleanor.

Morel, Francois, jt. auth. see Carrez, Maurice.

Morel, Hector V., tr. see Clymer, R. Swinburne.

Morelli, Elizabeth A., ed. see Lonergan, Bernard J. F.

Morelli, Mark D., ed. see Lonergan, Bernard J. F.

Moremen, William M. Developing Spiritually & Professionally. LC 84-5194. (The Pastor's Handbooks: Vol. 5). 120p. 1984. pap. 7.95 (ISBN 0-664-24604-4). Westminster.

Moreno, Antonio. Jung, Gods, & Modern Man. LC 73-122047. pap. 72.00 (ISBN 0-317-29683-3, 2022073). Bks Demand UMI.

Moreno, Francisco Jose. Between Faith & Reason: An Approach to Individual & Social Psychology. LC 76-56926. 1977. 20.00x (ISBN 0-8147-5416-3). NYU Pr.

Moreno, J. L. Words of the Father. 8.00 (ISBN 0-685-06817-X); pap. 6.00 (ISBN 0-685-06818-8). Beacon Hse.

Moreno, Maria L., jt. auth. see Marvel, Thomas S.

Morentz, Doris, jt. auth. see Morentz, Jim.

Morentz, James, jt. auth. see Albert, Harold.

Morentz, Jim & Morentz, Doris. Children's Object Lesson Sermons Based on the Common Lectionary Year. 112p. (Orig.). 1984. pap. 6.95 (ISBN 0-687-06499-6). Abingdon.

--Children's Object Lesson Sermons Based on the New Common Lectionary: Year C. 112p. (Orig.). 1985. pap. 6.95 (ISBN 0-687-06498-8). Abingdon.

--Minister's Annual: Preaching in 1987. 432p. 1986. 9.95 (ISBN 0-687-26990-3). Abingdon.

--Minister's Annual: Preaching in 1988. 496p. 1987. 12.95 (ISBN 0-687-26991-1). Abingdon.

--Our Time Together: Children's Sermons Based on Lectionary Series A. 112p. (Orig.). 1983. pap. 8.75 (ISBN 0-687-29775-3). Abingdon.

Morenz, Siegfried. Egyptian Religion. LC 73-8407. 395p. 1973. 39.95x (ISBN 0-8014-0782-6). Cornell U Pr.

Moret, A. & Davy, G. From Tribe to Empire: Social Organization among the Primitives & in the Ancient East. Childe, V. Gordon, tr. from Fr. LC 71-139997. (Illus.). 339p. 1971. Repr. of 1926 ed. lib. bdg. 24.50x (ISBN 0-8154-0368-2). Cooper Sq.

Morewedge, Parviz, ed. Islamic Philosophical Theology. LC 79-14405. 1979. 55.50x (ISBN 0-87395-242-1). State U NY Pr.

--Islamic Philosophy & Mysticism. LC 80-14364. (Studies in Islamic Philosophy & Science). 1981. 45.00x (ISBN 0-88206-302-2). Caravan Bks.

Morey, A., ed. see Foliot, G.

Morey, Charles R. Christian Art. (Illus.). 1958. pap. 3.95 (ISBN 0-393-00103-2, Norton Lib). Norton.

--Christian Art. (Illus.). 14.50 (ISBN 0-8446-2606-6). Peter Smith.

Morey, Clinton R. The Denial: A Play for Lent. 1980. 3.95 (ISBN 0-89536-412-3, 0420). CSS of Ohio.

Morey, Grace K., jt. auth. see Clymer, R. Swineburn.

Morey, Robert. A Christian Handbook for Defending the Faith. 1979. pap. 2.75 (ISBN 0-87552-336-6). Presby & Reformed.

--The New Atheism & the Erosion of Freedom. 180p. (Orig.). 1986. pap. 5.95 (ISBN 0-87123-889-6, 210889). Bethany Hse.

Morey, Robert A. Death & the Afterlife. 250p. 1984. pap. 11.95 (ISBN 0-87123-433-5). Bethany Hse.

--Horoscopes & the Christian. 64p. (Orig.). 1981. pap. 2.95 (ISBN 0-87123-202-2, 210202). Bethany Hse.

--How to Answer a Jehovah's Witness. LC 79-25502. 112p. (Orig.). 1980. pap. 3.95 (ISBN 0-87123-206-5, 210206). Bethany Hse.

--How to Answer a Mormon. 119p. (Orig.). 1983. pap. 3.95 (ISBN 0-87123-260-X, 210260). Bethany Hse.

--Reincarnation & Christianity. LC 80-24497. 60p. 1980. pap. 2.95 (ISBN 0-87123-493-9, 210493). Bethany Hse.

--When Is It Right to Fight? 160p. (Orig.). 1985. pap. 4.95 (ISBN 0-87123-810-1, 210810). Bethany Hse.

--Worship Is All of Life. LC 83-73375. (Illus.). 115p. (Orig.). 1984. pap. 5.45 (ISBN 0-87509-336-1). Chr Pubns.

Morey-Gaines, Ann-Janine. Apples & Ashes: Culture, Metaphor & Morality in the American Dream. LC 81-14346. (AAR Academy Ser.). 1982. 12.95 (ISBN 0-89130-535-1, 01-01-38). Scholars Pr GA.

Morfi, Fray J. History of Texas, Sixteen Seventy-Three to Seventeen Seventy-Nine, 2 pts. Castaneda, Carlos E., ed. LC 67-24718. (Quivira Society Publications Ser.: Vol. 6). 1967. Repr. of 1935 ed. 34.00 (ISBN 0-405-19053-0). Ayer Co Pubs.

Morford, Mark P. & Lenardon, Robert J. Classical Mythology. 3rd. ed. (Illus.). 644p. 1985. pap. text ed. 19.95x (ISBN 0-582-28541-0). Longman.

Morgan. Gospel According to John. 1984. 13.95 (ISBN 0-8007-0119-4). Revell.

--Gospel According to Luke. 1984. 13.95 (ISBN 0-8007-0120-8). Revell.

--Gospel According to Mark. 1984. 13.95 (ISBN 0-8007-0121-6). Revell.

--Gospel According to Matthew. 1984. 13.95 (ISBN 0-8007-0122-4). Revell.

Morgan, jt. auth. see Campbell, G.

Morgan, Bayard Q., ed. see St. Thomas Aquinas.

Morgan, Campbell G. Analyzed Bible. 256p. 1984. Isaiah I. pap. 5.95 (ISBN 0-8010-6171-7); Isaiah 2. pap. 5.95 (ISBN 0-8010-6172-5). Baker Bk.

--Analyzed Bible. Matthew. 6.95 (ISBN 0-8010-6159-8); Romans. pap. 5.95 (ISBN 0-8010-6149-0). Baker Bk.

--Analyzed Bible: John. 280p. 1984. pap. 6.95 (ISBN 0-8010-6173-3). Baker Bk.

--The Westminister Pulpits, 10 vols. 1983. Set. deluxe ed. 99.95 (ISBN 0-8010-6155-5). Baker Bk.

Morgan, Carl H. Layman's Introduction to the New Testament. LC 68-22756. (Illus.). 1968. pap. text ed. 4.95 (ISBN 0-8170-0399-1). Judson.

Morgan, Dale L. Dale Morgan on Early Mormonism: Correspondence & a New History. Walker, John P., ed. LC 86-60251. 414p. 1986. 20.95 (ISBN 0-941214-36-2). Signature Bks.

Morgan, Darold H. Personal Finances for Ministers. LC 85-17443. (Broadman Leadership Ser.). 1985. pap. 5.95 (ISBN 0-8054-6405-0). Broadman.

Morgan, Donn F. Wisdom in the Old Testament Traditions. LC 80-84653. 180p. 1982. 17.50 (ISBN 0-8042-0188-9); pap. 9.50 (ISBN 0-8042-0189-7). John Knox.

Morgan, E. S. Puritan Family. 14.75 (ISBN 0-8446-2609-0). Peter Smith.

Morgan, Edmund, ed. see Wigglesworth, Michael.

Morgan, Edmund S. The Gentle Puritan: A Life of Ezra Stiles, 1727-1795. LC 62-8257. (Institute of Early American History & Culture Ser.). 504p. 1962. 30.00x (ISBN 0-8078-1231-5). U of NC Pr.

--The Gentle Puritan: A Life of Ezra Stiles, 1727-1795. (Illus.). 512p. 1983. pap. 9.95 (ISBN 0-393-30126-5). Norton.

--The Puritan Dilemma: The Story of John Winthrop. (Library of American Biography). 224p. 1962. pap. 8.75 (ISBN 0-316-58286-7). Little.

--The Puritan Family: Religion & Domestic Relations in Seventeenth-Century New England. LC 80-18819. x, 196p. 1980. Repr. of 1966 ed. lib. bdg. 29.75x (ISBN 0-313-22703-9, MOPFA). Greenwood.

--Roger Williams: The Church & the State. 176p. 1987. pap. 5.95 (ISBN 0-393-30403-5). Norton.

--Visible Saints: The History of a Puritan Idea. LC 63-9999. 168p. 1965. pap. 6.95x (ISBN 0-8014-9041-3). Cornell U Pr.

Morgan, Edmund S., ed. Puritan Family: Religion & Domestic Relations in 17th-Century New England. rev. ed. pap. 6.95x (ISBN 0-06-131227-4, TB1227, Torch). Har-Row.

Morgan, Edward. John Elias: Life & Letters. 1973. 13.95 (ISBN 0-85151-174-0). Banner of Truth.

Morgan, Elise N. The Angel of the Presence. (Meditation Ser.). 1922. 3.50 (ISBN 0-87516-327-0). De Vorss.

--Communion. (Meditation Ser.). 1928. 3.50 (ISBN 0-87516-328-9). De Vorss.

--The Illimitable One. (Meditation Ser.). 1934. 3.50 (ISBN 0-87516-329-7). De Vorss.

--Now This Day. 1948. 3.50 (ISBN 0-87516-330-0). De Vorss.

--That We May Be Willing to Receive. (Meditation Ser.). 1938. 3.50 (ISBN 0-87516-331-9). De Vorss.

--The Way. (Meditation Ser.). 1972. 3.50 (ISBN 0-87516-332-7). De Vorss.

--Your Own Path. (Meditation Ser.). 1928. 4.50 (ISBN 0-87516-333-5). De Vorss.

Morgan, Ernest. Dealing Creatively with Death: A Manual of Death Education & Simple Burial. 10th ed. 1984. pap. 6.50. Continent Assn Funeral.

Morgan, Evan, tr. see Tzu, Huai-nan.

Morgan, Everett J., ed. Christian Witness in the Secular City. LC 75-133951. (Orig.). 1970. pap. 4.00 (ISBN 0-8294-0198-9). Loyola.

Morgan, Frank, Jr. Keys to Unlock Yourself. LC 84-21418. 1985. pap. 6.95 (ISBN 0-8054-5003-3). Broadman.

Morgan, G. Campbell. Acts of the Apostles. 560p. 1924. 17.95 (ISBN 0-8007-0000-7). Revell.

--Answers of Jesus to Job. (Morgan Library). 1973. pap. 3.95 (ISBN 0-8010-5917-8). Baker Bk.

--Corinthian Letters of Paul. 288p. 1946. 15.95 (ISBN 0-8007-0051-1). Revell.

--Discipleship. (Morgan Library). 1973. pap. 3.45 (ISBN 0-8010-5920-8). Baker Bk.

--Exposition of the Whole Bible. 544p. 1959. 17.95 (ISBN 0-8007-0088-0). Revell.

--God's Last Word to Man: Studies in Hebrew. (Morgan Library). pap. 4.95 (ISBN 0-8010-5955-0). Baker Bk.

--The Gospel According to John. Fang, Carl, tr. (G. Campbell Morgan's Expository Ser.). 1985. write for info. (ISBN 0-941598-94-2); pap. write for info. (ISBN 0-941598-18-7). Living Spring Pubns.

--The Gospel According to Luke. Chao, Lorna, tr. (G. Campbell Morgan's Expository Ser.). 1985. write for info. (ISBN 0-941598-95-0); pap. write for info. (ISBN 0-941598-17-9). Living Spring Pubns.

--The Gospel According to Mark. Chan, Silas, tr. from Eng. (G. Campbell Morgan's Expository Ser.). (Chinese.). 1984. write for info. (ISBN 0-941598-96-9); pap. write for info. (ISBN 0-941598-16-0). Living Spring Pubns.

--The Gospel According to Matthew. Chang, David, tr. from Eng. (G. Campbell Morgan's Expository Ser.). (Chinese.). 1984. write for info. (ISBN 0-941598-97-7); pap. write for info. (ISBN 0-941598-15-2). Living Spring Pubns.

--The Great Physician. 416p. 1982. Repr. 16.95 (ISBN 0-8007-0485-1). Revell.

--Handbook for Bible Teachers & Preachers. (Paperback Reference Library). 312p. 1985. pap. 8.95 (ISBN 0-8010-6190-3). Baker Bk.

--Hosea: The Heart & Holiness of God. (Morgan Library). 1974. pap. 4.50 (ISBN 0-8010-5952-6). Baker Bk.

--Isaiah. Chao, Lorna, tr. (G. Campbell Morgan's Expository Ser.). 1985. write for info (ISBN 0-941598-93-4); pap. write for info. (ISBN 0-941598-20-9). Living Spring Pubns.

--Life Problems. (Morgan Library). 1978. pap. 3.95 (ISBN 0-8010-6056-7). Baker Bk.

--Malachi's Message for Today. (Morgan Library). 131p. 1972. pap. 3.95 (ISBN 0-8010-5912-7). Baker Bk.

--Notes on the Psalms. 288p. 1947. 14.95 (ISBN 0-8007-0241-7). Revell.

--The Parable of the Father's Heart. (Morgan Library). 96p. 1981. pap. 2.95 (ISBN 0-8010-6118-0). Baker Bk.

--Parables & Metaphors of Our Lord. 352p. 1956. 15.95 (ISBN 0-8007-0245-X). Revell.

--Practice of Prayer. (Morgan Library). pap. 3.95 (ISBN 0-8010-5896-1). Baker Bk.

--Searchlights from the Word. 384p. 1956. 14.95 (ISBN 0-8007-0854-7). Revell.

--Searchlights from the Word. 1984. pap. 11.95 (ISBN 0-8010-6174-1). Baker Bk.

--The Simple Things of the Christian Life. 1984. pap. 2.25 (ISBN 0-915374-40-4). Rapids Christian.

--The Spirit of God. (Morgan Library). 240p. 1981. pap. 4.95 (ISBN 0-8010-6119-9). Baker Bk.

--Studies in the Four Gospels, 4 vols. Incl. The Gospel According to Matthew. 320p (ISBN 0-8007-0122-4); The Gospel According to Mark. 352p (ISBN 0-8007-0121-6); The Gospel According to Luke. 288p (ISBN 0-8007-0120-8); The Gospel According to John. 336p (ISBN 0-8007-0119-4). Set. 49.95 (ISBN 0-8007-0373-1); one-volume ed. 27.95 (ISBN 0-8007-0297-2); 13.95 ea. Revell.

--The Teaching of Christ. 352p. 1984. 16.95 (ISBN 0-8007-0395-2). Revell.

--Ten Commandments. (Morgan Library). 1974. pap. 3.95 (ISBN 0-8010-5954-2). Baker Bk.

--Voices of Twelve Hebrew Prophets. (Morgan Library). 128p. 1975. pap. 3.95 (ISBN 0-8010-5977-1). Baker Bk.

Morgan, G. Campbell, jt. auth. see Wood, Nathan R.

Morgan, Helen. Who'd Be a Missionary. 1972. pap. 1.50 (ISBN 0-87508-365-X). Chr Lit.

--Who'd Stay a Missionary. 1972. pap. 1.50 (ISBN 0-87508-366-8). Chr Lit.

Morgan, Howard M. The God-Man of Galilee. 1983. pap. 14.95 (ISBN 0-8359-2561-7). Reston.

Morgan, Howard M. & Morgan, John C. The God-Man of Galilee: Studies in Christian Living. 100p. 1986. Repr. of 1983 ed. 4.95 (ISBN 0-913029-14-9). Stevens Bk Pr.

Morgan, Irvonwy. Prince Charles's Puritan Chaplain, John Preston. LC 58-3992. 1957. 10.00x (ISBN 0-8401-1648-9). A R Allenson.

Morgan, J. & Cox, S. The Epistles of John. 612p. 1982. lib. bdg. 22.95 Smythe Sewn (ISBN 0-86524-133-3, 6202). Klock & Klock.

Morgan, James. The Biblical Doctrine of the Holy Spirit. 510p. 1985. Repr. lib. bdg. 19.00 (ISBN 0-86524-185-6, 8805). Klock & Klock.

Morgan, John. Godly Learning: Puritan Attitudes Towards Reason, Learning, & Education, 1560-1640. 378p. 1986. 49.50 (ISBN 0-521-23511-1) (ISBN 0-317-39807-5). Cambridge U Pr.

--You Can't Manage Alone: Practical Prayers for Conscientious Managers. 272p. 1986. gift ed. 12.95 (ISBN 0-310-33608-2). Zondervan.

Morgan, John, ed. see Johnson County Historical Society Staff.

Morgan, John C., jt. auth. see Morgan, Howard M.

Morgan, John H. Who Becomes a Bishop? A Study of Priests Who Become Bishops in the Episcopal Church (1960 to 1980) 65p. (Orig.). 1985. pap. 6.95x (ISBN 0-932269-28-1). Wyndham Hall.

--Women Priests: An Emerging Ministry in the Episcopal Church (1960 to 1980) 185p. (Orig.). 1985. pap. 12.95x (ISBN 0-932269-48-6). Wyndham Hall.

Morgan, John H., ed. Church Divinity, Nineteen Eighty Five. 109p. (Orig.). 1985. pap. 10.00x (ISBN 0-932269-61-3). Wyndham Hall.

Morgan, John S. & Philp, J. R. You Can't Manage Alone. 256p. (Orig.). 1985. pap. 4.95 (ISBN 0-310-33602-3, 12766P). Zondervan.

Morgan, Kenneth W. The Path of the Buddha: Buddhism Interpreted by Buddhists. 1986. 24.00X (ISBN 81-208-0030-3, Pub. by Motilal Banarsidass). South Asia Bks.

Morgan, Kenneth W. see McDermott, Robert A.

Morgan, Kenneth W., ed. Islam the Straight Path: Islam Interpreted by Muslims. LC 58-9807. pap. 115.80 (ISBN 0-317-08489-5, 2012383). Bks Demand UMI.

--The Religion of the Hindus: Interpreted by Hindus. LC 53-10466. Repr. of 1953 ed. 112.00 (ISBN 0-8357-9975-1, 2015620). Bks Demand UMI.

Morgan, Marabel. The Electric Woman. 224p. 1985. 11.95 (ISBN 0-8499-0497-8, 0497-8). Word Bks.

--The Electric Woman. 1986. 3.95 (ISBN 0-8499-4175-X). Word Bks.

--The Total Woman. 192p. 1973. spire bks. 3.50 (ISBN 0-8007-8218-6). Revell.

Morgan, Michael A. Sepher Ha-Razim: The Book of Mysteries. LC 82-25181. (Society of Biblical Literature Texts & Translations Ser.). 108p. 1983. pap. 10.95 (ISBN 0-89130-615-3, 06 02 25). Scholars Pr GA.

Morgan, Michael L. & Fackenheim, Emil, eds. The Jewish Thought of Emil Fackenheim: A Reader. LC 87-2116. 400p. 1987. 39.95X (ISBN 0-8143-1820-7); pap. 15.95X (ISBN 0-8143-1821-5). Wayne St U Pr.

Morgan, Nell & Chambers, Catherine. Preserving the Pentecostal Lady. Wallace, Mary H., ed. LC 86-28067. (Illus.). 134p. 1980. pap. 4.95 (ISBN 0-912315-50-4). Word Aflame.

Morgan, Peggy. Buddhism. (World Religions Ser.). (Illus.). 72p. 1987. 16.95 (ISBN 0-7134-5203-X, Pub. by Batsford England). David & Charles.

--Buddhism in the Twentieth Century. 1985. pap. 5.95 (ISBN 0-7175-1394-7). Dufour.

Morgan, Peter. Story Weaving. Lambert, Herbert, ed. LC 86-6079. 128p. (Orig.). 1986. pap. 8.95 (ISBN 0-8272-3423-6). CBP.

Morgan, R. W. St. Paul in Britain. LC 83-73168. 128p. 1984. pap. 4.50 (ISBN 0-934666-12-1). Artisan Sales.

Morgan, Richard E. The Supreme Court & Religion. LC 72-80077. 1972. 14.95 (ISBN 0-02-921970-1). Free Pr.

Morgan, Richard L. Is There Life after Divorce in the Church? LC 85-42825. 200p. 1985. pap. 12.95 (ISBN 0-8042-1123-X). John Knox.

Morgan, Robert. Advent Recollections: Five Dramatic Monologs. 1985. 3.50 (ISBN 0-89536-764-5, 5871). CSS of Ohio.

Morgan, Robert & Pye, Michael, eds. Ernst Troeltsch: Writings on Theology & Religion. LC 77-79596. 1977. 9.95 (ISBN 0-8042-0554-X). John Knox.

Morgan, Robert, jt. ed. see Pye, Michael.

Morgan, Roger & Silvestri, Stefano. Moderates & Conservatives in Western Europe. LC 83-5662. 288p. 1983. 27.50 (ISBN 0-8386-3201-7). Fairleigh Dickinson.

Morgan, Thomas. The Moral Philosopher in a Dialogue Between Philalethes, a Christian Deist, & Theophanes, a Christian Jew. LC 75-11239. (British Philosophers & Theologians of the 17th & 18th Centuries Ser.: Vol. 39). 463p. 1977. Repr. of 1737 ed. lib. bdg. 51.00 (ISBN 0-8240-1791-9). Garland Pub.

Morgan, Thomas B. Speaking of Cardinals. facs. ed. LC 70-134119. (Essay Index Reprint Ser). 1946. 18.00 (ISBN 0-8369-2002-3). Ayer Co Pubs.

Morgan, Trudy J. All My Love, Kate. Woolsey, Raymond H., ed. (Banner Ser.). 96p. (Orig.). 1986. pap. 6.50 (ISBN 0-8280-0318-1). Review & Herald.

Morgan, W. The Religion & Theology of Paul. 272p. 1917. 9.95 (ISBN 0-567-02200-5, Pub. by T & T Clark Ltd UK). Fortress.

Morgan, William. Freemasonry Exposed. 8.50 (ISBN 0-685-19475-2). Powner.

Morgan-Witts, Max, jt. auth. see Thomas, Gordon.

Morgenroth, Anton. Splendor of the Faith: Meditations on the Credo of the People of God. 206p. (Orig.). 1983. pap. 7.95 (ISBN 0-931888-14-X). Christendom Pubns.

Morgenstern, Julian. Rites of Birth, Marriage, Death, & Kindred Occasions Among the Semites. 1966. 20.00x (ISBN 0-87068-230-X). Ktav.

Mori, Masatoshi G. Buddhism & Faith. LC 78-70102. Repr. of 1928 ed. 21.50 (ISBN 0-404-17353-5). AMS Pr.

Moriarty. Numbers. (Bible Ser.). Pt. 1. pap. 1.00 (ISBN 0-8091-5101-4); Pt. 2. pap. 1.00 (ISBN 0-8091-5102-2). Paulist Pr.

Moriarty, Claire, jt. auth. see Reed, Evelyn.

Moriarty, Daniel P. How to Raise Money at Church Without Sales or Bingo. 1977. pap. 4.00 (ISBN 0-933968-00-0). D Moriarty.

Moriarty, Frederic L. First Book of Samuel. (Bible Ser.). 1971. pap. 1.00 (ISBN 0-8091-5135-9). Paulist Pr.

Moriarty, Frederick. Second Book of Samuel. (Bible Ser.). pap. 1.00 (ISBN 0-8091-5136-7). Paulist Pr.

Morice, Hyacinthe, jt. auth. see Pierre, Dom.

Morin, F. Dictionnaire de Philosophie et de Theologie Scolastiques, 2 vols. Migne, J. P., ed. (Troisieme et Derniere Encyclopedie Theologique Ser.: Vols. 21-22). (Fr.). 1496p. Repr. of 1865 ed. lib. bdg. 190.00x (ISBN 0-89241-304-2). Caratzas.

Morin, James, ed. see Canadian Christian Movement for Peace Staff, et al.

Morin, Jean. Commentarius de Sacris Ecclesiae Ordinationibus. 740p. Repr. of 1695 ed. text ed. 165.60 (ISBN 0-576-99716-1, Pub. by Gregg Intl Pubs England). Gregg Intl.

--Commentarius Historicus de Disciplina in Administratione Sacramenti Poenitentiae. 1020p. Repr. of 1682 ed. text ed. 248.40x (ISBN 0-576-99723-4, Pub. by Gregg Intl Pubs England). Gregg Intl.

Moringland Publications Inc, ed. see Sri, Patricia.

Morinis, E. Alan, ed. Pilgrimage in the Hindu Tradition: A Case Study of West Bengal. (Illus.). 1984. 34.95x (ISBN 0-19-561412-7). Oxford U Pr.

Morioka, Kiyomi. Religion in Changing Japanese Society. 231p. 1975. 29.50 (ISBN 0-86008-131-1, Pub. by U of Tokyo Japan). Columbia U Pr.

Morison, Frank. Quien Movio la Piedra? Ward, Rhode, tr. from Eng. LC 77-11752. Tr. of Who Moved the Stone? (Span.). 206p. 1977. pap. 4.95 (ISBN 0-89922-100-9). Edit Caribe.

--Who Moved the Stone. pap. 3.95 (ISBN 0-310-29562-9, 10371P). Zondervan.

Morison, James. Mark. 1981. lib. bdg. 21.00 (ISBN 0-86524-069-8, 4102). Klock & Klock.

--Matthew. 1981. lib. bdg. 24.95 (ISBN 0-86524-068-X, 4001). Klock & Klock.

Morison, James C. The Life & Times of St. Bernard of Clairvaux. 1977. lib. bdg. 59.95 (ISBN 0-8490-2162-6). Gordon Pr.

Morison, Richard. An Exhortation to Styre All Englyshe Men to the Defense of Theyr Countreye. LC 79-38211. (English Experience Ser.: No. 476). 64p. 1972. Repr. of 1539 ed. 9.50 (ISBN 90-221-0476-1). Walter J Johnson.

--Humanist Scholarship & Public Order: Two Tracts Against the Pilgrimage of Grace, & a Collection of Related Contemporary Documents. Berkowitz, David S., ed. LC 79-89983. 280p. 1983. text ed. 28.50 (ISBN 0-918016-01-0). Folger Bks.

--An Inuective Agenste Treason. LC 72-38212. (English Experience Ser.: No. 477). 104p. 1972. Repr. of 1539 ed. 9.50 (ISBN 90-221-0477-X). Walter J Johnson.

Morison, Robert S., jt. ed. see Lappe, Marc.

Morison, Samuel E. The Intellectual Life of Colonial New England. LC 79-20246. 1980. Repr. of 1956 ed. lib. bdg. 24.75x (ISBN 0-313-22032-8, MOIL). Greenwood.

Morison, Samuel E., ed. see Bradford, William.

Morison, Stanley. Likeness of Thomas More: An Iconographical Survey of Three Centuries. Barker, Nicolas, ed. (Illus.). 1964. 50.00 (ISBN 0-8232-0575-4). Fordham.

Morison, Susan A., intro. by see Abrams, Barbara C.

Morissey, Kirkie. In His Name. 132p. 1985. pap. 4.95 (ISBN 0-89109-056-8). NavPress.

Mork, Wulston. The Benedictine Way. 1987. pap. write for info. (ISBN 0-932506-48-8). St Bedes Pubns.

Morland, Samuel. History of the Evangelical Churches of the Valleys of Piemont. 1983. 32.00 (ISBN 0-686-42929-X). Church History.

Morley, John. Oliver Cromwell. 1977. Repr. of 1900 ed. lib. bdg. 25.00 (ISBN 0-8492-1850-0). R West.

Morley, John, ed. see Froude, James A.

Morley, John, ed. see Pattison, Mark.

Morley, John F. Vatican Diplomacy & the Jews During the Holocaust, 1939-1943. 1980. 25.00x (ISBN 0-87068-701-8). Ktav.

--Vatican Diplomacy & the Jews During the Holocaust 1939-1943. 320p. 25.00. ADL.

Morley, Lewis H. Now It Can Be Told. Wallace, Mary H., ed. LC 84-126606. (Illus.). 251p. (Orig.). 1983. pap. 5.95 (ISBN 0-912315-11-3). Word Aflame.

Morley, Raoul. Womanhood: The Feminine in Ancient Hellenism Gnosticism, Christianity & Islam. 119p. 1985. 16.95 (ISBN 0-9594165-0-1, Pub. by Delacroix Pr); pap. 8.95 (ISBN 0-317-41343-0). Intl Spec Bk.

Morley, Sylvanus G. & Brainerd, George W. The Ancient Maya. Rev., 4th ed. Sharer, Robert J., rev. by. LC 81-85451. (Illus.). xx, 708p. 1983. 38.50 (ISBN 0-8047-1137-2); pap. 14.95 (ISBN 0-8047-1288-3, SP 80). Stanford U Pr.

Mornay, Charlotte A. De see De Mornay, Charlotte A.

Mornay, Philippe de. A Work Concerning the Trewnesse of the Christian Religion. Sidney, Philip, tr. from Fr. LC 75-45384. 680p. 1976. Repr. of 1587 ed. lib. bdg. 90.00x (ISBN 0-8201-1166-X). Schol Facsimiles.

Mornay, Philippe De see Mornay, Philippe de.

Morneau, Robert F. Discovering God's Presence. LC 80-18590. 188p. (Orig.). 1980. pap. 3.95 (ISBN 0-8146-1197-4). Liturgical Pr.

--Mantras for the Evening. LC 82-83587. (Illus.). 116p. (Orig.). 1982. pap. text ed. 4.95 (ISBN 0-8146-1269-5). Liturgical Pr.

--Mantras for the Morning: An Introduction to Holistic Prayer. LC 81-1085. (Illus.). 120p. 1981. pap. 4.95 (ISBN 0-8146-1210-5). Liturgical Pr.

--Principles of Preaching. 1983. pap. 6.95 (ISBN 0-941850-11-0). Sunday Pubns.

--Spiritual Aids for Those in Renew: Ponderings, Poems & Promises. LC 84-12299. 111p. (Orig.). 1984. pap. 4.50 (ISBN 0-8189-0473-9). Alba.

--Themes & Theses of Six Recent Papal Documents: A Commentary. 160p. (Orig.). 1985. pap. 5.95 (ISBN 0-8189-0482-8). Alba.

--There Is a Season: An Inspirational Journal. LC 84-11622. (Illus.). 175p. 1984. 18.95 (ISBN 0-13-914755-1, Busn); pap. 9.95 (ISBN 0-13-914706-3). P-H.

--Trinity Sunday Revisted. LC 79-25097. 96p. 1980. pap. 3.50 (ISBN 0-8146-1084-6). Liturgical Pr.

Morner, Magnus. The Political & Economic Activities of the Jesuits in the Plata Region. 1976. lib. bdg. 59.95 (ISBN 0-8490-2451-X). Gordon Pr.

Morningland Publications, Inc., ed. Healing: As It Is, 2 vols. (Illus.). 320p. (Orig.). 1981. Set. pap. 10.00 (ISBN 0-935146-59-8). Morningland.

Morningland Publications, Inc., ed. see Donato, Sri.

Morningland Publications, Inc., ed. see Donato, Sri & Donato, Gopi G.

Morningland Publications, Inc., ed. see Patricia.

Morningstar, Jim. Family Awakening in Body, Mind, & Spirit. 60p. 1984. pap. 6.00 (ISBN 0-9604856-1-9). Transform Inc.

--Spiritual Psychology: A New Age Course for Body, Mind & Spirit. 2nd ed. (Illus.). 119p. 1981. pap. 10.00 (ISBN 0-9604856-0-0). Transform Inc.

Morrell, Gloria G. Lying...Not a Very Fun Thing. 1986. pap. 3.95 (ISBN 0-8054-4338-X). Broadman.

--Sally's Calendar Book. 1986. pap. 3.95 (ISBN 0-8054-4337-1). Broadman.

Morrell, Robert E. Sand & Pebbles: The Tales of Muju Ichien, a Voice for Pluralism in Kamakura Buddhism. (Series in Buddhist Studies). 337p. 1985. 44.50 (ISBN 0-88706-059-5); pap. 16.95x (ISBN 0-88706-060-9). State U NY Pr.

Morrice, William G. Joy in the New Testament. 144p. (Orig.). 1982. pap. 11.95 (ISBN 0-85364-340-7). Attic Pr.

Morrill, Sibley S. The Texas Cannibals, or, Why Father Serra Came to California. 28p. 1964. octavo wrappers 5.00 (ISBN 0-910740-04-6). Holmes.

Morris & Rohrer. Decade of Creation: Acts-Facts-Impacts, Vol. 4. LC 80-67426. 320p. 1980. pap. 7.95 (ISBN 0-89051-069-5). Master Bks.

Morris, jt. auth. see Diehl.

Morris, Brian. Anthropological Studies of Religion: An Introductory Text. (Illus.). 384p. 1987. 42.50 (ISBN 0-521-32794-6); pap. 12.95 (ISBN 0-521-33991-X). Cambridge U Pr.

Morris, Bryon T. A Charge to Keep. 1971. 4.00 (ISBN 0-87012-092-1). McClain.

Morris, Charles W. Paths of Life: Preface to a World Religion. LC 72-94732. 228p. 1973. pap. 2.25x (ISBN 0-226-53879-6, P541, Phoen). U of Chicago Pr.

--Symbolism & Reality: A Study in the Nature of Mind. LC 86-17602. (Foundations of Semiotics Ser.: No. 15). v, 150p. 1987. 34.00x (ISBN 90-272-3287-3). Benjamins North Am.

Morris, Christopher, ed. Anthems for Choirs Four. 1976. pap. 8.75x (ISBN 0-19-353018-X). Oxford U Pr.

Morris, Daniel. Beatitude Saints. LC 83-62423. 128p. (Orig.). 1984. pap. 4.95 (ISBN 0-87973-615-1, 615). Our Sunday Visitor.

Morris, Danny. Discovering Our Family Covenants. LC 81-51299. 1981. pap. 2.95x (ISBN 0-8358-0419-4). Upper Room.

Morris, Danny E. Any Miracle God Wants to Give. 1974. pap. 1.25x (ISBN 0-8358-0314-7). Upper Room.

Morris, E. The Bells of St. Mary's Twickenham. 1985. 11.25x (ISBN 0-317-54270-2, Pub. by J Richardson UK). State Mutual Bk.

Morris, Edward E. Milton: Tractate of Education. LC 73-13795. 1895. Repr. lib. bdg. 12.50 (ISBN 0-8414-6000-0). Folcroft.

Morris, Elias C. Sermons, Addresses & Reminiscences & Important Correspondence, with a Picture Gallery of Eminent Ministers & Scholars. Gaustad, Edwin S., ed. LC 79-52598. (The Baptist Tradition Ser.). (Illus.). 1980. Repr. of 1901 ed. lib. bdg. 27.50x (ISBN 0-405-12465-1). Ayer Co Pubs.

Morris, Frank. The Divine Epic. LC 72-96118. 539p. 1973. pap. 5.00 (ISBN 0-913382-18-3, 101-18). Prow Bks-Franciscan.

Morris, Frederick M. Bishop Pike: Ham, Heretic, or Hero. LC 67-28381. pap. 20.00 (ISBN 0-317-08443-7, 2012934). Bks Demand UMI.

Morris, George E. Rethinking Congregational Development. LC 84-71366. 144p. (Orig.). 1984. pap. 5.25 (ISBN 0-88177-012-4, DRO12B). Discipleship Res.

Morris, George E. & Fox, H. E. Faith Sharing: Dynamic Christian Witnessing By Invitation. LC 86-71913. 176p. (Orig.). 1986. pap. 6.95 ea. (ISBN 0-88177-039-6, DR039B). Discipleship Res.

Morris, George E., jt. auth. see Fox, H. Eddie.

Morris, H. Creation & Its Critics. LC 82-84483. 32p. 1982. 1.00 (ISBN 0-89051-091-1). Master Bks.

Morris, H. M., jt. auth. see Whitcomb, John C., Jr.

Morris, H. N. Flaxman, Blake, Coleridge, & Other Men of Genius Influenced by Swedenborg. 1973. Repr. of 1915 ed. lib. bdg. 20.00 (ISBN 0-8414-1555-3). Folcroft.

Morris, Harry. Last Things in Shakespeare. LC 85-1453. (Illus.). 360p. 1986. 30.00 (ISBN 0-8130-0794-1). U Presses Fla.

Morris, Hazel. My Family. LC 85-24334. (Bible & Me Ser.). (Illus.). 1986. 5.95 (ISBN 0-8054-4164-6). Broadman.

Morris, Henry. Amostra de Salmos. Orig. Title: Sampling the Psalms. (Port.). 1986. write for info. (ISBN 0-8297-0698-4). Life Pubs Intl.

--Biblical Cosmology & Modern Science. 1970. pap. 4.50 (ISBN 0-87552-349-8). Presby & Reformed.

--Psaumes Choisis. Tr. of Sampling the Psalms. (Fr.). 192p. 1986. pap. 3.50 (ISBN 0-8297-0697-6). Life Pubs Intl.

Morris, Henry M. Bible Has the Answer. pap. 8.95 (ISBN 0-8010-5905-4). Baker Bk.

--The Biblical Basis of Modern Science. 1984. 24.95 (ISBN 0-8010-6178-4). Baker Bk.

--Creation & the Modern Christian. 298p. 1985. pap. 8.95 (ISBN 0-89051-111-X). Master Bks.

--Days of Praise. (Illus.). 388p. (Orig.). 1986. pap. 9.95 (ISBN 0-89051-116-0). Master Bks.

--Education for the Real World. LC 77-78017. 1977. pap. 8.95 (ISBN 0-89051-093-8). Master Bks.

--Evolution & the Modern Christian. pap. 3.95 (ISBN 0-8010-5881-3). Baker Bk.

--Evolution & the Modern Christian. 1967. pap. 2.95 (ISBN 0-87552-337-4). Presby & Reformed.

--Genesis Record. 24.95 (ISBN 0-8010-6004-4). Baker Bk.

--History of Modern Creationism. LC 84-60865. 1984. 12.95 (ISBN 0-89051-107-1); pap. 9.95 (ISBN 0-89051-102-0). Master Bks.

--King of Creation. LC 80-80558. 1980. pap. 6.95 (ISBN 0-89051-059-8). Master Bks.

--Many Infallible Proofs. LC 74-81484. 384p. 1974. pap. 8.95 (ISBN 0-89051-005-9). Master Bks.

--Men of Science, Men of God. (Illus.). 1982. pap. 2.95 (ISBN 0-89051-080-6). Master Bks.

--The Remarkable Birth of Planet Earth. 124p. 1973. pap. 2.50 (ISBN 0-89051-000-8). Master Bks.

--The Revelation Record. 1983. 18.95 (ISBN 0-8423-5511-1). Tyndale.

--Sampling the Psalms. LC 78-55613. 1978. pap. 5.95 (ISBN 0-89051-049-0). Master Bks.

--Science & the Bible. rev., expanded ed. 1986. pap. 5.95 (ISBN 0-8024-0656-4). Moody.

--The Scientific Case for Creation. LC 77-78019. (Illus.). 1977. pap. 2.95 (ISBN 0-89051-037-7). Master Bks.

--The Troubled Waters of Evolution. 2nd ed. LC 82-15254. (Illus.). 225p. 1975. pap. 6.95 (ISBN 0-89051-087-3). Master Bks.

--Twilight of Evolution. LC 76-2265. 1963. pap. 4.95 (ISBN 0-8010-5862-7). Baker Bk.

--What is Creation Science. LC 82-70114. (Illus.). 1982. pap. 8.95 (ISBN 0-89051-081-4). Master Bks.

Morris, Henry M. & Clark, Martin. The Bible Has the Answer. LC 76-20206. 1976. pap. 9.95 (ISBN 0-89051-018-0). Master Bks.

Morris, Henry M. & Gish, Duane T. The Battle for Creation: Acts, Facts, Impacts, Vol. 2. LC 74-75429. (Illus.). 1976. pap. 5.95 (ISBN 0-89051-020-2). Master Bks.

Morris, Henry M., jt. auth. see Whitcomb, John C.

Morris, Henry M., et al, eds. Creation: The Cutting Edge-Acts, Facts, Impacts, Vol. 5. 240p. 1982. pap. 7.95 (ISBN 0-89051-088-1). Master Bks.

--Scientific Creationism. LC 74-14160. 1974. pap. 8.95 (ISBN 0-89051-003-2). Master Bks.

Morris, Henry M., 3rd. Baptism: How Important Is It? LC 77-87954. 1978. pap. 1.95 (ISBN 0-916406-72-5). Accent Bks.

Morris, Henry, 3rd. Explore the Word! LC 78-55611. 1978. pap. 7.95 (ISBN 0-89051-047-4). Master Bks.

Morris, Herbert. On Guilt & Innocence: Essays in Legal Philosophy & Moral Psychology. 1976. pap. 3.95 (ISBN 0-520-03944-0, 434). U of Cal Pr.

Morris, James W., tr. see Mulla Sadra.

Morris, Kenneth E. Bonhoeffer's Ethic of Discipleship: A Study in Social Psychology, Political Thought, & Religion. LC 85-31949. 144p. 1986. 17.95 (ISBN 0-271-00428-2). Pa St U Pr.

Morris, Laval S. The Gardens of Eden & Man. 1982. 5.95 (ISBN 0-8062-1973-4). Carlton.

Morris, Lawrence, tr. see Abd Allah Ansarti, Khwajih.

Morris, Leon. Apocalyptic. 88p. 1977. pap. 4.95 (ISBN 0-8028-1455-7). Eerdmans.

--Apostolic Preaching of the Cross. 1956. pap. 5.95 (ISBN 0-8028-1512-X). Eerdmans.

--The Atonement. LC 83-20649. 204p. 1984. pap. 8.95 (ISBN 0-87784-826-2). Inter-Varsity.

--Commentary on the Revelation of John. Tasker, R. V., ed. (Tyndale Bible Commentaries). 1957. pap. 5.95 (ISBN 0-8028-1419-0). Eerdmans.

--Creo En la Revelacion. Blanch, Miguel, tr. from Eng. (Serie Creo). Tr. of I Believe in the Revelation. (Span.). 223p. 1979. pap. 5.95 (ISBN 0-89922-140-8). Edit Caribe.

--First & Second Epistles to the Thessalonians. (New International Commentary of the New Testament). 1959. 14.95 (ISBN 0-8028-2187-1). Eerdmans.

--First & Second Thessalonians. rev. ed. Tasker, R. V., ed. (Tyndale New Testament Commentaries Ser.). 160p. 1984. pap. 4.95 (ISBN 0-8028-0034-3). Eerdmans.

--The First Epistle of Paul to the Corinthians. (Tyndale New Testament Commentary). 1958. pap. 5.95 (ISBN 0-8028-1406-9). Eerdmans.

--The Gospel According to St. Luke. (Tyndale New Testament Commentaries Ser.). 1974. pap. 5.95 (ISBN 0-8028-1402-6). Eerdmans.

--Gospel of John. (New International Commentary of the New Testament Ser.). 1970. 24.95 (ISBN 0-8028-2296-7). Eerdmans.

--Hebrews: Bible Study Commentary. 1986. pap. 5.95 (ISBN 0-310-45183-3, 12390P). Zondervan.

--I Believe in Revelation. (I Believe Ser.). 160p. 1976. pap. 6.95 (ISBN 0-8028-1637-1). Eerdmans.

--New Testament Theology. 448p. 1986. text ed. 19.95 (ISBN 0-310-45570-7, 12391, Pub. by Academie Bks). Zondervan.

--Reflections on the Gospel of John, Vol. 2. 208p. 1987. pap. 8.95 (ISBN 0-8010-6215-2). Baker Bk.

--Testaments of Love: A Study of Love in the Bible. (Orig.). 1981. 12.95 (ISBN 0-8028-3502-3). Eerdmans.

Morris, Leon, jt. auth. see Cundall, Arthur E.

Morris, Leon, et al. The Expositor's Bible Commentary, Vol. 12. 1986. cloth 19.95 (ISBN 0-88469-198-5). BMH Bks.

Morris, M. C., jt. auth. see Bosschere, Jean de.

Morris, Mary, tr. see Leibniz, Gottfried W. & Parkinson, G. H.

Morris, Pamela, tr. see Bernanos, Georges.

Morris, Peter M. & James, Edward. A Critical Word Book of Leviticus, Numbers, Deuteronomy. (Computer Bible Ser.: Vol. VIII). 1975. pap. 20.00 (ISBN 0-935106-13-8). Biblical Res Assocs.

--A Critical Word Book of the Pentateuch. (Computer Bible Ser.: Vol. XVII). 1980. pap. 25.00 (ISBN 0-935106-03-0). Biblical Res Assocs.

Morris, R., ed. The Blickiling Homilies, Pts. I-III. (EETS OS Ser.: Vols. 58 & 63, 73). 1874. 28.00 (ISBN 0-8115-3354-9). Kraus Repr.

Morris, R. K., jt. ed. see Butler, L. A.

Morris, Richard, ed. Old English Homilies & Homiletic Treatises, Pts. I & II. (EETS. OS Ser. I: No. 29, 31). Repr. of 1868 ed. 25.00 (ISBN 0-527-00029-9). Kraus Repr.

--Old English Homilies of the 13th Century. (EETS OS Ser. II: No. 53). Repr. of 1873 ed. 30.00 (ISBN 0-527-00048-5). Kraus Repr.

--The Puggala-Pannatti. LC 78-70109. Repr. of 1883 ed. 20.00 (ISBN 0-404-17359-4). AMS Pr.

Morris, Richard, jt. ed. see Addyman, Peter.

Morris, Richard, ed. see Buddhavamsa.

Morris, Richard B., et al, eds. Dissertations in American Biography Series, 38 bks. 1982. write for info. Ayer Co Pubs.

Morris, Robert. Freemasonry in the Holy Land: Handmarks of Hiram's Builders. Davis, Moshe, ed. LC 77-70731. (America & the Holy Land Ser.). (Illus.). 1977. Repr. of 1872 ed. lib. bdg. 46.50x (ISBN 0-405-10270-4). Ayer Co Pubs.

Morris, S. L. The Drama of Christianity: An Interpretation of the Book of Revelation. 152p. 1982. pap. 4.95 (ISBN 0-8010-6136-9). Baker Bk.

Morris, Thomas V. Anselmian Explorations: Essays in Philosophical Theology. LC 86-40239. 264p. 1987. text ed. 28.95 (ISBN 0-268-00616-4). U of Notre Dame Pr.

--The Logic of God Incarnate. LC 85-21252. (Illus.). 224p. 1986. text ed. 19.95x (ISBN 0-8014-1846-1). Cornell U Pr.

Morris, William D. The Christian Origins of Social Revolt. LC 78-14133. 1979. Repr. of 1949 ed. 19.50 (ISBN 0-88355-805-X). Hyperion Conn.

Morris, Woodrow W. The Greatest of These: Quotations on Fundamental Truths of Charity - The Teaching of Freemasonry. (Illus.). 132p. 1985. 8.75 (ISBN 0-88053-080-4). Macoy Pub.

Morrish, George. Concordance of the Septuagint. 17.95 (ISBN 0-310-20300-7, 6512). Zondervan.

Morrish, Ivor. Obeah, Christ, & Rastaman: Jamaica & Its Religion. 128p. 1982. 17.95 (ISBN 0-227-67831-1). Attic Pr.

Morrison. Morrison on James to Revelation. pap. 4.95 (ISBN 0-89957-563-3). AMG Pubs.

Morrison, Barrie M. Lalmai, a Cultural Center of Early Bengal: An Archaeological Report & Historical Analysis. LC 74-9892. (Publications on Asia of the School of International Studies: No. 24). (Illus.). 160p. 1974. 18.50x (ISBN 0-295-95342-X). U of Wash Pr.

Morrison, Charles C. Unfinished Reformation. facs. ed. LC 68-20322. (Essay Index Reprint Ser). 1953. 17.50 (ISBN 0-8369-0723-X). Ayer Co Pubs.

Morrison, Clinton. An Analytical Concordance to the Revised Standard Version of the New Testament. LC 77-26210. 800p. 1979. 45.00 (ISBN 0-664-20773-1). Westminster.

Morrison, Clinton D. Powers That Be: Earthly Rulers & Demonic Powers in Romans, Chapter 13, 1-7. LC 60-4219. (Studies in Biblical Theology: No. 29). 1960. pap. 10.00x (ISBN 0-8401-3029-5). A R Allenson.

Morrison, Clinton D. & Barnes, David H. New Testament Word Lists. 1964. pap. 3.95 (ISBN 0-8028-1141-8). Eerdmans.

Morrison, G. H. Morrison on Galations through Hebrews. LC 82-71841. (Glasgow Pulpit Ser.). 1982. pap. 4.95 (ISBN 0-89957-557-9). AMG Pubs.

--Morrison on John, Vol. I. new ed. (The Glasgow Pulpit Ser.). 1979. pap. 4.95 (ISBN 0-89957-534-X). AMG Pubs.

--Morrison on John, Vol. II. new ed. (The Glasgow Pulpit Ser.). 1979. pap. 4.95 (ISBN 0-89957-535-8). AMG Pubs.

--Morrison on Luke, Vol. I. new ed. (The Glasgow Pulpit Ser.). 1979. pap. 4.95 (ISBN 0-89957-532-3). AMG Pubs.

--Morrison on Luke, Vol. II. new ed. (The Glasgow Pulpit Ser.). 1979. pap. 4.95 (ISBN 0-89957-533-1). AMG Pubs.

--Morrison on Mark. new ed. (The Glasgow Pulpit Ser.). 1979. pap. 4.95 (ISBN 0-89957-531-5). AMG Pubs.

--Morrison on Matthew, Vol. I. new ed. (The Glasgow Pulpit Ser.). 1979. pap. 4.95 (ISBN 0-89957-528-5). AMG Pubs.

--Morrison on Matthew, Vol. II. new ed. (The Glasgow Pulpit Ser.). 1979. pap. 4.95 (ISBN 0-89957-529-3). AMG Pubs.

--Morrison on Matthew, Vol. III. new ed. (The Glasgow Pulpit Ser.). 1979. pap. 4.95 (ISBN 0-89957-530-7). AMG Pubs.

--Morrison on Romans & Corinthians. (Glasgow Pulpit Ser.). 96p. 1982. pap. 4.95 (ISBN 0-89957-547-1). AMG Pubs.

Morrison, G. H., ed. Morrison on Genesis. (Glasgow Pulpit Ser.). 72p. 1976. pap. 4.95 (ISBN 0-89957-520-X). AMG Pubs.

Morrison, George H. Christ in Shakespeare. 142p. 1981. Repr. of 1928 ed. lib. bdg. 30.00 (ISBN 0-89984-342-5). Century Bookbindery.

--Morrison on Acts. rev. ed. Zodhiates, Joan, ed. LC 80-69541. (Glasgow Pulpit Ser.). 1981. pap. 4.95 (ISBN 0-89957-050-X). AMG Pubs.

Morrison, J. H. Christian Faith & the Science of Today. 12.50 (ISBN 0-8414-6676-9). Folcroft.

Morrison, James H. Missionary Heroes of Africa. LC 79-89010. Repr. of 1922 ed. 22.50x (ISBN 0-8371-1738-0, MOM&, Pub. by Negro U Pr). Greenwood.

Morrison, Jim. American Prayer. 1983. pap. 8.95x (ISBN 0-915628-46-5). Zeppelin.

Morrison, John A. The Educational Philosophy of Saint John Bosco. LC 79-54817. 258p. (Orig.). 1979. pap. 8.95 (ISBN 0-89944-050-9). Don Bosco Multimedia.

Morrison, Karl E., ed. The Investiture Controversy: Issues, Ideals & Results. LC 77-15654. (European Problem Studies). 144p. 1976. pap. text ed. 5.95 (ISBN 0-88275-634-6). Krieger.

Morrison, Mary. The Journal & the Journey. LC 81-85559. (Pendle Hill Pamphlets Ser.). 32p. (Orig.). 1982. pap. 2.50x (ISBN 0-87574-242-4). Pendle Hill.

--Re-Conciliation: The Hidden Hyphen. LC 74-24007. 24p. (Orig.). 1974. pap. 2.50x (ISBN 0-87574-198-3, 198). Pendle Hill.

Morrison, Mary, ed. see Law, William.

Morrison, Mary C. Approaching the Gospels Together: A Leader's Guide to Group Gospels Study. LC 78-51385. 32p. (Orig.). 1978. pap. 2.50x (ISBN 0-87574-219-X, 219). Pendle Hill.

--Approaching the Gospels Together: A Leaders' Guide to Group Gospels Study. (Orig.). 1987. pap. 10.95 (ISBN 0-87574-910-0). Pendle Hill.

--The Way of the Cross. LC 85-60516. 32p. (Orig.). 1985. pap. 2.50x (ISBN 0-87574-260-2). Pendle Hill.

Morrison, Nathaniel. Human Roots, Fact or Fiction? 1983. 4.95 (ISBN 0-8062-2218-2). Carlton.

Morrison, Sarah L. The Modern Witch's Spellbook. LC 71-135588. 256p. 1973. pap. 5.95 (ISBN 0-8065-0372-6). Citadel Pr.

--The Modern Witch's Spellbook, Vol. 2. 224p. 1986. pap. 6.95 (ISBN 0-8065-1015-3). Citadel Pr.

Morrison, W. D., ed. see Pfleiderer, Otto.

Morrison-Reed, Mark. Black Pioneers in a White Denomination. LC 83-70747. 216p. 1983. pap. text ed. 9.95 (ISBN 0-8070-1601-2, BP 662). Beacon Pr.

Morriss, Frank. The Catholic As Citizen. 141p. 1980. 6.95 (ISBN 0-8199-0775-8). Franciscan Herald.

Morriss, Frank, ed. A Christmas Celebration: The Wanderer's Christmas Anthology. LC 83-51146. 334p. 1983. 14.95 (ISBN 0-915245-00-0). Wanderer Pr.

Morrissey, Gerard. The Crisis of Dissent. 128p. (Orig.). 1985. pap. 4.95 (ISBN 0-931888-19-0). Christendom Pubns.

--Defending the Papacy. 96p. (Orig.). 1984. pap. 4.95 (ISBN 0-931888-15-8). Christendom Pubns.

Morrissey, Kirkie. Designed by God: A Woman's Workshop on Wholeness. (Woman's Workshop Ser.). 160p. (Orig.). 1985. pap. 3.95 (ISBN 0-310-45011-X, 16246P). Zondervan.

--On Holy Ground. 144p. (Orig.). 1983. pap. 4.95 (ISBN 0-89109-051-7). NavPress.

--A Woman's Workshop on Forgiveness. (Woman's Workshop Ser.). 160p. 1982. pap. 3.95 (ISBN 0-310-44931-6, 16245P). Zondervan.

Morrow, Danny R. Silhouette of a Saint: Albert Pepper. 1985. 4.95 (ISBN 0-86544-027-1). Salv Army Suppl South.

Morrow, Glenn R. & Dillion, John M. Proclus' Commentary on Plato's "Parmenides". LC 85-43302. 712p. 1986. text ed. 80.00x (ISBN 0-691-07305-8). Princeton U Pr.

Morrow, Ralph E. Northern Methodism & Reconstruction. ix, 269p. 1956. 5.00 (ISBN 0-87013-018-8). Mich St U Pr.

Morrow, Steve, tr. see Shiv Brat Lal.

Morrow, Theodore, tr. see Boff, Leonardo.

Morrow, Theodore, tr. see Libanio, J. B.

Morschauer, Scott, jt. ed. see Kort, Ann.

Morse, Ann, jt. auth. see Morse, Charles.

Morse, Charles & Morse, Ann. Whobody There? 1977. pap. 4.95x (ISBN 0-8358-0350-3). Upper Room.

Morse, Charlotte C. The Pattern of Judgement in the "Queste" & "Cleanness". LC 77-25158. (Illus.). 248p. 1978. 19.00x (ISBN 0-8262-0242-X). U of Mo Pr.

Morse, Christopher. The Logic of Promise in Moltmann's Theology. LC 78-54556. 192p. 1979. 12.95 (ISBN 0-8006-0523-3, 1-523). Fortress.

Morse, Flo. The Shakers & the World's People. LC 79-27271. 1981. 17.95 (ISBN 0-396-07809-5). Dodd.

--The Story of the Shakers. (Illus.). 96p. 1986. pap. 6.95 (ISBN 0-88150-062-3). Countryman.

Morse, James K. Jedidiah Morse: A Champion of New England Orthodoxy. LC 39-11247. Repr. of 1939 ed. 10.00 (ISBN 0-404-04504-9). AMS Pr.

Morse, Joyce. Peter Sinks in the Water. (Books I Can Read). 32p. (Orig.). 1980. pap. 1.95 (ISBN 0-8127-0281-6). Review & Herald.

--Where Is Jesus? (Books I Can Read). 32p. 1980. pap. 1.95 (ISBN 0-8127-0280-8). Review & Herald.

Morse, Kenneth I. Move in Our Midst: Looking at Worship in the Life of the Church. 1977. pap. 2.95 (ISBN 0-87178-583-8). Brethren.

Morse, Lois. Two Blocks from Happiness. 176p. 1985. pap. 6.95 (ISBN 0-87239-860-9, 3005). Standard Pub.

Morse, Samuel F. Foreign Conspiracy Against the Liberties of the United States: The Numbers of Brutus. LC 76-46090. (Anti-Movements in America Ser.). 1977. lib. bdg. 18.00 (ISBN 0-405-09963-0). Ayer Co Pubs.

Morse-Boycott, Desmond L. Lead, Kindly Light. LC 70-107728. (Essay Index Reprint Ser). 1933. 16.00 (ISBN 0-8369-1529-1). Ayer Co Pubs.

Morselli, Henry. Suicide: An Essay on Comparative Moral Statistics. LC 74-25770. (European Sociology Ser.). 402p. 1975. Repr. 27.00x (ISBN 0-405-06524-8). Ayer Co Pubs.

Morson, John. Christ the Way: The Christology of Guerric of Igny. (Cistercian Studies: N0.25). 1978. 11.95 (ISBN 0-87907-825-1). Cistercian Pubns.

Mortensen, A. Russell, jt. ed. see Mulder, William.

Mortimer, Edward. Faith & Power: The Politics of Islam. (Illus.). 425p. 1982. 6.36 (ISBN 0-394-71173-4). Random.

Mortimer, Ernest. Blaise Pascal: The Life & Work of a Realist. 1979. Repr. of 1959 ed. lib. bdg. 25.00 (ISBN 0-8414-6341-7). Folcroft.

Morton, A. L. The Everlasting Gospel. 1978. Repr. of 1958 ed. lib. bdg. 15.00 (ISBN 0-8495-3736-3). Arden Lib.

--Everlasting Gospel. (Studies in Blake, No. 3). 1958. pap. 39.95x (ISBN 0-8383-0098-7). Haskell.

--The World of the Ranters: Religious Radicalism in the English Revolution. 232p. 1970. 14.95x (ISBN 0-8464-0980-1). Beekman Pubs.

Morton, A. Q. & Michaelson, S. A Critical Concordance to I, II Thessalonians. Baird, J. Arthur & Freedman, David N., eds. (The Computer Bible: Vol XXVI). 136p. (Orig.). 1983. pap. 25.00x (ISBN 0-935106-21-9). Biblical Res Assocs.

--Critical Concordance to the Pastoral Epistles, I, II Timothy, Titus, Philemon. Baird, J. Arthur & Freedman, David N., eds. (The Computer Bible Ser.: Vol. XXV). 1982. pap. 35.00 (ISBN 0-935106-20-0). Biblical Res Assocs.

Morton, A. Q. & Michaelson, Sidney. A Critical Concordance to the Acts of the Apostles. (Computer Bible Ser.: Vol. VII). 1976. pap. 15.00 (ISBN 0-935106-14-6). Biblical Res Assocs.

--Critical Concordance to the Letter of Paul to the Romans. Baird, J. Arthur & Freedman, David Noel, eds. (Computer Bible Ser: Vol. XIII). 1977. pap. 27.50 (ISBN 0-935106-08-1). Biblical Res Assocs.

Morton, A. Q., et al. Critical Concordance to the Letter of Paul to the Colossians. Baird, J. Arthur & Freedman, David, eds. (Computer Bible Ser.: Vol. 24). (Orig.). 1981. pap. text ed. 20.00 (ISBN 0-935106-19-7). Biblical Res Assocs.

--Critical Concordance to the Letter of Paul to the Philippians. Baird, J. Arthur & Freedman, David, eds. (Computer Bible Ser.: Vol. 23). (Orig.). 1980. pap. text ed. 20.00 (ISBN 0-935106-18-9). Biblical Res Assocs.

--A Critical Concordance to I & II Corinthians. (Computer Bible Ser.: Vol. XIX). 1979. pap. 30.00 (ISBN 0-935106-01-4). Biblical Res Assocs.

--A Critical Concordance to the Epistle of Paul to the Galatians. Baird, J. Arthur & Freedman, David, eds. (The Computer Bible Ser.: Vol. XXI). (Orig.). 1980. pap. text ed. 20.00 (ISBN 0-935106-16-2). Biblical Res Assocs.

--A Critical Concordance to the Letter of Paul to the Ephesians. Baird, J. Arthur & Freedman, David, eds. (The Computer Bible Ser.: Vol. XXII). (Orig.). 1980. pap. text ed. 20.00 (ISBN 0-935106-17-0). Biblical Res Assocs.

Morton, Bruce L., jt. auth. see Jicks, John M.

Morton, Craig & Burger, Robert. The Courage to Believe. (Epiphany Bks.). (Illus.). 1983. pap. 2.75 (ISBN 0-345-30564-7). Ballantine.

Morton, Daniel O. Memoir of Rev. Levi Parsons: Late Missionary to Palestine. Davis, Moshe, ed. (America & the Holy Land Ser.). 1977. Repr. of 1824 ed. lib. bdg. 33.00x (ISBN 0-405-10271-2). Ayer Co Pubs.

Morton, H. V. In the Steps of St. Paul. (Illus.). 440p. 1986. Repr. of 1936 ed. lib. bdg. 45.00 (ISBN 0-89984-770-6). Century Bookbindery.

--In the Steps of the Master. 1935. lib. bdg. 32.59 (ISBN 0-8414-6678-5). Folcroft.

--In the Steps of the Master. (Illus.). 408p. 1984. pap. 12.95 (ISBN 0-396-08415-X). Dodd.

Morton, James, ed. Ancren Riwle, a Treatise on the Rules & Duties of Monastic Life from a Semi-Saxon MS. of the Thirteenth Century. LC 72-158250. (Camden Society, London. Publications, First Series: No. 1). Repr. of 1853 ed. 55.00 (ISBN 0-404-50157-5). AMS Pr.

Morton, James, tr. Nuns' Rule or the Ancrew Riwle. LC 66-23314. (Medieval Library). Repr. of 1926 ed. 17.50x (ISBN 0-8154-0155-8). Cooper Sq.

Morton, James P., jt. auth. see Sandys, Edwina.

Morton, John. Redeeming Creation: A Christian World Evolving. (Illus.). 84p. (Orig.). 1984. pap. 9.95 (ISBN 0-318-20036-8, Pub. by Zealandia Pubns). ANZ Religious Pubns.

Morton, John B. Hilaire Belloc: A Memoir. LC 74-19265. 1974. Repr. of 1955 ed. lib. bdg. 25.00 (ISBN 0-8414-6149-X). Folcroft.

Morton, Leah, pseud. I Am a Woman & a Jew. (Masterworks of Modern Jewish Writing Ser.). (Illus.). 380p. 1986. pap. 9.95 (ISBN 0-910129-56-8, Distr. by Schocken Books). Wiener Pub Inc.

Morton, Nelle. The Journey Is Home: The Distinguished Feminist Theologian Traces the Development of Her Personal & Theoretical Vision. LC 85-42342. 285p. 1986. pap. 8.95 (ISBN 0-8070-1133-9, BP 718). Beacon Pr.

Morton, Richard, jt. auth. see Browning, John.

Morwood, J. H., ed. see Apuleius.

Mosala, Itumeleng & Tlhagale, Buti, eds. Hammering Swords Into Ploughshares: Essays in Honor of Archbishop Mpilo Desmond Tutu. 360p. (Orig.). 1987. pap. 12.95 (ISBN 0-8028-0269-9). Eerdmans.

Mosala, Itumeleng J. & Tlhagale, Buti, eds. The Unquestionable Right to Be Free: Black Theology from South Africa. 224p. (Orig.). 1986. pap. 11.95 (ISBN 0-88344-251-5). Orbis Bks.

Mosatche, Harriet S. Searching: Practices & Beliefs of the Religious Cults & Human Potential Movements. LC 83-4829. (Illus.). 437p. 1984. 14.95 (ISBN 0-87396-092-0). Stravon.

Moschus, Saint John. Spiritual Meadow: The Pratum Spirituale. pap. 1.25 (ISBN 0-686-16371-0). Eastern Orthodox.

Moscow Synod. Staff, ed. Bogojavlenije Gospodnje. Tr. of Theophany. 194p. pap. 8.00 (ISBN 0-317-29167-X). Holy Trinity.

--Preobrazhenije Gospodnje. Tr. of The Rransfiguration of the Lord. 128p. pap. 6.00 (ISBN 0-317-29169-6). Holy Trinity.

Moseley, James G. A Cultural History of Religion in America. LC 80-23609. (Contributions to the Study of Religion Ser.: No. 2). 216p. 1981. lib. bdg. 29.95 (ISBN 0-313-22479-X, MRA/). Greenwood.

Moseley, James G., ed. A Complex Inheritance. LC 75-8955. (American Academy of Religion. Dissertation Ser.). ix, 169p. 1975. pap. 9.95 (ISBN 0-89130-000-7, 010104). Scholars Pr GA.

Moseley, Rufus. Reverse Side of the Cross. pap. 0.65 ea. 2 for 1.00 (ISBN 0-910924-83-X). Macalester.

Moser, Mary T. The Evolution of the Option for the Poor in France, 1880-1965. (Illus.). 216p. (Orig.). 1985. lib. bdg. 24.00 (ISBN 0-8191-4814-8); pap. text ed. 11.75 (ISBN 0-8191-4815-6). U Pr of Amer.

Moses, A. Elfin & Hawkins, Robert O., Jr. Counseling Lesbian Women & Gay Men: A Life-Issues Approach. 263p. 1982. pap. text ed. 19.95 (ISBN 0-675-20599-9). Merrill.

Moses Ben Maimon. Eight Chapters of Maimonides on Ethics. (Columbia University. Oriental Studies: No. 7). Repr. of 1912 ed. 24.50 (ISBN 0-404-50497-3). AMS Pr.

Moses, Larry W. The Political Role of Mongol Buddhism. LC 81-622859. (Indiana University Uralic & Altaic Ser.: Vol. 133). x, 299p. 1977. 15.00 (ISBN 0-933070-01-2). Ind U Res Inst.

Moses, Sallee. Sallee. 140p. 1985. 5.95 (ISBN 0-89221-120-2). New Leaf.

Moses, Wilson J. Black Messiahs & Uncle Toms: Social & Literary Manipulations of a Religious Myth. LC 81-9645. 304p. 1982. 24.95x (ISBN 0-271-00294-8). Pa St U Pr.

Moshe, Beth. Judaism's Truth versus the Missionaries. 354p. 1987. 14.95 (ISBN 0-8197-0515-2). Bloch.

Moshe, Davis, jt. ed. see Fink, Reuben.

Mosher, Ralph, ed. Moral Education: A First Generation of Research & Development. LC 80-18607. 426p. 1980. 42.95 (ISBN 0-03-053961-7). Praeger.

Moskin, Marietta. In Search of God. LC 79-10493. (Illus.). 160p. 1979. 10.95 (ISBN 0-689-30719-5). Atheneum.

Moskop, John C. Divine Omniscience & Human Freedom: Thomas Aquinas & Charles Hartshorne. LC 84-1172. xviii, 105p. 1984. 14.95 (ISBN 0-86554-123-X, MUP/H102). Mercer Univ Pr.

Moskos, C. C., Jr. & Papajohn, J. C. Greek Orthodox Youth Today. Vaporis, N. M., intro. by. (Saints Peter & Paul Youth Ministry Lectures Ser.). 56p. (Orig.). 1983. pap. 3.00 (ISBN 0-916586-56-1). Holy Cross Orthodox.

Moskowitz, Ely. Lord, Make My Days Count. LC 83-2430. 231p. 1983. 14.95 (ISBN 0-8022-2423-7). Philos Lib.

Moskowitz, Jane M., jt. auth. see Bloomfield, Brynna C.

Moskowitz, Nachama S. Original Bulletin Boards on Jewish Themes. 128p. (Orig.). 1986. pap. text ed. 12.50 (ISBN 0-86705-019-5). AIRE.

Mosqueda, Lawrence J. Chicanos, Catholicism & Political Ideology. 228p. (Orig.). 1986. lib. bdg. 24.50 (ISBN 0-8191-5318-4); pap. text ed. 12.75 (ISBN 0-8191-5319-2). U Pr of Amer.

Moss, David, jt. auth. see Moss, Rosalyn.

Moss, Edward, jt. ed. see Llewelyn, Robert.

Moss, Jean D. Godded with God: Hendrik Niclaes & His Family of Love. LC 81-68192. (Transactions Ser.: Vol. 71, Pt. 8). 1981. 10.00 (ISBN 0-87169-718-1). Am Philos.

Moss, Jim, jt. auth. see Carney, Russell.

Moss, Michele & Brians, Charlene. Latter Rain. large print ed. 24p. 1984. pap. 5.00 (ISBN 0-914009-03-6). VHI Library.

Moss, Robert H. The Waters of Mormon. 176p. 1986. 9.95. Horizon Utah.

Moss, Rosalind, jt. auth. see Porter, Bertha.

Moss, Rosalyn & Moss, David. An Invitation to Shabbat. (Illus.). 160p. 1981. cancelled (ISBN 0-89961-013-7); pap. cancelled (ISBN 0-89961-014-5). SBS Pub.

Moss, Roy L. The Lord's Portion: A Scriptural Study of Tithing. (Illus.). 80p. (Orig.). 1980. pap. 2.95 (ISBN 0-912315-48-2). Word Aflame.

Mosse, George L. Germans & Jews. LC 68-9631. 260p. 1985. 25.00x. Fertig.

--Germans & Jews: The Right, the Left, & the Search for a 'Third Force' in Pre-Nazi Germany. LC 68-9631. 1970. 23.50 (ISBN 0-86527-081-3). Fertig.

--The Holy Pretence. LC 68-14552. 1968. 23.50x (ISBN 0-86527-099-6). Fertig.

--The Reformation. rev. ed. LC 63-11339. (Berkshire Studies in History). 1969. pap. text ed. 10.95 (ISBN 0-03-082836-8, HoltE). H Holt & Co.

Mosse, George L., jt. ed. see Vago, Bela.

Mosshammer, Alden A. The Chronicle of Eusebius & Greek Chronographic Tradition. LC 76-1029. 366p. 1979. 29.50 (ISBN 0-8387-1939-2). Bucknell U Pr.

Mossner, Ernest C. Bishop Butler & the Age of Reason. LC 69-13247. 1969. Repr. of 1936 ed. 15.00 (ISBN 0-405-08807-8, Pub. by Blom). Ayer Co Pubs.

Most, William G. The Consciousness of Christ. LC 80-68761. 232p. (Orig.). 1980. pap. text ed. 6.95 (ISBN 0-931888-03-4, Chr Coll Pr). Christendom Pubns.

--Free from All Error: Authorship, Inerrancy, Historicity of Scripture, Church Teaching, & Modern Scripture Scholars. 179p. (Orig.). 1985. pap. 11.95 (ISBN 0-913382-51-5, 101-31). Prow Bks-Franciscan.

--The Heart Has Its Reasons: The Sacred Heart of Jesus & the Immaculate Heart of Mary. 35p. (Orig.). 1985. pap. 1.50 (ISBN 0-913382-50-7, 105-40). Prow Bks-Franciscan.

Moster, Mary B. When the Doctor Says "It's Cancer". abr. ed. (Pocket Guides Ser.). 96p. 1986. 1.95 (ISBN 0-8423-7981-9). Tyndale.

Mostrom, Donald G. The Dynamics of Intimacy with God. 158p. 1983. pap. 5.95 (ISBN 0-8423-1701-5). Tyndale.

--Spiritual Privileges You Didn't Know Were Yours. LC 86-11383. 192p. (Orig.). 1986. pap. 5.95 (ISBN 0-87784-982-X). Inter-Varsity.

Mothe-Fenelon, Francois D. see De Salignac de la Mothe-Fenelon, Francoise.

Mother. The Sunlit Path. 194p. 1984. pap. 4.95 (ISBN 0-89071-318-9, Pub. by Sri Aurobindo Ashram India). Matagiri.

Mother, jt. auth. see Aurobindo, Sri.

Mother Angelica. Living Prayer. 126p. (Orig.). 1985. pap. 4.95 (ISBN 0-89283-280-0). Servant.

Mother Columba Hart, tr. Hadewijch: The Complete Works. LC 80-84500. (Classics of Western Spirituality Ser.). 404p. 1981. 13.95 (ISBN 0-8091-0311-7); pap. 10.95 (ISBN 0-8091-2297-9). Paulist Pr.

Mother Immaculata. Consecration & the Spirit of Carmel. LC 82-72203. (Living Meditation & Prayerbook Ser.). (Illus.). 270p. (Orig.). 1985. pap. text ed. 6.00 (ISBN 0-932406-08-4). AFC.

Mother Martha. Papa Nicholas Planas. Holy Transfiguration Monastery, ed. & tr. from Greek. (Orig.). 1981. pap. 5.50x (ISBN 0-913026-18-2). St Nectarios.

Mother Mary & Archimandrite Kallistos Ware, trs. The Festal Menaion. 248p. 1977. pap. 10.95 (ISBN 0-571-11137-8). Faber & Faber.

--The Lenten Triodion. LC 83-20750. 699p. (Orig.). 1984. pap. 17.95 (ISBN 0-571-13243-X). Faber & Faber.

Mother Mary Francis. Walled in Light: St. Colette. 1985. 9.50 (ISBN 0-8199-0889-4). Franciscan Herald.

Mother Teresa. Heart of Joy: The Transforming Power of Self-Giving. 140p. (Orig.). 1987. pap. 3.95 (ISBN 0-89283-342-4). Servant.

--Jesus, the Word to Be Spoken. 176p. (Orig.). 1986. pocket-size 3.95 (ISBN 0-89283-304-1). Servant.

--Jesus, the Word to Be Spoken: A Daily Devotional. 1987. 9.95 (ISBN 0-8027-2574-0). Walker & Co.

--Mother Teresa: Contemplative in the Heart of the World. 154p. 1985. pap. 8.95 (ISBN 0-89283-279-7). Servant.

--Words to Love By. LC 82-73373. (Illus.). 80p. (Orig.). 1983. pap. 4.95 (ISBN 0-87793-261-1). Ave Maria.

--Words to Love By. 160p. 1985. pap. 6.95 large print ed. (ISBN 0-8027-2478-7). Walker & Co.

Mother Teresa of Calcutta. Life in the Spirit: Reflections, Meditations, & Prayers. LC 82-48938. 128p. 1983. 10.45i (ISBN 0-06-066021-X, HarpR). Har-Row.

--The Love of Christ: Spiritual Counsels. LC 81-48216. 128p. 1982. 8.45 (ISBN 0-06-068229-9, HarpR). Har-Row.

--A Mother Teresa Treasury: Mother Teresa of Calcutta, 3 vols. Incl. Vol. 1. A Gift for God. 96p; Vol. 2. The Love of Christ. 128p; Vol. 3. Life in the Spirit. 96p. LC 85-42786. 1985. 19.95 (ISBN 0-06-068228-0, HarpR). Har-Row.

Mother Teresa of Calcutta & Roger of Taize. Meditations on the Way of the Cross. (Illus.). 64p. (Orig.). 1987. pap. 5.95 (ISBN 0-8298-0585-0). Pilgrim NY.

Mother Teresa of Calcutta & Spink, Kathryn. I Need Souls Like You Sharing in the Work of Charity Through Prayer & Suffering. LC 83-48984. 128p. 1984. 10.45 (ISBN 0-06-068236-1, HarpR). Har-Row.

Mother Thais. Zhitija Russkikh Svatikh, v 2 tom, 2 vols. LC 82-81204. Tr. of The Lives of the Russian Saints. Vol. 1. pap. 10.00 (ISBN 0-88465-012-X); Vol. 2. pap. 13.00 (ISBN 0-88465-020-0). Holy Trinity.

Motlagh, Hushidar, compiled by. Unto Him Shall We Return: Selections from the Baha'i Writings on the Reality & Immortality of the Human Soul. 144p. 1985. pap. 9.95 (ISBN 0-87743-201-5). Baha'i.

Motoyama, Hiroshi. Theories of the Chakras. LC 81-51165. 350p. (Orig.). 1982. pap. 8.95 (ISBN 0-8356-0551-5, Quest). Theos Pub Hse.

Mott, John R. The Evangelization of the World in This Generation. LC 76-38457. (Religion in America, Ser. 2). 258p. 1972. Repr. of 1900 ed. 17.00 (ISBN 0-405-04078-4). Ayer Co Pubs.

--Moslem World of Today. xv, 420p. 1986. text ed. 50.00x (ISBN 81-210-0016-5, Pub. by Inter India Pubns N Delhi). Apt Bks.

Mott, John R., et al. Student Mission Power: Report of the First International Convention of the Student Volunteer Movement for Foreign Missions, 1891. LC 79-92013. 1979. pap. 6.95 (ISBN 0-87808-736-2). William Carey Lib.

Mott, Michael. The Seven Mountains of Thomas Merton. LC 84-10944. 1984. 24.95 (ISBN 0-395-31324-4). HM.

--The Seven Mountains of Thomas Merton. 1986. pap. 12.95 (ISBN 0-395-40451-7). HM.

Mott, Stephen C. Biblical Ethics & Social Change. 1982. 21.95x (ISBN 0-19-502947-X); pap. 9.95x (ISBN 0-19-502948-8). Oxford U Pr.

Mott, Stephen C., jt. auth. see Bruland, Esther B.

Motta, Marcelo, jt. auth. see Crowley, Aleister.

Mottahedeh, Roy. The Mantle of the Prophet: Religion & Politics in Iran. LC 86-42737. 416p. 1986. pap. 9.95 (ISBN 0-394-74865-4). Pantheon.

Motte, G. Homilies for Sundays of the Year: Cycles B. 1976. 7.50 ea. (ISBN 0-8199-0575-5). Franciscan Herald.

Motte, Ganzague. Homilies for Sundays of the Year: Cycle A. 1974. 7.50 (ISBN 0-8199-0535-6). Franciscan Herald.

Motte, Gonzague. Homilies for Sundays of the Year Cycle 'C', 1974. Drury, John, tr. from Fr. Tr. of Homilies pour une annees. 312p. 1973. 10.00 (ISBN 0-8199-0461-9). Franciscan Herald.

Motte, Mary & Lang, Joseph R., eds. Mission in Dialogue: The Sedos Research Seminar on the Future of Mission. LC 82-2258. 704p. (Orig.). 1982. 35.00 (ISBN 0-88344-332-5). Orbis Bks.

Motter, Alton M., ed. Preaching about Death: Eighteen Sermons Dealing with the Experience of Death from the Christian Perspective. LC 74-26336. pap. 23.50 (2026862). Bks Demand UMI.

Mottola, Anthony, tr. see St. Ignatius.

Mottweiler, Jack. Adults As Learners. (C. E. Ministries Ser.). 95p. (Orig.). 1984. pap. 3.50 (ISBN 0-89367-098-7). Light & Life.

Motyer, Alec. The Message of James. Stott, John R., ed. LC 85-4316. (Bible Speaks Today Ser.). 156p. 1985. pap. 6.95 (ISBN 0-87784-292-2). Inter-Varsity.

--The Message of Philippians. Stott, John R., ed. LC 83-22684. (The Bible Speaks Today Ser.). 252p. 1983. pap. 7.95 (ISBN 0-87784-310-4). Inter-Varsity.

Motyer, J. A., ed. see Baldwin, Joyce G.

Motyer, J. A., ed. see Brown, Raymond.

Motyer, J. A., ed. see Kidner, Derek.

Motyer, J. A., ed. see Lucas, R. J.

Motyer, J. A., ed. see Prior, David.

Motyer, J. A., ed. see Stott, John R.

Motyer, J. A., ed. see Wilcock, Michael.

Mou-Lam, jt. tr. see Price, A. F.

Moule, A. C. Christians in China Before the Year 1550. 59.95 (ISBN 0-87968-865-3). Gordon Pr.

--Christians in China before the Year 1550. 1972. lib. bdg. 20.00x (ISBN 0-374-95972-2, Octagon). Hippocrene Bks.

Moule, C. F. The Birth of the New Testament. rev. ed. LC 81-47432. 336p. 1981. pap. 9.50 (ISBN 0-06-066029-5, RD 365, HarpR). Har-Row.

Moule, C. F., jt. ed. see Bammel, E.

Moule, C. F., jt. ed. see Farmer, William R.

Moule, Charles F. Epistles of Paul the Apostle to the Colossians & to Philemon. (Cambridge Greek Testament Ser.). 1959. text ed. 32.50 (ISBN 0-521-04252-6); pap. text ed. 10.95 (ISBN 0-521-09236-1). Cambridge U Pr.

--Essays in New Testament Interpretation. LC 81-10141. (Illus.). 260p. 1982. 42.50 (ISBN 0-521-23783-1). Cambridge U Pr.

--Gospel According to Mark. (Cambridge Bible Commentary on the New English Bible, New Testament Ser.). (Orig.). 1965. 15.50 (ISBN 0-521-04210-0); pap. 7.95x (ISBN 0-521-09288-4). Cambridge U Pr.

--Idiom Book of New Testament Greek. 2nd ed. 1959. 39.50 (ISBN 0-521-05774-4); pap. text ed. 13.95 (ISBN 0-521-09237-X). Cambridge U Pr.

--The Origin of Christology. LC 76-11087. 1977. 29.95 (ISBN 0-521-21290-1); pap. 11.95 (ISBN 0-521-29363-4). Cambridge U Pr.

Moule, H., jt. auth. see Pattison, R.

Moule, H. C. Romans. 1982. lib. bdg. 16.25 (ISBN 0-86524-086-8, 4502). Klock & Klock.

Moule, H. C. & Orr, J. The Resurrection of Christ. 1980. 20.00 (ISBN 0-86524-062-0, 9506). Klock & Klock.

Moule, H. C. G. Colossian & Philemon Studies. 1981. 12.00 (ISBN 0-86524-052-3, 7106). Klock & Klock.

--Studies in Colossians & Philemon. LC 77-79185. (Kregel Popular Commentary Ser.). 196p. 1977. kivar 6.95 (ISBN 0-8254-3217-0). Kregel.

--Studies in Ephesians. LC 77-79179. (Kregel Popular Commentary Ser.). 176p. 1977. kivar 7.95 (ISBN 0-8254-3218-9). Kregel.

--Studies in Hebrews. LC 77-79181. (Kregel Popular Commentary Ser.). 120p. 1977. kivar 5.95 (ISBN 0-8254-3223-5). Kregel.

--Studies in Philippians. LC 77-79184. (Kregel Popular Commentary Ser.). 136p. 1977. kivar 6.95 (ISBN 0-8254-3216-2). Kregel.

--Studies in Romans. LC 77-79180. (Kregel Popular Commentary Ser.). 270p. 1977. kivar 8.95 (ISBN 0-8254-3215-4). Kregel.

--Studies in Second Timothy. LC 77-79182. (Kregel Popular Commentary Ser.). 180p. 1977. kivar 6.95 (ISBN 0-8254-3219-7). Kregel.

Moule, Handley. Colossians. 1975. pap. 4.95 (ISBN 0-87508-361-7). Chr Lit.

--Ephesians. 1975. pap. 4.95 (ISBN 0-87508-363-3). Chr Lit.

--Philippians. 1975. pap. 4.95 (ISBN 0-87508-364-1). Chr Lit.

--Romans. 1975. pap. 4.95 (ISBN 0-87508-362-5). Chr Lit.

--Two, Corinthians. 1976. pap. 4.95 (ISBN 0-87508-359-5). Chr Lit.

Moulton, J. H. Treasure of the Magi: A Study of Modern Zoroastrianism. lib. bdg. 59.95 (ISBN 0-8490-2759-4). Gordon Pr.

Moulton, J. H. & Milligan, G. The Vocabulary of the Greek Testament: Illustrated from the Papyri & Other Non-Literary Sources, 2 vols. 1977. lib. bdg. 250.00 (ISBN 0-8490-2800-0). Gordon Pr.

Moulton, James H. Early Zoroastrianism. 1976. lib. bdg. 59.95 (ISBN 0-8490-1743-2). Gordon Pr.

--Early Zoroastrianism: Lectures Delivered at Oxford & in London, February to May, 1912. LC 77-27517. (Hibbert Lectures Ser.). Repr. of 1913 ed. 37.00 (ISBN 0-404-60414-5). AMS Pr.

--A Prolegomena to a Grammar of New Testament, Vol. I. (Moulton's Grammar of New Testament Greek Ser.). 320p. 1906. 19.95 (ISBN 0-567-01011-2, Pub. by T & T Clark Ltd UK). Fortress.

--Style, Vol. 4. (Moulton's Grammar of New Testament Greek Ser.). 184p. 1976. 14.95 (ISBN 0-567-01018-X, Pub. by T & T Clark Ltd Uk). Fortress.

--Treasure of the Magi: A Story of Modern Zoroastrianism. LC 73-173004. Repr. of 1917 ed. 21.75 (ISBN 0-404-04508-1). AMS Pr.

Moulton, James H. & Howard, Wilbert F. Accidence & Word Formation, Vol. 2. (Moulton's Grammar of New Testament Greek Ser.). 572p. 1929. 21.95 (ISBN 0-567-01012-0, Pub. by T & T Clark Ltd UK). Fortress.

Moulton, James H. & Milligan, George. Vocabulary of the Greek New Testament. (Gr.). 1949. 35.95 (ISBN 0-8028-2178-2). Eerdmans.

Moulton, Phillips P. The Living Witness of John Woolman. LC 72-94969. 36p. (Orig.). 1973. 2.50x (ISBN 0-87574-187-8, 187). Pendle Hill.

Moulton, Phillips P., ed. The Journal & Major Essays of John Woolman. (A Library of Protestant Thought). (Illus.). 336p. 1971. pap. text ed. 7.95 (ISBN 0-19-501419-7). Religious Soc Friends.

Moulton, R. G. The Literary Study of the Bible. 34.95 (ISBN 0-8490-0544-2). Gordon Pr.

Moulton, Richard G. The Literary Study of the Bible. LC 70-4534. 1898. 59.00x (ISBN 0-403-00113-7). Scholarly.

--A Short Introduction to the Literature of the Bible. 1978. Repr. of 1900 ed. lib. bdg. 25.00 (ISBN 0-8495-3729-0). Arden Lib.

--A Short Introduction to the Literature of the Bible. 1901. 25.00 (ISBN 0-8274-3404-9). R West.

Moulton, Richard G. & Bruce, A. B. The Bible As Literature. LC 78-1666. Repr. of 1899 ed. lib. bdg. 47.50 (ISBN 0-8414-6242-9). Folcroft.

Moum, Margaret R. Guidebook to the Aquarian Gospel of Jesus the Christ. 93p. 1974. pap. 3.95 (ISBN 0-917200-05-5). ESPress.

Mounce, Robert. A Living Hope: A Commentary on I & II Peter. 1982. pap. 4.95 (ISBN 0-8028-1915-X). Eerdmans.

Mounce, Robert H. The Book of Revelation. LC 77-7664. (New International Commentary on New Testament Ser.). 1977. 16.95 (ISBN 0-8028-2348-3). Eerdmans.

--Matthew: A Good News Commentary. LC 84-48775. (Good News Commentary Ser.). 288p. (Orig.). 1985. pap. 9.95 (ISBN 0-06-066032-5, HarpR). Har-Row.

--Pass It on. LC 78-68851. (Bible Commentary for Layman Ser.). 160p. 1979. pap. 3.50 (ISBN 0-8307-0667-4, S332108). Regal.

Mounce, Virginia N. An Archivists Guide to the Catholic Church in Mexico. LC 78-62226. 1979. perfect bdg. 10.95 (ISBN 0-88247-570-3). R & E Pubs.

Mounce, William D. Profiles in Faith. LC 84-9961. 1984. pap. 3.95 (ISBN 0-8307-0984-3, S382102). Regal.

Mount, Balfour M., jt. ed. see Ajemian, Ina.

Mount, Guy, jt. auth. see Modesto, Ruby.

Mountford, J. F. The Scholia Bembina in Terentium. 140p. 1934. text ed. 41.40x (ISBN 0-576-72270-7, Pub. by Gregg Intl Pubs England). Gregg Intl.

Mouradian, Kay. Reflective Meditation. LC 82-50163. 175p. (Orig.). 1982. pap. 4.50 (ISBN 0-8356-0565-5, Quest). Theos Pub Hse.

Mourant, John A., jt. auth. see Harshbarger, Luther H.

Mourot, Jean, jt. auth. see Chateaubriand, Rene de.

Mouton, Boyce. By This Shall All Men Know. LC 79-56541. 1980. pap. 2.95 (ISBN 0-89900-139-4). College Pr Pub.

--These Two Commandments. 2nd ed. (Orig.). 1978. pap. 2.95 (ISBN 0-89900-138-6). College Pr Pub.

Moutsopolous, Evanghelos, jt. ed. see De Nicolas, Antonio T.

Mouw, Richard. When Kings Come Marching In: Isaiah & the New Jerusalem. 96p. (Orig.). 1983. pap. 3.95 (ISBN 0-8028-1935-4). Eerdmans.

Mouw, Richard J. Called to Holy Worldliness. Gibbs, Mark, ed. LC 80-8047. (Laity Exchange). 160p. (Orig.). 1980. pap. 5.95 (ISBN 0-8006-1397-X, 1-1397). Fortress.
--Politics & the Biblical Drama. 1983. pap. 5.95 (ISBN 0-8010-6153-9). Baker Bk.
Movimiento Familiar Cristiano De Miami, tr. see Reilly, Terry & Reilly, Mimi.
Mow, Anna B. Springs of Love. LC 79-11186. 1979. pap. 1.95 (ISBN 0-87178-810-1). Brethren.
Mow, Merrill, ed. see Arnold, Eberhard.
Mower, A. Glenn, Jr. The United States, the United Nations, & Human Rights: The Eleanor Roosevelt & Jimmy Carter Eras. LC 78-22134. (Studies in Human Rights Ser.: No. 4). xii, 215p. 1979. lib. bdg. 29.95 (ISBN 0-313-21090-X, MUH/). Greenwood.
Mower, Richard K. Overcoming Depression. LC 85-29228. 160p. 1986. 8.95 (ISBN 0-87579-025-9). Deseret Bk.
Mowlana Jalal ud-Din Mohammad Rumi. Masnavi, Vol. 1. Estelami, Mohammad, ed. (Mazda Special Persian Language Publications). (Persian.). 580p. 1987. lib. bdg. 25.00 (ISBN 0-939214-40-7). Mazda Pubs.
Mowshowitz, Israel. A Rabbi's Rovings. 385p. 1985. 20.00 (ISBN 0-88125-069-4). Ktav.
Moxcey, Mary E. Some Qualities Associated with Success in the Christian Ministry. LC 76-177095. (Columbia University. Teachers College. Contributions to Education: No. 122). Repr. of 1922 ed. 22.50 (ISBN 0-404-55122-X). AMS Pr.
Moyd, Olin P. Redemption in Black Theology. LC 78-23816. 1979. soft cover 8.95 (ISBN 0-8170-0806-3). Judson.
Moyer, Elgin. Wycliffe Biographical Dictionary of the Church. 1982. 19.95 (ISBN 0-8024-9693-8). Moody.
Moyer, Katy. The Father the Son the Holy Spirit. 1983. pap. 1.25 (ISBN 0-910709-18-1). PTL Repro.
Moyes, Gordon. Discovering Jesus. (Illus.). 160p. (Orig.). 1984. pap. 9.95 (ISBN 0-86760-005-5, Pub. by Albatross Bks). ANZ Religious Pubns.
Moyes, Malcolm. Richard Rolle's Expositio Super Novem Lectiones Mortuorum. Hogg, James, ed. (Elizabethan & Renaissance Studies). (Orig.). 1984. pap. 15.00 (ISBN 3-7052-0753-9, Pub. by Salzburg Studies). Longwood Pub Group.
Moynahan, Michael. God of Seasons. LC 79-93127. 1980. pap. text ed. 4.95 (ISBN 0-89390-019-2). Resource Pubns.
Moynahan, Michael E. God of Untold Tales. LC 79-64823. 1979. pap. 4.95 (ISBN 0-89390-009-5). Resource Pubns.
--How the Word Became Flesh: Story Dramas for Education & Worship. LC 80-54874. 1981. pap. 10.95 (ISBN 0-89390-029-X). Resource Pubns.
--Once upon a Parable: Dramas for Worship & Religious Education. (Orig.). 1984. pap. 8.95 (ISBN 0-8091-2586-2). Paulist Pr.
Moynihan, Michael. God on Our Side: The British Padre in World War I. (Illus.). 196p. 1983. 19.95 (ISBN 0-436-29402-8, Pub. by Secker & Warburg UK). David & Charles.
Moyser, George, ed. Church & Politics Today. 320p. 1985. pap. 17.95 (ISBN 0-567-29350-5, Pub. by T&T Clark Ltd Uk). Fortress.
Mozaffari, Mehdi. Authority in Islam. Vale, Michel, tr. from Fr. Tr. of Pouvoic Islamique. 156p. 1987. 39.95 (ISBN 0-87332-388-2). M E Sharpe.
Mozeson, Isaac E. The Word: The English from Hebrew Dictionary. 1986. 16.95 (ISBN 0-933503-44-X). Shapolsky Pubs.
Mozley, E. N. The Theology of Albert Schweitzer. LC 73-16630. 108p. 1974. Repr. of 1950 ed. lib. bdg. 22.50x (ISBN 0-8371-7204-7, SCTH). Greenwood.
Mozley, E. N., ed. see Schweitzer, Albert.
Mozley, James F. John Foxe & His Book. LC 76-120651. 1970. Repr. of 1940 ed. lib. bdg. 18.50x (ISBN 0-374-95977-3, Octagon). Hippocrene Bks.
--William Tyndale. LC 70-109801. (Illus.). 1971. Repr. of 1937 ed. lib. bdg. 22.50x (ISBN 0-8371-4292-X, MOWT). Greenwood.
Mozumdar, A. K. Today & Tomorrow. 2nd ed. 1979. pap. 2.50 (ISBN 0-87516-369-6). De Vorss.
--The Triumphant Spirit. 1978. pap. 6.50 (ISBN 0-87516-261-4). De Vorss.
Mrosovsky, Kitty, tr. see Flaubert, Gustave.
Mrozinski, Ronald. Franciscan Prayer Life. 1983. 12.50 (ISBN 0-8199-0795-2). Franciscan Herald.
M. S. A. The Muslim Population of the World. pap. 1.00 (ISBN 0-686-18438-6). Kazi Pubns.
Mtshali, Oswald. Fireflames. (Illus.). 72p. (Orig.). 1983. pap. 6.95 (ISBN 0-88208-501-8). Lawrence Hill.
Muccie, Frank J., Jr. The Essene Humane Gospel of Jesus. 174p. pap. 4.95 (ISBN 0-938520-02-4). Edenite.
--I & the Father Are One. 180p. 1982. pap. 7.95 (ISBN 0-938520-01-6). Edenite.
--Jesus Was a Vegetarian. 62p. pap. 1.95 (ISBN 0-938520-03-2). Edenite.
Muck, Terry. Liberating the Leader's Prayer Life. 160p. 1985. 9.95 (ISBN 0-8499-0549-4, 0549-4). Word Bks.
--When to Take a Risk. (Leadership Library). 175p. 1987. 9.95 (ISBN 0-917463-12-9). Chr Today.
Muck, Terry C. Liberating the Leader's Prayer Life. (Leadership Library). 176p. 1985. 9.95 (ISBN 0-917463-05-6). Chr Today.
--When to Take a Risk, No. 9. 192p. 1987. 9.95 (ISBN 0-8499-0615-6). Word Bks.
Mud Flower Collective. God's Fierce Whimsy: Christian Feminism & Theological Education. Heyward, Carter, ed. (Orig.). 1985. pap. 11.95 (ISBN 0-8298-0546-X). Pilgrim NY.
Muddit, B. Howard, ed. Christian Worship (Hymns) 716p. 1976. text ed. 15.00x (ISBN 0-85364-194-3). Attic Pr.
Mudge, Lewis S., ed. see Ricoeur, Paul.
Mudge, Zachariah A. Sketches of Mission Life among the Indians of Oregon. 1983. 12.50 (ISBN 0-87770-308-6). Ye Galleon.
Mudroch, Vaclav. The Wyclyf Tradition. Reeves, A. Compton, ed. LC 77-92253. xvii, 91p. 1979. 15.00x (ISBN 0-8214-0403-2). Ohio U Pr.
Mudugula, I. S. The Acarya: Sandara of Kaladi - A Story. (Illus.). 142p. 1985. 16.00 (ISBN 0-317-46523-6, Pub. by Motilal Banarsidass India). Orient Bk Dist.
Muehl, William. Why Preach? Why Listen? LC 86-45216. 96p. 1986. pap. 4.95 (ISBN 0-8006-1928-5, 1-1928). Fortress.
Muehlenberg, Ekkehard. Psalmenkommentare aus der Katenenueberlieferung, Vol. 1. LC 73-91808. (Patristische Texte und Studien, Band 15). (Ger.). 1974. 58.40x (ISBN 3-11-004182-0). De Gruyter.
--Psalmenkommentare aus der Katenenueberlieferung: Untersuchungen zu den Psalmenkatenen, Vol. 3. (Patristische Texte und Studien: No. 19). 1978. 41.20x (ISBN 3-11-006959-8). De Gruyter.
--Psalmenkommentware aus Katenenveberlieferung, Vol. 2. (Patristische Texte und Studien: Vol. 16). 1977. 59.60x (ISBN 3-11-005717-4). De Gruyter.
Muelder, Walter G. The Ethical Edge of Christian Theology: Forty Years of Communitarian Personalism. LC 83-21935. (Toronto Studies in Theology: Vol. 13). 435p. 1984. 69.95x (ISBN 0-88946-754-4). E Mellen.
--Moral Law in Christian Social Ethics. LC 66-15972. 198p. lib. bdg. 19.95x (ISBN 0-88946-011-6). E Mellen.
Mueller, A. C. My Good Shepherd Bible Story Book. LC 70-89876. 1969. bds. 12.50 (ISBN 0-570-03400-0, 56-1126). Concordia.
Mueller, Charles S. Bible Reading for Teenagers. LC 81-52274. (Bible Readings Ser.). 112p. (Orig.). 1981. pap. 3.95 (ISBN 0-8066-1906-6, 10-0681). Augsburg.
--Christian Family Prepares for Christmas. 1965. laminated bdg. 3.75 (ISBN 0-570-03023-4, 6-1092). Concordia.
--Getting Along: A Guide for Teenagers. LC 80-65546. 128p. (Orig.). 1980. pap. 4.95 (ISBN 0-8066-1791-8, 10-2545). Augsburg.
--Thank God I Have a Teenager. LC 84-24363. 128p. (Orig.). 1985. pap. 5.95 (ISBN 0-8066-2126-5, 10-6239). Augsburg.
--Words of Faith: A Devotional Dictionary. 160p. (Orig.). 1985. pap. 5.95 (ISBN 0-570-03968-1, 12-3003). Concordia.
Mueller, Charles S. & Bardill, Donald R. Thank God I'm a Teenager. LC 76-3854. 1976. pap. 5.95 (ISBN 0-8066-1536-2, 10-6242). Augsburg.
Mueller, Daniel. Just Follow the Signs. 1984. 5.00 (ISBN 0-89536-676-2, 4851). CSS of Ohio.
Mueller, David. Karl Barth. Patterson, Bob E., ed. LC 70-188066. (Makers of the Modern Theological Mind Ser). 1972. 8.95 (ISBN 0-87680-254-4, 80254). Word Bks.
Mueller, David L. Karl Barth. 172p. 1984. pap. text ed. 8.95 (ISBN 0-8499-3002-2, 3002-2). Word Bks.
Mueller, Franz H. Church & the Social Question. 158p. 1984. 14.95 (ISBN 0-8447-3567-1). Am Enterprise.
Mueller, Friedrich M. Anthropological Religion. LC 73-18822. (Gifford Lectures: 1891). 1975. Repr. of 1892 ed. 34.00 (ISBN 0-404-11428-8). AMS Pr.
--Buddhist Texts from Japan, 3 pts. in 1 vol. LC 73-18824. (Illus.). Repr. of 1884 ed. 34.50 (ISBN 0-404-11430-X). AMS Pr.
--Lectures on the Origin & Growth of Religion, as Illustrated by the Religions of India. LC 73-18816. Repr. of 1882 ed. 34.50 (ISBN 0-404-11440-7). AMS Pr.
--Lectures on the Science of Religion: With a Paper on Buddhist Nihilism, & a Translation of the Dhammapada or Path of Virtue. LC 73-18818. Repr. of 1872 ed. 15.00 (ISBN 0-404-11444-X). AMS Pr.
--Life & Religion. LC 73-18821. Repr. of 1905 ed. 19.75 (ISBN 0-404-11448-2). AMS Pr.
--Natural Religion. LC 73-18810. (Gifford Lectures: 1888). Repr. of 1889 ed. 44.50 (ISBN 0-404-11450-4). AMS Pr.
--Physical Religion. LC 73-18811. (Gifford Lectures: 1890). Repr. of 1891 ed. 34.00 (ISBN 0-404-11451-2). AMS Pr.
--Ramakrishna, His Life & Sayings. LC 73-18812. Repr. of 1899 ed. 22.00 (ISBN 0-404-11452-0). AMS Pr.
--Rig-Veda-Samhita: The Sacred Hymns of the Brahmans, 4 vols. 2nd ed. LC 73-18831. 1892. Set. 176.00 (ISBN 0-404-11461-X); Vol. 1. (ISBN 0-404-11462-8); Vol. 2. (ISBN 0-404-11463-6); Vol. 3. (ISBN 0-404-11464-4); Vol. 4. (ISBN 0-404-11465-2). AMS Pr.
--Selected Essays on Language, Mythology & Religion, 2 vols. LC 73-18814. Repr. of 1881 ed. 87.50 set (ISBN 0-404-11456-3). AMS Pr.
--Theosophy: Or, Psychological Religion. LC 73-18830. (Gifford Lectures: 1892). Repr. of 1903 ed. 47.00 (ISBN 0-404-14460-8). AMS Pr.
Mueller, G., jt. ed. see Krause, G.
Mueller, Geo. God Answers Prayer. pap. 2.95 (ISBN 0-686-27009-6). Schmul Pub Co.
Mueller, George. Answers to Prayer. (Moody Classics Ser.). 1984. pap. 3.50 (ISBN 0-8024-0565-7). Moody.
Mueller, Hans-Peter, ed. Bibel und Alter Orient: Altorientische Beitrage zum Alten Testament von Wolfram von Soden. (Beihefte zur Zeitschrift fur die Alttestamentliche Wissenschaft Ser.: Band 162). xii, 224p. 1985. 50.50x (ISBN 3-11-010091-6). De Gruyter.
Mueller, J. J. What Are They Saying about Theological Method? LC 84-61031. (WATSA Ser.). 88p. (Orig.). 1985. pap. 4.95 (ISBN 0-8091-2657-5). Paulist Pr.
Mueller, J. Theodore, tr. see Luther, Martin.
Mueller, James R., jt. auth. see Charlesworth, James H.
Mueller, Janel. The Native Tongue & the Word: Developments in English Prose Style, 1380-1580. LC 83-15817. 512p. 1984. lib. bdg. 27.50x (ISBN 0-226-54562-8). U of Chicago Pr.
Mueller, John T. Christian Dogmatics. 1934. 18.95 (ISBN 0-570-03221-0, 15-1071). Concordia.
--Great Missionaries to China. LC 73-38329. (Biography Index Reprint Ser). Repr. of 1947 ed. 12.75 (ISBN 0-8369-8124-3). Ayer Co Pubs.
--Great Missionaries to the Orient. LC 78-38330. (Biography Index Reprint Ser). Repr. of 1948 ed. 14.75 (ISBN 0-8369-8125-1). Ayer Co Pubs.
Mueller, Mary L., jt. auth. see Cove, Mary K.
Mueller, Michael. The Sinner's Return to God: Or, the Prodigal Son. LC 82-74244. 224p. 1983. pap. 6.00 (ISBN 0-89555-205-1). TAN Bks Pubs.
Mueller, Robert. For People Just Like Us. Sherer, Michael L., ed. (Orig.). 1986. pap. 3.75 (ISBN 0-89536-834-X, 6848). CSS of Ohio.
Mueller, Ulrich B., jt. auth. see Seybold, Klaus.
Mueller, Virginia. What Is Faith? (A Happy Day Book). (Illus.). 24p. (Orig.). 1980. 1.59 (ISBN 0-87239-411-5, 3643). Standard Pub.
Mueller, Virginia, jt. auth. see Pape, Donna L.
Mueller, Walter. Grammatical Aids for Students of New Testament Greek. 1972. pap. 3.95 (ISBN 0-8028-1447-6). Eerdmans.
Mueller, William R. John Donne: Preacher. 1977. Repr. of 1962 ed. lib. bdg. 19.50x (ISBN 0-374-95988-9, Octagon). Hippocrene Bks.
Muenchow, Charles A., tr. see Westermann, Claus.
Muggeridge, Anne R. The Desolate City: Revolution in the Catholic Church. 256p. 1986. 16.95 (ISBN 0-06-066038-4, HarpR). Har-Row.
Muggeridge, Kitty. Gazing on Truth: Meditations on Reality. 96p. (Orig.). 1985. pap. 4.95 (ISBN 0-8028-0072-6). Eerdmans.
Muggeridge, Malcolm. The End of Christendom. 1980. pap. 2.95 (ISBN 0-8028-1837-4). Eerdmans.
--Jesus. LC 74-28794. 176p. 1976. pap. 9.95 (ISBN 0-06-066042-2, RD149, HarpR). Har-Row.
--Jesus Rediscovered. 1979. pap. 7.95 (ISBN 0-385-14654-X, Galilee). Doubleday.
--Something Beautiful for God. 312p. 1985. pap. 8.95 (ISBN 0-8027-2474-4). Walker & Co.
--Something Beautiful for God: Mother Teresa of Calcutta. 1977. pap. 3.50 (ISBN 0-385-12639-5, Im). Doubleday.
Muggeridge, Malcolm, et al. Christian Married Love. Dennehy, Raymond, ed. Englund, Sergia & Leiva, Erasmo, trs. LC 81-85047. Tr. of Christlicher Stand. 132p. (Orig.). 1981. pap. 8.95 (ISBN 0-89870-008-6). Ignatius Pr.
Muhaiyaddeen, Bawa. Maya Veeram or the Forces of Illusion. Marcus, Sharon, ed. Ganesan, K. & Ganesan, R., trs. from Tamil. (Illus.). 232p. 1982. pap. 10.95 (ISBN 0-87728-550-0). Weiser.
Muhaiyaddeen, M. R. Golden Words of a Sufi Sheikh. LC 82-11854. 472p. 1983. 15.95 (ISBN 0-914390-24-4). Fellowship Pr PA.
--Islam & World Peace. LC 87-11921. 150p. 1987. 6.95 (ISBN 0-914390-25-2). Fellowship Pr PA.
Muhaiyaddeen, M. R. Bawa. Sheikh & Disciple. LC 83-1565. (Illus.). 120p. 1983. 7.95 (ISBN 0-914390-26-0). Fellowship Pr PA.
Muhaiyaddeen, M. R. Bawa see Bawa Muhaiyaddeen, M. R.
Muhajir. Lessons from the Stories of the Quran. pap. 14.95 (ISBN 0-686-18515-3). Kazi Pubns.
Muhajir, A. M. Islam in Practical Life. 1968. 7.25x (ISBN 0-87902-067-9). Orientalia.
--Lessons from the Stories of the Quran. 1969. 14.95x (ISBN 0-87902-066-0). Orientalia.
--Tenets of Islam. 1969. 7.25x (ISBN 0-87902-107-1). Orientalia.
Muhajir, M. R. Islam in Practical Life. 12.50 (ISBN 0-686-18502-1). Kazi Pubns.
Muhammad. The Qur'an: A New Translation with a Critical Rearrangement of the Surahs, 2 vols. Bell, Richard, tr. 14.95 ea. (Pub. by T & T Clark Ltd UK). Vol. 1, 348 pgs (ISBN 0-567-02027-4). Vol. 2, 352 pgs (ISBN 0-567-02028-2). Fortress.
Muhammad-'Aliy-Salmani, Ustad. My Memories of Baha'u'llah: Ustad Muhammad-'Aliy-Salmani, the Barber. Gail, Marzieh, tr. from Persian. (Illus.). xii, 148p. 1982. 11.95 (ISBN 0-933770-21-9). Kalimat.
Muhiyaddin, Mohammed A. A Comparative Study of the Religions of Today. 1984. 15.95 (ISBN 0-533-05963-1). Vantage.
Muhlschlegel, Peter. Auguste Forel & the Baha'i Faith. Neri, Helene, tr. from Ger. 64p. 1979. pap. 3.50 (ISBN 0-85398-076-4). G Ronald Pub.
Muhlstein, Anka. Baron James: The Rise of the French Rothschilds. LC 84-40015. 224p. 1984. pap. 7.95 (ISBN 0-394-72608-1, Vin). Random.
Mui, Shan. The Seven Magic Orders. Tabrah, Ruth, ed. LC 72-86743. (Illus.). 1973. 5.95 (ISBN 0-89610-011-1). Island Heritage.
Muir, Edwin. John Knox: Portrait of a Calvinist. facsimile ed. LC 76-148892. (Select Bibliographies Reprint Ser). Repr. of 1929 ed. 21.00 (ISBN 0-8369-5656-7). Ayer Co Pubs.
--John Knox: Portrait of a Calvinist. 1978. Repr. of 1930 ed. lib. bdg. 30.00 (ISBN 0-8414-6246-1). Folcroft.
--John Knox: Portrait of a Calvinist. LC 78-159096. 1971. Repr. of 1929 ed. 28.00x (ISBN 0-8046-1639-6, Pub. by Kennikat). Assoc Faculty Pr.
Muir, Frank. Christmas Customs & Traditions. LC 77-76504. (Illus.). 1977. 7.95 (ISBN 0-8008-1552-1). Taplinger.
Muir, J. V., jt. ed. see Easterling, P. E.
Muir, P. H. A Bibliography of the First Editions of Books by Maurice Henry Hewlett. LC 73-14788. 1927. Repr. lib. bdg. 17.50 (ISBN 0-8414-5981-9). Folcroft.
Muir, Pearson M. Religious Writers of England. 1901. 20.00 (ISBN 0-8274-3264-X). R West.
Muir, W. The Caliphate: Its Rise, Decline & Fall. 624p. 1984. Repr. of 1891 ed. 90.00x (ISBN 0-317-39168-2, Pub. by Luzac & Co Ltd). State Mutual Bk.
Muir, William. Annals of the Early Caliphate from Original Sources. 1977. lib. bdg. 59.95 (ISBN 0-8490-1434-4). Gordon Pr.
--The Life of Mohammad from Original Sources. new rev. ed. Weir, Thomas H., ed. LC 78-180366. Repr. of 1923 ed. 57.50 (ISBN 0-404-56306-6). AMS Pr.
Muir, William K., Jr. Prayer in the Public Schools: Law & Attitude Change. LC 67-28851. 1967. U of Chicago Pr.
Muira, Ayako. Shiokari Pass. 1968. 4.95 (ISBN 9971-972-23-9). OMF Bks.
Mukenge, Ida R. The Black Church in Urban America: A Case Study in Political Economy. LC 83-14593. 256p. 1984. lib. bdg. 27.50 (ISBN 0-8191-3431-7); pap. text ed. 13.50 (ISBN 0-8191-3432-5). U Pr of Amer.
Mukerjee, Radhakamal, tr. The Song of the Self Supreme: Astavakra Gita. LC 74-24308. 293p. 1981. 9.95 (ISBN 0-913922-14-5). Dawn Horse Pr.
Mukerji, A. P. Doctrine & Practice of Yoga. 6.00 (ISBN 0-911662-23-5). Yoga.
--Yoga Lessons for Developing Spiritual Consciousness. 7.00 (ISBN 0-911662-24-3). Yoga.
Mukerji, P. N., tr. see Aranya, S. Hariharananda.
Mukherjee, Prabhat. The History of Medieval Vaishnavism in Orissa. 200p. 1986. Repr. 14.00X (ISBN 0-8364-1754-2, Pub. by Manohar India). South Asia Bks.
--History of the Chaitanya Faith in Orissa. 1979. 14.00x (ISBN 0-8364-0547-1). South Asia Bks.
Mukherji, Dhan G. The Face of Silence: A Biography of Rama Krishna. LC 85-22355. 264p. 1985. Repr. lib. bdg. 19.95x (ISBN 0-89370-584-5). Borgo Pr.

Mukhopadhyay, Somnath. Candi in Art & Iconography. 1984. 34.00x (ISBN 0-8364-1146-3, Pub. by Agam India). South Asia Bks.
Mukhyopadhyaya, Pramatha N. see Woodroffe, John.
Muktananda. I Love You. (Illus.). 40p. (Orig.). 1975. 1.75 (ISBN 0-914602-58-6). SYDA Found.
--Meditate. LC 80-20477. 84p. 1980. 9.95x (ISBN 0-87395-471-8); pap. 4.95x (ISBN 0-87395-472-6). State U NY Pr.
Muktananda, Swami. A Book for the Mind. 40p. (Orig.). 1976. pap. 1.75 (ISBN 0-685-99448-1). SYDA Found.
--En Busca del Ser. LC 81-50917. 140p. 1981. pap. 4.95 (ISBN 0-914602-71-3). SYDA Found.
--En Compania de un Siddha. LC 81-84263. 1981. pap. 5.95. SYDA Found.
--God Is with You. (Illus.). 40p. (Orig.). 1978. pap. 1.75 (ISBN 0-914602-57-8). SYDA Found.
--I Am That. rev. ed. 104p. 1983. pap. 3.95 (ISBN 0-914602-27-6). SYDA Found.
--I Welcome You All with Love. 40p. (Orig.). 1978. pap. 1.75 (ISBN 0-914602-59-4). SYDA Found.
--Perfect Relationship. LC 80-54457. 240p. 1980. pap. 6.95 (ISBN 0-914602-53-5). SYDA Found.
--Play of Consciousness. LC 78-15841. (Illus.). 1979. pap. 7.64 (ISBN 0-06-066044-9, RD 223, HarpR). Har-Row.
--Play of Consciousness. LC 78-62769. 322p. 1978. 9.95 (ISBN 0-914602-36-5); pap. 6.95 (ISBN 0-914602-37-3). SYDA Found.
--La Relacion Perfecta. LC 81-84261. 218p. 1982. pap. 6.95 (ISBN 0-914602-84-5). SYDA Found.
--Secret of the Siddhas. LC 80-53590. 256p. 1980. pap. 6.95 (ISBN 0-914602-52-7). SYDA Found.
Mulder, Alfred E. Happiness Is: An Introduction to Christian Life & Faith. 60p. 1983. pap. 3.25 (ISBN 0-933140-88-6). CRC Pubns.
Mulder, John M., jt. auth. see Wilson, John F.
Mulder, John M., jt. ed. see Kerr, Hugh T.
Mulder, John R., ed. Religion & Literature: The Convergence of Approaches. (AAR Thematic Studies). pap. 8.95_o.s. (ISBN 0-89130-676-5, 01-24-72). Scholars Pr GA.
Mulder, John T., jt. ed. see Kerr, Hugh T.
Mulder, Karen, jt. auth. see Jurries, Ginger.
Mulder, William. The Mormons in American History. (The University of Utah Frederick William Reynolds Lecture Ser.: No. 21). 1981. pap. 4.95 (ISBN 0-87480-184-2). U of Utah Pr.
Mulder, William & Mortensen, A. Russell, eds. Among the Mormons: Historic Accounts by Contemporary Observers. LC 58-5825. xiv, 496p. 1973. (Bison). U of Nebr Pr.
Muldoon, Maureen, ed. Abortion: An Annotated Indexed Bibliography. LC 79-91622. (Studies in Women & Religion: Vol. 3). 148p. 1980. 49.95x (ISBN 0-88946-972-5). E Mellen.
Muldrow, George M. Milton & the Drama of the Soul: A Study of the Theme of the Restoration of Man in Milton's Later Poetry. LC 76-89796. (Studies in English Literature: Vol. 51). 1970. text ed. 23.20x (ISBN 90-2790-530-4). Mouton.
Mulert, H. see Dilthey, Wilhelm.
Mulford, Elisha. The Republic of God: An Institute of Theology. LC 75-3291. Repr. of 1881 ed. 18.00 (ISBN 0-404-59277-5). AMS Pr.
Mulhearn, Timothy, ed. Getting It All Together: The Heritage of Thomas Merton. 1984. pap. 4.95 (ISBN 0-89453-380-0). M Glazier.
Mulholland, John. Beware Familiar Spirits. LC 78-66328. 1938. pap. 5.95 (ISBN 0-684-16181-8). Brown Bk.
Mulholland, Kenneth. Adventures in Training the Ministry. 1976. pap. 5.95 (ISBN 0-87552-340-4). Presby & Reformed.
Mulholland, M. Robert. Shaped by the Word. (Orig.). 1985. pap. 7.95 (ISBN 0-8358-0519-0). Upper Room.
Mulla Firuz Bin Kaus, tr. from Mahabhadian. The Desatir. LC 73-84045. (Secret Doctrine Reference Ser.). 208p. 1980. pap. 9.00 (ISBN 0-913510-33-5). Wizards.
Mullahy, Bernard. The Splendid Risk. LC 81-40445. 256p. 1982. text ed. 12.95 (ISBN 0-268-01705-0). U of Notre Dame Pr.
Mullaly, Columba. Trinity College, Washington, DC: The First Eighty Years, 1897-1977. 500p. 1987. 40.00 (ISBN 0-87061-140-2); pap. 35.00 (ISBN 0-87061-139-9). Chr Classics.
Mullan, Bob. Life as Laughter: Following Bhagwan Shree Rajneesh. (Illus.). 204p. 1984. 26.95x (ISBN 0-7102-0141-9); pap. 12.95 (ISBN 0-7102-0043-9). Methuen Inc.
Mulla Sadra. The Wisdom of the Throne: An Introduction to the Philosophy of Mulla Sadra. Morris, James W., tr. from Arabic. LC 81-47153. (Princeton Library of Asian Translations). 300p. 1981. 34.50x (ISBN 0-691-06493-8). Princeton U Pr.
Mullen, E. Theodore, Jr. The Assembly of the Gods: The Divine Council in Canaanite & Early Hebrew Literature. LC 80-10128. (Harvard Semitic Museum Monographs: No. 24). 1980. 10.50x (ISBN 0-89130-380-4, 04 00 24). Scholars Pr GA.
Mullen, Peter, jt. ed. see Martin, David.
Mullen, Sharon. When Jesus Was Born. LC 86-17558. (Bible-&-Me Ser.). 1987. 5.95 (ISBN 0-8054-4177-8). Broadman.
Mullen, Tom. Laughing Out Loud & Other Religious Experiences. 1983. 8.95 (ISBN 0-8499-0329-7). Word Bks.
Mullens, Leonard. Lord Teach Us to Pray. 1963. pap. 1.00 (ISBN 0-686-75248-1). Firm Foun Pub.
--Unity in Christ. 1958. 3.00 (ISBN 0-88027-053-5). Firm Foun Pub.
Muller, Alexander V., ed. & tr. from Russian. The Spiritual Regulation of Peter the Great. LC 74-4590. (Publications on Russia & Eastern Europe of the School of International Studies: No. 3). 188p. 1972. 16.50x (ISBN 0-295-95237-7); pap. 6.95x (ISBN 0-295-95282-2). U of Wash Pr.
Muller, Edward, ed. see Buddhaghosa.
Muller, F. & Oldenberg, H. Vedic Hymns. (Sacred Bks. of the East: Vols. 32, 46). both vols. 30.00 (ISBN 0-89581-529-X); 15.00 ea. Asian Human Pr.
Muller, F. M. Vedanta Philosophy. 182p. 1984. text ed. 27.00x. Coronet Bks.
Muller, F. Max. The Upanishads, 2 vols. 1974. lib. bdg. 250.00 (ISBN 0-8490-1252-X). Gordon Pr.
Muller, F. Max, ed. The Upanishads. (Sacred Bks. of the East: Vol 1 & 15). both vols. 30.00 (ISBN 0-686-97473-5); 15.00 ea. Asian Human Pr.
Muller, F. Max, ed. see Arya-Sura.
Muller, F. Max, ed. see Kasawara, Kenju.
Muller, F. Max, ed. see Legge, James.
Muller, F. Max, jt. auth. see Cowell, E. B.
Muller, Francis J. De Paroecia Domui Religiosae Commissa. 1956. 3.50 (ISBN 0-686-11580-5). Franciscan Inst.
Muller, Friedrich M. Introduction to the Science of Religion. Bolle, Kees W., ed. LC 77-79145. (Mythology Ser.). 1978. lib. bdg. 32.00x (ISBN 0-405-10554-1). Ayer Co Pubs.
Muller, Friedrich Max. Comparative Mythology: An Essay. rev. ed. Dorson, Richard M., ed. LC 77-70612. (International Folklore Ser.). 1977. Repr. of 1909 ed. lib. bdg. 22.00x (ISBN 0-405-10111-2). Ayer Co Pubs.
Muller, George. Autobiography of George Muller. Wayland, H. Lincoln, ed. (Giant Summit Books Ser.). 490p. 1981. pap. 11.95 (ISBN 0-8010-6105-9). Baker Bk.
--The Autobiography of George Muller. 300p. 1984. pap. 3.50 (ISBN 0-88368-159-5). Whitaker Hse.
--George Muller Treasury. Steer, Roger, ed. LC 86-72058. 192p. (Orig.). 1987. pap. 7.95 (ISBN 0-89107-416-3, Crossway Bks). Good News.
Muller, Herbert J. Religion & Freedom in the Modern World. LC 63-20911. 1963. pap. 1.50x (ISBN 0-226-54815-5, P193, Phoen). U of Chicago Pr.
Muller, Jacobus J. Epistles of Paul to the Philippians. (New International Commentary on the New Testament). 1985. 12.95 (ISBN 0-8028-2188-X). Eerdmans.
Muller, Karl O. Introduction to a Scientific System of Mythology. Bolle, Kees W., ed. LC 77-79144. (Mythology Ser.). 1978. Repr. of 1844 ed. lib. bdg. 30.00x (ISBN 0-405-10553-3). Ayer Co Pubs.
Muller, Lydia, ed. Glaubenszeugnisse Oberdeutscher. (Ger). 34.00 (ISBN 0-384-40404-9); pap. 28.00 (ISBN 0-384-40403-0). Johnson Repr.
Muller, Max. Chips from a German Workshop: Volume I: Essays on the Science of Religion. (Reprints & Translations). 1985. pap. 13.95 (ISBN 0-89130-890-3, 00-07-10). Scholars Pr GA.
Muller, Max, ed. Sacred Book of the East: Vedic Hymns, 2 vols. 250.00 (ISBN 0-87968-438-0). Krishna Pr.
--Sacred Books of China: Text of Taoism, 2 vols. lib. bdg. 250.00 (ISBN 0-87968-298-1). Krishna Pr.
--Sacred Books of the East, 50 vols. 1977-1980. Repr. of 1975 ed. Set. 630.00; 16.80 ea. (ISBN 0-89684-310-6). Orient Bk Dist.
Muller, Michael. Blessed Eucharist: Our Greatest Treasure. LC 79-112490. 1973. pap. 9.00 (ISBN 0-89555-040-7). TAN Bks Pubs.
--Prayer-the Key to Salvation. LC 85-52207. 226p. 1985. pap. 5.00 (ISBN 0-89555-287-6). Tan Bks Pubs.
Muller, Richard A. Christ & the Decree: Christology & Predestination in Reformed Theology from Calvin to Perkins. (Studies in Historical Theology: Vol. 2). 250p. 1986. lib. bdg. 30.00x (ISBN 0-939464-39-X). Labyrinth Pr.
--A Dictionary of Latin & Greek Theological Terms. 1985. 14.95 (ISBN 0-8010-6185-7). Baker Bk.
Muller, Robert. Most of All They Taught Me Happiness. LC 78-52110. 1985. pap. 7.95 (ISBN 0-385-19914-7, Im). Doubleday.
--A Plants of Hope. (Chrysalis Bk). (Illus.). 128p. 1986. pap. 7.95 (ISBN 0-916349-04-7). Amity Hous Inc.
Muller, W. Max. Egyptian Mythology & Indochinese Mythology. Bd. with Scott, James G. LC 63-19097. (Mythology of All Races Ser.: Vol. 12). (Illus.). Repr. of 1932 ed. 30.00x (ISBN 0-8154-0160-4). Cooper Sq.
Mullet, Rosa M. God's Marvelous Work, Bk. 1. 1980. Repr. of 1975 ed. write for info. (ISBN 0-686-11149-4); tchr's. ed. avail. (ISBN 0-686-11150-8). Rod & Staff.
--God's Marvelous Work, Bk. 2. 1981. write for info. (ISBN 0-686-25256-X); tchr's. ed. avail. (ISBN 0-686-25257-8). Rod & Staff.
Mullett, Michael. Radical Religious Movements in Early Modern Europe. (Early Modern Europe Today Ser.). 208p. 1980. text ed. 9.95 (ISBN 0-04-901028-X). Allen Unwin.
Mulligan, James J. Theologians & Authority Within the Living Church. 131p. (Orig.). 1986. pap. 13.95 (ISBN 0-935372-18-0). Pope John Ctr.
Mulligan, Robert W., tr. see St. Thomas Aquinas.
Mulliken, E. G., tr. see Kautsky, Karl.
Mulliken, Frances H. First Ladies of the Restoration. 1985. pap. 6.50 (ISBN 0-8309-0419-0). Herald Hse.
Mulliken, J. L., tr. see Kautsky, Karl.
Mullin, Glenn, et al. Selected Works of the Dalai Lama I: Bridging the Sutras & Tantras. Rev. ed. LC 85-8333. (Teachings of the Dalai Lamas Ser.). Orig. Title: Bridging the Sutras & Tantras. (Tibetan., Illus.). 288p. (Orig.). 1985. pap. 12.95 (ISBN 0-937938-27-0). Snow Lion.
Mullin, Glenn H. Selected Works of the Dalai Lama VII: Songs of Spiritual Change. Rev. ed. LC 85-8332. (Teachings of the Dalai Lamas Ser.). Orig. Title: Songs of Spiritual Change. (Tibetan., Illus.). 225p. 1985. pap. 10.95 (ISBN 0-937938-30-0). Snow Lion.
Mullin, Glenn H., et al. Selected Works of the Dalai Lama II: The Tantric Yogas of the Sister Niguma. LC 85-40081. (Teachings of the Dalai Lamas Ser.). (Tibetan., Illus.). 240p. (Orig.). 1985. pap. 10.95 (ISBN 0-937938-28-9). Snow Lion.
--Selected Works of the Dalai Lama III: Essence of Refined Gold. Rev. ed. LC 85-8359. (Teachings of the Dalai Lamas Ser.). Orig. Title: Essence of Refined Gold. (Tibetan.). 264p. 1985. pap. 10.95 (ISBN 0-937938-29-7). Snow Lion.
Mullin, Redmond. The Wealth of Christians. LC 84-7262. 256p. (Orig.). 1984. pap. 10.95 (ISBN 0-88344-709-6). Orbis Bks.
Mullin, Robert B. Episcopal Vision-American Reality: High Church Theology & Social Thought in Evangelical America. 1986. 20.00 (ISBN 0-300-03487-3). Yale U Pr.
Mullin, Robert B., jt. auth. see Ahlstrom, Sydney E.
Mullins, E. Y., jt. auth. see Hobbs, Herschel H.
Mullins, Edgar Y. Baptist Beliefs. 5.95 (ISBN 0-8170-0014-3); pap. 4.95. Judson.
--La Religion Cristiana En Su Expresion Doctrinal. Hale, Sara A., tr. Orig. Title: The Christian Religion in Its Doctrinal Expression. 522p. 1980. pap. 10.95 (ISBN 0-311-09042-7). Casa Bautista.
Mulloy, John J., ed. see Dawson, Christopher.
Mulqueen, Jack & Chatton, Ray. God's Mother Is My Mother. (Illus.). 28p. (Orig.). 1978. pap. 2.50 (ISBN 0-913382-49-3, 103-13). Prow Bks-Franciscan.
Mulryan, John, ed. Milton & the Middle Ages. LC 81-69400. 192p. 1982. 22.50 (ISBN 0-8387-5036-2). Bucknell U Pr.
Mulvey, Sr. Mary D. French Catholic Missionaries in the Present United States (1604-1791) LC 73-3578. (Catholic University of America. Studies in American Church History: No. 23). Repr. of 1936 ed. 23.00 (ISBN 0-404-57773-3). AMS Pr.
Mumford, Amy R. Help Me Understand. (Accent Expressions Ser.). 24p. (Orig.). 1984. pap. 4.95 (ISBN 0-89636-142-X). Accent Bks.
--It Only Hurts Between Paydays. LC 80-70679. 160p. 1986. pap. 5.95 (ISBN 0-89636-067-9). Accent Bks.
Mumford, Amy Ross. It Hurts to Lose a Special Person. (Accent Expressions Ser.). (Illus.). 24p. (Orig.). 1982. gift book 4.95 (ISBN 0-89636-093-8). Accent Bks.
Mumford, J. Psychosomatic Yoga. (Paths to Inner Power Ser.). 96p. 1974. 1.25 (ISBN 0-85030-208-0). Weiser.
Mumford, Lewis. The Human Way Out. 1983. pap. 2.50x (ISBN 0-87574-097-9, 097). Pendle Hill.
Mumford, Stephen D. American Democracy & the Vatican: Population Growth & National Security. LC 84-72500. 268p. (Orig.). 1984. 11.95 (ISBN 0-931779-00-6); pap. 7.95 (ISBN 0-931779-01-4). Humanist Pr.
--The Pope & the New Apocalypse: The Holy War Against Family Planning. (Illus.). 82p. (Orig.). 1986. 6.95 (ISBN 0-937307-00-9); pap. 3.95 (ISBN 0-937307-01-7). CRPS.
Munby, Denys L. God & the Rich Society: A Study of Christians in a World of Abundance. LC 85-21886. v, 218p. 1985. Repr. of 1961 ed. lib. bdg. 39.75x (ISBN 0-313-24925-3, MGRS). Greenwood.
Munce, R. H. Ruth. 117p. 1971. spral bdg 3.95x (ISBN 0-914674-00-5). Freelandia.
Munch, Peter A. Norse Mythology, Legends of Gods & Heroes. Hustvedt, Sigurd B., tr. LC 74-112002. 1970. Repr. of 1926 ed. 23.75 (ISBN 0-404-04538-3). AMS Pr.
Munck, Johannes. Paul & the Salvation of Mankind. LC 60-5412. 1977. pap. 8.95 (ISBN 0-8042-0373-3). John Knox.
Munck, Johannes, ed. Acts of the Apostles. LC 66-20918. (Anchor Bible Ser.: Vol. 31). 1967. 18.00 (ISBN 0-385-00914-3, Anchor Pr). Doubleday.
Munday, Anthony. The Englishe Romayne Lyfe. LC 76-38213. (English Experience Ser.: No. 478). 84p. 1972. Repr. of 1582 ed. 6.00 (ISBN 90-221-0478-8). Walter J Johnson.
Munday, Anthony & Shakespeare, William. Sir Thomas More. LC 74-133715. (Tudor Facsimile Texts. Old English Plays: No. 65). Repr. of 1910 ed. 49.50 (ISBN 0-404-53365-5). AMS Pr.
Mundfrom, Gerald F. Baptism, a Covenant. (Illus.). 140p. (Orig.). 1985. pap. text ed. 4.00x (ISBN 0-9615494-0-8). Mercy & Truth.
--The Depressed Christian. 115p. (Orig.). 1983. 2.50 (ISBN 0-318-19335-3). Mercy & Truth.
--My Experience with Clinical Depression. rev. ed. (Illus.). 184p. 1986. pap. 5.50x (ISBN 0-9615494-1-6). Mercy & Truth.
--Purged. 175p. Date not set. 5.00 (ISBN 0-318-19336-1). Mercy & Truth.
Mundhenk, N., jt. auth. see Clark, D. J.
Mundy, John H., et al. Essays in Medieval Life & Thought. LC 65-25472. 1955. 18.00 (ISBN 0-8196-0159-4). Biblo.
Munger, Robert B. My Heart-Christ's Home. rev. ed. 32p. 1986. pap. 0.75 (ISBN 0-87784-075-X). Inter-Varsity.
Muni Shri Nagraj Ji. The Contemporaneity & the Chronology of Mahavira & Buddha. 188p. 1975. 4.00 (ISBN 0-88065-163-6, Pub. by Messers Today & Tomorrows Printers & Publishers India). Scholarly Pubns.
Munitz, Milton, jt. ed. see Keifer, Howard.
Munitz, Milton K. Space, Time & Creation: Philosophical Aspects of Scientific Cosmology. 2nd ed. 11.75 (ISBN 0-8446-5908-8). Peter Smith.
Munitz, Milton K., ed. see International Philosophy Year Conferences, Brockport.
Munitz, Milton K., jt. ed. see Kiefer, Howard E.
Munjee, Aslam. The Rape of a Noble Ideology. 487p. 1986. write for info. (ISBN 0-9617573-0-2). First Amend Pubs.
Munk, Arthur W. A Synoptic Approach to the Riddle of Existence. LC 77-818. 264p. 1977. 15.00 (ISBN 0-87527-165-0). Fireside Bks.
Munk, Eli. The Seven Days of the Beginning. 8.95 (ISBN 0-87306-028-8). Feldheim.
Munk, Eli, jt. ed. see Munk, Michael L.
Munk, Elie. The World of Prayer, 2 vols. 19.95 set (ISBN 0-87306-080-6); Vol. 1. 9.50 (ISBN 0-87306-081-4); Vol. 2. 11.50 (ISBN 0-87306-082-2). Feldheim.
--The World of Prayer. Biberfeld, Henry & Oschry, Leonard, trs. from Ger. Orig. Title: Die Welt der Gebete. 1978. pap. 10.95 (ISBN 0-87306-170-5). Feldheim.
Munk, Michael L. & Munk, Eli, eds. Shechita: Religious & Historical Research on the Method of Slaughter. (Illus.). 1976. 9.95 (ISBN 0-87306-992-7). Feldheim.
Munk, S. Philosophy & Philosophical Authors of the Jews: A Historical Sketch with Explanatory Notes. Kalisch, Isidor, tr. (Reprints in Philosophy Ser.). Repr. of 1881 ed. lib. bdg. 26.50 (ISBN 0-697-00012-5). Irvington.
--Philosophy & Philosophical Authors of the Jews: A Historical Sketch With Explanatory Notes. Kalisch, Isidor, tr. (Reprints in Philosophy Ser.). 1986. pap. text ed. 6.95x (ISBN 0-8290-1881-6). Irvington.
Munk, Salomon. Melanges Philosophie Juive et Arabe. Katz, Steven, ed. LC 79-7148. (Jewish Philosophy, Mysticism & History of Ideas Ser.). 1980. Repr. of 1927 ed. lib. bdg. 51.50x (ISBN 0-405-12278-0). Ayer Co Pubs.
Munn, Elijah H. The Progress(?) of Woman. 84p. 6.95 (ISBN 0-9609828-0-9). EHM Pub.
Munn, Sherrill. Beacon Small-Group Bible Studies, Luke: Lessons on Discipleship, Vol. 2. 68p. (Orig.). 1981. pap. 2.50 (ISBN 0-8341-0689-2). Beacon Hill.

Munnick, Harriet D. Catholic Church Records of the Pacific Northwest: Oregon City, Salem & Jacksonville. LC 84-70844. (Illus.). 1984. 25.00 (ISBN 0-8323-0429-8). Binford-Metropolitan.
--Catholic Church Records of the Pacific Northwest: St. Louis, Gervais & Brooks. LC 72-71955. (Illus.). 1982. 25.00 (ISBN 0-8323-0408-5). Binford-Metropolitan.
--Catholic Church Records of the Pacific Northwest: Vancouver & Stellamaris Mission. LC 72-83958. (Illus.). 1972. 25.00 (ISBN 0-8323-0375-5). Binford-Metropolitan.
Munnick, Harriet D., compiled by. Catholic Church Records of the Pacific Northwest: Roseburg & Portland. LC 85-63221. (Illus.). 440p. 1986. 25.00 (ISBN 0-8323-0447-6). Binford-Metropolitan.
Munnick, Harriet D. & Beckham, Stephen D., eds. Catholic Church Records of the Pacific Northwest: Grand Ronde Register, 2 Vols. (Illus.). 1987. Set. 25.00 (ISBN 0-8323-0455-7). Vol. I. Vol.II. Binford-Metropolitan.
Munnick, Harriet D. & Beckman, Stephan D., eds. Catholic Church Records of the Pacific Northwest: Grand Ronde Register, 2 vols. (Illus.). 1987. Set. 25.00 (ISBN 0-8323-0455-7). Vol. I, (1860-1885) Vol. II, (1885-1898) Binford-Metropolitan.
Munnik, Len, illus. Nothing to Laugh About. (Illus.). 96p. (Orig.). 1983. pap. 6.95 (ISBN 0-8298-0694-6). Pilgrim NY.
Munoz, A. Lopez. Programas Para Dias Especiales Tomo I. 107p. 1984. pap. 1.95 (ISBN 0-311-07005-1). Casa Bautista.
--Programas Para Dias Especiales Tomo II. 64p. 1984. pap. 1.95 (ISBN 0-311-07006-X). Casa Bautista.
Munoz, Hector. Will You Hear My Confession? How to Make a Good Examination of Conscience & a Good Confession. Bair, Robert, tr. from Span. LC 82-20597. 162p. 1983. pap. 6.95 (ISBN 0-8189-0439-9). Alba.
Munoz, Hector, jt. auth. see Alessio, Luis.
Munro, Dana C. The Kingdom of the Crusaders. LC 65-20472. 1966. Repr. of 1935 ed. 22.50x (ISBN 0-8046-0326-X, Pub. by Kennikat). Assoc Faculty Pr.
Munro, Donald J., ed. Individualism & Holism: The Confucian & Taoist Philosophical Perspectives. (Michigan Monographs in Chinese Studies: No. 52). 399p. 1985. 25.00 (ISBN 0-89264-057-X); pap. 12.50 (ISBN 0-89264-058-8). U of Mich Ctr Chinese.
Munro, Eleanor. On Glory Roads: A Pilgrims Book about Pilgrimages. LC 86-50231. (Illus.). 286p. 1987. pap. 17.95 (ISBN 0-500-24127-9). Thames Hudson.
Munro, Winsome. Authority in Paul & Peter: The Identification of a Pastoral Stratum in the Pauline Corpus & Peter 1. LC 81-12216. (Society of New Testament Studies: No. 45). (Illus.). 230p. 1983. 32.50 (ISBN 0-521-23694-0). Cambridge U Pr.
Munson, jt. auth. see Hegstad.
Munson, Gorham B. Twelve Decisive Battles of the Mind: The Story of Propaganda During the Christian Era, with Abridged Versions of Texts That Have Shaped History. LC 72-167388. (Essay Index Reprint Ser.). Repr. of 1942 ed. 18.00 (ISBN 0-8369-2705-2). Ayer Co Pubs.
Munson, Henry, Jr. The House of Si Abd Allah: The Oral History of a Moroccan Family. LC 83-19837. 280p. 1984. 22.50x (ISBN 0-300-03084-3). Yale U Pr.
Munson, Thomas N. The Challenge of Religion: A Philosophical Appraisal. LC 85-10297. 238p. 1985. text ed. 21.00x (ISBN 0-8207-0179-3); pap. text ed. 10.00x (ISBN 0-8207-0181-5). Duquesne.
Muntz, Carrie, tr. see Graham, Billy.
Murad, Khurram, ed. see Nadwi, Abul H.
Murakami, Hiroshi, jt. tr. see Gibson, Morgan.
Murakami, Shigeyoshi. Japanese Religion in the Modern Century. Earhart, H. Byron, tr. 186p. 1979. 18.50x (ISBN 0-86008-260-1, Pub. by U of Tokyo Japan). Columbia U Pr.
Muramoto, Naboru. Healing Ourselves. Abehsera, Michael, compiled by. (Illus.). 150p. 1974. pap. 9.95 (ISBN 0-380-00900-5, 60168-0). Avon.
Muraoka, T. A Greek-Hebrew - Aramaic Index to I Esdras. LC 83-8690. (SBL-Septuagint & Cognate Studies). 94p. 1984. pap. 8.75 (ISBN 0-89130-631-5, 06 04 16). Scholars Pr GA.
--Modern Hebrew for Biblical Scholars: An Annotated Chrestomathy with an Outline Grammar & Glossary. (Journal for the Study of the Old Testament Ser.: Manuals 2). 220p. 1982. text ed. 25.00 (ISBN 0-905774-36-1, Pub. by JSOT Pr England); pap. text ed. 14.50 (ISBN 0-905774-37-X, Pub. by JSOT Pr England). Eisenbrauns.
Murat, Leonhard Von see Schmid, Walter & Von Murat, Leonhard.
Murata, Kiyoaki. Japan's New Buddhism: An Objective Account of Soka Gakkai. LC 74-83640. (Illus.). 216p. 1969. 8.50 (ISBN 0-8348-0040-3). Weatherhill.
Murav'Ev, Andrei N. A History of the Church of Russia. LC 76-133816. Repr. of 1842 ed. 29.45 (ISBN 0-404-04541-3). AMS Pr.
Murchie, Guy. Music of the Spheres: The Material Universe from Atom to Quasar, Simply Explained, 2 vols. (Illus.). 28.00 set (ISBN 0-8446-0815-7). Peter Smith.
Murchland, Bernard. The Dream of Christian Socialism: An Essay on its European Origins. 74p. 1982. pap. 4.25 (ISBN 0-8447-3470-5). Am Enterprise.
Murd, M. A. Intellectual Modernism of Shibli Nu'mani: An Exposition of His Religious & Political Ideas. pap. 19.95 (ISBN 0-317-46099-4). Kazi Pubns.
Murdick, Olin J. Achieving Shared Responsibility in the American Church. 14p. 1977. 1.55 (ISBN 0-686-39921-8). Natl Cath Educ.
Murdoch, Iris. The Sovereignty of Good. 116p. 1985. pap. 5.95 (ISBN 0-7448-0028-5, Ark Paperbks). Methuen Inc.
Murdoch, J. E., ed. see International Colloquium on Philosophy, Science, & Theology in the Middle Ages, 1st, Boston, Sept. 1973.
Murdoch, John. The Mahabharata. 160p. 1986. Repr. 14.00X (ISBN 0-8364-1762-3, Pub. by Manohar Inida). South Asia Bks.
Murdock, John E., ed. see International Colloquium on Philosophy, Science Theology in the Middle Ages, 1st, 1973.
Murdock, Kenneth B. Literature & Theology in Colonial New England. LC 78-104247. xi, 235p. Repr. of 1949 ed. lib. bdg. 22.50x (ISBN 0-8371-3990-2, MUCN). Greenwood.
Murdock, Kenneth B., ed. see Mather, Cotton.
Murdock, Mike. The Winner's World. (Orig.). 1986. pap. 4.95 (ISBN 0-89274-398-0). Harrison Hse.
Murgotten, Francis C. see Ahmad Ibn Yahya, Al-Baladuri.
Murnion, Philip J. The Catholic Priest & the Changing Structure of Pastoral Ministry. 40.00 (ISBN 0-405-10845-1, 11822). Ayer Co Pubs.
Murphet, Howard. Sai Baba Avatar: A New Journey into Power & Glory. LC 77-83643. 1977. 10.25 (ISBN 0-9600958-2-9); pap. 5.40 (ISBN 0-9600958-3-7). Birth Day.
--When Daylight Comes. LC 74-18958. (Illus.). 304p. (Orig.). 1975. cloth 8.95 (ISBN 0-8356-0461-6). Theos Pub Hse.
Murphey. Devotions for Travelers. 1.95 (ISBN 0-318-18171-1). WCTU.
Murphey, Cecil. But God Has Promised. LC 76-16283. 1976. pap. 2.95 (ISBN 0-88419-002-1). Creation Hse.
--Comforting Those Who Grieve. LC 78-71052. 64p. 1979. pap. 1.00 (ISBN 0-8042-1099-3). John Knox.
--Seven Daily Sins & What to Do about Them. 112p. (Orig.). 1981. pap. 2.95 (ISBN 0-89283-101-4). Servant.
Murphey, Cecil B. When in Doubt, Hug 'em: How to Develop a Caring Church. LC 77-15751. 1978. 5.95 (ISBN 0-8042-1890-0). John Knox.
Murphey, Cecil B., compiled by. The Encyclopedia for Today's Christian Woman. (Encyclopedias Ser.). 512p. 1984. 16.95 (ISBN 0-8007-1393-1). Revell.
Murphree, Jon T. A Loving God & a Suffering World. LC 81-11759. 144p. (Orig.). 1981. pap. 4.50 (ISBN 0-87784-877-7). Inter-Varsity.
--Made to Be Mastered: Managing Your Emotions Successfully--God's Way. 126p. (YA) 1984. pap. 5.95 (ISBN 0-8010-6169-5). Baker Bk.
--When God Says You're OK: A Christian Approach to Transactional Analysis. new ed. LC 75-21452. 132p. 1975. pap. 2.95 (ISBN 0-87784-716-9). Inter-Varsity.
Murphy, Anne, jt. auth. see Murphy, Chuck.
Murphy, Arlene W. The Liturgical Year in Puzzles. 1982. 9.95 (Pub. by Pflaum Pr). Peter Li.
Murphy, Campbell. David & I Talk to God. 1983. pap. 2.95 each (ISBN 0-686-45018-3). Cook.
Murphy, Carol. A Deeper Faith. 1983. pap. 2.50x (ISBN 0-87574-099-5, 099). Pendle Hill.
--The Examined Life. 1983. pap. 2.50x (ISBN 0-87574-085-5, 085). Pendle Hill.
--The Faith of An Ex-Agnostic. 1983. pap. 2.50x (ISBN 0-87574-046-4, 046). Pendle Hill.
--Four Women: Four Windows on Light. Mather, Eleanore P., ed. LC 81-80220. 26p. 1981. pap. 2.50x (ISBN 0-87574-236-X, 236). Pendle Hill.
--Holy Morality. LC 71-110286. (Orig.). 1970. pap. 2.50x (ISBN 0-87574-169-X). Pendle Hill.
--The Ministry of Counseling. 1983. pap. 2.50x (ISBN 0-87574-067-7, 067). Pendle Hill.
--Nurturing Contemplation. 1983. pap. 2.50x (ISBN 0-87574-252-1, 252). Pendle Hill.
--Religion & Mental Illness. 1983. pap. 2.50x (ISBN 0-87574-082-0, 082). Pendle Hill.
Murphy, Carol, ed. see Boulding, Kenneth E. & Mayer, Milton.
Murphy, Carol R. The Available Mind. LC 73-94186. (Orig.). 1974. pap. 2.50x (ISBN 0-87574-193-2). Pendle Hill.
--Man: The Broken Image. LC 68-30960. (Orig.). pap. 2.50x (ISBN 0-87574-158-4). Pendle Hill.
--Many Religions: One God. LC 66-30689. (Orig.). 1966. pap. 2.50x (ISBN 0-87574-150-9). Pendle Hill.
--O Inward Traveller. LC 77-91637. 31p. (Orig.). 1977. pap. 2.50x (ISBN 0-87574-216-5). Pendle Hill.
--Revelation & Experience. LC 64-22765. (Orig.). pap. 2.50x (ISBN 0-87574-137-1). Pendle Hill.
--The Roots of Pendle Hill. LC 78-1768. (Orig.). pap. 2.50x (ISBN 0-87574-223-8). Pendle Hill.
--The Sound of Silence: Moving with T'ai Chi. LC 75-41548. (Orig.). 1976. pap. 2.50x (ISBN 0-87574-205-X, 205). Pendle Hill.
--The Valley of the Shadow. LC 72-80095. 24p. (Orig.). 1972. pap. 2.50x (ISBN 0-87574-184-3). Pendle Hill.
Murphy Center for Liturgical Research. Made, Not Born: New Perspectives on Christian Initiation & the Catechumenate. 192p. 1976. pap. 6.95 (ISBN 0-268-01337-3). U of Notre Dame Pr.
Murphy, Chuck & Murphy, Anne. When the Saints Go Marching Out. 1987. pap. 5.95 (Chosen Bks). Revell.
Murphy, David, ed. What I Believe: Catholic College Students Discuss Their Faith. 164p. 1985. 11.95 (ISBN 0-88347-181-7). Thomas More.
Murphy, Elspeth. Everybody, Shout Hallelujah! (David & I Talk to God Ser.). (Illus.). 24p. 1981. pap. 2.50 (ISBN 0-89191-369-6, 53694). Cook.
--God Cares When I Do Something Stupid. (God's Word in My Heart Ser.). (Illus.). 24p. 1984. pap. 2.95 (ISBN 0-89191-792-6). Cook.
--God Cares When I Need to Talk to Somebody. (God's Word in My Heart Ser.). (Illus.). 24p. 1984. pap. 2.95 (ISBN 0-89191-887-6). Cook.
--God Cares When Somebody Hurts Me. (God's Word in My Heart Ser.). (Illus.). 24p. 1984. pap. 2.95 (ISBN 0-89191-790-X). Cook.
--Jesus & the Big Storm. (Tubable Hugable Ser.). (Illus.). 1984. pap. 2.95 (ISBN 0-89191-816-7). Cook.
--Noah's Ark. (Tubable Hugable Ser.). (Illus.). 1984. pap. 2.95 (ISBN 0-89191-820-5). Cook.
--Sometimes I Get Lonely. LC 80-70251. (David & I Talk to God Ser.). (Illus.). 24p. 1981. pap. 2.95 (ISBN 0-89191-367-X, 53678). Cook.
--Sometimes I Get Scared. (David & I Talk to God Ser.). (Illus.). 1980. pap. 2.95 (ISBN 0-89191-275-4). Cook.
--Sometimes I'm Good, Sometimes I'm Bad. (David & I Talk to God Ser.). (Illus.). 24p. 1981. pap. 2.95 (ISBN 0-89191-368-8, 53686). Cook.
--What Can I Say to You, God? (David & I Talk to God Ser.). (Illus.). 1980. pap. 2.95 (ISBN 0-89191-276-2). Cook.
--Where Are You, God? (David & I Talk to God Ser.). (Illus.). 1980. pap. 2.50 (ISBN 0-89191-274-6). Cook.
Murphy, Elspeth C. Chalkdust: Prayer Meditations for a Teacher. 1978. 5.95 (ISBN 0-8010-6065-6). Baker Bk.
--God Cares When I'm Disappointed. (God's Word in my Heart Ser.). (Illus.). 1983. 2.95 (ISBN 0-89191-725-X). Cook.
--God Cares When I'm Sorry. (God's Word in My Heart Ser.). (Illus.). 1983. 2.95 (ISBN 0-89191-724-1). Cook.
--God Cares When I'm Worried. LC 82-73572. (God's Word in My Heart Ser.). (Illus.). 1983. 2.95 (ISBN 0-89191-723-3). Cook.
--God Hears Me When I Pray. (Hardcover Psalm Books for Children). (Illus.). 96p. 1985. 7.95 (ISBN 0-89191-645-8, 56457). Cook.
--God Helps Me Everyday. (Hardcover Psalm Books for Children). (Illus.). 96p. 1985. 7.95 (ISBN 0-89191-642-3, 56424). Cook.
--God You Fill Us Up with Joy. (David & I Talk to God Ser.). (Illus.). 1987. pap. 2.95 (ISBN 1-55513-037-2, Chariot Bks). Cook.
--I'm Listening, God: Psalm 19. (David & I Talk to God Ser.). (Illus.). 1983. misc. format 2.50 (ISBN 0-89191-583-4). Cook.
--It's My Birthday, God: Psalm 90. (David & I Talk to God Ser.). (Illus.). 1982. misc. format 2.50 (ISBN 0-89191-580-X). Cook.
--Make Way for the King: Psalm 145 & 24. (David & I Talk to God Ser.). (Illus.). 1983. 2.95 (ISBN 0-89191-581-8). Cook.
--Sometimes Everything Feels Just Right. (David & I Talk to God Ser.). (Illus.). 1987. pap. 2.95 (ISBN 1-55513-038-0, Chariot Bks). Cook.
--Sometimes I Get Mad. (David & I Talk to God Ser.). 1981. pap. 2.95 (ISBN 0-89191-493-5, 54932). Cook.
--Sometimes I Have to Cry. (David & I Talk to God Ser.). (Illus.). 1981. pap. 2.95 (ISBN 0-89191-494-3, 54940). Cook.
--Sometimes I Need to Be Hugged. (David & I Talk to God Ser.). (Illus.). 1981. pap. 2.95 (ISBN 0-89191-492-7, 54924). Cook.
Murphy, Emmy L. Who Made God. 1978. pap. 2.25 (ISBN 0-915374-07-2, 07-2). Rapids Christian.
Murphy, Frederick. Breviary Lives of the Saints: A Translation into English. 1979. pap. 1.00 (ISBN 0-8198-1108-4). Dghtrs St Paul.
Murphy, Frederick J. Breviary Lives of the Saints, Vol. 1 Sept.- Jan., Vol. 2 Feb.-May. (Lat., Illus., Orig.). 1965. Vol. 1. pap. 2.50 (ISBN 0-8198-0012-0); Vol. 2. 3.50 (ISBN 0-8198-0013-9). Dghtrs St Paul.
--The Structure & Meaning of Second Baruch. 1985. 16.50 (ISBN 0-89130-844-X, 06-01-78); pap. 10.95 (ISBN 0-89130-845-8). Scholars Pr GA.
Murphy, G., ed. see Cohen, I. L.
Murphy, G. Ronald. Brecht & the Bible: A Study of Religious Nihilism & Human Weakness in Brecht's Plays. LC 80-20207. (Studies in Germanic Languages & Literatures: No. 96). xi, 107p. 12.50x (ISBN 0-8078-8096-5). U of NC Pr.
Murphy, George L. The Trademark of God. 110p. (Orig.). 1986. pap. 6.95 (ISBN 0-8192-1382-9). Morehouse.
Murphy, J. L., jt. ed. see Baker, Donald C.
Murphy, James G. Commentary on the Book of Exodus. 1979. 14.50 (ISBN 0-86524-014-0, 0201). Klock & Klock.
--Commentary on the Book of Genesis. xvi, 535p. 1986. Repr. of 1873 ed. lib. bdg. 27.50 (ISBN 0-89941-508-3). W S Hein.
Murphy, John W. The Social Philosophy of Martin Buber: The Social World as a Human Dimension. LC 82-21779. 176p. (Orig.). 1983. lib. bdg. 26.25 (ISBN 0-8191-2940-2); pap. text ed. 11.50 (ISBN 0-8191-2941-0). U Pr of Amer.
Murphy, Joseph. Amazing Laws of Cosmic Mind Power. 1965. pap. 4.95 (ISBN 0-13-023804-X, Reward). P-H.
--Great Bible Truths for Human Problems. 1976. pap. text ed. 7.00 (ISBN 0-87516-214-2). De Vorss.
--Healing Power of Love. pap. 1.00 (ISBN 0-87516-334-3). De Vorss.
--How to Pray with a Deck of Cards. pap. 0.75 (ISBN 0-87516-335-1). De Vorss.
--How to Use the Power of Prayer. pap. 1.50 (ISBN 0-87516-275-4). De Vorss.
--How to Use Your Healing Power. 158p. 1973. pap. 3.50 (ISBN 0-87516-186-3). De Vorss.
--Infinite Power for Richer Living. 1969. pap. 4.95 (ISBN 0-13-464396-8, Reward). P-H.
--Living Without Strain. 157p. 1973. pap. 3.95 (ISBN 0-87516-187-1). De Vorss.
--Love Is Freedom. pap. 1.25 (ISBN 0-87516-337-8). De Vorss.
--Magic of Faith. pap. 1.50 (ISBN 0-87516-291-6). De Vorss.
--Mental Poisons & Their Antidotes. pap. 1.50 (ISBN 0-87516-339-4). De Vorss.
--Peace Within Yourself. 300p. 1972. pap. 6.50 (ISBN 0-87516-188-X). De Vorss.
--Pray Your Way Through It. 171p. 1973. pap. 4.00 (ISBN 0-87516-190-1). De Vorss.
--Prayer Is the Answer. 190p. 1973. pap. 5.00 (ISBN 0-87516-189-8). De Vorss.
--Quiet Moments with God. pap. 2.00 (ISBN 0-87516-276-2). De Vorss.
--Songs of God. LC 79-52353. (Orig.). 1979. pap. 6.00 (ISBN 0-87516-379-3). De Vorss.
--Special Meditations for Health, Wealth, Love. pap. 1.50 (ISBN 0-87516-336-X). De Vorss.
--Supreme Mastery of Fear. pap. 0.75 (ISBN 0-87516-340-8). De Vorss.
--These Truths Can Change Your Life. 280p. 1982. pap. 7.50 (ISBN 0-87516-476-5). De Vorss.
--Within You Is the Power. LC 77-86026. 1978. pap. 6.00 (ISBN 0-87516-247-9). De Vorss.
Murphy, Judith K. Sharing Care: The Christian Ministry of Respite Care. (Illus.). 64p. (Orig.). 1986. pap. 3.95 (ISBN 0-8298-0575-3). Pilgrim NY.
Murphy, Leona S. Miracles & the Sumrall Family. 205p. (Orig.). 1984. pap. 6.95 (ISBN 0-89274-325-5). Harrison Hse.
Murphy, Sr. M. Gertrude. Saint Basil & Monasticism. LC 70-144661. Repr. of 1930 ed. 14.75 (ISBN 0-404-04543-X). AMS Pr.
Murphy, Paul E. Triadic Mysticism. 1986. 23.00X (ISBN 81-208-0010-9, Pub. by Motilal Banarsidass). South Asia Bks.
Murphy, Paul I. & Arlington, R. Rene. La Popessa. LC 82-61880. (Illus.). 296p. (Orig.). 1983. 16.50 (ISBN 0-446-51258-3). Warner Bks.
--La Popessa. 432p. 1985. pap. 3.95 (ISBN 0-446-32817-0). Warner Bks.
Murphy, Richard T. Background to the Bible: An Introduction to Scripture Study. (Illus.). 1978. pap. 5.95 (ISBN 0-89283-055-7). Servant.
Murphy, Robert, Jr. Psychotherapy Based on Human Longing. LC 60-14173. (Orig.). 1960. pap. 2.50x (ISBN 0-87574-111-8, 111). Pendle Hill.
Murphy, Roland, et al. Presence of God. LC 78-107214. (Concilium Ser.: Vol. 50). 215p. 7.95 (ISBN 0-8091-0116-5). Paulist Pr.

Murphy, Roland E. Ecclesiastes & Canticle of Canticles. (Bible Ser.). pap. 1.00 (ISBN 0-8091-5036-0). Paulist Pr.

--Exodus. (Bible Ser.). Pt. 1. pap. 1.00 (ISBN 0-8091-5043-3); Pt. 2. pap. 1.00 (ISBN 0-8091-5044-1). Paulist Pr.

--The Psalms, Job. LC 77-78637. (Proclamation Commentaries: the Old Testament Witnesses for Preaching). (Orig.). 1977. pap. 4.95 (ISBN 0-8006-0588-8, 1-588). Fortress.

--Wisdom Literature & Psalms: Interpreting Biblical Texts. Bailey, Lloyd R. & Furnish, Victor P., eds. 160p. (Orig.). 1983. pap. 8.95 (ISBN 0-687-45759-9). Abingdon.

--Wisdom Literature: Ruth, Esther, Job, Proverbs, Ecclesiastes, Canticles. (The Forms of the Old Testament Literature Ser.). (Orig.). 1981. pap. 12.95 (ISBN 0-8028-1877-3). Eerdmans.

Murphy, Roland E., ed. & intro. by. Medieval Exegesis of Wisdom Literature: Essays by Beryl Smalley. (Scholars Press Reprints & Translations Ser.). 1986. 13.95 (ISBN 1-55540-026-4, 00 07 16). Scholars Pr GA.

Murphy, Sheila M. Midlife Wanderer: The Woman Religious in Midlife Transition. LC 83-25806. 176p. (Orig.). 1983. pap. 8.00 (ISBN 0-89571-018-8). Affirmation.

Murphy-O'Connor, Jerome. Becoming Human Together: The Pastoral anthropology of St. Paul. (Good News Studies: Vol. 2). 224p. 1982. pap. 8.95 (ISBN 0-89453-075-5). M Glazier.

--First Corinthians. (New Testament Message Ser.: Vol. 10). 172p. 1980. 12.95 (ISBN 0-89453-198-0); pap. 7.95 (ISBN 0-89453-133-6). M Glazier.

--St. Paul's Corinth: Texts & Archaeology. (Good News Studies: Vol. 6). 1983. pap. 9.95 (ISBN 0-89453-303-7). M Glazier.

--What Is Religious Life? A Critical Reappraisal. pap. 4.95 (ISBN 0-89453-074-7). M Glazier.

Murrah, David J. C. C. Slaughter: Rancher, Banker, Baptist. (M. K. Brown Range Life Ser.: No. 15). (Illus.). 191p. 1981. 14.95 (ISBN 0-292-71067-4). U of Tex Pr.

Murray, Albert V. The State & the Church in a Free Society. LC 77-27134. (Hibbert Lectures: 1957). Repr. of 1958 ed. 27.50 (ISBN 0-404-60433-1). AMS Pr.

Murray, Andrew. Abide in Christ. 1968. 4.95 (ISBN 0-87508-371-4); pap. 2.95 (ISBN 0-87508-370-6). Chr Lit.

--Abide in Christ. (Large Print Christian Classic). 192p. 1983. Repr. 14.95 (ISBN 0-87983-334-3). Keats.

--Abide in Christ. 1980. pap. 2.95 (ISBN 0-88368-091-2). Whitaker Hse.

--Abide in Christ. (The Christian Library). 1985. Repr. text ed. 6.95 (ISBN 0-916441-10-5). Barbour & Co.

--Absolute Surrender. 1962. pap. 2.95 (ISBN 0-87508-398-6). Chr Lit.

--Absolute Surrender. (Andrew Murray Ser.). pap. 3.50 (ISBN 0-8024-0560-6). Moody.

--Absolute Surrender. 128p. 1981. pap. 3.50 (ISBN 0-88368-093-9). Whitaker Hse.

--Aids to Devotions. 1961. pap. 2.95 (ISBN 0-87508-378-1). Chr Lit.

--The Believer's Absolute Surrender. 150p. 1985. pap. 3.95 (ISBN 0-87123-827-6). Bethany Hse.

--The Believer's Call to Commitment. 110p. 1983. pap. 3.95 (ISBN 0-87123-289-8). Bethany Hse.

--Believer's Daily Renewal. LC 81-6143. 125p. 1981. pap. 3.95 (ISBN 0-87123-147-6, 210147). Bethany Hse.

--The Believer's Full Blessing of Pentecost. 112p. 1984. pap. 3.95 (ISBN 0-87123-597-8). Bethany Hse.

--The Believer's New Covenant. LC 83-21408. 128p. 1983. pap. 3.95 (ISBN 0-87123-406-8, 210406). Bethany Hse.

--The Believer's New Life. LC 83-3006. 208p. 1984. pap. 3.95 (ISBN 0-87123-431-9). Bethany Hse.

--The Believer's Prayer Life. rev. ed. LC 83-12254. (The Andrew Murray Prayer Library). 141p. 1983. pap. 3.95 (ISBN 0-87123-277-4). Bethany Hse.

--The Believer's School of Prayer. rev. ed. LC 82-4401. 201p. 1982. pap. 3.95 (ISBN 0-87123-195-6, 210195). Bethany Hse.

--The Believer's Secret of Holiness. LC 84-2973. 208p. 1984. pap. 3.95 (ISBN 0-87123-432-7). Bethany Hse.

--The Believer's Secret of Living Like Christ. 176p. (Orig.). 1985. pap. 3.95 (ISBN 0-87123-445-9). Bethany Hse.

--Believer's Secret of Obedience. LC 82-14603. (Andrew Murray Christian Maturity Library). 88p. 1982. pap. 3.95 (ISBN 0-87123-279-0, 210279). Bethany Hse.

--The Believer's Secret of the Master's Indwelling. rev. ed. 192p. 1986. pap. 3.95 (ISBN 0-87123-653-2, 210653). Bethany Hse.

--The Believer's Secret of Waiting on God. 169p. 1986. pap. 3.95 (ISBN 0-87123-886-1). Bethany Hse.

--The Best of Andrew Murray. (Best Ser.). pap. 4.95 (ISBN 0-8010-6069-9). Baker Bk.

--The Blessings of Obedience. Orig. Title: School of Obedience; Believer's Secret of Obedience. 107p. 1984. pap. text ed. 3.50 (ISBN 0-88368-155-2). Whitaker Hse.

--Blood of the Cross. 1968. pap. 2.95 (ISBN 0-87508-374-9). Chr Lit.

--The Blood of the Cross. 144p. 1981. pap. 3.50 (ISBN 0-88368-103-X). Whitaker Hse.

--Confession & Forgiveness. 176p. 1984. pap. 5.95 (ISBN 0-310-29731-1, 10366P, Clarion Class). Zondervan.

--Confession: The Road to Forgiveness. Orig. Title: Have Mercy Upon Me. 160p. 1983. pap. text ed. 3.50 (ISBN 0-88368-134-X). Whitaker Hse.

--Covenants & Blessings. 176p. 1984. pap. text ed. 3.50 (ISBN 0-88368-136-6). Whitaker Hse.

--Daily Secrets of Christian Living. LC 77-17187. 400p. 1978. pap. 7.95 (ISBN 0-87123-500-5, 210500). Bethany Hse.

--Daily Thoughts on Holiness. 1977. 6.95 (ISBN 0-87508-369-2). Chr Lit.

--Deeper Christian Life. Tucker, Lyman R., ed. 112p. 1986. pap. 5.95 (ISBN 0-310-29791-5, 10365P). Zondervan.

--Divine Healing. 1962. pap. 3.50 (ISBN 0-87508-375-7). Chr Lit.

--Divine Healing. 160p. 1982. pap. text ed. 3.50 (ISBN 0-88368-112-9). Whitaker Hse.

--Entrega Absoluta. 192p. 1981. 2.95 (ISBN 0-88113-079-6). Edit Betania.

--La Escuela de la Obediencia. Orig. Title: The School of Obedience. (Span.). 128p. 1984. pap. 3.25 (ISBN 0-317-14852-4). Kregel.

--Every Day with Andrew Murray. rev. ed. Tr. of God's Best Secret. 208p. 1986. pap. 3.95 (ISBN 0-89283-302-5, Pub. by Vine Books). Servant.

--Full Blessing of Pentecost. 1965. pap. 2.95 (ISBN 0-87508-376-5). Chr Lit.

--God's Best Secrets. 1986. pap. 9.95 (ISBN 0-310-29711-7, 10391P). Zondervan.

--Holiest of All: An Exposition of the Epistle to the Hebrews. 576p. 17.95 (ISBN 0-8007-0138-0). Revell.

--How to Be Perfect. 144p. 1982. pap. text ed. 3.50 (ISBN 0-88368-113-7). Whitaker Hse.

--How to Bring Your Children to Christ. 320p. 1984. pap. 3.95 (ISBN 0-88368-135-8). Whitaker Hse.

--How to Raise Your Children for Christ. LC 75-29344. 288p. 1975. pap. 4.95 (ISBN 0-87123-224-3, 210224). Bethany Hse.

--In Search of Spiritual Excellence. Orig. Title: The Full Blessing of Pentecost. 125p. 1984. pap. text ed. 3.50 (ISBN 0-88368-163-3). Whitaker Hse.

--The Inner Life. 1980. pap. 2.95 (ISBN 0-310-29752-4). Zondervan.

--The Inner Life. 144p. 1984. pap. 5.95 (ISBN 0-310-29751-6, 10364P, Clarion Class). Zondervan.

--The Inner Life. 160p. 1984. pap. text ed. 3.50 (ISBN 0-88368-138-2). Whitaker Hse.

--Insights for Daily Living: A Guide to Scriptural Prayer. rev. ed. 208p. Date not set. pap. 3.95 (ISBN 0-89283-329-7, Pub. by Vine Books). Servant.

--Jesus Christ: Prophet-Priest. 64p. 1967. pap. 2.95 (ISBN 0-87123-271-5, 200271). Bethany Hse.

--Jesus Himself. 27p. 1966. pap. 0.95 (ISBN 0-87509-096-6). Chr Pubns.

--Let Us Draw Nigh. 1962. pap. 2.95 (ISBN 0-87508-379-X). Chr Lit.

--Like Christ. 240p. 1981. pap. 2.95 (ISBN 0-88368-099-8). Whitaker Hse.

--Living the New Life. 256p. 1982. pap. text ed. 3.50 (ISBN 0-88368-108-0). Whitaker Hse.

--Living to Please God. 100p. 1985. pap. text ed. 3.50 (ISBN 0-88368-166-8). Whitaker Hse.

--The Master's Indwelling. LC 76-23363. 192p. 1977. pap. 2.95 (ISBN 0-87123-355-X, 200355). Bethany Hse.

--The Ministry of Intercession. 208p. 1982. pap. text ed. 3.50 (ISBN 0-88368-114-5). Whitaker Hse.

--The Ministry of Intercessory Prayer. rev. ed. LC 81-18011. 1981. pap. 3.95 (ISBN 0-87123-353-3, 210353). Bethany Hse.

--Money: Christ's Perspective on the Use & Abuse of Money. 80p. 1978. pap. 2.95 (ISBN 0-87123-382-7, 200382). Bethany Hse.

--Not My Will. Schoolland, Marian, tr. 1977. pap. 2.95 (ISBN 0-310-29722-2, 10381P). Zondervan.

--La Nueva Vida. 144p. 1979. 2.95 (ISBN 0-88113-220-9). Edit Betania.

--Power of the Blood. 1984. pap. 3.50 (ISBN 0-87508-428-1). Chr Lit.

--Power of the Blood of Jesus. LC 85-62802. 1985. pap. 3.50 (ISBN 0-88270-597-0). Bridge Pub.

--Prayer Life. (Andrew Murray Ser.). pap. 3.50 (ISBN 0-8024-6806-3). Moody.

--The Prayer Life. 160p. 1981. pap. 3.50 (ISBN 0-88368-102-1). Whitaker Hse.

--School of Obedience. (Andrew Murray Ser.). pap. 3.50 (ISBN 0-8024-7627-9). Moody.

--Secret Abiding Presence. (Secret Ser.). (Orig.). 1979. pap. 1.95 (ISBN 0-87508-382-X). Chr Lit.

--Secret of Adoration. (Secret Ser.). (Orig.). 1979. pap. 1.95 (ISBN 0-87508-384-6). Chr Lit.

--The Secret of Believing Prayer. LC 80-69320. 80p. 1980. pap. 3.50 (ISBN 0-87123-528-5, 200528). Bethany Hse.

--Secret of Brotherly Love. (Secret Ser.). (Orig.). 1980. pap. 1.95 (ISBN 0-87508-390-0). Chr Lit.

--Secret of Christ Our Life. (Secret Ser.). (Orig.). 1980. pap. 1.95 (ISBN 0-87508-385-4). Chr Lit.

--Secret of Fellowship. (Secret Ser.). (Orig.). 1980. pap. 1.95 (ISBN 0-87508-388-9). Chr Lit.

--Secret of Inspiration. (Secret Ser.). (Orig.). 1979. pap. 1.95 (ISBN 0-87508-386-2). Chr Lit.

--Secret of Intercession. (Secret Ser.). (Orig.). 1980. pap. 1.95 (ISBN 0-87508-391-9). Chr Lit.

--Secret of Power from on High. (Secret Ser.). (Orig.). 1980. pap. 1.95 (ISBN 0-87508-392-7). Chr Lit.

--Secret of the Cross. (Secret Ser.). (Orig.). 1980. pap. 1.95 (ISBN 0-87508-389-7). Chr Lit.

--Secret of the Faith Life. (Secret Ser.). (Orig.). 1979. pap. 1.95 (ISBN 0-87508-387-0). Chr Lit.

--Secret of the Throne of Grace. (Secret Ser.). (Orig.). 1980. pap. 1.95 (ISBN 0-87508-393-5). Chr Lit.

--Secret of United Prayer. (Secret Ser.). (Orig.). 1980. pap. 1.95 (ISBN 0-87508-394-3). Chr Lit.

--The Spirit of Christ. rev. ed. LC 79-51335. 288p. 1979. pap. 4.95 (ISBN 0-87123-589-7, 210589). Bethany Hse.

--Spirit of Christ. 1970. pap. 4.50 (ISBN 0-87508-395-1). Chr Lit.

--The Spirit of Christ. 2nd ed. 240p. 1984. pap. 3.50 (ISBN 0-88368-126-9). Whitaker Hse.

--State of the Church. 1983. pap. 2.95 (ISBN 0-87508-407-9). Chr Lit.

--True Vine. (Andrew Murray Ser.). pap. 3.50 (ISBN 0-8024-8798-X). Moody.

--The True Vine. 112p. 1983. pap. text ed. 3.50 (ISBN 0-88368-118-8). Whitaker Hse.

--Two Covenants. 1974. pap. 3.50 (ISBN 0-87508-396-X). Chr Lit.

--Waiting on God. (Andrew Murray Ser.). pap. 3.50 (ISBN 0-8024-0026-4). Moody.

--Waiting on God. 160p. 1981. pap. 3.50 (ISBN 0-88368-101-3). Whitaker Hse.

--With Christ in the School of Obedience. 108p. 1986. pap. 4.95 (ISBN 0-89693-281-8). Victor Bks.

--With Christ in the School of Prayer. 288p. 1981. pap. 3.50 (ISBN 0-88368-106-4). Whitaker Hse.

--With Christ in the School of Prayer. 288p. 1983. pap. 5.95 (ISBN 0-310-29771-0, 10527P, Clarion Class). Zondervan.

Murray, Andrew & Choy, Leona. Inner Chamber. (Orig.). 1980. pap. 2.50 (ISBN 0-87508-405-2). Chr Lit.

--Key to the Missionary Problem. (Orig.). 1980. pap. 3.95 (ISBN 0-87508-401-X). Chr Lit.

--Lord's Table. (Orig.). 1980. pap. 2.95 (ISBN 0-87508-380-3). Chr Lit.

Murray, Andrew, ed. see Law, William.

Murray, Andrew, et al. The Believer's Secret of the Abiding Presence. rev. ed. 144p. 1987. pap. 3.95 (ISBN 0-87123-899-3). Bethany Hse.

Murray, Christopher, jt. auth. see Murray, Kim.

Murray, Dick. Strengthening the Adult Sunday School Class. LC 81-3667. (Creative Leadership Ser.). 128p. (Orig.). 1981. pap. 6.95 (ISBN 0-687-39989-0). Abingdon.

--Teaching the Bible to Adults & Youth. (Creative Leadership Ser.). 176p. 1987. pap. 8.95 (ISBN 0-687-41082-7). Abingdon.

Murray, Donal. Life & Sacrament: Reflections on the Catholic Vision. (Theology & Life Ser.: Vol. 4). 1983. pap. 6.95 (ISBN 0-89453-299-5). M Glazier.

Murray, Dorothy G. Sister Anna: God's Captive to Set Others Free. 175p. (Orig.). 1983. pap. 7.95 (ISBN 0-87178-796-2). Brethren.

Murray, Douglas M., jt. ed. see Forrester, Duncan B.

Murray, Ferne H. A Journey into His Presence. LC 78-73439. (Illus.). 1979. pap. 3.95 (ISBN 0-932994-00-8). Day Star.

Murray, Frank S. The Sublimity of Faith. LC 81-81770. (Illus.). 952p. 1982. 25.00 (ISBN 0-910840-20-2). Kingdom.

Murray, Frank S., ed. Standard, Vols. 11-26. Incl. Vol. 11, o.s.i; Vol. 12; Vol. 13. 1961; Vol. 14. 1962 (ISBN 0-910840-62-8); Vol. 15. 1963 (ISBN 0-910840-63-6); Vol. 16. 1964 (ISBN 0-910840-64-4); Vol. 17. 1965 (ISBN 0-910840-65-2); Vol. 18. 1966 (ISBN 0-910840-66-0); Vol. 19. 1967 (ISBN 0-910840-67-9); Vol. 20. 1968 (ISBN 0-910840-68-7); Vol. 21. 1969 (ISBN 0-910840-69-5); Vol. 22. 1970 (ISBN 0-910840-70-9); Vol. 23. 1971 (ISBN 0-910840-71-7); Vol. 24. 1972 (ISBN 0-910840-72-5); Vol.25. 1973 (ISBN 0-910840-73-3); Vol. 26. 1974 (ISBN 0-910840-74-1). 2.00x ea. Kingdom.

--Standard, Vol. 30. 1978. 3.00x (ISBN 0-910840-78-4). Kingdom.

--The Standard Nineteen Seventy-Nine. 192p. 1979. 3.00x (ISBN 0-910840-79-2). Kingdom.

--The Standard 1982. (Sermons Ser.). 192p. 1982. 3.00x (ISBN 0-910840-82-2). Kingdom.

--The Standard 1983 Termination. (Sermons Ser.). 192p. 1983. 3.00x (ISBN 0-910840-83-0). Kingdom.

Murray, Gilbert. Five Stages of Greek Religion. LC 76-27675. 1976. Repr. of 1925 ed. lib. bdg. 22.50x (ISBN 0-8371-9080-0, MUFS). Greenwood.

--Five Stages of Greek Religion: Studies Based on a Course of Lectures Delivered in April 1912 at Columbia University. LC 75-41202. Repr. of 1925 ed. 12.50 (ISBN 0-404-14577-9). AMS Pr.

--Stoic, Christian & Humanist. LC 75-99712. (Essay Index Reprint Ser.). 1940. 17.00 (ISBN 0-8369-1363-9). Ayer Co Pubs.

Murray, Iain. Life of John Murray. 1984. pap. 6.95 (ISBN 0-85151-426-X). Banner of Truth.

--Spurgeon un Principe Olvidado. 2nd ed. (Span.). 156p. 1984. pap. 3.95 (ISBN 0-85151-439-1). Banner of Truth.

Murray, Iain, ed. see Houghton, S. M.

Murray, Iain H. The Forgotton Surgeon. 1978. pap. 5.45 (ISBN 0-85151-156-2). Banner of Truth.

--The Life of A. W. Pink. (Illus.). 272p. (Orig.). 1981. pap. 5.95 (ISBN 0-85151-332-8). Banner of Truth.

--The Puritan Hope. 1975. pap. 5.95 (ISBN 0-85151-037-X). Banner of Truth.

Murray, Iain H., ed. Diary of Kenneth Macrae. (Illus.). 535p. 1980. 19.95 (ISBN 0-85151-297-6). Banner of Truth.

Murray, John. Atonement. pap. 1.50 (ISBN 0-87552-342-0). Presby & Reformed.

--Christian Baptism. 1980. pap. 3.95 (ISBN 0-87552-343-9). Presby & Reformed.

--Collected Writings of John Murray: Claims of Truth, Vol. 1. 374p. 1976. 22.95 (ISBN 0-85151-241-0). Banner of Truth.

--The Collected Writings of John Murray: Lectures in Systematic Theology, Vol. 2. 1978. 24.95 (ISBN 0-85151-242-9). Banner of Truth.

--Collected Writings of John Murray: Studies in Theology, Vol. 4. 390p. 1983. 24.95 (ISBN 0-85151-340-9). Banner of Truth.

--The Collected Writings of John Murray: The Claims of Truth, 4 vols. 1976. Set. 88.95 (ISBN 0-85151-396-4). Banner of Truth.

--Epistle of Paul to the Romans. (New International Commentary on the New Testament). 1960. 19.95 (ISBN 0-8028-2286-X). Eerdmans.

--Imputation of Adam's Sin. 1977. pap. 2.95 (ISBN 0-87552-341-2). Presby & Reformed.

--Principles of Conduct. 1957. pap. 7.95 (ISBN 0-8028-1144-2). Eerdmans.

--Redemption: Accomplished & Applied. 1961. pap. 5.95 (ISBN 0-8028-1143-4). Eerdmans.

Murray, John, jt. auth. see Eisenhower, David.

Murray, John C. Problem of God: Yesterday & Today. (St. Thomas More Lectures Ser.: No. 1). (Orig.). 1964. pap. 5.95x (ISBN 0-300-00171-1, Y138). Yale U Pr.

Murray, John O. Catholic Heros & Heroines of America. 35.00 (ISBN 0-87968-818-1). Gordon Pr.

--Catholic Pioneers of America. 35.00 (ISBN 0-87968-819-X). Gordon Pr.

--Little Lives of the Great Saints. LC 82-50593. 495p. 1985. pap. 12.00 (ISBN 0-89555-190-X). Tan Bks Pubs.

Murray, Jon & O'Hair, Madalyn. All the Questions You Ever Wanted to Ask American Atheists with All the Answers. 2nd ed. 248p. (Orig.). 1986. pap. 7.00 (ISBN 0-910309-24-8). Am Atheist.

Murray, Jon G. Essays on American Atheism, Vol. I. 350p. (Orig.). 1986. pap. 8.00 (ISBN 0-910309-28-0). Am Atheist.

--Essays on American Atheism, Vol. II. 300p. (Orig.). 1986. pap. 8.00 (ISBN 0-910309-29-9). Am Atheist.

Murray, Jon G., ed. Essays of an Atheist Activist. 67p. (Orig.). 1981. pap. 3.25 (ISBN 0-911826-02-5). Am Atheist.

Murray, Kim & Murray, Christopher. Illuminations from the Bhagavad-Gita. LC 79-3834. (Illus.). 64p. (Orig.). pap. 8.95 (ISBN 0-06-090763-0, CN 763, PL). Har-Row.

Murray, Margaret A. Egyptian Religious Poetry. Cranmer-Byng, J. L., ed. LC 79-8714. (The Wisdom of the East Ser.). 120p. 1980. Repr. of 1949 ed. lib. bdg. 22.50x (ISBN 0-313-21012-8, MUER). Greenwood.

--Egyptian Temples. LC 75-41203. Repr. of 1931 ed. 27.50 (ISBN 0-404-14719-4). AMS Pr.

Murray, Nicholas. Letters to the Right Rev. John Hughes, Roman Catholic Bishop of New York. Grob, Gerald, ed. LC 76-46091. (Anti-Movements in America). 1977. Repr. of 1855 ed. 29.00 (ISBN 0-405-09964-9). Ayer Co Pubs.

Murray, Patrick, ed. Treasury of Irish Religious Verse. 1986. 17.95 (ISBN 0-8245-0776-2). Crossroad NY.

Murray, Paul. The Mysticism Debate. 1978. 6.26 (ISBN 0-8199-0722-7). Franciscan Herald.

Murray, R. Symbols of Church & Kingdom. LC 74-80363. 430p. 1975. 59.50 (ISBN 0-521-20553-0). Cambridge U Pr.

Murray, Robert H. Erasmus & Luther: Their Attitude to Toleration. LC 83-45659. (The Zodiac Club Ser.). Date not set. Repr. of 1920 ed. 57.50 (ISBN 0-404-19809-0). AMS Pr.

--Group Movements Throughout the Ages. LC 72-301. (Essay Index Reprint Ser.). Repr. of 1935 ed. 22.00 (ISBN 0-8369-2810-5). Ayer Co Pubs.

Murray, Stephen. Building Troyes Cathedral: The Late Gothic Campaigns. LC 85-45744. (Illus.). 272p. 1986. 47.50x (ISBN 0-253-31277-9). Ind U Pr.

Murray, Thomas. Pitcairn's Island. LC 72-281. (World History Ser., No. 48). 1972. Repr. of 1860 ed. lib. bdg. 52.95x (ISBN 0-8383-1410-4). Haskell.

Murray, Tom. A Higher Call. 1984. 12.95 (ISBN 0-533-06032-X). Vantage.

Murray, William J. My Life Without God. LC 83-14269. 252p. 1984. pap. 5.95 (ISBN 0-8407-5884-7). Nelson.

Murray-Aynsley, Harriet. Symbolism of the East & West. LC 74-118538. 1971. Repr. of 1900 ed. 25.50x (ISBN 0-8046-1162-9, Pub by Kennikat). Assoc Faculty Pr.

Murro, Jonathan. God-Realization Journal. (Illus.). 337p. 1975. 10.00 (ISBN 0-917187-16-4). A R C Pub.

Murro, Jonathan, jt. auth. see Colton, Ann R.

Murry, J. Middleton. The Challenge of Schweitzer. LC 72-190328. Repr. of 1948 ed. lib. bdg. 20.00 (ISBN 0-8414-6171-6). Folcroft.

--The Life of Jesus. 1982. Repr. of 1927 ed. lib. bdg. 35.00 (ISBN 0-8495-3939-0). Arden Lib.

Murry, John M. The Betrayal of Christ by the Churches. 59.95 (ISBN 0-87968-724-X). Gordon Pr.

Murthy, B. Srinivasa. Mother Teresa & India. LC 82-80522. (Illus.). 144p. (Orig.). 1983. pap. 6.95x (ISBN 0-941910-00-8). Long Beach Pubns.

Murthy, B. Srinivasa, tr. from Sanskrit. The Bhagavad Gita: Translated with Introduction & Notes. LC 84-82433. 150p. 1985. pap. 9.95 (ISBN 0-941910-01-6). Long Beach Pubns.

Murty, K. S. Revelation & Reason in Advaita Vedanta. 1974. Repr. 11.25 (ISBN 0-8426-0662-9). Orient Bk Dist.

Murwin, Susan A., jt. auth. see Payne, Suzzy C.

Mus, Paul. Barabudur: Esquisse d'une histoire du bouddhisme fondee sur la critique archeologique des textes, 2 vols. in 1. Bolle, Kees W., ed. LC 77-79146. (Mythology Ser.). (Fr.). 1978. Repr. of 1935 ed. lib. bdg. 82.50x (ISBN 0-405-10555-X). Ayer Co Pubs.

Musa, Adam, ed. Letters & Lectures of Idries Shah. 40p. 1981. pap. 4.95 (ISBN 0-86304-010-1, Pub. by Octagon Pr England). Ins Study Human.

Musallam, Basim. Sex & Society in Islam: Birth Control Before the Nineteenth Century. LC 82-23539. (Cambridge Studies in Islamic Civilization). 240p. 1983. 34.50 (ISBN 0-521-24874-4). Cambridge U Pr.

Musallam, Basim F. Sex & Society in Islam: Birth Control Before the Nineteenth Century. (Cambridge Studies in Islamic Civilization). 176p. 1986. pap. 12.95 (ISBN 0-521-33858-1). Cambridge U Pr.

Musaph-Andriesse, R. G. From Torah to Kabbalah: A Basic Introduction to the Writings of Judaism. 1982. pap. 4.95x (ISBN 0-19-520364-X). Oxford U Pr.

Musavi, Sayyed M. Western Civilization Through Muslim Eyes. Goulding, F. J., tr. from Persian. 146p. 1977. 4.95 (ISBN 0-941722-20-1); pap. 3.95 (ISBN 0-941722-06-6). Book-Dist-Ctr.

Muse, Charles B. The Catholic Sex Manual for Teenagers. (Illus.). 1980. 31.85 (ISBN 0-89266-217-4). Am Classical Coll Pr.

Muse, Dan T. The Song of Songs. 5.95 (ISBN 0-911866-78-7). Advocate.

Muses, C. A. Esoteric Teachings of the Tibetan Tantra. 319p. 1982. pap. 8.95 (ISBN 0-87728-307-9). Weiser.

Musgrove, Peggy. Who's Who Among Bible Women. LC 81-81126. 128p. (Orig.). 1981. 2.50 (ISBN 0-88243-883-2, 02-0883); teacher's ed. 3.95 (ISBN 0-88243-193-5, 32-0193). Gospel Pub.

Mushir-Ul-Hag. Islam in Secular India. (Indian Institute of Advanced Study Monographs Ser). 110p. 1972. 8.00x (ISBN 0-89684-426-9). Orient Bk Dist.

Musil, Alois. Northern Arabia, According to the Original Investigations of Alois Musil. LC 77-87092. (American Geographical Society. Oriental Explorations & Studies: Map Vol.). Repr. of 1928 ed. 30.00 (ISBN 0-404-60237-1). AMS Pr.

Musser, Benjamin F. Franciscan Poets. facs. ed. LC 67-26768. (Essay Index Reprint Ser). 1933. 17.25 (ISBN 0-8369-0732-9). Ayer Co Pubs.

Musser, Harlan C. Sex--Our Myth Theology? 196p. 1981. pap. 7.95 (ISBN 0-8059-2768-9). Dorrance.

Musser, Joe. A Skeptics Quest. 224p. (Orig.). 1984. pap. 6.95 (ISBN 0-86605-151-1). Campus Crusade.

Musser, Joe, jt. auth. see Eareckson, Joni.

Mussiett, Salomon C., tr. see Nelson, Edward W.

Mussner, Franz. Tractate on the Jews: The Significance of Judaism for the Christian Faith. Swidler, Leonard, tr. from German. LC 83-5699. 352p. 1983. 29.95 (ISBN 0-8006-0707-4, 1-707). Fortress.

Mussner, Franz, jt. auth. see Gnilka, Joachim.

Muste, A. J. Non-Violence in an Aggressive World. LC 76-137551. (Peace Movement in America Ser). 220p. 1972. Repr. of 1940 ed. lib. bdg. 15.95x (ISBN 0-89198-081-4). Ozer.

--Of Holy Disobedience. LC 52-1568. (Orig.). 1952. pap. 2.50x (ISBN 0-87574-064-2). Pendle Hill.

--Of Holy Disobedience. 23p. 1952-1964. pap. 1.25 (ISBN 0-934676-09-7). Greenlf Bks.

--Saints for This Age. LC 62-21962. (Orig.). 1962. pap. 2.50x (ISBN 0-87574-124-X, 124). Pendle Hill.

--War is the Enemy. 1983. pap. 2.50x (ISBN 0-87574-015-4, 015). Pendle Hill.

--The World Task of Pacifism. 1983. pap. 2.50x (ISBN 0-87574-013-8, 013). Pendle Hill.

Musto, Ronald G. The Catholic Peace Tradition. LC 86-12494. 464p. (Orig.). 1986. pap. 21.95 (ISBN 0-88344-263-9). Orbis Bks.

--The Peace Tradition in the Catholic Church: An Annotated Bibliography. LC 86-31950. (Garland Reference Library of Social Science). 500p. 1987. lib. bdg. 67.00 (ISBN 0-8240-8584-1). Garland Pub.

Muston, Alexis. The Israel of the Alps: A Complete History of the Waldenses & Their Colonies, 2 vols. Montgomery, John, tr. LC 77-84718. Repr. of 1875 ed. 84.50 set (ISBN 0-404-16140-5). AMS Pr.

Musurillo, Herbert. The Acts of the Christian Martyrs: Text & Translations. (Oxford Early English Texts Ser). 1972. 52.00x (ISBN 0-19-826806-8). Oxford U Pr.

Musurillo, Herbert A. Symbol & Myth in Ancient Poetry. LC 77-2395. 1977. Repr. of 1961 ed. lib. bdg. 24.75x (ISBN 0-8371-9554-3, MUSM). Greenwood.

Mutahhari, Ayatullah M. Fundamentals of Islamic Thought: God, Man & the Universe. Algar, Hamid, ed. Campbell, R., tr. (Comtemporary Islamic Thought Perian Ser.). Orig. Title: Per. 231p. (Orig.). 1985. 19.95 (ISBN 0-933782-14-4); pap. 8.95 (ISBN 0-933782-15-2). Mizan Pr.

--Social & Historical Change: An Islamic Perspective. Algar, Hamid, ed. Campbell, R., tr. from Persian. (Contemporary Islamic Thought, Persian Ser.). 156p. 1986. 18.95 (ISBN 0-933782-18-7); pap. 7.95 (ISBN 0-933782-19-5). Mizan Pr.

Mutahhari, Morteza. Man & Faith. Abri, Amir F. & Talebinejad, Mohammad, trs. from Arabic. LC 82-60360. 64p. 1985. pap. 3.95 (ISBN 0-940368-48-X). Tahrike Tarsile Quran.

--Religion & the World. Tawheedi, Mohammad S., tr. 44p. 1984. pap. 3.95 (ISBN 0-940368-34-X). Tahrike Tarsile Quran.

--Understanding the Quran. Tawheedi, Mohammad S., tr. from Persian. LC 84-50586. 64p. 1985. pap. 3.95 (ISBN 0-940368-35-8). Tahrike Tarsile Quran.

Mutahhari, Murtaza. The Nature of Imam Hussein'n Movement. Ali, Muhammed K., ed. Pazargadi, Alaedin, tr. 20p. 1984. pap. 2.95 (ISBN 0-940368-33-1). Tahrike Tarsile Quran.

Mutahhery, Murtaza. The Martyr. Ansari, M. A., tr. 62p. 1983. pap. 4.00 (ISBN 0-941724-13-1). Islamic Seminary.

--Master & Mastership. Ansari, M. A., tr. 124p. 1983. pap. 5.00 (ISBN 0-941724-15-8). Islamic Seminary.

--Monotheistic Point of View. 70p. 1984. pap. 3.95 (ISBN 0-940368-39-0). Tahrike Tarsile Quran.

--Rationality of Islam. Ansari, M. A., tr. 170p. 1983. pap. 6.00 (ISBN 0-941724-17-4). Islamic Seminary.

Mutlak, Suheil. In Memory of Kahil Gibran. (Arabic.). 1982. 14.00x (ISBN 0-86685-295-6). Intl Bk Ctr.

Muto, Susan. Approaching the Sacred. 4.95 (ISBN 0-87193-047-1). Dimension Bks.

--Blessings That Make Us Be: Living the Beatitudes. LC 82-13102. 176p. 1982. 7.95 (ISBN 0-8245-0516-6). Crossroad NY.

--The Journey Homeward. 6.95 (ISBN 0-87193-001-3). Dimension Bks.

--A Practical Guide to Spiritual Reading. 9.95 (ISBN 0-87193-046-3). Dimension Bks.

--Renewed at Each Awakening: The Formative Power of Sacred Words. 1985. pap. 4.95 (ISBN 0-87193-147-8). Dimension Bks.

--Steps Along the Way: The Path of Spiritual Reading. 4.95 (ISBN 0-87193-048-X). Dimension Bks.

Muto, Susan, jt. auth. see Kaam, Adrian van.

Muto, Susan, jt. auth. see Van Kaam, Adrian.

Muto, Susan A. Meditation in Motion. LC 86-4690. 144p. 1986. 5.95 (ISBN 0-385-23533-X, Im). Doubleday.

--Pathways of Spiritual Living. LC 84-1564. 192p. 1984. pap. 6.95 (ISBN 0-385-19473-0, Im). Doubleday.

Muto, Susan A. & Kaam, Adrian Van. Celebrating the Single Life. LC 81-43770. 1985. pap. 6.95 (ISBN 0-385-19915-5, Im). Doubleday.

Muto, Susan A., jt. auth. see Van Kamm, Adrian.

Mutrux, Robert. Great New England Churches: Sixty-Five Houses of Worship That Changed Our Lives. LC 81-80425. (Illus.). 288p. (Orig.). 1981. pap. 14.95 (ISBN 0-87106-950-4). Globe Pequot.

Mutschmann, H. Further Studies Concerning the Origin of Paradise Lost. LC 77-24899. lib. bdg. 10.00 (ISBN 0-8414-6211-9). Folcroft.

--Secret of John Milton. LC 72-194771. 1925. lib. bdg. 15.00 (ISBN 0-8414-6694-7). Folcroft.

Mutschmann, Heinrich. Studies Concerning the Origins of Milton's Paradise Lost. LC 79-163459. (Studies in Milton, No. 22). 1971. Repr. of 1924 ed. lib. bdg. 39.95x (ISBN 0-8383-1324-8). Haskell.

--Studies Concerning the Origins of Milton's Paradise Lost. 1924. Repr. 15.00 (ISBN 0-8274-3532-0). R West.

Mutschmann, Heinrich & Wentersdorf, Karl. Shakespeare & Catholicism. LC 71-105107. 1970. Repr. of 1952 ed. 31.50 (ISBN 0-404-04547-2). AMS Pr.

Muybridge, Eadweard. Muybridge's Complete Human & Animal Locomotion: All 781 Plates from the 1887 Animal Locomotion, 3 vols. Incl. Vol. 1. 33.34 (ISBN 0-486-23792-3); Vol. 2. 33.33 (ISBN 0-486-23793-1); Vol. 3. 33.33 (ISBN 0-486-23794-X). (Illus.). 1979. Repr. of 1887 ed. Set. 100.00. Dover.

Muyskens, James L. The Sufficiency of Hope: Conceptual Foundations of Religion. (Philosophical Monographs: 3rd Annual Ser.). 186p. 1979. 27.95 (ISBN 0-87722-162-6). Temple U Pr.

Muzaffar, Muhammad Rida Al see Al-Muzaffar, Muhammad Rida.

Muzorewa, Gwinyai H. The Origins & Development of African Theology. LC 84-14769. 160p. (Orig.). 1985. pap. 9.95 (ISBN 0-88344-351-1). Orbis Bks.

Muzzaffar, Muhammed R. Al see Al-Muzaffar, Muhammed R.

Muzzey, D. S. The Spiritual Franciscans. 59.95 (ISBN 0-8490-1113-2). Gordon Pr.

Muzzy, Ruth & Hughes, R. Kent. The Christian Wedding Planner. 320p. 1984. pap. 9.95 (ISBN 0-8423-0253-0). Tyndale.

Myer, Isaac. Qabbalah: The Philosophical Writings of Solomon Ben Yehudah Ibn Gabirol. 69.95 (ISBN 0-8490-0922-7). Gordon Pr.

Myerhoff, Barbara. Number Our Days. 1980. 8.95 (ISBN 0-671-25430-8, Touchstone). S&S.

Myerhoff, Barbara G. Peyote Hunt: The Sacred Journey of the Huichol Indians. LC 73-16923. (Symbol, Myth & Ritual Ser.). (Illus.). 288p. 1976. pap. 9.95x (ISBN 0-8014-9137-1). Cornell U Pr.

Myerhoff, Barbara G., jt. ed. see Moore, Sally F.

Myers, Aaron M. Representation & Misrepresentation of the Puritan in Elizabethan Drama. LC 76-20654. 1976. Repr. of 1931 ed. lib. bdg. 27.50 (ISBN 0-8414-6141-4). Folcroft.

Myers, Albert C., ed. see Wister, Sally.

Myers, Bill. Faith Workout. (Illus.). 144p. 1986. 3.95 (ISBN 0-89693-265-6). Victor Bks.

Myers, David C. The Human Puzzle: Psychological Research & Christian Belief. LC 77-15873. 1978. pap. 8.95x (ISBN 0-06-065558-5, RD 265, HarpR). Har-Row.

Myers, David G. The Inflated Self: Human Illusions & the Bibical Call to Hope. 176p. 1980. 12.95 (ISBN 0-8164-0459-3, HarpR); pap. 5.95 (ISBN 0-8164-2326-1). Har-Row.

Myers, David G., jt. auth. see Bolt, Martin.

Myers, Edith. The Mysteries of the Rosary. (Illus.). 41p. 1977. Repr. of 1968 ed. 2.50 (ISBN 0-912414-13-8). Stella Maris Bks.

Myers, Edward. When Parents Die: A Guide for Adults. 208p. 1986. 13.95 (ISBN 0-670-80771-0). Viking.

Myers, Edwards, jt. auth. see Turner, J. J.

Myers, Ernest, ed. Selected Prose Writings of John Milton. 1973. Repr. of 1904 ed. lib. bdg. 20.00 (ISBN 0-8414-6695-5). Folcroft.

Myers, Geoffrey M., et al, eds. Les Chetifs. LC 79-2565. (Old French Crusade Cycle Ser.: Vol. V). xxxvi, 352p. 1981. text ed. 35.00 (ISBN 0-8173-0023-6). U of Ala Pr.

Myers, Gustavus. Ye Olden Blue Laws. 274p. 1980. Repr. of 1921 ed. lib. bdg. 25.00 (ISBN 0-8495-3795-9). Arden Lib.

Myers, Jacob M. Hosea-Jonah. LC 59-10454. (Layman's Bible Commentary: Vol. 14). 1959. pap. 4.95 (ISBN 0-8042-3074-9). John Knox.

Myers, Jacob M., ed. Chronicles One. LC 65-17226. (Anchor Bible Ser.: Vol. 12). 1965. 14.00 (ISBN 0-385-01259-4, Anchor Pr). Doubleday.

--Chronicles Two. (Anchor Bible Ser.: Vol. 13). 1965. 14.00 (ISBN 0-385-03757-0, Anchor Pr). Doubleday.

--Ezra & Nehemiah. LC 65-23788. (Anchor Bible Ser.: Vol. 14). 1965. 16.00 (ISBN 0-385-04695-2, Anchor Pr). Doubleday.

Myers, James E., jt. auth. see Lehmann, Arthur C.

Myers, John B. Thomas J. Comber, Missionary Pioneer to the Congo. LC 74-98739. (Illus.). Repr. of 1888 ed. lib. bdg. cancelled (ISBN 0-8371-2769-6, MYC&, Pub. by Negro U Pr). Greenwood.

Myers, Margaret E. Meyersville, Md., Lutheran Baptisms. Russell, Donna V., ed. (Illus.). 70p. 1986. pap. 10.00 (ISBN 0-914385-04-6). Catoctin Pr.

Myers, Oma L., jt. auth. see Welch, Rosa P.

Myers, Rawley. The Book of Mary: Devotions for October & May. LC 84-61563. 208p. (Orig.). 1984. pap. 6.50 (ISBN 0-87973-804-9, 804). Our Sunday Visitor.

--God & Man: The Basic Truths. 1976. 0.50 (ISBN 0-8199-0606-9). Franciscan Herald.

--Jesus Is Here: Devotions to the Sacred Heart & Precious Blood. LC 85-63066. 144p. (Orig.). 1986. pap. 5.95 (ISBN 0-87973-520-1, XXX 520). Our Sunday Visitor.

--Journal of a Parish Priest. LC 81-82022. 144p. (Orig.). 1982. pap. 3.75 (ISBN 0-87973-675-5, 675). Our Sunday Visitor.

--Lent: A Journey to Resurrection Prayers & Reflections for the Penitential Season. LC 83-63084. 192p. 1984. pap. 5.95 (ISBN 0-87973-605-4). Our Sunday Visitor.

Myers, Robert J., ed. Religion & the State: The Struggle for Legitimacy & Power. LC 85-72100. (The Annals of the American Academy of Political & Social Science Ser.: Vol. 483). 1986. text ed. 15.00 (ISBN 0-8039-2538-7); pap. text ed. 7.95 (ISBN 0-8039-2539-5). Sage.

Myers, Robert M. Handel, Dryden & Milton. 1956. lib. bdg. 32.50 (ISBN 0-8414-6129-5). Folcroft.

--Handel's Messiah: A Touchstone of Taste. LC 72-159747. 338p. 1971. Repr. of 1948 ed. lib. bdg. 27.50x (ISBN 0-374-96035-6, Octagon). Hippocrene Bks.

Myers, Ruth, jt. auth. see Myers, Warren.

Myers, Sondra, jt. auth. see Rittner, Carol.

Myers, Thomas, ed. see Calvin, John.

Myers, Trevor C. The Essence of Rastafari Nationalism & Black Economic Development. 1986. 10.00 (ISBN 0-533-06629-8). Vantage.

Myers, Warren & Myers, Ruth. Pray: How to Be Effective in Prayer. LC 83-61679. 204p. 1984. pap. 5.95 (ISBN 0-89109-510-1). NavPress.

Myers, William F. The Brightness of His Presence: Theological Dissertation. LC 82-90351. 64p. 1982. 6.95 (ISBN 0-87948-049-1). Beatty.

Myerson, Joel. New England Transcendentalists & the DIAL: A History of the Magazine & Its Contributors. LC 78-66814. 400p. 1980. 35.00 (ISBN 0-8386-2294-1). Fairleigh Dickinson.

--Theodore Parker: A Descriptive Bibliography. LC 81-43354. 238p. 1981. lib. bdg. 33.00 (ISBN 0-8240-9279-1). Garland Pub.

Myerson, Joel, ed. The Transcendentalists: A Review of Research & Criticism. (Reviews of Research Ser.). 450p. 1984. 30.00x (ISBN 0-87352-260-5); pap. 20.00x (ISBN 0-87352-261-3). Modern Lang.

Myhrman, David V. Babylonian Hymns & Prayers. 59.95 (ISBN 0-87968-691-X). Gordon Pr.

Mykian, M. Numerology Made Easy. 1979. pap. 5.00 (ISBN 0-87980-376-2). Wilshire.

Mykoff, Moshe, ed. see Nachman & Nathan.

Mykoff, Moshe, tr. from Hebrew see Rabbi Nachman of Breslov.

Mykoff, Moshe, tr. see Rabbi Nachman of Breslov.

Mylander, Charles. Running Red Lights. LC 86-444. 250p. (Orig.). 1986. pap. 6.95 (ISBN 0-8307-1103-1, 5418666). Regal.

--Secrets for Growing Churches. LC 79-1764. 1979. pap. 4.95i (ISBN 0-06-066055-4, RD 302, HarpR). Har-Row.

Mylar, Isaac L. Early Days at the Mission San Juan Bautista. (Illus.). 208p. 1986. pap. 9.95 (ISBN 0-317-44751-3). Panorama West.

Mynors, R. A., tr. see Erasmus, Desiderius.

Myo-Bong, Master & Hye-Am Choi. Gateway to Patriarchal Son (Zen) Venerable Master Hye-Am's Dharma Talks. Myo-Bong, Master, tr. from Chinese & Korean. LC 86-50754. (Chinese Korean & Eng.). 450p. (Orig.). 1986. 18.00 (ISBN 0-938647-01-6). Western Son Acad.

Myo-Bong, Master, tr. see Myo-Bong, Master & Hye-Am Choi.

Myo-Bong Master. Gateway to Zen (Ch'an) Hye-Am Choi, ed. LC 86-50750. (Chinese Korean & Eng.). 355p. (Orig.). 1986. 18.00 (ISBN 0-938647-00-8). Western Son Acad.

Myra, Harold. The New You. 1980. pap. 3.95 (ISBN 0-88207-581-0). Victor Bks.

--Santa, Are You for Real? LC 77-23023. (Illus.). 6.95 (ISBN 0-8407-5122-2). Nelson.

Myring. First Guide to the Universe. (Let's Find Out About Ser.). 1982. 10.95 (ISBN 0-86020-611-4, Usborne-Hayes). EDC.

Myss, Caroline M., jt. auth. see Shealy, C. Norman.

Mystic Jhamom Publishers Staff, ed. Is Man a Fress Agent Illustrations Booklet: Supplement. (Conversations with a Mystic Ser.: No. 1). 12p. 1985. pap. 1.75 (ISBN 0-933961-02-2). Mystic Jhamom.

Mystic Jhamom Staff, ed. Jhamom's Story of Creation. (Conversations Mystic Ser.: No. 3). (Illus.). 136p. 1986. pap. 9.95 (ISBN 0-933961-07-3). Mystic Jhamom.

--The Phenomena of Life. (Conversations with a Mystic Ser.: No. 4). (Illus.). 1986. pap. write for info. (ISBN 0-933961-09-X). Mystic Jhamom.

--The Phenomena of Life Illustrations Booklet: Supplement. (Conversations with a Mystic Ser.: No. 4). (Illus.). 24p. 1986. pap. write for info. (ISBN 0-933961-10-3). Mystic Jhamom.

--Why? Psychic Development & How! (Conversations with a Mystic Ser.: No. 2). (Illus.). 176p. 1985. pap. 11.75 (ISBN 0-933961-05-7). Mystic Jhamom.

Mystic Jhamon Editors. Is Man a Free Agent. (Conversations with a Mystic: No. 1). (Illus.). 128p. 1985. pap. 9.95 (ISBN 0-933961-01-4). Mystic Jhamom.

N

Naamani, Israel T. The State of Israel. LC 79-12757. (Illus.). 1980. pap. 6.95x (ISBN 0-87441-278-1). Behrman.

Nabha, Kahan S. Sikhs We Are Not Hindus. Singh, Jarnail, tr. 152p. 1986. pap. 12.00x (ISBN 0-8364-1839-5). South Asia Bks.

Nabi, Malik B. The Quranic Phenomenon. Kirkari, Abu B., tr. from Fr. LC 82-70460. (Illus.). 187p. (Orig.). 1982. pap. 6.00 (ISBN 0-89259-023-8). Am Trust Pubns.

Nachant, Frances G. Song of Peace. 1969. cancelled (ISBN 0-8233-0126-5). Golden Quill.

Nachman & Nathan. Mayim. Mykoff, Moshe, ed. 64p. (Orig.). 1987. pap. 1.50 (ISBN 0-930213-28-9). Breslov Res Inst.

Nachman of Breslov. Rabbi Nachman's Stories. Kaplan, Aryeh, tr. from Hebrew. LC 83-70201. Tr. of Sippurey Ma'asioth. 552p. 1983. 15.00 (ISBN 0-930213-02-5). Breslov Res Inst.

--Rabbi Nachman's Tikkun: The Comprehensive Remedy. Greenbaum, Avraham, tr. from Hebrew. 240p. 1984. 10.00 (ISBN 0-930213-06-8). Breslov Res Inst.

--Rabbi Nachman's Wisdom. Rosenfeld, Zvi A., ed. Kaplan, Aryeh, tr. from Hebrew. Tr. of Shevachay HaRan-Sichos HaRan. (Illus.). 510p. 1984. 14.00 (ISBN 0-930213-00-9); pap. 11.00 (ISBN 0-930213-01-7). Breslov Res Inst.

Nachmani, Amikam. Great Power Discord in Palestine: The Anglo-American Committee of Inquiry into the Problems of European Jewry & Palestine 1945-1946. (Illus.). 296p. 1986. 30.00 (ISBN 0-7146-3298-8, F Cass Co). Biblio Dist.

Nachman of Breslov. Les Contes. Regnot, Franz, tr. from Yiddish. Tr. of Sippurey Ma'asioth. (Fr.). 180p. (Orig.). 1981. pap. 7.00 (ISBN 0-930213-22-X). Breslov Res Inst.

--The Gems of Rabbi Nachman. Rosenfeld, Tzvi A., ed. Kaplan, Ayreh, tr. from Hebrew. (Illus.). 186p. (Orig.). 1980. pap. 2.00 (ISBN 0-930213-10-6). Breslov Res Inst.

--Hitbodedouth: Ou La Porte du Ciel. Besancon, Its'hak, adapted by. (Fr.). 110p. (Orig.). 1982. pap. 2.00 (ISBN 0-930213-27-0). Breslov Res Inst.

--Rabbi Nachman's Stories: Skazochnniji Histori Rabbi Nechman iz Bratzlav. Avni, Baruch, tr. from Hebrew & Rus. Tr. of Sippurey Maasiot. (Illus.). 332p. (Orig.). 1987. pap. 10.00 (ISBN 0-930213-29-7). Breslov Res Inst.

Nachman of Breslov & Nathan of Breslov. Azamra (I Will Sing) Greenbaum, Avraham, tr. from Hebrew. 64p. (Orig.). 1984. pap. 1.50 (ISBN 0-930213-11-4). Breslov Res INst.

--Courage! Tr. of Meshivat Nefesh. 119p. (Orig.). 1983. pap. 3.00 (ISBN 0-930213-23-8). Breslov Res Inst.

--Outpouring of the Soul. Kaplan, Aryeh, tr. from Hebrew. Tr. of Hishtap'kuth HaNefesh. 96p. (Orig.). 1980. pap. 2.50 (ISBN 0-930213-14-9). Breslov Res Inst.

--Restore My Soul. Greenbaum, Avraham, tr. from Hebrew. Tr. of Meshivat Nefesh. 128p. (Orig.). 1980. pap. 3.00 (ISBN 0-930213-13-0). Breslov Res Inst.

Nachtrieb, Eric, jt. auth. see Slater, Michael.

Nacpil, Emerito, ed. The Human & the Holy: Asian Perspectives in Christian Theology. Elwood, Douglas J. 1978. pap. text ed. 10.00x (ISBN 0-686-23912-1, Pub. by New Day Pub). Cellar.

Nacpil, Emerito & Elwood, Douglas J., eds. The Human & the Holy: Asian Perspectives in Christian Theology. LC 80-14134. 384p. (Orig.). 1980. pap. 3.74 (ISBN 0-88344-195-0). Orbis Bks.

Nadal, J. C. Dictionnaire d'Eloquence Sacree, Vol. 6. Migne, J. P., ed. (Nouvelle Encyclopedie Theologique Ser.). (Fr.). 650p. Repr. of 1851 ed. lib. bdg. 83.00x (ISBN 0-89241-256-9). Caratzas.

Nadasdy, Dean. Gospel Dramas: Twelve Plays for Worship in Lent & Other Seasons. LC 85-22886. 96p. (Orig.). 1985. pap. 4.95 (ISBN 0-8066-2185-0, 10-2829). Augsburg.

Nadasdy, Dean, jt. auth. see Schroeder, Theodore W.

Nadawi, Abul H. Islam & the World. Kidwai, Mohammad A., tr. from Arabic. Tr. of Madha Khasira al-Alam bi-Inhtat al-Muslimin. 218p. (Orig.). 1977. pap. 5.95x (ISBN 0-939830-04-3, Pub. by IIFSO Kuwait). New Era Pubns MI.

--Madha Khasira al-Alam bi-Inhtat al-Muslimin. 4th ed. (Arabic.). 432p. (Orig.). 1978. pap. 8.50x (ISBN 0-939830-14-0, Pub. by IIFSO Kuwait). New Era Pubns MI.

Nadejda Gorodetzky. Saint Tikhon of Zadonsk: Inspirer of Dostoevsky. LC 76-49919. 320p. 1977. pap. 8.95 (ISBN 0-913836-32-X). St Vladimirs.

Naden, C. J., adapted by. Jason & the Golden Fleece. LC 80-50068. (Illus.). 32p. 1980. PLB 9.79 (ISBN 0-89375-360-2); pap. 2.50 (ISBN 0-89375-364-5). Troll Assocs.

--Pegasus, the Winged Horse. new ed. LC 80-50069. (Illus.). 32p. 1980. PLB 9.79 (ISBN 0-89375-361-0); pap. 2.50 (ISBN 0-89375-365-3). Troll Assocs.

--Perseus & Medusa. LC 80-50083. (Illus.). 32p. 1980. PLB 9.79 (ISBN 0-89375-362-9); pap. 2.50 (ISBN 0-89375-366-1). Troll Assocs.

--Theseus & the Minotaur. LC 80-50067. (Illus.). 32p. 1980. PLB 9.79 (ISBN 0-89375-363-7); pap. 2.50 (ISBN 0-89375-367-X). Troll Assocs.

Nadich, Judah. Jewish Legends of the Second Commonwealth. 508p. 1983. 25.00 (ISBN 0-8276-0212-X, 490). Jewish Pubns.

Nadui, A. H. Islam: The Perfect Religion & a Way of Life. pap. 1.00 (ISBN 0-686-18498-X). Kazi Pubns.

Nadui, S. M. A Geographical History of the Qur'an. 1970. 10.50 (ISBN 0-87902-300-7). Orientalia.

Nadvi. An Easy History of the Prophet of Islam. pap. 3.95 (ISBN 0-686-18309-6). Kazi Pubns.

--Saviors of Islamic Spirit, 3 Vols. 60.00 set (ISBN 0-686-18312-6); 20.00 ea. Kazi Pubns.

Nadvi, A. Islam: The Only Way. pap. 1.00 (ISBN 0-686-18499-8). Kazi Pubns.

Nadvi, A. H. Four Pillars of Islam. 14.95 (ISBN 0-686-18597-8). Kazi Pubns.

--A Geographical History of the Qur'an. 12.50 (ISBN 0-686-18521-8). Kazi Pubns.

--Islam & the World. 14.50 (ISBN 0-686-18625-7). Kazi Pubns.

--Only a Prophet Could Do It. pap. 1.00 (ISBN 0-686-18429-7). Kazi Pubns.

--Religion & Civilization. 4.00 (ISBN 0-686-18566-8). Kazi Pubns.

--Tales of the Prophets. pap. 2.50 (ISBN 0-686-18388-6). Kazi Pubns.

Nadvi, T. The Object of Life According to the Holy Qur'an. 1972. 3.50x (ISBN 0-87902-181-0). Orientalia.

Nadwi, Abul H. Muslims in the West: The Message & the Mission. Murad, Khurram, ed. 191p. (Orig.). 1983. pap. 6.95x (ISBN 0-86037-130-1, Pub by Islamic Found UK). New Era Pubns MI.

Nadzo, Stefan. There Is a Way. 129p. 1981. pap. 4.75 (ISBN 0-937226-00-9). Coleman Pub.

Nadzo, Stefan C. Take off Your Shoes. 120p. 1981. pap. 4.57 (ISBN 0-937226-01-7). Coleman Pub.

--Take off Your Shoes: A Guide to the Nature of Reality. LC 81-66185. 140p. (Orig.). 1981. pap. 5.95 (ISBN 0-937226-01-7). Eden's Work.

--There Is a Way: Meditations for a Seeker. LC 80-66831. (Illus.). 129p. (Orig.). 1980. pap. 5.95 (ISBN 0-937226-00-9). Eden's Work.

Naff, Thomas & Owen, Roger, eds. Studies in Eighteenth-Century Islamic History. LC 77-22012. 462p. 1977. 24.95x (ISBN 0-8093-0819-3). S Ill U Pr.

Nagarjuna. She-rab Dong-bu, or Prajnya Danda: A Metrical Translation in Tibetan of a Sanskirt Ethical Work. Campbell, W. L., ed. LC 78-70103. Repr. of 1919 ed. 22.00 (ISBN 0-404-17354-3). AMS Pr.

Nagarjuna & Gyatso, Tenzin. The Buddhism of Tibet & the Precious Garland. 212p. 1983. pap. 12.50 (ISBN 0-04-294127-X). Allen Unwin.

Nagarjuna & Pandit, Sakya. Elegant Sayings. LC 77-23433. (Tibetan Translation Ser.: Vol. 8). 1977. 10.95 (ISBN 0-913546-12-7); pap. 6.95 (ISBN 0-913546-13-5). Dharma Pub.

Nagatani, T., tr. see Bloom, Alred.

Nagel, Norman, tr. see Sasse, Herman.

Nagel, Stephan, ed. see Stoutzenberger, Joseph.

Nagel, T. Mortal Questions. LC 78-58797. 1979. 32.50 (ISBN 0-521-22360-1); pap. 10.95 (ISBN 0-521-29460-6). Cambridge U Pr.

Nageleisen, John A. Charity for the Suffering Souls. LC 82-83797. 375p. 1982. pap. 10.00 (ISBN 0-89555-200-0). TAN Bks Pubs.

Naglee, David I. From Font to Faith: John Wesley on Infant Baptism & the Nurture of Children. (American University Studies VII-Theology & Religion: Vol. 24). 272p. 1987. text ed. 26.00 (ISBN 0-8204-0375-X). P Lang Pubs.

--In Praise of More Folly. 208p. 1982. 10.00 (ISBN 0-682-49803-3, Banner). Exposition Pr FL.

Nagler, A. M. The Medieval Religious Stage: Shapes & Phantoms. LC 75-43328. (Illus.). 1976. 22.00x (ISBN 0-300-01986-6). Yale U Pr.

Nagpal, R. C. Modern Hindu Law. (Hindi.). 815p. 1984. 225.00x (Pub. by Eastern Bk India). State Mutual Bk.

--Modern Hindu Law. 992p. 1983. 360.00x (Pub. by Eastern Bk India). State Mutual Bk.

Nahon, Gerard, jt. ed. see Mechoulan, Henry.

Naiman, Charles S., ed. Proceedings of the Associations of the Associations of Orthodox Jewish Scientists, Vols. 8-9. (Illus.). 304p. (Orig.). 1987. pap. 14.95 (ISBN 0-87203-125-X). Hermon.

Naimy, Nadeem. The Lebanese Prophets of New York. 112p. 1985. text ed. 18.00x (ISBN 0-8156-6073-1, Am U Beirut). Syracuse U Pr.

Nain De Tillemont, Louis S. Le see Le Nain De Tillemont, Louis S.

Naipaul, V. S. Among the Believers: An Islamic Journey. LC 81-47503. 512p. 1981. 15.00 (ISBN 0-394-50969-2). Knopf.

Nair, P. T., ed. Bruton's Visit of Lord Jagannath 350 Years Ago: British Beginnings in Orissa. 1986. 14.00x (ISBN 0-8364-1610-4, Pub. by Minerva India). South Asia Bks.

Naismith, A. Twelve Hundred Scripture Outlines. (Source Book for Ministers). 1978. pap. 5.95 (ISBN 0-8010-6692-1). Baker Bk.

Najarian, Berge. Climbing on Top of Your Troubles. 1984. 6.50 (ISBN 0-8062-2283-2). Carlton.

Nakamura, Hajime. Gotama Buddha. LC 77-8589. 1977. 8.95x (ISBN 0-914910-05-1); pap. 6.95x (ISBN 0-914910-06-X). Buddhist Bks.

Nakamura, Hijime. Buddhism in Comparative Light. 1986. 15.00 (ISBN 81-208-0184-9, Pub. by Motilal Banarsidass). South Asia Bks.

--Indian Buddhism: A Survey with Bibliographical Notes. 440p. 1986. 28.00 (Pub. by Motilal Banarsidass). South Asia Bks.

Nakarai, Toyozo W. The Study of the Impact of Buddhism Upon Japanese Life As Revealed in the Order of Kokin-Shu. 59.95 (ISBN 0-8490-1156-6). Gordon Pr.

Nakhjavani, Bahiyyih. Four on an Island. 144p. 10.95 (ISBN 0-85398-173-6); pap. 5.95 (ISBN 0-85398-174-4). G Ronald Pub.

--Response. 144p. pap. 4.95 (ISBN 0-85398-107-8). G Ronald Pub.

--When We Grow up. 120p. 1979. 9.95 (ISBN 0-85398-085-3); pap. 4.95 (ISBN 0-85398-086-1). G Ronald Pub.

Nalanda Translation Committee, tr. see Heruka, Tsang N.

Nalanda Translation Committee, tr. see Trungpa, Chogyam.

Naman, Anne A. The Jew in the Victorian Novel: Some Relationships Between Prejudice & Art. LC 79-8634. (AMS Studies in the 19th Century: No. 1). 1980. 29.50 (ISBN 0-404-18023-X). AMS Pr.

Nanak, Guru. The Japji. Singh, Sangat, tr. from Punjabi. 128p. (Orig.). 1974. pap. 2.25 (ISBN 0-88253-317-7). Ind-US Inc.

Nanavaty, Jal J. Educational Thought, Vol. 1. 1973. pap. 10.00 (ISBN 0-89744-150-8, Pub. by Joshi & Lockhande India). Auromere.

Nanda, Jyotir M. Yoga Wisdom of the Upanishads: Kena..Mundaka..Prashna..Ishavasya. (Illus.). 1974. pap. 4.99 (ISBN 0-934664-36-6). Yoga Res Foun.

Nanda, Maya, jt. auth. see Swami, Jyotir.

Nanda-Nandana, Sri. The Secret Teachings of the Vedas: The Ancient Knowledge of the East. LC 86-51209. 320p. (Orig.). 1987. pap. 14.95 (ISBN 0-9617410-0-7). World Relief.

Nandi, R. N. Religious Institutions & Cults in the Deccan. 1973. 8.50 (ISBN 0-8426-0564-9). Orient Bk Dist.

Nandimath, S. C. A Handbook of Virasaivism. 1979. 15.00 (ISBN 0-89684-053-0, Pub. by Motilal Banarsidass India). Orient Bk Dist.

Nandy, Pritish, jt. auth. see Mirabai.

Nandy, Pritish, ed. The Lord is My Shepherd: Selections from the Psalms. (Vikas Library of Modern Morian Writing: No. 12). (Orig.). 1982. text ed. 5.95x (ISBN 0-7069-1492-9, Pub. by Vikas India). Advent NY.

Nane, Orville J. Nave's Topical Bible. 1616p. Date not set. 19.95 (ISBN 0-917006-02-X). Hendrickson MA.

Nanji, Azim. The Nizari Ismaili Tradition in the Indo-Pakistan Subcontinent. LC 78-12990. (Monographs in Islamic Religion & Theology). 1979. 30.00x (ISBN 0-88206-020-1). Caravan Bks.

Nanjio, Bunyiu, compiled by. A Short History of the Twelve Japanese Buddhist Sects. LC 78-70104. Repr. of 1886 ed. 23.00 (ISBN 0-404-17355-1). AMS Pr.

Nanjio, Bunyiu, tr. from Japanese. Short History of the Twelve Buddhist Sects. (Studies in Japanese History & Civilization). 1979. Repr. of 1886 ed. 19.75 (ISBN 0-89093-252-2). U Pubns Amer.

Napier, Alexander, ed. see Barrow, Isaac.

Napier, Arthur S., ed. History of the Holy Rood-Tree. (EETS, OS Ser.: No. 103). Repr. of 1894 ed. 12.00 (ISBN 0-527-00104-X). Kraus Repr.

Napier, B. D. On New Creation. LC 70-134553. (Rockwell Lectures). 1971. 14.95x (ISBN 0-8071-0524-4). La State U Pr.

Napier, B. Davie. Come Sweet Death. rev. ed. LC 80-27301. 64p. 1981. pap. 4.95 (ISBN 0-8298-0422-6). Pilgrim NY.

--Come Sweet Death: A Quintet from Genesis. LC 67-17793. 96p. 1975. 2 rec album 11.95 (ISBN 0-8298-0375-0). Pilgrim NY.

--Exodus. LC 59-10454. (Layman's Bible Commentary Ser: Vol. 3). 1963. write for info. (ISBN 0-8042-3003-X); pap. 4.95 (ISBN 0-8042-3063-3). John Knox.

Napier, C. K., rev. by see Natha, Prana & Chaudhuri, J. B.

Napier, Davie. Song of the Vineyard: A Guide Through the Old Testament. rev. ed. LC 78-14672. 360p. 1981. pap. 12.95 (ISBN 0-8006-1352-X, 1-1352). Fortress.

--Word of God, Word of Earth. LC 75-45312. 120p. 1976. 5.95 (ISBN 0-8298-0304-1); pap. 3.25 (ISBN 0-8298-0307-6). Pilgrim NY.

Napier, Davie, jt. auth. see Borsch, Frederick H.

Napier, Mark, ed. see Spottiswood, John.

Napoleone, Mary A. & Johanson, E. Jane. Spirits & Seasons. (Illus.). 83p. 1982. pap. 3.95 (ISBN 0-9610038-0-4). Heatherdown Pr.

Napper, Elizabeth, ed. see Fourteenth Dalai Lama His Holiness Tenzin Gyatso.

Napper, Elizabeth, ed. see Hopkins, Jeffrey.

Napper, Elizabeth, ed. see Hopkins, Jeffrey & Klein, Ann.

Napper, Elizabeth, ed. see Rinbochay, Lati.

Naqvi, Syed N. H. Ethics & Economics: An Islamic Synthesis. 176p. (Orig.). 1981. 17.25x (ISBN 0-86037-079-8, Pub by Islamic Found UK); pap. 9.95x (ISBN 0-86037-080-1). New Era Pubns MI.

Nara, I. S. Safarnama & Zafarnama. 327p. 1986. 25.00x (ISBN 0-8364-1793-3, Pub. by Minerva India). South Asia Bks.

Narada. The Bhakti Sutras of Narada. Sinha, Nandalal, tr. & intro. by. LC 73-3792. (Sacred Books of the Hindus: No. 7, Pt. 1). Repr. of 1911 ed. 17.00 (ISBN 0-404-57807-1). AMS Pr.

--Narada Bhakti Sutras: The Gospel of Divine Love. Tyagisananda, Swami, tr. (Sanskrit & Eng). pap. 4.95 (ISBN 0-87481-427-8). Vedanta Pr.

--Narada's Way of Divine Love: The Bhakti Sutras. 1st ed. Prabhavananda, Swami, tr. from Sansk. LC 75-161488. 1971. pap. 4.95 (ISBN 0-87481-508-8). Vedanta Pr.

Narang, A. S. Storm over the Sutlej: The Sikhs & Akali Politics. 1983. 24.00x (ISBN 0-8364-1079-3, Gitanjali). South Asia Bks.

Narasimha, N. S. & Babaji, Ramananda. The Way of Vaisnava Sages: A Medieval Story of South Indian Sadhus. LC 86-28251. (Sanskrit Notes of Visnu-vijay Swami). 422p. (Orig.). 1987. lib. bdg. 33.50 (ISBN 0-8191-6060-1); pap. text ed. 18.75 (ISBN 0-8191-6061-X). U Pr of Amer.

Narasimhan, Chakravarthi V., tr. The Mahabharata. LC 64-10347. 254p. (English Version Based on Selected Verses). 1973. pap. 12.00x (ISBN 0-231-08321-1). Columbia U Pr.

Narasu, P. Lakshmi. The Essence of Buddhism with an Introduction by Anagarika H. Dharmmapals. 212p. 1986. Repr. of 1907 ed. 15.00X (ISBN 0-8364-1748-8, Pub. by Manohar India). South Asia Bks.

Naravane, V. S. A Dictionary of Indian Mythology. 350p. Date not set. text ed. price not set (ISBN 0-7069-2463-0, Vikas India). Advent NY.

--Premchand: His Life & Work. 280p. 1980. text ed. 25.00x (ISBN 0-7069-1091-5, Pub. by Vikas India). Advent NY.

Narayan, B. K. Pan-Islamism. 232p. 35.00X (ISBN 0-317-52149-7, Pub. by S Chand Mutual). State Mutual Bk.

Narayan, R. K. My Dateless Diary. 1960. pap. 3.25 (ISBN 0-86578-118-4). Ind-US Inc.

--The Ramayana of R. K. Narayan: A Shortened Modern Prose Version of the Indian Epic, Suggested by the Tamil Version of Kamban. LC 79-189514. (Illus.). 192p. 1972. 13.95 (ISBN 0-670-58950-0). Viking.

--Swami & Friends. LC 80-16119. 192p. 1980. lib. bdg. 13.00x (ISBN 0-226-56829-6); pap. 6.95 (ISBN 0-226-56831-8). U of Chicago Pr.

Narayananda, Swami. The Primal Power in Man: The Kundalini Shakti Yoga. 155p. 1971. pap. 11.95 (ISBN 0-88697-027-X). Life Science.

Nardine, Arlene. In Search of the Yellow Submarine. 222p. 1985. pap. write for info. (ISBN 0-88144-065-5). Christian Pub.

Nargolkar, V. The Creed of Saint Vinoba. 320p. 1963. pap. 5.00 (ISBN 0-686-96938-3). Greenlf Bks.

Nariman, Gushtaspshah K. Literary History of Sanskrit Buddhism. LC 78-70106. Repr. of 1920 ed. 37.50 (ISBN 0-404-17356-X). AMS Pr.

Nariman, J. K. Literary History of Sanskrit Buddhism. 2nd ed. 1972. 13.95 (ISBN 0-8426-0453-7). Orient Bk Dist.

Narla, V. R. Gods, Goblins & Men. 1979. 12.00x (ISBN 0-8364-0559-5, Pub. by Minerva Associates). South Asia Bks.

Narot, Joseph R. For Whom the Rabbi Speaks. pap. 1.65 (ISBN 0-686-15800-8). Rostrum Bks.

--An Introduction to a Faith. pap. 1.00 (ISBN 0-686-15807-5). Rostrum Bks.

--Judaism Without Guilt. pap. 0.75 (ISBN 0-686-15811-3). Rostrum Bks.

--Letters to the Now Generation. pap. 1.95 (ISBN 0-686-15801-6). Rostrum Bks.

--The Lost Honesty. pap. 1.25 (ISBN 0-686-15804-0). Rostrum Bks.

--Old Wine in Old Bottles. pap. 0.75 (ISBN 0-686-15809-1). Rostrum Bks.

--A Preface to Well Being. pap. 1.00 (ISBN 0-686-15806-7). Rostrum Bks.

--A Primer for Temple Life. pap. 1.00 (ISBN 0-686-15808-3). Rostrum Bks.

--The Sermons of Joseph R. Narot. 6.00 (ISBN 0-686-15812-1). Rostrum Bks.

--What I Believe About God. pap. 0.95 (ISBN 0-686-15803-2). Rostrum Bks.

--Why I Am a Jew. pap. 0.95 (ISBN 0-686-15802-4). Rostrum Bks.

Narramore, Bruce. Parenting with Love & Limits. 312p. 1987. pap. 9.95 (ISBN 0-310-30541-1). Zondervan.

--Why Children Misbehave. 152p. 1984. pap. 5.95 (ISBN 0-310-30361-3). Zondervan.

Narramore, Bruce S. Parenting with Love & Limits. 176p. 1982. pap. 5.95 (ISBN 0-310-30351-6, 11240P). Zondervan.

Narramore, Bruce S. & Carter, John. The Integration of Psychology & Theology: An Introduction. (Rosemead Ser.). (Orig.). 1979. pap. 8.95 (ISBN 0-310-30341-9, 11190P). Zondervan.

Narramore, Clyde M. Counseling Youth. new ed. 128p. (Orig.). 1974. pap. 5.95 (ISBN 0-310-29891-1, 12229P). Zondervan.

--La Disciplina en el Hogar. Zorzoli, Ruben O., tr. from Eng. 32p. 1985. Repr. of 1982 ed. 1.50 (ISBN 0-311-46051-8). Casa Bautista.

--Psychology of Counseling. 13.95 (ISBN 0-310-29930-6, 10409). Zondervan.

Narramore, Kathy & Hill, Alice. Kindred Spirits. 144p. (Orig.). 1985. pap. 5.95 (ISBN 0-310-30531-4, 11245P). Zondervan.

Narramore, S. Bruce. Help! I'm a Parent. 1972. pap. 6.95 (ISBN 0-310-30321-4). Zondervan.

--No Condemnation: Rethinking Guilt Motivation in Counseling, Preaching & Parenting. 208p. 1984. pap. 8.95 (ISBN 0-310-30401-6, 11244P). Zondervan.

--An Ounce of Prevention: A Parent's Guide to Moral & Spiritual Growth in Children. 160p. 1973. pap. 6.95 (ISBN 0-310-30301-X, 11035P). Zondervan.

Narrell, Irena. Our City: The Jews of San Francisco. LC 80-21216. 1980. 25.00 (ISBN 0-8310-7122-2). Howell-North.

Narvaez, Jorge. Father Meroto. 160p. pap. text ed. 6.95 (ISBN 0-936123-03-6). NY Circus Pubns.

Nary, Rhoda, jt. auth. see McMakin, Jacqueline.

Nash, Arnold S., ed. Protestant Thought in the Twentieth Century: Whence & Whither? LC 78-5860. 1978. Repr. of 1951 ed. lib. bdg. 22.50x (ISBN 0-313-20484-5, NAPT). Greenwood.

Nash, Geoffrey. The Phoenix & the Ashes. 160p. 1985. pap. 6.95 (ISBN 0-85398-199-X). G Ronald Pub.

Nash, Gerald R. When Faith Meets the Impossible. (Outreach Ser.). pap. 1.25 (ISBN 0-686-78874-5). Pacific Pr Pub Assn.

--Why God Allows Trials & Disappointments. (Uplook Ser.). 31p. 1972. pap. 0.99 (ISBN 0-8163-0082-8, 23618-2). Pacific Pr Pub Assn.

--You & Your Conscience. (Outreach Ser.). 1981. pap. 1.25 (ISBN 0-8163-0428-9). Pacific Pr Pub Assn.

Nash, June. In the Eyes of the Ancestors: Belief & Behavior in a Mayan Community. (Illus.). 374p. 1985. pap. text ed. 11.95x (ISBN 0-88133-142-2). Waveland Pr.

Nash, Ron, ed. Liberation Theology. 1984. 15.95 (ISBN 0-88062-121-4). Mott Media.

Nash, Ronald. Christianity & the Hellenistic World. (CFUC Ser.). 1986. pap. 9.95 (ISBN 0-310-45210-4, 12383P). Zondervan.

--Concept of God. 1983. (cep) 5.95 (ISBN 0-310-45141-8, 12381P). Zondervan.

Nash, Ronald H. Christian Faith & Historical Understanding. 176p. 1984. pap. 5.95 (ISBN 0-310-45121-3, 12379P). Zondervan.

--Evangelicals in America: Who They Are, What They Believe. 128p. 1987. pap. 7.95 (ISBN 0-687-12177-9). Abingdon.

--The Light of the Mind: St. Augustine's Theory of Knowledge. LC 69-19765. Repr. of 1969 ed. 39.80 (ISBN 0-8357-9790-2, 2016099). Bks Demand UMI.

--Poverty & Wealth: The Christian Debate over Capitalism. LC 86-70291. 256p. (Orig.). 1986. pap. 8.95 (ISBN 0-89107-402-3, Crossway Bks). Good News.

--Social Justice & the Christian Church. 175p. 1983. 12.95 (ISBN 0-88062-008-0). Mott Media.

--The Word of God & the Mind of Man: The Crisis of Revealed Truth in Contemporary Theology. 176p. (Orig.). 1982. pap. 6.95 (ISBN 0-310-45131-0, 12380P). Zondervan.

Nash, Ronald H., ed. Liberation Theology. 1986. text ed. 15.95 (ISBN 0-8010-6745-6). Baker Bk.

--Social Justice & the Christian Church. 1986. pap. 7.95 (ISBN 0-8010-6746-4). Baker Bk.

Nash, Thomas. Pierce Penilesse, His Supplication to the Divell. Repr. of 1924 ed. lib. bdg. 22.50x (ISBN 0-8371-2919-2, NAPP). Greenwood.

Nasir, Jamal J. The Islamic Law of Personal Status. Date not set. 79.00 (ISBN 0-317-53173-5); deluxe ed. 132.00 (ISBN 0-86010-503-2). Graham & Trotman.

Nasn, S. H. Islamic Life & Thought. 232p. 1981. 35.00x (ISBN 0-317-39093-7, Pub. by Luzac & Co Ltd). State Mutual Bk.

Nasr, S. H. Muhammad: Man of Allah. 61p. 1982. 20.00x (ISBN 0-317-39130-5, Pub. by Luzac & Co Ltd). State Mutual Bk.

Nasr, Sayyed H. Sufi Essays. 1973. 34.50x (ISBN 0-87395-233-2); pap. 10.95 (ISBN 0-87395-389-4). State U NY Pr.

Nasr, Sayyed H., tr. see Tabatabai, Muhammad.

Nasr, Seyyed H. Islam & the Plight of Modern Man. LC 75-29014. (World of Islam Ser.). 1976. text ed. 26.00x (ISBN 0-582-78053-5). Longman.

--Islamic Life & Thought. LC 81-4723. 232p. 1981. 44.50 (ISBN 0-87395-490-4); pap. 14.95x (ISBN 0-87395-491-2). State U NY Pr.

--Muhammed: Man of Allah. 61p. (Orig.). 1986. pap. text ed. 9.95 (ISBN 0-7103-0154-5). Methuen Inc.

--Three Muslim Sages. LC 75-14430. 192p. 1976. pap. text ed. 10.00x (ISBN 0-88206-500-9). Caravan Bks.

--Traditional Islam in the Modern World. 320p. 1987. text ed. 39.95 (ISBN 0-7103-0177-4). Methuen Inc.

Nasr, Seyyed H., ed. Islamic Spirituality. (World Spirituality Ser.). (Illus.). 496p. 1987. 49.50x (ISBN 0-8245-0767-3). Crossroad NY.

--Knowledge & the Sacred. 228p. 1982. 17.50 (ISBN 0-8245-0095-4). Crossroad NY.

Nassau, Robert H. Fetishism in West Africa: Forty Years' Observation of Native Customs & Superstitions. LC 69-18995. (Illus.). Repr. of 1904 ed. 22.50x (ISBN 0-8371-0977-9, NAF&, Pub. by Negro U Pr). Greenwood.

Nast, Seyyed H., ed. The Essential Writings of Frithjof Schuon. (A Roots of Wisdom Bk). 512p. 1986. 34.95 (ISBN 0-916349-05-5). Amity Hous Inc.

Nast, Thomas. Thomas Nast's Christmas Drawings. (Illus.). 1978. pap. 4.50 (ISBN 0-486-23660-9). Dover.

Nast, Thomas, tr. see Dyer, Wayne W.

Nastick, Sharon. So You Think You've Got Problems: Twelve Stubborn Saints & Their Pushy Parents. LC 81-85454. (Illus.). 96p. (Orig.). 1982. pap. 3.95 (ISBN 0-87973-661-5, 661). Our Sunday Visitor.

Natale, Samuel M. Ethics & Morals in Business. LC 83-3200. 183p. 1983. text ed. 19.95 (ISBN 0-89135-036-5, Pub. by REP Bks). Religious Educ.

Natale, Samuel M., jt. auth. see Wilson, John B.

Nataraja Guru, tr. see Chaitanya Yati, Guru N.

Natarajan, B. The City of the Cosmic Dance. 193p. 1974. text ed. 15.00x (ISBN 0-86125-035-4). Apt Bks.

Nath, Lala B., tr. see Puranas, Brahmandapurana.

Nath, R. History of Decorative Art in Mughal Architecture. 1986. Repr. of 1977 ed. 16.50 (ISBN 81-208-0077-X, Pub. by Motilal Banarsidass India). Orient Bk Dist.

--Islamic Architecture & Culture in India. (Illus.). 228p. 1983. text ed. 40.00x (ISBN 0-86590-135-X). Apt Bks.

Natha, Prana & Chaudhuri, J. B. Catalogue of the Library of the India Office: Vol. 2, Oriental Languages, Pt. 1, Sanskrit Books. Rev. ed. Napier, C. K., rev. by. 3149p. 1957. Repr. of 1938 ed. 45.00 (ISBN 0-7123-0612-9, Pub. by British Lib). Longwood Pub Group.

Nathan, jt. auth. see Nachman.

Nathan, Hans. William Billings: Data & Documents. LC 75-33593. (Bibliographies in American Music: No. 2). 1976. 10.00 (ISBN 0-911772-67-7). Info Coord.

Nathan, Joan. The Children's Jewish Holiday Kitchen. LC 86-22016. (Illus.). 144p. 1987. plastic comb. 10.95 (ISBN 0-8052-0827-5). Schocken.

Nathan of Breslov. Advice. Greenbaum, Avraham, tr. from Hebrew. LC 83-70202. Tr. of Likutey Etzot. 522p. 1983. 13.00 (ISBN 0-930213-04-1). Breslov Res Inst.

Nathan, Peter E., ed. see Heillig, Roma J.

Nathan, Rabbi. Tzaddik. Greenbaum, Avraham, tr. from Hebrew. Orig. Title: Chayey Moharan. Date not set. price not set (ISBN 0-930213-17-3). Breslov Res Inst.

Nathanael Ibn Al-Fayyumi. Bustan Al-Ukul. Levine, David, tr. LC 8-4311. (American Geographical Society. Oriental Explorations & Studies: No. 6). 20.75 (ISBN 0-404-50496-5). AMS Pr.

Nathan of Breslov, jt. auth. see Nachman of Breslov.

Nathanson, Maurice, jt. auth. see Hodgson, Shadworth H.

National Association of Catholic Chaplains. Fear Not, I Am with You. 1970. pap. 0.75 (ISBN 0-685-22552-6). Alba.

National Catholic Educational Associations & National Conference of Directors of Religious Education. Hear the Word, Share the Word, Guide Your People. 48p. 1978. 4.80. Natl Cath Educ.

National Conference of Catholic Bishops. Building Economic Justice: The Bishops Pastoral Letter & Tools for Action. 112p. (Orig.). 1986. pap. 7.95 (ISBN 1-55586-122-9). US Catholic.

--The Challenge of Peace: God's Promise & Our Response. 116p. (Orig.). 1983. pap. 1.95 (ISBN 1-555868-63-0). US Catholic.

--Economic Justice for All: Pastoral Letter in Catholic Social Teaching & U. S. Economy. 192p. 1986. pap. 2.95 (ISBN 1-55586-101-6). US Catholic.

--Empowered by the Spirit: Campus Ministry Faces the Future. 56p. 1986. pap. 2.95 (ISBN 1-55586-981-5). US Catholic.

National Conference of Catholic Bishops Staff. To the Ends of the Earth: A Pastoral Statement on World Mission. 40p. (Orig.). pap. 3.95 (ISBN 1-55586-112-1). US Catholic.

--Together, a New People: Pastoral Statement on Migrants & Refugees. 40p. (Orig.). 1987. pap. 3.95 (ISBN 1-55586-147-4). US Catholic.

National Conference of Catholic Bishops, United States Catholic Conference. A Vision & Strategy: The Plan of Pastoral Action for Family Ministry. (Illus., Orig.). 1978. pap. 3.75 (ISBN 1-55586-961-0). US Catholic.

National Conference of Directors of Religious Education. That They All May Be One. 1977. 3.60 (ISBN 0-318-00800-9). Natl Cath Educ.

National Conference of Religious Vocation Directors. Ministries for the Lord: A Resource Guide & Directory of Catholic Church Vocations for Men, 1985. 128p. (Orig.). 1985. pap. 4.95 (ISBN 0-8091-2724-5). Paulist Pr.

National Conference on Religion & Race. Race: Challenge to Religion. Ahmann, Mathew, ed. LC 78-24276. 1979. Repr. of 1963 ed. lib. bdg. 22.50x (ISBN 0-313-20796-8, NCRA). Greenwood.

National Council of Churches of Christ. An Inclusive Language Lectionary: Readings for Year B. 192p. (Orig.). 1984. pap. 8.95 (ISBN 0-8298-0719-5). Pilgrim NY.

National Council of Churches Staff. Inclusive Language for Psalms. 1987. pap. 7.95. Pilgrim Pr.

--Inclusive-Language Psalms. 144p. (Orig.). 1987. pap. 7.95 (ISBN 0-8298-0747-0). Pilgrim NY.

National Council of Jewish Women. Abortion: Challenges Ahead. (Illus.). 25p. (Orig.). 1985. pap. text ed. 5.00 (ISBN 0-941840-19-0). NCJW.

--Family Life Education Program Idea Guide. (Illus.). 37p. 1985. pap. text ed. 3.00 (ISBN 0-941840-21-2). NCJW.

--Our Heritage Speaks: Applying Jewish Values to Contemporary Issues. (Module I - Care of Aging Parents). (Illus.). 30p. (Orig.). 1985. pap. 3.50 (ISBN 0-941840-23-9). NCJW.

--Self Help for Seniors. 30p. (Orig.). 1983. pap. text ed. 4.00 (ISBN 0-941840-14-X). NCJW.

National Council of Jewish Women Staff. Our Heritage Speaks: Applying Jewish Values to Contempary Issues. (Jewish Values Ser.: Choices in Action & Advocacy: Module II). 19p. (Orig.). pap. 3.50 (ISBN 0-941840-28-X). NCJW.

National Executive Committee of the MLP, USA, ed. see Marxist-Leninist Party, USA.

National Research Council. Science & Creationism: A View from the National Academy of Sciences. 28p. 1984. pap. 4.00 (ISBN 0-309-03440-X). Natl Acad Pr.

National Society of Colonial Dames of America. Church Music & Musical Life in Pennsylvania in the Eighteenth Century, 3 vols. in 4 pts. LC 79-38037. (Illus.). Repr. of 1926 ed. Set. 150.00 (ISBN 0-404-08090-1). AMS Pr.

National Study Conference of the Churches on a Just & Durable Peace 1st Ohio Wesleyan University 1942. A Basis for the Peace to Come. McConnell, Francis J., ed. 9.75 (ISBN 0-8369-7277-5, 8076). Ayer Co Pubs.

National Master Ch'ing Liang. Flower Adornment Sutra Preface. Bilingual ed. Tripitaka Master Hua, commentary by. Buddhist Text Translation Society, tr. from Chinese. (Illus.). 244p. (Orig.). 1980. pap. 7.00 (ISBN 0-917512-28-6). Buddhist Text.

--Flower Adornment Sutra Prologue: Vol. I, The First Door. Master Hua, Tripitaka, commentary by. Buddhist Text Translation Society, tr. from Chinese. (Illus.). 252p. (Orig.). 1981. pap. 10.00 (ISBN 0-917512-66-9). Buddhist Text.

--Flower Adornment Sutra Prologue: Vol. II, The Second Door, Part I. Tripitaka Master Hua, commentary by. Buddhist Text Translation Society, tr. from Chinese. (Illus.). 280p. (Orig.). 1981. pap. 10.00 (ISBN 0-917512-73-1). Buddhist Text.

--Flower Adornment Sutra Prologue: Vol. III: The Second Door, Part II. Tripitaka Master Hua, commentary by. Buddhist Text Translation Society Staff, tr. from Chinese. (Illus.). 220p. (Orig.). 1983. pap. 10.00 (ISBN 0-917512-98-7). Buddhist Text.

--Flower Adornment Sutra Prologue, Vol. IV: The Second Door, Part III. Buddhist Text Translation Society, tr. from Chinese. 170p. (Orig.). 1983. pap. 8.00 (ISBN 0-88139-009-7). Buddhist Text.

Natividad, Josephine C. My Oneness with God. 1984. 8.95 (ISBN 0-533-05995-X). Vantage.

Natoli, Charles M. Nietzsche & Pascal on Christianity. LC 83-49020. (American University Studies V (Philosophy): Vol. 3). 200p. (Orig.). 1984. pap. text ed. 24.25 (ISBN 0-8204-0071-8). P Lang Pubs.

Natu, Bal. Glimpses of the God-Man Meher, Baba, Vol. IV. LC 79-913293. (Illus.). 218p. (Orig.). 1984. pap. 7.95 (ISBN 0-913078-52-2). Sheriar Pr.

--Glimpses of the God-Man, Meher Baba: Vol. III, February 1952 - February 1953. LC 79-913293. (Illus.). 344p. (Orig.). 1982. pap. 7.95 (ISBN 0-913078-44-1). Sheriar Pr.

--Glimpses of the God-Man, Meher Baba, Vol. 2: Jan. 1949-Jan. 1952. (Illus.). 406p. 1979. pap. 7.95 (ISBN 0-913078-38-7). Sheriar Pr.

Nau, Erika S. Self-Awareness Through Huna-Hawaii's Ancient Wisdom. Grunwald, Stefan, ed. LC 80-27842. (Orig.). 1981. pap. 5.95 (ISBN 0-89865-099-2, Unilaw). Donning Co.

Naude, C. F. & Solle, Dorothee. Hope for Faith: A Conversation. 48p. (Orig.). 1986. pap. 3.95. Eerdmans.

--Hope for Faith: A Conversation. 1986. pap. 3.95 (ISBN 0-8028-0191-9). Eerdmans.

Nauert, Charles G., Jr. The Age of Renaissance & Reformation. LC 81-40034. 330p. 1982. lib. bdg. 30.25 (ISBN 0-8191-1861-3); pap. text ed. 12.75 (ISBN 0-8191-1862-1). U Pr of Amer.

Naujoks, Bob, jt. auth. see Jacobson, Dick.

Nauman, Eileen. American Book of Nutrition & Medical Astrology. Lee, Rebecca, ed. (Illus.). 304p. (Orig.). 1982. pap. 17.95 (ISBN 0-917086-28-7). A C S Pubns Inc.

Nauman, Elmo, Jr. Exorcism Through the Ages. (Illus.). 256p. 1974. pap. 3.95 (ISBN 0-8065-0450-1). Citadel Pr.

Naumani, M. What Islam Is? 10.50 (ISBN 0-686-18477-7). Kazi Pubns.

Navarro, Aurelia, ed. see Hatengdi, M. U.

Navarro, Dawn. The Los Angeles Times Book of Christmas Entertaining. Balsley, Betsy, compiled by. (Illus.). 176p. 1985. 24.95 (ISBN 0-8109-1290-2). Abrams.

Navasky, Victor. Naming Names. LC 80-15044. 468p. 1980. 15.95 (ISBN 0-670-50393-2). Viking.

Nave, Orville. Nave's Topical Bible. condensed ed. Moody Press Staff, ed. pap. 4.95 (ISBN 0-8024-0030-2). Moody.

Nave, Orville J. Nave's Study Bible. 24.95 (ISBN 0-8010-6696-4). Baker Bk.

--Nave's Topical Bible. LC 79-14111. 1979. 19.95 (ISBN 0-8407-4992-9). Nelson.

Nave, Orville J. & Coder, S. Maxwell. Nave's Topical Bible. enlarged ed. 1384p. 1975. 21.95 (ISBN 0-8024-5861-0). Moody.

Navia, Luis E. & Kelly, Eugene, eds. Ethics & the Search for Values. LC 80-82123. 530p. 1980. pap. text ed. 17.95 (ISBN 0-87975-139-8). Prometheus Bks.

Navickas. Consciousness & Reality. 1976. pap. 37.00 (ISBN 90-247-1775-2, Pub. by Martinus Nijhoff Netherlands). Kluwer Academic.

Navigators. Lessons on Christian Living. (Growing in Christ Ser.). 46p. 1982. pap. text ed. 2.45 (ISBN 0-934396-29-9). Churches Alive.

Navigators Staff. The Character of the Christian. rev. ed. (Design for Discipleship Ser.: Bk. 4). 49p. 1980. pap. text ed. 1.95 (ISBN 0-934396-19-1). Churches Alive.

--Design for Discipleship, 6 bks. rev. ed. 1980. pap. text ed. 9.35 (ISBN 0-934396-15-9). Churches Alive.

--Foundations for Faith. rev. ed. (Design for Discipleship Ser.: Bk. 5). 1980. pap. text ed. 1.95 (ISBN 0-934396-20-5). Churches Alive.

--Growing in Discipleship. rev. ed. (Design for Discipleship Ser.: Bk. 6). 1980. pap. text ed. 1.95 (ISBN 0-934396-21-3). Churches Alive.

--Lessons on Assurance. (Growing in Christ Ser.). 32p. 1982. pap. text ed. 2.45 (ISBN 0-934396-28-0). Churches Alive.

--The Navigator Bible Studies Handbook. x1979 ed. LC 79-87654. (Illus.). 132p. 1974. pap. 5.95 (ISBN 0-89109-075-4). Navpress.

--The Spirit-Filled Christian. rev. ed. (Design for Discipleship Ser.: Bk. 2). 1980. pap. text ed. cancelled (ISBN 0-934396-17-5). Churches Alive.

--Walking with Christ. rev. ed. (Design for Discipleship Ser.: Bk. 3). 1980. pap. text ed. 1.95 (ISBN 0-934396-18-3). Churches Alive.

--Your Life in Christ. rev. ed. (Design for Discipleship Ser.: Bk. 1). 1980. pap. text ed. 1.95 (ISBN 0-934396-16-7). Churches Alive.

Navigators Staff, ed. How to Lead Small Group Bible Studies. 72p. 1982. pap. 3.95 (ISBN 0-89109-124-6). NavPress.

Naville, E. The Text of the Old Testament. (British Academy, London, Schweich Lectures in Biblical Archaeology Series, 1915). pap. 19.00 (ISBN 0-8115-1257-6). Kraus Repr.

Navon, Robert, ed. see Proclus.

Navon, Yitzhak. The Six Days & the Seven Gates. 1980. 6.00 (ISBN 0-930832-57-4); pap. 4.00 (ISBN 0-686-70336-7). Herzl Pr.

Navone, John. Gospel Love: A Narrative Theology. (Good News Studies Ser.: Vol. 12). 1984. pap. 8.95 (ISBN 0-89453-437-8). M Glazier.

--Personal Witness. LC 67-13761. 1967. 4.95 (ISBN 0-685-42652-1, Pub-by Sheed). Guild Bks.

Nawsome, James D. Samuel One & Two. Hayes, James D., ed. (Knox Preaching Guide Ser.). 1983. pap. 5.95 (ISBN 0-8042-3211-3). John Knox.

Naylor, C. W. Heart Talks. 279p. 1982. pap. 2.50 (ISBN 0-686-36257-8). Faith Pub Hse.

--The Redemption of Howard Gray. 72p. pap. 0.50 (ISBN 0-686-29162-X). Faith Pub Hse.

Naylor, Harriet H. The Role of the Volunteer Director in the Care of the Terminal Patient & the Family. 17.00 (ISBN 0-405-13092-9). Ayer Co Pubs.

Naylor, Phyllis R. An Amish Family. 12.95 (ISBN 0-8488-0109-1, Pub. by Amereon Hse). Amereon Ltd.

--Getting Along with Your Friends. LC 79-22999. (Illus.). 1980. 8.75g (ISBN 0-687-14122-2). Abingdon.

--Never Born a Hero. LC 82-70950. 128p. pap. 3.95 (ISBN 0-8066-1925-2, 10-4647). Augsburg.

--A Triangle Has Four Sides: True-to-Life Stories Show How Teens Deal with Feelings & Problems. LC 83-72123. 128p. (Orig.). (YA) 1984. pap. 3.95 (ISBN 0-8066-2067-6, 10-6700). Augsburg.

Naylor, Robert E. Baptist Deacon. 1955. 7.50 (ISBN 0-8054-3501-8). Broadman.

Naylor, Thomas H. Strategic Planning Management. 156p. 1980. pap. 13.00 (ISBN 0-912841-15-X, 03). Planning Forum.

Nayyar, Adam, tr. see Jettmar, Karl.

Nayyar, Sushila. Kasturba, Wife of Gandhi. 1983. pap. 2.50x (ISBN 0-87574-000-6, 000). Pendle Hill.

Naz, R. Dictionnaire de Droit Canonique, 7 vols. (Fr.). 1965. Set. 695.00 (ISBN 0-686-57057-X, M-6423). French & Eur.

Nazigian, Arthur. Teach Them Diligently. 1986. pap. 2.95 (ISBN 0-8010-6747-2). Baker Bk.

Nazir-Ali, M. Islam: A Christian Perspective. 160p. (Orig.). 1982. pap. text ed. 9.95 cancelled (ISBN 0-85364-333-4). Attic Pr.

Nazir-Ali, Michael. Islam: A Christian Perspective. LC 84-3615. 186p. 1984. pap. 11.95 (ISBN 0-664-24527-7). Westminster.

Neagle, Larry. Underground Manual for Spiritual Survival. (Orig.). 1986. pap. 4.95 (ISBN 0-8024-9052-2). Moody.

Neal, Charles L. Parabolas del Evangelio. 144p. 1983. pap. 2.50 (ISBN 0-311-04338-0). Casa Bautista.

Neal, Daniel. The History of New-England... to the Year of Our Lord, 1700, 2 vols. LC 75-31125. Repr. of 1747 ed. Set. 64.00 (ISBN 0-404-13760-1). AMS Pr.

--History of the Puritans, 3 vols. 1979. 54.95 (ISBN 0-86524-011-6, 9401). Klock & Klock.

Neal, Emily G. Healing Ministry. 176p. 1985. pap. 7.95 (ISBN 0-8245-0688-X). Crossroad NY.

Neal, Julia. The Kentucky Shakers. LC 82-1871. (Illus.). 120p. 1982. 10.00 (ISBN 0-8131-1458-6). U Pr of Ky.

Neal, Marie A. Catholic Sisters in Transition: From the 1960's to the 1980's. (Consecrated Life Studies Ser.: Vol. 2). 1984. pap. 7.95 (ISBN 0-89453-444-0). M Glazier.

Neal, Marshall. Seven Churches. (Illus.). 108p. (Orig.). 1977. pap. 2.95 (ISBN 0-89084-062-8). Bob Jones Univ Pr.

Neale, J. E. The Age of Catherine de Medici. 272p. 1978. pap. 6.50 (ISBN 0-224-60566-6, Pub. by Jonathan Cape). Salem Hse Pubs.

Neale, John M. Essays on Liturgiology & Church History. LC 70-173070. Repr. of 1863 ed. 32.50 (ISBN 0-404-04667-3). AMS Pr.

--A History of the Holy Eastern Church, 5 vols. LC 74-144662. Repr. of 1850 ed. Set. 215.00 (ISBN 0-404-04670-3). AMS Pr.

--A History of the So-Called Jansenist Church of Holland. LC 71-133820. Repr. of 1858 ed. 26.50 (ISBN 0-404-04656-8). AMS Pr.

--Hymns of the Eastern Church. LC 77-173029. Repr. of 1862 ed. 17.95 (ISBN 0-404-04666-5). AMS Pr.

--Voices from the East: Documents of the Present State & Working of the Oriental Church. LC 75-173069. Repr. of 1859 ed. 18.00 (ISBN 0-404-04659-2). AMS Pr.

Neale, John M., ed. A Commentary on the Psalms from Primitive & Mediaeval Writers. LC 78-130990. 1976. Repr. of 1887 ed. 205.00 (ISBN 0-404-04680-0). AMS Pr.

Neale, John M., ed. see Durantis, Gulielmus.

Neale, Robert E. Loneliness, Solitude, & Companionship. LC 83-26065. 132p. (Orig.). 1984. pap. 9.95 (ISBN 0-664-24621-4). Westminster.

Neame, Alan, tr. The Hermitage Within: Spirituality of the Desert. 160p. 1982. pap. 6.95 (ISBN 0-8091-2428-9). Paulist Pr.

Neame, Alan, tr. see Camara, Dom H.

Neame, Alan, tr. see Carretto, Carlo.

Neander, Johann A. General History of the Christian Religion & Church, 9 vols. rev. ed. Torrey, Joseph, tr. from Ger. Repr. of 1858 ed. Set. lib. bdg. 495.00 (ISBN 0-404-09590-9); lib. bdg. 55.00 ea. AMS Pr.

Nearing, Helen & Nearing, Scott. Living the Good Life: How to Live Sanely & Simply in a Troubled World. LC 73-127820. (Illus.). 1971. pap. 5.25 (ISBN 0-8052-0300-1). Schocken.

Nearing, Scott, jt. auth. see Nearing, Helen.

Neary, Donal. The Calm Beneath the Storm: Reflections & Prayers for Young People. 80p. 1984. pap. 3.95 (ISBN 0-8294-0470-8). Loyola.

Nebeker, Helen. Jean Rhys: Woman in Passage. 250p. (Orig.). 1981. pap. 8.95 (ISBN 0-920792-04-9). Eden Pr.

Nebelsick, Harold. Theology & Science in Mutual Modification. 1981. text ed. 19.95x (ISBN 0-19-520273-2). Oxford U Pr.

Nebelsick, Harold P. Circles of God-Theology & Science from the Greeks to Copernicus. (Theology & Science at the Frontiers of Knowledge Ser.: Vol. 2). 312p. 1985. 24.00 (ISBN 0-7073-0448-2, Pub. by Scottish Academic Pr Scotland). Longwood Pub Group.

Nebenzahl, Kenneth. Maps of the Holy Land: Images of Terra Sancta Through Two Millennia. LC 86-675055. (Illus.). 164p. 1986. 55.00 (ISBN 0-89659-658-3). Abbeville Pr.

Nebesky-Wojkowitz, Rene De. Oracles & Demons of Tibet. 100.00 (ISBN 0-87968-463-1). Gordon Pr.

--Tibetan Religious Dances. Furer-Haimendorf, Christoph Von, ed. (Religion & Society: No. 2). 1976. text ed. 36.00x (ISBN 90-279-7621-X). Mouton.

Neblett, William. The Role of Feelings in Morals. LC 81-40105. 114p. (Orig.). 1981. lib. bdg. 24.75 (ISBN 0-8191-1752-8); pap. text ed. 9.75 (ISBN 0-8191-1753-6). U Pr of Amer.

Necheles, Ruth F. Abbe Gregoire, 1787-1831: The Odyssey of an Egalitarian. LC 75-105987. 1971. lib. bdg. 29.95 (ISBN 0-8371-3312-2, NAG/&). Greenwood.

Nederhood, Joel. Promises, Promises, Promises. LC 79-18889. (Orig.). 1979. pap. text ed. 4.50 (ISBN 0-933140-09-6). CRC Pubns.

Nee, Watchman. Aids to "Revelation". Kaung, Stephen, tr. 1983. pap. 2.75 (ISBN 0-935008-60-8). Christian Fellow Pubs.

--Assembling Together. Kaung, Stephen, tr. (Basic Lesson Ser.: Vol. 3). 1973. 4.50 (ISBN 0-935008-01-2); pap. 3.25 (ISBN 0-935008-02-0). Christian Fellow Pubs.

--A Balanced Christian Life. Koung, Stephen, tr. 1981. pap. 3.25 (ISBN 0-686-95516-1). Christian Fellow Pubs.

--The Better Covenant. Kaung, Stephen, tr. 1982. 4.75 (ISBN 0-935008-56-X); pap. 3.75 (ISBN 0-935008-55-1). Christian Fellow Pubs.

--The Body of Christ: A Reality. Kaung, Stephen, tr. 1978. pap. 2.50 (ISBN 0-935008-13-6). Christian Fellow Pubs.

--Changed into His Likeness. 1969. 4.95 (ISBN 0-87508-411-7); pap. 3.95 (ISBN 0-87508-410-9). Chr Lit.

--Christ the Sum of All Spiritual Things. Kaung, Stephen, tr. 1973. pap. 2.50 (ISBN 0-935008-14-4). Christian Fellow Pubs.

--The Church & the Work, 3 vols. Kaung, Stephen, tr. (Chinese.). 550p. 1982. 27.00 (ISBN 0-935008-57-8); pap. text ed. 15.00 (ISBN 0-935008-58-6). Christian Fellow Pubs.

--Come, Lord Jesus. Kaung, Stephen, tr. 1976. 5.50 (ISBN 0-935008-15-2); pap. 4.25 (ISBN 0-935008-16-0). Christian Fellow Pubs.

--Conhecimento Espiritual. Orig. Title: Spiritual Knowledge. (Port.). 1986. write for info. (ISBN 0-8297-0781-6). Life Pubs Intl.

--Conocimiento Espiritual. Orig. Title: Spiritual Knowledge. (Span.). 1986. write for info. (ISBN 0-8297-0782-4). Life Pubs Intl.

--Do All to the Glory of God. Kaung, Stephen, tr. (Basic Lesson Ser.: Vol. 5). 1974. 5.50 (ISBN 0-935008-03-9); pap. 4.25 (ISBN 0-935008-04-7). Christian Fellow Pubs.

--Full of Grace & Truth, Vol. II. Kaung, Stephen, tr. 1981. pap. 3.25 (ISBN 0-935008-51-9). Christian Fellow Pubs.

--Full of Grace & Truth, Vol. I. Kaung, Stephen, tr. 1980. pap. 3.25 (ISBN 0-935008-49-7). Christian Fellow Pubs.

--God's Plan & the Overcomers. Kaung, Stephen, tr. from Chinese. 1977. pap. 2.50 (ISBN 0-935008-19-5). Christian Fellow Pubs.

--God's Work. Kaung, Stephen, tr. 1974. pap. 2.25 (ISBN 0-935008-20-9). Christian Fellow Pubs.

--The Good Confession. Kaung, Stephen, tr. (Basic Lesson Ser.: Vol. 2). 1973. 4.25 (ISBN 0-935008-05-5); pap. 2.75 (ISBN 0-935008-06-3). Christian Fellow Pubs.

--Gospel Dialogue. Kaung, Stephen, tr. 1975. 5.25 (ISBN 0-935008-21-7); pap. 4.00 (ISBN 0-935008-22-5). Christian Fellow Pubs.

--Grace for Grace. Kaung, Stephen, tr. from Chinese. 1983. pap. text ed. 2.75 (ISBN 0-935008-59-4). Christian Fellow Pubs.

--Joyful Heart. 1977. pap. 3.95 (ISBN 0-87508-417-6). Chr Lit.

--The Joyful Heart. 1977. pap. 4.50 (ISBN 0-8423-1975-1). Tyndale.

--The Joyful Heart. Chen, Ruth T., tr. (Chinese.). 1985. write for info. (ISBN 0-941598-91-8); pap. write for info. (ISBN 0-941598-24-1). Living Spring Pubns.

--The King & the Kingdom of Heaven. Kaung, Stephen, tr. from Chinese. 1978. pap. 5.00 (ISBN 0-935008-24-1). Christian Fellow Pubs.

--The Latent Power of the Soul. Kaung, Stephen, tr. 1972. pap. 2.50 (ISBN 0-935008-25-X). Christian Fellow Pubs.

--Let Us Pray. Kaung, Stephen, tr. from Chinese. 1977. pap. 2.50 (ISBN 0-935008-26-8). Christian Fellow Pubs.

--La Liberacion del Espiritu. 112p. 1968. 2.95 (ISBN 0-88113-255-1). Edit Betania.

--The Life that Wins. Fader, Herbert L., ed. Kaung, Stephen, tr. from Chinese. & intro. by. 157p. (Orig.). 1986. 9.00 (ISBN 0-935008-65-9); pap. 4.00 (ISBN 0-935008-66-7). Christian Fellow Pubs.

--A Living Sacrifice. Kaung, Stephen, tr. (Basic Lesson Ser.: Vol. 1). 1972. 4.25 (ISBN 0-935008-07-1); pap. 2.75 (ISBN 0-935008-08-X). Christian Fellow Pubs.

--Love One Another. Kaung, Stephen, tr. (Basic Lesson Ser.: Vol. 6). 1975. 5.50 (ISBN 0-935008-09-8); pap. 4.25 (ISBN 0-935008-10-1). Christian Fellow Pubs.

--The Ministry of God's Word. Kaung, Stephen, tr. 1971. 5.50 (ISBN 0-935008-27-6); pap. 4.25 (ISBN 0-935008-28-4). Christian Fellow Pubs.

--The Mystery of Creation. Kaung, Stephen, tr. 1981. pap. 3.10 (ISBN 0-935008-52-7). Christian Fellow Pubs.

--Normal Christian Life. 1961-1963. pap. 4.50 (ISBN 0-87508-414-1). Chr Lit.

--The Normal Christian Life. 1977. pap. 4.95 (ISBN 0-8423-4710-0). Tyndale.

--Normal Christian Life Study Guide. Foster, ed. 1978. pap. 2.25 (ISBN 0-87508-418-4). Chr Lit.

--Not I, But Christ. Kaung, Stephen, tr. (Basic Lesson Ser.: Vol. 4). 1974. 4.50 (ISBN 0-935008-11-X); pap. 3.25 (ISBN 0-935008-12-8). Christian Fellow Pubs.

--Practical Issues of This Life. Kaung, Stephen, tr. 1975. pap. 3.25 (ISBN 0-935008-29-2). Christian Fellow Pubs.

--The Prayer Ministry of the Church. Kaung, Stephen, tr. 1973. pap. 2.75 (ISBN 0-935008-30-6). Christian Fellow Pubs.

--The Salvation of the Soul. Kaung, Stephen, tr. 1978. pap. 2.75 (ISBN 0-935008-31-4). Christian Fellow Pubs.

--Sit, Walk, Stand. 1964. pap. 2.50 (ISBN 0-87508-419-2). Chr Lit.

--Sit, Walk, Stand. 1977. pap. 2.95 (ISBN 0-8423-5893-5). Tyndale.

--Song of Songs. 1965-1967. pap. 2.95 (ISBN 0-87508-420-6). Chr Lit.

--The Spirit of Judgment. Fader, Herbert L., et al, eds. Kaung, Stephen, tr. from Chinese. 158p. (Orig.). 1984. pap. 3.25 (ISBN 0-935008-63-2). Christian Fellow Pubs.

--The Spirit of the Gospel. Fader, Herbert L., ed. Kaung, Stephen, tr. from Chinese. 100p. (Orig.). 1986. pap. 3.50 (ISBN 0-935008-67-5). Christian Fellow Pubs.

--Spiritual Authority. Kaung, Stephen, tr. 1972. 4.75 (ISBN 0-935008-34-9); pap. 3.75 (ISBN 0-935008-35-7). Christian Fellow Pubs.

--Spiritual Knowledge. Kaung, Stephen, tr. 1973. 4.00 (ISBN 0-935008-36-5); pap. 2.75 (ISBN 0-935008-37-3). Christian Fellow Pubs.

--Spiritual Man. Kaung, Stephen, tr. 1968. 12.50 (ISBN 0-935008-38-1); pap. 7.50 (ISBN 0-935008-39-X). Christian Fellow Pubs.

--Spiritual Reality or Obsession. Kaung, Stephen, tr. 1970. pap. 2.25 (ISBN 0-935008-41-1). Christian Fellow Pubs.

--Table in the Wilderness. 1969. pap. 4.95 (ISBN 0-87508-422-2). Chr Lit.

--Testimony of God. Kaung, Stephen, tr. 1979. pap. 2.75 (ISBN 0-935008-44-6). Christian Fellow Pubs.

--What Shall This Man Do. 1965. pap. 2.95 (ISBN 0-87508-427-3). Chr Lit.

--What Shall This Man Do? 1978. pap. 4.50 (ISBN 0-8423-7910-X). Tyndale.

--Whom Shall I Send? Kaung, Stephen, tr. 1979. pap. 2.25 (ISBN 0-935008-45-4). Christian Fellow Pubs.

--Ye Search the Scriptures. Kaung, Stephen, tr. 1974. 4.75 (ISBN 0-935008-46-2); pap. 3.75 (ISBN 0-935008-47-0). Christian Fellow Pubs.

Nee, Watchmans. Love Not the World. 1977. pap. 3.50 (ISBN 0-8423-3850-0). Tyndale.

Needham, David C. Birthright! Christian, Do You Know Who You Are? LC 79-90682. (Critical Concern Bks.). 293p. 1982. 10.95 (ISBN 0-930014-29-4); pap. 6.95 (ISBN 0-930014-75-8). Multnomah.

Needham, G. I., ed. Lives of Three English Saints. rev. ed. 119p. 1979. pap. text ed. 7.95x (ISBN 0-85989-076-7, Pub. by U Exeter UK). Humanities.

Needham, G. I., ed. see Aelfric.

Needham, Joseph. Moulds of Understanding: A Pattern of Natural Philosophy. LC 75-37252. 320p. 1976. 27.50 (ISBN 0-312-54950-4). St Martin.

--Time the Refreshing River: Science, Religion & Socialism & Other Essays. 292p. 1986. 39.95 (ISBN 0-85124-429-7, Pub. by Spokesman UK); pap. 12.50 (ISBN 0-85124-439-4, Pub. by Spokesman UK). Humanities.

Needham, Thomas L., ed. see Malony, H. Newton.

Needleman, Carla. The Work of Craft. 160p. 1987. pap. 8.95 (ISBN 1-85063-061-5, 30615, Ark Paperbks). Methuen Inc.

Needleman, Jacob. Lost Christianity: A Journey of Rediscovery. LC 84-48227. 224p. 1985. pap. 6.95 (ISBN 0-06-066102-X, HarpR). HarRow.

--New Religions. 276p. 1984. pap. 10.95 (ISBN 0-8245-0635-9). Crossroad NY.

Needleman, Jacob & Baker, George, eds. Understanding the New Religions. 1978. (HarpR); pap. 8.95 (ISBN 0-8164-2188-9). Har-Row.
Needleman, Jacob, et al. Religion for a New Generation. 2nd ed. Scott, Kenneth, ed. 576p. 1977. pap. text ed. write for info. (ISBN 0-02-385990-3). Macmillan.
Needleman, John, ed. The Sword of Gnosis: Metaphysics, Cosmology, Tradition, Symbolism. 448p. 1986. pap. 10.95 (ISBN 0-317-40557-8). Methuen Inc.
Neel, Peg. How to Pray According to God's Word. 72p. 1982. pap. 2.25 (ISBN 0-88144-004-3, CPS-004). Christian Pub.
Neeld, Elizabeth H., ed. see Harper, Tommie F.
Neely, Alan, tr. see Avila, Rafael.
Neely, Alan, tr. see Dussel, Enrique.
Neely, Keith. Daddy's Letter. (Color & Learn Bks.). (Orig.). pap. 2.25 (ISBN 0-8024-0502-9). Moody.
Neely, Mary, jt. auth. see Seay, Davin.
Neeson, Eoin. The First Book of Irish Myths & Legends. 128p. 1982. pap. 5.95 (ISBN 0-85342-130-7, Pub. by Mercier Pr Ireland). Irish Bks Media.
--The Second Book of Irish Myths & Legends. 128p. 1981. pap. 5.95 (ISBN 0-85342-131-5, Pub. by Mercier Pr Ireland). Irish Bks Media.
Neff, Kenneth, jt. auth. see Moore, John.
Neff, Larry M. & Weiser, Frederick S., eds. The Account Book of Conrad Weiser: Berks County, Pennsylvania, 1746-1760. LC 81-84666. (Sources & Documents of the Pennsylvania Germans Ser.: No. 6). (Illus.). 1981. 15.00 (ISBN 0-911122-43-5). Penn German Soc.
Neff, Lavonne. God's Gift Baby. (Arch Bks.: No. 14). 1977. pap. 0.99 (ISBN 0-570-06113-X, 59-1230). Concordia.
Neff, LaVonne, tr. see Ellul, Jacques.
Neff, Pauline. Tough Love: How Parents Can Deal with Drug Abuse. 160p. 1984. pap. 7.50 (ISBN 0-687-42407-0). Abingdon.
Negev, Abraham, ed. Dictionnaire Archeologique de la Bible. (Fr.). 350p. 1970. 47.50 (ISBN 0-686-57094-4, M-6117). French & Eur.
Negev, Avraham, ed. Archaeological Encyclopedia of the Holyland. LC 79-92775. (Illus.). 356p. 1980. Repr. of 1974 ed. 9.95 (ISBN 0-89961-004-8). SBS Pub.
Neggers, Gladys. Vocabulario Culto. 2nd ed. (Span.). 168p. 1977. pap. 8.75 (ISBN 84-359-0034-7, S-50023). French & Eur.
Negri, Giulio. Istoria Degli Scrittori Fiorentini. 570p. Date not set. Repr. of 1722 ed. text ed. 144.90x (ISBN 0-576-72205-7, Pub. by Gregg Intl Pubs England). Gregg Intl.
Negrin, S., ed. The Great Harmony: Teachings & Observations of the Way of the Universe. LC 77-77387. (Illus., Orig.). 1977. pap. 3.50 (ISBN 0-87810-033-4). Times Change.
Negus, Joan. Cosmic Combinations. 168p. (Orig.). 1982. pap. 7.95 (ISBN 0-917086-37-6). A C S Pubns Inc.
Nehemiah, Ezra. Daniel. Cohen, A., ed. 278p. 1951. 10.95 (ISBN 0-900689-36-6). Soncino Pr.
Neher, Andre. The Exile of the Word: From the Silence of the Bible to the Silence of Auschwitz. LC 80-12612. 224p. 1980. 17.95 (ISBN 0-8276-0176-X, 465). Jewish Pubns.
--Jewish Thought & the Scientific Revolution of the Sixteenth Century: David Gans (1541-1613) & His Times. Maisel, David, tr. (Littman Library of Jewish Civilization). (Illus.). 240p. 1986. 29.95x (ISBN 0-19-710057-0). Oxford U Pr.
Nehls, H. Michael. The Colors of Christmas. Sherer, Michael L., ed. (Orig.). 1986. pap. 3.95 (ISBN 0-89536-838-2, 6862). CSS of Ohio.
Nehmer, Nancy L. Celebrating Our Wedding. 96p. 1987. text ed. 14.95 (ISBN 0-8423-0273-5). Tyndale.
Neider, Charles, ed. see Twain, Mark.
Neie, Herbert. The Doctrine of the Atonement in the Theology of Wolfhart Panneberg. (Theologische Bibliothek Toepelmann: Vol. 36). 1978. 40.00x (ISBN 3-11-007506-7). De Gruyter.
Neighbour, Ralph. Contacto en el Espiritu. Martinez, Jose L., ed. Kratzig, Guillermo, tr. (Span.). 120p. 1983. pap. 2.50 (ISBN 0-311-09098-2). Casa Bautista.
Neighbour, Ralph W. This Gift Is Mine. LC 73-93907. 1974. 5.50 (ISBN 0-8054-5223-0). Broadman.
Neighbour, Ralph W., Jr. La Iglesia del Futuro. Martinez, Jose L., tr. from Eng. Orig. Title: Future Church. 256p. 1983. pap. 7.95 (ISBN 0-311-17024-2). Casa Bautista.
--The Seven Last Words of the Church. LC 79-51937. 1979. pap. 4.95 (ISBN 0-8054-5527-2). Broadman.
--Sigueme. 128p. 1986. Repr. of 1983 ed. reader ed. 2.75 (ISBN 0-311-13837-3); student ed. 2.65 (ISBN 0-311-13836-5). Casa Bautista.
--The Touch of the Spirit. LC 72-84243. 1977. pap. 4.25 (ISBN 0-8054-5158-7). Broadman.
Neighbour, Ralph W., Sr. The Searching Heart. 1986. pap. 5.95 (ISBN 0-937931-05-5). Global TN.
--The Shining Light. 1986. pap. 5.95 (ISBN 0-937931-03-9). Global TN.
--Thine Enemy. 1986. pap. 5.95 (ISBN 0-937931-06-3). Global TN.
--A Voice from Heaven. 1986. pap. 5.95 (ISBN 0-937931-04-7). Global TN.
Neil, Charles, jt. ed. see Wright, Charles.
Neil, William. The Acts of the Apostles. rev. ed. Black, Matthew, ed. (New Century Bible Commentary Ser.). 272p. 1981. pap. 9.95 (ISBN 0-8028-1904-4). Eerdmans.
--The Difficult Sayings of Jesus. 1977. pap. 2.95 (ISBN 0-8028-1668-1). Eerdmans.
--Harper's Bible Commentary. LC 63-7607. 544p. 1975. pap. 7.95 (ISBN 0-06-066090-2, RD 92, HarpR). Har-Row.
--Letter of Paul to the Galatians. (Cambridge Commmentary on the New English Bible, New Testament Ser.). (Orig.). 1967. pap. 6.95x (ISBN 0-521-09402-X). Cambridge U Pr.
Neil, William & Travis, Stephen. More Difficult Sayings of Jesus. 128p. (Orig.). 1982. pap. 5.95 (ISBN 0-8028-1937-0). Eerdmans.
Neil, William, tr. see Keller, Werner.
Neilan, Ruth E. American Military Movement Relating Sacred Dance. Adams, Doug, ed. & intro. by. (Orig.). 1985. pap. 3.00 (ISBN 0-941500-37-3). Sharing Co.
Neilands, David L. Studies in the Covenant of Grace. 1981. pap. 5.75 (ISBN 0-87552-365-X). Presby & Reformed.
Neill, Mary, jt. auth. see Chervin, Ronda.
Neill, Mary, et al. How Shall We Find the Father? Meditations for Mixed Voices. 160p. (Orig.). 1983. pap. 8.95 (ISBN 0-8164-2623-6, HarpR). Har-Row.
Neill, Merrily & Tangedahl, Joanne. A New Blueprint for Marriage. 256p. 1981. pap. 6.50 (ISBN 0-942494-65-2). Coleman Pub.
Neill, S. E. Lexikon Zur Weltmission. (Ger.). 48.00 (ISBN 3-7974-0054-3, M-7190). French & Eur.
Neill, Stephen. Anglicanism. 4th ed. 1977. pap. 10.95x (ISBN 0-19-520033-0). Oxford U Pr.
--Christian Faith & Other Faiths. LC 84-19123. 304p. 1984. pap. 9.95 (ISBN 0-87784-337-6). Inter-Varsity.
--History of Christian Missions. (History of the Church Ser.: Vol. 6). (Orig.). 1964. pap. 5.95 (ISBN 0-14-020628-0, Pelican). Penguin.
--A History of Christianity in India: The Beginnings to 1707. LC 82-23475. 600p. 1984. 85.00 (ISBN 0-521-24351-3). Cambridge U Pr.
--A History of Christianity in India 1707-1858. (Illus.). 592p. 1985. 79.50 (ISBN 0-521-30376-1). Cambridge U Pr.
--Interpretation of the New Testament, 1861-1961. 1964. pap. 10.95x (ISBN 0-19-283005-8). Oxford U Pr.
--Jesus Through Many Eyes: Introduction to the Theology of the New Testament. LC 75-36455. 228p. 1976. pap. 7.95 (ISBN 0-8006-1220-5, 1-1220). Fortress.
--The Pelican History of the Church: A History of the Christian Missions, Vol. 6. 512p. 1987. pap. 6.95 (ISBN 0-14-022736-9, Pelican). Penguin.
--The Supremacy of Jesus. LC 84-47740. (The Jesus Library Ser.). 216p. 1984. pap. 6.95 (ISBN 0-87784-928-5). Inter-Varsity.
Neill, Stephen, et al. When Will Ye Be Wise? Kilmister, C. A., ed. 208p. (Orig.). 1984. pap. 6.95. St Thomas.
Neilson, Francis. From UR to Nazareth: An Economic Inquiry into the Religious & Political History of Israel. 75.00 (ISBN 0-87700-010-7). Revisionist Pr.
--Teilhard de Chardin's Vision of the Future. 1979. lib. bdg. 39.50 (ISBN 0-685-96640-2). Revisionist Pr.
Neilson, N., ed. The Cartulary & Terrier of the Priory of Bilsongton, Kent. (British Academy, London, Records of the Social & Economic History of England & Wales Ser.: Vol. 7). pap. 36.00 (ISBN 0-8115-1247-9). Kraus Repr.
Neimark, Anne E. Damien, the Leper Priest. LC 80-15141. 160p. 1980. 11.25 (ISBN 0-688-22246-3); PLB 11.88 (ISBN 0-688-32246-8). Morrow.
--One Man's Valor: Leo Baeck & the Holocaust. (Jewish Biography Ser.). (Illus.). 128p. 1986. 14.95 (ISBN 0-525-67175-7, 01451-440). Lodestar Bks.
Neitz, Mary J. Charisma & Community: A Study of Religion in American Culture. 275p. 1987. 34.95 (ISBN 0-88738-130-8). Transaction Bks.
Nelkin, Dorothy. The Creation Controversy: Science or Scripture in the Schools. 256p. 1982. 16.95 (ISBN 0-393-01635-8). Norton.
--The Creation Controversy: Science or Scripture in the Schools? LC 83-45954. 242p. 1984. pap. 9.95x (ISBN 0-8070-3155-0, BP 675). Beacon Pr.
Nelkin, Dorothy & Pollak, Michael. The Atom Besieged: Extraparliamentary Dissent in France & Germany. (Illus.). 256p. 1981. 30.00x (ISBN 0-262-14034-9); pap. 8.95 (ISBN 0-262-64021-X). MIT Pr.
Nellen, Josephine F. Jesus & You. 1987. 8.95 (ISBN 0-533-07355-3). Vantage.
Nelli, Rene. Dictionnaire Des Heresies Meridionales. (Fr.). 384p. 18.50 (ISBN 0-686-56886-9, F-21110). French & Eur.
--Spiritualite de l'Heresie: le Catharisme. LC 78-63189. (Heresies of the Early Christian & Medieval Era: Second Ser.). Repr. of 1953 ed. 31.00 (ISBN 0-404-16226-6). AMS Pr.
Nelson, Alan H. The Medieval English Stage: Corpus Christi Pageants & Plays. LC 73-85247. (Patterns of Literary Criticism Ser). 288p. 1974. 21.00x (ISBN 0-226-57173-4). U of Chicago Pr.
Nelson, Barbara, ed. Christian Periodical Index. 88p. 3 yr. cumulative 45.00 (ISBN 0-318-17810-9); 10.00 ea. Assn Chr Libs.
Nelson, Byron C. After Its Kind. rev. ed. (Illus.). 1967. pap. 5.95 (ISBN 0-87123-008-9). Bethany Hse.
--Deluge Story in Stone. (Illus.). 1968. Repr. of 1931 ed. 5.95 (ISBN 0-87123-095-X, 210095). Bethany Hse.
Nelson, C. Ellis. Don't Let Your Conscience Be Your Guide. LC 77-94430. 120p. 1978. pap. 2.95 (ISBN 0-8091-2099-2). Paulist Pr.
--Where Faith Begins. pap. 8.95 (ISBN 0-8042-1471-9). John Knox.
Nelson, Carl G. The Prince of Peace. LC 79-63954. (Illus., Ltd. ed-600copies). 1979. 10.00 (ISBN 0-930954-11-4). Tidal Pr.
Nelson, Clifford, ed. see Kaasa, Harris & Rosholt, Malcolm.
Nelson, Dean, jt. auth. see Spencer, Dean.
Nelson, E. A., tr. see Von Balthasar, Hans U.
Nelson, E. Clifford, ed. Lutherans in North America. rev. ed. LC 74-26337. (Illus.). 576p. 1980. 22.50x (ISBN 0-8006-0409-1); pap. 16.95 (ISBN 0-8006-1409-7, 1-1409). Fortress.
--A Pioneer Churchman: J. W. C. Dietrichson in Wisconsin, 1844-1850. Rosholt, Malcolm & Kaasa, Harris, trs. from Norwegian. 1973. lib. bdg. 11.50 (ISBN 0-8057-5443-1, Twayne). G K Hall.
Nelson, Edward W. Music & Worship. 176p. 1985. spiral bdg. 13.50 (ISBN 0-311-72642-9). Casa Bautista.
--Que Mi Pueblo Adore. Mussiett, Salomon C., tr. from Eng. Tr. of Music & Worship. (Span.). 184p. 1986. pap. 5.00 (ISBN 0-311-17029-3). Casa Bautista.
Nelson, Ethel, jt. auth. see Kang, C. H.
Nelson, F. Burton. The Story of the People of God. (Illus.). 436p. 1971. pap. 5.50 (ISBN 0-910452-17-2). Covenant.
Nelson, Gerald E. & Lewak, Richard W. Who's the Boss? Love, Authority & Parenting. LC 85-8184. Orig. Title: The One-Minute Scolding. (Illus.). 164p. 1985. pap. 6.95 (ISBN 0-87773-342-2, 74223-0). Shambhala Pubns.
Nelson, Gertrud M. Clip-Art for Feasts & Seasons. expanded ed. (Illus.). 120p. (Orig.). 1982. pap. 10.95 (ISBN 0-916134-41-5). Pueblo Pub Co.
--To Dance with God: Family Ritual & Community Celebration. 176p. 1986. pap. 9.95 (ISBN 0-8091-2812-8). Paulist Pr.
Nelson, Harold H. Key Plans Showing Locations of Theban Temple Decorations. LC 42-21551. (Oriental Institute Pubns. Ser: No. 56). (Illus.). 1941. 30.00x (ISBN 0-226-62154-5, OIP56). U of Chicago Pr.
Nelson, Harold H. & Holscher, Uvo. Medinet Habu, Nineteen Twenty Four-Twenty Eight. LC 29-13423. (Illus.). 1929. pap. 5.00x (ISBN 0-226-62320-3, OIC5). U of Chicago Pr.
Nelson, J. Robert. Human Life: A Biblical Perspective for Bioethics. LC 83-48140. 208p. 1984. pap. 10.95 (ISBN 0-8006-1754-1, 1-1754). Fortress.
Nelson, James A. How to Enjoy Living. LC 82-70774. 160p. (Orig.). 1982. pap. 4.95 (ISBN 0-89636-087-3). Accent Bks.
Nelson, James B. Between Two Gardens: Reflections on Sexuality & Religious Experience. 160p. (Orig.). 1983. pap. 8.95 (ISBN 0-8298-0681-4). Pilgrim NY.
--Embodiment: An Approach to Sexuality & Christian Theology. LC 78-55589. 1979. pap. 11.95 (ISBN 0-8066-1701-2, 10-2071). Augsburg.
--Embodiment: An Approach to Sexuality & Christian Theology. 296p. 1978. 9.95 (ISBN 0-8298-0349-1). Pilgrim NY.
Nelson, James E. What We Know about Heaven. 80p. 1987. 2.95, paper (ISBN 0-8423-7921-5). Tyndale.
Nelson, James G. The Sublime Puritan: Milton & the Victorians. LC 74-8794. (Illus.). 209p. 1974. Repr. of 1963 ed. lib. bdg. 24.75x (ISBN 0-8371-7586-0, NESP). Greenwood.
Nelson, Jane S. Christ-Centered Crafts for Children's Classes. LC 81-8711. 1981. pap. 2.50 (ISBN 0-87227-078-5). Reg Baptist.
Nelson, Jean T., jt. auth. see Rippy, J. Fred.
Nelson, John O. The Christian Conscience & War. 47p. 1950. pap. 1.00 (ISBN 0-8361-1547-3). Herald Pr.
--Opportunities in Religious Service. (VGM Career Bks.). (Illus.). 160p. 1983. 9.95 (ISBN 0-8442-6600-0, 6600-0, Passport Bks); pap. 7.95 (ISBN 0-8442-6601-9, 6601-9). Natl Textbk.
Nelson, John W. Your God Is Alive & Well & Appearing in Popular Culture. LC 76-26092. 216p. 1976. softcover 5.95 (ISBN 0-664-24866-7). Westminster.
Nelson, Kristina. The Art of Reciting the Qur'an. (Modern Middle East Ser.: No. 11). 271p. 1986. text ed. 25.00x (ISBN 0-292-70367-8). U of Tex Pr.
Nelson, Lee & Nelson, Miriam. Concordance to the Kitab-i-Iqan. 350p. (Orig.). 1984. pap. 9.95 (ISBN 0-933770-29-4). Kalimat.
Nelson, Leonard. System of Ethics. 1956. 49.50x (ISBN 0-685-69846-7). Elliots Bks.
Nelson, Lowry. The Mormon Village: A Study in Social Origins. 59.95 (ISBN 0-8490-0673-2). Gordon Pr.
Nelson, Lynn, jt. auth. see Nelson, Virgil.
Nelson, Lynn H. & Shirk, Melanie. Liutprand of Cremona, Mission to Constantinople 968 A.D. 62p. 1972. pap. 1.00x (ISBN 0-87291-039-3). Coronado Pr.
Nelson, M. W. Los Testigos de Jehova. 130p. 1984. pap. 2.50 (ISBN 0-311-06352-7). Casa Bautista.
Nelson, Marlin L., ed. Readings in Third World Missions: A Collection of Essential Documents. LC 76-45803. 1976. pap. 6.95x (ISBN 0-87808-319-7). William Carey Lib.
Nelson, Martha. The Christian Woman in the Working World. LC 76-127198. 141p. 1975. pap. 1.50 (ISBN 0-8054-6915-X). Broadman.
--On Being a Deacon's Wife. LC 72-96150. 96p. 1973. 7.95 (ISBN 0-8054-3505-0). Broadman.
--On Being a Deacon's Wife: Study Guide. LC 72-96150. 1977. saddlewire 2.25 (ISBN 0-8054-3507-7). Broadman.
--This Call We Share. LC 76-29804. 1977. 8.50 (ISBN 0-8054-2701-5). Broadman.
Nelson, Miriam, jt. auth. see Nelson, Lee.
Nelson, P. C. The Letters of Paul: Complete Outlines & Notes on the Epistles of Paul. 144p. 1976. pap. 2.00 (ISBN 0-88243-546-9, 02-0546). Gospel Pub.
Nelson, Paul. Narrative & Morality: A Theological Inquiry. LC 86-43034. 192p. 1987. 21.50x (ISBN 0-271-00485-1). Pa St U Pr.
Nelson, Ralph C., tr. see Allard, Jean-Louis.
Nelson, Rob, jt. auth. see Powles, Cyril.
Nelson, Robert S. The Iconography of Preface & Miniature in the Byzantine Gospel Book. LC 80-15335. (College Art Association Monograph Ser.: Vol. 36). (Illus.). 180p. 1985. Repr. of 1980 ed. 30.00x (ISBN 0-271-00404-5). Pa St U Pr.
Nelson, Ruth Y. God's Song in My Heart: Daily Devotions. LC 56-11912. 432p. 1957. 8.95 (ISBN 0-8006-0254-4, 1-254). Fortress.
Nelson, Sarah. Ulster's Uncertain Defenders: Protestant Political, Paramilitary & Community Groups & the Northern Ireland Conflict. (Irish Studies). 206p. 1984. text ed. 32.00x (ISBN 0-8156-2316-X). Syracuse U Pr.
Nelson, Stanley A., compiled by. A Journey in Becoming. (Orig.). 1983. pap. 4.95 (ISBN 0-8054-6320-8). Broadman.
Nelson, Steven M. & Starkey, Frank L. Becoming One Flesh. 1979. pap. 2.95 (ISBN 0-89536-354-2, 0229). CSS of Ohio.
Nelson, Thomas. What Christians Believe about the Bible. 183p. 1985. pap. 7.95 (ISBN 0-317-43242-7). Ideals.
Nelson, Truman. God in Love: The Sexual Revolution of John Humphrey Noyes. write for info (ISBN 0-393-01636-6). Norton.
Nelson, Virgil & Nelson, Lynn. Catalog of Creative Ministries. 144p. 1983. pap. 9.95 (ISBN 0-8170-1017-3). Judson.
--Retreat Handbook. LC 75-23468. 128p. 1976. pap. 7.95 (ISBN 0-8170-0694-X). Judson.
Nelson, Welsley W. Don't Park Behind a Truck & Other Chapel Talks. 40p. 1982. pap. 2.95 (ISBN 0-910452-51-2). Covenant.
Nelson, Wesley W. Crying for My Mother: The Intimate Life of a Clergyman. 120p. 1975. pap. 4.00 (ISBN 0-910452-26-1). Covenant.
--God's Friends: Called to Believe & Belong. 1985. 15.95 (ISBN 0-910452-59-8); pastor's guide 19.95. Covenant.
--Liberation. 1974. pap. 2.95 (ISBN 0-910452-19-9). Covenant.
Nelson, William, jt. ed. see Ferguson, John.
Nelson, William S., ed. Christian Way in Race Relations. facs. ed. LC 79-134121. (Essay Index Reprint Ser). 1948. 20.00 (ISBN 0-8369-2004-X). Ayer Co Pubs.
Nelson, Wilton M. Protestantism in Central America. 96p. (Orig.). 1984. pap. 4.95 (ISBN 0-8028-0024-6). Eerdmans.
--El Protestantismo en Centro America. (Span.). 102p. (Orig.). 1982. pap. 2.50 (ISBN 0-89922-211-0). Edit Caribe.

Nelson, Wilton M., ed. Diccionario Ilustrado de la Biblia. (Span., Illus.). 735p. 1974. 29.95 (ISBN 0-89922-033-9); pap. 21.95 (ISBN 0-89922-099-1). Edit Caribe.

Nelson, Zev K. The Light Within. LC 78-56774. 1979. 8.95 (ISBN 0-88400-060-5). Shengold.

Nelson-Pallneyer, Jack. The Politics of Compassion: A Biblical Perspective on World Hunger, the Arms Race & U. S. Policy in Central America. LC 85-25809. 128p. (Orig.). 1986. pap. 8.95 (ISBN 0-88344-356-2). Orbis Bks.

Nemec, Ludvik. Antonin Cyril Stojan: Apostle of Unity. LC 83-70817. (Illus.). 256p. 1983. pap. 11.95 (ISBN 0-89944-068-1). Don Bosco Multimedia.

--Infant Jesus of Prague. (LargeType). 2.25 (ISBN 0-89942-129-6, 129/04). Catholic Bk Pub.

Nemeck, Francis K. Receptivity. 135p. 1985. 10.00 (ISBN 0-533-06057-5). Vantage.

Nemeck, Francis K. & Coombs, Marie T. Contemplation. (Ways of Prayer Ser.: Vol. 5). 151p. 1982. 8.95 (ISBN 0-89453-429-7); pap. 5.95 (ISBN 0-89453-276-6). M Glazier.

--The Way of Spiritual Direction. 1985. pap. 8.95 (ISBN 0-89453-447-5). M Glazier.

Nemeshegyi, Peter. The Meaning of Christianity. 128p. 1982. pap. 3.95 (ISBN 0-8091-2464-5). Paulist Pr.

Nemichandra, see Devendra Gani.

Nemmers, Erwin E. Twenty Centuries of Catholic Church Music. LC 78-17248. 1978. Repr. of 1949 ed. lib. bdg. 22.50x (ISBN 0-313-20542-6, NETW). Greenwood.

Nemoy, Leon, tr. Karaite Anthology: Excerpts from the Early Literature. (Judaica Ser.: No. 7). 1952. 45.00x (ISBN 0-300-00792-2). Yale U Pr.

Nennius. Nennius's "History of the Brittons". Wade-Evans, A. W., tr. Bd. with The Annals of Britons of Court Pedigree of Hywel the Good. (Church Historical Society, London, N. S.: No. 34). pap. 23.00 (ISBN 0-317-15134-7). Kraus Repr.

Nerenberg, Arnie. Love & Estrangement in the Baha'i Community. (Orig.). 1986. 9.95 (ISBN 0-933770-47-2). Kalimat.

Nerheim, Steven J., jt. auth. see Backmen, Richard J.

Neri, Helene, tr. see Muhlschlegel, Peter.

Neri, Helene M., tr. see Schaefer, Udo.

Nerney, Catherine. Called to Be Faithful: Reflections on Cycle B Readings for the Sundays of Lent. 1.95 (ISBN 0-8091-9339-6). Paulist Pr.

--Enrollment in the School of Discipleship. 1.50 (ISBN 0-8091-9331-0). Paulist Pr.

--The Experience of Lent with the Risen Christ. 1.95 (ISBN 0-8091-9308-6). Paulist Pr.

Nero, pseud. By My Laugh Its Jewish. 1982 ed. (Illus.). 110p. Date not set. 12.50x (ISBN 0-85303-197-5, Pub. by Vallentine Mitchell England); pap. 6.50x (ISBN 0-85303-198-3). Biblio Dist.

Nersoyan, H. J. Andre Gide: The Theism of an Atheist. LC 69-17717. 1969. 19.95x (ISBN 0-8156-2135-3). Syracuse U Pr.

Nersoyan, Tiran, jt. ed. see Fries, Paul R.

Nesdoly, Samuel J. Among the Soviet Evangelicals. (Orig.). 1986. pap. 6.45 (ISBN 0-85151-489-8). Banner of Truth.

Ness, Bethann Van see Van Ness, Bethann & De Clemente, Elizabeth M.

Ness Geotchius, Eugene Van see Van Ness Goetchius, Eugene.

Nester, Emery, jt. auth. see Baker, Don.

Nester, Lois M. Lady of Faith. (Illus.). 112p. 1987. 7.95 (ISBN 0-8059-3040-X). Dorrance.

Nestingen, James A. The Faith We Hold: The Living Witness of Luther & the Augsburg Confession. LC 83-70516. 96p. (Orig.). 1983. pap. 5.95 (ISBN 0-8066-2022-6, 10-2200). Augsburg.

--Martin Luther: His Life & Teachings. LC 82-71829. 80p. 1982. pap. 4.50 (ISBN 0-8006-1642-1, 1-1642). Fortress.

Nestorian Church. Liturgy & Ritual: The Liturgy of the Holy Apostles Adai & Mari. LC 79-131032. Repr. of 1893 ed. 14.50 (ISBN 0-404-03997-9). AMS Pr.

Nestorova, Tatyana. American Missionaries among the Bulgarians: 1858-1912. 160p. 1987. text ed. 20.00 (ISBN 0-88033-114-3, 218). East Eur Quarterly.

Nethery, Susan. A Mother Shares: Meditations on Parenting. 128p. 1981. 5.95 (ISBN 0-8010-6736-7). Baker Bk.

Netter, Thomas. Fasciculi Zizaniorium Magistri Johannis Wyclif Cum Tritico. Shirley, Walter W., ed. (Rolls Ser.: No. 5). Repr. of 1858 ed. 60.00 (ISBN 0-8115-1006-9). Kraus Repr.

Nettl, Paul. Mozart & Masonry. LC 78-114564. (Music Ser.). 1970. Repr. of 1957 ed. lib. bdg. 25.00 (ISBN 0-306-71922-3). Da Capo.

Nettles, Joseph E. So Beloved Cousins: The Life & Times of Solon B. Cousins, Jr. LC 82-23986. x, 178p. 1983. 12.95x (ISBN 0-86554-070-5, H53). Mercer Univ Pr.

Nettles, Tom, jt. auth. see Bush, Russ.

Nettleton, David. Chosen to Salvation: Select Thoughts on the Doctrine of Election. LC 83-11062. 1983. pap. 5.95 (ISBN 0-87227-094-7). Reg Baptist.

--Our Infallible Bible. LC 77-15540. (Illus.). 1978. pap. 1.75 (ISBN 0-87227-055-6); tchr's guide 4.50 (ISBN 0-87227-056-4). Reg Baptist.

Neubauer, A. Catalogue of the Hebrew Mss in the Jew's College, London. (Descriptive Catalogue of the Hewbrew Mss of the Montefiore Library). 274p. Repr. of 1904 ed. text ed. 74.52x (ISBN 0-576-80128-3, Pub. by Gregg Intl Pubs England). Gregg Intl.

Neuberger, Beth. Good News! (Happy Day Bks.). (Illus.). 24p. 1984. 1.59 (ISBN 0-87239-736-X, 3706). Standard Pub.

Neuberger, Julia. The Story of the Jews. (Cambridge Books for Children). (Illus.). 32p. 1987. 7.95 (ISBN 0-521-30601-9); pap. 3.95 (ISBN 0-521-31580-8). Cambridge U Pr.

Neufelder, Jerome. The Church Year in Prayer. LC 84-62162. 200p. (Orig.). 1985. pap. 7.95 (ISBN 0-87973-729-8, 729). Our Sunday Visitor.

Neufelder, Jerome N. & Coelho, Mary C., eds. Writings on Spiritual Direction by Great Christian Masters. 224p. (Orig.). 1982. pap. 11.95 (ISBN 0-8164-2420-9, HarpR). Har-Row.

Neufeldt, Ronald. Religious Studies in Alberta: A State-of-the-Art Review. (Study of Religion in Canada Ser.). 145p. 1983. pap. text ed. 10.00x (ISBN 0-317-03613-0, Pub. by Wilfrid Laurier Canada). Humanities.

Neufer, Sharon & Emswiler, Tom N. Wholeness in Worship. LC 79-2982. 192p. (Orig.). 1980. pap. 6.95 (ISBN 0-06-062247-4, RD 314, HarpR). Har-Row.

Neufer, Thomas, jt. auth. see Emswiler, Sharon.

Neugroschel, Joachim, tr. see Alt, Franz.

Neugroschel, Joachim, tr. see Ellul, Jacques.

Neugroschel, Joachim, tr. see Heschel, Abraham J.

Neugroschel, Joachim, tr. see Talec, Pierre.

Neuhaus, Richard J. Freedom for Ministry: A Critical Affirmation of the Church & Its Mission. LC 78-3352. 256p. 1984. pap. 7.95 (ISBN 0-06-066095-3, RD 505, HarpR). Har-Row.

--The Naked Public Square: Religion & Democracy in America. LC 84-6017. 288p. 1984. 16.95 (ISBN 0-8028-3588-0). Eerdmans.

--The Naked Public Square: Religion & Democracy in America. 280p. 1986. pap. 8.95 (ISBN 0-8028-0080-7). Eerdmans.

Neuhaus, Richard J., ed. Confession, Conflict, & Community. (The Encounter Ser.: Vol. 3). 128p. (Orig.). 1986. pap. 5.95 (ISBN 0-8028-0203-6). Eerdmans.

Neuhaus, Richard J. & Cromartie, Michael, eds. Confronting This World: Evangelicals, Fundamentalists, & Politics. (Orig.). 1986. text ed. 22.00 (ISBN 0-89633-107-5); pap. text ed. 14.00 (ISBN 0-89633-108-3). Ethics & Public Policy.

Neuhaus, Richard J., ed. see Billington, James, et al.

Neuhaus, Richard J., ed. see Johnson, Paul, et al.

Neuman, Abraham A. Jews in Spain: Their Social, Political & Cultural Life During the Middle Ages, 2 vols. LC 70-105964. 1970. Repr. of 1942 ed. lib. bdg. 54.50x (ISBN 0-374-96061-5, Octagon). Hippocrene Bks.

Neumann, Erich. Origins & History of Consciousness. Hull, R. F., tr. (Bollingen Ser.: Vol. 42). (Illus.). 1954. pap. 9.95 (ISBN 0-691-01761-1). Princeton U Pr.

Neumark, David. Geschichte der Judischen Philosophie des Mittelalters, 3 vols. Katz, Steven, ed. LC 79-7149. (Jewish Philosophy, Mysticism & History of Ideas Ser.). 1980. Repr. of 1928 ed. Set. lib. bdg. 120.00x (ISBN 0-405-12279-9); lib. bdg. 40.00x ea. Vol. 1 (ISBN 0-405-12280-2). Vol. 2, Pt. 1 (ISBN 0-405-12281-0). Vol. 2, Pt. 2 (ISBN 0-405-12282-9). Ayer Co Pubs.

Neuner, J. & Dupuis, J., eds. The Christian Faith. rev. ed. LC 82-22700. 740p. 1983. pap. 13.95 (ISBN 0-8189-0453-4). Alba.

Neusch, Marcel. The Sources of Modern Atheism: One Hundred Years of Debate over God. LC 82-60596. 1983. pap. 9.95 (ISBN 0-8091-2488-2). Paulist Pr.

Neuser, Jacob. Reading & Believing. (Brown Judaic Studies). 138p. 1986. 25.50 (ISBN 0-89130-976-4, 14-01-13); pap. 20.50 (ISBN 0-89130-977-2). Scholars Pr GA.

--Sifre to Numbers, Part I. (Brown Judaic Studies). 1986. text ed. 27.95 (ISBN 1-55540-008-6, 14-01-18); pap. 22.95 (ISBN 1-55540-009-4). Scholars Pr GA.

--Sifre to Numbers, Part II. (Brown Judaic Studies). 1986. text ed. 24.95 (ISBN 1-55540-010-8, 14-01-19); pap. 19.95 (ISBN 1-55540-011-6). Scholars Pr GA.

Neusner, J. The Tosefta Translated from the Hebrew: The Order of Purities, Pt. 6. 45.00x (ISBN 0-87068-430-2). Ktav.

Neusner, J., et al, eds. see Vermes, Pamela.

Neusner, Jacob. The Academic Study of Judaism: Essays & Reflections. LC 75-5782. (Brown Judaic Studies). pap. 16.50 (14-00-35). Scholars Pr GA.

--The Academic Study of Judaism: Essays & Reflections I. (Third Ser.). 20.00x (ISBN 0-87068-712-3). Ktav.

--American Judaism: Adventure in Modernity. pap. 9.95x (ISBN 0-87068-681-X). Ktav.

--Ancient Israel after Catastrophe: The Religious World View of the Mishnah. LC 82-15972. 82p. 1983. pap. 8.95x (ISBN 0-8139-0980-5). U Pr of Va.

--Ancient Judaism & Modern Category Formation: "Judaism," "Midrash," "Messianism," & Canon in the Past Quarter-Century. LC 85-30416. (Studies in Judaism Ser.). 138p. (Orig.). 1986. lib. bdg. 22.50 (ISBN 0-8191-5395-8, Pub. by Studies in Judaism); pap. text ed. 9.75 (ISBN 0-8191-5396-6). U Pr of Amer.

--Canon & Connection: Intertextuality in Judaism. (Studies in Judaism). 316p. (Orig.). 1987. lib. bdg. 27.50 (ISBN 0-8191-5796-1, Pub. by Studies in Judaism); pap. text ed. 15.75 (ISBN 0-8191-5797-X). U Pr of Amer.

--Comparative Midrash: The Plan & Program of Genesis Rabbah & Leviticus Rabbah. (Brown Judaic Studies). 1986. 27.95 (ISBN 0-89130-958-6, 14-01-11); pap. 22.95 (ISBN 0-89130-959-4). Scholars Pr GA.

--The Death & Birth of Judaism: The Impact of Christianity, Secularism & the Holocaust on Jewish Faith. LC 86-47733. 352p. 1987. 21.95 (ISBN 0-465-01577-8). Basic.

--The Enchantments of Judaism: Rites of Transformation from Birth Through Death. LC 87-47507. 192p. 1987. 15.95 (ISBN 0-465-01964-1). Basic.

--First-Century Judaism in Crisis: Yohanan ben Zakkai & the Renaissance of Torah. X ed. 1982. 14.95x (ISBN 0-87068-728-X). Ktav.

--Form-Analysis & Exegesis: A Fresh Approach to the Interpretation of Mishnah. 224p. 1981. 22.50 (ISBN 0-8166-0984-5); pap. 9.95x (ISBN 0-8166-0985-3). U of Minn Pr.

--Formative Judaism. LC 82-16746. (Brown Judaic Studies). 182p. 1982. pap. 13.50 (ISBN 0-89130-594-7, 14 00 37). Scholars Pr GA.

--Formative Judaism - Religious Historical & Literary Studies: Fourth Series - Problems of Classification & Composition. (Brown Judaic Studies: No. 76). 222p. 1984. 24.95 (ISBN 0-89130-782-6, 14 00 76); pap. 16.95 (ISBN 0-89130-783-4). Scholars Pr GA.

--Formative Judaism II. LC 82-25072. (Brown Judiac Studies). 198p. 1983. pap. 13.50 (ISBN 0-89130-614-5, 14 00 41). Scholars Pr GA.

--Formative Judaism: Religious, Historical, & Literary Studies. (Brown Judaic Studies). (Fifth Series Revisioning the Written Records of a Nascent Religion). 1985. 29.95 (ISBN 0-89130-850-4, 14-00-91); pap. 21.95 (ISBN 0-89130-851-2). Scholars Pr Ga.

--Formative Judaism: Religious, Historical & Literary Studies-Third Series. LC 83-8662. (Brown Judaic Studies). 212p. 1983. pap. 15.00 (ISBN 0-89130-633-1, 14 00 46). Scholars Pr GA.

--From Mishnah to Scripture: The Problem of the Unattributed Saying. LC 84-10527. (Brown Judaic Studies). 135p. 1984. 20.95 (ISBN 0-89130-759-1, 14 00 67); pap. 13.95 (ISBN 0-89130-749-4). Scholars Pr GA.

--From Politics to Piety: The Emergence of Pharisaic Judaism. pap. 9.95 (ISBN 0-87068-677-1). Ktav.

--Genesis & Judaism: The Perspective of Genesis Rabbah, an Analytical Anthology. 1985. 28.95 (ISBN 0-89130-940-3, 14-01-08); pap. 22.95 (ISBN 0-89130-941-1). Scholars Pr GA.

--Genesis Rabbah: The Judaic Commentary on the Book of Genesis, Vol. II. 1985. 34.95 (ISBN 0-89130-933-0, 14-01-05); pap. 29.55 (ISBN 0-89130-934-9). Scholars Pr GA.

--Genesis Rabbah: The Judaic Commentary to the Book of Genesis, Vol. III. 1985. 33.95 (ISBN 0-89130-935-7, 14-01-06); pap. 28.55 (ISBN 0-89130-936-5). Scholars Pr GA.

--Genesis Rabbah: The Judaic Commentary to the Book of Genesis, Vol. 1. 1985. 35.75 (ISBN 0-89130-931-4, 14-01-04); pap. 26.75 (ISBN 0-89130-932-2). Scholars Pr GA.

--History & Torah: Essays on Jewish Learning. 128p. 1965. text ed. 8.50x (ISBN 0-686-37017-1, Pub. by Vallentine Michell England). Biblio Dist.

--A History of the Jews in Babylonia: The Parthian Period. LC 84-5363. (Brown Judaic Studies). 292p. pap. 21.00 (ISBN 0-89130-738-9, 14 00 62). Scholars Pr GA.

--In Search of Talmudic Biography: The Problem of the Attributed Saying. LC 84-10526. (Brown Judaic Studies). 148p. 1984. 19.95 (ISBN 0-89130-752-4, 14 00 70); pap. 14.95 (ISBN 0-89130-758-3). Scholars Pr GA.

--In the Margins of the Yerushalmi: Glosses on the English Translation. LC 83-20113. (Brown Judaic Studies). 160p. 1983. pap. 14.00 (ISBN 0-89130-663-3, 14 00 55). Scholars Pr GA.

--The Integrity of Leviticus Rabbah: The Problem of the Autonomy of a Rabbinic Document. (Brown Judaic Studies). 1985. 25.95 (ISBN 0-89130-852-0, 14-00-93); pap. 21.50 (ISBN 0-89130-853-9). Scholars Pr Ga.

--Invitation to the Talmud. Rev. ed. LC 83-48422. 320p. 1984. 19.45 (ISBN 0-06-066099-6, HarpR). Har-Row.

--Israel & Iran in Talmudic Times: A Political History. (Illus.). 266p. (Orig.). 1987. lib. bdg. 27.50 (ISBN 0-8191-5729-5, Pub. by Studies in Judaism); pap. text ed. 14.75 (ISBN 0-8191-5730-9). U Pr of Amer.

--Israel's Politics in Sasanian Iran: Jewish Self-Government in Talmudic Times. (Studies in Judaism). (Illus.). 202p. (Orig.). 1987. lib. bdg. 24.75 (ISBN 0-8191-5725-2, Pub. by Studies in Judaism); pap. text ed. 12.25 (ISBN 0-8191-5726-0). U Pr of Amer.

--The Jewish War Against the Jews: Reflections on Golah, Shoah, & Torah. LC 84-9657. 157p. 1984. 12.95 (ISBN 0-88125-050-3). Ktav.

--Judaism & Scripture: The Evidence of Leviticus Rabbah. LC 85-20497. (CSHJ Ser.). 664p. 1986. 50.00x (ISBN 0-226-57614-0). U of Chicago Pr.

--Judaism, Christianity & Zoroastrianism in Talmudic Babylonia. (Studies in Judaism). 240p. (Orig.). 1987. lib. bdg. 26.50 (ISBN 0-8191-5727-9, Pub. by Studies in Judaism); pap. text ed. 13.50 (ISBN 0-8191-5728-7). U Pr of Amer.

--Judaism in Society: The Evidence of the Yerushalmi, Toward the Natural History of a Religion. LC 83-4916. (Chicago Studies in the History of Judaism). 272p. 1984. lib. bdg. 25.00x (ISBN 0-226-57616-7). U of Chicago Pr.

--Judaism in the American Humanities. LC 81-1798. (Brown Judaic Studies). 1981. pap. text ed. 20.00 (ISBN 0-89130-480-0, 14-00-28). Scholars Pr GA.

--Judaism in the American Humanities: Second Series. (Brown Judaic Ser.). 136p. 1983. pap. 13.50 (ISBN 0-89130-618-8, 14 00 42). Scholars Pr GA.

--Judaism in the Beginning of Christianity. LC 83-48000. 112p. 1984. pap. 5.95 (ISBN 0-8006-1750-9, 1-1750). Fortress.

--Judaism in the Matrix of Christianity. LC 85-45492. 160p. 1986. pap. 12.95 (ISBN 0-8006-1897-1, 1-1897). Fortress.

--Judaism: The Classical Statement, the Evidence of the Bavli. LC 85-28875. (CSHJ Ser.). 288p. 1986. 37.00 (ISBN 0-226-57620-5). U of Chicago Pr.

--Judaism: The Evidence of the Mishnah. LC 80-26080. xx, 420p. 1981. 25.00x (ISBN 0-226-57617-5); pap. 15.95 (ISBN 0-226-57619-1). U of Chicago Pr.

--Learn Mishnah. LC 78-5482. (Illus.). 1978. pap. 4.95x (ISBN 0-87441-310-9). Behrman.

--Learn Talmud. (Illus.). 1979. pap. 4.95x (ISBN 0-87441-292-7). Behrman.

--Major Trends in Formative Judaism: First Series. LC 83-20176. (Brown Judaic Studies). 126p. 1983. pap. 14.25 (ISBN 0-89130-668-4, 14 00 60). Scholars Pr GA.

--Major Trends in Formative Judaism: Second Series: Texts, Contents, & Contexts. LC 83-20176. (Brown Judaic Studies). 160p. 1984. pap. text ed. 15.00 (ISBN 0-89130-727-3, 14 00 61). Scholars Pr GA.

--Major Trends in Formative Judaism: Third Series: The Three Stages in the Formation of Judaism. (Brown Judaic St00553869x). 1985. 22.95 (ISBN 0-89130-898-9, 14-00-99); pap. 18.25 (ISBN 0-89130-899-7). Scholars Pr GA.

--The Memorized Torah: The Mnemonic System of the Mishnah. (Brown Judaic Studies). 1985. 22.95 (ISBN 0-89130-866-0, 14-00-96); pap. 17.95 (ISBN 0-89130-867-9). Scholars Pr GA.

--Messiah in Context: Israel's History & Destiny in Formative Judaism. LC 83-20542. (Foundations of Judaism Ser.). 304p. 1984. 26.95 (ISBN 0-8006-0716-3, 1-716). Fortress.

--Method & Meaning in Ancient Judaism. LC 79-9881. (Brown Judaic Ser.: No. 10). 1979. 18.00 (ISBN 0-89130-281-6, 140010); pap. 13.50 (ISBN 0-89130-300-6). Scholars Pr GA.

--Method & Meaning in Ancient Judaism II. LC 80-21781. (Brown Judaic Studies). 1981. pap. 27.50 (ISBN 0-89130-416-9, 140015). Scholars Pr GA.

--Method & Meaning in Ancient Judiasm III. LC 80-19449. (Brown Judaic Studies). 1981. pap. 27.50 (ISBN 0-89130-418-5, 14-00-16). Scholars Pr GA.

--Midrash in Context. LC 83-5705. 240p. 1983. 23.95 (ISBN 0-8006-0708-2, 1-708). Fortress.

--Mitzvah: Basic Jewish Ideas. (Ser.). (Orig.). 1981. pap. 4.95 (ISBN 0-940646-25-0). Rossel Bks.

--The Oral Torah: The Sacred Books of Judaism. LC 85-42788. 256p. 1986. 19.45 (ISBN 0-06-066103-8, HarpR). Har-Row.

--The Peripatetic Saying: The Problem of the Thrice-Told Tale in the Canon of Talmudic Literature. (Brown Judaic Studies: No. 89). 208p. 1985. 18.95 (ISBN 0-89130-830-X, 14 00 89); pap. 15.95 (ISBN 0-89130-831-8). Scholars Pr GA.

--The Pharisees: Rabbinic Perspectives. LC 85-5783. (Studies in Ancient Judaism). 300p. (Orig.). 1985. pap. text ed. 19.95x (ISBN 0-88125-067-8). Ktav.

--The Public Side of Learning: The Political Consequences of Scholorship in the Context of Judaism. (Studies in Religion). 1985. 17.95 (ISBN 0-89130-860-1); pap. 11.95 (ISBN 0-89130-861-X, 01-00-40). Scholars Pr GA.

--Religious Study of Judaism: Context, Text, Circumstance, Vol. 3. (Studies in Judaism). 234p. (Orig.). 1987. lib. bdg. 25.50 (ISBN 0-8191-6047-4, Pub. by Studies in Judaism); pap. 13.75 (ISBN 0-8191-6048-2, Pub. by Studies in Judaism). U Pr of Amer.

--The Religious Study of Judaism: Description, Analysis & Interpretation. LC 85-30411. (Studies in Judaism Ser.: Vol. 1). 188p. (Orig.). 1986. lib. bdg. 22.50 (ISBN 0-8191-5393-1, Pub. by Studies in Judaism); pap. text ed. 9.75 (ISBN 0-8191-5394-X). U Pr of Amer.

--The Religious Study of Judaism: Description, Analysis, Interpretation-The Centrality of Context. LC 85-30411. (Studies in Judaism: Vol. 2). 230p. (Orig.). 1986. lib. bdg. 24.50 (ISBN 0-8191-5450-4, Pub. by Studies in Judaism); pap. text ed. 12.75 (ISBN 0-8191-5451-2). U Pr of Amer.

--Self-Fulfilling Prophecy: Exile & Return As the History of Judaism. LC 86-47756. 320p. 1987. 25.00 (ISBN 0-8070-3606-4). Beacon Pr.

--Stranger at Home: "The Holocaust," Zionism, & American Judaism. LC 80-19455. x, 214p. 1985. pap. 8.95 (ISBN 0-226-57629-9). U of Chicago Pr.

--The Study of Ancient Judaism, 2 vols. 1982. Vol. I. 37.50x ea. (ISBN 0-87068-892-8). Vol. II (ISBN 0-87068-893-6). Ktav.

--There We Sat Down: Talmudic Judaism in the Making. pap. 9.95x (ISBN 0-87068-676-3). Ktav.

--Torah from Our Sages: Pirke Avot. 214p. 1986. 18.95 (ISBN 0-940646-39-0); pap. 9.95. Rossel Bks.

--Torah: From Scroll to Symbol in Formative Judaism. LC 84-45190. (Foundations of Judaism Trilogy Ser.). 208p. 1985. 24.95 (1-734). Fortress.

--Tosefta: Structure & Sources. (Brown University Ser.). 1986. 39.95 (ISBN 1-55540-049-3, 14-01-12). Scholars Pr GA.

--The Tosefta Translated from the Hebrew IV. Neziqin: The Order of Damages. 1981. 45.00x (ISBN 0-87068-692-5). Ktav.

--The Tosefta Translated from the Hebrew I. Zeraim: The Order of Seeds. 1986. 45.00x. Ktav.

--The Tosefta, Translated from the Hebrew: Pt. II. Moed. The Order of Appointed Times. 45.00x (ISBN 0-87068-691-7). Ktav.

--The Tosefta, Translated from the Hebrew: Pt. III Nashim. The Order of Women. 45.00x (ISBN 0-87068-684-4). Ktav.

--The Tosefta Translated from the Hebrew V. Qodoshim: The Order of Holy Things. 1980. 45.00x (ISBN 0-87068-340-3). Ktav.

--Tzedakah: Can Jewish Philanthropy Buy Jewish Survival? Altshuler, David, ed. (Basic Jewish Ideas Ser.). 160p. 1982. pap. 7.95 (ISBN 0-940646-07-2). Rossel Bks.

--Understanding American Judaism: Toward the Description of a Modern Religion, 2 vols. Incl. Vol. 1. The Synagogue & the Rabbi (ISBN 0-87068-279-2); Vol. 2. Reform, Orthodoxy, Conservatism, & Reconstructionism (ISBN 0-87068-280-6). pap. 11.95 ea. Ktav.

--Understanding Jewish Theology. 1973. pap. 11.95x (ISBN 0-87068-215-6). Ktav.

--Understanding Jewish Theology: Classsical Issues & Modern Perspective. 280p. pap. 9.95 (ISBN 0-686-95185-9). ADL.

--Understanding Rabbinic Judaism: From Talmudic to Modern Times. 1974. pap. 11.95x (ISBN 0-685-56200-X). Ktav.

--Understanding Seeking Faith: Essays on the Case of Judaism Vol. 1: Dabates on Method Reports of Results. (Brown University Ser.). 158p. 1986. 25.95 (ISBN 1-55540-053-1, 14-01-16). Scholars Pr GA.

--Vanquished Nation, Broken Spirit: The Virtues of the Heart in Formative Judaism. 208p. Date not set. price not set (ISBN 0-521-32832-2); pap. price not set (ISBN 0-521-33801-8). Cambridge U Pr.

--The Way of Torah: An Introduction to Judaism. 3rd ed. 164p. 1979. pap. text ed. write for info. (ISBN 0-87872-217-3). Wadsworth Pub.

--The Way of Torah: An Introduction to Judaism. 4th ed. Fullerton, Sheryl, ed. 192p. (Orig.). 1987. price not set. Wadsworth Pub.

Neusner, Jacob, jt. auth. see Silverman, Morris.

Neusner, Jacob, ed. Ancient Judaism: Debates & Disputes. LC 84-5532. (Brown Judaic Studies). 292p. 31.50 (ISBN 0-89130-755-9); pap. 20.95 (ISBN 0-89130-746-X, 14 00 64). Scholars Pr GA.

--Contemporary Judaic Fellowship in Theory & Practice. 1972. 20.00x (ISBN 0-87068-187-7). Ktav.

--Our Sages, God & Israel: An Anthology of the Jerusalem Talmud. LC 84-23793. 179p. 1985. 19.95 (ISBN 0-940646-18-8). Rossel Bks.

--Take Judaism, for Example: Studies Toward the Comparison of Religion. LC 82-16039. 1983. 22.50x (ISBN 0-226-57618-3). U of Chicago Pr.

--The Talmud of the Land of Israel: A Preliminary Translation & Explanation- Vol. 25, Gittin. (Chicago Studies in the History of Judaism). 270p. 1985. 33.00 (ISBN 0-226-57684-1). U of Chicago Pr.

--The Talmud of the Land of Israel: A Preliminary Translation & Explanation- Vol. 24, Nazir. (Chicago Studies in the History of Judaism). 268p. 1985. 33.00 (ISBN 0-226-57683-3). U of Chicago Pr.

Neusner, Jacob, ed. & tr. The Talmud of the Land of Israel: A Preliminary Translation & Explanation- Vol. 23, Nedarim. (Chicago Studies in the History of Judaism). 248p. 1985. 31.00 (ISBN 0-226-57682-5). U of Chicago Pr.

--The Talmud of the Land of Israel: A Preliminary Translation & Explanation: Hagigah & Moed Qatan, Vol. 20. LC 85-29037. (Chicago Studies in the History of Judaism). 242p. 1986. 35.00x (ISBN 0-226-57679-5). U of Chicago Pr.

Neusner, Jacob, ed. The Talmud of the Land of Israel: A Preliminary Translation & Explanation, Vol. 22: Ketubot. (Chicago Studies in the History of Judaism). 384p. 1985. lib. bdg. 49.00x (ISBN 0-226-57681-7). U of Chicago Pr.

Neusner, Jacob, ed. & tr. The Talmud of the Land of Israel: A Prelimninary Translation & Explanation-Vol. 26, Qiddushin. 1984. 25.00 (ISBN 0-226-57686-8). U of Chicago Pr.

--The Talmud of the Land of Israel: A Preliminary Translation & Explanation-Vol. 27, Sotah. 1984. 25.00 (ISBN 0-226-57687-6). U of Chicago Pr.

--The Talmud of the Land of Israel: A Preliminary Translation & Explanation-Vol. 28, Baba Qamma. 1984. 25.00 (ISBN 0-226-57688-4). U of Chicago Pr.

--The Talmud of the Land of Israel: A Preliminary Translation & Explanation-Vol. 29, Baba Mesia. 1984. 25.00 (ISBN 0-226-57689-2). U of Chicago Pr.

--The Talmud of the Land of Israel: A Preliminary Translation & Explanation-Vol. 30, Baba Batra. 1984. 25.00 (ISBN 0-226-57690-6). U of Chicago Pr.

--The Talmud of the Land of Israel: A Preliminary Translation & Explanation-Vol. 31, Sanhedrin & Makkot. 1984. 45.00 (ISBN 0-226-57691-4). U of Chicago Pr.

--The Talmud of the Land of Israel: A Preliminary Translation & Explanation-Vol. 33, Abodah Zarah. 1982. 27.00 (ISBN 0-226-57693-0). U of Chicago Pr.

--The Talmud of the Land of Israel: A Preliminary Translation & Explanation-Vol. 34, Horayot & Niddah. 1982. 29.00 (ISBN 0-226-57694-9). U of Chicago Pr.

--The Talmud of the Land of Israel: A Preliminary Translation & Explanation-Vol. 35, Introduction & Taxonomy. 1984. 19.00 (ISBN 0-226-57695-7). U of Chicago Pr.

Neusner, Jacob, ed. The Talmud of the Land of Israel: A Preliminary Translation & Explanation: Vol. 19, Megillah. LC 86-25284. (Chicago Studies in the History of Judaism). 200p. 1987. text ed. 27.50 (ISBN 0-226-57678-7). U of Chicago Pr.

Neusner, Jacob, ed. & tr. The Talmud of the Land of Israel: A Preliminary Translation & Explanation-Yebamot, Vol. 21. LC 86-11406. (Chicago Studies in the History of Judaism). 514p. 1987. text ed. 58.00x (ISBN 0-226-57680-9). U of Chicago Pr.

Neusner, Jacob & Frerichs, Ernest S., eds. Goodenough on the History of Religion & on Judaism. (Brown Judaic Studies). 168p. 1987. pap. 29.95 (ISBN 1-55540-062-0, 14-01-21). Scholars Pr GA.

--To See Ourselves As Others See Us: Christians Jews, "Others" in Late Antiquity. (Scholars Press Studies in the Humanities). (Orig.). 1985. 38.95 (ISBN 0-89130-819-9, 00-01-09); pap. 25.95 (ISBN 0-89130-820-2). Scholars Pr GA.

Neusner, Jacob, ed. see Bokser, Baruch M.

Neusner, Jacob, ed. see Jaffee, Martin.

Neusner, Jacob, ed. see Mandelbaum, Irving J.

Neusner, Jacob, ed. see Novak, David.

Neusner, Jacob, jt. ed. see Vermes, Geza.

Neusner, Jacob, tr. The Fathers According to Rabbi Nathan. (Brown Judaic Studies). 274p. 1986. 41.95 (ISBN 1-55540-051-5, 14-01-14). Scholars Pr GA.

--The Talmud of Babylonia: An American Translation XXIII: Tractate Sanhedrin-Chap. 9-11. (Brown Judiac Studies). 1985. 29.95 (ISBN 0-89130-803-2, 14-0087); pap. 23.00 (ISBN 0-89130-804-0). Scholars Pr GA.

Neusner, Jacob & Brooks, Roger, trs. Sifra: The Rabbinic Commentary on Leviticus. (Brown Judaic Studies). 1985. 22.95 (ISBN 0-89130-913-6, 14-01-02); pap. 18.25 (ISBN 0-89130-914-4). Scholars Pr Ga.

Neusner, Jacob, et al, eds. Judaic Perspectives on Ancient Israel. LC 86-45908. 356p. 1987. 34.95 (ISBN 0-8006-0832-1, 1-832). Fortress.

Neuss, Paula, ed. Aspects of Early English Drama. LC 83-21331. (Illus.). 176p. 1985. Repr. of 1983 ed. 42.50x (ISBN 0-389-20428-5, 07314). B&N Imports.

Nevaskar, Balwant S. Capitalists Without Capitalism: The Jains of India & the Quakers of the West. LC 72-98709. (Contributions in Sociology: No. 6). 1971. lib. bdg. 29.95 (ISBN 0-8371-3297-5, NCA/). Greenwood.

Neve, Felix. An Essay on the Myth of the Rbhus. Davanc, G. V., tr. from Fr. 370p. 1985. 42.50 (ISBN 81-202-0150-7, Pub. by Ajanta). South Asia Bks.

Neville. The Law & the Promise. 156p. 1984. pap. 5.50 (ISBN 0-87516-532-X). De Vorss.

--Your Faith Is Your Fortune. pap. 5.50 (ISBN 0-87516-078-6). De Vorss.

Neville, Gwen K. Kinship & Pilgrimage: Rituals of Reunion in American Protestant Culture. 1987. 18.95. Oxford U Pr.

Neville, Gwen K. & Westerhoff, John H., III. Learning Through Liturgy. 189p. 1983. pap. 6.95 (ISBN 0-8164-2423-3, HarpR). Har-Row.

Neville, Joyce. How to Share Your Faith Without Being Offensive. 160p. (Orig.). 1983. pap. 6.95 (ISBN 0-8164-2228-1, HarpR). Har-Row.

Neville, Robert C. Creativity & God: A Challenge to Process Theology. 192p. 1980. 12.95 (ISBN 0-8164-0120-9, HarpR). Har-Row.

--God the Creator: On the Transcendence & Presence of God. LC 68-13128. (Illus.). 1968. 12.50x (ISBN 0-226-57641-8). U of Chicago Pr.

--Soldier, Sage, Saint. LC 77-75798. 1978. 20.00 (ISBN 0-8232-1035-9); pap. 8.00 (ISBN 0-8232-1036-7). Fordham.

--The Tao & the Daimon: Segments of a Religious Inquiry. 304p. 1982. 44.50x (ISBN 0-87395-661-3); pap. 14.95x (ISBN 0-87395-662-1). State U NY Pr.

Nevin, John W. The Anxious Bench: Chambersburg, PA 1844. Kuklick, Bruce, ed. Bd. with The Mystical Presence (Philadelphia, PA 1846) 56p. (American Religious Thought of the 18th & 19th Centuries Ser.). 312p. 1987. lib. bdg. 45.00 (ISBN 0-8240-6970-6). Garland Pub.

Nevins, Albert J. Builders of Catholic America. LC 85-72363. 250p. (Orig.). 1985. pap. 7.95 (ISBN 0-87973-582-1, 582). Our Sunday Visitor.

--Called to Serve: A Guidebook for Altar Servers. LC 81-82546. 48p. 1981. pap. 13.95 pkg. of six (ISBN 0-87973-663-1, 663). Our Sunday Visitor.

--The Deuterocanonical Books (Paraphrase) 1976. pap. 1.25 (ISBN 0-87973-721-2). Our Sunday Visitor.

--Life after Death. LC 83-61888. 136p. (Orig.). 1983. pap. 5.95 (ISBN 0-87973-612-7, 612). Our Sunday Visitor.

--The Life of Jesus Christ. 248p. (Orig.). 1987. pap. 12.95 (ISBN 0-87973-500-7, 500). Our Sunday Visitor.

--A Saint for Your Name: Saints for Boys. LC 79-92504. (Illus.). 120p. (YA) 1980. pap. 5.95 (ISBN 0-87973-320-9, 320). Our Sunday Visitor.

--A Saint for Your Name: Saints for Girls. LC 79-92502. (Illus.). 104p. (YA) 1980. pap. 5.95 (ISBN 0-87973-321-7, 321). Our Sunday Visitor.

Nevins, Albert J., ed. Father Smith Instructs Jackson. rev. ed. LC 75-628. 278p. 1975. pap. 6.50 (ISBN 0-87973-864-2). Our Sunday Visitor.

Nevins, Ann. Super Stitches: A Book of Superstitions. LC 82-15875. (Illus.). 64p. 1983. reinforced bdg. 9.95 (ISBN 0-8234-0476-5). Holiday.

Nevins, William. Thoughts on Popery. Grob, Gerald, ed. LC 76-46093. (Anti-Movements in America). 1977. Repr. of 1836 ed. lib. bdg. 17.00x (ISBN 0-405-09966-5). Ayer Co Pubs.

Nevius, John. Planting & Development of Missionary Churches. 1974. pap. 2.45 (ISBN 0-87552-346-3). Presby & Reformed.

New England Society see Eames, Wilberforce.

New Jewish Agenda, ed. The Shalom Seders. 128p. 1984. pap. 12.95 (ISBN 0-531-09840-0). Watts.

New Jewish Agenda, compiled by. The Shalom Seders: Three Passover Haggadahs. LC 83-25857. (Illus.). 128p. 1984. pap. 12.95 (ISBN 0-915361-03-5, 09747-1, Dist. by Watts). Adama Pubs Inc.

New, John F. Anglican & Puritan: The Basis of Their Opposition, 1558-1640. 1964. 18.00x (ISBN 0-8047-0066-4). Stanford U Pr.

--The Renaissance & Reformation: A Short History. 2nd ed. 201p. 1977. pap. text ed. 11.00 (ISBN 0-394-34199-6, RanC). Random.

New, John F., ed. Oliver Cromwell: Pretender, Puritan, Statesman, Paradox? LC 76-23190. (European Prob. Studies Ser.). 128p. 1977. pap. text ed. 5.95 (ISBN 0-88275-457-2). Krieger.

New, Silva, jt. ed. see Lake, Kirsopp.

New York Academy Of Medicine. Ministry & Medicine in Human Relations. facs. ed. Galdston, Iago, ed. LC 77-142682. (Essay Index Reprint Ser). 1955. 17.00 (ISBN 0-8369-2120-8). Ayer Co Pubs.

New York CIRCUS Publications, Inc. Staff, ed. see Ezcurra, Ana M.

New York Public Library, Research Libraries. Dictionary Catalog of Jewish Collection, 14 Vols. 1960. Set. 1240.00 (ISBN 0-8161-0409-3, Pub. by Hall Library). G K Hall.

--Dictionary Catalog of the Jewish Collection, First Supplement, 8 vols. 5424p. 1975. Set. lib. bdg. 875.00 (ISBN 0-8161-0773-4, Hall Library). G K Hall.

Newbattle Abbey. Registrum S. Marie De Neubotle. Innes, Cosmo, ed. LC 74-173074. (Bannatyne Club, Edinburgh. Publications: No. 89). Repr. of 1849 ed. 42.50 (ISBN 0-404-52819-8). AMS Pr.

Newbigin, James E. The Reunion of the Church: A Defence of the South India Scheme. LC 79-4205. 1979. Repr. of 1960 ed. lib. bdg. cancelled (ISBN 0-313-20797-6, NERU). Greenwood.

Newbigin, Lesslie. Foolishness to the Greeks. 176p. (Orig.). 1986. pap. 7.95 (ISBN 0-8028-0176-5). Eerdmans.

--Unfinished Agenda: An Autobiography. (Illus.). 280p. (Orig.). 1985. pap. 11.95 (ISBN 0-8028-0091-2). Eerdmans.

Newbold, Robert T., Jr., ed. Black Preaching: Select Sermons in the Presbyterian Tradition. LC 77-4015. 180p. 1977. softcover 5.65 (ISBN 0-664-24323-1). Westminster.

Newburgh, Charles, tr. see Geiger, Abraham.

Newby, Grace, jt. auth. see Albritton, Clarice.

Newby, James R. Reflections from the Light of Christ: 5 Quaker Classics. LC 80-7477. 126p. 1980. 7.95 (ISBN 0-913408-55-7). Friends United.

Newcomb, Charles B. Psychic Philosophy & the Awakening of Spiritual Consciousness, 2 vols. (Illus.). 1985. Set. 187.65 (ISBN 0-89920-090-7). Am Inst Psych.

Newcomb, Robert T. Janissa. 1943. 8.00 (ISBN 0-685-08807-3). Destiny.

Newcombe, Jack, ed. A Christmas Treasury. LC 81-50583. (Illus.). 512p. 1982. 22.95 (ISBN 0-670-22110-4). Viking.

Newell, Arlo. The Church of God As Revealed in Scripture. 1983. pap. 1.95 (ISBN 0-87162-269-6, D4775). Warner Pr.

Newell, Arlo F. Receive the Holy Spirit. 1984. pap. 2.95 (ISBN 0-87162-409-5, D6431). Warner Pr.

Newell, Arlo F., ed. see Byrum, R. R.

Newell, Herbert M. & Newell, Jeanie P. History of Fayette County Baptist Association. 1968. 15.00 (ISBN 0-317-13829-4). Banner Pr AL.

Newell, Jeanie P., jt. auth. see Newell, Herbert M.

Newell, Linda K. & Avery, Valeen T. Mormon Enigma: Emma Hale Smith, Prophet's Wife, Elect Lady, Polygamy's Foe. LC 80-2400. (Illus.). 394p. 1984. 19.95 (ISBN 0-385-17166-8). Doubleday.

Newell, Norman D. Creation & Evolution: Myth or Reality? LC 81-21767. (Convergence Ser.). 232p. 1982. 24.00x (ISBN 0-231-05348-7). Columbia U Pr.

Newell, Theron A. My Friend God: This Amazing Universe! Who Made It? LC 82-73698. (Illus.). 92p. 1983. 9.95 (ISBN 0-9610080-0-8). Dentan Pr.

Newell, William L. The Secular Magi: Marx, Nietzsche, & Freud on Religion. 264p. (Orig.). 1986. pap. 13.95 (ISBN 0-8298-0579-6). Pilgrim NY.

--Struggle & Submission: R. C. Zaehner on Mysticisms. LC 80-6295. 402p. 1981. lib. bdg. 29.25 (ISBN 0-8191-1696-3); pap. text ed. 15.25 (ISBN 0-8191-1697-1). U Pr of Amer.

Newell, William R. Romans Verse by Verse. 1938. 19.95 (ISBN 0-8024-7385-7). Moody.

--Studies in Joshua-Job. LC 83-19899. (Old Testament Studies). 224p. 1983. kivar 7.95 (ISBN 0-8254-3314-2). Kregel.

--Studies in the Pentateuch. LC 83-19903. (Old Testament Studies). 272p. 1983. kivar 7.95 (ISBN 0-8254-3313-4). Kregel.

Newey, Paul, jt. auth. see Love, Bessie.

Newey, Vincent, ed. The Pilgrim's Progress: Critical & Historical Views. (English Texts & Studies). 302p. 1980. 30.00x (ISBN 0-389-20016-6). B&N Imports.

Newhouse, Flower A. Disciplines of the Holy Quest. 4th ed. LC 59-15553. (Illus.). 1959. 10.50 (ISBN 0-910378-05-3). Christward.

--Drama of Incarnation. 4th ed. 1948. 7.50 (ISBN 0-910378-04-5). Christward.

--Gateways into Light. 2nd ed. LC 74-75517. 160p. 1974. pap. 8.50 (ISBN 0-910378-09-6). Christward.

--Here Are Your Answers, Vol. I. 3rd ed. LC 49-16192. 1948. 9.50 (ISBN 0-910378-01-0). Christward.

--Here Are Your Answers, Vol. II. 2nd ed. LC 76-103410. 1969. 9.50 (ISBN 0-910378-06-1). Christward.

--Here Are Your Answers, Vol. III. Boult, Pamela, ed. 222p. 1983. 11.00 (ISBN 0-910378-18-5). Christward.

--The Meaning & Value of the Sacraments. LC 77-186123. 123p. 1971. 7.50 (ISBN 0-910378-07-X). Christward.

--Prayers of a Mystic. Boult, Pamela, compiled by. & intro. by. LC 86-71083. 100p. (Orig.). 1986. pap. 6.00 (ISBN 0-910378-21-5). Christward.

--Rediscovering the Angels & Natives of Eternity. 7th ed. (Illus.). 11.00 (ISBN 0-910378-02-9). Christward.

--The Sacred Heart of Christmas. 2nd ed. Bengtson, Athene, ed. LC 78-74956. (Illus.). 1978. pap. 7.00 (ISBN 0-910378-14-2). Christward.

--Songs of Deliverance. LC 72-94582. 250p. 1972. 9.50 (ISBN 0-910378-08-8). Christward.

--Through Lent to Resurrection. Bengtson, Melodie N., ed. LC 77-77088. (Illus.). 1977. pap. 5.00 (ISBN 0-910378-13-4). Christward.

--Travel with Inner Perceptiveness. (Illus.). 112p. (Orig.). 1979. pap. text ed. 7.00 (ISBN 0-910378-16-9). Christward.

Newhouse, Flower A., et al. Insights into Reality. 2nd ed. LC 75-36869. 1975. pap. 8.50 (ISBN 0-910378-10-X). Christward.

Newing, A. A Peal of Puzzles. 1985. 16.25x (ISBN 0-317-54301-6, Pub. by J Richardson UK). State Mutual Bk.

Newland, Guy. Compassion: A Tibetan Analysis. (A Wisdom Advanced Book: Blue Ser.). 168p. (Orig.). 1985. pap. 12.95 (ISBN 0-318-04680-6, Wisdom Pubns). Great Traditions.

--Compassion in Madhyamika Buddhism. (A Wisdom Advanced Book, Blue Ser.). 160p. (Orig.). 1984. pap. 10.95 (ISBN 0-86171-024-X, Wisdom Pubns). Great Traditions.

Newland, Mary R. The Saint Book: For Parents, Teachers, Homilists, Storytellers & Children. (Illus.). 206p. 1979. pap. 8.95 (ISBN 0-8164-0210-8, 7480, HarpR). Har-Row.

--The Saint Book: For Parents, Teachers, Homilists, Storytellers & Children. 206p. (Orig.). 1985. pap. 8.95 (ISBN 0-86683-979-8, 7480, HarpR). Har-Row.

Newland, Mary R., jt. ed. see Hill, Brennan.

Newlands, George M. Hilary of Poitiers: A Study in Theological Method. (European University Studies: Series 23, Vol. 108). xiii, 216p. 1978. pap. 25.25 (ISBN 3-261-03133-6). P Lang Pubs.

Newlin, Claude M. Philosophy & Religion in Colonial America. LC 68-23317. 1968. Repr. of 1962 ed. lib. bdg. cancelled (ISBN 0-8371-0184-0, NEPR). Greenwood.

Newman, Albert H. History of Anti-Pedobaptism: From the Rise of Pedobaptism to A.D. 1609. LC 71-144664. Repr. of 1897 ed. 26.45 (ISBN 0-404-04686-X). AMS Pr.

--A Manual of Church History, 2 vols. 1977. Set. lib. bdg. 250.00 (ISBN 0-8490-2205-3). Gordon Pr.

Newman, Aryeh, tr. see Meiseles, Meir.

Newman, B. M. & Nida, E. A. Translator's Handbook on Paul's Letter to the Romans. LC 75-2229. (Helps for Translators Ser.). 325p. 1973. 5.00x (ISBN 0-8267-0139-6, 08517, Pub. by United Bible). Am Bible.

--Translator's Handbook on the Gospel of John. LC 81-452133. (Helps for Translators Ser.). 681p. 1980. 7.00x (ISBN 0-8267-0137-X, 08620, Pub. by United Bible). Am Bible.

Newman, B. M., Jr. & Nida, E. A. Translator's Handbook on the Acts of the Apostles. LC 73-162720. (Helps for Translators Ser.). 542p. 1972. 6.00x (ISBN 0-8267-0138-8, 08514, Pub. by United Bible). Am Bible.

Newman, Barbara. Sister of Wisdom: St. Hildegard's Theology of the Feminine. 1987. 30.00. U of Cal Pr.

--Sister of Wisdom: St. Hildegard's Theology of the Feminine. 288p. 1987. 18.95 (ISBN 0-520-05810-0). U of Cal Pr.

Newman, Barclay M. A Concise Greek-English Dictionary of the New Testament. 203p. 1971. 3.25x (ISBN 3-438-06008-6, 56493, Pub. by United Bible). Am Bible.

Newman, Daisy. A Procession of Friends. 484p. 1980. pap. 11.95 (ISBN 0-913408-59-X). Friends United.

Newman, Graeme, jt. auth. see Marongiu, Pietro.

Newman, Graeme R. Understanding Violence. 1979. pap. text ed. 15.50 scp (ISBN 0-397-47396-6, HarpC). Har-Row.

Newman, Henry. Hymns. 1983. 9.95 (ISBN 0-87193-199-0). Dimension Bks.

Newman, Jay. Foundations of Religious Tolerance. 192p. 1982. 27.50x (ISBN 0-8020-5591-5); pap. 9.95 (ISBN 0-8020-6507-4). U of Toronto Pr.

--The Mental Philosophy of John Henry Newman. 224p. 1986. pap. 22.95x (ISBN 0-88920-186-2, Pub. by Wilfrid Laurier Canada). Humanities.

Newman, Jeremiah. Conscience Versus Law. 260p. 1972. 5.95 (ISBN 0-8199-0433-3). Franciscan Herald.

Newman, John H. Apologia Pro Vita Sua. Culler, A. D., ed. LC 56-2548. (YA) 1956. pap. 6.50 (ISBN 0-395-05109-6, RivEd). HM.

--Apologia Pro Vita Sua. DeLaura, David, ed. (Critical Editions Ser). 1968. pap. text ed. 11.95x (ISBN 0-393-09766-8, 9766, NortonC). Norton.

--Blessed Art Thou among Women. 1985. 4.95 (ISBN 0-87193-076-5). Dimension Bks.

--An Essay in Aid of a Grammar of Assent. LC 78-51523. 1979. text ed. 18.95 (ISBN 0-268-00999-6, NDP-214); pap. text ed. 9.95 (ISBN 0-268-01000-5). U of Notre Dame Pr.

--An Essay in Aid of a Grammar of Assent. Ker, Ian, ed. & intro. by. 480p. 1985. 59.95x (ISBN 0-19-812751-0). Oxford U Pr.

--Essays & Sketches. Harrold, Charles F., ed. Repr. of 1948 ed. lib. bdg. 41.00x (ISBN 0-8371-2842-0, NEER). Greenwood.

--The Kingdom Within: Discourses to Mixed Congregations. 1984. pap. 14.95 (ISBN 0-87193-216-4). Dimension Bks.

--The Letters & Diaries of John Henry Cardinal Newman: Consulting the Laity, January 1859-June 1861, Vol. 19. 38.50x (ISBN 0-19-920051-3). Oxford U Pr.

--The Letters & Diaries of John Henry Cardinal Newman: Ealing, Trinity, Oriel, February 1801 to December 1826, Vol. I. Ker, Ian & Gornall, Thomas, eds. 1978. 52.00x (ISBN 0-19-920102-1). Oxford U Pr.

--The Letters & Diaries of John Henry Cardinal Newman: The Oxford Movement, July 1833 to December 1834, Vol. IV. Ker, Ian & Gornall, Thomas, eds. 1980. 55.00x (ISBN 0-19-920112-9). Oxford U Pr.

--The Letters & Diaries of John Henry Newman: A Cardinal's Apostolate, October 1881-December 1884, Vol. 30. Dessain, Charles S., ed. 1976. 47.00x (ISBN 0-19-920060-2). Oxford U Pr.

--The Letters & Diaries of John Henry Newman: New Bearings, January 1832 to June 1833, Vol. 3. Ker, Ian & Gornall, Thomas, eds. 1979. 52.00x (ISBN 0-19-920109-9). Oxford U Pr.

--The Letters & Diaries of John Henry Newman: Standing Firm Amid Trials, July 1861-December 1863, Vol. 20. 38.50x (ISBN 0-19-920052-1). Oxford U Pr.

--The Letters & Diaries of John Henry Newman: The Cardinalate, January 1878-September 1881, Vol. 29. Dessain, Charles S. & Gornall, Thomas, eds. 1976. 47.00x (ISBN 0-19-920059-9). Oxford U Pr.

--The Letters & Diaries of John Henry Newman: The Last Years, January 1885 to August 1890, Vol.31. Dessain, Charles S. & Gornall, Thomas, eds. 1977. 52.00x (ISBN 0-19-920083-1). Oxford U Pr.

--The Letters & Diaries of John Henry Newman: Tutor of Oriel, January 1827 to December 1831, Vol. II. Ker, Ian & Gornall, Thomas, eds. 1979. 55.00x (ISBN 0-19-920108-0). Oxford U Pr.

--The Letters & Diaries of John Henry Newman. Dessain, Charles S. & Gornall, Thomas, eds. Incl. Vol. 23. Defeat at Oxford-Defence at Rome, January to December 1867. 38.50x (ISBN 0-19-920040-8); Vol. 24. A Grammar of Ascent, January 1868 to December 1869. 38.50x (ISBN 0-19-920043-2); Vol. 25. The Vatican Council, January 1870 to December 1871. 42.00x (ISBN 0-19-920055-6); Vol. 26. Aftermaths, January 1872 to December 1873. 42.00x (ISBN 0-19-920056-4). 1973. Oxford U Pr.

--The Letters & Diaries of John Henry Newman, Vols. 27 & 28. Dessain, Stephen & Gornall, Thomas, eds. Incl. Vol. 27. Controversy with Gladstone, January 1874-December 1875 (ISBN 0-19-920057-2); Vol. 28. Fellow of Trinity, January 1876-December 1878 (ISBN 0-19-920058-0). 1975. 38.50x ea. Oxford U Pr.

--Mary the Second Eve. 40p. 1982. pap. 1.50 (ISBN 0-89555-181-0). TAN Bks Pubs.

--A Packet of Letters: A Selection from the Correspondence of John Henry Newman. Suggs, Joyce, intro. by. LC 82-4444. (Illus.). 1983. 19.95x (ISBN 0-19-826442-9). Oxford U Pr.

--Parochial & Plain Sermons. LC 86-62927. 1734p. (Orig.). 1987. pap. 49.00 (ISBN 0-89870-136-8). Ignatius Pr.

--A Reason for the Hope Within: Sermons on the Theory of Religious Belief. 368p. 1985. pap. 14.95 (ISBN 0-87193-219-9). Dimension Bks.

--Taking on the Heart of Christ. 1985. Repr. 4.95 (ISBN 0-87193-114-1). Dimension Bks.

--The Theological Papers of John Henry Newman: On Biblical Inspiration & on Infallibility, Vol. 2. Holmes, J. Derek, ed. 1979. text ed. 22.50x (ISBN 0-19-920081-5). Oxford U Pr.

--The Theological Papers of John Henry Newman: On Faith & Certainty, Vol. 1. Holmes, Derek, ed. 1976. 22.50x (ISBN 0-19-920071-8). Oxford U Pr.

Newman, John H., tr. see Athanasius, St.

Newman, John H., et al, eds. Tracts for the Times, 6 Vols. 1833-1841. Set. lib. bdg. 295.00 (ISBN 0-404-19560-1). Vol. 1 (ISBN 0-404-04711-4). Vol. 2 (ISBN 0-404-04712-2). Vol. 3 (ISBN 0-404-04713-0). Vol. 4 (ISBN 0-404-04714-9). Vol. 5 (ISBN 0-404-04715-7). Vol. 6 (ISBN 0-404-04716-5). AMS Pr.

Newman, Cardinal John H. Characteristics from the Writings of John Henry Newman. LC 76-45366. 1976. Repr. of 1875 ed. lib. bdg. 49.50 (ISBN 0-8414-5813-8). Folcroft.

--A Newman Anthology. Lilly, W. S., ed. 1977. lib. bdg. 59.95 (ISBN 0-8490-2341-6). Gordon Pr.

Newman, Louis. Genesis: The Student's Guide, Pt. 2. pap. 4.95 (ISBN 0-8381-0404-5). United Syn Bk.

--Teacher's Supplement to Genesis the Student's Guide Pt. 1. pap. 2.95 (ISBN 0-8381-0403-7). United Syn Bk.

Newman, Louis, jt. auth. see Newman, Shirley.

Newman, Louis E. The Sanctity of the Seventh Year: A Study of Mishnah Tractate Shebiit. LC 83-8683. (Brown Judaic Studies). 276p. 1983. pap. 12.00 (ISBN 0-89130-630-7, 14 00 44). Scholars Pr GA.

Newman, Louis I. The Hasidic Anthology. 740p. 1987. 40.00 (ISBN 0-87668-968-3). Aronson.

--Jewish Influence on Christian Reform Movements. LC 26-883. (Columbia University. Oriental Studies: No. 23). Repr. of 1925 ed. 45.00 (ISBN 0-404-50513-9). AMS Pr.

Newman, Louis I., ed. & tr. from Hebrew, Yiddish & Ger. The Hasidic Anthology: Tales & Teachings of the Hasidim. LC 63-11041. 576p. 1987. pap. 12.95 (ISBN 0-8052-0836-4). Schocken.

Newman, Louis I., ed. Maggidim & Hasidim: Their Wisdom. 1962. 14.95x (ISBN 0-8197-0161-0). Bloch.

--The Talmudic Anthology. LC 45-9682. 1978. pap. text ed. 12.95x (ISBN 0-87441-303-6). Behrman.

Newman, P. R. Atlas of the English Civil War. (Illus.). 144p. 1985. text ed. 35.00x (ISBN 0-02-906540-2). Macmillan.

Newman, Richard. Black Power & Black Religion: Essays & Reviews. LC 86-20906. 1986. lib. bdg. 25.00 (ISBN 0-933951-03-5). Locust Hill Pr.

Newman, Richard, jt. auth. see Burkett, Randall K.

Newman, Richard, jt. ed. see Wills, David W.

Newman, Robert C. Baptists & the American Tradition. LC 76-7166. 1976. pap. 1.95 (ISBN 0-87227-008-4). Reg Baptist.

Newman, Robert C. & Eckelmann, Herman J., Jr. Genesis One & the Origin of the Earth. 156p. 1981. pap. 4.95 (ISBN 0-8010-6735-9). Baker Bk.

Newman, Shirley. A Child's Introduction to the Early Prophets. LC 75-14052. (Illus.). 128p. 1975. 6.95x (ISBN 0-87441-244-7). Behrman.

--Introduction to Kings, Later Prophets & Writings, Vol. 3. Rossel, Seymour, ed. (The Child's Introduction to Bible Ser.). (Illus.). 160p. (Orig.). 1981. pap. text ed. 6.95x (ISBN 0-87441-336-2); wkbk. by Morris Sugarman 3.50x; tchr's ed. 12.50x. Behrman.

Newman, Shirley & Newman, Louis. A Child's Introduction to Torah. LC 72-2056. (Illus.). 128p. 1972. text ed. 6.95x (ISBN 0-87441-067-3). 2.25x ea., wkbk in 2 pts. Behrman.

Newman, Stewart A. A Free Church Perspective: A Study in Ecclesiology. 113p. (Orig.). 1986. pap. 8.95 (ISBN 0-913029-12-2). Stevens Bk Pr.

Newman, William M. & Halvorson, Peter L. Patterns in Pluralism: A Portrait of American Religion, 1952-1971. LC 79-55177. 1980. pap. 6.50 (ISBN 0-914422-10-3). Glenmary Res Ctr.

Newman, William M., jt. auth. see Halvorson, Peter L.

Newport, John P. Demons, Demons, Demons. LC 78-189503. 1977. pap. 3.95 (ISBN 0-8054-5577-9). Broadman.

--The Lion & the Lamb. LC 85-29887. 1986. 11.95 (ISBN 0-8054-1324-3). Broadman.

--Paul Tillich. 320p. 1984. 12.95 (ISBN 0-8499-2952-0). Word Bks.

--What Is Christian Doctrine? LC 83-71266. (Layman's Library of Christian Doctrine Ser.). 1984. 5.95 (ISBN 0-8054-1631-5). Broadman.

Newsom, Carol. The Songs of the Sabbath Sacrifice: Edition, Translation, & Commentary. (Harvard Semitic Museum Ser.). 1985. 34.95 (ISBN 0-89130-837-7, 04-04-27). Scholars Pr GA.

Newsome, David. Bishop Westcott & the Platonic Tradition. LC 78-409427. (Bishop Westcott Memorial Lecture Ser.: Vol. 1968). pap. 20.00 (ISBN 0-317-12985-6, 2051381). Bks Demand UMI.

--Godliness & Good Learning: Four Studies on a Victorian Ideal. (Illus.). 1961. 21.00 (ISBN 0-7195-1015-5). Transatl Arts.

Newsome, David H. Wilberforces & Henry Manning: The Parting of Friends. LC 67-2. (Illus.). 1966. 30.00x (ISBN 0-674-95280-4, Belknap Pr). Harvard U Pr.

Newsome, James D., Jr. The Hebrew Prophets. LC 84-7601. 252p. (Orig.). 1984. pap. 12.95 (ISBN 0-8042-0113-7). John Knox.

--A Synoptic Harmony of Samuel, Kings, & Chronicles. 272p. 1986. text ed. 16.95 (ISBN 0-8010-6744-8). Baker Bk.

Newsome, Robert R. The Ministering Parish: Methods & Procedures for the Pastoral Organization. LC 81-85381. 128p. (Orig.). 1982. pap. 8.95 (ISBN 0-8091-2435-1). Paulist Pr.

Newstead, Helaine. Bran the Blessed in Arthurian Romance. LC 40-4360. Repr. of 1939 ed. 14.50 (ISBN 0-404-04687-8). AMS Pr.

Newton, A. Edward. Greatest Book in the World & Other Papers. LC 78-86572. (Essay & General Literature Index Reprint Ser). (Illus.). 1969. Repr. 31.50x (ISBN 0-8046-0579-3, Pub. by Kennikat). Assoc Faculty Pr.

Newton, Douglas, ed. see Bessieres, Albert.

Newton, John. Letters of John Newton. 1976. pap. 3.95 (ISBN 0-85151-120-1). Banner of Truth.

--Out of the Depths. LC 80-85340. (Shepherd Illustrated Classics Ser.). (Illus.). 1981. pap. 5.95 (ISBN 0-87983-243-6). Keats.

--Works of John Newton, 6 vols. 1985. Repr. of 1820 ed. Set. 125.00 (ISBN 0-85151-460-X). Banner of Truth.

Newton, Joseph F. The Builders: A Story & Study of Freemasonry. 9th printing ed. (Illus.). 345p. 1985. Repr. 11.95 (ISBN 0-88053-045-6). Macoy Pub.

--The Men's House: Masonic Papers & Addresses. 253p. 1969. text ed. 5.00 (ISBN 0-88053-037-5, M-86). Macoy Pub.

--Short Talks on Masonry. 255p. 1979. Repr. of 1969 ed. text ed. 6.95 (ISBN 0-88053-036-7, M-85). Macoy Pub.

--Some Living Masters of the Pulpit: Studies in Religious Personality. facsimile ed. LC 71-152203. (Essay Index Reprint Ser). Repr. of 1923 ed. 18.00 (ISBN 0-8369-2287-5). Ayer Co Pubs.

Newton, LaVose. The Church Library Handbook. Rev. ed. 1987. Repr. of 1972 ed. 12.95 (ISBN 0-89081-563-1). Harvest Hse.

Newton, Lucilda A. Big Peanuts. 1976. pap. 1.75 (ISBN 0-915374-17-X, 17-X). Rapids Christian.

--Big Peanuts in Trouble. 1976. pap. 1.75 (ISBN 0-915374-18-8, 18-8). Rapids Christian.

Newton, Michael. The Concept of Purity at Quaram & in the Letters of Paul. (Society of New Testament Studies Monograph: No. 53). 180p. 1985. 32.50 (ISBN 0-521-26583-5). Cambridge U Pr.

Newton, Richard. Bible Animals & the Lessons Taught by Them. 1978. Repr. of 1888 ed. lib. bdg. 42.50 (ISBN 0-8492-1958-2). R West.

Neyrey, Jerome. The Passion According to Luke. 232p. (Orig.). 1985. pap. 8.95 (ISBN 0-8091-2688-5). Paulist Pr.

Neyrey, Jerome H. Christ Is Community: The Christologies of the New Testament. (Good News Studies: Vol. 13). 1985. pap. 12.95 (ISBN 0-89453-465-3). M Glazier.

--First Timothy, Second Timothy, Titus, James, First Peter, Second Peter, Jude, No. 9. Karris, Robert J., ed. (Collegeville Bible Commentary Ser.). 112p. 1983. pap. 2.95 (ISBN 0-8146-1309-8). Liturgical Pr.

Nezu, Masuo, tr. see Niwano, Nikkyo.

NFCLC. The Cry of the People: Workshops for Christian Service. 318p. (Orig.). 1980. pap. 10.00 (ISBN 0-913605-06-9). NFCLC.

--NFCLC Formation Program. 150p. 1975. wkbk. 7.00x (ISBN 0-913605-02-6). NFCLC.

--NFCLC Formation Program: Leader's Manual. 80p. (Orig.). 1975. pap. 3.50x wkbk. (ISBN 0-913605-03-4). NFCLC.

--To Simplify Our Life. 150p. 1982. wkbk. & cassette 10.00x (ISBN 0-913605-04-2). NFCLC.

Ng, David. Developing Leaders for Youth Ministry. 64p. 1984. pap. 5.95 (ISBN 0-8170-1032-7). Judson.

--See It! Do It! Your Faith in Action. (Orig.). 1972. pap. 2.50 (ISBN 0-377-02401-5). Friend Pr.

--Youth in the Community of Disciples. 80p. 1984. pap. 3.95 (ISBN 0-8170-1015-7). Judson.

Ng, David & Thomas, Virginia. Children in the Worshipping Community. LC 80-84655. (Illus.). 128p. (Orig.). 1981. pap. 7.95 (ISBN 0-8042-1688-6). John Knox.

Ngah, Nor bin. Kitab Jawi: Islamic Thought of the Malay Muslim Scholars. 64p. (Orig.). 1982. pap. text ed. 7.50x (ISBN 9971-902-48-6, Pub. by Inst Southeast Asian Stud). Gower Pub Co.

Ngor Tharttse mKhanpo bSodnams rgyamtsho. Tibetan Mandalas: The Ngor Collection. Tachikawa, Musashi, ed. (Tibetan, Sanskrit, Japanese & Eng., Illus.). 1985. Set. boxed ltd. ed. 1500.00x (ISBN 0-87773-800-9). Vol. 1, 300p. Vol. 2, 340p. Shambhala Pubns.

Nhat Hanh, Thich. Being Peace. (Illus.). 120p. (Orig.). 1987. pap. 8.50 (ISBN 0-938077-00-7). Parallax Pr.

Ni, Hua-Ching. The Complete Works of Lao Tzu: Tao Teh Ching & Hua Hu Ching. LC 79-88745. (Illus.). 219p. (Orig.). 1979. pap. 9.50 (ISBN 0-937064-00-9). SEBT.

--Tao: The Subtle Universal Law & the Integral Way of Life. LC 79-91720. (Illus.). 166p. (Orig.). 1979. pap. text ed. 7.50 (ISBN 0-937064-01-7). SEBT.

--The Taoist Inner View of the Universe & the Immortal Realm. LC 79-92389. (Illus.). 218p. (Orig.). 1979. pap. text ed. 12.50 (ISBN 0-937064-02-5). SEBT.

Ni, Hua-Chung. Heavenly Way. LC 81-50158. (Illus.). 41p. (Orig.). 1981. pap. text ed. 2.50 (ISBN 0-937064-03-3). SEBT.

Niazi, Kausar. Towards Understanding Islam. 232p. (Orig.). 1981. pap. 12.50 (ISBN 0-88004-009-2). Sunwise Turn.

Nibley, Hugh. Enoch the Prophet. 1986. text ed. 15.95 (ISBN 0-87579-047-X). Deseret Bk.

--Old Testament & Related Studies. LC 85-27544. (Collected Works of Hugh Nibley Ser.). 304p. 1986. 15.95 (ISBN 0-87579-032-1). Deseret Bk.

--The World & the Profits: Mormanism & Earlt Christianity. 1987. 10.95 (ISBN 0-87579-078-X). Deseret Bk.

Nibley, Hugh C. Since Cumorah. 11.95 (ISBN 0-87747-240-8). Deseret Bk.

Niccacci, Rufino, jt. auth. see Ramati, Alexander.

Nicene & Post-Nicene Fathers. Writings of the Nicene & Post-Nicene Fathers, 28 vols. Incl. First Series, 14 Vols. 251.30 set (ISBN 0-8028-8114-9); St. Augustine only, 8 Vols. 143.60 set (ISBN 0-8028-8106-8); St. Chrysostom only, 6 Vols. 107.70 set (ISBN 0-8028-8113-0); Second Series, 14 Vols. 251.30 set (ISBN 0-8028-8129-7). 1952-56. Repr. 17.95 ea. Eerdmans.

Nicephorus. Nicephori Archiepiscopi Constantinopolitani Opuscula Historica. De Boor, Carl G., ed. LC 75-7311. (Roman History Ser.). (Gr.). 1975. Repr. 25.50x (ISBN 0-405-07193-0). Ayer Co Pubs.

Nichol, Christopher, ed. Women & the Church. 102p. (Orig.). 1984. pap. 8.95 (ISBN 0-318-20037-6, Pub. by Tertiary Christian Studies). ANZ Religious Pubns.

Nichol, Francis D. The Midnight Cry: A Defense of William Miller & the Millerites. LC 72-8249. Repr. of 1944 ed. 36.00 (ISBN 0-404-11003-7). AMS Pr.

Nichol, Jon. The First & Third Crusades. (Resource Units: Middle Ages, 1066-1485 Ser.). (Illus.). 24p. 1974. pap. text ed. 12.95 10 copies & tchr's guide (ISBN 0-582-39377-9). Longman.

Nichol, Todd. All These Lutherans: Three Paths Toward a New Lutheran Church. LC 86-3638. (Illus.). 128p. (Orig.). 1986. pap. 6.95 (ISBN 0-8066-2208-3, 10-0228). Augsburg.

Nicholas, Charles, illus. God Is My Co-Pilot. LC 78-50959. (Contemporary Motivators Ser.). (Illus.). 1978. pap. text ed. 1.95 (ISBN 0-88301-302-9). Pendulum Pr.

Nicholas, David R. Foundations of Biblical Inerrancy. pap. 2.50 (ISBN 0-88469-104-7). BMH Bks.

--What's a Woman to Do in Church? 148p. 1979. 7.95 (ISBN 0-88469-123-3). BMH Bks.

Nicholas, Ron, et al. Good Things Come in Small Groups. LC 85-778. 200p. 1985. pap. 6.95 (ISBN 0-87784-917-X). Inter-Varsity.

Nicholas, Tim & Touchton, Ken. More Than Just Talk. Furlow, Elaine S., ed. (Human Touch Photo-Text Ser.). (Illus.). 1977. 6.95g (ISBN 0-937170-16-X). Home Mission.

Nicholas, Tracy. Rastafari: A Way of Life. LC 77-76285. (Illus.). 1979. pap. 9.95 (ISBN 0-385-11575-X, Anch). Doubleday.

Nicholas Of Cusa. The Vision of God. Satter, Emma G., tr. LC 60-9104. pap. 3.95x (ISBN 0-8044-6594-0). Ungar.

Nicholl, Donald. Holiness. 176p. (Orig.). 1981. pap. 8.95 (ISBN 0-8164-2336-9, HarpR). Har-Row.

Nicholls, Bruce & Kantzer, Kenneth. In Word & Deed. 224p. 1986. pap. 10.95 (ISBN 0-8028-1965-6). Eerdmans.

Nichols, Harold. The Work of the Deacon & Deaconess. (Orig.). pap. 4.95 (ISBN 0-8170-0328-2). Judson.

Nichols, J. Randall. Building the Word: The Dynamics of Communication & Preaching. LC 79-3590. 176p. 1981. 10.00 (ISBN 0-06-066109-7, HarpR). Har-Row.

Nichols, James, ed. see Annesley, Samuel, et al.

Nichols, James, ed. see Annesley, Samuel.

Nichols, John. Some Account of the Alien Priories, & of Such Lands As They Are Known to Have Possessed in England & Wales, 2 Vols. in 1. LC 72-173079. Repr. of 1786 ed. 47.50 (ISBN 0-404-04689-4). AMS Pr.

Nichols, John A. & Shank, M. Thomas, eds. Medieval Religious Women I: Distant Echoes. (Cistercian Studies: No. 71). 1984. 29.95 (ISBN 0-87907-871-5); pap. 11.95 (ISBN 0-87907-971-1). Cistercian Pubns.

Nichols, John G., ed. Narrative of the Days of the Reformation, Chiefly from the Manuscripts of John Foxe the Martyrologist. Repr. of 1859 ed. 37.00 (ISBN 0-384-41460-5). Johnson Repr.

--Narrative of the Days of the Reformation. (Camden Society, London. Publications, First Ser.: No. 77). Repr. of 1859 ed. 37.00 (ISBN 0-404-50177-X). AMS Pr.

Nichols, Lonnie J. God, the Universe & Self. LC 82-74521. 96p. 1983. pap. 4.50 (ISBN 0-87516-515-X). De Vorss.

Nichols, Peter. The Pope's Divisions. 16.95 (ISBN 0-03-047576-7). Brown Bk.

Nichols, Robert L. & Stavrou, Theofanis G., eds. Russian Orthodoxy under the Old Regime. LC 78-3196. 1978. 16.50 (ISBN 0-8166-0846-6); pap. text ed. 8.95x (ISBN 0-8166-0847-4). U of Minn Pr.

Nichols, Roy. The Greening of the Gospel. 1985. 6.25 (ISBN 0-89536-745-9, 5851). CSS of Ohio.

Nichols, Stephen G., Jr., jt. ed. see Lyons, John D.

Nichols, Sue. Words on Target: For Better Christian Communication. LC 63-16410. (Illus., Orig.). 1963. pap. 5.50 (ISBN 0-8042-1476-X). John Knox.

Nicholson, tr. see Iqbal, Mohammad.

Nicholson, D. H. The Mysticism of St. Francis of Assissi. 1977. lib. bdg. 59.95 (ISBN 0-8490-2319-X). Gordon Pr.

Nicholson, Dan. From Hippie to Happy. (Orig.). 1984. pap. write for info. (ISBN 0-88144-026-4, CPS026). Christian Pub.

Nicholson, E. W. The Book of the Prophet Jeremiah: Chapters 1-25. LC 73-80477. (Cambridge Bible Commentary on the New English Bible, Old Testament Ser.). 200p. 1973. 27.95 (ISBN 0-521-08625-6); pap. 11.95 (ISBN 0-521-09769-X). Cambridge U Pr.

--The Book of the Prophet Jeremiah: Chapters 26-52. LC 74-80357. (Cambridge Bible Commentary on the New English Bible, Old Testament Ser.). 250p. 1975. 27.95 (ISBN 0-521-20497-6); pap. 12.95 (ISBN 0-521-09867-X). Cambridge U Pr.

Nicholson, E. W., jt. ed. see Baker, J.

Nicholson, Ernest W. God & His People: Covenant & Theology in the Old Testament. 240p. 1986. 36.00x (ISBN 0-19-826684-7). Oxford U Pr.

Nicholson, H. B. & Berger, Rainer. Two Aztec Wood Idols: Iconographic & Chronologic Analysis. LC 68-58701. (Studies in Pre-Columbian Art & Archaeology: No.5). (Illus.). 28p. 1968. pap. 3.00x (ISBN 0-88402-026-6). Dumbarton Oaks.

Nicholson, Irene. Mexican & Central American Mythology. LC 84-45598. (The Library of the World's Myths & Legends). (Illus.). 144p. 1985. 18.95 (ISBN 0-87226-003-8). P Bedrick Bks.

Nicholson, Joseph W., jt. auth. see Mays, Benjamin E.

Nicholson, R. A. The Essence of Sufism. 1984. pap. 3.95 (ISBN 0-916411-49-4, Near Eastern). Holmes Pub.

--Idea of Personality in Sufism. 12.50 (ISBN 0-686-18606-0). Kazi Pubns.

--Ideas of Personality in Sufism. 1970. 12.50 (ISBN 0-87902-180-2). Orientalia.

--The Kashf al-Mahjub: The Oldest Persian Treatise on Sufism by Ali B. Uthman al-Hullabi al-Hujwiri. 441p. 1976. Repr. 30.00x (ISBN 0-317-39100-3, Pub. by Luzac & Co Ltd). State Mutual Bk.

--The Sufi Doctrine of the Perfect Man. 1984. pap. 3.95 (ISBN 0-916411-48-6, Near Eastern). Holmes Pub.

Nicholson, R. A., tr. see Rumi, Jalalu'ddin.

Nicholson, Reynold A. The Mystics of Islam: An Introduction to Sufism. LC 75-10713. 192p. 1975. pap. 5.95 (ISBN 0-8052-0492-X). Schocken.

--Studies in Islamic Mysticism. LC 78-73958. 1979. pap. 16.95 (ISBN 0-521-29546-7). Cambridge U Pr.

Nicholson, Reynold A., tr. Translations of Eastern Poetry & Prose. Repr. of 1922 ed. lib. bdg. 22.50 (ISBN 0-8371-2301-1, NIEP). Greenwood.

Nicholson, Robert L. Joscelyn I, Prince of Edessa. LC 78-63352. (The Crusades & Military Orders: Second Ser.). 120p. Repr. of 1954 ed. 21.50 (ISBN 0-404-17025-0). AMS Pr.

Nicholson, Shirley, compiled by. Shamanism. LC 86-40405. 402p. (Orig.). 1987. pap. 7.50 (ISBN 0-8356-0617-1). Theos Pub Hse.

Nicholson, Shirley, ed. see Besant, Annie.

Nicholson, Shirley, ed. see Powell, Robert.

Nicholson, Vincent D. Cooperation & Coercion as Methods of Social Change. 1983. pap. 2.50x (ISBN 0-87574-001-4, 001). Pendle Hill.

Nicholson, W. R. Colossians. LC 73-81742. 284p. 1973. 7.95 (ISBN 0-8254-3301-0); pap. 5.95 (ISBN 0-8254-3300-2). Kregel.

Nicholson, William R. Six Miracles of Calvary. (Moody Classics Ser.). 1928. pap. 3.50 (ISBN 0-8024-7834-4). Moody.

Nickel, Margaret C. Dream of Spring. 256p. 1987. 12.95 (ISBN 0-89962-589-4). Todd & Honeywell.

Nickell, Joe. Inquest on the Shroud of Turin. LC 82-62457. (Illus.). 178p. 1982. 18.95 (ISBN 0-87975-194-0). Prometheus Bks.

Nickell, Judy. New Testament Herald. 1985. 1.25 (ISBN 0-89536-733-5, 5878). CSS of Ohio.

Nickelsburg, George W. Jewish Literature Between the Bible & the Mishnah: A Historical & Literary Introduction. LC 80-16176. 352p. 1981. 19.95 (ISBN 0-8006-0649-3, 1-649). Fortress.

Nickelsburg, George W. & Stone, Michael E. Faith & Piety in Early Judaism: Texts & Documents. LC 82-71830. 272p. 1983. 19.95 (ISBN 0-8006-0679-5). Fortress.

Nickelsburg, George W. & Kraft, Robert A., eds. Early Judaism & Its Modern Interpreters. LC 85-45491. (The Bible & its Modern Interpreters Ser.). 544p. 1986. 24.95 (ISBN 0-8006-0722-8). Fortress.

Nickelsburg, George W. & MacRal, George W., eds. Christians Among Jews & Gentiles: Essays in Honor of Krister Stendahl. pap. 19.95 (ISBN 0-317-52516-6). Fortress.

Nickelsburg, George W., jt. ed. see Collins, John J.

Nickelsburg, George W., Jr., ed. Studies on the Testament of Abraham. LC 76-44205. (Society of Biblical Literature. Septuagint & Cognate Studies). 1976. pap. 13.50 (ISBN 0-89130-117-8, 060406). Scholars Pr GA.

Nickerson, Jill, ed. Country Christmas Entertaining. LC 83-62128. 64p. 1983. pap. 5.95 (ISBN 0-89821-055-0). Reiman Assocs.

Nickle, Keith. Collection: A Study in Paul's Strategy. LC 66-72379. (Studies in Biblical Theology: No. 48). 1966. pap. 10.00x (ISBN 0-8401-3048-1). A R Allenson.

Nickle, Keith F. The Synoptic Gospels: An Introduction. LC 79-92069. (Orig.). 1980. pap. 9.95 (ISBN 0-8042-0422-5). John Knox.

Nicklesburg, George W., ed. Studies on the Testament of Joseph. LC 75-26923. (Society of Biblical Literature. Septurgint & Cognate Studies). 153p. 1975. pap. 13.50 (ISBN 0-89130-027-9, 060405). Scholars Pr GA.

Nicklin, J. Bernard. Testimony in Stone. 1961. 6.00 (ISBN 0-685-08818-9). Destiny.

Nicol, D. M. Church & Society in the Last Centuries of Byzantium. LC 78-72092. (The Birkbeck Lectures, 1977). 1979. 32.50 (ISBN 0-521-22438-1). Cambridge U Pr.

Nicolas, Antonio de see De Nicolas, Antonio.

Nicolas, Antonio T. de see De Nicolas, Antonio T. & Moutsopolous, Evanghelos.

Nicoll, Maurice. The Mark. LC 84-22116. 216p. 1985. pap. 9.95 (ISBN 0-87773-315-5, 72998-6). Shambhala Pubns.

--The New Man: An Interpretation of Some Parables & Miracles of Christ. LC 83-20279. 153p. (Orig.). 1984. pap. 9.95 (ISBN 0-87773-268-X). Shambhala Pubns.

--Psychological Commentaries on the Teaching of Gurdjieff & Ouspensky, Vol. 1. LC 83-25194. 371p. (Orig.). 1984. pap. 15.95 (ISBN 0-87773-269-8). Shambhala Pubns.

--Psychological Commentaries on the Teachings of Gurdjieff & Ouspensky, Vol. 2. LC 83-25194. 404p. (Orig.). 1984. pap. 18.95 (ISBN 0-87773-270-1). Shambhala Pubns.

--Psychological Commentaries on the Teachings of Gurdjieff & Ouspensky, Vol. 3. LC 83-25194. 447p. (Orig.). 1984. pap. 11.95 (ISBN 0-87773-271-X). Shambhala Pubns.

--Psychological Commentaries on the Teaching of Gurdjieff & Ouspensky, Vol. 4. LC 83-25194. 268p. 1984. pap. 11.95 (ISBN 0-87773-287-6, 72695-2). Shambhala Pubns.

--Psychological Commentaries on the Teaching of Gurdjieff & Ouspensky, Vol. 5. LC 83-25194. 253p. 1984. pap. 11.95 (ISBN 0-87773-288-4, 72694-4). Shambhala Pubns.

Nicoll, Mildred R., tr. see Steiner, Rudolf.

Nicoll, W. Robertson, ed. Expositor's Greek New Testament, 5 Vols. 1952. Set. 60.00 (ISBN 0-8028-2108-1). Eerdmans.

Nicosia, Francis R. The Third Reich & the Palestine Question. 335p. 1986. text ed. 35.00x (ISBN 0-292-72731-3). U of Tex Pr.

Nida, E. A., jt. auth. see Arichea, D. C., Jr.

Nida, E. A., jt. auth. see Bratcher, R. G.

Nida, E. A., jt. auth. see De Waard, J.

Nida, E. A., jt. auth. see Ellingworth, P.

Nida, E. A., jt. auth. see Loh, I.

Nida, E. A., jt. auth. see Newman, B. M.

Nida, E. A., jt. auth. see Newman, B. M., Jr.

Nida, Eugene A. Comment Traduire la Bible. Margot, J. C., tr. 279p. 1967. pap. 4.05x (ISBN 0-8267-0024-1, 51970, Pub. by United Bible). Am Bible.

--Customs & Cultures: Anthropology for Christian Missions. 2nd ed. LC 54-8976. (Applied Cultural Anthropology Ser.). 306p. 1975. Repr. of 1954 ed. 7.95x (ISBN 0-87808-723-0). William Carey Lib.

--Religion Across Cultures. LC 68-11733. (Applied Cultural Anthropology Ser). 1979. pap. text ed. 3.95x (ISBN 0-87808-738-9). William Carey Lib.

--Toward a Science of Translating: With Special Reference to Principles & Procedures Involved in Bible Translating. 1964. text ed. 39.95x (ISBN 0-391-02063-3). Humanities.

Nida, Eugene A. & Reyburn, William D. Meaning Across Cultures: A Study on Bible Translating. LC 81-38374. 96p. (Orig.). 1981. pap. 2.98 (ISBN 0-88344-326-0). Orbis Bks.

Nida, Eugene A., jt. auth. see Bratcher, Robert G.

Nida, Eugene A., jt. auth. see Ellingworth, Paul.

Nida, Eugene A., jt. auth. see Price, Brynmor F.

Nida, Eugene A., jt. auth. see Taber, Charles R.

Nida, Eugene A., jt. auth. see Waard, Jan de.

Nidditch, P. H., ed. see Hume, David.

Niditch, Susan. Chaos to Cosmos: Studies in Biblical Patterns of Creation. (Scholars Press Studies in the Humanities: No. 6). 1985. 13.95 (ISBN 0-89130-762-1, 00 01 06); pap. 9.25 (ISBN 0-89130-763-X). Scholars Pr GA.

--The Symbolic Vision in Biblical Tradition. LC 83-8643. (Harvard Semitic Monographs). 270p. 1983. 15.00 (ISBN 0-89130-627-7, 04 00 30). Scholars Pr GA.

Niebuhr, H. Richard. Christ & Culture. pap. 7.95x (ISBN 0-06-130003-9, TB3, Torch). Har-Row.

--Christ & Culture. 17.00 (ISBN 0-8446-2658-9). Peter Smith.

--Meaning of Revelation. 1967. pap. 5.95 (ISBN 0-02-087750-1, Collier). Macmillan.

--The Meaning of Revelation. 1983. 14.00 (ISBN 0-8446-6033-7). Peter Smith.

--The Purpose of the Church & Its Ministry. LC 76-62925. (Orig.). 1977. pap. 3.00i (ISBN 0-06-066174-7, RD 211, HarpR). Har-Row.

--Radical Monotheism in Western Culture. pap. 5.95x (ISBN 0-06-131491-9, TB1491, Torch). Har-Row.

--The Responsible Self. LC 63-15955. 1978. pap. 6.95xi (ISBN 0-06-066211-5, RD 266, HarpR). Har-Row.

Niebuhr, H. Richard & Williams, Daniel D., eds. The Ministry in Historical Perspectives. rev. ed. LC 80-8899. (Ministers Paperback Library). 384p. 1983. pap. 8.95 (ISBN 0-06-066232-8, RD 354, HarpR). Har-Row.

Niebuhr, H. Richard, jt. ed. see Beach, Waldo.

Niebuhr, Reinhold. Beyond Tragedy: Essays on the Christian Interpretation of History. facsimile ed. LC 76-167397. (Essay Index Reprint Ser). Repr. of 1937 ed. 23.95 (ISBN 0-8369-2437-1). Ayer Co Pubs.

--Beyond Tragedy: Essays on the Christian Interpretation of History. 1937. pap. text ed. 7.95 (ISBN 0-684-16410-8, SL38, ScribT). Scribner.

--Christian Realism & Political Problems. LC 75-128062. 1977. Repr. of 1953 ed. 19.50x (ISBN 0-678-02757-9). Kelley.

--Christianity & Power Politics. LC 69-12421. xi, 226p. 1969. Repr. of 1940 ed. 24.50 (ISBN 0-208-00740-7, Archon). Shoe String.

--The Contribution of Religion to Social Work. LC 74-172444. Repr. of 1932 ed. 5.00 (ISBN 0-404-04708-4). AMS Pr.

--Faith & History: A Comparison of Christian & Modern Views of History. (Lib. Rep. Ed.). 1949. 25.00 (ISBN 0-684-15318-1, ScribT). Scribner.

--An Interpretation of Christian Ethics. 1979. pap. 8.95 (ISBN 0-8164-2206-0, HarpR). Har-Row.

--Leaves from the Notebook of a Tamed Cynic. LC 79-2992. (Harper's Ministers Paperback Library). 224p. 1980. pap. 5.95i (ISBN 0-06-066231-X, RD 311, HarpR). Har-Row.

--Love & Justice: Selections from the Shorter Writings of Reinhold Niebuhr. Robertson, D. B., ed. 12.50 (ISBN 0-8446-2659-7). Peter Smith.

--Moral Man & Immoral Society. 16.75 (ISBN 0-8446-6221-6). Peter Smith.

--Moral Man & Immoral Society: A Study in Ethics & Politics. 1932. pap. 9.95 (ISBN 0-684-71857-X, ScribT). Scribner.

--Pious & Secular America. LC 79-128063. 1977. Repr. of 1958 ed. 17.50x (ISBN 0-678-02756-0). Kelley.

Niebuhr, Richard H. The Social Sources of Denominationalism. 1984. 17.50 (ISBN 0-8446-6150-3). Peter Smith.

Niedner, Frederick A., Jr., jt. auth. see Truemper, David G.

Niehaus, Thomas, et al. Resources for Latin American Jewish Studies: Essays on Using Jewish Reference Sources for the Study of Latin American Jewry; U. S. Library Collections on L. A. Jews; & U. S. Archival Resources for the Study of Jews in L. A. Elkin, Judith L., ed. LC 84-80219. (LAJSA Publication Ser.: No. 1). 59p. (Orig.). 1984. pap. text ed. 10.00 (ISBN 0-916921-00-X). Lat Am Jewish Assn.

Nield, Jonathan, tr. see Boutroux, Emile.

Nieli, Russell. Wittgenstein: From Mysticism to Ordinary Language: A Study of Viennese Positivism & the Thought of Ludwig Wittgenstein. (SUNY Series in Philosophy). 224p. 1987. 39.50x (ISBN 0-88706-397-7); pap. 12.95x (ISBN 0-88706-398-5). State U NY Pr.

Nielsen, Ernest D., ed. & tr. see Grundtvig, N. F.

Nielsen, H. A. Where the Passion Is: A Reading of Kierkegaard's Philosophical Fragments. LC 83-6923. 209p. 1983. 20.00 (ISBN 0-8130-0742-9). U Presses Fla.

Nielsen, Kai. Ethics Without God. (Skeptic's Bookshelf Ser.). 112p. 1973. pap. 9.95 (ISBN 0-87975-019-7). Prometheus Bks.

--An Introduction to the Philosophy of Religion. LC 82-16843. 200p. 1983. 22.50x (ISBN 0-312-43310-7). St Martin.

--The Philosophy & Atheism. (The Skeptic's Bookshelf Ser.). 231p. 1985. 20.95 (ISBN 0-87975-289-0). Prometheus Bks.

Nielsen, Kai E. Scepticism. LC 72-77776. (New Studies in the Philosophy of Religion Ser.). 96p. 1973. 18.95 (ISBN 0-312-70070-9). St Martin.

Nielsen, Margaret, ed. see MacHaffie, Ingeborg S.

Nielsen, Niels, et al, eds. Religions of Asia. LC 82-60477. 384p. 1983. pap. text ed. 17.95 (ISBN 0-312-67096-6). St Martin.

--Religions of the World. LC 81-51859. 688p. 1982. text ed. 28.95 (ISBN 0-312-67121-0); write for info. instructors manual. St Martin.

Nielson, Bill. Beacon Small-Group Bible Studies, I & II Thessalonians: The Distinguishing Marks of a Christian. 56p. 1982. pap. 2.50 (ISBN 0-8341-0738-4). Beacon Hill.

Nielson, Greg, jt. auth. see Toth, Max.

Nielson, John B. The Towel & the Cross. 118p. (Orig.). 1983. pap. 3.95 (ISBN 0-8341-0847-X). Beacon Hill.

--Zehariah-Malachi: Prisoners of Hope. 80p. (Orig.). 1986. pap. 2.50 (ISBN 0-8341-1100-4). Beacon Hill.

Nielson, John M. Beacon Small-Group Bible Studies, Romans: More than Conquerors. Wolf, Earl C., ed. 96p. (Orig.). 1984. pap. 2.50 (ISBN 0-8341-0944-1). Beacon Hill.

Nielson, Joseph F. You Can Be a Better Parent. (Christian Counseling Aids Ser.). 1977. pap. 0.95 (ISBN 0-8010-6691-3). Baker Bk.

Nielson, Larry. How Would You Like to See the Slides of My Mission? A Tasteful Collection of Missionary Humor. LC 80-82708. (Illus.). 158p. (Orig.). 1980. pap. 4.95 (ISBN 0-88290-153-2, 2040). Horizon Utah.

Nieman, Charles. Gods Plan for the Family. 58p. (Orig.). 1985. 4.95 (ISBN 0-914307-49-5). Word Faith.

--God's Plan for Your Financial Success. 230p. (Orig.). 1985. pap. text ed. 6.95 (ISBN 0-914307-34-7). Word Faith.

--The Life of Excellence. 32p. (Orig.). 1985. wkbk. 4.95 (ISBN 0-914307-37-1). Word Faith.

--Life of Jesus. 55p. (Orig.). 1984. wkbk. 2.75 (ISBN 0-914307-25-8). Word Faith.

--Prayer: An Invitation from God. 140p. (Orig.). 1983. pap. text ed. 4.95 (ISBN 0-914307-03-7, Dist. by Harrison Hse). Word Faith.

--Wisdom & Guidance. 206p. (Orig.). 1984. pap. text ed. 5.00 (ISBN 0-914307-19-3, Dist. by Harrison Hse). Word Faith.

Niemand, Jasper, ed. & intro. by see Judge, William Q.

Niemann, Martha M. The Single Life: A Christian Challenge. 144p. 1986. pap. 4.25 (ISBN 0-89243-254-3). Liguori Pubns.

Niemoller, Martin. Exile in the Fatherland: Martin Niemoller's Letters from Moabit Prison. Locke, Hubert G., ed. Kaemke, Ernst, tr. 212p. (Orig.). 1986. pap. 9.95 (ISBN 0-8028-0188-9). Eerdmans.

Niendorff, John S. Listen to the Light. 96p. 1983. pap. 4.50 (ISBN 0-911336-84-2). Sci of Mind.

Nies, Richard C. The Security of Salvation. LC 78-17523. (Waymark Ser.). 1978. pap. 2.50 (ISBN 0-8127-0187-9). Review & Herald.

Nieting, Lorenz. Lesser Festivals 4: Saints' Days & Special Occasions. Achtemeier, Elizabeth, et al, eds. LC 79-7377. (Proclamation Two Ser.: Aids for Interpreting the Lessons of the Church Year). 64p. (Orig.). 1981. pap. 3.75 (ISBN 0-8006-1396-1, 1-1396). Fortress.

Nieto, J. C. Mystic, Rebel, Saint: A Study on St. Joan of the Cross. (Illus.). 148p. (Orig.). 1979. pap. text ed. 38.00x (Pub. by Droz Switzerland). Coronet Bks.

Nietzsche, Friedrich. The Antichrist. LC 70-161338. (Atheist Viewpoint Ser). 60p. 1972. Repr. of 1930 ed. 13.00 (ISBN 0-405-03799-6). Ayer Co Pubs.

--The Antichrist & Twilight of the Gods. 1974. 100.00 (ISBN 0-87968-210-8). Gordon Pr.

--The Dawn of Day. 1974. 100.00 (ISBN 0-87968-204-3). Gordon Pr.

--Daybreak: Thoughts on the Prejudices of Morality. Hollingdale, R. J., tr. LC 81-18017. (Texts in German Philosophy). 220p. 1982. 22.95 (ISBN 0-521-24396-3); pap. 9.95 (ISBN 0-521-28662-X). Cambridge U Pr.

--A Nietzsche Reader. Hollingdale, R. J., tr. from Ger. (Classics Ser.). (Orig.). 1978. pap. 4.95 (ISBN 0-14-044329-0). Penguin.

--Nietzsche, Werke, Kritische Gesamtausgabe, Sect. 8, Vol. 1: Nachgelassene Fragmente, Herbst 1885 bis Herbst 1887. Colli, Giorgio & Montinari, Mazzino, eds. (Ger.). viii, 360p. 1974. 28.20x (ISBN 3-11-004741-1). De Gruyter.

--On the Genealogy of Morals. Kaufman, Walter, tr. Bd. with Ecce Homo. 1967. pap. 4.76 (ISBN 0-394-70401-0, Vin). Random.

Niewyk, Donald L. The Jews in Weimar Germany. LC 79-26234. 262p. 1980. 27.50x (ISBN 0-8071-0661-5). La State U Pr.

Niezabitowska, Malgorzata. Remnants: The Last Jews of Poland. Brand, William & Dobosiewicz, Hanna, trs. from Polish. LC 86-1468. (Illus.). 272p. 1986. 35.00 (ISBN 0-914919-05-9). Friendly Pr NY.

Niggemeyer, Vickie, jt. auth. see Ritchie, Judith.

Nighswander, Ada. The Little Martins Learn to Love. 6.50 (ISBN 0-686-30775-5). Rod & Staff.

Nightingale, Earl. Earl Nightingale's Greatest Discovery: The Strangest Secret...Revisited. (PMA Ser.). 1987. 17.95 (ISBN 0-396-08928-3). Dodd.

Nightingale, Ken. One Way Through the Jungle. pap. 2.50 (ISBN 0-85363-107-7). OMF Bks.

Nigosian, S. A. World Religions Series. (Comparative Religions Ser.). 1976. pap. text ed. 6.45 (ISBN 0-88343-688-4). McDougal-Littell.

Nigosian, Solomon. Islam. (Crucible Ser.). 208p. 1987. pap. 9.95 (ISBN 0-85030-490-3). Thorsons Pubs.

--Islam: The Way of Submission. 1987. pap. 9.95. Inner Tradit.

--Judaism. (Crucible Ser.). 208p. 1987. pap. 9.95 (ISBN 0-85030-429-6). Thorsons Pubs.

--Judaism: The Way of Holiness. 1987. pap. 9.95. Inner Tradit.

Niguidula, Lydia N. Celebration: a Sourcebook for Christian Worship. 1975. wrps. 6.50x (ISBN 0-686-18680-X). Cellar.

Ni Hua Ching. Eight Thousand Years of Wisdom: Conversations with Taoist Master Ni, Hua Ching, Bk. 1. LC 83-51082. 248p. (Orig.). 1983. pap. text ed. 12.50 (ISBN 0-937064-07-6). SEBT.

--Eight Thousand Years of Wisdom: Conversations with Taoist Master Ni, Hua Ching, Bk. 2. LC 83-51082. 248p. (Orig.). 1983. pap. text ed. 12.50 (ISBN 0-937064-08-4). SEBT.

--Workbook for Spiritual Development of All People. LC 83-51083. 240p. 1983. text ed. 12.50 (ISBN 0-937064-06-8). SEBT.

Ni Hua-Ching, Master & Hua-Ching. The Complete Works of Lao Tzu: Tao Teh Ching & Hua Hu Ching. LC 79-88745. 219p. 1979. pap. text ed. 7.50x (ISBN 0-937064-00-9). Wisdom Garden.

--Tao-The Subtle Universal Law & the Integral Way of Life. LC 79-91720. 166p. 1980. pap. text ed. 7.50 (ISBN 0-937064-01-7). Wisdom Garden.

--The Taoist Inner View of the Universe & the Immortal Realm. LC 79-91720. 218p. 1980. pap. text ed. 12.50x (ISBN 0-937064-02-5). Wisdom Garden.

Nijim, Basheer K., ed. American Church Politics & the Middle East. (Monograph: No. 15). 156p. (Orig.). 1982. pap. 7.50 (ISBN 0-937694-53-3). Assn Arab-Amer U Grads.

Nijsse, Marinus. Through Troubled Waters. (Children's Summit Bks.). pap. 1.95 (ISBN 0-8010-6728-6). Baker Bk.

Nikel, Johannes S. Ein Never Ninkarrak-Text. pap. 7.00 (ISBN 0-384-41600-4). Johnson Repr.

Nikhilananda, Swami. Hinduism: Its Meaning for the Liberation of the Spirit: a Survey of Hinduism. LC 58-6155. 189p. 5.50 (ISBN 0-911206-13-2). Ramakrishna.

--Holy Mother: Being the Life of Sri Sarada Devi, Wife of Sri Ramakrishna & Helpmate in His Mission. LC 62-13423. (Illus.). 384p. pap. 7.95 (ISBN 0-911206-20-5). Ramakrishna.

--Man in Search of Immortality. LC 68-101793. 112p. 4.95 (ISBN 0-911206-12-4). Ramakrishna.

--Vivekananda: A Biography. LC 53-7851. 364p. 5.95 (ISBN 0-911206-08-6). Ramakrishna.

Nikhilananda, Swami, jt. auth. see Tapasyananda, Swami.

Nikhilananda, Swami, tr. Drg-Drsya-Viveka. (Sanskrit & Eng.). pap. 1.50 (ISBN 0-87481-402-2). Vedanta Pr.

--Self-Knowledge: Sankara's "Atmabodha". LC 50-36440. 248p. with notes 7.00 (ISBN 0-911206-11-6). Ramakrishna.

Nikiforoff-Volgin, V. Dorozhnij Posokh. Tr. of A Staff for the Road. 188p. 1971. pap. 6.00 (ISBN 0-317-30421-6). Holy Trinity.

--Zemlja Imjeninnitsa. Tr. of The Feast of the Land. 182p. 1960. pap. 6.00 (ISBN 0-317-30418-6). Holy Trinity.

Nikiprowetzky, Valentin. La Troisieme Sibylle. (Etudes Juives: No. 9). 1970. pap. 34.40x (ISBN 0-686-21819-1). Mouton.

Niklas, Gerald R. The Making of a Pastoral Person. 159p. (Orig.). 1981. pap. 6.95 (ISBN 0-8189-0409-7). Alba.

Niklas, Gerals R. & Stefanics, Charlotte. Ministry to the Sick. LC 82-4083. 143p. (Orig.). 1982. pap. 7.95 (ISBN 0-8189-0429-1). Alba.

Niklaus, Phyllis M., jt. auth. see Patterson, Kathy C.

Niklaus, Robert, et al, eds. All for Jesus. LC 86-72007. (Illus.). 322p. 1986. 11.95 (ISBN 0-87509-383-3). Chr Pubns.

Nikopol, Georg R. The Artistic & Mystical Significance of Indian & Egyptian Temples. (Illus.). 187p. 1984. 137.45 (ISBN 0-86650-131-2). Gloucester Art.

Nilles, Nicolaus. Kalendarium Manuale Utriusque Ecclesiae Orientalis & Occidentalis. (Fr.). 1509p. Date not set. Repr. of 1897 ed. text ed. 310.50x (ISBN 0-576-99195-3, Pub by Gregg Intl Pubs England). Gregg Intl.

Nilsen, Mary. Real Living: A Small-Group Life Experience with the Gospel of Luke, Pt. 1. (Illus.). 1977. pap. text ed. 5.65 (ISBN 0-03-021856-X, HarpR); tchr's. ed. 7.95 (ISBN 0-03-021861-6). Har-Row.

Nilsen, Mary Y. Our Family Shares Advent: Scripture, Prayer, & Activities for Families. (Illus.). 64p. (Orig.). 1980. pap. 7.95 (ISBN 0-86683-637-3, 8129, HarpR). Har-Row.

--Real Living: A Small Group Life Experience with the Gospel of Luke, Pt. 2. (Illus.). 1978. pap. text ed. 5.65 (ISBN 0-03-022141-2, HarpR); tchr's. guide 7.95 (ISBN 0-03-022146-3). Har-Row.

--Real Living: A Small-Group Life Experience with the Gospel of Luke, Pt. 3. (Illus.). 1978. pap. text ed. 5.65 (ISBN 0-03-045696-7, HarpR); tchr's. guide 7.95 (ISBN 0-03-045701-7). Har-Row.

--Real Living: A Small-Group Life Experience with the Gospel of Luke, Pt. 4. Winston Press Editorial Staff, ed. (Illus.). 1979. pap. text ed. 5.65 (ISBN 0-03-045706-8, HarpR); tchr's. guide 7.95 (ISBN 0-03-045711-4). Har-Row.

--Tending the Family Tree: A Family-Centered, Bible-Based Experience for Church Groups. 80p. (Orig.). 1982. pap. 7.95 (ISBN 0-86683-169-X, HarpR). Har-Row.

Nilson, Jon. From this Day Forward. LC 83-73133. 88p. (Orig.). 1983. pap. 2.95 (ISBN 0-87029-192-0, 20284-6). Abbey.

Nilsson, Martin P. The Dionysiac Mysteries of the Hellenistic & Roman Age. facsimile ed. LC 75-10643. (Ancient Religion & Mythology Ser.). (Illus.). 1976. Repr. of 1957 ed. 13.00x (ISBN 0-405-07261-9). Ayer Co Pubs.

--Greek Folk Religion. 1972. pap. 10.95x (ISBN 0-8122-1034-4, Pa. Paperbacks). U of Pa Pr.

--The Minoan-Mycenaean Religion. LC 70-162300. 1950. 15.00 (ISBN 0-8196-0273-6). Biblo.

--The Mycenaean Origins of Greek Mythology. 16.50 (ISBN 0-8446-6208-9). Peter Smith.

--The Mycenaen Origins of Greek Mythology. (Sather Classical Lectures: Vol.80). 278p. 1983. pap. 7.95 (ISBN 0-520-05073-8, CAL 655). U of Cal Pr.

Nilus. Protocols of the Learned Elders of Zion. Marsden, Victor E., ed. & tr. 1977. lib. bdg. 59.95 (ISBN 0-8490-1388-7). Gordon Pr.

Nilus of Sinai. Selected Texts on Prayer. pap. 0.25 (ISBN 0-317-11390-9). Eastern Orthodox.

Nima, Ramy. The Wrath of Allah: Islamic Revolution & Reaction in Iran. 170p. (Orig.). 1983. pap. 9.50 (ISBN 0-86104-733-8, Pub by Pluto Pr). Longwood Pub Group.

Nimeth, Albert J. In Your Time of Sorrow. 1976. pap. 0.50 (ISBN 0-685-77503-8). Franciscan Herald.

--Of Course I Love You. 1973. 5.00 (ISBN 0-8199-0466-X). Franciscan Herald.

--Tenderly I Care. 1977. 5.00 (ISBN 0-685-85844-8). Franciscan Herald.

--To Listen Is to Heal. 1984. 5.00 (ISBN 0-317-46887-1). Franciscan Herald.

Nimick, John A. Be Still & Know. LC 67-11989. 1967. 7.95 (ISBN 0-8022-1222-0). Philos Lib.

Ninde, Edward S. The Story of the American Hymn. LC 72-1708. (Illus.). Repr. of 1921 ed. 29.75 (ISBN 0-404-09914-9). AMS Pr.

Nineham, Dennis. The Use & Abuse of the Bible. LC 76-15690. (Library of Philosophy & Religion Ser.). (Illus.). 295p. 1976. text ed. 28.50x (ISBN 0-06-495178-2). B&N Imports.

Nineham, Dennis E. The Gospel of St. Mark: Commentaries. (Orig.). 1964. pap. 7.95 (ISBN 0-14-020489-X, Pelican). Penguin.

Ninomiya, Sontoku. Sage Ninomiya's Evening Talks. Yamagata, Isoh, tr. Repr. of 1953 ed. lib. bdg. 22.50x (ISBN 0-8371-3134-0, NIEV). Greenwood.

Nipham, Lama. Calm & Clear. 1985. 20.00x (ISBN 0-317-39045-7, Pub. by Luzac & Co Ltd). State Mutual Bk.

Nipp, Susan, jt. auth. see Beall, Pam.

Nipp, Susan H., jt. auth. see Beall, Pamela C.

Nir, Yeshayahu. The Bible & the Image: The History of Photography in the Holy Land, 1839-1899. LC 84-21997. (Illus.). 1985. 39.95 (ISBN 0-8122-7981-6). U of Pa Pr.

Niramayananda. Call of the Spirit: Conversion with Swami Akhandananda. 170p. 1987. pap. text ed. 3.50 (ISBN 0-87481-538-X, Pub. by Ramakrishna Math Madras India). Vedanta Pr.

Nirodbaran. Twelve Years with Sri Aurobindo. 306p. 1973. 5.00 (ISBN 0-89071-245-X); pap. 4.00 (ISBN 0-89071-244-1). Matagiri.

Nisargadatta Maharaj. The Blissful Life: As Realized Through the Teachings of Sri Nisargadatta Maharaj. Powell, Robert, compiled by. ix, 84p. pap. 6.95 (ISBN 0-89386-014-X). Acorn NC.

--I Am That; Talks with Sri Nisargadatta Maharaj. Frydman, Maurice, tr. from Marathi. Dikshit, Sudhakar S., ed. LC 81-66800. xx, 550p. 1986. Repr. of 1982 ed. 19.50 (ISBN 0-89386-002-6). Acorn NC.

--Prior to Consciousness: Talks with Sri Nisargadatta Maharaj. Dunn, Jean, ed. LC 85-71544. ix, 159p. (Orig.). pap. 9.95 (ISBN 0-317-19710-X). Acorn NC.

Nisbet, Alexander. First & Second Peter. (Geneva Series Commentaries). 14.95 (ISBN 0-85151-338-7). Banner of Truth.

Nishikawa, Kyotaro & Sano, Emily J. The Great Age of Japanese Buddhist Sculpture, AD 600-1300. LC 82-82805. (Illus.). 152p. (Orig.). 1982. 45.00 (ISBN 0-912804-07-6, Dist by U of Wash Pr); pap. 24.95 (ISBN 0-912804-08-4). Kimbell Art.

Nishitani, Keiji. Religion & Nothingness. Bragt, Jan Van, tr. from Japanese. LC 81-4084. 366p. 1982. 35.95x (ISBN 0-520-04329-4); pap. 10.95x (ISBN 0-520-04946-2, CAL 634). U of Cal Pr.

Nissenbaum, Stephen, jt. auth. see Boyer, Paul.

Nissenbaum, Stephen, jt. ed. see Boyer, Paul.

Nissiotis, N. Interpreting Orthodoxy. 1980. pap. 2.95 (ISBN 0-937032-23-9). Light&Life Pub Co MN.

Nitchie, Elizabeth. Reverend Colonel Finch. LC 40-33650. Repr. of 1940 ed. 12.50 (ISBN 0-404-04777-7). AMS Pr.

Nitobe, Inazo. Bushido: The Soul of Japan. LC 77-83070. 1969. Repr. of 1905 ed. 7.25 (ISBN 0-8048-0693-4). C E Tuttle.

Nitti, Francesco. Catholic Socialism. 1976. lib. bdg. 69.95 (ISBN 0-8490-1586-3). Gordon Pr.

Nityaswarupananda, Swami, tr. see Astavakra.

Nivedita, Sr. Complete Works of Sister Nivedita, 4 vols. Incl. Vol. 1. Our Master & His Message, the Master As I Saw Him, Kali the Mother, Lectures & Articles (ISBN 0-87481-112-0); Vol. 2. The Web of Indian Life, an Indian Study on Love & Death, Studies from an Eastern Home, Lectures & Articles (ISBN 0-87481-113-9); Vol. 3. Indian Art, Cradle Tales of Hinduism, Religion & Dharma (ISBN 0-87481-114-7); Vol. 4. Footfalls of Indian History, Bodh-Gaya, Civic Ideal & Indian Nationality, Hints on National Education in India (ISBN 0-87481-115-5); Vol. V. Lectures & Writings (ISBN 0-87481-226-7). 60.00x set (ISBN 0-87481-216-X). Vedanta Pr.

--Cradle Tales of Hinduism. (Illus.). 329p. 1972. pap. 5.95 (ISBN 0-87481-131-7). Vedanta Pr.

--Master As I Saw Him. 6.95 (ISBN 0-87481-088-4). Vedanta Pr.

--Notes of Some Wanderings. 3.00 (ISBN 0-87481-185-6). Vedanta Pr.

--Siva & Buddha. pap. 0.50 (ISBN 0-87481-116-3). Vedanta Pr.

Nivedita, Sr., jt. auth. see Coomaraswamy, Ananda K.

Nivison, David S. & Wright, Arthur F., eds. Confucianism in Action. LC 59-7433. 1959. 30.00x (ISBN 0-8047-0554-2). Stanford U Pr.

Niwano, Nichiko. My Father My Teacher: A Spiritual Journey. Gage, Richard L., tr. from Jap. 143p. (Orig.). 1982. pap. 3.50 (ISBN 4-333-01095-0, Pub. by Kosei Pub Co Japan). C E Tuttle.

Niwano, Nikkyo. Buddhism for Today: A Modern Interpretation of the Threefold Lotus Sutra. LC 79-22383. 476p. 1976. pap. 10.95 (ISBN 0-8348-0147-7). Weatherhill.

--A Buddhist Approach to Peace. Nezu, Masuo, tr. from Japanese. (Illus.). 162p. 1977. 7.95 (ISBN 4-333-00308-3, Pub. by Kosei Publishing Co). C E Tuttle.

--Lifetime Beginner: An Autobiography. Gage, Richard L., tr. from Japanese. Orig. Title: Shoshin Issho & Niwano Nikkyo Jiden. (Illus.). 344p. 1978. 14.95 (Pub. by Kosei Publishing Co). C E Tuttle.

--Shakyamuni Buddha: A Narrative Biography. rev. ed. Davis, Rebecca M., ed. Miyazaki, Kojiro, tr. from Japanese. LC 80-154779. Orig. Title: Bukkyo No Inochi Hokeyo. (Illus.). 128p. 1980. pap. 3.50 (ISBN 4-333-01001-2, Pub. by Kosei Publishing Co). C E Tuttle.

Nix, Verolga & Cleveland, Jefferson, eds. Songs of Zion. LC 81-8039. 352p. (Orig.). 1981. pap. 7.95 accompanist ed. (ISBN 0-687-39121-0); pap. 7.95 (ISBN 0-687-39120-2). Abingdon.

Nix, William E., jt. auth. see Geisler, Norman L.

Nixon, David. The Year of the Locust. 138p. (Orig.). 1980. pap. 3.95 (ISBN 0-8341-0675-2). Beacon Hill.

Nixon, David L., jt. auth. see Jones, Terry L.

Nixon, E. Anna. A Century of Planting: A History of the American Friends Mission in India. LC 85-72070. (Illus.). 493p. (Orig.). 1985. 16.95x (ISBN 0-913342-55-6); pap. 11.95 (ISBN 0-913342-54-8). Barclay Pr.

Nizami. Layla & Majnun. Gelpke, R., ed. & tr. from Persian. LC 78-58219. 206p. 1978. pap. 8.95 (ISBN 0-87773-133-0). Shambhala Pubns.

Nizami, Ashraf F. Namaz the Yoga of Islam. (Illus.). xxiii, 46p. 1981. text ed. 5.95x (ISBN 0-86590-052-3, Pub. by Taraporevala India). Apt Bks.

N. J. Insurrection - Resurrection. (Illus.). 1976. pap. 1.25 (ISBN 0-686-16521-7). Working Peoples Art.

Noble, Bernard, tr. see Scheler, Max F.

Noble, E. Myron. The Gospel of Music: A Key to Understanding a Major Chord of Ministry. LC 85-63559. 159p. (Orig.). 1986. pap. 4.95 (ISBN 0-9616056-1-8). Mid Atl Reg Pr.

Noble, E. Myron, jt. ed. see DuPree, Sherry S.

Noble, M. E., jt. auth. see Coomaraswamy, A. K.

Noble, Margaret. Kali the Mother. 110p. 1985. pap. 2.00 (ISBN 0-87481-104-X, Pub. by Advaita Ashrama India). Vedanta Pr.

Noble, Margaret see Nivedita, Sr.

Noble, R. Shakespeare's Biblical Knowledge. 59.95 (ISBN 0-8490-1039-X). Gordon Pr.

Noble, Richmond. Shakespeare's Biblical Knowledge & Use of the Book of Common Prayer. 1970. lib. bdg. 20.00x (ISBN 0-374-96115-8, Octagon). Hippocrene Bks.

Noble, Richmond S. Shakespeare's Biblical Knowledge & Use of the Book of Common Prayer: As Exemplified in the Plays of the First Folio. 303p. 1980. Repr. of 1935 ed. lib. bdg. 37.50 (ISBN 0-8492-1971-X). R West.

Noble, Ruth A. Wow! God Made Me. 1981. 5.75 (ISBN 0-89536-479-4, 2330). CSS of Ohio.

Noble, Thomas F. X. The Republic of St. Peter: The Birth of the Papal State, 680-825. LC 83-21870. (The Middle Ages Ser.). (Illus.). 416p. 1984. 36.95x (ISBN 0-8122-7917-4); pap. 14.95. U of Pa Pr.

Noble, Vicki. Motherpeace: A Way to the Goddess Through Myth, Art & Tarot. LC 82-47752. (Illus.). 240p. (Orig.). 1982. pap. 12.95 (ISBN 0-06-066300-6, CN4039, HarpR). Har-Row.

Noblett, Robert A. A Main Street Gospel. 1983. 4.75 (ISBN 0-89536-608-8, 1341). CSS of Ohio.

Nobo, Jorge L. Whitehead's Metaphysics of Extension & Solidarity. (Philosophy Ser.). 544p. (Orig.). 1986. 49.50x (ISBN 0-88706-261-X); pap. 24.50x (ISBN 0-88706-262-8). State U NY Pr.

Nock, Arthur D. Essays on Religion & the Ancient World. Stewart, Zeph, ed. 1164p. 1986. Set. 98.00x (ISBN 0-19-814282-X). Oxford U Pr.

Noddings, Nel & Shore, Paul J. Awakening the Inner Eye: Intuition in Education. LC 83-1805. 236p. 1984. 26.95x (ISBN 0-8077-2751-2). Tchrs Coll.

Noe, Tom. The Sixth Day. LC 79-55296. (Illus.). 80p. (Orig.). 1979. pap. 2.95 (ISBN 0-87793-190-9). Ave Maria.

Noel, Daniel. Approaching Earth. (Chrysalis Bk.). 192p. (Orig.). 1986. pap. 14.95 (ISBN 0-916349-12-8). Amity Hous Inc.

Noel, Gerard. Cardinal Basil Hume. (Profiles Ser.). (Illus.). 64p. 1984. 8.95 (ISBN 0-241-11204-4, Pub. by Hamish Hamilton England). David & Charles.

Noer, Deliar. Administration of Islam in Indonesia. (Monograph Ser.). 1978. pap. 4.50 (ISBN 0-87763-002-X). Cornell Mod Indo.

Noerdlinger, Henry S. Moses & Egypt: The Documentation to the Motion Picture "the Ten Commandments". LC 56-12886. 202p. 1956. pap. 1.95 (ISBN 0-88474-007-2). U of S Cal Pr.

Noettl, Margaret, jt. auth. see Brusius, Ron.

Noffke, Suzanne, ed. Catherine of Siena: The Dialogue. LC 79-56755. (Classics of Western Spirituality Ser.). 416p. 1980. 13.95 (ISBN 0-8091-0295-1); pap. 10.95 (ISBN 0-8091-2233-2). Paulist Pr.

--Prayers of Catherine of Siena. LC 82-60746. 288p. 1983. pap. 9.95 (ISBN 0-8091-2508-0). Paulist Pr.

Noffsinger, John S. A Program for Higher Education in the Church of the Brethren. LC 78-177711. (Columbia University. Teachers College. Contributions to Education: No. 172). Repr. of 1925 ed. 22.50 (ISBN 0-404-55172-6). AMS Pr.

Nogent, Guibert De see De Nogent, Guibert.

Nohl, Frederick. Martin Luther: Hero of Faith. LC 62-14146. (Illus.). 1962. pap. 5.25 (ISBN 0-570-03727-1, 12-2629). Concordia.

Nolan, Albert. Jesus Before Christianity. LC 78-6708. 156p. (Orig.). 1978. pap. 8.95 (ISBN 0-88344-230-2). Orbis Bks.

Nolan, Hugh J., ed. Pastoral Letters of the United States Catholic Bishops: 1792-1983, 4 vols. 1890p. 1984. pap. 95.00 (ISBN 1-55586-897-5). US Catholic.

--Pastoral Letters of the United States Catholic Bishops, 1975-1983, Vol. IV. 616p. 1984. pap. 24.95 (ISBN 1-55586-875-4). US Catholic.

--Pastoral Letters of the United States Catholic Bishops, 1962-1974, Vol. III. 511p. 1984. pap. 24.95 (ISBN 1-55586-870-3). US Catholic.

--Pastoral Letters of the United States Catholic Bishops, 1941-1961, Vol. II. 271p. 1984. pap. 24.95 (ISBN 1-55586-885-1). US Catholic.

--Pastoral Letters of the United States Catholic Bishops, 1792-1940, Vol. I. 487p. 1984. pap. 24.95 (ISBN 1-55586-880-0). US Catholic.

Nolan, James L. Discovery of the Lost Art Treasures of California's First Mission. Pourade, Richard F., ed. LC 78-73173. (Illus.). 128p. 1978. 20.00 (ISBN 0-913938-20-3). Copley Bks.

Nolan, Richard T. & Kirkpatrick, Frank G. Living Issues in Ethics. 400p. 1982. pap. text ed. write for info. (ISBN 0-534-01140-3). Wadsworth Pub.

Nold, Liselotte, jt. auth. see Harupa, Gisela.

Nolde, O. Frederick, ed. Toward World-Wide Christianity. LC 70-86049. (Essay & General Literature Index Reprint Ser). 1969. Repr. of 1946 ed. 23.50x (ISBN 0-8046-0581-5, Pub by Kennikat). Assoc Faculty Pr.

Noll, Mark, jt. ed. see Lundin, Roger.

Noll, Mark A. Christians & the American Revolution. LC 77-23354. pap. 48.80 (ISBN 0-8357-9125-4, 2016042). Bks Demand UMI.

Noll, Mark A., ed. Charles Hodge: The Way of Life & Selected Writings. 1987. 12.95. Paulist Pr.

Noll, Mark A., compiled by. The Princeton Theology: An Anthology. 432p. (Orig.). 1983. pap. 14.95 (ISBN 0-8010-6737-5). Baker Bk.

Noll, Mark A., jt. ed. see Hatch, Nathan O.

Noll, Mark A., et al. The Search for Christian America. LC 83-71239. 168p. 1983. pap. 6.95 (ISBN 0-89107-285-3, Crossway Bks). Good News.

Noll, Mark A., et al, eds. Eerdmans' Handbook to Christianity in America. LC 83-1656. (Illus.). 544p. 1983. 24.95 (ISBN 0-8028-3582-1). Eerdmans.

Noll, Peter. On Death & Dying. 1987. price not set (ISBN 0-670-80703-6). Viking.

Nolt, Marilyn, jt. auth. see Peifer, Jane.

Nommensen, B. P. Comfort for the Sick. rev. ed. 1976. pap. 5.00 (ISBN 0-8100-0011-3, 06N0553). Northwest Pub.

Nomura, Yushi. Desert Wisdom: Sayings from the Desert Fathers. LC 82-45488. (Illus.). 128p. 1982. 14.95 (ISBN 0-385-18078-0). Doubleday.

--Desert Wisdom: Sayings from the Desert Fathers. LC 82-45488. (Illus.). 128p. 1984. pap. 8.95 (ISBN 0-385-18079-9, Im). Doubleday.

Noon, Scott. Building a Fort in the Family Tree. 1984. 3.50 (ISBN 0-89536-703-3, 4884). CSS of Ohio.

Noonan, Breda, ed. see Gaspar, Karl.

Noonan, Eileen. Books for Catholic Elementary Schools. pap. 2.50 (ISBN 0-87507-024-8). Cath Lib Assn.

Noonan, Hugh. Companion to the Clams. (Illus.). 1980. pap. 10.50 (ISBN 0-8199-0680-8). Franciscan Herald.

Noonan, John T. The Believer & the Powers That Are: Cases, History, & Other Data Bearing on the Relation of Religion & Government. LC 86-28440. 1987. 35.00 (ISBN 0-02-923161-2). Macmillan.

Noonan, John T., Jr. Power to Dissolve: Lawyers & Marriages in the Courts of the Roman Curia. LC 75-176044. (Illus.). 464p. 1972. 30.00x (ISBN 0-674-69575-5, Belknap Pr). Harvard U Pr.

Noonan, John T., Jr., intro. by. The Morality of Abortion: Legal & Historical Perspectives. LC 70-129118. 276p. 1970. pap. text ed. 6.95x (ISBN 0-674-58727-8). Harvard U Pr.

Noonan, John T., Jr., et al, eds. The Role & Responsibility of the Moral Philosopher: Proceedings, Vol. 56. LC 81-69068. 214p. 1983. pap. 15.00 (ISBN 0-918090-16-4). Am Cath Philo.

Noorbergen, Rene. Ellen G. White: Prophet of Destiny. LC 70-190456. 363p. 1970. text ed. 6.95 (ISBN 0-87983-014-X); pap. 2.50 (ISBN 0-87983-077-8); spanish version 1.95 (ISBN 0-87983-076-X). MMI Pr.

--Noah's Ark Found! The End of the Search. Golbitz, Pat, ed. LC 86-33162. (Illus.). 192p. 1987. 14.95 (ISBN 0-688-06456-6). Morrow.

Noord, Glenn Van, jt. auth. see Hendricks, William C.

Noordewier, Helen C. Missy Doe & Other Benjy Stories. (Voyager Ser.). 96p. (Orig.). 1981. pap. 2.50 (ISBN 0-8010-6732-4). Baker Bk.

Noordtzij, A. Bible Student's Commentary: Leviticus. (Bible Student's Commentary Ser.). 288p. 1982. 16.95 (ISBN 0-310-45090-X, 11757). Zondervan.

--Bible Student's Commentary: Numbers. (Bible Student's Commentary Ser.). 1986. 16.95 (ISBN 0-310-43980-9, 11758). Zondervan.

Norbeck, E. Religion in Human Life: Anthropological Views. LC 73-7862. (Basic Anthropology Unit Ser.). 1974. pap. text ed. 9.95 (ISBN 0-03-091284-9, HoltC). H HOlt & Co.

Norbeck, Edward. Religion & Society in Modern Japan. (Rice University Studies: Vol. 56, No. 1). 232p. 1970. pap. 10.00x (ISBN 0-89263-203-8). Rice Univ.

Norbert. Das Leben des Bischofs Benno der Zweiter von Osnabruck. Bd. with Ausfuehrliches Namenregister und Sachregister Mit Genauem Inhalsverzeichnis der Seither Erschienene Baende 1-90. (Die Geschichtschreiber der Deutschen Vorzeit Ser: Vol. 91). (Ger.). 12.00 (ISBN 0-384-41895-3). Johnson Repr.

Norbie, D. L. Baptism: The Church's Troubled Water. 1985. pap. 1.75 (ISBN 0-937396-66-4). Walterick Pubs.

Norbie, Don. New Testament Church Organization. pap. 2.50 (ISBN 0-937396-28-1). Walterick Pubs.

Norbie, Donald L. The Lord's Supper: The Church's Love Feast. 1986. pap. 2.25 (ISBN 0-937396-67-2). Walterick Pubs.

Norbu, Namkhai. The Crystal & the Way of Light: Meditation, Contemplation & Self Liberation. Shane, John, ed. (Illus.). 224p. 1986. pap. 14.95 (ISBN 0-7102-0833-2, 08332). Methuen Inc.

--The Cycle of Day & Night, Where One Proceeds along the Path of the Primordial Yoga: A Basic Text on the Practice of Dzog Chen. 80p. Date not set. 8.50 (ISBN 0-931892-09-0). B Dolphin Pub.

--The Cycle of Day & Night: Where One Proceeds Along the Path of the Primordial Yoga; A Basic Tibetan Text on the Practice of Dzogchen. Reynolds, John, ed. & tr. from Tibetan. (Illus.). 128p. 1987. pap. 9.95 (ISBN 0-88268-040-4). Station Hill Pr.

--Dzog Chen & Zen. Lipman, Kennard, ed. Norbu, Namkhai, tr. from Ital. (Illus.). 52p. (Orig.). 1987. pap. 5.00 (ISBN 0-931892-08-2). B Dolphin Pub.

Norbu, Namkhai, tr. see Manjusrimitra.

Norbu, Namkhai, tr. see Norbu, Namkhai.

Norbu, Tenzin, tr. see Gyatso, Geshe K.

Norbu, Thinley. A Brief Fantasy History of a Himalayan. LC 84-29754. (Orig.). Date not set. pap. 10.00 (ISBN 0-9607000-1-3). Jewel Pub Hse.

--Magic Dance: The Display of the Self-Nature of the Five Wisdom Dakinis. rev. ed. LC 85-59. 166p. (Orig.). 1981. pap. 10.00 (ISBN 0-9607000-0-5). Jewel Pub Hse.

--The Small Golden Key to the Treasure of the Various Essential Necessities of General & Extraordinary Buddhist Dharma. rev. ed. LC 84-29724. 111p. 1985. pap. 10.00 (ISBN 0-9607000-2-1). Jewel Pub Hse.

Norbu, Thinley, tr. see Rinpoche, Patrul.

Norbu, Thubten Jigme, tr. see Kaufmann, Walter.

Norbu, Tsampa Yeshe. Rasa Tantra: Blood Marriage, The Sacred Initiation, A Marriage of the Faiths of East & West. (Illus.). 36p. 1980. pap. 6.95 (ISBN 0-9609802-2-9). Life Science.

Nordau, Max. The Psychology of Mysticism, 2 Vols. 271p. 1985. Set. 249.50 (ISBN 0-89920-099-0). Am Inst Psych.

Norden, Eduard. Aus Altromischen Priesterbuchern. facsimile ed. LC 75-10644. (Ancient Religion & Mythology Ser.). (Ger.). 1976. Repr. of 1939 ed. 23.50x (ISBN 0-405-07019-5). Ayer Co Pubs.

Norden, Hugo. The Technique of Canon. 1982. pap. 9.00 (ISBN 0-8283-1839-5). Branden Pub Co.

Norden, John. A Pensive Mans Practise. LC 77-171776. (English Experience Ser.: No. 401). 192p. 1971. Repr. of 1584 ed. 18.50 (ISBN 90-221-0401-X). Walter J Johnson.

--Progress of Piety. Repr. of 1847 ed. 21.00 (ISBN 0-384-41910-0). Johnson Repr.

Norden, Rudolph. Introducing the Books of the Bible: A Devotional Summary. 64p. 1987. pap. 3.95 (ISBN 0-570-04452-9, 12-3061). Concordia.

Norden, Rudolph F. Day by Day with Jesus. 400p. (Orig.). 1985. pap. 10.95 (ISBN 0-570-03971-1, 12-3006). Concordia.

--Radiant Faith. Feucht, Oscar E., ed. 1966. pap. 1.60 study guide (ISBN 0-570-03527-9, 14-1330); pap. 1.95 leader's manual (ISBN 0-570-03528-7, 14-1331). Concordia.

--Symbols & Their Meaning. 1985. pap. 3.50 (ISBN 0-570-03949-5, 12-2883). Concordia.

Norden, Walter. Papsttum Und Byzanz: Das Problem Ihrer Wiedervereinigung Bis Zum Untergange Des Byzantinischen Reichs (1453) 1903. 40.50 (ISBN 0-8337-2571-8). B Franklin.

Nordenfalk, Carl, ed. Medieval & Renaissance Miniatures from the National Gallery of Art. LC 74-28397. (Illus.). pap. 8.95 (ISBN 0-89468-017-X). Natl Gallery Art.

Nordenhaug, Joseph, tr. see Blanke, Fritz.

Nordewin, Dr., tr. see Lorber, Jakob.

Nordheim, Eckhard von see Von Nordheim, Eckhard.

Nordon, Hugo, tr. Chorale Harmonization in the Church Modes. 1974. pap. 3.75 (ISBN 0-8008-1516-5, Crescendo). Taplinger.

Nordtvedt, Matilda. The Family Idea Book: Praying & Playing Together. (Orig.). 1984. pap. 5.95 (ISBN 0-8024-0436-7). Moody.

--Living Beyond Depression. LC 78-58082. 128p. 1978. pap. 3.50 (ISBN 0-87123-339-8, 200339). Bethany Hse.

Nordtvedt, Matilda & Steinkuehler, Pearl. Programs for Special Occasions. (Orig.). 1984. pap. 4.95 (ISBN 0-8024-1218-1). Moody.

Nordyke, Cyndy, jt. auth. see Nordyke, Spencer.

Nordyke, Spencer & Nordyke, Cyndy. Essentials of Basic Youth Ministry. 49p. (Orig.). 1984. wkbk. 4.95 (ISBN 0-914307-21-5). Word Faith.

Norelius, Eric. The Pioneer Swedish Settlements & Swedish Lutheran Churches in America 1845-1860. Bergendoff, Conrad, tr. from Swedish. LC 84-71391. (Publication Ser.: No. 31). Orig. Title: De Svenska Luterska Forsamlingarnas och Svenska Historia i Amerika. 419p. 1984. 15.00 (ISBN 0-910184-31-3). Augustana.

Norgren, William, et al, eds. What Can We Share? A Lutheran-Episcopal Resource & Study Guide. (Lutheran-Episcopal Dialogue Ser.). 88p. (Orig.). 1985. pap. 2.00 (ISBN 0-88028-047-6). Forward Movement.

Norheim, Karen. Mrs. Preacher. 160p. (Orig.). 1985. pap. 3.95 (ISBN 0-89900-204-8). College Pr Pub.

Norick, Sylvester. Outdoor Life in the Menominee Forest. 1979. 7.95 (ISBN 0-8199-0767-7). Franciscan Herald.

Norihiko Kikumura. Shinran: His Life & Thought. LC 70-172538. 192p. 1972. 9.95 (ISBN 0-685-65548-2). Nembutsu Pr.

Norman, Dwayne, ed. Your Beginning with God. 31p. 1982. pap. 1.95 (ISBN 0-88144-063-9). Christian Pub.

Norman, E. R. Christianity & the World Order. 1979. pap. 6.95x (ISBN 0-19-283019-8). Oxford U Pr.

Norman, Edward. Christianity in the Southern Hemisphere: The Churches in Latin America & South Africa. 1981. text ed. 38.95x (ISBN 0-19-821127-9). Oxford U Pr.

--The English Catholic Church in the Nineteenth Century. 1984. pap. 13.95x (ISBN 0-19-822955-0). Oxford U Pr.

--Roman Catholicism in England from the Elizabethan Settlement to the Second Vatican Council. (OPUS). 160p. 1985. 18.95x (ISBN 0-19-219181-0); pap. 9.95 (ISBN 0-19-281935-6). Oxford U Pr.

--The Victorian Christian Socialists. 210p. Date not set. price not set (ISBN 0-521-32515-3). Cambridge U Pr.

Norman, Edward R. & English, Raymond. Ethics & Nuclear Arms: European & American Perspectives. LC 85-10304. 1985. pap. 7.00 (ISBN 0-89633-095-8). Ethics & Public Policy.

Norman, Ernest L. The Anthenium. 1964. 4.95 (ISBN 0-932642-13-6). Unarius Pubns.

--Cosmic Continuum. 2nd ed. (Illus.). 1960. 7.95 (ISBN 0-932642-17-9). Unarius Pubns.

--The Elysium. (Illus.). 1956. 4.95 (ISBN 0-932642-14-4). Unarius Pubns.

Norman, H. C., ed. see Dhammapadatthakatha.

Norman, Louise. God's Power Versus Satan's Power: Christian Life Lessons. (Teaching Bks.). (Illus.). 64p. (Orig.). 1985. pap. text ed. 8.95 (ISBN 0-86508-062-3). BCM Intl Inc.

Norman, Richard. The Moral Philosophers: An Introduction to Ethics. 1983. 29.95x (ISBN 0-19-875060-9); pap. 10.95x (ISBN 0-19-875059-5). Oxford U Pr.

Norman, Ruth. Science, Politics & the Great Deception, Religion. 530p. (Orig.). 1987. text ed. 14.95 (ISBN 0-932642-93-4). Unarius Pubns.

Norman, Ruth & Spaegel, Charles. Principles & Practice of Past Life Therapy. (Illus.). 500p. 1984. 10.95 (ISBN 0-932642-79-9). Unarius Pubns.

Norman, Ruth, intro. by. Glowing Moments. 170p. (Orig.). 1982. pap. 4.95 (ISBN 0-932642-76-4). Unarius Pubns.

Norman, Ruth, ed. see Dallison, Dennis.

Norman, Ruth E. Bridge to Heaven. 1969. 8.95 (ISBN 0-932642-10-1). Unarius Pubns.

--History of the Universe, Vol. 2. (Illus.). 450p. 1982. 9.95x (ISBN 0-932642-72-1). Unarius Pubns.

--Keys to the Universe & the Mind. (Tesla Speaks Ser.: Vol. 11). (Illus.). 1977. 12.50 (ISBN 0-932642-34-9). Unarius Pubns.

--Mars Underground Cities Discovered. (Tesla Speaks Ser.: Vol. 12). (Illus.). 1977. 7.95 (ISBN 0-932642-35-7); pap. 6.95 (ISBN 0-932642-46-2). Unarius Pubns.

--Your Encounter with Life, Death & Immortality. (Illus.). 1978. pap. 2.00 (ISBN 0-932642-43-8). Unarius Pubns.

Norman, Ruth E., et al. The Masters Speak, 2 vols. (Tesla Speaks Ser.: No. 8). (Illus.). 1975. 8.95 ea.; Vol. 1. (ISBN 0-932642-30-6); Vol. 2. (ISBN 0-932642-29-2). Unarius Pubns.

Norquist, Marilyn. The Bible: Its Heroes & Its Message. 96p. 1985. pap. 2.95 (ISBN 0-89243-227-6). Liguori Pubns.

--Biblical Guidelines for Discovering God's Kingdom. LC 82-81769. 64p. 1982. pap. 4.25 (ISBN 0-89243-160-1). Liguori Pubns.

--Como Leer y Orar los Evangelios. McPhee, John, ed. Diaz, Olimpia, tr. from Eng. (Handbook of the Bible Ser.). Orig. Title: Hand. 64p. 1980. pap. 1.50 (ISBN 0-89243-127-X). Liguori Pubns.

--How to Read & Pray the Gospels. (Handbook of the Bible Ser.). 1979. pap. 1.95 (ISBN 0-89243-099-0). Liguori Pubns.

--How to Read & Pray the Prophets. (Handbook of the Bible Ser.). (Orig.). 1980. pap. 1.50 (ISBN 0-89243-122-9, 44900). Liguori Pubns.

--Jesus' Pattern for a Happy Life: The Beatitudes. 112p. 1986. pap. 3.50 (ISBN 0-89243-136-9). Liguori Pubns.

--Thy Kingdom Come: The Basic Teachings of Jesus. 64p. 1986. pap. 1.50 (ISBN 0-89243-244-6). Liguori Pubns.

Norris, Bill & Norris, Judy, eds. What the Bible Says about Families. (What the Bible Says Ser.). 425p. (Orig.). text ed. 13.95 (ISBN 0-89900-099-1). College Pr Pub.

Norris, Docia W. Religious Science for Youth. pap. 1.50 (ISBN 0-87516-153-7). De Vorss.

Norris, Elwood G. Be Not Deceived: A Scriptural Refutation of the Adam-God Theory. LC 78-70362. 141p. 1978. 8.95 (ISBN 0-88290-101-X). Horizon Utah.

Norris, John. Christian Blessedness (with) Reflections upon a Late Essay Concerning Human Understanding. Wellek, Rene, ed. LC 75-11241. (British Philosophers & Theologians of the 17th & 18th Centuries Ser.). 1978. Repr. of 1690 ed. lib. bdg. 51.00 (ISBN 0-8240-1793-5). Garland Pub.

--Treatises Upon Several Subjects. Wellek, Rene, ed. LC 75-11244. (British Philosophers & Theologians of the 17th & 18th Centuries Ser.). 1978. Repr. of 1698 ed. lib. bdg. 51.00 (ISBN 0-8240-1796-X). Garland Pub.

Norris, Judy, jt. ed. see Norris, Bill.

Norris, Margot. Beasts of the Modern Imagination: Darwin, Nietzsche, Kafka, & Lawrence. LC 84-21320. 256p. 1985. text ed. 26.50x (ISBN 0-8018-3252-7). Johns Hopkins.

Norris, Richard A. Understanding the Faith of the Church. (Church's Teaching Ser.: Vol. 4). 288p. 1979. 5.95 (ISBN 0-8164-0421-6, HarpR); pap. 3.95 (ISBN 0-8164-2217-6, Crossroad Bks); user guide .95 (ISBN 0-8164-2224-9). Har-Row.

Norris, Richard A., tr. see Norris, Richard A., Jr. & Rusch, William G.

Norris, Richard A., Jr. & Rusch, William G., eds. The Christological Controversy. Norris, Richard A., tr. LC 79-8890. (Sources of Early Christian Thought). 176p. 1980. pap. 7.95 (ISBN 0-8006-1411-9, 1-1411). Fortress.

Norrisey, Marie C., jt. auth. see Michael, Chester P.

North American Protestant Ministries Overseas. Mission Handbook. 13th ed. 1986. write for info. World Vision Intl.

North, Anthony. Islamic Arms. (The Victoria & Albert Introductions to Decorative Arts Ser.). (Illus.). 48p. 1986. 9.95 (ISBN 0-88045-078-9). Stemmer Hse.

North Berwick Priory. Carte Monialium De Northberwic. Innes, Cosmo, ed. LC 74-173799. (Bannatyne Club, Edinburgh. Publications: No. 84). Repr. of 1847 ed. 27.50 (ISBN 0-404-52809-0). AMS Pr.

North, Brownlow. The Rich Man & Lazarus. 1979. pap. 2.95 (ISBN 0-85151-121-X). Banner of Truth.

North, Gary. Backward, Christian Soldiers? 294p. 1984. pap. 4.95 (ISBN 0-930464-01-X). Dominion Pr.

--The Dominion Covenant: Genesis. 1982. 14.95 (ISBN 0-930464-03-6). Inst Christian.

--Honest Money. (The Biblical Blueprint Ser.). Date not set. pap. 6.95 (ISBN 0-8407-3094-2). Nelson.

--Moses & Pharaoh: Dominion Religion vs. Power Religion. 430p. 1985. pap. text ed. 12.50 (ISBN 0-930464-05-2). Inst Christian.

--Seventy-Five Bible Questions Your Instructors Pray You Won't Ask. 280p. (Orig.). 1984. pap. 4.95 (ISBN 0-930462-03-3). Am Bur Eco Res.

--Unconditional Surrender: God's Program for Victory. 2nd ed. LC 82-84385. 280p. 1983. pap. text ed. 9.95 (ISBN 0-939404-06-0). Geneva Ministr.

North, Gary, ed. Tactics of Christian Resistance. LC 83-81783. (Christianity & Civilization Ser.: No. 3). 528p. 1983. pap. 14.95 (ISBN 0-939404-07-9). Geneva Ministr.

North, Helen. From Myth to Icon: Reflections of Greek Ethical Doctrine in Literature & Art. LC 79-7619. (Cornell Studies in Classical Philology). (Illus.). 288p. 1979. 29.95x (ISBN 0-8014-1135-1). Cornell U Pr.

North, Ira. Balance, A Tried & Tested Formula for Church Growth. 1983. pap. 5.95 (ISBN 0-89225-270-7). Gospel Advocate.

North, J. B. From Pentecost to the Present. LC 82-74538. 520p. (Orig.). 1983. 18.95 (ISBN 0-89900-230-7). College Pr Pub.

North, James B. The Church of the New Testament. (Restoration Booklets Ser.). (Illus., Orig.). 1984. 0.75 (ISBN 0-87239-779-3, 3299). Standard Pub.

North, Robert. Psalms. (Bible Ser.). Pt. 3. pap. 1.00 (ISBN 0-8091-5125-1); Pt. 4. pap. 1.00 (ISBN 0-8091-5126-X); Pt. 5. pap. 1.00 (ISBN 0-8091-5127-8); Pt. 6. pap. 1.00 (ISBN 0-8091-5128-6). Paulist Pr.

Northbrooke, John. Treatise Against Dicing, Dancing, Plays & Interludes. LC 77-149667. Repr. of 1843 ed. 19.00 (ISBN 0-404-04793-9). AMS Pr.

Northcote, Hugh. Christianity & Sex Problems. 2nd ed. LC 72-9668. Repr. of 1916 ed. 49.50 (ISBN 0-404-57486-6). AMS Pr.

Northcutt, David L. Financial Management for Clergy. 192p. 1984. pap. 6.95 (ISBN 0-8010-6740-5). Baker Bk.

Northeast Center for Youth Ministry Staff, jt. auth. see Reynolds, Brian.

Northrup, Marguerite. Christmas Story: From the Gospels of Matthew & Luke. LC 65-23504. (Illus.). 1966. 8.95 (ISBN 0-87099-047-0, 139459, Pub. by Metro Mus Art). NYGS.

Northrup, Melvin. Toby's Gift. (Books I Can Read). 32p. (Orig.). 1980. pap. 1.95 (ISBN 0-8127-0291-3). Review & Herald.

Norton, Andrews. Discourse on the Latest Form of Infidelity. LC 71-122660. 1971. Repr. of 1839 ed. 18.00x (ISBN 0-8046-1309-5, Pub. by Kennikat). Assoc Faculty Pr.

Norton, Augustus R. Amal & the Shi'a: Struggle for the Soul of Lebanon. (Modern Middle East Ser.: No. 13). (Illus.). 264p. 1987. text ed. 25.00x (ISBN 0-292-73039-X); pap. 10.95 (ISBN 0-292-73040-3). U of Tex Pr.

Norton, Charles E. Historical Studies of Church-Building in the Middle Ages. LC 78-95072. (Select Bibliographies Reprint Ser.). 1902. 32.00 (ISBN 0-8369-5072-0). Ayer Co Pubs.

--Historical Studies of Church Building in the Middle Ages: Venice, Sienna, Florence. 1977. lib. bdg. 39.95 (ISBN 0-8490-1962-1). Gordon Pr.

--Historical Studies of Church-Building in the Middle Ages: Venice, Siena, Florence. LC 78-15869. 1978. Repr. of 1880 ed. lib. bdg. 35.00 (ISBN 0-89341-361-5). Longwood Pub Group.

Norton, Daniel S. & Rushton, Peters. Classical Myths in English Literature. Repr. of 1952 ed. lib. bdg. 39.75x (ISBN 0-8371-2440-9, NOCM). Greenwood.

Norton, David L. Personal Destinies: A Philosophy of Ethical Individualism. 1976. 47.50x (ISBN 0-691-07215-9); pap. 10.95x (ISBN 0-691-01975-4). Princeton U Pr.

Norton, Herman A. Religion in Tennessee, Seventeen Seventy-Seven to Nineteen Forty-Five. LC 81-1562. (Tennessee Three Star Ser.). (Illus.). 136p. 1981. pap. 3.50 (ISBN 0-87049-318-3). U of Tenn Pr.

Norton, John. Abel Being Dead, Yet Speaketh. LC 78-8184. 1978. Repr. of 1658 ed. 30.00x (ISBN 0-8201-1310-7). Schol Facsimiles.

--The Orthodox Evangelist. LC 78-280. (American Puritan Writings Ser.: No. 11). Repr. of 1654 ed. 67.50 (ISBN 0-404-60811-6). AMS Pr.

Norton, Wesley. Religious Newspapers in the Old Northwest to 1861: A History, Bibliography, & Record of Opinion. LC 75-36983. xi, 196p. 1977. 12.50x (ISBN 0-8214-0193-9). Ohio U Pr.

Norton, Wilbert H., jt. auth. see Engel, James F.

Norvell. Amazing Secrets of the Mystic East. cancelled 14.95 (ISBN 0-13-023754-X, Parker). P-H.

Norweb, Jeanne. The Forbidden Door. LC 82-84552. (Illus.). 216p. 1985. pap. 5.95 (ISBN 0-89191-937-6, 59378, Chariot Bks). Cook.

Norwell, Alexander. Catechism Written in Latin Together with the Same Catechism Translated into English. Repr. of 1853 ed. 25.00 (ISBN 0-384-42090-7). Johnson Repr.

Norwich England Diocese. Visitations of the Diocese of Norwich, A. D. 1492-1532. Jessopp, A., ed. Repr. of 1888 ed. 30.00 (ISBN 0-384-41985-2). Johnson Repr.

Norwood, Frederick A. & Carr, Jo. Young Reader's Book of Church History. LC 81-20505. (Illus.). 176p. 1982. 11.95 (ISBN 0-687-46827-2). Abingdon.

Norwood, Frederick A., ed. Sourcebook of American Methodism. 683p. (Orig.). 1982. 20.95 (ISBN 0-687-39140-7). Abingdon.

Norwood, John H. The Schism in the Methodist Episcopal Church, 1844. LC 76-10284. (Perspectives in American Hist. Ser.: No. 33). 255p. 1976. Repr. of 1923 ed. lib. bdg. 25.00x (ISBN 0-87991-357-6). Porcupine Pr.

Nosco, Peter, ed. Confucianism & Tokugawa Culture. LC 83-43086. 360p. 1984. 32.50x (ISBN 0-691-07286-8). Princeton U Pr.

Noser, A. A. Living with God in My Heart. 1980. 2.50 (ISBN 0-8198-4406-3); pap. 1.50 (ISBN 0-8198-4404-7). Dghtrs St Paul.

Noss, Davis S., jt. auth. see Noss, John B.

Noss, John B. & Noss, Davis S. Man's Religion. 7th ed. (Illus.). 608p. 1984. text ed. write for info. (ISBN 0-02-388470-3). Macmillan.

Noss, Philip A., ed. Grafting Old Rootstock. LC 81-51153. (International Museum of Cultures Publications: No. 14). (Illus.). 246p. (Orig.). 1982. pap. 12.00x (ISBN 0-88312-165-4); microfiche (3) 6.00x (ISBN 0-88312-990-6). Summer Inst Ling.

Nota, John H. Max Scheler: The Man & His Works. 1983. 12.00 (ISBN 0-8199-0852-5). Franciscan Herald.

Notaro, Thom. Van Til & the Use of Evidence. 1980. pap. 4.50 (ISBN 0-87552-353-6). Presby & Reformed.

Note, Gene Van see Van Note, Gene.

Notestein, Wallace. History of Witchcraft in England from 1558 to 1718. LC 65-18824. 1965. Repr. of 1911 ed. 16.00x (ISBN 0-8462-0649-8). Russell.

Noth, Martin. The Chronicler's History. (JSOT Supplement Ser.). 120p. 1987. text ed. 22.50x (ISBN 1-85075-043-2, Pub. by JSOT Pr England); pap. text ed. 9.50x (ISBN 1-85075-044-0, Pub. by JSOT Pr England). Eisenbrauns.

--The Deuteronomistic History. (Journal for the Study of the Old Testament, Supplement Ser.: No. 15). 1981. text ed. 20.95x (ISBN 0-905774-25-6, Pub. by JSOT Pr England); pap. text ed. 10.95x (ISBN 0-905774-30-2, Pub. by JSOT Pr England). Eisenbrauns.

--Exodus, a Commentary. LC 62-7940. (Old Testament Library). 284p. 1962. 17.95 (ISBN 0-664-20370-1). Westminster.

--History of Israel: Biblical History. 2nd ed. LC 58-5195. 1960. 16.95xi (ISBN 0-06-066310-3, HarpR). Har-Row.

--The Laws in the Pentateuch. 304p. pap. 13.95 (ISBN 0-317-31484-X, 30-870-259). Fortress.

Noth, Martin & Anderson, Berhard W. History of Pentateuchal Traditions. LC 80-24937. (Scholars Press Reproductions Ser.). 1981. 22.00_o.s. (ISBN 0-89130-446-0, 00-07-05); text ed. 17.50 (ISBN 0-89130-954-3). Scholars Pr GA.

Nothstein, Ira O., ed. & tr. The Planting of the Swedish Church in America: Graduation Dissertation of Tobias Eric Biorck. LC 43-18182. (Augustana College Library Publication Ser.: No. 19). 39p. 1943. pap. 3.00x (ISBN 0-910182-14-0). Augustana Coll.

Noton, Thomas A., jt. auth. see Quick, Daniel L.

Notovich, N. The Unknown Life of Jesus Christ. 69.95 (ISBN 0-87968-073-3). Gordon Pr.

Nott, C. S. Teachings of Gurdjieff: The Journal of a Pupil. (Illus., Orig.). 1974. pap. 7.95 (ISBN 0-87728-395-8). Weiser.

Nott, C. S., tr. see Attar, Farid Ud-Din.

Nottage, Isaiah L. The Biblical Mysteries Revealed. 1984. 9.95 (ISBN 0-8062-2315-4). Carlton.

Nottingham, Elizabeth K. Methodism & the Frontier: Indiana Proving Ground. LC 41-19465. Repr. of 1941 ed. 7.00 (ISBN 0-404-04798-X). AMS Pr.

--Religion: A Sociological View. LC 81-40769. 348p. 1981. pap. text ed. 13.50 (ISBN 0-8191-1813-3). U Pr of Amer.

Nottingham, William, tr. see Clevenot, Michel.

Nottingham, William J. Practice & Preaching of Liberation. Lambert, Herbert, ed. LC 85-18997. 96p. (Orig.). 1986. pap. 9.95 (ISBN 0-8272-2931-3). CBP.

Nouwen, Henri. With Open Hands. 96p. 1985. pap. 4.95 large print ed. (ISBN 0-8027-2475-2). Walker & Co.

Nouwen, Henri J. Behold the Beauty of the Lord: Praying with Icons. LC 86-72698. (Illus.). 80p. (Orig.). 1987. spiral binding 7.95 (ISBN 0-87793-356-1). Ave Maria.

--Clowning in Rome: Reflections on Solitude, Celibacy, Prayer & Contemplation. LC 78-22423. (Illus.). 1979. pap. 4.95 (ISBN 0-385-15129-2, Im). Doubleday.

--Creative Ministry. LC 73-139050. 1971. pap. 3.50 (ISBN 0-385-12616-6, Im). Doubleday.

--Cry for Mercy: Prayers from the Genesee. LC 80-2563. (Illus.). 175p. 1983. pap. 6.95 (ISBN 0-385-17508-6, Im). Doubleday.

--The Genesee Diary: Report from a Trappist Monastery. LC 80-23632. 192p. 1981. pap. 4.50 (ISBN 0-385-17446-2, Im). Doubleday.

--The Genesee Diary: Report from a Trappist Monastery. LC 85-7150. 352p. 1985. pap. 12.95 (ISBN 0-8027-2500-7). Walker & Co.

--Gracias! A Latin American Journal. LC 82-48935. 224p. 1983. 13.45 (ISBN 0-06-066318-9, HarpR). Har-Row.

--In Memoriam. LC 79-56690. 64p. 1980. pap. 2.50 (ISBN 0-87793-197-6). Ave Maria.

--A Letter of Consolation. LC 81-48212. 96p. 1982. 10.45 (ISBN 0-686-81488-6, HarpR). Har-Row.

--Lifesigns: Intimacy, Fecundity, Ecstasy in Christian Perspective. LC 86-4572. (Illus.). 128p. 1986. pap. 11.95 (ISBN 0-385-23627-1). Doubleday.

--The Living Reminder: Service & Prayer in Memory of Jesus Christ. 80p. 1981. pap. 4.95 (ISBN 0-86683-915-1, HarpR). Har-Row.

--Love in Fearful Land: A Guatemalan Story. LC 85-71913. (Illus.). 120p. (Orig.). 1985. pap. 5.95 (ISBN 0-87793-294-8). Ave Maria.

--Making All Things New: An Invitation to Life in the Spirit. LC 80-8897. 96p. 1981. 10.45 (ISBN 0-06-066326-X, HarpR). Har-Row.

--Out of Solitude. (Illus.). 64p. 1974. pap. 1.95 (ISBN 0-87793-072-4). Ave Maria.

--Reaching Out: The Three Movements of the Spiritual Life. LC 86-2901. (Illus.). 168p. 1986. pap. 5.95 (ISBN 0-385-23682-4, Im). Doubleday.

--Thomas Merton: Contemplative Critic. LC 80-8898. 176p. 1981. pap. 6.95 (ISBN 0-06-066324-3, RD 357, HarpR). Har-Row.

--The Way of the Heart. (Epiphany Bks.). 1983. pap. 2.50 (ISBN 0-345-30530-2). Ballantine.

--The Way of the Heart: Desert Spirituality & Contemporary Ministry. 96p. 1981. 8.95 (ISBN 0-86683-913-5, AY7443, HarpR). Har-Row.

--With Open Hands. LC 71-177600. (Illus.). 160p. 1972. pap. 3.95 (ISBN 0-87793-040-6). Ave Maria.

--The Wounded Healer: Ministry in Contemporary Society. LC 72-186312. 1979. pap. 3.50 (ISBN 0-385-14803-8, Im). Doubleday.

Nouwen, Henri J. M. The Genesee Diary: Report from a Trappist Monastery. LC 75-38169. 192p. 1976. 9.95 (ISBN 0-385-11368-4). Doubleday.

--Reaching Out: The Three Movements of the Spiritual Life. LC 74-9460. 120p. 1975. 9.95 (ISBN 0-385-03212-9). Doubleday.

Novak, David. Halakhah in a Theological Dimension: Essays on the Interpenetration of Law & Theology in Judaism. Neusner, Jacob, ed. LC 84-10661. (Brown Judaic Studies: No. 68). 1985. 19.75 (ISBN 0-89130-757-5, 14-00-68); pap. 16.25 (ISBN 0-89130-829-6). Scholars Pr GA.

--The Image of the Non-Jew in Judaism: An Historical & Constructive Study of the Noahide Laws. LC 83-21989. (Toronto Studies in Theology: Vol. 14). 500p. 1984. 69.95x (ISBN 0-88946-759-5). E Mellen.

--Suicide & Morality: The Theories of Plato, Aquinas & Kant & Their Relevance for Suicidology. LC 75-37543. x, 136p. 1976. lib. bdg. 7.50 (ISBN 0-685-69079-2). Scholars Studies.

Novak, David & Samuelson, Norbert, eds. Creation & the End of Days - Judaism & Scientific Cosmology: Proceedings of the 1984 Meeting of the Academy for Jewish Philosophy. LC 86-19062. 336p. (Orig.). 1986. 26.75 (ISBN 0-8191-5524-1, Pub. by Studies in Judaism); pap. text ed. 14.50 (ISBN 0-8191-5525-X, Pub. by Studies in Judaism). U Pr of Amer.

Novak, Michael. Ascent of the Mountain, Flight of the Dove: An Invitation to Religious Studies. rev. ed. LC 77-20463. 1978. pap. 5.95xi (ISBN 0-06-066322-7, RD 232, HarpR). Har-Row.

--Confession of a Catholic. LC 85-20367. 232p. 1986. pap. text ed. 12.25 (ISBN 0-8191-5023-1). U Pr of Amer.

--Experience of Nothingness. 1971. pap. 5.95x (ISBN 0-06-131938-4, TB 1938, Torch). Har-Row.

--Freedom with Justice: Catholic Social Thought & Liberal Institutions. LC 84-47731. 272p. 1984. 17.45 (ISBN 0-06-066317-0, HarpR). Har-Row.

Novak, Michael, ed. Democracy & Mediating Structures: A Theological Inquiry. 1980. 13.25 (ISBN 0-8447-2175-1); pap. 7.25 (ISBN 0-8447-2176-X). Am Enterprise.

Novak, William & Waldoks, Moshe. Big Book of Jewish Humor. LC 81-47234. (Illus.). 320p. 1981. pap. 14.95 (ISBN 0-06-090917-X, CN 917, PL). Har-Row.

Novakshonoff, V., tr. see Khrapovitsky, Antony.

Novakshonoff, Varlaam, tr. see Khrapovitsky, Antony.

Novitch, Miriam, ed. Sobibor: Martyrdom & Revolt. (Illus.). 168p. pap. 4.95 (ISBN 0-686-95087-9). ADL.

Nowak, Margaret & Durrant, Stephen. The Tale of the Nisan Shamaness: A Manchu Folk Epic. LC 76-49171. (Publications on Asia of the School of International Studies: No. 31). 192p. 1977. 15.00x (ISBN 0-295-95548-1). U of Wash Pr.

Nowak, Nancy C., jt. auth. see Furfine, Sandy S.

Nowell, Alexander. A Catechisme, or First Instruction & Learning of Christian Religion. LC 74-23570. 185p. 1975. Repr. of 1570 ed. lib. bdg. 30.00x (ISBN 0-8201-1143-0). Schol Facsimiles.

Nowell, Irene. Jonah, Tobit, Judith. (Collegeville Bible Commentary: Old Testament Ser.: Vol. 25). 112p. 1986. pap. 2.95 (ISBN 0-8146-1481-7). Liturgical Pr.

Nowlan, Connie W. A Man Who Wouldn't Listen. (Trailblazer Ser.). 1982. pap. 5.95 (ISBN 0-8163-0441-6). Pacific Pr Pub Assn.

Noy, Dov. Studies in Jewish Folklore. 1981. 25.00x (ISBN 0-915938-02-2). Ktav.

Noy, Dov, ed. Folktales of Israel. Baharav, Gene, tr. LC 63-16721. (Folktales of the World Ser). 1963. 14.00x (ISBN 0-226-59719-9); pap. 7.95x (ISBN 0-226-59720-2, FW8). U of Chicago Pr.

Noyce, Gaylord. The Art of Pastoral Conversation. LC 81-82350. 128p. 1982. pap. 3.99 (ISBN 0-8042-1131-0). John Knox.

Noyce, Gaylord, jt. auth. see Rossman, Peter.

Noyes, George R., tr. see Zielinski, Thaddeus.

Noyes, George W., ed. John Humphrey Noyes: The Putney Community. (Illus.). 1931. 30.00x (ISBN 0-8156-8059-7). Syracuse U Pr.

--Religious Experience of John Humphrey Noyes. 1923. 15.00x (ISBN 0-8156-8060-0). Syracuse U Pr.

Noyes, George W., ed. see Noyes, John H.

Noyes, John H. Berean. LC 74-83431. (Religion in America, Ser. 1). 1969. Repr. of 1847 ed. 32.00 (ISBN 0-405-00256-4). Ayer Co Pubs.

--Religious Experience of John Humphrey Noyes, Founder of the Oneida Community. facsimile ed. Noyes, George W., ed. (Select Bibliographies Reprint Ser). Repr. of 1923 ed. 26.50 (ISBN 0-8369-5750-4). Ayer Co Pubs.

--Salvation from Sin. 59.95 (ISBN 0-8490-0990-1). Gordon Pr.

--The Way of Holiness. LC 75-337. (The Radical Tradition in America Ser.). 230p. 1975. Repr. of 1838 ed. 21.50 (ISBN 0-88355-240-X). Hyperion Conn.

Nozick, M., ed. Miguel De Unamuno: The Agony of Belief. 1982. 23.50 (ISBN 0-691-06498-9); pap. 10.50x (ISBN 0-691-01366-7). Princeton U Pr.

Nozick, Martin, jt. ed. see Kerrigan, Anthony.

Nuermberger, Ruth K. Free Produce Movement. LC 73-110135. (Duke University. Trinity College Historical Society. Historical Papers: No. 25). Repr. of 1942 ed. 24.50 (ISBN 0-404-51775-7). AMS Pr.

Nugent, Christopher. Masks of Satan: The Demonic in History. 216p. 1984. 22.50 (ISBN 0-89860-128-2, Sheed & Ward). Eastview.

Nugent, Donald. Ecumenism in the Age of the Reformation: The Colloquy of Poissy. LC 73-80026. (Historical Studies: No. 89). 296p. 1974. text ed. 20.00x (ISBN 0-674-23725-0). Harvard U Pr.

Nugent, Robert, ed. A Challenge to Love: Gay & Lesbian Catholics in the Church. LC 82-19850. 256p. 1983. pap. 10.95 (ISBN 0-8245-0518-2). Crossroad NY.

Nukariva, K. The Religion of the Samurai: A Study of Zen Philosophy & Discipline in China & Japan. 253p. 1973. 30.00x (ISBN 0-317-39142-9, Pub. by Luzac & Co Ltd); pap. 20.00x (ISBN 0-317-39143-7). State Mutual Bk.

Null & Watts. A Little Bit of Everything Good. pap. 5.50 (ISBN 0-89137-619-4). Quality Pubns.

Nulman, Louis. What is Chanukah? A Programmed Text. text ed. 2.25 (ISBN 0-914131-73-7, A30). Torah Umesorah.

--What is Kosher? A Programmed Text. text ed. 2.50 (ISBN 0-914131-74-5, A40). Torah Umesorah.

Nu'man, Muhammad A. What Every American Should Know about Islam & the Muslims. 74p. (Orig.). 1985. pap. 5.00 (ISBN 0-933821-04-2). New Mind Prod.

Numbers, Ronald L. Creation by Natural Law: Laplace's Nebular Hypothesis in American Thought. LC 76-45810. 196p. 1977. 22.50x (ISBN 0-295-95439-6). U of Wash Pr.

Numbers, Ronald L. & Amundsen, Darrel W., eds. Caring & Curing: Historical Essays on Health, Medicine, & the Faith Traditions. 576p. 1986. text ed. 35.00x (ISBN 0-02-919270-6). Macmillan.

Numbers, Ronald L. & Butler, Jonathan M., eds. The Disappointed: Millerism & Millenarianism in the Nineteenth Century. (Religion in North America Ser.). 1987. 29.95 (ISBN 0-253-34299-6). Ind U Pr.

Numrich, Charles. Passion Play. 1983. 4.95 (ISBN 0-89536-601-0, 1627). CSS of Ohio.

Numrich, Charles H. For All Seasons. 43p. 1981. pap. text ed. 6.25 (ISBN 0-89536-490-5, 0600). CSS of Ohio.

Nunez, Emilio. Liberation Theology. 1985. text ed. 15.95 (ISBN 0-8024-4893-3). Moody.

Nunez, Emilio A. Reflexion Pastoral: El Pastor y Su Ministerio. Orig. Title: Pastoral Reflection. (Span.). Date not set. pap. 6.50 (ISBN 0-8254-1515-2). Kregel.

Nunn, Henry P. Short Syntax of New Testament Greek. 5th ed. 1931. text ed. 10.95 (ISBN 0-521-09941-2). Cambridge U Pr.

Nunn, T. Percy. Anthropomorphism & Physics. 1977. lib. bdg. 59.95 (ISBN 0-8490-1438-7). Gordon Pr.

Nunnally-Cox, Janice. Foremothers: Women of the Bible. 192p. (Orig.). 1981. pap. 6.95 (ISBN 0-8164-2329-6, HarpR). Har-Row.

Nuns of the Monastery of St. Clare, Balsbach, Germany, et al. The Celebration of the Eucharist: The Church's Festival of Love. Smith, David, tr. 1983. 6.00 (ISBN 0-8199-0866-5). Franciscan Herald.

Nuovo, Victor, tr. see Tillich, Paul.

Nurbakhsh, Ali-Reza, tr. see Nurbakhsh, Javad.

Nurbakhsh, Iavad. The Great Satan "EBLIS". Graham, Terry, et al, trs. 1986. pap. 6.00x (ISBN 0-933546-23-8). KhaniQahi-Nimatullahi-Sufi.

Nurbakhsh, Javad. In the Paradise of the Sufis. LC 79-83588. 1979. pap. 6.00x (ISBN 0-933546-01-7). KhaniQahi-Nimatullahi-Sufi.

--In the Tavern of Ruin: Seven Essays on Sufism. LC 78-102838. (Orig.). 1978. pap. 6.00x (ISBN 0-933546-00-9). KhaniQahi-Nimatullahi-Sufi.

--Masters of the Path: A History of the Masters of the Nimatullahi Sufi Order. LC 80-80902. (Illus.). 144p. 1980. pap. 6.00x (ISBN 0-933546-03-3). KhaniQahi-Nimatullahi-Sufi.

--Sufism: Fear & Hope, Contraction & Expansion, Gathering & Dispersion, Intoxication, & Sobriety, Annihilation & Subsistence. Chittick, William, tr. from Persian. (Orig.). 1982. pap. 6.00x (ISBN 0-933546-07-6). KhaniQahi-Nimatullahi-Sufi.

--Sufism-III: Submission, Contentment, Absence, Presence, Intimacy. Graham, Terry & Lewisohn, Leonard, trs. 133p. 1985. pap. 6.00x (ISBN 0-933546-19-X). KhaniQahi-Nimatullahi-Sufi.

--Sufism: Meaning, Knowledge, & Unity. Wilson, Peter, tr. from Persian. 128p. (Orig.). 1981. pap. 6.00x (ISBN 0-933546-05-X). Khaniqahi-Nimatullahi-Sufi.

--Traditions of the Prophet (Ahadith) Rothschild, Jeffrey, et al, eds. Lewisehn, Leonard & Nurbakhsh, Ali-Reza, trs. 104p. 1981. pap. 6.00x (ISBN 0-933546-06-8). KhaniQahi-Nimatullahi-Sufi.

--The Truths of Love. Lewisohn, Leonard, tr. 1982. pap. 6.00x (ISBN 0-933546-08-4). KhaniQahi Nimatullahi-Sufi.

Nurbakhsh, Dr. Javad. Sufi Symbolism, Vol. 1. Lewisohn, Leonard & Graham, Terry, trs. 260p. 1986. 20.00 (ISBN 0-933546-12-2). Khaniqahi-Nimatullahi-Sufi.

Nurbakhsh, Jawad. Traditions of the Prophet, Vol. 2. Lewisohn, Leonard & Graham, Terry, trs. 1984. pap. 6.00x (ISBN 0-933546-10-6). KhaniQahi-Nimatullahi-Sufi.

Nurenberger, M. J. The Scared & the Doomed: The Jewish Establishment vs. the Six Million. (Illus.). 320p. (Orig.). 1986. pap. 12.95 (ISBN 0-88962-289-2). Riverrun NY.

Nurmi, Martin. Blake's Marriage of Heaven & Hell. LC 72-6067. (Studies in Blake, No. 3). 1972. Repr. of 1957 ed. lib. bdg. 75.00x (ISBN 0-8383-1599-2). Haskell.

Nurser, John. The Reign of Conscience: Individual, Church & State in Lord Acton's History of Liberty. McNeill, William H. & Stansky, Peter, eds. (Modern European History Ser.). 225p. 1987. lib. bdg. 40.00 (ISBN 0-8240-7826-8). Garland Pub.

Nussey, Dora, tr. see Male, Emile.

Nutanhhery, Murtaza. Women & Her Rights. Ansari, M. A., tr. from Arabic. 286p. 1984. pap. 9.00 (ISBN 0-941724-30-1). Islamic Seminary.

Nutt, Alfred. Studies on the Legend of the Holy Grail with Special Reference to the Hypothesis of Its Celtic Origin. (Folk-Lore Society, London, Monographs: Vol. 23). pap. 29.00 (ISBN 0-8115-0510-3). Kraus Repr.

Nutt, Alfred T. Fairy Mythology of Shakespeare. LC 71-139169. (Popular Studies in Mythology, Romance & Folklore: No. 6). Repr. of 1900 ed. 5.50 (ISBN 0-404-53506-2). AMS Pr.

--Legends of the Holy Grail. LC 78-139176. (Popular Studies in Mythology, Romance & Folklore: No. 14). Repr. of 1902 ed. 5.50 (ISBN 0-404-53514-3). AMS Pr.

Nutt, Grady. Being Me. LC 71-145984. 1971. pap. 3.95 (ISBN 0-8054-6909-5, 4269-09). Broadman.

--The Gospel According to Norton. LC 73-91610. pap. 4.50 (ISBN 0-8054-5322-9, 4253-22). Broadman.

Nuttall, Clayton. The Weeping Church: Confronting the Crisis of Church Polity. LC 85-10760. 1985. pap. 5.95 (ISBN 0-87227-104-8). Reg Baptist.

Nuttall, Clayton L. The Conflict: The Separation of the Church & State. LC 80-21267. 144p. 1980. pap. 4.95 (ISBN 0-87227-076-9, RBP5088). Reg Baptist.

Nuttall, Geoffrey. Christian Pacifism in History. pap. 1.25 (ISBN 0-912018-13-5). World Without War.

Nuttall, Geoffrey F. Studies in Christian Enthusiasm. 1983. pap. 2.50x (ISBN 0-87574-041-3, 041). Pendle Hill.

--To the Refreshing of the Children of Light. 1983. pap. 2.50x (ISBN 0-87574-101-0, 101). Pendle Hill.

Nuttall, Geoffrey F. & Chadwick, O., eds. From Uniformity to Unity, 1662-1962. LC 63-2539. 1962. 20.00x (ISBN 0-8401-1746-9). A R Allenson.

Nuttall, Zelia. Fundamental Principles of Old & New World Civilization. (HU PMP Ser.). 1901. 51.00 (ISBN 0-527-01190-8). Kraus Repr.

--Penitential Rite of the Ancient Mexicans. (HU PMP Ser.). 1904. pap. 10.00 (ISBN 0-527-01189-4). Kraus Repr.

Nutting, George. Resurrection Is Not a Fairy Tale. 1981. 5.75 (ISBN 0-8062-1649-2). Carlton.

Nutting, George L. & Nutting, Ruth S. The Angel World. 115p. (Orig.). 1985. pap. 2.95 (ISBN 0-9612266-1-7). Numard Bks.

--A Parable of the Ninth Hour. 165p. (Orig.). 1983. pap. 2.95 (ISBN 0-9612266-0-9). Numard Bks.

Nutting, Ruth S., jt. auth. see Nutting, George L.

Nuys, Roscoe Van see Van Nuys, Roscoe.

Nuzum, C. The Life of Faith. 96p. 1956. pap. 1.95 (ISBN 0-88243-539-6, 02-0539). Gospel Pub.

Nyana, U. The Vipassana Dipani; or the Manual of Insight. LC 78-70107. Repr. of 1930 ed. 22.00 (ISBN 0-404-17357-8). AMS Pr.

Nyanatiloka. Buddhist Dictionary. LC 77-87508. Repr. of 1950 ed. 20.00 (ISBN 0-404-16846-9). AMS Pr.

Nyber, D. M. Help for Families with a Problem Child. LC 12-2822. (Trauma Bks.: Ser. 2). 1983. pap. 2.75 (ISBN 0-570-08259-5). Concordia.

Nyberg, Dorothea. We Still Love You, Bob. 144p. 1984. pap. 6.95 (ISBN 0-87178-925-6). Brethren.

Nyburg, Sidney L. The Chosen People. Sarna, Jonathan D., ed. (Masterworks of Modern Jewish Writing Ser.). 382p. 1986. pap. 9.95 (ISBN 0-910129-47-9, Distr. by Schcken Books). Wiener Pub Inc.

Nydahl, Ole. Entering the Diamond Way: My Path among the Lamas. Aronoff, Carol A. & Clemens, Paul M., eds. LC 85-73182. (Illus.). 256p. (Orig.). 1985. pap. 12.95 (ISBN 0-931892-03-1). B Dolphin Pub.

Nye, John. Between the Rivers: A History of United Methodism in Iowa. LC 86-80106. (Illus.). 350p. 1986. 12.95x (ISBN 0-9616298-0-0); pap. 10.95 (ISBN 0-9616298-1-9). IA Conf Com Arch.

Nye, Miriam B. But I Never Thought He'd Die: Practical Help for Widows. LC 78-9644. 150p. 1978. pap. 7.95 (ISBN 0-664-24208-1). Westminster.

Nye, Naomi S. Different Ways to Pray. LC 79-5470. 1980. pap. 6.95 (ISBN 0-932576-04-4). Breitenbush Bks.

Nygren, Anders. Commentary on Romans. Rasmussen, Carl, tr. LC 49-48317. 472p. 1949. pap. 6.95 (ISBN 0-8006-1684-7, 1-1684). Fortress.

Nygren, Bruce, jt. auth. see Hester, Glenn.

Nygren, Malcolm. The Lord of the Four Seasons. 144p. (Orig.). 1986. pap. 7.95 (ISBN 0-9617890-1-8). Doxology Lane.

Nyhus, Paul L., tr. see Oberman, Heiko A.

Nyingpo, Namkhay. Mother of Knowledge: The Enlightenment of Ye-shes Mtsho-Rgyal. Tulka, Tarthang, tr. (Translation Ser.). Orig. Title: Tibetan. (Illus.). 250p. 1983. 21.95 (ISBN 0-913546-90-9); pap. 12.95 (ISBN 0-913546-91-7). Dharma Pub.

Nykanen, Marita & Williams, Esther, trs. from Finnish. The Faith We Hold: Archbishop Paul. LC 80-10404. 96p. 1980. pap. 4.95 (ISBN 0-913836-63-X). St Vladimirs.

Nyquist, James F. & Kuhatschek, Jack. Leading Bible Discussions. rev. ed. 60p. 1985. pap. 2.95 (ISBN 0-8308-1000-5). Inter-Varsity.

Nystrom, Carolyn. Acts 1-12: Church on the Move. (Young Fisherman Bible Study Guide Ser.). 59p. 1979. tchrs. ed. 4.95 (ISBN 0-87788-126-X); student ed. 2.95 (ISBN 0-87788-125-1). Shaw Pubs.

--Angels & Me. (Children's Bible Basics Ser.). (Illus.). 1984. 4.95 (ISBN 0-8024-6017-8). Moody.

--At the Starting Line: Beginning a New Life. (Young Fisherman Bible Studyguides). 48p. 1985. pap. 2.95 student (ISBN 0-87788-053-0); pap. text ed. 4.95 Tchr's. (ISBN 0-87788-054-9). Shaw Pubs.

--Basic Beliefs: A Woman's Workshop on the Christian Faith. (Woman's Workshop Ser.). 124p. 1986. pap. 3.95 (ISBN 0-310-41971-9). Zondervan.

--Behold Your Christ: A Woman's Workshop on Jesus. (Woman's Workshop Ser.). 128p. (Orig.). 1985. pap. 3.95 (ISBN 0-310-41981-6, 11284P). Zondervan.

--Characters & Kings: A Woman's Workshop on the History of Israel, 2 pts. (Woman's Workshop Ser.). 240p. (Orig.). 1985. Part 1. pap. 2.95 (ISBN 0-310-41881-X, 11279P); Part 2. pap. 3.95 (ISBN 0-310-41871-2, 11283). Zondervan.

--Growing Jesus' Way. (Children's Bible Basics Ser.). 1982. 4.95 (ISBN 0-8024-5999-4). Moody.

--The Holy Spirit in Me. (Children's Bible Ser.). 32p. 1980. pap. 4.95 (ISBN 0-8024-5994-3). Moody.

--Jesus Is No Secret. (Children's Bible Basics Ser.). (Illus.). 1983. 4.95 (ISBN 0-8024-0193-7). Moody.

--Lord, I Want to Have a Quiet Time: Learning to Study the Bible for Yourself. 156p. 1984. pap. 6.95 (ISBN 0-87788-516-8). Shaw Pubs.

--Mark: God on the Move. (Young Fisherman Bible Studyguide Ser.). 96p. 1978. pap. 4.95 tchr's ed. (ISBN 0-87788-312-2); student ed. 2.95 (ISBN 0-87788-311-4). Shaw Pubs.

--Romans: Christianity on Trial. (Young Fisherman Bible Studyguide Ser.). (Illus.). 124p. 1980. pap. 4.95 tchr's ed. (ISBN 0-87788-899-X); student ed. 3.95 (ISBN 0-87788-898-1). Shaw Pubs.

--What Happens When We Die? (Children's Bible Basics Ser.). 32p. 1981. 4.95 (ISBN 0-8024-5995-1). Moody.

--What Is a Christian? (Children's Bible Basics Ser.). 32p. 1981. 4.95 (ISBN 0-8024-5997-8). Moody.

--What Is Prayer? (Children's Bible Basics Ser.). 32p. 1980. pap. 4.95 (ISBN 0-8024-5991-9). Moody.

--What Is the Bible? (Children's Bible Basics Ser.). 32p. 1982. 4.95 (ISBN 0-8024-0157-0). Moody.

--Who Is God? (Children's Bible Basics Ser.). 32p. 1980. pap. 4.95 (ISBN 0-8024-5992-7). Moody.

--Who Is Jesus? (Children's Bible Basics Ser.). 32p. 1980. pap. 4.95 (ISBN 0-8024-5993-5). Moody.

--Who Is Jesus? A Woman's Workshop on Mark. (Woman's Workshop Ser.). 144p. 1987. pap. 3.95 (ISBN 0-310-42001-6). Zondervan.

--Why Do I Do Things Wrong? (Children's Bible Basics Ser.). 32p. 1981. 4.95 (ISBN 0-8024-5996-X). Moody.

--A Woman's Workshop on David & His Psalms. (Woman's Workshop Ser.). 144p. 1982. pap. 3.95 (ISBN 0-310-41931-X, 11276P). Zondervan.

--A Woman's Workshop on Romans-Leader's Manual. 112p. (Orig.). 1981. pap. 3.95 (ISBN 0-310-41911-5, 11274P). Zondervan.

--A Woman's Workshop on Romans-Student's Manual. 144p. (Orig.). 1981. pap. 3.95 (ISBN 0-310-41921-2, 11275P). Zondervan.

Nystrom, Carolyn & Floding, Mathew. Who Am I? A Look in the Mirror. (Young Fisherman Bible Studyguides). 64p. (Orig.). (YA) 1987. pap. 4.95 tchr's. ed. (ISBN 0-87788-933-3); pap. 2.95 student ed. (ISBN 0-87788-932-5). Shaw Pubs.

Nystrom, Carolyn & Floding, Matthew. Relationships: Face to Face. (Young Fisherman Bible Studyguide Ser.). 64p. (Orig.). (YA) 1986. pap. 2.95 student ed. (ISBN 0-87788-722-5); tchr's ed. 4.95 (ISBN 0-87788-723-3). Shaw Pubs.

Nystrom, Carolyn & Fromer, Margaret. Acts 13-28: Missions Accomplished. (Young Fisherman Bible Studyguide). (Illus.). 93p. 1979. tchrs. ed. 4.95 (ISBN 0-87788-011-5); student ed. 2.95 (ISBN 0-87788-010-7). Shaw Pubs.
--People in Turmoil: A Woman's Workshop on First Corinthians. (Woman's Workshop Ser.). 128p. (Orig.). 1985. pap. 3.95 (ISBN 0-310-41891-7, 11278P). Zondervan.
--A Woman's Workshop on James. (Woman's Workshop Ser.). 144p. (Orig.). 1980. pap. 2.95 (ISBN 0-310-41901-8, 11273P). Zondervan.
Nystrom, Carolyn, jt. auth. see Fromer, Margaret.
Nyvall, David. My Father's Testament. 1974. pap. 5.95 (ISBN 0-910452-20-2). Covenant.

O

Oak, Henry L. A Visit to the Missions of Southern California in February & March 1874. Axe, Ruth F., et al, eds. LC 81-52830. (Illus.). 87p. 1981. 20.00 (ISBN 0-916561-66-6). Southwest Mus.
Oakeley, Hilda D., ed. Greek Ethical Thought from Homer to the Stoics. LC 79-173804. (Library of Greek Thought: No. 5). Repr. of 1925 ed. 10.00 (ISBN 0-404-07804-4). AMS Pr.
Oakes, Maud see Watts, Alan W.
Oakeshott, Walter. Sigena: Romanesque Paintings in Spain & the Winchester Bible Artists. (Illus.). 1972. 49.00x (ISBN 0-19-921006-3). Oxford U Pr.
Oakley, jt. auth. see Cooper.
Oakley, Francis. Omnipotence, Covenant & Order: An Excursion in the History of Ideas from Abelard to Leibniz. LC 83-45945. 168p. 1984. 18.50x (ISBN 0-8014-1631-0). Cornell U Pr.
--The Western Church in the Later Middle Ages. LC 79-7621. 352p. 1985. 32.50x (ISBN 0-8014-1208-0); pap. text ed. 9.95x (ISBN 0-8014-9347-1). Cornell U Pr.
Oakley, Thomas P. English Penitential Discipline & Anglo-Saxon Law in Their Joint Influence. LC 71-82243. (Columbia University. Studies in the Social Sciences: No. 242). Repr. of 1923 ed. 20.00 (ISBN 0-404-51242-9). AMS Pr.
Oaks, Dallin H. Trust Doctrines in Church Controversies. LC 83-25058. xiv, 125p. 1984. 13.95x (ISBN 0-86554-104-3, MUP/H96). Mercer Univ Pr.
Oaks, Dallin H., ed. Wall Between Church & State. LC 63-20897. 1963. pap. 1.95X (ISBN 0-226-61429-8, P137, Phoen). U of Chicago Pr.
Oakshott, Walter. The Two Winchester Bibles. (Illus.). 1981. 350.00x (ISBN 0-19-818235-X). Oxford U Pr.
Oates, Charles E., jt. auth. see Oates, Wayne E.
Oates, Wayne E. The Christian Pastor. Rev. 3rd ed. LC 82-4933. 298p. 1982. pap. 9.95 (ISBN 0-664-24372-X). Westminster.
--Convictions That Give You Confidence. LC 84-5193. (Potentials: Guides for Productive Living Ser.: Vol. 10). 110p. 1984. pap. 7.95 (ISBN 0-664-24529-3). Westminster.
--Introduction to Pastoral Counseling. 1959. 14.95 (ISBN 0-8054-2404-0). Broadman.
--Managing Your Stress. LC 85-47715. 64p. 1985. pap. 3.95 (ISBN 0-8006-1880-7, 1-1880). Fortress.
--Pastoral Care & Counseling in Grief & Separation. Clinebell, Howard J. & Stone, Howard W., eds. LC 75-13048. (Creative Pastoral Care & Counseling Ser.). 96p. 1976. pap. 4.50 (ISBN 0-8006-0554-3, 1-554). Fortress.
--Pastoral Counseling. LC 73-19719. 240p. 1982. pap. 8.95 (ISBN 0-664-24405-X). Westminster.
--Pastor's Handbook, Vol. II. LC 79-28639. (Christian Care Bks.). 120p. 1980. pap. 7.95 (ISBN 0-664-24330-4). Westminster.
--Pastor's Handbook, Vol. 1. LC 79-28639. (Christian Care Bks.). 120p. 1980. pap. 7.95 (ISBN 0-664-24300-2). Westminster.
--The Religious Care of the Psychiatric Patient. LC 78-18454. 252p. 1978. 13.95 (ISBN 0-664-21365-0). Westminster.
--The Struggle to Be Free: My Story & Your Story. LC 83-5904. 164p. 1983. pap. 7.95 (ISBN 0-664-24500-5). Westminster.
--Your Particular Grief. LC 81-3328. 114p. 1981. pap. 6.95 (ISBN 0-664-24376-2). Westminster.
--Your Right to Rest. LC 83-26045. (Potentials: Guides for Productive Living Ser.: Vol. 1). 104p. (Orig.). 1984. pap. 7.95 (ISBN 0-664-24517-X). Westminster.
Oates, Wayne E. & Oates, Charles E. People in Pain: Guidelines for Pastoral Care. LC 85-5403. 152p. 1985. pap. 8.95 (ISBN 0-664-24674-5). Westminster.
Oates, Wayne E., ed. Potentials: (Guides for Productive Living Ser.). 1984. pap. 7.95 ea. Westminster.
Oats, William N. A Question of Survival: Quakers in Australia in the Nineteenth Century. LC 84-2351. (Illus.). 409p. 1985. text ed. 35.00x (ISBN 0-7022-1708-5). U of Queensland Pr.
Obach, Robert E. & Kirk, Albert. A Commentary on the Gospel of John. LC 80-84505. 272p. 1981. pap. 7.95 (ISBN 0-8091-2346-0). Paulist Pr.
--A Commentary on the Gospel of Luke. 272p. (Orig.). 1986. pap. 8.95 (ISBN 0-8091-2763-6). Paulist Pr.
Obach, Robert E., jt. auth. see Kirk, Albert.
O'Barr, Ann G. First Light. LC 83-70211. (Orig.). 1984. pap. 5.95 (ISBN 0-8054-7305-X). Broadman.
Obayashi, Hiroshi. Agape & History: A Theological Essay on Historical Consciousness. LC 80-1683. 356p. (Orig.). 1981. pap. text ed. 15.25 (ISBN 0-8191-1713-7). U Pr of Amer.
Obelkevich, James, ed. Religion & the People, 800-1700. LC 78-7847. v, 336p. 1979. 30.00x (ISBN 0-8078-1332-X). U of NC Pr.
Obelkevich, Jim & Roper, Lyndal. Disciplines of Faith. 512p. 1987. 55.00 (ISBN 0-7102-0750-6, Pub. by Routledge UK); pap. 25.00 (ISBN 0-7102-0993-2). Methuen Inc.
Obenhaus, Victor. Ethics for an Industrial Age: A Christian Inquiry. LC 73-15317. 338p. 1975. Repr. of 1965 ed. lib. bdg. 22.50x (ISBN 0-8371-7189-X, OBIA). Greenwood.
Oberholzer, Emil, Jr. Delinquent Saints: Disciplinary Action in the Early Congregational Churches of Massachusetts. LC 70-76660. (Columbia University. Studies in the Social Sciences: No. 590). Repr. of 1956 ed. 14.50 (ISBN 0-404-51590-8). AMS Pr.
Oberman, H. A. Masters of the Reformation: Rival Roads to a New Ideology. Martin, D., tr. from German. 432p. 1981. 57.50 (ISBN 0-521-23098-5). Cambridge U Pr.
Oberman, Heiko A. The Dawn of the Reformation: Essays in Late Medieval & Early Reformation Thought. 352p. 1986. pap. 26.95 (ISBN 0-567-09371-9, Pub. by T & T Clark Ltd UK). Fortress.
--Forerunners of the Reformation: The Shape of Late Medieval Thought, Illustrated by Key Documents: Nyhus, Paul L., tr. LC 81-66518. pap. 86.80 (2027871). Bks Demand UMI.
--The Harvest of Medieval Theology: Gabriel Biel & Late Medieval Nominalism. xvi, 495p. 1983. pap. 17.50 (ISBN 0-939464-05-5). Labyrinth Pr.
--The Roots of Anti-Semitism: In the Age of Renaissance & Reformation. Porter, James I., tr. from Ger. LC 83-5695. 163p. 1983. 13.95 (ISBN 0-8006-0709-0, 1-709). Fortress.
Obermann, Julian, ed. Nissim Ibn Shahin: The Arabic Original of Ibn Shahin's Book of Comfort. LC 78-63561. (Yale Oriental Ser. Researches: No. 17). Repr. of 1933 ed. 72.50 (ISBN 0-404-60287-8). AMS Pr.
Obermayer, H. Kleines Stuttgarter-Bibellexikon. 3rd ed. (Ger.). 344p. 1976. 9.95 (ISBN 3-460-30053-1, M-7507, Pub. by Vlg. Katholisches Bibelwerk). French & Eur.
Obermayer, Heinz. Diccionario Biblico Manual. (Span.). 352p. 1975. pap. 7.95 (ISBN 84-7263-094-3, S-50212). French & Eur.
Obermiller, E. The Doctrine of Prajna-Paramita As Exposed in the Abhisamayalamkara of Maitreya. 153p. 1984. Repr. of 1932 ed. lib. bdg. 19.50x (ISBN 0-88181-002-9). Canon Pubns.
--The History of Buddhism in India & Tibet. 231p. 1986. Repr. of 1932 ed. 27.00 (ISBN 81-7030-026-6, Pub. by Sri Satguru Pubns India). Orient Bk Dist.
Obermiller, E., tr. see Maitreya, Aryasanga.
Oberndorfer, Anne, jt. auth. see Oberndorfer, Marx.
Oberndorfer, Marx & Oberndorfer, Anne. Noels: A Collection of Christmas Carols. 144p. 1932. complete gift edition 8.50 (ISBN 0-912222-05-0, R2582751); pap. 4.00 choral ed., carols only (ISBN 0-912222-06-9). FitzSimons.
Oberoi, A. S. Support of the Shaken Sangat: Meetings with Three Masters. Perkins, Russell, ed. LC 84-50911. (Illus.). 256p. (Orig.). 1984. pap. 15.00 (ISBN 0-89142-043-6). Sant Bani Ash.
Oberst, Bruce. Deuteronomy. LC 70-1070. (The Bible Study Textbook Ser.). 1968. 14.30 (ISBN 0-89900-009-6). College Pr Pub.
--Letters from Peter. LC 74-1071. (The Bible Study Textbook Ser.). (Illus.). 1962. 10.60 (ISBN 0-89900-046-0). College Pr Pub.
Obeyesekere, Gananath. The Cult of the Goddess Pattini. LC 83-5884. (Illus.). 629p. 1984. lib. bdg. 42.50x (ISBN 0-226-61602-9). U of Chicago Pr.
--Medusa's Hair: An Essay on Personal Symbols & Religious Experiences. LC 80-27372. (Illus.). 252p. 1981. lib. bdg. 22.50x (ISBN 0-226-61600-2). U of Chicago Pr.
Obold, Ruth. Prepare for Peace, Pt. I. (Illus.). 40p. 1986. 6.25 (ISBN 0-87303-116-4). Faith & Life.
--Prepare for Peace, Pt. II. (Illus.). 48p. 1986. 6.25 (ISBN 0-87303-117-2). Faith & Life.
--Prepare for Peace, Pt. III. (Illus.). 55p. (YA) 1986. 6.25 (ISBN 0-87303-118-0). Faith & Life.
Obolensky, D. Italy, Mount Athos & Muscovy: The Three Worlds of Maximos the Greek. (Raleigh Lectures on History). 1981. pap. 3.00 (ISBN 0-85672-323-1, Pub. by British Acad). Longwood Pub Group.
Obolensky, Dimitri, jt. auth. see Knowles, David.
Obrennen, Junius & Smith, Nopal. The Crystal Icon. (Illus.). vii, 200p. 1981. deluxe ed. 50.00 (ISBN 0-940578-03-4). Galahand Pr.
O'Brian, Patrick, tr. see Daniel-Rops, Henri.
O'Brien, Bonnie B & C, Chester. The Victory of the Lamb. 182p. 1982. pap. 12.75 (ISBN 0-311-72280-6). Casa Bautista.
O'Brien, Bonnie B. & Sample, Dorothy E. Life in the Fifth Dimension. 1984. pap. 6.50 (ISBN 0-8054-5214-1). Broadman.
O'Brien, Charles F. Sir William Dawson: A Life in Science & Religion. LC 71-153381. (American Philosophical Society, Memoirs: Vol. 84). pap. 54.30 (ISBN 0-317-20673-7, 2025140). Bks Demand UMI.
O'Brien, Christian. The Genius of the Few: The Story of Those who Founded the Garden of Eden. 320p. 1985. pap. 12.95 (ISBN 0-85500-214-X). Newcastle Pub.
O'Brien, Conor C. The Siege: The Saga of Israel & Zionism. 800p. 1986. 24.95 (ISBN 0-671-60044-3). S&S.
O'Brien, David, jt. auth. see Wood, Leon.
O'Brien, David J. The Renewal of American Catholicism. LC 72-85825. 320p. 1974. pap. 4.95 (ISBN 0-8091-1828-9). Paulist Pr.
O'Brien, David J. & Shannon, Thomas A., eds. Renewing the Earth: Catholic Documents on Peace, Justice & Liberation. LC 76-52008. 1977. pap. 6.95 (ISBN 0-385-12954-8, Im). Doubleday.
O'Brien, Gene & O'Brien, Judith T. Couples Praying: A Special Intimacy. 132p. 1986. pap. 3.95 (ISBN 0-8091-2816-0). Paulist Pr.
O'Brien, Gene, jt. auth. see O'Brien, Judith T.
O'Brien, George D. God & the New Haven Railway. LC 86-47554. 144p. 1986. 14.95 (ISBN 0-8070-1010-3). Beacon Pr.
O'Brien, Isidore. Francis of Assisi: Mirror Christ. 1978. 6.95 (ISBN 0-8199-0691-3). Franciscan Herald.
--St. Anthony of Padua. 1976. 5.00 (ISBN 0-8198-0472-X). Dghtrs St Paul.
O'Brien, J. Stephen, ed. Gathering God's People: Signs of a Successful Parish. LC 81-85241. 264p. (Orig.). 1982. pap. 7.95 (ISBN 0-87973-656-9, 656). Our Sunday Visitor.
O'Brien, Joachim. Parish Family Life & Social Action. LC 77-3573. 1977. pap. 1.50 (ISBN 0-8199-0673-5). Franciscan Herald.
O'Brien, Joan & Major, Wilfred. In the Beginning: Creation Myths from Ancient Mesopotamia, Israel, & Greece. LC 81-21311. (American Academy of Religion Academy Ser.). 1982. pap. 8.25 (ISBN 0-89130-559-9, 010311A). Scholars Pr GA.
O'Brien, John A. The Faith of Millions. rev. ed. LC 74-82119. 416p. 1974. pap. 6.50 (ISBN 0-87973-830-8). Our Sunday Visitor.
O'Brien, John M. Medieval Church. (Quality Paperback: No. 227). 120p. (Orig.). 1968. pap. 2.95 (ISBN 0-8226-0227-X). Littlefield.
O'Brien, Judith T. & O'Brien, Gene. A Redeeming State: A Handbook-Leader's Guide for Couples Planning Remarriage in the Church. 1984. leader's guide pamphlet 2.95 (ISBN 0-8091-5183-9); pap. 3.95 handbook-pamphlet (ISBN 0-8091-5182-0). Paulist Pr.
O'Brien, Judith T., jt. auth. see O'Brien, Gene.
O'Brien, Justin. Portrait of Andre Gide. 390p. 1976. Repr. of 1953 ed. lib. bdg. 29.00x (ISBN 0-374-96139-5, Octagon). Hippocrene Bks.
O'Brien, Lee. American Jewish Organizations & Israel. LC 85-29117. 330p. 1985. pap. 24.95 (ISBN 0-88728-153-2). Inst Palestine.
O'Brien, Marian M. Herbs & Spices of the Bible: How to Grow & Use Them. Lambert, Herbert, ed. LC 84-256. 128p. 1984. pap. 8.95 (ISBN 0-8272-1420-0). CBP.
O'Brien, Raymond C. Legal Education & Religious Perspective. LC 85-220822. (Illus.). 95p. Date not set. price not set. Cambridge U Pr.
O'Brien, Robert Y. Parish Adult Education in Five Practical Steps. 32p. 1985. pap. text ed. 1.50 (ISBN 0-89243-234-9). Liguori Pubns.
O'Brien, Thomas C., ed. see International Committee on English in the Liturgy.
O'Byrne, Cathal. From Green Hills of Galilee. facsimile ed. LC 71-167464. (Short Story Index Reprint Ser.). Repr. of 1935 ed. 14.00 (ISBN 0-8369-3990-5). Ayer Co Pubs.
Oca, V. Montes De see Dacruz, J.
O'Callaghan, Edmund B. List of Editions of the Holy Scriptures & Parts Thereof Printed in American Previous to 1860. LC 66-25690. 1966. Repr. of 1861 ed. 43.00x (ISBN 0-8103-3313-9). Gale.
O'Callaghan, Joseph F., ed. Heresies of the Early Christian & Medieval Era, 67 titles in 92 vols. (An AMS Reprint Ser.). 1965. Repr. of 1816 ed. write in info. (ISBN 0-404-16090-5). AMS Pr.
O'Callaghan, Joseph F., tr. see St. Ignatius Loyola.
O'Callaghan, P. O. An Eastern Orthodox Response to Evangelical Claims. 1984. pap. 2.95 (ISBN 0-937032-35-2). Light&Life Pub Co MN.
O'Callahan, J. F., ed. Studies in Cistercian Medieval History: Presented to Jeremiah F. O'Sullivan. LC 77-152486. (Cistercian Studies: No. 13). 1971. 7.95 (ISBN 0-87907-813-8). Cistercian Pubns.
O'Carroll, Michael. Pius XII: Greatness Dishonoured. 252p. 1980. 10.00 (ISBN 0-912414-41-3). Lumen Christi.
--Theotokos: A Theological Encyclopedia of the Blessed Virgin Mary. 1982. pap. 19.95 (ISBN 0-89453-268-5). M Glazier.
Ochs, Carol. An Ascent to Joy: Transforming Deadness of Spirit. LC 85-41019. 160p. 1986. text ed. 12.95x (ISBN 0-268-00615-6). U of Notre Dame Pr.
--Behind the Sex of God: Toward a New Consciousness - Transcending Matriarchy & Patriarchy. LC 76-48519. 1977. pap. 8.95x (ISBN 0-8070-1113-4, Pub. by Ariadne Bks, BPA12). Beacon Pr.
--Women & Spirituality. LC 83-3397. (New Feminist Perspectives Ser.). 166p. 1983. 18.95x (ISBN 0-8476-7232-8, Rowman & Allanheld); pap. 9.95x (ISBN 0-8476-7233-6). Rowman.
Ochshorn, Judith. The Female Experience & the Nature of the Divine. LC 81-47012. pap. 71.50 (2056237). Bks Demand UMI.
O'Collins, Gerald. Finding Jesus: Living Through Lent with John's Gospel. 64p. 1984. pap. 3.95 (ISBN 0-8091-2565-X). Paulist Pr.
--Foundations of Theology. LC 70-153756. 1971. pap. 3.95 (ISBN 0-8294-0201-2). Loyola.
--Fundamental Theology. LC 80-82809. 288p. (Orig.). 1981. pap. 8.95 (ISBN 0-8091-2347-9). Paulist Pr.
--Interpreting Jesus. 1983. pap. 9.95 (ISBN 0-8091-2572-2). Paulist Pr.
--Jesus Risen: An Historical, Fundamental & Systematic Examination of Christ's Resurrection. 240p. 1987. 13.95 (ISBN 0-8091-2849-7); pap. 16.95 (ISBN 0-8091-0393-1). Paulist Pr.
--A Month with Jesus. pap. 2.95 (ISBN 0-87193-097-8). Dimension Bks.
--The People's Christmas. (Orig.). 1984. pap. 3.50 (ISBN 0-8091-2660-5). Paulist Pr.
--The Resurrection of Jesus Christ. LC 73-2613. 160p. 1973. pap. 3.50 (ISBN 0-8170-0614-1). Judson.
--The Second Journey. LC 77-99303. 96p. 1978. pap. 3.95 (ISBN 0-8091-2209-X). Paulist Pr.
--What Are They Saying about Jesus? Rev. ed. LC 77-70640. 1982. pap. 3.95 (ISBN 0-8091-2521-8). Paulist Pr.
O'Collins, Gerald, jt. ed. see Latourelle, Rene.
O'Connell, Daniel M. A Cardinal Newman Prayerbook: Kindly Light. 352p. 1985. pap. 14.95 (ISBN 0-87193-220-2). Dimension Bks.
O'Connell, E. Patrick, tr. see De La Touche, Louise M.
O'Connell, George, jt. auth. see Gallup, George, Jr.
O'Connell, Jeremiah J. Catholicity in the Carolinas & Georgia: Leaves of Its History. LC 73-187371. (Illus.). 647p. 1972. Repr. of 1879 ed. 17.50 (ISBN 0-87152-099-0). Reprint.
O'Connell, Kevin G. The Theodotionic Revision of the Book of Exodus. LC 70-160026. (Semitic Monographs Ser: No. 3). 509p. 1972. 20.00x (ISBN 0-674-87785-3). Harvard U Pr.
O'Connell, M. R. Thomas Stapleton & the Counter Reformation. 1964. 49.50x (ISBN 0-685-69850-5). Elliots Bks.
O'Connell, Margaret. The Magic Cauldron: Witchcraft for Good & Evil. LC 75-26757. (Illus.). 256p. 1975. 15.95 (ISBN 0-87599-187-4). S G Phillips.
O'Connell, Mathew J., tr. see Gonzalez-Ruiz, Jose-Maria.
O'Connell, Mathew J., tr. see Sobrino, Jon.
O'Connell, Matthew, tr. see Belo, Fernando.
O'Connell, Matthew, tr. see Gatti, Enzo.
O'Connell, Matthew, tr. see Gutierrez, Gustavo.
O'Connell, Matthew, tr. see Latourelle, Rene.
O'Connell, Matthew, tr. see Martimort, A. G., et al.
O'Connell, Matthew, tr. see Schottroff, Luise & Stegemann, Wolfgang.
O'Connell, Matthew, tr. see Vaillancourt, Raymond.

O'Connell, Matthew J. Temple of the Holy Spirit. 345p. 1983. pap. 17.50 (ISBN 0-916134-64-4). Pueblo Pub Co.
O'Connell, Matthew J., tr. see Adam, Adolf.
O'Connell, Matthew J., tr. see Bakole Wa Ilunga.
O'Connell, Matthew J., tr. see Berger & Hollerweger.
O'Connell, Matthew J., tr. see Camara, Helder.
O'Connell, Matthew J., tr. see Deiss, Lucien.
O'Connell, Matthew J., tr. see Echegaray, Hugo.
O'Connell, Matthew J., tr. see Fischer, Balthasar.
O'Connell, Matthew J., tr. see Gutierrez, Gustavo.
O'Connell, Matthew J., tr. see Hamelin, Leonce.
O'connell, Matthew J., tr. see Jager, Willigis.
O'Connell, Matthew J., tr. see Martimort, A. G., et al.
O'Connell, Matthew J., tr. see Mazza, Enrico.
O'Connell, Matthew J., tr. see Metz, Rene & Schlick, Jean.
O'Connell, Matthew J., tr. see Pannenberg, Wolfhart.
O'Connell, Matthew J., tr. see Ratzinger, Joseph C.
O'Connell, Matthew J., tr. see Rordorf, Willy, et al.
O'Connell, Matthew J., tr. see Schelkle, Karl H.
O'Connell, Matthew J., tr. see Schulz, Hans-Joachim.
O'Connell, Matthew J., tr. see Von Allmen, et al.
O'Connell, Patrick. Original Sin in the Light of Modern Science. 128p. 1973. pap. 3.00 (ISBN 0-912414-15-4). Lumen Christi.
O'Connell, Patrick & Carty, Charles. The Holy Shroud & Four Visions: The Holy Shroud New Evidence Compared with the Visions of St. Bridget of Sweden, Maria d'Agreda, Anne Catherine Emmerich, & Teresa Neumann. (Illus.). 1974. pap. 1.50 (ISBN 0-89555-102-0). TAN Bks Pubs.
O'Connell, Patrick, tr. see St. Joseph Cafasso.
O'Connell, Patrick F. Collectanea Cartusiensia, No. 2. Hogg, James, ed. (Analecta Cartusiana Ser.: No. 82-2). (Fr. & Ger.). 118p. (Orig.). 1980. pap. 25.00 (ISBN 3-7052-0120-4, Pub. by Salzburg Studies). Longwood Pub Group.
O'Connell, Robert. Imagination & Metaphysics in St. Augustine. LC 85-82595. (Aquinas Lecture). 70p. 1986. 7.95 (ISBN 0-87462-227-1). Marquette.
O'Connell, Robert J. Art & the Christian Intelligence in St. Augustine. LC 78-546. 1978. 18.00x (ISBN 0-674-04675-7). Harvard U Pr.
--An Introduction to Plato's Metaphysics. LC 84-73309. xii, 235p. 1985. pap. 6.25 (ISBN 0-8232-1132-0). Fordham.
--Saint Augustine's Early Theory of Man, A. D. 386-391. LC 68-21981. 1968. text ed. 20.00x (ISBN 0-674-78520-7, Belknap Pr). Harvard U Pr.
O'Connell, Timothy E. Principles for a Catholic Morality. 1978. (HarpR); pap. 9.95 (ISBN 0-86683-885-6). Har-Row.
O'Conner, Fr. J., tr. see Claudel, Paul.
O'Connor, Brian, et al. The Role of the Minister in Caring for the Dying Patient & the Bereaved. 16.50 (ISBN 0-405-12504-6). Ayer Co Pubs.
O'Connor, Brian P., et al, eds. The Pastoral Role in Caring for the Dying & Bereaved: Pragmatic & Ecumenical. LC 86-545. (Foundation of Thanatology Ser.: Vol. 7). 245p. 1986. lib. bdg. 39.95 (ISBN 0-275-92153-0, C2153). Praeger.
O'Connor, David, jt. auth. see Hutchinson, John.
O'Connor, Edmund, ed. see Yapp, Malcolm.
O'Connor, Elizabeth. Call to Commitment. LC 63-10963. 224p. 1976. pap. 5.95 (ISBN 0-06-066330-8, RD131, HarpR). Har-Row.
--Journey Inward, Journey Outward. LC 75-9313. 192p. 1975. pap. 5.95 (ISBN 0-06-066332-4, RD100, HarpR). Har-Row.
--Letters to Scattered Pilgrims. LC 78-3361. 176p. 1982. (HarpR); pap. 8.95 (ISBN 0-06-066334-0, RD-374). Har-Row.
--Our Many Selves. LC 78-124699. 1971. pap. 4.95 (ISBN 0-06-066336-7, RD-36, HarpR). Har-Row.
--Search for Silence. rev. ed. Broucek, Marcia, ed. LC 86-114. 192p. 1986. pap. 8.95 (ISBN 0-931055-08-3). LuraMedia.
O'Connor, Flannery. The Habit of Being. Fitzgerald, Sally, ed. & intro. by. LC 78-11559. 639p. 1979. 15.00 (ISBN 0-374-16769-9). FS&G.
O'Connor, Francine & Boswell, Kathryn. ABC's of Faith, Bk. 3. (Illus.). 32p. (Orig.). 1980. pap. 1.95 (ISBN 0-89243-125-3). Liguori Pubns.
--ABC's of Faith, Bk. 4. (Illus.). 1981. pap. 1.95 (ISBN 0-89243-138-5). Liguori Pubns.
--ABC'S of Faith, Bk. 5. (Illus.). 32p. 1982. pap. 1.95 (ISBN 0-89243-165-2). Liguori Pubns.
--ABC's of Faith, Bk. 6. (Illus.). 32p. 1984. pap. 1.95 (ISBN 0-89243-214-4). Liguori Pubns.
O'Connor, Francine M. Special Friends of Jesus: New Testament Stories. 64p. 1986. pap. 3.95 (ISBN 0-89243-255-1). Liguori Pubns.
O'Connor, Francine M. & Boswell, Kathryn. The ABC's of Faith, 2 bks. 1979. Bk. 1. pap. 1.95 (ISBN 0-89243-113-X); Bk. 2. pap. 1.95 (ISBN 0-89243-114-8). Liguori Pubns.
--The ABC'S of the Rosary. (Illus.). 32p. 1984. pap. 1.95 (ISBN 0-89243-221-7). Liguori Pubns.
O'Connor, James. The Father's Son. 324p. 1984. 7.00 (ISBN 0-8198-2621-9); pap. 6.00 (ISBN 0-8198-2622-7). Dghtrs St Paul.
O'Connor, John, tr. see Biver, Paul.
O'Connor, John F., tr. see Leo, Pope.
O'Connor, John J. In Defense of Life. 1980. 4.00 (ISBN 0-686-74344-X); pap. 3.00 (ISBN 0-8198-3601-X). Dghtrs St Paul.
O'Connor, June. The Quest for Political & Spiritual Liberation: A Study in the Thought of Sri Aurobindo Ghose. LC 75-5249. 153p. 1976. 16.50 (ISBN 0-8386-1734-4). Fairleigh Dickinson.
O'Connor, Leo F. Religion in the American Novel: The Search for Belief, 1860-1920. LC 83-21842. 364p. (Orig.). 1984. lib. bdg. 31.00 (ISBN 0-8191-3683-2); pap. text ed. 14.50 (ISBN 0-8191-3684-0). U Pr of Amer.
O'Connor, M. & Freedman, David N. Backgrounds for the Bible. 1987. text ed. 17.50x (ISBN 0-931464-30-7). Eisenbrauns.
O'Connor, M., jt. ed. see Meyers, Carol L.
O'Connor, Sr. M. Catharine. Art of Dying Well. Repr. of 1942 ed. 15.00 (ISBN 0-404-04811-0). AMS Pr.
O'Connor, Michael. Hebrew Verse Structure. 1980. 18.75x (ISBN 0-931464-02-1). Eisenbrauns.
O'Connor, Nancy. Letting Go with Love: The Grieving Process. LC 84-61538. 186p. 1985. 18.95x (ISBN 0-9613714-1-2); pap. 9.95x (ISBN 0-9613714-0-4). La Mariposa.
O'Connor, Patricia. Therese of Lisieux: A Biography. LC 83-63169. 168p. 1984. pap. 5.95 (ISBN 0-87973-607-0, 607). Our Sunday Visitor.
O'Connor, Patrick, compiled by. Buddhists Find Christ: The Spiritual Quest of Thirteen Men & Women in Burma, China, Japan, Korea, Sri Lanka, Thailand, Vietnam. 240p. 1975. pap. 2.25 (ISBN 0-8048-1146-6). C E Tuttle.
O'Connor, Sarah H. The Nine Months Journey: A Christian Mother's Reflections on Pregnancy & Childbirth. 128p. (Orig.). 1984. pap. 6.95 (ISBN 0-687-28017-6). Abingdon.
O'Connor, Thomas H. Fitzpatrick's Boston, 1846-1866: John Bernard Fitzpatrick, Third Bishop of Boston. LC 83-23806. 308p. 1984. text ed. 22.95x (ISBN 0-930350-56-1). NE U Pr.
O'Connor, William R. Natural Desire for God: Aquinas Lectures. 1948. 7.95 (ISBN 0-87462-113-5). Marquette.
O'Conor, John F., tr. see Leo, Pope.
Oda, Stephanie C. Reaching for Joy. 48p. 1985. 4.95 (ISBN 0-8378-5402-4). Gibson.
Oda, Stephanie C., ed. Seasons of the Heart. (A Reader's Digest-C. R. Gibson Bk.). (Illus.). 96p. 1984. 8.00 (ISBN 0-8378-1806-0). Gibson.
O'Day, Gail R. Revelation in the Fourth Gospel: Narrative Mode & Theological Claim. LC 86-45217. 160p. 1986. pap. 9.95 (ISBN 0-8006-1933-1). Fortress.
O'Day, Rey & Powers, Edward. Theatre of the Spirit: A Worship Handbook. LC 80-14165. 190p. (Orig.). 1980. pap. 7.95 (ISBN 0-8298-0363-7). Pilgrim NY.
O'Day, Rosemary. The Debate on the English Reformation. 217p. 1986. text ed. 29.95 (ISBN 0-416-72670-4, 9794); pap. text ed. 9.95 (ISBN 0-416-72680-1, 9802). Methuen Inc.
O'Day, Rosemary, jt. auth. see Heal, Felicity.
O'Day, Rosemary & Heal, Felicity, eds. Princes & Paupers in the English Church: 1500-1800. 294p. 1981. 28.50x (ISBN 0-389-20200-2, 06982). B&N Imports.
Oddi, Silvie C. The Right of the Catechized to the Truth. 102p. 1983. pap. 2.00 (ISBN 0-8198-6407-2). Dghtrs St Paul.
Oddie, G. A. Social Protest in India: British Protestant Missionaries & Social Reforms, Eighteen Fifty to Nineteen Hundred. 1979. 17.50x (ISBN 0-8364-0195-6). South Asia Bks.
Oddo, Gilbert L. Freedom & Equality: Civil Liberties & the Supreme Court. LC 78-25592. 1979. pap. text ed. write for info. (ISBN 0-673-16262-1). Scott F.
Ode, James. Brass Instruments in Church Services. 1970. pap. 3.00 (ISBN 0-8066-1025-5, 11-9085). Augsburg.
O'Dea, Barbara. Of Fast & Festival: Celebrating Lent & Easter. 1982. pap. 3.95 (ISBN 0-8091-2426-2). Paulist Pr.
O'Dea, Thomas F. Mormons. LC 57-6984. 1964. pap. 10.00x (ISBN 0-226-61744-0, P162, Phoen). U of Chicago Pr.
Odeberg, Hugo. Enoch Three, or the Hebrew Book of Enoch. rev. ed. (Library of Biblical Studies). 1970. 39.50x (ISBN 0-87068-093-5). Ktav.
Oded, Arye. Islam in Uganda. 382p. 1974. casebound 19.95x (ISBN 0-87855-171-9). Transaction Bks.
Odell, Catherine. On Pilgrimage with Father Ralph Diorio: Following the Footpaths of Faith through the Holyland, Rome & Lourdes. LC 85-7083. (Illus.). 192p. 1986. 16.95 (ISBN 0-385-19908-2). Doubleday.
Odell, Catherine & Odell, William. The First Human Right: A Pro-Life Primer. LC 82-61466. 1983. pap. 4.95 (ISBN 0-87973-620-8, 620). Our Sunday Visitor.
Odell, Catherine M. Those Who Saw Her: The Apparitions of Mary. 200p. (Orig.). 1986. pap. 6.95 (ISBN 0-87973-720-4, 720). Our Sunday Visitor.
Odell, William, jt. auth. see McDonald, Perry.
Odell, William, jt. auth. see Odell, Catherine.
Oden, Thomas. Becoming a Minister. 256p. 1987. 17.95 (ISBN 0-8245-0825-4). Crossroad NY.
Oden, Thomas C. Agenda for Theology. LC 78-19506. 1979. pap. text ed. 11.00 (ISBN 0-06-066347-2, HarpR). Har-Row.
--Care of Souls in the Classic Tradition. LC 83-48912. (Theology & Pastoral Care Ser.). pap. 7.95 (ISBN 0-8006-1729-0, 1-729). Fortress.
--Conscience & Dividends: Church & the Multinationals. LC 85-1581. 192p. 1985. 15.00 (ISBN 0-89633-089-3); pap. 9.00 (ISBN 0-89633-090-7). Ethics & Public Policy.
--Crisis Ministries. 224p. 1985. 19.95 (ISBN 0-8245-0709-6). Crossroad NY.
--The Living God. 1986. 29.45 (ISBN 0-317-52383-X, HarpR). Har-Row.
--Pastoral Theology: Essentials of Ministry. LC 82-47753. 456p. (Orig.). 1983. 15.95 (ISBN 0-06-066353-7, RD 415, HarpR). Har-Row.
Oden, Thomas C., ed. see Wesley, John.
Odenheimer, William H. Jerusalem & Its Vicinity: Familiar Lectures on the Sacred Localities Connected with the Week Before the Resurrection. Davis, Moshe, ed. (America & the Holy Land Ser.). (Illus.). 1977. Repr. of 1855 ed. lib. bdg. 20.00x (ISBN 0-405-10272-0). Ayer Co Pubs.
Odens, Peter R. Father Garces: The Maverick Priest. (Illus.). 1980. pap. 3.50 (ISBN 0-9609484-3-0). P R Odens.
Odhner, Carl T. Michael Servetus, His Life & Teachings. LC 83-45626. Date not set. Repr. of 1910 ed. 18.50 (ISBN 0-404-19844-9). AMS Pr.
Odhner, Hugo L. The Moral Life. 142p. 1985. Repr. of 1957 ed. write for info. (ISBN 0-910557-08-X). Acad New Church.
--Swedenborg's System of Degrees. 25p. 1970. pap. 1.00 (ISBN 0-915221-16-0). Swedenborg Sci Assn.
Odhner, John D., ed. see Swedenborg, Emanuel.
Odier, Daniel. Nirvana-Tao: The Secret Meditation Techniques of the Taoist & Buddhist Masters. (Illus.). 208p. (Orig.). 1986. pap. 9.95 (ISBN 0-89281-045-9). Inner Tradit.
Odin, Steve. Process Metaphysics & Hua-Yen Buddhism: A Critical Study of Cumulative Penetration vs. Interpretation. LC 81-9388. 256p. 1982. 44.50 (ISBN 0-87395-568-4); pap. 16.95 (ISBN 0-87395-569-2). State U NY Pr.
Odo of Deuil. De Profectione Ludovici VII in Orientem: The Journey of Louis the Seventh to the East. Berry, Virginia G., ed. & tr. 1965. pap. 6.95x (ISBN 0-393-09662-9). Norton.
O'Doherty, E. F. see McNamee, Fintan.
Odom, Martha. The Making of a Missionary. Woolsey, Raymond H., ed. 128p. (Orig.). 1985. pap. 5.95 (ISBN 0-8280-0289-4). Review & Herald.
Odom, Stephen A., ed. Steady in an Unsteady World. 144p. 1986. pap. 7.95 (ISBN 0-8170-1097-1). Judson.
O'Donnell, Anne M., ed. see Erasmus.
O'Donnell, Desmond. Meet Jesus in Luke. LC 80-67126. (Praying the Scriptures Ser.). 56p. (Orig.). 1980. pap. 1.75 (ISBN 0-87793-206-9). Ave Maria.
O'Donnell, Desmond, jt. auth. see White, Thomas.
O'Donnell, Edward. Priestly People. 64p. 1982. pap. 1.50 (ISBN 0-89243-168-7). Liguori Pubns.
O'Donnell, J. D. Faith for Today. LC 65-29130. (Sunday School Workers Training Course Ser.: No. 5). 1974. pap. 3.95 (ISBN 0-89265-000-1). Randall Hse.
--Free Will Baptist Doctrines. 1974. pap. 4.95 (ISBN 0-89265-019-2). Randall Hse.
--Handbook for Deacons. 1973. pap. 3.95 (ISBN 0-89265-011-7). Randall Hse.
--The Preacher & His Preaching. 1974. pap. 3.95 (ISBN 0-89265-018-4). Randall Hse.
--A Survey of Church History. 1973. pap. 4.95 (ISBN 0-89265-009-5). Randall Hse.
O'Donnell, J. D. & Hampton, Ralph, Jr. A Survey of the Books of History. 1976. pap. 3.25 (ISBN 0-89265-032-X). Randall Hse.
--A Survey of the Books of Poetry. 1976. pap. 2.25 (ISBN 0-89265-033-8). Randall Hse.
O'Donnell, J. D., jt. auth. see Outlaw, Stanley.
O'Donnell, James J. Augustine. LC 84-28133. (World Author Ser.). 1985. lib. bdg. 19.95 (ISBN 0-8057-6609-X, Twayne). G K Hall.
O'Donnell, John H. The Catholic Hierarchy of the United States, 1790-1922. LC 73-3558. (Catholic University of America. Studies in American Church History: No. 4). Repr. of 1922 ed. 28.00 (ISBN 0-404-57754-7). AMS Pr.
O'Donnell, John J. Trinity & Temporality. (Oxford Theological Monographs). 1983. 32.50x (ISBN 0-19-826722-3). Oxford U Pr.
O'Donnell, Lydia, jt. auth. see Lein, Laura.
O'Donnell, Thomas J. Medicine & Christian Morality. LC 75-41471. 1976. 9.95 (ISBN 0-8189-0323-6). Alba.
O'Donoghue, Noel D. Heaven in Ordinarie. 1979. 14.95 (ISBN 0-87243-085-5). Templegate.
--The Holy Mountain: Approaches to the Mystery of Prayer. 9.95 (ISBN 0-89453-430-0); pap. 6.95 (ISBN 0-89453-300-2). M Glazier.
O'Donovan, Daniel, tr. Bernard of Clairvaux, Treatises III: On Grace & Free Choice, in Praise of the New Knighthood. (Cistercian Studies Ser.: No. 3). 1977. 10.95 (ISBN 0-87907-119-2); pap. 4.95 (ISBN 0-87907-719-0). Cistercian Pubns.
O'Donovan, L. J. A World of Grace. 1980. pap. 14.95x (ISBN 0-8245-0406-2). Crossroad NY.
O'Donovan, Oliver. The Problem of Self-Love in Saint Augustine. LC 80-5397. 208p. 1980. text ed. 23.50x (ISBN 0-300-02468-1). Yale U Pr.
--Resurrection & Moral Order: An Outline for an Evangelical Ethics. 320p. 1986. 18.95 (ISBN 0-8028-3610-0). Eerdmans.
Odor, Harold & Odor, Ruth. Becoming a Christian. (Illus.). 16p. 1985. 0.75 (ISBN 0-87239-901-X, 3301). Standard Pub.
--Sharing Your Faith. (Illus.). 16p. 1985. 0.75 (ISBN 0-87239-902-8, 3302). Standard Pub.
Odor, Ruth. Bible Adventures. (Flip-a-Bible-Story Bks.). (Illus.). 16p. (Orig.). 1982. pap. 3.95 (ISBN 0-87239-561-8, 2735). Standard Pub.
--Bible Heroes. (Flip-a-Bible-Story Bks.). (Illus.). 16p. (Orig.). 1982. pap. 3.95 (ISBN 0-87239-562-6, 2736). Standard Pub.
--Christmas Is a Time for Singing. LC 81-86706. (Happy Day Bks.). (Illus.). 24p. (Orig.). 1982. pap. 1.59 (ISBN 0-87239-535-9, 3581). Standard Pub.
--The Happiest Day. 1985. 5.95 (ISBN 0-89565-085-1, R4915). Standard Pub.
--Jesus & His Friends. (Flip-a-Bible-Story Bks.). (Illus.). 16p. (Orig.). 1982. pap. 3.95 (ISBN 0-87239-560-X, 2734). Standard Pub.
--The Life of Jesus. (Flip-a-Bible-Story Bks.). (Illus.). 16p. (Orig.). 1982. pap. 3.95 (ISBN 0-87239-559-6, 2733). Standard Pub.
--Prayers for Boys. 1985. pap. 0.69 pocket size (ISBN 0-87239-825-0, 2815). Standard Pub.
--Prayers for Girls. 1985. pap. 0.69 pocket size (ISBN 0-87239-826-9, 2816). Standard Pub.
--The Very Special Night. (A Happy Day Book). (Illus.). 24p. (Orig.). 1980. 1.59 (ISBN 0-87239-405-0, 3637). Standard Pub.
Odor, Ruth, jt. auth. see Odor, Harold.
O'Driscoll, Herbert. A Certain Life: Contemporary Meditations on the Way of Christ. 96p. (Orig.). 1980. pap. 5.95 (ISBN 0-8164-2040-8, HarpR). Har-Row.
--A Certain Life: Contemporary Meditations on the Way of Christ. 192p. 1985. pap. 8.95 large print ed. (ISBN 0-8027-2491-4); pap. cancelled (ISBN 0-8027-7274-9). Walker & Co.
--Crossroads: Times of Decision for People of God. 96p. 1983. pap. 5.95 (ISBN 0-8164-2432-2, HarpR). Har-Row.
--Portrait of a Woman. 96p. (Orig.). 1981. pap. 4.95 (ISBN 0-8164-2332-6, HarpR). Har-Row.
O'Duffy, E. Crusade in Spain. 69.95 (ISBN 0-87968-972-2). Gordon Pr.
Odulphi Van Den Eynde, jt. ed. see Damiani Van Den Eynde.
Oduyoye, Mercy A. Hearing & Knowing: Theological Reflections on Christianity in Africa. LC 85-29873. 176p. (Orig.). 1986. pap. 9.95 (ISBN 0-88344-258-2). Orbis Bks.
Oduyoye, Modupe. Sons of the Gods & Daughters of Men: An Afro-Asiatic Interpretation of Genesis 1-11. LC 83-6308. 126p. (Orig.). 1983. pap. 12.95 (ISBN 0-88344-467-4). Orbis Bks.
O'Dwyer, Barry W., tr. from Lat. Letters from Ireland, 1228-1229. (Cistercian Fathers Ser.: No. 28). Orig. Title: Registrum epistolarum Stephani de Lexinton abbatis de Stannlegia et de Saviagnaco. 1982. 24.95 (ISBN 0-87907-428-0). Cistercian Pubns.
O'Dwyer, Margaret M. The Papacy in the Age of Napoleon & the Restoration: Pius VII, 1800-1823. 296p. (Orig.). 1985. lib. bdg. 24.00 (ISBN 0-8191-4825-3); pap. text ed. 12.75 (ISBN 0-8191-4826-1). U Pr of Amer.
Oeconomos, Lysimaque. La Vie Religieuse Dans l'Empire Byzantin Au Temps Des Comnenes et Des Anges. LC 77-184705. (Research & Source Works Ser.). (Fr.). 252p. 1972. Repr. of 1918 ed. lib. bdg. 23.50 (ISBN 0-8337-2602-1). B Franklin.
Oecumenical Synod Seventh, jt. auth. see Damascene, John.

Oehler, Gustave. Theology of the Old Testament. 1978. 22.50 (ISBN 0-86524-125-2, 8702). Klock & Klock.

Oelman, Timothy, ed. & tr. Marrano Poets of the Seventeenth Century: An Anthology of the Poetry of Joao Pinto Delgado, Antonio Enriquez Gomez & Miguel de Barrios. (Littman Library of Jewish Civilization). (Illus.). 1985. 24.95x (ISBN 0-19-710047-3). Oxford U Pr.

Oesterle, John A., tr. see St. Thomas Aquinas.

Oesterley, William O. The Jewish Background of the Christian Liturgy. 1925. 11.75 (ISBN 0-8446-1329-0). Peter Smith.

--Jews & Judaism During the Greek Period: The Background of Christianity. LC 74-102580. 1970. Repr. of 1941 ed. 23.00x (ISBN 0-8046-0740-0, Pub. by Kennikat). Assoc Faculty Pr.

--A Short Survey of the Literature of Rabbinical & Medieval Judaism. LC 72-82352. 328p. 1973. Repr. of 1920 ed. lib. bdg. 24.50 (ISBN 0-8337-3944-1). B Franklin.

Oesterreich, T. K. Obsession & Possession. 1935. 11.00x (ISBN 0-685-00906-8). Wehman.

--Possession: Demoniacal & Other. 400p. 1974. pap. 4.95 (ISBN 0-8065-0436-6). Citadel Pr.

Oesterreich, Traugott K. Possession. 1966. 10.00 (ISBN 0-8216-0138-5). Univ Bks.

Oesterreicher, John M. Five in Search of Wisdom. abr. ed. Orig. Title: Walls Are Crumbling: Seven Jewish Philosophers Discover Christ. 1967. pap. 2.25x (ISBN 0-268-00100-6). U of Notre Dame Pr.

--The New Encounter Between Christians & Jews. LC 85-26033. 472p. 1986. 25.00 (ISBN 0-8022-2496-2). Philos Lib.

--The Unfinished Dialogue: Martin Buber & the Christian Way. LC 85-12410. 128p. 1986. 14.95 (ISBN 0-8022-2495-4). Philos Lib.

--Walls Are Crumbling. (Illus.). 10.00 (ISBN 0-8159-7201-6). Devin.

Oestreich, Nelson, jt. auth. see Perkins, James A.

Oetting, R. When Jesus Was a Lad. LC 68-56816. (Illus.). 1968. PLB 9.26x (ISBN 0-87783-047-9). Oddo.

O'Farrell, Padraic. Superstitions of the Irish Country People. rev. ed. 92p. 1982. pap. 5.95 (ISBN 0-85342-530-2, Pub. by Mercier Pr Ireland). Irish Bks Media.

O'Ferrall, F. Catholic Emancipation: Daniel O'Connell & the Birth of Irish Democracy. LC 85-14178. 350p. 1985. text ed. 38.50x (ISBN 0-391-03353-0). Humanities.

Office of Worship for the Presbyterian Church (U. S. A.) & the Cumberland Presbyterian Church Station. Christian Marriage. (Supplemental Liturgical Resource Ser.: 3). 120p. (Orig.). 1986. pap. 7.95 (ISBN 0-664-24033-X). Westminster.

Office of Worship for the Presbyterian Church (U. S. A.) & the Cumberland Presbyterian Church. The Funeral: A Service of Witness to the Resurrection. (Supplemental Liturgical Resource Ser.: 4). 120p. (Orig.). 1986. pap. write for info. (ISBN 0-664-24034-8). Westminster.

Office of Worship for the Presbyterian Church (U. S. A.) & Cumberland Presbyterian Church. A Psalm Sampler. LC 85-753089. (Illus.). 48p. 1986. pap. 4.95 ea. (ISBN 0-664-24681-8). Westminster.

Offner, Hazel. The Fruit of the Spirit. (LifeGuide Bible Studies). 64p. 1987. pap. 2.95. Inter-Varsity.

Offord, R. M., ed. Jerry McAuley, an Apostle to the Lost. facsimile ed. LC 75-124248. (Select Bibliographies Reprint Ser). (Illus.). Repr. of 1907 ed. 19.00 (ISBN 0-8369-5436-X). Ayer Co Pubs.

O'Fiaich, Tomas. St. Columbanus in His Own Words. pap. 4.95 (ISBN 0-686-05661-2). Eastern Orthodox.

O'Flaherty, Liam. The Ecstacy of Angus. 64p. 1978. Repr. of 1931 ed. 10.95 (ISBN 0-905473-18-3, Pub. by Wolfhound Pr Ireland). Irish Bks Media.

O'Flaherty, Vincent M. Who...Me? A Study in Identification by Seeking the Will of God. 200p. 1974. 4.95 (ISBN 0-8199-0540-2). Franciscan Herald.

O'Flaherty, Wendy. Rig Veda. (Pengiun Classic Ser.). 1982. pap. 5.95 (ISBN 0-14-044402-5). Penguin.

O'Flaherty, Wendy, tr. Hindu Myths. (Classics Ser.). 360p. 1975. pap. 5.95 (ISBN 0-14-044306-1). Penguin.

O'Flaherty, Wendy D. Dreams, Illusion, & Other Realities. LC 83-17944. (Illus.). xvi, 366p. 1986. pap. 13.95 (ISBN 0-226-61855-2). U of Chicago Pr.

--Karma & Rebirth in Classical Indian Traditions. LC 79-64475. 400p. 1980. 41.00x (ISBN 0-520-03923-8). U of Cal Pr.

--The Origins of Evil in Hindu Mythology Hermeneuties. (Studies in the History of Religions). 1977. pap. 6.95 (ISBN 0-520-04098-8, CAL 456). U of Cal Pr.

--Siva: The Erotic Ascetic. (Illus.). 1981. pap. 9.95 (ISBN 0-19-520250-3). Oxford U Pr.

Ofori, Patrick E. Christianity in Tropical Africa: A Selective Annotated Bibliography. 461p. 1977. lib. bdg. 48.00 (ISBN 3-262-00002-7). Kraus Intl.

--Islam in Africa South of the Sahara: A Select Bibliographic Guide. 223p. 1977. lib. bdg. 42.00 (ISBN 3-262-00003-5). Kraus Intl.

Ogden, Dunbar H. Wedding Bells. (Orig.). 1945. pap. 3.25 (ISBN 0-8042-1884-6). John Knox.

Ogden, Schubert M. Christ Without Myth: A Study Based on the Theology of Rudolf Bultmann. LC 79-102841. 1979. pap. 8.95x (ISBN 0-87074-172-1). SMU Press.

--On Theology. 180p. 1986. 19.50 (ISBN 0-86683-529-6, HarpR). Har-Row.

--The Point of Christology. LC 81-47842. 224p. 1982. 14.00i (ISBN 0-06-066352-9, HarpR). Har-Row.

--The Reality of God. LC 66-20783. 1977. pap. 4.95xi (ISBN 0-06-066351-0, RD 241, HarpR). Har-Row.

Ogden, Schubert M., ed. & tr. see Bultmann, Rudolf.

Ogg, Elizabeth. Facing Death & Loss. LC 85-51126. 106p. 1985. pap. 19.00 (ISBN 0-87762-423-2). Technomic.

Ogg, George. Chronology of the Public Ministry of Jesus. 1980. lib. bdg. 75.00 (ISBN 0-8490-3142-7). Gordon Pr.

Ogibenin, B. L. Structure d'un Mythe Vedique: Le Mythe Cosmogonique dans le Rgveda. (Approaches to Semiotics: No. 30). 1973. 27.20x (ISBN 0-686-21821-3). Mouton.

Ogier VIII. The Holy Jerusalem Voyage of Ogier VIII, Seigneure D'anglure. Browne, Roland A., tr. LC 75-4773. (Illus.). 163p. 1975. 10.00 (ISBN 0-8130-0513-2). U Presses Fla.

Ogilvie, Lloyd. Congratulations - God Believes in You. 128p. 1980. 5.95 (ISBN 0-8499-2994-6). Word Bks.

--Let God Love You. 1978. pap. 7.95 (ISBN 0-8499-2831-1, 2831-1). Word Bks.

Ogilvie, Lloyd, ed. see McKenna, David L.

Ogilvie, Lloyd J. Ask Him Anything. (QP Proven-Word Ser.). 244p. 1984. pap. 7.95 (ISBN 0-8499-2982-2). Word Bks.

--Autobiography of God. LC 78-53355. 324p. 1981. pap. 7.95 (ISBN 0-8307-0791-3, 5415106). Regal.

--The Beauty of Caring. LC 80-80464. 1981. pap. 5.95 (ISBN 0-89081-244-6). Harvest Hse.

--The Beauty of Friendship. LC 80-80463. 1980. pap. 5.95 (ISBN 0-89081-243-8). Harvest Hse.

--The Beauty of Love. LC 80-80465. (Orig.). 1980. pap. 5.95 (ISBN 0-89081-245-4). Harvest Hse.

--The Beauty of Sharing. LC 80-8880. (Orig.). 1981. pap. 5.95 (ISBN 0-89081-246-2). Harvest Hse.

--Caer en la Grandeza. Lievano, M. Francisco, tr. from Eng. Orig. Title: Falling into Greatness. (Span.). 190p. 1985. pap. 4.95 (ISBN 0-8297-0702-6). Life Pubs Intl.

--The Communicator's Commentary-Acts, Vol. 5. (The Communicator's Commentaries Ser.). 1982. 18.95 (ISBN 0-8499-0158-8). Word Bks.

--Discovering God's Will in Your Life. (Orig.). 1985. pap. 4.95 (ISBN 0-89081-468-6). Harvest Hse.

--L' Ecole des Psaumes. Cosson, Annie L., ed. Rousseau, Marie-Andre, tr. Tr. of Falling into Greatness. (Fr.). 208p. 1985. pap. 3.50 (ISBN 0-8297-0700-X). Life Pubs Intl.

--God's Best for My Life. LC 81-82390. 390p. (Orig.). 1981. text ed. 10.95 (ISBN 0-89081-293-4, 2934). Harvest Hse.

--If God Cares, Why Do I Still Have Problems? 208p. 1985. 12.95 (ISBN 0-8499-0454-4, 0454-4). Word Bks.

--Lord of the Impossible. 224p. (Orig.). 1984. pap. 9.95 (ISBN 0-687-22710-0). Abingdon.

--Loved & Forgiven. LC 76-29889. 160p. 1977. pap. 3.50 (ISBN 0-8307-0442-6, S313103). Regal.

--Praying with Power. LC 83-17742. 1983. 8.95 (ISBN 0-8307-0854-5, 5110309). Regal.

--Radiance of the Inner Splendor. LC 80-51524. 144p. 1980. pap. text ed. 4.95x (ISBN 0-8358-0405-4). Upper Room.

--A Sarca Ainda Arde. Orig. Title: The Bush Is Still Burning. (Port.). 1986. write for info. (ISBN 0-8297-1093-0). Life Pubs Intl.

--When God First Thought of You. 1980. pap. 9.95 (ISBN 0-8499-2945-8). Word Bks.

--Why Not? Accept Christ's Healing & Wholeness. 192p. 1984. 9.95 (ISBN 0-8007-1223-4). Revell.

--You've Got Charisma. 177p. 1983. pap. 4.35 (ISBN 0-687-47268-7). Abingdon.

--La Zarza Sique Ardiendo. Orig. Title: The Bush Is Still Burning. (Span.). 1986. write for info. (ISBN 0-8297-1094-9). Life Pubs Intl.

Ogilvie, Lloyd J., jt. auth. see Chafin, Kenneth L.

Ogilvie, Lloyd J., frwd. by. The Guideposts Family Topical Concordance to the Bible. LC 82-12412. 1982. 17.95 (ISBN 0-8407-4962-7). Nelson.

Ogilvie, Lloyd J., ed. see Cedar, Paul A.

Ogilvie, Lloyd J., ed. see Fredrikson, Roger L.

Ogilvie, Lloyd J., ed. see Larson, Bruce.

Ogilvie, Lloyd John. Freedom In the Spirit. LC 83-82318. 192p. 1984. pap. 4.95 (ISBN 0-89081-444-9). Harvest Hse.

--You Are Loved & Forgiven. rev. ed. LC 86-10186. 192p. 1986. text ed. 12.95 (ISBN 0-8307-1168-6, 5111616); pap. text ed. 4.95 (ISBN 0-8307-1110-4, S412117). Regal.

Ogilvie, Lloyde J. The Cup of Wonder: Communion Meditations. 142p. 1985. pap. 5.95 (ISBN 0-8010-6710-3). Baker Bk.

Ogilvie, Mary G., ed. see Stephen, Caroline.

Ogilvy, Carol & Tinkham, Trudy. Classy Christmas Concert. 112p. 1986. wkbk. 8.95 (ISBN 0-86653-349-4). Good Apple.

Ogle, Arthur. Canon Law in Mediaeval England: An Examination of William Lyndwood's Provinciale. LC 78-156390. (Research & Source Works Ser.: No. 731). 1971. Repr. of 1912 ed. lib. bdg. 20.50 (ISBN 0-8337-2603-X). B Franklin.

Oglesby, Enoch H. Ethics & Theology from the Other Side: Sounds of Moral Struggle. LC 79-62897. 1979. pap. text ed. 11.50 (ISBN 0-8191-0706-9). U Pr of Amer.

--God's Divine Arithematic. Jones, Amos, Jr., ed. LC 84-54498. 150p. (Orig.). 1986. pap. write for info. (ISBN 0-910683-06-9). Sunday School.

Oglesby, Stuart R. Prayers for All Occasions. 180p. 1983. pap. 5.95 (ISBN 0-8042-2485-4). John Knox.

Ogletree, Thomas W. Hospitality to The Stranger: Dimension of Moral Understanding. LC 84-18763. 176p. 1985. pap. 10.95 (ISBN 0-8006-1839-4, 1-1839). Fortress.

--The Use of the Bible in Christian Ethics. LC 83-5489. 240p. 1983. 19.95 (ISBN 0-8006-0710-4, 1-710). Fortress.

Oglivie, Lloyd J. Falling into Greatness. LC 84-1946. 224p. 1984. 11.95 (ISBN 0-8407-5326-8). Nelson.

O'Gorman, Denis. Scriptual Dramas for Children. LC 77-70632. 232p. 1977. pap. 8.95 (ISBN 0-8091-2021-6). Paulist Pr.

O'Gorman, Robert T., jt. auth. see Seymour, Jack L.

O'Grady, John. Catholic Charities in the United States: History & Problems. LC 71-137180. (Poverty U. S. A. Historical Record Ser). 1971. Repr. of 1930 ed. 32.00 (ISBN 0-405-03118-1). Ayer Co Pubs.

O'Grady, John F. Models of Jesus. LC 82-45076. (Illus.). 224p. 1982. pap. 4.95 (ISBN 0-385-17321-0, Im). Doubleday.

O'Grady, Ron. The Song of Jesus. (Illus.). 80p. (Orig.). 1984. pap. 9.95 (ISBN 0-85819-470-8, Pub. by JBCE). ANZ Religious Pubns.

Ogrodowski, William. A Catholic Book of the Mass. LC 84-60752. 168p. 1985. pap. 6.95 (ISBN 0-87973-600-3, 600). Our Sunday Visitor.

O'Guin, C. M. Special Occasion Helps. (Pulpit Library). 88p. 1983. pap. 2.95 (ISBN 0-8010-6650-6). Baker bk.

O'Hagan, Thomas. Essays on Catholic Life. facs. ed. LC 67-22106. (Essay Index Reprint Ser). 1916. 17.00 (ISBN 0-8369-1333-7). Ayer Co Pubs.

O'Hair, Madalyn. An Atheist Speaks. (American Atheist Radio Series Reprints). 321p. (Orig.). 1986. pap. 6.00 (ISBN 0-910309-27-2). Am Atheist.

--O'Hair on Prayer. 12p. (Orig.). 1980. saddle stiched 1.00 (ISBN 0-910309-30-2). Am Atheist.

--Why I Am An Atheist. rev. ed. 39p. 1980. Repr. of 1966 ed. 3.25 (ISBN 0-911826-12-2). Am Atheist.

O'Hair, Madalyn, jt. auth. see Murray, Jon.

O'Hair, Madalyn M. Atheist Epic: Bill Murray, the Bible & the Baltimore Board of Education. LC 71-88701. 316p. 1970. pap. 6.00 (ISBN 0-911826-01-7). Am Atheist.

--Atheist Magazines: A Sampling, 1927-1970. LC 72-171441. (Atheist Viewpoint Ser). 554p. 1972. Repr. of 1971 ed. 28.00 (ISBN 0-405-03812-7). Ayer Co Pubs.

--Freedom under Siege. 282p. cancelled (ISBN 0-911826-25-4). Am Atheist.

--Nobody Has a Prayer. 105p. (Orig.). 1982. pap. 3.00 (ISBN 0-910309-07-8). Am Atheist.

--War in Vietnam: The Religious Connection. 83p. (Orig.). 1982. pap. 4.00 (ISBN 0-911826-28-9). Am Atheist.

--What on Earth Is an Atheist? LC 71-88701. (Fifty-Two Programs from the American Atheist Radio Ser.). 282p. 1969. pap. 6.00 (ISBN 0-911826-00-9). Am Atheist.

--What on Earth Is an Atheist. LC 74-161339. (Atheist Viewpoint Ser). 288p. 1972. Repr. of 1969 ed. 18.00 (ISBN 0-405-03802-X). Ayer Co Pubs.

--Women & Atheism: The Ultimate Liberation. 23p. 1979. 2.50 (ISBN 0-911826-17-3). Am Atheist.

O'Hair, Madalyn M., ed. The Atheist Viewpoint, 25 bks. 1972. Set. 498.00 (ISBN 0-405-03620-5). Ayer Co Pubs.

--The Atheist Viewpoint. Date not set. cancelled (ISBN 0-405-03791-0, 395). Ayer Co Pubs.

O'Hair, Madalyn M., ed. see Lewis, Joseph.

O'Halloran, James. Living Cells: Developing Small Christian Community. LC 83-22076. 132p. (Orig.). 1984. pap. 4.95 (ISBN 0-88344-288-4). Orbis Bks.

Ohanneson, Joan. And They Felt No Shame: Christians Reclaim Their Sexuality. 200p. (Orig.). 1982. pap. 11.95 (ISBN 0-86683-676-4, HarpR). Har-Row.

--Woman: Survivor in the Church. (Orig.). 1980. pap. 6.95 (ISBN 0-86683-607-1, HarpR). Har-Row.

O'Hara, Edwin V. The Church & the Country Community. 14.00 (ISBN 0-405-10846-X, 11849). Ayer Co Pubs.

O'Hara, Jim & Walle, Grace. Collage; A Resource Book for Christian Youth Groups. 86p. (Orig.). 1976. pap. 4.00 (ISBN 0-9608124-5-8). Marianist Com Ctr.

O'Hara, Magdalen, ed. The Directory of Women Religious in the United States. 1985. 65.00 (ISBN 0-89453-528-5). M Glazier.

O'Hara, R. Philip, et al, trs. see Bultmann, Rudolf.

O'Hare, Padraic, ed. Tradition & Transformation in Religious Education. LC 78-27506. 114p. (Orig.). 1979. pap. 6.95 (ISBN 0-89135-016-0). Religious Educ.

O'Hear, Anthony. Experience, Explanation & Faith: An Introduction to the Philosophy of Religion. LC 83-15957. 266p. (Orig.). 1984. pap. 10.95 (ISBN 0-7100-9768-9). Methuen Inc.

O. Henry. The Gift of the Magi. LC 82-60896. (Illus.). 32p. 1982. 14.95 (ISBN 0-907234-17-8). Picture Bk Studio USA.

O. Henry, et al. Inspiration Three, Vol. 5: Three Famous Classics in One Book. LC 73-80032. (Pivot Family Reader Ser.). 1973. pap. 1.25 (ISBN 0-87983-045-X). Keats.

O'Heron, Edward J. Biblical Companions. LC 78-74625. 1979. pap. 3.95 (ISBN 0-87973-647-X). Our Sunday Visitor.

Ohlemacher, Janet. Beloved Alcoholic: What to Do When a Family Member Drinks. 128p. 1984. pap. 4.95 (ISBN 0-310-45531-6, 12480P). Zondervan.

Ohler, Annemarie. Studying the Old Testament. 400p. 33.95 (ISBN 0-567-09335-2, Pub. by T & T Clard Ltd UK). Fortress.

Ohlgren, Thomas H., compiled by. Insular & Anglo-Saxon Illuminated Manuscripts: An Iconographic Catalogue c. A.D. 625 to 1100. LC 85-20446. (Illus.). 480p. 75.00 (ISBN 0-8240-8651-1). Garland Pub.

Ohlsen, Woodrow. Perspectives on Old Testament Literature. LC 77-91012. (Illus.). 450p. 1978. 14.95 (ISBN 0-15-570484-2, HC). HarBraceJ.

Ohsberg, H. Oliver. Church & Persons with Handicaps. LC 82-80342. 128p. 1982. pap. 7.95 (ISBN 0-8361-1996-7). Herald Pr.

Oinas, Felix J. Essays on Russian Folklore & Mythology. (Illus.). 183p. (Orig.). 1985. pap. 12.95 (ISBN 0-89357-148-2). Slavica.

Okakura, Y. The Japanese Spirit. lib. bdg. 79.95 (ISBN 0-87968-549-2). Krishna Pr.

Okayama, Kotaro. Zur Grundlegung Christlicher Ethik Theologische Konzeptionen der Gegenwart im Lichte des Analogie-Problems. (Theologische Bibliothek Toepelmann: Vol. 30). 1977. 24.40x (ISBN 3-11-005812-X). De Gruyter.

Oke, Janette. Love's Abiding Joy. LC 83-15503. 224p. (Orig.). 1983. pap. 4.95 (ISBN 0-87123-401-7, 210401). Bethany Hse.

--Love's Abiding Joy. 217p. 1985. Large Print. pap. 6.95 (ISBN 0-317-20707-5). Bethany Hse.

--Love's Long Journey. 207p. 1985. Large Print. pap. 6.95 (ISBN 0-317-20714-8). Bethany Hse.

--Love's Unending Legacy. 224p. (Orig.). 1984. pap. 4.95 (ISBN 0-87123-616-8, 210616). Bethany Hse.

--Love's Unending Legacy. 224p. 1985. Large Print. pap. 6.95 (ISBN 0-87123-855-1). Bethany Hse.

--When Calls the Heart. LC 82-24451. 221p. (Orig.). 1983. pap. 5.95 (ISBN 0-87123-611-7, 210611). Bethany Hse.

--When Calls the Heart. Large type ed. (Canadian West Ser.). 221p. (Orig.). 1986. pap. 7.95 (ISBN 0-87123-885-3). Bethany Hse.

O'Keefe, Bernadette. Faith, Culture & the Dual System: A Comparative Study of Church & County Schools. 200p. 1986. 27.00x (ISBN 1-85000-110-3, Falmer Pr); pap. 15.00x (ISBN 1-85000-111-1, Falmer Pr). Taylor & Francis.

O'Keefe, Theodore J., ed. see Staeglich, Wilhelm.

O'Keeffe, Timothy J. Milton & the Pauline Tradition: A Study of Theme & Symbolism. LC 80-5842. 356p. (Orig.). 1982. PLB 32.25 (ISBN 0-8191-2453-2); pap. text ed. 15.75 (ISBN 0-8191-2454-0). U Pr of Amer.

O'Kelly, Bernard, ed. & tr. see Colet, John.

Oki, Masahiro. Zen Yoga Therapy. LC 79-1060. (Illus.). 1979. pap. 12.50 (ISBN 0-87040-459-8). Japan Pubns USA.

Oko, Adolph S., compiled by see Columbia University.

Okoroche, Cyril. The Meaning of Religious Conversion in Africa: The Case of the Igbo of Nigeria. 354p. 1987. text ed. 55.00x (ISBN 0-566-05030-7, Pub. by Gower Pub England). Gower Pub Co.

Olan, Levi A. Maturity in an Immature World. 1984. 15.00 (ISBN 0-88125-049-X). Ktav.

--Prophetic Faith & the Secular Age. LC 82-2903. 168p. 1982. 15.00x (ISBN 0-87068-888-X). Ktav.

Olbricht, Thomas. The Power to Be. LC 79-67136. (Journey Bks.). 1979. pap. 3.50 (ISBN 0-8344-0108-8). Sweet.

Olbricht, Thomas H. He Loves Forever. LC 80-52461. (Journey Bks). (Orig.). 1980. pap. 3.50 (ISBN 0-8344-0117-7). Sweet.

--Message of the New Testament-Ephesians & Colossians. LC 82-74323. (Way of Life Ser.: No. 170). 91p. 1983. pap. 3.95 (ISBN 0-89112-170-6, Biblo Res Pr). Abilene Christ U.

Olcott, Anthony, tr. see Markish, Shimon.

Olcott, Henry S. Buddhist Catechism. 1971. pap. 2.75 (ISBN 0-8356-0027-0, Quest). Theos Pub Hse.

--The Buddhist Catechism. 44th ed. xv, 115p. 1983. pap. 4.95 (ISBN 0-912181-07-9). East School Pr.

--Old Diary Leaves. 1973. 7.50 ea. Vol. I (ISBN 0-8356-7106-2). Vol. II (ISBN 0-8356-7123-2). Vol. III (ISBN 0-8356-7480-0). Vol. IV (ISBN 0-8356-7484-3). Vol. V (ISBN 0-8356-7487-8). Vol. VI (ISBN 0-8356-7491-6). Theos Pub Hse.

Olcott, William T. Sun Lore of All Ages. 1976. lib. bdg. 59.95 (ISBN 0-8490-2718-7). Gordon Pr.

Olcott, William Tyler. Sun Lore of All Ages. 346p. 1984. Repr. of 1914 ed. lib. bdg. 25.00 (ISBN 0-89341-148-5). Longwood Pub Group.

Old, Hughes O. Guides to the Reformed Tradition: Worship. Leith, John H. & Kuykendall, John W., eds. LC 83-19616. 194p. 1984. pap. 11.95 (ISBN 0-8042-3252-0). John Knox.

Oldani, Louis J., intro. by see McCabe, William H.

Oldenber. Buddha: His Life, Doctrine, Order. 1971. 28.00 (ISBN 0-89684-493-5). Orient Bk Dist.

Oldenberg, H., jt. auth. see Davids, T. W.

Oldenberg, H., jt. auth. see Muller, F.

Oldenberg, Hermann. Buddha: His Life, His Doctrine & His Order. 59.95 (ISBN 0-87968-800-9). Gordon Pr.

Oldenburg, Cornelius. Comfort Ye My People: Messages of Comfort for the Bereaved. (Solace Ser.). 1983. pap. 1.25 (ISBN 0-8010-6704-9). Baker Bk.

--My Grace Is Sufficient: Devotional Thoughts for Hospital Patients. (Solace Ser.). 1983. pap. 1.25 (ISBN 0-8010-6705-7). Baker Bk.

Older, Mrs. Fremont. California Missions & Their Romances. 314p. 1983. Repr. of 1938 ed. lib. bdg. 50.00 (ISBN 0-89987-620-X). Darby Bks.

Olderr, Steven. Symbolism: A Comprehensive Dictionary. LC 85-42833. 159p. 1986. lib. bdg. 25.95 (ISBN 0-89950-187-7). McFarland & Co.

Oldham, Bruce, ed. Footprints: Following Jesus for Junior Highers. 170p. (Orig.). 1983. pap. 4.50 (ISBN 0-8341-0863-1). Beacon Hill.

Oldham, Dale. Dale Oldham Memorial Trilogy. 1984. Set. pap. 3.95 (ISBN 0-317-38180-6, D5042). Giants along My Path (ISBN 0-87162-162-2, D3784). How to Grow Spiritually (ISBN 0-87162-142-8, D5043). Living Close to God (ISBN 0-87162-013-8, D5304). Warner Pr.

Oldham, Glenna. For He Delights in Me. 1982. gift, padded cover 9.95 (ISBN 0-87162-260-2, D1017). Warner Pr.

Oldham, J. H., jt. auth. see Hooft, W. A.

Oldham, Joseph H. Christianity & the Race Problem. LC 73-75534. Repr. of 1924 ed. 19.75x (ISBN 0-8371-1112-9, OLC&, Pub. by Negro U Pr). Greenwood.

Olds, Barbara M. Favorite Poems of Faith & Comfort. 1977. Repr. of 1947 ed. 25.00 (ISBN 0-89984-077-9). Century Bookbindery.

O'Leary, De Lacy E. Islam at the Cross Roads: A Brief Survey of the Present Position & Problems of the World of Islam. LC 80-1916. 1981. Repr. of 1923 ed. 26.50 (ISBN 0-404-18983-0). AMS Pr.

--The Saints of Egypt. (Church Historical Society, London, News Ser.: No. 27). Repr. of 1937 ed. 55.00 (ISBN 0-8115-3151-1). Kraus Repr.

O'Leary, Joseph S. Questioning Back: The Overcoming of Metaphysics in Christian Tradition. 224p. 1985. cancelled (ISBN 0-8245-0675-8). Crossroad NY.

Olen, Dale R. Teaching Life Skills to Children: A Practical Guide for Teachers & Parents. 1984. pap. 6.95 (ISBN 0-8091-2618-4). Paulist Pr.

Olf, Lillian. Their Name Is Pius. LC 74-107729. (Essay Index Reprint Ser). 1941. 27.50 (ISBN 0-8369-1768-5). Ayer Co Pubs.

Olford, A. Stephen. A Graca de Dar. Orig. Title: The Grace of Giving. (Port.). 1986. write for info. (ISBN 0-8297-1602-5). Life Pubs Intl.

Olford, Stephen. The Grace of Giving. 1984. pap. 4.95 (ISBN 0-8010-6703-0). Baker Bk.

--The Grace of Giving. 1986. write for info. (ISBN 0-8297-1263-1). Life Pubs Intl.

Olford, Stephen F. The Tabernacle: Camping with God. LC 78-173686. 1971. 8.95 (ISBN 0-87213-675-2). Loizeaux.

Olford, Stephen O. The Secret of Soul-Winning. 1978. pap. 5.95 (ISBN 0-8024-7684-8). Moody.

Olgilvie, Lloyd J. Lloyd John Ogilvie Anthology. 1987. 10.95 (ISBN 0-8307-1189-9, 5419003). Regal.

Oligny, Paul J., tr. see Lekeux, Martial.

Olin, Caroline & Olin, D. Caroline. Myths & Legends of the Indian Southwest, Bk 1. 1st ed. (Illus.). 1978. pap. 2.95 (ISBN 0-88388-049-0). Bellerophon Bks.

Olin, Caroline, jt. auth. see Dutton, Bertha P.

Olin, D. Caroline, jt. auth. see Olin, Caroline.

Olin, John C. Christian Humanism & the Reformation: Selected Writings of Erasmus. 2nd ed. LC 65-10218. (Illus.). xiv, 202p. 1975. pap. 9.00 (ISBN 0-8232-0988-1). Fordham.

--Six Essays on Erasmus & a Translation of Erasmus' Letter to Carondelet 1523. LC 76-18467. (Illus.). xiv, 125p. 1977. 17.50 (ISBN 0-8232-1023-5); pap. 8.00 (ISBN 0-8232-1024-3). Fordham.

Olin, John C., ed. Autobiography of St. Ignatius Loyola. 1974. pap. 6.95x (ISBN 0-06-131783-7, TB1783, Torch). Har-Row.

Olin, John C. & Smart, James D., eds. Luther, Erasmus & the Reformation: A Catholic-Protestant Reappraisal. LC 82-15500. x, 150p. 1982. Repr. of 1969 ed. lib. bdg. 22.50x (ISBN 0-313-23652-6, OLLE). Greenwood.

Olin, John C., ed. see Erasmus.

Oliner, Samuel P. Restless Memories: Recollections of the Holocaust Years. rev., 2nd ed. LC 85-82084. 215p. (Orig.). 1986. pap. 9.95 (ISBN 0-943376-28-9). Magnes Mus.

Oliphant, Margaret. Memoir of the Life of Laurence Oliphant & of Alice Oliphant, His Wife. LC 75-36915. (Occult Ser.). 1976. Repr. of 1892 ed. 32.00x (ISBN 0-405-07970-2). Ayer Co Pubs.

Oliphant, Margaret O. Jeanne d'Arc. LC 73-14460. (Heroes of the Nations Series). Repr. of 1896 ed. 30.00 (ISBN 0-404-58278-8). AMS Pr.

Olitzky, Kerry M., jt. auth. see Stevens, Joel.

Olive, Don. Wolfhart Pannenberg. 120p. 1984. pap. text ed. 8.95 (ISBN 0-8499-3003-0, 3003-0). Word Bks.

Oliveira, Joseph De. Jacinta, Flower of Fatima. 192p. 1972. pap. 3.95 (ISBN 0-911988-45-9). AMI Pr.

Oliver, Andrew & Peabody, James B. The Records of Trinity Church, Boston: Vol. II - 1728-1830. LC 80-68230. 571p. 1982. 30.00x (ISBN 0-8139-0982-1, Colonial Soc MA). U Pr of Va.

Oliver, Andrew & Peabody, James B., eds. The Records of Trinity Church, Boston, 1728-1830. LC 80-68230. 519p. 1980. 30.00x (ISBN 0-8139-0950-3, Colonial Soc Ma). U Pr of Va.

Oliver, Caroline. Western Women in Colonial Africa. LC 81-24194. (Contributions in Comparative Colonial Studies: No. 12). xv, 201p. 1982. lib. bdg. 29.95 (ISBN 0-313-23388-8, OWA/). Greenwood.

Oliver, Egbert S. Saints & Sinners: The Planting of New England Congregationalism in Portland, Oregon, 1851-1876. Pierce, Joe E., ed. (Illus.). 250p. 1987. pap. 4.95 (ISBN 0-913244-66-X). Hapi Pr.

Oliver, Fitch E., ed. see Pynchon, William.

Oliver, Frederick S., as told to see Phylos the Thibetan.

Oliver, Gerald. Stewardship: Lessons from the Bible. LC 84-62421. write for info. (ISBN 0-9614316-0-1). Natl Inst Phil.

Oliver, Harold H. Relatedness: Essays in Metaphysics & Theology. LC 84-1152. xvi, 178p. 1984. 14.50 (ISBN 0-86554-141-8, MUP/H132). Mercer Univ Pr.

Oliver, Harold H, tr. see Buri, Fritz.

Oliver, Libby H., et al. Colonial Williamsburg Decorates for Christmas. LC 81-10103. (Illus.). 80p. 1981. 11.95 (ISBN 0-03-060403-6). H Holt & Co.

Oliver, Lucille. Cry for the World. 1981. pap. 3.00 (ISBN 0-8309-0307-0). Herald Hse.

Oliver, Peter. The Puritan Commonwealth. LC 75-31127. Repr. of 1856 ed. 41.50 (ISBN 0-404-13606-0). AMS Pr.

--Saints of Chaos. facs. ed. LC 67-23255. (Essay Index Reprint Ser). 1934. 17.00 (ISBN 0-8369-0752-3). Ayer Co Pubs.

Oliver, Revilo P. Christianity & the Survival of the West. 1984. lib. bdg. 79.95 (ISBN 0-87700-599-0). Revisionist Pr.

Oliver, Robert T. History of Public Speaking in America. LC 78-13428. 1978. Repr. of 1965 ed. lib. bdg. 47.50 (ISBN 0-313-21152-3, OLPS). Greenwood.

Oliveri, Mario. The Representatives: The Real Nature & Function of Papal Legates. LC 81-108272. 192p. (Orig.). 1981. pap. 4.95 (ISBN 0-905715-20-9). Wanderer Pr.

Oliverus. The Capture of Damietta. Gavigan, John J., tr. LC 78-63353. (The Crusades & Military Orders: Second Ser.). Repr. of 1948 ed. 17.50 (ISBN 0-404-17026-9). AMS Pr.

Olivestone, Ceil & Olivestone, David. Let's Go to Synagogue. LC 81-516. (Illus.). 24p. 1981. 4.95 (ISBN 0-89961-018-8). SBS Pub.

Olivestone, David, jt. auth. see Olivestone, Ceil.

Olivier, D. Luther's Faith: The Cause of the Gospel in the Church. LC 12-2961. 1982. pap. 13.95 (ISBN 0-570-03868-5). Concordia.

Olivier, Daniel. The Trial of Luther. 1979. pap. 8.95 (ISBN 0-570-03785-9, 12-2743). Concordia.

Ollard, Sidney. The Anglo-Catholic Revival. 59.95 (ISBN 0-87968-634-0). Gordon Pr.

Ollenburger, Ben C. Zion, the City of the Great King: A Theological Symbol of the Jerusalem Cult. (JSOT Supplement Ser.: No. 41). 240p. 1986. text ed. 28.50x (ISBN 1-85075-015-7, Pub. by JSOT Pr England); pap. text ed. 13.50x (ISBN 1-85075-014-9). Eisenbrauns.

Olley, John W. Righteousness in the Septuagint of Isaiah: A Contextual Study. LC 78-3425. (Society of Biblical Literature, Septuagint & Cognate Studies: No. 8). 1979. pap. 9.95 (ISBN 0-89130-226-3, 06-04-08). Scholars Pr GA.

Olliver, C. W. An Analysis of Magic & Witchcraft: A Retrospective Introduction to the Study of Modern Metaphysics. 244p. 1985. Repr. of 1928 ed. Set. lib. bdg. 100.00 (ISBN 0-89984-775-7). Century Bookbindery.

Olliver, Jane. Doubleday Christmas Treasury. LC 86-6297. 128p. 1986. 14.95 (ISBN 0-385-23409-0). Doubleday.

Olmedo, Alfonso, tr. see Augsburger, David.

Olmedo, Alfonso, tr. see Benko, Stephen.

Olmstead, Nan. Ladybug & Country Preacher. LC 84-29264. 1985. pap. 3.95 (ISBN 0-8054-4297-9). Broadman.

Olsen, Alfa B., jt. auth. see Efron, Marshall.

Olsen, Carl. Book of the Goddess. 264p. 1985. pap. 9.95 (ISBN 0-8245-0689-8). Crossroad NY.

Olsen, Charles M. Cultivating Religious Growth Groups. LC 83-27328. (The Pastor's Handbook Ser.: Vol. 3). 118p. (Orig.). 1984. pap. 7.95 (ISBN 0-664-24617-6). Westminster.

Olsen, Del. Made in God's Image. 128p. (Orig.). 1986. pap. 5.95 (ISBN 0-310-46381-5, 18382P). Zondervan.

Olsen, Erling C. Psalms, Meditations in the Psalms. 1050p. 1975. Repr. 19.95 (ISBN 0-87213-680-9). Loizeaux.

Olsen, Frank H. Church Staff Support: Cultivating & Maintaining Staff Relationships. (Administration for Churches Ser.). 40p. (Orig.). 1982. pap. 3.95 (ISBN 0-8066-1964-3, 10-1370). Augsburg.

Olsen, Kermit. First Steps in Prayer. pap. 2.50 (ISBN 0-910924-49-X). Macalester.

Olsen, Mahlon E. History of the Origin & Progress of Seventh-Day Adventists. LC 76-134375. Repr. of 1925 ed. 46.50 (ISBN 0-404-08423-0). AMS Pr.

Olsen, Mary P. For the Greater Glory: A Church Needlepoint Handbook. (Illus.). 192p. 1980. 17.50 (ISBN 0-8164-0476-3, HarpR). Har-Row.

Olsen, Sue. Kate Magevney & the Christmas Miracle: A Child's Christmas in Memphis (1850) Easson, Roger R., ed. LC 84-11612. (A Child's Christmas in Memphis Ser.: Vol. 2). (Illus.). 48p. 1984. 9.95 (ISBN 0-918518-34-2). St Luke TN.

Olsen, V. N. The New Testament Logia on Divorce: A Study of their Interpretation from Erasmus to Milton. 167p. (Orig.). 1971. pap. 40.00x (Pub. by J. C. B. Mohr BRD). Coronet Bks.

Olsen, V. Norskov. John Foxe & the Elizabethan Church. 1973. 38.50x (ISBN 0-520-02075-8). U of Cal Pr.

Olsen, V. Norskov, et al, eds. The Advent Hope in Scripture & History. 272p. (Orig.). 1987. 22.95 (ISBN 0-8280-0311-4). Review & Herald.

Olshausen, Hermann. A Commentary on Paul's First & Second Epistle to the Corinthians. 388p. 1984. 14.75 (ISBN 0-86524-184-8, 4604). Klock & Klock.

--Studies in the Epistle to the Romans. 438p. 1983. lib. bdg. 16.50 (ISBN 0-86524-163-5, 4503). Klock & Klock.

Olson. Bruchko. LC 73-81494. 1977. pap. 5.95 (ISBN 0-88419-133-8). Creation Hse.

Olson, Adolf. A Centenary History As Related to the Baptist General Conference of America. Ganstad, Edwin S., ed. LC 79-52602. (The Baptist Tradition Ser.). (Illus.). 1980. Repr. of 1952 ed. lib. bdg. 55.50x (ISBN 0-405-12467-8). Ayer Co Pubs.

Olson, Alan M. Transcendence & Hermeneutics. (Studies in Philosophy & Religion: No. 2). 1979. lib. bdg. 35.00 (ISBN 90-247-2092-3, Pub. by Martinus Nijhoff Netherlands). Kluwer Academic.

Olson, Alan M., ed. Myth, Symbol & Reality. LC 80-11617. 189p. 1982. pap. text ed. 7.95 (ISBN 0-268-01349-7). U of Notre Dame Pr.

Olson, Alan M.. & Rouner, Leroy S., eds. Transcendence & the Sacred. LC 81-50456. 256p. 1981. 19.95 (ISBN 0-268-01841-3). U of Notre Dame Pr.

Olson, Arnold T. The Significance of Silence. LC 80-70698. (Heritage Ser.: Vol. 2). 208p. 1981. 8.95 (ISBN 0-911802-49-5). Free Church Pubns.

--Stumbling Toward Maturity. LC 81-66943. (Heritage Ser.: Vol. 3). 208p. 1981. 8.95 (ISBN 0-911802-50-9). Free Church Pubns.

--This We Believe. 2nd ed. LC 61-18801. 1965. Repr. of 1961 ed. 6.95 (ISBN 0-911802-01-0). Free Church Pubns.

Olson, Arnold T., ed. The Search for Identity. LC 80-66030. (Heritage Ser.: Vol. 1). 160p. 1980. 8.95 (ISBN 0-911802-46-0). Free Church Pubns.

Olson, Carl, ed. The Book of the Goddess, Past & Present: An Introduction to Her Religion. LC 82-23606. 275p. 1983. 14.95 (ISBN 0-8245-0566-2). Crossroad NY.

Olson, Chet, ed. Jesus Two: The Life & Wisdom of Jesus. 216p. 1982. 8.95 (ISBN 0-940298-04-X); pap. 5.95 (ISBN 0-940298-03-1). Spiritwarrior Pub.

Olson, Dennis T. The Death of the Old & the Birth of the New: Framework of the Book of Numbers & the Pentateuch. (Brown Judaic Ser.). 1985. 29.95 (ISBN 0-89130-885-7, 14-00-71); pap. 22.95 (ISBN 0-89130-886-5). Scholars Pr Ga.

Olson, G. Keith. Why Teenagers Act the Way They Do. (Orig.). 1987. pap. 15.95 (ISBN 0-931529-17-4). Group Bks.

Olson, James S. Catholic Immigrants in America. 260p. 1986. 26.95x01568129x (ISBN 0-8304-1037-6). Nelson-Hall.

Olson, Natanael. Como Ganar a Tu Familia Para Cristo. Villarello, Ildefonso, tr. from Eng. 182p. 1983. pap. 1.50 (ISBN 0-311-13801-2). Casa Bautista.

Olson, Nathanael. How to Win Your Family to Christ. LC 77-81561. pap. 3.95 (ISBN 0-89107-149-0). Good News.

Olson, Richard P. Changing Male Roles in Today's World: A Christian Perspective for Men - & the Women Who Care about Them. 160p. 1982. pap. 5.95 (ISBN 0-8170-0946-9). Judson.

Olson, Richard P. & Pia-Terry, Carole D. Help for Remarried Couples & Families. 160p. 1984. pap. 6.95 (ISBN 0-8170-0991-4). Judson.

--Ministry with Remarried Persons. 160p. 1984. pap. 6.95 (ISBN 0-8170-0990-6). Judson.

Olson, Robert G. Ethics: A Short Introduction. 1977. pap. text ed. 6.50 (ISBN 0-394-32033-6, RanC). Random.

Olson, Ruth L., ed. Hymns & Songs for Church Schools. LC 62-13898. (Illus.). 1962. 7.95 ea. (12-1500). 25 or more 7.65 ea. Augsburg.

Olson, Stuart A. Imagination Becomes Reality Vol. 1: One Hundred Fifty Posture Solo Dance. Kuehl, Gerald, ed. (T'ai Chi Ch'uan-the Teaching of Master T. T. Liang Ser.). (Illus., Orig.). 1986. pap. 19.94 (ISBN 0-938045-01-6). Bubbling Well.

--The Wind Sweeps Away the Plum Blossoms: The Principles & Techniques of Yang Style T'ai Chi Spear & Staff. Olson, Stuart A., tr. from Chinese. (Illus.). 150p. (Orig.). 1986. pap. 14.95 (ISBN 0-938045-00-8). Bubbling Well.

Olson, Stuart A., compiled by. & tr. from Chinese. Cultivating the Ch'i: Translated from Original Writings in the Pang Family's Secret Journal, Describing T'ai Chi Chi-Kung Exercises. (Illus.). 98p. 1986. pap. 10.95 (ISBN 0-938045-02-4). Bubbling-Well.

Olson, Terrance D., jt. ed. see Britsch, R. Lanier.

Olsson, Karl A. By One Spirit. (Illus.). 1962. pap. 9.95x (ISBN 0-910452-10-5). Covenant.

--A Family of Faith. 157p. 1975. cloth 5.45 (ISBN 0-910452-24-5). Covenant.

--Into One Body... by the Cross, Vol. 1. 1985. pap. 8.95 (ISBN 0-910452-62-8). Covenant.

Olsson, Rolf, jt. ed. see Tygstrup, Niels.

Olsvanger, Immanuel, ed. Royte Pomerantsen or How to Laugh in Yiddish. 1979. pap. 6.95 (ISBN 0-8052-0099-1). Schocken.

Olthuis, James H., et al. A Hermeneutics of Ultimacy: Peril or Promise? (Christian Studies Today). 90p. (Orig.). 1987. lib. bdg. 19.75 (ISBN 0-8191-5800-3, Pub. by Inst Chris Stud); pap. text ed. 8.25 (ISBN 0-8191-5801-1). U Pr of Amer.

Olum, Walam. The Lenape & Their Legends. Brinton, Daniel G., tr. LC 74-108462. 262p. 1973. Repr. of 1884 ed. 29.00 (ISBN 0-403-00449-7). Scholarly.

Omaha Section National Council of Jewish Women. The Kitchen Connection. Kutler, Sandy & Polikov, Sheila, eds. (Illus., Orig.). 1983. pap. 11.95 (ISBN 0-9612406-0-1). Omaha Sec Nat.

O'Mahoney, Gerald. Abba! Father! A Personal Catechism. 160p. 1982. 10.95 (ISBN 0-8245-0546-8); pap. 5.95 (ISBN 0-8245-0519-0). Crossroad NY.

O'Mahoney, Patrick J. The Fantasy of Human Rights. 192p. 1978. pap. 4.95 (ISBN 0-85597-256-4). Attic Pr.

O'Malley, J. Steven. Pilgrimage of Faith: The Legacy of the Otterbeins. LC 73-5684. (ATLA Monograph: No. 4). 226p. 1973. 18.00 (ISBN 0-8108-0626-6). Scarecrow.

O'Malley, John. Fifth Week. LC 75-43583. 1976. 2.95 (ISBN 0-8294-0248-9). Loyola.

O'Malley, John W., et al. Challenge. LC 58-6622. 1958. 4.95 (ISBN 0-8294-0062-1). Loyola.

O'Malley, Lewis S. Popular Hinduism: The Religion of the Masses. LC 70-142072. 1971. Repr. of 1935 ed. 24.00 (ISBN 0-384-43305-7). Johnson Repr.

O'Malley, William J. The Living Word: Scripture & Myth, Vol. 1. LC 80-80534. 180p. (Orig.). 1980. pap. text ed. 4.95 (ISBN 0-8091-9558-5). Paulist Pr.

--Meeting the Living God. 2nd, rev. ed. 1983. pap. 5.95 (ISBN 0-8091-9565-8). Paulist Pr.

--The Roots of Unbelief: In Defense of Everything. LC 75-34840. 96p. 1976. pap. 2.95 (ISBN 0-8091-1915-3). Paulist Pr.

--The Voice of the Blood. LC 79-90055. (Five Christian Martyrs of Our Time Ser.: No. 633). 195p. (Orig.). 1980. pap. 1.99 (ISBN 0-88344-539-5). Orbis Bks.

--Why Not? Daring to Live the Challenge of Christ. LC 86-14059. 169p. (Orig.). 1986. pap. 6.95 (ISBN 0-8189-0504-2). Alba.

Oman, J. C. Brahmans, Theists & Muslims of India. 1973. 24.00 (ISBN 0-89684-371-8). Orient Bk Dist.

--The Mystics, Ascetics & Saints of India: A Study of Sadhmaism with an Account of the Yogis, Sanyasis, Bairagis, & other Strange Hindu Sectarians. 308p. 1984. text ed. 38.50x (ISBN 0-89563-650-6). Coronet Bks.

Oman, John C. The Brahmans, Theists & Muslims of India. LC 76-179231. (Illus.). Repr. of 1907 ed. 31.50 (ISBN 0-404-54858-X). AMS Pr.

--Cults, Customs, & Superstitions of India: Being a Revised & Enlarged Edition of Indian Life, Religious & Social. LC 70-179232. (Illus.). Repr. of 1908 ed. 36.00 (ISBN 0-404-54859-8). AMS Pr.

--The Mystics, Ascetics & Saints of India. lib. bdg. 75.00 (ISBN 0-8490-0698-8). Gordon Pr.

Oman, John W. The Natural & the Supernatural. LC 79-39696. (Select Bibliographies Reprint Ser.). 1972. Repr. of 1931 ed. 20.75 (ISBN 0-8369-9941-X). Ayer Co Pubs.

Omar, H. A. The Great Warriors. 1984. pap. 15.00x (ISBN 0-7212-0631-X, Pub. by Regency Pr). State Mutual Bk.

--The Paragon of Human Perfection. 85p. 1984. 21.00x (ISBN 0-7212-0566-6, Pub. by Regency Pr). State Mutual Bk.

Omartian, Stormie. Greater Health God's Way. 208p. 1984. pap. 5.95 (ISBN 0-917143-00-0). Sparrow Pr CA.

--Stormie. 224p. (Orig.). 1986. pap. 6.95 (ISBN 0-89081-556-9). Harvest Hse.

O'Meadhra, U. Early Christian, Viking & Romanesque Art. (Illus.). 260p. (Orig.). 1979. pap. text ed. 30.00x (ISBN 91-22-00270-7, Pub. by Almqvist & Wiksell). Coronet Bks.

O'Meara, Carra F. The Iconography of the Facade of Saint-Gilles-Du-Gard. LC 76-23668. (Outstanding Dissertations in the Fine Arts - Medieval). (Illus.). 352p. 1977. Repr. of 1975 ed. lib. bdg. 63.00 (ISBN 0-8240-2717-5). Garland Pub.

O'Meara, Dominic J. Neoplatonism & Christian Thought. LC 81-5272. (Neoplatonism: Ancient & Modern Ser.). 270p. 1981. 44.50x (ISBN 0-87395-492-0); pap. 14.95x (ISBN 0-87395-493-9). State U NY Pr.

O'Meara, Dominic J., et al, trs. see Van Steenberghen, Fernand.

O'Meara, John J. The Voyage of Saint Brendan: Journey to the Promised Land. (Dolmen Texts: No. 1). (Illus.). 1978. pap. text ed. 9.95x (ISBN 0-85105-384-X). Humanities.

--The Young Augustine: An Introduction to the Confessions of St. Augustine. 224p. 1980. pap. text ed. 10.95x (ISBN 0-582-49110-X). Longman.

O'Meara, Thomas F. Romantic Idealism & Roman Catholicism: Schelling & the Theologians. LC 81-40449. 240p. 1982. 25.00 (ISBN 0-268-01610-0). U of Notre Dame Pr.

--Theology of Ministry. LC 82-60588. 1983. pap. 11.95 (ISBN 0-8091-2487-4). Paulist Pr.

Omer, Devorah. The Gideonites. 256p. 1968. 3.50 (ISBN 0-88482-750-X). Hebrew Pub.

--Once There Was a Hassid. (Illus.). 28p. 1987. 9.95 (ISBN 0-915361-73-6, Dist. by Watts). Adama Pubs Inc.

--Path Beneath the Sea. 192p. 1969. 3.50 (ISBN 0-88482-744-5). Hebrew Pub.

Omer, Mordechai. Turner & the Bible. 48p. 1981. 5.50x (ISBN 0-900090-79-0, Pub. by Ashmolean Museum). State Mutual Bk.

--Turner & the Bible. (Illus.). 48p. (Orig.). 1981. pap. 7.75 (ISBN 0-900090-90-1, Pub. by Ashmolean Mus). Longwood Pub Group.

Omi, Maurice M., ed. Work & Faith in Society. 96p. (Orig.). 1986. pap. 6.95 (ISBN 1-55586-988-2). US Catholic.

Ommen, Thomas B. The Hermeneutic of Dogma. LC 75-29493. (American Academy of Religion. Dissertation Ser.). 1975. pap. 9.95 (ISBN 0-89130-039-2, 010111). Scholars Pr GA.

Omoyajowo, Akin. Diversity in Unity: The Development & Expansion of the Cherubim & Seraphim Church in Nigeria. LC 83-21706. 126p. (Orig.). 1984. lib. bdg. 22.00 (ISBN 0-8191-3655-7). U Pr of Amer.

Omoyajowo, J. A. Cherubim & Seraphim: The History of an African Independent Church. LC 78-64624. 256p. (Orig.). 1982. 21.50x (ISBN 0-88357-068-8); pap. 8.95 (ISBN 0-88357-069-6). NOK Pubs.

Omrcanin, Ivo. Forced Conversions of Croatians to the Serbian Faith in History. 92p. (Orig.). 1985. pap. 6.00 (ISBN 0-9613814-1-8). Samizdat.

O'Neal, Debbie. Handbook for Church Nurseries. 32p. (Orig.). 1985. pap. 2.95 (ISBN 0-8066-2174-5, 10-2944). Augsburg.

O'Neal, Debbie T. An Easter People: Family Devotional Activities for Lent & Easter. 32p. (Orig.). 1986. pap. 3.95 (ISBN 0-8066-2255-5, 10-1990). Augsburg.

O'Neal, Glenn. Make the Bible Live. pap. 3.50 (ISBN 0-88469-020-2). BMH Bks.

Oneida Community. Bible Communism. LC 76-187475. (The American Utopian Adventure Ser.). 128p. 1973. Repr. of 1853 ed. lib. bdg. 17.50x (ISBN 0-87991-015-1). Porcupine Pr.

--Bible Communism: A Compilation from the Annual Reports & Other Publications of the Oneida Association & Its Branches. LC 72-2978. Repr. of 1853 ed. 8.50 (ISBN 0-404-10742-7). AMS Pr.

--Hand-book of the Oneida Community, with a Sketch of Its Founder, & an Outline of Its Constitution & Doctrines, 3 vols in 1. Incl. Hand-Book of the Oneida Community, Containing a Brief Sketch of Its Present Condition, Internal Economy & Leading Principles; Mutual Criticism. LC 72-2977. Repr. of 1876 ed. 23.50 (ISBN 0-404-10741-9). AMS Pr.

O'Neil, Charles J. Imprudence in Saint Thomas Aquinas. (Aquinas Lecture Ser.). 1955. 7.95 (ISBN 0-87462-120-8). Marquette.

O'Neil, Charles J. see St. Thomas Aquinas.

O'Neil, Floyd A., jt. ed. see Milner, Clyde A., II.

O'Neil, Gisela, ed. see Steiner, Rudolf.

O'Neil, Kevin. American Buddhist Directory. 2nd ed. 116p. (Orig.). 1985. pap. 20.00 (ISBN 0-86627-012-4). Crises Res Pr.

--The American Buddhist Directory, 1982. 96p. 1982. pap. 7.00 (ISBN 0-86627-003-5). Crises Res Pr.

--Awakening of Faith in Mahayana. (Orig.). 1984. pap. 14.95 (ISBN 0-86627-012-4). Crises Res Pr.

--Basic Buddhism. 41p. (Orig.). 1981. pap. 5.00 (ISBN 0-86627-006-X). Crises Res Pr.

--The Diamond Sutra. 1978. pap. 5.00 (ISBN 0-86627-004-3). Crises Res Pr.

--How to Protect Your Family from Terrorists. 106p. 1979. pap. 15.00 (ISBN 0-86627-007-8). Crises Res Pr.

--An Introduction to Nichiren Shoshu Buddhism. 111p. 1980. pap. 5.00 (ISBN 0-86627-002-7). Crises Res Pr.

--Realm of Totality. 49p. (Orig.). 1984. pap. 6.00 (ISBN 0-86627-011-6). Crises Res Pr.

O'Neil, Kevin, ed. The Sutra Spoken by Vimilakirti. pap. 6.00 (ISBN 0-86627-009-4). Crises Res Pr.

O'Neil, Kevin R. What to Tell Your Children about Cults. 52p. (Orig.). 1982. pap. 9.95 (ISBN 0-86627-001-9). Crises Res Pr.

O'Neil, Kevin R., ed. American Buddhist Newsletter: 1981-82, Vol. I. 136p. (Orig.). 1982. pap. 35.00 (ISBN 0-86627-000-0). Crises Res Pr.

O'Neil, Sunny. The Gift of Christmas Past: A Return to Victorian Traditions. LC 81-14961. (Illus.). 146p. 1981. 15.95 (ISBN 0-910050-55-4). AASLH Pr.

O'Neil, Terry, jt. auth. see Bleier, Rocky.

O'Neil, Thomas. Towards the Life Divine: Sri Aurobindo's Vision. 1979. 10.50x (ISBN 0-8364-0546-3). South Asia Bks.

O'Neill, Ana M. Etica Para la Era Atomica. facsimile ed. 10.00 (ISBN 0-8477-2815-3); pap. 9.00 (ISBN 0-8477-2807-2). U of PR Pr.

O'Neill, Colman. Sacramental Realism: A General Theory of the Sacraments. (Theology & Life Ser.: Vol. 2). 1983. 9.95 (ISBN 0-89453-297-9). M Glazier.

O'Neill, Colman E. Meeting Christ in the Sacraments. LC 64-20111. 1964. pap. 3.95 (ISBN 0-8189-0090-3). Alba.

O'Neill, Daniel. Troubadour for the Lord: The Story of John Michael Talbot. 192p. 1983. 9.95 (ISBN 0-8245-0567-0). Crossroad NY.

O'Neill, Daniel, jt. auth. see Vath, Raymond E.

O'Neill, Daniel W., jt. auth. see Vath, Raymond E.

O'Neill, Dennis. Lazarus Interlude: A Story of God's Healing Love in a Moment of Ministry. LC 83-60438. 80p. (Orig.). 1983. pap. 2.95 (ISBN 0-87793-271-9). Ave Maria.

O'Neill, Eugene. Moon for the Misbegotten. LC 74-5218. 1974. pap. 2.95 (ISBN 0-394-71236-6, Vin). Random.

O'Neill, Irene, jt. auth. see Mitchell, Joan.

O'Neill, James M. Catholicism & American Freedom. LC 78-21495. 1979. Repr. of 1952 ed. lib. bdg. cancelled (ISBN 0-313-21153-1, ONCA). Greenwood.

O'Neill, James Milton. Religion & Education Under the Constitution. LC 72-171389. (Civil Liberties in American History Ser). 338p. 1972. Repr. of 1949 ed. lib. bdg. 39.50 (ISBN 0-306-70228-2). Da Capo.

O'Neill, Judith. Martin Luther. LC 74-12959. (Cambridge Introduction to the History of Mankind). (Illus.). 48p. 1975. pap. text ed. 4.95 (ISBN 0-521-20403-8). Cambridge U Pr.

--Martin Luther. LC 78-56804. (Cambridge Topic Bks). (Illus.). 1978. PLB 8.95 (ISBN 0-8225-1215-7). Lerner Pubns.

Ong, Walter J. American Catholic Crossroads: Religious-Secular Encounters in the Modern World. LC 80-29660. xi, 160p. 1981. Repr. of 1959 ed. lib. bdg. 22.50x (ISBN 0-313-22467-6, ONAM). Greenwood.

Ono, Sokyo. Shinto: The Kami Way. LC 61-14033. 1962. 8.50 (ISBN 0-8048-0525-3). C E Tuttle.

Onslow-Ford, Gordon. Creation. (Illus.). 123p. 1978. text ed. 30.00 (ISBN 0-9612760-0-2). Bishop Pine.

Onstad, Esther. Courage for Today-Hope for Tomorrow: A Study of the Revelation. LC 75-2829. 144p. 1975. pap. 6.95 (ISBN 0-8066-1474-9, 10-1695). Augsburg.

Onyioha, K. O. African Godianism: A Revolutionary Religion for Mankind Through Direct Communication with God. 1980. 15.00 (ISBN 0-914970-31-3). Conch Mag.

Oort, H. A. van see Van Oort, H. A.

Oostdyk, Harv. Step One: The Gospel & the Ghetto. 342p. 1983. pap. 8.95 (ISBN 0-89221-094-X). New Leaf.

Oosten, Jarich G. The War of the Gods: The Social Code in Indo-European Mythology. (International Library of Anthropology). 240p. 1985. 32.50x (ISBN 0-7102-0289-X). Methuen Inc.

Oosterhouse, Kenneth, et al. Born of a Glorious Thunder: Real Life Accounts of Foreign Christian Work. Kortenhoeven, Helen, tr. 304p. (Orig.). 1986. pap. 6.95. West Indies Pub.

Oosterhuis, Huub. Times of Life: Prayers & Poems. Smith, N. D., tr. from Dutch. LC 79-89653. 128p. (Orig.). 1980. pap. 4.95 (ISBN 0-8091-2245-6). Paulist Pr.

--Your Word Is Near. Smith, N. D., tr. from Dutch. LC 68-20848. 192p. 1968. pap. 4.95 (ISBN 0-8091-1775-4, Deus). Paulist Pr.

Oosterveen, Gerald & Cook, Bruce L. Serving Mentally Impaired People. 52p. 1983. pap. 5.95 (ISBN 0-89191-764-0). Cook.

Oosterwal, Gottfried & Staples, Russell L. Servants for Christ: The Adventist Church Facing the 80's. vi, 162p. 1980. pap. 3.95 (ISBN 0-943872-78-2). Andrews Univ Pr.

Oosthuizen, G. C. The Church of Scientology Religious Philosophy, Religion, & Church. pap. 4.00 (ISBN 0-686-74641-4). Church of Scient Info.

Opal, Lyon. Parables. 1984. pap. 1.95 (ISBN 0-317-30409-7). Pacific Pr Pub Assn.

Opatz, Patrica G. The Pleasure of God's Company. 96p. 1985. pap. 3.95 (ISBN 0-8146-1437-X). Liturgical Pr.

Opatz, Patricia G. Be Still & Know That I Am God. 64p. 1981. softcover 2.95 (ISBN 0-8146-1231-8). Liturgical Pr.

--Nobody Says "Please" in the Psalms. 72p. (Orig.). 1984. pap. 2.95 (ISBN 0-8146-1326-8). Liturgical Pr.

Open Path. Namgyal Rinpoche: Unfolding Through Art. Wongmo, Karma C., ed. (Illus.). 157p. (Orig.). 1982. text ed. 30.00x (ISBN 0-9602722-2-4). Open Path.

Opfell, Olga S. The King James Bible Translators. LC 81-20885. (Illus.). 179p. 1982. lib. bdg. 18.95x (ISBN 0-89950-041-2). McFarland & Co.

Ophiel. The Art & Practice of Caballa Magic. 1977. pap. 8.95 (ISBN 0-87728-303-6). Weiser.

Opie, Robert. Rev'rund, Get Your Gun. LC 77-78851. 1978. pap. 3.50 (ISBN 0-88419-141-9). Creation Hse.

Opler, Morris E. Myths & Legends of the Lipan Apache Indians. LC 40-13687. (Amer. Folklore SocietyMemoirs Ser.). Repr. of 1940 ed. 21.00 (ISBN 0-527-01088-X). Kraus Repr.

--Myths & Tales of the Chiricahua Apache Indians. LC 43-2944. (Amer. Folklore Society Memoirs Ser.). Repr. of 1942 ed. 15.00 (ISBN 0-527-01089-8). Kraus Repr.

--Myths & Tales of the Jicarilla Apache Indians. LC 38-22477. (American Folklore Society Memoirs). Repr. of 1938 ed. 37.00 (ISBN 0-527-01083-9). Kraus Repr.

Oppenheim, Frank M., ed. The Reasoning Heart: Toward a North American Theology. 160p. (Orig.). 1986. pap. 9.95 (ISBN 0-87840-433-3); 17.95 (ISBN 0-87840-439-2). Georgetown U Pr.

Oppenheim, Janet. The Other World: Spiritualism & Physical Research in England, 1850-1914. (Illus.). 580p. 1985. 44.50 (ISBN 0-521-26505-3). Cambridge U Pr.

Oppenheim, Micha F., jt. auth. see Cutter, Charles.

Oppenheim, Michael. What Does Revelation Mean for the Modern Jew? LC 85-18929. (Symposium Ser.: Vol. 17). 152p. 1985. lib. bdg. 39.95x (ISBN 0-88946-708-0). E Mellen.

Oppenheimer, Oscar. God & Man. LC 79-64099. 1979. pap. text ed. 11.25 (ISBN 0-8191-0753-0). U Pr of Amer.

Oppermann, Charles J. English Missionaries in Sweden & Finland. LC 38-16784. (Church Historical Society Ser.: No. 26). 1937. 17.50x (ISBN 0-281-00240-1). A R Allenson.

Oppert, Gustav. On the Original Inhabitants of Bharatavarsa or India. Bolle, Kees W., ed. (Mythology Ser.). 1978. Repr. of 1893 ed. lib. bdg. 55.00x (ISBN 0-405-10557-6). Ayer Co Pubs.

Oppitz, Joseph. Autumn Memoirs of St. Alphonsus Liguori. 96p. 1986. pap. 3.95 (ISBN 0-89243-253-5). Liguori Pubns.

Optatus, Saint Optati Milevitani Libri Septum. (Corpus Scriptorum Ecclesiasticorum Latinorum Ser: Vol. 26). (Lat). pap. 50.00 (ISBN 0-384-43390-1). Johnson Repr.

Opton, Frank. Liberal Religion: Principles & Practices. LC 81-81129. (Library of Liberal Religion). 295p. 1981. 20.95 (ISBN 0-87975-155-X). Prometheus Bks.

O'Quinn, J. Frank, ed. Jesus' Lost Gospels: The Discovery at Nag Hammadi. (Illus.). 48p. 1981. pap. text ed. 6.95 (ISBN 0-9609802-0-2). Life Science.

Oraker, James & Meredith, Char. Almost Grown: A Christian Guide for Parents of Teenagers. LC 78-20585. 192p. 1982. pap. 6.95 (ISBN 0-06-066398-7, RD 380, HarpR). Har-Row.

Orange County Genealogical Committee Members & Hovemeyer, Gretchen A., eds. Early Records of the St. James Episcopal Church of Goshen, New York: Baptisms, Marriages, & Funerals, 1799-1911. 140p. (Orig.). 1985. pap. 20.00 (ISBN 0-9604116-4-X). Orange County Genealog.

Orange County Genealogical Society. Diagram & List of Goshen Presbyterian Church Pews, 1796. 1986. pap. text ed. 0.50 (ISBN 0-937135-02-X). Orange County Genealog.

Orbaker, Douglas & Blake, Robert A. Day of Redemption. Sherer, Michael L., ed. (Orig.). 1987. pap. 2.25 (ISBN 0-89536-848-X, 7807). CSS of Ohio.

Orban, A. P. Die Korrespondenz und die Liber Exhortacionis des Heinrich Von Kalkar: Eine Kritische Ausgabe. Hogg, James, ed. (Analecta Cartusiana Ser.: No. 111). 303p. (Orig.). 1984. pap. 25.00 (ISBN 0-317-42581-1, Pub. by Salzburg Studies). Longwood Pub Group.

Orbeliani, Sulkhan-Saba. The Book of Wisdom & Lies. Vivian, Katherine, tr. 1982. 14.95 (Pub. by Octagon Pr England). Ins Study Human.

Orbison, T. Tucker, ed. see Colloquium on Myth in Literature, Bucknell & Susquehanna Universities, Mar. 21-2, 1974, et al.

Orchard, Bernard & Riley, Harold. The Order of the Synoptics: Why Three Synoptic Gospels? 384p. 1987. 38.95 (ISBN 0-86554-222-8, MUP H-199). Mercer Univ Pr.

Orchard, Bernard, tr. see Vanhoye, Albert.

Orchard, D. B. & Longstaff, R. W., eds. J. J. Griesbach. LC 77-27405. (Society for New Testament Studies Monographs: No. 34). 1979. 32.50 (ISBN 0-521-21706-7). Cambridge U Pr.

Orchard, John B. A Synopsis of the Four Gospels in a New Translation: Arranged According to the Two Gospel Hypothesis. LC 81-18753. 319p. 1982. English 9.95 (ISBN 0-86554-024-1, MUP-H22); Greek 21.00 (ISBN 0-86554-061-6, MUP-H70). Mercer Univ Pr.

Orchard, R. E. This Is Our Hope. 150p. 1966. 3.95 (ISBN 0-88243-617-1, 02-0617). Gospel Pub.

Orchard, Richard E. Look Who's Coming. LC 74-33870. (Radiant Bks.). 128p. 1975. pap. 1.25 (ISBN 0-88243-541-8, 02-0541). Gospel Pub.

Orchard, Thomas N. Astronomy of Milton's Paradise Lost. LC 68-4178. (Studies in Milton, No. 22). (Illus.). 1969. Repr. of 1896 ed. lib. bdg. 75.00x (ISBN 0-8383-0672-1). Haskell.

Ordericus Vitalis. Ecclesiastical History of England & Normandy, 4 Vols. Forrester, T., tr. LC 68-57872. (Bohn's Antiquarian Library Ser). Repr. of 1856 ed. Set. 115.00 (ISBN 0-404-50040-4). AMS Pr.

Ordericus, Vitalis. Historiae Ecclesiasticae Libri Tredecim, 5 Vols. Le Prevost, A., ed. Set. 240.00 (ISBN 0-384-43511-4); Set. pap. 210.00 (ISBN 0-384-43512-2). Johnson Repr.

Ordonez, Francisco. Del Odio al Amor. 1983. pap. 1.50 (ISBN 0-311-08223-8). Casa Bautista.

--Repertorio de Navidad. 80p. 1986. pap. 1.75 (ISBN 0-311-08211-4). Casa Bautista.

O'Ree. Bible Games & Fun for Everyone. 1966. 0.60 (ISBN 0-88027-103-5). Firm Foun Pub.

O'Reilly, James. Lay & Religious States of Life. LC 76-43048. 1977. pap. text ed. 0.75 (ISBN 0-685-81233-2). Franciscan Herald.

--The Moral Problems of Contraception. (Synthesis Ser). 62p. 1975. pap. 0.75 (ISBN 0-8199-0363-9). Franciscan Herald.

--Reconciliation & Renewal. (Synthesis Ser). 36p. 1974. pap. 0.75 (ISBN 0-8199-0361-2). Franciscan Herald.

O'Reilly, Peter, tr. see Maritain, Jacques.

O'Reilly, Sean. Bioethics & the Limits of Science. 176p. (Orig.). 1980. pap. 9.95 (ISBN 0-931888-02-6, Chris. Coll. Pr.). Christendom Pubns.

--In the Image of God. 92p. 1982. 2.95 (ISBN 0-8198-3607-9, MS0308); pap. 1.95 (ISBN 0-8198-3608-7). Dghtrs St Paul.

--Our Name Is Peter. LC 77-380. 155p. 1977. 5.95 (ISBN 0-8199-0666-2). Franciscan Herald.

Orellana, Eugenio, tr. see Owen, Robert & Howard, David M.

Orelli, Hans C. von. The Prophecies of Jeremiah. 1977. 15.25 (ISBN 0-86524-102-3, 2401). Klock & Klock.

--The Twelve Minor Prophets. 1977. 15.50 (ISBN 0-86524-114-7, 7001). Klock & Klock.

Oren, Dan A. Joining the Club: A History of Jews & Yale. LC 85-14252. (The Yale Scene, University Ser.: No. 4). 448p. 1986. 29.95x (ISBN 0-300-03330-3). Yale U Pr.

Orenstein, Aviel, tr. see Ha-Cohen, Yisroel Meir.

Orenstein, Eugene, et al, trs. see Mahler, Raphael.

Orest. ONE. LC 76-47223. (Orig.). 1977. pap. 4.95 (ISBN 0-89407-002-9). Strawberry Hill.

Organ, Troy W. Hindu Quest for the Perfection of Man. x, 439p. 1970. pap. 14.00x (ISBN 0-8214-0575-6). Ohio U Pr.

Orgel, Stephen, ed. see Rastell, John.

Oriental Institute Staff. Persepolis & Ancient Iran. LC 76-7942. 1976. 55.00 (ISBN 0-226-69493-3, Chicago Visual Lib); 1 color & 11 black-&-white fiches incl. U of Chicago Pr.

Origen. Homilies on Genesis & Exodus. LC 82-4124. (Fathers of the Church Ser.: Vol. 71). 422p. 1982. 29.95x (ISBN 0-8132-0071-7). Cath U Pr.

Original Publications, tr. from Span. Helping Yourself With Selected Prayers. pap. 3.95 (ISBN 0-942272-01-3). Original Pubns.

Oring, Elliott. Israeli Humor: The Content & Structure of the Chizbat of the Palmah. LC 80-25483. (Modern Jewish Literature & Culture Ser.). 210p. 1981. 44.50 (ISBN 0-87395-512-9); pap. 14.95x (ISBN 0-87395-513-7). State U NY Pr.

Orlandis, Jose. A Short History of the Catholic Church. 163p. 1985. pap. 7.50 (ISBN 0-912414-43-X). Lumen Christi.

--A Short History of the Catholic Church. Adams, Michael, tr. from Span. Tr. of Historia breve del Cristianismo. 163p. (Orig.). 1985. pap. 7.95 (ISBN 0-906127-86-6, Pub. by Four Courts Pr Ireland). Scepter Pubs.

Orleans, Pierre J. D' see D'Orleans, Pierre J.

Orlinsky, H. M. Israel Exploration Journal Reader, 2 vols. (The Library of Biblical Studies). 1982. Set. 99.50x (ISBN 0-87068-267-9). Ktav.

Orlinsky, Harry M. Ancient Israel. 2nd ed. (Development of Western Civilization Ser.). (Illus.). 164p. (Orig.). 1960. pap. text ed. 5.95x (ISBN 0-8014-9849-X). Cornell U Pr.

--Ancient Israel. LC 82-2937. (The Development of Western Civilization Ser.). xii, 164p. 1982. Repr. of 1954 ed. lib. bdg. 24.75x (ISBN 0-313-23559-7, ORAN). Greenwood.

--Essays in Biblical & Jewish Culture & Bible Translation. 1973. 25.00x (ISBN 0-87068-218-0). Ktav.

--International Organization for Masoretic Studies, 1972 & 1973 Proceedings & Papers. LC 74-16568. (Society of Biblical Literature, Masoretic Studies). Repr. of 1974 ed. 33.30 (ISBN 0-8357-9573-X, 2017535). Bks Demand UMI.

--Understanding the Bible Through History & Archaeology. 1969. 12.50x (ISBN 0-87068-096-X). Ktav.

Orlinsky, Harry M., ed. Masoretic Studies. 10.00x (ISBN 0-685-56221-2). Ktav.

Orloff, Nicholas, tr. see Orthodox Eastern Church.

Ormerod, Oliver. The Picture of a Papist: Whereunto Is Annexed a Certain Treatise, Intituled Pagano-Papismus. LC 74-28878. (English Experience Ser.: No. 756). 1975. Repr. of 1606 ed. 18.50 (ISBN 90-221-0756-6). Walter J Johnson.

--The Picture of a Puritane: Or, a Relation of the Opinions - of the Anabaptists in Germanie, & of the Puritanes in England. LC 74-28879. (English Experience Ser.: No. 757). 1975. Repr. of 1605 ed. 9.50 (ISBN 90-221-0757-4). Walter J Johnson.

Ormond, Alexander T. The Philosophy of Religion: Lectures Written for the Elliott Lectureship at the Western Theological Seminary. 195p. 1982. Repr. of 1922 ed. lib. bdg. 50.00 (ISBN 0-8495-4219-7). Arden Lib.

Ormrod, J. A., tr. see Evola, Julius.

Ormsby, Eric. Theodicy in Islamic Thought. LC 84-3396. 320p. 1984. text ed. 30.00x (ISBN 0-691-07278-7). Princeton U pr.

Ornitz, Samuel. Alrightniks Row: The Making of a Professional Jew, Haunch, Paunch & Jowl. Gabriel, Milley, ed. LC 85-40730. (Masterworks of Modern Jewish Writing Ser.). 320p. 1986. 18.85 (ISBN 0-910129-49-5, Distributed by Schocken Books); pap. 9.95 (ISBN 0-910129-46-0). Wiener Pub Inc.

O'Rourke, Brian. The Conscience of the Race: Sex & Religion in Irish & French Novels 1941-1973. 72p. 1980. 15.00x (ISBN 0-906127-22-X, BBA 03641, Pub. by Irish Academic Pr Ireland). Biblio Dist.

O'Rourke, David K. The Holy Land As Jesus Knew It: Its People, Customs & Religion. 160p. 1983. pap. 4.95 (ISBN 0-89243-182-2). Liguori Pubns.

O'Rourke, Edward. Living Like a King. 1979. 3.95 (ISBN 0-87243-087-1). Templegate.

O'Rourke, John J. & Greenburg, S. Thomas, eds. Symposium on the Magisterium: A Positive Statement. 1978. 5.95 (ISBN 0-8198-0559-9); pap. 4.50 (ISBN 0-8198-0560-2). Dghtrs St Paul.

O'Rourke, Kevin D., jt. auth. see Ashley, Benedict M.

O'Rourke, Thomas P. The Franciscan Missions in Texas (1690-1793) LC 73-3559. (Catholic University of America. Studies in American Church History: No. 5). Repr. of 1927 ed. 19.50 (ISBN 0-404-57755-5). AMS Pr.

Orovitz, Norma A. Puzzled! The Jewish Word Search. LC 77-83177. 1977. pap. 3.95 (ISBN 0-8197-0022-3). Bloch.

Orozco, E. C. Republican Protestantism in Aztlan. LC 80-82906. 261p. 1980. 24.00x (ISBN 0-9606102-1-9); pap. 14.50x (ISBN 0-9606102-2-7). Petereins Pr.

Orozco, Julio, tr. see Kunz, Marilyn & Schell, Catherine.

Orozco, Julio, tr. see Lindskoog, Kathryn.

Orozco, Julio, tr. see Osborne, Cecil G.

Orozco, Julio, tr. see Reid, James.

Orr, Anna M. Proving Yourself: A Study of James. (Basic Bible Study Ser.). 64p. pap. 2.95 (ISBN 0-930756-75-4, 521015). Aglow Pubns.

Orr, Bill & Lutzer, Erwin. If I Could Change My Mom & Dad. 128p. 1983. pap. 3.50 (ISBN 0-8024-0174-0). Moody.

Orr, C. E. Food for Lambs. 168p. pap. 1.50 (ISBN 0-686-29109-3). Faith Pub Hse.

--Heavenly Life for Earthly Living. 60p. pap. 0.40 (ISBN 0-686-29111-5); pap. 1.00 3 copies (ISBN 0-686-34362-X). Faith Pub Hse.

--Helps to Holy Living. 64p. pap. 0.40 (ISBN 0-686-29112-3); pap. 1.00 3 copies (ISBN 0-686-29113-1). Faith Pub Hse.

--The Hidden Life. 112p. pap. 0.75 (ISBN 0-686-29149-2). Faith Pub Hse.

--How to Live a Holy Life. 112p. pap. 0.75 (ISBN 0-686-29120-4). Faith Pub Hse.

--Odors from Golden Vials. 78p. pap. 0.60 (ISBN 0-686-29131-X). Faith Pub Hse.

Orr, Dick & Bartlett, David L. Bible Journeys. 80p. 1980. pap. 4.95 (ISBN 0-8170-0898-5). Judson.

Orr, J., jt. auth. see Lidden, H. P.

Orr, J., jt. auth. see Moule, H. C.

Orr, J. B., jt. auth. see Beck, R. N.

Orr, James, ed. International Standard Bible Encyclopedia, 4 vols. 1930. 89.95 (ISBN 0-8028-8045-2). Eerdmans.

Orr, Leonard. The New Yoga. write for info. L Orr.

Orr, Leonard & Ray, Sondra. Rebirthing in the New Age. LC 76-53337. 1978. pap. 9.95 (ISBN 0-89087-134-5). Celestial Arts.

Orr, Robert G. Religion in China. (Orig.). 1980. pap. 4.95 (ISBN 0-377-00103-1). Friend Pr.

Orr, Robert P. The Meaning of Transcendence. Dietrich, Wendell, ed. LC 80-12872. (American Academy of Religion Dissertation Ser.). 172p. 1981. pap. 9.95 (ISBN 0-89130-408-8, 01 01 35). Scholars Pr GA.

Orr, William F. & Walther, James S. Corinthians I. LC 75-42441. (Anchor Bible Ser.: Vol. 32). 1976. 18.00 (ISBN 0-385-02853-9). Doubleday.

Orsen, Dennis. Focus for Evangelism: The Evangelical Implications of Ministry. 48p. (Orig.). 1985. pap. 3.95 (ISBN 0-8066-2199-0, 23-1601). Augsburg.

Orser, Evelyn. On My Back, Looking Up! Coffen, Richard W., ed. LC 83-13882. (A Banner Bk.). (Illus.). 94p. (Orig.). 1984. pap. 5.95 (ISBN 0-8280-0218-5). Review & Herald.

Orsi, Robert A. The Madonna of One Hundred Fifteenth Street: Faith & Community in Italian Harlem, 1880 to 1950. LC 85-10799. (Illus.). 366p. 1985. 29.95x (ISBN 0-300-03262-5). Yale U Pr.

Orso, Kathryn W. Parenthood: A Commitment in Faith. LC 75-5219. 64p. (Orig.). 1975. pap. text ed. 2.95 (ISBN 0-8192-1198-2); tchr's ed. 3.75 (ISBN 0-8192-1204-0); wkbk. 3.95 (ISBN 0-8192-1199-0). Morehouse.

Orsy, Ladislas. Evolving Church & the Sacrament of Penance. 1974. 6.95 (ISBN 0-87193-072-2). Dimension Bks.

--The Lord of Confusion. 5.00 (ISBN 0-87193-064-1). Dimension Bks.

Ortega, Pedro R. Christmas in Old Santa Fe. LC 73-90581. (Illus.). 1982. pap. 6.25 (ISBN 0-913270-25-3). Sunstone Pr.

Ortegel, Adelaide. Banners & Such. LC 86-62616. 1986. pap. 9.95 (ISBN 0-89390-016-8). Resource Pubns.

Ortego, Hasa. Christmas Eve on the Big Bayou. 1974. 3.95 (ISBN 0-87511-091-6). Claitors.

Orthodox Christian Educational Society, ed. see Livadeas, Themistocles & Charitos, Minas.

Orthodox Christian Educational Society, ed. see Makrakis, Apostolos.

Orthodox Christian Educational Society, ed. see Philaretos, S. D.

Orthodox Christian Educational Society, ed. see Philaretos, Sotirios D.

Orthodox Christian Educational Society, ed. see Photiou, Paul.

Orthodox Christian Educational Society, ed. see Vassilakos, Aristarchus.

Orthodox Eastern Church. The General Menaion, or the Book of Services Common to the Festivals of Our Lord Jesus Christ, of the Holy Virgin, & of the Different Orders of Saints. Orloff, Nicholas, tr. from Old Slavonic. pap. 15.00 (ISBN 0-686-25551-8). Eastern Orthodox.

--Liturgies of Saints Mark, James, Clement, Chrysostom, & the Church of Malabar. LC 76-83374. Repr. of 1859 ed. 18.50 (ISBN 0-404-04658-4). AMS Pr.

--Liturgies of Saints Mark, James, Clement, Chrysostom, Basil. LC 79-80721. (Gr). 1969. Repr. of 1859 ed. 18.50 (ISBN 0-404-04657-6). AMS Pr.

--Offices of the Oriental Church. LC 73-79805. Repr. of 1884 ed. 16.75 (ISBN 0-404-00874-7). AMS Pr.

--Service to a Fool for Christ Sake. pap. 0.75 (ISBN 0-686-05663-9). Eastern Orthodox.

--Synod of Sixteen Seventy-Two: Acts & Decrees of the Jerusalem Synod Held Under Dositheus, Containing the Confession Published Name of Cyril Lukaris. Robertson, J. N., tr. LC 78-81769. 1969. Repr. of 1899 ed. 18.50 (ISBN 0-404-03567-1). AMS Pr.

Orthodox Eastern Church-Synod of Jerusalem. Acts & Decrees of the Synod of Jerusalem, 1672. pap. 1.95 (ISBN 0-686-05637-X). Eastern Orthodox.

Ortiz, Alfonso, jt. auth. see Erodes, Richard.

Ortiz, Joe. Saved? What Do You Mean Saved? A Journalist's Report on Salvation. Feldstein, Mark D., ed. (Illus.). 95p. (Orig.). 1983. pap. 4.95 (ISBN 0-912695-00-5). GBM Bks.

Ortiz, Juan C. Cry of the Human Heart. LC 76-24099. 1977. pap. 4.95 (ISBN 0-88419-010-2). Creation Hse.

--The Disciple. LC 74-29650. 144p. 1975. pap. 4.95 (ISBN 0-88419-145-1). Creation Hse.

--Discipulo. 192p. 1978. 3.75 (ISBN 0-88113-065-6). Edit Betania.

--Living with Jesus Today. 1982. 4.95 (ISBN 0-88419-187-7). Creation Hse.

Ortiz, Juan Carlos. Jesus en Nuestras Vidas - Hoy. Araujo, Juan S., tr. from Eng. Tr. of Living with Jesus Today. (Span.). 160p. 1987. pap. 4.25 (ISBN 0-88113-157-1). Edit Betania.

Ortiz, Juan Carlos & Buckingham, Jamie. Call to Discipleship. LC 75-7476. 1975. pap. 4.95 (ISBN 0-88270-122-3). Bridge Pub.

Ortiz, Marcelino. Verdades que Cambian Vidas. (Span.). 96p. (Orig.). 1981. pap. 2.50 (ISBN 0-89922-173-4). Edit Caribe.

Ortiz, Victoria. Sojourner Truth. LC 73-22290. (Illus.). 160p. (YA) 1974. PLB 10.89 (ISBN 0-397-31504-X, Lipp Jr Bks). HarpJ.

Ortland, Anne. Disciplines of the Beautiful Woman. Gift ed. 131p. 1986. Repr. 9.95 (ISBN 0-8499-0551-6). Word Bks.

--Disciplines of the Heart. 1987. 12.95. Word Bks.

Ortlund, Anne. The Acts of Joanna. 160p. 1982. 7.95 (ISBN 0-8499-0283-5). Word Bks.

--Disciplines of the Beautiful Woman. (QP Proven-Word Ser.). 132p. 1984. pap. 5.95 (ISBN 0-8499-2983-0). Word Bks.

Ortlund, Anne, jt. auth. see Ortlund, Raymond.

Ortlund, Anne, et al. Yes, God...I Am a Creative Woman. LC 83-80610. 225p. (Orig.). 1983. pap. 4.50 (ISBN 0-935797-02-5). Harvest IL.

Ortlund, Raymond & Ortlund, Anne. The Best Half of Life. LC 76-21582. 1976. pap. 3.25 (ISBN 0-8307-0443-4, 5404193). Regal.

Ortlund, Raymond C. Be a New Christian All Your Life. 192p. 1983. 5.95 (ISBN 0-8007-5119-1, Power Bks). Revell.

--Lord, Make My Life a Miracle! LC 73-89714. (Orig.). 1974. pap. 3.50 (ISBN 0-8307-0284-9, 5011701); study guide 1.59 (ISBN 0-8307-0626-7, 6101305). Regal.

--Lord, Make My Life Count. LC 75-6188. 144p. 1975. pap. 3.50 (ISBN 0-8307-0348-9, S112175). Regal.

Ortmayer, Roger. Sing & Pray & Shout Hurray. 1974. pap. 2.75 (ISBN 0-377-00004-3). Friend Pr.

Orton, William A. Liberal Tradition. 1945. 12.50x (ISBN 0-686-83606-5). Elliots Bks.

Orvell, Miles. Invisible Parade: The Fiction of Flannery O'Connor. LC 72-91132. 246p. 1975. 27.95 (ISBN 0-87722-023-9). Temple U Pr.

Os, Henk van see Van Os, Henk.

Osb, Barrier, jt. auth. see Bruno, Soeur.

Osbeck, Kenneth W. Devotional Warm-ups for Church Choirs. LC 85-17222. 96p. (Orig.). 1985. pap. 2.95 (ISBN 0-8254-3421-1); pap. 29.00 dozen (ISBN 0-8254-3423-8). Kregel.

--Junior's Praise. LC 57-1012. 184p. 1981. 5.95x (ISBN 0-8254-3400-9). Kregel.

--Ministry of Music. LC 61-14865. 192p. 1975. pap. 5.95x (ISBN 0-8254-3410-6). Kregel.

--My Music Workbook. 144p. 1982. pap. 5.95x (ISBN 0-8254-3415-7). Kregel.

--One Hundred One Hymn Stories. LC 81-17165. 288p. 1982. pap. 8.95 (ISBN 0-8254-3416-5). Kregel.

--One Hundred One More Hymn Stories. LC 84-27847. 328p. (Orig.). 1985. pap. 9.95 (ISBN 0-8254-3420-3). Kregel.

--Pocket Guide for the Church Choir Member. 48p. 1984. pap. 1.25 (ISBN 0-8254-3408-4); Per Dozen. pap. 12.95 (ISBN 0-8254-3417-3). Kregel.

--Singing with Understanding: Including 101 Beloved Hymn Backgrounds. LC 78-19960. 324p. 1979. 14.95 (ISBN 0-8254-3414-9). Kregel.

Osborn, Arthur W. Cosmic Womb: An Interpretation of Man's Relationship to the Infinite. LC 69-17714. (Orig.). 1969. pap. 2.25 (ISBN 0-8356-0001-7, Quest). Theos Pub Hse.

Osborn, E. Ethical Patterns in Early Christian Thought. LC 75-10040. 288p. 1976. 39.50 (ISBN 0-521-20835-1). Cambridge U Pr.

Osborn, E. C. Word & History. 1967. pap. 2.60x (ISBN 0-85564-020-0, Pub. by U of W Austral Pr). Intl Spec Bk.

Osborn, Eric F. Ethical Patterns in Early Christian Thought. LC 75-10040. pap. 65.50 (2026351). Bks Demand UMI.

Osborn, R. R., ed. Grounds of Hope: Essays in Faith & Freedom. 184p. 1968. 3.95 (ISBN 0-87921-055-9). Attic Pr.

Osborn, Ronald, ed. see Leaders of the Christian Church Staff & Teegarden, Kenneth L.

Osborn, Ronald E. The Faith We Affirm. LC 79-21079. 1979. pap. 3.50 (ISBN 0-8272-1009-4). CBP.

Osborn, T. L. Faith Speaks. 1982. pap. 2.95 (ISBN 0-89274-226-7, HH-226). Harrison Hse.

--Healing the Sick. 420p. 1981. pap. 7.95 (ISBN 0-89274-187-2, HH-187). Harrison Hse.

--How to Be Born Again. 160p. pap. 2.95 (ISBN 0-89274-224-0, HH-224). Harrison Hse.

--How to Enjoy Plenty. pap. 2.95 (ISBN 0-89274-222-4, HH-222). Harrison Hse.

--Miracles: Proof of God's Power. 96p. (Orig.). 1981. pap. 1.50 (ISBN 0-89274-185-6, HH-185). Harrison Hse.

--Receive Miracle Healing. 1983. pap. 4.95 (ISBN 0-89274-221-6, HH221). Harrison Hse.

--Soulwinning: Out Where the People Are. rev. ed. (Illus.). 218p. (Orig.). 1982. pap. 3.95 (ISBN 0-317-44699-1). Harrison Hse.

Osborne, Arthur. The Incredible Sai Baba: The Life & Miracles of a Modern-Day Saint. 102p. 1985. pap. text ed. 5.00x (ISBN 0-86125-105-9, Pub. by Orient Longman Ltd India). Apt Bks.

Osborne, Arthur, ed. The Collected Works of Ramana Maharshi. 192p. 1970. pap. 9.95 (ISBN 0-87728-070-3). Weiser.

Osborne, Cecil. How to Have a Happier Wife. LC 85-14255. 64p. (Orig.). 1986. pap. 2.95 (ISBN 0-310-30622-1, 10478P). Zondervan.

Osborne, Cecil G. Amate Siquiera un Poco. Orozco, Julio, tr. from Eng. LC 78-57808. Tr. of The Art of Learning to Love Yourself. (Span.). 182p. 1978. pap. 4.95 (ISBN 0-89922-120-3). Edit Caribe.

--The Art of Getting Along With People. 192p. 1982. pap. 3.95 (ISBN 0-310-30612-4, 10477P). Zondervan.

--The Art of Learning to Love Yourself. 1976. 3.95 (ISBN 0-310-30572-1, 10475P). Zondervan.

--The Art of Understanding Yourself. 1986. pap. 4.95 (ISBN 0-310-30592-6, 10472P). Zondervan.

--The Joy of Understanding Your Faith. 192p. (Orig.). 1983. pap. 7.75 (ISBN 0-687-20594-8). Abingdon.

--You're in Charge. pap. write for info (ISBN 0-515-09688-1). Jove Pubns.

Osborne, Denis. The Andromedans & Other Parables of Science & Faith. LC 78-18550. (Illus.). 1978. pap. 2.50 (ISBN 0-87784-600-6). Inter-Varsity.

Osborne, Grant R. The Resurrection Narratives: A Redactional Study. 288p. 1984. pap. 11.95 (ISBN 0-8010-6708-1). Baker Bk.

Osborne, Grant R. & Woodward, Stephen B. Handbook for Bible Study. 188p. 1983. pap. 5.95 (ISBN 0-8010-6701-4). Baker Bk.

Osborne, Harold. South American Mythology. LC 85-28567. (The Library of the World's Myths & Legends). (Illus.). 144p. 1986. 18.95 (ISBN 0-87226-043-7). P Bedrick Bks.

Osborne, John. Luther. pap. 3.95 (ISBN 0-451-14474-0, Sig). NAL.

Osborne, Kenan B. The Christian Sacraments of Initiation, Baptism, Confirmation, Eucharist. 1987. pap. 12.95. Paulist Pr.

Osborne, Roy F. Great Preachers of Today. 212p. 1966. case bound 11.95 (ISBN 0-89112-207-9, Bibl Res Pr). Abilene Christ U.

Osburn, Charlie & Lilly, Fred. The Charlie Osburn Story: You Gotta Give It All to Jesus. 140p. 1986. pap. 4.95 (ISBN 0-89283-287-8). Servant.

Osburn, William, Jr. A Hebrew & English Lexicon to the Old Testament. 287p. 1981. pap. 6.95 (ISBN 0-310-20361-9, 6264P). Zondervan.

Oschry, Leonard. The Story of the Vilna Gaon. 1.50 (ISBN 0-914131-62-1, D52). Torah Umesorah.

Oschry, Leonard, tr. see Bachrach, Yehoshua.

Oschry, Leonard, tr. see Chaim, Chafetz.

Oschry, Leonard, tr. see Hayyim, Hafetz.

Oschry, Leonard, tr. see Kahana, Kalman.

Oschry, Leonard, tr. see Katz, Jacob.

Oschry, Leonard, tr. see Munk, Elie.

Osden, Russell. A Capsule View of the Bible. 1979. pap. 1.00 (ISBN 0-88469-045-8). BMH Bks.

Osee, Johan. Call of the Virgin at San Damiano. (Illus.). 1977. pap. 6.95 (ISBN 0-8158-0354-0). Chris Mass.

Osen, James L. Prophet & Peacemaker: The Life of Adolphe Monod. (Illus.). 420p. 1984. lib. bdg. 32.25 (ISBN 0-8191-3825-8); pap. text ed. 17.75 (ISBN 0-8191-3826-6). U Pr of Amer.

Oseney Abbey. The English Register of Oseney Abbey: Parts 1 & 2. (EETS, OS Ser.: No. 133, 144). 1907-1913. Repr. of 1907 ed. 22.00 (ISBN 0-527-00130-9). Kraus Repr.

Oser, Fritz, jt. ed. see Berkowitz, Marvin W.

Osgood, Charles G. Classical Mythology of Milton's English Poems. LC 64-8180. 198p. 1964. Repr. of 1900 ed. 17.50x (ISBN 0-87752-080-1). Gordian.

--Classical Mythology of Milton's English Poems. LC 65-15902. (Studies in Comparative Literature, No. 35). 1969. Repr. of 1900 ed. lib. bdg. 75.00x (ISBN 0-8383-0603-9). Haskell.

Osgood, Judy, ed. Mediations for Those Who Live with Alcoholism. 72p. 1987. pap. 5.95 (ISBN 0-916895-04-1). Gilgal Pubns.

--Meditations for Bereaved Parents. LC 86-15003. (Gilgal Meditations Ser.). 70p. (Orig.). 1984. pap. 5.95 (ISBN 0-916895-00-9). Gilgal Pubns.

--Meditations for the Divorced. (Gilgal Meditations Ser.). 167p. (Orig.). 1987. pap. text ed. 5.95 (ISBN 0-916895-02-5). Gilgal Pubns.

--Meditations for the Widowed. LC 86-15002. (Gilgal Meditations Ser.). 70p. (Orig.). 1985. pap. 5.95 (ISBN 0-916895-01-7). Gilgal Pubns.

O'Shaughnessy, Laura & Serra, Luis. The Church & Revolution in Nicaragua. LC 82-92625. (Monographs in International Studies, Latin America Ser.: No. 11). 118p. pap. 11.00x (ISBN 0-89680-126-8, Ohio U Ctr Intl). Ohio U Pr.

O'Shea, Kevin. The Way of Tenderness. LC 78-61728. (Orig.). 1978. pap. 2.95 (ISBN 0-8091-2166-2). Paulist Pr.

Osiek, Carolyn. Galatians. (New Testament Message Ser.: Vol. 12). 8.95 (ISBN 0-89453-200-6); pap. 5.95 (ISBN 0-89453-135-2). M Glazier.

--Rich & Poor in the Shepherd of Hermas: An Exegetical-Social Investigation. Vawter, Bruce, ed. LC 83-7385. (Catholic Biblical Quarterly Monographs: No. 15). xi, 184p. (Orig.). 1983. pap. 6.00x (ISBN 0-915170-14-0). Catholic Biblical.

--What Are They Saying about the Social Setting of the New Testament? (WATSA Ser.). (Orig.). 1984. pap. 4.95 (ISBN 0-8091-2625-7). Paulist Pr.

Osiek, Carolyn A. First Corinthians. (Read & Pray Ser.). 1980. 1.75 (ISBN 0-8199-0634-4). Franciscan Herald.

Osis, Karlis & Haraldsson, Erlendur. At the Hour of Death. 1985. pap. 3.95 (ISBN 0-380-49486-8, 49486-8, Discus). Avon.

Osler, Margaret J. & Farber, Paul L., eds. Religion, Science & Worldview: Essays in Honor of Richard S. Westfall. 320p. 1985. 49.50 (ISBN 0-521-30452-0). Cambridge U Pr.

Osmond, D. S. see Steiner, Rudolf.

Osmond, D. S., tr. see Steiner, Rudolf.

Osmond, Dorothy S., tr. see Steiner, Rudolf.

Osmond, Percy H. Mystical Poets of the English Church. LC 72-5166. 1919. lib. bdg. 48.50 (ISBN 0-8414-6542-8). Folcroft.

Oss, Adriaan C. van see Van Oss, Adriaan C.

Oss, Celia van see Lewis, C. S., et al.

Ossowska, M. Moral Norms: A Tentative Systemization. 264p. 1980. 47.00 (ISBN 0-444-85454-1, North-Holland). Elsevier.

Ost, Steve. How to Increase Your Faith. (Cornerstone Ser.). 32p. 1981. pap. 2.00 (ISBN 0-930756-61-4, 533003). Aglow Pubns.

--The Lord's Balance. 32p. 1979. pap. 0.95 (ISBN 0-930756-43-6, 541007). Aglow Pubns.

Osten-Sacken, Peter Von Der see Von Der Osten-Sacken, Peter.

Oster, Rose. Your Creative Workshop. 1977. pap. 0.75 (ISBN 0-87516-236-3). De Vorss.

Osterhaven, M. Eugene, jt. tr. see Miller, Allen O.

Osterreicher, John M. The Unfinished Dialogue: Martin Buber & the Christian Way. 136p. 1987. pap. 5.95 (ISBN 0-8065-1050-1). Citadel Pr.

Osthathios, Geervarghese M. Theology of a Classless Society. LC 79-27013. 160p. (Orig.). 1980. pap. 2.24 (ISBN 0-88344-500-X). Orbis Bks.

Ostling, Joan K., jt. auth. see Christopher, J. R.

Ostow, Mortimer. Psychoanalysis & Judaism. 1982. 25.00x (ISBN 0-87068-713-1). Ktav.

Ostow, Mortimer & Scharfstein, Ben-Ami. The Need to Believe: The Psychology of Religion. 1969. pap. text ed. 19.95 (ISBN 0-8236-8159-9, 23520). Intl Univs Pr.

Ostrander, Frederick C. Li Romans Dou Lis. Repr. of 1915 ed. 16.50 (ISBN 0-404-50616-X). AMS Pr.

Ostrom, Karl A. & Shriver, Donald W., Jr. Is There Hope for the City? LC 77-22187. (Biblical Perspectives on Current Issues). 204p. 1977. softcover 4.95 (ISBN 0-664-24147-6). Westminster.

Ostrom, William. In God We Live. (Orig.). 1986. pap. 2.50 (ISBN 0-87574-267-X). Pendle Hill.

Ostwald, Martin, tr. see Aristotle.

O'Sullivan, Jeremiah F., tr. see Idung Of Prufening.

O'Sullivan, Jeremiah F., tr. see Lackner, Bede K.

O'Sullivan, Kevin. Sunday Readings. Incl. Cycle A. 428p. 1971. (ISBN 0-8199-0481-3); Cycle B. 487p. 1972. (ISBN 0-8199-0482-1); Cycle C. 444p. 1970. (ISBN 0-8199-0483-X). LC 74-141766. 9.00 ea. Franciscan Herald.

O'Sullivan, Richard, tr. see Maritain, Jacques.

Oswald, H., ed. Luther's Works: Lectures on the Minor Prophets, 2: Jonah & Habakkuk, Vol. 19. LC 55-9893. 1974. 13.95 (ISBN 0-570-06419-8, 15-1761). Concordia.

Oswald, Hilton, ed. Luther's Works, Vol. 11. Bowman, Herbert J., tr. from Lat. LC 55-9893. 560p. 1976. 17.95 (ISBN 0-570-06411-2, 15-1753). Concordia.

Oswalt, John. The Leisure Crisis. 168p. 1987. pap. 5.95 (ISBN 0-89693-241-9). Victor Bks.

Oswalt, John N. The Book of Isaiah, Chapters 1-39. (New International Commentary on the Old Testament Ser.). 672p. 29.95 (ISBN 0-8028-2368-8). Eerdmans.

Otani, Kosho K. The Successor: My Life. LC 84-23016. (Illus.). 114p. 1985. 16.95x (ISBN 0-914910-50-7). Buddhist Bks.

Otis, George, Jr. The God They Never Knew. 244p. 1982. pap. 5.95 (ISBN 0-915134-84-5). Mott Media.

O'Toole, James. Guide to the Archives of the Archdiocese of Boston. LC 80-8989. 300p. 1981. lib. bdg. 61.00 (ISBN 0-8240-9359-3). Garland Pub.

O'Toole, R. Religion: Classic Sociological Approaches. 1984. text ed. 12.95 (ISBN 0-07-548560-5). McGraw.

O'Toole, Robert F. The Unity of Luke's Theology: An Analysis of Luke-Acts. (Good News Studies Ser.: Vol. 9). 1984. pap. 8.95 (ISBN 0-89453-438-6). M Glazier.

Ott, Heinrich. God. LC 73-5350. 128p. 1974. pap. 5.95 (ISBN 0-8042-0590-6). John Knox.

Ott, Ludwig. Fundamentals of Catholic Dogma. Bastible, James C., ed. Lynch, Patrick, tr. from Ger. Orig. Title: Grundriss der Katholischen Dogmatik. 1974. pap. 15.00 (ISBN 0-89555-009-1). TAN Bks Pubs.

Otte, Elmer. Engaging the Aging in Ministry. 1981. pap. 7.95 (ISBN 0-9602938-5-X). Retirement Res.

Otte, Elmer & Bergmann, Mark. Engaging the Aging in Ministry. LC 12-2798. 1981. pap. 6.95 (ISBN 0-570-03833-2). Concordia.

Ottensoser, Max & Roberg, Alex, eds. Israelitische Lehrerbildungsanstalt Wurzburg. LC 81-81930. (Illus.). 256p. 1982. 12.95 (ISBN 0-8187-0046-7). Harlo Pr.

Otterholt, Howard V. How to Be Your Own Good Samaritan. LC 81-3465. 1982. 15.95 (ISBN 0-87949-195-7). Ashley Bks.

Otting, Rae. When Jesus Was a Lad. (Illus.). 1978. pap. 1.25 (ISBN 0-89508-055-9). Rainbow Bks.

Ottman, F., jt. auth. see Ironside, H. A.

Otto, A. S. The Theologia Twenty-One Encyclopedia, 2 vols. 1985. Set. vinyl 39.95 (ISBN 0-912132-16-7). Dominion Pr.

Otto, A. S., ed. Chairman's Chat-Life Lines. 120p. 1981. vinyl 24.95 (ISBN 0-912132-11-6). Dominion Pr.

--Invisible Ministry Annual Reports. 60p. 1985. vinyl 19.95 (ISBN 0-912132-12-4). Dominion Pr.

Otto, Christian F. Space into Light: The Churches of Balthasar Neumann. (Illus.). 1979. 55.00x (ISBN 0-262-15019-0). MIT Pr.

Otto, Donna. All in Good Time. 240p. 1985. 12.95 (ISBN 0-8407-5963-0). Nelson.

Otto, Herbert A., ed. Marriage & Family Enrichment: New Perspectives & Programs. LC 75-30743. 1976. pap. 9.95 (ISBN 0-687-23620-7). Abingdon.

Otto, John A., tr. see Oury, Guy-Marie.

Otto, Rudolf. Idea of the Holy. 2nd ed. Harvey, John W., tr. 1950. pap. 8.95 (ISBN 0-19-500210-5). Oxford U Pr.

--Mysticism East & West. Bracey, Bertha L. & Payne, Richenda C., trs. 289p. 1987. pap. 8.75 (ISBN 0-8356-0619-8). Theos Pub Hse.

Otto, Von St. Blasien. Die Chronik Des Otto Von St. Blasien. Kohl, Horst, tr. (Ger). pap. 10.00 (ISBN 0-384-43970-5). Johnson Repr.

Otto, Walter F. Dionysus: Myth & Cult. Palmer, Robert B., tr. from Ger. LC 86-13742. (Dunquin Ser.: No. 14). xxi, 243p. 1981. pap. 13.00 (ISBN 0-88214-214-3). Spring Pubns.

--Gestez Urbild und Mythos. Bolle, Kees W., ed. LC 77-82281. (Mytholoy Ser.). (Ger.). 1978. Repr. of 1951 ed. lib. bdg. 17.00x (ISBN 0-405-10572-X). Ayer Co Pubs.

--The Homeric Gods: The Spiritual Significance of Greek Religion. Bolle, Kees W., ed. LC 77-79149. (Mythology Ser.). 1978. Repr. of 1954 ed. lib. bdg. 22.00x (ISBN 0-405-10558-4). Ayer Co Pubs.

--The Homeric Gods: The Spiritual Significance of Greek Religion. 1978. Repr. of 1954 ed. lib. bdg. 24.00x (ISBN 0-88254-845-X, Octagon). Hippocrene Bks.

Otto, Walter G. Priester und Tempel Im Hellenistischen Agypten: Ein Beitrag Zur Kulturgeschichte Des Hellenismus, 2 vols. in 1. facsimile ed. LC 75-10645. (Ancient Religion & Mythology Ser.). (Ger.). 1976. Repr. 62.00x (ISBN 0-405-07278-3). Ayer Co Pubs.

Otto Bishop of Freising. Der Chronik des Bischofs Otto, Von Freising, Sechstes und Siebentes Buch. Kohl, H., tr. (Ger.). pap. 10.00 (ISBN 0-384-43965-9). Johnson Repr.

Otwell, John H. And Sarah Laughed: The Status of Woman in the Old Testament. LC 76-54671. 222p. 1977. pap. 8.95 (ISBN 0-664-24126-3). Westminster.

Otzen, Benedikt, jt. ed. see Jeppesen, Knud.

Ouden, Bernard D. Essays on Reason, Will, Creativity, & Time: Studies in the Philosophy of Friedrich Nietzsche. LC 82-45042. 124p. (Orig.). 1982. PLB 23.75 o. p. (ISBN 0-8191-2449-4); pap. text ed. 9.50 (ISBN 0-8191-2450-8). U Pr of Amer.

Oudin, Casimir. Commentarius de Scriptoribus Ecclesiae Antiquis Illorumque Scriptis. 3296p. Date not set. Repr. of 1723 ed. text ed. 662.40x (ISBN 0-576-72229-4, Pub. by Gregg Intl Pubs England). Gregg Intl.

Ouellett, F. L' Etude des Religions dans les Ecoles: L'experience Americaine, Anglaise et Canadienne. (SR Editions Ser.: No. 7). (Fr.). 666p. 1985. pap. text ed. 20.50x (ISBN 0-88920-183-8, Pub. by Wilfrid Laurier Canada). Humanities.

Ouellette, Raymond. Holistic Healing & the Edgar Cayce Readings. LC 80-80446. 384p. 1980. 11.95 (ISBN 0-936450-07-X); pap. 7.75. Aero Pr.

Oulton, J. E. & Chadwick, Henry, eds. Alexandrian Christianity. LC 54-10257. (Library of Christian Classics). 472p. 1977. pap. 8.95 (ISBN 0-664-24153-0). Westminster.

Oursler, Fulton. Greatest Story Ever Told. 1949. pap. 4.95 (ISBN 0-385-08028-X, D121, Im). Doubleday.

--The Greatest Story Ever Told. 1981. pap. 2.95 (ISBN 0-671-44742-4). PB.

Oury, Guy-Marie. St. Benedict: Blessed by God. Otto, John A., tr. from Fr. LC 80-13253. Orig. Title: Ce que croyait Benoit. 92p. (Orig.). 1980. pap. text ed. 4.50 (ISBN 0-8146-1181-8). Liturgical Pr.

Ouseley, S. G. Colour Meditations. 96p. 1981. pap. 3.50 (ISBN 0-85243-062-0). Ariel OH.

Ouspensky, Leonid. Theology of the Icon. Meyendorff, Elizabeth, tr. from Fr. LC 77-11882. (Illus.). 232p. 1978. pap. 12.95 (ISBN 0-913836-42-7). St Vladimirs.

Ouspensky, Leonid, jt. auth. see Lossky, Vladimir.

Ouspensky, P. D. Fourth Way. 1971. pap. 7.95 (ISBN 0-394-71672-8, Vin). Random.

--A Further Record. 352p. 1987. pap. 13.95 (ISBN 1-85063-056-9, 30569, Ark Paperbks). Methuen Inc.

--In Search of the Miraculous: Fragments of an Unknown Teaching. 399p. 1965. pap. 6.95 (ISBN 0-15-644508-5, Harv). HarBraceJ.

Outka, Gene. Agape: An Ethical Analysis. LC 78-88070. (Publications in Religion Ser.: No. 17). 336p. 1972. 33.00x (ISBN 0-300-01384-1); pap. 8.95x (ISBN 0-300-02122-4). Yale U Pr.

Outlaw, et al. A Survey of the Old Testament. Harrison, Harrold D., ed. (Orig.). 1984. pap. 5.95 (ISBN 0-89265-089-3). Randall Hse.

--A Survey of the New Testament. Harrison, Harrold D., ed. (Orig.). 1984. pap. 4.95 (ISBN 0-89265-090-7). Randall Hse.

Outlaw, Stanley. Questions from Text of Old Testament. 1977. pap. 2.95 (ISBN 0-89265-049-4). Randall Hse.

--Questions from the Text of the New Testament. 36p. 1977. pap. 2.95 (ISBN 0-89265-050-8). Randall Hse.

--Survey of the Old Testament. 1977. pap. 2.75 (ISBN 0-89265-048-6). Randall Hse.

Outlaw, Stanley & O'Donnell, J. D. A Survey of the Pentateuch. 93p. 1975. pap. 2.95 (ISBN 0-89265-027-3). Randall Hse.

Outlaw, Stanley & Thigpen, Charles. A Survey of the Gospels. 1976. pap. 1.95 (ISBN 0-89265-031-1). Randall Hse.

Outlaw, Stanley, et al. A Survey of the General Epistles & Revelation. 1976. pap. 2.95 (ISBN 0-89265-036-2). Randall Hse.

Outler, Albert, ed. John Wesley. 1964. pap. 13.95 (ISBN 0-19-502810-4). Oxford U Pr.

Outler, Albert C. The Works of John Wesley, Volume 2: Sermons II, 34-70. 600p. 1985. 49.95 (ISBN 0-687-46211-8). Abingdon.

Outler, Albert C., et al. The Relationships Among the Gospels: An Interdisciplinary Dialogue. Walker, William O., Jr., ed. LC 78-52845. (Monograph Series in Religion). 359p. 1978. text ed. 15.00 (ISBN 0-911536-73-6). Trinity U Pr.

Ouweneel, W. J. Creation or Evolution-What Is the Truth? 58p. pap. 3.95 (ISBN 0-88172-145-X). Believers Bkshelf.

--What Is Election? pap. 2.25 (ISBN 0-88172-162-X). Believers Bkshelf.

--What Is the Christian's Hope? 53p. pap. 2.95 (ISBN 0-88172-116-6). Believers Bkshelf.

--What Is the Sonship of Christ? pap. 2.25 (ISBN 0-88172-170-0). Believers Bkshelf.

Over, Raymond Van see Van Over, Raymond.

Overall, John. Convocation Book of 1606. LC 77-173482. (Library of Anglo-Catholic Theology: No. 15). Repr. of 1844 ed. 27.50 (ISBN 0-404-52107-X). AMS Pr.

Overbeck, J. J. Catholic Orthodoxy & Anglo-Catholicism. LC 76-81771. Repr. of 1866 ed. 10.00 (ISBN 0-404-04839-0). AMS Pr.

Overbeck, Joy, jt. auth. see Pogzeba, Wolfgang.

Overberg, Kenneth R. To Comfort & Confront. 78p. (Orig.). 1983. pap. 2.95 (ISBN 0-914544-49-7). Living Flame Pr.

Overby, Coleman. Bible Women. 1936. pap. 2.95 (ISBN 0-88027-082-9). Firm Foun Pub.

Overduin, Daniel. Reflections Books, 4 vols. 1980. Set. pap. 6.95 (ISBN 0-570-03817-0, 12-2785). Concordia.

--Reflections on the Creed. 1980. pap. 1.95 (ISBN 0-570-03814-6, 12-2782). Concordia.

--Reflections on the Lord's Prayer. 1980. pap. 1.95 (ISBN 0-570-03815-4, 12-2783). Concordia.

--Reflections on the Sacraments. 1980. pap. 1.95 (ISBN 0-570-03816-2, 12-2784). Concordia.

--Reflections on the Ten Commandments. 1980. pap. 1.95 (ISBN 0-570-03813-8, 12-2781). Concordia.

Overholt, James. From Tiny Beginnings. 64p. 1987. pap. 4.95 (ISBN 0-87178-296-0). Brethren.

Overholt, Thomas. Threat of Falsehood: A Study in Jeremiah. LC 71-131589. (Studies in Biblical Theology, 2nd Ser: No. 16). pap. 10.00x (ISBN 0-8401-3066-X). A R Allenson.

Overholt, Thomas W. Prophecy in Cross Cultural Perspective: A Sourcebook for Biblical Researchers. (Society of Biblical Literature Ser.). 1985. pap. 26.95 (ISBN 0-89130-901-2, 06-03-17). Scholars Pr GA.
Overholt, Thomas W., jt. ed. see Culley, Robert C.
Overholt, Thomas W., jt. ed. see Merrill, Arthur L.
Overly, Fay. Missing: A Family's Triumph in the Tragedy No Parent Ever Wants to Face. LC 84-72590. 210p. (Orig.). 1985. pap. 6.95 (ISBN 0-89636-151-9). Accent Bks.
Overmyer, Daniel. The Religions of China. LC 85-42789. 128p. (Orig.). 1986. pap. 6.95 (ISBN 0-06-066401-0, HarpR). Har-Row.
Overmyer, Daniel L. Folk Buddhist Religion: Dissenting Sects in Late Traditional China. (Harvard East Asian Ser.: No.83). 256p. 1976. 15.00x (ISBN 0-674-30705-4). Harvard U Pr.
Overrein, Judy. The King's Daughters. 116p. (Orig.). 1982. pap. text ed. 3.00 (ISBN 0-941630-00-5). Freedom Pr.
Overton, Basil. Mule Musings. 6.95 (ISBN 0-89137-105-2); pap. 4.25. Quality Pubns.
--When Christ Was Preached to Christ. pap. 5.50 (ISBN 0-89137-545-7). Quality Pubns.
Overton, John H. The English Church in the Nineteenth Century (1800-1833) (Victorian Age Ser.). 1894. Repr. 35.00 (ISBN 0-8482-5454-6). Norwood Edns.
Overton, John H. & Relton, Frederic. English Church from the Accession of George First to the End of the Eighteenth Century, 1714-1800. (History of the English Church Ser.: No. 7). Repr. of 1906 ed. 29.50 (ISBN 0-404-50757-3). AMS Pr.
Oviatt, Fern & Oviatt, Joan. Mormon Mind Puzzlers. 60p. 1983. 1.99 (ISBN 0-934126-30-5). Randall Bk Co.
Oviatt, Joan, jt. auth. see Oviatt, Fern.
Ovid. Metamorphoseon. Pontanus, Jacobus, ed. LC 75-27868. (Renaissance & the Gods Ser.: Vol. 24). (Illus.). 1977. Repr. of 1618 ed. lib. bdg. 88.00 (ISBN 0-8240-2073-1). Garland Pub.
--Metamorphoses. Garth, et al, trs. LC 75-27884. (Renaissance & the Gods Ser.: Vol. 39). (Illus.). 1976. Repr. of 1732 ed. lib. bdg. 88.00 (ISBN 0-8240-2088-X). Garland Pub.
Owen, A. L. The Famous Druids: A Survey of Three Centuries of English Literature in the Druids. LC 78-13614. (Illus.). 1979. Repr. of 1962 ed. lib. bdg. 22.50x (ISBN 0-313-20629-5, OWFD). Greenwood.
Owen, Aloysius, tr. see Alessio, Luis & Munoz, Hector.
Owen, Aloysius, tr. see Bojorge, Horacio.
Owen, Aloysius, tr. see Philipon, M. M.
Owen, Bob. Ted Engstrom: Man with a Vision. 214p. 1984. pap. 5.95 (ISBN 0-8423-6942-2). Tyndale.
Owen, Dennis E., jt. auth. see Hill, Samuel S.
Owen, G. Frederick. Abraham Lincoln: The Man & His Faith. 232p. 1981. pap. 6.95 (ISBN 0-8423-0000-7). Tyndale.
Owen, Huw P. Christian Theism: A Study in Its Basic Principles. 184p. 1984. 19.95 (ISBN 0-567-09336-0, Pub. by T&T Clark Ltd Uk). Fortress.
Owen, Jackie & Laemmlen, Ann. Articles of Faith Learning Book. (Illus.). 64p. 1982. Bk. I. pap. 3.95 (ISBN 0-87747-878-3); Bk. II, 80pgs. pap. 3.95 (ISBN 0-87747-915-1); Bk. III, 80pgs. pap. 3.95 (ISBN 0-87747-922-4). Deseret Bk.
Owen, John. Death of Death. 1983. pap. 7.95 (ISBN 0-85151-382-4). Banner of Truth.
--Hebrews, the Epistle of Warning. LC 68-57719. 1973. pap. 9.95 (ISBN 0-8254-3407-6). Kregel.
--The Holy Spirit, His Gifts & Power. LC 60-16514. 1977. pap. 11.95 (ISBN 0-8254-3413-0). Kregel.
--Sin & Temptation. Houston, James M., ed. LC 83-791. (Classics of Faith & Devotion). 1983. 10.95 (ISBN 0-88070-013-0). Multnomah.
--Works of John Owen, Vol. I. 1980. 16.95 (ISBN 0-85151-123-6). Banner of Truth.
--Works of John Owen, Vol. II. 1980. 16.95 (ISBN 0-85151-124-4). Banner of Truth.
--Works of John Owen, Vol. III. 1980. 16.95 (ISBN 0-85151-125-2). Banner of Truth.
--Works of John Owen, Vol. IV. 1980. 16.95 (ISBN 0-85151-068-X). Banner of Truth.
--Works of John Owen, Vol. V. 1980. 16.95 (ISBN 0-85151-067-1). Banner of Truth.
--Works of John Owen, Vol. VI. 1980. 16.95 (ISBN 0-85151-126-0). Banner of Truth.
--Works of John Owen, Vol. VII. 1980. 16.95 (ISBN 0-85151-127-9). Banner of Truth.
--Works of John Owen, Vol. VIII. 1980. 16.95 (ISBN 0-85151-066-3). Banner of Truth.
--Works of John Owen, Vol. IX. 1980. 16.95 (ISBN 0-85151-065-5). Banner of Truth.
--Works of John Owen, Vol. X. 1980. 16.95 (ISBN 0-85151-064-7). Banner of Truth.
--Works of John Owen, Vol. XI. 1980. 16.95 (ISBN 0-85151-128-7). Banner of Truth.
--Works of John Owen, Vol. XII. 1980. 16.95 (ISBN 0-85151-129-5). Banner of Truth.
--Works of John Owen, Vol. XIII. 1980. 16.95 (ISBN 0-85151-063-9). Banner of Truth.
--Works of John Owen, Vol. XIV. 1980. 16.95 (ISBN 0-85151-062-0). Banner of Truth.
--Works of John Owen, Vol. XV. 1980. 16.95 (ISBN 0-85151-130-9). Banner of Truth.
--Works of John Owen, Vol. XVI. 1980. 16.95 (ISBN 0-85151-061-2). Banner of Truth.
--Works of John Owen, 16 vols. 1980. Set. 244.95 (ISBN 0-85151-392-1). Banner of Truth.
Owen, Lewis. The Running Register: Recording the State of the English Colledges in All Forraine Parts. LC 68-54654. (English Experience Ser.: No. 19). 118p. 1968. Repr. of 1626 ed. 13.00 (ISBN 90-221-0019-7). Walter J Johnson.
Owen, Mary A. Voodoo Tales As Told among the Negroes of the Southwest. facs. ed. LC 70-149874. (Black Heritage Library Collection). (Illus.). 1893. 17.00 (ISBN 0-8369-8754-3). Ayer Co Pubs.
--Voodoo Tales, As Told among the Negroes of the Southwest. LC 78-78773. (Illus.). Repr. of 1893 ed. cancelled (ISBN 0-8371-1395-4). Greenwood.
Owen, Pat H. The Genesis Principle for Parents. 224p. 1985. pap. 6.95 (ISBN 0-8423-0996-9). Tyndale.
Owen, R. J. The Moonies: A Critical Look at a Controversial Group. 1985. 20.00x (ISBN 0-7062-4149-5, Pub. by Ward Lock Educ Co Ltd). State Mutual Bk.
--Trial of Faith. 1.60 (ISBN 0-08-017609-7). Pergamon.
Owen, Ray. Listening to Life. Penoi, Mary & Condit, Kay, eds. 124p. (Orig.). 1987. pap. 5.95 (ISBN 0-942316-14-2). Pueblo Pub Pr.
Owen, Robert & Howard, David M. Victor el Victorioso. Orellana, Eugenio, tr. from Eng. Tr. of Victor. (Span.). 152p. 1981. pap. 3.25 (ISBN 0-89922-206-4). Edit Caribe.
Owen, Robert, jt. auth. see Carman, Stephen.
Owen, Robert D., jt. auth. see Knowlton, Charles.
Owen, Roger, jt. ed. see Naff, Thomas.
Owen, Valarie. In the Beginning God. 224p. (Orig.). 1983. pap. text ed. 6.95 (ISBN 0-914307-00-2, Dist. by Harrion Hse). Word Faith.
--Let My People Go. 395p. (Orig.). 1983. pap. text ed. 9.95 (ISBN 0-914307-10-X, Dist. by Harrison Hse). Word Faith.
--Possess the Land. 193p. (Orig.). 1984. pap. text ed. 6.95 (ISBN 0-914307-17-7, Dist. by Harrison Hse). Word Faith.
Owen, Valerie. Christ, Resurrection Life. 268p. (Orig.). 1985. pap. text ed. 7.95 (ISBN 0-914307-32-0). Word Faith.
Owen, William. The Cambrian Biography; or Historical Notices of Celebrated Men Among the Ancient Britons. Feldman, Burton & Richardson, Robert, eds. LC 78-60896. (Myth & Romanticism Ser.: Vol. 20). (Illus.). 1979. lib. bdg. 80.00 (ISBN 0-8240-3569-0). Garland Pub.
Owens, Bill. Health & Healing: God's Way. (Illus.). 124p. (Orig.). Date not set. pap. 5.00 (ISBN 0-936801-01-8). Christ Serv Ctrs.
Owens, Carolyn. Color Me...Cuddly! (Illus.). 32p. 1982. pap. 0.99 (ISBN 0-87123-695-8, 220695). Bethany Hse.
Owens, J. J., jt. auth. see Yates, Kyle M.
Owens, J. J., ed. see Yates, Kyle M.
Owens, Joanne. The Unofficial Sunday School Teacher's Handbook. (Illus.). 240p. (Orig.). 1987. pap. 7.95 (ISBN 0-916260-42-9). Meriwether Pub.
Owens, John G., jt. auth. see Fewkes, Jesse W.
Owens, Joseph. An Elementary Christian Metaphysics. LC 84-23888. 399p. 1985. pap. text ed. 12.95 (ISBN 0-268-00916-3, 85-09168, Dist. by Harper & Row). U of Notre Dame Pr.
--Human Destiny: Some Problems for Catholic Philosophy. LC 82-21496. 126p. 1985. 16.95 (ISBN 0-8132-0604-9); pap. 7.95 (ISBN 0-8132-0605-7). Cath U Pr.
--An Interpretation of Existence. LC 84-23805. 162p. 1985. pap. text ed. 7.95 (ISBN 0-268-01157-5, 85-11578, Dist. by Harper & Row). U of Notre Dame Pr.
--St. Thomas Aquinas on the Existence of God: Collected Papers of Joseph Owens. Catan, John R., ed. LC 79-13885. 1980. 44.50x (ISBN 0-87395-401-7); pap. 16.95x (ISBN 0-87395-446-7). State U NY Pr.
Owens, Joseph C. Saint Thomas & the Future of Metaphysics. (Aquinas Lecture). 1957. 7.95 (ISBN 0-87462-122-4). Marquette.
Owens, Laurella, jt. ed. see Brown, Virginia P.
Owens, Lillian. Handbook for Counselors: GMA. 161p. 1979. pap. 3.00 (ISBN 0-89114-023-9). Baptist Pub Hse.
Owens, Mary F. Layman's Bible Book Commentary: Ezra, Nehemiah, Esther, Job, Vol. 7. 1984. 5.95 (ISBN 0-8054-1177-1). Broadman.
--Salt from the Psalter. LC 80-67147. 1981. pap. 4.95 (ISBN 0-8054-1218-2). Broadman.
Owens, Milton E., Jr., ed. Outstanding Black Sermons, Vol. 3. 80p. 1982. pap. 4.95 (ISBN 0-8170-0973-6). Judson.
Owens, Valerie. The Holy Spirit of God. 168p. (Orig.). 1985. pap. text ed. 6.50 (ISBN 0-914307-39-8). Word Faith.
Owens, Virginia S. And the Trees Clap Their Hands: Faith, Perception & the New Physics. 148p. 1983. pap. 6.95 (ISBN 0-8028-1949-4). Eerdmans.
--Wind River Winter: How the World Dies. 288p. 1987. pap. 10.95 (ISBN 0-310-45861-7). Zondervan.
Owyang, Gregory R., jt. auth. see Chinn, Wilberta L.
Oxenham, John, ed. Appropriate Values & Education in Developing Nations. (Illus.). 304p. 1987. 22.95 (ISBN 0-89226-050-5, Pub. by ICUS). Paragon Hse.
Oxnam, Garfield B. Preaching in a Revolutionary Age. facsimile ed. LC 75-142687. (Essay Index Reprint Ser). Repr. of 1944 ed. 18.00 (ISBN 0-8369-2421-5). Ayer Co Pubs.
Oxtoby & Sandison. Once upon a Christmas. 1986. 14.95 (ISBN 0-8120-5755-4). Barron.
Oxtoby, Willard B. Some Inscriptions of the Safaitic Bedouin. (American Oriental Ser.: Vol. 50). (Illus.). 1968. pap. 8.00x (ISBN 0-940490-50-1). Am Orient Soc.
Oxtoby, Willard G. The Meaning of Other Faiths. LC 83-1090. (Library of Living Faith: Vol. 10). 120p. (Orig.). 1983. pap. 5.95 (ISBN 0-664-24443-2). Westminster.
Oyola, Eliezer, tr. see Dobbins, Richard D.
Oyola, Eliezer, tr. see Hayford, Jack W.
Ozak, Muzaffer. Dervish Virtues. 192p. (Orig.). 1987. pap. 9.00 (ISBN 0-939660-22-9). Threshold VT.
Ozanam, Frederick. Franciscan Poets of the Thirteenth Century. LC 68-26288. 1969. Repr. of 1914 ed. 24.50x (ISBN 0-8046-0342-1). Assoc Faculty Pr.
Ozeri, Zion M. Yemenite Jews: A Photographic Essay. (Illus.). 96p. 1985. 19.95 (ISBN 0-8052-3980-4). Schocken.
Ozment, Robert V. Love Is the Answer. 160p. 1986. pap. 5.95 (ISBN 0-8007-5227-9). Revell.
Ozment, Steven. When Fathers Ruled: Family Life in Reformation Europe. LC 83-6098. (Illus.). 238p. 1983. text ed. 17.50x (ISBN 0-674-95120-4). Harvard U Pr.
Ozment, Steven E. Mysticism & Dissent: Religious Ideology & Social Protest in the Sixteenth Century. LC 72-91316. 272p. 1973. 33.00x (ISBN 0-300-01576-3). Yale U Pr.
--The Reformation in the Cities: The Appeal of Protestantism to Sixteenth-Century Germany & Switzerland. LC 75-8444. 228p. 1975. 28.50x (ISBN 0-300-01898-3); pap. 7.95x (ISBN 0-300-02496-7). Yale U Pr.
Ozment, Steven E., ed. Reformation Europe: A Guide to Research. 390p. 1982. 18.50x (ISBN 0-910345-01-5); pap. 13.50x (ISBN 0-686-82436-9). Center Reform.
Ozols, Violet, tr. see Lorber, Jakob.
Ozols, Violet, tr. see Mohr, Victor.

P

Paamoni, Zev. Aaron, the High Priest. (Biblical Ser.). (Illus.). 1970. 4.00 (ISBN 0-914080-27-X). Shulsinger Sales.
--The Adventures of Jacob. (Biblical Ser.). (Illus.). 1970. 4.00 (ISBN 0-914080-26-1). Shulsinger Sales.
--Benjamin, the Littlest Brother. (Biblical Ser.). (Illus.). 1970. 4.00 (ISBN 0-914080-28-8). Shulsinger Sales.
--Yitzchak, Son of Abraham. (Biblical Ser.). (Illus.). 1970. 4.00 (ISBN 0-914080-25-3). Shulsinger Sales.
Paccard, Andre. Traditional Islamic Craft in Moroccan Architecture, 2 vols. 1980. 495.00x (ISBN 0-686-69970-X, Pub. by Editions Atelier England). State Mutual Bk.
Pace, Mildred M. Pyramids: Tombs for Eternity. (Illus.). 192p. 1981. 10.95 (ISBN 0-07-048054-0). McGraw.
Pache, Rene. Inspiration & Authority of Scripture. 1970. pap. 10.95 (ISBN 0-8024-4091-6). Moody.
--Person & Work of the Holy Spirit. 1960. pap. 7.50 (ISBN 0-8024-6471-8). Moody.
Pacheco, Josephine F., jt. auth. see Foner, Philip S.
Pachomius, St. History of the Monks at Tabenna. pap. 1.95 (ISBN 0-686-05644-2). Eastern Orthodox.
Pachomius, Saint Instructions of St. Pachomius. Budge, E. Wallis, tr. pap. text ed. 1.95 (ISBN 0-686-25553-4). Eastern Orthodox.
--Rule of St. Pachomius. Budge, E. A., tr. from Coptic. 1975. pap. 1.95 (ISBN 0-686-10939-2). Eastern Orthodox.
Pachow, W. Chinese Buddhism: Aspects of Interaction & Reinterpretation. LC 80-5432. 275p. 1980. lib. bdg. 27.00 (ISBN 0-8191-1090-6). U Pr of Amer.
Pachter, Marc, ed. Telling Lives: The Biographer's Art. LC 81-10312. 151p. 1981. pap. 10.95 (ISBN 0-8122-1118-9). U of Pa Pr.
Pacific School Of Religion. Religious Progress on the Pacific Slope: Addresses & Papers at the Celebration of the Semi-Centennial Anniversary of Pacific School of Religion, Berkeley, California. facs. ed. LC 68-22941. (Essay Index Reprint Ser). 1968. Repr. of 1917 ed. 19.00 (ISBN 0-8369-0820-1). Ayer Co Pubs.
Pacini, David S. The Cunning of Modern Religious Thought. LC 86-45201. 192p. 1986. 16.95 (ISBN 0-8006-0786-4, 1-786). Fortress.
Pack, Frank. Message of the New Testament: Revelation I & II, 2 vols. (Way of Life Ser.: No. 176 & 177). 1984. pap. 3.95 ea. (Bibl Res Pr). Vol. I (ISBN 0-89112-176-5). Vol. II (ISBN 0-89112-177-3). Abilene Christ U.
--Tongues & the Holy Spirit. (Way of Life Ser: No. 127). (Orig.). 1972. pap. text ed. 3.95 (ISBN 0-89112-127-7, Bibl Res Pr). Abilene Christ U.
Pack, Frank & Meador, Prentice A., Jr. Preaching to Modern Man. Thomas, J. D., ed. LC 73-75928. 1969. 10.95 (ISBN 0-89112-060-2, Bibl Res Pr). Abilene Christ U.
Packard, Dane. The Church Becoming Christ's Body: The Small Church's Manual of Dances for Holy Seasons. Adams, Doug, ed. 110p. (Orig.). 1985. pap. 7.95 (ISBN 0-941500-35-7). Sharing Co.
Packard, David W., jt. auth. see Lofstedt, Bengt M.
Packard, Dennis J. & Packard, Sandra. Feasting Upon the Word. LC 81-12446. 242p. 7.95 (ISBN 0-87747-879-1). Deseret Bk.
Packard, Jerrold M. Peter's Kingdom: Inside the Papal City. (Illus.). 352p. 1985. 17.95 (ISBN 0-684-18430-3, ScribT). Scribner.
Packard, Russell C. Come, Journey with Me: A Personal Story of Conversion & Ordination. LC 84-24356. 208p. (Orig.). 1984. pap. 8.00 (ISBN 0-89571-021-8). Affirmation.
Packard, Sandra, jt. auth. see Packard, Dennis J.
Packer, Boyd K. Eternal Love. LC 73-88635. 22p. 1973. 1.50 (ISBN 0-87747-514-8). Deseret Bk.
--Our Father's Plan. LC 84-72516. (Illus.). 64p. 1984. 8.95 (ISBN 0-87747-523-7). Deseret Bk.
Packer, Duane, jt. auth. see Roman, Sanaya.
Packer, J. I. The Apostle's Creed. 1983. pap. 3.95 (ISBN 0-8423-0051-1); Leader's Guide 2.95 (ISBN 0-8423-0052-X). Tyndale.
--Beyond the Battle for the Bible. LC 80-68331. 160p. 1980. text ed. 9.95 (ISBN 0-89107-195-4, Crossway Bks). Good News.
--God Has Spoken. rev. ed. LC 80-7789. (Orig.). 1980. pap. 4.95 (ISBN 0-87784-656-1). Inter-Varsity.
--I Want to Be a Christian. 1977. pap. 8.95 (ISBN 0-8423-1842-9). Tyndale.
--Knowing God. LC 73-81573. 1973. pap. 7.95 (ISBN 0-87784-770-3). Inter-Varsity.
--Knowing Man. LC 79-52495. 1979. pap. 3.95 (ISBN 0-89107-175-X, Crossway Bks). Good News.
--Meeting God. (LifeBuilder Bible Studies). 64p. (Orig.). 1986. pap. 2.95. Inter-Varsity.
--The Ten Commandments. 1982. pap. 3.95 (ISBN 0-8423-7004-8); leader's guide 2.95 (ISBN 0-8423-7005-6). Tyndale.
Packer, J. I. & Howard, Thomas. Christianity: The True Humanism. 1985. 9.95 (ISBN 0-8499-0316-5). Word Bks.
Packer, J. I. & Tenney, Merrill C., eds. The World of the New Testament. LC 82-12548. 1982. pap. 6.95 (ISBN 0-8407-5821-9). Nelson.
Packer, J. I., tr. see Luther, Martin.
Packer, J. I., et al, eds. All the People & Places of the Bible. LC 82-12564. 1982. pap. 6.95 (ISBN 0-8407-5819-7). Nelson.
--The World of the Old Testament. LC 82-12563. 1982. pap. 6.95 (ISBN 0-8407-5820-0). Nelson.
Packer, J. T. Keep in the Step with the Spirit. Date not set. pap. 7.95 (ISBN 0-8007-5235-X, Power Bks). Revell.
Packer, James I. Evangelism & the Sovereignty of God. LC 67-28875. 1961. pap. 3.95 (ISBN 0-87784-680-4). Inter-Varsity.
--Fundamentalism & the Word of God. 1958. pap. 6.95 (ISBN 0-8028-1147-7). Eerdmans.
--God in Our Midst: Seeking & Receiving Ongoing Revival. (Christian Essentials Ser.). 48p. (Orig.). 1987. pap. 1.95 (ISBN 0-89283-327-0). Servant.
--God's Words. LC 81-18683. 192p. (Orig.). 1982. pap. 5.95 (ISBN 0-87784-367-8). Inter-Varsity.
--Your Father Loves You: Daily Insights for Knowing God. Watson, Jean, ed. & compiled by. 392p. 1986. pap. 9.95 (ISBN 0-87788-975-9). Shaw Pubs.

Packer, James I., pref. by. Knowing God: Study Guide. 1975. pap. 2.95 (ISBN 0-87784-413-5). Inter-Varsity.

Packer, James I., et al, eds. The Bible Almanac: A Comprehensive Handbook of the People of the Bible & How They Lived. LC 79-23475. 792p. 1980. 16.95 (ISBN 0-8407-5162-1). Nelson.

--Public Life in Bible Times. 224p. 1985. pap. 6.95 (ISBN 0-8407-5984-3). Nelson.

Packer, John W. Acts of the Apostles. (Cambridge Bible Commentary on the New English Bible, New Testament Ser.). (Orig.). 1966. pap. 10.95 (ISBN 0-521-09383-X). Cambridge U Pr.

Packo, John E. Find & Use Your Spiritual Gifts. LC 80-69967. 117p. (Orig.). 1980. pap. 2.95 (ISBN 0-87509-293-4); Leader's Guide. 2.95 (ISBN 0-87509-294-2). Chr Pubns.

Packull, Werner O. Mysticism & the Early South German-Austrian Anabaptist 1525-1531. LC 76-46557. (Studies in the Anabaptist & Mennonite History: No. 19). 296p. 1977. 19.95x (ISBN 0-8361-1130-3). Herald Pr.

Packull, Werner O., jt. auth. see Stayer, James M.

Padberg, John W. Colleges in Controversy: The Jesuit Schools in France from Revival to Suppression, 1815-1880. LC 75-78523. (Historical Studies: No. 83). 1969. text ed. 22.50x (ISBN 0-674-14160-1). Harvard U Pr.

Padberg, John W., ed. Documents of the Thirty-First & Thirty-Second General Congregations of the Society of Jesus: An English Translation of the Official Latin Texts of the General Congregations & of the Accompanying Papal Documents. LC 77-70881. (Jesuit Primary Sources in English Translation: No. 2). 608p. 1977. pap. 6.00 smyth sewn (ISBN 0-912422-26-2). Inst Jesuit.

Paddock, Charles L. Going up. LC 53-107000078. (Dest Ser.). 1984. pap. 5.95 (ISBN 0-317-28316-2). Pacific Pr Pub Assn.

Padelford, Frederick M. Political & Ecclesiastical Allegory of First Book of the Faerie Queen. 1911. lib. bdg. 10.00 (ISBN 0-8414-9237-9). Folcroft.

--Political & Ecclesiastical Allegory of the First Book of the Fairie Queen. LC 70-111785. Repr. of 1911 ed. 5.00 (ISBN 0-404-04856-0). AMS Pr.

Paden, John N. Religion & Political Culture in Kano. LC 74-153548. 1973. 46.50x (ISBN 0-520-02020-0). U of Cal Pr.

Paden, W. D., tr. see Gronbech, Vilhelm.

Padgett, James E. True Gospel of Salvation Revealed Anew by Jesus, 3 Vols. Vol. I, III. pap. 7.50 ea. (ISBN 0-686-37147-X); Vols. II, III. pap. 9.00 ea. New Age Min Spiritualist.

Padilla, C. Rene, jt. ed. see Branson, Mark L.

Padilla, Gilbert. Refreshment in the Desert: Spiritual Connections in Daily Life. 144p. (Orig.). 1985. pap. 7.95 (ISBN 0-89622-228-4). Twenty-Third.

Padmarajiah, Y. J. A Comparative Study of the Jaina Theories of Reality & Knowledge. 460p. 1986. 22.00 (ISBN 81-208-0036-2, Pub. by Motilal Banarsidass India). South Asia Bks.

Padmasambhava, Guru. The Legend of the Great Stupa. LC 73-79059. (Tibetan Translation Ser., Vol. 2). (Illus.). 144p. 1973. pap. 6.95 (ISBN 0-913546-03-8). Dharma Pub.

Padovano, Anthony. Dawn Without Darkness. LC 82-45117. (Illus.). 272p. 1982. pap. 4.95 (ISBN 0-385-18183-3, Im). Doubleday.

Paelian, Frances. The Mystical Marriage of Science & Spirit. LC 81-70272. (Illus.). 200p. 1981. pap. 11.95 (ISBN 0-918936-11-X). Astara.

Paetkau, Paul, et al. God-Man-Land. LC 78-55244. 1978. 5.25 (ISBN 0-87303-008-7). Faith & Life.

Paetow, Louis J., ed. Crusades & Other Historical Essays, Presented to Dana C. Munro by His Former Students. facs. ed. LC 68-14902. (Essay Index Reprint Ser). 1928. 21.50 (ISBN 0-8369-0354-4). Ayer Co Pubs.

Paffard, Michael. The Unattended Moment: Excerpts from Autobiographies with Hints & Guesses. LC 76-368148. 1976. pap. text ed. 3.95x (ISBN 0-8401-1803-1). A R Allenson.

Paganuzzi, P. Pravda ob Ubijstvje Tsarskoj Semji. LC 80-84594. Tr. of The Truth About the Murder of the Royal Family. 234p. 1981. 15.00 (ISBN 0-317-29234-X); pap. 10.00 (ISBN 0-317-29235-8). Holy Trinity.

Paganuzzi, P. N. Visoko-Dechanskaja Lavra na Kosovje Polje (v Serbii) Tr. of The Visoko-Dechansky Monastery at Kosova Polija (in Serbia) 1976. pap. 1.00 (ISBN 0-317-30331-7). Holy Trinity.

Page, Carole. Carrie: Heartsong Books. 160p. (Orig.). 1984. pap. 2.95 (ISBN 0-87123-441-6). Bethany Hse.

Page, Carole G. Neeley Never Said Good-By. (Sensitive Issues Ser.). (Orig.). 1984. pap. 3.50 (ISBN 0-8024-0342-5). Moody.

Page, Carole G., jt. auth. see Hernandez, David.

Page, Jesse. The Black Bishop: Samuel Adjai Crowther. LC 75-106783. (Illus.). 1979. Repr. of 1908 ed. 32.00x (ISBN 0-8371-4610-0, PBB&, Pub. by Negro U Pr). Greenwood.

Page, Tom, ed. The Upper Room Disciplines, 1986. 382p. (Orig.). 1985. pap. 3.95 (ISBN 0-8358-0507-7). Upper Room.

Pagels, Elaine. Adam, Eve & the Serpent. 1987. 17.95 (ISBN 0-394-52140-4). Random.

--The Gnostic Gospels. LC 79-4764. 1979. 14.95 (ISBN 0-394-50278-7). Random.

Paget, Francis. An Introduction to the Fifth Book of Hooker's Treatise of the Laws of Ecclesiastical Polity. 265p. 1981. Repr. of 1899 ed. lib. bdg. 85.00 (ISBN 0-8495-4402-5). Arden Lib.

Paget, John. An Answer to the Unjust Complaints of W. Best: Also an Answer to Mr. John Davenport. LC 76-57403. (English Experience Ser.: No. 819). 1977. Repr. of 1635 ed. lib. bdg. 16.00 (ISBN 90-221-0819-8). Walter J Johnson.

Paget, M. Spirituals Reborn: Melody. LC 74-76574. 96p. 1976. Pt. 1. pap. text ed. 5.95 (ISBN 0-521-08714-7); Pt. 2. pap. text ed. 5.95 (ISBN 0-521-21332-0); choral 13.95 (ISBN 0-521-08713-9). Cambridge U Pr.

Paget, Wilkes M. Poverty, Revolution & the Church. 142p. (Orig.). 1982. pap. text ed. 10.95 (ISBN 0-85364-285-0). Attic Pr.

Pahl, Paul D., tr. Luther's Works, Vol. 6. LC 55-9893. 1969. 16.95 (ISBN 0-570-06406-6, 15-1748). Concordia.

--Luther's Works, Vol 7. LC 55-9893. 1964. 15.95 (ISBN 0-570-06407-4, 15-1749). Concordia.

--Luther's Works: Genesis Chapters 45-50, Vol. 8. LC 55-9893. 1965. 14.95 (ISBN 0-570-06408-2, 15-1750). Concordia.

Paige, Jeffrey M., jt. auth. see Paige, Karen E.

Paige, Karen E. & Paige, Jeffrey M. The Politics of Reproductive Ritual. 392p. 1981. 31.00x (ISBN 0-520-03071-0); pap. 8.95 (ISBN 0-520-04782-6, CAL 572). U of Cal Pr.

Paige, Roger. Dealing with Divorce. 1979. pap. 4.50 (ISBN 0-8309-0240-6). Herald Hse.

Pailin, David A. Attitudes to Other Religions: Comparative Religion in Seventeenth & Eighteenth-Century Britain. LC 83-20652. 368p. 1984. 49.00 (ISBN 0-7190-1065-9, Pub. by Manchester Univ Pr). Longwood Pub Group.

Paine, Mabel H. & Fisher, Betty J., eds. The Divine Art of Living. 272p. 1986. pap. 9.95 (ISBN 0-87743-194-9). Baha'i.

Painter, Desmond & Shepard, John. Religion. Yapp, Malcolm & Killinger, Margaret, eds. (World History Ser.). (Illus.). 32p. 1980. lib. bdg. 6.95 (ISBN 0-89908-145-2); pap. text ed. 2.45 (ISBN 0-89908-120-7). Greenhaven.

Painter, John. Theology As Hermeneutics: Rudolf Bultmann's Theology of the History of Jesus. (Historic Texts & Interpreters Ser.: No. 4). 220p. 1986. text ed. 23.95x (ISBN 1-85075-050-5, Pub. by Almond Pr England); pap. text ed. 14.95x (ISBN 1-85075-051-3). Eisenbrauns.

Painter, Muriel T. With Good Heart: Yaqui Beliefs & Ceremonies in Pascua, Village. Spicer, Edward H. & Kaemlein, Wilma, eds. LC 86-893. (Illus.). 533p. 1986. 35.00x (ISBN 0-8165-0875-5). U of Ariz Pr.

--A Yaqui Easter. LC 74-153706. 40p. 1971. pap. 3.95 (ISBN 0-8165-0168-8). U of Ariz Pr.

Painter, Sidney. Mediaeval Society. (Development of Western Civilization Ser). (Illus.). 109p. 1951. pap. 5.95x (ISBN 0-8014-9850-3). Cornell U Pr.

--Scourge of the Clergy: Peter of Dreux, Duke of Brittany. LC 76-96188. 1970. Repr. of 1937 ed. lib. bdg. 16.00x (ISBN 0-374-96175-1, Octagon). Hippocrene Bks.

Painter, Sidney, jt. auth. see Tierney, Brian.

Paisley Abbey. Registrum Monasterii De Passelet. Innes, Cosmo, ed. LC 75-174311. (Maitland Club. Glasgow. Publications: No. 17). Repr. of 1832 ed. 52.50 (ISBN 0-404-52954-2). AMS Pr.

Pak, Bo Hi. Truth Is My Sword. LC 78-74661. 110p. (Orig.). 1978. pap. 2.00 (ISBN 0-318-03063-2). HSA Pubns.

Pakuda, Bahya I. The Book of Direction to the Duties of the Heart. Mansoor, Menahem, et al, trs. from Arabic. (Littman Library of Jewish Civilization). 1973. 43.00x (ISBN 0-19-710020-1). Oxford U Pr.

Pal, P. Krishna: The Cowherd King. LC 70-185825. 1972. pap. 4.95x (ISBN 0-87587-048-1). LA Co Art Mus.

Pal, Pratapaditya. Bronzes of Kashmir. LC 75-902. (Illus.). 205p. 1975. lib. bdg. 40.00 (ISBN 0-87817-158-4). Hacker.

--Hindu Religion & Iconology According to the Tantrasara. LC 81-52893. (Tantric Tradition Ser.). Orig. Title: Tantrasara. (Illus.). 172p. 1982. pap. 10.95 (ISBN 0-941582-00-0). Vichitra Pr.

--Light of Asia: Buddha Sakyamuni in Asian Art. LC 84-788. (Illus.). 344p. 1984. 35.00 (ISBN 0-295-96123-6, Pub. by LA County Museum of Art). U of Wash Pr.

Pal, Pratapaditya, et al. Light of Asia: Buddha Sakyamuni in Asian Art. (Illus.). 332p. 1984. 35.00 (ISBN 0-87587-116-X, Dist. by U of Wash Pr); pap. 16.95 (ISBN 0-87587-116-X). LA Co Art Mus.

Palacios, Miguel A. Islam & the Divine Comedy. 295p. 1968. Repr. of 1926 ed. 30.00x (ISBN 0-7146-1995-7, F Cass Co). Biblio Dist.

Palairet, Michael, tr. see Emmerich, Anne C.

Palandro, Michael & Lestarjette, Steve. The Essentials of Christian Relationship. 56p. 1987. pap. text ed. 2.95 (ISBN 0-939079-00-3). Christlife Pubs.

Palassis, Neketas S., ed. St. Nectarios Orthodox Conference. LC 80-53258. 176p. (Orig.). 1981. pap. 15.00x (ISBN 0-913026-14-X). St Nectarios.

Palau, Gabriel. The Active Catholic. LC 84-50405. 224p. 1984. pap. 4.00 (ISBN 0-89555-238-8). TAN Bks Pubs.

Palau, Luis. Grito de Victoria! Calcada, Leticia, tr. from Eng. Tr. of The Moment to Shout! (Span.). 144p. 1986. pap. 5.50 (ISBN 0-311-46106-9). Casa Bautista.

--Heart after God. LC 78-57676. 200p. 1982. pap. 3.50 (ISBN 0-930014-83-9). Multnomah.

--The Moment to Shout. LC 77-4593. 250p. 1982. pap. 3.50 (ISBN 0-930014-84-7). Multnomah.

--My Response. 1985. pap. 3.95 (ISBN 0-8024-8782-3). Moody.

--Schemer & the Dreamer: God's Way to the Top. LC 77-4589. 1976. pap. 3.50 (ISBN 0-930014-12-X). Multnomah.

--Time to Stop Pretending. 156p. 1985. pap. 5.95 (ISBN 0-89693-332-6). Victor Bks.

--Walk on Water, Pete! LC 80-39955. 1974. pap. 2.95 (ISBN 0-930014-34-0). Multnomah.

Palazzini, Pietro, ed. Sin: Its Reality & Nature. 238p. 1964. 9.95 (ISBN 0-933932-25-1). Scepter Pubs.

Palestrina, Giovanni P. Ten Four-Part Motets for the Church's Year. Harman, Alec, tr. (Lat. & Eng.). 1964. 9.95 (ISBN 0-19-353332-4). Oxford U Pr.

Paley, Alan L. Confucius: Ancient Chinese Philosopher. Rahmas, D. Steve, ed. (Outstanding Personalities Ser.: No. 59). 32p. (Orig.). 1973. lib. bdg. 3.50 incl. catalog cards (ISBN 0-87157-559-0); pap. 1.95 vinyl laminated covers (ISBN 0-87157-059-9). SamHar Pr.

Paley, William. Natural Theology. 1986. lib. bdg. 30.00x (ISBN 0-935005-61-7); pap. 15.00x (ISBN 0-935005-62-5). Ibis Pub VA.

--The Principles of Moral & Political Philosophy. Wellek, Rene, ed. LC 75-11246. (British Philosophers & Theologians of the 17th & 18th Centuries Ser.: Vol. 45). 1977. Repr. of 1785 ed. lib. bdg. 51.00 (ISBN 0-8240-1797-8). Garland Pub.

Pallares, Jose C. A Poor Man Called Jesus: Reflections on the Gospel of Mark. Barr, Robert R., tr. from Span. LC 85-15339. 144p. (Orig.). 1986. pap. 8.95 (ISBN 0-88344-398-8). Orbis Bks.

Pallenberg, Esward H. The Amazing Discovery of the Holy Ghost. (Illus.). 98p. 1984. pap. 23.75 (ISBN 0-89266-487-8). Am Classical Coll Pr.

Palliere, Aime. The Unknown Sanctuary. Wise, Louise W., tr. LC 79-150294. 243p. 1985. pap. 8.95x (ISBN 0-8197-0498-9). Bloch.

Pallis, Marco. Peaks & Lamas. lib. bdg. 100.00 (ISBN 0-87968-327-9). Gordon Pr.

Palm, Franklin C. Calvinisim & the Religious Wars. LC 78-80579. 1971. Repr. 24.50x (ISBN 0-86527-020-1). Fertig.

--Calvinism & the Religious Wars. LC 83-45628. Date not set. Repr. of 1932 ed. 22.50 (ISBN 0-404-19880-5). AMS Pr.

--Politics & Religion in Sixteenth-Century France: A Study of the Career of Henry of Montmorency-Damville, Uncrowned King of the South. 13.25 (ISBN 0-8446-0835-1). Peter Smith.

Palma, Anthony D. Truth-Antidote for Error. LC 76-52177. (Radiant Life Ser.). 128p. 1977. pap. 2.50 (ISBN 0-88243-904-9, 02-0904); teacher's ed 3.95 (ISBN 0-88243-174-9, 32-0174). Gospel Pub.

Palmer, A. Smythe. The Samson Saga & Its Place in Comparative Religion. 1977. lib. bdg. 59.95 (ISBN 0-8490-2565-6). Gordon Pr.

Palmer, Aaron H. Documents & Facts Illustrating the Origin of the Mission to Japan. LC 72-82105. (Japan Library Ser.). 1973. Repr. of 1857 ed. lib. bdg. 11.00 (ISBN 0-8420-1399-7). Scholarly Res Inc.

Palmer, Abram S. Samson-Saga & Its Place in Comparative Religion. Dorson, Richard, ed. LC 77-70613. (International Folklore Ser.). 1977. Repr. of 1913 ed. lib. bdg. 23.50x (ISBN 0-405-10112-0). Ayer Co Pubs.

Palmer, Bernard. My Son, My Son. (Living Bks.). 288p. (Orig.). 1987. pap. 3.95 (ISBN 0-8423-4639-2). Tyndale.

Palmer, Bernard & Palmer, Marjorie. Light a Small Candle. LC 82-84439. 1982. 10.95 (ISBN 0-911802-54-1). Free Church Pubns.

Palmer, Bernard, jt. auth. see Dunn, Jerry G.

Palmer, C. Eddie, ed. see Chalfant, Paul H. & Beckley, Robert E.

Palmer, Cynthia, ed. see Huxley, Aldous.

Palmer, David S. In Search of Cumorah: New Evidences for the Book of Mormon from Ancient Mexico. LC 80-83866. (Illus.). 300p. 1981. 10.95 (ISBN 0-88290-169-9, 1063). Horizon Utah.

Palmer, E. H., ed. The Quran. (Sacred Books of the East: Vols. 6, 9). both vols. 30.00 (ISBN 0-686-97479-4); 15.00 ea. Asian Human Pr.

Palmer, E. H., ed. see Conder, Claude R.

Palmer, Earl. First & Second Thessalonians: A Good News Commentary. LC 82-48409. (Good News Commentary Ser.). 128p. (Orig.). 1983. pap. 6.95 (ISBN 0-06-066455-X, RD426, HarpR). Har-Row.

--In Search of a Faith That Works. LC 85-18421. (In Search of Ser.). 140p. 1985. write for info. (ISBN 0-8307-0889-8, 5110509). Regal.

Palmer, Earl F. The Intimate Gospel: Studies in John. 1978. pap. 5.95 (ISBN 0-8499-2941-5). Word Bks.

--Old Law New Life: Ten Commandments & New Testament Faith. 128p. (Orig.). 1984. pap. 7.95 (ISBN 0-687-28744-8). Abingdon.

Palmer, Edward H. The Desert of the Exodus: Journeys on Foot in the Wilderness of the Forty Years Wanderings, 2 vols. in one. Davis, Moshe, ed. (America & the Holy Land Ser.). (Illus.). lib. bdg. 51.00x (ISBN 0-405-10276-3). Ayer Co Pubs.

Palmer, Edwin H. Doctrinas Claves. 2.95 (ISBN 0-85151-407-3). Banner of Truth.

--Five Points of Calvinism: A Study Guide. 1972. pap. 4.95 (ISBN 0-8010-6926-2). Baker Bk.

--The Holy Spirit: His Person & Ministry. 200p. (Orig.). 1985. pap. 5.95 (ISBN 0-87552-367-6). Presby & Reformed.

Palmer, G. E. & Sherrard, Philip, trs. The Philokalia, Vol. 1: The Complete Text Compiled By St. Nikodimos of the Holy Mountain & St. Markarios of Corinth, Vol. 1. 384p. 1983. pap. 10.95 (ISBN 0-571-13013-5). Faber & Faber.

Palmer, G. E., tr. see Kadloubowsky, E.

Palmer, G. E., et al, eds. The Philokalia, Vol. 2: The Complete Text. 408p. 1981. 30.00 (ISBN 0-571-11725-2). Faber & Faber.

Palmer, Gordon. By Freedom's Holy Light. 1964. 9.95 (ISBN 0-8159-5110-8). Devin.

Palmer, Humphrey. Presupposition & Transcendental Inference. LC 84-18384. 108p. 1985. 27.50 (ISBN 0-312-64173-7). St Martin.

Palmer, Jerry. One God. (Contemporary Poets of Dorrance Ser.). 88p. 1981. 4.95 (ISBN 0-8059-2789-1). Dorrance.

Palmer, John M. Equipping for Ministry. LC 85-80220. 88p. (Orig.). 1985. pap. cancelled (ISBN 0-88243-802-6, 02-0802). Gospel Pub.

Palmer, King, jt. auth. see Rhys, Stephen.

Palmer, M. D. Henry VIII. 2nd ed. (Seminar Studies in History Ser.). (Illus.). 1983. pap. text ed. 6.95x (ISBN 0-582-35437-4). Longman.

Palmer, Marjorie. God Helps David. (My Bible Story Reader Ser.: Vol. 1). (Illus.). 1983. pap. 1.95 (ISBN 0-8024-0191-0). Moody.

Palmer, Marjorie, jt. auth. see Palmer, Bernard.

Palmer, Martin. Faiths & Festivals. (Ward Lock Educational Ser.). 25.00x (ISBN 0-7062-4293-9, Pub. by Ward Lock Educ Co Ltd). State Mutual Bk.

Palmer, Martin, tr. from Chinese. T'ung Shu. LC 85-2520. (Illus.). 240p. 1986. pap. 7.95 (ISBN 0-87773-346-5, 74221-4, Dist. by Random). Shambhala Pubns.

Palmer, Melba P. Are You Ready? 81p. (Orig.). 1984. pap. 7.95 (ISBN 0-942494-88-1). Coleman Pub.

Palmer, Michael. Paul Tillich's Philosophy of Art. LC 83-15056. (Theologische Bibliothek Toepelmann Ser.: Vol. 41). xxii, 217p. 1983. 49.50x (ISBN 3-11-009681-1). De Gruyter.

Palmer, Nehemiah M. Understanding Yourself, Society & Marriage. 288p. 1984. pap. 7.95 (ISBN 0-912315-82-2). Word Aflame.

Palmer, Otto. Rudolf Steiner on His Book, The Philosophy of Freedom. Spock, Marjorie, tr. from Ger. 1975. 4.50 (ISBN 0-910142-68-8). Anthroposophic.

Palmer, Parker J. The Company of Strangers: Christians & the Renewal of America's Public Life. 176p. 1983. pap. 7.95 (ISBN 0-8245-0601-4). Crossroad NY.

--In the Belly of a Paradox: The Thought of Thomas Merton. LC 78-71769. 1979. pap. 2.50x (ISBN 0-87574-224-6). Pendle Hill.

--A Place Called Community. LC 77-75909. (Orig.). 1977. pap. 2.50x (ISBN 0-87574-212-2). Pendle Hill.

--The Promise of Paradox. LC 80-68134. 128p. (Orig.). 1980. pap. 3.95 (ISBN 0-87793-210-7). Ave Maria.
Palmer, Phobe. Entire Devotion to God. 2.95 (ISBN 0-686-27774-0). Schmul Pub Co.
--Full Salvation. pap. 4.95 (ISBN 0-686-27772-4). Schmul Pub Co.
Palmer, Phoebe. The Devotional Writings of Phoebe Palmer. Dayton, Donald W., ed. (The Higher Christian Life Ser.). 640p. 1985. 80.00 (ISBN 0-8240-6431-3). Garland Pub.
--The Promise of the Father. Dayton, Donald W., ed. (The Higher Christian Life Ser.). 421p. 1985. 50.00 (ISBN 0-8240-6434-8). Garland Pub.
Palmer, Phoebe & Wheatley, Richard. The Life & Letters of Mrs. Phoebe Palmer. Dayton, Donald W., ed. (The Higher Christian Life Ser.). 636p. 1985. 80.00 (ISBN 0-8240-6432-1). Garland Pub.
Palmer, Phoebe & Dayton, Donald W., eds. Pioneer Experiences. (The Higher Christian Life Ser.). 368p. 1985. 45.00 (ISBN 0-8240-6433-X). Garland Pub.
Palmer, Richard E. Hermeneutics: Interpretation Theory in Schleiermacher, Dilthey, Heidegger, & Gadamer. LC 68-54885. (Studies in Phenomenology & Existential Philosophy). 1969. 22.95 (ISBN 0-8101-0027-4); pap. 9.95 (ISBN 0-8101-0459-8). Northwestern U Pr.
Palmer, Richard F. & Butler, Karl D. Brigham Young: The New York Years. Alexander, Thomas G. & Christy, Howard A., eds. (Charles Redd Monographs in Western History: No. 14). (Illus.). 106p. 1982. 9.95 (ISBN 0-941214-07-9, Dist. by Signature Bks). C Redd Ctr.
Palmer, Robert B., tr. see Otto, Walter F.
Palmer, Robert E. Roman Religion & Roman Empire: Five Essays. LC 73-89289. (Haney Foundation Ser.: No. 15). Repr. of 1974 ed. 36.40 (2055281). Bks Demand UMI.
Palmer, Spencer J. Confucian Rituals in Korea. (Religions of Asia Ser.). (Illus.). 270p. 1984. 30.00 (ISBN 0-89581-457-9). Asian Human Pr.
Palmer, Spencer W. The Expanding Church. LC 78-26082. 1979. 6.95 (ISBN 0-87747-732-9). Deseret Bk.
Palmer, W. Robert. How to Understand the Bible. 2nd ed. 118p. 1980. pap. 3.95 (ISBN 0-89900-140-8). College Pr Pub.
Palmour, Jody. On Moral Character: A Practical Guide to Aristotle's Virtues & Vices. 350p. (Orig.). 1986. 29.00 (ISBN 0-9616203-1-5); pap. 18.00 (ISBN 0-9616203-0-7). Archon Inst Leader Dev.
Palms. First Things First. 1983. 5.95 (ISBN 0-88207-290-0). Victor Bks.
Palms, Roger C. God Guides Your Tomorrows. Rev. ed. LC 86-27688. 96p. 1987. pap. 2.95 (ISBN 0-87784-572-7). Inter Varsity.
--Living on the Mountain. 288p. 1985. 11.95 (ISBN 0-8007-1449-0). Revell.
Palomeque, Carmen, tr. see Bender, Harold S. & Horsch, John.
Palotta, Joseph L. That Your Joy Might Be Full. 247p. 1981. pap. 6.95 (ISBN 0-9604852-1-X). Revelation Hse.
--True Riches. 319p. (Orig.). 1985. pap. 8.95 (ISBN 0-9604852-2-8). Revelation Hse.
Paloutzian, Raymond F. Invitation to the Psychology of Religion. 1983. pap. text ed. 13.50x (ISBN 0-673-15343-6). Scott F.
Pals, Daniel L. The Victorian "Lives" of Jesus. LC 82-81018. (Trinity University Monograph Series in Religion). 225p. 1982. 20.00 (ISBN 0-911536-95-7). Trinity U Pr.
Palsson, Hermann, tr. Hrafnkel's Saga. (Classics Ser). 1971. pap. 4.95 (ISBN 0-14-044238-3). Penguin.
Palsson, Mary D., jt. ed. see Dinnerstein, Leonard.
Panagopoulos, Beata K. Cistercian & Mendicant Monasteries in Medieval Greece. LC 78-10769. (Illus.). 1979. lib. bdg. 24.00x (ISBN 0-226-64544-4). U of Chicago Pr.
Pancheri, Francesco S. The Universal Primacy of Christ. Carol, Juniper B., tr. from Italian. Orig. Title: Il Primato universale de Christo. 144p. (Orig.). 1984. pap. 6.95 (ISBN 0-931888-16-6). Christendom Pubns.
Panciatichi, Ermenegildo. The Stations of the Cross of Our Lord & Master Jesus Christ. (Illus.). 156p. 1987. 88.85 (ISBN 0-86650-211-4). Gloucester Art.
Panda, Sadhu C. Naga Cult in Orissa. xx, 142p. 1986. text ed. 30.00x (ISBN 81-7018-356-1, Pub. by B. R. Pub Corp Delhi). Apt Bks.
Pande, G. C. Studies in the Origin of Buddhism. 2nd rev. ed. 1974. 30.00 (ISBN 0-8426-0547-9). Orient Bk Dist.
Pandey, Raj B. Hindu Sanskaras. 1976. Repr. 25.00 (ISBN 0-8426-0853-2). Orient Bk Dist.
Pandeya, R. C. Buddhist Studies in India. 1975. 12.50 (ISBN 0-8426-0806-0). Orient Bk Dist.
Pandit, M. P. Aditi & Other Deities in the Veda. 1979. 3.95 (ISBN 0-941524-01-9). Lotus Light.
--Dhyana. 1979. pap. 1.95 (ISBN 0-941524-03-5). Lotus Light.
--Dynamics of Yoga, Vol. I. 182p. 1979. 9.95 (ISBN 0-941524-05-1). Lotus Light.
--Dynamics of Yoga, Vol. II. 1979. 9.95 (ISBN 0-941524-06-X). Lotus Light.
--Dynamics of Yoga, Vol. III. 164p. 1980. 10.95 (ISBN 0-941524-07-8). Lotus Light.
--Kundalini Yoga. LC 79-88734. 1979. 4.95 (ISBN 0-89744-004-8); pap. 3.00 (ISBN 0-89744-005-6). Auromere.
--Kundalini Yoga. pap. 3.00 (ISBN 0-89744-106-0). Auromere.
--Lights on the Tantra. 3.95 (ISBN 0-89744-107-9, Pub. by Ganesh & Co. India). Auromere.
--More on Tantras. 152p. 1986. text ed. 22.50x (ISBN 81-207-0122-4, Pub. by Sterling Pubs India). Apt Bks.
--Mystic Approach to the Veda & the Upanishad. 4.25 (ISBN 0-89744-108-7, Pub. by Ganesh & Co. India). Auromere.
--Sadhana in Sri Aurobindo's Yoga. LC 78-59851. 1978. pap. 3.95 (ISBN 0-89744-000-5, Pub. by Atmaniketan Ashram). Auromere.
--Satsang. Golikhere, Vasanti R., ed. (Vol. I). 298p. (Orig.). 1979. pap. 11.00 (ISBN 0-941524-10-8). Lotus Light.
--Studies in the Tantras & the Veda. 1973. 3.95 (ISBN 0-89744-110-9, Pub. by Ganesh & Co India). Auromere.
--The Teaching of Sri Aurobindo. (Illus., Orig.). 1978. pap. 3.50 (ISBN 0-89744-982-7, Pub. by Bharatiya Vidya Bhavan India). Auromere.
--The Upanisads: Gateways of Knowledge. 2nd ed. 1968. 4.00 (ISBN 0-89744-111-7, Pub. by Ganesh & Co. India). Auromere.
--Yoga for the Modern Man. 115p. 1979. 4.00 (ISBN 0-941524-13-2). Lotus Light.
--The Yoga of Knowledge. LC 79-88735. (Talks at Centre Ser.: Vol. II). 1979. pap. 5.95 (ISBN 0-89744-003-X). Auromere.
--The Yoga of Knowledge: Talks at Centre, Vol. II. LC 86-80692. 282p. (Orig.). 1986. pap. 7.95 (ISBN 0-941524-23-X). Lotus Light.
--The Yoga of Works: Talks at Centre I. LC 85-50695. 192p. 1985. pap. 7.95 (ISBN 0-941524-21-3). Lotus Light.
Pandit, M. P., ed. Gems from the Tantras, 2nd Series. 1971. 3.95 (ISBN 0-89744-103-6, Pub. by Ganesh & Co. India). Auromere.
--Gems from the Veda. Aurobindo, Sri, tr. 102p. 1974. 3.95 (ISBN 0-89744-104-4, Pub. by Ganesh & Co. India). Auromere.
Pandit, M. P., tr. see Parasurama.
Pandit, Madhav P. The Yoga of Love. LC 81-86373. (Talks at Center Ser.: Vol. III). 112p. (Orig.). 1982. pap. 3.95 (ISBN 0-941524-16-7). Lotus Light.
--Yoga of Self-Perfection. LC 83-81299. (Talks at Centre Ser.: Vol. IV). 312p. (Orig.). 1983. pap. 7.95 (ISBN 0-941524-20-5). Lotus Light.
Pandit, Sakya, jt. auth. see Nagarjuna.
Pandit, Sri M. Japa. 41p. 1979. Repr. of 1959 ed. 1.95 (ISBN 0-941524-09-4). Lotus Light.
--Yoga in Sri Aurobindo's Epic Savitri. 236p. 1979. 7.95 (ISBN 0-941524-15-9). Lotus Light.
Pandit, Sri M., ed. see Aurobindo, Sri.
Pandurangarao, Malyala. Consecration of Idols. (Illus.). 32p. (Orig.). 1984. pap. 2.00x (ISBN 0-938924-21-4). Sri Shirdi Sai.
--Hanumaan Chaaleesa. (Illus.). 16p. (Orig.). 1984. pap. 2.00x (ISBN 0-317-07665-5). Sri Shirdi Sai.
Pandurangarao Malyaya. Model Building of Solar Systems. (Worship Technology Around the World Ser.: No. 1). Orig. Title: Sri Satyanarayana Katha. (Illus.). 100p. (Orig.). 1981. 9.99 (ISBN 0-938924-00-1). Sri Shirdi Sai.
Pang, Chia S. & Hock, Goh E. T'ai Chi: Ten Minutes to Health. LC 85-22388. (Illus.). 131p. (Orig.). 1986. pap. 12.95 (ISBN 0-916360-30-X). CRCS Pubns NV.
Pangborn, Cyrus R. Zoroastrianism. 178p. 1982. text ed. 15.95x (ISBN 0-89891-006-4). Advent NY.
Pang Jeng Lo, Benjamin, tr. see Chen Wei-Ming.
Pangrazzi, Arnaldo. Your Words in Prayer in Time of Illness. 72p. (Orig.). 1982. pap. 1.25 (ISBN 0-8189-0417-8). Alba.
Panichas, George A. The Reverent Discipline: Essays in Literary Criticism & Culture. LC 73-15749. 488p. 1974. 29.95x (ISBN 0-87049-149-0). U of Tenn Pr.
Panico, Edward J., ed. see Tixeront, J.
Panikkar, Raimundo. Intrareligious Dialogue. LC 78-58962. 136p. 1978. 6.95 (ISBN 0-8091-2728-8). Paulist Pr.
--Mantramanjari: An Anthology of the Veclas for Modern Man & Contemporary Celebration. 1977. 55.00x (ISBN 0-520-02854-6). U of Cal Pr.
--Myth, Faith & Hermeneutics: Toward Cross-Cultural Religious Understanding. LC 77-99306. 528p. 1980. 22.95 (ISBN 0-8091-0232-3). Paulist Pr.
--The Trinity & the Religious Experience of Man: Icon, Person, Mystery. LC 73-77329. pap. 24.50 (ISBN 0-317-26668-3, 2025122). Bks Demand UMI.
--The Unknown Christ of Hinduism. LC 81-2886. 208p. (Orig.). 1981. pap. 7.95 (ISBN 0-88344-523-9). Orbis Bks.
--Worship & Secular Man: An Essay on the Liturgical Nature of Man. LC 72-93339. pap. 29.80 (ISBN 0-317-26670-5, 2025123). Bks Demand UMI.
Panikkar, Raimundo, et al. Blessed Simplicity: The Monk as Universal Archetype. 224p. (Orig.). 1982. 17.95 (ISBN 0-8164-0531-X, HarpR). Har-Row.
Panitz, Esther L. The Alien in Their Midst: Image of Jews in English Literature. LC 78-75183. 192p. 1981. 20.00 (ISBN 0-8386-2318-2). Fairleigh Dickinson.
Pankey, William R. Edge of Paradise: Fifty Years in the Pulpit. 1972. 7.00 (ISBN 0-87012-111-1). McClain.
Pankiewicz, Tadeusz. The Cracow Ghetto Pharmacy. 1987. 16.95 (ISBN 0-89604-114-X); pap. 10.95 (ISBN 0-89604-115-8). Holocaust Pubns.
Panko, Stephen M. Martin Buber. Patterson, Bob E., ed. LC 76-2869. (Markers of the Modern Theological Mind Ser.). 1976. 8.95 (ISBN 0-87680-470-9, 80470). Word Bks.
Pannabecker, Samuel F. Open Doors. LC 75-9417. (Mennonite Historical Ser.). (Illus.). 432p. 1975. 18.50 (ISBN 0-87303-636-0). Faith & Life.
Pannell, Alastair D., tr. see Bucaille, Maurice.
Pannenberg, Wolfhart. Anthropology in Theological Perspective. O'Connell, Matthew J., tr. from German. LC 84-22048. 552p. 1985. 38.95 (ISBN 0-664-21399-5). Westminster.
--Basic Questions in Theology: Collected Essays, Vol. I. LC 82-15984. 256p. 1983. pap. 12.95 (ISBN 0-664-24466-1). Westminster.
--Basic Questions in Theology: Collected Essays, Vol. II. LC 82-15984. 258p. 1983. pap. 12.95 (ISBN 0-664-24467-X). Westminster.
--Christian Spirituality. LC 83-19662. 114p. (Orig.). 1983. pap. 8.95 (ISBN 0-664-24495-5). Westminster.
--The Church. Crim, Keith, tr. LC 82-23768. 176p. 1983. pap. 10.95 (ISBN 0-664-24460-2). Westminster.
--Ethics. Crim, Keith, tr. from Ger. LC 81-13051. Orig. Title: Ethik und Ekklesiologie. 222p. 1981. pap. 10.95 (ISBN 0-664-24392-4). Westminster.
--Faith & Reality. LC 77-682. 148p. 1977. softcover 6.50 (ISBN 0-664-24755-5). Westminster.
--The Idea of God & Human Freedom. LC 73-3165. 224p. 1973. 6.95 (ISBN 0-664-20971-8). Westminster.
--Jesus: God & Man. 2nd ed. Wilkins, Lewis L. & Priebe, Duane A., trs. LC 76-26478. 428p. 1982. pap. 13.95 (ISBN 0-664-24468-8). Westminster.
--Theology & the Kingdom of God. LC 69-12668. 144p. 1969. pap. 5.95 (ISBN 0-664-24842-X). Westminster.
--Theology & the Philosophy of Science. McDonagh, Francis, tr. LC 76-20763. 464p. 1976. 17.50 (ISBN 0-664-21337-5). Westminster.
Panniker, Raimundo. The Vedic Experience. 937p. 1983. 28.50 (ISBN 0-89744-011-0). Auromere.
Panning, Armin J. The Life of Christ. 1971. pap. 2.50 (ISBN 0-8100-0018-0, 09-0932). Northwest Pub.
Panofsky, Erwin. Gothic Architecture & Scholasticism. (Illus.). pap. 7.95 (ISBN 0-452-00834-4, Mer). NAL.
Panorelli, Dora. The Ultimate Relationship. 1985. 8.95 (ISBN 0-8062-2454-1). Carlton.
Panos, Chris. Double Agent. 1986. pap. 6.95 (ISBN 0-910311-43-9). Huntington Hse Inc.
Pantazopoulos, N. J. Church & Law in the Balkan Peninsula during the Ottoman Rule. (Illus.). 125p. 1983. pap. text ed. 24.00 (Pub. by A M Hakkert). Coronet Bks.
Pantin, W. A. The English Church in the Fourteenth Century. (Medieval Academy Reprints for Teaching Ser.). 1980. pap. 6.50 (ISBN 0-8020-6411-6). U of Toronto Pr.
Panzarella, Andrew. Religion & Human Experience. LC 73-87024. 1974. pap. 5.20x (ISBN 0-88489-058-9); tchr's. guide 3.00x (ISBN 0-88489-080-5). St Marys.
Panzion, Leo. The Pleasures of Being a Catholic. new ed. (Human Development Library Bk.). (Illus.). 1979. Set. 49.75 (ISBN 0-89266-155-0). Am Classical Coll Pr.
Paola, Tomie De see De Paola, Tomie.
Paola, Tomie de see De Paola, Tomie.
Paola, Tomie De see De Paola, Tomie.
Paoli, Arturo. Freedom to Be Free. Quinn, Charles U., tr. from It. LC 72-93340. Tr. of Dialogo Della Liberazione. 320p. (Orig.). 1973. pap. 2.48 (ISBN 0-88344-143-8). Orbis Bks.
--Gather Together in My Name: Reflections on Christianity & Community. Barr, Robert R., tr. LC 86-23806. 144p. (Orig.). 1987. pap. 9.95 (ISBN 0-88344-357-0). Orbis Bks.
Paolucci, Henry. Zionism, the Superpowers, & the P.L.O. LC 82-15728. 80p. 1982. pap. 7.95 (ISBN 0-918680-18-2, GHGP 708). Griffon Hse.
Paolucci, Henry, ed. see Saint Augustine.
Paone, Anthony J. My Life with Christ. LC 62-17359. 1962. pap. 4.95 (ISBN 0-385-03361-3, D185, Im). Doubleday.
Papadopoullos, Theodore H. Studies & Documents Relating to the History of the Greek Church & People Under Turkish Domination. LC 78-38759. Repr. of 1952 ed. 27.50 (ISBN 0-404-56314-7). AMS Pr.
Papadopoulos, Gerasimos. Orthodoxy, Faith & Life: Christ & the Church. 151p. 1981. 10.95 (ISBN 0-916586-48-0); pap. 5.95 (ISBN 0-916586-47-2). Holy Cross Orthodox.
--Orthodoxy, Faith & Life: Christ in the Gospels, Vol. 1. 164p. 1980. 9.50 (ISBN 0-916586-38-3); pap. 4.95 (ISBN 0-916586-37-5). Holy Cross Orthodox.
Papadopulos, Leonidas, et al, trs. see St. Nectarios Press.
Papadopulos, Leonidas J. & Lizardos, Georgia, trs. from Gr. The Life & Sufferings of Saint Catherine the Great Martyr. (Illus.). 1986. pap. 3.00 (ISBN 0-913026-63-8). St Nectarios.
Papajohn, J. C., jt. auth. see Moskos, C. C., Jr.
Papasogli, Giorgio. St. Teresa of Avila. LC 58-12223. 1973. Repr. 5.00 (ISBN 0-8198-0511-4). Dghtrs St Paul.
Pape, Donna L. & Mueller, Virginia. Bible Activities for Kids, No. 2. (Illus.). 60p. (Orig.). 1980. pap. 1.95 (ISBN 0-87123-149-2, 21049). Bethany Hse.
Pape, Donna L., et al. Bible Activities for Kids, No. 1. (Illus.). 64p. (Orig.). 1980. pap. 1.95 (ISBN 0-87123-148-4, 210148). Bethany Hse.
--Bible Activities for Kids, No. 3. (Illus.). 63p. (Orig.). 1981. pap. 1.95 (ISBN 0-87123-172-7, 210172). Bethany Hse.
--Bible Activities for Kids, No. 4. (Illus.). 59p. 1981. pap. 1.95 (ISBN 0-87123-173-5, 210173). Bethany Hse.
Papers Presented at the Conference, Convened by the American Jewish Historical Society & the Theodor Herzl Foundation in New York City, December 26-27,1955. Early History of Zionism in America: Proceedings. LC 77-70725. (America & the Holy Land Ser.). 1977. Repr. of 1958 ed. lib. bdg. 26.50x (ISBN 0-405-10268-2). Ayer Co Pubs.
Pappas, George S. & Swain, Marshall, eds. Essays on Knowledge & Justification. LC 77-10299. (Illus.). 384p. 1978. 42.50x (ISBN 0-8014-1086-X); pap. 10.95x (ISBN 0-8014-9865-1). Cornell U Pr.
Pappas, Michael G. Sweet Dreams for Little Ones. (Illus.). 64p. (Orig.). 1982. pap. 6.95 (ISBN 0-86683-641-1, AY8156, HarpR). Har-Row.
Papus. The Qabalah. 1977. pap. 12.95 (ISBN 0-85030-340-0). Weiser.
Paquet, jt. auth. see Carr.
Para Research. World Ephemeris for the Twentieth Century. 1983. Midnight calculations. pap. 12.95 (ISBN 0-914918-60-5); Noon calculations. pap. 12.95 (ISBN 0-914918-61-3). Para Res.
Paracelsus. Coelum Philosophorum: Or the Book of Vexations. Waite, A. E., tr. from Lat. pap. 2.95 (ISBN 0-916411-13-3, Pub. by Alchemical Pr). Holmes Pub.
Paradis, Lenora F. Hospice Handbook: A Guide for Managers & Planners. 420p. 1985. 46.50 (ISBN 0-87189-104-2). Aspen Pub.
Paradise, Valdemar. Preserving One's Own Life. 160p. 1986. 9.95 (ISBN 0-8059-3035-3). Dorrance.
Paramananda, Swami. Book of Daily Thoughts & Prayers. 1977. 9.50 (ISBN 0-911564-01-2); soft lexotone bdg. 7.50 (ISBN 0-911564-32-2). Vedanta Ctr.
--Christ & Oriental Ideals. 4th ed. 1968. 4.50 (ISBN 0-911564-14-4). Vedanta Ctr.
--Concentration & Meditation. 8th ed. 1974. pap. 3.50 (ISBN 0-911564-07-1). Vedanta Ctr.
--Emerson & Vedanta. 2nd ed. 1985. pap. 3.50 (ISBN 0-911564-13-6). Vedanta Ctr.
--Faith is Power. 2nd ed. Orig. Title: Faith as Constructive Force. 1961. 4.50 (ISBN 0-911564-09-8). Vedanta Ctr.
--Plato & Vedic Idealism. (Orig.). 1924. 4.50 (ISBN 0-911564-15-2). Vedanta Ctr.
--Principles & Purposes of Vedanta. 8th ed. 1937. pap. 1.00 (ISBN 0-911564-30-6). Vedanta Ctr.
--Reincarnation & Immortality. 2nd ed. 1961. 4.50 (ISBN 0-911564-05-5). Vedanta Ctr.
--Right Resolutions. 2nd ed. 1981. pap. 1.00 (ISBN 0-911564-29-2). Vedanta Ctr.
--Science & Practice of Yoga. 1918. pap. 0.50 (ISBN 0-911564-31-4). Vedanta Ctr.
--Silence as Yoga. 4th ed. 1974. pap. 3.50 (ISBN 0-911564-11-X). Vedanta Ctr.
--Spiritual Healing. 4th ed. 1975. pap. 3.50 (ISBN 0-911564-10-1). Vedanta Ctr.

--Srimad-Bhagavad-Gita. 7th ed. Orig. Title: Bhagavad-Gita, Srimad. 1981. 5.75 (ISBN 0-911564-03-9); lexitone bdg. 3.50. Vedanta Ctr.

--Vedanta in Practice. 3rd ed. 1985. pap. 3.50 (ISBN 0-911564-04-7). Vedanta Ctr.

--Way of Peace & Blessedness. 3rd ed. 1961. 4.50 (ISBN 0-911564-06-3). Vedanta Ctr.

Paramhansa, Yogananda. Sermon on the Mount Interpreted by Paramhansa Yogananada. LC 79-91531. 1980. pap. 8.95 (ISBN 0-937134-01-5). Amrita Found.

Paranjpe, V. G., tr. see Bergaigne, Abel.

Parasurama. Bases of Tantra Sadhana. Pandit, M. P., tr. (Sanskrit.). 52p. 1980. 2.00 (ISBN 0-941524-02-7). Lotus Light.

Parbury, Kathleen. Women of Grace: A Biographical Dictionary of British Women Saints, Martyrs & Reformers. 224p. 1985. 25.00x (ISBN 0-85362-213-2, Oriel). Methuen Inc.

Pardington, G. P. Studies in Christian Doctrine, 4 Vols. Freligh, H. M. & Schroeder, E. H., eds. 312p. 1964. pap. 1.95 ea. Vol. 1 (ISBN 0-87509-135-0). Vol. 2 (ISBN 0-87509-136-9). Vol. 3 (ISBN 0-87509-137-7). Vol. 4 (ISBN 0-87509-138-5). Chr Pubns.

--Twenty-Five Wonderful Years, Eighteen Eighty-Nine to Nineteen Fourteen: A Popular Sketch of the Christian & Missionary Alliance. Dayton, Donald W., ed. (The Higher Christian Life Ser.). 238p. 1985. 30.00 (ISBN 0-8240-6435-6). Garland Pub.

Pardington, George P. Outline Studies in Christian Doctrine. pap. 5.95 (ISBN 0-87509-116-4). Chr Pubns.

Pare, George. The Catholic Church in Detroit, 1701-1888. LC 83-67420. 733p. 1983. pap. 19.05x (ISBN 0-8143-1758-8). Wayne St U Pr.

Paredi, Angela. Saint Ambrose: His Life & Times. LC 63-19325. pap. 123.80 (ISBN 0-317-26143-6, 2024372). Bks Demand UMI.

Paregien, Stan. Twenty-Six Lessons on the Gospel of John. (Bible Student Study Guides Ser.). 1977. pap. 3.95 (ISBN 0-89900-152-1). College Pr Pub.

Paregien, Stanley. The Day Jesus Died. 1970. 3.00 (ISBN 0-88027-004-7). Firm Foun Pub.

Parent, Neil, ed. Christian Adulthood Nineteen Eighty-Seven. Date not set. pap. price not set (ISBN 1-55586-106-7). US Catholic.

Parent, Neil A., ed. Adult Learning & the Parish. 144p. 1985. pap. 6.95 (ISBN 0-697-02063-0). Wm C Brown.

--Christian Adulthood. 125p. 1985. pap. 6.95 (ISBN 1-55586-921-1). US Catholic.

--Christian Adulthood 1982. 130p. 1982. pap. 5.95 (ISBN 1-55586-827-4). US Catholic.

--Christian Adulthood 1983. 68p. 1983. pap. 4.95 (ISBN 1-55586-862-2). US Catholic.

--Christian Adulthood 1985-1986. 124p. 1985. pap. 8.95 (ISBN 1-55586-965-3). US Catholic.

--Serving Life & Faith: Adult Religious Education & the American Catholic Community. 72p. 1986. pap. 6.95 (ISBN 1-55586-982-3). US Catholic.

Parent, William, ed. & pref. by see Thomson, Judith J.

Parente, Pascal P. Beyond Space. 1977. pap. 4.50 (ISBN 0-89555-053-9). TAN Bks Pubs.

--City on a Mountain - Padre Pio. Orig. Title: Padre Pio. 154p. 1968. pap. 3.50 (ISBN 0-911988-35-1). AMI Pr.

Parfitt, Tudor. Operation Moses: The Untold Story of the Secret Exodus of the Falasha Jews from Ethiopia. LC 85-40240. (Illus.). 192p. 1986. 16.95 (ISBN 0-8128-3059-8). Stein & Day.

Parfitt, Tudor, jt. ed. see Abramson, Glenda.

Pargoire, Jules. Eglise Byzantine De 527 a 847. 1971. Repr. of 1905 ed. lib. bdg. 26.00 (ISBN 0-8337-2672-2). B Franklin.

Parham, Charles F. & Parham, Sarah E. The Life of Charles F. Parham, Founder of the Apostolic Faith Movement. (The Higher Christian Life Ser.). 468p. 1985. lib. bdg. 60.00 (ISBN 0-8240-6436-4). Garland Pub.

Parham, Sarah E., jt. auth. see Parham, Charles F.

Parihar, Subhash. Muslim Inscriptions in the Punjab, Haryana & Himachal Pradesh. (Illus.). 79p. 1986. text ed. 40.00x (ISBN 81-210-0017-3, Pub. by Inter India Pubns N Delhi). Apt Bks.

Parikh, Narahari D., ed. see Gandhi, Mohandas K.

Parimal, Ma P., ed. see Rajneesh, Bhagwan S.

Paris, Andrew. What the Bible Says about the Lords's Supper. LC 86-71103. (What the Bible Says Ser.). text ed. 13.95 (ISBN 0-89900-253-6). College Pr Pub.

Paris, Arthur E. Black Pentecostalism: Southern Religion in an Urban World. LC 81-16169. 192p. 1982. lib. bdg. 17.50x (ISBN 0-87023-353-X). U of Mass Pr.

Paris, Edmond. The Secret History of the Jesuits. rev. ed. 208p. 1982. pap. 5.95 (ISBN 0-937958-10-7). Chick Pubns.

Paris, Gaston, ed. see Guillaume De Berneville.

Paris, Ginette. Pagan Meditations: The Worlds of Aphrodite, Artemis, & Hestia. Moore, Gwendolyn, tr. from Fr. LC 86-6675. 204p. (Orig.). 1986. pap. 13.50 (ISBN 0-88214-330-1). Spring Pubns.

Paris, Howard. Clip-Art Panel Cartoons for Churches 2. 96p. 1987. pap. 4.95 (ISBN 0-8010-7098-8). Baker Bk.

Paris, Janelle A. Planning Bulletin Boards for Church & Synagogue Libraries. LC 83-7331. (CSLA Guide Two Ser. No. 11). (Orig.). 1983. pap. 6.95 (ISBN 0-915324-20-2); pap. 5.50 members. CSLA.

Paris, Paulin, ed. see De Villehardouin, Geoffroi.

Paris, Peter J. The Social Teaching of the Black Churches. LC 84-47930. 176p. 1985. pap. 8.95 (ISBN 0-8006-1805-X, 1-1805). Fortress.

Parish, Elijah, jt. auth. see M'Clure, David.

Parish, Peggy. December Decorations: A Holiday How-to Book. LC 75-14285. (Illus.). 64p. 1975. 9.95 (ISBN 0-02-769920-X). Macmillan.

Paritzky, Karen, tr. see Ehrmann, Naftali H.

Paritzky, Karen, tr. see Hirsch, Samson R.

Paritzky-Joshua, Karin, tr. see Hirsch, Sampson R.

Park, Edwards A. Selected Essays. Kuklick, Bruce, ed. (American Religious Thought of the 18th & 19th Centuries Ser.). 367p. 1987. lib. bdg. 55.00 (ISBN 0-8240-6957-9). Garland Pub.

Park, James. The Existential Christian, No. 1. (Existential Freedom Ser. No. 1). 1970. pap. 1.00x (ISBN 0-89231-001-4). Existential Bks.

--The Existential Christian, No. 2. (Existential Freedom Ser.: No. 2). 1971. pap. 5.00x (ISBN 0-89231-002-2). Existential Bks.

--An Existential Interpretation of Paul's Letters to the Romans. LC 83-8852. 1983. pap. 4.00x (ISBN 0-89231-200-9). Existential Bks.

Park, O'Hyun, tr. Essentials of Zen Buddhism. 143p. 1985. pap. 4.95 (ISBN 0-317-20880-2). CSA Pr.

Park, Polly, ed. To Save Their Heathen Souls: Voyage to & Life in Foochow, China, Based on Wentworth Diaries & Letters, 1854-1858. (Pittsburgh Theological Monographs: New Ser. 9). (Illus., Orig.). 1984. pap. 10.00 (ISBN 0-915138-66-2). Pickwick.

Park, Sung-Bae. Buddhist Faith & Sudden Enlightenment. LC 82-10459. 222p. 1983. 44.50x (ISBN 0-87395-673-7); pap. 12.95x (ISBN 0-87395-674-5). State U NY Pr.

Park, Thelma. The House of Neh. (Illus.). 178p. (Orig.). 1986. pap. 9.95 (ISBN 1-55630-023-9). Brentwood Comm.

Park, Willard Z. Shamanism in Western North America. LC 74-12553. 166p. 1975. Repr. of 1938 ed. lib. bdg. 22.50x (ISBN 0-8154-0497-2). Cooper Sq.

Parke, Caroline, ed. see Lodo, Venerable Larma.

Parke, Caroline M., ed. see Lodo, Venerable L.

Parke, David. The Epic of Unitarianism. 1957. pap. 3.50 (ISBN 0-933840-05-5). Unitarian Univ.

Parke, David, ed. The Right Time: The Best of Kairos. 1982. pap. 7.95 (ISBN 0-933840-13-6). Unitarian Univ.

Parke, H. W. Festivals of the Athenians. LC 76-12819. (Aspects of Greek & Roman Life Ser.). (Illus.). 288p. 1986. pap. text ed. 8.95x (ISBN 0-8014-9440-0). Cornell U Pr.

Parker, A. H., tr. see Steiner, Rudolf.

Parker, Arthur C. Seneca Myths & Folk Tales. LC 76-43803. (Buffalo Historical Society. Publication: Vol. 27). Repr. of 1923 ed. 35.00 (ISBN 0-404-15659-2). AMS Pr.

Parker, Clayton A. My Will Be Done. 201p. 1982. pap. 3.00 (ISBN 0-686-86578-2, 0-9606438). C A Parker Pubns.

Parker, D. Coffey. Feed My Sheep. (Illus.). 1983. 3.00. Harlo Pr.

Parker, De Witt. Human Values: An Interpretation of Ethics Based on a Study of Values. LC 75-3305. Repr. of 1931 ed. 42.50 (ISBN 0-404-59290-2). AMS Pr.

Parker, Diane, et al, eds. see Smith, Donald M.

Parker, Elizabeth C. The Descent from the Cross: Its Relation to the Extra-Liturgical Depositio Drama. LC 77-94713. (Outstanding Dissertations in the Fine Arts Ser.). 1978. lib. bdg. 41.00 (ISBN 0-8240-3245-4). Garland Pub.

Parker, Faye W. Mental, Physical, Spiritual Health. LC 79-56170. 80p. 1980. pap. 2.95 (ISBN 0-87516-397-1). De Vorss.

Parker, Francis H. Reason & Faith Revisited. (Aquinas Lecture 1971). 7.95 (ISBN 0-87462-136-4). Marquette.

Parker, Gail T. Mind Cure in New England: From the Civil War to World War I. LC 72-92704. 209p. 1973. 18.00x (ISBN 0-87451-073-2). U Pr of New Eng.

Parker, Gary. Life Before Birth. (Orig.). 1987. 9.95 (ISBN 0-89051-115-2); read-along cassette 5.95. Master Bks.

Parker, Gary E. From Evolution to Creation: A Personal Testimony. LC 77-78020. 1978. pap. 1.00 (ISBN 0-89051-035-0). Master Bks.

Parker, Gary E., jt. auth. see Bliss, Richard B.

Parker, George. Lexico-Concordancia del Nuevo Testamento en Griego y Espanol. (Span.). 1000p. 1982. pap. 19.95 (ISBN 0-311-42066-4). Casa Bautista.

Parker, Harold M., Jr., compiled by. Bibliography of Published Articles on American Presbyterianism, 1901-1980. LC 85-7987. (Bibliographies & Indexes in Religious Studies: No. 4). xv, 261p. 1985. lib. bdg. 37.50 (ISBN 0-313-24544-4, PBP/). Greenwood.

Parker, Helen. Light on a Dark Trail. LC 82-71560. 1982. pap. 4.95 (ISBN 0-8054-5430-6). Broadman.

Parker, Henry. The Rich & the Poor. LC 77-7419. (English Experience Ser.: No. 882). 1977. Repr. of 1493 ed. lib. bdg. 69.00 (ISBN 90-221-0882-1). Walter J Johnson.

Parker, Inez M. The Rise & Decline of the Program for Black Education in the United Presbyterian Church, U. S. A. 1865-1970. LC 76-49248. (Presbyterian Historical Ser.). 320p. 1977. 10.00 (ISBN 0-911536-66-3). Trinity U Pr.

Parker, James. The Concept of Apokatastasis in Acts: A Study in Primitive Christian Theology. 140p. 1981. pap. text ed. 5.95 (ISBN 0-931016-01-0). Schola Pr TX.

Parker, John see Duffy, John.

Parker, Joseph. Preaching Through the Bible, 14 vols. 189.50 (ISBN 0-8010-7032-5). Baker Bk.

Parker, Kenneth L. The English Sabbath: A Study of Doctrine & Practice from the Reformation to the Civil War. (Illus.). 224p. Date not set. price not set (ISBN 0-521-30535-7). Cambridge U Pr.

Parker, Lois. They of Rome. 128p. 1980. pap. 5.95 (ISBN 0-8127-0308-1). Review & Herald.

Parker, Margaret. Autobiography of God: Leader's Guide. (Study & Grow Electives). 64p. 1985. pap. 3.95 (ISBN 0-8307-1030-2, 6102058). Regal.

--Love, Acceptance & Forgiveness: Leader's Guide. LC 79-63763. 128p. 1984. pap. 3.95 (ISBN 0-8307-0989-4, 6101895). Regal.

--When You Feel Like a Failure. (Study & Grow Electives). 64p. 1985. pap. 3.95 leader's guide (ISBN 0-8307-1036-1, 6102073). Regal.

Parker, Marjorie. Bread from My Oven. (Quiet Time Bks). 128p. 1972. pap. 3.50 (ISBN 0-8024-0910-5). Moody.

Parker, Marjorie H. Fun Devotions for Kids, No. 2. 64p. 1985. pap. 2.50 (ISBN 0-87239-892-7, 2822). Standard Pub.

Parker, Mildred, jt. auth. see Allen, Charles L.

Parker, Paul E. & Enlow, David R. What's a Nice Person Like You Doing Sick? LC 74-82838. (Illus.). 80p. 1974. pap. 1.50 (ISBN 0-88419-082-X). Creation Hse.

Parker, Peggy, jt. auth. see Barrett, Ethel.

Parker, Richard B. & Sabin, Robin. The Islamic Monuments of Cairo: A Practical Guide. 3rd ed. Williams, Caroline, ed. 1986. pap. 12.50x (ISBN 977-424-036-7, Pub. by Am Univ Cairo Pr). Columbia U Pr.

Parker, Robert A. A Yankee Saint: John Humphrey Noyes & the Oneida Community. LC 75-187456. (The American Utopian Adventure Ser.). 322p. 1973. Repr. of 1935 ed. lib. bdg. 27.50x (ISBN 0-87991-009-7). Porcupine Pr.

--A Yankee Saint: John Humphrey Noyes & the Oneida Community. LC 73-2570. (Illus.). 332p. 1973. Repr. of 1935 ed. 29.50 (ISBN 0-208-01319-9, Archon). Shoe String.

Parker Society-London. Parker Society Publications, 55 Vols. Repr. of 1841 ed. Set. 2200.00 (ISBN 0-384-44880-1). Johnson Repr.

Parker, T. H. Calvin's Old Testament Commentaries. 256p. 1986. 28.95 (ISBN 0-567-09365-4, Pub. by T & T Clark Ltd UK). Fortress.

--Commentaries on Romans Fifteen Thirty-Two to Fifteen Forty-Two. 250p. 1986. 25.50 (ISBN 0-567-09366-2, Pub. by T & T Clark Ltd Uk). Fortress.

--John Calvin. Jenkins, Simon, ed. 240p. 1987. pap. 7.95 (ISBN 0-7459-1219-2). Lion USA.

--John Calvin: A Biography. LC 75-33302. (Illus.). 208p. 1976. 10.95 (ISBN 0-664-20810-X). Westminster.

Parker, T. H. see Calvin, John.

Parker, T. V. American Protestantism. 1956. 7.95 (ISBN 0-8022-1264-6). Philos Lib.

Parker, Theodore. A Discourse of Matters Pertaining to Religion. LC 72-4968. (Romantic Tradition in American Literature Ser.). 510p. 1972. Repr. of 1842 ed. 35.00 (ISBN 0-405-04639-1). Ayer Co Pubs.

--Works - Centenary Edition, 15 vols. LC 75-3307. Repr. of 1911 ed. 595.00 set (ISBN 0-404-59300-3). AMS Pr.

Parker, Thomas D., jt. ed. see Evans, Robert A.

Parker, Thomas W. The Knights Templars in England. LC 63-11983. pap. 48.80 (ISBN 0-317-08903-X, 2055370). Bks Demand UMI.

Parker, W. & St. Johns, E. Prayer Can Change Your Life. 1974. pap. 2.95 (ISBN 0-346-12137-X). Cornerstone.

Parker, William & St. Johns, Elaine. Prayer Can Change Your Life. 270p. 1983. pap. 4.95 (ISBN 0-13-694786-7, Reward). P-H.

Parker-Rhodes, Frederick. Wholesight. LC 77-95406. 30p. (Orig.). 1978. pap. 2.50x (ISBN 0-87574-217-3). Pendle Hill.

Parkes, Ellen, jt. auth. see Carlozzi, Carl G.

Parkes, Henry B. Jonathan Edwards, the Fiery Puritan. LC 75-3135. Repr. of 1930 ed. 30.00 (ISBN 0-404-59144-2). AMS Pr.

Parkes, James. Conflict of the Church & the Synagogue: A Study in the Origins of Antisemitism. LC 61-11472. (Temple Books). 1969. pap. text ed. 6.95x (ISBN 0-689-70151-9, T9). Atheneum.

Parkes, James W. Emergence of the Jewish Problem, 1878-1939. Repr. of 1946 ed. lib. bdg. 22.50x (ISBN 0-8371-2794-7, PJPR). Greenwood.

--The Jew in the Medieval Community. 456p. 1976. pap. 12.95 (ISBN 0-87203-060-1). Hermon.

Parke-Taylor, G. H. Yahweh: The Divine Name in the Bible. 134p. 1975. text ed. 14.95x (ISBN 0-88920-014-9, Pub. by Wilfrid Laurier Canada). Humanities.

Parkhill, Joe M. God Did Not Create Sickness or Disease. 160p. (Orig.). 1983. pap. text ed. 6.95 (ISBN 0-936744-05-7). Country Bazaar.

Parkhurst, Charles H. Pulpit & the Pew. 1913. 39.50x (ISBN 0-686-83717-7). Elliots Bks.

Parkhurst, G., ed. see Finney, Charles G.

Parkhurst, Genevieve. Glorious Victory Thru Healing Memories. 4.95 (ISBN 0-910924-55-4). Macalester.

--Healing & Wholeness. 6.95 (ISBN 0-910924-90-2). Macalester.

--Take a Walk with Jesus. pap. 0.40 ea. 3 for 1.00 (ISBN 0-910924-31-7). Macalester.

Parkhurst, Helen H. Cathedral: A Gothic Pilgrimage. 304p. 1980. Repr. of 1936 ed. lib. bdg. 40.00 (ISBN 0-8492-2174-9). R West.

Parkhurst, Henry M., ed. see Anti-Sabbath Convention Staff.

Parkhurst, L. B., jt. auth. see Finney, Charles G.

Parkhurst, L. G., ed. see Finney, Charles G.

Parkhurst, Louis, jt. auth. see Finney, Charles.

Parkhurst, Louis, ed. see Finney, Charles.

Parkhurst, Louis G., ed. see Finney, Charles G.

Parkhurst, Louis G., Jr., jt. auth. see Bunyan, John.

Parkhurst, Louis G., Jr., ed. see Finney, Charles G.

Parkinson, G. H., jt. auth. see Leibniz, Gottfried W.

Parkman, Francis. The Jesuits in North America. 586p. 1970. Repr. of 1895 ed. 22.50 (ISBN 0-87928-016-6). Corner Hse.

Parks, Helen J. Holding the Ropes. LC 83-70004. 156p. 1983. 6.95 (ISBN 0-8054-5194-3). Broadman.

Parks, Joyce. Single, but Not Sorry. rev. ed. 235p. 1986. pap. 3.95 (ISBN 0-89084-307-4). Bob Jones Univ Pr.

Parks, Keith H. First Things First. 2nd rev. ed. 32p. 1981. pap. 2.49 (ISBN 0-88151-012-2). Lay Leadership.

--Fishers of Men. 3rd rev. ed. 196p. 1981. pap. text ed. 17.00 (ISBN 0-88151-014-9). Lay Leadership.

--Fishers of Men: Home Study Guide. 3rd rev. ed. 64p. 1981. 8.00 (ISBN 0-88151-015-7). Lay Leadership.

--You Are Welcome. 2nd rev. ed. 32p. 1981. pap. 2.49 (ISBN 0-88151-013-0). Lay Leadership.

Parks, Sharon, jt. ed. see Dykstra, Craig.

Parlasca, Klans. Die Roemischen Mosaiken in Deutschland. (Illus.). 156p. 1970. Repr. of 1959 ed. 64.00x (ISBN 3-11-001212-X). De Gruyter.

Parlette, Ralph. The University of Hard Knocks. 1966. gift ed. 6.95 (ISBN 0-915720-05-1). Brownlow Pub Co.

Parley, Winifred A., ed. see Blavatsky, Helena P.

Parmalee, Alice. Introducing the Bible. (Epiphany Ser.). 128p. 1983. pap. 2.25 (ISBN 0-345-30575-2). Ballantine.

Parmelee, Alice. Guide to the New Testament. (All About the Bible Ser.: Bk. 3). (Illus.). 1980. pap. 5.95 (ISBN 0-8192-1255-5). Morehouse.

--Guide to the Old Testament & Apocrypha. (All About the Bible Ser.: Bk. 2). (Illus.). 1980. pap. 5.95 (ISBN 0-8192-1254-7). Morehouse.

--Highlights of the Story of Christianity, Bk. 5. LC 80-81098. (All About the Bible Ser.). 136p. (Orig.). 1980. pap. 5.95 (ISBN 0-8192-1274-1). Morehouse.

--A History of the People of Israel, Bk. 4. LC 80-81097. (All About the Bible). 148p. (Orig.). 1980. pap. 5.95 (ISBN 0-8192-1273-3). Morehouse.

--The Holy Land. LC 81-80630. (All About the Bible Ser.: Bk. 6). 136p. (Orig.). 1981. pap. 5.95 (ISBN 0-8192-1290-3). Morehouse.

--Introducing the Bible. (All About the Bible Ser.: Bk. 1). (Illus.). 1979. pap. 5.95 (ISBN 0-8192-1253-9). Morehouse.

Parmenter, Bruce. What the Bible Says about Self Esteem. LC 86-70211. (What the Bible Says Ser.). 405p. 13.95 (ISBN 0-89900-251-X). College Pr Pub.

Parmisano, Stan. Come to the Mountain: The Comtemporary Experience of Prayer. LC 86-70254. 96p. (Orig.). 1986. pap. 4.95 (ISBN 0-87793-337-5). Ave Maria.

Parot, Joseph J. Polish Catholics in Chicago, 1850-1920: A Religious History. LC 81-11297. 298p. 22.50 (ISBN 0-87580-081-5); pap. 10.00 (ISBN 0-87580-527-2). N Ill U Pr.

Parpola, Asko & Hansen, Bent S., eds. South Asian Religion & Society. (Studies on Asian Topics (Scandinavian Institute of Asian Studies): No. 11). 262p. (Orig.). 1986. pap. 18.00 (ISBN 0-913215-16-3). Riverdale Co.

Parr, Catharine. Prayers or Medytacions, Wherin the Mynde Is Styrred Patiently to Suffre All Afflictions Here. LC 76-57370. (English Experience Ser.: No. 788). 1977. Repr. of 1545 ed. PLB 6.00 (ISBN 90-221-0788-4). Walter J Johnson.

Parr, Micheal. Given & Shed for You. Sherer, Micheal L., ed. (Orig.). 1981. pap. 2.50 (ISBN 0-89536-847-1, 7806). CSS of Ohio.

Parr, Roger P. Matthieu de Vendome, ars Versificatoria. Robb, James, ed. LC 80-84768. 1981. pap. 9.95 (ISBN 0-87462-222-0). Marquette.

Parratt, Saroj Nalini. The Religion of Manipur. 1980. 13.00x (ISBN 0-8364-0594-3, Pub. by Mukhopadhyaya India). South Asia Bks.

Parrinder, Edward G. Book of World Religions. (Illus.). 1967. 12.50 (ISBN 0-7175-0443-3). Dufour.

Parrinder, Geoffrey. African Mythology. LC 85-22967. (Library of the World's Myths & Legends). (Illus.). 144p. 1986. 18.95 (ISBN 0-87226-042-9). P Bedrick Bks.

--African Traditional Religion. 3rd ed. LC 76-22490. (Illus.). 156p. 1976. Repr. of 1976 ed. lib. bdg. 25.00x (ISBN 0-8371-3401-3, PAF&, Pub. by Negro U Pr). Greenwood.

--Avatar & Incarnation. 1982. Repr. of 1970 ed. 15.95 (ISBN 0-19-520361-5). Oxford U Pr.

--Comparative Religion. LC 73-19116. 130p. 1975. Repr. of 1962 ed. lib. bdg. 45.00x (ISBN 0-8371-7301-9, PACR). Greenwood.

--A Dictionary of Non-Christian Religions. LC 73-4781. (Illus.). 320p. 1973. 10.95 (ISBN 0-664-20981-5). Westminster.

--Dictionary of Non-Christian Religions. 19.95 (ISBN 0-7175-0972-9). Dufour.

--Encounters in World Religions. 224p. 1987. 15.95 (ISBN 0-8245-0826-2). Crossroad NY.

--Introduction to Asian Religions. 1976. pap. 7.95 (ISBN 0-19-519858-1). Oxford U Pr.

--Mysticism in the World's Religions. 1976. pap. text ed. 6.95 (ISBN 0-19-502185-1). Oxford U Pr.

--Religion in an African City. LC 74-142921. (Illus.). Repr. of 1953 ed. 22.50x (ISBN 0-8371-5947-4, PAC&, Pub. by Negro U Pr). Greenwood.

--Sex in the World's Religions. 1980. pap. 9.95x (ISBN 0-19-520202-3). Oxford U Pr.

--The Wisdom of the Early Buddhists. LC 77-7945. (New Directions Wisdon Ser.). 1977. pap. 4.95 (ISBN 0-8112-0667-X, NDP444). New Directions.

--World Religions: From Ancient History to the Present. (Illus.). 224p. 1984. 29.95 (ISBN 0-87196-129-6). Facts on File.

--Worship in the World's Religions. 2nd ed. (Quality Paperback: No. 316). 239p. 1976. pap. 4.95 (ISBN 0-8226-0316-0). Littlefield.

Parrinder, Geoffrey, ed. World Religions: From Ancient History to the Present. (Illus.). 528p. 1985. pap. 14.95 (ISBN 0-8160-1289-X). Facts on File.

Parrinder, Geoffrey, tr. from Sanskrit. & intro. by. The Wisdom of the Forest: Selections from the Hindu Upanishads. LC 75-42114. (The Wisdom Bks). 96p. 1976. pap. 1.95 (ISBN 0-8112-0607-6, NDP414). New Directions.

Parris, Paula. Ruth: Woman of Courage. (BibLearn Ser.). (Illus.). 1977. bds. 5.95 (ISBN 0-8054-4229-4, 4242-29). Broadman.

Parrish, Annette, ed. see Finley, Tom.

Parrish, Katharine W. Dustmop Devotionals. (Orig.). 1986. pap. 7.00 (ISBN 0-915541-09-2). Star Bks Inc.

Parrish-Harra, Carol W. Messengers of Hope. 1983. pap. 7.95 (ISBN 0-87613-079-1). New Age.

--A New Age Handbook on Death & Dying: Death Is Life Too. LC 81-70369. 160p. 1982. pap. 5.95 (ISBN 0-87516-470-6). De Vorss.

Parrot, Andre. The Temple of Jerusalem. Hooke, Beatrice E., tr. from Fr. LC 85-8037. (Studies in Biblical Archaeology: No. 5). Tr. of Le Temple de Jerusalem. (Illus.). 112p. 1985. Repr. of 1957 ed. lib. bdg. 35.00x (ISBN 0-313-24224-0, PATJ). Greenwood.

Parrot, Friedrich. Journey to Ararat. LC 73-115576. (Russia Observed, Series I). 1970. Repr. of 1846 ed. 20.00 (ISBN 0-405-03057-6). Ayer Co Pubs.

Parrott, Bob W. God's Sense of Humor. LC 82-9142. 221p. 1984. 17.50 (ISBN 0-8022-2421-0). Philos Lib.

--Ontology of Humor. LC 81-80239. 96p. 1982. 10.95 (ISBN 0-8022-2387-7). Philos Lib.

Parrott, JoAnn. The Sunshine Tree. 1979. pap. 2.50 (ISBN 0-911739-14-9). Abbott Loop.

Parrott, Leslie. The Habit of Happiness. 192p. 1987. 10.95 (ISBN 0-8499-0607-5). Word Bks.

--Usher's Manual. 1969. pap. 2.95 (ISBN 0-310-30651-5, 10513P). Zondervan.

Parrott, Leslie, jt. auth. see Schmelzenbach, Elmer.

Parry, Betty, ed. The Unicorn & the Garden. LC 78-64531. (Illus.). 1978. perfect bdg. 10.00 (ISBN 0-915380-04-8). Word Works.

Parry, Danaan. The Essene Book of Days 1987. 400p. (Orig.). 1986. pap. 12.95 (ISBN 0-913319-02-3). Sunstone Pubns.

Parry, David. Households of God. (Cistercian Studies: No. 39). (Orig.). 1980. pap. 7.95 (ISBN 0-87907-939-8). Cistercian Pubns.

Parry, J. P. Democracy & Religion: Gladstone & the Liberal Party, 1867-1876. (Cambridge Studies in the History & Theory of Politics). 520p. 1986. 59.50 (ISBN 0-521-30948-4). Cambridge U Pr.

Parry, Jonathan, jt. ed. see Bloch, Maurice.

Parry, Michel, ed. The Devil's Children: Tales of Demons & Exorcists. LC 74-21721. 212p. 1975. 7.95 (ISBN 0-8008-2188-2). Taplinger.

Parry, W. H. Three Centuries of English Church Music. 1977. lib. bdg. 59.95 (ISBN 0-8490-2745-4). Gordon Pr.

Parshall, Phil. Beyond the Mosque. 312p. 1985. pap. 9.95 (ISBN 0-8010-7089-9). Baker Bk.

--Bridges to Islam: A Christian Perspective on Folk Islam. 120p. 1983. pap. 6.95 (ISBN 0-8010-7081-3). Baker Bk.

--New Paths in Muslim Evangelism: Evangelical Approaches to Contextualization. 200p. (Orig.). 1980. pap. 8.95 (ISBN 0-8010-7056-2). Baker Bk.

Parsley, Rod. The Someday Syndrome. 37p. 1986. pap. 2.95 (ISBN 0-88144-069-8). Christian Pub.

--Worshipping the Unknown God. 31p. 1986. pap. 2.75 (ISBN 0-88144-070-1). Christian Pub.

Parsons, Edward, ed. see Edwards, Jonathan.

Parsons, Elsie C. Hopi & Zuni Ceremonialism. LC 34-5260. (American Anthro. Associatiom Memoirs). 1933. 11.00 (ISBN 0-527-00538-X). Kraus Repr.

--Scalp Ceremonial of Zuni. LC 25-1663. (American Anthro. Association Memoirs). 1924. pap. 15.00 (ISBN 0-527-00530-4). Kraus Repr.

Parsons, Elsie W. Religious Chastity: An Ethnological Study, by John Main (Pseud.) LC 72-9672. Repr. of 1913 ed. 52.00 (ISBN 0-404-57489-0). AMS Pr.

Parsons, Francis. Six Men of Yale. facsimile ed. LC 72-156702. (Essay Index Reprint Ser). Repr. of 1939 ed. 18.00 (ISBN 0-8369-2329-4). Ayer Co Pubs.

Parsons, Howard L. Christianity Today in the U. S. S. R. LC 86-27320. 216p. (Orig.). 1987. pap. 6.95 (ISBN 0-7178-0651-0). Intl Pubs CO.

Parsons, Ramon M. La Moral en la Educacion. LC 83-10594. (Span.). 90p. 1984. write for info. (ISBN 0-8477-2746-7). U of PR Pr.

Parsons, Richard D. Adolescents in Turmoil, Parents under Stress: A Pastoral Ministry Primer. 160p. (Orig.). 1987. pap. 7.95 (ISBN 0-8091-2855-1). Paulist Pr.

Parsons, Richard E. Sir Edwyn Hoskyns As a Biblical Theologian. LC 85-25038. 152p. 1986. 25.00 (ISBN 0-312-72647-3). St Martin.

Parsons, Robert. The Judgment of a Catholicke English-Man Living in Banishment for His Religion. LC 57-9033. 1978. Repr. of 1608 ed. 30.00x (ISBN 0-8201-1240-2). Schol Facsimiles.

Parsons, Wilfrid. Early Catholic Americana. LC 77-91536. 1977. Repr. of 1939 ed. lib. bdg. 25.00 (ISBN 0-89341-469-7). Longwood Pub Group.

Partee, Charles, ed. Calvin & Classical Philosophy 1977. (Studies in the History of Christian Thought: Vol. 14). 30.00 (ISBN 90-04-04839-1). Heinman.

Partin, Malcolm O. Waldeck-Rousseau, Combes, & the Church: The Politics of Anticlericalism, 1899-1905. LC 74-76167. pap. 77.80 (ISBN 0-317-20441-6, 2023432). Bks Demand UMI.

--Waldeck-Rousseau, Combes, & the Church, 1899-1905: The Politics of Anticlericalism. LC 74-76167. (Duke Historical Publication Ser). 299p. 1969. 23.25 (ISBN 0-8223-0130-X). Duke.

Partridge, Edmund. Church in Perspective: Standard Course for Layreaders. rev. ed. 1976. 5.95 (ISBN 0-8192-1210-5). Morehouse.

Partridge, Eric. A New Testament Word Book: A Glossary. facsimile ed. LC 70-117907. (Select Bibliographies Reprint Ser). Repr. of 1940 ed. 19.00 (ISBN 0-8369-5359-2). Ayer Co Pubs.

Partridge, Jeannette. Losing a Loved One. 3.50 (ISBN 0-913420-86-7). Olympus Pub Co.

Parunak, H. van dyke see Van Dyke Parunak, H.

Parunak, Van Dyke H. Linguistic Density Plots in Ezekiel: The Computer Bible, Vol. XXVII A & B. Baird, Arthur J. & Freedman, David, eds. 528p. 1984. pap. 70.00x (ISBN 0-935106-22-7). Biblical Res Assocs.

Parvati, Jeannine. Prenatal Yoga & Natural Birth. rev. ed. (Illus.). 64p. 1986. pap. 7.95 (ISBN 0-938190-89-X). North Atlantic.

Parvey, Constance F., ed. The Community of Women & Men in the Church. LC 82-71831. 288p. (Orig.). 1982. pap. 14.95 (ISBN 0-8006-1644-8, 1-1644). Fortress.

Parvin, Earl. Missions U. S. A. (Orig.). 1985. pap. text ed. 14.95 (ISBN 0-8024-5975-7). Moody.

Pasachoff, Naomi E. Playwriters, Preachers & Politicians: A Study of Testament Dramas. Hogg, James, ed. (Elizabethan & Renaissance Studies). 162p. (Orig.). 1975. pap. 15.00 (ISBN 3-7052-0691-5, Pub. by Salzburg Studies). Longwood Pub Group.

Pascal. The Christian Mind. Houston, James, ed. (Classics of Faith & Devotion Ser.). cancelled (ISBN 0-88070-159-5). Multnomah.

Pascal, Blaise. Maximes et Pensees. 4.95 (ISBN 0-686-54848-5). French & Eur.

--The Mystery of Jesus & of the Jewish People, 2 vols. (Illus.). 245p. 1985. 207.50 (ISBN 0-89901-228-0). Found Class Reprints.

--Pensees. (Univers des Lettres). pap. 2.50 (ISBN 0-685-34246-8). French & Eur.

--Pensees, 2 vols. (Folios 936 & 937). 4.50 ea. French & Eur.

--Pensees. Desgranges, ed. 1962. pap. 9.95 (ISBN 0-685-11485-6). French & Eur.

--Pensees. Desgranges, ed. (Coll. Prestige). 16.95 (ISBN 0-685-34245-X). French & Eur.

--Pensees. Krailsheimer, A. J., tr. (Classics Ser.). (Orig.). 1966. pap. 3.95 (ISBN 0-14-044171-9). Penguin.

--Les Provinciales. 1966. 4.95 (ISBN 0-686-54852-3). French & Eur.

--The Thoughts, Letters, & Opuscules of Blaise Pascal. 1978. Repr. of 1864 ed. lib. bdg. 35.00 (ISBN 0-8492-2094-7). R West.

--The Thoughts of Blaise Pascal. LC 78-12814. 1978. Repr. of 1961 ed. lib. bdg. 24.25 (ISBN 0-313-20530-2, PATH). Greenwood.

Pascal, Blaise & Adam, Antoine. Lettres Escrites a un Provincial. 320p. 1967. 4.50 (ISBN 0-686-54847-7). French & Eur.

Pascal, Blaise & Lafuma, Louis. Deux Pieces Imparfaites sur la Grace et le Concile de Trente, Extraites du M. S. de l'Abbe Perier. 76p. 1947. 5.95 (ISBN 0-686-54845-0). French & Eur.

Pascal, E., tr. see Migne, J. P.

Pascal, Pierre. Avvakum et les Debuts Du Raskol. (Etudes Sur L'histoire, L'economie et la Sociologie Des Pays Slaves Ser.: No. 8). 1969. pap. 35.60x (ISBN 90-2796-293-6). Mouton.

Pascal, Roy. Social Basis of the German Reformation: Martin Luther & His Times. LC 68-30539. 1971. Repr. of 1933 ed. 25.00x (ISBN 0-678-00549-4). Kelley.

Paschal, George H., Jr. & Benner, Judith A. One Hundred Years of Challenge & Change: A History of the Synod of Texas of the United Presbyterian Church in the U. S. A. LC 68-20488. 259p. 1968. 4.00 (ISBN 0-911536-32-9). Trinity U Pr.

Paschal, Mrs. W. N. Life of a Rich Man. (Illus.). 180p. 1976. pap. 2.50 (ISBN 0-89114-075-1). Baptist Pub Hse.

Paschall, jt. ed. see Hobbs.

Pascher, Josef. Der Konigsweg Zu Wiedergeburt und Vergottung Bei Philon Von Alexandreia. Repr. of 1931 ed. 22.00 (ISBN 0-384-45050-4). Johnson Repr.

Paschos, Jacqueline & Destang, Francoise. Come to School. (Rejoice Ser.). pap. 0.35 (ISBN 0-8091-6505-8). Paulist Pr.

Pascual, Manuel, tr. see Killgallon, James J., et al.

Pashin, Gertrude, tr. see Einhorn, David.

Paske-Smith, Montague, ed. Japanese Traditions of Christianity: Being Some Old Translations from the Japanese, with British Consular Reports of the Persecutions of 1868-1872. (Studies in Japanese History & Civilization). 1979. Repr. of 1930 ed. 17.50 (ISBN 0-89093-257-3). U Pubns Amer.

Paskins, Barrie, ed. Ethics & European Security. 192p. 1986. 28.95x (ISBN 0-86569-146-0). Auburn Hse.

Pasquariello, Ronald D., et al, eds. Redeeming the City: Theology, Politics & Urban Policy. 224p. 1982. pap. 11.00 (ISBN 0-317-02300-4). Schalkenbach.

Pass, Gail. Zoe's Book. 224p. 1987. pap. 7.95 (ISBN 0-930044-95-9). Naiad Pr.

Passamaneck, Marge. People Are Different, People Are the Same. 1983. pap. 3.10 (ISBN 0-89536-615-0, 1629). CSS of Ohio.

Passamaneck, Stephen. The Traditional Jewish Law of Sale. 1983. 20.00x (ISBN 0-686-87788-8). Ktav.

Passamaneck, Stephen M., ed. see Bazak, Jacob.

Passamaneck, Stephen M., tr. see Karo, Joseph Ben Ephraim.

Passantino, Robert, et al. Answers to the Cultist at Your Door. LC 80-83850. 1981. pap. 5.95 (ISBN 0-89081-275-6). Harvest Hse.

Passavant, Anthony C. A Highly Informative History of the Renaissance Period of Italian Painting. (Illus.). 117p. 1984. pap. 23.75 (ISBN 0-86650-128-2). Gloucester Art.

Passmore, John. Perfectability of Man. LC 77-129625. 1970. 25.00x (ISBN 0-684-15521-4, ScribT). Scribner.

Pastoral Care Office. Empowered to Care. 1980. pap. 9.00 (ISBN 0-8309-0291-0). Herald Hse.

Pastoral Care Office, Reorganized Church of Jesus Christ of Latter Day Saints. Visiting: A Pastoral Care Ministry. 186p. (Orig.). 1985. pap. 10.25 (ISBN 0-8309-0429-8). Herald Hse.

Pastrovicchi, Angelo. Saint Joseph of Copertino. LC 79-91298. 135p. 1980. pap. 3.00 (ISBN 0-89555-135-7). TAN Bks Pubs.

Pastva, M. Loretta. Growing up to God: A Guide for Teenagers on the Sacrement of Reconciliation. LC 83-15538. 82p. (Orig.). 1983. pap. 4.95 (ISBN 0-8189-0455-0). Alba.

Pastva, Mary L. The Catholic Youth Retreat Book: Everything You Need to Plan Prayer Experiences for a Day, an Evening, a Weekend. (Illus.). 87p. 1984. pap. 7.95 (ISBN 0-86716-032-2). St Anthony Mess Pr.

--Great Religions of the World. (Illus.). 251p. (Orig.). 1986. pap. text ed. 9.95x (ISBN 0-88489-175-5). St Mary's.

Pasztory, Esther. The Iconography of the Teotihuacan Tlaloc. LC 74-16543. (Studies in Pre-Columbian Art & Archaeology: No. 15). (Illus.). 22p. 1974. pap. 3.00x (ISBN 0-88402-059-2). Dumbarton Oaks.

Patai, Raphael. Gates to the Old City. 928p. 1980. pap. 12.95 (ISBN 0-380-76091-6, 76091-6). Avon.

--The Hebrew Goddess. 1984. pap. 2.95 (ISBN 0-380-39289-5, 39289, Discus). Avon.

--The Jewish Mind. LC 76-58040. 1977. 14.95 (ISBN 0-684-14878-1, ScribT). Scribner.

--The Jewish Mind. 384p. 1985. pap. 14.95 (ISBN 0-684-16321-7, ScribT). Scribner.

--The Messiah Texts. 1979. pap. 7.95 (ISBN 0-380-46482-9, 46482-9). Avon.

--Messiah Texts: Jewish Legends of Three Thousound Years. LC 79-5387. 426p. 1979. 25.95x (ISBN 0-8143-1652-2). Wayne St U Pr.

--Nahum Goldmann: His Missions to the Gentiles. LC 85-24518. (Judaic Studies Ser.). (Illus.). 345p. 1987. 29.95 (ISBN 0-8173-0294-8). U of Ala Pr.

--The Seed of Abraham: Jews & Arabs in Contact & Conflict. 384p. 1986. 29.95 (ISBN 0-87480-251-2). U of Utah Pr.

Patai, Raphael, jt. auth. see Graves, Robert.

Patai, Raphael, ed. Herzl Year Book: Vol. 5, Studies in the History of Zionism in America. LC 72-117807. (Essay Index Reprint Ser.). 1963. 22.00 (ISBN 0-8369-1951-3). Ayer Co Pubs.

Patai, Raphael, et al. Studies in Biblical & Jewish Folklore. LC 72-6871. (Studies in Comparitive Literature: No. 35). 1972. Repr. of 1960 ed. lib. bdg. 49.95x (ISBN 0-8383-1665-4). Haskell.

Patanjali. Patanjali's Yoga Sutras. 2nd ed. Prasada, Rama, tr. from Sanskrit. 318p. 1981. Repr. of 1912 ed. 28.50 (ISBN 0-89744-220-2, Pub. by Orient Reprint India). Auromere.

--Patanjali's Yoga Sutras. (the Aphorisms of Yoga, by Patanjali.) with the Commentary of Vyasa & the Gloss of Vachaspati Misra. Rama Prasada, tr. LC 73-3789. Repr. of 1912 ed. 29.00 (ISBN 0-404-57804-7). AMS Pr.

--Raja Yoga Sutras. Swami Jyotir Maya Nanda, tr. from Sanskrit. (Illus.). 1978. pap. 2.99 (ISBN 0-934664-38-2). Yoga Res Foun.

--Yoga Sutras of Patanjali. 7th ed. Johnston, Charles, tr. from Sanskrit. 1984. pap. 6.00 (ISBN 0-914732-08-0). Bro Life Inc.

Patanjali, Bhagwan S. Aphorisms of Yoga. (Illus.). 96p. (Orig.). 1973. pap. 5.50 (ISBN 0-571-10320-0). Faber & Faber.

Patanjali, Swami S. The Ten Principal Upanishads. Yeats, W. B., tr. (Orig.). 1970. pap. 5.95 (ISBN 0-571-09363-9). Faber & Faber.

Patch, Howard R. Other World, According to Descriptions in Medieval Literature. LC 77-96164. 1970. Repr. of 1950 ed. lib. bdg. 27.50x (ISBN 0-374-96289-8, Octagon). Hippocrene Bks.

--The Tradition of the Goddess Fortuna in Medieval Philosophy & Literature. Repr. of 1922 ed. lib. bdg. 15.00 (ISBN 0-8414-6751-X). Folcroft.

--The Tradition of the Goddess Fortuna in Roman Literature & in the Transitional Period. LC 76-41188. 1976. Repr. of 1922 ed. lib. bdg. 15.50 (ISBN 0-8414-6753-6). Folcroft.

--The Tradition of the Goddess Fortuna in Roman Literature & in the Transitional Period. 1980. Repr. of 1912 ed. 15.00 (ISBN 0-8482-5593-3). Norwood Edns.

Pate, Don. He Shall Be Like a Tree. (Horizon Ser.). 128p. 1981. pap. 5.95 (ISBN 0-8127-0315-4). Review & Herald.

Pate, Ernest. Dreams for a Quiet Night. LC 83-73639. 80p. (Orig.). 1984. pap. 4.95 (ISBN 0-87516-535-4). De Vorss.

Patel, Ishwarbhai, ed. Sciences & the Vedas. 1986. 12.50X (ISBN 0-8364-1663-5, Pub. by Somaiya). South Asia Bks.

Patel, Satyavrata. Hinduism: Religion & Way of Life. 165p. 1980. 15.95x (ISBN 0-940500-25-6). Asia Bk Corp.

Pater, Calvin A. Karlstadt As the Father of the Baptist Movements. 350p. 1984. 37.50x (ISBN 0-8020-5555-9). U of Toronto Pr.

Pater, Walter. Cupid & Psyche. (Illus.). 48p. 1977. 9.95 (ISBN 0-571-11115-7). Faber & Faber.

Pateria, A. K. Modern Commentators of Veda. 120p. 1986. text ed. 22.50x (ISBN 81-7018-252-2, Pub. by B R Pub Corp Delhi). Apt Bks.

Paterson, Eugene H. Earth & Altar: The Community of Prayer in a Self-Bound Society. 180p. (Orig.). 1985. pap. 5.95 (ISBN 0-8091-2732-6). Paulist Pr.

Paterson, George. Helping Your Handicapped Child. LC 74-14185. 112p. (Orig.). 1975. pap. 5.95 (ISBN 0-8066-1467-6, 10-3005). Augsburg.

Paterson, George W. The Cardiac Patient. LC 78-52187. (Religion & Medicine Ser.). 1978. pap. 5.95 (ISBN 0-8066-1661-X, 10-0971). Augsburg.

Paterson, Isabel B. God of the Machine. LC 77-172225. (Right Wing Individualist Tradition in America Ser). 1972. Repr. of 1943 ed. 25.50 (ISBN 0-405-00434-6). Ayer Co Pubs.

Paterson, J. H. & Wiseman, D. J., eds. New Bible Atlas. 128p. 1985. 14.95 (ISBN 0-8423-4675-9). Tyndale.

Paterson, J. R. A Faith for the 1980s. 3.95x (ISBN 0-7152-0433-5). Outlook.

Paterson, James. The Liberty of the Press, Speech & Public Worship: Being Commentaries on the Liberty of the Subject & the Laws of England. xxxi, 568p. 1985. Repr. of 1880 ed. lib. bdg. 42.50x (ISBN 0-8377-1019-7). Rothman.

Paterson, John. How to Pray Together. pap. 0.75 (ISBN 0-87784-119-5). Inter-Varsity.

Paterson, John & Paterson, Katherine. Consider the Lilies: Flowers of the Bible. LC 85-43603. (Illus.). 96p. (YA) 1986. 13.70i (ISBN 0-690-04461-5, Crowell Jr Bks); PLB 13.89 (ISBN 0-690-04463-1). HarpJ.

Paterson, Katherine, jt. auth. see Paterson, John.

Paterson, Kathy, ed. see Kearns, Thomas F.

Paterson, Ruby. Fun with Bible Facts. pap. 1.75 (ISBN 0-89137-620-8). Quality Pubns.

--More Fun with Bible Facts. pap. 1.75 (ISBN 0-89137-617-8). Quality Pubns.

Paterson, William P. The Nature of Religion. LC 77-27202. (Gifford Lectures: 1924-25). Repr. of 1926 ed. 47.50 (ISBN 0-404-60476-5). AMS Pr.

Pathak, Sushil M. American Missionaries & Hinduism: A Study of Their Contacts from 1813-1918. 294p. 1967. text ed. 20.00x. Coronet Bks.

Patnaik, Deba, ed. Geography of Holiness: The Photography of Thomas Merton. LC 80-18604. 1980. 17.50 (ISBN 0-8298-0401-3). Pilgrim NY.

Paton, Alan. Instrument of Thy Peace. 124p. 1985. pap. text ed. 8.95 large print ed. (ISBN 0-8027-2494-9). Walker & Co.

Paton, David, ed. see Allen, Roland.

Paton, H. J., tr. see Kant, Immanuel.

Paton, Lewis B. A Critical & Exegetical Commentary on Esther. Driver, Samuel R., et al, eds. LC 8-30156. (International Critical Commentary Ser.). 360p. 1908. 22.95 (ISBN 0-567-05009-2, Pub. by T & T Clark Ltd UK). Fortress.

--The Early History of Syria & Palestine. LC 79-2878. (Illus.). 302p. 1981. Repr. of 1901 ed. 28.50 (ISBN 0-8305-0046-4). Hyperion Conn.

Patriarchal Institute for Patristic Studies, et al. The Treasures of Mount Athos, Volume 2: The Monasteries of Iveron, St. Panteleimon, Esphigmenou & Chilandari. (Illus.). 400p. 1976. cancelled (ISBN 0-89241-004-3). Caratzas.

Patricia. Jesus I: The Man. Morningland Publications, Inc., ed. (Ser. of Three Books Called Jesus). (Illus.). 439p. 1980. pap. 10.00 (ISBN 0-935146-15-6). Morningland.

--Jesus II: The Mission. Morningland Publications, Inc., ed. (Ser. of Three Books Called Jesus). (Illus.). 461p. 1980. pap. 10.00 (ISBN 0-935146-17-2). Morningland.

--Jesus III: The Return. Morningland Publications, Inc., ed. (Ser. of Three Books Called Jesus). (Illus.). 470p. (Orig.). 1980. pap. 10.00 (ISBN 0-935146-18-0). Morningland.

Patricia & Gyan, Gopi. Oneness, Vol. II. (Orig.). 1980. spiral bdg. 7.95 (ISBN 0-935146-24-5). Morningland.

Patricia, Sri & Gyan, Gopi. Oneness, Vol. I. 1979. pap. 3.95 (ISBN 0-935146-11-3). Morningland.

Patrick, Dale. Old Testament Law. LC 84-4418. 228p. (Orig.). 1984. 15.95 (ISBN 0-8042-0133-1). John Knox.

Patrick, J. Max & Sundell, Roger H. Milton & the Art of Sacred Song. LC 78-65014. 248p. 1979. 32.50x (ISBN 0-299-07830-2). U of Wis Pr.

Patrick, John M. Milton's Conception of Sin As Developed in Paradise Lost. 1930. Repr. 25.00 (ISBN 0-8274-2740-9). R West.

Patrick, Mary. The Love Commandment: How to Find Its Meaning for Today. Lambert, Herbert, ed. LC 84-7083. 112p. 1984. pap. 6.95 (ISBN 0-8272-2118-5). CBP.

Patrick, Priscilla. To Life! Yoga with Priscilla Patrick. LC 82-71187. (Illus.). 76p. (Orig.). 1982. pap. 9.95 (ISBN 0-943274-00-1). SC Ed Comm Inc.

Patrick, Saint Confession of St. Patrick. pap. 1.95 (ISBN 0-686-25547-X). Eastern Orthodox.

Patrick, Saint & Fiacc, Saint Writings of St. Patrick, with the Metrical Life of St. Patrick. pap. 2.95 (ISBN 0-686-25558-5). Eastern Orthodox.

Patrick, Ted & Dulack, Tom. Let Our Children Go! 1977. pap. 2.25 (ISBN 0-345-28343-0). Ballantine.

Patrides, C. A. Cambridge Platonists. (Stratford-Upon-Avon Library). 1969. 25.00x (ISBN 0-674-09125-6). Harvard U Pr.

--Milton & the Christian Tradition. LC 79-10846. xvi, 302p. 1979. Repr. 28.00 (ISBN 0-208-01821-2, Archon). Shoe String.

Patrides, C. A. & Wittreich, Joseph A., Jr., eds. The Apocalypse in English Renaissance Thought & Literature. LC 84-71281. 452p. (Orig.). 1985. 52.00x (ISBN 0-8014-1648-5); pap. 19.95x (ISBN 0-8014-9893-7). Cornell U Pr.

Patrinelis, C. G., jt. auth. see Medlin, W. K.

Patrinelis, Christos, et al. Stavronikita Monastery: History-Icons-Embroideries. (Illus.). 241p. 1974. 75.00 (ISBN 0-89241-076-0). Caratzas.

Patrizi, Agostino P. Caeremoniale Romanum of Agostino Patrizi Piccolomini. 310p. 1516. text ed. 66.24x (ISBN 0-576-99434-0, Pub. by Gregg Intl Pubs England). Gregg Intl.

Patsavos, L. J. & Charles, G. J. The Role of the Priest & the Apostolate of the Laity. Vaporis, N. M., ed. (Clergy Seminar Lectures Ser.). 63p. (Orig.). 1983. pap. 3.00 (ISBN 0-916586-57-X). Holy Cross Orthodox.

Patschovsky, Alexander. Die Anfaenge einer staendigen Inquisition in Boehmen: Ein Prager Inquisitoren-Handbuch aus der ersten Haelfte des 14 Jahrhunderts. (Beitraege zur Geschichte und Quellenkunde des Mittelalters, Vol. 3). (Illus.). xviii, 319p. 1975. 39.60x (ISBN 3-11-004404-8). De Gruyter.

Patt, Richard W. Partners in the Impossible. 1984. 4.95 (ISBN 0-89536-678-9, 4854). CSS of Ohio.

Patte, Daniel. Early Jewish Hermeneutic in Palestine. LC 75-22225. (Society of Biblical Literature. Dissertation Ser.: No. 22). Repr. of 1975 ed. 89.50 (ISBN 0-8357-9570-5, 2017666). Bks Demand UMI.

--The Gospel According to Matthew: A Structural Commentary on Matthew's Faith. LC 86-45218. 432p. 1986. pap. 19.95 (ISBN 0-8006-1978-1, 1-1978). Fortress.

--Paul's Faith & the Power of the Gospel: A Structural Introduction to the Pauline Letters. LC 82-7416. 432p. (Orig.). 1983. 21.95 (ISBN 0-8006-0683-3, 1-1682). Fortress.

--Preaching Paul. LC 84-47931. (Fortress Resources for Preaching Ser.). 96p. 1984. pap. 4.95 (ISBN 0-8006-1140-3). Fortress.

--What Is Structural Exegesis? Via, Dan O., Jr., ed. LC 75-36454. (Guides to Biblical Scholarship: New Testament Ser.). 96p. (Orig.). 1976. pap. 4.50 (ISBN 0-8006-0462-8, 1-462). Fortress.

Patte, Daniel, ed. Semiology & Parables: Exploration of the Possibilities Offered by Structuralism for Exegesis. Papers of the Vanderbilt University Conference, May 15-17, 1975. LC 76-20686. (Pittsburgh Theological Monographs: No. 9). 1976. pap. 9.95 (ISBN 0-915138-11-5). Pickwick.

Patten, Donald W. The Biblical Flood & the Ice Epoch. 1966. 9.00 (ISBN 0-686-70598-X); pap. 7.50 (ISBN 0-686-70599-8). Pacific Mer.

Patten, Donald W., ed. Symposium on Creation, No. 4. pap. 3.95 (ISBN 0-8010-6925-4). Baker Bk.

Patten, Simon. The Social Basis of Religion. (The Neglected American Economists Ser.). 1974. lib. bdg. 61.00 (ISBN 0-8240-1028-0). Garland Pub.

Patterson, Bessie. The Wise Woman Knows. 4.95 (ISBN 0-89137-422-1). Quality Pubns.

Patterson, Bob. Carl F. Henry, Makers of the Modern Theological Mind. 1983. pap. 8.95 (ISBN 0-8499-2951-2). Word Bks.

Patterson, Bob E. Reinhold Niebuhr. LC 76-46783. (Makers of the Modern Theological Mind Series). 1977. 8.95 (ISBN 0-87680-508-X). Word Bks.

Patterson, Bob E., ed. see Duncan, Elmer H.

Patterson, Bob E., ed. see Humphrey, J. Edward.

Patterson, Bob E., ed. see Mueller, David.

Patterson, Bob E., ed. see Panko, Stephen M.

Patterson, Bob E., ed. see Roark, Dallas M.

Patterson, Charles. Anti-Semitism: The Road to the Holocaust & Beyond. 160p. 1982. 11.95 (ISBN 0-8027-6470-3). Walker & Co.

Patterson, Charles H. New Testament Notes. (Orig.). 1965. pap. 3.25 (ISBN 0-8220-0880-7). Cliffs.

--Old Testament Notes. (Orig.). 1965. pap. 3.25 (ISBN 0-8220-0949-8). Cliffs.

Patterson, Chuck. There Is Something Else. Wallace, Mary H., ed. (Illus., Orig.). 1982. pap. 5.95 (ISBN 0-912315-23-7). Word Aflame.

Patterson, Daniel W. Nine Shaker Spirituals. (Illus.). 34p. 1981. pap. 2.00 (ISBN 0-937942-10-3). Shaker Mus.

--The Shaker Spiritual. LC 77-85557. (Illus.). 1979. text ed. 90.00x (ISBN 0-691-09124-2). Princeton U Pr.

Patterson, David. Faith & Philosophy. LC 81-43469. 162p. (Orig.). 1982. pap. text ed. 10.50 (ISBN 0-8191-2651-9). U Pr of Amer.

Patterson, Elizabeth, ed. see Baba, Meher, et al.

Patterson, Elizabeth C., ed. see Baba, Meher, et al.

Patterson, Mrs. Elmer. Wisely Train the Younger Women. 1973. pap. 4.95 (ISBN 0-89137-406-X). Quality Pubns.

Patterson, F. W. Manual de Finanzas Para Iglesias. (Illus.). 118p. 1986. pap. 2.50 (ISBN 0-311-17005-6). Casa Bautista.

Patterson, Frank A. Middle English Penitential Lyric. LC 11-26002. Repr. of 1911 ed. 17.50 (ISBN 0-404-04908-7). AMS Pr.

Patterson, Frank W. A Short History of Christian Missions. 176p. 1985. pap. 15.95 (ISBN 0-311-72663-1). Casa Bautista.

Patterson, George. Church Planting Through Obedience Oriented Teaching. LC 81-285. (Illus.). 64p. (Orig.). 1981. pap. 3.95x (ISBN 0-87808-910-1). William Carey Lib.

Patterson, Gordon N. Message from Infinity: A Space-Age Correlation of Science & Religion. (Illus.). 96p. 1984. 6.50 (ISBN 0-682-40149-8). Exposition Pr FL.

Patterson, J. B. The Christmas Star Was Jesus Himself: A Theological Work Showing any Theological Value in the Miracle Side Is also Found in the Non-Miracle Side of the New Testament. 3rd ed. LC 84-71886. 238p. 1986. pap. 7.50x (ISBN 0-9613670-2-4). Christmas Star.

Patterson, Kathy C. & Niklaus, Phyllis M. Stories for Communication. Communication & Learning Innovators, Ltd. Staff, et al, eds. (Bible Ser.). (Illus.). 13p. 1985. 6.00 (ISBN 0-932361-01-3). Comm & Learning.

Patterson, LeRoy. The Best Is Yet to Be. 192p. (Orig.). 1986. pap. 5.95 (ISBN 0-8423-0183-6). Tyndale.

--Good Morning, Lord: Devotions for Athletes. (Good Morning, Lord Ser.). 1979. 4.95 (ISBN 0-8010-7044-9). Baker Bk.

Patterson, Lillie. Christmas Feasts & Festivals. LC 68-14778. (Holiday Bks.). (Illus.). 64p. 1968. PLB 7.56 (ISBN 0-8116-6562-3). Garrard.

--Christmas in America. LC 69-11077. (Holiday Bks.). (Illus.). 64p. 1969. PLB 7.56 (ISBN 0-8116-6563-1). Garrard.

--Coretta Scott King. LC 76-19077. (American All Ser.). (Illus.). 96p. 1977. PLB 7.12 (ISBN 0-8116-4585-1). Garrard.

--David, the Story of a King. (Illus.). 96p. 1985. PLB 7.95 (ISBN 0-687-10280-4). Abingdon.

--Easter. LC 66-10150. (Holiday Bks.). (Illus.). 1966. PLB 7.56 (ISBN 0-8116-6559-3). Garrard.

Patterson, Morgan W. Baptist History Sourcebook. cancelled (ISBN 0-8054-6568-5). Broadman.

Patterson, Paige. Song of Solomon. (Everyman's Bible Commentary Ser.). (Orig.). 1986. pap. 5.95 (ISBN 0-8024-2057-5). Moody.

Patterson, Paulina G. De see De Patterson, Paulina G.

Patterson, Ray. House Beautiful. (Illus.). 118p. 1987. pap. 3.95 (ISBN 0-936369-05-1). Son-Rise Pubns.

Patterson, Robert. Pastoral Health Care: Understanding the Church's Healing Ministers. LC 83-1948. 30p. 1983. pap. 0.90 (ISBN 0-87125-080-2). Cath Health.

Patterson, Robert L. The Conception of God in the Philosophy of Thomas Aquinas. 508p. 1977. Repr. of 1935 ed. lib. bdg. 30.00 (ISBN 0-915172-27-5). Richwood Pub.

--Philosophy of Religion. LC 74-101130. 1970. 31.75 (ISBN 0-8223-0223-3). Duke.

Patterson, W. F., tr. see Robertson, A. T.

Patterson, Ward. The Morality Maze. LC 81-14539. 128p. (Orig.). 1982. pap. 2.25 (ISBN 0-87239-478-6, 41010). Standard Pub.

--Triumph over Temptation. (Illus.). 96p. (Orig.). 1984. pap. 2.95 (ISBN 0-87239-730-0, 39976). Standard Pub.

--Under His Wings. LC 86-70646. 160p. 1986. pap. 6.95 (ISBN 0-89636-216-7). Accent Bks.

--Wonders in the Midst. LC 78-62709. 96p. (Orig.). 1979. pap. 2.25 (ISBN 0-87239-237-6, 40076). Standard Pub.

Patterson, Yvonne. Doubting Thomas. (Arch Book Ser.: No. 18). 1981. pap. 0.99 (ISBN 0-570-06144-X, 59-1261). Concordia.

--God Made Birds. LC 82-62730. (Happy Day Bks.). (Illus.). 24p. 1983. 1.59 (ISBN 0-87239-634-7, 3554). Standard Pub.

--God Made Fish. (Happy Day Bks.). (Illus.). 24p. 1986. 1.59 (ISBN 0-87403-026-9, 3486). Standard Pub.

--Happy Hannah. (Happy Day Bible Stories Bks.). (Illus.). 24p. 1984. 1.59 (ISBN 0-87239-764-5, 3724). Standard Pub.

Pattie, Alice, jt. auth. see Kreis, Bernadine.

Pattie, Alice, jt. auth. see Kreis, Bernardine.

Pattie, T. S. Manuscripts of the Bible. (Illus.). 32p. (Orig.). 1979. pap. 2.95 (ISBN 0-904654-13-3, Pub. by British Lib). Longwood Pub Group.

Pattison, E. Mansell. Pastor & Parish: A Systems Approach. Clinebell, Howard J. & Stone, Howard W., eds. LC 76-62619. (Creative Pastoral Care & Counseling Ser.). 96p. 1977. pap. 0.50 (ISBN 0-8006-0559-4, 1-559). Fortress.

Pattison, Mark. Essays & Reviews: Tendencies of Religious Thought in England. Jowett, Benjamin, ed. 434p. 1982. Repr. of 1861 ed. lib. bdg. 75.00 (ISBN 0-89987-040-6). Darby Bks.

--Milton. Morley, John, ed. LC 68-58393. (English Men of Letters). Repr. of 1887 ed. lib. bdg. 12.50 (ISBN 0-404-51725-0). AMS Pr.

--Milton. 1896. Repr. 12.00 (ISBN 0-8274-2735-2). R West.

Pattison, R. & Moule, H. Exposition of Ephesians: Lessons in Grace & Godliness. 390p. 1983. lib. bdg. 14.75 Smythe Sewn (ISBN 0-86524-153-8, 4902). Klock & Klock.

Pattison, Seth A. see Seth, Pattison A.

Pattison, T. Harwood. The History of the English Bible. 1894. 20.00 (ISBN 0-8274-2521-X). R West.

Pattison Seth, A. see Seth, Pattison A.

Patton, Carl S. Sources of the Synoptic Gospels. 263p. 1980. Repr. of 1915 ed. lib. bdg. 50.00 (ISBN 0-89984-385-9). Century Bookbindery.

--Sources of the Synoptic Gospels. Repr. of 1915 ed. 37.00 (ISBN 0-384-38805-1). Johnson Repr.

Patton, John. Is Human Forgiveness Possible? A Pastoral Care Perspective. 192p. (Orig.). 1985. pap. 10.95 (ISBN 0-687-19704-X). Abingdon.

--Pastoral Counseling: A Ministry of the Church. 240p. (Orig.). 1983. pap. 12.95 (ISBN 0-687-30314-1). Abingdon.

Patton, John E. Case Against TM in the Schools. (Direction Bks.). 80p. 1976. pap. 1.45 (ISBN 0-8010-6957-2). Baker Bk.

Patton, Leslie K. The Purpose of Church-Related Colleges. LC 78-177145. (Columbia University. Studies in the Social Sciences: No. 783). Repr. of 1940 ed. 22.50 (ISBN 0-404-55783-X). AMS Pr.

Patzan, Flora, tr. see Bauman, Elizabeth.

Patzer, Jere. Bored Again Christian. (Quest Ser.). 16p. 1983. pap. 1.25 (ISBN 0-8163-0521-8). Pacific Pr Pub Assn.

Patzia, Arthur G. Colossians, Philemon, Ephesians. LC 83-48996. (Good News Commentary Ser.). 256p. (Orig.). 1984. pap. 8.95 (ISBN 0-06-066479-7, RD 506). Har-Row.

Pauck, Marion, jt. auth. see Pauck, Wilhelm.

Pauck, Marion, ed. see Pauck, Wilhelm.

Pauck, Wilhelm. From Luther to Tillich: The Reformers & Their Heirs. Pauck, Marion, ed. LC 84-48229. 144p. 1985. 19.45 (ISBN 0-06-066475-4, HarpR). Har-Row.

Pauck, Wilhelm & Pauck, Marion. Paul Tillich: His Life & Thought, Vol. 1: Life. LC 74-25709. (Illus.). 352p. 1976. 15.00 (ISBN 0-06-066474-6, HarpR). Har-Row.

Pauck, Wilhelm, ed. Luther: Lectures on Romans. LC 61-13626. (Library of Christian Classics). 502p. 1977. pap. 11.95 (ISBN 0-664-24151-4). Westminster.

--Melanchthon & Bucer. LC 69-12309. (Library of Christian Classics). 422p. 1980. pap. 9.95 (ISBN 0-664-24164-6). Westminster.

Paul, C. Kegan. The Thoughts of Blaise Pascal: Translated from the Text of M. Auguste Molinier. 1978. Repr. of 1888 ed. 30.00 (ISBN 0-8492-2095-5). R West.

Paul, C. Kegan, ed. see Huysmans, Joris K.

Paul, Cathy. God's Inspired Holy Word Says... 1981. 4.95 (ISBN 0-8062-1785-5). Carlton.

Paul, Cecil & Lanham, Jan. Choices: In Pursuit of Wholeness. 88p. 1982. pap. 3.95 (ISBN 0-8341-0807-0). Beacon Hill.

Paul, Diana. The Buddhist Feminine Ideal: Queen Srimala & the Tathagatagarbha American Academy of Religion. LC 79-12031. (Dissertation Ser.: No. 30). 1980. o.s. 14.00 (ISBN 0-89130-284-0, 01-01-30); pap. 9.95 (ISBN 0-89130-303-0). Scholars Pr GA.

--Women in Buddhism: Images of the Feminine in the Mahayana Tradition. 1985. 35.00x (ISBN 0-520-05445-8); pap. 10.95 (ISBN 0-520-05428-8, CAL 740). U of Cal Pr.

Paul, Ellen F., et al, eds. Nuclear Rights-Nuclear Wrongs. LC 85-26711. 248p. 1986. text ed. 24.95x (ISBN 0-631-14964-3). Basil Blackwell.

Paul, Frances L. Kahtahah. LC 76-17804. (Illus., Orig.). 1976. pap. 7.95 (ISBN 0-88240-058-4). Alaska Northwest.

Paul, G., jt. auth. see Hilbert, Frances F.

Paul, Garrett E., tr. see Jungel, Eberhard.

Paul, Harry W. The Edge of Contingency: French Catholic Reaction to Scientific Change from Darwin to Duhem. LC 78-11168. 1979. 15.00 (ISBN 0-8130-0582-5). U Presses Fla.

Paul, Iain. Science, Theology & Einstein. (Theology & Scientific Culture Ser.). 1982. 16.95x (ISBN 0-19-520378-X). Oxford U Pr.

Paul, James L., ed. The Exceptional Child: A Guidebook for Churches & Community Agencies. LC 82-16914. 176p. text ed. 22.00x (ISBN 0-8156-2287-2); pap. text ed. 12.95x (ISBN 0-8156-2288-0). Syracuse U Pr.

Paul, Kathleen. Taurus. (Sun Signs Ser.). (Illus.). 1978. PLB 7.95 (ISBN 0-87191-642-8); pap. 3.95 (ISBN 0-89812-072-1). Creative Ed.

Paul, Leslie. Sir Thomas More. facsimile ed. LC 75-128882. (Select Bibliographies Ser). Repr. of 1953 ed. 16.00 (ISBN 0-8369-5502-1). Ayer Co Pubs.

Paul, Leslie A. Meaning of Human Existence. LC 73-148642. 1971. Repr. of 1949 ed. lib. bdg. 22.50x (ISBN 0-8371-6008-1, PAHE). Greenwood.

Paul, Robert A. The Tibetan Symbolic World: Psychoanalytic Explorations. LC 81-16505. (Chicago Originals Ser.). (Illus.). 360p. 1982. lib. bdg. 14.00x (ISBN 0-226-64987-3). U of Chicago Pr.

Paul, Robert S. The Assembly of the Lord. (Illus.). 624p. 1985. 39.95 (ISBN 0-567-09341-7, Pub. by T&T Clark Ltd UK). Fortress.

--Freedom with Order: The Doctrine of the Church in the United Church of Christ. 160p. (Orig.). 1987. pap. 8.95 (ISBN 0-8298-0749-7). Pilgrim NY.

Pauley, William C. De see De Pauley, William C.

Pauley, William C. de see De Pauley, William C.

Pauli, Hertha. Her Name Was Sojourner Truth. (YA) 1976. pap. 1.50 (ISBN 0-380-00719-3, 29074). Avon.

Paulinus of Nola, Saint Letters of Saint Paulinus of Nola. Quasten & Burqhardt, eds. (Ancient Christian Writers Ser.: Nos. 35-36). Vol. 1. 11.95 (ISBN 0-8091-0088-6); Vol. 2. 13.95 (ISBN 0-8091-0089-4). Paulist Pr.

--Sancti Pontii Meropii Paulini Nolani Epistulae. (Corpus Scriptorum Ecclesiasticorum Latinorum Ser: Vol. 29). (Lat). Repr. of 1894 ed. 50.00 (ISBN 0-384-45195-0). Johnson Repr.

--Sancti Pontii Meropii Pavlini Nolani Carmina. (Corpus Scriptorum Ecclesiasticorum Latinorum Ser: Vol. 30). Repr. of 1894 ed. 46.00 (ISBN 0-384-45185-3). Johnson Repr.

Paulist Editorial Committee, ed. Liturgy Constitution. 192p. 1964. pap. 1.95 (ISBN 0-8091-1620-0, 192, Deus). Paulist Pr.

Paulk, Earl. Divine Runner. LC 78-71967. 142p. (Orig.). 1978. pap. 3.25 (ISBN 0-917595-00-9). K-Dimension.

--Held in the Heavens until... 256p. (Orig.). 1985. pap. 7.95 (ISBN 0-917595-07-6). K-Dimension.

--The Provoker. Weeks, Trisha, ed. 400p. (Orig.). 1986. pap. 9.95 (ISBN 0-917595-09-2). K-Dimension.

--To Whom Is God Betrothed? 200p. (Orig.). 1985. pap. 4.95 (ISBN 0-917595-10-6). K-Dimension.

--Ultimate Kingdom. 2nd ed. 264p. (Orig.). 1987. pap. 7.95 (ISBN 0-917595-13-0). K-Dimension.

--Wounded Body of Christ. 2nd ed. 160p. 1985. pap. 4.95 (ISBN 0-917595-06-8). K-Dimension.

Paulk, Earl P. Sunday School Evangelism. 1958. 4.95 (ISBN 0-87148-759-4). Pathway Pr.

Paul Of Venice. Logica Magna of Paul of Venice, Part 1, Fascicule 1. Kretzmann, Norman, ed. (British Academy Ser.). 1979. text ed. 98.00x (ISBN 0-19-725980-4). Oxford U Pr.

Paulsell, William & Kelty, Matthew. Letters from a Hermit. 1978. 7.95 (ISBN 0-87243-086-3). Templegate.

Paulsell, William O. Taste & See: A Personal Guide to the Spiritual Life. LC 76-5634. 1977. pap. 2.95 (ISBN 0-88489-093-7). St Mary's.

Paulsell, William O., ed. Sermons in a Monastery: Chapter Talks by Matthew Kelty Ocso, No. 59. (Cistercian Studies Series). 1983. 14.95 (ISBN 0-87907-858-8); pap. 6.00 (ISBN 0-87907-958-4). Cistercian Pubns.

Paulsen, Norman D. Christ Consciousness. 2nd, rev. ed. LC 84-72066. (Illus.). 496p. (Orig.). 1985. 16.95 (ISBN 0-941848-03-5); pap. 10.95 (ISBN 0-941848-04-3). Builders Pub.

Paul Sixth, Pope Ecclesiam Suam. pap. 0.50 (ISBN 0-8091-5035-2). Paulist Pr.

Paulson, Hank & Richardson, Don. Beyond the Wall. LC 81-84567. (Orig.). 1982. pap. 5.95 (ISBN 0-8307-0806-5, 5415708). Regal.

Paulson, Ivar. Old Estonian Folk Religion. LC 76-63029. (Uralic & Altaic Ser: Vol. 108). (Orig.). 1971. pap. text ed. 19.95x (ISBN 0-87750-154-8). Res Ctr Lang Semiotic.

Paulson, J. Sig. Here's a Thought. 67p. 1982. pap. 2.00 (ISBN 0-317-20869-1). CSA Pr.

--How to Love Your Neighbor. 184p. 1974. pap. 4.95 (ISBN 0-317-20873-X). CSA Pr.

--Living with Purpose. 142p. 1968. pap. 3.95 (ISBN 0-317-20871-3). CSA Pr.

--The Thirteen Commandments. 154p. 1964. pap. 3.95 (ISBN 0-317-20872-1). CSA Pr.

--Your Power Tube. 166p. 1969. pap. 3.95 (ISBN 0-317-20870-5). CSA Pr.

Paulson, Ronald. Book & Painting: Shakespeare, Milton, & the Bible. LC 82-2769. (Hodges Lectures Ser.). (Illus.). 248p. 1982. text ed. 23.50x (ISBN 0-87049-358-2). U of Tenn Pr.

Paulson, Ross E., ed. see Jackson, Gregory L.

Paulson, Sig, jt. auth. see Loomis, Evarts G.

Paulson, Wayne. Parish Secretary's Handbook. 192p. (Orig.). 1983. pap. 12.95 (ISBN 0-8066-1898-1, 10-4868). Augsburg.

Paulus Orosius. Seven Books of History Against the Pagans. LC 64-8670. (Fathers of the Church Ser: Vol. 50). 414p. 1964. 22.95x (ISBN 0-8132-0050-4). Cath U Pr.

Pauw, Berthold A. Religion in a Tswana Chiefdom. LC 85-21881. (Illus.). xii, 274p. 1985. Repr. of 1960 ed. lib. bdg. 75.00x (ISBN 0-313-24974-1, PRTC). Greenwood.

Pavitranananda, Swami. A Short Life of the Holy Mother. pap. 1.75 (ISBN 0-87481-122-8). Vedanta Pr.

Pavitrananda, Swami. Common Sense about Yoga. pap. 1.25 (ISBN 0-87481-105-8). Vedanta Pr.

Pavitrananda, Swami, tr. see Pushpadanta.

Pavlos, Andrew J. The Cult Experience. LC 81-13175. (Contributions to the Study of Religion: No. 6). xvi, 209p. 1982. lib. bdg. 29.95 (ISBN 0-313-23164-8, PEX/). Greenwood.

Pavlu, Ricki. Evolution: When Fact Became Fiction. LC 86-13144. (Illus.). 184p. (Orig.). 1986. pap. 6.95 (ISBN 0-932581-51-X). Word Aflame.

Pavry, Jal D. Zoroastrian Doctrine of a Future Life from Death to the Individual Judgment. 2nd. ed. LC 79-10518. Repr. of 1929 ed. 16.50 (ISBN 0-404-50481-7). AMS Pr.

Pawelzik, Fritz. I Sing Your Praise All the Day Long. (Illus., Orig.). 1967. pap. 1.50 (ISBN 0-377-37221-8). Friend Pr.

Pawley, B. The Second Vatican Council: Studies by Eight Anglican Observers. 12.00 (ISBN 0-8446-2713-5). Peter Smith.

Pawlikowski, John & Senior, Donald, eds. Biblical & Theological Reflections on the Challenge of Peace. (Theology & Life Ser.: Vol. 10). 1984. pap. 9.95 (ISBN 0-89453-433-5). M Glazier.

Pawlikowski, John T. Christ in the Light of the Christian-Jewish Dialogue. LC 81-83186. (Stimulus Bks.). 208p. (Orig.). 1982. pap. 7.95 (ISBN 0-8091-2416-5). Paulist Pr.

--What Are They Saying about Christian-Jewish Relations? LC 79-56135. 144p. (Orig.). 1980. pap. 3.95 (ISBN 0-8091-2239-1). Paulist Pr.

Pawsey, Margaret M. The Demon of Discord: Tensions in the Catholic Church of Victoria, 1853-1864. (Illus.). 200p. 1983. 25.00x (ISBN 0-522-84249-6, Pub. by Melbourne U Pr). Intl Spec Bk.

Pax, Noel. Simply Christmas. (Illus.). 72p. (Orig.). 1980. pap. 3.95 (ISBN 0-8027-7168-8); 5.95 (ISBN 0-8027-0672-X). Walker & Co.

Paxson, Ruth. Como Vivir en el Plano Superior. Orig. Title: Life on the Highest Plane. (Span.). 254p. 1984. pap. 4.95 (ISBN 0-8254-1551-9). Kregel.

--Life on the Highest Plane: A Study of the Spiritual Nature & Needs of Man. pap. 12.95 (ISBN 0-8010-7091-0). Baker Bk.

--Rios De Agua Viva. 96p. 1983. pap. 1.95 (ISBN 0-311-46065-8). Casa Bautista.

--Rivers of Living Water. (Moody Classics Ser.). 1984. pap. 3.50 (ISBN 0-8024-7367-9). Moody.

--Wealth, Walk & Warfare of the Christian. 224p. 1939. 11.95 (ISBN 0-8007-0340-5). Revell.

Paxton, Geoffrey J. El Zarandeo del Adventismo. Orig. Title: The Shaking of Adventism. (Span.). 172p. 1982. pap. 5.75 (ISBN 0-311-05604-0, Edit Mundo). Casa Bautista.

Paxton, Robert O., jt. auth. see Marrus, Michael R.

Payer, Pierre J., tr. see Damian, Peter.

Payne, Alfred C. A University at Prayer. LC 86-14613. (Illus.). 1987. 13.95x (ISBN 0-9617635-0-7). VA Tech Educ Found.

Payne, Daniel A. History of the African Methodist Episcopal Church. LC 69-18573. (American Negro: His History & Literature Ser., No. 2). 1969. Repr. of 1891 ed. 19.00 (ISBN 0-405-01885-1). Ayer Co Pubs.

--Recollections of Seventy Years. LC 68-29015. (American Negro: His History & Literature Ser., No. 1). (Illus.). 1968. Repr. of 1888 ed. 14.00 (ISBN 0-405-01834-7). Ayer Co Pubs.

--The Semi-Centenary & the Retrospection of the African Methodist Episcopal Church. facsimile ed. LC 76-37598. (Black Heritage Library Collection). Repr. of 1866 ed. 16.50 (ISBN 0-8369-8974-0). Ayer Co Pubs.

--Sermons & Addresses, 1853-1891. LC 70-38458. (Religion in America, Ser. 2). 1972. 19.00 (ISBN 0-405-04079-2). Ayer Co Pubs.

--Treatise on Domestic Education. facs. ed. LC 75-157373. (Black Heritage Library Collection Ser). 1885. 16.00 (ISBN 0-8369-8811-6). Ayer Co Pubs.

Payne, Darwin R. A Christmas Carol: A Playscript. LC 80-18827. (Illus.). 138p. 1981. pap. 4.95 net (ISBN 0-8093-0999-8). S Ill U Pr.

Payne, David F. Deuteronomy. LC 85-13653. (Daily Study Bible - Old Testament). 210p. 1985. 14.95 (ISBN 0-664-21832-6); pap. 7.95 (ISBN 0-664-24580-3). Westminster.

--First & Second Samuel. LC 82-16009. (The Daily Study Bible-Old Testament). 292p. 1982. 12.95 (ISBN 0-664-21806-7); pap. 6.95 (ISBN 0-664-24573-0). Westminster.

--Kingdoms of the Lord: A History of the Hebrew Kingdoms from Saul to the Fall of Jerusalem. LC 81-3197. (Illus.). pap. 85.00 (ISBN 0-317-11122-1, 2020852). Bks Demand UMI.

Payne, Dorothy. Life after Divorce. (Looking Up Ser.). 24p. (Orig.). 1982. pap. 1.25 booklet (ISBN 0-8298-0610-5). Pilgrim NY.

--Singleness. LC 83-10174. (Choices: Guides for Today's Woman Ser.: Vol. 4). 112p. 1983. pap. 7.95 (ISBN 0-664-24541-2). Westminster.

Payne, E. F., tr. see Schopenhauer, Arthur.

Payne, Elizabeth. Meet the Pilgrim Fathers. (Step-up Books Ser). (Illus.). 1966. PLB 5.99 (ISBN 0-394-90063-4, BYR). Random.

Payne, Ernest A., jt. auth. see Robinson, H. Wheeler.

Payne, Franklin E., Jr. Biblical-Medical Ethics. 1986. text ed. 19.95 (ISBN 0-8010-7099-6). Baker Bk.

Payne, Franklyn E., Jr. Biblical Medical Ethics. Goss, Leonard G., ed. 288p. 1985. write for info. (ISBN 0-88062-068-4). Mott Media.

Payne, J. Barton. Encyclopedia of Biblical Prophecy. 784p. 1980. pap. 18.95 (ISBN 0-8010-7051-1). Baker Bk.

--Theology of the Older Testament. 1962. 12.95 (ISBN 0-310-30721-X, 10545P). Zondervan.

Payne, John B., et al, trs. see Erasmus, Desiderius.

Payne, Joseph E., et al. Together at Baptism. LC 73-144040. (Illus.). 80p. (Orig.). 1971. pap. 1.50 (ISBN 0-87793-031-7). Ave Maria.

Payne, Leanne. The Broken Image. LC 81-65468. 188p. 1981. pap. 6.95 (ISBN 0-89107-215-2, Crossway Bks). Good News.

--Real Presence: The Holy Spirit in the Works of C. S. Lewis. LC 78-71945. 183p. 1979. pap. 6.95 (ISBN 0-89107-164-4, Crossway Bks). Good News.

Payne, Peggy. Teaching for Life-Changing Learning. (C. E. Ministries Ser.). 94p. (Orig.). 1984. pap. 3.50 (ISBN 0-89367-092-8). Light & Life.

Payne, Richard, ed. Letters to Young People: A World Spiritual Legacy for Our Future Earth. (Patterns of World Spirituality Ser.). 240p. pap. 9.95 (ISBN 0-913757-72-1). Paragon Hse.

Payne, Richenda C., tr. see Otto, Rudolf.

Payne, Robert. The Holy Fire. LC 79-27594. 328p. 1980. pap. 8.95 (ISBN 0-913836-61-3). St Vladimirs.

Payne, Suzzy C. & Murwin, Susan A. Creative American Quilting Inspired by the Bible. (Illus.). 192p. 1982. 18.95 (ISBN 0-8007-1402-4). Revell.

Paynell, Thomas, tr. see Erasmus, Desiderius.

Paz, D. G. The Priesthoods & Apostasies of Pierce Connally: A Study of Victorian Conversion & Anticatholicism. (Studies in American Religion: Vol. 18). 418p. 1986. lib. bdg. 69.95x (ISBN 0-88946-662-9). E Mellen.

Pazargadi, Alaedin, tr. see Mutahhari, Murtaza.

Pazargadi, Aluddin, tr. see Ayatollah Morteza Motahhari.

Pazargali, Alaedin, tr. see Ali, Muhammad K.

Pazdan, Mary M. Joel, Obadiah, Haggai, Zechariah, Malachi. (Collegevile Bible Commentary Ser.). 128p. 1986. pap. 2.95 (ISBN 0-8146-1424-8). Liturgical Pr.

Pazhayatil, Harshajan. Counseling & Health Care. LC 76-29068. 385p. 1977. pap. 8.00 (ISBN 0-8199-0623-9). Franciscan Herald.

Pe, Hla. Burma: Literature, Historiography, Scholarship, Language, Life & Buddhism. 224p. 1986. pap. text ed. 17.50 (ISBN 9971-988-00-3, Pub. by Inst Southeast Asian Stud). Gower Pub Co.

Peabody, Francis G. Reminiscences of Present-Day Saints. facsimile ed. LC 74-37525. (Essay Index Reprint Ser). Repr. of 1927 ed. 23.50 (ISBN 0-8369-2576-9). Ayer Co Pubs.

Peabody, James B., jt. auth. see Oliver, Andrew.

Peabody, James B., jt. ed. see Oliver, Andrew.

Peabody, Larry. Secular Word Is Full-Time Service Study Guide. 1976. pap. 1.50 (ISBN 0-87508-449-4). Chr Lit.

--Secular Work Is Full Time Service. 1974. pap. 2.95 (ISBN 0-87508-448-6). Chr Lit.

Peace Education Council & Sister Loretta Carey. Directions for Justice-Peace Education in the Catholic Elementary School. 44p. 1985. 4.80 (ISBN 0-318-20608-0). Natl Cath Educ.

Peace, Philip C. More Than Candlelighting: A Guide for Training Acolytes. LC 82-18973. (Illus.). 64p. (Orig.). 1983. pap. 4.95 (ISBN 0-8298-0642-3). Pilgrim NY.

Peace, Richard. Pilgrimage: A Workbook on Christian Growth. 1985. pap. 6.95 (ISBN 0-8010-7087-2). Baker Bk.

--Small Group Evangelism. rev. ed. 225p. 1983. pap. 6.95 (ISBN 0-87784-329-5). Inter-Varsity.

Peacham, Henry. Minerva Britanna, or a Garden of Heroical Devises. LC 73-171783. (English Experience Ser.: No. 407). 232p. 1971. Repr. of 1612 ed. 33.50 (ISBN 90-221-0407-9). Walter J Johnson.

Peachey, J. Lorne. How to Teach Peace to Children. 32p. (Orig.). 1981. pap. 1.45 (ISBN 0-8361-1969-X). Herald Pr.

Peachey, Paul, ed. Peace, Politics, & the People of God. LC 85-45490. 208p. 1986. pap. 12.95 (ISBN 0-8006-1898-X). Fortress.

--Die Soziale Herkunft Der Schweizer Taufer in Der Feformationszeit. (Ger.). 157p. (Orig.). 1954. pap. 4.50x (ISBN 0-8361-1160-5). Herald Pr.

Peachment, Brian. An Aeroplane or a Grave. 1974. pap. 1.85 (ISBN 0-08-017841-3). Pergamon.

--Devil's Island. 1974. pap. 1.60 (ISBN 0-08-017613-5). Pergamon.

--Down among the Dead Men. 1974. pap. 1.60 (ISBN 0-08-017615-1). Pergamon.

--Three Fighters for Freedom. 1974. pap. 1.60 (ISBN 0-08-017617-8). Pergamon.

Peacock, Heber F. A Translator's Guide to Selected Psalms. (Helps for Translators Ser.). 154p. 1981. pap. 3.30x (ISBN 0-8267-0299-6, 08737, Pub. by United Bible). Am Bible.

--A Translator's Guide to Selections from the First Five Books of the Old Testament. (Helps for Translators Ser.). 323p. 1982. pap. 4.30x (ISBN 0-8267-0298-8, 08765, Pub. by United Bible). Am Bible.

Peacock, James L. Muslim Puritans: Reformist Psychology in Southeast Asian Islam. LC 76-55571. 1978. 36.00x (ISBN 0-520-03403-1). U of Cal Pr.

Peacocke, A. R. Creation & the World of Science: The Bampton Lecturers. 1979. 22.50x (ISBN 0-19-826650-2). Oxford U Pr.

--Science & the Christian Experiment. 1971. pap. 8.95x (ISBN 0-19-213956-8). Oxford U Pr.

Peacocke, A. R., ed. The Sciences & Theology in the Twentieth Century. LC 81-14771. 309p. 1982. 25.00 (ISBN 0-268-01704-2). U of Notre Dame Pr.

Peacocke, Arthur. Intimations of Reality: Critical Realism in Science & Religion. LC 84-40357. (The Mendenhall Lectures). 96p. 1984. text ed. 10.95 (ISBN 0-268-01155-9, 85-11552); pap. text ed. 4.95 (ISBN 0-268-01156-7, 85-11560). U of Notre Dame Pr.

Peacocke, Arthur R. Creation & the World of Science. LC 79-40267. 408p. 1985. Repr. text ed. 9.95 (ISBN 0-268-00755-1, 85-07550, Dist. by Har-Row). U of Notre Dame Pr.

Peacocke, Arthur R., ed. The Sciences & Theology in the Twentieth Century. LC 81-14771. 327p. 1986. pap. 12.95 (ISBN 0-268-01725-5). U of Notre Dame Pr.

Peacocke, Christopher A. Holistic Explanation: Action, Space, Interpretation. 1979. 28.50x (ISBN 0-19-824605-6). Oxford U Pr.

Peake, A. S., et al. Germany in the Nineteenth Century. facs. ed. LC 67-30189. (Manchester University Publications Historical Ser.: No. 24). 1915. 15.00 (ISBN 0-8369-0472-9). Ayer Co Pubs.

Peake, Arthur S. A Critical Introduction to the New Testament. 242p. 1979. Repr. of 1909 ed. lib. bdg. 25.00 (ISBN 0-89987-009-0). Darby Bks.

--A Critical Introduction to the New Testament. 1914. lib. bdg. 25.00 (ISBN 0-8482-9974-4). Norwood Edns.

Peake, Harold, jt. auth. see Fleure, H. F.

Peale, John S. Biblical History As the Quest for Maturity. LC 85-5067. (Symposium Ser.: Vol. 15). 120p. 1985. 39.95x (ISBN 0-88946-706-4). E Mellen.

Peale, Norman V. Amazing Results of Positive Thinking. 1982. pap. 2.75 (ISBN 0-449-20304-2, Crest). Fawcett.

--Enthusiasm Makes the Difference. 1978. pap. 2.50 (ISBN 0-449-23698-6, Crest). Fawcett.

--A Guide to Confident Living. 1977. pap. 2.25 (ISBN 0-449-24173-4, Crest). Fawcett.

--Inspiring Messages for Daily Living. 1981. pap. 2.50 (ISBN 0-449-92383-5, Crest). Fawcett.

--The New Art of Living. 160p. 1977. pap. 2.50 (ISBN 0-449-23938-1, Crest). Fawcett.

--Norman Vincent Peale's Treasury of Courage & Confidence. 256p. 1985. pap. 3.50 (ISBN 0-515-08329-1). Jove Pubns.

--Norman Vincent Peale's Treasury of Joy & Enthusiasm. 192p. 1982. pap. 2.50 (ISBN 0-8007-8450-2). Revell.

--Positive Imaging: The Powerful Way to Change Your Life. 192p. 1981. pap. 2.95 (ISBN 0-8007-8484-7). Revell.

--The Positive Power of Jesus Christ. 1980. pap. 6.95 1981o. p. (ISBN 0-8423-4875-1); pap. 3.95 (ISBN 0-8423-4914-6). Tyndale.

--Power of Positive Thinking. 1954. pap. 9.95 (ISBN 0-13-686402-3). P-H.

--Power of Positive Thinking. 224p. 1966. pap. 3.50 (ISBN 0-8007-8033-7, Spire Bks). Revell.

--The Power of Positive Thinking. 552p. 1985. pap. 15.95 large print ed. (ISBN 0-8027-2465-5). Walker & Co.

--Power of the Plus Factor. 1987. 14.95 (ISBN 0-8007-1526-8). Revell.

--Sin, Sex & Self-Control. 1978. pap. 2.50 (ISBN 0-449-23921-7, Crest). Fawcett.

--Stay Alive All Your Life. 256p. 1978. pap. 2.25 (ISBN 0-449-23513-0, Crest). Fawcett.

--Treasury of Joy & Enthusiasm. 224p. 1982. pap. 2.50 (ISBN 0-449-24550-0, Crest). Fawcett.

Peale, Norman V. & Blanton, Smiley. The Art of Real Happiness. 1976. pap. 2.50 (ISBN 0-449-24062-2, Crest). Fawcett.

Peale, Norman Vincent. The True Joy of Positive Living. 480p. 1985. pap. 16.95 (ISBN 0-8027-2503-1). Walker & Co.

Peale, Ruth S. Secrets of Staying in Love. 272p. 1984. pap. 5.95 (ISBN 0-8407-5910-X). Nelson.

Pearce, Carol, tr. see Alexeyeva, Ludmilla.

Pearce, G. R. John Knox. 1936. Repr. 25.00 (ISBN 0-8274-3855-9). R West.

Pearce, J. Winston. Planning Your Preaching. LC 78-73135. 1979. pap. 6.25 (ISBN 0-8054-2108-4). Broadman.

--To Brighten Each Day. LC 83-70001. 1983. 9.95 (ISBN 0-8054-5220-6). Broadman.

Pearce, Jenny, jt. ed. see Beeson, Trevor.

Pearl, Chaim. The Medieval Jewish Mind. LC 76-184221. 208p. 1973. 8.95 (ISBN 0-87677-043-X). Hartmore.

Pearl, Chaim & Brookes, Reuben. The Guide to Jewish Knowledge. rev. ed. LC 75-25366. 142p. 1976. 8.95 (ISBN 0-87677-138-X). Hartmore.

Pearl, Cyril. The Girl with the Swansdown Seat: Aspects of Mid-Victorian Morality. 6.95 (ISBN 0-686-85784-4, Pub. by Quartet England). Charles River Bks.

Pearl, David, ed. see Fyzee, Asaf A.

Pearl, Patricia. Religious Books for Children: An Annotated Bibliography. (Orig.). 1983. pap. 5.95 (ISBN 0-915324-21-0); pap. 4.75 members. CSLA.

Pearlman, Moshe & Yannai, Yaacov. Historical Sites in the Holy Land. 286p. 1985. 16.95 (ISBN 0-8170-1086-6). Judson.

Pearlman, Myer. Knowing the Doctrines of the Bible. 400p. 1937. 7.95 (ISBN 0-88243-534-5, 02-0534). Gospel Pub.

--Let's Meet the Holy Spirit. (Radiant Bks.). 64p. 1975. pap. 0.95 (ISBN 0-88243-565-5, 02-0565). Gospel Pub.

--The Minister's Service Book. 4.95 (ISBN 0-88243-551-5, 02-0551). Gospel Pub.

--Seeing the Story of the Bible. 128p. 1930. pap. 2.95 (ISBN 0-88243-581-7, 02-0581). Gospel Pub.

--Successful Sunday School Teaching. 112p. 1935. pap. 1.35 (ISBN 0-88243-606-6, 02-0606). Gospel Pub.

--Through the Bible Book by Book, 4 vols. 1935. pap. 2.95 ea.; Vol. 1. (ISBN 0-88243-660-0, 02-0660); Vol. 2. (ISBN 0-88243-661-9, 02-0661); Vol. 3. (ISBN 0-88243-662-7, 02-0662); Vol. 4. (ISBN 0-88243-663-5, 02-0663). Gospel Pub.

Pearson, Arthur. In Christ Jesus. pap. 6.95 (ISBN 0-89957-573-0). AMG Pubs.

Pearson, Birger A. The Pneumatikos-Psychikos Terminology in First Corinthians. LC 73-92202. (Society of Biblical Literature. Dissertation Ser.). 1975. pap. 8.95 (ISBN 0-88414-034-2, 060112). Scholars Pr GA.

Pearson, Birger A. & Goehring, James E., eds. The Roots of Egyptian Christianity. LC 85-47736. (Studies in Antiquity & Christianity). 336p. 1986. 39.95 (ISBN 0-8006-3100-5, 1-3100). Fortress.

Pearson, Carol L. Good-Bye, I Love You. LC 85-23235. 240p. 1986. 15.95 (ISBN 0-394-55032-3). Random.

--A Lasting Peace. 110p. 1983. 7.95 (ISBN 0-934126-38-0). Randall Bk Co.

Pearson, Darrell. Parents As Partners in Youth Ministry. 64p. 1985. 5.95 (ISBN 0-89693-322-9). Victor Bks.

Pearson, Derek. We Wish You a Merry Christmas. 1983. 30.00x (ISBN 0-86334-017-2, Pub. by macdonald Pub UK). State Mutual Bk.

Pearson, D'Orsay W., ed. Pedro Ciruelo's A Treatise Reproving All Superstitions & Forms of Witchcraft: Very Necessary & Useful for All Good Christians Zealous for Their Salvation. Maio, Eugene & Pearson, D'Orsay W., trs. LC 74-4979. 366p. 1976. 27.50 (ISBN 0-8386-1580-5). Fairleigh Dickinson.

Pearson, D'Orsay W., tr. see Pearson, D'Orsay W.

Pearson, E. Norman. Space Time & Self. rev. ed. LC 71-1546. (Illus.). pap. 5.95 (ISBN 0-8356-0409-8, Quest). Theos Pub Hse.

Pearson, Esther. Early Churches of Washington State. LC 79-57216. (Illus.). 182p. 1980. 27.50 (ISBN 0-295-95713-1). U of Wash Pr.

Pearson, H. F., et al. Preliminary Report on the Synagogue at Dura-Europos. (Illus.). 1936. pap. 49.50x (ISBN 0-686-51290-1). Elliots Bks.

Pearson, Hesketh. The Smith of Smiths Being the Life, Wit & Humor of Sydney Smith. LC 73-145230. (Literature Ser.). (Illus.). 338p. 1972. Repr. of 1934 ed. 39.00x (ISBN 0-403-01146-9). Scholarly.

Pearson, J. D. & Behn, Wolfgang, eds. Index Islamicus, Fifth Supplement 1976-1980. 944p. 1983. Set. 159.00x (ISBN 0-7201-1650-3); Pt. 1: Articles. 96.00 (ISBN 0-7201-1669-4); Pt. 2: Monographs. 64.00 (ISBN 0-7201-1668-6). Mansell.

--Index Islamicus: First Supplement 1956-1960. 344p. 1978. Repr. of 1962 ed. 53.00x (ISBN 0-7201-0381-9). Mansell.

--Index Islamicus: Primary Sequence 1906-1955. 933p. 1958. 75.00x (ISBN 0-7201-0380-0). Mansell.

--Index Islamicus: Second Supplement, 1961-1965. 372p. 1967. 53.00 (ISBN 0-7201-0382-7). Mansell.

--Index Islamicus: Third Supplement 1966-1970. 420p. 1972. 53.00x (ISBN 0-7201-0282-0). Mansell.

Pearson, J. D. & Walsh, Ann, eds. Index Islamicus, Fourth Supplement: Part 2, 1972-73. 108p. 1974. 64.00 (ISBN 0-7201-0286-3). Mansell.

--Index Islamicus: Fourth Supplement, Part 4, 1974-1975. 128p. 1975. pap. 10.00x (ISBN 0-7201-0288-X). Mansell.

Pearson, Keith, ed. Worship in the Round: Patterns of Informative & Participative Worship. (Illus.). 88p. (Orig.). 1983. pap. 5.95 (ISBN 0-85819-343-4, Pub. by JBCE). ANZ Religious Pubns.

Pearson, Lionel. Popular Ethics in Ancient Greece. 1962. 20.00x (ISBN 0-8047-0102-4). Stanford U Pr.

Pearson, Mary R., ed. Fifty-Two Children's Programs. 224p. (Orig.). 1985. pap. 14.95 (ISBN 0-89636-189-6). Accent Bks.

Pearson, Mary Rose. More Children's Church Time. LC 82-70390. 220p. (Orig.). 1982. 14.95 (ISBN 0-89636-082-2). Accent Bks.

Pearson, Nancy, tr. see Corbin, Henry.

Peart-Binns, John S. Defender of the Church of England: A Biography of R. R. Williams, Bishop of Leicester. 172p. 1984. 30.00x (ISBN 0-317-43628-7, Pub. by Amate Pr. Ltd.). State Mutual Bk.

Pease, T. C. The Leveller Movement. 11.75 (ISBN 0-8446-1345-2). Peter Smith.

Peatling, John H. Religious Education in a Psychological Key. LC 81-8678. 439p. (Orig.). 1981. pap. 14.95 (ISBN 0-89135-027-6). Religious Educ.

Peatling, John H., ed. Annual Review of Research: Religious Education, Vol. 1. (Orig.). 1980. pap. 5.95 (ISBN 0-915744-23-6). Character Res.

--Annual Review of Research: Religious Education, Vol. 2. viii, 148p. (Orig.). 1981. pap. 6.95 (ISBN 0-915744-26-0). Character Res.

Peau, Andrew T. Le see Le Peau, Andrew T.

Pebworth, Ted-Larry, jt. auth. see Summers, Claude J.

Peccorini, Francisco L. On to the World of "Freedom": A Kantian Meditation on Finite Selfhood. LC 82-40233. 370p. (Orig.). 1982. lib. bdg. 30.25 o. p. (ISBN 0-8191-2643-8); pap. text ed. 15.75 (ISBN 0-8191-2644-6). U Pr of Amer.

Pechota, Vratislav. The Right to Know One's Human Rights: A Road Toward Marriage & Family. LC 83-72868. 52p. 1983. pap. 2.50 (ISBN 0-87495-056-2). Am Jewish Comm.

Peck, Abraham J., jt. auth. see Marcus, Jacob R.

Peck, Abraham J., ed. Jews & Christians after the Holocaust. LC 81-70665. pap. 31.80 (2029611). Bks Demand UMI.

Peck, Abraham J., jt. ed. see Marcus, Jacob R.

Peck, Alan. The Priestly Gift in Mishnah: A Study of Tractate Terumot. LC 81-2764. (Brown BJS Ser.). 1981. pap. 16.50 (ISBN 0-89130-488-6, 140020). Scholars Pr GA.

Peck, George. Pentecost 3. LC 84-18756. (Proclamation 3 A). 64p. 1987. pap. 3.75 (ISBN 0-8006-4124-8, 1-4124). Fortress.

--Simplicity: A Rich Quaker's View. LC 72-97851. (Orig.). 1973. pap. 2.50x (ISBN 0-87574-189-4). Pendle Hill.

--The Triple Way. LC 77-79824. 321p. (Orig.). 1977. pap. 2.50x (ISBN 0-87574-213-0). Pendle Hill.

Peck, George & Hoffman, John S., eds. The Laity in Ministry. 176p. 1984. pap. 7.95 (ISBN 0-8170-1041-6). Judson.

Peck, Jane C. Self & Family. LC 84-13166. (Choices: Guides for Today's Woman Ser.: Vol. 11). 118p. 1984. pap. 6.95 (ISBN 0-664-24547-1). Westminster.

Peck, John. What the Bible Teaches about the Holy Spirit. 1979. pap. 3.95 (ISBN 0-8423-7882-0). Tyndale.

Peck, John M. Father Clark: Or, The Pioneer Preacher. 285p. 1986. pap. text ed. 6.95x (ISBN 0-8290-1901-4). Irvington.

Peck, M. Scott. People of the Lie: The Hope for Healing Human Evil. LC 83-13631. 269p. 1983. 15.95 (ISBN 0-671-45492-7). S&S.

--People of the Lie: The Hope for Healing Human Evil. 1985. pap. 7.95 (ISBN 0-671-52816-5, Touchstone Bks). S&S.

--The Road Less Traveled. 448p. 1985. pap. 16.95 (ISBN 0-8027-2498-1). Walker & Co.

Peck, M. Scott, et al. What Return Can I Make? The Dimensions of the Christian Experience. LC 85-11945. 96p. 1985. 24.95 (ISBN 0-317-38030-3). S&S.

Peck, Paul L. Basic Spiritual Metaphysics. LC 78-61984. 1978. 14.50 (ISBN 0-87881-079-X). Mojave Bks.

--Footsteps along the Path. rev. ed. (Spiritual Metaphysics: Freeways to Divine Awareness Ser.). 164p. (Orig.). 1982. pap. 7.95 (ISBN 0-941600-01-7). Harmony Pr.

--Freeway to Health. (Spiritual Metaphysics: Freeways to Divine Awareness Ser.). 264p. (Orig.). 1982. pap. 7.95 (ISBN 0-941600-04-1). Harmony Pr.

--Freeway to Human Love. (Spiritual Metaphysics: Freeways to Divine Awareness Ser.). 264p. (Orig.). 1982. pap. 7.95 (ISBN 0-941600-06-8). Harmony Pr.

--Freeway to Personal Growth. (Spiritual Awareness: Freeways to Divine Awareness Ser.). 264p. (Orig.). 1982. pap. 7.95 (ISBN 0-941600-07-6). Harmony Pr.

--Freeway to Work & Health. (Spiritual Metaphysics: Freeways to Divine Awareness Ser.). 264p. (Orig.). 1982. pap. 7.95 (ISBN 0-941600-05-X). Harmony Pr.

--Inherit the Kingdom. rev. ed. (Spiritual Metaphysics: Freeways to Divine Awareness Ser.). (Orig.). 1982. pap. 7.95 (ISBN 0-941600-02-5). Harmony Pr.

--Intermediate Spiritual Metaphysics. LC 78-61985. (Spiritual Metaphysics Ser.: Vol. 2). 1979. 15.95 (ISBN 0-87881-081-1); pap. 13.50 (ISBN 0-87881-082-X). Mojave Bks.

--Milestones of the Way. rev. ed. (Spiritual Metaphysics: Freeways to Divine Awareness Ser.). 250p. (Orig.). 1982. pap. 7.95 (ISBN 0-941600-03-3). Harmony Pr.

Peck, Richard. Rock: Making Musical Choices. 174p. (Orig.). 1985. pap. 4.95 (ISBN 0-89084-297-3). Bob Jones Univ Pr.

Peck, Robert L. American Meditation & Beginning Yoga. 1976. 6.00 (ISBN 0-685-71846-8). Personal Dev Ctr.

Peck, William J., ed. New Studies in Bonhoeffer's Ethics. (Toronto Studies in Theology: Vol. 31). 284p. 1987. lib. bdg. 49.95 (ISBN 0-88946-775-7). E Mellen.

Peckham, Brian. The Composition of the Deuteronomic History. (Harvard Semitic Museum Monographs). 1985. 13.95 (ISBN 0-89130-909-8, 04-00-35). Scholars Pr GA.

Peckthall, Mardaduke, tr. Holy Quaran. 1986. Repr. of 1983 ed. 20.00x (ISBN 0-8364-1623-6, Pub. by Rajesh). South Asia Bks.

Pederson, Phillip E., ed. What Does This Mean? Luther's Catechisms Today. LC 79-50082. 1979. pap. 7.95 (ISBN 0-8066-1723-3, 10-7047). Augsburg.

Pedlow, J. C. Windows on the Holy Land. (Illus.). 150p. 1980. pap. 8.95 (ISBN 0-227-67839-7). Attic Pr.

Pedraz, Juan L. I Wish I Could Believe. Attanasio, Salvatore, tr. from Span. LC 82-20606. 201p. (Orig.). 1983. pap. 7.95 (ISBN 0-8189-0445-3). Alba.

Pedretti, Carlo & Brown, David A. Leonardo, 3 vols. (Illus.). 1985. Set. pap. 29.95 (ISBN 0-295-96323-9, Pub. by Natl Gallery of Art). U of Wash Pr.

Pedrick, Jean. Saints. (Chapbook Ser.: No. 1). 40p. (Orig.). 1980. pap. 4.95 (ISBN 0-937672-00-9). Rowan Tree.

Pedrini, Duilio T., jt. auth. see Pedrini, Lura.

Pedrini, Lura & Pedrini, Duilio T. Serpent Imagery & Symbolism. 1966. 10.95 (ISBN 0-8084-0274-9); pap. 6.95x (ISBN 0-8084-0275-7). New Coll U Pr.

Peel, J. D. & Stewart, Charles C., eds. Popular Islam South of the Sahara. (African Studies). 128p. 1986. pap. 15.00 (ISBN 0-7190-1975-3, Pub. by Manchester Univ Pr). Longwood Pub Group.

Peele, George. Samples from the Love of King David & Fair Bethsabe: With Reference Portions of the Bible. Dreher, G. K., ed. LC 79-56834. 71p. (Orig.). 1980. pap. 4.95 (ISBN 0-9601000-2-4). Longshanks Bk.

Peeler, E. F., tr. see Gurian, Waldemar.

Peelman, Nancy. The Beasts, Birds & Fish of the Bible. LC 75-14605. (Illus.). 40p. (Orig.). 1975. pap. 4.50 (ISBN 0-8192-1197-4). Morehouse.

--The Plants of the Bible. LC 75-14607. (Illus.). 40p. (Orig.). 1975. pap. 4.50 (ISBN 0-8192-1196-6). Morehouse.

Peerman, Dean G., jt. ed. see Marty, Martin E.

Peers, Allison, tr. see Lull, Ramon.

Peers, E. A. Studies of the Spanish Mystics, 3 vols. 1977. lib. bdg. 300.00 (ISBN 0-8490-2706-3). Gordon Pr.

Peers, E. Alison. The Life of Teresa of Jesus. 1960. pap. 5.50 (ISBN 0-385-01109-1, Im). Doubleday.

Peers, E. Allison. The Mystics of Spain. 1977. lib. bdg. 59.95 (ISBN 0-8490-2322-X). Gordon Pr.

--St. John of the Cross & Other Lectures & Addresses. 1977. lib. bdg. 59.95 (ISBN 0-8490-2558-3). Gordon Pr.

Peers, Edgar A. Behind That Wall. facs. ed. LC 72-90672. (Essay Index Reprint Ser). 1948. 15.00 (ISBN 0-8369-1210-1). Ayer Co Pubs.

--The Church in Spain, Seventeen Thirty-Seven to Nineteen Thirty-Seven. 1980. lib. bdg. 44.95 (ISBN 0-8490-3149-4). Gordon Pr.

--St. John of the Cross, & Other Lectures & Addresses, 1920-1945. facs. ed. LC 70-136650. (Biography Index Reprint Ser.). 1946. 16.00 (ISBN 0-8369-8045-X). Ayer Co Pubs.

Peet, Henry, ed. Register of Baptisms of the French Protestant Refugees Settled at Thorney, Cambridgeshire, 1654-1727. Bd. with Letters of Denization. Shaw, William A., ed. Repr. of 1911 ed; Registers of the French Church of Portarlington, Ireland. Le Fanu, Thomas P., ed. Repr. of 1908 ed; Registers of the French Churches of Bristol. Lart, Charles E., ed. Repr. of 1912 ed; Register of the French Church at Thorpe-le-Spoken. Waller, William C., ed. Repr. of 1912 ed. (Huguenot Society of London Publications Ser.: Vols. 17 & 20). Repr. of 1903 ed. 144.00 (ISBN 0-317-17885-7). Kraus Repr.

Peet, Stephen O. Myths & Symbols, or Aboriginal Religions in America. LC 76-27515. (Illus.). 1976. Repr. of 1905 ed. lib. bdg. 45.00 (ISBN 0-89341-039-X). Longwood Pub Group.

Peeters, Flor. Jubilate Deo Omnis Terra: Psalm 99, Score & Brass Parts Accompaniment 1954. pap. 20.00 (ISBN 0-317-09824-1, 2003407). Bks Demand UMI.

Peffley, Bill. Prayerful Pauses with Jesus & Mary. (Illus.). 96p. (Orig.). 1985. pap. 5.95 (ISBN 0-89622-251-9). Twenty-Third.

Pegis, Anton C. Saint Thomas & Philosophy. (Aquinas Lecture). 1964. 7.95 (ISBN 0-87462-129-1). Marquette.

--Saint Thomas & the Greeks. (Aquinas Lecture). 1939. 7.95 (ISBN 0-87462-103-8). Marquette.

Pegis, Anton C., ed. see St. Thomas Aquinas.

Pegis, Anton C. see St. Thomas Aquinas.

Pegoda, Dan, jt. auth. see Sims, Tim.

Pegram, Don R. America: Christian or Pagan. 1982. pap. 1.25 (ISBN 0-89265-082-6). Randall Hse.

--Great Churches-Today's Essentials. 1982. pap. 1.25 (ISBN 0-89265-083-4). Randall Hse.

--Sheep among Wolves. 1982. pap. 1.25 (ISBN 0-89265-084-2). Randall Hse.

--Sinning Against the Holy Spirit. 1982. pap. 1.25 (ISBN 0-89265-085-0). Randall Hse.

--Why We Do Not Speak in Tongues. 1982. pap. 1.25 (ISBN 0-89265-086-9). Randall Hse.

Pegues, Albert W. Our Baptist Ministers & Schools. Repr. of 1892 ed. 44.00 (ISBN 0-384-45660-X). Johnson Repr.

Pegues, Etta B. The Abundant Life. 1971. pap. 2.75 (ISBN 0-88027-081-0). Firm Foun Pub.

Peguy, Charles. Notre Seigneur. pap. 2.50 (ISBN 0-685-37032-1). French & Eur.

--Un Nouveau Theologien, M. Laudet. pap. 3.95 (ISBN 0-685-37044-5). French & Eur.

--Oeuvres en Prose: 1909-1914. Peguy, M., ed. (Bibl. de la Pleiade). 1957. 42.95 (ISBN 0-685-01987-X). French & Eur.

Peguy, M., ed. see Peguy, Charles.
Peifer, Jane & Nolt, Marilyn. Good Thoughts about Me. (Good Thoughts Ser.: No. 1). (Illus.). 24p. (Orig.). 1985. pap. 2.95 (ISBN 0-8361-3389-7). Herald Pr.
--Good Thoughts about People. (Good Thoughts Ser.: No. 3). (Illus.). 24p. (Orig.). 1985. pap. 2.95 (ISBN 0-8361-3390-0). Herald Pr.
--Good Thoughts at Bedtime. (Good Thoughts Ser.: No. 2). (Illus.). 24p. (Orig.). 1985. pap. 2.95 (ISBN 0-8361-3388-9). Herald Pr.
Peil, William. Affirmation: The Touch of Life. LC 82-20655. (Illus.). 48p. 1983. pap. 1.95 (ISBN 0-89571-026-9). Affirmation.
--The Big Way. 1983. 1.00 (ISBN 0-89536-952-4, 7503). CSS of Ohio.
Peile, James H. The Reproach of the Gospel: An Inquiry into the Apparent Failure of Christianity As a General Rule of Life & Conduct. 1977. lib. bdg. 59.95 (ISBN 0-8490-2516-8). Gordon Pr.
Peiris, William. The Western Contribution to Buddhism. 372p. 1974. lib. bdg. 79.95 (ISBN 0-87968-550-6). Krishna Pr.
--Western Contribution to Buddhism. 1973. 11.25 (ISBN 0-8426-0537-1). Orient Bk Dist.
Pelekanidis, S. M., et al. The Treasures of Mount Athos: Illuminated Manuscripts, Vol. 1. (Patriarchal Institute for Patristic Studies). (Illus.). 500p. 1975. cancelled (ISBN 0-89241-003-5). Caratzas.
Peletz, Michael G. Social History & Evolution in the Interrelationship of Adat & Islam in Rembau, Negeri Sembilan. 59p. (Orig.). 1981. pap. text ed. 9.50x (ISBN 9971-902-28-1, Pub. by Inst Southeast Asian Stud). Gower Pub Co.
Pelgrin, Mark. And a Time to Die. Moon, Sheila & Howes, Elizabeth, eds. LC 75-26836. 159p. 1976. pap. 2.95 (ISBN 0-8356-0305-9, Quest). Theos Pub Hse.
Pelham, R. W. A Shaker's Answer. 32p. 1981. pap. 1.50 (ISBN 0-937942-09-X). Shaker Mus.
Peli, Pinchas. Shabbat Shalom: A Renewed Encounter with the Sabbath. 120p. 1986. pap. 7.95 (ISBN 0-940646-37-4). Rossel Bks.
Peli, Pinchas, tr. see Soloveitchik, Joseph D.
Pelikan, Jaroslav. Bach among the Theologians. LC 86-45219. 176p. 1986. 14.95 (ISBN 0-8006-0792-9, 1-792). Fortress.
--The Christian Tradition, Vol. 1. LC 79-142042. 1971. pap. 12.95 (ISBN 0-226-65371-4, P644, Phoen). U of Chicago Pr.
--The Christian Tradition, a History of the Development of Doctrine: The Spirit of Eastern Christendom, 600-1700, Vol. 2. LC 79-142042. 1977. pap. 10.95 (ISBN 0-226-65373-0, P738, Phoen). U of Chicago Pr.
--The Christian Tradition: A History of the Development of Doctrine, Vol. 1: Emergence of the Catholic Tradition, 100-600. LC 79-142042. 1971. 25.00x (ISBN 0-226-65370-6). U of Chicago Pr.
--The Christian Tradition: A History of the Development of Doctrine Vol. III: the Growth of Medieval Theology (600-1300) LC 78-1501. 1978. 27.50x (ISBN 0-226-65374-9). U of Chicago Pr.
--The Christian Tradition: a History of the Development of Doctrine, Vol. 2: The Spirit of Eastern Christendom, 600-1700. LC 79-142042. xxv, 432p. 1974. 25.00x (ISBN 0-226-65372-2). U of Chicago Pr.
--The Christian Tradition: A History of the Development of Doctrine, Vol. 3, The Growth of Medieval Theology, 600-1300. LC 78-1501. xxviii, 336p. 1980. pap. 12.95 (ISBN 0-226-65375-7, P896). U of Chicago Pr.
--The Christian Tradition: A History of the Development of Doctrine, Vol. 4: Reformation of Church & Dogma (1300-1700) LC 79-142042. lii, 426p. 1985. 27.50x (ISBN 0-226-65376-5); pap. 14.95 (ISBN 0-226-65377-3). U of Chicago Pr.
--Development of Christian Doctrine: Some Historical Prolegomena. LC 69-14864. (St. Thomas More Lectures Ser.: No. 3). 174p. 1969. 18.50x (ISBN 0-300-01082-6). Yale U Pr.
--Jesus Through the Centuries: His Place in the History of Culture. LC 85-2428. (Illus.). 272p. 1985. 22.50 (ISBN 0-300-03496-2). Yale U Pr.
--Jesus Through the Centuries: His Place in the History of Culture. LC 86-45679. (Illus.). 288p. 1987. pap. 8.95 (ISBN 0-06-097080-4, PL 7080, PL). Har-Row.
Pelikan, Jaroslav, ed. Luther the Expositor. 1959. 13.95 (ISBN 0-570-06431-7, 15-1741). Concordia.
--Luther's Works, Vol. 9. LC 55-9893. 1960. 14.95 (ISBN 0-570-06409-0, 15-1751). Concordia.
--Luther's Works, Vol. 21. LC 55-9893. 16.95 (ISBN 0-570-06421-X, 15-1763). Concordia.
--Luther's Works, Vol. 22. Bertram, Martin, tr. LC 55-9893. 1957. 17.95 (ISBN 0-570-06422-8, 15-1764). Concordia.
--Luther's Works, Vol. 24. Bertram, Martin H., tr. LC 55-9893. 1961. 16.95 (ISBN 0-570-06424-4, 15-1766). Concordia.
--Luther's Works: Genesis Chapters 1-5, Vol. 1. Schick, George V., tr. LC 55-9893. 1958. 15.95 (ISBN 0-570-06401-5, 15-1743). Concordia.
--Luther's Works: Genesis Chapters 15-20, Vol. 3. Schick, George V., tr. LC 55-9893. 1961. 15.95 (ISBN 0-570-06403-1, 15-1745). Concordia.
--Luther's Works: Genesis Chapters 6-11, Vol. 2. Schick, George V., tr. LC 55-9893. 1960. 16.95 (ISBN 0-570-06402-3, 15-1744). Concordia.
Pelikan, Jaroslav, ed. see Luther, Martin.
Pelikan, Jaroslav see Luther, Martin.
Pelikan, Jaroslav, et al, trs. from Lat. Luther's Works, Vol. 15, Letters On Ecclesiastes, Song Of Solomon, & The Last Words Of David. LC 55-9893. 1971. 15.95 (ISBN 0-570-06415-5, 15-1757). Concordia.
Pelikan, Jaroslav J. The Shape of Death: Life, Death, & Immortality in the Early Fathers. LC 78-6030. 1978. Repr. of 1961 ed. lib. bdg. 22.50x (ISBN 0-313-20458-6, PESD). Greenwood.
Pelikan, Judy, illus. The Words of Christ. Golbitz, Pat, ed. LC 86-60824. (Illus.). 64p. 1986. 14.95 (ISBN 0-688-06240-7). Morrow.
Pell, Eve. The Big Chill: How the Reagan Administration, Corporate America & Religious Conservatives Are Subverting Free Speech & the Public's Right to Know. LC 83-71942. 278p. 1984. 22.50 (ISBN 0-8070-6160-3). Beacon Pr.
Pellegrin, Mignonette, ed. see Young, Robert & Young, Loy.
Pellegrino, Cardinal Michael. Give What You Command. flexible bdg 3.00 (ISBN 0-89942-580-1, 580/04). Catholic Bk Pub.
Pelletier, Joseph A. Sun Danced at Fatima. rev. ed. LC 83-45046. (Illus.). 240p. 1983. pap. 6.95 (ISBN 0-385-18965-6, Im). Doubleday.
Pelletier, Robert. Planets in Houses: Experiencing Your Environment Planets. Anderson, Margaret, ed. (Planets Ser.). (Illus.). 1978. pap. 19.95 (ISBN 0-914918-27-3). Para Res.
Pelley, Ronn T. In Word & Deed: A Student's Beginning Guide to Understanding the Luthern Worship Service. (Pass Along Ser.). (Illus.). 32p. 1986. pap. 2.95 (ISBN 0-933350-49-X). Morse Pr.
Pellman, Donald R., jt. auth. see Glick, Ferne P.
Peloubet, F. N., ed. see Smith, William.
Peloubet, Francis N. Everyday Bible Dictionary. 816p. 1967. 14.95 (ISBN 0-310-30850-X, 10551). Zondervan.
Peloubet, M. A., ed. see Smith, William.
Pelt, G. Van see Van Pelt, G.
Pelt, Gertrude W. Van see Van Pelt, Gertrude W.
Pelt, Nancy L. Van see Van Pelt, Nancy L.
Pelt, Nancy Van see Van Pelt, Nancy.
Pelt, Nancy Van see Van Pelt, Nancy L.
Peltier, A. C. Dictionnaire Universel et Complet des Conciles, 2 vols. Migne, J. P., ed. (Encyclopedie Theologique Ser.: Vols. 13-14). (Fr.). 1378p. Repr. of 1846 ed. lib. bdg. 175.00x (ISBN 0-89241-236-4). Caratzas.
Pelton, Donald. Spiritual Quest: Variations on a Theme. (Illus., Orig.). 1986. pap. 7.95 (ISBN 0-933169-02-7). Heldon Pr.
Pelton, Robert D. The Trickster in West Africa: A Study of Mythic Irony & Sacred Delight. LC 77-75396. (Hermeneutics: Studies in the History of Religions). 1980. 42.00x (ISBN 0-520-03477-5). U of Cal Pr.
Pelton, Robert W. The Devil & Karen Kingston: The Incredible Three-Day Exorcism That Brought Miraculous Deliverance to a Totally Demonized Young Girl. LC 76-12148. (Illus.). 1976. 7.50 (ISBN 0-916620-10-7). Portals Pr.
Pelton, Robert W., jt. auth. see Farley, G. M.
Pe Maung Tin, tr. see Buddhaghosa.
Pemberton, Larry. Called to Care. (Orig.). 1985. pap. text ed. 4.95 (ISBN 0-87148-183-9). Pathway Pr.
Pemberton, Prentiss L., jt. auth. see Finn, Daniel R.
Pendlebury, D. L., tr. see Shah Waliullah.
Pendlebury, David. Jami: Yusuf & Zulaika. 1980. 16.95 (ISBN 0-900860-77-4). Ins Study Human.
Pendleton, J. M. Compendio de Teologia Cristiana. Trevino, Alejandro, tr. Orig. Title: Christian Doctrines: Compendium of Theology. (Span.). 413p. 1983. pap. 5.95 (ISBN 0-311-09008-7). Casa Bautista.
Pendleton, James H. Christian Doctrines: A Compendium of Theology. 16.95 (ISBN 0-8170-0037-2). Judson.
Pendleton, James M. Baptist Church Manual. rev. ed. 1966. Repr. of 1867 ed. 8.50 (ISBN 0-8054-2510-1). Broadman.
Pendleton, Joe. The Joy of Bible Study. (Illus.). 64p. (Orig.). 1981. pap. 1.95 (ISBN 0-89114-106-5); P. 32. tchr's ed. 1.50 (ISBN 0-89114-107-3). Baptist Pub Hse.
Pendleton, Nathaniel D. The Glorification: Sermons & Papers. 2nd ed. 221p. 1985. Repr. of 1941 ed. 7.00 (ISBN 0-910557-10-1). Acad New Church.
--Selected Papers & Addresses. 251p. 1985. 7.00 (ISBN 0-910557-09-8). Acad New Church.
Pendleton, Winston K. Do It! Six Steps to Happiness. Lambert, Herbert, ed. LC 86-6112. 96p. (Orig.). 1986. pap. 5.95 (ISBN 0-8272-0613-5). CBP.
--How to Stop Worrying-Forever. LC 66-19811. 80p. 1975. Repr. of 1966 ed. 4.95 (ISBN 0-88289-083-2). Pelican.
Penelhum, Terence. God & Skepticism. 1983. lib. bdg. 34.95 (ISBN 90-277-1550-5, Pub. by Reidel Holland). Kluwer Academic.
Penelope, Sr., tr. William of St. Thierry: On Contemplating God, Prayer, Meditations. (Cistercian Fathers Ser.: No. 3). 1970. pap. 5.00 (ISBN 0-87907-903-7). Cistercian Pubns.
Penington, Isaac. The Inward Journey of Isaac Penington. Leach, Robert J., ed. LC 44-280. (Orig.). 1944. pap. 2.50x (ISBN 0-87574-029-4). Pendle Hill.
Penkower, Monty N. The Jews Were Expendable: Free World Diplomacy & the Holocaust. LC 82-17490. 446p. 1983. 27.50 (ISBN 0-252-00747-6). U of Ill Pr.
Penn, Bennett. The Path of Transcendence. 144p. 1987. pap. text ed. 10.00 (ISBN 0-682-40332-6). Exposition Pr FL.
Penn, Gregory E. Freedom, the Essence of Life. LC 78-75026. 1979. pap. 5.95 (ISBN 0-87516-288-6). De Vorss.
Penn, William. Fruits of Solitude. pap. 5.95 (ISBN 0-913408-39-5). Friends United.
--The Rise & Progress of the People Called Quakers. 1977. pap. 2.95 (ISBN 0-913408-32-8). Friends United.
Penn, William & Brinton, Anna. No Cross No Crown. 1983. pap. text ed. 2.50x (ISBN 0-87574-030-8, 030). Pendle Hill.
Pennel, Joe E., Jr. The Whisper of Christmas: Reflections for Advent & Christmas. LC 84-50839. 128p. (Orig.). 1984. pap. 4.95 (ISBN 0-8358-0492-5). Upper Room.
Pennell, Joseph. The Jew at Home: Impressions of Jewish Life in Russia & Austria. 1976. lib. bdg. 134.95 (ISBN 0-8490-2098-0). Gordon Pr.
Penner, Clifford & Penner, Joyce. The Gift of Sex. 1981. pap. 11.95 (ISBN 0-8499-2893-1). Word Bks.
Penner, Joyce, jt. auth. see Penner, Clifford.
Penniman, Josiah H. A Book about the English Bible. 1977. Repr. of 1920 ed. lib. bdg. 27.50 (ISBN 0-8492-2101-3). R West.
Pennington, Arthur R. The Life & Character of Erasmus. 1977. lib. bdg. 59.95 (ISBN 0-8490-2159-6). Gordon Pr.
Pennington, Basil. Challenges in Prayer. (Ways of Prayer Ser.: Vol. 1). 1982. 8.95 (ISBN 0-89453-425-4); pap. 4.95 (ISBN 0-89453-275-8). M Glazier.
--The Eucharist Yesterday & Today. 224p. 1984. 10.95 (ISBN 0-8245-0602-2). Crossroad NY.
--Eucharist: Yesterday & Today. 148p. pap. 6.95 (ISBN 0-8245-0690-1). Crossroad NY.
--The Last of the Fathers. LC 82-24098. 1983. pap. 14.95 (ISBN 0-932506-24-0). St Bedes Pubns.
--O Holy Mountain: Journal of a Retreat on Mount Athos. pap. 6.95 (ISBN 0-89453-382-7). M Glazier.
Pennington, Celeste, ed. see Creswell, Mike.
Pennington, Celeste, ed. see Durham, Jackie.
Pennington, Chester, jt. auth. see Kingsbury, Jack D.
Pennington, Kenneth. Pope & Bishops: A Study of the Papal Monarchy in the Twelfth & Thirteenth Centuries. LC 83-21799. (The Middle Ages Ser.). 227p. 1984. 31.50x (ISBN 0-8122-7918-2). U of Pa Pr.
Pennington, Kenneth, jt. ed. see Somerville, Robert.
Pennington, M. B. The Manual of Life: The New Testament for Daily Living. 128p. (Orig.). 1985. pap. 4.95 (ISBN 0-8091-2710-5). Paulist Pr.
Pennington, M. B., ed. One Yet Two: Monastic Tradition East & West. LC 75-26146. (Cistercian Studies Ser.: No. 29). 1976. 14.95 (ISBN 0-87907-800-6). Cistercian Pubns.
Pennington, M. Basil. Breaking Bread: The Table Talk of Jesus. LC 85-51008. 160p. 1986. 10.95 (ISBN 0-86683-489-3, HarpR). Har-Row.
--Centered Living: The Way of Centering Prayer. LC 85-27474. (Illus.). 216p. 1986. 15.95 (ISBN 0-385-23186-5). Doubleday.
--Centering Prayer: Renewing an Ancient Christian Prayer Form. LC 82-45077. 256p. 1982. pap. 4.50 (ISBN 0-385-18179-5, Im). Doubleday.
--Daily We Follow Him: Learning Discipleship from Peter. LC 86-20157. 160p. 1987. pap. 4.95 (ISBN 0-385-23535-6, Im). Doubleday.
--Daily We Touch Him: Practical Religious Experiences. LC 76-20836. 1977. pap. 3.50 (ISBN 0-385-14802-X, Im). Doubleday.
--In Peter's Footsteps: Learning to Be a Disciple. LC 85-1541. 144p. 1985. 12.95 (ISBN 0-385-19398-X). Doubleday.
--Jubilee: A Monk's Journal. LC 81-82336. 208p. (Orig.). 1981. 6.95 (ISBN 0-8091-2402-5). Paulist Pr.
--Mary Today: The Challenging Woman. LC 86-29183. (Illus.). 168p. 1987. 13.95 (ISBN 0-385-23609-3). Doubleday.
--Monastic Journey to India. 144p. (Orig.). 1982. pap. 9.95 (ISBN 0-8164-2398-9, HarpR). Har-Row.
--Place Apart: Monastic Prayer & Practice for Everyone. LC 81-43566. 168p. 1985. pap. 5.95 (ISBN 0-385-19706-3, Im). Doubleday.
--Pocket Book of Prayers. LC 85-12936. 192p. 1986. pap. 4.50 (ISBN 0-385-23298-5, Im). Doubleday.
--Prayertimes: Morning-Midday-Evening. LC 87-4212. 168p. 1987. pap. 3.95 (ISBN 0-385-24061-9, Im). Doubleday.
Pennington, M. Basil, ed. The Cistercian Spirit: A Symposium in Memory of Thomas Merton. (Cistercian Studies: No. 3). xvi, 286p. 1973. Repr. of 1972 ed. 7.95 (ISBN 0-87907-803-0). Cistercian Pubns.
--Saint Bernard of Clairvaux: Essays Commemorating the Eighth Centenary of His Canonization. LC 77-4487. (Cistercian Studies: No. 28). 1977. 14.95 (ISBN 0-87907-828-6). Cistercian Pubns.
Pennington, M. Basil, et al. The Living Testament: The Essential Writings of Christianity since the Bible. LC 85-42790. 400p. 1985. 22.45 (ISBN 0-06-066499-1, HarpR); pap. 14.95 (ISBN 0-06-066498-3). Har-Row.
Penn-Lewis, Jessie. All Things New. 1962. pap. 2.95 (ISBN 0-87508-990-9). Chr Lit.
--Awakening in Wales. 1962. pap. 3.95 (ISBN 0-87508-991-7). Chr Lit.
--Climax of the Risen Life. 1962. pap. 2.95 (ISBN 0-87508-992-5). Chr Lit.
--Communion with God. 1962. pap. 2.95 (ISBN 0-87508-993-3). Chr Lit.
--Cross: Touchstone of Faith. 1962. pap. 2.95 (ISBN 0-87508-994-1). Chr Lit.
--Dying to Live. 1962. pap. 2.25 (ISBN 0-87508-995-X). Chr Lit.
--Life in the Spirit. 1962. pap. 3.95 (ISBN 0-87508-948-8). Chr Lit.
--The Magna Charta of Woman. LC 75-28655. 112p. 1975. pap. 3.50 (ISBN 0-87123-377-0, 200377). Bethany Hse.
--Opened Heavens. 1962. pap. 2.95 (ISBN 0-87508-996-8). Chr Lit.
--Prayer & Evangelism. 1962. pap. 2.95 (ISBN 0-87508-952-6). Chr Lit.
--Spiritual Warfare. 1962. pap. 2.95 (ISBN 0-87508-997-6). Chr Lit.
--Story of Job. 1965. pap. 4.95 (ISBN 0-87508-954-2). Chr Lit.
--Thy Hidden Ones. 1962. pap. 4.50 (ISBN 0-87508-998-4). Chr Lit.
--Warfare with Satan. 1962. pap. 4.15 (ISBN 0-87508-999-2). Chr Lit.
Penn-Lewis, Jessie & Roberts, Evan. War on the Saints. 9th ed. 1986. Repr. of 1912 ed. 10.50 (ISBN 0-913926-02-7). T E Lowe.
Pennock, Michael. Christian Morality & You: Teacher Manual. Rev. ed. (High School Religion Text Program). 152p. 1984. 7.95 (ISBN 0-87793-311-1). Ave Maria.
--Jesus & You: Student Text. rev. ed. LC 84-70384. (High School Religion Text Ser.). (Illus.). 224p. 1984. pap. 5.95 (ISBN 0-87793-315-4). Ave Maria.
--Jesus & You: Teacher Manual. Rev. ed. (High School Religion Text Ser.). 144p. 1984. pap. 7.95 (ISBN 0-87793-316-2). Ave Maria.
--Moral Problems: Student Text. LC 79-51015. (Illus.). 240p. 1979. pap. text ed. 5.50 (ISBN 0-87793-177-1); tchr's manual 2.95 (ISBN 0-87793-178-X). Ave Maria.
--The New Testament: Student Text. LC 82-70088. (Illus.). 256p. (Orig.). 1982. pap. 5.50 (ISBN 0-87793-246-8). Ave Maria.
--The New Testament: Teacher's Manual. 112p. (Orig.). 1982. 2.95 (ISBN 0-87793-247-6). Ave Maria.
--Prayer & You. LC 85-70162. (Illus., Orig.). 1985. pap. text ed. 5.50 student ed., 160 pg. (ISBN 0-87793-284-0); tchr's. ed., 144 pg. 7.95 (ISBN 0-87793-285-9). Ave Maria.
--The Sacraments & You. LC 81-65227. (Illus.). 272p. 1981. pap. 5.50 (ISBN 0-87793-221-2); teachers ed. 2.95 (ISBN 0-87793-222-0). Ave Maria.
--Your Church & You. LC 83-70053. (Illus.). 288p. (Orig.). 1983. pap. 5.50 student text (ISBN 0-87793-268-9); tchr's. ed. 3.50 (ISBN 0-87793-269-7). Ave Maria.
--Your Faith & You. rev. ed. LC 86-70575. (Ave Maria Press' High School Religion Text Programs Ser.). (Illus.). 320p. 1986. pap. text ed. 6.95 (ISBN 0-87793-334-0). Ave Maria.
Pennock, Michael & Finley, James. Christian Morality & You: Student Text. Rev. ed. LC 83-73085. (High School Religion Text Programs). (Illus.). 200p. 1984. pap. 5.95 (ISBN 0-87793-308-1). Ave Maria.

Pennsylvania University Bicentennial Conference. Religion & the Modern World. Maritain, Jacques & Hromadka, Joseph, eds. LC 68-26204. Repr. of 1941 ed. 22.50x (ISBN 0-8046-0360-X, Pub. by Kennikat). Assoc Faculty Pr.

Penny, Nicholas. Church Monuments in Romantic England. LC 76-58912. (Studies in British Art). (Illus.). 1977. 47.00x (ISBN 0-300-02075-9). Yale U Pr.

Penoi, Mary, ed. see Owen, Ray.

Penrice, J. A Dictionary & Glossary of the Koran, with Copious Grammatical References & Explanations of the Text. 176p. 1978. text ed. 26.00. Coronet Bks.

Penrice, John. Dictionary & Glossary of the Koran. (Arabic & Eng.). 20.00x (ISBN 0-86685-088-0). Intl Bk Ctr.

--A Dictionary & Glossary of the Koran. 180p. 1985. 15.00x (ISBN 0-7007-0001-3, Pub. by Curzon Pr England). Humanities.

--Dictionary & Glossary of the Koran, with Copious Grammatical References & Explanations. LC 70-90039. (Arabic.). 1969. Repr. of 1873 ed. 20.00 (ISBN 0-8196-0252-3). Biblo.

--A Dictionary & Glossary of the Koran with Grammatical References & Explanations. 1980. lib. bdg. 55.00 (ISBN 0-8490-3123-0). Gordon Pr.

Pentar, Michael P. Building a Happy Marriage. pap. 2.95 (ISBN 0-8198-1114-9). Dghtrs St Paul.

Pentecost, Dwight. A Harmony of the Words & Works of Jesus Christ. 272p. 1981. 12.95 (ISBN 0-310-30950-6, 17016); pap. 8.95 (ISBN 0-310-30951-4, 17016P). Zondervan.

Pentecost, Edward C. Issues in Missiology. LC 82-70467. 192p. 1982. 11.95 (ISBN 0-8010-7071-6). Baker Bk.

Pentecost, J. Dwight. Design for Discipleship. 1977. pap. 4.95 (ISBN 0-310-30861-5, 17011P). Zondervan.

--God's Answers to Man's Problems. (Moody Press Electives Ser.). (Orig.). 1985. pap. text ed. 3.95 (ISBN 0-8024-0702-1); leader's guide 2.50 (ISBN 0-8024-0703-X). Moody.

--The Joy of Fellowship: A Study of First John. 1977. pap. 5.95 (ISBN 0-310-30921-2, 17013P). Zondervan.

--The Joy of Living: A Study of Philippians. 160p. 1973. pap. text ed. 6.95 (ISBN 0-310-30871-2, 17012P). Zondervan.

--The Parables of Jesus. 160p. 1982. 9.95 (ISBN 0-310-30960-3, 17017). Zondervan.

--Prophecy for Today. 224p. 1984. pap. 5.95 (ISBN 0-310-30981-6, 17018P). Zondervan.

--El Sermon del Monte. Orig. Title: The Sermon on the Mount. (Span.). 1981. pap. 4.75 (ISBN 0-8254-1556-X). Kregel.

--Things to Come. 1958. 18.95 (ISBN 0-310-30890-9, 6355, Pub by Dunhan). Zondervan.

--Things Which Become Sound Doctrine. 1970. Repr. 5.95 (ISBN 0-310-30901-8, 6504P). Zondervan.

--The Words & Works of Jesus Christ. 576p. 1981. 19.95 (ISBN 0-310-30940-9, 17015). Zondervan.

--Your Adversary the Devil. 192p. 1976. pap. 6.95 (ISBN 0-310-30911-5, 17010P). Zondervan.

Penter, John. Circumstantial Evidence. 144p. 1981. 11.95 (ISBN 0-939762-00-5). Faraday.

Pentz, Croft M. Expository Outlines from Romans. (Sermon Outline Ser.). 48p. (Orig.). 1980. pap. 2.50 (ISBN 0-8010-7057-0). Baker Bk.

--Expository Outlines on Hebrews. (Sermon Outline Ser.). pap. 1.95 (ISBN 0-8010-7045-7). Baker Bk.

--Outlines on Revelation. (Sermon Outline Ser.). 1978. pap. 2.50 (ISBN 0-8010-7030-9). Baker Bk.

--Outlines on the Holy Spirit. (Sermon Outline Ser.). 1978. pap. 2.50 (ISBN 0-8010-7029-5). Baker Bk.

--Outlines on the Parables of Jesus. (Sermon Outline Ser.). (Orig.). 1980. pap. 2.50 (ISBN 0-8010-7055-4). Baker Bk.

--Sermon Outlines for Special Days. (Sermon Outline Ser.). 1979. pap. 2.50 (ISBN 0-8010-7046-5). Baker Bk.

--Sermon Outlines from Acts. (Sermon Outline Ser.). 1978. pap. 2.50 (ISBN 0-8010-7039-2). Baker Bk.

Pepin, David. Discovering Cathedrals. 5th. ed. (Discovering Ser.: No. 112). (Illus.). 1985. pap. 4.95 (ISBN 0-85263-718-7, Pub. by Shire Pubns England). Seven Hills Bks.

--Discovering Shrines & Holy Places. (Discovering Ser.: No. 254). (Illus.). 80p. (Orig.). 1983. pap. 3.95 (ISBN 0-85263-514-1, Pub. by Shire Pubns England). Seven Hills Bks.

Pepler, C. The Basis of the Mysticism of St. Thomas Aquinas. 1977. lib. bdg. 59.95 (ISBN 0-8490-1479-4). Gordon Pr.

Pepper, Clayton, ed. First Steps in Faith. pap. 2.25 (ISBN 0-89137-206-7). Quality Pubns.

--Introduction to Soul Winning. pap. 2.25 (ISBN 0-89137-204-0). Quality Pubns.

--Keeping Converts & Restoring the Erring. pap. 2.25 (ISBN 0-89137-205-9). Quality Pubns.

--Total Evangelism. pap. 2.25 (ISBN 0-89137-203-2). Quality Pubns.

Pepper, Stephen. Bob Jones University Collection of Religious Art: Italian Paintings. (Illus.). 336p. (Orig.). 1984. pap. 55.00 (ISBN 0-89084-263-9). Bob Jones Univ Pr.

Peppler, Alice S. Divorced & Christian. LC 74-4505. 96p. 1974. pap. 3.75 (ISBN 0-570-03189-3, 12-2591). Concordia.

--Single Again--This Time with Children: A Christian Guide for the Single Parent. LC 81-52278. 128p. (Orig.). 1982. pap. 6.95 (ISBN 0-8066-1910-4, 10-5802). Augsburg.

Percha, Alex La see La Perchia, Alex.

Percheron, Maurice. Buddha & Buddhism. Stapleton, Edmund, tr. from Fr. LC 82-3471. (The Overlook Spiritual Masters Ser.). (Illus.). 192p. 1982. cloth 18.95 (ISBN 0-87951-157-5). Overlook Pr.

--Buddha & Buddhism. Stapleton, Edmund, tr. from Fr. LC 82-3471. (Spiritual Masters Ser.). (Illus.). 192p. 1983. pap. 9.95 (ISBN 0-87951-193-1). Overlook Pr.

Percival, Harold W. Man & Woman, & Child. LC 52-6126. 1979. pap. 6.95 (ISBN 0-911650-08-3). Word Foun.

--Masonry & Its Symbols, in Light of "Thinking & Destiny". LC 52-2237. 1979. pap. 3.95 (ISBN 0-911650-07-5). Word Foun.

Percival, Milton O. William Blake's Circle of Destiny. 1964. lib. bdg. 27.50x (ISBN 0-374-96384-3, Octagon). Hippocrene Bks.

Percy, Bishop. Bishop Percy's Folio Manuscript Ballards & Romances, 3 vols. Hales, John W., et al, eds. LC 67-23962. 1866p. 1968. Repr. of 1868 ed. 210.00x (ISBN 0-8103-3409-7). Gale.

Perdue, Leo G. & Kovacs, Brian W., eds. A Prophet to the Nations: Essays in Jeremiah Studies. xii, 391p. 1984. text ed. 25.00x (ISBN 0-931464-20-X). Eisenbrauns.

Pereira, Jose. Monolithic Jinas. 1977. 11.50 (ISBN 0-8426-1027-8, Pub. by Motilal Banarsidass India). Orient Bk Dist.

Perennes, F. Dictionnaire de Lecons et Exemples de Litterature Chretienne en Prose et en Verse, 2 vols. Migne, J. P., ed. (Troisieme et Derniere Encyclopedie Theologique Ser.: Vols. 61-62). (Fr.). 1510p. Repr. of 1864 ed. lib. bdg. 191.50x (ISBN 0-89241-326-3). Caratzas.

--Dictionnaire de Noels et de Cantiques. Migne, J. P., ed. (Troisieme et Derniere Encyclopedie Theologique Ser.: Vol. 63). (Fr.). 720p. Repr. of 1867 ed. lib. bdg. 91.50x (ISBN 0-89241-327-1). Caratzas.

Perennes, F., jt. auth. see Defeller, F. X.

Perennes, F M. Dictionnaire de Bibliographie Catholique, Presentant l'Indication et les Titres Complets de tous les Ouvrages qui Ontetes Publies dans les Trois Lanques Grecque, Latine et Francaise... Suivi d'un Dictionnaire de Bibliologie par G. Brunet (the Last 2 Vols., 6 vols. Migne, J. P., ed. (Troisieme et Derniere Encyclopedie Theologique Ser.: Vols. 39-44). (Fr.). 4001p. Repr. of 1866 ed. lib. bdg. 510.00x (ISBN 0-89241-318-2). Caratzas.

Perersen, William J. C. S. Lewis Had a Wife. 160p. (Orig.). 1985. pap. 2.95 (ISBN 0-8423-0202-6). Tyndale.

Peretz, David, et al, eds. Death & Grief: Selected Readings for the Medical Student. 270p. 1977. pap. 6.95 (ISBN 0-930194-82-9). Ctr Thanatology.

Perez, Belia. Tres Dramas De Navidad. 24p. 1985. pap. 0.80 (ISBN 0-311-08221-1). Casa Bautista.

Perez, Eugene. Kalumburu: The Benedictine Mission & the Aborigines 1908-1975. (Illus.). 1978. pap. 15.00x (ISBN 0-9596887-0-6, Pub. by U of W Austral Pr). Intl Spec Bk.

Perez, Guillermo H. Lo Que los Jovenes Deben Saber Acerca de las Drogas. 80p. 1983. pap. 1.10 (ISBN 0-311-46070-4). Casa Bautista.

Perez, J. Guillent. A Case of Conscience. 370p. (Orig.). 1985. pap. 12.95 (ISBN 0-9607590-2-6). Action Life Pubns.

Perez-Esclarin, Antonio. Atheism & Liberation. Drury, John, tr. from Sp. LC 78-731. Orig. Title: Ateismo Y Liberacion. 205p. (Orig.). 1978. pap. 1.99 (ISBN 0-88344-020-2). Orbis Bks.

Perez-Esquivel, Adolfo. Christ in a Poncho: Witnesses to the Nonviolent Struggles in Latin America. Barr, Robert R., tr. from Fr. LC 82-18760. Tr. of Le Christ au poncho, suivi de Temoignages de luttes nonviolentes en Amerique Latine. 139p. (Orig.). 1983. pap. 7.95 (ISBN 0-88344-104-7). Orbis Bks.

Perez-Ramon, Joacquin. Self & Non-Self in Early Buddhism. (Religon & Society Ser.: No. 17). 1980. 58.00x (ISBN 90-279-7987-1). Mouton.

Perigo, Grace, tr. Letters of Adam of Perseigne. LC 76-15486. (Cistercian Father Ser.: No. 21). 1976. 11.95 (ISBN 0-87907-621-6). Cistercian Pubns.

Perinbanayagam, R. S. The Karmic Theater: Self, Society & Astrology in Jaffna. LC 82-6997. 224p. 1982. lib. bdg. 22.50x (ISBN 0-87023-374-2). U of Mass Pr.

Perino, Renato. Call to Holiness: New Frontiers in Spirituality for Today's Religious. LC 85-28621. 160p. (Orig.). 1986. pap. 7.95 (ISBN 0-8189-0475-5). ALBA.

Perkins, Aeschliman. The Man Who Cried Justice. 1987. pap. 5.95 (ISBN 0-8307-1075-2, 5418545). Regal.

Perkins, Ethel R., ed. see Vogue, Adalbert de.

Perkins, Hal. Leadership Multiplication Books: Book A, World Vision. 30p. 1983. pap. 2.50 (ISBN 0-8341-0858-5); Set of 8 bks. pap. 19.95 (YD-1495). Beacon Hill.

--Leadership Multiplication Books: Book B, Knowing the Father. 30p. (Orig.). 1983. pap. 2.50 (ISBN 0-8341-0859-3); Set of 8 bks. pap. 19.95 (YD-1495). Beacon Hill.

--Leadership Multiplication Books: Book C, Coming to Jesus. (Bk. C). (Orig.). 1983. pap. 2.50 (ISBN 0-8341-0852-6). Beacon Hill.

--Leadership Multiplication Books: Book D, Following Jesus. 30p. (Orig.). (YA) 1983. pap. 2.50 (ISBN 0-8341-0860-7); Set of 8 bks. pap. 19.95 (YD-1495). Beacon Hill.

--Leadership Multiplication Books: Book E, Becoming Like Jesus. 30p. (Orig.). 1983. pap. 2.50 (ISBN 0-8341-0861-5); Set of 8 bks. pap. 19.95 (YD-1495). Beacon Hill.

--Leadership Multiplication Books: Book F, Making Leaders in Families. 30p. (Orig.). (YA) 1983. pap. 2.50 (ISBN 0-8341-0862-3); Set of 8 bks. pap. 19.95 (YD-1495). Beacon Hill.

--Leadership Multiplication Books: Book G, Making Leaders in the Church. 30p. (Orig.). (YA) 1983. pap. 2.50 (ISBN 0-8341-0866-6); Set of 8 bks. pap. 19.95 (YD-1495). Beacon Hill.

--Leadership Multiplication Books: Book H, Making Leaders in the World. 30p. (Orig.). (YA) 1983. pap. 2.50 (ISBN 0-8341-0867-4); Set of 8 bks. pap. 19.95 (YD-1495). Beacon Hill.

Perkins, J. A. The Concept of the Self in the French Enlightenment. 162p. (Orig.). 1969. pap. text ed. 24.50x (Pub. by Droz Switzerland). Coronet Bks.

Perkins, J. S. Geometry of Space & Consciousness. 2nd ed. 1973. 3.50 (ISBN 0-8356-7006-6). Theos Pub Hse.

Perkins, James A. & Oestreich, Nelson. The Amish: Two Perceptions Two. (Illus.). 24p. (Orig.). 1981. pap. 4.00 (ISBN 0-936014-10-5). Dawn Valley.

Perkins, James B. Richelieu & the Growth of French Power. 359p. 1982. Repr. of 1900 ed. lib. bdg. 40.00 (ISBN 0-89984-826-5). Century Bookbindery.

Perkins, James S. Experiencing Reincarnation. LC 77-5249. (Illus.). 1977. pap. 4.95 (ISBN 0-8356-0500-0, Quest). Theos Pub Hse.

--Through Death to Rebirth. new ed. LC 61-13301. (Illus.). 124p. 1974. pap. 4.25 (ISBN 0-8356-0451-9, Quest). Theos Pub Hse.

Perkins, Jim, jt. auth. see Perkins, Lee.

Perkins, John. With Justice for All. LC 80-50262. 216p. 1982. text ed. 10.95 (ISBN 0-8307-0754-9, 5108802); pap. 5.95 (ISBN 0-8307-0934-7, 5418181). Regal.

Perkins, John M. Let Justice Roll Down. LC 74-30172. 224p. 1976. pap. 5.95 (ISBN 0-8307-0345-4, 5404002). Regal.

Perkins, Judith, ed. see Singh, Ajaib.

Perkins, Lee & Perkins, Jim. Healthier & Happier Children Through Bedtime Meditations & Prayers, Bks. 1 & 2. 40p. 1982. book & tape set 14.95 (ISBN 0-87604-184-5). ARE Pr.

--Healthier & Happier Children Through Bedtime Meditations & Stories. rev. ed. 1975. with tape 7.95 (ISBN 0-87604-106-3). ARE Pr.

Perkins, M. L. The Moral & Political Philosophy of the Abbe de Saint-Pierre. 160p. (Orig.). 1959. pap. text ed. 20.00x (Pub. by Droz Switzerland). Coronet Bks.

Perkins, Mary, jt. auth. see Hainsworth, Phillip.

Perkins, Paul. Forgotten Is the Name. 1985. 7.95 (ISBN 0-89536-938-9, 7556). CSS of Ohio.

Perkins, Percy H., Jr. Gemstones of the Bible. 2nd ed. 1986. 17.95 (ISBN 0-9603090-2-0). P H Perkins Jr.

Perkins, Pheme. The Book of Revelation. Karris, Robert J., ed. (Collegeville Bible Commentary Ser.: No. 11). 96p. 1983. Vol. 11. pap. 2.95 (ISBN 0-8146-1311-X). Liturgical Pr.

--The Gnostic Dialogue: The Early Church & Crisis of Gnosticism. LC 80-81441. (Theological Inquiries Ser.). 256p. 1980. pap. 7.95 (ISBN 0-8091-2320-7). Paulist Pr.

--The Gospel According to St. John: A Theological Commentary. LC 77-12896. (Herald Scriptural Library). pap. 66.80 (ISBN 0-317-28173-9, 2022571). Bks Demand UMI.

--Gospel of St. John. (Read & Pray Ser.). 96p. 1975. pap. 1.75 (ISBN 0-685-55958-0). Franciscan Herald.

--Hearing the Parables of Jesus. LC 80-84508. 228p. (Orig.). 1981. pap. 7.95 (ISBN 0-8091-2352-5). Paulist Pr.

--Johannine Epistles. (New Testament Ser.: Vol. 21). 120p. 1980. 10.95 (ISBN 0-89453-209-X); pap. 6.95 (ISBN 0-89453-144-1). M Glazier.

--Lent: Series B. Achtemeier, Elizabeth, ed. LC 84-6010. (Proclamation 3: Aids for Interpreting the Lessons of the Church Year Ser.). 64p. 1984. pap. 3.75 (ISBN 0-8006-4103-5). Fortress.

--Love Commands in the New Testament. 144p. (Orig.). 1982. pap. 5.95 (ISBN 0-8091-2450-5). Paulist Pr.

--Ministering in the Pauline Churches: Partners for Christ. LC 82-60849. 1982. pap. 4.95 (ISBN 0-8091-2473-4). Paulist Pr.

--Reading the New Testament: An Introduction. LC 78-51892. 352p. 1978. pap. 5.95 (ISBN 0-8091-9535-6). Paulist Pr.

--Resurrection: New Testament Witness & Contemporary Reflection. LC 83-25473. 564p. 1984. 19.95 (ISBN 0-385-17256-7). Doubleday.

--What We Believe: A Biblical Catechism of the Apostles Creed. 144p. (Orig.). 1986. pap. 3.95 (ISBN 0-8091-2764-4). Paulist Pr.

Perkins, Pheme, jt. auth. see Fuller, Reginald.

Perkins, Russell, ed. see Kabir.

Perkins, Russell. The Impact of a Saint. LC 80-51959. 256p. 1980. pap. 7.50 (ISBN 0-89142-037-1). Sant Bani Ash.

Perkins, Russell, ed. Third World Tour of Kirpal Singh. (Illus.). 1974. pap. 2.50 (ISBN 0-89142-008-8). Sant Bani Ash.

Perkins, Russell, ed. see Oberoi, A. S.

Perkins, Russell, ed. see Singh, Ajaib.

Perkins, Russell, ed. see Singh, Kirpal.

Perkins, William. The Whole Treatise of the Cases of Conscience. LC 74-38218. (English Experience Ser.: No. 482). 690p. 1972. Repr. of 1606 ed. 43.00 (ISBN 90-221-0482-6). Walter J Johnson.

Perlin, Seymour, jt. auth. see Beauchamp, Thom.

Perlman, Alice. Torah Pointers in the Collection of the Judah L. Magnes Museum. (Illus.). 24p. (Orig.). 1987. pap. 4.95 (ISBN 0-943376-30-0). Magnes Mus.

Perlmann, Moshe, ed. & tr. from Arabic. Ibn Kammuna's Examination of the Three Faiths: A Thirteenth-Century Essay in the Comparative Study of Religion. LC 73-102659. 1971. 32.00x (ISBN 0-520-01658-0). U of Cal Pr.

Perlmann, Moshe, tr. see Al-Tabari.

Permuth, S., jt. auth. see Mawdsley, R.

Permuth, Steve, et al. The Law, the Student, & the Catholic School. 96p. 1981. 6.00 (ISBN 0-686-39898-X). Natl Cath Educ.

Perner, Bernard & Perner, Majorie. Mount to the Sky Like Eagles, Vol. 9. (Heritage Ser.). 1986. 10.95 (ISBN 0-911802-64-9). Free Church Pubns.

Perner, Majorie, jt. auth. see Perner, Bernard.

Pernoud, Regine. Joan of Arc: By Herself & Her Witnesses. LC 66-24807. 1969. pap. 10.95 (ISBN 0-8128-1260-3). Stein & Day.

Peroncel-Hugoz, Jean-Pierre. The Raft of Mohammed: Social & Human Consequences of the Return to Traditional Religion in the Arab World. 304p. 1987. 18.95 (ISBN 0-913729-31-0). Paragon Hse.

Perowne, Stewart. Roman Mythology. LC 84-6446. (The Library of the World's Myths & Legends). (Illus.). 144p. 1984. 18.95 (ISBN 0-911745-56-4). P Bedrick Bks.

Perpich, Sandra W. A Hermeneutic Critique of Structuralist Exegesis: With Specific Reference to Lk. 10.29-37. LC 83-21737. (Illus.). 264p. (Orig.). 1984. lib. bdg. 25.25 (ISBN 0-8191-3668-9); pap. text ed. 13.25 (ISBN 0-8191-3669-7). U Pr of Amer.

Perreiah, Alan, ed. Paul of Venice: Logica Magna, Tractatus De Suppositione. (Text Ser). 1971. 16.00 (ISBN 0-686-11560-0). Franciscan Inst.

Perrens, Francois T. Libertins en France au Dix-Septieme Siecle. LC 72-168701. (Fr.). 428p. 1973. Repr. of 1896 ed. lib. bdg. 29.00 (ISBN 0-8337-2728-1). B Franklin.

Perrier, Joseph L. Revival of Scholastic Philosophy in the Nineteenth Century. LC 9-10966. Repr. of 1909 ed. 17.50 (ISBN 0-404-04994-X). AMS Pr.

Perrin, Arnold. Out of Bondage. (Illus.). 52p. 1983. pap. 4.95 (ISBN 0-939736-45-4). Wings ME.

Perrin, Joseph-Marie. Mary Mother of Christ & of Christians. Finley, Jean D., tr. from Fr. LC 77-26608. (Illus.). 1978. pap. 3.50 (ISBN 0-8189-0367-8). Alba.

Perrin, Norman. Jesus & the Language of the Kingdom: Symbol & Metaphor in New Testament Interpretation. LC 80-20822. 240p. 1980. pap. 11.95 (ISBN 0-8006-1432-1, 1-1432). Fortress.

--Rediscovering the Teachings of Jesus. LC 67-11510. 1976. pap. 6.95xi (ISBN 0-06-066493-2, RD 151, HarpR). Har-Row.

--Resurrection According to Matthew, Mark, & Luke. LC 76-47913. 96p. (Orig.). 1977. pap. 3.95 (ISBN 0-8006-1248-5, 1-1248). Fortress.

--What Is Redaction Criticism? Via, Dan O., Jr., ed. LC 72-81529. (Guides to Biblical Scholarship). 96p. (Orig.). 1969. pap. 4.50 (ISBN 0-8006-0181-5, 1-181). Fortress.

Perrin, Norman & Duling, Dennis C. The New Testament: An Introduction. 2nd ed. (Illus.). 516p. (Orig.). 1982. pap. text ed. 15.95 (ISBN 0-15-565726-7, HC). HarBraceJ.

Perrin, Norman, jt. auth. see Abernathy, David.

Perrin, Norman, tr. see Jeremias, Joachim.

Perrin, Stuart. The Mystical Ferryboat. (The Metaphysics Ser.). 121p. (Orig.). 1987. 12.95 (ISBN 0-943920-67-1); pap. price not set (ISBN 0-943920-64-7). Metamorphous Pr.

Perris, George H. Emerson. 1973. Repr. of 1910 ed. 25.00 (ISBN 0-8274-0995-8). R West.

Perrone, Stephen P. & Spata, James P. Send in His Clowns. Zapel, Arthur L. & Pijanowski, Kathy, eds. (Illus.). 79p. (Orig.). 1985. pap. 7.95 (ISBN 0-916260-32-1). Meriwether Pub.

Perrotta, Kevin. Taming the TV Habit. 162p. (Orig.). 1982. pap. 6.95 (ISBN 0-89283-155-3). Servant.

Perrotta, Kevin, ed. see Colson, Charles, et al.

Perry, Bliss. Emerson Today. LC 69-19220. 140p. 1969. Repr. of 1931 ed. 18.00 (ISBN 0-208-00798-9, Archon). Shoe String.

Perry, Charles A. The Resurrection Promise: An Interpretation of the Easter Narratives. 152p. (Orig.). 1987. pap. 8.95 (ISBN 0-8028-0249-4). Eerdmans.

Perry, Charles E., Jr. Why Christians Burn Out. LC 82-2098. 168p. 1982. pap. 4.95 (ISBN 0-8407-5800-6). Nelson.

Perry, Earl & Perry, Wilma. Puppets Go to Church. 85p. 1975. pap. 2.50 (ISBN 0-8341-0385-0). Beacon Hill.

Perry, Edith W. Altar Guild Manual. (Orig.). 1945. pap. 2.95 (ISBN 0-8192-1067-6). Morehouse.

Perry, Frances B., ed. Let's Sing Together: Favorite Primary Songs of Members of the Church of Jesus Christ of Latter-day Saints. (Illus.). 96p. 1981. 10.98 (ISBN 0-941518-00-0). Perry Enterprises.

Perry, Frank L., Jr. Sex & the Bible. LC 82-72143. (Orig.). 1982. pap. 7.95 (ISBN 0-943708-00-1). Chr Educ Res Inst.

Perry, Frederick. Saint Louis: Louis IX of France, the Most Christian King. LC 73-14462. Repr. of 1901 ed. 30.00 (ISBN 0-404-58280-X). AMS Pr.

Perry, Iris, jt. auth. see Coombs, Robert S.

Perry, Jack. Light from Light. 208p. 1987. 11.95 (ISBN 0-310-23850-1). Zondervan.

Perry, Jeff C. Alter Worker's Manual. 2nd ed. 61p. 1982. pap. 3.00 (ISBN 0-933643-07-1). Grace World Outreach.

Perry, John R. A Dialogue on Personal Identity & Immortality. LC 78-52943. 60p. 1978. lib. bdg. 15.00 (ISBN 0-915144-91-3); pap. text ed. 2.95 (ISBN 0-915144-53-0). Hackett Pub.

Perry, John W; see Watts, Alan W.

Perry, Lewis. Radical Abolitionism: Anarchy & the Government of God in Anti-Slavery Thought. 328p. 1973. 27.50x (ISBN 0-8014-0754-0). Cornell U Pr.

Perry, Lloyd & Sell, Charles. Speaking to Life's Problems. 1983. pap. 12.95 (ISBN 0-8024-0170-8). Moody.

Perry, Lloyd M. Biblical Preaching for Today's World. LC 73-7471. 256p. 1973. 18.95 (ISBN 0-8024-0707-2). Moody.

--Manual for Biblical Preaching. pap. 12.95 (ISBN 0-8010-7047-3). Baker Bk.

--Predicacion Biblica para el Mundo Actual. Carrodeguas, Angel A., tr. from Eng. Orig. Title: Biblical Preaching for Today's World. (Span.). 176p. 1986. pap. 4.95 (ISBN 0-8297-0957-6). Life Pubs Intl.

Perry, Lloyd M. & Culver, Robert D. How to Get More from Your Bible. (Direction Bks). 1979. pap. 3.95 (ISBN 0-8010-7048-1). Baker Bk.

Perry, Lloyd M. & Lias, Edward J. Manual of Pastoral Problems & Procedures. 8.95 (ISBN 0-8010-7063-5). Baker Bk.

Perry, Lloyd M. & Shawchuck, Norman. Revitalizing the Twentieth Century Church. LC 81-16974. Date not set. pap. 7.95 (ISBN 0-8024-7318-0). Moody.

Perry, Lloyd M., jt. auth. see Wiersbe, Warren.

Perry, Ralph B. The Free Man & the Soldier. facsimile ed. LC 73-24250. (Select Bibliographies Reprint Ser.). Repr. of 1916 ed. 16.00 (ISBN 0-8369-5438-6). Ayer Co Pubs.

--Puritanism & Democracy. 688p. 1944. 19.50 (ISBN 0-8149-0180-8). Vanguard.

Perry, T. Anthony. Erotic Spirituality: The Integrative Tradition from Leone Ebreo to John Donne. 208p. 1980. 15.75 (ISBN 0-8173-0024-4). U of Ala Pr.

Perry, Thomas D. Moral Reasoning & Truth: An Essay in Philosophy & Jurisprudence. 1976. 38.00x (ISBN 0-19-824532-7). Oxford U Pr.

Perry, Whitall N. A Treasury of Traditional Wisdom. 1986. pap. 19.95 (ISBN 0-317-52385-6, PL 4136, HarpR). Har-Row.

Perry, William S. Historical Collections Relating to the American Colonial Church, 5 Pts. in 4 Vols. LC 75-99948. Repr. of 1878 ed. Set. 245.00 (ISBN 0-404-05070-0). Vol. 1 (ISBN 0-404-05071-9). Vol. 2 (ISBN 0-404-05072-7). Vol. 3 (ISBN 0-404-05073-5). Vol. 4 (ISBN 0-404-05074-3). AMS Pr.

Perry, Wilma, jt. auth. see Perry, Earl.

Perryman, F. J. How to Resist the Devil. 48p. pap. 0.50 (ISBN 0-686-29122-0). Faith Pub Hse.

Perschke, Louis M. Helps & Hints at Bible Study. 176p. 1981. 8.50 (ISBN 0-682-49733-9, Testament). Exposition Pr FL.

Pershing, Betty, jt. auth. see Hirschmann, Maria A.

Persinger, Michael A., et al. TM & Cult Mania. 208p. 1980. 10.95 (ISBN 0-8158-0392-3). Chris Mass.

Person, Laura, jt. auth. see Griffith, Nancy S.

Persons, Stow. Free Religion: An American Faith. 1947. 49.50x (ISBN 0-686-83554-9). Elliots Bks.

Persson, Norma J. God & Nature: A Book of Devotions for Christians Who Love Wildlife. 240p. 1984. pap. 6.95 (ISBN 0-13-357559-4). P-H.

Persuitte, David. Joseph Smith & the Origins of "The Book of Mormon". LC 84-42734. (Illus.). 303p. 1985. lib. bdg. 19.95x (ISBN 0-89950-134-6). McFarland & Co.

Perti, Giacomo Antonio. Laudate Pueri. Berger, Jean, ed. LC 65-26097. (Penn State Music Series, No. 10). 35p. 1965. pap. 4.00x (ISBN 0-271-73075-7). Pa St U Pr.

Peruvian Bishops' Commission for Social Action. Between Honesty & Hope: Documents from & about the Church in Latin America. LC 78-143185. (Maryknoll Documentation Ser.). pap. 67.80 (ISBN 0-317-26635-7, 2025116). Bks Demand UMI.

Pervan, Tomislav. Queen of Peace, Echo of the Eternal Word. (Illus.). 58p. (Orig.). 1986. pap. 3.50 (ISBN 0-940535-05-X). Franciscan U Pr.

Pervo, Richard I. Profit with Delight: The Literary Genre of the Acts of the Apostles. LC 86-45220. 224p. 1987. 16.95 (ISBN 0-8006-0782-1). Fortress.

Pervo, Richard I. & Carl, William J., III. Epiphany. Achtemeier, Elizabeth, et al, eds. LC 79-7377. (Proclamation 2: Aids for Interpreting the Lessons of the Church Year, Series C). 64p. 1979. pap. 3.75 (ISBN 0-8006-4085-3, 1-4085). Fortress.

Pesek-Marous, Georgia. The Bull: A Religious & Secular History of Phallus Worship & Male Homosexuality. (Illus.). 185p. (Orig.). 1984. pap. 9.95 (ISBN 0-916453-01-4). Tau Pr.

Peshkin, Alan. God's Choice: The Total World of a Fundamentalist Christian School. LC 85-24524. x, 350p. 1986. lib. bdg. 24.95 (ISBN 0-226-66198-9). U of Chicago Pr.

Pessin, Deborah. History of the Jews in America. (Illus.). 1957. pap. 4.95x (ISBN 0-8381-0189-5). United Syn Bk.

--Jewish People, 3 Vols. (Illus.). 1951-53. pap. 4.25x ea. Vol. I (ISBN 0-8381-0182-8). Vol. II (ISBN 0-8381-0185-2). Vol. III (ISBN 0-8381-0187-9). pap. 2.50x ea. pupils' activity bks. Vol. I Activity Bk (ISBN 0-8381-0183-6). Vol. II Activity Bk (ISBN 0-8381-0186-0). Vol. III Activity Bk (ISBN 0-8381-0188-7). United Syn Bk.

Pesta, Raymond J. The Christian Approach to Successful Selling. LC 81-68890. 92p. 1981. pap. 5.95 (ISBN 0-941280-00-4). Chr Acad Success.

Pestana, Carla G. Liberty of Conscience & the Growth of Religious Diversity in Early America, 1636-1786. (Illus.). 104p. 1986. pap. 30.00 (ISBN 0-916617-02-5); bibliographical suppl. 10.00 (ISBN 0-916617-03-3). J C Brown.

Petach, Heidi. Daniel & the Lions. (Happy Day Bible Stories Bks.). (Illus.). 24p. 1984. 1.59 (ISBN 0-87239-762-9, 3722). Standard Pub.

--The Lost Sheep. (Happy Day Bible Stories Bks.). (Illus.). 24p. 1984. 1.59 (ISBN 0-87239-765-3, 3725). Standard Pub.

Peter, John F; see David, Hans T.

Peter, Karl A. The Dynamics of Hutterite Society: An Analytical Approach. 250p. 1986. 27.50x (ISBN 0-88864-108-7, Univ of Atla Pr Canada); pap. 16.95x (ISBN 0-88864-109-5). U of Nebr Pr.

Peter, Lily. In the Beginning: Myths of the Western World. LC 82-20274. (Illus.). 96p. 1983. 19.00x (ISBN 0-938626-15-9); pap. 7.95 (ISBN 0-938626-18-3). U of Ark Pr.

Peter The Venerable. Letters of Peter the Venerable, 2 Vols. Constable, Giles, ed. LC 67-10086. (Historical Studies: No. 78). 1967. Set. 55.00x (ISBN 0-674-52775-5). Harvard U Pr.

Peterman, Mary E. Healing: A Spiritual Adventure. LC 74-80416. 104p. 1974. pap. 3.95 (ISBN 0-8006-1086-5, 1-1086). Fortress.

Peter of Waltham, ed. see Gregory the Great.

Peters, Barbarba & Samuels, Victoria, eds. Dialogue on Diversity: A New Agenda for Women. 88p. 1978. pap. 1.95 (ISBN 0-87495-003-1). Am Jewish Comm.

Peters, Dan, et al. Rock's Hidden Persuader: The Truth about Back Masking. 128p. 1985. pap. 3.95 (ISBN 0-87123-857-8, 200857). Bethany Hse.

--Why Knock Rock? 272p. (Orig.). 1984. pap. 6.95 (ISBN 0-87123-440-8, 210440). Bethany Hse.

Peters, David B. A Betrayal of Innocence. 160p. 1986. 11.95 (ISBN 0-8499-0502-8, 0502-8). Word Bks.

Peters, Dory. My God Is Real. 1984. pap. 3.95 (ISBN 0-938612-08-5). Revival Press.

Peters, Edward. The Magician, the Witch & the Law. LC 78-51341. (Middle Ages Ser.). 1982. 23.50x (ISBN 0-8122-7746-5); pap. 9.95x (ISBN 0-8122-1101-4). U of Pa Pr.

Peters, Edward, ed. Christian Society & the Crusades, 1198-1229: Sources in Translation, Including the Capture of Damietta. LC 78-163385. (Middle Ages Ser). 1971. 21.00x (ISBN 0-8122-7644-2); pap. 9.95x (ISBN 0-8122-1024-7, Pa Paperbks). U of Pa Pr.

--First Crusade: The Chronicle of Fulcher of Chartres & Other Source Materials. LC 74-163384. (Middle Ages Ser.). 1971. 21.00x (ISBN 0-8122-7643-4); pap. text ed. 9.95x (ISBN 0-8122-1017-4, Pa Paperbks). U of Pa Pr.

--Heresy & Authority in Medieval Europe. LC 79-5262. (Middle Ages Ser.). 384p. 1980. 39.00x (ISBN 0-8122-7779-1); pap. 15.95x (ISBN 0-8122-1103-0). U of Pa Pr.

--Monks, Bishops, & Pagans: Christian Culture in Gaul & Italy. Incl. Selections from the Minor Writings. Gregory Of Tours. McDermott, William C., ed. LC 74-33702. (Middle Ages Ser.). 252p. 1975. (Pa Paperbks); pap. text ed. 10.95x (ISBN 0-8122-1069-7). U of Pa Pr.

Peters, Edward, jt. ed. see Kors, Alan C.

Peters, Mrs. Edwin. Echoes from Beautiful Feet. (Illus.). 168p. 1975. pap. 1.95 (ISBN 0-89114-073-5). Baptist Pub Hse.

Peters, F. E. The Children of Abraham: Judaism, Christianity, Islam. LC 81-47941. 240p. 1983. 23.50 (ISBN 0-691-07267-1); pap. 8.50x (ISBN 0-691-02030-2). Princeton U Pr.

--Jerusalem & Mecca: The Typology of the Holy City in the Near East. 272p. 1987. 45.00 (ISBN 0-8147-6598-X). NYU Pr.

--Jerusalem: The Holy City in the Eyes of Chroniclers, Visitors, Pilgrims, & Prophets from the Days of Abraham to the Beginnings of Modern Times. LC 85-42699. (Illus.). 712p. 1985. 37.00 (ISBN 0-691-07300-7). Princeton U Pr.

Peters, George. A Biblical Theology of Missions. LC 72-77952. 384p. 1972. 11.95 (ISBN 0-8024-0706-4). Moody.

--A Theology of Church Growth. 368p. 1981. pap. 10.95 (ISBN 0-310-43101-8, 11285P). Zondervan.

Peters, George W. Foundations of Mennonite Brethren Missions. LC 83-72078. 262p. (Orig.). 1984. pap. 12.95 (ISBN 0-318-18902-X). Kindred Pr.

Peters, Heather, jt. auth. see Lyons, Elizabeth.

Peters, John L. Christian Perfection & American Methodism. 1985. pap. 9.95 (ISBN 0-310-31241-8, 17043P). Zondervan.

Peters, Kathleen, ed. see Bingham, Mindy, et al.

Peters, Madison C. Wit & Wisdom of the Talmud. 169p. 1980. Repr. of 1900 ed. lib. bdg. 20.00 (ISBN 0-8414-6852-4). Folcroft.

Peters, Melvin K. A Critical Edition of the Coptic (Bohairic) Pentateuch, Vol. 5. LC 83-3260. (SBL Septuagint & Cognate Studies). 126p. 1983. pap. 11.95 (ISBN 0-89130-617-X, 06 04 15). Scholars Pr GA.

--A Critical Edition of the Coptic (Bohairic) Pentateuch: Septuagint & Cognate Studies, Vol. 2, Exodus. 122p. 1986. 11.95 (ISBN 1-55540-030-2, 06-04-22); pap. 8.95 (ISBN 1-55540-031-0). Scholars Pr GA.

Peters, Rudilph. Islam & Colonialism. (Religion & Society Ser.). 1984. text ed. 37.75x (ISBN 90-279-3347-2); pap. 14.95 (ISBN 3-11-010022-3). Mouton.

Peters, Stanley J. The Church Unique. 1987. 12.95 (ISBN 0-533-06972-6). Vantage.

Peters, W. A. Gerard Manley Hopkins: A Tribute. 80p. 1984. pap. 5.95 (ISBN 0-8294-0456-2). Loyola.

Peters, William J. What Your Wedding Can Be. LC 80-65402. 136p. (Orig.). 1980. pap. 2.95 (ISBN 0-87029-163-7, 20350-5). Abbey.

Petersen, Bill. Those Curious New Cults in the Eighties. rev. ed. LC 72-93700. 1982. pap. text ed. 3.95 (ISBN 0-87983-317-3). Keats.

Petersen, Carol. Albert Camus. Gode, Alexander, tr. LC 68-31455. (Literature & Life Ser.). 1969. 12.95 (ISBN 0-8044-2691-0). Ungar.

Petersen, David L. Haggai & Zechariah 1-8, a Commentary. LC 84-7477. (Old Testament Library). 320p. 1984. 24.95 (ISBN 0-664-21830-X). Westminster.

Petersen, David L., ed. Prophecy in Israel: Search for an Identity. LC 85-45584. (Issues in Religion & Theology Ser.). 176p. 1986. pap. 7.95 (ISBN 0-317-47042-6, 1-773). Fortress.

Petersen, Evelyn & Petersen, J. Allan. For Women Only. pap. 7.95, 1974 (ISBN 0-8423-0896-2); pap. 3.95 1982 (ISBN 0-8423-0897-0). Tyndale.

Petersen, J. Allan. The Art of Being a Man. 1974. pap. 1.25 (ISBN 0-8423-0085-6). Tyndale.

--Before You Marry. 1974. pap. 3.95 (ISBN 0-8423-0104-6). Tyndale.

--For Families Only. 1981. pap. 2.95 (ISBN 0-8423-0879-2). Tyndale.

--For Men Only. 1982. pap. 3.95 (ISBN 0-8423-0892-X). Tyndale.

--The Myth of the Greener Grass. 1983. 8.95 (ISBN 0-8423-4656-2); pap. 6.95 (ISBN 0-8423-4651-1). Tyndale.

Petersen, J. Allan, jt. auth. see Petersen, Evelyn.

Petersen, J. Allan, compiled by. The Marriage Affair. 1971. pap. 9.95 (ISBN 0-8423-4171-4). Tyndale.

Petersen, J. Allan, et al. Two Become One. 1973. pap. 3.95 (ISBN 0-8423-7620-8). Tyndale.

Petersen, Jim. Evangelism As a Lifestyle. LC 80-83874. 144p. 1980. pap. 5.95 (ISBN 0-89109-475-X). NavPress.

--Evangelism for Our Generation. 216p. 1985. pap. 5.95 (ISBN 0-89109-476-8). NavPress.

Petersen, Mark E. Malachi & the Great & Dreadful Day. 76p. 1983. 5.95 (ISBN 0-87747-962-3). Deseret Bk.

--Noah & the Flood. LC 82-14947. 97p. 1982. 6.95 (ISBN 0-87747-935-6). Deseret Bk.

--The Sons of Mosiah. 125p. 1984. 6.95 (ISBN 0-87747-297-1). Deseret Bk.

--Three Kings of Israel. LC 80-36697. 179p. 1980. 6.95 (ISBN 0-87747-829-5). Deseret Bk.

Petersen, Norman. Rediscovering Paul: Philemon & the Sociology of Paul's Narrative World. LC 84-48730. 320p. 1985. 24.95 (ISBN 0-8006-0741-4, 1-741). Fortress.

Petersen, Norman R. Literary Criticism for New Testament Critics. Via, Dan O., Jr., ed. LC 77-15241. (Guides to Biblical Scholarship: New Testament Ser.). 96p. (Orig.). 1978. pap. 4.50 (ISBN 0-8006-0465-2, 1-465). Fortress.

Petersen, W. P. & Fehr, Terry. Meditation Made Easy. (Concise Guides Ser.). (Illus.). 1979. s&l 9.90 (ISBN 0-531-02894-1). Watts.

Petersen, William. Masonic Quiz. 12.00x (ISBN 0-685-22032-X). Wehman.

Petersen, William J. Catherine Marshall Had a Husband. (Living Books Ser.). 240p. (Orig.). 1986. mass 3.95 (ISBN 0-8423-0204-2). Tyndale.

--O Discipulado de Timoteo. Orig. Title: The Discipling of Timothy. (Port.). 1986. write for info. (ISBN 0-8297-0685-2). Life Pubs Intl.

--Jeremiah: The Prophet Who Wouldn't Quit. 168p. 1984. pap. 5.95 (ISBN 0-88207-243-9). Victor Bks.

--Martin Luther Had a Wife. 1983. pap. 3.95 (ISBN 0-8423-4104-8). Tyndale.

Peterseon, Evelyn H. Who Cares? A Handbook of Christian Counselling. 181p. 1982. pap. text ed. 6.95 (ISBN 0-85364-272-9). Attic Pr.

Petersham, Maud & Petersham, Miska. Christ Child. 63p. 1931. 12.95 (ISBN 0-385-07260-0); PLB (ISBN 0-385-07319-4); pap. 5.95 (ISBN 0-385-15841-6, Zephyr). Doubleday.

Petersham, Miska, jt. auth. see Petersham, Maud.

Peterson, Alan W., illus. Truth the Poet Sings. (Illus.). 220p. 1984. 5.95 (ISBN 0-87159-160-X). Unity School.

Peterson, Carolyn S. & Fenton, Ann D. Christmas Story Programs. (Illus.). 1981. 7.00 (ISBN 0-913545-01-5). Moonlight FL.

Peterson, Clifford, ed. Saint Erkenwald. new ed. LC 76-53197. (Haney Foundation Ser). 1977. 16.00x (ISBN 0-8122-7723-6). U of Pa Pr.

Peterson, David. Hebrews & Perfection: An Examination of the Concept of Perfection in the Epistle to the Hebrews. LC 82-4188. (Society for New Testament Monograph 47). 260p. 1982. 47.50 (ISBN 0-521-24408-0). Cambridge U Pr.

Peterson, David L. The Roles of Israel's Prophets. (Journal for the Study of the Old Testament: Supplement Ser. 17). 131p. 1982. text ed. 14.95 (ISBN 0-905774-32-9, Pub. by JSOT Pr England); (Pub. by JSOT Pr England). Eisenbrauns.

Peterson, Esther A. A Child's Life of Christ. (Illus.). 44p. 1987. 6.95 (ISBN 1-55523-045-8). Winston-Derek.

Peterson, Eugene. Psalms: Prayers of the Heart. (LifeGuide Bible Studies). 64p. (Orig.). 1987. pap. 2.95. Inter-Varsity.

--Run with the Horses. LC 83-13005. 216p. (Orig.). 1983. pap. 6.95 (ISBN 0-87784-905-6). Inter-Varsity.

--Traveling Light. LC 82-15314. 204p. (Orig.). 1982. pap. 5.25 (ISBN 0-87784-377-5). Inter-Varsity.

Peterson, Eugene, et al. Weddings, Funerals, Special Events. (Leadership Library). 175p. 1987. 9.95 (ISBN 0-917463-13-7). Chr Today.

Peterson, Eugene H. Five Smooth Stones for Pastoral Work. LC 79-87751. 1980. pap. 9.95 (ISBN 0-8042-1103-5). John Knox.

--Growing up in Christ. pap. 5.50 (ISBN 0-8042-2026-3). John Knox.

--A Long Obedience in the Same Direction. LC 79-2715. 1980. pap. 6.95 (ISBN 0-87784-727-4). Inter-Varsity.

--Working the Angles: A Trigonometry for Pastoral Work. 266p. (Orig.). 1987. pap. 7.95 (ISBN 0-8028-0265-6). Eerdmans.

Peterson, Evelyn. Who Cares? A Handbook of Christian Counselling. LC 82-60447. (Illus.). 192p. 1982. pap. 7.95 (ISBN 0-8192-1317-9). Morehouse.

Peterson, Gilbert A. The Christian Education of Adults. 1985. text ed. 16.95 (ISBN 0-8024-0496-0). Moody.

Peterson, James L. & Zill, Nicholas. American Jewish High School Students: A National Profile. LC 84-72249. vi, 32p. (Orig.). 1984. pap. 2.50 (ISBN 0-87495-065-1). Am Jewish Comm.

Peterson, Jan, ed. see Hurst, Jane.

Peterson, Jan, ed. see Hynes, Kathleen.

Peterson, John H. Healing Touch. LC 81-80629. 112p. (Orig.). 1981. pap. 5.95 (ISBN 0-8192-1291-1). Morehouse.

Peterson, Kim, ed. see Diamond, Carlin J.

Peterson, Levi S. Canyons of Grace. 135p. 1982. pap. 5.95 (ISBN 0-941214-26-5, Orion). Signature Bks.

Peterson, Levi S., ed. Greening Wheat: Fifteen Mormon Short Stories. 216p. (Orig.). 1983. pap. 5.95 (ISBN 0-941214-12-5, Orion). Signature Bks.

Peterson, Lorraine. If God Loves Me: Teacher's Guide. 128p. (Orig.). 1983. pap. 4.95 (ISBN 0-87123-586-2, 210586). Bethany Hse.

--If God Loves Me, Why Can't I Get My Locker Open? LC 80-27014. 141p. (Orig.). 1980. pap. 4.95 (ISBN 0-87123-251-0, 210251). Bethany Hse.

--Why Isn't God Giving Cash Prizes? (Devotionals for Teens Ser.: No. 3). (Illus.). 160p. 1982. pap. 4.95 (ISBN 0-87123-626-5, 210626). Bethany Hse.

Peterson, Mark E. The Teachings of Paul. LC 84-70647. 120p. 1984. 6.95 (ISBN 0-87747-843-0). Deseret Bk.

Peterson, Meg. Hymns for Auto Harp. 56p. 1978. wkbk 4.95 (ISBN 0-89228-053-0). Impact Bks MO.

Peterson, Michael L. Evil & the Christian God. LC 82-70465. 176p. (Orig.). 1982. pap. 7.95 (ISBN 0-8010-7070-8). Baker Bk.

Peterson, Owen. The Divine Discontent: The Life of Nathan S. S. Beman. (Illus.). xvii, 224p. 1985. text ed. 21.95 (ISBN 0-86554-170-1, MUP-H160). Mercer Univ Pr.

Peterson, Ralph H. Did Jesus Know What He Was Talking About? 112p. 1982. 6.95 (ISBN 0-8187-0045-9). Am Developing.

Peterson, Robert A. Calvin's Doctrine of the Atonement. 1983. pap. 4.95 (ISBN 0-87552-369-2). Presby & Reformed.

Peterson, Roland. Everyone Is Right. 352p. (Orig.). 1986. pap. 12.95 (ISBN 0-87516-565-6). De Vorss.

Peterson, Roy M. The Cults of Campania. LC 23-13673. (American Academy in Rome, Papers & Monographs: Vol. 1). pap. 103.30 (2026716). Bks Demand UMI.

Peterson, Thomas. Doing Something by Doing Nothing. 1985. 6.25 (ISBN 0-89536-747-5, 5853). CSS of Ohio.

--The Gospel Shines Through. (Orig.). 1987. pap. price not set (ISBN 0-89536-874-9, 7860). CSS of Ohio.

Peterson, Thomas D. Epoxy Epistles: Letters That Stick. Sherer, Michael L., ed. (Orig.). 1987. pap. 3.95 (ISBN 0-89536-868-4, 7827). CSS of Ohio.

Petin, L. M. Dictionnaire Hagiographique, 2 vols. Migne, J. P., ed. (Encyclopedie Theologique Ser.: Vols. 40-41). (Fr.). 1580p. Repr. of 1850 ed. lib. bdg. 240.00x (ISBN 0-89241-246-1). Caratzas.

Petri, Catharose de see De Petri, Catharose.

Petri, Catharose De see De Petri, Catharose.

Petri, Catharose De see Van Rijckenborgh, Jan & De Petri, Catharose.

Petrie, Arthur. Message of Daniel. pap. 2.95 (ISBN 0-87509-103-2). Chr Pubns.

Petrie, George. Church & State in Early Maryland. LC 78-63810. (Johns Hopkins University. Studies in the Social Sciences. Tenth Ser. 1892: 4). Repr. of 1892 ed. 11.50 (ISBN 0-404-61073-0). AMS Pr.

--Church & State in Early Maryland. 1973. pap. 9.00. Johnson Repr.

Petrie, William F. Religion & Conscience in Ancient Egypt. LC 72-83176. Repr. of 1898 ed. 24.50 (ISBN 0-405-08854-X). Ayer Co Pubs.

Petrini, Arnold, jt. auth. see Archenti, Augustine.

Petrocelli, Orlando R., ed. The Elbert Hubbard Notebook. rev ed. 192p. 1980. Repr. 10.00 (ISBN 0-89433-144-2). Petrocelli.

Petroff, Elizabeth. Consolation of the Blessed. (Illus.). 224p. 1980. 12.95 (ISBN 0-686-32835-3). Alta Gaia Bks.

Petrullo, Vincenzo. The Diabolic Root: A Study of Peyotism, the New Indian Religion, Among the Delawares. 185p. 1975. Repr. of 1934 ed. lib. bdg. 18.00x (ISBN 0-374-96411-4, Octagon). Hippocrene Bks.

Petrushevsky, I. P. Islam in Iran. Evans, Hubert, tr. (Series in Near Eastern Studies). 400p. 1985. 49.50x (ISBN 0-88706-070-6). State U NY Pr.

Petry, Ann. Tituba of Salem Village. LC 64-20691. (YA) 1964. 14.70i (ISBN 0-690-82677-X, Crowell Jr Bks). HarpJ.

Petry, Ray C. Francis of Assisi. LC 41-25932. Repr. of 1941 ed. 11.50 (ISBN 0-404-05017-4). AMS Pr.

Petry, Ray C., ed. A History of Christianity: Volume I, Readings in the History of the Early & Medieval Church. 576p. 1981. pap. 23.95 (ISBN 0-8010-7064-3). Baker Bk.

--Late Medieval Mysticism. LC 57-5092. (Library of Christian Classics). 420p. 1980. pap. 12.95 (ISBN 0-664-24163-8). Westminster.

Petry, Ronald D. Partners in Creation. 126p. (Orig.). 1979. pap. 4.95 (ISBN 0-87178-688-5). Brethren.

Petschenig, M., ed. see Cassianus, Johannes.

Pettazzoni, Raffaele & Bolle, Kees W., eds. Miti E. Leggende: Myths & Legends, 4 vols. in 1. LC 77-79151. (Mythology Ser.). (Ital.). 1978. Repr. of 1959 ed. lib. bdg. 186.00x (ISBN 0-405-10560-6). Ayer Co Pubs.

Pettazzoni, Rattaele. The All Knowing God: Researches into the Early Religion & Cultlure. Bolle, Kees W., ed. LC 77-79150. (Mythology Ser.). (Illus.). 1978. Repr. of 1956 ed. lib. bdg. 40.00x (ISBN 0-405-10559-2). Ayer Co Pubs.

Pettegree, Andrew. Foreign Protestant Communities in Sixteenth-Century London. (Historical Monographs). 280p. 1987. 49.50 (ISBN 0-19-822938-0). Oxford U Pr.

Pettersson, T. Retention of Religious Experiences. (Illus.). 158p. (Orig.). 1975. pap. text ed. 18.50x (Pub. Almqvist & Wiksell). Coronet Bks.

Pettigrew, Helen. Bible Word Quest. new ed. 96p. 1975. pap. 2.95 (ISBN 0-8010-6965-3). Baker Bk.

Pettingill, William L. Bible Questions Answered. 1932. 8.95 (ISBN 0-310-31131-4, Pub. by Dunham). Zondervan.

Pettit, Ed, jt. auth. see Schul, Bill.

Pettit, Hermon & Wessel, Helen. Beautiful on the Mountain. LC 84-70118. (Illus.). 144p. 1984. 10.95 (ISBN 0-933082-03-7). Bookmates Intl.

--God of the Wilderness. LC 84-70119. (Illus.). 176p. 1984. 10.95 (ISBN 0-933082-04-5). Bookmates Intl.

Pettit, Norman, ed. see Edwards, Jonathan.

Pettitt, Bryce. Worldwide Church of God. (Truthway Ser.). 26p. (Orig.). 1981. pap. text ed. 1.25 (ISBN 0-87148-916-3). Pathway Pr.

Pettitt, Walter R. The Evangelism Ministry of the Local Church. 119p. 1969. 5.25 (ISBN 0-87148-276-2); pap. 4.25 (ISBN 0-87148-277-0). Pathway Pr.

Petts, David. The Dynamic Difference: How the Holy Spirit Can Add an Exciting New Dimension to Your Life. LC 77-91483. 64p. 1978. pap. 0.95 (ISBN 0-88243-484-5, 02-0484, Radiant Bks). Gospel Pub.

Petty, Frances, jt. auth. see Petty, James.

Petty, James & Petty, Frances. That Door with the Lock. 1973. pap. 2.95 (ISBN 0-88428-023-3, 314). Parchment Pr.

Petty, Jo. An Apple a Day: Treasured Selections from Apples of Gold. 1979. 6.95 (ISBN 0-8378-5025-8). Gibson.

Petty, Thurman, Jr. Siege. (Orion Ser.). 144p. 1980. pap. 3.95 (ISBN 0-8127-0302-2). Review & Herald.

Petuchowski, jt. auth. see Falaturi, Abdoldjavad.

Petuchowski, Jacob, ed. New Perspectives on Abraham Geiger. pap. 2.50x (ISBN 0-87820-201-3, Pub. by Hebrew Union College Press). Ktav.

Petuchowski, Jacob J. Freedom of Expression in the Jewish Tradition. 34p. 1984. pap. 2.50 (ISBN 0-87495-062-7). Am Jewish Comm.

--Heirs of the Pharisees. LC 86-1496. (Brown Classics in Judaica Ser.). 214p. 1986. pap. text ed. 12.00 (ISBN 0-8191-5256-0). U Pr of Amer.

Petuchowski, Jacob J., ed. & tr. Theology & Poetry Studies in the Medieval Piyyut. (Littman Library of Jewish Civilization). 1978. 18.50x (ISBN 0-19-710014-7). Oxford U Pr.

Petuchowski, Jakob J. Ever since Sinai. 3rd ed. LC 79-64324. 1979. pap. text ed. 5.95 (ISBN 0-930038-11-8). Arbit.

--Our Masters Taught Rabbinic Stories & Sayings. LC 82-9999. 160p. 1982. 10.95 (ISBN 0-8245-0521-2). Crossroad NY.

--Prayerbook Reform in Europe: The Liturgy of European Liberal & Reform Judaism. LC 68-8262. (Illus.). 1969. 13.50 (ISBN 0-8074-0091-2, 387580, Pub. by World Union). UAHC.

--The Theology of Haham David Nieto. 1970. 10.00x (ISBN 0-87068-015-3). Ktav.

Petuchowski, Jakob J., ed. Understanding Jewish Prayer. 1972. pap. 7.95x (ISBN 0-87068-186-9). Ktav.

Petzold, Gertrud Von see Von Petzold, Gertrud.

Peukert, Helmut. Science, Action, & Fundamental Theology: Toward a Theology of Communicative Action. Bohman, James, tr. from Ger. (German Social Thought Ser.). 364p. 1984. text ed. 37.50x (ISBN 0-262-16095-1). MIT Pr.

--Science, Action, & Fundamental Theology: Toward a Theology of Communicative Action. Bohman, James, tr. (Studies in Contemporary German Social Thought Ser.). 360p. 1986. pap. text ed. 12.50x (ISBN 0-262-66060-1). MIT Pr.

Peusch, Leonard. The Three Crosses. 1978. 0.75 (ISBN 0-8199-0723-5). Franciscan Herald.

Pevarnik, Carrie & Chaney, Robert. Psalms: Prayer Power for Your Problems. LC 78-58146. (Illus.). 1978. pap. 9.95 (ISBN 0-918936-05-5). Astara.

Pevear, Richard, tr. see Alain.

Pevsner, Nikolaus & Metcalf, Priscilla. The Cathedrals of England: Midland, Eastern & Northern England, Vol. 2. 400p. 1985. 40.00 (ISBN 0-670-80125-9). Viking.

--The Cathedrals of England: Southern England, Vol. 1. 384p. 1985. 40.00 (ISBN 0-670-80124-0). Viking.

Peyravan, Abdosalam, tr. see Mah Talat Etemad Moghadam.

Peyret, Raymond. Marthe Robin: The Cross & the Joy. Faulhaber, Clare W., tr. from Fr. LC 83-15591. (Illus.). 135p. 1983. pap. 6.95 (ISBN 0-8189-0464-X). Alba.

Pez, Bernhard. Bibliotheca Asctica Antiquo-Nova, 12 Vols. 6600p. 1740. text ed. 414.00x (ISBN 0-576-72814-4, Pub. by Gregg Intl Pubs England). Gregg Intl.

Pfaff, Richard W. Medieval Latin Liturgy: A Select Bibliography. (Toronto Medieval Bibliographies Ser.). 128p. 1982. pap. 12.50 (ISBN 0-8020-6488-4). U of Toronto Pr.

Pfannmueller, Gustav. Handbuch der Islam-Literatur. (Ger.). viii, 436p. 1974. Repr. of 1923 ed. 68.00x (ISBN 3-11-002488-8). De Gruyter.

Pfarr, Anthony J. Seek His Face. LC 73-86211. 1973. 4.95 (ISBN 0-8198-0353-7); pap. 3.95 (ISBN 0-8198-0354-5). Dghtrs St Paul.

Pfatteicher, Carl F. John Redford: Organist & Almoner of St. Paul's Cathedral in the Reign of Henry VIII. LC 74-24184. Repr. of 1934 ed. 24.00 (ISBN 0-404-13088-7). AMS Pr.

Pfatteicher, Philip H. Commentary on the Occasional Services. LC 82-48542. 336p. 1983. 19.95 (ISBN 0-8006-0697-3, 1-1697). Fortress.

--Festivals & Commemorations: Handbook to the Calendar in Lutheran Book of Worship. LC 79-54129. 336p. 24.95 (ISBN 0-8066-1757-8, 10-2295). Augsburg.

--Foretaste of the Feast to Come: Devotions on Holy Communion. (Illus.). 64p. (Orig.). 1987. kivar paper 3.95 (ISBN 0-8066-2283-0, 10-2357). Augsburg.

Pfatteicher, Philip H. & Messerli, Carlos R. Manual on the Liturgy: Lutheran Book of Worship. LC 78-68179. 1979. 18.00 (ISBN 0-8066-1676-8, 12-2015). Augsburg.

Pfeffer, L. Religious Freedom. Haiman, Franklyn S., ed. (To Protect These Rights Ser.). 192p. 1983. pap. 12.95 (ISBN 0-8442-6001-0, 6001-0, Passport Bks.). Natl Textbk.

Pfeffer, Leo. Church, State & Freedom, 2 vols. 1987. lib. bdg. 75.00 ea. Vol. 1 (ISBN 0-379-20734-6). Vol. 2 (ISBN 0-379-20735-4). Oceana.

--Creeds in Competition: A Creative Force in American Culture. LC 78-2308. 1978. Repr. of 1958 ed. lib. bdg. 19.00x (ISBN 0-313-20349-0, PFCC). Greenwood.

--Religion, State & the Burger Court. LC 84-43056. 310p. 1985. 23.95 (ISBN 0-87975-275-0). Prometheus Bks.

Pfeffer, Leo, jt. auth. see Stokes, Anson.

Pfeifer, Carl J. Presences of Jesus. 2nd ed. 112p. 1984. pap. 4.95 (ISBN 0-89622-193-8). Twenty-Third.

Pfeifer, Carl J., jt. auth. see Manternach, Janaan.

Pfeiffer, Baldur, ed. The European Seventh-Day Adventists Mission in the Middle East 1879-1939. (European University Studies: Ser. 23, Vol. 161). 124p. 1981. pap. 16.45 (ISBN 3-8204-5918-9). P Lang Pubs.

Pfeiffer, Charles F. Baker's Bible Atlas. rev. ed. (Illus.). 1961. Repr. 15.95 (ISBN 0-8010-6930-0). Baker Bk.

--Between the Testaments. pap. 4.95 (ISBN 0-8010-6873-8). Baker Bk.

--The Bible Atlas. LC 60-15536. 1975. 16.95 (ISBN 0-8054-1129-1). Broadman.

--Book of Genesis. (Shield Bible Study). (Orig.). pap. 2.95 (ISBN 0-8010-6906-8). Baker Bk.

--Book of Leviticus: A Study Manual. (Shield Bible Study). (Orig.). pap. 2.95 (ISBN 0-8010-6889-4). Baker Bk.

--Dead Sea Scrolls & the Bible. rev. & enl. ed. (Baker Studies in Biblical Archaeology). (Illus.). 1969. pap. 5.95 (ISBN 0-8010-6898-3). Baker Bk.

--Epistle to the Hebrews. (Everyman's Bible Commentary Ser.). (Orig.). 1968. pap. 5.95 (ISBN 0-8024-2058-3). Moody.

--Old Testament History. 1973. 22.95 (ISBN 0-8010-6945-9). Baker Bk.

--Ras Shamra & the Bible. (Baker Studies in Biblical Archaeology). 1976. pap. 2.95 (ISBN 0-8010-7003-1). Baker Bk.

--Tell El-Amarna & the Bible. (Baker Studies in Biblical Archaeology). 1976. pap. 2.95 (ISBN 0-8010-7002-3). Baker Bk.

Pfeiffer, Charles F. & Vos, Howard F. Wycliffe Historical Geography of Bible Lands. 1967. 25.95 (ISBN 0-8024-9699-7). Moody.

Pfeiffer, Charles F., jt. auth. see Harrison, Everett.

Pfeiffer, Charles F., ed. see Gama, Roberto.

Pfeiffer, Charles F., jt. ed. see Harrison, Everett.

Pfeiffer, Charles F., et al, eds. Wycliffe Bible Encyclopedia, 2 vols. (Illus.). 1875p. 1975. 54.95 (ISBN 0-8024-9697-0). Moody.

Pfeiffer, Charles R. La Epistola a los Hebreos (Comentario Biblico Portavoz) Orig. Title: Epistle to the Hebrews (Everyman's Bible Commentary) (Span.). 128p. 1981. pap. 3.50 (ISBN 0-8254-1564-0). Kregel.

Pfeiffer, Franz. Meister Eckhart, 2 vols. 1977. lib. bdg. 250.00 (ISBN 0-8490-2222-3). Gordon Pr.

Pfeiffer, John E. The Creative Explosion: An Inquiry into the Origins of Art & Religion. LC 84-72675. (Illus.). 270p. (Orig.). 1985. pap. text ed. 12.95x (ISBN 0-8014-9308-0). Cornell U Pr.

Pfeiffer, Robert H. History of New Testament Times. LC 77-138125. 561p. 1972. Repr. of 1949 ed. lib. bdg. 23.00x (ISBN 0-8371-3559-1, PFNT). Greenwood.

Pfister, Friedrich. Der Reliquienkult im Altertum, 2 vols. in 1. Incl. Vol. 1. Das Objekt des Reliquienkultes; Vol. 2. Die Reliquien als Kultobjekt: Geschichte des Reliquienkultes. (Ger.). xii, 686p. 1974. Repr. of 1909 ed. 76.00x (ISBN 3-11-002453-5). De Gruyter.

Pfisterer, Karl D. The Prism of Scripture: Studies on History & Historicity in the Work of Jonathan Edwards, Vol. 1. (Anglo-American Forum Ser.: Vol. 1). 381p. 1975. pap. 31.55 (ISBN 3-261-00965-9). P Lang Pubs.

Pfleiderer, O. The Philosophy of Religion on the Basis of Its History, 4 vols. in 2. Repr. of 1886 ed. Set. 72.00 (ISBN 0-527-03238-7). Kraus Repr.

Pfleiderer, Otto. Lectures on the Influence of the Apostle Paul on the Development of Christianity. Smith, J. Frederick, tr. LC 77-27166. (Hibbert Lectures: 1885). Repr. of 1885 ed. 29.00 (ISBN 0-404-60406-4). AMS Pr.

--Philosophy & Development of Religion, 2 vols. LC 77-27229. (Gifford Lectures: 1894). Repr. of 1894 ed. Set. 65.00 (ISBN 0-404-60470-6). AMS Pr.

--Primitive Christianity, 4 vols. Morrison, W. D., ed. Montgomery, W., tr. LC 65-22085. (Library of Religious & Philosophical Thought). 1966. Repr. of 1906 ed. lib. bdg. 150.00x (ISBN 0-678-09954-5, Reference Bk Pubs). Kelley.

Pfordresher, John, jt. ed. see Dawson, Carl.

Pfrimmer, Mildred. Books to Learn & Live by, 5 bks. Incl. Bk. 1. The ABC's of Creation; Bk. 2. The ABC's of the Flood; Bk. 3. The Aardvark in the Art; Bk. 4. Elephant in Eden; Bk. 5. The Tale of the Whale. (The Little Talkers Ser.). 1977. Set. 17.50 (ISBN 0-685-80546-8). Triumph Pub.

Pfuetze, Paul. Self, Society, Existence: Human Nature & Dialogue in the Thought of George Herbert Mead & Martin Buber. 400p. 1973. Repr. of 1961 ed. lib. bdg. 22.50x (ISBN 0-8371-6708-6, PFSS). Greenwood.

Phaigh, Bethal. Gestalt & the Wisdom of the Kahunas. LC 82-50928. 112p. 1983. pap. 5.95 (ISBN 0-87516-498-6). De Vorss.

Phan, Peter C. Culture & Eschatology: The Iconographical Vision of Paul Evdokimov. LC 83-48751. (American University Studies VII (Theology & Religion): Vol. 1). 345p. 1984. text ed. 36.50 (ISBN 0-8204-0040-8). P Lang Pubs.

--Social Thought. (Message of the Fathers of the Church Ser.: Vol. 20). 15.95 (ISBN 0-89453-360-6); pap. 9.95 (ISBN 0-89453-331-2). M Glazier.

Phanuel, I. see Coscia, Louis W., pseud.

Phares, Ross. Bible in Pocket, Gun in Hand: The Story of Frontier Religion. LC 64-11375. viii, 182p. 1971. pap. 5.50 (ISBN 0-8032-5725-2, BB 524, Bison). U of Nebr Pr.

Phelan, Gerald B. Saint Thomas & Analogy. (Aquinas Lecture). 1941. 7.95 (ISBN 0-87462-105-4). Marquette.

Phelan, John L. Hispanization of the Philippines: Spanish Aims & Filipino Responses, 1565-1700. (Illus.). 234p. 1959. 30.00x (ISBN 0-299-01810-5). U of Wis Pr.

--The Millennial Kingdom of the Franciscans in the New World. 2nd rev ed. 1970. 35.95x (ISBN 0-520-01404-9). U of Cal Pr.

Phelan, Paul J. With a Merry Heart. 353p. 1981. Repr. of 1943 ed. lib. bdg. 25.00 (ISBN 0-89760-710-4). Telegraph Bks.

Phelan, Thomas P. Catholics in Colonial Days. LC 74-145706. Repr. of 1935 ed. 40.00x (ISBN 0-8103-3685-5). Gale.

Phelps, Austin. The Still Hour. 1979. pap. 3.45 (ISBN 0-85151-202-X). Banner of Truth.

Phelps, Austin, et al. Hymns & Choirs. LC 78-144671. Repr. of 1860 ed. 29.50 (ISBN 0-404-07207-0). AMS Pr.

Phelps, Myron H. The Master in Akka: Including Recollections of the Greatest Holy Leaf. Orig. Title: Abbas Effendi: His Life & Teachings. (Illus.). 1985. Repr. of 1912 ed. 12.95 (ISBN 0-933770-49-9). Kalimat.

Phelps, William L. Human Nature & the Gospel. 1977. Repr. of 1925 ed. lib. bdg. 30.00 (ISBN 0-8414-6807-9). Folcroft.

Phenix, Philip H. Religious Concerns in Contemporary Education. LC 59-11329. Repr. of 1959 ed. 29.50 (ISBN 0-8357-9605-1, 2016949). Bks Demand UMI.

Pherson, Dave Mac. The Incredible Cover-Up. 1975. 8.95 (ISBN 0-88270-143-6); pap. 3.95 (ISBN 0-88270-144-4). Omega Pubns Or.

Phifer, Kenneth G. A Book of Uncommon Prayer. LC 82-50945. 128p. 1983. pap. 5.95 (ISBN 0-8358-0451-8). Upper Room.

Philaretos, S. D. The Idea of the Being. Orthodox Christian Educational Society, ed. Cummings, D., tr. from Hellenic. 287p. 1963. 5.75x (ISBN 0-938366-09-2). Orthodox Chr.

Philaretos, Sotirios D. The Decalogue & the Gospel. Orthodox Christian Educational Society, ed. Cummings, D., tr. from Hellenic. 62p. (Orig.). 1957. pap. 2.00x (ISBN 0-938366-43-2). Orthodox Chr.

Philby, Harry S. Arabia of the Wahhabis. LC 73-6297. (The Middle East Ser.). Repr. of 1928 ed. 33.00 (ISBN 0-405-05355-X). Ayer Co Pubs.

Philip, James. Numbers, Vol. 4. 300p. 1987. 18.95 (ISBN 0-8499-0409-9). Word Bks.

Philip, John. Researches in South Africa, 2 vols. LC 77-82065. (Illus.). Repr. of 1828 ed. 33.00x (ISBN 0-8371-3855-8, PHR&). Greenwood.

Philip, Lotte B. The Ghent Altarpiece & the Art of Jan Van Eyck. LC 73-113007. (Illus.). 380p. 1981. pap. 16.50 (ISBN 0-691-00316-5). Princeton U Pr.

Philipon, M. M. Conchita: A Mother's Diary. Owen, Aloysius, tr. LC 78-1929. 1978. pap. 6.95 (ISBN 0-8189-0368-6). Alba.

Philippe, Thomas. The Fire of Contemplation: A Guide for Interior Souls. Doran, Verda C., tr. from Fr. LC 81-8099. 128p. (Orig.). 1981. pap. 4.95 (ISBN 0-8189-0414-3). Alba.

Philippi, Charles, tr. see Vogue, Adalbert de.

Philippus De Thame. Knights Hospitallers in England: Being the Report of Prior Phillip De Thame to the Grand Master Elyan De Villanova for A. D. 1338. Larking, Lambert B., ed. (Camden Society, London. Publications, First Ser.: No. 65). Repr. of 1857 ed. 37.00 (ISBN 0-404-50165-6). AMS Pr.

--Knights Hospitallers in England. Repr. of 1857 ed. 37.00 (ISBN 0-384-46330-4). Johnson Repr.

Philips, Gerard. Achieving Christian Maturity. 4.95 (ISBN 0-685-10957-7, L37990). Franciscan Herald.

Philips, John. Exploring the Psalms, Vol. 3. 318p. 1986. 14.95 (ISBN 0-87213-686-8). Loizeaux.

Philips, Mike, jt. auth. see Ryun, Jim.

Philipson, David. Jew in English Fiction. LC 76-42290. 1889. lib. bdg. 25.00 (ISBN 0-8414-6796-X). Folcroft.

--The Jew in English Fiction. LC 76-30568. (English Literature Ser, No. 33). 1977. lib. bdg. 47.95x (ISBN 0-8383-2150-X). Haskell.

--Old European Jewries. LC 74-178586. Repr. of 1895 ed. 27.50 (ISBN 0-404-56663-4). AMS Pr.

Philipson, David, ed. see Wise, Isaac.

Philipson, David, et al. Studies in Jewish Literature Issued in Honor of Professor Kaufmann Kohler, Ph.D. Katz, Steven, ed. LC 79-7167. (Jewish Philosophy, Mysticism & History of Ideas Ser.). 1980. Repr. of 1913 ed. lib. bdg. 26.50x (ISBN 0-405-12283-7). Ayer Co Pubs.

Phillimore, Robert. The Principal Ecclesiastical Judgments Delivered in the Court of Arches 1867 to 1875. xiii, 420p. 1981. Repr. of 1876 ed. lib. bdg. 35.00x (ISBN 0-8377-2504-6). Rothman.

Phillippo, James M. Jamaica: Its Past & Present State. LC 70-109998. (Illus.). Repr. of 1843 ed. 23.75x (ISBN 0-8371-4132-X, PIA&, Pub. by Negro U Pr). Greenwood.

Phillippou, Margaret J. Transcendental Dancing. 1982. pap. 3.00 (ISBN 0-941500-29-2). Sharing Co.

Phillippson, Ernst A. Germanisches Heidentum Bei Den Angelsachsen. Repr. of 1929 ed. 20.00 (ISBN 0-384-46310-X). Johnson Repr.

Phillips, ed. see Knoche, Keith.

Phillips, ed. see Wheeler, Penny.

Phillips, Allen. Nuggets for Happiness. 1959. 2.95 (ISBN 0-87148-625-3). Pathway Pr.

Phillips, Anthony. Deuteronomy. LC 73-77172. (Cambridge Bible Commentary on the New English Bible, Old Testament Ser.). (Illus.). 224p. 1973. pap. 29.95 (ISBN 0-521-08636-1); pap. 12.95 (ISBN 0-521-09772-X). Cambridge U Pr.

Phillips, Anthony C., jt. ed. see Coggins, R. J.

Phillips, Bernard, ed. & intro. by see Suzuki, Daisetz T.

Phillips, Bob. How Can I Be Sure: A Pre-Marriage Inventory. LC 77-94448. 160p. (Orig.). 1978. pap. 3.95 (ISBN 0-89081-073-7). Harvest Hse.

--In Search of Bible Trivia. (Orig.). 1985. pap. 4.95 (ISBN 0-89081-458-9). Harvest Hse.

--In Search of Bible Trivia II. pap. 4.95 (ISBN 0-89081-464-3). Harvest Hse.

--The World's Greatest Collection of Heavenly Humor. LC 81-82676. 192p. (Orig.). 1982. pap. text ed. 2.95 (ISBN 0-89081-297-7). Harvest Hse.

Phillips, Cara L. Doing Right Makes Me Happy. Mahany, Patricia, ed. LC 82-80028. (Happy Day Bks.). (Illus.). 24p. (Orig.). 1982. pap. 1.59 (ISBN 0-87239-536-7, 3582). Standard Pub.

Phillips, Carolyn. Michelle. 1982. 3.95 (ISBN 0-88113-205-5). Edit Betania.

Phillips, Charles H. The History of the Colored Methodist Episcopal Church in America: Comprising Its Organization, Subsequent Developments & Present Status. LC 73-38459. (Religion in America, Ser. 2). 252p. 1972. Repr. of 1898 ed. 17.00 (ISBN 0-405-04080-6). Ayer Co Pubs.

Phillips, Charles S. The Church in France, Seventeen Eighty-Seven to Eighteen Forty-Eight. (Church Historical Society London Ser.: No. 19A). Repr. of 1934 ed. 40.00 (ISBN 0-8115-3143-0). Kraus Repr.

--New Commandment: An Inquiry into the Social Precept & Practice of the Ancient Church. LC 31-31370. (Church Historical Society Ser.: No. 4). 1930. 10.00x (ISBN 0-8401-5004-0). A R Allenson.

--The New Commandment: An Inquiry into the Social Precept & Practice of the Ancient Church. (Church Historical Society London Ser.: No. 4). Repr. of 1930 ed. 40.00 (ISBN 0-8115-3128-7). Kraus Repr.

Phillips, Cheryl & Harvey, Bonnie C., eds. My Jesus Pocketbook of God's Fruit. LC 83-50194. (My Jesus Pocketbook Ser.). (Illus.). 32p. 1983. pap. 0.49 (ISBN 0-937420-08-5). Stirrup Assoc.

Phillips, Cheryl M. & Harvey, Bonnie C., eds. My Jesus Pocketbook of the Lord's Prayer. LC 83-50193. (My Jesus Pocketbook Ser.). (Illus.). 32p. 1983. pap. 0.49 (ISBN 0-937420-07-7). Stirrup Assoc.

Phillips, Cheryl M., ed. see Lee, Laurel.

Phillips, Cheryl M., ed. see Stirrup Associates, Inc.

Phillips, Cheryl M., ed. see Stirrup Associates Inc.

Phillips, Cheryl M., ed. see Stirrup Associates, Inc. Staff.

Phillips, D. Z. Belief, Change & Forms of Life. (Library of Philosophy & Religion). 144p. 1986. text ed. 29.95x (ISBN 0-391-03385-9). Humanities.

--R. S. Thomas: Poet of the Hidden God. (Princeton Theolographical Monograph Ser.: No. 2). 192p. (Orig.). 1986. pap. 18.00 (ISBN 0-915138-83-2). Pickwick.

Phillips, D. Z., et al, eds. see Fries, Jakob F.

Phillips, Dorothy B., et al, eds. The Choice Is Always Ours. rev. ed. 480p. (Orig.). 1975. pap. 3.95 (ISBN 0-8356-0302-4, Quest). Theos Pub Hse.

Phillips, E. Lee. Breaking Silence Before the Lord. (Pulpit Library). 160p. 1986. pap. 5.95 (ISBN 0-8010-7093-7). Baker Bk.

--Prayer for Our Day. LC 81-82349. 156p. 1982. pap. 4.95 (ISBN 0-8042-2583-4). John Knox.

--Prayers for Worship. 148p. 1985. pap. 4.95 (ISBN 0-8010-7090-2). Baker Bk.

Phillips, Evelyn M. The Illustrated Guidebook to the Frescoes in the Sistine Chapel. (Illus.). 124p. 1981. Repr. of 1901 ed. 69.85 (ISBN 0-89901-029-6). Found Class Reprints.

Phillips, Gary, tr. see Entrevernes Group.

Phillips, George S. see Searle, January, pseud.

Phillips, Gloria & Harrell, Irene B. A Heart Set Free. (Orig.). 1985. pap. 5.00 (ISBN 0-915541-02-5); study guide: Spiritual Warfare 5.00 (ISBN 0-915541-16-5); answer bk. avail. (ISBN 0-915541-17-3). Star Bks Inc.

Phillips, Harold R. & Firth, Robert E., eds. Cases in Denominational Administration: A Management Casebook for Decision-Making. vi, 314p. 1978. pap. text ed. 4.95 (ISBN 0-943872-75-8). Andrews Univ Pr.

Phillips, Helen, tr. see Galilea, Segundo.

Phillips, J. A. Eve: The History of an Idea. LC 83-48424. (Illus.). 192p. 1984. 12.45 (ISBN 0-06-066552-1, HarpR). Har-Row.

Phillips, J. B. The Living Gospels. 288p. 1981. 24.95 (ISBN 0-8317-3948-7, Rutledge Pr). Smith Pubs.

--The New Testament in Modern English. 1973. 8.95 (ISBN 0-02-088490-7). Macmillan.

--The Newborn Christian: 114 Readings. 240p. 1984. 5.95 (ISBN 0-02-088270-X, Collier). Macmillan.

--Peter's Portrait of Jesus. (Festival Ser.). 192p. 1981. pap. 1.95 (ISBN 0-687-30850-X). Abingdon.

--The Price of Success: An Autobiography. 288p. (Orig.). 1985. pap. 7.95 (ISBN 0-87788-659-8). Shaw Pubs.

Phillips, James D. Salem in the Eighteenth Century. LC 37-36381. (Illus.). 533p. 1969. Repr. of 1937 ed. 25.00 (ISBN 0-88389-017-8). Essex Inst.

Phillips, James M. From the Rising of the Sun: Christians & Society in Contemporary Japan. LC 80-24609. 320p. (Orig.). 1981. pap. 14.95 (ISBN 0-88344-145-4). Orbis Bks.

Phillips, John. The Bible Explorer's Guide. 320p. 1987. 9.95 (ISBN 0-87213-682-5). Loizeaux.

--Exploring Acts, Vol. 1. (Exploring Ser.). (Orig.). 1986. pap. 11.95 (ISBN 0-8024-2435-X). Moody.

--Exploring Genesis. LC 80-23685. 582p. 1980. pap. 9.95 (ISBN 0-8024-2430-9). Moody.

--Exploring Hebrews. LC 76-39908. 1977. pap. 9.95 (ISBN 0-8024-2431-7). Moody.

--Exploring Revelation. LC 74-15330. 288p. 1974. pap. 9.95 (ISBN 0-8024-2432-5). Moody.

--Exploring Revelation. rev. ed. (Exploring Ser.). 1987. pap. 11.95 (ISBN 0-8024-2497-X). Moody.

--Exploring Romans. 250p. 1971. pap. 9.95 (ISBN 0-8024-2433-3). Moody.

--Exploring Romans. rev. ed. (Exploring Ser.). 1987. pap. 11.95 (ISBN 0-8024-2429-5). Moody.

--Exploring the Future. LC 82-557. 400p. 1983. 14.95 (ISBN 0-8407-5275-X). Nelson.

--Exploring the Psalms, Vol. 4. 1987. 14.95 (ISBN 0-87213-687-6). Loizeaux.

--Exploring the Psalms, Vol. 5. 1987. 14.95 (ISBN 0-87213-688-4). Loizeaux.

--Exploring the Psalms: Vol. II, 42-72. 288p. 1986. 14.95 (ISBN 0-87213-685-X). Loizeaux.

--Exploring the Psalms: Volume 1 (Psalms 1-41) 318p. 1985. 14.95 (ISBN 0-87213-684-1). Loizeaux.

--Exploring the Scriptures. 1965. pap. 9.95 (ISBN 0-8024-2434-1). Moody.

--Exploring the Song of Solomon. 157p. 1984. pap. 6.95 (ISBN 0-87213-683-3). Loizeaux.

--Exploring the World of the Jew. LC 81-16844. 288p. 1982. pap. 9.95 (ISBN 0-8024-2411-2). Moody.

--How to Live Forever. (Teach Yourself the Bible Ser.). 1964. pap. 2.75 (ISBN 0-8024-3700-1). Moody.

--One Hundred Sermon Outlines from the New Testament. 1979. pap. 4.95 (ISBN 0-8024-7817-4). Moody.

--One Hundred Sermon Outlines from the Old Testament. 2nd ed. pap. 4.95 (ISBN 0-8024-7816-6). Moody.

Phillips, John A. Eve: The History of an Idea. LC 83-48424. (Illus.). 224p. 1985. pap. 7.95 (ISBN 0-06-250670-6, HarpR). Har-Row.

Phillips, John B. Your God Is Too Small. pap. 3.95 (ISBN 0-02-088540-7, Collier). Macmillan.

Phillips, Joseph W. Jedidiah Morse & New England Congregationalism. 305p. 1983. 30.00x (ISBN 0-8135-0982-3). Rutgers U Pr.

Phillips, Keith. The Making of a Disciple. LC 80-24908. 160p. 1983. 2.50 (ISBN 0-8007-8485-5, Spire Bks). Revell.

Phillips, Leona. A Christmas Bibliography. 1977. lib. bdg. 69.95 (ISBN 0-8490-1363-1). Gordon Pr.

Phillips, Leona R. Martin Luther & the Reformation: An Annotated Bibliography. 1985. lib. bdg. 79.95 (ISBN 0-8490-3242-3). Gordon Pr.

Phillips, McCandlish. The Bible, the Supernatural & the Jews. LC 77-92532. 1970. pap. 8.95 (ISBN 0-87123-036-4, 210036). Bethany Hse.

Phillips, Marcia, jt. auth. see Kaplan, David.

Phillips, Margaret. Songs of the Good Earth. LC 79-10731. 62p. 1980. pap. 4.95 (ISBN 0-88289-221-5). Pelican.

Phillips, Margaret M., ed. see Erasmus, Desiderius.

Phillips, Max, ed. see Cooper, Douglas.

Phillips, Michael. George MacDonald. 336p. 1987. 12.95 (ISBN 0-87123-944-2). Bethany Hse.

Phillips, Michael, ed. see MacDonald, George.

Phillips, Mike. Building Respect, Responsibility, & Spiritual Values in Your Child. LC 81-12225. 138p. (Orig.). 1981. pap. 3.95 (ISBN 0-87123-146-8, 210146). Bethany Hse.

--A Survival Guide for Tough Times. LC 79-4261. 176p. 1979. pap. 3.95 (ISBN 0-87123-498-X, 210498). Bethany Hse.

--A Vision for the Church. 110p. 1981. pap. 3.95 (ISBN 0-940652-02-1). Sunrise Bks.

Phillips, Nancy V. & Van Andel, Mary T. Journeying Together: A Study on the Psalms. write for info. (ISBN 0-916466-03-5). Reformed Church.

Phillips, Osborne, jt. auth. see Denning, Melita.

Phillips, Paul T., jt. ed. see Helmstadter, Richard J.

Phillips, Sheree. Mothers: At the Heart of Life. 140p. (Orig.). 1985. pap. 4.95 (ISBN 0-89283-274-6, Pub. by Vine Books). Servant.

Phillips, Stephen H. Aurobindo's Philosophy of Brahman. xii, 200p. 1986. 30.64 (ISBN 90-04-07765-0, Pub. by E J Brill). Heinman.

Phillips, Vera & Robertson, Edwin. J. B. Phillips: The Wounded Healer. 120p. (Orig.). 1985. pap. 5.95 (ISBN 0-8028-0073-4). Eerdmans.

Phillips, Wade H. God the Church & Revelation. 376p. (Orig.). 1986. pap. 8.95 (ISBN 0-934942-60-9, 4048). White Wing Pub.

--Perplexing Scriptures. 135p. (Orig.). 1984. pap. 4.50 (ISBN 0-934942-44-7, 2034). White Wing Pub.

Phillips, Walter. Defending "A Christian Country". Churchmen & Society in New South Wales in the 1880's & After. (Illus.). 332p. 1982. text ed. 39.95 (ISBN 0-7022-1539-2). U of Queensland Pr.

Phillips, William J. Carols, Their Origin, Music, & Connection with Mystery-Plays: A Greenwood Archival Edition. (Illus.). Repr. of 1921 ed. lib. bdg. 40.00x (ISBN 0-8371-4312-8, PHCA). Greenwood.

Philo. Philonis Alexandrini in Flaccum. Connor, W. R., ed. LC 78-18570. (Greek Texts & Commentaries Ser.). 1979. Repr. of 1939 ed. lib. bdg. 17.00x (ISBN 0-405-11414-1). Ayer Co Pubs.

Philp, Howard L. Freud & Religious Belief. LC 72-12635. 140p. 1974. Repr. of 1956 ed. lib. bdg. 22.50x (ISBN 0-8371-6682-9, PHFR). Greenwood.

Philp, J. R., jt. auth. see Morgan, John S.

Philpot, J. H. The Sacred Tree: The Tree in Religion & Myth. 1977. lib. bdg. 69.95 (ISBN 0-8490-2553-2). Gordon Pr.

--The Seceders. pap. 2.95 (ISBN 0-85151-132-5). Banner of Truth.

Philpot, William M. Best Black Sermons. LC 72-75358. 96p. 1972. pap. 4.95 (ISBN 0-8170-0533-1). Judson.

Phinney, William R., et al, eds. Thomas Ware, a Spectator at the Christmas Conference: A Miscellany on Thomas Ware & the Christmas Conference. LC 84-70457. (Illus.). 320p. (Orig.). 1984. pap. 8.95 smythsewn (ISBN 0-914960-48-2). Academy Bks.

Phipps, William E. Death: Confronting the Reality. LC 86-45405. 204p. (Orig.). 1987. pap. 11.95 (ISBN 0-8042-0487-X). John Knox.

--Encounter Through Questioning Paul: A Fresh Approach to the Apostle's Life & Letters. LC 82-17580. (Illus.). 114p. (Orig.). 1983. lib. bdg. 24.25 (ISBN 0-8191-2785-X); pap. text ed. 9.50 (ISBN 0-8191-2786-8). U Pr of Amer.

--Influential Theologians on Wo-Man. LC 79-5431. 1980. lib. bdg. 23.00 (ISBN 0-8191-1383-2); pap. text ed. 9.50 (ISBN 0-8191-0880-4). U Pr of Amer.

--Paul Against Supernaturalism. LC 85-19228. 177p. 1986. 17.95 (ISBN 0-8022-2501-2). Philos Lib.

--Was Jesus Married? The Distortion of Sexuality in the Christian Tradition. LC 85-32319. 250p. 1986. pap. text ed. 11.75 (ISBN 0-8191-5191-2). U Pr of Amer.

Photiadis, John D., ed. Religion in Appalachia. 1979. 10.75 (ISBN 0-686-26337-5). W Va U Ctr Exten.

Photiou, Paul. My Conversion to Christ. Orthodox Christian Educational Society, ed. (Gr., Orig.). 1970. Repr. of 1952 ed. 0.50x (ISBN 0-938366-41-6). Orthodox Chr.

Phu, Sam, jt. auth. see Friesen, Evelyn.

Phy, Allene S., ed. The Bible & Popular Culture in America. LC 83-11548. (Bible in American Culture Ser.). 1985. 15.95 (ISBN 0-89130-640-4, 06 12 02). Scholars Pr GA.

Phylos. A Dweller on Two Planets. LC 80-8896. (Harper's Library of Spiritual Wisdom). 424p. 1981. pap. 10.95 (ISBN 0-06-066565-3, CN 4010, HarpR). Har-Row.

--The Growth of a Soul. LC 76-15521. 10.00 (ISBN 0-912216-07-7). Angel Pr.

Phylos the Thibetan. A Dweller on Two Planets, or the Dividing of the Way, Vol. 12. Oliver, Frederick S., as told to. LC 73-94420. (Spiritual Science Library). (Illus.). 432p. 1983. lib. bdg. 18.00 (ISBN 0-89345-039-1). Garber Comm.

Phypers, David, jt. auth. see Bridge, Donald.

Physick, John. Victorian Church Art. (Illus.). 212p. (Orig.). 1984. pap. 12.95 (ISBN 0-901486-36-1, Pub. by Victoria & Albert Mus UK). Faber & Faber.

Piankoff, A. & Rambova, N., eds. The Tomb of Ramesses VI, 2 vols. LC 54-5646. (Bollingen Ser.: No. 40). Vol. 1- Texts. pap. 145.80 (ISBN 0-317-28638-2, 2051348); Vol. 2- Plates. pap. 53.00 (ISBN 0-317-28639-0). Bks Demand UMI.

Piarist Fathers. Constitutions of the Order of the Pious Schools. Cudinach, Salvidor, ed. & tr. from Lat. LC 85-60915. Tr. of Constitutiones Ordinis Scholarum Piarum. 110p. Date not set. price not set (ISBN 0-9614908-0-2). Piarist Father.

Pia-Terry, Carole D., jt. auth. see Olson, Richard P.

Piatigorsky, Alexander. The Buddhist Philosophy of Thought: Essays in Interpretation. LC 82-3987. 240p. 1984. text ed. 24.50x (ISBN 0-389-20266-5, 07084). B&N Imports.

Piatigorsky, Alexander, jt. auth. see Denwood, Philip.

Piatigorsky, Alexander, jt. ed. see Denwood, Philip.

Piatt, Larry. One Thousand One More Questions on the Bible. 96p. 1986. pap. 4.95 (ISBN 0-8010-7094-5). Baker Bk.

--One Thousand One Questions on the Bible. 50p. 1984. pap. 3.95 (ISBN 0-8010-7085-6). Baker Bk.

Picard, J. M. & De Pontlarcy, Y. Saint Patrick's Purgatory. 78p. 1985. pap. 7.00 (ISBN 0-912414-44-8). Lumen Christi.

Picasso, Juan R. Senderos de Navidad. 24p. 1980. pap. 0.80 (ISBN 0-311-08218-1). Casa Bautista.

Picchio, Riccardo & Goldblatt, Harvey, eds. Aspects of the Slavic Language Question: Church Slavonic-South Slavic-West Slavic, Vol. 1. (Yale Russian & East European Publications Ser.: No. 4a). 416p. 1984. 35.00 (ISBN 0-936586-03-6). Slavica.

--Aspects of the Slavic Language Question: Vol. 1, Church Slavonic-South Slavic-West Slavic. (Yale Russian & East European Publications Ser.: No. 4-a). 416p. 1984. 35.00 (ISBN 0-936586-03-6). Yale Russian.

Piche, Thomas, Jr., ed. see Sandys, Edwina & Morton, James P.

Picirilli, Robert. The Book of Galatians. 1973. pap. 3.95 (ISBN 0-89265-012-5). Randall Hse.

--The Book of Romans, 3 vols. 1974. Set. pap. 3.50 ea.; Vol. 1. pap. (ISBN 0-89265-015-X); Vol. 2. pap. (ISBN 0-89265-016-8); Vol. 3. pap. (ISBN 0-89265-017-6). Randall Hse.

--The Book of Romans. 324p. 1975. 8.95 (ISBN 0-89265-026-5). Randall Hse.

--Pauline Writings Notes. 1967. pap. 2.95 (ISBN 0-89265-001-X). Randall Hse.

--What the Bible Says about Tongues. 1981. pap. 0.95 (ISBN 0-89265-071-0). Randall Hse.

Picirilli, Robert & Hampton, Ralph, Jr. A Survey of the Major Prophets. 1976. pap. 1.50 (ISBN 0-89265-034-6). Randall Hse.

Picirilli, Robert, jt. auth. see Forlines, Leroy.

Picirilli, Robert E. Church Government & Ordinances. 1973. pap. 0.95 (ISBN 0-89265-102-4). Randall Hse.

--Doctrine of Last Things. 29p. 1973. pap. 0.95 (ISBN 0-89265-103-2). Randall Hse.

--Fundamentals of the Faith. 30p. 1973. pap. 0.95 (ISBN 0-89265-106-7). Randall Hse.

--Paul the Apostle. (Orig.). 1986. pap. 7.95 (ISBN 0-8024-6325-8). Moody.

--Paul the Apostle. 1986. pap. 7.95 (ISBN 0-89265-117-2). Randall Hse.

--Perseverance. 28p. 1973. pap. 0.95 (ISBN 0-89265-108-3). Randall Hse.

--Randall House Bible Commentary (1, 2 Corinthians) Harrison, H. D., ed. (Bible Commentary Ser.). 350p. 1986. 19.95 (ISBN 0-89265-118-0). Randall Hse.

Picirilli, Robert E., ed. History of Free Will Baptist State Associations. 1976. pap. 2.50 (ISBN 0-89265-061-3). Randall Hse.

Pick, Aaron. Dictionary of Old Testament Words for English Readers. LC 76-16230. 602p. 1977. kivar 14.95 (ISBN 0-8254-3511-0). Kregel.

Pick, Bernhard. The Apocryphal Acts of Paul, Peter, John, Andrew, & Thomas. 376p. 1909. 19.95 (ISBN 0-912050-60-8). Open Court.

--The Cabala. LC 13-26188. 115p. 1974. pap. 4.95 (ISBN 0-87548-199-X). Open Court.

Pickard, Bertram. Peacemakers' Dilemma. 1983. pap. 2.50x (ISBN 0-87574-016-2, 016). Pendle Hill.

Pickell, Charles N. Epistle to the Colossians: A Study Manual. (Shield Bible Study Ser). (Orig.). 1965. pap. 1.00 (ISBN 0-8010-6942-4). Baker Bk.

Picken, Stuart D. Buddhism: Japan's Cultural Identity. LC 81-84800. (Illus.). 80p. 1982. 19.95 (ISBN 0-87011-499-9). Kodansha.

--Christianity & Japan: Meeting, Conflict, Hope. LC 82-48787. (Illus.). 80p. 1983. 18.95 (ISBN 0-87011-571-5). Kodansha.

--Shinto: Japan's Spiritual Roots. LC 79-91520. (Illus.). 80p. 1980. 19.95 (ISBN 0-87011-410-7). Kodansha.

Pickering, Ernest. Biblical Separation: The Struggle for a Pure Church. LC 78-26840. 1979. 6.95 (ISBN 0-87227-069-6). Reg Baptist.

Pickering, Samuel, Jr. The Moral Tradition in English Fiction, 1785-1850. LC 74-12540. 194p. 1976. text ed. 16.00x (ISBN 0-87451-109-7). U Pr of New Eng.

Pickering, W. S. Durkheim's Sociology of Religion: Themes & Theories. 576p. 1984. 45.00x (ISBN 0-7100-9298-9). Methuen Inc.

--The Hutterists: Christians Who Practice a Communal Way of Life. 1985. 20.00 (ISBN 0-7062-4163-0, Pub. by Ward Lock Educ Co Ltd). State Mutual Bk.

Pickering, W. S., ed. Durkheim on Religion. 1983. pap. 10.95x (ISBN 0-7100-9074-9). Methuen Inc.

Pickering, Wilbur N. The Identity of the New Testament Text. rev. ed. LC 80-17369. 192p. 1980. pap. 8.95 (ISBN 0-8407-5744-1). Nelson.

Pickett, Margaret E. What's Keeping You, Santa? A Christmas Musical Program Package. (Illus.). 74p. (Program package incl. Production Guide with choir arranged songs, cassette tape of songs & thirty slides from book.). 1983. 44.95 (ISBN 0-913939-01-3). TP Assocs.

Pickett, Toni. Miracles. 1983. 5.95 (ISBN 0-8062-2201-8). Carlton.

Pickthall. The Holy Quran: Text & Explanatory Translation. 1983. 25.50 (ISBN 0-686-18527-7). Kazi Pubns.

--The Meaning of the Glorious Quran. pap. 4.95 (ISBN 0-686-18531-5). Kazi Pubns.

Pickthall, M., ed. Holy Quran. 1983. Repr. of 1977 ed. 18.50x (ISBN 0-8364-0989-2, Pub. by R Taj Co). South Asia Bks.

Pickthall, M. M., ed. Holy Quran with English Translation. 1976. Repr. 17.50x (ISBN 0-8364-0415-7). South Asia Bks.

Pickthall, M. M., tr. The Meaning of the Illustrious Qur'an: Arabic & English. 1970. 45.00x (ISBN 0-87902-182-9). Orientalia.

Pickthall, Marmaduke, ed. The Glorious Koran. bilingual ed. 1696p. 1976. text ed. 50.00x (ISBN 0-04-297036-9). Allen Unwin.

Pickthall, Mohammed M., tr. Meaning of the Glorious Koran. pap. 4.50 (ISBN 0-451-62305-3, ME2305, Ment). NAL.

Pickthall, Muhammad, tr. Qur'an: The Glorious. 767p. 1983. pap. 8.00 (ISBN 0-940368-30-7). Tahrike Tarsile Quran.

Pickthorn, William E., compiled by. Ministers Manual Ser, 3 vols. Incl. Vol. 1, Services for Special Occasions (ISBN 0-88243-547-7, 02-0547); Vol. 2, Services for Weddings & Funerals (ISBN 0-88243-548-5, 02-0548); Vol. 3, Services for Ministers & Workers (ISBN 0-88243-549-3, 02-0549). LC 65-13222. 1965. Set. 13.95 (ISBN 0-88243-544-2, 02-0544); 4.95 ea. Gospel Pub.

Pico, Juan H., jt. auth. see Sobrino, Jon.

Pico, Pancho. Matrimonio Sorprendente. 96p. 1981. pap. 1.90 (ISBN 0-311-37022-5). Casa Bautista.

Pico Della Mirandola, Giovanni. On the Dignity of Man. Wallis, Charles G., et al, trs. Bd. with On Being & Unity; Heptaplus. LC 65-26540. 1965. pap. 7.87 scp (ISBN 0-672-60483-3, LLA227). Bobbs.

--On the Imagination. Caplan, Harry, tr. & notes by. LC 72-113063. (Lat. & Eng.). ix, 102p. Repr. of 1930 ed. lib. bdg. 22.50x (ISBN 0-8371-4703-4, PIOI). Greenwood.

Picton, J. Allanson. Oliver Cromwell: The Man & His Mission. 1978. Repr. of 1883 ed. lib. bdg. 40.00 (ISBN 0-8482-2126-5). Norwood Edns.

--Pantheism. 96p. 1914. 0.95 (ISBN 0-317-40425-3). Open Court.

Pictor, Mike. Conversations with Christ. 73p. (Orig.). 1984. pap. 6.95 (ISBN 0-942494-84-9). Coleman Pub.

Piddington, Ralph, ed. see Williamson, Robert W.

Pie, A., et al. Mystery & Mysticism. 1956. 5.95 (ISBN 0-8022-1988-8). Philos Lib.

Piediscalzi, N., et al. Public Education Religion Studies: An Overview. Swyhart, B., ed. LC 76-26670. (American Academy of Religion. Section Papers). 1976. pap. 12.00 (ISBN 0-89130-082-1, 01-09-18). Scholars Pr GA.

Piediscalzi, Nicholas, jt. ed. see Barr, David.

Piediscalzi, Nicolas & Thobaben, Robert G., eds. Three Worlds of Christian Marxist Encounters. LC 84-48724. 240p. 1985. pap. 14.95 (ISBN 0-8006-1840-8, 1-1840). Fortress.

Piehl, Mel. Breaking Bread: The Catholic Worker & the Origin of Catholic Radicalism in America. LC 82-10327. 233p. 1982. 24.95 (ISBN 0-87722-257-6). Temple U Pr.

--Breaking Bread: The Catholic Worker & the Origin of Catholic Radicalism in America. 314p. 1984. pap. 12.95 (ISBN 0-87722-353-X). Temple U Pr.

Pieper, Francis. Christian Dogmatics, 4 Vols. Engelder, Theodore, et al, trs. 1950-1957. Vol. 1. 18.95 (ISBN 0-570-06712-X, 15-1001); Vol. 2. 18.95 (ISBN 0-570-06713-8, 15-1002); Vol. 3. 18.95 (ISBN 0-570-06714-6, 15-1003); Vol. 4. 25.95 (ISBN 0-570-06711-1, 15-1000); Set. 69.95 (ISBN 0-570-06715-4, 15-1852). Concordia.

Pieper, Josef. Belief & Faith: A Philosophical Tract. Winston, Richard & Winston, Clara, trs. from German. LC 75-31841. 106p. 1976. Repr. of 1963 ed. lib. bdg. 22.50x (ISBN 0-8371-8490-8, PIBF). Greenwood.

--Four Cardinal Virtues. 1966. pap. 5.95 (ISBN 0-268-00103-0). U of Notre Dame Pr.

--Guide to Thomas Aquinas. LC 86-40588. 192p. 1987. pap. text ed. 8.95x (ISBN 0-268-01013-7, Dist. by Har-Row). U of Notre Dame Pr.

--No One Could Have Known: An Autobiography-- The Early Years. Harrison, Graham, tr. from Ger. LC 86-72509. Tr. of Noch Wusste es Niemand. (Illus.). 227p. (Orig.). 1987. pap. 9.95 (ISBN 0-89870-131-7). Ignatius Pr.

--On Hope. McCarthy, Mary F., tr. from Ger. LC 85-82177. Orig. Title: Uber die Hoffnung. 99p. (Orig.). 1986. pap. 6.95 (ISBN 0-89870-067-1). Ignatius Pr.

Pieper, Josef & Raskop, Heinrich. What Catholics Believe: A Primer of the Catholic Faith. Van Heurck, Jan, tr. LC 82-1411. 116p. 1983. 8.50 (ISBN 0-8199-0796-0). Franciscan Herald.

Pieper, Josef, et al. Guide to Thomas Aquinas. Winston, Richard & Winston, Clara, trs. from Ger. 182p. 1982. Repr. of 1962 ed. lib. bdg. 20.50 (ISBN 0-374-96448-3, Octagon). Hippocrene Bks.

Piepkorn, Arthur C. Profiles in Belief: the Religious Bodies of North America, Vol. 1: Roman Catholic, Old Catholic & Eastern Orthodox. LC 76-9971. 1977. 20.00 (ISBN 0-06-066580-7, HarpR). Har-Row.

--Profiles in Belief: The Religious Bodies of the United States & Canada, Vols. 3 & 4. Incl. Vol. 3. Holiness & Pentecostal Bodies; Vol. 4. Evangelical, Fundamental, & Other Christian Bodies. 1979. Set. 25.45i (ISBN 0-06-066581-5, HarpR). Har-Row.

--Profiles in Belief, Vol. 2: Protestantism. LC 76-9971. 1978. 30.00 (ISBN 0-06-066582-3, HarpR). Har-Row.

Piepkorn, Arthur Carl. The Survival of the Historic Vestments in the Lutheran Church after Fifteen Fifty-Five. 120p. 1956. write for info. Concordia Schl Grad Studies.

Pierce, Charles R., Jr. The Religious Life of Samuel Johnson. LC 82-13938. 184p. 1982. lib. bdg. 21.50 (ISBN 0-208-01992-8, Archon). Shoe String.

Pierce, Glen A., ed. see Book, Doyle C.

Pierce, Gregory, jt. auth. see Droel, William.

Pierce, Gregory F. Activism that Makes Sense: Congregations & Community Organization. LC 83-82016. (Orig.). 1984. pap. 6.95 (ISBN 0-8091-2600-1). Paulist Pr.

Pierce, Joe E., ed. see Oliver, Egbert S.

Pierce, Rice A. How to Enjoy Bible Study with Others. LC 72-5250. 1972. 3.95 (ISBN 0-8407-5043-9). Religious Activ.

--Leading Dynamic Bible Study. LC 74-78835. 1979. 3.95 (ISBN 0-8054-3420-8). Religious Activ.

Pierce, Richard D., ed. Records of the First Church in Salem, Massachusetts, 1629-1736. LC 73-93302. 1974. 30.00 (ISBN 0-88389-050-X). Essex Inst.

Pierce, Ruth I. Single & Pregnant. LC 72-119678. 1970. pap. 3.95 (ISBN 0-8070-2779-0, BP407). Beacon Pr.

Pierce, William. Historical Introduction to the Marprelate Tracts: A Chapter in the Evolution of Religious & Civil Liberty in England. 1908. 23.50 (ISBN 0-8337-2762-1). B Franklin.

Pierradrd, Pierre. Larousse Des Prenoms et Des Saints. (Fr.). 256p. 1976. 42.50 (ISBN 0-686-57079-0, M-6454). French & Eur.

Pierrakos, Eva. Guide Lectures for Self-Transformation. LC 85-134343. 216p. (Orig.). 1985. 12.95 (ISBN 0-9614777-0-9); pap. 7.95 (ISBN 0-9614777-1-7). Pathwork Pr.

--Guide Lectures for Self Transformation. LC 85-134343. 195p. 1986. pap. 9.95 (ISBN 0-913299-32-4, Dist. by NAL). Stillpoint.

Pierrard, Pierre. Dictionnaire des Prenoms et des Saints. (Fr.). 224p. 1975. pap. 6.95 (ISBN 0-686-56861-3, M-6639). French & Eur.

Pierre, Dom & Morice, Hyacinthe. Histoire Ecclesiastique et Civile de Bretagne, 2 vols. 752p. Date not set. Repr. of 1756 ed. text ed. 310.50x (ISBN 0-576-78866-X, Pub. by Gregg Intl Pubs England). Gregg Intl.

Pierre du Moulin, the Elder. The Anatomy of Arminianisme. LC 76-57380. (English Experience Ser.: No. 797). 1977. Repr. of 1620 ed. lib. bdg. 46.00 (ISBN 90-221-0797-3). Walter J Johnson.

Pierre, Kenneth J., jt. auth. see Rocker, Dolore.

Pierre-Quint, Leon. Andre Gide. Richardson, Dorothy, tr. 1934. 30.00 (ISBN 0-8274-1865-5). R West.

Pierrot. Dictionnaire de Theologie Morale, 2 vols. Migne, J. P., ed. (Encyclopedie Theologique Ser.: Vols. 31-32). (Fr.). 1486p. Repr. of 1849 ed. lib. bdg. 188.50x (ISBN 0-89241-242-9). Caratzas.

Pierson, A. T. Acts of the Holy Spirit. 127p. 1980. pap. 3.25 (ISBN 0-87509-274-8). Chr Pubns.

Pierson, Arthur T. George Muller of Bristol. 336p. 1984. pap. 7.95 (ISBN 0-310-47091-9, 11669P, Clarion Class). Zondervan.

Pierson, Carlos C., tr. see Le Roy.

Pierson, Carlos C., tr. see Tidwell, J. B.

Pierson, Jack D. What a Teenager Ought to Know About Sex & God. (Teenager's Essential Education Library). (Illus.). 147p. 1981. 48.75 (ISBN 0-89266-288-3). Am Classical Coll Pr.

Pierson, Lance, jt. auth. see Mandeville, Sylvia.

Pierson, Paul E. Themes from Acts. LC 82-80153. (Bible Commentary for Laymen Ser.). (Orig.). 1982. pap. 3.50 (ISBN 0-8307-0819-7, S361107). Regal.

--A Younger Church in Search of Maturity: Presbyterianism in Brazil from 1910-1959. LC 73-89596. 306p. 1974. 8.00 (ISBN 0-911536-49-3). Trinity U Pr.

Pierson, Robert H. Here Comes Adventure. Wheeler, Gerald, ed. (Banner Ser.). (Illus.). 192p. (Orig.). 1984. pap. 5.95 (ISBN 0-8280-0244-4). Review & Herald.

Piet, John H. A Path Through the Bible. LC 81-2258. (Illus.). 318p. 1981. pap. 14.95 (ISBN 0-664-24369-X). Westminster.

Pieterisma, Albert. Chester Beatty Biblical Papyri IV & V: A New Edition with Text-Critical Analysis. LC 74-84103. 1974. 24.00 (ISBN 0-88866-016-2, 310016). Scholars Pr GA.

Pieters, A. Can We Trust Bible History? 2.50 (ISBN 0-686-23481-2). Rose Pub MI.

Pietrangeli, Carlo, et al. The Sistine Chapel: The Art, the History, & the Restoration. (Illus.). 272p. 1986. 60.00 (ISBN 0-517-56274-X, Harmony). Crown.

Piette, Charles J. Evocation de Junipero Serra, Foundateur de la Californie. (Fr., Illus.). 1946. 5.00 (ISBN 0-88382-251-2); pap. 5.00 (ISBN 0-88382-250-4). AAFH.

Piety, James. Chicago Historical Geographic Guide. (Illus.). 125p. (Orig.). 1983. pap. text ed. 6.80 wkbk. (ISBN 0-87563-290-4). Stipes.

Piggott, Juliet. Japanese Mythology. rev. ed. LC 83-71480. (The Library of the World's Myths & Legends). (Illus.). 144p. 1983. 18.95 (ISBN 0-911745-09-2). P Bedrick Bks.

--Japanese Mythology. (Library of the World's Myths & Legends). (Illus.). 144p. PLB 16.95 (ISBN 0-317-31009-7). Creative Ed.

Pigman, C. W., III. Grief & English Renaissance Elegy. 192p. 1985. 29.95 (ISBN 0-521-26871-0). Cambridge U Pr.

Pignatelli, Gaspare. The Christ Nobody Knows: A Sentimental Vision of His Life. (Illus.). 121p. 1987. 88.85 (ISBN 0-89266-576-9). Am Classical Coll Pr.

Pigott, Grenville. A Manual of Scandinavian Mythology: Containing a Popular Account of the Two Eddas & of the Religion of Odin. Bolle, Kees W., ed. LC 77-79152. (Mythology Ser.). 1978. Repr. of 1839 ed. lib. bdg. 27.50x (ISBN 0-405-10561-4). Ayer Co Pubs.

Pijanowski, Kathy, ed. see Perrone, Stephen P. & Spata, James P.

Pijanowski, Kathy, ed. see Qubein, Nido.

Pike, Diane K. Cosmic Unfoldment: The Individualizing Process as Mirrored in the Life of Jesus. LC 76-45344. 99p. 1976. pap. 2.00 (ISBN 0-916192-08-3). L P Pubns.

--My Journey into Self Phase One. LC 79-12179. 161p. 1979. pap. 4.95 (ISBN 0-916192-13-X). L P Pubns.

Pike, Edgar R. Slayers of Superstition. LC 78-102581. 1970. Repr. of 1931 ed. 16.50x (ISBN 0-8046-0741-9, Pub.by Kennikat). Assoc Faculty Pr.

Pike, Eunice V. Ken Pike: Scholar & Christian. LC 81-51058. (Illus.). 270p. (Orig.). 1981. pap. 5.00 (ISBN 0-88312-920-5); microfiche (3) 6.00 (ISBN 0-88312-986-8). Summer Inst Ling.

Pike, Fredrick B. The Politics of the Miraculous in Peru: Haya de la Torre & the Spiritualist Tradition. LC 85-1162. (Illus.). xviii, 391p. 1986. 32.50x (ISBN 0-8032-3672-7). U of Nebr Pr.

Pike, Gustavus D. Jubilee Singers, & Their Campaign for Twenty Thousand Dollars. LC 72-1692. Repr. of 1873 ed. 18.50 (ISBN 0-404-08329-3). AMS Pr.

--The Singing Campaign for Ten Thousand Pounds. rev. ed. LC 75-164392. (Black Heritage Library Collection). Repr. of 1875 ed. 18.25 (ISBN 0-8369-8851-5). Ayer Co Pubs.

Pike, James A. & Pittenger, W. Norman. Faith of the Church. 224p. (Orig.). 1951. pap. 1.00 (ISBN 0-8164-2019-X, SP3, HarpR). Har-Row.

Pike, Martha V. & Armstrong, Janice G. A Time to Mourn: Expressions of Grief in Nineteenth Century America. LC 80-15105. (Illus.). 192p. 1980. pap. 14.95 (ISBN 0-295-96325-5, Pub. by Museums at Stony Brook). U of Wash Pr.

Pike, Nelson. God & Evil: Reading on the Theological Problem of Evil. 1964. pap. 14.95 ref.ed. (ISBN 0-13-357665-5). P-H.

Pike, Nelson, ed. see Hume, David.

Pilch, John J. Wellness Spirituality. 112p. 1985. pap. 7.95 (ISBN 0-8245-0710-X). Crossroad NY.

--Wellness: Your Invitation to Full Life. Frost, Miriam, ed. Orig. Title: Wellness. 128p. (Orig.). 1981. pap. text ed. 5.95 (ISBN 0-86683-758-2, HarpR). Har-Row.

Pilch, John J. & Karris, Robert J. Galatians & Romans, No. 6. (Collegeville Bible Commentary Ser.). 80p. 1983. pap. 2.95 (ISBN 0-8146-1306-3). Liturgical Pr.

Pilgrim, Peace. Steps Toward Inner Peace: Suggested Uses of Harmonious Principles for Human Living. (Illus.). 36p. 1987. pap. 2.50 leatherette (ISBN 0-943734-07-X). Ocean Tree Bks.

Pilgrim, Richard, jt. auth. see Ellwood, Robert S.

Pilgrim, Richard B. Buddhism & the Arts of Japan. LC 81-8063. (Focus on Hinduism & Buddhism Ser.). 64p. (Orig.). 1981. pap. 4.95x (ISBN 0-89012-026-9). Anima Pubns.

Pilgrim, Walter E. Good News to the Poor: Wealth & Poverty in Luke-Acts. LC 81-65653. 208p. (Orig.). 1981. pap. 10.95 (ISBN 0-8066-1889-2, 10-2807). Augsburg.

Pilkington, James. Works of James Pilkington, Lord Bishop of Durham. 1842. Repr. of 1842 ed. 55.00 (ISBN 0-384-46530-7). Johnson Repr.

Pilkington, James P. Methodist Publishing House: A History, Vol. 1. LC 68-21894. (Illus.). 1968. 8.25 (ISBN 0-687-26700-5). Abingdon.

Pillai, A. K. Transcendental Self: A Comparative Study of Thoreau & the Psycho-Philosophy of Hinduism & Buddhism. LC 85-686. 130p. (Orig.). 1985. lib. bdg. 21.75 (ISBN 0-8191-4572-6). U Pr of Amer.

Pillai, Ananda R., et al. The Private Diary of Ananda Ranga Pillai in 12 Volumes. Price, J. F. & Rangachari, eds. Dupleix, Joseph F., tr. 1986. Repr. per Set 420.00X (PUb. by Abhinav by India). South Asia Bks.

Pillai, K. C. Light Through an Eastern Window. pap. 4.95 (ISBN 0-8315-0057-3). Speller.

--Light Through an Eastern Window. LC 85-51634. 144p. 1986. 4.95 (ISBN 0-910068-63-1). Am Christian.

--Orientalisms of the Bible, Vol. II. LC 84-50935. 141p. 1984. 3.95 (ISBN 0-910068-56-9). Am Christian.

--Orientalisms of the Bible, Vol. 1. 1969. 4.95x (ISBN 0-912178-02-7). Mor-Mac.

--Orientalisms of the Bible, Vol. 2. 1974. 4.95x (ISBN 0-912178-04-3). Mor-Mac.

Pillai, V. R. Temple Culture of South India. (Illus.). xii, 201p. 1986. text ed. 45.00x (ISBN 81-210-0168-4, Pub. by Inter India Pubns N Delhi). Apt Bks.

Pilley, Catherine M. & Wilt, Matthew R., eds. Catholic Subject Headings. rev. ed. 257p. 1981. pap. 25.00x (ISBN 0-87507-009-4). Cath Lib Assn.

Pinard, C. Dictionnaire des Objections Populaires contre le Dogme, la Morale, la Discipline et L'histoire de Eglise Catholique. Migne, J. P., ed. (Troisieme et Derniere Encyclopedie Theologique Ser.: Vol. 33). (Fr.). 756p. Repr. of 1858 ed. lib. bdg. 96.50x (ISBN 0-89241-312-3). Caratzas.

Pinay, M. The Plot Against the Catholic Church: Communism, Free Masonry & the Jewish Fifth Column in the Clergy. 1979. lib. bdg. 69.95 (ISBN 0-8490-2984-8). Gordon Pr.

Pinay, Maurice. The Plot Against the Church. 1978. 15.00x (ISBN 0-911038-39-6). Noontide.

Pincus-Witten, Robert. Occult Symbolism in France: Josephin Peladan & the Salons De la Rose-Croix. LC 75-23809. (Outstanding Dissertations in the Fine Arts-20th Century). (Illus.). 300p. 1976. lib. bdg. 50.00 (ISBN 0-8240-2003-0). Garland Pub.

Pine, Edward, ed. The Pauline Muses. 355p. 1981. Repr. of 1947 ed. lib. bdg. 25.00 (ISBN 0-8495-4395-9). Arden Lib.

Pines, Shlomo, tr. see Maimonides, Moses.

Pingree, D., jt. auth. see Reiner, Erica.

Pingree, David, tr. The Yavanajataka of Sphujidhvaja, 2 vols. (Harvard Oriental Ser: No. 48). 1978. Set. 80.00x (ISBN 0-674-96373-3). Harvard U Pr.

Pink, A. W. Los Atributos de Dios. 2.95 (ISBN 0-686-12561-4). Banner of Truth.

--Christian Liberty. pap. 0.50 (ISBN 0-685-88370-1). Reiner.

--A Fourfold Salvation. pap. 0.75 (ISBN 0-685-41831-6). Reiner.

--Letters of A. W. Pink. 1978. pap. 2.95 (ISBN 0-85151-262-3). Banner of Truth.

--The Life of Elijah. 1976. pap. 5.95 (ISBN 0-85151-041-8). Banner of Truth.

--Profiting from the Word. 1977. pap. 3.45 (ISBN 0-85151-032-9). Banner of Truth.

--La Soberania De Dios. 3.50 (ISBN 0-85151-416-2). Banner of Truth.

--The Sovereignty of God. 1976. pap. 3.95 (ISBN 0-85151-133-3). Banner of Truth.

--Studies in the Scriptures, 1946. pap. 9.45 (ISBN 0-85151-346-8). Banner of Truth.

--Studies in the Scriptures, 1947. 298p. pap. 9.45 (ISBN 0-85151-347-6). Banner of Truth.

--Tithing. pap. 0.50 (ISBN 0-686-48166-6). Reiner.

--La Vida de Elias. (Span.). 360p. 1984. pap. 4.95 (ISBN 0-85151-424-3). Banner of Truth.

Pink, Arthur W. The Antichrist. 1980. pap. 12.00 (ISBN 0-86524-000-0, 9802). Klock & Klock.

--Atonement. 10.95 (ISBN 0-685-19822-7). Reiner.

--Attributes of God. pap. 3.95 (ISBN 0-8010-6989-0). Baker Bk.

--The Beatitudes & the Lord's Prayer. 140p. 1982. pap. 4.95 (ISBN 0-8010-7073-2). Baker Bk.

--Christians in Romans Seven. pap. 0.50 (ISBN 0-685-00738-3). Reiner.

--Comfort for Christians. (Summit Bks.). 122p. 1976. pap. 2.95 (ISBN 0-8010-7062-7). Baker Bk.

--Comfort for Christians. pap. 3.95 (ISBN 0-685-19825-1). Reiner.

--The Divine Covenants: God's Seven Covenant Engagements with Man. 317p. 1984. pap. 7.95 (ISBN 0-8010-7082-1). Baker Bk.

--Divine Healing. pap. 0.75 (ISBN 0-685-00742-1). Reiner.

--Divine Inspiration of the Bible. pap. 4.50 (ISBN 0-685-19827-8). Reiner.

--Eternal Punishment. pap. 0.75 (ISBN 0-685-00734-0). Reiner.

--Exposition of Hebrews. 1954. 29.95 (ISBN 0-8010-6857-6). Baker Bk.

--Exposition of the Gospel of John, 4 Vols. in 1. 1945. 29.95 (ISBN 0-310-31180-2, 10566). Zondervan.

--Exposition on the Sermon on the Mount. 9.95 (ISBN 0-8010-7075-9). Baker Bk.

--Gleanings from Elisha. LC 79-181591. 288p. 1972. pap. 10.95 (ISBN 0-8024-3000-7). Moody.

--Gleanings from Paul. LC 67-14379. 1967. pap. 10.95 (ISBN 0-8024-3005-8). Moody.

--Gleanings from the Scriptures. LC 73-80942. 1970. pap. 10.95 (ISBN 0-8024-3006-6). Moody.

--Gleanings in Exodus. 1964. pap. 10.95 (ISBN 0-8024-3001-5). Moody.

--Gleanings in Genesis. 1922. pap. 10.95 (ISBN 0-8024-3002-3). Moody.

--Gleanings in Joshua. LC 64-20991. 1964. pap. 10.95 (ISBN 0-8024-3004-X). Moody.

--Gleanings in the Godhead. LC 75-15760. 256p. pap. 10.95 (ISBN 0-8024-3003-1). Moody.

--Holy Spirit. 1970. pap. 6.95 (ISBN 0-8010-7041-4). Baker Bk.

--The Life of David, 2 vols. in one. (Giant Summit Ser.). 768p. 1981. pap. 14.95 (ISBN 0-8010-7061-9). Baker Bk.

--Life of David. 14.95 (ISBN 0-685-19837-5). Reiner.

--New Birth. pap. 0.50 (ISBN 0-685-00739-1). Reiner.

--Practical Christianity. pap. 6.95 (ISBN 0-8010-6990-4). Baker Bk.

--Regeneration. pap. 0.75 (ISBN 0-685-00735-9). Reiner.

--Seven Sayings of Our Saviour on the Cross. (Summit Bks). 1977. pap. 4.95 (ISBN 0-8010-7084-8). Baker Bk.

--The Sovereignty of God. pap. 6.95 (ISBN 0-8010-7088-0). Baker Bk.

--Ten Commandments. pap. 2.50 (ISBN 0-685-00740-5). Reiner.

Pink, George L. The Unity of One. 160p. 1982. 8.00 (ISBN 0-682-49838-6). Exposition Pr FL.

Pinkard, Terry P., jt. ed. see Beauchamp, Tom L.

Pinkerton, Robert, tr. see Metropolitan Philaret of Moscow.

Pinkham, Mildred W. Woman in the Sacred Scriptures of Hinduism. LC 41-7015. Repr. of 1941 ed. 16.50 (ISBN 0-404-05055-7). AMS Pr.

Pinkney, David H., ed. see Cohen, Paul M.

Pinkston, Tom. A Spirit Soars. 34p. pap. 3.00 (ISBN 0-942494-47-4). Coleman Pub.

Pinkston, William S., Jr. With Wings As Eagles. (Illus.). 127p. 1983. pap. 5.95 (ISBN 0-89084-231-0). Bob Jones Univ Pr.

Pinkus, Benjamin. The Soviet Government & the Jews, Nineteen Forty-Eight to Nineteen Sixty-Seven: A Documented Study. 675p. 1984. 62.50 (ISBN 0-521-24713-6). Cambridge U Pr.

Pinnell, Lois M. French Creek Presbyterian Church. (Illus.). 1971. 10.00 (ISBN 0-87012-110-3). McClain.

Pinner, Mary T. & Shuard, Hilary. In-Service Education in Primary Mathematics. 208p. 1985. pap. 15.00x (ISBN 0-335-15023-3, Open Univ Pr). Taylor & Francis.

Pinnock, Clark. Defense of Biblical Infallibility. pap. 1.75 (ISBN 0-8010-6863-0). Baker Bk.

--Three Keys to Spiritual Renewal. 112p. 1986. pap. 4.95 (ISBN 0-87123-656-7). Bethany Hse.

Pinnock, Clark H. Biblical Revelation. 2nd ed. 272p. (Orig.). 1985. pap. 7.95 (ISBN 0-87552-371-4). Presby & Reformed.

--Defense of Biblical Infallibility. 1967. pap. 1.75 (ISBN 0-87552-350-1). Presby & Reformed.

--Grace Unlimited. LC 75-22161. 272p. 1975. pap. 8.95 (ISBN 0-87123-185-9, 210185). Bethany Hse.

--Reason Enough: A Case for the Christian Faith. 126p. 1986. pap. 4.95 (ISBN 0-85364-296-6, Pub. by Paternoster UK). Attic Pr.

--The Scripture Principle. LC 84-37732. 288p. 1985. 15.45i (ISBN 0-06-066620-X); 15.95. Har-Row.

Pinsent, John. Greek Mythology. rev. ed. LC 83-71479. (The Library of the World's Myths & Legends). (Illus.). 144p. 1983. 18.95 (ISBN 0-911745-08-4). P Bedrick Bks.

--Greek Mythology. (Library of the World's Myths & Legends). (Illus.). 144p. PLB 16.95 (ISBN 0-317-31010-0). Creative Ed.

Pinsker, Lev S. Road to Freedom. LC 70-162734. 142p. 1975. Repr. of 1944 ed. lib. bdg. 22.50x (ISBN 0-8371-6195-9, PIRF). Greenwood.

Pinsker, Sanford. Schlemiel As Metaphor: Studies in the Yiddish & American Jewish Novel. LC 77-132487. (Crosscurrents-Modern Critiques Ser.). 185p. 1971. 6.95x (ISBN 0-8093-0480-5). S Ill U Pr.

Pinsker, Sanford & Fischel, Jack, eds. America & the Holocaust, Vol. I. (Holocaust Studies Annual). 200p. 1984. lib. bdg. 15.00 (ISBN 0-913283-02-9). Penkevill.

Pinsker, Sanford, jt. ed. see Fischel, Jack R.

Pinson. The Local Church in Ministry. LC 73-75629. 7.50 (ISBN 0-8054-6304-6). Broadman.

Pinson, William M. Applying the Gospel: Suggestions for Christian Social Action in the Local Church. new ed. LC 75-8374. 160p. 1975. pap. 5.95 (ISBN 0-8054-6306-2). Broadman.

Pinson, William M., Jr. Ready to Minister. LC 84-3052. (Broadman Leadership Ser.). 1984. pap. 4.95 (ISBN 0-8054-3109-8). Broadman.

Pinto, De Solo, et al. The Tree of Life: An Anthology. 1981. Repr. of 1929 ed. lib. bdg. 35.00 (ISBN 0-89984-390-5). Century Bookbindery.

Pinto, Solo De see Pinto, De Solo, et al.

Pinto, Vivan De Sola. English Biography. 1973. lib. bdg. 10.00 (ISBN 0-8414-9259-X). Folcroft.

Pinto, Vivan De Sola see Pinto, Vivan De Sola.

Pinto, Vivian De Sola, ed. The Divine Vision. LC 68-24905. (Studies in Blake, No. 3). 1973. Repr. of 1957 ed. lib. bdg. 75.00x (ISBN 0-8383-0790-6). Haskell.

Pio, Padre. The Agony of Jesus. 40p. 1974. pap. 1.00 (ISBN 0-89555-097-0). TAN Bks Pubs.

--Meditation Prayer on Mary Immaculate. (Illus.). 28p. 1974. pap. 0.75 (ISBN 0-89555-099-7). Tan Bks Pubs.

Piovesan, Emilio, tr. & intro. by see Du Pont, Guigo.

Pipa, Joseph A. Leader's Guide for T. Norton Sterrett's "How to Understand Your Bible". A Teaching Manual for Use in Adult Study Groups. (Orig.). 1977. pap. 2.95 (ISBN 0-934688-06-0). Great Comm Pubns.

Pipe, Virginia E. Live & Learn with Your Teenager. LC 85-18451. (Family Life Ser.). 160p. 1985. pap. 6.95 (ISBN 0-8170-1069-6). Judson.

Piper, John. Desiring God: Meditations of a Christian Hedonist. (Critical Concern Ser.). 1987. 12.95 (ISBN 0-88070-169-2). Multnomah.

--The Justification of God: An Exegetical & Theological Study of Romans 9: 1-23. 312p. (Orig.). 1983. pap. 8.95 (ISBN 0-8010-7079-1). Baker Bk.

--Love Your Enemies. LC 77-95449. (Society for New Testament Studies: No. 38). 1980. 34.50 (ISBN 0-521-22056-4). Cambridge U Pr.

Pipes, Daniel. In the Path of God: Islam & Political Power. LC 83-70764. 373p. 1983. text ed. 22.50 (ISBN 0-465-03451-9). Basic.

--In the Path of God: Islam & Political Power. LC 83-70764. 384p. 1985. pap. 9.95 (ISBN 0-465-03452-7, PL-5138). Basic.

Pipes, William H. Say Amen Brother, Old-Time Negro Preaching: A Study in American Frustration. LC 73-111585. Repr. of 1951 ed. 22.50x (ISBN 0-8371-4611-9, PSA&, Pub. by Negro U Pr). Greenwood.

Pipkin, H. Wayne, compiled by. A Zwingli Bibliography. LC 73-153549. (Bibliographia Tripotamopolitana: No.7). 1972. 7.00x (ISBN 0-931222-06-0). Pitts Theolog.

Pipkin, H. Wayne, jt. ed. see Furchs, E. J.

Pipkin, Wayne H., tr. Huldrych Zwingli-Writings in Search of True Religion: Reformation, Pastoral & Eucharistic Writings, Vol. 2. (Pittsburgh Theological Monographs: No. 13). 1984. pap. 19.95 (ISBN 0-915138-59-X). Pickwick.

Pippert, Rebecca & Siemens, Ruth. Evangelism. (Lifebuilder Bible Studies). 64p. (Orig.). 1985. pap. text ed. 2.95 (ISBN 0-8308-1050-1). Inter-Varsity.

Pippert, Rebecca M. Out of the Saltshaker: Evangelism As a Way of Life. LC 79-1995. 1979. pap. 6.95 (ISBN 0-87784-735-5); study guide 2.95 (ISBN 0-87784-532-8). Inter-Varsity.

Pirenne, Henri. Mohammed & Charlemagne. (B & N Paperback Ser.). 239p. (Orig.). 1983. pap. 9.95x (ISBN 0-389-20134-0, 06641, 444). B&N Imports.

Pirola, Teresa. Empowered People. 48p. (Orig.). 1985. pap. text ed. 1.95 (ISBN 0-911905-26-X). Past & Mat Rene Ctr.

Pir Vilayat Inayat Khan. The Call of the Dervish. LC 81-52421. 224p. (Orig.). 1981. pap. 8.95 (ISBN 0-930872-26-6, 1013P). Omega Pr NM.

Pisani, Maria S. La Certosa di Serra San Bruno Nella Storia del Monachesimo. Hogg, James, ed. (Analcecta Cartusiana Ser.: No. 26-1). (Ital.). 131p. (Orig.). 1976. pap. 25.00 (ISBN 3-7052-0026-7, Pub. by Salzburg Studies). Longwood Pub Group.

Piscatori, James P., jt. auth. see Royal Institute of International Affairs.

Piscatori, James P., ed. Islam in the Political Process. LC 82-9745. 272p. 1983. 42.50 (ISBN 0-521-24941-4); pap. 16.95 (ISBN 0-521-27434-6). Cambridge U Pr.

Pissard, Hippolyte. La Guerre Sainte en Pays Chretien. LC 78-63357. (The Crusades & Military Orders: Second Ser.). Repr. of 1912 ed. 23.50 (ISBN 0-404-17027-7). AMS Pr.

Pitcairn, Harold F., ed. A Concordance of Selected Subjects Treated of in the Rational Psychology of Emmanuel Swedenborg. 337p. 1960. 7.00 (ISBN 0-915221-11-X). Swedenborg Sci Assn.

Pitcairne, Archibald. Babell. LC 75-174208. (Maitland Club, Glasgow. Publications Ser.: No. 6). Repr. of 1830 ed. 11.00 (ISBN 0-404-52931-3). AMS Pr.

Pitcher, Arthur. Memoirs of Peter. 1981. 3.95 (ISBN 0-86544-015-8). Salv Army Suppl South.

Pitcher, Arthur R. Christmas Remembered. 1985. pap. 5.25 (ISBN 0-86544-029-8). Salv Army Suppl South.

Pitcher, George. Berkeley. (The Arguments of the Philosophers Ser.). 300p. 1977. 24.95x (ISBN 0-7100-8685-7); pap. 14.95 (ISBN 0-7102-0391-8). Methuen Inc.

Pitcher, W. Alvin, jt. ed. see Amjad-Ali, Charles.

Pitirim, Monseigneur, et al. The Orthodox Church of Russia: A Millennial Celebration. LC 82-6933. (Illus.). 320p. 1982. 65.00 (ISBN 0-86565-029-2). Vendome.

Pitkin, Ron, jt. auth. see Ricker, Robert S.

Pitman, E. R. Ann H. Judson of Burma. 1974. pap. 2.95 (ISBN 0-87508-601-2). Chr Lit.

Pitman, Michael. Adam & Evolution. 269p. 1986. pap. 12.95 (ISBN 0-8010-7092-9). Baker Bk.

Pitman, Walter G. The Baptists & Public Affairs in the Province of Canada: 1840-1867. Gaustad, Edwin S., ed. LC 79-52576. (The Baptist Tradition Ser.). 1980. lib. bdg. 21.00x (ISBN 0-405-12444-9). Ayer Co Pubs.

Pitre, David W. To Martin Luther King, with Love: A Southern Quaker's Tribute. 1984. pap. 2.50x (ISBN 0-87574-254-8, 254). Pendle Hill.

Pitrone, Jean. Great Black Robe. (Illus.). 1965. 4.00 (ISBN 0-8198-0050-3); pap. 3.00 (ISBN 0-8198-0051-1). Dghtrs St Paul.

Pitt, Clifford S. Church, Ministry & Sacraments: A Critical Evaluation of the Thought of Peter Taylor Forsyth. LC 82-24817. 360p. (Orig.). 1983. lib. bdg. 31.25 (ISBN 0-8191-3027-3); pap. text ed. 15.75 (ISBN 0-8191-3028-1). U Pr of Amer.

Pitt, Theodore K. Premarital Counseling Handbook for Ministers. 192p. 1985. pap. 9.95 (ISBN 0-8170-1071-8). Judson.

Pittenger, Norman. After Death-Life in God. 96p. 1980. 4.95 (ISBN 0-8164-0108-X, HarpR). Har-Row.

--Before the Ending of the Day. 110p. 1985. pap. 5.95 (ISBN 0-8192-1365-9). Morehouse.

--Catholic Faith in a Process Perspective. LC 81-9615. 160p. (Orig.). 1981. pap. 1.74 (ISBN 0-88344-091-1). Orbis Bks.

--The Divine Trinity. LC 76-55002. 1977. 5.95 (ISBN 0-8298-0330-0). Pilgrim NY.

--Freed to Love: A Process Interpretation of Redemption. 1987. pap. 8.95. Morehouse.

--The Holy Spirit. LC 74-10839. 128p. 1974. 5.50 (ISBN 0-8298-0284-3). Pilgrim NY.

--Loving Says It All. 128p. 1978. 6.95 (ISBN 0-8298-0352-1). Pilgrim NY.

--The Lure of Divine Love. LC 79-15611. (Orig.). 1979. pap. 6.95 (ISBN 0-8298-0370-X). Pilgrim NY.

--Making Sexuality Human. LC 79-126862. 1979. pap. 4.95 (ISBN 0-8298-0368-8). Pilgrim NY.

--The Ministry of All Christians. 96p. 1983. pap. 5.95 (ISBN 0-8192-1323-3). Morehouse.

--The Pilgrim Church & the Easter People. LC 86-45327. 112p. (Orig.). 1987. pap. 8.95 (ISBN 0-89453-598-6). M Glazier.

--Preaching the Gospel. LC 83-62716. 108p. (Orig.). 1984. pap. 5.95 (ISBN 0-8192-1340-3). Morehouse.

Pittenger, Norman W. Passion & Perfection. 1985. pap. 2.00 (ISBN 0-88028-044-1). Forward Movement.

Pittenger, W. Norman. Trying to Be a Christian. LC 72-1567. 128p. 1972. 4.95 (ISBN 0-8298-0237-1). Pilgrim NY.

Pittenger, W. Norman, jt. auth. see Pike, James A.

Pittenger, William N. Christian Faith & the Question of History. LC 73-79353. pap. 39.00 (2026910). Bks Demand UMI.

Pittinger, W. Norman. Love & Control in Sexuality. LC 73-19833. 128p. 1974. 4.25 (ISBN 0-8298-0268-1). Pilgrim NY.

Pittman, Grace. Hospitality with Confidence. 128p. (Orig.). 1986. pap. 4.95 (ISBN 0-87123-858-6, 210858). Bethany Hse.

Pittman, Thomas B., 3rd. Reaching for the Sky. 1976. pap. 3.95 (ISBN 0-87148-731-4). Pathway Pr.

Pitts, Audre. Let Me Keep Laughter. 106p. 1986. pap. 3.95 (ISBN 0-8341-1090-3). Beacon Hill.

Pitts, David. How in the World Do I Get Along With My Parents? 40p. 1982. pap. 0.95 (ISBN 0-88144-046-9). Christian Pub.

Pitts, James M., ed. The Way of Faith. 176p. (Orig.). 1985. pap. 8.95 (ISBN 0-913029-10-6). Stevens Bk Pr.

Pitts, Joseph. A Faithful Account of the Religion & Manners of the Mahometans. 284p. Repr. of 1738 ed. text ed. 62.10x (ISBN 0-576-03333-2). Gregg Intl.

Pitts, Michael R., jt. auth. see Campbell, Richard H.

Pitts, V. Peter. Concept Development & the Development of the God Concept in the Child: A Bibliography. LC 77-70266. 1977. pap. 2.75 (ISBN 0-915744-07-4). Character Res.

Pitts, V. Peter, ed. Children's Pictures of God. LC 79-56298. (Illus.). 1979. pap. 3.95 (ISBN 0-915744-20-1). Character Res.

Pitt-Watson. A Primer for Preachers. 112p. 1987. 5.95 (ISBN 0-8010-7096-1). Baker Bk.

Pitt-Watson, Ian. Preaching: A Kind of Folly. LC 77-21983. 120p. 1978. pap. 3.95 (ISBN 0-664-24181-6). Westminster.

Pivar, David J. Purity Crusade: Sexual Morality & Social Control, 1868-1900. LC 70-179650. (Contributions in American History Ser.: No. 23). 308p. 1973. lib. bdg. 29.95 (ISBN 0-8371-6319-6, PPC/). Greenwood.

Pixley, George V. God's Kingdom: A Guide for Biblical Study. Walsh, Donald E., tr. from Sp. LC 81-3946. Tr. of Reino de Dios. 128p. (Orig.). 1981. pap. 5.95 (ISBN 0-88344-156-X). Orbis Bks.

--On Exodus: An Evangelical & Popular Commentary. Barr, Robert R., tr. from Span. 256p. (Orig.). 1987. 19.95 (ISBN 0-88344-560-3); pap. 9.95 (ISBN 0-88344-559-X). Orbis Bks.

Pixner, Bargil, et al. The Glory of Bethlehem. 75p. 1986. 11.95 (ISBN 0-8170-1109-9). Judson.

Placher, William C. A History of Christian Theology: An Introduction. LC 83-16778. 324p. 1983. pap. 16.95 (ISBN 0-664-24496-3). Westminster.

Plake, David C. & Plake, Roberta S. The Ministry of Teaching. LC 82-81509. (Workers Training Ser.). 128p. (Orig.). 1982. pap. 2.50 (ISBN 0-88243-567-1, 02-0567). Gospel Pub.

Plake, Roberta S., jt. auth. see Plake, David C.

Planchart, Alejandro. The Repertory of Tropes at Winchester, 2 vols. LC 76-3033. 1976. text ed. 63.00x (ISBN 0-691-09121-8). Princeton U Pr.

Planhol, Xavier de. The World of Islam. 153p. 1959. pap. 8.95x (ISBN 0-8014-9830-9). Cornell U Pr.

Plante, Julian G. Austrian Monasteries, Part 1: Gottweig, Heiligenkreuz, Herzogenburg,...Seitenstetten, & Wilhering. (Checklists of Manuscripts Microfilmed for the Hill Monastic Manuscript Library Ser.: Vol. I). iv, 52p. (Orig.). 1967. pap. 10.00 (ISBN 0-940250-26-8). Hill Monastic.

--Austrian Monasteries, Part 2: Admont, Altenburg,..."Osterreichische Nationalbibliothek, Universitatsbibliothek, Wilten, Zwettl. (Checklists of Manuscripts Microfilmed for the Hill Monastic Manuscript Library Ser.: Vol. I). viii, 296p. 1974. pap. 20.00 (ISBN 0-940250-27-6). Hill Monastic.

Plantinga, Alvin. Does God Have a Nature? LC 80-6585. (Aquinas Lecture Ser.). 1980. 7.95 (ISBN 0-87462-145-3). Marquette.

--God, Freedom, & Evil. 1978. pap. 7.95 (ISBN 0-8028-1731-9). Eerdmans.

Plantinga, Alvin & Wolterstorff, Nicholas, eds. Faith & Rationality: Reason & Belief in God. LC 83-14843. 336p. 1984. 24.95x (ISBN 0-268-00964-3, 85-09648); pap. text ed. 11.95x (ISBN 0-268-00965-1, 85-09655). U of Notre Dame Pr.

Plantinga, Cornelius, Jr. Beyond Doubt: A Devotional Response to Questions of Faith. LC 80-10647. (Illus.). 256p. (Orig.). 1980. pap. text ed. 8.95 (ISBN 0-933140-12-6); pap. text ed. 5.95 leader's guide (ISBN 0-933140-61-4). CRC Pubns.

--A Place to Stand: A Reformed Study of Creeds & Confessions. LC 79-371. (Illus.). 1979. pap. text ed. 8.95 (ISBN 0-933140-01-0). CRC Pubns.

--A Sure Thing. LC 86-8280. (Illus.). 300p. 1986. lib. bdg. 11.95 (ISBN 0-930265-27-0); incl. tchr's. manual 7.95 (ISBN 0-930265-28-9). CRC Pubns.

Plantinga, Theodore. Reading the Bible As History. 110p. (Orig.). 1980. pap. 4.25 (ISBN 0-932914-04-7). Dordt Coll Pr.

--Wait for the Lord: Meditations on the Christian Life. 137p. (Orig.). 1981. pap. 5.75 (ISBN 0-932914-12-8). Dordt Coll Pr.

Plaskow, Judith. Sex, Sin & Grace: Women's Experience & the Theologies of Reinhold Niebuhr & Paul Tillich. LC 79-5434. 1980. pap. text ed. 11.25 (ISBN 0-8191-0882-0). U Pr of Amer.

--Women & Religion. Arnold, Joan & Romero, Joan A., eds. LC 74-83126. (American Academy of Religion. Aids for the Study of Religion). Repr. of 1974 ed. 54.00 (ISBN 0-8357-9581-0, 2017557). Bks Demand UMI.

Plaskow, Judith, jt. auth. see Christ, Carol P.

Plass, Ewald. This Is Luther. 1984. pap. 8.95 (ISBN 0-570-03942-8, 12-2875). Concordia.

Plassmann, Thomas. The Upper Room: Retreat Readings for Priests. (Spirit & Life Ser). 1954. 4.50 (ISBN 0-686-11565-1). Franciscan Inst.

Plaster, David R. Ordinances: What Are They? 1985. pap. 5.95 (ISBN 0-88469-164-0). BMH Bks.

Plateaux, L., jt. auth. see Montenat, C.

Plater, Ormonde. The Deacon in the Liturgy. (Illus.). 60p. (Orig.). 1981. pap. 6.00 (ISBN 0-9605798-0-X). Natl Ctr Diaconate.

Plato. Dialogue of the Immortality of the Soul. LC 73-161797. Repr. of 1713 ed. 20.00 (ISBN 0-404-54134-8). AMS Pr.

--Phaedo. Church, F. J., tr. LC 51-10496. 1951. pap. 4.24 scp (ISBN 0-672-60192-3, LLA30). Bobbs.

--Phaedo. Grube, G. M., tr. LC 76-49565. 72p. 1977. pap. 2.50 (ISBN 0-915144-18-2). Hackett Pub.

--Plato's Phaedo. Bluck, R. S., tr. 1955. pap. 7.87 scp (ISBN 0-672-60308-X, LLA110). Bobbs.

Plato, jt. auth. see Socrates.

Platon. Orthodox Doctrine of the Apostolic Eastern Church. 1973. 5.00 (ISBN 0-686-05409-1). Eastern Orthodox.

--Orthodox Doctrine of the Apostolic Eastern Church: A Compendium of Christian Theology. LC 70-81772. Repr. of 1857 ed. 18.50 (ISBN 0-404-05058-1). AMS Pr.

--Present State of the Greek Church in Russia. LC 75-131031. Repr. of 1815 ed. 21.50 (ISBN 0-404-05059-X). AMS Pr.

Platt, Charles. Popular Superstitions. LC 70-167114. 244p. 1973. Repr. of 1925 ed. 46.00x (ISBN 0-8103-3170-5). Gale.

Platt, Colin. The Abbeys & Priories of Medieval England. LC 84-80387. (Illus.). xvii, 270p. 1984. 32.50 (ISBN 0-8232-1117-7); pap. 19.95 (ISBN 0-8232-1118-5). Fordham.

--Medieval England: A Social History & Archaeology from the Conquest to 1600 A. D. (Illus.). 1978. encore ed. 9.95 (ISBN 0-684-17247-X, ScribT). Scribner.

--Parish Churches of Medieval England. 1981. 34.95 (ISBN 0-436-37553-2, Pub. by Secker & Warburg UK); pap. 16.95 (ISBN 0-436-37554-0, Pub. by Secker & Warburg UK). David & Charles.

Platt, Nancy V. Pastoral Care to the Cancer Patient. 100p. 1980. pap. 9.75x (ISBN 0-398-04051-6). C C Thomas.

Platvoet, J. G. Comparing Religions: A Limitative Approach. (Religion & Reason Ser.: No. 24). xiv, 350p. 1982. 51.50x (ISBN 90-279-3170-4). Mouton.

Platzner, Robert S., jt. auth. see Gersh, Harry.

Plaut, W. Gunther. Commentary on Genesis. (Pardes Torah; Jewish Commentary on the Torah Ser.). 1974. 20.00 (ISBN 0-8074-0001-7, 381611). UAHC.

--Deuteronomy: The Torah. (A Modern Commentary Ser.). 528p. 1983. 20.00 (ISBN 0-8074-0045-9). UAHC.

--Exodus: A Modern Commentary. (The Torah Commentary Ser.). 571p. 1983. 20.00 (ISBN 0-8074-0040-8, 381606). UAHC.

--The Rise of Reform Judaism: A Sourcebook of Its European Origins. Incl. Growth of Reform Judaism: American & European Sources to 1948. 1965. 1963. 10.00 (ISBN 0-8074-0089-0, 382770, Pub. by World Union). UAHC.

--The Torah: A Modern Commentary: Numbers. (The Torah Commentary Ser.). 476p. 1980. 20.00 (ISBN 0-8074-0039-4, 381602). UAHC.

Plaut, W. Gunther & Bamberger, Bernard J. The Torah: A Modern Commentary. (Illus.). 1824p. 1981. 30.00 (ISBN 0-8074-0055-6). UAHC.

Plaut, W. Gunther, ed. Growth of Reform Judaism: American & European Sources Until 1948. 1965. 10.00 (ISBN 0-8074-0086-6, 382780). UAHC.

Plaut, W. Gunther, ed. see Bamberger, Bernard J.

Playfoot, Jane, jt. ed. see Gonzalez, Jose L.

Playfoot, Janet, jt. ed. see Gonzalez-Balado, Jose L.

Ple, Albert. Duty or Pleasure? A New Appraisal of Christian Ethics. 208p. 1986. 22.95 (ISBN 0-913729-24-8); pap. 12.95 (ISBN 0-913729-25-6). Paragon Hse.

Pleasance, Simon, tr. see Beonio-Brocchieri Fumagalli, M. T.

Plessis, David du see Du Plessis, David.

Plesur, Milton. Jewish Life in Twentieth Century America: Challenge & Accommodation. LC 81-11196. (Illus.). 264p. 1982. text ed. 21.95x (ISBN 0-88229-639-6). Nelson-Hall.

Plett, C. F. The Story of the Kimmer Mennonite Brethren Church. pap. 12.00 (ISBN 0-919797-51-2). Herald Pr.

Plewe, Lucille J. Wayfinders: For Believers & Non-Believers. LC 77-78794. 1977. pap. 5.00 (ISBN 0-89555-028-8). TAN Bks Pubs.

Pliskin, Jacqueline. The Animated Haggadah & Story of Passover. (Illus.). 1987. pap. 7.95. Shapolsky Pubs.

Ploeg Van, Kees der see Van Os, Henk.

Plongeon, Augustus Le see Le Plongeon, Augustus.

Plooij, D. Pilgrim Fathers from a Dutch Point of View. LC 71-100509. Repr. of 1932 ed. 8.50 (ISBN 0-404-05065-4). AMS Pr.

Plooij, Daniel. Pilgrim Fathers from a Dutch Point of View. LC 79-131801. 1970. Repr. of 1932 ed. 7.00x (ISBN 0-403-00688-0). Scholarly.

Plotinus. Opera: Enneades IV-V, Vol II. Schwyzer, H. R. & Henry, Paul, eds. (Oxford Classical Texts). 1977. 24.95x (ISBN 0-19-814582-9). Oxford U Pr.

--Plotinus: Essay on the Beautiful. Taylor, Thomas, tr. 1984. pap. 5.95 (ISBN 0-916411-86-9, Pub. by Alexandrian Pr). Holmes Pub.

Plotkin, Frederick. Faith & Reason: Essays in the Religious & Scientific Imagination. LC 72-97937. 1970. 6.00 (ISBN 0-8022-2322-2). Philos Lib.

--Milton's Inward Jerusalem: "Paradise Lost" & the Ways of Knowing. LC 76-159468. (Studies in English Literature: No. 72). 155p. 1971. text ed. 17.60x (ISBN 0-686-22493-0). Mouton.

Plou, Dafne C. De see Drakeford, John W.

Plow, Sabanes De see Simmons, Paul D. & Crawford, Kenneth.

Plueddemann, Carol, ed. Great Passages of the Bible. (Fisherman Bible Studyguide Ser.). 64p. (Orig.). 1987. pap. 2.95 (ISBN 0-87788-332-7). Shaw Pubs.

Plueger, Aaron L. Things to Come for Planet Earth. 1977. pap. 3.95 (ISBN 0-570-03762-X, 12-2691). Concordia.

Plugin, V. Frescoes of St. Demetrius' Cathedral. 44p. 1974. 25.00x (ISBN 0-569-08164-5, Pub. by Collets UK). State Mutual Bk.

Plumer, W. S. Psalms. (Geneva Commentaries Ser.). 1978. 32.95 (ISBN 0-85151-209-7). Banner of Truth.

Plumer, William S. Commentary on Romans. LC 73-155251. (Kregel Reprint Library). 646p. 1971. 18.95 (ISBN 0-8254-3501-3). Kregel.

Plummer, Alfred. The Church of the Early Fathers. 1892. 15.00 (ISBN 0-8414-9261-1). Folcroft.

--A Critical & Exegetical Commentary on the Gospel According to St. Luke. Driver, Samuel R. & Plummer, Alfred, eds. (International Critical Commentary Ser.). 688p. 1901. 24.95 (ISBN 0-567-05023-8, Pub. by T & T Clark Ltd UK). Fortress.

--A Critical & Exegetical Commentary on the Second Epistle of St. Paul to the Corinthians. Driver, Samuel R. & Briggs, Charles A., eds. (International Critical Commentary Ser.). 462p. 1915. 24.95 (ISBN 0-567-05028-9, Pub. by T & T Clark Ltd UK). Fortress.

--English Church History: From the Death of Archbishop Parker to the Death of King Charles I. 1977. lib. bdg. 59.95 (ISBN 0-8490-1772-6). Gordon Pr.

--The Epistles of Saint John. (Thornapple Commentaries Ser.). 302p. 1980. pap. 7.95 (ISBN 0-8010-7058-9). Baker Bk.

--An Exegetical Commentary on The Gospel According To Matthew. (Thornapple Commentaries Ser.). 497p. 1982. pap. 12.95 (ISBN 0-8010-7078-3). Baker Bk.

--The Gospel According to St. John. (Thornapple Commentaries Ser.). 380p. 1981. pap. 9.95 (ISBN 0-8010-7068-6). Baker Bk.

--The Gospel According to St. Mark. (Thornapple Commentaries Ser.). 448p. 1982. pap. 12.95 (ISBN 0-8010-7072-4). Baker Bk.

Plummer, Alfred, jt. auth. see Robertson, Archibald.

Plummer, Alfred, ed. see Barton, George A.

Plummer, Alfred, ed. see Bernard, J. H.

Plummer, Alfred, ed. see Charles, R. H.

Plummer, Alfred, ed. see Driver, Samuel R.

Plummer, Alfred, ed. see Gray, G. Buchanan.

Plummer, Alfred, ed. see Moffatt, James.

Plummer, Alfred, ed. see Montgomery, James A.

Plummer, Alfred, ed. see Plummer, Alfred.

Plummer, Alfred, ed. see Sanday, William & Headlam, Arthur C.

Plummer, Alfred, ed. see Smith, John M., et al.

Plummer, John, jt. ed. see Lavin, Irving.

Plummer, John, intro. by. The Hours of Catherine of Cleves. LC 66-23096. (Illus.). 360p. 1975. 50.00 (ISBN 0-8076-0379-1). Braziller.

Plummer, L. Gordon. By the Holy Tetrakyts: Symbol & Reality in Man & Universe. (Study Ser.: No. 9). (Illus.). 96p. (Orig.). 1982. pap. 5.75 (ISBN 0-913004-44-8). Point Loma Pub.

--From Atom to Kosmos: A Theosophical Study in Evolution. (Illus.). 134p. Date not set. price not set (ISBN 0-913004-49-9). Point Loma Pub.

--Mathematics of the Cosmic Mind. rev. ed. LC 77-114206. (Illus.). 1970. 18.95 (ISBN 0-8356-0030-0). Theos Pub Hse.

Plumpe, jt. ed. see Quasten.

Plumpe, J., ed. see Augustine, St.

Plumpe, J., jt. ed. see Kuasten, J.

Plunkett, Mark. John. (Standard Bible Study Workbooks Ser.). 80p. 1987. wkbk. 1.95 (ISBN 0-87403-184-2, 40204). Standard Pub.

Pluquet, F. A. Dictionnaire des Heresies des Erreurs et des Schismes, 2 vols. Migne, J. P., ed. (Encyclopedie Theologique Ser.: Vols. 11-12). (Fr.). 1374p. Repr. of 1847 ed. lib. bdg. 175.00x (ISBN 0-89241-235-6). Caratzas.

Plutarch. The Roman Questions of Plutarch. facsimile ed. Rose, Herbert J., ed. LC 75-14267. (Ancient Religion & Mythology Ser.). 1976. Repr. of 1924 ed. 17.00x (ISBN 0-405-07272-4). Ayer Co Pubs.

Pluth, Alphonsus & Koch, Carl. The Catholic Church: Our Mission in History. (Illus.). 330p. (Orig.). 1985. pap. text ed. 11.00x (ISBN 0-88489-161-5); teaching manual 18.95x (ISBN 0-88489-162-3). St Mary's.

Pluth, Alphonsus, ed. see Smith, Thomas.

Poage, Godfrey. In Garments All Red. 1977. 3.00 (ISBN 0-8198-0422-3); pap. 1.50 (ISBN 0-8198-0423-1). Dghtrs St Paul.

--Son of the Passion. 1977. 3.50 (ISBN 0-8198-0458-4); pap. 2.25 (ISBN 0-8198-0459-2). Dghtrs St Paul.

Pobee, John S. Persecution & Martyrdom: From Experience to Theology in Paul. (JSNT Supplement Ser.: No. 6). 150p. 1984. text ed. 28.50x (ISBN 0-905774-52-3, Pub. by JSOT Pr. England); pap. text ed. 13.50x (ISBN 0-905774-53-1, Pub. by JSOT Pr. England). Eisenbrauns.

Pochin-Mould, Daphne. Irish Pilgrimage. 1957. 12.95 (ISBN 0-8159-5816-1). Devin.

Pochmann, Henry A. New England Transcendentalism & St. Louis Hegelianism. LC 68-55163. (Studies in Comparative Literature, No. 35). 1969. Repr. of 1948 ed. lib. bdg. 39.95x (ISBN 0-8383-0610-1). Haskell.

Pocketpac Bks. Promises for the Golden Years. 96p. 1983. pap. 2.50 (ISBN 0-87788-320-3). Shaw Pubs.

Pocklington, John. Sunday No Sabbath: A Sermon. LC 74-28881. (English Experience Ser.: No. 759). 1975. Repr. of 1636 ed. 6.00 (ISBN 90-221-0759-0). Walter J Johnson.

Pocknee, Cyril E. Christian Altar in History & Today. LC 64-1983. 1962. text ed. 10.00x (ISBN 0-8401-1871-6). A R Allenson.

Pocock, N., ed. see Harpsfield, Nicholas.

Pocock, Nicholas, ed. Troubles Connected with the Prayer Book of 1549. 1884. 27.00 (ISBN 0-384-47030-0). Johnson Repr.

Poddar, Hanumanprasad. Gopis' Love for Sri Krishna. (Illus.). 51p. 1981. pap. 9.95 (ISBN 0-913922-51-X). Dawn Horse Pr.

Podgorski, Frank R. Ego: Revealer-Concealer, a Key to Yoga. (Illus.). 306p. 1985. lib. bdg. 27.50 (ISBN 0-8191-4345-6); pap. text ed. 14.50 (ISBN 0-8191-4346-4). U Pr of Amer.

--Hinduism: A Beautiful Mosaic. LC 85-51907. i, 61p. 1984. pap. text ed. 6.95x (ISBN 0-932269-12-5). Wyndham Hall.

Podgorski, John. Empowering the Catholic Teacher. 1987. pap. write for info. (ISBN 0-697-02242-0). Wm C Brown.

Podhaizer, Mary E. Following Christ: Activity Book. Puccetti, Patricia I., ed. (Faith & Life Ser.). 41p. (Orig.). 1985. pap. 2.50 (ISBN 0-89870-066-3). Ignatius Pr.

--Jesus Our Life: Activity Book. Puccetti, Patricia I., ed. (Faith & Life Ser.: bk. 2). 76p. (Orig.). 1984. pap. 2.50 (ISBN 0-89870-063-9). Ignatius Pr.

Podles, Mary S. & Porter, Vicki. A Guide to God's Minstrel: St. Francis of Assisi. Strohecker, Carol, ed. (Illus.). 24p. (Orig.). 1982. pap. 1.50 (ISBN 0-911886-23-0). Walters Art.

Podwal, Mark. A Book of Hebrew Letters. LC 78-70076. (Illus.). 64p. 1979. pap. 5.95 (ISBN 0-8276-0118-2, 435). Jewish Pubns.

Poehlman, William R., tr. see Lohse, Eduard.

Poel, Cornelius J. van Der see Van Der Poel, Cornelius J.

Poel, Cornelius J. Van Der see Van Der Poel, Cornelius J.

Poellet, Luther, tr. see Quenstedt, J. A.

Poellot, Luther, tr. see Chemitz, Martin.

Poewe, Karla, jt. auth. see Hexham, Irving.

Poffenberger, Nancy. Instant Piano Fun for Christmas. 24p. 1986. pap. text ed. 4.95 (ISBN 0-938293-28-1). Fun Pub OH.

Poganski, Donald J. Fifty Object Lessons. 1967. 4.50 (ISBN 0-570-03172-9, 12-2282). Concordia.

--Forty Object Lessons. LC 72-86233. 160p. 1973. pap. 4.50 (ISBN 0-570-03148-6, 12-2283). Concordia.

Poggi, Gianfranco. Calvinism & the Capitalist Spirit: Max Weber's "Protestant Ethic". LC 83-40103. 136p. 1983. lib. bdg. 13.50x (ISBN 0-87023-417-X); pap. text ed. 6.95x (ISBN 0-87023-418-8). U of Mass Pr.

--Catholic Action in Italy: Sociology of a Sponsored Organization. 1967. 25.00x (ISBN 0-8047-0292-6). Stanford U Pr.

Pogzeba, Wolfgang & Overbeck, Joy. Ranchos De Taos: San Francisco De Asis Church. LC 81-82257. (Illus.). 68p. (Orig.). 1981. pap. 7.95 (ISBN 0-913504-66-1). Lowell Pr.

Pohier, Jacques & Mieth, Dietmar, eds. One Faith, One Church, Man, Many Moralities, Vol. 150. (Concilium 1981). 128p. (Orig.). 1981. pap. 6.95 (ISBN 0-8164-2350-4, HarpR). Har-Row.

Pohier, Jacques, jt. ed. see Mieth, Dietmar.

Pohier, Jaques. God in Fragments. 384p. 1986. 22.50 (ISBN 0-8245-0744-4). Crossroad NY.

Pohle, Joseph. Eschatology. LC 72-109823. 1971. Repr. of 1917 ed. lib. bdg. 22.50x (ISBN 0-8371-4314-4, POES). Greenwood.

Pohle, Myrtle A. Truth Seekers. (Daybreak Ser.). 144p. 1983. pap. 4.95 (ISBN 0-8163-0529-3). Pacific Pr Pub Assn.

Pohlmann, Constantin. Francis, a Way: The Franciscan Alternative. Smith, Davie, tr. 1988. cancelled 12.50 (ISBN 0-8199-0865-7). Franciscan Herald.

Pointer, Lyle. Beginning Anew. (Christian Living Ser.). 32p. (Orig.). 1987. pap. write for info. (ISBN 0-8341-1189-6). Beacon Hill.

--Now That You Are Saved. (Christian Living Ser.). 32p. (Orig.). 1987. pap. 2.50 (ISBN 0-8341-1157-8). Beacon Hill.

--Welcome Back to Jesus. (Christian Living Ser.). 32p. (Orig.). 1987. pap. write for info. (ISBN 0-8341-1190-X). Beacon Hill.

Pois, Robert A. National Socialism & the Religion of Nature. LC 85-27615. 208p. 1986. 27.50 (ISBN 0-312-55958-5). St Martin.

Pojman, Louis P. The Logic of Subjectivity: Kierkegaard's Philosophy of Religion. LC 83-1053. 174p. 1984. 17.50x (ISBN 0-8173-0166-6). U of Ala Pr.

--Philosophy of Religion: An Anthology. King, Ken, ed. (Orig.). 1986. write for info. (ISBN 0-534-06672-0). Wadsworth Pub.

--Religious Belief & the Will. (Problems of Philosophy Ser.). 256p. 1986. text ed. 32.50 (ISBN 0-7102-0399-3). Methuen Inc.

Polack, W. G. The Handbook to the Lutheran Hymnal. 3rd rev. ed. 1975. Repr. of 1942 ed. lib. bdg. 16.95 (ISBN 0-8100-0003-2, 03-0700). Northwest Pub.

Poladian, Vartapet T., tr. see Gulleserian, Papken.

Polan, Gregory J. In the Ways of Justice Toward Salvation. (American University Studies VII - Theology & Religion: Vol. 13). 360p. 1986. text ed. 46.00 (ISBN 0-8204-0280-X). P Lang Pubs.

Polanco, Bermudez Y., tr. see Judge, William Q.

Poland, Lynn M. Literary Criticism & Biblical Hermeneutics. (American Academy of Religion Academy Ser.: No. 48). 1985. 15.25 (ISBN 0-89130-825-3, 01 01 48); pap. 10.25 (ISBN 0-89130-836-9). Scholars Pr GA.

Polcino, Anna, ed. Intimacy: Issues of Emotional Living in an Age of Stress for Clergy & Religious. LC 78-104617. 1978. pap. 5.00 (ISBN 0-89571-003-X). Affirmation.

Polcino, Anna, jt. auth. see Helldorfer, Martin C.

Pole, Kay, jt. ed. see Blake, Nigel.

Pole, Reginald. De Summo Pontifice. 330p. Repr. of 1569 ed. text ed. 62.10 (ISBN 0-576-99123-6, Pub. by Gregg Intl Pubs England). Gregg Intl.

Pole, Thomas. A History of the Origin & Progress of Adult Schools: With an Account of Some Beneficial Effects. (First Ser. in the Social History of Education: No. 8). 108p. 1968. Repr. of 1814 ed. 25.00x (ISBN 0-7130-0009-0, Pub. by Woburn Pr England). Biblio Dist.

Polek, David & Anderhub, Rita. Advent Begins at Home. 1979. pap. 1.50 (ISBN 0-89243-111-3). Liguori Pubns.

Polen, O. W. Editorially Speaking. 1975. pap. 2.25 (ISBN 0-87148-300-9). Pathway Pr.

--Editorially Speaking, Vol. 2. 58p. 1980. pap. 2.25 (ISBN 0-87148-296-7). Pathway Pr.

--Living by the Word. LC 77-79942. 1977. pap. 1.95 (ISBN 0-87148-509-5). Pathway Pr.

--The Sunday School Teacher. 1956. pap. 5.25 (ISBN 0-87148-765-9). Pathway Pr.

Polese, Richard, compiled by. Prayers of the World. 62p. 1987. pap. 5.00 (ISBN 0-943734-00-2). Ocean Tree Bks.

Poley, Irvin C. & Poley, Ruth V. Quaker Anecdotes. 1983. pap. 2.50x (ISBN 0-87574-033-2, 033). Pendle Hill.

Poley, Ruth V., jt. auth. see Poley, Irvin C.

Poliakov, Leon. Harvest of Hate. LC 78-71294. 350p. 1979. pap. 12.95 (ISBN 0-89604-006-2). Holocaust Pubns.

--Harvest of Hate: The Nazi Program for the Destruction of the Jews in Europe. LC 74-110836. 1971. Repr. of 1954 ed. lib. bdg. 22.50x (ISBN 0-8371-2635-5, POHH). Greenwood.

--Harvest of Hate: The Nazi Program for the Destruction of the Jews of Europe. rev ed. LC 78-71294. 1979. pap. 5.95 (ISBN 0-8052-5006-9, Pub. by Holocaust Library). Schocken.

--History of Anti-Semitism, Vol. 1: From the Time of Christ to the Court Jews. LC 65-10228. 340p. 1964. 19.50 (ISBN 0-8149-0186-7). Vanguard.

--The History of Anti-Semitism, Vol. 2: From Mohammed to the Marranos. Gerardi, Natalie, tr. from Fr. LC 65-10228. Tr. of Histoire De l'antisemitisme: De Mahomet Aux Marranes. 399p. 1974. 19.50 (ISBN 0-8149-0701-6). Vanguard.

--Jewish Barbers & the Holy See: From the Thirteenth to the Seventeenth-Century. Kochan, Miriam, tr. from Fr. (Littman Library of Jewish Civilization). 288p. 1977. 29.00x (ISBN 0-19-710028-7). Oxford U Pr.

Poliakov, Leon & Sabille, Jacques. Jews under the Italian Occupation. LC 81-22202. 208p. 1983. Repr. of 1955 ed. 23.50x (ISBN 0-86527-344-8). Fertig.

Polikov, Sheila, ed. see Omaha Section National Council of Jewish Women.

Poling, David, compiled by. Inspiration Three, Vol. 3: Three Famous Classics in One Book - Wisdom of Luther, Calvin & Wesley. LC 73-80032. (Pivot Family Reader Ser.). 1973. pap. 1.25 (ISBN 0-87983-043-3). Keats.

Poling, David, ed. This Great Company: A Treasury of Sermons by Outstanding Preachers of the Christian Tradition. LC 74-75977. (Illus.). 1976. 8.95 (ISBN 0-87983-123-5); pap. 4.95 (ISBN 0-87983-124-3). Keats.

Poling, James N. & Miller, Donald E. Foundations for a Practical Theology of Ministry. 192p. 1985. pap. 9.95 (ISBN 0-687-13340-8). Abingdon.

Poling, Tommy H., jt. auth. see Kenny, J. Frank.

Polish, Daniel F., jt. ed. see Fisher, Eugene J.

Polit, Gustavo, tr. see Schuon, Frithjof.

Polk, Thomas E., II. Saint-Denis, Noyon & the Early Gothic Choir: Methodological Considerations for the History of Early Gothic Architecture, Vol. 4. (Sanctuaries of the Gallic-Frankish Church Ser.). (Illus.). 220p. 1982. pap. 32.10 (ISBN 3-8204-6177-9). P Lang Pubs.

Polk, Timothy. The Prophetic Persona: The Language of Self-Reference in Jeremiah. (JSOT Supplement Ser.: No. 32). 240p. 1985. text ed. 28.50x (ISBN 0-905774-70-1, Pub. by JSOT Pr England); pap. text ed. 13.50x (ISBN 0-905774-71-X, Pub. by JSOT Pr England). Eisenbrauns.

Polka, Brayton. The Dialectic of Biblical Critique: Interpretation & Existence. LC 84-26216. 192p. 1986. 25.00 (ISBN 0-312-19874-4). St Martin.

Polkinghorne, John. One World: The Interaction of Science & Theology. 128p. 1987. 17.50 (ISBN 0-691-08459-9); pap. 7.95 (ISBN 0-691-02407-3). Princeton U Pr.

Poll, Solomon. Ancient Thoughts in Modern Perspective: A Contemporary View of the Bible. LC 68-22349. 136p. 1968. 6.95 (ISBN 0-8022-1998-5). Philos Lib.

Pollack, David. Zen Poems of the Five Mountains. LC 84-13910. (American Academy of Religion Studies in Religion). 1984. 22.50 (ISBN 0-89130-776-1, 01 00 37); pap. 14.95 (ISBN 0-89130-775-3). Scholars Pr GA.

Pollack, John. The Master: A Life of Jesus. 240p. 1985. 12.95 (ISBN 0-89693-315-6). Victor Bks.

Pollak, Gabriel, ed. Transliterated Haggadah: Passover Haggadah. (Heb. & Eng). deluxe ed. 18.50 leatherette bdg. (ISBN 0-87559-082-9). Shalom.

Pollak, Michael. Mandarins, Jews & Missionaries: The Jewish Experience in the Chinese Empire. LC 79-84732. (Illus.). 439p. 1983. pap. 10.95 (ISBN 0-8276-0229-4). Jewish Pubns.

Pollak, Michael, jt. auth. see Nelkin, Dorothy.

Pollak, P. S. Halel Vzimrah: Commentary in Hebrew on the Passover Haggadah. (Heb). 12.50 (ISBN 0-87559-100-0); pap. 9.50 (ISBN 0-87559-099-3). Shalom.

--Marbin Besimho. (Heb). 9.50 (ISBN 0-87559-083-7); pap. 5.00 saddle stitched (ISBN 0-87559-084-5). Shalom.

--Minhas Marheshes: Commentary on Genesis. (Heb). 9.50 (ISBN 0-87559-101-9). Shalom.

--Nefesh Hayah: Commentary & Interpretation on the Passover Haggadah with the Haggadah Text. (Hebrew.). 9.50 (ISBN 0-87559-091-8). Shalom.

--Shaare Rahmin: Sermon Material for the High Holidays in Hebrew. 7.50 (ISBN 0-87559-104-3). Shalom.

--Tal Hermon: Sermon Material for Yom Kippur & Eulogy in Hebrew. (Heb). 9.50 (ISBN 0-87559-086-1); pap. 5.00 (ISBN 0-87559-085-3). Shalom.

Pollard, Albert F. Thomas Cranmer & the English Reformation, 1849-1556. LC 83-45587. Date not set. Repr. of 1927 ed. 42.50 (ISBN 0-404-19905-4). AMS Pr.

Pollard, Alfred F. Jesuits in Poland. LC 76-116799. (Studies in Philosophy, No. 40). 1970. Repr. of 1902 ed. lib. bdg. 39.95x (ISBN 0-8383-1041-9). Haskell.

Pollard, Frank. Keeping Free. LC 82-73932. 1983. 4.95 (ISBN 0-8054-5216-8). Broadman.

Pollard, John F. The Vatican & Italian Fascism, Nineteen Twenty-Nine to Nineteen Thirty-Two: A Study in Conflict. 240p. 1985. 34.50 (ISBN 0-521-26870-2). Cambridge U Pr.

Pollard, Nina T. Nothing but a Footprint. LC 85-29049. 1986. pap. 3.25 (ISBN 0-8054-5716-X). Broadman.

Pollard, Stewart M. Tied to Masonic Apron Strings. Cook, Lewis C., ed. 1979. pap. 4.50 (ISBN 0-88053-059-6, M-322). Macoy Pub.

Pollard, T. E. Fullness of Humanity: Christ's Humanness & Ours. 128p. 1982. text ed. 19.95x (ISBN 0-907459-10-2, Pub. by Almond Pr England); pap. text ed. 9.95x (ISBN 0-907459-11-0, Pub. by Almond Pr England). Eisenbrauns.

Pollard, W. G. Transcendence & Providence: Reflections of a Physicist & Priest. (Theology & Science at the Frontiers of Knowledge Ser.: Vol. 6). 146p. 1986. 17.00 (ISBN 0-7073-0486-5, Pub. by Scot Acad Pr). Longwood Pub Group.

Pollen, John H. English Catholics in the Reign of Queen Elizabeth: A Study of Their Politics, Civil Life & Government. 1971. Repr. of 1920 ed. lib. bdg. 24.50 (ISBN 0-8337-2798-2). B Franklin.

Pollinger, Eileen. Building Christian Discipline. 96p. (Orig.). 1986. pap. 3.95 (ISBN 0-87123-877-2); tchr's guide 4.95 (ISBN 0-87123-878-0). Bethany Hse.

Pollins, Harold. Economic History of the Jews in England. (Littman Library of Jewish Civilization). 1983. 37.50x (ISBN 0-19-710048-1). Oxford U Pr.

Pollitt, Christopher. Manipulating the Machine: Changing the Pattern of Ministerial Departments, 1960-83. 296p. 1984. text ed. 29.95x (ISBN 0-04-351064-7). Allen Unwin.

Pollnow, Jim. My God, Why? A Mastectomy from a Husbands Point of View. LC 79-55888. 127p. 1980. pap. 2.95x (ISBN 0-9603708-0-3). J L Pollnow.

Pollock, Algernon J. La Paz con Dios. 2nd ed. Mahecha, Alberto, ed. Bautista, SAra, tr. from Eng. (La Serie Diamante). Tr. of Peace With God. (Span., Illus.). 48p. 1982. pap. 0.85 (ISBN 0-942504-09-7). Overcomer Pr.

Pollock, Algernon J. & Bennett, Gordon H. El Pecado Despues de la Conversion. 2nd ed. Bautista, Sara, tr. from Eng. (La Serie Diamante). Tr. of Sin After Conversion. (Span., Illus.). 36p. 1982. pap. 0.85 (ISBN 0-942504-04-6). Overcomer Pr.

Pollock, Ervin H. Human Rights: Amintaphil, Vol. 1. LC 70-173834. xviii, 419p. 1971. lib. bdg. 37.50 (ISBN 0-930342-65-8). W S Hein.

Pollock, Frederick. Spinoza: His Life & Philosophy. (Reprints in Philosophy Ser.). (Illus.). Repr. of 1880 ed. lib. bdg. 47.00x (ISBN 0-697-00055-9). Irvington.

Pollock, George. Mourning & Liberation. 1987. lib. bdg. price not set (ISBN 0-8236-3485-X). Intl Univs Pr.

Pollock, John. Apostle. Orig. Title: Man Who Shook the World. 244p. 1972. pap. 7.95 (ISBN 0-88207-233-1). Victor Bks.

--The Apostle: A Life of Paul. 312p. 1985. 11.95 (ISBN 0-89693-368-7). Victor Bks.

--Wilberforce. LC 77-86525. (Illus.). 1978. 26.00x (ISBN 0-312-87942-3). St Martin.

Pollock, Penny. Emily's Tiger. (Orig.). 1984. pap. 1.95 (ISBN 0-8091-6554-6). Paulist Pr.

Pollock, Shirley. Building Teen Excitement: A Youth Worker's Guide. LC 85-11256. 80p. (Orig.). 1985. pap. 8.95 (ISBN 0-687-03993-2). Abingdon.

Polman, A. D. Barth. (Modern Thinkers Ser.). pap. 2.25 (ISBN 0-87552-580-6). Presby & Reformed.

Polner, Murray. American Jewish Biographies. (Illus.). 500p. 1982. 39.95x (ISBN 0-87196-462-7). Facts on File.

Polner, Murray, ed. The Disarmament Catalogue. LC 82-13226. (Illus.). 224p. (Orig.). 1982. pap. 12.95 (ISBN 0-8298-0627-X). Pilgrim NY.

Polocino, Anna. The Adventure of Affirming: Reflections on Healing & Ministry. LC 86-8005. 111p. (Orig.). 1986. pap. 7.95 (ISBN 0-89571-030-7). Affirmation.

Poloma, Margaret M. The Charismatic Movement: Is There a New Pentecost? (Social Movements: Past & Present Ser.). 1982. lib. bdg. 18.95 (ISBN 0-8057-9701-7, Twayne). G K Hall.

--The Charismatic Movement: Is There a New Pentecost? (Social Movements Past & Present Ser.). 304p. 1987. pap. 9.95 (ISBN 0-8057-9721-1, Twayne). G K Hall.

Polome, Edgar C., ed. Essays in Honor of Karl Kerenyi. (Journal of Indo-European Studies Monographs: No. 4). (Illus.). 144p. (Orig.). 1984. pap. 30.00x (ISBN 0-941694-20-8). Inst Study Man.

Polonsky, Antony, et al. The Jews in Poland. 288p. 1986. 24.95 (ISBN 0-631-14857-4). Basil Blackwell.

Pols, Edward. Whitehead's Metaphysics: A Critical Examination of Process & Reality. LC 67-10721. 217p. 1967. 8.95x (ISBN 0-8093-0280-2). S Ill U Pr.

Polsky, Michael. V Zashchitu Pravoslavnoj Vjeri ot Sektantov. Tr. of In Defence of Orthodoxy Against Sectarians. 1950. pap. 1.00 (ISBN 0-317-30261-2). Holy Trinity.

Polston, Don. Living Without Losing. LC 75-27142. 1976. pap. 5.95 (ISBN 0-89081-015-X). Harvest Hse.

--There Can Be a New You: A Positive Approach to Life. LC 77-84892. 160p. 1980. pap. 3.95 (ISBN 0-89081-099-0, 0990). Harvest Hse.

Polston, Donald H. Where There's a Wall, There's a Way. (Living Books). 224p. 1985. pap. 2.95 (ISBN 0-8423-8204-6). Tyndale.

Polyzoides, G. History & Teachings of the Eastern Greek Orthodox Church. (Illus.). 96p. 4.00 (ISBN 0-686-83964-1). Divry.

--Stories from the New Testament. (Illus.). 112p. 3.20 (ISBN 0-686-83966-8). Divry.

--Stories from the Old Testament. (Gr., Illus.). 71p. 3.20 (ISBN 0-686-80434-1). Divry.

--What We See & Hear in a Greek Eastern Orthodox Church. 92p. 4.00 (ISBN 0-686-83965-X). Divry.

Polyzoides, M. Catechism of Eastern Greek Orthodox Church. 96p. 4.00 (ISBN 0-686-79625-X). Divry.

Polzer, Charles. Kino Guide II. LC 82-50218. (Illus.). 76p. 1982. pap. 5.00 (ISBN 0-915076-07-1). SW Mission.

--Rules & Precepts of the Jesuit Missions of Northwestern New Spain. LC 75-8456. 141p. 1976. pap. 4.50 (ISBN 0-8165-0488-1). U of Ariz Pr.

Polzer, Charles W., jt. auth. see Cabat, Erni.

Polzer, Charles W., ed. see Cabat, Erni.

Polzin, Robert M. Moses & the Deuteronomist: A Literary Study of the Deuteronomic History. 224p. 1981. 17.95 (ISBN 0-8164-0456-9, HarpR); pap. 8.95 (ISBN 0-8164-2284-2). Har-Row.

Polzin, Robert M. & Rothman, Eugene, eds. The Biblical Mosaic: Changing Perspectives. LC 81-67307. (Semeia Studies). 1982. pap. 9.95 (ISBN 0-8006-1510-7, Co-Pub by Fortress Pr). Fortress.

Pomazansky, Michael. The Old Testament in the New Testament Church. 40p. (Orig.). 1977. pap. 2.00 (ISBN 0-317-30281-7). Holy Trinity.

Pomeau, Rene, ed. see Voltaire.

Pomerans, Arno, tr. see Hillesum, Etty.

Pomerans, Arnold, tr. see Hillesum, Etty.

Pomerville, Paul. The Third Force in Missions. 196p. 1986. pap. 9.95 (ISBN 0-913573-15-9). Hendrickson MA.

Pomey, Antoine. The Pantheon. LC 75-27879. (Renaissance & the Gods Ser.: Vol. 34). (Illus.). 1976. Repr. of 1694 ed. lib. bdg. 88.00 (ISBN 0-8240-2083-9). Garland Pub.

Pomiane, Edouard de see De Pomiane, Edouard.

Pomian-Srzednicki, Maciej. Religious Changes in Contemporary Poland: Secularization & Politics. (International Library of Sociology). 227p. 1982. 27.95x (ISBN 0-7100-9245-8). Methuen Inc.

Pommert, John. Thirteen Lessons on Timothy & Titus. (Bible Student Study Guides). 2.95 (ISBN 0-89900-162-9). College Pr Pub.

Ponce, Charles. Kabbalah. LC 78-7385. (Illus.). 1978. pap. 6.50 (ISBN 0-8356-0510-8, Quest). Theos Pub Hse.

Poncet, Rene. Les Privileges des Clercs Au Moyen-Age. (Fr.). 230p. Repr. of 1901 ed. lib. bdg. 42.50x. Coronet Bks.

Poncins, Leon De see De Poncins, Leon.

Ponder, Catherine. Dare to Prosper. LC 82-74520. 80p. 1983. pap. 3.00 (ISBN 0-87516-511-7). De Vorss.

--Dynamic Laws of Healing. 1972. pap. 6.95 (ISBN 0-87516-156-1). De Vorss.

--The Healing Secrets of the Ages. rev. ed. LC 67-26503. 278p. 1985. pap. 6.95 (ISBN 0-87516-550-8). De Vorss.

--The Millionaire from Nazareth. (The Millionaires of the Bible Ser.). 1979. pap. 6.95 (ISBN 0-87516-370-X). De Vorss.

--The Millionaire Joshua. LC 77-86719. (The Millionaires of the Bible Ser.). 1978. pap. 5.95 (ISBN 0-87516-253-3). De Vorss.

--The Millionaire Moses. LC 77-71459. (The Millionaires of the Bible Ser.). 1977. pap. 5.95 (ISBN 0-87516-232-0). De Vorss.

--The Millionaires of Genesis. (The Millionaires of the Bible Ser.). 1976. pap. 4.95 (ISBN 0-87516-215-0). De Vorss.

--Open Your Mind to Prosperity. rev. ed. LC 70-155720. 184p. 1984. pap. 5.50 (ISBN 0-87516-531-1). De Vorss.

--Open Your Mind to Receive. LC 82-74283. 128p. 1983. pap. 4.50 (ISBN 0-87516-507-9). De Vorss.

--The Prospering Power of Love. rev. ed. LC 66-25849. 126p. 1984. pap. 3.50 (ISBN 0-87516-525-7). De Vorss.

--The Prospering Power of Prayer. 80p. 1983. pap. 3.00 (ISBN 0-87516-516-8). De Vorss.

Pontanus, Jacobus, ed. see Ovid.

Pontas, J. Dictionnaire de Cas de Conscience ou Decisions, 2 vols. Migne, J. P., ed. (Encyclopedie Theologique Ser.: Vols. 18-19). (Fr.). 1326p. Repr. of 1847 ed. lib. bdg. 169.00x (ISBN 0-89241-238-0). Caratzas.

Pontifical Council for the Family. Family Hope for the World. 71p. pap. 3.50 (ISBN 0-317-46615-1). New City.

Pontifical Council for the Laity. A Festival of Hope. 179p. pap. 6.00 (ISBN 0-317-46617-8). New City.

Pontifical Institute of Medieval Studies, Ontario. Dictionary Catalogue of the Library of the Pontifical Institute of Medieval Studies, 5 vols. 1972. Set. lib. bdg. 505.00 (ISBN 0-8161-0970-2, Hall Library). G K Hall.

Pontious, Alfred E. Feed My Sheep. 26p. pap. text ed. 1.95 (ISBN 0-940227-01-0). Liberation Pub.

Pontlarcy, Y. de see Picard, J. M. & De Pontlarcy, Y.

Pontus, St. Life of St. Cyprian. pap. 1.50 (ISBN 0-686-05651-5). Eastern Orthodox.

Ponzan, Mrs. Joe, jt. auth. see Ponzani, Joe.

Ponzani, Joe & Ponzan, Mrs. Joe. Susanna Wesley, a Study Guide. 1983. 1.75 (ISBN 0-89536-607-X, 1930). CSS of Ohio.

Pool, S. L. Orations of Mohammad. pap. 2.00 (ISBN 0-686-18347-9). Kazi Pubns.

Poole, Cecil A. The Eternal Fruits of Knowledge. 3rd ed. LC 76-352583. 162p. 1978. 6.95 (ISBN 0-912057-27-0, G524). AMORC.

--Mysticism - the Ultimate Experience. LC 81-86628. 166p. 1982. 8.95 (ISBN 0-912057-33-5, G-647). AMORC.

Poole, Matthew. A Commentary on the Holy Bible, 3 vols. 1979. Set. 92.95 (ISBN 0-85151-211-9); 35.95 ea. Vol.1, Genesis through Job (ISBN 0-85151-054-X). Vol. 2, Psalms through Malachi (ISBN 0-85151-134-1). Vol. 3, Matthew through Revelation (ISBN 0-85151-135-X). Banner of Truth.

Poole, Reginald L. Wycliffe & Movements for Reform. LC 77-84729. Repr. of 1889 ed. 28.00 (ISBN 0-404-16129-4). AMS Pr.

Poole, Stafford & Slawson, Douglas J. Church & Slave in Perry County, Missouri, 1818-1865. (Studies in American Religion: Vol. 22). (Illus.). 240p. lib. bdg. 49.95x (ISBN 0-88946-666-1). E Mellen.

Poor, Laura E. Sanskrit & Its Kindred Literatures. LC 76-27525. 1976. Repr. of 1880 ed. lib. bdg. 35.00 (ISBN 0-89341-038-1). Longwood Pub Group.

Poortvliet, Rien. He Was One of Us: The Life of Jesus of Nazareth. LC 85-29270. 128p. 1986. 14.95 (ISBN 0-385-13576-9). Doubleday.

Poovey, W. A. Prodigals & Publicans: Dramas & Meditations on Six Parables. LC 79-54111. 100p. 1979. pap. 5.95 (ISBN 0-8066-1763-2, 10-5247). Augsburg.

Poovey, W. A., ed. Planning a Christian Funeral: A Minister's Guide. LC 78-52198. 1978. pap. 7.95 (ISBN 0-8066-1668-7, 10-4990). Augsburg.

Pope, Earl. New England Calvinism & the Disruption of the Presbyterian Church. Kuklick, Bruce, ed. (American Religious Thought of the 18th & 19th Centuries Ser.). 400p. 1987. lib. bdg. 50.00 (ISBN 0-8240-6969-2). Garland Pub.

Pope John Center Staff. Technological Powers & the Person: Nuclear Energy & Reproductive Technology. Lossing, Larry D. & Bayer, Edward J., eds. (Illus.). 370p. (Orig.). 1983. pap. 15.95 (ISBN 0-935372-12-1). Pope John Ctr.

Pope John Paul II, jt. auth. see Frossard, Andre.

Pope, Leigh. Dreams & Visions. 96p. (Orig.). 1982. pap. 7.95 (ISBN 0-85819-339-6, Pub. by JBCE). ANZ Religious Pubns.

Pope, Liston. Millhands & Preachers: A Study of Gastonia. (Studies in Religious Education: No. 15). (Illus.). 1965. pap. 11.95x (ISBN 0-300-00182-7). Yale U Pr.

Pope, Marvin H., ed. Job. rev. ed. (Anchor Bible Ser.: Vol. 15). 1973. 18.00 (ISBN 0-385-00894-5, Anchor Pr). Doubleday.

Pope, Marvin H., tr. Song of Songs. LC 72-79417. (Anchor Bible Ser.: Vol. 7C). (Illus.). 1977. 18.00 (ISBN 0-385-00569-5, Anchor Pr). Doubleday.

Pope Paul VI. Humanae Vitae. 2nd, rev. ed. Caligari, Marc, tr. from Lat. 1983. pap. 1.95 (ISBN 0-89870-000-0). Ignatius Pr.

Pope, Robert G. Half-Way Covenant: Church Membership in Puritan New England. Repr. of 1969 ed. 63.30 (ISBN 0-8357-9500-4, 2011473). Bks Demand UMI.

Pope, Robert G., ed. The Notebook of the Reverand John Fiske: 1644 to 1675. LC 74-81447. 256p. 1974. 17.50 (ISBN 0-88389-052-6). Essex Inst.

Pope, Robert H. Incidental Grace. 176p. 1985. pap. 6.95 (ISBN 0-310-34651-7, 12743P). Zondervan.

Pope Gregory VII. The Epistolae Vagantes of Pope Gregory Seven. Cowdrey, H. E., ed. (Oxford Medieval Texts). (Eng. & Lat.). 1972. 42.00x (ISBN 0-19-822220-3). Oxford U Pr.

Pope-Hennessy, John. Luca della Robbia. LC 79-13566. (Illus.). 282p. 1980. 125.00x (ISBN 0-8014-1256-0). Cornell U Pr.

Pope John Paul. Puebla: A Pilgrimage of Faith. 1979. pap. 2.00 (ISBN 0-8198-0629-3). Dghtrs St Paul.

Pope John Paul, II. Pope John Paul II: On Jews & Judiasm, 1979-1986. (Orig.). Date not set. pap. price not set (ISBN 1-55586-151-2). US Catholic.

Pope John Paul I. The Lesson of the Christmas Donkey. Smith, David & Cunningham, Robert, trs. LC 79-21337. 104p. 1982. 6.95 (ISBN 0-8199-0774-X). Franciscan Herald.

Pope John Paul II. Africa: Apostolic Pilgrimage. 1980. 8.00 (ISBN 0-8198-0708-7); pap. 7.00 (ISBN 0-8198-0709-5). Dghtrs St Paul.

--Brazil, Journey in the Light of the Eucharist. 1980. 8.00 (ISBN 0-8198-1102-5); pap. 7.00 (ISBN 0-8198-1103-3). Dghtrs St Paul.

--Canada: Celebrating Our Faith. 370p. 1985. 7.00 (ISBN 0-317-18636-1); pap. 6.00 (ISBN 0-8198-1441-5). Dghtrs St Paul.

--Faithfulness to the Gospel. Daughters of St. Paul, compiled by. 335p. 1982. 4.50 (ISBN 0-8198-2614-6, EP0482); pap. 3.50 (ISBN 0-8198-2615-4). Dghtrs St Paul.

--The Far East Journey of Peace & Brotherhood. write for info. Dghtrs St Paul.

--Germany-Pilgrimage of Unity & Peace. 1981. 6.00 (ISBN 0-8198-3013-5); pap. 5.00 (ISBN 0-8198-3014-3). Dghtrs St Paul.

--I Believe in Youth, Christ Believes in Youth. 1981. 4.95 (ISBN 0-8198-3602-8); pap. 3.95 (ISBN 0-8198-3603-6). Dghtrs St Paul.

--Ireland: In the Footsteps of St. Patrick. 1979. 3.95 (ISBN 0-8198-0624-2); pap. 2.95 (ISBN 0-8198-0625-0). Dghtrs St Paul.

--Light of Christ. 256p. 1987. pap. 9.95 (ISBN 0-8245-0820-3). Crossroad NY.

--Lord & Giver of Life. 144p. (Orig.). 1986. pap. 3.95 (ISBN 1-55586-103-2). US Catholic.

--Love & Responsibility. Willetts, H. T., tr. 320p. 1981. 15.00 (ISBN 0-374-19247-2); pap. 7.95 (ISBN 0-374-51685-5). FS&G.

--On Human Work. 62p. 1981. pap. 3.95 (ISBN 1-55586-825-8). US Catholic.

--Original Unity of Man & Woman. 184p. 1981. 4.00 (ISBN 0-8198-5405-0); pap. 3.00 (ISBN 0-686-78419-7). Dghtrs St Paul.

--Reflections on Humanae Vitae. 96p. 1984. 3.76 (ISBN 0-8198-6409-9); pap. 2.75 (ISBN 0-8198-6410-2). Dghtrs St Paul.

--Sacred in All Its Forms. 482p. 1984. 7.50 (ISBN 0-8198-6845-0); pap. 6.50 (ISBN 0-8198-6846-9). Dghtrs St Paul.

--To the U. S. Bishops at Their Ad Ldmina Visita. 108p. 1984. 3.50 (ISBN 0-8198-0723-0); pap. 2.50 (ISBN 0-8198-0724-9). Dghtrs St Paul.

--Toward a Philosophy of Praxis. Bloch, A. & Czuczka, G. T., eds. LC 80-21239. 152p. 1981. 10.95 (ISBN 0-8245-0033-4). Crossroad NY.

--Turkey: Ecumenical Pilgrimage. 3.50 (ISBN 0-8198-0650-1); pap. 2.50 (ISBN 0-8198-0651-X). Dghtrs St Paul.

--U. S. A. The Message of Justice, Peace & Love. 1979. 5.95 (ISBN 0-8198-0630-7); pap. 4.95 (ISBN 0-8198-0631-5). Dghtrs St Paul.

--Visible Signs of the Gospel. 1980. 4.00 (ISBN 0-8198-8000-0); pap. 2.95 (ISBN 0-8198-8001-9). Dghtrs St Paul.

--The Whole Truth About Man. 1981. 7.95 (ISBN 0-686-73822-5); pap. 6.95 (ISBN 0-8198-8202-X). Dghtrs St Paul.

--Witnesses of Christ. 398p. 1983. 5.50 (ISBN 0-8198-8206-2); pap. 4.25 (ISBN 0-8198-8207-0). Dghtrs St Paul.

--Words of Certitude. 266p. 1985. pap. 7.95 large print ed. (ISBN 0-8027-2477-9). Walker & Co.

--Words of Certitude: Excerpts from His Talks & Writings As Bishop & Pope. Buono, Anthon, tr. from It. LC 80-81440. 136p. 1980. pap. 3.95 (ISBN 0-8091-2302-9). Paulist Pr.

--You Are My Favorites. 1980. 6.95 (ISBN 0-8198-8701-3). Dghtrs St Paul.

--You Are the Future You Are My Hope. 1979. pap. 3.95 (ISBN 0-8198-0633-1). Dghtrs St Paul.

Pope John Paul II & Frossard, Andre. Be Not Afraid: Pope John Paul II Speaks Out on His Life, His Beliefs, & His Inspiring Vision for Humanity. LC 85-2322. 216p. 1985. pap. 7.95 (ISBN 0-385-23151-2, Im). Doubleday.

Popejoy, Bill. The Case for Divine Healing. LC 75-43155. 64p. 1976. pap. 0.95 (ISBN 0-88243-478-0, 02-0478). Gospel Pub.

Popelka, Jan, jt. auth. see Lineman, Rose.

Pope Paul II. Pope John Paul II & the Family & Text. LC 82-13308. 416p. 1983. 15.00 (ISBN 0-8199-0851-7). Franciscan Herald.

Pope Paul Sixth. On Evangelization in the Modern World. 70p. 1975. pap. 2.95 (ISBN 1-55586-129-6). US Catholic.

Pope Paul the Sixth. Devotion to the Blessed Virgin Mary. 1974. pap. 0.35 (ISBN 0-8198-0295-6). Dghtrs St Paul.

--Who Is Jesus? LC 72-80446. pap. 2.25 (ISBN 0-8198-0325-1). Dghtrs St Paul.

Pope Paul VI. Mary God's Mother & Ours. 1979. 4.75 (ISBN 0-8198-0571-8); pap. 3.50 (ISBN 0-8198-0572-6). Dghtrs St Paul.

--On Christian Joy. 1975. pap. 0.30 (ISBN 0-8198-0448-7). Dghtrs St Paul.

--On Evangelization in the Modern World. 1976. pap. text ed. 0.40 (ISBN 0-8198-0409-6). Dghtrs St Paul.

Pope Pius Eleventh. Essays in History, Written Between the Years 1896-1912. facs. ed. LC 67-26771. (Essay Index Reprint Ser.). 1934. 17.00 (ISBN 0-8369-0791-4). Ayer Co Pubs.

Pope Pius Tenth. Recipe for Holiness. 125p. 1971. 4.00 (ISBN 0-912414-04-9). Lumen Christi.

Pope Pius Twelfth. Addresses of Pius the Twelfth to Cloistered Religious. pap. 1.25 (ISBN 0-8198-0006-6). Dghtrs St Paul.

--Directives to Lay Apostles: Eighty-Six Pronouncements. Monks Of Solesmes, ed. 1964. 4.00 (ISBN 0-8198-0035-X); pap. 3.00 (ISBN 0-8198-0036-8). Dghtrs St Paul.

Pope Pius X. On the Doctrine of the Modernists. 1973. pap. 0.50 (ISBN 0-8198-0248-4). Dghtrs St Paul.

Popieluszko, Jerzy. The Way of My Cross: The Masses & Homilies of Father Jerzy Popieluszko. Wren, Michael, tr. from Polish & Fr. 200p. pap. 9.95 (ISBN 0-89526-806-X). Regnery Bks.

Popkin, Richard H. The History of Scepticism from Erasmus to Spinoza. LC 78-65469. 1979. 37.00x (ISBN 0-520-03827-4); pap. 9.50x (ISBN 0-520-03876-2, CAMPUS NO. 226). U of Cal Pr.

Popkin, Richard H. & Signer, Michael, eds. Spinoza's Earliest Publication? 100p. 1987. 17.50 (ISBN 90-232-2223-7, Pub. by Van Gorcum Holland). Longwood Pub Group.

Popkin, Richard H., ed. see Hume, David.

Popley, H. A., ed. & tr. The Sacred Kural. 2nd. ed. Orig. Title: The Tamil Veda of Tiruvalluvar. 159p. pap. 2.80 (ISBN 0-88253-386-X). Ind-US Inc.

Popoff, Irmis B. Gurdjieff Group Work with Wilhem Nyland. (Illus.). 80p. 1983. pap. 4.95 (ISBN 0-87728-580-2). Weiser.

Popoff, Peter. America's Family Crisis. Tanner, Don, ed. LC 82-82843. 80p. 1982. pap. 2.00 (ISBN 0-938544-15-2). Faith Messenger.

--Calamities, Catastrophies, & Chaos. Tanner, Don, ed. LC 80-69974. (Illus.). 108p. 1980. pap. 2.50 (ISBN 0-938544-01-2). Faith Messenger.

--Demons At Your Doorstep. Tanner, Don, ed. LC 82-82842. (Illus.). 56p. 1982. pap. 1.50 (ISBN 0-938544-13-6). Faith Messenger.

--A New Fire Is Blazing. Tanner, Don, ed. LC 80-67993. (Illus.). 194p. (Orig.). 1980. pap. 4.95 (ISBN 0-938544-02-0). Faith Messenger.

--Set Free from Satan's Slavery. Tanner, Don, ed. LC 82-83455. 64p. 1982. pap. 2.00 (ISBN 0-938544-17-9). Faith Messenger.

--Seven Delivery Systems for God's Healing Power. Tanner, Don, ed. LC 81-69730. (Illus.). 70p. 1981. pap. 1.50 (ISBN 0-938544-07-1). Faith Messenger.

--Six Things Satan Uses to Rob You of God's Abundant Blessings. Tanner, Don, ed. LC 81-86521. (Illus.). 96p. 1982. pap. 2.00 (ISBN 0-938544-11-X). Faith Messenger.

--Three Steps to Answered Prayer. Tanner, Don, ed. LC 81-70342. 92p. 1981. pap. 2.00 (ISBN 0-938544-10-1). Faith Messenger.

--Twenty-Seven Things the Church Must Go Through Before the Great Tribulation. Tanner, Don, ed. LC 81-68675. (Illus.). 50p. 1981. pap. 1.00 (ISBN 0-938544-08-X). Faith Messenger.

--Ye Shall Receive Power: The Amazing Miracle of Holy Spirit Baptism. Tanner, Don, ed. LC 82-71629. (Illus.). 96p. 1982. pap. 2.00 (ISBN 0-938544-14-4). Faith Messenger.

Popov, Haralan. Tortured for His Faith. pap. 3.95 (ISBN 0-310-31262-0, 18070P). Zondervan.

Poppel, Stephen M. Zionism in Germany 1897-1933: The Shaping of a Jewish Identity. LC 76-14284. 229p. 1977. 7.95 (ISBN 0-8276-0085-2, 395). Jewish Pubns.

Poppelbaum, Hermann. New Light on Heredity & Evolution. Macbeth, Norman, tr. 1977. pap. 6.95 (ISBN 0-916786-15-3). St George Bk Serv.

Popson, Martha. That We Might Have Life. LC 80-2080. 128p. 1981. pap. 2.95 (ISBN 0-385-17438-1, Im). Doubleday.

Porath, Jonathan D. Jews in Russia: The Last Four Centuries. 1973. pap. 3.75x (ISBN 0-8381-0220-4). United Syn Bk.

Porrath, Samuel. Life Beyond the Final Curtain. 250p. text ed. 17.95 (ISBN 0-88125-083-X). Ktav.

Portalie, Eugene. A Guide to the Thought of Saint Augustine. Bastian, Ralph J., tr. from Fr. LC 75-1182. 428p. 1975. Repr. of 1960 ed. lib. bdg. 25.50x (ISBN 0-8371-7992-0, POGS). Greenwood.

Porte, Jacques. Encyclopedie Des Musiques Sacrees, 3 vols. (Fr.). 1978. Set. 95.00 (ISBN 0-686-57145-2, M-6202). French & Eur.

Porten, Bezalel. Archives from Elephantine: The Life of an Ancient Jewish Military Colony. (Illus.). 1968. 47.50x (ISBN 0-520-01028-0). U of Cal Pr.

Porteous, A. Forest Folklore, Mythology & Romance. 1977. lib. bdg. 59.95 (ISBN 0-8490-1858-7). Gordon Pr.

Porteous, A. J., et al, eds. see Smith, Norman K.

Porteous, Norman W. Daniel, a Commentary. LC 65-21071. (Old Testament Library). 174p. 1965. 14.95 (ISBN 0-664-20663-8). Westminster.

Porter, A. Kingsley. Romanesque Sculpture of the Pilgrimage Roads, 10 Vols. in 3. LC 67-4262. (Illus.). 1986. Repr. of 1923 ed. 250.00 set (ISBN 0-87817-020-0). Hacker.

Porter, Alan. You've Really Got Me, God! (Direction Bks.). pap. 1.45 (ISBN 0-8010-7019-8). Baker Bk.

Porter, Alyene. Papa Was a Preacher. 192p. 1979. 3.50 (ISBN 0-8007-8359-X, Spire Bks). Revell.

Porter, Arthur K. Crosses & Culture of Ireland. LC 68-56480. (Illus.). 1969. Repr. of 1931 ed. 33.00 (ISBN 0-405-08860-4, Pub. by Blom). Ayer Co Pubs.

Porter, Bertha & Moss, Rosalind. Theban Temples, Vol. 2. rev ed. (Topographical Bibliography of Ancient Egyptian Hieroglyphic Texts, Reliefs & Paintings Ser.). 586p. 1972. text ed. 60.00 (ISBN 0-900416-18-1, Pub. by Aris & Phillips UK). Humanities.

--Upper Egypt Chief Temples, Six. (Topographical Bibliography of Ancient Egyptian Hieroglyphic Texts, Reliefs & Paintings Ser.: Vol. 6). 264p. 1939. text ed. 38.50 (ISBN 0-900416-30-0, Pub. by Aris & Phillips UK). Humanities.

Porter, Burton F. Deity & Morality-with Regard to the Naturalistic Fallacy. LC 68-16017. 1968. text ed. 7.95x (ISBN 0-04-100012-9). Humanities.

--The Good Life: Alternatives in Ethics. (Illus.). 1980. pap. text ed. write for info. (ISBN 0-02-396120-1). Macmillan.

Porter, Caryl. To Make All Things New. (Orig.). 1987. 9.95 (ISBN 0-8054-7324-6). Broadman.

Porter, Catherine, tr. see Todorov, Tzvetan.

Porter, David. Mother Teresa: The Early Years. 120p. (Orig.). 1986. pap. 5.95 (ISBN 0-8028-0185-4). Eerdmans.

--The Practical Christianity of Malcolm Muggeridge. LC 83-26442. 132p. 1984. pap. 4.95 (ISBN 0-87784-971-4). Inter-Varsity.

Porter, Gene S. Birds of the Bible. 1986. Repr. lib. bdg. 35.95x (ISBN 0-89966-529-2). Buccaneer Bks.

Porter, H. Boone. Keeping the Church Year. 1978. pap. 5.95 (ISBN 0-8164-2161-7, HarpR). Har-Row.

--The Song of Creation: Selections from the First Article. 120p. (Orig.). 1986. pap. 6.95 (ISBN 0-936384-34-4). Cowley Pubns.

Porter, H. C. Reformation & Reaction in Tudor Cambridge. LC 77-179573. (Illus.). xv, 462p. 1972. Repr. of 1958 ed. 35.00 (ISBN 0-208-01228-1, Archon). Shoe String.
Porter, H. C., ed. Puritanism in Tudor England. LC 75-145532. (History in Depth Ser). xvi, 312p. 1971. 17.95x (ISBN 0-87249-222-2); pap. 7.95x (ISBN 0-87249-223-0). U of SC Pr.
Porter, J. R. Leviticus. LC 75-20831. (Cambridge Bible Commentary on the New English Bible, Old Testament Ser.). (Illus.). 250p. 1976. 29.95 (ISBN 0-521-08638-8); pap. 11.95x (ISBN 0-521-09773-8). Cambridge U Pr.
Porter, J. R., jt. ed. see Durham, John I.
Porter, Jack N. Confronting History & Holocaust: Collected Essays: 1972-1982. LC 83-3572. (Illus.). 168p. (Orig.). 1983. lib. bdg. 26.00 (ISBN 0-8191-3107-5); pap. text ed. 11.25 (ISBN 0-8191-3108-3). U Pr of Amer.
--Handbook of Cults, Sects, & Self-Realization Groups. 95p. (Orig.). 1982. pap. 6.95 (ISBN 0-932270-03-4). Spencer Pr.
Porter, Jack N. & Doress, Irvin. Kids in Cults: Why They Join, Why They Stay, Why They Leave. Rev. ed. 22p. (Orig.). 1982. pap. 2.95 (ISBN 0-932270-02-6). Spencer Pr.
Porter, Jack N., ed. Jewish Partisans: A Documentary of Jewish Resistance in the Soviet Union During World War II, Vol. II. LC 81-40258. 314p. (Orig.). 1982. lib. bdg. 29.00 (ISBN 0-8191-2537-7); pap. text ed. 14.25 (ISBN 0-8191-2538-5). U Pr of Amer.
Porter, Jack N., compiled by. Jews & the Cults: Bibliography-Guide. LC 81-67448. 50p. 1981. pap. 3.50 (ISBN 0-9602036-4-8). Biblio NY.
Porter, Jack W. & Stineman, William F. The Catholic Church in Greencastle, Putnam County, Indiana 1848-1978. LC 78-65724. (Illus.). 1979. 14.95 (ISBN 0-9602352-0-5). St Paul the Apostle.
Porter, Jack W., jt. auth. see Stineman, William F.
Porter, James I., tr. see Oberman, Heiko A.
Porter, John F., ed. see Maurice, Frederick D.
Porter, Kingsley A. Construction of Lombard & Gothic Vaults. 1911. 75.00x (ISBN 0-685-69851-3). Elliots Bks.
Porter, Larry. Illustrated Stories from Church History, 16 vols. Cheesman, Paul R., ed. (Illus.). write for info (ISBN 0-911712-21-6). Promised Land.
Porter, Robert, ed. Emigrants at Worship: One Hundred & Twenty-Five Years of Chisago Lake Methodism. (Illus.). 85p. (Orig.). 1983. pap. 8.75 (ISBN 0-933565-02-X). Porter Pub Co.
Porter, Valerie. Seek Ye First the Kingdom of God. 1984. 6.75 (ISBN 0-8062-2258-1). Carlton.
Porter, Vicki, jt. auth. see Podles, Mary S.
Porterfield, Amanda. Feminine Spirituality in America: From Sarah Edwards to Martha Graham. 248p. 1980. 29.95 (ISBN 0-87722-175-8). Temple U Pr.
Porterfield, Kay M. Keeping Promises: The Challenge of the Sober Parent. 172p. (Orig.). 1984. pap. 4.95 (ISBN 0-89486-245-6). Hazelden.
Porterfield, P. & Spradlin, W. W. The Search for Certainty. 290p. 1983. pap. 28.50 (ISBN 0-387-90889-7). Springer-Verlag.
Portes Gil, Emilio. The Conflict Between the Civil Power & the Clergy: Historical & Legal Essay. 1976. lib. bdg. 59.95 (ISBN 0-87968-928-5). Gordon Pr.
Portier, William L. Isaac Hecker & the First Vatican Council, Including Hecker's Notes in Italy: 1869-1870. LC 85-3034. (Studies in American Religion: Vol. 15). 360p. 1984. 59.95x (ISBN 0-88946-653-X). E Mellen.
Portilla, Lorraine. He Brought Me Out of a Horrible Pit. DeLellis, Leatrice, ed. (Orig.). Date not set. pap. 5.00 (ISBN 0-9616892-0-X). Your New Beginning.
Portillo, Carlos E. Eternal Security Is Conditional. LC 85-52117. 150p. (Orig.). 1987. pap. write for info. (ISBN 0-937365-03-3). WCP Pubns.
--Evil Side of Good. LC 85-52117. 200p. (Orig.). Date not set. pap. price not set (ISBN 0-937365-04-1). WCP Pubns.
--His Revelation from Apocalypses. LC 85-52117. 150p. (Orig.). 1987. pap. write for info. (ISBN 0-937365-02-5). WCP Pubns.
--That Unknown Day. LC 85-52117. (Illus.). 400p. (Orig.). 1986. 14.95 (ISBN 0-937365-00-9); pap. 9.95 (ISBN 0-937365-01-7). WCP Pubns.
Portner, Balthasar. Die Agyptischen Totenstelen Als Zeugen Des Sozialen und Religiosen Lebens Ihrer Zeit. pap. 8.00 (ISBN 0-384-47040-8). Johnson Repr.
Porto, Humberto & Schlesinger, Hugo. Prayers of Blessing & Praise for All Occasions. Leipsiger, Michael, tr. from Port. Tr. of Dialogando com Deus. 128p. 1987. 9.95 (ISBN 0-89622-311-6). Twenty-Third.
Porton, Gary G. Understanding Rabbinic Midrash. 1985. 14.95 (ISBN 0-88125-056-2). Ktav.
Portwood, Doris. Commonsense Suicide: The Final Right. 142p. 1983. pap. 8.00 (ISBN 0-394-62013-5). Hemlock Soc.
Posel, Norman S., tr. see Epstein, Simon.
Poser, Hans. Philosophie und Mythos. 1979. text ed. 35.20x (ISBN 3-11-007601-2). De Gruyter.
Posey, Walter B. The Development of Methodism in the Old Southwest: 1783-1824. LC 73-18408. (Perspectives in American History Ser.: No. 19). (Illus.). 1974. Repr. of 1933 ed. lib. bdg. 22.50x (ISBN 0-87991-339-8). Porcupine Pr.
Poslusney, Venard. Attaining Spiritual Maturity for Contemplation (According to St. John of the Cross) (Orig.). 1973. pap. 1.50 (ISBN 0-914544-04-7). Living Flame Pr.
--Prayer of Love: The Art of Aspiration. 128p. (Orig.). 1975. pap. 2.95 (ISBN 0-914544-06-3). Living Flame Pr.
--Union with the Lord in Prayer: Beyond Meditation to Affective Prayer, Aspiration & Contemplation. (Illus., Orig.). 1973. pap. 1.50 (ISBN 0-914544-03-9). Living Flame Pr.
Posner, Raphael, et al, eds. Jewish Liturgy: Prayer & Synagogue Service Through the Ages. (Illus.). 1976. 25.00 (ISBN 0-8148-0596-5). L Amiel Pub.
Posner, Zalman I. Think Jewish: A Contemporary View of Judaism, a Jewish View of Today's World. LC 78-71323. 1979. 8.95 (ISBN 0-9602394-0-5); pap. 4.95 (ISBN 0-9602394-1-3). Kesher.
Pospielovsky, Dimitry. The Russian Church under the Soviet Regime. 533p. Set. 18.95 (ISBN 0-88141-033-0); Vol. I, 248 pgs. 9.95 (ISBN 0-88141-015-2); Vol. II, 285 pgs. 9.95 (ISBN 0-88141-016-0). St Vladimirs.
Poss, Sylvia. Towards Death with Dignity: Caring for Dying People. 1981. 33.75x (ISBN 0-317-05777-4, Pub. by Natl Soc Work). State Mutual Bk.
Post, Elizabeth L. Emily Post on Weddings. LC 86-12094. (Illus.). 192p. (Orig.). 1987. pap. 2.95 (ISBN 0-06-080812-8, P 812, PL). Har-Row.
Post, Jonathan F. Henry Vaughan: The Unfolding Vision. LC 82-47609. 264p. 1983. 26.50 (ISBN 0-691-06527-6). Princeton U Pr.
Post, Levi A. The Vatican Plato & Its Relations. (APA Philological Monographs). 22.50 (ISBN 0-89130-704-4, 40-00-04). Scholars Pr GA.
Post, Stephen G. Christian Love & Self-Denial: A Historical & Normative Study of Jonathan Edwards, Samuel Hopkins & American Theological Ethics. 138p. (Orig.). 1987. lib. bdg. 22.50 (ISBN 0-8191-5261-7); pap. text ed. 8.75 (ISBN 0-8191-5262-5). U Pr of Amer.
Post, W. Ellwood. Saints, Signs & Symbols. (Illus.). 96p. 1974. pap. 6.50 (ISBN 0-8192-1171-0). Morehouse.
Postal, Bernard & Koppman, Lionel. American Jewish Landmarks: A Travel Guide & History, Vol. 1. LC 76-27401. (Orig.). 1977. 25.00 (ISBN 0-8303-0151-8); pap. 15.00 (ISBN 0-8303-0152-6). Fleet.
--American Jewish Landmarks: A Travel Guide & History, the South & Southwest, Vol. II. LC 76-27401. 1979. 21.95 (ISBN 0-8303-0155-0); pap. 11.95 (ISBN 0-8303-0157-7). Fleet.
--Jewish Landmarks of New York: A Travel Guide & History. LC 76-27400. (Orig.). 1978. 15.95 (ISBN 0-8303-0153-4). Fleet.
Postan, Elizabeth, jt. ed. see Holbrook, David.
Postema, Donald H. Space for God: Leader's Guide. 120p. 1983. pap. 3.95 (ISBN 0-933140-47-9). CRC Pubns.
--Space for God, Study & Practice of Spirituality & Prayer. LC 83-15504. 180p. 1983. pap. 9.95 (ISBN 0-933140-46-0). CRC Pubns.
Posterski, Don. Why Am I Afraid to Tell You I'm a Christian? LC 83-12958. 112p. (Orig.). 1983. pap. 2.95 (ISBN 0-87784-847-5). Inter-Varsity.
Post Laurens Van, De see Van Der Post, Laurens.
Postol, Bernard, jt. auth. see Koppman, Lionel.
Pote, Lawrence. Acceptance. pap. 1.50 (ISBN 0-8010-7050-3). Baker Bk.
Poteat, Hubert M. Practical Hymnology. LC 72-1693. Repr. of 1921 ed. 14.50 (ISBN 0-404-09912-2). AMS Pr.
Potgieter, Pieter. Victory: The Work of the Spirit. 42p. 1984. pap. 1.45 (ISBN 0-85151-430-8). Banner of Truth.
Pothen, S. Divorce: Its Causes & Consequences in Hindu Society. 320p. 1986. text ed. 35.00x (ISBN 0-7069-2932-2, Pub. by Vikas India). Advent NY.
Potocki, Andrzej, tr. see Wojtyla, Cardinal Karol.
Potok, Chaim. Wanderings: Chaim Potok's History of the Jews. LC 78-54915. 1978. 29.95 (ISBN 0-394-50110-1). Knopf.
Pott, Constance M. Francis Bacon & His Secret Society. LC 71-174282. Repr. of 1891 ed. 32.50 (ISBN 0-404-05096-4). AMS Pr.
Pott, John, tr. see Hebly, J. A.
Potter, C. F. The Lost Years of Jesus Revealed. 1982. pap. 2.25 (ISBN 0-449-12468-1, GM). Fawcett.
Potter, G. R., jt. auth. see Milton, John.
Potter, G. R. & Greengrass, M., eds. John Calvin. LC 82-23088. (Documents of Modern History Ser.). 180p. 1983. 20.00x (ISBN 0-312-44277-7). St Martin.
Potter, George R., ed. see Donne, John.
Potter, Henry C. Principles of Religious Education. (Educational Ser.). 1900. Repr. 10.00 (ISBN 0-8482-5585-2). Norwood Edns.
Potter, Irving. The Cause of Anti-Jewism in the United States. 1982. lib. bdg. 59.95 (ISBN 0-87700-394-7). Revisionist Pr.
Potter, Karl H., ed. Advaita Vedanta Up to Samkara & His Pupils: Encyclopedia of Indian Philosophies, Vol. 3. LC 77-8558. 648p. 1982. 63.00x (ISBN 0-691-07182-9). Princeton U Pr.
Potter, L. J., ed. see Milton, John.
Potter, Ralph B. War & Moral Discourse. LC 69-18111. (Orig.). 1969. pap. 3.95 (ISBN 0-8042-0863-8). John Knox.
Potterbaum, Charlene. Thanks Lord, I Needed That. 1979. Repr. of 1977 ed. pocket size 2.95 (ISBN 0-88270-411-7, Pub. by Logos). Bridge Pub.
Potthast, A., tr. see Walahfrid Strabo.
Potts, Kenneth C., jt. auth. see Jones, Jeffrey D.
Potts, Thomas. Potts' Discovery of Witches in the County of Lancaster. Repr. of 1745 ed. 31.00 (ISBN 0-384-47430-6). Johnson Repr.
Potvin, Raymond H. Seminarians of the Eighties: A National Survey. 64p. 1986. 5.65 (ISBN 0-318-20579-3). Natl Cath Educ.
Poujol, F. A. Dictionnaire des Facultes Intellectuelles et Affectives de l'ame ou l'on Traite des Passions, des Vertus, des Vices, des Defauts. Migne, J. P., ed. (Encyclopedie Theologique Ser.: Vol. 39). (Fr.). 560p. Repr. of 1849 ed. lib. bdg. 72.00x (ISBN 0-89241-245-3). Caratzas.
Poulain, Jacques. Logique & Religion: L'Atomisme Logique de L. Wittgenstein & la Possibilite des Propositions Religieuses. (Religion & Reason: No. 7). 1974. 18.40x (ISBN 90-2797-284-2). Mouton.
Poulos, George. Footsteps in the Sea: A Biography of Archbishop Athenagoras Cavadas. (Illus.). 186p. 1979. 7.95 (ISBN 0-916586-36-7); pap. 10.95 (ISBN 0-916586-35-9). Holy Cross Orthodox.
Poulos, Nellie. Life's Story & Healings. 160p. pap. 1.50 (ISBN 0-686-29128-X). Faith Pub Hse.
Poultney, James W. The Bronze Tables of Iguvium. (APA Philological Monographs). 37.50 (ISBN 0-89130-745-1, 40-00-18). Scholars Pr GA.
Pounders, Margaret. Laws of Love. LC 79-64898. 1979. 5.95 (ISBN 0-87159-083-2). Unity School.
Pountney, Michael. Getting a Job. LC 84-9039. 160p. (Orig.). 1984. pap. 4.95 (ISBN 0-87784-935-8). Inter-Varsity.
Pourade, Richard F., ed. see Nolan, James L.
Poussard, Wendy, jt. auth. see Eastman, Moira.
Pousset, Edouard. Life in Faith & Freedom: An Essay Presenting Gaston Fessard's Analysis of the Dialectic of the Spiritual Exercises of St. Ignatius. Ganss, G. E., frwd. by. LC 79-84200. (Modern Scholarly Studies About Jesuits, in English Translation Ser.: No. 4). 286p. 1980. 9.00 (ISBN 0-912422-41-6); pap. 8.00 smythsewn (ISBN 0-912422-40-8); pap. 7.00 (ISBN 0-912422-39-4). Inst Jesuit.
Poussin, J. C. & Garnier, J. C. Dictionnaire de la Tradition Pontificale, Patristique et Conciliaire, 2 vols. Migne, J. P., ed. (Troisieme et Derniere Encyclopedie Theologique Ser.: Vol. 12-13). (Fr.). 1464p. Repr. of 1855 ed. lib. bdg. 186.00x (ISBN 0-89241-296-8). Caratzas.
Pouwels, Randall L. Horn & Crescent: Cultural Change & Traditional Islam on the East African Coast, 800-1900. (African Studies Ser.: No. 53). (Illus.). 288p. Date not set. price not set (ISBN 0-521-32308-8). Cambridge U Pr.
Powell. Etheric Double. 12.50 (ISBN 0-8356-5068-5). Theos Pub Hse.
--Stand Tough. 1983. 3.95 (ISBN 0-88207-592-6). Victor Bks.
Powell, A. E. Causal Body. 1972. 18.95 (ISBN 0-8356-5034-0); pap. 11.75 (ISBN 0-8356-5302-1). Theos Pub Hse.
--Mental Body. 1975. 11.95 (ISBN 0-8356-5504-0). Theos Pub Hse.
Powell, Adam C., Sr. Against the Tide: An Autobiography. Gaustad, Edwin S., ed. LC 79-52603. (The Baptist Tradition Ser.). 1980. Repr. of 1938 ed. 27.50x (ISBN 0-405-12468-6). Ayer Co Pubs.
Powell, Adriana, tr. see Decker, Ed & Hunt, Dave.
Powell, Arthur E. Etheric Double. (Illus.). 1969. pap. 3.95 (ISBN 0-8356-0075-0, Quest). Theos Pub Hse.
Powell, B. Athenian Mythology: Erichthonius & the Three Daughters of Cecrops. (Illus.). 90p. 1976. 15.00 (ISBN 0-89005-121-6). Ares.
Powell, Carol & Powell, David. How to Bring Up Children in the Catholic Faith. 240p. 1984. 12.95 (ISBN 0-13-402537-7). P-H.
Powell, David, jt. auth. see Powell, Carol.
Powell, David, tr. see Schaeffer, Edith.
Powell, David, tr. see Sisson, Richard, et al.
Powell, David E. Antireligious Propaganda in the Soviet Union: A Study of Mass Persuasion. LC 74-34127. 206p. 1975. pap. 8.95x (ISBN 0-262-66042-3). MIT Pr.
Powell, Edgar & Trevelyan, G. M., eds. The Peasants' Rising & the Lollards. LC 78-63202. (Heresies of the Early Christian & Medieval Era: Second Ser.). Repr. of 1899 ed. 24.00 (ISBN 0-404-16238-X). AMS Pr.
Powell, Elsie R. Romanenghi de see Fletcher, William M.
Powell, F. J., jt. auth. see Innes, A. T.
Powell, Gabriel. The Catholikes Supplication Unto the King's Majestie, for Toleration of Catholike Religion in England. LC 76-57406. (English Experience Ser.: No. 822). 1977. lib. bdg. 6.00 (ISBN 90-221-0822-8). Walter J Johnson.
Powell, Ivor. The Amazing Acts. 1987. 18.95 (ISBN 0-8254-3526-9). Kregel.
--Bible Highways. LC 85-8097. 192p. 1985. pap. 5.95 (ISBN 0-8254-3521-8). Kregel.
--Bible Treasures. LC 84-25090. 192p. (Orig.). 1985. pap. 5.95 (ISBN 0-8254-3518-8). Kregel.
--Bible Windows. LC 85-8103. 188p. 1985. pap. 5.95 (ISBN 0-8254-3522-6). Kregel.
--John's Wonderful Gospel. LC 83-16192. 448p. 1983. 16.95 (ISBN 0-8254-3514-5). Kregel.
--Luke's Thrilling Gospel. LC 84-9637. 508p. 1984. 18.95 (ISBN 0-8254-3513-7). Kregel.
--Matthew's Majestic Gospel. LC 86-10401. 528p. 1986. 18.95 (ISBN 0-8254-3525-0). Kregel.
Powell, Ivor C. Bible Gems. LC 86-27525. 172p. (Orig.). 1987. pap. 5.95 (ISBN 0-8254-3527-7). Kregel.
--Mark's Superb Gospel. LC 85-25615. 432p. 1986. 16.95 (ISBN 0-8254-3523-4). Kregel.
--What in the World Will Happen Next? LC 85-7579. 176p. (Orig.). 1985. pap. 5.95 (ISBN 0-8254-3524-2). Kregel.
Powell, James M. Anatomy of a Crusade, Twelve Thirteen to Twelve Twenty-One. (Middle Ages Ser.). (Illus.). 336p. 1986. text ed. 34.95x (ISBN 0-8122-8025-3). U of Pa Pr.
Powell, James N. Mandalas: The Dynamics of Vedic Symbolism. Ghai, S. K., ed. 127p. 1980. 9.95 (ISBN 0-914794-36-1). Wisdom Garden.
--The Tao of Symbols. 1982. 11.50 (ISBN 0-688-01351-1). Morrow.
Powell, John. Fully Human, Fully Alive. LC 76-41586. 1976. pap. 3.95 (ISBN 0-913592-77-3). Argus Comm.
--He Touched Me: My Pilgrimage of Prayer. 1974. pap. 2.75 (ISBN 0-913592-47-1). Argus Comm.
--A Reason to Live, a Reason to Die. rev. ed. LC 75-24848. (Illus.). 208p. 1972. pap. 3.95 (ISBN 0-913592-61-7). Argus Comm.
--The Secret of Staying in Love. LC 74-84712. (Illus.). 1974. pap. 3.95 (ISBN 0-913592-29-3). Argus Comm.
--Why Am I Afraid to Love? rev. ed. (Illus.). 120p. 1972. pap. 3.50 (ISBN 0-913592-03-X). Argus Comm.
--Why Am I Afraid to Tell You Who I Am? LC 70-113274. (Illus.). 168p. 1969. pap. 2.95 (ISBN 0-913592-02-1). Argus Comm.
Powell, John S. The Christian Vision: The Truth That Sets Us Free. LC 83-73231. (Illus.). 155p. 1984. pap. 5.95. Argus Comm.
Powell, Jouett L. Three Uses of Christian Discourse in John Henry Newman. LC 75-29423. (American Academy of Religion. Dissertation Ser.). 1975. pap. 9.95 (ISBN 0-89130-042-2, 010110). Scholars Pr GA.
Powell, Larry. I Hear the Rolling Thunder. 1986. 9.25 (ISBN 0-89536-803-X, 6821). CSS of Ohio.
--On His Way. 1984. 5.00 (ISBN 0-89536-681-9, 4857). CSS of Ohio.
Powell, Larry D. Christianity Is a Verb. 1984. 5.95 (ISBN 0-89536-650-9, 0392). CSS of Ohio.
Powell, Margaret J., ed. Bible, N. T. Epistles of Paul: The Pauline Epistles Contained in Ms. (EETS, ES Ser.: No. 116). Repr. of 1916 ed. 35.00 (ISBN 0-527-00320-4). Kraus Repr.
Powell, Paul. When the Hurt Won't Go Away. 144p. 1986. pap. 4.95 (ISBN 0-89693-365-2). Victor Bks.
--Wherever He Leads I'll Go: The Story of B. B. McKinney. 50p. (Orig.). 1974. pap. 2.00 (ISBN 0-914520-04-0). Insight Pr.
Powell, Paul W. Beyond Conversion. LC 77-80942. 1978. pap. 3.95 (ISBN 0-8054-5260-5). Broadman.
--The Complete Disciple. 120p. 1982. pap. 4.95 (ISBN 0-88207-307-9). Victor Bks.
--Dynamic Discipleship. LC 84-11388. 1984. pap. 5.95 (ISBN 0-8054-5004-1). Broadman.
--Go-Givers in a Go-Getter World. 1986. pap. 5.95 (ISBN 0-8054-2546-2). Broadman.
--How to Make Your Church Hum. LC 76-47791. 1977. pap. 3.95 (ISBN 0-8054-2528-4). Broadman.

--I Like Being a Christian. LC 82-73370. (Orig.). 1982. pap. 5.50 (ISBN 0-8054-5212-5). Broadman.

--Jesus Is for Now! LC 85-4115. 1985. pap. 3.75 (ISBN 0-8054-5006-8). Broadman.

--The Nuts & Bolts of Church Growth. LC 81-68926. 1982. pap. 5.95 (ISBN 0-8054-2542-X). Broadman.

--The Saint Peter Principle. LC 81-67372. 1982. 5.50 (ISBN 0-8054-5299-0). Broadman.

--Why Me, Lord? 120p. 1981. pap. 4.95 (ISBN 0-89693-007-6). Victor Bks.

Powell, Raphael P. No Black-White Church. 1984. 7.50 (ISBN 0-8062-2295-6). Carlton.

Powell, Robert. Depopulation Arranged, Convicted & Condemned by the Lawes of God & Man. LC 76-57407. (English Experience Ser.: No. 823). 1977. Repr. of 1636 ed. lib. bdg. 16.00 (ISBN 90-221-0823-6). Walter J Johnson.

--The Great Awakening. Nicholson, Shirley, ed. LC 83-70688. Orig. Title: Zen & Reality. 179p. 1983. pap. 6.50 (ISBN 0-8356-0577-9, Quest). Theos Pub Hse.

Powell, Robert, compiled by see Nisargadatta Maharaj.

Powell, Ruth. Walking with a Hero: Children's Bible Studies for Children's Church. 96p. (Orig.). 1982. pap. 7.95 (ISBN 0-87239-593-6, 3375). Standard Pub.

Powell, Terry. Heroes & Zeroes. 144p. 1987. pap. 3.95 (ISBN 0-89693-570-1). Victor Bks.

--Nobody's Perfect. LC 78-65556. 116p. 1979. pap. 3.95 (ISBN 0-88207-577-2). Victor Bks.

--Welcome to the Church. (Lay Action Ministry Program Ser.). 96p. 1987. pap. 4.95 (ISBN 0-89191-514-1). Cook.

--Welcome to Your Ministry. (Lay Action Ministry Program Ser.). 96p. 1987. pap. 4.95 (ISBN 0-89191-515-X). Cook.

--You Want Me to Know What? 2nd ed. (Foundation Ser.). (Illus.). 142p. (Orig.). 1986. pap. 2.95 (ISBN 0-935797-04-1). Harvest IL.

Powell, Timothy M. You've Gotta Hand It to God! LC 84-73557. 128p. 1985. 2.95 (ISBN 0-88243-859-X, 02-0859); tchr's. ed. 3.95 (ISBN 0-88243-199-4, 32-0199). Gospel Pub.

Powell, Walter. The Intimate Notebook of a Recent Convert to Catholicism: The Confessions of an Anguished Soul. (Illus.). 1977. 41.45 (ISBN 0-89266-079-1). Am Classical Coll Pr.

Powell, Walter W., ed. see Simmel, Georg.

Powell, William F. The Record of Tung Shan. LC 86-4305. (Classics in East Asian Buddism: No. 1). 112p. 1986. pap. text ed. 8.50x (ISBN 0-8248-1070-8). UH Pr.

Powellson, Jack. Holistic Economics & Social Protest. 1983. pap. 2.50x (ISBN 0-87574-250-5, 250). Pendle Hill.

Power. Heritage Series. 1976. pap. 8.00 (ISBN 0-8298-0313-0). Pilgrim NY.

Power, David & Collins, Mary, eds. Blessing & Power, Vol. 178. (Concilium Ser.). 128p. pap. 6.95 (ISBN 0-567-30058-7, Pub. by T & T Clark Ltd UK). Fortress.

Power, David, jt. ed. see Collins, Mary.

Power, David, jt. ed. see Maldonado, Luis.

Power, David N. Gifts That Differ: Lay Ministries Established & Unestablished. (Studies in the Reformed Rites of the Catholic Church: Vol. 8). (Orig.). 1980. pap. 9.95 (ISBN 0-916134-43-1). Pueblo Pub Co.

--The Sacrifice We Offer: Tridentine Dogma & Its Reinterpretation. 240p. 1987. 16.95 (ISBN 0-8245-0743-6). Crossroad NY.

--Unsearchable Riches. 160p. (Orig.). 1984. pap. 9.95 (ISBN 0-916134-62-8). Pueblo Pub Co.

Power, M. Susan. Before the Convention: Religion & the Founders. LC 84-12004. 268p. (Orig.). 1984. lib. bdg. 26.25 (ISBN 0-8191-4133-X); pap. text ed. 13.25 (ISBN 0-8191-4134-8). U Pr of Amer.

Power, Michael. Religion in the Reich. LC 78-63706. (Studies in Fascism: Ideology & Practice). 1979. Repr. of 1939 ed. 28.00 (ISBN 0-404-16976-7). AMS Pr.

Power, P. B. A Book of Comfort. 1974. pap. 2.95 (ISBN 0-85151-203-8). Banner of Truth.

--The I Wills of Christ. 382p. 1984. pap. 5.95 (ISBN 0-85151-429-4). Banner of Truth.

--The I Wills of the Psalms. 395p. 1985. pap. 5.95 (ISBN 0-85151-445-6). Banner of Truth.

Powers, B. Ward. Learn to Read the Greek New Testament. 300p. 1982. 21.00 (ISBN 0-85364-291-5); pap. text ed. 13.95 cancelled (ISBN 0-85364-292-3). Attic Pr.

Powers, Betty & Mall, E. Jane. Church Office Handbook for Ministers. 80p. 1983. pap. 3.95 (ISBN 0-8170-1011-4). Judson.

Powers, Bruce P. Christian Leadership. LC 78-72841. 1979. 8.50 (ISBN 0-8054-3227-2). Broadman.

--Church Administration Handbook. LC 84-29249. 1985. pap. 9.95 (ISBN 0-8054-3112-8). Broadman.

--Growing Faith. LC 81-66990. 1982. pap. 5.50 (ISBN 0-8054-3230-2). Broadman.

Powers, Bruce P., ed. Christian Education Handbook. LC 80-69522. 1981. pap. 9.95 (ISBN 0-8054-3229-9). Broadman.

Powers, Darden. Blessings from Jehovah-Rophe: The Lord Doth Heal. LC 83-90951. 173p. 1984. 11.95 (ISBN 0-533-05957-7). Vantage.

Powers, David S. Studies in Qur'an & Hadith: The Formation of the Islamic Law of Inheritance. 1986. text ed. 30.00x (ISBN 0-520-05558-6). U of Cal Pr.

Powers, Edward, jt. auth. see O'Day, Rey.

Powers, Edward A. In Essentials, Unity: An Ecumenical Sampler. (Orig.). 1982. pap. 4.95 (ISBN 0-377-00117-1). Friend Pr.

Powers, Elvin M. Building a Caring-Sharing Community of Believers. 128p. 1983. pap. 3.95 (ISBN 0-8341-0822-4). Beacon Hill.

Powers, Isaias. Letters from an Understanding Friend: Jesus on the Way to Jerusalem. 112p. (Orig.). 1985. pap. 4.95 (ISBN 0-89622-215-2). Twenty-Third.

--Quiet Places with Jesus. LC 78-64452. 128p. 1978. pap. 4.95 (ISBN 0-89622-086-9). Twenty-Third.

--Quiet Places with Mary. 160p. (Orig.). 1986. pap. 4.95 (ISBN 0-89622-297-7). Twenty-THird.

Powers, John. Coping with a Gentle God. 1984. pap. 6.95 (ISBN 0-89453-443-2). M Glazier.

Powers, Mala. Follow the Year: A Family Celebration of Christian Holidays. LC 85-42791. (Illus.). 128p. 1985. 14.45 (ISBN 0-06-066693-5, HarpR). Har-Row.

Powers, Susan. The Inspirational Series, 12 bks. (Illus.). 1980. 2.95 ea. (Mayflower Bks). Smith Pubs.

Powers, Thomas E. Invitation to a Great Experiment. 3rd ed. LC 74-16887. Orig. Title: First Questions on the Life of the Spirit. (Illus.). 238p. 1986. pap. 8.95 (ISBN 0-914896-33-4). East Ridge Pr.

Powers, Ward. Learn to Read the Greek New Testament. 336p. 1982. 19.95 (ISBN 0-8028-3578-3). Eerdmans.

Powers, William. Sacred Language: The Nature of Supernatural Discourse in Lakota. LC 86-40079. (Civilization of the American Indians Ser.: Vol. 179). (Illus.). 320p. 1986. 24.95x (ISBN 0-8061-2009-6). U of Okla Pr.

Powers, William K. Oglala Religion. LC 76-30614. (Illus.). xxii, 237p. 1977. pap. 6.95 (ISBN 0-8032-8706-2, BB 802, Bison). U of Nebr Pr.

Powicke, Frederick J. The Cambridge Platonists. LC 79-151196. (Illus.). x, 219p. 1971. Repr. of 1926 ed. 23.00 (ISBN 0-208-01088-2, Archon). Shoe String.

--Cambridge Platonists, a Study. Repr. of 1926 ed. lib. bdg. 22.50x (ISBN 0-8371-3999-6, POPL). Greenwood.

Powicke, Frederick M. The Christian Life in the Middle Ages & Other Essays. LC 78-6723. (Illus.). vi, 176p. Repr. of 1935 ed. lib. bdg. 22.50x (ISBN 0-8371-9304-4, POCL). Greenwood.

--Ways of Medieval Life & Thought. LC 64-13394. (Illus.). 1949. 12.00 (ISBN 0-8196-0137-3). Biblo.

Powles, Cyril & Nelson, Rob. Mission Impossible-Unless... (Orig.). 1973. pap. 2.95 (ISBN 0-377-03009-0). Friend Pr.

Powlison, Paul S. Yagua Mythology: Epic Tendencies in a New World Mythology. Merrifield, William R., ed. LC 84-63152. (International Museum of Cultures Publications: No. 16). (Illus.). 132p. (Orig.). 1985. pap. 14.00 (ISBN 0-88312-172-7); microfiche (2) 4.00 (ISBN 0-88312-254-5). Summer Inst Ling.

Powys, Llewelyn. The Pathetic Fallacy. LC 77-828. 1977. Repr. of 1930 ed. lib. bdg. 25.00 (ISBN 0-8414-6797-8). Folcroft.

--Rats in the Sacristy. facs. ed. LC 67-30226. (Essay Index Reprint Ser). 1937. 17.00 (ISBN 0-8369-0798-1). Ayer Co Pubs.

Poyner, Alice. From the Campus to the World. LC 86-3024. 150p. (Orig.). 1986. pap. 6.95 (ISBN 0-87784-947-1). Inter-Varsity.

Pozdneyev, Aleksei M. Religion & Ritual in Society: Lamaist Buddhism in Late 19th-Century Mongolia. Krueger, John R., ed. Raun, Alo & Raun, Linda, trs. from Rus. (Occasional Papers Ser.: No. 10). Orig. Title: Ocherki Byta Buddiiskikh Monastyrei. pap. 15.00x (ISBN 0-910980-50-0). Mongolia.

Poziemski, Christine L., jt. auth. see Gustafson, J. Louise.

Pozo, Candido. Mary & Scripture. Date not set. price not set (ISBN 0-8199-0906-8). Franciscan Herald.

Prabhavananda, Swami. Bhagavatam, Srimad: The Wisdom of God. 1978. Repr. of 1943 ed. 5.95 (ISBN 0-87481-483-9). Vedanta Pr.

--Bhagavatam, Srimad: The Wisdom of God. 1979. pap. 5.95 (ISBN 0-87481-490-1). Vedanta Pr.

--Eternal Companion: Brahmananda, His Life & Teachings. 3rd ed. LC 72-113256. 1960. pap. 7.95 (ISBN 0-87481-024-8). Vedanta Pr.

--Religion in Practice. 6.95 (ISBN 0-87481-016-7). Vedanta Pr.

--The Sermon on the Mount According to Vedanta. 1972. pap. 3.95 (ISBN 0-451-62509-9, ME2338, Ment). NAL.

--Sermon on the Mount According to Vedanta. LC 64-8660. 6.95 (ISBN 0-87481-002-7). Vedanta Pr.

--Spiritual Heritage of India. LC 63-10517. 1979. pap. 8.95 (ISBN 0-87481-035-3). Vedanta Pr.

--Vedic Religion & Philosophy. 3.95 (ISBN 0-87481-411-1). Vedanta Pr.

--Yoga & Mysticism: An Introduction to Vedanta. 53p. 1984. pap. 3.95 (ISBN 0-87481-020-5). Vedanta Pr.

Prabhavananda, Swami & Isherwood, Christopher. How to Know God: The Yoga Aphorisms of Patanjali. 1969. pap. 2.95 (ISBN 0-451-62330-4, ME2330, Ment). NAL.

Prabhavananda, Swami, tr. Memories of a Loving Soul. (Orig.). 1968. pap. 4.95 (ISBN 0-87481-015-9). Vedanta Pr.

Prabhavananda, Swami & Isherwood, Christopher, trs. from Sanskrit. How to Know God: The Yoga Aphorisms of Patanjali. 224p. 1983. pap. 6.95 (ISBN 0-87481-041-8). Vedanta Pr.

Prabhavananda, Swami & Manchester, Frederick, trs. Upanishads: Breath of the Eternal. LC 48-5935. pap. 6.95 (ISBN 0-87481-040-X). Vedanta Pr.

Prabhavananda, Swami, tr. see Bhagavad-Gita.

Prabhavananda, Swami, tr. see Narada.

Prabhu, Krishna, ed. see Bhagwan Shree Rajneesh.

Prabhu, R. K., ed. see Gandhi, M. K. & Tagore, Rabindranath.

Prabhu, Swami Krishna, ed. see Bhagwan Shree Rajneesh.

Prabhu, Swami Krishna, ed. see Rajneesh, Bhagwan Shree.

Pradera, Victor. The New State. Malley, B., tr. LC 79-180421. Repr. of 1939 ed. 29.50 (ISBN 0-404-56196-9). AMS Pr.

Pradhan, Ayoda P. The Buddha's System of Meditation: Phase (I-VIII, 4 vols. 1986. text ed. 150.00x (ISBN 81-207-0140-2, Pub. by Sterling Pubs India). Apt Bks.

Prado, Carlos G. Illusions of Faith: A Critique of Non-Credal Religion. (Orig.). 1980. pap. text ed. 9.95 (ISBN 0-8403-2176-7). Kendall-Hunt.

Pradt, Mary A., jt. auth. see Slavin, Stephen L.

Praeder, Susan M. Miracle Stories in Christian Antiquity. LC 86-45909. 288p. 1987. pap. 22.95 (ISBN 0-8006-2115-8, 1-2115). Fortress.

Praem, O., jt. auth. see McBride, Alfred.

Praetz, Helen. Building a School System. 178p. 1980. 28.00x (ISBN 0-522-84213-5, Pub. by Melbourne U Pr Australia). Intl Spec Bk.

Pragai, Michael J. Faith & Fulfillment: Christians & the Return to the Promised Land. (Illus.). 326p. 1985. 24.00x (ISBN 0-85303-210-6, Vallentine Mitchell England); pap. 12.50x (ISBN 0-85303-211-4). Biblio Dist.

Prager, Dennis & Telushkin, Joseph. Nine Questions People Ask About Judaism. 1981. 14.95 (ISBN 0-671-42593-5). S&S.

--The Nine Questions People Ask about Judaism. 1986. pap. 7.95 (ISBN 0-671-62261-7, Touchstone Bks). S&S.

--Why the Jews? The Reason for Anti-Semitism. 224p. 1983. 14.95 (ISBN 0-671-45270-3). S&S.

Prager, Moshe. Rabbi Yisroel Baal Shem Tov. (Hebrew., Illus.). 1.75 (ISBN 0-914131-51-6, D50). Torah Umesorah.

Pragman, James H. Traditions of Ministry. LC 12-2982. (Continued Applied Christianity Ser.). 1983. pap. 15.95 (ISBN 0-570-03900-2, 12-2982). Concordia.

Prahlow, Lois, jt. auth. see Rathert, Donna.

Prainatis. The Talmud Unmasked. 1979. lib. bdg. 59.95 (ISBN 0-8490-3010-2). Gordon Pr.

Prajnanananda. Christ the Savior & Christ Myth. rev. ed. 7.95 (ISBN 0-87481-652-1, Pub. by Ramakrishna Math Madras India). Vedanta Pr.

Prajnanananda, Swami. Christ the Savior & Christ Myth. rev. ed. 7.59. Vedanta Pr.

Prajnananda, Swami. The Philosophical Ideas of Swami Abhenananda: A Critical Study (A Guide to the Complete Works of Swami Abhedananda) (Illus.). 7.95 (ISBN 0-87481-623-8). Vedanta Pr.

Prakash, Swami S. & Vidyalankar, Pandit S. Rigveda Samhita, 10 vols. (Eng.). vol. 17.00 ea. (Pub. by S Chand India). State Mutual Bk.

Praktikos. Evagrius Ponticus. Bamberger, John E., tr. from Gr. & Syriac. LC 76-152483. (Cistercian Studies: No. 4). xciv, 88p. 1970. pap. 4.00 (ISBN 0-87907-804-9). Cistercian Pubns.

Prange, Erwin C. A Time for Intercession. LC 76-20085. 176p. 1979. pap. 3.95 (ISBN 0-87123-561-7, 210561). Bethany Hse.

Prange, Erwin E. The Gift Is Already Yours. LC 79-55545. 1980. pap. 2.95 (ISBN 0-87123-189-1, 200189). Bethany Hse.

Prange, Victor H. Why So Many Churches. 1985. pap. 2.95 (ISBN 0-8100-0188-8, 15N0413). Northwest Pub.

Prasad, R. C. Lifting the Veil (Kundalini Yoga) A Compendium of Rajneesh's Essential Teachings. 1975. pap. 6.50 (ISBN 0-89684-244-4). Orient Bk Dist.

Prasad, Ram Chandra. Rajneesh: The Mystic of Feeling. 2nrev. ed. 1978. 10.95 (ISBN 0-89684-023-9, Pub. by Motilal Banarsidass India). Orient Bk Dist.

Prasad, Yuvaraj D. The Indian Muslims & World War I. 1985. 20.00x (ISBN 0-8364-1489-6, Pub. by Nanaki Prakashan). South Asia Bks.

Prasada, Ajit, ed. & tr. see Amritachandra.

Prasada, Rama, tr. see Patanjali.

Prasch, Billy. Alcoholism Recovery. 60p. 1984. pap. 2.00 (ISBN 0-8198-0725-7). Dghtrs St Paul.

Prater, Arnold. Learning to Pray. 144p. (Orig.). 1986. pap. 6.50 (ISBN 0-687-21330-4). Abingdon.

Prather, Hugh. A Book of Games: A Course in Spiritual Play. LC 80-2840. (Illus.). 192p. 1981. pap. 6.95 (ISBN 0-385-14779-1, Dolp). Doubleday.

--There Is a Place Where You Are Not Alone. LC 80-912. 224p. 1980. pap. 6.95 (ISBN 0-385-14778-3, Dolp). Doubleday.

Pratima, Ma Yoga, ed. see Rajneesh, Bhagwan Shree.

Pratney, Winkey. El Joven y Su Dios. (El Joven y Sus Inquietudes Ser.). 1982. 2.95 (ISBN 0-88113-163-6). Edit Betania.

--El Joven y Su Mundo. (El Joven y Sus Inquietudes). 1982. 2.50 (ISBN 0-88113-164-4). Edit Betania.

--El Joven y Sus Amigos. (El Joven y Sus Inquietudes Ser). 1982. 2.25 (ISBN 0-88113-162-8). Edit Betania.

--El Joven y Sus Dilemas. (El Joven y Sus Inquietudes). 1982. 2.50 (ISBN 0-88113-165-2). Edit Betania.

--Youth Aflame. 448p. (Orig.). 1983. pap. 7.95 (ISBN 0-87123-659-1, 210659). Bethany Hse.

Pratney, Winkie. Devil Take the Youngest. Keith, Bill, ed. 300p. (Orig.). 1985. pap. 6.95 (ISBN 0-910311-29-3). Huntington Hse Inc.

--Doorways to Discipleship. LC 77-80008. 272p. 1977. pap. 5.95 (ISBN 0-87123-106-9, 210106). Bethany Hse.

--A Handbook for Followers of Jesus. LC 76-44385. 336p. 1976. pap. 6.95 (ISBN 0-87123-378-9, 210378). Bethany Hse.

--Revival: Principles to Change the World. 320p. (Orig.). 1983. pap. 3.95 (ISBN 0-88368-124-2). Whitaker Hse.

Pratt, Sr. Antoinette M. The Attitude of the Catholic Church Toward Witchcraft & the Allied Practices of Sorcery & Magic. LC 79-8116. 144p. Repr. of 1945 ed. 22.50 (ISBN 0-404-18429-4). AMS Pr.

Pratt, David H. English Quakers & the First Industrial Revolution: A Study of the Quaker Community in Four Industrial Counties; York, Warwick, & Gloucester, 1750-1830. LC 84-46009. (British Economic History Ser.). 236p. 1985. lib. bdg. 28.00 (ISBN 0-8240-6689-8). Garland Pub.

Pratt, Henry J. Liberalization of American Protestantism: A Case Study in Complex Organizations. LC 74-38837. 345p. 1972. 24.95 (ISBN 0-8143-1475-9). Wayne St U Pr.

Pratt, James B. Adventures in Philosophy & Religion. LC 75-3323. Repr. of 1931 ed. 16.00 (ISBN 0-404-59319-4). AMS Pr.

--The Pilgrimage of Buddhism & a Buddhist Pilgrimage. LC 75-3325. (Philosophy of America Ser.). Repr. of 1928 ed. 57.50 (ISBN 0-404-59320-8). AMS Pr.

--The Pilgrimage of Buddhism & a Buddhist Pilgrimage. 758p. 1982. Repr. of 1928 ed. lib. bdg. 45.00 (ISBN 0-89984-828-1). Century Bookbindery.

--The Psychology of Religious Belief. LC 75-3326. (Philosophy of America Ser.). Repr. of 1907 ed. 34.00 (ISBN 0-404-59321-6). AMS Pr.

--The Religious Consciousness: A Psychological Study. 1971. Repr. of 1920 ed. 21.95x (ISBN 0-02-850350-3). Hafner.

Pratt, Josiah, ed. Thought of the Evangelical Leaders: John Newton, Thomas Scott, Charles Simeon, Etc. 1978. 18.95 (ISBN 0-85151-270-4). Banner of Truth.

Pratt, Leonard, tr. see Shen Fu.

Pratt, Louis. Sing Praises to His Name. Sherer, Michael L., ed. (Orig.). 1986. pap. 6.75 (ISBN 0-89536-831-5, 6845). CSS of Ohio.

--Worship the Lord. 1983. 4.35 (ISBN 0-89536-580-4, 2332). CSS of Ohio.

Pratt, Orson, ed. see Smith, Joseph.

Pratt, Parley P. Autobiography of Parley P. Pratt. Pratt, Parley P., Jr., pref. by. LC 85-10264. (Classics in Mormon Literature Ser.). (Illus.). 475p. 1985. 14.95 (ISBN 0-87747-740-X). Deseret Bk.

Pratt, Waldo S. Music of the French Psalter of 1562. LC 40-4909. Repr. of 1939 ed. 15.00 (ISBN 0-404-05119-7). AMS Pr.

--The Music of the Pilgrims: A Description of the Psalm-Book Brought to Plymouth in Sixteen Twenty. 1980. lib. bdg. 59.00 (ISBN 0-8490-3180-X). Gordon Pr.

--Musical Ministries in the Church. LC 74-24193. Repr. of 1923 ed. 18.75 (ISBN 0-404-13095-X). AMS Pr.

Pratt, Yvonne K. Especially for the Single Woman. 1980. pap. 2.25 (ISBN 0-87148-295-9). Pathway Pr.

Pratto, David J., jt. auth. see Rallings, E. M.

Prawer, Joshua. Crusader Institutions. (Illus.). 1980. 89.00x (ISBN 0-19-822536-9). Oxford U Pr.

Prawer, S. S. Heine's Jewish Comedy: A Study of His Portraits of Jews & Judaism. 846p. 1986. pap. 19.95x (ISBN 0-19-815834-3). Oxford U Pr.

Prebish, Charles S. Buddhist Monastic Discipline: The Sanskrit Pratimoksa Sutras of the Mahasamghikas & Mulasarvastivadins. LC 74-10743. (Institute for Advanced Study of World Religions Ser.). 1975. 22.50x (ISBN 0-271-01171-8). Pa St U Pr.

Prebish, Charles S., ed. Buddhism: A Modern Perspective. LC 74-300085. 346p. 1975. 24.95x (ISBN 0-271-01185-8); pap. 14.95x (ISBN 0-271-01195-5). Pa St U Pr.

Predmore, Helen R. Chester, N.Y. Presbyterian Church: A History. LC 73-89297. (Illus.). 377p. 1975. 9.45 (ISBN 0-912526-11-4). Lib Res.

Pree, Gladis de see De Pree, Gordon & De Pree, Gladis.

Pree, Gordon De see De Pree, Gordon & De Pree, Gladis.

Preedy, George R. The Life of John Knox. 1940. Repr. 35.00 (ISBN 0-8274-2933-9). R West.

Preger, Theodorus, ed. Scriptores Originum Constantino-Politanarum. LC 75-7335. (Roman History Ser.). (Gr.). 1975. Repr. 32.00x (ISBN 0-405-07054-3). Ayer Co Pubs.

Preibisch, P. Two Studies on the Roman Pontifices. LC 75-10647. (Ancient Religion & Mythology Ser.). 1976. 12.00x (ISBN 0-405-07271-6). Ayer Co Pubs.

Preiss, Theo. Life in Christ. LC 55-1608. (Studies in Biblical Theology: No. 13). 1954. pap. 10.00x (ISBN 0-8401-3013-9). A R Allenson.

Preister, Steven & Young, James J. Catholic Remarriage: Pastoral Issues & Preparation Models. 224p. (Orig.). 1986. pap. 12.95 (ISBN 0-8091-2808-X). Paulist Pr.

Preister, Steven, ed. see Schervish, Paul, et al.

Prelinger, Catherine M. Charity, Challenge, & Change: Religious Dimensions of the Mid-Nineteenth Century Women's Movement in Germany. LC 86-19432. (Contributions in Women's Studies Ser.: No. 75). 225p. 1987. lib. bdg. 29.95 (ISBN 0-313-25401-X, PCY). Greenwood.

Preller, Ludwig. Griechische Mythology. Bolle, Kees W., ed. LC 77-79153. (Mythology Ser.). (Ger.). 1978. lib. bdg. 62.00x (ISBN 0-405-10562-2). Ayer Co Pubs.

--Romische Mythologie: Roman Mythology. Bolle, Kees W., ed. LC 77-79154. (Mythology Ser.). (Ger.). 1978. Repr. of 1865 ed. lib. bdg. 53.00x (ISBN 0-405-10563-0). Ayer Co Pubs.

Preller, Victor. Divine Science & the Science of God: A Reformulation of Thomas Aquinas. LC 66-21838. pap. 72.80 (ISBN 0-317-08468-2, 2010543). Bks Demand UMI.

Prem, Krishna. Initiation into Yoga. LC 76-10790. (Orig.). 1976. pap. 3.25 (ISBN 0-8356-0484-5, Quest). Theos Pub Hse.

Prem, Krishna Sri see Krishna Prem, Sri.

Prem, Ma A., ed. see Rajneesh, Bhagwan S.

Prem, Ma Ananda, ed. see Rajneesh, Bhagwan Shree.

Prem, Sri K. & Ashish, Sri Madhava. Man: The Measure of All Things. LC 74-87256. 1969. 8.50 (ISBN 0-8356-0006-8). Theos Pub Hse.

Prem, Swami Krishna, ed. see Rajneesh, Bhagwan Shree.

Preminger, Alex, jt. ed. see Greenstein, Edward L.

Premm, Mattias. Dogmatic Theology for the Laity. 1977. pap. 12.00 (ISBN 0-89555-022-9). TAN Bks Pubs.

Premoe, David, jt. auth. see Premoe, Deborah.

Premoe, David, ed. Zion, the Growing Symbol. 1980. pap. 6.00 (ISBN 0-8309-0301-1). Herald Hse.

Premoe, Deborah & Premoe, David. Multiple Faith Relationships. (Pastoral Care Office Pamphlet Ser.). 84p. 1984. pap. text ed. 5.00 (ISBN 0-8309-0390-9). Herald Hse.

Premoli, Orazio M. Contemporary Church History. 1977. lib. bdg. 59.95 (ISBN 0-8490-1669-X). Gordon Pr.

Prenter, Regin. Luther's Theology of the Cross. Anderson, Charles S., ed. LC 71-152368. (Facet Bks.). 32p. 1971. pap. 2.50 (ISBN 0-8006-3062-9, 1-3062). Fortress.

Prentice, Marjorie G., jt. auth. see Brown, Marion E.

Prentice, Robert P. Psychology of Love According to St. Bonaventure. (Philosophy Ser). 1957. 8.00 (ISBN 0-686-11536-8). Franciscan Inst.

Prentiss, Elizabeth. Stepping Heavenward. pap. 6.95 (ISBN 0-685-99369-8). Reiner.

Prentiss, George L. The Life & Letters of Elizabeth Prentiss. Gifford, Carolyn D. & Dayton, Donald, eds. (Women in American Protestant Religion 1800-1930 Ser.). 573p. 1987. lib. bdg. 80.00 (ISBN 0-8240-0672-0). Garland Pub.

Presbyterian Church In The United States Of America. Records of the Presbyterian Church in the United States of America, 1706-1788. LC 75-83434. (Religion in America, Ser. 1). 1969. Repr. of 1904 ed. 30.00 (ISBN 0-405-00259-9). Ayer Co Pubs.

Prescott, D. M. Noah & His Ark. (Very First Bible Stories Ser.). 1984. 1.59 (ISBN 0-87162-273-4, D8502). Warner Pr.

Prescott, Hilda F. Once to Sinai. LC 78-63358. (The Crusades & Military Orders: Second Ser.). Repr. of 1957 ed. 27.00 (ISBN 0-404-17028-5). AMS Pr.

Prescott, Roger. Hello, My Friend. 1981. 6.75 (ISBN 0-89536-474-3, 0800). CSS of Ohio.

--The Promise of Life. 1984. 4.75 (ISBN 0-89536-683-5, 4859). CSS of Ohio.

--The Second Mile. 1985. 4.95 (ISBN 0-89536-739-4, 5823). CSS of Ohio.

Preston, Daniel. The Church Triumphant. pap. 4.95 (ISBN 0-934942-30-7). White Wing Pub.

--The Era of A. J. Tomlinson. 206p. (Orig.). 1984. pap. 6.95 (ISBN 0-934942-41-2, 1925). White Wing Pub.

Preston, Daniel D. The Life & Work of the Minister. 1968. 5.95 (ISBN 0-934942-11-0). White Wing Pub.

Preston, David G., tr. see Blocher, Henri.

Preston, Elizabeth, ed. see Blavatsky, Helena P.

Preston, James J. Cult of the Goddess: Social & Religious Change in a Hindu Temple. (Illus.). 109p. 1985. pap. text ed. 6.95x (ISBN 0-88133-135-X). Waveland Pr.

Preston, James J., ed. Mother Worship: Theme & Variations. LC 81-3336. (Studies in Religion). xxiv, 360p. 1982. text ed. 29.00x (ISBN 0-8078-1471-7). U of NC Pr.

--Mother Worship: Theme & Variations. (Studies in Religion). xxiv, 360p. 1983. pap. text ed. 9.95x (ISBN 0-8078-4114-5). U of NC Pr.

Preston, John. Breastplate of Faith & Love. Facs. ed. 241p. 1979. Repr. of 1630 ed. 22.95 (ISBN 0-85151-289-5). Banner of Truth.

--The Saints Daily Exercise. LC 76-57409. (English Experience Ser.: No. 824). 1977. Repr. of 1629 ed. lib. bdg. 16.00 (ISBN 90-221-0824-4). Walter J Johnson.

Preston, Mary Jane. Getting Your House in Order. 130p. 1986. pap. 8.95 (ISBN 0-941478-48-3). Paraclete Pr.

Preston, William H., ed. Fathers Are Special. LC 76-39715. (Illus.). 1977. 8.95 (ISBN 0-8054-5622-8, 4256-22). Broadman.

Prestwich, Menna, ed. International Calvinism. (Illus.). 414p. 1985. 49.95x (ISBN 0-19-821933-4). Oxford U Pr.

Pretzel, Ulrich. Fruhgeschichte Des Deutschen Reims. (Ger). 27.00 (ISBN 0-384-47740-2); pap. 22.00 (ISBN 0-685-02131-9). Johnson Repr.

Preus, Herman A. A Theology to Live By. 1977. pap. 7.95 (ISBN 0-570-03739-5, 12-2643). Concordia.

Preus, J. A., tr. see Chemnitz, Martin.

Preus, James S. From Shadow to Promise: Old Testament Interpretation from Augustine to the Young Luther. LC 69-12732. (Illus.). xii, 301p. 1969. 20.00x (ISBN 0-674-32610-5, Belkap Pr). Harvard U Pr.

Preus, Mary. Eloquence & Ignorance in Augustine's "On the Nature & Origin of the Soul". (AAR Academy Ser.). 1986. 19.95 (ISBN 0-89130-927-6, 01-01-51); pap. 15.25 (ISBN 0-89130-928-4). Scholars Pr Ga.

Preus, Robert. Getting into the Theology of Concord. 1978. pap. 3.75 (ISBN 0-570-03767-0, 12-2702). Concordia.

Preus, Robert D. Theology of Post-Reformation Lutheranism: A Study of Theological Prolegomena. LC 70-121877. 1970. 16.95 (ISBN 0-570-03211-3, 15-2110). Concordia.

--Theology of Post-Reformation Lutheranism, Vol. 2. 350p. 1972. 16.95 (ISBN 0-570-03226-1, 15-2123). Concordia.

Preus, Robert D., jt. ed. see Radmacher, Earl D.

Preuss, Arthur, ed. see Grisar, Hartmann.

Preuss, Julius. Biblical & Talmudic Medicine. Rosner, Fred, tr. from Ger. 1978. 45.00x (ISBN 0-88482-861-1, Sandhedrin Pr). Hebrew Pub.

--Biblisch-Talmudische Medizin. rev. ed. (Ger). 1970. 150.00 (ISBN 0-87068-121-4). Ktav.

Prevallet, Elaine. Reflections on Simplicity. LC 82-80439. 31p. 1982. pap. 2.50x (ISBN 0-87574-244-0). Pendle Hill.

Previtali, David R. The Life of Grace. (Faith & Life). (Illus.). 176p. (Orig.). 1985. pap. 7.50 (ISBN 0-89870-083-3); pap. 2.50 activity bk. (ISBN 0-89870-084-1). Ignatius Pr.

Previte-Orton, C. W. Outlines of Medieval History. 2nd ed. LC 64-25837. 1916. 12.00 (ISBN 0-8196-0147-0). Biblo.

Previte-Orton, C. W., ed. The Shorter Cambridge Medieval History, 2 vols. Incl. Vol. 1. The Later Roman Empire to the Twelfth Century. (Illus.). 644p. 74.50 (ISBN 0-521-20962-5); pap. 23.95 (ISBN 0-521-09976-5); Vol. 2. The Twelfth Century to the Renaissance. (Illus.). 558p. 74.50 (ISBN 0-521-20963-3); pap. 23.95 (ISBN 0-521-09977-3). (Medieval History Ser). 1975. pap. 18.95 ea. Set. 135.00 (ISBN 0-521-05993-3); Set. pap. 39.50 (ISBN 0-521-08758-9). Cambridge U Pr.

Prevost, A. Le see Ordericus, Vitalis.

Prevot, Andre. Love, Peace & Joy: Devotion to the Sacred Heart of Jesus According to St. Gertrude. LC 84-51822. 224p. 1985. pap. 4.00 (ISBN 0-89555-255-8). Tan Bks Pubs.

Prezelski, Carmen V., tr. see Cabat, Erni.

Prezelski, Carmen V., tr. see Cabat, Erni & Polzer, Charles W.

Price, A. F. & Mou-Lam, trs. from Sanskrit & Chinese. The Diamond Sutra & the Sutra of Hui Neng. (The Clear Light Ser.). 190p. 1969. pap. 7.95 (ISBN 0-87773-005-9). Shambhala Pubns.

Price, Brena. Giving, Christian Stewardship: Teaching Bks. (Illus.). 14p. 1971. pap. text ed. 2.95 (ISBN 0-86508-154-9). BCM Intl Inc.

Price, Brynmor F. & Nida, Eugene A. A Translator's Handbook on the Book of Jonah. (Helps for Translators Ser.). 95p. 1978. 3.30x (ISBN 0-8267-0199-X, 08552, Pub. by United Bible). Am Bible.

Price, Carl E. Through Other Eyes: Vivid Narratives of Some of the Bible's Most Notable Characters. 144p. (Orig.). 1987. pap. 6.95 (ISBN 0-8358-0555-7). Upper Room.

--Writings in the Dust. 112p. (Orig.). 1984. pap. 4.75 (ISBN 0-8358-0474-7). Upper Room.

Price, Charles P. A Matter of Faith. LC 83-50559. 80p. 1983. pap. 5.95 (ISBN 0-8192-1335-7). Morehouse.

Price, Charles P. & Weil, Louis. Liturgy for Living. (Church's Teaching Ser.: Vol. 5). 1979. 5.95 (ISBN 0-8164-0422-4, HarpR); pap. 4.95 (ISBN 0-8164-2218-4); user guide 1.50 (ISBN 0-8164-2225-7). Har-Row.

Price, Charles P., jt. auth. see Goetchius, Eugene V.

Price, Charles P., jt. auth. see MacRae, George W.

Price, Charles S. Real Faith: One of the Classic Faith-Builders. 1972. pap. 4.95 (ISBN 0-88270-000-6). Bridge Pub.

Price, David. Mahommedan History, 3 vols. Orig. Title: Chronological Retrospect or the Principal Events of Mahommedan History. (Illus.). 2291p. 1984. Repr. of 1811 ed. Set. text ed. 400.00x (ISBN 0-86590-393-X, Inter India Pubns Delhi). Apt Bks.

Price, E. B. Is It the Watchtower? LC 67-30889. 1967. pap. 1.25 (ISBN 0-8163-0106-9, 09665-1). Pacific Pr Pub Assn.

Price, E. W. Acts in Prayer. LC 74-15278. 1974. pap. 0.95 (ISBN 0-8054-9209-7). Broadman.

Price, Eugenia. Another Day. LC 84-7697. 168p. 1984. 9.95 (ISBN 0-385-27660-5, Dial). Doubleday.

--Beloved World: The Story of God & People. (Illus.). 1979. pap. 9.95 (ISBN 0-310-31271-X, 10540P). Zondervan.

--The Burden Is Light. 272p. 1985. pap. 11.95 (ISBN 0-8027-2514-7). Walker & Co.

--The Burden is Light: The Autobiography of a Transformed Pagan. 176p. pap. 2.95 (ISBN 0-8007-8583-5, Spire Bks). Revell.

--Early Will I Seek Thee. 160p. pap. 2.95 (ISBN 0-8007-8584-3, Spire Bks). Revell.

--Early Will I Seek Thee: Journal of a Heart That Longed & Found. LC 82-22179. 188p. 1983. pap. 6.95 (ISBN 0-385-27864-0, Dial). Doubleday.

--God Speaks to Women Today. 192p. 1984. pap. 6.95 (ISBN 0-310-31301-5, 10530P). Zondervan.

--Leave Yourself Alone. 128p. 1982. pap. 5.95 (ISBN 0-310-31431-3, 16244P). Zondervan.

--Make Love Your Aim. 192p. 1983. pap. 5.95 (ISBN 0-310-31311-2, 16243P). Zondervan.

--No Pat Answers. 144p. 1983. pap. 5.95 (ISBN 0-310-31331-7, 16244P). Zondervan.

--The Unique World of Women. 248p. 1982. pap. 7.95 (ISBN 0-310-31351-1, 16216P). Zondervan.

--What Is God Like? 192p. 1982. pap. 5.95 (ISBN 0-310-31441-0, 16242P). Zondervan.

--What Really Matters. LC 82-25236. (Illus.). 120p. 1983. 7.95 (ISBN 0-385-27659-1, Dial). Doubleday.

--What Really Matters. 160p. 1985. pap. 2.95 (ISBN 0-515-08989-3). Jove Pubns.

--Woman to Woman. pap. 3.95 (ISBN 0-310-31392-9, 10589P). Zondervan.

--A Woman's Choice: Living Through Your Problems. 192p. 1983. pap. 5.95 (ISBN 0-310-31381-3, 16217P). Zondervan.

Price, Frederick. Como Obra la Fe. 111p. 1980. pap. 2.95 (ISBN 0-89274-157-0). Harrison Hse.

Price, Frederick K. Faith, Foolishness, or Presumption. 160p. (Orig.). 1979. pap. 4.95 (ISBN 0-89274-103-1). Harrison Hse.

--The Holy Spirit the Missing Ingredient. 1978. pap. text ed. 1.95 (ISBN 0-89274-081-7). Harrison Hse.

--How Faith Works. 128p. (Orig.). 1979. pap. 3.95 (ISBN 0-89274-001-9). Harrison Hse.

--How to Obtain Strong Faith: Six Principles. 184p. pap. 4.95 (ISBN 0-89274-042-6). Harrison Hse.

--Is Healing for All? 127p. (Orig.). 1979. pap. 3.95 (ISBN 0-89274-005-1). Harrison Hse.

--Now Faith Is. 32p. 1984. pap. 0.75 (ISBN 0-89274-302-6). Harrison Hse.

--Thank God for Everything. 31p. pap. 0.75 mini-bk. (ISBN 0-89274-056-6). Harrison Hse.

Price, Harry. No Respecter of Persons. 128p. 1981. pap. 4.95 (ISBN 0-8059-2797-2). Dorrance.

Price, J. F., ed. see Pillai, Ananda R., et al.

Price, J. M. & Estudio, Guias de. Guia de Estudios Sobre Jesus el Maestro. 50p. 1982. pap. 3.25 (ISBN 0-311-43501-7). Casa Bautista.

Price, James L. The New Testament. 544p. 1986. lib. bdg. write for info. (ISBN 0-02-396610-6). Macmillan.

Price, John R. Practical Spirituality. 160p. (Orig.). 1985. pap. 6.95 (ISBN 0-942082-06-0). Quartus Bks.

Price, Katheryn. Applied Christianity for Today's Christian Woman. 1978. pap. 3.50 (ISBN 0-88027-045-4). Firm Foun Pub.

Price, Leo. The Tree That Always Said No. LC 73-90617. (Illus.). 1973. plastic bdg. 2.75 (ISBN 0-8198-0330-8); pap. 1.75 (ISBN 0-8198-0331-6). Dghtrs St Paul.

Price, Milburn, jt. auth. see Reynolds, William J.

Price, Nelson L. Called to Splendor. LC 84-17506. 1984. pap. 4.95 (ISBN 0-8054-5007-6). Broadman.

--The Destruction of Death. LC 82-72464. 1983. 4.50 (ISBN 0-8054-1528-9). Broadman.

--The Emmanuel Factor. 1987. 8.95 (ISBN 0-8054-5050-5). Broadman.

--Farewell to Fear. (Orig.). 1983. pap. 5.95 (ISBN 0-8054-5533-7). Broadman.

--Only the Beginning. LC 79-55662. 1980. 7.95 (ISBN 0-8054-5331-8, 4253-31). Broadman.

Price, R. M., tr. see Theodoret.

Price, Richard. A Free Discussion of the Doctrine of Materialism and Philosophical Necessity, 1778. Wellek, Rene, ed. LC 75-11247. (British Philosophers & Theologians of the 17th & 18th Centuries Ser.). 1978. lib. bdg. 51.00 (ISBN 0-8240-1798-6). Garland Pub.

--Review of the Principal Questions in Morals. LC 73-179398. 516p. 1974. Repr. of 1787 ed. lib. bdg. 32.50 (ISBN 0-8337-2831-8). B Franklin.

Price, S. R. Rituals & Power: The Roman Imperial Cult in Asia Minor. (Illus.). 316p. 1986. pap. 14.95 (ISBN 0-521-31268-X). Cambridge U Pr.

Price, Steven, jt. auth. see Gibson, Eva.

Price, Theron D. Revelation & Faith: Theological Reflections on the Knowing & Doing of Faith. 192p. 1987. 29.95 (ISBN 0-86554-260-0, MUP H-221); pap. 14.95 (ISBN 0-86554-261-9, MUP P-45). Mercer Univ Pr.

Price, Vladimir, ed. see Hume, David.

Price, Walter K. The Coming Antichrist. 240p. 1985. pap. 6.95 (ISBN 0-87213-695-7). Loizeaux.

Price, Wendell W. Contemporary Problems of Evangelism. LC 76-12941. 1976. 3.95 (ISBN 0-87509-070-2); pap. 2.00 (ISBN 0-87509-071-0). Chr Pubns.

Prichard, Harold A. Moral Obligation & Duty & Interest: Essays & Lectures. (Oxford Paperbacks Ser). (Orig.). 1968. pap. 4.95x (ISBN 0-19-881151-9). Oxford U Pr.

Prichard, Robert W., ed. Readings from the History of the Episcopal Church. 192p. (Orig.). 1986. pap. 14.95 (ISBN 0-8192-1383-7). Morehouse.

Prickett, Stephen. Romanticism & Religion. LC 75-2254. 320p. 1976. 49.50 (ISBN 0-521-21072-0). Cambridge U Pr.

--Words & the Word: Language Poetics, & Biblical Interpretation. 288p. 1986. 39.50 (ISBN 0-521-32248-0). Cambridge U Pr.

Priddis, Ronald, jt. auth. see Bergera, Gary J.

Priddy, Linda. The Bible & Me: Writing Fun for Kids Series. (Illus.). 24p. (Orig.). 1982. pap. 1.50 (ISBN 0-87239-482-4, 2101). Standard Pub.

Pride, Mary. The Way Home Beyond Feminism, Back to Reality. LC 84-73078. 240p. (Orig.). 1985. pap. 7.95 (ISBN 0-89107-345-0, Crossway Bks). Good News.

Pridham, Arthur. Notes on Romans. 1983. 13.95 (ISBN 0-8254-3519-6). Kregel.

Pridham, Geoffrey. Christian Democracy in Western Germany. LC 77-9235. 1978. 27.50x (ISBN 0-312-13396-0). St Martin.
Priebe, Duane A., tr. see Pannenberg, Wolfhart.
Priesand, Sally. Judaism & the New Woman. LC 75-21951. (Jewish Concepts & Issues Ser.). 162p. (Orig.). 1975. pap. 2.50x (ISBN 0-87441-230-7). Behrman.
Priest, Ames. Governmental & Judicial Ethics in the Bible & Rabbinic Literature. 1980. 20.00x (ISBN 0-87068-697-6). Ktav.
Priest, James E. Governmental & Judicial Ethics in the Bible & Rabbinic Literature. LC 79-23423. 312p. 1980. 17.95x (ISBN 0-87068-697-6). Pepperdine U Pr.
Priest, Josiah & Brown, W. S. Bible Defence of Slavery. LC 74-92439. 1851. 79.00 (ISBN 0-403-00171-4). Scholarly.
Priestley, Denise M. Bringing Forth in Hope: Being Creative in a Nuclear Age. 80p. (Orig.). 1983. pap. 4.95 (ISBN 0-8091-2551-X). Paulist Pr.
Priestley, Joseph. Disquisitions Relating to Matter & Spirit. LC 74-26285. (History, Philosophy & Sociology of Science Ser). 1975. Repr. 27.00x (ISBN 0-405-06612-0). Ayer Co Pubs.
--An Examination of Dr. Reid's Inquiry into the Human Mind. Wellek, Rene, ed. LC 75-11249. (British Philosophers & Theologians of the 17th & 18th Centuries Ser.). 1978. Repr. of 1774 ed. lib. bdg. 51.00 (ISBN 0-8240-1800-1). Garland Pub.
--The Theological & Miscellaneous Works, 25 vols. in 26. Repr. Set. 1352.00 (ISBN 0-527-72751-2). Kraus Repr.
Priestly, Joseph L. The Way Jesus Walked: Spontaneous Reflections on the Way of the Cross. 224p. (Orig.). 1982. pap. 6.95 (ISBN 0-89962-252-6). Todd & Honeywell.
Priest Nikolai Deputatov. Revnitel' Blagotchestija 19-go vjeka, Episkop Theofan Zatvornik. Tr. of A Zealot for Piety in the 19th Century Bishop Theophan the Recluse. 71p. 1971. pap. 3.00 (ISBN 0-317-29261-7). Holy Trinity.
Prime, Derek. Baker's Bible Study Guide. (Baker's Paperback Reference Library). 296p. 1982. pap. 8.95 (ISBN 0-8010-7076-7). Baker Bk.
Prime, Wendell. Fifteenth Century Bibles. LC 77-85626. 1977. Repr. of 1888 ed. lib. bdg. 15.00 (ISBN 0-89341-320-8). Longwood Pub Group.
Prime, William C. Tent Life in the Holy Land. Davis, Moshe, ed. LC 77-70734. (America & the Holy Land Ser.). (Illus.). 1977. Repr. of 1857 ed. lib. bdg. 38.50x (ISBN 0-405-10278-X). Ayer Co Pubs.
Primeaux, Patrick. Richard R. Niebuhr on Christ & Religion: The Four-Stage Development of His Thought. (Toronto Studies in Theology: Vol. 4). (Illus.). xiv, 288p. 1981. 49.95x (ISBN 0-88946-973-3). E Mellen.
Prince, Derek. Baptism in the Holy Spirit. 1966. pap. 1.95 (ISBN 0-934920-07-9, B-19). Derek Prince.
--Eternal Judgment. (Foundation Ser.: Bk. VII). 1965-66. pap. 2.95 (ISBN 0-934920-06-0, B-16). Derek Prince.
--Expelling Demons. 1969. pap. 0.25 (ISBN 0-934920-18-4, B70). Derek Prince.
--Faith to Live by. 1977. pap. 5.95 (ISBN 0-934920-25-7, B-29). Derek Prince.
--Foundation for Faith. (Foundation Ser.: Bk. I). 1965-66. pap. 2.95 (ISBN 0-934920-00-1, B-10). Derek Prince.
--From Jordan to Pentecost, Bk. III. (Foundation Ser.). pap. 2.95 (ISBN 0-934920-02-8, B-12). Derek Prince.
--The Grace of Yielding. 1977. pap. 2.50 (ISBN 0-934920-20-6, B-30). Derek Prince.
--How to Fast Successfully. 1976. pap. 2.50 (ISBN 0-934920-19-2, B-28). Derek Prince.
--Laying on of Hands. (Foundation Ser.: Bk. V). 1965-66. pap. 1.95 (ISBN 0-934920-04-4, B-14). Derek Prince.
--Philosophy, the Bible & the Supernatural. 1969. pap. 0.10 (ISBN 0-934920-22-2, B71). Derek Prince.
--Praying for the Government. 1970. pap. 1.50 (ISBN 0-934920-11-7, B-20). Derek Prince.
--Purposes of Pentecost. (Foundation Ser.: Bk. IV). 1965-66. pap. 3.95 (ISBN 0-934920-03-6). Derek Prince.
--Repent & Believe. (Foundation Ser.: Bk. II). 1965-66. pap. 2.95 (ISBN 0-934920-01-X, B-11). Derek Prince.
--Resurrection of the Dead. (Foundation Ser.: Bk. VI). 1965-66. pap. 2.95 (ISBN 0-934920-05-2, B-15). Derek Prince.
--Self Study Bible Course. 1969. pap. 5.95 (ISBN 0-934920-08-7, B-90). Derek Prince.
--Shaping History Through Prayer & Fasting. 1973. 9.95 (ISBN 0-934920-23-0, B-24); pap. 5.95 (ISBN 0-686-12766-8, B-25). Derek Prince.
Prince, Derek & Prince, Ruth. God Is a Matchmaker. 1986. pap. 5.95 (ISBN 0-8007-9058-8, B35). Revell.
Prince, F. T., ed. see Milton, John.
Prince, Harold B., compiled by. A Presbyterian Bibliography. LC 83-10116. (ATLA Bibliography Ser.: No. 8). 466p. 1983. pap. 35.00 (ISBN 0-8108-1639-3). Scarecrow.
Prince, Lydia. Appointment in Jerusalem. 1975. 9.95 (ISBN 0-934920-24-9, B-26); pap. 5.95 (ISBN 0-934920-27-3, B 26A). Derek Prince.
Prince, Matthew. Winning Through Caring: The Handbook on Friendship Evangelism. 96p. (Orig.). 1981. pap. 3.95 (ISBN 0-8010-7065-1). Baker Bk.
Prince, Ruth, jt. auth. see Prince, Derek.
Prince, Soledad G., tr. see Garbee, Ed & Van Dyke, Henry.
Princehouse, Nona T. The Creator & the Creature. (Illus.). 96p. 1986. 9.95 (ISBN 0-89962-530-4). Todd & Honeywell.
Pringle, Cyrus. Civil War Diary of Cyrus Pringle: Record of Quaker Conscience. LC 62-18328. Orig. Title: Record of a Quaker Conscience. (Orig.). 1962. pap. 2.50x (ISBN 0-87574-122-3, 122). Pendle Hill.
Pringle, M. A. Journey in East Africa: Towards the Mountains of the Moon. new ed. LC 72-3957. (Black Heritage Library Collection Ser.). Repr. of 1886 ed. 27.50 (ISBN 0-8369-9105-2). Ayer Co Pubs.
Prinsloo, Willem S. The Theology of the Book of Joel. (Beihefte zur Zeitschrift fur die Alttestamentliche Wissenschaft: Vol. 163). viii, 136p. 1985. 43.75x (ISBN 3-11-010301-X). De Gruyter.
Prinzing, Fred W. Handling Church Tensions Creatively. LC 86-80687. 216p. (Orig.). 1986. pap. 4.95 (ISBN 0-935797-23-8). Harvest IL.
Prior, Arthur N. Logic & the Basis of Ethics. 1949. 17.95x (ISBN 0-19-824157-7). Oxford U Pr.
--Papers in Logic & Ethics. Geach, P. T. & Kenny, A. J., eds. LC 76-9376. 238p. 1976. 15.00x (ISBN 0-87023-213-4). U of Mass Pr.
Prior, Brenda. Little Sleeping Beauty. (Arch Bks: Set 6). 1969. laminated bdg. 0.99 (ISBN 0-570-06041-9, 59-1156). Concordia.
Prior, David. The Message of I Corinthians. Stott, John R. & Motyer, J. A., eds. LC 85-239. (The Bible Speaks Today Ser.). 270p. 1985. pap. 7.95 (ISBN 0-87784-297-3). Inter-Varsity.
--Parish Renewal at the Grassroots. 1987. 12.95 (ISBN 0-310-38370-6). Zondervan.
Prior, Edward S. The Cathedral Builders in England. LC 77-94613. 1978. Repr. of 1905 ed. lib. bdg. 25.00 (ISBN 0-89341-247-3). Longwood Pub Group.
Prior, William J. Unity & Development in Plato's Metaphysics. LC 85-5073. 202p. 1985. 24.95 (ISBN 0-8126-9000-1). Open Court.
Prip-Moller, J. Chinese Buddhist Monasteries: Their Plan & Its Function As a Setting for Buddhist Monastic Life. (Illus.). 400p. 1983. Repr. of 1937 ed. 100.00 (ISBN 0-295-96085-X). U of Wash Pr.
Prital, David. In Search of Self: The Soviet Jewish Intelligentsia & the Exodus. 282p. 1983. pap. text ed. 25.00x (ISBN 965-223-420-6, Pub. by Magnes Pr Israel). Humanities.
Pritchard, Arnold. Catholic Loyalism in Elizabethan England. LC 78-10208. xiii, 243p. 1979. 22.50x (ISBN 0-8078-1345-1). U of NC Pr.
Pritchard, B., tr. see Ferrero, Guglielmo.
Pritchard, Gretchen W. Go, Tell It on the Mountain: Three Christmas Pageants for Church Schools. (Illus.). 63p. (Orig.). 1985. pap. 12.50x (ISBN 0-9614022-1-0). Sunday Paper.
--New Life: The Sunday Paper's Baptism Book. (Illus.). 80p. (Orig.). 1986. pap. 5.75x (ISBN 0-9614022-2-9). Sunday Paper.
Pritchard, James B. Archaeology & the Old Testament. LC 58-10053. pap. 69.80 (ISBN 0-317-08485-2, 2016011). Bks Demand UMI.
--Gibeon, Where the Sun Stood Still: The Discovery of a Biblical City. 1962. 31.50 (ISBN 0-691-03517-2); pap. 9.50x (ISBN 0-691-00210-X). Princeton U Pr.
--Hebrew Inscriptions & Stamps from Gibeon. (University Museum Monographs: No. 17). (Illus.). 32p. 1959. 5.00 (ISBN 0-934718-10-5). Univ Mus of U PA.
--Palestinian Figurines in Relation to Certain Goddesses Known Through Literature. (American Oriental Ser.: Vol. 24). 1943. 11.00 (ISBN 0-527-02698-0). Kraus Repr.
Pritchard, James B., ed. Ancient Near East in Pictures with Supplement. 2nd ed. Incl. Ancient Near Eastern Texts Relating to the Old Testament with Supplement. 3rd ed. Set. text ed. 60.50x ea. (ISBN 0-691-03503-2, 035032T); pictures 66.25x (032024T). 1969. deluxe ed. 68.50x ea. (ISBN 0-691-03502-4); Set. 126.75x (ISBN 0-686-66606-2). Princeton U Pr.
Pritchard, John P. A Literary Approach to the New Testament. (Illus.). 350p. 1972. 17.95x (ISBN 0-8061-1011-2); pap. 11.95x (ISBN 0-8061-1710-9). U of Okla Pr.
Pritchett, John P. Black Robe & Buckskin. 1960. 12.95x (ISBN 0-8084-0063-0); pap. 8.95 (ISBN 0-8084-0064-9). New Coll U Pr.
Pritchett, W. Douglas. The Children of God-Family of Love: An Annotated Bibliography. Melton, J. Gordon, ed. LC 83-48223. (Sects & Cults in America: Bibliographical Guides Ser.). 250p. 1984. lib. bdg. 33.00 (ISBN 0-8240-9043-8). Garland Pub.
Pritsak, Omeljan, jt. auth. see Golb, Norman.
Pritt, Ann F. How to Make an L.D.S. Quiet Book. 38p. 1976. pap. 3.95 (ISBN 0-87747-116-9). Deseret Bk.
Probstein, Bobbie. Return to Center. LC 85-70723. (Illus.). 256p. (Orig.). 1985. pap. 9.95 (ISBN 0-87516-554-0). De Vorss.
Procko, Bohdan P. Ukrainian Catholics in America: A History. LC 81-43718. 184p. (Orig.). 1982. lib. bdg. 27.75 (ISBN 0-8191-2409-5); pap. text ed. 11.50 (ISBN 0-8191-2410-9). U Pr of Amer.
Proclus. The Platonic Theology, Vol. II: Bks IV-VI. rev. ed. Navon, Robert, ed. Taylor, Thomas, tr. from Gr. LC 84-52789. (Great Works of Philosophy: Vol. II). Tr. of The Six Books of Proclus on the Theology of Plato. 292p. 1986. text ed. 35.00 (ISBN 0-933601-05-0); pap. text ed. 22.50 (ISBN 0-933601-06-9). Selene Bks.
--The Platonic Theology: Vol. 1 - Books I-III. Rev. ed. Navon, Robert, ed. Taylor, Thomas, tr. from Greek. (Great Works of Philosophy Ser.: Vol. I). xxvi, 222p. 1985. text ed. 35.00 (ISBN 0-9609866-7-7); pap. text ed. 22.50 (ISBN 0-9609866-6-9). Selene Bks.
Procter, Evelyn S. Curia & Cortes in Leon & Castille, Ten Seventy-Two to Twelve Ninety-Five. LC 79-51750. (Cambridge Iberian & Latin American Studies). (Illus.). 350p. 1980. 44.50 (ISBN 0-521-22639-2). Cambridge U Pr.
Procter, Marjorie. The Little Grey Donkey. (Very First Bible Stories Ser.). 1984. 1.59 (ISBN 0-87162-272-6, D8501). Warner Pr.
--The Little Lost Lamb. (Very First Bible Stories Ser.). 1984. 1.59 (ISBN 0-87162-276-9, D8505). Warner Pr.
Proctor, F. B. Treasury of Quotations on Religious Subjects. LC 76-15741. 832p. 1976. 21.95 (ISBN 0-8254-3500-5). Kregel.
Proctor, Jesse H., ed. Islam & International Relations. LC 80-1914. 1981. Repr. of 1965 ed. 27.50 (ISBN 0-404-18969-5). AMS Pr.
Proctor, Percy M. Star Myths & Stories: From Andromeda to Virgo. (Illus.). 1972. 8.50 (ISBN 0-682-47470-3, Banner). Exposition Pr FL.
Proctor, Samuel, et al, eds. Jews of the South: Selected Essays. LC 83-25060. viii, 131p. 1984. 12.95 (ISBN 0-86554-102-7, H94). Mercer Univ Pr.
Proctor, Samuel D. & Watley, William D. Sermons from the Black Pulpit. 128p. 1984. pap. 7.95 (ISBN 0-8170-1034-3). Judson.
Proctor, Wesley, tr. see Meredith, Howard & Milan, Virginia E.
Proctor, William. An Interview with Chiara Lubich. 72p. (Orig.). 1983. pap. 4.95 (ISBN 0-911782-44-3). New City.
Proctor, William, jt. auth. see Boa, Kenneth.
Proctor, William, jt. auth. see Mickey, Paul.
Proctor, William, jt. auth. see Robertson, Pat.
Proffer, Ellendea. Mikhail Bulgakov: Life & Work. LC 83-16199. 1984. 45.00 (ISBN 0-88233-198-1). Ardis Pubs.
Proffer, Ellendea, ed. Bulgakov Photographic Bibliography. 140p. 1984. 35.00 (ISBN 0-88233-812-9); pap. 15.00 (ISBN 0-88233-813-7). Ardis Pubs.
Progoff, Ira. The Practice of Process Meditation: The Intensive Journal Way to Spiritual Experience. LC 80-68847. 343p. 1980. 18.95 (ISBN 0-87941-008-6); pap. 9.95, 1980 (ISBN 0-87941-008-6). Dialogue Hse.
--Well & the Cathedral. 5th ed. LC 76-20823. (Entrance Meditation Ser.). 166p. 1983. 4.95; pap. 11.50 incl. cassette (ISBN 0-87941-005-1). Dialogue Hse.
--The White Robed Monk. 3rd, rev. & enl. ed. LC 79-1553. (Entrance Meditation Ser.). 111p. 1983. pap. 3.95 (ISBN 0-87941-007-8); pap. 11.50 incl. cassette. Dialogue Hse.
Prokes, M. Timothy. Women's Challenge: Ministry in the Flesh. 2.95 (ISBN 0-87193-006-4). Dimension Bks.
Prokop, Phyllis S. The Positive Power of the Ten Commandments. LC 86-31043. (Orig.). 1987. 7.95 (ISBN 0-8054-5037-8). Broadman.
Prompsault, J. H. Dictionnaire Raisonne de Droit et de Jurisprudence en Matiere Civile Ecclesiastique, 3 vols. Migne, J. P., ed. (Encyclopedie Theologique Ser.: Vols. 36-38). (Fr.). 1948p. Repr. of 1849 ed. lib. bdg. 248.00x (ISBN 0-89241-244-5). Caratzas.
Pronzato, Alessandro. Meditation on the Sand. LC 82-24513. (Ital.). 104p. (Orig.). 1983. pap. 5.95 (ISBN 0-8189-0457-7). Alba.
Prophet, Elizabeth, jt. auth. see Prophet, Mark.
Prophet, Elizabeth, jt. ed. see Prophet, Elizabeth C.
Prophet, Elizabeth, jt. ed. see Prophet, Mark.
Prophet, Elizabeth C. Forbidden Mysteries of Enoch. LC 82-62445. (Illus.). 504p. 1983. pap. 12.95 (ISBN 0-916766-60-8). Summit Univ.
--The Lost Years of Jesus. (Illus.). 401p. 1984. pap. 14.95 (ISBN 0-916766-61-6). Summit Univ.
--Where the Eagles Gather: Vol. 24, Bks. I & II. LC 81-86682. 636p. 1982. 35.90; Bk. I. 17.95 (ISBN 0-916766-49-7); Bk. II. 17.95 (ISBN 0-916766-57-8). Summit Univ.
Prophet, Elizabeth C., jt. auth. see Prophet, Mark L.
Prophet, Elizabeth C., ed. Mysteries of the Holy Grail: Archangel Gabriel. LC 83-51154. (Illus.). 430p. 1984. pap. 12.95 (ISBN 0-916766-64-0). Summit Univ.
--Pearls of Wisdom: A Prophecy of Karma, to the Earth & Her Evolutions, Vol. 23. LC 81-50418. 540p. 1980. 14.95 (ISBN 0-916766-41-1). Summit Univ.
--Pearls of Wisdom 1975: El Morya-On Discipleship East & West, Vol. 18. LC 79-64047. 349p. 1979. 18.95 (ISBN 0-916766-15-2). Summit Univ.
--Pearls of Wisdom 1976, Vol. 19. LC 76-52850. 13.95 (ISBN 0-916766-24-1). Summit Univ.
Prophet, Elizabeth C., intro. by. Prayer & Meditation. LC 76-28086. (Illus.). 306p. (Orig.). 1978. pap. 9.95 (ISBN 0-916766-19-5). Summit Univ.
Prophet, Elizabeth C. & Prophet, Elizabeth, eds. Pearls of Wisdom 1971: Masters of the Far East-On the Pillars of Eternity, Vol. 14. LC 78-60619. 234p. 14.95 (ISBN 0-916766-31-4). Summit Univ.
Prophet, Elizabeth C., ed. see El Morya.
Prophet, Elizabeth C., jt. ed. see Prophet, Mark L.
Prophet, Mark & Prophet, Elizabeth. Climb the Highest Mountain. LC 72-175101. (Illus.). 516p. 1978. pap. 16.95 (ISBN 0-916766-26-8). Summit Univ.
--My Soul Doth Magnify the Lord! rev. ed. (Illus.). 350p. 1980. pap. 7.95 (ISBN 0-916766-35-7). Summit Univ.
Prophet, Mark & Prophet, Elizabeth, eds. Pearls of Wisdom 1965: The Mechanization Concept. LC 79-89833. 297p. 1979. 16.95 (ISBN 0-916766-35-7). Summit Univ.
--Pearls of Wisdom 1969: Kuthumi-On Selfhood, Vol. 12. LC 79-53229. 314p. 1979. 17.95 (ISBN 0-916766-34-9). Summit Univ.
--Pearls of Wisdom, 1978: Spoken by Elohim, Vol. 21. LC 79-66985. 513p. 1980. 14.95 (ISBN 0-916766-36-5). Summit Univ.
Prophet, Mark L. & Prophet, Elizabeth C. The Lost Teachings of Jesus, Vol. I. LC 81-52784. (Illus.). 425p. (Orig.). 1986. 19.95 (ISBN 0-916766-45-4). Summit Univ.
--The Lost Teachings of Jesus, Vol. 1. LC 81-52784. (Illus.). 425p. (Orig.). pap. 14.95 (ISBN 0-916766-71-3). Summit Univ.
--The Lost Teachings of Jesus, Vol. 2. LC 81-52784. (Illus.). 598p. (Orig.). 1986. pap. 21.95 (ISBN 0-916766-72-1). Summit Univ.
Prophet, Mark L. & Prophet, Elizabeth C., eds. Corona Class Lessons. LC 83-51445. 455p. (Orig.). 1986. pap. 12.95 (ISBN 0-916766-65-9). Summit Univ.
Prophet Pearl. Weight Group Therapist: Spiritual Gifts. large type ed. 32p. 1984. pap. 6.00 (ISBN 0-914009-16-8). VHI Library.
Propst, Rebecca L. Psychotherapy in a Religious Framework. LC 86-27582. 208p. 1987. text ed. 29.95 (ISBN 0-89885-350-8). Human Sci Pr.
Prose, Francine. Stories from Our Living Past. new ed. Harlow, Jules, ed. LC 74-8514. (Illus.). 128p. 1974. 6.95x (ISBN 0-87441-081-9). Behrman.
Proske, Karl, ed. Musica Divina Selectus Novus Missarum, 10 vols in 8. 1973. Repr. of 1855 ed. 545.00 (ISBN 0-384-48055-1). Johnson Repr.
Proskouriakoff, Tatiana, jt. ed. see Knorozov, Yuri V.
Prospo, R. C. de. Theism in the Discourse of Jonathan Edwards. LC 84-40406. 296p. 1985. 37.50 (ISBN 0-87413-281-9). U Delaware Pr.
Prosser, Eleanor. Drama & Religion in the English Mystery Plays: A Re-Evaluation. 1961. 18.50x (ISBN 0-8047-0060-5). Stanford U Pr.
Proten, C. Introduction to the Fante & Accra (GA) Languages & J. E. J. (Capiteins Fante Catechism Ser.). 69p. 1971. 19.00x (ISBN 0-317-39089-9, Pub. by Luzac & Co Ltd). State Mutual Bk.
Proterra, Michael. Homo Spiritualis Nititur Fide: Martin Luther & Ignatius of Loyola, an Analytical & Comparative Study of a Hermeneutic Based on the Heuristic Structure of Discretio. LC 82-21837. 92p. (Orig.). 1983. lib. bdg. 22.00 (ISBN 0-8191-2938-0); pap. text ed. 8.50 (ISBN 0-8191-2939-9). U Pr of Amer.
Protoierei, pref. by see Pushkarev, Sergei.
Protopresbyer Michael Pomazansky. V Mire Molitvi. Tr. of Prayer in the World. 148p. 1957. pap. 5.00 (ISBN 0-317-29096-7). Holy Trinity.

Protopresbyter Michael Polsky. Novije Mutcheniki Rossijskije, tom 2, Vol. 2. Tr. of The New Martyrs of Russia. 329p. 1957. pap. 11.00 (ISBN 0-317-29207-2). Holy Trinity.

Protopresbyter Michael Pomazansky. Bog Nash na Njbesi i na zjemli. Tr. of Our God is in Heaven & on Earth. 140p. 1985. pap. 5.00 (ISBN 0-317-29087-8). Holy Trinity.

--O Zhizni o Vjere o Tzerkvje, 2 vols. Tr. of On Life, Faith & the Church. 650p. 1976. pap. 23.00 (ISBN 0-317-29072-X). Holy Trinity.

--Pravosavnoje Dogmaticheskoje Bogoslovije. Tr. of Orthodox Dogmatic Theology. 280p. 1963. pap. text ed. 20.00 (ISBN 0-317-29309-5). Holy Trinity.

--Vjetkhij Zavjet v Novozavjetnoi Tserkvi. Tr. of The Old Testament in the New Testament Church. 38p. 1961. pap. 2.00 (ISBN 0-317-29101-7). Holy Trinity.

Proud, Robert. The History of Pennsylvania, 2 Vols. LC 66-25101. 1967. Repr. of 1797 ed. 20.00 ea. Vol. 1 (ISBN 0-87152-031-1). Vol. 2 (ISBN 0-87152-032-X). Set. 40.00 (ISBN 0-87152-305-1). Reprint.

Proudfoot, Wayne. God & the Self: Three Types of Philosophy of Religion. LC 75-28983. 241p. 1976. 22.50 (ISBN 0-8387-1769-1). Bucknell U Pr.

--Religious Experience. LC 84-23928. 1985. 30.00x (ISBN 0-520-05143-2). U of Cal Pr.

Prout, E. Double Counterpoint & Canon. LC 68-25300. (Studies in Music, No. 42). 1969. Repr. of 1893 ed. lib. bdg. 48.95x (ISBN 0-8383-0312-9). Haskell.

Prout, Ebenezer. Double Counterpoint & Canon. Repr. of 1893 ed. lib. bdg. 22.50x (ISBN 0-8371-2265-1, PRDC). Greenwood.

Provonsha, Jack. Is Death for Real? (Outreach Ser.). 1981. pap. 3.95 (ISBN 0-8163-0406-8). Pacific Pr Pub Assn.

Provost, James & Walf, Knut, eds. Canon Law--Church Reality. (Concilium Nineteen Eighty-Six Ser.). 120p. 1986. pap. 6.95 (ISBN 0-567-30065-X, Pub. by T & T Clark Ltd UK). Fortress.

Provost, James, jt. ed. see Albergio, Giuseppe.

Provost, James H., ed. Church As Communion. (Permanent Seminar Studies: No. 1). 245p. 1984. pap. 8.00 (ISBN 0-943616-23-9). Canon Law Soc.

--Church As Mission. (Permanent Seminar Studies: No. 2). 288p. 1984. pap. 8.00 (ISBN 0-943616-24-7). Canon Law Soc.

--Code, Community, Ministry: Selected Studies for the Revised Code of Canon Law. vi, 116p. (Orig.). 1983. pap. 4.50 (ISBN 0-943616-15-8). Canon Law Soc.

Prozesky, Martin. Religion & Ultimate Well-Being: An Explanatory Theory. LC 84-3340. 224p. 1984. 22.50 (ISBN 0-312-67057-5). St Martin.

Prucha, Francis P. Churches & the Indian Schools, 1888-1912. LC 79-12220. (Illus.). xiv, 278p. 1979. 21.50x (ISBN 0-8032-3657-3). U of Nebr Pr.

Pruden, Leo, tr. Karmasiddhi Prakarana of Vasubandhu. 1987. 20.00 (ISBN 0-89581-907-4). Asian Human Pr.

Prudentius. Poems, Vol. 1. LC 63-5499. (Fathers of the Church Ser: Vol. 43). 343p. 1962. 16.95x (ISBN 0-8132-0043-1). Cath U Pr.

--Poems, Vol. 2. LC 63-5499. (Fathers of the Church Ser: Vol. 52). 224p. 1965. 15.95x (ISBN 0-8132-0052-0). Cath U Pr.

Pruett, Gordon E. The Meaning & End of Suffering for Freud & the Buddhist Tradition. LC 86-26735. 524p. 1987. lib. bdg. 34.50 (ISBN 0-8191-5758-9). U Pr of Amer.

Pruett, John H. The Parish Clergy under the Later Stuarts: The Leicestershire Experience. LC 78-8174. 203p. 1978. 19.95 (ISBN 0-252-00662-3). U of Ill Pr.

Pruitt, Fred. A Great Sacrifice. 31p. 1982. pap. 0.25 (ISBN 0-686-36262-4); pap. 1.00 5 copies (ISBN 0-686-37284-0). Faith Pub Hse.

--The New Testament Church & Its Symbols. 131p. 1.00 (ISBN 0-686-29157-3). Faith Pub Hse.

--Past, Present & Future of the Church. 72p. pap. 0.60 (ISBN 0-686-29133-6). Faith Pub Hse.

Pruitt, Fred & Pruitt, Lawrence. God's Gracious Dealings. (Illus.). 496p. 5.00 (ISBN 0-686-29110-7). Faith Pub Hse.

Pruitt, Lawrence, jt. auth. see Pruitt, Fred.

Pruitt, Raymond M. Fundamentals of the Faith. 1981. 16.95 (ISBN 0-934942-21-8). White Wing Pub.

Pruitt, Rhonda R. Flames of Fire: Biographical Accounts of Pentecost Through the Centuries. (Orig.). pap. text ed. write for info. Faith Print.

Pruitt, Robert J. And Then Shall the End Come. 1979. pap. 1.95 (ISBN 0-934942-20-X). White Wing Pub.

--The Death of the Third Nature. 1975. pap. 1.95 (ISBN 0-934942-04-8). White Wing Pub.

--The Kingdom of God & the Church of God. 1977. pap. 1.95 (ISBN 0-934942-09-9). White Wing Pub.

Prupas, Marilynne, jt. auth. see Rosenfeld, Linda.

Prusan, Peretz. Guide to Hebrew Lettering. (Illus.). 64p. 1982. pap. 5.95 (ISBN 0-8074-0155-2, 282800). UAHC.

Pruser, Friedrich. England und Die Schmalkaldener, 1535-1540. 34.00 (ISBN 0-384-48058-6); pap. 28.00 (ISBN 0-384-48057-8). Johnson Repr.

Prussner, Frederick, jt. auth. see Hayes, John H.

Pruter, Hugo R. Neo-Congregationalism. LC 85-13416. 90p. 1985. Repr. lib. bdg. 19.95x (ISBN 0-89370-598-5). Borgo Pr.

--The Theology of Congregationalism. LC 85-12844. 100p. 1985. Repr. lib. bdg. 19.95x (ISBN 0-89370-597-7). Borgo Pr.

Pruter, Karl. Bishops Extraordinary. LC 86-2284. 60p. 1985. Repr. lib. bdg. 19.95x (ISBN 0-89370-544-6). Borgo Pr.

--Directory of Autocephalous Anglican, Catholic, & Orthodox Bishops. 3rd ed. LC 86-34289. 53p. 1986. lib. bdg. 19.95x (ISBN 0-89370-528-4). Borgo Pr.

--A History of the Old Catholic Church. LC 85-13418. 76p. 1985. Repr. lib. bdg. 19.95x (ISBN 0-89370-594-2). Borgo Pr.

--Jewish Christians in the U. S. A Bibliography. LC 84-48881. 250p. 1985. lib. bdg. 30.00 (ISBN 0-8240-8741-0). Garland Pub.

--Jewish Christians in the United States: A Bibliography Sects & Cults in America. LC 86-48881. (Garland Reference Library of Social Sciences Ser.). 1987. lib. bdg. 38.00. Garland Pub.

--The Teachings of the Great Mystics. LC 85-13306. 118p. 1985. Repr. lib. bdg. 19.95x (ISBN 0-89370-595-0). Borgo Pr.

Pruter, Karl & Melton, J. Gordon. The Old Catholic Sourcebook. LC 83-47610. 254p. 1983. 39.00 (ISBN 0-8240-9111-6). Garland Pub.

Pruyser, Paul W. The Minister As Diagnostician: Personal Problems in Pastoral Perspective. LC 76-8922. 144p. 1976. pap. 7.95 (ISBN 0-664-24123-9). Westminster.

Pryke, E. J. Redactional Style in the Marcan Gospel. LC 76-52184. (Society for New Testament Studies Monographs: No. 33). 1978. 44.50 (ISBN 0-521-21430-0). Cambridge U Pr.

Prynne, William. Mount-Orgueil. LC 83-20361. 1984. Repr. of 1641 ed. 40.00x (ISBN 0-8201-1392-1). Schol Facsimiles.

--The Unlovelinesse of Love-Lockes. LC 76-57410. (English Experience Ser.: No. 825). 1977. Repr. of 1628 ed. lib. bdg. 10.50 (ISBN 90-221-0825-2). Walter J Johnson.

Pryor, Neale. You Can Trust Your Bible. 3.95 (ISBN 0-89137-524-4). Quality Pubns.

Pryor, R. Louis, ed. One Gospel: Taken Literally from the Four Gospels in the Authorized King James Version of the Bible. LC 85-42545. 381p. 1985. 29.95x (ISBN 0-89950-184-2); pap. 19.95x (ISBN 0-89950-192-3). McFarland & Co.

Pryse, James M. The Apocalypse Unsealed. LC 76-41124. (Illus.). 1977. pap. 4.95 (ISBN 0-685-59031-3). Sym & Sign.

Przybylski, Benno. Righteousness in Matthew & His World of Thought. LC 79-41371. (Society for New Testament Studies Monographs: No. 41). 240p. 1981. 32.50 (ISBN 0-521-22566-3). Cambridge U Pr.

Pubek, Ronald E. The Metaphysical Imperative: A Critique of the Modern Approach to Science. LC 82-40244. 166p. (Orig.). 1983. lib. bdg. 26.00 (ISBN 0-8191-2663-2); pap. text ed. 11.25 (ISBN 0-8191-2664-0). U Pr of Amer.

Puccetti, Patricia I. Credo: I Believe: Activity Book. 46p. (Orig.). 1985. pap. 2.50 (ISBN 0-89870-082-5). Ignatius Pr.

Puccetti, Patricia I., ed. see Podhaizer, Mary E.

Puccetti, Patricia I., ed. see Sockey, Daria M.

Pucillo, Gladys, compiled by. God, Grant Me Serenity. 1982. 4.95 (ISBN 0-8378-2030-8). Gibson.

Puckett, Newbell N. Folk Beliefs of the Southern Negro. LC 68-55780. (Criminology, Law Enforcement, & Social Problems Ser.: No. 22). (Illus.). 1968. Repr. of 1926 ed. 18.00x (ISBN 0-87585-022-7). Patterson Smith.

Puech, Henri-Charles. Histoire des Religions, 3 vols. (Historique Ser.). Vols. 1 & 2. 59.95 ea.; Vol. 2. 69.95 (ISBN 0-686-56461-8). French & Eur.

Puffenberger, Allen. Words for the Weary. (Orig.). 1987. pap. price not set (ISBN 0-89536-875-7, 7861). CSS of Ohio.

Pugh, J. T. For Preachers Only. LC 86-10976. 192p. (Orig.). 1971. pap. 5.95 (ISBN 0-912315-35-0). Word Aflame.

--How to Receive the Holy Ghost. 63p. (Orig.). 1969. pap. 1.95 (ISBN 0-912315-45-8). Word Aflame.

Pugh, Nathanael. Dating Tips. Wallace, Mary H., ed. (Illus.). 120p. 1983. pap. 4.95 (ISBN 0-912315-00-8). Word Aflame.

--Living in the Tower. LC 86-18888. 96p. (Orig.). 1986. pap. 4.95 (ISBN 0-932581-01-3). Word Aflame.

--Music: Does It Really Matter? 2nd ed. Wallace, Mary H., ed. (Illus.). 79p. 1984. pap. 2.50 (ISBN 0-912315-73-3). Word Aflame.

--Running Free: Conquering Fear & Shyness. Wallace, Mary H., ed. 96p. (Orig.). 1984. pap. 4.50 (ISBN 0-912315-69-5). Word Aflame.

Pugsley, Richard. Window into Chant. 1987. pap. 5.95 (ISBN 0-941478-50-5). Paraclete Pr.

Puhalo, L. Lives of the Saints, Vols. 2. 1977. pap. 2.50x ea.; Vol. 2. (ISBN 0-913026-75-1); St Nectarios.

Puhalo, L., tr. see Khrapovitsky, Antony.

Puhalo, Lazar. Creation & Fall. 36p. (Orig.). 1986. pap. text ed. 4.00 (ISBN 0-913026-97-2). Synaxis Pr.

--Innokenty of Alaska. 86p. (Orig.). 1986. pap. 5.00 (ISBN 0-913026-86-7). Synaxis Pr.

--Missionary Handbook. 49p. (Orig.). 1985. pap. text ed. 3.00 (ISBN 0-911523-00-6). Synaxis Pr.

Puhalo, Lazar, tr. see Khrapovitsky, Antony.

Puhalo, Lev. Lives of Saints for Young People, Vol. 1. 1975. pap. 2.50x (ISBN 0-913026-11-5). St Nectarios.

Puhl, Louis J. The Spiritual Exercises of St. Ignatius Based on Studies in the Language of the Autograph. (Request Reprint). 1968. pap. 4.00 (ISBN 0-8294-0065-6). Loyola.

Puhvel, Jaan. Comparative Mythology. LC 86-20882. (Illus.). 304p. 1987. text ed. 29.50x (ISBN 0-8018-3413-9). Johns Hopkins.

Puig, Enric. Lord, I Am One of Your Little Ones. 93p. 1987. 5.95 (ISBN 0-8294-0545-3). Loyola.

Puligandla, R. The Fundamentals of Indian Philosophy. LC 85-20195. 364p. 1985. pap. text ed. 14.75 (ISBN 0-8191-4891-1). U Pr of Amer.

Pullan, Brian. The Jews of Europe & The Inquisition of Venice, 1550-1670. LC 83-7147. 364p. 1983. 32.50x (ISBN 0-389-20414-5). B&N Imports.

Pullan, Leighton. The History of the Book of Common Prayer. LC 77-15663. 1901. 20.00 (ISBN 0-8414-6848-6). Folcroft.

--The History of the Book of Common Prayer. 330p. 1981. Repr. of 1901 ed. lib. bdg. 35.00 (ISBN 0-8492-2167-6). R West.

Pullapilly, Cyriac K. Caesar Baronius: Courtier-Reformation Historian. 1975. 21.95x (ISBN 0-268-00501-X). U of Notre Dame Pr.

Pullar, Philippa, jt. auth. see Bek, Lilla.

Pullen-Burry, Henry B. Qabalism. 167p. 1972. Repr. of 1925 ed. 10.00 (ISBN 0-911662-45-6). Yoga.

Pulley, Leland E. Reaching Up, Reaching Out. LC 85-90071. (Orig.). 1985. pap. 5.95 (ISBN 0-9611282-1-6). Stewardship Enters.

Pullias, Athens C. Sermons of Athens Clay Pullias. Thomas, J. D., ed. (Great Preachers Ser). 1962. 11.95 (ISBN 0-89112-203-6, Bibl Res Pr). Abilene Christ U.

Puls, Joan. Every Bush Is Burning: A Spirituality for Today. 2nd ed. 112p. 1986. pap. 5.95 (ISBN 0-89622-280-2). Twenty-Third.

Pummer, Reinhard, jt. ed. see Sethi, Amarjit S.

Punito, Ma, ed. see Rajneesh, Bhagwan Shree.

Punke, Harold H. Mythology in American Education. 480p. 1981. pap. 14.75x (ISBN 0-8134-2136-5). Inter Print Pubs.

Punshon, John. Alternative Christianity. 1982. pap. 2.50x (ISBN 0-87574-245-9, 245). Pendle Hill.

--Encounter with Silence: Reflections from the Quaker Tradition. 156p. (Orig.). 1987. pap. 6.95 (ISBN 0-913408-96-4). Friends United.

Punt, Neal. Unconditional Good News: Toward An Understanding of Biblical Universalism. LC 80-10458. pap. 40.80 (ISBN 0-317-20014-3, 2023222). Bks Demand UMI.

--Unconditional Good News: Toward an Understanding of Biblical Universalism. LC 80-10458. pap. 44.80 (ISBN 0-317-39671-4, 2023222). Bks Demand UMI.

Punta, Frncesco del see Del Punta, Francesco.

Punto, Francesco del see Del Punta, Francesco.

Puranas, Bhagavatapurana. The Bhakti-Ratnavali: With the Commentary of Visnu Puri. LC 73-3794. (Sacred Books of the Hindus: No. 7 Pt.3). Repr. of 1912 ed. 25.00 (ISBN 0-404-57835-7). AMS Pr.

Puranas, Brahmandapurana. The Adhyatma Ramayana. Nath, Lala B., tr. LC 73-3828. (Sacred Books of the Hindus: Extra Vol. 1). Repr. of 1913 ed. 25.00 (ISBN 0-404-57846-2). AMS Pr.

Purani, A. B. The Life of Sri Aurobindo. (Illus.). 1978. 13.50 (ISBN 0-89071-230-1); pap. 11.25 (ISBN 0-89071-229-8). Matagiri.

Purce, Jill. The Mystic Spiral: Journey of the Soul. (Art & Imagination Ser.). (Illus.). 128p. 1980. pap. 10.95 (ISBN 0-500-81005-2). Thames Hudson.

--The Mystic Spiral: Journey of the Soul. 1983. 17.00 (ISBN 0-8446-5993-2). Peter Smith.

Purce, Jill, ed. see Bancroft, Anne.

Purce, Jill, ed. see Halifax, Joan.

Purce, Jill, ed. see Lamy, Lucie.

Purce, Jill, ed. see Lawlor, Robert.

Purce, Jill, ed. see Matthews, John.

Purcell, Edmund S. Life of Cardinal Manning, Archbishop of Westminster, 2 vols. LC 70-126605. (Europe 1815-1945 Ser.). 1534p. 1973. Repr. of 1896 ed. Set. lib. bdg. 115.00 (ISBN 0-306-70050-6). Da Capo.

--Life of Cardinal Manning, Archbishop of Westminster, 2 vols. 1973. Repr. of 1896 ed. 50.00 set (ISBN 0-8274-1075-1). R West.

Purcell, M. Papal Crusading Policy, Twelve Hundred Forty-Four to Twelve Hundred Ninety-One. 1975. 40.00 (ISBN 90-04-04317-9). Heinman.

Purcell, Mary. The First Jesuit. rev. ed. 225p. 1981. 10.00 (ISBN 0-8294-0371-X). Loyola.

--Matt Talbot: His Life & Times. 250p. 1977. 7.00 (ISBN 0-8199-0657-3). Franciscan Herald.

--The Quiet Companion: Peter Favre S. J., 1506-1546. vi, 198p. 1981. 8.95 (ISBN 0-8294-0377-9). Loyola.

Purcell, Royal. Ethics, Morality, & Mores. 177p. (Orig.). 1986. pap. 9.95 (ISBN 0-933189-01-X). Purcell Pub.

Purcell, William. Martyrs of Our Time. Lambert, Herbert, ed. LC 85-4104. 1985. pap. 9.95 (ISBN 0-8272-2317-X). CBP.

Purchas, Samuel. Purchas His Pilgrim Microcosmus: Or The Historie of Man. LC 76-25513. (English Experience Ser.: No. 146). 820p. 1969. Repr. of 1619 ed. 69.00 (ISBN 90-221-0146-0). Walter J Johnson.

Purdom, C. B. The God-Man: The Life, Journeys & Work of Meher Baba with an Interpretation of His Silence & Spiritual Teaching. LC 72-175960. (Illus.). 464p. 1971. 9.95 (ISBN 0-913078-03-4). Sheriar Pr.

--The Perfect Master. (Illus.). 330p. 1976. pap. 3.95 (ISBN 0-913078-24-7). Sheriar Pr.

Purdom, Charles, jt. auth. see Schloss, Malcolm.

Purdue, A. W., jt. auth. see Golby, J. M.

Purdy, A. C., jt. auth. see MacGregor, G. H.

Purdy, Alexander. The Reality of God: Thoughts on the Death of God Controversy. LC 67-23314. (Orig.). pap. 2.50x (ISBN 0-87574-154-1). Pendle Hill.

Purdy, Dorothy, jt. auth. see Spiegelberg, Nancy.

Purdy, Dwight H. Joseph Conrad's Bible. LC 83-40331. 160p. 1984. 16.95x (ISBN 0-8061-1876-8). U of Okla Pr.

Purdy, Edna I. The Walk down the Road to Tomorrow. 1983. 6.95 (ISBN 0-8062-2172-0). Carlton.

Purdy, J. David. Dads Are Special, Too. 96p. 1985. pap. 3.95 (ISBN 0-8423-0503-3). Tyndale.

Purdy, John C. Parables at Work. LC 84-17323. 132p. 1986. 10.95 (ISBN 0-664-21268-9); pap. 7.95 (ISBN 0-664-24640-0). Westminster.

Purdy, John C., ed. Always Being Reformed: The Future of Church Education. LC 85-953. 120p. 1985. pap. 7.95 (ISBN 0-664-24655-9, A Geneva Press Publication). Westminster.

Purdy, Susan. Christmas Gifts for You to Make. LC 76-10160. (Illus.). 1976. PLB 12.89 (ISBN 0-397-31695-X, Lipp Jr Bks); pap. 4.95 o. p. (ISBN 0-397-31696-8). HarpJ.

Purefoy, George W. History of the Sandy Creek Baptist Association, from Its Organization in A. D. 1758 to 1858. Gaustad, Edwin S., ed. LC 79-52604. (The Baptist Tradition Ser.). (Illus.). 1980. Repr. of 1859 ed. lib. bdg. 26.50x (ISBN 0-405-12469-4). Ayer Co Pubs.

Purgraski. Sorting Life Out. LC 60-9573. 1978. 24.00x (ISBN 0-930004-00-0); free student packet, 36 pgs. C E M Comp.

Puri, Ishwar C. Beyond Logic & Reason. Ingram, Leonard, ed. 59p. 1983. pap. 3.00 (ISBN 0-937067-00-8). Inst Study Hum Aware.

--Go Within. Scott, Edward D., ed. 177p. (Orig.). 1986. pap. 6.00 (ISBN 0-937067-07-5). Inst Study Hum Aware.

--Journey to Totality. Scott, Edward D., ed. 121p. (Orig.). 1985. pap. 6.00 (ISBN 0-937067-05-9). Inst Study Hum Aware.

--Know Thyself. Ingram, Leonard, ed. 66p. 1983. pap. 3.00 (ISBN 0-937067-01-6). Inst Study Hum Aware.

--New Age-Old Path. Scott, Edward D., ed. 54p. (Orig.). 1985. pap. 3.00 (ISBN 0-937067-04-0). Inst Study Hum Aware.

--On Love. Scott, Edward D., ed. 28p. (Orig.). 1984. pap. 2.00 (ISBN 0-937067-03-2). Inst Study Hum Aware.

--Spirituality & Total Health. Scott, Edward D., ed. 29p. (Orig.). 1986. pap. 2.00 (ISBN 0-937067-08-3). Inst Study Hum Aware.

Puri, Vishnu. Bhakti Ratnavali: An Anthology from the Bhagavata. Tapasyananda, Swami, tr. from Sanskrit. 256p. 1980. pap. 5.95 (ISBN 0-87481-499-5). Vedanta Pr.

Purinton, Herbert R. Literature of the Old Testament. 1926. 20.00 (ISBN 0-8274-2966-5). R West.

Purintun, Ann-Elizabeth, jt. auth. see Kraft, Robert A.

Purkiser. The Church in a Changing World. pap. 1.00 (ISBN 0-686-12910-5). Schmul Pub Co.

Purkiser, W. T. Beacon Bible Expositions: Hebrews, James, Peter, Vol. 11. Greathouse, William M. & Taylor, Willard H., eds. 1974. 8.95 (ISBN 0-8341-0322-2). Beacon Hill.
--Called unto Holiness, Vol. 2. 368p. 1983. 14.95 (ISBN 0-8341-0868-2). Beacon Hill.
--Exploring Christian Holiness, Vol. I: The Biblical Foundations, 3 Vols. (Exploring Christian Holiness Ser.). 280p. 1983. 10.95 (ISBN 0-8341-0843-7). Beacon Hill.
--Interpreting Christian Holiness. 70p. (Orig.). 1971. pap. 1.95 (ISBN 0-8341-0221-8). Beacon Hill.
--The Lordship of Jesus. 70p. (Orig.). 1986. pap. 2.95 (ISBN 0-8341-1135-7). Beacon Hill.
--A Primer on Prayer. (Christian Living Ser.). 32p. (Orig.). 1987. pap. write for info. (ISBN 0-8341-1191-8). Beacon Hill.
--These Earthen Vessels. 118p. 1985. pap. 4.95 (ISBN 0-8341-0977-8). Beacon Hill.
Purnananda, Swami, jt. auth. see Smart, Ninian.
Purnell, Dick. Beating the Break-up Habit. 128p. (Orig.). 1983. pap. 5.95 (ISBN 0-89840-059-7). Heres Life.
--Faith: A Thirty-One-Day Experiment. 60p. (Orig.). 1985. pap. 2.95 (ISBN 0-89840-076-7). Heres Life.
--The Thirty-One Day Experiment. LC 83-49023. 63p. (Orig.). 1984. pap. 2.95 (ISBN 0-89840-058-9). Heres Life.
Purnell, Douglas. Exploring Your Family Story. (Illus.). 156p. (Orig.). 1983. pap. 9.95 (ISBN 0-85819-415-5, Pub. by JBCE). ANZ Religious Pubns.
Purple, Samuel S. Records of the Dutch Reformed Church in New Amsterdam & New York. 50.00 (ISBN 0-8490-0936-7). Gordon Pr.
Pursell, Cleo. Triumph Over Suffering. 1982. pap. 1.50 (ISBN 0-89265-079-6). Randall Hse.
Pursey, Barbara. The Gifts of the Holy Spirit. 40p. 1984. 1.95 (ISBN 0-934421-02-1). Presby Renewal Pubns.
Pursey, Barbara A. The Charismatic Renewal & You. Orig. Title: The Holy Spirit, the Church & You. 43p. (Orig.). 1987. pap. 2.95 (ISBN 0-934421-08-0). Presby Renewal Pubns.
Purtill, Richard. Thinking about Ethics. 160p. 1976. pap. text ed. write for info. (ISBN 0-13-917716-7). P-H.
--Thinking about Religion: A Philosophical Introduction to Religion. 1978. pap. text ed. write for info (ISBN 0-13-917724-8). P-H.
Purtle, Carol J. The Marian Paintings of Jan Van Eyck. LC 81-47943. (Illus.). 288p. 1982. 52.50x (ISBN 0-691-03989-5). Princeton U Pr.
Purucker, G. De see De Purucker, G.
Purucker, G De see De Purucker, G.
Purucker, G. De see De Purucker, G.
Purucker, G. de see De Purucker, G.
Purucker, G. De see De Purucker, G.
Purucker, G. De see De Purucker, G. & Tingley, Katherine.
Purves. King David. (Ladybird Ser.). 1980. 2.50 (ISBN 0-87508-843-0). Chr Lit.
Purves, George T. The Testimony of Justin Martyr to Early Christianity. 1977. lib. bdg. 59.95 (ISBN 0-8490-2735-7). Gordon Pr.
Purves, Jock. The Unlisted Legion. 1978. pap. 4.45 (ISBN 0-85151-245-3). Banner of Truth.
Puryear, Herbert B. Reflections on the Path. 224p. 1986. pap. 3.50 (ISBN 0-553-25659-9). Bantam.
--Sex & the Spiritual Path. 256p. 1986. pap. 3.50 (ISBN 0-553-25635-1). Bantam.
Puryear, Herbert B. & Thurston, Mark. Meditation & the Mind of Man. rev. ed. 1975. pap. 6.95 (ISBN 0-87604-105-5). ARE Pr.
Puryear, Meredith. Healing Through Meditation & Prayer. 1978. pap. 5.95 (ISBN 0-87604-104-7). ARE Pr.
Pusch, Hans. Working Together on Rudolf Steiner's Mystery Dramas. LC 80-67024. (Steiner's Mystery Dramas Ser.). (Illus.). 144p. (Orig.). 1980. 15.95 (ISBN 0-910142-90-4); pap. 9.95 (ISBN 0-910142-91-2). Anthroposophic.
Pusch, Hans, tr. see Steiner, Rudolf.
Pusch, Ruth, tr. see Steiner, Rudolf.
Pusey, Edward B. Daniel the Prophet. 1978. 19.50 (ISBN 0-86524-103-1, 2701). Klock & Klock.
--The Minor Prophets: With a Commentary Explanatory & Practical & Introductions to the Several Books, 2 vols. 1986. Repr. of 1885 ed. Set. lib. bdg. 45.00 (ISBN 0-89941-505-9). W S Hein.
Pusey, Merlo. Builders of the Kingdom. LC 81-10005. 1981. 10.95 (ISBN 0-8425-1968-8). Brigham.
Pushkarev, Sergei. Rol' Pravoslavnoi Tserkvi V Istorii Rosii: The Role of the Orthodox Church in Russian History. Protoierei, pref. by. LC 85-80831. (Rus.). 125p. 1985. 9.50 (ISBN 0-911971-13-0). Effect Pub.
Pushpadanta. Siva-Mahimna Stotram (the Hymn on the Greatness of Siva) Pavitrananda, Swami, tr. pap. 1.50 (ISBN 0-87481-148-1). Vedanta Pr.
Puthenpurakal, Joseph. Baptist Missions in Nagaland. 1984. 22.50x (ISBN 0-8364-1138-2, Pub. by Mukhopadhyaya). South Asia Bks.
Putman, Bob, jt. auth. see Johnson, Gordon G.
Putnam, George H. The Censorship of the Church of Rome, 2 vols. 200.00 (ISBN 0-87968-826-2). Gordon Pr.
--Censorship of the Church of Rome & Its Influence upon the Production & Distribution of Literature, 2 Vols. LC 67-12455. 1967. Repr. of 1906 ed. 55.00 (ISBN 0-405-08869-8); 27.50 ea. Vol. 1 (ISBN 0-405-08870-1). Vol. 2 (ISBN 0-405-08871-X). Ayer Co Pubs.
Putnam, Joanne. A Time to Grow. Wallace, Mary, ed. LC 85-20190. (Illus.). 112p. (Orig.). 1985. pap. 4.95 (ISBN 0-912315-92-X). Word Aflame.
Putnam, Roy C. In It to Win It. 1973. pap. 2.95 (ISBN 0-87508-440-0). Chr Lit.
--Those He Came to Save. LC 77-13764. Repr. of 1978 ed. 35.50 (ISBN 0-8357-9029-0, 2016414). Bks Demand UMI.
Putrill, Richard L. C. S. Lewis's Case for the Christian Faith. LC 81-47435. 160p. 1985. pap. 6.68 (ISBN 0-06-066713-3, HarpR). Har-Row.
Putte, Walter Van De see Jamart, Francois.
Pyarelal, et al. Gandhian Thought & Contemporary Society. Mathur, J. S., ed. 285p. 1983. 18.00 (ISBN 0-934676-31-3). Greenlf Bks.
Pyatt. Youth Empowerment in the Church. 1983. pap. 5.95 (ISBN 0-8298-0605-9). Pilgrim NY.
Pye, Michael. The Buddha. 148p. 1979. 18.00 (ISBN 0-7156-1302-2, Pub. by Duckworth London); pap. 8.95 (ISBN 0-7156-1387-1). Longwood Pub Group.
--Skilful Means: A Concept in Mahayana Buddhism. 211p. 1978. 75.00 (ISBN 0-7156-1266-2, Pub. by Duckworth London). Longwood Pub Group.
--Zen & Modern Japanese Religions. 1985. 13.00 (ISBN 0-7062-3148-1, Pub. by Ward Lock Educ Co Ltd). State Mutual Bk.
Pye, Michael & Morgan, Robert, eds. The Cardinal Meaning: Essays in Comparative Hermeneutics, Buddhism & Christianity. (Religion & Reason Ser: No. 6). 203p. 1973. text ed. 23.25x (ISBN 90-2797-228-1). Mouton.
Pye, Michael, jt. ed. see Morgan, Robert.
Pylant, Agnes D. Threescore & Ten-Wow. LC 70-151621. 1971. pap. 2.75 (ISBN 0-8054-5213-3). Broadman.
Pyle, Hershal. America's Favorite Carols. Date not set. 2.50 (ISBN 0-317-20179-4). Campus.
--Carols for the Holidays. Date not set. 2.25 (ISBN 0-317-20177-8). Campus.
--A Festival of Holiday Songs. Date not set. pap. 2.95 (ISBN 0-317-20180-8). Campus.
Pynchon, William. The Diary of William Pynchon of Salem. Oliver, Fitch E., ed. LC 75-31131. Repr. of 1890 ed. 28.50 (ISBN 0-404-13608-7). AMS Pr.
Pyron, Bernard. The Great Rebellion: A Biblical Scrutiny of the Popular Culture of 1962-85 & Its Christian Versions. 212p. (Orig.). 1985. pap. text ed. 7.00 (ISBN 0-9615024-0-1). Rebound Pubns.
Pyron, Bernard, ed. National Sin & the Decline of American Advantages: Loss of the American Edge in War. 230p. (Orig.). 1986. pap. text ed. 7.00 (ISBN 0-9615024-1-X). Rebound Pubns.

Q

Qaderi, M. Taleem-Ul-Islam, 4. pap. 7.50 (ISBN 0-686-18387-8). Kazi Pubns.
Qadri, A. A. Islamic Jurisprudence in the Modern World. 45.00 (ISBN 0-317-46102-8). Kazi Pubns.
Qamar, J. God's Existence & Contemporary Science. pap. 1.00 (ISBN 0-686-18452-1). Kazi Pubns.
Qayyum, A. On Striving to Be a Muslim. pap. 12.50 (ISBN 0-686-63908-1). Kazi Pubns.
Qazi, M. A. ABC Islamic Reader. pap. 2.50 (ISBN 0-686-83566-2). Kazi Pubns.
--Alif Ba Ta Islamic Reader. pap. 2.00 (ISBN 0-686-83570-0). Kazi Pubns.
--Bilal in Hadith. pap. 1.25 (ISBN 0-686-18324-X). Kazi Pubns.
--Bilal: The First Muadhdhin of the Prophet of Islam. pap. 4.50 (ISBN 0-686-18325-8). Kazi Pubns.
--Miracles of Prophet Muhammad. pap. 3.50 (ISBN 0-686-18629-X). Kazi Pubns.
--What's in a Muslim Name? pap. 3.50 (ISBN 0-686-18582-X). Kazi Pubns.
Qimron, Elisha. The Hebrew of the Dead Sea Scrolls. (Harvard Semitic Ser.: No. 29). 1986. text ed. 13.95 (ISBN 0-89130-989-6, 04-04-29). Scholars Pr GA.
Quade, Quentin L., ed. The Pope & Revolution: John Paul II Confronts Liberation Theology. LC 82-4971. 205p. 1982. 12.00 (ISBN 0-89633-059-1); pap. 7.00 (ISBN 0-89633-054-0). Ethics & Public Policy.
Quadri, A. A. Islamic Jurisprudence in the Modern World. 35.00 (ISBN 0-317-01602-4). Kazi Pubns.
Quadrupani, R. P. Light & Peace. LC 79-67860. 193p. 1980. pap. 3.50 (ISBN 0-89555-133-0). TAN Bks Pubs.
Quanbeck, Philip A., II, tr. see Gunkel, Hermann.
Quantin, M. Dictionnaire Raisonne de Diplomatie Chretienne, Vol. 47. Migne, J. P., ed. (Encyclopedie Theologique Ser.). (Fr.). 578p. Repr. of 1846 ed. lib. bdg. 74.00x (ISBN 0-89241-251-8). Caratzas.
Quaraishi, M. Tariq, ed. Some Aspects of Prophet Muhammad's Life. LC 83-71409. 89p. (Orig.). Date not set. pap. 4.50 (ISBN 0-89259-045-9). Am Trust Pubns.
Quarles, J. C., tr. see Sullivan, James L.
Quarles, Jaime C., tr. see Brown, Jamieson-Fausett.
Quarles, Jaime C., tr. see Latourette, Kenneth S.
Quarles, Lemuel C., tr. see Brown, Jamieson-Fausett.
Quarles, Lemuel C., tr. see Latourette, Kenneth S.
Quasem, M. A. Salvation of the Soul & Islamic Devotion. 200p. (Orig.). 1984. pap. 12.95 (ISBN 0-7103-0033-6, Kegan Paul). Methuen Inc.
Quasem, Mohammad A. The Ethics of Al-Ghazali. LC 78-15259. (Monographs in Islamic Religion & Theology). 1978. 35.00x (ISBN 0-88206-021-X). Caravan Bks.
Quasem, Muhammad A. The Ethics of al-Ghazali: A Composite Ethics in Islam. 1975. 17.85 (ISBN 0-686-18952-3); pap. 9.00 (ISBN 0-686-18953-1). Quasem.
--The Jewels of the Qur'an: Al-Ghazali's Theory. 1977. 12.00 (ISBN 0-686-23467-7). Quasem.
--The Jewels of the Qur'an: Al-Ghazali's Theory. 240p. (Orig.). 1984. pap. 12.95 (ISBN 0-7103-0034-4, Kegan Paul). Methuen Inc.
--The Recitation & Interpretation of the Qur'an. 1979. 12.00 (ISBN 0-318-00410-0). Quasem.
Quasten & Plumpe, eds. Epistles of St. Clement of Rome & St. Ignatius of Antioch. Kleist, James A., tr. (Ancient Christian Writers Ser.: No. 1). 1946. 12.95 (ISBN 0-8091-0038-X). Paulist Pr.
Quasten, ed. see Jerome, Saint.
Quasten, ed. see Paulinus of Nola, Saint.
Quasten, J., ed. Poems of St. Paulinus of Nola. Walsh, P. G., tr. (Ancient Christian Writers Ser.: Vol. 40). 1975. 14.95 (ISBN 0-8091-0197-1). Paulist Pr.
Quasten, J., ed. see Augustine, St.
Quasten, J., ed. see St. Augustine.
Quasten, Johannes. Patrology, 3 vols. 1514p. 1983. Set. pap. 50.00 (ISBN 0-87061-084-8); Vol. 1. pap. 15.00 (ISBN 0-87061-084-8); Vol. 2. pap. 18.00 (ISBN 0-87061-085-6); Vol. 3. pap. 21.00 (ISBN 0-87061-091-0); Set of 4 vols. pap. 85.00. Chr Classics.
Quasten, Johannes & Di Berardino, Angelo, eds. Patrology, Vol. IV: The Golden Age of Latin Patristic Literature. Solari, Placid, tr. 1986. 48.00 (ISBN 0-87061-126-7); pap. 39.95 (ISBN 0-87061-127-5); Set of 4 vols. pap. 85.00. Chr Classics.
Quaytman, Wilfred, ed. Holocaust Survivors: Psychological & Social Sequelae. LC 80-80071. (A Special Issue of Journal of Contemporary Psychotherapy: Vol. 11, No. 1). 88p. 1981. pap. 9.95 (ISBN 0-89885-016-9). Human Sci Pr.
Qubein, Nido. What Works & What Doesn't in Youth Ministry. Zapel, Arthur L. & Pijanowski, Kathy, eds. (Illus.). 211p. 1986. pap. 7.95 (ISBN 0-916260-40-2). Meriwether Pub.
Quebedeaux, Richard. The New Charismatics II: How a Christian Renewal Movement Became a Part of the American Religious Mainstream. LC 82-48417. 228p. 1983. pap. 8.95 (ISBN 0-06-066723-0, RD379, HarpR). Har-Row.
Quebedeaux, Richard, ed. Lifestyle: Conversations with Members of the Unification Church. LC 82-50799. (Conference Ser.: No. 13). (Orig.). 1982. 12.95 (ISBN 0-932894-18-6, Pub. by New Era Bks); pap. 9.95 (ISBN 0-932894-13-5, Pub. by New Era Bks). Paragon Hse.
--Lifestyles. LC 82-50799. 214p. (Orig.). 1982. 14.95; pap. 10.95. Rose Sharon Pr.
Quebedeaux, Richard & Sawatsky, Rodney, eds. Evangelical-Unification Dialogue. LC 79-89421. (Conference Ser.: No. 3). 374p. (Orig.). 1979. pap. text ed. 7.95 (ISBN 0-932894-02-X, Pub. by New Era Bks). Paragon Hse.
--Evangical-Unification Dialog. LC 79-89421. 374p. (Orig.). pap. 7.95. Rose Sharon Pr.
Queck, Lynn. Leader's Guide: Meeting Jesus in Holy Communion. 96p. 1985. pap. 3.95 (ISBN 0-89243-224-1). Liguori Pubns.
Queller, Donald E. The Fourth Crusade. LC 77-81454. (Middle Ages Ser). 1977. pap. 10.95x (ISBN 0-8122-1098-0). U of Pa Pr.
Quennell, Peter. John Ruskin: The Portrait of a Prophet. 1973. Repr. of 1949 ed. 35.00 (ISBN 0-8274-0472-7). R West.
Quenon, Paul. Carved in Stone. (Illus.). 40p. 1979. pap. 2.50 (ISBN 0-87793-195-X). Ave Maria.
Quenstedt, J. A. The Nature & Character of Theology. Poellet, Luther, tr. 208p. 1986. 12.95 (ISBN 0-570-03984-3, 12-3011). Concordia.
Querido, R. M., tr. see Steiner, Rudolf.
Querido, Rene. Questions & Answers on Reincarnation & Karma. 1977. pap. 3.50 (ISBN 0-916786-18-8). St George Bk Serv.
Quesnell, John G. Holy Terrors & Holy Parents. 228p. 1976. 7.95 (ISBN 0-8199-0561-5). Franciscan Herald.
Quesnell, John Q. The Family Planning Dilemma Revisited. (Synthesis Ser.). 64p. 1975. pap. 1.75 (ISBN 0-8199-0364-7). Franciscan Herald.
--The Message of Christ & the Counselor. (Synthesis Ser). 1975. 2.00 (ISBN 0-8199-0534-8). Franciscan Herald.
Quesnell, Quentin. The Gospel in the Church: A Catechetical Commentary on the Lectionary Cycle C: the Creed. LC 82-9951. 176p. 1982. 12.95 (ISBN 0-8245-0454-2); pap. 5.95 (ISBN 0-8245-0476-3). Crossroad NY.
Quezada, Adolfo. A Desert Place. (Illus.). 96p. (Orig.). 1982. pap. 2.95 (ISBN 0-914544-40-3). Living Flame Pr.
--Good-Bye, My Son, Hello. LC 84-72629. 64p. (Orig.). 1985. pap. 2.95 (ISBN 0-87029-196-3). Abbey.
--Wholeness: The Legacy of Jesus. 89p. (Orig.). 1983. pap. 2.95 (ISBN 0-914544-48-9). Living Flame Pr.
Quicherat, Jules, ed. see Jeanne D'Arc, Saint.
Quick, Daniel L. & Noton, Thomas A. Cry from the Mountain. 159p. 1986. pap. 5.95 (ISBN 0-89066-064-6). World Wide Pubs.
Quigley, Carol, ed. Turning Points in Religious Life. LC 85-45565. 180p. (Orig.). 1987. pap. 8.95 (ISBN 0-89453-545-5). M Glazier.
Quigley, Robert, jt. auth. see Sears, William.
Quigley, Thomas E., ed. American Catholics & Vietnam. LC 68-54102. pap. 49.30 (ISBN 0-317-07878-X, 2012814). Bks Demand UMI.
Quilan, Hamid, ed. see Sabiq, Sayyed.
Quillin, Roger T. Meeting Christ in Handel's Messiah: Lent & Easter Messages Based on Handel's Texts & Music. 96p. 1984. pap. 4.95 (ISBN 0-8066-2118-4, 10-4318). Augsburg.
Quimby, Ian M., ed. Winterthur Portfolio No. 8: Thematic Issue on Religion in America. (A Winterthur Bk.). (Illus.). 1973. 15.00X (ISBN 0-226-92134-4). U of Chicago Pr.
Quincer, Sheldon B., ed. Matthew Henry's Sermon Outlines. 1955. pap. 5.95 (ISBN 0-8028-1155-8). Eerdmans.
Quine, W. V. & Ullian, J. S. The Web of Belief. 2nd ed. 1978. pap. text ed. 7.00 (ISBN 0-394-32179-0, RanC). Random.
Quinlan, Hamid, ed. see Abdul Fattah Rashid Hamid.
Quinlan, Hamid, ed. see Abu-Saud, Mahmoud.
Quinlan, Hamid, ed. see Ali-Nadawi, Abul H.
Quinlan, Hamid, ed. see Badawi, Gamal A.
Quinlan, Hamid, ed. see Izzidien, Mouel Y.
Quinlan, Hamid, ed. see Kishta, Leila.
Quinlan, Hamid, ed. see Siddiqui, Zeba.
Quinley, Ernest & Quinley, Rachel. Lets Have Church, Children, No. 1. 1981. pap. 7.95 (ISBN 0-87148-512-5). Pathway Pr.
--Let's Have Church, Children, No. 2. 1981. pap. 7.95 (ISBN 0-87148-513-3). Pathway Pr.
Quinley, Harold E. & Glock, Charles Y. Anti-Semitism in America. LC 78-20649. 1979. 11.95 (ISBN 0-02-925640-2). Free Pr.
Quinley, Rachel, jt. auth. see Quinley, Ernest.
Quinn, Arthur, jt. auth. see Kikawada, Isaac M.
Quinn, Bernard. Distribution of Catholic Priests in the United States: 1971. 1975. pap. 3.50x (ISBN 0-914422-04-9). Glenmary Res Ctr.
--The Small Rural Parish. LC 79-56508. (Orig.). 1980. pap. 3.50x (ISBN 0-914422-11-1). Glenmary Res Ctr.
Quinn, Bernard & Booker-Feister, John. Apostolic Regions of the United States: 1980. LC 78-67012. (Illus.). 1985. pap. text ed. 4.00x (ISBN 0-914422-08-1). Glenmary Res Ctr.
Quinn, Bernard, jt. auth. see Byers, David M.
Quinn, Charles U., tr. see Bouyer, Louis.
Quinn, Charles U., tr. see Moeller, Charles.
Quinn, Charles U., tr. see Paoli, Arturo.
Quinn, D. Michael. Early Mormonism & the Magic World View. 250p. 1987. 14.95 (ISBN 0-941214-46-X). Signature Bks.
Quinn, Edward, tr. see Kung, Hans.
Quinn, Esther C. The Penitence of Adam: (A Study of the Andrius MS., No. 36. Dufau, Micheline, tr. LC 79-19056. 192p. 1980. 21.00x (ISBN 84-499-3367-6). Romance.

Quinn, John M. Praise in St. Augustine: Readings & Reflections. 220p. pap. 8.95 (ISBN 0-8158-0430-X). Chris Mass.

Quinn, Mark. Jesus of the Gospels: A Worktext Approach to Understanding Scripture. (YA) 1987. pap. text ed. write for info. (ISBN 0-697-02233-1); write for info. tchr's. ed. (ISBN 0-697-02234-X). Wm C Brown.

Quinn, P. E. Cry Out! Inside the Terrifying World of an Abused Child. 208p. 1984. 10.95 (ISBN 0-687-10015-1). Abingdon.

Quinn, Phil E. Renegade Saint: A Story of Hope by a Child Abuse Survivor. 1986. 12.95 (ISBN 0-687-36130-3). Abingdon.

Quinn, Philip L. Divine Commands & Moral Requirements. (Clarendon Library of Logic & Philosophy). 1978. text ed. 36.00x (ISBN 0-19-824413-4). Oxford U Pr.

Quinn, R. M. Fernando Gallego & the Retablo of Ciudad Rodrigo. LC 60-15915. (Span. & Eng., Illus.). 117p. 1961. 8.50x (ISBN 0-8165-0034-7). U of Ariz Pr.

Quinones de Dailey, Eva, ed. Vision Clara de Dios. (Span.). pap. 4.95 (ISBN 0-87148-884-1). Pathway Pr.

Quint, Emanuel & Hecht, Neil S. Jewish Jurisprudence: Its Sources & Modern Applications Ser, Vol. 1. (Jurisprudence-Its Sources & Modern Applications Ser.). 268p. 1980. 46.25 (ISBN 3-7186-0054-4); pap. 13.95 (ISBN 3-7186-0055-2). Harwood Academic.

Quint, Emanuel B. & Hecht, Neil S. Jewish Jurisprudence: Its Sources & Modern Applications. (Jewish Jurisprudence Ser.: Vol. 2). 193p. 1986. text ed. 65.00 (ISBN 3-7186-0064-1); pap. text ed. 18.00 (ISBN 3-7186-0293-8). Harwood Academic.

Quintero, Roberto, ed. see Cornish, Patty Jo.

Quinton, Margaret, jt. ed. see Tomlinson, Peter.

Quirk, Robert E. The Mexican Revolution & the Catholic Church, 1910-1929. LC 85-30209. 276p. 1986. Repr. of 1973 ed. lib. bdg. 45.00x (ISBN 0-313-25121-5, QUMC). Greenwood.

Quirk, Thomas, ed. see Howard, Leon.

Quiros, T. E. Por Sendas Biblicas. (Span.). 162p. 1985. pap. 3.25 (ISBN 0-311-08753-1). Casa Bautista.

Quispel, Gilles & Scholem, Gershom. Jewish & Gnostic Man. LC 85-26137. (Eranos Lectures Ser.: No. 3). 46p. (Orig.). 1986. pap. 7.50 (ISBN 0-88214-403-0). Spring Pubns.

Quistorp, Heinrich. Calvin's Doctrine of the Last Things. John Knox.

--Calvin's Doctrine of the Last Things. Knight, Harold, tr. LC 83-45629. Date not set. Repr. of 1955 ed. 27.50 (ISBN 0-404-19846-5). AMS Pr.

Quitoriano, James H. The Psychology of the Soul. (Illus.). 1979. 47.50 (ISBN 0-89266-204-2). Am Classical Coll Pr.

Quoist, Michael. Prayers. 1975. pap. 5.95 (ISBN 0-380-00406-2, 60244-X). Avon.

Quoist, Michel. The Breath of Love. 167p. (Orig.). 1987. pap. 8.95 (ISBN 0-8245-0801-7). Crossroad NY.

--Living Words. 5.95 (ISBN 0-87193-196-6). Dimension Bks.

--Meeting God. 1985. 4.95 (ISBN 0-87193-222-9). Dimension Bks.

--With Open Heart. 264p. (Orig.). 1983. pap. 8.95 (ISBN 0-8245-0569-7). Crossroad NY.

Quraishi, M. Tariq, ed. Islam, A Way of Life & a Movement. LC 83-71408. 221p. (Orig.). 1986. pap. 9.50 (ISBN 0-89259-055-6). Am Trust Pubns.

Qureshi, A. I. Fiscal System of Islam. 1981. 10.50 (ISBN 0-686-97866-8). Kazi Pubns.

Qureshi, Hafiz M. The Qur'an and Slavery. Siddique, Kaukab, tr. from Urdu. 39p. (Orig.). 1984. pap. 2.00 (ISBN 0-942978-07-2). Am Soc Ed & Rel.

Qureshi, Regula B. Sufi Music of India & Pakistan: Sound, Context & Meaning in Qawwali. (Cambridge Studies in Ethnomusicology). (Illus.). 300p. 1987. 69.50 (ISBN 0-521-26767-6); cassette 18.96 (ISBN 0-521-32598-6). Cambridge U Pr.

Qutb, M. Islam: The Misunderstood Religion. pap. 8.50 (ISBN 0-686-18500-5). Kazi Pubns.

Qutb, Muhammad. Islam: The Misunderstood Religion. Tr. of Shubuhat haul al-Islam. 199p. (Orig.). 1977. pap. 5.95 (ISBN 0-939830-05-1, Pub. by IIFSO Kuwait). New Era Pubns MI.

--Shubuhat Haul al-Islam. (Arabic.). 203p. (Orig.). 1977. pap. 4.75x (ISBN 0-939830-15-9, Pub. by IIFSO Kuwait). New Era Pubns MI.

Qutb, S. In the Shade of the Qur'an, 30th Part. pap. 14.95 (ISBN 0-317-46111-7). Kazi Pubns.

--Milestone. 1981. pap. 7.50 (ISBN 0-686-77426-4). Kazi Pubns.

Qutb, Sayyed. Islam & Universal Peace. LC 77-89635. 1977. pap. 2.85 (ISBN 0-89259-007-6). Am Trust Pubns.

Qutb, Sayyid. Al-Mustaqbal li-hadha ad-Din. (Arabic.). 118p. (Orig.). 1978. pap. 2.35x (ISBN 0-939830-16-7, Pub. by IIFSO Kuwait). New Era Pubns MI.

--Hadha ad-Din. (Arabic.). 96p. (Orig.). 1978. pap. 1.75x (ISBN 0-939830-18-3, Pub. by IIFSO Kuwait). New Era Pubns MI.

--Ma alim fi at-Tariq. (Arabic.). 186p. (Orig.). 1978. pap. 3.75x (ISBN 0-939830-17-5, Pub. by IIFSO Kuwait). New Era Pubns MI.

--Milestones. Tr. of Ma alim fi at-Tariq. 303p. (Orig.). 1978. pap. 5.95 (ISBN 0-939830-07-8, Pub. by IIFSO Kuwait). New Era Pubns MI.

--This Religion of Islam. Tr. of Hadha ad-Din. 104p. (Orig.). 1977. pap. 2.95x (ISBN 0-939830-08-6, Pub. by IIFSO Kuwait). New Era Pubns MI.

R

R. R. Bowker Co. Staff, ed. Religious & Inspirational Books & Serials in Print 1987. 1700p. 1987. 89.00 (ISBN 0-8352-2320-5). Bowker.

Raabe, Paul J. The Scientific & Humorous Revelations of God. 2nd rev. ed. 1981. 4.00 (ISBN 0-682-49415-1). Exposition Pr FL.

Raban, S. Mortmain Legislation & the English Church, 1279-1500. LC 81-21685. (Cambridge Studies in Medieval Life & Thought: No. 17). (Illus.). 244p. 1982. 47.50 (ISBN 0-521-24233-9). Cambridge U Pr.

Rabassa, Gregory, tr. see Benet, Juan.

Rabbani, Ruhiyyih. Prescription for Living. 2nd, rev. ed. 272p. 4.75 (ISBN 0-85398-002-0). G Ronald Pub.

--The Priceless Pearl. (Illus.). 1969. pap. 8.95 (ISBN 0-900125-03-9, 331-048). Baha'i.

Rabbath, Antoine. Documents Inedits Pour Servir a l'Histoire Du Christianisme En Orient, 2 Vols. LC 72-174293. Repr. of 1911 ed. Set. lib. bdg. 95.00 (ISBN 0-404-05202-9). AMS Pr.

Rabbi Aryeh Kaplan. Unitl the Mashiach: The Life of Rabbi Nachman. Shapiro, Dovid, ed. 379p. 1986. text ed. 15.00 (ISBN 0-930213-08-4). Breslov Res Inst.

Rabbi Nachman of Breslov. The Aleph-Bet Book. Mykoff, Moshe, tr. from Hebrew. & intro. by. Tr. of Sefer HaMiddot. 268p. 1986. text ed. 12.00 (ISBN 0-930213-15-7). Breslov Res Inst.

--Likutey Moharan, Vol. 1. Bergman, Simcha & Mykoff, Moshe, trs. from Hebrew. 213p. 1986. pap. text ed. 10.00 (ISBN 0-930213-76-9). Breslov Res Inst.

--TSOHAR. Greenbaum, Avraham, tr. from Hebrew. 64p. (Orig.). 1986. pap. text ed. 1.50 (ISBN 0-930213-26-2). Breslov Res Inst.

Rabbi Nachman of Breslov & Rabbi Nathan of Breslov. Rabbi Nachman De Breslov. Dimermanas, Alon, ed. (Illus.). 442p. 1986. text ed. 18.00 (ISBN 0-930213-19-X); pap. 15.00 (ISBN 0-930213-20-3). Breslov Res Inst.

Rabbi Nathan of Breslov, jt. auth. see Rabbi Nachman of Breslov.

Rabbi Alon I. Tolwin. Taryag: The Six Hundred Thirteenth Mitzvos. 106p. 1983. pap. 5.95 (ISBN 0-87306-378-3). Feldheim.

Rabbi Mindy Avra Portnoy. Ima on the Bima: My Mommy is a Rabbi. LC 86-3023. (Illus.). 32p. 1986. 10.95 (ISBN 0-930494-54-7); pap. 4.95 (ISBN 0-930494-55-5). Kar Ben.

Rabbi Nachman. Le Tikoun Haklali. Dimermanas, Alon, tr. from Hebrew. (Fr.). 125p. 1986. pap. text ed. 3.00 (ISBN 0-930213-24-6). Breslov Res Inst.

Rabbinowitz, Joseph, ed. see Marmorstein, Arthur.

Rabbi Yehoshja Y. Neuwirth. Shemirath Sabbath. Grangewood, W., tr. from Hebrew. Tr. of Shemirath Sabbath Kehilchathah. 360p. 1984. 11.95 (ISBN 0-87306-298-1); pap. 8.95 (ISBN 0-87306-375-9). Feldheim.

Rabe, Valentin H. The Home Base of American China Missions, 1880-1920. (Harvard East Asian Monographs: Vol. 75). 1978. 21.00x (ISBN 0-674-40581-1). Harvard U Pr.

Rabil, Albert. Erasmus & the New Testament: The Mind of a Christian Humanist. LC 71-184768. (Trinity University Monograph Series in Religion: Vol. 1). pap. 51.50 (ISBN 0-317-08044-X, 2022565). Bks Demand UMI.

Rabin. Jewish Lights: Substitute Teachers Kit. 1984. 3.00x (ISBN 0-940646-28-5). Rossel Bks.

Rabin, Chaim. Hebrew. 1977. Repr. of 1949 ed. lib. bdg. 17.00 (ISBN 0-8492-2311-3). R West.

--Qumran Studies. LC 76-40116. (Scripta Judaica: No. 2). 1976. Repr. of 1957 ed. lib. bdg. 22.50x (ISBN 0-8371-9060-6, RAQS). Greenwood.

Rabin, Chaim, tr. see Maimonodes, Moses.

Rabinbach, Anson & Zipes, Jack D., eds. Germans & Jews since the Holocaust: The Changing Situation in West Germany. 300p. 1986. text ed. 37.50 (ISBN 0-8419-0924-5); pap. text ed. 17.95 (ISBN 0-8419-0925-3). Holmes & Meier.

Rabinonwitz, C. D. A Teacher's Guide for Sefer Yehoshua. (Hebrew.). 4.00 (ISBN 0-914131-68-0, B41). Torah Umesorah.

Rabinovitch, Nachum L. Probability & Statistical Inference in Ancient & Medieval Jewish Literature. LC 79-187394. pap. 54.80 (ISBN 0-317-08544-1, 2014349). Bks Demand UMI.

Rabinowicz, Harry. Hasidism & the State of Israel. (Littman Library of Jewish Civilization). (Illus.). 1982. 24.95x (ISBN 0-19-710049-X). Oxford U Pr.

Rabinowicz, Oscar K. Winston Churchill on Jewish Problems. LC 74-43. 231p. 1974. Repr. of 1960 ed. lib. bdg. 22.50x (ISBN 0-8371-7357-4, RAWC). Greenwood.

Rabinowitz, C. D. A Teacher's Guide for Melachim I: A Teacher's Guide. 5.00 (ISBN 0-914131-66-4, B45). Torah Umesorah.

--The Teaching of Prayer: A Teacher's Guide. 2.25 (ISBN 0-914131-71-0, B50). Torah Umesorah.

Rabinowitz, Chaim D. Divrei Y'mei Yisroel: In Hebrew. text ed. 10.00 (ISBN 0-914131-18-4, A80). Torah Umesorah.

Rabinowitz, Dorothy. About the Holocaust: What We Know & How We Know It. LC 79-51801. (Illus.). 48p. 1979. pap. 1.50 (ISBN 0-87495-014-7). Am Jewish Comm.

Rabinowitz, Jacob J. see Maimonides, Moses.

Rabinowitz, Jan. The Tzedakah Workbook. (Illus.). 32p. (Orig.). 1986. pap. text ed. 3.95 (ISBN 0-933873-07-7). Torah Aura.

Rabinowitz, Louis I. Torah & Flora. (Illus.). 1977. 11.95 (ISBN 0-88482-917-0, Sanhedrin Pr). Hebrew Pub.

Rabinowitz, Louis I. see Maimonides, Moses.

Rabinowitz, Oskar K. Arnold Toynbee on Judaism & Zionism: A Critique. 372p. 1975. 17.95x (ISBN 0-8464-0149-5). Beekman Pubs.

Rabinsky, Leatrice & Mann, Gertrude. Journey of Conscience: Young People Respond to the Holocaust. 112p. Repr. 1.50 (ISBN 0-686-95073-9). ADL.

Rabten, Geshe. Echoes of Voidness. Batchelor, Stephen, ed. (Intermediate Book: White Ser.). (Illus.). 148p. (Orig.). 1983. pap. 8.95 (ISBN 0-86171-010-X, Pub. by Wisdom Pubns). Great Traditions.

--The Essential Nectar. Wilson, Martin, ed. (A Wisdom Basic Book, Orange Ser.). 304p. (Orig.). 1984. pap. 11.95 (ISBN 0-86171-013-4, Wisdom Pubns). Great Traditions.

Raburn, Terry. Under the Guns in Beirut. LC 80-65308. 160p. 1980. pap. 2.50 (ISBN 0-88243-634-1, 02-0634). Gospel Pub.

Rabuzzi, Kathryn A. The Sacred & the Feminine: Toward a Theology of Housework. 224p. 1982. 15.95 (ISBN 0-8164-0509-3, HarpR). Har-Row.

Raccagni, Michelle. The Modern Arab Woman: A Bibliography. LC 78-15528. 272p. 1978. lib. bdg. 19.00 (ISBN 0-8108-1165-0). Scarecrow.

Race, Alan. Christians & Religious Pluralism: Patterns in the Christian Theology of Religions. 192p. (Orig.). 1983. pap. 8.95 (ISBN 0-88344-101-2). Orbis Bks.

Rachlin & Marriott. Plains Indian Mythology. 224p. 1977. pap. 3.95 (ISBN 0-452-00766-6, Mer). NAL.

Rachlin, Carol K., jt. auth. see Marriott, Alice.

Rachlis, Eugene, jt. ed. see Levine, Mark.

Racine, Louis. Life of Milton. LC 74-16189. 1930. lib. bdg. 17.00 (ISBN 0-8414-7258-0). Folcroft.

Rad, Gerhard von see Von Rad, Gerhard.

Rad, Gerhard Von see Von Rad, Gerhard.

Rad, Gerhard von see Von Rad, Gerhard.

Rada, jt. auth. see Warren, Mary P.

Radau, Hugo. Ninib, the Determiner of Fates from the Temple Library of Nippur. (Publications of the Babylonian Section, Ser. D: Vol. 5-2). (Illus.). x, 73p. 1910. bound 5.00xsoft (ISBN 0-686-11919-3). Univ Mus of U PA.

Radcliffe, Florence J. A Simple Matter of Justice: The Phyllis Wheatly YWCA Story. 304p. 1985. 13.00 (ISBN 0-682-40199-4). Exposition Pr FL.

Radday, Yehuda & Levi, Yaakov. An Analytical Linguistic Key-Word-in-Context Concordance to the Book of Exodus. Baird, Arthur J. & Freedman, David, eds. (The Computer Bible Ser.: Vol. 28). (Orig.). 1985. 45.00 (ISBN 0-935106-23-5). Biblical Res Assocs.

Radday, Yehuda T. An Analytical Linguistic Concordance to the Book of Isaiah. (Computer Bible Ser: Vol. II). 1975. 20.00 (ISBN 0-935106-15-4). Biblical Res Assocs.

--An Analytical, Linguistic Key-Word-in-Context Concordance to the Book of Judges. (Computer Bible Ser.: Vol. XI). 1977. pap. 20.00 (ISBN 0-935106-10-3). Biblical Res Assocs.

Radecke, Mark. In Christ: A New Creation. Sherer, Michael L., ed. (Orig.). 1986. pap. 6.25 (ISBN 0-89536-821-8, 6830). CSS of Ohio.

Radecke, Mark W. In Many & Various Ways. 1985. 5.75 (ISBN 0-89536-721-1, 5806). CSS of Ohio.

Rademacher, William J. Answers for Parish Councillors. LC 81-51429. 1981. pap. 6.95 (ISBN 0-89622-134-2). Twenty-Third.

Rademaker, C. S. Life & Work of Gerardus Joannes Vossius 1577-1649. (Respublica Literaria Neerlandica: No. 5). 472p. 1981. text ed. 39.50 (ISBN 90-232-1785-3, Pub. by Van Gorcum Holland). Longwood Pub Group.

Rader, Rosemary. Breaking Boundaries: Male-Female Friendship in Early Christian Communities. (Theological Inquiries Ser.). 144p. 1983. pap. 6.95 (ISBN 0-8091-2506-4). Paulist Pr.

Rader, William. The Church & Racial Hostility: A History of Interpretation of Ephesians. 1978. 71.50x (ISBN 3-16-140112-3). Adlers Foreign Bks.

Radford, Edwin & Radford, Mona A. Encyclopedia of Superstitions. Repr. of 1949 ed. lib. bdg. 45.00x (ISBN 0-8371-2115-9, RASU). Greenwood.

Radford, Mona A., jt. auth. see Radford, Edwin.

Radha, Sivananda. Kundalini Yoga for the West. LC 81-40488. (Illus.). 379p. 1981. pap. 14.95 (ISBN 0-87773-211-6). Shambhala Pubns.

Radha, Swami S. The Divine Light Invocation. 54p. 1982. pap. 5.00 (ISBN 0-931454-08-5). Timeless Bks.

Radhakrishnan, S. Eastern Religions & Western Thought. 2nd ed. 1975. pap. text ed. 10.95x (ISBN 0-19-560604-3). Oxford U Pr.

--Hindu View of Life. (Unwin Paperbacks Ser.). 92p. 1980. pap. 4.95 (ISBN 0-04-294115-6). Allen Unwin.

--Indian Religions. (Orient Paperbacks Ser.). 196p. 1981. pap. 3.95 (ISBN 0-86578-084-6); 8.95 (ISBN 0-86578-117-6). Ind-US Inc.

--Indian Religions. 1979. 7.00x (ISBN 0-8364-0367-3). South Asia Bks.

--Living with a Purpose. 136p. 1982. 9.00 (ISBN 0-86578-204-0); pap. 4.25 (ISBN 0-86578-137-0). Ind-US Inc.

Radhakrishnan, S., tr. see Badarayana.

Radhakrishnan, Sarvepalli. Recovery of Faith. Repr. of 1955 ed. lib. bdg. 22.50x (ISBN 0-8371-0197-2, RARF). Greenwood.

Radin, Max. The Jews Among the Greeks & Romans. LC 73-2224. (The Jewish People; History, Religion, Literature Ser.). Repr. of 1915 ed. 33.00 (ISBN 0-405-05286-3). Ayer Co Pubs.

Radin, Paul. Literary Aspects of North American Mythology. 1979. Repr. of 1915 ed. lib. bdg. 15.50 (ISBN 0-8414-7304-8). Folcroft.

--Literary Aspects of North American Mythology. (Folklore Ser). 20.00 (ISBN 0-8482-5887-8). Norwood Edns.

--Primitive Religion: Its Nature & Origin. 1937. pap. text ed. 5.95 (ISBN 0-486-20393-X). Dover.

--Road of Life & Death. (Bollingen Ser.: Vol. 5). 1945. 33.00 (ISBN 0-691-09819-0). Princeton U Pr.

--Trickster: A Study in American Indian Mythology. Repr. of 1956 ed. lib. bdg. 28.75x (ISBN 0-8371-2112-4, RATT). Greenwood.

--The Trickster: A Study in American Indian Mythology. LC 74-88986. 223p. 1972. pap. 6.95 (ISBN 0-8052-0351-6). Schocken.

Radin, Pual. Primitive Religion. 15.25 (ISBN 0-8446-2775-5). Peter Smith.

Radius, Marianne. New Testament Story Sermons for Children's Church. 120p. 1984. pap. 5.95 (ISBN 0-8010-7723-0). Baker Bk.

--Ninety Story Sermons for Children's Church. 286p. 1976. pap. 7.95 (ISBN 0-8010-7641-2). Baker Bk.

--One Hundred & Twenty Dramatic Story Sermons for Children's Church. 368p. 1985. pap. 8.95 (ISBN 0-8010-7730-3). Baker Bk.

Radl, Shirley. Mother's Day Is over. 288p. 1987. 17.95 (ISBN 0-87795-864-5). Arbor Hse.

Radl, Shirley R. The Invisible Woman: Target of the Religious New Right. LC 83-5345. 264p. 1983. 17.95 (ISBN 0-385-29232-5, Sey Lawr). Delacorte.

--The Invisible Woman: Target of the Religious New Right. LC 83-5345. 264p. 1983. pap. 9.95 (ISBN 0-385-29210-4, Delta). Dell.

Radler, William. The Church & Racial Hostility. 282p. 1978. lib. bdg. 45.00x (Pub. by J C B Mohr BRD). Coronet Bks.

Radmacher, Earl D. & Preus, Robert D., eds. Hermeneutics, Inerrancy, & the Bible: Papers from ICBI Summit II. LC 83-12314. 928p. (Orig.). 1984. pap. 16.95 (ISBN 0-310-37081-7, 12314P). Zondervan.

Radspieler, A., tr. see Bardon, Franz.

Rady, Martyn C. Medieval Buda. 1985. 32.00 (ISBN 0-88033-074-0). East Eur Quarterly.

Radzinowics, Mary Ann, ed. see Milton, John.

Radzinowicz, Mary Ann. Toward Samson Agonistes: The Growth of Milton's Mind. LC 77-85559. 1978. 50.00x (ISBN 0-691-06357-5). Princeton U Pr.

Rae, Daphne. Love Until It Hurts: The Work of Mother Teresa & Her Missionaries of Charity. LC 81-47424. (Illus., Orig.). 1981. pap. 9.95 (ISBN 0-06-066729-X, RD 368, HarpR). Har-Row.

Raffalovich, Isaiah. Our Inheritance: A Collection of Sermons & Addresses for All the Sabbaths & Festivals. 272p. 32.50 (ISBN 0-87559-146-9). Shalom.

Raffan, John, tr. see Burkert, William.

Raftery, Francis. The Teacher in the Catholic School. 61p. 1986. 6.60 (ISBN 0-318-20567-X). Natl Cath Educ.

Ragg, Lonsdale. Tree Lore in the Bible. Repr. of 1935 ed. lib. bdg. 30.00 (ISBN 0-8495-4528-5). Arden Lib.

Raghavan, K. Yoga, Facts & Fancies. 1983. 7.50x (ISBN 0-8364-0950-7, Pub. by Mukhopadhyay India). South Asia Bks.

Raghavan, V., ed. The Ramayana Tradition in Asia. 1982. 18.00x (ISBN 0-8364-0899-3, Pub. by National Sahitya Akademi). South Asia Bks.

Raglan, FitzRoy. The Hero: A Study in Tradition, Myth, & Drama. LC 75-23424. 296p. 1975. Repr. of 1956 ed. lib. bdg. 45.00x (ISBN 0-8371-8138-0, RATH). Greenwood.

Ragland, Margaret. Full of Joy. 1980. pap. 5.25 (ISBN 0-89137-415-9). Quality Pubns.

--What's It Worth? Probing Our Values with Questions Jesus Asked. 1977. pap. 4.95 (ISBN 0-89137-409-4). Quality Pubns.

Ragsdale, John P. Protestant Mission Education in Zambia: Eighteen Eighty to Nineteen Fifty-Four. LC 85-40505. 192p. 1986. 26.50x (ISBN 0-941664-09-0). Susquehanna U Pr.

Ragusa, Isa & Green, Rosalie B., eds. Meditations on the Life of Christ: An Illustrated Manuscript of the Fourteenth Century. (Monographs in Art & Archeology: No. 35). (Illus.). 501p. 1975. 52.50x (ISBN 0-691-03829-5). Princeton U Pr.

Rahaman, A. Quranic Sciences. pap. 14.95 (ISBN 0-317-46103-6). Kazi Pubns.

Rahbar, Daud, ed. & tr. from Urdu. Urdu Letters of Mirza Asadu'llah Khan Ghalib. 628p. 1987. 48.50 (ISBN 0-88706-412-4). State U NY Pr.

Rahim, Abdur. The Principles of Muhammadan Jurisprudence According to the Hanali, Maliki, Shafi'i & Hanbali Schools. LC 79-2879. 443p. 1981. Repr. of 1911 ed. 34.50 (ISBN 0-8305-0047-2). Hyperion Conn.

Rahman, A. Encyclopaedia of Seerah I-IV. 55.00 ea. (ISBN 0-317-46105-2). Kazi Pubns.

--Essentials of Islam. pap. 4.95 (ISBN 0-686-67786-2). Kazi Pubns.

--Muhammad as a Military Leader. pap. 12.50 (ISBN 0-317-46107-9). Kazi Pubns.

--Prayer, Its Significance & Benefits. pap. 12.50 (ISBN 0-317-46106-0). Kazi Pubns.

--Subject Index of Holy Quran. 29.00 (ISBN 0-317-14644-0). Kazi Pubns.

--Utility of Prayers. pap. 3.50 (ISBN 0-686-18590-0). Kazi Pubns.

Rahman, F., ed. see Avicenna.

Rahman, Fazlur. Health & Medicine in the Islamic Tradition. 176p. 1987. 16.95x (ISBN 0-8245-0797-5). Crossroad NY.

--Islam. 2nd ed. LC 78-68547. 1979. pap. 9.95 (ISBN 0-226-70281-2, P806, Phoen). U of Chicago Pr.

--Islam & Modernity: Transformation of an Intellectual Tradition. LC 82-2720. (Publications of the Center for Middle Eastern Studies: No. 15). 184p. 1984. pap. 6.95x (ISBN 0-226-70284-7). U of Chicago Pr.

--Major Themes of the Qur'an. LC 79-54189. 1980. 30.00x (ISBN 0-88297-026-7); pap. 16.00x (ISBN 0-88297-027-5). Bibliotheca.

--The Philosophy of Mulla Sadra Shirazi. LC 75-31693. 1976. 39.50x (ISBN 0-87395-300-2). State U NY Pr.

--Prophecy in Islam: Philosophy & Orthodoxy. LC 78-66082. (Midway Reprints Ser.). 1979. pap. text ed. 9.00x (ISBN 0-226-70282-0). U of Chicago Pr.

Rahman, M. From Consultation to Confrontation: A Study of the Muslim League in British Indian Politics, 1906-1912. 313p. 1985. 52.00x (ISBN 0-317-39069-4, Pub. by Luzac & Co Ltd). State Mutual Bk.

Rahman, S. A. Punishment of Apostasy in Islam. pap. 7.50 (ISBN 0-686-18551-X). Kazi Pubns.

Rahmas, D. Steve, ed. see Paley, Alan L.

Rahming, Philip A. Martin Luther King, Jr. His Religion, His Philosophy. LC 86-911950. 96p. (Orig.). 1986. pap. text ed. 10.00 (ISBN 0-682-40301-6). Exposition Pr FL.

Rahn, Carl. Science & the Religious Life. 1928. 39.50x (ISBN 0-685-69853-X). Elliots Bks.

Rahner & Vorgrimmler. Kleines Theologisches Woerterbuch. (Ger.). 460p. 1976. 11.95 (ISBN 0-686-56624-6, M-7508, Pub. by Herder). French & Eur.

Rahner, Hugo. Greek Myths & Christian Mystery. LC 79-156736. (Illus.). 1971. Repr. of 1963 ed. 18.00 (ISBN 0-8196-0270-1). Biblo.

--The Spirituality of St. Ignatius Loyola: An Account of Its Historical Development. Smith, Francis J., tr. LC 53-5586. (Request Reprint). 1968. 3.50 (ISBN 0-8294-0066-4). Loyola.

Rahner, K. Herders Theologisches Taschenlexikon. (Ger.). 3180p. 1976. pap. 99.50 (ISBN 0-686-56481-2, M-7463, Pub. by Herder). French & Eur.

Rahner, Karl. Anointing of the Sick. 1979. 1.50 (ISBN 0-87193-108-7). Dimension Bks.

--Baptism. 1.50 (ISBN 0-87193-120-6). Dimension Bks.

--Christian at the Crossroads. Moiser, Jeremy, tr. from Ger. 250p. 1976. 5.95 (ISBN 0-8245-0207-8). Crossroad NY.

--Concern for the Church: Theological Investigations Vol. 20. (Theological Investigations Ser.). (Ger.). 272p. 1981. 16.95 (ISBN 0-8245-0027-X). Crossroad NY.

--Confirmation. 1.50 (ISBN 0-87193-123-0). Dimension Bks.

--Dictionary of Theology. 548p. 1985. pap. 17.50 (ISBN 0-8245-0691-X). Crossroad NY.

--Eternal Yes. 1.50 (ISBN 0-87193-119-2). Dimension Bks.

--Eucharist. 1970. 1.50 (ISBN 0-87193-106-0). Dimension Bks.

--Faith & Ministry. (Theological Investigations Ser.: Vol. 19). 352p. 1983. 24.50x (ISBN 0-8245-0572-7). Crossroad NY.

--Foundations of Christian Faith: An Introduction to the Idea of Christianity. LC 82-4663. 492p. 1982. pap. 16.95 (ISBN 0-8245-0523-9). Crossroad NY.

--Free Speech in the Church. LC 79-8717. Orig. Title: Das Freie Wort in der Kirche. 112p. 1981. Repr. of 1959 ed. lib. bdg. 22.50x (ISBN 0-313-20849-2, RAFS). Greenwood.

--God & Revelation, Vol. 18. (Theological Investigations Ser.). 352p. 1983. 24.50x (ISBN 0-8245-0571-9). Crossroad NY.

--Is Christian Life Possible Today? 1984. pap. 6.95 (ISBN 0-87193-210-5). Dimension Bks.

--Karl Rahner in Dialogue. 352p. 1986. 18.95 (ISBN 0-8245-0749-5). Crossroad NY.

--The Love of Jesus & the Love of Neighbor. LC 82-23523. 96p. 1983. pap. 5.95 (ISBN 0-8245-0570-0). Crossroad NY.

--Marriage. 1.50 (ISBN 0-87193-118-4). Dimension Bks.

--Meditations on Freedom & the Spirit. 1978. pap. 3.95 (ISBN 0-8245-0325-2). Crossroad NY.

--Meditations on Hope & Love. LC 77-76614. 1977. pap. 3.95 (ISBN 0-8245-0326-0). Crossroad NY.

--The Practice of Faith: A Handbook of Contemporary Spirituality. 354p. 1983. 19.50 (ISBN 0-8245-0603-0); pap. 14.95. Crossroad NY.

--The Practice of Faith: A Handbook of Contemporary Spirituality. rev. ed. 336p. 1986. pap. 14.95 (ISBN 0-8245-0779-7). Crossroad NY.

--Prayers & Meditations: An Anthology of the Spiritual Writings of Karl Rahner. Griffiths, John, ed. 128p. 1980. pap. 4.95 (ISBN 0-8245-0053-9). Crossroad NY.

--Prayers for a Lifetime. 256p. 1984. 12.95 (ISBN 0-8245-0678-2). Crossroad NY.

--Prayers for a Lifetime. 256p. 1986. pap. 8.95 (ISBN 0-317-42453-X). Crossroad NY.

--The Religious Life Today. 1976. 5.95 (ISBN 0-8245-0371-6). Crossroad NY.

--Shape of the Church to Come. 1974. 10.95 (ISBN 0-8245-0372-4). Crossroad NY.

--The Spirit in the Church. 1979. pap. 3.95 (ISBN 0-8245-0399-6). Crossroad NY.

--Theological Investigations, Vols. 1-17, 20. Incl. Vol. 1. 22.50x (ISBN 0-8245-0377-5); Vol. 2. Man & the Church. 22.50x (ISBN 0-8245-0378-3); Vol. 3. Theology of the Spiritual Life. 24.50x (ISBN 0-8245-0379-1); Vol. 4. More Recent Writings. 24.50x (ISBN 0-8245-0380-5); Vol. 5. Later Writings. 27.50x (ISBN 0-8245-0381-3); Vol. 6. Concerning Vatican Council II. 24.50x (ISBN 0-8245-0382-1); Vol. 7. Further Theology of the Spiritual Life I. 19.50x (ISBN 0-8245-0383-X); Vol. 8. Further Theology of the Spiritual Life II. 19.50x (ISBN 0-8245-0384-8); Vol. 9. Writings of 1965-1967, I. 19.50x (ISBN 0-8245-0385-6); Vol. 10. Writings of 1965-1967, II. 22.50x (ISBN 0-8245-0386-4); Vol. 11. Confrontation I. 22.50 (ISBN 0-8245-0387-2); Vol. 12. Confrontations II. 22.50x (ISBN 0-8245-0388-0); Vol. 13. Theology Anthropology, Christology. 22.50x (ISBN 0-8245-0389-9); Vol. 14. In Dialogue with the Future. 22.50 (ISBN 0-8245-0390-2); Penance in the Early Church. 500p. 29.50x (ISBN 0-8245-0025-3); Vol. 16. Experience of the Spirit: Source of Theology. 1979. 19.50x (ISBN 0-8245-0392-9); Vol. 17. Jesus, Man & the Church. 19.50x (ISBN 0-8245-0026-1); Vol. 20. Concern for the Church. 14.50x (ISBN 0-8245-0027-X). Crossroad NY.

--Theological Investigations, Vol. 22: Humane Society & the Church of Tomorrow. 288p. 1987. 24.50 (ISBN 0-8245-0802-5). Crossroad NY.

--Words of Faith. 96p. 1986. pap. 5.95 (ISBN 0-8245-0788-6). Crossroad NY.

Rahner, Karl & Metz, Johann B. The Courage to Pray. 112p. (Orig.). 1980. pap. 3.95 (ISBN 0-8245-2024-6). Crossroad NY.

Rahner, Karl & Thusing, Wilhelm. A New Christology. 256p. 1980. 12.95 (ISBN 0-8245-0333-3). Crossroad NY.

Rahner, Karl & Weger, Karl-Heinz. Our Christian Faith: Answers for the Future. 208p. (Orig.). 1980. 10.95 (ISBN 0-8245-0361-9); pap. 4.95 (ISBN 0-8245-0362-7). Crossroad NY.

Rahner, Karl, jt. auth. see Fries, Heinrich.

Rahner, Karl, ed. Encyclopedia of Theology: The Concise Sacramentum Mundi. rev., abr. ed. LC 82-7285. 1536p. 1975. 49.50x (ISBN 0-8245-0303-1). Crossroad NY.

--Pastoral Mission of the Church. LC 76-57341. (Concilium Ser.: Vol. 3). 192p. 7.95 (ISBN 0-8091-0108-4). Paulist Pr.

--Renewal of Preaching. LC 68-22795. (Concilium Ser.: Vol. 33). 204p. 7.95 (ISBN 0-8091-0126-2). Paulist Pr.

Rahner, Karl S. Pastoral Approach to Atheism. LC 67-21347. (Concilium Ser.: Vol. 23). 189p. 7.95 (ISBN 0-8091-0107-6). Paulist Pr.

Rahula, Bhikku T. A Critical Study of the Mahavastu. 1978. 24.95 (ISBN 0-89684-018-2, Pub. by Motilal Banarsidass India). Orient Bk Dist.

Rahula, Walpola. Buddhist Studies in Honour of Walpola Rahula. 308p. 1981. 75.00x (ISBN 0-86092-030-5, Pub. by Fraser Bks). State Mutual Bk.

--What the Buddha Taught. rev. ed. (Illus.). 168p. 1974. pap. 6.95 (ISBN 0-394-17827-0, E641, Ever). Grove.

--Zen & the Taming of the Bull: Towards the Definition of Buddhist Thought. 1978. text ed. 17.50x (ISBN 0-900406-69-0). Humanities.

Rai, Amrit. A House Divided: The Origin & Development of Hindi-Hindavi. 1985. 29.95x (ISBN 0-19-561643-X). Oxford U Pr.

Rai, Raghu, jt. auth. see Singh, Khushwant.

Raine, James, ed. The Historians of the Church of York & Its Archbishops, 3 vols. (Rolls Ser.: No. 71). Repr. of 1894 ed. Set. 180.00 (ISBN 0-8115-1139-1). Kraus Repr.

Raine, Linnea P. The International Implications of the Papal Assassination Attempt: A Case of State-Sponsored Terrorism. (Significant Issues Ser.: Vol. VI, No. 20). 32p. (Orig.). 1985. pap. text ed. 6.95 (ISBN 0-8191-5935-2, Pub. by CSIS). U Pr of Amer.

Raines, John C. & Day-Lower, Donna C. Modern Work & Human Meaning. LC 85-26370. (Illus.). 152p. (Orig.). 1986. pap. 12.95 (ISBN 0-664-24703-2). Westminster.

Raines, Robert. A Faithing Oak. 128p. 1984. pap. 6.95 (ISBN 0-8245-0636-7). Crossroad NY.

--Going Home. LC 84-23210. 154p. 1985. pap. 6.95 (ISBN 0-8245-0692-8). Crossroad NY.

Raines, Robert A. A Faithing Oak: Meditations from the Mountain. LC 82-12720. 128p. 1982. 9.95 (ISBN 0-8245-0485-2). Crossroad NY.

--New Life in the Church. rev. ed. LC 61-5267. (Harper's Ministers Paperback Library). 192p. 1980. pap. 4.50i (ISBN 0-06-066773-7, RD 309, HarpR). Har-Row.

--To Kiss the Joy. 160p. 1983. pap. 4.35 (ISBN 0-687-42185-3). Abingdon.

Rainey, Albert. Cosmic Visions. LC 85-90309. 56p. (Orig.). 1986. pap. write for info. (ISBN 0-932971-01-6). Al Rainey Pubns.

Rainey, Anson F., tr. see Aharoni, Yohanan.

Raisanen, Heikki. Paul & the Law. 332p. 1986. pap. 19.95 (ISBN 0-8006-1915-3, 1-1915). Fortress.

--Paul & the Law. 330p. 1983. lib. bdg. 67.50x (ISBN 3-16-144629-1, Pub. by J C B Mohr BRD). Coronet Bks.

Raisin, Jacob S. The Haskalah Movement in Russia. 1976. Repr. of 1913 ed. 40.00 (ISBN 0-8274-2471-X). R West.

Raistrick, Arthur. Quakers in Science & Industry. LC 68-18641. (Illus.). 1968. Repr. of 1950 ed. 35.00x (ISBN 0-678-05622-6). Kelley.

Raitt, Jill. The Eucharistic Theology of Theodore Beza: Development of the Reformed Doctrine. LC 74-188907. (American Academy of Religion. Studies in Religion). 1972. pap. 9.95 (ISBN 0-89130-156-9, 010004). Scholars Pr GA.

Raitt, Jill, ed. Shapers of Religious Traditions in Germany, Switzerland, & Poland, Fifteen Sixty to Sixteen Hundred. LC 80-23287. 256p. 1981. text ed. 28.50x (ISBN 0-300-02457-6). Yale U Pr.

Raitt, Jill, et al, eds. Christian Spirituality, Vol. 11. (World Spirituality Ser.: Vol. 17). 528p. 1987. 49.50x (ISBN 0-8245-0765-7). Crossroad NY.

Raj, Veni. A Diamond in the Darkness. (Illus.). 32p. 1984. pap. 3.50 (ISBN 0-85398-161-2). G Ronald Pub.

Raja, C. Kunhan. Poet Philosophers of the Rig Veda. (Sanskrit & eng.). 10.00 (ISBN 0-89744-121-4, Pub. by Ganesh & Co. India). Auromere.

Rajagapalachari, Chakravarti, tr. see Vyasa.

Rajagopal, D., ed. Commentaries on Living: 2nd Series. 1959. 14.95 (ISBN 0-575-00417-7, Pub. by Gollancz England). David & Charles.

--Commentaries on Living: 3rd Series. 1961. 14.95 (ISBN 0-575-00229-8, Pub. by Gollancz England). David & Charles.

Rajagopal, D., ed. see Krishnamurti, Jiddu.

Rajagopalachari, C. Ramakrishna Upanishad. pap. 1.95 (ISBN 0-87481-430-8). Vedanta Pr.

--Ramayana. 1979. pap. 5.95 (ISBN 0-89744-930-4). Auromere.

Rajagopalachari, Chakravarti, ed. & tr. see Valmiki.

Rajagopalachari, Chakravarti, ed. see Vyasa.

Rajak, Tessa. Josephus: The Historian & His Society. LC 83-16538. 256p. 1984. 24.95 (ISBN 0-8006-0717-1, 1-717). Fortress.

Rajan, Balachandra, ed. Paradise Lost: A Tercenenary Tribute. LC 77-429833. pap. 38.50 (ISBN 0-317-27001-X, 2023659). Bks Demand UMI.

Rajan, K. V. Indian Temple Styles: The Personality of Hindu Architecture. (Illus.). 194p. 1972. 22.50x (ISBN 0-89684-420-X). Orient Bk Dist.

--India's Religious Art: Ideas & Ideals. (Illus.). 1982. text ed. 45.00x (ISBN 0-391-02916-9). Humanities.

Raj Gupta, Giri, ed. Religions in Modern India. (Main Currents in Indian Sociology Ser.: Vol. 5). 368p. 1983. text ed. 37.50x (ISBN 0-7069-0793-0, Pub. by Vikas India). Advent NY.

Rajneesh. Pointing the Way. 1979. text ed. 10.95 (ISBN 0-89684-070-0, Pub. by Motilal Banarsidass Delhi). Orient Bk Dist.

Rajneesh Academy Staff, ed. see Rajneesh, Baghwan S.

Rajneesh Academy Staff, ed. see Rajneesh, Bhagwan S.

Rajneesh, Acharya. The Mysteries of Life & Death. Bisen, Malini, tr. from Hindi. 1978. pap. 3.50 (ISBN 0-89684-045-X, Pub. by Motilal Banarsidass India). Orient Bk Dist.

Rajneesh, Baghwan S. The Rajneesh Bible, Vol. 1. Rajneesh Academy Staff, ed. LC 85-42539. 800p. (Orig.). 1985. pap. 6.95 (ISBN 0-88050-200-2). Chidvilas Found.

Rajneesh, Bhagwan S. And Now, & Here, Vol. II. Vedant, Swami S., ed. LC 84-42798. (Early Writings & Discourses Ser.). 384p. (Orig.). 1985. pap. 4.95 (ISBN 0-88050-712-8). Chidvilas Found.

--The Beginning of the Beginning. 3rd ed. Parimal, Ma P., ed. vi, 113p. (Orig.). 1982. pap. 2.95x (ISBN 0-7069-2123-2, Pub. by Vikas India). Advent NY.

--The Book: An Introduction to the Teachings of Bhagwan Shree Rajneesh, Series III, R-Z. Rajneesh Academy Staff, ed. LC 84-42616. (Academy Ser.). 576p. (Orig.). 1984. pap. 5.95 (ISBN 0-88050-704-7). Chidvilas Found.

--The Book: An Introduction to the Teachings of Bhagwan Shree Rajneesh, Series I, A-H. Rajneesh Academy Staff, ed. LC 84-42616. (Academy Ser.). 620p. (Orig.). 1984. pap. 5.95 (ISBN 0-88050-702-0). Chidvilas Found.

--The Book: An Introduction to the Teachings of Bhagwan Shree Rajneesh, Series II, I-Q. Rajneesh Academy Staff, ed. (Academy Ser.). 576p. (Orig.). 1984. pap. 5.95 (ISBN 0-88050-703-9). Chidvilas Found.

--The Book of the Books, Vol. 1. Rajneesh Foundation International, ed. LC 82-50462. (Buddha Ser.). 360p. (Orig.). 1982. pap. 15.95 (ISBN 0-88050-513-3). Chidvilas Found.

--Book of the Books, Vol. 2. Asha, Ma P., ed. LC 82-50462. (Buddha Ser.). 352p. (Orig.). 1983. pap. 4.95 (ISBN 0-88050-514-1). Chidvilas Found.

--The Book of the Books, Vol. 3. Ma P. Karima, ed. LC 82-50462. (Buddha Ser.). 352p. (Orig.). 1984. pap. 4.95 (ISBN 0-88050-515-X). Chidvilas Found.

--The Book of the Books, Vol. 4. Krishna, Swami P., ed. LC 82-50462. (Buddha Ser.). 384p. (Orig.). 1985. pap. 4.95 (ISBN 0-88050-516-8). Chidvilas Found.

--The Book of the Secrets. pap. 8.95 (ISBN 0-06-090564-6, CN 564, PL). Har-Row.

--Book of the Secrets, Vol. IV. 2nd ed ed. Rajneesh Foundation International, ed. LC 75-36733. (Tantra Ser.). 408p. 1982. pap. 7.95 (ISBN 0-88050-528-1). Chidvilas Found.

--The Book of the Secrets Two. LC 75-39733. 1979. pap. 8.95 (ISBN 0-06-090668-5, CN 668, PL). Har-Row.

--Book of the Secrets, Vol. V. 2nd ed. Ma Prema Veena, ed. LC 75-36733. (Tantra Ser.). 400p. 1984. pap. 4.95 (ISBN 0-88050-529-X). Chidvilas Found.

--Book of Wisdom, Vol. I. Rajneesh Foundation International, ed. LC 82-23142. (Buddhist Masters Ser.). 420p. (Orig.). 1983. pap. 9.95 (ISBN 0-88050-530-3). Chidvilas Found.

--The Book of Wisdom, Vol. 2. Swami Krishna Prabhu, ed. LC 82-23142. (Buddhist Masters Ser.). 416p. (Orig.). 1984. pap. 5.95 (ISBN 0-88050-531-1). Chidvilas Found.

--A Cup of Tea. 2nd ed ed. Somendra, Swami Anand, ed. LC 83-43215. (Early Discourses & Writings Ser.). 272p. 1983. pap. 4.95 (ISBN 0-88050-538-9). Chidvilas Found.
--The Grass Grows by Itself. (Illus.). 1978. pap. 4.95 (ISBN 0-87516-251-7). De Vorss.
--Hammer on the Rock: A Darshan Diary. (Illus.). 464p. 1979. pap. 8.95 (ISBN 0-394-17090-3, E730, Ever). Grove.
--Just Around the Corner. Mahasattva, Swami Krishna, ed. LC 84-42870. (Initiation Talks Ser.). 224p. (Orig.). 1984. pap. 3.95 (ISBN 0-88050-588-5). Chidvilas Found.
--Meditation: The Art of Ecstasy. Bharti, Ma S., ed. 1978. pap. 3.50 (ISBN 0-06-080394-0, P394, PL). Har-Row.
--Mystic Experience. Prem, Ma A., ed. Diddee, Dolly, tr. 543p. 1977. text ed. 25.00 (ISBN 0-89684-292-4, Pub. by Motilal Banarsidass India). Orient Bk Dist.
--The Passion for the Impossible. Maneesha, Ma P., ed. LC 83-181944. (Initiation Talks Ser.). (Illus.). 464p. (Orig.). 1978. 18.95 (ISBN 0-88050-111-1). Chidvilas Found.
--The Rajneesh Bible, Vol. II. Rajneesh Academy Staff, ed. LC 85-42539. 839p. (Orig.). 1985. pap. 7.95x (ISBN 0-88050-201-0, 201-0). Chidvilas Found.
--The Rajneesh Bible, Vol. III. Rajneesh Academy Staff, ed. LC 85-42539. 1072p. (Orig.). 1985. pap. 6.95 (ISBN 0-88050-202-9). Chidvilas Found.
--The Rajneesh Upanishad. Ma Deva Sarito, ed. 1032p. 1986. pap. 9.95 (ISBN 3-907757-00-9). Rajneesh Neo-Sannyas Intl.
--Roots & Wings: Talks on Zen. (Orig.). 1979. pap. 9.95 (ISBN 0-7100-0420-6). Methuen Inc.
--The Secret. Chinmaya, Swami P., ed. LC 83-185068. (Sufi Ser.). (Illus.). 760p. (Orig.). 1980. 23.95 (ISBN 0-88050-127-8). Chidvilas Found.
--The Secret of Secrets, Vol. 1. Rajneesh Foundation International, ed. LC 82-50464. (Tao Ser.). 588p. (Orig.). 1982. pap. 16.95 (ISBN 0-88050-628-8). Chidvilas Found.
--The Secret of Secrets, Vol. 2. Sudha, Ma Y., ed. LC 82-50464. (Tao Ser.). 528p. (Orig.). 1983. pap. 4.95 (ISBN 0-88050-629-6). Chidvilas Found.
--The Shadow of the Whip. Maneesha, Ma Prem, ed. LC 82-230735. (Initiation Talks Ser.). (Illus.). 554p. (Orig.). 1978. 18.95 (ISBN 0-88050-131-6). Chidvilas Found.
--The Supreme Doctrine: Discourses on the Kenopanishad. 356p. (Orig.). 1980. pap. 12.95 (ISBN 0-7100-0572-5). Methuen Inc.
--The Way of Tao: Part II. Didi, Dolli, tr. 1979. 24.00 (ISBN 0-89684-056-5, Pub. by Motilal Banarsidass India). Orient Bk Dist.
--Wings of Love & Random Thought. 1979. pap. 4.50 (ISBN 0-89684-031-X, Pub. by Motilal Barnarsidass India). Orient Bk Dist.
--Zorba the Buddha. Maneesha, Ma Prem, ed. LC 82-50463. (Initiation Talks Ser.). (Illus.). 344p. 1982. pap. 21.95 (ISBN 0-88050-694-6). Chidvilas Found.

Rajneesh, Bhagwan Shree. Above All, Don't Wobble. Maneesha, Ma Prem, ed. LC 83-81247. (Initiation Talks Ser.). (Illus.). 488p. (Orig.). 1976. 21.95 (ISBN 0-88050-001-8). Chidvilas Found.
--Ah This! Rajneesh Foundation International, ed. LC 82-24026. (Zen Ser.). 268p. (Orig.). 1982. pap. 8.95 (ISBN 0-88050-502-8). Chidvilas Found.
--Ancient Music in the Pines. Veena, Ma Prem, ed. LC 78-901931. (Zen Ser.). (Illus.). 298p. (Orig.). 1977. 15.50 (ISBN 0-88050-003-4). Chidvilas Found.
--And Now, & Here, Vol. 1. Mahasattva, Swami Satya, ed. LC 84-42798. (Early Discourses & Writings Ser.). 320p. (Orig.). 1984. pap. 4.95 (ISBN 0-88050-709-8). Chidvilas Found.
--And the Flowers Showered. Somendra, Swami Anand, ed. LC 83-181344. (Zen Ser.). (Illus.). 288p. (Orig.). 1975. 16.95 (ISBN 0-88050-004-2); pap. 5.95 (ISBN 0-88050-504-4). Chidvilas Found.
--The Art of Dying. Veena, Ma Prema, ed. LC 78-905608. (Hasidism Ser.). (Illus.). 284p. (Orig.). 1978. 14.95 (ISBN 0-88050-005-0). Chidvilas Found.
--Be Realistic: Plan for a Miracle. Maneesha, Ma Prem, ed. LC 78-902296. (Initiation Talks Ser.). (Illus.). 418p. (Orig.). 1977. 19.95 (ISBN 0-88050-010-7). Chidvilas Found.
--Be Still & Know. Anurag, Ma Yoga, ed. (Question & Answer Ser.). (Illus.). 364p. (Orig.). 1981. pap. 13.95 (ISBN 0-88050-511-7). Chidvilas Found.
--Believing the Impossible Before Breakfast. Maneesha, Ma Prem, ed. LC 82-229302. (Initiation Talks Ser.). (Illus.). 266p. (Orig.). 1981. 22.95 (ISBN 0-88050-006-9). Chidvilas Found.
--The Beloved, 2 vols. Sudha, Ma Yoga, ed. LC 78-903022. (Baul Mystics Ser.). (Illus., Orig.). 1977. Vol. I, 324 pgs. 15.95 ea. (ISBN 0-88050-007-7). Vol. II, 288 pgs. 1978. Chidvilas Found.
--Beloved of My Heart. Maneesha, Ma Prem, ed. (Initiation Talks Ser.). (Illus.). 356p. (Orig.). 1978. 19.95 (ISBN 0-88050-009-3). Chidvilas Found.
--Blessed are the Ignorant. Maneesha, Ma Prem, ed. LC 83-181704. (Initiation Talks Ser.). (Illus.). 566p. (Orig.). 1979. 19.95 (ISBN 0-88050-012-3). Chidvilas Found.
--Books I Have Loved. Sambuddha, Swami Devaraj & Mahasattva, Swami Devageet, eds. LC 85-43070. (Biography Ser.). 288p. (Orig.). 1985. pap. 3.95 (ISBN 0-88050-716-0). Chidvilas Found.
--The Buddha Disease. Ma Prem Maneesha, ed. LC 83-181256. (Initiation Talks Ser.). (Illus.). 642p. (Orig.). 1979. 21.50 (ISBN 0-88050-032-8). Chidvilas Found.
--Come Follow Me, Vol. III. Swami Deva Paritosh, ed. LC 80-8343. (Jesus Ser.). (Illus.). 272p. (Orig.). 1976. 12.95 (ISBN 0-88050-036-0). Chidvilas Found.
--Come Follow Me, Vol. IV. Ma Yoga Sudha, ed. LC 80-8343. (Jesus Ser.). (Illus.). 286p. (Orig.). 1977. 12.95 (ISBN 0-88050-037-9). Chidvilas Found.
--Come Follow Me, Vol. II. Ma Satya Bharti, ed. LC 80-8343. (Jesus Ser.). (Illus.). 316p. (Orig.). 1977. 12.95 (ISBN 0-88050-035-2). Chidvilas Found.
--Come Follow Me, Vol. I. Ma Satya Bharti, ed. LC 80-8343. (Jesus Ser.). (Illus.). 292p. (Orig.). 1976. 12.95 (ISBN 0-88050-034-4). Chidvilas Found.
--The Cypress in the Courtyard. Maneesha, Ma Prem, ed. LC 83-181284. (Initiation Talks Ser.). (Illus.). 466p. (Orig.). 1978. 18.95 (ISBN 0-88050-039-5). Chidvilas Found.
--Dance Your Way to God. Maneesha, Ma Prem, ed. LC 78-907936. (Initiation Talks Ser.). (Illus.). 384p. (Orig.). 1978. 19.95 (ISBN 0-88050-041-7). Chidvilas Found.
--Dang Dang Doko Dang. Veena, Ma Prem, ed. LC 77-907636. (Zen Ser.). (Illus.). 290p. (Orig.). 1977. 14.50 (ISBN 0-88050-042-5). Chidvilas Found.
--The Diamond Sutra. Pratima, Ma Yoga, ed. LC 82-185071. (Buddha Ser.). (Illus.). 492p. (Orig.). 1979. 19.50 (ISBN 0-88050-043-3). Chidvilas Found.
--The Discipline of Transcendence, 4 vols. Vandana, Ma Ananda & Pratima, Ma Yoga, eds. LC 78-906087. (Buddha Ser.). (Illus., Orig.). 1978. Vol. I, 324 pgs. 16.50 ea. (ISBN 0-88050-045-X). Vol. II, 348 pgs (ISBN 0-88050-046-8). Vol. III, 320 pgs (ISBN 0-88050-047-6). Vol. IV, 376 pgs (ISBN 0-88050-048-4). Chidvilas Found.
--The Divine Melody. Bhasha, Ma Deva, ed. LC 83-174697. (Kabir Ser.). (Illus.). 284p. (Orig.). 1978. 16.50 (ISBN 0-88050-049-2). Chidvilas Found.
--Don't Bite My Finger, Look Where I Am Pointing. Maneesha, Ma Prem, ed. LC 82-21602. (Initiation Talks Ser.). 232p. (Orig.). 1982. pap. 14.95 (ISBN 0-88050-550-8). Chidvilas Found.
--Don't Just Do Something, Sit There. Maneesha, Ma Prem, ed. (Initiation Talks Ser.). (Illus.). 370p. (Orig.). 1980. 25.50 (ISBN 0-88050-052-2). Chidvilas Found.
--Don't Let Yourself Be Upset by the Sutra: Rather Upset the Sutra Yourself. Prabhu, Swami Krishna, ed. LC 85-43054. (Initiation Talks Ser.). 560p. (Orig.). 1985. pap. 5.95 (ISBN 0-88050-584-2). Chidvilas Found.
--Don't Look Before You Leap. Rajneesh Foundation International, ed. LC 83-3282. (Initiation Talks Ser.). 480p. (Orig.). 1983. pap. 4.95 (ISBN 0-88050-554-0). Chidvilas Found.
--Ecstasy: The Forgotten Language. Chinmaya, Swami Prem, ed. LC 83-179587. (Kabir Ser.). (Illus.). 332p. (Orig.). 1978. 16.50 (ISBN 0-88050-055-7). Chidvilas Found.
--Far Beyond the Stars. Maneesha, Ma Prem, ed. LC 82-229145. (Initiation Talks Ser.). (Illus.). 306p. (Orig.). 1980. 20.95 (ISBN 0-88050-059-X). Chidvilas Found.
--The First Principle. Chinmaya, Swami Prem, ed. LC 83-179587. (Zen Ser.). (Illus.). 386p. (Orig.). 1979. 17.95 (ISBN 0-88050-061-1). Chidvilas Found.
--The Fish in the Sea is Not Thirsty. Anurag, Ma Yoga, ed. LC 82-244585. (Kabir Ser.). (Illus.). 524p. (Orig.). 1980. 22.95 (ISBN 0-88050-062-X). Chidvilas Found.
--For Madmen Only: Price of Admission: Your Mind. Maneesha, Ma Prem, ed. LC 83-186152. (Initiation Talks Ser.). (Illus.). 616p. (Orig.). 1979. 19.50 (ISBN 0-88050-063-8). Chidvilas Found.
--From Sex to Superconsciousness. Prem, Swami Krishna, ed. LC 77-20821. (Early Discourses & Writings Ser.). (Illus.). 256p. (Orig.). 1979. 15.50 (ISBN 0-88050-064-6). Chidvilas Found.
--The Further Shore. Maneesha, Ma Prem, ed. LC 83-181220. (Initation Talks Ser.). (Illus.). 288p. (Orig.). 1980. 22.95 (ISBN 0-88050-065-4). Chidvilas Found.
--Get Out of Your Own Way. Pratima, Ma Yoga, ed. LC 83-181935. (Initation Talks Ser.). (Illus.). 374p. (Orig.). 1977. 18.95 (ISBN 0-88050-066-2). Chidvilas Found.
--Glimpses of a Golden Childhood. Sambuddha, Swami Devaraj & Mahasattva, Swami Devageet, eds. LC 85-43069. (Biography Ser.). 788p. (Orig.). 1985. pap. 6.95 (ISBN 0-88050-715-2). Chidvilas Found.
--God Is Not for Sale. Pratima, Ma Yoga, ed. LC 82-244555. (Initiation Talks Ser.). (Illus.). 450p. (Orig.). 1978. 18.95 (ISBN 0-88050-067-0). Chidvilas Found.
--God's Got a Thing about You. Maneesha, Ma Prem, ed. LC 83-11237. (Initiation Talks Ser.). 576p. (Orig.). 1983. pap. 4.95 (ISBN 0-88050-568-0). Chidvilas Found.
--The Goose Is Out. Rajneesh Foundation International, ed. LC 82-60497. (Question & Answer Ser.). 324p. (Orig.). 1982. pap. 10.95 (ISBN 0-88050-571-0). Chidvilas Found.
--The Grass Grows by Itself. Veena, Ma Prema, ed. LC 77-905411. (Zen Ser.). (Illus.). 254p. (Orig.). 1978. 15.50 (ISBN 0-88050-072-7); pap. 4.95 (ISBN 0-88050-572-9). Chidvilas Found.
--The Great Nothing. Maneesha, Ma Prem, ed. LC 83-173216. (Initation Talks Ser.). (Illus.). 488p. (Orig.). 1978. 18.95 (ISBN 0-88050-073-5). Chidvilas Found.
--Guest. Sudha, Ma Yoga, ed. LC 82-203740. (Kabir Ser.). (Illus.). 604p. (Orig.). 1981. pap. 15.95 (ISBN 0-88050-574-5). Chidvilas Found.
--Guida Spirituale. Rajneesh Foundation International, ed. LC 83-4435. (Western Mystics Ser.). 400p. (Orig.). 1983. pap. 4.95 (ISBN 0-88050-575-3). Chidvilas Found.
--Hallelujah! Maneesha, Ma Prem, ed. LC 83-180760. (Initiation Talks Ser.). (Illus.). 364p. (Orig.). 1981. 25.95 (ISBN 0-88050-076-X); pap. 18.95 (ISBN 0-88050-576-1). Chidvilas Found.
--Hammer on the Rock. Maneesha, Ma Prem, ed. LC 79-52012. (Initiation Talks Ser.). 464p. (Orig.). 1976. 22.50 (ISBN 0-88050-077-8). Chidvilas Found.
--The Heart Sutra. Sudha, ma Yoga, ed. LC 78-908490. (Buddha Ser.). (Illus.). 332p. (Orig.). 1978. 16.95 (ISBN 0-88050-078-6). Chidvilas Found.
--The Hidden Harmony. Anurag, Ma Yoga, ed. LC 83-184618. (Western Mystics Ser.). (Illus.). 364p. (Orig.). 1976. 16.95 (ISBN 0-88050-079-4). Chidvilas Found.
--Hsin Hsin Ming: The Book of Nothing. 2nd ed. Punito, Ma, ed. LC 83-17783. (Zen Master Ser.). 320p. 1983. pap. 4.95 (ISBN 0-88050-597-4). Chidvilas Found.
--I Am That. Ma Prem Apa, ed. LC 84-42809. (Upanishads Ser.). 416p. (Orig.). 1984. pap. 5.95 (ISBN 0-88050-580-X). Chidvilas Found.
--I Say unto You, 2 vols. Asha, Ma Prem, ed. LC 82-245650. (Jesus Ser.). (Illus., Orig.). 1980. Vol. I, 384. 19.50 (ISBN 0-88050-085-9); Vol. II. pap. 15.95 (ISBN 0-88050-586-9); pap. 4.95 wkbk. (ISBN 0-88050-585-0). Chidvilas Found.
--In Search of the Miraculous, Vol. 1. Sambuddha, Swami Anand, ed. LC 84-42869. (Early Discourses & Writings Ser.). 368p. (Orig.). 1984. pap. 4.95 (ISBN 0-88050-710-1). Chidvilas Found.
--Just Like That. Somendra, Swami Anand, ed. (Sufi Ser.). (Illus.). 488p. (Orig.). 1975. 19.50 (ISBN 0-88050-089-1). Chidvilas Found.
--Krishna: The Man & His Philosophy. Sambuddha, Swami Anand, ed. LC 85-43055. (Early Writings & Discourses Ser.). 880p. 1985. pap. 5.95 (ISBN 0-88050-713-6). Chidvilas Found.
--The Last Testament, Vol. I. Svadesh, Swami, et al, eds. LC 85-63289. (Interview Ser.). (Illus.). 832p. (Orig.). 1986. pap. 7.95x (ISBN 0-88050-250-9, 250-9). Chidvilas Found.
--Let Go! Maneesha, Ma Prem, ed. LC 83-181279. (Initiation Talks Ser.). (Illus.). 654p. (Orig.). 1980. 22.95 (ISBN 0-88050-091-3). Chidvilas Found.
--The Long & the Short & the All. Prabhu, Swami Krishna, ed. LC 84-42806. (Early Writings & Discourses Ser.). 320p. 1984. pap. 4.95 (ISBN 0-88050-708-X). Chidvilas Found.
--Madman's Guide to Enlightenment. Maneesha, Ma Prem, ed. (Initiation Talks Ser.). (Illus.). 388p. (Orig.). 1980. pap. 18.95 (ISBN 0-88050-593-1). Chidvilas Found.
--The Mustard Seed. rev. ed. Prabhu, Swami Krishna, ed. LC 84-43009. (Jesus Ser.). 560p. 1984. pap. 5.95 (ISBN 0-88050-595-8). Chidvilas Found.
--My Way: The Way of the White Clouds. rev. ed. Teertha, Swami Ananda, ed. LC 79-2303. (Questions & Answers Ser.). (Illus.). 640p. 1975. 29.95 (ISBN 0-88050-096-4). Chidvilas Found.
--Neither This Nor That. Pratima, Ma Yoga, ed. LC 83-181238. (Zen Ser.). (Illus.). 280p. (Orig.). 1975. 14.95 (ISBN 0-88050-097-2). Chidvilas Found.
--The New Alchemy: To Turn You On. Bharti, Ma Satya, ed. LC 83-181814. (Western Mystics Ser.). (Illus.). 308p. (Orig.). 1978. 15.50 (ISBN 0-88050-098-0). Chidvilas Found.
--The Ninety-Nine Names of Nothingness. Maneesha, Ma Prem, ed. (Initiation Talks Ser.). (Illus.). 596p. (Orig.). 1980. pap. 18.95 (ISBN 0-88050-599-0). Chidvilas Found.
--Nirvana: The Last Nightmare. Pratima, Ma Yoga, ed. LC 77-902717. (Zen Ser.). (Illus.). 290p. (Orig.). 1976. 17.50 (ISBN 0-88050-101-4). Chidvilas Found.
--The No Book: No Buddha, No Teaching, No Discipline. Maneesha, Ma Prem, ed. (Initation Talks Ser.). (Illus.). 354p. (Orig.). 1981. 26.95 (ISBN 0-88050-102-2). Chidvilas Found.
--No Water, No Moon. 2nd ed. Anurag, Ma Yoga, ed. LC 75-907472. (Zen Ser.). (Illus.). 260p. 1978. 14.50 (ISBN 0-88050-105-7). Chidvilas Found.
--No Water, No Moon. Prabhu, Swami Krishna, ed. LC 84-42871. (Zen Ser.). 320p. 1984. pap. 4.95 (ISBN 0-88050-605-9). Chidvilas Found.
--Notes of a Madman. Sambuddha, Swami Devaraj & Mahasattva, Swami Devageet, eds. LC 85-43071. (Biography Ser.). 140p. (Orig.). 1985. pap. 4.50 (ISBN 0-88050-714-4). Chidvilas Found.
--Nothing to Lose but Your Head. Maneesha, Ma Prem, ed. LC 78-901075. (Initiation Talks Ser.). (Illus.). 408p. (Orig.). 1977. 19.50 (ISBN 0-88050-104-9). Chidvilas Found.
--Only Losers Can Win In This Game. Maneesha, Ma Prem, ed. LC 82-229469. (Initation Talks Ser.). 610p. (Orig.). 1981. 23.50 (ISBN 0-88050-107-3). Chidvilas Found.
--The Open Door. Maneesha, Ma Prem, ed. LC 83-181263. (Initiation Talks Ser.). (Illus.). 336p. (Orig.). 1980. 18.95 (ISBN 0-88050-608-3). Chidvilas Found.
--The Open Secret. Maneesha, Ma Prem, ed. LC 83-180822. (Initiation Talks Ser.). 382p. (Orig.). 1980. 25.50 (ISBN 0-88050-109-X). Chidvilas Found.
--The Orange Book: The Meditation Techniques of Bhagwan Shree Rajneesh. 2nd ed. Rajneesh Foundation International, ed. LC 82-63117. (Meditation Ser.). 256p. 1983. pap. 3.95 (ISBN 0-88050-697-0). Chidvilas Found.
--The Path of Love. Sudha, Ma Yoga, ed. LC 83-181255. (Kabir Ser.). (Illus.). 350p. (Orig.). 1978. 16.50 (ISBN 0-88050-112-X); pap. 12.95 358p (ISBN 0-88050-612-1). Chidvilas Found.
--The Perfect Master, 2 vols. Anurag, Ma Yoga, ed. LC 83-172954. (Sufi Ser.). (Illus.). 1980. Vol. I, 380 pgs. 19.95 ea. (ISBN 0-88050-113-8). Vol. II, 368 pgs. 1981 (ISBN 0-88050-114-6). Chidvilas Found.
--Philosophia Perennis, Vol. 1. Anurag, Ma Yoga, ed. (Western Mystics Ser.). (Illus.). 392p. (Orig.). 1981. 19.95 (ISBN 0-88050-115-4); pap. 15.95 428p (ISBN 0-88050-615-6). Chidvilas Found.
--Philosophia Perennis, Vol. 2. Anurag, Ma Yoga, ed. (Western Mystics Ser.). (Illus.). 436p. (Orig.). 1981. pap. 15.95 (ISBN 0-88050-616-4). Chidvilas Found.
--Philosophia Ultima. Anurag, Ma Yoga, ed. LC 83-43216. (Upanishads Ser.). 384p. (Orig.). 1983. pap. 4.95 (ISBN 0-88050-617-2). Chidvilas Found.
--The Rajneesh Bible, Vol. IV. LC 85-42539. (Illus.). 800p. (Orig.). 1987. pap. 9.95x (ISBN 3-907757-02-5). Chidvilas Found.
--Returning to the Source. Sudha, Ma Yoga, ed. LC 83-182149. (Zen Ser.). (Illus.). 402p. (Orig.). 1976. 15.95 (ISBN 0-88050-120-0). Chidvilas Found.
--The Revolution. Vandana, Ma Ananda, ed. LC 83-181203. (Kabir Ser.). (Illus.). 424p. (Orig.). 1979. 16.95 (ISBN 0-88050-121-9). Chidvilas Found.
--A Rose Is a Rose Is a Rose. Pratima, Ma Yoga, ed. (Initiation Talks Ser.). (Illus.). 428p. (Orig.). 1978. 18.95 (ISBN 0-88050-123-5). Chidvilas Found.
--Sacred Yes. Ma Prem Maneesha, ed. LC 83-17665. (Initiation Talks Ser.). 448p. (Orig.). 1983. pap. 4.95 (ISBN 0-88050-624-5). Chidvilas Found.
--The Shadow of the Bamboo. Maneesha, Ma Prem, ed. LC 84-42807. (Initiation Talks Ser.). 240p. (Orig.). 1984. pap. 3.95 (ISBN 0-88050-630-X). Chidvilas found.
--Snap Your Fingers, Slap Your Face & Wake Up! Sarito, Ma Deva, ed. LC 84-43011. (Initiation Talks Ser.). 256p. (Orig.). 1984. pap. 3.95 (ISBN 0-88050-632-6). Chidvilas Found.
--The Sound of One Hand Clapping. Pratima, Ma Yoga, ed. (Initiation Talks Ser.). (Illus.). 632p. (Orig.). 1981. pap. 22.50 (ISBN 0-88050-633-4). Chidvilas Found.
--The Sound of Running Water. Asha, Ma Prem, ed. LC 83-180798. (Photobiography Ser.). (Illus.). 564p. 1980. 100.00 (ISBN 0-88050-134-0). Chidvilas Found.

--A Sudden Clash of Thunder. Anurag, Ma Yoga, ed. LC 78-901998. (Zen Ser.). (Illus.). 284p. (Orig.). 1977. 16.50 (ISBN 0-88050-135-9). Chidvilas Found.

--Sufis: The People of the Path, 2 vols. Veena, Ma Prema, ed. (Sufi Ser.). (Illus., Orig.). 1979. Vol. I, 552 pgs. 18.50 (ISBN 0-88050-136-7); Vol. II, 552 pgs. 1980. 19.50 (ISBN 0-88050-137-5). Chidvilas Found.

--The Sun Behind the Sun Behind the Sun. Maneesha, Ma Prem, ed. LC 83-181209. (Initiation Talks Ser.). (Illus.). 648p. (Orig.). 1980. 21.95 (ISBN 0-88050-138-3). Chidvilas Found.

--The Sun Rises in the Evening. Asha, Ma Prem, ed. LC 83-181196. (Zen Ser.). (Illus.). 372p. (Orig.). 1980. 17.95 (ISBN 0-88050-139-1). Chidvilas Found.

--Take It Easy, 2 vols. Anurag, Ma Yoga & Vandana, Ma Ananda, eds. LC 83-177521. (Zen Ser.). (Illus., Orig.). 1979. Vol. I, 584 pgs. 21.95 ea. (ISBN 0-88050-141-3). Vol. II, 584 pgs (ISBN 0-88050-142-1). Chidvilas Found.

--Tantra, Spirituality & Sex. 2nd ed. Anurag, Ma Yoga, ed. LC 83-16036. (Tantra Ser.). 160p. 1983. pap. 3.95 (ISBN 0-88050-696-2). Chidvilas Found.

--Tantra: The Supreme Understanding. 2nd ed. Apa, Ma Prem & Vadan, Ma Anand, eds. LC 84-42797. (Tantra Ser.). 336p. 1984. pap. 4.95 (ISBN 0-88050-643-1). Chidvilas Found.

--The Tantra Vision, 2 vols. Anurag, Ma Yoga, ed. (Tantra Ser.). (Illus., Orig.). 1978. Vol. I, 340 pgs. 16.50 ea. (ISBN 0-88050-144-8). Vol. II, 344 pgs (ISBN 0-88050-145-6). Chidvilas Found.

--Tao: The Golden Gate, Vol. 1. Asha, Ma Prem, ed. LC 84-42615. (Tao Ser.). 336p. (Orig.). 1984. pap. 4.95 (ISBN 0-88050-646-6). Chidvilas Found.

--Tao: The Pathless Path, 2 vols. Asha, Ma Prem & Veena, Ma Prema, eds. LC 82-232884. (Tao Ser.). (Illus.). 1979. Vol. I, 432 pgs. 17.95 ea. (ISBN 0-88050-148-0). Vol. II, 540 pgs (ISBN 0-88050-149-9). Vol. I, 440p. pap. 15.95 (ISBN 0-88050-648-2); Vol. II, 1978, 542p. pap. write for info. (ISBN 0-88050-649-0). Chidvilas Found.

--Tao: The Three Treasures, 4 vols. Veena, Ma Prema & Somendra, Swami Anand, eds. LC 76-905202. (Tao Ser.). (Illus., Orig.). 1977. Vol. II, 346 pgs., 1976. 15.95 ea. (ISBN 0-88050-151-0). Vol. III, 404 pgs. 1976 (ISBN 0-88050-152-9). Vol. IV, 422 pgs. 1977 (ISBN 0-88050-153-7). Chidvilas Found.

--Theologia Mystica. Asha, Ma Prem, ed. LC 83-11086. (Western Mystics Ser.). 400p. (Orig.). 1983. pap. 4.95 (ISBN 0-88050-655-5). Chidvilas Found.

--This Is It. Maneesha, ma Prem, ed. LC 82-230731. (Initiation Talks Ser.). (Illus.). 672p. (Orig.). 1979. 19.95 (ISBN 0-88050-156-1). Chidvilas Found.

--This Very Body the Buddha. Vandana, Ma Ananda, ed. LC 79-904227. (Zen Ser.). (Illus.). 360p. (Orig.). 1978. 16.95 (ISBN 0-88050-157-X). Chidvilas Found.

--This Very Place the Lotus Paradise. Madyapa, Swami Anand, ed. LC 84-42805. (Photobiography Ser.). 568p. (Orig.). 1984. 100.00x (ISBN 0-88050-705-5). Chidvilas Found.

--The Tongue-Tip Taste of Tao. Maneesha, Ma Prem, ed. (Initiation Talks Ser.). (Illus.). 350p. 1981. 26.95 (ISBN 0-88050-158-8). Chidvilas Found.

--The True Sage. Chaitanya, Swami Christ, ed. LC 83-183323. (Hasids Ser.). (Illus.). 410p. (Orig.). 1976. 16.50 (ISBN 0-88050-159-6). Chidvilas Found.

--Turn on, Tune in & Drop the Lot. Maneesha, Ma Prem, ed. (Initiation Talks Ser.). (Illus.). 312p. (Orig.). 1980. pap. 18.95 (ISBN 0-88050-660-1). Chidvilas Found.

--The Ultimate Alchemy, 2 vols. Prem, Ma Ananda, ed. LC 75-905370. (Upanishad Ser.). (Illus.). 1976. Vol. I, 442 pgs. 18.95 ea. (ISBN 0-88050-161-8). Vol. II, 424 pgs (ISBN 0-88050-162-6). Chidvilas Found.

--Unio Mystica, 2 vols. 2nd ed. Vandana, Ma Ananda, ed. LC 82-245842. (Sufi Ser.). (Illus.). 1980. Vol. I 384p. 17.95 ea. (ISBN 0-88050-163-4). Vol. II (ISBN 0-88050-164-2). Vol. I. pap. 13.95 ea. (ISBN 0-88050-663-6). Vol. II 368p 1981 (ISBN 0-88050-664-4). Chidvilas Found.

--Until You Die. Anurag, Ma Yoga, ed. LC 77-900984. (Sufi Ser.). (Illus.). 280p. (Orig.). 1976. 15.95 (ISBN 0-88050-165-0). Chidvilas Found.

--Vedanta: Seven Steps to Samadhi. Pratima, Ma Yoga, ed. LC 77-904425. (Upanishad Ser.). (Illus.). 518p. (Orig.). 1976. 16.50 (ISBN 0-88050-166-9). Chidvilas Found.

--Walk Without Feet, Fly Without Wings, & Think Without Mind. Anurag, Ma Yoga, ed. LC 83-181337. (Questions & Answers Ser.). (Illus.). 384p. (Orig.). 1979. 16.50 (ISBN 0-88050-167-7). Chidvilas Found.

--Walking in Zen, Sitting in Zen. Rajneesh Foundation International, ed. LC 82-24025. (Questions & Answers Ser.). 444p. (Orig.). 1982. pap. 10.95 (ISBN 0-88050-668-7). Chidvilas Found.

--What Is Is, What Ain't, Ain't. Maneesha, Ma Prem, ed. LC 83-177697. (Initiation Talks Ser.). (Illus.). 624p. (Orig.). 1980. 18.95 (ISBN 0-88050-670-9). Chidvilas Found.

--When the Shoe Fits. Veena, Ma Prema, ed. LC 76-904914. (Zen Masters Ser.). (Illus.). 388p. (Orig.). 1976. 16.50 (ISBN 0-88050-171-5). Chidvilas Found.

--The White Lotus. Asha, Ma Prem, ed. LC 81-903266. (Zen Ser.). (Illus.). 430p. 1981. 17.95 (ISBN 0-88050-172-3); pap. 13.95 (ISBN 0-88050-672-5). Chidvilas Found.

--The Wild Geese & the Water. Prabhu, Swami Krishna, ed. LC 85-43053. (Responses to Questions Ser.). 416p. (Orig.). 1985. pap. 4.95 (ISBN 0-88050-673-3). Chidvilas Found.

--The Wisdom of the Sands, 2 vols. Sudha, Ma Yoga, ed. LC 80-903299. (Sufi Ser.). (Illus., Orig.). 1980. Vol. I, 380 pgs. 19.95 ea. (ISBN 0-88050-174-X). Vol. II, 404 pgs. 1980 (ISBN 0-88050-175-8). Vol.1 386p 1980. pap. 15.95 ea. (ISBN 0-88050-674-1). Chidvilas Found.

--Won't You Join the Dance. Maneesha, Ma Prem, ed. LC 83-43217. (Initiation Talks Ser.). 320p. (Orig.). 1983. pap. 4.95 (ISBN 0-88050-676-8). Chidvilas Found.

--Yoga: The Alpha & the Omega, 10 vols, Vols. 1-5. Prem, Ma Ananda & Sudha, Ma Yoga, eds. LC 76-902396. (Yoga Ser.). (Illus., Orig.). 1976. Vol I, 272 pgs. 16.95 ea. (ISBN 0-88050-177-4). Vol II, 266 pgs. 1976 (ISBN 0-88050-178-2). Vol. III, 298 pgs. 1976 (ISBN 0-88050-179-0). Vol. IV, 280 pgs. 1976 (ISBN 0-88050-180-4). Vol. V, 266 pgs. 1976 (ISBN 0-88050-181-2). Chidvilas Found.

--Yoga: The Alpha & the Omega, 10 vols, Vols. 6-10. Chinmaya, Swami Prem & Sudha, Ma Yoga, eds. LC 76-902396. (Yoga Ser.). (Illus., Orig.). 1977. Vol. VI, 270 pgs. 16.95 ea. (ISBN 0-88050-182-0). Vol. VII250p 1977 (ISBN 0-88050-183-9). Vol. VIII, 298 pgs. 1977 (ISBN 0-88050-184-7). Vol. IX, 346 pgs. 1978 (ISBN 0-88050-185-5). Vol. X, 270 pgs. 1978 (ISBN 0-88050-186-3). Chidvilas Found.

--Yoga: The Science of the Soul, Vol. 1. 2nd ed. Mahasattva, Swami Krishna, ed. LC 84-42812. (Yoga Ser.). 304p. 1984. pap. 4.95 (ISBN 0-88050-677-6). Chidvilas Found.

--You Ain't Seen Nothing Yet. Maneesha, Ma Prem, ed. LC 84-42614. (Initiation Talks Ser.). 304p. (Orig.). 1984. pap. 4.95 (ISBN 0-88050-687-3). Chidvilas Found.

--Zen: The Path of Paradox, 3 vols. Veena, Ma Prema & Vandana, Ma Ananda, eds. LC 82-246214. (Zen Ser.). (Illus.). 1978. Vol. I, 376 pgs. 16.95 ea. (ISBN 0-88050-188-X). Vol. II, 372pgs 1979 (ISBN 0-88050-189-8). Vol. III, 392 pgs. 1979 (ISBN 0-88050-190-1). Chidvilas Found.

--Zen: The Special Transmission. Ma Prem Rajo & Ma Deva Sarito, eds. LC 84-43010. (Zen Ser.). 368p. (Orig.). 1984. pap. 4.95 (ISBN 0-88050-691-1). Chidvilas Found.

--Zen: Zest, Zip Zap & Zing. Asha, Ma Prem, ed. LC 83-183222. (Question & Answer Ser.). (Illus.). 472p. (Orig.). 1981. pap. 19.95 468p 1981 (ISBN 0-88050-692-X). Chidvilas Found.

--The Zero Experience. Maneesha, Ma Prem, ed. (Initiation Talks Ser.). (Illus.). 632p. (Orig.). 1979. 21.50 (ISBN 0-88050-193-6). Chidvilas Found.

Rajneesh, Bhagwan Shree & Sudha, Ma Yoga. The Wisdom of the Sands. LC 80-903299. (Sufi Ser.: Vol. II). 412p. (Orig.). 1980. pap. 15.95 (ISBN 0-88050-675-X). Chidvilas Found.

Rajneesh, Bhagwan Sri. Nirvana: The Last Nightmare. Rajneesh Foundation, ed. (Illus.). 278p. (Orig.). 1981. pap. 8.95 (ISBN 0-914794-37-X). Wisdom Garden Bks.

Rajneesh Foundation, ed. see Rajneesh, Bhagwan Sri.

Rajneesh Foundation International, ed. see Rajneesh, Bhagwan S.

Rajneesh Foundation International, ed. see Rajneesh, Bhagwan Shree.

Rajneesh Foundation International, ed. see Rajneesh, Bhagwan S.

Raju, P. T. Spirit, Being & Self. (Studies in Indian & Western Philosophy). 285p. 1982. 29.95 (ISBN 0-940500-98-1, Pub. by S. Asian Pubs India). Asia Bk Corp.

--Structural Depths of Indian Thought. (Philosophy Ser.). 600p. 1985. 49.50x (ISBN 0-88706-139-7); pap. 24.50x (ISBN 0-88706-140-0). State U NY Pr.

Rakel, Michael & Bremke, Maryann. New Testament Times. 1984. 9.95 (ISBN 0-89837-100-7, Pub. by Pflaum Press). Peter Li.

--Old Testament Times. 1984. 9.95 (ISBN 0-89837-099-X, Pub. by Pflaum Press). Peter Li.

Rakov, Lois E. My First Haggadah. new ed. (Illus.). 1978. 3.95 (ISBN 0-87243-075-8). Templegate.

Raleigh, Alexander. The Book of Esther. 1980. 9.75 (ISBN 0-86524-037-X, 1701). Klock & Klock.

Raleigh, Walter A. Milton. LC 67-13336. 1967. Repr. of 1900 ed. 17.00 (ISBN 0-405-08873-6). Ayer Co Pubs.

--Milton. 1973. 10.00 (ISBN 0-8274-1323-8). R West.

Ralli, Augustus. Christians at Mecca. LC 70-118545. 1971. Repr. of 1909 ed. 27.00x (ISBN 0-8046-1170-X, Pub. by Kennikat). Assoc Faculty Pr.

--Poetry & Faith. LC 76-16831. 1976. Repr. of 1951 ed. lib. bdg. 20.00 (ISBN 0-8414-7316-1). Folcroft.

Rallings, E. M. & Pratto, David J. Two-Clergy Marriages: A Special Case of Dual Careers. 126p. (Orig.). 1985. 24.00 (ISBN 0-8191-4343-X); pap. text ed. 9.50 (ISBN 0-8191-4344-8). U Pr of Amer.

Ralph, Margaret. Historias Que Jesus Conto. (Serie Jirafa). Orig. Title: Stories Jesus Told. 28p. 1979. 3.95 (ISBN 0-311-38537-0, Edit Mundo). Casa Bautista.

--Jesus: Historias de su Vida. LaValle, Teresa, tr. (Serie Jirafa). Orig. Title: The Life of Jesus. (Illus.). 28p. 1979. 3.95 (ISBN 0-311-38536-2, Edit Mundo). Casa Bautista.

--Personas Escogidas de Dios. (Serie Jirafa). Orig. Title: God's Special People. 28p. 1979. 3.95 (ISBN 0-311-38535-4, Edit Mundo). Casa Bautista.

Ralston, W. R. Songs of the Russian People: As Illustrative of Slavonic Mythology & Russian Social Life. LC 77-132444. (Studies in Music, No. 42). 1970. Repr. of 1872 ed. lib. bdg. 69.95x (ISBN 0-8383-1224-1). Haskell.

Ram, Sri. Thoughts for Aspirants. Series II. 3.95 (ISBN 0-8356-7449-5). Theos Pub Hse.

Rama, Swami. Exercise Without Movement. (Illus.). 88p. (Orig.). pap. 5.95 (ISBN 0-89389-089-8). Himalayan Pubs.

--Freedom from the Bondage of Karma. 2nd ed. 92p. pap. 5.95 (ISBN 0-89389-031-6). Himalayan Pubs.

--Lectures on Yoga. LC 79-114571. (Illus.). 208p. pap. 7.95 (ISBN 0-89389-050-2); 6.95 (ISBN 0-89389-051-0). Himalayan Pubs.

Ramachandran. Sri Sankara Vijayam. 1977. pap. 2.25 (ISBN 0-89744-123-0, Pub. by Ganesh & Co. India). Auromere.

Ramacharaka, Yogi. Fourteen Lessons in Yoga Philosophy. 8.00 (ISBN 0-911662-01-4). Yoga.

--Gnani Yoga. 8.00 (ISBN 0-911662-04-9). Yoga.

--Hatha Yoga. 8.00 (ISBN 0-911662-06-5). Yoga.

--Hindu-Yogi Practical Water Cure. leatherette 3.00 (ISBN 0-911662-12-X). Yoga.

--The Hindu Yogi Science of Breath. 88p. 1905. pap. text ed. 5.95 (ISBN 0-88697-047-4). Life Science.

--Mystic Christianity. 8.00 (ISBN 0-911662-08-1). Yoga.

--Philosophies & Religions of India. 8.00 (ISBN 0-911662-05-7). Yoga.

--Raja Yoga. 8.00 (ISBN 0-911662-03-0). Yoga.

Ramadhan, S. Islam & Nationalism. pap. 1.00 (ISBN 0-686-18586-2). Kazi Pubns.

Ramaiah, G. Sundara. A Philosophical Study of the Mysticism of Sankara. 1983. 12.00x (ISBN 0-686-88924-X, Pub. by KP Bagchi India). South Asia Bks.

Ramakrishna Math Staff, ed. Sadhanas for Spiritual Life. 166p. pap. 2.75 (ISBN 0-87481-507-X). Vedanta Pr.

Ramakrishna, Sri. Sayings of Sri Ramakrishna. 5.50 (ISBN 0-87481-431-6). Vedanta Pr.

--Tales & Parables of Sri Ramakrishna. pap. 5.00 (ISBN 0-87481-493-6). Vedanta Pr.

--Teachings of Sri Ramakrishna. pap. 4.95 (ISBN 0-87481-133-3). Vedanta Pr.

--Words of the Master. Brahmananda, Swami, ed. pap. 1.50 (ISBN 0-87481-135-X). Vedanta Pr.

Ramakrishna, Swami. Tales from Ramakrishna. (Illus.). 54p. (Orig.). 1975. pap. 2.75 (ISBN 0-87481-152-X). Vedanta Pr.

Ramakrishna Gopala Bhanddarkar. Commemorative Essays Presented to Sir Ramakrishna Gopal Bhandarkar. LC 78-70111. Repr. of 1917 ed. 44.00 (ISBN 0-404-17366-7). AMS Pr.

Ramakrishnananda, Swami. The Ancient Quest. 112p. pap. 1.00 (ISBN 0-87481-412-X). Vedanta Pr.

--Krishna: Pastoral & Kingmaker. pap. 2.25 (ISBN 0-87481-447-2). Vedanta Pr.

Ramakrishna's Disciples. Message of Our Master. pap. 1.95 (ISBN 0-87481-102-3). Vedanta Pr.

--Spiritual Talks. 5.95 (ISBN 0-87481-103-1). Vedanta Pr.

Ramakrisnananda, Swami. Life of Sri Ranauja. 1979. pap. 8.95 (ISBN 0-87481-446-4). Vedanta Pr.

Ramanathan, P. The Western Approach to the Law & the Prophets of the Ancient World. (Illus.). 188p. 1984. 88.95 (ISBN 0-89920-113-X). Am Inst Psych.

Ramanayyan, Venkata. An Essay on the Origin of the South Indian Temples. (Illus.). 92p. 1986. Repr. 15.00X (ISBN 0-8364-1725-9, Pub. by Manohar India). South Asia Bks.

Ramanuja Research Society. Vishishtadvaita: Philosophy & Religion. 273p. 1975. 10.75 (ISBN 0-88253-683-4). Ind-US Inc.

Ramanujachari, C., tr. see Tyagaraja.

Ramanujan, A. K., tr. Speaking of Siva. (Classics Ser.). 200p. 1973. pap. 5.95 (ISBN 0-14-044270-7). Penguin.

Rama Prasada, tr. see Patanjali.

Ramati, Alexander & Niccacci, Rufino. The Assisi Underground. 1978. 3.50 (ISBN 0-8128-8135-4). Stein & Day.

Rambo, Lewis. The Divorcing Christian. 96p. (Orig.). 1983. pap. 5.25 (ISBN 0-687-10994-9). Abingdon.

Rambova, N., jt. ed. see Piankoff, A.

Rameshwar Rao, S., tr. The Mahabharata. 2nd ed. Orig. Title: The Children's Mahabharata. 219p. 1976. pap. text ed. cancelled (ISBN 0-89253-041-3). Ind-US Inc.

Ramet, Pedro, ed. Religion & Nationalism in Soviet & East European Politics. (Policy Studies). v, 282p. 1985. text ed. 35.00 (ISBN 0-8223-0608-5). Duke.

Ramientos, Nene. Contemporary Christian Issues. 71p. 1982. pap. 4.00 (ISBN 971-10-0013-X, Pub. by New Day Philippines). Cellar.

Ramirez de Arellano, Annette B. & Seipp, Conrad. Colonialism, Catholicism, & Contraception: A History of Birth Control in Puerto Rico. LC 82-13646. xiv, 219p. 1983. 25.00x (ISBN 0-8078-1544-6). U of NC Pr.

Ramm, Bernard. Christian View of Science & Scripture. 1954. pap. 4.95 (ISBN 0-8028-1429-8). Eerdmans.

--Diccionario de Teologia Contemporanea. Valle, Roger V., tr. 143p. 1984. pap. 3.75 (ISBN 0-311-09064-8). Casa Bautista.

--An Evangelical Christology: Ecumenic & Historic. 224p. 1985. 14.95 (ISBN 0-8407-7518-0). Nelson.

--Hermeneutics. (Practical Theology Ser.). pap. 3.95 (ISBN 0-8010-7605-6). Baker Bk.

--Offense to Reason: The Theology of Sin. LC 84-48777. 288p. 1985. 15.45 (ISBN 0-06-066792-3, HarpR). Har-Row.

--Protestant Biblical Interpretation. 9.95 (ISBN 0-8010-7600-5). Baker Bk.

--Protestant Biblical Interpretation. Chan, Silas, tr. from Eng. (Chinese.). 1984. pap. write for info. (ISBN 0-941598-10-1). Living Spring Pubns.

--Varieties of Christian Apologetics. (Twin Brooks Ser.). pap. 5.95 (ISBN 0-8010-7610-2). Baker Bk.

Ramm, Bernard L. After Fundamentalism: The Future of Evangelical Theology. LC 82-47792. 226p. 1984. text ed. 14.37i (ISBN 0-06-066791-5, RD 473, HarpR); pap. 9.95 (HarpR). Har-Row.

--God's Way Out. rev. ed. Stewart, Ed, ed. 214p. 1987. pap. 5.95 (ISBN 0-8307-1215-1, 5416514). Regal.

Ramm, Charles A. Meditations on the Mystery of Christmas. Lilly, Sr. Catherine M., ed. LC 59-15709. (Illus.). 1959. 6.95 (ISBN 0-87015-092-8). Pacific Bks.

Rammohun Roy, R. The English Works of Raja Ramohun Roy. Ghose, Jogendra C., ed. LC 75-41220. Repr. of 1906 ed. 49.50 (ISBN 0-404-14738-0). AMS Pr.

Ramos, Dominga D. Moncado. 1985. 9.75 (ISBN 0-8062-2452-5). Carlton.

Rampa, Mama S. Tigerlily. 1978. pap. 2.95 (ISBN 0-552-10735-2). Weiser.

Rampa, T. Lobsang. Living with the Lama. pap. 2.95 (ISBN 0-552-08408-5). Weiser.

--The Rampa Story. pap. 2.95 (ISBN 0-552-11413-8). Weiser.

--Third Eye. 1974. pap. 2.50 (ISBN 0-345-29023-2). Ballantine.

Ramprasad. Ramprasad: The Melodius Mystic. Buddhananda, tr. 72p. 1985. pap. 2.00 (ISBN 0-87481-568-1, Pub. by Ramakrishna Math Madras India). Vedanta Pr.

Ramras-Rauch, Gila & Michman-Melkman, Joseph, eds. Facing the Holocaust. 1986. 16.95 (ISBN 0-8276-0253-7). Jewish Pubns.

Ramsay, DeVere. God's People Our Story: Bible Stories from the New Testament. LC 83-51404. 128p. 1984. 12.95 (ISBN 0-8358-0480-1). Upper Room.

--The Old Testament: God's People-Our Story. LC 84-51829. (Illus.). 1985. 12.95 (ISBN 0-8358-0500-X). Upper Room.

Ramsay, W. M. The Church in the Roman Empire Before A. D. 170. LC 77-6997. 1977. Repr. of 1904 ed. 50.00 (ISBN 0-89341-216-3). Longwood Pub Group.

--Pauline & Other Studies in Early Christian History. 1977. lib. bdg. 59.95 (ISBN 0-8490-2416-1). Gordon Pr.

Ramsay, W. M. & Bell, Gertrude L. The Thousand & One Churches. (Illus.). xvi, 580p. 1985. Repr. of 1905 ed. lib. bdg. 80.00x (ISBN 0-89241-121-X). Caratzas.

Ramsay, William H. Historical Commentary on the Epistle to the Galatians. 1978. 17.75 (ISBN 0-86524-107-4, 4801). Klock & Klock.

Ramsay, William M. The Education of Christ. LC 80-84438. (Shepherd Illustrated Classics Ser.). (Illus.). 168p. 1981. pap. 5.95 (ISBN 0-87983-236-3). Keats.

--Four Modern Prophets: Walter Rauschenbusch, Martin Luther King, Jr., Gustavo Gutierrez, Rosemary Radford Ruether. LC 86-45351. 108p. (Orig.). 1986. pap. 6.95 (ISBN 0-8042-0811-5). John Knox.

--The Layman's Guide to the New Testament. LC 79-87742. (Layman's Bible Commentary Ser.). 273p. (Orig.). 1980. pap. 11.95 (ISBN 0-8042-0322-9). John Knox.

--Letters to the Seven Churches. (William M. Ramsay Library). 476p. 1985. pap. 12.95 (ISBN 0-8010-7681-1). Baker Bk.

--St. Paul the Traveller & Roman Citizen. (William M. Ramsay Library Ser.). 1979. pap. 14.95 (ISBN 0-8010-7613-7). Baker Bk.

Ramsden, E. C., tr. see Undset, Sigrid.

Ramsden, William E. The Church in a Changing Society. LC 79-24274. (Into Our Third Century Ser.). (Orig.). 1980. pap. 4.95 (ISBN 0-687-08250-1). Abingdon.

--Ministries Through Non-Parish Institutions. LC 80-22294. (Into Our Third Century Ser.). 96p. (Orig.). 1981. pap. 4.95 (ISBN 0-687-27037-5). Abingdon.

Ramsey, A. Michael & Suenens, Leon J. Future of the Christian Church. (Orig.). 1970. pap. 3.95 (ISBN 0-8192-1124-9). Morehouse.

Ramsey, Boniface. Beginning to Read the Fathers. 288p. (Orig.). 1985. pap. 9.95 (ISBN 0-8091-2691-5). Paulist Pr.

Ramsey, Dale E. Sing Praises! Management of Church Hymns. 30p. (Orig.). 1983. pap. 3.50 (ISBN 0-8272-3300-0). CBP.

Ramsey, Evelyn. Show Me, Lord. 178p. 1982. pap. 4.95 (ISBN 0-8341-0781-3). Beacon Hill.

Ramsey, George W. Quest for the Historical Israel. LC 80-82188. 208p. (Orig.). 1981. pap. 13.95 (ISBN 0-8042-0187-0). John Knox.

Ramsey, I. T., ed. see Locke, John.

Ramsey, James B. Revelation: An Exposition of the First Eleven Chapters. (Geneva Commentary Ser.). 1977. 17.95 (ISBN 0-85151-256-9). Banner of Truth.

Ramsey, Johnny, ed. Story of the Bible. pap. 3.95 (ISBN 0-89137-543-0). Quality Pubns.

Ramsey, Michael. Be Still & Know: A Study in the Life of Prayer. 128p. (Orig.). 1983. pap. 6.95 (ISBN 0-8164-2473-X, HarpR). Har-Row.

Ramsey, Paul. Basic Christian Ethics. LC 78-56925. 424p. 1980. pap. text ed. 14.00x (ISBN 0-226-70383-5). U of Chicago Pr.

--Deeds & Rules in Christian Ethics. LC 83-10257. 256p. 1983. pap. text ed. 13.25 (ISBN 0-8191-3355-8). U Pr of Amer.

--Faith & Ethics: The Theology of H. Richard Niebuhr. 11.25 (ISBN 0-8446-2778-X). Peter Smith.

--Study of Religion in Colleges & Universities. Wilson, John F., ed. LC 70-90957. 336p. 1970. 37.00x (ISBN 0-691-07161-6). Princeton U Pr.

--The Truth of Value. 139p. 1985. text ed. 15.00x (ISBN 0-391-03058-2). Humanities.

--War & the Christian Conscience: How Shall Modern War Be Conducted Justly? LC 61-10666. xxiv, 331p. 1985. pap. 9.95 (ISBN 0-8223-0361-2). Duke.

--War & the Christian Conscience: How Shall Modern War be Conducted Justly? LC 61-10666. pap. 88.30 (ISBN 0-317-26099-5, 2023766). Bks Demand UMI.

Ramsey, Paul, ed. Contemporary Religious Poetry. 1987. pap. 7.95. Paulist Pr.

Ramsey, Paul, ed. see Edwards, Jonathan.

Ramsey, Paul, jt. ed. see McCormick, Richard A.

Ramsey, Russell. God's Joyful Runner: The Story of Eric Liddell. (Orig.). 1987. pap. 9.95 (ISBN 0-88270-624-1, P624-1). Bridge Pub.

--A Lady, A Healer. Graves, Helen, ed. LC 85-40891. 213p. (Orig.). 1986. pap. 3.95 (ISBN 1-55523-006-7). Winston-Derek.

Ramseyer, Robert L. Mission & the Peace Witness. LC 79-16738. (Christian Peace Shelf Ser.: No. 7). 144p. 1979. pap. 6.95 (ISBN 0-8361-1896-0). Herald Pr.

Ramshaw, Elaine. Ritual & Pastoral Care. LC 85-45487. (Theology and Pastoral Care Ser.). 128p. 1987. pap. 7.95 (ISBN 0-8006-1738-X). Fortress.

Ramshaw-Schmidt, Gail. Christ in Sacred Speech: The Meaning of Liturgical Language. LC 85-45486. 144p. 1986. pap. 9.95 (ISBN 0-8006-1907-2, 1-1907). Fortress.

--Letters for God's Name. (Illus.). 1984. pap. 4.95 (ISBN 0-86683-880-5, 7458, HarpR). Har-Row.

Ramtha. Ramtha. Weinberg, Steven L., ed. LC 85-61768. 224p. 1986. 19.95 (ISBN 0-932201-11-3). Sovereignty.

--Ramtha: A Treasure Chest of Wisdom. Fazio, Sue A. & Weischedel, Randall, eds. 250p. 1987. 16.95 (ISBN 0-932201-23-7). Sovereignty.

--Ramtha in Audience. 300p. 1987. 15.95 (ISBN 0-932201-90-3); pap. 9.95 (ISBN 0-932201-82-2). Sovereignty.

--Ramtha: Select Teachings. Weinberg, Steven L., ed. 150p. 1987. pap. 8.95 (ISBN 0-932201-19-9). Sovereignty.

Ranade, R. D. Mysticism in India: The Poet Saints of Maharashtra. LC 82-10458. (Illus.). 534p. 1982. 44.50x (ISBN 0-87395-669-9); pap. 12.95 (ISBN 0-87395-670-2). State U NY Pr.

Ranaghan, Dorothy. A Day in Thy Courts. LC 84-70866. 144p. (Orig.). 1984. pap. 4.95 (ISBN 0-943780-05-5, 8055). Charismatic Ren Servs.

Ranaghan, Dorothy, jt. auth. see Ranaghan, Kevin.

Ranaghan, Kevin & Ranaghan, Dorothy. Catholic Pentecostals Today. rev. ed. LC 83-70963. 196p. 1983. pap. 4.95 (ISBN 0-943780-03-9, 8039). Charismatic Ren Servs.

Rananujan, A. K., tr. from Tamil. Hymns for the Drowning: Poems for Vishnu by Nammalvar. LC 81-47151. (Princeton Library of Asian Translations). 145p. 1982. 23.50 (ISBN 0-691-06492-X); pap. 8.00 (ISBN 0-691-01385-3). Princeton U Pr.

Rand, Benjamin, ed. The Classical Moralists: Selections Illustrating Ethics from Socrates to Martineau. 16.50 (ISBN 0-8446-1374-6). Peter Smith.

Rand, Edward K. Cicero in the Courtroom of Saint Thomas Aquinas. (Aquinas Lecture Ser.). 1945. 7.95 (ISBN 0-87462-109-7). Marquette.

--Founders of the Middle Ages. 1928. pap. 7.95 (ISBN 0-486-20369-7). Dover.

Rand, Howard B. Behold, He Cometh. 1955. 5.00 (ISBN 0-685-08798-0). Destiny.

--Digest of the Divine Law. 1943. 8.00 (ISBN 0-685-08802-2). Destiny.

--Hour Cometh. 1966. 5.00 (ISBN 0-685-08805-7). Destiny.

--Marvels of Prophecy. 1959. 5.00 (ISBN 0-685-08810-3). Destiny.

--Primogenesis. 1953. 15.00 (ISBN 0-685-08813-8). Destiny.

--Study in Daniel. 1948. 12.00 (ISBN 0-685-08814-6). Destiny.

--Study in Hosea. 1955. 8.00 (ISBN 0-685-08815-4). Destiny.

--Study in Jeremiah. 1947. 12.00 (ISBN 0-685-08816-2). Destiny.

--Study in Revelation. 1941. 12.00 (ISBN 0-685-08817-0). Destiny.

Rand, Richard, tr. see Derrida, Jacques.

Rand, W. W. Diccionario de la Santa Biblia. (Span., Illus.). 768p. 1969. pap. 15.50 (ISBN 0-89922-003-7). Edit Caribe.

Randall, Alice E. Sources of Spenser's Classical Mythology. 1896. Repr. 10.00 (ISBN 0-8274-3476-6). R West.

Randall, Daniel R. A Puritan Colony in Maryland. LC 78-63763. (Johns Hopkins University. Studies in the Social Sciences. Fourth Ser. 1886: 6). Repr. of 1886 ed. 11.50 (ISBN 0-404-61031-5). AMS Pr.

--A Puritan Colony in Maryland. 1973. pap. 9.00 (ISBN 0-384-49568-0). Johnson Repr.

Randall, Doanda, compiled by. Buddhist & Hindu Art in the Collection of John H. Mann. (Illus.). 285p. (Orig.). 1981. 65.00x (ISBN 0-940492-01-6). Asian Conserv Lab.

Randall, Emilius O. History of the Zoar Society. 3rd ed. LC 75-134427. 1972. Repr. of 1904 ed. 14.50 (ISBN 0-404-08467-2). AMS Pr.

Randall, Gerald. Church Furnishing & Decoration in England & Wales. LC 80-11125. (Illus.). 240p. 1980. text ed. 42.50x (ISBN 0-8419-0602-5). Holmes & Meier.

--The English Parish Church. 192p. 1982. 35.00 (ISBN 0-8419-6402-5). Holmes & Meier.

Randall, John. Wisdom Instructs Her Children: The Power of the Spirit & the Word. 128p. (Orig.). 1981. pap. 3.95 (ISBN 0-914544-36-5). Living Flame Pr.

Randall, John, et al. Mary: Pathway to Fruitfulness. (Orig.). 1978. pap. 2.95 (ISBN 0-914544-28-4). Living Flame Pr.

Randall, John H. Hellenistic Ways of Deliverance & the Making of the Christian Synthesis. LC 74-137339. 1970. 28.00x (ISBN 0-231-03327-3). Columbia U Pr.

Randall, John H., Jr. The Role of Knowledge in Western Religion. 160p. 1986. pap. text ed. 10.75 (ISBN 0-8191-5167-X). U Pr of Amer.

Randall, Louise A. Scripture Stories for Tiny Tots: Read-Aloud Stories from the Bible for Children 1 to 6. LC 83-83429. 38p. (Orig.). 1983. pap. 3.95 (ISBN 0-88290-209-1). Horizon Utah.

Randall, Margaret. Christians in the Nicaraguan Revolution. (Illus.). 240p. (Orig.). 1984. 15.95 (ISBN 0-919573-14-2, Pub. by New Star Bks BC); pap. 7.95 (ISBN 0-919573-15-0, Pub. by New Star Bks BC). Left Bank.

Randall, Max W. The Great Awakenings & the Restoration Movement. LC 82-74537. 442p. (Orig.). 1983. pap. 9.95 (ISBN 0-89900-229-3). College Pr Pub.

Randall, Peter, tr. see Boesak, Allan.

Randall, Robert L. Pastors & Parishes. LC 86-27176. 184p. 1987. text ed. 29.95 (ISBN 0-89885-348-6). Human Sci Pr.

--Putting the Pieces Together: Guidance from a Pastoral Psychologist. 80p. (Orig.). 1986. pap. 4.95 (ISBN 0-8298-0583-4). Pilgrim NY.

Randall, Steve, ed. see Tarthang Tulku.

Randel, Don M. An Index to the Chant of the Mozarabic Rite. LC 72-5384. (Princeton Studies in Music Ser.: No. 6). pap. 160.00 (ISBN 0-317-09926-4, 2011400). Bks Demand UMI.

Rando, Therese A., ed. Loss & Anticipatory Grief. LC 85-45082. 256p. 1986. 27.00 (ISBN 0-669-11144-9). Lexington Bks.

Randolph, Boris. Bible Verses in Verse. LC 80-67992. 144p. 1980. pap. 3.95 (ISBN 0-87516-424-2). De Vorss.

Randolph, J., tr. see Trismegistus, Hermes.

Randolph, Paschal B. After Death: The Immortality of Man. 272p. 1970. write for info. (ISBN 0-932785-00-X). Philos Pub.

--Ravalette: The Rosicrucian's Story. 283p. 1939. 7.95 (ISBN 0-932785-40-9). Philos Pub.

--Soul! The Soul World! Clymer, R. Swinburne, ed. 246p. 1932. 9.95 (ISBN 0-932785-45-X). Philos Pub.

Randour, Mary L. Women's Psyche, Women's Spirit: The Reality of Relationships. LC 86-17180. 240p. 1987. 25.00x (ISBN 0-231-06250-8). Columbia U Pr.

Rangachari, ed. see Pillai, Ananda R., et al.

Ranganathananda, Swami. Ramakrishna Math & Mission: Its Ideals & Activities. (Illus.). pap. 1.00 (ISBN 0-87481-448-0). Vedanta Pr.

--Science & Religion. 1979. pap. 3.75 (ISBN 0-87481-190-2). Vedanta Pr.

Range, Cornelius. Heal Me or Kill Me! LC 85-71350. 1985. pap. 5.95 (ISBN 0-88270-592-X). Bridge Pub.

Ranger, T. O. & Weller, John, eds. Themes in the Christian History of Central Africa. 1974. 44.00x (ISBN 0-520-02536-9). U of Cal Pr.

Ranieri, Ralph F. Christian Living: Ten Basic Virtues. 64p. 1983. pap. 1.50 (ISBN 0-89243-193-8). Liguori Pubns.

Rank, Maureen. Free to Grieve: Coping with the Trauma of Miscarriage. 176p. 1985. pap. 5.95 (ISBN 0-87123-806-3, 210806). Bethany Hse.

Rank, Maureen, jt. auth. see Johnston, Russ.

Rank, Otto. The Psychology of the Soul, 2 vols. (Illus.). 201p. 1986. Set. 147.55 (ISBN 0-89920-127-X). Am Inst Psych.

Ranke, Leopold Von see Von Ranke, Leopold.

Rankin, David, jt. auth. see Christensen, Alice.

Rankin, Eric. Cockburnspath: A Documentary History of a Border Parish. Bulloch, James, ed. (Illus.). 166p. 1981. 16.95 (ISBN 0-567-09316-6, Pub. by T&T Clark Ltd UK). Fortress.

Rankin, Oliver S. Jewish Religious Polemic. rev. ed. 1969. 20.00x (ISBN 0-87068-007-2). Ktav.

Rankin, Peg. Glorify God & Enjoy Him Forever. LC 81-51742. 176p. 1981. pap. 5.95 (ISBN 0-8307-0796-4, 5415209). Regal.

--Yet Will I Trust Him. LC 79-91705. 160p. 1980. 5.95 (ISBN 0-8307-0741-7, 5412005). Regal.

Rankin, Robert, ed. see Bloy, Myron B., Jr., et al.

Ransom, John C. God Without Thunder: An Unorthodox Defense of Orthodoxy. LC 65-17410. x, 334p. 1965. Repr. of 1930 ed. 29.50 (ISBN 0-208-00085-2, Archon). Shoe String.

Ransom, Ralph. Steps on the Stairway. LC 81-66408. 96p. 1981. 8.95 (ISBN 0-8119-0424-5). Fell.

Ranum, Patricia, tr. see Aries, Philippe.

Rao, K. L. Mahatma Gandhi & Comparative Religion. 1979. 15.00x (ISBN 0-89684-034-4). South Asia Bks.

Rao, N. R., tr. see Vyasa.

Rao, P. Nagaraja. Epistemology of Dvaita Vedanta. 6.50 (ISBN 0-8356-7442-8). Theos Pub Hse.

Rao, S. K. Tantra Mantra Yantra: The Tantra Psychology. (Illus.). 1977. text ed. 12.50x (ISBN 0-391-01286-X). Humanities.

--Tibetan Tantrik Tradition. (Illus.). 1977. text ed. 10.50x (ISBN 0-391-01105-7). Humanities.

Rao, Sethu, jt. auth. see Bouvier, Leon.

Rapaport, et al. Early Child Care in Israel. (International Monograph on Early Child Care). 212p. 1976. 38.50 (ISBN 0-677-05270-7). Gordon & Breach.

Rapaport, Chanan, jt. auth. see Charny, Israel W.

Raphael, Audrey M. Growing Pains. (Illus.). 68p. 1985. 6.95 (ISBN 0-533-06210-1). Vantage.

Raphael, Bishop. Anglican-Orthodox Intercommunion. pap. 0.25 (ISBN 0-686-05405-9). Eastern Orthodox.

Raphael, Chaim. Encounters with the Jewish People. LC 79-14424. 1979. pap. text ed. 6.95x (ISBN 0-87441-282-X). Behrman.

--Memoirs of a Special Case. rev. ed. LC 62-9548. 208p. 1985. 12.95 (ISBN 0-940646-16-1); pap. 7.95 (ISBN 0-940646-17-X). Rossel Bks.

--The Road from Babylon: The Story of the Sephardic & Oriental Jews. LC 85-42587. (Illus.). 320p. 1986. 22.45i (ISBN 0-06-039048-4, C&M Bessie Bks). Har-Row.

--The Springs of Jewish Life. LC 82-70853. 1982. 16.50 (ISBN 0-465-08192-4). Basic.

Raphael, Chaim, tr. The Passover Haggadah. LC 78-52362. (Illus.). 1978. pap. 3.95 (ISBN 0-87441-312-5). Behrman.

Raphael, D. D. Moral Philosophy. (Oxford Paperbacks University Ser.). (Orig.). 1981. pap. text ed. 8.95x (ISBN 0-19-289136-7). Oxford U Pr.

Raphael, D. D., ed. British Moralists, Sixteen Fifty to Eighteen Hundred, 2 vols. 1969. Set. pap. 18.95x (ISBN 0-19-875010-2). Oxford U Pr.

Raphael, David D. Moral Judgment. LC 77-28440. 1978. Repr. of 1955 ed. lib. bdg. 22.25x (ISBN 0-313-20246-X, RAMJ). Greenwood.

Raphael, Marc L. Jews & Judaism in a Midwestern Community: Columbus, Ohio, 1840-1975. (Illus.). 296p. 1979. 10.00 (ISBN 0-318-00876-9). Ohio Hist Soc.

--Profiles in American Judaism: The Reform, Conservative, Orthodox & Reconstructionist Traditions in Historical Perspective. LC 84-47734. 288p. 1985. 20.45 (ISBN 0-06-066801-6, HarpR). Har-Row.

--Understanding American Jewish Philanthropy. 20.00x (ISBN 0-87068-689-5). Ktav.

Raphael, Marc L., ed. Approaches to Modern Judaism, Vol. II. (Brown Judaic Studies: No. 56). 128p. 1985. 19.95 (ISBN 0-89130-793-1, 14 00 56); pap. 16.95 (ISBN 0-89130-794-X). Scholars Pr GA.

--Jews & Judaism in the United States: A Documentary History. 352p. 1983. pap. text ed. 9.95x (ISBN 0-87441-347-8). Behrman.

Rappaport, Elana, ed. see Carlebach, Shlomo.

Rappaport, Ernest A. Anti-Judaism: A Psychohistory. LC 75-36297. 312p. 1976. 12.50 (ISBN 0-9603382-0-9). Perspective Chicago.

Rappaport, Jon, ed. see Donnelly, Mark & Fenton, Nina.

Rappoport, Angelo S. Folklore of the Jews. LC 71-167125. Repr. of 1937 ed. 40.00x (ISBN 0-8103-3864-5). Gale.

--The Love Affairs of the Vatican. 35.00 (ISBN 0-8490-0561-2). Gordon Pr.

--Mediaeval Legends of Christ. LC 76-15555. 1976. Repr. of 1934 ed. lib. bdg. 32.50 (ISBN 0-8414-7346-3). Folcroft.

--Myth & Legend of Ancient Israel, 3 Vols. rev. ed. 1966. Set. 39.50x (ISBN 0-87068-099-4). Ktav.

--Superstitions of Sailors. LC 71-158207. 1971. Repr. of 1928 ed. 43.00x (ISBN 0-8103-3739-8). Gale.

Rappoport, Leon H., jt. auth. see Kren, George M.

Raschke, Carl, ed. see Fehr, Wayne L.

Raschke, Carl A. The Alchemy of the Word: Language & the End of Theology. LC 79-15490. (American Academy of Religion, Studies in Religion: No. 20). 1979. 14.00 (ISBN 0-89130-319-7, 01-00-20); pap. 9.95 (ISBN 0-89130-320-0). Scholars Pr GA.

--The Bursting of New Wineskins: Reflection on Religion & Culture at the End of Affluence. LC 78-16604. (Pittsburgh Theological Monographs: No. 24). 1978. 10.75 (ISBN 0-915138-34-4). Pickwick.

--The Interruption of Eternity: Modern Gnosticism & the Origins of the New Religious Consciousness. LC 79-16460. 280p. 1980. 21.95x (ISBN 0-88229-374-5). Nelson-Hall.

Raschke, Carl A., ed. New Dimensions in Philosophical Theology. (AAR Thematic Studies). 19.50 (ISBN 0-89130-682-X, 01-24-91). Scholars Pr GA.

Raser, Harold E. Phoebe Palmer: Her Life & Thought. LC 86-31251. (Studies in Women & Religion: Vol. 22). 392p. 1987. 59.95 (ISBN 0-88946-527-4). E Mellen.

Rashdall, H. Conscience & Christ: Six Lectures on Christian Ethics. LC 17-2649. 1916. 26.00 (ISBN 0-527-73900-6). Kraus Repr.

Rashdall, Hastings. Philosophy & Religion: Six Lectures Delivered at Cambridge. Repr. of 1910 ed. lib. bdg. 22.50x (ISBN 0-8371-3025-5, RAPR). Greenwood.

Rashid, Khalid. Muslim Law. 376p. 1985. 60.00x (Pub. by Eastern Bk India). State Mutual Bk.

Rashid, M. S. Iqbal's Concept of God. 120p. 1986. pap. text ed. 12.95 (ISBN 0-7103-0004-2). Methuen Inc.

Rasi, Humberto. Life of Jesus. 9.95 ea. (ISBN 0-8163-0573-0). No.1, 1984. No.2, 1985 (ISBN 0-8163-0602-8). No. 3, 1985 (ISBN 0-8163-0607-9). Pacific Pr Pub Assn.

Raskas, Bernard S. Heart of Wisdom, Bk. III. 10.50. United Synagogue.

--Heart of Wisdom-One. 1962. 8.50 (ISBN 0-8381-2102-0). United Syn Bk.

--Heart of Wisdom-Two. 1979. 9.50 (ISBN 0-8381-2104-7). United Syn Bk.

Raskas, Bernard S., ed. Living Thoughts. LC 76-22418. 1976. 12.50 (ISBN 0-87677-145-2). Hartmore.

Raskop, Heinrich, jt. auth. see Pieper, Josef.

Rasmussen, B. H., tr. see Keller, Werner.

Rasmussen, Carl, tr. see Nygren, Anders.

Rasmussen, John H., tr. see Grane, Leif.

Rasmussen, Larry L., jt. auth. see Birch, Bruce C.

Rasmussen, Royal. How New Evidence of God Can Bring You Joy. (Illus.). 228p. 1986. 14.95 (ISBN 0-936223-01-4). Sunshine Pr.

Rasooli, Jay M. & Allen, Cady H. Dr. Sa'eed of Iran: Kurdish Physician to Princes & Peasants, Nobles & Nomads. LC 57-13245. (Illus.). 192p. 1983. pap. 6.95 (ISBN 0-87808-743-5). William Carey Lib.

Raspa, Anthony. The Emotive Image: Jesuit Poetics in the English Renaissance. LC 83-502. 173p. 1983. 19.50x (ISBN 0-912646-65-9). Tex Christian.

Raspa, Anthony, ed. see Donne, John.

Rasputin, Maria. My Father. 1970. 5.00 (ISBN 0-8216-0120-2). Univ Bks.

Rassieur, Charles L. Christian Renewal: Living Beyond Burnout. LC 83-26064. (Potentials: Guides for Productive Living: Vol. 5). 120p. (Orig.). 1984. pap. 7.95 (ISBN 0-664-24611-7). Westminster.

--The Problem Clergymen Don't Talk About. LC 75-40306. 156p. 1976. pap. 5.95 (ISBN 0-664-24790-3). Westminster.

--Stress Management for Ministers. LC 81-16458. 168p. 1982. pap. 8.95 (ISBN 0-664-24397-5). Westminster.

Rast, Harold W., ed. see Heinecken, Martin J.

Rast, Harold W., ed. see Jeske, Richard L.

Rast, Walter E. Joshua, Judges, Samuel, Kings. McCurley, Foster R., ed. LC 78-54559. (Proclamation Commentaries: the Old Testament Witnesses for Preaching). 132p. 1978. pap. 4.95 (ISBN 0-8006-0594-2, 1-594). Fortress.

--Tradition History & the Old Testament. Tucker, Gene M., ed. LC 70-171509. (Guides to Biblical Scholarship: Old Testament Ser.). 96p. (Orig.). 1972. pap. 4.50 (ISBN 0-8006-1460-7, 1-1460). Fortress.

Rastell, John. A Critical Edition of John Rastell's "The Pastyme of People" & " A New Book of Purgatory". Gertiz, Albert J. & Orgel, Stephen, eds. (The Renaissance Imagination Ser.). 509p. 1985. lib. bdg. 28.00 (ISBN 0-8240-5459-8). Garland Pub.

Rastogi, Navjivan. Introduction to the Tantraloka. 400p. 1986. 22.00 (ISBN 81-208-0180-6, Pub. by Motilal Banarsidass). South Asia Bks.

Rasul, M. G. Origin & Development of Muslim Historiography. 1970. 5.00x (ISBN 0-87902-183-7). Orientalia.

Ratcliffe, A. The Truth about Hitler & the Roman Catholic Church. 1982. lib. bdg. 59.95 (ISBN 0-87700-362-9). Revisionist Pr.

Rathert, Donna & Prahlow, Lois. Time for Church. 24p. 1985. pap. 2.95 (ISBN 0-570-04129-5, 56-1540). Concordia.

Rathert, Donna R. Lent Is for Remembering. LC 56-1613. 24p. (Orig.). 1987. pap. 2.95 (ISBN 0-570-04147-3). Concordia.

Rathwick, Clyde W. God's Co-Workers: Your Importance to God. 1985. 10.00 (ISBN 0-682-40223-0). Exposition Pr FL.

Ratiu, A. Stolen Church. 192p. 1982. pap. 4.95 (ISBN 0-88264-155-7). Diane Bks.

Ratner, Elaine, ed. see Roman, Sanaya.

Rattey, B. K. A Short History of the Hebrews: From the Patriarchs to Herod the Great. 3rd ed. (Illus.). 1976. pap. 11.50x (ISBN 0-19-832121-X). Oxford U Pr.

Ratzinger, Cardinal J. Seek That Which Is Above. Harrison, Graham, tr. from German. LC 86-81553. Tr. of Suchen was Droben Ist. 132p. 1986. 9.95 (ISBN 0-89870-101-5). Ignatius Pr.

Ratzinger, J. Theology of History According to St. Bonaventure. 12.50 (ISBN 0-8199-0415-5). Franciscan Herald.

Ratzinger, Joseph. Behold the Pierced One. Tr. of Schauen auf den Durchbohrten. 128p. 1986. pap. 7.95 (ISBN 0-89870-087-6). Ignatius Pr.

--Daughter Zion. McDermott, John M., tr. from Ger. LC 82-84579. Orig. Title: Tochter Zion. 83p. (Orig.). 1983. pap. 5.95 (ISBN 0-89870-026-4). Ignatius Pr.

--The Feast of Faith. Harrison, Graham, tr. from Ger. LC 85-82175. Orig. Title: Das Fest des Glaubens. 175p. (Orig.). 1986. pap. 8.95 (ISBN 0-89870-056-6). Ignatius Pr.

--Introduction to Christianity. 1970. 8.95 (ISBN 0-8245-0319-8). Crossroad NY.

--Journey Towards Easter. 160p. 1987. 12.95 (ISBN 0-8245-0803-3). Crossroad NY.

Ratzinger, Joseph & Lehmann, Karl. Living with the Church. Hayes, Zachary, tr. from Ger. LC 78-15509. Orig. Title: Mit der Kirche Leben. 53p. 1978. pap. 1.50 (ISBN 0-8199-0742-1). Franciscan Herald.

Ratzinger, Joseph & Messori, Vittorio. The Ratzinger Report. Attanasio, Salvator & Harrison, Graham, trs. LC 85-81218. Tr. of Rapporto sulla Fede. (Ger. & Ital.). 197p. (Orig.). 1985. pap. 9.95 (ISBN 0-89870-080-9). Ignatius Pr.

Ratzinger, Joseph, et al. Principles of Christian Morality. Harrison, Graham, tr. from Ger. LC 85-82176. Orig. Title: Prinzipien Chrislicher Moral. 104p. (Orig.). 1986. pap. 6.95 (ISBN 0-89870-086-8). Ignatius Pr.

--Church Today. Ignatius, May, tr. 79p. pap. 1.25 (ISBN 0-8199-0396-5). Franciscan Herald.

Ratzinger, Joseph C. Dogma & Preaching. O'Connell, Matthew J., tr. 1983. 9.95 (ISBN 0-8199-0819-3). Franciscan Herald.

--Principles of Catholic Theology: Building Stones for Fundamental Theology. McCarthy, Mary F., tr. from Ger. LC 86-83133. Tr. of Theologische Prinzipienlehre. 320p. (Orig.). 1986. 24.95 (ISBN 0-89870-133-3). Ignatius Pr.

Ratzinger, Joseph Cardinal. The God of Jesus Christ. Cunningham, Robert, tr. from Fr. Tr. of Le Dieu de Jesus Christ. 1978. 6.95 (ISBN 0-8199-0697-2). Franciscan Herald.

Ratzlaff, Don, jt. auth. see Johnson, Rose.

Ratzlaff, Erich. Ein Leben Fur Den Herrn. 171p. (Orig.). 1985. pap. 6.75 (ISBN 0-919797-37-7). Kindred Pr.

Ratzlaff, Ruben M. & Butler, Paul T. Ezra-Nehemiah-Esther. (Bible Study Textbook Ser.). 1979. 14.30 (ISBN 0-89900-014-2). College Pr Pub.

Ratzsch, Del. Philosophy of Science. Evans, C. Stephen, ed. LC 86-178. (Contours of Christian Philosophy Ser.). 128p. (Orig.). 1986. pap. 6.95 (ISBN 0-87784-344-9). Inter-Varsity.

Rau, Albert G. & David, Hans T. Catalogue of Music by American Moravians, 1742-1842. LC 76-134283. Repr. of 1938 ed. 14.00 (ISBN 0-404-07206-2). AMS Pr.

Rau, Lois. Very Special Day. (Redwood Ser.). 1982. pap. 2.95 (ISBN 0-8163-0447-5). Pacific Pr Pub Assn.

--Very Special Person. (Sunshine Ser.). 1982. pap. 2.95 (ISBN 0-8163-0445-9). Pacific Pr Pub Assn.

--Very Special Planet. (Sunshine Ser.). 1982. pap. 2.95 (ISBN 0-8163-0446-7). Pacific Pr Pub Assn.

--Very Special Promise. (Sunshine Ser.). 1982. pap. 2.95 (ISBN 0-8163-0448-3). Pacific Pr Pub Assn.

Raub, Joyce. Cain & Abel. (Arch Bks.). (Illus.). 24p. 1986. pap. 0.99 saddlestitched (ISBN 0-570-06199-7, 59-1422). Concordia.

Rauch, Gerry. Handling Conflicts: Taking the Tension Out of Difficult Relationships. (Living as a Christian Ser.). 160p. (Orig.). 1985. pap. 3.95 (ISBN 0-89283-187-1). Servant.

Rauch, Rufus W., ed. A Chesterton Celebration at the University of Notre Dame. LC 85-3592. (Illus.). 96p. 1983. 9.95 (ISBN 0-268-00744-6, 83-07444). U of Notre Dame Pr.

Rauf, A. Hadith for Children. pap. 5.95 (ISBN 0-686-63901-4). Kazi Pubns.

--Story of Islamic Culture. 1981. 2.50 (ISBN 0-686-97868-4). Kazi Pubns.

Rauf, A., jt. auth. see Farook, Omar.

Rauf, Abdul. Bilal Ibn Rabah. LC 76-49691. 1977. pap. 3.95 (ISBN 0-89259-008-4). Am Trust Pubns.

Rauf, M. A. Islamic Religious Knowledge, 3 vols. 9.50 (ISBN 0-686-18392-4). Kazi Pubns.

Rauman, Richard. For the Reputation of Truth: Politics, Religion, & Conflict Among the Pennsylvanian Quakers, 1750-1800. LC 79-143626. pap. 70.00 (ISBN 0-317-39712-5, 2025828). Bks Demand UMI.

Raun, Alo, tr. see Pozdneyev, Aleksei M.

Raun, Linda, tr. see Pozdneyev, Aleksei M.

Rausch, David A. Arno C. Gaebelein, Eighteen Sixty-One to Nineteen Forty-Five: Irenic Fundamentalist & Scholar. LC 83-9364. (Studies in American Religion: Vol. 10). (Illus.). 318p. 1984. 49.95x (ISBN 0-88946-652-1). E Mellen.

--A Legacy of Hatred: Why Christians Must Not Forget the Holocaust. 1984. 9.95 (ISBN 0-8024-0341-7). Moody.

--Messianic Judaism: Its History, Theology & Polity. LC 82-20382. (Texts & Studies in Religion: Vol. 14). 304p. 1983. 49.95x (ISBN 0-88946-802-8). E Mellen.

--Zionism Within Early American Fundamentalism, 1878-1918: A Convergence of Two Traditions. LC 79-66371. (Texts & Studies in Religion: Vol. 4). viii, 386p. 1980. 59.95x (ISBN 0-88946-875-3). E Mellen.

Rausch, David A., ed. Eminent Hebrew Christians of the Nineteenth Century: Brief Biographical Sketches. LC 83-22013. (Texts & Studies in Religion: Vol. 17). 184p. lib. bdg. 39.95x (ISBN 0-88946-806-0). E Mellen.

Rausch, Robert A. Creative Discipline. Brooks, Frances, ed. 1986. pap. 5.95 (ISBN 0-939697-05-X). Graded Pr.

Rauschenbusch, Walter. For God & the People. LC 77-8615. 1977. lib. bdg. 22.00 (ISBN 0-8414-7332-3). Folcroft.

--Prayers of the Social Awakening. LC 77-8615. 1909. 22.00 (ISBN 0-8414-7332-3). Folcroft.

--The Social Principles of Jesus. LC 76-50566. 1976. Repr. of 1916 ed. lib. bdg. 22.00 (ISBN 0-8414-7308-0). Folcroft.

Rauschenbusch, Walter, jt. auth. see Luccock, Halford E.

Rautkallio, Hannu. Finland & the Holocaust: The Finnish Experience. 1987. 20.95 (ISBN 0-89604-120-4); pap. 13.95 (ISBN 0-89604-121-2). Holocaust Pubns.

Raven, Charles. Apollinarianism: An Essay on the Christology of the Early Church. LC 77-84706. Repr. of 1923 ed. 38.00 (ISBN 0-404-16113-8). AMS Pr.

Raven, Charles E. Christian Socialism, Eighteen Forty-Eight to Eighteen Fifty-Four. 396p. 1968. Repr. of 1920 ed. 35.00x (F Cass Co). Biblio Dist.

--Christian Socialism, Eighteen Forty-Eight to Eighteen Fifty-Four. LC 68-56058. 1968. Repr. of 1920 ed. 35.00x (ISBN 0-678-05148-8). Kelley.

--Natural Religion & Christian Theology: First & Second Series, 2 vols. LC 77-27176. (Gifford Lectures: 1951-52). Repr. of 1953 ed. Set. 37.50 (ISBN 0-404-60540-0). AMS Pr.

--War & the Christian. LC 75-147675. (Library of War & Peace; Relig. & Ethical Positions on War). 1972. lib. bdg. 46.00 (ISBN 0-8240-0432-9). Garland Pub.

Ravenhill, Leonard. America Is Too Young to Die. LC 79-19229. 128p. 1979. pap. 4.95 (ISBN 0-87123-013-5, 210013). Bethany Hse.

--The Judgement Seat of Christ: Your Day in Court. 200p. (Orig.). 1986. pap. 6.95 (ISBN 0-910311-34-X). Huntington Hse Inc.

--Meat for Men. 144p. 1979. pap. 4.95 (ISBN 0-87123-362-2, A-510418). Bethany Hse.

--Porque No Llega el Avivamiento. 144p. 1980. 2.75 (ISBN 0-88113-250-0). Edit Betania.

--Revival God's Way. LC 83-15589. 128p. 1983. text ed. 7.95 (ISBN 0-87123-580-3). Bethany Hse.

--Revival God's Way. 128p. (Orig.). 1983. pap. 7.95 (210620). Bethany Hse.

--Revival Praying. 176p. 1962. pap. 4.95 (ISBN 0-87123-482-3, 210482). Bethany Hse.

--Sodom Had No Bible. 208p. 1979. pap. 4.95 (ISBN 0-87123-496-3, 210496). Bethany Hse.

--Tried & Transfigured. LC 81-71752. 144p. 1982. pap. 4.95 (ISBN 0-87123-544-7, 210544). Bethany Hse.

--Why Revival Tarries. 176p. 1979. pap. 4.95 (ISBN 0-87123-607-9, 210607). Bethany Hse.

Ravenscroft, Trevor. The Cup of Destiny: The Quest for the Grail. LC 82-60160. 194p. 1982. pap. 6.95 (ISBN 0-87728-546-2). Weiser.

--The Spear of Destiny: The Occult Power Behind the Spear Which Pierced the Side of Christ... & How Hitler Inverted the Force in a Bid to Conquer the World. LC 82-60165. 384p. 1982. pap. 9.95 (ISBN 0-87728-547-0). Weiser.

Raverty, H. C., tr. see Al-din, Minhaj.

Ravier, Andre. Ignatius of Loyola & the Founding of Society of Jesus. Daly, Maura, et al, trs. from Fr. Tr. of Ignace de Loyola Fonde la Compagnie de Jesus. 498p. (Orig.). 1987. 29.95 (ISBN 0-89870-036-1). Ignatius Pr.

Raviez, Marilyn E. Early Colonial Religious Drama in Mexico: From Tzompantli to Golgotha. LC 77-76157. pap. 68.30 (2029506). Bks Demand UMI.

Ravindra. The White Lotus: At the Feet of the Mother. (Illus.). 1978. 8.50x (ISBN 0-89684-466-8). Orient Bk Dist.

Ravindra, Ravi. Whispers from the Other Shore. LC 84-40164. 170p. (Orig.). 1984. pap. 6.50 (ISBN 0-8356-0589-2, Quest). Theos Pub Hse.

Ravitch, Norman. Sword & Mitre: Government & Episcopate in France & England in the Age of Aristocracy. 1966. text ed. 18.40x (ISBN 0-686-22467-1). Mouton.

Rawding, F. W. The Buddha. LC 74-14436. (Cambridge Introduction to the History of Mankind Ser.). (Illus.). 48p. (YA) 1975. pap. 5.95 (ISBN 0-521-20368-6). Cambridge U Pr.

--The Buddha. LC 78-56789. (Cambridge Topic Bks). (Illus.). PLB 8.95 (ISBN 0-8225-1212-2). Lerner Pubns.

Rawlings, James S., jt. auth. see Davis, Vernon P.

Rawlings, Maurice. Beyond Death's Door. 1979. pap. 3.50 (ISBN 0-553-25204-6). Bantam.

Rawlings, Meridel. Honor Thy Father. Keith, Bill, ed. (Orig.). 1986. pap. 6.95 (ISBN 0-910311-39-0). Huntington Hse Inc.

Rawlins, Winifred. The Inner Islands. 1983. pap. 2.50x (ISBN 0-87574-073-1, 073). Pendle Hill.

Rawlinson, G., jt. auth. see Kirk, T.

Rawlinson, George. The Story of Ancient Egypt. 1887. Repr. 50.00 (ISBN 0-8482-5897-5). Norwood Edns.

Rawlinson, Ian. Yoga for the West: A Manual for Designing Your Own Practice. McNeilage, Alastair, ed. (Illus.). 200p. (Orig.). 1987. lib. bdg. 12.95 (ISBN 0-916360-26-1). CRCS Pubns NV.

Rawlyk, G. A. Ravished by the Spirit: Religious Revivals, Baptists, & Henry Alline. 190p. 1984. 19.95x (ISBN 0-7735-0439-7); pap. 7.95 (ISBN 0-7735-0440-0). McGill-Queens U Pr.

Rawson & Carlwright. Witches. (Story Book). 1979. 6.95 (ISBN 0-86020-341-7, Usborne-Hayes); PLB 11.96 (ISBN 0-88110-057-9); pap. 2.95 (ISBN 0-86020-340-9). EDC.

Rawson & Lloyd. The Miracles of Jesus. (Children's Picture Bible Ser.). 1982. 7.95 (ISBN 0-86020-518-5, Usborne-Hayes); PLB 12.96 (ISBN 0-88110-099-4); pap. 4.95 (ISBN 0-86020-523-1). EDC.

Rawson, jt. auth. see Cartwright.

Rawson, Claude, ed. The Character of Swift's Satire: A Revised Focus. LC 81-72062. 344p. 1983. 34.50 (ISBN 0-87413-209-6). U Delaware Pr.

Rawson, Natasha. Search for Truth. LC 80-85047. 150p. 1981. 14.95 (ISBN 0-89896-149-1, Pub. by the Linolean Press). Larksdale.

Rawson, Philip. Tantra: The Indian Cult of Ecstasy. (Art & Imagination Ser.). (Illus.). 1984. pap. 10.95f (ISBN 0-500-81001-X). Thames Hudson.

Rawson, Philip & Legeza, Laszlo. Tao: The Chinese Philosophy of Time & Change. (Art & Imagination Ser.). (Illus.). 1984. pap. 10.95f (ISBN 0-500-81002-8). Thames Hudson.

Rawson, Raymond. The Way Home. LC 84-90242. 113p. 1985. 10.95 (ISBN 0-533-06294-2). Vantage.

Ray, Angeln. Angels Ascending & Descending. 176p. 1984. 12.95 (ISBN 0-915763-00-1). Starseed Pubns.

Ray, Ann, ed. see Herzog, Stephanie.

Ray, Ann, ed. see Hills, Christopher.

Ray, Benjamin C. African Religions: Symbol, Ritual & Community. 1976. pap. write for info. (ISBN 0-13-018622-8). P-H.

Ray, Bruce. Withhold Not Correction. pap. 3.45 (ISBN 0-8010-7687-0). Baker Bk.

--Withhold Not Correction. 1978. pap. 3.45 (ISBN 0-87552-400-1). Presby & Reformed.

Ray, C. A. La Vida Responsable: Orientacion Biblica Sobre Nuestro Estilo De Vivir. Lopez, Albert C., tr. Orig. Title: Living the Responsible Life. 160p. 1982. Repr. of 1980 ed. 3.75 (ISBN 0-311-46079-8). Casa Bautista.

Ray, Charles. Marvelous Ministry. 100p. 1985. pap. 2.95. Pilgrim Pubns.

--Mrs. C. H. Spurgeon. 1979. pap. 2.50 (ISBN 0-686-09102-7). Pilgrim Pubns.

Ray, D. B. The Baptist Succession. 1984. Repr. of 1912 ed. 22.00 (ISBN 0-317-11348-8). Church History.

Ray, David R. Small Churches Are the Right Size. LC 82-11256. 224p. (Orig.). 1982. pap. 7.95 (ISBN 0-8298-0620-2). Pilgrim NY.

Ray, Eric. Sofer: The Story of a Torah Scroll. LC 85-52420. (Illus.). 32p. (Orig.). 1986. pap. text ed. 4.95 (ISBN 0-933873-04-2). Torah Aura.

Ray, Irene R. & Gupta, Mallika C. Story of Vivekananda. (Illus.). 1971. pap. 3.00 (ISBN 0-87481-125-2). Vedanta Pr.

Ray, John. Three Physico-Theological Discourses: Primitive Chaos, & Creation of the World, the General Deluge, Its Causes & Effects. Albritton, Claude C., Jr., ed. LC 77-6538. (History of Geology Ser.). 1978. Repr. of 1713 ed. lib. bdg. 34.50x (ISBN 0-405-10457-X). Ayer Co Pubs.

--The Wisdom of God Manifested in the Works of the Creation. LC 75-11250. (British Philosophers & Theologians in the 17th & 18th Century Ser.). 247p. 1979. lib. bdg. 51.00 (ISBN 0-8240-1801-X). Garland Pub.

--The Wisdom of God Manifested in the Works of the Creation: Heavenly Bodies, Elements, Meteors, Fossils, Vegetables, Animals. Egerton, Frank N., 3rd, ed. LC 77-74250. (History of Ecology Ser.). 1978. Repr. of 1717 ed. lib. bdg. 40.00x (ISBN 0-405-10419-7). Ayer Co Pubs.

Ray, Mary A. American Opinion of Roman Catholicism in the Eighteenth Century. 456p. 1974. Repr. of 1936 ed. lib. bdg. 26.00x (ISBN 0-374-96723-7, Octagon). Hippocrene Bks.

Ray, Nihar-Ranjan. Brahmanical Gods in Burma: A Chapter of Indian Art & Iconography. LC 77-87020. Repr. of 1932 ed. 16.50 (ISBN 0-404-16852-3). AMS Pr.

--An Introduction to the Study of Theravada Buddhism in Burma: A Study of Indo-Burmese Historical & Cultural Relations from the Earliest Times to the British Conquest. LC 77-87021. Repr. of 1946 ed. 25.00 (ISBN 0-404-16853-1). AMS Pr.

--Sanskrit Buddhism in Burma. LC 78-70112. Repr. of 1936 ed. 22.00 (ISBN 0-404-17367-5). AMS Pr.

Ray, Randolph, ed. One Hundred Great Religious Poems. LC 78-80378. (Granger Index Reprint Ser). 1951. 15.00 (ISBN 0-8369-6060-2). Ayer Co Pubs.

Ray, Sandy F. Journeying Through a Jungle. LC 79-84787. 1979. 5.50 (ISBN 0-8054-5169-2). Broadman.

Ray, Sondra. Celebration of Breath. LC 83-1770. 192p. 1983. pap. 8.95 (ISBN 0-89087-355-0). Celestial Arts.

Ray, Sondra, jt. auth. see Orr, Leonard.

Raya, Joseph. Acathist Hymn to the Name of Jesus. Vinck, Jose D., ed. 40p. 1983. 6.00x (ISBN 0-911726-45-4). Alleluia Pr.

Raya, Joseph & Vinck, Jose D. Apostolos: Byzantine Epistles Lectionary. 550p. 1981. 87.50x (ISBN 0-911726-37-3); folded sheets 67.50x (ISBN 0-911726-38-1). Alleluia Pr.

--Byzantine Altar Gospel. 350p. 1979. 87.50x (ISBN 0-911726-34-9). Alleluia Pr.

--Musical Setting for the Liturgy of St. John Chrysostom. (Illus.). 44p. 1971. pap. 2.00 (ISBN 0-911726-05-5). Alleluia Pr.

Rayburn, Jim, III. Dance, Children, Dance. 192p. 1984. 9.95 (ISBN 0-8423-0515-7). Tyndale.

Rayburn, John. Gregorian Chant: A History of Controversy Concerning Its Rhythm. LC 80-27616. xiv, 90p. 1981. Repr. of 1964 ed. lib. bdg. 22.50x (ISBN 0-313-22811-6, RAGR). Greenwood.

Rayburn, Robert G. O Come, Let Us Worship: Corporate Worship in the Evangelical Church. LC 79-55192. 1980. 11.95 (ISBN 0-8010-7690-0); pap. 8.95 (ISBN 0-8010-7728-1). Baker Bk.

Rayds, John, jt. auth. see Fishel, Kent.

Rayez, Andre. Dictionnaire de Spiritualite, 12 vols. (Fr.). 1970. Set. 1195.00 (ISBN 0-686-57101-0, M-6125). French & Eur.

Rayford, Julian Lee. The First Christmas Dinner. (Illus.). 35p. 1947. 7.50 (ISBN 0-940882-03-5). Haunted Bk Shop.

Raymond, E. The Gem Stones in the Breastplate. (Illus.). 48p. (Orig.). 1987. pap. price not set (ISBN 0-934666-18-0). Artisan Sales.

Raymond, Ernest. In the Steps of St. Francis. 380p. 1975. pap. 4.95 (ISBN 0-8199-0557-7). Franciscan Herald.

Raymond, Irving W. Teaching of the Early Church on the Use of Wine & Strong Drink. LC 79-120207. (Columbia University. Studies in the Social Sciences: No. 286). Repr. of 1927 ed. 14.50 (ISBN 0-404-51286-0). AMS Pr.

Raymond, Jeanette. Implementing Pastoral Care in Schools. LC 85-14978. 304p. 1985. 33.00 (ISBN 0-7099-2273-6, Pub. by Croom Helm Ltd); pap. 14.95 (ISBN 0-7099-4211-7). Methuen Inc.

Raymond, John. Twenty-Six Lessons on Matthew, Vol. II. (Bible Student Study Guide Ser.). 130p. 1981. pap. 2.95 (ISBN 0-89900-171-8). College Pr Pub.

--Twenty-Six Lessons on Matthew, Vol. 1. LC 80-67734. (Bible Student Study Guides). 130p. (Orig.). 1980. pap. 2.95 (ISBN 0-89900-167-X). College Pr Pub.

Raymond of Cupua. Saint Catherine of Siena. 30.00 (ISBN 0-89453-151-4). M Glazier.

Raz, Simcha. A Tzaddik in Our Time. Wengrow, Charles, tr. from Hebrew. (Illus.). 1976. 13.95 (ISBN 0-87306-130-6). Feldheim.

--A Tzaddik in Our Time: Life & Times of Rav Aryeh Levin of Jerusalem, Celebrated Tzaddik of Jerusalem. Wengrov, Charles, tr. from Hebrew. Tr. of Ish Tzaddik Hayah. (Illus.). 1978. pap. 10.95 (ISBN 0-87306-986-2). Feldheim.

Raza, A. Musa. Muhammad in the Holy Quran. 15.95 (ISBN 0-317-14646-7). Kazi Pubns.

Raza, M. S. Introducing the Prophets. 1970. 5.00x (ISBN 0-87902-184-5). Orientalia.

Razwy, Sayed A. Salman el-Farsi. 1985. pap. 3.95 (ISBN 0-933543-02-6). Aza Khana.

Razwy, Sayed A., ed. The Holy Koran. rev. ed. Ali, A. Yusuf, tr. 424p. 1986. pap. 4.50 (ISBN 0-940368-77-3). Tahrike Tarsile Quran.

Rea, Alayna, jt. auth. see Rea, John D.

Rea, Hope. Rembrandt Van Ryn. Repr. of 1903 ed. 20.00 (ISBN 0-8482-5893-2). Norwood Edns.

Rea, John D. & Rea, Alayna. The Twelve Days of Christmas: The Twelve Stages of a Soul (The Creation of a Universe) 40p. (Orig.). 1987. pap. 4.95 (ISBN 0-938183-04-4). Two Trees Pub.

Read, David. I Am Persuaded. (The Scholar As Preacher Ser.). 192p. 1961. 12.95 (ISBN 0-567-04430-0, Pub. by T & T Clark Ltd UK). Fortress.

Read, David H. The Christian Faith. LC 85-10473. 256p. 1985. pap. 9.95 (ISBN 0-8027-2515-5). Walker & Co.

--This Grace Given. 144p. (Orig.). 1984. pap. 7.95 (ISBN 0-8028-0025-4). Eerdmans.

Read, Jesse, jt. auth. see Burkitt, Lemuel.

Read, John. Humour & Humanism in Chemistry. LC 79-8621. Repr. of 1947 ed. 42.50 (ISBN 0-404-18487-1). AMS Pr.

Read, Lenet H. How We Got the Bible. LC 85-72842. 140p. 1985. 8.95 (ISBN 0-87747-799-X). Deseret Bk.

Read, Opie. Confessions of a Negro Preacher. LC 73-18597. Repr. of 1928 ed. 21.50 (ISBN 0-404-11408-3). AMS Pr.

Read, Ralph H., ed. Younger Churchmen Look at the Church. facsimile ed. LC 74-156708. (Essay Index Reprint Ser). Repr. of 1935 ed. 21.50 (ISBN 0-8369-2330-8). Ayer Co Pubs.

Read, William M. Michigan Manuscript 18 of the Gospels. LC 44-13750. (Publications in Language & Literature Ser.: No. 11). (Illus.). 75p. 1942. pap. 5.00x (ISBN 0-295-95219-9). U of Wash Pr.

Reader, J. The Divine Mystery. 79p. pap. 4.95 (ISBN 0-88172-117-4). Believers Bkshelf.

Reader's Digest Editors. Atlas of the Bible: An Illustrated Guide to the Holy Land. LC 80-53426. (Illus.). 256p. 1981. 21.95 (ISBN 0-89577-097-0, Pub. by RD Assn). Random.

--Book of Christmas. LC 73-84158. (Illus.). 304p. 1973. 21.95 (ISBN 0-89577-013-X, Pub. by RD Assn). Random.

--Family Guide to the Bible: A Concordance & Reference Companion to the King James Version. LC 84-13261. (Illus.). 832p. 1984. 24.50 (ISBN 0-89577-192-6, Pub. by RD Assn). Random.

--Great People of the Bible & How They Lived. LC 73-86027. (Illus.). 1974. 21.99 (ISBN 0-89577-015-6). RD Assn.

--Mysteries of the Unexplained. LC 82-60791. (Illus.). 320p. 1983. 21.95 (ISBN 0-89577-146-2, Pub. by RD Assn). Random.

Reading, Lucile C. Shining Moments: Stories for Latter-day Saint Children. LC 85-1655. 158p. 1985. 6.95 (ISBN 0-87747-687-X). Deseret Bk.

Ready, Dolores. Joan, the Brave Soldier: Joan of Arc. LC 77-86597. (Stories About Christian Heroes). (Illus.). 1977. pap. 1.95 (ISBN 0-86683-764-7, HarpR). Har-Row.

--John's Magic: John Bosco. LC 77-86595. (Stories About Christian Heroes). (Illus.). 1977. pap. 1.95 (ISBN 0-86683-765-5, HarpR). Har-Row.

Ready, Dolores, jt. auth. see Riehle, Mary C.

Reagan, Charles E. & Stewart, David, eds. The Philosophy of Paul Ricoeur: An Anthology of His Work. LC 77-75444. 1978. pap. 11.95x (ISBN 0-8070-1517-2, BPA15, Pub. by Ariadne Bks). Beacon Pr.

Reamer, Frederic G. Ethical Dilemmas in Social Service. LC 81-18071. 304p. 1982. 22.50x (ISBN 0-231-05188-3). Columbia U Pr.

Reamer, Judy. Feelings Women Rarely Share. Arthur, Donna, ed. 150p. (Orig.). 1987. pap. text ed. 3.50 (ISBN 0-88368-186-2). Whitaker Hse.

Reapsome, James. Romans: A Daily Dialogue With God. (Personal Bible Studyguide Ser.). 120p. pap. 4.95 (ISBN 0-87788-731-4). Shaw Pubs.

Reapsome, James & Reapsome, Martha. Marriage: God's Design for Intimacy. (LifeBuilder Bible Studies). 64p. (Orig.). 1986. pap. 2.95 (ISBN 0-8308-1056-0). Inter-Varsity.

Reapsome, Martha. A Woman's Path to Godliness. 176p. 1986. 10.95 (ISBN 0-8407-9067-8). Oliver-Nelson.

Reapsome, Martha, jt. auth. see Jim.

Reapsome, Martha, jt. auth. see Reapsome, James.

Reardon, B. Liberalism & Tradition. LC 75-7214. 320p. 1975. Cambridge U Pr.

Reardon, Bernard. Religious Thoughts in the Reformation. 1981. pap. text ed. 14.95 (ISBN 0-582-49031-6). Longman.

Reardon, Bernard M. Religion in the Age of Romanticism: Studies in Early Nineteenth Century Thought. 320p. 1985. 39.50 (ISBN 0-521-30088-6); pap. 14.95 (ISBN 0-521-31745-2). Cambridge U Pr.

--Religious Thought in the Nineteenth Century. (Orig.). 1966. 49.50 (ISBN 0-521-06049-4); pap. 16.95x (ISBN 0-521-09386-4). Cambridge U Pr.

--Religious Thought in the Victorian Age: A Survey from Coleridge to Gore. (Illus.). 512p. 1980. pap. text ed. 15.95x (ISBN 0-582-49126-6). Longman.

Reardon, Bernard M., ed. Liberal Protestantism. 1968. 18.50x (ISBN 0-8047-0647-6). Stanford U Pr.

--Roman Catholic Modernism. 1970. 20.00x (ISBN 0-8047-0750-2). Stanford U Pr.

Reason, Joyce. Quaker Cavalier: William Penn. 1971. pap. 2.95 (ISBN 0-87508-618-7). Chr Lit.

--Searcher for God (Isabel Kuhn) 1963. pap. 2.95 (ISBN 0-87508-621-7). Chr Lit.

--To Be a Pilgrim (John Bunyan) 1961. pap. 2.95 (ISBN 0-87508-625-X). Chr Lit.

Reaver, J. Russell. Emerson As Mythmaker. LC 54-8431. 1954. pap. 4.00 (ISBN 0-8130-0195-1). U Presses Fla.

Reay, B., ed. see McGregor, J. F.

Reay, Barry. The Quakers & the English Revolution. LC 84-22355. 200p. 1985. 22.50 (ISBN 0-312-65808-7). St Martin.

Reay, Lee. Incredible Passage: Through the Hole-in-the-Rock. Hechtle, Ranier, ed. (Illus.). 128p. (Orig.). 1981. 5.95 (ISBN 0-934826-05-6); pap. 4.50 (ISBN 0-934826-06-4). Meadow Lane.

Rebecque, Constant De see De Rebecque, Constant & Benjamin, Henri.

Rebhun, Joseph. God & Man in Two Worlds. 1985. lib. bdg. 16.95 (ISBN 0-9614162-1-1). OR Pub.

Recinos, Adrian & Goetz, Delia, trs. Popol Vuh: The Sacred Book of the Ancient Quiche Maya: Spanish Version of the Original Maya. (Civilization of the American Indian Ser.: No. 29). (Eng). 1983. Repr. of 1950 ed. 16.95 (ISBN 0-8061-0205-5). U of Okla Pr.

Reck, Carleen & Coreil, Judith. School Evaluation for the Catholic Elementary School: An Overview. 56p. 1983. 3.00 (ISBN 0-318-00791-6). Natl Cath Educ.

--Verifying the Vision: A Self-Evaluation Instrument for the Catholic Elementary School. 160p. 1984. 12.00 (ISBN 0-318-17778-1). Natl Cath Educ.

Recker, Colane. All the Days of Lent. LC 78-73825. (Illus.). 64p. 1978. pap. 2.45 (ISBN 0-87793-168-2). Ave Maria.

Recob, James B., jt. auth. see Amy, William O.

Rector, Connie. Sustaining. 79p. 1985. 7.95 (ISBN 0-934126-59-3). Randall Bk Co.

Rector, Hartman, Jr. Already to Harvest. 91p. 1985. 7.95 (ISBN 0-934126-67-4); pap. 4.95 (ISBN 0-934126-73-9). Randall Bk Co.

Red. Pilgrim Hymnal. 1958. 9.95x (ISBN 0-8298-0107-3). Pilgrim NY.

Reddan, Minnie & Clapham, Alfred W. The Church of St. Helen, Bishopsgate, Pt. 1. LC 74-6179. (London County Council Survey of London: No. 9). Repr. of 1924 ed. 74.50 (ISBN 0-404-51659-9). AMS Pr.

Reddin, Opal. Have It His Way. LC 78-73143. 128p. 1980. pap. 1.95 (ISBN 0-88243-717-8, 02-0717); tchr's ed 2.95 (ISBN 0-88243-332-6, 02-0332). Gospel Pub.

Redding, David A., et al. The Prayers I Love. LC 78-17798. (Illus., Orig.). 1978. pap. 6.95 (ISBN 0-89407-025-8). Strawberry Hill.

Reddish, Robert O., Jr. The Burning Burning Bush. LC 73-85938. (Illus.). 1974. 11.95 (ISBN 0-686-05480-6). Rorge Pub Co.

--John Wesley, His Way of Knowing God. 1972. soft cover 4.00 (ISBN 0-686-08730-5). Rorge Pub Co.

--Satan, God & Saint Teresa. (Illus.). 1967. soft cover 5.00 (ISBN 0-686-08728-3). Rorge Pub Co.

Reddy, C. Mookka. The Tirumalavadi Temple: History & Culture Through the Ages. xii, 236p. 1986. text ed. 30.00x (ISBN 81-7018-329-4, Pub. by B. R. Pub Corp Delhi). Apt Bks.

Reddy, C. Narayana. Viswambhara. 66p. 1987. text ed. 12.50x (ISBN 81-207-0578-5, Pub. by Sterling Pubs India). Apt Bks.

Reddy, T. J. Poems in One Part Harmony. 60p. 1980. pap. 4.00 (ISBN 0-932112-07-2). Carolina Wren.

Reddy, V. Narayan. The East West Understanding of Man. 320p. 1985. text ed. 40.00x (ISBN 0-86590-704-8, Pub. by B R Pub Corp India). Apt Bks.

Redeker, Martin see Dilthey, Wilhelm.

Redekop, Calvin. Strangers Become Neighbors. LC 80-13887. (Studies in Anabaptist & Mennonite History Ser.: No. 22). (Illus.). 312p. 1980. 24.95x (ISBN 0-8361-1228-8). Herald Pr.

Redekop, Calvin, jt. ed. see Burkholder, J. R.

Redekop, Calvin W. The Old Colony Mennonites: Dilemmas of Ethnic Minority Life. LC 69-13192. (Illus.). 302p. 1969. 22.00x (ISBN 0-8018-1020-5). Johns Hopkins.

--The Old Colony Mennonites: Dilemmas of Ethnic Minority Life. LC 69-13192. pap. 80.50 (ISBN 0-317-08392-9, 2021737). Bks Demand UMI.

Redekop, John H. Two Sides, the Best of Personal Opinion, 1964-1984. 306p. (Orig.). 1984. pap. 9.95 (ISBN 0-919797-13-X). Kindred Pr.

Redemptorist Pastoral Publication. How You Live with Jesus: Catechism for Today's Young Catholic. LC 81-80097. 96p. 1981. pap. 3.50 (ISBN 0-89243-137-7). Liguori Pubns.

--The Illustrated Catechism. LC 80-84312. 112p. (Orig.). 1981. pap. 3.95 (ISBN 0-89243-135-0). Liguori Pubns.

--Jesus Loves You. 80p. 1983. 4.95 (ISBN 0-89243-175-X). Liguori Pubns.

--Manual para el Catolico de Hoy. 1978. pap. 1.95 (ISBN 0-89243-091-5). Liguori Pubns.

Redemptorist Pastoral Publication Staff. Jesus Loves You: A Catholic Catechism for the Primary Grades. LC 82-8000658. 96p. 1982. pap. 4.95 (ISBN 0-89243-157-1). Liguori Pubns.

Redemptorists, jt. auth. see Liguori, Alfonso M.

Redford, D. B., jt. ed. see Wevers, John W.

Redford, F. J. Planting New Churches. LC 78-55694. 1979. 8.50 (ISBN 0-8054-6314-3). Broadman.

Redgrove, H. Stanley. Alchemy, Ancient & Modern. (Illus.). 141p. 1980. 20.00 (ISBN 0-89005-344-8). Ares.

Rediger, G. Lloyd. Coping with Clergy Burnout. 112p. 1982. pap. 5.95 (ISBN 0-8170-0956-6). Judson.

--Lord, Don't Let Me Be Bored. LC 85-26379. 132p. 1986. pap. 9.95 (ISBN 0-664-24700-8). Westminster.

Reding, Andrew, ed. Christianity & Revolution: Tomas Borge's Theology of Life. LC 86-23788. (Illus.). 160p. (Orig.). 1987. pap. 8.95 (ISBN 0-88344-411-9). Orbis Bks.

Redman, B. R., tr. see Gobineau, Joseph A.

Redmond, Howard. A Philosophy of the Second Advent. Goss, Leonard G., ed. 160p. 1985. write for info. (ISBN 0-88062-070-6); pap. write for info. (ISBN 0-88062-067-6). Mott Media.

Redmond, Howard A. Philosophy of the Second Advent. 1986. text ed. 12.95 (ISBN 0-8010-7740-0). Baker Bk.

Redpath, Alan. Blessings Out of Buffetings: Studies in Second Corinthians. 256p. 1965. 11.95 (ISBN 0-8007-0026-0). Revell.

--Making of a Man of God: Studies in the Life of David. 256p. 1962. 12.95 (ISBN 0-8007-0189-5). Revell.

--Royal Route to Heaven: Studies in First Corinthians. 256p. 1960. 12.95 (ISBN 0-8007-0279-4). Revell.

--Victorious Christian Faith. 192p. 9.95 (ISBN 0-8007-1208-0). Revell.

--Victorious Christian Living: Studies in the Book of Joshua. 256p. 1955. 10.95 (ISBN 0-8007-0336-7). Revell.

--Victorious Christian Service: Studies in the Book of Nehemiah. 192p. 9.95 (ISBN 0-8007-0337-5). Revell.

Redpath, Henry A., jt. auth. see Hatch, Edwin.

Redpath, Peter A. The Moral Wisdom of St. Thomas: An Introduction. LC 83-3590. 216p. (Orig.). 1983. lib. bdg. 26.00 (ISBN 0-8191-3144-X); pap. text ed. 11.00 (ISBN 0-8191-3145-8). U Pr of Amer.

--A Simplified Introduction to the Wisdom of St. Thomas. LC 80-5230. 180p. 1980. lib. bdg. 24.00 (ISBN 0-8191-1058-2); pap. text ed. 10.50 (ISBN 0-8191-1059-0). U Pr of Amer.

Redstone, Lilian J., ed. Parish of All Hallows, Pt. 1. LC 74-138273. (London County Council. Survey of London: No. 12). Repr. of 1929 ed. 74.50 (ISBN 0-404-51662-9). AMS Pr.

Redwood, John. Reason, Ridicule & Religion. 1976. 16.50x (ISBN 0-674-74953-7). Harvard U Pr.

Reece, Benny R. Sermones Ratherii Episcopi Veronensis. 5.00 (ISBN 0-686-23377-8). Classical Folia.

Reece, Colleen. Honor Bound. 176p. 1983. 3.95 (ISBN 0-8024-0153-8). Moody.

Reece, Colleen L. Comrades of the Trail. Wheeler, Gerald, ed. (Banner Ser.). 96p. (Orig.). 1987. pap. 6.50 (ISBN 0-8280-0355-6). Review & Herald.

--Last Page in the Diary. Wheeler, Gerald, ed. (Banner Ser.). 128p. (Orig.). 1986. pap. 6.50 (ISBN 0-8280-0304-1). Review & Herald.

--The Other Nine. (Orig.). 1981. pap. 7.50 (ISBN 0-8309-0288-0). Herald Hse.

Reece, Louise. Thank You Lord. (Illus.). 164p. (Orig.). 1983. pap. 3.95x (ISBN 0-9614264-0-3). Lovejoy Pr.

Reece, Nancy, ed. see Stadler, Bernice.

Reeck, Darrell. Ethics for the Professions: A Christian Perspective. LC 81-52282. 176p. (Orig.). 1982. pap. 11.95 (ISBN 0-8066-1914-7, 10-2088). Augsburg.

Reed, A. W. Myths & Legends of Australia. LC 72-779. (Illus.). 1973. 7.50 (ISBN 0-8008-5463-2). Taplinger.

Reed, Bika. Rebel in the Soul. LC 78-15791. (Illus.). 1979. pap. 9.95 (ISBN 0-89281-004-1). Inner Tradit.

Reed, Bobbie. Christian Family Activities for One-Parent Families. LC 82-5704. (Illus.). 96p. (Orig.). 1982. pap. 4.95 (ISBN 0-87239-571-5, 2966). Standard Pub.

--Making the Most of Single Life. 1980. pap. 3.95 (ISBN 0-570-03809-X, 12-2918). Concordia.

--Single on Sunday: A Manual for Successful Single Adult Ministries. 1979. pap. 5.95 (ISBN 0-570-03781-6, 12-2735). Concordia.

Reed, Bobbie, jt. auth. see Marlowe, Monroe.

Reed, Bobbie, jt. auth. see Reed, C. Edward.

Reed, C. Edward & Reed, Bobbie. A Creative Bible Learning for Youth: Grades 7-12. LC 77-76205. 1977. pap. 3.95 (ISBN 0-8307-0479-5, 9700102). Regal.

Reed, Carlynn. And We Have Danced: The History of the Sacred Dance Guild, 1958-1978. Adams, Doug, ed. 1978. 5.95 (ISBN 0-941500-00-4). Sharing Co.

Reed, David A. Jehovah's Witnesses Answered Verse By Verse. 1987. pap. 5.95 (ISBN 0-8010-7739-7). Baker Bk.

Reed, Douglas. Behind the Scene. (Pt. 2 of Far & Wide). 1976. pap. 3.50x (ISBN 0-911038-41-8). Noontide.

Reed, Evelyn & Moriarty, Claire. Abortion & the Catholic Church: Two Feminists Defend Women's Rights. 1973. pap. 0.35 (ISBN 0-87348-288-3). Path Pr NY.

Reed, Gordon K. Living Life By God's Law. 124p. (Orig.). 1984. pap. 6.00 (ISBN 0-317-03221-6). Word Ministries.

Reed, Gwendolyn. Adam & Eve. LC 68-27712. (Illus.). 1968. PLB 11.88 (ISBN 0-688-51256-9). Lothrop.

Reed, Lyman E. Preparing Missionaries for Intercultural Communication. LC 84-23060. (Illus.). 224p. (Orig.). 1985. pap. text ed. 6.95x (ISBN 0-87808-438-X). William Carey Lib.

Reed, Margaret C. The Church-Related Pre-School. 128p. 1985. pap. 7.95 (ISBN 0-687-08334-6). Abingdon.

Reed, Oscar F. Beacon Bible Expositions: Vol. 7, Corinthians. Greathouse, William M. & Taylor, Willard H., eds. 1976. 8.95 (ISBN 0-8341-0318-4). Beacon Hill.

Reed, Roy A., jt. auth. see Browning, Robert L.

Reed, Sampson. Observations on the Growth of the Mind Including GENIUS. 5th ed. LC 72-4971. (The Romantic Tradition in American Literature Ser.). 110p. 1972. Repr. of 1859 ed. 18.00 (ISBN 0-405-04641-3). Ayer Co Pubs.

Reed, Susan M. Church & State in Massachusetts, 1691-1740. (University of Illinois Studies in the Social Sciences: Vol. 3, No. 4). 210p. Repr. of 1914 ed. 15.00 (ISBN 0-384-50110-9). Johnson Repr.

Reed, Will L., ed. Second Treasury of Christmas Music. LC 68-16193. 1968. 12.95 (ISBN 0-87523-165-9). Emerson.

--Treasury of Easter Music & Music for Passiontide. 1963. 12.95 (ISBN 0-87523-142-X). Emerson.

Reeder, Rachel. Liturgy: Advent, Christmas, Epiphany, Vol. 4, No. 3. (The Quarterly Journal of the Lit. Conference Ser.). (Illus.). 88p. (Orig.). 1984. pap. 7.95 (ISBN 0-918208-36-X). Liturgical Conf.

--Liturgy: Holy Places. (The Quarterly Journal of the Liturgical Conference: Vol. 3, No. 4). (Illus.). 96p. (Orig.). 1983. pap. text ed. 7.95 (ISBN 0-918208-32-7). Liturgical Conf.

Reeder, Rachel, ed. Liturgy: Celebrating Marriage, Vol. 4, No. 2. (Illus.). 80p. 1984. pap. text ed. 7.95 (ISBN 0-918208-34-3). Liturgical Conf.

--Liturgy: Diakonia. (Journal of The Liturgical Conference: Vol. 2, No. 4). (Illus.). 84p. (Orig.). 1982. pap. 7.95 (ISBN 0-918208-28-9). Liturgical Conf.

--Liturgy: Dressing the Church. (The Quarterly Journal of the Liturgical Conference Ser.: Vol.5, No. 4). (Illus.). 103p. (Orig.). Date not set. pap. 7.95 (ISBN 0-918208-40-8). Liturgical Conf.

--Liturgy: Easter's Fifty Days. (Journal of The Liturgical Conference: Vol. 3, No. 1). (Illus.). 72p. 1982. pap. text ed. 7.95 (ISBN 0-918208-29-7). Liturgical Conf.

--Liturgy: Feasts & Fasting. (The Quarterly Journal of the Liturgical Conference: Vol. 2, No. 1 of Liturgy). (Illus.). 80p. (Orig.). 1981. pap. text ed. 7.95 (ISBN 0-918208-25-4). Liturgical Conf.

--Liturgy: In Spirit & Truth. (The Quarterly Journal of the Liturgical Conference: Vol. 5, No. 3). (Illus.). 96p. (Orig.). pap. text ed. 7.95 (ISBN 0-918208-39-4). Liturgical Conf.

--Liturgy: Language & Metaphor, Vol. 4, No.4. (The Quarterly Journal of the Lit. Conference Ser.). (Illus.). 95p. (Orig.). 1985. pap. 7.95 (ISBN 0-918208-35-1). Liturgical Conf.

--Liturgy: Ministries to the Sick. (Quarterly Journal of the Liturgical Conference Ser.: Vol. 2, No. 2 of Liturgy). (Illus.). 80p. 1982. 7.95 (ISBN 0-918208-26-2). Liturgical Conf.

--Liturgy: One Church, Many Churches. (Quarterly Journal of The Liturgical Conference: Vol. 3, No. 2). (Illus.). 96p. (Orig.). 1983. pap. text ed. 7.95 (ISBN 0-918208-30-0). Liturgical Conf.

--Liturgy: Putting on Christ, Vol. 4, No. 1. (Illus.). 80p. 1983. pap. text ed. 7.95 (ISBN 0-918208-33-5). Liturgical Conf.

--Liturgy: Scripture & the Assembly. (Quarterly Journal of the Liturgical Conference Ser.: Vol. 2, No. 3 of Liturgy). (Illus.). 80p. 1982. 7.95 (ISBN 0-918208-27-0). Liturgical Conf.

--Liturgy: Teaching Prayer. (The Quarterly Journal of the Liturgical Conference Ser.: Vol. 5, No. 1). (Illus.). 96p. (Orig.). pap. text ed. 7.95 (ISBN 0-918208-37-8). Liturgical Conf.

--Liturgy: The Church & Culture. (The Quarterly Journal of the Liturgical Conference Ser.: Vol. 6, No. 1). (Illus.). 96p. (Orig.). Date not set. pap. 7.95 (ISBN 0-918208-41-6). Liturgical Conf.

--Liturgy: With All the Saints. (The Quarterly Journal of the Liturgy Conference Ser.: Vol. 5, No. 2). (Illus.). 112p. (Orig.). pap. text ed. 7.95 (ISBN 0-918208-38-6). Liturgical Conf.

--Liturgy: With Lyre & Harp. (Quarterly Journal of the Liturgical Conference: Vol. 3, No. 3). (Illus.). 88p. (Orig.). 1983. pap. text ed. 7.95 (ISBN 0-918208-31-9). Liturgical Conf.

Reeder, W. Donald. Letters of John & Jude. (Teach Yourself the Bible Ser.). 1965. pap. 2.75 (ISBN 0-8024-4674-4). Moody.

Reeds, Roger C. Biblical Graphics. 1977. 7.95 (ISBN 0-89265-058-3); pap. 5.95 (ISBN 0-89265-042-7). Randall Hse.

--Pupil Profiles. (Sunday School Workers Training Course Ser.: No. 3). 1973. pap. 3.95 (ISBN 0-89265-010-9). Randall Hse.

Reedy, William J., ed. Becoming a Catholic Christian. 198p. pap. 5.95 (ISBN 0-8215-9326-9). Sadlier.

Re'emi, P., jt. auth. see Martin-Achard, R.

Rees, Daniel, jt. auth. see English Benedictine Congregation Members.

Rees, James. Shakespeare & the Bible. LC 70-174307. Repr. of 1876 ed. 16.00 (ISBN 0-404-05235-5). AMS Pr.

--Shakespeare & the Bible. LC 72-14367. 1973. lib. bdg. 15.50 (ISBN 0-8414-1348-7). Folcroft.

Rees, Seth C. Miracles in the Slums. (The Higher Christian Life Ser.). 301p. 1985. lib. bdg. 40.00 (ISBN 0-8240-6440-2). Garland Pub.

Rees, U., ed. The Cartulary of Haughmond Abbey. 304p. 1985. text ed. 39.95x (ISBN 0-7083-0907-0, Pub. by U of Wales). Humanities.

Rees, William. A History of the Order of St. John of Jerusalem in Wales & on the Welsh Border: Including an Account of the Templars. LC 76-29839. (Illus.). Repr. of 1947 ed. 26.50 (ISBN 0-404-15427-1). AMS Pr.

Reese, Alexander. Approaching Advent of Christ. LC 73-85374. 328p. 1975. 8.95 (ISBN 0-8254-3610-9). Kregel.

Reese, Edward, compiled by. The Reese Chronological Bible. 1620p. 1980. Repr. of 1977 ed. 26.95 (ISBN 0-87123-115-8, 230115). Bethany Hse.

Reese, Gareth. New Testament History-Acts. 5th ed. (The Bible Study Textbook Ser.). (Illus.). 1976. 19.95 (ISBN 0-89900-055-X). College Pr Pub.

Reese, James. The Book of Wisdom, Song of Songs. (Old Testament Message Ser.: Vol. 20). 12.95 (ISBN 0-89453-420-3); pap. 8.95 (ISBN 0-89453-254-5). M Glazier.

Reese, James M. Experiencing the Good News: The New Testament as Communication. (Good News Studies Ser.: Vol. 10). 1984. pap. 9.95 (ISBN 0-89453-448-3). M Glazier.

--First & Second Thessalonians. (New Testament Message Ser.: Vol. 16). 130p. 1980. 10.95 (ISBN 0-89453-204-9); pap. 5.95 (ISBN 0-89453-139-5). M Glazier.

Reese, Loretta. Fifty-Four Crafts with Easy Patterns. LC 78-62788. (Illus.). 1979. pap. 4.95 (ISBN 0-87239-175-2, 2134). Standard Pub.

Reese, William L. Dictionary of Philosophy & Religion: Eastern & Western Thought. text ed. 29.95x 648p. 1980 (ISBN 0-391-00688-6); pap. text ed. 19.95x 644p. 1981 (ISBN 0-391-00941-9). Humanities.

Reese, William L., jt. auth. see Hartshorne, Charles.

Reese, William L. & Freeman, Eugene, eds. Process & Divinity: The Hartshorne Festschrift. LC 64-13547. 644p. 1964. 32.95 (ISBN 0-87548-054-3). Open Court.

Reesing, John. Milton's Poetic Art: A Mask, Lycidas, & Paradise Lost. LC 68-17632. Repr. of 1968 ed. 55.50 (ISBN 0-8357-9166-1, 2017011). Bks Demand UMI.

Reesman, Richard T. Contributions of the Major Philosophers into the Problem of Body Resurrection & Personal Immortality. (Illus.). 117p. 1981. 61.85 (ISBN 0-89920-021-4). Am Inst Psych.

Reeve, Pamela. Faith Is. 1970. pap. 4.95 (ISBN 0-930014-05-7). Multnomah.

--La Fe Es. Orig. Title: Faith Is. (Span.). 50p. 1983. spiral bd 4.95 (ISBN 0-930014-96-0). Multnomah.

--Parables by the Sea. LC 77-6209. (Illus.). 1976. gift ed. o.p. 5.95 (ISBN 0-930014-10-3); pap. 5.95 (ISBN 0-930014-11-1). Multnomah.

Reeves, A. Compton, ed. see Mudroch, Vaclav.

Reeves, J. B. The Hymn As Literature. 59.95 (ISBN 0-8490-0378-4). Gordon Pr.

Reeves, James, jt. auth. see Weekley, James.

Reeves, Kenneth V. The Godhead. Rev. ed. Wallace, Mary H., ed. 1984. pap. 4.50 (ISBN 0-912315-64-4). Word Aflame.

--The Rivers of Living Water. (Illus.). 78p. (Orig.). 1980. pap. 3.00 (ISBN 0-912315-65-2). Word Aflame.

--The Supreme Godhead. Wallace, Mary H., ed. (Illus.). 100p. (Orig.). 1984. pap. 5.50 (ISBN 0-912315-74-1). Word Aflame.

Reeves, Marjorie. The Medieval Monastery: Then & There Ser. (Illus.). 90p. (Orig.). 1980. pap. text ed. 4.75 (ISBN 0-582-20372-4). Longman.

Reeves, Marjorie, ed. see Cubitt, Heather.

Reeves, Marjorie, ed. see McWilliam, H. O.

Reeves, Marjorie, ed. see Williams, Ann.

Reeves, R. Daniel & Jenson, Ronald. Always Advancing. LC 83-73182. 196p. (Orig.). 1984. pap. 8.95 (ISBN 0-86605-120-1, 403188). Campus Crusade.

Reeves, Troy D. An Annotated Index to the Sermons of John Donne: Index to Proper Names, Vol. II. Hogg, James, ed. (Elizabethan & Renaissance Studies). 148p. (Orig.). 1980. pap. 15.00 (ISBN 0-317-40117-3, Pub by Salzburg Studies). Longwood Pub Group.

--An Annotated Index to the Sermons of John Donne: Index to the Scriptures, Vol. I. Hogg, James, ed. (Elizabethan & Renaissance Studies). 229p. (Orig.). 1979. pap. 15.00 (ISBN 0-317-40114-9, Pub by Salzburgh Studies). Longwood Pub Group.

--An Annotated Index to the Sermons of John Donne: Index to Topics, Vol. III. Hogg, James, ed. (Elizabethan & Renaissance Studies). 226p. (Orig.). 1981. pap. 15.00 (ISBN 0-317-40118-1, Pub by Salzburg Studies). Longwood Pub Group.

Reeves, Una G. Writing Verse As a Hobby. 1962. 6.95 (ISBN 0-8158-0172-6). Chris Mass.

Reeves, William, ed. see Adamnan, Saint.

Reff, Theodore, ed. Exhibitions of the Rosicrucian Salon. (Modern Art in Paris 1855 to 1900 Ser.). 354p. 1981. lib. bdg. 53.00 (ISBN 0-8240-4730-3). Garland Pub.

Reformed Church in America. Rejoice in the Lord: A Hymn Companion to the Scriptures. Routley, Erik, ed. 608p. 1985. 12.95x (ISBN 0-8028-9009-1). Eerdmans.

Reftery, Larry, ed. Worship His Majesty. 32p. 1981. pap. 0.75 (ISBN 0-88144-056-6). Christian Pub.

Regamey, Constantin, tr. from Sanskrit & Tibetan. Three Chapters from the Samadhirajasutra. 112p. 1984. Repr. of 1938 ed. lib. bdg. 17.50x (ISBN 0-88181-003-7). Canon Pubns.

Regamey, Pius R. Renewal in the Spirit. 1980. 5.95 (ISBN 0-8198-6402-1); pap. 4.95 (ISBN 0-8198-6403-X). Dghtrs St Paul.

Regan, Cronan. Signpost: Questions About the Church & Religion You Always Wanted Answered. LC 70-169056. (Illus.). 340p. 1972. 7.50 (ISBN 0-8199-0432-5). Franciscan Herald.

Regan, Geoffrey B. Israel & the Arabs: Cambridge Introduction to the History of Mankind. (Illus.). 48p. 1984. pap. 4.95 (ISBN 0-521-27580-6). Cambridge U Pr.

Regan, Jane, jt. auth. see Cove, Mary.

Regan, Richard J., ed. see St. Thomas Acquinas.

Regan, Tom. Bloomsbury's Prophet: G. E. Moore & the Development of His Moral Philosophy. 328p. 1986. 29.95 (ISBN 0-87722-446-3). Temple U Pr.

Regan, Tom, ed. Matters of Life & Death: New Introductory Essays in Moral Philosophy. 368p. 1980. 32.95 (ISBN 0-87722-181-2). Temple U Pr.

Regan, Tom & Van DeVeer, Donald, eds. And Justice for All: New Introductory Essays in Ethics & Public Policy. LC 81-23446. (Philosophy & Society Ser.). 320p. 1982. 34.00x (ISBN 0-8476-7059-7); pap. 12.50x (ISBN 0-8476-7060-0). Rowman.

Regardie, Israel. Ceremonial Magic: A Guide to the Mechanism of Ritual. LC 86-18389. 176p. 1986. lib. bdg. 19.95x (ISBN 0-8095-7013-0). Borgo Pr.

--Energy, Prayer & Relaxation. LC 82-83292. 80p. 1982. pap. 5.95 (ISBN 0-941404-02-1). Falcon Pr Az.

--A Garden of Pomegranates. LC 74-18984. (High Magick Ser.). (Illus.). 176p. 1985. pap. 6.95 (ISBN 0-87542-690-5, L-690). Llewellyn Pubns.

Regardie, Israel, et al. Mysticism, Psychology & Oedipus. LC 85-81908. 96p. (Orig.). 1986. pap. 6.95 (ISBN 0-941404-38-2). Falcon Pr AZ.

Regazzi, John J. & Hines, Theodore C. A Guide to Indexed Periodicals in Religion. LC 75-22277. 328p. 1975. 20.00 (ISBN 0-8108-0868-4). Scarecrow.

Regehr, Lydia. Bible Riddles of Birds & Beasts & Creeping Things. (Illus.). 36p. (Orig.). 1982. pap. 1.50 (ISBN 0-89323-030-8). Bible Memory.

Regehr, Margaret. The Golden Thread. (Illus.). 209p. (Orig.). 1985. pap. text ed. 7.00 (ISBN 0-9614486-0-1). M Regehr.

Regel, Vasilii E., ed. Analecta Byzantino-Russica. 1964. Repr. of 1891 ed. 23.50 (ISBN 0-8337-2919-5). B Franklin.

Regelson, Abraham, tr. The Deluxe Haggadah. 1961. velour bound 30.00 (ISBN 0-914080-34-2). Shulsinger Sales.

--The Haggadah-Kleinman. 1965. pap. 1.99 (ISBN 0-914080-33-4). Shulsinger Sales.

Regency Press Ltd. Staff, ed. Secret of the Golden Hours. 112p. 1984. 40.00 (ISBN 0-7212-0656-5, Pub. by Regency Pr). State Mutual Bk.

Regenmorter, John Van see Van Regenmorter, John & Van Regenmorter, Sylvia.

Regenmorter, Sylvia Van see Van Regenmorter, John & Van Regenmorter, Sylvia.

Regis, Louis-Marie. Saint Thomas & Epistemology. (Aquinas Lecture Ser.). 1946. 7.95 (ISBN 0-87462-110-0). Marquette.

Regnot, Franz, tr. see Nachman of Breslov.

Rehman, A. Muhammad the Educator. pap. 15.00 (ISBN 0-686-18433-5). Kazi Pubns.

Rehork, Joachim, ed. see Keller, Werner.

Rehrer, Ronald. Now What Do I Do? 1982. pap. 4.95 (ISBN 0-570-03854-5, 12-2809). Concordia.

Rehwinkel, Alfred M. Flood. 2nd ed. (Orig.). (YA) 1951-1957. pap. 9.95 (ISBN 0-570-03183-4, 12-2103). Concordia.

--The Wonders of Creation. LC 74-8416. 288p. 1973. pap. 7.95 (ISBN 0-87123-649-4, 210649). Bethany Hse.

Reich, Bernard. Israel: Land of Tradition & Conflict. (Profiles-Nations of the Contemporary Middle East Ser.). 240p. 1985. 28.00x (ISBN 0-8133-0211-0); pap. text ed. 13.95x (ISBN 0-8133-0215-3). Westview.

Reichard, Gladys. Navajo Medicine Man Sand Paintings. (Illus.). 1977. pap. 8.95 (ISBN 0-486-23329-4). Dover.

Reichard, Gladys A. Analysis of Coeur D'Alene Indian Myths. LC 48-2411. (AFS M). Repr. of 1947 ed. 21.00 (ISBN 0-527-01093-6). Kraus Repr.

--Navaho Religion: A Study of Symbolism. LC 83-5082. 804p. 1983. pap. 19.95x (ISBN 0-8165-0834-8). U of Ariz Pr.

Reichel-Dolmatoff, Gerardo. Amazonian Cosmos: The Sexual & Religious Symbolism of the Tukano Indians. Reichel-Dolmatoff, Gerardo, tr. from Span. LC 73-133491. xxiv, 290p. 1974. pap. 7.95X (ISBN 0-226-70732-6, P574, Phoen). U of Chicago Pr.

Reichelt, Hans. Avesta Reader. 1968. Repr. of 1911 ed. 38.80x (ISBN 3-11-000159-4). De Gruyter.

Reichelt, Karl. Truth & Tradition in Chinese Buddhism. 59.95 (ISBN 0-8490-1234-1). Gordon Pr.

Reichenbach, Bodo A., tr. see Bo Yin Ra.

Reichenbach, Bruce. Evil & a Good God. LC 82-71120. xviii, 198p. 1982. 22.50 (ISBN 0-8232-1080-4); pap. 9.00 (ISBN 0-8232-1081-2). Fordham.

Reichenbach, Bruce R. The Cosmological Argument: A Reassessment. (Illus.). 160p. 1972. 16.00x (ISBN 0-398-02387-5). C C Thomas.

Reichert, Richard. Adult Education Ministry: A Parish Manual. 1986. pap. 5.95 (ISBN 0-697-02206-4). Wm C Brown.

--Born in the Spirit of Jesus. 84p. (Orig.). 1980. pap. text ed. 3.20 (ISBN 0-697-01725-7); tchr's manual 4.00 (ISBN 0-697-01726-5); spirit masters 10.95. Wm C Brown.

--Born in the Spirit of Jesus. (YA) 1985. pap. text ed. 4.50 (ISBN 0-697-02120-3); tchr's. ed. 5.50 (ISBN 0-697-02121-1); spirit masters 10.95 (ISBN 0-697-01727-3). Wm C Brown.

--Community of the Spirit. 120p. 1982. pap. 3.60 (ISBN 0-697-01796-6); tchr's manual 4.00 (ISBN 0-697-01797-4); spirit masters 10.95 (ISBN 0-697-01798-2). Wm C Brown.

--Confronting Christianity: Adults & Authority. LC 78-53634. 44p. 1978. pap. 9.95 (ISBN 0-88489-102-X). St Marys.

--Confronting Christianity: Faith & Religion. LC 78-53634. 44p. 1978. pap. 9.95 (ISBN 0-88489-100-3). St Marys.

--Confronting Christianity: Moral Issues. LC 78-53634. 44p. 1978. pap. 9.95 (ISBN 0-88489-099-6). St Marys.

--Growing Within, Changing Without. (New Creation Ser.). 96p. 1985. pap. text ed. 4.05 (ISBN 0-697-01993-4); tchr's. ed. 4.50 (ISBN 0-697-01994-2). Wm C Brown.

--Making Moral Decisions. rev. ed. LC 83-60316. (Illus.). 1983. pap. text ed. 7.20x (ISBN 0-88489-150-X); tchrs. guide 9.00x (ISBN 0-88489-151-8). St Marys.

--New Creation People. (New Creation Ser.). 96p. 1985. pap. text ed. 4.25 (ISBN 0-697-01997-7); tchr's. ed. 4.50 (ISBN 0-697-01998-5). Wm C Brown.

--On Our Way. (New Creation Ser.). 96p. 1985. pap. text ed. 4.25 (ISBN 0-697-01995-0); tchr's. ed. 4.50 (ISBN 0-697-01996-9). Wm C Brown.

--Sexuality & Dating. LC 81-51011. (Illus.). 160p. 1981. pap. 5.00x (ISBN 0-88489-133-X); tchrs' guide 9.00x (ISBN 0-88489-138-0); student workbook 2.00 (ISBN 0-88489-139-9). St Mary's.

--Simulation Games for Religious Education. LC 75-142. 1975. pap. 4.50 (ISBN 0-88489-060-0). St Marys.

Reichert, Richard J. A Learning Process for Religious Education. LC 74-14308. (Orig.). 1974. pap. 3.95 (ISBN 0-8278-0001-0, Pub. by Pflaum Pr). Peter Li.

Reichley, A. James. Religion in American Public Life. LC 85-21312. 402p. 1985. 31.95 (ISBN 0-8157-7378-1); pap. 11.95 (ISBN 0-8157-7377-3). Brookings.

Reichter, Arlo, et al. The Group Retreat Book. LC 82-62532. (Illus.). 400p. (Orig.). 1983. pap. 15.95 (ISBN 0-936664-08-8). Group Bks.

Reicke, Bo. The New Testament Era: The World of the Bible from 500 B.C. to A.D. 100. LC 68-15864. 352p. 1974. pap. 8.95 (ISBN 0-8006-1080-6, 1-1080). Fortress.

--The Roots of the Synoptic Gospels. LC 85-45485. 224p. 1986. 22.95 (ISBN 0-8006-0766-X, 1-766). Fortress.

Reicke, Bo I. The Disobedient Spirits & Christian Baptism: Study of First Peter, III-19 & Its Context. LC 79-8117. 288p. 1984. Repr. of 1946 ed. 41.50 (ISBN 0-404-18430-8). AMS Pr.

Reicke, Bo I., ed. Epistles of James, Peter & Jude. LC 63-8221. (Anchor Bible Ser.: Vol. 37). 1964. 14.00 (ISBN 0-385-01374-4, Anchor Pr). Doubleday.

Reid, Charles. Choice & Action: An Introduction to Ethics. 1981. pap. text ed. write for info. (ISBN 0-02-399180-1). Macmillan.

Reid, Charles J., Jr., ed. Peace in a Nuclear Age: The Bishops' Pastoral Letter in Perspective. 1986. 44.95 (ISBN 0-8132-0624-3). Cath U Pr.

Reid, David P. What Are They Saying about the Prophets? LC 80-80869. 112p. (Orig.). 1980. pap. 3.95 (ISBN 0-8091-2304-5). Paulist Pr.

Reid, David R. Devotions for Growing Christians. 256p. (Orig.). 1986. pap. 4.95 (ISBN 0-87213-701-5). Loizeaux.

--Thoughts for Growing Christians. LC 82-7913. 160p. 1982. pap. 3.95 (ISBN 0-8024-2200-4). Moody.

Reid, Donald M. The Odyssey of Farah Antun: A Syrian Christian's Quest for Secularism. LC 74-80598. (Studies in Middle Eastern History: No. 2). 1975. 25.00x (ISBN 0-88297-009-7). Bibliotheca.

Reid, Doris F., ed. A Treasury of Edith Hamilton. LC 70-90989. 1969. 5.00 (ISBN 0-393-04313-4). Norton.

Reid, Garnett. How to Grow in Grace. 1982. pap. 1.50 (ISBN 0-89265-077-X). Randall Hse.

--How to Know God's Will. 1982. pap. 1.50 (ISBN 0-89265-078-8). Randall Hse.

--How to Know You're Saved. 1982. pap. 1.50 (ISBN 0-89265-075-3). Randall Hse.

Reid, Gilbert. A Christian's Appreciation of Other Faiths. 305p. 1921. 22.95 (ISBN 0-87548-219-8). Open Court.

Reid, Helen F., jt. auth. see Hamilton, Michael P.

Reid, J. K., ed. Calvin: Theological Treatises. LC 54-9956. (Library of Christian Classics). 352p. 1978. softcover 8.95 (ISBN 0-664-24156-5). Westminster.

Reid, J. K., tr. see Calvin, John.

Reid, James. Dios, el Atomo, y el Universo. Orozco, Julio, tr. from Eng. LC 76-55491. Tr. of God, the Atom & the Universe. (Span.). 240p. (Orig.). 1977. pap. 5.95 (ISBN 0-89922-083-5). Edit Caribe.

Reid, James D. The Telegraph in America: Its Founders, Promoters & Noted Men. LC 74-7493. (Telecommunications Ser). (Illus.). 926p. 1974. Repr. of 1879 ed. 63.00 (ISBN 0-405-06056-4). Ayer Co Pubs.

Reid, John C. God's Promises & My Needs. 80p. (Orig.). 1986. pap. 2.50 (ISBN 0-914733-06-0). Desert Min.

--The Grumpy Prophet & 22 other Bible Stories to Read & Tell. 80p. 1986. casebound 7.95 (ISBN 0-87239-917-6, 3370). Standard Pub.

--Parables from Nature. 1954. 3.95 (ISBN 0-8028-4025-6). Eerdmans.

--Thirty Favorite Bible Stories with Discussion Questions. LC 81-21514. (Illus.). 192p. (Orig.). 1982. pap. 4.95 (ISBN 0-87239-498-0, 3373). Standard Pub.

--Twenty-Two More Object Talks for Children's Worship. (Illus.). 80p. 1987. pap. 3.50 (ISBN 0-87403-239-3, 2879). Standard Pub.

Reid, John K. The Authority of Scripture: A Study of the Reformation & Post-Reformation Understanding of the Bible. LC 79-8716. 286p. 1981. Repr. of 1962 ed. lib. bdg. 25.00x (ISBN 0-313-22191-X, REAS). Greenwood.

Reid, Muriel F. Speak the Thought: How to Read & Speak in Public, with Bible-Lesson Applications. 2nd, exp. ed. 64p. 1984. 7.00 (ISBN 0-915878-05-4). Joseph Pub Co.

Reid, Richard & Crum, Milton, Jr. Lesser Festivals 3: Saints' Days & Special Occasions. Achtemeier, Elizabeth, et al, eds. LC 79-7377. (Proclamation 2: Aids for Interpreting the Lessons of the Church Year). 64p. (Orig.). 1981. pap. 3.75 (ISBN 0-8006-1395-3, 1-1395). Fortress.

Reid, Russell L. A Romance with Reality. 1983. 5.75 (ISBN 0-8062-2185-2). Carlton.

Reid, Stuart J. The Life & Times of Sydney Smith. Repr. of 1901 ed. lib. bdg. 30.00 (ISBN 0-8495-4533-1). Arden Lib.

--A Sketch of the Life & Times of Sydney Smith. 59.95 (ISBN 0-8490-1060-8). Gordon Pr.

--A Sketch of the Life & Times of the Rev. Sydney Smith. 1977. Repr. of 1885 ed. lib. bdg. 30.00 (ISBN 0-8495-4512-9). Arden Lib.

Reid, Thomas. Essays on the Active Powers of Man. Wellek, Rene, ed. LC 75-11251. (British Philosophers & Theologians of the 17th & 18th Centuries: Vol. 50). 1977. Repr. of 1788 ed. lib. bdg. 51.00 (ISBN 0-8240-1802-8). Garland Pub.

Reid, Thomas F., et al. Seduction?? A Biblical Response. rev. ed. Biros, Florence K. & Williams, Carole, eds. (Illus.). 1986. pap. 6.95 (ISBN 0-936369-02-7). Son-Rise Pubns.

Reid, W. Stanford. Trumpeter of God: A Biography of John Knox. 372p. 1982. pap. 8.95 (ISBN 0-8010-7708-7). Baker Bk.

Reid, William. Blood of Jesus. pap. 1.50x (ISBN 0-914053-02-7). Liberty Bell Pr.

Reid, William, ed. Authentic Records of Revival, Now in Progress in the United Kingdom. (Revival Library). viii, 478p. 1980. Repr. of 1860 ed. lib. bdg. 15.95 (ISBN 0-940033-17-8). R O Roberts.

Reider, Rimma. Jewish Ceremonial Designs. (International Design Library). (Illus.). 48p. 1987. pap. 3.95 (ISBN 0-88045-087-8). Stemmer Hse.

Reidt, Wilford H. & Lake, John G. Jesus God's Way of Healing & Power to Promote Health. 171p. 1981. pap. 5.95 (ISBN 0-89274-197-X). Harrison Hse.

Reierson, Gary B., jt. auth. see Campbell, Thomas C.

Reif, Joseph A. & Levinson, Hanna. FSI Hebrew Basic Course. 1976. pap. text ed. 15.00X (ISBN 0-686-10730-6); 35 cassettes 210.00x (ISBN 0-686-10731-4). Intl Learn Syst.

--Spoken Modern Hebrew. (Spoken Language Ser.). 590p. 1980. pap. 15.00x (ISBN 0-87950-683-0); cassettes, 31 dual track 180.00x (ISBN 0-87950-684-9); text & cassettes 190.00x (ISBN 0-87950-685-7). Spoken Lang Serv.

Reif, Stefan C., jt. ed. see Emerton, J. A.

Reiff, Stephanie A. Secrets of Tut's Tomb & the Pyramids. LC 77-22770. (Great Unsolved Mysteries). (Illus.). 1977. PLB 14.65 (ISBN 0-8172-1051-2). Raintree Pubs.

Reigle, David. The Books of Kiu-Te in the Tibetan Buddhist Tantras. LC 83-60416. (Secret Doctrine Reference Ser.). (Illus.). 80p. (Orig.). 1983. pap. 5.00 (ISBN 0-913510-49-1). Wizards.

Reik, Theodor. Dogma & Compulsion. LC 72-9369. 332p. 1973. Repr. of 1951 ed. lib. bdg. 45.00x (ISBN 0-8371-6577-6, REDC). Greenwood.

Reik, Theodore. Ritual. pap. text ed. 19.95 (ISBN 0-8236-8269-2, 025840). Intl Univs Pr.

Reiling, J. & Swellengrebel, J. L. Translator's Handbook on the Gospel of Luke. LC 72-856530. (Helps for Translators Ser.). 798p. 1971. 8.40x (ISBN 0-8267-0198-1, 08512, Pub. by United Bible). Am Bible.

Reilly, Barbara. Children's Bulletin Sundays of Easter. 1979. pap. 7.55 (ISBN 0-88479-008-8). Arena Lettres.

Reilly, Bernard F. Santiago, St. Denis, & St. Peter: The Reception of the Roman Liturgy in Leon-Castile in 1080. (Illus.). xvi, 216p. 1985. 37.50 (ISBN 0-8232-1125-8). Fordham.

Reilly, Cyril A. Song of Creation. 64p. 1983. pap. 9.95 (ISBN 0-86683-710-8, HarpR). Har-Row.

Reilly, Daniel F. School Controversy Eighteen Ninety-One to Eighteen Ninety-Three. LC 76-89221. (American Education: Its Men, Institutions & Ideas, Ser. 1). 1969. Repr. of 1943 ed. 24.00 (ISBN 0-405-01460-0). Ayer Co Pubs.

Reilly, Mary V. & Wetterer, Margaret K. From Thy Bounty: Holiday Foods Around from the World. (Illus.). 44p. (Orig.). 1982. pap. 4.95 (ISBN 0-8192-1299-7). Morehouse.

--The Seeds of Paradise: A Garland of Holiday Projects. (Illus.). 44p. (Orig.). 1982. pap. 4.95 (ISBN 0-8192-1298-9). Morehouse.

--Voices of Praise. (Illus., Orig.). 1980. pap. 4.95 (ISBN 0-8192-1276-8). Morehouse.

Reilly, Mary V., et al. Wait in Joyful Hope! (Illus., Orig.). 1980. pap. 4.95 (ISBN 0-8192-1275-X). Morehouse.

Reilly, Mimi, jt. auth. see Reilly, Terry.

Reilly, Robert, ed. The Transcendent Adventure: Studies of Religion in Science Fiction-Fantasy. LC 84-542. (Contributions to the Study of Science Fiction & Fantasy Ser.: No. 12). x, 266p. 1985. lib. bdg. 35.00 (ISBN 0-313-23062-5, RET/). Greenwood.

Reilly, Terry & Reilly, Mimi. Family Nights: Advent-Christmas. 1977. pap. 1.45 (ISBN 0-87029-135-1, 20161-6). Abbey.

--Family Nights: Lent-Easter. 1977. pap. 1.45 (ISBN 0-87029-130-0, 20158-2). Abbey.

--Family Nights: Summer-Vacation. 1977. pap. 1.45 (ISBN 0-87029-134-3, 20160-8). Abbey.

--Noches Para la Familia. Movimiento Familiar Cristiano De Miami, tr. LC 81-65209. (Span., Illus.). 64p. 1981. pap. 2.95 (ISBN 0-87029-175-0, 20249-9). Abbey.

Reimer, G. C., tr. see Freytag, Gustav.

Reimer, Larry, jt. auth. see Reimer, Sandy.

Reimer, Lawrence D. Living at the Edge of Faith. 96p. 1984. pap. 6.95 (ISBN 0-8170-1023-8). Judson.

Reimer, Sandy & Reimer, Larry. The Retreat Handbook. 192p. 1987. pap. 9.95. Morehouse.

Reimherr, Otto, ed. Quest for Faith, Quest for Freedom: Aspects of Pennsylvania's Religious Experience. LC 86-61790. (Illus.). 208p. 1987. 28.50x (ISBN 0-941664-26-0). Susquehanna U Pr.

Reinecke, Elisabeth, tr. see Rudin, Josef.

Reiner, Erica & Pingree, D. Babylonian Planetary Omens, Enuma Anu Enlil, Tablet 50-51. LC 79-67168. (Bibliotheca Mesopotamica Ser.: Vol. 2, Pt. 2). 100p. (Orig.). 1980. pap. 15.00x (ISBN 0-89003-049-9). Undena Pubns.

Reinerman, Alan J. Austria & the Papacy in the Age of Metternich: Between Conflict & Cooperation, 1809-1830. LC 79-774. (Vol. 1). 254p. 1979. 27.95x (ISBN 0-8132-0548-4). Cath U Pr.

Reinertson, Kristen E. The Holy City with Signs & Wonders. LC 86-90554. (Illus.). 150p. (Orig.). 1987. pap. text ed. 11.95 (ISBN 0-9617564-5-4). Skoglie Storevik Pubs.

Reines, Alvin J. Maimonides & Abravanel on Prophecy. 1971. 15.00x (ISBN 0-87820-200-5, Pub. by Hebrew Union). KTAV.

--Polydoxy: Explorations in a Philosophy of Liberal Religion. 200p. 1987. 29.95 (ISBN 0-87975-399-4). Prometheus Bks.

Reinhart, Dietrich, jt. auth. see Kwatera, Michael.

Reinhart, J. R. The Power of Knowing Who I Am in Christ. LC 82-73254. 220p. 1983. pap. 7.95 (ISBN 0-918060-04-4). Burn-Hart.

Reinharz, Jehuda, ed. Living with Antisemitism: Modern Jewish Responses. (Tauber Institute Ser.: No. 6). 1987. 45.00 (ISBN 0-87451-388-X). U Pr of New Eng.

Reinharz, Jehuda & Schatzberg, Walter, eds. The Jewish Response to German Culture: From the Enlightenment to the Second World War. LC 85-14185. 368p. 1985. 32.50x (ISBN 0-87451-345-6). U Pr of New Eng.

Reinharz, Jehuda, et al, eds. Mystics, Philosophers, & Politicians: Essays in Jewish Intellectual History in Honor of Alexander Altman. LC 81-5540. (Duke Monographs in Medieval & Renaissance Studies: No. 5). xv, 372p. 1982. 36.75 (ISBN 0-8223-0446-5). Duke.

Reinhold, H. A. The Soul Afire: Revelations of the Mystics. 1977. Repr. of 1944 ed. 30.00 (ISBN 0-89984-099-X). Century Bookbindery.

Reining, Priscilla & Tinker, Irene, eds. Population: Dynamics, Ethics & Policy. 1975. pap. 19.00 (ISBN 0-12-586751-4). Acad Pr.

Reinisch, Leonhard, ed. Theologians of Our Time. 1964. 17.95x (ISBN 0-268-00271-1); pap. 7.95x (ISBN 0-268-00378-5). U of Notre Dame Pr.

Reinitz, R. Tensions in American Puritanism. LC 70-100325. (Problems in American History Ser.). pap. 52.00 (ISBN 0-8357-9991-3, 2019292). Bks Demand UMI.

Reinitz, Richard. Irony & Consciousness: American Historiography & Reinhold Niebuhr's Vision. LC 77-92574. 232p. 23.50 (ISBN 0-8387-2062-5). Bucknell U Pr.

Reis, Elizabeth M. A Deeper Kind of Truth: Biblical Tales for Life & Prayer. 112p. (Orig.). 1987. pap. 5.95 (ISBN 0-8091-2858-6). Paulist Pr.

Reis, Richard H. George MacDonald. LC 71-125820. (Twayne's English Authors Ser.). 1972. lib. bdg. 17.95 (ISBN 0-8057-1356-5). Irvington.

Reischauer, A. K. Studies in Japanese Buddhism. LC 73-107769. Repr. of 1917 ed. 24.50 (ISBN 0-404-05237-1). AMS Pr.

Reischauer, August. Studies in Japanese Buddhism. 75.00 (ISBN 0-8490-1147-7). Gordon Pr.

Reischauer, August K. Nature & Truth of the Great Religions: Toward a Philosophy of Religion. LC 65-20612. 1966. 19.50 (ISBN 0-8048-0420-6). C E Tuttle.

Reischauer, Edwin O., tr. Ennin's Diary: The Record of a Pilgrimage to China in Search of the Law. LC 55-5553. (Illus.). pap. 119.50 (ISBN 0-8357-9521-7, 2012366). Bks Demand UMI.

Reiser, Oliver. Cosmic Humanism & World Unity. new ed. LC 73-86468. (World Institute Creative Findings Ser.). (Illus.). 286p. 1975. 49.50 (ISBN 0-677-03870-4); pap. 21.00 (ISBN 0-677-03875-5). Gordon & Breach.

Reiser, William. Into the Needle's Eye. LC 83-72741. 144p. (Orig.). 1984. pap. 4.50 (ISBN 0-87793-306-5). Ave Maria.

--An Unlikely Catechism: Some Challenges for the Creedless Catholic. 184p. (Orig.). 1985. pap. 6.95 (ISBN 0-8091-2706-7). Paulist Pr.

Reiser, William E. What Are They Saying about Dogma? LC 78-58955. 1978. pap. 3.95 (ISBN 0-8091-2127-1). Paulist Pr.

Reisinger, Ernest C. The Carnal Christian: What Should We Think of the Carnal Christian? 75p. 1.20 (ISBN 0-85151-389-1). Banner of Truth.

--Today's Evangelism: It's Message & Methods. 1982. pap. 4.95 (ISBN 0-87552-417-6). Presby & Reformed.

Reisman, Bernard. The Chavurah: A Contemporary Jewish Experience. 1977. pap. 7.50 (ISBN 0-8074-0048-3, 140050). UAHC.

--The Jewish Experiential Book: The Quest for Jewish Identity. 1979. 35.00x (ISBN 0-87068-688-7). Ktav.

Reisman, Bernard & Rosen, Gladys. Single-Parent Families at Camp: The Essence of an Experience. LC 84-70480. 54p. 1984. pap. 2.50 (ISBN 0-87495-061-9). Am Jewish Comm.

Reisman, W. Michael. Folded Lies: Bribery, Crusades, & Reforms. LC 78-3207. 1979. 12.95 (ISBN 0-02-926280-1). Free Pr.

Reisner, G. A. Excavations at Kerma, Pts. I-V. Hooton, E. A. & Bates, Natica I., eds. (Harvard African Studies: Vol. 5). Pts. I-III. lib. bdg. 118.00set (ISBN 0-527-01028-6); Pts. IV-V. lib. bdg. 69.00 set (ISBN 0-527-01029-4). Kraus Repr.

Reisner, George A. A Provincial Cemetery of the Pyramid Age, Naga-Ed-Der, Pt. 3. (Publications in Egyptian Archaeology: Vol. 6). 1932. 110.00x (ISBN 0-520-01060-4). U of Cal Pr.

Reiss, Edmund. Boethius. (World Authors Ser.). 1982. lib. bdg. 19.95 (ISBN 0-8057-6519-0, Twayne). G K Hall.

Reiss, Walter. Thank God for My Breakdown. 1980. 4.95 (ISBN 0-8100-0114-4, 12N1717). Northwest Pub.

Reist, Thomas. Saint Bonaventure As a Biblical Commentator: A Translation & Analysis of His "Commentary on Luke," XVIII,34-XIX,42. 284p. (Orig.). 1985. lib. bdg. 24.00 (ISBN 0-8191-4578-5); pap. text ed. 12.75 (ISBN 0-8191-4579-3). U Pr of Amer.

Reith, George. St. John, 2 vols, Vol. I & 2. Whyte, A. & Moffatt, J., eds. (Handbooks for Bible Classes & Private Students Ser.). 1889. 8.95 ea. (Pub. by T & T Clark Ltd UK). Vol. 1, 200 pgs (ISBN 0-567-08114-1). Vol. 2, 180 pgs (ISBN 0-567-08115-X). Fortress.

Reitlinger, Gerald. The Final Solution: The Attempt to Exterminate the Jews of Europe 1939-45. 622p. 1987. Repr. of 1953 ed. 40.00 (ISBN 0-87668-951-9). Aronson.

Reitzenstein, Richard. The Hellenistic Mystery-Religions. Steely, John E., tr. from Ger. LC 77-12980. (Pittsburgh Theological Monographs: No. 15). Orig. Title: Die Hellenistischen Mysterienreligionen Nach Ihren Arundgedanken und Wirkungen. 1978. pap. text ed. 17.75 (ISBN 0-915138-20-4). Pickwick.

Rejwan, Nissim. The Jews of Iraq. 288p. 1986. 30.00 (ISBN 0-8133-0348-6). Westview.

Rele, V. G. Human Mind Power: Secrets of the Vedic Gods. 136p. 1983. pap. text ed. 5.95x (ISBN 0-86590-231-3, Pub. by Taraporevala India). Apt Bks.

Relfe, Mary S. The New Money System. 271p. 1982. pap. 6.95 (ISBN 0-9607986-1-7). Ministries.

--When Your Money Fails. 234p. (Orig.). 1981. pap. text ed. 5.95 (ISBN 0-9607986-0-9). Ministries.

Religious Education Commission. All Are Called. 1984. pap. 5.75 (ISBN 0-8309-0391-7). Herald Hse.

Religious Education Staff. The Spirit Alive in Prayer: Spirit Masters. 1979. 9.95 (ISBN 0-697-01699-4). Wm C Brown.

--The Spirit Alive in Service: Spirit Masters. 1979. 9.95 (ISBN 0-697-01712-5). Wm C Brown.

--The Spirit Alive in Vocations: Spirit Masters. 1980. 9.95 (ISBN 0-697-01755-9). Wm C Brown.

Religous Education Staff. The Spirit Alive in Liturgy: Spirit Masters. 1981. 9.95 (ISBN 0-686-84105-0). Wm C Brown.

--The Spirit Alive in You: Spirit Masters. 1982. 9.95 (ISBN 0-697-01805-9). Wm C Brown.

Relton, Frederic, jt. auth. see Overton, John H.

Rembrandt. Drawings of Rembrandt, 2 Vols. Slive, Seymour, ed. (Illus.). pap. 12.50 ea.; Vol. 1. pap. (ISBN 0-486-21485-0); Vol. 2. pap. (ISBN 0-486-21486-9). Dover.

Rembrandt, Elaine. Heroes, Heroines, & Holidays: Plays for Jewish Youth. LC 81-67027. 148p. (Orig.). 1981. pap. 6.50 (ISBN 0-86705-002-0). AIRE.

Remus, Harold. Pagan-Christian Conflict over Miracle in the Second Century. LC 83-6729. (Patristic Monograph: No. 10). xiii, 371p. 1983. pap. 11.00 (ISBN 0-915646-09-9). Phila Patristic.

Remy, Jules & Brenchley, Julius. A Journey to Great Salt-Lake City, 2 vols. LC 75-134399. (Illus.). Repr. of 1861 ed. Set. 49.50 (ISBN 0-404-08441-9). Vol. 1 (ISBN 0-404-08442-7). Vol. 2 (ISBN 0-404-08443-5). AMS Pr.

Renan, Ernest. Lectures on the Influence of the Institutions, Thought & Culture of Rome, on Christianity & the Development of the Catholic Church. Beard, Charles, tr. LC 77-27170. (Hibbert Lectures: 1880). Repr. of 1898 ed. 24.50 (ISBN 0-404-60402-1). AMS Pr.

Renard, John, tr. IBN Abbad of Ronda, Letters on the Sufi Path. (Classics of Western Spirituality Ser.: No. 49). 256p. 1986. 12.95 (ISBN 0-8091-0365-6); pap. 9.95 (ISBN 0-8091-2730-X). Paulist PR.

Renard, Pierre. The Solar Revolution & the Prophet. (Testimonials Ser.). (Illus.). 193p. (Orig.). 1980. pap. 9.95 (ISBN 2-85566-135-8, Pub. by Prosveta France). Prosveta USA.

Renberg, Dalia H. The Complete Family Guide to Jewish Holidays. (Illus.). 256p. 1984. pap. 15.95 (ISBN 0-531-09408-1). Watts.

--The Complete Family Guide to Jewish Holidays. LC 84-11008. (Illus.). 1985. pap. 15.95 (ISBN 0-915361-09-4, 09408-1, Dist. by Watts). Adama Pubs Inc.

Rendahl, J. Stanley. Working with Older Adults. LC 84-80708. (Equipping Ser.). (Illus., Orig.). 1984. pap. 5.95 (ISBN 0-935797-08-4). Harvest IL.

Rendall, K. Norline. Just a Taste of Honey. (Quiet Time Bks.). 1975. pap. 3.50 (ISBN 0-8024-4494-6). Moody.

Rendel, Peter. Introduction to the Chakras. (Paths to Inner Power Ser). (Illus.). 1981. pap. 3.50 (ISBN 0-85030-161-0). Weiser.

Rendsburg, Gary, et al. The Bible World: Essays in Honor of Cyrus H. Gordon. 1981. 45.00x (ISBN 0-87068-758-1). Ktav.

Rendsburg, Gary A. Redaction of Genesis. xii, 132p. 1986. text ed. 12.50x (ISBN 0-931464-25-0). Eisenbrauns.

Rendtorff, Rolf. The Old Testament: An Introduction. Bowden, John, tr. LC 85-47728. (Ger.). 1986. 22.95 (ISBN 0-8006-0750-3). Fortress.

Rendtorff, Trutz. Ethics, Vol. 1: Basic Elements & Methodology in an Ethical Theology. Crimm, Keith, tr. LC 85-45484. 208p. 1986. 19.95 (ISBN 0-8006-0767-8, 1-767). Fortress.

Renee, Janine, jt. auth. see Fitch, Ed.

Rene-Jacques. Mont Saint-Michel. (Panorama Bks.). (Fr.). 62p. 3.95 (ISBN 0-685-23348-0). French & Eur.

Rengers, Christopher. The Youngest Prophet: The Life of Jacinta Marto, Fatima Visionary. LC 85-30789. 144p. (Orig.). 1986. pap. 5.95 (ISBN 0-8189-0496-8). Alba.

Renirkens, Clement. Love with Your Eyes Open. Lucas, Marc & Lucas, Claudia, trs. from Fr. LC 85-28669. 145p. (Orig.). 1986. pap. 7.95 (ISBN 0-8189-0491-7). Alba.

Renn, Walter, et al. The Treatment of the Holocaust in Textbooks: The Federal Republic of Germany, Israel, the United States. (Holocaust Studies). 288p. 1987. text ed. 30.00 (ISBN 0-88033-955-1). East Eur Quarterly.

Renner, Louis L. Father Tom of the Artic. LC 85-71951. (Illus.). 176p. (Orig.). 24.95 (ISBN 0-8323-0445-X); pap. 10.95 (ISBN 0-8323-0443-3). Binford-Metropolitan.

--The Knom: Father Jim Poole Story. LC 85-71950. (Illus.). 184p. (Orig.). 1985. pap. 8.95 (ISBN 0-8323-0444-1). Binford-Metropolitan.

Renno, John R. Circumstances That Caused Me to Leave the Amish Church. 54p. 1987. pap. 3.00 (ISBN 1-55618-021-7). Brunswick Pub.

Renou, Louis. Religions of Ancient India. 147p. Repr. of 1953 ed. text ed. 19.95x. Coronet Bks.

Renouf, Peter L. Lectures on the Origin & Growth of Religion as Illustrated by the Religion of Ancient Egypt. 2nd ed. LC 77-27171. (Hibbert Lectures: 1879). Repr. of 1884 ed. 30.00 (ISBN 0-404-60401-3). AMS Pr.

Renshaw, Betty, et al. Values & Voices. 3rd ed. 334p. 1986. pap. text ed. 16.95 (ISBN 0-03-071039-1, HoltC). HR&W.

Renu, Ma, ed. see Dass, Baba Hari.

Renwick, A. M. & Harman, A. M. The Story of the Church. 2nd. enl. ed. 272p. (Orig.). 1985. pap. 8.95 (ISBN 0-8028-0092-0). Eerdmans.

Reorganized Church of Jesus Christ of Latter Day Saints, Board of Publication Staff. Doctrine & Covenants. LC 78-134922. 1978. 14.00 (ISBN 0-8309-0204-X). Herald Hse.

Repass, Mary E. Faith Within the Hills. (Heritage Group Ser.). (Illus.). 1873. text ed. 15.00 (ISBN 0-940502-03-8). Foxhound Ent.

Repath, Ann, ed. see Schweitzer, Albert.

Reporting Tribunal Jurisprudence Committee. Matrimonial Jurisprudence United States, 1975-1976: Summaries of Selected Cases. 158p. (Orig.). 1977. pap. 3.50 (ISBN 0-943616-11-5). Canon Law Soc.

Reps, Paul. Square Sun Square Moon: A Collection of Prose Essays. LC 67-14277. (Illus., Orig.). 1967. pap. 6.50 (ISBN 0-8048-0544-X). C E Tuttle.

--Ten Ways to Meditate. LC 70-83639. (Illus.). 64p. 1981. 9.95 (ISBN 0-8348-0163-9). Weatherhill.

--Unwrinkling Plays. LC 65-12270. (Illus., Orig.). 1965. pap. 4.75 (ISBN 0-8048-0607-1). C E Tuttle.

--Zen Flesh, Zen Bones. LC 57-10199. (Illus.). 1957. 11.50 (ISBN 0-8048-0644-6). C E Tuttle.

--Zen Telegrams: Seventy-Nine Picture Poems. LC 59-8189. (Illus.). 1959. pap. 7.95 (ISBN 0-8048-0645-4). C E Tuttle.

Reps, Paul, ed. Zen Flesh, Zen Bones: A Collection of Zen & Pre-Zen Writings. pap. 3.95 (ISBN 0-385-08130-8, A233, Anch). Doubleday.

Rescher, Nicholas. Essays in Philosophical Analysis. LC 82-45160. (Illus.). 438p. 1982. pap. text ed. 17.75 (ISBN 0-8191-2459-1). U Pr of Amer.

--Pascal's Wager: A Study of Practical Reasoning in Philosophical Theology. LC 84-40820. 176p. 1985. text ed. 19.95 (ISBN 0-268-01556-2, 85-15561). U of Notre Dame Pr.

--Scepticism: A Critical Reappraisal. LC 79-22990. 265p. 1980. 30.00x (ISBN 0-8476-6240-3). Rowman.

Reschke, Meier M. Hugo Zuckermann: A Great Jewish Leader. LC 84-90055. 45p. 1985. 7.95 (ISBN 0-533-06136-9). Vantage.

Resource Publications, Inc. Staff. MusiCatalog. Cunningham, W. P., ed. 1978. pap. 54.90x (ISBN 0-89390-013-3). Resource Pubns.

Ressler, Martin E., et al. Lancaster County Churches in the Revolutionary War Era. Harrison, Matthew W., Jr., ed. LC 76-21210. (Illus.). 96p. 1976. pap. 3.50 (ISBN 0-915010-11-9, Co-Pub by Lancaster County Bicentennial Committee). Sutter House.

Rest, Friedrich. Fourteen Messages of Hope. (Pulpit Library). 96p. 1985. pap. 3.95 (ISBN 0-8010-7733-8). Baker Bk.

--Funeral Handbook. 144p. 1982. 9.95 (ISBN 0-8170-0929-9). Judson.

--Our Christian Symbols. LC 53-9923. (Illus.). 96p. 1954. pap. 3.25 (ISBN 0-8298-0099-9). Pilgrim NY.

--Our Christian Worship: Advent-Christmas. 1985. 4.75 (ISBN 0-89536-761-0, 5868). CSS of Ohio.

Rest, James R. Moral Development: Advances in Research & Theory. LC 86-21708. 241p. 1986. lib. bdg. 36.95 (ISBN 0-275-92254-5, C2254). Praeger.

Restivo, Sal. The Social Relations of Physics, Mysticism & Mathematics. 1983. lib. bdg. 49.50 (ISBN 90-277-1536-X, Pub. by Reidel Holland). Kluwer Academic.

--The Social Relations of Physics, Mysticism & Mathematics. (Pallas Paperbacks Ser.). 1985. pap. 14.95 (ISBN 90-277-2084-3, Pub. by Reidel Holland). Kluwer Academic.

Retzer, Fernon. You Can Understand the Bible. 1984. pap. 1.95 (ISBN 0-317-28295-6). Pacific Pr Pub Assn.

Reu, Johann M. The Augsburg Confession. LC 83-45650. Date not set. Repr. of 1930 ed. 76.50 (ISBN 0-404-19859-7). AMS Pr.

--Luther's German Bible. LC 83-45651. Date not set. Repr. of 1934 ed. 75.00 (ISBN 0-404-19860-0). AMS Pr.

--Thirty-Five Years of Luther Research. LC 79-13505. (Illus.). Repr. of 1917 ed. 16.50 (ISBN 0-404-05284-3). AMS Pr.

Reuchlin, Abelard. The True Authorship of the New Testament. 1979. pap. 4.00 (ISBN 0-930808-02-9). Vector Assocs.

Reuchlin, Johann. De Arte Cabbalistica. Goodman, Martin, tr. LC 77-86231. (Bilingual Editions of Classics in Philosophy & Science Ser.: No. 1). 1983. 20.00 (ISBN 0-913870-56-0). Abaris Bks.

Reuman, Robert E. Walls: Physical & Psychological. LC 66-24444. (Orig.). pap. 2.50x (ISBN 0-87574-147-9). Pendle Hill.

Reumann, John. Jesus in the Church's Gospels: Modern Scholarship & the Earliest Sources. LC 68-10983. 564p. 1973. pap. 9.95 (ISBN 0-8006-1091-1, 1-1091). Fortress.

--Righteousness in the New Testament: Justification in Lutheran-Catholic Dialogue. LC 81-43086. 320p. 1982. pap. 13.95 (ISBN 0-8006-1616-2, 1-1616). Fortress.

--Righteousness in the New Testament: Justification in Lutheran-Catholic Dialogue. LC 81-85385. 320p. (Orig.). 1982. pap. 13.95 (ISBN 0-8091-2436-X). Paulist Pr.

--The Supper of the Lord: The New Testament, Ecumenical Dialogues & Faith & Order on "Eucharist". LC 84-47932. 224p. 1984. pap. 13.95 (ISBN 0-8006-1816-5). Fortress.

Reumann, John, ed. see Conzelmann, Hans.

Reumann, John, ed. see Gunkel, Hermann.

Reumann, John, ed. see Hahn, Ferdinand.

Reumann, John, ed. & tr. see Jeremias, Joachim.

Reumann, John, ed. see Jeremias, Joachim.

Reumann, John, ed. see Lewis, C. S.

Reumann, John, ed. see Stendahl, Krister.

Reumann, John, et al, eds. Studies in Lutheran Hermeneutics. LC 78-14673. 352p. 1979. 15.95 (ISBN 0-8006-0534-9, 1-534). Fortress.

Reumann, John H., jt. ed. see Taylor, Walter F., Jr.

Reuss, Josef. The First Epistle to Timothy & the Second Epistle to Timothy. McKenzie, John L., ed. LC 81-605. (New Testament for Spiritual Reading Ser.). 171p. 1981. pap. 4.95 (ISBN 0-8245-0128-4). Crossroad NY.

Reutemann, Charles. Let's Pray: Fifty Services for Praying Communities. LC 75-197. 1975. pap. 5.95 (ISBN 0-9600824-1-7). St Marys.

--Let's Pray Two. LC 82-60612. (Illus.). 224p. (Orig.). 1982. pap. 6.95 (ISBN 0-88489-148-8). St Mary's.

Reuter, Timothy, ed. The Greatest Englishman: Essays on St. Boniface & the Church at Crediton. 140p. 1980. text ed. 15.00 (ISBN 0-85364-277-X). Attic Pr.

Reuterdahl, Arvid. Scientific Theism. 1926. 10.00 (ISBN 0-8159-6805-1). Devin.

Reutersward, Patrik. Forgotten Symbols of God: Five Essays Reprinted from Konsthistorisk Tidskrift. (Stockholm Studies in History of Art: No. 35). (Illus.). 152p. (Orig.). 1986. pap. text ed. 22.00x (Pub. by SPN Yugoslavia). Coronet Bks.

Revealed Book. Qur'an Made Easy. 132p. 1983. pap. 6.00 (ISBN 0-941724-09-3). Islamic Seminary.

Revell, E. J. Biblical Texts with Palestinian Pointing & Their Accents. LC 77-8893. (Society of Biblical Literature. Masoretic Studies). 1977. pap. 10.95 (ISBN 0-89130-141-0, 060504). Scholars Pr GA.

Revell, Peter. Fifteenth-Century English Prayers & Meditations: A Bibliography of Manuscripts Preserved at the British Museum Library. LC 75-6579. (Reference Library of Humanities: Vol. 19). 150p. 1975. lib. bdg. 28.00 (ISBN 0-8240-1098-1). Garland Pub.

Reventlow, Henning G. The Authority of the Bible & the Rise of the Modern World. Bowden, John, tr. from German. LC 83-48921. 688p. 1984. 42.95 (ISBN 0-8006-0288-9, 1-288). Fortress.

--Problems of Biblical Theology in the 20th Century. LC 86-4722. 1986. pap. 14.95 (ISBN 0-8006-1935-8, 1-1935). Fortress.

--Problems of Old Testament Theology in the Twentieth Century. Bowden, John, tr. LC 84-21178. 96p. 1985. 14.95 (ISBN 0-8006-1875-0, 1-1875). Fortress.

Reverend James Hawker & Sr. Thea Bowman. The Non-Catholic in the Catholic School. 1984. 4.20 (ISBN 0-318-18580-6); member 3.15. Natl Cath Educ.

Reverend Laurence Mancuso, tr. see Monks of New Skete.

Reverend Laurence Mancuso, tr. see Monks of New Skete Staff.

Reverend Mother Ruth. In Wisdom Thou Hast Made Them. Galanter, Patricia, ed. (Illus.). 141p. 1986. 15.95x (ISBN 0-937431-01-X). Adams Bannister Cox.

Revesz, Therese R. Witches. LC 77-10626. (Myth, Magic, & Superstition Ser.). (Illus.). 1977. PLB 14.65 (ISBN 0-8172-1034-2). Raintree Pubs.

Rev. Frederick K. Jelly. Madonna: Mary in the Catholic Tradition. LC 86-61598. 210p. (Orig.). 1986. pap. 7.50 (ISBN 0-87973-536-8, 536). Our Sunday Visitor.

Rev. Gene Ulses. The Wisdom of the Lord: Homilies for Weekdays & Feast Days. LC 86-60910. 254p. (Orig.). 1986. 12.95 (ISBN 0-87973-512-0, 512). Our Sunday Visitor.

Revill, Joseph N., jt. auth. see Larson, Clinton F.

Reville, Albert. The Life & Writings of Theodore Parker. 59.95 (ISBN 0-8490-0525-6). Gordon Pr.

--The Native Religions of Mexico & Peru: Hibbert Lectures. Wicksteed, Phillip H., tr. LC 77-27167. 224p. 1983. Repr. of 1884 ed. 29.50 (ISBN 0-404-60405-6). Ams Pr.

Reville, Albert D. Lectures on the Origin & Growth of Religion as Illustrated by the Native Religions of Mexico & Peru. 1977. lib. bdg. 59.95 (ISBN 0-8490-2140-5). Gordon Pr.

Reville, John C. Herald of Christ Louis Bourdaloue, S. J. 1978. Repr. of 1922 ed. lib. bdg. 25.00 (ISBN 0-8492-2270-2). R West.

Revoir, Trudie W. Christmas Workshop for the Church Family. 96p. 1982. pap. 6.95 (ISBN 0-8170-0963-9). Judson.

--Legends & Traditions of Christmas. (Illus.). 112p. 1985. pap. 5.95 (ISBN 0-8170-1082-3). Judson.

Rev. Robert Paul Mohan. A Book of Comfort: Thoughts in Late Evening. LC 86-60911. 118p. (Orig.). 1986. pap. 5.95 (ISBN 0-87973-541-4, 541). Our Sunday Visitor.

Rev. William F. Maestri. Living Securely with Insecurity. LC 86-60328. 185p. (Orig.). 1986. pap. 6.95 (ISBN 0-87973-543-0, 543). Our Sunday Visitor.

Rev. William Kramer. Evolution & Creation: A Catholic Understanding. LC 86-60907. 168p. (Orig.). 1986. pap. 6.95 (ISBN 0-87973-511-2, 511). Our Sunday Visitor.

Rew, Lois J. God's Green Liniment. LC 81-84183. (Illus.). 208p. (Orig.). 1981. pap. 5.95 (ISBN 0-938462-02-4). Green Leaf CA.

Rew, Lois J., ed. see Shannon, Foster H.

Rex, Barbara. Saints & Innocents. 1972. 6.95 (ISBN 0-393-08664-X). Norton.

Rexine, John E. An Explorer of Realms of Art, Life, & Thought: A Survey of the Works of Philosopher & Theologian Constantine Cavarnos. LC 85-81278. (Illus.). 184p. 1985. 9.00 (ISBN 0-914744-69-0, 85-81278); pap. 6.00 (ISBN 0-914744-70-4). Inst Byzantine.

--Religion in Plato & Cicero. LC 68-28581. 72p. Repr. of 1959 ed. lib. bdg. 22.50x (ISBN 0-8371-0198-0, RERP). Greenwood.

Rexroat, Stephen V. The Sunday School Spirit. LC 79-51833. (Workers Training Book of the Year Ser.). 128p. (Orig.). 1979. pap. 1.50 (ISBN 0-88243-594-9, 02-0594). Gospel Pub.

Rexroth, Kenneth, ed. The Buddhist Writings of Lafcadio Hearn. LC 77-2496. 312p. 1977. lib. bdg. 12.95 (ISBN 0-915520-05-2). Ross-Erikson.

Rey, Greta. Good Morning, Lord: Devotions for Young Teens. (Good Morning, Lord Ser.). 96p. 1983. 4.95 (ISBN 0-8010-7719-2). Baker Bk.

Reyburn, Hugh Y. John Calvin: His Life, Letters & Work. LC 83-45630. Date not set. Repr. of 1914 ed. 45.00 (ISBN 0-404-19847-3). AMS Pr.

Reyburn, William D., jt. auth. see Nida, Eugene A.

Reyes, Benito F. Dialogues with God: Sonnet Psalms on the Significance of Being Human. LC 78-244706. 139p. 1969. pap. 7.50 (ISBN 0-939375-37-0). World Univ Amer.

--The Essence of All Religions. 25p. 1983. pap. 3.00 (ISBN 0-939375-14-1). World Univ Amer.

--The Eternal Christ: Sonnet Prayer for the Second Coming. 18p. 1977. pap. 5.50 (ISBN 0-939375-00-1). World Univ Amer.

--Meditation: Cybernetics of Consciousness. Volz, Fred J., ed. 152p. 1978. pap. 7.50 (ISBN 0-939375-04-4). World Univ Amer.

--Moments Without Self. 4th ed. LC 61-21760. 198p. Date not set. Repr. of 1970 ed. 10.00 (ISBN 0-939375-36-2). World Univ Amer.

--Scientific Evidence of the Existence of the Soul. rev. ed. LC 70-122432. 1970. (Quest); pap. 7.50 (ISBN 0-8356-0404-7, Dist. by World Univ Amer). Theos Pub Hse.

Reymond, Robert. Brunner's Dialectic. 1967. pap. 0.75 (ISBN 0-87552-404-4). Presby & Reformed.

--The Justification of Knowledge. 1976. pap. 6.95 (ISBN 0-87552-406-0). Presby & Reformed.

Reyner, J. H. Gurdjieff in Action. 117p. 1982. 12.95 (ISBN 0-04-294117-2). Allen Unwin.

--Ouspensky: The Unsung Genius. 115p. 1982. 14.95 (ISBN 0-04-294122-9). Allen Unwin.

Reynolds, A., ed. see Huggett, Joyce.

Reynolds, A., ed. see Warren, Norman.

Reynolds, Blair. Manner & Method: A Translation of the French Reformed Church's Liturgy. 85p. (Orig.). 1985. pap. 6.95x (ISBN 0-932269-40-0). Wyndham Hall.

Reynolds, Bonnie J., jt. auth. see Choudhury, Bikram.

Reynolds, Brian & Northeast Center for Youth Ministry Staff. A Chance to Serve: Peer Minister's Handbook. (Illus.). 75p. (Orig.). 1983. pap. 4.95 (ISBN 0-88489-154-2); pap. 9.95 leader's manual (ISBN 0-88489-153-4). St Mary's.

Reynolds, David K. Naikan Psychotherapy: Meditation for Self-Development. LC 82-21862. 184p. 1983. 17.50x (ISBN 0-226-71029-7). U of Chicago Pr.

Reynolds, David S. Faith in Fiction: The Emergence of Religious Literature in America. LC 80-20885. 304p. 1981. text ed. 25.00x (ISBN 0-674-29172-7). Harvard U Pr.

Reynolds, E. E. The Life of Saint Francis of Assisi. 128p. 1983. pap. 5.95 (ISBN 0-87061-081-3). Chr Classics.

Reynolds, E. E., ed. see More, Thomas.

Reynolds, Erma. Bible Events Quiz Book. (Quiz & Puzzle Bks.). 96p. 1985. pap. 3.50 (ISBN 0-8010-7734-6). Baker Bk.

--Bible People Quiz Book. (Quiz & Puzzle Books). 1979. pap. 2.95 (ISBN 0-8010-7692-7). Baker Bk.

--Intriguing Bible Quizzes. (Quiz & Puzzle Books). 112p. 1976. pap. 2.95 (ISBN 0-8010-7640-4). Baker Bk.

--One Hundred One Bible Action Games. 64p. 1986. pap. 3.95 (ISBN 0-87403-017-X, 2801). Standard Pub.

Reynolds, Ernest E. Thomas More & Erasmus. LC 65-26739. x, 260p. 1966. 25.00 (ISBN 0-8232-0670-X). Fordham.

Reynolds, Frank E. & Capps, Donald, eds. The Biographical Process: Studies in the History & Psychology of Religion. (Religion & Reason, Method & Theory in the Study & Interpretation of Religion: No. 11). 1976. text ed. 51.50x (ISBN 90-2797-522-1). Mouton.

Reynolds, Frank E., jt. ed. see Moore, Robert L.

Reynolds, Frank E., et al. Guide to Buddhist Religion. 440p. 1981. lib. bdg. 57.50 (ISBN 0-8161-7900-X, Hall Reference). G K Hall.

Reynolds, George & Sjodahl, Janne M. Commentary on the Book of Mormon, 7 vols. Vol. 1. 9.95 (ISBN 0-87747-039-1); Vol. 2. 9.95 (ISBN 0-87747-040-5); Vol. 3. 9.95 (ISBN 0-87747-041-3); Vol. 4. 9.95 (ISBN 0-87747-042-1); Vol. 5. 9.95 (ISBN 0-87747-043-X); Vol. 6. 9.95 (ISBN 0-87747-044-8); Vol. 7. 9.95 (ISBN 0-87747-045-6). Deseret Bk.

--Commentary on the Pearl of Great Price. 9.95 (ISBN 0-87747-046-4). Deseret Bk.

Reynolds, James A. Catholic Emancipation Crisis in Ireland, 1823-1829. Repr. of 1954 ed. lib. bdg. 22.50x (ISBN 0-8371-3141-3, RECE). Greenwood.

Reynolds, John, ed. & tr. see Norbu, Namkhai.

Reynolds, Joyce. Puppet Shows That Reach & Teach Children, 3 vols. LC 73-185586. (Illus.). 1974. Vol. 1. pap. 3.50 (ISBN 0-88243-740-2, 02-0740); Vol. 2. pap. 3.50 (ISBN 0-88243-741-0, 02-0741); Vol. 3. pap. 3.50 (ISBN 0-88243-744-5, 02-0744). Gospel Pub.

--The Search for the True Meaning of Christmas. (Illus.). 1977. pap. text ed. 2.25 (ISBN 0-88243-100-5, 30-0100). Gospel Pub.

Reynolds, Lillian R. No Retirement: Devotions on Christian Discipleship for Older People. LC 83-48916. 96p. 1984. pap. 4.50 (ISBN 0-8006-1779-7, 1-1779). Fortress.

Reynolds, Louis B. We Have Tomorrow. Woolsey, Raymond H., ed. 480p. 1984. 19.95 (ISBN 0-8280-0232-0). Review & Herald.

Reynolds, R. & Ekstrom, Rosemary. Concise Catholic Dictionary Shortened Titles on Reprints. 224p. 1982. pap. 3.95 (ISBN 0-89622-159-8). Twenty-Third.

Reynolds, R. Gene. Assurance. 128p. 1982. pap. 3.95 (ISBN 0-8423-0088-0). Tyndale.

Reynolds, Ralph V. All Things to All Men. Wallace, Mary H., ed. 128p. 1983. pap. 4.95 (ISBN 0-912315-01-6). Word Aflame.

--Truth Shall Triumph. 9th ed. 111p. 1983. pap. 2.95 (ISBN 0-912315-07-5). Word Aflame.

--Upon the Potter's Wheel. Wallace, Mary H., ed. LC 85-31583. 144p. (Orig.). 1981. pap. 4.95 (ISBN 0-912315-22-9). Word Aflame.

Reynolds, Reginald. John Woolman & the Twentieth Century. 1983. pap. 2.50x (ISBN 0-87574-096-0, 096). Pendle Hill.

--The Wisdom of John Woolman: With a Selection from His Writings As a Guide to the Seekers of Today. LC 79-8724. xii, 178p. 1981. Repr. of 1948 ed. lib. bdg. 22.50x (ISBN 0-313-22190-1, REJW). Greenwood.

Reynolds, Roger E. The Ordinals of Christ from Their Origins to the Twelfth Century. 1978. 55.00x (ISBN 3-11-007058-8). De Gruyter.

Reynolds, Thomas L., Jr. Youth's Search for Self. LC 82-70866. (Orig.). 1983. pap. 4.50 (ISBN 0-8054-5338-5, 4253-38). Broadman.

Reynolds, Vernon & Tanner, Ralph E. The Biology of Religion. LC 82-6573. (Illus.). 321p. 1983. text ed. 31.95x (ISBN 0-582-30021-5). Longman.

Reynolds, William J. Companion to Baptist Hymnal: 1975 Edition. LC 75-39449. 480p. 1976. bds. 16.95 (ISBN 0-8054-6808-0). Broadman.

--Hymns of Our Faith. LC 64-14049. 1964. 18.95 (ISBN 0-8054-6805-6). Broadman.

Reynolds, William J. & Price, Milburn. A Joyful Sound: Christian Hymnody. 2nd ed. LC 77-12048. 1978. 26.95 (ISBN 0-03-040831-8, HoltC). HR&W.

Reznikoff, Charles, tr. see Benjamin, Israel B.

Rezy, Carol. Liturgies for Little Ones: Thirty-Eight Complete Celebrations for Grades One Through Three. LC 78-59926. (Illus.). 160p. 1978. pap. 4.95 (ISBN 0-87793-160-7). Ave Maria.

Rhein, Francis B. Understanding the New Testament. LC 65-23532. 1974. pap. text ed. 6.95 (ISBN 0-8120-0027-7). Barron.

Rhie, Marylin M. Fo-Kuang Ssu: Literary Evidences & Buddhist Images. LC 76-23690. (Outstanding Dissertations in the Fine Arts - Far Eastern). (Illus.). 1977. Repr. of 1970 ed. lib. bdg. 55.00 (ISBN 0-8240-2721-3). Garland Pub.

Rhoades, Gale R. Waybill to Lost Spanish Signs & Symbols. (Illus., Orig.). 1982. pap. 6.00 (ISBN 0-942688-02-3). Dream Garden.

Rhoads, David, jt. auth. see Michie, Donald.

Rhodes, Arnold B. Mighty Acts of God. (Orig.). 1964. pap. 7.95 (ISBN 0-8042-9010-5); tchrs' ed. 6.95 (ISBN 0-8042-9012-1). John Knox.

--Psalms. LC 59-10454. (Layman's Bible Commentary Ser: Vol. 9). 1960. 4.25 (ISBN 0-8042-3009-9); pap. 4.95 (ISBN 0-8042-3069-2). John Knox.

Rhodes, Bennie. Calculator Word Games. LC 77-8870. 1977. pap. 2.95 (ISBN 0-915134-39-X). Mott Media.

Rhodes, Erroll F., tr. see Aland, Kurt & Aland, Barbara.

Rhodes, Erroll F., tr. see Wurthwein, Ernst.

Rhodes, H. T. The Satanic Mass. 256p. 1974. 7.95 (ISBN 0-8065-0405-6). Citadel Pr.

--The Satanic Mass. 254p. 1975. pap. 3.95 (ISBN 0-8065-0484-6). Citadel Pr.

Rhodes, John, ed. Christmas: A Celebration. 1986. 15.95 (ISBN 0-571-13752-0). Faber & Faber.

Rhodes, Royal W., jt. auth. see Baly, Denis.

Rhodin, Victoria, tr. see Zink, Jorg.

Rhymes, Douglas A. Through Prayer to Reality. LC 74-81813. 1976. pap. 3.95 (ISBN 0-88489-088-0). St Mary's.

Rhyne, C. Thomas. Faith Establishes the Law. Kee, Howard, ed. LC 81-1794. (Society of Biblical Literature Dissertation Ser.). 1981. pap. 13.50 (ISBN 0-89130-483-5, 06-01-55). Scholars Pr GA.

Rhys, John. Lectures on the Origin & Growth of Religion as Illustrated by Celtic Heathendom. LC 77-27165. (Hibbert Lectures: 1886). Repr. of 1898 ed. 53.00 (ISBN 0-404-60407-2). AMS Pr.

Rhys, Stephen & Palmer, King. ABC of Church Music. LC 73-83175. 1969. 7.50 (ISBN 0-8008-0010-9, Crescendo). Taplinger.

Riano, J. F. Critical & Biographical Notes on Early Spanish Music. LC 79-158958. (Music Ser.). 1971. Repr. of 1887 ed. lib. bdg. 29.50 (ISBN 0-306-70193-6). Da Capo.

Ribadeneira, Pedro. Bibliotheca Scriptorum Societatis Jesu. 1022p. Date not set. Repr. of 1676 ed. text ed. 207.00x (ISBN 0-576-78529-6, Pub. by Gregg Intl Pubs England). Gregg Intl.

Ribalow, Harld V. & Ribalow, Meir. The Jewish Baseball Stars. (Illus.). 1984. 12.95 (ISBN 0-88254-898-0). Hippocrene Bks.

Ribalow, Harold, jt. auth. see Caplan, Samuel.

Ribalow, Meir, jt. auth. see Ribalow, Harld V.

Ribberbos, Herman N. Coming of the Kingdom. 1962. pap. 11.95 (ISBN 0-87552-408-7). Presby & Reformed.

Ribuffo, Leo. The Old Christian Right: The Protestant Far Right from the Great Depression to the Cold War. 277p. 1983. 29.95 (ISBN 0-87722-297-5). Temple U Pr.

Ricapito, Joseph V., tr. from Span. see Valdes, Alfonso de.

Ricard, Robert. The Spiritual Conquest of Mexico: An Essay on the Apostolate & the Evangelizing Methods of the Mendicant Orders in New Spain, 1523-1572. Simpson, Lesley B., tr. from Sp. (California Library Reprint Ser.: No. 57). (Illus.). 435p. 1974. pap. 9.95 (ISBN 0-520-04784-2, CAL 593). U of Cal Pr.

Riccardo, Martin V. Mystical Consciousness: Exploring an Extraordinary State of Awareness. 1977. pap. 5.00 (ISBN 0-686-19170-6). MVR Bks.

Ricci, Matteo. The True Meaning of the Lord of Heaven. Lancashire, Douglas & Hu Kuo-chen, Peter, trs. Malatesta, Edward J., ed. LC 84-80944. (Jesuit Primary Sources in English Translations Series I: No. 6). (Eng. & Chinese., Illus.). 300p. 1985. 39.00 (ISBN 0-912422-78-5); smyth sewn 34.00 (ISBN 0-912422-77-7). Inst Jesuit.

Ricciardi, Antonio. St. Maximilian Kolbe. Daughters of St. Paul, tr. from Ital. (Illus.). 314p. 1982. 7.95 (ISBN 0-8198-6838-8, ST0283); pap. 6.50 (ISBN 0-8198-6837-X). Dghtrs St Paul.

Rice, Cathy. Singing in Signs. LC 81-18830. 160p. 1982. 7.95 (ISBN 0-8407-9006-6). Nelson.

Rice, Charles, jt. auth. see Collins, Adela Y.

Rice, Charles E. Beyond Abortion: The Origin & Future of the Secular State. 1978. 5.25 (ISBN 0-8199-0696-4). Franciscan Herald.

Rice, David G. & Stambaugh, John E. Sources for the Study of Greek Religion. LC 79-18389. (Society of Biblical Literature. Sources for Biblical Study Ser.: No. 14). 1979. pap. 9.95 (ISBN 0-89130-347-2, 060314). Scholars Pr GA.

Rice, Don, ed. The New Testament: A Pictorial Archive from Nineteenth-Century Sources. (Pictorial Archive Ser.). (Illus.). 192p. (Orig.). 1986. pap. 7.95 (ISBN 0-486-25073-3). Dover.

Rice, Edward. American Saints & Seers: American-Born Religions & the Genius Behind Them. LC 81-15293. (Illus.). 240p. 1982. 11.95 (ISBN 0-02-775980-6, Four Winds). Macmillan.

--Ten Religions of the East. LC 78-6186. (Illus.). 160p. 1978. 8.95 (ISBN 0-02-776210-6, Four Winds). Macmillan.

Rice, Edwin W. Sunday-School Movement, 1780-1917, & the American Sunday-School Union, 1817-1917. LC 70-165728. (American Education Ser, No. 2). (Illus.). 1971. Repr. of 1917 ed. 36.00 (ISBN 0-405-03717-1). Ayer Co Pubs.

Rice, Eugene F., Jr. Saint Jerome in the Renaissance. LC 84-21321. (Symposia in Comparative History Ser.: No. 13). (Illus.). 272p. 1985. text ed. 24.00x (ISBN 0-8018-2381-1). Johns Hopkins.

Rice, F. Philip. Sexual Problems in Marriage: Help from a Christian Counselor. LC 77-27443. 252p. 1978. softcover 6.95 (ISBN 0-664-24194-8). Westminster.

Rice, George. Luke, a Plagiarist. (Anchor Ser.). 1984. pap. 6.95 (ISBN 0-8163-0542-0). Pacific Pr Pub Assn.

Rice, George E. Christ in Colision. (Harvest Ser.). 112p. 1982. pap. 4.95 (ISBN 0-8163-0473-4). Pacific Pr Pub Assn.

Rice, Helen S. Everyone Needs Someone: Poems of Love & Friendship. 80p. 1973. 8.95 (ISBN 0-8007-0966-7). Revell.

--Heart Gifts from Helen Steiner Rice. LC 68-28438. (Illus.). 96p. 1968. 8.95 (ISBN 0-8007-0133-X). Revell.

--In the Vineyard of the Lord. (Illus.). 160p. 1979. 12.95 (ISBN 0-8007-1036-3). Revell.

--Life Is Forever. (Illus.). 32p. 1974. 8.95 (ISBN 0-8007-0681-1). Revell.

--Love. (Illus.). 128p. 1980. 12.95 (ISBN 0-8007-1072-X). Revell.

--Loving Promises. (Illus.). 128p. 1975. 12.95 (ISBN 0-8007-0736-2); large-print ed., 176p. 12.95 (ISBN 0-8007-1333-8). Revell.

--Mothers are a Gift of Love. (Illus.). 128p. 1980. 12.95 (ISBN 0-8007-1135-1). Revell.

--Somebody Loves You. 128p. 1976. 12.95 (ISBN 0-8007-0818-0); large-print ed. 10.95 (ISBN 0-8007-1120-3). Revell.

--Someone Cares: The Collected Poems of Helen Steiner Rice. 128p. 1972. 12.95 (ISBN 0-8007-0524-6); large-print ed. 12.95 (ISBN 0-8007-0959-4). Revell.

Rice, Helen S., jt. auth. see Allen, Charles L.

Rice, Hugh A. L. Thomas Ken: Bishop & Non-Juror. LC 58-4172. 1958. 10.00x (ISBN 0-8401-2008-7). A R Allenson.

Rice, John R. When a Christian Sins. 1954. pap. 3.50 (ISBN 0-8024-9434-X). Moody.

Rice, Joyce G. Love Never Ends. pap. 3.95 (ISBN 0-89036-147-9). Hawkes Pub Inc.

Rice, Max M. Your Rewards in Heaven. LC 80-68885. 160p. 1981. pap. 4.95 (ISBN 0-89636-063-6). Accent Bks.

Rice, Max M. & Rice, Vivian B. When Can I Say, "I Love You"? LC 76-54926. 1977. pap. 4.95 (ISBN 0-8024-9436-6). Moody.

Rice, N. L., jt. auth. see Blanchard, Jonathan.

Rice, Paul & Rice, Valeta. Cancer: Through the Numbers. 40p. 1983. pap. 2.00 (ISBN 0-87728-568-3). Weiser.

Rice, Philip B. On the Knowledge of Good & Evil. LC 75-8968. 299p. 1975. Repr. of 1955 ed. lib. bdg. 22.50x (ISBN 0-8371-8124-0, RIGE). Greenwood.

Rice, Richard. God's Foreknowledge & Man's Free Will. 128p. (Orig.). 1985. pap. 4.95 (ISBN 0-87123-845-4, 210845). Bethany Hse.

--The Reign of God: An Introduction to Christian Theology from a Seventh-Day Adventist Perspective. LC 85-70344. 400p. 1985. text ed. 23.95 (ISBN 0-943872-90-1). Andrews Univ Pr.

--When Bad Happens to God's People. 1984. pap. 4.95 (ISBN 0-8163-0570-6). Pacific Pr Pub Assn.

Rice, Valeta, jt. auth. see Rice, Paul.

Rice, Vivian B., jt. auth. see Rice, Max M.

Rice, Wayne. Great Ideas for Small Youth Groups. 256p. (Orig.). 1985. pap. 7.95 (ISBN 0-310-34891-9, 10823P). Zondervan.

--Junior High Ministry. 220p. 1987. text ed. 12.95 (ISBN 0-310-34970-2). Zondervan.

--Junior High Ministry: A Guidebook for the Leading & Teaching of Early Adolescents. 1978. pap. 6.95 (ISBN 0-310-34971-0, 10825P). Zondervan.

--The Youth Specialties Clip Art Book. 240p. (Orig.). 1985. pap. 14.95 (ISBN 0-310-34911-7, 10824P). Zondervan.

Rice, Wayne & Yaconelli, Mike. Far Out Ideas for Young Groups. 96p. 1975. pap. 6.95 (ISBN 0-310-34941-9, 10797P). Zondervan.

--Incredible Ideas for Youth Groups. 160p. (Orig.). 1982. pap. 7.95 (ISBN 0-310-45231-7, 11370P). Zondervan.

--Play It: Team Games for Groups. 256p. 1986. pap. 10.95 (ISBN 0-310-35191-X, 10799). Zondervan.

--Right-on Ideas for Youth Groups. (Illus.). 96p. 1973. pap. 6.95 (ISBN 0-310-34951-6, 10796P). Zondervan.

--Super Ideas for Youth Groups. (Orig.). 1979. pap. 6.95 (ISBN 0-310-34981-8, 10773P). Zondervan.

--Tension Getters. 128p. (Orig.). (YA) 1985. pap. 6.95 (ISBN 0-310-45241-4, 11371P). Zondervan.

--Tension Getters II. rev. ed. (Orig.). 1985. pap. 6.95 (ISBN 0-310-34931-1, 10774P). Zondervan.

--Way Out Ideas for Youth Groups. pap. 6.95 (ISBN 0-310-34961-3, 10795P). Zondervan.

Rice, Wayne, jt. auth. see Yaconelli, Mike.

Rice, Wayne, ed. Ideas, 39 vols. (Ideas Library). (Illus.). 52p. (Orig.). pap. 7.95 ea.; Set. pap. 140.00 (ISBN 0-910125-00-7); index o.p. 6.95 (ISBN 0-910125-01-5). Youth Special.

Rice, Wayne, compiled by. The Youth Specialties Clip Art Book, Vol. II. 112p. 1987. pap. 14.95 (ISBN 0-310-39791-X). Zondervan.

Rice, Wayne, et al. Fun-N-Games. 1977. pap. 6.95 (ISBN 0-310-35001-8, 10798P). Zondervan.

Rice, William C., jt. auth. see Lovelace, Austin C.

Rice Handford, Elisabeth see Handford, Elisabeth R.

Rich, Charles. The Embrace of the Soul: Reflections on the Song of Songs. LC 83-23066. 1984. pap. 3.50 (ISBN 0-932506-31-3). St Bedes Pubns.

Rich, Elaine S. Mennonite Women: A Story of God's Faithfulness. LC 82-15452. 256p. 1983. pap. 9.95 (ISBN 0-8361-3311-0). Herald Pr.

Rich, George. God Pursues a Priest. 60p. (Orig.). 1986. pap. 2.95 (ISBN 0-87227-109-9). Reg Baptist.

Rich, Jane K. & Blake, Nelson M., eds. A Lasting Spring: Jessie Catherine Kinsley, Daughter of the Oneida Community. LC 82-19200. (York State Bks.). (Illus.). 300p. (Orig.). 1983. 32.00x (ISBN 0-8156-0183-2); pap. 14.95 (ISBN 0-8156-0176-X). Syracuse U Pr.

Rich, Marion K. Where Love is Found. 124p. (Orig.). 1984. pap. 5.95 (ISBN 0-8341-0922-0). Beacon Hill.

Rich, Russell R. Ensign to the Nations: A History of the LDS Church from 1846 to 1972. LC 72-91730. (Illus.). 680p. 1972. pap. 9.95 (ISBN 0-8425-0671-3). Brigham.

Rich, Vera, jt. auth. see Blum, Jakub.

Richabhchand. Integral Yoga of Sri Aurobindo. 2nd ed. 1979. 20.00 (ISBN 0-89744-939-8); pap. 16.00 (ISBN 0-89744-940-1). Auromere.

Richard, Dwight Peter, jt. auth. see Gentle, Jimmie.

Richard, Earl. Acts Six: One to Eight, Four - The Authors Method of Composition. LC 78-12926. (Society of Biblical Literature. Dissertation Ser.: No. 41). (Orig.). 1978. pap. 10.95 (ISBN 0-89130-261-1, 06-01-41). Scholars Pr GA.

Richard, H. M. Skeptic & the Ten Commandments. (Uplook Ser.). 1981. pap. 0.99 (ISBN 0-686-79998-4). Pacific Pr Pub Assn.

Richard, J. The Latin Kingdom of Jerusalem, 2 Pts. (Europe in the Middle Ages Selected Studies: Vol. 11). 514p. 1978. Set. 91.50 (ISBN 0-444-85092-9, North-Holland). Elsevier.

Richard, James W. The Confessional History of the Lutheran Church. LC 83-45672. Date not set. Repr. of 1909 ed. 62.50 (ISBN 0-404-19861-9). AMS Pr.

--Philip Melanchthon, the Protestant Preceptor of Germany. LC 72-82414. 1974. Repr. of 1898 ed. lib. bdg. 25.50 (ISBN 0-8337-4341-4). B Franklin.

Richard, Jean. Le Royaume Latin de Jerusalem. LC 78-63359. (The Crusades & Military Orders: Second Ser.). Repr. of 1953 ed. 28.50 (ISBN 0-404-17029-3). AMS Pr.

Richard, Lucien. What Are They Saying about Christ & World Religions? LC 81-80878. 96p. (Orig.). 1981. pap. 4.95 (ISBN 0-8091-2391-6). Paulist Pr.

Richard, Lucien J. A Kenotic Christology: In the Humanity of Jesus the Christ, the Compassion of Our God. LC 80-40915. 342p. (Orig.). 1982. lib. bdg. 32.00 (ISBN 0-8191-2199-1); pap. text ed. 14.50 (ISBN 0-8191-2200-9). U Pr of Amer.

Richard Of St. Victor, et al. Cell of Self-Knowledge. Gardner, E. G., ed. LC 66-25702. (Medieval Library). Repr. of 1926 ed. 17.50x (ISBN 0-8154-0188-4). Cooper Sq.

Richard, Pablo, et al. The Idols of Death & the God of Life: A Theology. Campbell, Barbara E. & Shepard, Bonnie, trs. from Span. LC 83-6788. Tr. of La Lucha de los Dioses: la Idolos de la Opresion y la Busqueda del Dios Liberador. 240p. (Orig.). 1983. pap. 12.95 (ISBN 0-88344-048-2). Orbis Bks.

Richard, Paul. Seven Steps to the New Age. 1979. pap. 3.95 (ISBN 0-89744-131-1, Pub. by Ganesh & Co India). Auromere.

Richard, Van Den Tak see Van Den Tak, Richard.

Richards, Colin, ed. New Directions in Primary Education. 310p. 1982. text ed. 30.00x (ISBN 0-905273-27-3, Falmer Pr); pap. 16.00x (ISBN 0-905273-26-5). Taylor & Francis.

Richards, D. S. Islamic Civilization, Nine Fifty - Eleven Fifty. 284p. 1983. 50.00x (ISBN 0-317-39090-2, Pub. by Luzac & Co Ltd). State Mutual Bk.

Richards, David A. Toleration & the Constitution. LC 86-2358. 288p. 1986. 29.95x (ISBN 0-19-504018-X). Oxford U Pr.

Richards, Elton P., Jr. Outreach Preaching: The Role of Preaching in Evangelism. 56p. (Orig.). 1986. pap. 4.25 (ISBN 0-8066-2232-6, 10-4859). Augsburg.

Richards, Franklin D. The Challenge & the Harvest. LC 82-74368. 208p. 1983. 7.95 (ISBN 0-87747-939-9). Deseret Bk.

Richards, Gertrude R., ed. see Davison, Ellen S.

Richards, Glyn, ed. A Source Book of Modern Hinduism. 220p. 1985. 20.00 (ISBN 0-7007-0173-7). Salem Hse Pubs.

Richards, H. M., Jr. Angels: Secret Agents of God & Satan. LC 80-22223. (Flame Ser.). 64p. 1980. pap. 0.99 (ISBN 0-8127-0313-8). Review & Herald.

--Faith & Prayer. (Uplook Ser.). 32p. 1971. pap. 0.79 (ISBN 0-8163-0071-2, 06010-3). Pacific Pr Pub Assn.

Richards, Harold. Earthquake. LC 79-13559. (Flame Ser.). 1979. pap. 0.99 (ISBN 0-8127-0240-9). Review & Herald.

Richards, Harriet. Light Your Own Lamp. LC 66-26971. 1967. 5.95 (ISBN 0-8022-1333-2). Philos Lib.

Richards, Hubert J. Death & After: What Will Really Happen? (What Really Happened? Ser.). 1987. pap. 5.95 (ISBN 0-89622-288-8). Twenty-Third.

--The First Christmas: What Really Happened? (What Really Happened? Ser.). 128p. 1986. pap. 5.95 (ISBN 0-89622-289-6). Twenty-Third.

--The First Easter: What Really Happened? (What Really Happened? Ser.). 144p. 1986. pap. 5.95 (ISBN 0-89622-282-9). Twenty-Third.

--The Miracles of Jesus: What Really Happened? (What Really Happened? Ser.). 128p. 1986. pap. 5.95 (ISBN 0-89622-287-X). Twenty-Third.

Richards, Jean. We Can Share God's Love. 80p. 1984. pap. 2.95 (ISBN 0-8170-1010-6). Judson.

Richards, Jean H. A Boy Named Jesus. LC 77-71036. (Illus.). 1978. 3.95 (ISBN 0-8054-4415-7, 4244-15); film & cassette 19.00 (4436-38). Broadman.

--Jesus Went about Doing Good. LC 80-70475. 1983. 5.95 (ISBN 0-8054-4289-8, 4242-89). Broadman.

Richards, Jeffrey. Consul of God. 1980. 27.95x (ISBN 0-7100-0346-3). Methuen Inc.

Richards, Katharine L. How Christmas Came to the Sunday-Schools: The Observance of Christmas in the Protestant Church Schools of the United States. LC 70-159860. 1971. Repr. of 1934 ed. 40.00x (ISBN 0-8103-3793-2). Gale.

Richards, Ken. Walking Through the Bible with H. M. S. Richards. 384p. 1983. 9.95 (ISBN 0-8163-0433-5). Pacific Pr Pub Assn.

Richards, Kent, ed. Society of Biblical Literature Nineteen Eighty-One: Seminar Papers. (SBL Seminar Papers & Abstracts). pap. 9.00 (ISBN 0-89130-548-3, 06-09-20). Scholars Pr GA.

Richards, Kent, ed. see Crossan, John D.

Richards, Kent, ed. see Hynes, William J.

Richards, Kent H., ed. Society of Biblical Literature: Seminar Papers Nineteen Eighty-Four. 412p. 1984. pap. 15.00 (ISBN 0-89130-810-5, 06 09 23). Scholars Pr GA.

--Society of Biblical Literature: Seminar Papers Nineteen Eighty-Three. (SBL Seminar Papers). 490p. 1983. pap. 15.00 (ISBN 0-89130-607-2, 06 09 22). Scholars Pr GA.

Richards, Larry. The Dictionary of Basic Bible Truths. 528p. 1987. pap. 14.95 (ISBN 0-310-43521-8). Zondervan.

--International Children's Bible Handbook. LC 86-5995. (Illus.). 1986. 13.95 (ISBN 0-8344-0133-9, BB600C). Sweet.

--Love Your Neighbor: A Woman's Workshop on Fellowship. Kobobel, Janet, ed. 144p. 1986. pap. 3.95 (18139). Zondervan.

--Pass It on. LC 77-87260. (Bible Alive Ser.). (Illus.). 1978. pap. text ed. 2.95 (ISBN 0-89191-089-1); tchr's ed. 3.95 (ISBN 0-89191-090-5). Cook.

--Personal Ministry Handbook. 224p. 1986. pap. 9.95 (ISBN 0-8010-7736-2). Baker Bk.

--Teaching Youth. 156p. 1982. pap. 4.95 (ISBN 0-8341-0776-7). Beacon Hill.

--Tomorrow Today. 132p. 1986. pap. 4.95 (ISBN 0-89693-505-1). Victor Bks.

--When It Hurts Too Much to Wait: Understanding God's Timing. 160p. 1985. 9.95 (ISBN 0-8499-0489-7, 0489-7). Word Bks.

--Years of Darkness, Days of Glory. LC 76-6582. (Bible Alive Ser). (Illus.). 1977. pap. text ed. 2.95 (ISBN 0-912692-97-9); tchr's. ed. o.p. 3.95 (ISBN 0-912692-96-0). Cook.

Richards, Lawrence & Martin, Gib. Theology of Personal Ministry. 272p. 1981. 17.95 (ISBN 0-310-31970-6, 18137). Zondervan.

Richards, Lawrence O. The Believer's Guidebook from Aspirin to Zoos. 528p. 1983. 9.95 (ISBN 0-310-43470-X, 18163). Zondervan.

--The Believer's Praise Book. 1986. pap. 2.50 (ISBN 0-310-43512-9, 18204P). Zondervan.

--The Believer's Prayer Book. 1986. pap. 2.50 (ISBN 0-310-43602-8, 18213P). Zondervan.

--Believer's Promise Book. 80p. (Orig.). 1984. pap. 2.50 (ISBN 0-310-43462-9, 18144P). Zondervan.

--The Christian Man's Promise Book. 1986. pap. 2.50 (ISBN 0-310-43582-X, 18211P). Zondervan.

--The Christian Woman's Promise Book. 1986. pap. 2.50 (ISBN 0-310-43592-7, 18212P). Zondervan.

--Creative Bible Study. 1979. pap. 5.95 (ISBN 0-310-31911-0, 10711P). Zondervan.

--Creative Bible Teaching. LC 74-104830. 1970. 12.95 (ISBN 0-8024-1640-3). Moody.

--Expository Dictionary of Bible Words. 596p. 1985. 24.95 (ISBN 0-310-39000-1, 18300). Zondervan.

--How Far I Can Go. (Answers for Youth Ser.). 1980. pap. 4.95 (ISBN 0-310-38951-8, 18025P). Zondervan.

--How I Can Be Real. (Answers for Youth Ser.). 1980. pap. 4.95 (ISBN 0-310-38971-2, 18207P). Zondervan.

--How I Can Experience God. (Answers for Youth Ser.). 1980. pap. 4.95 (ISBN 0-310-38991-7, 18209P). Zondervan.

--How I Can Make Decisions. (Answers for Youth Ser.). 1980. pap. 4.95 (ISBN 0-310-38981-X, 18208P). Zondervan.

--Love Your Neighbour: A Woman's Workshop on Fellowship. (Woman's Workshop Ser.). 160p. (Orig.). 1981. pap. 3.95 (ISBN 0-310-43451-3, 18139P). Zondervan.

--Sixty Nine Ways to Start a Study Group & Keep It Growing. 2nd ed. 144p. 1980. pap. 3.95 (ISBN 0-310-31981-1, 18138P). Zondervan.

--A Theology of Christian Education. 320p. 1975. 17.95 (ISBN 0-310-31940-4, 18135). Zondervan.

--The Word Bible Handbook. 1982. 10.95 (ISBN 0-8499-0279-7). Word Bks.

--The Word Parents Handbook. 1983. 9.95 (ISBN 0-8499-0328-9). Word Bks.

--Youth Ministry: Its Renewal In the Local Church. rev. ed. 1972. 15.95 (ISBN 0-310-32010-0). Zondervan.

Richards, Lawrence O. & Hoeldtke, Clyde. A Theology of Church Leadership. (Illus.). 352p. 1980. 17.95 (ISBN 0-310-31960-9, 18136). Zondervan.

Richards, Lawrence O. & LeFever, Marlene D. Nurturing My Students. (Complete Teacher Training Meeting Ser.). 48p. 1985. pap. text ed. 9.95 (ISBN 0-317-38010-9). Cook.

Richards, LeGrand. Marvelous Work & a Wonder. 5.95 (ISBN 0-87747-161-4); pocket black leather o.p. 8.50 (ISBN 0-87747-163-0); pocket brown leather o.p. 11.95 (ISBN 0-87747-383-8). Deseret Bk.

Richards, M. Ross & Richards, Marie C. New Testament Charts. pap. 2.95 (ISBN 0-87747-446-X). Deseret Bk.

--Old Testament Charts. pap. 1.95 (ISBN 0-87747-447-8). Deseret Bk.

Richards, Marie C., jt. auth. see Richards, M. Ross.

Richards, Mary C. Toward Wholeness: Rudolf Steiner Education in America. LC 80-14905. 210p. 1980. 16.00 (ISBN 0-8195-5049-3); pap. 9.95 (ISBN 0-8195-6062-6). Wesleyan U Pr.

Richards, Michael. Nature & Necessity of Christ's Church. LC 83-2596. 142p. 1983. pap. 7.95 (ISBN 0-8189-0458-5). Alba.

Richards, Steve. The Traveller's Guide to the Astral Plane. 112p. 1984. pap. 7.95 (ISBN 0-85030-337-0). Newcastle Pub.

Richards, Sue & Hagemeyer, Stanley. Ministry to the Divorced: Guidance, Structure & Organization That Promote Healing in the Church. 112p. 1986. text ed. 6.95 (ISBN 0-310-20051-2, 9604P). Zondervan.

Richards, Theodora, jt. auth. see Winter, Dina S.

Richards, William L. The Classification of the Greek Manuscripts of the Johannine Epistles. LC 77-23469. (Society of Biblical Literature. Dissertation Ser.). 1977. pap. 9.95 (ISBN 0-89130-140-2, 060135). Scholars Pr GA.

Richardson, Alan. Creeds in the Making: A Short Introduction to the History of Christian Doctrine. LC 81-43073. 128p. 1981. pap. 5.95 (ISBN 0-8006-1609-X, 1-1609). Fortress.

--Gate of Moon: Mythical & Magical Doorways to the Otherworld. 160p. 1984. pap. 9.95 (ISBN 0-85030-365-6). Newcastle Pub.

--An Introduction to the Mystical Qabalah. (Paths to Inner Power Ser). 1974. pap. 3.50 (ISBN 0-85030-264-1). Weiser.

--Science, History & Faith. LC 86-22863. 216p. 1986. Repr. of 1950 ed. lib. bdg. 39.75x (ISBN 0-313-25325-0, RISHF). Greenwood.

--Theological Word Book of the Bible. 1962. 7.95 (ISBN 0-02-603060-8). Macmillan.

--Theological Wordbook of the Bible. 1962. pap. 7.95 (ISBN 0-02-089090-7, Collier). Macmillan.

Richardson, Alan & Bowden, John, eds. The Westminster Dictionary of Christian Theology. LC 83-14521. 632p. 1983. 24.95 (ISBN 0-664-21398-7). Westminster.

Richardson, Alice M. Index to Stories of Hymns. LC 72-1690. Repr. of 1929 ed. 11.50 (ISBN 0-404-09911-4). AMS Pr.

Richardson, Arleta. Sixteen & Away from Home. (Grandma's Attic Ser.). 1985. pap. 3.50 (ISBN 0-89191-933-3, 59337). Cook.

Richardson, Beth, ed. Seasons of Peace. 72p. (Orig.). 1986. pap. 3.95 (ISBN 0-8358-0548-4). Upper Room.

Richardson, Carol. Bible Programs & Dramas for Children. 64p. (Orig.). 1983. pap. 2.95 (ISBN 0-87239-665-7, 3350). Standard Pub.

Richardson, Cyril C. Christianity of Ignatius of Antioch. LC 35-7948. Repr. of 1935 ed. 14.50 (ISBN 0-404-05297-5). AMS Pr.

--The Church Through the Centuries. LC 72-6726. Repr. of 1938 ed. 21.00 (ISBN 0-404-10645-5). AMS Pr.

Richardson, Cyril C., ed. Early Christian Fathers. (Library of Christian Classics: Vol. 1). 1970. pap. 9.95 (ISBN 0-02-088980-1, Collier). Macmillan.

Richardson, David, jt. auth. see Emmons, Michael.

Richardson, Don. Peace Child. LC 75-26356. (Illus.). 288p. 1975. Repr. of 1974 ed. digest 6.95 (ISBN 0-8307-0415-9, 5403006). Regal.

Richardson, Don, jt. auth. see Paulson, Hank.

Richardson, Donald. Great Zeus & All His Children: Greek Mythology for Adults. 312p. 1984. 16.95 (ISBN 0-13-364950-4); pap. 7.95 (ISBN 0-13-364943-1). P-H.

Richardson, Dorothy, tr. see Pierre-Quint, Leon.

Richardson, E. Allen. Islamic Cultures in North America. LC 81-2876. 84p. (Orig.). 1981. pap. 3.95 (ISBN 0-8298-0449-8). Pilgrim NY.

Richardson, Edward. Love Yourself. 1970. pap. 1.50 (ISBN 0-89243-028-1, 28849). Liguori Pubns.

Richardson, Frank H. Solo para Muchachos. 112p. 1986. pap. 1.95 (ISBN 0-311-46929-9). Casa Bautista.

Richardson, Henry G. The English Jewry under Angevin Kings. LC 83-18539. ix, 313p. 1983. Repr. of 1960 ed. lib. bdg. 35.00x (ISBN 0-313-24247-X, RIEJ). Greenwood.

Richardson, Herbert. New Religions & Mental Health. 177p. 1980. pap. 11.95. Rose Sharon Pr.

--Ten Theologians Respond to the Unification Church. LC 81-70679. 199p. 1981. pap. 10.95. Rose Sharon Pr.

Richardson, Herbert, ed. Constitutional Issues in the Case of Rev. Moon: Amicus Briefs Presented to the United States Supreme Court. (Studies in Religion & Society: Vol. 10). 710p. 1984. 69.95x (ISBN 0-88946-873-7). E Mellen.

--Constitutional Issues in the Case of Reverend Moon: Amicus Briefs Presented to the United States Supreme Court. 699p. 1984. pap. 19.95. Rose Sharon Pr.

--Ten Theologians Respond to the Unification Church. LC 81-70679. (Conference Ser.: No. 10). xv, 199p. (Orig.). 1981. pap. text ed. 9.95 (ISBN 0-932894-10-0, Pub. by New Era Bks). Paragon Hse.

Richardson, Herbert, ed. see Anselm Of Canterbury.

Richardson, Herbert, tr. see Anselm Of Canterbury.

Richardson, Herbert, tr. see Hopkins, Jasper.

Richardson, Herbert W. Nun, Witch, Playmate: The Americanization of Sex. 2nd ed. xii, 147p. 1977. Repr. of 1974 ed. 19.95x (ISBN 0-88946-950-4). E Mellen.

--Toward an American Theology. (Richard Ser.: No. 2). 1967. 29.95 (ISBN 0-88946-028-0). E Mellen.

Richardson, Herbert W., jt. auth. see Bryant, M. Darrol.

Richardson, Herbert W., ed. New Religions & Mental Health: Understanding the Issues. (Symposium Ser.: Vol. 5). 240p. (Orig.). 1980. 39.95x (ISBN 0-88946-910-5). E Mellen.

Richardson, Herbert W., jt. ed. see Clark, Elizabeth.

Richardson, Hugh, jt. auth. see Snellgrove, David.

Richardson, I. M. The Adventures of Eros & Psyche. LC 82-16057. (Illus.). 32p. 1983. PLB 9.79 (ISBN 0-89375-861-2); pap. text ed. 2.50 (ISBN 0-89375-862-0). Troll Assocs.

--Prometheus & the Story of Fire. LC 82-15979. (Illus.). 32p. 1983. PLB 9.79 (ISBN 0-89375-859-0); pap. text ed. 2.50 (ISBN 0-89375-860-4). Troll Assocs.

Richardson, I. M., adapted by see Homer.

Richardson, J. & Co. Staff. Book of Kant, Vol. 5. 1983. 57.50x (ISBN 0-317-54273-7, Pub. by J Richardson UK); pap. 40.00x (ISBN 0-317-54274-5). State Mutual Bk.

--Moral Philosophy, Vol. 9. 1982. 62.50x (ISBN 0-317-54279-6, Pub. by J Richardson UK); pap. 47.50x (ISBN 0-317-54280-X, Pub. by J Richardson UK). State Mutual Bk.

Richardson, James. The God Who Shows Up. LC 81-47889. 55p. (Orig.). 1981. pap. 3.00 (ISBN 0-914520-16-4). Insight Pr.

--Narrative of a Mission to Central Africa: 1850-1851, 2 vols. (Illus.). 704p. 1970. Repr. of 1853 ed. 95.00x set (ISBN 0-7146-1848-9, BHA-01848, F Cass Co). Biblio Dist.

Richardson, James T., et al. Organized Miracles: A Study of a Contemporary, Youth, Communal, Fundamentalist Organization. LC 78-55937. 368p. 1979. 19.95 (ISBN 0-87855-284-7). Transaction Bks.

Richardson, Jim. Foundations for Living. LC 82-74215. 1983. pap. 9.95 (ISBN 0-911739-13-0). Abbott Loop.

--Praying in the Holy Ghost. 1983. pap. 1.75 (ISBN 0-911739-02-5). Abbott Loop.

Richardson, Jim, jt. auth. see Benjamin, Dick.

Richardson, Jim, jt. auth. see Benjamin, Rick.

Richardson, Jim, jt. auth. see Fick, Mike.

Richardson, Jim, jt. auth. see Gularte, Frank.

Richardson, Jim, jt. auth. see Wilkinson, Jerry.

Richardson, Joe M. Christian Reconstruction: The American Missionary Association & Southern Blacks, 1861-1890. LC 85-13946. (Illus.). 352p. 1986. 30.00x (ISBN 0-8203-0816-1). U of GA Pr.

Richardson, John. Caring Enough to Confront. LC 73-83400. (Caring Enough Ser.). 1984. pap. 3.95 (ISBN 0-8307-0990-8, 6101903). Regal.

--The Measure of a Man. (Study & Grow Electives). 64p. 1985. pap. 3.95 (ISBN 0-8307-1018-3, 6102023). Regal.

Richardson, John R. What Happens After Death? Some Musing on -- Is God Through with a Person After Death? LC 81-52115. 1981. 6.95 (ISBN 0-686-79843-0). St Thomas.

Richardson, Jonathan & Richardson, Jonathan, Jr. Explanatory Notes & Remarks on Milton's Paradise Lost. LC 77-174317. Repr. of 1734 ed. 37.50 (ISBN 0-404-05298-3). AMS Pr.

Richardson, Marilyn. Black Women & Religion. 1980. 17.50 (ISBN 0-8161-8087-3, Hall Reference). G K Hall.

Richardson, Neville. The World Council of Churches & Race Relations. (IC-Studies in the Intercultural History of Christianity: Vol. 9). 78p. 1977. pap. 15.65 (ISBN 3-261-01718-X). P Lang Pubs.

Richardson, Otis D. God in the High Country. 1980. 10.00 (ISBN 0-682-49644-8). Exposition Pr FL.

Richardson, P. & Hurd, J. From Jesus to Paul: Studies in Honour of Francis Wright Beare. 256p. 1984. pap. text ed. 16.50x (ISBN 0-88920-138-2, Pub. by Wilfrid Laurier Canada). Humanities.

Richardson, P. & Granskou, D., eds. Anti-Judaism in Early Christianity: Vol. 1, Paul & the Gospels. 240p. 1984. pap. text ed. 17.95x (ISBN 0-88920-167-6, Pub. by Wilfrid Laurier Canada). Humanities.

Richardson, Robert, ed. see Anquetil-Duperron, A. H.

Richardson, Robert, ed. see Bryant, Jacob.

Richardson, Robert, ed. see Owen, William.

Richardson, Robert D., jt. auth. see Feldman, Burton.

Richardson, Robert D., ed. see Beausobre, Isaac de.

Richardson, Robert D., ed. see Bell, John.

Richardson, Robert D., ed. see Davies, Edward.

Richardson, Robert D., ed. see Dupuis, Charles.

Richardson, Robert D., ed. see Faber, George S.

Richardson, Robert D., ed. see Godwin, William.

Richardson, Robert D., ed. see Maurice, Thomas.

Richardson, Robert D., ed. see Moor, Edward.

Richardson, Robert D., ed. see Rowlands, Henry.

Richardson, Robert D., ed. see Stukeley, William.

Richardson, Robert D., ed. see Volney, C. F.

Richardson, Robert D., Jr. Myth & Literature in the American Renaissance. LC 77-23638. 320p. 1978. 22.50x (ISBN 0-253-33965-0). Ind U Pr.

Richardson, Stewart, ed. see Gorbachev, Mikail S.

Richardson, Valeria, ed. God's Promises for Today's Believer. 100p. (Orig.). 1986. write for info. (ISBN 0-88368-162-5). Whitaker Hse.

Richardson, W. Christian Doctrine: The Faith... Once Delivered. LC 82-25598. (Bible College Textbooks Ser.). 448p. (Orig.). 1983. pap. 9.95 (ISBN 0-87239-610-X, 88588). Standard Pub.

Richardson, Wally G. & Huett, Lenora. The Spiritual Value of Gem Stones. LC 79-54728. 168p. 1980. pap. 6.50 (ISBN 0-87516-383-1). De Vorss.

Richardson, William. The Restoring Father. 64p. 1987. pap. price not set (ISBN 0-87403-257-1, 39966). Standard Pub.

Riches, John. Jesus & the Transformation of Judaism. 264p. (Orig.). 1982. pap. 10.95 (ISBN 0-8164-2361-X, HarpR). Har-Row.

Riches, John, ed. The Analog of Beauty: Essays for Hans Urs von Balthasar at Eighty. 256p. 1986. 19.95 (ISBN 0-567-09351-4, Pub. by T & T Clark Ltd UK). Fortress.

Riches, John, ed. see Best, Ernest.

Riches, John, ed. see Hubner, Hans.

Riches, John, ed. see Maddox, Robert.

Riches, John, ed. see Theissen, Gerd.

Riches, John, ed. see Von Balthasar, Hans U.

Riches, John, tr. see Ritter, Gerhard.

Riches, Pierre. Back to Basics: Catholic Faith in Today's World. 176p. 1984. pap. 7.95 (ISBN 0-8245-0646-4). Crossroad NY.

Richesin, L. Dale, ed. The Challenge of Liberation Theology: A First World Response. Mahan, Brian. LC 81-9527. 152p. (Orig.). 1981. pap. 7.95 (ISBN 0-88344-092-X). Orbis Bks.

Richesin, L. Dale & Bouchard, Larry D., eds. Interpreting Disciples: Practical Theology in the Disciples of Christ. LC 86-30072. 295p. (Orig.). 1987. pap. text ed. 14.95x (ISBN 0-87565-072-4). Tex Christian.

Richie, David S. Memories & Meditations of a Workcamper. LC 73-84213. 36p. (Orig.). 1973. pap. 2.50x (ISBN 0-87574-190-8, 189). Pendle Hill.

Richie, Donald. Zen Inklings: Some Stories, Fables, Parables, Sermons & Prints with Notes & Commentaries. LC 82-2561. (Illus.). 162p. 1982. 17.95 (ISBN 0-8348-0170-1). Weatherhill.

Richman, Paula. Women, Branch Stories, & Religious Rhetoric in a Tamil Buddhist Text. (Foreign & Comparative Studies-South Asian Ser.: No. 12). (Orig.). 1987. pap. write for info. (ISBN 0-915984-90-3). Syracuse U Foreign Comp.

Richmond, Hugh M. The Christian Revolutionary: John Milton. 1974. 32.50x (ISBN 0-520-02443-5). U of Cal Pr.

--Puritans & Libertines: Anglo-French Literary Relations in the Reformation. 400p. 1981. 35.95x (ISBN 0-520-04179-8). U of Cal Pr.

Richmond, Mary L., compiled by. Shaker Literature: A Bibliography, 2 vols. LC 75-41908. 656p. 1976. Set. 60.00x (ISBN 0-87451-117-8). U Pr of New Eng.

Richmond, Mary L., ed. see Filley, Dorothy M.

Richmond, Olney H. The Mystic Test Book. (Orig.). 1983. pap. 9.95 (ISBN 0-87877-064-X). Newcastle Pub.

Richmond-Garland, Diana S. & Garland, David E. Beyond Companionship-Christians in Marriage. LC 86-7767. 192p. 1986. pap. 12.95 (ISBN 0-664-24018-6). Westminster.

Richstatter, Thomas. Liturgical Law Today: New Style, New Spirit. LC 77-3008. pap. 67.80 (ISBN 0-317-28483-5, 2019104). Bks Demand UMI.

Richter, Anton H., tr. see Eisenberg, C. G.

Richter, Betts. Something Special Within. 2nd ed. (Illus.). 48p. 1982. pap. 4.50 (ISBN 0-87516-488-9). De Vorss.

Richter, Don, jt. ed. see Wyckoff, D. Campbell.

Richter, Gottfried. Art & Human Consciousness. Frohlich, Margaret & Channer, Burley, trs. from Ger. (Illus.). 300p. (Orig.). 1985. 30.00 (ISBN 0-88010-108-3). Anthroposophic.

Richter, Julius. History of Protestant Missions in the Near East. LC 79-133822. Repr. of 1910 ed. 29.50 (ISBN 0-404-05331-9). AMS Pr.

Richter, Robert L. The Last Enemy. 1983. 3.75 (ISBN 0-89536-960-5, 7511). CSS of Ohio.

Richter, Will, ed. see Schwartz, Eduard.

Richterkessing, Sue. Devotions for Your Preschool Classroom. 1983. pap. 4.95 (ISBN 0-570-03913-4, 12-2854). Concordia.

Rickard, Garth, jt. auth. see Cox, Heather.

Rickard, Marvin G. Let It Grow: Your Church Can Chart a New Course. LC 84-22733. 1985. pap. 5.95 (ISBN 0-88070-074-2). Multnomah.

Ricke, Herbert, et al. Beit El-Wali Temple of Ramesses Second. portfolio ed. LC 67-18437. (Oriental Institute Nubian Expedition Pubns. Ser.: Vol. 1). (Illus.). 1967. 30.00x (ISBN 0-226-62365-3, OINE1). U of Chicago Pr.

Rickenborgh, Jan Van see Van Rijckenborgh, Jan.

Rickenborgh, Jan Van see Van Rijckenborgh, Jan & De Petri, Catharose.

Ricker, Robert S. & Pitkin, Ron. Soulsearch: Hope for Twenty-First Century Living from Ecclesiastes. rev. ed. LC 85-21594. (Bible Commentary for Laymen Ser.). 168p. 1985. pap. 4.25 (ISBN 0-8307-1100-7, S393118). Regal.

Rickerson, Wayne. Christian Family Activities for Families with Children. LC 82-10385. (Illus.). 96p. (Orig.). 1982. pap. 4.95 (ISBN 0-87239-569-3, 2964). Standard Pub.

--Christian Family Activities for Families with Preschoolers. LC 82-5583. (Illus.). 96p. (Orig.). 1982. pap. 4.95 (ISBN 0-87239-568-5, 2963). Standard Pub.

--Christian Family Activities for Families with Teens. LC 82-5833. (Illus.). 96p. (Orig.). 1982. pap. 4.95 (ISBN 0-87239-570-7, 2965). Standard Pub.

--Family Fun Times: Activities That Bind Marriages, Build Families, & Develop Christian Leaders. 80p. Date not set. pap. 7.95 (ISBN 0-87403-207-5, 3187). Standard Pub.

--Newly Married. (Family Ministry Ser.). 96p. 1986. pap. 19.95 (ISBN 0-89191-967-8). Cook.

--Strengthening the Family. 128p. 1987. pap. 5.95 (ISBN 0-87403-206-7, 3186). Standard Pub.

Rickert, Corinne H. Case of John Darrell: Minister & Exorcist. LC 62-62828. (University of Florida Humanities Monographs: No. 9). 1962. pap. 3.50 (ISBN 0-8130-0197-8). U Presses Fla.

Ricketts, Sarah, jt. auth. see Bubna, Donald.

Ricks, Chip. Carol's Story. 192p. 1981. pap. 6.95 (ISBN 0-8423-0208-5). Tyndale.

--John & One John. 1982. pap. 2.50 (ISBN 0-8423-1890-9). Tyndale.

Ricks, Chip & Marsh, Marilyn. How to Write for Christian Magazines. LC 84-23025. 1985. pap. 7.50 (ISBN 0-8054-7910-4). Broadman.

Ricks, Eldin. Book of Mormon Study Guide. 1976. pap. 4.95 (ISBN 0-87747-567-9). Deseret Bk.

Ricks, George R. Some Aspects of the Religious Music of the United States Negro. Dorson, Richard M., ed. LC 77-70621. (International Folklore Ser.). 1977. Repr. of 1977 ed. lib. bdg. 36.50x (ISBN 0-405-10123-6). Ayer Co Pubs.

Ricks, Stephen D., jt. ed. see Brinner, William M.

Ricoeur, Paul. Essays on Biblical Interpretation. Mudge, Lewis S., ed. LC 80-8052. 192p. (Orig.). 1980. pap. 8.95 (ISBN 0-8006-1407-0, 1-1407). Fortress.

--The Reality of the Historical Past. LC 84-60012. (Aquinas Lecture Ser.). 51p. 1984. 7.95 (ISBN 0-87462-152-6). Marquette.

--Symbolism of Evil. Buchanan, Emerson, tr. LC 67-11506. 1969. pap. 11.95x (ISBN 0-8070-1567-9, BPA18). Beacon Pr.

Ricoeur, Paul, jt. auth. see MacIntyre, Alasdair.

Riddell, Carole & Wallingford, Kay. Helpful Hints for Fun-filled Parenting. LC 84-2056. 128p. 1984. pap. 6.95 spiral (ISBN 0-8407-5880-4). Nelson.

Riddell, Walter A. Rise of Ecclesiastical Control in Quebec. (Columbia University. Studies in the Social Sciences: No. 174). Repr. of 1916 ed. 17.50 (ISBN 0-404-51174-0). AMS Pr.

Ridder, Herman. Membership in the Reformed Church. pap. 1.65 (ISBN 0-686-23484-7). Rose Pub MI.

Ridderbos, Bernhard. Saint & Symbol: Images of Saint Jerome in Early Italian Art. (Illus.). xv, 126p. 1984. pap. 18.00x (ISBN 90-6088-087-0, Pub. by Boumas Boekhuis Netherlands). Benjamins North AM.

Ridderbos, H. N. Bultmann. (Modern Thinkers Ser.). 1960. pap. 2.00 (ISBN 0-87552-581-4). Presby & Reformed.

Ridderbos, Herman N. Epistle of Paul to the Churches of Galatia. (New International Commentary on the New Testament Ser.). 1953. 12.95 (ISBN 0-8028-2191-X). Eerdmans.

--Paul. DeWitt, J. Richard, tr. 587p. 1975. 23.95 (ISBN 0-8028-3438-8). Eerdmans.

Ridderbos, J. Bible Student's Commentary: Deuteronomy. (Bible Student's Commentary Ser.). 336p. 1984. 16.95 (ISBN 0-310-45260-0, 11760). Zondervan.

--Bible Student's Commentary: Isaiah. (Bible Student's Commentary Ser.). 528p. 1985. 24.95 (ISBN 0-310-45270-8, 11761). Zondervan.

Ridderbos, N. H. Die Psalmen: Stilistische Verfahren und Aufbau mit besonderer Beruecksichtigung von Ps. 1-41. Mittring, Karl E., tr. from Dutch. (Beiheft 117 zur Zeitschrift fuer die alttestamentliche Wissenschaft). 305p. 1972. 41.60x (ISBN 3-11-001834-9). De Gruyter.

Ridding, Laura, ed. Travels of Macarius: Extracts from the Diary of the Travels of Macarius, Patriarch of Antioch. LC 77-115577. (Russia Observed Ser). 1971. Repr. of 1936 ed. 12.00 (ISBN 0-405-03089-4). Ayer Co Pubs.

Riddle, Donald W. Early Christian Life As Reflected in Its Literature. 256p. 1981. Repr. of 1936 ed. lib. bdg. 40.00 (ISBN 0-8495-4646-X). Arden Lib.

Riddle, Pauline, jt. auth. see Andrews, Mildred.

Ridenhour, Lynn. Seasonings for Sermons, Vol. 2. 1982. 4.75 (ISBN 0-89536-577-4, 1916). CSS of Ohio.

Ridenhour, Thomas E., jt. auth. see Micks, Marianne H.

Ridenhour, Thomas E., Sr. Promise of Peace, Call for Justice. Sherer, Michael L., ed. (Orig.). 1986. pap. 6.75 (ISBN 0-89536-822-6, 6831). CSS of Ohio.

Ridenour, Crea. Ocupate en Ensenar. 48p. 1983. pap. 1.50 (ISBN 0-311-11031-2). Casa Bautista.

Ridenour, Fritz. Faith It or Fake It? LC 73-120783. 176p. 1978. pap. 3.50 (ISBN 0-8307-0441-8, S114186). Regal.

--How Do You Handle Life? LC 77-140941. 192p. 1976. pap. 3.50 (ISBN 0-8307-0430-2, S104156). Regal.

--How to Be a Christian in an Unchristian World. rev. ed. LC 72-169603. 192p. (Orig.). 1972. pap. 3.50 (ISBN 0-8307-0611-9, S123150). Regal.

--How to Be a Christian Without Being Perfect. LC 86-6479. 250p. (Orig.). 1986. text ed. 12.95 (5111607); pap. text ed. 6.95 (ISBN 0-8307-1106-6, 5418680). Regal.

--How to Be a Christian Without Being Religious. 1971. pap. 5.95 (ISBN 0-8423-1450-4). Tyndale.

--How to Be a Christian Without Being Religious. 2nd ed. LC 72-169603. 176p. 1984. pap. 4.95 (ISBN 0-8307-0982-7, 5418331); Leaders Guide, Doug Van Bronkhorst 3.95 (ISBN 0-8307-0993-2, 6101930). Regal.

--How to Be a Christian Without Being Religious. (Illus.). 166p. 1985. pap. 3.95 (ISBN 0-8307-1026-4, S182104). Regal.

--How to Decide What's Really Important. LC 78-68146. 160p. 1978. 3.50 (ISBN 0-8307-0266-0, S122154). Regal.

--I'm a Good Man, But. LC 75-96702. 1969. pap. 3.50 (ISBN 0-8307-0429-9, S102153). Regal.

--So What's the Difference? rev. ed. LC 67-31426. 1979. 5.95 (ISBN 0-8307-0721-2, 5414008). Regal.

Ridick, Joyce. Treasures in Earthen Vessels: The Vows, a Wholistic Approach. LC 84-2817. 166p. 1984. pap. 9.95 (ISBN 0-8189-0467-4). Alba.

Ridley, F. A. The Assassins: A Study of the Cult of the Assassins in Persia and Islam. (Islam Ser.). 1980. lib. bdg. 59.95 (ISBN 0-8490-3077-3). Gordon Pr.

Ridley, Francis A. The Jesuits: A Study in Counter-Reformation. LC 83-45595. Date not set. Repr. of 1938 ed. 35.00 (ISBN 0-404-19888-0). AMS Pr.

--The Papacy & Fascism: The Crisis of the 20th Century. LC 72-180422. (Studies in Fascism, Ideology & Practice). Repr. of 1937 ed. 24.50 (ISBN 0-404-56156-X). AMS Pr.

Ridley, Gustave. From Boredom to Bliss. Campbell, Jean, ed. (Illus.). 160p. (Orig.). 1983. pap. 8.95 (ISBN 0-9610544-0-9). Harmonious Pr.

Ridley, Jasper. Thomas Cranner. 450p. 1983. Repr. of 1962 ed. lib. bdg. 65.00 (ISBN 0-89987-737-0). Darby Bks.

Ridley, Nicholas. Works of Nicholas Ridley, D.D., Sometime Lord Bishop of London, Martyr, 1555. Repr. of 1841 ed. 41.00 (ISBN 0-384-50840-5). Johnson Repr.

Ridolfi, Roberto. The Life of Girolamo Savonarola. LC 76-8001. (Illus.). 1976. Repr. of 1959 ed. lib. bdg. 65.00x (ISBN 0-8371-8873-3, RIGS). Greenwood.

Ridout, Lionel J. Renegade, Outcast & Maverick: Three Pioneer California Clergy 1847-1893. 1973. 7.95x (ISBN 0-916304-10-8). SDSU Press.

Ridout, S. King Saul, Man after the Flesh. 8.50 (ISBN 0-88172-118-2). Believers Bkshelf.

Ridout, Samuel. The Church & Its Order According to Scripture. 1915. pap. 2.75 (ISBN 0-87213-711-2). Loizeaux.

--Job. 1919. pap. 3.95 (ISBN 0-87213-719-8). Loizeaux.

--Judges & Ruth. rev. ed. 415p. 1981. pap. 7.25 (ISBN 0-87213-720-1). Loizeaux.

--Lectures on the Tabernacle. (Illus.). 1973. Repr. of 1914 ed. 13.95 (ISBN 0-87213-715-5); chart only 0.15 (ISBN 0-87213-716-3). Loizeaux.

Ridpath, George. The Stage Condemn'd. LC 79-170443. (The English Stage Ser.: Vol. 29). 1973. lib. bdg. 61.00 (ISBN 0-8240-0612-7). Garland Pub.

Riegel, O. U. Crown of Glory: Life of J. J. Strang, Moses, of the Mormons. 1935. 59.50x (ISBN 0-685-69857-2). Elliots Bks.

Riegert, Lillian, jt. auth. see Kunath, Anne.

Riegler, Gordon A. The Socialization of the New England Clergy Eighteen Hundred to Eighteen Sixty. LC 79-13027. (Perspectives in American History Ser.: No. 37). 187p. 1980. Repr. of 1945 ed. lib. bdg. 25.00x (ISBN 0-87991-361-4). Porcupine Pr.

Riehle, Mary C. & Ready, Dolores. Happy Together, 1977. rev. ed. 1977. pap. text ed. 4.95 (ISBN 0-86683-110-X, HarpR); tchr's. ed. 7.55 (ISBN 0-86683-113-4). Har-Row.

Rieman, T. Wayne, jt. auth. see Bhagat, Shantilal P.

Riemer, Jack, ed. Jewish Reflections on Death. LC 74-18242. 192p. 1976. pap. 5.95 (ISBN 0-8052-0516-0). Schocken.

Riemer, Jack & Stampfer, Nathaniel, eds. Ethical Wills: A Jewish Tradition. LC 82-19160. 192p. 1983. 16.95 (ISBN 0-8052-3839-5). Schocken.

Rienecker, Fritz. Lexikon Zur Bibel. 3rd ed. (Ger.). 1974. 40.00 (ISBN 3-417-00403-9, M-7192). French & Eur.

Rienecker, Fritz & Rogers, Cleon. Linquistic Key to the Greek New Testament. 912p. 1982. 29.95 (ISBN 0-310-32050-X, 6277). Zondervan.

Riepe, Dale M. The Naturalistic Tradition in Indian Thought. LC 82-9185. xii, 308p. 1982. Repr. of 1961 ed. lib. bdg. 35.00x (ISBN 0-313-23622-4, RINA). Greenwood.

Riesen, Richard A. Criticism & Faith in Late Victorian Scotland: A. B. Davidson, William Robertson Smith & George Adam Smith. LC 85-5388. 490p. (Orig.). 1985. lib. bdg. 30.50 (ISBN 0-8191-4655-2); pap. text ed. 18.75 (ISBN 0-8191-4656-0). U Pr of Amer.

Riesener, Ingrid. Der Stamm Awad in Alten Testament. (Beiheft zur Zeitschrift Fuer die Alttestamentliche Wissenschaft: Vol. 149). 1979. 62.00x (ISBN 3-11-007260-2). De Gruyter.

Rietcheck, Robert & Korn, Daniel. Sunday Mass: What Part Do You Play? 32p. 1985. pap. 1.50 (ISBN 0-89243-235-7). Liguori Pubns.

Rieu, Richard, jt. ed. see Cecil, Robert.

Riezler, Sigmund. Die Literarischen Widersacher der Paepste Zur Zeit Ludwig Des Baiers. 336p. 1874. Repr. 25.50 (ISBN 0-8337-2994-2). B Franklin.

Rife, Carl B. Confirmation Resources. 1982. pap. 5.25 tchr's. guide (ISBN 0-89536-537-5, 0356). CSS of Ohio.

Rife, Carl B. & Bishop, Carolyn. The Church Is You & I. 1984. 1.95 (ISBN 0-89536-658-4, 0394). CSS of Ohio.

Rife, J. Merle. The Nature & Origin of the New Testament. LC 74-80276. 1975. 9.95 (ISBN 0-8022-2148-3). Philos Lib.

Riffert, George R. Great Pyramid Proof of God. 1932. 8.00 (ISBN 0-685-08804-9). Destiny.

Rifkin, Jeremy. Declaration of a Heretic. 150p. 1985. 19.95 (ISBN 0-7102-0709-3); pap. 7.95 (ISBN 0-7102-0710-7). Methuen Inc.

Rifkin, Jeremy & Howard, Ted. The Emerging Order: God in the Age of Scarcity. (Epiphany Bks.). 1983. pap. 2.95 (ISBN 0-345-30464-0). Ballantine.

Rifkin, Natalie S., ed. see Krutch, Joseph W., et al.

Rifkind, Simon H., et al. The Basic Equities of the Palestine Problem. Davis, Moshe, ed. LC 77-70736. (America & the Holy Land Ser.). 1977. Repr. of 1947 ed. lib. bdg. 17.00x (ISBN 0-405-10279-8). Ayer Co Pubs.

Riforgiato, Leonard R. Missionary of Moderation: Henry Melchior Muhlenberg & the Lutheran Church in English America. LC 78-75203. 256p. 23.50 (ISBN 0-8387-2379-9). Bucknell U Pr.

Riga, Peter J. Human Rights as Human & Christian Realities. LC 81-69244. (New Studies on Law & Society). 165p. (Orig.). 1982. 26.00x (ISBN 0-86733-016-3, 5016). Assoc Faculty Pr.

Rigaud, Milo. Secrets of Voodoo. Cross, Robert B., tr. from Fr. (Illus.). 256p. 1985. pap. 7.95 (ISBN 0-87286-171-6). City Lights.

Rigby, Peter. Persistent Pastoralists: Nomadic Societies in Transition. 208p. 1985. 26.25x (ISBN 0-86232-226-X, Pub. by Zed Pr England); pap. 9.95 (ISBN 0-86232-227-8, Pub. by Zed Pr England). Humanities.

Rigby, Stephen, tr. see Bessieres, Albert.

Rigdon, Raymond M., jt. auth. see Colson, Howard P.

Riggans, Walter. Numbers. LC 83-7007. (Daily Study Bible-Old Testament). 262p. (Orig.). 1983. 14.95 (ISBN 0-664-21393-6); pap. 7.95 (ISBN 0-664-24474-2). Westminster.

Riggins, John & Winter, Jack. Gameplan: The Language & Strategy of Pro Football. Rev. ed. Halsey, Alexandra, ed. LC 84-40402. (Illus.). 240p. 1984. pap. 12.95x (ISBN 0-915643-08-1). Santa Barb Pr.

Riggins, William, tr. see Steiner, Rudolf.

Riggle, H. M. Beyond the Tomb. 288p. 4.00 (ISBN 0-686-29100-X). Faith Pub Hse.

--Christian Baptism, Feet Washing & the Lord's Supper. 264p. 3.50 (ISBN 0-686-29105-0). Faith Pub Hse.

--The Christian Church: Its Rise & Progress. 488p. 5.00 (ISBN 0-686-29144-1). Faith Pub Hse.

--Jesus Is Coming Again. 111p. pap. 1.00 (ISBN 0-686-29123-9). Faith Pub Hse.

--The Kingdom of God & the One Thousand Years Reign. 160p. pap. 1.50 (ISBN 0-686-29153-0). Faith Pub Hse.

--The Sabbath & the Lord's Day. 160p. pap. 1.50 (ISBN 0-686-29165-4). Faith Pub Hse.

--The Two Works of Grace. 56p. pap. 0.40 (ISBN 0-686-29168-9); pap. 1.00 3 copies (ISBN 0-686-29169-7). Faith Pub Hse.

Riggle, H. M., jt. auth. see Speck, Von S.

Riggle, H. M., jt. auth. see Warner, D. S.

Riggle, H. M., jt. ed. see Speck, S. L.

Riggs, Jack R. Hosea's Heartbreak. 1984. pap. 5.95 (ISBN 0-87213-724-4). Loizeaux.

Riggs, Ralph M. Living in Christ. LC 67-25874. 1967. pap. 1.50 (ISBN 0-88243-538-8, 02-0538). Gospel Pub.

--So Send I You. 130p. 1965. 1.25 (ISBN 0-88243-587-6, 02-0587). Gospel Pub.

--The Spirit-Filled Pastor's Guide. 1948. pap. 5.95 (ISBN 0-88243-588-4, 02-0588). Gospel Pub.

--The Spirit Himself. 210p. 1949. 5.50 (ISBN 0-88243-590-6, 02-0590). Gospel Pub.

--The Story of the Future. LC 67-31330. 1968. 2.95 (ISBN 0-88243-742-9, 02-0742). Gospel Pub.

--We Believe. 184p. 1954. 3.50 (ISBN 0-88243-780-1, 02-0780). Gospel Pub.

Riggs, Robert F. The Apocalypse Unsealed. LC 80-81698. 328p. 1981. pap. 9.95 (ISBN 0-8022-2367-2). Philos Lib.

Riggs, Stephen R. Tah-Koo Wah-Kan; Or, the Gospel Among the Dakotas. LC 78-38460. (Religion in America, Ser. 2). 534p. 1972. Repr. of 1869 ed. 33.00 (ISBN 0-405-04081-4). Ayer Co Pubs.

Riggs, William G. The Christian Poet in Paradise Lost. 1972. 30.00x (ISBN 0-520-02081-2). U of Cal Pr.

Rigney, Barbara H. Lilith's Daughters: Women & Religion in Contemporary Fiction. LC 81-70012. 136p. 1982. 17.50x (ISBN 0-299-08960-6). U of Wis Pr.

Rigsbee, Ron & Bakker, Dorothy. The Agony of Deception. LC 83-81285. 288p. (Orig.). 1983. pap. 6.95 (ISBN 0-910311-07-2). Huntington Hse Inc.

Rijckenborgh, Jan van see Van Rijckenborgh, Jan.

Rijckenborgh, Jan Van see Van Rijckenborgh, Jan.

Rijckenborgh, Jan van see Van Rijckenborgh, Jan.

Rijckenborgh, Jan Van see Van Rijckenborgh, Jan.

Rijckenborgh, Jan van see Van Rijckenborgh, Jan & De Petri, Catharose.

Rijckenborgh, Jan Van see Van Rijckenborgh, Jan & De Petri, Catharose.

Rijkenborgh, Jan van see Van Rijckenborgh, Jan.

Rijn, J. C. Van see Van Rijn, J. C.

Rijn, J. C. van see Van Rijn, J. C.

Rijn, Rembrandt Van see Van Rijn, Rembrandt.

Rijn Rembrandt, Hermansz Van see Van Rijn Rembrandt, Hermansz.

Rikhof, Herwi. The Concept of Church: A Methodological Inquiry into the Use of Metaphors in Ecclesiology. LC 80-84751. xvi, 304p. 1981. 35.00x (ISBN 0-915762-11-0). Patmos Pr.

Riley, Betty. A Veil Too Thin: Reincarnation Out of Control. LC 84-50090. 96p. 1984. pap. 2.95 (ISBN 0-911842-37-3). Valley Sun.

Riley, Edith M., tr. see Beguin, Albert.

Riley, H. T., tr. see Ingulf, Abbot.

Riley, Harold, jt. auth. see Orchard, Bernard.

Riley, Hugh M. Christian Initiation: A Comparative Study of the Interpretation of the Baptismal Liturgy in the Mystagogical Writing of Cyril of Jerusalem, John Chrysostom, Theodore of Mopsuetia, & Ambrose of Milan. LC 74-11191. (Catholic University of America Studies in Christian Antiquity: No. 17). pap. 128.80 (ISBN 0-317-27922-X, 2025126). Bks Demand UMI.

Riley, Isaac H. The Meaning of Mysticism. LC 75-26512. 1975. lib. bdg. 20.00 (ISBN 0-8414-7227-0). Folcroft.

Riley, Isaac W. American Thought from Puritanism to Pragmatism & Beyond: A Greenwood Archival Edition. 2nd ed. Repr. of 1923 ed. lib. bdg. 65.00x (ISBN 0-8371-2391-7, RIAT). Greenwood.

Riley, Jeannie C. & Buckingham, Jamie. From Harper Valley to the Mountain Top. (Epiphany Bks.). (Illus.). 1983. pap. 2.75 (ISBN 0-345-30481-0). Ballantine.

Riley, Kelly. Celebrate Easter. (Celebrate Ser.). (Illus.). 144p. 1987. pap. 9.95 (ISBN 0-86653-385-0). Good Apple.

Riley, Patrick. The General Will Before Fousseau: The Transformation of the Divine into the Civic. (Studies in Moral, Political, & Legal Philosophy). 272p. 1986. text ed. 27.50 (ISBN 0-691-07720-7). Princeton U Pr.

--Kant's Political Philosophy. LC 82-573. (Philosophy & Society Ser.). 224p. 1983. text ed. 31.50x (ISBN 0-8476-6763-4). Rowman.

Riley, Philip B., jt. ed. see Fallon, Timothy P.

Riley, William. The Bible Study Group: An Owner's Manual. LC 85-70362. (Illus.). 152p. 1985. pap. 7.95 (ISBN 0-87793-286-7). Ave Maria.

--Tale of Two Testaments. 176p. 1985. pap. 5.95 (ISBN 0-89622-240-3). Twenty Third.

Riley, Woodbridge. American Thought from Puritanism to Pragmatism. 11.75 (ISBN 0-8446-1385-1). Peter Smith.

Riley-Smith, Jonathan, jt. auth. see Riley-Smith, Louise.

Riley-Smith, Louise & Riley-Smith, Jonathan. The Crusades: Idea & Reality, 1095-1274. (Documents in Medieval History). 208p. 1981. pap. text ed. 17.95 (ISBN 0-7131-6348-8). E Arnold.

Rilliet, Albert. Calvin & Servetus: The Reformer's Share in the Trial of Michael Servetus Historically Ascertained. Tweedie, W. K., tr. from Fr. LC 83-45631. Date not set. Repr. of 1846 ed. 31.50 (ISBN 0-404-19848-1). AMS Pr.

Rimmer, C. Brandon. Religion in Shreds. LC 73-82861. pap. 1.25 (ISBN 0-88419-046-3, Co-Pub by Crection Hse). Aragorn Bks.

Rinaldi, Peter M. By Love Compelled. (Illus., Orig.). 1973. pap. 3.25 (ISBN 0-89944-032-0). Don Bosco Multimedia.

--I Saw the Holy Shroud. LC 83-71121. (Illus.). 112p. 1983. 4.95 (ISBN 0-89944-072-X); pap. 2.85 (ISBN 0-89944-069-X). Don Bosco Multimedia.

--In Verdant Pastures: From a Pastor's Diary. LC 85-72837. 228p. (Orig.). 1985. pap. 7.95 (ISBN 0-89944-202-1). Don Bosco Multimedia.

--Man with a Dream. (Illus.). 1978. pap. 2.95 (ISBN 0-89944-035-5). Don Bosco Multimedia.

--When Millions Saw the Shroud. LC 79-53065. (Illus.). 1979. 6.95 (ISBN 0-89944-023-1); pap. 2.95 (ISBN 0-89944-024-X). Don Bosco Multimedia.

Rinbochay, Khetsun S. Tantric Practice in Nying-ma. Hopkins, Jeffery & Klein, Anne, eds. LC 86-3762. 238p. (Orig.). 1983. lib. bdg. 16.00 cancelled (ISBN 0-937938-13-0); pap. text ed. 12.50 (ISBN 0-937938-14-9). Snow Lion.

Rinbochay, Lati. Mind in Tibetan Buddhism. Napper, Elizabeth, ed. LC 86-3799. 172p. (Orig.). 1980. lib. bdg. 12.95 cancelled (ISBN 0-937938-03-3); pap. 10.95 (ISBN 0-937938-02-5). Snow Lion.

Rinbochay, Lati & Hopkins, Jeffrey. Death, Intermediate State & Rebirth in Tibetan Buddhism. LC 80-80130. 86p. 1980. lib. bdg. cancelled (ISBN 0-937938-01-7); pap. 6.95 (ISBN 0-937938-00-9). Snow Lion.

Rinbochay, Lati, et al. Meditative Status in Tibetan Buddhism. Zahler, Leah, ed. Hopkins, Jeffrey, tr. from Tibetan. (Wisdom Advanced Book: Blue Ser.). (Illus.). 288p. (Orig.). 1983. pap. 10.95 (ISBN 0-86171-011-8, Pub. by Wisdom Pubns). Great Traditions.

Rindzinski, Milka, tr. see Augsburger, Myron S.

Rindzinski, Milka, tr. see Wenger, J. C.

Rindzinsky, Milka, tr. from English. Confesion de fe las Iglesias Menonitas. 32p. (Orig.). 1983. pap. 0.60x (ISBN 0-8361-1258-X). Herald Pr.

Rinehart, Alice D. Mortals in the Immortal Profession: An Oral History of Teaching. LC 82-17200. 410p. 1983. pap. text ed. 19.95x (ISBN 0-8290-1049-1). Irvington.

Rinehart, Paula, jt. auth. see Rinehart, Stacy.

Rinehart, Stacy & Rinehart, Paula. Choices: Finding God's Way in Dating, Sex, Singleness & Marriage. LC 82-62071. 170p. 1983. pap. 3.95 (ISBN 0-89109-494-6). NavPress.

Rinehart, Stacy, jt. auth. see Christian Character Library Staff.

Rinere, Elissa. New Law & Life: Sixty Practical Questions & Answers on the New Code of Canon Law. 103p. (Orig.). 1985. pap. 4.50 (ISBN 0-943616-28-X). Canon Law Soc.

Ringe, Sharon H. Jesus, Liberation & the Biblical Jubilee: Images for Ethics & Christology. LC 85-4609. (Overtures to Biblical Theology Ser.). 144p. 1985. pap. 8.95 (ISBN 0-8006-1544-1). Fortress.

Ringelblum, Emmanuel. Polish-Jewish Relations During the Second World War. Allon, Dafna, et al, trs. LC 76-1394. 330p. 1976. 35.00x (ISBN 0-86527-155-0). Fertig.

Ringelheim, Joan & Katz, Esther, eds. Catalogue of Audio & Video Testimonies of the Holocaust. (Occasional Papers from the Institute for Research in History Ser.: No. 5). 150p. (Orig.). Date not set. pap. 7.50 (ISBN 0-913865-04-4). Inst Res Hist.

Ringelheim, Joan M., jt. auth. see Katz, Esther.

Ringgren, Helmer. Israelite Religion. Green, David E., tr. from Ger. LC 66-10757. 408p. 1975. pap. 7.95 (ISBN 0-8006-1121-7, 1-1121). Fortress.

--Religions of the Ancient Near East. Sturdy, John, tr. LC 72-8587. (Illus.). 208p. 1972. 7.50 (ISBN 0-664-20953-X). Westminster.

Ringgren, Helmer, jt. ed. see Botterweck, G. Johannes.

Rinker, Rosalind. Prayer: Conversing with God. pap. 3.50 (ISBN 0-310-32092-5, 10716P). Zondervan.

--You Can Witness with Confidence. pap. 2.95 (ISBN 0-310-32152-2). Zondervan.

--You Can Witness with Confidence. 112p. 1984. pap. 5.95 (ISBN 0-310-32151-4, 10714P). Zondervan.

Rinpoche, Bikshu. Buddhism: An Introduction to the Living Spiritual Tradition. 160p. (Orig.). 1987. pap. 8.95 (ISBN 0-913757-71-3, Pub. by New Era Bks). Paragon Hse.

Rinpoche, Patrul. The Propitious Speech from the Beginning, Middle & End. Norbu, Thinley, tr. from Tibetan. 46p. (Orig.). 1984. pap. 7.00 (ISBN 0-9607000-6-4). Jewel Pub Hse.

Rinpoche, Thubten K., et al, trs. see Dalai Lama, IV.

Rinpoche, Zopa, jt. auth. see Yeshe, Lama.

Riols, Noreen. Eye of the Storm. 176p. 1985. pap. 2.95 (ISBN 0-345-32716-0). Ballantine.

Ripa, Cesare. Iconologia. LC 75-27865. (Renaissance & the Gods Ser.: Vol. 21). (Illus.). 581p. 1976. Repr. of 1611 ed. lib. bdg. 88.00 (ISBN 0-8240-2070-7). Garland Pub.

Ripa, Cesare see Marolles, Michel de.

Ripley, Francis J. Mary, Mother of the Church: What Recent Popes Have Said about the Blessed Mother's Role in the Church. 1973. pap. 2.00 (ISBN 0-89555-094-6). TAN Bks Pubs.

--This Is the Faith. 317p. 1973. pap. 5.95 (ISBN 0-903348-02-0). Lumen Christi.

Riplinger, Thomas. An American Vision of the Church: The Church in American Protestant Theology 1937-1967, Vol. 76. (European University Studies: Ser. 23). vi, 320p. 1977. pap. 33.95 (ISBN 3-261-02093-8). P Lang Pubs.

Rippey, Mari. It's Tough Being a Mother. 32p. 1983. pap. 2.95 (ISBN 0-8170-0995-7). Judson.

Rippin, A. & Knappert, J., eds. Islam (Textual Sources for the Study of Islam) LC 86-22190. (Textual Sources for the Study of Religion). 256p. 1986. 23.50x (ISBN 0-389-20677-6); pap. 11.75 (ISBN 0-389-20678-4). B&N Imports.

Ripple, Paula. Called to Be Friends. LC 80-67402. 160p. (Orig.). 1980. pap. 3.95 (ISBN 0-87793-212-3). Ave Maria.

--Growing Strong at Broken Places. LC 86-71124. 184p. (Orig.). 1986. pap. 5.95 (ISBN 0-87793-341-3). Ave Maria.

--The Pain & the Possibility. LC 78-67745. 144p. 1978. pap. 2.95 (ISBN 0-87793-162-3). Ave Maria.

--Walking with Loneliness. LC 82-73048. 176p. (Orig.). 1982. pap. 4.95 (ISBN 0-87793-259-X). Ave Maria.

--Walking with Loneliness. 318p. 1985. pap. 9.95 large print ed. (ISBN 0-8027-2490-6). Walker & Co.

Rippy, J. Fred & Nelson, Jean T. Crusaders of the Jungle. LC 76-123495. 1971. Repr. of 1936 ed. 31.50x (ISBN 0-8046-1382-6, Pub. by Kennikat). Assoc Faculty Pr.

Rischer, Carol. Insights for Young Mothers. pap. 5.95 (ISBN 0-89081-485-6). Harvest Hse.

Rischin, Moses. The Promised City: New York's Jews, 1870-1914. (Illus.). 342p. 1977. pap. 8.95x (ISBN 0-674-71501-2); text ed. 22.50x (ISBN 0-674-71502-0). Harvard U Pr.

Rischin, Moses, ed. The Jews of the West: The Metropolitan Years. (Illus.). 1979. 5.95 (ISBN 0-911934-11-1). Am Jewish Hist Soc.

--The Jews of the West: The Metropolitan Years. (Illus.). 156p. 1975. pap. 5.95 (ISBN 0-943376-10-6). Magnes Mus.

--Modern Jewish Experience, 59 vols. 1975. Set. 1630.50x (ISBN 0-405-06690-2). Ayer Co Pubs.

Rischin, Moses, ed. see Hapgood, Hutchins.

Risedorf, Gwen. Born Today, Born Yesterday: Reincarnation. LC 77-21406. (Myth, Magic & Superstition). (Illus.). 1977. PLB 14.65 (ISBN 0-8172-1045-8). Raintree Pubs.

Rishabchand. Sri Aurobindo: His Life Unique. (Illus.). 427p. 1981. 20.00 (ISBN 0-89071-326-X, Pub. by Sri Aurobindo Ashram India); pap. 15.00 (ISBN 0-89071-325-1, Pub. by Sri Aurobindo Ashram India). Matagiri.

Rishabhchand. The Integral Yoga of Sri Aurobindo. 473p. 1974. pap. 5.30 (ISBN 0-89071-281-6). Matagiri.

Riskin, Shlomo. The Wife's Role in Initiating Divorce in Jewish Law & the Agunah Problem: A Halakhic Solution. 1987. 17.95 (ISBN 0-88125-122-4); pap. 11.95 (ISBN 0-88125-132-1). Ktav.

Rist, J. M. On the Independence of Matthew & Mark. LC 76-40840. (Society for New Testament Studies Monographs: No. 22). 1978. 24.95 (ISBN 0-521-21476-9). Cambridge U Pr.

Ristow, Kate S. & Comeaux, Maureen N. Harvest: A Faithful Approach to Life Issues for Junior High People. (Illus.). 167p. 1984. pap. 24.50 (ISBN 0-940634-20-1). Puissance Pubns.

Ritajananda, Swami. Swami Turiyananda. (Illus.). pap. 1.95 (ISBN 0-87481-473-1). Vedanta Pr.

Ritchie, Carson I. Frontier Parish: An Account of the Society for the Propagation of the Gospel & the Anglican Church in America, Drawn from the Records of the Bishop of London. LC 75-3564. 210p. 1976. 18.50 (ISBN 0-8386-1735-2). Fairleigh Dickinson.

Ritchie, George G. & Sherrill, Elizabeth. Return from Tomorrow. 128p. 1981. pap. 2.95 (ISBN 0-8007-8412-X, Spire Bks). Revell.

Ritchie, John. Feasts of Jehovah. LC 82-182. 80p. 1982. pap. 3.95 (ISBN 0-8254-3613-3). Kregel.

--Five Hundred Children's Sermon Outlines. LC 86-27396. 128p. 1987. pap. 4.95 (ISBN 0-8254-3623-0). Kregel.

--Five Hundred Evangelistic Sermon Outlines. LC 86-27200. 128p. 1987. pap. 4.95 (ISBN 0-8254-3619-2). Kregel.

--Five Hundred Gospel Sermon Illustrations. LC 86-27201. 152p. 1987. pap. 5.95 (ISBN 0-8254-3620-6). Kregel.

--Five Hundred Gospel Sermon Outlines. LC 86-27760. 128p. 1987. pap. 4.95 (ISBN 0-8254-3621-4). Kregel.

--Five Hundred Sermon Outlines on Basic Bible Truths. LC 86-27541. 128p. 1987. pap. 4.95 (ISBN 0-8254-3618-4). Kregel.

--Five Hundred Sermon Outlines on the Christian Life. LC 86-27759. 120p. 1987. pap. 4.95 (ISBN 0-8254-3622-2). Kregel.

--From Egypt to Canaan. LC 82-220. 102p. 1982. pap. 4.50 (ISBN 0-8254-3614-1). Kregel.

--The Tabernacle. LC 82-178. 122p. 1982. pap. 4.50 (ISBN 0-8254-3616-8). Kregel.

--El Tabernaculo en el Desierto. Orig. Title: The Tabernacle in the Desert. (Span.). 144p. Date not set. pap. 3.95 (ISBN 0-8254-1616-7). Kregel.

Ritchie, Judith & Niggemeyer, Vickie. Holy Days: Holidays. LC 78-23841. (Illus.). 1978. 7.95 (ISBN 0-915134-48-9). Mott Media.

Ritschl, Dietrich. The Logic of Theology. Bowden, John, tr. LC 86-45920. 336p. 1987. pap. 24.95 (ISBN 0-8006-1975-7). Fortress.

Ritter, Gerhard. Luther: His Life & Work. Riches, John, tr. from Ger. LC 78-2717. 1978. Repr. of 1963 ed. lib. bdg. 24.25x (ISBN 0-313-20347-4, RILU). Greenwood.

Ritter, K. Comparative Geography of Palestine & the Sinaitic Peninsula, 4 Vols. LC 68-26367. (Reference Ser., No. 44). 1969. Repr. of 1865 ed. Set. lib. bdg. 159.95x (ISBN 0-8383-0180-0). Haskell.

Ritter, Karl. The Comparative Geography of Palestine, 4 vols. 1865. Set. 65.00x (ISBN 0-403-03564-3). Scholarly.

--Comparative Geography of Palestine & the Sinaitic Peninsula, 4 Vols. Gage, William L., tr. LC 69-10151. 1969. Repr. of 1866 ed. Set. lib. bdg. 71.00x (ISBN 0-8371-0638-9, RISP). Greenwood.

Rittmayer, Jane F. Life, Time. 1st ed. pap. 31.80 (ISBN 0-317-26230-0, 2055572). Bks Demand UMI.

Rittner, Carol & Myers, Sondra. Courage to Care: Rescuers of Jews During the Holocaust. 176p. 1986. 24.95 (ISBN 0-8147-7397-4). NYU Pr.

Riva, Anna. Powers of the Psalms. 128p. (Orig.). 1982. pap. 3.95 (ISBN 0-943832-07-1). Intl Imports.

--Spellcraft, Hexcraft & Witchcraft. (Illus.). 64p. 1977. pap. 3.50 (ISBN 0-943832-00-4). Intl Imports.

Rivas, Jose G., tr. see Torrey, R. A.

Rivera, Roberto A., ed. Apocalipsis. (Span.). 96p. 1980. pap. 3.25 (ISBN 0-87148-028-X). Pathway Pr.

--El Nacimiento del Mesias. (Span.). 172p. 1983. pap. 4.95 (ISBN 0-87148-308-4). Pathway Pr.

Rivers, Caryl. Virgins. 256p. 1984. 12.95 (ISBN 0-312-84951-6, Pub. by Marek). St Martin.

Rivers, Elias, ed. see Lincoln, Victoria.

Rivers, Gloria R. Cosmic Consciousness: The Highway to Wholeness. Cramer, Owen, ed. (Orig.). 1987. pap. text ed. 12.00 (ISBN 0-918341-01-9). Temple Pubns.

Rives, Elsie. Abraham: Man of Faith. (BibLearn Ser.). (Illus.). 1976. 5.95 (ISBN 0-8054-4223-5, 4242-23). Broadman.

--The Shoemakes: God's Helpers. LC 86-4148. (Meet the Missionary Ser.). 1986. pap. 5.50 (ISBN 0-8054-4328-2). Broadman.

Rivet, Mother Mary M. Influence of the Spanish Mystics on the Works of Saint Francis De Sales. LC 79-115355. (Catholic University of America. Studies in Romance Languages & Literatures: No. 22). Repr. of 1941 ed. 20.00 (ISBN 0-404-50322-5). AMS Pr.

Rivkin, Ellis. A Hidden Revolution: The Pharisee's Search for the Kingdom Within. LC 78-17180. 1978. 13.95 (ISBN 0-687-16970-4). Abingdon.

--What Crucified Jesus? The Political Execution of a Charismatic. 128p. 1984. pap. 7.50 (ISBN 0-687-44637-6). Abingdon.

Rivkin, Nacha. Reishis Chochmah. (Illus.). 64p. text ed. 3.50 (ISBN 0-914131-54-0, A01); wkbk. 3.00 (ISBN 0-914131-55-9). Torah Umesorah.

--Reishis Chochmah, Vol. II. (Illus.). 100p. 4.75 (ISBN 0-914131-56-7, A03). Torah Umesorah.

Rix, Herbert D. Martin Luther: The Man & the Image. 335p. 1983. text ed. 37.50x (ISBN 0-8290-0554-4). Irvington.

Rizvi, Allama S. Element of Islamic Studies. Anwarali, Maulana, ed. Rizvi, Saeed A., tr. LC 84-52745. 60p. 1984. pap. 3.95 (ISBN 0-940368-44-7). Tahrike Tarsile Quran.

Rizvi, S. Muhammad, tr. see Ar-Razi, Al-Kulayni.

Rizvi, S. Saeed, tr. see At-Tabatabai, S. Muhammad.

Rizvi, S. Saeed, tr. see Husayn at-Tabatabai, S. Muhammad.

Rizvi, Saeed A., tr. see Rizvi, Allama S.

Rizzuto, Ana-Maria. The Birth of the Living God: A Psychoanalytic Study. LC 78-10475. (Illus.). 246p. 1981. pap. 8.50x (ISBN 0-226-72102-7). U of Chicago Pr.

Roach, Joyce G., jt. ed. see Alter, Judy.

Roach, Michael L. Outreach Through Neighborhood Bible Study. 54p. 1986. 3.50 (ISBN 0-317-52739-8). Herald Hse.

Roadcup, David. Ministering to Youth. LC 79-92586. (Bible College Textbooks Ser.). 256p. (Orig.). 1980. pap. text ed. 6.95 (ISBN 0-87239-395-X, 88582). Standard Pub.

Roadcup, David, jt. ed. see Underwood, Jon.

Roark, Dallas M. Christian Faith: Introduction to Christian Thought. 1977. pap. 4.95 (ISBN 0-8010-7652-8). Baker Bk.

--Dietrich Bonhoeffer. Patterson, Bob E., ed. LC 72-76439. (Makers of the Modern Theological Mind Ser.). 140p. 1972. 8.95 (ISBN 0-87680-253-6, 80253). Word Bks.

Roback, A. A. The Story of Yiddish Literature. 75.00 (ISBN 0-87968-084-9). Gordon Pr.

Roback, A. A., ed. The Albert Schweitzer Jubilee Book. LC 79-97392. (Illus.). 508p. Repr. of 1945 ed. lib. bdg. 24.50x (ISBN 0-8371-2670-3, ASJB). Greenwood.

Robb, Anita P. Encounter. (Illus.). 153p. (Orig.). 1982. pap. 3.95 (ISBN 0-89216-048-9). Salvation Army.

Robb, Carol S., jt. ed. see Deats, Paul.

Robb, Carol S., intro. by see Harrison, Beverly W.

Robb, Ed & Robb, Julia. Betrayal of the Church: Apostasy & Renewal in the Mainline Denominations. LC 86-71006. 304p. (Orig.). 1986. pap. 8.95 (ISBN 0-89107-403-1, Crossway Bks). Good News.

Robb, J. Wesley. The Reverent Skeptic. LC 79-83609. 238p. 1979. 12.50 (ISBN 0-8022-2245-5). Philos Lib.

Robb, James, ed. see Parr, Roger P.

Robb, James H. Man As Infinite Spirit. (Aquinas Lecture). 1974. 7.95 (ISBN 0-87462-139-9). Marquette.

--Saint Thomas Aquinas: Questions on the Soul. (Medieval Philosophical Texts in Translation: NO. 27). 1984. 24.95 (ISBN 0-87462-226-3). Marquette.

Robb, Julia, jt. auth. see Robb, Ed.

Robb, R. I., ed. see Bhashycharaya, Pundit M.

Robb, Richard I., ed. The Secret Doctrine of H. P. Blavatsky: First International Symposium, July 1984. 112p. 1984. pap. 7.00 (ISBN 0-913510-52-1). Wizards.

Robbert, G. S. Luther As Interpreter of Scripture. LC 12-2960. 1982. pap. 9.95 (ISBN 0-570-03867-7). Concordia.

Robbins, Duffy. Programming to Build Disciples. 64p. 1987. pap. 4.95 (ISBN 0-89693-573-6). Victor Bks.

Robbins, Edward M. The Christian Church & the Equal Rights Amendment. Graves, Helen, ed. LC 85-40892. 80p. 1986. pap. 6.95 (ISBN 0-938232-95-9, Dist. by Baker & Taylor Co.). Winston-Derek.

Robbins, James R. At The River I Stand. 5.95 (ISBN 0-8062-2426-6). Carlton.

Robbins, Jhan. Marriage Made in Heaven: The Story of Billy & Ruth Graham. 192p. 1983. 13.95 (ISBN 0-399-12849-2, Putnam). Putnam Pub Group.

Robbins, John W. Cornelius VanTil: The Man & the Myth. (Trinity Papers: No. 15). 40p. (Orig.). 1986. pap. 2.45 (ISBN 0-940931-15-X). Trinity Found.

--Scripture Twisting in the Seminaries, Part 1: Feminism. (Trinity Papers: No. 10). 116p. (Orig.). 1985. pap. 5.95 (ISBN 0-940931-10-9). Trinity Found.

--War & Peace: A Christian Foreign Policy. (Trinity Papers: No. 1). 250p. (Orig.). 1987. pap. 8.95 (ISBN 0-940931-21-4). Trinity Found.

Robbins, John W., ed. & intro. by see Machen, J. Gresham.

Robbins, Keith, ed. Religion & Humanism: Papers Read at the Eighteenth Summer Meeting & the Nineteenth Winter Meeting of the Ecclesiastical History Society. (Studies in Church History: Vol. 17). (Illus.). 378p. 1981. 45.00x (ISBN 0-631-18050-8). Basil Blackwell.

Robbins, Ray F. The Revelation of Jesus Christ. LC 75-1739. 240p. 1976. bds. 6.50 (ISBN 0-8054-1354-5). Broadman.

Robbins, Richard S. Bible Stories in Action for Children. 1981. 4.50 (ISBN 0-89536-475-1, 0209). CSS of Ohio.

Robbins, Rossell H., jt. auth. see Brown, Carleton.

Robbins, Thomas & Anthony, Dick, eds. In Gods We Trust: New Patterns of Religious Pluralism in America. LC 79-66441. 224p. 1980. pap. text ed. 12.95 (ISBN 0-87855-746-6). Transaction Bks.

Robbins, Thomas & Robertson, Roland, eds. Church-State Relations: Tensions & Transitions. 380p. 1986. 29.95 (ISBN 0-88738-108-1); pap. 14.95 (ISBN 0-88738-651-2). Transaction Bks.

Robbins, Thomas, et al, eds. Cults, Culture & the Law: Perspectives on New Religious Movements. (American Academy of Religion Studies in Religion: No. 36). 1985. 18.95 (ISBN 0-89130-832-6, 01 00 36); pap. 13.50 (ISBN 0-89130-833-4). Scholars Pr GA.

Robbins, Vernon K. Jesus the Teacher: A Socio-Rhetorical Interpretation of Mark. LC 83-16504. 256p. 1984. 23.95 (ISBN 0-8006-0719-8, 1-719). Fortress.

Robbins, William. Newman Brothers: An Essay in Comparative Intellectual Biography. LC 66-4976. (Illus.). 1966. 15.00x (ISBN 0-674-62200-6). Harvard U Pr.

Robeck, Cecil M., jt. ed. see Dayton, Donald W.

Robeck, Nesta de see De Robeck, Nesta.

Roberg, Alex, jt. ed. see Ottensoser, Max.

Robert. Dictionnaire de Proverbes & Dictons. 45.00 (ISBN 0-317-45633-4). French & Eur.

Robert, Carl. Bild und Lied: Archaologische Beitrage Zur Geschichte der Griechischen Heldensage. facsimile ed. LC 75-10653. (Ancient Religion & Mythology Ser.). (Ger., Illus.). 1976. Repr. of 1881 ed. 20.00x (ISBN 0-405-07277-5). Ayer Co Pubs.

Robert, Charles, ed. Manipulated Man: The Power of Man Over Man, Its Risks & Its Limits. European Studies. Strasbourg, September 24-29, 1973. Frank, C. P., tr. LC 77-24330. (Pittsburgh Theological Monographs: No. 16). 1977. pap. 8.00 (ISBN 0-915138-21-2). Pickwick.

Robert L. Humphrey, J. D., & Associates Staff. Paradigm Shift: Teach the Universal Values. LC 83-83386. (Illus.). 100p. 1984. pap. 7.95 (ISBN 0-915761-00-9). Life Values Pr.

Roberto, D. The Love of Mary. LC 83-51545. 240p. 1985. pap. 5.00 (ISBN 0-89555-235-3). Tan Bks Pubs.

Roberto, John, ed. Creative Communication & Community Building. LC 81-83635. (Creative Resources for Youth Ministry Ser.: Vol. 1). (Illus.). 108p. (Orig.). 1981. pap. 8.95 (ISBN 0-88489-135-6). St Mary's.

--Creative Learning Experiences. LC 81-83636. (Creative Resources for Youth Ministry Ser.: Vol. 2). (Illus.). 144p. (Orig.). 1981. pap. 8.95 (ISBN 0-88489-136-4). St Mary's.

--Creative Projects & Worship Experiences. LC 81-86367. (Creative Resources for Youth Ministry Ser.: Vol. 3). (Illus.). 80p. (Orig.). 1981. pap. 8.95 (ISBN 0-88489-137-2). St Mary's.

Roberts. Witches & Witch-Hunters. 1978. Repr. of 1973 ed. lib. bdg. 27.50 (ISBN 0-8414-2928-6). Folcroft.

Roberts, jt. auth. see Kruschwitz.

Roberts, A., ed. see Ante-Nicene Fathers.

Roberts, Alexander, jt. tr. see Donaldson, James.

Roberts, Allen E. The Craft & Its Symbols. 5th printing ed. LC 73-89493. (Illus.). 92p. 1985. Repr. text ed. 7.50 (ISBN 0-88053-058-8). Macoy Pub.

--Freemasonry in American History. (Illus.). 504p. 1985. text ed. 20.00 (ISBN 0-88053-078-2). Macoy Pub.

--How to Conduct a Leadership Seminar. 11p. 1970. pap. 1.00 (ISBN 0-88053-013-8). Macoy Pub.

Roberts, Anne F. & Cockrell, Marcia W., eds. Historic Albany: Its Churches & Synagogues. (Illus.). 415p. (Orig.). 1986. pap. 15.00 (ISBN 0-941237-00-1). Libr Commns Servs.

Roberts, Arthur O. Move over, Elijah. LC 67-24903. 161p. 1967. 3.50 (ISBN 0-913342-11-4). Barclay Pr.

Roberts, Augustine. Centered on Christ. LC 79-4036. 1979. pap. 7.95 (ISBN 0-932506-03-8). St Bedes Pubns.

Roberts, B. H. Comprehensive History of The Church of Jesus Christ of Latter-day Saints, 6 vols plus index. (Illus.). 1965. Vols. 1-6. 12.95 ea.; Vol. 1. (ISBN 0-8425-0299-8); Vol. 2. (ISBN 0-8425-0300-5); Vol. 3. (ISBN 0-8425-0301-3); Vol. 4. (ISBN 0-8425-0482-6); Vol. 5. (ISBN 0-8425-0304-8); Vol. 6. (ISBN 0-8425-0305-6); Index. 9.95 (ISBN 0-8425-0627-6). Brigham.

--Outlines of Ecclesiastical History. LC 79-9744. 1979. 7.95 (ISBN 0-87747-748-5). Deseret Bk.

--Studies of the Book of Mormon. Madsen, Brigham D., ed. LC 84-236. (Illus.). 412p. 1985. 21.95 (ISBN 0-252-01043-4). U of Ill Pr.

Roberts, B. H., intro. by. History of the Church, 7 vols. Incl. Vol. 1 (1820-1834) 511p. 1974 (ISBN 0-87747-074-X); Vol. 2 (1834-1837) 543p. 1974 (ISBN 0-87747-075-8); Vol. 3 (1834-1839) 478p (ISBN 0-87747-076-6); Vol. 4 (1839-1842) 620p (ISBN 0-87747-077-4); Vol. 5 (1842-1843) 563p (ISBN 0-87747-078-2); Vol. 6 (1843-1844) 641p (ISBN 0-87747-079-0); Vol. 7 (period 2, The Apostolic Interregnum) 640p (ISBN 0-87747-080-4). 15.95 ea.; index 15.95 (ISBN 0-87747-291-2). Deseret Bk.

Roberts, B. T. Why Another Sect? (The Higher Christian Life Ser.). 321p. 1985. lib. bdg. 40.00 (ISBN 0-8240-6441-0). Garland Pub.

Roberts, Bernadette. The Experience of No-Self: A Contemplative Journey. LC 84-5500. 204p. 1984. pap. 9.95 (ISBN 0-87773-289-2, 72693-6). Shambhala Pubns.

--The Path to No-Self: Life at the Center. LC 84-19340. 224p. (Orig.). 1985. pap. 9.95 (ISBN 0-87773-306-6, 72999-4). Shambhala Pubns.

Roberts, Brigham H. Mormon Doctrine of Deity: The Roberts-Van der Donckt Discussion. 296p. 1975. 9.95 (ISBN 0-88290-058-7). Horizon Utah.

Roberts, Cara. Teaching with Object Talks. (Illus.). 48p. (Orig.). 1982. pap. 2.95 (ISBN 0-87239-533-2, 2889). Standard Pub.

Roberts, D. S. Faith, Hope & Love: Learning about I Corinthians 13. LC 56-1397. (Concept Books Series Four). 1983. pap. 3.95 (ISBN 0-570-08526-8). Concordia.

Roberts, Debbie. Rejoice: A Biblical Study of the Dance. 98p. 1982. pap. 3.95 (ISBN 0-938612-02-6). Revival Press.

Roberts, Dennis. Islam: A Concise Introduction. LC 81-47845. 224p. 1982. pap. 7.95 (ISBN 0-06-066880-6, CN 4026, HarpR). Har-Row.

--Well... Excuse Me. LC 80-84233. 48p. (Orig.). 1980. pap. 1.50 (ISBN 0-89081-265-9). Harvest Hse.

Roberts, Don. Prayers for the Young Child. 1981. pap. 7.95 (ISBN 0-570-04051-5, 56-1717). Concordia.

Roberts, Donald. Grace: God's Special Gift. 1982. pap. 3.95 (ISBN 0-570-04060-4, 56-1363). Concordia.

Roberts, Donald L. The Perfect Church. LC 79-56331. 95p. (Orig.). 1980. pap. 2.95 (ISBN 0-87509-267-5). Chr Pubns.

--The Practicing Church. LC 1-67318. 100p. (Orig.). 1981. pap. 2.95 (ISBN 0-87509-303-5). Chr Pubns.

Roberts, Douglas. To Adam with Love. pap. write for info (ISBN 0-515-09536-2). Jove Pubns.

Roberts, Evan, jt. auth. see Penn-Lewis, Jessie.

Roberts, Frances J. Come Away, My Beloved. 1970. 9.95 (ISBN 0-932814-01-8); pap. 6.95 (ISBN 0-932814-02-6). Kings Farspan.

--Dialogues with God. 1968. 6.95 (ISBN 0-932814-07-7); pap. 4.95 (ISBN 0-932814-08-5). Kings Farspan.

--Launch Out! 1964. 2.95 (ISBN 0-932814-21-2). Kings Farspan.

--Learn to Reign. 1963. 2.95 (ISBN 0-932814-22-0). Kings Farspan.

--Listen to the Silence. 1964. 2.95 (ISBN 0-932814-23-9). Kings Farspan.

--Living Water. 1965. 2.95 (ISBN 0-932814-20-4). Kings Farspan.

--Lovest Thou Me? 1967. 2.95 (ISBN 0-932814-19-0). Kings Farspan.

--On the Highroad of Surrender. 1973. 6.95 (ISBN 0-932814-14-X); pap. 4.95 (ISBN 0-932814-15-8). Kings Farspan.

--Progress of Another Pilgrim. 1970. 6.95 (ISBN 0-932814-10-7); pap. 4.95 (ISBN 0-932814-11-5). Kings Farspan.

--Sounding of the Trumpet. 1966. 2.95 (ISBN 0-932814-24-7). Kings Farspan.

--When the Latch Is Lifted. 1970. 3.95 (ISBN 0-932814-18-2). Kings Farspan.

Roberts, Frank. To All Generations, a Study of Church History. 276p. (Orig.). 1981. pap. text ed. 10.95 (ISBN 0-933140-17-7); leader's guide 7.95 (ISBN 0-933140-18-5). CRC Pubns.

Roberts, Frank, ed. Songs of Joyful Praise. 1975. pap. 2.00x (ISBN 0-88027-060-8). Firm Foun Pub.

Roberts, Helen M. Mission Tales: Stories of the Historic California Missions: Missions San Diego, San Luis Rey, San Juan Capistrano, Vol. 1. LC 62-11254. (Illus.). 91p. 1962. 5.95x (ISBN 0-87015-244-0). Pacific Bks.

--Mission Tales: Stories of the Historic California Missions: Missions San Gabriel, San Fernando Rey, San Buenaventura, Vol. 2. LC 62-11254. (Illus.). 92p. 1962. 5.95x (ISBN 0-87015-245-9). Pacific Bks.

--Mission Tales: Stories of the Historic California Missions: Missions Santa Barbara, Santa Ines, Purisima, Vol. 3. LC 62-11254. (Illus.). 95p. 1962. 5.95x (ISBN 0-87015-246-7). Pacific Bks.

--Mission Tales: Stories of the Historic California Missions: Missions San Luis Obispo, San Miguel, San Antonio, Vol. 4. LC 62-11254. (Illus.). 92p. 1962. 5.95x (ISBN 0-87015-247-5). Pacific Bks.

--Mission Tales: Stories of the Historic California Missions: Missions Soledad, San Carlos, San Juan Bautista, Vol. 5. LC 62-11254. (Illus.). 88p. 1962. 5.95x (ISBN 0-87015-248-3). Pacific Bks.

Roberts, Howard W. The Lasting Words of Jesus. LC 85-12288. 1986. pap. 4.95 (ISBN 0-8054-2257-9). Broadman.

--Learning to Pray. LC 82-74296. 1984. pap. 4.95 (ISBN 0-8054-5195-1). Broadman.

--Redemptive Responses of Jesus. (Orig.). 1987. pap. 5.95 (ISBN 0-8054-5715-1). Broadman.

Roberts, J. Deotis. Black Theology in Dialogue. LC 86-15665. 132p. (Orig.). 1987. pap. 12.95 (ISBN 0-664-24022-4). Westminster.

--Roots of a Black Future: Family & Church. LC 80-16788. 152p. 1980. pap. 8.95 (ISBN 0-664-24333-9). Westminster.

Roberts, J. Deotis, jt. ed. see Gardiner, James J.

Roberts, J. J., jt. auth. see Miller, Patrick D., Jr.

Roberts, J. J., jt. ed. see Goedicke, Hans.

Roberts, J. J. M., jt. auth. see Miller, Patrick D.

Roberts, James D. Black Theology Today: Liberation & Contextualization. LC 83-17246. (Toronto Studies in Theology: Vol. 12). 218p. 1984. 49.95x (ISBN 0-88946-755-2). E Mellen.

Roberts, Jane. How to Develop Your ESP Power. new ed. LC 66-17331. 264p. 1980. pap. 7.95 (ISBN 0-8119-0379-6). Fell.

Roberts, Jim & Scheck, Joann. Bible Pop-O-Rama Books, 2 vols. Incl. The Brightest Star (ISBN 0-8066-1601-6, 10-0915); When Jesus Was a Boy (ISBN 0-8066-1602-4, 10-7064). (Illus.). 1978. laminated 1.95 ea. Augsburg.

Roberts, Keith A. Religion in Sociological Perspective. 466p. 1984. 31.00x (ISBN 0-256-03127-4). Dorsey.

Roberts, Kenneth J. The Evangelizers. Waters, Anna M., ed. (Illus.). 100p. (Orig.). 1984. pap. text ed. 3.50 (ISBN 0-9610984-2-2). PAX Tapes.

--Mary, the Perfect Prayer Partner. Waters, Anna Marie, ed. LC 83-61151. (Illus.). 128p. (Orig.). 1983. pap. 3.95 (ISBN 0-9610984-1-4). Pax Tapes.

--Playboy to Priest. LC 78-169145. 304p. 1974. pap. 4.95 (ISBN 0-87973-782-4). Our Sunday Visitor.

--Pray It Again, Sam. Ruskin, Anna Marie, ed. LC 83-61243. 116p. (Orig.). 1983. pap. 3.95 (ISBN 0-9610984-0-6). Pax Tapes.

--You Better Believe It. LC 77-84944. (Illus.). 1977. pap. 5.95 (ISBN 0-87973-750-6). Our Sunday Visitor.

Roberts, Oral. The Call. 1982. pap. 1.25 (ISBN 0-380-01078-X, 10678). Avon.

--Your Road to Recovery. 224p. 1986. 12.95 (ISBN 0-8407-9058-9). Oliver-Nelson.

Roberts, Patricia, ed. Parenting Alone. 1980. pap. 4.50 (ISBN 0-8309-0297-X). Herald Hse.

Roberts, Peg. Devotions for New Parents. 85p. 1984. 4.95 (ISBN 0-8010-7727-3). Baker Bk.

--Good Morning, Lord: Devotions for Today's Homemakers. 96p. 1982. 4.95 (ISBN 0-8010-7718-4). Baker Bk.

Roberts, Peter. In Search of Early Christian Unity. 1985. 18.00 (ISBN 0-533-05859-7). Vantage.

Roberts, Ransom. How to Have a Happier Year: Take a Number (Nonsense Numerology) LC 81-90709. (Illus.). 128p. (Orig.). 1982. pap. 5.95 (ISBN 0-9607834-0-7). Uptown Bks.

Roberts, Richard. From Eden to Eros: Origins of the Put down of Women. (Illus.). 167p. (Orig.). 1985. pap. 8.95x (ISBN 0-942380-05-3). Vernal Equinox.

--Jesus of Poets & Prophets. LC 74-118546. 1971. Repr. of 1919 ed. 22.50x (ISBN 0-8046-1171-8, Pub. by Kennikat). Assoc Faculty Pr.

--The Jesus of Poets & Prophets. 1977. Repr. of 1920 ed. lib. bdg. 25.00 (ISBN 0-8492-2312-1). R West.

Roberts, Richard O. Revival! 186p. 1982. pap. 6.95 (ISBN 0-8423-5575-8). Tyndale.

Roberts, Robert. The Social Laws of the Qoran. 136p. 1982. text ed. 11.95x (ISBN 0-7007-0009-9, Pub. by Curzon Pr England). Apt Bks.

Roberts, Robert C. Spirituality & Human Emotion. 134p. 1983. pap. 5.95 (ISBN 0-8028-1939-7). Eerdmans.

--The Strengths of a Christian. LC 84-3498. (Spirituality & the Christian Life Ser.: Vol. 2). 118p. 1984. pap. 7.95 (ISBN 0-664-24613-3). Westminster.

Roberts, Roger. Holiness: Every Christian's Calling. LC 85-11330. 1985. pap. 5.95 (ISBN 0-8054-1956-X). Broadman.

Roberts, Roger L., ed. see Julian of Norwich.

Roberts, Roy R. God Has a Better Idea: The Home. pap. 4.95 (ISBN 0-88469-023-7). BMH Bks.

--Life in the Pressure Cooker: Studies in James. pap. 4.95 (ISBN 0-88469-033-4). BMH Bks.

Roberts, S. C. Doctor Watson: Prolegomena to the Study of a Biographical Problem. LC 73-16388. lib. bdg. 10.00 (ISBN 0-8414-7268-8). Folcroft.

Roberts, S. C., ed. see Browne, T. & Johnson, Samuel.

Roberts, Samuel K., jt. auth. see Bakke, Raymond J.

Roberts, Sharon L. Somebody Lives Inside: The Holy Spirit. (Concept Ser.). (Illus.). 24p. (Orig.). 1986. pap. 3.95 saddlestitched (ISBN 0-570-08530-6, 56-1557). Concordia.

Roberts, Ted. Failing Forward. 1985. pap. 4.95 (ISBN 0-89081-432-5). Harvest Hse.

Roberts, Ursula. Reminiscences: A Lifetime of Spiritualism. 115p. 1985. 20.00x (ISBN 0-7212-0726-X, Pub. by Regency Pr). State Mutual Bk.

Roberts, W. Rhys. Dionysius of Halicarnassus, on Literary Composition & Dionysius of Halicarnassus: The Three Literary Letters (EP. AD Ammaeum I, EP. AD Popeium, EP. AD Ammaeum II, 2 vols. Taran, Leonardo, ed. (Ancient Greek Literature Ser.). 616p. 1987. lib. bdg. 90.00 (ISBN 0-8240-7766-0). Garland Pub.

Roberts, Wes, jt. auth. see Wright, Norman.

Roberts, William O. Initiation to Adulthood: An Ancient Rite of Passage in Contemporary Form. LC 82-18544. 208p. (Orig.). 1983. pap. 7.95 (ISBN 0-8298-0629-6). Pilgrim NY.

Roberts, William P. Encounters with Christ: An Introduction to the Sacraments. 256p. (Orig.). 1985. pap. 8.95 (ISBN 0-8091-2707-5). Paulist Pr.

--Marriage: Sacrament of Hope & Challenge. 136p. 1983. pap. text ed. 4.75 (ISBN 0-86716-019-5). St Anthony Mess Pr.

--Touchstones for Prayer. 98p. 1983. pap. text ed. 2.95 (ISBN 0-86716-023-3). St Anthony Mess Pr.

Roberts, William P., ed. Commitment to Partnership: Exploring the Theology of Marriage. 1987. pap. 10.95. Paulist Pr.

Robertson, A. T. Una Armonia De los Cuatro Evangelios. Patterson, W. F., tr. from Eng. Orig. Title: Harmony of the Four Gospels. (Span.). 259p. 1986. pap. 4.95 (ISBN 0-311-04302-X). Casa Bautista.

--Estudios en el Nuevo Testamento. Hale, Sara A., tr. from Eng. Orig. Title: Studies in the New Testament. (Span.). 224p. 1983. pap. 3.50 (ISBN 0-311-03629-5). Casa Bautista.

--A Harmony of the Gospels. 1932. 12.45i (ISBN 0-06-066890-3, HarpR). Har-Row.

--Word Pictures in the New Testament, 6 vols. 1982. 75.00 (ISBN 0-8010-7710-9). Baker Bk.

Robertson, A. T. & Davis, W. Hersey. New Short Grammar of the Greek New Testament. 10th ed. 1977. pap. 12.95 (ISBN 0-8010-7656-0). Baker Bk.

Robertson, A. T., jt. auth. see Monser, Harold E.

Robertson, Alec. Interpretation of Plainchant: A Preliminary Study. Repr. of 1937 ed. lib. bdg. 22.50x (ISBN 0-8371-4322-5, ROPL). Greenwood.

Robertson, Archibald. Morals in World History. LC 74-6354. (World History Ser., No. 48). 1974. lib. bdg. 49.95x (ISBN 0-8383-1918-1). Haskell.

--Word Pictures in the New Testament, 6 vols. Incl. Vol. 1. Matthew & Mark (ISBN 0-8054-1301-4); Vol. 2. Luke (ISBN 0-8054-1302-2); Vol. 3. Acts (ISBN 0-8054-1303-0); Vol. 4. Epistles of Paul (ISBN 0-8054-1304-9); Vol. 5. John & Hebrews (ISBN 0-8054-1305-7); Vol. 6. Genesis, Epistles, Revelation & John (ISBN 0-8054-1306-5). 1943. 11.95 ea.; Set. 67.50 (ISBN 0-8054-1307-3). Broadman.

Robertson, Archibald & Plummer, Alfred. A Critical & Exegitical Commentary on the First Epistle of St. Paul to the Corinthians. Driver, Samuel R. & Briggs, Charles A., eds. (International Critical Commentary Ser.). 496p. 1914. 24.95 (ISBN 0-567-05027-0, Pub. by T & T Clark Ltd UK). Fortress.

Robertson, Archibald T. Grammar of the Greek New Testament in the Light of Historical Research. 1947. 45.00 (ISBN 0-8054-1308-1). Broadman.

--That Old-Time Religion. LC 78-24159. 1979. Repr. of 1950 ed. lib. bdg. 24.75x (ISBN 0-313-20823-9, ROOT). Greenwood.

Robertson, Arthur. Matthew. (Everyman's Bible Commentary Ser.). (Orig.). 1983. pap. 5.95 (ISBN 0-8024-0233-X). Moody.

Robertson, C. Alton. Is God Still Here: Q-Book No. 15. (Orig.). 1968. pap. 0.75 (ISBN 0-377-86371-8). Friend Pr.

Robertson, C. N. Oneida Community Profiles. (Illus.). 1977. 10.00x (ISBN 0-8156-0140-9). Syracuse U Pr.

Robertson, Constance N. Oneida Community: The Breakup, 1876 - 1881. LC 72-38405. (New York State Studies). (Illus.). 330p. 1972. 14.95x (ISBN 0-8156-0086-0). Syracuse U Pr.

Robertson, D. B. Reinhold Niebuhr's Works: A Bibliography. LC 83-16840. 282p. 1984. lib. bdg. 25.50 (ISBN 0-8191-3592-5); pap. text ed. 12.75 (ISBN 0-8191-3593-3). U Pr of Amer.

Robertson, D. B., ed. see Niebuhr, Reinhold.

Robertson, D. W., Jr., tr. see Saint Augustine.

Robertson, Dede. The New You. 1984. 12.95 (ISBN 0-8407-5408-6). Nelson.

Robertson, Edwin, jt. auth. see Phillips, Vera.

Robertson, Edwin H., tr. see Lienhard, Marc.

Robertson, Edwin H., tr. see Lochman, Jan M.

Robertson, Everett, compiled by. The Ministry of Clowning. LC 82-71444. 1983. pap. 5.95 (ISBN 0-8054-7522-2). Broadman.

Robertson, Everett, ed. Puppet Scripts for Use at Church. LC 78-72843. 1979. pap. 6.95 (ISBN 0-8054-7516-8). Broadman.

--Puppet Scripts for Use at Church, No. 2. LC 78-72843. 1980. saddle-wire 6.95 (ISBN 0-8054-7519-2). Broadman.

--Using Puppetry in the Church. LC 78-72842. 1979. pap. 6.95 (ISBN 0-8054-7517-6). Broadman.

Robertson, Frederick W. Sermons on Religion & Life. 332p. 1981. Repr. of 1906 ed. lib. bdg. 15.00 (ISBN 0-89984-437-5). Century Bookbindery.

--Sermons on Religion & Life. 332p. 1983. Repr. of 1982 ed. lib. bdg. 20.00 (ISBN 0-89987-731-1). Darby Bks.

--Sermons on the Bible. 1978. Repr. of 1906 ed. lib. bdg. 35.00 (ISBN 0-8482-2315-2). Norwood Edns.

Robertson, Ian W., tr. see Barth, Karl.

Robertson, Irvine G. What the Cults Believe. rev. ed. 1966. pap. 5.95 (ISBN 0-8024-9411-0). Moody.

Robertson, J. M. Christ & Krishna. 59.95 (ISBN 0-87968-422-4). Gordon Pr.

Robertson, J. N., tr. see Orthodox Eastern Church.

Robertson, James C. & Sheppard, J. B., eds. Materials for the History of Thomas Becket, 7 vols. (Rolls Ser.: No. 67). Repr. of 1885 ed. Set. 308.00 (ISBN 0-8115-1135-9). Kraus Repr.

Robertson, James C., ed. see Bargrave, John.

Robertson, Jenny. Enciclopedia de Historias Biblicas. LaValle, Maria T., tr. Tr. of Encyclopedia of Bible Stories. (Span., Illus.). 272p. 1984. 12.95 (ISBN 0-311-03671-6). Casa Bautista.

--The Landybird Bible Storybook. (Illus.). 384p. 1983. 14.95 (ISBN 0-310-44440-3, 11361). Zondervan.

Robertson, John. Here I Am, God, Where Are You? 1975. pap. 2.50 (ISBN 0-8423-1416-4). Tyndale.

Robertson, John G. Milton's Fame on the Continent. Repr. of 1908 ed. lib. bdg. 8.50 (ISBN 0-8414-7462-1). Folcroft.

Robertson, John M. Comfort: Prayers & Promises for Times of Sorrow. 1977. pap. 2.95 (ISBN 0-8423-0432-0). Tyndale.

--Pardoned: Prayers & Promises for Prisoners. 1983. pap. 2.50 (ISBN 0-8423-4831-X). Tyndale.

--Perdonado. Lumpuy, Luis B., tr. from Eng. Orig. Title: Pardoned. (Span., Illus.). 64p. 1985. pap. 0.95 (ISBN 0-8297-0909-6). Life Pubs Intl.

--Roots & Wings: Prayers & Promises for Parents. 84p. 1983. pap. 2.50 (ISBN 0-8423-5712-2). Tyndale.

--Together: Prayers & Promises for Newlyweds. 64p. 1982. pap. 2.50 (ISBN 0-8423-7282-2). Tyndale.

Robertson, Joseph, ed. Concilia Scotiae, 2 Vols. LC 77-39875. (Bannatyne Club, Edinburgh. Publications: No. 113). Repr. of 1866 ed. 65.00 (ISBN 0-404-52866-X). AMS Pr.

Robertson, Leroy J., ed. Hymns from the Crossroads. (Illus.). 51p. 1965. pap. 6.00 (ISBN 0-8258-0137-0, 0-4516). Fischer Inc NY.

Robertson, O. D. Sold on Sunday School. (Orig.). 1984. pap. text ed. 3.95 (ISBN 0-87148-808-6). Pathway Pr.

Robertson, O. Palmer. The Christ of the Covenants. 1981. pap. 9.95 (ISBN 0-87552-418-4). Presby & Reformed.

Robertson, Pat. Answers to Two Hundred of Life's Most Probing Questions. 1987. pap. 3.95. Bantam.

--Le Royaume Secret. Cosson, Annie L., ed. Gimenez, Anne, tr. Tr. of The Secret Kingdom. (Fr.). 261p. 1985. pap. 2.75 (ISBN 0-8297-1277-1). Life Pubs Intl.

Robertson, Pat & Buckingham, Jamie. Shout It from the Housetops: The Story of the Founder of the Christian Broadcasting Network. LC 72-76591. 248p. 1972. pap. 3.95 (ISBN 0-88270-097-9). Bridge Pub.

Robertson, Pat & Proctor, William. Beyond Reason: How Miracles Can Change Your Life. LC 84-61470. 192p. 1984. 12.95 (ISBN 0-688-02214-6). Morrow.

--Beyond Reason: How Miracles Can Change Your Life. (Religion Ser.). 176p. 1986. pap. 3.50 (ISBN 0-553-25415-4). Bantam.

Robertson, Pat & Slosser, Bob. The Secret Kingdom: A Promise of Hope & Freedom in a World of Turmoil. LC 83-14268. 96p. 1983. 13.95 (ISBN 0-8407-5272-5). Nelson.

Robertson, Roland, jt. ed. see Robbins, Thomas.

Robertson, Roy. The Timothy Principle. 120p. 1986. pap. 4.95 (ISBN 0-89109-550-0). NavPress.

Robertson, Tomas. Baja California & Its Missions. (Illus.). 1978. pap. 3.95 (ISBN 0-910856-66-4). La Siesta.

Robertson, W. On Christian Doctrine: Augustine. 1958. pap. text ed. write for info. (ISBN 0-02-402150-4). Macmillan.

Robicsek, Francis. The Smoking Gods: Tobacco in Maya Art, History, & Religion. LC 78-64904. (Illus.). 1978. 39.50 (ISBN 0-8061-1511-4). U of Okla Pr.

Robicsek, Francis & Hale, Donald. The Maya Book of the Dead: The Ceramic Codex. LC 81-86395. (Illus.). 288p. 48.50 (ISBN 0-8061-9911-3). U of Okla Pr.

Robillard, Edmond. Reincarnation: Illusion or Reality. LC 82-1638. 182p. (Orig.). 1982. pap. 5.95 (ISBN 0-8189-0432-1). Alba.

Robillard, St. John A. Religion & the Law: Religious Liberty in Modern English Law. LC 83-197990. 224p. 1984. pap. 42.50 (ISBN 0-7190-0956-1, Pub. by Manchester Univ Pr). Longwood Pub Group.

Robinet, Jean F. Le Mouvement religieux a Paris pendant la Revolution: 1789-1801, 2 vols. LC 70-174331. (Collection de documents relatifs a l'histoire de Paris pendant la Revolution francaise). Repr. of 1898 ed. Set. 169.00 (ISBN 0-404-52567-9); 84.50 ea. Vol. 1 (ISBN 0-404-52568-7). Vol. 2 (ISBN 0-404-52569-5). AMS Pr.

Robinson, A. E. Layman & the Book. pap. 1.95 (ISBN 0-911866-58-2). Advocate.

Robinson, Alfred. Life in California Before the Conquest. LC 68-30553. (American Scene Ser). (Illus.). 1969. Repr. of 1846 ed. lib. bdg. 39.50 (ISBN 0-306-71142-7). Da Capo.

Robinson, Arthur W. The Personal Life of the Christian. 1981. pap. 7.95X (ISBN 0-19-213427-2). Oxford U Pr.

Robinson, Benjamin W. The Life of Paul. 1918. 20.00 (ISBN 0-8414-7468-0). Folcroft.

--Life of Paul. 2nd ed. LC 18-19810. (Midway Reprint Ser). 1973. pap. 16.00x (ISBN 0-226-72261-9). U of Chicago Pr.

Robinson, Charles E. A Concise History of the United Society of Believers Called Shakers. LC 75-342. (The Radical Tradition in America Ser.). 134p. 1975. Repr. of 1893 ed. 16.50 (ISBN 0-88355-245-0). Hyperion Conn.

Robinson, Daniel S. Crucial Issues in Philosophy. 1955. 6.95 (ISBN 0-8158-0177-7). Chris Mass.

Robinson, Daniel S., ed. see Gomperz, Heinrich.

Robinson, Darrell W. Total Church Life. LC 85-7900. 1985. 7.95 (ISBN 0-8054-6250-3). Broadman.

Robinson, David. Apostle of Culture: Emerson As Preacher & Lecturer. LC 81-16228. 200p. 1982. 21.00x (ISBN 0-8122-7824-0). U of Pa Pr.

--The Unitarians & the Universalists. LC 84-9031. (Denominations in America Ser.: No. 1). xiii, 368p. 1985. lib. bdg. 37.50 (ISBN 0-313-20946-4, RUN/). Greenwood.

Robinson, David, ed. Concordance to the Good News Bible: Today's English Version. 1416p. 1984. 24.95 (ISBN 0-8407-4956-2). Nelson.

--William Ellery Channing: Selected Writings. LC 84-62567. (Source of American Spirituality Ser.: Vol. 2). 320p. 1985. 12.95 (ISBN 0-8091-0359-1). Paulist Pr.

Robinson, Donald. Faith's Framework: The Structure of New Testament Theology. 152p. 1986. pap. 9.95 (ISBN 0-85364-317-2, Pub. by Paternoster UK). Attic Pr.

Robinson, Edna M. Tennyson's Use of the Bible. 119p. 1968. Repr. of 1917 ed. 12.50x (ISBN 0-87752-093-3). Gordian.

Robinson, Edward. The Original Vision: A Study of the Religious Experience of Childhood. 192p. (Orig.). 1983. pap. 7.95 (ISBN 0-8164-2439-X, HarpR). Har-Row.

Robinson, Edward, tr. see Gesenius, William.

Robinson, Edward S., tr. see Jaeger, Werner W.

Robinson, Forbes & Kilpack, Gilbert. An Inward Legacy. 1983. pap. 5.00x (ISBN 0-87574-092-8, 092). Pendle Hill.

Robinson, Forbes, tr. Coptic Apocryphal Gospels. (Texts & Studies: No. 1, Vol. 4-Pt. 2). pap. 19.00 (ISBN 0-8115-1693-8). Kraus Repr.

Robinson, Francis. Separatism among Indian Muslims: The Politics of the United Provinces' Muslims, 1860-1923. LC 73-93393. (Cambridge South Asian Studies: No. 16). pap. 121.80 (ISBN 0-317-26379-X, 2024521). Bks Demand UMI.

Robinson, Fred C. Beowulf & the Appositive Style. LC 84-11889. (Hodges Lecture Ser.). 120p. 1985. text ed. 12.95x (ISBN 0-87049-444-9); pap. 6.95x (ISBN 0-87049-531-3). U of Tenn Pr.

Robinson, Gail. God Made Only One Me. 32p. 1986. 4.95 (ISBN 0-570-04148-1). Concordia.

Robinson, Generalee. Have You Heard from Heaven Lately: Sermons for All Occasions. 1984. 8.95 (ISBN 0-533-05804-X). Vantage.

Robinson, George L. Book of Isaiah. pap. 4.50 (ISBN 0-8010-7609-9). Baker Bk.

--Twelve Minor Prophets. 5.95 (ISBN 0-8010-7669-2). Baker Bk.

--The Twelve Minor Prophets. 203p. 1981. Repr. of 1926 ed. lib. bdg. 35.00 (ISBN 0-89984-434-0). Century Bookbindery.

Robinson, H., jt. ed. see Foster, J.

Robinson, H. P. Redemption, Conceived & Revealed. 3.95 (ISBN 0-911866-59-0); pap. 2.95 (ISBN 0-911866-89-2). Advocate.

Robinson, H. Wheeler. The Christian Doctrine of Man. 368p. 1958. 19.95 (ISBN 0-567-22219-5, Pub. by T & T Clark Ltd UK). Fortress.

--History of Israel. rev. ed. Brockington, L. H., ed. (Studies in Theology: No. 42). 1964. pap. 8.95x (ISBN 0-8401-6042-9). A R Allenson.

--The History of Israel. (Studies in Theology). 206p. 1967. pap. 13.50 (ISBN 0-7156-0163-6, Pub. by Duckworth London). Longwood Pub Group.

--The Life & Faith of the Baptists. 158p. 1985. pap. 6.95 (ISBN 0-913029-09-2). Stevens Bk Pr.

Robinson, H. Wheeler & Payne, Ernest A. British Baptists: An Original Anthology. Gaustad, Edwin S., ed. LC 79-52583. (The Baptist Tradition Ser.). 1980. lib. bdg. 30.00x (ISBN 0-405-12450-3). Ayer Co Pubs.

Robinson, Haddon. Biblical Preaching. LC 80-66776. 1980. 10.95 (ISBN 0-8010-7700-1). Baker Bk.

--The Good Shepherd: Reflections on Psalm 23. 1987. pap. 1.95 (ISBN 0-8024-6688-5). Moody.

Robinson, Haddon, jt. ed. see Litfin, Duane.

Robinson, Haddon W. Grief. 24p. 1976. pap. 3.50 (ISBN 0-310-32261-8, 9772P). Zondervan.

Robinson, Henry W. Inspiration & Revelation in the Old Testament. LC 78-9891. 1979. Repr. of 1946 ed. lib. bdg. 24.75x (ISBN 0-313-21068-3, ROIR). Greenwood.

Robinson, Herbert S. & Wilson, Knox. Myths & Legends of All Nations. (Quality Paperback Ser.: No. 319). 244p. 1978. pap. 5.95 (ISBN 0-8226-0319-5). Littlefield.

Robinson, Ian S. Authority & Resistance in the Investiture Contest. LC 78-9110. 189p. 1978. text ed. 44.50x (ISBN 0-8419-0407-3). Holmes & Meier.

Robinson, Ira, ed. Cyrus Adler: Selected Letters. 1000p. 1985. 2 vols. boxed 50.00 (ISBN 0-8276-0224-3). Jewish Pubns.

Robinson, J., ed. The First Book of Kings. LC 72-80592. (Cambridge Bible Commentary on the New English Bible, Old Testament Ser.). (Illus.). 228p. 1972. pap. 12.95 (ISBN 0-521-09734-7). Cambridge U Pr.

--The Second Book of Kings. LC 75-39371. (Cambridge Bible Commentary on the New English Bible, Old Testament Ser.). (Illus.). 1976. pap. 12.95x (ISBN 0-521-09774-6). Cambridge U Pr.

Robinson, J. A. Euthaliana, Studies of Euthalius: Codex H of the Pauline Epistles & the Armenian Version. (Texts & Studies Ser.: No. 1, Vol. 3, Pt. 3). pap. 19.00 (ISBN 0-8115-1690-3). Kraus Repr.

Robinson, J. A., ed. The Passion of S. Perpetua. (Texts & Studies Ser.: No. 1, Vol. 1,Pt. 2). pap. 13.00 (ISBN 0-8115-1680-6). Kraus Repr.

Robinson, J. Armitage. Commentary on Ephesians. LC 78-59143. (Kregel Ltd Ed. Library). 320p. 1979. 14.95 (ISBN 0-8254-3612-5). Kregel.

Robinson, Jacob. Guide to Jewish History Under Nazi Impact. 1974. 45.00x (ISBN 0-87068-231-8). Ktav.

Robinson, Jacob & Sachs, Henry. The Holocaust: The Nuremberg Evidence, Part I: Documents, Digest, Index & Chronological Tables. (Yad Vashem-Yivo. Joint Documentary Projects). 1976. 30.00 (ISBN 0-914512-37-4). Yivo Inst.

Robinson, James. A Cup Running Over. (Orig.). 1987. pap. price not set (ISBN 0-89536-873-0, 7859). CSS of Ohio.

Robinson, James & Cox, Jimmie. In Search of a Father. 1979. pap. 1.95 (ISBN 0-8423-1634-5). Tyndale.

Robinson, James, tr. see Abhayadatta.

Robinson, James D. How to Use The Bible. 1982. pap. 3.25 (ISBN 0-570-03853-7, 12-2808). Concordia.

Robinson, James H. & Darline, R. One Hundred Bible Quiz Activities for Church School Classes. 1981. pap. 3.95 (ISBN 0-570-03829-4, 12-2794). Concordia.

Robinson, James M. The Nag Hammadi Library. 1978. 23.03i (ISBN 0-06-066929-2, HarpR); pap. 11.95 (CN4008). Har-Row.

--A New Quest of the Historical Jesus & Other Essays. LC 82-48586. 224p. 1983. pap. 12.95 (ISBN 0-8006-1698-7). Fortress.

Robinson, James M. & Koester, Helmut. Trajectories through Early Christianity. LC 79-141254. 312p. 1971. pap. 9.95 (ISBN 0-8006-1362-7, 1-1362). Fortress.

Robinson, James M. & Cobb, John B., Jr., eds. The Later Heidegger & Theology. LC 78-23619. 1979. Repr. of 1963 ed. lib. bdg. 22.50x (ISBN 0-313-20783-6, ROLH). Greenwood.

Robinson, James M., et al. Bultmann School of Biblical Interpretation: New Directions. Funk, Robert W. & Ebeling, Gerhard, eds. 1965. lib. bdg. 17.50x (ISBN 0-88307-242-4). Gannon.

Robinson, James W. The Beauty of Being Prepared. 1982. 4.25 (ISBN 0-89536-548-0, 0213). CSS of Ohio.

Robinson, Jessie B., jt. auth. see Eisenberg, Azriel.

Robinson, Jo Ann. A. J. Muste: Pacifist & Prophet. Mather, Eleanore P., ed. LC 81-80219. 31p. 1981. pap. 2.50x (ISBN 0-87574-235-1, 235). Pendle Hill.

Robinson, John. A Justification of Separation from the Church of England. LC 77-7427. (English Experience Ser.: No. 888). 1977. Repr. of 1610 ed. lib. bdg. 46.00 (ISBN 90-221-0888-0). Walter J Johnson.

Robinson, John A. The Body: A Study in Pauline Theology. LC 77-7221. 96p. 1977. pap. 3.95 (ISBN 0-664-24149-2). Westminster.

--Exploration into God. LC 67-26529. 1967. 4.95 (ISBN 0-8047-0322-1). Stanford U Pr.

--Honest to God. LC 63-13819. 144p. 1963. pap. 7.95 (ISBN 0-664-24465-3). Westminster.

--The Human Face of God. LC 73-78. 282p. 1979. softcover 5.95 (ISBN 0-664-24241-3). Westminster.

--Jesus & His Coming. 2nd ed. LC 79-14078. 192p. 1979. pap. 6.95 (ISBN 0-664-24278-2). Westminster.

--The Priority of John. 464p. 1987. pap. 19.95 (ISBN 0-940989-01-8). Meyer Stone Bks.

--Truth Is Two-Eyed. LC 79-25774. 174p. 1980. pap. 6.95 (ISBN 0-664-24316-9). Westminster.

--Wrestling with Romans. LC 79-11645. 160p. 1979. pap. 5.95 (ISBN 0-664-24275-8). Westminster.

Robinson, John A. T. Redating the New Testament. LC 76-17554. 384p. 1976. 15.00 (ISBN 0-664-21336-7). Westminster.

Robinson, John M. Pagan Christs. 1967. 5.95 (ISBN 0-8216-0136-9). Univ Bks.

Robinson, Joseph A. Gilbert Crispin, Abbot of Westminster: A Study of the Abby Under Norman Rule. LC 80-2211. Repr. of 1911 ed. 37.50 (ISBN 0-404-18785-4). AMS Pr.

Robinson, Lillian H. Psychiatry & Religion: Overlapping Concerns (Clinical Insights Monograph) LC 85-28728. 192p. 1986. pap. text ed. 12.00x (ISBN 0-88048-099-8, 48-099-8). Am Psychiatric.

Robinson, Lydia, tr. see Garbe, Richard.

Robinson, N. F. Monasticism in the Orthodox Church. LC 72-131506. Repr. of 1916 ed. 18.50 (ISBN 0-404-05375-0). AMS Pr.

Robinson, Paschal, tr. see Frances D'Assisi, Saint.

Robinson, Percy J., tr. see Du Creux, Francois.

Robinson, Peter S., ed. Foundation Guide for Religious Grant Seekers. LC 79-19006. (Scholars Press Handbooks in Humanities Ser.: No. 1). 1979. 10.50 (ISBN 0-89130-339-1, 001501); pap. 9.95 (ISBN 0-89130-340-5). Scholars Pr GA.

Robinson, Philip S. Sinners & Saints. LC 75-134400. Repr. of 1883 ed. 25.00 (ISBN 0-404-08444-3). AMS Pr.

Robinson, Ras. Free Indeed! (Illus.). 1983. pap. 1.00 (ISBN 0-937778-08-7). Fulness Hse.

--How to Receive God's Anointing. (Illus.). 88p. 1985. pap. text ed. 3.95 (ISBN 0-937778-10-9). Fulness Hse.

Robinson, Ras, ed. The Finest of Fulness. 192p. 1979. pap. 4.00 (ISBN 0-937778-00-1). Fulness Hse.

--Spiritual Warfare. (Illus.). 72p. 1982. pap. 3.00 (ISBN 0-937778-05-2). Fulness Hse.

Robinson, Ray & Winold, Allen. The Choral Experience: Literature, Materials, & Methods. 1976. text ed. 25.50 scp (ISBN 0-06-161419-X, HarpC). Har-Row.

Robinson, Richard H. Early Madhyamika in India & China. 1976. Repr. 18.50 (ISBN 0-8426-0904-0). Orient Bk Dist.

--Early Madhyamika in India & China. 346p. 1978. pap. 6.95 (ISBN 0-87728-433-4). Weiser.

Robinson, Richard H. & Johnson, Willard L. The Buddhist Religion: A Historical Introduction. 3rd ed. 304p. 1982. pap. text ed. write for info (ISBN 0-534-01027-X). Wadsworth Pub.

Robinson, Richard H., tr. see Cranmer-Byng, J. L.

Robinson, Robert. Ecclesiastical Researches. 1984. Repr. of 1792 ed. 37.00 (ISBN 0-317-11349-6). Church History.

Robinson, Russell D. Teaching the Scriptures: A Syllabus for Bible Study. (Illus.). 156p. 1977. 11.95 (ISBN 0-9600154-3-4); pap. 9.95 (ISBN 0-9600154-4-2). Bible Study Pr.

Robinson, S. J., jt. auth. see Urwin, J.

Robinson, Stephen E. The Testament of Adam: An Examination of the Syriac & Greek Traditions. LC 80-12209. (Society of Biblical Literature Dissertation Ser.: No. 52). pap. 13.50 (ISBN 0-89130-399-5, 06-01-52). Scholars Pr GA.

Robinson, Stewart M. And We Mutually Pledge. LC 64-17287. pap. 3.25 (ISBN 0-912806-19-2). Long Hse.

Robinson, T. The Life & Death of Mary Magdalene. Sommer, H. O., ed. (EETS ES Ser.: Vol. 78). pap. 15.00 (ISBN 0-8115-3401-4). Kraus Repr.

Robinson, T. H. Decline & Fall of the Hebrew Kingdoms. LC 74-137284. Repr. of 1926 ed. 21.50 (ISBN 0-404-05376-9). AMS Pr.

Robinson, T. H., et al, eds. Megilloth. (Biblia Hebraica Stuttgartensia Ser.). 62p. 1975. pap. 2.50x (ISBN 3-438-05213-X, 61304, Pub. by United Bible). Am Bible.

Robinson, Theodore H. The Poetry of the Old Testament. LC 75-41233. Repr. of 1947 ed. 15.00 (ISBN 0-404-14593-0). AMS Pr.

Robinson, Thomas. Studies in Romans: A Suggestive Commentary on Paul's Epistle to the Romans, 2 vols. in 1. LC 82-7795. (Kregel Bible Study Classics Ser.). 912p. 1982. 24.95 (ISBN 0-8254-3625-7). Kregel.

Robinson, Virgil. James White. LC 75-16921. (Illus.). 1976. 9.95 (ISBN 0-8280-0049-2). Review & Herald.

Robinson, Wayne. Questions Are the Answer. LC 80-36780. 110p. 1980. pap. 5.95 (ISBN 0-8298-0409-9). Pilgrim NY.

Robinson, Wayne B. The Transforming Power of the Bible. LC 83-23680. 240p. (Orig.). 1984. pap. 9.95 (ISBN 0-8298-0706-3). Pilgrim NY.

Robison, James. Attack on the Family. 1980. pap. 2.95 (ISBN 0-8423-0092-9). Tyndale.

Robison, James & Cox, Jim. Save America to Save the World. 1980. pap. 1.95 (ISBN 0-8423-5823-4). Tyndale.

Robison, John. Proofs of a Conspiracy. 1967. pap. 4.95 (ISBN 0-88279-121-4). Western Islands.

Robison, Pamela. Abinadi, Man of God. (Orig.). 1981. pap. 4.00 (ISBN 0-8309-0324-0). Herald Hse.

--Alma. 90p. 1985. pap. 5.75 (ISBN 0-8309-0409-3). Herald Hse.

Robison, R. Warren. Louisiana Church Architecture. LC 84-70619. (USL Architecture Ser.: No. 2). 90p. 1984. 19.95 (ISBN 0-940984-20-2). U of SW LA Ctr LA Studies.

Robleto, Adolfo. Catecismo Biblico y Doctrinal Para el Nuevo Creyente. 164p. 1985. pap. 1.95 (ISBN 0-311-09088-5). Casa Bautista.

--Conozca Quienes Son. (Span.). 112p. 1986. pap. 3.25 (ISBN 0-311-05764-0). Casa Bautista.

--Sermones para Dias Especiales, Tomo II. 96p. 1985. Repr. of 1984 ed. 2.75 (ISBN 0-311-07011-6). Casa Bautista.

--Sermones para Dias Especiales, Tomo I. (Span.). 112p. 1986. Repr. of 1983 ed. 2.50 (ISBN 0-311-07009-4). Casa Bautista.

Robleto, Adolfo, tr. see Conner, T.

Robleto, Adolfo, tr. see Cowman, Mrs. Charles E.

Robleto, Adolfo, tr. see Dana, H. E.

Robleto, Adolfo, tr. see Dana, H. E. & Mantey, J. R.

Robleto, Un Adolfo. Un Vistazo a la Doctrina Romana. 128p. 1984. pap. 2.95 (ISBN 0-311-05319-X). Casa Bautista.

Roboz, Helga, tr. see Marion-Wild, E. C.

Roboz, Steven & Steiner, Rudolf. Islam: Study Notes. Roboz, Steven, ed. 33p. 1980. pap. 2.95 (ISBN 0-88010-050-8, Pub. by Steiner Book Centre Canada). Anthroposophic.

Roboz, Steven, ed. The Holy Grail: From the Works of Rudolf Steiner. 2nd ed. 1984. pap. 4.75 (ISBN 0-919924-24-7, Steiner Bk Ctr). Anthroposophic.

Roboz, Steven, ed. see Roboz, Steven & Steiner, Rudolf.

Roboz, Steven, tr. see Marion-Wild, E. C.

Robson. Eternal Truths of Life. 4.75 (ISBN 0-8356-7030-9). Theos Pub Hse.

Robson, J., tr. Mishkat Al-Masabih, 2 vols. Set. 65.00x (ISBN 0-87902-068-7); Vol. 1. 35.00 (ISBN 0-87902-297-3); Vol. 2. 35.00 (ISBN 0-87902-298-1). Orientalia.

Robson, J. M., ed. see Mill, John S.

Robson, Ralph & Billings, Jean. Christian Cross-Cultural Communication. (Mini Bible Studies). (Illus.). 1978. pap. 2.50 instructor (ISBN 0-87239-202-3, 88555); pap. 1.95 student (ISBN 0-87239-198-1, 88551). Standard Pub.

Robson, W., tr. see Michaud, Joseph F.

Robson, Walter. An English View of American Quakerism: The Journal of Walter Robson 1842-1929 Written During the Fall of 1877, While Traveling Among American Friends. Bronner, Edwin B., ed. LC 71-107345. (American Philosophical Society Memoirs Ser.: Vol. 79). pap. 43.80 (ISBN 0-317-27898-3, 2025135). Bks Demand UMI.

Robynson, R., tr. see More, Thomas.

Roca, Paul M. Spanish Jesuit Churches in Mexico's Tarahumara. LC 78-14467. 369p. 1979. pap. 11.50x (ISBN 0-8165-0572-1). U of Ariz Pr.

Roccapriore, Maria. Anointing the Sick. LC 80-65722. (Illus.). 144p. (Orig.). 1980. pap. 2.95 (ISBN 0-8189-1160-3, 160, Pub. by Alba Bks). Alba.

Rocco, Sha. Sex Mythology. (Illus.). 55p. 1982. Repr. of 1874 ed. 3.00. Am Atheist.

Rocco, Sha see Sha Rocco.

Rochais, G. Les Recits de Resurrection des Morts dans le Nouveau Testament. LC 79-41615. (Society for New Testament Studies Monographs: No. 40). (Fr.). 240p. 1981. 39.50 (ISBN 0-521-22381-4). Cambridge U Pr.

Rochau, Dair. How to Raise Self Esteem. (Life Ser.). 1983. pap. 5.95 (ISBN 0-8163-0504-8). Pacific Pr Pub Assn.

Roche, Jerome. North Italian Church Music in the Age of Monteverdi. (Illus.). 1984. 45.00x (ISBN 0-19-316118-4). Oxford U Pr.

Roche de Coppens, Peter. The Nature & Use of Ritual for Spiritual Attainment. Rossner, John, ed. LC 85-10270. (Llewellyn's Spiritual Perspectives Ser.). (Illus.). 250p. (Orig.). 1985. pap. 9.95 (ISBN 0-87542-675-1, L-675). Llewellyn Pubns.

Roche de Coppens, Peter, et al, eds. see Winterhalter, Robert.

Rochelle, Jay C., tr. see Bonhoeffer, Dietrich.

Rocher, Ludo, ed. Ezourvedam: A French Veda of the Eighteenth Century. LC 84-6308. (University of Pennsylvania Studies on Southeast Asia: No. 1). 250p. 1984. 34.00x (ISBN 0-915027-05-4); pap. 16.00 (ISBN 0-915027-06-2). Benjamins North Am.

Rochester, Stuart I. American Liberal Disillusionment in the Wake of World War I. LC 76-47613. 1977. 22.50x (ISBN 0-271-01233-1). Pa St U Pr.

Rochlin, Harriett. Pioneer Jews: A New Life in the Far West. LC 83-12647. (Illus.). 1984. 17.95 (ISBN 0-395-31832-7). HM.

Rock, Francis J. J. Ross Browne: A Biography. 90p. 1984. Repr. of 1929 ed. 22.00x (ISBN 0-939738-21-X). Zubal Inc.

Rock, Judith. Theology in the Shape of Dance: Using Dance in Worship & Theological Process. 1977. 2.50 (ISBN 0-941500-16-0). Sharing Co.

Rock, Judith, jt. auth. see Adams, Doug.

Rock, Judith, jt. auth. see Mealy, Norman.

Rockaway, Robert. The Jews of Detroit: From the Beginning, 1762-1914. LC 86-15866. (Illus.). 175p. 1986. 15.95X (ISBN 0-8143-1808-8). Wayne St U Pr.

Rocke, Herman H. Check Your Panoply. 240p. 1977. pap. text ed. 4.00 (ISBN 0-910424-71-3). Concordant.

Rockefeller, Stephen C., jt. ed. see Lopez, Donald S., Jr.

Rocker, Dolore & Pierre, Kenneth J. Shared Ministry: An Integrated Approach to Leadership & Service. (Illus.). 245p. (Orig.). 1984. pap. 18.95 (ISBN 0-88489-158-5). St Mary's.

Rockhill, William H., ed. Udanavarga: A Collection of Verses from the Buddhist Canon. Repr. of 1883 ed. text ed. 20.00 (ISBN 0-89644-342-6, Pub. by Chinese Matl Ctr). Coronet Bks.

Rockhill, William W., ed. The Life of Buddha & the Early History of His Order. 285p. Repr. of 1884 ed. text ed. 19.50x (ISBN 0-89563-149-0, Pub. by Chinese Matl Ctr). Coronet Bks.

Rockland, Mae S. The Hanukkah Book. (Illus.). 190p. 1985. pap. 9.95 (ISBN 0-8052-0792-9). Schocken.

--The Jewish Party Book: A Contemporary Guide to Customs, Crafts & Foods. LC 78-54387. (Illus.). 284p. 1987. pap. 10.95 (ISBN 0-8052-0829-1). Schocken.

Rockwell, Hays H., jt. auth. see Clifford, Richard J.

Rockwell, Margaret. Stepping Out, Sharing Christ in Everyday Circumstances. LC 84-47804. 134p. 1984. pap. 5.95 (ISBN 0-89840-072-4). Heres Life.

Rockwood, Irving, ed. see Elder, Charles D. & Cobb, Roger W.

Rockwood, Raymond O., ed. Carl Becker's Heavenly City Revisited. LC 68-11256. xxxii, 227p. 1968. Repr. of 1958 ed. 23.00 (ISBN 0-208-00421-1, Archon). Shoe String.

Rodd, Cyril S., ed. The Pastor's Problems. 168p. pap. 11.65 Canada (ISBN 0-317-31449-1); pap. 8.95 (ISBN 0-317-31450-5, 30-29117-1902). Fortress.

Rodda, Dorothy, jt. auth. see Kohl, Rachel.

Roddy, Lee, jt. auth. see Douglass, Stephen B.

Rodehaver, Gladys K., jt. ed. see Easu.

Rodeheaver, Homer A. Hymnal Handbook for Standard Hymns & Gospel Songs. LC 72-1686. Repr. of 1931 ed. 17.50 (ISBN 0-404-09913-0). AMS Pr.

--Singing Black. LC 72-1681. Repr. of 1936 ed. 12.50 (ISBN 0-404-08330-7). AMS Pr.

Roden, Eva, jt. auth. see Roden, Rudolph G.

Roden, Rudolph G. & Roden, Eva. Lives on Borrowed Time. 1984. 6.95 (ISBN 0-8062-2316-2). Carlton.

Roden, Shelly. When Puppets Talk, Everybody Listens. LC 78-55265. 72p. 1978. pap. 4.95 (ISBN 0-88207-266-8). Victor Bks.

Rodenbery, C., tr. see Eugippius.

Rodes, Robert. Lay Authority & Reformation in the English Church. LC 82-7038. 319p. 1982. 25.00 (ISBN 0-268-01265-2). U of Notre Dame Pr.

Rodes, Robert E. Law & Liberation. LC 85-41011. 240p. 1986. text ed. 24.95 (ISBN 0-268-01279-2). U of Notre Dame Pr.

Rodes, Robert E., Jr. Ecclesiastical Admininstration in Medieval England: The Anglo-Saxons to the Reformation. LC 73-22584. 1977. text ed. 19.95x (ISBN 0-268-00903-1). U of Notre Dame Pr.

Rodgers, Peter. Knowing Jesus. LC 82-14832. 64p. (Orig.). pap. 1.95 (ISBN 0-87784-383-X). Inter-Varsity.

Rodgers, Susan, jt. ed. see Kipp, Rita S.

Rodin, Auguste. Cathedrals of France. rev. ed. Geissbuhler, Elisabeth C., tr. from Fr. (Art of the Middle Ages Ser.). Tr. of Cathedrales de France. (Illus.). 278p. 1981. 25.00 (ISBN 0-933806-07-8). Black Swan CT.

Rodinson, Maxime. Cult, Ghetto, & State: The Persistence of the Jewish Question. Rothschild, Jon, tr. from Fr. 239p. (Orig.). 1984. pap. 10.95 (ISBN 0-86356-020-2, Pub. by Al Saqi UK). Evergreen Dist.

--Muhammad. Carter, Anne, tr. LC 69-20189. 1980. pap. 9.95 (ISBN 0-394-73822-5). Pantheon.

Rodley, Lyn. Cave Monasteries of Byzantine Cappadocia. (Illus.). 284p. 1986. 79.50 (ISBN 0-521-26798-6). Cambridge U Pr.

Rodman, Hyman, et al. The Abortion Question. 250p. 1987. 25.00 (ISBN 0-231-05332-0). Columbia U Pr.

Rodman, Julius S. The Kahuna Sorcerers of Hawaii, Past & Present: With a Glossary of Ancient Religious Terms & the Books of the Hawaiian Royal Dead. (Illus.). 1979. 20.00 (ISBN 0-682-49196-9, Banner). Exposition Pr FL.

Rodrigue, Beryl. A Convert Looks at the Catholic Church & the World Crisis. 1981. 6.50 (ISBN 0-8062-1833-9). Carlton.

Rodrigues, Otilio, jt. tr. see Kavanaugh, Kieran.

Rodriguez, Alfonso. La Estructura Mitica del Popol Vuh. LC 84-81886. (Coleccion Polymita Ser.). (Span.). 108p. (Orig.). 1985. pap. 10.00 (ISBN 0-89729-360-6). Ediciones.

Rodriguez, Angel M. Substitution in the Hebrew Cultus, Vol. 3. (Andrews University Seminary Doctoral Dissertation Ser.). xiv, 339p. (Orig.). 1982. pap. 10.95 (ISBN 0-943872-35-9). Andrews Univ Pr.

Rodriguez, Cookie. Please Make Me Cry! 1974. pap. 2.95 (ISBN 0-88368-042-4). Whitaker Hse.

Rodriguez, Jorge A., tr. see Westberg, Granger.

Rodriguez, Oscar E., tr. see Rusbuldt, Richard E., et al.

Rodriguez, Otilio, jt. tr. see Kavanaugh, Kieran.

Rodriguez, P. Pedro. Matrimono y Familia Cristiana. LC 84-7000069. 116p. 1984. pap. 2.95 (ISBN 0-915388-20-0). Buckley Pubns.

Rodriquez, Otillo, jt. tr. see Kavanaugh, Kieran.

Rodwell, J. M., ed. & tr. Koran. 1978. pap. 3.50x (ISBN 0-460-01380-7, Evman). Biblio Dist.

Rodwell, Warwick. The Archaeology of the English Church. (Illus.). 192p. 1981. 34.95 (ISBN 0-7134-2590-3, Pub. by Batsford England). David & Charles.

Rodzianko, M. The Truth about the Russian Church Abroad. Hilko, Michael P., tr. from Rus. LC 74-29321. (Illus.). 48p. (Orig.). 1975. pap. 1.50 (ISBN 0-88465-004-9). Holy Trinity.

Roe, Earl O., ed. see Dowley, Tom.

Roe, Peter G. The Cosmic Zygote: Cosmology in the Amazon Basin. (Illus.). 451p. 1982. 42.00x (ISBN 0-8135-0896-7). Rutgers U Pr.

Roebling, Karl. Christian Science-Kingdom or Cult? 190p. 1984. 12.95 (ISBN 0-942910-09-5). Paragon-Dynapress.

--Pentecostal Origins & Trends Early & Modern. 3rd, rev. ed. LC 85-63631. 112p. 8.95 (ISBN 0-942910-12-5). Paragon-Dynapress.

--Prophecy from Here to Two Thousand. 144p. 1983. pap. 4.95 (ISBN 0-942910-06-0). Paragon DynaPress.

Roeck, Alan L. Twenty-Four Hours a Day for Everyone. LC 78-52007. 383p. (Orig.). 1977. pap. 5.95 (ISBN 0-89486-040-2). Hazelden.

Roeda, Jack. Decisions: A Study of Christian Ethics. LC 80-189628. (Orig.). 1980. pap. text ed. 4.50 (ISBN 0-933140-14-2); tchr's. manual 5.95 (ISBN 0-933140-15-0). CRC Pubns.

Roehrich, Gustave G. Essay on the Life, the Writings, & the Doctrine of the Anabaptist, Hans Denk. Foster, Claude R., et al, trs. from Fr. & Ger. LC 83-10295. 54p. (Orig.). 1983. pap. text ed. 5.50 (ISBN 0-8191-3347-7). U Pr of Amer.

Roehrs & Franzmann. Concordia Self-Study Commentary. LC 15-2721. 1979. 21.95 (ISBN 0-570-03277-6). Concordia.

Roelker, W. Greene, ed. see David, Ebenezer.

Roemer, Theodore. The Ludwig-Missionsverein & the Church in the United States (1838-1918) LC 73-3571. (Catholic University of America. Studies in American Church History: No. 16). Repr. of 1933 ed. 22.00 (ISBN 0-404-57766-0). AMS Pr.

Roerich, Helena. Foundations of Buddhism. 1971. Repr. index 8.00 (ISBN 0-686-79661-6). Agni Yoga Soc.

Roerich, Nicholas. Shambhala. softcover 12.00 (ISBN 0-686-79666-7); 16.00. Agni Yoga Soc.

Roes, Carol. Four Negro Spirituals. 1975. pap. 3.75 (ISBN 0-930932-24-2); record incl. M Loke.

Roesel, Carol. Impressions. (Illus., Orig.). 1982. pap. 3.95 (ISBN 0-89081-317-5). Harvest Hse.

Roetzel, Calvin J. The Letters of Paul: Conversations in Context. 2nd ed. LC 81-85334. (Biblical Foundations Ser.). 144p. 1982. pap. 9.95 (ISBN 0-8042-0209-5). John Knox.
--The World That Shaped the New Testament. LC 85-12492. 180p. 1985. pap. 11.95 (ISBN 0-8042-0455-1). John Knox.
Rofe, Husein. The Path of Subud. 69.95 (ISBN 0-8490-0805-0). Gordon Pr.
Rogahn, Kenneth & Schoedel, Walter. Parables from the Cross. 1981. pap. 5.95 (ISBN 0-570-03847-2, 12-2950). Concordia.
Rogahn, Kenneth W. Begin with Prayer: Prayers & Devotional Outlines for Church Meetings. 112p. 1985. 6.95 (ISBN 0-570-03962-2, 15-2178). Concordia.
Rogal, Samuel J. Guide to the Hymns & Tunes of American Methodism. LC 85-27114. (Music Reference Collection Ser.: No. 7). 337p. 1986. lib. bdg. 45.00 (ISBN 0-313-25123-1, RGH/). Greenwood.
--John & Charles Wesley. (English Authors Ser.: No. 368). 197p. 1983. lib. bdg. 16.95 (ISBN 0-8057-6854-8, Twayne). G K Hall.
Rogal, Samuel J., compiled by. The Children's Jubliee: A Bibliographical Survey of Hymnals for Infants, Youth & Sunday Schools Published in Britain & American, 1655-1900. LC 83-1661. (Illus.). xliv, 91p. 1983. lib. bdg. 35.00 (ISBN 0-313-23880-4, RCJ/). Greenwood.
Roger of Taize. Awakened from Within: Meditations on the Christian Life. LC 86-19615. 144p. 1987. 12.95 (ISBN 0-385-23536-4). Doubleday.
Roger of Taize, jt. auth. see Mother Teresa of Calcutta.
Rogers & Thatcher. The Home Stretch. 160p. 1986. 9.95 (ISBN 0-8499-0344-0). Word Bks.
Rogers, jt. auth. see Turner.
Rogers, Adrian P. God's Way to Health, Wealth & Wisdom. 1987. 9.95 (ISBN 0-8054-5048-3). Broadman.
Rogers, Arthur K. Morals in Review. LC 72-126697. Repr. of 1927 ed. 31.50 (ISBN 0-404-05379-3). AMS Pr.
Rogers, Barbara. God Rescues His People Activity Book. 72p. (Orig.). 1983. pap. 3.00 (ISBN 0-8361-3338-2). Herald Pr.
--God's Chosen King Activity Book. 88p. (Orig.). 1984. pap. 3.00 (ISBN 0-8361-3370-6). Herald Pr.
Rogers, Bruce A., jt. auth. see Rogers, Kristine M.
Rogers, Carl R. Therapist's View of Personal Goals. LC 60-11607. (Orig.). 1960. pap. 2.50x (ISBN 0-87574-108-8). Pendle Hill.
Rogers, Charles R. Joy. 1979. pap. 1.00 (ISBN 0-89841-001-0). Zoe Pubns.
Rogers, Cleon, jt. auth. see Rienecker, Fritz.
Rogers, Dale E. Angel Unaware. (Orig.). 1984. pap. 2.50 (ISBN 0-515-08952-4). Jove Pubns.
--God in the Hard Times. LC 85-10479. 160p. 1985. pap. 8.95 (ISBN 0-8027-2516-3). Walker & Co.
--Let Us Love. 1982. 8.95 (ISBN 0-8499-0298-3). Word Bks.
Rogers, Donald B. In Praise of Learning. LC 79-26829. (Into Our Third Century Ser.). (Orig.). 1980. pap. 3.95 (ISBN 0-687-18910-1). Abingdon.
Rogers, Donald B., jt. auth. see Berg, Kay K.
Rogers, Elizabeth F. Peter Lombard & the Sacramental System. 250p. 1976. Repr. of 1927 ed. lib. bdg. 19.50x (ISBN 0-915172-22-4). Richwood Pub.
Rogers, Francine, jt. auth. see Cirino, Andre.
Rogers, Francis M. The Quest for Eastern Christians: Travels & Rumor in the Age of Discovery. LC 62-18138. pap. 58.30 (ISBN 0-317-41750-9, 2055901). Bks Demand UMI.
Rogers, H., ed. see Howe, John.
Rogers, Jack. Presbyterian Creeds: A Guide to the Book of Confessions. LC 84-22001. 252p. (Orig.). 1985. pap. 8.95 (ISBN 0-664-24627-3). Westminster.
Rogers, Jack & McKim, Donald. The Authority & Interpretation of the Bible: An Historical Approach. LC 78-20584. 1979. 23.50 (ISBN 0-06-066696-X, HarpR). Har-Row.
Rogers, Jack, et al. Case Studies in Christ & Salvation. LC 76-53765. 176p. 1977. pap. 7.95 (ISBN 0-664-24133-6). Westminster.
Rogers, James A. Richard Furman: Life & Legacy. (Illus.). xxxii, 336p. 1985. 24.95 (ISBN 0-86554-151-5, MUP/H142). Mercer Univ Pr.
Rogers, Janice, jt. auth. see Cunningham, Loren.
Rogers, John B. The Birth of God: Recovering the Mystery of Christmas. 112p. 1987. pap. 6.95 (ISBN 0-687-03554-6). Abingdon.
Rogers, John B., Jr. Pentecost Three: Proclamation 3B. LC 84-18756. (Proclamation Ser.). 64p. 1985. pap. 3.75 (ISBN 0-8006-4108-6, 1-4108). Fortress.
Rogers, John T. Communicating Christ to the Cults. LC 83-4421. 1983. pap. 3.95 (ISBN 0-87227-091-2). Reg Baptist.
Rogers, Joyce. The Wise Woman. LC 80-68538. 1981. 8.95 (ISBN 0-8054-5289-3). Broadman.
Rogers, Kristine M. & Rogers, Bruce A. Paths to Transformation: A Study of the General Agencies of the United Methodist Church. LC 81-17565. (Into Our Third Century Ser.). 96p. (Orig.). 1982. pap. 3.50 (ISBN 0-687-30094-0). Abingdon.
Rogers, L. W. The Ghosts in Shakespeare. LC 72-3658. (Studies in Shakespeare, No. 24). 1972. Repr. of 1925 ed. lib. bdg. 75.00x (ISBN 0-8383-1567-4). Haskell.
Rogers, Liz, jt. auth. see Hill, Harold.
Rogers, Maggie & Hawkins, Judith. The Glass Christmas Ornament: Old & New. 2nd, rev. ed. (Illus.). 126p. (Orig.). 1983. pap. 12.95 (ISBN 0-917304-79-9). Timber.
Rogers, Patrick V. Colossians. (New Testament Message Ser.: Vol. 15). 10.95 (ISBN 0-89453-138-7); pap. 5.95 (ISBN 0-89453-203-0). M Glazier.
Rogers, Richard. Hallelujah Anyway. 57p. (Orig.). 1980. pap. text ed. 2.50 (ISBN 0-931097-03-7). Sentinel Pub.
--Holy Spirit of God. 85p. (Orig.). 1980. pap. text ed. 3.50 (ISBN 0-931097-04-5). Sentinel Pub.
--The Love of Christ. 26p. 1981. pap. text ed. 1.50 (ISBN 0-931097-12-6). Sentinel Pub.
Rogers, Richard & Ward, Samuel. Two Elizabethan Puritan Diaries. Knappen, Marshall M., ed. 1933. 11.75 (ISBN 0-8446-1387-8). Peter Smith.
Rogers, Robert W., ed. Cuneiform Parallels to the Old Testament. 1977. lib. bdg. 69.95 (ISBN 0-8490-1695-9). Gordon Pr.
Rogers, Roy, et al. Roy Rogers-Dale Evans: Happy Trails. 1979. 2.50 (ISBN 0-8499-0086-7); 13.95. Word Bks.
Rogers, Spencer. The Shamans Healing Way. 1976. pap. 4.95 (ISBN 0-916552-06-3). Acoma Bks.
Rogers, T., tr. see Buddhaghosa.
Rogers, Theresa F., jt. auth. see Friedman, Natalie.
Rogers, Theresa F., jt. auth. see Friedman, Nathalie.
Rogers, Thomas. The Catholic Doctrine of the Church of England. Repr. of 1854 ed. 31.00 (ISBN 0-384-51710-2). Johnson Repr.
Rogers, Thomas F. God's Fools. 233p. (Orig.). 1983. pap. 5.95 (ISBN 0-941214-14-1, Eden Hill Pub). Signature Bks.
Rogers, W. R. You Can Give a Chalk Talk. LC 80-65775. 1981. saddlewire 5.25 (ISBN 0-8054-6931-1). Broadman.
Rogerson, J. W. Anthropology & the Old Testament. (The Biblical Seminar Ser.: No. 1). 128p. 1984. pap. text ed. 8.95x (ISBN 0-905774-82-5, Pub. by JSOT Pr England). Eisenbrauns.
--Myth in Old Testament Interpretation. LC 73-78234. (Beiheft zur Zeitschrift fuer die Alttestamentliche Wissenschaft). 1974. 50.00x (ISBN 3-11-004220-7). De Gruyter.
Rogerson, John. Atlas of the Bible. 240p. 1985. text ed. 40.00 (ISBN 0-8407-5462-0). Nelson.
Rogerson, John, ed. Beginning Old Testament Study. LC 82-20210. 164p. 1983. pap. 8.95 (ISBN 0-664-24451-3). Westminster.
Rogerson, John W. Old Testament Criticism in the Nineteenth Century. LC 84-47933. 448p. 1985. 29.95 (ISBN 0-8006-0737-6, 1-737). Fortress.
--Psalms, 1-50. LC 76-27911. (Cambridge Bible Commentary on the New English Bible, Old Testament Ser.). 1977. 37.50 (ISBN 0-521-21463-7); pap. 11.95 (ISBN 0-521-29160-7). Cambridge U Pr.
--Psalms, 101-150. LC 76-27911. (Cambridge Bible Commentary on the New English Bible, Old Testament Ser.). 1977. 37.50 (ISBN 0-521-21465-3); pap. 11.95 (ISBN 0-521-29162-3). Cambridge U Pr.
--Psalms, 51-100. LC 76-27911. (Cambridge Bible Commentary on the New English Bible, Old Testament Ser.). 1977. 37.50 (ISBN 0-521-21464-5); pap. 11.95 (ISBN 0-521-29161-5). Cambridge U Pr.
Rogge, O. John. Why Men Confess. LC 74-22067. (Quality Paperbacks Ser.). iv, 298p. 1975. pap. 5.95 (ISBN 0-306-80006-3). Da Capo.
Roggenkamp. Stave Churches in Norway. 17.95 (ISBN 0-85440-205-5). Anthroposophic.
Rogger, Hans. Jewish Policies & Right-Wing Politics in Imperial Russia. LC 85-1006. 1985. 30.00x (ISBN 0-520-04596-3). U of Cal Pr.
Rogler, LLoyd H., jt. auth. see Farber, Anne.
Rogness, Alvin N. Book of Comfort. LC 78-66943. 1979. kivar 7.95 (ISBN 0-8066-1677-6, 10-0795). Augsburg.
--The Jesus Life: A Guide for Young Christians. LC 72-90260. 112p. (Orig.). (YA) 1973. pap. 5.95 (ISBN 0-8066-1307-6, 10-3521). Augsburg.
--Remember the Promise. LC 76-27082. 1977. kivar 2.95 (ISBN 0-8066-1567-2, 10-5480). Augsburg.
--Remember the Promise. LC 76-27082. 1978. gift ed. 7.50 (ISBN 0-8066-1619-9, 10-5481). Augsburg.
--Today & Tomorrow. LC 77-84095. 1978. pap. 6.95 (ISBN 0-8066-1621-0, 10-6660). Augsburg.
--The Word for Every Day: Three Hundred & Sixty-Five Devotional Reading. LC 81-65650. 376p. 1981. kivar 12.95 (ISBN 0-8066-1886-8, 10-7284). Augsburg.
Rogness, Michael. The Hand That Holds Me. LC 84-14447. 112p. (Orig.). 1984. pap. 5.95 (ISBN 0-8066-2093-5, 10-2943). Augsburg.
Rogo, D. Scott. Man Does Survive Death. 1977. pap. 3.95 (ISBN 0-8065-0582-6). Citadel Pr.
--The Search for Yesterday: A Critical Examination of the Evidence for Reincarnation. 288p. 1985. 22.95 (ISBN 0-13-797036-6); pap. 10.95 (ISBN 0-13-797028-5). P H.
Rogrbaugh, Dennis, jt. ed. see Strauss, Herbert A.
Roguet, A. M. Homilies for the Celebration of Baptism. Du Charme, Jerome, tr. from Fr. LC 76-53546. 1977. pap. 2.75 (ISBN 0-8199-0655-7). Franciscan Herald.
--Homilies for the Celebration of Marriage. Du Charme, Jerome, tr. from Fr. LC 76-53538. 1977. pap. 3.50 (ISBN 0-8199-0656-5). Franciscan Herald.
--The New Mass. 2.95 (ISBN 0-89942-130-X, 130/05). Catholic Bk Pub.
Rohatyn, Dennis. The Reluctant Naturalist: A Study of G.E. Moore's Principia Ethica. 150p. (Orig.). 1987. lib. bdg. 22.50 (ISBN 0-8191-5767-8); pap. text ed. 9.75 (ISBN 0-8191-5768-6). U Pr of Amer.
Rohde, Erwin. Psyche: The Cult of Souls & Belief in Immortality Among the Greeks. facsimile ed. LC 75-37911. (Select Bibliographies Reprint Ser). Repr. of 1920 ed. 32.00 (ISBN 0-8369-6749-6). Ayer Co Pubs.
Rohde, Peter P., ed. see Kierkegaard, Soren.
Rohe, Fred. The Zen of Running. 1975. pap. 5.95 (ISBN 0-394-73038-0). Random.
Roheim, Geza. Eternal Ones of the Dream: Myth & Ritual, Dreams & Fantasies-Their Role in the Lives of Primitive Man. 1970. pap. text ed. 19.95 (ISBN 0-8236-8044-4, 021760). Intl Univs Pr.
--The Riddle of the Sphinx, or Human Origins. Money-Kryle, R., tr. 10.75 (ISBN 0-8446-5238-5). Peter Smith.
Rohling, A. The Jew According to the Talmud. 1982. lib. bdg. 69.95 (ISBN 0-87700-361-0). Revisionist Pr.
Rohnet, Nancy, jt. auth. see Amenta, Madalon.
Rohr, Janelle, ed. Death & Dying. 2nd, rev. ed. (Opposing Viewpoints Ser.). (Illus.). 1987. 12.95 (ISBN 0-317-53944-2); pap. 6.95. Greenhaven.
Rohr, John Von see Von Rohr, John.
Rohrbach, Peter T. Conversation with Christ. LC 82-50586. 171p. 1982. pap. 5.00 (ISBN 0-89555-180-2). TAN Bks Pubs.
Rohrer, jt. auth. see Morris.
Rohrer, Daniel M. Freedom of Speech & Human Rights: An International Perspective. 1979. pap. text ed. 12.95 (ISBN 0-8403-1987-8, 40198701). Kendall-Hunt.
Rohrer, Norman. Open Arms. 256p. (Orig.). 1987. pap. 6.95 (ISBN 0-8423-4754-2). Tyndale.
Rohrer, Norman B. Mom LeTourneau. Throop, Isabel A., ed. 144p. 1985. 6.95 (ISBN 0-8423-4502-7). Tyndale.
Rohrer, Norman B. & Sutherland, S. Philip. Why Am I Shy? Turning Shyness into Confidence. LC 78-52182. 1978. pap. 6.95 (ISBN 0-8066-1656-3, 10-7130). Augsburg.
Rohwer, Lee O. What Is God Like? (Illus.). 64p. (Orig.). 1986. pap. 5.95 (ISBN 0-9617788-0-6). Damon Pub.
Roiter, Howard, jt. auth. see Kohn, Nahum.
Rojas, Juan, tr. see Graham, Billy.
Rokeach, Milton. Beliefs, Attitudes & Values: A Theory of Organization & Change. LC 68-21322. (Social & Behavioral Science Ser.). 1968. 25.95x (ISBN 0-87589-013-X). Jossey-Bass.
--Understanding Human Values: Individual & Societal. LC 78-24753. (Illus.). 1979. 14.95 (ISBN 0-02-926760-9). Free Pr.
Rokem, Galit Hasan see Hasan-Rokem, Galit & Dundes, Alan.
Roland, Michael L. Sabbath at Sea. (Destiny II Ser.). 108p. 1984. pap. 6.50 (ISBN 0-8163-0547-1). Pacific Pr Pub Assn.
Roland, Timothy. First Steps. 1984. pap. 1.95 (ISBN 0-88207-450-4). Victor Bks.
Rolando, Mary J. Recognizing & Helping the Learning Disabled Child in Your Classroom. 24p. 1978. 2.40 (ISBN 0-686-39949-8). Natl Cath Educ.
Rolfe, Eugene, tr. see Meier, C. A.
Rolheiser, Ronald. The Loneliness Factor: Its Religious & Spiritual Meaning. 8.95 (ISBN 0-87193-168-0). Dimension Bks.
Roll, William G. Theory & Experiment in Psychical Research. new ed. LC 75-7398. (Perspectives in Psychical Research Ser.). (Illus.). 1975. 38.50x (ISBN 0-405-07047-0). Ayer Co Pubs.
Rolland, Romain. Life of Ramakrishna. 5.95 (ISBN 0-87481-080-9). Vedanta Pr.
--Life of Vivekananda. 1987. 7.95 (ISBN 0-87481-090-6, Pub. by Advaita Ashrama). Vedanta Pr.
--La Vie de Ramakrishna. 1978. 16.95 (ISBN 0-686-55279-2). French & Eur.
--La Vie de Vivekananda. 352p. 1978. 16.95 (ISBN 0-686-55280-6). French & Eur.
Rolle, Richard. The Contra Amatores Mundi of Richard Rolle of Hampole. Theiner, Paul F., ed. LC 68-64641. 196p. 1983. Repr. of 1968 ed. lib. bdg. 19.95x (ISBN 0-89370-791-0). Borgo Pr.
--The Fire of Love. Wolters, Clifton, tr. (Classics Ser.). 192p. 1972. pap. 4.95 (ISBN 0-14-044256-1). Penguin.
--The Fire of Love & the Mending of Life. Comper, Francis M., ed. Misyn, Richard, tr. 1920. Repr. 25.00 (ISBN 0-8274-2346-2). R West.
--The Mending of Life: Being an Anonymous Version of about A. D. 1400 from the De Emendatione Vitae of Richard Rolle of Hampole. 95p. 1981. Repr. of 1913 ed. lib. bdg. 30.00 (ISBN 0-89987-374-X). Darby Bks.
Roller, Karen L., ed. Women Pray. 96p. (Orig.). 1986. pap. 3.95 (ISBN 0-8298-0737-3). Pilgrim NY.
Rolleston, T. W. Myths & Legends of the Celtic Race. (Illus.). 457p. 1985. 14.95 (ISBN 0-8052-3996-0). Schocken.
Rollins, Marion J. The God of the Old Testament in Relation to War. LC 72-176551. (Columbia University. Teachers College. Contributions to Education Ser.: No. 263). Repr. of 1927 ed. 22.50 (ISBN 0-404-55263-3). AMS Pr.
Rollins, Wayne G. Jung & the Bible. LC 82-48091. 156p. 1983. pap. 10.95 (ISBN 0-8042-1117-5). John Knox.
Rolls, Charles J. His Glorious Name. (Names & Titles of Jesus Christ Ser.: No. 5). 267p. 1986. pap. 5.95 (ISBN 0-87213-735-X). Loizeaux.
--The Indescribable Christ. Rev. ed. 1984. pap. 5.95 (ISBN 0-87213-731-7). Loizeaux.
--Name above Every Name: The Names & Titles of Jesus Christ Beginning with P-S. rev. ed. LC 65-26585. 1985. pap. 5.95 (ISBN 0-87213-734-1). Loizeaux.
--Time's Noblest Name: The Names & Titles of Jesus Christ, L-O. New rev. ed. pap. 5.95 (ISBN 0-87213-733-3). Loizeaux.
--The World's Greatest Name, Names & Titles of Jesus Christ Beginning with H-K. rev. ed. 183p. 1985. pap. 5.95 (ISBN 0-87213-732-5). Loizeaux.
Roloff, Marvin L., ed. Education for Christian Living: Strategies for Nurture Based on Biblical & Historical Foundations. LC 86-28756. 224p. (Orig.). 1986. pap. 12.95 (ISBN 0-8066-2238-5, 10-2003). Augsburg.
Rolston, Holmes. First Thessalonians-Philemon. LC 59-10454. (Layman's Bible Commentary Ser: Vol. 23). pap. 4.95 (ISBN 0-8042-3083-8). John Knox.
Rolston, Holmes, III. John Calvin Vs. the Westminster Confession. LC 75-37422. (Orig.). 1972. pap. 4.95 (ISBN 0-8042-0488-8). John Knox.
--Religious Inquiry: Participation & Detachment. LC 83-24602. 323p. 1985. 22.50 (ISBN 0-8022-2450-4). Philos Lib.
--Science & Religion: A Critical Survey. 368p. 1986. 34.95 (ISBN 0-87722-437-4). Temple U Pr.
--Science & Religion: An Introduction. 200p. 1987. pap. text ed. 11.50 (ISBN 0-394-36327-2, RanC). Random.
Rolte, J., tr. Palatinate-a Full Declaration of the Faith & Ceremonies Professed in the Dominions of Prince Fredericke, 5. Prince Elector Palatine. LC 79-84129. (English Experience Ser.: No. 947). 208p. 1979. Repr. of 1614 ed. lib. bdg. 20.00 (ISBN 90-221-0947-X). Walter J Johnson.
Rolwing, Richard J. A Philosophy of Revelation: According to Karl Rahner. LC 78-63067. 1978. pap. text ed. 8.50 (ISBN 0-8191-0609-7). U Pr of Amer.
Romain, Philip S. Growing in Inner Freedom: A Guide for Today. 64p. 1986. pap. 1.95 (ISBN 0-89243-259-4). Liguori Pubns.
Romain, Philip St. see St. Romain, Philip.
Romaine, William. Life, Walk & Triumph of Faith: With an Account of His Life and Work by Peter Toon. 439p. 1970. 14.00 (ISBN 0-227-67744-7). Attic Pr.
Roman, Sanaya. Living with Joy: Keys to Personal Power & Spiritual Transformation. Ratner, Elaine, ed. (Earth Life Ser.). 216p. (Orig.). 1986. pap. 9.95 (ISBN 0-915811-03-0). H J Kramer Inc.
Roman, Sanaya & Packer, Duane. Opening to Channel: How to Connect with Your Guide. Armstrong, Gregory, ed. (Birth into Light Ser.). 280p. (Orig.). 1987. pap. 12.95 (ISBN 0-915811-05-7). H J Kramer Inc.

Romanell, Patrick. Croce Versus Gentile: A Dialogue on Contemporary Italian Philosophy. LC 78-63709. (Studies in Fascism: Ideology & Practice). (Illus.). 80p. Repr. of 1947 ed. 18.00 (ISBN 0-404-16979-1). AMS Pr.

Romanenghi de Powell, Elsie R., tr. see Fletcher, William M.

Romanides, John S. Franks, Romans, Feudalism, & Doctrine: An Interplay Between Theology & Society. (Patriarch Athenagoras Memorial Lectures Ser.). 98p. (Orig.). 1982. pap. text ed. 4.95 (ISBN 0-916586-54-5). Holy Cross Orthodox.

Romano, Elio. A Generation of Wrath. 228p. 1986. 14.95 (ISBN 0-7278-2039-7). Salem Hse Pubs.

Romashkevitch, P. A., ed. Polnij Russkij Orthograficheskij Slovar' Tr. of Complete Russian Orthographic Dictionary. 264p. pap. 10.00 (ISBN 0-317-29290-0). Holy Trinity.

Romb, Anselm. Franciscan Charism. LC 79-91837. 122p. 1969. 3.00 (ISBN 0-8199-0477-5); pap. 1.95 (ISBN 0-685-77516-X). Franciscan Herald.

--Kolbe Reader. (Orig.). Date not set. pap. price not set (ISBN 0-913382-35-3, 101-35). Prow Bks-Franciscan.

--Man of Peace: Casimir Michael Cypher, OFM Conv: His Meaning in Life Was Found in Death. (Illus.). 67p. (Orig.). 1985. pap. 3.75 (ISBN 0-913382-17-5, 105-42). Prow Bks-Franciscan.

--Total Consecration to Mary, Spouse of the Holy Spirit. 64p. 1982. pap. 1.50 (ISBN 0-913382-13-2, 105-37). Prow Bks-Franciscan.

Romero, Joan A., ed. see Plaskow, Judith.

Romero, Sidney J. Religion in the Rebel Ranks. (Illus.). 226p. (Orig.). 1983. lib. bdg. 27.00 (ISBN 0-8191-3327-2); pap. text ed. 12.50 (ISBN 0-8191-3328-0). U Pr of Amer.

Romig, Robert E. Reasonable Religion: A Commonsense Approach. LC 84-42823. 200p. 1984. 18.95 (ISBN 0-87975-252-1). Prometheus Bks.

Romig, Walter, ed. Book of Catholic Authors, Fourth Series: Informal Self-Portraits of Famous Modern Catholic Writers. LC 70-179740. (Biography Index Reprint Ser.). Repr. of 1948 ed. 27.50 (ISBN 0-8369-8108-1). Ayer Co Pubs.

Romig, Walter, ed. see Catholic Library Association Staff.

Rommel, Kurt. Our Father Who Art in Heaven. Cooperrider, Edward A., tr. from Ger. LC 80-2373. Tr. of Einladung zum Gesprach mit Gott: Gedanken uber das Vaterunser. 96p. 1981. pap. 4.95 (ISBN 0-8006-1448-8, 1-1448). Fortress.

Rommen, Heinrich A. State in Catholic Thought: A Treatise in Political Philosophy. Repr. of 1945 ed. lib. bdg. 26.25x (ISBN 0-8371-2437-9, ROCT). Greenwood.

Ronaldson, Dolores, ed. see Witter, Evelyn.

Ronan & Hanisch. Epistolario de Juan Ignacio Molina. (Span.). 1980. 11.60 (ISBN 0-8294-0360-4). Loyola.

Ronan, Charles E. Francisco Javier Clavigero, S. J., Figure of the Mexican Enlightment: His Life & Work. 1978. pap. 26.00x (ISBN 88-7041-340-3). Jesuit Hist.

Ronan, Patrick J. Religion & Rural Life: A Mission Statement for the Religion & Rural Life Council of Rural America. 1982. 1.90 (ISBN 0-318-01734-2). Rural America.

Ronayne. Freemasonry Handbook. 9.00x (ISBN 0-685-21949-6). Wehman.

Ronayne, E. Ma-Ha-Bone: Ritual. 11.00x (ISBN 0-685-22019-2). Wehman.

Ronayne, Edmond. Blue Lodge & Chapter. 1947. 11.00 (ISBN 0-685-19465-5). Powner.

--Chapter Degrees. 8.50 (ISBN 0-685-19469-8). Powner.

--Handbook of Freemasonry. 9.00 (ISBN 0-685-19476-0). Powner.

--Mah Hah Bone. 11.00 (ISBN 0-685-19485-X). Powner.

--Master's Carpet. 9.00 (ISBN 0-685-19490-6). Powner.

Rongstad, James. How to Respond to the Lodge. (The Response Ser.). 1977. 1.95 (ISBN 0-570-07677-3, 12-2660). Concordia.

Ronk, A. T. History of Brethren Missionary Movements. LC 70-184490. 1971. pap. 2.25x (ISBN 0-934970-02-5). Brethren Ohio.

--History of the Brethren Church. LC 68-23554. 1968. 10.95x (ISBN 0-934970-03-3). Brethren Ohio.

--A Search for Truth. LC 73-82191. 1973. pap. 1.00x (ISBN 0-934970-04-1). Brethren Ohio.

Ronsvalle, John & Ronsvalle, Sylvia. Hidden Billions: The Potential of the Church in the U. S. 175p. (Orig.). 1984. pap. 8.00 (ISBN 0-914527-18-5). C-Four Res.

Ronsvalle, Sylvia, jt. auth. see Ronsvalle, John.

Roof, Wade C. Community & Commitment: Religious Plausibility in a Liberal Protestant Church. 278p. 1978. 28.00 (ISBN 0-444-99038-0). Elsevier.

--Community & Commitment: Religious Plausibility in a Liberal Protestant Church. LC 77-16329. 288p. pap. 10.95 (ISBN 0-8298-0669-5). Pilgrim NY.

Roof, Wade C. & McKinney, William. America Mainline Religion: Its Changing Shape of the Religious Establishment. 272p. 1987. text ed. 27.00 (ISBN 0-8135-1215-8); pap. text ed. 10.00 (ISBN 0-8135-1216-6). Rutgers U Pr.

Roof, Wade C., jt. auth. see Michaelsen, Robert S.

Roohan, James E. American Catholics & the Social Question, 1865-1900. LC 76-6364. (Irish Americans Ser). 1976. 37.50 (ISBN 0-405-09356-X). Ayer Co Pubs.

Rooker, C. Keith, jt. auth. see Hill, Marvin S.

Room, M. B. Wanted Your Daily Life. 1976. pap. 2.50 (ISBN 0-87508-011-1). Chr Lit.

Rooney, John, tr. see Thomas a Kempis.

Rooney, Laurel. Stations of the Cross. 1984. 9.95 (ISBN 0-89837-094-9, Pub. by Pflaum Press). Peter Li.

Rooney, Lucy & Faricy, Robert. Mary, Queen of Peace: Is the Mother of God Appearing in Medjugorje? 98p. (Orig.). 1985. pap. 4.95 (ISBN 0-317-19369-4). Alba.

Rooney, Lucy, jt. auth. see Fancy, Robert.

Roop, Eugene F. Genesis. (The Believers Church Bible Comentary Ser.: No. 2). 344p. (Orig.). 1987. pap. 17.95 (ISBN 0-8361-3443-5). Herald Pr.

Roos, Paavo. Survey of Rook-Cut Chamber-Tombs in Caria, Pt. I: Southeastern Caria & the Lyco-Carian Borderland. (Studies in Mediterranean Archaeology). (Illus.). 132p. (Orig.). 1985. pap. text ed. 82.50X (Pub. by Almqvist & Wiksell). Coronet Bks.

Roos, Richard. Christwalk. 208p. (Orig.). 1985. pap. 7.95 (ISBN 0-8091-2667-2). Paulist Pr.

Roosen-Runge, Heinz. The Rolin-Madonna of Jan Van Eyck. (Illus.). 56p. 1973. pap. 9.75 (ISBN 0-8390-0125-8). Abner Schram Ltd.

Roosevelt, Eleanor. You Learn by Living. LC 83-6838. 224p. 1983. pap. 9.95 (ISBN 0-664-24494-7). Westminster.

Root, H. E., ed. see Hume, David.

Root, Orrin. Standard Bible Atlas. (Illus.). 32p. 1973. pap. 3.50 (ISBN 0-87239-251-1, 3169). Standard Pub.

--Training for Service: A Survey of the Bible. Daniel, Eleanor, rev. by. 128p. 1983. pap. 3.95 (ISBN 0-87239-704-1, 3212); tchr's. ed. 4.95 (ISBN 0-87239-703-3, 3211). Standard Pub.

Roozen, David A. Churched & Unchurched in America: A Comparative Profile. LC 77-94682. 1978. pap. 2.00 (ISBN 0-914422-07-3). Glenmary Res Ctr.

Roozen, David A. & McKinney, Wiliam. Varieties of Religious Presence: Mission in Public Life. 400p. (Orig.). 1984. pap. 12.95 (ISBN 0-8298-0724-1). Pilgrim NY.

Roozen, David A., jt. ed. see Hoge, Dean R.

Roper, D. A Christian Philosophy of Culture. Date not set. pap. 3.95x cancelled (ISBN 0-86990-540-6). Radix Bks.

Roper, Gayle G. Mother's World. (Ultra Bks Ser). 96p. 1975. 3.50 (ISBN 0-8010-7631-5). Baker Bk.

Roper, Lyndal, jt. auth. see Obelkevich, Jim.

Roper, William. The Life of Sir Thomas More. pap. 6.95 (ISBN 0-87243-118-5). Templegate.

Roper, William see Sylvester, Richard S. & Harding, Davis P.

Ropes, James H. A Critical & Exegetical Commentary on the Epistle of St. James. LC 16-6543. (International Critical Commentary Ser.). 336p. 1916. 22.95 (ISBN 0-567-05035-1, Pub. by T & T Clark Ltd UK). Fortress.

--Singular Problem of the Epistle to the Galatians. (Harvard Theological Studies). 1929. pap. 15.00 (ISBN 0-527-01014-6). Kraus Repr.

Ropp, Harry L. The Mormon Papers. rev. ed. LC 77-2681. (Illus., Orig.). 1987. pap. 5.95 (ISBN 0-87784-469-0). Inter-Varsity.

Roque, Marichelle, jt. auth. see Arienda, Roger.

Rordorf, Willy, et al. The Eucharist of the Early Christians. O'Connell, Matthew J., tr. from Fr. 1978. pap. 9.95 (ISBN 0-916134-33-4). Pueblo Pub Co.

Rorick, William G. Your Brain & the Mind of Christ. LC 84-50081. 140p. 1984. 4.95 (ISBN 0-938232-43-6). Winston-Derek.

Rosadi, Giovanni. The Trial of Jesus. 1977. lib. bdg. 59.95 (ISBN 0-8490-2767-5). Gordon Pr.

Rosage, David. Climbing Higher: Reflections on Our Spiritual Journey. 112p. (Orig.). 1983. pap. 4.95 (ISBN 0-89283-147-2). Servant.

--Rejoice in Me: A Pocket Guide to Daily Scriptural Prayer. 256p. 1986. pocket-size 3.95 (ISBN 0-89283-298-3). Servant.

Rosage, David E. Abide in Me: A Pocket Guide to Daily Scriptural Prayer. 240p. (Orig.). 1985. pap. 3.95 (ISBN 0-89283-243-6). Servant.

--The Bread of Life. (Orig.). 1979. pap. 2.50 (ISBN 0-89283-067-0). Servant.

--Encountering the Lord in Daily Life. 160p. (Orig.). 1983. pap. 4.50 (ISBN 0-914544-45-4). Living Flame Pr.

--Follow Me: A Pocket Guide to Daily Scriptural Prayer. 240p. 1982. pap. 3.95 (ISBN 0-89283-168-5). Servant.

--A Lenten Pilgrimage: Scriptural Meditations in the Holy Land. (Orig.). 1980. pap. 3.50 (ISBN 0-89283-081-6). Servant.

--Linger with Me: Moments Aside with Jesus. 212p. (Orig.). 1979. pap. 3.95 (ISBN 0-914544-29-2). Living Flame Pr.

--Listen to Him. 112p. (Orig.). 1981. pap. 3.50 (ISBN 0-89283-108-1). Servant.

--Living Here & Hereafter. (Christian Dying, Death & Resurection Ser.). 128p. (Orig.). 1982. pap. 2.95 (ISBN 0-914544-44-6). Living Flame Pr.

--The Lord Is My Shepherd: Praying the Psalms. 196p. (Orig.). 1984. pap. 3.50 (ISBN 0-89283-196-0). Servant.

--The Pocket Book of Bible Prayers. 224p. (Orig.). 1987. compact ed. 5.95 (ISBN 0-89283-320-3). Servant.

--Praying with Scripture in the Holy Land: Daily Meditations with the Risen Jesus. 184p. (Orig.). 1977. pap. 3.95 (ISBN 0-914544-14-4). Living Flame Pr.

--Reconciliation: The Sacramental Path to Peace. 144p. (Orig.). 1984. pap. 5.95 (ISBN 0-914544-56-X). Living Flame Pr.

--Scriptural Prayer Journal. 150p. (Orig.). 1987. pap. 4.95 (ISBN 0-89283-341-6). Servant.

--Speak, Lord, Your Servant Is Listening. 1977. pap. 2.95 (ISBN 0-89283-046-8). Servant.

Rosales, Antonio. A Study of a Sixteenth-Century Tagalog Manuscript on the Ten Commandments: Its Significance & Implications. (Illus.). 166p. 1985. text ed. 16.00x (ISBN 0-8248-0971-8). UH Pr.

Rosato, Philip. The Spirit as Lord. 240p. 1981. 20.95 (ISBN 0-567-09305-0, Pub. by T&T Clark Ltd UK). Fortress.

Roscher, Wilhelm & Hillman, James. Pan & the Nightmare: Two Essays. (Dunquin Ser.: No. 4). lxiii, 88p. 1972. pap. 8.50 (ISBN 0-88214-204-6). Spring Pubns.

Roscoe, Thomas, ed. see Roscoe, William.

Roscoe, William. Life & Pontificate of Pope Leo the Tenth, 2 vols. rev. ed. 6th ed. Roscoe, Thomas, ed. LC 75-174965. Repr. of 1853 ed. 92.50 (ISBN 0-404-05430-7). AMS Pr.

Rose, Anne C. Transcendentalism As a Social Movement, 1830-1850. LC 81-3340. 288p. 1986. pap. 11.95x (ISBN 0-300-03757-0). Yale U Pr.

Rose, E. Cases of Conscience. LC 74-76947. 272p. 1975. 44.50 (ISBN 0-521-20462-3). Cambridge U Pr.

Rose, Elliot. Cases of Conscience: Alternatives Open to Recusants & Puritans under Elizabeth I & James I. LC 74-76947. pap. 68.50 (2027243). Bks Demand UMI.

Rose, H. J., tr. see Schmidt, W.

Rose, Herbert J. Handbook of Greek Mythology. 1959. pap. 7.95 (ISBN 0-525-47041-7, 0772-230). Dutton.

Rose, Herbert J., ed. see Plutarch.

Rose, Jack H. Christianity & Education: A Manifesto. LC 86-90551. 302p. (Orig.). 1986. pap. 29.95 (ISBN 0-9617430-0-X). J H Rose.

Rose, June, jt. auth. see Blue, Lionel.

Rose, Larry L. & Hadaway, C. Kirk, eds. The Urban Challenge. LC 82-71026. 1982. pap. 5.95 (ISBN 0-8054-6238-4). Broadman.

Rose, Larry L., et al. An Urban World. LC 84-12649. 1984. pap. 8.95 (ISBN 0-8054-6339-9). Broadman.

Rose, Martial, ed. Wakefield Mystery Plays. 1969. pap. 10.95x (ISBN 0-393-00483-X, Norton Lib). Norton.

Rose, Morton F. The Shadow of the Cross. LC 86-9630. (Orig.). 1986. pap. 3.25 (ISBN 0-8054-5030-0). Broadman.

Rose, N. A. Gentile Zionists: Study in Anglo-Zionist Diplomacy 1929-1939. 246p. 1973. 29.50x (ISBN 0-7146-2940-5, F Cass Co). Biblio Dist.

Rose, P. L. Bodin & the Great God of Nature: The Moral & Religious Universe of a Judaiser. 200p. (Orig.). 1980. pap. text ed. 48.50x (Pub. by Droz Switzerland). Coronet Bks.

Rose, Paul L., ed. see Bodin, J.

Rose, Peter I. Strangers in Their Midst: Small-Town Jews & Their Neighbors. 1977. lib. bdg. 12.95 (ISBN 0-915172-32-1). Richwood Pub.

Rose, Ron, jt. auth. see Allen, Roger.

Rose, Stephen. Jesus & Jim Jones. LC 79-17285. (Orig.). 1979. 8.95 (ISBN 0-8298-0379-3); pap. 6.95 (ISBN 0-8298-0373-4). Pilgrim NY.

Rose, Stewart. Ignatius Loyola & the Early Jesuits. LC 83-45596. Date not set. Repr. of 1870 ed. 52.00 (ISBN 0-404-19889-9). AMS Pr.

Rose, Tom. Economics: Principles & Policy from a Christian Perspective. 2nd ed. LC 85-72235. (Illus.). 380p. 1985. text ed. 18.95 (ISBN 0-9612198-5-8); instrs' manual 7.00 (ISBN 0-9612198-1-5). A E P.

Rose, Tom & Metcalf, Robert. The Coming Victory. (The Coronation Ser.: No. 5). 206p. (Orig.). 1980. pap. 6.95x (ISBN 0-686-28757-6). Chr Stud Ctr.

Roseberry, Eric, ed. The Faber Book of Carols & Christmas Songs. 118p. 1983. 8.95 (ISBN 0-571-09249-7); pap. 6.95 (ISBN 0-571-13189-1). Faber & Faber.

Rosel, Paul. Silent Night, Holy Night. (Illus.). 1969. 3.25 (ISBN 0-8066-0928-1, 11-9388). Augsburg.

Rosemergy, Jim. A Recent Revelation. LC 81-50146. 137p. 1981. 5.95 (ISBN 0-87159-002-6). Unity School.

Rosen, Anne, et al. Family Passover. LC 79-89298. 64p. 1980. 6.95 (ISBN 0-8276-0169-7, 452). Jewish Pubns.

Rosen, Bernard & Caplan, Arthur L. Ethics in the Undergraduate Curriculum. LC 80-12351. (The Teaching of Ethics Ser.). 67p. 1980. pap. 4.00 (ISBN 0-916558-13-4). Hastings Ctr.

Rosen, Ceil & Rosen, Moishe. Christ in the Passover. LC 77-10689. 1978. pap. 4.95 (ISBN 0-8024-1392-7). Moody.

Rosen, Gerald. Zen in the Art of J. D. Salinger. LC 77-72494. (Modern Authors Monograph Ser.: No. 3). 40p. 1977. pap. 3.50 (ISBN 0-916870-06-5). Creative Arts Bk.

Rosen, Gladys. Jewish Life in America: Historical Perspectives. 12.50x (ISBN 0-87068-346-2); pap. 9.95 (ISBN 0-686-52683-X). Ktav.

Rosen, Gladys, jt. auth. see Reisman, Bernard.

Rosen, Gladys L., ed. Jewish Life in America: Historical Perspectives. LC 78-16560. 198p. 1978. pap. 6.95 (ISBN 0-686-74514-0). Am Jewish Comm.

Rosen, Harold. Religious Education & Our Ultimate Committment: An Application of Henry Nelson Wieman's Philosophy of Creative Interchange. LC 84-19651. 196p. (Orig.). 1985. lib. bdg. 24.25 (ISBN 0-8191-4341-3, Unitarian Univ Assn); pap. text ed. 10.75 (ISBN 0-8191-4342-1, Unitarian Univ. Assn.). U Pr of Amer.

Rosen, Michael. Hegel's Dialectic & Its Criticism. LC 81-24211. 210p. 1982. 29.95 (ISBN 0-521-24484-6). Cambridge U Pr.

Rosen, Moishe. Share the New Life with a Jew. LC 76-7627. 1976. pap. 3.95 (ISBN 0-8024-7898-0). Moody.

--Y'shua. 128p. (Orig.). 1983. pap. 3.50 (ISBN 0-8024-9842-6). Moody.

Rosen, Moishe, jt. auth. see Rosen, Ceil.

Rosen, Oded, ed. The Encyclopedia of Jewish Institutions: United States & Canada. 512p. 1983. 55.00 (ISBN 0-913185-00-0). Mosadot Pubns.

Rosen, Steven. Food for the Spirit: Vegetarianism & the World Religions. Greene, Joshua M., ed. (Illus.). 144p. (Orig.). 1987. 9.95 (ISBN 0-89647-022-9); pap. 6.95 (ISBN 0-89647-021-0). Bala Bks.

Rosenau, William. Hebraisms in the Authorized Version of the Bible. LC 76-9047. 1976. Repr. of 1903 ed. lib. bdg. 25.00 (ISBN 0-8414-7247-5). Folcroft.

--Jewish Ceremonial Institutions & Customs. rev. ed. 3rd. ed. LC 70-78222. (Illus.). 1971. Repr. of 1925 ed. 35.00x (ISBN 0-8103-3402-X). Gale.

Rosenbach, Abraham S. An American Jewish Bibliography: Being a List of Books & Pamphlets by Jews, or Relating to Them, Printed in the United States from the Establishment of the Press in the Colonies until 1850. (American Jewish Historical Society Publications: No. 30). (Illus.). pap. 127.30 (ISBN 0-317-09938-8, 2017816). Bks Demand UMI.

Rosenbaum, Brenda. How to Avoid the Evil Eye: Five Thousand Years of Jewish Superstition. (Illus.). 96p. 1985. pap. 5.95 (ISBN 0-312-39584-1). St Martin.

Rosenbaum, Ernest, et al. Nutrition for the Cancer Patient. (Orig.). 1980. pap. 7.95 (ISBN 0-915950-38-3). Bull Pub.

Rosenbaum, Ernest H., et al. Rehabilitation Exercises for the Cancer Patient. (Illus., Orig.). 1980. pap. 4.95 (ISBN 0-915950-37-5). Bull Pub.

--Sexuality & Cancer. (Orig.). 1980. pap. 2.95 (ISBN 0-915950-39-1). Bull Pub.

Rosenbaum, Fred. Architects of Reform: Congregation & Community Leadership, Emanuel of San Francisco. 1849-1980. LC 80-54032. 241p. 1980. 19.95 (ISBN 0-943376-14-9); pap. 9.95 (ISBN 0-943376-13-0). Magnes Mus.

Rosenbaum, I. Holocaust & Halakhah. (Library of Jewish Law & Ethics: No. 2). 15.00x (ISBN 0-87068-296-2); pap. 9.95. Ktav.

Rosenbaum, Larry. You Shall Be My Witnesses: How to Reach Your City for Christ. LC 86-90426. 144p. (Orig.). 1986. pap. 5.00 (ISBN 0-938573-00-4). SOS Minist Pr.

Rosenbaum, M., jt. auth. see Silbermann, A. M.

Rosenbaum, S. E. A Voyage to America in Eighteen Forty-Seven: The Diary of a Bohemian Jew on His Voyage from Hamburg to New York in 1847. (Studies in Judaica & the Holocaust: No. 3). 60p. 1987. lib. bdg. 19.95x (ISBN 0-89370-371-0); pap. text ed. 9.95x (ISBN 0-89370-471-7). Borgo Pr.

Rosenberg, A. Nicolas Gueudeville & His Work Sixteen Fifty-Two to Seventeen Twenty-Five. 1982. 49.50 (ISBN 90-247-2533-X, Pub. by Martinus Nijhoff Netherlands). Kluwer Academic.

Rosenberg, A. J. Book of Jeremiah, Vol. 1. (Books of the Prophet Ser.). 460p. 1985. 12.95 (ISBN 0-910818-59-2). Judaica Pr.

--Book of Kings 2. 480p. 1980. 12.95 (ISBN 0-910818-31-2). Judaica Pr.

--Book of Twelve Prophets, Vol. II. (Book of the Prophets Ser.). 270p. 1987. 14.95. Judaica Pr.

--Megillath Esther. 86p. 1985. pap. 6.95 (ISBN 0-900689-97-8). Soncino Pr.

Rosenberg, A. J., ed. Book of Isaiah 1. 261p. 1982. 12.95 (ISBN 0-910818-50-9). Judaica Pr.

--Book of Isaiah 2. 554p. 1983. 12.95 (ISBN 0-910818-52-5). Judaica Pr.

--Book of Jeremiah, Bk. II. 442p. 1985. 12.95 (ISBN 0-910818-60-6). Judaica Pr.

--Book of Joshua. 350p. 1984. 12.95 (ISBN 0-910818-08-8). Judaica Pr.

--Book of Judges. 400p. 1979. 12.95 (ISBN 0-910818-17-7). Judaica Pr.

--Book of Kings 1. 512p. 1980. 12.95 (ISBN 0-910818-30-4). Judaica Pr.

--Book of Samuel 1. 525p. 1981. 12.95 (ISBN 0-910818-07-X). Judaica Pr.

--Book of Samuel 2. 540p. 1982. 12.95 (ISBN 0-910818-11-8). Judaica Pr.

--Book of Twelve Prophets, Vol. 1. (Books of the Prophets Ser). 465p. 1986. 14.95 (ISBN 0-910818-70-3). Judaica Pr.

Rosenberg, Amye. Mitzvot. (Illus.). 30p. pap. text ed. 2.95x (ISBN 0-87441-387-7). Behrman.

--Tzedakah. (Jewish Awareness Ser.). (Illus.). 1979. pap. text ed. 2.95x (ISBN 0-87441-279-X). Behrman.

Rosenberg, Avrohom Y. The Mishnah-Seder Moed, Vol. 4. (Art Scroll Mishnah Ser.). 352p. 1979. 14.95 (ISBN 0-89906-258-X); pap. 11.95 (ISBN 0-89906-259-8). Mesorah Pubns.

Rosenberg, Charles E., ed. Healing & History: Essays for George Rosen. 1979. lib. bdg. 27.00 (ISBN 0-88202-180-X). Watson Pub Intl.

Rosenberg, Edgar. From Shylock to Svengali: Jewish Stereotypes in English Fiction. (Illus.). 1960. 27.50x (ISBN 0-8047-0586-0). Stanford U Pr.

Rosenberg, Israel. The World of Words. 224p. 1973. 8.95 (ISBN 0-8022-2101-7). Philos Lib.

Rosenberg, Joel. King & Kin: Political Allegory in the Hebrew Bible. LC 85-45160. (Indiana Studies in Biblical Literature: Midland Bks: No. 396). 256p. 1986. 29.50x (ISBN 0-253-14624-0); pap. 10.95x (ISBN 0-253-20396-1). Ind U Pr.

Rosenberg, Roy A. Who Was Jesus? LC 85-29523. 132p. (Orig.). 1986. lib. bdg. 23.75 (ISBN 0-8191-5177-7); pap. 9.25 (ISBN 0-8191-5178-5). U Pr of Amer.

Rosenberg, Stuart E. The Christian Problem: A Jewish View. 304p. 1986. 15.95 (ISBN 0-87052-284-1). Hippocrene Bks.

--Christians & Jews: The Eternal Bond. rev. ed. 200p. 1985. 13.95 (ISBN 0-8044-5800-6). Ungar.

--Judaism. 159p. pap. 2.45 (ISBN 0-686-95139-5). ADL.

--New Jewish Identity in America. LC 84-10938. 384p. 1985. 19.95 (ISBN 0-88254-997-9). Hippocrene Bks.

--The Real Jewish World: A Rabbi's Second Thoughts. LC 83-17455. 434p. 1984. 19.95 (ISBN 0-8022-2439-3). Philos Lib.

Rosenblatt. The High Ways to Perfection by Abraham Maimonides, 2 vols. 35.00 (ISBN 0-87306-113-6). Feldheim.

--Under the Nuptial Canopy. 1975. 6.00 (ISBN 0-87306-109-8). Feldheim.

Rosenblatt, Bernard A. Two Generations of Zionism. LC 67-18134. 1967. 7.95 (ISBN 0-88400-017-6). Shengold.

Rosenblatt, Paul. John Woolman. (Great American Thinkers Ser.). 1969. lib. bdg. 17.95 (ISBN 0-89197-813-5). Irvington.

Rosenblatt, Paul C., et al. Grief & Mourning in Cross-Cultural Perspective. LC 76-29270. (Comparative Studies Ser.). 242p. 1976. pap. 7.00x (ISBN 0-87536-334-2). HRAFP.

Rosenblatt, Samuel. Hear, Oh Israel. 1958. 7.50 (ISBN 0-87306-106-3). Feldheim.

Rosenblatt, Samuel, tr. Saadia Gaon Book of Beliefs & Opinions. (Judaica Ser.: No. 1). 1948. 55.00x (ISBN 0-300-00865-1). Yale U Pr.

Rosenblatt, Samuel, tr. see Abraham Ben Moses Ben Maimon.

Rosenbloom, Joseph R. Conversion to Judaism: From the Biblical Period to the Present. 20.00x (ISBN 0-87820-113-0). Ktav.

Rosenblum, Richard. My Bar Mitzvah. LC 84-16685. (Illus.). 32p. 1985. 10.25 (ISBN 0-688-04143-4, Morrow Junior Books); PLB 10.88 (ISBN 0-688-04144-2, Morrow Junior Books). Morrow.

Rosenfeld, Alvin H. A Double Dying: Reflections on Holocaust Literature. LC 79-3006. 224p. 1980. 17.50x (ISBN 0-253-13337-8). Ind U Pr.

Rosenfeld, Alvin H. & Greenberg, Irving, eds. Confronting the Holocaust: The Impact of Elie Wiesel. LC 78-15821. pap. 61.80 (ISBN 0-317-27853-3, 2056054). Bks Demand UMI.

Rosenfeld, Israel. Gemorah L'mas'chillim. 4.75 (ISBN 0-914131-23-0, A40); tchr's. guide 3.00 (ISBN 0-914131-24-9, A41). Torah Umesorah.

--Targilon for Sefer Bamidbar, Vol. 1. text ed. 4.00 (ISBN 0-914131-64-8, A23). Torah Umesorah.

--Targilon for Sefer Bemidbar, Vol. II. text ed. 4.00 (ISBN 0-914131-65-6, A24). Torah Umesorah.

Rosenfeld, Linda & Prupas, Marilynne. Left Alive: After a Suicide Death in the Family. 120p. 1984. 20.75 (ISBN 0-398-04953-X). C C Thomas.

Rosenfeld, Max, tr. see Blinkin, Meir.

Rosenfeld, Max, tr. see Emiot, Israel.

Rosenfeld, Max, tr. see Smolar, Hersh.

Rosenfeld, Sidney, ed. see Amery, Jean.

Rosenfeld, Sidney, tr. see Amery, Jean.

Rosenfeld, Stella, tr. see Amery, Jean.

Rosenfeld, Stella P., ed. see Amery, Jean.

Rosenfeld, Stella P., tr. see Amery, Jean.

Rosenfeld, Tzvi A., ed. see Nachman of Breslov.

Rosenfeld, Zvi A., ed. see Nachman of Breslov.

Rosenfield, Abraham. Kinot for the Ninth of Av. 482p. 1956. 12.95 (ISBN 0-910818-16-9). Judaica Pr.

--Selichot for the Whole Year. 832p. 1956. 13.95 (ISBN 0-910818-10-X). Judaica Pr.

Rosenfield, John M. & Ten Grotenhuis, Elizabeth. Journey of the Three Jewels: Japanese Buddhist Paintings from Western Collections. LC 79-15072. (Illus.). 1979. 19.95 (ISBN 0-87848-054-4). Asia Soc.

Rosenius, C. O. Romans, a Devotional Commentary. 1978. pap. 5.45 (ISBN 0-910452-42-3). Covenant.

Rosenkrans, B., compiled by. My Book of Christmas Carols. (All Aboard Bks.). (Illus.). 32p. 1986. pap. 1.95 (ISBN 0-448-19079-6, G&D). Putnam Pub Group.

Rosensaft, Jean. Chagall & the Bible. (Illus.). 160p. 1987. 24.95 (ISBN 0-87663-653-9). Universe.

Rosensaft, Menachem Z. The Legal Status of Soviet Jewry: De Jure Equality & De Facto Discrimination. 30p. 1.00 (ISBN 0-686-74962-6). ADL.

Rosenstock-Huessy, Eugen. Applied Science of the Soul. 40p. 1984. pap. text ed. 3.95 (ISBN 0-910727-04-X). Golden Phoenix.

--The Fruit of Lips or Why Four Gospels? LC 78-8524. (Pittsburgh Theological Monographs: No. 19). 1978. pap. 6.25 (ISBN 0-915138-31-X). Pickwick.

--I Am an Impure Thinker. 1970. 10.00 (ISBN 0-912148-03-9); pap. 6.95 (ISBN 0-912148-04-7). Argo Bks.

--Multiformity of Man. 1973. pap. 3.50 (ISBN 0-912148-06-3). Argo Bks.

Rosenstock-Huessy, Eugen & Battles, Ford L. Magna Carta Latina: The Privilege of Singing, Articulating & Reading a Language & Keeping It Alive. 2nd ed. LC 75-23378. (Pittsburgh Reprint Ser.: No. 1). 1975. pap. text ed. 9.95 (ISBN 0-915138-07-7). Pickwick.

Rosenthal, Abigail L. A Good Look at Evil. 264p. 1987. 24.95 (ISBN 0-87722-456-0). Temple U Pr.

Rosenthal, Curt, tr. see Simmel, Georg.

Rosenthal, Donald A. La Grande Maniere: Religious & Historical Painting in France, 1700-1800. (Illus.). 200p. 1987. pap. 24.95 (ISBN 0-295-96475-8). U of Wash Pr.

Rosenthal, Erwin I. Political Thought in Medieval Islam: An Introductory Outline. LC 85-21909. ix, 345p. 1985. Repr. of 1958 ed. lib. bdg. 47.50x (ISBN 0-313-25094-4, JA82). Greenwood.

--Studia Semitica, 2 vols. Incl. Vol. 1. Jewish Themes. 59.50 (ISBN 0-521-07958-6); Vol. 2. Islamic Themes. 49.50 (ISBN 0-521-07959-4). (Oriental Publications Ser.: Nos. 16 & 17). Cambridge U Pr.

Rosenthal, Erwin I. & Katz, Steven, eds. Saadya Studies: In Commemoration of the One Thousandth Anniversary of the Death of R. Saadya Gaon. LC 79-7170. (Jewish Philosophy, Mysticism & History of Ideas Ser.). 1980. Repr. of 1943 ed. lib. bdg. 25.50x (ISBN 0-405-12284-5). Ayer Co Pubs.

Rosenthal, F., jt. auth. see Brann, M.

Rosenthal, Gilbert S. Contemporary Judaism: Patterns of Survival. 2nd ed. 401p. 1986. 39.95 (ISBN 0-89885-260-9, Dist. by Independent Publishers Group); pap. 16.95 (ISBN 0-89885-277-3). Human Sci Pr.

--The Many Faces of Judaism. Rossel, Seymour, ed. LC 78-25898. 1979. pap. 4.95x (ISBN 0-87441-311-7). Behrman.

Rosenthal, Joan. Lord Is My Strength. 1976. pap. 1.25 (ISBN 0-89129-086-9). Jove Pubns.

Rosenthal, Ludwig. The Final Solution to the Jewish Question: Mass-Murder or Hoax? (Illus.). 145p. (Orig.). 1984. pap. 9.95 (ISBN 0-318-04673-3). Magnes Mus.

Rosenthal, Raymond, tr. see Chastel, Andre.

Rosenthal, Stanley. One God or Three? 1978. pap. text ed. 2.25 (ISBN 0-87508-464-8). Chr Lit.

Rosenthal, Ted. How Could I Not Be Among You? LC 73-80922. (Illus.). 80p. 1987. pap. 9.95 (ISBN 0-89255-117-8). Persea Bks.

Rosenwein, Barbara H. Rhinoceros Bound: Cluny in the Tenth Century. LC 81-43525. (Middle Ages Ser.). 192p. 1982. 24.00x (ISBN 0-8122-7830-5). U of Pa Pr.

Rosenzweig, Franz. The Star of Redemption. Hallo, William W., tr. from Ger. LC 84-40833. 464p. 1985. text ed. 30.00 (ISBN 0-268-01717-4, 85-17179); pap. text ed. 12.95 (ISBN 0-268-01718-2, 85-17187). U of Notre Dame Pr.

Rosenzweig, Rachel. Solidaritaet mit den Leidenden im Judentum. (Studia Judaica: Vol. 10). 1978. 46.40x (ISBN 3-11-005939-8). De Gruyter.

Rose-Troup, Frances. Massachusetts Bay Company & Its Predecessors. LC 68-56574. 1973. Repr. of 1930 ed. 22.50x (ISBN 0-678-00871-X). Kelley.

Rosett, Arthur, jt. auth. see Dorff, Elliot N.

Roseveare, Helen. Living Holiness. 192p. (Orig.). 1987. pap. 5.95 (ISBN 0-87123-952-3). Bethany Hse.

Rosewaike, Ira. The Edge of Greatness: A Portrait of American Jewry in the Early National Period. (Illus.). 1985. 25.00 (ISBN 0-87820-013-4, Pub. by Am Jewish Archives). Ktav.

Rosewell, Pamela. The Five Silent Years of Corrie Ten Boom. Hazzard, David, ed. 192p. 1986. pap. 6.95 (ISBN 0-310-61121-0, 13228P). Zondervan.

Rosher, Grace. Beyond the Horizon: Being New Evidence from the Other Side of Life. 154p. 1961. 10.95 (ISBN 0-227-67412-X). Attic Pr.

Rosholt, Malcolm, jt. tr. see Kaasa, Harris.

Rosholt, Malcolm, tr. see Nelson, E. Clifford.

Rosicrucian Foundation. The Brotherhood of the Rosy Cross. 76p. 1935. 5.95 (ISBN 0-932785-06-9). Philos Pub.

Rosik, Christopher H. & Malony, H. Newton, eds. The Nineteen Eighty-Three Travis Papers in the Integration of Psychology & Theology. 1986. pap. 10.00 (ISBN 0-9609928-5-5). Integ Pr.

Rosin, Jacob. In God's Image. LC 75-86507. 1969. 6.00 (ISBN 0-8022-2299-4). Philos Lib.

Roskies, David G. Against the Apocalypse: Responses to Catastrophe in Modern Jewish Culture. LC 83-18663. (Illus.). 392p. 1986. pap. 9.95 (ISBN 0-674-00916-9). Harvard U Pr.

Roskies, David G, jt. auth. see Roskies, Diane K.

Roskies, Diane. Teaching the Holocaust to Children: A Review & Bibliography. pap. 7.50x (ISBN 0-87068-469-8). Ktav.

Roskies, Diane K. & Roskies, David G. The Shtetl Book. rev ed. pap. 9.95x (ISBN 0-87068-455-8). Ktav.

Rosler, Margarete. Die Fassungen der Alexius-Legende. Repr. of 1905 ed. 25.00 (ISBN 0-384-51670-X). Johnson Repr.

Rosman, Abraham, jt. auth. see Rubel, Paula G.

Rosmini, Antonio. Talks to Priests. Ingoldsby, Mary F., tr. from Ital. LC 82-61099. Tr. of Confrerenze Sui Doveri Ecclesiastici. 368p. 1983. 18.00 (ISBN 0-911782-43-5). New City.

Rosner. Maimonides' Commentary on the Mishnah. cancelled (ISBN 0-87306-083-0). Feldheim.

Rosner, F. Medicine in the Bible & the Talmud: Selections from Classical Jewish Sources. (Library of Jewish Law & Ethics: Vol. 5). 9.95x (ISBN 0-87068-326-8). Ktav.

Rosner, Fred. Maimonides' Commentary on Mishnah Sanhedrin. LC 81-51800. 224p. 1981. 14.95 (ISBN 0-87203-099-7). Hermon.

--Medicine in the Mishneh Torah of Maimonides. 1983. 20.00x (ISBN 0-88125-020-1); pap. 11.95 (ISBN 0-88125-021-X). Ktav.

--Modern Medicine & Jewish Ethics. LC 86-2910. 1986. text ed. 22.50 (ISBN 0-88125-091-0); pap. text ed. 14.95 (ISBN 0-88125-102-X). Ktav.

--Modern Medicine & Jewish Law: Studies in Torah Judaism. 1972. 9.95x (ISBN 0-8197-0389-3). Bloch.

--Sex Ethics in the Writings of Moses Maimonides. LC 74-75479. 225p. 1974. 7.95x (ISBN 0-8197-0365-6). Bloch.

Rosner, Fred, ed. see Association of Orthodox Jewish Scientists.

Rosner, Fred, ed. see Associations of Orthodox Jewish Scientists Staff.

Rosner, Fred, tr. Moses Maimonides' Treatise on Resurrection. 12.50x (ISBN 0-87068-764-6); pap. 7.95. Ktav.

Rosner, Fred, tr. see Preuss, Julius.

Rosner, Fred, et al. Jewish Bioethics. 1979. (Sanhedrin Pr); pap. 11.95 (ISBN 0-88482-935-9, Sanhedrin Pr). Hebrew Pub.

Rosny, Eric de see De Rosny, Eric.

Rosoff, David. The Tefillin Handbook. (Orig.). 1984. pap. 4.95 (ISBN 0-87306-373-2). Feldheim.

Ross, A. C. Arnica: The Amazing Healer. 96p. (Orig.). 1986. pap. 2.50 (ISBN 0-7225-0374-1, Dist. by Inner Traditions International). Thorsons Pubs.

Ross, Aileen D. The Hindu Family in Its Urban Setting. LC 62-2801. pap. 84.80 (ISBN 0-317-09747-4, 2014388). Bks Demand UMI.

Ross, Alan. The Jesus Messages. Boster, Gregory, ed. (Illus.). 24p. (Orig.). pap. 3.49 (ISBN 0-9617038-0-6). Divine Love Pub.

Ross, Alf. On Guilt, Responsibility & Punishment. LC 73-94446. 1974. 33.00x (ISBN 0-520-02717-5). U of Cal Pr.

Ross, Bette M. Hannah's Daughters. Date not set. pap. 5.95 (ISBN 0-8007-5232-5, Power Bks). Revell.

--Journey of No Return. Date not set. pap. 5.95 (ISBN 0-8007-5231-7, Power Bks). Revell.

--Our Special Child. rev. ed. 256p. 1984. pap. 8.95 (ISBN 0-8007-1230-7). Revell.

Ross, Bob L. Acts Two: Thirty-Eight. 1976. 2.25 (ISBN 0-686-09114-0). Pilgrim Pubns.

--Baptism & Restoration Movement. 1979. pap. 1.00 (ISBN 0-686-28281-7). Pilgrim Pubns.

--Campbellism: Its History & Heresies. 1981. 2.90 (ISBN 0-686-09113-2). Pilgrim Pubns.

--Introduction to C. H. Spurgeon. 1985. pap. 0.95 (ISBN 0-686-18093-3). Pilgrim Pubns.

--Killing Effects of Calvinism. 1980. pap. 1.25 (ISBN 0-686-29039-9). Pilgrim Pubns.

--Old Landmarkism & the Baptists. 1979. pap. 3.95 (ISBN 0-686-26196-8). Pilgrim Pubns.

--Pictorial Biography of C. H. Spurgeon. 1981. 5.95 (ISBN 0-686-16830-5); pap. 3.95 (ISBN 0-686-16831-3). Pilgrim Pubns.

--Salvation by Grace Through Faith in Contrast to the Restorationist Doctrine. 1979. pap. 1.00 (ISBN 0-686-35836-8). Pilgrim Pubns.

Ross, Charles. The Inner Sanctuary. 1967. pap. 2.95 (ISBN 0-85151-042-6). Banner of Truth.

Ross, Charlotte. Who Is the Minister's Wife? A Search for Personal Fulfillment. LC 79-24027. 132p. 1980. pap. 6.95 (ISBN 0-664-24302-9). Westminster.

Ross, Dan. Acts of Faith: A Journey to the Fringes of Jewish Identity. LC 83-40468. (Illus.). 256p. 1984. pap. 8.95 (ISBN 0-8052-0759-7). Schocken.

Ross, E. Denison, tr. see Lammens, Henri.

Ross, Estelle. Martin Luther. LC 83-45673. (Illus.). Date not set. Repr. of 1927 ed. 28.00 (ISBN 0-404-19862-7). AMS Pr.

Ross, Floyd H. Shinto, the Way of Japan. LC 83-12970. (Illus.). xvii, 187p. 1983. Repr. of 1965 ed. lib. bdg. 35.00x (ISBN 0-313-24240-2, RSHI). Greenwood.

Ross, Floyd H. & Hills, Tynette. Great Religions By Which Men Live. Orig. Title: Questions That Matter Most Asked by the World's Religions. 1977. pap. 2.50 (ISBN 0-449-30825-1, Prem). Fawcett.

Ross, Frederick. Slavery Ordained of God. LC 70-95445. (Studies in Black History & Culture, No. 54). 1970. Repr. of 1959 ed. lib. bdg. 48.95x (ISBN 0-8383-1202-0). Haskell.

Ross, Frederick A. Slavery Ordained by God. facs. ed. LC 74-83876. (Black Heritage Library Collection Ser). 1857. 14.25 (ISBN 0-8369-8647-4). Ayer Co Pubs.

Ross, G. R., ed. see Descartes, Rene.

Ross, Harriet, compiled by. Heroes & Heroines of Many Lands. (Illus.). 160p. 1981. PLB 7.95 (ISBN 0-87460-214-9). Lion Bks.

--Myths & Legends of Many Lands. new ed. (Illus.). 160p. 1984. PLB 7.95. Lion Bks.

--Myths of Ancient Greece. (Illus.). 160p. 1984. PLB 7.95 (ISBN 0-87460-383-8). Lion Bks.

Ross, J. Elliott. Christian Ethics. 1951. 10.50 (ISBN 0-8159-5202-3). Devin.

Ross, James F. Philosophical Theology. 366p. 1982. 15.50 (ISBN 0-8290-0335-5). Irvington.

--Philosophical Theology. 366p. 1982. pap. 7.95 (ISBN 0-8290-1764-X). Irvington.

Ross, Joe. NESFA Hymnal. 2nd ed. 220p. pap. 10.00 (ISBN 0-915368-69-2). New Eng SF Assoc.

Ross, John E. Truths to Live by. facsimile ed. LC 72-37834. (Essay Index Reprint Ser). Repr. of 1929 ed. 19.00 (ISBN 0-8369-2622-6). Ayer Co Pubs.

Ross, Lydia & Ryan, Charles J. Theosophia: An Introduction. 1974. pap. 1.75 (ISBN 0-913004-13-8). Point Loma Pub.

Ross, Maggie. Fire of Your Life: A Solitude Shared. LC 82-61420. 128p. 1983. pap. 6.95 (ISBN 0-8091-2513-7). Paulist Pr.

Ross, Malcolm M. Poetry & Dogma. LC 78-86284. 1969. Repr. of 1954 ed. lib. bdg. 18.50x (ISBN 0-374-96973-6, Octagon). Hippocrene Bks.

Ross, Nancy W. Buddhism: A Way of Life & Thought. LC 80-7652. (Illus.). 224p. 1980. 15.95 (ISBN 0-394-49286-2). Knopf.

--Buddhism: A Way of Life & Thought. LC 81-40081. (Illus.). 224p. 1981. pap. 6.95 (ISBN 0-394-74754-2, Vin). Random.

--Three Ways of Asian Wisdom: Hinduism, Buddhism, Zen. (Illus.). 1978. pap. 12.95 (ISBN 0-671-24230-X, Touchstone Bks). S&S.
Ross, Nancy W., ed. World of Zen. (Illus.). 1960. pap. 8.95 (ISBN 0-394-70301-4, Vin). Random.
Ross, Pearl, ed. Jesus the Pagan. 84p. 1972. 7.00 (ISBN 0-8022-2097-5). Philos Lib.
Ross, Robert R. N. The Non-Existence of God: Linguistic Paradox in Tillich's Thought. LC 78-65486. (Toronto Studies in Theology: Vol. 1). xiv, 216p. 1978. 39.95x (ISBN 0-88946-905-9). E Mellen.
Ross, Robert W. So It Was True: The American Protestant Press & the Nazi Persecution of the Jews. LC 80-196. 1980. 20.00 (ISBN 0-8166-0948-9); pap. 9.95 (ISBN 0-8166-0951-9). U of Minn Pr.
--So It Was True: The American Protestant Press & the Nazi Persecution of the Jews. 374p. pap. 9.95 (ISBN 0-686-95052-6). ADL.
Ross, Stephen D. Transition to an Ordinal Metaphysics. 162p. 1980. 44.50x (ISBN 0-87395-434-3); pap. 16.95x (ISBN 0-87395-435-1). State U NY Pr.
Ross, Uta O. The Boy Who Wanted to Be a Missionary. (Illus.). 48p. (Orig.). 1984. pap. 11.95 (ISBN 0-687-03910-X). Abingdon.
Ross, Vicki. Hunger & Discipleship. (Orig.). 1982. pap. 8.00 (ISBN 0-8309-0346-1). Herald Hse.
Ross, Sir William D. Kant's Ethical Theory: A Commentary on the Grundlegung zur Metaphysik der Sitten. LC 78-6730. 1978. Repr. of 1954 ed. lib. bdg. 22.50x (ISBN 0-8371-9059-2, ROKE). Greenwood.
Ross-Bryant, Lynn. Imagination & the Life of the Spirit: An Introduction to the Study of Religion & Literature. LC 79-28464. (Scholars Press General Ser.: Vol. 2). pap. 7.95x (ISBN 0-89130-378-2, 00 03 02). Scholars Pr GA.
Rossel, Seymour. Introduction to Jewish History. Kozodoy, Neil, ed. (Illus.). 128p. 1981. pap. text ed. 5.95x (ISBN 0-87441-335-4). Behrman.
--Israel: Covenant People, Covenant Land. (Illus.). 256p. 1985. pap. 8.95 (ISBN 0-941232-06-9, 147500). UAHC.
--Journey Through Jewish History, Vol. II. (Illus.). 128p. 1983. pap. text ed. 5.95x (ISBN 0-87441-366-4). Behrman.
--When a Jew Prays. Borowitz, Eugene B. & Chanover, Hyman, eds. LC 73-1233. (Illus.). 192p. 1973. pap. text ed. 6.95x (ISBN 0-87441-093-2). Behrman.
--When a Jew Seeks Wisdom: The Sayings of the Fathers. LC 75-14119. (Jewish Values Ser.). pap. 6.95x (ISBN 0-87441-089-4). Behrman.
Rossel, Seymour, ed. see Kozodoy, Ruth.
Rossel, Seymour, ed. see Langer, Jiri.
Rossel, Seymour, ed. see Newman, Shirley.
Rossel, Seymour, ed. see Rosenthal, Gilbert S.
Rosset, Hannelore, ed. see Batchelor, Stephen.
Rossetti, Stephen J. I Am Awake: A Guide to the Contemplative Life. 1987. pap. 3.95. Paulist Pr.
Rossi, Ernest L., ed. see Erickson, Milton H., et al.
Rossi, Ino. From the Sociology of Symbols to the Sociology of Signs. LC 83-5261. 1983. 49.50 (ISBN 0-231-04844-0); pap. 17.50 (ISBN 0-231-04845-9). Columbia U Pr.
Rossi, Leandro & Valsecchi, Ambrogio. Diccionario Enciclopedico De Teologia Moral. 3rd ed. (Span.). 1488p. 1978. 38.95 (ISBN 84-285-0468-7, S-50077); pap. 32.95 (ISBN 84-285-0467-9, S-50078). French & Eur.
--Diccionario Enciclopedico De Teologia Moral: Suplemento. (Span.). 256p. 1978. 13.95 (ISBN 84-285-0709-0, S-50079). French & Eur.
Rossi, Peter H., jt. auth. see Greeley, Andrew M.
Rossi, Philip. Together Toward Hope: A Journey to Moral Theology. LC 83-1279. 224p. 1983. 16.95x (ISBN 0-268-01844-8, 85-18441). U of Notre Dame Pr.
Rossi, Vinio. Andre Gide. LC 68-54458. (Columbia Essays on Modern Writers Ser.: No. 35). (Orig.). 1968. pap. 3.00 (ISBN 0-231-02960-8). Columbia U Pr.
Rossier, H. Meditations on Joshua. 7.25 (ISBN 0-88172-119-0). Believers Bkshelf.
--Que Pasa Despues de la Muerte? 2nd ed. Bennett, Gordon H., ed. Bautista, Sara, tr. from Eng. (La Serie Diamante). Tr. of What Happens After Death? (Span., Illus.). 36p. 1982. pap. 0.85 (ISBN 0-942504-07-0). Overcomer Pr.
Rossignol, Elaine. You Are What You Swallow. LC 86-83406. 220p. (Orig.). 1987. pap. 9.95 (ISBN 0-89896-240-4). Larksdale.
Rossini, Lillian M. Rabbi Letters, No. 1. (Illus.). 32p. 1986. 5.95 (ISBN 0-89962-506-1). Todd & Honeywell.
Rossman, Douglas A. Where Legends Live. (Illus.). 48p. (Orig.). 1986. pap. 5.00x (ISBN 0-935741-10-0). Cherokee Pubns.
Rossman, Heribert. Bibliographie Zur Geschichte Des Karatauser-Spirit-Ualitat: Im Deutschen Sprachraum Und Nachbargebieten. Hogg, James, ed. (Analecta Cartusiana Ser.: No. 67). (Orig.). 1987. pap. 25.00 (ISBN 3-7052-0099-2, Pub. by Salzburg Studies). Longwood Pub Group.
Rossman, Parker, jt. auth. see Bedell, Kenneth.
Rossman, Peter & Noyce, Gaylord. Helping People Care on the Job. 144p. 1985. pap. 5.95. Judson.
Rossmann, Heribert. Bibliographie Zur Geschichte Des Kartauser-Ordens: Im Deutschen Sprachraum Und Nachbargebieten. Hogg, James, ed. (Analecta Cartusiana Ser.: No. 67). (Orig.). 1987. pap. 25.00 (ISBN 3-7052-0098-4, Pub. by Salzburg Studies). Longwood Pub Group.
Rossner, John. Toward Recovery of the Primordial Tradition: Ancient Insights & Modern Discoveries, 2 bks, Vol. 1. Incl. Bk. 1. From Ancient Magic to Future Technology. LC 79-66892. 14.75 (ISBN 0-8191-0861-8); Bk. 2. Toward a Parapsychology of Religion: from Ancient Religion to Future Science. LC 79-66893. 14.25 (ISBN 0-8191-0862-6). 1979. U Pr of Amer.
--Towards Recovery of the Primordial Tradition: Ancient Insights & Modern Discoveries, Vol. II. LC 83-14753. (The Primordial Tradition in Contemporary Experience Ser.: Bk. 2). 152p. 1984. PLB 27.00 (ISBN 0-8191-3519-4); pap. 13.50 (ISBN 0-8191-3520-8). U Pr of Amer.
Rossner, John, ed. see Roche de Coppens, Peter.
Rossow, Francis. Preaching the Creative Gospel Creatively. 1983. pap. 8.95 (ISBN 0-570-03917-7, 12-2856). Concordia.
Rossow, Francis & Aho, Gerhard. Lectionary Preaching Resources. (Illus.). 224p. 1987. pap. 14.95 (ISBN 0-570-04468-5). Concordia.
Rost, Leonhard. The Succession to the Throne of David. (Historic Texts & Interpreters Ser: No. 1). Orig. Title: Die Uberlieferung von der Thronnachfolge Davids. 160p. 1982. text ed. 25.95x (ISBN 0-907459-12-9, Pub. by Almond Pr England); pap. text ed. 12.95x (ISBN 0-907459-13-7, Pub. by Almond Pr England). Eisenbrauns.
Rosten, Leo. Joys of Yiddish. 1968. 19.95 (ISBN 0-07-053975-8). McGraw.
--Joys of Yiddish. 534p. 1970. pap. 4.95 (ISBN 0-671-47349-2). WSP.
Rosten, Leo, ed. Religions of America. LC 74-11705. 1975. pap. 11.95 (ISBN 0-671-21971-5, Touchstone Bks). S&S.
Roston, Murray. Prophet & Poet: The Bible & the Growth of Romanticism. 1979. Repr. of 1965 ed. lib. bdg. 27.50 (ISBN 0-8495-4610-9). Arden Lib.
Roston, Scott. Nightmare in Israel. 1987. 14.95 (ISBN 0-533-07157-7). Vantage.
Rostron, Hilda L. Animals, Birds & Plants of the Bible. (Ladybird Ser). (Illus.). 1964. bds. 2.50 (ISBN 0-87508-830-9). Chr Lit.
--Baby Jesus. (Ladybird Ser.). (Illus.). 1961. bds. 2.50 (ISBN 0-87508-832-5). Chr Lit.
--Stories About Children of the Bible. (Ladybird Ser). (Illus.). 1962. bds. 2.50 (ISBN 0-87508-860-0). Chr Lit.
--Stories About Jesus the Friend. (Ladybird Ser). (Illus.). 1961. bds. 2.50 (ISBN 0-87508-862-7). Chr Lit.
--Stories About Jesus the Helper. (Ladybird Ser). (Illus.). 1961. bds. 2.50 (ISBN 0-87508-864-3). Chr Lit.
Rostron, S. Nowell. The Christology of St. Paul. 1977. lib. bdg. 59.95 (ISBN 0-8490-1620-7). Gordon Pr.
Roswell, Steve C., tr. see Epictetus.
Roszak, Theodore. Unfinished Animal. 1977. pap. 5.95 (ISBN 0-06-090537-9, CN 537, PL). Har-Row.
Rotberg, Robert I. Christian Missionaries & the Creation of Northern Rhodesia, 1880-1924. 1965. 30.50x (ISBN 0-691-03009-X). Princeton U Pr.
Rotelle, John. Augustine Day by Day. (Orig.). 1986. pap. 4.50 (ISBN 0-89942-170-9, 170-09). Catholic BK Pub.
Rotelle, John E., ed. Augustine's Heritage: Readings from the Augustinian Tradition, 3 vols. Vol. 1. 1.50 (ISBN 0-89942-701-4, 701-04). Vol. 2 (ISBN 0-89942-702-2, 702-04). Vol. 3 (ISBN 0-89942-703-0, 703-04). Catholic Bk Pub.
Rotenberg, Mordechai. Damnation & Deviance: The Protestant Ethic & the Spirit of Failure. LC 77-18432. 1978. 12.95 (ISBN 0-02-927490-7). Free Pr.
--Dialogue with Deviance: The Hasidic Ethic & the Theory of Social Contraction. LC 81-13309. 224p. 1983. text ed. 27.50 (ISBN 0-89727-031-2). ISHI PA.
Rotenstreich, Nathan. Practice & Realization. 1979. lib. bdg. 29.00 (ISBN 90-247-2112-1, Pub. by Martinus Nijhoff Netherlands). Kluwer Academic.
Rotenstreich, Nathan, ed. Essays on Zionism & the Contemporary Jewish Condition. 1981. write for info. Herzl Pr.
Roth, Bette, jt. auth. see Grad, Eli.
Roth, C., intro. by. The Sarajevo Haggadah. 50.00 (ISBN 0-87068-761-1). Ktav.
Roth, Catharine P., tr. see St. John Chrysostom.
Roth, Catherine, tr. St. Theodore the Studite on the Holy Icons. LC 81-18319. 115p. (Orig.). pap. 4.95 (ISBN 0-913836-76-1). St Vladimirs.
Roth, Cecil. Dead Sea Scrolls: A New Historical Approach. 1966. pap. 3.95x (ISBN 0-393-00303-5, Norton Lib). Norton.
--Dona Gracia of the House of Nasi. LC 77-92984. 208p. 1978. pap. 4.95 (ISBN 0-8276-0099-2, 415). Jewish Pubns.
--Gleanings: Essays in Jewish History, Letters & Art. 1967. 10.00x (ISBN 0-8197-0178-5). Bloch.
--The Haggadah. 109p. 1975. pap. 4.95 (ISBN 0-900689-72-2). Soncino Pr.
--A History of the Jews: From Earliest Times Through the Six Day War. rev. ed. LC 74-121042. 1970. pap. 8.95 (ISBN 0-8052-0009-6). Schocken.
--A History of the Marranos. LC 74-10149. 448p. 1974. pap. 10.95 (ISBN 0-8052-0463-6). Schocken.
--The Jewish Contribution to Civilizaton. 1978. pap. 5.95 (ISBN 0-85222-217-3, East & West Lib). Hebrew Pub.
--The Jews in the Renaissance. LC 59-8516. (Illus.). 378p. 1978. pap. 8.95 (ISBN 0-8276-0103-4, 321). Jewish Pubns.
--Short History of the Jewish People. rev. ed. 1969. 14.95; pap. 6.95 (ISBN 0-87677-183-5). Hartmore.
--Soncino Haggadah. 4.95x (ISBN 0-685-01039-2). Bloch.
--Spanish Inquisition. (Illus., Orig.). 1964. pap. 7.95 (ISBN 0-393-00255-1, Norton Lib). Norton.
Roth, Cecil, jt. auth. see Wurmbrand, Max.
Roth, Cecil & Widoger, Geoffrey, eds. The Concise Jewish Encyclopedia. 576p. (Orig.). 1980. pap. 8.95 (ISBN 0-452-00526-4, F526, Mer). NAL.
Roth, Charles. Mind: The Master Power. 1984. 5.95 (ISBN 0-87159-099-9). Unity School.
--More Power to You! LC 82-50122. 158p. 1982. 5.95 (ISBN 0-87159-093-X). Unity School.
--A New Way of Thinking. LC 78-64751. 1979. 5.95 (ISBN 0-87159-113-8). Unity School.
Roth, Guenther, tr. see Schluchter, Wolfgang.
Roth, Joel. The Halakhic Process: A Systemic Analysis. (Moreshet Ser.: Vol. 13). 1987. 35.00 (ISBN 0-87334-035-3). Jewish Sem.
Roth, John & Sontag, Fredrick E., eds. The Defense of God. LC 84-25592. (God Ser.). 196p. (Orig.). 1985. text ed. 21.95 (ISBN 0-913757-26-8, Pub. by New Era Bks); pap. text ed. 12.95 (ISBN 0-913757-27-6, Pub. by New Era Bks). Paragon Hse.
Roth, Joseph. Job: The Story of a Simple Man. Thompson, Dorothy, tr. from Ger. LC 81-18901. (A Tusk Bk.). 252p. 1985. 22.50 (ISBN 0-87951-149-4); pap. 8.95 (ISBN 0-87951-202-4). Overlook Pr.
Roth, Leon. Judaism, a Portrait. LC 61-5918. 240p. 1972. pap. 4.95 (ISBN 0-8052-0344-3). Schocken.
--Spinoza. LC 78-14139. 1986. Repr. of 1954 ed. 23.75 (ISBN 0-88355-813-0). Hyperion Conn.
Roth, Martin & Stevens, John. Zen Guide: Where to Meditate in Japan. (Illus.). 152p. pap. 7.50 (ISBN 0-8348-0202-3). Weatherhill.
Roth, Norman D. Maimonides: Essays & Texts, 850th Anniversary. 1986. 10.00x (ISBN 0-942260-59-7). Hispanic Seminary.
Roth, Robert P. The Theater of God: Story in Christian Doctrine. LC 84-48725. 208p. 1985. pap. 10.95 (ISBN 0-8006-1841-6, 1-1841). Fortress.
Roth, Samuel. Jews Must Live. 1980. lib. bdg. 69.95 (ISBN 0-8490-3204-0). Gordon Pr.
Roth, Walter E. An Inquiry into the Animism & Folklore of the Guiana Indians. LC 16-9897. (Landmarks in Anthropology Ser). Repr. of 1915 ed. 23.00 (ISBN 0-384-52130-4). Johnson Repr.
Roth, Wolfgang & Ruether, Rosemary R. The Liberating Bond: Covenants Biblical & Contemporary. (Orig.). 1978. pap. 2.95 (ISBN 0-377-00076-0). Friend Pr.
Rothchild, Sylvia. A Special Legacy: An Oral History of Soviet Jewish Emigres in the United States. 336p. 1986. pap. 8.95 (ISBN 0-671-62817-8, Touchstone). S&S.
Rothchild, Sylvia, ed. Voices from the Holocaust. 464p. 1982. pap. 10.95 (ISBN 0-452-00860-3, Mer). NAL.
Rothenberg, Benno, ed. Archaeological Haggadah. LC 86-1052. (Illus.). 1986. 12.95 (ISBN 0-915361-36-1, 09713-7, Dist. by Watts). Adama Pubs Inc.
Rothenberg, Jerome. Abulafia's Circles. 1979. pap. 2.00 (ISBN 0-87924-034-2). Membrane Pr.
Rothenberg, Joshua. The Jewish Religion in the Soviet Union. 1971. 20.00x (ISBN 0-87068-156-7). Ktav.
Rother, Kathleen & Gosse, Carol A. National Catholic Rural Life Conference Idea Book for Small Town Churches. LC 76-2333. 106p. 1976. pap. 2.50x (ISBN 0-914422-05-7). Glenmary Res Ctr.
Rotherham, Joseph B. Studies in Psalms, Vol. I. DeWelt, Don, ed. (The Bible Study Textbook Ser.). (Illus.). 1970. Repr. 14.30 (ISBN 0-89900-016-9). College Pr Pub.
--Studies in Psalms, Vol. II. rev. ed. DeWelt, Don, ed. (The Bible Study Textbook Ser.). (Illus.). 1971. Repr. of 1901 ed. 14.30 (ISBN 0-89900-017-7). College Pr Pub.
Rothes, John L. Relation of Proceedings Concerning the Affairs of the Kirk of Scotland. LC 79-174966. (Bannatyne Club, Edinburgh. Publications: No. 37). Repr. of 1830 ed. 28.00 (ISBN 0-404-52743-4). AMS Pr.
Rothfuss, Frank. Journey to Jerusalem. 1982. pap. 9.25 (ISBN 0-89536-522-7, 1015). CSS of Ohio.
Rothkirchen, L., jt. ed. see Gutman, Y.
Rothman, David J. & Rothman, Sheila M., eds. First Ten Annual Reports 1871-1880, Young Women's Christian Association, New York, 1871-1880. (Women & Children First Ser.). 375p. 1986. lib. bdg. 45.00 (ISBN 0-8240-7682-6). Garland Pub.
Rothman, Eugene, jt. ed. see Polzin, Robert M.
Rothman, Frances. My Father, Edward Branston: His Life & Letters. (Illus.). 109p. 1983. pap. 5.00 (ISBN 0-943376-18-1). Magnes Mus.
Rothman, Sheila M., jt. ed. see Rothman, David J.
Rothrock, George A. The Huguenots: A Biography of a Minority. LC 78-23476. (Illus.). 228p. 1979. 21.95x (ISBN 0-88229-277-3). Nelson-Hall.
Rothschild, Jeffrey, et al, eds. see Nurbakhsh, Javad.
Rothschild, Jon, tr. see Rodinson, Maxime.
Rothschild, Zeev. Knowing Your Tefilen & Mezuzos: A Layman's Guide to Understanding & Appreciating Tefilin & Mezuzos. 80p. (Orig.). 1982. pap. 2.50 (ISBN 0-686-76528-1). Feldheim.
Rothstein, Chaya L. The Mentchkins Make Shabbos. (Sifrei Rimon Ser.). 1986. pap. 2.50 (ISBN 0-317-42728-8). Feldheim.
Rothstein, Joseph, ed. Meeting Life's Challenges with Pastoral Counseling. 1986. 14.95 (ISBN 0-533-06612-3). Vantage.
Rothstein, Raphael. The Story of Masada. (Illus.). 296p. 1983. cancelled (ISBN 0-89961-012-9). SBS Pub.
Rothwell, Mel-Thomas. Preaching Holiness Effectively. 160p. 1982. pap. 4.95 (ISBN 0-8341-0784-8). Beacon Hill.
Rotman, Jayne. If Your Doctor's Busy, Call on God: A Spiritual Journey Through Ecological Illness. 190p. (Orig.). Date not set. pap. price not set (ISBN 0-931515-05-X). Triumph Pr.
Rotondo, Antonio, ed. Camillo Renato: Opere, Documenti E Testimonianze. LC 72-3454. (Corpus Reformatorum Italicorum & Biblioteca Ser.). (Lat. & Ital., Illus.). 353p. 1968. 25.00 (ISBN 0-87580-034-3). N Ill U Pr.
Rott, H. G., jt. ed. see Krebs, Manfred.
Rottschafer, Joyce. My Bible Number Book. LC 81-50675. (A Happy Day Book). (Illus.). 24p. (Orig.). 1981. pap. 1.59 (ISBN 0-87239-465-4, 3598). Standard Pub.
Roudiez, Leon S., tr. see Kristeva, Julia.
Rouet, Albert. A Short Dictionary of the New Testament. (Illus.). 128p. 1982. pap. 6.95 (ISBN 0-8091-2400-9). Paulist Pr.
Rough, Worth S. Synopsis: Past-Present-Future. LC 84-90177. 84p. 1984. 17.95 (ISBN 0-533-06227-6). Vantage.
Rouillard, Dom P. Diccionario De los Santos De Cada Dia. (Span.). 472p. 1966. 15.75 (ISBN 84-281-0062-4, S-50020). French & Eur.
Rouiller, Gregoire, jt. ed. see Bovon, Francois.
Roumani, Judith, tr. see De Felice, Renzo.
Round, Graham, illus. Elijah & the Great Drought. (Illus.). 16p. 1982. pap. 0.99 (ISBN 0-86683-662-4, AY8239, HarpR). Har-Row.
--Miriam & the Princess of Egypt. (Illus.). 16p. 1982. pap. 0.99 (ISBN 0-86683-659-4, AY8240, HarpR). Har-Row.
--Naaman & the Little Servant Girl. (Illus.). 1982. pap. 0.99 (ISBN 0-86683-660-8, AY8242, HarpR). Har-Row.
--Nehemiah Builds a City. (Illus.). 16p. 1982. pap. 0.99 (ISBN 0-86683-661-6, AY8241, HarpR). Har-Row.
Rouner, Arthur A., Jr. How to Love. (Contemporary Discussion Ser.). 1974. pap. 1.25 (ISBN 0-8010-7622-6). Baker Bk.
--Receiving the Spirit at Old First Church. LC 81-19959. 96p. (Orig.). 1982. pap. 5.95 (ISBN 0-8298-0492-7). Pilgrim NY.
--Struggling With Sex: Serious Call to Marriage-Centered Sexual Life. LC 86-32028. 128p. (Orig.). (YA) 1986. pap. 6.50 (ISBN 0-8066-2243-1, 10-6096). Augsburg.

Rouner, Leroy S. Knowing Religiously. LC 85-8689. (Boston University Studies in Philosophy & Religion: Vol. 7). 240p. 1985. text ed. 22.95x (ISBN 0-268-01224-5, 85-12246, Dist. by Har-Row). U of Notre Dame Pr.
--Within Human Experience: The Philosophy of William Ernest Hocking. LC 71-75433. (Illus.). 1969. text ed. 20.00x (ISBN 0-674-95380-0). Harvard U Pr.
Rouner, Leroy S., ed. Civil Religion & Political Theology. LC 86-11242. (Boston University Studies in Philosophy & Religion: Vol. 8). 240p. 1986. text ed. 24.95x (ISBN 0-268-00757-8). U of Notre Dame Pr.
--On Nature. LC 84-7502. (Boston University Studies in Philosophy & Religion: Vol. 6). 224p. 1984. text ed. 20.95 (ISBN 0-268-01499-X, 85-14994). U of Notre Dame Pr.
--Religious Pluralism. LC 84-7431. (Boston University Studies in Philosphy & Religion: Vol. 5). 256p. 1984. text ed. 22.95 (ISBN 0-268-01626-7, 85-16262). U of Notre Dame Pr.
Rouner, Leroy S., jt. ed. see Olson, Alan M..
Roupp, Harold W. One Life Isn't Enough. 3.50 (ISBN 0-910924-44-9). Macalester.
Rouse, Jerry L. Church Building: The Ministry of Leadership in the Body of Christ. 0.75 (ISBN 0-911802-57-6). Free Church Pubns.
Rouse, John E., Jr., et al, eds. The Political Role of Religion on the U. S. (Special Study Ser.). 300p. 1985. pap. text ed. 24.50x (ISBN 0-8133-7030-2). Westview.
Rouse, Richard & Rouse, Susan. The Last Week. 1985. 1.00 (ISBN 0-89536-726-2, 5810). CSS of Ohio.
Rouse, Susan, jt. auth. see Rouse, Richard.
Rouse, W. D., tr. see Santideva.
Rouse, W. H. Gods, Heroes & Men of Ancient Greece. 192p. (YA) 1971. pap. 3.50 (ISBN 0-451-62366-5, Ment). NAL.
Rouse, W. H., jt. ed. see Bendall, Cecil.
Rouse, William H. Greek Votive Offerings: An Essay in the History of Greek Religion. facsimile ed. LC 75-10654. (Ancient Religion & Mythology Ser.). (Illus.). 1976. Repr. of 1902 ed. 36.50x (ISBN 0-405-07262-7). Ayer Co Pubs.
Rousseau, George S. Tobias Smollett. 210p. 1982. 18.95 (ISBN 0-567-09330-1, Pub. by T&T Clark Ltd UK). Fortress.
Rousseau, Jean-Jacques. Lettre a M. d'Alembert sur les Spectacles. 208p. 1948. 7.95 (ISBN 0-686-55352-7). French & Eur.
Rousseau, Marie-Andre, tr. see Ogilvie, Lloyd J.
Rousseau, Mary & Gallagner, Chuck. Sex Is Holy. (A Chrysalis Bk). 160p. (Orig.). 1986. pap. 9.95 (ISBN 0-916349-11-X). Amity Hous Inc.
Rousseau, Phillip. Ascetics, Authority, & the Church in the Age of Jerome & Cassian. (Historical Monographs). 1978. 39.95x (ISBN 0-19-821870-2). Oxford U Pr.
Rousseau, Richard, ed. Christianity & Judaism: The Deepening Dialogue. (Modern Theological Themes: Selections from the Literature Ser.: Vol. 3). (Orig.). 1983. pap. 15.00 (ISBN 0-940866-02-1). Ridge Row.
Rousseau, Richard W., ed. Interreligious Dialogue: Facing the Next Frontier. LC 81-52035. (Modern Theological Themes Ser.: Selection from the Literature: Vol. I). 234p. (Orig.). 1981. pap. 13.50 (ISBN 0-940866-00-5). Ridge Row.
Rousset, David. The Other Kingdom. Guthrie, Ramon, tr. from Fr. LC 81-12572. 173p. 1982. Repr. of 1947 ed. lib. bdg. 21.50 (ISBN 0-86527-339-1). Fertig.
Rousset, Paul. Les Origines et les caracteres de la premiere croisade. LC 76-29837. (Fr.). Repr. of 1945 ed. 25.00 (ISBN 0-404-15428-X). AMS Pr.
Rousso, Nira. The Passover Gourmet. (Illus.). 192p. 1987. 19.95 (ISBN 0-915361-66-3, Dist. by Watts). Adama Pubs Inc.
Routh, Harold V. God, Man & Epic Poetry: A Study in Comparative Literature, 2 Vols. LC 69-10152. (Illus.). 1968. Repr. of 1927 ed. lib. bdg. 37.50x (ISBN 0-8371-0206-5, ROEP). Greenwood.
--Towards the Twentieth Century. facs. ed. LC 69-17587. (Essay Index Reprint Ser). 1937. 19.00 (ISBN 0-8369-0091-X). Ayer Co Pubs.
Routley, Erik. Christian Hymns Observed: When in Our Music God Is Glorified. LC 82-61841. 121p. (Orig.). 1982. pap. text ed. 12.95 (ISBN 0-911009-00-0). Prestige Pubns.
--Church Music & the Christian Faith. LC 78-110219. 156p. 1978. pap. 7.95 (ISBN 0-916642-10-0). Agape IL.
--Church Music & the Christian Faith. LC 78-110219. 1979. 7.95 (ISBN 0-916642-11-9, Agape). Hope Pub.
--Creeds & Confessions: The Reformation & Its Modern Ecumenical Implications. LC 63-3127. (Studies in Theology: No. 62). 1962. text ed. 8.50x (ISBN 0-8401-6062-3). A R Allenson.
--The English Carol. LC 73-9129. (Illus.). 272p. 1973. Repr. of 1959 ed. lib. bdg. 22.50x (ISBN 0-8371-6989-5, ROEC). Greenwood.
--Exploring the Psalms. LC 74-20674. 170p. 1975. pap. 3.95 (ISBN 0-664-24999-X). Westminster.
--The Musical Wesleys. LC 75-36511. (Illus.). 1976. Repr. of 1968 ed. text ed. 22.50x (ISBN 0-8371-8644-7, ROMW). Greenwood.
Routley, Erik & Young, Carlton R. Music Leadership in the Church. 136p. 1985. pap. text ed. 6.95 (ISBN 0-916642-24-0). Agape IL.
Routley, Erik, ed. see Reformed Church in America.
Routtenberg, Lilly S. & Seldin, Ruth R. The Jewish Wedding Book: A Practical Guide to the Traditions & Social Customs of the Jewish Wedding. LC 67-13723. (Illus.). 1969. pap. 6.95 (ISBN 0-8052-0186-6). Schocken.
Routtenberg, Max J. One in a Minyan & Other Studies. 1979. pap. 6.95x (ISBN 0-87068-342-X). Ktav.
Rover, Dave & Fickett, Harold. Welcome Home, Davey. 208p. 1986. 12.95 (ISBN 0-8499-0553-2). Word Bks.
Row, John & Row, William. Historie of the Kirk of Scotland, 2 Vols. LC 70-174969. (Maitland Club. Glasgow. Publications: No. 55). Repr. of 1842 ed. Set. 57.50 (ISBN 0-404-53039-7). AMS Pr.
Row, Subba T. Esoteric Writings. 17.95 (ISBN 0-8356-7544-0). Theos Pub Hse.
Row, T. Subba. Consciousness & Immortality. (Sangam Texts Ser.). 96p. (Orig.). 1983. pap. 8.75 (ISBN 0-88695-012-0). Concord Grove.
--Notes on the Bhagavad-Gita. LC 77-88628. 1978. 6.00 (ISBN 0-911500-81-2); pap. 3.50 (ISBN 0-911500-82-0). Theos U Pr.
Row, William, jt. auth. see Row, John.
Rowan, John. The Horned God. 160p. 1987. pap. 13.95 (ISBN 0-7102-0674-7, 06747, Ark Paperbks). Methuen Inc.
Rowatt, G. Wade, Jr. & Rowatt, Mary Jo. The Two-Career Marriage. LC 79-28408. (Christian Care Bks.: Vol. 5). 120p. 1980. pap. 7.95 (ISBN 0-664-24298-7). Westminster.
Rowatt, Mary Jo, jt. auth. see Rowatt, G. Wade, Jr.
Rowe, Clarence J., jt. ed. see Sipe, A. W.
Rowe, David. Thunder & Trumpets: The Millerite Movement & Dissenting Religion in Upstate New York, 1800-1850. (American Academy of Religion Studies in Religion: No. 38). 1985. 24.95 (ISBN 0-89130-770-2, 01 00 38); pap. 16.95 (ISBN 0-89130-769-9). Scholars Pr GA.
Rowe, Frederick A. I Launch at Paradise: A Consideration of John Donne, Poet & Preacher. LC 65-84641. 1964. 10.00x (ISBN 0-8401-2055-9). A R Allenson.
--I Launch at Paradise: A Consideration of John Donne Poet & Preacher. 253p. 1983. lib. bdg. 40.00 (ISBN 0-89984-841-9). Century Bookbindery.
Rowe, H. Edward. The Day They Padlocked the Church. LC 83-80608. 86p. (Orig.). 1983. pap. 3.50 (ISBN 0-910311-05-6). Huntington Hse Inc.
--New Age Globalism: Humanist Agenda for Building a New World Without God. 95p. (Orig.). 1985. pap. 4.95 (ISBN 0-931225-11-6). Growth Pub.
Rowe, Henry K. Modern Pathfinders of Christianity: The Lives & Deeds of Seven Centuries of Christian Leaders. facs. ed. LC 68-16973. (Essay Index Reprint Ser). 1928. 15.00 (ISBN 0-8369-0839-2). Ayer Co Pubs.
Rowe, Kenneth E. Methodist Union Catalog: Pre-1976 Imprints, Vol. V:G-Haz. LC 75-33190. 371p. 1981. 29.00 (ISBN 0-8108-1454-4). Scarecrow.
Rowe, Kenneth E., ed. Methodist Union Catalog: Pre-1976 Imprints, 20 vols, Vol. I, A-bj. LC 75-33190. 438p. 1975. 29.00 (ISBN 0-8108-0880-3). Scarecrow.
--Methodist Union Catalog: Pre-1976 Imprints, Vol. VI: He-I. LC 75-33190. 360p. 1985. 29.00 (ISBN 0-8108-1725-X). Scarecrow.
--Methodist Union Catalog: Pre-1976 Imprints, Vol. 3, Che-Dix. LC 75-33190. 431p. 1978. 29.00 (ISBN 0-8108-1067-0). Scarecrow.
--The Place of Wesley in the Christian Tradition: Essays Delevered at Drew University in Celebration of the Commencement of the Publication of the Oxford Edition of the Works of John Wesley. LC 76-27659. 168p. 1976. 16.50 (ISBN 0-8108-0981-8). Scarecrow.
--United Methodist Studies: Basic Bibliographies. 40p. (Orig.). 1982. pap. 2.00 (ISBN 0-687-43109-3). Abingdon.
Rowe, Lois. On Call. 1984. 8.95 (ISBN 0-8010-7724-9). Baker Bk.
Rowe, Sherlie. Decisions. Vol. 1. pap. 3.95 (ISBN 0-89137-806-5); Vol. 2. pap. 3.95 (ISBN 0-89137-807-3). Quality Pubns.
Rowe, Stephen, ed. Living Beyond Crisis: Essays on Discovery & Being in the World. LC 80-18135. 261p. 1980. pap. 8.95 (ISBN 0-8298-0402-1). Pilgrim NY.
Rowe, William. Philosophy of Religion: An Introduction. 207p. 1985. pap. text ed. write for info. (ISBN 0-8221-0208-0). Wadsworth Pub.
Rowe, William L. & Wainwright, William J., eds. Philosophy of Religion: Selected Readings. 489p. 1973. pap. text ed. 16.95 (ISBN 0-15-570580-6, HC). HarBraceJ.
Rowell, Cy. Thankful Praise: A Studyguide. 24p. (Orig.). 1987. pap. 2.50 (ISBN 0-8272-3651-4). CBP.
Rowell, Edmon L., Jr. Apostles: Jesus' Special Helpers. (BibLearn Ser.). (Illus.). 1979. 5.95 (ISBN 0-8054-4246-4, 4242-46). Broadman.
Rowell, Geoffrey. The Vision Glorious: Themes & Personalities of the Catholic Revival in Anglicanism. 280p. 1983. text ed. 27.00x (ISBN 0-19-826443-7). Oxford U Pr.
Rowell, Geoffrey, ed. Tradition Renewed: The Oxford Movement Conference Papers. (Princeton Theological Monograph Ser.: No. 3). (Orig.). 1986. pap. 30.00 (ISBN 0-915138-82-4). PickWick.
Rowen, Samuel F., jt. ed. see Conn, Harvie M.
Rowland, Alfred. Studies in First Timothy. 302p. 1985. smythe sewn 12.00 (ISBN 0-86524-194-5, 5402). Klock & Klock.
Rowland, Benjamin, Jr. The Evolution of the Buddha Image. LC 74-27420. (Asia Society Ser.). (Illus.). 1979. Repr. of 1963 ed. lib. bdg. 31.00x (ISBN 0-405-06568-X). Ayer Co Pubs.
Rowland, Christopher. Christian Origins: From Messianic Movement to Christian Religion. LC 85-70241. 448p. (Orig.). 1985. pap. 19.95 (ISBN 0-8066-2173-7, 10-1175). Augsburg.
--The Open Heaven: The Study of Apocalyptic in Judaism & Early Christianity. LC 82-7409. 540p. 1982. 29.50x (ISBN 0-8245-0455-0). Crossroad NY.
Rowland, Cynthia, tr. see Cristiani, Leon.
Rowland, F. V. Daniel & the Revelation. 1984. 11.95 (ISBN 0-533-05996-8). Vantage.
Rowland, Jacqueline. Fifty-Two Middler-Junior Crafts. 48p. (Orig.). 1984. pap. 2.95 (ISBN 0-87239-727-0, 2107). Standard Pub.
Rowland, May. Dare to Believe. 1961. 5.95 (ISBN 0-87159-024-7). Unity School.
Rowland, Robert C. The Rhetoric of Menachem Begin: The Myth of Redemption Through Return. 330p. (Orig.). 1985. lib. bdg. 29.50 (ISBN 0-8191-4735-4); pap. text ed. 14.75 (ISBN 0-8191-4736-2). U Pr of Amer.
Rowland, Roy V. The Psychological Search for God. (Illus.). 1980. 44.75 (ISBN 0-89920-003-6). Am Inst Psych.
Rowland-Entwistle, Theodore. Confucius & Ancient China. (Life & Times Ser.). (Illus.). 64p. 1987. lib. bdg. 11.40 (ISBN 0-531-18101-4, Pub. by Bookwright Pr). Watts.
Rowlands, Gerald. Coming Alive in the Spirit: The Spirit-led Life. (Basic Bible Study). Orig. Title: The Holy Spirit & His Fruit. 64p. 1985. pap. 2.95 (ISBN 0-930756-90-8, 521019). Aglow Pubns.
--The Holy Spirit & His Gifts. Sekowsky, Jo Anne, ed. (Aglow Basic Bible Study Ser.). 64p. 1984. pap. 2.95 (ISBN 0-930756-83-5, 521017). Aglow Pubns.
--How to Be Alive in the Spirit. (Aglow Cornerstone Ser.). 38p. 1982. pap. 2.50 (ISBN 0-930756-69-X). Aglow Pubns.
--How to Know the Fullness of the Spirit. (Cornerstone Ser.). (Illus.). 32p. 1982. pap. 2.00 (ISBN 0-930756-68-1, 533005). Aglow Pubns.
--How to Minister God's Healing Power. (Cornerstone Ser.). 32p. pap. 2.00 (ISBN 0-930756-73-8, 533007). Aglow Pubns.
Rowlands, Henry. Mona Antiqua Restaurata. Feldman, Burton & Richardson, Robert D., eds. LC 78-60894. (Myth & Romanticism Ser.: Vol. 21). 399p. 1979. lib. bdg. 80.00 (ISBN 0-8240-3570-4). Garland Pub.
Rowlett, Martha G. In Spirit & in Truth: A Guide to Praying. LC 82-50944. 112p. 1983. pap. 5.95 (ISBN 0-8358-0448-8). Upper Room.
Rowley, Gwyn, ed. Israel into Palestine. LC 83-22167. 198p. 1983. 31.00x (ISBN 0-7201-1674-0). Mansell.
Rowley, H. H. From Joseph to Joshua: Biblical Traditions in the Light of Archaeology. (Schweich Lectures on Biblical Archaeology). 212p. 1970. Repr. of 1948 ed. 8.25 (ISBN 0-85672-720-2, Pub. by British Acad). Longwood Pub Group.
--Job. rev. ed. (New Century Bible Ser.). 302p. 1976. 9.95 (ISBN 0-551-00596-3). Attic Pr.
--New Century Bible Commentary on Job. rev. ed. Clements, Ronald E., ed. 304p. 1980. pap. 7.95 (ISBN 0-8028-1838-2). Eerdmans.
--Rediscovery of the Old Testament. 224p. 1946. 14.00 (ISBN 0-227-67576-2). Attic Pr.
--The Relevance of Apocalyptic. 3rd, rev. ed. LC 64-12221. 240p. 1980. pap. text ed. 7.95 (ISBN 0-87921-061-3). Attic Pr.
Rowley, H. H., jt. auth. see Black, Matthew.
Rowley, H. H., ed. Student's Bible Atlas. 40p. 1984. pap. 3.95 (ISBN 0-8170-1022-X). Judson.
Rowley, H. H., ed. see Manson, T. W.
Rowley, Harold H. Prophecy & Religion in Ancient China & Israel. LC 56-12074. 1956. 12.00x (ISBN 0-8401-2059-1). A R Allenson.
--Re-Discovery of the Old Testament. facs. ed. LC 75-76912. (Essay Index Reprint Ser). 1946. 19.00 (ISBN 0-8369-1154-7). Ayer Co Pubs.
--The Unity of the Bible. LC 78-2684. 1978. Repr. of 1953 ed. lib. bdg. 22.50x (ISBN 0-313-20346-6, ROUB). Greenwood.
Rowlison, Bruce A. Creative Hospitality As a Means of Evangelism. rev. ed. LC 81-84182. (Illus.). 144p. 1982. pap. 5.95 (ISBN 0-938462-03-2). Green Leaf CA.
Rowlison, Bruce A., jt. auth. see Wiebe, Ronald W.
Rowntree, Arthur. Whittier: Crusader & Prophet. LC 73-13660. 1946. Repr. 15.00 (ISBN 0-8414-7230-0). Folcroft.
Rowse, A. L. Milton the Puritan: Portrait of a Mind. 298p. 1985. pap. text ed. 12.50 (ISBN 0-8191-4778-8). U Pr of Amer.
Rowthorn, Anne. Samuel Seabury: A Bicentennial Biography. 160p. 1983. 14.95 (ISBN 0-8164-0517-4, HarpR). Har-Row.
Rowthorn, Anne W. The Liberation of the Laity. 232p. (Orig.). 1986. pap. 9.95 (ISBN 0-8192-1395-0). Morehouse.
Rowthorn, Jeffrey W. The Wideness of God's Mercy: Litanies to Enlarge Our Prayer, 2 vols. Set. pap. 29.95 (ISBN 0-86683-789-2, HarpR). Har-Row.
Roy, A. K. A History of the Jainas. 1984. 22.50x (ISBN 0-8364-1136-6, Pub. by Gitanjali Prakashan). South Asia Bks.
Roy, Alexander Le see Le Roy, Alexander.
Roy, Anilbaran, ed. see Aurobindo, Sri.
Roy, Anilbaran, ed. see Sri Aurobindo.
Roy, Asim. The Islamic Syncretistic Tradition in Bengal. LC 83-42574. 312p. 1984. 31.50x (ISBN 0-691-05387-1). Princeton U Pr.
Roy, Buddhaved. Marriage Rituals & Songs of Bengal. 1985. 6.50x (ISBN 0-8364-1290-7, Pub. by Mukhopadhyaya India). South Asia Bks.
Roy, Cristina. Sunshine Country. 160p. (YA) 6.50 (ISBN 0-686-05594-2); pap. 4.35 (ISBN 0-686-05595-0). Rod & Staff.
Roy, Dilip K., jt. auth. see Devi, Indira.
Roy, Dilipkumar. Bhagavad Gita, a Revelation. 190p. 1975. 9.95 (ISBN 0-88253-698-2). Ind-US Inc.
Roy, Elmer L. Work of Holy Spirit. pap. 2.50 (ISBN 0-89315-108-4). Lambert Bk.
Roy, Girish C. Indian Culture. 1977. write for info. (ISBN 0-686-22664-X). Intl Bk Dist.
Roy, Marie L., jt. auth. see Wood, Robert.
Roy, Maurice. The Parish & Democracy in French Canada. LC 52-1123. (University of Toronto, Duncan & John Gray Memorial Lecture Ser.). pap. 20.00 (2026546). Bks Demand UMI.
Roy, Olivier. Islam & Resistance in Afghanistan. (Cambridge Middle East Library). (Illus.). 256p. 1986. 24.95 (ISBN 0-521-32833-0). Cambridge U Pr.
Roy, Paul S. Building Christian Communities for Justice. LC 81-80050. 188p. (Orig.). 1981. pap. 9.95 (ISBN 0-8091-2380-0). Paulist Pr.
Roy, Rustrum. Experimenting with Truth: The Fusion of Religion with Technology Needed for Humanity's Survival. (The Hibbert Lectures: 1979). (Illus.). 228p. 1981. 32.00 (ISBN 0-08-025820-4); pap. 10.00 (ISBN 0-08-025819-0). Pergamon.
Roy, Shibani. The Dawoodi Bohras: An Anthropological Perspective. (Illus.). xv, 191p. 1984. text ed. 27.50x (ISBN 0-86590-324-7, Pub. by B R Publishing Corp). Apt Bks.
Roy, W., tr. see Erasmus, Desiderius.
Roy, William. Rede Me & Be Nott Wrothe for I Say No Thynge but Trothe. LC 76-38221. (English Experience Ser.: No. 485). 144p. 1972. Repr. of 1528 ed. 13.00 (ISBN 90-221-0485-0). Walter J Johnson.
Royal Institute of International Affairs & Piscatori, James P. Islam in a World of Nation-States. LC 86-8275. 1986. 34.50 (ISBN 0-521-32985-X); pap. 12.95 (ISBN 0-521-33867-0). Cambridge U Pr.
Royce, Josiah. Conception of Immortality. 1968. Repr. of 1900 ed. lib. bdg. 22.50x (ISBN 0-8371-0207-3, ROCI). Greenwood.
--Problem of Christianity. LC 68-16716. 1968. 25.00x (ISBN 0-226-73058-1). U of Chicago Pr.
--The Religious Philosophy of Josiah Royce. Brown, Stuart G., ed. LC 76-4496. 239p. 1976. Repr. of 1952 ed. lib. bdg. 22.50x (ISBN 0-8371-8810-5, RORP). Greenwood.
--Sources of Religious Insight. LC 76-56454. 1977. Repr. lib. bdg. 20.00x (ISBN 0-374-96989-2, Octagon). Hippocrene Bks.
Roy-Chaudhury, P. C. Gandhi & His Contemporaries. 336p. 1972. 25.00x (ISBN 0-89684-394-7). Orient Bk Dist.
Royer, Fanchon. The Life of St. Anthony Mary Claret. LC 85-52248. 302p. (Orig.). 1985. pap. 8.00 (ISBN 0-89555-288-4). Tan Bks Pubs.
Royer, Katherine. Happy Times with Nursery Children at Home & Church. 192p. (Orig.). 1971. pap. 7.95x (ISBN 0-8361-1275-X). Herald Pr.

--Nursery Stories of Jesus. (Illus.). 48p. 1957. pap. 2.95 (ISBN 0-8361-1276-8). Herald Pr.

Royer, Katherine, ed. Nursery Songbook. (Illus.). 48p. 1957. pap. 2.95x (ISBN 0-8361-1278-4). Herald Pr.

Roys, Ralph L., ed. Book of Chilam Balam of Chumayel. (Civilization of the American Indian Ser.: No. 87). (Illus.). 1973. pap. 19.95x (ISBN 0-8061-0735-9). U of Okla Pr.

Rozanow, Gora Z. Cultural Heritage of Jasna Gora. (Illus.). 1977. 14.00 (ISBN 0-912728-44-2). Newbury Bks.

Rozenblit, Marsha L. The Jews of Vienna, 1867-1914: Assimilation & Identity. (Modern Jewish History Ser.). 368p. 1984. 44.50 (ISBN 0-87395-844-6); pap. 16.95 (ISBN 0-87395-845-4). State U NY Pr.

Rozentals, Janis. Promise of Eternal Life: Biblical Witness to Christian Hope. LC 86-26456. 112p. (Orig.). 1987. pap. 6.50 (ISBN 0-8066-2254-7, 10-5257). Augsburg.

Roziner, Felix. Shcharansky: The Man. 1986. 16.95 (ISBN 0-318-21401-6); pap. 10.95. Shapolsky Pubs.

Roziner, Felix, ed. The Shcharansky Chronicles: A Complete Documentary. 1986. 18.95 (ISBN 0-318-21399-0); pap. 11.95. Shapolsky Pubs.

Rozman, Deborah, ed. see Hills, Christopher.

Rozman, Deborah A. Meditating with Children: New Age Meditations for Children. LC 76-10480. (Illus.). 160p. (Orig.). 1975. pap. 7.95 (ISBN 0-916438-23-6). Univ of Trees.

Ruark, J., ed. see Criswell, W. A.

Ruark, J., ed. see Howard, J. Grant.

Ruark, James, ed. see Snyder, Howard A. & Runyon, Daniel V.

Ruark, Jim, ed. see Bisagno, John.

Rubadeau, Joan. The Little Book of Good: Spiritual Values for Parents & Children. 58p. 1986. pap. 7.00 (ISBN 0-913105-19-8). PAGL Pr.

Rubadeau, Joan, jt. auth. see Linthorst, Jan.

Rubel, Paula G. & Rosman, Abraham. Your Own Pigs You May Not Eat. LC 78-7544. (Illus.). 1978. lib. bdg. 30.00x (ISBN 0-226-73082-4). U of Chicago Pr.

Rubenstein, Hymie. It's Getting Gooder & Gooder. (Orig.). 1976. pap. 4.95 (ISBN 0-89350-006-2). Fountain Pr.

Rubenstein, Richard. The Cunning of History: The Holocaust & the American Future. price not set (ISBN 0-8446-5860-X). Peter Smith.

--Reflections on Religion & Public Policy. (Monographs). 1984. 1.95 (ISBN 0-88702-002-X, Pub. by Wash Inst DC). Paragon Hse.

Rubenstein, Richard J. After Auschwitz: Essays in Contemporary Judaism. (Orig.). 1966. pap. 10.28 scp (ISBN 0-672-61150-3). Bobbs.

Rubenstein, Richard L. After Auschwitz: Radical Theology & Contemporary Judism. 1966. pap. text ed. write for info. (ISBN 0-02-404210-2). Macmillan.

--Power Struggle. LC 86-16000. 214p. 1986. pap. text ed. 12.75 (ISBN 0-8191-5428-8). U Pr of Amer.

--The Religious Imagination: A Study in Psychoanalysis & Jewish Theology. LC 85-15825. (Brown Classics in Judaica Ser.). 276p. 1985. pap. text ed. 12.50 (ISBN 0-8191-4539-4). U Pr of Amer.

Rubenstein, Richard L., ed. The Worldwide Impact of Religion on Comtemporary Politics. 224p. 1987. 21.95 (ISBN 0-88702-203-0, Pub. by Wash Inst DC); pap. 12.95 (ISBN 0-88702-211-1, Pub.by Wash Inst DC). Paragon Hse.

Rubin, Abba. Images in Transition: The English Jew in English Literature, 1660-1830. LC 83-22730. (Contributions of the Study of World Literature Ser.: No. 4). iv, 157p. 1984. lib. bdg. 29.95 (ISBN 0-313-23779-4, RUJ/). Greenwood.

Rubin, Alvan D., jt. auth. see Efron, Benjamin.

Rubin, Barry, jt. ed. see Laqueur, Walter.

Rubin, Gail. Psalmist with a Camera. LC 79-5086. (Illus.). 116p. 1979. 19.95 (ISBN 0-89659-076-3); pap. 14.95 (ISBN 0-89659-071-2). Abbeville Pr.

Rubin, Gershon. The Hebrew Saga. LC 84-1745. 204p. 1984. 15.00 (ISBN 0-8022-2451-2). Philos Lib.

Rubin, Ruth. Voices of a People: The Story of Yiddish Folksong. LC 79-84679. 558p. 1979. pap. 8.95 (ISBN 0-8276-0121-2, 445). Jewish Pubns.

Rubin, Theodore I. Reconciliations: Inner Peace in an Age of Anxiety. 1983. pap. 3.50 (ISBN 0-425-06312-7). Berkley Pub.

Rubin, William S. Modern Sacred Art & the Church of Assy. LC 61-15469. (Illus.). pap. 61.30 (ISBN 0-317-10614-7, 2051858). Bks Demand UMI.

Rubinow, Isaac M. Economic Conditions of the Jews in Russia. facsimile ed. LC 74-29519. (Modern Jewish Experience Ser.). 1975. Repr. of 1907 ed. 15.00x (ISBN 0-405-06744-5). Ayer Co Pubs.

Rubinstein, Amnon. The Zionist Dream Revisited: From Herzl to Gush Emunim & Back. LC 83-40471. 224p. 1984. 14.95 (ISBN 0-8052-3886-7). Schocken.

--The Zionist Dream Revisited: From Herzl to Gush Emunim & Back. LC 83-40470. 224p. 1987. pap. 8.95 (ISBN 0-8052-0835-6). Schocken.

Rubinstein, Aryeh, ed. Hasidism. 128p. pap. 4.50 (ISBN 0-686-95129-8). ADL.

Rubinstein, Erna F. The Survivor in Us All: Four Young Sisters in the Holocaust. 185p. 1986. 19.50 (ISBN 0-208-02025-X, Archon); pap. 12.50x (ISBN 0-208-02128-0). Shoe String.

Rubinstein, Leon. The First Swallows. LC 83-45138. (Illus.). 216p. 1986. 14.50 (ISBN 0-8453-4758-6, Cornwall Bks). Assoc Univ Prs.

Ruble, Richard, ed. Christian Perspectives on Psychology. LC 75-15956. 147p. 1975. pap. text ed. 14.95x (ISBN 0-8422-0456-3). Irvington.

Ruch, Dr. Velma. The Signature of God. 1986. pap. 25.00 (ISBN 0-8309-0428-X). Herald Hse.

Rucker, Gilbert W. The Mystery of... America's Future... Destruction... Revealed! 1985. 6.95 (ISBN 0-8062-2440-1). Carlton.

Rucker, Ruby, et al. The Fourth Dimension: A Guided Tour of Higher Universes. (Illus.). 228p. 1985. pap. 8.95 (ISBN 0-395-39388-4). HM.

Rudavsky, David. Modern Jewish Religious Movements. 3rd rev. ed. LC 79-11266. 1979. pap. text ed. 9.95x (ISBN 0-87441-286-2). Behrman.

Rudavsky, Tamar, ed. Divine Omniscience & Omnipotence in Medieval Philosophy. 1984. lib. bdg. 54.00 (ISBN 90-277-1750-8, Pub. by Reidel Holland). Kluwer Academic.

Rudder, Lena E. White Roots & the Mysteries of God: About the Dead Sea Scrolls. (Illus.). 144p. (Orig.). 1986. pap. write for info. (ISBN 0-937581-00-3). Zarathustrotemo Pr.

--White Roots & the Mysteries of God: And the Dead Sea Scrolls. rev. ed. (Illus.). 144p. (Orig.). 1986. write for info. (ISBN 0-937581-01-1). Zarathustrotemo Pr.

Rudel, Joan, tr. see Steiner, Rudolf.

Ruderman, David, jt. auth. see Hallo, William.

Ruderman, David, jt. ed. see Hallo, William.

Rudhyar, Dane. Culture, Crisis & Creativity. LC 76-43008. (Orig.). 1977. pap. 4.25 (ISBN 0-8356-0487-X, Quest). Theos Pub Hse.

--The Fullness of Human Experience. LC 85-40771. 272p. (Orig.). 1986. pap. 7.75 (ISBN 0-8356-0606-6, Quest). Theos Pub Hse.

--The Rebirth of Hindu Music. 112p. 1980. pap. 4.95 (ISBN 0-87728-448-2). Weiser.

--White Thunder. 1976. pap. 3.50 (ISBN 0-916108-07-4). Seed Center.

Rudhyar, Leyla Rael. The Lunation Process. pap. 3.95 (ISBN 0-943358-15-9). Aurora Press.

Rudick, Michael, jt. ed. see Battin, Margaret.

Rudin, A. James. Israel for Christians. LC 82-7241. 160p. (Orig.). 1983. pap. 8.95 (ISBN 0-8006-1643-X, 1-1643). Fortress.

Rudin, A. James & Rudin, Marcia R. Prison or Paradise? The New Religious Cults? LC 80-10210. 168p. 1980. 4.95 (ISBN 0-8006-1937-4, 1-1937). Fortress.

Rudin, A. James & Gillen, Ann, eds. The Struggle for Religious Survival in the Soviet Union. LC 86-72630. 76p. 1986. pap. 5.00 (ISBN 0-87495-085-6). Am Jewish Comm.

Rudin, Jacob. Haggadah for Children. 1973. 2.25x (ISBN 0-8197-0032-0). Bloch.

Rudin, Jacob P. Very Truly Yours. 1971. 6.50x (ISBN 0-8197-0279-X). Bloch.

Rudin, James, et al. Twenty Years of Jewish-Catholic Relations. 336p. (Orig.). 1986. pap. 11.95 (ISBN 0-8091-2762-8). Paulist Pr.

Rudin, Josef. Fanaticism. LC 69-14813. (Ger). 1969. Repr. of 1965 ed. 17.95 (ISBN 0-268-00318-1). U of Notre Dame Pr.

--Psychotherapy & Religion. Bailey, Paul C. & Reinecke, Elisabeth, trs. LC 68-12291. 1968. pap. 7.95x (ISBN 0-268-00226-6). U of Notre Dame Pr.

Rudin, Marcia R., jt. auth. see Rudin, A. James.

Rudman, Jack. Senior Field Representative (Human Rights) (Career Examination Ser.: C-2563). (Cloth bdg. avail. on request). pap. 14.00 (ISBN 0-8373-2563-3). Natl Learning.

Rudnick, Milton L. Christian Ethics for Today: An Evangelical Approach. LC 79-53924. 1979. pap. 8.95 (ISBN 0-8010-7738-9). Baker Bk.

--Christianity Is for You. 1961. pap. 3.25 (ISBN 0-570-03503-1, 14-1271). Concordia.

--Speaking the Gospel Through the Ages: A History of Evangelism. 1984. 24.95 (ISBN 0-570-04204-6, 15-2172). Concordia.

Rudnytzky, Leonid, jt. ed. see Labunka, Miroslav.

Rudolf, Anthony, jt. ed. see Schwartz, Howard.

Rudolph, Albert see Rudrananda, Swami, pseud.

Rudolph, Erwin, ed. William Law on Christian Perfection. 146p. 1981. pap. 3.95 (ISBN 0-87123-117-4, 210117). Bethany Hse.

Rudolph, Kurt. Gnosis: The Nature & History of Gnosticism. LC 81-47437. 411p. 1982. 28.45 (ISBN 0-06-067017-7, HarpR); pap. 14.95 (ISBN 0-06-067018-5, PL 4122). Har-Row.

Rudolph, L. C. Francis Asbury. 240p. (Orig.). 1983. pap. 8.95 (ISBN 0-687-13461-7). Abingdon.

--Hoosier Zion: The Presbyterians in Early Indiana. LC 62-8261. (Yale Publications in Religion Ser.: No. 5). (Illus.). pap. 49.00 (ISBN 0-317-09434-3, 2009008). Bks Demand UMI.

Rudolph, L. C. & Endelman, Judith E. Religion in Indiana: A Guide to Historical Resources. LC 84-43186. 224p. 1986. 22.50x (ISBN 0-253-34960-5). Ind U Pr.

Rudowski, Peter. The Gospel in Madison Avenue. 1983. 3.85 (ISBN 0-89536-644-4, 0741). CSS of Ohio.

Rudrananda, Swami, pseud. Behind the Cosmic Curtain: The Further Writings of Swami Rudrananda. Mann, John, ed. (Illus.). 176p. (Orig.). pap. 9.95x (ISBN 0-9613477-0-8). Neolog.

Rudrum, Alan, ed. John Milton. LC 71-127553. (Modern Judgement Ser). 1978. pap. text ed. 2.50 (ISBN 0-87695-100-0). Aurora Pubs.

Rudwick, Elliot. Race Riot at East St. Louis, July 2, 1917. LC 64-13634. (Studies in American Negro Life). 1972. pap. text ed. 3.95x (ISBN 0-689-70336-8, NL31). Atheneum.

Rudwin, Maximilian. The Devil in Legend & Literature. LC 73-85284. (Illus.). 365p. 1973. 22.95 (ISBN 0-87548-247-3); pap. 9.95 (ISBN 0-87548-248-1). Open Court.

Rudwin, Maximilian J. Devil in Legend & Literature. LC 71-111780. (Illus.). Repr. of 1931 ed. 14.50 (ISBN 0-404-05451-X). AMS Pr.

Rue, Pierre De La see De La Rue, Pierre.

Rueckert, Hanns see Luther, Martin.

Ruef, John. Paul's First Letter to Corinth. LC 77-24086. (Westminster Pelican Commentaries). 224p. 1978. 10.00 (ISBN 0-664-21348-0); softcover 5.45 (ISBN 0-664-24183-2). Westminster.

Ruegg, Lawrence. When Someone You Love Dies. 1984. 0.95 (ISBN 0-89536-659-2, 2355). CSS of Ohio.

Ruegsegger, Ronald W., ed. Reflections on Francis Schaeffer. 336p. 1986. pap. 12.95 (ISBN 0-310-37091-4, 12355P). Zondervan.

Rueter, Alvin. The Freedom to Be Wrong. 1985. 6.25 (ISBN 0-89536-749-1, 5855). CSS of Ohio.

--Personnel Management in the Church: Developing Personnel Policies & Practices. (Church Administration Ser.). 56p. (Orig.). 1984. pap. 3.95 (ISBN 0-8066-2072-2, 10-4920). Augsburg.

Ruether, Rosemary. Faith & Fratricide: The Theological Roots of Anti-Semitism. 1974. pap. 8.95 (ISBN 0-8164-2263-X, HarpR). Har-Row.

--Liberation Theology: Human Hope Confronts Christian History & American Power. LC 72-92263. Repr. of 1972 ed. 50.50 (ISBN 0-8357-9487-3, 2015212). Bks Demand UMI.

Ruether, Rosemary & McLaughlin, Eleanor. Women of Spirit. 1979. pap. 10.95 (ISBN 0-671-24805-7, Touchstone Bks). S&S.

Ruether, Rosemary R. Disputed Questions: On Being a Christian. LC 81-12718. (Journeys in Faith Ser.). 144p. 1982. 9.95 (ISBN 0-687-10950-7). Abingdon.

--Mary-the Feminine Face of the Church. LC 77-7652. 106p. 1977. pap. 6.95 (ISBN 0-664-24759-8). Westminster.

--New Woman-New Earth: Sexist Ideologies & Human Liberation. 255p. 1978. pap. 9.95 (ISBN 0-8164-2185-4, HarpR). Har-Row.

--The Radical Kingdom: The Western Experience of Messianic Hope. LC 70-109080. 324p. 1975. pap. 5.95 (ISBN 0-8091-1860-2). Paulist Pr.

--Religion & Sexism. 1974. pap. 10.95 (ISBN 0-671-21693-7, Touchstone Bks). S&S.

--Sexism & God-Talk: Toward a Feminist Theology. LC 82-72502. 300p. (Orig.). 1984. pap. 9.95 (ISBN 0-8070-1105-3, BP680); 18.95x (ISBN 0-8070-1104-5). Beacon Pr.

--To Change the World: Christology & Cultural Criticism. LC 81-9703. 96p. 1983. pap. 5.95 (ISBN 0-8245-0573-5). Crossroad NY.

--Womanguides: Readings Toward a Feminist Theology. LC 84-14508. 286p. 1986. 21.95 (ISBN 0-8070-1202-5); pap. 10.95 (ISBN 0-8070-1203-3, BP 726). Beacon Pr.

--Women-Church. 1986. 16.45 (ISBN 0-06-066834-2). Har-Row.

Ruether, Rosemary R., jt. auth. see Roth, Wolfgang.

Ruether, Rosemary R. & Keller, Rosemary S., eds. Women & Religion in America: Nineteen Hundred to Nineteen Sixty-Eight, Vol. 3. (Illus.). 452p. 1986. 26.45 (ISBN 0-06-066833-4, HarpT). Har-Row.

--Women & Religion in America: The Colonial & Revolutionary Period, Vol. II. LC 80-8346. (Illus.). 448p. 1983. 24.45 (ISBN 0-06-066832-6, HarpR). Har-Row.

Ruffcorn, Kevin E. Bible Readings for Growing Christians. LC 84-18424. 112p. (Orig.). 1984. pap. 3.95 (ISBN 0-8066-2131-1, 10-0685). Augsburg.

Ruffin, Bernard. Fanny Crosby. (Heroes of the Faith Ser.). 1985. Repr. of 1976 ed. 6.95 (ISBN 0-916441-16-4). Barbour & Co.

Ruffin, C. Bernard. The Days of the Martyrs. LC 85-60517. 200p. (Orig.). 1985. pap. 7.95 (ISBN 0-87973-595-3, 595). Our Sunday Visitor.

--Padre Pio: The True Story. LC 81-81525. (Illus.). 348p. (Orig.). 1982. pap. 8.95 (ISBN 0-87973-673-9, 673). Our Sunday Visitor.

--The Twelve: The Lives of the Apostles After Calvary. LC 83-63168. 194p. (Orig.). 1984. pap. 7.95 (ISBN 0-87973-609-7, 609). Our Sunday Visitor.

Ruffo-Fiore, Silvia. Niccolo Machiavelli. (World Authors Ser.). 1982. lib. bdg. 15.95 (ISBN 0-8057-6499-2, Twayne). G K Hall.

Ruffolo, Marina E., ed. The Dynamic Voice of Vatican II. 1977. 4.50 (ISBN 0-8198-0405-3); pap. 2.95 (ISBN 0-8198-0406-1). Dghtrs St Paul.

Rufinius, Tyrannius. Opera Pars 1. Orationum Gregorii Nazianzeni Novem Interpretation. Engelbrecht, A., ed. Repr. of 1910 ed. 40.00 (ISBN 0-384-52540-7). Johnson Repr.

Rufus, Jones M. Studies in Mystical Religion. 1978. Repr. of 1919 ed. lib. bdg. 45.00 (ISBN 0-8492-1257-X). R West.

Rugh, Charles E. Moral Training in the Public Schools. 203p. 1980. Repr. lib. bdg. 25.00 (ISBN 0-8492-7749-3). R West.

Ruhe, David S. Door of Hope: A Century of the Baha'i Faith in the Holy Land. 254p. 19.95 (ISBN 0-85398-149-3); pap. 13.50 (ISBN 0-85398-150-7). G Ronald Pub.

Ruhe, Margaret. Some Thoughts on Marriage. 36p. 1982. pap. 1.95 (ISBN 0-933770-23-5). Kalimat.

Ruhnau, Helena E. Journeys into the Fifth Dimension. LC 75-149286. (Illus.). 1975. 12.95 (ISBN 0-941036-02-2). Colleasius Pr.

--Let There Be Light - Words of the Christ. (Illus.). 220p. (Orig.). 1987. pap. text ed. 9.95 (ISBN 0-941036-60-X). Colleasius Pr.

--Light on a Mountain. (Illus.). 1976. 12.95 (ISBN 0-941036-00-6); pap. 6.50 (ISBN 0-941036-01-4). Colleasius Pr.

--Reappearance of the Dove. LC 75-27625. (Illus.). 1978. 12.95 (ISBN 0-941036-03-0). Colleasius Pr.

Ruhnke, Robert. For Better & for Ever: Sponsor Couple Program for Christian Marriage Preparation. 1981. pap. 3.95 (ISBN 0-89243-143-1); dialogue packet wkbk. 3.75 (ISBN 0-89243-144-X). Liguori Pubns.

--Nos Amaremos Toda la Vida: Paquete de Hojas para el Dialogo. Diaz, Olimpia, tr. (Span.). 96p. 1983. 3.75 (ISBN 0-89243-185-7). Liguori Pubns.

Ruiz, Hugo. Hermanos, Ahora Cartas del Diablo. 64p. 1986. pap. 1.40 (ISBN 0-311-46045-3). Casa Bautista.

Ruiz, Mario, ed. Manual de Ceremonias Matrimoniales. (Span.). 184p. 1982. 6.95 (ISBN 0-87148-581-8). Pathway Pr.

Ruiz de Alarcon, Hernando. Treatise on the Heathen Superstitions that Today Live among the Indians Native to this New Spain, 1629. Andrews, J. Richard & Hassig, Ross, eds. LC 83-47842. (The Civilization of the American Indian Ser.: Vol. 164). (Illus.). 540p. 1984. text ed. 48.50x (ISBN 0-8061-1832-6). U of Okla Pr.

Rukhadze, Avtandil. Jews in the U. S. S. R. Figures, Facts, Comment. 112p. 1984. pap. 5.00x (ISBN 0-317-53875-6, Pub. by Collets (UK)). State Mutual Bk.

Ruland, Vernon. Eight Sacred Horizons: The Religious Imagination East & West. 240p. 1985. 19.95x (ISBN 0-317-18117-3). MacMillan.

--Horizons of Criticism: An Assessment of Religious-Literary Options. LC 75-20162. pap. 68.80 (ISBN 0-317-29363-X, 2024203). Bks Demand UMI.

Rule, Paul A. K'ung-Tzu or Confuscius? The Jesuit Interpretation of Confucianism. 292p. (Orig.). 1987. pap. text ed. 18.95x (ISBN 0-86861-913-2). Allen Unwin.

Rulla, Luigi M. Depth Psychology & Vocation: A Psycho-Social Perspective. LC 70-146938. 1971. 28.00 (ISBN 88-7652-374-X). Loyola.

--Entering & Leaving Vocation: Intrapsychic Dynamics. 1976. 20.00 (ISBN 88-7652-407-X). Loyola.

Rumbaut, Ruben D. John of God: His Place in the History of Psychiatry & Medicine. LC 77-91668. 1978. pap. 8.00 (ISBN 0-89729-198-0). Ediciones.

Rumble, Dale. Windows of the Soul. (Orig.). 1977. pap. 3.50 (ISBN 0-89350-017-8). Fountain Pr.

Rumble, L. A Brief Life of Christ. 54p. 1974. pap. 1.50 (ISBN 0-89555-096-2). TAN Bks Pubs.

Rumble, Leslie. The Incredible Creed of the Jehovah Witnesses. 1977. pap. 0.60 (ISBN 0-89555-025-3). TAN Bks Pubs.

Rumble, Leslie & Carty, Charles M. Radio Replies, 3 vols. LC 79-51938. 1979. Set. pap. 27.00 (ISBN 0-89555-159-4). Vol. 1 (ISBN 0-89555-089-X). Vol. 2 (ISBN 0-89555-090-3). Vol. 3 (ISBN 0-89555-091-1). TAN Bks Pubs.

Rumi, Jalalu'ddin. The Mathnawi of Jalalu'ddin Rumi, 3 vols. Nicholson, R. A., tr. from Persian. 1444p. 1985. 175.00x (ISBN 0-317-39128-3, Pub. by Luzac & Co Ltd). State Mutual Bk.

Rump, Ariane & Chan, Wing-Tsit, trs. Commentary on the Lao Tzu by Wang Pi. LC 79-11212. (Society for Asian & Comparative Philosophy Monograph: No. 6). 266p. 1979. pap. text ed. 8.00x (ISBN 0-8248-0677-8). UH Pr.

Rumpf, David A., jt. auth. see Rumpf, Oscar J.

Rumpf, Oscar J. & Rumpf, David A. Fourteen Witnesses. 1985. 5.95 (ISBN 0-89536-722-X, 5805). CSS of Ohio.

Rumscheidt, H. Martin. Karl Barth in Review: Posthumous Works Introduced & Assessed. (Pittsburgh Theological Monograph: No. 30). xxviii, 118p. (Orig.). 1981. pap. 11.75 (ISBN 0-915138-33-6). Pickwick.

Rumscheidt, H. Martin, ed. The Way of Theology in Karl Barth: Essays & Comments. (Princeton Theological Monograph Ser.: No. 8). 1986. pap. 9.90 (ISBN 0-915138-61-1). Pickwick.

Rumscheidt, H. Martin, tr. see Feil, Ernst.

Rumscheidt, Martin, tr. see Zellweger-Barth, Max.

Rumsey, Peter L. Acts of God & the People, 1620-1730. Miles, Margaret R., ed. LC 86-19292. (Studies in Religion: No. 2). 182p. 1986. 39.95 (ISBN 0-8357-1761-5). UMI Res Pr.

Rumsey, Thomas R. Men & Women of the Renaissance & Reformation 1300-1600. 487p. (Orig.). 1981. pap. text ed. 10.95 (ISBN 0-686-81286-7). Ind Sch Pr.

Runcie, Robert A. Seasons of the Spirit: The Archbishop of Canterbury at Home & Abroad. LC 83-1734. pap. 68.00 (ISBN 0-317-30160-8, 2025342). Bks Demand UMI.

Runciman, Steven. The Byzantine Theocracy. LC 76-47405. (Weil Lectures Ser.). 1977. 32.50 (ISBN 0-521-21401-7). Cambridge U Pr.

--The Eastern Schism. LC 78-63367. (The Crusades & Military Orders: Second Ser.). 200p. Repr. of 1956 ed. 24.50 (ISBN 0-404-16247-9). AMS Pr.

--The Great Church in Captivity: A Study of the Patriarchate of Constantinople from the Eve of the Turkish Conquest to the Greek War of Independence. 465p. Date not set. pap. price not set. Cambridge U Pr.

--The Great Church in Captivity: A Study of the Patriarchate of Constantinople from the Eve of the Turkish Conquest to the Greek War of Independence. LC 68-29330. pap. 116.30 (ISBN 0-317-26393-5, 2024531). Bks Demand UMI.

--The Medieval Manichee: A Study of the Christian Dualist Heresy. LC 82-4123. 224p. 1982. 39.50 (ISBN 0-521-06166-0); pap. 13.95 (ISBN 0-521-28926-2). Cambridge U Pr.

Runeberg, Anne. Witches, Demons & Fertility Magic. 273p. 1980. Repr. of 1947 ed. lib. bdg. 30.00 (ISBN 0-8414-7399-4). Folcroft.

Runeberg, Arne. Witches, Demons & Fertility Magic. LC 74-3091. (Folklore Ser). 39.50 (ISBN 0-88305-560-0). Norwood Edns.

Runes, Dagobert D. Dictionary of Judaism. 236p. 1981. 5.95 (ISBN 0-8065-0787-X). Citadel Pr.

--Jew & the Cross. 1966. pap. 0.95 (ISBN 0-8065-0111-1, 216). Citadel Pr.

--Let My People Live. LC 74-75083. 84p. 1975. 6.00 (ISBN 0-8022-2141-6). Philos Lib.

--Of God, the Devil & the Jews. 1952. 5.00 (ISBN 0-8022-1444-4). Philos Lib.

Runia, Klaus. The Present-Day Christological Debate. Marshall, I. Howard, ed. LC 84-6554. (Issues in Contemporary Theology Ser.). 120p. 1984. pap. 7.95 (ISBN 0-87784-937-4). Inter-Varsity.

Runk, Wesley. What Color Is Your Balloon? (Orig.). 1987. pap. price not set (ISBN 0-89536-883-8, 7869). CSS of Ohio.

--You're God's Masterpiece. 1985. 4.50 (ISBN 0-89536-757-2, 5863). CSS of Ohio.

Runk, Wesley T. Captivating Object Lessons. (Object Lesson Ser). 1979. pap. 3.95 (ISBN 0-8010-7671-4). Baker Bk.

--Let's Share Jesus-Together. 1982. 4.50 (ISBN 0-89536-554-5, 1243). CSS of Ohio.

--Object Lessons from the Bible. (Object Lessons Ser.). 96p. 1980. pap. 3.95 (ISBN 0-8010-7698-6). Baker Bk.

--On Jesus' Team. Sherer, Michael L., ed. (Orig.). 1986. pap. 5.25 (ISBN 0-89536-809-9, 6838). CSS of Ohio.

--On the Move with Jesus. 1984. 4.50 (ISBN 0-89536-670-3, 1511). CSS of Ohio.

--People Who Knew Paul. 1985. 2.00 (ISBN 0-89536-185-X, 1610). CSS of Ohio.

--Shiny New Lives. 108p. (Orig.). 1975. pap. 4.50 (ISBN 0-89536-224-4, 1938). CSS of Ohio.

--Speaking with Signs. 1975. 2.50 (ISBN 0-89536-216-3, 1920). CSS of Ohio.

--Standing Up for Jesus. 1985. 4.50 (ISBN 0-89536-725-4, 5809). CSS of Ohio.

Runnalls, Graham A., jt. ed. see Elliott, John R., Jr.

Runner, E. H. The Relation of the Bible to Learning. 1974. pap. 4.95 (ISBN 0-686-11988-6). Wedge Pub.

--Scriptural Religion & Political Task. 1974. pap. 2.95 (ISBN 0-686-11989-4). Wedge Pub.

Runyon, Daniel V., jt. auth. see Snyder, Howard A.

Runyon, Randolph. Fowles, Irving, Barthes: Canonical Variations on an Apocryphal Theme. LC 81-11125. (Illus.). 134p. 1982. 17.50x (ISBN 0-8142-0335-3). Ohio St U Pr.

Runyon, Theodore H., ed. Sanctification & Liberation: Liberation Theologies in Light of the Wesleyan Tradition. LC 80-20287. 1981. pap. 6.95 (ISBN 0-687-36810-3). Abingdon.

Runzo, Joseph. Reason, Relativism & God. LC 85-27893. 308p. 1986. 29.95x (ISBN 0-312-66538-5). St Martin.

Runzo, Joseph & Ihara, Graig K., eds. Religious Experience & Religious Belief: Essays in the Epistemology of Religion. LC 86-1614. 160p. 1986. lib. bdg. 23.50 (ISBN 0-8191-5292-7); pap. text ed. 10.75 (ISBN 0-8191-5293-5). U Pr of Amer.

Ruoff, Norman D., ed. Writings of President Frederick M. Smith, Vol. 1. LC 78-6428. 1978. pap. 10.00 (ISBN 0-8309-0215-5). Herald Hse.

--The Writings of President Frederick M. Smith, Vol. 2. LC 78-6428. 1979. pap. 10.00 (ISBN 0-8309-0239-2). Herald Hse.

--The Writings of President Frederick M. Smith, Vol. III: The Zionic Enterprise. 1981. pap. 10.00 (ISBN 0-8309-0300-3). Herald Hse.

Ruopp, Phillips. Private Testimony & Public Policy. 1983. pap. 2.50x (ISBN 0-87574-105-3, 105). Pendle Hill.

Ruotolo, Lucio P. Six Existential Heroes: The Politics of Faith. LC 72-86386. 192p. 1973. 12.50x (ISBN 0-674-81025-2). Harvard U Pr.

Rupcic, Ljudevit, jt. auth. see Laurentin, Rene.

Rupp, E. G. & Drewery, Benjamin, eds. Martin Luther. (Documents of Modern History Ser.). 1970. pap. text ed. 11.95 (ISBN 0-312-51660-6). St Martin.

Rupp, E. Gordon & Watson, Philip S., eds. Luther & Erasmus: Free Will & Salvation. LC 76-79870. (Library of Christian Classics). 356p. 1978. softcover 10.95 (ISBN 0-664-24158-1). Westminster.

Rupp, Ernest G. Six Makers of English Religion, Fifteen Hundred to Seventeen Hundred. (Essay Index Reprint Ser.). Repr. of 1957 ed. 16.75 (ISBN 0-518-10159-2). Ayer Co Pubs.

Rupp, George. Beyond Existentialism & Zen: Religion in a Pluralistic World. 1979. 14.95x (ISBN 0-19-502462-1). Oxford U Pr.

--Christologies & Cultures: Toward a Typology of Religious Worldviews. (Religion & Reason Ser: No. 10). 269p. 1974. text ed. 23.75x (ISBN 90-2797-641-4). Mouton.

--Culture-Protestantism: German Liberal Theology at the Turn of the Twentieth Century. LC 77-13763. (American Academy of Religion. Studies in Religion: No. 15). 1977. pap. 8.95 (ISBN 0-89130-197-6, 010015). Scholars Pr GA.

Rupp, Gordon. Religion in England: 1688-1781. (History of the Christian Church Ser.). 520p. 1987. 79.00x (ISBN 0-19-826918-8). Oxford U Pr.

Rupp, Gordon, et al. The People Called Methodist. LC 84-72360. (Pan-Methodist Lectures). 96p. (Orig.). 1985. DR016B. pap. 3.95 (ISBN 0-88177-016-7). Discipleship Res.

Rupp, Israel D. He Pasa Ekklesia: An Original History of the Religious Denominations at Present Existing in the United States Containing Authentic Accounts of Their Rise, Progress, Statistics. 30.00 (ISBN 0-8369-7149-3, 7981). Ayer Co Pubs.

--The Religious Denominations in the United States: Their Past History, Present Condition, & Doctrines. LC 72-2943. Repr. of 1861 ed. 67.50 (ISBN 0-404-10709-5). AMS Pr.

Rupp, Joyce. Fresh Bread & Other Gifts of Spiritual Nourishment. LC 85-70020. 160p. (Orig.). 1985. pap. 4.95 (ISBN 0-87793-283-2). Ave Maria.

Rupp, Richard H. Getting Through College. LC 84-60726. 223p. 1984. pap. 9.95 (ISBN 0-8091-2627-3). Paulist Pr.

Ruppert, Hoover. God Will See You Through. 1976. pap. 0.75x (ISBN 0-8358-0351-1). Upper Room.

Ruppin, Arthur. The Agricultural Colonization of the Zionist Organization in Palestine. Feiwel, R. J., tr. from Ger. LC 75-6451. (The Rise of Jewish Nationalism & the Middle East Ser). vii, 209p. 1975. Repr. of 1926 ed. 20.35 (ISBN 0-88355-337-6). Hyperion Conn.

--Three Decades of Palestine: Speeches & Papers on the Upbuilding of the Jewish National Home. LC 70-97301. (Illus.). 342p. 1975. Repr. of 1936 ed. lib. bdg. 22.50x (ISBN 0-8371-2629-0, RUPA). Greenwood.

Rupprecht, David & Rupprecht, Ruth. Radical Hospitality. 110p. 1983. 7.95 (ISBN 0-87552-421-4); pap. 4.95 (ISBN 0-87552-420-6). Presby & Reformed.

Rupprecht, Konrad. Der Tempel Von Jerusalem. (Beihefte 144 Zur Zeitschrift Fuer die Alttestamentliche Wissenschaft). 1976. text ed. 22.80x (ISBN 3-11-006619-X). De Gruyter.

Rupprecht, Ruth, jt. auth. see Rupprecht, David.

Rusbuldt, Richard E. Basic Leader Skills: Handbook for Church Leaders. 64p. 1981. pap. 5.95 (ISBN 0-8170-0920-5). Judson.

--Basic Teacher Skills: Handbook for Church School Teachers. 144p. 1981. pap. 5.95 (ISBN 0-8170-0919-1). Judson.

--Evangelism on Purpose. 48p. 1980. pap. 2.95 (ISBN 0-8170-0894-2). Judson.

--Hello-Is God There? 64p. 1984. pap. 5.95 (ISBN 0-8170-1043-2). Judson.

Rusbuldt, Richard E., jt. auth. see McIntosh, Duncan.

Rusbuldt, Richard E., et al. Local Church Planning Manual. 1977. pap. 14.95 (ISBN 0-8170-0753-9). Judson.

--Medidas Principales en la Planificacion de la Iglesia Local: Key Steps in Local Church Planning. Rodriguez, Oscar E., tr. from Eng. (Span.). 134p. 1981. pap. 5.95 (ISBN 0-8170-0933-7). Judson.

Rusch, William G. Ecumenism: A Movement Toward Church Unity. LC 84-48707. 96p. 1985. pap. 6.95 (ISBN 0-8006-1847-5, 1-1847). Fortress.

--The Later Latin Fathers. (Studies in Theology). 214p. 1977. pap. 13.50 (ISBN 0-7156-1674-9, Pub. by Duckworth London). Longwood Pub Group.

Rusch, William G., ed. The Trinitarian Controversy. LC 79-8889. (Sources of Early Christian Thought Ser.). 192p. 1980. pap. 7.95 (ISBN 0-8006-1410-0, 1-1410). Fortress.

Rusch, William G., jt. ed. see Norris, Richard A., Jr.

Rusche, Franz. Blut, Leben und Seele, Ihr Verhaeltnis Nach Auffassung der Griechischen und Hellenistischen Antike, der Bibel und der Alten Alexandrinischen Theologen. Repr. of 1930 ed. 34.00 (ISBN 0-384-52515-6). Johnson Repr.

Rush, Alfred C. Death & Burial in Christian Antiquity. 59.59 (ISBN 0-8490-0009-2). Gordon Pr.

Rush, Alfred C., ed. Autobiography of St. John Neumann. 1977. 3.50 (ISBN 0-8198-0384-7); pap. 2.50 (ISBN 0-8198-0385-5). Dghtrs St Paul.

Rush, Anne K. Moon, Moon. 1976. pap. 7.95 (ISBN 0-394-73230-8). Random.

Rush, James E. Toward a General Theory of Healing. LC 80-8264. (Illus.). 314p. (Orig.). 1982. lib. bdg. 25.75 (ISBN 0-8191-1880-X); pap. text ed. 13.50 (ISBN 0-8191-1881-8). U Pr of Amer.

Rush, Myron. Burnout. 156p. 1987. pap. 6.95 (ISBN 0-89693-242-7). Victor Bks.

--Lord of the Marketplace. 192p. 1986. pap. 7.95 (ISBN 0-89693-278-8). Victor Bks.

Rush, Myron D. Management: A Biblical Approach. 1983. pap. 7.95 (ISBN 0-88207-607-8). Victor Bks.

Rush, Vincent E. The Responsible Christian: A Guide for Moral Decision Making According to Classical Tradition. 288p. 1984. 9.95 (ISBN 0-8294-0448-1). Loyola.

Rushd, Ibn. Epistle on the Possibility of Conjunction with the Active Intellect. Bland, Kalman P., ed. & tr. (Moreshet Ser: No. 7). 35.00x (ISBN 0-87334-005-1). Ktav.

Rushdoony, Rousas J. The Institutes of Biblical Law. 1973. 24.00 (ISBN 0-87552-410-9). Presby & Reformed.

--Intellectual Schizophrenia. 1961. pap. 5.50 (ISBN 0-87552-411-7). Presby & Reformed.

--Thy Kingdom Come: Studies in Daniel & Revelation. pap. 7.95 (ISBN 0-87552-413-3). Presby & Reformed.

Rushing, Philip. Empty Sleeves. LC 83-11322. 224p. (Orig.). 1984. 9.95 (ISBN 0-310-28820-7, 11322). Zondervan.

Rushmore, Louis. The Cost of Discipleship. 1986. pap. 4.00 (ISBN 0-89137-563-5). Quality Pubns.

Rushton, Peters, jt. auth. see Norton, Daniel S.

Ruskin, Anna Marie, ed. see Roberts, Kenneth J.

Ruskin, John. The Bible References of John Ruskin. LC 77-13181. 1977. Repr. lib. bdg. 30.00 (ISBN 0-8414-4608-3). Folcroft.

--The Queen of the Air: A Study of the Greek Myths of Cloud & Storm. LC 78-58190. 1978. Repr. of 1869 ed. lib. bdg. 25.00 (ISBN 0-89341-322-4). Longwood Pub Group.

Ruskin, John, et al. An Illustrated Architectural History of the Greatest Cathedrals of the World, 2 vols. (Illus.). 311p. 1986. Set. 187.75 (ISBN 0-86650-201-7). Gloucester Art.

Ruskowski, Leo F. French Emigre Priests in the United States (1791-1815) LC 73-3586. (Catholic University of America. Studies in American Church History: No. 32). Repr. of 1940 ed. 21.00 (ISBN 0-404-57782-2). AMS Pr.

Russ, Esther. The Eternal Echo of Easter: A Choral Drama. 1980. 4.50 (ISBN 0-89536-423-9, 0515). CSS of Ohio.

Russel, Jeffrey B. Witchcraft in the Middle Ages. (Illus.). 1976. pap. 5.95 (ISBN 0-8065-0504-4). Citadel Pr.

Russell. My First Bible Wordbook. 1984. 8.95 (ISBN 0-528-82421-X). Macmillan.

Russell, A., ed. see Blake, William.

Russell, A. G., jt. ed. see MacLagan, E. R.

Russell, A. J. God Calling. (Christian Library). 1985. Repr. 6.95 (ISBN 0-916441-22-9). Barbour & Co.

--God Calling. (The Christian Library). 249p. 1986. Repr. leatherette 3.95 (ISBN 0-916441-45-8). Barbour & Co.

--A Treasury of Devotion. 432p. 1986. 16.95 (ISBN 0-396-08885-6). Dodd.

Russell, A. J., ed. God Calling. 192p. 1972. pap. 3.50 (ISBN 0-8007-8096-5, Spire Bks). Revell.

--God Calling. 208p. 1987. pap. 3.50 (ISBN 0-515-09026-3). Jove Pubns.

Russell, Allan M., jt. auth. see Gerhart, Mary.

Russell, Arthur J. Their Religion. facs. ed. LC 78-128308. (Essay Index Reprint Ser). 1935. 20.00 (ISBN 0-8369-2131-3). Ayer Co Pubs.

Russell, Arthur J., ed. God at Eventide. 1950. 9.95 (ISBN 0-396-03183-8). Dodd.

--God at Eventide. 156p. 1974. pap. 2.75 (ISBN 0-8007-8154-6, Spire Bks). Revell.

--God Calling: A Devotional Diary. 10.95 (ISBN 0-396-02621-4). Dodd.

Russell, B., et al. If I Could Preach Just Once. facsimile ed. LC 73-167364. (Essay Index Reprint Ser). Repr. of 1929 ed. 17.00 (ISBN 0-8369-2457-6). Ayer Co Pubs.

Russell, Bert. Hardships & Happy Times. LC 78-75104. (Oral History Ser.: No. 1). 1982. 9.95 (ISBN 0-930344-04-9); pap. 7.95 (ISBN 0-930344-01-4). Lacon Pubs.

Russell, Bertrand. Am I an Atheist or an Agnostic. 32p. pap. cancelled (ISBN 0-911826-96-3). Am Atheist.

--Atheism: Collected Essays, 1943-1949. LC 71-169217. (Atheist Viewpoint Ser). 232p. 1972. Repr. of 1971 ed. 15.00 (ISBN 0-405-03808-9). Ayer Co Pubs.

--Common Sense & Nuclear Warfare. LC 68-54291. Repr. of 1959 ed. 18.00 (ISBN 0-404-05465-X). AMS Pr.

--Human Society in Ethics & Politics. 1954. text ed. 18.50x (ISBN 0-04-172004-0). Allen Unwin.

--Mysticism & Logic & Other Essays. 2nd ed. LC 81-119829. 168p. 1981. pap. 8.95x (ISBN 0-389-20135-9, 06657). B&N Imports.

--Religion & Science. 1961. pap. 8.95 (ISBN 0-19-500228-8). Oxford U Pr.

--Why I Am Not a Christian & Other Essays on Religion & Related Subjects. 1967. pap. 6.95 (ISBN 0-671-20323-1, Touchstone Bks). S&S.

Russell, Colin A. Cross-Currents: Interaction Between Science & Faith. 272p. 1985. pap. 10.95 (ISBN 0-8028-0163-3). Eerdmans.

Russell, D. S. Apocalyptic: Ancient & Modern. LC 78-54561. 96p. 1978. pap. 4.25 (ISBN 0-8006-1342-2, 1-1342). Fortress.

--Between the Testaments. LC 77-74742. 176p. 1960. pap. 5.95 (ISBN 0-8006-1856-4, 1-1856). Fortress.

--Daniel. LC 81-1777. (The Daily Study Bible - Old Testament Ser.). 244p. 1981. 12.95 (ISBN 0-664-21800-8); pap. 6.95 (ISBN 0-664-24567-6). Westminster.

--From Early Judaism to Early Church. LC 85-31776. 1986. pap. 5.95 (ISBN 0-8006-1921-8). Fortress.

--The Jews from Alexander to Herod. 1967. pap. 13.95x (ISBN 0-19-836913-1). Oxford U Pr.

--Method & Message of Jewish Apocalyptic. LC 64-18683. (Old Testament Library). 464p. 1964. 19.95 (ISBN 0-664-20543-7). Westminster.

Russell, Donna V., ed. see Myers, Margaret E.

Russell, Dora. The Religion of the Machine Age. 232p. 1985. 27.95 (ISBN 0-7100-9547-3). Methuen Inc.

Russell, Elbert. History of Quakerism. LC 79-53169. 612p. 1980. pap. 14.95 (ISBN 0-913408-52-2). Friends United.

Russell, George W. The Ascending Cycle. (Sangam Texts Ser.). 105p. (Orig.). 1983. pap. 8.75 (ISBN 0-88695-013-9). Concord Grove.

Russell, George W. see AE, pseud.

Russell, George W., ed. see Wood, Edward L.

Russell, George W. E. Sydney Smith. 1973. lib. bdg. 20.00 (ISBN 0-8414-7488-5). Folcroft.

--Sydney Smith. LC 79-156929. 1971. Repr. of 1905 ed. 35.00x (ISBN 0-8103-3720-7). Gale.

Russell, H. Africa's Twelve Apostles. 1980. 6.95 (ISBN 0-8198-0702-8); pap. 5.50 (ISBN 0-8198-0703-6). Dghtrs St Paul.

Russell, James D., ed. see Hughes, Leonard V., Jr.

Russell, Jeffrey. History of Medieval Christianity. LC 68-9743. 1968. pap. 8.95x (ISBN 0-88295-761-9). Harlan Davidson.

Russell, Jeffrey B. The Devil: Perceptions of Evil from Antiquity to Primitive Christianity. LC 77-3126. (Illus.). 288p. 1977. 27.50x (ISBN 0-8014-0938-1). Cornell U Pr.

--Dissent & Reform in the Early Middle Ages. LC 78-63178. (Heresies of the Early Christian & Medieval Era: Second Ser.). 344p. Repr. of 1965 ed. 36.00 (ISBN 0-404-16196-0). AMS Pr.

--A History of Witchcraft: Sorcerers, Heretics & Pagans. (Illus.). 1982. pap. 10.95f (ISBN 0-500-27242-5). Thames Hudson.

--Lucifer: The Devil in the Middle Ages. LC 84-45153. (Illus.). 384p. 1984. 24.95x (ISBN 0-8014-1503-9). Cornell U Pr.

--Lucifer: The Devil in the Middle Ages. LC 84-45153. (Illus.). 360p. 1986. pap. text ed. 12.95x (ISBN 0-8014-9429-X). Cornell U Pr.

--Mephistopheles: The Devil in the Modern World. LC 86-47648. (Illus.). 352p. 1986. text ed. 24.95x (ISBN 0-8014-1808-9). Cornell U Pr.

Russell, Jim, illus. Moses of the Bullrushes: Retold by Catherine Storr. (People of the Bible Ser.). (Illus.). 32p. 1984. 10.65 (ISBN 0-8172-1990-0, Raintree Children's Books Belitha Press Ltd. - London). Raintree Pubs.

Russell, Joseph. The Daily Lectionary-Year 1: Advent-Easter. (Orig.). 1986. pap. 2.50 (ISBN 0-88028-057-3). Forward Movement.

Russell, Joseph P. The Daily Lectionary: A Weekly Guide for Daily Bible Readings, the Sundays After Pentecost Year One. (Daily Lectionary Ser.). 136p. (Orig.). 1987. pap. 3.25 (ISBN 0-88028-060-3). Forward Movement.

Russell, Joseph P., ed. see Ingram, Kristen J.

Russell, Lester F. Black Baptist Secondary Schools in Virginia, 1887-1957: A Study in Black History. LC 80-22414. 218p. 1981. 18.00 (ISBN 0-8108-1373-4). Scarecrow.

Russell, Letty M. Becoming Human. LC 81-23121. (Library of Living Faith: Vol. 2). 114p. 1982. pap. 5.95 (ISBN 0-664-24408-4). Westminster.

--The Future of Partnership. LC 78-20805. 198p. 1979. pap. 8.95 (ISBN 0-664-24240-5). Westminster.

--Household of Freedom: Authority in Feminist Theology. 132p. (Orig.). 1987. pap. 8.95 (ISBN 0-664-24017-8). Westminster.

--Human Liberation in a Feminist Perspective: A Theology. LC 74-10613. 214p. 1974. pap. 8.95 (ISBN 0-664-24991-4). Westminster.

Russell, Letty M., ed. Changing Contexts of Our Faith. LC 85-4418. 112p. 1985. pap. 4.95 (ISBN 0-8006-1862-9). Fortress.

--Feminist Interpretation of the Bible. LC 84-17342. 166p. (Orig.). 1985. pap. 10.95 (ISBN 0-664-24639-7). Westminster.

--The Liberating Word: A Guide to Non-Sexist Interpretation of the Bible. LC 76-18689. 120p. 1976. pap. 7.95 (ISBN 0-664-24751-2). Westminster.

Russell, Marjorie. The Arcadia Story. LC 85-40651. 265p. 1985. pap. 9.95 (ISBN 0-938232-83-5, Dist. by Baker & Taylor Co.). Winston-Derek.

Russell, Marjorie H. Handbook of Christian Meditation. 1978. pap. 5.95 (ISBN 0-8159-5713-0). Devin.

--A Handbook of Christian Meditation. (Illus.). pap. 5.95 (ISBN 0-8159-6110-3). Devin.

--Oneness of All Life. 160p. 1984. 5.95 (ISBN 0-87159-123-5). Unity School.

--Revelation: Your Future Prophesied. (Illus.). 60p. (Orig.). 1985. pap. 7.98 (ISBN 0-9614745-0-5). Arcadia Corp.

Russell, Michael, ed. see Spottiswood, John.

Russell, Norman, tr. The Lives of the Desert Fathers. 192p. 1981. 40.00x (ISBN 0-264-66581-3, Pub. by Mowbrays Pub Div). State Mutual Bk.

Russell, Norman, jt. tr. see Ward, Benedicta.

Russell, Olga W. Humor in Pascal. 1977. 8.95 (ISBN 0-8158-0343-5). Chris Mass.

Russell, Paul A. Lay Theology in the Reformation: Popular Pamphleteers in Southwest Germany, 1521-1525. (Illus.). 303p. 1986. 39.50 (ISBN 0-521-30727-9). Cambridge U Pr.

Russell, Peter. The TM Technique: A Skeptic's Guide to the TM Program. 1977. pap. 7.95 (ISBN 0-7100-0337-4). Methuen Inc.

Russell, Peter, tr. see Corbin, Henry.

Russell, Ralph D., ed. Essays in Reconstruction. LC 68-15835. 1968. Repr. of 1946 ed. 21.50x (ISBN 0-8046-0398-7, Pub. by Kennikat). Assoc Faculty Pr.

Russell, Robert. The Answer Will Come. 91p. 1981. pap. 3.00 (ISBN 0-87516-440-4). De Vorss.

Russell, Robert A. Dry Those Tears. 133p. 1975. pap. 4.95 (ISBN 0-87516-203-7). De Vorss.

--God Works Through Faith. 1957. pap. 3.95 (ISBN 0-87516-325-4). De Vorss.

--God Works Through You. 1977. pap. 3.95 (ISBN 0-87516-217-7). De Vorss.

--Making the Contact. 90p. 1980. Repr. of 1956 ed. lexitone cover 3.95 (ISBN 0-87516-391-2). De Vorss.

--You Too Can Be Prosperous. 162p. 1975. pap. 3.95 (ISBN 0-87516-205-3). De Vorss.

--You Try It. 1953. pap. 5.50 (ISBN 0-87516-326-2). De Vorss.

Russell, Robert L. The Making of a Leader. 256p. 1987. pap. price not set (ISBN 0-87403-267-9, 3181). Standard Pub.

Russell, Susan. Fifty-Two Teen Crafts. 48p. (Orig.). 1984. pap. 2.95 (ISBN 0-87239-728-9, 2108). Standard Pub.

Russo-Alesi, Anthony I. Martyrology Pronouncing Dictionary. LC 79-167151. 1973. Repr. of 1939 ed. 35.00x (ISBN 0-8103-3272-8). Gale.

Russon, Robb. Letters to a New Elder: The Melchizedek Priesthood, Its Duty & Fulfillment. pap. 2.95 (ISBN 0-89036-144-4). Hawkes Pub Inc.

Rust, Brian & McLeish, Barry. The Support-Raising Handbook: A Guide for Christian Workers. LC 84-22448. 156p. (Orig.). 1984. pap. 9.95 (ISBN 0-87784-326-0). Inter-Varsity.

Rust, Eric C. Judges, Ruth, First & Second Samuel. LC 59-10454. (Layman's Bible Commentary Ser: Vol. 6). 1961. pap. 4.95 (ISBN 0-8042-3066-8). John Knox.

--Religion, Revelation & Reason. LC 81-2760. vi, 192p. 1981. 14.50x (ISBN 0-86554-006-3). Mercer Univ Pr.

--The Word & Words: Towards a Theology of Preaching. LC 82-8032. xii, 131p. 1982. 10.95 (ISBN 0-86554-055-1, MUP-H36). Mercer Univ Pr.

Rust, Henry. Christians As Peacemakers. 54p. (Orig.). 1983. pap. 5.95 (ISBN 0-940754-21-5). Ed Ministries.

Rust, Henry R. James: The Most American Book in the Bible. 70p. (Orig.). 1985. pap. 6.95 (ISBN 0-940754-31-2). Ed Ministries.

Rutenber, Culbert G. The Price & the Prize. LC 81-65392. 1981. 6.95 (ISBN 0-8054-6230-9). Broadman.

Ruth, Eddie. The Right to Be Here. (Illus.). 28p. (Orig.). 1981. pap. 2.00 (ISBN 0-911826-27-0). Am Atheist.

Ruth, John L. Conrad Grebel: Son of Zurich (Biography) LC 75-8829. 160p. 1975. 9.95 (ISBN 0-8361-1767-0). Herald Pr.

--Maintaining the Right Fellowship. LC 83-18579. (Anabaptist & Mennonite History Ser.: No. 26). 608p. 1984. 24.95x (ISBN 0-8361-1259-8). Herald Pr.

--Mennonite Identity & Literary Art. 72p. 1978. pap. 1.95 (ISBN 0-8361-1861-8). Herald Pr.

--A Quiet & Peaceable Life. rev. ed. LC 85-70284. (People's Place Booklet: No. 2). (Illus.). 96p. (Orig.). 1985. pap. 4.50 (ISBN 0-934672-25-3). Good Bks PA.

--Twas Seeding Time. LC 76-41475. 220p. 1976. pap. 5.95 (ISBN 0-8361-1800-6). Herald Pr.

Ruthen, Gerald C., retold by. Daniel & the Silver Flute: An Old Hassidic Tale. (Illus.). 32p. 11.95. United Synagogue.

Rutherford, Richard. The Death of a Christian: The Rite of Funerals. (Studies in the Reformed Rites of the Catholic Church: Vol. 7). 1980. pap. 9.95 (ISBN 0-916134-40-7). Pueblo Pub Co.

Rutherford, Samuel. Letters of Samuel Rutherford. 1985. Repr. 17.95 (ISBN 0-85151-388-3). Banner of Truth.

Rutherford, Ward. The Druids: Magicians of the West. 176p. 1984. pap. 7.95 (ISBN 0-85030-346-X). Newcastle Pub.

--The Druids: Magicians of the West. LC 86-18803. 176p. 1986. lib. bdg. 19.95x (ISBN 0-8095-7007-6). Borgo Pr.

Ruthler, George W. Beyond Modernity: Reflections of a Post-Modern Catholic. LC 86-82636. 227p. (Orig.). 1986. pap. 11.95 (ISBN 0-89870-135-X). Ignatius Pr.

Rutland, Jonathan. Take a Trip to Israel. (Take a Trip to Ser.). (Illus.). 32p. 1981. lib. bdg. 9.90 (ISBN 0-531-04318-5). Watts.

Rutland, Robert A. The First Amendment: The Legacy of George Mason. LC 85-2958. (Illus.). 208p. 1985. 15.00 (ISBN 0-913969-05-2, Pub. by G Mason U Pr). U Pr of Amer.

Rutledge, Dom D. In Search of a Yogi: Himalayan Pilgrimage. lib. bdg. 69.95 (ISBN 0-8490-0392-X). Gordon Pr.

Rutledge, Don & Furlow, Elaine S. The Human Touch. LC 75-2365. (Human Touch Ser.). (Illus.). 1975. 5.95 (ISBN 0-937170-13-5). Home Mission.

Rutledge, Don, tr. see Martin, Dan.

Rutman, Darrett B., ed. The Great Awakening: Event & Exegesis. LC 77-10540. 208p. 1977. pap. text ed. 8.00 (ISBN 0-88275-605-2). Krieger.

Rutstein, Nathan. He Loved & Served: The Story of Curtis Kelsey. (Illus.). 208p. 12.95 (ISBN 0-85398-120-5); pap. 7.95 (ISBN 0-85398-121-3). G Ronald Pub.

--Teaching the Baha'i Faith: Spirit in Action. 192p. 11.95 (ISBN 0-85398-175-2); pap. 6.95 (ISBN 0-85398-176-0). G Ronald Pub.

Rutten, Felix. Die Victorverehrung Im Christlichen Altertum. Repr. of 1936 ed. 15.00 (ISBN 0-384-52655-1). Johnson Repr.

Rutter, Eldon. The Holy Cities of Arabia, 2 vols. LC 78-63477. Repr. of 1928 ed. Set. 49.50 (ISBN 0-404-16543-5). AMS Pr.

Ruttner, John, jt. ed. see Willcocks, David.

Ruyle, Gene. Making a Life: Career, Commitment & the Life Process. 144p. (Orig.). 1983. pap. 7.95 (ISBN 0-8164-2408-X, HarpR). Har-Row.

Ryan, Alvan, ed. Newman & Gladstone: The Vatican Decrees. 1962. 13.95 (ISBN 0-268-00190-1). U of Notre Dame Pr.

Ryan, Arthur H. Mirroring Christ's Splendour. Rev. ed. 216p. 1984. pap. 7.00 (ISBN 0-912414-40-5). Lumen Christi.

Ryan, Charles J. H. P. Blavatsky & the Theosophical Movement. 2nd,rev. ed. Knoche, Grace F., ed. LC 75-4433. (Illus.). 1975. 9.00 (ISBN 0-911500-79-0); pap. 6.00 (ISBN 0-911500-80-4). Theos U Pr.

--H. P. Blavatsky & the Theosophical Movement: With 7 Appendixes. Small, W. Emmett & Todd, Helen, eds. (Illus.). 484p. 1975. pap. 7.00 (ISBN 0-913004-25-1). Point Loma Pub.

--What Is Theosophy? A General View of Occult Doctrine. rev. ed. Small, W. Emmett & Todd, Helen, eds. (Theosophical Manual: No. 1). 92p. 1975. pap. 2.25 (913004-18-9). Point Loma Pub.

Ryan, Charles J., jt. auth. see Ross, Lydia.

Ryan, George E. Figures in Our Catholic History. 1979. 4.00 (ISBN 0-8198-0608-0); pap. 2.50 (ISBN 0-8198-0609-9). Dghtrs St Paul.

Ryan, James. Bible Promises for Growing Christians. LC 84-22953. 1985. pap. 2.25 (ISBN 0-8054-5014-9). Broadman.

Ryan, James M. Conversations with God: A Voice That Will Drive You Sane. Lambert, Herbert, ed. LC 84-7620. 96p. 1984. pap. 6.95 (ISBN 0-8272-0444-2). CBP.

Ryan, John. Irish Monasticism: Origins & Early Development. 520p. 1986. 60.00x (ISBN 0-7165-2374-4, Pub. by Irish Academic Pr Ireland). Biblio Dist.

Ryan, John A. Questions of the Day. facs. ed. LC 67-26779. (Essay Index Reprint Ser). 1931. 20.00 (ISBN 0-8369-0846-5). Ayer Co Pubs.

Ryan, John B., jt. auth. see Crotty, Robert.

Ryan, John J. Jesus People. 1970. text ed. 2.95 (ISBN 0-914070-03-7). ACTA Found.

--The Nature, Structure, & Function of the Church in William of Ockham. LC 78-2891. (American Academy of Religion: Studies in Religion, 16). 1979. pap. 9.95 (ISBN 0-89130-230-1, 1010016). Scholars Pr GA.

Ryan, John K. John Duns Scotus, Twelve Sixty Five-Nineteen Sixty Five. Bonansea, Bernardine M., ed. LC 61-66336. (Studies in Philosophy & the History of Philosophy Ser.: Vol. 3). pap. 98.00 (ISBN 0-317-08040-7, 2022584). Bks Demand UMI.

Ryan, John K., ed. Studies in Philosophy & the History of Philosophy, Vol. 4. LC 61-66336. Repr. of 1969 ed. 59.50 (ISBN 0-8357-9057-6, 2017279). Bks Demand UMI.

Ryan, John K. & Benard, Edmond, eds. American Essays for the Newman Centennial. LC 47-30528. pap. 64.50 (ISBN 0-317-07851-8, 2005379). Bks Demand UMI.

Ryan, John K., ed. see St. Francis De Sales.

Ryan, John K., tr. see St. Francis de Sales.

Ryan, Kevin. Questions & Answers on Moral Education. LC 81-80011. (Fastback Ser.: No. 153). 1981. pap. 0.90 (ISBN 0-87367-153-8). Phi Delta Kappa.

Ryan, Mary P. How Sacraments Celebrate Our Story. LC 78-53635. (Journeys Ser). 1978. pap. text ed. 6.00x (ISBN 0-88489-104-6); tchrs. guide 6.00x (ISBN 0-88489-108-9). St Mary's.

Ryan, Michael D., ed. Human Responses to the Holocaust: Perpetrators, Victims, Bystanders & Resisters-Papers of the 1979 Bernhard E. Olson Scholar's Conference on the Church Struggle & the Holocaust Sponsored by the National Conference of Christians & Jews. LC 81-38331. (Texts & Studies in Religion: Vol. 9). 300p. 1981. 49.95x (ISBN 0-88946-902-4). E Mellen.

Ryan, Pat & Ryan, Rosemary. Lent Begins at Home. 1979. pap. 1.50 (ISBN 0-89243-101-6). Liguori Pubns.

Ryan, Roberta. The George Lozuks: Doers of the Word. LC 85-6615. (Meet the Missionary Ser.). 1985. 5.50 (ISBN 0-8054-4293-6, 4242-93). Broadman.

Ryan, Rosemary, jt. auth. see Ryan, Pat.

Ryan, Roy. Strong Sunday Schools-Strong Churches: The Pastor's Role. LC 86-71810. 72p. (Orig.). 1987. pap. 4.95 (ISBN 0-88177-035-3, DR035B). Discipleship Res.

Ryan, Thomas. Fasting Rediscovered: A Guide to Health & Wholeness for Your Body-Spirit. LC 80-81581. 160p. (Orig.). 1981. pap. 6.95 (ISBN 0-8091-2323-1). Paulist Pr.

--Wellness, Spirituality & Sports. LC 86-4923. 224p. 1986. pap. 8.95 (ISBN 0-8091-2801-2). Paulist Pr.

Ryan, Thomas J., ed. Critical History & Biblical Faith: New Testament Perspectives. (Annual Publication of the College Theology Society Ser.). 242p. 1984. pap. text ed. 8.25 (ISBN 0-8191-4157-7). U Pr of Amer.

Ryan, Thomas P. Tales of Christian Unity: The Adventures of An Ecumenical Pilgrim. LC 82-60748. 224p. 1983. pap. 9.95 (ISBN 0-8091-2502-1). Paulist Pr.

Ryazhsky, A. Uchjebnik Tserkovnago Penija. Tr. of Textbook of Sacred Singing. 105p. 1966. pap. 5.00 (ISBN 0-317-30382-1). Holy Trinity.

Rybolt, John E. Wisdom. (Collegeville Bible Commentary: Old Testament Ser.: Vol. 20). 112p. 1986. pap. 2.95 (ISBN 0-8146-1477-9). Liturgical Pr.

Rycaut, Paul. Present State of the Greek & Armenian Churches. LC 75-13321. Repr. of 1679 ed. 32.50 (ISBN 0-404-05476-5). AMS Pr.

Rydberg, Denny. Building Community in Youth Groups. LC 85-17645. (Illus.). 177p. (Orig.). 1985. pap. 11.95 (ISBN 0-931529-06-9). Group Bks.

Ryder, Andrew. Prayer: The Eastern Tradition. (Orig.). 1983. pap. 2.95 (ISBN 0-914544-47-0). Living Flame Pr.

Ryder, Lew. Why J. R.? A Psychiatrist Discusses the Villain of Dallas. LC 82-82836. 153p. (Orig.). 1983. pap. 4.95 (ISBN 0-910311-02-1). Huntington Hse Inc.

Rye, Jennifer. The Story of the Christians. (Cambridge Books for Children). (Illus.). 32p. 1987. 7.95 (ISBN 0-521-30118-1); pap. 3.95 (ISBN 0-521-31748-7). Cambridge U Pr.

Ryel, D., jt. auth. see Dahlstrom, J.

Ryken, Leland. Culture in Christian Perspective: A Door to Understanding & Enjoying the Arts. LC 86-1442. 1986. 13.95 (ISBN 0-88070-115-3). Multnomah.

--How to Read the Bible As Literature. 200p. (Orig.). 1985. pap. text ed. 7.95 (ISBN 0-310-39021-4, 11158P). Zondervan.

--Wordly Saints: The Puritans As They Really Were. 272p. 1986. 18.95 (ISBN 0-310-32500-5). Zondervan.

--Worlds of Delight: A Literary Introduction to the Bible. 372p. 1987. pap. 17.95 (ISBN 0-8010-7743-5). Baker Bk.

Ryken, Leland, ed. The Christian Imagination: Essays on Literature & the Arts. LC 80-70154. 344p. (Orig.). 1981. pap. 13.95 (ISBN 0-8010-7702-8). Baker Bk.

--The New Testament in Literary Criticism. (A Library of Literary Criticism). 450p. 1985. 45.00 (ISBN 0-8044-3271-6). Ungar.

Ryken, Leland, jt. ed. see Sims, James H.

Rylaarsdam, Coert, ed. see Habel, Norman C.

Rylaarsdam, J. Coert. Proverbs, Ecclesiastes, Song of Solomon. LC 59-10454. (Layman's Bible Commentary Ser: Vol. 10). 1964. pap. 4.95 (ISBN 0-8042-3070-6). John Knox.

Rylaarsdam, J. Coert, ed. Transitions in Biblical Scholarship. LC 68-9135. (Essays in Divinity Ser: Vol. 6). 1968. 25.00x (ISBN 0-226-73287-8). U of Chicago Pr.

Rylaarsdam, J. Coert, ed. see Tucker, Gene M.

Rylaarsdam, John C. Revelation in Jewish Wisdom Literature. (Midway Reprint Ser.). pap. 35.00 (ISBN 0-317-26582-2, 2024065). Bks Demand UMI.

Ryle, J. C. Christian Leaders of the Eighteenth Century: Includes Whitefield, Wesley, Grimshaw, Romaine, Rowlands, Berridge, Venn, Walker, Harvey, Toplady, & Fletcher. 1978. pap. 7.45 (ISBN 0-85151-268-2). Banner of Truth.

--Expository Thoughts on the Gospels, 3 vols. Incl. St. Matthew. 426p. 1974. Repr. 9.95 (ISBN 0-227-67697-1); St. Mark. 384p. 1973. Repr. 9.95 (ISBN 0-227-67698-X); St. Luke. 540p. Repr. of 1983 ed. 19.95 (ISBN 0-227-67877-X); St. John. write for info. (ISBN 0-227-67453-7); Vol. 2. 9.95 (ISBN 0-227-67454-5); Matthew-Mark. 380p. Repr. of 1983 ed. 19.95 (ISBN 0-227-67874-5). Set. 65.00 (ISBN 0-227-67874-5). Attic Pr.

--Five English Reformers. rev. ed. 156p. (Orig.). 1981. pap. text ed. 3.95 (ISBN 0-85151-138-4). Banner of Truth.

--Holiness. 352p. 1977. Repr. of 1959 ed. 12.50 (ISBN 0-227-67482-0). Attic Pr.

--Holiness. (Giant Summit Bks.). pap. 11.95 (ISBN 0-8010-7686-2). Baker Bk.

--Luke. (Expository Thoughts on the Gospel Ser.: Vol. 2). 530p. 1986. pap. 6.95 (ISBN 0-85151-498-7). Banner of Truth.

--Luke. (Expository Thoughts on the Gospel Ser.: Vol. 1). 390p. 1986. pap. 5.95 (ISBN 0-85151-497-9). Banner of Truth.

--Mark. 370p. 1984. pap. 5.95 (ISBN 0-85151-441-3). Banner of Truth.

--Matthew. (Expository Thoughts on the Gospel Ser.). 368p. 1986. pap. 5.95 (ISBN 0-85151-483-9). Banner of Truth.

--No Uncertain Sound: Charges & Addresses. 384p. 1984. pap. 10.95 (ISBN 0-85151-444-8). Banner of Truth.

--Practical Religion: Being Plain Papers on Daily Duties, Experience Dangers, & Privileges of Professing Christianity. 334p. 1977. Repr. of 1959 ed. 12.95 (ISBN 0-227-67569-X). Attic Pr.

--The Upper Room. 1983. pap. 9.95 (ISBN 0-85151-017-5). Banner of Truth.

Ryle, John C. Holiness. 352p. 1979. 12.95 (ISBN 0-8007-1066-5). Revell.

--Old Paths: Being Plain Statements on Some of the Weightier Matters of Christianity. 553p. 1977. 12.95 (ISBN 0-227-67821-4). Attic Pr.

Ryle, John Charles. Knots Untied: Being Plain Statements on Some of the Weightier Matters of Christianity. 342p. 1977. Repr. of 1964 ed. 12.95 (ISBN 0-227-67511-8). Attic Pr.

Rynberg, Elbert. Lithuania Calling Collect: An Exploration of the Roads to Love. 160p. 1983. 8.50 (ISBN 0-682-49970-6). Exposition Pr FL.

Rynkiewich, Michael A. & Spradley, James P. Ethics & Anthropology. LC 81-3698. 198p. 1981. Repr. of 1976 ed. lib. bdg. 14.50 (ISBN 0-89874-349-4). Krieger.

Ryre, Charles C. What You Should Know about Inerrancy. (Current Christian Issues Ser.). pap. 4.50 (ISBN 0-8024-8785-8). Moody.

Ryrie, jt. auth. see Steele.

Ryrie, Charles. Acts of the Apostles. (Everyman's Bible Commentary Ser.). 1967. pap. 5.95 (ISBN 0-8024-2044-3). Moody.

--Neo-Orthodoxy. 1978. pap. 2.50 (ISBN 0-937396-27-3). Walterick Pubs.

--Ryrie's Concise Guide to the Bible. LC 83-71924. 163p. (Orig.). 1983. pap. 5.95 (ISBN 0-86605-121-X). Heres Life.

--We Believe in Creation. 62p. 1976. pap. 0.50 (ISBN 0-937396-54-0). Walterick Pubs.

Ryrie, Charles C. Apocalipsis (Comentario Biblico Portavoz) Orig. Title: Revelation (Everyman's Bible Commentary) (Span.). 128p. 1981. pap. 3.50 (ISBN 0-8254-1625-6). Kregel.

--Balancing the Christian Life. 1969. pap. 5.95 (ISBN 0-8024-0452-9). Moody.

--Las Bases de la Fe Premilenial. Orig. Title: The Basis of the Premillennial Faith. (Span.). 224p. 1984. pap. 3.95 (ISBN 0-8254-1626-4). Kregel.

--Basic Theology. 544p. 1986. 16.95 (ISBN 0-89693-814-X). Victor Bks.

--Basis of the Premillennial Faith. 1954. pap. 4.95 (ISBN 0-87213-741-4). Loizeaux.

--Biblical Theology of the New Testament. LC 59-11468. 1959. 12.95 (ISBN 0-8024-0712-9). Moody.

--Dispensacionalismo, Hoy. Orig. Title: Dispensationalism Today. (Span.). 256p. 1974. pap. 4.75 (ISBN 0-8254-1627-2). Kregel.

--Dispensationalism Today. LC 65-14611. 211p. 1973. pap. 6.95 (ISBN 0-8024-2256-X). Moody.

--Equilibrio en la Vida Cristiana. Orig. Title: Balancing the Christian Life. (Span.). 208p. 1983. pap. 5.95 (ISBN 0-8254-1628-0). Kregel.

--El Espiritu Santo. Orig. Title: The Holy Spirit. (Span.). 192p. 1978. pap. 3.95 (ISBN 0-8254-1629-9). Kregel.

--The Final Countdown. 120p. 1982. pap. 4.95 (ISBN 0-88207-347-8). Victor Bks.

--First & Second Thessalonians. (Everyman's Bible Commentary Ser.). 1968. pap. 5.95 (ISBN 0-8024-2052-4). Moody.

--The Grace of God. rev., new ed. 128p. 1975. pap. 4.95 (ISBN 0-8024-3250-6). Moody.

--La Gracia de Dios. Orig. Title: The Grace of God. (Span.). 160p. 1979. pap. 3.50 (ISBN 0-8254-1630-2). Kregel.

--Los Hechos de los Apostoles (Comentario Biblico Portavoz) Orig. Title: The Acts of the Apostles (Everyman's Bible Commentary) (Span.). 96p. 1981. pap. 2.95 (ISBN 0-8254-1631-0). Kregel.

--Holy Spirit. LC 65-14610. (Orig.). 1965. pap. 5.95 (ISBN 0-8024-3565-3). Moody.

--Making the Most of Life. 1983. pap. 3.95 (ISBN 0-88207-587-X). SP Pubns.

--Object Lessons. 96p. 1981. pap. 3.95 (ISBN 0-8024-6024-0). Moody.

--Primera y Segunda Tesalonicenses (Comentario Biblico Portavoz) Orig. Title: First & Second Thessalonians (Everyman's Bible Commentary) (Span.). 104p. 1981. pap. 2.95 (ISBN 0-8254-1634-5). Kregel.

--Revelation. (Everyman's Bible Commentary Ser.). (Orig.). 1968. pap. 5.95 (ISBN 0-8024-2066-4). Moody.

--The Role of Women in the Church. LC 58-8329. 1979. pap. 5.95 (ISBN 0-8024-7371-7). Moody.

--Sintesis de Doctrina Biblica. Orig. Title: Survey of Bible Doctrine. (Span.). 208p. 1979. pap. 4.95 (ISBN 0-8254-1637-X). Kregel.

--Survey of Bible Doctrine. LC 72-77958. 192p. 1972. pap. 5.95 (ISBN 0-8024-8435-2). Moody.

--Understanding Bible Doctrine. rev. ed. (Elective Ser.). 1983. pap. 3.95 (ISBN 0-8024-0258-5). Moody.

--What You Should Know about Social Responsibility. LC 81-16804. (Current Christian Issues Ser.). 1982. pap. 4.50 (ISBN 0-8024-9417-X). Moody.

--What You Should Know about the Rapture. LC 81-4019. (Current Christian Issues Ser.). 128p. 1981. pap. 4.50 (ISBN 0-8024-9416-1). Moody.

--You Mean the Bible Teaches That. 1974. pap. 5.95 (ISBN 0-8024-9828-0). Moody.

Rys, Janet Van see Van Rys, Janet.

Ryun, Jim & Philips, Mike. In Quest of Gold: The Jim Ryun Story. LC 84-47735. (Illus.). 224p. 1984. 12.45i (ISBN 0-06-067021-5, HarpR). Har-Row.

Ryuzo, Nagao. Chinese Folklore: Belief & Marriage. (Asian Folklore & Social Life Monograph: No. 14). (Japanese.). 1938. 14.00 (ISBN 0-89986-035-4). Oriental Bk Store.

Rywkin, Michael. Moscow's Muslim Challenge: Soviet Central Asia. LC 81-14414. (Illus.). 232p. 1982. pap. 13.95 (ISBN 0-87332-262-2). M E Sharpe.

S

S. P. Publications Editors. What Is the Church? Leader's Guide. Chao, Lorna Y., tr. (Basic Doctrine Ser.). 1986. pap. write for info. (ISBN 0-941598-35-7). Living Spring Pubns.

Saalfeld, Lawrence J. Forces of Prejudice in Oregon, Nineteen Twenty to Nineteen Twenty-Five. LC 84-14599. (Oregon Catholic History Ser.). (Orig.). 1984. pap. 8.95 (ISBN 0-9613644-0-8). Archdiocesan.

Saalman, Howard. Filippo Brunelleschi: The Cupola of Santa Maria del Fiore. Harris, John & Laing, Alastair, eds. (Studies in Architecture: No. XX). (Illus.). 420p. 1986. 95.00 (ISBN 0-302-02784-X, Pub. by Zwemmer Bks UK). Sotheby Pubns.

Sabanes De Plou, Dafne, tr. see Simmons, Paul D. & Crawford, Kenneth.

Sabar, Yona, ed. The Folk Literature of the Kurdistani Jews: An Anthology. LC 81-43605. (Judaica Ser.: No. 23). 320p. 1982. 35.00x (ISBN 0-300-02698-6). Yale U Pr.

Sabarin, Leopold, jt. auth. see Lyonnet, Stanislas.

Sabatier, A. The Apostle Paul: A History of the Development of the Doctrine of St. Paul. 1977. lib. bdg. 59.95 (ISBN 0-8490-1442-5). Gordon Pr.

Sabatier, Paul. Life of St. Francis of Assisi. 1977. lib. bdg. 59.95 (ISBN 0-8490-2167-7). Gordon Pr.

Sabatini, Rafael. Heroic Lives. facs. ed. LC 70-99648. (Essay Index Reprint Ser.). 1934. 19.50 (ISBN 0-8369-2071-6). Ayer Co Pubs.

Sabbah, Fatna A. Woman in the Muslim Unconscious. LC 84-11343. (Athene Ser.). 188p. 1984. 27.00 (ISBN 0-08-031626-3); pap. 11.00 (ISBN 0-08-031625-5). Pergamon.

Sabbath, Linda. The Radiant Heart. 1986. Repr. of 1985 ed. 4.95 (ISBN 0-87193-003-X). Dimension Bks.

Sabet, Huschmand. The Heavens Are Cleft Asunder. rev. ed. Coburn, Oliver, tr. from Ger. Orig. Title: Gespaltene Himmel. (Eng.). 1975. pap. 6.25 (ISBN 0-85398-055-1, 332-014). G Ronald Pub.

Sabille, Jacques, jt. auth. see Poliakov, Leon.

Sabin, Robin, jt. auth. see Parker, Richard B.

Sabini, J. Islam: A Primer. 127p. 1984. 30.00x (ISBN 0-317-39197-6, Pub. by Luzac & Co Ltd). State Mutual Bk.

Sabini, John. Islam: A Primer. LC 83-61987. (Illus.). 127p. 1983. pap. 7.50x (ISBN 0-918992-05-2). Middle East Edit.

Sabini, Jon & Silver, Maury. Moralities of Everyday Life. 1982. 22.50x (ISBN 0-19-503016-8); pap. 8.95 (ISBN 0-19-503017-6). Oxford U Pr.

Sabins, Walter E. With Bible & Spade. (Orig.). 1987. pap. price not set (ISBN 0-89536-897-8, 7883). CSS of Ohio.

Sabiq, Sayyed. Figh Al Sunnah. Quilan, Hamid, ed. Izzidien, Movel Y., tr. from Arabic. LC 82-70450. 1700p. (Orig.). 1983. text ed. 30.00 (ISBN 0-89259-033-5); pap. 20.00 (ISBN 0-686-81828-8). Am Trust Pubns.

Sable, Martin H. Latin American Jewry: A Research Guide. LC 77-18527. (Bibliographica Judaica: No. 6). Repr. of 1978 ed. 160.00 (ISBN 0-317-42036-4, 2025695). Bks Demand UMI.

Sabourin, Leopold. Christology: Basic Texts in Focus. LC 84-12304. 259p. (Orig.). 1984. pap. 9.95 (ISBN 0-8189-0471-2). ALBA.

--The Psalms: Their Origin & Meaning. LC 73-16459. 560p. (Orig.). 1974. pap. 12.95 (ISBN 0-8189-0121-7). Alba.

Sabsovich, Katherine. Adventures in Idealism: A Personal Record of the Life of Professor Sabsovich. facsimile ed. LC 74-29520. (Modern Jewish Experience Ser.). (Illus.). 1975. Repr. of 1922 ed. 23.50x (ISBN 0-405-06745-3). Ayer Co Pubs.

Sabzavari, Hadi Ibn Mahdi. The Metaphysics of Haji Mulla Hadi Sabzavari. Izutsu, Toshihiku & Mohaghegh, Mehdi, trs. from Persian. LC 76-18174. 248p. 1977. lib. bdg. 35.00x (ISBN 0-88206-011-2). Caravan Bks.

Sachar, A. L. History of the Jews. rev. ed. 1967. 20.00 (ISBN 0-394-42871-4). Knopf.

Sachar, Abram. The Redemption of the Unwanted: The Post-Holocaust Years. 334p. 1985. pap. 9.95 (ISBN 0-312-66730-2, Pub. by Marek). St Martin.

Sachar, Abram L. The Redemption of the Unwanted: From the Liberation of the Death Camps to the Founding of Israel. LC 83-3025. (Illus.). 320p. 1983. 19.95 (ISBN 0-312-66729-9, Pub. by Marek). St Martin.

Sachar, Howard M. Diaspora: An Inquiry into the Contemporary Jewish World. LC 84-48190. 480p. 1985. 27.00i (ISBN 0-06-015403-9, HarpT). Har-Row.

--Diaspora: An Inquiry into the Contemporary Jewish World. LC 84-48190. (Illus.). 539p. 1986. pap. 10.95 (ISBN 0-06-091347-9, PL-1347, PL). Har-Row.

--A History of Israel: From the Rise of Zionism to Our Time. LC 76-13710. (Illus.). 1979. 14.95 (ISBN 0-394-73679-6). Knopf.

Sachar, Howard M., ed. see Klieman, Aaron.

Sachau, Edward C., tr. see Al-Biruni.

Sachau, Edward C., tr. see Embree, Ainslie.

Sachdeva, I. P. Yoga & Depth Psychology. 269p. 1978. 16.95x (ISBN 0-317-12334-3, Pub. by Motilal Banarsi). Asia Bk Corp.

Sachedina, Abdulaziz A. Islamic Messianism: The Idea of Mahdi in Twelver Shi'ism. LC 80-16767. 1980. 49.50x (ISBN 0-87395-442-4); pap. 19.95x (ISBN 0-87395-458-0). State U NY Pr.

Sacher, Harry, ed. Zionism & the Jewish Future. LC 75-6452. (The Rise of Jewish Nationalism & the Middle East Ser.). viii, 252p. 1975. Repr. of 1916 ed. 25.85 (ISBN 0-88355-338-4). Hyperion Conn.

Sacher-Masoch, L. Jewish Tales. 59.95 (ISBN 0-8490-0445-4). Gordon Pr.

Sachs, Abraham S. Worlds That Passed. facsimile ed. Berman, Harold & Joffe, Judah, trs. from Yiddish. LC 74-29521. (Modern Jewish Experience Ser.). (Eng.). 1975. Repr. of 1928 ed. 24.50x (ISBN 0-405-06746-1). Ayer Co Pubs.

Sachs, Henry, jt. auth. see Robinson, Jacob.

Sachs, Michael. Die Religiose Poesie der Juden in Spanien. Katz, Steven, ed. LC 79-7150. (Jewish Philosophy, Mysticism & History of Ideas Ser.). 1980. Repr. of 1901 ed. lib. bdg. 37.00x (ISBN 0-405-12285-3). Ayer Co Pubs.

Sachs, Viola. La Contre-Bible de Melville: Moby-Dick Dechiffre. 122p. 1975. pap. text ed. 13.60x (ISBN 90-2797-586-8). Mouton.

Sachs, William L., jt. auth. see Trigg, Joseph W.

Sachse, Julius F. German Pietists of Provincial Pennsylvania, 1694-1708. LC 70-134384. (Communal Societies Ser.). Repr. of 1895 ed. 32.50 (ISBN 0-404-07204-6). AMS Pr.

--Music of the Ephrata Cloister. LC 77-134386. (Communal Societies Ser.). Repr. of 1903 ed. 15.00 (ISBN 0-404-05500-1). AMS Pr.

Sack, Benjamin G. History of the Jews in Canada. LC 65-1899. pap. 79.00 (ISBN 0-317-28422-3, 2022315). Bks Demand UMI.

Sack, John. The Wolf in Winter: A Story of Francis Assisi. LC 85-60296. 128p. (Orig.). 1985. pap. 4.95 (ISBN 0-8091-6556-2). Paulist Pr.

Sackville-West, V. Saint Joan of Arc. LC 84-9125. 416p. 1984. pap. 7.95 (ISBN 0-8398-2856-X, Gregg). G K Hall.

Sacred Congregation for Divine Worship. Rites of the Catholic Church, Vol. 1. rev. ed. International Committee on English in the Liturgy, tr. from Lat. 1983. 14.50 (ISBN 0-916134-15-6). Pueblo Pub Co.

--The Rites of the Catholic Church, Vol. 2. International Commission on English in the Liturgy, tr. from Lat. 1980. pap. 11.50 (ISBN 0-916134-37-7). Pueblo Pub Co.

Sacred Congregation of the Clergy, Official English Translation of the Latin Document April 11, 1971. General Catechetical Directory. pap. 3.75 (ISBN 1-55586-173-3, V-173). US Catholic.

Sadananda. Vedantasara of Sadananda. pap. 3.00 (ISBN 0-87481-073-6). Vedanta Pr.

Sader, Kathy. Let Earth Receive Its King: Christmas Service for Children. (Orig.). 1986. pap. 0.90 (ISBN 0-8066-9202-2, 23-1682). Augsburg.

Sadha, Mouni. Samadhi: The Superconsciousness of the Future. (Unwin Paperbacks). 1977. pap. 5.95 (ISBN 0-04-149039-8). Allen Unwin.

Sadhu. Meditation. pap. 7.00 (ISBN 0-87980-096-8). Wilshire.

Sadhu, M. Concentration: A Guide to Mental Mastery. pap. 5.00 (ISBN 0-87980-023-2). Wilshire.

Sadhu, Mouni. Tarot. pap. 8.00 (ISBN 0-87980-157-3). Wilshire.

Sadler, A. W. In Quest of the Historical Buddha & the White Cranes of Sri Ramakrishna. LC 84-48565. (Illus.). 1984. pap. 6.50x sewn bdg. (ISBN 0-910913-02-1). Laughing B P.

--The Journey of Western Spirituality. 234p. 1986. lib. bdg. 23.00 (ISBN 0-8191-5722-8, Pub. by College Tehology Society); pap. text ed. 13.00 (ISBN 0-8191-5618-3). U Pr of Amer.

Sadler, A. W., ed. The Journey of Western Spirituality: CTS Annual Publication, 1980. LC 81-5831. 1981. text ed. 18.00 (ISBN 0-89130-505-X, 34 10 80). Scholars Pr GA.

Sadler, Williams S., Jr. A Study of the Master Universe. LC 68-58958. (Illus.). 150p. 1968. 13.00 (ISBN 0-686-05760-0); pap. write for info. (ISBN 0-686-05761-9). Second Soc Foun.

Sadoleto, Jacopo, jt. ed. see Calvin, John.

Sadowski, Frank, ed. The Church Fathers on the Bible. 1987. pap. write for info. (ISBN 0-8189-0510-7). Alba.

Sadowy, Chester P. Benjamin Colman's "Some of the Glories of Our Lord & Saviour Jesus Christ," Exhibited in Twenty Sacramental Discourses (1928) 1979. lib. bdg. 35.00 (ISBN 0-8482-6210-7). Norwood Edns.

Sadr, Muhammad B. Introduction to Islamic Political System. Ansari, M. A., tr. 112p. 1985. pap. 6.00 (ISBN 0-941724-34-4). Islamic Seminary.

Sadr, Muhhammad B. A Short History of Iluml Usul. Ansari, M. A., tr. from Arabic. 130p. 1985. pap. 5.00 (ISBN 0-941724-37-9). Islamic Seminary.

Sadtler, Barbara. The Echo is of God. 96p. (Orig.). 1986. pap. 1.90 (ISBN 0-88028-052-2). Forward Movement.

Saeed, M. Studies in Muslim Philosophy. 12.00 (ISBN 0-686-18601-X). Kazi Pubns.

Saeeed, M. A Dictionary of Muslim Philosophy. 14.50 (ISBN 0-686-18370-3). Kazi Pubns.

Safa-Isfahani, Nezhat. The Rivayat-i Hemit-i Asawahistan: A Study in Zoroastrian Law. (Harvard Iranian Ser.: No. 2). 304p. 1981. text ed. 25.00x (ISBN 0-674-77305-5). Harvard U Pr.

Safed. Safed Spirituality: Rules of Mystical Piety, the Beginning of Wisdom. Fine, Lawrence, tr. (Classics of Western Spirituality Ser.). 1984. 12.95 (ISBN 0-8091-0349-4); pap. 9.95 (ISBN 0-8091-2612-5). Paulist Pr.

Saffen, Wayne. The Second Season: Lent, Easter, Ascension. LC 72-87064. pap. 24.00 (2026827). Bks Demand UMI.

Safley, Thomas M. Let No Man Put Asunder: The Control of Marriage in the German Southwest, 1550-1600. (Studies and Essays: Vol. II). 210p. 1984. 25.00x (ISBN 0-940474-02-6). Sixteenth Cent.

Safran, Alexander. Israel in Space & Time: Basic Themes in Jewish Spirituality. 1987. 25.00. Feldheim.

Safran, Bezalel, ed. Hasidism: Continuity or Innovation? (Harvard Judaic Texts & Studies: No. V). 60p. 1985. text ed. 5.00x (ISBN 0-674-38120-3). Harvard U Ctr Jewish.

Safranski, Scott R. Managing God's Organization: The Catholic Church in Society. Farmer, Richard, ed. LC 85-16540. (Research for Business Decisions: No. 79). 200p. 1985. 44.95 (ISBN 0-8357-1669-4). UMI Res Pr.

Safwat, Nabil, tr. see Widad El Sakkakini.

Sagard-Theodat, Gabriel. Long Journey to the Country of the Hurons. Wrong, George M., ed. Langton, H. H., tr. LC 68-28613. 1968. Repr. of 1939 ed. lib. bdg. 29.25x (ISBN 0-8371-3861-2, SAJC). Greenwood.

Sage, Gerald S. The End of False Religion-When? LC 87-80323. (Illus.). 192p. (Orig.). 1987. pap. 9.95 (ISBN 0-941813-00-2). Elite Pubs.

Sage, Wilfred Le see Le Sage, Wilfred.

Sager, Harold G. Rebel for God. 1983. 5.75 (ISBN 0-8062-1868-1). Carlton.

Sahagun, Bernardino de. Florentine Codex, General History of the Things of New Spain, 13 bks. Anderson, Arthur J. & Dibble, Charles E., trs. Incl. Introductory Volume: Introductions, Sahagun's Prologues & Interpolations, General Bibliography, General Indices. 1982. 35.00x (ISBN 0-87480-165-6); Bk. 1. Gods. rev., 2nd ed. 1970. 17.50 (ISBN 0-87480-000-5); Bk. 2. Ceremonies. rev., 2nd ed. 1981. 40.00x (ISBN 0-87480-194-X); Bk. 3. Origins of the Gods. rev., 2nd ed. 1979. 17.50x (ISBN 0-87480-002-1); Bks. 4 & 5. The Soothsayers, the Omens. Repr. of 1979 ed. 40.00x (ISBN 0-87480-003-X); Bk. 6. Rhetoric & Moral Philosophy. 1976. 40.00x (ISBN 0-87480-010-2); Bk. 7. Sun, Moon & Stars, & the Binding of the Years. Repr. of 1977 ed. 17.50 (ISBN 0-87480-004-8); Bk. 8. Kings & Lords. Repr. of 1979 ed. 20.00x (ISBN 0-87480-005-6); Bk. 9. Merchants. Repr. of 1976 ed. 20.00x (ISBN 0-87480-006-4); Bk. 10. People. Repr. of 1974 ed. 30.00x (ISBN 0-87480-007-2); Bk. 11. Earthly Things. Repr. of 1975 ed. 45.00x (ISBN **0-87480-008-0); Bk. 12. Conquest of Mexico. rev., 2nd ed. 1975. 27.50x (ISBN 0-87480-096-X). 1982. Set. 350.00x (ISBN 0-87480-082-X). U of Utah Pr.**

Sahagun, Fray B. De see Sahagun, Bernardino de.

Sahas, Daniel. Katechesis. 70p. 1981. pap. 3.00 (ISBN 0-916586-45-6). Holy Cross Orthodox.

Sahay, R. R. Religious Philosophy of William James. 1980. text ed. 18.95x. Coronet Bks.

Saher, P. J. Eastern Wisdom & Western Thought: A Comparative Study in the Modern Philosophy of Religion. LC 72-441621. pap. 73.50 (ISBN 0-317-09011-9, 2012165). Bks Demand UMI.

--Zen Yoga. 1976. 15.00 (ISBN 0-8426-0822-2). Orient Bk Dist.

Saher, Parwez J. The Conquest of Suffering. 1977. 12.50 (ISBN 0-89684-189-8, Pub. by Motilal Banarsidass India). Orient Bk Dist.

Sahn, Seung. Only Don't Know: The Teaching Letters of Zen Master Seung Sahn. LC 82-17380. (Wheel Ser.: No. 3). 205p. (Orig.). 1982. pap. 7.95 (ISBN 0-87704-054-0). Four Seasons Foun.

Sahni, K. A Mind in Ferment: Mikhail Bulgakov's Prose. 251p. 1984. text ed. 12.50x (ISBN 0-391-03201-1, Pub. by Arnold Heinemann). Humanities.

Sahukar, Mani. Sai Baba, the Saint of Shirdi. LC 75-29273. 1977. 3.95 (ISBN 0-913922-11-0). Dawn Horse Pr.

Saia, Mary J. & Boyle, Judith. Our Growing Child. 112p. (Orig.). 1985. pap. 5.95 (ISBN 0-89622-221-7). Twenty-Third.

Saia, Mary J., et al. Awakenings. (Education to Wonder Ser.: Pre-School Program). 1973. program director's handbook 3.50 (ISBN 0-8091-9075-3); tchr dev. handbook 3.50 (ISBN 0-8091-9074-5); tchr. guidebk. 4 yr. olds 6.95 (ISBN 0-8091-9071-0); tchr. guidebk. 5 yr. olds 6.95 (ISBN 0-8091-9072-9). parent-tchr. dev. kit 75.00 (ISBN 0-8091-9073-7); child-parent kit 4 yr. olds 5.95 (ISBN 0-8091-9077-X); child-parent kit 5 yr. olds 5.95 (ISBN 0-8091-9078-8). Paulist Pr.

Said, Abdul. Human Rights & World Order. LC 78-62438. 170p. 1978. pap. 5.95 (ISBN 0-87855-718-0). Transaction Bks.

Said, Labib As see As-Said, Labib.

Said, Marie-Bernard, tr. see Bernard Of Clairvaux.

Saidi, Margaret D., tr. see Cabanis, Pierre J.

Saiedi, Nader, ed. Beyond Marxism: Baha'i Perspectives on a New World Order. (Orig.). 1988. pap. 9.95 (ISBN 0-933770-59-6). Kalimat.

Sailes, Samuel. Self-Help. Bull, George & Joseph, Keith, eds. 240p. 1986. pap. 6.95 (ISBN 0-14-009100-9). Penguin.

Sailhamer, John. First & Second Chronicles. (Everyman's Bible Commentary Ser.). (Orig.). 1983. pap. 5.95 (ISBN 0-8024-2012-5). Moody.

Saillens, E. Les Sonnets Anglais et Italians De Milton. LC 74-12230. 1930. lib. bdg. 28.50 (ISBN 0-8414-7784-1). Folcroft.

Sain, Uggar, tr. & intro. by see Kundakunda Acharya.

Saini, Uma A. Valdika Mantras with Transliteration & Translation. LC 85-52267. (Sanskrit.). 288p. 1986. text ed. 19.00 (ISBN 0-9616357-0-3). U & K Pub.

St. Alphonsus de Liguori. The Glories of Mary. LC 79-112485. 1977. pap. 13.50 (ISBN 0-89555-021-0). TAN Bks Pubs.

--Uniformity with God's Will. 1977. pap. 1.00 (ISBN 0-89555-019-9). TAN Bks Pubs.

St. Amour, Sr. M. Paulina. Study of the "Villancico" up to Lope De Vega. LC 78-94170. (Catholic University of America Studies in Romance Languages & Literatures Ser: No. 21). Repr. of 1940 ed. 22.00 (ISBN 0-404-50321-7). AMS Pr.

St. Anthanasius. St. Athanasius on the Incarnation. 120p. 1977. pap. 4.95 (ISBN 0-913836-40-0). St Vladimirs.

St. Augustine. Against Julian. LC 77-81347. (Fathers of the Church Ser.: Vol. 35). 407p. 1957. 21.95x (ISBN 0-8132-0035-0). Cath U Pr.

--The City of God. LC 58-5717. pap. 6.50 (ISBN 0-385-02910-1, Im). Doubleday.

--City of God. Knowles, David, ed. (Classics Ser.). 1984. pap. 12.95 (ISBN 0-14-044426-2). Penguin.

--The City of God. Dods, Marcus, tr. LC 54-5465. 1950. 10.95 (ISBN 0-394-60397-4). Modern Lib.

--City of God, Bks. 1-7. LC 63-19613. (Fathers of the Church Ser.: Vol. 8). 401p. 1950. 29.95x (ISBN 0-8132-0008-3). Cath U Pr.

--Eighty-Three Different Questions. LC 81-2546. (Fathers of the Church Ser.: Vol. 70). 257p. 1982. 29.95x (ISBN 0-8132-0070-9). Cath U Pr.

--Immortality of the Soul & Other Works. (Fathers of the Church Ser.: Vol. 4). 489p. 1947. 29.95x (ISBN 0-8132-0004-0). Cath U Pr.

--Letters: 165-203. (Fathers of the Church Ser.: Vol. 30). 421p. 1955. 21.95x (ISBN 0-8132-0030-X). Cath U Pr.

--Letters: 204-270. (Fathers of the Church Ser.: Vol. 32). 317p. 1956. 17.95x (ISBN 0-8132-0032-6). Cath U Pr.

--St. Augustine on the Psalms: Vol. 2. Quasten, J. & Burghardt, W. J., eds. Hebgin, D. Scholastica & Corrigan, D. Felicitas, trs. LC 60-10722. (Ancient Christian Writers Ser.: No. 30). 425p. 1961. 14.95 (ISBN 0-8091-0105-X). Paulist Pr.

--Sermons on the Liturgical Seasons. (Fathers of the Church Ser.: Vol. 38). 1959. 29.95x (ISBN 0-8132-0038-5). Cath U Pr.

--The Theory of Free Will. (Illus.). 117p. 1984. 66.55 (ISBN 0-89266-466-5). Am Classical Coll Pr.

St. Basil The Great. On the Holy Spirit. Anderson, David, tr. from Gr. LC 80-25502. 118p. (Orig.). 1980. pap. 4.95 (ISBN 0-913836-74-5). St Vladimirs.

St. Bonaventure. What Manner of Man. (Sermons on Christ Ser). 1974. 5.95 (ISBN 0-8199-0497-X). Franciscan Herald.

St. Catherine of Siena. The Dialogue of St. Catherine of Siena. Thorold, Algar, tr. from It. & intro. by. 1976. pap. 6.00 (ISBN 0-89555-037-7). TAN Bks Pubs.

St. Clair. Following Jesus. 1983. 4.95 (ISBN 0-88207-301-X). Victor Bks.

St. Clair, Barry. Giving Away Your Faith. (Moving Toward Maturity Ser.: No. 4). 132p. 1985. pap. 4.95 (ISBN 0-317-16074-5). Victor Bks.

--Growing On. (Moving Toward Maturity Ser.: No. 5). 144p. 1986. pap. 4.95 (ISBN 0-88207-305-2). Victor Bks.

--Joy Explosion. 128p. 1986. pap. 9.95 (ISBN 0-88207-306-0). Victor Bks.

--Leadership. 1984. pap. 9.95 (ISBN 0-88207-193-9). Victor Bks.

--Making Jesus Lord. 1983. pap. 4.95 (ISBN 0-88207-303-6). Victor Bks.

--Spending Time Alone with God. 144p. 1984. pap. 4.95 (ISBN 0-88207-302-8). Victor Bks.

St. Cormac, Bishop of Munster. The Rule of St. Cormac: Irish Monastic Rules. (Vol. III). pap. 1.50 (ISBN 0-317-11386-0). Eastern Orthodox.

St. Cyprian of Carthage. The Lord's Prayer. Bonin, Edmond, ed. 112p. (Orig.). 1983. pap. 6.95 (ISBN 0-87061-076-7). Chr Classics.

St. Cyres, Viscount. Francois de Fenelon. LC 72-113319. 1970. Repr. of 1901 ed. 25.50x (ISBN 0-8046-0998-5, Pub. by Kennikat). Assoc Faculty Pr.

--Pascal. 1909. Repr. 25.00 (ISBN 0-8274-3103-1). R West.

St. Cyril, Bishop of Jerusalem. Five Instructions on the Sacraments. 1974. pap. 1.25 (ISBN 0-686-10197-9). Eastern Orthodox.

St. Cyril of Jerusalem. Oglasytel' Nija i Tajnovodstennija Pouchenija. Tr. of Prochatechisis & Mystagogical Catechesis. (Rus.). 376p. (Orig.). 1976. 18.00x (ISBN 0-88465-024-3); pap. 13.00x (ISBN 0-88465-025-1). Holy Trinity.

St. Cyril of Alexandria. Letters, 1-50. (The Fathers of the Church: Vol. 76). 350p. 1987. 29.95x (ISBN 0-8132-0076-8). Cath U Pr.

St. Dimitry of Rostov. The Assumption of Our Lady. 1976. pap. 1.50 (ISBN 0-317-30435-6). Holy Trinity.

St. Dorotheos of Gaza. Dushepoljeznija Pouchjenija. Tr. of Spiritual Teachings. (Rus.). 300p. (Orig.). 1970. 15.00x (ISBN 0-88465-035-9); pap. 10.00x (ISBN 0-88465-036-7). Holy Trinity.

St. Francis de Sales. Daily Readings with St. Francis de Sales. LLewelyn, Robert, ed. (Daily Readings Ser.). 1986. pap. 4.95 (ISBN 0-87243-147-9). Templegate.

--Introduction to the Devout Life. rev. ed. Ryan, John K., ed. 1972. pap. 5.50 (ISBN 0-385-03009-6, IM). Doubleday.

--Treatise on the Love of God, 2 vols. Ryan, John K., tr. 1975. Set. pap. 10.00 (ISBN 0-89555-064-4); Vol. 1. pap. (ISBN 0-89555-062-8, 166-I); Vol. 2. pap. (ISBN 0-89555-063-6). TAN Bks Pubs.

St. Francis of Sales. The Sermons of St. Francis de Sales on Our Lady. Fiorelli, Lewis S., ed. LC 85-51662. 197p. 1985. pap. 7.00 (ISBN 0-89555-259-0). Tan Bks Pubs.

St. Germanus of Constantinople. On the Divine Liturgy. Meyendorff, Paul, tr. from Gr. LC 84-27615. 107p. 1984. pap. text ed. 4.95 (ISBN 0-88141-038-1). St Vladimirs.

St. Gertrude. The Life & Revelations of St. Gertrude. 570p. 1983. pap. 15.00 (ISBN 0-87061-079-1). Chr Classics.

St. Gregory & Balfour, David. Discourse on the Tranfiguration. LC 85-13299. 170p. 1985. Repr. lib. bdg. 19.95x (ISBN 0-89370-862-3). Borgo Pr.

St. Herman of Alaska Brotherhood Staff, ed. see Herman, Abbot.

St. Hilary Troitsky. Christianity or the Church? 48p. (Orig.). 1985. pap. 2.00 (ISBN 0-317-30269-8). Holy Trinity.

St. Ignatius. Spiritual Exercises of St. Ignatius. Mottola, Anthony, tr. pap. 3.95 (ISBN 0-385-02436-3, D170, Im). Doubleday.

St. Ignatius of Antioch & St. Polycarp of Simirna. Poslanije Saviatago Ignatija Antiokhiskago i Sviatago Polykarpa Smirnskago. Tr. of Letters of St. Ignatius of Antioch & of St. Polycarp of Smirna. (Rus.). 80p. (Orig.). 1975. pap. 2.00x (ISBN 0-88465-023-5). Holy Trinity.

St. Ignatius Loyola. The Autobiography of St. Ignatius Loyola, with Related Documents. O'Callaghan, Joseph F., tr. 16.00 (ISBN 0-8446-5240-7). Peter Smith.

St. Johh-Stevas, Norman. The Two Cities. 352p. 1984. 27.50 (ISBN 0-571-13083-6). Faber & Faber.

St. John, P. Infant & Junior Scripture Lesson. 274p. 1956. 4.00 (ISBN 0-227-67493-6). Attic Pr.

St. John, Patricia. If You Love Me. 1984. pap. 3.50 (ISBN 0-8024-5962-5). Moody.

--The Runaway. 1985. pap. 3.95 (ISBN 0-8024-9159-6). Moody.

--Twice Freed: The Story of Onesimus, a Runaway Slave. (Orig.). 1985. pap. 3.95 (ISBN 0-8024-8848-X). Moody.

St. John, Robert. Tongue of the Prophets. pap. 7.00 (ISBN 0-87980-166-2). Wilshire.

--Tongue of the Prophets: The Life Story of Eliezer Ben Yehuda. LC 77-97303. 377p. 1972. Repr. of 1952 ed. lib. bdg. 22.50x (ISBN 0-8371-2631-2, STTP). Greenwood.

St. John Chrysostom. Homilies on Genesis 1-17. Hill, Robert C., tr. from Gr. (The Fathers of the Church Ser.: Vol. 74). 1986. 29.95 (ISBN 0-8132-0074-1). Cath U Pr.

--On Wealth & Poverty. Roth, Catharine P., tr. from Gr. LC 84-22920. 140p. 1984. pap. text ed. 5.95 (ISBN 0-88141-039-X). St Vladimirs.

--Sermon on the Decollation of St. John the Baptist, & on Herodias, & on Good & Evil Women. (Early Slavic Literatures, Studies, Texts, & Seminar Materials: Vol. 3). Orig. Title: V 29 den' mesiatsa avgusta slovo Ioanna Zlatoustogo na useknovenie glavy. (Slavic & Gr.). 45p. 1982. pap. 4.00 (ISBN 0-933884-23-0). Berkeley Slavic.

St. John of Kronstadt. On Prayer. (Orig.). 1985. pap. 3.00 (ISBN 0-317-30263-9). Holy Trinity.

St. John of the Cross. Daily Readings with St. John of the Cross. Llewelyn, Robert, ed. (Daily Readings Ser.). 1986. pap. 4.95 (ISBN 0-87243-148-7). Templegate.

--Dark Night of the Soul. 1959. pap. 3.95 (ISBN 0-385-02930-6, D78, Im). Doubleday.

--The Poems of St. John of the Cross. Barnstone, Willis, tr. & intro. by. LC 68-14597. (Eng. & Span.). 144p. 1972. pap. 4.95 (ISBN 0-8112-0449-9, NDP341). New Directions.

St. Johns, A. R. No Good-byes: My Search Into Life Beyond Death. 1981. 10.95 (ISBN 0-07-054450-6). McGraw.

St. John-Stevas, Norman. Life, Death & the Law: A Study of the Relationship Between Law & Christian Morals in the English & American Legal Systems. 375p. 1981. Repr. of 1961 ed. lib. bdg. 32.50x (ISBN 0-8377-1119-3). Rothman.

St. John Vianney. Thoughts of the Cure d'Ars. LC 84-50404. 79p. 1984. pap. 1.50 (ISBN 0-89555-240-X). TAN Bks Pubs.

St. Joseph Cafasso. The Priest the Man of God: His Dignity & Duties. O'Connell, Patrick, tr. from It. LC 79-112472. 1971. Repr. of 1892 ed. 7.00 (ISBN 0-89555-041-5). TAN Bks Pubs.

St. Leonard. The Hidden Treasure: Holy Mass. 1971. pap. 2.50 (ISBN 0-89555-036-9). TAN Bks Pubs.

St. Louis De Montfort. Secret of the Rosary. pap. 1.00 (ISBN 0-910984-04-2). Montfort Pubns.

Saint Mary's College - Holy Cross - Indiana. College Goes to School. facs. ed. LC 68-58811. (Essay Index Reprint Ser). 1945. 15.00 (ISBN 0-8369-0125-8). Ayer Co Pubs.

St. Mary's College, Kansas, Jesuit Fathers. The Church Teaches: Documents of the Church in English Translation. Clarkson, John F., et al, eds. 1973. pap. 10.00 (ISBN 0-89555-011-3). TAN Bks Pubs.

St. Maximus the Confessor. The Church, the Liturgy & the Soul of Man. Stead, Dom J., tr. from Gr. LC 82-10545. 1982. pap. 6.95 (ISBN 0-932506-23-2). St Bedes Pubns.

St. Nectarios Press, ed. New Martyrs of the Turkish Yoke. Papadopulos, Leonidas, et al, trs. from Gr. LC 84-50974. 400p. (Orig.). 1985. pap. 12.50x (ISBN 0-913026-57-3); pap. 15.00x after January 1986. St Nectarios.

St. Nicodemos the Hagiorite, ed. Dobrotoljubije, Tom Pjatij: Philokalia, Vol. 5. Govoroff, Theophan, tr. from Greek. (Rus.). 350p. (Orig.). 1966. 20.00x (ISBN 0-88465-030-8); pap. 15.00x (ISBN 0-88465-029-4). Holy Trinity.

--Dobrotoljubije, Tom Tchetvjortij: Philokalia, Vol. 4. Govoroff, Theofan, tr. from Greek. (Rus.). 495p. (Orig.). 1965. 25.00x (ISBN 0-88465-027-8); pap. 20.00x (ISBN 0-88465-028-6). Holy Trinity.

St. Paul. The Epistles of Paul in Modern English: A Paraphrase. Stevens, George B., tr. from Gr. 1980. Repr. of 1898 ed. 10.95 (ISBN 0-939464-03-9). Labyrinth Pr.

--The Writings of St. Paul. Meeks, Wayne, ed. (Critical Edition Ser). 1972. 12.95 (ISBN 0-393-04338-X); pap. 9.95x (ISBN 0-393-09979-2). Norton.

St. Paul, George A. Here & Hereafter. LC 56-9839. (Loyola Request Reprint Ser.). Repr. of 1963 ed. 59.30 (ISBN 0-8357-9427-X, 2015061). Bks Demand UMI.

St. Peter Chrysologos & St. Valerian. Selected Works. LC 65-27500. (Fathers of the Church Ser.: Vol. 17). 454p. 1953. 29.95x (ISBN 0-8132-0017-2). Cath U Pr.

St. Philastrius Bishop of Brescia. Sancti Filastrii Episcopi Brixiensis Diversarum Hereseon Liber. Repr. of 1898 ed. 50.00 (ISBN 0-384-46225-1). Johnson Repr.

St. Polycarp of Simirna, jt. auth. see St. Ignatius of Antioch.

St. Romain, Philip. Becoming a New Person: Twelve Steps to Christian Growth. 96p. 1984. pap. 2.95 (ISBN 0-89243-200-4). Liguori Pubns.

--Catholic Answers to Fundamentalists' Questions. 64p. 1984. pap. 1.95 (ISBN 0-89243-220-9). Liguori Pubns.

--Faith & Doubt Today. LC 85-82033. 128p. (Orig.). 1986. pap. 3.25 (ISBN 0-89243-245-4). Liguori Pubns.

--How to Form a Christian Growth Support Group. 48p. (Orig.). 1985. pap. 2.95 (ISBN 0-89243-242-X). Liguori Pubns.

--Jesus Alive in Our Lives. LC 85-71676. 104p. (Orig.). 1985. pap. 4.95 (ISBN 0-87793-293-X). Ave Maria.

--Praying the Daily Gospels: A Guide to Meditation. LC 84-71186. 248p. (Orig.). 1984. pap. 5.95 (ISBN 0-87793-314-6). Ave Maria.

St. Symeon. St. Symeon, the New Theologian: Theological & Practical Discourses & Three Theological Discourses. Bell, David N., ed. McGuckin, Paul, tr. from Greek. (Cistercian Studies: No. 41). 1982. write for info. (ISBN 0-87907-841-3); pap. 8.00 (ISBN 0-87907-941-X). Cistercian Pubns.

St. Teresa of Avila. The Life of Prayer. Houston, James M., ed. LC 83-12185. (Classics of Faith & Devotion). 1983. 11.95 (ISBN 0-88070-022-X). Multnomah.

--Daily Readings with St. Teresa of Avila. LLewelyn, Robert, ed. (Daily Readings Ser.). 1986. pap. 4.95 (ISBN 0-87243-146-0). Templegate.

--Interior Castle. 1972. pap. 4.50 (ISBN 0-385-03643-4, Im). Doubleday.

--Way of Perfection. pap. 4.95 (ISBN 0-385-06539-6, D176, Im). Doubleday.

St. Teresa of Lisieux. Autobiography of Saint Therese of Lisieux: The Story of a Soul. 1957. pap. 3.95 (ISBN 0-385-02903-9, D56, Im). Doubleday.

St. Thomas Acquinas. On Law, Morality, & Politics. Regan, Richard J. & Baumgarth, William P., eds. (HPC Classics Ser.). 300p. 1987. 27.50 (ISBN 0-87220-032-9); pap. text ed. 7.95 (ISBN 0-87220-031-0). Hackett Pub.

St. Thomas Aquinas. Aquinas on Politics & Ethics. Sigmund, Paul e., ed. (Norton Critical Edition Ser.). pap. write for info. (ISBN 0-393-95243-6). Norton.

--Commentary on St. Paul's Epistle to the Ephesians. Lamb, M. L., tr. LC 66-19307. (Aquinas Scripture Ser.). 1966. Vol. 2. 10.00x (ISBN 0-87343-022-0). Magi Bks.

--Commentary on St. Paul's Epistle to the Galatians. Larcher, F. R., tr. LC 66-19306. (Aquinas Scripture Ser.). 1966. Vol. 1. 10.00x (ISBN 0-87343-021-2). Magi Bks.

--Commentary on Saint Paul's Epistle to the Philippians & First Thessalonians. LC 66-19306. (Aquinas Scripture Ser.: Vol. 3). 1969. lib. bdg. 10.00x (ISBN 0-87343-047-6); pap. 6.00x (ISBN 0-87343-028-X). Magi Bks.

--Commentary on the Gospel of St. John, Pt. 1. Weisheipl, James A., ed. Larcher, Fabian R., tr. from Lat. LC 66-19306. (Aquinas Scripture Ser.: Vol. 4). (Illus.). 512p. 1980. 35.00x (ISBN 0-87343-031-X). Magi Bks.

--The Grace of Christ. (Summa Theologiae Ser.: Vol. 49). 1974. 18.95 (ISBN 0-07-002024-8). McGraw.

--Introduction to Saint Thomas Aquinas. Pegis, Anton C., ed. (Modern Library College Editions Ser.). 1965. pap. 3.75x (ISBN 0-394-30974-X, T74, RanC). Random.

--Middle High German Translation of the "Summa Theologica". Morgan, Bayard Q. & Strothmann, Friedrich W., eds. LC 50-8471. (Stanford University. Stanford Studies in Language & Literature: No. 8). (Lat. & Ger., Glossary). Repr. of 1950 ed. 42.50 (ISBN 0-404-51816-8). AMS Pr.

--Political Ideas of St. Thomas Aquinas: A Selection from His Writings. 1973. pap. 9.95x (ISBN 0-317-30522-0). Free Pr.

--Political Ideas of St. Thomas Aquinas. Bigongiari, Dino, ed. (Library of Classics Ser.: No. 15). 1973. pap. text ed. 7.95x (ISBN 0-02-840380-0). Hafner.

--Providence & Predestination: Questions 5 & 6 of "Truth". Mulligan, Robert W., tr. 154p. 1961. pap. 5.95 (ISBN 0-89526-937-6). Regnery Bks.

--Saint Thomas Aquinas: On Charity. Kendzierski, Lotti H., tr. (Medieval Philosophical Texts in Translation: No. 10). 1960. pap. 7.95 (ISBN 0-87462-210-7). Marquette.

--Saint Thomas Aquinas: On Spiritual Creatures. Fitzpatrick, Mary C., tr. (Medieval Philosophical Texts in Translation: No. 5). 1949. pap. 7.95 (ISBN 0-87462-205-0). Marquette.

--St. Thomas Aquinas: Philosophical Texts. Gilby, Thomas, ed. xxiv, 406p. 1982. pap. 12.50x (ISBN 0-939464-06-3). Labyrinth Pr.

--St. Thomas Aquinas: Theological Texts. Gilby, Thomas, ed. 444p. 1982. pap. 12.50x (ISBN 0-939464-01-2). Labyrinth Pr.

--Selected Writings of St. Thomas Aquinas. Goodwin, Robert P., tr. Incl. The Principles of Nature; On Being & Essence; On the Virtues in General; On Free Choice. LC 65-26529. (Orig.). 1965. pap. 4.24 scp (ISBN 0-672-60469-8, LLA217). Bobbs.

--Summa Contra Gentiles, 4 bks. Incl. Bk. 1. God. Pegis, Anton C., tr. 317p. pap. 7.45x (ISBN 0-268-01678-X); Bk. 2. Creation. Anderson, James F., tr. 351p. text ed. 16.95 (ISBN 0-268-01679-8); pap. 7.45 (ISBN 0-268-01680-1); Bk. 3. Providence, 2 bks. in 1. Bourke, Vernon J., tr. 560p. text ed. 35.00x (ISBN 0-268-01681-X); pap. 15.00x (ISBN 0-268-01682-8); Bk. 4. Salvation. O'Neil, Charles J., tr. 360p. text ed. 16.95 (ISBN 0-268-01683-6); pap. 8.95x (ISBN 0-268-01684-4). LC 75-19883. 1975. Set. pap. 35.00. U of Notre Dame Pr.

--Summa Theologica, 5 vols. 3057p. 1982. 225.00 (ISBN 0-87061-063-5); pap. 150.00 (ISBN 0-87061-069-4). Chr Classics.

--Treatise on Happiness. Oesterle, John A., tr. LC 83-17091. 224p. 1983. text ed. 15.95x (ISBN 0-268-01848-0, 85-18482); pap. text ed. 5.95x (ISBN 0-268-01849-9, 85-18490). U of Notre Dame Pr.

--Treatise on the Virtues. Oesterle, John A., tr. LC 84-10691. 171p. 1984. pap. text ed. 7.95 (ISBN 0-268-01855-3, 85-18557). U of Notre Dame Pr.

Saint Athanasius. Zhitie Prepodobnago Antonija Velikago. Tr. of The Life of St. Anthony the Great. 47p. pap. 2.00 (ISBN 0-317-29181-5). Holy Trinity.

Saint Augustine. Against the Academicians. Garvey, Sr. M. Patricia, tr. (Mediaeval Philosophical Texts in Translation). 1957. pap. 7.95 (ISBN 0-87462-202-6). Marquette.

--The Confessions of Saint Augustine. LC 60-13725. 6.50 (ISBN 0-385-02955-1, Im). Doubleday.

--Enchiridion on Faith, Hope & Love. Paolucci, Henry, ed. 177p. 1961. pap. 4.95 (ISBN 0-89526-938-4). Regnery Bks.

--The Essential Augustine. Bourke, Vernon J., commentary by. 274p. 1973. 15.00 (ISBN 0-915144-08-5); pap. text ed. 4.95 (ISBN 0-915144-07-7). Hackett Pub.

--On Christian Doctrine. Robertson, D. W., Jr., tr. LC 58-9956. 1958. pap. 7.20 scp (ISBN 0-672-60262-8). Bobbs.

--On Free Choice of the Will. Benjamin, A. S. & Hackstaff, L. H., trs. LC 63-16932. (Orig.). 1964. pap. 7.20 scp (ISBN 0-672-60368-3, LLAS150). Bobbs.

--Political Writings of St. Augustine. Paolucci, Henry, ed. 358p. pap. 5.95 (ISBN 0-89526-941-4). Regnery Bks.

--Rule of Saint Augustine. Canning, Raymond, tr. LC 85-20760. 128p. 1986. pap. 3.95 (ISBN 0-385-23241-1, Im). Doubleday.

Saint-Beuve. Port Royal, 3 vols. Vol. 1. 37.50 (ISBN 0-686-56564-9); Vol. 2. 37.50 (ISBN 0-686-56565-7); Vol. 3. 35.95 (ISBN 0-686-56566-5). French & Eur.

St. Blasien, Otto Von see Otto, Von St. Blasien.

St. Clair, Mae G., jt. auth. see Turner, Gladys D.

Saint Dimitri Rostov. Zhitija Svjatikh v 12 tomov, 12 vols. Tr. of The Lives of the Saints. 10000p. Repr. of 1968 ed. 360.00 (ISBN 0-317-29175-0). Holy Trinity.

Sainte Marthe, DEnis de see De Sainte Marthe, Denis.

Saint Ephrem. The Harp of the Spirit: Eighteen Poems of Saint Ephrem. Brock, Sebastian, tr. LC 84-285. 89p. 1984. Repr. of 1983 ed. lib. bdg. 19.95x (ISBN 0-89370-776-7). Borgo Pr.

Saint-Exupery, Saint Antoine De. The Wisdom of the Sands. Gilbert, Stuart, tr. from Fr. LC 79-15938. 1979. pap. 10.95 (ISBN 0-226-73372-6, P826). U of Chicago Pr.

Saint German, Christopher. The Addicion of Salem & Byzance. LC 73-6157. (English Experience Ser.: No. 619). 152p. 1973. Repr. of 1534 ed. 10.50 (ISBN 90-221-0619-5). Walter J Johnson.

--A Treatise Concernynge the Division Betwene the Spiritualitie & Temporalitie. LC 72-6027. (English Experience Ser.: No. 453). 94p. 1972. Repr. of 1532 ed. 14.00 (ISBN 90-221-0453-2). Walter J Johnson.

St. Goar, Maria, tr. see Kuhlewind, Georg.

St. Goar, Maria, tr. see Steiner, Rudolf.

Saint Hilacion Troitsky. Khristianstvo ili Tserkov. Tr. of Christianity or the Church. 64p. pap. 2.00 (ISBN 0-317-28982-9). Holy Trinity.

Saint-Hilaire, J. B. Buddha & His Religion. 59.95 (ISBN 0-87968-798-3). Gordon Pr.

Saint-Hilaire, J. Barthelemy. Buddhism in India & Sri Lanka. LC 75-907912. 1975. Repr. of 1975 ed. 10.50x (ISBN 0-89684-373-4). Orient Bk Dist.

Saint-Hilaire, P. B., ed. see Aurobindo, Sri.

Saint-Hilaire, P. B., ed. & intro. by see Sri Aurobindo & The Mother.

Saint John Bosco. St. Joseph Cafasso: Priest of the Gallows. LC 82-50979. Orig. Title: A Saint Speaks for Another Saint. 80p. 1983. pap. 2.00 (ISBN 0-89555-194-2). TAN Bks Pubs.

Saint John Climacus. Lestvitsa. Tr. of The Ladder. 363p. 18.00 (ISBN 0-317-28895-4); pap. 13.00 (ISBN 0-317-28896-2). Holy Trinity.

Saint John Kronstadt. Misli o Bogosluzhenii Pravoslavnoi Tserkvi. Tr. of Thoughts on the Divine Services of the Orthdox Church. 141p. 1954. 5.00 (ISBN 0-317-28907-1). Holy Trinity.

Saint John Moschus. Trorenija Svatago Efrema Sirina, Vol. 1. Tr. of The Works of St. Works of Ephraim. 475p. 21.00 (ISBN 0-317-28899-7); pap. 16.00 (ISBN 0-317-28900-4). Holy Trinity.

Saint John of Kronstadt. My Life in Christ. Goulaeff, E. E., tr. from Rus. LC 84-81775. 558p. 1984. 25.00 (ISBN 0-88465-018-9); pap. 20.00 (ISBN 0-88465-017-0). Holy Trinity.

St. Johns, E., jt. auth. see Parker, W.

St. Johns, Elaine, jt. auth. see Parker, William.

Saint-Jure, Jean B. & De La Colombiere, Claude. Trustful Surrender to Divine Providence: The Secret of Peace & Happiness. LC 83-50252. 139p. 1983. pap. 3.00 (ISBN 0-89555-216-7). TAN Bks Pubs.

Saint-Martin, Louis-Claude de see De Saint-Martin, Louis-Claude.

Saint Nicodemos the Hagiorite. Njevidimaja Bran' Tr. of Unseen Warfare. 288p. 15.00 (ISBN 0-317-28905-5); pap. 10.00 (ISBN 0-317-28906-3). Holy Trinity.

St. Therese of Lisieux, jt. auth. see Thomas a Kempis.

Saint Thomas. The Gospel According to Thomas. (Sacred Texts Ser.). Orig. Title: Coptic. vii, 88p. 1983. pap. 8.75 (ISBN 0-88695-005-8). Concord Grove.

Saint Thomas Aquinas. Truth & the Disputed Questions on Truth. (Illus.). 107p. 1987. 117.50 (ISBN 0-89266-582-3). Am Classical Coll Pr.

St. Valerian, jt. auth. see St. Peter Chrysologos.

Saint-Vallier, Jean B. Estat Present De L'eglise & De la Colonie Francoise Dans la Nouvelle France Par M. L'eveque De Quebec. (Canadiana Avant 1867: No. 20). 1967. 18.40x (ISBN 90-2796-332-0). Mouton.

Saint Victor Of Vita. Historia Persecutionis Africanae Provinciae. (Corpus Scriptorum Ecclesiasticorum Latinorum Ser.: Vol. 7). 1881. 30.00 (ISBN 0-384-64540-2). Johnson Repr.

Sajkovic, Olivera, ed. see Da Silva, Andrew J.

Sakade, Florence, ed. see Leggett, Trevor.

Sakakibara, Tokuso, et al. Bodhisattvas Everywhere. Tabrah, Ruth, ed. Arai, Toshikazu, tr. from Japanese. 120p. (Orig.). 1983. pap. 6.95 (ISBN 0-938474-03-0). Buddhist Study.

Sakenfeld, Katharine D. Faithfulness in Action: Loyalty in Biblical Perspective. LC 84-18738. (Overtures to Biblical Theology Ser.). 176p. 1985. pap. 8.95 (ISBN 0-8006-1540-9, 1-1540). Fortress.

Sakkas, Basil Priest. The Calendar Question. 96p. (Orig.). 1973. pap. 4.00 (ISBN 0-317-30294-9). Holy Trinity.

Saklatvala, Beram. The Christian Island. LC 75-92561. (Illus.). 150p. 1970. 15.00 (ISBN 0-8386-7571-9). Fairleigh Dickinson.

Sakoian, Frances & Acker, Louis S. The Astrologer's Handbook. LC 78-160647. (Illus.). 480p. (YA) 1973. 17.45i (ISBN 0-06-013734-7, HarpT). Har-Row.

Sakr, A. Names of Quran in Holy Quran. pap. 2.50 (ISBN 0-317-01599-0). Kazi Pubns.

Saksena, S. K. Nature of Consciousness in Hindu Philosophy. 2nd ed. 1971. 5.95 (ISBN 0-89684-284-3). Orient Bk Dist.

Sala, Harold. My Favorite Verse. LC 86-72986. (My Favorite Verse Ser.). 24p. 1987. pap. 4.95 (ISBN 0-89636-228-0). Accent Bks.

Sala, Harold J. Guidelines for Living. (Direction Bks.). 80p. (Orig.). 1982. pap. 2.95 (ISBN 0-8010-8219-6). Baker Bk.

Salajan, Ioanna. Zen Comics. LC 74-35679. 88p. 1974. pap. 4.95 (ISBN 0-8048-1120-2). C E Tuttle.

Salamon, Avrohon Y. Akdamus. (The Art Scroll Mesorah Ser.). 160p. 1978. 11.95 (ISBN 0-89906-154-0); pap. 8.95 (ISBN 0-89906-155-9). Mesorah Pubns.

Salamon, Lester M., jt. auth. see Clotfelter, Charles T.

Salaquarda, Joerg, ed. see Weischedel, Wilhelm, et al.

Salbstein, Michail. The Emancipation of the Jews in Britain: The Question of Admission of the Jews to Parliament, 1828-1860. (Littman Library of Jewish Civilization). 1982. 24.95x (ISBN 0-19-710050-3). Oxford U Pr.

Saldarini, Anthony J. Jesus & Passover. (Orig.). 1984. pap. 4.95 (ISBN 0-8091-2595-1). Paulist Pr.

--Scholastic Rabbinism: A Literary Study of the Fathers According to Rabbi Nathan. LC 81-13564. (Brown Judaic Studies). 1982. pap. text ed. 12.00 (ISBN 0-89130-523-8, 14-00-14). Scholars Pr GA.

Sale, J. Russell. Filipino Lippi's Strozzi Chapel in Santa Maria Novella. Freedberg, Sydney J., ed. LC 78-74376. (Outstanding Dissertations in the Fine Arts Ser.). (Illus.). 1979. lib. bdg. 57.00 (ISBN 0-8240-3963-7). Garland Pub.

Saleem, M., jt. auth. see Khan, M. Z.

Salem, Elie A. Political Theory & Institutions of the Khawarij. LC 78-64226. (Johns Hopkins University. Studies in the Social Sciences. Seventy-Fourth Ser. 1956: 2). Repr. of 1956 ed. 15.50 (ISBN 0-404-61328-4). AMS Pr.

Salem, Luis. El Dios de Nuestros Libertadores. LC 77-165. (Span., Illus.). 172p. (Orig.). 1977. pap. 3.25 (ISBN 0-89922-093-2). Edit Caribe.

--Hogares de la Biblia. (Span.). 107p. (Orig.). pap. 2.50 (ISBN 0-89922-079-7). Edit Caribe.

--Rimas del Pesebre. LC 77-82265. (Span.). 86p. (Orig.). 1978. pap. 2.50 (ISBN 0-89922-118-1). Edit Caribe.

Salemson, Harold J., tr. see Fesquet, Henri.

Salerno, Tony. Life in Christ. 128p. (Orig.). 1985. pap. 9.95 (ISBN 0-87123-887-X, 210887). Bethany Hse.

Sales, Francis de see De Sales, Francis.

Sales, Francois De see De Sales, Saint Francoise.

Sales, George & Wherry, E. M., eds. Comprehensive Commentary on the Qur'an, 4 Vols. LC 79-153620. Repr. of 1896 ed. Set. 145.00 (ISBN 0-404-09520-8); 27.50 ea. Vol. 1 (ISBN 0-404-09521-6). Vol. 2 (ISBN 0-404-09522-4). Vol. 3 (ISBN 0-404-09523-2). Vol. 4 (ISBN 0-404-09524-0). AMS Pr.

Sales, Lorenzo. Jesus Appeals to the World. 1955. 5.95 (ISBN 0-8189-0069-5). Alba.

Saleska, E. J. Let Not Your Heart Be Troubled. 1945. 0.95 (ISBN 0-570-03676-3, 74-1001). Concordia.

--Strength from Above. 1946. 0.95 (ISBN 0-570-03677-1, 74-1002). Concordia.

Saleska, Edward J., jt. ed. see Gockel, Herman W.

Saletore, R. N. Encyclopaedia of Indian Culture, V-Z, Vol. 5. 324p. 1985. text ed. 50.00x (ISBN 0-391-02978-9, Pub. by Sterling India). Humanities.

--Indian Witchcraft. 216p. 1981. text ed. 17.50x (ISBN 0-391-02480-9). Humanities.

Saliba, John A. Religious Cults Today: A Challenge to Christian Families. 48p. 1983. pap. 1.50 (ISBN 0-89243-189-X). Liguori Pubns.

Salibi, Kamal. The Bible Came from Arabia. (Illus.). 224p. 1986. 18.95 (ISBN 0-224-02830-8, Pub. by Jonathan Cape). Salem Hse Pubs.

Saliers, Don E. The Soul in Paraphrase: Prayer & the Religious Affections. 160p. 1980. 8.95 (ISBN 0-8164-0121-7, HarpR). Har-Row.

--Worship & Spirituality. LC 84-7211. (Spirituality & the Christian Life Ser.: Vol. 5). 114p. 1984. pap. 7.95 (ISBN 0-664-24634-6). Westminster.

Saliers, Don E., jt. auth. see Brown, Schuyler.

Saliers, Don E., ed. see Barth, Karl.

Salimbene Di Adam. From Saint Francis to Dante: Translations from the Chronicle of the Franciscan Salimbene (1221-88) Coulton, G. G., ed. & tr. from It. LC 68-10910. 462p. 1972. pap. 10.95x (ISBN 0-8122-1053-0, Pa Paperbks). U of Pa Pr.

Salin, Mary W. No Other Light. 224p. 1986. 14.95 (ISBN 0-8245-0748-7). Crossroad NY.

Salisbury, Joyce E. Iberian Popular Religion, Six Hundred B. C. to Seven Hundred A. D. Celts, Romans & Visigoths. (Texts & Studies in Religion: Vol. 20). 340p. 1985. 59.95x (ISBN 0-88946-809-5). E Mellen.

Salko, N. The Illustrious Relic of the Kulikovo Battle. 1985. 39.00x (ISBN 0-569-08567-5, Pub. by Collets (UK)). State Mutual Bk.

Salley, Christopher & Behm, Ronald. What Color Is Your God? Black Consciousness & the Christian Faith. LC 81-6758. 132p. (Orig.). 1981. pap. 4.50 (ISBN 0-87784-791-6). Inter-Varsity.

Salls, Betty R. Greatest of These-Love. pap. 1.75 (ISBN 0-686-12744-7). Grace Pub Co.

--My Love Remembers. pap. 1.75 (ISBN 0-686-12740-4). Grace Pub Co.

Salluste, A. Marxism & Judaism. 1982. lib. bdg. 69.95 (ISBN 0-87700-329-7). Revisionist Pr.

Salmi, Mario, intro. by. The Grimani Breviary. LC 74-78138. (Illus.). 276p. 1974. 195.00 (ISBN 0-87951-022-6). Overlook Pr.

Salmon, James F., jt. ed. see King, Thomas M.

Salmon, Pierre. The Abbot in Monastic Tradition. Lavoie, Claire, tr. from Fr. LC 78-158955. (Cistercian Studies: No. 14). Tr. of L Abbe' dans la Tradition Monastique. 148p. 1972. 9.95 (ISBN 0-87907-814-6). Cistercian Pubns.

Salmond, S. D. The Biblical Doctrine of Immortality. 718p. 1984. lib. bdg. 26.95 (ISBN 0-86524-164-3, 8804). Klock & Klock.

Salmond, S. D., ed. see Davidson, A. B.

Saloff-Astakhoff, N. I. Judith. 160p. 1980. 1.00 (ISBN 0-88113-290-X). Edit Betania.

Salomon, George & Feitelson, Rose. The Many Faces of Anti-Semitism. 44p. 1978. 1.50 (ISBN 0-87495-045-7). Am Jewish Comm.

Salomon, Michel. Future Life. 384p. 1983. 19.95 (ISBN 0-02-606770-6). Macmillan.

Salpointe, J. B. Soldiers of the Cross. 1977. Repr. of 1898 ed. lib. bdg. 24.95x (ISBN 0-89712-063-9). Documentary Pubns.

--Soldiers of the Cross: Notes on the Ecclesiastical History of New Mexico, Arizona, & Colorado. LC 67-29317. 299p. 1982. lib. bdg. 44.95x (ISBN 0-89370-733-3). Borgo Pr.

Salsbury, Barbara G. Just Add Water: How to Use Dehydrated Foods & TVP. 92p. 1972. 5.50 (ISBN 0-88290-011-0). Horizon Utah.

Salter, Darius L. Spirit & Intellect: Thomas Upham's Holiness Theology. LC 86-10048. (Studies in Evangelicalism: No. 7). 283p. 1986. 27.50 (ISBN 0-8108-1899-X). Scarecrow.

Salter, Elizabeth. Nicolas Love's Myrrour of the Blessed Lyf of Jesu Christ. Hogg, James, ed. (Analecta Carusiana Ser.: No. 10). (Orig.). 1974. pap. 25.00 (ISBN 3-7052-0011-9, Pub by Salzburg Studies). Longwood Pub Group.

Salter, H. E., jt. ed. see Turner, G. J.

Saltkill, Sue. Christmas Classics. (Illus.). 1985. pap. 6.95 (ISBN 0-943574-32-3). That Patchwork.

Saltus, Edgar. Lords of the Ghostland: A History of the Ideal. LC 71-116003. Repr. of 1907 ed. 17.50 (ISBN 0-404-05539-7). AMS Pr.

--Mary Magdalen. LC 78-116002. Repr. of 1891 ed. 17.50 (ISBN 0-404-05517-6). AMS Pr.

Saltzgaber, Jan M., jt. auth. see Altschuler, Glenn C.

Salvado, Rosendo. The Salvado Memoirs: Historical Memoirs of Australia & Particularly of the Benedictine Mission of New Norcia & of the Habits & Customs of the Australian Natives. Stormon, E. J., tr. 1978. pap. 10.95x (ISBN 0-85564-114-2, Pub. by U of W Austral Pr). Intl Spec Bk.

Salvation Army Literary Staff, ed. It's Beautiful & Other Salvationist Verse. (Illus.). 105p. (Orig.). 1984. pap. 3.50 (ISBN 0-89216-052-7). Salvation Army.

Salverte, Eusebe. The Philosophy of Magic. large type ed. pap. 6.95 (ISBN 0-910122-41-5). Amherst Pr.

Salvian the Presbyter. Complete Writings. (Fathers of the Church Ser.: Vol. 3). 396p. 1947. 34.95x (ISBN 0-8132-0003-2). Cath U Pr.

Salzman, Marcus, tr. see Ahimaaz Ben Paltiel.

Salzmann, Laurence, jt. auth. see Gursan-Salzmann, Ayse.

Salzmann, Regina A. Catholic Press Directory, 1986. 208p. 1986. pap. 25.00 (ISBN 0-318-18711-6). Cath Pr Assn.

Samartha, S. J. Courage for Dialogue: Ecumenical Issues in Inter-Religious Relationships. LC 81-16936. 172p. (Orig.). 1982. pap. 4.48 (ISBN 0-88344-094-6). Orbis Bks.

Samartha, S. J., ed. Living Faith & Ultimate Goals: Salvation & World Religions. LC 75-7610. 119p. (Orig.). 1975. pap. 1.98 (ISBN 0-88344-297-3). Orbis Bks.

Samay, Sebastian. Reason Revisited: The Philosophy of Karl Jaspers. LC 72-160423. pap. 79.50 (ISBN 0-317-26140-1, 2024371). Bks Demand UMI.

Sambhi, Piara S., jt. auth. see Cole, W. Owen.

Sambuddha, Swami Anand, ed. see Rajneesh, Bhagwan Shree.

Sambuddha, Swami Devaraj, ed. see Rajneesh, Bhagwan Shree.

Saminsky, Lazare. Music of the Ghetto & the Bible. LC 74-24220. Repr. of 1934 ed. 16.00 (ISBN 0-404-12833-5). AMS Pr.

Sammon, Sean D. Growing Pains in Ministry. LC 83-9991. 240p. (Orig.). 1983. pap. 8.00 (ISBN 0-89571-016-1). Affirmation.

--Growing Pains in Ministry. LC 83-9991. 240p. 1983. 12.95 (ISBN 0-89571-027-7); study guide, 77p 3.95 (ISBN 0-89571-029-3). Affirmation.

Sammon, Sean D., ed. see Helldorfer, Martin C. & Polcino, Anna.

Sammon, Sean D., et al. Fidelity: Issues of Emotional Living in an Age of Stress for Clergy & Religious. Hart, Joseph L., ed. LC 81-533. 148p. (Orig.). 1981. pap. 5.00 (ISBN 0-89571-011-0). Affirmation.

Sammons, Martha C. A Guide Through Narnia. LC 78-26476. (Wheaton Literary Ser.). 164p. 1979. pap. 3.95 (ISBN 0-87788-325-4). Shaw Pubs.

Samms, Robert L. How to Study the Bible, Pt. I. (Lay Action Ministry Program Ser.). 96p. 1987. pap. 4.95 (ISBN 0-89191-516-8). Cook.

--How to Study the Bible, Pt. II. (Lay Action Ministry Program Ser.). 96p. 1987. pap. 4.95 (ISBN 0-89191-517-6). Cook.

Sampey, R. Estudios sobre el Antiguo Testamento. 226p. 1983. pap. 3.50 (ISBN 0-311-03627-9). Casa Bautista.

Sample, Dorothy E., jt. auth. see O'Brien, Bonnie B.

Sample, Tex. Blue-Collar Ministry. 192p. 1984. pap. 9.95 (ISBN 0-8170-1029-7). Judson.

Sampley, J. Paul. Pauline Partnership in Christ: Christian Community & Commitment in Light of Roman Law. LC 79-8895. 144p. 1980. 2.00 (ISBN 0-8006-0631-0, 1-631). Fortress.

Sampley, J. Paul, jt. auth. see Francis, Fred O.

Sampley, J. Paul, et al. Ephesians, II Colossians, Thessalonians: Pastoral Epistles. LC 77-78652. (Proclamation Commentaries: the New Testament Witness for Preaching). 128p. 1978. pap. 4.95 (ISBN 0-8006-0589-6, 1-589). Fortress.

Sampson, Alden. Studies in Milton & an Essay on Poetry. LC 71-126686. 1970. Repr. of 1913 ed. 24.00 (ISBN 0-404-05555-9). AMS Pr.

Sampson, Gloria. Historic Churches & Temples of Georgia. (Illus.). 144p. 1987. 24.95 (ISBN 0-86554-242-2, MUP-H212). Mercer Univ Pr.

Sampson, H. Grant. The Anglican Tradition in Eighteenth Century Verse. (De Proprietatibus Litterarum, Ser. Practica: No. 33). 1971. pap. text ed. 27.20x (ISBN 90-2791-907-0). Mouton.

Sampson, Tom S. Only by Grace: A Candid Look at the Life of a Minister. Lambert, Herbert, ed. LC 85-29916. 144p. (Orig.). 1986. pap. 9.95 (ISBN 0-8272-2707-8). CBP.

Sampson, William. The Coming of Consolation. (Orig.). 1986. pap. 8.95 (ISBN 0-87061-132-1). Chr Classics.

Samra, Cal. Jesus Put on a Happy Face: The Healing Power of Joy & Humor. LC 85-60257. (Illus.). 234p. (Orig.). 1985. pap. 7.95 (ISBN 0-933453-00-0). Rosejoy Pubns.

--The Joyful Christ: The Healing Power of Humor. 1986. pap. 7.95 (ISBN 0-06-067032-0). Har-Row.

Sams, Earnell, Jr. The Aorist Participle of Antecedent Action. LC 81-67641. 1982. pap. write for info. (ISBN 0-940068-01-X). Doctrine Christ.

--Doctrine on Divine Healing. (Orig.). 1982. pap. write for info. (ISBN 0-940068-02-8). Doctrine Christ.

Sams, Henry W., ed. Autobiography of Brook Farm. 15.25 (ISBN 0-8446-4056-5). Peter Smith.

Samskriti & Franks, Judith. Hatha Yoga Manual II. 176p. plastic comb bdg. 9.95 (ISBN 0-89389-043-X). Himalayan Pubs.

Samskrti & Veda. Hatha Yoga Manual I. 2nd ed. (Illus.). 187p. plastic comb. 9.95 (ISBN 0-89389-053-7). Himalayan Pubs.

Samson Raphael Hirsch Publication Society Staff, tr. see Hirsch, Samson R.

Samuel, D. N., ed. The Evangelical Succession. 144p. 1979. pap. 5.95 (ISBN 0-227-67834-6). Attic Pr.

Samuel, Edith. Your Jewish Lexicon. (Hebrew.). 192p. (Orig.). 1982. 10.00 (ISBN 0-8074-0054-8); pap. 5.95 (ISBN 0-8074-0061-0). UAHC.

Samuel, Geoffrey, tr. see Heissig, Walther.

Samuel, Herbert L. A Century's Changes of Outlook. LC 77-7136. (Hibbert Lectures: 1953). Repr. of 1953 ed. 11.00 (ISBN 0-404-60432-3). AMS Pr.

Samuel, L. The Impossibility of Agnosticism. pap. 0.75 (ISBN 0-87784-125-X). Inter-Varsity.

Samuel, Leith. Share Your Faith. (Contemporary Discussion Ser.). 104p. 1981. pap. 2.95 (ISBN 0-8010-8187-4). Baker Bk.

--There Is an Answer. pap. 2.50 (ISBN 0-87508-469-9). Chr Lit.

Samuel, Maurice. Certain People of the Book. 1977. pap. 7.50 (ISBN 0-8074-0082-3, 388350). UAHC.

--Gentleman & the Jew. LC 77-6666. pap. 5.95x (ISBN 0-87441-264-1). Behrman.

--Harvest in the Desert. LC 82-985. 316p. 1982. Repr. lib. bdg. 27.50x (ISBN 0-313-23354-3, SAHA). Greenwood.

--The World of Sholom Aleichem. LC 86-47697. 344p. 1986. pap. 9.95 (ISBN 0-689-70709-6, 343). Atheneum.

Samuel, Maurice, tr. see Fleg, Edmond.

Samuel, Maurice, tr. see Levin, Shmarya.

Samuel, Rinna. Israel: Promised Land to Modern State. (Illus.). 175p. 1971. Repr. of 1969 ed. 18.50x (ISBN 0-85303-135-5, Pub. by Vallentine Mitchell England). Biblio Dist.

Samuel, Vinay & Sugden, Chris, eds. Sharing Jesus in the "Two Thirds" World. 432p. (Orig.). 1984. pap. 10.95 (ISBN 0-8028-1997-4). Eerdmans.

Samuel, William. The Child Within Us Lives! 412p. 1986. 24.95 (ISBN 0-938747-01-0); pap. 15.95 (ISBN 0-938747-00-2). Mntn Brook Pubns.

Samuelian, Thomas J., ed. see Koghbatsi, Yeznik.

Samuels, Daniel G. Old Testament Truth Sermons by Jesus. pap. 12.50 (ISBN 0-686-34378-6). New Age Min Spiritualist.

--Old Testament Truth Sermons on Jeremiah by Jesus. pap. 5.00 (ISBN 0-686-12713-7). New Age Min Spiritualist.

Samuels, David G. Birth & Youth of Jesus, by Mary, Mother of Jesus. 5.00 (ISBN 0-686-12714-5). New Age Min Spiritualist.

Samuels, Maurice. You Gentiles. pap. 3.00x (ISBN 0-911038-08-6). Noontide.

Samuels, Ruth. Bible Stories for Jewish Children, 2 vols, No. 1. (Illus.). 1958. 7.95x (ISBN 0-87068-356-X). Ktav.

--Bible Stories for Jewish Children, 2 vols, No. 2. (Illus.). 1973. 7.95x (ISBN 0-87068-965-7). Ktav.

--Pathways Through Jewish History. rev ed. (Illus.). 1977. pap. 9.00x (ISBN 0-87068-520-1). Ktav.

Samuels, Victoria, jt. ed. see Peters, Barbarba.

Samuelson, Norbert, jt. ed. see Novak, David.

Samuelson, Norbert, tr. see Daud, Abraham I.

Samuelson, Sue. Christmas: An Annotated Bibliography of Analytical Scholarship. Dundes, Alan, ed. LC 82-48083. (Garland Folklore Bibliographies Ser.). 200p. 1982. lib. bdg. 31.00 (ISBN 0-8240-9263-5). Garland Pub.

Sanadi, Lalita. Mantra Meditation. rev. ed. D'Auri, Laura, ed. (Illus.). 160p. pap. cancelled (ISBN 0-87407-204-2, FP-4). Thor.

Sanborn, Franklin B. Ralph Waldo Emerson. LC 72-7220. Repr. of 1901 ed. lib. bdg. 15.00 (ISBN 0-8414-0262-0). Folcroft.

Sanborn, Franklin B., ed. Genius & Character of Emerson. LC 72-122663. 1971. Repr. of 1885 ed. 27.50x (ISBN 0-8046-1312-5, Pub. by Kennikat). Assoc Faculty Pr.

Sanborn, Patricia F. Existentialism. 192p. 1984. text ed. 22.00x (ISBN 0-8290-1015-7); pap. text ed. 9.95x (ISBN 0-8290-1016-5). Irvington.

Sanchez, Benjamin M. Israel & the Prophecies. pap. 3.10 (ISBN 0-913558-06-0). Educator Pubns.

Sanchez, Jorge, tr. see Smedes, Lewis.

Sanchez, Jose M. Anticlericalism: A Brief History. LC 72-3504. 256p. 1973. text ed. 14.95 (ISBN 0-268-00471-4). U of Notre Dame Pr.

--The Spanish Civil War As a Religious Tragedy. LC 86-40581. 272p. 1987. text ed. 22.95x (ISBN 0-268-01726-3, Dist. by Har-Row). U of Notre Dame Pr.

Sanchez, Julio. The Community of the Holy Spirit: A Movement of Change in a Covent of Nuns in Puerto Rico. 190p. (Orig.). 1984. lib. bdg. 25.25 (ISBN 0-8191-3367-1); pap. text ed. 11.75 (ISBN 0-8191-3368-X). U Pr of Amer.

Sanchez, Pedro. Memories of the Life of the Priest Don Antonio Jose Martinez. De Aragon, Ray J., tr. LC 78-51462. (Span. & Eng.). 1978. 12.00 (ISBN 0-89016-044-9); pap. 6.95 (ISBN 0-89016-045-7). Lightning Tree.

Sanchez, Zayda N., tr. see Cummins, D. Duane.

Sanchez-Perez, J. M. Engrammes of the Universe: Extra-Cerebral Memory, Reincarnation & Demonic Possession. 1980. 8.50 (ISBN 0-682-49474-7). Exposition Pr FL.

Sand, Faith A. The Travels of Faith. LC 85-17751. (Illus.). 152p. (Orig.). 1986. pap. 4.95 (ISBN 0-932727-03-4). Hope Pub Hse.

Sandal, Mohan L. Introduction to the Mimamsa Sutras of Jaimini. LC 73-3821. (Sacred Books of the Hindus: No. 28). Repr. of 1925 ed. 24.50 (ISBN 0-404-57828-4). AMS Pr.

--Philosophical Teachings in the Upanisats. LC 73-3831. (Sacred Books of the Hindus: Extra Vol. 5). Repr. of 1926 ed. 17.00 (ISBN 0-404-57849-7). AMS Pr.

Sandal, Mohan L., tr. see Jaimini.

Sandal, Mohan L., jt. tr. see Vidyarnava, Srisa Chandra.

Sandalgian, Joseph. Histoire documentaire de l'Armenie, 2 Vols. LC 79-175431. 1917. Repr. of 1917 ed. Set. 70.00 (ISBN 0-404-05557-5). AMS Pr.

Sandall, Robert & Wiggins, Arch. The History of the Salvation Army, 6 vols. 2093p. (Orig.). 1979. pap. 10.00 set (ISBN 0-318-04018-2). Vol. 1 (ISBN 0-89216-030-6). Vol. 2 (ISBN 0-89216-031-4). Vol. 3 (ISBN 0-89216-032-2). Vol. 4 (ISBN 0-89216-033-0). Vol. 5 (ISBN 0-89216-034-9). Vol. 6 (ISBN 0-89216-035-7). Salvation Army.

Sanday, William & Headlam, Arthur C. A Critical & Exegetical Commentary on the Epistle to the Romans. Driver, Samuel R. & Plummer, Alfred, eds. (International Critical Commentary Ser.). 568p. 1902. 22.95 (ISBN 0-567-05026-2, Pub. by T & T Clark Ltd UK). Fortress.

Sandberg, Craig. Simple Life Coloring Book. 1983. 2.25 (ISBN 0-87813-519-7). Christian Light.

Sandberg, Jessie R. Preparing Your Children for Greatness. (Joyful Living Ser.). 1987. pap. 1.50 (ISBN 0-912623-05-5). Joyful Woman.

Sandberg, Karl C. At the Crossaroads of Faith & Reason: An Essay on Pierre Bayle. LC 66-18531. pap. 33.80 (ISBN 0-317-51991-3, 2027388). Bks Demand UMI.

Sandberg, Neil C. Jewish Life in Los Angeles: A Window to Tomorrow. LC 86-11025. (Illus.). 224p. 1986. lib. bdg. 17.50 (ISBN 0-8191-5439-3). U Pr of Amer.

Sande, Gene. Bible - Man's Book of Realization. 1981. pap. 2.50 (ISBN 0-87613-095-3). New Age.

Sandeen, Ernest, ed. The Bible & Social Reform. LC 81-9294. (SBL The Bible In American Culture Ser.). 1982. 12.95 (ISBN 0-89130-531-9, 061206, Co-pub. by Fortress Pr). Scholars Pr GA.

Sandeen, Ernest R., ed. The Bible & Social Reform. LC 81-71386. (The Bible in American Culture Ser.). 196p. 1982. 12.95 (ISBN 0-8006-0611-6, 1-611). Fortress.

Sandeen, Ernest R. & Hale, Frederick, eds. American Religion & Philosophy: A Guide to Information Sources. LC 73-17562. (American Studies Information Guide: Vol. 5). 1978. 62.00x (ISBN 0-8103-1262-X). Gale.

Sandell, Mary. Building an Effective Church School. 1986. pap. 10.00 (ISBN 0-8309-0441-7). Herald Hse.

Sander, Emilie T., tr. see Stendahl, Krister.

Sanderlin, David. Putting on the New Self: A Guide to Personal Development & Community Living. 1986. pap. 12.95 (ISBN 0-87061-125-9). Chr Classics.

Sanders, Andrew. Charles Dickens, Resurrectionist. LC 81-21246. 1982. 26.00 (ISBN 0-312-13014-7). St Martin.

Sanders, Bill. Tough Turf. 168p. (Orig.). 1985. pap. 5.95 (ISBN 0-8007-5212-0). Revell.

Sanders, E. P. Jesus & Judaism. LC 84-48806. 448p. 1985. 19.95 (ISBN 0-8006-0743-0, 1-743). Fortress.

--Paul & Palestinian Judaism: A Comparison of Patterns of Religion. LC 76-62612. 648p. 1977. pap. 19.95 (ISBN 0-8006-1899-8, 1-1899). Fortress.

--Paul, the Law & the Jewish People. LC 82-17487. 240p. 1983. pap. 9.95 (ISBN 0-8006-1878-5, 1-1878). Fortress.

Sanders, E. P., ed. Jewish & Christian Self-Definition, Vol. 1: The Shaping of Christianity in the Second & Third Centuries. LC 79-7390. 336p. 1980. 5.00 (ISBN 0-8006-0578-0, 1-578). Fortress.

Sanders, E. P., jt. ed. see Meyer, Ben F.

Sanders, E. P., et al, eds. Jewish & Christian Self-Definition, Vol. 2: Aspects of Judaism in the Greco-Roman Period. LC 79-7390. 450p. 1981. 5.00 (ISBN 0-8006-0660-4, 1-660). Fortress.

Sanders, Frank K., ed. see Kent, Charles F.

Sanders, Henry A. New Testament Manuscripts in the Freer Collection. Repr. of 1918 ed. 37.00 (ISBN 0-384-38809-4). Johnson Repr.

--Old Testament Manuscripts in the Freer Collection. Repr. of 1917 ed. 37.00 (ISBN 0-384-38808-6). Johnson Repr.

Sanders, Henry A., ed. Roman History & Mythology. Repr. of 1910 ed. 37.00 (ISBN 0-384-38804-3). Johnson Repr.

Sanders, J. O. Paul the Leader. LC 83-62737. 192p. 1984. pap. 5.95 (ISBN 0-89109-515-2). NavPress.

Sanders, J. Oswald. Best That I Can Be. 1976. pap. 1.95 (ISBN 9971-83-873-7). OMF Bks.

--Certainties of Christ's Coming. 128p. 1984. pap. 2.95 (ISBN 0-87788-111-1). Shaw Pubs.

--Le Christ Incomparable. Tr. of The Incomparable Christ. (Fr.). 1986. pap. 3.90 (ISBN 0-8297-1344-1). Life Pubs Intl.

--Consider Him. 2nd ed. 1979. pap. 1.50 (ISBN 9971-83-778-1). OMF Bks.

--Effective Faith. Orig. Title: Mighty Faith. 1980. pap. 1.00 (ISBN 9971-83-833-8). OMF Bks.

--Effective Prayer. pap. write for info. (ISBN 0-8024-0781-1). Moody.

--Effective Prayer. 1961. pap. 1.00 (ISBN 9971-83-818-4). OMF Bks.

--Enjoying Intimacy with God. LC 80-21398. 218p. 1980. pap. 5.95 (ISBN 0-8024-2346-9). Moody.

--Holy Spirit & His Gifts. (Contemporary Evangelical Perspectives Ser). kivar 5.95 (ISBN 0-310-32481-5, 6520P). Zondervan.

--In Pursuit of Maturity. 256p. 1986. pap. text ed. 7.95 (ISBN 0-310-32511-0). Zondervan.

--The Incomparable Christ. rev. ed. 256p. 1982. pap. 8.95 (ISBN 0-8024-4081-9). Moody.

--Just Like Us: Twenty-One Character Studies from the Bible. 1985. pap. 6.95 (ISBN 0-8024-6516-1). Moody.

--Pablo, el Lider. Tr. of Paul the Leader. (Span.). 208p. 1986. pap. 3.50 (ISBN 0-8297-0760-3). Life Pubs Intl.

--Paulo, o Lider. Orig. Title: Paul the Leader. (Port.). 1986. write for info. (ISBN 0-8297-0756-5). Life Pubs Intl.

--Prayer Power Unlimited. (Moody Press Electives Ser.). (Orig.). 1984. pap. 3.95 (ISBN 0-8024-6675-3); pap. 2.50 leader's guide (ISBN 0-8024-6676-1). Moody.

--Promised-Land Living. 1984. pap. 5.95 (ISBN 0-8024-0372-7). Moody.

--Satan Is No Myth. LC 74-15358. 1983. pap. 5.95 (ISBN 0-8024-7525-6). Moody.

--Spiritual Leadership. rev. ed. LC 67-14387. (J. Oswald Sanders Ser.). 160p. 1974. pap. 3.95 (ISBN 0-8024-8221-X). Moody.

--Spiritual Leadership. 5th ed. 1986. text ed. 9.95 (ISBN 0-8024-8246-5). Moody.

--Spiritual Maturity. Chao, Samuel & Chao, Lorna, trs. from Eng. (Chinese.). 1983. pap. write for info. (ISBN 0-941598-08-X). Living Spring Pubns.

Sanders, J. Oswald & Gould, Dana. Spiritual Leadership: Leader's Guide. (Orig.). 1987. pap. 4.95 (ISBN 0-8024-8226-0). Moody.

Sanders, Jack T. Ben Sira & Demotic Wisdom. LC 82-21464. (SBL Monograph). 134p. 1983. pap. 19.50 (ISBN 0-89130-586-6). Scholars Pr GA.

--The Jews in Luke-Acts. LC 86-45926. 432p. 1987. pap. 19.95 (ISBN 0-8006-0837-2, 1-1969). Fortress.

Sanders, James. Fun-in-Learning About Chanukah. LC 76-189390. (Illus.). 1972. 3.95 (ISBN 0-8246-0135-1). Jonathan David.

Sanders, James A. Canon & Community: A Guide to Canonical Criticism. LC 83-18483. (Guides to Biblical Scholarship). 96p. 1984. pap. 4.50 (ISBN 0-8006-0468-7, 1-468). Fortress.

--From Sacred Story to Sacred Text: Canon As Paradigm. LC 85-45483. 240p. 1987. 18.95 (ISBN 0-8006-0805-4). Fortress.

--God Has a Story Too: Biblical Sermons in Context. LC 77-15244. 160p. 1979. pap. 6.95 (ISBN 0-8006-1353-8, 1-1353). Fortress.

--Torah & Canon. LC 72-171504. 144p. (Orig.). 1972. pap. 5.95 (ISBN 0-8006-0105-X, 1-105). Fortress.

Sanders, Marjorie L. Getting Away. LC 83-70214. 1984. pap. 5.95 (ISBN 0-8054-7523-0). Broadman.

Sanders, Randolph K. & Malony, H. Newton. Speak up! Christian Assertiveness. LC 84-20806. 118p. (Orig.). 1985. pap. 7.95 (ISBN 0-664-24551-X). Westminster.

--Speak up! Christian Assertiveness. 1986. pap. 2.95 (Pub. by Ballantine-Epiphany). Ballantine.

Sanders, Ronald & Gillon, Edmund V. The Lower East Side: A Guide to Its Jewish Past with Ninety-Nine New Photographs. (Illus.). 1980. pap. 5.95 (ISBN 0-486-23871-7). Dover.

Sanders, Rostelle. When the Working Men Rise & Shine. 1984. 4.95 (ISBN 0-8062-2136-4). Carlton.

Sanders, Stephen. To Him Who Conquers. LC 73-111183. 210p. 1970. 25.00 (ISBN 0-385-06306-7). Fellowship Crown.

Sanders, Thomas G. Protestant Concepts of Church & State. 19.50 (ISBN 0-8446-6185-6). Peter Smith.

--Secular Consciousness & National Conscience: The Church & Political Alternatives in Southern Europe. Spitzer, Manon, ed. LC 77-6457. 144p. 1977. pap. text ed. 6.50 (ISBN 0-910116-90-3). U Field Staff Intl.
Sanderson, J. B., tr. see Hegel, Georg W.
Sanderson, John W. The Fruit of the Spirit. 192p. 1985. pap. 3.95 (ISBN 0-87552-431-1). Presby & Reformed.
Sanderson, Joyce. Why Are You Here Now? 83p. (Orig.). 1981. pap. 6.95 (ISBN 0-942494-10-5). Coleman Pub.
Sanderson, Judith E. An Exodus Scroll from Qumran: 4QpaleoExodm & the Samaritan Tradition. (Harvard Semitic Studies). 378p. 1986. 20.95 (ISBN 1-55540-036-1, 04-04-30). Scholars Pr GA.
Sanderson, Margaret H. Cardinal of Scotland - David Beaton 1494-1546. 324p. 1986. 39.95x (ISBN 0-85976-110-X, Pub. by John Donald Pub UK). Humanities.
Sanderson, Richard N. The Islamic Movement & the Threat to Western Civilization. (Illus.). 141p. 1980. deluxe ed. 67.45x (ISBN 0-930008-59-6). Inst Econ Pol.
--The Islamic Movement & the Threat to Western Civilization, 2 vols. (Illus.). 309p. 1985. Set. 227.50 (ISBN 0-86722-113-5). Inst Econ Finan.
Sandford, Frank W. Art of War for the Christian Soldier. 2nd ed. LC 66-29707. 1966. 4.00 (ISBN 0-910840-12-1). Kingdom.
--Majesty of Snowy Whiteness. 1963. pap. 1.50 (ISBN 0-910840-10-5). Kingdom.
Sandford, Frank W., intro. by. Warrior Songs for the White Cavalry. 4th ed. 1972. 7.50 (ISBN 0-910840-14-8). Kingdom.
Sandford, John & Sandford, Paula. Elijah Task. LC 77-82331. 252p. (Orig.). 1986. pap. 5.95 (ISBN 0-932081-11-8). Victory Hse.
--Healing the Wounded Spirit. LC 85-71640. 510p. 1986. pap. 8.95 (ISBN 0-932081-14-2). Victory Hse.
--Restoring the Christian Family. LC 79-64977. 336p. 1986. pap. 6.95 (ISBN 0-932081-12-6). Victory Hse.
--The Transformation of the Inner Man. LC 82-72007. 432p. 1986. pap. 6.95 (ISBN 0-932081-13-4). Victory Hse.
Sandford, Paula, jt. auth. see Sandford, John.
Sandifer, Kevin. Facts, Baptist History: Sixteen Hundred to Nineteen Eighty. Bryan, Lydia & Gill, Rowland, eds. LC 83-80441. (Illus.). 144p. (Orig.). 1983. pap. 6.50 (ISBN 0-910653-01-1). Archival Servs.
--Religious Archives, a Complete Technical Look for the Layman. Gill, Rowland P., ed. 96p. (Orig.). 1985. pap. text ed. 5.50 (ISBN 0-910653-03-8, 8101-C). Archival Servs.
Sandifer, Kevin W. A Fellowship of Love, the Heritage of First Baptist Church of Blanchard, Louisiana. Tippett, Donald C., ed. (Illus.). 1986. lib. bdg. 2.50 (ISBN 0-910653-02-X). Archival Servs.
--The Importance of the Ark of Covenant in Christianity. Sibley, J. Ashley, Jr., ed. 112p. (Orig.). 1986. pap. 6.25 (ISBN 0-910653-13-5, 8101M). Archival Servs.
--Introduction to Religious Archival Science. Gill, Rowland P., ed. 16p. (Orig.). 1985. students guide 3.50 (ISBN 0-910653-05-4, 8101-F). Archival Servs.
--A Layman's Look at Starting a Religious Archives. Hall, Renee, et al, eds. 48p. (Orig.). 1982. pap. text ed. 4.50 (ISBN 0-910653-00-3, 8101-A). Archival Servs.
Sandin, Robert T. The Search for Excellence: The Christian College in an Age of Educational Competition. LC 82-12482. vi, 242p. 1982. text ed. 13.50x (ISBN 0-86554-037-3, MUP-H39). Mercer Univ Pr.
Sandison, jt. auth. see Oxtoby.
Sandle, Marjorie, tr. see D'Epinay, Christian L.
Sandler, Lucy F. The Peterborough Psalter in Brussels & Other Fenland Manuscripts. (Illus.). 1974. 49.00x (ISBN 0-19-921005-5). Oxford U Pr.
--The Psalter of Robert de Lisle. (Harvey Miller Publication Ser.). (Illus.). 1983. 105.00x (ISBN 0-19-921028-4). Oxford U Pr.
Sandmel, Samuel. Enjoyment of Scripture: The Law, the Prophets, & the Writings. (Illus.). 1972. pap. 8.95 (ISBN 0-19-501783-8). Oxford U Pr.
--The Hebrew Scriptures: An Introduction to Their Literature & Religious Ideas. 1978. pap. 16.95x (ISBN 0-19-502369-2). Oxford U Pr.
--A Jewish Understanding of the New Testament. 1974. 11.95x (ISBN 0-87068-102-8); pap. 9.95x (ISBN 0-87068-262-8). Ktav.
--A Jewish Understanding of the New Testament. 356p. pap. 9.95 (ISBN 0-686-95179-4). ADL.
--Judaism & Christian Beginnings. pap. 11.95x (ISBN 0-19-502282-3). Oxford U Pr.
--A Little Book on Religion: For People Who Are Not Religious. LC 75-1831. 1975. pap. ~~3.95 cancelled (ISBN 0-89012-002-1).~~ Anima Pubns.
--Philo of Alexandria: An Introduction. 1979. pap. 9.95 (ISBN 0-19-502515-6). Oxford U Pr.
--The Several Israels. 1971. 12.50x. Ktav.
--We Jews & Jesus. LC 65-11529. 1965. pap. 7.95 (ISBN 0-19-501676-9). Oxford U Pr.
Sandmel, Samuel, jt. auth. see Crenshaw, James L.
Sandover, Oswald D. The Catholic Church, the Peace of the World & the Foreign Policy of the United States. (Illus.). 117p. 1983. 99.45x (ISBN 0-86722-055-4). Inst Econ Pol.
Sandoz, Ellis, ed. Eric Voegelin's Thought: A Critical Appraisal. LC 81-43591. xv, 208p. 1982. 24.75 (ISBN 0-8223-0465-1). Duke.
Sandoz, Luis Mojica see Mojica Sandoz, Luis.
Sandri-White, Alex. Guide to Religious Education. 7.95x (ISBN 0-685-22753-7). Aurea.
Sands, P. C. Literary Genius of the New Testament. 1932. 20.00 (ISBN 0-8274-2953-3). R West.
Sands, Percy C. Literary Genius of the New Testament. Repr. of 1932 ed. lib. bdg. 22.50x (ISBN 0-8371-4328-4, SANT). Greenwood.
--Literary Genius of the Old Testament. LC 75-35756. 1975. Repr. of 1924 ed. lib. bdg. 27.50 (ISBN 0-8414-7646-2). Folcroft.
Sandstrom, Alan R. Traditional Curing & Crop Fertility Rituals Among Otomi Indians of the Sierra de Puebla, Mexico: The Lopez Manuscripts. (Occasional Papers & Monographs: No. 3). (Illus.). vi, 104p. 1981. 4.00 (ISBN 0-9605982-0-0). W H Mathers Mus.
Sandstrom, Alan R. & Sandstrom, Pamela E. Traditional Papermaking & Paper Cult Figures of Mexico. LC 85-40947. (Illus.). 336p. 1986. 24.95 (ISBN 0-8061-1972-1). U of Okla Pr.
Sandstrom, David H. Landmarks of the Spirit: One Man's Journey. 192p. (Orig.). 1984. pap. 11.95 (ISBN 0-8298-0726-8). Pilgrim NY.
Sandstrom, Pamela E., jt. auth. see Sandstrom, Alan R.
Sandweiss, Samuel H. Sai Baba: The Holy Man & the Psychiatrist. LC 75-28784. 1975. 10.25 (ISBN 0-9600958-0-2); pap. 6.30 (ISBN 0-9600958-1-0). Birth Day.
--Spirit & the Mind. 1985. pap. 6.30 (ISBN 0-9600958-9-6). Birth Day.
Sandys, Edwin. Sermons of Edwin Sandys D. D. Repr. of 1841 ed. 41.00 (ISBN 0-384-53200-4). Johnson Repr.
Sandys, Edwina & Morton, James P. Women of the Bible: Sculpture. Piche, Thomas, Jr., ed. LC 86-83188. (Illus.). 24p. (Orig.). 1986. pap. text ed. write for info. (ISBN 0-914407-07-4). Everson Mus.
Sandys, William. Christmas Carols, Ancient & Modern. LC 76-30740. 1977. Repr. of 1833 ed. lib. bdg. 32.50 (ISBN 0-8414-7779-5). Folcroft.
--Christmas Carols: Ancient & Modern. 69.95 (ISBN 0-87968-866-1). Gordon Pr.
--Christmastide: Its History, Festivities & Carols. 69.95 (ISBN 0-87968-867-X). Gordon Pr.
Sanford, Agnes. Behold Your God. 5.95 (ISBN 0-910924-35-X); pap. 4.50 (ISBN 0-910924-63-5). Macalester.
--Healing Gifts of the Spirit. 1983. pap. 2.75 (ISBN 0-515-07621-X). Jove Pubns.
--Healing Light. pap. 4.50 (ISBN 0-910924-37-6). pocketsize o.p. 2.50 (ISBN 0-910924-52-X). Macalester.
--Healing Power of the Bible. 224p. 1984. pap. 2.50 (ISBN 0-515-07104-8). Jove Pubns.
--The Healing Power of the Bible. 1983. pap. 2.50 (ISBN 0-8007-8475-8, Spire Bks). Revell.
--The Healing Power of the Bible. LC 83-48999. 1984. pap. 6.95 (ISBN 0-06-067053-3, RD 520, HarpR). Har-Row.
--The Healing Touch of God. (Epiphany Ser.). 224p. 1983. pap. 2.50 (ISBN 0-345-30661-9). Ballantine.
--Sealed Orders: The Autobiography of a Christian Mystic. LC 72-76592. 312p. 1972. (Pub. by Logos); pap. 7.95 (ISBN 0-88270-048-0). Bridge Pub.
Sanford, Agness. The Healing Gifts of the Spirit. LC 83-48998. 240p. 1984. pap. 6.95 (ISBN 0-06-067052-5, RD 519, HarpR). Har-Row.
Sanford, Charles B. The Religious Life of Thomas Jefferson. LC 83-21649. 246p. 1984. 13.95x (ISBN 0-8139-0996-1). U Pr of Va.
Sanford, James H. Zen-Man Ikkyu. LC 81-5724. (Harvard Studies in World Religions). 1981. 18.00 (ISBN 0-89130-499-1, 030002); pap. 13.50 (ISBN 0-89130-500-9). Scholars Pr GA.
Sanford, John. The Color of the Air: Scenes from the Life of an American Jew, Vol. 1. 305p. (Orig.). 1985. 20.00 (ISBN 0-87685-644-X); pap. 12.50 (ISBN 0-87685-643-1). Black Sparrow.
--The Waters of Darkness: Scenes from the Life of an American Jew, Vol. 2. 294p. (Orig.). 1986. 20.00 (ISBN 0-87685-672-5); signed cloth 30.00 (ISBN 0-87685-673-3); pap. 12.50 (ISBN 0-87685-671-7). Black Sparrow.
Sanford, John A. Dreams: God's Forgotten Language. (Crossroad Paperback Ser.). 224p. 1982. pap. 9.95 (ISBN 0-8245-0456-9). Crossroad NY.
--Evil: The Shadow Side of Reality. 176p. 1981. 10.95 (ISBN 0-8245-0037-7); pap. 9.95 (ISBN 0-8245-0526-3). Crossroad NY.
--Invisible Partners. LC 79-56604. 139p. (Orig.). 1980. pap. 6.95 (ISBN 0-8091-2277-4). Paulist Pr.
--King Saul, the Tragic Hero: A Study in Individuation. LC 84-61023. 160p. (Orig.). 1985. pap. 7.95 (ISBN 0-8091-2658-3). Paulist Pr.
--Kingdom Within: A Study of the Inner Meaning of Jesus' Sayings. LC 77-105548. 1970. Har-Row.
--The Man Who Lost His Shadow. LC 82-62414. 1983. 6.95 (ISBN 0-8091-0337-0). Paulist Pr.
--The Man Who Wrestled with God: Light from the Old Testament on the Psychology of Individuation. LC 80-84829. 128p. 1981. pap. 7.95 (ISBN 0-8091-2367-3). Paulist Pr.
--Ministry Burnout. 144p. 1982. 5.95 (ISBN 0-8091-2465-3). Paulist Pr.
Sanford, John A., intro. by. Fritz Kunkel: Selected Writings. 400p. 1984. pap. 12.95 (ISBN 0-8091-2558-7). Paulist Pr.
Sanford, Ruth. Do You Feel Alone in the Spirit? 1978. pap. 1.95 (ISBN 0-89283-056-5). Servant.
--The First Years Together. 140p. (Orig.). 1983. pap. 5.95 (ISBN 0-89283-134-0). Servant.
--More Than Survivors: God's Way of Restoration for Women. 200p. (Orig.). 1981. pap. 4.95 (ISBN 0-89283-102-2). Servant.
Sanger, C. Bert. The Art of Travel by Soul: An Out of Body Experience. (Illus.). 150p. 1986. 15.00 (ISBN 0-9615362-0-9). Popular Pubns.
Sanghavi, Vilas. Jaina Community. 2nd ed. 455p. 1980. 29.95 (ISBN 0-317-12346-7, Pub. by Popular Pubns India). Asia Bk Corp.
Sangster, Margaret E. Fairest Girlhood. 224p. 1987. pap. 5.95 (ISBN 0-310-34471-9). Zondervan.
Sangster, Paul. A History of the Free Churches. (Illus.). 224p. 1984. 29.95 (ISBN 0-434-41330-5, Pub. by W Heinemann Ltd). David & Charles.
Sangster, W. E. The Craft of Sermon Illustration. (Notable Books on Preaching). 1973. pap. 7.95 (ISBN 0-8010-8214-5). Baker Bk.
--Teach Me to Pray. 1959. pap. 1.50x (ISBN 0-8358-0125-X). Upper Room.
Sankalia, H. D. The Ramayana in Historical Perspective. 1983. 18.50x (ISBN 0-8364-0997-3, Pub. by Macmillan India). South Asia Bks.
Sankaracarya. Saudaryalahari or, Flood of Beauty. Brown, William N., ed. LC 57-9072. (Oriental Ser: No. 43). (Illus.). 1958. 16.50x (ISBN 0-674-78990-3). Harvard U Pr.
Sankaracharya. Bhagavad Gita with Commentary of Sri Sankaracharya. Sastry, Alladi M., tr. 1979. 16.00 (ISBN 0-89744-188-5). Auromere.
Sankaracharya, Sri. Dakshinamurti Stotra. Sastri, Alladi M., tr. 1979. 12.00 (ISBN 0-89744-189-3). Auromere.
Sankey, Ira D. My Life & the Story of the Gospel Hymns & of Sacred Songs & Solos. LC 72-1682. Repr. of 1907 ed. 32.50 (ISBN 0-404-08332-3). AMS Pr.
Sankey, Ira D., et al. Gospel Hyms, 6 vols, No. 1-6. facsimile ed. LC 70-171076. (Earlier American Music Ser.: No. 5). 512p. 1972. Repr. of 1895 ed. lib. bdg. 37.50 (ISBN 0-306-77305-8). Da Capo.
Sanks, T. Howland. Authority in the Church: A Study in Changing Paradigms. LC 74-16565. (American Academy of Religion. Dissertation Ser.: No. 2). Repr. of 1974 ed. 37.10 (ISBN 0-8357-9564-0, 2017555). Bks Demand UMI.
Sanneh, Lamin. West African Christianity: The Religious Impact. 304p. (Orig.). 1983. pap. 11.95 (ISBN 0-88344-703-7). Orbis Bks.
Sannella, Lee. The Kundalini Experience: Psychosis or Transcendence. rev. ed. (Illus.). 160p. 1987. pap. 9.95 (ISBN 0-941255-29-8). Integral Pub.
Sanner, A. E & Harper, A. F. Exploring Christian Education. 504p. 1978. 15.95 (ISBN 0-8341-0494-6). Beacon Hill.
Sanner, A. Elwood & Greathouse, William M. Beacon Bible Expositions, Vol. 2: Mark. 1978. 8.95 (ISBN 0-8341-0313-3). Beacon Hill.
Sanning, Walter N. The Dissolution of Eastern European Jewry: An Analysis of the Six Million Myth. 1983. lib. bdg. 79.95 (ISBN 0-87700-463-3). Revisionist Pr.
--The Dissolution of Eastern European Jewry. (Illus.). 239p. 1986. pap. 8.00 (ISBN 0-317-53010-0). Noontide.
Sano, Emily J., jt. auth. see Nishikawa, Kyotaro.
Sano, Roy I. From Every Nation Without Number: Racial & Ethnic Diversity in United Methodism. LC 81-20610. (Into Our Third Century Ser.). (Orig.). 1982. pap. 3.95 (ISBN 0-687-13642-3). Abingdon.
Sansoucie, Larry A. The Ecumenical Lectionary. 111p. (Orig.). 1986. pap. 9.95 (ISBN 0-937505-04-8). Glyndwr Resc.
Sant Bani Ashram School Children, tr. Book of Jonah. LC 84-50924. (Illus.). 1984. pap. 6.95 (ISBN 0-89142-044-4). Sant Bani Ash.
Santa, Ana Julio De see De Santa Ana, Julio.
Santa, George F. A Modern Study in the Book of Proverbs: Charles Bridges Classic Revised for Today's Reader. LC 78-7667. (Illus.). 1978. kiver bdg. 17.95 (ISBN 0-915134-27-6); incl. study guide (ISBN 0-915134-49-7). Mott Media.
Santa-Maria, Maria L. Growth Through Meditation & Journal Writing: A Jungian Perspective on Christian Spirituality. 1983. pap. 8.95 (ISBN 0-8091-2570-6). Paulist Pr.
Santas, Gerasimos X. Socrates. 1982. pap. 10.95 (ISBN 0-7100-9327-6). Methuen Inc.
Santayana, George. The Idea of Christ in the Gospels: Or, God in Man, a Critical Essay. LC 75-3338. Repr. of 1946 ed. 30.00 (ISBN 0-404-59341-0). AMS Pr.
--Interpretations of Poetry & Religion. 11.25 (ISBN 0-8446-0893-9). Peter Smith.
--The Intimate Analysis of a Lost Life, 2 vols. (Illus.). 285p. 1986. 147.55 (ISBN 0-86650-196-7). Gloucester Art.
--The Life of Reason: Reason in Religion, Vol. 3. 288p. 1982. pap. 5.95 (ISBN 0-486-24253-6). Dover.
--Reason in Religion. 1983. 14.50 (ISBN 0-8446-5927-4). Peter Smith.
--Scepticism & Animal Faith. 14.75 (ISBN 0-8446-2863-8). Peter Smith.
--Scepticism & Animal Faith: Introduction to a System of Philosophy. 1955. pap. text ed. 6.00 (ISBN 0-486-20236-4). Dover.
Santer, M., jt. ed. see Wiles, Maurice.
Santideva. The Path of Light. LC 78-70117. Repr. of 1909 ed. 20.00 (ISBN 0-404-17374-8). AMS Pr.
Santideva, compiled by. Siksha-Samuccaya, a Compendium of Buddhist Doctrine. Bendall, Cecil & Rouse, W. D., trs. LC 78-70114. Repr. of 1922 ed. 33.50 (ISBN 0-404-17368-3). AMS Pr.
Santillana, Giorgio. The Crime of Galileo. LC 55-7400. (Midway Reprint Ser). (Illus.). xvi, 339p. 1955. pap. 14.00x (ISBN 0-226-73481-1). U of Chicago Pr.
Santillana, Giorgio De see Santillana, Giorgio.
Santis, Zerlina De see De Santis, Zerlina.
Sant Keshavadas, Satguru see Keshavadas, Satguru S.
Santmire, H. Paul. South African Testament: From Personal Encounter to Theological Challenge. 266p. (Orig.). 1987. pap. 7.95 (ISBN 0-8028-0266-4). Eerdmans.
--The Travail of Nature: The Ambiguous Ecological Promise of Christian Theology. LC 84-47934. 288p. 1985. 16.95 (ISBN 0-8006-1806-8, 1-1806). Fortress.
Santo, Charles De see De Santo, Charles.
Santo, Lori, ed. Jews & Hispanics in America: The Meeting of Two Historic Cultures. 31p. 1982. pap. 2.50 (ISBN 0-87495-061-9). Am Jewish Comm.
Santoni, Ronald E., ed. Religious Language & the Problem of Religious Knowledge. LC 68-27352. Repr. of 1968 ed. 95.50 (ISBN 0-8357-9238-2, 2017640). Bks Demand UMI.
Sanua, Victor D., ed. Fields of Offerings: Studies in Honor of Raphael Patai. LC 82-21072. (Illus.). 352p. 1983. 28.50 (ISBN 0-8386-3171-1). Fairleigh Dickinson.
Sao Paulo, Brazil Mission Team. Steps into the Mission Field. 1978. 5.95 (ISBN 0-88027-019-5). Firm Foun Pub.
Saperstein, Marc. Decoding the Rabbis: A Thirteenth-Century Commentary on the Aggadah. LC 80-13166. (Judaic Monographs: No. 3). 298p. 1980. text ed. 20.00x (ISBN 0-674-19445-4). Harvard U Pr.
Saphir, Adolph. The Divine Unity of Scripture. LC 84-9642. (Adolph Saphir Study Ser.). 376p. 1984. pap. 10.95 (ISBN 0-8254-3747-4). Kregel.
--Epistle to the Hebrews, 2 vols. in 1. LC 83-4390. 924p. 1983. 21.95 (ISBN 0-8254-3728-8). Kregel.
--Our Lord's Pattern for Prayer. LC 84-9710. (Adolph Saphir Study Ser.). 432p. 1984. pap. 11.95 (ISBN 0-8254-3748-2). Kregel.
Sapone, Edith. To You Mom. (Illus.). 1961. 3.00 (ISBN 0-8198-0162-3); pap. 2.00 (ISBN 0-8198-0163-1). Dghtrs St Paul.
Saporetti, C. Assur 14446: La famiglia "A". (Cybernetica Mesopotamica, Data Sets: Cuneiform Texts Ser.: Vol. 1). 140p. 1979. pap. 12.00x soft only (ISBN 0-89003-036-7). Undena Pubns.
Sapp, Gary L., ed. Handbook of Moral Development. 296p. 1986. pap. 14.95 (ISBN 0-89135-054-3). Religious Educ.
Sapp, Stephen. Sexuality, the Bible & Science. LC 76-62617. pap. 38.00 (2026976). Bks Demand UMI.

Sappington, Roger. The Brethren in the New Nation. (Illus.). 1976. 13.95 (ISBN 0-87178-113-1). Brethren.

Sappington, Roger E. The Brethren in Industrial America. 512p. 1985. 24.95 (ISBN 0-87178-111-5). Brethren.

Saradananda, Swami. Ramakrishna, Sri: The Great Master, Pts. 1 & 2. rev. ed. Swami Jagadananda, tr. (Illus.). 1980. Pt. 1, 563p. pap. 8.50x ea. (ISBN 0-87481-495-2). Pt. 2 (ISBN 0-87481-496-0). Vedanta Pr.

Saradeshananda. The Mother as I Saw Her. Dey, J. N., tr. from Bengali. 247p. 1985. pap. 4.95 (ISBN 0-87481-530-4, Pub. by Ramakrishna Math Madras India). Vedanta Pr.

Sarasohn, Lisa, ed. see Desai, Yogi A.

Saraswati, Baidyanath. Brahmanic Ritual Traditions. Malik, S. C., ed. LC 78-901135. (Illus.). 1977. 15.00 (ISBN 0-89684-478-1). Orient Bk Dist.

Saraydarian, Haroutiun. Christ, Avatar of Sacrificial Love. LC 74-11760. 1974. 9.00 (ISBN 0-911794-38-7); pap. 8.00 (ISBN 0-911794-39-5). Aqua Educ.

--Science of Meditation. LC 77-158995. 1971. 11.00 (ISBN 0-911794-29-8); pap. 9.00 (ISBN 0-911794-30-1). Aqua Educ.

Saraydarian, Haroutiun, tr. Bhagavad Gita. LC 74-11759. 1974. 9.00 (ISBN 0-911794-36-0); pap. 7.00 (ISBN 0-911794-37-9). Aqua Educ.

Saraydarian, Torkom. Challenge for Discipleship. LC 86-70417. 25.00 (ISBN 0-911794-50-6); pap. 20.00 (ISBN 0-911794-51-4). Aqua Educ.

--A Daily Discipline of Worship. 1986. pap. 1.00 (ISBN 0-911794-52-2). Aqua Educ.

--Dialogue with Christ. LC 77-86722. 1979. pap. 4.00 (ISBN 0-911794-42-5). Aqua Educ.

--Five Great Mantrams of the New Age. LC 73-39431. 1975. pap. 2.00 (ISBN 0-911794-19-0). Aqua Educ.

--Flame of Beauty, Culture, Love, Joy. LC 80-67681. 1980. pap. 10.00 (ISBN 0-911794-02-6). Aqua Educ.

--Hierarchy & the Plan. LC 75-39432. 1975. pap. 2.00 (ISBN 0-911794-20-4). Aqua Educ.

--I Was. LC 77-86723. 1981. pap. 5.00 (ISBN 0-911794-43-3). Aqua Educ.

--Legend of Shamballa. LC 76-12895. 1976. 12.00 (ISBN 0-911794-40-9); pap. 10.00 (ISBN 0-911794-41-7). Aqua Educ.

--Psyche & Psychism, 2 vols. LC 80-67684. 1981. Set. 60.00 (ISBN 0-911794-06-9). Aqua Educ.

--Questioning Traveller & Karma. 1979. pap. 2.50 (ISBN 0-911794-45-X). Aqua Educ.

--Talks on Agni. LC 86-722414. 1987. pap. price not set (ISBN 0-911794-56-5). Aqua Educ.

--Torchbearers. 1981. pap. 2.50 (ISBN 0-911794-49-2). Aqua Educ.

--Triangles of Fire. LC 77-82155. 1977. pap. 3.00 (ISBN 0-911794-35-2). Aqua Educ.

--The Unusual Court. LC 77-86720. 1979. pap. 4.00 (ISBN 0-911794-44-1). Aqua Educ.

--Woman - Torch of the Future. LC 80-67680. 1980. pap. 8.00 (ISBN 0-911794-00-X). Aqua Educ.

Sardar, Ziauddin. The Future of Muslim Civilisation. 224p. 1979. 25.00 (ISBN 0-85664-800-0, Pub. by Croom Helm Ltd). Methuen Inc.

--Islam: Outline of a Classification Scheme. 81p. 1979. 17.50 (ISBN 0-85157-285-5, Pub. by Bingley England). Shoe String.

Sardar, Ziauddin, ed. The Touch of Midas: Science, Values & the Environment in Islam & the West. LC 83-22262. 253p. 1984. 38.50 (ISBN 0-7190-0974-X, Pub. by Manchester Univ Pr). Longwood Pub Group.

Sarfeh, Rustam, tr. see Abd Allah Ansarti, Khwajih.

Sargeant, Phillip W. Witches & Warlocks. 1976. 20.00x (ISBN 0-7158-1028-6). Charles River Bks.

Sargeant, Winthrop. The Bhagavad Gita. Chapple, Christopher, ed. (SUNY Ser. in Cultural Perspectives). 777p. 1984. 44.50x (ISBN 0-87395-831-4); pap. 14.95x (ISBN 0-87395-830-6). State U NY Pr.

Sargent, Daniel. Four Independents. facs. ed. LC 68-55856. (Essay Index Reprint Ser.). 1935. 18.00 (ISBN 0-8369-0850-3). Ayer Co Pubs.

--Thomas More. facs. ed. LC 71-119963. (Select Bibliographies Reprint Ser). 1933. 19.00 (ISBN 0-8369-5406-8). Ayer Co Pubs.

Sargent, John. Life & Letters of Henry Martyn. 496p. 1985. pap. 6.95 (ISBN 0-85151-468-5). Banner of Truth.

Sargent, Lucy. Tincraft for Christmas. (Illus.). 1969. 7.95 (ISBN 0-688-02638-9); pap. 5.95 (ISBN 0-688-07638-6). Morrow.

Sargent, Michael & Hogg, James. Nicholas Love: The Myrrour of the Blessed LYF of Jesu Christ, 2 Vols. (Analecta Cartusiana Ser.: No. 91). (Orig.). 1987. pap. 50.00 (ISBN 3-7052-0159-X, Pub. by Salzburg Studies). Longwood Pub Group.

Sargent, Michael, jt. auth. see Hogg, James.

Sargent, Michael G. James Grenehalgh As Textual Critic. Hogg, James, ed. (Analecta Cartusiana Ser.: No. 85/1&2). 589p. (Orig.). 1984. pap. 50.00 (ISBN 3-7052-0142-5, Pub. by Salzburg Studies). Longwood Pub Group.

Sargent, Richard B. & Benson, John E. Computers in the Church: Practical Assistance in Making the Computer Decision. (Administration Series for Churches). 112p. (Orig.). 1986. pap. 10.95 (ISBN 0-8066-2231-8, 10-1625). Augsburg.

Sargent, Virginia A., jt. ed. see McCay, Gracie R.

Sarito, Ma Deva, ed. see Rajneesh, Bhagwan Shree.

Sarkar, Benoy K. Folk-Element in Hindu Culture: A Contribution to Socio-Religious Studies in Hindu Folk Institutions. LC 72-907790. 332p. 1972. Repr. of 1917 ed. 24.00 (ISBN 0-89684-387-4). Orient Bk Dist.

--The Positive Background of Hindu Sociology, 2 vols. LC 73-3807. (Sacred Books of the Hindus: Nos. 16 & 25). Repr. of 1926 ed. Set. 74.50 (ISBN 0-404-57839-X). AMS Pr.

--The Positive Background of Hindu Sociology: Introduction to Hindu Positivism. LC 74-17338. (Sacred Books of the Hindus: 32). Repr. of 1937 ed. 74.50 (ISBN 0-404-57850-0). AMS Pr.

Sarkar, H. Studies in Early Buddhist Architecture of India. (Illus.). 1966. 16.00x. Coronet Bks.

Sarkar, J. N. Hindu-Muslim Relations in Medieval Bengal. 130p. 1986. 15.00x (ISBN 0-8364-1806-9, Pub. by Chanakya India). South Asia Bks.

Sarkar, R. M. Regional Cults & Rural Traditions: An Interacting Pattern of Divinity & Humanity in Rural Bengal. (Illus.). xx, 351p. 1986. text ed. 50.00x (ISBN 81-210-0095-5, Pub. by Inter India Pubns N Delhi). Apt Bks.

Sarma, D. S. The Master & the Disciple. pap. 1.00 (ISBN 0-87481-466-9). Vedanta Pr.

--A Primer of Hinduism. 170p. 1987. pap. 3.25 (ISBN 0-87481-532-0, Pub. by Ramakrishna Math Madras India). Vedanta Pr.

Sarma, Sreeramula R., tr. see Hillebrandt, Alfred.

Sarna, Jonathan D. The American Jewish Experience. 336p. 1986. text ed. 35.00x (ISBN 0-8419-0934-2); pap. text ed. 19.50x (ISBN 0-8419-0935-0). Holmes & Meier.

--Jacksonian Jew: The Two Worlds of Mordecai Noah. LC 79-24379. 245p. 1981. text ed. 35.00x (ISBN 0-8419-0567-3). Holmes & Meier.

Sarna, Jonathan D., ed. People Walk on Their Heads: Moses Weinberger's Jews & Judaism in New York. 137p. 1982. text ed. 24.50x (ISBN 0-8419-0707-2); pap. text ed. 12.95x (ISBN 0-8419-0731-5). Holmes & Meier.

Sarna, Jonathan D., ed. see Antin, Mary.

Sarna, Jonathan D., ed. see Heine, Heinrich.

Sarna, Jonathan D., ed. see Nyburg, Sidney L.

Sarna, Jonathan D., et al. Jews & the Founding of the Republic. LC 85-40513. (American History in Documents Ser.). (Illus.). 240p. (Orig.). 1985. pap. text ed. 14.50x (ISBN 0-910129-44-4). Wiener Pub Inc.

Sarna, Lazar, jt. ed. see Bovarsky, Abraham.

Sarna, Nahum M. Exploring Exodus: The Heritage of Biblical Israel. LC 85-18445. 288p. 1987. pap. 8.95 (ISBN 0-8052-0830-5). Schocken.

--Understanding Genesis: The Heritage of Biblical Israel. LC 66-23626. 1970. pap. 7.50 (ISBN 0-8052-0253-6). Schocken.

Sarno, Ronald, jt. auth. see Badia, Leonard F.

Sarno, Ronald A. Using Media in Religious Education. LC 86-33844. 230p. (Orig.). 1987. pap. 13.95 (ISBN 0-89135-058-6). Religious Educ.

Saroja, G. V. Tilak & Sankara on Bhagvad Gita. 200p. 1985. text ed. 20.00x (ISBN 0-86590-571-1, Pub. by Sterling Pubs India). Apt Bks.

Sarolea, Charles. Cardinal Newman. 174p. 1980. Repr. of 1908 ed. lib. bdg. 30.00 (ISBN 0-89987-759-1). Darby Bks.

Sarre, Alicia, tr. see Fritz, Patricia.

Sarre, Winifred. Perce Judd: Man of Peace. (Illus.). 176p. 1983. pap. 10.00 (ISBN 0-8309-0377-1). Herald Hse.

Sartain, E. M. Jajal Al-Din Al-Suywti, 2 vols. Incl. Vol. 1. Biography & Background. 230p. 44.50 (ISBN 0-521-20547-6); Vol. 2. Al-Tahadduth bini'mat allah. 370p. 52.50 (ISBN 0-521-20546-8). LC 74-82226. (Oriental Publications Ser.: Nos. 23 & 24). 1975. Set. 86.00 (ISBN 0-521-20633-2). Cambridge U Pr.

Sartakov, S. Siberian Stories. 607p. 1979. 9.45 (ISBN 0-8285-1621-9, Pub. by Progress Pubs USSR). Imported Pubns.

Sartelle, John P. Infant Baptism: What Christian Parents Should Know. 32p. 1985. pap. 1.95 (ISBN 0-87552-429-X); shrinkwrapped package of 12 19.50 (ISBN 0-87552-438-9). Presby & Reformed.

Sartorio, Enrico C. Social & Religious Life of Italians in the United States. LC 73-13520. 1974. Repr. of 1918 ed. 19.50x (ISBN 0-678-01364-0). Kelley.

Sartre, Jean-Paul. Anti-Semite & Jew. LC 48-9237. 1965. pap. 4.95 (ISBN 0-8052-0102-5). Schocken.

--Reflexions Sur la Question Juive. 1962. pap. 3.95 (ISBN 0-685-11523-2). French & Eur.

Sarvananda, Swami, tr. Aitareyopanisad. (Sanskrit & English). pap. 1.00 (ISBN 0-87481-463-4). Vedanta Pr.

--Isavasyopanisad. (Sanskrit & English). pap. 1.00 (ISBN 0-87481-456-1). Vedanta Pr.

--Kathopanisad. (Sanskrit & English). pap. 1.00 (ISBN 0-87481-458-8). Vedanta Pr.

--Kenopanisad. (Sanskrit & Eng.). pap. 1.00 (ISBN 0-87481-457-X). Vedanta Pr.

--Mundakopanisad. (Sanskrit & English). pap. 1.00 (ISBN 0-87481-460-X). Vedanta Pr.

--Prasnopanisad. (Sanskrit & English). pap. 1.00 (ISBN 0-87481-459-6). Vedanta Pr.

Sarvin, Margaret M. Hope for Families. 6.95 (ISBN 0-8215-9902-X). Sadlier.

Sarwar, H. G. Philosophy of the Quran. 4.50 (ISBN 0-686-18604-4). Kazi Pubns.

--Philosophy of the Qur'an. 1969. 7.25x (ISBN 0-87902-187-X). Orientalia.

Sarwar, Shaikh M. Religious Teachings for Children, Bk. 1. 44p. pap. 5.00 (ISBN 0-941724-03-4). Islamic Seminary.

--Religious Teachings for Children, Bk. 2. 66p. pap. 5.00 (ISBN 0-941724-04-2). Islamic Seminary.

--Religious Teachings for Children, Bk. 3. 80p. pap. 5.00 (ISBN 0-941724-05-0). Islamic Seminary.

--Religious Teachings for Children, Bk. 4. 72p. 1981. pap. 5.00 (ISBN 0-941724-06-9). Islamic Seminary.

Sasaki, Ruth F., jt. auth. see Miura, Isshu.

Sasaki, Ruth F., et al, trs. A Man of Zen: The Recorded Sayings of Layman P'ang. LC 77-157273. (Illus.). 124p. 1976. 6.95 (ISBN 0-8348-0057-8); pap. 4.95 (ISBN 0-8348-0121-3). Weatherhill.

Sasaki, Sokei-an. Zen Eye. Farkas, Mary, ed. LC 84-48129. 136p. (Orig.). Date not set. pap. 10.95 (ISBN 0-87011-696-7). Kodansha.

Sasek, Lawrence A. Literary Temper of the English Puritans. Repr. of 1961 ed. lib. bdg. 22.50x (ISBN 0-8371-2333-X, SAEP). Greenwood.

Saso, Michael & Chappell, David W., eds. Buddhist & Taoist Studies Number One. (Asian Studies at Hawaii: No. 18). (Illus.). 174p. 1977. pap. text ed. 10.50x (ISBN 0-8248-0420-1). UH Pr.

Saso, Michael R. Taoism & the Rite of Cosmic Renewal. (Illus.). 1972. pap. 4.00x (ISBN 0-87422-011-4). Wash St U Pr.

Sass, Lorna J. Christmas Feasts from History. Atcheson, Jean, ed. LC 81-68835. (Great American Cooking Schools Ser.). (Illus.). 84p. 1981. pap. 5.95 (ISBN 0-941034-01-1). I Chalmers.

Sasse, Herman. We Confess: The Sacraments. (We Confess Ser.: Vol. II). 160p. 1985. 11.95 (ISBN 0-570-03982-7, 12-2899). Concordia.

--We Confess, Vol. 1: Jesus Christ. Nagel, Norman, tr. 1984. pap. 10.95 (ISBN 0-570-03941-X, 12-2877). Concordia.

Sasser, Nancy L. Around the Advent Wreath: Devotions for Families Using the Advent Wreath. 40p. (Orig.). 1984. pap. 2.95 (ISBN 0-8066-2074-9, 23-1064). Augsburg.

Sassoon, David S. A History of the Jews in Baghdad. LC 77-87645. (Illus.). 264p. Repr. of 1949 ed. 34.00 (ISBN 0-404-16427-7). AMS Pr.

Sassoon, George. The Kabbalah Decoded. Dale, Rodney, ed. 240p. 1978. pap. 9.95 (ISBN 0-7156-1289-1). US Games Syst.

Sassoon, George, tr. see Dale, Rodney.

Sastri, A. Mahadeva. The Vedanta Doctrine of Sri Sankaracharya. 245p. 1986. Repr. of 1899 ed. lib. bdg. 16.95 (ISBN 81-7030-029-0, Pub. by Sri Satguru Pubns India). Orient Bk Dist.

Sastri, Alladi M., tr. see Sankaracharya, Sri.

Sastri, S. Subrahmanya. Samgraha-Cudamani of Govinda. 4.75 (ISBN 0-8356-7354-5). Theos Pub Hse.

Sastry, Alladi M., tr. Taitiriya Upanishad. 93p. 1980. 36.00 (ISBN 0-89744-145-1, Pub. by Samata Bks India). Auromere.

Sastry, Alladi M., tr. see Sankaracharya.

Satchidanada, Sri Swam i. Beyond Words. Alexander, Lester, ed. LC 76-29896. (Illus.). 190p. 1977. pap. 5.95 (ISBN 0-03-016911-9). Integral Yoga Pubns.

Satchidanada, Sri Swami. Peace is Within Our Reach. LC 85-14384. 96p. (Orig.). 1985. pap. 4.95 (ISBN 0-932040-29-2). Integral Yoga Pubns.

Satchidananda, S., ed. Living Yoga. (Psychic Studies). 336p. 1977. 30.95 (ISBN 0-677-05230-8). Gordon & Breach.

Satchidananda, Sri Swami. Kailash Journal: Pilgrimage into the Himalayas. LC 84-25296. 1984. pap. 6.95 (ISBN 0-932040-25-X). Integral Yoga Pubns.

Satchidandanda, Swami. To Know Yourself: The Essential Teachings of Swami Satchidananda. LC 77-80901. 1978. pap. 7.95 (ISBN 0-385-12613-1, Anch). Doubleday.

Satir, Virginia. Meditations & Inspirations. LC 85-13302. 96p. (Orig.). 1985. pap. 5.95 (ISBN 0-89087-421-2). Celestial Arts.

Satisa Chandra Vidyabhusana, tr. see Gotama.

Sato, Chiaki. Inspirational Lines. 1986. 5.95 (ISBN 0-533-06789-8). Vantage.

Sato, Koji. The Zen Life: Daily Life in a Zen Monastery. Victoria, Ryojun, tr. LC 79-185602. (Illus.). 194p. 1983. pap. 7.50 (ISBN 0-8348-1517-6). Weatherhill.

Satprakashananda, Swami. The Goal & the Way: The Vedantic Approach to Life's Problems. LC 77-75279. 302p. 1977. 12.50 (ISBN 0-916356-56-6). Vedanta Soc St Louis.

--Hinduism & Christianity: Jesus Christ & His Teachings in the Light of Vedanta. LC 75-32598. 196p. 1975. 8.95 (ISBN 0-916356-53-1). Vedanta Soc St Louis.

--Meditation: Its Process, Practice, & Culmination. LC 76-15722. 264p. 1976. 10.00 (ISBN 0-916356-55-8). Vedanta Soc St Louis.

--Methods of Knowledge According to Advaita Vedanta. 366p. 1975. Repr. of 1965 ed. 10.00 (ISBN 0-87481-154-6). Vedanta Pr.

--Sri Ramakrishna's Life & Message in the Present Age: With the Author's Reminiscences of Holy Mother & Some Direct Disciples. LC 75-46386. 208p. 1976. 6.00 (ISBN 0-916356-54-X). Vedanta Soc St Louis.

--Swami Vivekananda's Contribution to the Present Age. (Illus.). 249p. 1978. 9.50 (ISBN 0-916356-58-2, 77-91628). Vedanta Soc St Louis.

Satprem. Mother or the New Species. LC 83-4370. Orig. Title: Mere Ou L'espece Nouvelle. 530p. 1983. pap. 8.95 (ISBN 0-938710-03-6). Inst Evolutionary.

Satre, Lowell J., ed. see Melanchthon, Philipp.

Satsvarupa dasa Goswami. The Life Story of His Divine Grace A. C. Bhaktivedanta Swami Prabhupada. 32p. 1984. saddlestitch 3.50 (ISBN 0-89647-019-9). Bala Bks.

--A Lifetime in Preparation: Srila Prabhupada-lilamrta, Vol. 1. (Illus.). 357p. 1980. 12.95 (ISBN 0-686-71685-X). Bhaktivedanta.

Sattar, M. A. It Removes the Misconceptions about Caliphs' Caliphate. 416p. 1985. pap. 19.00 (ISBN 0-941724-36-0). Islamic Seminary.

Sattenfield, Charles L. Let's Grow & Make Disciples! 92p. (Orig.). 1980. 2.75 (ISBN 0-88027-080-2). Firm Foun Pub.

Satter, Emma G., tr. see Nicholas Of Cusa.

Satterlee, Allen. Notable Quotables (A Compendium of Quotes by Salvation Army Authors) 1985. 15.95 (ISBN 0-86544-028-X). Salv Army Suppl South.

Sattler, Gary. God's Glory, Neighbor's Good: Francke's Biography & Sermons. 272p. 1982. pap. 8.95 (ISBN 0-910452-50-4). Covenant.

Sattler, Helen. Bible Puzzle Trails. (Pelican Activity Ser.). 32p. 1977. pap. 0.89 (ISBN 0-8010-7900-4). Baker Bk.

Sattler, Helen R. The Smallest Witch. LC 81-2202. (Illus.). 32p. 1982. 6.75 (ISBN 0-525-66747-4). Dandelion Pr.

Saturday Evening Post Editors. The Saturday Evening Post Christmas Book. LC 76-24034. (Illus.). 160p. 1976. 14.95 (ISBN 0-89387-001-3, Co-Pub by Sat Eve Post). Curtis Pub Co.

--The Saturday Evening Post Christmas Stories. LC 80-67058. (Illus.). 144p. 1980. 14.95 (ISBN 0-89387-046-3, Co-Pub by Sat Eve Post). Curtis Pub Co.

Satyaprakash. Buddhism: A Select Bibliography. 1986. Repr. of 1976 ed. 28.50x (ISBN 0-8364-1828-X, Pub. by Indian Doc Serv India). South Asia Bks.

--Christianity: A Select Bibliography. 1986. 18.50x (ISBN 0-8364-1829-8, Pub. by Indian Doc Serv India). South Asia Bks.

--Jainism: A Select Bibliography. 1984. 12.50x (ISBN 0-8364-1224-9, Pub. by Indian Doc Serv India). South Asia Bks.

--Muslims in India: A Bibliography of Their Religious, Socio-Economic & Political Literature. 1986. 34.00x (ISBN 0-8364-1558-2, Pub. by Indian Doc Serv India). South Asia Bks.

Satyaprakash, ed. Buddhism: A Selection Bibliography. 1977. 11.00 (ISBN 0-88386-956-X). South Asia Bks.

--Hinduism: A Select Bibliography. 1984. 46.50x (ISBN 0-8364-1121-8, Pub. by Indian Doc Serv India). South Asia Bks.

Satyavrata, Siddhantalankar. Glimpses of the Vedas. 140p. 1980. 9.95 (ISBN 0-940500-12-4, Pub. by Milind Pubns India). Asia Bk Corp.

Saucy, Richard L. Is Bible Reliable, Bk. 2. Wong, Ernest, tr. (Basic Doctrine Ser.). (Chinese.). 1985. pap. write for info. (ISBN 0-941598-28-4). Living Spring Pubns.

Saucy, Robert L. The Church in God's Program. LC 70-175496. (Handbook of Bible Doctrine). 1972. pap. 7.95 (ISBN 0-8024-1544-X). Moody.

Saud, M. A. Concepts of Islam. pap. 6.95 (ISBN 0-317-01600-8). Kazi Pubns.

Sauer, E. E., tr. see Koehler, J.

Sauer, Erich. La Aurora de la Redencion del Mundo. Orig. Title: The Dawn of World Redemption. (Span.). 320p. 1967. pap. 7.95 (ISBN 0-8254-1652-3). Kregel.

--De Eternidad a Eternidad. Orig. Title: From Eternity to Eternity. (Span.). 1977. pap. 4.95 (ISBN 0-8254-1653-1). Kregel.

--The King of the Earth. 256p. 1979. pap. 10.95 (ISBN 0-85364-009-2). Attic Pr.

--El Triunfo del Crucificado. Orig. Title: The Triumph of the Crucified. (Span.). 288p. 1980. pap. 6.50 (ISBN 0-8254-1655-8). Kregel.

Sauer, Val J., Jr. The Eschatology Handbook: The Bible Speaks to Us about Endtimes. (Illus.). 180p. (Orig.). 1981. pap. 3.99 (ISBN 0-8042-0066-1). John Knox.

Sauerman, Thomas H. & Schomaker, Linda, eds. Starting a Church-Sponsored Weekday Preschool Program: A Manual of Guidance. LC 80-14160. 128p. (Orig.). 1980. pap. 6.95 (ISBN 0-8006-1377-5, 1-1377). Fortress.

Saulcy, L. F. Dictionnaire les Antiquites Bibligues. Migne, J. P., ed. (Troisieme et Derniere Encyclopedie Theologique Ser.: Vol. 45). (Fr.). 516p. Repr. of 1859 ed. lib. bdg. 66.50x (ISBN 0-89241-319-0). Caratzas.

Saulex, William H. The Romance of the Hebrew Language. 243p. 1983. Repr. of 1913 ed. lib. bdg. 30.00 (ISBN 0-8482-6303-0). Norwood Edns.

Saulez, William H. The Romance of the Hebrew Language. 1979. Repr. of 1913 ed. lib. bdg. 27.50 (ISBN 0-8414-8013-3). Folcroft.

Saulson, Scott B. Institutionalized Language Planning: Documents & Analysis of the Revival of Hebrew. (Contributions to the Sociology of Language Ser.: No. 23). 1979. text ed. 24.80x (ISBN 90-279-7567-1). Mouton.

Saumur, Lucien. The Humanist Evangel. LC 81-85573. 128p. 1982. 16.95 (ISBN 0-87975-172-X); pap. 13.95 (ISBN 0-87975-114-2). Prometheus Bks.

Saunders, E. Dale. Buddhism in Japan: With an Outline of Its Origins in India. LC 77-24539. 1977. Repr. of 1964 ed. lib. bdg. 25.75x (ISBN 0-8371-9746-5, SABJ). Greenwood.

--Mudra: A Study of Symbolic Gestures in Japanese Buddhist Sculpture. (Bollingen Ser.: Vol. 58). (Illus.). 1960. 37.00x (ISBN 0-691-09796-8). Princeton U Pr.

Saunders, Ernest W. Searching the Scriptures: A History of the Society of Biblical Literature 1880-1980. LC 82-10818. (Society of Biblical Literature - Biblical Scholarship in North America Ser.). 15.00 (ISBN 0-89130-591-2, 06-11-08). Scholars Pr GA.

--Thessalonians, Philippians, & Philemon One & Two. Hayes, John, ed. (Knox Preaching Guides Ser.). 1983. pap. 4.95. John Knox.

Saunders, Ernest W. & Craddock, Fred B. Epiphany. Achtemeier, Elizabeth, et al, eds. LC 79-7377. (Proclamation 2: Aids for Interpreting the Lessons of the Church Year, Series B). 64p. 1981. pap. 3.75 (ISBN 0-8006-4069-1, 1-4069). Fortress.

Saunders, J. J. A History of Medieval Islam. (Illus.). 1978. pap. 9.95x (ISBN 0-7100-0050-2). Methuen Inc.

Saunders, K. J. Story of Buddhism. 69.95 (ISBN 0-8490-1129-9). Gordon Pr.

Saunders, Kenneth J. Epochs in Buddhist History; the Haskell Lectures, 1921. LC 78-70118. Repr. of 1924 ed. 32.00 (ISBN 0-404-17375-6). AMS Pr.

--Gotama Buddha: A Biography. LC 78-70119. Repr. of 1922 ed. 18.00 (ISBN 0-404-17376-4). AMS Pr.

Saunders, Kenneth J., ed. The Heart of Buddhism: Being an Anthology of Buddhist Verse. LC 78-70120. Repr. of 1915 ed. 17.00 (ISBN 0-404-17377-2). AMS Pr.

Saunders, Landon B. The Power of Receiving. (Twentieth Century Sermons Ser.). 1979. 11.95 (ISBN 0-89112-312-1, Bibl Res Pr). Abilene Christ U.

Saunders, T. Bailey, tr. see Schopenhauer, Arthur.

Saunders, Tao T. Dragons, Gods & Spirits from Chinese Mythology. (World Mythologies Ser.). (Illus.). 132p. 1983. 16.95 (ISBN 0-8052-3799-2). Schocken.

Sauneron, Serge. The Priests of Ancient Egypt. LC 59-10792. (Illus.). 192p. 1980. pap. 3.50 (ISBN 0-394-17410-0, B433, BC). Grove.

Saurat, D. Milton, Man & Thinker. LC 76-121151. (Studies in Milton, No. 22). 1970. Repr. of 1925 ed. lib. bdg. 49.95x (ISBN 0-8383-1093-1). Haskell.

Saurat, Denis. Literature & Occult Traditions. LC 68-759. (Studies in Comparative Literature, No. 35). 1969. Repr. of 1930 ed. lib. bdg. 49.95x (ISBN 0-8383-0617-9). Haskell.

--Literature & the Occult Tradition. Bolton, D., tr. LC 65-27133. 1930. Repr. 23.00x (ISBN 0-8046-0405-3, Pub. by Kennikat). Assoc Faculty Pr.

--Milton: Man & Thinker. LC 73-153352. Tr. of La Pensee De Milton. Repr. of 1925 ed. 24.50 (ISBN 0-404-05565-6). AMS Pr.

Saussaye, P. Chantepie De La see De La Saussaye, P. Chantepie.

Sautter, Cynthia D. Irish Dance & Spirituality: Relating Folkdance & Faith. Adams, Doug, ed. (Orig.). 1986. pap. text ed. 3.00 (ISBN 0-941500-39-X). Sharing Co.

Saux, Henri Le see Le Saux, Henri.

Savacool, John K., ed. see Desroche, Henri.

Savacool, John K., ed. & tr. see Desroche, Henri.

Savage, Alma H. Dogsled Apostles. facs. ed. LC 68-55857. (Essay Index Reprint Ser). 1942. 18.00 (ISBN 0-8369-0851-1). Ayer Co Pubs.

Savage, D. S. Mysticism & Aldous Huxley. LC 77-23247. 1947. lib. bdg. 12.50 (ISBN 0-8414-7805-8). Folcroft.

Savage, Robert C. Pocket Praise. (Pocket Ser.). 176p. 1985. pap. 2.95 (ISBN 0-8423-4931-6). Tyndale.

--Pocket Prayers: Seven Hundred & Seventy-Seven Bible Ways to Pray. 1982. pap. 2.95 (ISBN 0-8423-4849-2). Tyndale.

Savage, Thomas G. And Now a Word from Our Creator. LC 72-1370. 1972. 5.95 (ISBN 0-8294-0213-6). Loyola.

Savalan, Karen O. Suicide. 248p. 1982. 10.00 (ISBN 0-86690-210-4, 2363-01). Am Fed Astrologers.

Savary, Lou, jt. auth. see Scheing, Theresa.

Savary, Louis M. Psychological Themes in the Golden Epistle of William Saint-Thierry to the Carthusians of Mont-Dieu. Hogg, James, ed. (Analecta Cartusiana Ser.: No. 8). 198p. (Orig.). 1973. pap. 25.00 (ISBN 3-7052-0009-7, Pub by Salzburg Studies). Longwood Pub Group.

Savary, Louis M. & Berne, Patricia H. Prayerways: For Those Who Feel Discouraged or Distraught, Frightened or Frustrated, Angry or Anxious, Powerless or Purposeless, Over-Extended or Under-Appreciated, Burned Out or Just Plain Worn Out. LC 80-7737. 176p. 1984. pap. 7.95 (ISBN 0-06-067064-9, RD 526, HarpR). Har-Row.

Savary, Louis M. & Scheihing, Theresa O. Our Treasured Heritage: Teaching Christian Meditation to Children. LC 81-7818. 176p. 1981. 9.95 (ISBN 0-8245-0078-4). Crossroad NY.

Savary, Louis M., et al. Dreams & Spiritual Growth: A Christian Approach to Dreamwork. LC 84-60566. 241p. pap. 9.95 (ISBN 0-8091-2629-X). Paulist Pr.

Savas, Savas J. The Treasury of Orthodox Hymnology: The Triodion. 1983. pap. 4.95 (ISBN 0-937032-32-8). Light&Life Pub Co MN.

Savelle, Jerry. Energizing Your Faith. 64p. 1984. pap. 2.25 (ISBN 0-89274-285-2, HH-285). Harrison Hse.

--Fruits of Righteousness. 32p. (Orig.). 1980. pap. 1.95 (ISBN 0-89274-069-8). Harrison Hse.

--If Satan Can't Steal Your Joy, He Can't Have Your Goods. 160p. 1983. pap. 3.95 (ISBN 0-89274-262-3). Harrison Hse.

--Living in Divine Prosperity. 256p. 1983. pap. 4.95 (ISBN 0-89274-247-X). Harrison Hse.

--Man's Crown of Glory. 96p. (Orig.). 1983. pap. 2.75 (ISBN 0-89274-169-4, HH-169). Harrison Hse.

--A Right Mental Attitude. 138p. (Orig.). 1981. pap. 3.25 (ISBN 0-89274-159-7). Harrison Hse.

--Sharing Jesus Effectively. 125p. (Orig.). 1982. pap. 3.95 (ISBN 0-89274-251-8). Harrison Hse.

--Sowing in Famine. 32p. (Orig.). 1982. pap. 1.50 (ISBN 0-686-83911-0). Harrison Hse.

--Spirit of Might. 77p. (Orig.). 1982. pap. 2.50 (ISBN 0-89274-242-9, HH-242). Harrison Hse.

Save-Soderbergh, Torgny, ed. Temples & Tombs of Ancient Nubia. LC 86-50517. (Illus.). 1987. 29.95 (ISBN 0-500-01392-6). Thames Hudson.

Savoy, Gene. Jamil: The Child Christ. LC 73-92360. (Sacred Teachings of Light Ser.: Codex I). 118p. 1976. text ed. 25.00 (ISBN 0-936202-00-9). Intl Comm Christ.

--The Lost Gospel of Jesus: The Hidden Teachings of Christ. authorized millennium ed. LC 78-71277. (The Sacred Teachings of Light, Codex VIII Ser.). (Illus.). xv, 91p. 1984. text ed. 39.50 (ISBN 0-936202-08-4). Intl Comm Christ.

--The Millennium Edition of the Decoded New Testament: Origins & History of the Paradosis or Secret Tradition of the Oral Law Called the Gospel, with Commentary on the Canonical New Testament, Apocrypha, Pseudepigrapha, Old Testament, Dead Sea Scrolls, Ancient Fragments, & Other Religious Texts. Revised ed. LC 83-80523. (The Sacred Teachings of Light, Codex II Ser.). Orig. Title: The Decoded New Testament. (Illus.). 207p. 1983. text ed. 39.50 (ISBN 0-936202-06-8). Intl Comm Christ.

--The Millennium Edition of the Essaei Document: Secrets of an Eternal Race. Revised ed. LC 83-83221. Orig. Title: The Essaei Document. (Illus.). xii, 140p. 1983. text ed. 39.50 (ISBN 0-936202-07-6). Intl Comm Christ.

--The Miracle of the Second Advent: The Emerging New Christianity. LC 84-81232. (Illus.). 68p. 1984. text ed. 14.50 (ISBN 0-936202-04-1). Intl Comm Christ.

Savran, George. Quoted Direct Speech. (Studies in Biblical Literature). Date not set. price not set. Ind U Pr.

Sawar, G. Muhammad the Holy Prophet. pap. 14.50 (ISBN 0-686-18432-7). Kazi Pubns.

Saward, John. Perfect Fools. 1980. text ed. 29.95x (ISBN 0-19-213230-X). Oxford U Pr.

Sawatsky, Rodney, jt. ed. see Quebedeaux, Richard.

Sawatsky, Walter. Soviet Evangelicals: Since World War II. LC 81-94121. 560p. 1981. 19.95x (ISBN 0-8361-1238-5); pap. 14.95x (ISBN 0-8361-1239-3). Herald Pr.

Sawicki, Marianne. Faith & Sexism: Guidelines for Religious Educators. 112p. 1979. pap. 4.95 (ISBN 0-8164-0105-5, HarpR). Har-Row.

Sawin, Margaret M. Family Enrichment with Family Clusters. 1979. pap. 6.95 (ISBN 0-8170-0830-6). Judson.

Sawyer, David. R. Work of the Church: Getting the Job Done in Boards & Committees. 128p. 1987. pap. 6.95 (ISBN 0-8170-1116-1). Judson.

Sawyer, Jane. Why Stay Married? (Outreach Ser.). 1982. pap. 1.25 (ISBN 0-8163-0443-2). Pacific Pr Pub Assn.

Sawyer, John F. Isaiah, Vol. I, Chs. 1-32. LC 84-22098. (The Daily Study Bible Ser. Old Testament). 280p. 1984. 14.95 (ISBN 0-664-21812-1); pap. 7.95 (ISBN 0-664-24579-X). Westminster.

--A Modern Introduction to Biblical Hebrew. (Orig.). 1976. pap. 14.95x (ISBN 0-85362-159-4, Oriel). Methuen Inc.

--Prophecy & Prophets of the Old Testament. 1987. pap. 8.95. Oxford U Pr.

--Semantics in Biblical Research: New Methods of Defining Hebrew Words for Salvation. LC 72-75901. (Studies in Biblical Theology, Second Ser.: No. 24). 1972. pap. text ed. 12.00x (ISBN 0-8401-3074-0). A R Allenson.

Sawyer, Kieran. Confirming Faith. LC 82-71984. (Illus.). 208p. (Orig.). 1982. pap. text ed. 9.75 directors manual (ISBN 0-87793-251-4). Ave Maria.

--Confirming Faith: Participant Book. LC 82-71984. (Illus.). 96p. (Orig.). 1982. pap. text ed. 3.75 (ISBN 0-87793-252-2). Ave Maria.

--Developing Faith. LC 78-72942. (Illus.). 152p. 1978. pap. text ed. 5.95 (ISBN 0-87793-164-X). Ave Maria.

--The Jesus Difference: And Other Youth Ministry Activities. LC 86-72571. 168p. (Orig.). 1987. spiral binding 8.95 (ISBN 0-87793-353-7). Ave Maria.

Sawyer, Michael E., compiled by. A Bibliographical Index of Five English Mystics: Richard Rolle, Julian of Norwich, The Author of the Cloud of Unknowing, Walter Hilton, Margery Kempe. LC 73-110788. 1978. 10.00 (ISBN 0-931222-09-5). Pitts Theolog.

Sawyer, Peter, ed. Domesday Book: A Reassessment. 224p. 1985. 49.95 (ISBN 0-7131-6440-9). E Arnold.

Sawyer, W. C. Teutonic Legends in the Nibelungen Lied & the Nibelungen Ring. 1976. lib. bdg. 59.95 (ISBN 0-8490-2736-5). Gordon Pr.

Sawyers, Lindell, ed. Faith & Families. 208p. (Orig.). 1986. pap. 12.95 (ISBN 0-664-24038-0). Westminster.

Saxby, Trevor J. Pilgrims of a Common Life. LC 86-27043. 208p. (Orig.). 1987. pap. 17.95 (ISBN 0-8361-3426-5). Herald Pr.

Saxena, K. P. Muslim Law. 4th ed. 1306p. 1963. 105.00x (Pub. by Eastern Bk India). State Mutual Bk.

Saxton, et al, eds. The Changing Family: Views from Theology & Social Sciences in the Light of the Aspostolic Exhortation "Familiaris Consortio". 224p. 1984. 12.95 (ISBN 0-8294-0458-9). Loyola.

Say, Lauren E., et al. Youth Ministries Ideas Two. (Orig.). 1985. pap. 6.00 (ISBN 0-8309-0427-1). Herald Hse.

Sayama, Mike. Samadhi: Self Development in Zen, Swordsmanship, & Psychotherapy. (Transpersonal & Humanistic Psychology). 147p. 1985. 34.50x (ISBN 0-88706-146-X); pap. 10.95 (ISBN 0-88706-147-8). State U NY Pr.

Sayce, A. H., ed. Records of the Past: Being English Translations of the Ancient Monuments of Egypt & Western Asia, 6 vols. in 2. LC 72-83175. Repr. of 1888 ed. Set. 71.00 (ISBN 0-405-08918-X); 35.75 ea. Vol. 1 (ISBN 0-405-08919-8). Vol. 2 (ISBN 0-405-08922-8). Ayer Co Pubs.

Sayce, Archibald H. The Religions of Ancient Egypt & Babylonia. LC 77-27223. (Gifford Lectures: 1902). Repr. of 1903 ed. 46.50 (ISBN 0-404-60457-9). AMS Pr.

Sayer, Elisabeth. Be Ye Also Ready. LC 80-82065. (Orig.). 1980. pap. text ed. 3.50 (ISBN 0-932050-07-7). New Puritan.

Sayer, George. Jack: C. S. Lewis & His Times. LC 84-48778. (Illus.). 416p. 1985. 25.95 (ISBN 0-06-067072-X, HarpR). Har-Row.

Sayers, Dorothy L. The Man Born to Be King. 343p. 1983. 13.95 (ISBN 0-575-00366-9, Pub. by Gollancz England). David & Charles.

--Mind of the Maker. Repr. of 1941 ed. lib. bdg. 22.50x (ISBN 0-8371-3372-6, SAMM). Greenwood.

Sayers, Jane E. Papal Government & England During the Pontificate of Honorius III (1216-1227) LC 84-1853. (Cambridge Studies in Medieval Life & Thought: 3rd Ser., Vol. 21). 1985. 49.50 (ISBN 0-521-25911-8). Cambridge U Pr.

Sayers, Stanley. Lord Went with Them. pap. 2.50 (ISBN 0-89315-143-2). Lambert Bk.

Sayers, Stanley E. Drink from the Deeper Wells. 7.50 (ISBN 0-89225-079-8). Gospel Advocate.

--The Nature of Things to Come. 1972. 7.95 (ISBN 0-88027-013-6). Firm Foun Pub.

Sayers, William T. Body, Soul & Blood: Recovering the Human in Medicine. LC 79-56194. 112p. 1980. pap. 5.95 (ISBN 0-935718-00-1). Asclepiad.

Sayili, Aydin. The Observatory in Islam. Cohen, I. Bernard, ed. LC 80-2144. (Development of Science Ser.). (Illus.). 1981. lib. bdg. 45.00x (ISBN 0-405-13951-9). Ayer Co Pubs.

Sayler, Gwendolyn B. Have the Promises Failed: A Literary Analysis of 2 Baruch. LC 83-16336. (SBL Dissertation Ser.). 180p. 15.75 (ISBN 0-89130-651-X, 060172); pap. 10.50 (ISBN 0-89130-781-8). Scholars Pr GA.

Sayler, Mary H. Why Are You Home, Dad? 1983. 4.95 (ISBN 0-8054-4276-6, 4242-76). Broadman.

Saylor, Dennis. And You Visited Me. LC 79-88403. 1979. pap. 7.95 (ISBN 0-933350-21-X). Morse Pr.

Saypol, Judyth & Wikler, Madeline. My Very Own Haggadah. Rev. ed. LC 83-6. (Illus.). 32p. pap. text ed. 2.95 (ISBN 0-930494-23-7). Kar Ben.

Saypol, Judyth & Wikler, Madeline, illus. My Very Own Simchat Torah. (Illus.). 24p. 1981. pap. 2.95 (ISBN 0-930494-11-3). Kar Ben.

Saypol, Judyth R. & Wikler, Madeline. Come Let Us Welcome Shabbat. LC 83-25638. (Illus.). 32p. 1978. pap. 2.95 (ISBN 0-930494-04-0). Kar Ben.

--My Very Own Chanukah Book. LC 77-23682. (Illus.). 32p. 1977. pap. 2.95 (ISBN 0-930494-03-2). Kar-Ben.

--My Very Own Megillah. (Illus.). 32p. 1977. pap. 2.95 (ISBN 0-930494-01-6). Kar Ben.

--My Very Own Sukkot Book. LC 83-26738. (Illus.). 40p. 1980. pap. 2.95 (ISBN 0-930494-09-1). Kar Ben.

--My Very Own Yom Kippur Book. (Illus.). 32p. 1978. pap. 2.95 (ISBN 0-930494-05-9). Kar Ben.

Sayre, John L. & Hamburger, Roberta, eds. Tools for Theological Research. rev. 7th ed. LC 85-11979. 120p. (Orig.). 1985. pap. 5.00x (ISBN 0-912832-22-3). Seminary Pr.

Scaer, David. Getting into the Story of Concord. 1978. pap. 3.95 (ISBN 0-570-03768-9, 12-2703). Concordia.

Scaglione, Aldo. The Liberal Arts & the Jesuit College System. LC 86-17507. (Paperback Ser.: No. 6). (Illus.). v, 229p. 1986. 44.00x (ISBN 0-915027-76-3); pap. 20.00x (ISBN 0-915027-77-1). Benjamins North Am.

Scales, John L., ed. see Koll, Elsie.

Scalf, Cherie & Waters, Kenneth. Dating & Relating. 160p. 1982. pap. 7.95 (ISBN 0-8499-2890-7). Word Bks.

Scally, John, jt. ed. see Kakonis, Tom E.

Scammon, John H. Proverbs: Good Advice for Good Living. LC 78-24505. 1979. pap. 3.95 (ISBN 0-8170-0819-5). Judson.

Scanlan, J. F., tr. see Maritain, Jacques.

Scanlan, J. P., jt. ed. see De George, R. T.

Scanlan, Michael. Inner Healing. LC 74-81901. 96p. (Orig.). 1974. pap. 3.95 (ISBN 0-8091-1846-7). Paulist Pr.

--Let the Fire Fall. 180p. 1986. pap. 6.95 (ISBN 0-89283-296-7). Servant.

--The Power in Penance. 64p. 1972. pap. 0.95 (ISBN 0-87793-092-9). Ave Maria.

Scanlan, Michael & Cirner, Randall J. Deliverance from Evil Spirits: A Weapon for Spiritual Warfare. 125p. (Orig.). 1980. pap. 4.95 (ISBN 0-89283-091-3). Servant.

Scanlan, Michael & Shields, Ann T. And Their Eyes Were Opened. 1976. pap. 3.95 (ISBN 0-89283-035-2). Servant.

Scanlan, Michael, ed. see Kraljevic, Sveosar.

Scantlebury, R. E., tr. see Constant, Gustave L.

Scanzoni, Letha & Mollenkott, Virginia R. Is the Homosexual My Neighbor? Another Christian View. LC 77-20445. 176p. 1980. pap. 8.95 (ISBN 0-06-067076-2, RD 337, HarpR). Har-Row.

Scanzoni, Letha D. Sexuality. LC 83-27375. (Choices: Guides for Today's Woman: Vol. 8). 114p. (Orig.). 1984. pap. 6.95 (ISBN 0-664-24548-X). Westminster.

Scarborough, Lee R. With Christ after the Lost. rev. ed. Head, E. D., ed. 1953. 12.95 (ISBN 0-8054-6203-1). Broadman.

Scarborough, Peggy. Hallelujah Anyway, Tim. 1976. pap. 3.95 (ISBN 0-87148-405-6). Pathway Pr.

--The Treasures of Age. (International Correspondence Program Ser.). (Orig.). 1985. pap. text ed. 6.95 (ISBN 0-87148-856-6). Pathway Pr.

Scarisbrick, J. J. Henry VIII. LC 68-10995. (English Monarchs Series). (Illus.). 1968. pap. 8.95 (ISBN 0-520-01130-9, CAL195). U of Cal Pr.

--The Reformation & the English People. 214p. 1986. pap. text ed. 12.95x (ISBN 0-631-14755-1). Basil Blackwell.

Scarlett, William, ed. see Brooks, Phillips.

Scarpaci, Jean, ed. The Interaction of Italians & Jews in America. 1974. 9.95 (ISBN 0-934675-07-4). Am Italian.

Scazzero, Peter, jt. auth. see Sterk, Andrea.

Scentouri Staff. Catering Service Potpourri for Centerpieces, Etc. 16p. 1985. pap. text ed. 3.75 (ISBN 0-318-04421-8, Pub. by Scentouri). Prosperity & Profits.

Schaaf, James L., tr. see Aland, Kurt.

Schaaf, James L., tr. see Brecht, Martin.

Schaal, John H. Feed My Sheep. 1972. pap. 1.95 (ISBN 0-8010-7958-6). Baker Bk.

Schaap, James C. CRC Family Portrait: Sketches of Ordinary Christians in a 125-Year-Old Church. LC 82-22625. 287p. (Orig.). 1983. pap. 4.95 (ISBN 0-933140-60-6). CRC Pubns.

Schaar, Claes. Critical Studies in Cynewulf Group. LC 67-30824. (Beowulf & the Literature of the Anglo Saxons Ser., No. 2). 1969. Repr. of 1949 ed. lib. bdg. 75.00x (ISBN 0-8383-0740-X). Haskell.

Schaberg, Jane. The Father, the Son & the Holy Spirit: An Investigation of the Origin & Meaning of the Triadic Phrase in Matt 28: 19b. LC 81-14466. (SBL Dissertation Ser.). 1982. pap. 18.00 (ISBN 0-89130-543-2, 060161). Scholars Pr GA.

--The Illegitimacy of Jesus: A Feminist Theological Interpretation. 240p. 1985. 16.95 (ISBN 0-86683-972-0, HarpR). Har-Row.

Schach, Paul, tr. from Old Norse. The Saga of Tristram & Isond. LC 73-76351. (Illus.). xxiv, 148p. 1973. 14.95x (ISBN 0-8032-0832-4); pap. 3.95x (ISBN 0-8032-5847-X, BB 608, Bison). U of Nebr Pr.

Schacher, James A. Conversational Bible Studies. (Contemporary Discussion Ser). 112p. 1975. 1.65 (ISBN 0-8010-8054-1). Baker Bk.

Schachnowitz, Selig. Avrohom ben Avrohom: The Famous Historical Novel About the Ger Tzedek of Vilna. (YA) 7.95 (ISBN 0-87306-134-9); pap. 5.95. Feldheim.

--Light from the West. Leftwich, Joseph, tr. 7.95 (ISBN 0-87306-124-1). Feldheim.

Schacht, Joseph. Introduction to Islamic Law. 1964. pap. 18.95x (ISBN 0-19-825473-3). Oxford U Pr.

Schacht, Joseph & Bosworth, C. E., eds. The Legacy of Islam. 2nd ed. (Legacy Ser). (Illus.). 1974. text ed. 29.95x (ISBN 0-19-821913-X). Oxford U Pr.

--The Legacy of Islam. 2nd ed. (Illus.). 1974. pap. 8.95 (ISBN 0-19-285081-4). Oxford U Pr.

Schacht, Richard. Nietzsche. (Arguments of the Philosophers Ser.). 560p. 1983. 35.00x (ISBN 0-7100-9191-5); pap. 17.50 (ISBN 0-7102-0544-9). Methuen Inc.

Schachter, Zalman M. & Hoffman, Edward. Sparks of Light: Counseling in the Hasidic Tradition. LC 83-42804. 208p. (Orig.). 1983. pap. 9.95 (ISBN 0-87773-240-X). Shambhala Pubns.

Schackel, James. O Come, O Come, Emmanuel. (Candlelight Ser.). 1984. 2.25 (ISBN 0-89536-691-6, 4867). CSS of Ohio.

Schaeder, Grete. The Hebrew Humanism of Martin Buber. Jacobs, Noah J., tr. from Ger. LC 70-39691. (Schaver Publication Fund for Jewish Studies Ser.). 504p. 1973. 29.95x (ISBN 0-8143-1483-X). Wayne St U Pr.

Schaefer, Christopher & Voors, Tijno. Vision in Action: The Art of Taking & Shaping Initiatives. 199p. (Orig.). 1986. pap. text ed. 12.95 (ISBN 0-88010-150-4). Anthroposophic.

Schaefer, Peter. Rivalitaet zwischen Engeln und Menschen: Untersuchungen zur rabbinischen Engelvorstellung. (Studia Judaica, Vol. 8). xiv, 280p. 1975. 38.80x (ISBN 3-11-004632-6). De Gruyter.

Schaefer, Udo. The Imperishable Dominion. 320p. pap. 11.95 (ISBN 0-85398-142-6). G Ronald Pub.

--The Light Shineth in Darkness: Five Studies in Revelation after Christ. Neri, Helene M. & Coburn, Oliver, trs. 208p. 1977. 15.95 (ISBN 0-85398-091-8); pap. 9.95 (ISBN 0-85398-072-1). G Ronald Pub.

Schaefer-Lichtenberger, Christa. Stadt und Eidgenossenschaft im Alten Testament: Eine Auseinandersetzung mit Max Webers Studie "Das Antike Judentum". (Ger.). 485p. 1983. 43.20 (ISBN 3-11-008591-7). De Gruyter.

Schaeffer, Edith. Affliction. 256p. 1978. 10.95 (ISBN 0-8007-0926-8); 7.95 (ISBN 0-8007-5150-7). Revell.

--The Art of Life. 1987. 10.95 (Crossway Bks). Good News.

--Christianity Is Jewish. 1977. pap. 6.95 (ISBN 0-8423-0242-5). Tyndale.

--Common Sense Christian Living. LC 83-8263. 272p. 1983. 13.95 (ISBN 0-8407-5280-6). Nelson.

--Diez Pasos a la Vida. Powell, David, tr. from Eng. Orig. Title: Lifelines. (Span.). 192p. 1987. pap. 4.95 (ISBN 0-88113-251-9). Edit Betania.

--Everybody Can Know. 1978. 8.95 (ISBN 0-8423-0786-9). Tyndale.

--The Hidden Art of Homemaking. (Living Studies). 216p. 1985. pap. 6.95 (ISBN 0-8423-1398-2); Leader's Guide 2.95 (ISBN 0-8423-1399-0). Tyndale.

--Lifelines: God's Frame Work For Christian Living. LC 83-71240. 224p. (Orig.). 1982. (Crossway Bks); pap. 6.95 (ISBN 0-89107-294-2). Good News.

--A Way of Seeing. 256p. 1977. pap. 6.95 (ISBN 0-8007-5036-5, Power Bks). Revell.

--What Is a Family? 256p. 1982. pap. 7.95 (ISBN 0-8007-5088-8, Power Bks). Revell.

Schaeffer, Francis. Basic Bible Studies. 1972. pap. 2.95 (ISBN 0-8423-0103-8). Tyndale.

--He Is There & He Is Not Silent. 1972. pap. 4.95 (ISBN 0-8423-1413-X). Tyndale.

--True Spirituality. 1972. pap. 6.95 (ISBN 0-8423-7351-9). Tyndale.

Schaeffer, Francis A. Art & the Bible. LC 73-75891. 64p. 1973. pap. 2.95 (ISBN 0-87784-443-7). Inter-Varsity.

--A Christian Manifesto. LC 81-69737. 192p. 1981. pap. 5.95 (ISBN 0-89107-233-0, Crossway Bks). Good News.

--The Church at the End of the Twentieth Century: The Church Before the Watching World. 2nd ed. LC 85-71893. 160p. 1985. pap. 6.95 (ISBN 0-89107-368-X, Crossway Bks). Good News.

--The Complete Works of Francis A. Schaeffer. LC 84-72010. 2250p. 1985. (Crossway Bks); pap. 59.95 (ISBN 0-89107-331-0). Good News.

--Genesis in Space & Time. LC 72-78406. 144p. 1972. pap. 6.95 (ISBN 0-87784-636-7). Inter-Varsity.

--God Who Is There. LC 68-29304. 1968. pap. 7.95 (ISBN 0-87784-711-8). Inter-Varsity.

--The Great Evangelical Disaster. LC 83-73125. 192p. 1984. 14.95 (ISBN 0-89107-309-4, Crossway Bks); pap. 7.95 (ISBN 0-89107-308-6). Good News.

--How Should We Then Live? LC 83-70956. 288p. 1983. pap. 9.95 (ISBN 0-89107-292-6, Crossway BKs). Good News.

--Joshua & the Flow of Biblical History. LC 74-31847. 216p. 1975. pap. text ed. 7.95 (ISBN 0-87784-773-8). Inter-Varsity.

--Mark of the Christian. pap. 2.50 (ISBN 0-87784-434-8). Inter-Varsity.

Schaeffer, Francis A., jt. auth. see Koop, C. Everett.

Schaeffer, Franky. Addicted to Mediocrity. LC 80-85325. (Illus.). 128p. 1981. pap. 5.95 (ISBN 0-89107-214-4, Crossway Bks). Good News.

--Bad News for Modern Man. LC 84-70082. (Illus.). 192p. (Orig.). 1984. 14.95 (ISBN 0-89107-323-X, Crossway Bks); pap. 7.95 (ISBN 0-89107-311-6). Good News.

--A Time for Anger. LC 82-71981. 192p. 1982. pap. 6.95 (ISBN 0-89107-263-2, Crossway Bks). Good News.

Schaeffer, Franky, ed. Is Capitalism Christian? LC 85-70471. 400p. (Orig.). 1985. pap. 9.95 (ISBN 0-89107-362-0, Crossway Bks). Good News.

Schaeffer, Henry. The Social Legislation of the Primitive Semites. LC 70-174369. Repr. of 1915 ed. 16.00 (ISBN 0-405-08929-5). Ayer Co Pubs.

Schaeffer, Sue. Mine to Choose. LC 78-73144. 128p. 1979. 2.50 (ISBN 0-88243-553-1, 02-0553, Radiant Bks.); tchr's manual 2.50 (ISBN 0-88243-337-7, 02-0337). Gospel Pub.

Schafer, Edward H. Mirages in the Sea of Time: The Taoist Poetry of Ts'ao T'ang. 1985. 18.00x (ISBN 0-520-05429-6). U of Cal Pr.

--Pacing the Void: T'ang Approaches to the Stars. LC 76-48362. 1978. 49.50x (ISBN 0-520-03344-2). U of Cal Pr.

Schaff, D. S. John Huss. 59.95 (ISBN 0-8490-0451-9). Gordon Pr.

Schaff, Philip. Church & State in the U. S.; or, the American Idea of Religious Liberty & Its... LC 75-38462. (Religion in America, Ser. 2). 188p. 1972. Repr. of 1888 ed. 17.00 (ISBN 0-405-04083-0). Ayer Co Pubs.

--The Creeds of Christendom, 3 vols. 1983. 75.00 (ISBN 0-8010-8232-3). Baker Bk.

--History of the Christian Church, 8 vols. Incl. Vol. 1. Apostolic Christianity. 17.95 (ISBN 0-8028-8047-9); Vol. 2. Ante-Nicene. 100-325. 17.95 (ISBN 0-8028-8048-7); Vol. 3. Nicene & Post-Nicene. 311-600. 17.95 (ISBN 0-8028-8049-5); Vol. 4. Medieval Christianity. 590-1073. 17.95 (ISBN 0-8028-8050-9); Vol. 5. Middle Ages. 1049-1294. 17.95 (ISBN 0-8028-8051-7); Vol. 6. Middle Ages. 1295-1517. 17.95 (ISBN 0-8028-8052-5); Vol. 7. German Reformation. 17.95 (ISBN 0-8028-8053-3); Vol. 8. Swiss Reformation. 17.95 (ISBN 0-8028-8054-1). 1960. Repr. 17.95 ea.; 143.60 (ISBN 0-8028-8046-0). Eerdmans.

--The Principle of Protestantism: Chambersburg, PA 1845. Kuklick, Bruce, ed. Bd. with What Is Church History? Philadelphia, PA 1846. 215p. (American Religious Thought of the 18th & 19th Centuries Ser.). 343p. 1987. lib. bdg. 50.00. Garland Pub.

--The Principles of Protestantism. Thompson, Bard & Bricker, George H., eds. 1964. pap. 6.95 (ISBN 0-8298-0348-3). Pilgrim NY.

--Through Bible Lands: Notes on Travel in Egypt, the Desert, & Palestine. Davis, Moshe, ed. LC 77-70740. (America & the Holy Land Ser.). 1977. Repr. of 1878 ed. lib. bdg. 30.00x (ISBN 0-405-10286-0). Ayer Co Pubs.

Schaffer, James & Todd, Colleen. Christian Wives: Women Behind the Evangelists. LC 87-5291. (Illus.). 168p. 1987. 12.95 (ISBN 0-385-23581-X, Dolp). Doubleday.

Schaffer, Patricia. Chag Sameach! A Jewish Holiday Book for Children. (Illus.). 28p. (Orig.). 1985. pap. 4.95 (ISBN 0-935079-16-5). Tabor Sarah Bks.

Schaffer, Ulrich. For the Love of Children. LC 79-2984. 128p. (Orig.). 1980. pap. 3.95i (ISBN 0-06-067084-3, RD 310, HarpR). Har-Row.

--Growing into the Blue. LC 83-48463. (Illus.). 96p. (Orig.). 1984. pap. 14.95 (ISBN 0-06-067089-4, RD 509, HarpR). Har-Row.

Schaffner, Franklin J. Worthington Miner: A Directors Guild of America Oral History. LC 84-22184. 323p. 1985. 22.50 (ISBN 0-8108-1757-8). Scarecrow.

Schain, Richard. A Contemporary Logos. 20p. (Orig.). 1984. pap. 2.00 (ISBN 0-9609922-2-7). Garric Pr.

Schalit, Abraham. Koenig Herodes: Der Mann und sein Werk. Amir, Jehoshua, tr. (Studia Judaica, No. 4). (Ger). 1969. 80.00x (ISBN 3-11-001346-0). De Gruyter.

Schalk, Carl. The Hymn of the Day & Its Use in Lutheran Worship. 48p. (Orig.). 1983. pap. 2.50 (ISBN 0-570-01322-4, 99-1252). Concordia.

--Music in Lutheran Worship. 16p. (Orig.). 1983. pap. 1.25 (ISBN 0-570-01323-2, 99-1253). Concordia.

--The Pastor & the Church Musicians: Thoughts on Aspects of a Common Ministry. 12p. (Orig.). 1984. pap. 1.50 (ISBN 0-570-01330-5, 99-1256). Concordia.

Schall, J. V. The Church, the State & Society in the Thought of John Paul II. 1982. 7.50 (ISBN 0-8199-0838-X). Franciscan Herald.

Schall, James. Christianity & Politics. 1981. 6.95 (ISBN 0-8198-1406-7); pap. 5.95 (ISBN 0-8198-1407-5). Dghtrs St Paul.

Schall, James V. Christianity & Life. LC 79-89759. 133p. (Orig.). 1981. pap. 7.95 (ISBN 0-89870-004-3). Ignatius Pr.

--Liberation Theology in Latin America. LC 80-82266. 412p. (Orig.). 1982. pap. 13.95 (ISBN 0-89870-006-X). Ignatius Pr.

--The Politics of Heaven & Hell: Christian Themes from Classical, Medieval & Modern Political Philosophy. LC 84-7409. 360p. (Orig.). 1984. lib. bdg. 26.00 (ISBN 0-8191-3991-2); pap. text ed. 13.50 (ISBN 0-8191-3992-0). U Pr of Amer.

--Unexpected Meditations Late in the Twentieth Century. 142p. 1986. 9.95 (ISBN 0-8199-0885-1). Franciscan Herald.

Schall, James V., jt. ed. see Carey, George W.

Schall, James V., jt. ed. see Hanus, Jerome J.

Schaller, John. Biblical Christology. 1981. 10.95 (ISBN 0-8100-0126-8, 15N0372). Northwest Pub.

Schaller, Lyle E. Activating the Passive Church: Diagnosis & Treatment. LC 81-3460. 160p. (Orig.). 1981. pap. 6.95 (ISBN 0-687-00716-X). Abingdon.

--Assimilating New Members. LC 77-18037. (The Creative Leadership Ser.). 1978. pap. 7.50 (ISBN 0-687-01938-9). Abingdon.

--The Change Agent: The Strategy of Innovative Leadership. LC 77-185544. 208p. (Orig.). 1972. pap. 7.95 (ISBN 0-687-06042-7). Abingdon.

--Effective Church Planning. LC 78-26462. 1979. 6.95 (ISBN 0-687-11530-2). Abingdon.

--Getting Things Done: Concepts & Skills for Leaders. 144p. (Orig.). 1986. pap. 10.95 (ISBN 0-687-14142-7). Abingdon.

--Growing Plans: Strategies to Increase Your Church's Membership. 176p. 1983. pap. 7.95 (ISBN 0-687-15962-8). Abingdon.

--It's a Different World! The Challenge for Today's Pastor. 240p. 1987. pap. 10.95 (ISBN 0-687-19729-5). Abingdon.

--Looking in the Mirror: Self-Appraisal in the Local Church. 208p. 1984. pap. 9.50 (ISBN 0-687-22635-X). Abingdon.

--The Middle-Sized Church: Problems & Prescriptions. 160p. (Orig.). 1985. pap. 6.95 (ISBN 0-687-26948-2). Abingdon.

--The Multiple Staff & the Larger Church. LC 79-20796. 1980. pap. 6.95 (ISBN 0-687-27297-1). Abingdon.

--The Pastor & the People: Building a New Partnership for Effective Ministry. LC 72-8567. 176p. (Orig.). 1973. pap. 7.95 (ISBN 0-687-30136-X). Abingdon.

--The Small Church is Different. LC 82-1830. 192p. (Orig.). 1982. pap. 7.95 (ISBN 0-687-38717-5). Abingdon.

--Survival Tactics in the Parish. LC 76-54751. (Orig.). 1977. pap. 8.75 (ISBN 0-687-40757-5). Abingdon.

Schaller, Lyle E., ed. Women As Pastors. LC 81-20667. (Creative Leadership Ser.). (Orig.). 1982. pap. 5.95 (ISBN 0-687-45957-5). Abingdon.

Schaller, Lyle E., ed. see Hunter, Kent R.

Schaller, Lyle E., ed. see Sheek, G. William.

Schalow, Frank. Imagination & Existence: Heidegger's Retrieval of the Kantian Ethic. 192p. (Orig.). 1986. lib. bdg. 24.75 (ISBN 0-8191-5114-9); pap. text ed. 11.75 (ISBN 0-8191-5115-7). U Pr of Amer.

Schamoni, Wilhelm. Face of the Saints. Fremantle, Anne, tr. LC 70-38328. (Biography Index Reprint Ser). Repr. of 1947 ed. 26.50 (ISBN 0-8369-8128-6). Ayer Co Pubs.

Schantz, Daniel D. Barton W. Stone. (Restoration Booklets Ser.). (Illus., Orig.). 1984. pap. 0.75 (ISBN 0-87239-775-0, 3295). Standard Pub.

--Raccoon John Smith. (Restoration Booklets). (Illus.). 16p. (Orig.). 1984. pap. 0.75 (ISBN 0-87239-778-5, 3298). Standard Pub.

--Walter Scott. (Restoration Booklets Ser.). (Illus.). 16p. (Orig.). 1984. pap. 0.75 (ISBN 0-87239-777-7, 3297). Standard Pub.

Schanz, John P. Introduction to the Sacraments. 180p. (Orig.). 1983. pap. 9.95 (ISBN 0-916134-57-1). Pueblo Pub Co.

Schaper, Robert. In His Presence: Appreciating Your Worship Tradition. LC 84-1305. 204p. 1984. pap. 5.95 (ISBN 0-8407-5887-1). Nelson.

Schapiro, Jacob S. Social Reform & the Reformation. LC 74-127456. (Columbia University Studies in the Social Sciences: No. 90). 1970. Repr. of 1909 ed. 16.50 (ISBN 0-404-51090-6). AMS Pr.

Schapiro, Meyer. Late Antique, Early Christian & Mediaeval Art: Selected Papers, Vol. III. (Illus.). 422p. 1979. 25.00 (ISBN 0-8076-0927-7). Braziller.

Schaps, Hilda W., jt. auth. see Schutz, Albert.

Scharfstein, Ben-Ami, jt. auth. see Ostow, Mortimer.

Scharfstein, Ben-Ami, ed. Philosophy East-Philosophy West: A Critical Comparison of Indian, Chinese, Islamic & European Philosophy. 1978. 25.00x (ISBN 0-19-520064-0). Oxford U Pr.

Scharfstein, Eythe & Scharfstein, Sol. Book of Chanukah. (Illus.). 1959. 5.95x (ISBN 0-87068-357-8). Ktav.

Scharfstein, Sol. What to Do on a Jewish Holiday? 1985. 6.95 (ISBN 0-88125-170-4). Ktav.

Scharfstein, Sol, jt. auth. see Scharfstein, Eythe.

Scharkemann, Martin N. Stephen: A Singular Saint. 207p. 1968. write for info. Concordia Schl Grad Studies.

Scharlemann, Martin H. The Making of a Theologian. 182p. 1984. pap. 6.50 (ISBN 0-911770-54-2). Concordia Schl Grad Studies.

--Qumran & Corinth. 1962. pap. 5.95x (ISBN 0-8084-0358-3). New Coll U Pr.

--Qumran & Corinth. 78p. 1962. write for info. Concordia Schl Grad Studies.

Scharlemann, Robert P. The Being of God: Theology & the Experience of Truth. 224p. 1981. 14.95 (ISBN 0-8164-0494-1, HarpR). Har-Row.

--Reflection & Doubt in the Thought of Paul Tillich. LC 79-81430. Repr. of 1969 ed. 45.60 (ISBN 0-8357-9481-4, 2013185). Bks Demand UMI.

Scharlemann, Robert P., ed. Naming God. (The Contemporary Discussion Ser.). 224p. (Orig.). 1986. 21.95 (ISBN 0-913757-22-5, Pub. by New Era Bks.); pap. 12.95 (ISBN 0-913757-23-3, Pub. by New Era Bks). Paragon Hse.

Scharper, Philip & Sharper, Sally, eds. The Gospel in Art by the Peasants of Solentiname. Walsh, Donaldly, tr. from Span. (Illus.). 70p. 1984. 10.95 (ISBN 0-88344-382-1). Orbis Bks.

Scharper, Philip J., jt. ed. see Cassidy, Richard J.

Scharper, Philip J., jt. ed. see Eagleson, John.

Schatz, Elihu A. Proof of the Accuracy of the Bible. LC 73-10726. (Illus.). xxvi, 740p. 1973. 15.00x (ISBN 0-8246-0161-0). Jonathan David.

Schatzberg, Walter, jt. ed. see Reinharz, Jehuda.

Schatzman, Siegfried. A Pauline Theology of Charismata. 150p. 1986. pap. 7.95 (ISBN 0-913573-45-0). Hendrickson MA.

Schaub, Edward J. Spinoza: The Man & His Thought. 61p. 1933. pap. 0.95 (ISBN 0-317-40400-8). Open Court.

Schauer, Ken. Two Fish to You. 65p. 1985. pap. 4.95 (ISBN 0-933350-46-5). Morse Pr.

Schaumberg, Ethel L. Judas: The Unforgiven Man. 1981. 4.75 (1002). CSS of Ohio.

Schaupp, Jack. Creating & Playing Games with Students. (Orig.). 1981. pap. 6.50 (ISBN 0-687-09809-2). Abingdon.

Schauss, Hayyim. Jewish Festivals: From Their Beginnings to Our Own Day. rev. ed. (Illus.). (YA) 1969. 8.00 (ISBN 0-8074-0095-5, 383202); course syll. 1.25 (ISBN 0-686-66555-4, 247330). UAHC.

--The Jewish Festivals: History & Observance. LC 62-13140. 1973. pap. 7.50 (ISBN 0-8052-0413-X). Schocken.

--Lifetime of a Jew: Throughout the Ages of Jewish History. rev. ed. (Illus.). (YA) 1976. pap. 7.95 (ISBN 0-8074-0096-3, 383473). UAHC.

Schaya, Leo. The Universal Meaning of the Kabbalah. 1972. 6.95 (ISBN 0-8216-0167-9). Univ Bks.

Schechter, Solomon. Aspects of Rabbinic Theology: Major Concepts of the Talmud. LC 61-14919. 1961. pap. 8.95 (ISBN 0-8052-0015-0). Schocken.

--Seminary Addresses. 1959. pap. 2.45 (ISBN 0-8381-2109-8). United Syn Bk.

--Seminary Addresses & Other Papers. LC 79-83435. (Religion in America, Ser. 1). 1969. Repr. of 1915 ed. 19.00 (ISBN 0-405-00260-2). Ayer Co Pubs.

--Seminary Addresses & Other Papers. 270p. Date not set. Repr. of 1915 ed. text ed. 62.10x (ISBN 0-576-80119-4, Pub by Gregg Intl Pubs England). Gregg Intl.

--Studies in Judaism. facsimile ed. LC 78-38775. (Essay Index Reprint Ser). Repr. of 1896 ed. 19.50 (ISBN 0-8369-2670-6). Ayer Co Pubs.

Scheck, Joann. Three Men Who Walked in Fire. (Arch Bks: Set 4). 1967. laminated bdg. 0.99 (ISBN 0-570-06026-5, 59-1137). Concordia.

Scheck, Joann, jt. auth. see Roberts, Jim.

Schecter, Solomon. Documents of Jewish Sectaries, 2 Vols. in 1. rev. ed. (Library of Biblical Studies Ser). (Illus.). 1970. 35.00 (ISBN 0-87068-016-1). Ktav.

Scheer, Gladys E. The Church Library: Tips & Tools. LC 73-10093. (Orig.). 1973. pap. 3.95 (ISBN 0-8272-0435-3). CBP.

Scheffczyk, Leo, ed. Faith in Christ & the Worship of Christ. Harrison, Graham, tr. from Ger. LC 85-82174. Orig. Title: Christusglaube und Christusverehrung. 216p. (Orig.). 1986. pap. 9.95 (ISBN 0-89870-057-4). Ignatius Pr.

Schefski, Harold K., ed. & tr. see Leskov, Nikolai.

Scheiber, Alexander. Essays on Jewish Folklore & Comparative Literature. (Illus.). 456p. 1985. 55.00x (ISBN 963-05-3944-6, Pub. by Akademiai Kiado Hungary). Humanities.

Scheiber, Sr. Mary M. Ludwig Tieck & the Medieval Church. LC 74-140028. (Catholic University Studies in German: No. 12). Repr. of 1939 ed. 22.00 (ISBN 0-404-50232-6). AMS Pr.

Scheick, William J. The Writings of Jonathan Edwards: Theme, Motif, & Style. LC 75-18689. 192p. 1975. 14.50x (ISBN 0-89096-004-6). Tex A&M Univ Pr.

Scheidler, Bill. New Testament Church & Its Ministries. (Illus.). 120p. 1980. pap. 8.95 (ISBN 0-914936-43-3). Bible Temple.

Scheidler, Joseph M. Closed: Ninety-Nine Ways to Stop Abortion. LC 85-42646. 350p. (Orig.). 1985. pap. 9.95 (ISBN 0-89107-346-9, Crossway Bks). Good News.

--Closed: Ninety-Nine Ways to Stop Abortion. LC 85-61055. 350p. (Orig.). 1985. pap. 9.95 (ISBN 0-89870-075-2). Ignatius Pr.

Scheidt, David L., tr. see Soelle, Dorothee.

Scheihing, Theresa O., jt. auth. see Savary, Louis M.

Schein, Bruce E. Following the Way: The Setting of John's Gospel. LC 79-54121. 224p. 1980. 14.95 (ISBN 0-8066-1758-6, 10-2348). Augsburg.

Schein, Jeffrey L. & Staub, Jacob J., eds. Creative Jewish Education. 256p. (Orig.). 1985. pap. 7.95 (ISBN 0-940646-33-1). Rossel Bks.

Scheiner, Irwin. Christian Converts & Social Protest in Meiji Japan. LC 74-94981. (Center for Japanese Studies). 1970. 35.00x (ISBN 0-520-01585-1). U of Cal Pr.

Scheing, Theresa & Savary, Lou. Our Treasured Heritage. 176p. 1986. pap. 8.95 (ISBN 0-8245-0731-2). Crossroad NY.

Scheke, Linda & Miller, Mary E. Blood of Kings: Dynasty & Ritual in Maya Art. 1986. 50.00 (ISBN 0-8076-1159-X). Braziller.

Schelbert, Leo. Swiss Migration to America: The Swiss Mennonites. Cordasco, Francesco, ed. LC 80-891. (American Ethnic Groups Ser.). 1981. lib. bdg. 38.50x (ISBN 0-405-13452-5). Ayer Co Pubs.

Scheler, Max. Formalism in Ethics & Non-Formal Ethics of Values: A New Attempt Toward the Foundation of an Ethical Personalism. Frings, Manfred S. & Funk, Roger L., trs. from Ger. LC 72-97416. (Studies in Phenomenology & Existential Philosophy). Orig. Title: Der Formalismus der Ethik und die Materiale Wertethik. 750p. 1973. text ed. 29.95 (ISBN 0-8101-0415-6); 14.95 (ISBN 0-8101-0620-5). Northwestern U Pr.

Scheler, Max F. On the Eternal in Man. Noble, Bernard, tr. LC 72-6599. 480p. 1972. Repr. of 1960 ed. 35.00 (ISBN 0-208-01280-X, Archon). Shoe String.

Schelkle, Karl H. The Spirit & the Bride: Woman in the Bible. Schneider, John, ed. O'Connell, Matthew J., tr. from Ger. LC 79-16976. 191p. (Orig.). 1979. pap. 3.50 (ISBN 0-8146-1008-0). Liturgical Pr.

Schell, Catherine, jt. auth. see Kunz, Marilyn.

Schell, William G. Biblical Trace of the Church. 173p. pap. 1.50 (ISBN 0-686-29103-4). Faith Pub Hse.

--The Ordinances of the New Testament. 67p. pap. 0.50 (ISBN 0-686-29158-1). Faith Pub Hse.

Schellenberger, Bernadin. Nomad of the Spirit: Reflections of a Young Monastic. 112p. 1981. 8.95 (ISBN 0-8245-0075-X). Crossroad NY.

Schellhas, P. Representation of Deities of the Maya Manuscripts. (Hupmaen Ser.: Vol. 4, No. 1). (Illus.). 1904. pap. 15.00 (ISBN 0-527-01198-3). Kraus Repr.

Schellman, James M. Ecumenical Services of Prayer: Consultation on Common Texts. 80p. 1983. pap. 1.95 (ISBN 0-8091-5180-4). Paulist Pr.

Schenk, Fredrick J. & Anderson, James V. Aging Together, Serving Together: A Guide to Congregational Planning for the Aging. LC 10-185. 40p. (Orig.). 1982. pap. 3.50 (ISBN 0-8066-1963-5, 10-0185). Augsburg.

Schenke, Ludger. Glory & the Way of the Cross: The Gospel of St. Mark. Karris, Robert, ed. Scroggs, Robin, tr. (Herald Biblical Bklts). 1972. pap. 1.25 (ISBN 0-8199-0517-8). Franciscan Herald.

Schenker, Walter. Die Sprache Huldrych Zwinglis im Kontrast zur Sprache Luthers. (Studia Linguistica Germanica: Vol. 14). (Illus.). 1977. 66.00x (ISBN 3-11-006605-X). De Gruyter.

Scherer, James A. Global Living Here & Now. 1974. pap. 2.25 (ISBN 0-377-00003-5). Friend Pr.

--Gospel, Church, & Kingdom: Comparative Studies in World Mission Theology. 256p. (Orig.). 1987. pap. 14.95 (ISBN 0-8066-2280-6, 10-2828). Augsburg.

Scherer, Lester B. A Short History of Religion in America. (Illus.). 145p. (Orig.). 1980. pap. 8.95x (ISBN 0-89894-011-7). Advocate Pub Group.

Scherer, Ross P., ed. American Denominational Organization: A Sociological View. LC 80-13859. 378p. 1980. pap. 14.95x (ISBN 0-87808-173-9, Ecclesia). William Carey Lib.

Scherman, Nosson. Bircas Hamazon-Grace after Meals. (Art Scroll Mesorah Ser.). 96p. 1977. 7.50 (ISBN 0-89906-152-4); pap. 5.50 (ISBN 0-89906-153-2). Mesorah Pubns.

--The Haggadah Treasury. (The Art Scroll Mesorah Ser.). 200p. 1978. 10.95 (ISBN 0-89906-200-8); pap. 7.95 (ISBN 0-89906-201-6). Mesorah Pubns.

--Kaddish. (Art Scroll Mesorah Ser.). 64p. 1980. 6.95 (ISBN 0-89906-160-5). Mesorah Pubns.

--Siddur: Sabbath Eve Service. 1980. 10.95 (ISBN 0-686-68764-7); pap. 7.95 (ISBN 0-686-68765-5). Mesorah Pubns.

--Zemiroth - Sabbath Songs. Zlotowitz, Meir, ed. (Artscroll Mesorah Ser.). 1979. 13.95 (ISBN 0-89906-156-7); pap. 10.95 (ISBN 0-89906-157-5). Mesorah Pubns.

Scherman, Nosson, tr. The Family Haggadah. (Artscroll Mesorah Ser.). 96p. (Orig.). 1981. pap. 2.75 (ISBN 0-89906-178-8). Mesorah Pubns.

Schermann, Theodor. Agyptische Abendmahlsliturgien Des Ersten Jahrtausends. Repr. of 1912 ed. 19.00 (ISBN 0-384-53730-8). Johnson Repr.

--Die Allgemeine Kirchenordnung Fruehchristliche Liturgien und Kirchliche Uberlieferung, 3 pts. Repr. of 1914 ed. Set. 55.00 (ISBN 0-384-53740-5). Johnson Repr.

Schermerhorn, Elizabeth W. Malta of the Knights. LC 76-29838. Repr. of 1929 ed. 40.00 (ISBN 0-404-15429-8). AMS Pr.

Scherpbier, H. Milton in Holland. LC 76-41928. 1933. lib. bdg. 30.00 (ISBN 0-8414-7580-6). Folcroft.

Schervish, Paul, et al. Families, the Economy & the Church: A Book of Readings & Discussion Guide. Brigham, Frederick & Preister, Steven, eds. 144p. (Orig.). 1987. pap. 5.95 (ISBN 1-55586-136-9). US Catholic.

Scheuer, Joseph F., jt. auth. see Wakin, Edward.

Scheuerman, Richard D. Pilgrims on the Earth. 165p. 1976. 12.00 (ISBN 0-87770-128-8). Ye Galleon.

Schiappa, Barbara D. Mixing: Catholic-Protestant Marriages in the 1980's. LC 81-84387. 144p. (Orig.). 1982. pap. 5.95 (ISBN 0-8091-2443-2). Paulist Pr.

Schiavo, Giovanni E. Italian-American History: The Italian Contribution to the Catholic Church in America. LC 74-17948. (Italian American Experience Ser: Vol. No. 2). (Illus.). 1975. Repr. 70.50x (ISBN 0-405-06429-2). Ayer Co Pubs.

Schibilla, Linda, jt. auth. see Christman, Ronald.

Schiblin, Richard. The Bible, the Church, & Social Justice. 64p. 1983. pap. 1.50 (ISBN 0-89243-187-3). Liguori Pubns.

Schick, Eduard. The Revelation of St. John, Vol. I. McKenzie, John L., ed. LC 81-605. (New Testament for Spiritual Reading Ser.). 112p. 1981. pap. 4.95 (ISBN 0-8245-0133-0). Crossroad NY.

--The Revelation of St. John, Vol. II. McKenzie, John L., ed. LC 81-605. (New Testament for Spiritual Reading Ser.). 112p. 1981. 10.00 (ISBN 0-8245-0359-7); pap. 4.95 (ISBN 0-8245-0134-9). Crossroad NY.

Schick, Edwin A. Revelation - the Last Book of the Bible. LC 76-62602. pap. 20.00 (2029617). Bks Demand UMI.

Schick, G. V., tr. Luther's Works: Genesis Chapters 21-25, Vol. 4. LC 55-9893. 1964. 16.95 (ISBN 0-570-06404-X, 15-1746). Concordia.

Schick, George V., tr. see Pelikan, Jaroslav.

Schiefen, Richard J. Nicholas Wiseman & the Transformation of English Catholicism. (Illus.). 416p. 1984. 32.50x (ISBN 0-915762-15-3). Patmos Pr.

Schieffelin, Edward L. The Sorrow of the Lonely & the Burning of the Dancers. LC 75-10999. (Illus.). 256p. 1975. pap. text ed. 9.95 (ISBN 0-312-74550-8). St Martin.

Schieffer, Rudolphus. Acta Conciliorum Oecumenicorum Tomus 4, Volumen 3: Index Generalis Tomorum 1-4, Pars 1; Indices Codicum et. LC 74-79318. 579p. 1974. 136.00x (ISBN 3-11-004449-8). De Gruyter.

Schield, Dean C. More Effective Choir Ministry: A Manual for Church Musicians. LC 86-42932. 32p. (Orig.). 1986. pap. 4.00 (ISBN 0-937021-02-4). Sagamore Bks MI.

Schierse, F. J. The Epistle to the Hebrews & the Epistle of St. James. McKenzie, John L., ed. LC 81-605. (New Testament for Spiritual Reading Ser.). 246p. 1981. pap. 4.95 (ISBN 0-8245-0130-6). Crossroad NY.

Schievella, Pasqual S. Hey! Is That You, God? Crystal, Richard O., ed. Date not set. 16.95. Sebastian LI.

Schiff, Gary S. Tradition & Politics: The Religious Parties of Israel. LC 77-5723. 267p. 1977. 25.00x (ISBN 0-8143-1580-1). Wayne St U Pr.

Schiff, Marty, jt. auth. see Baumgartner, Keith A.

Schiff, Ze'ev, jt. ed. see Fabian, Larry L.

Schiffhorst, Gerald J., ed. The Triumph of Patience: Medieval & Renaissance Studies. LC 77-12732. (Illus.). 1978. 10.00 (ISBN 0-8130-0590-6). U Presses Fla.

Schiffman, Harvey R. Sensation & Perception: An Integrated Approach. 2d ed. LC 81-19770. 540p. 1982. write for info. (ISBN 0-471-08208-2). Wiley.

Schiffman, Joseph, ed. see Bellamy, Edward.

Schiffman, L. H., ed. see Grossfeld, Bernard.

Schiffman, Lawrence. Sectarian Laws in the Dead Sea Scrolls: Courts, Testimony & the Penal Code. LC 82-837. (Brown Judaic Studies). 294p. 1983. pap. 27.50 (ISBN 0-89130-569-6). Scholars Pr GA.

Schiffman, Lawrence H. Who Was Jew: Rabbinic & Halakhic Perspectives on the Jewish-Christian Schism. (Illus.). 140p. 1985. 14.95 (ISBN 0-88125-053-8); pap. 8.95 (ISBN 0-88125-054-6). Ktav.

Schild, Philip, jt. ed. see Kramer, Ralph M.

Schilder, Klass. The Trilogy, 3 vols. 1978. Set. 48.00 (ISBN 0-86524-126-0, 9501). Klock & Klock.

Schillebeeck, Edward. God among Us. 256p. 1986. pap. 9.95 (ISBN 0-8245-0732-0). Crossroad NY.

Schillebeeckx, Edward. Christ: The Experience of Jesus As Lord. 928p. 1983. pap. 17.95 (ISBN 0-8245-0605-7). Crossroad NY.

--Church with a Human Face: New & Expanded Theology of Ministry. Bowden, John, tr. 400p. 1985. 19.95 (ISBN 0-8245-0693-6). Crossroad NY.

--God among Us: The Gospel Proclaimed. LC 82-23575. 278p. 1983. 12.95 (ISBN 0-8245-0575-1). Crossroad NY.

--God Is New Each Moment: Conversations with Huub Oosterhuis & Piet Hoogeveen. LC 83-614. 160p. (Orig.). 1983. pap. 7.95 (ISBN 0-8164-2475-6, HarpR). Har-Row.

--Interim Report on the Books Jesus & Christ. 160p. 1980. 9.95 (ISBN 0-8245-0029-6). Crossroad NY.

--Jesus: An Experiment in Christology. 1979. pap. 12.95 (ISBN 0-8245-0405-4). Crossroad NY.

--Ministry. 160p. 1981. 12.95 (ISBN 0-8245-0030-X). Crossroad NY.

--Ministry. Bowden, John, tr. 176p. 1984. pap. 9.95 (ISBN 0-8245-0638-3). Crossroad NY.

--On Christian Faith. 128p. 1987. 12.95 (ISBN 0-8245-0827-0). Crossroad NY.

--On Christian Faith: The Spiritual, Ethical & Political Dimensions. 1987. 12.95. Crossroad NY.

--Paul the Apostle. (Illus.). 128p. 1983. 14.95 (ISBN 0-8245-0574-3). Crossroad NY.

--Schillebeeckx Reader. Schreiter, Robert, ed. 1987. pap. 16.95 (ISBN 0-8245-0828-9). Crossroad NY.

Schillebeeckx, Edward & Baptist-Metz, Johannes. Martyrdom Today. (Concilium 1983: Vol. 163). 128p. 1983. pap. 6.95 (ISBN 0-8164-2443-8, HarpR). Har-Row.

Schillebeeckx, Edward & Metz, Johannes B. God & Father, Vol. 143. (Concilium 1981). 128p. (Orig.). 1981. pap. 6.95 (ISBN 0-8164-2310-5, HarpR). Har-Row.

Schillebeeckx, Edward. Church & Mankind. LC 65-15249. (Concilium Ser.: Vol. 1). 196p. 1965. 7.95 (ISBN 0-8091-0015-0). Paulist Pr.

--The Movement of Theology since the Council. (Concilium 1983: Vol. 170). 128p. (Orig.). 1983. pap. 6.95 (ISBN 0-8164-2450-0, HarpR). Har-Row.

Schillebeeckx, Edward & Metz, Johann B., eds. The Right of the Community to a Priest: New Concilium 1980, No. 133. 128p. 1980. pap. 5.95 (ISBN 0-8164-2275-3, HarpR). Har-Row.

Schillebeeckx, Edward & Metz, Johannes-Baptist, eds. Jesus, Son of God? (Concilium Ser.: Vol. 153). 128p. 1982. pap. 6.95 (ISBN 0-8164-2384-9, HarpR). Har-Row.

Schillebeeckx, Edward & Willems, Boniface, eds. Man As Man & Believer. LC 67-17789. (Concilium Ser.: Vol. 21). 188p. 7.95 (ISBN 0-8091-0093-2). Paulist Pr.

--Problem of Eschatology. LC 79-76195. (Concilium Ser.: Vol. 41). 175p. 1969. 7.95 (ISBN 0-8091-0117-3). Paulist Pr.

Schillebeeckx, Edward, jt. ed. see Metz, Johannes-Baptist.

Schillebeeckx, Edward, jt. ed. see Kung, Hans.

Schiller, Friedrich Von see Von Schiller, Friedrich.

Schiller, Mayer. The Road Back: A Discovery of Judaism Without Embellishments. new ed. 1978. 9.95 (ISBN 0-87306-164-0). Feldheim.

Schilling, S. Paul. The Faith We Sing. LC 82-21749. 262p. 1983. pap. 14.95 (ISBN 0-664-24434-3). Westminster.

--God & Human Anguish. LC 77-5857. Repr. of 1977 ed. 76.00 (ISBN 0-8357-9009-6, 2016362). Bks Demand UMI.

Schilpp, Paul, ed. Theology & Modern Life. LC 70-117852. (Essay Index Reprint Ser). 1940. 19.00 (ISBN 0-8369-1727-8). Ayer Co Pubs.

Schilpp, Paul A., ed. Theology & Modern Life: Essays in Honor of Harris Franklin Rall. (Essay Index Reprint Ser.). 307p. 1982. Repr. of 1940 ed. lib. bdg. 18.00 (ISBN 0-686-79705-1). Irvington.

Schilpp, Paul A. & Friedman, Maurice, eds. The Philosophy of Martin Buber. LC 65-14535. (The Library of Living Philosophers: Vol. XII). 831p. 1967. 37.95 (ISBN 0-87548-129-9). Open Court.

Schimel, David, jt. auth. see Brafman, Morris.

Schimidt, Marilee. Could I Be a Teacher. 1985. 2.95 (ISBN 0-8100-0200-0, 16N0782). Northwest Pub.

Schimmel. The Oral Law. cancelled (ISBN 0-87306-088-1). Feldheim.

Schimmel, Annemarie. And Muhammad Is His Messenger: The Veneration of the Prophet in Islamic Piety. LC 84-17374. (Studies in Religion). (Illus.). xii, 377p. 1985. 32.00x (ISBN 0-8078-1639-6); pap. 9.95x (ISBN 0-8078-4128-5). U of NC Pr.

--As Through a Veil: Mystical Poetry in Islam. 359p. 1987. pap. text ed. 14.50 (ISBN 0-231-05247-2). Columbia U Pr.

--Islamic Calligraphy. (Illus.). 1970. 103.25x (ISBN 0-685-00757-X). Adlers Foreign Bks.

--Mystical Dimensions of Islam. LC 73-16112. (Illus.). xxi, 506p. 1975. 30.00x (ISBN 0-8078-1223-4); pap. 8.95x (ISBN 0-8078-1271-4). U of NC Pr.

Schimmel, Harold, tr. see Yeshurun, Avoth.

Schimmels, Cliff. The First Three Years of School: A Survivor's Guide. 160p. (Orig.). 1984. pap. 5.95 (ISBN 0-8007-5175-2, Power Bks). Revell.

Schindler, David L., ed. Beyond Mechanism: The Universe in Recent Physics & Catholic Thought. 166p. (Orig.). 1986. lib. bdg. 22.75 (ISBN 0-8191-5357-5, Pub. by Communio Intl Cth Review); pap. text ed. 10.75 (ISBN 0-8191-5358-3). U Pr of Amer.

Schindler, Harold. Orrin Porter Rockwell: Man of God, Son of Thunder. 2nd ed. (University of Utah Publications in the American West: Vol. 15). (Illus.). 1983. 24.95 (ISBN 0-87480-204-0). U of Utah Pr.

Schindler, Marian, jt. auth. see Schindler, Robert.

Schindler, Regine. Hannah at the Manger. (Illus.). 31p. 1983. pap. 9.95 printed binding (ISBN 0-687-16627-6). Abingdon.

--The Lost Sheep. LC 80-68546. Orig. Title: Das Verlorene Shaf. (Illus.). 32p. 1982. Repr. 7.95g (ISBN 0-687-22780-1). Abingdon.

--A Miracle for Sarah. Tr. of Und Sara Lacht. (Illus.). 28p. 1985. 7.95 (ISBN 0-687-27044-8). Abingdon.

Schindler, Robert & Schindler, Marian. Mission Possible. 168p. 1984. pap. 5.95 (ISBN 0-88207-618-3). Victor Bks.

Schipani, Daniel S. Conscientization & Creativity: Paulo Freire & Christian Education. 224p. (Orig.). 1984. lib. bdg. 26.00 (ISBN 0-8191-3881-9); pap. text ed. 12.25 (ISBN 0-8191-3882-7). U Pr of Amer.

--El Reino de Dios y el Ministerio Educativo de la Iglesia. (Span.). 213p. 1984. pap. 5.50 (ISBN 0-89922-232-3). Edit Caribe.

Schirer, Marshall E. & Forehand, Mary A. Cooperative Ministry: Hope for Small Churches. 96p. 1984. pap. 3.95 (ISBN 0-8170-1030-0). Judson.

Schischa, A. The Blessing of Eliyahu: Rabbi Munk. 1983. 35.00x (ISBN 0-88125-016-3). Ktav.

Schiwetz, E. M. Six Spanish Missions in Texas: A Portfolio of Paintings. Memorial ed. (Illus.). 1984. 60.00 (ISBN 0-292-77597-0). U of Tex Pr.

Schlabach, Chris. Lecciones...la Vida Victoriosa. Orig. Title: Lessons in Victorious Living. (Span.). 1986. write for info. (ISBN 0-8297-0730-1). Life Pubs Intl.

--Lessons in Victorious Living. 160p. (Orig.). 1984. pap. 3.95 (ISBN 0-88368-141-2). Whitaker Hse.

Schlabach, Theron F. Gospel Versus Gospel. LC 79-15888. 352p. 1980. 17.95x (ISBN 0-8361-1220-2). Herald Pr.

Schlafly, Phyllis, jt. auth. see Vecsey, Joseph.

Schlagintweit, Emil. Buddhism in Tibet. 69.95 (ISBN 0-87968-802-5). Gordon Pr.

Schlamm, J. Vera & Friedman, Bob. Pursued. rev. ed. LC 86-600. 189p. 1986. pap. 3.95 (ISBN 0-8307-1146-5, 5018631). Regal.

Schlatter, Richard B. Social Ideas of Religious Leaders, Sixteen Sixty to Sixteen Sixty-Eight. LC 77-120663. 1970. Repr. lib. bdg. 18.50x (ISBN 0-374-97102-1, Octagon). Hippocrene Bks.

Schlegl, William. Bible Christmas Puzzles. (Illus.). 48p. 1987. pap. 5.95 (ISBN 0-86653-409-1). Good Apple.

--Bible Trivia. (Bible Baffler Ser.). 48p. 1986. wkbk. 4.95 (ISBN 0-86653-368-0). Good Apple.

Schleiermacher, F. Aus Schleiermachers Leben, in Briefen, 4 vols. (Ger.). xxxvi, 2006p. 1974. Repr. of 1863 ed. 190.00x (ISBN 3-11-002261-3). De Gruyter.

Schleiermacher, Friedrich. The Christian Faith. MacKintosh, H. R. & Sterwart, J. S., eds. Tr. of Der Christliche Glaube. 772p. 1928. 18.95 (ISBN 0-567-02239-0, Pub. by T&T Clark Ltd UK). Fortress.

--Hermeneutics: The Handwritten Manuscripts. Kimmerle, Heinz, ed. Duke, James & Forstman, Jack, trs. from Ger. LC 77-13969. (American Academy of Religion. Text & Translations Ser.: No. 1). 1978. pap. text ed. 10.25 (ISBN 0-89130-186-0, 010201). Scholars Pr GA.

--On Religion: Speeches to Its Cultured Despisers. pap. 8.95x (ISBN 0-06-130036-5, TB36, Torch). Har-Row.

--On Religion: Speeches to Its Cultured Despisers. 18.25 (ISBN 0-8446-2878-6). Peter Smith.

--On the Glaubenslehre: Two Letters to Dr. Lucke. Massey, James A., ed. Duke, James & Fiorenza, Francis S., trs. from Ger. LC 80-20717. (American Academy of Religion, Texts & Translations Ser.: No. 3). Orig. Title: Sendschreiben Uber Seine Glaubenslehre an Lucke. 1981. pap. 9.95 (ISBN 0-89130-420-7, 01-02-03). Scholars Pr GA.

--Die Praktische Theologie nach den Grundsatzen. (Ger.). 845p. 1983. 96.00 (ISBN 3-11-009699-4). De Gruyter.

Schleiermacher, Friedrich D. Kritische Gesamtausgabe: Erste Abteilung (Schriften und Entwuerfe), Band 7, Teil 3 - Der Christliche Glaube, 1821-1822. (Ger.). 1984. 128.00 (ISBN 3-11-008593-3). De Gruyter.

--Kritische Gesamtausgabe: Fuenfte Abteilung (Briefwechsel & Biographische Dokumente) Briefwechsel, 1774-1796, Band 1. Arndt, Andreas & Virmond, Wolfgang, eds. (Illus.). lxxii, 489p. 1986. 120.00x (ISBN 3-11-008595-X). De Gruyter.

Schleiermacher, Friedrich E. Schleiermacher's Soliloques. Friess, Horace L., tr. LC 78-59040. 1984. Repr. of 1926 ed. 23.00 (ISBN 0-88355-712-6). Hyperion Conn.

Schlein, Miriam. Our Holidays. (Illus.). 128p. 1983. pap. text ed. 4.95x (ISBN 0-87441-382-6). Behrman.

Schleiner, Winfried. The Imagery of John Donne's Sermons. LC 70-91655. Repr. of 1970 ed. 66.00 (2027523). Bks Demand UMI.

Schlesinger, Benjamin. The Jewish Family: A Survey & Annotated Bibliography. Strakhovsky, Florence, ed. LC 79-151389. pap. 46.80 (ISBN 0-317-09749-0, 2014401). Bks Demand UMI.

Schlesinger, G. Religion & Scientific Method. 1977. lib. bdg. 29.00 (ISBN 90-277-0815-0, Pub. by Reidel Holland); pap. 10.50 (ISBN 90-277-0816-9, Pub. by Reidel Holland). Kluwer Academic.

Schlesinger, Hugo, jt. auth. see Porto, Humberto.

Schlesselman, R. & Ahrens, L. Dear Father in Heaven. rev. ed. (Illus.). 1977. pap. 2.25 (ISBN 0-570-03469-8, 56-1301). Concordia.

Schleunes, Karl A. The Twisted Road to Auschwitz: Nazi Policy Toward German Jews, 1933-1939. LC 74-102024. pap. 72.00 (ISBN 0-317-11169-8, 2011134). Bks Demand UMI.

Schlick, Jean, ed. see Cerdic Colloquium Staff.

Schlick, Jean, jt. ed. see Metz, Rene.

Schlieben, Richard. Christliche Theologie und Philologie in der Spaetantike: Die schulwissenschaftlichen Methoden der Psalmenexegese Cassiodors. LC 74-77213. (Arbeiten zur Kirchengeschichte, Vol. 46). (Ger.). 132p. 1974. 19.00x (ISBN 3-11-004634-2). De Gruyter.

Schlink, Basilea. Allah or the God of the Bible: What Is the Truth? 1984. pap. 2.50 (ISBN 0-551-01140-8, Pub. by Marshall Morgan & Scott UK). Evang Sisterhood Mary.

--Asi Seremos Diferentes. 224p. 1976. 3.75 (ISBN 0-88113-004-4). Edit Betania.

--At the Side of Our Saviour: A Walk Through the Garden of Jesus' Sufferings. First English ed. (Illus.). 28p. (Orig.). 1982. pap. 1.50 gift edition (ISBN 3-87209-627-3). Evang Sisterhood Mary.

--Behold His Love. 144p. 1973. pap. 3.50 (ISBN 0-87123-039-9). Bethany Hse.

--Blessings of Illness. 1973. pap. 2.50 (ISBN 0-551-00446-0, Pub. by Marshall Morgan & Scott UK). Evang Sisterhood Mary.

--Countdown to World Disaster: Hope & Protection for the Future. 1976. pap. 0.50 (ISBN 3-87209-620-6). Evang Sisterhood Mary.

--Dear Brothers & Sisters in Christ: Five Letters of Comfort. 1978. pap. 0.95 (ISBN 3-87209-622-2). Evang Sisterhood Mary.

--Father of Comfort. 128p. 1971. pap. 3.50 (ISBN 0-87123-156-5, 200156). Bethany Hse.

--God Laments & Our Response. Tr. of Gott Klagt und Unsere Antwort. 64p. 1981. 0.50 (ISBN 3-87209-625-7). Evang Sisterhood Mary.

--The Grace of Love. 1974. gift edition 0.95 (ISBN 3-87209-662-1). Evang Sisterhood Mary.

--Hidden in His Hands. LC 79-52346. 96p. 1979. pap. 2.95 (ISBN 0-87123-208-1, 200208). Bethany Hse.

--The Holy Land Today. rev. ed. 1975. 4.50 (ISBN 3-87209-610-9). Evang Sisterhood Mary.

--I Want to Console You. 72p. 1981. pap. 1.50 (ISBN 3-87209-626-5). Evang Sisterhood Mary.

--If I Only Love Jesus. 1973. pap. 0.95 (ISBN 0-551-05288-0). Evang Sisterhood Mary.

--Jesus, My Lord So Hated Today. 1978. pap. 0.50 (ISBN 3-87209-653-2). Evang Sisterhood Mary.

--The Joy of My Heart. 1978. pap. 0.95 (ISBN 3-87209-623-0). Evang Sisterhood Mary.

--Let Me Stand at Your Side. 1975. 2.95 (ISBN 3-87209-614-1). Evang Sisterhood Mary.

--More Precious Than Gold. 1978. pap. 4.95 (ISBN 0-88419-178-8). Creation Hse.

--My All for Him. 160p. 1971. pap. 3.95 (ISBN 0-87123-370-3, 200370). Bethany Hse.

--My Father I Trust You. 1976. pap. 1.00 (ISBN 3-87209-617-6). Evang Sisterhood Mary.

--O None Can Be Loved Like Jesus. 1974. pap. 1.00 (ISBN 3-87209-651-6). Evang Sisterhood Mary.

--Patmos: When the Heavens Opened. LC 76-24522. 1976. pap. 1.95 (ISBN 0-88419-012-9). Creation Hse.

--Praying Our Way Through Life. 32p. 1970. pap. 0.95 (ISBN 0-87123-455-6, 260455). Bethany Hse.

--Repentance: The Joy Filled Life. LC 83-23774. 96p. 1984. pap. 3.95 (ISBN 0-87123-592-7, 210592). Bethany Hse.

--Ruled by the Spirit. 144p. 1970. pap. 3.50 (ISBN 0-87123-483-1, 200483). Bethany Hse.

--Secreto de la Oracion Diaria. 96p. 2.50 (ISBN 0-88113-201-2). Edit Betania.

--Songs & Prayers of Victory. 1978. pap. 1.50 (ISBN 3-87209-652-4). Evang Sisterhood Mary.

--Those Who Love Him. LC 69-11639. 96p. 1981. pap. 2.95 (ISBN 0-87123-609-5, 200609). Bethany Hse.

--The Weapon of Prayer. 1974. Gift ed. 0.95 (ISBN 3-87209-658-3). Evang Sisterhood Mary.

--What Made Them So Brave? (Illus.). 1978. gift edition 2.25 (ISBN 3-87209-655-9). Evang Sisterhood Mary.

--Why Doesn't God Intervene? Evangelical Sisterhood of Mary, tr. from Ger. 32p. 1982. pap. 0.50 (ISBN 3-87209-629-X). Evang Sisterhood Mary.

--You Will Never Be the Same. 192p. 1972. pap. 3.50 (ISBN 0-87123-661-3, 200661). Bethany Hse.

Schlink, Mother Basilea. I Found the Key to the Heart of God. LC 75-23920. 416p. 1975. pap. 5.95 (ISBN 0-87123-239-1, 200239). Bethany Hse.

--In Our Midst. 1973. pap. 0.95 (ISBN 0-551-05289-9). Evang Sisterhood Mary.

--Realities of Faith. 144p. (Orig.). 1983. pap. 3.95 (ISBN 0-87123-299-5). Bethany Hse.

Schlink, Edmund. The Doctrine of Baptism. Bouman, Herbert, tr. from Ger. LC 78-159794. 256p. 1972. pap. 10.95 (ISBN 0-570-03726-3, 12-2628). Concordia.

Schlitzer, Albert L. Our Life in Christ. (University Theology Ser.: Vols. 1 & 2). 1962. Set. 12.95 (ISBN 0-268-00201-0). U of Notre Dame Pr.

--Prayerlife of the Church. 1962. 7.95x (ISBN 0-268-00214-2). U of Notre Dame Pr.

Schlitzer, Albert L., ed. Spirit & Power of Christian Secularity. LC 75-75154. 1969. 12.95 (ISBN 0-268-00321-1). U of Notre Dame Pr.

Schloegl, Irmgard, ed. The Wisdom of the Zen Masters. LC 75-42115. (The Wisdom Bks.). 96p. 1976. pap. 5.95 (ISBN 0-8112-0610-6, NDP415). New Directions.

Schloss, Malcolm & Purdom, Charles. Three Incredible Weeks with Meher Baba. Frederick, Filis, ed. LC 80-109542. (Illus.). 165p. 1979. pap. 5.95 (ISBN 0-913078-36-0). Sheriar Pr.

Schluchter, Wolfgang. The Rise of Western Rationalism: Max Weber's Developmental History. Roth, Guenther, tr. from Ger. LC 81-2763. 300p. 1981. 24.50x (ISBN 0-520-04060-0); pap. 9.95 (ISBN 0-520-05464-4, CAL 747). U of Cal Pr.

Schmahl, Phillip. Logic of Faith. LC 65-20327. 250p. 1965. 5.95 (ISBN 0-8022-1503-3). Philos Lib.

Schmalenberg, Erich. Das Todesverstaendnis bei Simone de Beauvoir: Eine Theologische Untersuchung. LC 72-77421. (Theologische Bibliothek Toepelmann, No. 25). 1972. 20.80x (ISBN 3-11-004036-0). De Gruyter.

Schmalenberger & Crotts. From Sunday to Sunday. (Orig.). 1986. pap. 4.25 (ISBN 0-937172-63-4). JLJ Pubs.

Schmalenberger, Jerry. Advent & Christmas Saints. 1984. 3.75 (ISBN 0-89536-685-1, 4861). CSS of Ohio.

--Saints Who Shaped the Church. Sherer, Michael L., ed. (Orig.). 1987. pap. 6.50 (ISBN 0-89536-856-0, 7815). CSS of Ohio.

--Stewards of Creation. (Orig.). 1987. pap. price not set (ISBN 0-89536-894-3, 7880). CSS of Ohio.

Schmalenberger, Jerry L. The Good News Way of Life. 1985. 4.75 (ISBN 0-89536-735-1, 5819). CSS of Ohio.

--The Good News Way of Life: Study Book. 1982. pap. 0.50 (ISBN 0-89536-531-6, 0729). CSS of Ohio.

--The Good News Way of Life: Teacher's Guide. 1982. pap. 3.00 (ISBN 0-89536-530-8, 0728). CSS of Ohio.

--Why Belong to the Church? 1971. 3.50 (ISBN 0-89536-261-9). CSS of Ohio.

Schmaus, Michael. Dogma, 6 vols. Incl. Vol. 1. God in Revelation (ISBN 0-87061-098-8); Vol. 2. God & Creation (ISBN 0-87061-099-6); Vol. 3. God & His Christ (ISBN 0-87061-100-3); Vol. 4. The Church (ISBN 0-87061-101-1); Vol. 5. Church As Sacrament (ISBN 0-87061-102-X); Vol. 6. Justification & the Last Things (ISBN 0-87061-103-8). 1984. Set. pap. 60.00 (ISBN 0-87061-095-3); pap. 10.00 ea. Chr Classics.

--Essence of Christianity. 288p. 1966. pap. 2.50 (ISBN 0-933932-16-2). Scepter Pubs.

Schmelig, Leddy & Schmelig, Randolph. Steps in Self-Knowledge. LC 79-64038. 1979. 5.95 (ISBN 0-87159-144-8). Unity School.

Schmelig, Randolph, jt. auth. see Schmelig, Leddy.

Schmeling, William A. Creation Versus Evolution--Not Really. 2nd ed. LC 76-19997. (Illus.). 1977. pap. text ed. 5.25 (ISBN 0-915644-12-6). Clayton Pub Hse.

Schmelz, U. O. Studies in Jewish Demography. 1983. 25.00x (ISBN 0-88125-013-9). Ktav.

Schmelzenbach, Elmer & Parrott, Leslie. Sons of Africa. 217p. 1979. 8.95 (ISBN 0-8341-0601-9). Beacon Hill.

Schmelzer, Menahem. Isaac ben Abraham ibn Ezra Poems (in Hebrew) 15.00x (ISBN 0-87334-011-6). Ktav.

Schmelzer, Menahem, ed. see Mekhilta, Munich.

Schmemann, Alexander. Church, World, Mission. LC 79-27597. 227p. 1979. pap. 7.95 (ISBN 0-913836-49-4). St Vladimirs.

--For the Life of the World: Sacraments & Orthodoxy. 151p. 1973. pap. 5.95 (ISBN 0-913836-08-7). St Vladimirs.

--Great Lent: Journey to Pascha. 1974. pap. 5.95 (ISBN 0-913836-04-4). St Vladimirs.

--Historical Road of Eastern Orthodoxy. LC 77-12074. 343p. 1977. pap. 8.95 (ISBN 0-913836-47-8). St Vladimirs.

--Introduction to Liturgical Theology. LC 66-69197. 170p. 1966. pap. 9.95 (ISBN 0-913836-18-4). St Vladimirs.

--Of Water & the Spirit: A Liturgical Study of Baptism. LC 74-30061. 170p. 1974. pap. 7.95 (ISBN 0-913836-10-9). St Vladimirs.

Schmemann, Alexander, ed. Ultimate Questions: An Anthology of Modern Russian Religious Thought. 310p. 1977. pap. 8.95 (ISBN 0-913836-46-X). St Vladimirs.

Schmerling, Hilda L. Finger of God: Religious Thought & Themes in Literature from Chaucer to Kafka. 1977. lib. bdg. 69.95 (ISBN 0-8490-1358-5). Gordon Pr.

Schmid, Georg. Principles of Integral Science of Religion. (Religion & Reason Ser.). 1979. text ed. 33.75 (ISBN 90-279-7864-6). Mouton.

Schmid, Heinrich. Doctrinal Theology of the Evangelical Lutheran Church. LC 66-13052. 1961. 25.95 (ISBN 0-8066-0107-8, 10-1930). Augsburg.

Schmid, Walter & Von Murat, Leonhard. Quellen zur Geschichte der Taufer in der Schweiz, Vol. 1: Zurich. 428p. 1952. PLB 9.00x (ISBN 0-8361-1152-4). Herald Pr.

Schmidt, Charles G. Histoire et Doctrine de la Secte des Cathares ou Albigeois, 2 vols. LC 78-63191. (Heresies of the Early Christian & Medieval Era: Second Ser.). 1979. Repr. of 1849 ed. 57.50 set (ISBN 0-404-16180-4). AMS Pr.

Schmidt, Dan. Follow the Leader. 144p. 1986. pap. 3.95 (ISBN 0-89693-629-5). Victor Bks.

Schmidt, Dorothy M. Pursuing Life's Adventures. LC 85-40650. 168p. 1985. pap. 5.95 (ISBN 0-938232-84-3, Dist. by Baker & Taylor Co.). Winston-Derek.

Schmidt, Elisabeth. Do We Hear the Song of This Joy? Meditations on the Acts of the Apostles. Hackett, Allen, tr. from Fr. 120p. (Orig.). 1983. pap. 6.95 (ISBN 0-8298-0680-6). Pilgrim NY.

--When God Calls a Woman: The Struggle of a Woman Pastor in France & Algeria. Hackett, Allen, tr. from Fr. LC 81-12009. 224p. (Orig.). 1981. pap. 7.95 (ISBN 0-8298-0430-7). Pilgrim NY.

Schmidt, Erik. Hegels System der Theologie. LC 73-81703. (Theologische Bibliothek Toepelmann 26). 210p. 1974. 26.80x (ISBN 3-11-004463-3). De Gruyter.

Schmidt, Henry J., ed. Witnesses to a Third Way. 160p. (Orig.). 1986. pap. 5.95 (ISBN 0-87178-940-X). Brethren.

Schmidt, J. David. Graffiti: Devotions for Girls. new ed. (Illus.). 128p. (Orig.). (YA) 1983. pap. 4.95 (ISBN 0-8007-5115-9, Power Bks). Revell.

--Graffiti: Devotions for Guys. new ed. (Illus.). 128p. (Orig.). (YA) 1983. pap. 4.95 (ISBN 0-8007-5114-0, Power Bks). Revell.

--More Graffiti: Devotions for Girls. (Illus.). 128p. (Orig.). 1984. pap. 4.95 (ISBN 0-8007-5143-4, Power Bks). Revell.

--More Graffiti: Devotions for Guys. (Illus.). 128p. 1984. pap. 4.95 (ISBN 0-8007-5142-6, Power Bks). Revell.

Schmidt, Jerry A. Do You Hear What You're Thinking? 1983. pap. 5.95 (ISBN 0-88207-381-8). Victor Bks.

Schmidt, John. Utopia II: An Investigation into the Kingdom of God. (Orig.). 1986. pap. 3.50 (ISBN 0-89540-154-1). Sun Pub.

Schmidt, John D. Ramesses II: A Chronological Structure of His Reign. LC 72-6558. (Near Eastern Studies). Repr. of 1973 ed. 56.00 (ISBN 0-8357-9282-X, 2011503). Bks Demand UMI.

Schmidt, Joseph. Praying Our Experience. (Illus.). 56p. (Orig.). 1980. pap. 1.95 (ISBN 0-88489-113-5). St Mary's.

Schmidt, Ludwig. De Deo: Studien Zur Literaturkritik und Thelogie des Buches Jona, des Gespraechs zwischen Abraham und Jahiwe in Gen. 18, 22ff. (Beiheft 143 zur Zeitschrift Fuer die Alttestamentliche Wissenschaft Ser.). 1976. 41.60x (ISBN 3-11-006618-1). De Gruyter.

Schmidt, Margaret F. Passion's Child: The Extraordinary Life of Jane Digby. 5.95 (ISBN 0-7043-3202-7, Pub. by Quartet England). Charles River Bks.

Schmidt, Marilee. Could I Be a Pastor. 1985. 2.95 (ISBN 0-8100-0199-3, 16N0781). Northwest Pub.

Schmidt, Martin, jt. auth. see Stephan, Horst.

Schmidt, Orlando. Sing & Rejoice! LC 79-84367. 192p. 1979. 6.95x (ISBN 0-8361-1210-5); pap. 5.95x (ISBN 0-8361-1211-3). Herald Pr.

Schmidt, Paul, jt. auth. see Belasic, David.

Schmidt, Paul F. Buddhist Meditation on China. LC 84-81398. (Illus.). 74p. 1984. lib. bdg. 15.00 (ISBN 0-912998-06-7); pap. 6.00 (ISBN 0-912998-07-5). Hummingbird.

--Coping with Difficult People. LC 79-27486. (Christian Care Bks.: Vol. 6). 120p. 1980. pap. 7.95 (ISBN 0-664-24299-5). Westminster.

--Religious Knowledge. LC 79-8726. ix, 147p. 1981. Repr. of 1961 ed. lib. bdg. 22.50x (ISBN 0-313-22188-X, SCRK). Greenwood.

Schmidt, Steffen W., et al. Friends, Followers & Factions: A Reader in Political Clientelism. LC 73-93060. 1977. 48.50x (ISBN 0-520-02696-9); pap. 12.95x (ISBN 0-520-03156-3, CAMPUS 167). U of Cal Pr.

Schmidt, W. The Origin & Growth of Religion: Facts & Theories. Rose, H. J., tr. from Ger. LC 74-184909. xvi, 302p. 1972. Repr. of 1931 ed. lib. bdg. 22.50x (ISBN 0-8154-0408-5). Cooper Sq.

Schmidt, Walter. Lay Evangelism Calling: Participants Manual. 1986. 4.50 (ISBN 0-89536-805-6, 6825); training manual 2.95 (ISBN 0-89536-800-5, 6818). CSS of Ohio.

Schmidt, Walter A. Recruiting Evangelism Callers: Enlisting & Coordinating Workers. 64p. (Orig.). 1984. pap. 3.95 (ISBN 0-8066-2069-2, 23-1830). Augsburg.

Schmidt, Werner H. Einfuehrung in das Alte Testament: Dritte, Erweiterte Auflage. (Ger.). x, 394p. 1985. 19.20x (ISBN 3-11-010403-2). De Gruyter.

--The Faith of the Old Testament: A History. Sturdy, John, tr. LC 82-21780. 312p. (Orig.). 1983. 25.00 (ISBN 0-664-21826-1); pap. 12.95 (ISBN 0-664-24456-4). Westminster.

Schmidt, William J. Architect of Unity. 1978. cloth 14.95 (ISBN 0-377-00080-9); pap. 9.95 (ISBN 0-377-00079-5). Friend Pr.

Schmier, Louis, ed. Reflections of Southern Jewry: The Letters of Charles Wessolowsky. LC 81-16995. viii, 184p. 1982. 12.95 (ISBN 0-86554-020-9, MUP-H15). Mercer Univ Pr.

Schmithals, Walter. Einleitung in die Drei Ersten Evangelien. 512p. 1985. 23.20x (ISBN 3-11-010263-3). De Gruyter.

Schmitt, Abraham. The Art of Listening with Love. (Festival Bks.). 176p. 1982. pap. 4.50 (ISBN 0-687-01836-6). Abingdon.

--Before I Wake: Listening to God in Your Dreams. 160p. 1984. pap. 7.95 (ISBN 0-687-02605-9). Abingdon.

--Turn Again to Life. LC 86-33581. 136p. (Orig.). 1987. pap. 8.95 (ISBN 0-8361-3436-2). Herald Pr.

Schmitt, Abraham & Schmitt, Dorothy. Renewing Family Life. LC 84-22504. (Orig.). 1985. pap. 6.95 (ISBN 0-8361-3384-6). Herald Pr.

--When a Congregation Cares. LC 84-19294. 128p. (Orig.). 1984. pap. 6.95 (ISBN 0-8361-3410-9). Herald Pr.

Schmitt, Carl. Political Theology: Four Chapters on the Concept of Sovereignity. Schwab, George, tr. from Ger. (German Social Thought Ser.). 75p. 1985. 15.00x (ISBN 0-262-19244-6). MIT Pr.

Schmitt, Dorothy, jt. auth. see Schmitt, Abraham.

Schmitt, F. S., jt. ed. see Southern, R. W.

Schmitt, Hans-Christoph. Die Nichtpriesterliche Josephsgeschichte (Gen 37-50) 1979. 34.40 (ISBN 3-11-007834-1). De Gruyter.

Schmitt, Keith R. Death & After-Life in the Theologies of Karl Barth & John Hick: A Comparative Study. (Amsterdam Studies in Theology Ser.: Vol. 5). 230p. 1985. pap. 32.50x (ISBN 90-6203-528-0, Pub. by Rodopi Holland). Humanities.

Schmitt, Robert C. The Missionary Censuses of Hawaii. (Pacific Anthropological Records: No. 20). 50p. pap. 5.00 (ISBN 0-910240-66-3). Bishop Mus.

Schmitz, Kenneth L. The Gift: Creation. (Aquinas Lecture Ser.). 160p. 1982. 12.95 (ISBN 0-87462-149-6). Marquette.

Schmitz, Robert E., jt. auth. see Luebering, Carol.

Schmoeger, C. E., ed. see Emmerich, Anne C.

Schmoger, Carl E. The Life of Anne Catherine Emmerich, 2 vols. 1976. Set. pap. 33.00 (ISBN 0-89555-061-X); Vol. 1. pap. 12.00 (ISBN 0-89555-059-8); Vol. 2. pap. 24.00 (ISBN 0-89555-060-1). TAN Bks Pubs.

Schmoger, Carl E., ed. see Emmerich, Anne C.

Schmucker, Samuel S. American Lutheran Church, Historically, Doctrinally, & Practically Delineated in Several Discourses. LC 72-83436. (Religion in American Ser). 1969. Repr. of 1851 ed. 20.00 (ISBN 0-405-00261-0). Ayer Co Pubs.

Schnackenburg, Rudolf. The Gospel According to St. John, 2 vols. 1980. 39.50x ea. Vol. 1 (ISBN 0-8245-0311-2). Vol. 2 (ISBN 0-8245-0312-0). Crossroad NY.

--The Gospel According to St. John, Vol. 3. 566p. 1982. 39.50x (ISBN 0-8245-0098-9). Crossroad NY.

--The Gospel According to St. Mark, Vol. II. McKenzie, John L., ed. LC 81-605. (The New Testament for Spiritual Reading Ser.). 182p. 1981. pap. 4.95 (ISBN 0-686-85824-7). Crossroad NY.

--Moral Teaching of the New Testament. pap. 7.95 (ISBN 0-8245-0329-5). Crossroad NY.

--Present & Future: Modern Aspects of New Testament Theology. 1966. 11.95x (ISBN 0-268-00215-0). U of Notre Dame Pr.

Schnakenburg, Rudolf. The Gospel According to St. Mark, Vol. I. McKenzie, John L., ed. LC 81-605. (The New Testament for Spiritual Reading Ser.). 182p. pap. 4.95 (ISBN 0-8245-0112-8). Crossroad NY.

Schnapper, Dominique. Jewish Identities in France: An Analysis of Contemporary French Jewry. Goldhammer, Arthur, tr. LC 82-17495. (Illus.). 224p. 1983. lib. bdg. 25.00x (ISBN 0-226-73910-4). U of Chicago Pr.

Schnaus, Urban, tr. see Kemmer, Alfons.

Schneeberger, Pierre-F. Japanese Lacquer: Selected Pieces. Watson, K., tr. (The Baur Collection Ser.). (Illus.). 193p. 1985. 195.00 (ISBN 0-7102-0320-9). Methuen Inc.

Schneemelcher, Wilhelm, ed. Bibliographia Patristica: Internationale Patristische Bibliographie. Incl. Vol. 1. Erscheinungen des Jahres 1956. xxviii, 103p. 1959. 13.80x (ISBN 3-11-001248-0); Vol. 2. Erscheinungen des Jahres 1957. xxx, 115p. 1959. 13.80 (ISBN 3-11-001249-9); Vol. 3. Erscheinungen des Jahres 1958. xxxi, 119p. 1960. 13.80x (ISBN 3-11-001250-2); Vol. 4. Erscheinungen des Jahres 1959. xxxiii, 126p. 1961. 9.20x (ISBN 3-11-001251-0); Vol. 5. Erscheinungen des Jahres 1960. xxxiii, 114p. 1962. 9.20x (ISBN 3-11-001252-9); Vol. 6. Erscheinungen des Jahres 1961. xxxiii, 98p. 1963. 9.20x (ISBN 3-11-001253-7); Vol. 7. Erscheinungen des Jahres 1962. xxxiv, 108p. 1964. 9.20x (ISBN 3-11-001254-5); Vol. 8. Erscheinungen des Jahres 1963. xxxiv, 120p. 1966. 12.00x (ISBN 3-11-001255-3); Vol. 9. Erscheinungen des Jahres 1964. xxxiv, 157p. 1967. 12.00x (ISBN 3-11-001256-1); Vol. 10. Erscheinungen Des Jahres 1965. xxxiv, 127p. 1969. 12.00x (ISBN 3-11-001257-X); Vol. 11. Erscheinungen Des Jahres 1966. 1971. **28.80x (ISBN 3-11-003531-6); Vols. 12 & 13. Erscheinungen Des Jahres 1967-68. 1975. 28.80x (ISBN 3-11-004631-8). De Gruyter.**

Schneewind, J. B. Sidgwick's Ethics & Victorian Moral Philosophy. 1977. 49.95x (ISBN 0-19-824552-1). Oxford U Pr.

Schneewind, J. B., ed. see Hume, David.

Schneid, Hayyim, ed. The Family. LC 73-11760. (Popular Judaica Library). (Illus.). 120p. 1974. pap. 3.95 (ISBN 0-8276-0029-1, 341). Jewish Pubns.

Schneider, A. M., jt. auth. see Meyer-Plath.

Schneider, Albert. Communion with the Saints. 1983. 25.00 (ISBN 0-686-45785-4). Franciscan Herald.

Schneider, Bernard. Holy Spirit & You. pap. 4.95 (ISBN 0-88469-119-5). BMH Bks.

Schneider, Bernard N. Deuteronomy: A Favored Book of Jesus. pap. 5.95 (ISBN 0-88469-051-2). BMH Bks.

--The Love of God. 1985. pap. 5.95 (ISBN 0-88469-167-5). BMH Bks.

--The World of Unseen Spirits. pap. 5.95 (ISBN 0-88469-024-5). BMH Bks.

Schneider, Claire. Inspirations Unlimited. 48p. (Orig.). 1985. pap. 4.95 (ISBN 0-9601982-2-9). Greenwood Hse.

Schneider, D. Douglas. Symbolically Speaking. Michael, ed. (Illus.). 85p. 1987. pap. 5.95 (ISBN 0-939169-01-0). World Peace Univ.

Schneider, Dick, jt. auth. see Jaworski, Leon.

Schneider, Edward D., ed. Questions about the Beginning of Life. LC 85-15617. 192p. (Orig.). 1985. pap. 8.95 (ISBN 0-8066-2167-2, 10-5360). Augsburg.

Schneider, Gerhard. The Epistle to the Galatians. McKenzie, John L., ed. LC 81-605. (New Testament for Spiritual Reading Ser.). 142p. 1981. pap. 4.95 (ISBN 0-8245-0124-1). Crossroad NY.

Schneider, Hans. Der Konziliarismus als Problem der Neueren Katholischen Theologie. (Arbeiten Zur Kirchengeschichte Ser.). 1976. 50.80x (ISBN 3-11-005744-1). De Gruyter.

Schneider, Herbert & Lawton, George. Prophet & a Pilgrim. LC 78-134433. (Illus.). Repr. of 1942 ed. 36.50 (ISBN 0-404-05610-5). AMS Pr.

Schneider, Herbert W. Morals for Mankind. LC 60-14882. 96p. 1960. 5.00x (ISBN 0-8262-0006-0). U of Mo Pr.

--Religion in Twentieth Century America. LC 52-8219. (The Library of Congress Ser. in American Civilization). (Illus.). 1952. 16.50x (ISBN 0-674-75700-9). Harvard U Pr.

Schneider, Herbert W., jt. auth. see Friess, Horace L.

Schneider, Johannes. Church & World in the New Testament. 59p. 1983. pap. 5.45 (ISBN 0-86554-063-2, P11). Mercer Univ Pr.

Schneider, John, ed. see Schelkle, Karl H.

Schneider, Kent E. The Creative Musician in the Church. 1976. pap. 8.95 (ISBN 0-89390-014-1). Resource Pubns.

Schneider, Laurence A. A Madman of Ch'u: The Chinese Myth of Loyalty & Dissent. LC 78-54800. (Center for Chinese Studies). 1980. 35.95x (ISBN 0-520-03685-9). U of Cal Pr.

Schneider, Louis & Dornbusch, Sanford M. Popular Religion: Inspirational Books in America. LC 58-11958. (Midway Reprint Ser.). pap. 46.50 (2026741). Bks Demand UMI.

Schneider, Reinhold. Messages from the Depths: (Selections from the Writings of Reinhold Schneider) Winterhalter, Curt, ed. Cunningham, Robert, tr. from Ger. 1977. pap. 2.50 (ISBN 0-8199-0683-2). Franciscan Herald.

Schneider, Terrance L. Advent: Twenty-Eight Ways to Celebrate the Holy in the Holiday Rush. (Illus.). 37p. 1982. pap. text ed. 1.95 (ISBN 0-86716-017-9). St Anthony Mess Pr.

Schneider, Yvonne. Life's Candle Light. 82p. pap. 5.95 (ISBN 0-942494-29-6). Coleman Pub.

Schneiderman, Leo. The Psychology of Myth, Folklore & Religion. LC 81-9471. 232p. 1981. text ed. 21.95x (ISBN 0-88229-659-0); pap. text ed. 10.95x (ISBN 0-88229-783-X). Nelson-Hall.

Schneiders, Sandra M. New Wineskins: Reimagining Religious Life Today. 320p. (Orig.). 1986. pap. 10.95 (ISBN 0-8091-2765-2). Paulist Pr.

Schnell, Ursula. Das Verhaeltnis von Amt und Gemeinde im Neueren Katholizismus. (Theologische Bibliothek Toepolmann: Vol. 29). 1977. pap. 41.20x (ISBN 3-11-004929-5). De Gruyter.

Schnell, William J. How to Witness to a Jehovah's Witness. Orig. Title: Christians, Awake! 160p. 1975. pap. 3.95 (ISBN 0-8010-8048-7). Baker Bk.

--Jehovah's Witnesses Errors Exposed. pap. 6.95 (ISBN 0-8010-8074-6). Baker Bk.

--Thirty Years a Watchtower Slave. (Direction Bks). pap. 3.95 (ISBN 0-8010-7933-0). Baker Bk.

Schner, George P. The Church Renewed: The Documents of Vatican II Reconsidered. 164p. (Orig.). 1986. lib. bdg. 24.50 (ISBN 0-8191-5505-5, Pub. by Regis College Toronto CN); pap. text ed. 10.75 (ISBN 0-8191-5506-3). U Pr of Amer.

Schneweis, Emil. Angels & Demons According to Lactantius. LC 79-8121. (Satanism Ser.). 192p. Repr. of 1944 ed. 26.00 (ISBN 0-404-18433-2). AMS Pr.

Schnitzler, Arthur. Some Day Peace Will Return: Notes on War & Peace. Weiss, Robert O., tr. from Ger. LC 78-15807. 1971. 8.50 (ISBN 0-8044-2803-4). Ungar.

Schochet, Eli. Animal Life in Jewish Tradition. LC 83-12015. 379p. 1983. 25.00x (ISBN 0-88125-019-8). Ktav.

Schochet, Elijah J. Taz Rabbi David Halevi. 10.00x (ISBN 0-87068-687-9). Ktav.

Schochet, Elijah Judah. Bach: Rabbi Joel Sirkes, His Life, Works & Times. 13.95 (ISBN 0-87306-031-8). Feldheim.

Schodde, tr. Book of Jubilees. LC 80-53467. 96p. 1980. pap. 4.00 (ISBN 0-934666-07-5). Artisan Sales.

Schodde, George H., intro. by. The Book of Enoch Translated from the Ethiopic. 1982. Repr. of 1882 ed. 39.00x (ISBN 0-403-08997-2, Regency). Scholarly.

Schoder, Raymond V., tr. from Gr. & intro. by. Paul Wrote from the Heart. (Gr. & Eng.). 64p. 1987. 24.50 (ISBN 0-86516-181-X). Bolchazy-Carducci.

Schoedel, Walter, jt. auth. see Rogahn, Kenneth.

Schoedel, William. Ignatius of Antioch: A Commentary on the Seven Letters of Ignatius. LC 84-48731. (Hermeneia Ser.). 320p. 1985. 34.95 (ISBN 0-8006-6016-1, 20-6016). Fortress.

Schoedel, William R., ed. see Athenagoras.

Schoen, Edward L. Religious Explanations: A Model from the Sciences. LC 84-24237. xiv, 226p. 1985. text ed. 24.75 (ISBN 0-8223-0616-6). Duke.

Schoenberg, Wilfred. Paths to the Northwest: A Jesuit History of the Oregon Province. 477p. 1983. 27.50 (ISBN 0-8294-0405-8). Loyola.

Schoenbrod, Gilbert A. The Anatomy of God & Man. (Illus.). 272p. 27.00 (ISBN 0-942494-02-4). Coleman Pub.

Schoene, Albrecht see Henkel, Arthur.

Schoeneberg, Lynn A., jt. auth. see Kaplan, Steven K.

Schoenfeld, Joachim. Holocaust Memoirs: Jews in the Lwow Ghetto, the Janowski Concentration Camp, & as Deportees in Siberia. 1985. text ed. 17.50x (ISBN 0-88125-074-0). Ktav.

--Shtetl Memoirs: Jewish Life in Galicia under the Austro-Hungarian Empire & in the Polish Republic, 1898-1939. 400p. 1985. text ed. 17.50x (ISBN 0-88125-075-9). Ktav.

Schoenfeld, Stuart, et al. Bar Mitzvah. LC 85-4412. (Illus.). 192p. 1985. 50.00 (ISBN 0-385-19826-4). Doubleday.

Schoenhals, Lawrence R. Companion to Hymns of Faith & Life. (Orig.). 1980. pap. 6.95 (ISBN 0-89367-040-5). Light & Life.

Schoenhals, Roger, ed. When Trouble Comes: How to Find God's Help in Difficult Times. (Orig.). 1978. pap. 2.95 (ISBN 0-89367-027-8). Light & Life.

Schoenl, William J. The Intellectual Crisis in English Catholicism: Liberal Catholics, Modernists, & the Vatican in the Late Nineteenth & Early Twentieth Centuries. Stanmsky, Peter & Hume, Leslie, eds. LC 81-48368. 360p. 1982. lib. bdg. 52.00 (ISBN 0-8240-5164-5). Garland Pub.

Schoenle, Volker. Johannes, Jesus und die Juden. (Beitroge zur Biblischen Exegese und Theologie: Vol. 17). (Ger.). 288p. 1982. 40.00 (ISBN 3-8204-5877-8). P Lang Pubs.

Schoeps, Hans J. Paul: The Theology of the Apostle in the Light of Jewish Religious History. Knight, Harold, tr. LC 61-10284. 304p. 1979. Repr. of 1961 ed. softcover 7.95 (ISBN 0-664-24273-1). Westminster.

Schoer, Karl J., compiled by. Christmas Plays From Oberufer. 3rd ed. Harwood, A. C., tr. & intro. by. 64p. 1973. pap. 3.50 (ISBN 0-85440-279-9, Pub. by Steinerbooks). Anthroposophic.

Schoffeleers, J. Matthew, jt. ed. see Van Binsbergen, Wim M. J.

Schoffler, Herbert. Abendland und Altes Testament. pap. 10.00 (ISBN 0-384-54210-7). Johnson Repr.

--Anfange Des Puritanismus. Repr. of 1932 ed. 16.00 (ISBN 0-384-54220-4). Johnson Repr.

Schofield, William H., tr. see Bugge, Sophus.

Scholem, Gersham G. Jewish Gnosticism, Merkabah Mysticism & Talmudic Tradition. 1960. 10.00x (ISBN 0-685-31427-8, Pub. by Jewish Theol Seminary). Ktav.

Scholem, Gershom. Kabbalah. 1978. pap. 10.95 (ISBN 0-452-00791-7, Mer). NAL.

--Major Trends in Jewish Mysticism. 3rd ed. LC 61-8991. 1961. pap. 8.95 (ISBN 0-8052-0005-3). Schocken.

--The Messianic Idea in Judaism: And Other Essays on Jewish Spirituality. LC 70-130212. 384p. 1972. pap. 8.95 (ISBN 0-8052-0362-1). Schocken.

--Messianic Idea in Judaism & Other Essays on Jewish Spirituality. 376p. pap. 7.95 (ISBN 0-686-95141-7). ADL.

--On Jews & Judaism in Crisis: Selected Essays. Dannhauser, Werner J., ed. LC 75-37010. 1978. 16.50 (ISBN 0-8052-3613-9). Schocken.

--On the Kabbalah & Its Symbolism. LC 65-11575. 1969. pap. 6.95 (ISBN 0-8052-0235-8). Schocken.

--Origins of the Kabbalah. Werblowsky, R. J., ed. Arkush, Allan, tr. 500p. 1987. 47.50 (ISBN 0-691-07314-7). Princeton U Pr.

--Sabbatai Sevi: The Mystical Messiah. Werblowski, R. Zwi, tr. from Hebrew. LC 75-166389. (Bollingen Series, Vol. 93). (Illus.). 1040p. 1973. 71.00x (ISBN 0-691-09916-2); pap. 22.50x (ISBN 0-691-01809-X). Princeton U Pr.

--Walter Benjamin: The Story of a Friendship. Zohn, Harry, tr. from Ger. LC 81-11790. (Illus.). 240p. 1981. 13.95 (ISBN 0-8276-0197-2). Jewish Pubns.

Scholem, Gershom, jt. auth. see Quispel, Gilles.

Scholem, Gershom, ed. Zohar-The Book of Splendor: Basic Readings from the Kabbalah. LC 63-11040. 1963. pap. 3.95 (ISBN 0-8052-0045-2). Schocken.

Scholer, David M. Basic Bibliographic Guide for New Testament. pap. 3.95 (ISBN 0-8028-1503-0). Eerdmans.

Scholer, David M., ed. Perspectives in Churchmanship: Essays in Honor of Robert G. Torbet. (Festschriften Ser.: No. 3). vi, 108p. 1986. write for info. (ISBN 0-86554-268-6, MUP/H231). NABPR.

Scholer, David M., ed. see Mills, Watson E.

Schollmeyer, Anastasius, ed. Sumerisch-Babylonische Hymnen und Gebete an Samas. Repr. of 1912 ed. 12.00 (ISBN 0-384-54240-9). Johnson Repr.

Scholz, Heinrich. Religionsphilosophie. rev. ed. (Ger.). xi, 332p. 1974. Repr. of 1922 ed. 36.80x (ISBN 3-11-002217-6). De Gruyter.

Scholz, Joachim J. Blake & Novalis. (European University Studies: Series 18, Comparative Literature, Vol. 19). 404p. 1978. 40.40 (ISBN 3-261-02576-X). P Lang Pubs.

Schomaker, Linda, jt. ed. see Sauerman, Thomas H.

Schomas, Rhonda. My Book of Gospel Treasures. (Illus.). 63p. (Orig.). 1980. pap. 3.95 (ISBN 0-87747-839-2). Deseret Bk.

Schon, James F. & Crowther, Samuel. Journals of the Rev. James Frederick Schon & Mr. Samuel Crowther Who with the Sanction of Her Majesty's Government; Accompanied the Expedition Up the Niger in 1841 on Behalf of the Church Missionary Society. 2nd ed. 394p. 1970. 37.50x (ISBN 0-7146-1877-2, F Cass Co). Biblio Dist.

Schonauer, Betty, jt. auth. see Wilkerson, Gwen.

Schonborn, Johann P. Von. Die Psalmen Des Koniglichen Propheten Davids. xl, 872p. Repr. of 1658 ed. 62.00. Johnson Repr.

Schonfeld-Brand, Rebecca, tr. see Meiseles, Meir.

Schonfield, Hugh J. The Politics of God. 2nd ed. LC 78-9024. (Illus.). 264p. 1978. pap. 9.95 (ISBN 0-916438-14-7). Univ of Trees.

--Popular Dictionary of Judaism. 1966. pap. 1.75 (ISBN 0-8065-0075-1, 232). Citadel Pr.

Schonfield, Hugh J., ed. & tr. from Gr. The Original New Testament: A Radical Translation & Reinterpretation. LC 85-42792. 628p. 1985. 19.45 (ISBN 0-06-250776-1, HarpR). Har-Row.

Schoof, Ted, ed. The Schillebeeckx Case. (Orig.). 1984. pap. 7.95 (ISBN 0-8091-2607-9). Paulist Pr.

School of Philosophy Editorial Committee. The Physical & Transcendental Analysis of the Soul. 74p. 1986. 47.50 (ISBN 0-89266-565-3). Am Classical Coll Pr.

Schoolcraft, H. R. Myth of Hiawatha, & Other Oral Legends, Mythologic & Allegoric, of the North American Indians. Repr. of 1856 ed. 28.00 (ISBN 0-527-80350-2). Kraus Repr.

Schoolland, Marian, tr. see Murray, Andrew.

Schoolland, Marian M. Leading Little Ones to God: A Child's Book of Bible Teaching. rev., 2nd ed. (Illus.). 96p. 1981. 14.95 (ISBN 0-8028-4035-3). Eerdmans.

--Marian's Big Book of Bible Stories. 1947. 12.95 (ISBN 0-8028-5003-0). Eerdmans.

--Marian's Favorite Bible Stories. 1948. 5.95 (ISBN 0-8028-5002-2); pap. 3.95 (ISBN 0-8028-5007-3). Eerdmans.

Schoonenberg, Piet. Covenant & Creation. LC 74-75119. 1969. 11.95 (ISBN 0-268-00311-4). U of Notre Dame Pr.

--Man & Sin: A Theological View. 1965. 7.95 (ISBN 0-268-00167-7). U of Notre Dame Pr.

Schopen, Gregory, ed. see Jong, J. W. De.

Schopenhauer, Arthur. The Essence of Religion. (Illus.). 109p. 1985. 98.85 (ISBN 0-89266-505-X). Am Classical Coll Pr.

--Free Will & Fatalism. (Illus.). 131p. 1985. 97.85 (ISBN 0-89266-508-4). Am Classical Coll Pr.

--On the Basis of Morality. Payne, E. F., tr. LC 65-26525. (Orig.). 1965. pap. write for info. (ISBN 0-02-392400-4, LLA203). Macmillan.

--Pantheism & the Christian System. (Illus.). 119p. 1987. 117.50 (ISBN 0-89266-588-2). Am Classical Coll Pr.

--Religion: A Dialogue, & Other Essays. 3rd ed. Saunders, T. Bailey, tr. LC 72-488. (Essay Index Reprint Ser.). Repr. of 1891 ed. 13.00 (ISBN 0-8369-2820-2). Ayer Co Pubs.

--Religion: A Dialogue, & Other Essays. Saunders, T. Bailey, tr. LC 72-11305. 140p. 1973. Repr. of 1899 ed. lib. bdg. 25.00x (ISBN 0-8371-6652-7, SCRE). Greenwood.

Schornbaum, Karl. Quellen zur Geschichte der Taufer. 34.00 (ISBN 0-384-54246-8); pap. 28.00 (ISBN 0-384-54245-X). Johnson Repr.

--Quellen zur Geschichte der Wiedertaufer. 34.00 (ISBN 0-384-54249-2); pap. 28.00 (ISBN 0-384-54248-4). Johnson Repr.

Schorsch, Anita & Greif, Martin. The Morning Stars Sang: The Bible in Popular & Folk Art. LC 78-52197. (Illus.). 128p. 1980. 12.95x (ISBN 0-87663-316-5); pap. 8.95 (ISBN 0-87663-985-6). Universe.

Schossberger, Emily M., tr. see Maier, Hans.

Schostak, Zev. Taharath Hamishpacha: Jewish Family Laws. 1982. 3.95 (ISBN 0-87306-100-4). Feldheim.

Schoterman, J. A., ed. The Yonitantra. 1985. 11.00x (ISBN 0-8364-1326-1, Pub. by Manohar India). South Asia Bks.

Schott, Carl P. Physical Education in the Colleges of the United Lutheran Church of America: A Survey & Program. (Columbia University. Teachers College. Contributions to Education: No. 379). Repr. of 1929 ed. 22.50 (ISBN 0-404-55379-6). AMS Pr.

Schottroff, Luise & Stegemann, Wolfgang. Jesus & the Hope of the Poor. O'Connell, Matthew, tr. from Ger. LC 86-5435. (Jesus von Nazareth-Hoffnung der Armen Ser.). 144p. (Orig.). 1986. pap. 9.95 (ISBN 0-88344-255-8, CIP). Orbis Bks.

Schottroff, Willy & Stegemann, Wolfgang, eds. God of the Lowly: Socio-Historical Interpretation of the Bible. LC 84-5152. Tr. of Der Gott der Kleinen Leute. 192p. (Orig.). 1984. pap. 9.95 (ISBN 0-88344-153-5). Orbis Bks.

Schoun, Benjamin D. Helping Pastors Cope: A Psycho-social Support System for Pastors. viii, 259p. 1982. pap. 9.95 (ISBN 0-943872-86-3). Andrews Univ Pr.

Schouppe, F. X. Purgatory--Explained by the Lives & Legends of the Saints. LC 86-50579. 427p. (Orig.). 1986. pap. 5.00 (Pulp Pocketbook (ISBN 0-89555-301-5). Tan Bks Pubs.

Schous, Gerald P. The Extramural Sanctuary of Demeter & Persephone at Cyrene, Libya, Final Reports: Volume II: The East Greek, Island, & Laconian Pottery. White, Donald, ed. (University Museum Monograph: No. 56). (Illus.). xxi, 121p. 1986. 45.00 (ISBN 0-934718-55-5). Univ Mus of U PA.

Schoville, Keith N. Biblical Archaeology in Focus. LC 78-62914. 24.95 (ISBN 0-8010-8112-2). Baker Bk.

Schraff, Anne E. Caught in the Middle. (Voyager Ser.). 80p. (Orig.). (YA) 1981. pap. 2.95 (ISBN 0-8010-8200-5). Baker Bk.

Schraff, Francis, et al. Learning about Jesus. rev. ed. 80p. 1980. pap. 1.95 (ISBN 0-89243-129-6). Liguori Pubns.

Schraffenberger, Nancy, jt. auth. see Herrick, Joy F.

Schrag, Calvin O. Communicative Praxis & the Space of Subjectivity. LC 84-48647. (Studies in Phenomenology & Existential Philosophy). 232p. 1986. 27.50x (ISBN 0-253-31383-X). Ind U Pr.

Schrage, Alice. Birth of the King. LC 80-53874. (Bible Biography Ser.). 128p. 1981. pap. 2.50 (ISBN 0-8307-0765-4, 5810507). Regal.

--The King Who Lives Forever. LC 81-50590. (Bible Biography Ser.). 128p. 1981. pap. text ed. 1.95 (ISBN 0-8307-0766-2, 5810604). Regal.

Schrage, Wolfgang. Ethics of the New Testament. Green, David E., tr. LC 86-45922. 384p. 1987. pap. 29.95 (ISBN 0-8006-0835-6, 1-835). Fortress.

Schrage, Wolfgang, jt. auth. see Gerstenberger, Erhard S.

Schram, Peninnah. Jewish Stories One Generation Tells Another. 350p. 1987. 30.00 (ISBN 0-87668-967-5). Aronson.

Schramm, Carol H. What Is a Freckle? 1975. pap. 1.25 (ISBN 0-8198-0484-3). Dghtrs St Paul.

Schramm, Edmund, jt. auth. see Cortes, Juan D.

Schramm, John & Schramm, Mary. Things That Make for Peace: A Personal Search for a New Way of Life. LC 76-3861. 96p. (Orig.). 1976. pap. 5.95 (ISBN 0-8066-1537-0, 110-6400). Augsburg.

Schramm, Mary, jt. auth. see Schramm, John.

Schramm, Mary R. Gifts of Grace. LC 82-70946. 1982. pap. 5.95 (ISBN 0-8066-1921-X, 10-2551). Augsburg.

Schramm, Tim. Der Markus-Stoff Bei Lukas. LC 79-96099. (New Testament Studies Monographs: No. 14). (Ger). 1971. 34.50 (ISBN 0-521-07743-5). Cambridge U Pr.

Schrank, Jeffrey. Teaching Human Beings: One Hundred One Subversive Activities for the Classroom. LC 73-179154. 288p. (Orig.). 1972. 9.95x (ISBN 0-8070-3176-3); pap. 5.95x (ISBN 0-8070-3177-1, BP425). Beacon Pr.

Schreck, Alan. Catholic & Christian. 240p. (Orig.). 1984. pap. 6.95 (ISBN 0-89283-181-2). Servant.

--Catholic & Christian Study Guide. 64p. (Orig.). 1985. pap. 2.95 (ISBN 0-89283-249-5). Servant.

--The Compact History of the Catholic Church. 192p. (Orig.). 1987. pap. 5.95 (ISBN 0-89283-328-9). Servant.

Schreck, Harley & Barrett, David, eds. Unreached Peoples '86: Clarifying the Task. pap. write for info. (ISBN 0-912552-58-1). Missions Adv Res Com Ctr.

Schreck, Nancy & Leach, Maureen. Psalms Anew. 208p. (Orig.). 1986. pap. 6.95 (ISBN 0-88489-174-7). St Mary's.

--Surrender: A Guide to Prayer. (Take & Receive Ser.). 165p. (Orig.). 1986. pap. 6.95t (ISBN 0-88489-171-2). St Mary's.

Schreiber, Aaron. Jewish Law & Decision-Making: A Study Through Time. 456p. 1980. lib. bdg. 39.95 (ISBN 0-87722-120-0). Temple U Pr.

Schreiber, B. C. Meditations for Mature Christians. LC 85-90050. 1985. 13.95 (ISBN 0-533-06578-X). Vantage.

Schreiber, Clara S. Katherine: Life of Luther. 1981. 6.95 (ISBN 0-8100-0144-6, 15N0385). Northwest Pub.

Schreiber, Mordecai, tr. see Gorodetsky, Benjamin.

Schreiber, Suzanne L. Yoga for the Fun of It! Hatha Yoga for Preschool Children. 2nd ed. (Illus.). 54p. (Orig.). 1981. pap. 6.00 (ISBN 0-9608320-0-9). Sugar Marbel Pr.

Schreiter, Robert, ed. see Schillebeeckx, Edward.

Schreiter, Robert J. Constructing Local Theologies. LC 84-14797. 240p. (Orig.). 1985. pap. 8.95 (ISBN 0-88344-108-X). Orbis Bks.

Schreivogel, Paul A. Small Prayers for Small Children. LC 76-135226. (Illus.). 32p. 1980. pap. 3.95 (ISBN 0-8066-1804-3, 10-5836). Augsburg.

Schreur, Clarence. Genesis & Common Sense. 109p. 1983. 12.50 (ISBN 0-942078-03-9). R Tanner Assocs Inc.

Schrieber, Angela. Our First Communion: A Growing-up Moment. Fischer, Carl, ed. 1986. dupl. masterbk 9.95 (ISBN 0-89837-107-4). Peter Li.

Schrieber, William I. Our Amish Neighbors. LC 62-17137. (Illus.). 1978. pap. 5.95 (ISBN 0-226-74035-8). U of Chicago Pr.

Schrier, Nettie V. see Vander Shrier, Nettie.

Schriner, Chris & Mauck, Sue I. Confident Living: Practical Psychology & the Christian Faith. (Illus.). 101p. (Orig.). 1982. pap. text ed. 6.00 (ISBN 0-914527-17-7). C-Four Res.

Schrodt, Paul. The Problem of the Beginning of Dogma in Recent Theology: Theology. (European University Studies: Ser. 23, Vol. 103). xxvi, 339p. 1978. pap. 40.40 (ISBN 3-261-02464-X). P Lang Pubs.

Schroeder, A., jt. auth. see Bonnet, L.

Schroeder, David. Faith Refined by Fire. LC 85-80428. (Faith & Life Bible Studies). 143p. (Orig.). 1985. pap. 4.95 (ISBN 0-87303-103-2). Faith & Life.

--Solid Ground: Facts of the Faith for Young Christians. Bubna, Paul, frwd. by. 255p. 1982. pap. 4.95 (ISBN 0-87509-323-X); Leader's guide 2.95 (ISBN 0-87509-326-4). Chr Pubns.

Schroeder, E. H., ed. see Freligh, H. M.

Schroeder, E. H., ed. see Mangham, Evelyn.

Schroeder, E. H., ed. see Pardington, G. P.

Schroeder, Frederick & Meyers, Craig. The Potential for Spiritual Direction in the New Rite of Penance. 1.85 (ISBN 0-89942-530-5, 530/04). Catholic Bk Pub.

Schroeder, Gordon H., jt. auth. see Knight, A. R.

Schroeder, H. J., tr. Canons & Decrees of the Council of Trent. LC 78-66132. 293p. 1978. pap. 8.00 (ISBN 0-89555-074-1). TAN Bks Pubs.

Schroeder, Janet E. Dialogue with the Other: Martin Buber & the Quaker Experience. LC 73-92486. 32p. (Orig.). 1973. pap. 2.50x (ISBN 0-87574-192-4). Pendle Hill.

Schroeder, L. Celebrate-While We Wait. (Illus.). 1977. pap. 4.95 (ISBN 0-570-03052-8, 6-1177). Concordia.

Schroeder, L. Bonnet A. Juan y Hechos: Tomo II. Cativiela, A., tr. 1986. Repr. of 1983 ed. 14.95 (ISBN 0-311-03051-3). Casa Bautista.

Schroeder, M. J. Mary-Verse in "Meistergesang". (Catholic University Studies in German: No. 16). 1970. Repr. of 1942 ed. 30.00 (ISBN 0-404-50236-9). AMS Pr.

Schroeder, Phil, ed. Ministry with the Community College: A Lutheran Perspective. (Illus.). 75p. 1982. pap. text ed. 2.75 (ISBN 0-9609438-0-3). Luth Coun IL.

Schroeder, Theodore W. I Don't Want to Complain, But: Teen Conversations with God. 112p. (Orig.). 1985. pap. 4.95 (ISBN 0-570-03964-9, 12-2999). Concordia.

--Let's Look at This the Right Way: A Guide for Christian Parents in Conflict with Their Teens. 112p. (Orig.). 1986. pap. 4.95 (ISBN 0-570-03987-8, 12-3015). Concordia.

--Pastor's Counseling Manual for Ministry to Those Who Must Sustain a Loved One in Crisis. 1981. pap. 2.75 (ISBN 0-570-08250-1, 12YY2922). Concordia.

Schroeder, Theodore W. & Nadasdy, Dean. Questions Teens Are Asking Today. 1987. pap. 5.95 (ISBN 0-570-04454-5). Concordia.

Schroeder, W. Widick. Cognitive Structures & Religious Research. xiii, 211p. 1971. 7.50 (ISBN 0-87013-150-8). Mich St U Pr.

Schroeder, W. Widick, jt. ed. see Lefevre, Perry.

Schroeder, W. Widick, jt. ed. see LeFevre, Perry.

Schroeder, W. Widick, et al. Suburban Religion: Churches & Synagogues in the American Experience. LC 74-82113. (Studies in Religion & Society). 1974. 19.95x (ISBN 0-913348-05-8); pap. 10.95x (ISBN 0-913348-11-2). Ctr Sci Study.

Schrolder, A. & Bonnet, L. Hebreos-Apocalipsis: Tomo IV. Cotiviela, A., tr. from Eng. (Comentario Sobre el Nuevo Testamento). 540p. 1986. Repr. of 1983 ed. 14.95 (ISBN 0-311-03053-X). Casa Bautista.

Schroll, Sr. M. Alfred. Benedictine Monasticism As Reflected in the Warnefrid-Hildemar Commentaries on the Rule. LC 77-140026. (Columbia University. Studies in the Social Sciences: No. 478). Repr. of 1941 ed. 20.00 (ISBN 0-404-51478-2). AMS Pr.

Schubert, Hans Von see Von Schubert, Hans.

Schubert, Joe D. Marriage, Divorce & Purity. (Way of Life Ser: No. 101). 1966. pap. 3.95 (ISBN 0-89112-101-3, Bibl Res Pr). Abilene Christ U.

Schubert, Kurt. Dead Sea Community: Its Origin & Teachings. Doberstein, John W., tr. LC 73-15245. 178p. 1974. Repr. of 1959 ed. lib. bdg. 22.50x (ISBN 0-8371-7169-5, SCDS). Greenwood.

Schubring, Walther. The Doctrine of the Jainas. Buerlen, Wolfgang, tr. 1978. Repr. 15.00 (ISBN 0-89684-005-0, Pub. by Motilal Banarsidass India). Orient Bk Dist.

Schuchert, Richard, tr. see Endo, Shusaku.

Schuck, Marjorie M., ed. see Eggstein, Kurt.

Schuckman, Roy. Puerto Rican Neighbor. 1983. pap. 2.50x (ISBN 0-87574-075-8, 075). Pendle Hill.

Schucman, Helen. Gifts of God. LC 81-70309. 1982. 20.00 (ISBN 0-9606388-1-4). Found Inner Peace.

Schuetze, A. Basic Doctrines of the Bible. 1969. pap. 2.50 (ISBN 0-8100-0016-4, 09N0921). Northwest Pub.

Schuetze, Armin W. & Habezk, Irwin J. The Shepherd Under Christ. LC 74-81794. 1974. text ed. 14.95 (ISBN 0-8100-0046-6, 15N0351). Northwest Pub.

Schufreider, Gregory. An Introduction to Anselm's Argument. 131p. 1978. 29.95 (ISBN 0-87722-133-2); pap. 14.95 (ISBN 0-87722-129-4). Temple U Pr.

Schug, John A. A Padre Pio Profile. (Orig.). 1987. pap. 4.95 (ISBN 0-932506-56-9). St Bedes Pubns.

Schul, Bill & Pettit, Ed. Pyramids & the Second Reality. 1979. pap. 4.95 (ISBN 0-449-90008-8, Columbine). Fawcett.

--Secret Power of Pyramids. 1987. pap. 3.50 (ISBN 0-449-13986-7, GM). Fawcett.

Schuler, Eugenia, ed. see Chadwick, Enid M.

Schuler, G. H., ed. Egypt & Nuclear Technology: The Peace Divident. (Significant Issues Ser.: Vol. V, No. 9). 24p. (Orig.). 1983. pap. text ed. 6.95 (ISBN 0-8191-5924-7, Pub. by CSIS). U Pr of Amer.

Schuller, Arvella. The Positive Family. 1983. pap. 2.75 (ISBN 0-8007-8474-X, Spire Bks). Revell.

Schuller, Arvella, jt. auth. see Schuller, Robert H.

Schuller, Bruno. Wholly Human: Essays on the Theory & Language of Morality. Heinegg, Peter, tr. from Ger. Orig. Title: Der Menschliche Mensch. 256p. (Orig.). 1986. 17.95 (ISBN 0-87840-427-9); pap. 9.95 (ISBN 0-87840-422-8). Georgetown U Pr.

Schuller, Eileen M. Non-Canonical Psalms from Qumran: A Pseudepigraphic Collection. (Harvard Semitic Studies). 1987. 23.95 (ISBN 0-89130-943-8, 04-04-28). Scholars Pr GA.

Schuller, Robert. The Be-Happy Attitudes. 1985. 12.95 (ISBN 0-8499-0363-7). Word Bks.

--The Be-Happy Attitudes. lg. print ed. 1986. 12.95 (ISBN 0-8499-3055-3). Word Bks.

--Daily Power Thoughts. 384p. 1984. pap. 3.95 (ISBN 0-515-08164-7). Jove Pubns.

--God's Way to the Good Life. (Religion Ser.). 144p. 1987. pap. 2.95 (ISBN 0-553-26803-1). Bantam.

--Power Ideas for a Happy Family. 1982. pap. 1.95 (ISBN 0-515-06499-8). Jove Pubns.

--Tough Times Never Last but Tough People Do! 256p. 1984. pap. 3.95 (ISBN 0-553-24245-8). Bantam.

Schuller, Robert A., ed. Robert Schuller's Life Changers. 192p. 1981. 2.75 (ISBN 0-8007-8476-6, Spire Bks). Revell.

Schuller, Robert A., ed. see Schuller, Robert H.

Schuller, Robert H. Be Happy - You Are Loved! 224p. 1986. 15.95 (ISBN 0-8407-5517-1). Nelson.

--Daily Power Thoughts. LC 77-68012. 1978. 9.95 (ISBN 0-89081-131-8); pap. 6.95 (ISBN 0-89081-123-7). Harvest Hse.

--Discover Freedom. (Orig.). 1978. pap. 1.25 (ISBN 0-89081-155-5). Harvest Hse.

--Discover How Tou Can Turn Activity into Energy. (Orig.). 1978. pap. 1.25 (ISBN 0-89081-135-0). Harvest Hse.

--Discover Self-Love. (Orig.). 1978. pap. 1.25 (ISBN 0-89081-134-2). Harvest Hse.

--Discover Your Possibilities. (Orig.). 1980. pap. 3.95 (ISBN 0-89081-214-4). Harvest Hse.

--God's Way to the Good Life. LC 74-18978. (Pivot Family Reader Ser). 128p. 1974. pap. 1.75 (ISBN 0-87983-098-0). Keats.

--Living Powerfully One Day at a Time. 400p. 1983. pap. 7.95 (ISBN 0-8007-5113-2, Power Bks). Revell.
--Move Ahead with Possibility Thinking. 224p. 1973. pap. 2.95 (ISBN 0-8007-8105-8, Spire Bks). Revell.
--Power Ideas for a Happy Family. 1987. 8.95 (ISBN 0-8007-1528-4). Revell.
--Reach Out for New Life. 1979. pap. 3.50 (ISBN 0-553-25222-4). Bantam.
--Robert H. Schuller Tells You How to Be an Extraordinary Person in an Ordinary World. Schuller, Robert A., ed. 1987. 16.95 (Large Print Bks). G K Hall.
--Self-Esteem: The New Reformation. 144p. 1982. 3.95 (ISBN 0-8499-4172-5). Word Bks.
--Self-Love. 160p. 1975. pap. 2.95 (ISBN 0-8007-8195-3, Spire Bks). Revell.
--Tough-Minded Faith for Tender-Hearted People. LC 83-22144. 384p. 1984. 14.95 (ISBN 0-8407-5358-6). Nelson.
--Tough Minded Faith for Tender Hearted People. Date not set. 16.95 (ISBN 0-8161-3806-0, Large Print Bks); pap. 9.95 (ISBN 0-8161-3815-X). G K Hall.
--Tough Times Never Last, but Tough People Do! LC 83-4160. (Illus.). 240p. 1983. 12.95 (ISBN 0-8407-5287-3); pap. text ed. 5.95 (ISBN 0-8407-5936-3). Nelson.
--Tough Times Never Last, but Tough People Do! (General Ser.). 1984. lib. bdg. 13.95 (ISBN 0-8161-3677-7, Large Print Bks). G K Hall.
--Turning Your Stress into Strength. LC 77-88865. 144p. 1978. pap. 4.95 (ISBN 0-89081-113-X). Harvest Hse.
--You Can Become the Person You Want to Be. 160p. 1976. pap. 2.95 (ISBN 0-8007-8235-6, Spire Bks). Revell.
--Your Church Has a Fantastic Future. LC 86-11906. 364p. (Orig.). 1986. pap. 7.95 (ISBN 0-8307-1126-0, 5418785). Regal.
--Your Church Has a Fantastic Future! A Possibility Thinker's Guide to a Successful Church. rev. ed. LC 86-11906. (Illus.). 336p. 1986. pap. 14.95 (ISBN 0-8307-1180-5, 5111659). Regal.

Schuller, Robert H. & Schuller, Arvella. The Courage of Carol: Pearls from Tears. LC 78-65619. 1978. pap. 2.50 (ISBN 0-89081-182-2). Harvest Hse.

Schulman, Elias. A History of Jewish Education in the Soviet Union, 1918-1948. 1971. 25.00x (ISBN 0-87068-145-1). Ktav.
--The Holocaust in Yiddish Literature. 96p. 1983. pap. 4.00 (ISBN 0-318-20364-2). Workmen's Circle.

Schulman, Martin. Karmic Astrology: Retrogrades & Reincarnation. LC 83-104490. (Vol. 2). 1977. pap. 5.95 (ISBN 0-87728-345-1). Weiser.
--Karmic Relationships. LC 84-51376. 1984. pap. 7.95 (ISBN 0-87728-508-X). Weiser.

Schulman, Michael & Mekler, Eva. Bringing up a Moral Child: A New Approach for Teaching Your Child to Be Kind, Just & Responsible. LC 84-18472. 1985. 19.95 (ISBN 0-201-16442-6); pap. 12.95 (ISBN 0-201-16443-4). Addison-Wesley.

Schulte, Hannelis. Die Entstehung der Geschichtsschreibung Im Alten Israel. (Beiheft 128 zur Zeitschrift fuer die altestamentliche Wissenschaft). 1972. 36.40x (ISBN 3-11-003960-5). De Gruyter.

Schultenover, David G. George Tyrrell: In Search of Catholicism. LC 81-38406. (Illus.). xiv, 505p. 1981. 32.50x (ISBN 0-915762-13-7). Patmos Pr.

Schultheis, Michael J., et al. Our Best Kept Secret: The Rich Heritage of Catholic Social Teaching. (Illus.). 60p. (Orig.). 1985. pap. text ed. 3.50 (ISBN 0-934255-01-6). Center Concern.
--Our Best Kept Secret: The Rich Heritage of Catholic Social Teaching. rev. & expanded ed. 75p. (Orig.). 1987. pap. text ed. 4.50 (ISBN 0-934255-03-2). Center Concern.

Schultheis, Rob. Bone Games: One Man's Search for the Ultimate Athletic High. LC 84-42622. 240p. 1985. 15.95 (ISBN 0-394-53967-2). Random.

Schultz, Albert L. God's Call: Exodus Second Part. Bartlett, Kenneth, ed. (Books of Oral Tradition: No. 4). 80p. (Orig.). 1986. pap. 9.85 (ISBN 0-936596-11-2). Quantal.

Schultz, Douglas G. Eight Sculptors. LC 79-50457. (Illus.). 1979. pap. 6.50 (ISBN 0-914782-25-8). Buffalo Acad.

Schultz, H. Milton & Forbidden Knowledge. (MLA RFS). 1955. 22.00 (ISBN 0-527-80600-5). Kraus Repr.

Schultz, Joani, jt. auth. see Schultz, Thom.

Schultz, Joani, et al. Youth Ministry Cargo. LC 86-14836. (Illus.). 410p. (Orig.). 1986. 18.95 (ISBN 0-931529-14-X). Group Bks.

Schultz, Kathleen, et al, eds. The Radical Preacher's Sermon Book. (Illus.). 96p. 1983. pap. 4.00 (ISBN 0-9612114-0-7). Inst People's Church.

Schultz, Paul. A History of the Apostolic Succession of Archbishop Emile F. Rodriguez-Fairfield from the Mexican National Catholic Church. 100p. Date not set. Repr. lib. bdg. 19.95x (ISBN 0-89370-557-8). Borgo Pr.

Schultz, Robert C. & Lehmann, Helmut T., eds. Luther's Works: The Christian in Society III, Vol. 46. LC 55-9893. 1967. 19.95 (ISBN 0-8006-0346-X, 1-346). Fortress.

Schultz, Robert C., tr. see Althaus, Paul.

Schultz, Robert C., tr. see Lohse, Bernhard.

Schultz, Samuel. Deuteronomy. (Everyman Bible Commentary Ser). 128p. (Orig.). 1971. pap. 5.95 (ISBN 0-8024-2005-2). Moody.
--Ley e Historia del Antiguo Testamento. Villalobos, Fernando P., tr. from Eng. (Curso Para Maestros Cristianos Ser.: No. 1). (Span., Illus.). 122p. 1972. pap. 3.50 (ISBN 0-89922-008-8); instructor's manual 1.50 (ISBN 0-89922-009-6). Edit Caribe.

Schultz, Samuel J. Deuteronomio: El Evangelio del Amor (Comentario Biblico Portavoz) Orig. Title: Deuteronomy (Everyman's Bible Commentary) (Span.). 122p. 1979. pap. 3.50 (ISBN 0-8254-1658-2). Kregel.
--The Gospel of Moses. 1979. 6.95 (ISBN 0-8024-3198-4). Moody.
--Leviticus. (Everyman's Bible Commentary Ser.). (Orig.). 1983. pap. 5.95 (ISBN 0-8024-0247-X). Moody.
--The Old Testament Speaks. 3rd ed. LC 80-7740. (Illus.). 448p. 1980. 17.95xi (ISBN 0-06-067134-3, HarpR). Har-Row.
--Old Testament Survey: Law & History. rev. ed. LC 64-10037. 96p. 1968. pap. text ed. 4.95 (ISBN 0-910566-01-1); Perfect bdg. instr's. guide 5.95 (ISBN 0-910566-20-8). Evang Tchr.

Schultz, Thom & Schultz, Joani. Involving Youth in Youth Ministry. 200p. (Orig.). 1987. pap. 9.95 (ISBN 0-931529-20-4). Group Bks.

Schultz, Thom, ed. The Best of Try This One. (Illus.). 80p. (Orig.). 1977. pap. 5.95 (ISBN 0-936664-01-0). Group Bks.
--More...Try This One. LC 80-80947. (Illus.). 80p. (Orig.). 1980. pap. 5.95 (ISBN 0-936664-00-2). Group Bks.

Schultz, W. A. Sermon Outlines. 3.95 (ISBN 0-88027-092-6). Firm Foun Pub.

Schultze, Lilli. Shadow of Death. 1981. 3.50 (ISBN 0-87813-516-2). Christian Light.

Schulweis, Harold M. Evil & the Morality of Ged. (Hebrew Union College Jewish Perspectives Ser.: No. 3). 1984. 15.00 (ISBN 0-87820-502-0). Hebrew Union Coll Pr.

Schulweis, Harold M., jt. ed. see Bronstein, Daniel J.

Schulz, Hans-Joachim. The Byzantine Liturgy. O'Connell, Matthew J., tr. from Ger. (Orig.). 1986. pap. 17.50 (ISBN 0-916134-72-5). Pueblo Pub Co.

Schulz, Reuel J. Idols: Dead or Alive? 7.95 (ISBN 0-686-91886-X, 12N1724). Northwest Pub.

Schulz, Thomas. Charis: The Meaning of Grace in the New Testament. 78p. 1971. pap. 3.95 (ISBN 0-911620-06-0). Westcott.

Schulzinger, Morris S. The Tale of a Litvak. LC 84-7693. (Illus.). 379p. 1985. 24.95 (ISBN 0-8022-2454-7). Philos Lib.

Schumacher, Claire W. This Is Our St. Rose Church in Proctor Minnesota. (Illus.). 100p. 1976. pap. 3.00 (ISBN 0-917378-02-4). Schumacher Pubns.

Schumacher, E. F. & Gillingham, Peter N. Good Work. LC 76-5528. 1980. pap. 6.95x (ISBN 0-06-132053-6, TB 2053, Torch). Har-Row.

Schumacher, Evelyn A. Covenant Love: Reflections on the Biblical Covenant Theme. (Orig.). 1981. pap. 2.95 (ISBN 0-914544-38-1). Living Flame Pr.

Schumacher, Evelyn Ann, Sr. Presence Through the Word. 144p. (Orig.). 1983. pap. 2.95 (ISBN 0-914544-46-2). Living Flame Pr.

Schumacher, John N. Revolutionary Clergy: The Filipino Clergy & the Nationalist Movement, 1850-1903. 306p. 1982. (Pub. by Ateneo De Manila U Pr Philippines); pap. 17.50. Cellar.

Schumacher, Marigwen, tr. see Bonaventure, Saint.

Schumacher, Philip, tr. see Knecht, F. J.

Schumacher, Philip, tr. see Schuster, Ignatius.

Schumacher, Verle C. Anniversaries to Celebrate. LC 83-2228. 128p. (Orig.). 1982. pap. 7.95 (ISBN 0-8298-0628-8). Pilgrim NY.

Schumacher, William A. Roman Replies, 1983. 24p. (Orig.). 1983. pap. 3.00 (ISBN 0-943616-21-2). Canon Law Soc.

Schumacher, William A. & Cuneo, J. James, eds. Roman Replies & CLSA Advisory Opinions, 1985. 68p. (Orig.). 1985. pap. 5.50 (ISBN 0-943616-30-1). Canon Law Soc.

Schuman, Verne B. Washington University Papyri I: Non-Literary Texts, Nos. 1-16. LC 79-14199. (American Society of Papyrologists Ser.: No. 310017). 15.00 (ISBN 0-89130-286-7, 310017). Scholars Pr GA.

Schumann, Hans W. Buddhism. Fenerstein, Georg, tr. from Ger. LC 74-6302. (Illus.). 200p. 1974. pap. 7.95 (ISBN 0-8356-0457-8). Theos Pub Hse.

Schuon, Frithjof. Christianity - Islam: Essays on Esoteric Ecumenicism. LC 84-52674. (The Library of Traditional Wisdom). 270p. 1985. pap. 12.00 (ISBN 0-941532-05-4). Wrld Wisdom Bks.
--Esoterism as Principle & as Way. 240p. 1981. pap. 7.50 (ISBN 0-900588-23-3). Wrld Wisdom Bks.
--From the Divine to the Human: Survey of Metaphyisics & Epistemology. LC 82-50333. (The Library of Traditional Wisdom). 156p. 1982. pap. 7.00 (ISBN 0-941532-01-1). Wrld Wisdom Bks.
--Sufism: Veil & Quintessence. LC 81-69573. (The Library of Traditional Wisdom). 163p. pap. 7.00 (ISBN 0-941532-00-3). Wrld Wisdom Bks.
--Survey of Metaphysics & Esoterism. Polit, Gustavo, tr. from Fr. LC 86-13261. (The Library of Traditional Wisdom). Orig. Title: Resume de Metaphysique Integral Sur les Traces de la Religion Perenne. 224p. (Orig.). 1986. pap. 12.00 (ISBN 0-941532-06-2). Wrld Wisdom Bks.
--The Transcendent Unity of Religions. Rev. ed. LC 84-239. 165p. 1984. pap. 7.95 (ISBN 0-8356-0587-6, Quest). Theos Pub Hse.
--Understanding Islam. Matheson, D. M., tr. (Unwin Paperback Ser.). 1976. pap. 5.95 (ISBN 0-04-297035-0). Allen Unwin.

Schupack, Joseph. The Dead Years: Surviving the Holocaust. LC 86-81286. 1987. 16.95 (ISBN 0-89604-066-6); pap. 10.95 (ISBN 0-89604-067-4). Holocaust Pubns.

Schuppert, Mildred. Digest & Index of the Minutes of General Synod, 1958-1977. pap. 10.95 (ISBN 0-8028-1774-2). Eerdmans.

Schure, Edouard. From Sphinx to Christ: An Occult History, Vol. 16. 2nd ed. LC 70-130818. (Spiritual Science Library). 288p. 1981. lib. bdg. 16.00 (ISBN 0-89345-011-1). Garber Comm.
--The Great Initiates: A Study of the Secret History of Religions. LC 79-3597. (Harper Library of Spiritual Wisdom). (Fr.). 528p. 1980. pap. 9.95 (ISBN 0-06-067125-4, RD 400, HarpR). Har-Row.

Schure, Edward. Great Initiates: Secret History of Religions, Vol. 3. LC 61-8623. (Spiritual Science Library). 528p. 1982. Repr. of 1961 ed. lib. bdg. 23.00 (ISBN 0-89345-025-1, Spiritual Sci Lib). Garber Comm.
--Krishna & Orpheus. 69.95 (ISBN 0-8490-0475-6). Gordon Pr.

Schure, Edward, jt. auth. see Steiner, Rudolf.

Schurer, Emil. History of the Jewish People in the Age of Jesus Christ, Vol. 3, Pt. 2. Vermes, Geza, et al, eds. 250p. 1986. 29.95 (ISBN 0-567-09373-5, Pub. by T & T Clark Ltd UK). Fortress.
--History of the Jewish People in the Age of Jesus Christ, Vol. 3, Pt. 1. Vermes, Geza, et. al, eds. 704p. 1986. 48.50 (ISBN 0-567-02244-7, Pub. by T & T Clark Ltd UK). Fortress.
--A History of the Jewish People in the Time of Jesus. Glatzer, Nahum N., ed. LC 61-8195. 1961. pap. 7.95 (ISBN 0-8052-0008-8). Schocken.
--Schurer's History of the Jewish People in the Age of Jesus Christ, 2 vols. Vermes, Geza, et al, eds. 42.95 ea. (Pub. by T & T Clark Ltd UK). Vol. 1, 1973, 608 pgs (ISBN 0-567-02242-0). Vol. 2, 1979, 608 pgs (ISBN 0-567-02243-9). Fortress.

Schurhammer. Indonesia & India, Fifteen Forty-Five to Fifteen Forty-Nine. 726p. (Orig.). 1980. 40.00 (ISBN 0-8294-0356-6). Loyola.

Schurhammer, Georg. Francis Xavier, His Life, His Times. Costelloe, M. Joseph, tr. Incl. Vol. 1. Europe, 1506-1541. (Illus.). xxxii, 791p. 1973. 35.00 (ISBN 0-8294-0354-X); Vol. 2. India, 1541-1545. (Illus.). xvi, 759p. 1977. 35.00 (ISBN 0-8294-0355-8); Vol. 3. Indonesia & India, 1545-1549. xiv, 726p. 1980. 40.00 (ISBN 0-8294-0356-6); Vol. 4. Japan, India & China, 1549-1552. xii, 713p. 1982. 45.00 (ISBN 0-8294-0357-4). LC 72-88247. (Illus.). Jesuit Hist.

Schurmann, Heinz, et al. The First & Second Epistle to the Thessalonians. McKenzie, John L., ed. LC 81-605. (New Testament for Spiritual Reading Ser.). 168p. 1981. pap. 4.95 (ISBN 0-8245-0127-6). Crossroad NY.

Schurmann, Reiner, tr. see Eckhart, Meister.

Schuster, Clara S., ed. Jesus Loves Me, Too. 160p. (Orig.). 1985. pap. 6.95 (ISBN 0-8341-1074-1). Beacon Hill.

Schuster, George N. Catholic Authors, Crown Edition. (Illus.). (YA) 1952. pap. 3.95 (ISBN 0-910334-23-4). Cath Authors.

Schuster, Ignatius. Bible History. Heck, H. J., ed. Schumacher, Philip, tr. (Illus.). 1974. pap. 8.00 (ISBN 0-89555-006-7). TAN Bks Pubs.

Schuster, Louis A., et al, eds. see More, St. Thomas.

Schutte, Josef F. Valignano's Mission Principles for Japan: Vol. I (1573-1582), Pt. I - The Problem (1573-1580) Coyne, John J., tr. from Ger. LC 78-69683. (Modern Scholarly Studies About the Jesuits, in English Translations, Ser. II: No. 3). (Illus.). xxiv, 428p. 1980. 14.00 (ISBN 0-912422-36-X); pap. 12.00 smyth sewn (ISBN 0-912422-35-1). Inst Jesuit.
--Valignano's Mission Principles for Japan: Vol. I (1573-1582), Pts. I & II: The Problem 1573-1580 & The Solution 1580 to 1582. Ganss, G. E. & Fischer, P. C., eds. LC 78-69683. (Modern Scholarly Studies about the Jesuits, in English Translations: No. 5). Orig. Title: Valignanos Missionsgrundsatze Fur Japan. Tr. of Ger. 398p. 1985. 16.00 (ISBN 0-912422-76-9); pap. 14.00 sewn (ISBN 0-912422-75-0). Inst Jesuit.

Schutz, Albert & Schaps, Hilda W. Kosher Yoga: Cabalistic Roots of Western Mysticism. LC 83-60144. 128p. (Orig.). 1983. 12.95 (ISBN 0-936596-09-0); pap. 8.95 (ISBN 0-936596-08-2). Quantal.

Schutz, Albert L. Call Adonoi: Manual of Practical Cabalah & Gestalt Mysticism. LC 80-50264. (Illus.). 200p. (Orig.). 1980. 11.95 (ISBN 0-936596-01-5); pap. 8.95 (ISBN 0-936596-00-7). Quantal.
--Exodus-Exodus, Cabalistic Bible: Part I, Slavery & the Coming of Moses. (Orig.). 1984. pap. 6.95 (ISBN 0-936596-10-4). Quantal.

Schutz, J. H. Paul & the Anatomy of Apostolic Authority. LC 74-76573. (Society for New Testament Studies, Monographs: No. 26). 1975. 59.50 (ISBN 0-521-20464-X). Cambridge U Pr.

Schutz, John H., tr. see Theissen, Gerd.

Schutz, Roger. A Life We Never Dared Hope For. 80p. (Orig.). 1981. pap. 3.95 (ISBN 0-8164-2322-9, HarpR). Har-Row.
--Living Today for God. 80p. (Orig.). 1981. pap. 3.95 (ISBN 0-8164-2323-7, HarpR). Har-Row.

Schutz, Susan P. Creeds to Live By, Dreams to Follow. LC 86-7318. (Illus.). 64p. (Orig.). 1987. pap. 4.95 (ISBN 0-88396-248-9). Blue Mtn Pr Co.

Schutz, Wilhelm W. Pens under the Swastika. LC 70-118415. 1971. Repr. of 1946 ed. 19.95x (ISBN 0-8046-1192-0, Pub. by Kennikat). Assoc Faculty Pr.

Schuyler, Montgomery. Index Verborum of the Fragments of the "Avesta". LC 2-15630. (Columbia University. Indo-Iranian Ser.: No. 4). Repr. of 1901 ed. 14.50 (ISBN 0-404-50474-4). AMS Pr.

Schwab, George, tr. see Schmitt, Carl.

Schwab, Gustav. Gods & Heroes. LC 47-873. 1977. pap. 9.95 (ISBN 0-394-73402-5). Pantheon.

Schwab, Moise. Repertoire des Articles Relatifs a l'Histoire et a la Litterature Juives Parus dans les Periodiques De 1665 a 1900. rev. ed. (Fr.). 1971. 79.50 (ISBN 0-87068-163-X). Ktav.

Schwab, Richard C. Let the Bible Speak...About Tongues. LC 85-8098. (Illus.). 144p. (Orig.). 1985. pap. 6.95 (ISBN 0-8254-3753-9). Kregel.

Schwab, Simon. These & Those. 3.50 (ISBN 0-87306-076-8). Feldheim.

Schwaller, John F. The Origins of Church Wealth in Mexico: Ecclesiastical Revenues & Church Finances, 1523-1600. LC 85-1122. (Illus.). 241p. 1985. 22.50x (ISBN 0-8263-0813-9). U of NM Pr.

Schwaller De Lubicz, Isha. Her-Bak Egyptian Initiate. Fraser, Ronald, tr. from Fr. (Illus.). 400p. 1982. pap. 9.95 (ISBN 0-89281-002-5). Inner Tradit.

Schwaller de Lubicz, R. A. The Egyptian Miracle: The Wisdom of the Temple. VandenBroeck, A. & VandenBroeck, G., trs. from Fr. (Illus.). 320p. 1985. 14.95 (ISBN 0-89281-008-4). Inner Tradit.
--Nature-Word. Lawlor, Deborah & Lawlor, Robert, trs. from Fr. LC 82-81069. 160p. 1982. pap. 8.95 (ISBN 0-89281-036-X). Inner Tradit.
--Nature Word: Verbe Nature. Lawlor, Deborah, tr. from Fr. & intro. by. LC 82-81069. (Illus.). 160p. (Orig.). 1982. pap. 6.95 (ISBN 0-940262-00-2, Lindisfarne Pr). Inner Tradit.
--The Temple in Man: Sacred Architecture & the Perfect Man. Lawlor, Robert & Lawlor, Deborah, trs. from Fr. LC 81-13374. (Illus.). 132p. 1981. pap. 6.95 (ISBN 0-89281-021-1). Inner Tradit.

Schwan, S. Marie, jt. auth. see Bergan, Jacqueline.

Schwank, Benedikt. First & Second Epistles of St. Peter. McKenzie, John T., ed. LC 81-605. (New Testament for Spiritual Reading Ser.). 192p. 1981. pap. 4.95 (ISBN 0-8245-0131-4). Crossroad NY.

Schwanktfeld, Kurt W. The Hegel-Kierkegaard Cosmology of the Spirit. (Illus.). 103p. 1984. 87.85 (ISBN 0-89266-497-5). Am Classical Coll Pr.

Schwantes, Dave. Taming Your TV & Other Media. LC 79-16848. (Orion Ser.). 1979. pap. 3.95 (ISBN 0-8127-0246-8). Review & Herald.

Schwartz, Amy. Yossel Zissel & the Wisdom of Chelm. (Illus.). 32p. 9.95 (ISBN 0-8276-0258-8). Jewish Pubns.

Schwartz, Benjamin I. The World of Thought in Ancient China. (Illus.). 456p. 1985. text ed. 27.50x (ISBN 0-674-96190-0, Belknap Pr). Harvard U Pr.

Schwartz, Charles D. & Schwartz, Ouida D. A Flame of Fire: The Story of Troy Annual Conference. LC 82-70624. (Illus.). 376p. (Orig.). 1982. pap. text ed. 15.00x (ISBN 0-914960-38-5). Academy Bks.

Schwartz, David. Hanukkah Latkes & Rothschild's Millions. 1961. 14.95x (ISBN 0-8084-0036-3). New Coll U Pr.

Schwartz, Earl. Moral Development: A Practical Guide for Jewish Teachers. LC 83-70196. 188p. 1983. pap. text ed. 10.00 (ISBN 0-86705-037-3). AIRE.

Schwartz, Eduard. Ethik der Griechen. facsimile ed. Richter, Will, ed. LC 75-13293. (History of Ideas in Ancient Greece Ser.). (Ger.). 1976. Repr. of 1951 ed. 17.00x (ISBN 0-405-07337-2). Ayer Co Pubs.

Schwartz, Faye & Mohr, David. Creative Worship. 1982. 4.50 (ISBN 0-89536-567-7, 0376). CSS of Ohio.

Schwartz, Faye, jt. auth. see Mohr, David.

Schwartz, Gary. Sect Ideologies & Social Status. LC 72-120598. 1970. 18.00x (ISBN 0-226-74216-4). U of Chicago Pr.

Schwartz, Gary E. & Shapiro, David, eds. Consciousness & Self-Regulation: Advances in Research & Theory. Incl. Vol. 1. 422p. 1976. 35.00x (ISBN 0-306-33601-4); Vol. 2. 470p. 1978. 35.00x (ISBN 0-306-33602-2). LC 76-8907. (Illus., Plenum Pr). Plenum Pub.

Schwartz, Grace H. Monarch Notes on Shaw's Saint Joan. (Orig.). pap. 2.95 (ISBN 0-671-00725-4). Monarch Pr.

Schwartz, Hillel. The French Prophets: The History of a Millenarian Group in Eighteenth-Century England. LC 78-65459. (Illus.). 1980. 42.00x (ISBN 0-520-03815-0). U of Cal Pr.

--Knaves, Fools, Madmen & That Subtile Effluvium: A Study of the Opposition to the French Prophets in England, 1706-1710. LC 78-1692. (University of Florida Social Sciences Monographs: No. 62). 1978. pap. 5.50 (ISBN 0-8130-0505-1). U Presses Fla.

Schwartz, Howard & Rudolf, Anthony, eds. Voices Within the Ark. 1983. pap. 15.95 (ISBN 0-380-76109-2, 80119). Avon.

Schwartz, Howard, ed. see Freehof, Lillian S.

Schwartz, Mark F., et al, eds. Sex & Gender: A Theological & Scientific Inquiry. 385p. (Orig.). 1984. pap. 19.95 (ISBN 0-935372-13-X). Pope John Ctr.

Schwartz, Michael. The Case Against Planned Parenthood. 200p. (Orig.). Date not set. pap. cancelled (ISBN 0-87973-539-2, 539). Our Sunday Visitor.

--The Persistent Prejudice: Anti-Catholicism in America. LC 84-60746. 240p. 1984. pap. 6.95 (ISBN 0-87973-715-8, 715). Our Sunday Visitor.

Schwartz, Ouida D., jt. auth. see Schwartz, Charles D.

Schwartz, Paul, tr. see Flood, David & Matura, Thadee.

Schwartz, Paul, tr. see Leclerc, Eloi.

Schwartz, Paul, tr. see Matura, Thaddee.

Schwartz, Paul, tr. see Vorreux, Damien.

Schwartz, Richard B. Samuel Johnson & the Problem of Evil. LC 74-27314. 128p. 1975. 27.50x (ISBN 0-299-06790-4). U of Wis Pr.

Schwartz, Toby D. Mercy Lord, My Husband's in the Kitchen & Other Equal Opportunity Conversations with God. 96p. 1982. pap. 2.95 (ISBN 0-380-57943-X, 57943-X). Avon.

Schwartzbach, B. E. Voltaire's Old Testament Criticism. 275p. (Orig.). 1970. pap. text ed. 24.00x (Pub. by Droz Switzerland). Coronet Bks.

Schwartzfuchs, Simon. Napoleon, the Jews & the Sanhedria. (Littman Library of Jewish Civilization). 1979. 24.00x (ISBN 0-19-710023-6). Oxford U Pr.

Schwartzman, Sylvan D. & Spiro, Jack D. Living Bible: A Topical Approach to the Jewish Scriptures. (Illus.). 1962. text ed. 5.00 (ISBN 0-8074-0097-1, 161751). UAHC.

Schwarz, A. Z., jt. auth. see Aptowitzer, V.

Schwarz, Hans. Beyond the Gates of Death: A Biblical Examination of Evidence for Life After Death. LC 80-67805. 136p. 1981. pap. 6.95 (ISBN 0-8066-1868-X, 10-0647). Augsburg.

--Divine Communication: Word & Sacrament in Biblical, Historical & Contemporary Perspective. LC 84-48732. 176p. 1985. pap. 10.95 (ISBN 0-8006-1846-7, 1-1846). Fortress.

--What Christians Believe. LC 86-45923. 112p. 1987. pap. 4.95 (ISBN 0-8006-1959-5). Fortress.

Schwarz, Jack. Human Energy Systems. (Illus.). 1980. pap. 7.95 (ISBN 0-525-47556-7, 0772-230). Dutton.

--The Path of Action. LC 77-2247. 1977. pap. 8.95 (ISBN 0-525-48231-8, 0869-260). Dutton.

--Voluntary Controls: Exercises for Creative Meditation & for Activating the Potential of the Chakras. 1978. pap. 7.95 (ISBN 0-525-47494-3, 0772-230). Dutton.

Schwarz, Leo W., ed. Great Ages & Ideas of the Jewish People. LC 83-5464. 7.95 (ISBN 0-394-60413-X). Modern Lib.

Schwarz, Richard, ed. Internationales Jahrbuch fuer interdisziplinaere Forschung, Vol. 1: 1974. Wissenschaft als interdisziplinaeres Problem. 1974. 44.00x (ISBN 3-11-004633-4). De Gruyter.

Schwarz, Solomon M. The Jews in the Soviet Union. LC 72-4298. (World Affairs Ser.: National & International Viewpoints). 398p. 1972. Repr. of 1951 ed. 22.00 (ISBN 0-405-04589-1). Ayer Co Pubs.

Schwarzbaum, Haim. Studies in Jewish & World Folklore. (Fabula Supplement Ser., No. B 3). 1968. 97.50x (ISBN 3-11-000393-7). De Gruyter.

Schwarzkopf, Friedemann, tr. see Emmichoven, F. W.

Schwebel, Ivan. The Arena of Jerusalem. LC 86-3570. (Illus.). 1987. 39.95 (ISBN 0-915361-43-4, Dist. by Watts). Adama Pubs Inc.

Schweer, G. William. Personal Evangelism for Today. LC 83-70003. 1984. 10.95 (ISBN 0-8054-6241-4). Broadman.

Schweid, ELiezer. Judaism & Mysticism According to Gershom Scholem: A Critical Analysis & Programmatic Discussion. Weiner, David A., tr. (Reprints & Translations). 1985. 22.95 (ISBN 0-89130-982-9, 00-07-09); pap. 16.95 (ISBN 0-89130-887-3). Scholars Pr Ga.

Schweinfurth, Georg. Studies in Jewish Bibliography & Related Subjects in Memory of Abraham Solomon Freidus (1867-1923) 814p. 1929. Repr. text ed. 124.20x (ISBN 0-576-80130-5, Pub. by Gregg Intl Pubs England). Gregg Intl.

Schweitzer, Albert. Albert Schweitzer. Repath, Ann, ed. Winston, Richard & Winston, Clara, trs. (Living Philosophies Ser.). (Illus.). 32p. (YA) 1985. PLB 8.95 (ISBN 0-88682-013-8). Creative Ed.

--Essence of Faith. pap. 0.95 (ISBN 0-685-19400-0, 127, WL). Citadel Pr.

--Indian Thought & Its Development. 1962. 11.00 (ISBN 0-8446-2893-X). Peter Smith.

--The Light Within Us. (Philosophical Paperback Ser.). 58p. 1985. pap. 3.95 (ISBN 0-8022-2484-9). Philos Lib.

--The Mystery of the Kingdom of God: The Secret of Jesus' Messiahship & Passion. LC 85-60625. 174p. 1985. pap. 11.95 (ISBN 0-87975-294-7). Prometheus Bks.

--On the Edge of the Primeval Forest & More from the Primeval Forest: Experiences & Observations of a Doctor in Equatorial Africa. LC 75-41244. (Illus.). 1976. Repr. of 1948 ed. 18.50 (ISBN 0-404-14598-1). AMS Pr.

--Psychiatric Study of Jesus. 14.75 (ISBN 0-8446-2894-8). Peter Smith.

--Reverence for Life. Fuller, Reginald H., tr. LC 71-85052. 1980. Repr. of 1969 ed. 14.95 (ISBN 0-89197-920-4). Irvington.

--The Theology of Albert Schweitzer for Christian Inquirers. Mozley, E. N., ed. 1977. lib. bdg. 59.95 (ISBN 0-8490-2740-3). Gordon Pr.

--Thoughts for Our Times. Anderson, Erica, ed. (Illus.). 64p. 1981. Repr. of 1975 ed. 3.95 (ISBN 0-8298-0448-X). Pilgrim NY.

Schweitzer, Albert & A. J. The Problem of the Lord's Supper. LC 81-22590. xiv, 144p. 1982. 10.95 (ISBN 0-86554-025-X, MUP-H25). Mercer Univ Pr.

Schweizer, Eduard. The Good News According to Luke. Green, David E., tr. LC 83-22237. 1984. 23.95 (ISBN 0-8042-0249-4). John Knox.

--Good News According to Mark. Madvig, Donald, tr. LC 77-93828. 1970. 18.95 (ISBN 0-8042-0250-8). John Knox.

--Good News According to Matthew. Green, David E., tr. LC 74-3717. 1975. 19.95 (ISBN 0-8042-0251-6). John Knox.

--Jesus. LC 76-107322. 1979. pap. 7.95 (ISBN 0-8042-0331-8). John Knox.

--Jesus Christ: The Man from Nazareth & the Exalted Lord. Gloer, Hulitt, ed. 128p. (Orig.). 1986. 14.95 (ISBN 0-86554-225-2, MUP-H201); pap. 9.95 (ISBN 0-86554-226-0, MUP-P30). Mercer Univ Pr.

Schweizer, Edward. The Letter to the Colossians: A Commentary. Chester, Andrew, tr. LC 81-65657. 352p. (Orig.). 1982. pap. 14.95 (ISBN 0-8066-1893-0, 10-3823). Augsburg.

Schweltzer, Frederick. A History of the Jews Since the First Century A. D. 319p. pap. 1.95 (ISBN 0-686-95171-9). ADL.

Schwenckfeld, Caspar. Commentary on the Augsburg Confession. Grater, Fred A., tr. 182p. 1982. pap. 5.00 (ISBN 0-935980-02-4). Schwenkfelder Lib.

Schwengel, Georgius. Propago Sacri Ordinis Cartusienses per Germaniam Pars 2, 2 Vols. Hogg, James, ed. (Analecta Cartusiana Ser.: No. 90/4). 378p. 1982. pap. 50.00 (ISBN 3-7052-0151-4, Pub. by Salzburg Studies). Longwood Pub Group.

--Propago Sacri Ordinis Cartusiensis-Appartus Annales Sacri Ordinis Cartusiensis, 3 Vols. Hogg, James, ed. (Analecta Cartusiana Ser.: No. 90/9). 534p. (Orig.). 1983. pap. 85.00 (ISBN 3-7052-0156-5, Pub. by Salzburg Studies). Longwood Pub Group.

--Propago Sacri Ordinis Cartusiensis: Appendix ad Tom I, 2 Vols. Hogg, James, ed. (Analecta Cartusiana Ser.: No. 90/5). 440p. (Orig.). 1983. pap. 50.00 (ISBN 3-7052-0152-2, Pub. by Salzburg Studies). Longwood Pub Group.

--Propago Sacri Ordinis Cartusiensis: Appendis ad Tom II, 2 Vols. Hogg, James, ed. (Analecta Cartusiana: No. 90/6). 397p. (Orig.). 1983. pap. 50.00 (ISBN 0-317-42583-8, Pub. by Salzburg Studies). Longwood Pub Group.

--Propago Sacri Ordinis Cartusiensis: Appendix ad Tom III, 2 vols. Hogg, James, ed. (Analecta Cartusiana Ser.: No. 90/7). 357p. (Orig.). 1983. pap. 50.00 (ISBN 3-7052-0154-9, Pub. by Salzburg Studies). Longwood Pub Group.

--Propago Sacri Ordinis Cartusiensis: Appendix ad Tom IV, 2 Vols. Hogg, James, ed. (Analecta Cartusiana: No. 90/8). 412p. (Orig.). 1983. pap. 50.00 (ISBN 3-7052-0155-7, Pub. by Salzburg Studies). Longwood Pub Group.

--Propago Sacri Ordinis Cartusiensis de Provinciis Burgundiae, Franciae, Picardiae, Teutoniae et Angliae. Hogg, James, ed. (Analecta Cartusiana Ser.: No. 90/2). 276p. (Orig.). 1981. pap. 25.00 (ISBN 3-7052-0149-2, Pub. by Salzburg Studies). Longwood Pub Group.

--Propago Sacri Ordinis Cartusiensis-Diplomata Poloniae et Prussiae, 2 Vols. Hogg, James, ed. (Analecta Cartusiana Ser.: No. 90/11). 256p. (Orig.). 1982. pap. 50.00 (ISBN 3-7052-0158-1, Pub. by Salzburg Studies). Longwood Pub Group.

--Propago Sacri Ordinis Cartusiensis per Franciam, 2 Vols. Hogg, James, ed. (Analecta Cartusiana Ser.: No. 90/1). 300p. (Orig.). 1984. pap. 50.00 (ISBN 3-7052-0148-4, Pub. by Salzburg Studies). Longwood Pub Group.

--Propago Sacri Ordinis Cartusiensis per Germaniam. Hogg, James, ed. (Analecta Cartusiana Ser.: No. 90/3). 480p. (Orig.). 1981. pap. 25.00 (ISBN 3-7052-0150-6, Pub. by Salzburg Studies). Longwood Pub Group.

Schwertner, Siegfried. Internationales Abkuerzungsverzeichnis fuer Theologie und Grenzgebiete. LC 72-77418. 1974. pap. 35.20x (ISBN 3-11-004027-1). De Gruyter.

Schwickerat, Robert. Jesuit Education. 59.95 (ISBN 0-8490-0442-X). Gordon Pr.

Schwiebert, E. G. Luther's Ninety-Five Theses. pap. 0.75 (ISBN 0-570-03519-8, 14-1253). Concordia.

Schwiebert, Ernest G. Luther & His Times: The Reformation from a New Perspective. (Illus.). 1950. 24.95 (ISBN 0-570-03246-6, 15-1164). Concordia.

Schwieder, Dorothy, jt. auth. see Schwieder, Elmer.

Schwieder, Elmer & Schwieder, Dorothy. A Peculiar People: Iowa's Old Order Amish. facs. ed. (Illus.). 188p. 1975. 9.95x (ISBN 0-8138-0105-2). Iowa St U Pr.

Schwieters, Elsa S., tr. see Watson, David.

Schwing, Sally A. Do You Think It Snows In Heaven? Graves, Helen, ed. 213p. 1987. 12.95 (ISBN 1-55523-049-0). Winston-Derek.

Schwizer, Eduard. Luke: A Challenge to Present Theology. LC 81-85332. 144p. 1982. pap. 10.50 (ISBN 0-8042-0686-4). John Knox.

Schwyzer, H. R., ed. see Plotinus.

Sciacca, Francis. To Walk & Not Grow Weary. 84p. 1985. pap. 3.95 (ISBN 0-89109-034-7). NavPress.

Sciaparelli, Giovanni. Astronomy in the Old Testament. 59.95 (ISBN 0-87968-673-1). Gordon Pr.

Scipione, George C. Timothy, Titus & You: A Workbook for Church Leaders. 96p. 1986. pap. 3.95 (ISBN 0-87552-439-7). Presby & Reformed.

Scofield, C. I. The New Life in Christ Jesus. 1975. pap. 1.95 (ISBN 0-915374-41-2, 41-2). Rapids Christian.

--Rightly Dividing the Word of Truth. pap. 1.50 (ISBN 0-87213-770-8). Loizeaux.

--Rightly Dividing the Word of Truth. 72p. (Orig.). 1974. pap. 2.95 (ISBN 0-310-32662-1, 6364P). Zondervan.

--Traza Bien la Palabra de Verdad. Orig. Title: Rightly Dividing the Word of Truth. (Span.). 92p. 1971. pap. 3.25 (ISBN 0-8254-1660-4). Kregel.

Scofield, Willard A. Teaching the Bible: Creative Techniques for Bringing Scripture to Life. 112p. 1986. pap. 6.95 (ISBN 0-8170-1094-7). Judson.

Scoggan, Nita. God's Plan to Enjoy Your Children. Tolliver, Alice, ed. LC 84-60581. (Illus.). 52p. 1985. pap. 2.95 (ISBN 0-910487-03-0). Royalty Pub.

Scotish Missions Promotion. St. Andrews Seven. (Orig.). 1985. pap. 5.95 (ISBN 0-85151-428-6). Banner of Truth.

Scotland. Registrum Episcopatus Moraviensis. Innes, Cosmo N., ed. LC 71-172742. (Bannatyne Club, Edinburgh. Publications: No. 58). Repr. of 1837 ed. 47.50 (ISBN 0-404-52768-X). AMS Pr.

Scotland, Nigel. Can We Trust the Gospels? 54p. 1979. pap. 1.95 (ISBN 0-85364-249-4). Attic Pr.

Scott, Albert C. Mini Miracles & Words with a Little Wisdom. 1984. 6.95 (ISBN 0-8062-2320-0). Carlton.

Scott, Anna M. Day Dawn in Africa: Or Progress of the Protestant Episcopal Mission at Cape Palmas, West Africa. LC 69-18659. (Illus.). Repr. of 1858 ed. cancelled (ISBN 0-8371-5091-4, SCD&, Pub. by Negro U Pr). Greenwood.

Scott, Archibald. Buddhism & Christianity. LC 78-118547. 1970. Repr. of 1890 ed. 29.50x (ISBN 0-8046-1172-6, Pub. by Kennikat). Assoc Faculty Pr.

Scott, Bernard B. Jesus, Symbol-Maker for the Kingdom. LC 80-2388. pap. 47.50 (2029610). Bks Demand UMI.

--The Word of God in Words: Reading & Preaching the Gospels. LC 85-5227. (Fortress Resources for Preaching). 96p. 1985. pap. 4.95 (ISBN 0-8006-1142-X). Fortress.

Scott, Bernice. Junipero Serra: Pioneer of the Cross. (Illus.). 248p. 1985. pap. 9.95 (ISBN 0-317-44750-5). Panorama West.

Scott, Carolyn. Dr. Who Never Gave up, Ida Scudder. (Stories of Faith & Fame Ser.). (YA) 1975. pap. 2.95 (ISBN 0-87508-607-1). Chr Lit.

Scott, Clinton L. These Live Tomorrow. 1964. pap. write for info. (ISBN 0-933840-06-3). Unitarian Univ.

Scott, David H., ed. see Miller, Madeleine S. & Miller, J. Lane.

Scott, Donald M. From Office to Profession: The New England Ministry, 1750-1850. LC 77-20304. 1978. 21.00x (ISBN 0-8122-7737-6). U of Pa Pr.

Scott, Doug, tr. see Zimmerli, Walther.

Scott, Edward D., ed. see Puri, Ishwar C.

Scott, Ernest. The People of the Secret. 1983. 16.95 (ISBN 0-86304-027-6, Pub. by Octagon Pr England); pap. 8.95 (ISBN 0-86304-038-1). Ins Study Human.

Scott, Ernest F. The Literature of the New Testament. Evans, Austin P., ed. LC 84-25243. (Records of Civilization Sources & Studies: No. xv). xv, 312p. 1985. Repr. of 1936 ed. lib. bdg. 45.00x (ISBN 0-313-24743-9, SCNT). Greenwood.

--Paul's Epistle to the Romans. LC 79-4204. 1979. Repr. of 1947 ed. lib. bdg. 22.50x (ISBN 0-313-20800-X, SCPE). Greenwood.

Scott, Frances M., jt. auth. see Scott, William.

Scott, Franklyn D., ed. see Hale, Frederick.

Scott, Gini G. Cult & Countercult: A Study of a Spiritual Growth Group & a Witchcraft Order. LC 79-54057. (Contributions in Sociology: No. 38). (Illus.). 1980. lib. bdg. 29.95x (ISBN 0-313-22074-3, SCC/). Greenwood.

Scott, Hildreth. Alone, Again! (Uplook Ser.). 1976. pap. 0.99 (ISBN 0-8163-0251-0, 01496-9). Pacific Pr Pub Assn.

Scott, Ida B. My Hopes Were Shattered at Age Six: Read How God Blessed Me. 1981. 4.95 (ISBN 0-8062-1837-1). Carlton.

Scott, Jack, ed. see Witherspoon, John.

Scott, Jack B. Missions: A Family Affair. 1985. pap. 4.95 (ISBN 0-934688-15-X). Great Comm Pubns.

--Revelation Unfolded. pap. 2.95 (ISBN 0-8423-5510-3). Tyndale.

Scott, James G; see Muller, W. Max.

Scott, John C. How to Start Your Romance with God. 1987. 7.95. Franciscan Herald.

Scott, John H. God Reveals Himself. 1987. 7.95 (ISBN 0-533-07061-9). Vantage.

Scott, Keith, jt. ed. see Kawamura, Leslie S.

Scott, Kenneth. The Imperial Cult Under the Flavians. facsimile ed. LC 75-10655. (Ancient Religion & Mythology Ser.). 1976. Repr. of 1936 ed. 17.00x (ISBN 0-405-07263-5). Ayer Co Pubs.

Scott, Kenneth, ed. see Needleman, Jacob, et al.

Scott, Kenneth J., ed. see Tyson, Joseph B.

Scott, Lane A. & Hynson, Leon O., eds. Christian Ethics. (Wesleyan Theological Perspectives Ser.: Vol. III). 1983. 14.95 (ISBN 0-87162-267-X, D4852). Warner Pr.

Scott, Latayne. Time, Talents, Things: A Woman's Workshop on Christian Stewardship. Sloan, J., ed. (Woman's Workshop Ser.). 96p. (Orig.). 1987. pap. 3.95 (ISBN 0-310-38771-X). Zondervan.

Scott, Latayne C. The Mormon Mirage. 276p. 1982. pap. 7.95 (ISBN 0-310-38911-9, 10450P). Zondervan.

--Open up Your Life: A Woman's Workshop on Christian Hospitality. 144p. 1983. pap. 2.95 (ISBN 0-310-38901-1, 10451P). Zondervan.
--To Love Each Other: A Woman's Workshop on First Corinthians. (Woman's Workshop Ser.). 112p. (Orig.). 1985. pap. 3.95 (ISBN 0-310-38921-6, 10454P). Zondervan.
Scott, Mary. Kundalini in the Physical World. (Illus.). 240p. (Orig.). 1983. pap. 11.95 (ISBN 0-7100-9417-5). Methuen Inc.
Scott, Nathan A., Jr. Reinhold Niebuhr. (Pamphlets on American Writers Ser: No. 31). (Orig.). 1963. pap. 1.25x (ISBN 0-8166-0305-7, MPAW31). U of Minn Pr.
Scott, Nathan A., Jr., ed. Adversity & Grace: Studies in Recent American Literature. LC 68-16717. (Essays in Divinity Ser: Vol. 4). 1968. 9.50x (ISBN 0-226-74283-0). U of Chicago Pr.
--Legacy of Reinhold Niebuhr. LC 74-30714. xxiv, 124p. 1975. 10.00X (ISBN 0-226-74297-0). U of Chicago Pr.
Scott, Orange. Grounds of Secession from the M. E. Church. LC 71-82219. (Anti-Slavery Crusade in America Ser). 1969. Repr. of 1848 ed. 14.00 (ISBN 0-405-00659-4). Ayer Co Pubs.
Scott, R. B. Way of Widsom. 1972. pap. 7.95 (ISBN 0-02-089280-2, Collier). Macmillan.
Scott, R. B., ed. Proverbs & Ecclesiastes. LC 65-13988. (Anchor Bible Ser.: No. 18). 1965. 14.00 (ISBN 0-385-02177-1, Anch). Doubleday.
Scott, Ralph W. A New Look at Biblical Crime. LC 78-27535. 232p. 1979. 18.95x (ISBN 0-88229-416-4). Nelson-Hall.
Scott, Raymond L. The Hiding God: Jesus in the Old Testament. 192p. 1982. pap. 4.95 (ISBN 0-8010-8221-8). Baker Bk.
Scott, Robert L., Jr. God Is Still My Co-Pilot. 1967. 25.00 (ISBN 0-317-17716-8). Beachcomber Bks.
Scott, S. P. History of the Moorish Empire in Europe, 3 vols. 1977. Set. lib. bdg. 300.00 (ISBN 0-8490-2004-2). Gordon Pr.
Scott, Samuel H., jt. ed. see Soderlund, G. F.
Scott, Stephen. Why Do They Dress That Way? LC 86-81058. (People's Place Booklet Ser.: No. 7). (Illus.). 160p. (Orig.). 1986. pap. 5.50 (ISBN 0-934672-18-0). Good Bks PA.
Scott, Steve, jt. auth. see Smalley, Gary.
Scott, Thomas. Christs Politician & Solomon's Puritan: Two Sermons. LC 73-6159. (English Experience Ser.: No. 622). 1973. Repr. of 1616 ed. 6.00 (ISBN 90-221-0622-5). Walter J Johnson.
--Force of Truth. 1984. pap. 3.45 (ISBN 0-85151-425-1). Banner of Truth.
--The Interpreter, Wherein Three Principal Terms of State Are Clearly Unfolded. LC 74-80194. (English Experience Ser.: No. 673). 1974. Repr. of 1624 ed. 3.50 (ISBN 90-221-0281-5). Walter J Johnson.
Scott, Thomas, jt. auth. see Henry, Mathew.
Scott, Thomas, jt. auth. see Henry, Matthew.
Scott, W. Bible Handbook, 2 vols. 18.00 (ISBN 0-88172-123-9). Believers Bkshelf.
Scott, W. A. Wedge of Gold. 1974. pap. 3.95 (ISBN 0-685-52824-3). Reiner.
Scott, Waldron. Bring Forth Justice. LC 80-15992. 304p. 1980. pap. 11.95 (ISBN 0-8028-1848-X). Eerdmans.
--Karl Barth's Theology of Mission. Bockmuehl, Klaus, ed. (World Evangelical Fellowship: Outreach & Identity Theological Monograph). 40p. 1978. pap. 1.95 (ISBN 0-87784-541-7). Inter-Varsity.
Scott, Walter. Demonology & Witchcraft. 1970. 7.95 (ISBN 0-8065-0213-4). Citadel Pr.
--Exposition of the Revelation of Jesus Christ. LC 79-88736. 1979. Repr. 16.95 (ISBN 0-8254-3731-8). Kregel.
--Letters on Demonology & Witchcraft. 1887. Repr. 25.00 (ISBN 0-8274-2850-2). R West.
Scott, Walter, ed. & tr. Hermetica: The Ancient Greek & Latin Writings Which Contain Religious or Philosophic Teachings Ascribed to Hermes Trismegistus, 4 vols. LC 85-8198. 1985. Vol 1; 549p. pap. 15.95 (ISBN 0-87773-338-4); Vol. 2; 482p. pap. 15.95 (ISBN 0-87773-339-2); Vol. 3; 632p. pap. 17.95 (ISBN 0-87773-340-6); Vol. 4; 576p. pap. 17.95 (ISBN 0-87773-341-4). Shambhala Pubns.
Scott, Sir Walter. The Life of John Dryden. Kreissman, Bernard, ed. LC 63-8121. xx, 471p. 1963. pap. 5.95x (ISBN 0-8032-5177-7, BB 157, Bison). U of Nebr Pr.
Scott, Wilfrid, jt. auth. see Beckwith, Roger T.
Scott, Willard. The Joy of Living. (Epiphany Bks.). 192p. (Orig.). 1983. pap. 2.50 (ISBN 0-345-31073-X). Ballantine.
Scott, William & Scott, Frances M. The Church Then & Now: Cultivating a Sense of Tradition. 108p. (Orig.). 1985. pap. 3.95 (ISBN 0-934134-30-8, Leaven Pr). Sheed & Ward MO.
Scott-Craig, T. S. K. A Guide to Pronouncing Biblical Names. LC 81-84713. 112p. (Orig.). 1982. pap. 3.50 (ISBN 0-8192-1292-X). Morehouse.
Scotti, Juliet & Linksman, Ricki. Kirpal Singh: The Story of a Saint. 2nd ed. LC 77-79840. (Children's Ser.: No. 1). (Illus.). 96p. 1982. pap. 4.95 (ISBN 0-918224-05-5). Sawan Kirpal Pubns.
Scott-Maxwell, Florida. The Measure of My Days. 1979. pap. 5.95 (ISBN 0-14-005164-3). Penguin.
Scotto, Dominic. The Liturgy of the Hours. 1986. pap. 9.95 (ISBN 0-932506-48-8). St Bedes Pubns.
Scotus, Joannes D. Opera Omnia, 26 vols. 18302p. 1895. text ed. 4843.80x (ISBN 0-576-99127-9, Pub. by Gregg Intl Pubs England). Gregg Intl.
Scourby, Alice. Third Generation Greek Americans: A Study of Religious Attitudes. Cordasco, Francesco, ed. LC 80-893. (American Ethnic Groups Ser.). lib. bdg. 16.00x (ISBN 0-405-13454-1). Ayer Co Pubs.
Scovil, Elizabeth R., jt. auth. see Alleman, Herman.
Scoyoc, Nancy Van see Van Scoyoc, Nancy.
Scragg, W. R. The In-Between God. Wheeler, Gerald, ed. 128p. pap. price not set (ISBN 0-8280-0374-2). Review & Herald.
Scragg, Walter R. Directions: A Look at the Paths of Life. LC 77-78101. (Horizon Ser.). 1977. pap. 5.95 (ISBN 0-8127-0136-4). Review & Herald.
--Such Bright Hopes. Woolsey, Raymond, ed. 377p. 1987. price not set (ISBN 0-8280-0389-0). Review & Herald.
Scragg, Walter R. L. The God Who Says Yes. Wheeler, Gerald, ed. 128p. (Orig.). 1986. pap. 6.95 (ISBN 0-8280-0376-9). Review & Herald.
Scribner, R. The German Reformation. LC 85-19732. (Studies in European History). 88p. 1986. pap. text ed. 7.95x (ISBN 0-391-03362-X). Humanities.
Scribner, R. W. For the Sake of Simple Folk: Popular Propaganda for the German Reformation. (Cambridge Studies in Oral & Literate Culture: No. 2). (Illus.). 350p. 1981. Cambridge U Pr.
Scriven, Charles W. Jubilee of the World: The Sabbath As a Day of Gladness. (Flame Ser.). 1978. pap. 0.99 (ISBN 0-8127-0188-7). Review & Herald.
Scrivener, Frederick H., ed. see Beza, Theodore.
Scrocco, Jean L., ed. A Christmas Treasury. LC 84-8798. (Illus.). 48p. 1985. 11.95 (ISBN 0-88101-017-0). Unicorn Pub.
Scroggie, W. Graham. Fascination of Old Testament Story. Date not set. 7.95 (ISBN 0-8254-3726-1). Kregel.
--Guide to the Gospels. 664p. 1975. 23.95 (ISBN 0-8007-0127-5). Revell.
--How to Pray. rev. ed. LC 80-8076. (W. Graham Scroggie Library). 112p. 1981. pap. 4.50 (ISBN 0-8254-3736-9). Kregel.
--Joshua in the Light of the New Testament. LC 80-8074. (W. Graham Scroggie Library). 88p. 1981. pap. 4.50 (ISBN 0-8254-3734-2). Kregel.
--Know Your Bible. 608p. 1965. 23.95 (ISBN 0-8007-0169-0). Revell.
--Love Life: I Cor. 13. LC 79-2551. (W. Graham Scroggie Library). 96p. 1980. pap. 4.50 (ISBN 0-8254-3733-4). Kregel.
--Paul's Prison Prayers. LC 80-8077. (W. Graham Scroggie Library). 78p. 1981. pap. 4.50 (ISBN 0-8254-3737-7). Kregel.
--Studies in Philemon. LC 77-79186. (W. Graham Scroggie Library). 136p. 1982. pap. 4.50 (ISBN 0-8254-3739-3). Kregel.
--Tested by Temptation. LC 79-2559. (W. Graham Scroggie Library). 76p. 1980. pap. 4.50 (ISBN 0-8254-3732-6). Kregel.
--W. Graham Scroggie Library Series, 7 vols. 1981. pap. 28.00 (ISBN 0-8254-3740-7). Kregel.
Scroggie, William G. Luke-John. 1981. pap. 4.95 (ISBN 0-87508-485-0). Chr Lit.
Scroggins, Clara J. Silver Christmas Ornaments: A Collector's Guide. LC 79-15323. (Illus.). 208p. 1980. 25.00 (ISBN 0-498-02385-0). A S Barnes.
Scroggs, Robin. The New Testament & Homosexuality. LC 82-48588. 160p. 1984. pap. 8.95 (ISBN 0-8006-1854-8, 1-1854). Fortress.
--Paul for a New Day. LC 76-9719. 96p. 1977. pap. 3.95 (ISBN 0-8006-1242-6, 1-1242). Fortress.
Scroggs, Robin, tr. see Schenke, Ludger.
Scrogie, William G. Matthew-Mark. 1981. pap. 4.95 (ISBN 0-87508-484-2). Chr Lit.
Scrogin, Michael. Does the Gospel Make Sense Today? 128p. 1983. pap. 7.95 (ISBN 0-8170-0967-1). Judson.
--Practical Guide to Christian Living. 144p. 1985. pap. 6.95 (ISBN 0-8170-1053-X). Judson.
Scruggs, Julius R. God Is Faithful. 96p. 1985. pap. 6.95 (ISBN 0-8170-1060-2). Judson.
Scruggs, Rachael I. Come Follow Me. LC 80-52620. 142p. 1983. 7.95 (ISBN 0-533-04769-2). Vantage.
Scullard, H. H. Festivals & Ceremonies of the Roman Republic. LC 80-70447. (Aspects of Greek & Roman Life Ser.). (Illus.). 288p. 1981. 32.50x (ISBN 0-8014-1402-4). Cornell U Pr.
Scullard, H. H., ed. see Toynbee, J. M.
Scullion, John. Isaiah Forty to Sixty-Six. (Old Testament Message Ser.: Vol. 12). 1982. 12.95 (ISBN 0-89453-412-2); pap. 9.95 (ISBN 0-89453-246-4). M Glazier.
Scullion, John J., tr. see Westermann, Claus.
Scullion, John S., tr. see Westermann, Claus.
Scully. The Earth, the Temple, & the Gods. LC 79-12717. 1979. pap. 16.95x (ISBN 0-300-02397-9, Y-346). Yale U Pr.
Scully, Michael. The Best of This World. 416p. (Orig.). 1987. lib. bdg. 32.50 (ISBN 0-8191-5605-1, Pub. by IEA); pap. text ed. 19.75 (ISBN 0-8191-5606-X). U Pr of Amer.
Scult, Mel, ed. see Kaplan, Mordecai M.
Scuola, Editrice, Brescia, Italy, tr. see Bettoni, Efrem.
Scupoli, Lawrence. The Spiritual Combat. LC 78-61668. (The Spiritual Masters Ser.). 256p. 1978. pap. 4.95 (ISBN 0-8091-2158-1). Paulist Pr.
Scupoli, Lorenzo. Unseen Warfare. 280p. 1978. pap. 8.95 (ISBN 0-913836-52-4). St Vladimirs.
Scwab, Penny V. Thirteen Going on Twenty. LC 83-12292. 144p. (Orig.). 1983. pap. 4.95 (ISBN 0-87123-587-0, 210587). Bethany Hse.
Scwartz, Ronald A. see Browman, David L.
Scwarz, Hans. Responsible Faith: Christian Theology in the Light of 20th-Century Questions. LC 85-26657. 448p. 1986. text ed. 23.95 (ISBN 0-8066-2188-5, 10-5483). Augsburg.
Sczepanski, David, jt. auth. see Anfuso, Joseph.
Sczesniak, Lenny, tr. see Zanzucchi, Annamaria.
Seaburg, Carl. Celebrating Christmas. 1983. pap. 12.00 (ISBN 0-933840-17-9). Unitarian Univ.
--Great Occasions. 1968. pap. 9.95 (ISBN 0-933840-09-8). Unitarian Univ.
Seader, Ruth, ed. The New Life: Kirpal Singh. (Teachings of Kirpal Ser.: Vol. 3). 1976. pap. 3.50 (ISBN 0-89142-030-4). Sant Bani Ash.
--The Teachings of Kirpal Singh, 3 vols. Vol. I, The Holy Path, 104 pp. 3.00 (ISBN 0-318-03046-2); Vol. III, The New Life, 200 pp. 3.50 (ISBN 0-318-03047-0); One-Volume Ed., 474 pp. 7.95 (ISBN 0-318-03048-9). Sant Bani Ash.
Seader, Ruth, ed. see Singh, Kirpal.
Seadle, Michael. Quakers in Nazi Germany. (Studies in Quakerism: No. 5). 44p. (Orig.). 1978. pap. 2.00 (ISBN 0-89670-006-2). Progresiv Pub.
Seagren, Daniel R. Easter Is a Time. (Contempo Ser.). pap. 0.95 (ISBN 0-8010-8140-8). Baker Bk.
--Love Carved in Stone. LC 82-23195. 1983. pap. text ed. 3.50 (ISBN 0-8307-0840-5, S371101). Regal.
--To Dad. (Contempo Ser.). 1978. pap. 0.95 (ISBN 0-8010-8113-0). Baker Bk.
--Togetherness. (Contempo Ser.). 32p. 1978. pap. 0.95 (ISBN 0-8010-8114-9). Baker Bk.
--Uncommon Prayers for Couples. 1980. pap. 3.95 (ISBN 0-8010-8173-4). Baker Bk.
--Uncommon Prayers: For Young Adults at Work. 3.50 (ISBN 0-8010-8129-7). Baker Bk.
Seagrist, Edward M. More Word Search Puzzles. (Quiz & Puzzle Bks.). 80p. 1986. pap. 3.95 (ISBN 0-8010-8263-3). Baker Bk.
Seal, Brajendranath. The Positive Sciences of the Ancient Hindus. 313p. 1986. Repr. 19.00x (ISBN 0-8364-1575-2, Pub. by Motilal Banarsidass). South Asia Bks.
Seale, Ervin. Learn to Live. 256p. 1966. pap. 6.95 (ISBN 0-911336-08-7). Sci of Mind.
--Ten Words That Will Change Your Life. 192p. 1972. pap. 6.95 (ISBN 0-911336-38-9). Sci of Mind.
Seale, M. S. Qur'an & Bible: Studies in Interpretation & Dialogue. 124p. 1978. 23.50 (ISBN 0-85664-818-3, Pub. by Croom Helm Ltd). Methuen Inc.
Sealey, John. Religious Education: Philosophical Perspectives. Snelders, Philip & Wringe, Colin, eds. (Introductory Studies in the Philosophy of Education). 120p. 1985. text ed. 19.95x (ISBN 0-04-370130-2); pap. text ed. 7.95x (ISBN 0-04-370131-0). Allen Unwin.
Seals, Thomas L. Proverbs: Wisdom for All Ages. 5.50 (ISBN 0-89137-529-5). Quality Pubns.
Sealy, Shirley. Within My Heart. 168p. 1983. 7.95 (ISBN 0-934126-37-2). Randall Bk Co.
Seaman, Joanna S. Thirty Days to Victorious Living: A Devotional Workbook. 84p. (Orig.). 1986. pap. write for info. (ISBN 0-939113-00-7). Ansley Pubns.
Seaman, John E. Moral Paradox of Paradise Lost. LC 74-135665. (Studies in English Literature: Vol. 61). 1971. text ed. 17.00x (ISBN 90-2791-715-9). Mouton.
Seamands, David A. Healing for Damaged Emotions. 1981. pap. 5.95 (ISBN 0-88207-228-5). Victor Bks.
--Healing of Memories. 156p. 1985. text ed. 11.95 (ISBN 0-89693-532-9); pap. 6.95 (ISBN 0-89693-169-2). Victor Bks.
--Putting Away Childish Things. 144p. 1982. pap. 5.95 (ISBN 0-88207-308-7). Victor Bks.
Seamands, J. T. Tell It Well. 236p. (Orig.). 1981. pap. 6.95 (ISBN 0-8341-0684-1). Beacon Hill.
Seamands, John T. On Tiptoe with Love. (Direction Bk). pap. 1.95 (ISBN 0-8010-7991-8). Baker Bk.
--Power for the Day: 108 Meditations from Matthew. LC 75-45044. Repr. of 1976 ed. 28.00 (ISBN 0-8357-9020-7, 2016391). Bks Demand UMI.
Search Institute Staff. There Is a Season. Williams, Dorothy, ed. 1985. program manual 24.95 (ISBN 0-697-02047-9); pap. 4.95 parent book (ISBN 0-697-02046-0); video cassettes avail. Wm C Brown.
Searcy, W. B. The Proper Way to Study the Bible. 1982. 6.75 (ISBN 0-8062-1943-2). Carlton.
Seargent, Lewis. John Wycliffe: Last of the Schoolmen & First of the English Reformers. 1908. 30.00 (ISBN 0-8274-2629-1). R West.
Searle, January, pseud. Emerson: His Life & Writings. LC 76-40142. 1973. lib. bdg. 10.00 (ISBN 0-8414-7813-9). Folcroft.
Searle, Mark. Christening: The Making of Christians. LC 80-19454. (Illus.). 185p. (Orig.). 1980. pap. text ed. 6.50 (ISBN 0-8146-1183-4). Liturgical Pr.
--Liturgy Made Simple. LC 81-4807. 96p. (Orig.). 1981. pap. 2.95 (ISBN 0-8146-1221-0). Liturgical Pr.
Searle, Mark, ed. Liturgy & Social Justice. LC 80-27011. 102p. 1980. pap. 5.50 (ISBN 0-8146-1209-1). Liturgical Pr.
--Parish: A Place for Worship. LC 81-13655. 192p. (Orig.). 1981. pap. 5.95 (ISBN 0-8146-1236-9). Liturgical Pr.
--Sunday Morning: A Time for Worship. LC 82-15306. 200p. (Orig.). 1982. pap. 5.95 (ISBN 0-8146-1259-8). Liturgical Pr.
Searle, William. The Saint & the Skeptics: Joan of Arc in the World of Mark Twain, Anatole France, & Bernard Shaw. LC 75-26709. 178p. 1976. text ed. 22.50x (ISBN 0-8143-1541-0). Wayne St U Pr.
Searless, John E., jt. auth. see McDonald, William.
Sears, Buddy. Purpose: A Little Gift in the Adventure of Life. 169p. (Orig.). 1986. pap. 6.95 (ISBN 0-87418-023-6, 160). Coleman Pub.
Sears, Clara E. Gleanings from Old Shaker Journals. LC 75-345. (The Radical Tradition in America Ser). (Illus.). 311p. 1975. Repr. of 1916 ed. 30.25 (ISBN 0-88355-247-7). Hyperion Conn.
Sears, Lloyd C. Eyes of Jehovah: Life of James A. Harding. 8.50 (ISBN 0-89225-089-5). Gospel Advocate.
Sears, William. Christian Parenting & Child Care. 544p. 1985. 19.95 (ISBN 0-8407-5422-1). Nelson.
--A Cry from the Heart: The Baha'is in Iran. (Illus.). 224p. 1982. pap. 3.95 (ISBN 0-85398-134-5). G Ronald Pub.
--God Loves Laughter. 182p. 1960. o.p. (ISBN 0-85398-018-7); pap. 6.95 (ISBN 0-85398-019-5). G Ronald Pub.
--Thief in the Night. 320p. 1961. 8.95 (ISBN 0-85398-096-9); pap. 3.95 (ISBN 0-85398-008-X). G Ronald Pub.
--The Wine of Astonishment. 192p. 1963. pap. 3.95 (ISBN 0-85398-009-8). G Ronald Pub.
Sears, William & Quigley, Robert. The Flame. 144p. 1972. 7.95 (ISBN 0-85398-031-4); pap. 3.50 (ISBN 0-85398-030-6). G Ronald Pub.
Seashore, Gladys. I Am a Possibility. 80p. 1979. pap. 1.95 (ISBN 0-911802-44-4). Free Church Pubns.
--Jesus & Me. 1975. pap. 2.25 (ISBN 0-911802-37-1). Free Church Pubns.
--Let's Talk About Jesus. (Illus.). 1978. pap. 1.75 (ISBN 0-911802-40-1). Free Church Pubns.
--The New Me. 1972. pap. 1.75 (ISBN 0-911802-31-2). Free Church Pubns.
--Women of Faith. 1983. pap. 2.25 (ISBN 0-911802-55-X). Free Church Pubns.
Seasoltz, R., ed. Living Bread, Saving Cup: Readings on the Eucharist. LC 81-20813. 350p. 1982. pap. 12.95 (ISBN 0-8146-1257-1). Liturgical Pr.
Seasoltz, R. Kevin. New Liturgy, New Laws. LC 79-27916. 256p. 1980. pap. 7.95 (ISBN 0-8146-1077-3). Liturgical Pr.
Seaton, Alexander A. The Theory of Toleration under the Later Stuarts. 1972. lib. bdg. 23.00x (ISBN 0-374-97233-8, Octagon). Hippocrene Bks.
Seaton, Edith B., jt. auth. see Seaton, Ronald S.
Seaton, J. A Reading of Vergil's "Georgics". 222p. 1983. lib. bdg. 33.00x (Pub. by A M Hakkert). Coronet Bks.
Seaton, Jack. The Five Points of Calvinism. 1979. pap. 1.20 (ISBN 0-85151-264-X). Banner of Truth.

Seaton, Jerome, tr. The Wine of Endless Life: Taoists Drinking Songs. 1985. 6.00 (ISBN 0-934834-59-8). White Pine.

Seaton, Linda K. Scriptural Choreography: Biblical Dance Forms in Shaping Contemporary Worship. 1979. 2.50 (ISBN 0-941500-15-2). Sharing Co.

Seaton, Ronald S. & Seaton, Edith B. Here's How: Health Education by Extension. LC 76-40599. 1976. pap. 3.95 (ISBN 0-87808-150-X). William Carey Lib.

Seaver, George. Charles Kingsley: Poet. LC 73-1252. 1973. lib. bdg. 10.00 (ISBN 0-8414-1540-4). Folcroft.

Seaver, Paul S. The Puritan Lectureships: The Politics of Religious Dissent, 1560-1662. LC 71-93497. 1970. 30.00x (ISBN 0-8047-0711-1). Stanford U Pr.

--Wallington's World: A Puritan Artisan in Seventeenth-Century London. LC 84-40447. 272p. 1985. 29.50x (ISBN 0-8047-1267-0). Stanford U Pr.

Seay, Davin & Neely, Mary. Stairway to Heaven: The Spiritual Roots of Rock & Roll. 384p. 1986. pap. 9.95 (ISBN 0-345-33022-6, Pub. by Ballantine Epiphany). Ballantine.

Sebald, H. Witchcraft: The Heritage of a Heresy. 262p. 1978. pap. 15.50 (ISBN 0-444-99059-3). Elsevier.

Sebba, Helen, tr. see Bastide, Roger.

Sebeok, Thomas A., ed. Myth: A Symposium. LC 65-29803. (Midland Bks.: No. 83). 192p. 1955. pap. 4.95 (ISBN 0-253-20083-0). Ind U Pr.

Sechi, Antonietta A. La Certosa Di Trisulti Da Innocenzo III: Al Concilio Di Costanza 1204-1414. Hogg, James, ed. (Analecta Cartusiana Ser.). (Ital.). 197p. (Orig.). 1981. pap. 25.00 (ISBN 3-7052-0109-3, Pub. by Salzburg Studies). Longwood Pub Group.

Sechi, Stephan M., jt. auth. see Cordovano, Steven.

Sechrist, Alice S., ed. Dictionary of Bible Imagery. LC 79-63409. 1972. 3.95 (ISBN 0-87785-118-2). Swedenborg.

Sechrist, Elsie. Meditation: Gateway to Light. rev. ed. 53p. 1972. pap. 3.95 (ISBN 0-87604-062-8). ARE Pr.

Seckel, Al, ed. Bertrand Russell on God & Religion. 345p. pap. 12.95 (ISBN 0-87975-323-4). Prometheus Bks.

Seculoff, James. Holy Hour for a New People. LC 76-27491. (Orig.). 1976. pkg. of 10 17.00 (ISBN 0-87973-645-3). Our Sunday Visitor.

Seculoff, James F. Catholic Home Devotions. LC 85-72535. 160p. (Orig.). 1986. pap. 5.50 (ISBN 0-87973-584-8, 584). Our Sunday Visitor.

Sedano, Maruja, et al. El Libro De Formacion De Catequistas: Creciendo y Compartiendo. 1982. pap. 7.95 (ISBN 0-8091-2439-4). Paulist Pr.

Sedano, Maruja, jt. auth. see Boyd, Don.

Seddon, R. G., ed. see Steiner, Rudolf.

Sedgwick, Alexander. Jansenism in Seventeenth-Century France: Voices from the Wilderness. LC 77-2812. 243p. 1977. 20.00x (ISBN 0-8139-0702-0). U Pr of Va.

Sedgwick, Alexander C. Ralliement in French Politics, Eighteen Ninety to Eighteen Ninety-Eight. LC 65-12828. (Historical Studies: No. 74). 1965. 14.00x (ISBN 0-674-74751-8). Harvard U Pr.

Sedgwick, Henry D. Ignatius Loyola. LC 83-45597. Date not set. Repr. of 1923 ed. 42.50 (ISBN 0-404-19890-2). AMS Pr.

Sedgwick, Timothy F. Sacramental Ethics: Paschal Identity & the Christian Life. LC 86-45925. 128p. 1987. pap. text ed. 7.95 (ISBN 0-8006-1965-X, 1-1965). Fortress.

Sedulius. Opera Omnia. Huemer, Iohnnes, ed. (Corpus Scriptorum Ecclesiasticorum Latinorum Ser: Vol. 10). Repr. of 1885 ed. 50.00 (ISBN 0-384-54730-3). Johnson Repr.

Seduro, Vladimir. Dostoevsky in Russian & World Theatre. 1977. 17.50 (ISBN 0-8158-0347-8). Chris Mass.

See, Maura, ed. Daily Readings with St. Augustine. 1987. pap. 4.95 (ISBN 0-87243-152-5). Templegate.

Seebohm, Frederic. Era of the Protestant Revolution. LC 77-147114. Repr. of 1903 ed. 7.50 (ISBN 0-404-05695-4). AMS Pr.

--The Era of the Protestant Revolution. 1902. 25.00 (ISBN 0-8495-6274-0). Arden Lib.

Seebohm, Frederick. The Oxford Reformers. Incl. Oxford Wit & Humour. 1914. Repr. 20.00 (ISBN 0-8274-3094-9). R West.

Seeger, Daniel A. The Seed & the Tree: Reflections on Non-Violence. (Orig.). 1986. pap. 2.50x (ISBN 0-87574-269-6). Pendle Hill.

Seeger, Elizabeth. Eastern Religions. LC 73-10206. (Illus.). 1973. 14.70 (ISBN 0-690-25342-7, Crowell Jr Bks). HarpJ.

Seel, David J. Challenge & Crisis in Missionary Medicine. LC 79-16015. (Illus.). 1979. pap. 3.95 (ISBN 0-87808-172-0). William Carey Lib.

Seele, Keith C. Tomb of Tjanefer at Thebes. LC 59-14285. (Oriental Institute Pubns. Ser: No. 86). (Illus.). 1959. 22.00x (ISBN 0-226-62187-1, OIP86). U of Chicago Pr.

Seeley, Burns K. Meditations on St. John. Coniker, Jerome F. & Francis, Dale, eds. LC 81-65808. (Living Meditation & Prayerbook Ser.). (Illus.). 245p. (Orig.). 1981. pap. text ed. 5.00 (ISBN 0-932406-03-3). AFC.

--Meditations on St. Paul. Coniker, Jerome F., ed. LC 82-72201. (Living Meditation & Prayerbook Ser.). (Illus.). 270p. (Orig.). 1982. pap. text ed. 5.00 (ISBN 0-932406-06-8). AFC.

--Reflections on St. Paul. Coniker, Jerome F., ed. LC 82-72202. (Living Meditation & Prayerbook Ser.). (Illus.). 270p. (Orig.). 1982. pap. text ed. 5.00 (ISBN 0-932406-07-6). AFC.

Seeley, John R. Ecce Homo. 1970. Repr. of 1908 ed. 12.95x (ISBN 0-460-00305-4, Evman). Biblio Dist.

Seeliger, Wes. Western Theology. LC 72-96685. 103p. 1985. pap. 6.95 (ISBN 0-915321-00-9). Pioneer Vent.

Seely, Edward D. Teaching Early Adolescents Creatively: A Manual for Church School Teachers. 222p. 1971. Westminster.

Seelye, Kate C., tr. see Abd-Al-Kahir Ibn-Tahir Ibn Muhammad, Abu M.

Seerveld, C. Rainbows for the Fallen World. 1980. pap. 9.95x (ISBN 0-919071-01-5). Radix Bks.

Seerveld, Calvin. Balaam's Apocalyptic Prophecies: A Study in Reading Scripture. pap. 3.95 (ISBN 0-88906-110-6). Wedge Pub.

Seesholtz, Anna G. Friends of God: Practical Mystics of the Fourteenth Century. 1970. Repr. of 1934 ed. 14.50 (ISBN 0-404-05697-0). AMS Pr.

Segal, Abraham. One People: A Study in Comparative Judaism. Zlotowitz, Bernard M., ed. 160p. (Orig.). 1983. pap. text ed. 6.95 (ISBN 0-8074-0169-2, 140025). UAHC.

Segal, Abraham, jt. auth. see Charry, Elias.

Segal, Abraham, jt. auth. see Essrig, Harry.

Segal, Alan F. Rebecca's Children: Judaism & Christianity in the Roman World. LC 85-17656. 216p. 1986. text ed. 20.00x (ISBN 0-674-75075-6). Harvard U Pr.

Segal, Judah B. Hebrew Passover from the Earliest Times to A.D. 70. 1963. 24.95x (ISBN 0-19-713529-3). Oxford U Pr.

Segal, M. H. A Grammar of Mishnaic Hebrew. 1978. pap. text ed. 15.95x (ISBN 0-19-815454-2). Oxford U Pr.

Segal, Robert. Responsive Singing: Sabbath Morning Service. 184p. 1972. 4.50x (ISBN 0-8381-0218-2). United Syn Bk.

Segal, Robert A. Joseph Campbell on Myth: An Introduction. LC 84-45374. (Reference Library on the Humanities). 125p. 1987. lib. bdg. 18.00 (ISBN 0-8240-8827-1). Garland Pub.

--The Poimandres As Myth: Scholarly Theory & Gnostic Meaning. (Religion & Reason Ser.: No. 33). 216p. 1986. lib. bdg. 58.00x (ISBN 0-89925-146-3). Mouton.

Segal, Yocheved. Our Sages Showed the Way, Vol. 1. Falk, Esther, tr. (Hebrew.). pap. 9.95 (ISBN 0-87306-289-2). Feldheim.

--Our Sages Showed the Way, Vol. 2. Falk, Esther, tr. from Hebrew. (Jewish Youth Classics Ser.). (Illus.). 192p. 1982. text ed. 9.95 (ISBN 0-87306-200-0). Feldheim.

Segerman, Sue K. Hiding the Word in Your Heart: How to Memorize Scripture. (Cornerstone Ser.). 40p. 1986. pap. 2.95 (ISBN 0-932305-24-5, 533012). Aglow Pubns.

Segler, Franklin. Christian Worship: Its Theology & Practice. LC 67-22034. 1975. pap. 8.95 (ISBN 0-8054-2309-5). Broadman.

Segler, Franklin M. Broadman Minister's Manual. LC 68-26920. 1968. 9.95 (ISBN 0-8054-2307-9). Broadman.

--Theology of Church & Ministry. LC 60-14146. 1960. bds. 11.95 (ISBN 0-8054-2506-3). Broadman.

Segovia, Fernando F., ed. Discipleship in the New Testament. LC 85-47730. 240p. 1985. pap. 16.95 (ISBN 0-8006-1873-4, 1-1873). Fortress.

Segraves, Daniel. The Search For the Word of God: A Defense of King James Version. Wallace, Mary, ed. 328p. (Orig.). 1984. pap. 7.95 (ISBN 0-912315-70-9). Word Aflame.

Segraves, Daniel L. The Search for the Word of God: A Defense of the King James Versions. 1982. pap. 6.00x (ISBN 0-912315-70-9). Freedom Univ-FSP.

Segraves, Judy. Come on into My House. Wallace, Mary, ed. (Illus.). 90p. (Orig.). 1985. pap. 4.95 (ISBN 0-912315-87-3). Word Aflame.

Segre, Dan V. Memoirs of a Fortunate Jew: An Italian Story. LC 86-17495. 274p. 1987. 16.95 (ISBN 0-917561-32-5). Adler & Adler.

Segreti, Mario M., jt. auth. see Simi, Gino J.

Seguin, Mary A. Petaled Sun. 48p. (Orig.). 1986. pap. 3.25 (ISBN 0-9616951-0-2). M A Seguin.

Segundo, Jean L. Grace & the Human Condition. Drury, John, tr. from Span. LC 72-85794. (A Theology for Artisans of a New Humanity Ser.: Vol. 2). Orig. Title: Gracia y Condicion Humana. 221p. 1973. pap. 7.95 (ISBN 0-88344-488-7). Orbis Bks.

Segundo, Juan L. The Community Called Church. Drury, John, tr. from Span. LC 72-85795. (A Theology for Artisans of a New Humanity Ser., Vol. 1). Orig. Title: Esa communidad Lleamasha Iglesia. 181p. 1973. 7.95x (ISBN 0-88344-481-X); pap. 4.95x (ISBN 0-88344-487-9). Orbis Bks.

--Evolution & Guilt. Drury, John, tr. from Span. LC 73-89054. (A Theology for Artisans of a New Humanity Ser.: Vol. 5). Orig. Title: Evolucion y Culpa. 154p. (Orig.). 1974. 7.95 (ISBN 0-88344-485-2). Orbis Bks.

--The Hidden Motives of Pastoral Action: Latin American Reflections. Drury, John, tr. from Sp. LC 77-13420. Orig. Title: Accion Pastoral latinoamericana: Sus motivos ocultos. 141p. 1977. 12.95 (ISBN 0-88344-185-3). Orbis Bks.

--The Historical Jesus of the Synoptics. Drury, John, tr. from Span. LC 85-7146. (Jesus of Nazareth Yesterday & Today Ser.: Vol. II). Tr. of Historia y Actualidad: Sinopticos y Pablo El Hombre de Hoy Ante Jesus de Nazareth. 240p. (Orig.). 1985. pap. 9.95 (ISBN 0-88344-220-5). Orbis Bks.

--The Humanist Christology of Paul: Jesus of Nazareth Yesterday & Today, Vol. 3. Drury, John, tr. from Span. LC 86-8480. 256p. (Orig.). 1986. pap. 14.95 (ISBN 0-88344-221-3). Orbis Bks.

--Jesus of Nazareth Yesterday & Today. Drury, John, tr. from Span. LC 83-19386. (Faith & Ideologies Ser.: Vol. 1). Tr. of El Hombre de Hoy Ante Jesus de Nazaret: Fe e Ideologia Ser. 368p. (Orig.). 1984. pap. 14.95 (ISBN 0-88344-127-6). Orbis Bks.

--The Liberation of Theology. Drury, John, tr. from Spanish. LC 76-7049. Orig. Title: Liberation de la Tealogia. 248p. (Orig.). 1976. pap. 10.95 (ISBN 0-88344-286-8). Orbis Bks.

--Our Idea of God. Drury, John, tr. from Span. LC 73-77358. (Theology for Artisans of a New Humanity Ser.: Vol. 3). Orig. Title: Nuestra idea de Dios. 212p. (Orig.). 1974. 7.95x (ISBN 0-88344-483-6); pap. 4.95 o. p. (ISBN 0-88344-489-5). Orbis Bks.

--The Sacraments Today. Drury, John, tr. from Span. LC 73-77359. (Theology for Artisans of a New Humanity Ser.: Vol. 4). Orig. Title: Los Sacramentos Hay y. 192p. (Orig.). 1974. pap. 4.95x (ISBN 0-88344-490-9). Orbis Bks.

--Theology & the Church: A Response to Cardinal Ratzinger. LC 85-51459. 175p. 1985. 14.95 (ISBN 0-86683-491-5, HarpR). Har-Row.

Seguy, J. Les Assemblees Anabaptistes-Mennonites de France. 1977. 64.00x (ISBN 90-279-7524-8). Mouton.

Seguy, Marie-Rose. The Miraculous Journey of Mahomet. LC 77-5140. (Library of Illuminated Manuscripts). (Illus.). 1977. 40.00 (ISBN 0-8076-0868-8). Braziller.

Sehnert, Keith W. Selfcare-Wellcare. LC 85-15622. 240p. (Orig.). 1985. text ed. 12.95 (ISBN 0-8066-2179-6, 10-5644); pap. 3.95 (ISBN 0-8066-2180-X, 10-5645). Augsburg.

Seidel, Anna, jt. ed. see Welch, Holmes.

Seidel, Linda. Romanesque Sculpture from the Cathedral of Saint-Etienne, Toulouse. LC 76-23646. (Outstanding Dissertations in the Fine Arts). (Illus.). 1977. Repr. of 1965 ed. lib. bdg. 63.00 (ISBN 0-8240-2729-9). Garland Pub.

Seidel, Linda, ed. see Dixon, Laurinda S.

Seidel, Linda, ed. see Kaplan, Paul H.

Seidman, Bradley. Absent at the Creation. LC 83-90254. 1984. 10.95 (ISBN 0-87212-175-5). Libra.

Seifert, Lois. Our Family Night In: Workbook of Covenant Living. LC 80-54803. 200p. (Orig.). pap. 4.95x (ISBN 0-8358-0420-8). Upper Room.

Seiler, Sr. M. Hilarine. Anne De Marquets, Poetesse Religieuse De Seizieme Siecle. LC 75-94200. (Catholic University of America. Studies in Romance Languages & Literatures: No. 4). (Fr). Repr. of 1931 ed. 21.00 (ISBN 0-404-50304-7). AMS Pr.

Seilhamer, Frank H. No Empty Phrases. 1985. 4.25 (ISBN 0-89536-732-7, 5816). CSS of Ohio.

--Prophets & Prophecy: Seven Key Messengers. LC 76-62603. pap. 23.80 (2027878). Bks Demand UMI.

Seilhamer, Frank S. Adventure in Faith. 1983. 7.95 (ISBN 0-89536-675-4, 0125). CSS of Ohio.

Seipp, Conrad, jt. auth. see Ramirez de Arellano, Annette B.

Seipt, A. A. Schwenkfelder Hymnology. LC 77-134414. Repr. of 1909 ed. 14.50 (ISBN 0-404-09908-4). AMS Pr.

Seiss, Joseph. The Apocalypse. LC 86-27393. 536p. 1987. Repr. 24.95 (ISBN 0-8254-3754-7). Kregel.

--Gospel in Leviticus. LC 80-8078. 408p. 1981. 12.95 (ISBN 0-8254-3743-1). Kregel.

--The Great Pyramid: A Miracle in Stone. LC 72-81590. (Illus.). 256p. 1973. pap. 5.00 (ISBN 0-89345-218-1, Steinerbks). Garber Comm.

Seiss, Joseph A. The Gospel in the Stars. LC 72-86676. (Illus.). 1986. pap. 10.95 (ISBN 0-8254-3755-5). Kregel.

--The Great Pyramid: A Miracle in Stone. LC 80-8341. (Harper's Library of Spiritual Wisdom). 256p. 1981. pap. 5.95i (ISBN 0-06-067211-0, CN4005, HarpR). Har-Row.

Seivertson, Genevah D. The Christ Highway. LC 81-69023. 184p. 1982. pap. 7.25 (ISBN 0-87516-465-X). De Vorss.

Seixas, Gershom M. A Religious Discourse: Thanksgiving Day Sermon, November 26, 1789. LC 77-7298. (Illus.). 1977. pap. 2.00 (ISBN 0-916790-00-2). Jewish Hist.

Sekida, Katsuki. Zen Training: Methods & Philosophy. Grimstone, A. V., ed. LC 75-17573. (Illus.). 264p. 1975. 12.50 (ISBN 0-8348-0111-6); pap. 9.95 (ISBN 0-8348-0114-0). Weatherhill.

Sekida, Katsuki, tr. see Grimstone, A. V.

Sekkizhaar. Periya Puranam. Mahalingam, N., ed. Vanmikanathan, G., tr. from Tamil. 612p. 1985. text ed. 11.95x (ISBN 0-87481-534-7, Pub. by RamaKrishna Math). Vedanta Pr.

Sekowsky, Jo Anne. Essentials of Our faith: What Christians Believe. (Basic Bible Study Ser.). (Orig.). 1987. pap. 2.95 (ISBN 0-932305-37-7, 521023). Aglow Pubns.

Sekowsky, Jo Anne, jt. auth. see Dull, Elaine.

Sekowsky, Jo Anne, ed. see Rowlands, Gerald.

Sekowsky, Jo Anne, ed. see Wood, George.

Sekowsky, JoAnne. Forgiveness-A Two-Way Street. LC 53-3011. (Cornerstone Ser.). 40p. 1985. pap. 2.75 (ISBN 0-930756-95-9). Aglow Pubns.

--How to Walk in the Spirit. 32p. 1976. pap. 0.95 (ISBN 0-930756-17-7, 541004). Aglow Pubns.

--Restored Value: A Woman's Status in Christ. (Encourager Ser.). 32p. 1985. pap. 2.25 (ISBN 0-932305-01-6, 523001). Aglow Pubns.

--Spiritual Warfare...Strategy for Winning. (Workbook Ser.). 80p. pap. 4.95 (ISBN 0-930756-74-6, 581004). Aglow Pubns.

Sekowsky, JoAnne, jt. auth. see Collingridge, Ruth.

Selby, D. J. Introduction to the New Testament: The Word Became Flesh. 1971. text ed. write for info. (ISBN 0-02-408870-6). Macmillan.

Selby, D. J. & West, J. K. Introduction to the Bible, 2 Vols. 1971. Set. text ed. write for info. (ISBN 0-02-408850-1). Macmillan.

Selby, Donald J. Toward the Understanding of St. Paul. 1962. ref. ed. 26.67 (ISBN 0-13-925693-8). P-H.

Selby, Thomas G. The Holy Spirit & the Christian Privilege. 1978. Repr. lib. bdg. 20.00 (ISBN 0-8495-4858-6). Arden Lib.

Selby-Bigge, L. A., ed. British Moralists: Being Selections from Writers Principally of the Eighteenth Century, 2 vols. in 1. LC 64-20242. 1964. 74.50 (ISBN 0-672-51067-7); pap. text ed. 17.95x (ISBN 0-8290-1894-8). Irvington.

Selden, Edward G. In the Time of Paul. 1900. 10.00 (ISBN 0-8414-8134-2). Folcroft.

Selden, John. The History of Tithes. LC 75-25833. (English Experience Ser.: No. 147). 1968. Repr. of 1618 ed. 49.00 (ISBN 90-221-0147-9). Walter J Johnson.

Seldin, Mariam. Monarch Notes on Milton's Paradise Lost. (Orig.). pap. 3.50 (ISBN 0-671-00513-8). Monarch Pr.

Seldin, Ruth. Teacher's Guide to Jews & Their Religion. 150p. 5.95 (ISBN 0-88464-041-8); pap. 2.95 (ISBN 0-686-99468-X). ADL.

Seldin, Ruth, jt. auth. see Singer, David.

Seldin, Ruth R., jt. auth. see Routtenberg, Lilly S.

Seldon, Eric. The God of the Present Age. LC 80-26149. 1981. pap. 9.00 (ISBN 0-8309-0305-4). Herald Hse.

Selement, George. Keepers of the Vineyard: The Puritan Ministry & Collective Culture in Colonial New England. 128p. (Orig.). 1984. lib. bdg. 22.00 (ISBN 0-8191-3876-2); pap. text ed. 9.50 (ISBN 0-8191-3877-0). U Pr of Amer.

Self, Carolyn S. & Self, William L. Confessions of a Nomad: A Devotional Guide. LC 83-61913. 168p. 1983. 1.98 (ISBN 0-931948-47-9). Peachtree Pubs.

--A Survival Kit for Marriage. LC 81-66091. 1981. pap. 5.95 (ISBN 0-8054-5643-0). Broadman.

Self-Realization Fellowship. God Alone: The Life & Letters of a Saint - Sri Gyanamata. LC 84-52361. (Illus.). 324p. 1984. 8.50 (ISBN 0-87612-200-4, 1805). Self Realization.

--Paramahansa Yogananda: In Memoriam. (Illus.). 127p. 1986. pap. 2.50 (ISBN 0-87612-170-9). Self Realization.

Self-Realization Fellowship Editorial Staff, jt. auth. see Yogananda, Paramahansa.

Self, William L., jt. auth. see Self, Carolyn S.
Seligman, Charles G. Egypt & Negro Africa: Study in Divine Kingship. LC 74-15088. (Frazer Lecture: 1933). (Illus.). Repr. of 1934 ed. 21.50 (ISBN 0-404-12138-1). AMS Pr.
Seliktar, Ofira. New Zionism & the Foreign Policy System of Israel. 256p. cancelled (ISBN 0-7099-3341-X, Pub. by Croom Helm Ltd). Methuen Inc.
--New Zionism & the Foreign Policy System of Israel. (Middle East Research Institute Special Studies). 272p. 1986. text ed. 32.50x (ISBN 0-8093-1287-5). S Ill U Pr.
Selinger, Suzanne. Calvin Against Himself: An Inquiry in Intellectual History. LC 83-21330. 238p. 1984. 29.50 (ISBN 0-208-01948-0, Archon). Shoe String.
Sell, Alan P. Robert Mackintosh: Theologian of Integrity. (European University Studies: Ser. 23, Vol. 95). 107p. 1977. pap. 16.95 (ISBN 3-261-03008-9). P Lang Pubs.
--Saints: Visible, Orderly & Catholic: The Congregational Idea of the Church. (Princeton Theological Monograph Ser.: No. 7). (Orig.). 1986. pap. 15.00 (ISBN 0-915138-89-1). Pickwick.
--Theology in Turmoil: The Roots, Course & Significance of the Conservative-Liberal. 144p. 1984. pap. 9.95 (ISBN 0-8010-8246-3). Baker Bk.
Sell, Charles. The House on the Rock. 168p. 1987. pap. 5.95 (ISBN 0-89693-048-3). Victor Bks.
Sell, Charles, jt. auth. see Perry, Lloyd.
Sell, Charles M. Family Ministry: Family Life Through the Church. 272p. 15.95 (ISBN 0-310-42580-8, 12335). Zondervan.
Sell, Jesse. The Knowledge of the Truth - Two Doctrines: The Book of Thomas the Contender(CGII, 7) & the False Teachers in the Pastoral Epistles. (European University Studies Ser.: No. 23, Vol. 194). 114p. 1982. pap. 14.20 (ISBN 3-8204-7224-X). P Lang Pubs.
Sellar, Robert. Tragedy of Quebec. LC 72-1429. (Select Bibliographies Reprint Ser.). 1972. Repr. of 1907 ed. 17.25 (ISBN 0-8369-6836-0). Ayer Co Pubs.
Sellars, Roy W. The Next Step in Religion: An Essay Toward the Coming Renaissance. LC 75-3360. Repr. of 1918 ed. 24.50 (ISBN 0-404-59358-5). AMS Pr.
--Religion Coming of Age. LC 75-3362. Repr. of 1928 ed. 20.50 (ISBN 0-404-59359-3). AMS Pr.
Sellers, Ian. Nineteenth Century Nonconformity. (Foundations of Modern History Ser.). 110p. 1977. pap. text ed. 14.50x (ISBN 0-8419-5802-5). Holmes & Meier.
Sellers, James H. & Milam, Edward E. Accounting Student Perceptions of Business & Professional Ethics. 50p. (Orig.). 1981. pap. 4.50 (ISBN 0-938004-00-X). U MS Bus Econ.
Sellers, Ovid R. & Voigt, E. E. Biblical Hebrew for Beginners. 12th corr ed. 1963. pap. 3.95x (ISBN 0-8401-2163-6). A R Allenson.
Sellers, Robert V. Two Ancient Christologies: A Study in the Christological Thought of the Schools of Alexandria & Antioch in the Early History of Christian Doctrine. (Church Historical Society London N. S. Ser.: No. 39). Repr. of 1940 ed. 50.00 (ISBN 0-8115-3162-7). Kraus Repr.
Sellery, G. C. & Krey, A. C. Medieval Foundations of Western Civilization. LC 68-24116. (World History Ser., No. 48). (Illus.). 1968. Repr. 74.95x (ISBN 0-8383-0926-7). Haskell.
Sellner, Edward S. Christian Ministry & the Fifth Step. 32p. 1981. pap. 1.95 (ISBN 0-89486-130-1). Hazelden.
Sells, L. Ray, jt. auth. see LaSuer, Donald F.
Sells, Ray, jt. auth. see Crandall, Ronald.
Selmer, Carl, ed. & intro. by see Benedictus, Saint.
Selms, A. Van see Van Selms, A.
Selness, Craig. When Your Mountain Won't Move. 156p. 1984. pap. 5.95 (ISBN 0-88207-619-1). Victor Bks.
Seltman, Charles T. Women in Antiquity. LC 78-20490. 1981. Repr. of 1956 ed. 25.85 (ISBN 0-88355-867-X). Hyperion Conn.
Seltzer, Robert M. Jewish People, Jewish Thought. (Illus.). 1980. text ed. write for info. (ISBN 0-02-408950-8). Macmillan.
Seltzer, Sandford. Jews & Non-Jews Falling in Love. 1976. 4.00 (ISBN 0-8074-0098-X, 164050). UAHC.
Seltzer, Sanford. Jews & Non-Jews: Getting Married. 1984. pap. 4.00 (ISBN 0-8074-0300-8, 164055). UAHC.
Selvidge, Marla J., ed. Fundamentalism Today: What Makes It So Attractive? 144p. (Orig.). 1984. pap. 7.95 (ISBN 0-87178-297-9). Brethren.
Selwyn, Edward G. The First Epistle of St. Peter. 2nd ed. (Thornapple Commentaries Ser.). 517p. 1981. pap. 10.95 (ISBN 0-8010-8199-8). Baker Bk.
Selwyn, Edward G., ed. Essays, Catholic & Critical. facs. ed. LC 75-142695. (Essay Index Reprint Ser). 1926. 24.50 (ISBN 0-8369-2075-9). Ayer Co Pubs.
Selzer, Michael. Politics & Jewish Purpose. 45p. 1972. pap. 2.50 (ISBN 0-934676-12-7). Greenlf Bks.
Selznick, Gertude J. & Steinberg, Stephen. The Tenacity of Prejudice: Anti-Semitism in Contemporary America. LC 78-31365. (Univ of California Five-Year Study of Anti-Semitism). (Illus.). 1979. Repr. of 1969 ed. lib. bdg. 24.75x (ISBN 0-313-20965-0, SETP). Greenwood.
Semarians, Beer-Shiba, tr. see Hubbard, David.
Semenoff-Tian-Chansky, Alexander. Father John of Kronstadt: A Life. 160p. 1979. pap. 7.95 (ISBN 0-913836-56-7). St Vladimirs.
Semenov, E. P. The Russian Government & the Massacres. LC 70-97304. (Judaica Ser.). 265p. 1972. Repr. of 1907 ed. lib. bdg. 29.75 (ISBN 0-8371-2632-0, SERG). Greenwood.
Semonche, John E. Religion & Constitutional Government in the United States: A Historical Overview with Sources. (Constitutional Bookshelf Ser.). 250p. (Orig.). 1985. pap. 14.95 (ISBN 0-930095-09-X). Signal Bks.
--Religion & Law in American History. LC 85-201489. (Church, State, & the First Amendment, a North Carolina Dialogue: No. 2). 125p. Date not set. price not set. U of NC Pr.
Semple, Robert. History of the Rise & Progress of the Baptists in Virginia. 1976. Repr. of 1894 ed. 15.00 (ISBN 0-686-12331-X). Church History.
Sen, Debabrata. The Concept of Knowledge: Indian Theories. 1985. 24.00x (ISBN 0-8364-1398-9, Pub. by KP Bagchi India). South Asia Bks.
Sen, Kshitimohan M. Hinduism. (Orig.). 1962. pap. 5.95 (ISBN 0-14-020515-2, Pelican). Penguin.
Sena, Patrick. The Apocalypse: Biblical Revelation Explained. LC 83-22299. 116p. (Orig.). 1983. pap. 6.95 (ISBN 0-8189-0454-2). Alba.
Sencourt, Robert. The Life of Newman. 1973. Repr. of 1948 ed. 30.00 (ISBN 0-8274-1085-9). R West.
Sender, Ruth M. The Cage. LC 86-8562. 252p. 1986. 13.95 (ISBN 0-02-781830-6). Macmillan.
Seneca. Moral Letters, 3 vols. (Loeb Classical Library: No. 75-77). 12.50x (ISBN 0-686-76874-4). Vol. 1 (ISBN 0-674-99084-6). Vol. 2 (ISBN 0-674-99085-4). Vol. 3 (ISBN 0-674-99086-2). Harvard U Pr.
Seneviratne, H. L. Rituals of the Kandyan State. LC 77-80842. (Cambridge Studies in Social Anthropology: No. 22). (Illus.). 1978. 37.50 (ISBN 0-521-21736-9). Cambridge U Pr.
Seneviratne, Lionel J. Kharma, Rebirth, God, & Computers. 1987. 6.95 (ISBN 0-533-07145-3). Vantage.
Senior, Donald. First & Second Peter. (New Testament Message Ser.: Vol. 20). 10.95 (ISBN 0-89453-208-1); pap. 6.95 (ISBN 0-89453-143-3). M Glazier.
--God the Son. LC 81-69109. (Illus.). 95p. 1982. pap. 5.95 (ISBN 0-89505-065-X). Argus Comm.
--The Gospel of Matthew. (Read & Pray Ser.). 1974. 1.75 (ISBN 0-8199-0518-6). Franciscan Herald.
--Jesus: A Gospel Portrait. 192p. (Orig.). 1975. pap. 2.95 (ISBN 0-8278-9003-6, Pub. by Pflaum Pr). Peter Li.
--Mathew: A Gospel for the Church. 1976. pap. 1.25 (ISBN 0-685-77500-3). Franciscan Herald.
--The Passion of Jesus in the Gospel of Mark. (Passion Ser.: Vol. 2). 1984. pap. 8.95 (ISBN 0-89453-436-X). M Glazier.
--Passion of Jesus in the Gospel of Matthew. (Passion Ser.: Vol. 1). 1985. pap. 8.95 (ISBN 0-89453-460-2). M Glazier.
--What Are They Saying about Matthew? LC 82-62967. (WATSA Ser.). 96p. (Orig.). 1983. pap. 3.95 (ISBN 0-8091-2541-2). Paulist Pr.
Senior, Donald & Stuhlmueller, Carroll. The Biblical Foundations for Mission. LC 82-22430. 384p. (Orig.). 1983. 12.50 (ISBN 0-88344-046-6); pap. 14.95 (ISBN 0-88344-047-4). Orbis Bks.
Senior, Donald, jt. ed. see Pawlikowski, John.
Senior, Elizabeth, jt. auth. see Kitzinger, Ernst.
Senior, H. L. John Milton: The Supreme Englishman. lib. bdg. 15.50 (ISBN 0-8414-8126-1). Folcroft.
Senior, John. The Death of Christian Culture. 1978. 12.95 (ISBN 0-87000-416-6). Educator Pubns.
--The Restoration of Christian Culture. LC 82-83497. 244p. (Orig.). 1983. pap. 9.95 (ISBN 0-89870-024-8). Ignatius Pr.
--Way Down & Out: The Occult in Symbolist Literature. LC 68-23326. (Illus.). 1968. Repr. of 1959 ed. lib. bdg. 22.50x (ISBN 0-8371-0218-9, SESL). Greenwood.
Senn, Frank C. Christian Worship & Its Cultural Setting. LC 82-48587. 160p. 1983. pap. 9.95 (ISBN 0-8006-1700-2, 1-1700). Fortress.
Senn, Frank C., ed. Protestant Spiritual Traditions. 288p. (Orig.). 1986. pap. 9.95 (ISBN 0-8091-2761-X). Paulist Pr.
Seno, William J., jt. ed. see Adams, Charles R.
Sensabaugh, George. Milton in Early America. LC 79-14332. 322p. 1979. 32.50x (ISBN 0-87752-180-8). Gordian.
Senter, Mark, III. The Art of Recruiting Volunteers. 96p. 1983. pap. 9.95 (ISBN 0-88207-297-8). Victor Bks.
Senter, Ruth. The Seasons of Friendship: A Search for Intimacy. 160p. 1982. 9.95 (ISBN 0-310-38830-9, 11226). Zondervan.
--So You're the Pastor's Wife. 1979. pap. 4.95 (ISBN 0-310-38821-X). Zondervan.
--Startled by Silence. 160p. 1985. 10.95 (ISBN 0-310-38840-6, 11227). Zondervan.
Sepharial. The Kabala of Numbers. LC 80-53342. 423p. 1980. Repr. of 1974 ed. lib. bdg. 16.95x (ISBN 0-89370-627-2). Borgo Pr.
--The Kabala of Numbers. LC 74-6128. 425p. 1974. pap. 6.95 (ISBN 0-87877-027-5, P-27). Newcastle Pub.
--Your Fortune in Your Name; or Kabalistic Astrology. LC 81-21658. 200p. 1981. Repr. of 1981 ed. lib. bdg. 15.95x (ISBN 0-89370-656-6). Borgo Pr.
Septimus, Bernard. Hispano-Jewish Culture in Transition: The Career & Controversies of Ramah. LC 81-13275. (Harvard Judiac Monographs: No. 4). 192p. 1982. text ed. 20.00x (ISBN 0-674-39230-2). Harvard U Pr.
Septimus, Bernard, jt. ed. see Twersky, Isadore.
Seraphim, Mary. Clare: Her Light & Her Song. 44p. 1983. 18.00 (ISBN 0-8199-0870-3). Franciscan Herald.
Serapion, Saint Against the Manichees. Casey, Robert P., ed. (Harvard Theological Studies). 1931. pap. 15.00 (ISBN 0-527-01015-4). Kraus Repr.
Seraydarian, Patricia M. The Church Secretary's Handbook. 159p. 1982. pap. 5.95 (ISBN 0-8423-0281-6). Tyndale.
Sereni, Ezo H. & Ashery, R. E., eds. Jews & Arabs in Palestine: Studies in a National & Colonial Problem. LC 75-6455. (The Rise of Jewish Nationalism & the Middle East Ser). 416p. 1975. Repr. of 1936 ed. 31.35 (ISBN 0-88355-341-4). Hyperion Conn.
Sergeant, Lewis. John Wycliffe. LC 73-14468. (Heroes of the Nations Ser.). Repr. of 1893 ed. 30.00 (ISBN 0-404-58286-9). AMS Pr.
Sergeant, Philip W. Witches & Warlocks. LC 72-82208. (Illus.). Repr. of 1936 ed. 24.50 (ISBN 0-405-08898-1). Ayer Co Pubs.
--Witches & Warlocks. LC 72-164055. (Illus.). 290p. 1975. Repr. of 1936 ed. 34.00x (ISBN 0-8103-3979-X). Gale.
--Witches & Warlocks. 1972. 24.50 (ISBN 0-405-08950-3, 1457). Ayer Co Pubs.
Sergent, Bernard. Homosexuality in Greek Myth. Goldhammer, Arthur, tr. from Fr. LC 85-73369. 360p. 1986. 21.95 (ISBN 0-8070-5700-2). Beacon Pr.
Sergijevsky, N. Svjatitel' Tikhon, Episkop Voronjezhskij i Zadonskij. Tr. of St. Tikhon, Bishop pf Voronezh & Zadonsk. 213p. pap. 8.00 (ISBN 0-317-29184-X). Holy Trinity.
Sergio, Lisa. Jesus & Woman: An Exciting Discovery of What He Offered Her. LC 75-4365. 139p. 1980. pap. 4.95 (ISBN 0-914440-44-6). EPM Pubns.
Serig, Joseph A., jt. ed. see Hughes, Richard.
Seripando, Girolamo. In D. Pauli Epistolas ad Romanos et Galatas Commentaria. 568p. Repr. of 1601 ed. text ed. 99.36 (ISBN 0-576-99309-3, Pub. by Gregg Intl Pubs England). Gregg Intl.
Sernau, Scott. Please Don't Squeeze the Christian. 150p. (Orig.). 1987. pap. 4.95 (ISBN 0-87784-571-9). Inter Varsity.
Sernett, Milton C., ed. Afro-American Religious History: A Documentary Witness. LC 84-24686. xii, 506p. 1985. text ed. 46.50 (ISBN 0-8223-0591-7); pap. text ed. 16.95 (ISBN 0-8223-0594-1). Duke.
Serra, Luis, jt. auth. see O'Shaughnessy, Laura.
Serrano, Antonio, jt. auth. see Cowman, Charles E.
Serruya, Colette. Lake Kinneret: Lake of Tiberias, Sea of Galilee. (Monographiae Biologicae: No.32). 1978. lib. bdg. 68.50 (ISBN 90-619-3085-5, Pub. by Junk Pubs Netherlands). Kluwer Academic.
Servetus, Michael. Two Treatises of Servetus on the Trinity. Wilbur, Earl M., tr. (Harvard Theological Studies). 1932. 24.00 (ISBN 0-527-01016-2). Kraus Repr.
Servier, Andre. Islam & the Psychology of the Musulman. 1977. lib. bdg. 59.95 (ISBN 0-8490-2079-4). Gordon Pr.
Sessions, Barbara, tr. see Seznec, Jean.
Sessions, Kyle & Bebb, Phillip. Pietas et Societas, New Trends in Reformation Social History: Essays in Memory of Harold J. Grimm. (Sixteenth Century Essays & Studies: Vol. IV). (Illus.). 240p. 1985. Smyth Sewn 25.00x (ISBN 0-940474-04-2). Sixteenth Cent.
Sessler, John J. Communal Pietism Among Early American Moravians. LC 70-134387. Repr. of 1933 ed. 19.50 (ISBN 0-404-08430-3). AMS Pr.
Seters, John Van see Van Seters, John.
Seters, Virginia A. van see Van Seters, Virginia A.
Seth, Andrew. The Development from Kant to Hegel. 1975. lib. bdg. 49.95 (ISBN 0-8490-0020-3). Gordon Pr.
--The Development from Kant to Hegel, with Chapters on the Philosophy of Religion. Beck, Lewis W., ed. LC 75-32044. (The Philosophy of Immanuel Kant Ser.: Vol. 7). 1976. Repr. of 1882 ed. lib. bdg. 24.00 (ISBN 0-8240-2331-5). Garland Pub.
Seth, Pattison A. Idea of God in the Light of Recent Philosophy: Gifford Lectures Delivered in the University of Aberdeen, 1912 & 1913. 2nd ed. rev. ed. Repr. of 1920 ed. 29.00 (ISBN 0-527-81500-4). Kraus Repr.
--Idea of Immortality. Repr. of 1922 ed. 18.00 (ISBN 0-527-81506-3). Kraus Repr.
Seth, S. J. The Divinity of Krishna. 1984. text ed. 14.00x. Coronet Bks.
Sethi, A. S. Universal Sikhism. 1972. 5.95 (ISBN 0-88253-767-9). Ind-US Inc.
Sethi, Amarjit S. & Pummer, Reinhard, eds. Comparative Religion. 1979. text ed. 18.95x (ISBN 0-7069-0810-4, Pub. by Vikas India). Advent NY.
Sethi, V. K. Kabir: The Weaver of God's Name. 762p. 1986. 23.00X (ISBN 0-8364-1673-2, Pub. by Manohar India). South Asia Bks.
Sethna, K. D. The Spirituality of the Future: A Search Apropos of R. C. Zaehner's Study in Sri-Aurobindo & Teilhard de Chardin. LC 76-14764. 320p. 1981. 32.50 (ISBN 0-8386-2028-0). Fairleigh Dickinson.
Seth Pringle-Pattison, A. Studies in the Philosophy of Religion. LC 77-27204. (Gifford Lectures: 1923). Repr. of 1930 ed. 30.00 (ISBN 0-404-60474-9). AMS Pr.
Seth Pringle Pattison, Andrew. Philosophical Radicals & Other Essays. 1907. 23.50 (ISBN 0-8337-4388-0). B Franklin.
Seton, Bernard E. Our Heritage of Hymns: A Swift Survey. LC 84-71734. 160p. (Orig.). 1984. pap. 10.95 (ISBN 0-943872-89-8). Andrews Univ Pr.
Seton, Julia M. Symbols of Numerology. 304p. 1984. pap. 9.95 (ISBN 0-87877-071-2). Newcastle Pub.
--Symbols of Numerology. LC 84-9183. 304p. 1984. Repr. of 1984 ed. lib. bdg. 19.95x (ISBN 0-89370-671-X). Borgo Pr.
Seton, W. W. Some New Sources for the Life of Blessed Agnes of Bohemia. 184p. 1815. text ed. 33.12 (ISBN 0-576-99207-0, Pub. by Gregg Intl Pubs England). Gregg Intl.
Seton-Sears, Julia. Key to Health, Wealth, & Love. 32p. 1976. pap. 4.95 (ISBN 0-88697-025-3). Life Science.
Setton, Kenneth M. Christian Attitudes Towards the Emperor in the Fourth Century. LC 41-13567. (Columbia University. Studies in Social Sciences: No. 482). Repr. of 1941 ed. 20.00 (ISBN 0-404-51482-0). AMS Pr.
--The Papacy & the Levant, Twelve Hundred Four to Fifteen Seventy-One, Vol. Two: The Fifteenth Century. LC 75-25476. (Memoirs Ser.: Vol. 127). (Illus.). 1978. 40.00 (ISBN 0-87169-127-2). Am Philos.
--The Papacy & the Levant Twelve Hundred Four to Fifteen Seventy-One Vol I: The Thirteenth & Fourteenth Centuries. LC 75-25476. (Memoirs Ser.: Vol. 114). 1976. 35.00 (ISBN 0-87169-114-0). Am Philos.
--The Papacy & the Levant, Twelve Hundred Four to Fifteen Seventy-One, Vols. III & IV. LC 75-25476. (Memoirs Ser.: Vols. 161 & 162). 1984. Vol. 161. 45.00 (ISBN 0-87169-161-2); Vol. 162. 45.00 (ISBN 0-87169-162-0). Am Philos.
Setton, Kenneth M., ed. History of the Crusades, 5 vols. Incl. Vol. 1. The First Hundred Years. Baldwin, Marshall W., ed. (Illus.). 740p. 1969. Repr. of 1955 ed (ISBN 0-299-04831-4); Vol. 2. The Later Crusades, 1189 to 1311. 2nd ed. Wolff, Robert L. & Hazard, Harry W., eds. (Illus.). 896p. Repr. of 1962 ed (ISBN 0-299-04841-1); Vol. 3. The Fourteenth & Fifteenth Centuries. Hazard, Harry W. & Setton, Kenneth M., eds. (Illus.). 836p. 1975 (ISBN 0-299-06670-3); Vol. 4. The Art & Architecture of the Crusader States. Hazard, Harry W. & Setton, Kenneth M., eds. (Illus.). 444p. 1977 (ISBN 0-299-06820-X); Vol. 5. The Impact of the Crusades on the Near East. Setton, Kenneth M. & Zacour, Norman P., eds. (Illus.). 512p. 1985 (ISBN 0-299-09140-6). LC 68-9837. 40.00x ea. U of Wis Pr.
Setton, Kenneth M. see Setton, Kenneth M.
Seuflow, August R., tr. see Walther, C. F.

Seung, T. K. Semiotics & Thematics in Hermeneutics. LC 82-4345. 256p. 1982. 27.50 (ISBN 0-231-05410-6). Columbia U Pr.

Seven Archangels. The Vials of the Seven Last Plagues. LC 76-28083. 156p. (Orig.). 1977. pap. 5.95 (ISBN 0-916766-23-3). Summit Univ.

Seventh-Day Baptist General Conference. Seventh-Day Baptists in Europe & America: A Series of Historical Papers Written in Commemoration of the One Hundred Anniversary of the Organization, 2 vols. Gaustad, Edwin S., ed. LC 79-52605. (The Baptist Tradition Ser.). (Illus.). 1980. Repr. of 1910 ed. lib. bdg. 160.00x set (ISBN 0-405-12470-8). Ayer Co Pubs.

Seventh-Day Baptists General Conference. Seventh-Day Baptists in Europe & America, Vol. 1. 80.00 (ISBN 0-405-12478-3). Ayer Co Pubs.

--Seventh-Day Baptists in Europe & America, Vol. 2. 80.00 (ISBN 0-405-12479-1). Ayer Co Pubs.

Seventy First Infantry Division, U.S. Army. The Seventy-First Came to Gunskirchen Lager. Crawford, Fred R., intro. by. LC 79-51047. (Witness to the Holocaust Ser.: No. 1). (Illus.). 28p. 1983. pap. 1.50 (ISBN 0-89937-036-5). Witness Holocaust.

Severance, W. Murray. Pronouncing Bible Names. rev. ed. 96p. 5.95 (ISBN 0-87981-657-0, 4691-03). Holman Bible Pub.

Severinghaus, Leslie R. Religions & History: A Textbook for the Enlightenment of 12th Graders in our Tax-Supported Public High Schools. 1985. 13.95 (ISBN 0-533-06577-1). Vantage.

Severus, Sulpicius. The Life of Saint Martin of Tours. pap. 1.95 (ISBN 0-686-05653-1). Eastern Orthodox.

--Sulpicii Severi Libri Qui Supersunt. Halm, Carolus, ed. (Corpus Scriptorum Ecclesiasticorum Latinorum Ser: Vol. 1). (Lat). unbound 50.00 (ISBN 0-384-54955-1). Johnson Repr.

Sevestre, A. Dictionnaire de Patrologie, 4 vols. in 5. Migne, J. P., ed. (Nouvelle Encyclopedie Theologique Ser.: Vols. 20-23b). (Fr.). 3830p. Repr. of 1859 ed. lib. bdg. 485.00x (ISBN 0-89241-267-4). Caratzas.

Sevidge, Marla J. Daughters of Jerusalem. LC 87-7437. 176p. (Orig.). 1987. pap. 9.95 (ISBN 0-8361-3440-0). Herald Pr.

Sevillias, Errikos. Athens-Auschwitz. 109p. 1984. 11.95 (ISBN 0-930685-00-8). Cadmus Press.

Sewall, Penne, jt. auth. see Shaffer, Floyd.

Sewall, Samuel. Letter-Book of Samuel Sewall, 1685-1729, 2 vols. LC 75-31101. Repr. of 1838 ed. 67.50 set (ISBN 0-404-13580-3). AMS Pr.

Seward, Harold A. Freedom's Holy Light. (Illus.). 88p. 1986. 10.95 (ISBN 0-8059-3021-3). Dorrance.

Seward, Jack. Hara-Kiri: Japanese Ritual Suicide. LC 68-11973. 1968. pap. 7.95 (ISBN 0-8048-0231-9). C E Tuttle.

Sewell, Arthur. Study in Milton's Christian Doctrine. LC 72-193159. 1939. lib. bdg. 25.00 (ISBN 0-8414-8118-0). Folcroft.

--A Study in Milton's Christian Doctrine. LC 67-26661. xiii, 214p. 1967. Repr. of 1939 ed. 22.50 (ISBN 0-208-00416-5, Archon). Shoe String.

Sewell, Brocard, jt. ed. see Woolf, Cecil.

Sewell, Daisy M. The Home As God Would Have It. 1937. pap. 4.25 (ISBN 0-88027-047-0). Firm Foun Pub.

--Ideal Womanhood. 1947. pap. 1.50 (ISBN 0-88027-048-9). Firm Foun Pub.

Sewell, H. & Bulfinch, Thomas. Book of Myths. LC 42-25450. (Illus.). 128p. 1969. 11.95 (ISBN 0-02-782280-X). Macmillan.

Sewell, Jesse P., ed. The Church & Her Ideal Educational Situation. Speck, Henry E. 1933. 2.50 (ISBN 0-88027-083-7); pap. 1.50 (ISBN 0-88027-084-5). Firm Foun Pub.

Sewell, Jesse P. & Speck, Henry E., eds. The Church & the Children. 1935. 1.50 (ISBN 0-88027-104-3). Firm Foun Pub.

--The Church & the Young People. 1935. 1.50 (ISBN 0-88027-105-1). Firm Foun Pub.

Sexson, Lynda. Ordinarily Sacred. LC 82-17145. 144p. 1982. 9.95 (ISBN 0-8245-0530-1). Crossroad NY.

Sexton, Lydia. Autobiography of Lydia Sexton, the Story of Her Life Through a Period of over Seventy-Five Years from 1799 to 1872: Her Early Privations, Adventures, & Reminiscences. Gifford, Carolyn D. & Dayton, Donald, eds. (Women in American Protestant Religion 1800-1930 Ser.). 655p. 1987. lib. bdg. 95.00 (ISBN 0-8240-0673-9). Garland Pub.

Sextus Empiricus Staff. Sextus Empiricus: Selections from the Major Writings on Scepticism, Man, & God. rev. ed. Hallie, Phillip P., ed. Etheridge, Sanford G., tr. from Gr. LC 85-27059. 256p. 1985. lib. bdg. 27.50 (ISBN 0-87220-007-8); pap. 6.95 (ISBN 0-87220-006-X). Hackett Pub.

Sextus Empiricus. Scepticism, Man & God: Selections from the Major Writings Of Sextus Empiricus. Hallie, Philip P., ed. Etheridge, Sanford G., tr. LC 64-22377. pap. 62.00 (ISBN 0-317-08988-9, 2001959). Bks Demand UMI.

Seybold, Klaus & Mueller, Ulrich B. Sickness & Healing. Stott, Douglas W., tr. from Ger. LC 81-3663. (Biblical Encounter Ser.). 208p. (Orig.). 1981. pap. 9.95 (ISBN 0-687-38444-3). Abingdon.

Seyda, Robert. Transforming Love. LC 82-91022. 162p. 1984. 12.50 (ISBN 0-533-05687-X). Vantage.

Seymour, Barbara. Portrait of a Place: San Luis Obispo. (Illus.). 120p. (Orig.). 1986. pap. 12.95 (ISBN 0-9617522-0-3). Garden Creek Pubns.

Seymour, Charles, Jr. Notre-Dame of Noyon in the Twelfth Century: A Study in the Early Development of Gothic Architecture. (Illus.). 1968. pap. 3.95x (ISBN 0-393-00464-3, Norton Lib). Norton.

Seymour, Charles, Jr., ed. & intro. by. Michelangelo: The Sistine Chapel Ceiling. (Critical Studies in Art History). (Illus.). 243p. 1972. pap. 7.95x (ISBN 0-393-09889-3). Norton.

Seymour, Jack L. From Sunday School to Church School: Continuities in Protestant Church Education in the United States, 1860-1929. LC 82-15977. 188p. 1982. lib. bdg. 26.25 o. p. (ISBN 0-8191-2726-4); pap. text ed. 11.50 (ISBN 0-8191-2727-2). U Pr of Amer.

Seymour, Jack L. & Miller, Donald E. Contemporary Approaches to Christian Education. LC 81-14899. 176p. (Orig.). 1982. pap. 8.75 (ISBN 0-687-09493-3). Abingdon.

Seymour, Jack L. & O'Gorman, Robert T. The Church in the Education of the Public: Refocusing the Task of Religious Education. 160p. 1984. pap. 10.95 (ISBN 0-687-08252-8). Abingdon.

Seymour, Malcolm. Puritan Migration to Connecticut: The Saga of the Seymour Family, 1129-1746. LC 82-548. (Illus.). 136p. 1982. 29.50 (ISBN 0-914016-85-7). Phoenix Pub.

Seymour, Peter. Peter Spier's Little Bible Storybooks. (Illus.). 1983. 7.95 (ISBN 0-385-19061-1). Doubleday.

Seymour, Peter, compiled by. Moments Bright & Shining: Three Hundred & Sixty-Five Thoughts to Enjoy Day by Day. (Illus.). 1979. 6.95 (ISBN 0-8378-1706-4). Gibson.

Seymour, Richard. The Gift of God. pap. 1.50 (ISBN 0-686-12746-3). Grace Pub Co.

Seymour, William K. & Smith, John, eds. Happy Christmas. LC 68-26877. 256p. 1979. Repr. of 1968 ed. Westminster.

Seznec, Jean. The Survival of the Pagan Gods: The Mythological Tradition & Its Place in Renaissance Humanism & Art. Sessions, Barbara, tr. (Bollingen Ser.: Vol. 38). (Illus.). 108p. 1972. pap. 9.50x (ISBN 0-691-01783-2). Princeton U Pr.

SGam po pa. The Jewel Ornament of Liberation. Guenther, Herbert V., tr. LC 86-11839. 353p. (off). 1986. pap. 14.95 (ISBN 0-87773-378-3). Shambhala Pubns.

Shaanan, Alexander. Dear God, Is Justice Still With You? (Illus.). 144p. 1983. 8.95 (ISBN 0-89962-306-9). Todd & Honeywell.

Shaban, M. A. Islamic History: A.D. 750 to 1055, (A.H. 132 to 448) New Interpretation II. LC 75-39390. (Illus.). 190p. 1976. 49.50 (ISBN 0-521-21198-0); pap. 16.95 (ISBN 0-521-29453-3). Cambridge U Pr.

Shackle, C. An Introduction to the Sacred Language of the Sikhs. 1983. pap. 25.00x (ISBN 0-8364-1009-2, Pub. by London U Pr). South Asia Bks.

Shad, A. R. Do's & Do Nots in Islam. Tr. of Al-Halal wal-Haram. 15.95 (ISBN 0-317-01588-5). Kazi Pubns.

--From Adam to Muhammad. 16.95 (ISBN 0-317-01593-1). Kazi Pubns.

--Muslim Etiquettes. 1981. 16.50 (ISBN 0-686-77429-9). Kazi Pubns.

--Prescribed Islamic Prayers. pap. 5.50 (ISBN 0-686-18593-5). Kazi Pubns.

--Riadh-us-Salihin. (Eng. & Arabic.). 29.00 (ISBN 0-317-01590-7). Kazi Pubns.

Shafer, Carl. Excellence in Teaching with the Seven Laws: A Contemporary Abridgment of Gregory's Seven Laws of Teaching. 80p. 1985. pap. 4.95 (ISBN 0-8010-8261-7). Baker Bk.

Shafer, Robert. Christianity & Naturalism: Essays in Criticism. LC 68-26206. 1969. Repr. of 1926 ed. 25.50x (ISBN 0-8046-0413-4, Pub. by Kennikat). Assoc Faculty Pr.

Shaffer, Floyd. If I Were a Clown. LC 84-11000. 112p. (Orig.). 1984. pap. 5.95 (ISBN 0-8066-2082-X, 10-3198). Augsburg.

Shaffer, Floyd & Sewall, Penne. Clown Ministry. LC 84-80322. 112p. (Orig.). 1984. pap. 7.95 (ISBN 0-936664-18-5). Group Bks.

Shaffer, Kenneth, jt. auth. see Snyder, Graydon.

Shaffer, Thomas L. On Being a Christian & a Lawyer. LC 80-25215. 288p. 1981. 12.95 (ISBN 0-8425-1833-9). Brigham.

Shaffer, Wilma. Fourteen Women's Programs: Making Your House a Home. 96p. (Orig.). 1984. pap. 3.95 (ISBN 0-87239-743-2, 2974). Standard Pub.

Shah, A. Miftah-ul-Quran: Glossary of Quran, 2 vols. 22.50 (ISBN 0-686-18525-0). Kazi Pubns.

Shah, Adries. Seeker after Truth: A Handbook of Sufi Tales & Teachings. LC 82-48401. 232p. (Orig.). 1982. pap. 7.64 (ISBN 0-06-067257-9, CN-4049, HarpR). Har-Row.

Shah, Ahmed. The Bijak or the Complete Works of Kabir. 1981. Repr. 16.50x (ISBN 0-89684-256-8, Pub. by Asian Pubn India). Orient Bk Dist.

Shah, Idries. The Book of the Book. 146p. 1976. 9.95 (ISBN 0-900860-12-X, Pub. by Octagon Pr England). Ins Study Human.

--Caravan of Dreams. 207p. 1968. 14.95 (ISBN 0-900860-14-6, Pub. by Octagon Pr England). Ins Study Human.

--The Dermis Probe. 191p. 1980. 15.95 (ISBN 0-900860-83-9, Pub. by Octagon Pr England). Ins Study Human.

--The Elephant in the Dark. 76p. 1982. 9.95 (ISBN 0-900860-36-7, Pub. by Octagon Pr England). Ins Study Human.

--Learning How to Learn. 302p. 1978. 14.95 (ISBN 0-900860-59-6, Pub. by Octagon Pr England). Ins Study Human.

--Learning How to Learn: Psychology & Spirituality in the Sufi Way. LC 80-8892. 304p. 1981. pap. 9.95 (ISBN 0-06-067255-2, CN4015, HarpR). Har-Row.

--The Magic Monastery. 208p. 1972. 16.95 (ISBN 0-900860-89-8, Pub. by Octagon Pr England). Ins Study Human.

--Neglected Aspects of Sufi Study. 83p. 1977. 9.95 (ISBN 0-900860-56-1, Pub. by Octagon Pr England). Ins Study Human.

--A Perfumed Scorpion. 193p. 1982. 14.95 (ISBN 0-900860-62-6, Pub. by Octagon Pr England). Ins Study Human.

--Seeker after Truth. 1982. 16.95 (ISBN 0-900860-91-X, Pub. by Octagon Pr England). Ins Study Human.

--Special Illumination: The Sufi Use of Humour. 64p. 1977. 9.95 (ISBN 0-900860-57-X, Pub. by Octagon Pr England). Ins Study Human.

--Special Problems in the Study of Sufi Ideas. 45p. 1978. pap. 5.95 (ISBN 0-900860-21-9, Pub by Octagon Pr England). Ins Study Human.

--Sufis. LC 64-11299. 1971. pap. 6.95 (ISBN 0-385-07966-4, Anch). Doubleday.

--The Sufis. 1983. 19.95 (ISBN 0-86304-020-9, Pub. by Octagon Pr England). Ins Study Human.

--A Veiled Gazelle: Seeing How to See. 103p. 1977. 9.95 (ISBN 0-900860-58-8, Pub. by Octagon Pr England). Ins Study Human.

--Way of the Sufi. 1970. pap. 8.95 (ISBN 0-525-47261-4, 0869-260). Dutton.

--The Way of the Sufi. 1983. 16.95 (ISBN 0-900860-80-4, Pub. by Octagon Pr England). Ins Study Human.

--The World of the Sufi. 1979. 18.95 (ISBN 0-900860-66-9). Ins Study Human.

Shah, Idries, ed. The Exploits of the Incomparable Mulla Nasrudin. 1983. Repr. of 1968 ed. 14.95 (ISBN 0-86304-022-5, Pub. by Octagon Pr England). Ins Study Human.

Shah, Priyabala. Tilaka: Hindu Marks. (Illus.). 108p. 1985. 29.95x (ISBN 0-318-20319-7, Pub. by New Order Bk Co India). Humanities.

Shah, Sayed M., tr. see Al-Qaradawl, Yusuf.

Shah, Sirdar I. A. The Golden Caravan. 1983. 15.95 (ISBN 0-86304-026-8, Pub. by Octagon Pr England). Ins Study Human.

Shahak, Israel, jt. tr. see Yinon, Oded.

Shaham, Nathan. The Other Side of the Wall: Three Novellas. Gold, Leonard, tr. from Hebrew. 256p. 1983. 13.95 (ISBN 0-8276-0223-5, 607). Jewish Pubns.

Shahan, Robert W. & Kovach, Francis J. Bonaventure & Aquinas: Enduring Philosophers. LC 75-40963. (Illus.). 200p. 1976. pap. 8.95x (ISBN 0-8061-1349-9). U of Okla Pr.

Shahan, Robert W. & Biro, J. I., eds. Spinoza: New Perspectives. LC 77-18541. 1980. 16.50x (ISBN 0-8061-1459-2); pap. text ed. 8.95x (ISBN 0-8061-1647-1). U of Okla Pr.

Shahan, Robert W., jt. ed. see Kovach, Francis J.

Shaheen, David. Growing a Junior High Ministry. LC 86-19410. 300p. (Orig.). 1986. pap. 12.95 (ISBN 0-931529-15-8). Group Bks.

Shaheen, Naseeb. Biblical References in Shakespeare's Tragedies. LC 85-40636. 248p. 1987. 29.50x (ISBN 0-87413-293-2). U Delaware Pr.

Shahrastani, Muhammad B. Moslem Sects & Divisions: The Section on Muslim Sects in Kitab Al-Milal Wa L-Nihal. Kazi, A. K. & Flynn, J. G., trs. 180p. 1984. 29.95x (ISBN 0-7103-0063-8, Kegan Paul). Methuen Inc.

Shahrivar, Mitra, tr. see Mah Talat Etemad Moghadam.

Shah Waliullah. The Sacred Knowledge: The Altaf Al-Quds of Shah Waliullah. Jalbani, G. N. & Pendlebury, D. L., trs. 1982. 13.95 (ISBN 0-900860-93-6, Pub. by Octagon Pr England). Ins Study Human.

Shaikh Muhammad Sarwar. Arabic Alphabet & Daily Prayer. 34p. 1981. pap. 3.00 (ISBN 0-941724-07-7). Islamic Seminary.

Shaikh Muhammad Sarwar, tr. from Arabic. The Holy Qur'an. 418p. pap. 10.00 (ISBN 0-941724-00-X). Islamic Seminary.

Shaikh Muhammad Sarwar, tr. see Ayatullah Al-Khu'i.

Shain, Ruchoma. All for the Boss. 439p. 1984. 13.95 (ISBN 0-87306-346-5). Feldheim.

Shainberg, Maurice. Breaking from the K. G. B. 1986. 15.95 (ISBN 0-933503-54-7). Shapolsky Pubs.

Shairo, Chava, compiled by. Learn While You Play. 20p. 1.50 (B68). Torah Umesorah.

Shairp, J. C. Culture & Religion in Some of Their Relations: The Literary Theory of Culture. 1978. Repr. of 1872 ed. lib. bdg. 30.00 (ISBN 0-8492-8044-3). R West.

--John Keble: An Essay on the Author of the 'Christian Year' 1866. Repr. 15.00 (ISBN 0-8274-3919-9). R West.

Shakarian, Demos. The Happiest People on Earth. 192p. 1979. 2.95 (ISBN 0-8007-8362-X, Spire Bks). Revell.

Shaked, Haim, jt. ed. see Legum, Colin.

Shakers. A Collection of Millennial Hymns Adapted to the Present Order of the Church. LC 72-2991. (Communal Societies in America Ser). Repr. of 1847 ed. 21.50 (ISBN 0-404-10753-2). AMS Pr.

--The Constitution of the United Societies of Believers (Called Shakers) Containing Sundry Covenants & Articles of Agreement, Definitive of the Legal Grounds of the Institution. LC 72-2992. Repr. of 1833 ed. 16.00 (ISBN 0-404-10754-0). AMS Pr.

--A Summary View of the Millennial Church, or United Society of Believers, Commonly Called Shakers. LC 72-2993. Repr. of 1848 ed. 26.00 (ISBN 0-404-10755-9). AMS Pr.

--Testimonies in the Life, Character, Revelations, & Doctrines of Mother Ann Lee. 2nd ed. LC 72-2994. Repr. of 1888 ed. 20.00 (ISBN 0-404-10756-7). AMS Pr.

Shakespeare, William, jt. auth. see Munday, Anthony.

Shakhnazarov, G. Socialist Democracy. 150p. 1974. pap. 2.95 (ISBN 0-8285-0412-1, Pub. by Progress Pubs USSR). Imported Pubns.

Shakin, M. H. Holy Quran. (Arabic & Eng.). 634p. 1982. 49.00x (ISBN 0-317-39404-5, Pub. by Luzac & Co Ltd). State Mutual Bk.

Shakir, H. M., tr. Koran. LC 85-51993. (Arabic & Eng.). 672p. 1985. pap. text ed. 6.00 (ISBN 0-940368-56-0). Tahrike Tarsile Quran.

Shakir, M. H., tr. from Arabic. Holy Qur'an. LC 82-60299. 440p. 1982. pap. 3.95 (ISBN 0-940368-18-8). Tahrike Tarsile Quran.

Shakir, M. H., tr. Holy Quran. (Eng. & Arabic.). 660p. 1982. 15.00 (ISBN 0-940368-17-X); pap. 9.00 (ISBN 0-940368-16-1). Tahrike Tarsile Quran.

Shakir, M. H., tr. from Arabic. Koran. 440p. 1985. 15.00 (ISBN 0-933543-05-0); pap. 9.00 (ISBN 0-933543-04-2). Aza Khana.

Shakir, Mahomodali H. The Holy Qur'an. 320p. 1986. text ed. 29.95 (ISBN 0-7103-0162-6); pap. text ed. 20.00 (ISBN 0-7103-0161-8). Methuen Inc.

Shakir, Moin. Islam in Indian Politics. 1983. 11.00x (ISBN 0-8364-1032-7, Pub. by Ajanta). South Asia Bks.

Shakow, Zara, compiled by. Curtain Time: Plays, Readings, Sketches, Cantatas, & Poems for Jewish Programs. 1985. pap. 9.95 (ISBN 0-8246-0310-9). Jonathan David.

Shaku, Soyen. Sermons of a Buddhist Abbot. 35.00 (ISBN 0-8490-1026-8). Gordon Pr.

--Zen for Americans: Including the Sutra of Forty-Two Chapters. Suzuki, D. T., tr. 220p. 1974. pap. 6.95 (ISBN 0-87548-273-2). Open Court.

Shalaby, Ibrahim. Education of a Black Muslim. 1980. pap. 1.25 (ISBN 0-686-32639-3). Impresora Sahuaro.

Shalders, E. W., ed. see Godet, F. L.

Shalm, George. Spiritual Gifts. 131p. 1983. pap. 4.95 (ISBN 0-912315-04-0). Word Aflame.

Shalom of Safed. Images From The Bible: The Paintings of Shalom of Safed, the Words of Elie Wiesel. LC 79-51032. (Illus.). 112p. 1980. 40.00 (ISBN 0-87951-107-9); limited, signed 400.00 (ISBN 0-87951-108-7). Overlook Pr.

Shalvi, Alice. The Relationship of Renaissance Concepts of Honour to Shakespeares Problem Plays. Hogg, James, ed. (Jacobean Drama Studies). 362p. (Orig.). 1972. pap. 15.00 (ISBN 3-7052-0306-1, Pub. by Salzburg Studies). Longwood Pub Group.

Shamblin, Steve. How To Grow Up Spiritually. (Orig.). 1986. pap. 5.95 (ISBN 0-910311-44-7). Huntington Hse Inc.

Shamir, Ruth. All Our Vows. LC 82-61795. 1983. 11.95 (ISBN 0-88400-090-7). Shengold.

Shanabruch, Charles. Chicago's Catholics: An Evolution of an American Identity. LC 80-53071. (Studies in American Catholicism: Vol. 4). 288p. 1981. text ed. 22.95 (ISBN 0-268-01840-5). U of Notre Dame Pr.

Shanahan, William O. German Protestants Face the Social Question: The Conservative Phase, 1815-1871. 1954. 22.95 (ISBN 0-268-00110-3). U of Notre Dame Pr.

Shane, John, ed. see Norbu, Namkhai.

Shaner, David E. The Bodymind Experience in Japanese Buddhism: A Phenomenological Study of Kukai & Dogen. (Series in Buddhist Studies). 202p. 1986. 44.50x (ISBN 0-88706-061-7); pap. 14.95x (ISBN 0-88706-062-5). State U NY Pr.

Shaner, Dorcas D. Short Dramas for the Church. 224p. 1980. pap. 10.95 (ISBN -08170-0883-7). Judson.

Shangle, Robert D., ed. see Foster, Lee.

Shank, M. Thomas, jt. ed. see Nichols, John A.

Shank, Robert. Elect in the Son: A Study of the Doctrine of Election. LC 74-114957. 256p. 1970. 7.95 (ISBN 0-911620-02-8). Westcott.

--God's Tomorrow: The Life Beyond Death. (Orig.). 1975. pap. 1.95 (ISBN 0-911620-03-6). Westcott.

--Life in the Son: A Study of the Doctrine of Perseverance. LC 59-15488. 380p. 1960. 8.95 (ISBN 0-911620-01-X). Westcott.

--Sources of Power of the Apostolic Witness. 125p. 1982. pap. 3.95 (ISBN 0-911620-05-2). Westcott.

--Until: The Coming of Messiah & His Kingdom. LC 81-72098. 520p. 1982. pap. 11.95 (ISBN 0-911620-04-4). Westcott.

Shank, Robert, tr. Jesus, His Story: The Four Gospels As One Narrative in Language for Today. LC 62-17864. (Illus.). 256p. 1962. 7.95 (ISBN 0-911620-00-1). Westcott.

Shank, Stanley, ed. Test Your Bible Power: A Good Book Quiz. (Epiphany Bks.). 1983. pap. 1.95 (ISBN 0-345-30663-5). Ballantine.

Shankar, Bhavani. The Doctrine of the Bhagavad Gita: Sangam Texts Ser. Iyer, Raghavan, ed. 131p. (Orig.). 1984. pap. 8.75 (ISBN 0-88695-031-7). Concord Grove.

Shankara. Aparokshanubhuti (Self-Realization) Vimuktananda, Swami, tr. (Sanskrit & Eng). pap. 2.50 (ISBN 0-87481-065-5). Vedanta Pr.

--Bhagavad Gita, Srimad Bhasya of Sri Sankaracarya. Warrier, A. G., tr. from Sanskrit. 652p. (Orig.). 1984. pap. 16.00x (ISBN 0-87481-526-6, Pub. by Ramakrishna Math Madras India). Vedanta Pr.

--Brahma-Sutra Bhasya of Sankaracarya. Gambhirananda, Swami, tr. (Sanskrit & Eng.). 20.00 (ISBN 0-87481-066-3). Vedanta Pr.

--Laghu-Vakya-Vritti. (Sanskrit & English). pap. 1.50 (ISBN 0-87481-067-1). Vedanta Pr.

--Panchikaranam. (Sanskrit & English). pap. 2.00 (ISBN 0-87481-068-X). Vedanta Pr.

--Sivananda Lahari of Sri Sankara. Tapasyananda, tr. from Sanskrit. 87p. 1987. pap. 2.25 (ISBN 0-87481-545-2, Pub. by Ramakrishna Math Madras India). Vedanta Pr.

--Upadesa Sahasri: A Thousand Teachings. Jagadananda, Swami, tr. (Sanskrit & Eng). pap. 4.95 (ISBN 0-87481-423-5). Vedanta Pr.

--Vakyavritti & Atmajnanopadeshavidhi. (Sanskrit & Eng). pap. 1.95 (ISBN 0-87481-424-3). Vedanta Pr.

--Vivekachudamani of Shri Shankaracharya. Madhavananda, Swami, tr. (Sanskrit & Eng.). pap. 3.50 (ISBN 0-87481-147-3). Vedanta Pr.

Shankaranarayanan, S. Sri Chakra. 1979. 14.95 (ISBN 0-941524-11-6). Lotus Light.

Shann, G. V. Book of the Needs of the Holy Orthodox Church. LC 77-82258. 1969. Repr. of 1894 ed. 19.45 (ISBN 0-404-05951-1). AMS Pr.

--Euchology: A Manual of Prayers of the Holy Orthodox Church. LC 75-82260. 1969. Repr. of 1891 ed. 32.50 (ISBN 0-404-05952-X). AMS Pr.

Shannon, Albert C. The Medieval Inquisition. 168p. 1983. 15.00 (ISBN 0-9612336-0-5, 83-72869); pap. 10.00 (ISBN 0-9612336-1-3). Augustinian Coll Pr.

--The Popes & Heresy in the Thirteenth Century. LC 78-63192. (Heresies of the Early Christian & Medieval Era: Second Ser.). Repr. of 1949 ed. 31.00 (ISBN 0-404-16228-2). AMS Pr.

Shannon, Foster H. God Is Light. LC 80-83606. (Illus.). 240p. (Orig.). 1981. pap. 6.95 (ISBN 0-938462-00-8). Green Leaf CA.

--The Green Leaf Bible Series, Year One. Rew, Lois J., ed. 1982. pap. 12.50 (ISBN 0-938462-06-7). Green Leaf CA.

--Green Leaf Bible Series, Year Two. (Orig.). 1984. pap. 12.50 (ISBN 0-938462-11-3). Green Leaf CA.

Shannon, J. Michael, jt. auth. see Shannon, Robert.

Shannon, Michael, jt. auth. see Shannon, Robert.

Shannon, Robert & Shannon, J. Michael. Expository Preaching. 128p. (Orig.). 1982. pap. 5.95 (ISBN 0-87239-605-3, 3020). Standard Pub.

Shannon, Robert & Shannon, Michael. Celebrating the Birth of Christ. 112p. 1985. pap. 4.95 (ISBN 0-87239-916-8, 3022). Standard Pub.

--Celebrating the Resurrection. (Illus.). 112p. (Orig.). 1984. pap. 5.95 (ISBN 0-87239-754-8, 3021). Standard Pub.

--Stewardship Source Book. 160p. 1987. pap. price not set (ISBN 0-87403-250-4, 3180). Standard Pub.

Shannon, Robert, et al. Sixty-Eight Communion Meditations & Prayers. 120p. (Orig.). 1984. pap. 3.95 (ISBN 0-87239-770-X, 3033). Standard Pub.

Shannon, Robert C., jt. auth. see Eubanks, David L.

Shannon, Thomas. Bioethics. 2nd ed. LC 76-18054. 646p. 1976. pap. 14.95 (ISBN 0-8091-1970-6). Paulist Pr.

Shannon, Thomas & Manfra, Jo Ann. Law & Bioethics: Selected Cases. LC 81-80876. 448p. (Orig.). 1981. pap. 14.95 (ISBN 0-8091-2353-3). Paulist Pr.

Shannon, Thomas A. An Introduction to Bioethics. 2nd. ed. 160p. 1987. pap. 6.95. Paulist Pr.

--What Are They Saying about Peace & War? (WATSA Ser.). 128p. 1983. pap. 4.95 (ISBN 0-8091-2499-8). Paulist Pr.

Shannon, Thomas A. & Faso, Charles N. Let Them Go Free: A Family Prayer Service & Guidelines for the Withdrawal of Life Support Systems. 1987. pap. 2.95. Paulist Pr.

Shannon, Thomas A., jt. ed. see O'Brien, David J.

Shannon, William H. Thomas Merton's Dark Path. rev. ed. 260p. 1987. pap. 8.95 (ISBN 0-374-52019-4). FS&G.

Shannon, William H., ed. see Merton, Thomas.

Shannon-Thornberry, Milo, ed. The Alternate Celebrations Catalogue. LC 82-3638. (Illus.). 192p. 1982. pap. 8.95 (ISBN 0-8298-0601-6). Pilgrim NY.

Shantaraksita. Tattva-Sangraha of Santaraksita with Commentary of Kamalasila. Jha, Ganganath, tr. 1593p. 1986. Repr. of 1937 ed. Set. 85.00 (ISBN 0-317-46526-0, Pub. by Motilal Banarsidass India); Vol. 1. 50.00 (ISBN 81-208-0059-1); Vol. 2. 50.00 (ISBN 81-208-0060-5). South Asia Bks.

Shapiro, Alexander M. & Cohen, Burton I. Studies in Jewish Education & Judaica in Honor of Louis Newman. 1984. 20.00 (ISBN 0-317-13172-9). Ktav.

Shapiro, Alexander M., ed. Lilmod u-Lelamed: Studies in Jewish Education & Judaica in Honor of Louis Newman. 1984. 20.00x (ISBN 0-88125-038-4). Ktav.

Shapiro, Barbara J. John Wilkins, Sixteen Fourteen to Sixteen Seventy-Two: An Intellectual Biography. LC 73-84042. 1969. 40.00x (ISBN 0-520-01396-4). U of Cal Pr.

Shapiro, Carl. Freethought Versus Religion: The Atheist Challenge. 50p. 1977. 8.00x (ISBN 0-914937-06-5). Ind Pubns.

--Why I Am an Atheist. 14p. (Orig.). 1979. write for info. (ISBN 0-914937-02-2); incl. cassette 10.00 (ISBN 0-317-18464-4). Ind Pubns.

Shapiro, David, jt. ed. see Schwartz, Gary E.

Shapiro, Deane H., Jr. Meditation: Self-Regulation Strategy & Altered States of Consciousness. LC 80-66454. 318p. 1980. 28.95x (ISBN 0-202-25132-2). De Gruyter Aldine.

Shapiro, Deane H., Jr. & Walsh, Roger N., eds. Meditation: Classic & Contemporary Perspectives. LC 84-300. 722p. 1984. lib. bdg. 64.95x (ISBN 0-202-25136-5). De Gruyter Aldine.

Shapiro, Dovid, ed. see Rabbi Aryeh Kaplan.

Shapiro, Harry L. The Jewish People: A Biological History. 1978. lib. bdg. 59.95 (ISBN 0-685-62297-5). Revisionist Pr.

Shapiro, Linda, jt. auth. see Donoghue, Quentin.

Shapiro, Max S., ed. see Hendricks, Rhoda A.

Shapiro, R. Gary. Exhaustive Concordance of the Book of Mormon, Doctrine & Covenants & Pearl of Great Peace. Orig. Title: Triple Concordance. 1977. 17.95 (ISBN 0-89036-085-5). Hawkes Pub Inc.

Shapiro, Rabbi R. ALEF-Bet: A Primer for a Davenen Universe. (Illus.). 70p. 1983. pap. 9.95 (ISBN 0-911511-00-8). ENR Word.

Shapiro, Sidney, ed. Jews in Old China: Studies by Chinese Historians. (Illus.). 224p. 1984. 15.95 (ISBN 0-88254-996-0). Hippocrene Bks.

Shapiro, Yonathan. Leadership of the American Zionist Organization, 1897-1930. LC 71-126521. pap. 77.50 (ISBN 0-317-11047-0, 2022265). Bks Demand UMI.

Shapolsky, Ian. The Beginners' Jewish Book of Why & What. (YA) 1987. 11.95. Shapolsky Pubs.

--The Jewish Trivia & Information Book. 400p. 1985. pap. 5.95 (ISBN 0-317-39894-6). Shapolsky Pubs.

--The Second Jewish Trivia & Information Book. (Illus.). 400p. 1986. pap. 6.95 (ISBN 0-933503-45-8). Shapolsky Pubs.

Sharafuddin, Sadruddin. Ammar Yasir. Haq, M. Fazal, tr. Orig. Title: Halif al-Makhzum. 264p. 1985. pap. 9.00 (ISBN 0-941724-40-9). Islamic Seminary.

Sharer, Robert J., rev. by see Morley, Sylvanus G. & Brainerd, George W.

Sharf, Andrew. Byzantium Jewry from Justinian to the Fourth Crusade. (Littman Library of Jewish Civilization). (Illus.). 1971. 24.00x (ISBN 0-19-710021-X). Oxford U Pr.

Shargel, Baila R. Practical Dreamer: Israel Friedlaender & the Shaping of American Judaism. (Illus.). 1985. text ed. 20.00 (ISBN 0-87334-025-6, Pub. by Jewish Theol Seminary). Ktav.

Shariati, Ali. An Approach to Understanding of Islam. Kiavantash, Venus, tr. from Persian. 26p. 1980. pap. 1.00x (ISBN 0-941722-14-7). Book-Dist-Ctr.

--Art Awaiting the Saviour. Fardjadi, Homa, tr. from Persian. 23p. 1980. pap. 1.00x (ISBN 0-941722-16-3). Book Dist Ctr.

--Culture & Ideology. Marjani, Fathollah, tr. from Persian. 23p. 1980. pap. 1.00x (ISBN 0-941722-12-0). Book-Dist-Ctr.

--Fatima Is Fatima. Bakhtiar, Laleh, tr. from Arabic. LC 81-52831. 226p. 1982. pap. 4.95 (ISBN 0-940368-09-9). Tahrike Tarsile Quran.

--From Where Shall We Begin & Machine in the Captivity of Machinism. Marjani, Fathollah, tr. from Persian. 51p. 1980. pap. 1.95x (ISBN 0-941722-10-4). Book-Dist-Ctr.

Shari'Ati, Ali. Hajj. Somayyah & Yaser, trs. 1984. pap. 5.95 (ISBN 0-686-78719-6). Mizan Pr.

Shariati, Ali. Hajj. 2nd ed. Behzadnia, A., tr. from Persian. 162p. 1978. pap. 4.95 (ISBN 0-941722-09-0). Book-Dist-Ctr.

--Man & Islam. Marjani, Fathollah, tr. from Persian. 150p. (Orig.). 1981. 9.95 (ISBN 0-941722-02-3); pap. 4.95 (ISBN 0-941722-00-7). Book Dist Ctr.

Shari'ati, Ali. On the Sociology of Islam. 3rd ed. Algar, Hamid, tr. from Persian. LC 79-83552. 1980. 15.95 (ISBN 0-933782-01-2); pap. 5.95 (ISBN 0-933782-00-4). Mizan Pr.

Shariati, Ali. One Followed by Eternity of Zeros. Ghasemy, A. Asghar, tr. 23p. 1980. pap. 1.00 (ISBN 0-941722-15-5). Book-Dist-Ctr.

--Red Shi'ism. Shirazi, Habib, tr. from Persian. 1980. pap. 1.00 (ISBN 0-941722-17-1). Book-Dist-Ctr.

--Reflection of Humanity. 2nd ed. Marjani, Fathollah, tr. from Persian. 37p. 1984. pap. 2.00 (ISBN 0-941722-11-2). Book-Dist-Ctr.

--Selection & Election. Ghasemy, Ali A., tr. from Persian. 12p. 1980. pap. 0.75 (ISBN 0-941722-13-9). Book-Dist-Ctr.

--The Visage of Muhammad. 28p. (Orig.). 1979. pap. 1.25 (ISBN 0-318-03828-5). Book-Dist-Ctr.

Sharif, M. Islamic Social Framework. 14.50 (ISBN 0-686-18446-7). Kazi Pubns.

Sharif, Regina S. Non-Jewish Zionism: Its Roots in Western History. 160p. 1983. 18.75x (ISBN 0-86232-151-4, Pub. by Zed Pr England); pap. 8.75 (ISBN 0-86232-152-2). Humanities.

Shariff, A. A. Muslim Thought, Its Origin & Achievements. pap. 10.50 (ISBN 0-317-46100-1). Kazi Pubns.

Sharkey, Don. The Woman Shall Conquer. rev. ed. 258p. 1976. pap. 4.95 (ISBN 0-913382-01-9, 101-1). Prow Bks-Franciscan.

Sharkey, John. Celtic Mysteries: Art & Imagination Ser. (Illus.). 1987. pap. text ed. 10.95 (ISBN 0-500-81009-5). Thames Hudson.

Sharkey, Paul W., ed. Philosophy, Religion & Psychotherapy: Essays in the Philosophical Foundations of Psychotherapy. LC 81-40828. 242p. (Orig.). 1982. lib. bdg. 29.00 (ISBN 0-8191-2331-5); pap. text ed. 12.50 (ISBN 0-8191-2332-3). U Pr of Amer.

Sharma, Arvind. The Hindu Gita: Ancient & Classical Interpretations of the Bhagavadgita. LC 85-21520. 250p. 1986. 28.95 (ISBN 0-8126-9013-3). Open Court.

--Textual Studies in Hinduism. 1980. lib. bdg. 14.95x (ISBN 0-914914-15-4). New Horizons.

--Textual Studies in Hinduism. 1985. 12.50x (ISBN 0-8364-1291-5, Pub. by Manohar India). South Asia Bks.

Sharma, Arvind, jt. auth. see French, Hal W.

Sharma, Arvind, ed. Women in World Religions. (McGill Studies in the History of Religions). 256p. (Orig.). 1986. 34.50x (ISBN 0-88706-374-8); pap. 10.95x (ISBN 0-88706-375-6). State U NY Pr.

Sharma, B. N. History of the Dvaita School of Vedant & Its Literature. 2nd ed. 1981. 48.00x (ISBN 0-8364-0754-7, Pub. by Motilal Banarsidass). South Asia Bks.

--Iconography of Sadasiva. LC 76-902916. 1976. 12.50 (ISBN 0-88386-823-7). South Asia Bks.

Sharma, Gopi. The Science of Numbers. 1984. 11.50x (ISBN 0-8364-1133-1, Pub. by Ajanta). South Asia Bks.

Sharma, H. L. The Psychodynamics of Yoga. 160p. 1981. 16.95x (ISBN 0-317-12326-2, Pub. by G D K Pubns India). Asia Bk Corp.

Sharma, I. C. Cayce, Karma & Reincarnation. LC 81-23214. 186p. 1982. pap. 5.50 (ISBN 0-8356-0563-9, Quest). Theos Pub Hse.

Sharma, K. P. Hindu Vidhi (Hindu Law in Hindi) 390p. 1980. 90.00x (Pub. by Eastern Bk India). State Mutual Bk.

Sharma, Kamalesh. Role of Muslims in Indian Politics, 1857-1947. 295p. 1986. text ed. 45.00x (ISBN 81-210-0028-9, Pub. by Inter India Pubns N Delhi). Apt Bks.

Sharma, R. N. Brahmins Through the Ages. 1977. 18.00x (ISBN 0-686-22659-3). Intl Bk Dist.

Sharma, Shubhra. Life in the Upanishads. 1985. 15.00x (ISBN 81-7017-202-0, Pub. by Abhinav India). South Asia Bks.

Sharma, T. N. Religious Thought in India. 1980. 11.00x (ISBN 0-8364-0619-2, Pub. by Ramneek). South Asia Bks.

Sharma, V. S., tr. see Mensching, G.

Sharner, Mariann V. The Holy Spirit Came at 3 AM. 1983. 4.95 (ISBN 0-8062-2156-9). Carlton.

Sha Rocco. The Masculine Cross & Ancient Sex Worship. (Illus.). 65p. 1873. pap. 7.95 (ISBN 0-88697-014-8). Life Science.

Sharon, Douglas. Wizard of the Four Winds: A Shaman's Story. LC 78-3204. (Illus.). 1978. 19.95 (ISBN 0-02-928580-1). Free Pr.

Sharon, Ruth. Arts & Crafts the Year Round, 2 Vols. (Illus.). 1965. Set. 29.00x (ISBN 0-8381-0213-1). United Syn Bk.

Sharot, Stephen. Judaism: A Sociology. LC 75-37727. 240p. 1976. text ed. 29.50x (ISBN 0-8419-0250-X). Holmes & Meier.

--Messianism, Mysticism, & Magic: A Sociological Analysis of Jewish Religious Movements. LC 81-11688. (Studies in Religion). ix, 306p. 1987. pap. 12.95x (ISBN 0-8078-4170-6). U of NC Pr.

Sharp, C. J. New Training for Service. rev. ed. (Illus.). 128p. (Orig.). 1942. pap. 2.95 (ISBN 0-87239-334-8, 3059). Standard Pub.

Sharp, Corona, tr. see Von Speyr, Adrienne.

Sharp, Florence A., ed. see Erickson, Milton H., et al.

Sharp, Frank C. Ethics. LC 75-3365. Repr. of 1928 ed. 45.50 (ISBN 0-404-59362-3). AMS Pr.

Sharp, John K. Old Priest Remembers, Eighteen Ninety-Two to Nineteen Seventy-Eight. 2nd ed. 1978. 10.00 (ISBN 0-682-49183-7). Exposition Pr FL.

Sharp, Watson. The Catholic & the Jewish Approach to Sex & Their Relative Influence Upon the Cultural Character of Our Society. (Illus.). 1976. 47.75 (ISBN 0-89266-012-0). Am Classical Coll Pr.

Sharpe, Bertie W. Only God Cast out the Anti-Christ. 1983. 4.95 (ISBN 0-8062-2214-X). Carlton.

Sharpe, Charles K. Historical Account of the Belief in Witchcraft in Scotland. LC 74-8196. 1974. Repr. of 1884 ed. 48.00x (ISBN 0-8103-3590-5). Gale.

Sharpe, Eric J. Comparative Religion: A History. LC 86-2380. 330p. 1987. 31.95 (ISBN 0-8126-9032-X); pap. 14.95 (ISBN 0-8126-9041-9). Open Court.

--Understanding Religion. LC 82-25055. 160p. 1984. 19.95 (ISBN 0-312-83208-7). St Martin.

Sharpe, J. Edward, ed. American Indian Prayers & Poetry. (Illus.). 32p. 1985. pap. 3.00 (ISBN 0-935741-09-7). Cherokee Pubns.

Sharpe, K. J. & Ker, J. M., eds. Religion Nature: With Charles Birch & Others. (Illus.). 116p. (Orig.). 1984. pap. 11.95 (ISBN 0-9597672-0-7, Pub. by Auckland Univ Chaplaincy). ANZ Religious Pubns.

Sharpe, Kevin J. From Science to An Adequate Mythology. (Science, Religion & Society Ser.). 156p. (Orig.). 1984. pap. 11.95 (ISBN 0-86474-000-X, Pub. by Interface Press). ANZ Religious Pubns.

Sharper, Sally, jt. ed. see Scharper, Philip.

Sharrock, Roger. John Bunyan. LC 84-6728. 163p. 1984. Repr. lib. bdg. 25.00x (ISBN 0-313-24528-2, SHJO). Greenwood.

Shastra, M. N. Hindu Metaphysics. 247p. 1978. Repr. of 1904 ed. text ed. 15.00 (ISBN 0-89684-121-9, Pub. by Cosmo Pubns India). Orient Bk Dist.

Shastri, jt. auth. see Ballantyne.

Shastri, J. L. Puranas: Ancient Indian Tradition & Mythology. 1978-82. Shiva Purana: 4 Vols. 60.00 (ISBN 0-89581-343-2); Bhagavata Purana: 5 Vols. 75.00 (ISBN 0-89581-536-2); Linga Purana: 2 Vols. 45.00 (ISBN 0-89581-537-0); Garuda Purana: 3 Vols. 45.00 (ISBN 0-89581-538-9); Narada Purana: 5 Vols. 75.00 (ISBN 0-89581-539-7). Asian Human Pr.

--The Vedas of Raja Rammohan Rai. rev. ed. 1977. 7.95 (ISBN 0-89684-335-1). Orient Bk Dist.

Shastri, J. L., ed. Brahma Purana, Pt. I. (Ancient Tradition & Mythology Ser.: Vol. 33). 240p. 1985. 18.50 (ISBN 81-208-0003-6, Pub. by Motilal Banarsidass India). Orient Bk Dist.

Shastri, J. L., tr. Siva Purana, Vol. 1. cancelled (ISBN 0-89581-343-2). Asian Human Pr.

--Siva Purana, Vol. 2. cancelled (ISBN 0-89581-475-7). Asian Human Pr.
--Siva Purana, Vol. 3. cancelled (ISBN 0-89581-476-5). Asian Human Pr.
--Siva Purana, Vol. 4. cancelled (ISBN 0-89581-476-5). Asian Human Pr.

Shastri, Lakshmana, jt. auth. see Avalon, Arthur.

Shattock, E. H. The Rangoon, Burma, Thathana Yeiktha Meditation Course. 175p. 1985. 137.50 (ISBN 0-89920-094-X). Am Inst Psych.

Shattuck, Gardiner H., Jr. A Shield & Hiding Place: The Religious Life of the Civil War Armies. (Illus.). 192p. 1987. 24.95 (ISBN 0-86554-273-2, H236). Mercer Univ Pr.

Shatz, David, jt. ed. see Cahn, Stephen M.

Shatzky, Jacob. Geshikhte Fun Yidn in Varshe, 3 vols. LC 48-15791. (Yiddish.). 1953. Set. 10.00 (ISBN 0-914512-27-7); 10.00 ea. Vol. 1 (ISBN 0-914512-32-3). Vol. 2 (ISBN 0-914512-33-1). Vol. 3 (ISBN 0-914512-34-X). Yivo Inst.

Shatzmiller, Joseph. Recherches sur la Communaute Juive De Manosque Au Moyen Age (1241-1329) (Etudes Juives: No. 15). 1973. pap. 14.00x (ISBN 90-2797-188-9). Mouton.

Shaughnessy, Gerald. Has the Immigrant Kept the Faith. LC 76-83438. (Religion in America Ser). 1969. Repr. of 1925 ed. 20.00 (ISBN 0-405-00262-9). Ayer Co Pubs.

Shaver, Charles. Beacon Small-Group Bible Studies, Gospel of John, Pt. II: That You Might Have Life. Wolf, Earl C., ed. 64p. (Orig.). 1984. pap. 2.50 (ISBN 0-8341-0881-X). Beacon Hill.
--Beacon Small-Group Bible Studies, John: That All Might Believe, Vol. 1. 68p. (Orig.). 1980. pap. 2.50 (ISBN 0-8341-0651-5). Beacon Hill.

Shaver, Elizabeth. A Is for Apple. (Illus.). 36p. 1986. pap. 2.50. Shaker Her Soc.
--Watervliet Shaker Meeting House. 6p. 1986. pap. 2.50. Shaker Her Soc.

Shaver, Elizabeth D. Watervliet Shaker Cemetery, Albany, N. Y. 1986. pap. 2.50. Shaker Her Soc.

Shavit, Yaacov. The New Hebrew Nation: A Study in Israeli Heresy & Fantasy. 1987. 29.50 (ISBN 0-7146-3302-X, F Cass Co). Biblio Dist.

Shaw, Amy. Our Family Lenten Experience. 1983. 4.95 (ISBN 0-89536-590-1, 1506). CSS of Ohio.

Shaw, Barnabas. Memorials of South Africa. LC 71-109358. Repr. of 1840 ed. cancelled (ISBN 0-8371-3737-3, SMS&, Pub. by Negro U Pr). Greenwood.

Shaw, Bernard. Saint Joan, a Screenplay. Dukore, Bernard F., ed. LC 68-11039. (Illus.). 224p. 1968. 15.00x (ISBN 0-295-97885-6); pap. 5.95x (ISBN 0-295-95072-2, WP56). U of Wash Pr.
--Saint Joan, Major Barbara, Androcles. Bd. with Major Barbara; Androcles & the Lion. LC 56-5413. 6.95 (ISBN 0-394-60480-6). Modern Lib.

Shaw, Duncan, jt. ed. see Cowan, Ian B.

Shaw, George B. St. Joan. (Modern Critical Interpretations--Modern British Literature Ser.). 1987. 19.95 (ISBN 1-55546-030-5). Chelsea Hse.

Shaw, George Bernard. Saint Joan. (Penguin Plays Ser.). (YA) 1950. pap. 2.95 (ISBN 0-14-048005-6). Penguin.

Shaw, George P. Patriarch & Patriot: William Grant Broughton 1788-1853: Colonial Statesman & Ecclesiastic. 1978. 28.50x (ISBN 0-522-84122-8, Pub. by Melbourne U Pr). Intl Spec Bk.

Shaw, Graham. The Cost of Authority: Manipulation & Freedom in the New Testament. LC 82-48545. 320p. 1983. pap. 16.95 (ISBN 0-8006-1707-X). Fortress.

Shaw, James. Twelve Years in America Being Observations on the Country, the People, Institutions, & Religion. text ed. 25.50 (ISBN 0-8369-9234-2, 9088). Ayer Co Pubs.

Shaw, James B. Drawings by Old Masters at Christ Church, Oxford, 2 vols. (Illus.). 1976. 150.00x (ISBN 0-19-817323-7). Oxford U Pr.

Shaw, Jean. Greater Love: A Woman's Workshop on Friendship. 96p. 1984. pap. 2.95 (ISBN 0-310-43531-5, 9596P). Zondervan.
--Second Cup of Coffee: Proverbs for Today's Woman. 192p. (Orig.). 1981. pap. 3.95 (ISBN 0-310-43542-0, 9609P). Zondervan.

Shaw, John. Travels in England: A Ramble with the City & Town Missionaries. LC 84-48282. (The Rise of Urban Britain Ser.). 393p. 1985. 50.00 (ISBN 0-8240-6284-1). Garland Pub.

Shaw, John M. The Poetry of Sacred Song. 1972. 3.00 (ISBN 0-9607778-6-5). Friends Fla St.
--The Resurrection of Christ. 218p. 1920. 10.95 (ISBN 0-567-02252-8, Pub. by T & T Clark Ltd UK). Fortress.

Shaw, Joseph M. Pulpit under the Sky: A Life of Hans Nielson Hauge. LC 78-12391. 1979. Repr. of 1955 ed. lib. bdg. 24.75x (ISBN 0-313-21123-X, SHPU). Greenwood.

Shaw, Joseph M., et al, eds. Readings in Christian Humanism. LC 82-70963. (Orig.). 1982. pap. 24.95 (ISBN 0-8066-1938-4, 10-5400). Augsburg.

Shaw, Judy. Little Faith Builders. 30p. (Orig.). 1983. pap. 0.75 (ISBN 0-89274-290-9). Harrison Hse.

Shaw, Lee H., Jr. How to Live Forever in the New Jerusalem. 56p. (Orig.). (YA) 1985. pap. 3.00x (ISBN 0-9614311-0-5). Elijah-John.

Shaw, Luci. Colossians: Focus on Christ. (Fisherman Bible Studyguide). 56p. 1982. saddle-stitched 2.95 (ISBN 0-87788-132-4). Shaw Pubs.
--The Sighting. LC 81-9342. (The Wheaton Literary Ser.). (Illus.). 95p. 1981. pap. 5.95 (ISBN 0-87788-768-3). Shaw Pubs.

Shaw, Luci, ed. see Boom, Corrie ten.

Shaw, M. R., tr. see Villehardouin, Joinville.

Shaw, Margaret R., tr. see De Villehardouin, Geoffrey & De Joinville, Jean.

Shaw, Martin, ed. see Dearmer, Percy.

Shaw, Naomi. Let the Hallelujahs Roll. LC 76-52280. (YA) 1977. pap. 1.95 (ISBN 0-89221-028-1). New Leaf.

Shaw, Opal, jt. auth. see Hansen, Vee.

Shaw, Robert B. The Call of God: The Theme of Vocation in the Poetry of Donne & Herbert. LC 81-66126. (Cowley Lectures). 123p. (Orig.). 1981. pap. 6.00 (ISBN 0-936384-04-2). Cowley Pubns.

Shaw, Russell. Does Suffering Make Sense? LC 86-62613. 180p. (Orig.). 1987. pap. 4.95 (ISBN 0-87973-834-0). Our Sunday Visitor.
--Permanent Deacons. rev. ed. 40p. 1986. pap. 1.95 (ISBN 1-55586-989-0). US Catholic.
--Signs of the Times: Questions Catholics Ask Today. (Orig.). 1985. pap. 8.95 (ISBN 0-87061-133-X). Chr Classics.
--Why We Need Confession. LC 85-63153. 125p. (Orig.). 1986. pap. 4.95 (ISBN 0-87973-537-6, 537). Our Sunday Visitor.

Shaw, Russell, jt. auth. see Grisez, Germain.

Shaw, S. B., ed. Echoes of the General Holiness Assembly. (The Higher Christian Life Ser.). 345p. 1985. lib. bdg. 45.00 (ISBN 0-8240-6442-9). Garland Pub.

Shaw, Thomas, ed. Ways to Pray. LC 84-71180. (Sermon Ser.: No. 4). 92p. (Orig.). 1984. pap. 5.00 (ISBN 0-936384-19-0). Cowley Pubns.

Shaw, W. Frank. Chapters of Symbolism. 1979. Repr. of 1897 ed. lib. bdg. 45.00 (ISBN 0-8495-4902-7). Arden Lib.

Shaw, William A. Bibliography of the Historical Works of Dr. Creighton, Dr. Stubbs, Dr. S. R. Gardiner, & the Late Lord Acton. 1969. 17.50 (ISBN 0-8337-3242-0). B Franklin.
--A History of the English Church During the Civil Wars & under the Commonwealth, 1640-1660. LC 78-184708. 1974. Repr. of 1900 ed. lib. bdg. 57.50 (ISBN 0-8337-4389-9). B Franklin.

Shaw, William A. see Peet, Henry.

Shawchuck, Norman. How to Be a More Effective Church Leader: A Special Edition for Pastors & Other Church Leaders. (Illus.). 69p. 1981. pap. 9.95 (ISBN 0-938180-07-X). Org Resources Pr.
--How to be a More Effective Church Leader: A Special Edition for Pastors & Other Church Leaders. Orig. Title: Taking a Look at Your Leadership Styles. (Illus.). 69p. 1981. pap. 9.95 (ISBN 0-938180-07-X). Spiritual Growth.
--How to Manage Conflict in the Church: Conflict Interventions & Resources, Vol. II. (Illus.). 51p. (Orig.). 1983. pap. 9.95 (ISBN 0-938180-11-8). Org Resources Pr.
--How to Manage Conflict in the Church: Understanding & Managing Conflict, Vol. I. (Illus.). 51p. (Orig.). 1983. pap. 9.95 (ISBN 0-938180-10-X). Org Resources Pr.
--What It Means to Be a Church Leader: A Biblical Point of View. (Illus.). 71p. (Orig.). 1984. pap. 7.95 (ISBN 0-938180-13-4). Org Resources Pr.

Shawchuck, Norman & Lindgren, Alvin J. Management for Your Church: How to Realize Your Church's Potential Through a Systems Approach. (Illus.). 160p. 1985. pap. 8.95 (ISBN 0-938180-14-2). Org Resources Pr.

Shawchuck, Norman, jt. auth. see Job, Reuben.

Shawchuck, Norman, jt. auth. see Job, Rueben P.

Shawchuck, Norman, jt. auth. see Lindgren, Alvin J.

Shawchuck, Norman, jt. auth. see Perry, Lloyd M.

Shawchuck, Norman, et al. How to Conduct a Spiritual Life Retreat. (Orig.). 1986. pap. 5.95 (ISBN 0-8358-0527-1, ICN 608805, Dist. by Abingdon Pr). Upper Room.

Shawcross, John T., ed. see Milton, John.

Shea, David & Troyer, Anthony. The Religion of the Sufis. 1979. 11.95 (ISBN 0-900860-65-0). Ins Study Human.

Shea, John. The Challenge of Jesus. (Encore Edition Ser.). 192p. 1984. pap. 8.95 (ISBN 0-88347-169-8). Thomas More.
--The Hour of the Unexpected. LC 77-73648. 1977. pap. 4.95 (ISBN 0-913592-85-4). Argus Comm.
--Stories of Faith. 1980. pap. 9.95 (ISBN 0-88347-112-4). Thomas More.
--Stories of God: An Unauthorized Biography. 1978. pap. 8.95 (ISBN 0-88347-085-3). Thomas More.

Shea, John D. A Bibliographical Account of Catholic Bibles, Testaments & Other Portions of Scripture Translated from the Latin Vulgate. 1980. lib. bdg. 49.95 (ISBN 0-8490-3114-1). Gordon Pr.
--History of the Catholic Church in the United States, 4 vols. 216.00 (ISBN 0-405-10852-4, 11855). Ayer Co Pubs.
--History of the Catholic Missions Among the Indian Tribes of the United States, 1529-1854. LC 73-175853. Repr. of 1855 ed. 28.50 (ISBN 0-404-07176-7). AMS Pr.

Shea, John G. History of the Catholic Missions Among the Indian Tribes of the United States, 1529-1854. LC 70-83436. (Religion in America, Ser. 1). 1969. Repr. of 1857 ed. 26.50 (ISBN 0-405-00263-7). Ayer Co Pubs.

Shea, John J. Religious Experiencing: William James & Eugene Gendlin. 156p. (Orig.). 1987. lib. bdg. 22.50 (ISBN 0-8191-6136-5); pap. text ed. 10.75 (ISBN 0-8191-6137-3). U Pr of Amer.

Shea, Leo Martin. Lowell's Religious Outlook. 124p. 1983. Repr. of 1926 ed. 16.00x (ISBN 0-939738-13-9). Zubal Inc.

Shea, William M. The Naturalists & the Supernatural: Studies in Horizon & an American Philosophy of Religion. LC 84-14686. xvi, 242p. 1984. 21.50 (ISBN 0-86554-116-7, MUP/H98). Mercer Univ Pr.

Sheaf, J. P., Jr., jt. auth. see Alger, Horatio, Sr.

Shealy, C. Norman & Myss, Caroline M. The Creation of Health: The Merger of Traditional Medical Diagnosis with Clairvoyant Insight. 270p. 1987. 14.95 (ISBN 0-913299-40-5). Stillpoint.

Shearburn, Wally M. Jacob's Ladder: A Choral Reading. 1980. 4.00 (ISBN 0-89536-441-7, 1014). CSS of Ohio.

Shearer, Ann, tr. see Vanier, Vean.

Shearman, Hugh. Desire & Fulfillment. 1.75 (ISBN 0-8356-7054-6). Theos Pub Hse.
--Passionate Necessity. 3.50 (ISBN 0-8356-0200-1). Theos Pub Hse.

Shearman, J. The Vatican Stanze: Functions & Decoration. (Italian Lectures). 1971. pap. 2.50 (ISBN 0-85672-062-3, Pub. by British Acad). Longwood Pub Group.

Shearman, John, ed. see Wilde, Johannes.

Shearn, Carol R. The Church Office Handbook: A Basic Guide to Keeping Order. 288p. pap. 12.95 (ISBN 0-8192-1391-8). Morehouse.

Shear-Yashuv, Aharon. The Theology of Salomon Ludwig Steinheim. (Studies in Judaism in Modern Times: Vol. 7). (Illus.). x, 115p. 1986. 27.23 (ISBN 90-04-07670-0, Pub. by E J Brill). Heinman.

Shechtman, Stephen A., jt. auth. see Singer, Mark J.

Shedd, Charlie. Devotions for Dieters. 1983. 8.95 (ISBN 0-8499-0330-0). Word Bks.

Shedd, Charlie & Shedd, Martha. Bible Study in Duet. 144p. 1984. 8.95 (ISBN 0-310-42380-5, 18360). Zondervan.
--Bible Study Together: Making Marriage Last. 144p. 1987. pap. 5.95 (ISBN 0-310-42381-3). Zondervan.
--Praying Together: Making Marriage Last. 128p. 1987. pap. 5.95 (ISBN 0-310-43291-X). Zondervan.

Shedd, Charlie W. How to Develop a Tithing Church. (Orig.). 1961. pap. 5.95 (ISBN 0-687-17798-7). Abingdon.
--Letters to Philip. (Orig.). 1985. pap. 2.95 (ISBN 0-515-08465-4). Jove Pubns.
--Letters to Philip. 128p. 1969. pap. 2.95 (ISBN 0-8007-8025-6, Spire Bks). Revell.
--You Can Be a Great Parent. LC 76-128353. 1982. pap. 2.25 (ISBN 0-8499-4166-0, 98070). Word Bks.

Shedd, Martha, jt. auth. see Shedd, Charlie.

Shedd, W. G. The Doctrine of Endless Punishment. 1980. 8.25 (ISBN 0-86524-019-1, 9803). Klock & Klock.
--Sermons to the Natural Man. 1977. 13.95 (ISBN 0-85151-260-7). Banner of Truth.
--Theological Essays. 1981. lib. bdg. 26.00 (ISBN 0-86524-079-5, 8602). Klock & Klock.

Shedd, William G. Commentary on Romans: A Classic Commentary from the Reformed Perspective. (Thornapple Commentaries Ser.). 1980. pap. 8.95 (ISBN 0-8010-8175-0). Baker Bk.

Sheed, F. J. Death into Life: A Conversation. 1977. pap. 1.95 (ISBN 0-88479-005-3). Arena Lettres.
--The Holy Spirit in Action. 148p. 1981. pap. 3.95 (ISBN 0-89283-109-X). Servant.
--Map of Life. 1979. pap. 2.95 (ISBN 0-88479-017-7). Arena Lettres.
--Our Hearts Are Restless: The Prayer of St. Augustine. 96p. 1976. pap. 4.95 (ISBN 0-8164-2127-7, HarpR). Har-Row.
--Theology & Sanity. rev. ed. LC 78-62340. 1978. pap. 6.95 (ISBN 0-87973-854-5). Our Sunday Visitor.
--Theology for Beginners. Rev. ed. 200p. 1982. pap. 6.95 (ISBN 0-89283-124-3). Servant.
--To Know Christ Jesus. 1980. pap. 4.95 (ISBN 0-89283-080-8). Servant.

Sheed, Francis J. Sidelights on the Catholic Revival. facs. ed. LC 74-99649. (Essay Index Reprint Ser). 1940. 18.00 (ISBN 0-8369-2176-3). Ayer Co Pubs.

Sheed, Frank. What Difference Does Jesus Make? LC 76-162382. 264p. 1982. pap. 6.95 (ISBN 0-87973-810-3, 810). Our Sunday Visitor.

Sheed, Rosemary, tr. see De Surgy, Paul.

Sheed, Wilfrid. Frank & Maisie: A Memoir with Parents. 304p. 1986. pap. 7.95 (ISBN 0-671-62813-5, Touchstone Bks). S&S.

Sheedy, Charles E. The Eucharistic Controversy of the Eleventh Century Against the Background of Pre-Scholastic Theology. LC 78-63179. (Heresies of the Early Christian & Medieval Era: Second Ser.). Repr. of 1947 ed. 30.00 (ISBN 0-404-16197-9). AMS Pr.

Sheehan, John. Religion & Cult. 240p. pap. 6.95 (ISBN 0-87462-446-0). Marquette.

Sheehan, John F. On Becoming Whole in Christ: An Interpretation of the Spiritual Exercises. 1978. pap. 3.95 (ISBN 0-8294-0278-0). Loyola.

Sheehan, Lawrence. A Blessing of Years: The Memoirs of Lawrence Cardinal Sheehan. LC 82-19965. (Illus.). 314p. 1984. pap. text ed. 9.95 (ISBN 0-317-11856-0, 85-06743). U of Notre Dame Pr.

Sheehan, Maurice W., ed. St. Francis of Assisi: Essays in Commemoration, 1982. 10.00. Franciscan Inst.

Sheehan, Thomas, ed. The Knight-Errant of Assisi. Little, B., tr. Repr. 7.00. Franciscan Inst.

Sheek, G. William. The Word on Families: A Bibical Guide to Family Well-Being. Schaller, Lyle E., ed. 160p. (Orig.). 1985. pap. 7.50 (ISBN 0-687-46135-9). Abingdon.

Sheeley, Jill. Christmas in Aspen. (Illus.). 1982. Repr. write for info (ISBN 0-9609108-0-8). Columbine Pr.

Sheen, Fulton. Through the Year with Fulton Sheen: Inspiration Selections for Each Day of the Year. 213p. 1985. pap. 6.95 (ISBN 0-89283-236-3). Servant.

Sheen, Fulton J. Cross-Ways: A Book of Inspiration. LC 83-45272. (Illus.). 80p. 1984. pap. 7.95 (ISBN 0-385-19205-3, Im). Doubleday.
--God Love You. LC 80-23085. 224p. 1981. pap. 4.50 (ISBN 0-385-17486-1, Im). Doubleday.
--Jesus, Son of Mary: A Book for Children. (Illus.). 32p. 1980. 8.95 (ISBN 0-8164-0470-4, HarpR). Har-Row.
--Life Is Worth Living. 1978. pap. 4.50 (ISBN 0-385-14510-1, Im). Doubleday.
--The Life of All Living. 1979. pap. 3.50 (ISBN 0-385-15458-5, Im). Doubleday.
--Life of Christ. LC 77-81295. 1977. pap. 8.95 (ISBN 0-385-13220-4, Im). Doubleday.
--Lift up Your Heart. 280p. 1975. pap. 4.50 (ISBN 0-385-09001-3, Im). Doubleday.
--Moral Universe: A Preface to Christian Living. facs. ed. LC 67-28766. (Essay Index Reprint Ser). 1936. 15.00 (ISBN 0-8369-0873-2). Ayer Co Pubs.
--Peace of Soul. 1954. pap. 4.95 (ISBN 0-385-02871-7, D8, Im). Doubleday.
--Power of Love. 1968. pap. 2.95 (ISBN 0-385-01090-7, D235, Im). Doubleday.
--Rejoice. LC 84-45271. (Illus.). 80p. 1984. pap. 8.95 (ISBN 0-385-19164-2, Im). Doubleday.
--The Seven Last Words. 1982. pap. 2.95 (ISBN 0-8189-0438-0). Alba.
--Those Mysterious Priests. 1979. pap. 10.00 (ISBN 0-385-08102-2). Lumen Christi.
--Treasure in Clay: The Autobiography of Fulton J. Sheen. LC 81-43271. (Illus.). 384p. 1980. 15.95 (ISBN 0-385-15985-4). Doubleday.
--Treasure in Clay: The Autobiography of Fulton J. Sheen. LC 81-43271. (Illus.). 384p. 1982. pap. 8.95 (ISBN 0-385-17709-7, Im). Doubleday.
--The Way of the Cross: Giant Print Edition. rev. ed. (Illus.). 64p. 1982. pap. 2.50 (ISBN 0-87973-659-3, 659); roncote pocket-size 2.50 (ISBN 0-87973-660-7, 660). Our Sunday Visitor.
--The World's First Love. 240p. 1976. 4.50 (ISBN 0-385-11559-8, Im). Doubleday.
--The World's Great Love: The Prayer of the Rosary. (Illus.). 1978. pap. 4.95 (ISBN 0-8164-2182-X, HarpR). Har-Row.

Sheeran, Michael J. Beyond Majority Rule: Voteless Decisions in the Religious Society of Friends. (Illus.). 153p. (Orig.). 1983. pap. 4.95 (ISBN 0-941308-04-9). Religious Soc Friends.

Sheerin, John B., jt. ed. see Stransky, Thomas F.

Sheets, John. The Spirit Speaks in Us. 210p. 1986. 8.95 (ISBN 0-87193-250-4). Dimension Bks.

Sheets, John R. To Believe Is to Exist. 1986. pap. 14.95 (ISBN 0-87193-247-4). Dimension Bks.

Shehaden, Raja. Samed. 172p. 1984. pap. 9.95 (ISBN 0-531-09839-7). Watts.
Shehadi, Fadlou. Metaphysics in Islamic Philosophy. LC 81-18069. 1983. 35.00x (ISBN 0-88206-049-X). Caravan Bks.
Sheheen, Dennis, ed. A Child's Picture English-Hebrew Dictionary. (Children's Picture Dictionaries Ser.). (Illus.). 1987. 9.95 (ISBN 0-915361-75-2, Dist. by Watts). Adama Pubs Inc.
Sheik, Ali B. Islam: A Cultural Orientation. 10.00x (ISBN 0-8364-0802-0, Pub. by Macmillan India). South Asia Bks.
Sheikh, M. Saeed. Islamic Philosophy. 1982. 16.95 (ISBN 0-900860-50-2, Pub. by Octagon Pr England). Ins Study Human.
--Studies in Muslim Philosophy. 248p. (Orig.). 1981. pap. 11.75 (ISBN 0-88004-008-4). Sunwise Turn.
Sheil, Leonard. Pray Like This: Pray with Saint Paul. 1963. 3.00 (ISBN 0-8198-0128-3). Dghtrs St Paul.
Sheils, W. J., ed. Monks, Hermits & the Ascetic Tradition. (Studies in Church History: Vol. 22). 500p. 1985. 45.00x (ISBN 0-631-14351-3). Basil Blackwell.
--Persecution & Toleration. (Studies in Church History: Vol. 21). 500p. 1984. 45.00x (ISBN 0-631-13601-0). Basil Blackwell.
Sheils, W. J. & Baker, Derek, eds. The Church & Healing: Papers Read at the Twentieth Summer Meeting & the Twenty-First Winter Meeting. (Studies in Church History: Vol. 19). 400p. 1984. text ed. 45.00x (ISBN 0-631-13117-5). Basil Blackwell.
Sheils, W. J. & Wood, Diana, eds. Voluntary Religion, Vol. 23. 544p. 1987. text ed. 49.95 (ISBN 0-631-15054-4). Basil Blackwell.
Sheiner, Ben. Intellectual Mysticism. LC 78-50531. (Illus.). 120p. 1978. 8.95 (ISBN 0-8022-2228-5). Philos Lib.
Sheingold, Carl, jt. auth. see Mayer, Egon.
Sheinkin, David. The Path of the Kabbalah: An Introduction to the Living Jewish Spiritual Tradition. (Patterns of World Spirituality Ser.). 224p. 1986. pap. 9.95 (ISBN 0-913757-69-1, Pub. by New Era Bks). Paragon Hse.
Sheinkopf, David I. Gelatin & Jewish Law. 132p. 1983. pap. 7.95x (ISBN 0-8197-0488-1). Bloch.
Shekhawat, Virenda. Yoga: The Technique of Liberation. 90p. 1979. text ed. 7.50 (ISBN 0-89684-264-9, Pub. by Sterling India). Orient Bk Dist.
Shelby, Donald J. Bold Expectations of the Gospel. LC 82-50943. 96p. (Orig.). 1983. pap. 3.95 (ISBN 0-8358-0454-2). Upper Room.
--Forever Beginning: Exploration of the Faith for New Believers. 160p. (Orig.). 1987. pap. 5.95 (ISBN 0-8358-0557-3). Upper Room.
--Meeting the Messiah. LC 79-57363. 96p. (Orig.). 1980. pap. 3.50x (ISBN 0-8358-0398-8). Upper Room.
Sheldon, Charles. In His Steps. pap. 5.95, 250p. (ISBN 0-8007-5011-X, Power Bks); pap. 3.50, 192p. (ISBN 0-8007-8022-1, Spire Bks). Revell.
Sheldon, Charles L. In His Steps. 1980. pap. 3.95 (ISBN 0-88368-090-4). Whitaker Hse.
Sheldon, Charles M. Bible Stories. LC 74-4817. (Illus.). 1978. pap. 4.95 (ISBN 0-448-14612-6, G&D). Putnam Pub Group.
--In His Steps. (One Evening Christian Classic Ser.). 1962. pap. 2.95 (ISBN 0-89107-231-4). Good News.
--In His Steps. (Pivot Family Reader Ser). 256p. 1972. pap. 1.95 (ISBN 0-87983-012-3). Keats.
--In His Steps. 1977. large print kivar 8.95 (ISBN 0-310-32797-0, 12561L). Zondervan.
--In His Steps. 1982. gift ed. 7.95 (ISBN 0-915720-66-3). Brownlow Pub Co.
--In His Steps. 1985. pap. 4.95 (ISBN 0-916441-23-7). Barbour & Co.
--In His Steps. 243p. 1985. pap. 3.95 (ISBN 0-310-32751-2, Clarion Class). Zondervan.
Sheldon, Jean. Ribbon of Lies, Knife of Truth. McFarland, Ken, ed. (Harvest Ser.). 96p. 1982. pap. 3.95 (ISBN 0-8163-0449-1). Pacific Pr Pub Assn.
Sheley, Donald B., ed. Beggar at the Banquet: The Story of Dr. Woo Jun Hong. LC 81-13971. (Illus.). 178p. (Orig.). pap. 5.95 (ISBN 0-88289-306-8). Pelican.
Shelhamer. Holiness: How Obtained & Retained. 2.50 (ISBN 0-686-12878-8). Schmul Pub Co.
Shelhamer, E. E., ed. see Finney, Charles G.
Shell, Harvey. The Gods of China. Chamberlin, Roxanna, ed. (Illus.). 1985. pap. 4.95 (ISBN 0-914347-02-0). Ahio Pub Co.
--The Gods of Japan. (Illus.). 1984. pap. 4.95 (ISBN 0-914347-01-2). Ahio Pub Co.
Shell, Joy. The Ministry of Angels. 1977. pap. 3.95 (ISBN 0-8065-0586-9). Citadel Pr.
Shell, Rubel. Heavenly Patters for Happy Homes. 2.50 (ISBN 0-89315-109-2). Lambert Bk.
Shell, Susan M. The Rights of Reason: A Study of Kant's Philosophy & Politics. LC 79-19801. 1979. 23.50x (ISBN 0-8020-5462-5). U of Toronto Pr.
Shellenberger, Susie. There's Sheep in My Mirror. 108p. 1985. pap. 4.50 (ISBN 0-8341-1054-7). Beacon Hill.
Shelley, Bruce L. Christian Theology in Plain Language. 256p. 1985. 12.95 (ISBN 0-8499-0381-5, 0381-5). Word Bks.
Shelley, Lore, ed. Secretaries of Death: Accounts by Former Prisoners Who Worked in the Administrative Offices of Auschwitz. LC 85-43608. 450p. 1986. 20.00 (ISBN 0-88400-123-7). Shengold.
Shelley, Marshall. Helping Those Who Don't Want Help. (Leadership Library). 175p. 1986. 9.95 (ISBN 0-917463-10-2). Chr Today.
Shelley, Marshall see Merrill, Dean.
Shelley, Marshall, jt. ed. see Merrill, Dean.
Shelley, Percy Bysshe. Selected Essays on Atheism. LC 72-161341. (Atheist Viewpoint Ser). 100p. 1972. Repr. 13.00 (ISBN 0-405-03794-5). Ayer Co Pubs.
Shelley, Violet M. Reincarnation Unnecessary. 1979. pap. 5.95 (ISBN 0-87604-112-8). ARE Pr.
Shelly, Bruce. Church History in Plain Language. 512p. 1982. pap. 12.95 (ISBN 0-8499-2906-7). Word Bks.
--The Miracle of Anne. 90p. 1974. pap. 4.50 (ISBN 0-911336-55-9). Sci of Mind.
Shelly, Bruce L. What Is the Church, Bk. 3. Chao, Lorna Y., tr. (Basic Doctrine Ser.). (Chinese.). 1985. pap. write for info. (ISBN 0-941598-25-X). Living Spring Pubns.
Shelly, Judith A. Caring in Crisis: Bible Studies for Helping People. LC 78-13878. 1979. pap. 4.95 (ISBN 0-87784-563-8). Inter-Varsity.
--Not Just a Job: Serving Christ in Your Work. LC 84-29676. 140p. (Orig.). 1985. pap. 4.95 (ISBN 0-87784-332-5). Inter-Varsity.
--The Spiritual Needs of Children. LC 82-7223. (Orig.). 1982. pap. 5.95 (ISBN 0-87784-381-3). Inter-Varsity.
Shelly, Judith A., jt. auth. see Fish, Sharon.
Shelly, Judith Allen. Spiritual Care Workbook. 1978. pap. 5.95 (ISBN 0-87784-507-7). Inter-Varsity.
Shelly, Maynard. New Call for Peacemakers. (Illus.). 109p. 1980. pap. text ed. 2.00 (ISBN 0-87303-031-1). Faith & Life.
Shelly, Maynard, ed. see Janzen, Waldemar.
Shelly, Rubel. In Step with the Spirit: A Study of the Fruit of the Spirit, Galatians 5: 22-23. 1987. pap. price not set (ISBN 0-8010-8276-5). Baker Bk.
--Minor Prophets. pap. 2.50 (ISBN 0-89315-161-0). Lambert Bk.
Shelp, Earl E. Theology & Bioethics: Exploring the Foundation & Frontiers. 1985. lib. bdg. 39.50 (ISBN 90-277-1857-1, Pub. by Reidel Holland). Kluwer Academic.
Shelp, Earl E. & Sunderland, Ronald H. The Pastor As Servant. 112p. (Orig.). 1986. pap. 8.95 (ISBN 0-8298-0580-X). Pilgrim NY.
Shelp, Earl E. & Sunderland, Ronald H., eds. The Pastor As Priest. (Pastoral Ministry Ser.). 160p. (Orig.). 1987. pap. 9.95 (ISBN 0-8298-0751-9). Pilgrim NY.
Shelp, Earl E. & Sutherland, Ronald H., eds. The Pastor As Prophet. 172p. 1985. pap. 9.95 (ISBN 0-8298-0547-8). Pilgrim NY.
Shelton, Austin J. Igbo-Igala Borderland: Religion & Social Control in Indigenous African Colonialism. LC 70-141493. 1971. 44.50 (ISBN 0-87395-082-8). State U NY Pr.
Shelton, Charles M. Adolescent Spirituality: Pastoral Ministry for High School & College Youth. rev. ed. 1983. 15.00 (ISBN 0-8294-0422-8). Loyola.
Shelton, Ingrid. The Lord's Prayer. (Arch Bks.). 1982. pap. 0.99 (ISBN 0-570-06161-X, 59-1308). Concordia.
Shelton, Joan A. Stone Turning into Star: Prayer & Meditations for Lent. 168p. (Orig.). 1986. pap. 5.95 (ISBN 0-8091-2736-9). Paulist Pr.
Shelton, R. L., jt. ed. see Hartley, John E.
Shelton, Robert R. Loving Relationships. 272p. (Orig.). 1987. pap. 11.95 (ISBN 0-87178-542-0). Brethren.
Shen, C. T. Mayflower II: On Buddhist Voyage to Liberation. LC 83-81198. (Basic Buddhism Ser.). (Illus.). 1983. pap. 4.95 (ISBN 0-915078-03-1, P-02). Inst Adv Stud Wld.
Shen Fu. Six Records of a Floating Life. Pratt, Leonard, tr. 176p. 1983. pap. 3.95 (ISBN 0-14-044429-7). Penguin.
Sheng-Yen, Chang. Getting the Buddha Mind. LC 82-73979. 147p. (Orig.). 1982. pap. text ed. 5.95 (ISBN 0-9609854-0-9). Dharma Drum Pubs.
Shenk, Barbara K. The God of Sarah, Rebekah, & Rachel. LC 85-5503. 132p. 1985. 19.95 (ISBN 0-8361-3392-7). Herald Pr.
Shenk, Joseph C., as told to see Kisare.
Shenk, Lois L. Out of Mighty Waters. LC 81-20116. 192p. (Orig.). 1982. 10.95 (ISBN 0-8361-1987-8); pap. 6.95 (ISBN 0-8361-1988-6). Herald Pr.
Shenk, Michel, tr. see Trocme, Andre.
Shenk, Sara W. And Then There Were Three. LC 85-13936. 208p. (Orig.). 1985. pap. 8.95 (ISBN 0-8361-3398-6). Herald Pr.
Shenk, Wilbert. Anabaptism & Mission. LC 84-12863. (Missionary Study: No. 10). 264p. (Orig.). 1984. pap. 12.95 (ISBN 0-8361-3367-6). Herald Pr.
Shenk, Wilbert R. The Church in Mission. LC 84-81231. (Mennonite Faith Ser.: Vol. 15). 1984. pap. 1.50 (ISBN 0-8361-3377-3). Herald Pr.
--Exploring Church Growth. 336p. 1983. pap. 10.95 (ISBN 0-8028-1962-1). Eerdmans.
--Henry Venn: Missionary Statesman. LC 82-18779. 192p. (Orig.). 1983. pap. 2.49 (ISBN 0-88344-181-0). Orbis Bks.
Shenk, Wilbert R., compiled by. Bibliography of Henry Venn's Printed Writings. (Mennonite Missionary Studies: Pt. 4). 100p. 1975. pap. 3.75x (ISBN 0-8361-1203-2). Herald Pr.
Shenk, Wilbert R., ed. The Challenge of Church Growth. (Mennonite Missionary Studies: Pt. 1). 112p. 1973. pap. 4.95 (ISBN 0-8361-1200-8). Herald Pr.
--Mission Focus: Current Issues. LC 80-15686. pap. 122.00 (ISBN 0-317-26607-1, 2025420). Bks Demand UMI.
Shenkel, James D. Chronology & Recensional Development in the Greek Text of Kings. LC 68-21983. (Semitic Monographs: No. 1). (Illus.). 1968. text ed. 10.00x (ISBN 0-674-13050-2). Harvard U Pr.
Shenker, Israel. Coat of Many Colors: Pages from Jewish Life. LC 82-45338. 408p. 1985. 19.95 (ISBN 0-385-15811-4). Doubleday.
Shepard, Andrea J. Sing a New Song. 96p. (Orig.). 1986. pap. 4.95 (ISBN 0-310-34302-X, 12352P). Zondervan.
Shepard, Annis. The Wrong Kind of Dragon. LC 83-6023. (Illus.). 48p. (Orig.). 1983. pap. 4.50 (ISBN 0-687-46569-9). Abingdon.
Shepard, Bonnie, tr. see Richard, Pablo, et al.
Shepard, J. W. see Gospel Advocate.
Shepard, John, jt. auth. see Painter, Desmond.
Shepard, John W. Christ of the Gospels. rev. ed. 1946. 15.95 (ISBN 0-8028-1779-3). Eerdmans.
Shepard, Leslie. How to Protect Yourself Against Black Magic & Witchcraft. 1978. 7.95 (ISBN 0-8065-0646-6). Citadel Pr.
Shepard, Leslie, ed. see Dave, H. T.
Shepard, Richard F., et al. Live & Be Well: A Celebration of Yiddish Culture in America from the First Immigrants to the Second World War. (Illus.). 192p. 1982. 19.50 (ISBN 0-345-30752-6); pap. 9.95 (ISBN 0-345-29435-1). Ballantine.
Shepard, Sanford. Shem Tov: His World & His Words. LC 76-62685. (Coleccion De Estudios Hispanicos). 1978. pap. 10.00 (ISBN 0-89729-189-1). Ediciones.
Shepard, Thomas. Works, 3 vols. Albro, John A., ed. LC 49-1393. Repr. of 1853 ed. Set. 85.00 (ISBN 0-404-05990-2). Vol. 1 (ISBN 0-404-05991-0). Vol. 2 (ISBN 0-404-05992-9). Vol. 3 (ISBN 0-404-05993-7). AMS Pr.
Sheperd, A. P., tr. see Steiner, Rudolf.
Sheperd, Jack. Apocalypso: Revelations in Theatre. LC 70-178680. (Orig.). pap. 2.50x (ISBN 0-87574-180-0). Pendle Hill.
Shepherd, A. P. The Incarnation. 14p. (Orig.). 1976. pap. 1.50 (ISBN 0-88010-098-2). Anthroposophic.
Shepherd, Coulson. Jewish Holy Days: Their Prophetic & Christian Significance. LC 61-16660. 1961. pap. 3.25 (ISBN 0-87213-780-5). Loizeaux.
Shepherd, Gary, jt. auth. see Shepherd, Gordon.
Shepherd, Gordon & Shepherd, Gary. A Kingdom Transformed: Themes in the Development of Mormonism. 320p. 1984. 19.95 (ISBN 0-87480-233-4). U of Utah Pr.
Shepherd, J. Barrie. Diary of Daily Prayer. LC 74-14176. 136p. (Orig.). 1975. pap. 5.95 (ISBN 0-8066-1459-5, 10-1900). Augsburg.
--A Diary of Prayer: Daily Meditations on the Parables of Jesus. LC 80-27037. 132p. 1981. pap. 5.95 (ISBN 0-664-24352-5). Westminster.
--Encounters: Poetic Meditations on the Old Testament. LC 82-22422. 176p. (Orig.). 1983. pap. 8.95 (ISBN 0-8298-0637-7). Pilgrim NY.
--Prayers from the Mount. LC 85-26400. 144p. 1986. pap. 8.95 (ISBN 0-664-24699-0). Westminster.
Shepherd, J. W. Church, Falling Away & Restoration. 8.95 (ISBN 0-89225-065-8). Gospel Advocate.
Shepherd, J. W. see Gospel Advocate.
Shepherd, J. W see Gospel Advocate.
Shepherd, Massey H. Oxford American Prayer Book Commentary. 1950. 27.50 (ISBN 0-19-501202-X). Oxford U Pr.
Shepherd, Massey H., Jr. Companion of Prayer for Daily Living. LC 78-62063. 1978. pap. 3.95 kivar (ISBN 0-8192-1230-X). Morehouse.
Shepherd, Naomi. A Refuge from Darkness: Wilfrid Israel & the Rescue of the Jews. LC 83-22000. 18.45 (ISBN 0-394-52503-5). Pantheon.
Shepherd, R. A. The Religious Poems of Richard Crashaw with an Introductory Study. 1979. Repr. of 1914 ed. lib. bdg. 35.00 (ISBN 0-8495-4942-6). Arden Lib.
Shepherd, Silas H., et al. Little Masonic Library, 5 vols. 1977. Repr. cloth 35.00 set (ISBN 0-88053-005-7, M-5). Macoy Pub.
Shepherd, T. B. Methodism & the Literature of the 18th Century. LC 68-4718. (Studies in Comparative Literature, No. 35). 1969. Repr. of 1940 ed. lib. bdg. 75.00x (ISBN 0-8383-0680-2). Haskell.
Shepherd, Victor A. The Nature & Function of Faith in the Theology of John Calvin. LC 82-24899. vii, 248p. 1983. pap. 17.45 (ISBN 0-86554-066-7, P07). Mercer Univ Pr.
--The Nature & Function of Faith in the Theology of John Calvin. (Dissertation Ser.: No. 2). viii, 248p. 1982. pap. 17.45 (ISBN 0-86554-066-7). NABPR.
Shepherd, William C. Secure the Blessings of Liberty: American Constitutional Law & the New Religious Movement. LC 84-1347. (American Academy of Religion Studies in Religion: No. 35). 1984. 16.95 (ISBN 0-89130-733-8, 01-00-35); pap. 9.95 (ISBN 0-89130-824-5). Scholars Pr GA.
--To Secure the Blessings of Liberty: American Constitutional Law & the New Religious Movements. 128p. 1985. 12.95 (ISBN 0-8245-0664-2); pap. 8.95 (ISBN 0-8245-0670-7). Crossroad NY.
Sheppard, Donna. A Williamsburg Christmas. LC 80-7487. (Illus.). 84p. 1980. 11.95 (ISBN 0-03-057639-3). H Holt & Co.
Sheppard, Donna C. Williamsburg Christmas. LC 80-17179. (World of Williamsburg Ser.). (Illus.). 78p. (Orig.). 1980. pap. 6.95 (ISBN 0-87935-054-7). Williamsburg.
Sheppard, Gerald T. Wisdom as a Hermeneutical Construct: A Study in the Sapientalizing of the Old Testament. (Beihefte Zur Zeitschrift Fuer Die Alttestamentliche Wissenschaft: No. 151). 1979. 41.00x (ISBN 3-1100-7504-0). De Gruyter.
Sheppard, J. B., jt. ed. see Robertson, James C.
Sheppard, Jennifer M. The Giffard Bible. Freedberg, S. J., ed. (Outstanding Dissertations in Fine Arts Ser.). (Illus.). 450p. 1985. Repr. of 1983 ed. 60.00 (ISBN 0-8240-6867-X). Garland Pub.
Sheppard, Joseph B., ed. Christ Church Letters. Repr. of 1877 ed. 27.00 (ISBN 0-384-55120-3). Johnson Repr.
Sheppard, W. Great Hymns & Their Stories. lib. bdg. 69.95 (ISBN 0-87968-350-3). Gordon Pr.
Sheppard, W. L. Great Hymns & Their Stories. 1979. pap. 4.95 (ISBN 0-87508-492-3). Chr Lit.
Sher, Richard B. Church & University in the Scottish Enlightenment: The Moderate Literati of Edinburgh. LC 85-17911. (Illus.). 1985. text ed. 47.50x (ISBN 0-691-05445-2). Princeton U Pr.
Sherburn, George. The Early Popularity of Milton's Minor Poems. LC 73-14758. 1974. Repr. of 1919 ed. lib. bdg. 8.50 (ISBN 0-8414-7647-0). Folcroft.
Sherburne, Donald W., ed. A Key to Whitehead's "Process & Reality". LC 81-11661. 264p. 1981. pap. 10.00x (ISBN 0-226-75293-3). U of Chicago Pr.
Sherer, Michael, jt. auth. see Campbell, Robert.
Sherer, Michael, ed. see Bansemer, Richard.
Sherer, Michael L. And God Said... Yes! 1983. 5.75 (ISBN 0-89536-634-7, 0123). CSS of Ohio.
--Good News for Children. LC 80-65554. (Visual Messages on Epistle Texts, Ser. A). 128p. pap. 6.95 (ISBN 0-8066-1798-5, 10-2808). Augsburg.
--Good News for Children: Object Lessons on Epistle Texts. LC 81-65655. (Series B). 128p. (Orig.). 1981. pap. 6.95 (ISBN 0-8066-1891-4, 10-2809). Augsburg.
--Good News for Children: Object Lessons on Epistle Texts. LC 82-70957. (Series C). 128p. (Orig.). 1982. pap. 6.95 (ISBN 0-8066-1932-5, 10-2810). Augsburg.
--It's My Life: True-to-Life Stories for Young Teens. (Illus.). 112p. (Orig.). 1986. pap. 3.95 (ISBN 0-8066-2216-4, 10-3454). Augsburg.
--Six Who Dared. 1984. 6.50 (ISBN 0-89536-663-0, 1971). CSS of Ohio.
--Stewards of the Mysteries of God: Group Leader's Guide. 1985. 2.50 (ISBN 0-89536-780-7, 5831). CSS of Ohio.
--Stewards of the Mysteries of God: Master Planning Guide. 1985. 1.75 (ISBN 0-89536-779-3, 5830). CSS of Ohio.
--Stewards of the Mysteries of God: Worship Resources. 1985. 2.75 (ISBN 0-89536-781-5, 5832). CSS of Ohio.
Sherer, Michael L., jt. auth. see Bloom, James M.
Sherer, Michael L., ed. Drama Anthology. (Orig.). 1987. pap. price not set (ISBN 0-89536-890-0, 7876). CSS of Ohio.
--Excellence in Ministry. (Orig.). 1987. pap. 8.75 (ISBN 0-89536-866-8, 7825). CSS of Ohio.
--The Lectionary Series from the Common Lectionary: Series A (RSV) rev. ed. 1986. 14.25 (ISBN 0-89536-810-2, 6839). CSS of Ohio.

--The Lectionary Series from the Common Lectionary: Series A (TEV) rev. ed. 1986. 14.25 (ISBN 0-89536-811-0, 6840). CSS of Ohio.

--The Lectionary Series from the Common Lectionary: Series B (RSV) (Orig.). 1987. pap. price not set (ISBN 0-89536-884-6, 7870). CSS of Ohio.

Sherer, Michael L., ed. see Albrecht, Earl.

Sherer, Michael L., ed. see Bass, George.

Sherer, Michael L., ed. see Beck, Norman.

Sherer, Michael L., ed. see Braaten, John.

Sherer, Michael L., ed. see Brokhoff, Barbara.

Sherer, Michael L., ed. see Budd, Leonard H. & Talbott, Roger G.

Sherer, Michael L., ed. see Burton, Laurel A.

Sherer, Michael L., ed. see Chinn, Edward.

Sherer, Michael L., ed. see Corl, Heth H.

Sherer, Michael L., ed. see Detrick, R. Blaine.

Sherer, Michael L., ed. see Erickson, Craig D.

Sherer, Michael L., ed. see Exman, Gary.

Sherer, Michael L., ed. see Godshall, C. David.

Sherer, Michael L., ed. see Gray, G. Franklin & Woods, Charles A.

Sherer, Michael L., ed. see Grimbol, William.

Sherer, Michael L., ed. see Hamilton, Ronald R.

Sherer, Michael L., ed. see Hegele, Paul.

Sherer, Michael L., ed. see Henley, Gurden.

Sherer, Michael L., ed. see Jennings, Shirley.

Sherer, Michael L., ed. see Kalas, J. Ellsworth.

Sherer, Michael L., ed. see Lacy, Donald C.

Sherer, Michael L., ed. see Lybrand, R. E., Jr.

Sherer, Michael L., ed. see McCabe, Kendall K.

Sherer, Michael L., ed. see Mann, Leonard.

Sherer, Michael L., ed. see Mocko, George P.

Sherer, Michael L., ed. see Mueller, Robert.

Sherer, Michael L., ed. see Nehls, H. Michael.

Sherer, Michael L., ed. see Orbaker, Douglas & Blake, Robert A.

Sherer, Michael L., ed. see Peterson, Thomas D.

Sherer, Michael L., ed. see Pratt, Louis.

Sherer, Michael L., ed. see Radecke, Mark.

Sherer, Michael L., ed. see Ridenhour, Thomas E., Sr.

Sherer, Michael L., ed. see Runk, Wesley T.

Sherer, Michael L., ed. see Schmalenberger, Jerry.

Sherer, Michael L., ed. see Tapley, William.

Sherer, Michael L, ed. see Thulin, Richard L.

Sherer, Michael L., ed. see Tozer, Tom & Dessem, Ralph E.

Sherer, Michael L., ed. see Watts, P. Mark.

Sherer, Michael L., ed. see Weekley, James & Reeves, James.

Sherer, Michael L., ed. see Werman, Linda J.

Sherer, Micheal L., ed. see Parr, Micheal.

Sherer, Mike. Growing in Grace. 1986. 5.50 (ISBN 0-89536-798-X, 6816). CSS of Ohio.

Sherer, Mike & Aaseng, Nathan. Night of Wonder: Service-Story for Christmas Eve. 1985. 2.75 (ISBN 0-89536-762-9, 5869). CSS of Ohio.

Sheridan, Daniel P. The Advaitic Theism of the Bhagavata Purana. 1986. 14.00 (ISBN 81-208-0179-2, Pub. by Motilal Banarsidass). South Asia Bks.

Sheridan, John V. A Lay Psalter: Selections from the Psalms with Meditations. LC 84-62159. 216p. (Orig.). 1985. pap. 7.50 (ISBN 0-87973-716-6, 716). Our Sunday Visitor.

--Tourist in His Footsteps. LC 79-53024. (Presence Ser., Vol. 1). (Orig.). 1979. pap. 2.95 (ISBN 0-89003-034-0). Undena Pubns.

Sheridan, Mary A. And Some Fell on Good Ground. 1981. 9.95 (ISBN 0-8062-1806-1). Carlton.

Sheridan, Philip A., jt. auth. see Liptak, David Q.

Sherif, Faruq, ed. A Guide to the Contents of the Qur'an. (Middle East Cultures Ser.: No. 9). 172p. 1985. 25.00 (ISBN 0-86372-030-7, Pub. by Ithaca Pr UK). Humanities.

Sherif, Mohamed A. Ghazali's Theory of Virtue. LC 71-38000. 200p. 1975. 44.50 (ISBN 0-87395-206-5). State U NY Pr.

Sheriff, John K. The Good-Natured Man: The Evolution of a Moral Ideal, 1660-1800. LC 81-14758. 144p. 1982. text ed. 13.50 (ISBN 0-8173-0097-X). U of Ala Pr.

Sherley-Price, tr. see Bede the Venerable.

Sherley-Price, Leo, tr. see Bede the Venerable.

Sherlock, Connie. Bible Families. (Think 'n Check Quizzes Ser.). (Illus.). 16p. (Orig.). 1983. pap. 1.95 (ISBN 0-87239-688-6, 2792). Standard Pub.

--Life of Jesus. (Think 'N Check Quizzes Ser.). (Illus.). 16p. (Orig.). 1983. pap. 1.95 (ISBN 0-87239-689-4, 2793). Standard Pub.

Sherlock, Richard. Preserving Life: Public Policy & the Life Not Worth Living. LC 86-21347. 1987. 15.95 (ISBN 0-8294-0526-7). Loyola.

Sherlock, Therese, jt. auth. see Mitchell, Joan.

Sherlock, Thomas. The Tryal of the Witnesses of the Resurrection of Jesus. 2nd ed. Wellek, Rene, ed. Bd. with The Use & Extent of Prophecy. LC 75-25131. (British Philosophers & Theologians of the 17th & 18th Centuries Ser.). 348p. 1979. lib. bdg. 51.00 (ISBN 0-8240-1761-7). Garland Pub.

Sherman, Cecil E. A Kingdom of Surprises. LC 85-4699. (Orig.). 1985. pap. 3.75 (ISBN 0-8054-1533-5). Broadman.

Sherman, Franklin & Lehman, Helmut T., eds. Luther's Works: The Christian in Society IV, Vol. 47. LC 55-9893. 1971. 19.95 (ISBN 0-8006-0347-8, 1-347). Fortress.

Sherman, H., jt. auth. see Bristol, C.

Sherman, Harold. How to Use the Power of Prayer. 192p. 1985. 5.95 (ISBN 0-87159-061-1). Unity School.

--You Live after Death. 176p. 1987. pap. 2.95 (GM). Fawcett.

Sherman, Johanna. The Sacred Rose Tarot. 56p. 1982. pap. 12.00 incl. card deck (ISBN 0-88079-012-1). US Games Syst.

Sherman, John. Arab-Israeli Conflict, Nineteen Forty-Five to Nineteen Seventy-One: A Bibliography. LC 77-83360. (Reference Library of Social Science Ser.). 1978. lib. bdg. 63.00 (ISBN 0-8240-9829-3). Garland Pub.

Sherman, R. J. Pastor of the Range. (Illus.). 224p. 1985. 13.00 (ISBN 0-682-40225-7). Exposition Pr FL.

Sherman, Ruth W. & Wakefield, Robert S. Plymouth Colony Probate Guide: Where to Find Wills & Related Data for 800 People of Plymouth Colony, 1620-1691. LC 83-2362. (Plymouth Colony Research Group Ser.: No.2). xxi, 167p. 1983. 21.00x (ISBN 0-910233-01-2). Plymouth Col.

Sherman, Ruth W., ed. Peleg Burroughs's Journal, 1778-1798: The Tiverton R. I. Years of the Humbly Bold Baptist Minister. LC 80-39673. (Illus.). xxvi, 404p. 1981. 19.00x (ISBN 0-9604144-0-1). RI Genealogical.

Sherman, Shlomoh. Escape from Jesus: One Man's Search for a Meaningful Judaism. 1983. 14.95 (ISBN 0-915474-03-4). Effective Learn.

Sherman, Stuart P. Matthew Arnold: How to Know Him. 1973. lib. bdg. 20.00 (ISBN 0-8414-8083-4). Folcroft.

--Matthew Arnold, How to Know Him. 326p. 1968. Repr. of 1917 ed. 29.50 (ISBN 0-208-00453-X, Archon). Shoe String.

Sheron, Carole. The Rise & Fall of Superwoman. LC 79-26704. (Orion Ser.). 96p. 1980. pap. 3.50 (ISBN 0-8127-1270-6). Review & Herald.

Sherrard, Liadain, tr. see Mantzaridis, Georgios I.

Sherrard, Philip. The Eclipse of Man & Nature: Spiritual Anthroposophy. 160p. (Orig.). Date not set. pap. 8.95 (Lindisfarne Pr). Inner Tradit.

Sherrard, Philip & Ware, Kallistos, trs. The Philokalia, Vol. 3. LC 82-202671. 432p. 1984. 29.95 (ISBN 0-571-11726-0). Faber & Faber.

Sherrard, Philip, jt. tr. see Palmer, G. E.

Sherrer, Quin. How to Pray for Your Children. (Book Ser.). 112p. 1986. pap. 5.95 (ISBN 0-932305-33-4, 531022). Aglow Pubns.

Sherrill, Ceretha C. see Cee Cee, pseud.

Sherrill, Elizabeth, jt. auth. see Ritchie, George G.

Sherrill, Helen H., jt. auth. see Sherrill, Lewis J.

Sherrill, J., et al. God's Smuggler. 1968. pap. 2.95 (ISBN 0-451-13254-8, AE3254, Sig). NAL.

Sherrill, John. They Speak with Other Tongues. 144p. 1966. pap. 3.50 (ISBN 0-8007-8041-8, Spire Bks). Revell.

Sherrill, John, jt. auth. see Blair, Charles.

Sherrill, Lewis J. Presbyterian Parochial Schools, 1846-1870. LC 74-89234. (American Education: Its Men, Institutions & Ideas, Ser. 1). 1969. Repr. of 1932 ed. 11.50 (ISBN 0-405-01471-6). Ayer Co Pubs.

Sherrill, Lewis J. & Sherrill, Helen H. Becoming a Christian. 1943. pap. 1.49 (ISBN 0-8042-1548-0). John Knox.

Sherrill, Lou. Jovita Galan: Unselfish Teacher. LC 86-6110. (Meet the Missionary Ser.). 1986. 5.50 (ISBN 0-8054-4326-6). Broadman.

Sherring. Hindu Tribes & Castes, 3 vols. 1219p. 1974. Repr. of 1881 ed. Set. text ed. 120.00. Vol. 1, Benares. Vol. 2, Mohamedan Tribes of the North West Frontier & Aboriginal Tribes of the Central Provinces. Vol. 3 Natural History of the Hindu Caste, Unity of the Hindu Race. Coronet Bks.

Sherrod, Paul. Successful Soul Winning. (Illus.). 1978. 6.95 (ISBN 0-686-14476-7, 1730394523). P Sherrod.

Sherry, Gerard E. The Catholic Shrines of Europe. LC 86-62664. (Illus.). 119p. 1986. pap. 5.95 (ISBN 0-87973-548-1, 548). Our Sunday Visitor.

Sherry, Patrick. Spirit, Saints & Immortality. 200p. 1984. 39.50x (ISBN 0-87395-755-5); pap. 14.95x (ISBN 0-87395-756-3). State U NY Pr.

Sherwin, Byron & Ament, Susan. Encountering the Holocaust: An Interdisciplinary Survey. LC 79-9126. 500p. 1979. 22.50 (ISBN 0-88482-936-7). Impact Pr IL.

Sherwin, Byron, jt. auth. see Dresner, Samuel.

Sherwin, Byron L. Mystical Theology & Social Dissent: The Life & Works of Judah Loew of Prague. (Littman Library of Jewish Civilization). 256p. 1982. 24.95x (ISBN 0-19-710051-1). Oxford U Pr.

Sherwin-White, A. N. Roman Society & Roman Law in the New Testament. (Twin Brooks Ser.). 1978. pap. 7.95 (ISBN 0-8010-8148-3). Baker Bk.

Sherwood, John R. & Wagner, John C. Sources & Shapes of Power. LC 80-28125. (Into Our Third Century Ser.). (Orig.). 1981. pap. 3.95 (ISBN 0-687-39142-3). Abingdon.

Sherwood, Terry G. Fulfilling the Circle: A Study of John Donne's Thought. 231p. 1984. 27.50x (ISBN 0-8020-5621-0). U of Toronto Pr.

Sherwood, Zalmon. Kairos: Confessions of a Gay Priest. 150p. (Orig.). 1987. pap. 7.95 (ISBN 1-55583-102-8). Alyson Pubns.

Shestov, Lev. In Job's Balances: On the Sources of the Eternal Truths. Coventry, Camilla & Macartney, C. A., trs. from Ger. LC 73-92902. (Eng.). l, 379p. 1975. 20.00x (ISBN 0-8214-0143-2, 82-81461). Ohio U Pr.

--Potestas Clavium. Martin, Bernard, tr. LC 67-24282. 1968. 15.00x (ISBN 0-8214-0040-1). Ohio U Pr.

Shetler, Sanford G. Paul's Letter to the Corinthians 55 A.D. (Compact Commentary Ser). 1971. 7.80 (ISBN 0-87813-504-9); pap. 4.65 (ISBN 0-87813-503-0). Christian Light.

--Preacher of the People. LC 81-13387. 288p. 1982. 16.95x (ISBN 0-8361-1247-4); pap. 13.95x (ISBN 0-8361-1248-2). Herald Pr.

Shetter, Janette. Rhythms of the Ecosystem. LC 76-26392. (Illus., Orig.). 1976. pap. 2.50x (ISBN 0-87574-208-4). Pendle Hill.

Shevkenek, Alice. Things the Baptism in the Holy Spirit Will Do for You. 1976. pap. 1.00 (ISBN 0-89350-005-4). Fountain Pr.

Shewring, Walter, ed. see St Jerome.

Shibany, Roy. Status of Muslim Women in North India. 1979. 21.00x (ISBN 0-8364-0353-3). South Asia Bks.

Shibayama, Zenkei. Zen Comments on the Mumonkan. LC 73-18692. (Illus.). 384p. 1984. pap. 10.95 (ISBN 0-06-067278-1, CN 4091, HarpR). Har-Row.

Shiblak, Abbas. The Lure of Zion--the Case of the Iraqi Jews. 178p. 1986. 29.95 (ISBN 0-86356-121-7, Pub. by Al Saqi Bks UK); pap. 9.95 (ISBN 0-86356-033-4, Pub. by Al Saqi Bks UK). Humanities.

Shibley, David & Shibley, Naomi. More Special Times with God. LC 84-3485. 168p. 1984. 5.95 (ISBN 0-8407-5363-2). Nelson.

--Special Times with God. LC 81-14116. 160p. 1981. 5.95 (ISBN 0-8407-5780-8). Nelson.

Shibley, Naomi, jt. auth. see Shibley, David.

Shideler, Mary M. In Search of the Spirit. 272p. (Orig.). 1985. 11.95 (ISBN 0-345-32107-3, Pub. by Ballantine Epiphany). Ballantine.

Shields, Ann. Yielding to the Power of God: The Importance of Surrender, Abandonment, & Obedience to God's Will. 48p. (Orig.). 1987. pap. 1.95 (ISBN 0-89283-348-3). Servant.

Shields, Ann T., jt. auth. see Scanlan, Michael.

Shields, Carmel R., jt. auth. see Glathorn, Allan A.

Shields, Steven. Divergent Paths of the Restoration: 1984 Supplement. (Orig.). Date not set. pap. cancelled (ISBN 0-942284-02-X). Restoration Re.

Shields, Steven L. Divergent Paths of the Restoration. 282p. 1982. 12.95 (ISBN 0-941214-48-6). Signature Bks.

--Divergent Paths of the Restoration: A History of the Latter Day Saint Movement. 3rd, rev., enlarged ed. LC 81-86304. (Illus.). 282p. 1982. 12.95 (ISBN 0-942284-00-3). Restoration Re.

--No Greater Sacrifice: The Atonement & Redemption of Christ. LC 80-83864. 140p. 1980. 7.95 (ISBN 0-88290-166-4, 1059). Horizon Utah.

--The Restored Church. 16p. (Orig.). 1982. pap. 1.00 (ISBN 0-942284-01-1). Restoration Re.

Shiels, William E. Gonzalo De Tapia, 1561-1594: Founder of the First Permanent Jesuit Mission in North America. LC 74-12835. (U. S. Catholic Historical Society Monograph: No. XIV). 1978. Repr. of 1934 ed. lib. bdg. 22.50x (ISBN 0-8371-7758-8, SHGT). Greenwood.

Shienbaum, Kim E., ed. Legislating Morality: Private Choices on the Public Agenda. 256p. 1987. 28.95 (ISBN 0-87073-689-2); pap. 18.95 (ISBN 0-87073-690-6). Schenkman Bks Inc.

Shifrin, Adah. Meher Baba Is Love. 2nd ed. (Illus.). 56p. pap. 6.95. Sheriar Pr.

Shigaraki, Takamaro. The World of Buddhist Awakening. 96p. 1983. pap. 6.95 (ISBN 0-938474-03-0). Buddhist Study.

Shigematsu, Soiku. A Zen Forest: Sayings of the Masters. LC 81-31. (Illus.). 200p. 1981. 19.95 (ISBN 0-8348-0159-0). Weatherhill.

Shilder, Joyce. God's Special Baby. (Little Learner Ser.). 24p. 1985. 5.95 (56-1553); pap. 2.95 (ISBN 0-570-04088-4). Concordia.

Shim, Steve S. Korean Immigrant Churches Today in Southern California. LC 76-24724. 1977. soft bdg. 11.00 (ISBN 0-88247-426-X). R & E Pubs.

Shimada, Shigeo. A Stone Cried Out. 208p. 1986. pap. 7.95 (ISBN 0-8170-1111-0). Judson.

Shimmoni, Gideon, jt. ed. see International Center for University Teaching of Jewish Civilization Staff.

Shimoni, Emanuel, tr. see Avni, Haim.

Shimoni, S. Legends of Abraham the Patriarch. (Biblical Ser.). (Illus.). 1975. 3.00 (ISBN 0-914080-07-5). Shulsinger Sales.

--Legends of Daniel. (Biblical Ser.). (Illus.). 1975. 3.00 (ISBN 0-914080-14-8). Shulsinger Sales.

--Legends of Elijah. (Biblical Ser.). (Illus.). 1975. 3.00 (ISBN 0-914080-13-X). Shulsinger Sales.

--Legends of Joseph & His Brothers. (Biblical Ser.). (Illus.). 1975. 3.00 (ISBN 0-914080-11-3). Shulsinger Sales.

--Legends of Joshua. (Biblical Ser.). (Illus.). 1975. 3.00 (ISBN 0-914080-12-1). Shulsinger Sales.

Shin, Nan. Diary of a Zen Nun. LC 85-27576. (Illus.). 192p. 1986. 15.95 (ISBN 0-525-24408-5, 01549-460). Dutton.

Shin'ar, Uri. The Animated Hagaddah. Date not set. 14.95. Jonathan David.

Shine, Hill. Carlyle & the Saint Simonians. LC 71-120666. 1970. Repr. lib. bdg. 17.00x (ISBN 0-374-97360-1, Octagon). Hippocrene Bks.

Shiner, Margaret. Good Morning, Lord: Prayers & Promises for Teens. (Good Morning, Lord Ser.). 96p. 1976. 4.95 (ISBN 0-8010-8079-7). Baker Bk.

Shinn, Duane. How to Play Twelve Christmas Carols on the Piano - This Christmas - with the Visualized Chord System. 1976. pap. 6.95 (ISBN 0-912732-19-9). Duane Shinn.

--Super-Chords Made Super-Simple. 1976. pap. 6.95 (ISBN 0-912732-20-2). Duane Shinn.

Shinn, Duane & Hoffman, Diane. Evangelistic Embellishments: How to Make Hymns & Gospel Songs Come Alive. 1980. spiral bdg. 49.95 (ISBN 0-912732-49-0). Duane Shinn.

Shinn, Florence S. The Secret Door to Success. 1978. pap. 2.50 (ISBN 0-87516-258-4). De Vorss.

--Your Word Is Your Wand. 1978. pap. 2.50 (ISBN 0-87516-259-2). De Vorss.

Shinn, George. The American Dream Still Works. 1981. pap. 3.50 (ISBN 0-8423-0061-9). Tyndale.

Shinn, Larry, jt. ed. see Goswami, Shrivatsa.

Shinn, Larry D. The Dark Lord: Cult Images & the Hare Krishnas in America. 204p. (Orig.). 1987. pap. 16.95 (ISBN 0-664-24170-0). Westminster.

Shinn, Roger L. Forced Options. 272p. 1985. pap. 10.95 (ISBN 0-8298-0552-4). Pilgrim NY.

--Forced Options: Social Decisions for the 21st Century. LC 82-47755. (Religious Perspective Ser.). 256p. 1982. 16.30 (ISBN 0-06-067282-X, HarpR). Har-Row.

--Sermon on the Mount. LC 62-19785. 112p. (Orig.). 1984. pap. 3.95 (ISBN 0-8298-0120-0). Pilgrim NY.

Shiplett, Gary R. Worship & Hymnody. (Illus.). 122p. (Orig.). 1980. pap. text ed. 8.95 (ISBN 0-916260-08-9). Meriwether Pub.

Shipp, Richard C. Champions of Light. 118p. 1983. 7.95 (ISBN 0-934126-32-1). Randall Bk Co.

Shipps, Jan. Mormonism: The Story of a New Religious Tradition. LC 84-2672. (Illus.). 232p. 1985. 14.50 (ISBN 0-252-01159-7). U of Ill Pr.

Shipps, Jan, et al. After One Hundred Fifty Years: The Latter-Day Saints in Sesquicentennial Perspective. Alexander, Thomas G. & Embry, Jessie L., eds. (Charles Redd Monographs in Western History: No. 13). (Illus.). 207p. (Orig.). 1983. pap. 6.95 (ISBN 0-941214-08-7, Dist. by Signature Bks). C Redd Ctr.

Shipps, Kenneth W., jt. ed. see Carpenter, Joel A.

Shirazi, Habib, tr. see Shariati, Ali.

Shirk, Melanie, jt. auth. see Nelson, Lynn H.

Shirley, Ralph. Occultists & Mystics of All Ages. 176p. 1974. pap. 2.95 (ISBN 0-8065-0419-6). Citadel Pr.

Shirley, Samuel, tr. see Spinoza, Baruch.

Shirley, Walter W., ed. see Netter, Thomas.

Shirokogorov, Sergei M. Psychomental Complex of the Tungus. LC 76-44788. 488p. Repr. of 1935 ed. 120.00 (ISBN 0-404-15879-X). AMS Pr.

Shirts, R. Garry. Where Do You Draw the Line. 1977. 29.00 (ISBN 0-686-10238-X). Simile II.

Shissler, Barbara. New Testament in Art. LC 70-84411. (Fine Art Books). (Illus.). 1970. PLB 5.95 (ISBN 0-8225-0169-4). Lerner Pubns.

Shiva Das Floating Eagle Feather. Kiss of God. (Illus.). 100p. 1979. pap. 3.50 (ISBN 0-686-95426-2). Ananda Marga.

Shivananda, Swami. For Seekers of God: Spiritual Talks of Mahapurush Swami Shivananda. Vividishananda, Swami & Gambhirananda, Swami, trs. from Bengali. 186p. 1972. 10.00 (ISBN 0-87481-169-4); pap. 7.50 (ISBN 0-87481-130-9). Vedanta Pr.

Shivanandan, Mary. When Your Wife Wants to Work. LC 79-51278. (When Bks). (Illus.). 1980. pap. 2.45 (ISBN 0-87029-151-3, 20237-4). Abbey.

Shiv Brat Lal. Light on Ananda Yoga. Morrow, Steve, tr. LC 82-61990. 134p. 1982. pap. 10.00 (ISBN 0-89142-041-X). Sant Bani Ash.

Shivkumar, Muni. The Doctrine of Liberation in Indian Religion. 1984. text ed. 14.00x (ISBN 0-89563-286-1). Coronet Bks.

Shlemon, Barbara. Living Each Day by the Power of Faith. 140p. (Orig.). 1986. pap. 4.95 (ISBN 0-89283-289-4). Servant.

Shlemon, Barbara L. Healing Prayer. LC 75-36056. 88p. 1975. pap. 1.95 (ISBN 0-87793-108-9). Ave Maria.

--Healing the Hidden Self. LC 81-70022. (Illus.). 128p. 1982. pap. 3.50 (ISBN 0-87793-244-1). Ave Maria.

Shlemon, Barbara L., et al. To Heal As Jesus Healed. LC 78-54126. 112p. 1978. pap. 2.95 (ISBN 0-87793-152-6). Ave Maria.

Shmuelevitz, A. The Jews of the Ottoman Empire in the Late Fifteenth & the Sixteenth Centuries. 201p. 1984. pap. text ed. 35.00x (ISBN 90-04-07071-0, Pub. by EJ Brill Holland). Humanities.

Shneiderman, S. L. The River Remembers. LC 77-93935. (Illus.). 1978. 8.95 (ISBN 0-8180-0821-0). Horizon.

Shneidman, Edwin S., ed. On the Nature of Suicide. LC 78-92890. (Jossey-Bass Behavioral Science Ser.). pap. 40.00 (ISBN 0-317-08618-9, 2013857). Bks Demand UMI.

Shockey, Richard W. Training for Hospital Visitation: A Three-Week Course for Laypersons. LC 86-42930. 40p. (Orig.). 1986. pap. 4.00 (ISBN 0-937021-01-6). Sagamore Bks MI.

Shockley, Ann. Say Jesus & Come to Me. 288p. 1985. pap. 2.95 (ISBN 0-380-79657-0, 79657-0, Bard). Avon.

Shockley, Ann A. Say Jesus & Come to Me. 288p. 1986. pap. 8.95 (ISBN 0-930044-98-3). Naiad Pr.

Shockley, Grant S., et al. Black Pastors & Churches in United Methodism. 1976. pap. 1.00 (ISBN 0-89937-005-5). Ctr Res Soc Chg.

Shoemaker, Albert M. Birds & Scripture. (Illus.). 1984. pap. 2.50 (ISBN 0-913976-07-5). Discovery Bks.

Shoemaker, Dennis E. Heritage & Hope: A People of Hope. write for info. (ISBN 0-916466-04-3). Reformed Church.

Shoemaker, Donald. Abortion, the Bible, & the Christian. (Direction Bks). 1977. pap. text ed. 1.25 (ISBN 0-8010-8109-2). Baker Bk.

Shoemaker, Donald P. Abortion, the Bible & the Christian. 1976. 4.00 (ISBN 0-910728-15-1); pap. 1.25 (ISBN 0-910728-08-9). Hayes.

Shoemaker, H. Stephen. Retelling the Biblical Story. LC 85-16650. 1985. pap. 6.95 (ISBN 0-8054-2114-9). Broadman.

Shoemaker, Helen S. The Magnificent Promise: The Unifying Power of Prayer. 128p. (Orig.). 1985. pap. 6.95 (ISBN 0-687-22904-9). Abingdon.

--The Secret of Effective Prayer. LC 67-19306. 1976. pap. 1.95 (ISBN 0-87680-869-0, 91004, Key Word Bks). Word Bks.

Shoemaker, Kathryn E., illus. Children, Go Where I Send Thee: An American Spiritual. (Illus.). 32p. (Orig.). 1980. pap. 6.95 (ISBN 0-03-056673-8, HarpR). Har-Row.

Shoemaker, Mary E. Anno Domini Number One. (Orig.). 1981. pap. 2.95 (ISBN 0-937172-25-1). JLJ Pubs.

--Easter: A Promise Kept. (Orig.). 1981. pap. 1.75 (ISBN 0-937172-19-7). JLJ Pubs.

--Main Route to Bethlehem. (Orig.). 1981. pap. 4.50 (ISBN 0-937172-26-X). JLJ Pubs.

--Meanwhile, Back at the Flock: A Christmas Puppet Play. (Orig.). 1980. pap. 1.85 (ISBN 0-937172-09-X). JLJ Pubs.

Shoemaker, Stephen H. The Jekyll & Hyde Syndrome. (Orig.). 1987. text ed. 9.95 (ISBN 0-8054-1538-6). Broadman.

Shofner, David. Soul Winning. (Illus.). 96p. (Orig.). 1980. pap. 2.95 (ISBN 0-89957-051-8). AMG Pubs.

Shofner, Myra. The Ark Book of Riddles. LC 79-57214. (Illus.). 1980. pap. 2.50 (ISBN 0-89191-250-9). Cook.

--Second Ark Book of Riddles. (Illus.). 1981. pap. 2.50 (ISBN 0-89191-531-1, 55319). Cook.

Shoghi Effendi, tr. see Baha'u'llah.

Shoham, S. Giora. Rebellion, Creativity & Revelation. Cherns, Albert, intro. by. 320p. 1986. 29.95 (ISBN 0-905927-61-3). Transaction Bks.

Shore, Paul J., jt. auth. see Noddings, Nel.

Shore, Sally R., tr. John Chrysostom: On Virginity; Against Remarriage. Clark, Elizabeth A. LC 83-8193. (Studies in Women & Religion: Vol. 9). 200p. 1984. 49.95x (ISBN 0-88946-543-6). E Mellen.

Shorney, George H, Jr., jt. auth. see Hustad, Donald P.

Shorr, Philip. Science & Superstition in the Eighteenth Century: A Study of the Treatment of Science in Two Encyclopedias of 1725-1750. LC 33-3916. (Columbia University. Studies in the Social Sciences: No. 364). Repr. of 1932 ed. 10.00 (ISBN 0-404-51364-6). AMS Pr.

Shorris, Earl. Jews without Mercy: A Lament. 1982. 14.95 (ISBN 0-385-17853-0). Brown Bk.

Short, Beth. Memorizing Bible Verses with Games & Crafts. LC 12-2872. 1984. pap. 4.95 teacher's material (ISBN 0-570-03937-1). Concordia.

Short, Ernest H. The House of God: A History of Religious Architecture & Symbolism. 75.00 (ISBN 0-8490-0374-1). Gordon Pr.

Short, Ray E. Sex, Dating, & Love: Seventy-Seven Questions Most Often Asked. LC 83-72122. 144p. (Orig.). 1984. pap. 3.95 (ISBN 0-8066-2066-8, 10-5648). Augsburg.

--Sex, Love, or Infatuation: How Can I Really Know? LC 78-52180. 1978. pap. 3.95 (ISBN 0-8066-1653-9, 10-5650). Augsburg.

Short, Robert L. Gospel According to Peanuts. pap. 6.95 (ISBN 0-8042-1968-0). John Knox.

--The Gospel from Outer Space. LC 82-48936. (Illus.). 128p. (Orig.). 1983. pap. 5.95 (ISBN 0-06-067376-1, CN4064, HarpR). Har-Row.

--Something to Believe in. LC 75-36754. (Illus.). 1977. pap. 5.95i (ISBN 0-06-067381-8, RD 169, HarpR). Har-Row.

--A Time to Be Born, A Time to Die. pap. 6.95i (ISBN 0-06-067677-9, RD 52, HarpR). Har-Row.

Short, Roy H. The Episcopal Leadership Role in United Methodism. 224p. 1985. text ed. 9.95 (ISBN 0-687-11965-0). Abingdon.

Short, Stephen N. Pentecost: The Christian Student Movement from Howard University. (Illus., Orig.). 1987. pap. 6.95 (ISBN 0-9616056-2-6). Mid Atl Reg Pr.

Shorter, A. W. The Egyptian Gods: A Handbook. 1978. pap. 7.50 (ISBN 0-7100-0982-8). Methuen Inc.

Shorter, Alan W. The Egyptian Gods. (Mythology Library: Vol. 5). 300p. 1985. pap. 7.95 (ISBN 0-87877-082-8). Newcastle Pub.

--The Egyptian Gods: A Handbook. LC 85-26911. (Newcastle Mythology Library: Vol. 5). 300p. 1985. Repr. lib. bdg. 17.95x (ISBN 0-89370-682-5). Borgo Pr.

Shorter, Aylward. African Christian Theology: Adaptation or Incarnation? LC 77-23325. 180p. (Orig.). 1977. 7.95 (ISBN 0-88344-002-4); pap. 4.95 (ISBN 0-88344-003-2). Orbis Bks.

--African Culture & the Christian Church: An Introduction to Social & Pastoral Anthropology. LC 73-79481. pap. 60.30 (ISBN 0-317-26684-5, 2025114). Bks Demand UMI.

--Jesus & the Witchdoctor: An Approach to Healing & Wholeness. 268p. (Orig.). 1985. pap. 10.95 (ISBN 0-88344-225-6). Orbis Bks.

--Prayer in the Religious Traditions of Africa. 1975. pap. 7.95 (ISBN 0-19-519848-4). Oxford U Pr.

--Revelation & Its Interpretation. 280p. 1984. pap. text ed. 14.95 (ISBN 0-225-66356-2, AY8482, HarpR). Har-Row.

Shorter, Edward. The Making of the Modern Family. LC 75-7266. (Illus.). 1975. pap. 13.50x (ISBN 0-465-09722-7, TB-5042). Basic.

Shortland, Edward. Maori Religion & Mythology. LC 75-35268. Repr. of 1882 ed. 22.50 (ISBN 0-404-14437-3). AMS Pr.

--Traditions & Superstitions of the New Zealanders. 2nd ed. LC 75-35270. Repr. of 1856 ed. 32.50 (ISBN 0-404-14439-X). AMS Pr.

Shoshuk, Levi & Eisenberg, Azriel, eds. Momentous Century: Personal & Eyewitness Accounts of the Rise of the Jewish Homeland & State, 1875-1978. LC 81-86164. (Illus.). 472p. 1984. 25.00 (ISBN 0-8453-4748-9, Cornwall Bks). Assoc Univ Prs.

Shotaro, Lida, jt. ed. see Hurvitz, Leon.

Shotwell, Berenice M. Getting Better Acquainted with Your Bible. LC 75-173349. (Illus.). 1976. pap. 16.50 (ISBN 0-9603026-1-1). Shadwold.

--Getting Better Acquainted with Your Bible. LC 75-173349. (Illus.). 1972. 24.95 (ISBN 0-9603026-0-3). Shadwold.

Shotwell, James T. & Loomis, Louis R., eds. See of Peter. 1965. lib. bdg. 49.00x (ISBN 0-374-97391-1, Octagon). Hippocrene Bks.

Shotwell, Malcolm G. Creative Programs for the Church Year. 96p. 1986. pap. 7.95 (ISBN 0-8170-1102-1). Judson.

Shotwell, Willis A. Biblical Exegesis of Justin Martyr. LC 66-8998. 1965. pap. 10.00x (ISBN 0-8401-2173-3). A R Allenson.

Shoulson, Abraham B., ed. Marriage & Family Life: A Jewish View. 19.95x (ISBN 0-8084-0378-8). New Coll U Pr.

Shouppe, F. X. Purgatory: Explained by the Lives & Legends of the Saints. LC 79-112489. 1973. pap. 8.50 (ISBN 0-89555-042-3). TAN Bks Pubs.

Shourie, Arun. Hinduism: Essence & Consequence. 1980. text ed. 40.00x (ISBN 0-7069-0834-1, Pub. by Vikas India). Advent NY.

Shovers, Aaron H. Visions of Peace: The Story of the Messianic Expectation. LC 81-86206. 237p. (Orig.). 1985. pap. 12.75 (ISBN 0-9613613-0-1); wkbk. 8.75 (ISBN 0-9613613-1-X). Three Dimensional.

Showalter, G. H. & Cox, Frank L. A Book of Prayers. 1940. pap. 1.00 (ISBN 0-88027-063-2). Firm Foun Pub.

Showalter, G. H. & Davis, W. M. New Bible Studies. 1949. pap. 1.50 (ISBN 0-88027-027-6). Firm Foun Pub.

--Simplified Bible Lessons on the Old & New Testaments. 1944. pap. 2.75 (ISBN 0-88027-039-X). Firm Foun Pub.

Showalter, J. Stuart, jt. auth. see Moraczewski, Albert S.

Showalter, Lester. Investigating God's Orderly World, Bk. 1. (YA) 1970. write for info. (ISBN 0-686-05588-8); tchr's. ed. avail. (ISBN 0-686-05589-6). Rod & Staff.

--Investigating God's Orderly World, Bk 2. (YA) 1975. write for info. (ISBN 0-686-11144-3); tchr's. ed. avail. (ISBN 0-686-11145-1). Rod & Staff.

Showalter, Lester E., jt. auth. see Martin, John D.

Showalter, Mary E. Favorite Family Recipes. 128p. 1972. pap. 2.95 (ISBN 0-8361-1682-8). Herald Pr.

Showalter, Nathan, jt. auth. see Bontrager, G. Edwin.

Showers, Renald E. What on Earth Is God Doing? Satan's Conflict with God. LC 73-81551. 1973. pap. 3.95 (ISBN 0-87213-784-8). Loizeaux.

--What on Earth Is God Doing? Satan's Conflict with God: Study Guide. 48p. 1983. pap. 3.50 (ISBN 0-87213-785-6). Loizeaux.

Shrader-Frechette, K. S. Nuclear Power & Public Policy: The Social & Ethical Problems of Fission Technology. (Pallas Paperbacks Ser.: No. 15). 220p. 1980. lib. bdg. 20.00 (ISBN 90-277-1054-6, Pub. by Reidel Holland); pap. 10.50 (ISBN 90-277-1080-5). Kluwer Academic.

Shrady, Maria. The Mother Teresa Story. 1987. pap. 2.50. Paulist Pr.

Shree, Swami, jt. auth. see Yeats, William B.

Shrii Prabhat Rainjain Sarkar. Problem of the Day. 64p. 1968. pap. 1.00 (ISBN 0-686-95454-8). Ananda Marga.

Shringy, R. K. Philosophy of J. Krishnamurti: A Systematic Study. LC 78-670076. 1977. 24.00x (ISBN 0-89684-442-0). Orient Bk Dist.

Shriver, Donald W., Jr. The Lord's Prayer: A Way of Life. LC 83-9843. 108p. (Orig.). 1983. pap. 4.95 (ISBN 0-8042-2409-9). John Knox.

Shriver, Donald W., Jr., jt. auth. see Ostrom, Karl A.

Shriver, Donald W., Jr., ed. Medicine & Religion: Strategies of Care. LC 79-23420. (Contemporary Community Health Ser.). 1980. 14.95x (ISBN 0-8229-3412-4). U of Pittsburgh Pr.

Shriver, George H. Philip Schaff: Christian Scholar & Ecumenical Prophet. xii, 136p. 1987. 19.95 (ISBN 0-86554-234-1). Mercer Univ Pr.

Shriver, Peggy L. The Bible Vote: Religion & the New Right. LC 81-7389. 170p. 1981. pap. 5.95 (ISBN 0-8298-0465-X). Pilgrim NY.

Shriver, William P. Immigrant Forces: Factors in the New Democracy. LC 74-145493. (The American Immigration Library). 312p. 1971. Repr. of 1913 ed. lib. bdg. 20.95x (ISBN 0-89198-026-1). Ozer.

Shropshire, Marie. In Touch with God: How God Speaks to a Prayerful Heart. (Orig.). 1985. pap. 4.95 (ISBN 0-89081-447-3). Harvest Hse.

Shropshire, Rebecca, ed. see Watts, Alan.

Shryock, John K. The Temples of Anking & Their Cults, a Study of Modern Chinese Religion. LC 70-38083. Repr. of 1931 ed. 26.00 (ISBN 0-404-56947-1). AMS Pr.

Shryock, Richard H., jt. auth. see Beall, Otho T.

Shuard, Hilary, jt. auth. see Pinner, Mary T.

Shuart, Adele K. Signs in Judaism: A Resource Book for the Jewish Deaf Community. 196p. 1986. pap. 16.95x (ISBN 0-8197-0505-5). Bloch.

Shubin, Daniel H., ed. Spirit & Life, Book of the Sun. Volkov, John W., tr. from Russian. 768p. 1984. 40.00 (ISBN 0-318-20027-9). D H Shubin.

Shuffelton, Frank. Thomas Hooker, 1586-1647. LC 76-45912. 1977. 38.00x (ISBN 0-691-05249-2). Princeton U Pr.

Shuker, Nancy F. Martin Luther King. (World Leaders: Past & Present Ser.). (Illus.). 112p. 1985. lib. bdg. 16.95x (ISBN 0-87754-567-7). Chelsea Hse.

Shukri, Ahmed. Muhammedan Law of Marriage & Divorce. (Columbia University. Contributions to Oriental History & Philology: No. 7). Repr. of 1917 ed. 15.25 (ISBN 0-404-50537-6). AMS Pr.

Shuler, J. L. Power for a Finished Work. LC 78-53212. (Stories That Win Ser.). 1978. pap. 0.99 (ISBN 0-8163-0208-1, 16416-0). Pacific Pr Pub Assn.

Shuler, John L. Wonders of Salvation. 1985. pap. 5.95 (ISBN 0-8163-0591-9). Pacific Pr Pub Assn.

Shuler, Philip L. A Genre for the Gospels: The Biographical Character of Matthew. LC 81-71384. 144p. 1982. 3.50 (ISBN 0-8006-0677-9). Fortress.

--A Genre for the Gospels: The Biographical Character of Matthew. LC 81-71384. pap. 35.30 (2029606). Bks Demand UMI.

Shull, Barbara. How to Become a Skilled Intercessor. 32p. 1978. pap. 2.00 (ISBN 0-930756-35-5, 533001). Aglow Pubns.

Shull, Eva & Shull, Russell. CFO Songs. 1972. pap. 2.50 (ISBN 0-910924-53-8); pap. 3.95 spiral bdg. (ISBN 0-910924-54-6). Macalester.

Shull, Russell. Letters to Eva in Heaven. 3.95 (ISBN 0-910924-51-1). Macalester.

--Wonderfully Made for This Life & the Next. 1980. pap. 0.50 (ISBN 0-910924-70-8). Macalester.

Shull, Russell, jt. auth. see Shull, Eva.

Shulman, Abraham. The Adventures of a Yiddish Lecturer. LC 79-28734. 1980. 7.95 (ISBN 0-8298-0391-2). Pilgrim NY.

--The Case of Hotel Polski. LC 81-81519. 240p. 1982. 16.95 (ISBN 0-89604-033-X); pap. 10.95 (ISBN 0-89604-034-8). Holocaust Pubns.

Shulman, Albert M. Gateway to Judaism, 2 vols. 30.00 set (ISBN 0-8453-6896-6, Cornwall Bks). Assoc Univ Prs.

--The Religious Heritage of America. LC 81-3594. (Illus.). 480p. 1982. 25.00 (ISBN 0-498-02162-9). A S Barnes.

Shulman, Avi. Criticizing Children: A Parents Guide to Helping Children. (Dynamics of Personal Achievement Ser.). 48p. (Orig.). 1984. pap. 2.95 (ISBN 0-87306-365-1). Feldheim.

--A Guide to the Bais Hamikosh. rev. ed. 2.75 (ISBN 0-914131-25-7, B20). Torah Umesorah.

--How to Teach, Enjoy & Survive Primary Grades. 2.50 (ISBN 0-914131-34-6, B65). Torah Umesorah.

--Time Is Life. (Dynamics of Personal Achievement Ser.). 96p. (Orig.). 1985. pap. 4.95 (ISBN 0-87306-927-7). Feldheim.

Shulman, David D. Tamil Temple Myths: Sacrifice & Divine Marriage in the South Indian Saiva Tradition. LC 79-17051. 1980. 45.00x (ISBN 0-691-06415-6). Princeton U Pr.

Shulman, Jason, jt. auth. see Charlton, Jim.

Shulman, Nisson E. Authority & Community: Polish Jewry in the Sixteenth Century. 288p. 1986. text ed. 20.00x (ISBN 0-88125-101-1). Ktav.

Shulman, Shaindy. Torah Teddy Learns Colors. 1985. 3.95 (ISBN 0-87306-942-0). Feldheim.

--Torah Teddy Learns to Count. 1985. 3.95 (ISBN 0-87306-943-9). Feldheim.

Shultz, Ellen, ed. see Crosby, Sumner M., et al.

Shultz, Leland G. The Bible & the Christian Life. LC 82-82701. (Radiant Life Ser.). 128p. (Orig.). 1984. pap. 2.50 (ISBN 0-88243-857-3, 02-0857); tchr's guide 3.95 (ISBN 0-88243-198-6, 32-0198). Gospel Pub.

Shulvass, Moses A. The History of the Jewish People, Vol. 1: The Antiquity. LC 81-85564. 250p. 1982. 14.95 (ISBN 0-89526-660-1). Regnery Bks.

Shumacher, William A. Roman Replies, 1982. 42p. (Orig.). 1982. pap. 3.00 (ISBN 0-943616-13-1). Canon Law Soc.

Shumaker, W. Unpremeditated Verse Feeling & Perception in Milton's Paradise Lost. 1967. 26.00x (ISBN 0-691-06134-3). Princeton U Pr.

Shumsky, Abraham. Sabbath Service: Shaharit L'Shabbat. Date not set. pap. 3.95x (ISBN 0-940646-35-8). Rossel Bks.

Shumsky, Abraham & Shumsky, Adaia. Ahavat Chesed - Love Mercy: Reader. (Mah Tov Hebrew Teaching Ser.: Bk. 2). (Illus.). 1970. text ed. 5.50 (ISBN 0-8074-0175-7, 405304); tchrs'. guide 3.50 (ISBN 0-8074-0176-5, 205305); wkbk. 5.00 (ISBN 0-8074-0177-3, 405303). UAHC.

--Alef-Bet: A Hebrew Primer. (Illus.). 1979. pap. text ed. 6.00 (ISBN 0-8074-0026-2, 405309). UAHC.

--Asot Mishpat. (Mah Tov Hebrew Teaching Ser.: Bk. 1). (Illus.). 1969. text ed. 5.50 (ISBN 0-8074-0178-1, 405301); tchrs'. guide 3.50 (ISBN 0-8074-0179-X, 205302); wkbk. 5.00 (ISBN 0-8074-0180-3, 405300). UAHC.

--Hatznea Lechet: Walk Humbly. Spiro, Jack D., ed. (Mah Tov Hebrew Teaching Ser.: Bk. 3). (Illus.). 1971. text ed. 5.00 (ISBN 0-8074-0181-1, 405307); tchrs'. guide 3.50 (ISBN 0-8074-0182-X, 205308); wkbk. 5.00 (ISBN 0-8074-0183-8, 405306). UAHC.

Shumsky, Adaia, jt. auth. see Shumsky, Abraham.

Shunami, S. Bibliography of Jewish Bibliographies. enl. 2nd ed. 1969. 50.00x (ISBN 0-87068-882-0). Ktav.

Shupe, Anson, jt. auth. see Bromley, David.

Shupe, Anson, jt. auth. see Heinerman, John.

Shupe, Anson, jt. ed. see Hadden, Jeffrey K.

Shupe, Anson D., jt. auth. see Darrand, Tom C.

Shupe, Anson D., Jr. Six Perspectives on New Religions: A Case Study Approach. LC 81-9464. (Studies in Religion & Society: Vol. 1). 246p. 1981. 49.95x (ISBN 0-88946-983-0). E Mellen.

Shupe, Anson D., Jr., jt. auth. see Bromley, David G.

Shur, Irene G. & Littell, Franklin H. Reflection on the Holocaust. Lambert, Richard D., ed. LC 80-66618. (The Annals of the American Academy of Political & Social Science: No. 450). 272p. 1980. pap. text ed. 7.95 (ISBN 0-87761-253-6). Am Acad Pol Soc Sci.

Shurden, Walter B. Not a Silent People: Controversies That Have Shaped Southern Baptists. LC 79-178066. 128p. 1972. 6.50 (ISBN 0-8054-8801-4). Broadman.

Shurden, Walter B., ed. The Life of Baptists in the Life of the World. LC 85-1401. 1985. pap. 7.95 (ISBN 0-8054-6582-0). Broadman.

Shurin, Israel. Morei Ha'umah, Bk. 2. (Illus.). 4.00 (ISBN 0-914131-46-X, D45). Torah Umesorah.

Shurr, William H. Rappaccini's Children: American Writers in a Calvinist World. LC 79-57573. 176p. 1981. 16.00x (ISBN 0-8131-1427-6). U Pr of Ky.

Shuster, George N. Catholic Spirit in Modern English Literature. facs. ed. LC 67-26785. (Essay Index Reprint Ser). 1922. 20.00 (ISBN 0-8369-0878-3). Ayer Co Pubs.

--Religion Behind the Iron Curtain. LC 78-13547. 1978. Repr. of 1954 ed. lib. bdg. 22.50x (ISBN 0-313-20634-1, SHRB). Greenwood.

Shutt, V. Gladys. Food for Thought from God's Kettle. 1982. 8.95 (ISBN 0-533-05178-9). Vantage.

Shutte, A. J. Printed Italian Vernacular Religious Books 1465-1550: A Finding List. 484p. (Orig.). 1983. pap. text ed. 65.00x (Pub. by Droz Switzerland). Coronet Bks.

Shutts, Mark. Walking to Jesus: Scenes from My Journey. LC 84-91288. (Illus.). 80p. (Orig.). 1984. pap. 3.98 (ISBN 0-9614077-1-9). Shutts Minist.

Sia, Santiago, ed. Word & Spirit VIII. (Studies in Process Theology). 1986. pap. 7.00 (ISBN 0-932506-46-1). St Bedes Pubns.

Sias, Twila. You Can Teach Children Successfully. (Training Successful Teachers Ser.). 48p. (Orig.). 1984. pap. 2.95 (ISBN 0-87239-806-4, 3206). Standard Pub.

Sibbes, Richard. Exposition of St. Paul's Epistles. (Works of Sibbes: Vol. 5). 1978. Repr. 16.95 (ISBN 0-85151-246-1). Banner of Truth.

--Works of Richard Sibbes, Vol. VI. 560p. 1983. Repr. 16.95 (ISBN 0-85151-372-7). Banner of Truth.

--Works of Richard Sibbes, Vol. IV. 527p. 1983. Repr. 16.95 (ISBN 0-85151-371-9). Banner of Truth.

--Works of Richard Sibbes, Vol. 1. 1979. 16.95 (ISBN 0-85151-169-4). Banner of Truth.

--Works of Richard Sibbes, Vol. 3. 543p. 1981. 16.95 (ISBN 0-85151-329-8). Banner of Truth.

Sibbett, Ed, Jr. Easy-to-Make Christmas & Holiday Lightcatchers: With Full-Size Template for 66 Stained Glass Projects. 64p. 1984. pap. 4.50 (ISBN 0-486-24706-6). Dover.

--Ready-to-Use Christmas Designs. (Clip Art Ser.). (Illus.). 1979. pap. 3.50 (ISBN 0-486-23900-4). Dover.

Siberry, Elizabeth. Criticism of Crusading, Ten Ninety-Five to Twelve Seventy-Four. 1985. 37.00x (ISBN 0-19-821953-9). Oxford U Pr.

Sibley, Brian. C. S. Lewis Through the Shadowlands. LC 86-13096. (Illus.). 160p. 1986. pap. text ed. 10.95 (ISBN 0-8007-1509-8). Revell.

Sibley, J. Ashley, Jr., ed. see Sandifer, Kevin W.

Sibthorpe, Robert. Apostolike Obedience: A Sermon. LC 76-57418. (English Experience Ser.: No. 831). 1977. Repr. of 1627 ed. lib. bdg. 6.00 (ISBN 90-221-0831-7). Walter J Johnson.

Sica, Joseph F. God So Loved the World. LC 81-40441. 120p. (Orig.). 1981. lib. bdg. 21.00 o. p. (ISBN 0-8191-1677-7); pap. text ed. 9.25 (ISBN 0-8191-1678-5). U Pr of Amer.

Siccardi, Mirtha F. Luz Que No Se Apaga. Tr. of The Bright Light. (Span.). 256p. 1983. pap. 4.75 (ISBN 0-8254-1665-5). Kregel.

Sicher, Efraim. Beyond Marginality: Anglo-Jewish Literature after the Holocaust. (Modern Jewish Literature & Culture Ser.). 224p. 1985. 44.50x (ISBN 0-87395-976-0); pap. 14.95x (ISBN 0-87395-975-2). State U NY Pr.

Sichrovsky, Peter. Strangers in Their Own Land: Young Jews in Germany & Austria Today. Steinberg, Jean, tr. LC 85-43108. 208p. 1986. 14.95 (ISBN 0-465-08211-4). Basic.

Siddheswarananda, Swami. Meditation According to Yoga-Vedanta. pap. 4.95 (ISBN 0-87481-467-7). Vedanta Pr.

--Some Aspects of Vedanta Philosophy. Bhakti, Krishna & Marar, K. Narayana, trs. 318p. (Orig.). 1976. pap. 4.50 (ISBN 0-87481-471-5). Vedanta Pr.

Siddigi, K. N. The Qur'An & the World Today. 295p. 1971. 7.25x (ISBN 0-87902-249-3). Orientalia.

Siddigui, A. H. The Islamic Concept of Religion & Its Revival. 1981. 19.00 (ISBN 0-686-77428-0). Kazi Pubns.

Siddiq, Akhtar H. The Muslim World: A Selected Bibliography on Its Socio-Economic Development. (Public Administration Ser.: P 1372). 74p. 1984. pap. 11.25 (ISBN 0-88066-832-6). Vance Biblios.

Siddiqi, Amir H. Caliphate & Kingship in Mediaeval Persia. LC 77-10621. (Studies in Islamic History: No. 14). 112p. 1978. Repr. of 1937 ed. lib. bdg. 17.50x (ISBN 0-87991-463-7). Porcupine Pr.

Siddiqi, Muhammad N. Muslim Economic Thinking: A Survey of Contemporary Literature. 130p. (Orig.). 1981. 10.50x (ISBN 0-86037-082-8, Pub. by Islamic Found UK); pap. 5.25x (ISBN 0-86037-081-X). New Era Pubns MI.

Siddique, Kaukab. Islam and Revolution: Basic Issues Facing the Muslim World. LC 82-154032. 112p. 1981. pap. 10.00 (ISBN 0-942978-00-5). Am Soc Ed & Rel.

--Islam-the Wave of the Future. LC 82-83624. 75p. (Orig.). 1983. pap. 2.00 (ISBN 0-942978-04-8). Am Soc Ed & Rel.

--The Struggle of Muslim Women. LC 86-70641. 152p. (Orig.). 1986. pap. 9.95 (ISBN 0-942978-10-2). Am Soc Ed & Rel.

--Towards Understanding the Basics of Islam: Texts from Qur'an & Hadith. 52p. (Orig.). 1986. pap. 2.50 (ISBN 0-942978-01-3). Am Soc Ed & Rel.

Siddique, Kaukab, intro. by. & t see Ala Maudoodi, Abul.

Siddique, Kaukab, tr. see Qureshi, Hafiz M.

Siddiqui, A. A. Elementary Teachings of Islam. pap. 4.50 (ISBN 0-686-18397-5). Kazi Pubns.

Siddiqui, A. H. The Democracy & the Islamic State. 2.50 (ISBN 0-686-83892-0). Kazi Pubns.

--The Holy Quran: Text, Translation & Explanatory Notes, I-VIII. (Avail. in sep. parts). pap. 4.00 ea. Kazi Pubns.

--Islam & Remaking of Humanity. 14.95 (ISBN 0-686-83885-8); pap. 9.95 (ISBN 0-686-83886-6). Kazi Pubns.

--Islam & the Remaking of Humanity. pap. 9.95 (ISBN 0-686-63904-9). Kazi Pubns.

--Jehad in Islam. pap. 2.75 (ISBN 0-686-63906-5). Kazi Pubns.

--Life of Muhammad. 15.50 (ISBN 0-686-18307-X). Kazi Pubns.

--Philosophical Interpretation of History. 14.95 (ISBN 0-686-83884-X). Kazi Pubns.

--Prayers of the Prophet with Arabic Text. pap. 2.00 (ISBN 0-686-18345-2). Kazi Pubns.

--Prophethood in Islam. pap. 4.95 (ISBN 0-686-18344-4). Kazi Pubns.

--Selections from Quran & Hadith. pap. 22.50 ea. (ISBN 0-686-63914-6). Kazi Pubns.

--What Islam Gave to Humanity? pap. 2.50 (ISBN 0-686-63918-9). Kazi Pubns.

Siddiqui, M. I. Animal Sacrifice in Islam. pap. 2.75 (ISBN 0-686-63893-X). Kazi Pubns.

--Economic Security in Islam. 1981. 19.95 (ISBN 0-686-97853-6). Kazi Pubns.

--The Family Laws of Islam. Date not set. 22.00. Kazi Pubns.

--Penal Law of Islam. 1980. 16.50 (ISBN 0-686-64662-2). Kazi Pubns.

--Qualities of Holy Quran. 1981. 2.50 (ISBN 0-686-97854-4). Kazi Pubns.

--Rights of Allah & Human Rights. 1981. 15.95 (ISBN 0-686-97876-5). Kazi Pubns.

--What Agitates the Mind of the East. 1981. 1.25 (ISBN 0-686-97862-5). Kazi Pubns.

--Why Islam Forbids Free Mixing of Men & Women. 19.95. Kazi Pubns.

--Why Islam Forbids Intoxicants & Gambling. 1981. 15.75 (ISBN 0-686-97852-8). Kazi Pubns.

Siddiqui, M. M. Development of Islamic State & Society. 1986. 22.50 (ISBN 0-317-46088-9). Kazi Pubns.

--Women in Islam. 10.50 (ISBN 0-686-18462-9). Kazi Pubns.

--Women in Islam. 1969. 10.50 (ISBN 0-87902-069-5). Orientalia.

Siddiqui, M. S. Blessed Women of Islam. 16.95 (ISBN 0-686-83898-X). Kazi Pubns.

--Call to Islam. pap. 2.00 (ISBN 0-686-63897-2). Kazi Pubns.

--Islamic Sharia & the Muslims. pap. 2.50 (ISBN 0-686-63905-7). Kazi Pubns.

Siddiqui, Mohammed M., et al, trs. see Al-Qaradawi, Yusuf.

Siddiqui, Muhammad A. Elementary Teachings of Islam. Date not set. 1.75 (ISBN 0-89259-022-X). Am Trust Pubns.

Siddiqui, N. Muhammad the Benefactor of Humanity. pap. 9.50 (ISBN 0-686-18434-3). Kazi Pubns.

Siddiqui, Najib. Twelve Years with the Sufi Herb Doctors. 1983. 4.95 (ISBN 0-86304-014-4, Pub. by Octagon Pr England). Ins Study Human.

Siddiqui, Zeba. Kareem & Fatimah. Quinlan, Hamid, ed. LC 82-70452. (Illus.). 50p. 1982. pap. 3.50 (ISBN 0-89259-032-7). Am Trust Pubns.

Sidebottom, E. M. James, Jude & II Peter. (New Century Bible Ser). 142p. 1967. 7.50 (ISBN 0-551-00590-4). Attic Pr.

--James, Jude, II Peter. Black, Matthew, ed. (The New Century Bible Commentary Ser.). 130p. 1982. pap. 5.95 (ISBN 0-8028-1936-2). Eerdmans.

Sider, E. Morris. Messenger of Grace: A Biography of C. N. Hostetter Jr. LC 82-71583. 1982. cloth 7.95 (ISBN 0-916035-06-9); pap. 5.95 (ISBN 0-916035-07-7). Evangel Indiana.

Sider, E. Morris & Hostetler, Paul. Lantern in the Dawn: Selections from Writings of John E. Zercher. 1980. 6.95 (ISBN 0-916035-08-5). Evangel Indiana.

Sider, Robert D. The Gospel & Its Proclamation. (Message of the Fathers of the Church Ser.: Vol. 10). 15.95 (ISBN 0-89453-350-9); pap. 9.95 (ISBN 0-89453-321-5). M Glazier.

Sider, Robert D., ed. see Erasmus, Desiderius.

Sider, Ronald J. Christ & Violence. LC 79-9239. (Christian Peace Shelf Ser.). 104p. 1979. pap. 4.95 (ISBN 0-8361-1895-2). Herald Pr.

--Cry Justice: The Bible Speaks on Hunger & Poverty. LC 80-82133. 224p. 1980. pap. 3.95 (ISBN 0-8091-2308-8). Paulist Pr.

--Rich Christians in an Age of Hunger: A Biblical Study. LC 76-45106. 254p. 1977. pap. 5.95 (ISBN 0-8091-2015-1). Paulist Pr.

--Rich Christians in an Age of Hunger: A Biblical Study. 2nd, rev. ed. LC 84-4549. (Illus.). 257p. 1984. pap. 7.95 (ISBN 0-87784-977-3). Inter-Varsity.

Sider, Ronald J. & Taylor, Richard K. Nuclear Holocaust & Christian Hope. (Illus.). 492p. (Orig.). 1982. pap. 7.95 (ISBN 0-87784-386-4). Inter-Varsity.

--Nuclear Holocaust & Christian Hope: A Book for Christian Peacemakers. 360p. 1983. pap. 6.95 (ISBN 0-8091-2512-9). Paulist Pr.

Sider, Ronald J., jt. auth. see Evangelicals for Social Action Staff.

Sider, Ronald J., ed. Evangelicals & Development: Toward a Theology of Social Change. LC 82-6970. (Contemporary Issues in Social Ethics Ser.). 122p. 1982. pap. 6.95 (ISBN 0-664-24445-9). Westminster.

--Lifestyle in the Eighties: An Evangelical Commitment to Simple Lifestyle. LC 82-7067. (Contemporary Issues in Social Ethics Ser.). 258p. 1982. pap. 10.95 (ISBN 0-664-24437-8). Westminster.

--Living More Simply. LC 79-3634. (Orig.). 1980. pap. 4.95 (ISBN 0-87784-808-4). Inter-Varsity.

Sider, Ronald J. & Brubaker, Darrel J., eds. Preaching on Peace. LC 82-10958. 96p. 1982. pap. 0.50 (ISBN 0-8006-1681-2). Fortress.

Sidgwick, Henry. The Methods of Ethics. LC 81-85772. (Philosophical Classics Ser.). 568p. 1981. 30.00 (ISBN 0-915145-29-4); pap. 12.50 (ISBN 0-915145-28-6). Hackett Pub.

Sidney, Edwin. The Life of the Rev. Rowland Hill, A. M. 1978. Repr. of 1834 ed. lib. bdg. 25.00 (ISBN 0-8495-4870-5). Arden Lib.

Sidney, Philip, tr. see Mornay, Philippe de.

Sidon, Ephraim. The Animated Megillah. (Animated Holydays Ser.). 54p. 1987. 14.95 (ISBN 0-8246-0324-9). Jonathan David.

Sidorsky, David, et al, eds. Essays on Human Rights: Contemporary Issues & Jewish Perspectives. LC 78-1170. 416p. 1978. 12.00 (ISBN 0-8276-0107-7, 420). Jewish Pubns.

Sieben, Hermann J. Voces: Eine Bibliographie zu Woertern und Begriffen aus der Patristik (1918-1978) (Bibliographia Patristica). 461p. 1979. text ed. 55.20x (ISBN 3-11-007966-6). De Gruyter.

Siebers, Tobin. The Mirror of Medusa. LC 82-20071. (Illus.). 180p. 1983. text ed. 26.95x (ISBN 0-520-04856-3). U of Cal Pr.

Siebert, Rudolf J. The Critical Theory of Religion: The Frankfurt School from Universal Pragmatic to Political Theology. (Religion & Reason Ser.: Vol. 29). xvi, 722p. 1985. 112.00x (ISBN 0-89925-119-6). Mouton.

--Horkheimer's Critical Sociology of Religion: The Relative & the Transcendent. LC 78-66280. 1979. pap. text ed. 9.50 (ISBN 0-8191-0688-7). U Pr of Amer.

Siecke, Ernst. Drachenkampfe: Untersuchungen Sagenkunde, Vol. 1-pt. 1. Bolle, Kees W., ed. LC 77-79155. (Mythology Ser.). (Ger.). 1978. Repr. of 1907 ed. lib. bdg. 14.00x (ISBN 0-405-10564-9). Ayer Co Pubs.

Siegel, Beatrice. A New Look at the Pilgrims: Why They Came to America. LC 76-57060. (Illus.). 96p. 1987. Repr. of 1977 ed. o. p. 5.95 (ISBN 0-8027-6291-3); PLB 12.85 (ISBN 0-8027-6292-1). Walker & Co.

--Sam Ellis's Island. LC 85-42799. (Illus.). 128p. 1985. PLB 11.95 (ISBN 0-02-782720-8, Four Winds). Macmillan.

Siegel, Ben. The Controversial Sholem Asch: An Introduction to His Fiction. LC 76-43446. 1976. 12.95 (ISBN 0-87972-076-X); pap. 7.95 (ISBN 0-87972-170-7). Bowling Green Univ.

Siegel, James T. The Rope of God. LC 69-15942. (Center for South & Southeast Asia Studies, California Library Reprint Ser.: No. 96). 1978. Repr. of 1969 ed. 35.00x (ISBN 0-520-03714-6). U of Cal Pr.

Siegel, Jonathan P. The Severus Scroll & 1Q1SA. LC 75-28372. (Society of Biblical Literature, Masoretic Studies). 1975. pap. 8.95 (ISBN 0-89130-028-7, 060502). Scholars Pr GA.

Siegel, Martin, jt. ed. see Zeik, Michael.

Siegel, Paul N. The Meek & the Militant: Religion & Power Across the World. 260p. 1986. 35.00 (ISBN 0-86232-349-5, Pub. by Zed Pr UK); pap. 12.50 (ISBN 0-86232-350-9, Pub. by Zed Pr UK). Humanities.

Siegel, Robert. The Kingdom of Wundle. 48p. 1982. 8.95 (ISBN 0-89107-261-6, Crossway Bks). Good News.

Siegel, S., ed. Conservative Judaism & Jewish Law. 20.00x (ISBN 0-87068-428-0); pap. 9.95. Ktav.

Siegel, Seymour & Gertel, Elliot. God in the Teachings of Conservative Judaism. 278p. 1985. 20.00 (ISBN 0-88125-066-X). Ktav.

Siegel, Seymour, jt. auth. see Dresner, Samuel.

Siegelman, Jim, jt. auth. see Conway, Flo.

Siegfried. Beginning to Beginning. LC 84-90251. 65p. 1985. 6.95 (ISBN 0-533-06286-1). Vantage.

Siegl, Helen. Clip Art-Block Prints for the Gospel of Cycles A, B, C. (Illus.). 216p. (Orig.). pap. 11.95 (ISBN 0-916134-66-0). Pueblo Pub Co.

Siegle, Bernad A. Marriage: According to the New Code of Canon Law. LC 86-10806. 297p. (Orig.). 1986. pap. 14.95 (ISBN 0-8189-0497-6). Alba.

Siegle, Bernard. Marriage: According to the New Code of Canon Law. new ed. LC 72-4055. 297p. (Orig.). Date not set. pap. 14.95 (ISBN 0-8189-0497-6). Alba.

Siegman, Edward F. Ezechiel. (Bible Ser.). pap. 1.00 ea.; Pt. 1. pap. (ISBN 0-8091-5045-X); Pt. 2. pap. (ISBN 0-8091-5046-8). Paulist Pr.

Siemens, Ruth, jt. auth. see Pippert, Rebecca.

Sienkewicz, Thomas J. Classical Gods & Heroes in the National Gallery of Art. LC 82-23818. (Illus.). 50p. (Orig.). 1983. pap. text ed. 9.75 (ISBN 0-8191-2967-4). U Pr of Amer.

Sienkiewicz, Henryk. Quo Vadis. (Classics Ser). 1968. pap. 2.50 (ISBN 0-8049-0188-0, CL-188). Airmont.

Sienkiewicz, Magdalen, jt. auth. see Hunter, Lea A.

Sieur de Moleon. Voyages Liturgiques de France. 694p. Repr. of 1718 ed. text ed. 165.60x (ISBN 0-576-99713-7, Pub. by Gregg Intl Pubs England). Gregg Intl.

Siev, Asher, ed. see Katz, Yoseph.

Sievers, Eduard. Murbacher Hymnen, nach den Handschriften Herausgegeben. Repr. of 1874 ed. 27.00 (ISBN 0-384-55359-1). Johnson Repr.

Siewert, Alan E. An Unlikely Cast: Dramatic Monologues for Advent. 1976. pap. 3.50 (ISBN 0-89536-245-7, 2107). CSS of Ohio.

Siewert, John, jt. auth. see Wilson, Samuel.

Sifford, Darrell. Father & Son. LC 82-11063. 270p. 1982. 9.95 (ISBN 0-664-27004-2, A Bridgebooks Publication). Westminster.

Sigal, Gerald. The Jew & the Christian Missionary: A Jewish Response to Missionary Christianity. 1981. 20.00x (ISBN 0-87068-886-3). Ktav.

Sigal, Phillip. The Emergence of Contemporary Judaism: From Medievalism to Proto-Modernity in the 16th & 17th Century, Vol. 3. (Pittsburgh Theological Monographs New Ser.: No. 17). 1986. pap. text ed. 31.90 (ISBN 0-915138-57-3). Pickwick.

--Emergence of Contemporary Judaism: The Foundation of Judaism from Biblical Origins to the Sixth Century A. D, Vol. 1, Pts. 1 & 2. Incl. Pt. 1. From the Origins to the Separation of Christianity. (Pittsburgh Theological Monographs: No. 29). pap. text ed. 22.25 (ISBN 0-915138-30-1); Pt. 2. Rabbinic Judaism. (Pittsburgh Theological Monographs: No. 29a). pap. text ed. 20.25 (ISBN 0-915138-46-8). 1980. pap. text ed. 39.75 set (ISBN 0-915138-46-8). Pickwick.

--The Halakah of Jesus of Nazareth According to the Gospel of Matthew. 282p. (Orig.). 1986. lib. bdg. 23.75 (ISBN 0-8191-5210-2); pap. text ed. 13.25 (ISBN 0-8191-5211-0). U Pr of Amer.

Sigmund, Paul e., ed. see St. Thomas Aquinas.

Signer, Michael, jt. ed. see Popkin, Richard H.

Sigstedt, Cyriel O. Swedenborg Epic. LC 78-137269. (Illus.). Repr. of 1952 ed. 34.50 (ISBN 0-404-05999-6). AMS Pr.

Siirala, Aarne. Divine Humanness. Kantonen, T. A., tr. LC 70-99460. pap. 48.00 (2026964). Bks Demand UMI.

--The Voice of Illness. 225p. 1981. Repr. of 1964 ed. 49.95 (ISBN 0-88946-995-4). E Mellen.

Sikking, Robert P. A Matter of Life & Death. 1978. pap. 4.95 (ISBN 0-87516-256-8). De Vorss.

Sikking, Sue. God Always Says Yes. 143p. 1984. pap. 5.95 (ISBN 0-87516-545-1). De Vorss.

Sikora, R. I. & Barry, Brian, eds. Obligations to Future Generations. LC 78-5495. (Philosophical Monographs: Second Annual Ser.). 272p. 1978. 14.95 (ISBN 0-87722-132-4); pap. 12.95 (ISBN 0-87722-128-6). Temple U Pr.

Sikorsky, Igor I. Message of the Lord's Prayer. 1963. 10.95 (ISBN 0-8392-1068-X). Astor-Honor.

Silacara, Bhikkhu, tr. see Dahlke, Paul.

Silber, Edward S. God Is Otherwise Engaged. 317p. 1984. 10.95 (ISBN 0-89697-158-9). Intl Univ Pr.

Silberg, Moshe. Talmudic Law & the Modern State. 1973. 9.00x (ISBN 0-8381-3112-3). United Syn Bk.

Silberman, Charles. A Certain People: American Jews & Their Lives Today. 1985. 19.95 (ISBN 0-671-44761-0). Summit Bks.

Silberman, Charles E. A Certain People: American Jews & Their Lives Today. 464p. 1986. pap. 9.95 (ISBN 0-671-62877-1). Summit Bks.

Silberman, Mark, ed. see Kubie, Nora B.

Silberman, Shoshana. A Family Haggadah. 1987. pap. 3.95; Songs for a Family Seder. cassette 6.95. Kar Ben.

Silbermann, A. M. & Rosenbaum, M. Pentateuch with Rashi, 5 vols. LC 30-11064. 1973. 44.95 (ISBN 0-87306-019-9); slipcased ed. 46.95. Feldheim.

Silbermann, A. M., ed. The Children's Haggadah. Wartski, Isidore & Super, Arthur S., trs. (Illus.). 100p. 1972. 14.95 (ISBN 0-87306-984-6). Feldheim.

Silbermann, Eileen Z. The Savage Sacrament: A Theology of Marriage after American Feminism. 128p. (Orig.). 1983. pap. 5.95 (ISBN 0-89622-165-2). Twenty-Third.

Silberschlag, Eisig. From Renaissance to Renaissance: Hebrew Literature 1492-1967, Vol. I. 1972. 25.00x (ISBN 0-87068-184-2). Ktav.

Silberschlag, Eisig, compiled by. An Exhibition of Judaica & Hebraica. (Illus.). 26p. 1973. pap. 3.50 (ISBN 0-87959-034-3). U of Tex H Ransom Ctr.

Silcock, Thomas H. Words & Testimonies. LC 72-80097. (Orig.). 1972. pap. 2.50x (ISBN 0-87574-186-X). Pendle Hill.

Silcox, Claris E. Catholics, Jews, & Protestants: A Study of Relationships in the United States & Canada. LC 78-21101. 1979. Repr. of 1934 ed. lib. bdg. 24.75x (ISBN 0-313-20882-4, SICJ). Greenwood.

Sill, Gertrude G. Handbook of Symbols in Christian Art. (Illus.). 1975. pap. 10.95 (ISBN 0-02-000850-3, Collier). Macmillan.

Sill, Sterling W. Christmas Sermons. LC 73-86165. 184p. 1973. 8.95 (ISBN 0-87747-503-2). Deseret Bk.

--The Law of the Harvest. 392p. 1980. 10.95 (ISBN 0-88290-142-7). Horizon Utah.

--The Majesty of Books. LC 74-81407. 336p. 1974. 9.95 (ISBN 0-87747-532-6). Deseret Bk.

--Our World of Wonders. 96p. 1986. 7.95 (ISBN 0-88290-287-3). Horizon Utah.

--The Power of Poetry. LC 83-83267. 141p. 1984. 7.95 (ISBN 0-88290-238-5). Horizon Utah.

Silva, Andrew J. da see Da Silva, Andrew J.

Silva, Jose D., tr. see Eastman, Dick.

Silva, Moises. Biblical Interpretation: Its History. (Foundations in Hermeneutics Ser.: Vol. 1). 176p. Date not set. pap. 7.95 (ISBN 0-8407-7524-5). Nelson.

--Biblical Words & Their Meaning: An Introduction to Lexical Semantics. 1986. pap. 8.95 (ISBN 0-310-45671-1, 11630P). Zondervan.

Silva, Owen F., tr. Mission Music of California. Bienbar, Arthur, ed. LC 77-16531. (Music Reprint Ser.). (Illus.). 1978. Repr. of 1941 ed. lib. bdg. 39.50 (ISBN 0-306-77524-7). Da Capo.

Silva, Owen F. da see Silva, Owen F.

Silver, Abba H. History of Messianic Speculation in Israel from the First Through the Seventeenth Centuries. 11.75 (ISBN 0-8446-2937-5). Peter Smith.

--Where Judaism Differed. 1972. pap. 5.95 (ISBN 0-02-089360-4, Collier). Macmillan.

--Where Judaism Differed. 318p. 1987. Repr. of 1956 ed. 25.00 (ISBN 0-87668-957-8). Aronson.

Silver, Arthur M. Passover Haggadah: The Complete Seder. 1980. 10.95 (ISBN 0-932232-06-X). Menorah Pub.

Silver, Daniel B., jt. auth. see Fabrega, Horacio, Jr.

Silver, Daniel J. Images of Moses. LC 82-70854. 1982. 16.95 (ISBN 0-465-03201-X). Basic.

--Judaism & Ethics. 1970. 20.00x (ISBN 0-87068-010-2). Ktav.

Silver, Daniel J. & Martin, Bernard. History of Judaism, 2 vols. Incl. Vol. 1. From Abraham to Maimonides; Vol. 2. Europe & the New World. pap. 10.95 o.s.i (ISBN 0-465-03005-X). LC 73-90131. 1974. Basic.

Silver, James W. Confederate Morale & Church Propaganda. 1967. pap. 1.35x (ISBN 0-393-00422-8, Norton Lib). Norton.

Silver, Maury, jt. auth. see Sabini, Jon.

Silverman, Hillel E. From Week to Week. LC 74-16211. 1975. 10.95x (ISBN 0-87677-156-8). Hartmore.

Silverman, Joseph H., jt. auth. see Armistead, Samuel G.

Silverman, Kenneth, ed. see Mather, Cotton.

Silverman, Maida. My Bible Alphabet. (Golden Storytime Book). (Illus.). 24p. 1987. pap. 2.95 (ISBN 0-307-11968-8, Golden Bks). Western Pub.

Silverman, Morris. Evening Service for Yom Kippur. large type ed. 17.50 (ISBN 0-87677-073-1). Prayer Bk.

--Hartford Jews: Sixteen Fifty-Nine to Nineteen Seventy. (Illus.). 449p. 1970. 10.00 (ISBN 0-940748-21-5). Conn Hist Soc.

--High Holiday Prayer Book. 12.00 (ISBN 0-87677-051-0); simulated leather 13.50 (ISBN 0-87677-012-X). Prayer Bk.

--Memorial Service at the Cemetery. pap. 0.95 (ISBN 0-685-64878-8). Prayer Bk.

--Prayers of Consolation. 1972. 8.95x (ISBN 0-87677-062-6); pap. 6.95x (ISBN 0-87677-063-4). Prayer BK.

Silverman, Morris & Arzt, Max. Selihot Service. rev. ed. pap. 2.95x (ISBN 0-87677-066-9). Prayer Bk.

Silverman, Morris & Hillel. Tishah B'av Service. pap. 2.95x (ISBN 0-87677-068-5). Prayer Bk.

Silverman, Morris & Neusner, Jacob. Complete Purim Service. pap. 2.95 (ISBN 0-87677-064-2). Prayer Bk.

Silverman, Morris & United Synagogue. Weekday Prayer Book. 8.95 (ISBN 0-87677-071-5). Prayer Bk.

Silverman, Morris, ed. Passover Haggadah. pap. 4.95 (ISBN 0-87677-029-4). Hartmore.

--Passover Haggadah. rev. ed. (Illus.). 1986. 10.00 (ISBN 0-87677-025-1); pap. 4.95 (ISBN 0-87677-029-4). Prayer Bk.

Silverman, Phyllis R. Helping Women Cope with Grief. (Sage Human Services Guides Ser.: Vol. 25). 111p. 1981. pap. 9.95 (ISBN 0-8039-1735-X). Sage.

--Widow-to-Widow. 240p. 1986. text ed. 19.95 (ISBN 0-8261-5030-6). Springer Pub.

Silverman, William B. Basic Reform Judaism. LC 69-15531. 308p. 1970. 15.00 (ISBN 0-8022-2332-X). Philos Lib.

--Judaism & Christianity. LC 68-27330. pap. 5.95x (ISBN 0-87441-016-9). Behrman.

Silverstein, Baruch. Unclaimed Treasures. 1983. 15.00x (ISBN 0-88125-029-5). Ktav.

Silverstein, Herma, jt. auth. see Arnold, Caroline.

Silverstein, Shraga, tr. see Luzzatto, Mosche Chaim.

Silverstein, Shragu. Antidote. 1980. pap. 3.95 (ISBN 0-87306-173-X). Feldheim.

Silvert, Kalman H., ed. Churches & States: The Religious Institution & Modernization. LC 67-22384. 224p. 1967. 7.50 (ISBN 0-910116-64-4). U Field Staff Intl.

Silvestre, Lucio B. The End of the World, A.D. 2133. LC 83-90813. 233p. 1985. 12.95 (ISBN 0-533-05822-8). Vantage.

Silvestri, Stefano, jt. auth. see Morgan, Roger.

Silvey, D. O. Lord's Unconquerable Church. 256p. 1972. 4.95 (ISBN 0-89114-052-2); pap. 2.95 (ISBN 0-89114-051-4). Baptist Pub Hse.

--Welcome, New Church Member. 20p. 1964. pap. 0.60 (ISBN 0-89114-112-X). Baptist Pub Hse.

Silvey, James L., ed. see Jensen, Vi.

Simcox, Carroll. Eternal You. 112p. (Orig.). 1986. pap. 7.95 (ISBN 0-8245-0745-2). Crossroad NY.

Simcox, Carroll E. Prayer: The Divine Dialog. LC 84-28930. 108p. (Orig.). 1985. pap. 4.95 (ISBN 0-87784-527-1). Inter-Varsity.

Simeon, Charles. Evangelical Preaching: An Anthology of Sermons. Houston, James M., ed. LC 85-28389. (Classics of Faith & Devotion Ser.). 1986. 12.95 (ISBN 0-88070-120-X); pap. 9.95. Multnomah.

Simeone, William E. The Episcopal Church in Alaska: A Catalog of Photographs from the Archives & Historical Collections of the Episcopal Church. (Alaska Historical Commission Studies in History: No. 19). 152p. (Orig.). 1981. pap. text ed. 8.00 (ISBN 0-943712-08-4); microfiche 4.50 (ISBN 0-943712-07-6). Alaska Hist.

Simi, Gino J. & Segreti, Mario M. St. Francis of Paola: God's Miracle Worker Supreme. LC 77-78097. 1977. pap. 4.50 (ISBN 0-89555-065-2). TAN Bks Pubs.

Simler, Joseph. Catechism of Mental Prayer. LC 84-51901. 69p. 1985. pap. 1.50 (ISBN 0-89555-256-6). Tan Bks Pubs.

Simma, Maria. My Personal Experiences with the Poor Souls. Helena, M., tr. from Ger. 1978. 6.95 (ISBN 0-8199-0744-8). Franciscan Herald.

Simmel, Georg. Sociology of Religion. Coser, Lewis A. & Powell, Walter W., eds. Rosenthal, Curt, tr. from Ger. LC 79-7021. (Perennial Works in Sociology Ser.). 1979. Repr. of 1959 ed. lib. bdg. 15.00x (ISBN 0-405-12120-2). Ayer Co Pubs.

Simmonds, A. J. The Gentile Comes to Cache Valley. LC 72-80615. 143p. 1976. 8.95. Utah St U Pr.

Simmonds, James D. Masques of God: Form & Theme in the Poetry of Henry Vaughan. LC 78-170144. 1972. 24.95x (ISBN 0-8229-3236-9). U of Pittsburgh Pr.

Simmonds, James D., ed. Milton Studies, Vol. III. LC 69-12335. (Milton Studies). 1971. 32.95x (ISBN 0-8229-3218-0). U of Pittsburgh Pr.

--Milton Studies, Vol. II. LC 69-12335. (Milton Studies). 1970. 32.95x (ISBN 0-8229-3194-X). U of Pittsburgh Pr.

--Milton Studies, Vol. V. LC 69-12335. (Milton Studies). 1973. 32.95x (ISBN 0-8229-3272-5). U of Pittsburgh Pr.

--Milton Studies, Vol. VI. LC 69-12335. (Milton Studies). 1974. 32.95x (ISBN 0-8229-3288-1). U of Pittsburgh Pr.

--Milton Studies, Vol. VIII. LC 69-12335. (Milton Studies). 1975. 39.95x (ISBN 0-8229-3310-1). U of Pittsburgh Pr.

--Milton Studies, Vol. IX. LC 69-12335. (Milton Studies). 1976. 32.95x (ISBN 0-8229-3329-2). U of Pittsburgh Pr.

Simmons, A. LeRoi. Ephemeris Nineteen Fifty to Nineteen Seventy-Five. (Illus.). 375p. 1977. 14.00 (ISBN 0-9605126-1-6). Aquarian Bk Pubs.

Simmons, Arthur G. & Simmons, Beborah T. Create in Me: Young Adult Bible Study. 1985. 5.75 (ISBN 0-89536-765-3, 5872). CSS of Ohio.

Simmons, Beborah T., jt. auth. see Simmons, Arthur G.

Simmons, Billy E. A Functioning Faith. 144p. 1983. pap. 4.00 (ISBN 0-914520-18-0). Insight Pr.

--Galatians. 128p. 1983. pap. 3.00 (ISBN 0-914520-20-2). Insight Pr.

--The Incomparable Christ. 128p. 1983. pap. 4.00 (ISBN 0-914520-21-0). Insight Pr.

--Resplendent Themes. 70p. 1983. pap. 4.00 (ISBN 0-914520-19-9). Insight Pr.

Simmons, D. R. Iconography of New Zealand Maori Religion. (Iconography of Religions Ser.: Pt. II/1). (Illus.). ix, 33p. 1986. pap. 27.25 (ISBN 90-04-07588-7, Pub. by E J Brill). Heinman.

Simmons, David. Whakairo: Maori Tribal Art. (Illus.). 1985. 34.95x (ISBN 0-19-558119-9). Oxford U Pr.

Simmons, H. L., tr. see Symeon of Thessalonike.

Simmons, Leo W. The Role of the Aged in Primitive Society. LC 78-103998. (Illus.). 317p. 1970. Repr. of 1945 ed. 28.00 (ISBN 0-208-00824-1, Archon). Shoe String.

Simmons, Marc. Witchcraft in the Southwest: Spanish & Indian Supernaturalism on the Rio Grande. LC 79-18928. (Illus.). xiv, 184p. 1980. pap. 5.50 (ISBN 0-8032-9116-7, BB 729, Bison). U of Nebr Pr.

Simmons, Patricia A. Between You & Me, God. LC 74-79486. 1974. pap. 5.95 (ISBN 0-8054-4412-2, 4244-12). Broadman.

Simmons, Paul D. Birth & Death: Bioethical Decision-Making. LC 82-20160. (Biblical Perspectives on Current Issues). 270p. 1983. pap. 13.95 (ISBN 0-664-24463-7). Westminster.

Simmons, Paul D. & Crawford, Kenneth. Mi Desarrollo Sexual. Sabanes De Plou, Dafne, tr. from Eng. (El Sexo En la Vida Cristiana). (Span.). 96p. 1985. pap. 2.50 (ISBN 0-311-46257-X, Edit Mundo). Casa Bautista.

Simmons, Paul D., ed. Issues in Christian Ethics. LC 79-52983. 1980. pap. 8.95 (ISBN 0-8054-6122-1). Broadman.

Simmons, T. F., ed. The Lay Folks Mass Book: Four Texts. (EET OS Ser.: Vol. 71). Repr. of 1879 ed. 63.00 (ISBN 0-8115-3359-X). Kraus Repr.

Simmons, William S. Cautantowwit's House: An Indian Burial Ground on the Island of Conanicut in Narragansett Bay. LC 77-111456. (Illus.). pap. 49.50 (ISBN 0-317-41779-7, 2025642). Bks Demand UMI.

Simms, Carolynne. Letters from a Roman Catholic. 27p. 1987. pap. 3.00 (ISBN 0-911826-11-4). Am Atheist.

Simms, James M. First Colored Baptist Church in North America. LC 70-82074. (Illus.). Repr. of 1888 ed. 22.50x (ISBN 0-8371-1561-2, SIC&, Pub. by Negro U Pr). Greenwood.

Simms, Laura & Kozodoy, Ruth. Exploring Our Living Past. Harlow, Jules, ed. (Our Living Past Ser). (Illus.). 1978. pap. 6.95x (ISBN 0-87441-309-5). Behrman.

Simon, Arthur. Bread for the World. rev. ed. LC 84-238017. 219p. 1985. pap. 4.95 (ISBN 0-8091-2670-2). Paulist Pr.

Simon, Bennet. Kosher Konnection: The Los Angeles Dining Guide to the Best of Kosher, Delis & Natural Foods. LC 79-67671. (Orig.). 1980. pap. 4.95 (ISBN 0-935618-00-7). Rossi Pubns.

Simon, Charlie M. Christmas Every Friday & Other Christmas Stories. Hagen, Lyman B., ed. LC 81-65364. (Illus.). 68p. 1981. 7.95 (ISBN 0-935304-21-5). August Hse.

Simon, Edith. The Piebald Standard. LC 76-29836. Repr. of 1959 ed. 40.00 (ISBN 0-404-15419-0). AMS Pr.

Simon, Erika. Festivals of Attica: An Archaeological Commentary. LC 81-70160. 160p. 1983. text ed. 26.50x (ISBN 0-299-09180-5). U of Wis Pr.

Simon, Ethelyn, ed. see Anderson, Joseph.

Simon, Ethelyn, ed. see Anderson, Joseph, et al.

Simon, Gerhard. Church, State & Opposition in U. S. S. R. LC 73-87754. 1974. 37.95x (ISBN 0-520-02612-8). U of Cal Pr.

Simon, Henry A. Treasury of Christmas Songs & Carols. 2nd ed. 1973. 16.95 (ISBN 0-395-17786-3); pap. 9.95 (ISBN 0-395-17785-5). HM.

Simon, Joseph, ed. see Klein, Herbert A.

Simon, Julius. Certain Days: Zionist Memoirs & Selected Papers. Friesel, Evyatar, ed. 388p. 1971. casebound 12.95x (ISBN 0-87855-183-2). Transaction Bks.

Simon, Leon. Studies in Jewish Nationalism. LC 75-6458. (The Rise of Jewish Nationalism & the Middle East Ser.). xi, 174p. 1975. Repr. of 1920 ed. 19.80 (ISBN 0-88355-343-0). Hyperion Conn.

Simon, Marcal. Verus Israel. McKeating, H., tr. 592p. 1985. 57.00x (ISBN 0-19-710035-X). Oxford U Pr.

Simon, Martin P., jt. auth. see Jahsmann, Allan H.

Simon, Maurice & Levertoff, Paul, trs. Zohar. 1934. 75.00 (ISBN 0-900689-39-0); pap. 55.00. Soncino Pr.

Simon, Merill. Jerry Falwell & the Jews. LC 83-22266. 172p. 1983. 12.50 (ISBN 0-8246-0300-1). Jonathan David.

Simon, Norma. Every Friday Night. (Festival Series of Picture Story Booxs). (Illus.). plastic cover 4.50 (ISBN 0-8381-0708-7). United Syn Bk.

--Hanukah in My House. (Festival Series of Picture Story Books). (Illus.). 1960. plastic cover 4.50 (ISBN 0-8381-0705-2). United Syn Bk.

--Hanukkah. LC 66-10065. (Holiday Ser.). (Illus.). 1966. PLB 12.89 (ISBN 0-690-36953-0, Crowell Jr Bks). HarpJ.

--Happy Purim Night. (Festival Series of Picture Story Books). (Illus.). plastic cover 4.50 (ISBN 0-8381-0706-0, 10-706). United Syn Bk.

--My Family Seder. (Festival Series of Picture Story Books). (Illus.). 1961. plastic cover 4.50 (ISBN 0-8381-0710-9, 10-710). United Syn Bk.

--Our First Sukkah. (Festival Series of Picture Story Books). (Illus.). 1959. plastic cover 4.50 (ISBN 0-8381-0703-6). United Syn Bk.

--Passover. LC 65-11644. (Holiday Ser.). (Illus.). 1965. PLB 12.89 (ISBN 0-690-61094-7, Crowell Jr Bks). HarpJ.

--Purim Party. (Festival Series of Picture Story Books). (Illus.). 1959. plastic cover 4.50 (ISBN 0-8381-0707-9). United Syn Bk.

--Rosh Hashanah. (Festival Series of Picture Story Books). (Illus.). 1961. plastic cover 4.50 (ISBN 0-8381-0700-1). United Syn Bk.

--Simhat Torah. (Festival Series of Picture Story Books). (Illus.). 1960. bds. 4.50 lam. (ISBN 0-8381-0704-4). United Syn Bk.

--Tu Bishvat. (Festival Series of Picture Story Books). (Illus.). 1961. plastic cover 4.50 (ISBN 0-8381-0709-5). United Syn Bk.

--Yom Kippur. (Festival Series of Picture Story Books). (Illus.). 1959. plastic cover 4.50 (ISBN 0-8381-0702-8). United Syn Bk.

Simon, Paule, et al, trs. see De Lubac, Henry.

Simon, Pierre J. & Simon-Barouh, Ida. Hau Bong: Un Culte Vietnamien De Possession Transplante En France. (Cahiers De L'homme, Nouvelle Serie: No. 13). (Illus.). 1973. pap. 9.20x (ISBN 90-2797-185-4). Mouton.

Simon, Raphael. The Glory of Thy People. 1986. pap. 6.95 (ISBN 0-932506-47-X). St Bedes Pubns.

Simon, Rita J., ed. New Lives: The Adjustment of Soviet Jewish Immigrants in the United States & Israel. 208p. 1985. 19.95 (ISBN 0-669-09767-5). Lexington Bks.

Simon, Solomon. Adventures of Simple Shmerl. (Illus.). 1942. 4.95 (ISBN 0-87441-127-0). Behrman.

--More Wise Men of Helm. LC 65-14594. (Illus., Orig.). 1979. pap. 4.95 (ISBN 0-87441-126-2). Behrman.

--Wise Men of Helm. 1942. pap. 4.95 (ISBN 0-87441-125-4). Behrman.

Simon, Thomas G. & Fitzpatrick, James M. The Ministry of Liturgical Environment. 48p. (Orig.). 1984. pap. 1.25 (ISBN 0-8146-1354-3). Liturgical Pr.

Simon, Yves R., jt. auth. see Griffin, John H.

Simon-Barouh, Ida, jt. auth. see Simon, Pierre J.

Simonde De Sismondi, Jean C. History of the Crusades Against the Albigenses in the Thirteenth Century. LC 72-178564. Repr. of 1826 ed. 30.00 (ISBN 0-404-56672-3). AMS Pr.

Simone, R. Thomas & Sugarman, Richard I. Reclaiming the Humanities: The Roots of Self-Knowledge in the Greek & Biblical Worlds. 226p. (Orig.). 1986. lib. bdg. 25.75 (ISBN 0-8191-5093-2); pap. text ed. 9.75 (ISBN 0-8191-5094-0). U Pr of Amer.

Simoneau, Karin, jt. ed. see Wilbert, Johannes.

Simonet, Andre. Apostles for Our Time: Thoughts on Apostolic Spirituality. Bouchard, M. Angeline, tr. from Fr. LC 77-8537. 1977. pap. 4.95 (ISBN 0-8189-0354-6). Alba.

Simoni, Felix De see De Simoni, Felix.

Simons, C. P. Valuing Suffering As a Christian: Some Psychological Perspectives. (Synthesis Ser.). 1976. pap. 0.75 (ISBN 0-8199-0708-1). Franciscan Herald.

Simons, Eleanor, jt. auth. see Kapilla, Cleo.

Simons, Frans. Man Kann Wieder Christ Sein: Eine Abrechnung mit der Theologie und der "kritischen" Bibelwissenschaft. 231p. 1978. 27.80 (ISBN 3-261-03011-9). P Lang Pubs.

Simons, George E. The Standard Masonic Monitor. 248p. 1984. pap. 7.50 enlarged type (ISBN 0-88053-010-3). Macoy Pub.

--Standard Monitor. 7.50 (ISBN 0-685-19502-3). Powner.

Simons, George F. Faces & Facets: A Workbook for the Liturgical Celebrant. LC 77-78972. 1977. pap. 3.95 (ISBN 0-914070-11-8). ACTA Found.

--How Big Is a Person? A Book for Loving Out Loud. LC 82-61423. 72p. 1983. 3.95 (ISBN 0-8091-0336-2). Paulist Pr.

--Journal for Life: Discovering Faith & Values Through Journal Keeping-Theology from Experience, Pt. 2, Pt. 2. LC 75-17161. (Illus.). 1977. pap. 1.95 (ISBN 0-914070-10-X). ACTA Found.

Simons, John & Ward, Kay. Noah & His Great Ark. Ward, Kay, ed. (Bible Stories for Today Ser.). (Illus.). 16p. (Orig.). 1987. pap. text ed. 2.50 (ISBN 0-937039-00-4). Sun Pr FL.

Simons, Richard. Cynewulfs Wortshatz. 1899. 65.00 (ISBN 0-8274-2126-5). R West.

Simons, Thomas G. Blessings: A Reappraisal of Their Nature, Purpose, & Celebration. LC 80-54275. 1981. pap. 9.95 (ISBN 0-89390-026-5). Resource Pubns.

--Blessings for God's People: A Book of Blessings for All Occasions. LC 82-62045. 112p. (Orig.). 1983. pap. 5.95 (ISBN 0-87793-264-6). Ave Maria.

Simonsohn, S. History of the Jews in the Duchy of Mantua. 35.00x (ISBN 0-87068-341-1). Ktav.

Simonson, Harold P. Radical Discontinuities: American Romanticism & Christian Consciousness. LC 81-72051. 180p. 1983. 24.50 (ISBN 0-8386-3159-2). Fairleigh Dickinson.

Simonson, Harold P., ed. see Edwards, Jonathan.

Simoons, Elizabeth S., jt. auth. see Simoons, Frederick J.

Simoons, Frederick J. & Simoons, Elizabeth S. Ceremonial Ox of India: The Mithan in Nature, Culture, & History. LC 68-9023. (Illus.). 340p. 1968. 40.00x (ISBN 0-299-04980-9). U of Wis Pr.

Simpler, Steven. Roland H. Bainton: An Examination of His Reformation Historiography. LC 85-21567. (Texts & Studies in Religion: Vol. 24). 266p. 1985. PLB 49.95x (ISBN 0-88946-812-5). E Mellen.

Simpson, A. B. The Best of Simpson. Bailey, Keith M., compiled by. 1987. pap. write for info. (ISBN 0-87509-314-0). Chr Pubns.

--Christ in the Tabernacle. LC 85-70720. 150p. 1985. 4.95 (ISBN 0-87509-361-2). Chr Pubns.

--Danger Lines in the Deeper Life. 133p. 1966. pap. 2.00 (ISBN 0-87509-007-9). Chr Pubns.

--El Evangelio Cuadruple: Fourfold Gospel, Spanish. Bucher, Dorothy, tr. from Eng. 96p. 1981. pap. 2.00 (ISBN 0-87509-268-3). Chr Pubns.

--The Gentle Love of the Holy Spirit. 157p. 1983. pap. 5.95 (ISBN 0-87509-334-5). Chr Pubns.

--The Gospel of Healing. rev. ed. LC 86-70736. 180p. 1986. pap. 5.45 (ISBN 0-87509-376-0). Chr Pubns.

--Holy Spirit, 2 Vols. 7.95; Vol. 1. 7.95 ea. (ISBN 0-87509-015-X). Vol. 2 (ISBN 0-87509-016-8). pap. 5.95 ea. Vol. 1 (ISBN 0-87509-018-4). Vol. 2 (ISBN 0-87509-019-2). Chr Pubns.

--Is Life Worth Living? 30p. pap. 0.95 (ISBN 0-87509-045-1). Chr Pubns.

--Life of Prayer. 122p. 1975. pap. 2.50 (ISBN 0-87509-164-4). Chr Pubns.

--Santificados por Completo-Wholly Sanctified. (Eng., Illus.). 136p. 1981. 2.50 (ISBN 0-87509-307-8). Chr Pubns.

--Spirit Filled Church in Action. 112p. 1975. 2.00 (ISBN 0-87509-037-0). Chr Pubns.

--Walking in Love. 1975. Repr. 2.95 (ISBN 0-87509-040-0). Chr Pubns.

--Wholly Sanctified: Legacy Edition. Rev. ed. King, L. L., intro. by. 136p. 1982. pap. 4.95 (ISBN 0-87509-306-X). Chr Pubns.

Simpson, Alan. Puritanism in Old & New England. LC 55-13637. (Walgreen Foundation Lecture Ser). 1961. pap. 4.00x (ISBN 0-226-75929-6, P66, Phoen). U of Chicago Pr.

Simpson, Albert B. The Christ Life. LC 80-69301. 96p. pap. 2.25 (ISBN 0-87509-291-8). Chr Pubns.

--Christ of the Forty Days. pap. 1.25 (ISBN 0-87509-004-4). Chr Pubns.

--Days of Heaven on Earth. rev. ed. LC 84-70154. 369p. 1984. pap. 7.95 (ISBN 0-87509-346-9). Chr Pubns.

--Divine Emblems. pap. 2.95 (ISBN 0-87509-009-5). Chr Pubns.

--Echoes of the New Creation. pap. 1.25 (ISBN 0-87509-010-9). Chr Pubns.

--Four-Fold Gospel. rev. ed. 1984. pap. 4.95 (ISBN 0-87509-347-7). Chr Pubns.

--Larger Christian Life. 3.95 (ISBN 0-87509-025-7); pap. 3.45 mass market (ISBN 0-87509-026-5). Chr Pubns.

--Old Faith & the New Gospels. pap. 1.25 (ISBN 0-87509-031-1). Chr Pubns.

--Self Life & the Christ Life. pap. 1.95 (ISBN 0-87509-034-6). Chr Pubns.

--When the Comforter Came. pap. 2.95 (ISBN 0-87509-042-7). Chr Pubns.

Simpson, Charles. The Challenge to Care: A Fresh Look at How Pastors & Lay Leaders Relate to the People of God. 196p. 1986. pap. 5.95 (ISBN 0-89283-269-X, Pub. by Vine Books). Servant.

Simpson, Cuthbert A. Revelation & Response in the Old Testament. LC 73-76022. Repr. of 1947 ed. 15.00 (ISBN 0-404-06056-0). AMS Pr.

Simpson, Douglas. The Apocalypse: A Premillennial Interpretation of the Book of Revelation. 1975. pap. 3.95 (ISBN 0-89265-029-X). Randall Hse.

Simpson, Douglas J. The Book of Daniel. 1974. pap. 3.95 (ISBN 0-89265-023-0). Randall Hse.

--The Maturing Christian. 1977. pap. 1.50 (ISBN 0-89265-047-8). Randall Hse.

Simpson, Douglas J., ed. Christian Education: An Introduction to Its Scope. 1979. 7.95 (ISBN 0-89265-053-2). Randall Hse.

Simpson, Evelyn M., ed. & intro. by. see Donne, John.

Simpson, Evelyn M., ed. see Donne, John.

Simpson, F. Dale. Leading the First Century Church in the Space Age. 1972. 8.75 (ISBN 0-89137-003-X); pap. 5.95. Quality Pubns.

--Seven Steps along the Way. 1981. pap. 7.45 (ISBN 0-89137-527-9). Quality Pubns.

Simpson, Floyd & Hill, Glynn, eds. How to Repair Books & Maintain Audiovisuals. LC 84-9618. (Orig.). 1984. pap. 2.95 (ISBN 0-8054-3708-8). Broadman.

Simpson, Frances. Beacon Small-Group Bible Studies, Ruth-Esther: Faith That Risks All. Wolf, Earl C., ed. 96p. (Orig.). 1984. pap. 2.50 (ISBN 0-8341-0941-7). Beacon Hill.

Simpson, George E. Black Religions in the New World. LC 78-16892. (Illus.). 1978. 40.00x (ISBN 0-231-04540-9). Columbia U Pr.

Simpson, J. A., ed. The Concise Oxford Dictionary of Proverbs. (Paperback Reference Ser.). 1983. pap. 6.95 (ISBN 0-19-281880-5). Oxford U Pr.

Simpson, James, jt. ed. see Kratzmann, Gregory.

Simpson, James Y. Landmarks in the Struggle Between Science & Religion. LC 75-118549. 1971. Repr. of 1925 ed. 26.50x (ISBN 0-8046-1174-2, Pub. by Kennikat). Assoc Faculty Pr.

Simpson, Lesley B., ed. & tr. see Gomara, Francisco Lopez de.

Simpson, Lesley B., tr. see Ricard, Robert.

Simpson, M. A. Dying, Death, & Grief: A Critically Annotated Bibliography & Source Book of Thanatology & Terminal Care. LC 78-27273. 300p. 1979. 35.00x (ISBN 0-306-40147-9, Plenum Pr). Plenum Pub.

Simpson, Matthew. Encyclopedia of Methodism, 2 vols. 1977. lib. bdg. 250.00 (ISBN 0-8490-1766-1). Gordon Pr.

Simpson, Michael, tr. Gods & Heroes of the Greeks: The "Library" of Apollodorus. LC 75-32489. (Illus.). 320p. 1976. pap. 10.95x (ISBN 0-87023-206-1). U of Mass Pr.

Simpson, Peggy. Hospitality: In the Spirit of Love. 1980. pap. 4.95 (ISBN 0-89137-416-7). Quality Pubns.

Simpson, Peggy, ed. see Associated Women's Organization, Mars Hill Bible School.

Simpson, Richard. Religion of Shakespeare. Bowden, Henry S., ed. LC 74-176025. Repr. of 1899 ed. 17.50 (ISBN 0-404-00961-1). AMS Pr.

--Religion of Shakespeare. 1973. Repr. of 1899 ed. 17.45 (ISBN 0-8274-1094-8). R West.

Simpson, Robert D., ed. American Methodist Pioneer: The Life & Journals of the Rev. Freeborn Garrettson 1752-1827. LC 83-72532. (Illus.). 444p. 1983. text ed. 25.00 (ISBN 0-914960-49-0). Academy Bks.

Simpson, W. S., ed. see London - St. Paul'S Cathedral.

Simpson, William. The Jonah Legend: A Suggestion of Interpretation. LC 72-177422. (Illus.). vi, 182p. 1971. Repr. of 1899 ed. 35.00x (ISBN 0-8103-3820-3). Gale.

Simpson, William J. A Study of Bossuet. (Church Historical Society London N. S. Ser.: No. 22). pap. 23.00 (ISBN 0-8115-3146-5). Kraus Repr.

Simpson, William K. Heka-Nefer & the Dynastic Material from Toshka & Arminna. (Pubns of the Penn-Yale Expedition to Egypt: No. 1). (Illus.). xiv, 53p. 1963. 16.50x (ISBN 0-686-17767-3). Univ Mus of U PA.

--The Terrace of the Great God at Abydos: The Offering Chapels of Dynasties 12 & 13, Vol. 5. LC 73-88231. 1974. 25.00 (ISBN 0-686-05519-5). Penn-Yale Expedit.

Simpson, Winifred R. Hello, World, You're Mine? (Illus.). 1987. pap. 3.95 (ISBN 0-570-03643-7). Concordia.

Sims, Albert E. & Dent, George. Who's Who in the Bible. 1979. pap. 2.95 (ISBN 0-8065-0705-5). Citadel Pr.

--Who's Who in the Bible. 1982. pap. 4.95 (ISBN 0-8022-1577-7). Philos Lib.

Sims, Edward R. A Season with the Savior: Meditations on Mark. 1979. 6.95 (ISBN 0-8164-0413-5, HarpR); pap. 3.95 (ISBN 0-8164-2195-1). Har-Row.

Sims, James H. Dramatic Uses of Biblical Allusions in Marlowe & Shakespeare. LC 66-64917. (University of Florida Humanities Monographs: No. 24). 1966. pap. 3.50 (ISBN 0-8130-0206-0). U Presses Fla.

Sims, James H. & Ryken, Leland, eds. Milton & Scriptural Tradition: The Bible into Poetry. LC 83-16781. 192p. 1984. text ed. 19.50x (ISBN 0-8262-0427-9). U of MO Pr.

Sims, John. Power with Purpose. 1985. text ed. 8.95 (ISBN 0-87148-717-9); pap. text ed. 7.95 (ISBN 0-87148-716-0). Pathway Pr.

Sims, Tim & Pegoda, Dan. One Hundred & One Things to Do During a Dull Sermon. 85p. (Orig.). pap. 6.95 (ISBN 0-910125-05-8). Youth Special.

Simson, Otto Von see Von Simson, Otto.

Simundson, Daniel J. The Message of Job: A Theological Commentary. LC 84-24214. (Augsburg Old Testament Studies). 192p. (Orig.). 1986. pap. 9.95 (ISBN 0-8066-2218-0, 10-4349). Augsburg.

--Where Is God In My Praying? Biblical Responses to Eight Searching Questions. LC 86-22294. 96p. (Orig.). 1986. pap. 5.50 (ISBN 0-8066-2241-5, 10-7096). Augsburg.

--Where Is God in My Suffering? Biblical Responses to Seven Searching Questions. LC 83-72108. 80p. 1984. pap. 4.95 (ISBN 0-8066-2052-8, 10-7071). Augsburg.

Simundson, Danile J. Faith under Fire: Biblical Interpretations of Suffering. LC 79-54119. 158p. 1980. pap. 7.95 (ISBN 0-8066-1756-X, 10-2195). Augsburg.

Sinai, Anne & Sinai, Robert I., eds. Israel & the Arabs: Prelude to the Jewish State. LC 78-161364. (A Facts on File Publication). pap. 64.00 (2025158). Bks Demand UMI.

Sinai, Robert I., jt. ed. see Sinai, Anne.

Sinclair, Donna M. The Pastor's Wife Today. LC 80-26076. (Creative Leadership Ser.). 128p. (Orig.). 1981. pap. 5.95 (ISBN 0-687-30269-2). Abingdon.

Sinclair, E. M., tr. see Strauss, Leo.

Sinclair, George. Satan's Invisible World Discovered. LC 68-17017. 1969. Repr. of 1685 ed. 45.00x (ISBN 0-8201-1068-X). Schol Facsimiles.

Sinclair, John H., ed. Protestantism in Latin America: A Bibliographical Guide. rev. ed. LC 73-12837. 1976. pap. text ed. 8.95x (ISBN 0-87808-126-7). William Carey Lib.

Sinclair, Keith V. Prieres en Ancien Francais. LC 78-137. 208p. 1978. 35.00 (ISBN 0-208-01741-0, Archon). Shoe String.

Sinclair, Keith V., compiled by. French Devotional Texts of the Middle Ages: A Bibliographic Manuscript Guide. LC 79-7587. 1979. lib. bdg. 49.95x (ISBN 0-313-20649-X, SFT/). Greenwood.

Sinclair, Keith V., ed. French Devotional Texts of the Middle Ages: A Bibliographic Manuscript Guide, First Supplement. LC 82-11773. xvi, 234p. 1982. lib. bdg. 65.00 (ISBN 0-313-23664-X, SIF/). Greenwood.

Sinclair, Upton B. Profits of Religion. LC 73-120566. 1970. Repr. of 1918 ed. 22.50 (ISBN 0-404-06093-5). AMS Pr.

Sindevitch, Heinrich. Kamo Grjadeshi: Quo Vadis. 523p. 23.00 (ISBN 0-317-30246-9); pap. 18.00 (ISBN 0-317-30247-7). Holy Trinity.

Sinding-Larsen, Staale. Iconography & Ritual: A Study of Analytical Perspectives. 260p. 1985. 30.00x (ISBN 82-00-07184-7). Oxford U Pr.

Sine, Tom. The Mustard Seed Conspiracy. 1981. 7.95 (ISBN 0-8499-2939-3). Word Bks.

--Taking Discipleship Seriously. 80p. 1985. pap. 4.95 (ISBN 0-8170-1085-8). Judson.

Sinetar, Marsha. Do What You Love, the Money Will Follow. 1987. pap. 9.95. Paulist Pr.

Sinfield, Alan. Literature in Protestant England: 1560-1660. LC 82-18408. 168p. 1983. text ed. 26.50x (ISBN 0-389-20341-6, 07185). B&N Imports.

Singer, Betty J. Friends of the Jews. (Illus.). 1976. pap. text ed. 2.75 (ISBN 0-917400-01-1). Options.

Singer, C. C., jt. auth. see Evans, G. R.

Singer, C. Gregg. From Rationalism to Irrationality. 1979. pap. 14.50 (ISBN 0-87552-428-1). Presby & Reformed.

Singer, C Gregg. A Theological Interpretation of American History. rev. ed. 1981. pap. 7.95 (ISBN 0-87552-426-5). Presby & Reformed.

Singer, Charles. Religion & Science: Considered in Their Historical Relations. 78p. 1980. Repr. lib. bdg. 15.00 (ISBN 0-89987-756-7). Darby Bks.

Singer, David. Focus on the Jewish Family: A Selected Annotated Bibliography, 1970-1982. 32p. 1984. pap. 2.00 (ISBN 0-87495-058-9). Am Jewish Comm.

Singer, David & Seldin, Ruth. American Jewish Year Book, 1987. 1986. write for info. Am Jewish Comm.

Singer, David, jt. ed. see Himmelfarb, Milton.

Singer, Gregg. A Theological Interpretation of American History. kivar 7.95 (ISBN 0-934532-23-0). Presby & Ref.

Singer, I., ed. The Jewish Encyclopedia, 12 vols. 1976. Set. lib. bdg. 998.95 (ISBN 0-8490-2101-4). Gordon Pr.

Singer, Isaac B. Love & Exile: A Memoir. LC 79-7211. (Illus.). 384p. 1984. 17.95 (ISBN 0-385-14060-6). Doubleday.

--The Power of Light: Eight Stories for Hanukkah. LC 80-20263. (Illus.). 87p. 1980. 10.95 (ISBN 0-374-36099-5). FS&G.

Singer, Marcus G. Generalization in Ethics: An Essay in the Logic of Ethics with the Rudiments of a System of Moral Philosophy. LC 70-152539. (With a new introduction). 1971. Repr. of 1961 ed. 11.00x (ISBN 0-8462-1612-4). Russell.

Singer, Mark J. & Shechtman, Stephen A. The Missing Link: Building Quality Time with Teens. 176p. 1985. pap. 7.95 (ISBN 0-687-27078-2). Abingdon.

Singer, Milton, ed. Krishna: Myths, Rites, & Attitudes. LC 65-20585. 1969. pap. 12.00x (ISBN 0-226-76101-0, P329, Phoen). U of Chicago Pr.

--Traditional India: Structure & Change. (American Folklore Society Bibliographical & Special Ser.: No. 10). 356p. 1959. pap. 9.95x (ISBN 0-292-73504-9). U of Tex Pr.

Singer, Milton B., ed. Krishna: Myths, Rites, & Attitudes. LC 80-29194. xvii, 277p. 1981. Repr. of 1966 ed. lib. bdg. 27.50x (ISBN 0-313-22822-1, SIKR). Greenwood.

Singer, Peter. The Expanding Circle: Ethics & Sociobiology. 190p. 1981. 10.95 (ISBN 0-374-15112-1). FS&G.

--Practical Ethics. LC 79-52328. 1980. 37.50 (ISBN 0-521-22920-0); pap. 10.95 (ISBN 0-521-29720-6). Cambridge U Pr.

Singer, Phillip B. In Prison You Came to Me. (Looking Up Ser.). 24p. (Orig.). 1984. pap. 1.25 (ISBN 0-8298-0473-0). Pilgrim NY.

Singer, S. Prayer Book. Repr. of 1962 ed. 10.95x (ISBN 0-8197-0057-6). Bloch.

Singerman, Robert. Antisemitic Propaganda: An Annotated Bibliography & Research. LC 81-43363. (History, Political Science, International Affairs, Area Studies). 220p. 1982. lib. bdg. 73.00 (ISBN 0-8240-9270-8, SS112). Garland Pub.

--Jewish & Hebrew Onomastics: A Bibliography. (Reference Library of the Humanities: Vol. 92). (LC 76-052684). 1977. lib. bdg. 23.00 (ISBN 0-8240-9881-1). Garland Pub.

--Jewish Serials of the World: A Research Bibliography of Secondary Sources. LC 86-344. 399p. 1986. lib. bdg. 55.00 (ISBN 0-313-24493-6, SJE/). Greenwood.

--The Jews in Spain & Portugal: A Bibliography. LC 75-1166. (Reference Library of Social Science: No. 11). 376p. 1975. lib. bdg. 52.00 (ISBN 0-8240-1089-2). Garland Pub.

Singh, Ajaib. The Jewel of Happiness: The Sukhmani of Guru Arjan. Perkins, Russell & Perkins, Judith, eds. Bagga, Raaj K., tr. LC 84-50910. (Illus.). 384p. (Orig.). 1984. pap. 15.00 (ISBN 0-89142-042-8). Sant Bani Ash.

--Streams in the Desert. Perkins, Russell & Perkins, Judith, eds. LC 81-85843. (Illus.). 468p. (Orig.). 1982. pap. 12.00 (ISBN 0-89142-038-X). Sant Bani Ash.

Singh, B. Hindu Ethics. 200p. 1984. text ed. 22.50 (ISBN 0-391-02933-9). Humanities.

--The Philosophy of Upanishads. 160p. 1983. text ed. 10.50x (ISBN 0-391-02935-5). Humanities.

Singh, Balbir. Hindu Metaphysics. 256p. 1986. text ed. 25.00x (ISBN 0-391-03408-1). Humanities.

Singh, Bhagat. The Story of Krishna. (Illus.). 20p. (Orig.). 1976. pap. 1.75 (ISBN 0-89744-135-4, Pub. by Hemkunt India). Auromere.

Singh, Charu S. & Hogg, James. The Chariot of Fire: A Study of William Blake In the Light of Hindu Thought. (Romantic Reassessment Ser.). 194p. (Orig.). 1981. pap. 15.00 (ISBN 3-7052-0577-3, Pub. by Salzburg Studies). Longwood Pub Group.

Singh, Daljeet. Sikhism. 1979. text ed. 17.95 (ISBN 0-89684-074-3, Pub. by Sterling New Delhi). Orient Bk Dist.

Singh, Daljit & Smith, Angela. The Sikh World. (Religions of the World Ser.). (Illus.). 48p. 1985. PLB 14.96 (ISBN 0-382-09158-2); pap. 9.25 (ISBN 0-382-09159-0). Silver.

Singh, Darshan. Spiritual Awakening. LC 81-50726. (Illus.). 338p. (Orig.). 1982. pap. 6.50 (ISBN 0-918224-11-X). Sawan Kirpal Pubns.

Singh, Devendra, tr. see Thakar, Vimala.

Singh, Fauja. Guru Amar Das. 196p. 1979. text ed. 9.95 (ISBN 0-89684-080-8, Pub. by Sterling New Delhi). Orient Bk Dist.

Singh, Fauja, ed. Perspectives on Guru Amardas. 1985. 8.50x (ISBN 0-8364-1518-3, Pub. by Punjabi U India). South Asia Bks.

Singh, Gopal. Guru Gobind Singh. (National Biography Ser.). (Orig.). 1979. pap. 2.50 (ISBN 0-89744-206-7). Auromere.

Singh, Harbans. Guru Gobind Singh. 1979. text ed. 6.95 (ISBN 0-89684-073-5, Pub. by Sterling New Delhi). Orient Bk Dist.

--The Heritage of the Sikhs. 1983. 26.00x (ISBN 0-8364-1006-8); text ed. 16.00x (ISBN 0-8364-1007-6). South Asia Bks.

Singh, Jaideva. Siva Sutras: The Yoga of Supreme Identity. 1979. 16.95 (ISBN 0-89684-057-3, Pub. by Motilal Banarsidass India); pap. 12.50 (ISBN 0-89684-063-8, Pub. by Motilal Banarsidass India). Orient Bk Dist.

Singh, Jarnail. Sikh Symposium 1985. 121p. 1986. 8.00 (ISBN 0-8364-1840-9). South Asia Bks.

Singh, Jarnail, tr. see Nabha, Kahan S.

Singh, Khushwant. Gurus, Godman & Good People. (Illus.). 134p. 1975. text ed. 13.95x (ISBN 0-86125-087-7, Pub. by Orient Longman India). Apt Bks.

--A History of the Sikhs, 2 vols. LC 63-7550. (Illus.). 1984. Vol. 1, 1469-1839, 430 pgs. pap. 13.50 (ISBN 0-691-00803-5); Vol. 2, 1839-1964, 408 pgs. pap. 13.50 (ISBN 0-691-00804-3); Set. pap. 25.00 (ISBN 0-691-00805-1). Princeton U Pr.

Singh, Khushwant & Rai, Raghu. Sikhs. LC 85-22359. 300p. 1985. Repr. lib. bdg. 44.95x (ISBN 0-89370-891-7). Borgo Pr.

Singh, Khushwant & Singh, Suneet V. Homage to Guru Gobind Singh. 1970. pap. 2.75 (ISBN 0-88253-088-7). Ind-US Inc.

Singh, Khushwant, ed. & tr. Hymns of Guru Nanak. Repr. of 1969 ed. cancelled (ISBN 0-8364-0302-9, Orient Longman). South Asia Bks.

Singh, Kirpal. Baba Jaimal Singh: His Life & Teachings. (Illus.). 168p. 3.00 (ISBN 0-318-03045-4). Sant Bani Ash.

--The Crown of Life: A Study of Yoga. (Illus.). xv, 255p. 1980. pap. 7.00 (ISBN 0-89142-000-2). Sant Bani Ash.

--The Crown of Life: A Study of Yoga. 4th ed. LC 79-67543. (Illus.). 256p. pap. 6.95 (ISBN 0-918224-09-8). Sawan Kirpal Pubns.

--Godman: Finding a Spiritual Master. 2nd ed. LC 78-68503. (Illus.). 1979. pap. 5.95 (ISBN 0-918224-07-1). Sawan Kirpal Pubns.

--The Holy Path. Seader, Ruth, ed. (The Teachings of Kirpal Singh Ser., Vol. 1). (Illus.). viii, 94p. (Orig.). 1974. pap. 3.00 (ISBN 0-89142-013-4). Sant Bani Ash.

--The Light of Kirpal. LC 80-52537. xv, 446p. 1984. pap. 12.00 (ISBN 0-89142-033-9). Sant Bani Ash.

--Naam or Word. 4th ed. LC 81-51512. (Illus.). 335p. 1982. pap. 5.50 (ISBN 0-918224-12-8). Sawan Kirpal Pubns.

--Prayer: Its Nature & Technique. 4th ed. LC 81-50727. (Illus.). 149p. 1982. pap. 5.95 (ISBN 0-918224-10-1). Sawan Kirpal Pubns.

--Spirituality: What It Is. 3rd ed. LC 81-52000. (Illus.). 112p. 1982. pap. 3.50 (ISBN 0-918224-16-0). Sawan Kirpal Pubns.

--The Way of the Saints: The Collected Short Writings of Kirpal Singh. Perkins, Russell, ed. LC 76-21987. 402p. 1978. 8.00 (ISBN 0-89142-026-6). Sant Bani Ash.

Singh, Kirpal, ed. & tr. Jap Ji: Message of Guru Nanak. 5th ed. 182p. 1976. pap. 3.50 (ISBN 0-89142-029-0). Sant Bani Ash.

Singh, Krushwant, tr. see Iqbal, Mohammed.

Singh, Mala. The Story of Guru Nanak. (Illus.). 1979. 6.25 (ISBN 0-89744-138-9). Auromere.

Singh, Pratap, tr. see Kabir.

Singh, Pritam, ed. Sikh Concept of the Divine. 1986. 15.00x (ISBN 0-8364-1607-4, Pub. by Nanak Dev Univ India). South Asia Bks.

--Sikh Concept of the Divine. 223p. 1986. 15.00X (ISBN 0-8364-1670-8, Pub. by Abhinav India). South Asia Bks.

Singh, Puran. The Book of the Ten Masters. 1984. 6.00X (ISBN 0-8364-1159-5, Pub. by Punjabi). South Asia Bks.

--Spirit of the Sikhs, 3 vols. 1984. Repr. of 1920 ed. Pt.1. 7.50x (ISBN 0-8364-1115-3, Pub. by Punjabi); Pt.2, v.1. 7.50x (ISBN 0-8364-1116-1); Pt.2, Vol.2. 7.50x (ISBN 0-8364-1117-X). South Asia Bks.

Singh, R. B. Jainism in Early Medieval Karnataka. 1976. 9.95 (ISBN 0-8426-0981-4). Orient Bk Dist.

Singh, Sangat, tr. see Nanak, Guru.

Singh, Sohan, ed. The Ballad of God & Man: Asa Di Var. 1984. 9.00x (ISBN 0-8364-1220-6, Pub. by Nanak Dev Univ India). South Asia Bks.

Singh, Suneet V., jt. auth. see Singh, Khushwant.

Singh, Tara. Commentaries on A Course in Miracles. LC 86-18350. (Orig.). 1986. 16.95 (ISBN 1-55531-015-X); pap. 12.95 (ISBN 1-55531-016-8). Life Action Pr.

--A Course in Miracles - A Gift for All Mankind. LC 86-12073. (Orig.). 1986. 12.95 (ISBN 1-55531-013-3); pap. 7.95 (ISBN 1-55531-014-1). Life Action Pr.

--Dialogues on A Course in Miracles. LC 86-82912. (Orig.). 1987. 19.95 (ISBN 1-55531-130-X); pap. 14.95 (ISBN 1-55531-131-8). Life Action Pr.

--How to Learn from a Course in Miracles. rev. ed. LC 85-24790. (Orig.). 1985. 8.95 (ISBN 1-55531-000-1); pap. 4.50 (ISBN 1-55531-001-X). Life Action Pr.

--How to Raise a Child of God. 2nd ed. LC 86-82911. (Orig.). 1987. 19.95 (ISBN 1-55531-008-7); pap. 14.95 (ISBN 1-55531-009-5). Life Action Pr.

--Love Holds No Grievances: The Ending of Attack. 2nd ed. LC 86-14834. 1986. 8.95 (ISBN 1-55531-120-2); pap. 4.95 (ISBN 1-55531-007-9). Life Action Pr.

--Our Story of Bringing a Course in Miracles into Application. (Orig.). Date not set. price not set (ISBN 1-55531-127-X); pap. price not set (ISBN 1-55531-128-8). Life Action Pr.

Singh, Wazir. Philosophy of Sikh Religion. 127p. 1981. 13.95x (ISBN 0-940500-09-4, Pub. by Ess Ess Pubns India). Asia Bk Corp.

Singha, H. S. Junior Encyclopedia of Sikhism. 181p. 1985. text ed. 12.50x (ISBN 0-7069-2844-X, Pub. by Vikas India). Advent NY.

Singh Talib, Gurbachan see Gurbachan Singh Talib.

Sinha, B. C. Hinduism & Symbol Worship. 1985. 17.50x (ISBN 0-8364-1297-4, Pub. by Agam Kala Prakashan). South Asia Bks.

Sinha, Nandalal, tr. & intro. by see Kanada.

Sinha, Nandalal, tr. & intro. by see Narada.

Sinha, Phulgenda. Yoga: Meaning, Values & Practice. 1973. pap. 2.50 (ISBN 0-88253-259-6). Ind-US Inc.

Sinha, V. K. Secularism in India. 1968. 6.25 (ISBN 0-89684-521-4). Orient Bk Dist.

Sinishta, Gjon. The Fulfilled Promise: A Documentary Account of Religious Persecution in Albania. LC 76-57433. (Illus.). 253p. (Orig.). pap. 10.00 (ISBN 0-317-18715-5). Albanian Cath Info.

Sinistrari, Ludovico M. Demoniality. LC 72-83751. Repr. of 1927 ed. lib. bdg. 22.00 (ISBN 0-405-08976-7, Pub. by Blom). Ayer Co Pubs.

Sinkler, Lorainne, ed. see Goldsmith, Joel S.

Sinkler, Lorraine, ed. see Goldsmith, Joel S.

Sinnett. Esoteric Buddhism. 11.25 (ISBN 0-8356-5230-0). Theos Pub Hse.

Sinnett, A. P. Esoteric Buddhism. 5th ed. LC 73-76091. (Secret Doctrine Reference Ser.). 240p. 1981. pap. 8.00 (ISBN 0-913510-45-9). Wizards.

--Occult World. 9th ed. 1969. 12.95 (ISBN 0-8356-5019-7). Theos Pub Hse.

--Tennyson an Occultist. LC 72-2102. (Studies in Tennyson, No. 27). 1972. Repr. of 1920 ed. lib. bdg. 46.95x (ISBN 0-8383-1485-6). Haskell.

Sinnett, Alfred P., ed. Incidents in the Life of Madame Blavatsky. facsimile ed. LC 75-36919. (Occult Ser.). Repr. of 1886 ed. 25.50x (ISBN 0-405-07974-5). Ayer Co Pubs.

Sinsheimer, Hermann. Shylock: The History of a Character. LC 63-23188. (Illus.). Repr. of 1947 ed. 15.00 (ISBN 0-405-08977-5, Pub. by Blom). Ayer Co Pubs.

Siou, Lily. Chi-Kung: The Art of Mastering the Unseen Life Force. LC 75-32212. 1975. 17.50 (ISBN 0-8048-1169-5). C E Tuttle.

Sipe, A. W. & Rowe, Clarence J., eds. Psychiatry, Ministry, & Pastoral Counseling. rev ed. Orig. Title: Psychiatry, the Clergy, & Pastoral Counseling. 384p. 1984. pap. 12.95 (ISBN 0-8146-1324-1). Liturgical Pr.

Sipley, Richard M. Understanding Divine Healing. 168p. 1986. pap. 5.95 (ISBN 0-89693-263-X). Victor Bks.

Sipowicz, A. Edwin, tr. see Graham, Billy.

Sipowicz, Edwin, tr. see Graham, Billy.

Sipowicz, Edwin, tr. see Warren, Max.

Sirat, Colette. A History of Jewish Philosophy in the Middle Ages. 476p. 1985. 59.50 (ISBN 0-521-26087-6). Cambridge U Pr.

Sircar, D. C. Studies in the Religious Life of Ancient & Medieval India. 1971. 9.95 (ISBN 0-89684-326-2). Orient Bk Dist.

Sircar, M. Hindu Mysticism According to the Upanisads. 1974. text ed. 19.00x. Coronet Bks.

Sircar, M. N. Mysticism in the Bhagavad-Gita. 1977. 12.00x (ISBN 0-686-22667-4). Intl Bk Dist.

Sirdar Ikbal Ali Shah. Selections from the Koran. 1980. 10.85 (ISBN 0-900860-85-5, Pub. by Octagon Pr England). Ins Study Human.

Sire, J. W. Program for a New Man. pap. 0.75 (ISBN 0-87784-146-2). Inter-Varsity.

Sire, James W. Beginning with God. LC 81-14305. 128p. (Orig.). 1981. pap. 3.50 (ISBN 0-87784-369-4). Inter-Varsity.

--Scripture Twisting: Twenty Ways the Cults Misread the Bible. LC 80-19309. 216p. (Orig.). 1980. pap. 6.95 (ISBN 0-87784-611-1). Inter-Varsity.

--The Universe Next Door: A Basic World View Catalog. LC 75-32129. 240p. (Orig.). 1976. pap. 7.95 (ISBN 0-87784-772-X). Inter-Varsity.

Siriwardena, R., ed. Equality & the Religious Traditions of Asia. 300p. 1987. 29.95 (ISBN 0-312-00401-X). St Martin.

Sirr, Henry C. China & the Chinese: Their Religion, Culture, Customs, & Manufactures; The Evils Arising from the Opium Trade, 2 vols. 915p. Repr. of 1849 ed. Set. text ed. 38.00x (ISBN 0-89644-564-X, Pub. by Chinese Matl Ctr). Coronet Bks.

Sisam, Kenneth. Cynewulf & His Poetry. LC 75-1103. Repr. of 1933 ed. lib. bdg. 12.50 (ISBN 0-8414-7838-4). Folcroft.

Sisemore, J. T. Practiquemos la Visitacion. Gonzalez, Ananias, ed. Grijalva, Josue, tr. Orig. Title: The Ministry of Visitation. 1981. Repr. of 1979 ed. 2.50 (ISBN 0-311-11034-7). Casa Bautista.

Sisemore, John T. Blueprint for Teaching. LC 64-12413. 1964. 8.95 (ISBN 0-8054-3405-4). Broadman.

--Church Growth Through the Sunday School. LC 82-70870. (Orig.). 1983. pap. 6.50 (ISBN 0-8054-6237-6). Broadman.

--The Ministry of Visitation. LC 54-2969. 1954. 1.25 (ISBN 0-88243-550-7, 02-0550). Gospel Pub.

--Rejoice, You're a Sunday School Teacher. LC 76-20053. 1977. 9.50 (ISBN 0-8054-5147-1). Broadman.

Siskin, Edgar E. Washo Shamans & Peyotists: Religious Conflict in an American Indian Tribe. (Illus.). 300p. 1983. 25.00x (ISBN 0-87480-223-7). U of Utah Pr.

Sismondi, Jean C. Simonde De see Simonde De Sismondi, Jean C.

Sisson, C. H. Anglican Essays. 142p. 1983. 20.00 (ISBN 0-85635-456-2). Carcanet.

Sisson, Richard. Answering Christianity's Most Puzzling Questions, Vol. 2. 240p. (Orig.). 1983. pap. 8.95 (ISBN 0-8024-5148-9). Moody.

--Training for Evangelism. 1979. pap. 12.95 (ISBN 0-8024-8792-0). Moody.

Sisson, Richard, et al. Preparese Para Evangelizar: Un Programa De Evangelizacion Personal. Powell, David & Ditmore, Esteban, trs. Tr. of Training for Evangelism - A Program for Personal Evangelism. (Span.). 224p. (Orig.). 1984. pap. 5.95. Casa Bautista.

Sister Loretta Carey, jt. auth. see Peace Education Council.

Sisters of the Community of Jesus. Jericho Walls. (Illus.). 72p. (Orig.). 1984. pap. 7.95 incl. cassette (ISBN 0-941478-18-1). Paraclete Pr.

--Miracle at the Manger. LC 84-62045. (Illus., Orig.). 1984. pap. 9.95 (ISBN 0-941478-32-7). Paraclete Pr.

--Red Sea Waters. LC 82-61465. (Illus.). 72p. (Orig.). 1983. pap. 7.95 incl. cassette (ISBN 0-941478-08-4). Paraclete Pr.

Sit, Amy. The Rib. LC 76-22278. 1977. pap. 3.95 (ISBN 0-89221-026-5). New Leaf.

--Sing It! 1979. pap. 3.50 (ISBN 0-917726-39-1). Hunter Bks.

Sitaramiah, V. Valmiki Ramayanan. 1982. Repr. 7.00x (ISBN 0-317-47015-9, Pub. by National Sahitya Akademi). South Asia Bks.

Sitjar, Buenaventura. Vocabulary of the Language of San Antonio Mission, California. LC 10-26367. (Library of American Linguistics: No. 7). (Span.). Repr. of 1861 ed. 28.50 (ISBN 0-404-50987-8). AMS Pr.

Sitoy, T. Valentino, Jr. A History of Christianity in the Philippines: The Initial Encounter, Vol. 1. (Illus.). 384p. (Orig.). 1985. pap. 18.50x (ISBN 971-10-0254-X, Pub by New Day Philippines). Cellar.

Sittler, Joseph. Gravity & Grace: Reflections & Provocations. Delloff, Linda Marie, ed. LC 86-3547. 128p. (Orig.). 1986. pap. 6.95 (ISBN 0-8066-2205-9, 10-2888). Augsburg.

Sittler, Joseph A. Grace Notes & Other Fragments. Herhold, Robert M. & Delloff, Linda M., eds. LC 80-8055. 128p. (Orig.). 1981. pap. 5.95 (ISBN 0-8006-1404-6, 1-1404). Fortress.

Sittser, Jerry. The Adventure: Putting Energy into Your Work with God. LC 85-19695. 236p. 1985. pap. 6.95 (ISBN 0-87784-335-X). Inter-Varsity.

Sitwell, Sacheverell. Great Temples of the East. 1962. 12.95 (ISBN 0-8392-1041-8). Astor-Honor.

Siudy. Worship. 1980. 5.50 (ISBN 0-8298-0393-9). Pilgrim NY.

Sivan, Emmanuel. Interpretations of Islam: Past & Present. LC 84-70415. 256p. 1985. 19.95 (ISBN 0-87850-049-9). Darwin Pr.

--Radical Islam. LC 84-20999. 224p. 1987. pap. 9.95x (ISBN 0-300-03888-7). Yale U Pr.

--Radical Islam: Medieval Theology & Modern Politics. LC 84-20999. 224p. 1985. 20.00x (ISBN 0-300-03263-3). Yale U Pr.

Sivan, Reuven & Levenston, Edward A. The New Bantam-Megiddo Hebrew & English Dictionary. LC 77-75289. (Hebrew & Eng.). 1977. 24.95 (ISBN 0-8052-3666-X). Schocken.

Sivan, Reuven, jt. auth. see Levenston, Edward A.

Sivanada, Swami. Brahma Sutras. 2nd ed. 1977. pap. 28.00 (ISBN 0-89684-181-2, Pub. by Motilal Banarsidass India). Orient Bk Dist.

Sivananda, Swami. Divine Nectar. 2nd rev. ed. 1976. pap. 14.00 (ISBN 0-89684-196-0). Orient Bk Dist.

--Practice of Karma Yoga. 1974. 7.95 (ISBN 0-8426-0675-0); pap. 3.50 (ISBN 0-686-67764-1). Orient Bk Dist.

Sivananda Yoga Center. The Sivananda Companion to Yoga. 1983. pap. 9.95 (ISBN 0-671-47088-4). S&S.

Sivananda Radha, Swami. Kundalini Yoga for the West. LC 78-1857. (Illus.). 1978. 24.95 (ISBN 0-931454-01-8). Timeless Bks.

Sivapriyananda, S. Secret Power of Tantrik Breathing. 80p. 1983. text ed. 15.00 (ISBN 0-391-02899-5, Pub. by Abhinav Pubs India). Humanities.

Sivaraman, K. Saivism in Philosophical Perspective. 1973. 17.95 (ISBN 0-8426-0538-X). Orient Bk Dist.

Sivewright, Gary. Following. 32p. 1986. pap. 1.50 (ISBN 0-8341-1127-6). Beacon Hill.

Sivric, Ivo. Bishop J. G. Strossmayer: New Light on Vatican I. 1975. 7.95 (ISBN 0-8199-0491-0). Franciscan Herald.

Sivry, L. De see De Sivry, L.

Six, Jean-Francois. Is God Endangered by Believers? A Critical Study of the Gap Between Religion & Real Faith. 1983. 11.95 (ISBN 0-87193-207-5). Dimension Bks.

Sizemore, Denver. Thirteen Lessons in Christian Doctrine. 11th ed. 1968. pap. 2.95 (ISBN 0-89900-136-X). College Pr Pub.

--Trece Lecciones de Doctrina Biblica. Martinez, Raul, tr. from Eng. Tr. of Thirteen Lessons in Christian Doctrine. (Span.). 114p. pap. 1.95 (ISBN 0-89900-300-1). College Pr Pub.

Sizer, Sandra S. Gospel Hymns & Social Religion: The Rhetoric of Nineteenth-Century Revivalism. LC 78-10165. (American Civilization Ser.). 222p. 1979. lib. bdg. 27.95 (ISBN 0-87722-142-1). Temple U Pr.

Sjodahl, Janne M., jt. auth. see Reynolds, George.

Sjodahl, Janne M., jt. auth. see Smith, Hyrum M.

Sjogren, Per-Olof. The Jesus Prayer. Linton, Sydney, tr. from Swedish. LC 75-18789. 96p. 1975. pap. 3.95 (ISBN 0-8006-1216-7, 1-1216). Fortress.

Sjoo, Monica & Mor, Barbara. The Great Cosmic Mother. 1986. pap. 14.95 (ISBN 0-317-52386-4, PL 4115, HarpR). Har-Row.

Skaballanovitch, M. Pjatidesjatnitsa. Tr. of Pentacost. 176p. pap. 6.00 (ISBN 0-317-29163-7). Holy Trinity.

--Rozhdestvo Khristovo. Tr. of The Nativity of Christ. 195p. pap. 7.00 (ISBN 0-317-29162-9). Holy Trinity.
--Rozhdestvo Presvjatia Bogoroditsi. Tr. of The Nativity of the Holy Mother of God. 134p. pap. 5.00 (ISBN 0-317-29149-1). Holy Trinity.
--Uspenije Presvjatija Bogorodits. Tr. of The Dormition of the Mother of God. 114p. pap. 4.00 (ISBN 0-317-29164-5). Holy Trinity.
--Vozdvizhenije Tchestnago Krjesta Gospodnja. Tr. of The Exaltation of the Life Giving Cross. 173p. pap. 6.00 (ISBN 0-317-29152-1). Holy Trinity.
--Vvedenije vo Khram Presvjatija Bogoroditsi. Tr. of The Entrance of the Mother of God into the Temple. 115p. pap. 4.00 (ISBN 0-317-29157-2). Holy Trinity.
Skaggs, Merrill M., jt. auth. see Barber, Virginia.
Skane, Edward R. God's Man-Satan's Trap. 180p. Repr. of 1984 ed. 12.95 (ISBN 0-917655-00-1). Dane Bks.
Skariah, Matthew. Crispy Christians. LC 85-50245. 184p. (Orig.). 1985. pap. 2.75 (ISBN 0-933495-00-5). World Prayer.
--Free, but Not Cheap. LC 85-91360. 144p. (Orig.). 1986. pap. 3.50 (ISBN 0-933495-01-3). World Prayer.
Skarin, Annalee. Celestial Song of Creation. 1962p. pap. 5.95 (ISBN 0-87516-090-5). De Vorss.
--Man Triumphant. 1966p. pap. 5.95 (ISBN 0-87516-091-3). De Vorss.
--Secrets of Eternity. 1960. pap. 5.95 (ISBN 0-87516-092-1). De Vorss.
--Temple of God. pap. 5.95 (ISBN 0-87516-093-X). De Vorss.
--To God the Glory. pap. 5.95 (ISBN 0-87516-094-8). De Vorss.
--Ye Are Gods. 343p. 1973. pap. 5.95 (ISBN 0-87516-344-0). De Vorss.
Skatrud-Mickelson, Ellen. Draw Near the Cross: Lenten Devotions for Children & Those Who Love Them. 48p. (Orig.). 1985. pap. 2.95 (ISBN 0-8066-2200-8, 23-1604). Augsburg.
Skeat, T. C., jt. ed. see Bell, H. Idris.
Skeat, W. W., ed. Aelfric's Lives of Saints, Vol. II, Pts. III-IV. (EETS OS Ser.: Vols. 94 & 114). Repr. of 1900 ed. 22.00 (ISBN 0-8115-3365-4). Kraus Repr.
Skeat, Walter W. John Milton's Epitaphium Damonis. LC 75-44069. 1933. lib. bdg. 15.00 (ISBN 0-8414-7644-6). Folcroft.
--Malay Magic: Being an Introduction to the Folklore & Popular Religion of the Malay Peninsula. LC 70-174437. (Illus.). 1973. Repr. of 1900 ed. lib. bdg. 28.00 (ISBN 0-405-08980-5). Ayer Co Pubs.
Skeat, Walter W. & Blagden, Charles O. Pagan Races of the Malay Peninsula, 2 vols. new ed. (Illus.). 1966. 95.00x set (ISBN 0-7146-2027-0, F Cass Co). Biblio Dist.
Skeel, Emily E., ed. see Weems, Mason L.
Skeem, Jeanette L., ed. see Skeem, Kenneth A.
Skeem, Kenneth A. In the Beginning... Skeem, Jeanette L., ed. LC 81-68054. (Illus.). 256p. 1981. 12.00 (ISBN 0-9606782-0-4). Behemoth Pub.
Skeireins. Gothic Commentary on the Gospel of John. Bennett, W. H., tr. (MLA MS). 1960. 14.00 (ISBN 0-527-83350-9). Kraus Repr.
Skelly, Herbert & Skelly, Margaret. An Advent Event. (Illus.). 32p. (Orig.). 1973. pap. 3.25 (ISBN 0-8192-1148-6); kit 13.95 (ISBN 0-8192-1283-0). Morehouse.
Skelly, Margaret, jt. auth. see Skelly, Herbert.
Skelton, Eugene A. The Ministry of the Small Group Leader. 48p. 1986. pap. 1.25 (ISBN 0-8146-1487-6). Liturgical Pr.
Skelton, Mary L., ed. see Desikachar, T. K.
Skhi-Igumen, John. Christ Is in Our Midst: Letters from a Russian Monk. Williams, Esther, tr. from Rus. LC 80-10530. 168p. (Orig.). 1980. pap. 4.95 (ISBN 0-913836-64-8). St Vladimirs.
Skiba, Richard J. The Faithful City: A Biblical Study. 68p. 1976. 1.25 (ISBN 0-8199-0704-9). Franciscan Herald.
Skidmore, Janet. Redemptive Dancing: Prayer Dance & Congregational Dance in the Life of the Contemporary Church. Adams, Doug, ed. pap. 2.50 (ISBN 0-941500-46-2). Sharing Co.
Skillen, James, ed. see Hatfield, Mark, et al.
Skillen, James W. Christians Organizing for Political Service: A Study Guide Based on the Work of the Association for Public Justice. LC 80-66190. 113p. (Orig.). 1982. pap. 3.95 (ISBN 0-936456-01-9). Assn Public Justice.
Skilton, John H. The New Testament Student & Bible Translation. (New Testament Student Ser.). 1978. pap. 5.00 (ISBN 0-87552-436-2). Presby & Reformed.
--The New Testament Student & His Field. (New Testament Student Ser.). 318p. 1982. pap. 9.95 (ISBN 0-87552-437-0). Presby & Reformed.
Skinner, Clarence R., ed. Free Pulpit in Action. facsimile ed. LC 71-156718. (Essay Index Reprint Ser.). Repr. of 1931 ed. 22.00 (ISBN 0-8369-2333-2). Ayer Co Pubs.
Skinner, Craig. Lamplighter & Son. LC 82-82947. 1984. 13.95 (ISBN 0-8054-5705-4). Broadman.
--Teaching Ministry of the Pulpit: Its History, Theology, Psychology & Practice for Today. 1979. pap. 6.95 (ISBN 0-8010-8165-3). Baker Bk.
Skinner, Donna. File Folder Learning Centers. LC 81-84001. 160p. (Orig.). 1982. pap. 7.95 (ISBN 0-87239-492-1, 3071). Standard Pub.
Skinner, John. A Critical & Exegetical Commentary on Genesis. Driver, Samuel R., et al, eds. (International Critical Commentary Ser.). 640p. 1930. 24.95 (ISBN 0-567-05001-7, Pub. by T & T Clark Ltd UK). Fortress.
Skinner, John E. The Christian Disciple. LC 83-21772. 92p. (Orig.). 1984. lib. bdg. 20.50 (ISBN 0-8191-3657-3); pap. text ed. 7.75 (ISBN 0-8191-3658-1). U Pr of Amer.
--The Meaning of Authority. LC 82-25098. 88p. (Orig.). 1983. lib. bdg. 22.00 (ISBN 0-8191-3044-3, Co-pub. by Episcopal Div Sch); pap. text ed. 8.50 (ISBN 0-8191-3045-1). U Pr of Amer.
Skinner, Paul H. Self Power. 194p. pap. 7.95 (ISBN 0-942494-44-X). Coleman Pub.
Skinner, Tom. Words of Revolution: A Call Involvement in the Real Revolution. 44p. 1971. pap. 4.25 (ISBN 0-85364-113-7). Attic Pr.
Skipper, States, jt. auth. see Minirth, Frank B.
Skipwith, Ashkain, jt. auth. see Arnander, Primose.
Sklare, Marshall. America's Jews. 1971. pap. 9.00 (ISBN 0-394-31645-2, RanC). Random.
--Conservative Judaism: An American Religious Movement. cancelled. Transaction Bks.
--Conservative Judaism: An American Religious Movement. (Illus.). 336p. 1985. pap. text ed. 12.75 (ISBN 0-8191-4480-0, Co-Pub. by Ctr Jewish Comm Studies). U Pr of Amer.
Sklare, Marshall, ed. American Jews. 352p. 1983. pap. text ed. 9.95x (ISBN 0-87441-348-6). Behrman.
--Understanding American Jewry. LC 81-14795. 300p. 1982. text ed. 21.95x (ISBN 0-87855-454-8). Transaction Bks.
Sklare, Marshall, et al. Not Quite at Home: How an American Jewish Community Lives with Itself & Its Neighbors. LC 77-81092. (Institute of Human Relations Press Paperback Ser). x, 85p. (Orig.). 1969. pap. 1.00 (ISBN 0-87495-017-1). Am Jewish Comm.
Skoglund, Elizabeth. Can I Talk to You? 1977. pap. 3.25 (ISBN 0-8307-0557-0, 5407508). Regal.
--Coping. LC 79-65538. 128p. 1980. pap. 3.95 (ISBN 0-8307-0727-1, 5413109). Regal.
--Growing through Rejection. 1983. pap. 3.95 (ISBN 0-8423-1239-0). Tyndale.
--Safety Zones: Finding Refuge in Times of Turmoil. 220p. 1987. 12.95 (ISBN 0-8499-0555-9). Word Bks.
Skoglund, Herbert H. The World Seen. LC 85-80101. 120p. (Orig.). 1985. pap. 3.95 (ISBN 0-935797-18-1). Harvest IL.
Skoglund, John E. The Baptists. 1967. pap. 1.50 (ISBN 0-8170-0386-X). Judson.
Skogsbergh, Helga. From These Shores. (Illus.). 1975. pap. 1.50 (ISBN 0-910452-22-9). Covenant.
Skold, Betty W. I'm Glad You're Open Weekdays: Everyday Prayers to the God Who Works Between Sundays. LC 85-3923. 112p. (Orig.). 1985. pap. 5.95 (ISBN 0-8066-2129-X, 10-3201). Augsburg.
--The Kids Are Gone, Lord, but I'm Still Here: Prayers for Mothers. LC 80-67801. 96p. (Orig.). 1981. pap. 5.95 (ISBN 0-8066-1863-9, 10-3703). Augsburg.
--Lord, I Need an Answer: Story Devotions for Girls. LC 81-52279. 112p. (Orig.). 1982. pap. 3.95 (ISBN 0-8066-1911-2, 10-4099). Augsburg.
Skoor, Susan. Christian Education in the Family. 1984. pap. text ed. 6.00 (ISBN 0-8309-0392-5). Herald Hse.
Skoss, Solomon, ed. Hebrew-Arabic Dictionary of the Bible Known As Kitab Jami-Al-Alfaz, 2 vols. (Yale Oriental Researches Ser.: No. XX, XXI). (Hebrew & Arabic.). 1945. 50.00x ea.; 95.00x set (ISBN 0-686-57837-6). Elliots Bks.
Skoss, Solomon L., ed. see David Ben Abraham.
Skousen, Cleon W. Isaiah Speaks to Modern Times. 800p. 1984. 15.95 (ISBN 0-910558-25-6). Ensign Pub.
Skousen, W. Cleon. The First Two Thousand Years. 1953. 8.95 (ISBN 0-88494-029-2). Bookcraft Inc.
--The Fourth Thousand Years. LC 66-29887. 1966. 13.95 (ISBN 0-88494-147-7). Bookcraft Inc.
--The Third Thousand Years. 1964. 12.95 (ISBN 0-88494-122-1). Bookcraft Inc.
Skudlarek, William. The Word in Worship. LC 80-25525. (Abingdon Preacher's Library). 128p. (Orig.). 1981. pap. 6.95 (ISBN 0-687-46131-6). Abingdon.
Skudlarek, William, ed. The Continuing Quest for God: Monastic Spirituality in Tradition & Transition. LC 81-23614. x, 302p. (Orig.). 1982. pap. 8.95 (ISBN 0-8146-1235-0). Liturgical Pr.
Skurski, Roger. New Directions in Economic Justice. LC 83-1254. 304p. 1983. text ed. 20.95x (ISBN 0-268-01460-4, 85-14606); pap. text ed. 10.95x (ISBN 0-268-01461-2, 85-14614). U of Notre Dame Pr.
Slaate, Howard A. Contemporary Philosophies of Religion. LC 86-13148. 252p. (Orig.). 1986. pap. text ed. 14.50 (ISBN 0-8191-5492-X). U Pr of Amer.
Slaatte, Howard A. Fire in the Brand: An Introduction to the Creative Work & Theology of John Wesley. LC 83-16721. 158p. 1983. pap. text ed. 11.25 (ISBN 0-8191-3552-6). U Pr of Amer.
--The Seven Ecumenical Councils. LC 80-5755. 55p. 1980. pap. text ed. 7.25 (ISBN 0-8191-1204-6). U Pr of Amer.
--Time & Its End: A Comparative Existential Interpretation of Time & Eschatology. LC 80-7814. 298p. 1980. pap. text ed. 13.25 (ISBN 0-8191-1070-1). U Pr of Amer.
Slack, Kenneth. The United Reformed Church. 1978. pap. 3.15 (ISBN 0-08-021414-2). Pergamon.
Slack, S. B. Early Christianity. 94p. 1914. 0.95 (ISBN 0-317-40436-9). Open Court.
Sladden, John C. Boniface of Devon: Apostle of Germany. 254p. 1980. text ed. 18.75 (ISBN 0-85364-275-3). Attic Pr.
Slade, Afton, jt. auth. see Lande, Nathaniel.
Slafter, Edmund F. & Slafter, Edmund F., eds. John Checkley, or, Evolution of Religious Tolerance in Massachusetts, 2 vols. (Prince Soc. Pubns: Nos. 22 & 23). 1966. 39.00 (ISBN 0-8337-0553-9). B Franklin.
Slater, G. The Dravidian Element in Indian Culture. (Illus.). 192p. 1986. Repr. 14.00X (ISBN 0-8364-1706-2, Pub. by Manohar India). South Asia Bks.
Slater, Herman, ed. A Book of Pagan Rituals, Vol. 1. 1978. pap. 9.95 (ISBN 0-87728-348-6). Weiser.
Slater, John, jt. auth. see Smith, T. Roger.
Slater, Michael. Stretcher Bearers. LC 85-8389. 168p. 1985. pap. write for info. (ISBN 0-8307-1044-2, 5418505). Regal.
Slater, Michael & Nachtrieb, Eric. Stretcher Bearers. 64p. 1985. pap. 3.95 (ISBN 0-8307-1056-6, 6102137). Regal.
Slater, Peter. The Dynamics of Religion: Meaning & Change in Religious Traditions. LC 78-4426. 1978. pap. 6.95x (ISBN 0-685-53934-2, RD 280, HarpR). Har-Row.
Slater, Peter, ed. Religion & Culture in Canada. 568p. pap. text ed. 9.75x (ISBN 0-919812-06-6, Pub. by Wilfrid Laurier Canada). Humanities.
Slater, Peter G. Children in the New England Mind: In Death & in Life. LC 77-7352. 248p. 1977. 27.50 (ISBN 0-208-01652-X, Archon). Shoe String.
Slater, Philip. Footholds: Understanding the Shifting Family & Sexual Tensions in Our Culture. LC 77-12124. 1978. 13.95x (ISBN 0-8070-4160-2). Beacon Pr.
Slater, Philip E. Glory of Hera: Greek Mythology & the Greek Family. LC 68-24373. 540p. 1985. pap. 14.95x (ISBN 0-8070-5795-9, BPA12, Pub. by Ariadne Bks). Beacon Pr.
Slater, Robert. Great Jews in Sports. LC 82-19953. (Illus.). 304p. 1983. 14.95 (ISBN 0-8246-0285-4). Jonathan David.
Slater, Robert H. World Religions & World Community. LC 63-9805. (Lectures on the History of Religions Ser.: No. 6). 1963. 28.00x (ISBN 0-231-02615-3). Columbia U Pr.
Slater, Rosalie J. Teaching & Learning America's Christian History. LC 65-26334. 1965. lib. bdg. 10.00 (ISBN 0-912498-02-1). Found Am Christ.
Slater, Samuel. Keynes Schumpeter & the Effort to Save Capitalism from Total Collapse. (Illus.). 137p. 1984. 93.00x (ISBN 0-86654-134-9). Inst Econ Finan.
Slater, Wallace. Raja Yoga: A Simplified & Practical Course. LC 71-3051. 1969. pap. 4.50 (ISBN 0-8356-0131-5, Quest). Theos Pub Hse.
--Simplified Course in Hatha Yoga. 1967. pap. 2.75 (ISBN 0-8356-0138-2, Quest). Theos Pub Hse.
Slatoff, Walter J. The Look of Distance: Reflections on Suffering & Sympathy in Modern Literature - Auden to Agee, Whitman to Woolf. LC 85-10447. 309p. 1985. 25.00x (ISBN 0-8142-0385-X). Ohio St U Pr.
Slatte, Howard A. The Paradox of Existentialist Theology: The Dialectics of a Faith-Subsumed Reason-in-Existence. LC 81-43508. 272p. 1982. lib. bdg. 29.00 (ISBN 0-8191-2187-8); pap. text ed. 13.25 (ISBN 0-8191-2188-6). U Pr of Amer.
Slattery, Kathryn, jt. auth. see Blackwood, Cheryl P.
Slattery, Kathryn, jt. auth. see Wilson, William P.
Slaughter, James N., Jr. & Jackson, David J. Where Grown Men Cry: An Endeavor to Free the Spirit. LC 86-32665. (Illus.). 176p. 1986. pap. 12.95 (ISBN 0-9617749-0-8). Cormac Inc.
Slavens, Thomas P. Theological Libraries at Oxford. 160p. 1984. pap. text ed. 32.50 (ISBN 3-598-10563-0). K G Saur.
Slavens, Thomas P., jt. ed. see Wilson, John F.
Slavin, Stephen L. & Pradt, Mary A. The Einstein Syndrome: Corporate Anti-Semitism in America Today. LC 81-43767. (Illus., Orig.). 1982. lib. bdg. 26.25 (ISBN 0-8191-2370-6); pap. text ed. 11.25 (ISBN 0-8191-2371-4). U Pr of Amer.
Slavitz, Harriet, ed. see Lad, Vasant.
Slawson, Douglas J., jt. auth. see Poole, Stafford.
Slay, James L. Esto Creemos Curzo de Doctrina Biblica Para Ninos. (Span., Orig.). pap. 1.00 (ISBN 0-87148-311-4). Pathway Pr.
--Rescue the Perishing. 1961. 6.95 (ISBN 0-87148-729-2). Pathway Pr.
--This We Believe. 1963. pap. 4.95 (ISBN 0-87148-832-9). Pathway Pr.
Slay, James L., ed. Esto Creemos. (Span.). 156p. 1963. pap. 4.95 (ISBN 0-87148-309-2). Pathway Pr.
Sledge, Linda C. Shivering Babe, Victorious Lord: The Nativity in Poetry & Art. LC 81-9728. pap. 49.80 (ISBN 0-317-30162-4, 2025344). Bks Demand UMI.
Sleeman, Margaret, tr. see Meredith, Peter & Tailby, John.
Sleeper, C. Freeman & Spivey, Robert A. The Study of Religion in Two-Year Colleges. LC 75-28158. (American Academy of Religion, Individual Volumes). 1975. pap. 8.95 (ISBN 0-89130-031-7, 010801). Scholars Pr GA.
Sleeper, Sarah. Memoir of the Late Martha Hazeltine Smith. Gifford, Carolyn D. & Dayton, Donald, eds. (Women in American Protestant Religion 1800-1930 Ser.). 294p. 1987. lib. bdg. 40.00 (ISBN 0-8240-0686-0). Garland Pub.
Sleeth, Natalie. Adventures for the Soul. 139p. 1987. pap. 5.95 (ISBN 0-916642-30-5, 785). Hope Pub.
Sleeth, Ronald E. God's Word & Our Words: Basic Homiletics. LC 85-23777. 120p. (Orig.). 1986. pap. 7.95 (ISBN 0-8042-1577-4). John Knox.
--Look Who's Talking: A Guide for Lay Speakers in the Church. LC 77-1171. 1982. pap. 5.50 (ISBN 0-687-22630-9). Abingdon.
--Persuasive Preaching. LC 55-8527. viii, 96p. 1981. pap. 4.95 (ISBN 0-943872-81-2). Andrews Univ Pr.
Sleigh, Bernard. Witchcraft. 69.95 (ISBN 0-8490-1311-9). Gordon Pr.
Slemming, Charles W. Bible Digest. LC 68-27671. 906p. 1975. 27.95 (ISBN 0-8254-3706-7). Kregel.
--Bible Digest Charts. LC 64-17168. 1974. pap. 12.95 (ISBN 0-8254-3701-6). Kregel.
--Made According to Pattern. 1964. pap. 2.95 (ISBN 0-87508-506-7). Chr Lit.
--These Are the Garments. 1963. pap. 2.95 (ISBN 0-87508-507-5). Chr Lit.
--Thus Shalt Thou Serve. 1966. pap. 2.95 (ISBN 0-87508-508-3). Chr Lit.
Slesinski, Robert. Pavel Florensky: A Metaphysics of Love. LC 83-27130. 256p. 1984. pap. text ed. 12.95 (ISBN 0-88141-032-2). St Vladimirs.
Slingerland, H. Dixon. The Testaments of the Twelve Patriarchs: A Critical History of Research. LC 75-34233. (Society of Biblical Literature. Monograph). 1977. 13.50 (ISBN 0-89130-084-8, 060021); pap. 9.95 (ISBN 0-89130-062-7). Scholars Pr GA.
Slive, Seymour, ed. see Rembrandt.
Sloan, Frank, ed. see Lawton, Clive.
Sloan, Irving J. The Jews in America 1621-1977: A Chronology & Fact Book. 2nd ed. LC 77-26768. (No. 3). 1978. lib. bdg. 8.50 (ISBN 0-379-00530-1). Oceana.
Sloan, J., ed. see Scott, Latayne.
Sloan, John, ed. see Edwards, Judson.
Sloan, John, ed. see Estes, Steve & Estes, Verna.
Sloan, Johnny W., jt. auth. see Vaughn, Nancy R.
Sloan, Robert B. The Favorable Year of the Lord: A Study of Jubilary Theology in the Gospel of Luke. 213p. (Orig.). 1977. pap. 6.95 (ISBN 0-931016-02-9). Schola Pr TX.
Sloan, W. H. & Lerin, A. Concordancia Alfabetica De la Biblia. 1024p. 1981. pap. 14.95 (ISBN 0-311-42054-0). Casa Bautista.
Sloane, Kennedy W. John Greenleaf Whittier: His Life, Genius & Writings. 373p. 1982. Repr. of 1903 ed. lib. bdg. 25.00 (ISBN 0-89760-432-6). Telegraph Bks.
Sloane, Thomas O. Donne, Milton, & the End of Humanist Rhetoric. LC 83-24315. 1985. 38.50x (ISBN 0-520-05212-9). U of Cal Pr.
Sloat, John W. Lord, Make Us One. 144p. 1986. pap. 7.95 (ISBN 0-8170-1101-3). Judson.
Sloath, Donald E. The Dangers of Growing up in a Christian Home. 224p. 1986. pap. 8.95 (ISBN 0-8407-3064-0). Nelson.

Slobin, Mark, ed. Old Jewish Folk Music: The Collections & Writings of Moshe Beregovski. LC 81-43526. (Illus.). 640p. (Orig.). 1982. 45.00x (ISBN 0-8122-7833-X); pap. 18.95x (ISBN 0-8122-1126-X). U of Pa Pr.

Slochower, Harry. Mythopoesis: Mythic Patterns in the Literary Classics. LC 96-11337. (Waynebooks Ser: No. 35). 363p. 1970. 29.95x (ISBN 0-8143-1395-7); pap. text ed. 9.95x (ISBN 0-8143-1511-9). Wayne St U Pr.

--Three Ways of Modern Man. LC 37-17328. 1968. Repr. of 1937 ed. 20.00 (ISBN 0-527-83656-7). Kraus Repr.

Slocum, Robert. Ordinary Christians in a High-Tech World. 224p. 1986. 10.95 (ISBN 0-8499-0490-0, 0490-0); pap. 9.95 (ISBN 0-8499-3046-4). Word Bks.

Slomowitz, Samuel W. Jesus Christ-Sam. 1987. 7.95 (ISBN 0-533-07158-5). Vantage.

Slonimsky, Henry. Essays. 10.00x (ISBN 0-87068-884-7). Ktav.

Slosser, Bob. Miracle in Darien. LC 79-83791. 1979. 5.95 (ISBN 0-88270-355-2). Bridge Pub.

Slosser, Bob, jt. auth. see Atkins, Susan.

Slosser, Bob, jt. auth. see Robertson, Pat.

Slosson, Edwin E. Major Prophets of To-Day. facs. ed. LC 68-8493. (Essay Index Reprint Ser.). 1914. 20.00 (ISBN 0-8369-0882-1). Ayer Co Pubs.

--Six Major Prophets. facsimile ed. LC 71-167421. (Essay Index Reprint Ser). Repr. of 1917 ed. 23.00 (ISBN 0-8369-2571-8). Ayer Co Pubs.

Slote, Michael. Common-Sense Morality & Consequentialism. (International Library of Philosophy). 160p. 1985. 24.95x (ISBN 0-7102-0309-8). Methuen Inc.

Slotkin, Richard & Folsom, James K., eds. So Dreadful a Judgment: Puritan Responses to King Philip's War, 1676-1677. LC 77-14847. 1978. 27.00x (ISBN 0-8195-5027-2); pap. 13.00x (ISBN 0-8195-6058-8). Wesleyan U Pr.

Slover, Luella, ed. Life after Youth. 1981. pap. 4.50 (ISBN 0-8309-0303-8). Herald Hse.

Slover, Luella H. Ministry with Young Adults. 1980. pap. 4.00 (ISBN 0-8309-0283-X). Herald Hse.

Slover, Luella H., ed. Ministry with the Confined. (Orig.). 1981. pap. 4.50 (ISBN 0-8309-0318-6). Herald Hse.

Sloyan, Gerard. Rejoice & Take It Away: Sunday Preaching from the Scriptures, 2 vols. 1984. 15.00 (ISBN 0-89453-381-9). M Glazier.

Sloyan, Gerard S. Advent-Christmas. LC 84-18756. (Proclamation 3 C Ser.). 64p. 1985. pap. 3.75 (ISBN 0-8006-4125-6). Fortress.

--Commentary on the New Lectionary. LC 75-22781. 444p. 1975. pap. 11.95 (ISBN 0-8091-1895-5). Paulist Pr.

--Is Christ the End of the Law? LC 77-27454. (Biblical Perspectives on Current Issues). 210p. 1978. softcover 4.95 (ISBN 0-664-24190-5). Westminster.

--Jesus in Focus: A Life in Its Setting. 207p. (Orig.). 1983. pap. 7.95 (ISBN 0-89622-191-1). Twenty-Third.

--Jesus on Trial: The Development of the Passion Narratives & Their Historical & Ecumenical Implications. (Illus.). 156p. pap. 3.75 (ISBN 0-686-95173-5). ADL.

--The Jesus Tradition: Images of Jesus in the West. 128p. (Orig.). 1986. pap. 5.95 (ISBN 0-89622-285-3). Twenty-Third.

--Worshipful Preaching. LC 83-48911. (Fortress Resources for Preaching Ser.). 80p. 1984. pap. 3.95 (ISBN 0-8006-1781-9, 1-1781). Fortress.

Sloyan, Gerard S., jt. ed. see Swidler, Leonard.

Sloyan, Virginia, ed. Signs, Songs & Stories. (Illus.). 160p. 1982. pap. 8.50 (ISBN 0-8146-1285-7). Liturgical Pr.

Sloyan, Virginia, jt. ed. see Huck, Gabe.

Sluglett, Peter, compiled by. Theses on Islam, Middle East, & Northwest Africa, 1880-1978. 160p. 1983. 27.00x (ISBN 0-7201-1651-1). Mansell.

Slusser, Gerald H. From Jung to Jesus: Myth & Consciousness in the New Testament. LC 85-45792. 180p. 1986. pap. 10.95 (ISBN 0-8042-1111-6). John Knox.

Smail, R. C. Crusading Warfare, 1097-1193: A Contribution to Medieval Military History. LC 67-26956. (Cambridge Studies in Medieval Life & Thought Ser: No. 3). 1967. pap. 16.95 (ISBN 0-521-09730-4). Cambridge U Pr.

Smail, T. A. see Calvin, John.

Small, Dwight H. Marriage As Equal Partnership. 1980. pap. 3.95 (ISBN 0-8010-8177-7). Baker Bk.

--No Rival Love. 201p. (Orig.). 1985. pap. 4.95 (ISBN 0-87508-495-8). Chr Lit.

--Remarriage & God's Renewing Grace. 184p. 1986. pap. 7.95 (ISBN 0-8010-8264-1). Baker Bk.

--Your Marriage Is God's Affair. 352p. 1979. pap. 7.95 (ISBN 0-8007-5024-1, Power Bks): Revell.

Small, Emmett, ed. see De Purucker, G.

Small, Emmett, ed. see Wright, Leoline L., et al.

Small, Jacquelyn. Transformers-The Therapists of the Future. 272p. 1984. pap. 11.95 (ISBN 0-87516-529-X). De Vorss.

Small, Jocelyn P. Cacus & Marsyas in Etrusco-Roman Legend. LC 82-47614. (Princeton Monographs in Art & Archaeology: No. 45). (Illus.). 208p. 1982. 31.50x (ISBN 0-691-03562-8). Princeton U Pr.

Small, John, ed. English Metrical Homilies from Manuscripts of the Fourteenth Century. LC 79-178504. Repr. of 1862 ed. 22.50 (ISBN 0-404-56674-X). AMS Pr.

Small, Leonard R. No Other Name. 192p. 1966. 12.95 (ISBN 0-567-02257-9, Pub. by T & T Clark Ltd UK). Fortress.

Small, Lucile J. Not by Prescription. 64p. pap. 3.50 (ISBN 0-686-82633-7). Review & Herald.

Small, T. A., tr. see Barth, Karl, et al.

Small, W. Emmett, ed. see Benjamin, Elsie.

Small, W. Emmett, ed. see De Purucker, G. & Tingley, Katherine.

Small, W. Emmett, ed. see De Zirkoff, Boris.

Small, W. Emmett, ed. see Edge, Henry T.

Small, W. Emmett, ed. see Ryan, Charles J.

Small, W. Emmett, ed. see Tingley, Katherine.

Small, W. Emmett, ed. see Van Pelt, G.

Small, W. Emmett, ed. see Van Pelt, Gertrude W.

Small, W. Emmett, ed. see Wright, Leoline L.

Smalley, Beryl. Study of the Bible in the Middle Ages. 1964. pap. 9.95x (ISBN 0-268-00267-3). U of Notre Dame Pr.

Smalley, Gary. Joy That Lasts: How to Have an Overflowing Life. 144p. 1986. pap. 11.95 (ISBN 0-310-46290-8, 18254). Zondervan.

--The Key to Your Child's Heart. 160p. 1984. 10.95 (ISBN 0-8499-0433-1, 0433-1). Word Bks.

Smalley, Gary & Scott, Steve. For Better or for Best. 160p. 1982. pap. 5.95 (ISBN 0-310-44871-9, 18246P). Zondervan.

--If Only He Knew: A Valuable Guide to Knowing, Understanding, & Loving Your Wife. 144p. 1982. pap. 5.95 (ISBN 0-310-44881-6, 18247P). Zondervan.

--The Joy of Committed Love: A Valuable Guide to Knowing, Understanding & Loving Each Other. LC 83-18248. 336p. 1984. 12.95 (ISBN 0-310-44900-6, 18248). Zondervan.

Smalley, Gary & Trent, John. The Blessing: Giving & Gaining Family Approval. 224p. 1986. pap. text ed. 14.95 (ISBN 0-8407-3066-7). Nelson.

Smalley, Gary, et al. Decide to Love. 64p. (Orig.). 1985. tchr's. manual 19.95 (ISBN 0-310-44861-1, 18249P); student's manual 2.95 (ISBN 0-310-44331-8, 18253P). Zondervan.

Smalley, S. S., jt. auth. see Lindars, B.

Smalley, Stephen S. John: Evangelist & Interpreter. 285p. 1983. cancelled; pap. 10.95 (ISBN 0-85364-345-8). Attic Pr.

Smalley, W. A., jt. auth. see De Waard, J.

Smalley, William A., ed. Readings in Missionary Anthropology II. 2nd rev. enl. ed. LC 78-6009. (Applied Cultural Anthropology Ser.). 1978. pap. text ed. 13.95x (ISBN 0-87808-731-1). William Carey.

Smalley, William A., ed. see Loewen, Jacob A.

Smallwood, E. Mary, ed. see Josephus, Flavius.

Smally, Beryl. Studies in Medieval Thought & Learning from Abelard to Wyclif. (Illus.). 455p. 1982. 45.00 (ISBN 0-9506882-6-6). Hambledon Press.

Smarananda, Swami. The Story of Ramakrishna. (Illus., Orig.). 1976. pap. 2.25 (ISBN 0-87481-168-6). Vedanta Pr.

Smart, James D. The Cultural Subversion of the Biblical Faith: Life in the 20th Century under the Sign of the Cross. LC 77-22063. 126p. 1977. pap. 5.95 (ISBN 0-664-24148-4). Westminster.

--The Past, Present, & Future of Biblical Theology. LC 79-16943. 162p. 1979. softcover 8.95 (ISBN 0-664-24284-7). Westminster.

--The Rebirth of Ministry: A Study of the Biblical Character of the Church's Ministry. LC 60-6189. 192p. 1978. pap. 4.95 (ISBN 0-664-24206-5). Westminster.

--The Strange Silence of the Bible in the Church: A Study in Hermeneutics. LC 72-118323. 184p. 1970. pap. 8.95 (ISBN 0-664-24894-2). Westminster.

--The Teaching Ministry of the Church: An Examination of Basic Principles of Christian Education. LC 54-10569. 208p. 1971. pap. 6.95 (ISBN 0-664-24910-8). Westminster.

Smart, James D., jt. ed. see Olin, John C.

Smart, Ninian. Concept & Empathy. Wiebe, Donald, ed. LC 85-18957. 240p. 1986. 35.00. NYU Pr.

--A Dialogue of Religions. LC 79-8730. (The Library of Philosophy & Theology). 142p. 1981. Repr. of 1960 ed. lib. bdg. 22.50x (ISBN 0-313-22187-1, SMDR). Greenwood.

--The Philosophy of Religion. 1979. pap. 7.95x (ISBN 0-19-520139-6). Oxford U Pr.

--Religion & the Western Mind. 1986. 39.50 (ISBN 0-88706-382-9); pap. 12.95 (ISBN 0-88706-383-7). State U NY Pr.

--The Religious Experience of Mankind. 3rd ed. (Scribner Press Ser.). (Illus.). 656p. 1984. 30.00 (ISBN 0-684-18077-4, ScribT). Scribner.

--The Religious Experience of Mankind. 3rd ed. LC 83-20169. (Illus.). 634p. 1984. pap. text ed. 17.95 (ISBN 0-02-412130-4, Pub. by Scribner). Macmillan.

--The Science of Religion & the Sociology of Knowledge: Some Methodological Questions. LC 72-12115. 176p. 1973. 20.00x (ISBN 0-691-07191-8); pap. 8.50x (ISBN 0-691-01997-5). Princeton U Pr.

--Teacher & Christian Belief. 208p. 1966. 6.95 (ISBN 0-227-67703-X). Attic Pr.

--Worldviews. LC 82-16877. 190p. 1983. pap. 7.95x (ISBN 0-684-17812-5). Scribner.

--Worldviews: Crosscultural Explorations in Human Beliefs. (Illus.). 224p. 1983. 13.95 (ISBN 0-684-17811-7, ScribT). Scribner.

Smart, Ninian & Hecht, Richard. Sacred Texts of the World. 496p. 1984. pap. 16.95 (ISBN 0-8245-0639-1). Crossroad NY.

Smart, Ninian & Purnananda, Swami. Prophet of the New Hindu Age: The Life & Times of Archarya Pranavananda. (Illus.). 256p. 1985. 15.00 (ISBN 0-04-922032-2); pap. 9.50 (ISBN 0-04-922033-0). Allen Unwin.

Smart, Ninian see Merkl, Peter H.

Smart, Ninian & Hecht, Richard, eds. Sacred Texts of the World: A Universal Anthology. LC 82-7375. 1982. 27.50x (ISBN 0-8245-0483-6). Crossroad NY.

Smart, Ninian & Hecht, Richard B., eds. Sacred Texts of the World: A Universal Anthology. (Illus.). 496p. 1987. pap. 17.00 (ISBN 0-8334-1001-6, Freedeeds Bks). Garber Comm.

Smart, Ninian, ed. see Jayatilleke, K. N.

Smart, Ninian, et al. Nineteenth Century Religious Thought in the West, Vols. 2 & 3. 368p. Vol. 2, 08/1985. 49.50 (ISBN 0-521-22832-8); Vol. 3, 10/1985. 49.50 (ISBN 0-521-30114-9). Cambridge U Pr.

Smart, Ninian, et al, eds. Nineteenth Century Religious Thought in the West, Vol. 1. 350p. 1985. 49.50 (ISBN 0-521-22831-X). Cambridge U Pr.

Smart, Peter. The Vanitie & Downe-Fall of Superstitious Popish Ceremonies. LC 77-7428. (English Experience Ser.: No. 894). 1977. Repr. of 1628 ed. lib. bdg. 6.00 (ISBN 90-221-0894-5). Walter J Johnson.

Smart, Thomas B. Bibliography of Matthew Arnold, Eighteen Ninety-Two. 1974. lib. bdg. 18.50 (ISBN 0-8414-7634-9). Folcroft.

Smead, Jane. Chateaubriand et la Bible, Contribution a L'etude Des Sources Des "Martyrs". 1973. Repr. of 1924 ed. 15.00 (ISBN 0-384-56347-3). Johnson Repr.

Smeaton, George. Doctrine of the Holy Spirit. 1980. 15.95 (ISBN 0-85151-187-2). Banner of Truth.

Smedes, Lewis. Sexologia para Cristianos. Sanchez, Jorge, tr. from Eng. Tr. of Sex for Christians. 288p. 1982. pap. 5.95 (ISBN 0-89922-175-0). Edit Caribe.

Smedes, Lewis B. How Can It Be All Right When Everything Is All Wrong. LC 82-47756. 128p. (Orig.). 1982. pap. 6.95 (ISBN 0-06-067409-1, RD398, HarpR). Har-Row.

--Love Within Limits: A Realist's View of I Corinthians 13. 1978. pap. 4.95 (ISBN 0-8028-1753-X). Eerdmans.

--Mere Morality: What God Expects from Ordinary People. 292p. 1987. pap. 9.95 (ISBN 0-8028-0257-5). Eerdmans.

--Sex for Christians. 176p. 1976. pap. 5.95 (ISBN 0-8028-1618-5). Eerdmans.

--Union with Christ: A Biblical View of the New Life in Jesus Christ. rev. ed. Orig. Title: All Things Made New. 208p. 1983. pap. 4.95 (ISBN 0-8028-1963-X). Eerdmans.

Smedes, Lewis B., ed. see Verkuyl, Johannes.

Smeeton, Donald. Lollard Themes in Reformation Theology of William Tyndale. (Sixteenth Century Essays & Studies: Vol. VI). (Illus.). 240p. 1986. smyth sewn 30.00x (ISBN 0-940474-06-9). Sixteenth Cent.

Smelser, Georgia. Nathaniel A. Urshan: Champion of the Faith & Legend in Our Time. (Illus.). 160p. (Orig.). 1985. pap. 15.00 (ISBN 0-912315-95-4). Word Aflame.

--OMA. LC 85-31579. (Illus.). 254p. (Orig.). 1981. pap. 5.95 (ISBN 0-912315-16-4). Word Aflame.

Smelser, Georgia & Enloe, Eilene. Two Hundred Two Bulletin Boards for All Ages. LC 85-26522. (Illus.). 176p. (Orig.). 1986. pap. 5.50 (ISBN 0-912315-96-2). Word Aflame.

Smelser, Georgia & Westberg, Barbara. Fifty-Two Visualized Talks for Children's Church. (Illus., Orig.). 1981. pap. 4.50 tchr's ed (ISBN 0-912315-13-X). Word Aflame.

Smet, Pierre J. De see De Smet, Pierre J.

Smet, Pierre-Jean De see De Smet, Pierre-Jean.

Smiley, Emma. Bread of Life. 1972. pap. 1.00 (ISBN 0-87516-157-X). De Vorss.

--Search for Certainty. 1972. pap. 2.50 (ISBN 0-87516-159-6). De Vorss.

Smirnoff, Eugene. Russian Orthodox Missions. pap. 8.95 (ISBN 0-686-01299-2). Eastern Orthodox.

Smirnoff, Peter. Instruction in God's Law. 1974. pap. 5.00 (ISBN 0-686-10199-5). Eastern Orthodox.

Smirnov, P. S. Istoriia Russkago Raskola Starobriadstva. 314p. Repr. of 1895 ed. text ed. 62.10x (ISBN 0-576-99245-3, Pub. by Gregg Intl Pubs England). Gregg Intl.

Smirnov, S. Drevne-Russkii Dukhovnik: Izsledovnatie Po Istorii Tserkovnago Byta. 870p. Repr. of 1914 ed. text ed. 74.52 (ISBN 0-576-99178-3, Pub. by Gregg Intl Pubs England). Gregg Intl.

Smit, John. Saint Pius the Tenth. 1965. 4.00 (ISBN 0-8198-0140-2); pap. 3.00 (ISBN 0-8198-0141-0). Dghtrs St Paul.

Smit, William, jt. auth. see DeJong, Peter.

Smith. Christian Secret of a Happy Life. 2.50 (ISBN 0-318-18169-X). WCTU.

--Spiritual Living. 1978. pap. 2.95 (ISBN 0-8423-6410-2). Tyndale.

Smith & Smith. Growing Love in Christian Marriage: Pastors's Manual. 1981. pap. 4.75 (ISBN 0-687-15930-X). Abingdon.

Smith, Adam. The Theory of Moral Sentiments. (Glasgow Edition of the Works & Correspondence of Adam Smith Ser.). (Illus.). 1976. 54.00x (ISBN 0-19-828189-7). Oxford U Pr.

Smith, Adeline, jt. auth. see Meredith, Howard.

Smith, Agnes, jt. auth. see Waddell, Genny.

Smith, Alfred J. Deacon's Upholding the Pastor's Arms. 96p. 1983. pap. 4.00 (ISBN 0-686-46044-8). Prog Bapt Pub.

Smith, Alvin O. There is a Solution. 1983. 5.95 (ISBN 0-8062-1951-3). Carlton.

Smith, Amanda. Autobiography. LC 71-99407. 1969. Repr. of 1893 ed. lib. bdg. 25.00 (ISBN 0-8411-0080-2). Metro Bks.

Smith, Amanda B. An Autobiography: The Story of the Lord's Dealings with Mrs. Amanda Smith, The Colored Evangelist, Containing an Account of Her Life Work of Faith, & Her Travels in America, England, Ireland, Scotland, India & Africa, as an Independent Missionary. Gifford, Carolyn D. & Dayton, Donald, eds. (Women in American Protestant Religion 1800-1930 Ser.). 506p. 1987. lib. bdg. 70.00 (ISBN 0-8240-0674-7). Garland Pub.

Smith, Angela, jt. auth. see Singh, Daljit.

Smith, Antoinette & Smith, Leon. Preparing for Christian Marriage: Pastor's Edition. LC 80-28001. 112p. 1982. 7.75 (ISBN 0-687-33918-9). Abingdon.

Smith, Arthur L. Church & State in the Middle Ages. new ed. 245p. 1964. 28.50x (ISBN 0-7146-1514-5, F Cass Co). Biblio Dist.

Smith, Austine. Haiti Is Waiting. 78p. 1985. pap. 3.50 (ISBN 0-88144-035-3). Christian Pub.

--If That Isn't Love. 132p. 1985. pap. 5.95 (ISBN 0-88144-036-1). Christian Pub.

Smith, B., jt. ed. see Constable, G.

Smith, B. W. Jacques Maritain, Antimodern or Ultramodern? 1976. 27.95 (ISBN 0-444-99013-5, SIM/, Pub. by Elsevier). Greenwood.

Smith, Bailey E. Nothing but the Blood. (Orig.). 1987. pap. 6.95 (ISBN 0-8054-1537-8). Broadman.

--Real Christianity. LC 79-50336. 1980. 9.95 (ISBN 0-8054-5168-4). Broadman.

--Real Evangelism. LC 77-92283. 1978. 8.95 (ISBN 0-8054-6220-1). Broadman.

--Real Revival Preaching. LC 81-86667. 1982. 8.50 (ISBN 0-8054-6235-X). Broadman.

Smith, Barbara. The Westminster Concise Bible Dictionary. LC 80-25771. (Illus.). 188p. 1981. pap. 5.95 (ISBN 0-664-24363-0). Westminster.

Smith, Bardwell L., ed. Religion & Legitimation of Power in Sri Lanka. LC 77-7449. 1978. pap. 7.95 (ISBN 0-89012-008-0). Anima Pubns.

--Religion & Legitimation of Power in Thailand, Laos & Burma. LC 77-7444. 1978. pap. 7.95 (ISBN 0-89012-009-9). Anima Pubns.

Smith, Barrie & Smith, Ruth. Youth Ministries Handbook. 120p. 1984. pap. text ed. 12.50 (ISBN 0-8309-0402-6). Herald Hse.

Smith, Bert K. Aging in America. LC 72-6232. 256p. 1973. pap. 5.95 (ISBN 0-8070-2769-3, BP502). Beacon Pr.

Smith, Bertha. Go Home & Tell. LC 65-10342. (Orig.). 1964. pap. 5.50 (ISBN 0-8054-7202-9). Broadman.

--How the Spirit Filled My Life. LC 73-87068. 7.50 (ISBN 0-8054-5540-X). Broadman.

--Our Lost World. LC 80-68537. 1981. pap. 4.95 (ISBN 0-8054-6324-0). Broadman.

Smith, Betsy. Breakthrough: Women in Religion. LC 78-3016. (Breakthrough Ser.). 1978. 7.95 (ISBN 0-8027-6286-7). Walker & Co.

Smith, Betty, ed. see Eisenhower, David & Murray, John.

Smith, Billy K. Layman's Bible Book Commentary: Vol. 13 Hosea, Joel, Amos, Abadiah, Jonah. LC 80-68536. 1982. 5.95 (ISBN 0-8054-1183-6). Broadman.

Smith, Bradford. Dear Gift of Life: A Man's Encounter with Death. LC 65-24496. (Orig.). 1965. pap. 2.50x (ISBN 0-87574-142-8). Pendle Hill.

Smith, Brian H. The Church & Politics in Chile: Challenges to Modern Catholicism. LC 81-47951. 416p. 1982. 37.00x (ISBN 0-691-07629-4); pap. 13.50x L.P.E. (ISBN 0-691-10119-1). Princeton U Pr.

Smith, C. Henry. Story of the Mennonites. Krahn, Cornelius, ed. LC 81-65130. (Illus.). 589p. 1981. pap. 17.95 (ISBN 0-87303-069-9). Faith & Life.

Smith, C. Henry, jt. ed. see Bender, Harold S.

Smith, Carl T. Chinese Christians: Elites, Middlemen, & the Church in Hong Kong. (Illus.). 264p. 1986. 27.00x (ISBN 0-19-583973-0). Oxford U Pr.

Smith, Carleton S., ed. Psalmody in Seventeenth Century America: Series 1, the Ainsworth Psalter. price on application (ISBN 0-685-18958-9, Dist. by C. F. Peters Corp). NY Pub Lib.

Smith, Carolyn. Rebirth of Music: Training Course. 76p. 1985. pap. 4.95 (ISBN 0-938612-10-7). Revival Press.

Smith, Charles, jt. auth. see Bolton, Barbara.

Smith, Charles D. Islam & the Search for Social Order in Modern Egypt: A Biography of Muhammad Husayn Haykal. (Middle East Studies). 256p. 1983. 49.50 (ISBN 0-87395-710-5); pap. 18.95 (ISBN 0-87395-711-3). State U NY Pr.

Smith, Charles E. Innocent Three, Church Defender. LC 79-88939. 1971. Repr. of 1951 ed. lib. bdg. 55.00x (ISBN 0-8371-3145-6, SMIN). Greenwood.

--Papal Enforcement of Some Medieval Marriage Laws. LC 40-12564. pap. 59.30 (ISBN 0-317-28663-3, 2055314). Bks Demand UMI.

Smith, Charles H. The Coming of the Russian Mennonites: An Episode in the Settling of the Last Frontier, 1874-1884. 18.25 (ISBN 0-8369-7123-X, 7957). Ayer Co Pubs.

Smith, Charles R. Can You Know God's Will for Your Life? 1979. pap. 1.00 (ISBN 0-88469-044-X). BMH Bks.

--Did Christ Die Only for the Elect? 1979. pap. 1.00 (ISBN 0-88469-025-3). BMH Bks.

--The New "Life after Death" Religion. 1980. pap. 1.00 (ISBN 0-88469-125-X). BMH Bks.

--Tongues in Biblical Perspective. pap. 4.95 (ISBN 0-88469-005-9). BMH Bks.

Smith, Charles S. History of the African Methodist Episcopal Church, 1856-1922. 1922. 27.00 (ISBN 0-384-45261-2). Johnson Repr.

Smith, Charles W. The Jesus of the Parables. LC 74-26816. 255p. 1975. 8.95 (ISBN 0-8298-0267-3). Pilgrim NY.

Smith, Christine. The Baptistery of Pisa. LC 77-94715. (Outstanding Dissertations in the Fine Arts Ser.). (Illus.). 432p. 1978. lib. bdg. 53.00 (ISBN 0-8240-3249-7). Garland Pub.

Smith, Chuck. The Answer for Today, Vol. 1. 72p. (Orig.). 1980. pap. 1.95 (ISBN 0-936728-09-4). Word for Today.

--Answers for Today, Vol. II. (Answers for Today Ser.). 80p. (Orig.). 1986. pap. write for info. (ISBN 0-936728-28-0). Word for Today.

--Charisma vs. Charismania. LC 82-2241. 176p. (Orig.). 1983. pap. 3.95 (ISBN 0-89081-353-1). Harvest Hse.

--Effective Prayer Life. LC 78-27511. 96p. 1980. pap. 1.95 (ISBN 0-936728-03-5). Word for Today.

--Family Relationships. 48p. (Orig.). 1980. pap. 0.95 (ISBN 0-936728-04-3). Word for Today.

--Future Survival. (Illus.). 112p. (Orig.). 1980. pap. 1.50 (ISBN 0-936728-02-7). Word for Today.

--The Gospel According to Grace. 176p. 1981. pap. 3.95 (ISBN 0-936728-12-4). Word for Today.

--New Testament Study Guide. 224p. (YA) 1982. pap. 2.95 (ISBN 0-936728-33-7). Word For Today.

--The Tribulation & the Church. 64p. (Orig.). 1980. pap. 1.50 (ISBN 0-936728-01-9). Word for Today.

--What the World Is Coming To. LC 77-3186. 224p. 1980. pap. 1.95 (ISBN 0-936728-00-0). Word for Today.

Smith, Clifford N. Nineteenth-Century Emigration of "Old Lutherans" from Eastern Germany (Mainly Pomerania & Lower Silesia) to Australia, Canada, & the United States. (German-American Genealogical Research Monograph: No. 7). 1979. pap. 14.00 (ISBN 0-915162-06-7). Westland Pubns.

Smith, Cushing. I Can Heal Myself & I Will. new ed. LC 62-14344. 315p. 1980. pap. 7.95 (ISBN 0-8119-0384-2). Fell.

Smith, D. Fasting. 1973. 3.95 (ISBN 0-87508-516-4); pap. 2.95 (ISBN 0-87508-515-6). Chr Lit.

Smith, D. M., tr. see Barrett, C. K.

Smith, D. M., tr. see Barrett, Charles K.

Smith, D. Moody. John. 2nd, rev., & enl. ed. Krodel, Gerhard, ed. LC 75-13046. (Proclamation Commentaries: The New Testament Witnesses for Preaching Ser.). 144p. 1986. pap. 7.95 (ISBN 0-8006-1917-X, 1-1917). Fortress.

Smith, Daniel see McDermott, Robert A.

Smith, Daniel H. How to Lead a Child to Christ. (Orig.). 1987. pap. 2.95 (ISBN 0-8024-4622-1). Moody.

Smith, Danny, jt. auth. see Chmykhaler, Timothy.

Smith, David. Marx's Kapital for Beginners. (Illus.). 1982. pap. 3.95 (ISBN 0-394-71265-X). Pantheon.

Smith, David, ed. The Life & Letters of Saint Paul. 1977. lib. bdg. 69.95 (ISBN 0-8490-2161-8). Gordon Pr.

Smith, David, tr. see Congar, Yves.

Smith, David, tr. see Hardick, Lothar, et al.

Smith, David, tr. see Kasper, Walter.

Smith, David, tr. see Kloppenburg, Bonaventure.

Smith, David, tr. see Laun, Hellmut.

Smith, David, tr. see Nuns of the Monastery of St. Clare, Balsbach, Germany, et al.

Smith, David, tr. see Pope John Paul I.

Smith, David, tr. see Van Moorselaar, Corinne.

Smith, David H. Health & Medicine in Anglican Tradition. 140p. 1986. 15.95x (ISBN 0-8245-0716-9). Crossroad NY.

Smith, David L. Horace Bushnell: Selected Writings on Language, Religion & American Culture. LC 83-6678. (AAR Studies in Religion). 196p. 1984. pap. 9.75 (ISBN 0-89130-636-6, 01 00 33). Scholars Pr GA.

--Symbolism & Growth: The Religious Thought of Horace Bushnell. Dietrich, Wendell S., ed. LC 80-14600. (AAR Dissertation Ser.). pap. 9.95 (ISBN 0-89130-410-X, 01 01 36). Scholars Pr GA.

Smith, David M. English Episcopal Acta I: Lincoln 1067-1185. (English Episcopal Acta Ser.). (Illus.). 312p. 1980. 67.50 (ISBN 0-85672-645-1, Pub. by British Acad). Longwood Pub Group.

Smith, Davie, tr. see Pohlmann, Constantin.

Smith, Defost. Martyrs of the Oblong & Little Nine. 1948. 6.00 (ISBN 0-910294-11-9). Brown Bk.

Smith, Delia. A Feast for Advent. 2nd ed. 96p. 1985. pap. 4.95 (ISBN 0-89622-219-5). Twenty-Third.

--A Feast for Lent. 96p. pap. 3.95 (ISBN 0-89622-220-9). Twenty-Third.

Smith, Don I. By the River of No Return. LC 85-60311. (Illus.). 112p. 1985. pap. 5.95 (ISBN 0-932773-00-1). High Country Bks.

Smith, Donald. How to Cure Yourself of Positive Thinking. LC 77-70191. 1977. 7.95 (ISBN 0-912458-80-1). E A Seemann.

Smith, Donald E. Religion, Politics & Social Change in the Third World. LC 73-143516. 1951. 14.95 (ISBN 0-02-929490-8); pap. text ed. 6.95 (ISBN 0-02-929460-6). Free Pr.

Smith, Donald E., ed. Religion & Political Modernization. LC 73-86917. pap. 87.50 (ISBN 0-317-29714-7, 2022041). Bks Demand UMI.

Smith, Donald M. The Letter. Parker, Diane, et al, eds. LC 83-91201. (Illus.). 217p. 20.00 (ISBN 0-914731-00-9). DMS Publishing Co.

Smith, Donald P. Congregations Alive. LC 81-1371. 198p. 1981. pap. 10.95 (ISBN 0-664-24370-3). Westminster.

Smith, Donna, jt. auth. see Averett, Joy.

Smith, Dwight M. Interpreting the Gospels for Preaching. LC 79-8900. pap. 32.00 (2029609). Bks Demand UMI.

Smith, E. Brooks & Meredith, Robert. The Coming of the Pilgrims. 1964. 11.45 (ISBN 0-316-80048-1). Little.

--Pilgrim Courage. (Illus.). 1962. 6.95 (ISBN 0-316-80045-7). Little.

Smith, Ebbie C. Balanced Church Growth. LC 84-6456. 1984. pap. 5.95 (ISBN 0-8054-6246-5). Broadman.

Smith, Edward J. There Is No Happiness Without a Feeling. 119p. 1984. 20.00 (ISBN 0-682-40130-7). Exposition Pr FL.

Smith, Edward P. Gerty's Papa's Civil War. Armstrong, William H., ed. (Illus.). 128p. (Orig.). 1984. pap. 7.95 (ISBN 0-8298-0703-9). Pilgrim NY.

Smith, Edwin W. Great Lion of Bechuanaland: The Life and Times of Roger Price, Missionary. LC 57-36876. 1957. text ed. 20.00x (ISBN 0-8401-2210-1). A R Allenson.

Smith, Elias. The Life, Conversion, Preaching, Travels & Suffering of Elias Smith. Gaustad, Edwin S., ed. LC 79-52606. (The Baptist Tradition Ser.). 1980. Repr. of 1816 ed. lib. bdg. 34.50x (ISBN 0-405-12471-6). Ayer Co Pubs.

Smith, Elisabeth E., jt. auth. see Whitall, Hannah.

Smith, Eliza R. Biography & Family Record of Lorenzo Snow. 1975. Repr. 15.00 (ISBN 0-914740-15-6). Western Epics.

Smith, Elva S. & Hazeltine, Alice I.compiled by. Christmas in Legend & Story: A Book for Boys & Girls Illustrated from Famous Paintings. LC 72-39390. (Granger Index Reprint Ser.). Repr. of 1915 ed. 18.00 (ISBN 0-8369-6353-9). Ayer Co Pubs.

Smith, Elwyn A. The Religion of the Republic. LC 70-130326. pap. 76.00 (2026890). Bks Demand UMI.

--A Spiritual Exercise for New Parents. LC 85-47714. 64p. 1985. pap. 3.50 (ISBN 0-8006-1863-7, 1-1863). Fortress.

--A Spiritual Exercise for the Grieving. LC 84-47935. 64p. 1984. pap. 3.50 (ISBN 0-8006-1807-6, 1-1807). Fortress.

--A Spiritual Exercise for the Sick. LC 83-48141. 64p. 1983. pap. 3.50 (ISBN 0-8006-1751-7, 1-1751). Fortress.

Smith, Eric. Some Versions of the Fall: The Myth of the Fall of Man in English Literature. LC 75-185025. (Illus.). 1973. 22.95x (ISBN 0-8229-1107-8). U of Pittsburgh Pr.

Smith, Ervin. The Ethics of Martin Luther King Jr. LC 81-18976. (Studies in American Religion: Vol. 2). 226p. 1982. 49.95x (ISBN 0-88946-974-1). E Mellen.

Smith, Ester M. & Sutton, Maurice L. The Last Eight Days. LC 85-40202. 125p. (Orig.). 1985. pap. 6.95 (ISBN 0-938232-82-7). Winston-Derek.

Smith, F. G. The Last Reformation. 256p. 5.00 (ISBN 0-686-29154-9); pap. 3.50 (ISBN 0-686-29155-7). Faith Pub Hse.

--Prophetic Lectures on Daniel & Revelations. 260p. pap. 3.50 (ISBN 0-686-29136-0). Faith Pub Hse.

--The Revelation Explained. 464p. Repr. 5.50 (ISBN 0-686-29163-8). Faith Pub Hse.

--What the Bible Teaches. 576p. Repr. of 1914 ed. 5.50 (ISBN 0-686-29174-3). Faith Pub Hse.

--What the Bible Teaches. 1970. pap. 4.95 (ISBN 0-87162-104-5, D8850). Warner Pr.

Smith, F. H. Outline of Hinduism. 59.95 (ISBN 0-8490-0788-7). Gordon Pr.

Smith, F. LaGard. Insights for Today: The Wisdom of the Proverbs. LC 85-80483. 1985. leather 19.95 (ISBN 0-89081-499-6). Harvest Hse.

--The Narrated Bible in Chronological Order. 1984. text ed. 34.95 (ISBN 0-89081-408-2). Harvest Hse.

Smith, Floy, jt. auth. see Smith, Ken.

Smith, Floy, jt. auth. see Smith, Kenneth G.

Smith, Forrest M. Orange Morgan's 38, 325 Mornings. 1978. 7.00 (ISBN 0-918626-10-2); pap. 4.00 (ISBN 0-918626-07-2). Word Serv.

Smith, Francis J. First Prelude. (Illus.). 64p. 1981. pap. 5.95 (ISBN 0-8294-0387-6). Loyola.

Smith, Francis J., tr. see Rahner, Hugo.

Smith, Frank J. History of the PCA: Continuing Church Movement. 260p. 1985. 20.00 (ISBN 0-9612862-1-0). R E F Typesetting Pub.

Smith, Fred. Learning to Lead. (Leadership Library). 182p. 1986. write for info. (ISBN 0-917463-08-0). Chr Today.

Smith, G. B., jt. auth. see Tozer, A. W.

Smith, G. B., ed. see Tozer, A. W.

Smith, G. Barnett. William Tyndale & the Translation of the English Bible. 20.00 (ISBN 0-8274-3719-6). R West.

Smith, G. Barnett & Martin, Dorothy. John Knox: Apostle of the Scottish Reformation. LC 82-12608. (Golden Oldies Ser.). 128p. 1982. pap. 3.95 (ISBN 0-8024-4354-0). Moody.

Smith, G. Dallas, ed. Outlines of Bible Study: An Easy-to-Follow Guide to Greater Bible Knowledge. 120p. 1986. pap. text ed. 3.95 (ISBN 0-89225-287-1). Gospel Advocate.

Smith, Gary. A Commentary on the Book of Amos. 268p. 1986. 24.95 (ISBN 0-8407-5423-X). Nelson.

--Songs for My Fathers. LC 83-82775. 78p. 1984. pap. 5.00 perf. bnd. (ISBN 0-916418-55-3). Lotus.

Smith, Gary S. The Seeds of Secularization: Calvinism, Culture, & Pluralism in America, 1870-1915. 248p. (Orig.). 1985. pap. 14.95x (ISBN 0-8028-0058-0). Eerdmans.

Smith, Gary S., jt. ed. see Hoffecker, W. Andrew.

Smith, George. The Chaldean Account of Genesis. LC 77-73714. (Secret Doctrine Reference Ser.). (Illus.). 340p. 1977. Repr. of 1876 ed. 15.00 (ISBN 0-913510-26-2). Wizards.

Smith, George A. The Early Poetry of Israel in Its Physical & Social Origins. (British Academy, London, Schweich Lectures on Biblical Archaeology Series, 1910). pap. 19.00 (ISBN 0-8115-1252-5). Kraus Repr.

--Historical Geography of the Holy Land. 13.25 (ISBN 0-8446-2956-1). Peter Smith.

Smith, George D., tr. see Faulhaber.

Smith, George H. Atheism: The Case Against God. LC 79-2726. (Skeptic's Bookshelf Ser.). 355p. 1979. pap. 10.95 (ISBN 0-87975-124-X). Prometheus Bks.

Smith, George M. Hebron Church Register 1750-1825, Madison, Virginia, 2 vols. 1981. pap. 13.00 set (ISBN 0-917968-08-5). Shenandoah Hist.

Smith, George M., tr. see Wust, Klaus.

Smith, Gerald, ed. see Tozer, W.

Smith, Gerald B., compiled by. Jesus, Our Man in Glory. Date not set. pap. price not set (ISBN 0-87509-390-6). Chr Pubns.

Smith, Gerald B., ed. Religious Thought in the Last Quarter-Century. LC 71-107739. (Essay Index Reprint Ser). 1927. 12.00 (ISBN 0-8369-1583-6). Ayer Co Pubs.

Smith, Gerald B., jt. ed. see Mathews, Shailer.

Smith, Gerald B., ed. see Tozer, A. W.

Smith, Gerard. Christian Philosophy & Its Future. 144p. 8.95 (ISBN 0-87462-439-8). Marquette.

--Freedom in Molina. 1966. 2.25 (ISBN 0-8294-0070-2). Loyola.

--A Trio of Talks. 44p. pap. 4.95 (ISBN 0-87462-440-1). Marquette.

Smith, Gerard, ed. Jesuit Thinkers of the Renaissance. 1939. 8.95 (ISBN 0-87462-431-2). Marquette.

Smith, Gerrit. Sermons & Speeches of Gerrit Smith. LC 73-82222. (Anti-Slavery Crusade in America Ser). 1969. Repr. of 1861 ed. 11.50 (ISBN 0-405-00660-8). Ayer Co Pubs.

Smith, Glen C. Evangelizing Adults. 404p. (Orig.). 1985. pap. 12.95 (ISBN 0-8423-0793-1). Tyndale.

Smith, Glenn C. Evangelizing Youth. 352p. (Orig.). 1985. pap. 12.95 (ISBN 0-8423-0791-5). Tyndale.

Smith, Grafton E. Ancient Egyptians & the Origin of Civilization. facs. ed. LC 79-133534. (Select Bibliographies Reprint Ser.). 1923. 17.00 (ISBN 0-8369-5566-8). Ayer Co Pubs.

Smith, Graham. The Casino of Pius IV. LC 76-3017. (Illus.). 1976. 44.50x (ISBN 0-691-03915-1). Princeton U Pr.

Smith, Gregory F. The Ministry of Ushers. 32p. (Orig.). 1980. pap. 1.25 (ISBN 0-8146-1207-5). Liturgical Pr.

Smith, Gregory M. The Fire in Their Eyes: Spiritual Mentors for the Christian Life. 1984. pap. 4.95 (ISBN 0-8091-2620-6). Paulist Pr.

Smith, H. Gleanings on the Church. 85p. pap. 4.95 (ISBN 0-88172-150-6). Believers Bkshelf.

--The Last Words. pap. 4.75 (ISBN 0-88172-124-7). Believers Bkshelf.

--An Outline of the Book of Nehemiah. pap. 4.25 (ISBN 0-88172-125-5). Believers Bkshelf.

Smith, H. Augustine. Lyric Religion: The Romance of Immortal Hymns. 517p. Repr. of 1931 ed. lib. bdg. 75.00 (ISBN 0-918377-84-6). Russell Pr.

Smith, H. Daniel. Reading the Ramayana: A Bibliographic Guide for Students & College Teachers. Indian Variants on the Rama Theme in English Translations. (Foreign & Comparative Studies Program, South Asian Special Publications: No. 4). (Orig.). 1983. pap. text ed. 6.50x (ISBN 0-915984-87-3). Syracuse U Foreign Comp.

Smith, H. Shelton, et al. American Christianity: An Historical Interpretation with Representative Documents. lib. rep. ed. 1960. Vol. I. 45.00x (ISBN 0-684-15744-6, ScribT); Vol. II. 45.00x (ISBN 0-684-15745-4). Scribner.

Smith, Hannah. Religious Fanaticism. Strachey, Ray, ed. & intro. by. LC 72-8252. Orig. Title: Group Movements of the Past & Experiments in Guidance. Repr. of 1928 ed. 21.50 (ISBN 0-404-11005-3). AMS Pr.

Smith, Hannah W. Christian's Secret of a Happy Life. 256p. 1968. o. p. 8.95 (ISBN 0-8007-0044-9); pap. 6.95 (ISBN 0-8007-5004-7, Power Bks); pap. 3.50 (ISBN 0-8007-8007-8, Spire Bks). Revell.

--The Christian's Secret of a Happy Life. 240p. 1983. pap. text ed. 3.50 (ISBN 0-88368-132-3). Whitaker Hse.

--The Christian's Secret of a Happy Life. (Christian Library). 1985. 6.95 (ISBN 0-916441-21-0); pap. 3.95 (ISBN 0-916441-27-X). Barbour & Co.

--The Christian's Secret of a Happy Life. 224p. 1986. pap. 2.50 (ISBN 0-345-33586-4, Pub. by Ballantine Epiphany). Ballantine.

--Daily Devotions from the Christian's Secret of a Happy Life. Hill, Robert C., ed. 288p. (Orig.). 1984. pap. 5.95 (ISBN 0-8007-5139-6, Power Bks). Revell.

--God Is Enough. Dieter, Melvin & Dieter, Hallie, eds. 320p. 1986. 10.95 (ISBN 0-310-46260-6). Zondervan.

--The God of All Comfort. (One Evening Christian Classic Ser.). pap. 2.50 (ISBN 0-89107-008-7). Good News.

--God of All Comfort. 1956. pap. 4.50 (ISBN 0-8024-0018-3). Moody.

--Living Confidently in God's Love. Orig. Title: Living in the Sunshine the God of All Comfort. 192p. 1984. pap. text ed. 3.50 (ISBN 0-88368-150-1). Whitaker Hse.

--El Secreto de una Vida Feliz. 224p. 1980. 2.75 (ISBN 0-88113-270-5). Edit Betania.

--The Unselfishness of God & How I Discovered It. (The Higher Christian Life Ser.). 312p. 1985. lib. bdg. 40.00 (ISBN 0-8240-6443-7). Garland Pub.

Smith, Harmon L. Ethics & the New Medicine. LC 76-124756. Repr. of 1970 ed. 43.50 (ISBN 0-8357-9005-3, 2016356). Bks Demand UMI.

Smith, Harold I. I Wish Someone Understood My Divorce: A Practical Cope-Book. LC 86-28874. 160p. (Orig.). 1987. pap. 7.95 (ISBN 0-8066-2246-6, 10-3194). Augsburg.

--Life-Changing Answers to Depression. 192p. (Orig.). 1986. 9.95 (ISBN 0-89081-529-1). Harvest Hse.

--More Than "I Do". An Engaged Couple's Premarital Handbook. (Orig.). 1983. pap. 2.95 (ISBN 0-8341-0864-X). Beacon Hill.

--More Than "I Do". Devotions for the Engaged Couple. 1983p. (Orig.). 1983. pap. 2.95 (ISBN 0-8341-0805-4). Beacon Hill.

--Pastoral Care for Single Parents. 158p. 1982. pap. 3.95 (ISBN 0-8341-0782-1). Beacon Hill.

--Single & Feeling Good. 160p. 1987. pap. 9.95 (ISBN 0-687-38552-0). Abingdon.

--Tear Catchers. 160p. (Orig.). 1984. pap. 9.50 (ISBN 0-687-41184-X). Abingdon.

--You & Your Parents: Strategies for Building an Adult Relationship. 176p. (Orig.). 1987. pap. 8.95 (ISBN 0-8066-2267-9, 10-7407). Augsburg.

Smith, Harold I., compiled by. The Quotable Bresee. 280p. (Orig.). 1983. pap. 5.95 (ISBN 0-8341-0835-6). Beacon Hill.

Smith, Harry D. The Secret of Instantaneous Healing. 1965. 8.95 (ISBN 0-13-797951-7, Reward); pap. 4.95 (ISBN 0-13-797936-3). P-H.

Smith, Hattie. Let's Talk it Over God! LC 84-50077. 105p. 1984. 5.95 (ISBN 0-938232-46-0). Winston-Derek.

Smith, Helmer, ed. The Khuddaka-Patha. LC 78-72454. Repr. of 1915 ed. 28.50 (ISBN 0-404-17323-3). AMS Pr.

Smith, Helmer, jt. ed. see Andersen, Dines.

Smith, Henry. A Preparative to Mariage: Whereunto Is Annexed a Treatise of the Lords Supper, & Another of Usurie. LC 74-28885. (English Experience Ser.: No. 762). 1975. Repr. of 1591 ed. 16.00 (ISBN 90-221-0762-0). Walter J Johnson.

--Three Sermons: The Benefit of Contentation, the Affinitie of the Faithful, the Lost Sheep Is Found. LC 76-57418. (English Experience Ser.: No. 832). 1977. Repr. of 1599 ed. lib. bdg. 7.00 (ISBN 90-221-0832-5). Walter J Johnson.

Smith, Henry B. Faith & Philosophy: New York, 1877. Kuklick, Bruce, ed. (American Religious Thought of the 18th & 19th Centuries Ser.). 496p. 1987. lib. bdg. 70.00 (ISBN 0-8240-6967-6). Garland Pub.

Smith, Henry J. Time of the End. (International Correspondence Program Ser.). 159p. (Orig.). pap. 6.95 (ISBN 0-87148-853-1). Pathway Pr.

Smith, Henry P. A Critical & Exegetical Commentary on First & Second Samuel. Driver, Samuel R., et al, eds. LC 99-1607. (International Critical Commentary Ser.). 462p. 1898. 22.95 (ISBN 0-567-05005-X, Pub. by T & T Clark Ltd UK). Fortress.

Smith, Herbert F. Sexual Inversion: The Questions-with Catholic Answers. 1979. 2.95 (ISBN 0-8198-0612-9); pap. 1.95 (ISBN 0-8198-0613-7). Dghtrs St Paul.

Smith, Hilary D. Preaching in the Spanish Golden Age: A Study of Some Preachers of the Reign of Philip III. (Modern Language & Literature Monographs). 1979. 29.95x (ISBN 0-19-815532-8). Oxford U Pr.

Smith, Hilary S. Changing Conceptions of Original Sin: A Study in American Theology since 1750. Kuklick, Bruce, ed. (American Religious Thought of the 18th & 19th Centuries Ser.). 242p. 1987. lib. bdg. 35.00 (ISBN 0-8240-6954-4). Garland Pub.

Smith, Huston. Forgotten Truth: The Primordial Tradition. 1977. pap. 6.95x (ISBN 0-06-132054-4, TB 2054, Torch). Har-Row.

--Religions of Man. pap. 7.95 (ISBN 0-06-090043-1, CN43, PL). Har-Row.

--Religions of Man. 1965. pap. 5.95 (ISBN 0-06-080021-6, P21, PL). Har-Row.

Smith, Hyrum, III, jt. auth. see Kenney, Scott G.

Smith, Hyrum M. & Sjodahl, Janne M. Doctrine & Covenants Commentary. 14.95 (ISBN 0-87747-070-7). Deseret Bk.

Smith, J. Alfred. Preach On! LC 84-8439. 1984. pap. 4.95 (ISBN 0-8054-2112-2). Broadman.

Smith, J. Alfred, ed. Outstanding Black Sermons. LC 76-2084. 96p. 1976. pap. 4.95 (ISBN 0-8170-0664-8). Judson.

Smith, J. B. Greek-English Concordance. LC 55-12260. 430p. 1955. 29.95 (ISBN 0-8361-1368-3). Herald Pr.

Smith, J. Frederick, tr. see Pfleiderer, Otto.

Smith, Jackie M. Women, Faith, & Economic Justice. (Illus.). 80p. (Orig.). 1985. pap. 5.95 (ISBN 0-664-24600-1). Westminster.

Smith, James. Handfuls on Purpose, 5 vols. 1943. 69.95 set (ISBN 0-8028-8139-4). Eerdmans.

Smith, James E. Divided We Fall. LC 79-67439. 96p. (Orig.). 1980. pap. 2.25 (ISBN 0-87239-381-X, 40086). Standard Pub.

--Ezekiel. (Bible Study Textbook Ser.). 1979. 14.30 (ISBN 0-89900-024-X). College Pr Pub.

--First & Second Kings. LC 78-300507. (The Bible Study Textbook Ser.). (Illus.). 1975. 17.50 (ISBN 0-89900-012-6). College Pr Pub.

--Jeremiah & Lamentations. LC 72-97951. (The Bible Study Textbook Ser.). (Illus.). 1972. 18.95 (ISBN 0-89900-023-1). College Pr Pub.

--What the Bible Says about the Promised Messiah. (What the Bible Says Ser.). 530p. 1984. 13.95 (ISBN 0-89900-095-9). College Pr Pub.

Smith, James M., ed. see Harper, William R.

Smith, Jane I. & Haddad, Yvonne Y. Islamic Understanding of Death & Resurrection. LC 80-21303. 270p. 1981. 49.50x (ISBN 0-87395-506-4); pap. 19.95 (ISBN 0-87395-507-2). State U NY Pr.

Smith, Jane I., ed. The Precious Pearl: A Translation from the Arabic. LC 79-140. (Studies in World Religions: No. 1). 1979. 15.00 (ISBN 0-89130-278-6, 030001); pap. 8.95 05539067x (ISBN 0-89130-305-7). Scholars Pr GA.

Smith, Jane S. & Carlson, Betty. A Gift of Music. LC 83-70798. 255p. 1983. pap. 7.95 (ISBN 0-89107-293-4, Crossway Bks). Good News.

Smith, Jean. Tapu Removal in Maori Religion. 96p. 1974. text ed. 12.00x (ISBN 0-8248-0591-7). UH Pr.

Smith, Jim L. He Arose. 1973. pap. 1.75 (ISBN 0-88428-026-8, 317). Parchment Pr.

Smith, Joanmarie, jt. auth. see Durka, Gloria.

Smith, Jody B. Image of Guadalupe: Myth or Miracle? LC 80-2066. (Illus.). 216p. 1984. pap. 6.95 (ISBN 0-385-19705-5, Im). Doubleday.

Smith, John. Select Discourses. Wellek, Rene, ed. LC 75-11252. (British Philosophers & Theologians of the 17th & 18th Centuries Ser.). 1978. Repr. of 1660 ed. lib. bdg. 51.00 (ISBN 0-8240-1803-6). Garland Pub.

Smith, John, jt. ed. see Seymour, William K.

Smith, John C. Church Woodcarvings: A West Country Study. LC 79-77874. (Illus.). 1969. 17.95x (ISBN 0-678-05533-5). Kelley.

--From Colonialism to World Community: The Church's Pilgrimage. LC 82-12138. 334p. 1982. pap. 8.95 (ISBN 0-664-24452-1, Pub. by Geneva Press). Westminster.

Smith, John E. Experience & God. 1968. 11.95x (ISBN 0-19-501207-0). Oxford U Pr.

--Experience & God. LC 68-18566. 1974. pap. 6.95 (ISBN 0-19-501847-8). Oxford U Pr.

--Reason & God: Encounters of Philosophy with Religion. LC 77-13887. 1978. Repr. of 1961 ed. lib. bdg. 22.50x (ISBN 0-8371-9867-4, SMRG). Greenwood.

--Religion & Empiricism. (Aquinas Lecture Ser.). 1967. 7.95 (ISBN 0-87462-132-1). Marquette.

Smith, John E., ed. see Edwards, Jonathan.

Smith, John, Jr. The Relational Self: Ethics & Therapy from a Black Church Perspective. 256p. (Orig.). 1982. pap. 11.95 (ISBN 0-687-35945-7). Abingdon.

Smith, John M. The Origin & History of Hebrew Law. LC 79-1620. 1980. Repr. of 1960 ed. 23.65 (ISBN 0-88355-924-2). Hyperion Conn.

--Prophets & Their Times. rev ed. Irwin, William A., ed. LC 25-6864. 1941. 20.00x (ISBN 0-226-76356-0). U of Chicago Pr.

Smith, John M., et al. A Critical & Exegetical Commentary on Micah, Zephaniah, Nahum, Habakkuk, Obadiah & Joel. Driver, Samuel R. & Plummer, Alfred, eds. (International Critical Commentary Ser.). 560p. 1895. 24.95 (ISBN 0-567-05019-X, Pub. by T & T Clark Ltd UK). Fortress.

Smith, John W. Brief History of the Church of God Reformation Movement. 1976. pap. 3.95 (ISBN 0-87162-188-6, D2350). Warner Pr.

--I Will Build My Church. 1985. pap. 3.95 (ISBN 0-87162-411-7, D4320). Warner Pr.

Smith, Jonathan R. The First Crusade & the Idea of Crusading. LC 86-1608. (Middle Ages Ser.). 224p. 1986. text ed. 29.95x (ISBN 0-8122-8026-1). U of Pa Pr.

Smith, Jonathan Z. Imagining Religion: From Babylon to Jonestown. LC 82-2734. (Studies in the History of Judaism). 1982. 17.50x (ISBN 0-226-76358-7). U of Chicago Pr.

Smith, Joseph. Doctrine & Covenants of the Church of Jesus Christ of Latter-Day Saints: Containing the Revelations Given to Joseph Smith, Jun, the Prophet, for the Building up of the Kingdom of God in the Last Days. Pratt, Orson, ed. LC 69-14082. 1971. Repr. of 1880 ed. lib. bdg. 29.75x (ISBN 0-8371-4101-X, SMCC). Greenwood.

--Lectures on Faith. LC 84-73495. 96p. 1985. 6.95 (ISBN 0-87747-897-X). Deseret Bk.

Smith, Joseph F. Gospel Doctrine. 553p. 1975. 10.95. Deseret Bk.

--Gospel Doctrine. 1986. text ed. 10.95 (ISBN 0-87579-063-1). Deseret Bk.

--Teachings of the Prophet Joseph Smith. LC 76-111624. 437p. 1977. pap. 2.50 (ISBN 0-87747-778-7). Deseret Bk.

--Teachings of the Prophet Joseph Smith. 1976. 9.95 (ISBN 0-87747-626-8). Deseret Bk.

--The Way to Perfection. 365p. 1972. 8.95 (ISBN 0-87747-300-5). Deseret Bk.

Smith, Joseph, Jr., tr. The Book of Mormon. LC 66-15423. 414p. 1973. pap. 4.00 (ISBN 0-8309-0273-2). Herald Hse.

--Book of Mormon: First Edition Facsimile. 590p. 1980. 9.99 (ISBN 0-87747-808-2). Deseret Bk.

Smith, Josie, tr. see Hill, Tomas.

Smith, Josie De. Senor: No Me Dejes Rodar. (Illus.). 96p. 1986. pap. 2.50 (ISBN 0-311-40042-6). Casa Bautista.

Smith, Josie de see De Smith, Josie.

Smith, Joyce M. Becoming God's Woman. 1979. pap. 2.50 (ISBN 0-8423-0130-5). Tyndale.

--Celebration of Womanhood. (New Life Bible Studies). 64p. 1985. pap. 2.95 (ISBN 0-8423-0254-9). Tyndale.

--Coping with Life & Its Problems. 1976. pap. 2.95 (ISBN 0-8423-0434-7). Tyndale.

--Demons, Doubters & Dead Men. (Good Life Bible Studies Book). 64p. (Orig.). 1986. 2.95wkbk. (ISBN 0-8423-0542-4). Tyndale.

--Esther, a Woman of Courage. 1981. pap. 2.95 (ISBN 0-8423-0729-X). Tyndale.

--Fulfillment: Bible Studies for Women. 1975. pap. 2.95 (ISBN 0-8423-0980-2). Tyndale.

--Giants, Lions & Fire. 1981. pap. 2.95 (ISBN 0-8423-1022-3). Tyndale.

--Growing in Faith. 1982. pap. 2.95 (ISBN 0-8423-1227-7). Tyndale.

--Growing When You Don't Feel Like It. (Good Life Bible Studies). 64p. (YA) 1985. pap. 2.95 (ISBN 0-8423-1229-3). Tyndale.

--Learning to Talk with God. 1976. pap. 2.95 (ISBN 0-8423-2140-3). Tyndale.

--A Listening Heart. 1981. pap. 2.95 (ISBN 0-8423-2375-9). Tyndale.

--A Rejoicing Heart. 1979. pap. 2.95 (ISBN 0-8423-5418-2). Tyndale.

--Ruth: A Woman of Worth. 1979. pap. 2.50 (ISBN 0-8423-5810-2). Tyndale.

--Understanding Your Emotions. 1977. pap. 2.95 (ISBN 0-8423-7770-0). Tyndale.

--Walking in the Light. 1980. pap. 2.95 (ISBN 0-8423-7813-8). Tyndale.

--A Woman's Priorities. 1976. pap. 2.95 (ISBN 0-8423-8380-8). Tyndale.

--Young Disciples. 50p. 1983. pap. 2.95 (ISBN 0-8423-8599-1). Tyndale.

Smith, Joyce Marie. The Significance of Jesus. 1976. pap. 2.95 (ISBN 0-8423-5887-0). Tyndale.

Smith, Judith E. Family Connections: A History of Italian & Jewish Immigrant Lives in Providence, Rhode Island, 1900-1940. (SUNY Series in American Social History). 256p. 1985. 44.50 (ISBN 0-87395-964-7); pap. 16.95 (ISBN 0-87395-965-5). State U NY Pr.

Smith, Judith S., jt. auth. see Stephan, Eric.

Smith, Judy G. Celebrating Special Days in the Church School Year. Zapel, Arthur L., ed. LC 81-83441. (Illus.). 125p. (Orig.). 1981. pap. text ed. 8.95 (ISBN 0-916260-14-3). Meriwether Pub.

--Developing a Child's Spiritual Growth: Through Sight, Sound, Taste, Touch & Smell. 80p. (Orig.). 1983. pap. 8.75 (ISBN 0-687-10499-8). Abingdon.

--Drama Through the Church Year. Zapel, Arthur L., ed. LC 84-61476. 164p. (Orig.). 1984. pap. 7.95 (ISBN 0-916260-26-7). Meriwether Pub.

--Joyful Teaching - Joyful Learning. LC 86-71007. 104p. (Orig.). 1986. pap. 6.95 (ISBN 0-88177-031-0, DR031B). Discipleship Res.

--Teaching with Music Through the Church Year. 1979. pap. 7.95 (ISBN 0-687-41133-5). Abingdon.

Smith, Julia E. Abby Smith & Her Cows: With a Report of the Law Case Decided Contrary to Law. LC 72-2622. (American Women Ser: Images & Realities). 98p. 1972. Repr. of 1877 ed. 13.00 (ISBN 0-405-04478-X). Ayer Co Pubs.

Smith, Katherine V. Chickens, Cookies, & Cuzzin George. 144p. (Orig.). 1983. pap. text ed. 7.75 (ISBN 0-687-06485-6). Abingdon.

Smith, Kelly M. Social Crisis Preaching. LC 84-6656. x, 125p. 1984. 9.95x (ISBN 0-86554-111-6, MUP/H106); pap. 9.95 (ISBN 0-86554-246-5, MUP-P38). Mercer Univ Pr.

Smith, Ken & Smith, Floy. Learning to Be a Family: Leader's Guide. (Orig.). 1985. pap. 3.95 (ISBN 0-934688-17-6). Great Comm Pubns.

Smith, Kenneth, jt. auth. see McKibbens, Thomas R., Jr.

Smith, Kenneth B., jt. ed. see Bass, Dorothy C.

Smith, Kenneth G. & Smith, Floy. Learning to Be a Woman. LC 76-127932. (Orig.). 1970. pap. 3.95 (ISBN 0-87784-693-6). Inter-Varsity.

Smith, Kenneth L. The Last Warning. LC 79-53625. 1979. pap. 4.95 (ISBN 0-89412-030-1). Aegean Park Pr.

Smith, Kent D. Faith: Reflections on Experience, Theology & Fiction. 114p. (Orig.). 1984. lib. bdg. 22.00 (ISBN 0-8191-3634-4); pap. text ed. 9.25 (ISBN 0-8191-3635-2). U Pr of Amer.

Smith, L. T., ed. see Kyngeston, Richard.

Smith, Leon, jt. auth. see Smith, Antoinette.

Smith, Louis A. & Barndt, Joseph R. Beyond Brokenness. (Orig.). 1980. pap. 2.95 (ISBN 0-377-00100-7). Friend Pr.

Smith, Louise P., tr. see Bultmann, Rudolf.

Smith, Lucy M. Biographical Sketches of Joseph Smith, the Prophet & His Progenitors for Many Generations. LC 73-83439. (Religion in America, Ser. 1). 1969. Repr. of 1853 ed. 15.00 (ISBN 0-405-00264-5). Ayer Co Pubs.

Smith, Lucy T., ed. York Plays: The Plays Performed on the Day of Corpus Christi in the 14th, 15th, & 16th Centuries. LC 63-15180. (Illus.). 1963. Repr. of 1885 ed. 21.00x (ISBN 0-8462-0313-8). Russell.

Smith, M., ed. see Crabtree, T. T.

Smith, M. B., jt. auth. see Smith-Savage, E.

Smith, M. Blaine. Knowing God's Will. LC 78-24756. 1979. pap. 4.95 (ISBN 0-87784-610-3). Inter-Varsity.

--One of a Kind: A Biblical View of Self-Acceptance. LC 84-574. 140p. 1984. pap. 3.95 (ISBN 0-87784-921-8). Inter-Varsity.

Smith, Macklin. Prudentius 'Psychomachia' A Re-examination. LC 75-37192. 1976. 30.50x (ISBN 0-691-06299-4). Princeton U Pr.

Smith, Margaret. An Early Mystic of Baghdad: A Study of the Life & Teaching of Harith B. Asad al-Muhasibi, A.D. 781-A.D. 857. LC 76-180379. Repr. of 1935 ed. 16.50 (ISBN 0-404-56324-4). AMS Pr.

--An Introduction to the History of Mysticism. 69.95 (ISBN 0-87968-437-2). Gordon Pr.

--Rabi'a the Mystic & Her Fellow-Saints in Islam. 2nd ed. 256p. 1984. 37.50 (ISBN 0-521-26779-X); pap. 13.95 (ISBN 0-521-31863-7). Cambridge U Pr.

--The Way of the Mystics: The Early Christian Mystics & the Rise of the Sufis. 1978. pap. 6.95 (ISBN 0-19-519967-7). Oxford U Pr.

Smith, Marian W. Puyallup-Nisqually. LC 73-82360. (Columbia Univ. Contributions to Anthropology Ser.: Vol. 32). 1969. Repr. of 1940 ed. 34.50 (ISBN 0-404-50582-1). AMS Pr.

Smith, Marilyn A. Christmas Programs for Church Groups. (Paperback Program Ser). (Orig.). 1968. pap. 3.95 (ISBN 0-8010-7910-1). Baker Bk.

Smith, Martin L. Reconciliation: Preparing for Confession in the Episcopal Church. LC 85-21271. 121p. (Orig.). 1985. pap. 8.95 (ISBN 0-936384-30-1). Cowley Pubns.

Smith, Martin L., ed. Benson of Cowley. 153p. 1983. pap. 8.00 (ISBN 0-936384-12-3). Cowley Pubns.

Smith, Mary, tr. see Buhlmann, Walbert.

Smith, Mary P. The Story of Jesus. (Illus.). 32p. (Orig.). 1980. pap. 1.95 (ISBN 0-87516-420-X). De Vorss.

Smith, Matthew J., jt. auth. see Conley, Patrick T.

Smith, Michael, jt. auth. see Johnston, Leonard.

Smith, Michael, ed. see Adams, Jay E.

Smith, Michael K. The Church Under Siege. LC 76-12304. (Illus.). 1976. pap. 5.95 (ISBN 0-87784-855-6). Inter-Varsity.

Smith, Mont. What the Bible Says about the Covenant. 2nd ed. LC 81-65516. (What the Bible Says Ser.). 472p. 1981. 13.95 (ISBN 0-89900-083-5). College Pr Pub.

Smith, Moody D. Johannine Christianity: Essays on Its Setting, Sources, & Theology. 233p. 1985. 19.95x (ISBN 0-87249-449-7). U of SC Pr.

Smith, Moody D., jt. auth. see Spivey, Robert A.

Smith, Morton. Clement of Alexandria, & a Secret Gospel of Mark. LC 72-148938. 1973. 30.00x (ISBN 0-674-13490-7). Harvard U Pr.

--Jesus the Magician. LC 76-9986. 224p. 1982. pap. 12.95 (ISBN 0-06-067413-X, RD 372, HarpR). Har-Row.

--The Secret Gospel: The Discovery & Interpretation of the Secret Gospel According to Mark. LC 82-73215. 157p. pap. 7.95 (ISBN 0-913922-55-2). Dawn Horse Pr.

Smith, Morton, jt. auth. see Hadas, Moses.

Smith, N. D., tr. see Oosterhuis, Huub.

Smith, Nathan D. Roots, Renewal & the Brethren. 152p. (Orig.). 1986. text ed. 12.95 (ISBN 0-932727-09-3); pap. 6.95 (ISBN 0-932727-08-5). Hope Pub Hse.

Smith, Nelson M. What Is This Thing Called Love. 1970. 8.75 (ISBN 0-89137-505-8); pap. 4.95 (ISBN 0-89137-504-X). Quality Pubns.

Smith, Nopal, jt. auth. see Obrennen, Junius.

Smith, Norman K. Credibility of Divine Existence. Porteous, A. J., et al, eds. 1969. 27.50 (ISBN 0-312-17185-4). St Martin.

Smith, Norman K., ed. see Hume, David.

Smith, Oswald J. Pasion por las Almas. Orig. Title: Passion for Souls. (Span.). 208p. 1985. pap. 4.25 (ISBN 0-8254-1672-8). Kregel.

Smith, P. Key to the Colloquies of Erasmus. (Harvard Theological Studies). 1927. pap. 15.00 (ISBN 0-527-01013-8). Kraus Repr.

Smith, Page. Religious Origins of the American Revolution. LC 76-13157. (American Academy of Religion, Aids for the Study of Religion). 1976. pap. 8.95 (ISBN 0-89130-121-6, 010303). Scholars Pr GA.

Smith, Pauline. Christmas. 32p. 1985. pap. 1.50 (ISBN 0-908175-83-3, Pub. by Boolarong Pubn Australia). Intl Spec Bk.

Smith, Peter. The Babi & Baha'i Religions: From Messianic Sh'ism to a World Religion. (Illus.). 225p. Date not set. price not set (ISBN 0-521-30128-9). Cambridge U Pr.

--Nursling of Mortality: A Study of the Homeric Hymn to Aphrodite. (Studien zur klassischen Philologie: Vol. 3). 155p. 1980. pap. 20.65 (ISBN 3-8204-6111-6). P Lang Pubs.

Smith, Peter, ed. & intro. by. Studies in Babi & Baha'i History Volume 3: In Iran. (Illus.). 1986. 19.95 (ISBN 0-933770-46-4). Kalimat.

Smith, Peter, ed. Studies in Babi & Baha'i History, Vol. 6: Baha'is in the West. Date not set. 19.95 (ISBN 0-933770-64-2). Kalimat.

Smith, Peter & Lee, Anthony A., eds. Faith & Reason: Some Baha'i Perspectives. (Orig.). 1987. pap. 9.95 (ISBN 0-933770-56-1). Kalimat.

Smith, Pierre, jt. ed. see Izard, Michel.

Smith, Preserved. Luther's Table Talk. LC 78-127457. (Columbia University Studies in the Social Sciences: No. 69). 1970. Repr. of 1907 ed. 14.50 (ISBN 0-404-51069-8). AMS Pr.

--A Short History of Christian Theophagy. 223p. 1922. 16.95 (ISBN 0-87548-241-4). Open Court.

Smith, R. Pearsall. Walking in the Light. 128p. 1987. pap. 4.95 (ISBN 0-310-20921-8). Zondervan.

Smith, R. W. Pakua. pap. 8.25x (ISBN 0-685-22068-0). Wehman.

Smith, Richard H. A Concise Coptic-English Lexicon. 81p. 1983. 10.95x (ISBN 0-8028-3581-3). Eerdmans.

Smith, Richard K. Forty-Nine & Holding. LC 75-11179. (Illus.). 1975. 10.00 (ISBN 0-89430-023-7). Palos Verdes.

Smith, Robert, tr. see Chen Wei-Ming.

Smith, Robert C. & Lounibos, John, eds. Pagan & Christian Anxiety: A Response to E. R. Dodds. LC 83-27345. 248p. 1984. lib. bdg. 25.25 (ISBN 0-8191-3823-1); pap. text ed. 12.25 (ISBN 0-8191-3824-X). U Pr of Amer.

Smith, Robert H. Augsburg Commentary on the New Testament: Hebrews. LC 83-72125. (Augsburg Commentary New Testament Ser.). 192p. (Orig.). 1984. pap. 8.95 kivar (ISBN 0-8066-8876-9, 10-9034). Augsburg.

--Easter Gospels: The Resurrection of Jesus According to the Four Evangelists. LC 83-70518. 272p. (Orig.). 1983. pap. 15.95 (ISBN 0-8066-2024-2, 10-1988). Augsburg.

Smith, Robert H., jt. ed. see Groh, John E.

Smith, Robert J. Ancestor Worship in Contemporary Japan. LC 74-82780. (Illus.). xxii, 266p. 1974. 29.50x (ISBN 0-8047-0873-8). Stanford U Pr.

Smith, Robert O. A Biography of Jesus Christ. 1987. 14.95 (ISBN 0-533-07232-8). Vantage.

Smith, Robert S. In the Image of God. 150p. (Orig.). 1987. pap. 5.95 (ISBN 0-938999-01-X). Yuganta Pr.

Smith, Robert W. Secrets of Shaolin Temple Boxing. LC 64-22002. (Illus.). 1964. 7.95 (ISBN 0-8048-0518-0). C E Tuttle.

--Shaolin Temple Boxing Secrets. 7.95x (ISBN 0-685-22107-5). Wehman.

Smith, Robert W., jt. auth. see Cheng, Man-Ch'ing.

Smith, Rodney K. Public Prayer & the Constitution: A Case Study in Constitutional Interpretation. 320p. 1987. 35.00 (ISBN 0-8420-2260-0). Scholarly Res Inc.

Smith, Roland A. Before You Build Your Church. LC 76-73134. 1979. pap. 2.50 (ISBN 0-8054-3511-5). Broadman.

Smith, Ronald G., ed. see Ebeling, Gerhard.

Smith, Ruth, jt. auth. see Smith, Barrie.

Smith, Ruth S. Getting the Books Off the Shelves: Making the Most of Your Congregation's Library, No. 12. rev. ed. LC 85-11650. (CSLA Guide Ser.). (Illus.). 40p. 1985. pap. 6.95X (ISBN 0-915324-22-9). CSLA.

--Running a Library: Managing the Congregation's Library with Care, Confidence, & Common Sense. 144p. (Orig.). 1982. pap. 7.95 (ISBN 0-8164-2413-6, HarpR). Har-Row.

Smith, S. G., tr. see Buber, Martin, et al.

Smith, Sammireh A., tr. see Khanum, Munirih.

Smith, Sandra, tr. see Stehle, Hansjakob.

Smith, Sherwood. Thirteen Lessons on Romans, Vol. II. LC 81-65030. (Bible Student Study Guides Ser.). 114p. 1981. pap. 2.95 (ISBN 0-89900-170-X). College Pr Pub.

--Thirteen Lessons on Romans, Vol. I. LC 79-55509. (Bible Student Study Guides). 113p. (Orig.). 1980. pap. 2.95 (ISBN 0-89900-164-5). College Pr Pub.

Smith, Sidney. Isaiah Chapters XL-LV: Literary Criticism & History. (British Academy, London, Schweich Lectures on Biblical Archaeology Series, 1940). pap. 28.00 (ISBN 0-8115-1282-7). Kraus Repr.

--Ten Super Sunday Schools in the Black Community. LC 86-926. 1986. pap. 5.95 (ISBN 0-8054-6252-X). Broadman.

Smith, Steve, ed. Ways of Wisdom: Readings on the Good Life. (Illus.). 312p. (Orig.). 1983. lib. bdg. 29.75 (ISBN 0-8191-3387-6); pap. text ed. 14.25 (ISBN 0-8191-3388-4). U Pr of Amer.

Smith, Steven A. Satisfaction of Interest & the Co- ept of Morality. LC 73-8305. 165p. 1975. 18.00 (ISBN 0-8387-1383-1). Bucknell U Pr.

Smith, Sydney. Wit & Wisdom of the Rev. Sydney Smith. 1880. Repr. 25.00 (ISBN 0-8274-3728-5). R West.

Smith, Sydney D. Grapes of Conflict: The Faith Community & Farm Workers. 160p. 1987. 16.95 (ISBN 0-932727-12-3); pap. 9.95 (ISBN 0-932727-14-X); special ed. 25.00 (ISBN 0-932727-13-1). Hope Pub Hse.

Smith, T. Roger & Slater, John. Architecture, Classic & Early Christian. 1980. Repr. of 1893 ed. lib. bdg. 35.00 (ISBN 0-89341-364-X). Longwood Pub Group.

Smith, Tedra G. How Is Your Public Image? (Orig.). 1977. pap. 2.75 (ISBN 0-89536-096-9, 0823). CSS of Ohio.

Smith, Terrence V. Petrine Controversies in Early Christianity: Attitudes Towards Peter in Christian Writings for the First Two Centuries. 259p. (Orig.). 1985. pap. 52.50x (ISBN 3-16-144876-6, Pub. by J C B Mohr BRD). Coronet Bks.

Smith, Thomas. Alive in the Spirit: The Church in the Acts of the Apostles. (Orig.). 1976. pap. text ed. 5.65x (ISBN 0-88489-081-3); tchr's. ed. 3.00x (ISBN 0-88489-083-X). St Marys.

--The Good News about Jesus As Told by Mark. Pluth, Alphonsus, ed. LC 77-89324. (Illus.). 1977. pap. 3.95 (ISBN 0-88489-095-3); tchrs' ed 1.00 (ISBN 0-88489-116-X). St Mary's.

Smith, Thomas A. Discovering Discipleship: A Resource for Home Bible Studies. LC 80-54073. (Illus.). 64p. (Orig.). 1981. pap. 2.75 (ISBN 0-87239-438-7, 88570). Standard Pub.

Smith, Thomas A., Sr., jt. auth. see Taylor, William W.

Smith, Thomas J. Jesus Alive! The Mighty Message of Mark. LC 73-81824. 1973. pap. 6.00x (ISBN 0-88489-015-5); teaching guide 3.00x (ISBN 0-88489-117-8). St Marys.

Smith, Tilman R. Boards: Purposes, Organization, Procedures. LC 78-62628. 64p. 1978. pap. 1.95 (ISBN 0-8361-1862-6). Herald Pr.

Smith, Timothy. Revivalism & Social Reform: American Protestantism on the Eve of the Civil War. LC 80-8114. 272p. 1980. pap. text ed. 8.95x (ISBN 0-8018-2477-X). Johns Hopkins.

Smith, Timothy, ed. see Brunton, Paul.

Smith, Timothy L. Called unto Holiness, Vol. 1. LC 62-11409. 416p. 1962. 14.95 (ISBN 0-8341-0282-X). Beacon Hill.

--Revivalism & Social Reform: American Protestantism on the Eve of the Civil War. 11.25 (ISBN 0-8446-2960-X). Peter Smith.

--Whitefield & Wesley on the New Birth. 544p. 1986. pap. 7.95 (ISBN 0-310-75151-9). Zondervan.

Smith, Timothy L., ed. see Finney, Charles G.

Smith, Vincent A. History of India from the Sixth Century B.C. to the Mohammedan Conquest, Including the Invasion of Alexander the Great. LC 72-14391. (History of India Ser.: No. 2). Repr. of 1906 ed. 32.00 (ISBN 0-404-09002-8). AMS Pr.

Smith, Virginia W. The Single Parent: Revised, Updated & Expanded. 192p. 1983. pap. 5.95 (ISBN 0-8007-5105-1, Power Bks). Revell.

Smith, W. Have You Considered Him? pap. 0.75 (ISBN 0-87784-108-X). Inter-Varsity.

Smith, W. Alan. Children Belong in Worship: A Guide to the Children's Sermon. Lambert, Herbert, ed. LC 84-5840. 128p. 1984. pap. 7.95 (ISBN 0-8272-0445-0). CBP.

Smith, W. C. Modern Islam in India. 1985. Repr. of 1946 ed. 18.50x (ISBN 0-8364-1338-5, Pub. by Usha). South Asia Bks.

Smith, W. Douglas. Toward Continuous Misson: Strategizing for the Evangelization of Bolivia. LC 77-21490. 1978. pap. 4.95 (ISBN 0-87808-321-9). William Carey Lib.

Smith, W. R. Glorifying God. rev. ed. (Way of Life Ser.: No. 134). 1979. 3.95 (ISBN 0-89112-134-X, Bibl Res Pr). Abilene Christ U.

Smith, W. Robertson. Prophets of Israel & Their Place in History to the Close of the Eighth Century B. C. 1979. Repr. of 1895 ed. lib. bdg. 50.00 (ISBN 0-8495-4905-1). Arden Lib.

Smith, W. Thomas. Augustine: His Life & Thought. LC 79-92071. (Illus.). 190p. (Orig.). 1980. pap. 10.95 (ISBN 0-8042-0871-9). John Knox.

Smith, Wallace C. The Church in the Life of the Black Family. (Family Life Ser.). 160p. 1985. pap. 8.50 (ISBN 0-8170-1040-8). Judson.

Smith, Warren. The Secret Forces of the Pyramids. 220p. 1975. pap. 1.75 (ISBN 0-89083-114-9). Zebra.

Smith, Warren S., ed. Religious Speeches of Bernard Shaw. LC 63-18890. 1963. 19.95x (ISBN 0-271-73095-1). Pa St U Pr.

Smith, Warren T. Journey in Faith. 1984. 5.50 (ISBN 0-89536-679-7, 4855). CSS of Ohio.

Smith, Webster. The Farnese Hours. LC 76-4041. (Library of Illuminated Manuscripts). (Illus.). 168p. 1976. slipcase 45.00 (ISBN 0-8076-0856-4). Braziller.

Smith, Wilbur. Therefore Stand. LC 81-81096. (The Shepherd Illustrated Classics Ser.). (Illus.). 660p. 1982. pap. 9.95 (ISBN 0-87983-260-6). Keats.

Smith, Wilfred C. Belief & History. LC 75-50587. 138p. 1977. pap. 7.95x (ISBN 0-8139-1086-2). U Pr of Va.

--Faith & Belief. LC 78-63601. 1979. 35.50x (ISBN 0-691-07232-9). Princeton U Pr.

--Faith & Belief. 360p. 1987. pap. 12.50 (ISBN 0-691-02040-X). Princeton U Pr.

--The Faith of Other Men. 144p. 1972. pap. 6.95x (ISBN 0-06-131658-X, TB1658, Torch). Har-Row.

--Islam in Modern History. 1957. 37.00 (ISBN 0-691-03030-8); pap. 10.50x (ISBN 0-691-01991-6). Princeton U Pr.

--The Meaning & End of Religion. LC 77-20440. 1978. pap. 9.95 (ISBN 0-06-067465-2, RD 252, HarpR). Har-Row.

--Modern Islam in India: A Social Analysis. LC 70-179243. Repr. of 1946 ed. 17.00 (ISBN 0-404-54869-5). AMS Pr.

--On Understanding Islam. (Religion & Reason Ser.: No. 19). 352p. 1984. 55.50 (ISBN 90-279-3448-7); pap. 19.95 (ISBN 3-11-010020-7). Mouton.

--Religious Diversity. (Crossroad Paperback Ser.). 224p. 1982. pap. 7.95 (ISBN 0-8245-0458-5). Crossroad NY.

--Towards a World Theology: Faith & the Comparative History of Religion. LC 80-50826. 212p. 1981. 20.00 (ISBN 0-664-21380-4). Westminster.

Smith, Willard H. Mennonites in Illinois, No. 24. LC 83-152. (Studies in Anabaptist & Mennonite History Ser.). 616p. 1983. 24.95x (ISBN 0-8361-1253-9). Herald Pr.

Smith, William. New Smith's Bible Dictionary. rev. ed. LC 78-69668. 1979. pap. 9.95 (ISBN 0-385-14652-3, Galilee). Doubleday.

--Old Testament History. Fields, Wilbur, ed. LC 78-1072. (The Bible Study Textbook Ser.). (Illus.). 1967. Repr. of 1901 ed. 17.50 (ISBN 0-89900-001-0). College Pr Pub.

--A Proclamation: Eighteen Forty-Five. (Orig.). 1983. pap. 1.50 (ISBN 0-942284-03-8). Restoration Re.

--Smith's Bible Dictionary. rev. ed. 9.95 (ISBN 0-87981-033-5); thumb-indexed 14.95 (ISBN 0-87981-035-1); pap. 6.95 (ISBN 0-87981-489-6). Holman Bible Pub.

--Smith's Bible Dictionary. (Family Library). (YA) 1984. pap. 5.95 (ISBN 0-515-08507-3). Jove Pubns.

--Smith's Bible Dictionary. Peloubet, F. N. & Peloubet, M. A., eds. 1979. 8.95 (ISBN 0-8407-5542-2); pap. 5.95 (ISBN 0-8407-3085-3). Nelson.

--Smith's Bible Dictionary. 800p. pap. 4.95 (ISBN 0-8007-8039-6, Spire Bks). Revell.

--Smith's Bible Dictionary. (Illus.). 818p. 1981. pap. 7.95 (ISBN 0-310-32871-3, 10820P). Zondervan.

--Smith's Bible Dictionary. (Illus.). 1955. 10.95 (ISBN 0-310-32870-5, 10820). Zondervan.

--Smith's Bible Dictionary. 912p. Date not set. 10.95 (ISBN 0-917006-24-0). Hendrickson MA.

Smith, William & Cheetham, Samuel, eds. Dictionary of Christian Antiquities: Being a Continuation of the Dictionary of the Bible, 2 Vols. LC 17-21174. (LM). (Illus.). 1968. Repr. of 1880 ed. Set. 148.00 (ISBN 0-527-84150-1). Kraus Repr.

Smith, William & Wace, Henry, eds. Dictionary of Christian Biography, Literature, Sects & Doctrines: Being a Continuation of the Dictionary of the Bible, 4 Vols. LC 12-3122. 1968. Repr. of 1877 ed. Set. 375.00 (ISBN 0-527-84200-1). Kraus Repr.

Smith, William, tr. see Fichte, Johann G.

Smith, William A. Giovanni Gentile on the Existence of God. Matczak, S. A., ed. & intro. by. LC 70-111087. (Philosophical Questions Ser.: No. 7). 1970. 18.00 (ISBN 0-912116-04-8). Learned Pubns.

Smith, William C. Concerning Handel: His Life & Works. LC 78-59044. (Encore Music Editions). (Illus.). 1979. Repr. of 1948 ed. 27.50 (ISBN 0-88355-716-9). Hyperion Conn.

Smith, William H. St. Clair Papers: The Life & Public Services of Arthur St. Clair, 2 Vols. facs. ed. LC 77-117894. (Select Bibliographies Reprint Ser). 1881. Set. 62.00 (ISBN 0-8369-5347-9). Ayer Co Pubs.

Smith, William R. The Prophets of Israel. (Social Science Classics Ser.). 446p. text ed. cancelled (ISBN 0-87855-700-8); pap. text ed. cancelled (ISBN 0-686-68060-X). Transaction Bks.

--The Prophets of Israel: And Their Place in History to the Close of the Eighth Century, B.C. LC 77-87666. 504p. Repr. of 1907 ed. 47.50 (ISBN 0-404-16403-X). AMS Pr.

Smithline, Arnold. Natural Religion in American Literature. 1966. 11.95x (ISBN 0-8084-0227-7); pap. 7.95x (ISBN 0-8084-0228-5). New Coll U Pr.

Smith-Perkins, Staunton E. Satan in the Pulpit. (Illus.). 104p. (Orig.). 1982. pap. 4.95 (ISBN 0-943982-00-6, Dis. by Book Carrier). SES Development.

Smith-Savage, E. & Smith, M. B. Islamic Geomancy & a Thirteenth-Century Divinatory Device. LC 79-65001. (Studies in Near Eastern Culture & Society: Vol. 2). 91p. 1981. pap. 15.25x (ISBN 0-89003-038-3). Undena Pubns.

Smithson, Carma L. & Euler, Robert C. Havasupai Religion & Mythology. (Utah Anthropological Papers: No. 68). Repr. of 1964 ed. 14.00 (ISBN 0-404-60668-7). AMS Pr.

--Havasupai Religion & Mythology. viii, 112p. Repr. of 1964 ed. 19.00 (ISBN 0-384-56210-8). Johnson Repr.

Smithson, George A. Old English Christian Epic. LC 75-128192. 128p. 1971. Repr. of 1910 ed. 12.50x (ISBN 0-87753-050-5). Phaeton.

Smithson, Sandra. To Be the Bridge: A Black Perspective on White Catholicism in America. LC 84-50080. 200p. 1984. pap. 8.95 (ISBN 0-938232-48-7). Winston-Derek.

Smits, Edme R. Peter Abelard, Letters IX-XIV. xii, 315p. (Orig.). 1983. pap. 18.00x (ISBN 90-6088-085-4, Pub. by Boumas Boekhuis Netherlands). Benjamins North AM.

Smitty, William H. Three Hundred Sermon Outlines From the New Testament. LC 81-86666. (Orig.). 1983. pap. 4.50 (ISBN 0-8054-2246-3). Broadman.

Smock, Martha. Este Es el Tiempo para la Fe. Tr. of Now Is the Time for Faith. 1984. 5.95 (ISBN 0-87159-033-6). Unity School.

--Listen, Beloved. LC 80-50624. 177p. 1980. 5.95 (ISBN 0-87159-101-4). Unity School.

--Meet It with Faith. 1966. 5.95 (ISBN 0-87159-097-2). Unity School.

--Turning Points. LC 75-41954. 1976. 5.95 (ISBN 0-87159-156-1). Unity School.

Smoke, Jim. Every Single Day. 256p. 1983. 6.95 (ISBN 0-8007-5120-5, Power Bks). Revell.

--Suddenly Single. 120p. 1984. pap. 5.95 (ISBN 0-8007-5152-3, Power Bks). Revell.

--Turning Points. 192p. (Orig.). 1985. pap. 5.95 (ISBN 0-89081-484-8). Harvest Hse.

Smoke, Jim & Guest, Lisa. Growing Through Divorce: Working Guide. 96p. (Orig.). 1985. pap. 3.25 (ISBN 0-89081-477-5). Harvest Hse.

Smoke, Jim & McAfee, Lisa. Living Beyond Divorce: Working Guide. LC 83-82321. (Orig.). 1985. pap. 5.95 (ISBN 0-89081-407-4); working guide 3.95 (ISBN 0-89081-467-8). Harvest Hse.

Smolar, Hersh. The Minsk Ghetto. Rosenfeld, Max, tr. from Yiddish. 1987. 18.95 (ISBN 0-89604-068-2); pap. 13.95 (ISBN 0-89604-069-0). Holocaust Pubns.

Smolar, Leivy, jt. auth. see Churgin, Pinchas.

Smolarski, Dennis C. How Not to Say Mass: Guidebook for All Concerned about Authentic Worship. 96p. 1986. pap. 5.95 (ISBN 0-8091-2811-X). Paulist Pr.

Smoldon, W. L., jt. ed. see Greenberg, Noah.

Smothermon, Ron. Winning Through Enlightenment. 2nd ed. 226p. 1982. pap. 9.95 (ISBN 0-932654-01-0). Context Pubns.

Smuck, Harold. Friends in East Africa. 120p. (Orig.). 1987. pap. 8.95 (ISBN 0-913408-92-1). Friends United.

Smuck, Harold V. I Do Not Climb This Mountain Alone. (Illus.). 48p. (Orig.). 1985. pap. 3.00 (ISBN 0-913408-88-3). Friends United.

Smucker, Barbara C. Henry's Red Sea. LC 55-7810. (Christian Peace Shelf Ser.). (Illus.). 108p. 1955. 3.95 (ISBN 0-8361-1372-1). Herald Pr.

Smullyan, Raymond M. The Tao Is Silent. LC 76-62939. (Orig.). 1977. 8.95 (ISBN 0-685-75421-9, HarpR); pap. 4.95i (ISBN 0-06-067469-5, RD 206, HarpR). Har-Row.

Smuth, J. Paterson. The Ancient Documents & the Modern Bible. 212p. 1979. Repr. of 1920 ed. lib. bdg. 40.00 (ISBN 0-8495-4885-3). Arden Lib.

Smylie, James H. American Presbyterians: A Pictorial History. 1985. write for info. (ISBN 0-664-24679-6). Westminster.

Smyly, Barbara J., jt. auth. see Smyly, Glenn A.

Smyly, Glenn A. & Smyly, Barbara J. All in the Name of Love. 116p. 1986. 17.95 (ISBN 0-9616707-0-3); pap. 9.95 (ISBN 0-9616707-1-1). Alivening Pubns.

Smyres, Roy S. The Thoughts of Chairman Smyres: Chairman, under God, of His Own Life & Thought. vi, 146p. (Orig.). 1986. pap. 8.00 (ISBN 0-9616952-0-X). Smyres Pubns.

Smyth, Alexander. The True Life of Jesus of Nazareth - the Confessions of St. Paul. (Illus.). 1968. 7.95 (ISBN 0-932642-15-2); pap. write for info. (ISBN 0-932642-56-X). Unarius Pubns.

Smyth, Bernard T. Paul: Mystic & Missionary. LC 80-14041. 191p. (Orig.). 1980. pap. 3.98 (ISBN 0-88344-380-5). Orbis Bks.

Smyth, Charles H. Cranmer & the Reformation under Edward VI. Repr. of 1926 ed. lib. bdg. 22.50x (ISBN 0-8371-4025-0, SMCR). Greenwood.

Smyth, John. The Differences of the Churches of the Seperation Containing a Description of the Leitourgie & Ministerie of the Visible Church. LC 73-6161. (English Experience Ser.: No. 624). 32p. 1973. Repr. of 1608 ed. 5.00 (ISBN 90-221-0624-1). Walter J Johnson.

Smyth, John P. How We Got Our Bible. LC 77-24190. 1977. Repr. of 1912 ed. lib. bdg. 20.00 (ISBN 0-8414-7793-0). Folcroft.

Smyth, Mary Co. Biblical Quotations in Middle English Literature Before 1350. LC 74-18317. 1974. Repr. of 1910 ed. lib. bdg. 37.50 (ISBN 0-8414-7825-2). Folcroft.

Smyth, Mary W. Biblical Quotations in Middle English Literature, 2 vols. 105.00 (ISBN 0-87968-730-4). Gordon Pr.

Smyth, Norman. Story of Church Unity: The Lambeth Conference of Anglican Bishops & the Congregational-Episcopal Approaches. 1923. 29.50x (ISBN 0-686-83788-6). Elliots Bks.

Smyth, Norman & Walker, Williston. Approaches Toward Church Unity. 1919. 34.50x (ISBN 0-686-37862-8). Elliots Bks.

Smyth, Piazzi. Our Inheritance in the Great Pyramid, Vol. 8. LC 77-5284. (Illus.). 672p. 1980. Repr. of 1877 ed. lib. bdg. 45.00 (ISBN 0-89345-029-4, Spiritual Sci Lib). Garber Comm.

Smyth, Thomas. Calvin & His Enemies: A Memoir of the Life, Character & Principles of Calvin. rev. & enl. ed. LC 83-45632. Date not set. Repr. of 1909 ed. 28.00 (ISBN 0-404-19849-X). AMS Pr.

Snaith, John G., ed. Ecclesiasticus: Or, the Wisdom of Jesus Son of Sirach. LC 73-82459. (Cambridge Bible Commentary on the New English Bible, Old Testament Ser.). 180p. 1974. 32.50 (ISBN 0-521-08657-4); pap. 10.95 (ISBN 0-521-09775-4). Cambridge U Pr.

Snderson, H. George, et al, eds. Justification by Faith: Lutherans & Catholics in Dialogue VII. LC 84-28412. 320p. (Orig.). 1984. pap. 6.95 (ISBN 0-8066-2103-6, 10-3626). Augsburg.

Sneath, E. Hershey, ed. Evolution of Ethics. 1927. 49.50x (ISBN 0-685-69867-X). Elliots Bks.

Sneck, William J. Charismatic Spiritual Gifts: A Phenomenological Analysis. LC 80-8291. 312p. (Orig.). 1981. lib. bdg. 29.25 (ISBN 0-8191-1765-X); pap. text ed. 14.50 (ISBN 0-8191-1766-8). U Pr of Amer.

Sneen, Donald. Through Trials & Triumphs: A History of Augustana College. 192p. 1985. 17.00 (ISBN 0-931170-29-X). Ctr Western Studies.

Sneersohn, Haym Z. Palestine & Roumania: A Description of the Holy Land & the Past & Present State of Roumania & the Roumanian Jews. Davis, Moshe, ed. LC 77-70745. (America & the Holy Land Ser.). 1977. Repr. of 1872 ed. lib. bdg. 17.00x (ISBN 0-405-10291-7). Ayer Co Pubs.

Snelders, Philip, ed. see Sealey, John.

Snell, Beatrice S. Joint & Visible Fellowship. LC 65-19207. (Orig.). 1965. pap. 2.50x (ISBN 0-87574-140-1). Pendle Hill.

Snell, F. J. Wesley & Methodism. 243p. 1983. Repr. of 1900 ed. lib. bdg. 43.50 (ISBN 0-8495-4977-9). Arden Lib.

Snellgrove, David. Indo-Tibetan Buddhism: Indian Buddhists & Their Tibetan Successors. LC 85-2453. (Illus.). 550p. 1986. Vol. I. pap. 18.95 (ISBN 0-87773-311-2); Vol. II. pap. 18.95 (ISBN 0-87773-379-1). Shambhala Pubns.

Snellgrove, David & Richardson, Hugh. A Cultural History of Tibet. LC 85-27861. (Illus.). 307p. 1986. pap. 12.95 (ISBN 0-87773-353-8, 74380-6, Dist. by Random). Shambhala Pubns.

Snellgrove, David L. Hevajra Tantra, 2 Vols. 1959. 59.00x (ISBN 0-19-713516-1). Oxford U Pr.

Snelling, George. Allow Divine Energy to Help You. 181p. pap. 4.95 (ISBN 0-934142-03-3). Vancento Pub.

--The Divine Breakthrough. 92p. 1981. pap. 2.95 (ISBN 0-934142-01-7). Vancento Pub.

Snelling, John. Buddhism. (Religions of the World Ser.). (Illus.). 48p. 1986. PLB 10.90 (ISBN 0-531-18065-4, Pub. by Bookwright). Watts.

Snider, Denton J. A Biography of Ralph Waldo Emerson: Set Forth As His Life Essay. LC 77-9617. 1977. Repr. of 1921 ed. lib. bdg. 40.00 (ISBN 0-8414-7671-3). Folcroft.

--The Life of Emerson. 1973. Repr. of 1921 ed. 30.00 (ISBN 0-8274-0462-X). R West.

Snider, Joel P. The Cotton Patch Gospel: The Proclamation of Clarence Jordan. LC 85-6224. 112p. (Orig.). 1985. lib. bdg. 22.00 (ISBN 0-8191-4680-3); pap. text ed. 9.50 (ISBN 0-8191-4681-1). U Pr of Amer.

Snider, Theodore M. The Continuity of Salvation: A Study of Paul's Letter to the Romans. LC 84-42602. 200p. 1984. lib. bdg. 18.95x (ISBN 0-89950-126-5). McFarland & Co.

Snodgrass, John, tr. see Heine, Heinrich.

Snodgrass, Klyne. The Parable of the Wicked Tenants: An Inquiry into Parable Interpretation. 150p. 1983. pap. 48.00x (Pub. by J. C. B. Mohr BRD). Coronet Bks.

Snoek, J. Diedrich. Hunger for Community. LC 72-97850. (Orig.). 1973. pap. 2.50x (ISBN 0-87574-188-6). Pendle Hill.

Snook, Lee N. The Anonymous Christ: Jesus As Savior in Modern Theology. LC 86-14117. 192p. (Orig.). 1986. pap. 10.95 (ISBN 0-8066-2220-2, 10-0370). Augsburg.

Snow, Helen F. Totemism, the T'AO-T'iEH & the Chinese Ritual Bronzes. enl. ed. 100p. 1986. 35.00 (ISBN 0-686-64038-1). H F Snow.

Snow, Michael. Christian Pacifism. LC 81-69724. 98p. (Orig.). 1982. pap. 6.95 (ISBN 0-913408-67-0). Friends United.

Snowden, Rita. Christianity Close to Life. (Crossroad Paperback Ser.). 160p. 1982. pap. 5.95 (ISBN 0-8245-0459-3). Crossroad NY.

--Prayers in Later Life. 1981. pap. 3.50 (ISBN 0-8358-0435-6). Upper Room.

Snowman, Joel. The Legends of Israel. Levner, J. B., tr. from Hebrew. (Illus.). 233p. 1983. Repr. of 1946 ed. lib. bdg. 85.00 (ISBN 0-8495-5060-2). Arden Lib.

Snyder, Bernadet M. Dear God, I Have This Terrible Problem: A Housewife's Secret Letters. 96p. 1983. pap. 2.95 (ISBN 0-89243-188-1). Liguori Pubns.

Snyder, Bernadette. Graham Crackers, Galoshes & God. LC 82-82654. 96p. 1982. pap. 2.95 (ISBN 0-89243-164-4). Liguori Pubns.

--Hoorays & Hosannas. LC 80-66937. (Illus.). 56p. (Orig.). 1980. pap. 3.95 (ISBN 0-87793-205-0). Ave Maria.

Snyder, Bernadette M. Everyday Prayers for Everyday People. LC 83-63165. 132p. 1984. pap. 4.95 (ISBN 0-87973-604-6, 604). Our Sunday Visitor.

--Heavenly Hash: A Tasty Mix of a Mother's Meditations. LC 85-71564. 140p. (Orig.). 1985. pap. 6.95 (ISBN 0-87973-583-X, 583). Our Sunday Visitor.

--The Kitchen Sink Prayer Book. 96p. 1984. pap. 3.25 (ISBN 0-89243-217-9). Liguori Pubns.

--More Graham Crackers, Galoshes, & God. LC 85-80929. 96p. (Orig.). 1985. pap. 2.95 (ISBN 0-89243-243-8). Liguori Pubns.

Snyder, Bernadette M. & Terry, Hazelmai M. Decorations for Forty-Four Parish Celebrations: Enhancing Worship Experiences Tastefully & Simply. (Illus., Orig.). 1982. pap. 9.95 (ISBN 0-89622-167-9). Twenty-Third.

Snyder, C. Arnold. The Life & Thought of Michael Sattler. LC 83-22835. (Studies in Anabaptist & Mennonite History: No. 27). 264p. 1984. 19.95x (ISBN 0-8361-1264-4). Herald Pr.

Snyder, C. Arnoldo, tr. see Klaassen, Walter.

Snyder, Charles R. Alcohol & the Jews: A Cultural Study of Drinking & Sobriety. LC 77-24885. (Arcturus Books Paperbacks). 240p. 1978. pap. 6.95x (ISBN 0-8093-0846-0). S Ill U Pr.

Snyder, Chuck. Other Than That I Have No Opinion. 240p. (Orig.). 1985. pap. 5.95 (ISBN 0-8423-4763-1). Tyndale.

Snyder, Gary. He Who Hunted Birds in His Father's Village: The Dimensions of a Haida Myth. LC 78-16935. 154p. 1979. pap. 5.95 (ISBN 0-912516-38-0). Grey Fox.

Snyder, Graydon & Shaffer, Kenneth. Texts in Transit. (Orig.). 1976. pap. 2.95 (ISBN 0-685-61334-8). Brethren.

Snyder, Helen L. Five Dollar Convention. (Orig.). 1982. pap. 2.95 (ISBN 0-937172-31-6). JLJ Pubs.

--Shall We Take Down the Steeple? (Orig.). 1982. pap. 2.95 (ISBN 0-937172-42-1). JLJ Pubs.

--Why Be Without a Gripe? 1978. pap. 5.00 (ISBN 0-89536-310-0, 2344). CSS of Ohio.

Snyder, Howard. Comunidad del Rey. (Span.). 232p. (Orig.). 1983. pap. 5.50 (ISBN 0-317-00691-6). Edit Caribe.

--The Radical Wesley. LC 80-18197. 180p. (Orig.). 1980. pap. 5.95 (ISBN 0-87784-625-1). Inter-Varsity.

Snyder, Howard A. The Community of the King. LC 77-6030. (Illus.). 1977. pap. 7.95 (ISBN 0-87784-752-5). Inter-Varsity.

--A Kingdom Manifesto. LC 85-10725. 108p. (Orig.). 1985. pap. 5.95 (ISBN 0-87784-408-9). Inter-Varsity.

--Liberating the Church: The Ecology of Church & Kingdom. 280p. (Orig.). 1982. pap. 8.95 (ISBN 0-87784-385-6); cloth 12.95 (ISBN 0-87784-894-7). Inter-Varsity.

--The Problem of Wineskins: Church Renewal in Technological Age. LC 74-31842. (Illus.). 216p. 1975. pap. text ed. 6.95 (ISBN 0-87784-769-X). Inter-Varsity.

Snyder, Howard A. & Runyon, Daniel V. The Divided Flame: Wesleyans & the Charismatic Renewal. Ruark, James, ed. 128p. 1986. pap. 6.95 (ISBN 0-310-75181-0, 17082P). Zondervan.

--Foresight: Ten Major Trends That Will Dramatically Affect the Future of Christians & the Church. 176p. 1986. 12.95 (ISBN 0-8407-5531-7). Nelson.

Snyder, John. Reincarnation vs Resurrection. (Orig.). 1984. pap. 4.95 (ISBN 0-8024-0321-2). Moody.

Snyder, John I. The Promise of His Coming. LC 85-52310. 192p. 1986. pap. text ed. 12.50 (ISBN 0-936029-01-3). Western Bk Journ.

Snyder, Pam. A Life Styled by God: A Woman's Workshop on Spiritual Discipline for Weight Control. (Woman's Workshop Ser.). 112p. (Orig.). 1985. pap. 2.95 (ISBN 0-310-42791-6, 11378P). Zondervan.

Snyder, Phillip V. The Christmas Tree Book: The History of the Christmas Tree & Antique Christmas Tree Ornaments. LC 76-40224. (Large Format Ser.). (Illus.). 176p. 1977. pap. 10.95 (ISBN 0-14-004518-X). Penguin.

--December Twenty-Fifth: The Joy of Christmas Past. (Illus.). 346p. 1985. 17.95 (ISBN 0-396-08588-1). Dodd.

Snyder, Ross, ed. Openings into Ministry. LC 77-92707. (Studies in Ministry & Parish Life). 1977. 13.95x (ISBN 0-913552-10-0); pap. 5.95x (ISBN 0-913552-11-9). Exploration Pr.

Soames, Henry. The Anglo-Saxon Church: Its History, Revenues & General Character. 4th ed. LC 80-2212. Repr. of 1856 ed. 39.50 (ISBN 0-404-18786-2). AMS Pr.

Soards, Marion J. Thinking about Paul: His Life, Letters, & Theology. 224p. (Orig.). 1987. pap. 8.95 (ISBN 0-8091-2864-0). Paulist Pr.

Soards, Marion L. The Apostle Paul: An Introduction to His Writings & Teaching. 1987. pap. 8.95. Paulist Pr.

--The Passion According to Luke: The Special Material of Luke 22. (JSOT Supplement Ser.: No. 14). 150p. 1987. text ed. 24.50x (ISBN 1-85075-036-X, Pub. by JSOT Pr England); pap. text ed. 11.95x (ISBN 1-85075-037-8, Pub. by JSOT Pr England). Eisenbrauns.

Sobel, Jyoti, ed. see Aurobindo, Sri & Mother.

Sobel, Mechal. Trabelin' On: The Slave Journey to an Afro-Baptist Faith. LC 77-84775. (Contributions in Afro-American & African Studies: No. 36). 1978. lib. bdg. 35.00 (ISBN 0-8371-9887-9, STO/). Greenwood.

Sobel, Prem, ed. see Aurobindo, Sri & Mother.

Sobel, Ronald & Wallach, Sidney. Justice, Justice, Shalt Thou Pursue. 10.00x (ISBN 0-87068-458-2). Ktav.

Sobini, John. Armies in the Sand: The Struggle for Mecca & Medina. (Illus.). 223p. 11.95 (ISBN 0-500-01246-6). Brown Bk.

Sobrino, Jon. Christology at the Crossroads: A Latin American Approach. Drury, John, tr. from Span. LC 77-25025. Orig. Title: Cristologia desde America Latina. 458p. (Orig.). 1978. pap. 13.95 (ISBN 0-88344-076-8). Orbis Bks.

--Jesus in Latin America. LC 86-23485. Tr. of Jesus en America Latina: Su significada para la fe y la cristologia. 192p. (Orig.). 1987. pap. 11.95 (ISBN 0-88344-412-7). Orbis Bks.

--The True Church & the Poor. O'Connell, Mathew J., tr. from Span. LC 84-5661. Orig. Title: Resureccion de la Verdadera Iglesia, Los Pobres Lugar Teologica de la Eclesiologia. 384p. (Orig.). 1984. pap. 13.95 (ISBN 0-88344-513-1). Orbis Bks.

Sobrino, Jon & Pico, Juan H. Theology of Christian Solidarity. Berryman, Phillip, tr. from Span. LC 84-16533. Orig. Title: Teologia de la Solidaridad Chrisiana. 112p. (Orig.). 1985. pap. 7.95 (ISBN 0-88344-452-6). Orbis Bks.

Soby, James T. Georges Rouault: Paintings & Prints. LC 70-169317. (Museum of Modern Art Publications in Reprint). Repr. of 1947 ed. 24.50 (ISBN 0-405-01575-5). Ayer Co Pubs.

Society for Psychical Report. Report on Theosophical Society. LC 75-36920. (Occult Ser.). (Illus.). 1976. 26.50x (ISBN 0-405-07975-3). Ayer Co Pubs.

Society for the Right to Die. Handbook of Living Will Laws 1976-1980. rev. ed. Orig. Title: Handbook of Enacted Laws 1981 Handbook. 64p. pap. cancelled (ISBN 0-9613825-3-8). Soc Right to Die.

--Handbook of 1985 Living Will Laws. 128p. (Orig.). 1986. pap. 5.00x (ISBN 0-9613825-2-X). Soc Right to Die.

Society of Biblical Literature & Achtemeier, Paul J., eds. Harper's Bible Dictionary. LC 85-42767. (Illus.). 1194p. 1985. thumb indexed 29.95 (ISBN 0-06-069863-2, HarpR); 27.50 (ISBN 0-06-069862-4). Har-Row.

Society of Brothers, tr. see Arnold, Emmy.

Society of Metaphysicians Staff, ed. Etheric Heliang. 12.00x (ISBN 0-317-43573-6, Pub. by Soc of Metaphysicians). State Mutual Bk.

Sockey, Daria. Our Heavenly Father. (Faith & Life Ser.: Bk. 1). (Illus.). 125p. 1987. pap. text ed. 4.95; activity book 2.50. Ignatius Pr.

Sockey, Daria M. Credo: I Believe. Puccetti, Patricia I., ed. (Faith & Life Ser.). (Illus.). 132p. 1985. pap. 6.20 (ISBN 0-89870-081-7). Ignatius Pr.

Socrates & Plato. The Psychology of Fate & of Free Will. (Illus.). 121p. 1983. 75.85 (ISBN 0-89920-067-2). Am Inst Psych.

Soden, R. W. A Guide to Welsh Parish Churches. 149p. 1985. 40.50x (ISBN 0-86383-082-X, Pub. by Gomer Pr). State Mutual Bk.

Soderblom, Nathan. The Living God: Basal Forms of Personal Religion. LC 77-27196. (Gifford Lectures: 1931). Repr. of 1933 ed. 40.00 (ISBN 0-404-60485-4). AMS Pr.

Soderholm, Marjorie. Explaining Salvation to Children. 8th ed. 1979. pap. 1.50 (ISBN 0-911802-13-4). Free Church Pubns.

--Prayers That Make a Difference. rev. ed. Orig. Title: A Study Guide to Bible Prayers. 96p. 1980. pap. 2.50 (ISBN 0-911802-49-5). Free Church Pubns.

--Salvation, Then What. 1968. pap. 1.75 (ISBN 0-911802-14-2). Free Church Pubns.

Soderholm, Marjorie E. Understanding the Pupil, 3 pts. Incl. Pt. 1. The Pre-School Child; Pt. 2. The Primary & Junior Child; Pt. 3. The Adolescent. pap. 2.50 (ISBN 0-8010-7922-5). pap. Baker Bk.

Soderlund, G. F. & Scott, Samuel H., eds. Examples of Gregorian Chant & Other Sacred Music of the 16th Century. LC 70-129090. (Orig.). 1971. 27.95 (ISBN 0-13-293753-0). P-H.

Soderlund, Jean R. Quakers & Slavery: A Divided Spirit. LC 85-42707. (Illus.). 240p. 1985. text ed. 27.50x (ISBN 0-691-04732-4). Princeton U Pr.

Soderlund, Jean R. & Dunn, Richard S., eds. William Penn & the Founding of Pennsylvania, 1680-1684: A Documentary History. (Illus.). 380p. 1983. 26.50x (ISBN 0-8122-7862-3); pap. 10.95x (ISBN 0-8122-1131-6). U of Pa Pr.

Soderlund, Sven. The Greek Text of Jeremiah: A Revised Hypothesis. (JSOT Supplement Ser.: No. 47). 304p. 1986. text ed. 27.50x (ISBN 1-85075-028-9, Pub. by JSOT Pr England); pap. text ed. 13.50 (ISBN 0-317-46787-5). Eisenbrauns.

Soderman, Danuta. A Passion for Living. 1987. 11.95 (ISBN 0-8007-1534-9). Revell.

Sodipo, J. O., jt. auth. see Hallen, Barry.

Soekmono, Dr. Chandi Borobudur: A Monument of Mankind. (Illus.). 53p. (Co-published with Van Gorcum, Amsterdam). 1976. pap. 8.25 (ISBN 92-3-101292-4, U69, UNESCO). Bernan-Unipub.

Soelle, Dorothee. Choosing Life. Kohl, Margaret, tr. from Ger. LC 81-43082. Tr. of Wahlt das Leben. 128p. 1981. 9.95 (ISBN 0-8006-0667-1, 1-667). Fortress.

--Death by Bread Alone: Texts & Reflections on Religious Experience. Scheidt, David L., tr. from Ger. LC 77-78643. 168p. 1978. 2.00 (ISBN 0-8006-0514-4, 1-514). Fortress.

--The Strength of the Weak: Towards a Christian Feminist Identity. Kimber, Rita & Kimber, Robert, trs. LC 83-27348. 184p. (Orig.). 1984. pap. 9.95 (ISBN 0-664-24623-0). Westminster.

--Suffering. Kalin, Everett R., tr. from Ger. LC 75-13036. 192p. 1975. 10.95 (ISBN 0-8006-1813-0, 1-813); pap. 5.95. Fortress.

Soelle, Dorothee & Cloyes, Shirley A. To Work & to Love: A Theology of Creation. LC 84-47936. 160p. 1984. pap. 7.95 (ISBN 0-8006-1782-7). Fortress.

Soelle, Dorothee & Steffensky, Fulbert. Not Just Yes & Amen: Christians with a Cause. LC 84-48708. 96p. 1985. pap. 3.50 (ISBN 0-8006-1828-9, 1-1828). Fortress.

Sogaard, Viggo B. Everything You Need to Know for a Cassette Ministry. LC 74-20915. 224p. 1975. pap. 7.95 (ISBN 0-87123-125-5, 210125). Bethany Hse.

Sogen, Omori & Katsujo, Terayama. Zen & the Art of Calligraphy. Stevens, John, tr. from Japanese. (Illus.). 128p. (Orig.). 1983. pap. 13.95 (ISBN 0-7100-9284-9). Methuen Inc.

Sogen, Yamakami. Systems of Buddhist Thought. 385p. Repr. of 1912 ed. text ed. 28.50x (ISBN 0-89644-474-0, Pub. by Chinese Matl Ctr). Coronet Bks.

Soggin, J. Albert. A History of Ancient Israel. Bowden, John, tr. from Italian. LC 84-27010. (Illus.). 452p. 1985. 29.95 (ISBN 0-664-21258-1). Westminster.

Soggin, J. Alberto. Introduction to the Old Testament. Rev. ed. Bowden, John, tr. LC 81-3422. (Old Testament Library). 544p. 1982. 27.50 (ISBN 0-664-21385-5). Westminster.
--Joshua: A Commentary. Wilson, R. A., tr. LC 72-76954. (Old Testament Library). 264p. 1972. 14.95 (ISBN 0-664-20938-6). Westminster.
--Judges: A Commentary. Bowden, John, tr. from Ital. LC 81-7600. (Old Testament Library). 324p. 1981. text ed. 21.95 (ISBN 0-664-21368-5). Westminster.
Soghoian, Richard J. The Ethics of G. E. Moore & David Hume: The Treatise as a Response to Moore's Refutation of Ethical Naturalism. LC 79-88306. 1979. pap. text ed. 9.50 (ISBN 0-8191-0774-3). U Pr of Amer.
Sohl, Robert & Carr, Audrey. Games Zen Masters Play: The Writings of R. H. Blyth. 1976. pap. 3.50 (ISBN 0-451-62416-5, Ment). NAL.
Sohl, Robert & Carr, Audrey, eds. Gospel According to Zen: Beyond the Death of God. (Orig.). 1970. pap. 2.95 (ISBN 0-451-62184-0, ME2184, Ment). NAL.
Soho, Takuan. The Unfettered Mind: Writings of the Zen Master to the Sword Master. LC 86-45072. 92p. 1986. 12.95 (ISBN 0-87011-776-9). Kodansha.
Sokol, Dolly, jt. auth. see Geaney, Dennis J.
Sokoloff, D. Archpriest. Manual of the Orthodox Church's Divine Services. 172p. (Orig.). 1975. pap. 6.00 (ISBN 0-317-30302-3). Holy Trinity.
Sokolosky, Barbara A., ed. American Sunday School Union Papers, 1817-1915: A Guide to the Microfilm Edition. 154p. (Orig.). 1980. pap. text ed. 50.00 (ISBN 0-667-00582-X). Microfilming Corp.
Sokolosky, Valerie. Seasons of Success. 1985. pap. 3.95 (ISBN 0-89274-382-4). Harrison Hse.
Sokolov, P. Russkii Arkhierei iz Vizantii i Pravo Ego Naznacheniia do Nachala XV Veka. 582p. 1913. text ed. 74.52x (ISBN 0-576-99187-2, Pub. by Gregg Intl Pubs England). Gregg Intl.
Sokolow, Nahum. History of Zionism, 2 Vols. in 1. rev. ed. LC 68-19730. (Illus.). 1969. 45.00x (ISBN 0-87068-107-9). Ktav.
Sokolowski, Robert. The God of Faith & Reason: Foundations of Christian Theology. LC 81-19813. 192p. 1982. 15.95 (ISBN 0-268-01006-4); pap. text ed. 6.95 (ISBN 0-268-01007-2). U of Notre Dame Pr.
Sola, Carla de see De Sola, Carla.
Sola Pinto, Vivan De see Pinto, Vivan De Sola.
Solari, Placid, tr. see Quasten, Johannes & Di Berardino, Angelo.
Solberg, Richard W. Lutheran Higher Education in North America. LC 85-28757. 400p. (Orig.). 1985. pap. 9.95 (ISBN 0-8066-2187-7, 10-4168). Augsburg.
Solberg, Richard W. & Strommen, Merton P. How Church-Related Are Church-Related Colleges? Answers Based on a Comprehensive Survey of Supporting Constituencies of 18 LCA Colleges. LC 80-13833. 96p. (Orig.). 1980. pap. 3.95 (ISBN 0-8006-1388-0, 1-1388). Fortress.
Solberg, Winton U. Cotton Mather, the Christian Philosopher & the Classics. 44p. 1987. pap. write for info. (ISBN 0-912296-90-9). Am Antiquarian.
--Redeem the Time: The Puritan Sabbath in Early America. (Illus.). 1977. 25.00x (ISBN 0-674-75130-2). Harvard U Pr.
Sole-Leris, Amadeo. Tranquillity & Insight: An Introduction to the Oldest Form of Buddhist Meditation. LC 86-11834. 176p. 1986. pap. 7.95 (ISBN 0-87773-385-6). Shambhala Pubns.
Solignac, Pierre. Christian Neurosis. 256p. 1982. 12.95 (ISBN 0-8245-0108-X). Crossroad NY.
Solle, Dorothee. Of War & Love. Kimber, Robert & Kimber, Rita, trs. from Ger. LC 83-8252. Orig. Title: Im Hause Des Menschenfressers. 172p. (Orig.). 1983. pap. 7.95 (ISBN 0-88344-350-3). Orbis Bks.
Solle, Dorothee, jt. auth. see Naude, C. F.
Sollmann, F. W. Religion & Politics. 1983. pap. 2.50x (ISBN 0-87574-014-6, 014). Pendle Hill.
Sollmann, William F. Zwischen Krieg und Frieden. 1983. pap. 2.50x (ISBN 0-87574-045-6, 045). Pendle Hill.
Sollov, Jacques. Reborn Again in the Kingdom. LC 81-71382. (The Temple of Love Ser.). (Illus.). 128p. (Orig.). 1982. pap. 10.95 (ISBN 0-941804-04-6). White Eagle Pub.
Solmsen, Friedrich. Plato's Theology. 1942. 24.00 (ISBN 0-384-56600-6). Johnson Repr.
Soloff, Mordecai I. The Covenant People, Vol. 1: The First 2,000 Years of Jewish Life. LC 72-97080. (Illus.). 1973. 3.95x (ISBN 0-8246-0154-8); tchr's guide 8.95x (ISBN 0-685-30240-7); wkbk 2.95x (ISBN 0-8246-0155-6). Jonathan David.
--The Covenant People, Vol. 2: The Battle for Survival from Talmudic Times to the End of World War I. LC 72-97080. (Illus.). 1974. 3.95x; tchr's guide 8.95x (ISBN 0-685-47972-2); wkbk 2.95x (ISBN 0-8246-0155-6). Jonathan David.
Solomon, Bernard A. The Zaddick Christ: A Suite of Wood Engravings. (Illus.). 84p. 1974. 16.95 (ISBN 0-87921-022-2). Attic Pr.
Solomon, C. R. Hacia la Felicidad: Como Vivir una Vida Victoriosa y Practicar la Terapia Espiritual. 1983. Repr. of 1979 ed. 3.75 (ISBN 0-311-42060-5). Casa Bautista.
Solomon, Charles. Handbook to Happiness. 1982. pap. 5.95 (ISBN 0-8423-1281-1); leader's guide 2.95 (ISBN 0-8423-1282-X). Tyndale.
Solomon, Charles R. Counseling with the Mind of Christ: The Dynamics of Spirituotherapy. 160p. 1977. pap. 5.95 (ISBN 0-8007-5049-7, Power Bks). Revell.
--The Rejection Syndrome. 144p. 1982. pap. 5.95 (ISBN 0-8423-5417-4). Tyndale.
Solomon, Charmaine & Huxley, Dee. Love & a Wooden Spoon. LC 83-25446. 168p. 1985. pap. 10.00 (ISBN 0-385-19387-4). Doubleday.
Solomon, Dorothy A. In My Father's House. LC 84-11964. 312p. 1984. 17.95 (ISBN 0-531-09763-3). Watts.
Solomon, Frieda, tr. see Steiner, Rudolf.
Solomon, Robert C. In the Spirit of Hegel: A Study of G. W. F. Hegel's "Phenomenology of Spirit". (Illus.). 1983. 32.50x (ISBN 0-19-503169-5); pap. 14.95x (ISBN 0-19-503650-6). Oxford U Pr.
--The Passions. xxv, 448p. 1983. text ed. 22.95x (ISBN 0-268-01551-1); pap. text ed. 9.95x (ISBN 0-268-01552-X). U of Notre Dame Pr.
Soloveitchik, Aaron. The Fire of Sinai. (Annual Fryer Memorial Lecture Ser.). 1.00 (ISBN 0-914131-20-6, I32). Torah Umesorah.
--Law & Morality in Modern Society. (Annual Fryer Memorial Lecture Ser.). 0.75 (ISBN 0-914131-40-0, I33). Torah Umesorah.
Soloveitchik, Joseph B. Halakhic Man. Kaplan, Lawrence, tr. from Hebrew. 182p. 1984. 12.95 (ISBN 0-8276-0222-7, 606). Jewish Pubns.
--The Halakhic Mind: Rabbinic Judaism & Modern Thought. 128p. 1986. 16.95 (ISBN 0-02-930040-1). Free Pr.
Soloveitchik, Joseph D. Soloveitchik on Repentance. Peli, Pinchas, tr. 320p. 1984. 11.95 (ISBN 0-8091-2604-4). Paulist Pr.
Solovyev, Vladimir. God, Man & the Church. Attwater, Donald, tr. from Rus. 192p. 1975. 10.95 (ISBN 0-227-67690-4). Attic Pr.
--Lectures in Godmanhood. 214p. 1981. 37.00x (ISBN 0-234-77047-3, Pub. by Dobson Bks England). State Mutual Bk.
Solovyoff, Vsevolod S. A Modern Priestess of Isis. Leaf, Walter, tr. LC 75-36921. (Occult Ser.). 1976. Repr. of 1895 ed. 26.50x (ISBN 0-405-07976-1). Ayer Co Pubs.
Solovyov, Vladimir. The Meaning of Love. rev. ed. 144p. 1985. pap. 7.95 (ISBN 0-89281-068-8, Lindisfarne Pr). Inner Tradit.
Solowsky, Alan S. God & the American Corporation. (International Council for Excellence in Management Library). (Illus.). 1980. deluxe ed. 69.95 (ISBN 0-89266-266-2). Am Classical Coll Pr.
Solt, Leo F. Saints in Arms. LC 74-153355. (Stanford University. Stanford Studies in History, Economics & Political Science: No. 18). Repr. of 1959 ed. 19.00 (ISBN 0-404-50976-2). AMS Pr.
Soltau, Henry W. Holy Vessels & Furniture of the Tabernacle. LC 74-85428. (Illus.). 148p. 1986. pap. 12.95 (ISBN 0-8254-3751-2). Kregel.
--Tabernacle, Priesthood & the Offerings. LC 72-88590. 486p. 1974. 14.95 (ISBN 0-8254-3703-2); Published 1986. pap. 12.95 (ISBN 0-8254-3750-4). Kregel.
Somadeva, Bhatta. The Buddhist Legend of Jimutavahana. LC 78-70116. Repr. of 1911 ed. 20.50 (ISBN 0-404-17373-X). AMS Pr.
Somayyah, tr. see Shari'Ati, Ali.
Sombart, Werner. Jews & Modern Capitalism. LC 81-16152. (Social Science Classics Ser.). 475p. 1982. pap. 19.95 (ISBN 0-87855-837-3). Transaction Bks.
Some, Robert. A Godly Treatise Containing & Deciding Certaine Questions. LC 74-80231. (English Experience Ser.: No. 696). 204p. 1974. Repr. of 1588 ed. 20.00 (ISBN 90-221-0696-9). Walter J Johnson.
Somendra, Swami Anand, ed. see Rajneesh, Bhagwan S.
Somendra, Swami Anand, ed. see Rajneesh, Bhagwan Shree.
Somerset, Douglas P. The Destructive Conception of God in Kant's "Philosophy of Man". (Illus.). 129p. 1982. 73.45 (ISBN 0-89266-355-3). Am Classical Coll Pr.
Somervill, Charles. Leadership Strategies for Ministers. Cummings, H. Wayland, ed. LC 86-26788. 132p. (Orig.). 1987. pap. 8.95 (ISBN 0-664-24062-3). Westminster.
Somerville, Robert. Pope Alexander III & the Council of Tours (1163) A Study of Ecclesiastical Politics & Institutions in the Twelfth Century. (Center for Medieval & Renaissance Studies, UCLA: Publications No. 12). 1978. 24.50x (ISBN 0-520-03184-9). U of Cal Pr.
Somerville, Robert, ed. Scotia Pontificia: Papal Letters to Scotland Before the Pontificate of Innocent III, 1198 to 1216. 1981. 65.00x (ISBN 0-19-822433-8). Oxford U Pr.
Somerville, Robert & Pennington, Kenneth, eds. Law, Church, & Society: Essays in Honor of Stephan Kuttner. LC 76-53199. 1977. 27.95x (ISBN 0-8122-7726-0). U of Pa Pr.
Sommer, Fedor. The Iron Collar. Berky, Andrew S., tr. 261p. 1982. pap. 4.00 (ISBN 0-935980-01-6). Schwenkfelder Lib.
Sommer, H. O., ed. see Robinson, T.
Sommerdfeldt, John R., ed. Simplicity & Ordinariness: Studies in Medieval Cistercian History, Vol. IV. (Cistercian Studies: No. 61). (Orig.). 1980. pap. text ed. 8.95 (ISBN 0-87907-861-8). Cistercian Pubns.
Sommerfeldt, J. R., ed. Studies in Medieval Cistercian History, Vol. 2. (Studies Ser.: No. 24). 1977. pap. 10.95 (ISBN 0-87907-824-3). Cistercian Pubns.
Sommerfeldt, John R., ed. ABBA: Guides to Wholeness & Holiness East & West. (Cistercian Studies: No. 38). 1982. 22.95 (ISBN 0-87907-838-3). Cistercian Pubns.
--Cistercian Ideals & Reality. LC 78-16615. (Cistercian Studies: No. 60). 1978. pap. 8.95 (ISBN 0-87907-860-X). Cistercian Pubns.
Sommerville, C. John. Popular Religion in Restoration England. LC 77-7618. (University of Florida Social Sciences Monographs: No. 59). 1977. pap. 4.50 (ISBN 0-8130-0564-7). U Presses Fla.
Sonderegger-Kummer, Irene. Transparenz der Wirklichkeit: Edzard Schaper und die innere Spannung in der christlichen Literatur des zwanzigstes Jahrhunderts. (Quellen und Forschungen zur Sprach- und Kulturgeschichte der germanischen Voelker, No. 37). (Ger). 1971. 48.40x (ISBN 3-11-001845-4). De Gruyter.
Sondhi, Krishan. Communication & Values. 1986. 22.50X (Pub. by Somaiya). South Asia Bks.
Sondrup, Steven P., ed. Arts & Inspiration: Mormon Perspectives. LC 80-21927. (Illus.). 240p. 1980. pap. 7.95 (ISBN 0-8425-1845-2). Brigham.
Song, C. S. Tell Us Our Names: Story Theology from an Asian Perspective. LC 84-5139. (Illus.). 224p. (Orig.). 1984. pap. 10.95 (ISBN 0-88344-512-3). Orbis Bks.
--Theology from the Womb of Asia. 256p. (Orig.). 1986. pap. 12.95 (ISBN 0-88344-518-2, 85-31008). Orbis Bks.
Song, Choan-Seng. The Compassionate God. LC 81-16972. 304p. (Orig.). 1982. pap. 12.95 (ISBN 0-88344-095-4). Orbis Bks.
--The Tears of Lady Meng: A Parable of People's Political Theology. LC 82-2295. (Illus.). 80p. (Orig.). 1982. pap. 4.95 (ISBN 0-88344-505-0). Orbis Bks.
--Third-Eye Theology: Theology in Formation in Asian Settings. LC 79-4208. pap. 72.00 (ISBN 0-317-26666-7, 2025121). Bks Demand UMI.
Song, Grace Y., et al, eds. The Bible Compiled for A Blessed Life. LC 83-26389. 680p. (Orig.). 1984. pap. 4.95 (ISBN 0-916075-00-1). Intl Life Mess.
Sonne, Conway B. Ships, Saints, & Mariners: A Maritime Encyclopedia of Mormon Migration, 1830-1890. 256p. 1987. 19.50x (ISBN 0-87480-270-9). U of Utah Pr.
Sonneck, Oscar G. Francis Hopkinson, the First American Poet-Composer, & James Lyon, Patriot, Preacher, Psalmodist. 2nd ed. LC 65-23393. (Music Reprint Ser.). 213p. 1966. Repr. of 1905 ed. lib. bdg. 32.50 (ISBN 0-306-70918-X). Da Capo.
Sonnenfeld, Albert. Crossroads: Essays on the Catholic Novelists. 138p. 1982. 13.95 (ISBN 0-917786-24-6). Summa Pubns.
Sonnenfeld, Jean, jt. auth. see McMullen, Eleanor.
Sonnier, Isadore L., ed. Methods & Techniques of Holistic Education. (Illus.). 184p. 1985. 21.50 (ISBN 0-398-05054-6). C C Thomas.
Sonsino, Rifat. Motive Clauses in Hebrew Law: Biblical Forms & Near Eastern Parallels. LC 79-15024. (Society of Biblical Literature Dissertation Ser.: No. 45). 15.95 (ISBN 0-89130-317-0, 060145); pap. 10.95 (ISBN 0-89130-318-9). Scholars Pr GA.
Sonsino, Rifat & Syme, Daniel B. Finding God. 1986. 7.95 (ISBN 0-8074-0312-1, 571200). UAHC.
Sontag, Frederick. A Kierkegaard Handbook. LC 79-87741. 1980. pap. 7.25 (ISBN 0-8042-0654-6). John Knox.
Sontag, Frederick & Bryant, Darrol, eds. God, the Contemporary Discussion. LC 82-70771. 419p. (Orig.). 1982. pap. 13.95 (ISBN 0-318-03629-0). Rose Sharon Pr.
Sontag, Frederick & Bryant, M. Darrol, eds. God: The Contemporary Discussion. LC 82-70771. (Conference Ser.: No. 12). vi, 419p. (Orig.). 1982. pap. text ed. 12.95 (ISBN 0-932894-12-7, Pub. by New Era Bks). Paragon Hse.
Sontag, Fredrick E., jt. ed. see Roth, John.
Sookhdeo, Patrick. Jesus Christ the Only Way: Christian Responsibility in the Multicultural Society. 159p. 1978. pap. 5.95 (ISBN 0-85364-236-2). Attic Pr.
Sookhdeo, Patrick, intro. by. Christianity & Other Faiths. 48p. 1983. pap. 2.95 (ISBN 0-85364-363-6, Pub. by Paternoster UK). Attic Pr.
Soothill, W. E. The Lotus of the Wonderful Law, or the Lotus Gospel. (Illus.). 288p. 1987. pap. 9.95 (ISBN 0-391-03465-0, Pub. by Curzon Pr England). Humanities.
Soothill, William E. The Three Religions of China. LC 73-899. (China Studies: from Confucius to Mao Ser.). (Illus.). 271p. 1973. Repr. of 1929 ed. 28.00 (ISBN 0-88355-093-8). Hyperion Conn.
Sopa, Geshe Lhundup & Hopkins, Jeffrey. The Practice & Theory of Tibetan Buddhism. LC 75-42898. 1976. pap. 4.95 (ISBN 0-394-17905-6, E672, Ever). Grove.
Soper, Alexander C. The Evolution of Buddhist Architecture in Japan. LC 76-26054. (Illus.). 1978. Repr. of 1942 ed. lib. bdg. 75.00 (ISBN 0-87817-196-7). Hacker.
Soper, Charlton W. The Important Muromachi, Momoyama & Edo Periods in the Growth of Buddhist Architecture in Japan. (Illus.). 101p. 1987. 127.50 (ISBN 0-86650-218-1). Gloucester Art.
--The Kamakura Period in the Evolution of Buddhist Architecture in Japan. (Illus.). 143p. 1987. 147.75 (ISBN 0-86650-217-3). Gloucester Art.
Soper, David W. Men Who Shape Belief. LC 76-86061. (Essay & General Literature Index Reprint Ser). 1969. Repr. of 1955 ed. 24.00x (ISBN 0-8046-0588-2, Pub. by Kennikat). Assoc Faculty Pr.
Soper, Donald. Calling for Action: An Autobiographical Enquiry. LC 84-129410. (Illus.). 172p. 1985. 16.00 (ISBN 0-86051-265-7). Salem Hse Pubs.
Soper, Kate. Humanism & Anti-Humanism. 154p. 1986. 9.95 (ISBN 0-8126-9017-6). Open Court.
Sophrony, Archimandrite. His Life Is Mine. Edmonds, Rosemary, tr. from Russian. LC 76-56815. 128p. 1977. pap. 5.95 (ISBN 0-913836-33-8). St Vladimirs.
--The Monk of Mount Athos: Staretz Silouan 1866-1938. LC 61-4333. 124p. 1975. pap. 4.95 (ISBN 0-913836-15-X). St Vladimirs.
--Wisdom from Mount Athos: The Writings of Staretz Silouan, 1866-1938. 124p. 1974. pap. 5.95 (ISBN 0-913836-17-6). St Vladimirs.
Sorauf, Frank J. The Wall of Separation: The Constitutional Politics of Church & State. LC 75-3476. 420p. 1976. 40.00x (ISBN 0-691-07574-3). Princeton U Pr.
Sordi, Marta. The Christians & the Roman Empire. Bedini, Annabel, tr. LC 86-40081. 224p. 1986. 22.50x (ISBN 0-8061-2011-8). U of Okla Pr.
Sorensen, David A. The Friendship Olympics: A Young Christian Book for Boys. LC 86-32259. 112p. 1987. pap. 4.95 (ISBN 0-8066-2248-2, 10-2430). Augsburg.
--It's a Mystery to Me, Lord: Bible Devotions for Boys. LC 85-22993. (Young Readers Ser.). 112p. (Orig.). 1985. pap. 3.95 (ISBN 0-8066-2183-4, 10-3445). Augsburg.
Sorensen, S. An Index to the Names in the Mahabharata. 1978. Repr. 30.00 (ISBN 0-89684-011-5, Pub. by Motilal Banarsidass India). Orient Bk Dist.
Sorenson, Amanda, jt. auth. see Sorenson, Stephen.
Sorenson, Jane. Five Minutes with God, No. 2. (Illus.). 64p. 1985. pap. 2.50 (ISBN 0-87239-894-3, 2824). Standard Pub.
--Time Out for God. 64p. 1985. pap. 2.50 (ISBN 0-87239-895-1, 2825). Standard Pub.
--Time Out for God, No. 2. 64p. 1985. pap. 2.50 (ISBN 0-87239-896-X, 2826). Standard Pub.
Sorenson, John. An Ancient American Setting for the Book of Mormon. 400p. 1985. 14.95 (ISBN 0-87747-608-X). Deseret Bk.
Sorenson, Stephen. Growing Up Isn't Easy, Lord: Story Devotions for Boys. LC 79-50080. 1979. pap. 3.95 (ISBN 0-8066-1713-6, 10-2904). Augsburg.
--Lord, Teach Me Your Ways: Children's Stories with Biblical Parallels. LC 81-2067. 96p. 1982. 6.95 (ISBN 0-687-22660-0). Abingdon.
Sorenson, Stephen & Sorenson, Amanda. When Easy Answers Play Hard to Get: Decision Making for Young Teens. LC 84-11123. (Young Teens Ser.). 128p. (Orig.). 1984. pap. 3.95 (ISBN 0-8066-2084-6, 10-7080). Augsburg.
Sorenson, Stephen, jt. auth. see Kopp, Ruth.
Sorenson, Stephen W. Lord, I Want to Know You Better: Story Devotions for Boys. LC 81-52280. 112p. (Orig.). 1982. pap. 3.95 (ISBN 0-8066-1912-0, 10-4103). Augsburg.
Sorg, Henry C. Rosegger's Religion. LC 78-140029. (Catholic University Studies in German Ser.: No. 11). 1970. Repr. of 1938 ed. 24.00 (ISBN 0-404-50231-8). AMS Pr.

Sorge, Bob. Exploring Worship: Practical Guide to Praise & Worship. 304p. (Orig.). 1987. pap. 5.95 (ISBN 0-936369-04-3). Son-Rise Pubns.

Sork, David, et al. The Catechist Formation Book. LC 80-84507. 200p. (Orig.). 1981. pap. 7.95 (ISBN 0-8091-2365-7). Paulist Pr.

Sorley, Imogene, jt. auth. see Carr, Jo.

Sorley, William R. Moral Values & the Idea of God. LC 77-27215. (Gifford Lectures: 1914-15). 1978. Repr. of 1918 ed. 37.50 (ISBN 0-404-60465-X). AMS Pr.

Sorlien, Sandra. Bulletin Board Ideas: Creative Ways to Communicate the Gospel. (Illus.). 40p. (Orig.). 1980. pap. 4.95 (ISBN 0-8066-1778-0, 10-0949). Augsburg.

--Bulletin Boards That Communicate: Creative Ideas for the Congregation. 56p. (Orig.). 1984. pap. 4.95 (ISBN 0-8066-2073-0, 10-0950). Augsburg.

Sorokin, P. A. Forms & Techniques of Altruistic & Spiritual Growth: A Symposium. Repr. of 1954 ed. 28.00 (ISBN 0-527-84810-7). Kraus Repr.

Sorrill, Bobbie. Annie Armstrong: Dreamer in Action. LC 83-70842. 1984. 8.95 (ISBN 0-8054-6333-X). Broadman.

Sosland, Henry Adler. Guide for Preachers on Composing & Delivering Sermons. (Illus.). 1987. text ed. 20.00 (ISBN 0-87334-026-4, Pub. by Jewish Theol Seminary). Ktav.

Sotheby, S. L. Ramblings in the Elucidation of the Autograph of Milton. 1974. Repr. of 1861 ed. lib. bdg. 100.00 limited ed. (ISBN 0-8414-8008-7). Folcroft.

Soto, Domingo de see De Soto, Domingo.

Sottovagina, Hugh. The History of the Church of York, 1066-1127. Johnson, Charles, tr. from Lat. & intro. by. LC 80-2227. Repr. of 1961 ed. 38.00 (ISBN 0-404-18764-1). AMS Pr.

Soulen, Richard, tr. see Westermann, Claus.

Soulen, Richard N. Care for the Dying. LC 74-19968. 120p. 1975. pap. 6.50 (ISBN 0-8042-1098-5). John Knox.

--Handbook of Biblical Criticism. rev. ed. LC 76-12398. 225p. 1981. pap. 11.95 (ISBN 0-8042-0045-9). John Knox.

Sourd, Leonard Le see Marshall, Catherine & Le Sourd, Leonard.

Souter, A. Pegaluis's Expositions on Thirteen Epistles of St. Paul, 3 pts. in 1 vol. (Texts & Studies Ser. 1: Vol. 9). pap. 83.00 (ISBN 0-8115-1712-8). Pt. 1: Introduction. Kraus Repr.

Souter, A., ed. see Augustinus, Saint Aurelius.

Souter, Alexander, ed. Pocket Lexicon to the Greek New Testament. 1916. 17.95x (ISBN 0-19-864203-2). Oxford U Pr.

Souter, John. Love. (Campus Magazine Ser.). 96p. (Orig.). 1985. pap. 4.95 (ISBN 0-8423-3851-9). Tyndale.

--Moods. 96p. (Orig.). 1986. 4.95 (ISBN 0-8423-4498-5). Tyndale.

--What's the Good Word? The All New Super Incredible Bible Study Book for Junior Highs. 64p. 1983. pap. 3.50 (ISBN 0-310-45891-9, 12474P). Zondervan.

Souter, John & Souter, Susan. Youth Bible Study Notebook. 1977. pap. 5.95 (ISBN 0-8423-8790-0). Tyndale.

Souter, John C. The All-New Super Incredible Bible Study Book on Mark. 144p. (Orig.). 1985. pap. 3.95 (ISBN 0-310-45881-1, 12475P). Zondervan.

--Growing Stronger-Advanced. 1980. study guide 2.95 (ISBN 0-8423-1234-X). Tyndale.

--How to Grow New Christians. 1979. pap. 3.95 (ISBN 0-8423-1486-5). Tyndale.

--Temptation (Magazine Format, No. 3. 64p. 1984. 4.95 (ISBN 0-8423-6957-0). Tyndale.

--The Word. 96p. 1985. 4.95 (ISBN 0-8423-8394-8). Tyndale.

Souter, Susan, jt. auth. see Souter, John.

Souter, Susan J. How to Be a Confident Woman: A Bible Study Guide for Women. LC 78-51904. 80p. 1978. pap. 2.95 (ISBN 0-89081-124-5). Harvest Hse.

South African Evangelicals. Evangelical Witness in South Africa: An Evangelical Critique of Evangelical Theology & Practice. 46p. (Orig.). 1987. pap. 3.95 (ISBN 0-8028-0291-5). Eerdmans.

South Ctr. of Theos. Devas & Men. 8.95 (ISBN 0-8356-7518-1). Theos Pub Hse.

South, Robert. Sermons Preached upon Various Occasions, 8 vols. LC 73-175991. Repr. of 1842 ed. Set. 155.00 (ISBN 0-404-06180-X). AMS Pr.

Southard, Samuel. Pastoral Evangelism. LC 80-82196. 192p. 1981. pap. 4.50 (ISBN 0-8042-2037-9). John Knox.

--Religious Inquiry: An Introduction to the Why & How. LC 76-20449. Repr. of 1976 ed. 24.20 (ISBN 0-8357-9024-X, 2016398). Bks Demand UMI.

--Training Church Members for Pastoral Care. 96p. 1982. pap. 4.95 (ISBN 0-8170-0944-2). Judson.

Southaud, Samuel, ed. see Malony, H. Newton.

Souther, Sheila, jt. auth. see Call, Betty.

Souther, Shelia. Children Can Worship, Bk. 1. (Orig.). 1986. pap. 10.95 (ISBN 0-87148-185-5). Pathway Pr.

Southerm, R. W. Western Society & the Church in the Middle Ages. (History of the Church). (Orig.). 1970. pap. 5.95 (ISBN 0-14-020503-9, Pelican). Penguin.

Southern, Paul. New Testament in Survey. pap. 2.70 (ISBN 0-89137-550-3). Quality Pubns.

Southern, R. W. Medieval Humanism: And Other Stories. (Illus.). 288p. 1984. pap. 12.95x (ISBN 0-631-13649-5). Basil Blackwell.

--Western Views of Islam in the Middle Ages. LC 62-13270. 1978. 12.50x (ISBN 0-674-95055-0); pap. 4.95x (ISBN 0-674-95065-8). Harvard U Pr.

Southern, R. W. & Schmitt, F. S., eds. Memorials of Saint Anselm, Vol. I. (Auctores Britannici Medii Aevi). 370p. 1969. 22.50 (ISBN 0-85672-693-1, Pub. by British Acad). Longwood Pub Group.

Southern, R. W., ed. & tr. see Eadmer.

Southern, Richard. Robert Grosseteste: The Growth of an English Mind in Medieval Europe. 300p. 1986. 55.00x (ISBN 0-19-826450-X). Oxford U Pr.

Southern, Richard W. Making of the Middle Ages. (Illus.). 1953. pap. 8.95x 1961 (ISBN 0-300-00230-0, Y46). Yale U Pr.

--Saint Anselm & His Biographer: A Study of Monastic Life & Thought, 1059c-1130. (Birkbeck Lectures: 1959). pap. 101.30 (ISBN 0-317-09510-2, 2022473). Bks Demand UMI.

Southgate, Wyndham M. John Jewel & the Problem of Doctrinal Authority. LC 62-9430. (Historical Monographs: No. 49). (Illus.). 1962. 16.50x (ISBN 0-674-47750-2). Harvard U Pr.

Southwell Cathedral. Visitations & Memorials of Southwell Minister. Leach, Arthur F., ed. Repr. of 1891 ed. 27.00 (ISBN 0-384-56770-3). Johnson Repr.

Southwell, P. Ezra-Job. 1983. pap. 4.95 (ISBN 0-87508-156-8). Chr Lit.

Southwell, Robert. An Epistle of Comfort. Waugh, Margaret, ed. LC 66-22384. 1966. 3.95 (ISBN 0-8294-0072-9). Loyola.

--Marie Magdalens Funeral Teares. LC 74-22099. 180p. 1975. 30.00x (ISBN 0-8201-1144-9). Schol Facsimiles.

Southwold, Martin. Buddhism in Life: The Anthropological Study of Religion & the Sinhalese Practice of Buddhism. LC 83-9890. (Themes in Social Anthropology Ser.). 232p. 1984. 36.00 (ISBN 0-7190-0971-5, Pub. by Manchester Univ Pr). Longwood Pub Group.

Souza, Allan de see De Souza, Allan.

Sovenson, Lois B. What Does It Mean to Believe in Jesus. (Cornerstone Ser.). 32p. 1981. pap. 2.00 (ISBN 0-930756-64-9, 533004). Aglow Pubns.

Sovik, Edward A. Architecture for Worship. LC 73-78254. (Illus.). 112p. (Orig.). 1973. pap. 5.95 (ISBN 0-8066-1320-3, 10-0425). Augsburg.

Spaegel, Charles, jt. auth. see Norman, Ruth.

Spaeth, Barbara J. Laurie Miracle by Miracle. 48p. 1986. 6.95 (ISBN 0-317-43316-4). Todd & Honeywell.

Spaeth, Robert L. The Church & a Catholic's Conscience. 96p. 1985. pap. 6.50 (ISBN 0-86683-869-4, 8456, HarpR). Har-Row.

Spain, Rufus B. At Ease in Zion: A Social History of Southern Baptists, 1865-1900. LC 66-10367. 1967. 12.95x (ISBN 0-8265-1096-5). Vanderbilt U Pr.

Spalding, Baird T. Life & Teaching of the Masters of the Far East, 5 vols. pap. 4.00 ea. Vol. 1 (ISBN 0-87516-363-7). Vol. 2 (ISBN 0-87516-364-5). Vol.3 (ISBN 0-87516-365-3). Vol. 4 (ISBN 0-87516-366-1). Vol. 5 (ISBN 0-87516-367-X). 20.00 set (ISBN 0-87516-538-9). De Vorss.

Spalding, H. D., ed. Joys of Jewish Humor. LC 84-23822. (Illus.). 360p. 1985. pap. 8.95 (ISBN 0-8246-0257-9). Jonathan David.

Spalding, Henry D. Jewish Laffs. LC 82-9990. (Illus.). 96p. 1982. pap. 3.95 (ISBN 0-8246-0290-0). Jonathan David.

--A Treasure-Trove of American Jewish Humor. LC 75-40192. 429p. 1976. 16.95 (ISBN 0-8246-0204-8). Jonathan David.

Spalding, Henry D., ed. Encyclopedia of Jewish Humor. LC 68-21429. 1978. 16.95 (ISBN 0-8246-0021-5). Jonathan David.

Spalding, J. Howard. Introduction to Swedenborg's Religious Thought. LC 77-78682. 1973. pap. 2.95 (ISBN 0-87785-121-2). Swedenborg.

Spalding, John H. The Kingdom of Heaven As Seen by Swedenborg. LC 72-8245. Repr. of 1916 ed. 18.00 (ISBN 0-404-11006-1). AMS Pr.

Spalding, John L. The Religious Mission of the Irish People & Catholic Colonization. 17.00 (ISBN 0-405-10859-1, 11857). Ayer Co Pubs.

Spalding, Martin. Sketches of the Early Catholic Missions of Kentucky; from Their Commencement in 1787 to the Jubilee of 1826-7. LC 70-38548. (Religion in America, Ser. 2). 328p. 1972. Repr. of 1844 ed. 22.00 (ISBN 0-405-04087-3). Ayer Co Pubs.

Spalding, Martin J. Sketches of the Life, Times, - Character of Right Reverend Benedict Joseph Flaget, First Bishop of Louisville. LC 71-83441. (Religion in America, Ser. 1). 1969. Repr. of 1852 ed. 21.00 (ISBN 0-405-00266-1). Ayer Co Pubs.

Spalding, T. A. Elizabeth Demonology. 1880. lib. bdg. 27.50 (ISBN 0-8414-1620-6). Folcroft.

Spalding, Thomas W. Martin John Spalding: American Churchman. LC 74-171040. pap. 96.80 (2029524). Bks Demand UMI.

Spangenberg, Wolfhart. Samtliche Werke: Anbind-oder Fangbriefe. Gelegenheitsdichtungen. Beschreibung des Gluckhafens, Vol. 4, Pt. 1. Vizkelety & Bircher, eds. (Ger.). iv, 393p. 1981. 120.00 (ISBN 3-11-008030-3). De Gruyter.

Spangler, Ann. Bright Legacy: Portraits of Ten Outstanding Christian Women. 196p. 1985. pap. 6.95 (ISBN 0-89283-278-9, Pub. by Vine Books). Servant.

Spangler, Ann, ed. Bright Legacy: Portraits of Ten Outstanding Christian Women. 204p. 1983. 10.95 (ISBN 0-89283-167-7, Pub. by Vine Bks). Servant.

Spangler, David. Emergence: The Rebirth of the Sacred. LC 83-7626. 160p. (Orig.). 1984. pap. 10.95 (ISBN 0-385-29311-9, Delta). Dell.

Spangler, Wanda L. Marantha: The Mouse in the Tomb. 1986. 6.95 (ISBN 0-8062-2500-9). Carlton.

Spaniol, LeRoy J., jt. auth. see Lannan, Paul A.

Spanjaard, Barry. Don't Fence Me In: An American Teenager in the Holocaust. 8th ed. Spanjaard, Bunnie J., ed. LC 81-68713. (Illus.). 224p. (Orig.). 1981. pap. 8.95 (ISBN 0-9607008-0-3). B & B Pub CA.

Spanjaard, Bunnie J., ed. see Spanjaard, Barry.

Spann, J. Richard, ed. Christian Faith & Secularism. LC 70-86062. (Essay & General Literature Index Reprint Ser). 1969. Repr. of 1948 ed. 28.50x (ISBN 0-8046-0589-0, Pub. by Kennikat). Assoc Faculty Pr.

Sparagna, Aniceto. Personal Evangelism among Roman Catholics. (Orig.). 1978. pap. 3.95 (ISBN 0-89900-122-X). College Pr Pub.

Spargo, Emma J. The Category of the Aesthetic in the Philosophy of Saint Bonaventure. (Philosophy Ser). 1953. 8.00 (ISBN 0-686-11541-4). Franciscan Inst.

Sparkman, G. Temp. The Salvation & Nurture of the Child of God. 1983. 9.95 (ISBN 0-8170-0985-X). Judson.

--To Live with Hope. 112p. 1985. pap. 5.95 (ISBN 0-8170-1062-9). Judson.

--Writing Your Own Worship Materials. 1980. pap. 2.95 (ISBN 0-8170-0857-8). Judson.

Sparkman, G. Temp, ed. Knowing & Helping Youth. LC 77-75621. 1978. 8.50 (ISBN 0-8054-3219-1, 4232-19). Broadman.

Sparks, H. F. The Apocryphal Old Testament. 990p. 1984. 44.50x (ISBN 0-19-826166-7); pap. 19.95x (ISBN 0-19-826177-2). Oxford U Pr.

Sparks, Irving A. The Pastoral Epistles: Introduction & Commentary. LC 85-10925. (Orig.). 1985. pap. 6.00 (ISBN 0-934743-01-0). Inst Biblical.

Sparks, Judith, ed. Standard Christmas Program Book, No. 45. 48p. 1984. pap. 1.95 (ISBN 0-87239-749-1, 8645). Standard Pub.

Sparks, Judith A., compiled by. Bible Programs & Dramas for Youth & Adults. 64p. (Orig.). 1983. pap. 2.95 (ISBN 0-87239-671-1, 3351). Standard Pub.

Sparks, Judy, ed. Away in a Manger. (Happy Day Bks.). (Illus.). 24p. 1985. 1.59 (ISBN 0-87239-871-4, 3671). Standard Pub.

--Baby Jesus ABC Storybook. (Happy Day Bk.). (Illus.). 24p. 1979. 1.59 (ISBN 0-87239-354-2, 3624). Standard Pub.

--Christmas Programs for the Church, No. 16. 64p. 1983. pap. 2.95 (ISBN 0-87239-614-2, 8616). Standard Pub.

--Yes!, Jesus Loves Me. (Happy Day Bks.). (Illus.). 24p. 1985. 1.59 (ISBN 0-87239-882-X, 3682). Standard Pub.

Sparks, Lee, ed. Try This One... Too. LC 82-81331. (Illus.). 80p. (Orig.). 1982. pap. 5.95 (ISBN 0-936664-05-3). Group Bks.

--The Youth Group How-To Book. LC 81-81966. (Illus.). 224p. (Orig.). 1981. pap. 14.95 (ISBN 0-936664-03-7). Group Bks.

--The Youth Worker's Personal Management Handbook. LC 84-73152. 264p. 1985. 16.95 (ISBN 0-931529-03-4). Group Bks.

Sparks, Merla J. Creative Christian Home. pap. 1.95 (ISBN 0-8010-8050-9). Baker Bk.

Sparrow, Carroll M. Voyages & Cargoes. 1947. 3.00 (ISBN 0-685-09018-3). Dietz.

Sparrow, Lynn E. Edgar Cayce & the Born Again Christian. 237p. (Orig.). 1985. pap. 6.95 (ISBN 0-87604-158-6). ARE Pr.

Sparrow, Wilfred, jt. auth. see Khan, Gazanfar A.

Spasskii, A. Isotoriia Dogmaticheskikh Divhenii v Epokhu Vselenskikh Soborov. 656p. Repr. of 1914 ed. text ed. 74.52x (ISBN 0-576-99173-2, Pub. by Gregg Intl Pubs England). Gregg Intl.

Spata, James P., jt. auth. see Perrone, Stephen P.

Spatz, Jacob W. The Speaker's Bible. 2nd ed. 288p. 1986. pap. 10.00 (ISBN 0-938033-00-X). Alert Pubs.

Speaight, Robert. Life of Hilaire Belloc. facs. ed. LC 78-136655. (Biography Index Reprint Ser.). 1957. 29.00 (ISBN 0-8369-8050-6). Ayer Co Pubs.

--The Life of Hilaire Belloc. 552p. 1981. Repr. of 1957 ed. lib. bdg. 35.00 (ISBN 0-89987-773-7). Darby Bks.

Speake, Jennifer, ed. Biblical Quotations. LC 83-1511. 208p. 1983. 17.95 (ISBN 0-87196-241-1). Facts on File.

Speaks, R. L. The Prelude to Pentecost. 200p. 1985. 11.95 (ISBN 0-682-40229-X). Exposition Pr FL.

Spear, Tziporah. Kosher Calories. 1985. 12.95 (ISBN 0-317-38550-X); pap. 9.95 (ISBN 0-317-38551-8). Mesorah Pubns.

Spears, Cleola I., jt. auth. see Jackson, Anne A.

Spears, W. Eugene Jr. The Church on Assignment. LC 84-15541. 1985. pap. 3.25 (ISBN 0-8054-5011-4). Broadman.

Spears, W. H., Jr. Constantine's Triumph: A Tale of the Era of the Martyrs. LC 63-19710. 1964. 3.95 (ISBN 0-9600106-1-0). Spears.

Speas, Ralph. How to Deal with How You Feel. LC 80-65316. 1980. pap. 4.50 (ISBN 0-8054-5278-8). Broadman.

Specht, Walter, jt. auth. see Kubo, Sakae.

Speck, Frank G. Oklahoma Delaware Ceremonies, Feasts & Dances. LC 76-43845. (Memoirs of the American Philosophical Sociey: Vol. 7). Repr. of 1937 ed. 21.50 (ISBN 0-404-15696-7). AMS Pr.

--Penobscot Shamanism. LC 20-13167. (AAA Memoirs Ser.: No. 25). 1919. pap. 15.00 (ISBN 0-527-00527-4). Kraus Repr.

--A Study of the Delaware Indian Big House Ceremony: In Native Text Dictated by Witapanoxwe. LC 76-43846. (Publications of the Pennsylvania Historical Commission: Vol. 2). Repr. of 1931 ed. 24.00 (ISBN 0-404-15698-3). AMS Pr.

Speck, Henry E. see Sewell, Jesse P.

Speck, Henry E., jt. ed. see Sewell, Jesse P.

Speck, S. L. & Riggle, H. M., eds. Bible Readings for Bible Students & for the Home & Fireside. 432p. 1902. 5.00 (ISBN 0-686-29102-6). Faith Pub Hse.

Speck, Von S. & Riggle, H. M. Biblische Lehren. 343p. 1982. pap. 4.00 (ISBN 0-686-36267-5). Faith Pub Hse.

Speck, Winsome. Too Late to Hide. (Lifline Ser.). 140p. 1984. pap. 7.95 (ISBN 0-8163-0541-2). Pacific Pr Pub Assn.

Speckner, Killian. The Prayers of Father Killian. 384p. 1986. pap. 8.95 (ISBN 0-941478-56-4). Paraclete Pr.

Spector, Sheila A. Jewish Mysticism: An Annotated Bibliography on the Kabbalah in English. LC 83-48224. (Reference Library of Social Science Ser.). 1984. lib. bdg. 45.00 (ISBN 0-8240-9042-X). Garland Pub.

Speelman, Marlene & Adams, Janiece. Bible Busy Book. 10p. 1986. 15.95 (ISBN 0-8407-6711-0). Nelson.

Speer, Michael L. A Complete Guide to the Christian's Budget. new ed. LC 74-80341. 160p. 1975. pap. 3.25 (ISBN 0-8054-5227-3). Broadman.

Speer, Robert E. Five Minutes a Day. LC 43-16427. 384p. 1977. softcover 3.95 (ISBN 0-664-24139-5). Westminster.

--Some Great Leaders in the World Movement. facs. ed. LC 67-26786. (Essay Index Reprint Ser). 1911. 18.00 (ISBN 0-8369-0895-3). Ayer Co Pubs.

Speeth, Kathleen R. & Friedlander, Ira. Gurdjieff: The Early Years. LC 78-24696. (Illus.). 1979. pap. 5.95 (ISBN 0-06-090693-6, CN-693, PL). Har-Row.

Speidel, Michael P. Mithras-Orion: Greek Hero & Roman Army God. (Illus.). 56p. 1980. pap. text ed. 19.95 (ISBN 90-04-06055-3). Humanities.

Speight, Harold E. The Life & Writings of John Bunyan. 1928. 40.00 (ISBN 0-8274-2916-9). R West.

--The Life & Writings of John Bunyan. 224p. 1983. lib. bdg. 50.00 (ISBN 0-8495-5063-7). Arden Lib.

Speirs, E. B., tr. see Hegel, Georg W.

Speiser, E. A., ed. Genesis. LC 64-21724. (Anchor Bible Ser.: Vol. 1). 1964. 16.00 (ISBN 0-385-00854-6, Anchor Pr). Doubleday.

Speiser, Ephraim A. Oriental & Biblical Studies: Collected Writings of E. A. Speiser. Greenberg, Moshe & Finkelstein, Jacob J., eds. LC 65-21779. pap. 154.00 (ISBN 0-317-08338-4, 2003802). Bks Demand UMI.

Spell, Leonard, Sr. House of Prayer for All Nations. 174p. 1986. 12.95x (ISBN 0-9615439-1-4, 133997); pap. 9.95x (ISBN 0-9615439-2-2). Spell Assoc.

Speller, Jon P. Seed Money in Action. LC 65-26790. 1965. pap. 3.00 (ISBN 0-8315-0007-7). Speller.

Spellman, Norman W. Growing a Soul: The Story of A. Frank Smith. LC 78-20876. 1979. 17.95x (ISBN 0-87074-171-3). SMU Press.

Spellman, Peter W., jt. auth. see Askew, Thomas A., Jr.

Spence, Clark C. The Salvation Army Farm Colonies. LC 85-8763. 151p. 1985. 19.95x (ISBN 0-8165-0897-6). U of Ariz Pr.

Spence, H. D. & Exell, T. S. The Pulpit Commentary, 23 vols. Incl. Old Testament only, 14 Vols. 320.00 (ISBN 0-8028-8056-8, 2209); New Testament only, 8 Vols. 200.00 (ISBN 0-8028-8057-6, 2210). 1959. Repr. Set. 520.00 (ISBN 0-8028-8055-X); 0er vol 22.95. Eerdmans.

Spence, H. D. & Exell, Joseph S., eds. The Pulpit Commentary, 23 vols. 26612p. Date not set. Set. 520.00 (ISBN 0-917006-32-1). Hendrickson MA.

Spence, Hersey E. Old Testament Dramas. LC 74-175994. 1976. Repr. of 1936 ed. 15.50 (ISBN 0-404-06176-1). AMS Pr.

Spence, Jonathan D. The Memory Palace of Matteo Ricci. (Nonfiction Ser.). 368p. 1985. pap. 7.95 (ISBN 0-14-008098-8). Penguin.

Spence, Joseph. Polymetis. LC 75-27886. (Renaissance & the Gods Ser.: Vol. 41). (Illus.). 1976. Repr. of 1747 ed. lib. bdg. 88.00 (ISBN 0-8240-2090-1). Garland Pub.

Spence, Keith & McVeigh, Shaun. Cathedrals & Abbeys of England & Wales. (Blue Guides Ser.). (Illus.). 1984. 29.95 (ISBN 0-393-01664-1); pap. 16.95 (ISBN 0-393-30071-4). Norton.

Spence, L. The Gods of Mexico. 34.95 (ISBN 0-8490-0243-5). Gordon Pr.

--Myths & Legends of the North American Indian. LC 72-81598. (Illus.). 396p. 1975. pap. cancelled (ISBN 0-8334-1745-2, Steinerbks). Garber Comm.

Spence, Lewis. The Minor Traditions of British Mythology. LC 72-84001. Repr. of 1948 ed. 31.00 (ISBN 0-405-08989-9). Ayer Co Pubs.

--The Mythologies of Ancient Mexico & Peru. 80p. 1983. Repr. of 1907 ed. lib. bdg. 30.00 (ISBN 0-89987-949-7). Darby Bks.

--The Mythologies of Ancient Mexico & Peru. 80p. 1921. 0.95 (ISBN 0-317-40437-7). Open Court.

--Myths & Legends of Babylonia & Assyria. LC 77-167199. (Illus.). 414p. 1975. Repr. of 1916 ed. 53.00x (ISBN 0-8103-4089-5). Gale.

--Myths of Mexico & Peru. 1976. lib. bdg. 60.00 (ISBN 0-8490-0700-3). Gordon Pr.

--The Myths of Mexico & Peru. LC 76-27516. (Illus.). 1976. Repr. of 1914 ed. lib. bdg. 45.00 (ISBN 0-89341-031-4). Longwood Pub Group.

--The Outlines of Mythology. LC 77-3223. 1977. Repr. of 1944 ed. lib. bdg. 17.50 (ISBN 0-8414-7803-1). Folcroft.

--Popol Vuh: Mythic & Heroic Sagas of the Kiches of Central America. LC 75-139178. (Popular Studies in Mythology, Romance & Folklore: No. 16). Repr. of 1908 ed. 5.50 (ISBN 0-404-53516-X). AMS Pr.

Spence-Jones, H. D. The Early Christians in Rome. 1977. lib. bdg. 56.95 (ISBN 0-8490-1737-8). Gordon Pr.

Spencer, Aida B. Beyond the Curse: Women Called to Ministry. 224p. 1985. 10.95 (ISBN 0-8407-5482-5). Nelson.

Spencer, Anita. Mothers Are People Too: A Contemporary Analysis of Motherhood. 1984. pap. 5.95 (ISBN 0-8091-2616-8). Paulist Pr.

--Seasons: Women's Search for Self Through Life's Stages. LC 81-85379. 128p. (Orig.). 1982. pap. 4.95 (ISBN 0-8091-2437-8). Paulist Pr.

Spencer, Barbara H. The Book of Mag. 202p. pap. 7.95 (ISBN 0-942494-40-7). Coleman Pub.

Spencer, Bonnell. They Saw the Lord: The Resurrection Appearances. LC 83-61765. 235p. 1983. pap. 8.95 (ISBN 0-8192-1332-2). Morehouse.

Spencer, Dean & Nelson, Dean. God Never Said We'd Be Leading at the Half. 116p. (Orig.). 1980. pap. 2.95 (ISBN 0-8341-0766-X). Beacon Hill.

Spencer, Donald A. Hymn & Scripture Selection Guide. LC 76-48529. 1977. text ed. 9.85 (ISBN 0-8170-0705-9). Judson.

Spencer, Duane. Ephesians for the Family: A Daily Devotional Commentary. 336p. 1984. 12.95 (ISBN 0-8059-2942-8). Dorrance.

Spencer, Duane E. Holy Baptism: Word Keys Which Unlock the Covenant. LC 84-81663. 170p. 1984. 9.95 (ISBN 0-939404-08-7). Geneva Ministr.

--Tulip: Five Points of Calvinism. LC 78-73445. (Direction Bks). pap. 2.95 (ISBN 0-8010-8161-0). Baker Bk.

Spencer, Geoffrey. The Burning Bush. LC 74-84762. 1974. pap. 6.50 (ISBN 0-8309-0129-9). Herald Hse.

Spencer, Geoffrey F. Strangers & Pilgrims. 221p. (Orig.). 1984. pap. text ed. 12.50 (ISBN 0-8309-0399-2). Herald Hse.

Spencer, H. S. The Mysteries of God in the Universe: Including the Reincarnation & Karma in the Gathas, the Bible, & Koran, 2 vols. Repr. of 1967 ed. Set. text ed. 35.00x. Coronet Bks.

Spencer, Herbert. The Principles of Ethics, 2 vols. LC 77-71453. 550p. 1980. Set. pap. 8.00 (ISBN 0-913966-34-7, Liberty Clas); Vol. I. pap. (ISBN 0-913966-77-0); Vol. II. pap. (ISBN 0-913966-75-4). Liberty Fund.

--The Principles of Ethics, 2 vols. LC 77-71453. 1978. Repr. Set. 20.00 (ISBN 0-913966-33-9, Liberty Clas); Vol. I. (ISBN 0-913966-76-2); Vol. II. (ISBN 0-913966-74-6). Liberty Fund.

Spencer, J. H. The History of the Kentucky Baptists from 1769 to 1885, 2 vols. 1984. Repr. of 1886 ed. 54.00 (ISBN 0-686-12335-2). Church History.

Spencer, Jack, jt. auth. see Chartock, Roselle.

Spencer, James R. Have You Witnessed to a Mormon Lately? 1987. pap. 6.95 (Chosen Bks). Revell.

Spencer, Katherine. Mythology & Values: An Analysis of Navaho Chantway Myths. (American Folklore Society Memoir Ser: No. 48). 248p. 1957. pap. 6.95x (ISBN 0-292-73528-6). U of Tex Pr.

--Reflections of Social Life in the Navaho Origin Myth. LC 76-43850. (Univ. of New Mexico. Publications in Anthropology: No. 3). 1983. Repr. of 1947 ed. 20.00 (ISBN 0-404-15705-X). AMS Pr.

Spencer, Patricia. The Egyptian Temple: A Lexicographical Study. 300p. 1984. 50.00x (ISBN 0-7103-0065-4, Kegan Paul). Methuen Inc.

Spencer, Philip. Politics of Belief in Nineteenth-Century France. LC 77-80592. 284p. 1973. Repr. of 1954 ed. 24.50x (ISBN 0-86527-156-9). Fertig.

Spencer, Richard A. The Fire of Truth. LC 82-71218. (Orig.). 1982. pap. 6.95 (ISBN 0-8054-2248-X). Broadman.

Spencer, Richard A., ed. Orientation by Disorientation: Studies on Literary Criticism & Biblical Literary Criticism Presented in Honor of William A. Beardslee. (Pittsburgh Theological Monograph Ser.: No. 35). 1980. pap. text ed. 15.00 (ISBN 0-915138-44-1). Pickwick.

Spencer, Sidney. Mysticism in World Religion. 11.75 (ISBN 0-8446-0927-7). Peter Smith.

Spencer, Sydney, ed. see Law, William.

Spencer, Theodore, ed. A Garland for John Donne 1631-1931. 11.25 (ISBN 0-8446-1418-1). Peter Smith.

Spener, Philip J. Pia Desideria. Tappert, Theodore G., ed. & tr. LC 64-12995. 1964. pap. 5.95 (ISBN 0-8006-1953-6, 1-1953). Fortress.

Sperber, Johnathan. Popular Catholicism in Nineteenth-Century Germany. LC 84-42559. 552p. 1984. text ed. 45.00x (ISBN 0-691-05432-0). Princeton U Pr.

Sperling, Abraham I. Reasons for Jewish Customs & Traditions. Matts, Abraham, tr. LC 68-31711. cancelled. (ISBN 0-8197-0184-X); pap. cancelled (ISBN 0-8197-0008-8). Bloch.

Spero, Moshe. Handbook of Psychotherapy & Jewish Ethics. 1986. 19.95 (ISBN 0-87306-406-2). Feldheim.

Spero, Moshe H. Judaism & Psychology: Halakhic Perspectives. 25.00x (ISBN 0-87068-693-3). Ktav.

Spero, Moshe H., jt. auth. see Bulka, Reuven P.

Spero, Moshe H., ed. Psychotherapy of the Religious Patient. 250p. 1985. 32.75 (ISBN 0-398-05058-9). C C Thomas.

Spero, Shubert. Morality, Halakha & the Jewish Tradition. 1983. 20.00x (ISBN 0-87068-727-1). Ktav.

--The Story of the Chasam Sofer. (Illus.). 80p. 2.00 (ISBN 0-914131-61-3, D53). Torah Umesorah.

Sperry, Sidney B. Book of Mormon Chronology. pap. 1.00 (ISBN 0-87747-408-7). Deseret Bk.

--The Spirit of the Old Testament. LC 70-119330. (Classics in Mormon Literature Ser.). 246p. 1980. Repr. 6.95 (ISBN 0-87747-832-5). Deseret Bk.

Sperry Symposium, ed. Hearken, O Ye People. 297p. 1984. 9.95 (ISBN 0-934126-56-9). Randall Bk Co.

Sperry Symposium Staff, ed. Principles of the Gospel in Practice. 257p. Date not set. 10.95 (ISBN 0-934126-75-5). Randall Bk Co.

Sperry, Willard L. The Paradox of Religion. LC 77-27146. (Hibbert Lectures: 1927). Repr. of 1927 ed. 20.00 (ISBN 0-404-60424-2). AMS Pr.

--Signs of These Times: The Ayer Lectures of the Colgate Rochester Divinity School for 1929. facs. ed. LC 68-29247. (Essay Index Reprint Ser). 1968. Repr. of 1929 ed. 15.00 (ISBN 0-8369-0897-X). Ayer Co Pubs.

--What We Mean by Religion. facsimile ed. LC 78-128316. (Essay Index Reprint Ser.). Repr. of 1940 ed. 17.00 (ISBN 0-8369-2370-7). Ayer Co Pubs.

Sperry, Willard L., ed. Religion & Our Divided Denominations. facs. ed. LC 74-128315. (Essay Index Reprint Ser). 1945. 14.00 (ISBN 0-8369-2201-8). Ayer Co Pubs.

Sperry, Willard L., et al, eds. Religion in the Post-War World. facsimile ed. LC 76-142698. (Essay Index Reprints - Religion & Education Ser.: Vol. 4). Repr. of 1945 ed. 14.00 (ISBN 0-8369-2202-6). Ayer Co Pubs.

Speybrouck, Edward Van see Van Speybrouck, Edward.

Speyer, J. C., tr. see Arya-Sura.

Speyr, Adrienne von. Handmaid of the Lord. LC 85-60468. Tr. of Magd des Herrn. 178p. 1985. 9.95 (ISBN 0-89870-042-6). Ignatius Pr.

Speyr, Adrienne von see Von Speyr, Adrienne.

Spicer, Edward H., ed. see Painter, Muriel T.

Spicer, Stephen, jt. auth. see Kenny, James.

Spickard, Anderson & Thompson, Barbara R. Dying for a Drink: What You Should Know about Alcoholism. 192p. 1985. 11.95 (ISBN 0-8499-0467-6, 0467-6). Word Bks.

Spidlik, Tomas. The Spirituality of the Christian East: A Systematic Handbook. Gythiel, Anthony P., tr. from Fr. (Cistercian Studies Ser.: No. 79). Tr. of La Spritiualite de l'Orient Chritienne. 1986. 48.95 (ISBN 0-87907-879-0); pap. 17.00 (ISBN 0-87907-979-7). Cistercian Pubns.

Spiegel, Marcia C. & Kremsdorf, Deborah L., eds. Women Speak To God: The Prayers & Poems of Jewish Women. LC 86-51498. 100p. (Orig.). 1987. pap. 9.98 (ISBN 0-9608054-6-X). Womans Inst-Cont Jewish Ed.

Spiegel, Shalom. The Last Trial: On the Legend & Lore of the Command to Abraham to Offer Isaac As a Sacrifice - the Akedah. LC 79-12664. (The Jewish Legacy Ser.). 1979. pap. 7.95x (ISBN 0-87441-290-0). Behrman.

Spiegel, Shalom, jt. auth. see Torrey, Charles C.

Spiegelberg, Nancy & Purdy, Dorothy. Fanfare: A Celebration of Belief. LC 80-25519. (Illus., Orig.). 1981. pap. 6.95 (ISBN 0-930014-56-1). Multnomah.

Spiegelman, J. Marvin & Miyuki, Mokusen. Buddhism & Jungian Psychology. 224p. (Orig.). 1985. pap. 8.95 (ISBN 0-941404-37-4). Falcon Pr AZ.

Spiegelman, J. Marvin & Jacobson, Abraham, eds. A Modern Jew in Search of a Soul. 320p. 1986. pap. 12.95 (ISBN 0-941404-33-1). Falcon Pr AZ.

Spiegelstein, Max. Paul, the Saint Who Ain't. 1980. 12.50 (ISBN 0-89962-017-5). Todd & Honeywell.

Spiegler, Gerhard E., jt. ed. see Fu, Charles W.

Spier, Leslie. The Prophet Dance of the Northwest & Its Derivatives: The Source of the Ghost Dance. LC 76-43853. Repr. of 1935 ed. 18.00 (ISBN 0-404-15708-4). AMS Pr.

Spier, Peter. Book of Jonah. LC 85-1676. (Illus.). 40p. 1985. 11.95 (ISBN 0-385-19334-3); PLB 11.95 (ISBN 0-385-19335-1). Doubleday.

--Noah's Ark. LC 76-43630. (Illus.). 44p. 1977. 11.95 (ISBN 0-385-09473-6); PLB 11.95 (ISBN 0-385-12730-8). Doubleday.

--Noah's Ark. 48p. 1981. pap. 4.95 (ISBN 0-385-17302-4, Zephyr). Doubleday.

Spiers, Richard P., jt. auth. see Anderson, William J.

Spiess, Margaret B. Gather Me Together, Lord: And Other Prayers for Mothers. 96p. 1982. 4.95 (ISBN 0-8010-8229-3). Baker Bk.

--Hold Me Steady, Lord: And Other Prayers for Mothers. 112p. 1986. text ed. 7.95 (ISBN 0-8010-8266-8). Baker Bk.

Spiker, Louis. Children Together. 128p. 1980. pap. 9.50 (ISBN 0-8170-0824-1). Judson.

Spiker, Louise C. No Instant Grapes in God's Vineyard. 112p. 1982. pap. 5.95 (ISBN 0-8170-0955-8). Judson.

Spilka, Bernard, et al. The Psychology of Religion: An Empirical Approach. (Illus.). 400p. 1985. text ed. write for info. (ISBN 0-13-736398-2). P-H.

Spilly, Alphonse. The First & Second Maccabees. (Bible Commentary Ser.). 136p. 1985. pap. 2.95 (ISBN 0-8146-1419-1). Liturgical Pr.

Spindle, Richard. They Never Stopped Teaching. 96p. 1982. pap. 2.50 (ISBN 0-8341-0735-X). Beacon Hill.

Spink, Kathryn. The Miracle of Love: Mother Teresa of Calcutta, Her Missionaries of Charity, & Her Co-Workers. LC 81-47717. (Illus.). 256p. 1982. 15.00 (ISBN 0-06-067497-0, HarpR). Har-Row.

--A Universal Heart: The Life & Vision of Brother Roger of Taize. LC 86-45027. (Illus.). 192p. 1986. 14.95 (ISBN 0-06-067504-7, HarpR). Har-Row.

Spink, Kathryn, jt. auth. see Mother Teresa of Calcutta.

Spinka, Matthew. Christian Thought: From Erasmus to Berdyaev. LC 78-11967. 1979. Repr. of 1962 ed. lib. bdg. 24.75x (ISBN 0-313-21122-1, SPCT). Greenwood.

--John Hus: A Biography. LC 78-14366. (Illus.). 1978. Repr. of 1968 ed. lib. bdg. 37.50 (ISBN 0-313-21050-0, SPJH). Greenwood.

Spinks, Bryan D. Freedom or Order? The Eucharistic Liturgy in English Congregationalism 1645-1980. (Pittsburgh Theological Monographs: New Ser. 8). (Orig.). 1984. pap. 22.50 (ISBN 0-915138-33-6). Pickwick.

Spinoza, B. De. Ethics & on the Improvement of the Understanding. 1974. 7.95x (ISBN 0-02-852650-3). Hafner.

Spinoza, Baruch. The Collected Works of Spinoza, Vol. I. Curley, Edwin, ed. LC 84-11716. (Illus.). 720p. 1985. text ed. 45.00x (ISBN 0-691-07222-1). Princeton U Pr.

--The Ethics & Selected Letters. Feldman, Seymour, intro. by. Shirley, Samuel, tr. from Lat. & Heb. LC 81-7199. 268p. 1982. lib. bdg. 19.50 (ISBN 0-915145-18-9); pap. text ed. 4.95 (ISBN 0-915145-19-7). Hackett Pub.

--The Ethics of Spinoza. 1976. pap. 4.95 (ISBN 0-8065-0536-2). Citadel Pr.

Spinoza, Benedict. Theologico-Political Treatise: Political Treatise. Elwes, R. H., tr. pap. text ed. 6.95 (ISBN 0-486-20249-6). Dover.

Spinoza, Benedict D. Works of Spinoza, 2 Vols. Elwes, tr. Set. 29.50 (ISBN 0-8446-2986-3). Peter Smith.

Spira, Andreas & Klock, Christoph. The Easter Sermons of Gregory of Nyssa: A Translation & Commentary. LC 81-84108. (Patristic Monograph Ser.: No. 9). 384p. 1981. pap. 11.00 (ISBN 0-915646-08-0). Phila Patristic.

Spiro, Jack. A Time to Mourn. LC 67-30744. 160p. 1985. pap. text ed. 8.95 (ISBN 0-8197-0497-0). Bloch.

Spiro, Jack D. Time to Mourn: Judaism and the Psychology of Bereavement. 1968. 8.95 (ISBN 0-8197-0185-8). Bloch.

Spiro, Jack D., jt. auth. see Schwartzman, Sylvan D.

Spiro, Jack D., ed. see Shumsky, Abraham & Shumsky, Adaia.

Spiro, Melford E. Buddhism & Society: A Great Tradition & Its Burmese Vicissitudes. 2nd, exp. ed. LC 81-18522. 530p. 1982. 40.00x (ISBN 0-520-04671-4); pap. 10.95x (ISBN 0-520-04672-2, CAMPUS 298). U of Cal Pr.

--Burmese Supernaturalism. enlarged ed. LC 77-17280. pap. 84.00 (ISBN 0-317-42082-8, 2025708). Bks Demand UMI.

Spittler, Russell P. The Church. LC 77-83982. (Radiant Life Ser.). 126p. 1977. pap. 2.50 (ISBN 0-88243-910-3, 02-0910); tchr's. ed. 3.95 (ISBN 0-88243-180-3, 32-0180). Gospel Pub.

--Corinthian Correspondence. LC 75-43157. (Radiant Life Ser.). 128p. 1976. pap. 2.50 (ISBN 0-88243-892-1, 02-0892); tchr's. ed. 3.95 (ISBN 0-88243-166-8, 32-0166). Gospel Pub.

Spitz, Lewis W. Protestant Reformation. (Orig.). 1966. pap. 3.95x (ISBN 0-13-731638-0, Spec). P-H.

--The Protestant Reformation, Fifteen Seventeen to Fifteen Fifty-Nine: The Rise of Modern Europe. LC 83-48805. (Illus.). 448p. 1986. pap. 8.95 (ISBN 0-06-091277-4, PL 1277, PL). Har-Row.

--The Protestant Reformation 1517-1559. LC 83-48805. (The Rise of Modern Europe Ser.). (Illus.). 444p. 1984. 22.45i (ISBN 0-06-013958-7, HarpT). Har-Row.

--Renaissance & Reformation, 2 vols. Incl. Vol. 1. The Renaissance. LC 12-2759 (ISBN 0-570-03818-9); Vol. 2. The Reformation. LC 12-2760 (ISBN 0-570-03819-7). 1980. pap. 15.50 ea. Concordia.

Spitz, Lewis W., ed. Reformation: Basic Interpretations. 2nd ed. (Problems in European Civilization Ser.). 1972. pap. text ed. 5.95 (ISBN 0-669-81620-5). Heath.

Spitz, Lewis W. & Lehmann, Helmut T., eds. Luther's Works: Career of the Reformer IV, Vol. 34. LC 55-9893. 1960. 19.95 (ISBN 0-8006-0334-6, 1-334). Fortress.

Spitz, Lewis W., Sr. Life of Doctor C. F. W. Walther. (Illus.). 1961. 3.95 (ISBN 0-570-03247-4, 15-1246). Concordia.

Spitzer, Leo & Brody, Jules. Approaches Textuelles des "Memoires" de Saint-Simon. (Etudes Litteraires Francaise: No. 9). (Fr.). 107p. (Orig.). 1980. pap. 12.00 (ISBN 3-87808-888-4). Benjamins North Am.

Spitzer, Manon, ed. see Sanders, Thomas G.

Spivack, Bernard. Shakespeare & the Allegory of Evil: The History of a Metaphor in Relation to His Major Villains. LC 57-12758. pap. 130.30 (ISBN 0-317-28960-8, 2017840). Bks Demand UMI.

Spivey, Robert A. & Smith, Moody D. Anatomy of the New Testament: A Guide to Its Structure & Meaning. 3rd ed. 544p. 1981. text ed. write for info. (ISBN 0-02-415300-1). Macmillan.

Spivey, Robert A., jt. auth. see Sleeper, C. Freeman.

Spizzirri, Linda, jt. auth. see Spizzirri Publishing, Inc. Staff.

Spizzirri Publishing, Inc. Staff & Spizzirri, Linda. California Missions: An Educational Coloring Book. (Illus.). 32p. 1985. pap. 1.49 (ISBN 0-86545-062-5). Spizzirri.

Splaine, Mike. How to Build a Christian Lecture Series. (Illus.). 50p. 1982. wkbk. & cassette 5.00x (ISBN 0-913605-05-0). NFCLC.

Splitter, Russell P. God the Father. LC 76-20888. (Radiant Life Ser.). 128p. 1976. pap. 2.50 (ISBN 0-88243-898-0, 02-0898, Radiant Bks); teacher's ed 3.95 (ISBN 0-88243-170-6, 32-0170). Gospel Pub.

Spock, Marjorie. Eurythmy. (Illus.). 148p. (Orig.). 1980. 15.95 (ISBN 0-88010-023-0); pap. 9.95 (ISBN 0-910142-88-2). Anthroposophic.

--Reflections on Community Building. 1984. pap. 3.25 (ISBN 0-916786-67-6). St George Bk Serv.

--To Look on Earth with More Than Mortal Eyes. 1985. pap. 5.95 (ISBN 0-916786-79-X). St George Bk Serv.

Spock, Marjorie, tr. see Palmer, Otto.

Spock, Marjorie, tr. see Steiner, Rudolf.

Spoer, Hans H. Aid for Churchmen, Episcopal & Orthodox. LC 71-79152. Repr. of 1930 ed. 12.50 (ISBN 0-404-06197-4). AMS Pr.

Spohn, David, illus. Today's Gift. (Meditation Ser.). 400p. (Orig.). 1985. pap. 5.95 (ISBN 0-89486-302-9). Hazelden.

Spohn, William C. What Are They Saying about Scripture & Ethics? (WATSA Ser.). (Orig.). 1984. pap. 4.95 (ISBN 0-8091-2624-9). Paulist Pr.

Spong, John & Haines, Denise. Beyond Moralism. 204p. (Orig.). 1986. pap. 9.95 (ISBN 0-86683-514-8, HarpR). Har-Row.

Spong, John S. The Easter Moment. 176p. 1980. 9.95 (ISBN 0-8164-0133-0, HarpR). Har-Row.

--Into the Whirlwind: The Future of the Church. 224p. 1983. 9.95 (ISBN 0-86683-899-6, HarpR). Har-Row.

--This Hebrew Lord. 1976. pap. 4.95 (ISBN 0-8164-2133-1, HarpR). Har-Row.

Sponheim, Paul R. God: The Question & the Quest. LC 85-47737. 224p. 1986. 19.95 (ISBN 0-8006-0756-2). Fortress.

Spooner, jt. auth. see Coggin.

Spooner, W. A. Bishop Butler. 1979. Repr. of 1901 ed. lib. bdg. 30.00 (ISBN 0-8492-8086-9). R West.

Spottiswood, John. History of the Church of Scotland, 3 Vols. Russell, Michael & Napier, Mark, eds. LC 76-176004. (Bannatyne Club, Edinburgh. Publications: No. 93). Repr. of 1851 ed. Set. 145.00 (ISBN 0-404-52840-6). AMS Pr.

Spotts, Dwight & Veerman, David. Reaching Out to Troubled Youth. 204p. 1987. pap. 11.95 (ISBN 0-89693-296-6). Victor Bks.

Spotts, Frederic. The Churches & Politics in Germany. LC 72-11050. 419p. 1973. 25.00x (ISBN 0-8195-4059-5). Wesleyan U Pr.

Spradley, James P., jt. auth. see Rynkiewich, Michael A.

Spradley, Ruth. Women's Bible Studies--Colossians. (Women's Bible Studies Ser.). (Illus.). 144p. 1987. pap. 4.95 (ISBN 0-87403-232-6, 39932). Standard Pub.

--Women's Bible Studies--Philippians. (Women's Bible Studies Ser.). (Illus.). 144p. 1987. pap. 4.95 (ISBN 0-87403-231-8, 39931). Standard Pub.

Spradlin, W. W., jt. auth. see Porterfield, P.

Sprague, Betty. The Little Blank Book. (Illus.). 64p. 1982. pap. 5.95 (ISBN 0-942494-24-5). Coleman Pub.

Sprague, Betty W. The Inner Voice Speaks. 59p. pap. 7.95 (ISBN 0-942494-30-X). Coleman Pub.

Sprague, Jane, ed. see Woman's Institute for Continuing Jewish Education.

Sprague, Sidney. A Year with the Baha'is of India & Burma. (Historical Reprint Ser.). (Illus.). 1986. 8.95 (ISBN 0-933770-57-X). Kalimat.

Sprague, William B. Annals of the American Pulpit - Or, Commemorative Notices of Distinguished American Clergymen of Various Denominations, from the Early Settlement of the Country to the Close of the Year 1855, with Historical Introductions, 9 Vols. LC 75-83442. (Religion in America Ser). 1969. Repr. of 1857 ed. Set. 300.00 (ISBN 0-405-00267-X). Ayer Co Pubs.

Spratt, Dora F. Christmas Week at Bigler's Mill: A Sketch in Black & White. LC 72-2171. (Black Heritage Library Collection Ser.). Repr. of 1895 ed. 13.25 (ISBN 0-8369-9065-X). Ayer Co Pubs.

Spray, Pauline. Confessions of a Preacher's Wife. 174p. (Orig.). 1986. pap. 4.95 (ISBN 0-8341-0939-5). Beacon Hill.

Spray, Pauline E. Coping with Tension. (Direction Bks). 136p. 1981. pap. 2.95 (ISBN 0-8010-8189-0). Baker Bk.

Spray, Russell E. Blessed Assurance Sermon Outlines. (Pulpit Library). 80p. 1985. pap. 3.95 (ISBN 0-8010-8255-2). Baker Bk.

--Concise Sermon Outlines. (Paperback Library). 72p. 1985. pap. 3.95 (ISBN 0-8010-8258-7). Baker Bk.

--Easy-to-Use Sermon Outlines. (Sermon Outline Ser.). 1978. pap. 2.45 (ISBN 0-8010-8143-2). Baker Bk.

--How To-Sermon Outlines. (Pulpit Library). 96p. 1984. pap. 4.50 (ISBN 0-8010-8252-8). Baker Bk.

--Instant Sermons for Busy Pastors. (Sermon Outline Ser.). (Orig.). 1981. pap. 1.95 (ISBN 0-8010-8192-0). Baker Bk.

--Practical Sermon Outlines. 80p. 1984. pap. 3.95 (ISBN 0-8010-8240-4). Baker Bk.

--Ready to Use Sermon Outlines. 80p. 1987. pap. 3.95 (ISBN 0-8010-8268-4). Baker Bk.

--Scriptural Sermon Outlines. 64p. 1987. pap. price not set (ISBN 0-8010-8277-3). Baker Bk.

--Simple Outlines on the Christian Faith. (Dollar Sermon Library). 1977. pap. 1.95 (ISBN 0-8010-8120-3). Baker Bk.

--Soul Building Sermon Outlines. (Dollar Sermon Library). 1977. pap. 1.95 (ISBN 0-8010-8118-1). Baker Bk.

--Special Day Sermon Outlines. 80p. 1984. pap. 3.95 (ISBN 0-8010-8241-2). Baker Bk.

--Time-Saving Sermon Outlines. (Sermon Outline Ser.). (Orig.). 1981. pap. 2.50 (ISBN 0-8010-8193-9). Baker Bk.

--Why Sermon Outlines. (Sermon Outline Ser.). 48p. (Orig.). 1980. pap. 2.50 (ISBN 0-8010-8188-2). Baker Bk.

Sprenger, James, jt. auth. see Kramer, Heinrich.

Sprengling, Martin & Graham, William C., eds. Barhebraeus' Scholia on the Old Testament Pt. 1: Genesis 2nd Samuel. LC 32-461. (Oriental Institute Pubns. Ser: No. 13). 1931. 28.00x (ISBN 0-226-62107-3). U of Chicago Pr.

Spretnak, Charlene. Lost Goddesses of Early Greece: A Collection of Pre-Hellenic Myths. LC 84-45068. 132p. 1984. pap. 6.95 (ISBN 0-8070-1345-5, BP682). Beacon Pr.

--Politics of Women's Spirituality: Essays on the Rise of Spiritualist Power Within the Feminist Movement. LC 80-2876. 624p. 1982. pap. 14.95 (ISBN 0-385-17241-9, Anch). Doubleday.

--The Spiritual Dimension of Green Politics. LC 86-70255. 96p. (Orig.). 1986. pap. 4.95 (ISBN 0-939680-29-7). Bear & Co.

Sprietsma, Cargill. We Imperialists: Notes on Ernest Seilliere's "Philosophy of Imperialism". LC 70-176005. Repr. of 1931 ed. 16.50 (ISBN 0-404-06198-2). AMS Pr.

Sprigg, June. By Shaker Hands. (Illus.). 1975. pap. 15.95 (ISBN 0-394-73143-3). Knopf.

Springer, Kevin, jt. auth. see Wimber, John.

Springer, Nelson & Klassen, A. J., eds. Mennonite Bibliography, 2 vols. LC 77-9105. 1977. 78.00x ea. Vol. 1 (ISBN 0-8361-1206-7). Vol. 2 (ISBN 0-8361-1207-5). Set. 147.50. Herald Pr.

Springer, Rebecca. Within Heaven's Gates. 128p. 1984. pap. 3.50 (ISBN 0-88368-125-0). Whitaker Hse.

Springer, Rebecca R. Intra Muros: My Dream of Heaven. LC 78-67820. 1985. pap. 1.75 (ISBN 0-932484-01-8). Book Searchers.

Springsted, Eric O. Simone Weil & the Suffering of Love. 131p. (Orig.). 1986. pap. 8.95 (ISBN 0-936384-33-6). Cowley Pubns.

Sproul, Barbara C. Primal Myths: Creating the World. LC 78-4429. 1979. pap. 9.95x (ISBN 0-06-067501-2, HarpR, RD 230, HarpR). Har-Row.

Sproul, R. C. Basic Training: Plain Talk on the Key Truths of the Faith. 176p. (Orig.). 1982. pap. 5.95 (ISBN 0-310-44921-9, 12371P). Zondervan.

--Chosen by God. 1986. 10.95 (ISBN 0-8423-0282-4). Tyndale.

--Effective Prayer. 96p. 1984. 2.50 (ISBN 0-8423-0735-4). Tyndale.

--Ethics & the Christian. 94p. 1983. pap. 2.95 (ISBN 0-8423-0775-3). Tyndale.

--God's Will & the Christian. 96p. 1984. 2.95 (ISBN 0-8423-1096-7). Tyndale.

--The Holiness of God. 256p. 1985. 10.95 (ISBN 0-8423-1493-8). Tyndale.

--In Search of Dignity. LC 82-18576. (In Search Of Ser.). 1983. 10.95 (ISBN 0-8307-0869-3, 5110407). Regal.

--The Intimate Marriage. 160p. (Orig.). 1986. pap. 5.95 (ISBN 0-8423-1595-0). Tyndale.

--Knowing Scripture. LC 77-11364. 1977. pap. text ed. 5.95 (ISBN 0-87784-733-9). Inter-Varsity.

--One Holy Passion: The Consuming Thirst to Know God. 1987. 13.95. Nelson.

--Reason to Believe. 160p. 1982. pap. 5.95 (ISBN 0-310-44911-1, 12370P). Zondervan.

--Who Is Jesus? 96p. 1983. pap. 2.95 (ISBN 0-8423-8216-X). Tyndale.

Sproul, R. C., et al. Classical Apologetics: A Rational Defense of the Christian Faith & a Critique of Presuppositional Apologetics. LC 83-12372. 432p. (Orig.). 1984. pap. 12.95 (ISBN 0-310-44951-0, 12372P). Zondervan.

Sproul, R. C., Jr. Money Matters. 192p. (Orig.). 1985. pap. 5.95 (ISBN 0-8423-4540-X). Tyndale.

Sproule, John A. In Defense of Pretribulationism. 56p. (Orig.). 1980. pap. 2.95 (ISBN 0-88469-133-0). BMH Bks.

Spruce, James R. Come, Let Us Worship. 118p. 1986. pap. 3.95 (ISBN 0-8341-1028-8). Beacon Hill.

Spruce, Jim. Beacon Small-Group Bible Studies, Mark: Getting in on the Action. 80p. (Orig.). 1980. pap. 2.50 (ISBN 0-8341-0650-7). Beacon Hill.

Sprung, G. M., ed. The Problems of Two Truths in Buddhism & Vedanta. LC 73-83570. 1973. lib. bdg. 26.00 (ISBN 90-277-0335-3, Pub. by Reidel Holland). Kluwer Academic.

Sprunger, Keith. Dutch Puritanism. (Studies in the History of Christian Thought: Vol. 31). 485p. 1982. text ed. 90.00x (ISBN 90-04-06793-0, Pub. by E J Brill Holland). Humanities.

Sprunger, Keith L. The Learned Doctor William Ames: Dutch Backgrounds of English & American Puritanism. LC 77-175172. pap. 76.30 (ISBN 0-317-08400-3, 2020215). Bks Demand UMI.

Sprunger, W. Frederic. TEE in Japan: A Realistic Vision: the Feasibility of Theological Education by Extension for Churches in Japan. LC 81-7739. (Illus., Orig.). 1981. pap. 15.95x (ISBN 0-87808-434-7). William Carey Lib.

Spry, Toni, jt. auth. see Beardsley, Lou.

Spuler, Bertold, ed. The Muslim World: A Historical Survey of Modern Times, Pt. IV, Fascicule 1. x, 370p. 1981. text ed. 49.95x (ISBN 90-04-06196-7, Pub. by E J Brill Holland). Humanities.

Spurgen, C. H. Teaching Children. 1983. pap. 0.95 (ISBN 0-686-40816-0). Pilgrim Pubns.

--Treasury of David, 7 vols. 1983. Set. 75.00 (ISBN 0-686-40818-7). Pilgrim Pubns.

Spurgeon, C. H. Able to the Uttermost. 240p. 1985. pap. 5.95. Pilgrim Pubns.

--According to Promise. 106p. pap. 2.00 (ISBN 0-89323-003-0, 442). Bible Memory.

--According to Promise. 1979. pap. 2.50 (ISBN 0-686-26192-5). Pilgrim Pubns.

--All of Grace. 1978. pap. 2.25 (ISBN 0-686-00497-3). Pilgrim Pubns.

--All of Grace. 144p. 1981. pap. 2.95 (ISBN 0-88368-097-1). Whitaker Hse.

--All Round Ministry. 1978. pap. 7.45 (ISBN 0-85151-181-3). Banner of Truth.

--An All-Round Ministry. 1983. pap. 4.95 (ISBN 0-686-09107-8). Pilgrim Pubns.

--Around the Wicket Gate. 1973. pap. 2.50 (ISBN 0-686-09098-5). Pilgrim Pubns.

--Assurance. 1976. pap. 1.50 (ISBN 0-686-16842-9). Pilgrim Pubns.

--Baptism. 1976. pap. 1.50 (ISBN 0-686-18091-7). Pilgrim Pubns.

--Baptismal Regeneration. 1979. 1.50 (ISBN 0-686-09097-7). Pilgrim Pubns.

--The Beatitudes. 1978. pap. 2.75 (ISBN 0-686-00504-X). Pilgrim Pubns.

--The Best of C. H. Spurgeon. 256p. 1986. pap. 6.95 (ISBN 0-8010-8267-6). Baker Bk.

--The Bible & the Newspaper. 1973. pap. 2.50 (ISBN 0-686-09104-3). Pilgrim Pubns.

--C. H. Spurgeon's Prayers. 192p. Date not set. pap. price not set. Pilgrim Pubns.

--A Catechism. 32p. 1985. pap. 0.95. Pilgrim Pubns.

--Cheque-Book of the Book of Faith. 1982. pap. 4.95 (ISBN 0-686-16836-4). Pilgrim Pubns.

--Christ Crucified. 1978. pap. 0.95 (ISBN 0-686-26193-3). Pilgrim Pubns.

--Christ's Incarnation-"Good Tidings of Great Joy". 1978. pap. 2.50 (ISBN 0-686-00498-1). Pilgrim Pubns.

--Come Ye Children. 1979. pap. 2.95 (ISBN 0-686-16840-2). Pilgrim Pubns.

--The Comforter. 1978. pap. 0.95 (ISBN 0-686-26194-1). Pilgrim Pubns.

--Complete Index to C. H. Spurgeon's Sermons. 1980. 5.95 (ISBN 0-686-27983-2). Pilgrim Pubns.

--Conversion & Experiences After Conversion. 1977. pap. 1.50 (ISBN 0-686-17969-2). Pilgrim Pubns.

--Death. 1978. pap. 1.95 (ISBN 0-686-23024-8). Pilgrim Pubns.

--The DownGrade Controversy. 1978. pap. 2.75 (ISBN 0-686-00493-0). Pilgrim Pubns.

--Eccentric Preachers. 1978. pap. 3.25 (ISBN 0-686-00496-5). Pilgrim Pubns.

--Election. 1978. pap. 1.50 (ISBN 0-686-00503-1). Pilgrim Pubns.

--Evening by Evening. 368p. 1984. pap. text ed. 3.95 (ISBN 0-88368-154-4). Whitaker Hse.

--Exposition of the Doctrines of Grace. 1975. 1.50 (ISBN 0-686-09096-9). Pilgrim Pubns.

--Farm Sermons. 328p. Date not set. pap. write for info. Pilgrim Pubns.

--Feathers for Arrows. 1973. pap. 3.25 (ISBN 0-686-09105-1). Pilgrim Pubns.

--Go in Peace. 1978. pap. 0.50 (ISBN 0-685-36795-9). Reiner.

--God's Providence. pap. 0.75 (ISBN 0-685-00749-9). Reiner.

--The Golden Alphabet (on Psalm 119) 1980. pap. 4.25 (ISBN 0-686-09094-2). Pilgrim Pubns.

--The Gospel of the Kingdom (Matthew) 1978. pap. 4.95 (ISBN 0-686-09110-8). Pilgrim Pubns.

--Grace. 1976. pap. 1.50 (ISBN 0-686-16843-7). Pilgrim Pubns.

--Greatest Fight in the World. 64p. Date not set. pap. write for info. Pilgrim Pubns.

--Holy Spirit. 1978. pap. 1.95 (ISBN 0-686-23025-6). Pilgrim Pubns.

--Immutability of God. 1977. pap. 0.95 (ISBN 0-686-23221-6). Pilgrim Pubns.

--Infant Salvation. 1981. pap. 0.95 (ISBN 0-686-37176-3). Pilgrim Pubns.

--John Ploughman's Pictures. 1974. pap. 2.50 (ISBN 0-686-10526-5). Pilgrim Pubns.

--John Ploughman's Talk. 1975. pap. 2.50 (ISBN 0-686-16833-X). Pilgrim Pubns.

--Kingly Priesthood of the Saints. 1978. pap. 0.95 (ISBN 0-686-26195-X). Pilgrim Pubns.

--Looking Unto Jesus. 1976. pap. 0.10 (ISBN 0-686-16841-0). Pilgrim Pubns.

--Memories of Stambourne. 1975. pap. 1.95 (ISBN 0-686-16838-0). Pilgrim Pubns.

--Metropolitan Tabernacle Pulpit, 1861-1917, Vols. 7-63. (C. H. Spurgeon's Sermon Ser.). Repr. black or gold bdgs. (vols. 7-61) 12.95 ea.; (vols. 62-63 combined) 15.95 (ISBN 0-686-31695-9). Pilgrim Pubns.

--Un Ministerio Ideal, 2 vols, Vols. 1 & 2. Vol. 1. 3.95 (ISBN 0-85151-410-3); Vol. 2. 3.95 (ISBN 0-85151-411-1). Banner of Truth.

--Morning by Morning. 368p. 1984. pap. text ed. 3.95 (ISBN 0-88368-156-0). Whitaker Hse.

--New Park Street Pulpit Index. 1976. pap. 1.50 (ISBN 0-686-16848-8). Pilgrim Pubns.

Spurgeon, C H. New Park Street Pulpit 1855-1860, 6 vols. 1981. Set. 60.00 (ISBN 0-686-16847-X). Pilgrim Pubns.

Spurgeon, C. H. Only a Prayer Meeting. 1976. pap. 4.25 (ISBN 0-686-09106-X). Pilgrim Pubns.

--The Pastor in Prayer. 3.75 (ISBN 0-686-09092-6). Pilgrim Pubns.

--Pastor in Prayer. 192p. Date not set. pap. write for info. Pilgrim Pubns.

--Personality of the Holy Ghost. 1977. pap. 0.95 (ISBN 0-686-23222-4). Pilgrim Pubns.

--Remembrance of Christ. 1977. pap. 0.95 (ISBN 0-686-23223-2). Pilgrim Pubns.

--Saint & His Savior. Date not set. pap. write for info. Pilgrim Pubns.

--The Salt-Cellars. 1976. pap. 7.75 (ISBN 0-686-16837-2). Pilgrim Pubns.

--Sanctification. 1976. pap. 1.50 (ISBN 0-686-16844-5). Pilgrim Pubns.

--Satan. 1978. pap. 1.95 (ISBN 0-686-23026-4). Pilgrim Pubns.

--Scriptures. 1978. pap. 1.95 (ISBN 0-686-23027-2). Pilgrim Pubns.

--Security. 1976. pap. 1.50 (ISBN 0-686-16846-1). Pilgrim Pubns.

--Sermons on Unusual Occasions. 1978. pap. 6.25 (ISBN 0-686-00494-9). Pilgrim Pubns.

--Sin of Unbelief. 1977. pap. 0.95 (ISBN 0-686-23224-0). Pilgrim Pubns.

--Soul Winner. 1978. pap. 2.50 (ISBN 0-686-02430-3). Pilgrim Pubns.

--Speeches at Home & Abroad. 1974. 3.50 (ISBN 0-686-09111-6). Pilgrim Pubns.

--Spiritual Liberty. 1978. pap. 0.95 (ISBN 0-686-26197-6). Pilgrim Pubns.

--Sweet Comfort for Feeble Saints. 1978. pap. 0.95 (ISBN 0-686-28282-5). Pilgrim Pubns.

--Sword & Trowel, 5 vols. 1985. pap. 7.50 ea. Pilgrim Pubns.

--Teachings of Nature in the Kingdom of Grace. 1976. pap. 3.95 (ISBN 0-686-18094-1). Pilgrim Pubns.

--Textual & Subject Indexes of C. H. Spurgeon's Sermons. (Key to the Metropolitan Tabernacle Pulpit set). 1971. 2.95 (ISBN 0-686-09095-0). Pilgrim Pubns.

--Till He Come. 1978. pap. 4.25 (ISBN 0-686-09089-6). Pilgrim Pubns.

--Twelve Sermons on Holiness. pap. 3.75 (ISBN 0-685-88395-7). Reiner.

--The Two Wesleys. 1975. pap. 1.95 (ISBN 0-686-16834-8). Pilgrim Pubns.

--We Endeavor. 1975. pap. 2.25 (ISBN 0-686-16835-6). Pilgrim Pubns.

--What the Stones Say. 1975. pap. 2.50 (ISBN 0-686-18095-X). Pilgrim Pubns.

--Words of Cheer for Daily Life. 1978. pap. 2.50 (ISBN 0-686-09101-9). Pilgrim Pubns.

--Words of Counsel for Christian Workers. 160p. 1985. pap. 2.95. Pilgrim Pubns.

--Words of Jesus Christ from the Cross. 1978. pap. 2.75 (ISBN 0-686-23028-0). Pilgrim Pubns.
--Words of Warning for Daily Life. 1980. pap. 2.50 (ISBN 0-686-09100-0). Pilgrim Pubns.
--Words of Wisdom for Daily Life. pap. 2.50 (ISBN 0-686-09099-3). Pilgrim Pubns.
--Works. 1976. pap. 1.50 (ISBN 0-686-16845-3). Pilgrim Pubns.

Spurgeon, Carlos M. Discursos a Mis Estudiantes. 352p. 1981. pap. 5.75 (ISBN 0-311-42006-0). Casa Bautista.

Spurgeon, Charles. All of Grace. Chen, Ruth T. & Chou, Peter, trs. (Chinese.). 142p. 1984. pap. write for info. (ISBN 0-941598-22-5). Living Spring Pubns.

Spurgeon, Charles H. All of Grace. (Moody Classics Ser.). 1984. pap. 3.50 (ISBN 0-8024-0001-9). Moody.
--Apuntes de Sermones. Orig. Title: Spurgeon's Sermon Notes. (Span.). 432p. 1975. pap. 8.95 (ISBN 0-8254-1675-2). Kregel.
--Charles Haddon Spurgeon - Autobiography: The Early Years, 1834-1860, Vol. 1. 1976. 18.95 (ISBN 0-85151-076-0). Banner of Truth.
--Charles Haddon Spurgeon - Autobiography: The Full Harvest, 1861-1892, Vol. 2. 1975. 18.95 (ISBN 0-85151-182-1). Banner of Truth.
--Christ's Words from the Cross. (Spurgeon Library Ser.). 120p. 1981. pap. 4.95 (ISBN 0-8010-8207-2). Baker Bk.
--Daily Help. 1959. 4.95 (ISBN 0-399-12825-5, G&D). Putnam Pub Group.
--Faith's Checkbook. pap. 3.95 (ISBN 0-8024-0014-0). Moody.
--Gleanings among the Sheaves. 1974. pap. 1.95 (ISBN 0-87509-085-0). Chr Pubns.
--Guide to Commentaries. 0.50 (ISBN 0-85151-400-6). Banner of Truth.
--Lectures to My Students. 1977. pap. 12.95 (ISBN 0-8010-8097-5). Baker Bk.
--Lectures to My Students. 2nd ed. 443p. 1980. pap. 9.95 (ISBN 0-310-32911-6, 10845P). Zondervan.
--Metropolitan Tabernacle Pulpit. 1971. Vol. 31. 14.95. Banner of Truth.
--Morning & Evening. 736p. 1980. Repr. 13.95 (ISBN 0-310-32940-X, 10873); large print kivar 11.95 (ISBN 0-310-32927-2). Zondervan.
--Morning & Evening. 774p. Date not set. 13.95 (ISBN 0-917006-26-7). Hendrickson MA.
--My Sermon Notes, 4 vols. (Spurgeon Library). 1981. Set. pap. 21.95 (ISBN 0-8010-8201-3); pap. 5.95 ea. Baker Bk.
--Psalms. Fuller, David O., ed. LC 76-12085. 704p. 1977. kivar 14.95 (ISBN 0-8254-3714-8). Kregel.
--Sermons for Special Days & Occasions. 160p. 1984. pap. 4.95 (ISBN 0-8010-8247-1). Baker Bk.
--Sermons for Special Occasions. Cook, Charles T, ed. 256p. 1977. Repr. of 1958 ed. limp bk. 5.95 (ISBN 0-551-05573-1). Attic Pr.
--Sermons on Revival: Kelvedon. Cook, Charles T., ed. 256p. 1977. Repr. of 1958 ed. limp bk. 5.95 (ISBN 0-551-05575-8). Attic Pr.
--Sermons on the Miracles. Cook, Charles T, ed. 256p. 1977. Repr. of 1958 ed. limp bk. 5.95 (ISBN 0-551-05576-6). Attic Pr.
--Sermons on the Parables. Cook, Charles T, ed. 256p. 1977. Repr. of 1958 ed. limp bk. 5.95 (ISBN 0-551-05574-X). Attic Pr.
--Solamente Por Gracia. (Span.). 128p. 1982. pap. 3.25 (ISBN 0-8254-1678-7). Kregel.
--The Soulwinner. (Orig.). 1963. pap. 4.95 (ISBN 0-8028-8081-9). Eerdmans.
--Spurgeon's Devotional Bible. 1974. Repr. 19.95 (ISBN 0-8010-8043-6). Baker Bk.
--Spurgeon's Expository Encyclopedia, 15 vols. 1977. 195.00 (ISBN 0-8010-8104-1). Baker Bk.
--Spurgeon's Sermons, 10 vols. (Charles H. Spurgeon Library). 1983. pap. 99.95 (ISBN 0-8010-8231-5). Baker Bk.
--Spurgeon's Sermons on Christ's Names & Titles. Cook, Charles T., ed. 1965. Repr. of 1961 ed. 7.95 (ISBN 0-87921-033-8). Attic Pr.
--Treasury of David, 2 vols. 1983. Set. 45.00 (ISBN 0-8010-8256-0). Baker Bk.
--The Treasury of David, 2 vols. 1984. Repr. Psalms 1-78, Vol. I, 1440p. 39.95 set (ISBN 0-8407-5425-6). Psalms 79-150, Vol. II, 1464p. Nelson.
--The Treasury of David - A Commentary on the Psalms, 3 vols. 2912p. Date not set. 49.95 (ISBN 0-917006-25-9). Hendrickson MA.

Spurrell, Helen. Old Testament Translation. 840p. 1987. 29.95 (ISBN 0-8254-3757-1). Kregel.

Spurrier, Joseph H. Great Are the Promises unto the Isle of the Sea: The Church of Jesus Christ of Latter-Day Saints in the Hawaiian Islands. (Orig.). 1978. pap. 2.95 (ISBN 0-89036-114-2). Hawkes Pub Inc.

Spykman, Gordon. Never On Your Own. 125p. 1983. pap. 4.95 (ISBN 0-933140-85-1); Pt. 1, 48pgs. student manual 1.95 (ISBN 0-933140-86-X); Pt. 2, 48pgs. student manual 1.95 (ISBN 0-933140-87-8). CRC Pubns.

Spykman, Gordon, et al. Society, State, & Schools: A Case for Structural & Confessional Pluralism. 224p. (Orig.). 1981. pap. 9.95 (ISBN 0-8028-1880-3). Eerdmans.

Spykman, Gordon J., jt. auth. see Grissen, Lillian V.

Squier, Ephraim G. The Serpent Symbol & the Worship of the Reciprocal Principles of Nature in America. LC 17-25223. 1975. Repr. of 1851 ed. 21.00 (ISBN 0-527-03228-X). Kraus Repr.

Squire, Aelred. Aelred of Rievaulx: A Study. (Cistercian Studies Ser.: No. 50). 192p. 1981. 10.95 (ISBN 0-87907-850-2); pap. 5.00 (ISBN 0-686-85802-6). Cistercian Pubns.

Squire, Aelred, ed. & tr. Fathers Talking: An Anthology. (Studies: No. 93). 1986. 12.95 (ISBN 0-87907-893-6); pap. 6.95 (ISBN 0-87907-993-2). Cistercian Pubns.

Squire, Charles. Celtic Myth & Legend. LC 74-26575. (Newcastle Mythology Library: Vol. 1). 450p. 1975. pap. 6.95 (ISBN 0-87877-030-5). Newcastle Pub.
--Celtic Myth & Legend, Poetry & Romance. LC 80-53343. (Newcastle Mythology Library: Vol. 1). 450p. 1980. Repr. of 1975 ed. lib. bdg. 16.95x (ISBN 0-89370-630-2). Borgo Pr.
--Celtic Myth & Legend, Poetry & Romance. LC 77-6985. 1977. Repr. of 1910 ed. lib. bdg. 45.00 (ISBN 0-89341-164-7). Longwood Pub Group.
--The Mythology of Ancient Britain & Ireland. LC 73-13769. 1974. Repr. of 1909 ed. lib. bdg. 17.50 (ISBN 0-8414-7650-0). Folcroft.
--Mythology of the British Islands. LC 77-94622. 1979. Repr. of 1905 ed. lib. bdg. 45.00 (ISBN 0-89341-306-2). Longwood Pub Group.

Sr. Carole MacKenthun. Biblical Bulletin Boards. (Helping Hand Ser.). 48p. 1984. wkbk. 4.95 (ISBN 0-86653-197-1). Good Apple.

Sr. Clare. Journey Out of Chaos. LC 81-22885. 248p. (Orig.). 1981. pap. 8.00 (ISBN 0-89571-012-9). Affirmation.

Sri Aurobindo. The Mother. 62p. 1980. 19.00 (ISBN 0-89744-914-2, Pub. by Sri Aurobindo Ashram Trust India); pap. 2.00 (ISBN 0-89744-915-0, Pub. by Sru Aurobindo Ashram Trust India); pap. 1.00 miniature size 1980 (ISBN 0-89744-148-6). Auromere.

Sri Aurobindo Ashram Publications Department Staff & Aurobindo, Sri. On Women. 126p. (Orig.). Date not set. pap. 6.00 (ISBN 0-89744-236-9, Pub. by Sri Aurobindo Ashram Trust India). Auromere.

Sri, Patricia. Revelations: As It Is. Moringland Publications Inc, ed. (Illus.). 635p. (Orig.). 1979. pap. 10.00 (ISBN 0-935146-08-3). Morningland.

Sri, Prem Krishna see Krishna Sri, Prem.

SriAnanda. The Complete Book of Yoga: Harmony of Body & Mind. 175p. 1980. 11.95x (ISBN 0-317-12476-5, Pub. by Vision Bks India). Asia Bk Corp.

Sri Aurobindo. Essays on the Gita. 1976. 12.50 (ISBN 0-89071-231-X). Matagiri.
--Essays on the Gita. 1976. pap. 8.75 (ISBN 0-89071-222-0). Matagiri.
--Essays on the Gita. (Life Companion Library). 763p. 1983. 21.95 (ISBN 0-89744-006-4). Auromere.
--Glossary of Terms in Sri Aurobindo's Writings. 1978. 10.00 (ISBN 0-89071-271-9). Matagiri.
--Guidance from Sri Aurobindo: Letters to a Young Disciple. Doshi, Nagin, ed. 285p. 1974. 6.00 (ISBN 0-89071-205-0). Matagiri.
--The Immortal Fire. Jhunjhuniwala, Shyam S., ed. 216p. (Orig.). 1974. pap. 4.50 (ISBN 0-89071-209-3). Matagiri.
--Isha Upanishad. Aurobindo, Sri, tr. 1979. pap. 6.00 (ISBN 0-89744-922-3). Auromere.
--Kena Upanishad. Sri Aurobindo, tr. (Life Companion Library). 1979. pap. 5.95 (ISBN 0-89744-923-1). Auromere.
--Letters on Yoga, 3 vols. 1979. Vol. 1. 11.25 (ISBN 0-89071-236-0); Vol. 2. 12.50 (ISBN 0-89071-238-7); Vol. 3. 14.50 (ISBN 0-89071-240-9); Vol. 1. pap. 10.00 (ISBN 0-89071-237-9); Vol. 2. pap. 11.25 (ISBN 0-89071-239-5); Vol. 3. pap. 12.50 (ISBN 0-89071-241-7). Matagiri.
--Light for Students: Compiled from the Writings of Sri Aurobindo & the Mother. 1984. pap. 3.50 (ISBN 0-89071-272-7). Matagiri.
--Lights on Yoga. 1979. pap. 3.00 (ISBN 0-89744-916-9). Auromere.
--The Message of the Gita: With Text, Translation & Notes As Interpreted by Sri Aurobindo. Roy, Anilbaran, ed. 1984. pap. 7.95 (ISBN 0-89071-225-5). Matagiri.
--On Yoga II: Letters on Yoga Tome I. 1979. 15.00 (ISBN 0-89744-911-8). Auromere.
--A Practical Guide to Integral Yoga. (Illus.). 1985. 9.00 (ISBN 0-89071-217-4); pap. 6.95. Matagiri.
--The Problem of Rebirth. 1979. pap. 15.00 (ISBN 0-89744-913-4). Auromere.
--Sri Aurobindo & the Mother on Education. 6th, Special ed. 1978. pap. 16.00 (ISBN 0-89744-955-X). Auromere.
--Sri Aurobindo on Himself. 1979. 20.00 (ISBN 0-89744-917-7). Auromere.
--Thoughts & Aphorisms. 1979. pap. 6.00 (ISBN 0-89744-927-4). Auromere.
--Yoga of Divine Works. 2nd ed. (Life Companion Library). (Illus.). 270p. Date not set. pap. 8.95 (ISBN 0-89744-015-3). Auromere.

Sri Aurobindo & The Mother. Sri Aurobindo & the Mother on Education. 168p. 1973. pap. 3.50 (ISBN 0-89071-249-2). Matagiri.
--Sri Aurobindo & the Mother on Love. Saint-Hilaire, P. B., ed. & intro. by. 49p. 1973. pap. 2.00 (ISBN 0-89071-275-1). Matagiri.

Sri Chinmoy. Earth's Cry Meets Heaven's Smile, Bk. 2. 145p. (Orig.). 1975. Bk. 2. pap. 3.00 (ISBN 0-88497-143-0). Aum Pubns.
--Eternity's Silence-Heart. 200p. (Orig.). 1974. pap. 3.00 (ISBN 0-88497-106-6). Aum Pubns.
--Europe Blossoms. 1000p. (Orig.). 1974. pap. 15.00 (ISBN 0-88497-077-9). Aum Pubns.
--Father & Son. 100p. (Orig.). 1975. pap. 2.00 (ISBN 0-88497-119-8). Aum Pubns.
--Fifty Freedom-Boats to One Golden Shore, Pt. 5. 68p. (Orig.). 1975. pap. 2.00 (ISBN 0-88497-229-1). Aum Pubns.
--Flame-Waves, Pt. 1. 52p. (Orig.). 1975. pap. 2.00 (ISBN 0-88497-213-5). Aum Pubns.
--Flame-Waves, Pt. 2. 47p. (Orig.). 1975. pap. 2.00 (ISBN 0-88497-214-3). Aum Pubns.
--Flame-Waves, Pt. 3. 47p. (Orig.). 1975. pap. 2.00 (ISBN 0-88497-215-1). Aum Pubns.
--Flame-Waves, Pt. 4. 53p. (Orig.). 1975. pap. 2.00 (ISBN 0-88497-216-X). Aum Pubns.
--Flame-Waves, Pt. 5. 50p. (Orig.). 1975. pap. 2.00 (ISBN 0-88497-217-8). Aum Pubns.
--Fortune-Philosophy. 69p. (Orig.). 1974. pap. 2.00 (ISBN 0-88497-138-4). Aum Pubns.
--From the Source to the Source. (Orig.). 1978. pap. 8.00 (ISBN 0-88497-431-6). Aum Pubns.
--The Garden of Love-Light. 50p. (Orig.). 1974. pap. 2.00 (ISBN 0-88497-109-0). Aum Pubns.
--Kundalini: The Mother - Power. 2nd rev. ed. 1974. pap. 3.95 (ISBN 0-88497-104-X). Aum Pubns.
--Lord, I Ask You for One Favour. 50p. (Orig.). 1975. pap. 2.00 (ISBN 0-685-61224-4). Aum Pubns.
--Lord, I Need You. 50p. 1975. pap. 2.00 (ISBN 0-88497-211-9). Aum Pubns.
--Matsyendranath & Gorakshanath: Two Spiritual Lions. 64p. (Orig.). 1974. pap. 2.00 (ISBN 0-88497-093-0). Aum Pubns.
--My Flute. (Orig.). 1972. pap. 3.00 (ISBN 0-88497-227-5). Aum Pubns.
--My Promise to God. 50p. (Orig.). 1975. pap. 2.00 (ISBN 0-88497-222-4). Aum Pubns.
--A Soulful Cry Versus a Fruitful Smile. (Orig.). 1977. pap. 10.00 (ISBN 0-88497-402-2). Aum Pubns.
--Sound Becomes, Silence Is. 200p. (Orig.). 1975. pap. 3.00 (ISBN 0-88497-118-X). Aum Pubns.
--Supreme, I Sing Only for You. 105p. (Orig.). 1974. pap. 2.00 (ISBN 0-88497-079-5). Aum Pubns.
--Supreme, Teach Me How to Cry. 100p. (Orig.). 1974. pap. 2.00 (ISBN 0-88497-120-1). Aum Pubns.
--Supreme, Teach Me How to Surrender. 100p. (Orig.). 1975. pap. 2.00 (ISBN 0-88497-237-2). Aum Pubns.
--The Vision of God's Dawn. 67p. 1974. pap. 2.00 (ISBN 0-685-53062-0). Aum Pubns.
--When God-Love Descends. 50p. 1975. pap. 2.00 (ISBN 0-88497-210-0). Aum Pubns.
--When I Left God in Heaven. 50p. (Orig.). 1975. pap. 2.00 (ISBN 0-88497-223-2). Aum Pubns.

Sridhara, Swami B. The Loving Search for the Lost Servant. Goswami, B. S. & Mahayogi, B. V., eds. (Illus.). 120p. 1987. pap. text ed. 9.95 (ISBN 0-940431-05-X). Guardian Devot Pr.

Srinivasachari, P. N. Ethical Philosophy of the Gita. 2.00 (ISBN 0-87481-454-5). Vedanta Pr.
--Philosophy of Bhedabheda. 6.95 (ISBN 0-8356-7253-0). Theos Pub Hse.
--Synthetic View of Vedanta. 2.75 (ISBN 0-8356-7512-2). Theos Pub Hse.

Srinivasadasa. Yatindramatadipika. Adidevananda, Swami, tr. (Sanskrit & Eng.). 2.75 (ISBN 0-87481-428-6). Vedanta Pr.

Srinivasan, A. V. A Hindu Primer: Yaksha Prashna. (Illus.). 78p. 1984. pap. 7.70 (ISBN 0-86578-249-0, 6203). Ind-US Inc.

Srinivasan, Doris. Concept of Cow in the Rig Veda. 1979. 9.95 (ISBN 0-89684-060-3, Pub. by Motilal Banarsidass India). Orient Bk Dist.

Srinivasau, Nirmala. Identity Crisis of Muslims: Profiles of Lucknow Youth. 140p. 1981. text ed. 15.00x (ISBN 0-391-02279-2, Pub. by Concept Pubs India). Humanities.

Sri Ram, N. Approach To Reality. 5.75 (ISBN 0-8356-7339-1). Theos Pub Hse.
--Human Interest. 2nd ed. 1968. 2.50 (ISBN 0-8356-7170-4). Theos Pub Hse.
--Life's Deeper Aspects. 1968. 3.50 (ISBN 0-8356-7172-0). Theos Pub Hse.
--Thoughts for Aspirants. 7th ed. (Series 2). 1969. 4.25 (ISBN 0-8356-7195-X). Theos Pub Hse.

Sri Ramatherio, rev. by. Unto Thee I Grant. 32nd ed. LC 49-15007. 96p. 1979. 8.95 (ISBN 0-912057-02-5, G-505). AMORC.

Srisang, Koson. Perspectives on Political Ethics: An Ecumenical Inquiry. 196p. 1983. pap. 8.95 (ISBN 0-87840-407-4). Georgetown U Pr.

Sri Sarada Devi. The Gospel of the Holy Mother. 409p. 1986. pap. 7.50X (ISBN 0-8364-1667-8, Pub. by Mukhopadhyaya India). South Asia Bks.

Sri Swami Satchidananda. The Golden Present. 448p. (Orig.). Date not set. pap. write for info. (ISBN 0-932040-30-6). Integral Yoga Pubns.
--Guru & Disciple. 1977. pap. 1.95 (ISBN 0-932040-18-7). Integral Yoga Pubns.
--Integral Yoga: The Yoga Sutras of Patanjali. Pocket ed. LC 85-125. 124p. (Orig.). 1985. pap. 3.95 (ISBN 0-932040-28-4). Integral Yoga Pubns.
--The Living Gita. LC 84-27861. (Orig.). Date not set. pap. price not set (ISBN 0-932040-27-6). Integral Yoga Pubns.
--The Mother Is the Baby's First Guru: Pregnancy, Infant Care & Yoga. 1976. pap. 3.95 (ISBN 0-932040-15-2). Integral Yoga Pubns.

Srivastava. Mother Goddess in Indian Art, Archaeology & Literature. 1980. 32.00x (ISBN 0-686-65576-1, Pub. by Agam India). South Asia Bks.

Srivastava, Rama. Comparative Religion. LC 74-904268. 1974. 14.00x (ISBN 0-88386-565-3). South Asia Bks.

Srivastava, Rama S. Contemporary Indian Philosophy. 1983. text ed. 24.00x. Coronet Bks.

Sr. Thea Bowman, jt. auth. see Reverend James Hawker.

Sr. Vincent Regnault. St. Louise de Marillac: Servant of the Poor. LC 83-50058. 136p. 1984. pap. 3.50 (ISBN 0-89555-215-9). TAN Bks Pubs.

S. Saeed, Akhtar-Rizvi, jt. auth. see Husayn at-Tabatabai, S. Muhammad.

Ssu Shu. Chinese Classical Work Commonly Called the Four Books, 1828. Collie, David, ed. LC 75-122487. 1970. Repr. of 1828 ed. 50.00x (ISBN 0-8201-1079-5). Schol Facsimiles.

Staack, Hagen. Lectionary Preaching Workbook on the Psalms. (Ser. C). 1982. 14.25 (ISBN 0-89536-573-1, 1263). CSS of Ohio.
--A Study Guide for Genesis. 1984. pap. 3.95 (ISBN 0-9613270-0-6). G McBride.

Staal, Frits. Exploring Mysticism: A Methodological Essay. LC 74-76391. (Center for South & Southeast Asia Studies). 1975. 42.00x (ISBN 0-520-02726-4); pap. 4.95 (ISBN 0-520-03119-9, CAL 313). U of Cal Pr.

Staal, J. F. Nambudiri Veda Recitation. (Disputationes Rheno-Trajectinae: No. 5). (Illus.). pap. 13.60 (ISBN 90-2790-031-0). Mouton.

Stace, W. T. Mysticism & Philosophy. 1960. text ed. 17.50x (ISBN 0-333-08274-5). Humanities.
--Mysticism & Philosophy. 384p. 1987. pap. 10.95 (ISBN 0-87477-416-0). J P Tarcher.

Stace, Walter T. Concept of Morals. 11.25 (ISBN 0-8446-2990-1). Peter Smith.
--Religion & the Modern Mind. LC 80-24093. 285p. 1980. Repr. of 1952 ed. lib. bdg. 24.75x (ISBN 0-313-22662-8, STRM). Greenwood.
--Time & Eternity: An Essay in the Philosophy of Religion. Repr. of 1952 ed. lib. bdg. 22.50x (ISBN 0-8371-1867-0, STTE). Greenwood.

Stacey. Jeddah Old & New. (Illus.). 1980. 45.00x (ISBN 0-686-47159-8). Intl Bk Ctr.

Stacey, John. John Wycliffe & Reform. LC 78-63199. (Heresies of the Early Christian & Medieval Era: Second Ser.). 1979. Repr. of 1964 ed. 24.50 (ISBN 0-404-16239-8). AMS Pr.

Stacey, W. David. Groundwork of Biblical Studies. LC 82-70961. 448p. 1982. pap. 14.95 (ISBN 0-8066-1936-8, 10-2898). Augsburg.

Stack, George J. Kierkegaard's Existential Ethics. LC 75-16344. (Studies in Humanities: No. 16). 240p. 1977. 15.00 (ISBN 0-8173-6624-5); pap. 5.50 (ISBN 0-8173-6626-1). U of Ala Pr.

Stackhouse, Max. Ethics & the Urban Ethos: An Essay in Social Theory & Theological Reconstruction. LC 77-179155. 240p. 1974. pap. 4.95x (ISBN 0-8070-1137-1, BP479). Beacon Pr.

Stackhouse, Max L. Creeds, Society, & Human Rights: A Study in Three Cultures. 320p. 1984. 19.95 (ISBN 0-8028-3599-6). Eerdmans.
--Public Theology & Political Economy: Christian Stewardship in Modern Society. 192p. (Orig.). 1987. pap. 8.95 (ISBN 0-8028-0267-2). Eerdmans.

Stackhouse, Max L., ed. see Adams, James L.

Stacpoole, Alberic, ed. Mary's Place in Christian Dialogue. LC 83-61204. 282p. (Orig.). 1983. pap. 10.95 (ISBN 0-8192-1333-0). Morehouse.

Stacpoole, Dom A., ed. Vatican Two Revisited: By Those Who Were There. 448p. 1986. 24.50 (ISBN 0-86683-531-8, HarpR). Har-Row.

Stacy, John. Sermons That Should Be in Print. (Illus.). 104p. (Orig.). 1986. pap. 9.95. Brentwood Comm.

--Soul Touching Sermons. (Illus.). 114p. (Orig.). 1986. pap. 9.95 (ISBN 1-55630-015-8). Brentwood Comm.

Stadelmann, Luis I. Hebrew Conception of the World. (Analecta Biblica: Vol. 39). 1970. pap. 15.00 (ISBN 88-7653-039-8). Loyola.

Stadler, Bernice. Celebrations of the Word for Children: Cycle A. Reece, Nancy, ed. 88p. (Orig.). 1986. pap. 9.95 (ISBN 0-89622-308-6). Twenty-Third.

Stadler, Richard H. Living As a Winner. Fischer, William E., ed. (Bible Class Course for Young Adults Ser.). (Illus.). 64p. 1985. pap. 2.95 leaders guide (ISBN 0-938272-23-3); pap. 2.95 students guide (ISBN 0-938272-22-5). WELS Board.

--Meet the Lord & His Church. Fischer, William E., ed. (Bible Class Course for Young Adults Ser.). (Illus.). 64p. (Orig.). 1987. pap. text ed. 2.95 (ISBN 0-938272-26-8); tchr's ed. 2.95 (ISBN 0-938272-27-6). Wels Board.

Stadtler, Bea. The Holocaust: A History of Courage & Resistance. Bial, Morrison D., ed. LC 74-11469. Orig. Title: The Test. (Illus.). 210p. 1975. pap. text ed. 5.50x (ISBN 0-87441-231-5). Behrman.

--The Holocaust: A History of Courage & Resistance. 210p. Repr. 5.50 (ISBN 0-686-95067-4). ADL.

Staebler, Warren. Ralph Waldo Emerson. (World Leaders Ser.). 1973. lib. bdg. 12.50 (ISBN 0-8057-3674-3, Twayne). G K Hall.

Staeglich, Wilhelm. The Auschwitz Myth. O'Keefe, Theodore J., ed. Francis, Thomas, tr. from Ger. Tr. of Der Auschwitz Mythos. (Illus.). 408p. 1986. 19.95 (ISBN 0-939484-23-4). Inst Hist Rev.

Staehelin, Ernst. Das Theologische Lebenswerk Johannes Oekolampads. 61.00 (ISBN 0-384-57419-X); pap. 55.00 (ISBN 0-384-57418-1). Johnson Repr.

Staehlin, Jakob Von Storcksburg see Von Storcksburg Staehlin, Jakob.

Staffeld, Jean, et al. Thirty-Eight Recipes for Bulletin Boards & Art Projects That Christian Kids Can Make. (Illus.). 1978. pap. 4.95 (ISBN 0-570-03774-3, 12-2721). Concordia.

Stafford, Bill. The Adventure of Giving. Griffin, Ted, ed. 128p. (Orig.). 1985. pap. 4.95 (ISBN 0-8423-0036-8). Tyndale.

Stafford, Gilbert W. The Life of Salvation. 1979. pap. 3.95 (ISBN 0-87162-216-5, D5210). Warner Pr.

Stafford, Linda. Mind Invaders. (YA) 1982. pap. 1.95. Victor Bks.

Stafford, Tim. The Friendship Gap: Reaching Out Across Cultures. LC 84-6725. 152p. (Orig.). 1984. pap. 5.95 (ISBN 0-87784-975-7). Inter-Varsity.

--Knowing the Face of God. 256p. Date not set. pap. 8.95 (ISBN 0-310-32851-9). Zondervan.

--Knowing the Face of God: The Search for a Personal Relationship with God. 256p. 1986. text ed. 12.95 (ISBN 0-310-32850-0, 10836). Zondervan.

Stafford, William S. Domesticating the Clergy: The Inception of the Reformation in Strasbourg 1522-1524. LC 76-15567. (American Academy of Religion, Dissertation Ser.). 1976. pap. 9.95 (ISBN 0-89130-109-7, 010117). Scholars Pr GA.

Stafford Poole, C. M. Pedro Moya de Contreras: Catholic Reform & Royal Power in New Spain, 1571-1591. LC 86-1410. 350p. 1987. text ed. 30.00 (ISBN 0-520-05551-9). U of Cal Pr.

Stagg, Evelyn & Stagg, Frank. Woman in the World of Jesus. LC 77-28974. 292p. 1978. pap. 9.95 (ISBN 0-664-24195-6). Westminster.

Stagg, Frank. The Bible Speaks on Aging. LC 81-66092. 1981. softcover 6.50 (ISBN 0-8054-5292-3). Broadman.

--Book of Acts. 1955. 14.50 (ISBN 0-8054-1311-1). Broadman.

--Galatians & Romans. LC 79-92066. (Knox Preaching Guides Ser.). 128p. (Orig., John Hayes series editor). 1980. pap. 4.95 (ISBN 0-8042-3238-5); pap. 4.95. John Knox.

--The Holy Spirit Today. LC 73-85701. 1974. pap. 3.75 (ISBN 0-8054-1919-5). Broadman.

--New Testament Theology. LC 62-15328. 1962. 13.95 (ISBN 0-8054-1613-7). Broadman.

--Teologia del Nuevo Testamento. Canclini, Arnoldo, tr. 346p. 1985. pap. 9.95 (ISBN 0-311-09077-X). Casa Bautista.

Stagg, Frank, jt. auth. see Stagg, Evelyn.

Stahl, Carolyn. Opening to God: Guided Imagery Meditation on Scripture. LC 77-87403. 1977. 3.50x (ISBN 0-8358-0357-0). Upper Room.

Stahl, John. Arcane Commentaries. 9p. 1973. pap. 2.00 (ISBN 0-318-21744-9). Evanescent Pr.

--An Original Commentary on the I Ching. 32p. 1976. 10.00 (ISBN 0-318-21738-4). Evanescent Pr.

--Patterns of Illusion & Change. (Illus.). 24p. 1984. pap. 3.50 (ISBN 0-318-21732-5). Evanescent Pr.

--Theophany. 24p. deluxe ed. 100.00 (ISBN 0-318-21735-X). Evanescent Pr.

--Theophany. (Illus.). 24p. 100.00 (ISBN 0-318-21736-8); Proofs of main edition, 1979. 20.00; Early manuscript edition, 1978. 20.00. Evanescent Pr.

--The World Union Company. 60p. 1980. pap. 5.00 (ISBN 0-318-21734-1). Evanescent Pr.

Stahl, Martha D. By Birth or by Choice. LC 86-33643. 136p. (Orig.). 1987. pap. 5.95 (ISBN 0-8361-3437-0). Herald Pr.

Stahl, Paul H. Household, Village, & Village Confederation in Southeastern Europe. (East European Monographs: No. 200). 252p. 1986. 25.00 (ISBN 0-88033-094-5). East Eur Quarterly.

Stahl, Rachel K., jt. auth. see Fisher, Sara E.

Stainer, John. Music of the Bible. LC 74-100657. (Music Ser). (Illus.). 1970. Repr. of 1914 ed. lib. bdg. 32.50 (ISBN 0-306-71862-6). Da Capo.

Stair, Rolland. Be Reconciled. 48p. 1981. softcover 0.75 (ISBN 0-8146-1233-4). Liturgical Pr.

Stakeman, Randolph. The Cultural Politics of Religious Change: A Study of the Sanoyea Kpelle in Liberia. (African Studies: Vol. 3). 264p. text ed. 49.95x (ISBN 0-88946-177-5). E Mellen.

Stakeman, Richard. Religious Change in an African Town: A Sociological Study of God's Town, Liberia. 1987. 49.95. E Mellen.

Staley, David E. The Devil's Classroom. 1984. 7.95 (ISBN 0-89536-972-9, 7532). CSS of Ohio.

Staley, Vernon. The Catholic Religion. 320p. 1983. pap. 9.95 (ISBN 0-8192-1327-6). Morehouse.

Stalker, D. M. Genesis One to Twelve. 0.50x (ISBN 0-685-33497-X). Outlook.

Stalker, D. M., tr. see Bornkamm, Gunther.

Stalker, D. M., tr. see Von Rad, Gerhard.

Stalker, David M., tr. see Westermann, Claus.

Stalker, James. The Example of Jesus Christ: Imago Christi. LC 80-82322. (Shepherd Illustrated Classics Ser.). (Orig.). 1980. pap. 5.95 (ISBN 0-87983-231-2). Keats.

--The Life of Jesus Christ. Whyte, A. & Moffatt, J., eds. (Handbooks for Bible Classes & Private Students Ser.). 160p. 1922. pap. 7.95 (ISBN 0-567-28130-2, Pub. by T & T Clark Ltd UK). Fortress.

--Living the Christ Life. LC 81-81097. (The Shepherd Illustrated Classics Ser.). (Illus.). 1981. pap. 5.95 (ISBN 0-87983-259-2). Keats.

--Vida de Jesucristo. (Span.). 177p. pap. 3.50. Edit Caribe.

--Vida de San Pablo. (Span.). 160p. 1973. pap. 3.50 (ISBN 0-89922-025-8). Edit Caribe.

Stalker, James A. The Life of Jesus Christ. (Stalker Trilogy Ser.). 160p. 1984. pap. 5.95 (ISBN 0-310-44191-9, 12618P). Zondervan.

--The Life of St. Paul. (Stalker Trilogy Ser.). 176p. 1984. pap. 5.95 (ISBN 0-310-44181-1, 12617P). Zondervan.

Stalker, James M. Life of Jesus Christ. 160p. 10.95 (ISBN 0-8007-0177-1). Revell.

Stallo, Johann B., et al. Bible in Public Schools. 2nd ed. LC 67-27464. (Law, Politics & History Ser). 1967. Repr. of 1870 ed. lib. bdg. 39.50 (ISBN 0-306-70963-5). Da Capo.

Stambaugh, Joan. The Real Is Not the Rational. (Buddhist Studies). 142p. (Orig.). 1986. 34.50 (ISBN 0-88706-166-4); pap. 10.95 (ISBN 0-88706-167-2). State U NY Pr.

Stambaugh, John E. & Balch, David L. The New Testament in Its Social Environment. LC 85-15516. (Library of Early Christianity: Vol. 2). (Illus.). 208p. 1986. 16.95 (ISBN 0-664-21906-3). Westminster.

Stambaugh, John E., jt. auth. see Rice, David G.

Stambaugh, Ria, ed. Teufelbuecher in Auswahl, 3 vols. (Ausgaben Deutscher Literatur des 15. bis 18. Jahrh). (Ger). Vol. 1, 1970. write for info (ISBN 3-11-006388-3); Vol. 2, 1972. 112.00x (ISBN 3-11-003924-9); Vol. 3, 1973. 141.00x (ISBN 3-11-004127-8). De Gruyter.

Stamey, Joseph, jt. auth. see Monk, Robert C.

Stamm, Millie. Be Still & Know. 384p. 1981. pap. 7.95 (ISBN 0-310-32991-4, 10844P). Zondervan.

--Beside Still Waters: Meditation Moments on the Psalms. 144p. 1983. gift edition 9.95 (ISBN 0-310-33060-2, 10743). Zondervan.

--Meditation Moments for Women. 1967. pap. 7.95 (ISBN 0-310-32981-7). Zondervan.

Stamoolis, James J. Eastern Orthodox Mission Theology Today. LC 85-15596. 208p. (Orig.). 1986. pap. 18.95 (ISBN 0-88344-215-9). Orbis Bks.

Stamp, Josiah. Christian Ethic As An Economic Factor. facsimile ed. LC 70-102256. (Select Bibliographies Reprint Ser). 1926. 17.00 (ISBN 0-8369-5141-7). Ayer Co Pubs.

Stampfer, Nathaniel, jt. ed. see Riemer, Jack.

Stamwitz, Alicia von see Von Stamwitz, Alicia.

Stancliffe, Clare. St. Martin & His Hagiographer: History & Miracle in Sulpicius Severus. (Oxford Historical Monographs). (Illus.). 1983. 45.00x (ISBN 0-19-821895-8). Oxford U Pr.

Standhardt, Robert T. Journey to the Magical City: A Quadriplegic Person's Reflections on Suffering & Love. LC 83-80413. 96p. (Orig.). 1983. pap. 4.50 (ISBN 0-8358-0458-5). Upper Room.

Standiford, Deborah, jt. auth. see Standiford, Steven.

Standiford, Steven & Standiford, Deborah. Sudden Family. 160p. 1986. 9.95 (ISBN 0-8499-0567-2). Word Bks.

Stanesby, Derek. Science, Reason & Religion. 210p. 1985. 34.50 (ISBN 0-7099-3360-6, Pub. by Croom Helm Ltd). Methuen Inc.

Stanfield, Vernon L., rev. by see Broadus, John A.

Stanford, Donald, ed. see Masefield, John.

Stanford, Gwendolyn C. Legende Doree Ou Legenda Aurea: The First Ten Chapters. LC 85-90222. 125p. 1986. 8.95 (ISBN 0-533-06725-1). Vantage.

Stanford, Julian C. Reflection: Diary of a German Jew in Hiding. 1965. 4.50 (ISBN 0-943376-00-9). Magnes Mus.

Stanford, Miles J. The Complete Green Letters. 368p. 1984. pap. 9.95 (ISBN 0-310-33051-3, 9480, Clarion Class). Zondervan.

--The Green Letters: Principals of Spiritual Growth. 128p. 1975. pap. 3.95 (ISBN 0-310-33001-7, 9473P). Zondervan.

Stanford, Neal. I Do Windows. 48p. 1982. 6.00 (ISBN 0-682-49865-3). Exposition Pr FL.

--Open Windows. 80p. 1984. 8.00 (ISBN 0-682-40172-2). Exposition Pr FL.

Stanford, Susan. Will I Cry Tomorrow? 1987. 9.95 (ISBN 0-8007-1512-8). Revell.

Stanford, Sylvia. I'm Growing. (Bible & Me Ser.). (Illus.). 1986. 5.95 (ISBN 0-8054-4167-0). Broadman.

Stange, Charles D. British Unitarians Against American Slavery, 1833-1865. LC 82-48436. 256p. 1984. 29.50 (ISBN 0-8386-3168-1). Fairleigh Dickinson.

Stanger, Frank B. Gifts of the Spirit. 1974. pap. 0.95 (ISBN 0-87509-084-2). Chr Pubns.

Stangl, Jean. Bible Cut & Tell Stories: Old & New Testaments. (Illus.). 40p. 1987. pap. 2.95 (ISBN 0-87403-154-0, 2874 (OLD TESTAMENT)); pap. 2.95 (ISBN 0-87403-155-9, 2875 (NEW TESTAMENT)). Standard Pub.

Staniforth, Maxwell, tr. Early Christian Writings: The Apostolic Fathers. (Classics Ser.). 240p. 1968. pap. 5.95 (ISBN 0-14-044197-2). Penguin.

--Early Christian Writings: The Apostolic Fathers. 208p. 1987. 5.95 (ISBN 0-14-044475-0). Penguin.

Staniforth, Maxwell, tr. see Apostolic Fathers.

Staniland, Wake C., jt. auth. see Westropp, Hodder M.

Staniloae, Dumitru. Theology & the Church. Barringer, Robert, tr. from Romanian. LC 80-19313. 240p. 1980. pap. 7.95 (ISBN 0-913836-69-9). St Vladimirs.

Stanislawski, Michael. Tsar Nicholas I & the Jews: The Transformation of Jewish Society in Russia, 1825-1855. (Illus.). 272p. 1983. 18.95 (ISBN 0-8276-0216-2, 497). Jewish Pubns.

Stankes, M. Thomas. Confronting Cults, Old & New. pap. 6.95 (ISBN 0-317-12202-9). AMG Pubs.

Stankiewicz, W. J. Politics & Religion in Seventeenth-Century France. LC 76-2075. 269p. 1976. Repr. of 1960 ed. lib. bdg. 22.50x (ISBN 0-8371-8770-2, STPR). Greenwood.

Stanksy, Peter, ed. see Holland, Mary G.

Stanley, A. Knighton. The Children Is Crying. LC 78-26544. 1979. 8.95 (ISBN 0-8298-0347-5). Pilgrim NY.

Stanley, Arthur P. Epistles of Paul to the Corinthians. 1981. 20.95 (ISBN 0-86524-051-5, 7105). Klock & Klock.

--Essays Chiefly on Questions of Church & State from 1850 to 1870. 656p. Repr. of 1870 ed. text ed. 74.52x (ISBN 0-576-02173-3). Gregg Intl.

--Life & Correspondence of Thomas Arnold D. D, 2 vols. LC 75-29624. Repr. of 1845 ed. Set. 72.50 (ISBN 0-404-13980-9). AMS Pr.

Stanley, Carlton W. Matthew Arnold. 1978. Repr. of 1938 ed. 20.00 (ISBN 0-8492-2595-7). R West.

Stanley, Charles. Handle with Prayer. 120p. 1982. pap. 4.95 (ISBN 0-88207-309-5). Victor Bks.

--How to Listen to God. 160p. 1985. 10.95 (ISBN 0-8407-9041-4). Oliver-Nelson.

Stanley, Charles F. Confronting Casual Christianity. LC 85-7764. 1985. 7.95 (ISBN 0-8054-5022-X). Broadman.

--A Man's Touch. LC 77-80948. 120p. 1977. pap. 3.95 (ISBN 0-88207-753-8). Victor Bks.

Stanley, David. Life with Elvis. (Illus.). 1986. 12.95 (ISBN 0-8007-1490-3). Revell.

Stanley, David M. Apostolic Church in the New Testament. LC 65-19453. 500p. 1965. 7.95 (ISBN 0-8091-0002-9). Paulist Pr.

--I Encountered God! The Spiritual Exercises with the Gospel of St. John. Ganss, George E., ed. LC 84-82164. (Original Studies, Composed in English: Ser. III, No. 7). 348p. 1986. 14.00 (ISBN 0-912422-72-6); pap. 11.00 Smyth sewn (ISBN 0-912422-71-8). Inst Jesuit.

--A Modern Scriptural Approach to the Spiritual Exercises. Ganss, George E., frwd. by. LC 67-25219. (Series III: No. 1). xviii, 358p. 1986. pap. 6.95 (ISBN 0-912422-07-6). Inst Jesuit.

Stanley, Gary. The Garimus File. LC 82-72301. (Illus., Orig.). 1983. pap. 6.95 (ISBN 0-86605-107-4). Heres Life.

Stanley, Hugh P. The Challenge of Fatherhood. LC 82-73132. 96p. (Orig.). 1982. pap. 2.45 (ISBN 0-87029-185-8, 20279-6). Abbey.

Stanley, Linda, ed. see Associated Women's Organization, Mars Hill Bible School.

Stanley, Phyllis & Yih, Miltinnie. Celebrate the Seasons! 119p. (Orig.). 1986. pap. 4.95 (ISBN 0-89109-116-5). NavPress.

Stanley, W. P. The Student. 1957. 4.95 (ISBN 0-87148-756-X). Pathway Pr.

Stanmsky, Peter, ed. see Schoenl, William J.

Stannard, David E. The Puritan Way of Death: A Study in Religion, Culture & Social Change. LC 76-42647. (Illus.). 1977. 19.95x (ISBN 0-19-502226-2). Oxford U Pr.

--The Puritan Way of Death: A Study in Religion, Culture, & Social Change. LC 76-42647. (Illus.). 1977. pap. 8.95 (ISBN 0-19-502521-0). Oxford U Pr.

Stansell, Gary, tr. see Wolff, Hans W.

Stansky, Peter, ed. see Donovan, Robert K.

Stansky, Peter, ed. see Gunnin, Gerry C.

Stansky, Peter, ed. see Hein, Virginia H.

Stansky, Peter, ed. see Klaus, Robert J.

Stansky, Peter, ed. see Nurser, John.

Stansky, Thomas, jt. auth. see Anderson, Gerald H.

Stansky, Thomas F., jt. ed. see Anderson, Gerald H.

Stanton, Elizabeth C. The Original Feminist Attack on the Bible. LC 74-9343. 258p. 1974. 6.95 (ISBN 0-405-05997-3). Ayer Co Pubs.

--The Woman's Bible, 2 vols. in 1. LC 72-2626. (American Women Ser: Images & Realities). 380p. 1972. Repr. of 1895 ed. 25.50 (ISBN 0-405-04481-X). Ayer Co Pubs.

--The Woman's Bible. 1974. Repr. 12.95 (ISBN 0-9603042-1-5). Coalition Women-Relig.

Stanton, G. N. Jesus of Nazareth in New Testament Preaching. LC 73-92782. (Society of New Testament Studies: No. 27). 228p. 1975. 44.50 (ISBN 0-521-20465-8). Cambridge U Pr.

Stanton, Graham, ed. The Interpretation of Matthew. LC 83-5508. (Issues in Religion & Theology Ser.). 176p. 1983. pap. 7.95 (ISBN 0-8006-1766-5, 1-1766). Fortress.

Stanton, H. U. Teaching of the Qur'An, with an Account of Its Growth & Subject Index. LC 74-90040. 1969. Repr. 18.00 (ISBN 0-8196-0253-1). Biblo.

Stanton, Madeline E., jt. auth. see Fulton, John F.

Stanton, Robert L. The Church & the Rebellion. facsimile ed. LC 70-168521. (Black Heritage Library Collection). Repr. of 1864 ed. 31.25 (ISBN 0-8369-8873-6). Ayer Co Pubs.

Stanton, Sybil. The Twenty-Five Hour Woman. 256p. 1986. 9.95 (ISBN 0-8007-1487-3). Revell.

Stanwood, P. G., ed. see Hooker, Richard.

Stanwood, Paul & Warren, Austin, eds. William Law: A Serious Call to a Devout & Holy Life & the Spirit of Love. LC 78-61418. (Classics of Western Spirituality). 542p. 1978. 14.95 (ISBN 0-8091-0265-X); pap. 9.95 (ISBN 0-8091-2144-1). Paulist Pr.

Staples, Russell L., jt. auth. see Oosterwal, Gottfried.

Stapleton. The Life & Illustrious Martyrdom of Sir Thomas More. LC 66-23617. 206p. 1984. 7.50 (ISBN 0-8232-0731-5). Fordham.

Stapleton, Edmund, tr. see Percheron, Maurice.

Stapleton, Michael. The Concise Dictionary of Greek & Roman Mythology. LC 85-15101. (Orig.). 1986. pap. 4.95 (ISBN 0-87226-006-2). P Bedrick Bks.

--The Illustrated Dictionary of Greek & Roman Mythology. LC 85-30692. (The Library of the World's Myths & Legends). (Illus.). 224p. 1986. 17.95 (ISBN 0-87226-063-1). P Bedrick Bks.

Stapleton, Ruth. Power Through Release. pap. 0.50 (ISBN 0-910924-39-2); 3 for 1.00 (ISBN 0-685-04195-6). Macalester.

Stapleton, Ruth C. & Cochran, Robert. How Do You Face Disappointments? LC 77-78468. (Lifeline Ser.). 1977. pap. 0.95 (ISBN 0-88419-136-2). Creation Hse.

Stapleton, Thomas, tr. see Bede the Venerable.

Starcke, Walter. This Double Thread. 160p. 1969. 12.95 (ISBN 0-227-67738-2). Attic Pr.

Stargel, Gloria C. The Healing. (Orig.). 1982. pap. 2.50 (ISBN 0-8423-1425-3). Tyndale.

Starhawk. The Spiral Dance: Rebirth of the Ancient Religion of the Goddess. (Orig.). 1979. pap. 10.95 (ISBN 0-06-067535-7, RD 301, HarpR). Har-Row.

Stark, Claude. God of All. 1982. 20.00 (ISBN 0-89007-000-8); pap. 6.00 (ISBN 0-89007-102-0). Branden Pub Co.

Stark, Freya. The Valleys of the Assassins. rev. ed. (Illus.). 1972. 28.50 (ISBN 0-7195-2429-6). Transatl Arts.

Stark, Joan, jt. auth. see Stark, Tom.

Stark, Rodney & Bainbridge, William S. The Future of Religion: Secularization, Revival & Cult Formation. LC 83-18221. (Illus.). 600p. 1985. pap. 40.00x (ISBN 0-520-04854-7); 14.95 (ISBN 0-520-05731-7, CAMPUS 406). U of Cal Pr.

Stark, Rodney & Foster, Bruce D. Wayward Shepards: Prejudice & the Protestant Clergy. 130p. pap. 6.95 (ISBN 0-686-95186-7). ADL.

Stark, Rodney & Glock, Charles Y. American Piety: The Nature of Religious Commitment. 1968. 35.95x (ISBN 0-520-01210-0); pap. 2.65 (ISBN 0-520-01756-0, CAL197). U of Cal Pr.

Stark, Rodney, jt. auth. see Glock, Charles Y.

Stark, Rodney, ed. Religious Movements: Genesis, Exodus, & Numbers. LC 85-9539. (Sociology of Religion Ser.). 369p. 1986. 24.95 (ISBN 0-913757-43-8, Pub by New Era Bks); pap. 12.95 (ISBN 0-913757-44-6, Pub. by New Era Bks). Paragon Hse.

Stark, Tom & Stark, Joan. Guidance & God's Will. (Fisherman Bible Studyguide). 60p. 1978. saddle stitch 2.50 (ISBN 0-87788-324-6). Shaw Pubs.

Stark, Werner. Social Bond, an Investigation into the Bases of Law-Abidingness, Vol. IV: Safeguards of the Social Bond: Ethos & Religion. viii, 288p. 1983. 25.00 (ISBN 0-8232-1083-9); pap. 12.50 (ISBN 0-8232-1084-7). Fordham.

--The Sociology of Religion: A Study of Christendom, 5 vols. Incl. Vol. 1. Established Religion. xii, 235p. 1967. 20.00 (ISBN 0-8232-0720-X); Vol. 2. Sectarian Religion. viii, 357p. 1967. 22.50 (ISBN 0-8232-0735-8); Vol. 3. The Universal Church. x, 454p. 1967. 25.00 (ISBN 0-8232-0760-9); Vol. 4. Types of Religious Man. xii, 340p. 1970. 22.50 (ISBN 0-8232-0855-9); Vol. 5. Types of Religious Culture. x, 453p. 1972. 25.00 (ISBN 0-8232-0935-0). LC 66-27652. Set (ISBN 0-8232-0719-6). Fordham.

Starkes, M. Thomas. Confronting Popular Cults. LC 72-79177. 1972. pap. 4.25 (ISBN 0-8054-1805-9, 42-1805). Broadman.

--The Dual Ministry. 1986. pap. 3.95 (ISBN 0-937931-01-2). Global TN.

--The Foundation for Missions. LC 80-67460. 1981. pap. 5.50 (ISBN 0-8054-6325-9). Broadman.

--God's Commissioned People. LC 84-4968. 1984. pap. 12.95 (ISBN 0-8054-6338-0). Broadman.

--Today's World Religions. 1986. 10.95 (ISBN 0-937931-02-0); pap. 7.95. Global TN.

--Toward a Theology of Missions. 1984. pap. 5.95 (ISBN 0-89957-055-0). AMG Pubs.

Starkey, Edward D. Judaism & Christianity: A Guide to the Reference Literature. (Reference Sources in the Humanities Ser.). 250p. 1987. lib. bdg. 27.50 (ISBN 0-87287-533-4). Libs Unl.

Starkey, Frank L., jt. auth. see Nelson, Steven M.

Starkey, Marion. The Visionary Girls: Witchcraft in Salem Village. 1973. 15.45i (ISBN 0-316-81087-8). Little.

Starkey, Marion L. Devil in Massachusetts: A Modern Enquiry into the Salem Witch Trials. LC 49-10395. 1969. pap. 5.95 (ISBN 0-385-03509-8, Anch). Doubleday.

--Devil in Massachusetts: A Modern Inquiry into the Salem Witch Trials. 15.00 (ISBN 0-8446-2996-0). Peter Smith.

Starks, Arthur E. Combined Concordances to the Scriptures. 1978. 33.00 (ISBN 0-8309-0255-4). Herald Hse.

Starling, Allan, ed. Seeds of Promise: World Consultation on Frontier Missions, Edinburgh '80. LC 81-69488. (Illus.). 272p. (Orig.). 1981. pap. 8.95 (ISBN 0-87808-186-0). William Carey Lib.

Starnes, DeWitt T. & Talbert, Ernest W. Classical Myth & Legend in Renaissance Dictionaries. LC 73-11753. (Illus.). 517p. 1973. Repr. of 1955 ed. lib. bdg. 42.50x (ISBN 0-8371-7086-9, STCM). Greenwood.

Staron, Stanislaw, jt. ed. see Hilberg, Raul.

Starr, Edward C. A Baptist Bibliography, Vols. 1-25. Incl. Vol. 1. Authors A. 1947. 13.25x (ISBN 0-910056-00-5); Vol. 2. Authors B-Biloxi. 1952. 16.55x (ISBN 0-910056-01-3); Vol. 3. Authors Bin-Bz. 1953. 21.20x (ISBN 0-910056-02-1); Vol. 4. Authors C-Colby. 1954. 16.55x (ISBN 0-910056-03-X); Vol. 5. Authors Colchester-Cz. 1957. 13.25x (ISBN 0-910056-04-8); Vol. 6. Authors D. 1958. 13.25x (ISBN 0-910056-05-6); Vol. 7. Authors E-Flynt. 1961. 13.25x (ISBN 0-910056-06-4); Vol. 8. Authors Fo-Glazier. 1963. 16.55x (ISBN 0-910056-07-2); Vol. 9. Authors Gleason-Halko. 1964. 16.55x (ISBN 0-910056-08-0); Vol. 10. Authors Hall-Hill, Joseph. 1965. 16.55x (ISBN 0-910056-09-9); Vol. 11. Authors Hill, Kizard. 1966. 13.25x (ISBN 0-910056-10-2); Vol. 12. Authors J. 1967. 13.25x (ISBN 0-910056-11-0); Vol. 13. Authors K-Layton. 1968. 16.55x (ISBN 0-910056-12-9); Vol. 14. Authors Lea-McGuire. 1969. 16.55x (ISBN 0-910056-13-7); Vol. 15. Authors McIlvain-Merrill. 1970. 16.55x (ISBN 0-910056-14-5); Vol. 16. Authors **Merrimac-Nevin. 1971. 16.55x (ISBN 0-910056-15-3); Vol. 17. Authors New-Pastors. 1972. 16.55x (ISBN 0-910056-16-1); Vol. 18. Authors Pate-Poynton. 1972. 16.55x (ISBN 0-910056-17-X); Vol. 19. Authors Pra-Rives. 1973. 16.55x (ISBN 0-910056-18-8); Vol. 20. Authors Ro-Sardis. 1974. 13.25x (ISBN 0-685-24442-3); Vol. 21. Authors Sare-Smith, S. 1974. 16.55x (ISBN 0-685-24443-1); Vol. 22. Authors Smith, T.-Steude. 1975. 16.55x (ISBN 0-685-24444-X); Vol. 23. Authors Steven-Torbet. 1976. 16.55x (ISBN 0-685-24445-8); Vol. 24. Authors Torey-Wa. 1976. 16.55x (ISBN 0-685-24446-6); Vol. 25. Authors We-Z. 1976. 21.20x (ISBN 0-910056-24-2). Set. 400.00. Am Baptist.**

Starr, Frank. Light for the Way: Old Testament, 2 bks. (Illus.). 96p. 1987. pap. 2.95 ea. Bk. 3 (ISBN 0-570-04450-2, 12-3057). Bk. 4 (ISBN 0-570-04451-0, 12-3058). Concordia.

Starr, Frank, jt. auth. see Heintzen, Erich H.

Starr, Frederick. Korean Buddhism: History-Condition-Art: Three Lectures. LC 78-70123. Repr. of 1918 ed. 25.00 (ISBN 0-404-17379-9). AMS Pr.

Starr, G. A. Defoe & Casuistry. LC 75-113010. 1971. 25.50x (ISBN 0-691-06192-0). Princeton U Pr.

Starr, Irina. The Sound of Light. LC 69-20335. 1977. pap. 3.50 (ISBN 0-87516-220-7). De Vorss.

Starr, Joshua. Romania: The Jewries of the Levant After the Fourth Crusade. 1943. 10.00x (ISBN 0-87068-108-7). Ktav.

Starr, Lee A. The Bible Status of Women. Gifford, Carolyn D. & Dayton, Donald, eds. (Women in American Protestant Religion 1800-1930 Ser.). 416p. 1987. lib. bdg. 60.00 (ISBN 0-8240-0675-5). Garland Pub.

Starr, Paul D., jt. auth. see Alamuddin, Nura S.

Starratt, Alfred B. Your Self, My Self & the Self of the Universe. LC 79-9971. (Illus.). 192p. 1979. 12.95 (ISBN 0-916144-38-0); pap. 4.95 (ISBN 0-916144-39-9). Stemmer Hse.

Startup, Kenneth M. See His Banner Go: A Centennial History of the First Baptist Church, Paragould, Arkansas. LC 84-73475. (Illus.). 100p. 1985. write for info. (ISBN 0-935304-93-2). August Hse.

Staten, Ralph. Perseverance in Preservation. 36p. 1975. pap. 0.95 (ISBN 0-89265-109-1). Randall Hse.

Statler, Oliver. Japanese Pilgrimage. (Illus.). 352p. 1985. pap. 9.95 (ISBN 0-688-04834-X, Quill). Morrow.

Staton, Julia. What the Bible Says about Women. LC 80-66128. (What the Bible Says Ser.). 400p. 1980. 13.95 (ISBN 0-89900-079-7). College Pr Pub.

Staton, Knofel. Bible Keys for Today's Family. LC 83-9239. 144p. (Orig.). 1984. pap. 2.95 (ISBN 0-87239-669-X, 41024). Standard Pub.

--Check Your Commitment: Instructor. 160p. 1985. pap. 3.50 (ISBN 0-87239-828-5, 39982). Standard Pub.

--Check Your Commitment: Student. 128p. 1985. pap. 2.95 (ISBN 0-87239-829-3, 39983). Standard Pub.

--Check Your Discipleship. LC 81-9411. 116p. (Orig., Student's & instructor's ed. bnd. together). 1982. pap. 2.25 student ed. (ISBN 0-87239-424-7, 39991); instructor's ed. 2.50 (ISBN 0-87239-423-9, 39990). Standard Pub.

--Check Your Homelife. LC 82-19600. 176p. (Orig.). 1983. pap. 4.95 (ISBN 0-87239-649-5, 39973). Standard Pub.

--Check Your Life in Christ. 160p. pap. 2.95x (ISBN 0-89900-203-X). College Pr Pub.

--Check Your Morality. LC 83-418. 194p. (Orig.). 1983. pap. 3.95 (ISBN 0-87239-630-4, 39971). Standard Pub.

--Discovering My Gifts for Service. rev. ed. 48p. 1984. 2.50 (ISBN 0-87239-810-2, 39978). Standard Pub.

--First Corinthians. (Standard Bible Studies). (Illus.). 272p. 1987. pap. price not set (ISBN 0-87403-167-2, 40107). Standard Pub.

--God's Plan for Church Leadership. LC 82-3378. 160p. (Orig.). 1982. pap. 5.95 (ISBN 0-87239-566-9, 39987). Standard Pub.

--Grow, Christian, Grow: Student. LC 77-82120. (New Life Ser.). (Illus.). 1978. pap. 2.25 (ISBN 0-87239-177-9, 39999). Standard Pub.

--How to Know the Will of God. LC 78-62707. 96p. (Orig.). 1979. pap. 2.95 (ISBN 0-87239-985-0, 39948). Standard Pub.

--The Servant's Call. LC 75-7462. (Illus.). 96p. 1976. pap. 2.25 (ISBN 0-87239-051-9, 40024). Standard Pub.

--Spiritual Gifts for Christians Today. 118p. (Orig.). 1973. pap. 3.50 (ISBN 0-89900-134-3). College Pr Pub.

--Struggle for Freedom. LC 76-18381. 96p. 1977. pap. 2.25 (ISBN 0-87239-063-2, 40034). Standard Pub.

--Thirteen Lessons on I, II, III John. LC 80-69722. (Bible Student Study Guide Ser.). 149p. 1980. pap. 2.95 (ISBN 0-89900-169-6). College Pr Pub.

--What to Do till Jesus Comes. LC 81-14594. 112p. 1983. pap. 2.25 (ISBN 0-87239-481-6, 41016). Standard Pub.

Staub, Jacob. The Creation of the World According to Gersonides. LC 81-13523. (Brown Judiac Studies). 1982. pap. 20.00 (ISBN 0-89130-526-2, 14-00-24). Scholars Pr GA.

Staub, Jacob J., jt. auth. see Alpert, Rebecca T.

Staub, Jacob J., jt. ed. see Schein, Jeffrey L.

Staudacher, Joseph M. Lector's Guide to Biblical Pronunciations. LC 75-14609. 72p. (Orig.). 1975. pap. 2.95 (ISBN 0-87973-773-5). Our Sunday Visitor.

Stauderman, Albert P. Facts about Lutherans. 32p. 1959. pap. 0.95, 10 for 5.50 (ISBN 0-8006-1832-7, 1-1832). Fortress.

--Let Me Illustrate: Stories & Quotations for Christian Communicators. LC 83-70511. 192p. (Orig.). 1983. pap. 9.95 (ISBN 0-8066-2017-X, 10-3817). Augsburg.

Stauffer, J. Mark, ed. Our Hymns of Praise. (Illus.). 168p. 1958. 4.95x (ISBN 0-8361-1126-5). Herald Pr.

Stauffer, Richard. The Quest for Church Unity: From John Calvin to Isaac d'Huisseau. (Pittsburgh Theological Monographs: No. 19). (Orig.). 1986. pap. 14.00 (ISBN 0-915138-63-8). Pickwick.

Stauffer, Romaine H. Hidden Riches. 1983. 4.70 (ISBN 0-87813-520-0). Christian Light.

Stauffer, S. Anita. The Altar Guild: A Guide for the Ministry of Liturgical Preparations. 64p. 1978. pap. 2.95 (ISBN 0-8006-1321-X, 1-1321). Fortress.

--Altar Guild Handbook. LC 85-47713. 128p. 1985. pap. 5.95 (ISBN 0-8006-1868-8, 1-1868). Fortress.

Stauffer, Vernon. New England & the Bavarian Illuminati. LC 66-27153. 1967. Repr. of 1918 ed. 8.50x (ISBN 0-8462-0953-5). Russell.

Staupitz, Johann Von see Von Staupitz, Johann.

Stauter, Patrick C. & Delaney, Howard L. The Willging Years: Seventeen Years with the First Catholic Bishop of Pueblo. (Illus., Orig.). 1987. pap. text ed. 24.95 (ISBN 0-9617847-0-9). P C Stauter.

Staveley, A. L. Memories of Gurdjieff. LC 78-56109. 1978. 8.95 (ISBN 0-89756-000-0). Two Rivers.

Stavely, Lilian. The Golden Fountain or the Soul's Love for God. LC 82-70082. (The Library of Traditional Wisdom). 95p. 1982. pap. 4.75 (ISBN 0-941532-02-X). Wrld Wisdom Bks.

Stavropoulos, C. Partakers of Divine Nature. 1976. pap. 4.95 (ISBN 0-937032-09-3). Light&Life Pub Co MN.

Stavrou, Theofanis G., jt. ed. see Nichols, Robert L.

Stavroulakis, Nikos, illus. Jeremiah: A New Translation. (Illus.). 92p. 1973. 12.50 (ISBN 0-8276-0027-5). Jewish Pubns.

Stavsky. Thou Art Consecrated Unto Me. 1.50 (ISBN 0-87306-101-2). Feldheim.

Stavsky, David. For Thou Art with Me: A Manual of Mourning. 1965. pap. 1.50 (ISBN 0-87306-093-8). Feldheim.

Stayer, James M. Anabaptists & the Sword. 2nd rev. ed. 1976. 15.00 (ISBN 0-87291-081-4). Coronado Pr.

Stayer, James M. & Packull, Werner O. The Anabaptists & Thomas Muntzer. 176p. 1980. pap. text ed. 13.95 (ISBN 0-8403-2235-6). Kendall-Hunt.

Stcherbatskoi, F. I. The Conception of Buddhist Nirvana. lib. bdg. 100.00 (ISBN 0-87968-058-X). Krishna Pr.

Stcherbatsky, T. Buddhist Logic, 2 Vols. 1958. Repr. of 1932 ed. Set. text ed. 74.00x (ISBN 90-2790-060-4). Mouton.

--Central Conception of Buddhism. 1979. Repr. 12.50 (ISBN 0-89684-183-9). Orient Bk Dist.

Stcherbatsky, Theodore. Buddhist Logic, 2 vols. 1930. pap. text ed. 8.95 ea.; Vol. 1. pap. text ed. (ISBN 0-486-20955-5); Vol. 2. pap. text ed. (ISBN 0-486-20956-3). Dover.

--Conception of Buddhist Nirvana. 2nd rev. ed. 1977. 13.95 (ISBN 0-89684-187-1). Orient Bk Dist.

--The Conception of Buddhist Nirvana. 408p. 1979. pap. 6.95 (ISBN 0-87728-427-X). Weiser.

Stead, Dom J., tr. see St. Maximus the Confessor.

Stead, G. C. Divine Substance. (Illus.). 1966. 49.50x (ISBN 0-19-826630-8). Oxford U Pr.

Stead, Julian. There Shines Forth Christ. 1983. pap. 8.95 (ISBN 0-932506-29-1). St Bedes Pubns.

Stead, W. T. Borderland: A Casebook of True Supernatural Stories. LC 69-16361. 358p. 1970. 5.95 (ISBN 0-8216-0058-3). Univ Bks.

Steadman, John M. The Lamb & the Elephant: Ideal Imitation & the Context of Renaissance Allegory. LC 73-93874. 254p. 1974. 29.95 (ISBN 0-87328-062-8). Huntington Lib.

Steadman, Victoria, tr. see Evdokimov, Paul.

Stealey, Sydnor L. & Gaustad, Edwin S., eds. A Baptist Treasury. LC 79-52607. (The Baptist Tradition Ser.). 1980. Repr. of 1958 ed. lib. bdg. 27.50x (ISBN 0-405-12472-4). Ayer Co Pubs.

Stearn, Jess. Yoga, Youth & Reincarnation. (Illus.). 352p. 1986. pap. 3.95 (ISBN 0-553-26057-X). Bantam.

Stearns, Bill. If the World Fits, You're the Wrong Size. 1981. pap. 2.95 (ISBN 0-88207-588-8). SP Pubns.

--If the World Fits, You're the Wrong Size. 1981. pap. 3.95 (ISBN 0-88207-588-8). Victor Bks.

Stebbing, Henry, tr. see Henry, Paul E.

Stebbing, L. Encyclopedia of Numbers: Their Essence of Meaning. 1973. lib. bdg. 79.95 (ISBN 0-87968-553-0). Krishna Pr.

Stebbing, Rita, tr. see Steiner, Rudolf.

Stebbins, George C. Reminiscences & Gospel Hymn Stories. LC 74-144689. Repr. of 1924 ed. 24.50 (ISBN 0-404-07203-8). AMS Pr.

Stebbins, Madeline, tr. see Couer de Jesus d' Elbee, Jean du.

Steblin-Kamenskij, M. I. Myth. 165p. 1981. 15.50 (ISBN 0-89720-053-5); pap. 8.50 (ISBN 0-89720-054-3). Karoma.

Stedman, Jon, jt. auth. see Foster, Lewis.

Stedman, Ray C. Authentic Christianity: A Fresh Grip on Life. LC 84-20536. (Authentic Christianity Bks.). 182p. 1985. pap. 6.95 (ISBN 0-88070-072-6). Multnomah.

--From Guilt to Glory: The Message of Romans 9-16. LC 85-29659. (Authentic Christianity Bks.). 1986. pap. 7.95 (ISBN 0-88070-124-2). Multnomah.

--From Guilt to Glory: The Message of Romans 1-8. LC 85-29657. (Authentic Christianity Bks.). 1985. pap. 8.95 (ISBN 0-88070-123-4). Multnomah.

--Highlights of the Bible: Genesis-Nehemiah. LC 79-65423. 256p. 1979. pap. 3.50 (ISBN 0-8307-0656-9, S333147). Regal.

--Highlights of the Bible: Poets & Prophets. LC 81-50589. (Bible Commentary for Laymen Ser.). 224p. 1981. pap. text ed. 3.50 (ISBN 0-8307-0774-3, S352108). Regal.

--The Man of Faith: Learning from the Life of Abraham. LC 85-21772. (Authentic Christianity Bks.). 1985. pap. 7.95 (ISBN 0-88070-125-0). Multnomah.

--Solomon's Secret: Enjoying Life, God's Good Gift. LC 85-8967. (Authentic Christianity Bks.). 1985. pap. 6.95 (ISBN 0-88070-076-9). Multnomah.

--Spiritual Warfare: Winning the Daily Battle with Satan. LC 85-2893. (Authentic Christianity Ser.). 145p. 1985. pap. 6.95 (ISBN 0-88070-094-7). Multnomah.

--Talking to My Father: What Jesus Teaches on Prayer. LC 84-20783. (Authentic Christianity Bks.). 184p. 1985. pap. 6.95 (ISBN 0-88070-075-0). Multnomah.

--Understanding Man. LC 86-16463. (Authentic Christianity Ser.). (Orig.). 1986. pap. 6.95 (ISBN 0-88070-156-0). Multnomah.

--What More Can God Say? 2nd ed. LC 74-176002. 256p. 1977. pap. 3.95 (ISBN 0-8307-0457-4, S283123). Regal.

--What's This World Coming To? LC 86-6439. 1986. pap. 5.95 (ISBN 0-8307-1154-6, 5418825). Regal.

Steed, Robert P., jt. ed. see Baker, Tod A.

Steel, David. Preaching Through the Year. LC 80-82191. 168p. 1980. pap. 1.79 (ISBN 0-8042-1801-3). John Knox.

Steel, Valetta & Erny, Ed. Thrice Through the Valley. (Living Books). 112p. 1986. 2.95 (ISBN 0-8423-7146-X). Tyndale.

Steele. Gospel of the Comforter. pap. 5.95 (ISBN 0-686-12870-2). Schmul Pub Co.

--Half Hours with St. John. pap. 5.95 (ISBN 0-686-12871-0). Schmul Pub Co.

--Half Hours with St. Paul. pap. 5.95 (ISBN 0-686-12872-9). Schmul Pub Co.

--Jesus Exultant. pap. 2.95 (ISBN 0-686-12885-0). Schmul Pub Co.

--Love Enthroned. kivar 4.95 (ISBN 0-686-12891-5). Schmul Pub Co.

Steele & Ryrie. Meant to Last. 1983. 5.95 (ISBN 0-686-46323-4). Victor Bks.

Steele, Ashbel. Chief of the Pilgrims: Or, the Life & Time of William Brewster. facs. ed. LC 72-133535. (Select Bibliographies Reprint Ser). (Illus.). 1857. 23.50 (ISBN 0-8369-5567-6). Ayer Co Pubs.

Steele, D. Steele's Answers. 6.95 (ISBN 0-686-27781-3). Schmul Pub Co.

Steele, Daniel. A Substitute for Holiness, Or Antinomianism Revived. (The Higher Christian Life Ser.). 370p. 1985. lib. bdg. 45.00 (ISBN 0-8240-6445-3). Garland Pub.

Steele, David. God Must Have a Sense of Humor, He Made Aadvarks & Orangutans..., & Me! LC 82-84780. (Illus., Orig.). 1983. pap. 6.00 (ISBN 0-937088-09-9). Illum Pr.

Steele, David A. Images of Leadership & Authority for the Church: Biblical Principles & Secular Models. LC 86-24589. 206p. (Orig.). 1987. lib. bdg. 23.50 (ISBN 0-8191-5710-4); pap. text ed. 13.25 (ISBN 0-8191-5711-2). U Pr of Amer.

Steele, David H. & Curtis, Thomas C. Five Points of Calvinism. 1963. pap. 2.50 (ISBN 0-87552-444-3). Presby & Reformed.

Steele, David H. & Thomas, Curtis C. Interpretive Outline of Romans. (Illus.). 1963. pap. 5.95 (ISBN 0-87552-443-5). Presby & Reformed.

Steele, David N. & Thomas, Curtis C. Five Points of Calvinism. (Biblical & Theological Studies). pap. 2.50 (ISBN 0-8010-7919-5). Baker Bk.

--Romans. pap. 5.95 (ISBN 0-8010-8018-5). Baker Bk.

Steele, James. Bible Solutions to Problems of Daily Living. 132p. 1983. 10.95 (ISBN 0-13-078022-7); pap. 4.95 (ISBN 0-13-078014-6). P-H.

Steele, Nicola, jt. auth. see Detrich, Richard L.

Steele, Philip. Joseph & the Coat of Many Colors. LC 85-40309. (Bible Stories Ser.). (Illus.). 24p. 1985. 5.45 (ISBN 0-382-09091-8); PLB 6.96 (ISBN 0-382-09088-8). Silver.

Steele, Philip, adapted by. Joseph & His Brothers. LC 85-40308. (Bible Stories Ser.). (Illus.). 24p. 1985. 5.45 (ISBN 0-382-09092-6); PLB 6.96 (ISBN 0-382-09089-6). Silver.

Steele, Phillip W. Ozark Tales & Superstitions. LC 82-22425. (Illus.). 96p. 1983. pap. 4.95 (ISBN 0-88289-404-8). Pelican.

Steele, Sharon A. Keys to Contentment. (Aglow Bible Study Basic Ser.). 80p. 1981. pap. 2.95 (ISBN 0-930756-65-7, 521013). Aglow Pubns.

--A New Commandment: Loving As Jesus Loved. (Basic Bible Study). 64p. 1986. pap. 2.95 (ISBN 0-932305-21-0, 521021). Aglow Pubns.

Steelman, Robert B. What God Has Wrought: A History of the Southern New Jersey Conference of the United Methodist Church. LC 86-70275. 368p. (Orig.). 1986. text ed. 12.50x (ISBN 0-914960-60-1); pap. text ed. 10.00x (ISBN 0-914960-56-3). Academy Bks.

Steely, John E., jt. auth. see Hays, Brooks.

Steely, John E., ed. see De Jonge, Marinus.

Steely, John E., tr. see Conzelmann, Hans.

Steely, John E., tr. see Flesseman-Van Leer, E.

Steely, John E., tr. see Lohse, Edward.

Steely, John E., tr. see Reitzenstein, Richard.

Steely, John E., tr. see Von Harnack, Adolf.

Steeman, T. What's Wrong with God. McNamee, Fantan, ed. (Synthesis Ser.). pap. 0.75 (ISBN 0-8199-0391-4). Franciscan Herald.

Steen, Shirley & Edwards, Anne. A Child's Bible. 1986. 9.95 (ISBN 0-8091-2867-5). Paulist Pr.

Steenberghen, Fernand Van see Van Steenberghen, Fernand.

Steer, John L. & Dudley, Cliff. Vietnam, Curse or Blessing. LC 82-82016. (Illus.). 192p. (Orig.). 1982. pap. 5.95 (ISBN 0-89221-091-5). New Leaf.

Steer, Roger. George Muller: Delighted in God! rev. ed. LC 81-52600. 320p. 1981. pap. 3.95 (ISBN 0-87788-304-1). Shaw Pubs.

Steer, Roger, selected by. Spiritual Secrets of George Muller. 2nd ed. 126p. 1987. pap. 5.95 (ISBN 0-87788-782-9). Shaw Pubs.

Steer, Roger, ed. see Muller, George.

Steere, Douglas. Together in Solitude. LC 82-14918. 160p. 1983. 12.95 (ISBN 0-8245-0531-X). Crossroad NY.

--Together in Solitude. rev. ed. 208p. 1985. pap. 8.95 (ISBN 0-8245-0715-0). Crossroad NY.

Steere, Douglas, tr. see Kierkegaard, Soren.

Steere, Douglas V. Bethlehem Revisited. LC 65-26995. (Orig.). 1965. pap. 2.50x (ISBN 0-87574-144-4, 144). Pendle Hill.

--Community & Worship. 1983. pap. 2.50x (ISBN 0-87574-010-3, 010). Pendle Hill.

--Contemplation & Leisure. rev. ed. LC 74-30803. 32p. 1975. pap. 2.50x (ISBN 0-87574-199-1, 199). Pendle Hill.

--Gleanings: A Random Harvest. 144p. (Orig.). 1986. pap. 6.95 (ISBN 0-8358-0543-3). Upper Room.

--The Hardest Journey. 1983. pap. 2.50x (ISBN 0-87574-163-0, 163). Pendle Hill.

--Mutual Irradiation: A Quaker View of Ecumenism. LC 73-146680. (Orig.). 1971. pap. 2.50x (ISBN 0-87574-175-4). Pendle Hill.

--On Being Present Where You Are. LC 67-12913. (Orig.). 1967. pap. 2.50x (ISBN 0-87574-151-7, 151). Pendle Hill.

--On Speaking out of the Silence: Vocal Ministry. LC 72-182983. 24p. (Orig.). 1972. pap. 2.50x (ISBN 0-87574-182-7). Pendle Hill.

--Prayer & Worship. LC 78-70480. 1978. pap. 3.95 (ISBN 0-913408-44-1). Friends United.

--Prayer in the Contemporary World. LC 80-82942. 32p. pap. 2.50x (ISBN 0-87574-907-0). Pendle Hill.

Steere, Douglas V., ed. Quaker Spirituality: Selected Writings. (Classics of Western Spirituality Ser.). 384p. 1984. 12.95 (ISBN 0-8091-0335-4); pap. 9.95 (ISBN 0-8091-2510-2). Paulist Pr.

Stefanics, Charlotte, jt. auth. see Niklas, Gerals R.

Steffensky, Fulbert, jt. auth. see Soelle, Dorothee.

Steficek, Carol. A Future & a Hope. 1985. 2.95 (ISBN 0-89536-940-0, 7560). CSS of Ohio.

Stegall, Neil & Bernard, David. A New Birth: A Study Guide. 120p. (Orig.). 1987. pap. 5.95 spiral bd. (ISBN 0-932581-15-3). Word Aflame.

Stegemann, Wolfgang. The Gospel & the Poor. Elliott, Dietlinde, tr. from Ger. LC 83-48915. 80p. 1984. pap. 3.95 (ISBN 0-8006-1783-5, 1-1783). Fortress.

Stegemann, Wolfgang, jt. auth. see Schottroff, Luise.

Stegemann, Wolfgang, jt. ed. see Schottroff, Willy.

Stegner, Wallace. Mormon Country. LC 81-3410. x, 362p. 1981. 25.50x (ISBN 0-8032-4129-1); pap. 8.50 (ISBN 0-8032-9125-6, BB 778, Bison). U of Nebr Pr.

Stehle, Hansjakob. Eastern Politics of the Vatican, 1917-1979. Smith, Sandra, tr. from Ger. LC 80-15236. Orig. Title: Die Ostpolitik Des Vatikans, 1917-1975. (Illus.). 1981. 28.95x (ISBN 0-8214-0367-2); pap. 14.95 (ISBN 0-8214-0564-0). Ohio U Pr.

Stehlin, Stewart A. Weimar & the Vatican, 1919-1933. LC 83-42544. (Illus.). 512p. 1986. pap. 19.95x (ISBN 0-691-10195-7); text ed. 52.50x (ISBN 0-691-05399-5). Princeton U Pr.

Steidl, G. Basics of Assembly Life. pap. 3.75 (ISBN 0-88172-126-3). Believers Bkshelf.

Steidl, G. S. By Faith. 48p. pap. 3.25 (ISBN 0-88172-127-1). Believers Bkshelf.

Steidl, Paul M. Earth, the Stars, & the Bible. 1979. pap. 5.95 (ISBN 0-87552-430-3). Presby & Reformed.

Steiger, Brad. American Indian Magic: Sacred Pow Wows & Hopi Prophecies. (Illus.). 210p. 1986. 17.95 (ISBN 0-938294-19-9); pap. 9.95 (ISBN 0-938294-20-2). Global Comm.

--In My Soul I Am Free. 206p. 1968. pap. 5.95 (ISBN 0-88155-003-5). IWP Pub.

Steigert, Hermann, jt. auth. see Bickel, Margot.

Steimle, Edmund A. God the Stranger: Reflections About Resurrection. LC 78-14674. 80p. 1979. pap. 4.95 (ISBN 0-8006-1354-6, 1-1354). Fortress.

Steimle, Edmund A., et al. Preaching the Story. LC 78-14675. 208p. 1980. 9.95 (ISBN 0-8006-0538-1, 1-538). Fortress.

Stein, Arnold. The Art of Presence: The Poet & Paradise Lost. 1977. 30.95x (ISBN 0-520-03167-9). U of Cal Pr.

Stein, Arthur, jt. auth. see Weisbord, Robert G.

Stein, Aurel. The Thousand Buddhas. LC 77-94623. 1979. Repr. of 1921 ed. lib. bdg. 10.00 (ISBN 0-89341-249-X). Longwood Pub Group.

Stein, Edward V., ed. Fathering: Fact or Fable? LC 76-56840. Repr. of 1977 ed. 47.50 (ISBN 0-8357-9007-X, 2016357). Bks Demand UMI.

Stein, Gordon. Freethought in the United Kingdom & the Commonwealth: A Descriptive Bibliography. LC 80-1792. xxiii, 193p. 1981. lib. bdg. 39.95 (ISBN 0-313-20869-7, SFU/). Greenwood.

Stein, Gordon, ed. An Anthology of Atheism & Rationalism. LC 80-81326. (The Skeptic's Bookshelf Ser.). 354p. 1984. pap. 15.95 (ISBN 0-87975-267-X). Prometheus Bks.

Stein, Harry. Ethics & Other Liabilities. 160p. 1982. 10.95 (ISBN 0-312-26557-3). St Martin.

--Ethics & Other Liabilities: Trying to Live Right in an Amoral World. 176p. 1983. pap. 4.95 (ISBN 0-312-26544-1). St Martin.

Stein, Jock & Taylor, Howard. In Christ All Things Hold Together: An Introduction to Christian Doctrine. 176p. (Orig.). 1985. pap. 5.95 (ISBN 0-8028-0083-1). Eerdmans.

Stein, Jock, ed. Ministers for the Nineteen Eighties. 120p. 1980. pap. 6.00x (ISBN 0-905312-09-0, Pub. by Scot Acad Pr). Longwood Pub Group.

Stein, Joshua B. Claude G. Montefiore on the Ancient Rabbis: The Second Generation on Reform Judaism in Britain. LC 77-13194. (Brown University. Brown Judaic Studies: No. 4). 85p. 1977. pap. 9.00 (ISBN 0-89130-190-9, 140004). Scholars Pr GA.

Stein, Murray. Jung's Treatment of Christianity: The Psychotherapy of a Religious Tradition. 2nd ed. LC 85-4739. 194p. 1985. 24.95 (ISBN 0-933029-14-4). Chiron Pubns.

Stein, Murray & Moore, Robert, eds. Jung's Challenge to Contemporary Religion. 175p. 1987. pap. 14.95 (ISBN 0-933029-09-8). Chiron Pubns.

Stein, Murray, tr. see Kerenyi, Karl.

Stein, R. Conrad. The Holocaust. LC 85-31415. (World at War Ser.). (Illus.). 48p. 1986. PLB 10.60 (ISBN 0-516-04767-1); pap. 2.95 (ISBN 0-516-44767-X). Childrens.

--Warsaw Ghetto. LC 84-23202. (World at War Ser.). (Illus.). 48p. 1985. lib. bdg. 10.60 (ISBN 0-516-04779-5). Childrens.

Stein, Robert H. Difficult Passages in the Gospels. 139p. 1984. pap. 6.95 (ISBN 0-8010-8249-8). Baker Bk.

--Difficult Sayings in the Gospels: Jesus's Use of Overstatement & Hyperbole. 96p. pap. 4.95 (ISBN 0-8010-8262-5). Baker Bk.

--An Introduction to the Parables of Jesus. LC 81-11564. 180p. 1981. pap. 8.95 (ISBN 0-664-24390-8). Westminster.

--The Method & Message of Jesus' Teachings. LC 78-16427. 202p. 1978. pap. 8.95 (ISBN 0-664-24216-2). Westminster.

--Synoptic Problem. 280p. 1987. pap. 17.95 (ISBN 0-8010-8272-2). Baker Bk.

Stein, Walter. Nuclear Weapons & Christian Conscience. 165p. (Orig.). 1981. pap. 6.75 (ISBN 0-85036-112-5, Pub. by Merlin Pr UK). Longwood Pub Group.

Stein, Walter J. The Principle of Reincarnation. 1986. pap. 2.50 (ISBN 0-916786-85-4). St George Bk Serv.

Steinberg, Aaron. History As Experience. 1983. 35.00x (ISBN 0-88125-001-5). Ktav.

Steinberg, David. Welcome Brothers: Poems of a Changing Man's Consciousness. (Illus.). 1976. pap. 3.00 (ISBN 0-914906-04-6). Red Alder.

Steinberg, Hardy W. The Church of the Spirit. (Charismatic Bk.). 64p. 1972. pap. 0.69 (ISBN 0-88243-922-7, 02-0922). Gospel Pub.

Steinberg, Jean, tr. see Sichrovsky, Peter.

Steinberg, Jeff & Hefley, James C. Masterpiece in Progress. 288p. 1986. 11.95 (ISBN 0-8423-4194-3). Tyndale.

Steinberg, M. W., ed. see Klein, A. M.

Steinberg, Milton. As a Driven Leaf. LC 75-32237. 1939. pap. 7.95x (ISBN 0-87441-074-6). Behrman.

--Basic Judaism. LC 47-30768. 1965. pap. 3.95 (ISBN 0-15-610698-1, Harv). HarBraceJ.

--Basic Judaism. 180p. 1987. 22.00 (ISBN 0-87668-975-6). Aronson.

--Believing Jew: The Selected Writings. facsimile ed. LC 76-152215. (Essay Index Reprint Ser). Repr. of 1951 ed. 18.00 (ISBN 0-8369-2256-5). Ayer Co Pubs.

--The Making of the Modern Jew. (Brown Classics in Judaica Ser.). 318p. 1987. pap. text ed. 14.50 (ISBN 0-8191-4492-4). U Pr of Amer.

--A Partisan Guide to the Jewish Problem. LC 86-1509. (Brown Classics in Judaica). 312p. 1986. pap. text ed. 13.50 (ISBN 0-8191-4493-2). U Pr of Amer.

Steinberg, Ronald. Fra Girolamo Savonarola, Florentine Art & Renaissance Historiography. LC 76-8304. (Illus.). 151p. 1977. 14.00x (ISBN 0-8214-0202-1). Ohio U Pr.

Steinberg, Samuel. Living Hebrew. (YA) 1958. 17.95 (ISBN 0-517-00133-0); records, manual & dictionary incl. Crown.

Steinberg, Stephen, jt. auth. see Selznick, Gertude J.

Steinberg, Theodore L. Mendele Mocher Seforim. (World Authors Ser.). 1977. lib. bdg. 16.95 (ISBN 0-8057-6308-2, Twayne). G K Hall.

Steinberger, G. In the Footprints of the Lamb. Christensen, Bernard, tr. LC 78-73416. 96p. 1979. pap. 2.95 (ISBN 0-87123-237-5, 200237). Bethany Hse.

Steinberger, Heidi. Let's Learn About Jewish Symbols. LC 68-9347. (Illus.). 1969. pap. text ed. 6.00 (ISBN 0-8074-0144-7, 101035). UAHC.

Steinbrecher, Edwin. The Inner Guide Meditation: A Spiritual Technology for the 21st Century. 240p. (Orig.). 1987. pap. 7.95 (ISBN 0-87728-657-4). Weiser.

Steinbrecher, Edwin C. The Inner Guide Meditation. 4th ed. LC 78-60489. (Illus.). 1978. 12.95 (ISBN 0-685-65266-1); pap. 6.75 (ISBN 0-685-65267-X). Blue Feather.

Steinbron, Melvin J. Can the Pastor Do It Alone. 1987. pap. 7.95 (ISBN 0-8307-1171-6, 5418925). Regal.

Steinby, M., jt. auth. see Gecseq, F.

Steindam, Harold. As the Twig Is Bent: Sermons for Children. (Illus.). 128p. (Orig.). 1983. pap. 6.95 (ISBN 0-8298-0679-2). Pilgrim NY.

--Pastor at Work. (Illus.). 128p. 1985. pap. 7.95 (ISBN 0-8298-0562-1). Pilgrim NY.

Steindl-Rast, David. Gratefulness, the Heart of Prayer: An Approach to Life in Fullness. 144p. 1984. pap. 7.95 (ISBN 0-8091-2628-1). Paulist Pr.

Steiner, Bernard C., ed. see Bray, Thomas.

Steiner, Erich G. The Story of "Patria". LC 81-85302. 224p. 1982. 16.95 (ISBN 0-8052-5036-0); pap. 10.95 (ISBN 0-8052-5037-9). Holocaust Pubns.

Steiner, Johannes. Therese Neumann. LC 66-27536. (Illus.). 1967. pap. 5.95 (ISBN 0-8189-0144-6). Alba.

--The Visions of Therese Newmann. LC 75-34182. 245p. 1976. pap. 5.95 (ISBN 0-8189-0318-X). Alba.

Steiner, Moses J. Satan in the Woods. LC 78-54567. 1978. 10.95 (ISBN 0-88400-057-5). Shengold.

Steiner, Robert A. The Truth Shall Make You Free: An Inquiry into the Legend of God. LC 80-80646. (Illus.). 56p. (Orig.). 1980. pap. 3.95 (ISBN 0-9604044-0-6). Penseur Pr.

Steiner, Rudolf. Ahrimanic Deception. 20p. (Orig.). 1985. pap. 2.95 (ISBN 0-88010-146-6). Anthroposophic.

--Ancient Myths: Their Meaning & Connection with Evolution. Cotterell, M., tr. from Ger. 1978. pap. 5.95 (ISBN 0-919924-07-7). Anthroposophic.

--And It Came to Pass: An Old Testament, Reader for Children. 1973. lib. bdg. 79.95 (ISBN 0-87968-556-5). Krishna Pr.

--Anthroposophy: An Introduction. Burnett, V. Compton, tr. from Ger. 130p. 1983. pap. 7.00 (ISBN 0-85440-387-6, Pub by Steinerbooks). Anthroposophic.

--Anthroposophy & Christianity. Tr. of Christus und die menschliche Seele, Ueber den sinn deslebens, Theosophische Moral, Anthroposophie und Christentum, German. 26p. (Orig.). 1985. pap. 2.95 (ISBN 0-88010-149-0). Anthroposophic.

--Apocalypse of St. John. 2nd ed. Tr. of Die Apokalypse des Johannes. 227p. 1985. pap. 12.95 (ISBN 0-88010-131-8). Anthroposophic.

--Art as Seen in the Light of Mystery Wisdom. 2nd ed. Tr. of Kunst im Lichte der Mysterienweisheit. 182p. 1984. pap. 9.95 (ISBN 0-85440-416-3, Pub. by Steinerbooks). Anthroposophic.

--The Arts & Their Mission. Monges & Moore, trs. from German. 125p. 1986. pap. 8.95 (ISBN 0-88010-154-7). Anthroposophic.

--Aspects of Human Evolution. Stebbing, Rita, tr. 1986. 20.00 (ISBN 0-88010-251-9); pap. 9.95 (ISBN 0-88010-252-7). Anthroposophic.

--At the Gates of Spiritual Science. Tr. of Vor dem Tore der Theosophie. 160p. 1986. 20.00 (ISBN 0-88010-224-1); pap. 8.95 (ISBN 0-88010-135-0). Anthroposophic.

--Awakening to Community. Spock, Marjorie, tr. from Ger. LC 74-81153. 178p. 1975. 14.00 (ISBN 0-910142-61-0). Anthroposophic.

--Background to the Gospel of St. Mark. 2nd ed. Tr. of Exkurse in das Gebiet des Markus-Evangeliums. 200p. 1986. pap. 10.95 (ISBN 0-88010-145-8). Anthroposophic.

--Balance in World & Man: Lucifer & Ahriman. pap. 2.75 (ISBN 0-919924-05-0). Anthroposophic.

--The Being of Man & His Future Evolution. Wehrle, Pauline, tr. from Ger. 148p. 1981. 18.00 (ISBN 0-85440-402-3, Pub. by Steinerbooks); pap. 11.95 (ISBN 0-85440-405-8). Anthroposophic.

--The Boundaries of Natural Science. Amrine, Frederick, tr. from Ger. LC 83-9943. 144p. 1983. 14.95 (ISBN 0-88010-018-4). Anthroposophic.

--The Bridge Between Universal Spirituality & the Physical Constitution of Man. 2nd ed. Osmond, Dorothy S., tr. from Ger. 64p. (Orig.). 1979. pap. 3.95 (ISBN 0-910142-03-3). Anthroposophic.

--Building Stones for an Understanding of the Mystery of Golgotha. 240p. 1972. 10.95 (ISBN 0-85440-263-2). Anthroposophic.

--The Calendar of the Soul. Pusch, Ruth & Pusch, Hans, trs. from Ger. 62p. 1982. 7.95 (ISBN 0-88010-009-5). Anthroposophic.

--The Change in the Path to Supersensible Knowledge. 22p. 1982. pap. 3.00 (ISBN 0-919924-18-2, Pub. by Steiner Book Centre Canada). Anthroposophic.

--Christ & the Human Soul. 4th ed. 81p. 1984. pap. 6.50 (ISBN 0-85440-013-3, Pub. by Steinerbooks). Anthroposophic.

--Christ in Relation to Lucifer & Ahriman. Mollenhauer, Peter, tr. 1978. pap. 2.00 (ISBN 0-910142-77-7). Anthroposophic.

--Christianity As Mystical Fact. Tr. of Das Christentum als mystische Tatsache und die Mysterien des Altertums. 195p. 1986. pap. 8.95 (ISBN 0-88010-160-1). Anthroposophic.

--Christianity As Mystical Fact & the Mysteries of Antiquity. write for info. (ISBN 0-910142-04-1). Anthroposophic.

--Christianity in Human Evolution. 1979. pap. 2.00 (ISBN 0-88010-095-8). Anthroposophic.

--The Christmas Foundation Meeting of the Anthroposophical Society. Seddon, R. G., ed. 37p. (Orig.). 1980. pap. 3.00 (ISBN 0-88010-094-X, Pub. by Steinerbooks). Anthroposophic.

--The Concepts of Original Sin & Grace. Osmond, D. S., tr. from Ger. 32p. 1973. pap. 1.95 (ISBN 0-85440-275-6, Pub. by Steinerbooks). Anthroposophic.

--The Constitution of the School of Spiritual Science. 2nd ed. Adams, George & Rudel, Joan, trs. from Ger. 78p. 1980. pap. 5.00x (ISBN 0-88010-039-7, Pub. by Anthroposophical Society London). Anthroposophic.

--Course of My Life. Wannamaker, Olin D., tr. from Ger. Tr. of Mein Lebensgang. 400p. 1986. pap. 18.00 (ISBN 0-88010-159-8). Anthroposophic.

--Curative Eurythmy. 132p. 1984. pap. 9.95 (ISBN 0-85440-398-1, Pub. by Steinerbooks). Anthroposophic.

--The Dead Are with Us. Osmond, D. S., tr. from Ger. 32p. 1973. pap. 2.95 (ISBN 0-85440-274-8, Pub. by Steinerbooks). Anthroposophic.

--The Deed of Christ & the Opposing Spiritual Powers Lucifer, Ahriman, Mephistopheles, Asuras. 2.75 (ISBN 0-919924-02-6, Pub by Steiner Book Centre Canada). Anthroposophic.

--Deeper Secrets in Human History in the Light of the Gospel of St. Matthew. 2nd ed. Tr. of Die tieferen Geheimmnisse des Menschheitswerdens im Lichte der Evangelien. 60p. 1985. pap. 6.95 (ISBN 0-88010-132-6). Anthroposophic.

--Discussions with Teachers. Fox, Helen, tr. from Ger. 166p. 1983. pap. 11.00 (ISBN 0-85440-404-X, Pub by Steinerbooks). Anthroposophic.

--Earthly & Cosmic Man. Garber, Bernard J., ed. LC 85-80915. (Spiritual Science Library: Vol. 27). 176p. 1986. lib. bdg. 14.00 (ISBN 0-89345-055-3, Spiritual Sci Lib). Garber Comm.

--Egyptian Myths & Mysteries. Macbeth, Norman, tr. from Ger. 1971. 15.00 (ISBN 0-910142-09-2); pap. 7.95 (ISBN 0-910142-10-6). Anthroposophic.

--Esoteric Christianity & the Mission of Christian Rosenkreutz. 2nd ed. Wehrle, Pauline, tr. from Ger. 200p. 1984. pap. 9.95 (ISBN 0-88440-413-7, Pub. by Steinerbooks). Anthroposophic.

--The Etherisation of the Blood: The Entry of the Etheric Christ into the Evolution of the Earth. 4th ed. Freeman, Arnold & Osmond, D. S., trs. from Ger. 42p. 1985. pap. 3.95 (ISBN 0-85440-248-9, Pub. by Steinerbooks). Anthroposophic.

--The Evolution of the Earth & the Influence of the Stars. Hahn, Gladys, tr. from Ger. Tr. of Die Schoepfung der Welt und des Menschen Erdenleben und Sternenwirken. (Illus.). 200p. 1987. 20.00 (ISBN 0-88010-181-4); pap. 10.95 (ISBN 0-88010-180-6). Anthroposophic.

--Exoteric & Esoteric Christianity. 17p. 1983. pap. 3.00 (ISBN 0-919924-20-4). Anthroposophic.

--Facing Karma. 1977. 2.00 (ISBN 0-910142-64-5). Anthroposophic.

--The Festival & Their Meaning. 399p. 1981. 21.00 (ISBN 0-85440-370-1, Pub. by Steinerbooks); pap. 15.00 (ISBN 0-85440-380-9). Anthroposophic.

--The Fifth Gospel. Davy, C. & Osmond, D. S., trs. from Ger. Tr. of Aus der Akkasha Forschung: Das Fuenfte Evangelium. 168p. 1985. pap. 9.95 (ISBN 0-85440-520-8, Pub. by Steinerbooks). Anthroposophic.

--The Foundation Stone. 72p. 1979. pap. 5.50x (ISBN 0-85440-346-9, Pub. by Steinerbooks). Anthroposophic.

--The Four Mystery Plays. Bittleston, Adam, tr. from Ger. 512p. (Orig.). 1982. pap. text ed. 16.00 (ISBN 0-85440-403-1). Anthroposophic.

--The Four Sacrifices of Christ. 2nd ed. Church, Gilbert, ed. Laird-Brown, May, tr. from Ger. 20p. (Orig.). 1981. pap. 1.00 (ISBN 0-88010-026-5). Anthroposophic.

--From Buddha to Christ. Church, Gilbert, ed. Tr. of Das Esoterische Christentum & die geistige Fuehrung der Menschheit. 103p. 1987. pap. 5.95 (ISBN 0-88010-178-4). Anthroposophic.

--From Jesus to Christ. 185p. 1973. 16.95 (ISBN 0-85440-277-2). Anthroposophic.

--Fruits of Anthroposophy. Meuss, Anna R., tr. from Ger. Tr. of Anthroposophie, ihre Erkenntniswurzeln und Lebensfruechete. 76p. 1986. 20.00 (ISBN 0-88010-203-9); pap. 7.95 (ISBN 0-88010-202-0). Anthroposophic.

--Fundamentals of Therapy: An Extension of the Art of Healing Through Spiritual Knowledge. 4th ed. Frommer, Eva A. & Josephson, J. M., trs. from Ger. Tr. of Grundlegendes fur eine Erweiterung der Heilkunst nach geisteswissenschaftlichen Erkenntnissen. 128p. 1983. pap. 7.95 (ISBN 0-85440-423-6, Pub. by Steinerbooks). Anthroposophic.

--Genesis: Secrets of the Bible Story of Creation. Lenn, Dorothy, et al, trs. from Ger. 139p. 1982. pap. 9.95 (ISBN 0-85440-391-4, Pub by Steinerbooks). Anthroposophic.

--The Gospel of St. John. Monges, Maud B., tr. from Ger. LC 63-1084. (Illus.). 192p. 1984. 14.95 (ISBN 0-88010-107-5); pap. 8.95 (ISBN 0-910142-13-0). Anthroposophic.

--Gospel of St. John. (Russian Language Ser.). 294p. 1985. pap. 12.00 (ISBN 0-89345-900-3, Steiner). Garber Comm.

--Gospel of St. John. (Russian Language Ser.). 196p. 1985. pap. 10.00 (ISBN 0-89345-906-2, Steiner). Garber Comm.

--The Gospel of St. John & In Relation to the Other Gospels. rev. ed. Easton, Stewart, ed. Lockwood, Samuel & Lockwood, Loni, trs. from Ger. 298p. 1982. 14.00 (ISBN 0-88010-015-X); pap. 8.95 (ISBN 0-88010-014-1). Anthroposophic.

--Gospel of St. Luke. 1964. 14.95 (ISBN 0-85440-042-7). Anthroposophic.

--Gospel of St. Luke. (Russian Language Ser.). 202p. 1985. pap. 10.00 (ISBN 0-89345-902-X, Steiner). Garber Comm.

--Gospel of St. Matthew. 2nd ed. Tr. of Matthaeus-Evangelium. 230p. 1985. pap. 10.95 (ISBN 0-88010-134-2). Anthroposophic.

--Health & Illness, Vol. 1. St. Goar, Maria, tr. from German. (Illus.). 155p. (Orig.). 14.00 (ISBN 0-88010-028-1); pap. 8.95 (ISBN 0-88010-000-1). Anthroposophic.

--How Can Mankind Find the Christ Again? 2nd ed. Hahn, Galdys, ed. Dawson, Frances E. & Hahn, Gladys, trs. from Ger. 1984. 15.00 (ISBN 0-88010-078-8); pap. 8.95 (ISBN 0-88010-079-6). Anthroposophic.

--The Human Soul & the Universe. (q). Orig. Title: Cosmic & Human Metamorphoses. 24p. 1982. pap. 2.95 (ISBN 0-919924-17-4, Pub. by Steiner Book Centre Canada). Anthroposophic.

--The Human Soul in Relation to World Evolution. Stebbing, Rita, tr. from Ger. LC 84-21703. 180p. (Orig.). 1985. 16.00 (ISBN 0-88010-114-8); pap. 9.95 (ISBN 0-88010-113-X). Anthroposophic.

--The Influences of Lucifer & Ahriman: Man's Responsibility for the Earth. Osmond, D. S., tr. from Ger. 84p. 1976. pap. 6.95 (ISBN 0-919924-00-X). Anthroposophic.

--Initiation & Its Results. 134p. 1984. pap. 8.00 (ISBN 0-89540-148-7, SB-148). Sun Pub.

--Inner Impulses of Human Evolution: The Mexican Mysteries & the Knights Templar. Church, Gilbert, et al, eds. 180p. (Orig.). 1984. 16.00 (ISBN 0-88010-119-9); pap. 9.95 (ISBN 0-88010-118-0). Anthroposophic.

--Jesus & Christ. 1976. pap. 2.00 (ISBN 0-910142-74-2). Anthroposophic.

--The Karma of Materialism. Tr. of Menschliche und menschheitliche Entwicklungswanrheiten. 173p. (Orig.). 1986. 20.00 (ISBN 0-88010-130-X); pap. 9.95 (ISBN 0-88010-129-6). Anthroposophic.

--The Karma of Vocation. 2nd ed. Mollenhauer, Peter & Church, Gilbert, eds. Wannamaker, Olin, et al, trs. from Ger. 270p. 1984. 17.00 (ISBN 0-88010-085-0); pap. 10.95 (ISBN 0-88010-086-9). Anthroposophic.

--Karmic Relationships, 8 vols. Incl. Vol. 1. 205p. 14.50 (ISBN 0-85440-260-8); Vol. 2. 1974. 14.50 (ISBN 0-85440-281-0); Vol. 3. 12.95 (ISBN 0-85440-313-2); Vol. 4. 157p. 1983. 14.00 (ISBN 0-85440-412-0); Vol. 5. 10.95 (ISBN 0-685-36131-4); Vol. 6. 14.50 (ISBN 0-85440-242-X); Vol. 7. 140p. 1973. 9.95 (ISBN 0-85440-276-4); Vol. 8. 102p. 1975. 9.95 (ISBN 0-85440-018-4). Anthroposophic.

--Karmic Relationships: Esoteric Studies, Vol. I. Adams, George, tr. from Ger. 205p. 1981. 14.50 (ISBN 0-85440-260-8, Pub. by Steinerbooks). Anthroposophic.

--Karmic Relationships: Esoteric Studies, Vol. 2. Adams, George & Cotterell, M., trs. from Ger. Davy, C. & Osmond, D. S. 1974. 14.50 (ISBN 0-85440-281-0, Pub. by Steinerbooks). Anthroposophic.

--Karmic Relationships: Esoteric Studies, Vol. 4. 2nd ed. Adams, George, et al, trs. 157p. 1983. 14.00 (ISBN 0-85440-412-0, Pub by Steinerbooks). Anthroposophic.

--Karmic Relationships: Esoteric Studies, Vol. 7. Osmond, D. S., tr. from Ger. 140p. 1973. 9.95 (ISBN 0-85440-276-4, Pub. by Steinerbooks). Anthroposophic.

--Karmic Relationships: Esoteric Studies, Vol. 8. Osmond, D. S., tr. from Ger. Orig. Title: Cosmic Christianity & the Impulse of Michael. 102p. 1975. 9.95 (ISBN 0-85440-018-4, Pub. by Steinerbooks). Anthroposophic.

--Karmic Relationships: Esoteric Studies (The Karmic Relationships of the Anthroposophics Movement, Vol. 3. 3rd ed. Adams, George, tr. 179p. 1977. 12.95 (ISBN 0-85440-313-2, Pub. by Steinerbooks). Anthroposophic.

--Knowledge & Initiation: Cognition of the Christ through Anthroposophy. Adams, George, tr. from Ger. 31p. 1983. pap. 3.25 (ISBN 0-919924-21-2). Anthroposophic.

--Knowledge of the Higher Worlds & Its Attainment. 3rd ed. Monges, Henry B., tr. 1969. pap. 6.95 (ISBN 0-910142-20-3). Anthroposophic.

--Knowledge of the Higher Worlds & Its Attainment. Metaxa, George & Monges, Henry B., trs. from Ger. LC 79-101595. 224p. 1983. 14.00 (ISBN 0-88010-045-1); pap. 6.95 (ISBN 0-88010-046-X). Anthroposophic.

--Life Between Death & New Birth. (Russian Language Ser.). 90p. 1985. pap. 6.00 (ISBN 0-89345-904-6, Steiner). Garber Comm.

--Life Between Death & Rebirth. Querido, R. M., tr. from Ger. LC 68-57429. 308p. (Orig.). 1975. pap. 9.95 (ISBN 0-910142-62-9). Anthroposophic.

--The Life, Nature & Cultivation of Anthroposophy. Adams, George, tr. from Ger. 68p. 1976. pap. 5.95 (ISBN 0-85440-061-3, Pub. by Steinerbooks). Anthroposophic.

--The Lord's Prayer: An Esoteric Study. McKnight, Floyd, tr. from Ger. 26p. 1977. pap. 2.95 (ISBN 0-88010-029-X). Anthroposophic.

--Macrocosm & Microcosm. Tr. of Makrokosmos und Mikosmos. Seelenfragen, Lebensfragen, Geistesfragen. 205p. 1986. 20.00 (ISBN 0-88010-201-2); pap. 10.95 (ISBN 0-88010-200-4). Anthroposophic.

--Man as a Being of Sense & Perception. Lenn, Dorothy, tr. from Ger. 53p. 1981. pap. 6.00 (ISBN 0-919924-11-5, Pub. by Steiner Book Centre Canada). Anthroposophic.

--Man as a Picture of the Living Spirit. Adams, George, tr. from Ger. 31p. (Orig.). 1972. pap. 1.95 (ISBN 0-85440-253-5, Pub. by Steinerbooks). Anthroposophic.

--Man in the Past, the Present, & the Future: The Sun-Initiation of the Druid Priest & His Moon-Science. Goddard, E., tr. from Ger. 82p. 1982. pap. 5.00 (ISBN 0-85440-403-1, Pub by Steinerbooks). Anthroposophic.

--Manifestations of Karma. 3rd ed. 262p. 1984. pap. 10.95 (ISBN 0-317-18543-8, Pub. by Steinerbooks). Anthroposophic.

--Man's Being, His Destiny & World Evolution. 3rd ed. McArthur, Erna & Riggins, William, trs. from Ger. 123p. (Orig.). 1984. pap. 7.95 (ISBN 0-88010-090-7). Anthroposophic.

--Metamorphoses of the Soul: Path of Experience, 2 vols. 2nd ed. Davy, Charles & Von Arnim, Christian, trs. from Ger. 1983. Set. pap. 12.00 ea. (ISBN 0-317-13485-X). Vol. 1: 171 pgs (ISBN 0-85440-414-7, Pub. by Steinerbooks). Vol. 2: 150 pgs (ISBN 0-85440-415-5, Pub. by Steinerbooks). Anthroposophic.

--The Michael Mystery: Letters to the Members of the Anthroposophical Society with Their Accompanying Guidelines. Spock, Marjorie, tr. 1985. 15.95 (ISBN 0-916786-77-3); pap. 9.95 (ISBN 0-317-30085-7). St George Bk Serv.

--Mysticism at the Dawn of the Modern Age. (Russian Language Ser.). 102p. 1985. pap. 7.00 (ISBN 0-89345-901-1, Steiner). Garber Comm.

--Mysticism at the Dawn of the Modern Age, Vol. 6. 2nd ed. Allen, Paul M., ed. Zimmer, Karl E., tr. from Ger. LC 60-15703. (The Major Writings of Rudolf Steiner in English Translation Ser.: The Centennial Edition). 256p. 1981. lib. bdg. 16.00 (ISBN 0-89345-026-X, Spiritual Sci Lib); pap. 9.50 (ISBN 0-89345-206-8, Steinerbks). Garber Comm.

--Newborn Might & Strength Everlasting: A Christmas Offering. Church, Gilbert, ed. (Illus.). 19p. (Orig.). 1977. pap. 2.00 (ISBN 0-88010-100-8). Anthroposophic.

--Nutrition & Health. Hahn, Gladys, tr. from Ger. Tr. of Die Schoepfung der Welt und des Menschen. Erdenleben und Stennenwirken. (Illus.). 35p. 1987. pap. 3.95 (ISBN 0-88010-182-2). Anthroposophic.

--On the Life of the Soul. O'Neil, Gisela & Howard, Alan, eds. Borton, Samuel L., tr. 18p. (Orig.). 1985. pap. 3.50 (ISBN 0-88010-076-1). Anthroposophic.

--The Origin of Suffering, The Origin of Evil, Illness & Death. Cotterell, Mabel & Watkin, V. E., trs. (Ger.). 31p. 1980. pap. 2.95 (ISBN 0-919924-12-3, Pub. by Steiner Book Centre Canada). Anthroposophic.

--Origins of Natural Science. Tr. of Der Entstehungsoment der Naturwissenchaft in der Weltgeschichte und ihre seitherige Entwickelung. 159p. (Orig.). 1985. 20.00 (ISBN 0-317-38883-5); pap. 9.95 (ISBN 0-88010-140-7). Anthroposophic.

--Outline of Occult Science. 352p. 1972. 16.00 (ISBN 0-910142-26-2); pap. 9.95 (ISBN 0-910142-75-0). Anthroposophic.

--Pastoral Medicine. Hahn, Gladys, tr. from Ger. Tr. of Pastoral-Medizinischer Kurs. 1987. 20.00 (ISBN 0-88010-250-0); pap. 9.95 (ISBN 0-88010-253-5). Anthroposophic.

--Philosophy, Cosmology & Religion: Ten Lectures. Easton, Stewart C., et al, eds. 180p. (Orig.). 1984. 16.00 (ISBN 0-88010-109-1); pap. 9.95 (ISBN 0-88010-110-5). Anthroposophic.

--Philosophy of Freedom. Wilson, Michael, tr. from Ger. 226p. 1973. pap. 7.95 (ISBN 0-910142-52-1). Anthroposophic.

--Philosophy of Spiritual Activity, Vol. 2. 2nd ed. LC 80-65627. (Spiritual Science Library). 304p. 1980. lib. bdg. 16.00 (ISBN 0-89345-030-8, Spiritual Sci Lib); pap. 9.50 (ISBN 0-89345-208-4). Garber Comm.

--Prayer. 1966. pap. 2.00 (ISBN 0-910142-30-0). Anthroposophic.

--Prayers for Mothers & Children. 3rd. ed. Hersey, Eileen V. & Von Arnim, Christian, trs. from Ger. 76p. 1983. pap. 5.00 (ISBN 0-85440-195-4, Pub. by Steinerbooks). Anthroposophic.

--Pre-Earthly Deeds of Christ. 16p. 1976. pap. 2.75 (ISBN 0-919924-01-8, Pub. by Steiner Book Centre Canada). Anthroposophic.

--Preparing for the Sixth Epoch. Orig. Title: How Anthroposophic Groups Prepare for the Sixth Epoch. 1976. pap. 2.00 (ISBN 0-910142-72-6). Anthroposophic.

--The Principle of Spiritual Economy. Mollenhauer, Peter, tr. Tr. of Das Prinzip der Spirituellen Okonomie im Zusammenhang mit Wiederverkorperungsfragen. 220p. 1986. 20.00 (ISBN 0-88010-163-6); pap. 9.95 (ISBN 0-88010-162-8). Anthroposophic.

--The Reappearance of Christ in the Etheric. rev. ed. 190p. (Orig.). 1983. 14.00 (ISBN 0-88010-017-6); pap. 8.95 (ISBN 0-88010-016-8). Anthroposophic.

--The Redemption of Thinking: A Study in the Philosophy of Thomas Aquinas. Sheperd, A. P. & Nicoll, Mildred R., trs. from Ger. Orig. Title: Die Philosophie des Thomas von Aquino. 191p. 1983. pap. text ed. 8.95 (ISBN 0-88010-044-3). Anthroposophic.

--Reincarnation & Immortality. 3rd ed. LC 77-130817. 224p. 1970. pap. 5.00 (ISBN 0-89345-221-1, Steinerbks). Garber Comm.

--Reincarnation & Karma: Their Significance in Modern Culture. Osmond, D. S. & Davy, Charles, trs. (Ger.). 95p. 1977. pap. 6.50 (ISBN 0-919924-06-9, Pub. by Steiner Book Centre Canada). Anthroposophic.

--Road to Self Knowledge. 1975. 10.95 (ISBN 0-85440-290-X, Pub by Steinerbooks); pap. 6.95 o. p. (ISBN 0-85440-291-8). Anthroposophic.

--Rosicrucian Esotericism. Osmond, Dorothy S., tr. from Ger. 122p. 1978. 14.00 (ISBN 0-910142-78-5). Anthroposophic.

--Rosicrucianism & Modern Initiation: Mystery Centres of the Middle Ages. 3rd. ed. Adams, Mary, tr. 98p. 1982. pap. 9.95 (ISBN 0-85440-381-7, Pub by Steinerbooks). Anthroposophic.

--Rudolf Steiner: An Autobiography, Vol. 1. 2nd ed. LC 72-95242. (Spiritual Science Library). (Illus.). 560p. 1980. lib. bdg. 25.00 (ISBN 0-89345-031-6); pap. 17.00 (ISBN 0-89345-210-6). Garber Comm.

--The Significance of Spiritual Research for Moral Action. Cottrell, Alan P., tr. from Ger. 17p. 1981. pap. 2.00 (ISBN 0-88010-101-6). Anthroposophic.

--The Social Future. new rev. ed. Monges, Henry B., tr. from Ger. LC 72-87742. 151p. 1972. pap. text ed. 7.95 (ISBN 0-910142-34-3). Anthroposophic.

--Soul Economy & Waldorf Education. Tr. of Die gesunde Entwicklung des Leiblich-Physischen als Grundlage der freien Enfaltung. 320p. (Orig.). pap. 20.00 (ISBN 0-88010-138-5); 30.00 (ISBN 0-88010-139-3). Anthroposophic.

--The Spiritual Being in the Heavenly Bodies & in the Kingdoms of Nature. (Ger.). 210p. 1981. pap. 9.95 (ISBN 0-919924-14-X, Pub. by Steiner Book Centre Canada). Anthroposophic.

--The Spiritual Foundation of Morality. Cotterell, Mabel, tr. 90p. 1979. pap. 4.75 (ISBN 0-919924-09-3, Pub. by Steiner Book Centre Canada). Anthroposophic.

--The Spiritual Guidance of Man. 1983. pap. 5.95 (ISBN 0-910142-35-1). Anthroposophic.

--Spiritual Science As a Foundation for Social Forms. Howard, Alan, ed. St. Goar, Maria, tr. from Ger. Tr. of Geisteswissenschaft als Erkenntnis der Grundimpulse sozialer Gestaltung. 300p. 1986. 30.00 (ISBN 0-88010-153-9); pap. 20.00 (ISBN 0-88010-152-0). Anthroposophic.

--The Stages of Higher Knowledge. 64p. 1974. pap. 4.50 (ISBN 0-910142-37-8). Anthroposophic.

--Temple Legend. Wood, John, tr. from German. 1986. 28.00 (ISBN 0-85440-780-4, Pub by Steinerbooks). Anthroposophic.

--The Ten Commandments & the Sermon on the Mount. Solomon, Frieda, tr. from Ger. 44p. 1978. pap. 2.00 (ISBN 0-910142-79-3). Anthroposophic.

--Theosophy: An Introduction to Supersensible Knowledge. rev. ed. LC 78-135997. 195p. (Orig.). 1971. 14.00 (ISBN 0-910142-65-3); pap. 6.95 (ISBN 0-910142-39-4). Anthroposophic.

--Theosophy: An Introduction to the Supersensible Knowledge of the World & the Destination of Man. Monges, Henry B., tr. from Ger. Tr. of Theosophie: Einfuehrung in uebersinnliche Welterkenntnis und Menschenbestimmung. 200p. 1987. pap. 6.95 (ISBN 0-88010-179-2). Anthroposophic.

--Theosophy: Introduction to the Supersensible Knowledge of the World & the Destination of Man. Church, Gilbert, ed. Monges, Henry B., tr. Tr. of Theosophie: Einfuehrung in uebersinnliche Welterkenntnis und Mmenschenbestimmung. (Ger.). 195p. 1986. pap. cancelled (ISBN 0-910142-39-4). Anthroposophic.

--Theosophy of the Rosicrucian. Cotterell, Mabel & Osmond, D. S., trs. (Ger.). 168p. 1981. 15.95 (ISBN 0-85440-113-X, Pub. by Steinerbooks); pap. 11.95 (ISBN 0-85440-401-5). Anthroposophic.

--Three Lectures on the Mystery Dramas. Pusch, Ruth, tr. from Ger. 101p. (Orig.). 1983. pap. 7.95 (ISBN 0-88010-060-5). Anthroposophic.

--True & False Paths in Spiritual Investigation. Parker, A. H., tr. from Ger. Tr. of Das Initiaten-Bewusstsein. Die wahren und die falschen Wege der geistigen Forschung. 222p. 1986. pap. 10.95 (ISBN 0-88010-135-0). Anthroposophic.

--Truth & Knowledge: Introduction to "Philosophy of Spiritual Activity", Vol. 14. 2nd ed. Allen, Paul M., ed. Stebbing, Rita, tr. from Ger. LC 81-51762. (The Major Writings of Rudolf Steiner in English Translation Ser.). 112p. 1981. Repr. of 1963 ed. lib. bdg. 10.00 (ISBN 0-89345-008-1, Spiritual Sci Lib). Garber Comm.

--Truth, Beauty & Goodness. 1986. pap. 1.50 (ISBN 0-916786-86-2). St George Bk Serv.

--Universe Earth & Man. (Russian Language Ser.). 136p. 1985. pap. 8.00 (ISBN 0-89345-903-8, Steiner). Garber Comm.

--Verses & Meditations. Adams, George & Adams, Mary, trs. (Ger.). 253p. 1979. Repr. of 1961 ed. 9.95 (ISBN 0-85440-119-9, Pub. by Steinerbooks). Anthroposophic.

--The Waking of the Human Soul & the Forming of Destiny - The Need for Understanding Christ. Wannamaker, Olin D., tr. (Ger.). 25p. 1983. pap. 3.00 (ISBN 0-919924-19-0, Pub by Steiner Book Centre Canada). Anthroposophic.

--Wonders of the World, Ordeals of the Soul, Revelations of the Spirit. Lenn, Dorothy, et al, trs. from Ger. 190p. 1983. pap. 11.00 (ISBN 0-85440-363-9, Pub by Steinerbooks). Anthroposophic.

--World History in the Light of Anthroposophy: And As a Foundation for Knowledge of the Human Spirit. new ed. Adams, George & Adams, Mary, trs. from Ger. 159p. 1977. 12.50 (ISBN 0-85440-315-9); pap. 9.00 (ISBN 0-85440-316-7). Anthroposophic.

--The World of the Senses & the World of the Spirit. (Ger.). 88p. 1979. pap. 4.95 (ISBN 0-919924-10-7, Pub. by Steiner Book Centre Canada). Anthroposophic.

--The Year Participated. Barfield, Owen, tr. from Ger. Tr. of Anthroposophischer Seelenkalender. 52p. 1986. pap. 7.95 (ISBN 0-85440-790-1, Pub. by Steinerbooks). Anthroposophic.

Steiner, Rudolf & Schure, Edward. The East in the Light of the West: The Children of Lucifer & the Brothers of Christ & Antique Drama in 5 Acts, Vol. 28. Garber, Bernard J., ed. LC 85-80914. (Spiritual Science Library Ser.: Vol. 28). 384p. 1986. lib. bdg. 21.00 (ISBN 0-89345-056-1, Spiritual Sci Lib). Garber Comm.

Steiner, Rudolf, jt. auth. see Roboz, Steven.

Steiner, Rudolf, jt. auth. see Von Goethe, J. W.

Steiner, Rudolf, et al. Education As an Art, Vol. 13. Allen, Paul M., ed. Tapp, Michael & Tapp, Elizabeth, trs. from Ger. LC 73-130816. (Spiritual Science Library). 128p. (Orig.). 1981. lib. bdg. 11.00 (ISBN 0-89345-024-3); pap. 6.00 (ISBN 0-89345-202-5, Steinerbks). Garber Comm.

Steiner, Susan C. Joining the Army That Sheds No Blood. LC 82-81510. (Christian Peace Shelf Ser.). 176p. (Orig.). 1982. pap. 6.95 (ISBN 0-8361-3305-6). Herald Pr.

Steiner, Zara, ed. The Times Survey of the Foreign Ministries of the World. (Illus.). 1982. 87.50x (ISBN 0-930466-37-3). Meckler Pub.

Steinglass, Peter, et al. The Alcoholic Family. LC 86-47741. 320p. 1987. 22.95x (ISBN 0-465-00097-5). Basic.

Steinhart, Lawrence M. Beauty Through Health: From the Edgar Cayce Readings. LC 73-91501. 1974. 7.95 (ISBN 0-87795-078-4). Arbor Hse.

Steinheim, Salomon L. Die Offenbarung nach dem Lehrbegriffe der Synagoge, 4 vols. Katz, Steven, ed. LC 79-7151. (Jewish Philosophy, Mysticism & History of Ideas Ser.). 1980. Repr. of 1865 ed. Set. lib. bdg. 160.00x (ISBN 0-405-12286-1); lib. bdg. 40.00x ea. Vol. 2 (ISBN 0-405-12288-8). Vol. 3 (ISBN 0-405-12220-9). Vol. 4 (ISBN 0-405-12221-7). Ayer Co Pubs.

Steinhorn, Harriet. Shadows of the Holocaust. LC 83-14887. 80p. 1983. pap. text ed. 8.95 (ISBN 0-930494-25-3). Kar Ben.

Steinilber-Oberlin, Emile. Buddhist Sects of Japan: Their Histories, Philosophical Doctrines & Sanctuaries. Loge, Marc, tr. 1977. lib. bdg. 39.95 (ISBN 0-8490-1559-6). Gordon Pr.

--The Buddhist Sects of Japan, Their History, Philosophical Doctrines & Sanctuaries. Loge, Marc, tr. LC 78-109854. (Illus.). 303p. Repr. of 1938 ed. lib. bdg. 22.50x (ISBN 0-8371-4349-7, STBS). Greenwood.

Steinke, Frank F. Greater Works Shall Ye Do. 101p. (Orig.). 1980. pap. 2.25 (ISBN 0-686-73996-5). Impact Bks Mo.

Steinke, Peter L. Preaching the Theology of the Cross: Sermons & Worship Ideas for Lent & Easter. LC 82-72638. 128p. (Orig.). 1983. pap. 6.95 (ISBN 0-8066-1944-9, 10-5144). Augsburg.

Steinkraus, Warren, ed. see Brightman, Edgar S.

Steinkraus, Warren E., ed. New Studies in Berkeley's Philosophy. LC 81-40866. 218p. 1982. lib. bdg. 27.75 (ISBN 0-8191-2006-5); pap. text ed. 12.75 (ISBN 0-8191-2007-3). U Pr of Amer.

Steinkuehler, Pearl, jt. auth. see Nordtvedt, Matilda.

Steinmetz, David. Luther in Context. LC 85-45313. (Midland Bks: No. 405). 160p. 1986. 25.00x (ISBN 0-253-33647-3); pap. 7.95x (ISBN 0-253-20405-4). Ind U Pr.

Steinmetz, David C. Luther & Staupitz: An Essay in the Intellectual Origins of the Protestant Reformation. LC 80-23007. (Duke Monographs in Medieval & Renaissance Studies: No. 4). xi, 149p. 1980. 18.50 (ISBN 0-8223-0447-3). Duke.

--Reformers in the Wings. (Twin Brooks Ser.). 240p. 1981. pap. 7.95 (ISBN 0-8010-8208-0). Baker Bk.

Steinmetz, George H. The Royal Arch: Its Hidden Meaning. (Illus.). 145p. 1979. Repr. of 1946 ed. text ed. 9.50 (M-302). Macoy Pub.

Steinmetz, Paul. Meditations with Native Americans: Lakota Spirituality. LC 83-71961. (Meditations with Ser.). (Illus.). 144p. (Orig.). 1984. pap. 6.95 (ISBN 0-939680-13-0). Bear & Co.

Steinmetz, Urban G. I Will. LC 71-84816. (Illus.). 136p. 1969. pap. 1.75 (ISBN 0-87793-010-4). Ave Maria.

--Strangers, Lovers, Friends. LC 80-69479. (Illus.). 176p. (Orig.). 1981. pap. 3.95 (ISBN 0-87793-217-4). Ave Maria.

Steinmetzer, Franz X. Die Babylonischen Kudurru Als Urkundenform. Repr. of 1922 ed. 22.00 (ISBN 0-384-57850-0). Johnson Repr.

Steinmueller, John E. The Sword of the Spirit. 108p. 1977. pap. 3.00 (ISBN 0-912103-00-0). Stella Maris Bks.

Steinsaltz, Adin. Beggars & Prayers: Adin Steinsaltz Retells the Tales of Rabbi Nahman of Bratslav. LC 78-54502. 186p. 1985. pap. 6.95 (ISBN 0-465-00581-0, PL-5139). Basic.

--Biblical Images: Men & Women of the Book. LC 83-46081. (Illus.). 256p. 1984. 16.95 (ISBN 0-465-00670-1). Basic.

--Biblical Images: Men & Women of the Book. LC 83-46081. 256p. 1985. pap. 6.95 (ISBN 0-465-00671-X, PL-5158). Basic.

--Essential Talmud. LC 75-36384. 1982. pap. 8.95 (ISBN 0-465-02063-1, CN-5112). Basic.

--Teshuvah: A Guide for the Newly Observant Jew. 192p. 1987. 19.95 (ISBN 0-02-931150-0). Free Pr.

Steinschneider, Moritz. Gesammelte Schriften. Katz, Steven, ed. LC 79-7152. (Jewish Philosophy, Mysticism & History of Ideas Ser.). 1980. Repr. of 1925 ed. lib. bdg. 55.50x (ISBN 0-405-12289-6). Ayer Co Pubs.

--Die Geschichtsliteratur der Juden. Katz, Steven, ed. LC 79-7153. (Jewish Philosophy, Mysticism & History of Ideas Ser.). 1980. Repr. of 1905 ed. lib. bdg. 16.00x (ISBN 0-405-12290-X). Ayer Co Pubs.

Steinwede, Dietrich. Reformation: A Picture Story of Martin Luther. Cooperrider, Edward A., tr. from German. LC 82-49055. (Illus.). 56p. 1983. pap. 6.95 (ISBN 0-8006-1710-X, 1-1710). Fortress.

Stell, C. Hallelujah: Recording Chapels & Meeting Houses. (Illus.). 48p. 1985. pap. text ed. 7.95 (ISBN 0-906780-49-7, Pub. by Council British Archaeology). Humanities.

Stella, Pietro. Don Bosco & the Death of Charles. Drury, John, tr. from Italian. (Don Bosco in the History of Catholic Religious Thought & Practice Ser.). 56p. (Orig.). 1985. pap. 5.95 (ISBN 0-89944-080-0). Don Bosco Multimedia.

--Don Bosco: Life & Work. Drury, John, tr. from Italian. (Don Bosco in the History of Catholic Religious Thought & Practice Ser.). Tr. of Don Bosco Nella Storia della Religiosita Cattolica: Vita e Opere. 336p. (Orig.). 1985. 24.95 (ISBN 0-89944-081-9). Don Bosco Multimedia.

Steltenkamp, Michael. The Sacred Vision: Native American Religion & Its Practice Today. LC 82-60594. 1983. pap. 5.95 (ISBN 0-8091-2481-5). Paulist Pr.

Steltz, Nancy. A Christmas Pageant. (Orig.). 1987. pap. price not set (ISBN 0-89536-889-7, 7875). CSS of Ohio.

Stelzer, Theodore G. Child's Garden of Song. (Concordia Primary Religion Ser). 1949. 9.95 (ISBN 0-570-03479-5, 56-1003). Concordia.

Stenbock, Evelyn, jt. auth. see Eifert, Frank.

Stenbock, Evelyn A. Beacon Small-Group Bible Studies, Ecclesiastes: "Faith or Futility?". Wolf, Earl C., ed. 96p. (Orig.). 1985. pap. 2.50 (ISBN 0-8341-0964-6). Beacon Hill.

Stendahl, Brita. The Force of Tradition: A Case Study of Women Priests in Sweden. LC 84-48713. (Illus.). 208p. 1985. pap. 14.95 (ISBN 0-8006-1808-4, 1-1808). Fortress.

Stendahl, Krister. The Bible & the Role of Women: A Case Study in Hermeneutics. Reumann, John, ed. Sander, Emilie T., tr. LC 66-25262. (Facet Bks). 64p. 1966. pap. 3.95 (ISBN 0-8006-3030-0, 1-3030). Fortress.

--Holy Week Preaching. LC 84-48714. (Resources for Preaching Ser.). 64p. 1985. pap. 3.95 (ISBN 0-8006-1851-3, 1-1851). Fortress.

--Meanings: The Bible As Document & Guide. LC 83-5601. 240p. 1984. pap. 14.95 (ISBN 0-8006-1752-5, 1-1752). Fortress.

--Paul Among Jews & Gentiles & Other Essays. LC 75-36450. 144p. 1976. pap. 4.95 (ISBN 0-8006-1224-8, 1-1224). Fortress.

Stenerson, Ruth. Bible Reading for Singles. LC 80-65543. (Bible Reading Ser.). 112p. (Orig.). 1980. pap. 3.95 (ISBN 0-8066-1788-8, 10-0678). Augsburg.

--Bible Reading for Teachers. LC 81-52275. (Bible Readings Ser.). 112p. (Orig.). 1982. pap. 3.95 (ISBN 0-8066-1907-4, 10-0680). Augsburg.

--Bible Readings for Students. LC 85-30771. 112p. (Orig.). 1986. pap. 3.95 (ISBN 0-8066-2190-7, 10-0691). Augsburg.

Stengel, Paul. Die Griechischen Kultusaltertumer. facsimile ed. LC 75-10656. (Ancient Religion & Mythology Ser.). (Ger.). 1976. Repr. of 1920 ed. 22.00x (ISBN 0-405-07264-3). Ayer Co Pubs.

Stensland, Vivian, ed. Daily Light from the New American Standard Bible. 416p. 1975. 9.95 (ISBN 0-8024-1740-X). Moody.

Stephan, Eric & Smith, Judith S. What Happy Families Are Doing. LC 81-15151. 131p. 1981. 7.95 (ISBN 0-87747-877-5). Deseret Bk.

Stephan, Horst & Schmidt, Martin. Geschichte der Evangelischen Theologie in Deutschland seit dem Idealismus. 3rd ed. (De Gruyter Lehrbuch). 1973. 24.80x (ISBN 3-11-003752-1). De Gruyter.

Stephanides Brothers. Greek Mythology, 6 vols. (Series A.). (Eng.). Set. 50.00x (ISBN 0-916634-25-6). Double M Pr.

Stephanopoulos, Robert G., ed. see Trempelas, Panagiotes N.

Stephanou, Archimandrite E., tr. see Makrakis, Apostolos.

Stephanus, Eddius. The Life of Bishop Wilfrid. Colgrave, Bertram, ed. 207p. 1985. 37.50 (ISBN 0-521-30927-1); pap. 12.95 (ISBN 0-521-31387-2). Cambridge U Pr.

Stephany, Konrad. Ludwig Schaffrath, Stained Glass & Mosaic. LC 77-79948. 1977. write for info. (ISBN 0-686-05497-0). C & R Loo.

Stephen, Caroline. Quaker Strongholds. Ogilvie, Mary G., ed. LC 51-4625. 32p. (Orig.). 1951. pap. 2.50x (ISBN 0-87574-059-6, 059). Pendle Hill.

Stephens, Bruce M. God's Last Metaphor: The Doctrine of the Trinity in New England Theology. LC 80-11421. (American Academy of Religion Studies in Religion). pap. 11.95 (ISBN 0-89130-386-3, 01-00-24). Scholars Pr GA.

Stephens, Don. Trial by Trial: Destiny of a Believer. LC 85-80485. 176p. (Orig.). 1985. pap. 6.95 (ISBN 0-89081-498-8). Harvest Hse.

Stephens, Evan. Eight Favorite Anthems. 1972. pap. 1.95 (ISBN 0-87747-350-1). Deseret Bk.

Stephens, Jack H., et al. Maui Now. (Illus., Orig.). 1969. pap. 1.70 (ISBN 0-941200-02-7). Aquarius.

Stephens, John F. Spirit Filled Family, No. 11. 48p. (Orig.). 1980. pap. 1.95 (ISBN 0-89841-008-8). Zoe Pubns.

Stephens, Joseph R., et al. Chartism & Christianity. Thompson, Dorothy, ed. (Chartism, Working-Class Politics in the Industrial Revolution Ser.). 132p. 1987. lib. bdg. 25.00 (ISBN 0-8240-5593-4). Garland Pub.

Stephens, Julius H. The Churches & the Kingdom. LC 78-5676. 1978. Repr. of 1959 ed. lib. bdg. cancelled (ISBN 0-313-20488-8, STCK). Greenwood.

Stephens, Lynn. As God Intended. 1973. pap. 1.25 (ISBN 0-89114-045-X). Baptist Pub Hse.

Stephens, Susan, jt. ed. see Lateiner, Donald.

Stephens, W. P. The Theology of Huldrych Zwingli. 360p. 1985. 52.00x (ISBN 0-19-826677-4). Oxford U Pr.

Stephens, William H. Elijah. 1979. pap. 3.95 (ISBN 0-8423-4023-8). Tyndale.

--Where Jesus Walked. LC 80-67422. 1981. soft cover 14.95 (ISBN 0-8054-1138-0). Broadman.

Stephens, William R. English Church from the Norman Conquest to the Accession of Edward First, 1066-1272. LC 2-21443. (History of the English Church Ser.: No. 2). Repr. of 1901 ed. 29.50 (ISBN 0-404-50752-2). AMS Pr.

Stephens, William R., et al. History of the English Church, 8 vols. in 9. Repr. of 1910 ed. Set. 265.50 (ISBN 0-404-50750-6); 29.50 ea. AMS Pr.

Stephenson, Alan M. First Lambeth Conference. LC 67-95915. (Church Historical Society Ser.: No. 88). 1967. 22.50x (ISBN 0-8401-5088-1). A R Allenson.

Stephenson, George M. The Puritan Heritage. LC 78-10512. 1978. Repr. of 1952 ed. lib. bdg. 22.50x (ISBN 0-313-20733-X, STPU). Greenwood.

--Religious Aspects of Swedish Immigration: A Study of Immigrant Churches. LC 69-18790. (American Immigration Collection Ser., No. 1). (Illus.). 1969. Repr. of 1932 ed. 22.50 (ISBN 0-405-00539-3). Ayer Co Pubs.

--Religious Aspects of Swedish Immigration. LC 71-137294. Repr. of 1932 ed. 14.00 (ISBN 0-404-06257-1). AMS Pr.

Stephenson, James. Prophecy on Trial. 1984. 10.50 (ISBN 0-317-03380-8). Lucis.

Sterk, Andrea & Scazzero, Peter. Christian Character. (Lifebuilder Bible Studies). 60p. (Orig.). 1985. pap. text ed. 2.95 (ISBN 0-8308-1054-4). Inter-Varsity.

--Christian Disciplines: Living the Way God Wants You to Live. (LifeBuilder Bible Studies). 64p. (Orig.). 1986. pap. 2.95 (ISBN 0-8308-1055-2). Inter-Varsity.

Stern, et al. Islamic Philosophy & the Classical Tradition. 549p. 1972. 100.00x (ISBN 0-317-39094-5, Pub. by Luzac & Co Ltd). State Mutual Bk.

Stern, Chaim. Gates of Forgiveness: Selichot. 1980. pap. 1.00 ea. Eng. Ed (ISBN 0-916694-57-7). Hebrew Ed (ISBN 0-916694-74-7). Central Conf.

--Gates of Freedom: A Passover Haggadah. LC 81-84191. (Illus.). 130p. 1986. pap. 6.95 (ISBN 0-940646-21-8). Rossel Bks.

--Gates of Freedom: A Passover Haggadah. 1986. pap. 6.95 (ISBN 0-317-42655-9). Shapolsky Pubs.

--Gates of the House. 1977. cancelled (ISBN 0-916694-42-9); lib. bdg. cancelled. Central Conf.

--Isaac: The Link in the Chain. 1977. text ed. 9.95 (ISBN 0-8315-0077-8). Speller.

Stern, Chaim, ed. Gates of Prayer. pulpit ed. 1975. English ed. 20.00 (ISBN 0-916694-46-1); Hebrew 20.00 (ISBN 0-916694-03-8). Central Conf.

--Gates of Prayer. 1978. Gift edition. 25.00 (ISBN 0-916694-69-0). Central Conf.

--Gates of Prayer for Weekdays & at a House of Mourning. 1975. pap. 2.75 (ISBN 0-916694-04-6). Central Conf.

--Gates of Prayer: The New Union Prayerbook. 1975. English ed. 15.00 (ISBN 0-916694-01-1); Hebrew ed. 16.00 (ISBN 0-916694-00-3). Central Conf.

--Gates of Repentance. 1978. 16.00 (ISBN 0-916694-38-0); pulpit ed. 20.00 (ISBN 0-916694-40-2); Hebrew ed. 15.00 (ISBN 0-916694-39-9); Hebrew pulpit ed. 20.00 (ISBN 0-686-77334-9). Central Conf.

Stern, David E., ed. see McMillen, S. I.

Stern, E. Mark, ed. Carl Jung & Soul Psychology. Tr. of Voices: The Art & Science of Psychotherapy. 196p. (Orig.). Repr. of 1986 ed. text ed. write for info. (ISBN 0-86656-632-5). Haworth Pr.

--Psychotherapy & the Religiously Committed Patient. LC 84-25276. (The Psychotherapy Patient Ser.: Vol. 1, No. 3). 158p. 1985. text ed. 19.95 (ISBN 0-86656-394-6); pap. text ed. 14.95 (ISBN 0-86656-396-2). Haworth Pr.

Stern, Elizabeth G. see Morton, Leah, pseud.

Stern, Frederick C. F. O. Matthiessen: Christian Socialist As Critic. LC 80-29013. xv, 281p. 1981. 27.50x (ISBN 0-8078-1478-4). U of NC Pr.

Stern, Henri. Les Mosaiques De la Grande Mosquee De Cordoue. (Madrider Forschungen, Ser., Vol. 11). (Illus.). 55p. 1976. 64.00x (ISBN 3-11-002126-9). De Gruyter.

Stern, Herman I. The Gods of Our Fathers: A Study of Saxon Mythology. LC 77-85623. 1977. Repr. of 1898 ed. lib. bdg. 30.00 (ISBN 0-89341-303-8). Longwood Pub Group.

Stern, Jean, ed. The Cross & the Sword. LC 76-9415. Tr. of La Cruz y la Espada. (Eng. & Span., Illus.). 144p. 1982. pap. 10.00 (ISBN 0-295-95916-9, Pub. by San Diego Museum Art). U of Wash Pr.

Stern, Marvin. Death, Grief & Friendship in the Eighteenth Century: Edward Gibbon & Lord Sheffield. 1985. pap. 11.95 (ISBN 0-930194-35-7). Ctr Thanatology.

Stern, Menahem. The Sun & the Clouds. 1972. 6.95x (ISBN 0-87068-389-6). Ktav.

Stern, S. M., ed. & tr. see Goldziher, Ignac.

Stern, Selma. The Court Jew: A Contribution to the History of Absolutism in Europe. 316p. 1985. 29.95 (ISBN 0-88738-019-0). Transaction Bks.

Stern, Shirley. Exploring Jewish History. 1978. pap. 8.95x (ISBN 0-87068-651-8). Ktav.

Stern, Stephen. The Sephardic Jewish Community of Los Angeles: A Study in Folklore & Ethnic Identity. Dorson, Richard M., ed. LC 80-734. (Folklore of the World Ser.). 1980. lib. bdg. 40.00x (ISBN 0-405-13324-3). Ayer Co Pubs.

Sternberg, G. Stefanesti: Portrait of a Romanian Shtetl. (Illus.). 320p. 1984. 30.00 (ISBN 0-08-030840-6). Pergamon.

Sternberg, Meir. Poetics of Biblical Narrative. (Literary Biblical Ser.). 380p. cancelled (ISBN 0-8245-0640-5). Crossroad NY.

--The Poetics of Biblical Narrative: Ideological Literature & the Drama of Reading. LC 85-42752. (Indiana Studies in Biblical Literature). 596p. 1985. 57.50x (ISBN 0-253-34521-9). Ind U Pr.

Sternberg, Patricia. Be My Friend: The Art of Good Relationships. LC 83-10254. 192p. 1983. pap. 8.95 (ISBN 0-664-26007-1, A Bridgebooks Publication). Westminster.

Sternberg, Robert J. & Wagner, Richard K., eds. Practical Intelligence: Origins of Competence in the Everyday World. (Illus.). 240p. 1986. 49.50 (ISBN 0-521-30253-6); pap. 15.95 (ISBN 0-521-31797-5). Cambridge U Pr.

Sterner, Eugene. God's Caring People. 1981. pap. 3.95 (ISBN 0-87162-251-3, D3839). Warner Pr.

--Healing & Wholeness. (Doctrinal Material of the Church of God Ser.: No. 2). 1978. pap. text ed. 3.95 (ISBN 0-87162-201-7, D4285). Warner Pr.

Sterner, John. Growing Through Mid-Life Crises. 112p. 1985. 8.95 (ISBN 0-570-04220-8, 15-2181). Concordia.

--How to Become Super-Spiritual: Or Kill Yourself Trying. LC 82-6636. 160p. (Orig.). 1982. pap. 7.50 (ISBN 0-687-17760-X). Abingdon.

Sterrett, T. Norton. How to Understand Your Bible. LC 74-78674. 180p. 1974. pap. 6.95 (ISBN 0-87784-638-3). Inter-Varsity.

Sterwart, J. S., ed. see Schleiermacher, Friedrich.

Steuart, Robert H. Diversity in Holiness. facs. ed. LC 67-28770. (Essay Index Reprint Ser). 1937. 17.00 (ISBN 0-8369-0906-2). Ayer Co Pubs.

Steuer, Alexel D. & McClendon, James W., Jr., eds. Is God God? LC 81-1927. 288p. (Orig.). 1981. pap. 10.95 (ISBN 0-687-19703-1). Abingdon.

Steven, Hugh. To the Ends of the Earth. 2nd ed. 142p. 1986. pap. 3.10 (ISBN 0-938978-31-4). Wycliffe Bible.

Steven, Robert K., jt. auth. see Stevens, Revalee R.

Stevens, Abel. The Women of Methodism: Its Three Foundresses, Susanna Wesley, the Countess of Huntingdon, & Barbara Heck. Gifford, Carolyn D. & Dayton, Donald, eds. (Women in American Protestant Religion 1800-1930 Ser.). 304p. 1987. lib. bdg. 45.00 (ISBN 0-8240-0676-3). Garland Pub.

Stevens, Beulah F. Dear Georgia. LC 78-13546. 1979. pap. 0.75 (ISBN 0-8127-0204-2). Review & Herald.

Stevens, Carolyn S. Children's Favorites: Inspirational Songs Arranged for the Piano. 40p. 1986. pap. 7.95 (ISBN 0-88290-275-X). Horizon Utah.

Stevens, Clifford. The Blessed Virgin. LC 84-60745. 160p. 1985. pap. 6.95 (ISBN 0-87973-704-2, 704). Our Sunday Visitor.

--A Life of Christ. LC 83-60102. 196p. (Orig.). 1983. pap. 5.95 (ISBN 0-87973-617-8, 617). Our Sunday Visitor.

--Man of Galilee. LC 79-88086. 1979. pap. 2.50 (ISBN 0-87973-302-0). Our Sunday Visitor.

Stevens, Courtenay E. Sidonius Apollinaris & His Age. LC 78-21112. 1979. Repr. of 1933 ed. lib. bdg. 24.75x (ISBN 0-313-20850-6, STSA). Greenwood.

Stevens, David H. Milton Papers. LC 75-176438. Repr. of 1927 ed. 5.00 (ISBN 0-404-06262-8). AMS Pr.

--Milton Papers. LC 76-27340. 1927. lib. bdg. 12.00 (ISBN 0-8414-7615-2). Folcroft.

Stevens, Denis. Tudor Church Music. LC 73-4335. (Music Reprint Ser.). 144p. 1973. Repr. of 1955 ed. lib. bdg. 25.00 (ISBN 0-306-70579-6). Da Capo.

Stevens, Denis, ed. see Handel, George F.

Stevens, Douglas. Called to Care. (YA) 1985. 12.95 (ISBN 0-310-28461-9, 11366, Pub. by Youth Spec). Zondervan.

Stevens, Edward. Business Ethics. LC 79-91409. 248p. (Orig.). 1979. pap. 9.95 (ISBN 0-8091-2244-8). Paulist Pr.

--Making Moral Decisions. rev. ed. LC 81-80877. 96p. 1981. pap. 4.95 (ISBN 0-8091-2397-5). Paulist Pr.

--The Morals Game. LC 74-18855. 216p. 1975. pap. 5.95 (ISBN 0-8091-1852-1). Paulist Pr.

--The Religion Game, American Style. LC 76-9367. 168p. 1976. pap. 5.95 (ISBN 0-8091-1951-X). Paulist Pr.

Stevens, Elliot. Rabbinic Authority. 1982. 15.00x (ISBN 0-916694-88-7). Ktav.

Stevens, Elliot L., ed. CCAR Yearbook. Incl. Vol. 86. 1976. 1977. 15.00 (ISBN 0-916694-36-4); Vol. 88. 1978. Weber, Donald R., ed. 1979. 15.00 (ISBN 0-916694-58-5); Vol. 89. 1979. 1980. 15.00. Central Conf.

--Rabbinic Authority. 184p. 1982. 15.00 (ISBN 0-317-01466-8). Central Conf.

Stevens, Elliot L. & Weber, Donald A., eds. CCAR Yearbook: 1978, Vol. 88. 1979. 15.00 (ISBN 0-916694-58-5). Central Conf.

Stevens, George B. The Epistles of Paul in Modern English: A Paraphrase. viii, 331p. 1980. Repr. of 1898 ed. 10.95 (ISBN 0-940033-26-7). R O Roberts.

--The Theology of the New Testament. 636p. 1918. 19.95 (ISBN 0-567-07215-0, Pub. by T & T Clark Ltd UK). Fortress.

Stevens, George B., tr. see St. Paul.

Stevens, James S. Whittier's Use of the Bible. LC 74-13173. 1974. Repr. of 1930 ed. lib. bdg. 15.00 (ISBN 0-8414-7798-1). Folcroft.

Stevens, Jim, jt. auth. see Jenson, Ron.

Stevens, Joel & Olitzky, Kerry M. An Index to the Sound Recordings Collection of the American Jewish Arichives. 1980. 7.50x (ISBN 0-87820-009-6). Ktav.

Stevens, John, jt. auth. see Roth, Martin.

Stevens, John, tr. see Bede the Venerable.

Stevens, John, tr. see Sogen, Omori & Katsujo, Terayama.

Stevens, Margaret M. Prosperity Is God's Idea. (Illus.). 1978. pap. 4.50 (ISBN 0-87516-264-9). De Vorss.

--Stepping Stones for Boys & Girls. (Illus.). 1977. pap. 3.00 (ISBN 0-87516-248-7). De Vorss.

Stevens, Mark. Land Rush: The Secret World of Real Estate's Super Brokers & Developers. 1985. pap. 6.95 (ISBN 0-07-061274-9). McGraw.

Stevens, Paul. Imagination & the Presence of Shakespeare in Paradise Lost. LC 85-40378. 256p. 1985. text ed. 32.50x (ISBN 0-299-10420-6). U of Wis Pr.

--Revelation: The Triumph of God. (LifeBuilder Bible Studies). 64p. (Orig.). 1987. pap. 2.95 (ISBN 0-8308-1021-8). Inter-Varsity.

Stevens, R. David. Five Steps to Freedom. 60p. 1980. pap. 2.25 (ISBN 0-87516-400-5). De Vorss.

Stevens, R. Paul. Liberating the Laity. LC 85-10856. 192p. (Orig.). 1985. pap. 5.95 (ISBN 0-87784-613-8). Inter-Varsity.

--Married for Good. LC 86-2881. 220p. (Orig.). 1986. pap. 5.95 (ISBN 0-87784-603-0). Inter-Varsity.

Stevens, Revalee R. & Steven, Robert K. The Protestant Cemetery of Rome. LC 81-84484. (North American Records in Italy). (Illus.). 110p. (Orig.). 1982. pap. 9.00 (ISBN 0-88127-003-2). Oracle Pr LA.

Stevens, Richard J. Community Beyond Division: Chrisitan Life under South Africa's Apartheid System. 1984. 8.95 (ISBN 0-533-05729-9). Vantage.

Stevens, Richard P. American Zionism & U. S. Foreign Policy, 1942-1947. 236p. 1970. Repr. of 1962 ed. 6.00 (ISBN 0-88728-095-1). Inst Palestine.

Stevens, Sherrill. Layman's Bible Book Commentary: Genesis, Vol.1. LC 78-50377. 1978. 5.95 (ISBN 0-8054-1171-2). Broadman.

Stevens, Velma D. God Is Faithful. LC 86-921. 1986. pap. 3.25 (ISBN 0-8054-5028-9). Broadman.

Stevens, W. C. The Book of Daniel. 190p. 1915. pap. 3.25 (ISBN 0-87509-061-3). Chr Pubns.

Stevens, Weston A. Jesus As We Knew Him. LC 85-73771. (Illus.). 137p. 1986. pap. 5.95 (ISBN 0-9605818-2-0). John Alden Bks.

Stevens, William A. & Burton, Ernest D. A Harmony of the Gospels for Historical Study. 283p. 1930. text ed. write for info. (ISBN 0-02-417240-5, Pub. by Scribner). Macmillan.

Stevens, William O. The Cross in the Life & Literature of the Anglo-Saxons. 69.95 (ISBN 0-87968-970-6). Gordon Pr.

Stevens, William W. Doctrines of the Christian Religion. LC 77-83282. 1977. pap. 10.95 (ISBN 0-8054-1706-0). Broadman.

--A Guide for New Testament Study. LC 76-62920. 1977. pap. 13.95 (ISBN 0-8054-1360-X). Broadman.

--A Guide for Old Testament Study. LC 73-91606. pap. 10.50 (ISBN 0-8054-1210-7). Broadman.

Stevens, Woodie. How to Fill the Emptiness. (Christian Living Ser.). 32p. (Orig.). 1987. pap. write for info. (ISBN 0-8341-1188-8). Beacon Hill.

Stevens-Arroyo, Antonio, ed. Prophets Denied Honor: An Anthology on the Hispanic Church in the U. S. LC 79-26847. 397p. (Orig.). 1982. pap. 12.95 (ISBN 0-88344-395-3). Orbis Bks.

Stevenson, Arthur L. Story of Southern Hymnology. LC 72-1676. Repr. of 1931 ed. 17.50 (ISBN 0-404-08334-X). AMS Pr.

Stevenson, Burton. A Guide to Biography. 1973. Repr. of 1910 ed. 25.00 (ISBN 0-8274-0867-6). R West.

Stevenson, Burton, ed. American History in Verse. Abridged ed. 494p. 1975. pap. 7.00 (ISBN 0-89084-024-5). Bob Jones Univ Pr.

Stevenson, Charles. Ethics & Language. LC 75-41263. Repr. of 1944 ed. 22.50 (ISBN 0-404-14806-9). AMS Pr.

Stevenson, Dwight E. & Diehl, Charles F. Reaching People from the Pulpit: A Guide to Effective Sermon Delivery. (Notable Books on Preaching). 1978. pap. 4.50 (ISBN 0-8010-8133-5). Baker Bk.

Stevenson, F. S. Robert Grosseteste, Bishop of Lincoln: A Contribution to the Religious, Political & Intellectual History of the Thirteenth Century. (Medieval Studies Ser.). Repr. of 1899 ed. lib. bdg. 39.50 (ISBN 0-697-00018-4). Irvington.

Stevenson, J. The Catacombs: Rediscovered Monuments of Early Christianity. (Ancient Peoples & Places Ser.). (Illus.). 1978. 19.95 (ISBN 0-500-02091-4). Thames Hudson.

Stevenson, J. Sinclair. The Friend of Little Children: Story of Our Lord's Life Told for Children. 1978. Repr. lib. bdg. 25.00 (ISBN 0-8495-4876-4). Arden Lib.

Stevenson, Joseph. The Church Histories of England. 59.95 (ISBN 0-87968-869-6). Gordon Pr.

Stevenson, Kenneth & Habermas, Gary B. Verdict on the Shroud: Evidence for the Death & Resurrection of Jesus Christ. (Illus.). 220p. 1981. pap. 6.95 (ISBN 0-89283-174-X). Servant.

Stevenson, Kenneth, ed. Nuptial Blessing: A Study of Christian Marriage Rites. 1983. 22.50x (ISBN 0-19-520418-2); pap. 9.95x (ISBN 0-19-520419-0). Oxford U Pr.

--Proceedings of the Nineteen Seventy-Seven United States Conference of Research on the Shroud of Turin. (Illus.). 244p. (Orig.). 1980. pap. 10.00 (ISBN 0-9605516-0-3). Shroud of Turin.

Stevenson, Kenneth W. Eucharist & Offering. 300p. (Orig.). 1986. pap. 17.50 (ISBN 0-916134-77-6). Pueblo Pub Co.

Stevenson, Robert. Shakespeare's Religious Frontier. LC 73-16102. 1974. Repr. of 1958 ed. lib. bdg. 25.00 (ISBN 0-8414-7699-3). Folcroft.

--Spanish Cathedral Music in the Golden Age. LC 76-1013. (Illus.). 523p. 1976. Repr. of 1961 ed. lib. bdg. 39.50x (ISBN 0-8371-8744-3, STSP). Greenwood.

Stevenson, Robert Louis. The Book of Selected Prayers by Robert Louis Stevenson. Rev. ed. (Illus.). 99p. 1982. 47.85 (ISBN 0-89901-066-0). Found Class Reprints.

--Prayers Written at Vailima. xi, 61p. 1973. 40.00 (ISBN 0-317-11648-7). Dawsons.

--Selected Prayers by Robert Louis Stevenson. (Illus.). 1980. Repr. of 1904 ed. 39.75 (ISBN 0-89901-004-0). Found Class Reprints.

Stevenson, Robert M. Patterns of Protestant Church Music. LC 53-8271. viii, 219p. 1953. 20.50 (ISBN 0-8223-0168-7). Duke.

--Patterns of Protestant Church Music. LC 53-8271. pap. 56.80 (ISBN 0-317-26858-9, 2023455). Bks Demand UMI.

Stevenson, W. B. Crusaders in the East. 16.00x (ISBN 0-86685-035-X). Intl Bk Ctr.

Stevenson, Warren. Divine Analogy: A Study of the Creation Motif in Blake & Coleridge. Hogg, James, ed. (Romantic Reassessment Ser.). 403p. (Orig.). 1972. pap. 15.00 (ISBN 0-317-40044-4, Pub. by Salzburg Studies). Longwood Pub Group.

Stevenson, William R., Jr. Christian Love & Just War: Moral Paradox & Political Life in St. Augustine & His Modern Interpreters. 256p. 1987. 29.95 (ISBN 0-86554-272-4, H235). Mercer Univ Pr.

Stevevson, Robert. Exposition of the Pilgrim's Progress, with Illustrative Quotations from Bunyan's Minor Works. LC 77-24243. 1977. Repr. of 1912 ed. lib. bdg. 27.50 (ISBN 0-8414-7933-X). Folcroft.

Steward-Wallace, John, jt. ed. see Ghanananda, Swami.

Stewart, Avy. The Travelers. (Orig.). 1982. pap. 2.95 (ISBN 0-937172-36-7). JLJ Pubs.

Stewart, Charles C., jt. ed. see Peel, J. D.

Stewart, Charles P., jt. auth. see Stewart, Frances T.

Stewart, Claude Y., Jr. Nature in Grace: A Study in the Theology of Nature. LC 83-8196. xx, 318p. 1983. pap. 21.50 (ISBN 0-86554-068-3, P08). Mercer Univ Pr.

Stewart, D. Exploring the Philosophy of Religion. (Illus.). 1980. pap. text ed. write for info. (ISBN 0-13-297366-9). P-H.

Stewart, David, jt. ed. see Reagan, Charles E.

Stewart, Don. Ninety-Nine Questions People Ask Most about the Bible. 160p. (Orig.). 1987. pap. 5.95 (ISBN 0-8423-5107-8). Tyndale.

--One Hundred & One Questions People Ask Most about Jesus. 224p. (Orig.). 1987. pap. 5.95 (ISBN 0-8423-4748-8). Tyndale.

--One Hundred & Three Questions People Ask about God. 188p. 1987. pap. 5.95 (ISBN 0-8423-4747-X). Tyndale.

Stewart, Don, jt. auth. see McDowell, Josh.

Stewart, Dugald. Outlines of the Moral Philosophy. LC 75-11255. (British Philosophers & Theologians of the 17th & 18th Centuries: Vol. 54). 322p. 1976. Repr. of 1793 ed. lib. bdg. 51.00 (ISBN 0-8240-1805-2). Garland Pub.

Stewart, Ed. Here Comes Jesus. LC 77-90584. 160p. 1977. pap. 3.50 (ISBN 0-8307-0553-8, S101157). Regal.

Stewart, Ed & Fishwick, Nina M. Group Talk. LC 85-30142. 162p. (Orig.). 1986. pap. 5.95 (ISBN 0-8307-1139-2, S411103). Regal.

Stewart, Ed, ed. Outreach to Youth. 1978. pap. 1.50 (ISBN 0-8307-0503-1, 9770402). Regal.

--Teaching Adults Through Discussion. 32p. 1978. pap. 1.50 (ISBN 0-8307-0508-2, 9970401). Regal.

Stewart, Ed, ed. see Ramm, Bernard L.

Stewart, Frances T. & Stewart, Charles P. The Birth of Jesus. (Stick & Learn Book Ser.). (Orig.). 1985. pap. 6.95 (ISBN 0-8054-4171-9). Broadman.

--Noah & the Rainbow Promise. (Stick & L Book Ser.). (Illus.). 1986. pap. 6.95 (ISBN 0-8054-4187-5). Broadman.

Stewart, George, Jr. History of Religious Education in Connecticut to the Middle of the Nineteenth Century. LC 79-89238. (American Education: Its Men, Institutions & Ideas, Ser. 1). 1969. Repr. of 1924 ed. 17.00 (ISBN 0-405-01475-9). Ayer Co Pubs.

Stewart, George R. Year of the Oath. LC 77-150422. (Civil Liberties in American History Ser). 1971. Repr. of 1950 ed. lib. bdg. 22.50 (ISBN 0-306-70103-0). Da Capo.

Stewart, H. F. Blaise Pascal. 1973. Repr. of 1942 ed. 6.00 (ISBN 0-8274-1623-7). R West.

--The Holiness of Pascal. 1977. lib. bdg. 59.95 (ISBN 0-8490-2015-8). Gordon Pr.

Stewart, Helen H. The Supernatural in Shakespeare. LC 72-13282. 1972. Repr. of 1908 ed. lib. bdg. 22.50 (ISBN 0-8414-1168-9). Folcroft.

Stewart, Hugh F. Blaise Pascal. LC 77-16601. 1977. Repr. of 1942 ed. lib. bdg. 12.50 (ISBN 0-8414-7801-5). Folcroft.

--Boethius: An Essay. LC 74-20524. 1975. Repr. of 1891 ed. 23.50 (ISBN 0-8337-4935-8). B Franklin.

Stewart, James, ed. & intro. by see Kinzie, Frederick E. & Kinzie, Vera D.

Stewart, James H. American Catholic Leadership: A Decade of Turmoil, 1966-76. (Religion & Society Ser.: No. 13). 1978. pap. 13.00x (ISBN 90-279-7884-0). Mouton.

Stewart, James S. The Gates of New Life. (The Scholar As Preacher Ser.). 262p. 1976. pap. text ed. 11.95 (ISBN 0-567-24426-1, Pub. by T & T Clark Ltd UK). Fortress.

--The Life & Teaching of Jesus Christ. 1982. pap. 3.95 (ISBN 0-687-21744-X, Festival). Abingdon.

--Man in Christ. (James S. Stewart Library). 1975. pap. 7.95 (ISBN 0-8010-8045-2). Baker Bk.

--The Strong Name. (The Scholar As Preacher Ser.). 268p. 1940. 12.95 (ISBN 0-567-04427-0, Pub. by T & T Clark Ltd UK). Fortress.

--The Wind of the Spirit. 192p. 1984. pap. 6.95 (ISBN 0-8010-8250-1). Baker Bk.

Stewart, Jane L., jt. auth. see Faraone, Joseph J.

Stewart, John. Nestorian Missionary Enterprise. LC 78-63172. (Heresies of the Early Christian & Medieval Era: Second Ser.). Repr. of 1928 ed. 46.50 (ISBN 0-404-16187-1). AMS Pr.

Stewart, John & Wust, Klaus. Davidsburg Church Baptisms 1785-1845 New Market, Virginia. Stewart, John, tr. from Virginia German. 44p. 1983. pap. 6.75 (ISBN 0-917968-10-7). Shenandoah Hist.

Stewart, John, tr. see Stewart, John & Wust, Klaus.

Stewart, John J. How to Gain a Testimony of the Gospel of Jesus Christ. LC 78-52122. 74p. 1978. 5.50 (ISBN 0-88290-097-8). Horizon Utah.

--Mormonism & the Negro. LC 78-52123. 92p. 1978. 5.50 (ISBN 0-88290-098-6). Horizon Utah.

Stewart, K. K. God Made Me Special. LC 82-62731. (Happy Day Bks.). (Illus.). 24p. 1983. 1.59 (ISBN 0-87239-635-5, 3555). Standard Pub.

Stewart, Ken. Divorce & Remarriage. 141p. (Orig.). 1984. pap. 4.95 (ISBN 0-89274-343-3). Harrison Hse.

--Do's & Don'ts for an Overnight Stay in the Lion's Den. 31p. write for info. (ISBN 0-89274-043-4). Harrison Hse.

--Doubt: The Enemy of Faith. 32p. (Orig.). 1984. pap. 1.95 (ISBN 0-89274-034-5). Harrison Hse.

Stewart, Leon. Too Late. pap. 5.95 (ISBN 0-911866-66-3). Advocate.

Stewart, Linda, ed. Christmas Is Coming! 1986: Holiday Projects for Children & Parents. (Illus.). 128p. 1986. 17.95 (ISBN 0-8487-0688-9). Oxmoor Hse.

Stewart, Marjorie. Looking at Jesus with Luke. 24p. 1978. pap. 0.75 (ISBN 0-88243-756-9, 02-0756). Gospel Pub.

--Women in Neighborhood Evangelism. LC 77-93410. 128p. 1978. pap. 1.50 (ISBN 0-88243-723-2, 02-0723, Radiant Books). Gospel Pub.

Stewart, Omer C., ed. Peyotism in the West: A Historical & Cultural Perspective. (Anthropological Papers: No. 108). (Illus.). 168p. (Orig.). 1984. pap. 17.50x (ISBN 0-87480-235-0). U of Utah Pr.

Stewart, R. J. The Underworld Initiation: A Journey Towards Psychic Transformation. 272p. 1985. pap. 11.95 (ISBN 0-85030-399-0). Newcastle Pub.

Stewart, Rosemarie see Hanson, Virginia.

Stewart, Stan & Hubner, Pauline. Talking about Something Important. 128p. (Orig.). 1981. pap. 7.95 (ISBN 0-85819-328-0, Pub. by JBCE). ANZ Religious Pubns.

Stewart, V. Mary. Sexual Freedom. pap. 0.75 (ISBN 0-87784-111-X). Inter-Varsity.

Stewart, W. A. Quakers & Education. LC 76-115330. 1971. Repr. of 1953 ed. 32.50x (ISBN 0-8046-1121-1, Pub. by Kennikat). Assoc Faculty Pr.

Stewart, W. Grant. The Popular Superstitions & Festive Amusements of the Highlanders of Scotland. 1978. Repr. of 1851 ed. lib. bdg. 37.50 (ISBN 0-8492-8007-9). R West.

Stewart, Zeph, ed. see Nock, Arthur D.

Stiansen, Peder. History of the Norwegian Baptists in America. Gaustad, Edwin S., ed. LC 79-52608. (The Baptist Tradition Ser.). (Illus.). 1980. Repr. of 1939 ed. lib. bdg. 32.50x (ISBN 0-405-12473-2). Ayer Co Pubs.

Stibbs, Alan. How to Understand Your Bible. Wenham, David & Wenham, Clare, eds. LC 77-72351. Orig. Title: Understanding God's Word. 77p. 1978. pap. 1.95 (ISBN 0-87788-365-3). Shaw Pubs.

Stibbs, Alan M. First Epistle of Peter. (Tyndale Bible Commentaries). 1959. 4.95 (ISBN 0-8028-1416-6). Eerdmans.

--So Great Salvation: The Meaning & Message of the Letter to the Hebrews. 118p. 1970. pap. 4.95 (ISBN 0-85364-102-1). Attic Pr.

Stibbs, Alan M., ed. Search the Scriptures. rev. ed. 9.95 (ISBN 0-87784-856-4). Inter-Varsity.

Sticca, Sandro, ed. The Medieval Drama. LC 78-152517. (Illus.). 154p. 1972. 39.50 (ISBN 0-87395-085-2). State U NY Pr.

Stickelberger, E. Calvin. Gelser, David, tr. 174p. 1977. Repr. of 1959 ed. 12.95 (ISBN 0-227-67424-3). Attic Pr.

Stickly, Caroline. Broken Snare. 1975. pap. 3.75 (ISBN 0-85363-102-6). OMF Bks.

Stickney, Doris. Water Bugs & Dragonflies: Explaining Death to Children. (Illus.). 24p. 1982. pap. 1.25 (ISBN 0-8298-0609-1). Pilgrim NY.

Stiebner, Erhardt D. & Urban, Dieter. Signs & Emblems. LC 83-14793. (Illus.). 352p. 1984. 17.95 (ISBN 0-442-28059-9). Van Nos Reinhold.

Stiefel, Janice. How to Plan a Bible Treasure Hunt. (Illus.). 50p. (Orig.). 1981. pap. 3.50 (ISBN 0-9605858-0-X). Second Hand.

Stiehl, Ruth, jt. auth. see Altheim, Franz.

Stier, Rudolf E. Commentary on the Epistle of James. 278p. 1982. lib. bdg. 10.25 Smythe Sewn (ISBN 0-86524-157-0, 5903). Klock & Klock.

--Words of the Apostles. 1982. lib. bdg. 18.75 (ISBN 0-86524-087-6, 4403). Klock & Klock.

--Words of the Risen Christ. 1982. lib. bdg. 8.25 (ISBN 0-86524-088-4, 9512). Klock & Klock.

Stifle, J. M. ABC Bible Characters. 1982. pap. 3.95 (ISBN 0-570-04062-0, 56-1365). Concordia.

--ABC Bible Stories. 1982. pap. 3.95 (ISBN 0-570-04063-9, 56-1366). Concordia.

--ABC Book About Christmas. 1981. pap. 3.95 (ISBN 0-570-04053-1, 56-1714). Concordia.

--ABC Book About Jesus. 1981. pap. 3.95 (ISBN 0-570-04054-X, 56-1715). Concordia.

Still, William. Letters of Still. (Religious Ser.). 192p. (Orig.). 1984. pap. 5.95x (ISBN 0-85151-378-6). Banner of Truth.

Stiller, Gunther. J. S. Bach & Liturgical Life in Liepzig. Leaver, Robin A., ed. Boutman, Herbert J., et al, trs. from Ger. Tr. of Johann Sebastian Bach und das Leipziger Gottesdienstliche Leben Seiner Zeit. (Illus.). 312p. (Orig.). 1984. pap. 24.95 (ISBN 0-570-01320-8, 99-1247). Concordia.

Stillman, Mildred W., tr. see Fenelon, Francois.

Stillman, Norman A. The Jews of Arab Lands: A History & Source Book. LC 78-70078. (Illus.). 416p. 1979. 10.95 (ISBN 0-8276-0116-6, 426). Jewish Pubns.

Stillman, Peter G., ed. Hegel's Philosophy of Spirit. (SUNY Series in Hegelian Studies). 223p. 1986. 39.50x (ISBN 0-88706-476-0); pap. 12.95x (ISBN 0-88706-477-9). State U NY Pr.

Stillman, Peter R. Introduction to Myth. 1977. pap. text ed. 9.25x (ISBN 0-8104-5890-X). Boynton Cook Pubs.

Stilson, Max. Who? What? Where? Bible Quizzes. (Quiz & Puzzle Bks.). 96p. 1980. pap. 2.95 (ISBN 0-8010-8012-6). Baker Bk.

Stimson, J. F. Tuamotuan Religion. (BMB Ser.). Repr. of 1933 ed. 21.00 (ISBN 0-527-02209-8). Kraus Repr.

Stine, Alan. Love Power: New Dimensions for Building Strong Families. LC 78-70360. 1978. 8.95 (ISBN 0-88290-105-2). Horizon Utah.

Stineman, William F. & Porter, Jack W. Saint John the Evangelist Church, Indianapolis, Indiana: A Photographic Essay of the Oldest Catholic Church in Indianapolis & Marion County. LC 85-63564. (Illus.). 80p. 1986. 39.95 (ISBN 0-9616134-0-8). ST John Evang.

Stineman, William F., jt. auth. see Porter, Jack W.

Stinespring, William, tr. see Klausner, Joseph.

Stinger, Charles L. Humanism & the Church Fathers: Ambrogio Traversari (1386-1439) & the Revival of Patristic Theology in the Early Italian Renaissance. LC 76-21699. 1977. 49.50x (ISBN 0-87395-304-5). State U NY Pr.

Stinson, Linda L. Process & Conscience: Toward a Theology of Human Emergence. 202p. (Orig.). 1986. lib. bdg. 22.50 (ISBN 0-8191-5206-4); pap. text ed. 11.50 (ISBN 0-8191-5207-2). U Pr of Amer.

Stirling, James H. Philosophy & Theology. LC 77-27233. (Gifford Lectures: 1890). 1978. Repr. of 1890 ed. 39.00 (ISBN 0-404-60451-X). AMS Pr.

Stirling, Leader. Tanzanian Doctor. LC 78-316167. pap. 38.50 (ISBN 0-317-26454-0, 2023860). Bks Demand UMI.

Stirrup Associates Inc. All about Love. Phillips, Cheryl M. & Harvey, Bonnie C., eds. LC 84-50915. (Child's Paraphrase Ser.). (Illus.). 32p. 1984. pap. 1.49 (ISBN 0-937420-16-6). Stirrup Assoc.

--Beautiful Attitudes Matthew 5: 3-12. Phillips, Cheryl M. & Harvey, Bonnie C., eds. LC 84-50914. (Child's Paraphrase Ser.). (Illus.). 32p. 1984. pap. 1.49 (ISBN 0-937420-17-4). Stirrup Assoc.

--My Jesus Pocketbook of a Very Special Birth Day. Harvey, Bonnie C. & Phillips, Cheryl M., eds. LC 84-50919. (My Jesus Pocketbook Ser.). (Illus.). 32p. 1984. pap. 0.49 (ISBN 0-937420-15-8). Stirrup Assoc.

--My Jesus Pocketbook of Daniel in the Lion's Den. Harvey, Bonnie C. & Phillips, Cheryl M., eds. LC 84-50916. (My Jesus Pocketbook Ser.). (Illus.). 32p. (Orig.). 1984. pap. text ed. 0.49 (ISBN 0-937420-12-3). Stirrup Assoc.

Stirrup Associates, Inc. My Jesus Pocketbook of Jonah & the Big Fish. Harvey, Bonnie C. & Phillips, Cheryl M., eds. LC 83-51679. (My Jesus Pocketbook Ser.). (Illus.). 32p. 1984. pap. 0.49 (ISBN 0-937420-09-3). Stirrup Assoc.

--My Jesus Pocketbook of Noah & the Floating Zoo. Harvey, Bonnie C. & Phillips, Cheryl M., eds. LC 83-51680. (My Jesus Pocketbook Ser.). (Illus.). 32p. 1984. pap. 0.49 (ISBN 0-937420-10-7). Stirrup Assoc.

--My Jesus Pocketbook of Scripture Pictures. LC 82-80351. (Illus.). 32p. (Orig.). 1982. pap. 0.49 (ISBN 0-937420-02-6). Stirrup Assoc.

Stirrup Associates Inc. My Jesus Pocketbook of the Beginning. Harvey, Bonnie C. & Phillips, Cheryl M., eds. LC 84-50918. (Jesus Pocketbook Ser.). (Illus.). 32p. (Orig.). 1984. pap. 0.49 (ISBN 0-937420-14-X). Stirrup Assoc.

--My Jesus Pocketbook of the Big Little Person: The Story of Zacchaeus. Phillips, Cheryl M. & Harvey, Bonnie C., eds. LC 84-50917. (My Jesus Pocketbook Ser.). (Illus.). 32p. 1984. pap. 0.49 (ISBN 0-937420-13-1). Stirrup Assoc.

Stirrup Associates, Inc. Staff. My Jesus Pocketbook of Li'l Critters. Phillips, Cheryl M., ed. LC 82-63139. (Illus.). 32p. (Orig.). 1983. pap. text ed. 0.49 (ISBN 0-937420-05-0). Stirrup Assoc.

--My Jesus Pocketbook of Manners. Phillips, Cheryl M., ed. LC 82-63141. (Illus.). 32p. 1983. pap. 0.49 (ISBN 0-937420-06-9). Stirrup Assoc.

--My Jesus Pocketbook of the 23rd Psalm. Phillips, Cheryl M., ed. LC 82-63140. (Illus.). 32p. (Orig.). 1983. pap. text ed. 0.49 (ISBN 0-937420-04-2). Stirrup Assoc.

Stitskin, Leon D. Jewish Philosophy: A Study in Personalism. 1976. 15.00x (ISBN 0-685-84458-7). Bloch.

Stivers, Robert L. Hunger, Technology & Limits to Growth: Christian Responsibility for Three Ethical Issues. LC 83-72120. 176p. (Orig.). 1984. pap. 9.95 (ISBN 0-8066-2064-1, 10-3184). Augsburg.

St Jerome. St. Paul the First Hermit: His Life by St. Jerome. Shewring, Walter, ed. Hawkins, tr. from Lat. 48p. 1987. 1.50 (ISBN 0-916375-07-2). Press Alley.

Stob, George. That I May Know. 128p. 1982. pap. 3.95 (ISBN 0-933140-51-7); pap. 3.95 student wkbk (ISBN 0-933140-52-5). CRC Pubns.

Stob, Henry. Sin, Salvation & Service. (Orig.). 1984. pap. 2.95 (ISBN 0-933140-98-3). CRC Pubns.

--Theological Reflections: Essays on Related Themes. LC 81-1472. pap. 69.30 (ISBN 0-317-20015-1, 2023223). Bks Demand UMI.

Stobbe, Leslie H. Living with Others. 1986. pap. 4.95 (ISBN 0-8010-8275-7). Baker Bk.

--Preteen Bible Exploration. 1987. pap. 4.95 (ISBN 0-8010-8273-0). Baker Bk.

Stochl, Susan, ed. Easter People, Grade 5: Gather. (Easter People Ser.). (Illus.). 1979. pap. text ed. 5.65 (ISBN 0-03-050761-8, HarpR); tchr's manual 7.60 (ISBN 0-03-050771-5); wkbk. 3.90 (ISBN 0-03-050776-6); parent bk. 2.25 (ISBN 0-03-050766-9). Har-Row.

Stochl, Susan, et al, eds. Easter People, Grade 4: Remember. (The Easter People Ser). (Illus.). 1978. pap. text ed. 4.75 (ISBN 0-03-042801-7, HarpR); tchr's. manual 7.60 (ISBN 0-03-042796-7); activity pack 3.90 (ISBN 0-03-042911-0); parent book 2.25 (ISBN 0-03-042791-6). Har-Row.

--Easter People, Grade 1: Welcome. (Easter People Ser.). 1977. pap. text ed. 3.34 (ISBN 0-03-020356-2, 161, HarpR); tchr's. ed. 7.60 (ISBN 0-03-020366-X, 163); activity pack 3.90 (ISBN 0-03-020371-6, 162); parent bk. 2.25 (ISBN 0-03-020361-9, 164). Har-Row.

--Easter People, Grade 2: Belong. (Easter People Ser). 1977. pap. text ed. 3.34 (ISBN 0-03-020376-7, 165, HarpR); tchr's. ed. 7.60 (ISBN 0-03-020386-4, 167); activity pack 3.90 (ISBN 0-03-020391-0, 166); parent bk. 2.25 (ISBN 0-03-020381-3, 168). Har-Row.

--Easter People, Grade 3: Journey. (Easter People Ser). (Illus.). 1977. pap. text ed. 3.34 (ISBN 0-03-020396-1, 169, HarpR); tchr's. ed. 7.60 (ISBN 0-03-020406-2, 171); parent wkbk. 2.25 (ISBN 0-03-020401-1, 172); activity pack 3.90 (ISBN 0-03-020411-9, 170). Har-Row.

Stock, Augustine. Call to Discipleship: A Literary Study of Mark's Gospel. (Good News Studies: Vol. 1). 1982. pap. 9.95 (ISBN 0-89453-273-1). M Glazier.

Stock, Eugene. Practical Truths from the Pastoral Epistles. LC 83-6113. 352p. 1983. 14.95 (ISBN 0-8254-3746-6). Kregel.

Stock, G., jt. auth. see Conybeare, Frederick C.

Stock, George, jt. ed. see Conybeare, F. C.

Stock, R. D. The Holy & the Daemonic from Sir Thomas Browne to William Blake. LC 81-11974. (Illus.). 416p. 1981. 31.50 (ISBN 0-691-06495-4). Princeton U Pr.

Stocker, Fern N. Adoniram Judson: Following God's Plan. (Guessing Bks.). (Orig.). 1986. pap. 3.95 (ISBN 0-8024-4384-2). Moody.

--Billy Sunday: Baseball Preacher. (Preteen Biography Ser.). (Orig.). 1985. pap. text ed. 3.95 (ISBN 0-8024-0442-1). Moody.

--David Livingstone: Glorifying God, Not Himself. (Guessing Bks.). (Orig.). 1986. pap. 3.95 (ISBN 0-8024-4758-9). Moody.

--Hudson Taylor: Trusting God No Matter What. (Guessing Bks.). (Orig.). 1986. pap. 3.95 (ISBN 0-8024-8575-8). Moody.

--Sammy Morris: Believing in God's Power. (Guessing Bks.). (Orig.). 1986. pap. 3.95 (ISBN 0-8024-5443-7). Moody.

Stocklin, Ulrich V. Psalteria Wessofontana. Dreves, Guido M., ed. Repr. of 1902 ed. 60.00 (ISBN 0-384-58320-2). Johnson Repr.

--Udalricus Wessofontanus. Dreves, Guido M., ed. Repr. 60.00 (ISBN 0-384-58330-X). Johnson Repr.

Stockman, Robert H. The Baha'i Faith in America: Origins, 1892-1900, Vol. 1. (Illus.). 225p. 1985. 24.95 (ISBN 0-87743-199-X). Baha'i.

Stockums, Wilhelm. The Priesthood. 242p. 1982. pap. 7.00 (ISBN 0-89555-170-5). TAN Bks Pubs.

Stoddard, Andrea. How to Bind & Loose in Spiritual Conflict. 56p. (Orig.). 1986. 3.95 (ISBN 0-936371-00-5). Spirit Faith.

Stoddard, Charles W. St. Anthony, the Wonder-Worker of Padua. 2nd ed. 1971. pap. 2.50 (ISBN 0-89555-039-3). TAN Bks Pubs.

Stoddard, Sandol. Doubleday Illustrated Children's Bible. LC 82-45340. (Illus.). 384p. 1984. deluxe ed. 22.95 (ISBN 0-385-18541-3). Doubleday.

--Doubleday Illustrated Children's Bible. LC 82-45340. (Illus.). 384p. 1983. 14.95 (ISBN 0-385-18521-9). Doubleday.

--God's Little House. (Orig.). 1984. pap. 1.95 (ISBN 0-8091-6553-8). Paulist Pr.

Stoddard, Solomon, jt. auth. see Mather, Increase.

Stoddard, Whitney S. Art & Architecture in Medieval France. (Icon Editions Ser.). Orig. Title: Monastery & Cathedral in Medieval France. (Illus.). 436p. 1972. pap. 14.95xi (ISBN 0-06-430022-6, IN-22, HarpT). Har-Row.

--The Facade of Saint-Gilles-du-Gard: Its Influence on French Sculpture. LC 72-3696. (Illus.). 341p. 1973. pap. 17.50 (ISBN 0-8195-6068-5). Wesleyan U Pr.

--Monastery & Cathedral in France: Medieval Architecture, Sculpture, Stained Glass, Manuscripts, the Art of the Church Treasuries. LC 66-23923. 412p. 1966. 35.00x (ISBN 0-8195-3071-9). Wesleyan U Pr.

Stoddart, Janet T. The New Testament in Life & Literature. 1973. 40.00 (ISBN 0-8274-0860-9). R West.

Stodder, Joseph H. Moral Perspective in Webster's Major Tragedies. Hogg, James, ed. (Jacobean Drama Studies). 164p. (Orig.). 1974. pap. 15.00 (ISBN 3-7052-0343-6, Salzburg Studies). Longwood Pub Group.

Stoeckle, Bernard, ed. The Concise Dictionary of Christian Ethics. 1979. 19.50 (ISBN 0-8245-0300-7). Crossroad NY.

Stoeckli, Walter A. Church-State & School in Switzerland & the U. S. A Study in Comparative Constitutional Law. (European University Studies: Series 2, Law: Vol. 23). 50p. 1969. 5.85 (ISBN 3-261-00081-3). P Lang Pubs.

Stoeffer, F. Ernest, tr. see Lohse, Bernhard.

Stoehr, Taylor. Nay-Saying in Concord: Emerson, Alcott & Thoreau. LC 78-25580. 179p. 1979. 21.50 (ISBN 0-208-01767-4, Archon). Shoe String.

Stoesz, Cheryl & Brandt, Gilbert. Struggle of Love. 110p. (Orig.). 1983. pap. 4.95 (ISBN 0-919797-08-3). Kindred Pr.

Stoesz, Samuel. Church & Membership Awareness. rev. ed. pap. 2.95 (ISBN 0-87509-332-9). Chr Pubns.

Stoesz, Samuel J. Church & Membership Awareness. pap. 2.95 (ISBN 0-87509-066-4); leaders guide 0.95 (ISBN 0-87509-067-2). Chr Pubns.

--Church & Missions Alive. 1975. pap. 2.50 (ISBN 0-87509-068-0); leaders guide 0.95 (ISBN 0-87509-069-9). Chr Pubns.

--Understanding My Church. rev. ed. LC 82-73214. 216p. 1983. pap. 5.95 (ISBN 0-87509-325-6); leader's guide 2.95 (ISBN 0-87509-331-0). Chr Pubns.

Stoesz, Samuel S. Life Is for Growth. 1977. pap. 2.25 (ISBN 0-87509-102-4); leaders guide 1.25 (ISBN 0-87509-169-5). Chr Pubns.

Stoever, William K. A Faire & Easie Way to Heaven: Covenant Theology & Antinomianism in Early Massachusetts. LC 77-14851. 251p. 1978. 22.00x (ISBN 0-8195-5024-8). Wesleyan U Pr.

Stoevesand, Hinrich, ed. see Barth, Karl.

Stoffel, Ernest L. The Dragon Bound: Revelation Speaks to Our Times. 120p. (Orig.). 1981. pap. 5.25 (ISBN 0-8042-0227-3). John Knox.

Stoger, Alois. The Gospel According to St. Luke, Vol. I. McKenzie, John L., ed. LC 81-605. (New Testament for Spiritual Reading Ser.). 182p. 1981. pap. 4.95 (ISBN 0-8245-0114-4). Crossroad NY.

--The Gospel According to St. Luke, Vol. II. McKenzie, John L., ed. LC 81-605. (New Testament for Spiritual Reading Ser.). 182p. 1981. pap. 4.95 (ISBN 0-8245-0115-2). Crossroad NY.

Stohlker, Friedrich. Die Kartause Buxheim, 2 Vols. Hogg, James, ed. (Analecta Cartusiana Ser.: No. 96). (Orig.). 1985. pap. 50.00 (ISBN 3-7052-0167-0, Pub. by Salzburg Studies). Longwood Pub Group.

Stokes, Allison. Ministry after Freud. (Illus.). 256p. 1985. pap. 10.95 (ISBN 0-8298-0569-9). Pilgrim NY.

Stokes, Anson & Pfeffer, Leo. Church & State in the United States. rev. ed. LC 73-15318. 660p. 1975. Repr. of 1964 ed. lib. bdg. 47.50x (ISBN 0-8371-7186-5, STCI). Greenwood.

Stokes, George G. Natural Theology. LC 77-27232. (Gifford Lectures: 1891). Repr. of 1891 ed. 30.00 (ISBN 0-404-60452-8). AMS Pr.

Stokes, Mack B. The Bible in the Wesleyan Heritage. LC 80-23636. 96p. (Orig.). 1981. pap. 4.95 (ISBN 0-687-03100-1). Abingdon.

--Major United Methodist Beliefs. rev. & enl. ed. LC 77-173955. 128p. (Orig.). 1971. pap. 2.00 (ISBN 0-687-22923-5). Abingdon.

Stokes, Margaret. Early Christian Art in Ireland. LC 70-39211. (Select Bibliographies Reprint Ser.). Repr. of 1911 ed. 23.50 (ISBN 0-8369-6813-1). Ayer Co Pubs.

Stokes, Penelope. Ruth & Daniel: God's People in an Alien Society. (Fisherman Bible Studyguide Ser.). 64p. (Orig.). 1986. pap. 2.95 (ISBN 0-87788-735-7). Shaw Pubs.

Stokes, Whitley, ed. Tripartite Life of St. Patrick, with Other Documents Related to the Saint with Translation & Indexes, 2 vols. (Rolls Ser.: No. 89). Repr. of 1888 ed. Set. 88.00 (ISBN 0-8115-1165-0). Kraus Repr.

Stokes, William L. The Genesis Answer: A Scientist's Testament of Divine Creation. 1984. pap. 14.95 (ISBN 0-317-03128-7). P-H.

Stoll, David. Fishers of Men or Founders of Empire: The Wycliffe Bible Translators in Latin America. (Illus.). 352p. 1983. 29.50x (ISBN 0-86232-111-5, Pub. by Zed Pr England); pap. 10.75 (ISBN 0-86232-112-3, Pub. by Zed Pr England). Humanities.

Stone, Barbara. The Open Moment. 400p. (Orig.). 1985. pap. 11.95 (ISBN 0-87418-021-X, 158). Coleman Pub.

Stone, Barton W. The Biography of Eld. Barton Warren Stone, Written by Himself: With Additions & Reflections. LC 79-38463. (Religion in America, Ser. 2). 476p. 1972. Repr. of 1847 ed. 27.00 (ISBN 0-405-04089-X). Ayer Co Pubs.

Stone, Charles J. Christianity Before Christ. 1977. lib. bdg. 59.95 (ISBN 0-8490-1616-9). Gordon Pr.

Stone, Clara R., ed. Library Manual for Missionaries. LC 79-116205. (Illus., Orig.). 1979. pap. 4.95 (ISBN 0-686-31591-X). Assn Chr Libs.

Stone, Doris Van see Lutzer, Erwin & Van Stone, Doris.

Stone, Eric P. Medicine Among the American Indians. LC 75-23657. (Clio Medica: 7). (Illus.). Repr. of 1932 ed. 20.00 (ISBN 0-404-58907-3). AMS Pr.

Stone, Frank A. Academies for Anatolia: A Study of the Rationale, Program & Impact of the Educational Institutions Sponsored by the American Board in Turkey: 1830-1980. (Illus.). 384p. 1984. lib. bdg. 32.75 (ISBN 0-8191-4064-3). U Pr of Amer.

Stone, Glenn C., jt. ed. see LaFontaine, Charles V.

Stone, H. Lynn. Sing a New Song. LC 81-85596. 123p. (Orig.). 1981. pap. text ed. 3.00 (ISBN 0-87148-798-5). Pathway Pr.

Stone, Hal. Embracing Heaven & Earth: A Personal Odyssey. LC 84-72044. 179p. 1985. pap. 8.95 (ISBN 0-87516-547-8). De Vorss.

Stone, Howard E., ed. see Stone, Howard W.

Stone, Howard W. The Caring Church: A Guide for Lay Pastoral Care. LC 82-48415. 116p. (Orig.). 1983. pap. 6.95 (ISBN 0-06-067695-7, RD420, HarpR). Har-Row.

--Crisis Counseling. Clinebell, Howard J., ed. LC 75-13047. (Creative Pastoral Care & Counseling Ser.). 96p. (Orig.). 1976. pap. 5.95 (ISBN 0-8006-0553-5, 1-553). Fortress.

--Using Behavioral Methods in Pastoral Counseling. Clinebell, Howard J. & Stone, Howard E., eds. LC 79-2287. (Creative Pastoral Care & Counseling Ser.). 96p. 1980. pap. 0.50 (ISBN 0-8006-0563-2, 1-563). Fortress.

Stone, Howard W., ed. see Augsburger, David W.

Stone, Howard W., ed. see Clements, William M.

Stone, Howard W., ed. see Clinebell, Charlotte H.

Stone, Howard W., ed. see Clinebell, Howard J.

Stone, Howard W., ed. see Cobb, John B., Jr.

Stone, Howard W., ed. see Colston, Lowell G.

Stone, Howard W., ed. see Irwin, Paul B.

Stone, Howard W., ed. see Leas, Speed & Kittlaus, Paul.

Stone, Howard W., ed. see Oates, Wayne E.

Stone, Howard W., ed. see Pattison, E. Mansell.

Stone, Hoyt. The Inner Quest. 1980. pap. 6.25 (ISBN 0-87148-435-8). Pathway Pr.

Stone, Hoyt E. Dare to Live Free. 132p. 1984. pap. 4.95 (ISBN 0-88207-617-5). Victor Bks.

--Using Our Gifts. 38p. (Orig.). 1981. pap. text ed. 1.00 (ISBN 0-87148-880-9). Pathway Pr.

--Yet Will I Serve Him. 1976. pap. 3.95 (ISBN 0-87148-931-7). Pathway Pr.

Stone, J. David. Creative Movement Ministry, Vol. I. Brooks, Frances, ed. (Orig.). 1986. pap. 5.95 (ISBN 0-939697-04-1). Graded Pr.

--Spiritual Growth in Youth Ministry. LC 85-12623. 213p. 1985. 12.95 (ISBN 0-931529-04-2). Group Bks.

Stone, J. David & Keefauver, Larry. Friend to Friend: How You Can Help a Friend Through a Problem. LC 83-80942. (Illus.). 80p. (Orig.). 1983. pap. 5.95 (ISBN 0-936664-11-8). Group Bks.

Stone, J. David, ed. Catching the Rainbow: A Total Concept Youth Ministry. LC 81-12705. (The Complete Youth Ministries Handbook: Vol. II). 256p. (Orig.). 1981. pap. 19.95 (ISBN 0-687-04730-7); leadership training kit, includes book, 2 cassettes & leader's guide 24.95 (ISBN 0-687-04731-5). Abingdon.

--The Complete Youth Ministries Handbook, Vol. 1. 256p. (Orig.). 1980. pap. 14.95 (ISBN 0-687-09340-6). Abingdon.

Stone, James. The Church of God of Prophecy: History & Polity. 1977. 12.95 (ISBN 0-934942-02-1). White Wing Pub.

--How to Become a Great Man of God. 1981. pap. 1.95 (ISBN 0-934942-28-5). White Wing Pub.

--How to Become a Star. (How To Ser.). 72p. (Orig.). pap. 2.50 (ISBN 0-934942-38-2). White Wing Pub.

--How to Have a Powerful Prayer Life. (How To Ser.). 73p. (Orig.). 1985. pap. 2.50 (ISBN 0-934942-50-1, 2467). White Wing Pub.

--How to Have Powerful Daily Devotions. (How To Ser.). 81p. (Orig.). 1983. pap. 2.50 (ISBN 0-934942-33-1). White Wing Pub.

--How to Understand the Church of God. 1981. pap. 1.95 (ISBN 0-934942-27-7). White Wing Pub.

--How to Worship God. 60p. (Orig.). 1982. pap. 1.95 (ISBN 0-934942-32-3). White Wing Pub.

--Introduction to Basic Theology. 123p. (Orig.). 1983. pap. text ed. 5.95 (ISBN 0-934942-39-0). White Wing Pub.

Stone, James, ed. And He Gave Some Pastors Teachers. 324p. (Orig.). 1986. pap. text ed. 9.95 (ISBN 0-934942-61-7, 4052). White Wing Pub.

Stone, Jean M. Reformation & Renaissance. LC 83-45670. (Illus.). Date not set. Repr. of 1904 ed. 76.50 (ISBN 0-404-19820-1). AMS Pr.

Stone, Jeff, et al. Growing up Catholic: An Infinitely Funny Guide for the Faithful, the Fallen & Everyone in Between. LC 83-25394. 144p. 1985. pap. 5.95 (ISBN 0-385-19240-1, Dolp). Doubleday.

Stone, Justin F. Meditation for Healing: Particular Meditations for Particular Results. rev. ed. LC 86-61661. (Illus.). 192p. 1986. pap. 11.95 (ISBN 0-937277-01-0). Satori Resources.

--T'ai Chi Chih! Joy Thru Movement. rev. ed. (Illus.). 136p. 1986. pap. 9.95 (ISBN 0-937277-02-9). Satori Resources.

Stone, Lee A. The Story of Phallicism, with Other Essays on Related Subjects by Eminent Authorities. LC 72-9682. Repr. of 1927 ed. 49.50 (ISBN 0-404-57500-5). AMS Pr.

Stone, Martha. At the Sign of Midnight: The Concheros Dance Cult of Mexico. LC 73-76303. (Illus.). 262p. 1975. pap. 7.45x (ISBN 0-8165-0507-1). U of Ariz Pr.

Stone, Merlin. When God Was a Woman. LC 77-16262. (Illus.). 265p. 1978. pap. 6.95 (ISBN 0-15-696158-X, Harv). HarBraceJ.

Stone, Michael. Signs of the Judgement, Onomastica Sacra & the Generations from Adam. LC 80-28371. (University of Pennsylvania Armenian Texts & Studies). 1981. text ed. 16.50 (ISBN 0-89130-460-6, 21-02-03); pap. 12.00 (ISBN 0-89130-461-4). Scholars Pr GA.

Stone, Michael E. Scriptures, Sects & Visions: A Profile of Judaism from Ezra to the Jewish Revolts. LC 78-54151. 160p. 1980. 11.95 (ISBN 0-8006-0641-8, 1-641). Fortress.

--The Testament of Abraham. LC 72-88770. (Society of Biblical Literature. Texts & Translation-Psuedepigrapha Ser.). 1972. pap. 8.95 (ISBN 0-89130-170-4, 060202). Scholars Pr GA.

Stone, Michael E. & Strugnell, John. The Books of Elijah, Pts. 1 & 2. LC 79-15153. (Pseudepigrapha Ser.: No. 8). 1979. 13.50 (ISBN 0-89130-315-4, 060218); pap. 8.95 o.s. (ISBN 0-89130-316-2). Scholars Pr GA.

Stone, Michael E., jt. auth. see Nickelsburg, George W.

Stone, Michael E., ed. The Armenian Version of IV Ezra. LC 78-17084. 1979. 15.00 (ISBN 0-89130-287-5); pap. 10.50 (ISBN 0-89130-255-7, 210201). Scholars Pr GA.

--Jewish Writings of the Second Temple Period: Apocrypha, Pseudipigrapha, Qumran, Sectarian Writings, Philo, Josephus. LC 83-48926. (Compendia Rerum Iudaicarum ad Novum Testamentum Ser.). 656p. 1984. 35.95 (ISBN 0-8006-0603-5, 1-603). Fortress.

Stone, Michael E., ed. see Cox, Claude E.

Stone, Naomi B., et al, eds. see Merton, Thomas.

Stone, Nathan. Names of God. 1944. pap. 3.50 (ISBN 0-8024-5854-8). Moody.

Stone, Peter C. The First Book of the Lamb. 110p. 1987. 15.00 (ISBN 0-934469-01-6). Gabriel Pr CA.

--The Second Book of the Lamb. 233p. 1987. 22.00 (ISBN 0-934469-02-4). Gabriel Pr CA.

Stone, Ronald H. Paul Tillich's Radical Social Thought. 180p. 1986. pap. text ed. 10.75 (ISBN 0-8191-5152-1). U Pr of Amer.

--Realism & Hope. 1977. pap. text ed. 11.75 (ISBN 0-8191-0128-1). U Pr of Amer.

Stone, Ronald H., ed. Reformed Faith & Politics: Essays Prepared for the Advisory Council on Church & Society of the United Presbyterian Church in the U. S. A. & the Council on Theology & Culture of the Presbyterian Church in the U. S. LC 83-10513. 210p. (Orig.). 1983. lib. bdg. 22.00 (ISBN 0-8191-3295-0); pap. text ed. 8.50 (ISBN 0-8191-3296-9). U Pr of Amer.

Stone, Sam E. The Christian Minister. LC 79-63601. (Bible College Textbooks Ser.). 256p. (Orig.). 1980. pap. text ed. 6.95 (ISBN 0-87239-348-8, 88580). Standard Pub.

--How to be an Effective Church Leader. (Illus.). 96p. 1987. pap. price not set (ISBN 0-87403-268-7, 3182). Standard Pub.

Stone, Wilfred. Religion & Art of William Hale White (Mark Rutherford) 1979. Repr. of 1954 ed. lib. bdg. 30.00 (ISBN 0-8492-8233-0). R West.

Stone, Wilfred H. Religion & Art of William Hale White. LC 79-176447. Repr. of 1954 ed. 28.00 (ISBN 0-404-51822-2). AMS Pr.

Stoneburner, Carol, jt. ed. see Stoneburner, John.

Stoneburner, John & Stoneburner, Carol, eds. The Influence of Quaker Women on American Society: Biographical Studies. (Studies in Women & Religion: Vol. 21). 496p. 1986. text ed. 69.95x (ISBN 0-88946-528-2). E Mellen.

Stonecipher, Judy. Creation: For Kids & Other People Too. LC 82-62362. (Accent Discoveries Ser.). (Illus.). 64p. (Orig.). 1982. gift book 4.50 (ISBN 0-89636-095-4). Accent Bks.

Stonehouse, Merlin. John Wesley North & the Reform Frontier. LC 65-15075. pap. 73.00 (ISBN 0-317-29473-3, 2055921). Bks Demand UMI.

Stonehouse, Ned B. Origins of the Synoptic Gospels. (Twin Brooks Ser.). 1979. pap. 5.95 (ISBN 0-8010-8180-7). Baker Bk.

--Witness of the Synoptic Gospels to Christ. (Twin Brooks Ser.). 1979. pap. 8.95 (ISBN 0-8010-8181-5). Baker Bk.

Stoner, Laura M. Jesus: A Story Color Book. (Illus.). 80p. (Orig.). 1985. pap. 3.95 wkbk. (ISBN 0-934426-07-4). Napsac Reprods.

Stookey, Lawrence H. Baptism: Christ's Act in the Church. LC 81-17590. 208p. (Orig.). 1982. pap. 9.95 (ISBN 0-687-02364-5). Abingdon.

Stoop, David. Self Talk. 160p. 1981. pap. 5.95 (ISBN 0-8007-5074-8, Power Bks). Revell.

Stoops, John A. Religious Values in Education. LC 67-25689. 1967. text ed. 4.95x (ISBN 0-8134-0950-0, 950). Inter Print Pubs.

Stopler, Pinchas. Jewish Alternatives in Love, Dating & Marriage. 100p. (Orig.). 1985. lib. bdg. 10.50 (ISBN 0-8191-4475-4); pap. text ed. 5.95 (ISBN 0-8191-4476-2). U Pr of Amer.

Stoppe, Richard L. Leadership Communication. 254p. (Orig.). 1982. pap. text ed. 5.95 (ISBN 0-87148-519-2). Pathway Pr.

Storcksburg Staehlin, Jakob Von see Von Storcksburg Staehlin, Jakob.

Storer, Morris B., ed. Humanist Ethics. LC 80-7456. 313p. 1980. 19.95 (ISBN 0-87975-117-7); pap. 13.95 (ISBN 0-87975-118-5). Prometheus Bks.

Storer, Ronald. Creation & the Character of God. 204p. 1986. 39.00X (ISBN 0-7223-1973-8, Pub. by A H Stockwell England). State Mutual BK.

Storey, John W. Texas Baptist Leadership & Social Christianity, 1900-1980. LC 85-40747. (Texas A&M Southwestern Studies: No. 5). (Illus.). 237p. 1986. 22.50x (ISBN 0-89096-251-0). Tex A&M Univ Pr.

Storey, William, jt. auth. see McNally, Thomas.

Storey, William G. Lest We Forget. 176p. (Orig.). 1985. pap. 4.95 (ISBN 0-8091-2718-0). Paulist Pr.

--Praise Him: A Prayerbook for Today's Christian. 224p. (Orig.). 1973. pap. 2.95 (ISBN 0-87793-056-2). Ave Maria.

Storey, William G., jt. ed. see McNally, Thomas.

Stormon, E. J., tr. see Salvado, Rosendo.

Storms, C. Samuel. The Grandeur of God. 80p. 1985. pap. 6.95 (ISBN 0-8010-8254-4). Baker Bk.

--Tragedy in Eden: Original Sin in the Theology of Jonathan Edwards. LC 85-17866. 328p. 1986. lib. bdg. 27.25 (ISBN 0-8191-4936-5); pap. text ed. 12.75 (ISBN 0-8191-4937-3). U Pr of Amer.

Storms, E. M. Should a Christian Be a Mason? LC 80-83598. (Orig.). 1980. pap. text ed. 2.50 (ISBN 0-932050-08-5). New Puritan.

Storms, Kathleen. Simplicity of Life As Lived in the Everyday. LC 83-16812. 322p. (Orig.). 1984. lib. bdg. 27.75 (ISBN 0-8191-3601-8); pap. text ed. 13.75 (ISBN 0-8191-3602-6). U Pr of Amer.

Storms, Samuel C. Chosen For Life. 160p. 1987. pap. 6.95 (ISBN 0-8010-8270-6). Baker Bk.

Storr, Catherine. Abraham & Isaac. LC 84-18076. (People of the Bible Ser.). (Illus.). 32p. 1985. PLB 10.65 (ISBN 0-8172-1994-3). Raintree Pubs.

--David & Goliath. LC 84-18138. (People of the Bible Ser.). (Illus.). 32p. 1985. PLB 10.65 (ISBN 0-8172-1995-1). Raintree Pubs.

--Jesus Begins His Work. LC 82-9037. (People of the Bible). (Illus.). 32p. 1982. PLB 10.65 (ISBN 0-8172-1978-1). Raintree Pubs.

--Joan of Arc. LC 84-18346. (Raintree Stories Ser.). (Illus.). 32p. 1985. PLB 14.65 (ISBN 0-8172-2111-5); pap. 9.27 (ISBN 0-8172-2254-5). Raintree Pubs.

--Moses & the Plagues. LC 84-18077. (People of the Bible Ser.). (Illus.). 32p. 1985. PLB 10.65 (ISBN 0-8172-1999-4). Raintree Pubs.

--Noah & His Ark. Storr, Catherine, retold by. LC 82-7712. (People of the Bible Ser.). (Illus.). 32p. 1982. PLB 10.65 (ISBN 0-8172-1975-7). Raintree Pubs.

--St. Peter & St. Paul. LC 84-18078. (People of the Bible Ser.). (Illus.). 32p. 1985. PLB 10.65 (ISBN 0-8172-1998-6). Raintree Pubs.

Storr, Catherine, retold by. Adam & Eve. LC 82-23060. (People of the Bible). (Illus.). 32p. 1983. PLB 10.65 (ISBN 0-8172-1981-1). Raintree Pubs.

Storr, Catherine, as told by. Jesus & John the Baptist. (People of the Bible Ser.). (Illus.). 32p. 1985. PLB 10.65 (ISBN 0-8172-2037-2). Raintree Pubs.

--Jesus the Healer. (People of the Bible Ser.). (Illus.). 32p. 1985. PLB 10.65 (ISBN 0-8172-2041-0). Raintree Pubs.

Storr, Catherine, retold by. Jonah & the Whale. LC 82-23023. (People of the Bible). (Illus.). 32p. 1983. PLB 10.65 (ISBN 0-8172-1984-6). Raintree Pubs.

--Joseph & His Brothers. LC 82-9087. (People of the Bible). (Illus.). 32p. 1982. PLB 10.65 (ISBN 0-8172-1976-5). Raintree Pubs.

Storr, Catherine, as told by. Joseph & the Famine. (People of the Bible Ser.). (Illus.). 32p. 1985. PLB 10.65 (ISBN 0-8172-2038-0). Raintree Pubs.

--King David. (People of the Bible Ser.). (Illus.). 32p. 1985. PLB 10.65 (ISBN 0-8172-2042-9). Raintree Pubs.

Storr, Catherine, retold by. Miracles by the Sea. LC 82-23022. (People of the Bible). (Illus.). 32p. 1983. PLB 10.65 (ISBN 0-8172-1983-8). Raintree Pubs.

Storr, Catherine, ed. Moses in the Wilderness. (People of the Bible Ser.). (Illus.). 32p. 1985. PLB 10.65 (ISBN 0-8172-2039-9). Raintree Pubs.

Storr, Catherine, retold by. The Prodigal Son. LC 82-23011. (People of the Bible). (Illus.). 32p. 1983. PLB 10.65 (ISBN 0-8172-1982-X). Raintree Pubs.

Storr, Catherine, as told by. Ruth's Story. (Peoples of the Bible Ser.). (Illus.). 32p. 1985. PLB 10.65 (ISBN 0-8172-2043-7). Raintree Pubs.

--Samson & Delilah. (People of the Bible). (Illus.). 32p. 1985. PLB 10.65 (ISBN 0-8172-2044-5). Raintree Pubs.

--The Trials of Daniel. (People of the Bible Ser.). (Illus.). 32p. 1985. PLB 10.65 (ISBN 0-8172-2040-2). Raintree Pubs.

Storrs, Richard S. Bernard of Clairvaux: The Times, the Man & His Work. 598p. 1981. Repr. of 1893 ed. lib. bdg. 65.00 (ISBN 0-8495-4974-4). Arden Lib.

Stortz, Diane. Zaccheus Meets Jesus. (Happy Day Bible Stories Bks.). (Illus.). 24p. 1984. 1.59 (ISBN 0-87239-766-1, 3726). Standard Pub.

Story, Bettie Wilson see Wilson Story, Bettie.

Story, Cullen I K. Greek to Me: An Easy Way to Learn New Testament Greek Through Memory Visualization. LC 79-1769. (Illus.). 1979. pap. text ed. 12.45 (ISBN 0-06-067705-8, RD 307, HarpR). Har-Row.

Story, G. M., jt. ed. see Halpert, Herbert.

Story, Grace C. Footprints on the Sands of China. pap. 2.25 (ISBN 0-686-13722-1). Crusade Pubs.

Story, Ronald. Guardian of the Universe? 1980. 8.95 (ISBN 0-312-35216-6). St Martin.

Stott, Clifford L. Search for Sanctuary: Brigham Young & the White Mountain Expedition. (American West Ser.: Vol. 19). (Illus.). 272p. 1984. 19.95 (ISBN 0-87480-237-7). U of Utah Pr.

Stott, Doug, tr. see Westermann, Claus.

Stott, Douglas W., tr. see Gerstenberger, Erhard S. & Schrage, Wolfgang.

Stott, Douglas W., tr. see Seybold, Klaus & Mueller, Ulrich B.

Stott, J. R., ed. see Lucas, R. J.

Stott, John. Involvement, Vol. I: Being a Responsible Christian in a Non-Christian Society. (Crucial Questions Ser.). 224p. 1985. 13.95 (ISBN 0-8007-1418-0). Revell.

--One People. Rev. ed. 128p. 1982. pap. 4.95 (ISBN 0-8007-5099-3, Power Bks). Revell.

Stott, John & Miller, Nick, eds. Crime & the Responsible Community. LC 81-110661. (London Lectures in Contemporary Christianity: 1979). pap. 47.80 (ISBN 0-317-09298-7, 2019339). Bks Demand UMI.

Stott, John R. The Authentic Jesus. LC 85-23831. 96p. 1986. pap. 2.95 (ISBN 0-87784-619-7). Inter-Varsity.

--The Authority of the Bible. pap. 0.75 (ISBN 0-87784-147-0). Inter-Varsity.

--Baptism & Fullness: The Work of the Holy Spirit Today. LC 76-21457. 1976. pap. 2.95 (ISBN 0-87784-648-0). Inter-Varsity.

--Basic Christianity. 1957. pap. 2.95 (ISBN 0-8028-1189-2). Eerdmans.

--Basic Christianity. LC 58-13513. (Orig.). pap. 3.95 (ISBN 0-87784-690-1). Inter-Varsity.

--Basic Introduction to the New Testament. pap. 5.95 (ISBN 0-8028-1190-6). Eerdmans.

--Becoming a Christian. pap. 0.75 (ISBN 0-87784-100-4). Inter-Varsity.

--Being a Christian. pap. 0.75 (ISBN 0-87784-101-2). Inter-Varsity.

--Bible Book for Today. Chan, Silas, tr. (Chinese.). 1985. pap. write for info. (ISBN 0-941598-23-3). Living Spring Pubns.

--Christian Mission in the Modern World. LC 75-21455. 128p. (Orig.). 1976. pap. 5.95 (ISBN 0-87784-485-2). Inter-Varsity.

--The Cross of Christ. LC 86-21293. 480p. (Orig.). 1986. Repr. 14.95 (ISBN 0-87784-998-6). Inter-Varsity.

--Epistles of John. (Tyndale Bible Commentaries). Orig. Title: Johannine Epistles. 1964. pap. 4.95 (ISBN 0-8028-1418-2). Eerdmans.

--God's Book for God's People. LC 82-21203. 96p. 1982. pap. 2.95 (ISBN 0-87784-396-1). Inter-Varsity.

--Men Made New: An Exposition of Romans 5-8. 108p. 1984. pap. 4.95 (ISBN 0-8010-8244-7). Baker Bk.

--The Message of Ephesians. Motyer, J. A., ed. (The Bible Speaks Today Ser.). 1980. pap. text ed. 7.95 (ISBN 0-87784-287-6). Inter-Varsity.

--The Message of Galatians. pap. 6.95 (ISBN 0-87784-288-4). Inter-Varsity.

--The Message of Second Timothy. LC 73-75890. (Bible Speaks Today Ser.). 144p. 1973. text ed. 5.95 (ISBN 0-87784-295-7). Inter-Varsity.

--The Message of the Semon on the Mount. LC 84-27763. (Bible Speaks Today Ser.). 1978. pap. 6.95 (ISBN 0-87784-296-5). Inter-Varsity.

--One People. LC 84-72468. 127p. pap. 4.95 (ISBN 0-87509-324-8); leader's guide 2.95 (ISBN 0-87509-358-2). Chr Pubns.

--Preacher's Portrait in the New Testament. 1964. pap. 4.95 (ISBN 0-8028-1191-4). Eerdmans.

--Sed Llenos del Espiritu Santo. rev. ed. Cook, David A., tr. from Eng. LC 77-162. Tr. of Be Filled with the Holy Spirit. (Span.). 112p. 1977. pap. 3.50 (ISBN 0-89922-084-3). Edit Caribe.

--The Sermon on the Mount. (LifeGuide Bible Studies). 64p. 1987. pap. 2.95. Inter-Varsity.

--Understanding the Bible. rev. ed. 256p. 1982. pap. 6.95 (ISBN 0-310-41451-2, 12610P). Zondervan.

--Understanding the Bible. 2nd ed. 192p. 1985. pap. 6.95 (ISBN 0-310-41431-8). Zondervan.

--Your Mind Matters. LC 72-94672. 64p. 1973. pap. 3.50 (ISBN 0-87784-441-0). Inter-Varsity.

Stott, John R. & Coote, Robert. Down to Earth: Studies in Christianity & Culture. 2nd ed. (Orig.). 1980. pap. 9.95 (ISBN 0-8028-1827-7). Eerdmans.

Stott, John R., ed. The Year Two Thousand. LC 83-12871. 179p. 1983. pap. 7.95 (ISBN 0-87784-845-9). Inter-Varsity.

Stott, John R. & Meeking, Basil, eds. The Evangelical-Roman Catholic Dialogue on Mission, 1977-1984. 80p. (Orig.). 1986. pap. 4.95 (ISBN 0-8028-0184-6). Eerdmans.

Stott, John R., ed. see Baldwin, Joyce G.

Stott, John R., ed. see Brown, Raymond.

Stott, John R., ed. see Kidner, Derek.

Stott, John R., ed. see Motyer, Alec.

Stott, John R., ed. see Prior, David.

Stott, John R., ed. see Wilcock, Michael.

Stoudemire, Sterling A., tr. see De Cordoba, Pedro.

Stoudt, John J., tr. see Boehme, Jacob.

Stough, Richard H. Bequests, Endowments, & Special Gifts. (Orig.). 1981. pap. 1.75 (ISBN 0-937172-27-8). JLJ Pubs.

--Dial-A-Prayer. (Orig.). 1983. pap. 4.50 (ISBN 0-937172-44-8). JLJ Pubs.

Stoughton, John. History of Religion in England, 8 vols. 1977. lib. bdg. 800.00 (ISBN 0-8490-1984-2). Gordon Pr.

Stout, Harry S. The New England Soul: Preaching & Religious Culture in Colonial New England. LC 85-29853. 352p. 1986. 29.95x (ISBN 0-19-503958-0). Oxford U Pr.

Stout, Jeffrey. Flight from Authority: Religion, Morality & the Quest for Autonomy. LC 81-2340. (Revisions Ser.: Vol. 1). 307p. 1987. pap. text ed. 12.95x (ISBN 0-268-00971-6, Dist. by Har-Row). U of Notre Dame Pr.

Stout, John L. What the Bible Does Not Say. LC 80-84340. (Illus.). 208p. 1981. 10.95 (ISBN 0-8187-0042-4). Harlo Pr.

Stout, Martha G., jt. auth. see Ward, Patricia A.

Stoutzenberger, Joseph. Celebrating Sacraments. Nagel, Stephan, ed. (Illus.). 240p. (Orig.). 1984. pap. text ed. 8.25x (ISBN 0-88489-159-3); teaching manual 12.00 (ISBN 0-88489-160-7); spiritmasters 18.95. St Mary's.

--The Christian Call to Justice & Peace. (Illus.). 250p. (Orig.). 1987. pap. text ed. 11.00 (ISBN 0-88489-180-1). St Mary's.

Stover, Ruby E. Life's Golden Gleanings. 94p. pap. 1.00 (ISBN 0-686-29127-1). Faith Pub Hse.

Stowe, David M. When Faith Meets Faith. rev. ed. 1972. pap. 2.95 (ISBN 0-377-37201-3). Friend Pr.

Stowe, Faye C. The Whole Woman: Fashioned in His Image. 135p. 1984. pap. 4.95 (ISBN 0-8341-0913-1). Beacon Hill.

Stowe, W. McFerrin. If I Were a Pastor. 112p. (Orig.). 1983. pap. 6.50 (ISBN 0-687-18655-2). Abingdon.

Stowell, Gordon. Jesus Alimenta. De Martinez, Violeta S., tr. from Span. (Libros Pescaditos Sobre Jesus). Tr. of Jesus Feeds the People. (Illus.). 24p. pap. 0.60 (ISBN 0-311-38614-8). Casa Bautista.

--Jesus Ama. De Martinez, Violeta S., tr. from Span. (Libros Pescaditos Sobre Jesus). Tr. of Jesus Loves. (Illus.). 24p. 1984. pap. 0.60 (ISBN 0-311-38611-3). Casa Bautista.

--Jesus & the Fisherman. (Little Fish Bks.: Bk. II). (Illus.). 14p. 1982. pap. 0.59 (ISBN 0-8307-0831-6, 5608150). Regal.

--Jesus Cuenta. De Martinez, Violeta S., tr. from Span. (Libros Pescaditos Sobre Jesus). Tr. of Jesus Tells Stories. (Illus.). 24p. 1984. pap. 0.60 (ISBN 0-311-38613-X). Casa Bautista.

--Jesus Ensena. De Martinez, Violeta S., tr. from Span. (Libros Pescaditos Sobre Jesus). Tr. of Jesus Teaches. (Illus.). 24p. 1984. pap. 0.60 (ISBN 0-311-38609-1). Casa Bautista.

--Jesus Feeds the People. (Little Fish Bks.: Bk. II). (Illus.). 14p. 1982. pap. 0.59 (ISBN 0-8307-0832-4, 5608167). Regal.

--Jesus Heals. (Little Fish Bks.: Bk. II). (Illus.). 14p. 1982. pap. 0.59 (ISBN 0-8307-0828-6, 5608122). Regal.

--Jesus Is Born. (Little Fish Bks.: Bk. II). (Illus.). 14p. 1982. pap. 0.59 (ISBN 0-8307-0827-8, 5608119). Regal.

--Jesus Lives. (Little Fish Bks.: Bk. II). (Illus.). 14p. 1982. pap. 0.59 (ISBN 0-8307-0834-0, 5608181). Regal.

--Jesus Llama. De Martinez, Violeta S., tr. from Span. (Libros Pescaditos Sobre Jesus). Tr. of Jesus & the Fisherman. (Illus.). 24p. 1984. pap. 0.60 (ISBN 0-311-38612-1). Casa Bautista.

--Jesus Loves. (Little Fish Bks.: Bk. II). 14p. 1982. pap. 0.59 (ISBN 0-8307-0830-8, 5608145). Regal.

--Jesus Nace. De Martinez, Violeta S., tr. from Span. (Libros Pescaditos Sobre Jesus). Tr. of Jesus Is Born. (Illus.). 24p. 1984. pap. 0.60 (ISBN 0-311-38608-3). Casa Bautista.

--Jesus Sana. De Martinez, Violeta S., tr. from Eng. (Libros Pescaditos Sobre Jesus). Tr. of Jesus Heals. (Illus.). 24p. 1984. pap. 0.60 (ISBN 0-311-38610-5). Casa Bautista.

--Jesus Teaches. (Little Fish Bks.: Bk. II). (Illus.). 14p. 1982. pap. 0.59 (ISBN 0-8307-0829-4, 5608138). Regal.

--Jesus Tells Some Stories. (Little Fish Bks.: Bk. II). (Illus.). 14p. 1982. pap. 0.59 (ISBN 0-8307-0833-2, 5608176). Regal.

--Jesus Vive. De Martinez, Violeta S., tr. from Span. (Libros Pescaditos Sobre Jesus). Tr. of Jesus Lives. (Illus.). 24p. 1984. pap. 0.60 (ISBN 0-311-38615-6). Casa Bautista.

--Please God. (Little Fish Books About You & Me: III). 14p. 1984. mini-bk 0.59 (ISBN 0-8307-0954-1, 5608381). Regal.

--Thank You God. (Little Fish Books About You & Me Ser.: III). 14p. 1984. mini-bk 0.59 (ISBN 0-8307-0960-6, 5608436). Regal.

Stowell, Joseph. Tongue in Check. 132p. pap. 4.95 (ISBN 0-88207-293-5). Victor Bks.

Stowell, Joseph M. Fan the Flame: Living Out Your First Love for Christ. (Orig.). 1986. pap. 5.95 (ISBN 0-8024-2528-3). Moody.

--Kingdom Conflict. 156p. 1984. pap. 5.95 (ISBN 0-89693-376-8). Victor Bks.

--Through the Fire. 156p. 1985. pap. 5.95 (ISBN 0-89693-601-5). Victor Bks.

Stowers, Stanley K. Letter Writing in Greco-Roman Antiquity. LC 86-9082. (Library of Early Christianity: Vol. 5). 192p. 1986. 18.95 (ISBN 0-664-21909-8). Westminster.

Straalen, Alice van see Van Straalen, Alice.

Strachan, James. Early Bible Illustrations: A Short Study Based on Some Fifteenth & Early Sixteenth Century Printed Texts. LC 58-571. pap. 44.80 (ISBN 0-317-10120-X, 2050748). Bks Demand UMI.

Strachen, Richard, tr. see Dechanet, Jean M.

Strachey, James, ed. see Freud, Sigmund.

Strachey, James, tr. see Freud, Sigmund.

Strachey, Lytton. Eminent Victorians. 354p. 1969. pap. 6.95 (ISBN 0-15-628697-1, Harv). HarBraceJ.

Strachey, Ray, ed. & intro. by see Smith, Hannah.

Strack, Hermann L. Introduction to the Talmud & Midrash. LC 59-7191. (Temple Books). 1969. pap. text ed. 8.95x (ISBN 0-689-70189-6, T10). Atheneum.

--Petrograd Codex of the Hebrew Bible: The Latter Prophets, Prophetarum Posteriorum. rev. ed. (Library of Biblical Studies Ser). 1970. 50.00x (ISBN 0-87068-111-7). Ktav.

Strahan, James. Hebrew Ideals in Genesis (Genesis 11-50) LC 82-7785. 360p. 1982. 14.95 (ISBN 0-8254-3729-6). Kregel.

Strahan, Loretta. Beside the Still Waters. Hughes, Jeff, ed. 108p. (Orig.). 1986. pap. 3.45 (ISBN 0-910653-18-6, 8101T). Archival Servs.

Strain, Charles R., jt. auth. see McCann, Dennis P.

Strait, C. Neil. Beacon Small-Group Bible Studies, Ezra-Nehemiah: God's Faithfulness & Man's Obedience. Wolf, Earl C., ed. 96p. (Orig.). 1985. pap. 2.50 (ISBN 0-8341-0927-1). Beacon Hill.

--The Conquering Christ. 56p. 1975. pap. 1.25 (ISBN 0-8341-0273-0). Beacon Hill.

Strakhovsky, Florence, ed. see Schlesinger, Benjamin.

Strand, Robert J. Evangelism: The Unfinished Task. LC 81-80303. (Workers Training Ser.). 128p. (Orig.). 1981. pap. 2.25 (ISBN 0-88243-513-2, 02-0513). Gospel Pub.

Strandness, T. B. Samuel Sewall: A Puritan Portrait. viii, 250p. 1967. 7.50 (ISBN 0-87013-119-2). Mich St U Pr.

Strang, Stephen, et al, eds. Solving the Ministry's Toughest Problems, 2 vols. 432p. 1984. Vol. I. 24.95 (ISBN 0-930525-00-0); Vol. II. write for info. (ISBN 0-930525-01-9). Strang Comms Co.

Strange, James F., jt. auth. see Frank, Harry T.

Strange, John O., jt. auth. see Bailey, D. Waylon.

Strange, John O., jt. auth. see Cothen, Joe H.

Strange, Marcian. Amos, Osee & Michae. (Bible Ser.). pap. 1.00 (ISBN 0-8091-5002-6). Paulist Pr.

Strange, Roderick. The Catholic Faith. 192p. 1986. 24.95 (ISBN 0-19-826685-5); pap. 8.95 (ISBN 0-19-283051-1). Oxford U Pr.

--Newman & the Gospel of Christ. (Oxford Theological Monographs). 1981. 39.00x (ISBN 0-19-826718-5). Oxford U Pr.

Stranges, Frank E. The Authority of Jesus Christ. 12p. 1985. pap. text ed. 2.00 (ISBN 0-933470-08-8). Intl Evang.

--Heaven. 16p. (Orig.). 1985. pap. text ed. 2.00 (ISBN 0-933470-03-7). Intl Evang.

--Mystery Man of Darkness No. 666. 16p. 1985. pap. text ed. 2.00 (ISBN 0-933470-05-3). Intl Evang.

--Pre-Eternal Rest. 12p. 1985. pap. text ed. 2.00 (ISBN 0-933470-07-X). Intl Evang.

--The Secret Place of the Most High. 12p. 1985. pap. text ed. 2.00 (ISBN 0-933470-09-6). Intl Evang.

--The Star of Bethlehem. 20p. (Orig.). 1985. pap. text ed. 2.00 (ISBN 0-933470-06-1). Intl Evang.

--The White Planet. 24p. 1985. pap. text ed. 2.00 (ISBN 0-933470-04-5). Intl Evang.

Stranks, C. J. The Life & Writings of Jeremy Taylor. LC 73-11259. 1973. lib. bdg. 35.00 (ISBN 0-8414-7595-4). Folcroft.

Stranskey, Thomas F., jt. auth. see Anderson, Gerald H.

Stransky, Thomas & Anderson, Gerald H., eds. Mission Trends: Liberation Theologies, No. 4. LC 78-70827. (Mission Trend Ser.). 304p. 1979. pap. 4.95 (ISBN 0-8091-2185-9). Paulist Pr.

Stransky, Thomas, jt. ed. see Anderson, Gerald.

Stransky, Thomas, ed. see Vatican Council Two.

Stransky, Thomas F., jt. auth. see Henry, Patrick.

Stransky, Thomas F. & Sheerin, John B., eds. Doing the Truth in Charity: Statements of Popes Paul VI, John Paul I, John Paul II & the Secretariat for Promoting Christian Unity. LC 81-85384. 400p. (Orig.). 1982. 12.95 (ISBN 0-8091-2398-3). Paulist Pr.

Stransky, Thomas F., jt. ed. see Anderson, Gerald H.

Strasheim, Linda & Bence, Evelyn. Something Beautiful. 160p. (Orig.). 1985. pap. 5.95 (ISBN 0-310-29391-X, 10467P). Zondervan.

Strassfeld, Michael. Jewish Holidays. LC 84-48196. (Illus.). 1985. 24.45i (ISBN 0-06-015406-3, HarpT); pap. 15.95 (ISBN 0-06-091225-1). Har-Row.

--A Shabbat Haggadah for Celebration & Study. LC 80-83430. 124p. 1980. pap. 5.50 (ISBN 0-87495-025-2). Am Jewish Comm.

Strassfeld, Michael & Strassfeld, Sharon, eds. The Second Jewish Catalog: Sources & Resources. LC 73-11759. (Illus.). 464p. 1976. 8.95 (ISBN 0-8276-0084-4, 391). Jewish Pubns.

Strassfeld, Michael, jt. ed. see Strassfeld, Sharon.

Strassfeld, Michael, et alcompiled by. The Jewish Catalog: A Do-It Yourself Kit. LC 73-11759. (Illus.). 1973. pap. 8.95 (ISBN 0-8276-0042-9, 338). Jewish Pubns.

Strassfeld, Sharon & Kurzweil, Arthur. Behold a Great Image. LC 78-1168. (Illus.). 224p. 1978. 22.95 (ISBN 0-8276-0105-0, 417). Jewish Pubns.

Strassfeld, Sharon & Strassfeld, Michael, eds. Third Jewish Catalog: Creating Community. LC 80-19818. (Illus.). 416p. 1980. 9.95 (ISBN 0-8276-0183-2, 466). Jewish Pubns.

Strassfeld, Sharon, jt. ed. see Strassfeld, Michael.

Stratford, Philip. Faith & Fiction: Creative Process in Greene & Mauriac. 1964. pap. 9.95x (ISBN 0-268-00379-3). U of Notre Dame Pr.

Stratman, Carl J. Bibliography of Medieval Drama. LC 78-163141. 1047p. 1972. 100.00 (ISBN 0-8044-3272-4). Ungar.

Stratman, Chrysostemos. To the Orthodox Christians of the U. S. A. 6p. 1949. pap. 1.00 (ISBN 0-317-30430-5). Holy Trinity.

Stratman, Chrysostomos H. & Makrakis, Apostolos. The Roman Rite in Orthodoxy, Part I: Additional Testimonies, Pt. II. 62p. 1957. pap. 1.00x (ISBN 0-938366-38-6). Orthodox Chr.

Stratman, Gary D. Pastoral Preaching: Timeless Truth for Changing Needs. 112p. (Orig.). 1983. pap. 8.75 (ISBN 0-687-30139-4). Abingdon.

Straub, Gerald T. Salvation for Sale: An Insider's View of Pat Robertson's Ministry. (Illus.). 300p. 1986. 18.95 (ISBN 0-87975-357-9). Prometheus Bks.

Strauch, Alexander. Biblical Eldership: A Study Guide. 100p. (Orig.). 1987. pap. price not set (ISBN 0-936083-01-8). Lewis Roth.

--Biblical Eldership: An Urgent Call to Restore Biblical Church Leadership. 425p. 1986. 12.95 (ISBN 0-936083-00-X). Lewis-Roth.

Straughn, Harold. Five Divorces of a Healthy Marriage. Lambert, Herbert, ed. LC 85-29923. 160p. (Orig.). 1986. pap. 10.95 (ISBN 0-8272-2318-8). CBP.

Straughn, R. A. Meditation Techniques of the Kabalists, Vedantins & Taoists. (Illus.). 1976. pap. 6.95 (ISBN 0-917650-02-6). Maat Pub.

--The Realization of Neter Nu: A Kabalistical Guide to the Realization of Self. 1975. pap. 8.00 (ISBN 0-917650-01-8). Maat Pub.

Straus, Carrie. The Catholic Church. 288p. 1987. 14.95 (ISBN 0-87052-312-0). Hippocrene Bks.

Straus, Oscar S. Roger Williams, the Pioneer of Religious Liberty. facs. ed. LC 76-137385. (Select Bibliographies Reprint Ser). 1936. 20.00 (ISBN 0-8369-5586-2). Ayer Co Pubs.

Strauss. The Rosenbaums of Zell. cancelled (ISBN 0-685-48598-6). Feldheim.

Strauss, C. T. Buddha & His Doctrine. LC 70-102584. 1970. Repr. of 1923 ed. 16.50x (ISBN 0-8046-0744-3, Pub. by Kennikat). Assoc Faculty Pr.

Strauss, David F. Life of Jesus Critically Examined, 2 Vols. Evans, Marian, tr. LC 74-107193. 1970. Repr. of 1860 ed. Set. 59.00x (ISBN 0-403-00238-9). Scholarly.

Strauss, Gerald. Law, Resistance & the State: The Opposition to Roman Law in Reformation Germany. LC 85-43315. 312p. 1986. text ed. 34.50 (ISBN 0-691-05469-X). Princeton U Pr.

--Luther's House of Learning: Indoctrination of the Young in the German Reformation. LC 77-18705. pap. 101.30 (ISBN 0-317-20464-5, 2023003). Bks Demand UMI.

Strauss, Herbert, ed. Jewish Immigrants of the Nazi Period in the U. S. A, 6 Vols. Set. lib. bdg. 130.00 (ISBN 0-317-11838-2); Vol. 1. 35.00 (ISBN 3-598-08006-9). Vol. 2 (ISBN 3-598-08007-7). Vol. 3, Pt. 1 (ISBN 3-598-08008-5). Vol. 3, Pt. 2 (ISBN 3-598-08013-1). K G Saur.

Strauss, Herbert A., ed. Jewish Immigrants of the Nazi Period in the U. S. A. Essays on the History, Persecution, & Emigration of the German Jews. (Jewish Immigrants of the Nazi Period in the U. S. A. Ser.: Vol. 6). 430p. 1987. lib. bdg. 74.00 (ISBN 3-598-08011-5). K G Saur.

Strauss, Herbert A. & Kampe, Norbert, eds. Jewish Immigrants of the Nazi Period in the U. S. A. The Expulsion & Migration of German Jews 1933-45 - Annotated Sources. (Jewish Immigrants of the Nazi Period in the U. S. A. Ser.: Vol. 4). 225p. 1988. lib. bdg. 50.00 (ISBN 3-598-08009-3). K G Saur.

Strauss, Herbert A. & Rogrbaugh, Dennis, eds. Jewish Immigrants of the Nazi Period in the U. S. A. An Oral History Record. (Jewish Immigrants of the Nazi Period in the U. S. A. Ser.: Vol. 5). 308p. 1986. lib. bdg. 60.00 (ISBN 3-598-08010-7). K G Saur.

Strauss, James D. Job Shattering of Silence. LC 77-155412. (The Bible Study Textbook Ser.). (Illus.). 1976. 15.90 (ISBN 0-89900-015-0). College Pr Pub.

--Revelation - the Seer, the Saviour, & the Saved. rev. ed. (The Bible Study Textbook Ser.). (Illus.). 1972. 15.90 (ISBN 0-89900-048-7). College Pr Pub.

Strauss, Lehman. Certainties for Today. 1956. pap. 3.25 (ISBN 0-87213-810-0). Loizeaux.

--Daniel: Prophecies. LC 70-85293. Orig. Title: Prophecies of Daniel. 1969. 9.95 (ISBN 0-87213-812-7). Loizeaux.

--Demons, Yes - but Thank God for Good Angels. LC 75-38804. 1976. pap. 2.95 (ISBN 0-87213-831-3). Loizeaux.

--Epistles of John. LC 62-17542. 1962. pap. 3.95 (ISBN 0-87213-821-6). Loizeaux.

--First Person. LC 67-20931. 1967. 7.95 (ISBN 0-87213-815-1). Loizeaux.

--Galatians & Ephesians. 1957. 8.95 (ISBN 0-87213-817-8). Loizeaux.

--In God's Waiting Room. rev. ed. 1985. pap. text ed. 4.95 (ISBN 0-8024-3827-X). Moody.

--James. 1956. 8.95 (ISBN 0-87213-818-6). Loizeaux.

--Listen! Our Dying Savior Speaks. Orig. Title: The Day God Died. 113p. 1987. pap. 5.95 (ISBN 0-87213-828-3). Loizeaux.

--Philippians: Studies. 1959. 7.50 (ISBN 0-87213-823-2). Loizeaux.

--Prophetic Mysteries Revealed: The Prophetic Significance of the Parables of Matthew 13 & the Letters of Revelation 2-3. LC 80-17540. 256p. 1980. 9.95 (ISBN 0-87213-832-1). Loizeaux.

--Revelation. LC 64-8641. Orig. Title: Book of the Revelation. 9.95 (ISBN 0-87213-825-9). Loizeaux.

--Second Person. 1951. 7.95 (ISBN 0-87213-826-7). Loizeaux.

--Sense & Nonsense about Prayer. 128p. 1974. 4.95 (ISBN 0-8024-7700-3). Moody.

--Sense & Nonsense about Prayer. 1976. pap. 3.95 (ISBN 0-8024-7702-X). Moody.

--Third Person. 1954. 7.95 (ISBN 0-87213-827-5). Loizeaux.

--We Live Forever. 1947. pap. 5.95 (ISBN 0-87213-830-5). Loizeaux.

--When Loved Ones Are Taken in Death. pap. 2.50 (ISBN 0-310-33102-1, 6340P). Zondervan.

Strauss, Leo. Persecution & the Art of Writing. LC 73-1407. 204p. 1973. Repr. of 1952 ed. lib. bdg. 19.75 (ISBN 0-8371-6801-5, STPA). Greenwood.

--Philosophy & Law: Essays Toward the Understanding of Maimonides His Predecessors. Baumann, Fred, tr. from Ger. Tr. of Philosophie und Gesetz. 120p. 1987. 18.95 (ISBN 0-8276-0273-1). Jewish Pubns.

--Spinoza's Critique of Religion. Sinclair, E. M., tr. from Ger. LC 65-10948. 364p. 1982. pap. 8.50 (ISBN 0-8052-0704-X). Schocken.

Strauss, Richard. Famous Couples of the Bible. 1982. pap. 4.95 (ISBN 0-8423-0836-9); pap. 2.95 leader's guide (ISBN 0-8423-0837-7). Tyndale.

--How to Really Know the Will of God. 1982. pap. 5.95 (ISBN 0-8423-1537-3); 2.95 (ISBN 0-8423-1538-1). Tyndale.

--Win the Battle for Your Mind. 132p. 1986. pap. 5.95 (ISBN 0-87213-835-6). Loizeaux.

Strauss, Richard L. Famous Couples of the Bible. Chen, Ruth T., tr. (Chinese.). 1985. pap. write for info. (ISBN 0-941598-29-2). Living Spring Pubns.

--The Joy of Knowing God. 305p. 1984. pap. 8.95 (ISBN 0-87213-834-8). Loizeaux.

--Marriage Is for Love. 1982. pap. 4.95 (ISBN 0-8423-4178-1); leader's guide 2.95 (ISBN 0-8423-4179-X). Tyndale.

Strauss, Ruby, jt. auth. see Kurzweil, Arthur.

Strauss, Ruby G., ed. If Grandma Had Wheels: Jewish Folk Sayings. LC 85-7466. (Illus.). 64p. 1985. 8.95 (ISBN 0-689-31156-7, Childrens Bk). Macmillan.

Strauss, Walter, ed. Signs of Life: Jews from Wuerttemberg-Reports for the Period after 1933 in Letters & Descriptions. 25.00x. Ktav.

Stravinskas, Peter. Essentials of Religious Life Today. (Orig.). pap. price not set (ISBN 0-913382-34-5, 101-34). Prow Bks-Franciscan.

Stravinskas, Peter M. The Catholic Church & the Bible. LC 87-60217. 120p. (Orig.). 1987. pap. 5.95 (ISBN 0-87973-515-5). Our Sunday Visitor.

--The Catholic Response. LC 84-62435. 208p. (Orig.). 1985. pap. 5.95 (ISBN 0-87973-594-5, 594). Our Sunday Visitor.

--Prayer Book of the Bible: Reflection on the Old Testament. LC 83-63171. 160p. 1984. pap. 5.95 (ISBN 0-87973-606-2, 606). Our Sunday Visitor.

Stravinskas, Peter M. & McBain, Robert A. The Church After the Council: A Primer for Adults. LC 75-4720. 113p. (Orig.). 1975. pap. 2.95 (ISBN 0-8189-0316-3). Alba.

Strawson, P. F. Individuals: An Essay in Descriptive Metaphysics. 1964. pap. 12.95x (ISBN 0-416-68310-X, NO. 2535). Methuen Inc.

Strayer, Joseph R. Administration of Normandy Under Saint Louis. LC 72-171362. Repr. of 1932 ed. 16.00 (ISBN 0-404-06297-0). AMS Pr.

Strean, Herbert S., jt. auth. see Freeman, Lucy C.

Streaty, Anne, jt. auth. see Wimberly, Edward P.

Streebing, Cecilian. Devout Humanism as a Style. LC 70-128930. (Catholic University. Romance Literature: No. 50). Repr. of 1954 ed. 23.80 (ISBN 0-404-50350-0). AMS Pr.

Street, George E. Gothic Architecture in Spain, 2 Vols. King, Georgiana G., ed. LC 68-56490. (Illus.). 1968. Repr. of 1914 ed. Set. 55.00 (ISBN 0-405-09008-0); 27.50 ea. Vol. 1 (ISBN 0-405-09009-9). Vol. 2 (ISBN 0-405-09010-2). Ayer Co Pubs.

Streeter, B. H. The Buddha & the Christ. 59.95 (ISBN 0-87968-799-1). Gordon Pr.

--The Primitive Church: Studies in the Origin of the Christian Ministry. 1977. lib. bdg. 59.95 (ISBN 0-8490-2473-0). Gordon Pr.

Streeter, Burnett H. Buddha & the Christ. LC 72-102585. 1970. Repr. of 1932 ed. 29.50x (ISBN 0-8046-0745-1, Pub. by Kennikat). Assoc Faculty Pr.

--Foundations: A Statement of Christian Belief in Terms of Modern Thought by 70 Oxford Men. facs. ed. (Essay Index Reprint Ser). 1912. 20.50 (ISBN 0-8369-2189-5). Ayer Co Pubs.

Streeter, Burnett H., et al. Immortality: An Essay in Discovery, Co-Ordinating Scientific, Physical, & Biblical Research. 1977. Repr. of 1917 ed. lib. bdg. 27.50 (ISBN 0-8492-2418-7). R West.

Streeter, Carole S. Finding Your Place after Divorce: How Women Can Find Healing. 144p. 1986. pap. 5.95 (ISBN 0-310-41691-4, 10816P). Zondervan.

Streett, R. Alan. The Effective Invitation. 1984. pap. 6.95 (ISBN 0-8007-5170-1, Power Bks). Revell.

Strege, Merle D., ed. Baptism & Church: A Believers' Church Vision. LC 85-43567. 224p. (Orig.). 1986. pap. 12.50 (ISBN 0-937021-00-8). Sagamore Bks MI.

Streib, Betty. Light to Light. 1981. 10.00 (ISBN 0-89536-486-7, 1238). CSS of Ohio.

Streiker, Lowell D. Cults: The Continuing Threat. 144p. 1983. pap. 3.95 (ISBN 0-687-10069-0). Abingdon.

--The Gospel Time Bomb. 200p. 20.95 (ISBN 0-87975-259-9). Prometheus Bks.

Strelka, Joseph P., ed. Literary Criticism & Myth. LC 79-15111. (Yearbook of Comparative Criticism Ser.: Vol. 9). 1980. text ed. 25.00x (ISBN 0-271-00225-5). Pa St U Pr.

Strelley, Kate. The Ultimate Game: The Rise & Fall of Bhagwan Shree. 1987. 18.95. Har-Row.

Strem, George G. Agnosticism Is Also Faith. LC 85-90970. 1986. 15.00 (ISBN 0-87212-194-1). Libra.

Streng. Understanding Religious Life. 3rd ed. 1984. write for info. (ISBN 0-534-03699-6). Wadsworth Pub.

Streng, Frederick J., jt. ed. see Ingram, Paul O.

Streng, Frederick J., et al. Ways of Being Religious: Readings for a New Approach to Religion. (Illus.). 608p. 1973. 34.00 (ISBN 0-13-946277-5). P-H.

Streng, William D. Faith for Today: A Brief Outline of Christian Thought. LC 75-2843. 48p. (Orig.). 1975. pap. 2.95 (ISBN 0-8066-1488-9, 10-2180). Augsburg.

Strewart, Don. You Be the Judge. 96p. (Orig.). 1983. 2.95 (ISBN 0-89840-055-4). Heres Life.

Strharsky, Harry, ed. Must We Choose Sides? (Christian Committment for the '80s: Vol. 1). (Illus.). 128p. (Orig.). 1980. pap. 5.95 (ISBN 0-936476-01-X). Inter-Religious Task.

Stricker, William F. Keeping Christmas: An Edwardian-Age Memoir. LC 81-9406. (Illus.). 128p. 1981. 15.00 (ISBN 0-916144-60-7). Stemmer Hse.

Strickland, Reba C. Religion & the State in Georgia in the Eighteenth Century. LC 40-4840. (Columbia University Studies in the Social Sciences: No. 460). Repr. of 1939 ed. 18.50 (ISBN 0-404-51460-X). AMS Pr.

Strickland, Rennard. Fire & the Spirits: Cherokee Law From Clan to Court. LC 74-15903. (Illus.). 260p. 1982. pap. 10.95 (ISBN 0-8061-1619-6). U of Okla Pr.

Strickling, James E., Jr. Origins: Today's Science, Tomorrow's Myth. 1986. 11.95 (ISBN 0-317-40170-X). Vantage.

Stringer, Leslea & Bowman, Lea. Crafts Handbook for Children's Church: Graded Activities for Ages 3-7. (Teaching Help Ser.). (Orig.). 1981. pap. 8.95 (ISBN 0-8010-8197-1). Baker Bk.

Stringfellow, Bill. The Ultimate Ripoff. LC 81-49329. 176p. 1981. pap. 3.95 (ISBN 0-939286-00-9). Concerned Pubns.

Stringfellow, William. Instead of Death: New & Expanded Edition. rev. ed. 1976. pap. 3.95 (ISBN 0-8164-2120-X, HarpR). Har-Row.

--The Politics of Spirituality. LC 84-10434. (Spirituality & the Christian Life Ser.: Vol. 4). 90p. 1984. pap. 7.95 (ISBN 0-664-24633-8). Westminster.

Strobel, August. Der Spaetbronzezeitliche Seevoelkersturm: Ein Forschungsueberblick mit Folgerungen zur biblischen Exodusthematik. (Beiheft 145 Zur Zeitschrift fuer die Alttestamentliche Wissenschaft Ser). 1976. 61.00x (ISBN 3-11-006761-7). De Gruyter.

Strode, Muriel. My Little Book of Prayer. 73p. 1942. pap. 1.95 (ISBN 0-87548-237-6). Open Court.

Stroh, Guy W. American Ethical Thought. LC 79-891. 336p. 1979. 23.95x (ISBN 0-88229-356-7). Nelson-Hall.

Stroh, Luella. Aamot. 320p. (Orig.). 1987. pap. 9.95 (ISBN 0-939213-02-8). Oasis Bks.

Strohecker, Carol, ed. see Podles, Mary S. & Porter, Vicki.

Strom, Kay M. Chosen Families. 240p. 1985. 10.95 (ISBN 0-310-33590-6, 11715). Zondervan.

--Helping Women in Crisis: A Handbook for People-Helpers. 208p. 1986. pap. 7.95 (ISBN 0-310-33641-4, 11716P). Zondervan.

Strom, Yale & Blue, Brian. The Last Jews of Eastern Europe. LC 86-25354. (Illus.). 250p. 1986. 29.95 (ISBN 0-8022-2520-9). Philos Lib.

Strombeck, J. F. So Great Salvation. 26th ed. LC 81-85530. 160p. 1982. pap. 3.95 (ISBN 0-89081-215-2). Harvest Hse.

Stromberg, Peter G. Symbols of Community: The Cultural System of a Swedish Church. LC 85-30229. (Anthropology of Form & Meaning Ser.). 127p. 1986. 17.95x (ISBN 0-8165-0967-0). U of Ariz Pr.

Stromberg, Peter L., et al. The Teaching of Ethics in the Military. LC 81-86583. (The Teaching of Ethics in Higher Education Ser.: Vol. XII). 85p. (Orig.). 1982. pap. 5.00 (ISBN 0-916558-16-9). Hastings Ctr.

Strommen, Merton P. Five Cries of Youth. LC 73-18690. 192p. 1974. pap. 8.95 (ISBN 0-06-067748-1, RD224, HarpR). Har-Row.

--Five Shaping Forces: Using Organizational Dynamics to Do More with Less. 104p. 1982. 9.60 (ISBN 0-686-39889-0). Natl Cath Educ.

Strommen, Merton P., jt. auth. see Solberg, Richard W.

Strong, Augustus H. American Poets & Their Theology. facs. ed. LC 68-26477. (Essay Index Reprint Ser). 1968. Repr. of 1916 ed. 21.50 (ISBN 0-8369-0910-0). Ayer Co Pubs.

--Systematic Theology, 3 Vols in 1. 21.95 (ISBN 0-8170-0177-8). Judson.

--Systematic Theology. Incl. The Doctrine of God; The Doctrine of Man; The Doctrine of Salvation. 1168p. 24.95 (ISBN 0-8007-0302-2). Revell.

Strong, D. M., tr. from Pali. The Udana, or the Solemn Utterances of the Buddha. LC 78-70131. Repr. of 1902 ed. 20.50 (ISBN 0-404-17399-3). AMS Pr.

Strong, Donald S. Organized Anti-Semitism in America: The Rise of Group Prejudice During the Decade 1930-1940. LC 78-26198. 1979. Repr. of 1941 ed. lib. bdg. 22.50x (ISBN 0-313-20883-2, STOA). Greenwood.

Strong, Eugenia. Apotheosis & after Life. facsimile ed. LC 78-103668. (Select Bibliographies Reprint Ser). 1915. 33.00 (ISBN 0-8369-5168-9). Ayer Co Pubs.

Strong, James. Strong's Exhaustive Concordance. LC 78-73138. 1978. pap. 15.95 (ISBN 0-8054-1134-8). Broadman.

--Strong's Exhaustive Concordance of the Bible with the Exclusive Key-Word Comparison. rev. ed. 1980. 23.95 (ISBN 0-687-40030-9); thumb-indexed 28.95 (ISBN 0-687-40031-7). Abingdon.

--Strong's Exhaustive Concordance of the Bible. 1552p. Date not set. 20.95 (ISBN 0-917006-01-1). Hendrickson MA.

--The Strong's New Concordance of the Bible: Popular Edition. 784p. 1985. text ed. 10.95 (ISBN 0-8407-4951-1). Nelson.

--Tabernacle of Israel. LC 85-8100. (Illus.). 208p. 1987. pap. 10.95 (ISBN 0-8254-3745-8). Kregel.

Strong, James, jt. auth. see Berry, George R.

Strong, James, jt. auth. see McClintock, John.

Strong, James, ed. The New Strong's New Exhaustive Concordance of the Bible. 2nd ed. 1984. 24.95 (ISBN 0-8407-5360-8); indexed 28.95 (ISBN 0-8407-5442-6). Nelson.

--Strong's Exhaustive Concordance of the Bible. 1552p. 1986. text ed. 10.95 (ISBN 0-529-06334-4); Thumb indexed ed. text ed. 13.95 (ISBN 0-529-06335-2). World Bible.

Strong, John S. The Legend of King Asoka: A Study & Translation of the Asokavadana. LC 83-42579. (Princeton Library of Asian Translations). 336p. 1984. 30.00x (ISBN 0-691-06575-6). Princeton U Pr.

Strong, June. A Little Journey. Wheeler, Gerald, ed. 126p. (Orig.). 1984. pap. 5.95 (ISBN 0-8280-0236-3). Review & Herald.

--Where Are We Running? LC 78-26271. (Orion Ser.). 1979. pap. 3.50 (ISBN 0-8127-0207-7). Review & Herald.

Strong, Kendrick. Coping Is Not Enough. LC 86-23260. (Orig.). 1987. text ed. 7.95 (ISBN 0-8054-5042-4). Broadman.

Strong, William E. Story of the American Board: An Account of the First Hundred Years of the American Board for Foreign Missions. LC 79-83443. (Religion in America Ser). 1969. Repr. of 1910 ed. 26.50 (ISBN 0-405-00277-7). Ayer Co Pubs.

Stronstad, Roger. The Charismatic Theology of St. Luke. 96p. 1985. pap. 4.95 (ISBN 0-913573-11-6). Hendrickson MA.

Strothmann, F. W., ed. see Calvin, John.

Strothmann, F. W., ed. see Feuerbach, Ludwig.

Strothmann, Friedrich W., ed. see St. Thomas Aquinas.

Strothmann, Werner. Johannes von Apamea. (Patristische Texte und Studien 11). 1972. 48.40x (ISBN 3-11-002457-8). De Gruyter.

Stroud, Marion. Our Baby: The First Five Years. (Illus.). 48p. 1986. 11.95 (ISBN 0-7459-1119-6). Lion USA.

--Please Tell Me How You Feel. LC 83-22410. 160p. 1984. pap. 4.95 (ISBN 0-87123-427-0, 210427). Bethany Hse.

Stroud, Matthew D., tr. see De la Barca, Pedro C.

Stroud, Ronald, jt. auth. see Bookidis, Nancy.

Stroup, George W. Jesus Christ for Today. LC 82-13494. (Library of Living Faith: Vol. 7). 116p. 1982. pap. 5.95 (ISBN 0-664-24450-5). Westminster.

--The Promise of Narrative Theology: Recovering the Gospel in the Church. LC 80-84654. 216p. (Orig.). 1982. pap. 9.95 (ISBN 0-8042-0683-X). John Knox.

Stroup, Herbert W. & Wood, Norma S. Sexuality & the Counseling Pastor. LC 73-88344. pap. 33.50 (2027176). Bks Demand UMI.

Stroupe, Henry S. Religious Press in the South Atlantic States, 1802-1865. (Duke University. Trinity College Historical Socity. Historical Papers: No. 32). Repr. of 1956 ed. 24.50 (ISBN 0-404-51782-X). AMS Pr.

Strubhar, Daniel. Penmanship for Christian Writing. 1981. write for info.; tchr's. ed. avail. Rod & Staff.

Strubhar, Roy A., compiled by. Sing Unto God. 1972. pap. 1.00x (ISBN 0-87813-108-6). Park View.

Strugnell, John, jt. auth. see Stone, Michael E.

Struhl, Karsten J., jt. ed. see Struhl, Paula R.

Struhl, Paula R. & Struhl, Karsten J., eds. Ethics in Perspective: A Reader. 3rd ed. 1980. pap. text ed. 13.00 (ISBN 0-394-32354-8, RanC). Random.

Strunk, Orlo, Jr. The Secret Self. LC 76-14780. Repr. of 1976 ed. 27.50 (ISBN 0-8357-9025-8, 2016404). Bks Demand UMI.

Strutt, Edward C. Fra Filippo Lippi. LC 78-176460. Repr. of 1901 ed. 11.50 (ISBN 0-404-06299-7). AMS Pr.

Strutt, Malcolm. Wholistic Health & Living Yoga. LC 77-85790. (Illus.). 320p. (Orig.). 1978. pap. 9.95 (ISBN 0-916438-08-2). Univ of Trees.

Strutynski, Udo, ed. see Dumezil, Georges.

Struzzo, John A., et al. Suffering: Issues of Emotional Living in an Age of Stress for Clergy & Religious. Gilmartin, Richard J., ed. LC 84-9334. 144p. 1984. pap. 8.00 (ISBN 0-89571-020-X). Affirmation.

Strygler, Rosa. Rosa: A Story of Two Survivals. 190p. 15.95 (ISBN 0-88400-125-3). Shengold.

Stryk, Lucien. Encounter with Zen: Writings on Poetry & Zen. LC 81-9611. x, 259p. 1982. 26.95x (ISBN 0-8040-0405-6, Pub. by Swallow); pap. 10.95 (ISBN 0-8040-0406-4, Pub. by Swallow). Ohio U Pr.

--World of the Buddha: An Introduction to Buddhist Literature. 1982. pap. 9.95 (ISBN 0-394-17974-9, E803, Ever). Grove.

Stryk, Lucien & Ikemoto, Takashi, trs. from Japanese. Zen: Poems, Prayers, Sermons, Anecdotes, Interviews. LC 81-50909. 210p. 1982. 18.95x (ISBN 0-8040-0377-7, 82-75232, Pub by Swallow); pap. 8.95 (ISBN 0-8040-0378-5, 82-75240, Pub by Swallow). Ohio U Pr.

Strype, John. Annals of the Reformation & Establishment of Religion & Other Various Occurrences in the Church of England, 4 vols. in 7. 2nd ed. LC 66-20694. 1708-09. Repr. 255.00 (ISBN 0-8337-3444-X). B Franklin.

--Historical Collections of the Life & Acts of John Aylmer, Bishop of London, in the Reign of Queen Elizabeth. LC 74-979. 244p. 1974. Repr. of 1821 ed. lib. bdg. 22.50 (ISBN 0-8337-4427-5). B Franklin.

Strzygowski, Josef. Early Church Art in Northern Europe. LC 77-73725. (Illus.). 1980. Repr. of 1928 ed. lib. bdg. 30.00 (ISBN 0-87817-246-7). Hacker.

Stuart, Clara. Latimer: Apostle to the English. 320p. 1986. 15.95 (ISBN 0-310-41370-2). Zondervan.

Stuart, Douglas. Favorite Old Testament Passages: A Popular Commentary for Today. LC 85-5148. 130p. 1985. pap. 8.95 (ISBN 0-664-24676-1). Westminster.

--Old Testament Exegesis: A Primer for Students & Pastors. 2nd, rev. & enl. ed. LC 84-10431. 142p. 1984. pap. 7.95 (ISBN 0-664-24559-5). Westminster.

Stuart, Douglas, jt. auth. see Fee, Gordon.

Stuart, Friend. Adventures in Consciousness. 1962. pap. 6.95 (ISBN 0-912132-00-0). Dominion Pr.

--How to Conquer Physical Death. 1980. vinyl 29.95 (ISBN 0-912132-02-7). Dominion Pr.

--Master Thoughts, 3 vols. 600p. 1985. Set. vinyl 50.00 (ISBN 0-912132-05-1). Dominion Pr.

--The Revenant Christ. 1983. pap. 4.95 (ISBN 0-912132-15-9). Dominion Pr.

--Twenty Years of Tidings. 180p. 1986. vinyl 29.95 (ISBN 0-912132-10-8). Dominion Pr.

--What the Bible Says about Sex. 40p. 1985. pap. 4.95 (ISBN 0-912132-17-5). Dominion Pr.

Stuart, G. On the Shores of the Infinite. pap. 4.95 (ISBN 0-910122-34-2). Amherst Pr.

Stuart, Jamie. A Scots Gospel. LC 86-45544. 87p. (Orig.). 1986. pap. 4.95 (ISBN 0-8042-0421-7); 60 min. cassette 7.95 (ISBN 0-8042-0424-1). John Knox.

Stuart, Micheline, tr. see Suares, Carlo.

Stuart, Sally. All-Occasion Craft & Gift Book. (Illus.). 96p. (Orig.). 1984. pap. 5.95 (ISBN 0-87239-709-2, 2138). Standard Pub.

Stuart, Sally E. Teaching & Reaching: Junior Resources. 1983. pap. 7.95 (ISBN 0-87162-285-8, D5702). Warner Pr.

Stuart, Vincent, tr. see Suares, Carlo.

Stuart, Vincent G. Changing Mind. LC 80-53447. 80p. 1981. 6.95 (ISBN 0-87773-206-X). Shambhala Pubns.

Stuart-Fox, Martin, jt. auth. see Bucknell, R. S.

Stubbe, Arlon. The Phantom Church. 1986. 7.95 (ISBN 0-89536-802-1, 6820). CSS of Ohio.

Stubblebine, James, ed. Giotto: The Arena Chapel Frescoes. LC 67-17689. (Critical Studies in Art History Ser). (Illus.). 1969. pap. text ed. 7.95x (ISBN 0-393-09858-3, NortonC). Norton.

Stubblefield, Jerry M. A Church Ministering to Adults. LC 86-2299. (Orig.). 1986. pap. 9.95 (ISBN 0-8054-3235-3). Broadman.

Stubbs, Charles W. Charles Kingsley & the Christian Social Movement. LC 70-148310. Repr. of 1899 ed. 17.50 (ISBN 0-404-08914-3). AMS Pr.

--The Christ of English Poetry. LC 73-1787. 1973. lib. bdg. 25.00 (ISBN 0-8414-2621-X). Folcroft.

Stubbs, William. Historical Introduction to the Rolls Series. LC 77-158211. Repr. of 1902 ed. 11.50 (ISBN 0-404-06302-0). AMS Pr.

Stuckey, Debra. God Made Everything. (God's Creature Ser.). (Illus.). 4.95 (ISBN 0-570-04109-0, 56-1484). Concordia.

--God Made Me. (God's Creature Ser.). (Illus.). 1985. 4.95 (ISBN 0-570-04108-2, 56-1483). Concordia.

Stuckey, Debra K. God Made Families. (God's Creature Ser.). (Illus.). 24p. 1986. 4.95 (ISBN 0-570-04118-X). Concordia.

--God Made Prayer. (God Made Ser.). (Illus.). 24p. 1985. 4.95 (ISBN 0-570-04117-1, 56-1528). Concordia.

Stucki, Margaret E. War on Light: The Destruction of the Image of God in Man Through Modern Art. 1975. 15.00 (ISBN 0-686-23419-7). Birds' Meadow Pub.

--War on Light: The Destruction of the Image of God in Man Through Modern Art. 5.95 (ISBN 0-686-18059-3). Freedom Univ-FSP.

Stucky, Solomon. For Conscience' Sake. LC 83-98283. 240p. (Orig.). pap. 9.95 (ISBN 0-8361-3333-1). Herald Pr.

Students of Bais Yaakov Academy. Growing with Doniel. 1987. 9.95; pap. 7.95. Feldheim.

Studer, Gerald C. After Death, What? LC 75-38074. 160p. 1976. pap. 1.95 (ISBN 0-8361-1792-1). Herald Pr.

Studwell, William E. Christmas Carols: A Reference Guide. LC 84-48240. 320p. 1984. lib. bdg. 29.00 (ISBN 0-8240-8899-9). Garland Pub.

Studzinski, Raymond. Spiritual Direction & Mid-Life Development. 1985. 12.95 (ISBN 0-8294-0480-5). Loyola.

Stuenkel, Omar. Marriage is for Two: How to Build a Marriage That Lasts & Works. LC 81-65640. 96p. (Orig.). 1981. pap. 4.95 (ISBN 0-8066-1876-0, 10-4290). Augsburg.

Stugard, Christine. Living Bread. (Illus.). 80p. (Orig.). 1983. pap. 4.95 (ISBN 0-88028-023-9). Forward Movement.

Stuhlmacher, Peter. Reconciliation, Law & Righteousness: Essays in Biblical Theology. Kalin, Everett R., tr. LC 85-45482. 240p. 1986. 24.95 (ISBN 0-8006-0770-8, 1-770). Fortress.

Stuhlmacher, Peter, jt. auth. see Lapide, Pinchas.

Stuhlman, Daniel D. Library of Congress Headings for Judaica. LC 82-73398. (Orig.). 1983. pap. 5.00 (ISBN 0-934402-13-2); pap. 1.50 (ISBN 0-934402-15-9). BYLS Pr.

--My Own Hanukah Story. (Illus., Orig.). 1980. pap. 3.95 personalized version (ISBN 0-934402-07-8); decorations 1.00 (ISBN 0-934402-08-6); trade version 2.50 (ISBN 0-934402-12-4). BYLS Pr.

--My Own Pesah Story. (My Own Holiday Stories: No. 2). (Illus., Orig.). 1981. Personalized Version. pap. 3.95x (ISBN 0-934402-09-4); Trade Version. pap. 3.00 (ISBN 0-934402-10-8); Seder cards 1.50 (ISBN 0-934402-11-6). BYLS Pr.

Stuhlmeuller, Carroll. Biblical Meditations for Ordinary Time. 416p. (Orig.). 1984. Pt. II, Weeks 10-22. pap. 5.95 (ISBN 0-8091-2645-1); Pt. III, Weeks 23-34. pap. 5.95 (ISBN 0-8091-2648-6). Paulist Pr.

--Biblical Meditations for Ordinary Time: Pt. I, Weeks 1-9. 320p. (Orig.). 1984. pap. 4.95 (ISBN 0-8091-2644-3). Paulist Pr.

Stuhlmueller, Carroll. Aggai, Zacharia, Malachia, Jona, Joel, Abdia. (Bible Ser.). pap. 1.00 (ISBN 0-8091-5000-X). Paulist Pr.

--Amos, Hosea, Micah, Nahum, Zephaniah, Habakkuk. (Collegeville Bible Commentary Ser.). 120p. 1986. pap. 2.95 (ISBN 0-8146-1422-1). Liturgical Pr.

--Biblical Meditations for Advent & the Christmas Season. LC 80-82083. (Biblical Meditations Ser.: Vol. 3). 288p. (Orig.). 1980. pap. 4.95 (ISBN 0-8091-2318-5). Paulist Pr.

--Biblical Meditations for Lent. rev. ed. LC 77-91366. 190p. 1978. pap. 4.95 (ISBN 0-8091-2089-5). Paulist Pr.

--Isaiah. 1976. 1.75 (ISBN 0-8199-0628-X). Franciscan Herald.

--Leviticus. (Bible Ser.). pap. 1.00 (ISBN 0-8091-5082-4). Paulist Pr.

--The Psalms. (Read & Pray Ser.). 1979. 1.75 (ISBN 0-8199-0631-X). Franciscan Herald.

--Psalms One. (Old Testament Message Ser.: Vol. 21). 16.95 (ISBN 0-89453-421-1); pap. 12.95 (ISBN 0-89453-255-3). M Glazier.

--Psalms Two. (Old Testament Message Ser.: Vol. 22). 15.95 (ISBN 0-89453-422-X); pap. 10.95 (ISBN 0-89453-257-X). M Glazier.

--Reconciliation: A Biblical Call. (Biblical Booklets Ser). 68p. 1975. pap. 1.25 (ISBN 0-8199-0522-4). Franciscan Herald.

Stuhlmueller, Carroll, jt. auth. see Senior, Donald.

Stuhmueller, Carroll C. Biblical Meditations for the Easter Season. LC 80-81030. 256p. 1980. pap. 4.95 (ISBN 0-8091-2283-9). Paulist Pr.

Stuhr, Robert L. & Jarc, Jerry A. Annual Fund Estate Planning. (How to Ser.). 1984. 4.80. Natl Cath Educ.

Stuhr, Walter M., Jr. The Public Style: A Study of the Community Participation of Protestant Ministers. LC 72-89687. (Studies in Religion & Society Ser.). 1972. 14.95x (ISBN 0-913348-12-0); pap. 8.95x (ISBN 0-913348-02-3). Ctr Sci Study.

Stukeley, William. Stonehenge, a Temple Restored to the British Druids; Abury, a Temple of the British Druids. Feldman, Burton & Richardson, Robert D., eds. LC 78-60898. (Myth & Romanticism Ser.). 1984. lib. bdg. 80.00 (ISBN 0-8240-3572-0). Garland Pub.

Stulken, Marilyn K. Hymnal Companion to the Lutheran Book of Worship. LC 81-707. 672p. 1981. 34.95 (ISBN 0-8006-0300-1, 1-300). Fortress.

Stulman, Louis. The Other Text of Jeremiah: A Reconstruction of the Hebrew Text Underlying the Greek Version of the Prose Sections of Jeremiah with English Translation. LC 85-20278. 178p. (Orig.). 1986. lib. bdg. 25.75 (ISBN 0-8191-4988-8); pap. text ed. 12.75 (ISBN 0-8191-4989-6). U Pr of Amer.

--The Prose Sermons of the Book of Jeremiah: A Redescription of the Correspondence with Deuteronomistic Literature in Light of Recent Text-Critical Research. (Society of Biblical Literature Dissertation Ser.). 166p. 1987. 17.25 (ISBN 0-89130-960-8, 06-01-83); pap. 13.25 (ISBN 0-89130-961-6). Scholars Pr GA.

Stultz, Roberta, ed. see Tompkins, Iverna.

Stum, Stephen B. Beyond Inspiration. 128p. 1984. 5.95 (ISBN 0-87159-011-5). Unity School.

Stumme, John R. Socialism in Theological Perspective: A Study of Paul Tillich, Nineteen Eighteen to Nineteen Thirty-Three. LC 78-3675. (American Academy of Religion. Dissertation Ser.: No. 21). 1978. pap. 9.95 (ISBN 0-89130-232-8, 010121). Scholars Pr GA.

Stumme, Wayne. Christians & the Many Faces of Marxism. LC 84-10980. 176p. (Orig.). 1984. pap. 8.95 (ISBN 0-8066-2087-0, 10-1195). Augsburg.

Stumme, Wayne, ed. Bible & Mission: Biblical Foundations & Working Models for Congregational Ministry. LC 86-22167. (Mission in the U. S. A. Series). 208p. (Orig.). 1986. pap. 10.95 (ISBN 0-8066-2237-7, 10-0705). Augsburg.

Stummer, Friedrich. Summerisch-Akkadische Parallelen Zum Aufbau Alttestamentlicher Psalmen. Repr. of 1922 ed. 15.00 (ISBN 0-384-58710-0). Johnson Repr.

Stump, Donald V. & Arieti, James A., eds. Hamartia: The Concept of Error in the Western Tradition. LC 83-13087. (Texts & Studies in Religion: Vol. 16). 320p. 1984. 59.95x (ISBN 0-88946-805-2). E Mellen.

Stump, Gladys S. About God's People, Bk. 4. (Special Ser.). 144p. 1983. pap. 7.95 (ISBN 0-8163-0461-0). Pacific Pr Pub Assn.

--About People for a Special Time. 1981. pap. 7.95 (ISBN 0-8163-0353-3). Pacific Pr Pub Assn.

--About the Beginning, Bk. 1. LC 78-78070. 1979. pap. 7.95 (ISBN 0-8163-0380-0, 01055-3). Pacific Pr Pub Assn.

--About When Satan Tried to Rule, Bk. 2. LC 79-84610. 1980. pap. 7.95 (ISBN 0-8163-0381-9, 01056-1). Pacific Pr Pub Assn.

--Baby Jesus. (Books I Can Read Ser.). (Illus.). 1978. pap. 1.95 (ISBN 0-8127-0160-7). Review & Herald.

--Baby Moses. (Books I Can Read Ser.). (Illus.). 1978. pap. 1.95 (ISBN 0-8127-0164-X). Review & Herald.

--Elisha's Room. (Books I Can Read). (Illus.). 1978. pap. 1.95 (ISBN 0-8127-0162-3). Review & Herald.

--Mordecai's Ride. (Books I Can Read). (Illus.). 1978. pap. 1.95 (ISBN 0-8127-0161-5). Review & Herald.

--Paul. (Books I Can Read). (Illus.). 1978. pap. 1.95 (ISBN 0-8127-0165-8). Review & Herald.

Stumpf, Samuel E. Democratic Manifesto: The Impact of Dynamic Christianity Upon Public Life & Government. LC 54-4773. 1954. 7.95x (ISBN 0-8265-1039-6). Vanderbilt U Pr.

Stunden, Clifford. How to Raise a Child You Can Live With: And What to Do If You Haven't. 160p. 1987. 10.95 (ISBN 0-8499-0552-4). Word Bks.

Stupperich, Martin. Osiander in Preussen (1549-1552) (Arbeiten Zur Kirchengeschichte, Vol. 44). 402p. 1973. 30.80x (ISBN 3-11-004221-5). De Gruyter.

Stupperich, Robert. Erasmus Von Rotterdam und Seine Welt. 1977. 19.20x (ISBN 3-11-007085-5). De Gruyter.

Sturdy, John. Numbers. LC 75-39373. (Cambridge Bible Commentary on the New English Bible, Old Testament Ser.). 1976. pap. 11.95 (ISBN 0-521-09776-2). Cambridge U Pr.

Sturdy, John, tr. see Ringgren, Helmer.

Sturdy, John, tr. see Schmidt, Werner H.

Sturge, Jane, tr. see Gebler, Karl Von.

Sturges, Betty, jt. auth. see Gent, Barbara.

Sturlaugson, Mary F. A Soul So Rebellious. 88p. 1980. 8.95 (ISBN 0-87747-841-4). Deseret Bk.

Sturluson, S. Prose Edda. Brodeur, A. G., tr. 1916. 12.50x (ISBN 0-89067-000-5). Am Scandinavian.

Sturluson, Snorri. The Prose Edda of Snorri Sturluson: Tales from Norse Mythology. Young, Jean I., tr. 1964. pap. 5.95x (ISBN 0-520-01232-1, CAMPUS55). U of Cal Pr.

Sturz, Harry A. The Byzantine Text-Type & New Testament Textual Criticism. 320p. 1984. 18.95 (ISBN 0-8407-4958-9). Nelson.

Sturzo, Luigi. Church & State, Two Vols. (Vol. 2, O.P.). 1962. Set. pap. 11.90x (ISBN 0-268-00047-6). U of Notre Dame Pr.

Stutfield, Hugh E. Mysticism & Catholicism. 1977. lib. bdg. 59.95 (ISBN 0-8490-2318-1). Gordon Pr.

Stutley, James, jt. auth. see Stutley, Margaret.

Stutley, Margaret. The Illustrated Dictionary of Hindu Iconography. (Illus.). 200p. 1985. 36.95 (ISBN 0-317-17180-1). Methuen Inc.

Stutley, Margaret & Stutley, James. Harper's Dictionary of Hinduism: Its Mythology, Folklore, Philosophy, Literature & History. LC 76-9999. 400p. 1984. pap. 16.95 (ISBN 0-06-067767-8, RD 479, HarpR). Har-Row.

Stutman, Suzanne, jt. auth. see Epstein, David.

Stutsman, Gerald. Transcendency. LC 81-69736. 96p. 1982. pap. 4.75 (ISBN 0-87516-466-8). De Vorss.

Stutzman, Terry, ed. see Goossen, Rachel W.

Stylianopoulos, Theodore. The Gospel of Christ. 32p. 1981. pap. 1.95 (ISBN 0-916586-84-7). Hellenic Coll Pr.

Styll, John, ed. see Christian, Chris.

Suares, Carlo. Krishnamurti & the Unity of Man. 1974. lib. bdg. 69.95 (ISBN 0-8490-0476-4). Gordon Pr.

--The Qabala Trilogy. Stuart, Micheline & Stuart, Vincent, trs. from Fr. LC 85-8179. 565p. 1985. pap. 17.95 (ISBN 0-87773-337-6, 74220-6). Shambhala Pubns.

Suarez, F. Mary of Nazareth. 259p. 1979. pap. 4.95x (ISBN 0-933932-42-1). Scepter Pubs.

Suarez, Federico. About Being a Priest. 229p. 1979. 7.00 (ISBN 0-912414-27-8). Lumen Christi.

--Joseph of Nazareth. Mascarenhas, Ives & Kearns, Patrick, trs. from Span. Tr. of Jose, Esposo de Maria. 222p. (Orig.). 1984. pap. 7.95 (ISBN 0-906138-08-6). Scepter Pubs.

Suarez, Oscar S. Liberating the Pulpit: Selected Sermons. 164p. (Orig.). 1984. pap. 8.25 (ISBN 0-318-20555-6, Pub. by New Day Philippines). Cellar.

Suassure, Eric de see De Suassure, Eric.

Subbotin, N. The Acts of the Moscow Councils of the Years 1666 & 1667. 358p. 1893. text ed. 62.10x (ISBN 0-576-99199-6, Pub. by Gregg Intl Pubs England). Gregg Intl.

Subercaseaux, Pedro E. Life of Saint Francis. 1977. buckram 25.00 (ISBN 0-8199-0615-8). Franciscan Herald.

Subhan, S. A. Islam: Its Belief & Practices. 1938. 5.25x (ISBN 0-87902-190-X). Orientalia.

Subhani, Jafar. The Message. Haq, M. Fazal, tr. from Persian. 784p. 1985. pap. 25.00 (ISBN 0-941724-38-7). Islamic Seminary.

Subrahmanian, N. S. Encyclopedia of the Upanishads. 564p. 1986. text ed. 50.00x (ISBN 0-86590-771-4, Pub. by Sterling Pubs India). Apt Bks.

Subramaniam, K. Brahmin Priest of Tamil Nadu. LC 74-13072. 183p. 1975. 19.95x (ISBN 0-470-83535-4). Halsted Pr.

Subramaniam, K. R. Origin of Saivism & Its Development in the Tamil Land. 88p. 1986. Repr. 15.00X (ISBN 0-8364-1715-1, Pub. by Usha). South Asia Bks.

Subramaniam, V. Buddhism, Dance & Drama. 1985. 12.00x (ISBN 0-8364-1322-9, Pub. by Ashish India). South Asia Bks.

Subramanian, Anna A. Saints of India. (Illus.). 1978. pap. 3.25 (ISBN 0-87481-479-0). Vedanta Pr.

Subramuniya. The Clear White Light. (On the Path Ser.). (Illus.). 1979. pap. 2.00 (ISBN 0-87516-350-5). De Vorss.

--The Fine Art of Meditation. pap. 1.00 (ISBN 0-87516-356-4). De Vorss.

--Gems of Wisdom. (Illus.). 234p. 1973. 7.00 (ISBN 0-87516-346-7); pap. 5.00 (ISBN 0-87516-345-9). De Vorss.

--I'm All Right, Right Now. pap. 1.00 (ISBN 0-87516-355-6). De Vorss.

--The Lotus of the Heart. (On the Path Ser.). (Illus.). 72p. 1972. pap. 2.00 (ISBN 0-87516-352-1). De Vorss.

--The Meditator. (On the Path Ser.). (Illus.). 72p. 1973. pap. 2.00 (ISBN 0-87516-351-3). De Vorss.

--On the Brink of the Absolute. pap. 1.00 (ISBN 0-87516-359-9). De Vorss.

--The Power of Affirmation. pap. 1.00 (ISBN 0-87516-357-2). De Vorss.

--Raja Yoga. (Illus.). 193p. 1973. 7.00 (ISBN 0-87516-348-3). De Vorss.

--Reflections. (On the Path Ser.). (Illus.). 72p. 1969. pap. 2.00 (ISBN 0-87516-354-8). De Vorss.

--The River of Life. pap. 1.00 (ISBN 0-87516-360-2). De Vorss.

--The Search Is Within. (On the Path Ser.). (Illus.). 1973. pap. 2.00 (ISBN 0-87516-349-1). De Vorss.

--The Self God. (On the Path Ser.). 72p. 1959. pap. 2.00 (ISBN 0-87516-353-X). De Vorss.

Suchla, Peter. Kritischer Rationalismus In Theologischer Pruefung. (European University Studies Series No. 23: Vol. 187). (Ger.). 443p. 1982. 41.60 (ISBN 3-8204-5828-X). P Lang Pubs.

Suchocki, Marjorie. God-Christ-Church: A Practical Approach to Process Theology. 224p. 1982. pap. 10.95 (ISBN 0-8245-0464-X). Crossroad NY.

Sudbrack, Josef. Spiritual Guidance. 1984. pap. 3.95 (ISBN 0-8091-2571-4). Paulist Pr.

Sudha, Ma Y., ed. see Rajneesh, Bhagwan S.

Sudha, Ma Yoga, jt. auth. see Rajneesh, Bhagwan Shree.

Sudha, Ma Yoga, ed. see Rajneesh, Bhagwan Shree.

Sudha, ma Yoga, ed. see Rajneesh, Bhagwan Shree.

Sudha, Ma Yoga, ed. see Rajneesh, Bhagwan Shree.

Suelflow, August R. Religious Archives: An Introduction. LC 80-17159. (SAA Basic Archival Manual Ser.). 1980. pap. text ed. 7.00 (ISBN 0-931828-20-1). Soc Am Archivists.

Suelflow, August R., ed. see Concordia Historical Institute Staff & Lutheran Historical Conference Staff.

Sueltz, Arthur F. New Directions from the Ten Commandments. LC 75-36744. 128p. (Orig.). 1976. pap. 3.95i (ISBN 0-06-067760-0, RD145, HarpR). Har-Row.

Suenens, Leon J. Nature & Grace: A Vital Unity. (Malines Document Ser.: No. V). (Fr.). 80p. (Orig.). 1986. pap. 5.95 (ISBN 0-89283-303-3). Servant.

--Open the Frontiers. 1981. 8.95 (ISBN 0-8164-0489-5, HarpR). Har-Row.

Suenens, Leon J., jt. auth. see Ramsey, A. Michael.

Suffling, Ernest R. English Church Brasses from the 13th to the 17th Century, a Manual for Antiquaries, Archaeologists & Collectors. LC 73-126133. (Illus.). 456p. 1970. Repr. of 1910 ed. 22.50 (ISBN 0-8063-0437-5). Genealog Pub.

Sugarman, Allan S., jt. auth. see Greenberg, Sidney.

Sugarman, Joan, jt. auth. see Freeman, Grace.

Sugarman, Morris J., ed. see Elon, Amos.

Sugarman, Norman A., jt. auth. see Treusch, Paul E.

Sugarman, Richard I., jt. auth. see Simone, R. Thomas.

Sugden, Chris, jt. ed. see Samuel, Vinay.

Sugden, E. H., ed. see Wesley, John.

Sugden, Howard F. & Wiersbe, Warren W. Confident Pastoral Leadership. (Orig.). 1977. pap. 6.95 (ISBN 0-8024-1598-9). Moody.

Sugg, Joyce. Snapdragon: The Story of John Henry Newman. LC 81-85242. (Illus.). 192p. 1982. pap. 3.95 (ISBN 0-87973-653-4, 653). Our Sunday Visitor.

Suggs, Joyce, intro. by see Newman, John H.

Suggs, M. Jack. Wisdom, Christology, & Law in Matthew's Gospel. LC 75-95930. Repr. of 1970 ed. 36.00 (ISBN 0-8357-9185-8, 2017749). Bks Demand UMI.

Suggs, Roy A. Expository Sermon Outlines to Saints & Sinners. 1981. pap. 2.75 (ISBN 0-934942-24-2). White Wing Pub.

Sugiyama, Jiro. Classic Buddhist Sculpture. LC 82-80738. (Japanese Arts Library: Vol. 11). (Illus.). 200p. 1982. 25.00 (ISBN 0-87011-529-4). Kodansha.

Suhl, Yuri. They Fought Back: The Story of Jewish Resistance in Nazi Europe. 316p. Repr. 7.95 (ISBN 0-686-95093-3). ADL.

Suhrawardi, Shihabuddin Yahya. The Mystical & Visionary Treatises of Shihabuddin Yahya Suhrawardi. Thackston, W. H., Jr., tr. 1982. 16.95 (ISBN 0-900860-92-8, Pub. by Octagon Pr England). Ins Study Human.

Sukenik, E. L. Ancient Synagogues in Palestine & Greece. (British Academy, London, Schweich Lectures on Biblical Archaeology Series, 1930). pap. 19.00 (ISBN 0-8115-1272-X). Kraus Repr.

Suksamran, Somboon. Buddhism & Politics in Thailand. 180p. (Orig.). 1982. pap. text ed. 25.00 (ISBN 9971-902-43-5, Pub. by Inst Southeast Asian Stud). Gower Pub Co.

--Political Buddhism in Southeast Asia: The Role of the Sangha in the Modernization of Thailand. LC 77-77606. (Illus.). 1977. 20.00x (ISBN 0-312-62137-X). St Martin.

Sullender, R. Scott. Grief & Growth: Pastoral Resources for Emotional & Spiritual Growth. LC 84-61024. 240p. (Orig.). 1985. pap. 9.95 (ISBN 0-8091-2652-4). Paulist Pr.

--Peter: A Journey in Faith. 47p. (Orig.). 1986. pap. 6.95 (ISBN 0-940754-37-1). Ed Ministries.

Sullivan, Barbara. Page a Day for Lent 1987. 56p. (Orig.). 1987. pap. 2.95 (ISBN 0-8091-2852-7). Paulist Pr.

Sullivan, Bill M., jt. ed. see Johnston, Jon.

Sullivan, Clayton. Called to Preach, Condemned to Survive: The Education of Clayton Sullivan. xiv, 237p. 1985. 19.95 (ISBN 0-86554-173-6, MUP-H163). Mercer Univ Pr.

Sullivan, Daniel & Andrews, Judy. Sunday Scriptures. 4.95 (ISBN 0-8091-9336-1). Paulist Pr.

Sullivan, Eugene T. & Sullivan, Marilynn C., eds. Celebrate! No. V. LC 75-24148. 1978. pap. 11.99 (ISBN 0-912696-22-2). Wilton.

Sullivan, F. Russell. Faith & Reason in Kierkegaard. LC 78-60695. 1978. pap. text ed. 9.50 (ISBN 0-8191-0559-7). U Pr of Amer.

Sullivan, Francis. Tragic Psalms. 1987. pap. 5.95. Pastoral Pr.

Sullivan, Francis A. Charisms & Charismatic Renewal: A Biblical & Theological Study. 182p. 1982. pap. 8.95 (ISBN 0-89283-121-9). Servant.

--Magisterium: Teaching Authority in the Catholic Church. 1984. pap. 9.95 (ISBN 0-8091-2577-3). Paulist Pr.

Sullivan, Francis P. Lyric Psalms: Half a Psalter. (Illus.). 192p. (Orig.). 1983. pap. 5.95 (ISBN 0-9602378-8-7). Pastoral Pr.

Sullivan, George. Pope John Paul II: The People's Pope. LC 83-40395. (Illus.). 120p. 1984. 11.95 (ISBN 0-8027-6523-8). Walker & Co.

Sullivan, James L. Baptist Polity as I See It. LC 83-70940. 1983. 9.95 (ISBN 0-8054-6575-8). Broadman.

--Juan Testifica de Jesus. Quarles, J. C., tr. from Eng. Orig. Title: John's Witness to Jesus. 128p. 1986. pap. 3.25 (ISBN 0-311-04324-0). Casa Bautista.

Sullivan, Jessie. This Is God Speaking: Twenty-Six Lessons for Children's Church. LC 81-18476. (Illus.). 112p. (Orig.). 1982. pap. 7.95 (ISBN 0-87239-496-4, 3371). Standard Pub.

Sullivan, Jessie P. Object Lessons & Stories for the Children's Church. (Object Lesson Ser.). 160p. 1974. pap. 4.95 (ISBN 0-8010-8037-1). Baker Bk.

--Object Lessons: With Easy-to-Find Objects. (Object Lesson Ser.). 128p. (Orig.). 1981. pap. 3.95 (ISBN 0-8010-8190-4). Baker Bk.

--Puppet Scripts for Children's Church. (Paperback Program Ser.). 1978. pap. 4.50 (ISBN 0-8010-8124-6). Baker Bk.

Sullivan, John. Carmelite Studies II: Carmel & Psychology. LC 82-1091. 320p. pap. 6.95x (ISBN 0-935216-00-6). ICS Pubns.

--Chesterton: Contenary Appraisal. 243p. 1974. 12.50 (ISBN 0-06-496591-0). Lumen Christi.

Sullivan, John, intro. by. Carmelite Studies III: Centenary of Saint Theresa. LC 84-4498. 240p. (Orig.). 1984. pap. 6.95x (ISBN 0-935216-03-0). ICS Pubns.

Sullivan, John E. Ideas of Religion: A Prolegomenon to the Philosophy of Religion. LC 79-66230. 1979. pap. text ed. 12.25 (ISBN 0-8191-0808-1). U Pr of Amer.

Sullivan, Kevin. Joyce among the Jesuits. LC 84-25241. x, 259p. 1985. Repr. of 1957 ed. lib. bdg. 39.75x (ISBN 0-313-24745-5, SUJJ). Greenwood.

Sullivan, Marilynn C., jt. ed. see Sullivan, Eugene T.

Sullivan, Mary C., jt. auth. see Golden, Robert.

Sullivan, Mary L. Mother Cabrini: Italian Immigrant of the Century. 250p. 1987. 19.50 (ISBN 0-934733-06-6). Ctr Migration.

Sullivan, Michael. The Cave Temples of Maichishan. LC 69-15829. (Illus.). 1969. 70.00x (ISBN 0-520-01448-0). U of Cal Pr.

Sullivan, Patrick J. Blue Collar-Roman Collar-White Collar: U. S. Catholic Involvement in Labor Management Controversies, 1960-1980. LC 86-24593. 358p. (Orig.). 1987. lib. bdg. 26.75 (ISBN 0-8191-5704-X); pap. text ed. 16.75 (ISBN 0-8191-5705-8). U Pr of Amer.

--U. S. Catholic Institutions & Labor Unions, 1960-1980. LC 85-20171. 550p. (Orig.). 1986. lib. bdg. 40.50 (ISBN 0-8191-4970-5); pap. text ed. 22.75 (ISBN 0-8191-4971-3). U Pr of Amer.

Sullivan, Peter. Christ: The Answer. (Orig.). pap. 1.95 (ISBN 0-8198-0026-0). Dghtrs St Paul.

Sullivan, Robert E. John Toland & the Deist Controversy: A Study in Adaptations. LC 81-7137. (Harvard Historical Studies: 101). (Illus.). 384p. 1982. text ed. 27.50x (ISBN 0-674-48050-3). Harvard U Pr.

Sullivan, Shaun J. Killing in Defense of Private Property: The Development of a Roman Catholic Moral Teaching, Thirteenth to Eighteenth Centuries. LC 75-38843. (American Academy of Religion. Dissertation Ser.). (Illus.). 1976. pap. 9.95 (ISBN 0-89130-067-8, 010115). Scholars Pr GA.

Sullivan, Susan & Kawiak, Matthew. Parents Talk Love: The Catholic Family Handbook on Sexuality. LC 84-80361. 164p. (Orig.). 1984. pap. 7.95 (ISBN 0-8091-2639-7). Paulist Pr.

Sumarti, Muljanto. Islamic Education in Indonesia: A Bibliography. 133p. (Orig.). 1984. pap. text ed. 21.00x (ISBN 9971-902-57-5, Pub. by Inst Southeast Asian Stud). Gower Pub Co.

Summerhill, Louise. The Story of Birthright: The Alternative to Abortion. LC 72-96117. 1973. pap. 3.50 (ISBN 0-913382-06-X, 101-4). Prow Bks-Franciscan.

Summer Rain, Mary. Spirit Song. Friedman, Robert, ed. LC 85-15894. 200p. (Orig.). 1985. pap. 7.95 (ISBN 0-89865-405-X, Unilaw). Donning Co.

Summers, Claude J. & Pebworth, Ted-Larry. Bright Shootes of Everlastingnesse: The Seventeenth-Century Religious Lyric. LC 86-16132. 208p. 1987. text ed. 24.00 (ISBN 0-8262-0618-2, 83-36265). U of Mo Pr.

Summers, Georgianna. The Ladies, God Bless 'Em. 1983. 3.75 (ISBN 0-89536-581-2, 1264). CSS of Ohio.

--The Light Shines in the Darkness. (Orig.). 1987. pap. price not set (ISBN 0-89536-888-9, 7874). CSS of Ohio.

--Night of Miracles. 1982. pap. 4.95 (ISBN 0-89536-552-9, 1411). CSS of Ohio.

--Stress! How Christian Parents Cope. LC 86-71746. 80p. (Orig.). 1986. pap. 5.95 (ISBN 0-88177-032-9, DR032B). Discipleship Res.

--Teaching as Jesus Taught. LC 83-70161. 96p. (Orig.). 1983. pap. 4.50 (ISBN 0-88177-000-0, DR000B). Discipleship Res.

Summers, Jessica de see De Summers, Jessica.

Summers, Jester. Joseph: the Forgiver. (BibLearn Ser.). (Illus.). 1976. bds. 5.95 (ISBN 0-8054-4224-3, 4242-24). Broadman.

--The Two Nichols: Spent for Missions. LC 81-70910. (Meet the Missionary Ser.). 1982. 5.50 (ISBN 0-8054-4279-0, 4242-79). Broadman.

Summers, JoAn. God's Little Animals: Easy Illustrations & Bible Parallels. (Illus.). 32p. 1969. pap. 1.95 (ISBN 0-88243-718-6, 02-0718). Gospel Pub.

Summers, Larry, jt. auth. see Middlebrook, J. D.

Summers, Montague. The Geography of Witchcraft. 624p. 1973. pap. 4.95 (ISBN 0-8065-0391-2). Citadel Pr.

--History of Witchcraft. 1970. pap. 5.95 (ISBN 0-8065-0209-6, 0209-6). Citadel Pr.

--History of Witchcraft & Demonology. (Illus.). 370p. 1973. pap. 8.95 (ISBN 0-7100-7613-4). Methuen Inc.

--Malleus Maleficarum. 288p. 1971. pap. 7.50 (ISBN 0-486-22802-9). Dover.

--Supernatural Omnibus. 624p. 1982. 22.50 (ISBN 0-575-03120-4, Pub. by Gollancz England). David & Charles.

--The Werewolf. 308p. 1973. pap. 3.95 (ISBN 0-8065-0392-0). Citadel Pr.

Summers, Montague, ed. & tr. Malleus Maleficarum. LC 68-57193. 1969. Repr. of 1928 ed. 27.50 (ISBN 0-405-09016-1, Pub. by Blom). Ayer Co Pubs.

Summers, Montague, tr. see Kramer, Heinrich & Sprenger, James.

Summers, Ray. Behold the Lamb. LC 78-67924. 1979. 12.95 (ISBN 0-8054-1374-X). Broadman.

--Digno es el Cordero. Lerin, Alfredo, tr. from Eng. Orig. Title: Worthy is the Lamb. (Span.). 287p. 1981. pap. 4.95 (ISBN 0-311-04305-4). Casa Bautista.

--Ephesians: Pattern for Christian Living. LC 73-87069. pap. 4.25 (ISBN 0-8054-1345-6). Broadman.

--Essentials of New Testament Greek. 1950. text ed. 11.95 (ISBN 0-8054-1309-X). Broadman.

--Life Beyond. LC 83-20874. 1973. pap. 8.95 (ISBN 0-8054-1608-0). Broadman.

--Worthy Is the Lamb. 1951. 11.95 (ISBN 0-8054-1314-6). Broadman.

Summers, William H. The Lollards of the Chiltern Hills. LC 80-12770. (Heresies of the Early Christian & Medieval Era: Second Ser.). Repr. of 1906 ed. 31.51 (ISBN 0-404-16245-2). AMS Pr.

Sumner, David E. The Episcopal Church's History: 1945-1985. 1987. 24.95. Morehouse.

Sumner, Robert L. After the Revival-What? 1980. pap. 3.95 (ISBN 0-914012-22-3, Pub. by Bibl Evang Pr). Sword of Lord.

--Armstrongism: The Worldwide Church of God Examined in the Searching Light of Scripture. 424p. 1974. 12.95 (ISBN 0-914012-15-0, Pub. by Bibl Evang Pr). Sword of Lord.

--Biblical,Evangelism in Action. 1966. pap. 6.50 (ISBN 0-914012-29-0, Pub. by Bibl Evang Pr). Sword of Lord.

--Evangelism: The Church on Fire! 220p. 1960. 3.25 (ISBN 0-87398-211-8, Pub. by Bibl Evang Pr). Sword of Lord.

--Hell Is No Joke. 1959. pap. 3.25 (ISBN 0-914012-28-2, Pub.by Bibl Evang Pr). Sword of Lord.

--Powerhouse. 1978. pap. 3.95 (ISBN 0-914012-18-5, Pub. by Bibl Evang Pr). Sword of Lord.

--Saved by Grace...for Service. 1979. 8.95 (ISBN 0-87398-797-7, Pub. by Bibl Evang Pr). Sword of Lord.

Sumner, William G. Forgotten Man's Almanac: Rations of Common Sense from William Graham Sumner. Keller, A. G., ed. LC 70-141268. 1971. Repr. of 1943 ed. lib. bdg. 22.50x (ISBN 0-8371-5828-1, SUFM). Greenwood.

Sumners, Bill. Displaying & Exhibiting Your Church's History. Deweese, Charles W., ed. (Resource Kit for Your Church's History Ser.). 1984. 0.50 (ISBN 0-939804-22-0). Hist Comm S Baptist.

Sumners, Roxanne. Trust Is the Key. (Illus.). 52p. (Orig.). 1983. pap. 4.95 (ISBN 0-913627-00-3). Agadir Pr.

Sumrall, Lester. Faith to Change the World. 173p. (Orig.). 1983. pap. 4.95 (ISBN 0-89274-306-9, HH-306). Harrison Hse.

--The Gifts & Ministries of the Holy Spirit. 1982. pap. 7.95 (ISBN 0-89274-189-9, HH-189). Harrison Hse.

--One Hundred & One Questions & Answers on Demon Powers. 145p. (Orig.). 1983. pap. 3.25 (ISBN 0-89274-261-5). Harrison Hse.

--Take It, It's Yours. 140p. (Orig.). 1986. pap. text ed. 3.95 (ISBN 0-88368-174-9). Whitaker Hse.

--Victory & Dominion Over Fear. 104p. 1982. pap. 2.75 (ISBN 0-89274-233-X, HH-233). Harrison Hse.

Sumrall, Velma & Germany, Lucille. Telling the Story of the Local Church: The Who, What, When, Where & Why of Communication. (Orig.). 1979. pap. 5.00 (ISBN 0-8164-2193-5, HarpR); wkbk. avail. (ISBN 0-685-59466-1). Har-Row.

Sun, Hugo S., tr. see Forster, Roger & Marston, Paul.

Sunday Times, London. Seven Deadly Sins. LC 75-117848. (Essay Index Reprint Ser). 1962. 14.00 (ISBN 0-8369-1722-7). Ayer Co Pubs.

Sundberg, A. C., Jr. Old Testament of the Early Church: A Study of Canon. (Harvard Theological Studies). 1964. 24.00 (ISBN 0-527-01020-0). Kraus Repr.

Sundberg, Gunnar. Toward Pacifism. 1983. pap. 2.50x (ISBN 0-87574-056-1, 056). Pendle Hill.

Sundell, Roger H., jt. auth. see Patrick, J. Max.

Sunderland, La Roy. Testimony of God Against Slavery, or a Collection of Passages from the Bible, Which Show the Sin Holding Property in Man. LC 73-92444. 1970. Repr. of 1835 ed. 17.00x (ISBN 0-403-03707-7, 403-00183-8). Scholarly.

Sunderland, Ronald H., jt. auth. see Shelp, Earl E.

Sunderland, Ronald H., jt. ed. see Shelp, Earl E.

Sundquist, Ralph R., Jr. Whom God Chooses: The Child in the Church. rev. ed. 94p. 1973. pap. 1.65 (ISBN 0-664-71004-2, Pub. by Geneva Pr). Westminster.

Sunim, Kusan. The Way of Korean Zen. Fages, Martine, tr. (Illus.). 182p. pap. 12.50 (ISBN 0-8348-0201-5). Weatherhill.

Sunoo, Harold H. China of Confucius: A Critical Interpretation. LC 85-7639. (Illus.). 208p. 1985. lib. bdg. 28.95 (ISBN 0-912617-00-4); pap. 12.95 (ISBN 0-912617-01-2). Heritage Res Hse.

Sunset Editors. California Missions. 2nd ed. LC 79-88016. (Illus.). 320p. 1979. pap. 12.95 (ISBN 0-376-05172-8, Sunset Bks). Sunset-Lane.

Super, Arthur S., tr. see Silbermann, A. M.

Super, R. H., ed. see Arnold, Matthew.

Supraner, Robyn. Merry Christmas: Things to Make & Do. LC 80-23884. (Illus.). 48p. 1981. PLB 9.49 (ISBN 0-89375-422-6); pap. 1.95 (ISBN 0-89375-423-4). Troll Assocs.

Supreme Commander for the Allied Powers. Civil Information & Education Section. Religions in Japan: Buddhism, Shinto, Christianity. LC 77-13855. 1978. Repr. of 1955 ed. lib. bdg. 22.50x (ISBN 0-8371-9874-7, SURJ). Greenwood.

Surath, Sri. God Is Now Here. 1976. 5.00 (ISBN 0-685-58439-9). Ranney Pubns.

--Holy Spirit - the Living Love. 1978. pap. 3.00 (ISBN 0-685-58453-4). Ranney Pubns.

--To God Through Faith: From Christ to Sri Ramakrishna. 1978. pap. 3.00 (ISBN 0-685-58452-6). Ranney Pubns.

Sure, Heng & Chau, Heng. With One Heart Bowing to the City of Ten Thousand Buddhas, Vol. III. (Illus.). 154p. (Orig.). 1980. pap. 5.00 (ISBN 0-917512-89-8). Buddhist Text.

--With One Heart Bowing to the City of Ten Thousand Buddhas, Vol. VII. (Illus.). 160p. (Orig.). 1982. pap. 5.00 (ISBN 0-917512-99-5). Buddhist Text.

--With One Heart Bowing to the City of Ten Thousand Buddhas, Vol. VIII. (Illus.). 232p. (Orig.). 1982. pap. 7.50 (ISBN 0-917512-53-7). Buddhist Text.

--With One Heart Bowing to the City of Ten Thousand Buddhas, Vol. V. (Illus.). 127p. (Orig.). 1981. pap. 4.00 (ISBN 0-917512-91-X). Buddhist Text.

Surgy, Paul De see De Surgy, Paul.

Surin, Kenneth. Theology & the Problem of Evil. (Signposts in Theology Ser.). 192p. 1986. text ed. 39.95 (ISBN 0-631-14664-4); pap. text ed. 14.95 (ISBN 0-631-14663-6). Basil Blackwell.

Suring, Margit L. The Horn-Motif in the Hebrew Bible & Related Ancient Near Eastern Literature & Iconography. (Andrews University Seminary Doctoral Dissertation Ser.: Vol. 4). (Illus.). xxvi, 533p. 1982. pap. 12.95 (ISBN 0-943872-36-7). Andrews Univ Pr.

Suriyabongs, Luang. The Buddhas' Doctrine of Truth: Dhamma & Buddhist Religion As Practiced by the Holy Brotherhood in Siam. Bunnag, Krachang, tr. LC 77-87512. Repr. of 1936 ed. 14.50 (ISBN 0-404-16870-1). AMS Pr.

Surrey, Peter J. The Small Town Church. LC 81-622. (Creative Leadership Ser.). 128p. (Orig.). 1981. pap. 6.95 (ISBN 0-687-38720-5). Abingdon.

Susag, S. O. Personal Experiences of S. O. Susag. 191p. pap. 1.75 (ISBN 0-686-29134-4). Faith Pub Hse.

Suso, Henry. The Life of the Servant. 144p. 1983. pap. 11.95 (ISBN 0-227-67862-1, Pub. by J Clarke UK). Attic Pr.

Sussman, Cornelia & Sussman, Irving. Thomas Merton. LC 80-924. 176p. 1980. pap. 3.95 (ISBN 0-385-17172-2, Im). Doubleday.

Sussman, Cornelia, jt. auth. see Sussman, Irving.

Sussman, Henry. The Hegelian Aftermath: Readings in Hegel, Kierkegaard, Freud, Proust & James. LC 82-47971. 172p. 1982. text ed. 22.50x (ISBN 0-8018-2852-X). Johns Hopkins.

Sussman, Irving & Sussman, Cornelia. This Train Is Bound for Glory. 1969. 4.95 (ISBN 0-8199-0154-7, L38874). Franciscan Herald.

Sussman, Irving, jt. auth. see Sussman, Cornelia.

Sussman, Marvin B., jt. ed. see Marciano, Teresa.

Sussman, Varda. Ornamented Jewish Oil Lamps. (Illus.). 144p. 1982. pap. text ed. 55.00x (ISBN 0-85668-164-4, Pub. by Aris & Phillips UK). Humanities.

Sustar, T. David. A Sure Foundation. LC 80-84008. 124p. (Orig.). 1980. pap. text ed. 3.00 (ISBN 0-87148-795-0); 2.00 (ISBN 0-87148-436-6). Pathway Pr.

--Witnessing to Jehovah's Witnessess. (Truthway Ser.). 31p. (Orig.). 1981. pap. text ed. 1.25 (ISBN 0-87148-915-5). Pathway Pr.

Sutcliffe, Matthew. The Examination of T. Cartwrights Late Apologie. LC 72-7837. (English Experience Ser.: No. 558). 120p. 1973. Repr. of 1596 ed. 13.00 (ISBN 90-221-0558-X). Walter J Johnson.

--A Treatise of Ecclesiastical Discipline. LC 73-7082. (English Experience Ser.: No. 626). 1973. Repr. of 1590 ed. 21.00 (ISBN 90-221-0626-8). Walter J Johnson.

Suter, David W. Tradition & Composition in the Parables of Enoch. LC 79-17441. (Society of Biblical Literature. Dissertation Ser.: No. 47). 1979. pap. 9.95 (ISBN 0-89130-336-7, 060147). Scholars Pr GA.

Suther, Judith D. Essays on Camus' Exile & the Kingdom. LC 80-36800. (Romance Monographs: No. 41). 329p. 1982. 30.00x (ISBN 84-499-4725-1). Romance.

Sutherland, Arthur E. Church Shall Be Free: A Glance at Eight Centuries of Church & State. LC 65-24000. pap. 15.00 (2017808). Bks Demand UMI.

Sutherland, Charles W. Disciples of Destruction. 325p. 1986. 22.95 (ISBN 0-87975-349-8). Prometheus Bks.

Sutherland, Donald, tr. see Euripides.

Sutherland, N. M. The Huguenot Struggle for Recognition. LC 79-64070. 1980. text ed. 40.00x (ISBN 0-300-02328-6). Yale U Pr.

--Princes, Politics & Religion, 1547-1589. (No. 31). 240p. 1984. 30.00 (ISBN 0-907628-44-3). Hambledon Press.

Sutherland, Ronald H., jt. ed. see Shelp, Earl E.

Sutherland, S. Philip, jt. auth. see Rohrer, Norman B.

Sutherland, Stewart see Hebblethwaite, Brian L.

Sutherland, Stewart R. God, Jesus & Belief: The Legacy of Theism. 160p. 1984. 29.95x (ISBN 0-631-13548-0); pap. 12.95 (ISBN 0-631-13591-X). Basil Blackwell.

Sutphen, Dick. Past Lives, Future Loves. 1982. pap. 3.50 (ISBN 0-671-54363-6). PB.

--Reincarnation-The Unanswered Questions. 100p. 1983. pap. 2.95 (ISBN 0-686-47947-5). Valley Sun.

Sutphen, Dick & Taylor, Lauren L. Past Life Therapy in Action. 100p. 1983. pap. 2.95 (ISBN 0-911842-32-2). Valley Sun.

Sutphin, Stanley T. Options in Contemporary Theology. 1978. pap. text ed. 10.75 (ISBN 0-8191-0277-6). U Pr of Amer.

--Options in Contemporary Theology. rev. ed. LC 86-28199. 176p. 1987. lib. bdg. 22.50 (ISBN 0-8191-6058-X); pap. text ed. 10.75 (ISBN 0-8191-6059-8). U Pr of Amer.

Sutra, Buddhist. The Voice of the Buddha: The Beauty of Compassion, 2 vols. Bays, Gwendolyn, tr. from Fr. (Translation Ser.). (Illus.). 704p. 1983. Set. 60.00. Vol. I (ISBN 0-913546-84-4). Vol. II (ISBN 0-913546-85-2). Dharma Pub.

Sutra, Jaina. Self-Purification. (Illus.). 8.75 (ISBN 0-88695-020-1). Concord Grove.

Suttapitaka. Prakrit Dhammapada. LC 78-70127. Repr. of 1921 ed. 31.50 (ISBN 0-404-17386-1). AMS Pr.

Sutton, Anthony C. The Secret Cult of the Order. 140p. (Orig.). 1984. pap. text ed. 9.95 (ISBN 0-914981-09-9). Res Pubns AZ.

Sutton, Brett. Primitive Baptist Hymns of the Blue Ridge. (American Folklore Recordings Ser.). 28p. 1982. pap. 15.00x incl. records (ISBN 0-8078-4083-1). U of NC Pr.

Sutton, Eric A. The Living Thoughts of Swedenborg. 122p. 1981. Repr. of 1944 ed. lib. bdg. 20.00 (ISBN 0-8495-5041-6). Arden Lib.

Sutton, Hilton. The Devil Ain't What He Used to Be. 78p. (Orig.). 1982. pap. 2.25 (ISBN 0-89274-255-0). Harrison Hse.

--He's Coming! 149p. (Orig.). 1983. pap. 2.95 (ISBN 0-89274-256-9). Harrison Hse.

--Revelation: God's Grand Finale. 280p. (Orig.). 1984. pap. 6.95 (ISBN 0-89274-298-4). Harrison Hse.

--Revelation Teaching Syllabus. 1985. 10.00 (ISBN 0-89274-318-2). Harrison Hse.

Sutton, Joseph A. D. Magic Carpet: Aleppo in Flatbush: The Story of a Unique Ethnic Jewish Community. 3rd ed. LC 79-65516. (Illus.). 336p. 1986. text ed. 19.95x (ISBN 0-686-27080-0). Thayer-Jacoby.

Sutton, Maurice L., jt. auth. see Smith, Ester M.

Sutton, Michael. Nationalism, Positivism & Catholicism: The Politics of Charles Maurras & French Catholics, 1890-1914. LC 82-4360. (Cambridge Studies in the History & Theory of Politics). 320p. 1983. 47.50 (ISBN 0-521-22868-9). Cambridge U Pr.

Sutton, Ray R. Who Owns the Family. (The Biblical Blueprint ser.). 1986. pap. 6.95 (ISBN 0-8407-3097-7). Nelson.

Sutton, Rosalind, jt. auth. see Ife, Elaine.

Sutton, Rosalind & Ife, Elaine, eds. Moses the Leader. (Now You Can Read Stories from the Bible Ser.). (Illus.). 24p. 1985. 2.50 (ISBN 0-8407-5391-8). Nelson.

Sutton, Rosalind, jt. ed. see Ife, Elaine.

Suttor, T. L. Hierarchy & Democracy in Australia, 1788-1870: The Formation of Australian Catholicism. 1965. 22.00x (ISBN 0-522-83753-0, Pub. by Melbourne U Pr). Intl Spec Bk.

Suzuki, D. T. Essays in Zen Buddhism. 1961. pap. 5.95 (ISBN 0-394-17230-2, E309, Ever). Grove.

--Introduction to Zen Buddhism. 1964. pap. 3.95 (ISBN 0-394-17474-7, B341, BC). Grove.

--Living by Zen. pap. 5.95 (ISBN 0-87728-194-7). Weiser.

--Manual of Zen Buddhism. (Orig.). 1960. pap. 5.95 (ISBN 0-394-17224-8, E231, Ever). Grove.

--Mysticism: Christian & Buddhist. 160p. 1982. pap. 5.95 (ISBN 0-04-149053-3). Allen Unwin.

--Zen & Japanese Culture. (Bollingen Ser.: Vol. 64). (Illus.). 1959. 52.00x (ISBN 0-691-09849-2); pap. 10.95x (ISBN 0-691-01770-0). Princeton U Pr.

--Zen Buddhism: Selected Writings of D. T. Suzuki. 1956. pap. 5.50 (ISBN 0-385-09300-4, A90, Anch). Doubleday.

--Zen Doctrine of No Mind. 1981. pap. 8.50 (ISBN 0-87728-182-3). Weiser.

Suzuki, D. T., tr. see Asvaghosha.

Suzuki, D. T., tr. see Lao Tze.

Suzuki, D. T., tr. see Shaku, Soyen.

Suzuki, Daisetz T. The Essentials of Zen Buddhism. Phillips, Bernard, ed. & intro. by. LC 61-5041. 544p. 1973. Repr. of 1962 ed. lib. bdg. 45.00x (ISBN 0-8371-6649-7, SUEZ). Greenwood.

--Mysticism: Christian & Buddhist. LC 75-31442. 214p. 1976. Repr. of 1957 ed. lib. bdg. 25.00x (ISBN 0-8371-8516-5, SUMY). Greenwood.

--Studies in the Lankavatara Sutra: An Elucidation & Analysis of One of the Most Important Texts of Mahayana Buddhism, in Which Almost All Its Principal Tenets Are Presented Including the Teaching of Zen. 1968. Repr. of 1930 ed. 31.00 (ISBN 0-7100-6330-X). Methuen Inc.

Suzuki, Daisetz T., tr. The Lankavatara Sutra: A Mahayana Text. (Illus.). 1972. Repr. of 1932 ed. 27.00 (ISBN 0-7100-2165-8). Methuen Inc.

Suzuki, David A. Crisis in Japanese Buddhism: Case of the Otani Sect. 285p. 1985. 19.50 (ISBN 0-914910-51-5). Buddhist Bks.

Suzuki, Shunryu. Zen Mind, Beginner's Mind. Dixon, Trudy, ed. LC 70-123326. 132p. 1970. 9.95 (ISBN 0-8348-0052-7); pap. 5.95 (ISBN 0-8348-0079-9). Weatherhill.

Suzuki, Teitaro, tr. see Carus, Paul.

Svadesh, Swami, et al, eds. see Rajneesh, Bhagwan Shree.

Svami Kripalvananda. The Sadhak's Companion. Darshana Shakti Ma, ed. Gauri Modi, tr. from Gujarati. Orig. Title: Guru Vachanamrit. (Illus., Orig.). 1977. pap. text ed. 2.95 (ISBN 0-933116-04-7). Sanatana.

Svarupa dasa, Ravindra. Encounters with the Lord of the Universe. Swami, Jayadvaita & Dravida dasa, eds. 130p. 1985. pap. text ed. 3.50 (ISBN 0-911233-20-2). Gita Nagari.

Sven Eek. Damodar & the Pioneers of the Theosophical Movement. 19.95 (ISBN 0-8356-7003-1). Theos Pub Hse.

Svensson, Borje. Great Miracles of Jesus. (Change-the-Picture Storybooks). (Illus.). 10p. 1985. 6.95 (ISBN 0-89191-940-6, 59402, Chariot Bks). Cook.

--Great Stories from the Bible. (Change-the-Picture Storybooks). (Illus.). 10p. 1985. 6.95 (ISBN 0-89191-939-2, 59394, Chariot Bks). Cook.

Svirelin, Alexander. Tserkovnij Ustav. Tr. of Church Services. 143p. 1981. pap. text ed. 6.00 (ISBN 0-317-30282-5). Holy Trinity.

Swadley, Elizabeth. Your Christian Wedding. LC 66-15149. 1966. 8.95 (ISBN 0-8054-7902-3). Broadman.

Swafford, Mrs. A. W. Knowing God. rev. ed. (God & Us Ser.). Tr. of God & Us. 32p. 1980. tchrs' ed. 2.00 (ISBN 0-89114-090-5). Baptist Pub Hse.

Swafford, Mrs. Z. W. He Will Come. 3rd ed. (Illus.). 128p. 1974. pap. 2.00 (ISBN 0-89114-009-3). Baptist Pub Hse.

--This We Believe. (Illus.). 109p. (Orig.). 1983. pap. 2.50 (ISBN 0-89114-115-4). Baptist Pub Hse.

Swafford, Z. W. Bible Gems. 1974. pap. 0.75 (ISBN 0-89114-034-4). Baptist Pub Hse.

--Living for God. (God & Us Ser.). 32p. 1981. pap. 2.00 (ISBN 0-89114-099-9); coloring book 0.69 (ISBN 0-89114-102-2). Baptist Pub Hse.

--Serving God. (God & Us Ser.). 32p. 1981. pap. 2.00 (ISBN 0-89114-097-2); pap. 0.69 coloring bk. (ISBN 0-89114-098-0). Baptist Pub Hse.

Swafford, Mrs. Z. W. Worshiping God. (God & Us Ser.). 32p. 1983. pap. 2.00 (ISBN 0-89114-103-0); coloring book 0.69 (ISBN 0-89114-104-9). Baptist Pub Hse.

Swahananda, Swami. Meditation & Other Spiritual Disciplines. 171p. 6.50 (ISBN 0-87481-214-3, Pub. by Advaita Ashrama India). Vedanta Pr.

--Service & Spirituality. 211p. (Orig.). 1980. pap. 4.95 (ISBN 0-87481-500-2). Vedanta Pr.

Swahananda, Swami, tr. see Vidyaranya, Swami.

Swails, John W. The Holy Spirit & the Messianic Age. 4.95 (ISBN 0-911866-73-6). Advocate.

Swaim, J. Carter. War, Peace & the Bible. LC 81-16889. 144p. (Orig.). 1982. pap. 3.48 (ISBN 0-88344-752-5). Orbis Bks.

Swaim, Kathleen. Before & After the Fall: Contrasting Modes in "Paradise Lost". LC 85-28925. 312p. 1986. lib. bdg. 27.50X (ISBN 0-87023-504-4). U of Mass Pr.

Swain, Bernard F. Liberating Leadership: Practical Styles of Pastoral Ministry. 96p. (Orig.). 1986. pap. 6.95 (ISBN 0-86683-483-4, HarpR). Har-Row.

Swain, Clara A. A Glimpse of India, Being a Collection of Extracts from the Letters of Dr. Clara A. Swain. Gifford, Carolyn D. & Dayton, Donald, eds. (Women in American Protestant Religion 1800-1930 Ser.). 366p. 1987. lib. bdg. 50.00 (ISBN 0-8240-0677-1). Garland Pub.

Swain, Clark. Enriching Your Marriage: A Tune-up for Partners in Love. LC 80-84568. 250p. 1982. 9.95 (ISBN 0-88290-171-0, 2015). Horizon Utah.

Swain, Dorothy G. Teach Me to Teach. pap. 4.95 (ISBN 0-8170-0316-9). Judson.

Swain, Jasper. From My World to Yours: A Young Man's Account of the Afterlife. Langley, Noel, ed. LC 76-52573. 103p. 1984. pap. 7.95 (ISBN 0-8027-7257-9). Walker & Co.

Swain, Joseph R. What Does God Do All Day? 1977. 7.00 (ISBN 0-682-48919-0, Testament). Exposition Pr FL.

Swain, Joseph W., tr. see Durkheim, Emile.

Swain, Kathleen M., jt. ed. see Ingram, William.

Swain, Lionel. Ephesians. (New Testament Message Ser.: Vol. 13). 10.95 (ISBN 0-89453-201-4); pap. 5.95 (ISBN 0-89453-136-0). M Glazier.

Swain, Lionel, et al. Last Writings. LC 71-173033. (Scripture Discussion Commentary Ser.: Pt. 12). 192p. 1972. pap. text ed. 4.50 (ISBN 0-87946-011-3). ACTA Found.

Swain, Marshall, jt. ed. see Pappas, George S.

Swain, Peter, tr. see Bianco, Enzo.

Swami, Bhakivedanta. Srimad Bhagavatam: Eleventh Canto, 4 Vols. (Illus.4). 416p. 1983. 12.95 ea. (ISBN 0-89213-125-X). Bhaktivedanta.

Swami, Bhaktivedanta. Bhagavat Gita As It Is. 6.95 (ISBN 0-89213-134-9). Bhaktivedanta.

Swami, Jayadvaita, ed. see Svarupa dasa, Ravindra.

Swami, Jyotir & Nanda, Maya. Yoga Essays for Self-Improvement. LC 81-65248. 248p. 1981. pap. 4.99 (ISBN 0-934664-39-0, 030). Yoga Res Foun.

Swami Kuvalayananda. Popular Yoga Asanas. LC 76-130420. (Illus.). (YA) 1972. Repr. of 1931 ed. 12.50 (ISBN 0-8048-0673-X). C E Tuttle.

Swami, Shri P., tr. The Geeta. 96p. (Orig.). 1965. pap. 5.95 (ISBN 0-571-06157-5). Faber & Faber.

Swami Swahananda. Hindu Symbology & Other Essays. 266p. (Orig.). 1983. pap. 4.95 (ISBN 0-87481-526-6, Pub. by Ramakrishna Math Madras India). Vedanta Pr.

Swami Tapasyananda, tr. see Valmiki.

Swami Abhayananda. History of Mysticism. 464p. (Orig.). 1987. pap. 11.95 (ISBN 0-914557-04-1). Atma Bks.

Swami Abhedanenda. True Psychology. 1987. 6.50 (ISBN 0-87481-613-0, Pub. by Ramakrishna Math Madras India). Vedanta Pr.

Swami Amar Jyoti. Spirit of Himalaya: The Story of a Truth Seeker. 2nd rev. ed. LC 85-50206. (Illus.). 128p. 1985. pap. 5.95 (ISBN 0-933572-06-9). Truth Consciousness.

Swami Bhaktivedanta. Sri Isopanisad: Discovering the Original Person. 1985. 7.95; pap. 2.95 (ISBN 0-89213-138-1). Bhaktivedanta.

Swami Bhashyananda. From the Unreal to the Real. Date not set. price not set. Vivekananda.

Swami Chetanananda. Dynamic Stillness: A Practice Guide to Kundalini Yoga. 208p. 1987. pap. 9.95 (ISBN 0-915801-06-X). Rudra Pr.

--The Logic of Love. 288p. 1987. pap. 10.95 (ISBN 0-915801-05-1). Rudra Pr.

Swami Chetanananda, compiled by see Swami Vivekananda.

Swami Chidvilasananda, tr. see Swami Mukananda.

Swami Deva Paritosh, ed. see Rajneesh, Bhagwan Shree.

Swami Durgananda. Where Are You Going? A Guide to the Spiritual Journey. LC 81-52192. 176p. (Orig.). 1981. pap. 6.95 (ISBN 0-914602-75-6). SYDA Found.

Swami Durgananda, ed. see Swami Mukananda.

Swami Jagadananda, tr. see Saradananda, Swami.

Swami Jyotir, Maya N. Integral Yoga Today. 96p. (Orig.). 1983. pap. 2.50 (ISBN 0-934664-43-9). Yoga Res Foun.

Swami Jyotir Maya Nanda. The Mystery of the Soul: Katha Upanishad. (Illus.). 1976. pap. 1.99 (ISBN 0-934664-07-2). Yoga Res Foun.

--Srimad Bhagavad Gita: Pocket Book Edition. (Illus.). 384p. 1986. pap. 3.00 (ISBN 0-934664-44-7). Yoga Res Foun.

--The Way to Liberation: Moksha Dharma of Mahabharata, 2 vols. (Illus.). 1976. Ea. pap. 4.99 (ISBN 0-934664-11-0). Yoga Res Foun.

--Yoga Integral. (Span., Illus.). 112p. 1984. pap. 2.85 (ISBN 0-934664-51-X). Yoga Res Foun.

--Yoga of Divine Love: A Commentary on Narada Bhakti Sutras. 1982. pap. 4.99 (ISBN 0-934664-42-0). Yoga Res Foun.

Swami Jyotir Maya Nanda, tr. see Patanjali.

Swami Karunananda Ma, ed. Lotus Prayer Book. LC 86-10384. 224p. (Orig.). 1986. pap. 9.95 (ISBN 0-932040-33-0). Integral Yoga Pubns.

Swami Krishna Prabhu, ed. see Rajneesh, Bhagwan S.

Swami Kriyananda. Lessons in Yoga: Fourteen Steps to Higher Awareness. 2nd, rev. ed. 1979. pap. write for info. (ISBN 0-916124-16-9). Dawn Pubns CA.

Swami Kriyananda. Keys to the Bhagavad Gita. 48p. 1979. pap. 3.00 (ISBN 0-916124-15-0). Dawn Pubns CA.

Swami Mukananda. I Have Become Alive: Secrets of the Inner Journey. Swami Durgananda, ed. Swami Chidvilasananda, tr. LC 85-50040. 240p. (Orig.). 1985. pap. 6.95 (ISBN 0-914602-89-6). SYDA Found.

Swami Muktananda. Does Death Really Exist? LC 81-50161. 64p. 1983. pap. 3.95 (ISBN 0-914602-56-X). SYDA Found.

--Getting Rid of What You Haven't Got. LC 74-19579. 64p. 1974. 3.25 (ISBN 0-914602-44-6). SYDA Found.

--In the Company of a Siddha: Interviews & Conversations with Swami Muktananda. rev. ed. LC 78-65085. 192p. 1978. 5.95. SYDA Found.

--Kundalini Stavaha. 45p. 1980. pap. 2.50 (ISBN 0-914602-55-1). SYDA Found.

--Kundalini: The Secret of Life. (Illus.). 64p. (Orig.). 1983. pap. 3.95 (ISBN 0-914602-47-0). SYDA Found.

--Lalleshwari. LC 81-50160. 92p. 1981. pap. 3.95. SYDA Found.

--Light on the Path. LC 81-51377. 112p. 1972. 4.95 (ISBN 0-914602-54-3). SYDA Found.

--Mukteshwari, Vol. II. LC 79-101943. 188p. 1973. 6.00 (ISBN 0-914602-62-4). SYDA Found.

--Mystery of the Mind. LC 81-50159. (Illus.). 64p. (Orig.). 1983. pap. 3.95 (ISBN 0-914602-70-5). SYDA Found.

--Paramartha Katha Prasang: Spiritual Conversations with Swami Muktananda. 356p. 6.95 (ISBN 0-914602-90-X). SYDA Found.

--Reflections of the Self: Poems of Spiritual Life. LC 80-50391. (Illus.). 205p. (Orig.). 1980. pap. 5.95 (ISBN 0-914602-50-0). SYDA Found.

--Swami Muktananda American Tour 1970. LC 76-670007. 103p. 1974. 2.95 (ISBN 0-914602-25-X). SYDA Found.

--To Know the Knower. 40p. 1.75 (ISBN 0-317-03900-8). SYDA Found.

Swami Muktananda, tr. from Sanskrit. Shree Guru Gita. LC 81-51183. 128p. (Orig.). 1981. pap. 3.95 (ISBN 0-914602-73-X). SYDA Found.

Swami Nikhilananda, compiled by. Vivekananda: The Yogas & Other Works. LC 53-7534. (Illus.). 1018p. includes biography 19.95 (ISBN 0-911206-04-3). Ramakrishna.

Swami Premdharma, ed. see Zorba the Buddha Rajneesh Restaurants & Staff.

Swami Radha Sivananda. Seeds of Light. LC 76-67719. (Illus.). 116p. 1985. pap. 9.95 (ISBN 0-931454-11-5). Timeless Bks.

Swami Rama. Choosing a Path. 200p. (Orig.). pap. 8.95 (ISBN 0-89389-077-4). Himalayan Pubs.

--Inspired Thoughts of Swami Rama. 260p. (Orig.). pap. 8.95 (ISBN 0-89389-086-3). Himalayan Pubs.

--Path of Fire & Light: Advanced Practices of Yoga. 180p. (Orig.). 1986. pap. 8.95 (ISBN 0-89389-097-9). Himalayan Pubs.

--A Practical Guide to Holistic Health. 152p. 8.95 (ISBN 0-89389-066-9); pap. 6.95 (ISBN 0-89389-065-0). Himalayan Pubs.

Swami Rama, et al. Yoga & Psychotherapy: The Evolution of Consciousness. 332p. 13.95 (ISBN 0-89389-000-6); pap. 9.95 (ISBN 0-89389-036-7). Himalayan Pubs.

Swami Rudrananda. Spiritual Cannibalism. 208p. (Orig.). 1987. pap. 9.95 (ISBN 0-915801-07-8). Rudra Pr.

Swami Satchidananda, see Satchidandanda, Swami.

Swami Satprakashananda. The Universe, God, & God-Realization: From the Viewpoint of Vedanta. LC 77-79829. 310p. 1977. 12.50 (ISBN 0-916356-57-4). Vedanta Soc St Louis.

Swami Sivananda. Karma Yoga. Swami Venkatesananda, ed. (Life & Works of Swami Sivananda). 192p. (Orig.). 1985. pap. 6.95 (ISBN 0-949027-05-7). Integral Yoga Pubns.

Swami Sivananda & Swami Venkatesananda. Health & Hatha Yoga. (Life & Works of Swami Sivananda). (Illus.). 350p. (Orig.). 1985. pap. 9.95 (ISBN 0-949027-03-0). Integral Yoga Pubns.

Swami Sivananda Radha. Gods Who Walk the Rainbow. LC 81-9410. (Illus.). 240p. (Orig.). 1981. pap. 7.95 (ISBN 0-931454-07-7). Timeless Bks.

--Mantras: Words of Power. LC 80-10293. (Illus.). 150p. 1980. pap. 7.95 (ISBN 0-931454-05-0). Timeless Bks.

--Radha: Diary of a Woman's Search. LC 80-26470. (Illus.). 230p. (Orig.). 1981. pap. 7.95 (ISBN 0-931454-06-9). Timeless Bks.

Swami Venkatesananda, jt. auth. see Swami Sivananda.

Swami Venkatesananda, ed. Sivananda: Biography of a Modern Sage. (Life & Works of Swami Sivananda). (Illus.). 448p. (Orig.). 1985. pap. 9.95 (ISBN 0-949027-01-4). Integral Yoga Pubns.

Swami Venkatesananda, ed. see Swami Sivananda.

Swami Virajananda. Toward the Goal Supreme. LC 73-87782. 155p. 1973. pap. 3.50 (ISBN 0-87481-029-9). Vedanta Pr.

Swami Vireshwarananda. Brahma Sutra Sri Bhasya. 1979. 10.00 (ISBN 0-87481-189-9). Vedanta Pr.

Swami Vishnudevananda. Complete Illustrated Book of Yoga. 1981. pap. 3.50 (ISBN 0-671-44787-4). PB.

Swami Vishwashrayananda. Swami Vijnanananda: His Life & Sayings. Devavrata Basu Ray, tr. from Bengoli. 72p. 1981. pap. 1.95 (ISBN 0-87481-502-9). Vedanta Pr.

Swami Vivekananda. Bhakti-Yoga: The Yoga of Love & Devotion. pap. 1.50 (ISBN 0-87481-157-0). Vedanta Pr.

--Complete Works of Swami Vivekananda, 8 Vols. 75.00x (ISBN 0-87481-092-2); Vol. 1. 10.95x (ISBN 0-87481-137-6); Vol. 2. 10.00x (ISBN 0-87481-138-4); Vol. 3. 10.95x (ISBN 0-87481-139-2); Vol. 4. 10.95x (ISBN 0-87481-140-6); Vol. 5. 10.95x (ISBN 0-87481-141-4); Vol. 6. 10.95x (ISBN 0-87481-142-2); Vol. 7. 10.95x (ISBN 0-87481-143-0); Vol. 8. 10.95x (ISBN 0-87481-144-9). Vedanta Pr.

--Complete Works of Swami Vivekananda, 8 vols. pap. 55.00x (ISBN 0-87481-176-7). Vedanta Pr.

--Education. pap. 1.95 (ISBN 0-87481-451-0). Vedanta Pr.

--In Search of God & Other Poems. pap. 3.75 (ISBN 0-87481-121-X). Vedanta Pr.

--Jnana-Yoga. pap. 4.95 (ISBN 0-87481-158-9). Vedanta Pr.

--Karma-Yoga. pap. 1.50 (ISBN 0-87481-159-7). Vedanta Pr.

--Karma-Yoga & Bhakti-Yoga. LC 55-8657. 336p. pocket ed. 6.95 (ISBN 0-911206-07-8); pap. 6.95 large size (ISBN 0-911206-22-1). Ramakrishna.

--Lectures from Colombo to Almora. pap. 8.95 (ISBN 0-87481-171-6). Vedanta Pr.

--Meditation & Its Methods According to Swami Vivekananda. Swami Chetanananda, compiled by. LC 75-36392. (Orig.). 1976. pap. 4.95 (ISBN 0-87481-030-2). Vedanta Pr.

--Practical Vedanta. pap. 2.00 (ISBN 0-87481-124-4). Vedanta Pr.

--Raja-Yoga. LC 55-12231. 320p. pocket ed. 6.95 (ISBN 0-911206-06-X); pap. 6.95 large size (ISBN 0-911206-23-X). Ramakrishna.

--Ramakrishna & His Message. (Orig.). 1971. pap. 2.00 (ISBN 0-87481-126-0). Vedanta Pr.

--Ramakrishna As Swamiji Saw Him. (Orig.). 1970. pap. 1.00 (ISBN 0-87481-452-9). Vedanta Pr.

--Religion of Love. 114p. pap. 2.50 (ISBN 0-87481-129-5). Vedanta Pr.

--Selections from Swami Vivekananda. 10.00x (ISBN 0-87481-094-9); pap. 6.95 (ISBN 0-87481-174-0). Vedanta Pr.

--Teachings of Swami Vivekananda. 1971. pap. 3.95 (ISBN 0-87481-134-1). Vedanta Pr.

--Vivekananda: A Biography in Pictures. 2nd ed. Advaita Ashrama Staff, ed. (Illus.). 1974. 30.00x (ISBN 0-87481-136-8). Vedanta Pr.

--What Religion Is in the Words of Vivekananda. Yale, John, ed. pap. 5.95 (ISBN 0-87481-213-5). Vedanta Pr.

Swami Vivekananda, tr. Raja-Yoga: The Yoga Aphorisms of Patanjali. pap. 3.25 (ISBN 0-87481-160-0). Vedanta Pr.

Swami Vivekananda, et al. Thus Spake Library: Teachings of Vivekananda, Ramakrishna, Sri Sarada Devi, Rama, Krishna, Buddha, Christ, Muhammad, Shankara & Guru Nanak. pap. 3.50 set 10 bklts (ISBN 0-87481-444-8). Vedanta Pr.

Swan, Howard. Music in the Southwest, 1825-1950. LC 77-5421. (Music Reprint Ser.). 1977. Repr. of 1952 ed. lib. bdg. 39.50 (ISBN 0-306-77418-6). Da Capo.

Swan, M. L. The New Harp of Columbia. Horn, Dorothy D., et al, eds. LC 78-5504. (Tennesseana Editions Ser.). (Facsimile of 1867 Ed.). 1978. 18.95x (ISBN 0-87049-251-9). U of Tenn Pr.

Swancara, Frank. Obstruction of Justice by Religion: A Treatise on Religious Barbarities of the Common Law, & a Review of Judicial Oppressions of the Non-Religious in the U. S. LC 70-139581. (Civil Liberties in American History Ser). (Illus.). 1971. Repr. of 1936 ed. lib. bdg. 32.50 (ISBN 0-306-71964-9). Da Capo.

--Separation of Church & State. 346p. pap. 3.00. Truth Seeker.

Swank, George W. Living in God's Power. 112p. 1983. pap. 5.95 (ISBN 0-8170-0968-X). Judson.

Swank, J. Grant, Jr. Beacon Small-Group Bible Studies, I & II Peter: A Faith for Testing Times. (Beacon Small-Group Bible Studies). 80p. 1982. pap. 2.50 (ISBN 0-8341-0790-2). Beacon Hill.

Swanson, Allen J. Mending the Nets: Taiwan Church Growth & Loss in the 1980's. LC 86-47704. 320p. 1986. pap. 7.95 (ISBN 0-87808-207-7, WCL 207-7). William Carey Lib.

Swanson, Guy E. Birth of the Gods: The Origin of Primitive Beliefs. 1960. pap. 4.95 (ISBN 0-472-06093-7, 93, AA). U of Mich Pr.

Swanson, James R. & Tanner, Don. The Invincible Power of Praise. LC 86-19151. (Illus.). 64p. 1986. pap. 2.95 (ISBN 0-88005-004-7). Uplift Bks.

Swanson, Mary E., jt. auth. see Foster, Marshall E.

Swanson, R. N. Universities, Academics & the Great Schism. LC 78-56764. (Cambridge Studies in Medieval Life & Thought: 3rd Ser., No. 12). 1979. 49.50 (ISBN 0-521-22127-7). Cambridge U Pr.

Swanson, Reuben J. The Horizontal Line Synopsis of the Gospels. LC 75-20997. 608p. 1984. Repr. of 1980 ed. 24.95 (ISBN 0-87808-744-3). William Carey Lib.

--The Horizontal Line Synopsis of the Gospels: Volume I, The Gospel of Mathew. 1982. 29.95 (ISBN 0-915948-10-9). Bks Distinction.

--Roots out of Dry Ground. 1979. 8.50 (ISBN 0-915948-06-0); pap. 6.50 (ISBN 0-686-57420-6). Bks Distinction.

Swanson, Richard. Spare Your People! LC 85-73213. 1986. pap. 3.50 (ISBN 0-88270-596-2). Bridge Pub.

Swanson, Steve. Bible Readings for Men. LC 83-72116. 112p. (Orig.). 1984. pap. 3.95 (ISBN 0-8066-2060-9, 10-0682). Augsburg.

--Biblical Pictures of Water. 1986. 3.95 (ISBN 0-89536-784-X, 6802). CSS of Ohio.

--What Does God Want Me to Do with My Life? How to Decide about School, Job, Friends, Sex, Marriage. LC 79-50086. 104p. 1979. pap. 3.95 (ISBN 0-8066-1722-5, 10-7046). Augsburg.

Swanson, Steve, et al. Faith Prints: Youth Devotions for Every Day of the Year. LC 85-13466. 224p. (Orig.). 1985. pap. 4.95 (ISBN 0-8066-2178-8, 10-2189). Augsburg.

Swanson, Steven. Biblical Pictures of Bread. 1985. 3.95 (ISBN 0-89536-718-1, 5802). CSS of Ohio.

Swanston, Hamish. Histories Two. Bright, Laurence, ed. LC 71-173033. (Scripture Discussion Commentary Ser.: Pt. 5). 224p. 1971. pap. text ed. 4.50 (ISBN 0-87946-005-9). ACTA Found.

--Ideas of Order: Anglicans & the Renewal of Theological Method in the Middle Years of the 19th Century. 256p. 1974. pap. text ed. 22.00 (ISBN 90-232-1124-3, Pub. by Van Gorcum Holland). Longwood Pub Group.

Swanston, Hamish & Bright, Laurence. Histories One. LC 71-173033. (Scriptures Discussion Commentary Ser.: Pt. 3). 182p. 1971. pap. text ed. 4.50 (ISBN 0-87946-002-4). ACTA Found.

Swanston, Hamish F. A Language for Madness: The Abuse & the Use of Christian Creeds. 154p. 1976. pap. text ed. 12.50 (ISBN 90-232-1426-9, Pub. by Van Gorcum Holland). Longwood Pub Group.

Swanton, John R. Haida Texts & Myths: Skidegate Dialect. LC 5-41613. (Landmarks in Anthropology Ser). Repr. of 1905 ed. 34.00 (ISBN 0-384-59020-9). Johnson Repr.

--Myths & Tales of the Southeastern Indians. LC 74-9011. (Smithsonian Institution. Bureau of American Enthnology. Bulletin: 88). Repr. of 1929 ed. 20.00 (ISBN 0-404-11908-5). AMS Pr.

--Tlingit Myths & Texts. Repr. of 1909 ed. 34.00 (ISBN 0-384-59050-0). Johnson Repr.

--Tlingit Myths & Texts. Repr. of 1909 ed. 49.00 (ISBN 0-403-03710-7). Scholarly.

Swardson, Harold R. Poetry & the Fountain of Light: Observations on the Conflict Between Christian & Classical Traditions in Seventeenth-Century Poetry. LC 62-9993. 1962. 4.50x (ISBN 0-8262-0015-X). U of Mo Pr.

Swarte, Carolyn G. de see Acornley, John H.

Swarte, Carolyn G. de see Andrews, C. W.

Swarte, Carolyn G. de see Baker, Frances J.

Swarte, Carolyn G. de see Bethune, Joanna.

Swarte, Carolyn G. de see Brown, George.

Swarte, Carolyn G. de see Brown, Oswald E. & Brown, Anna M.

Swarte, Carolyn G. de see Coppin, Fanny J.

Swarte, Carolyn G. de see De Swarte, Carolyn G.

Swarte, Carolyn G. de see De Swarte, Carolyn G. & Dayton, Donald.

Swarthmore College. Catalog of the Friends Historical Library Book & Serial Collections, 6 vols. 1982. Set. lib. bdg. 655.00 (ISBN 0-8161-0376-3, Hall Library). G K Hall.

Swartley, Willard. Slavery, Sabbath, War & Women: Case Issues in Biblical Interpretation. LC 82-23417. (Conrad Grebel Lecture Ser.). 320p. (Orig.). 1983. pap. 15.95 (ISBN 0-8361-3330-7). Herald Pr.

Swartley, Willard M. Mark: The Way for All Nations. rev. ed. LC 78-27917. 224p. 1981. pap. 9.95 (ISBN 0-8361-1977-0). Herald Pr.

Swartley, Willard M., ed. Essays on War & Peace: Bible & Early Church. (Occasional Papers Ser.: No. 9). 154p. 1986. pap. text ed. 6.50 (ISBN 0-936273-09-7). Inst Mennonite.

Swartz, Lois B. Soaring Beyond Problems: Meditations for Difficult Times. (Illus.). 72p. (Orig.). 1987. pap. 6.95 (ISBN 0-940045-00-1). Walnut Knoll Assocs.

Swartz, Merlin L., et al. Studies on Islam. 1981. 22.50x (ISBN 0-19-502716-7); pap. 10.95x (ISBN 0-19-502717-5). Oxford U Pr.

Swarup, Ram. Understanding Islam Through Hadis: Religious Faith or Fanaticism? 1983. 13.95 (ISBN 0-682-49948-X). Exposition Pr FL.

Swarzenski, Hanns. An Eighteenth Century Creche. LC 66-25450. (Illus.). 1966. pap. 2.00 (ISBN 0-87846-142-6, Pub. by Mus Fine Arts Boston). C E Tuttle.

--Monuments of Romanesque Art: The Art of Church Treasures in North-Western Europe. 2nd ed. LC 55-937. (Illus.). 1967. 40.00x (ISBN 0-226-78605-6). U of Chicago Pr.

Swatos, William. Into Denominationalism. LC 79-53776. (Monograph: No. 2). 1979. pap. 5.50 (ISBN 0-932566-01-4). Soc Sci Stud Rel.

Swatos, William H., Jr. Faith of the Fathers: Science, Religion, & Reform in the Development of Early American Sociology. vi, 102p. 1985. pap. text ed. 6.95x (ISBN 0-932269-11-7). Wyndham Hall.

Swearer, Donald K. Buddhism & Society in Southeast Asia. LC 81-8048. (Focus on Hinduism & Buddhism Ser.). 64p. 1981. pap. 4.95x (ISBN 0-89012-023-4). Anima Pubns.

--Dialogue: The Key to Understanding Other Religions. LC 77-3964. (Biblical Perspectives on Current Issues). 172p. 1977. soft cover 4.95 (ISBN 0-664-24138-7). Westminster.

--Wat Haripunjaya: A Study of the Royal Temple of the Buddha's Relic, Lamphun, Thailand. LC 75-33802. (American Academy of Religion. Studies in Religion). 1976. pap. 9.95 (ISBN 0-89130-052-X, 010010). Scholars Pr GA.

Sweatte, Appolles T. Marriage, Divorce, & the Believer. LC 85-91361. 53p. 1986. 6.95. Vantage.

Sweazey, George E. The Church As Evangelist. LC 77-20452. 272p. 1984. pap. 7.95 (ISBN 0-06-067777-5, RD 502, HarpR). Har-Row.

--Preaching the Good News. 368p. 1976. 24.95 (ISBN 0-13-694802-2). P-H.

Swedenborg, Emanuel. Apocalypse Explained, 6 vols. Student ed. LC 76-46145. 12.00 ea. Vol. 1 (ISBN 0-87785-000-3). Vol. 2 (ISBN 0-87785-001-1). Vol. 3 (ISBN 0-87785-002-X). Vol. 4 (ISBN 0-87785-003-8). Vol. 5 (ISBN 0-87785-004-6). Vol. 6 (ISBN 0-87785-005-4). 72.00 set (ISBN 0-87785-006-2). Swedenborg.

--Apocalypse Revealed, 2 vols. LC 78-5623. 1974. Vol. 1. Vol. 2. student ed. set 11.00 (ISBN 0-87785-017-8); student ed. 12.00 ea. Vol. 1 (ISBN 0-87785-015-1). Vol. 2 (ISBN 0-87785-016-X). pap. 7.00 (ISBN 0-87785-014-3). Swedenborg.

--Arcana Coelestia (Heavenly Secrets, Vol. 1. pap. 3.95 (ISBN 0-87785-053-4). Swedenborg.

--Arcana Coelestia (Heavenly Secrets) Student Edition, 12 vols. Incl. 12.00 ea. Vol. 1 (ISBN 0-87785-021-6). Vol. 2 (ISBN 0-87785-022-4). Vol. 3 (ISBN 0-87785-023-2). Vol. 4 (ISBN 0-87785-024-0). Vol. 5 (ISBN 0-87785-025-9). Vol. 6 (ISBN 0-87785-026-7); Vol. 7 (ISBN 0-87785-027-5). Vol. 8 (ISBN 0-87785-028-3). Vol. 9 (ISBN 0-87785-029-1). Vol. 10 (ISBN 0-87785-030-5). Vol. 11 (ISBN 0-87785-031-3). Vol. 12 (ISBN 0-87785-032-1). LC 63-1828. 1977. Set. 144.00 (ISBN 0-87785-033-X). Swedenborg.

--Conjugal Love. Student ed. LC 79-93407. 12.00 (ISBN 0-87785-054-2). Swedenborg.

--Divine Love & Wisdom. LC 75-37094. student ed. 12.00 (ISBN 0-87785-056-9). Swedenborg.

--Divine Love & Wisdom. Dole, George, tr. LC 85-50918. 1986. pap. 6.95 (ISBN 0-87785-129-8). Swedenborg.

--Divine Providence. LC 74-30441. 1974. trade ed. o.p. 10.00 (ISBN 0-87785-060-7); student ed. 12.00 (ISBN 0-87785-059-3); pap. 3.95 (ISBN 0-87785-061-5). Swedenborg.

--Emanuel Swedenborg: Universal Human & Soul Body Interaction. (Classic of Western Spirituality Ser.). 258p. 1984. 12.95 (ISBN 0-8091-0344-3); pap. 9.95 (ISBN 0-8091-2554-4). Paulist Pr.

--Emanuel Swedenborg's Journal of Dreams. LC 86-70341. 1986. pap. 8.95 (ISBN 0-87785-133-6). Swedenborg.

--Experientiae Spirituales, 6 Vols. 2nd ed. Odhner, John D., ed. (Lat.). 3600p. 1982. Set. 270.00 (ISBN 0-910557-00-4). Acad New Church.

--Four Doctrines. LC 67-1465. 1971. student ed. 12.00 (ISBN 0-87785-063-1); pap. 2.95 (ISBN 0-87785-064-X). Swedenborg.

--Four Leading Doctrines of the New Church. LC 71-134426. Repr. of 1882 ed. 21.00 (ISBN 0-404-08466-4). AMS Pr.

--Heaven & Hell. large print ed. LC 81-52785. 800p. 8.25 (ISBN 0-87785-130-1). Swedenborg.

--Heaven & Hell. LC 77-93044. cancelled (ISBN 0-87785-167-0); student ed. 12.00 (ISBN 0-87785-066-6); pap. 5.95 (ISBN 0-87785-153-0). Swedenborg.

--Marital Love. LC 38-13542. 760p. 1974. student ed. 12.00 (ISBN 0-87785-150-6). Swedenborg.

--Miscellaneous Theological Works. LC 76-46143. 1970. cancelled (ISBN 0-87785-071-2); student ed. 12.00 (ISBN 0-87785-070-4). Swedenborg.

--Posthumous Theological Works, 2 vols. LC 38-24293. 634p. Vol. 1. Set. cancelled (ISBN 0-87785-078-X); student ed. 12.00 ea. Vol. 1 (ISBN 0-87785-073-9). Vol. 2 (ISBN 0-87785-074-7). Set. 24.00 (ISBN 0-87785-075-5). Swedenborg.

--Spiritual Diary of Emanuel Swedenborg, 6 vols. lib. bdg. 700.00 (ISBN 0-87968-560-3). Krishna Pr.

--Spiritual Life - the Word of God. pap. 1.95 (ISBN 0-87785-083-6). Swedenborg.

--The Spiritual World Laid Open. lib. bdg. 79.95 (ISBN 0-87968-561-1). Krishna Pr.

Swedenborg, Emmanuel. On the Means Which Conduce to True Philosophy & on the True Philosopher. Clissold, Augustus, tr. from Lat. 42p. pap. 1.00 (ISBN 0-915221-15-2). Swedenborg Sci Assn.

--The Principia: Or the First Princples of Natural Things, Vols. I & II. Clissold, Augustus, tr. from Lat. & intro. by. (Illus.). 1976. Repr. of 1846 ed. Set. 15.00 (ISBN 0-915221-20-9). Vol. I, 380p (ISBN 0-915221-37-3). Vol. II, 413p (ISBN 0-915221-38-1). Swedenborg Sci Assn.

--The Theory of the Soul, 2 vols. (Illus.). 245p. 1986. Set. 187.45 (ISBN 0-89901-261-2). Found Class Reprints.

Sweeney, Frances. Every Man My Brother. 1976. 4.00 (ISBN 0-8198-0410-X); pap. 3.00 (ISBN 0-8198-0411-8). Dghtrs St Paul.

Sweeney, Patrick & Crewe, Sarah. Visionary Spires: The Most Beatiful Churches That Never Were. LC 85-43038. (Illus.). 144p. 1985. 25.00 (ISBN 0-8478-0660-X). Rizzoli Intl.

Sweeney, Terrance A. God &... Thirty Interviews. 240p. 1985. pap. 8.95 (ISBN 0-86683-804-X, 8404, HarpR). Har-Row.

Sweeny, Z. T. Spirit & the Word. 1982. pap. 3.95 (ISBN 0-89225-264-2). Gospel Advocate.

Sweet, Charles F. Champion of the Cross. LC 76-144692. Repr. of 1894 ed. 27.50 (ISBN 0-404-07202-X). AMS Pr.

Sweet, Henry. King Alfred's West-Saxon Version of Gregory's Pastoral Care. 1979. Repr. of 1871 ed. lib. bdg. 200.00 (ISBN 0-8492-8102-4). R West.

Sweet, J. P. Revelation. LC 78-26383. (Westminster Pelican Commentaries). 378p. 1979. 14.95 (ISBN 0-664-21375-8); softcover 9.95 (ISBN 0-664-24262-6). Westminster.

Sweet, Leonard. The Minister's Wife: Her Role in Nineteenth Century American Evangelicalism. 323p. 1983. text ed. 29.95 (ISBN 0-87722-283-5). Temple U Pr.

Sweet, Leonard I. New Life in the Spirit. LC 81-23112. (Library of Living Faith: Vol. 4). 120p. (Orig.). 1982. pap. 5.95 (ISBN 0-664-24414-9). Westminster.

Sweet, Leonard I., ed. The Evangelical Tradition in America. LC 84-6723. x, 320p. 1984. 25.95 (ISBN 0-86554-092-6, MUP/H84). Mercer Univ Pr.

Sweet, William W. American Culture & Religion. LC 72-78372. ix, 114p. 1972. Repr. of 1951 ed. lib. bdg. 19.50x (ISBN 0-8154-0421-2). Cooper Sq.

--Religion on the American Frontier. Incl. Vol. 1. The Baptists, 1783-1830. 652p. Repr. of 1931 ed; Vol. 2. The Presbyterians, 1783-1840. (Illus.). 939p. 1964. Repr. of 1936 ed. 37.50x (ISBN 0-8154-0223-6); Vol. 3. The Congregationalists, 1783-1850. (Illus.). 435p. 1964. Repr. of 1934 ed. 37.50x (ISBN 0-8154-0224-4); Vol. 4. The Methodists, 1783-1840. (Illus.). 800p. 1964. Repr. of 1946 ed. 37.50x (ISBN 0-8154-0225-2). LC 63-21092. 1964. Repr. of 1946 ed. Cooper Sq.

--Revivalism in America. 1944. 12.75 (ISBN 0-8446-1430-0). Peter Smith.

Sweeting, Donald, jt. auth. see Sweeting, George.

Sweeting, George. The Basics of the Christian Life. rev. ed. (Moody Press Electives Ser.). 1983. pap. 3.95 (ISBN 0-8024-0259-3); Leader's Guide. pap. 2.50 (ISBN 0-8024-0309-3). Moody.

--Catch the Spirit of Love. 120p. 1983. pap. 4.95 (ISBN 0-88207-108-4). Victor Bks.

--Como Iniciar la Vida Cristiana. Orig. Title: How to Begin the Christian Life. (Span.). 1977. pap. 3.50 (ISBN 0-8254-1697-3). Kregel.

--Faith that Works: Study of the Book of James. 1983. pap. 3.95 (ISBN 0-8024-0276-3). Moody.

--How to Begin the Christian Life. LC 75-31674. 128p. 1976. pap. 3.50 (ISBN 0-8024-3626-9). Moody.

--How to Witness Successfully. LC 78-1959. 1978. pap. 3.95 (ISBN 0-8024-3791-5). Moody.

--Special Sermons by George Sweeting. 1985. pap. 11.95 (ISBN 0-8024-8211-2). Moody.

--Your Future: George Sweeting on Bible Prophecy. 1984. 6.95 (ISBN 0-8024-0404-9). Moody.

Sweeting, George & Sweeting, Donald. Acts of God. (Orig.). 1986. pap. 6.95 (ISBN 0-8024-0497-9). Moody.

Sweeting, George W. You Can Climb Higher: The Christian Persuit of Excellence. 192p. 1985. 10.95 (ISBN 0-8407-5424-8). Nelson.

Sweetman, James W. Islam & Christian Theology: A Study of the Interpretations of Theological Ideas in the Two Religions, 3 vols. 1980. Set. lib. bdg. 229.95 (ISBN 0-8490-3136-2). Gordon Pr.

Sweetser, Thomas P. The Catholic Parish: Shifting Membership in a Changing Church. LC 74-84543. (Studies in Religion & Society). 1974. 15.95x (ISBN 0-913348-06-6); pap. 8.95x (ISBN 0-913348-13-9). Ctr Sci Study.

--Successful Parishes: How They Meet the Challenge of Change. 204p. 1983. pap. 9.95 (ISBN 0-86683-694-2, HarpR). Har-Row.

Sweetser, Thomas P. & Holden, Carol W. Leadership in a Successful Parish. LC 86-45386. 160p. 1986. pap. 8.95 (ISBN 0-86683-517-2, RD 569, HarpR). Har-Row.

Swellengrebel, J. L., jt. auth. see Reiling, J.

Swenson, Ana M., tr. see Jauncey, J. H.

Swenson, Ana M., tr. see Valentine, Foy.

Swenson, D. F., tr. see Kierkegaard, Soren.

Swenson, Keith M. The Blessings Cup: A Guide to Family Devotions for Lent. 32p. (Orig.). 1984. pap. 2.75 (ISBN 0-8066-2033-1, 23-1120). Augsburg.

Swenson, Roger, ed. The Serious Season. LC 86-25876. 116p. (Orig.). 1987. pap. 7.95 (ISBN 0-8189-0512-3). Alba.

Swete, H. B. The Apostles' Creed, Its Relation to Primitive Christianity. 112p. 1981. Repr. of 1905 ed. lib. bdg. 50.00 (ISBN 0-89984-447-2). Century Bookbindery.

Swete, Henry B. Commentary on Mark. LC 77-79193. (Kregel Reprint Library). 554p. 1978. 18.95 (ISBN 0-8254-3715-6). Kregel.

--Commentary on Revelation. LC 77-79192. (Kregel Reprint Library). Orig. Title: Apocalypse of John. 562p. 1979. text ed. 18.95 (ISBN 0-8254-3716-4). Kregel.

Swetmon. Does the Bible Contradict Itself. 1985. pap. 3.95 (ISBN 0-89225-276-6). Gospel Advocate.

Swetmon, Bill. A Giving Heart. 162p. (Orig.). 1986. pap. 3.95 (ISBN 0-89225-288-X). Gospel Advocate.

Swidler, Arlene, ed. Human Rights in Religious Traditions. LC 82-15014. 128p. (Orig.). 1982. pap. 8.95 (ISBN 0-8298-0633-4). Pilgrim NY.

Swidler, Arlene & Conn, Walter E., eds. Mainstreaming: Feminist Research for Teaching Religious Studies. 96p. (Orig.). 1985. lib. bdg. 20.25 (ISBN 0-8191-4724-9, Co-Pub by College Theo Soc); pap. text ed. 7.75 (ISBN 0-8191-4725-7). U Pr of Amer.

Swidler, Arlene, tr. see Van Der Meer, Haye S.

Swidler, Leonard. Aufklarung Catholicism Seventeen Eighty to Eighteen Fifty: Liturgical & Other Reforms in the Catholic Aufklarung. LC 78-2736. 1978. pap. 9.95 (ISBN 0-89130-227-1, 01-00-17). Scholars Pr GA.

--Biblical Affirmations of Woman. LC 79-18886. 382p. 1979. 19.50 (ISBN 0-664-21377-4); softcover 10.95 (ISBN 0-664-24285-5). Westminster.

--Blood Witness for Unity & Peace: The Life of Max Joseph Metzger. 3.95 (ISBN 0-87193-077-3). Dimension Bks.

Swidler, Leonard, jt. auth. see Fernando, Antony.

Swidler, Leonard, ed. Authority in the Church & the Schillebeeckx Case. LC 82-73005. 224p. (Orig.). 1982. pap. 9.95 (ISBN 0-8245-0543-3). Crossroad NY.

--Consensus in Theology? A Dialogue with Hans Kung & Edward Schillebeeckx. LC 80-65385. 180p. 1980. 12.95 (ISBN 0-664-21379-0). Westminster.

--Religious Liberty & Human Rights in Nations & in Religions. 255p. (Orig.). 1986. pap. 9.95 (ISBN 0-931214-06-8). Ecumenical Phila.

Swidler, Leonard & Sloyan, Gerard S., eds. The Oberammergau Passionsspiel Nineteen Eighty-Four. 104p. pap. 5.00 (ISBN 0-686-95110-7). ADL.

Swidler, Leonard, tr. see Mussner, Franz.

Swidler, Leonard, tr. see Van Der Meer, Haye S.

Swietochowski, T. Russian Azerbaijan, Nineteen Five to Nineteen Twenty. 255p. 1985. 125.00 (ISBN 0-317-40712-0, Pub. by Collets UK). State Mutual Bk.

Swift, Emerson H. Roman Sources of Christian Art. (Illus.). Repr. of 1951 ed. lib. bdg. 22.50x (ISBN 0-8371-3430-7, SWCA). Greenwood.

Swift, Helen. In Search of Peace. 1983. pap. 3.75 (ISBN 0-89243-192-X). Liguori Pubns.

Swift, Helen C. How Blest You Are: A Living-Room Retreat Based on the Beatitudes. 85p. 1984. pap. 3.50 (ISBN 0-86716-033-0). St Anthony Mess Pr.

--A Living-Room Retreat: Meditations for Home Use with a 12-Week Plan for Group Sharing. 100p. 1981. pap. text ed. 3.25 (ISBN 0-912228-95-4). St Anthony Mess Pr.

Swift, Louis J. The Early Fathers on War & Military Service. (Message of the Fathers of the Church Ser.: Vol. 19). 1984. 15.95 (ISBN 0-89453-359-2); pap. 9.95 (ISBN 0-89453-330-4). M Glazier.

Swihart, Judson J. How to Treat Your Family As Well As You Treat Your Friends. LC 82-11234. 1982. pap. 5.95 (ISBN 0-8307-0855-3, 5417605). Regal.

Swimme, Brian. The Universe Is a Green Dragon: A Cosmic Creation Story. LC 84-72255. (Illus.). 173p. (Orig.). 1984. pap. 8.95 (ISBN 0-939680-14-9). Bear & Co.

Swimme, Brian, jt. auth. see Fox, Matt.

Swinburne, Irene, jt. auth. see Swinburne, Laurence.

Swinburne, Laurence & Swinburne, Irene. Ancient Myths: The First Science Fiction. LC 77-10915. (Myth, Magic & Superstition Ser.). (Illus.). 1977. PLB 14.65 (ISBN 0-8172-1042-3). Raintree Pubs.

Swinburne, Richard. The Coherence of Theism. (Clarendon Library of Logic & Philosophy). 1977. 42.00x (ISBN 0-19-824410-X). Oxford U Pr.

--The Evolution of the Soul. 320p. 1986. 45.00x (ISBN 0-19-824915-2). Oxford U Pr.

--The Existence of God. 1979. 42.00x (ISBN 0-19-824611-0); pap. 10.95x (ISBN 0-19-824778-8). Oxford U Pr.

--Faith & Reason. 1981. pap. 10.95X (ISBN 0-19-824725-7). Oxford U Pr.

Swindler, Arlene, tr. see Lapide, Pinchas.

Swindoll, Charles. Afirme Sus Valores. Araujo, Juan, tr. from Eng. Orig. Title: Strengthening Your Grip. (Span.). 256p. 1987. pap. 4.95 (ISBN 0-88113-087-7). Edit Betania.

--Hand Me Another Brick: Principles of Effective Leadership: How to Motivate Yourself & Others. LC 78-4170. 1978. pap. 6.95 (ISBN 0-8407-5650-X). Nelson.

--Living above the Level of Mediocrity: A Commitment to Excellence. 256p. 1987. 14.95 (ISBN 0-8499-0564-8). Word Bks.

--Living on the Ragged Edge: Ecclesiastes. 224p. 1985. 12.95 (ISBN 0-8499-0463-3, 0463-3). Word Bks.

--Strengthening Your Grip. 1986. deluxe ed. 9.95 (ISBN 0-8499-3852-X). Word Bks.

Swindoll, Charles A. Dropping Your Guard. 1986. deluxe ed. 9.95 (ISBN 0-8499-3850-3). Word Bks.

Swindoll, Charles R. Baje la Guardia! Araujo, Juan S., tr. from Eng. Tr. of Dropping Your Guard. (Span.). 176p. 1987. pap. 4.95 (ISBN 0-88113-016-8). Edit Betania.

--Come Before Winter & Share my Hope. LC 85-11590. 352p. 1985. 14.95 (ISBN 0-88070-110-2). Multnomah.

--Dropping Your Guard. 224p. 1987. pap. 3.50 (ISBN 0-553-26324-2). Bantam.

--For Those Who Hurt. LC 77-4594. (Illus.). 1977. pap. 3.95 (ISBN 0-930014-13-8). Multnomah.

--Growing Deep in the Christian Life: Returning to Our Roots. LC 86-8661. 1986. 14.95 (ISBN 0-88070-154-4). Multnomah.

--Growing Strong in the Seasons of Life. LC 83-11466. 350p. 1983. 14.95 (ISBN 0-88070-026-2). Multnomah.

--Improving Your Serve: The Art of Unselfish Living. 1981. 10.95 (ISBN 0-8499-0267-3). Word Bks.

--Killing Giants, Pulling Thorns. LC 78-57675. (Illus.). 1978. pap. 9.95 (ISBN 0-930014-25-1). Multnomah.

--Pasame Otro Ladrillo. 208p. 1980. 3.75 (ISBN 0-88113-315-9). Edit Betania.

--Standing Out: Being Real in an Unreal World. LC 82-24595. Orig. Title: Home: Where Life Makes Up Its Mind. 105p. 1983. pap. 9.95 (ISBN 0-88070-014-9). Multnomah.

--Starting over: Fresh Hope for the Road Ahead. LC 82-24636. 1983. pap. 5.95 (ISBN 0-88070-015-7). Multnomah.

--Strenghtening Your Grip. 272p. 1986. pap. 3.50 (ISBN 0-553-25923-7). Bantam.

--Strengthening Your Grip. 236p. 1982. 12.95 (ISBN 0-8499-0312-2). Word Bks.

--Strengthening Your Grip. 1986. 3.50 (ISBN 0-8499-4176-8). Word Bks.

--Strike the Original Match. LC 80-15639. 1980. pap. 6.95 (ISBN 0-930014-37-5); study guide 2.95 (ISBN 0-930014-49-9). Multnomah.

--Three Steps Forward, Two Steps Back. 320p. 1985. pap. 11.95 (ISBN 0-8027-2506-6). Walker & Co.

--Three Steps Forward, Two Steps Back: Persevering Through Pressure. LC 80-11892. 176p. 1980. 9.95 (ISBN 0-8407-5187-7); pap. 5.95 (ISBN 0-8407-5723-9). Nelson.

--You & Your Child. 2nd ed. 1982. pap. 4.95 (ISBN 0-8407-5616-X). Nelson.

Swindoll, Chuck. Compassion: Life Maps. 64p. 1984. 5.95 (ISBN 0-8499-0443-9, 0443-9). Word Bks.

--Improving Your Serve. 1986. deluxe ed. 9.95 (ISBN 0-8499-3851-1). Word Bks.

--Victory: Life Maps. 64p. 1984. 5.95 (ISBN 0-8499-0442-0, 0442-0). Word Bks.

Swindoll, Luci. My Favorite Verse. LC 85-73591. (My Favorite Verse Ser.). 24p. 1986. pap. 4.95 (ISBN 0-89636-204-3). Accent Bks.

--You Bring the Confetti. 160p. 1986. 9.95 (ISBN 0-8499-0527-3). Word Bks.

Swinger, Marlys. Kingdom of God's Justice: As Foretold by Isaiah. 60p. (Choral edition). 1972. pap. 2.50 (ISBN 0-87486-012-1); L.P. Record-Mono 4.95. Plough.

Swinger, Marlys, jt. auth. see Gick, Georg J.

Swischuk, Leonard. Emergency Radiology of the Acutely Ill or Injured Child. 2nd ed. (Illus.). 656p. 1985. text ed. 78.50 (ISBN 0-683-08049-0). Williams & Wilkins.

Switzer, David K. & Switzer, Shirley A. Parents of the Homosexual, Vol. 11. LC 80-13748. (Christian Care Bks.). 118p. 1980. pap. 7.95 (ISBN 0-664-24327-4). Westminster.

Switzer, David L. The Minister as Crisis Counselor. rev. ed. 304p. 1986. pap. 13.95 (ISBN 0-687-26954-7). Abingdon.

Switzer, Jennie B. Elder Northfield's Home; or, Sacrificed on the Mormon Altar. facsimile ed. LC 71-164576. (American Fiction Reprint Ser). Repr. of 1882 ed. 25.50 (ISBN 0-8369-7053-5). Ayer Co Pubs.

Switzer, Shirley A., jt. auth. see Switzer, David K.

Swomley, John M. Religious Liberty & the Secular State. 140p. 1987. 16.95x (ISBN 0-87975-373-0); pap. 10.95 (ISBN 0-87975-398-6). Prometheus Bks.

Swope, Mary R. Are You Sick & Tired? 176p. (Orig.). 1984. pap. 3.95 (ISBN 0-88368-149-8). Whitaker Hse.

Swor, Chester E. The Best of Chester Swor. LC 81-67202. 1981. pap. 6.95 (ISBN 0-8054-5293-1). Broadman.

Swords, Liam, ed. Funeral Homilies. 2.95 (ISBN 0-8091-2784-9). Paulist Pr.

--Marriage Homilles. 2.95. Paulist Pr.

Swyhart, B., ed. see Piediscalzi, N., et al.

Swyhart, Barbara A. Bioethical Decision-making: Releasing Religion from the Spiritual. LC 75-13040. pap. 35.00 (2026973). Bks Demand UMI.

Syama-Sankara, Hara C. Buddha & His Sayings. LC 78-70128. Repr. of 1914 ed. 18.00 (ISBN 0-404-17387-X). AMS Pr.

Sychterz, Terre. The Bible & Me! Zapel, Arthur L., ed. (Illus.). 40p. 1986. pap. 3.95 (ISBN 0-916260-39-9). Meriwether Pub.

SYDA Foundation. The Nectar of Chanting. 3rd, rev. ed. LC 78-68854. 216p. 7.95 (ISBN 0-914602-16-0). SYDA Found.

Sydnor, James R. Hymns & Their Uses. LC 81-71795. 155p. (Orig.). 1982. pap. 6.95 (ISBN 0-916642-18-6). Hope Pub.

Sydnor, William. Jesus According to Luke. 144p. (Orig.). 1982. pap. 7.95 (ISBN 0-8164-2393-8, HarpR). Har-Row.

--Looking at the Episcopal Church. LC 80-81103. 142p. (Orig.). 1981. pap. 5.95 (ISBN 0-8192-1279-2). Morehouse.

Sykes, Christopher. Crossroads to Israel 1917-1948. LC 72-93912. (Midland Bks.: No. 165). 416p. 1973. pap. 8.95x (ISBN 0-253-20165-9). Ind U Pr.

Sykes, Egerton. Everyman's Dictionary of Non-Classical Mythology. rev. ed. (Everyman's Reference Library). (Illus.). 298p. 1977. Repr. of 1968 ed. 13.50x (ISBN 0-460-03010-8, Pub. by J. M. Dent England). Biblio Dist.

Sykes, Norman. Church & State in England Since the Reformation. 1979. Repr. of 1929 ed. lib. bdg. 12.50 (ISBN 0-8482-6392-8). Norwood Edns.

--The English Religious Tradition: Sketches of Its Influence on Church, State & Society. LC 78-59045. 1986. Repr. of 1953 ed. 15.00 (ISBN 0-88355-717-7). Hyperion Conn.

--From Sheldon to Secker: Aspects of English Church History, 1660-1768. LC 59-2371. (The Ford Lectures: 1958). pap. 62.50 (ISBN 0-317-20808-X, 2024534). Bks Demand UMI.

Sykes, Reverend William G. Visions of Faith: An Anthology of Reflections. 544p. 1986. 19.95 (ISBN 0-920792-25-1). Eden Pr.

Sykes, S. W. Karl Barth: Studies of His Theological Method. 1979. text ed. 34.95x (ISBN 0-19-826649-9). Oxford U Pr.

Sykes, S. W. & Clayton, J. P. Christ, Faith & History. LC 70-176257. (Cambridge Studies in Christology). (Illus.). 280p. 1972. pap. text ed. 14.95 (ISBN 0-521-29325-1). Cambridge U Pr.

Sykes, S. W., ed. England & Germany: Studies in Theological Diplomacy. (IC-Studies in the Intercultural History of Christianity: Vol. 25). 170p. 1981. pap. 22.15 (ISBN 3-8204-5854-9). P Lang Pubs.

Sykes, Stephen. The Identity of Christianity. LC 83-48907. 256p. 1984. 21.95 (ISBN 0-8006-0720-1, 1-720). Fortress.

Sylla, E. D., ed. see International Colloquium on Philosophy, Science, & Theology in the Middle Ages, 1st, Boston, Sept. 1973.

Sylla, Edith D., ed. see International Colloquium on Philosophy, Science Theology in the Middle Ages, 1st, 1973.

Sylvester, Diane & Wiemann, Mary. Mythology, Archeology, Architecture. (Gifted & Talented Ser.). 112p. 1982. 8.95 (ISBN 0-88160-081-4, LW 901). Learning Wks.

Sylvester, Richard S. & Harding, Davis P., eds. Two Early Tudor Lives. Incl. The Life & Death of Cardinal Wolsey. Cavendish, George; The Life of Sir Thomas More. Roper, William. xxi, 260p. 1962. pap. 8.95x (ISBN 0-300-00239-4, Y81). Yale U Pr.

Sylvester, Richard S., tr. see More, St. Thomas.

Sylwester, R. The Puppet & the Word. LC 12-2966. 1982. pap. 4.95 (ISBN 0-570-03873-1). Concordia.

Sylwester, Roland. Teaching Bible Stories More Effectively with Puppets. (Illus.). 64p. 1976. pap. 3.95 (ISBN 0-570-03731-X, 12-2633). Concordia.

Syme, Charlotte U., jt. auth. see Syme, George S.

Syme, Daniel B., jt. auth. see Sonsino, Rifat.

Syme, Daniel B., ed. see Bearman, Jane.

Syme, Daniel B., ed. see Bial, Morrison D.

Syme, Daniel B., ed. see Marcus, Audrey F. & Zwerin, Raymond A.

Syme, George S. & Syme, Charlotte U. The Scripture of Truth. 121p. 1983. pap. 5.95 (ISBN 0-88062-019-6). Mott Media.

--Scripture of Truth. 1986. pap. 5.95 (ISBN 0-8010-8274-9). Baker Bk.

Syme, Ronald. Some Arval Brethren. 1980. 36.00x (ISBN 0-19-814831-3). Oxford U Pr.

Symeon of Thessalonike. A Treatise on Prayer: An Explanation of the Services of the Orthodox Church. Vaporis, N. M., intro. by. Simmons, H. L., tr. from Gr. (The Archbishop Iakovos Library of Ecclesiastical & Historical Sources: No. 9). Orig. Title: Peri Theias Kai Hieras Proseuches. (Orig.). 1984. 12.95; pap. text ed. 7.95 (ISBN 0-917653-05-X). Hellenic Coll Pr.

Symington, Thomas A. Religious Liberals & Conservatives: A Comparison of Those Who Are Liberal in Their Religious Thinking & Those Who Are Conservative. LC 70-177727. (Columbia University. Teachers College. Contributions to Education: No. 640). Repr. of 1935 ed. 22.50 (ISBN 0-404-55640-X). AMS Pr.

Symmank, Leo, jt. auth. see Kaiser, Eldor.

Symmons, Charles. Life of John Milton. 3rd ed. LC 71-128979. 1970. Repr. of 1822 ed. 25.50 (ISBN 0-404-06325-X). AMS Pr.

Symonds, Henry E. The Church Universal & the See of Rome: A Study of the Relations Between the Episcopate & the Papacy up to the Schism Between East & West. (Church Historical Society London N. S. Ser.: No. 36). pap. 60.00 (ISBN 0-8115-3159-7). Kraus Repr.

Symonds, John A. Problem in Greek Ethics. LC 71-163126. (Studies in Philosophy, No. 40). 1971. lib. bdg. 31.95x (ISBN 0-8383-1253-5). Haskell.

--Studies in Sexual Inversion. LC 72-9683. Repr. of 1928 ed. 32.50 (ISBN 0-404-57503-X). AMS Pr.

Synan, J. A. The Trinity, or the Tri-Personal Being of God. pap. 2.95 (ISBN 0-911866-00-0). Advocate.

Synan, Joseph A. Christian Life in Depth. 3.95 (ISBN 0-911866-60-4); pap. 2.95 (ISBN 0-911866-87-6). Advocate.

--A Good Minister of Jesus Christ. pap. 1.50 (ISBN 0-911866-81-7). Advocate.

--Shape of Things to Come. 1969. 3.95 (ISBN 0-911866-52-3); pap. 2.95 (ISBN 0-911866-90-6). Advocate.

Synan, Vinson. Aspects of Pentecostal-Charismatic Origins. LC 75-2802. 1975. 6.95 (ISBN 0-88270-111-8); pap. 6.95. Bridge Pub.

--The Holiness-Pentecostal Movement. 1972. pap. 9.95 (ISBN 0-8028-1728-9). Eerdmans.

--In the Latter Days: The Outpouring of the Holy Spirit in the Twentieth Century. 168p. (Orig.). 1984. pap. 4.95 (ISBN 0-89283-191-X). Servant.

--Old Time Power. 6.95 (ISBN 0-911866-67-1). Advocate.

Syndor, James R. Hymns: A Congregational Study. 100p. (Orig.). 1983. pap. text ed. 4.95 (ISBN 0-916642-19-4, 778); tchrs' ed 2.95 (ISBN 0-916642-20-8, 779). Agape Il.

Synge, Ursula. The Giant at the Ford & Other Legends of the Saints. LC 79-23020. (Illus.). 176p. 1980. 9.95 (ISBN 0-689-50168-4, McElderry Bk). Macmillan.

--The People & the Promise. LC 74-10661. 192p. 1974. 12.95 (ISBN 0-87599-208-0). S G Phillips.

Synnestvedt, Sig. Essential Swedenborg. LC 76-57901. 3.95 (ISBN 0-87785-116-6); pap. 2.95 (ISBN 0-87785-152-2). Swedenborg.

Syrmia, Edmond De see De Syrmia, Edmond.

Syrop, Konrad, tr. see Andrzejewski, Jerzy.

Syrtsov, V. L. The Insurrection of the Old-Ritualist Monks at the Solovetsk Monastery in the Seventeenth Century. 316p. Repr. of 1888 ed. text ed. 33.12 (ISBN 0-576-99180-5, Pub. by Gregg Intl Pubs England). Gregg Intl.

Syverson, Betty G. Bible Readings for Caregivers. (Bible Readings Ser.). 112p. (Orig.). 1987. pap. 3.95 (ISBN 0-8066-2276-8, 10-0695). Augsburg.

Syverud, Genevieve W. This Is My Song of Songs. (Orig.). 1966. pap. 2.95 (ISBN 0-8066-0613-4, 11-9495). Augsburg.

Szafar, Tadeusz, tr. see Banas, Josef.

Szajkowski, Bogdan. Next to God...Poland: Politics & Religion in Contemporary Poland. LC 83-40151. 258p. 1983. 25.00 (ISBN 0-312-57233-6). St Martin.

Szajkowski, Soza. Analytical Franco-Jewish Gazetteer, 1939-1945. 1966. 50.00 (ISBN 0-87068-112-5). Ktav.

--An Illustrated Sourcebook on the Holocaust, Vols. 1 & 2. Incl. Vol. 1. Prelude to Holocaust: the Jew Must Disappear. o. p 50.00 (ISBN 0-87068-294-6); Vol. 2. The Ghetto & Death Camp Walls Speak (ISBN 0-87068-295-4). 45.00x ea. Ktav.

--Jews & the French Revolution of 1789, 1830 & 1848. 1969. 59.50x (ISBN 0-87068-112-5). Ktav.

--Jews in the French Foreign Legion. 25.00x (ISBN 0-87068-285-7). Ktav.

Szajkowski, Z. An Illustrated Sourcebook of Russian Antisemitism 1881-1977, 2 vols. Vol. 1, The Nineteenth Century. 50.00x (ISBN 0-87068-347-0); Vol. 2, The Twentieth Century. 45.00x (ISBN 0-87068-348-9). Ktav.

Szajkowski, Zosa. An Illustrated Sourcebook on the Holocaust, Vol. III. 1979. 40.00x (ISBN 0-87068-690-9). Ktav.

Szarmach, Paul E., ed. Aspects of Jewish Culture in the Middle Ages: Papers from the Eighth Annual CEMERS Conference. 230p. 10.00 (ISBN 0-87395-165-4, Pub. by SUNY Pr). Medieval & Renaissance NY.

--Aspects of Jewish Culture in the Middle Ages. LC 77-29046. (Illus.). 208p. 1979. 44.50 (ISBN 0-87395-165-4). State U NY Pr.

--An Introduction to the Medieval Mystics of Europe. 368p. 1984. 44.50 (ISBN 0-87395-834-9); pap. 14.95x (ISBN 0-87395-835-7). State U NY Pr.

Szarnicki, Zygmunt V. Faith Leads to Salvation: The Truths of the Nicene Creed. 137p. (Orig.). 1984. pap. 9.95 (ISBN 0-939332-08-6). J Pohl Assocs.

--Mankind's Greatest Life. 188p. (Orig.). 1985. pap. 9.95 (ISBN 0-939332-12-4). J Pohl Assocs.

Szasz, Ferenc M. The Divided Mind of Protestant America, 1880-1930. LC 81-7597. 216p. 1982. text ed. 19.95 (ISBN 0-8173-0080-5). U of Ala Pr.

Szczesny, Gerhard. The Future of Unbelief. LC 60-1665. 1961. pap. 2.95 (ISBN 0-8076-0375-9). Braziller.

Szekely, Edmond B. Biogenic Meditation: Biogenic Self-Analysis, Creative Microcosmos. (Illus.). 40p. 1978. pap. 1.80 (ISBN 0-89564-051-1). IBS Intl.

--The Cosmotherapy of the Essenes. (Illus.). 64p. 1975. pap. 3.50 (ISBN 0-89564-012-0). IBS Intl.

--Creative Work: Karma Yoga. (Illus.). 32p. 1973. pap. 2.95 (ISBN 0-89564-066-X). IBS Intl.

--The Dialectical Method of Thinking. (Illus.). 40p. 1973. pap. 2.95 (ISBN 0-89564-063-5). IBS Intl.

--The Discovery of the Essene Gospel of Peace: The Essenes & the Vatican. (Illus.). 96p. 1977. pap. 4.80 (ISBN 0-89564-004-X). IBS Intl.

--The Essene Book of Asha: Journey to the Cosmic Ocean. (Illus.). 140p. 1976. pap. 7.50 (ISBN 0-89564-008-2). IBS Intl.

--The Essene Book of Creation. (Illus.). 86p. 1975. pap. 4.50 (ISBN 0-89564-005-8). IBS Intl.

--The Essene Code of Life. (Illus.). 44p. 1978. pap. 3.50 (ISBN 0-89564-013-9). IBS Intl.

--The Essene Communions with the Infinite. (Illus.). 64p. 1979. pap. 3.95 (ISBN 0-89564-009-0). IBS Intl.

--The Essene Gospel of Peace, Bk. 1. (Illus.). 72p. 1981. pap. 1.00 (ISBN 0-89564-000-7). IBS Intl.

--The Essene Gospel of Peace, Bk. 2. (Illus.). 132p. 1981. pap. 5.80 (ISBN 0-89564-001-5). IBS Intl.

--The Essene Gospel of Peace, Bk. 3: Lost Scrolls of the Essene Brotherhood. (Illus.). 144p. 1981. pap. 5.60 (ISBN 0-89564-002-3). IBS Intl.

--The Essene Gospel of Peace, Bk. 4: Teachings of the Elect. (Illus.). 40p. 1981. pap. 4.50 (ISBN 0-89564-003-1). IBS Intl.

--The Essene Jesus. (Illus.). 72p. 1977. pap. 4.50 (ISBN 0-89564-007-4). IBS Intl.

--The Essene Origins of Christianity. (Illus.). 184p. 1981. pap. 8.50 (ISBN 0-89564-015-5). IBS Intl.

--The Essene Science of Fasting & the Art of Sobriety. (Illus.). 48p. 1981. pap. 3.50 (ISBN 0-89564-011-2). IBS Intl.

--The Essene Science of Life. (Illus.). 64p. 1976. pap. 3.50 (ISBN 0-89564-010-4). IBS Intl.

--The Essene Teachings of Zarathurstra. (Illus.). 32p. 1974. pap. 2.95 (ISBN 0-89564-016-3). IBS Intl.

--The Essene Way: Biogenic Living. (Illus.). 200p. 1981. pap. 8.80 (ISBN 0-89564-019-8). IBS Intl.

--The Essene Way: World Pictures & Cosmic Symbols. (Illus.). 40p. 1978. pap. 1.80 (ISBN 0-89564-050-3). IBS Intl.

--The Essenes, by Josephus & His Contemporaries. (Illus.). 32p. 1981. pap. 2.95 (ISBN 0-89564-014-7). IBS Intl.

--The Evolution of Human Thought. (Illus.). 44p. 1971. pap. 2.50 (ISBN 0-89564-062-7). IBS Intl.

--Father, Give Us Another Chance. (Illus.). 62p. 1969. pap. 6.80 (ISBN 0-89564-071-6). IBS Intl.

--The Fiery Chariots. (Illus.). 96p. 1971. pap. 4.80 (ISBN 0-89564-017-1). IBS Intl.

--The First Essene. (Illus.). 240p. 1981. pap. 9.50 (ISBN 0-89564-018-X). IBS Intl.

--The Great Experiment. (Search for the Ageless Ser.: Vol. 2). (Illus.). 328p. 1977. pap. 8.80 (ISBN 0-89564-023-6). IBS Intl.

--I Came Back Tomorrow. (Illus.). 32p. 1976. pap. 3.50 (ISBN 0-89564-073-2). IBS Intl.

--The Living Buddha. (Illus.). 70p. 1977. pap. 4.50 (ISBN 0-89564-059-7). IBS Intl.

--Man in the Cosmic Ocean. (Illus.). 56p. 1970. pap. 3.50 (ISBN 0-89564-054-6). IBS Intl.

--My Unusual Adventures on the Five Continents in Search for the Ageless. (Search for the Ageless Ser.: Vol. 1). (Illus.). 212p. 1977. pap. 7.80 (ISBN 0-89564-022-8). IBS Intl.

--Pilgrim of the Himalayas. (Illus.). 32p. 1974. pap. 2.95 (ISBN 0-89564-061-9). IBS Intl.

--Talks by Edmond Bordeaux Szekely. 48p. 1972. pap. 2.95 (ISBN 0-89564-067-8). IBS Intl.

--The Teachings of the Essenes from Enoch to the Dead Sea Scrolls. (Illus.). 112p. 1981. pap. 4.80 (ISBN 0-89564-006-6). IBS Intl.

--The Tender Touch: Biogenic Fulfillment. (Illus.). 120p. 1977. text ed. 5.50 (ISBN 0-89564-020-1). IBS Intl.

--Toward the Conquest of the Inner Cosmos. (Illus.). 64p. 1969. pap. 6.80 (ISBN 0-89564-053-8). IBS Intl.

--The Zend-Avesta of Zarathustra. (Illus.). 100p. 1973. pap. 4.80 (ISBN 0-89564-058-9). IBS Intl.

Szentkeresti, Karen, jt. auth. see Tighe, Jeanne.

Szews, George R. We Will Celebrate a Church Wedding. 88p. 1983. pap. 1.50 (ISBN 0-8146-1288-1). Liturgical Pr.

Szirmai, Julia C. La Bible Anonyme du Ms. Paris B. N. F. Fr, No. 763. (Faux Titre Ser.: No. 22). 402p. 1985. pap. text ed. 55.00x (ISBN 90-6203-927-8, Pub. by Rodopi Holland). Humanities.

Szittya, Penn R. The Antifraternal Tradition in Medieval Literature. LC 85-43316. (Illus.). 320p. 1986. text ed. 40.00x (ISBN 0-691-06680-9). Princeton U Pr.

Szittya, Ruth O. That's My Brother. LC 82-70603. (Illus.). 32p. (Orig.). 1982. pap. 3.95 (ISBN 0-913408-74-3). Friends United.

Szjakowski, Soza. Jews, War & Communism. Incl. Vol. 1. The Attitude of American Jews to World War I, the Russian Revolution of 1917, and Communism, 1917 to 1945. 1972. 35.00x (ISBN 0-87068-182-6); Vol. 2. 1974. 35.00x (ISBN 0-87068-239-3). Ktav.

Szlakmann, Charles. Judaism for Beginners. (Documentary Comic Bks.). (Illus.). 189p. Date not set. pap. 6.95 (ISBN 0-86316-101-4). Writers & Readers.

Sztorc, Mary V. Student's Values in Drugs & Drug Abuse. 1976. pap. 2.00 (ISBN 0-87507-000-0). Cath Lib Assn.

Szyk, Arthur. Megillah: Book of Esther. 1974. 25.00x (ISBN 0-685-84454-4). Bloch.

T

Taafaki, Irene. The Horse of the Moonlight. (Illus.). 40p. pap. 3.50 (ISBN 0-85398-111-6). G Ronald Pub.

--Thoughts: Education for Peace & One World. (Illus.). 336p. 1986. 19.95 (ISBN 0-85398-221-X); pap. text ed. 9.95 (ISBN 0-85398-222-8). G Ronald Pub.

Tabachnick, A. Dass, ed. see Dass, B. Hari.

Tabak, Israel. Judaic Lore in Heine. LC 78-19266. 25.50 (ISBN 0-405-10632-7). Ayer Co Pubs.

Tabari, Azar & Yeganeh, Nahid, eds. In the Shadow of Islam: The Women's Movement in Iran. 256p. 1983. 24.75x (ISBN 0-86232-022-4, Pub. by Zed Pr England); pap. 10.25 (ISBN 0-86232-039-9). Humanities.

Tabataba'i, Allamah, jt. ed. see Chittick, W. C.

Tabatabai, Hossein M. Introduction to Shii Law: A Bibliographical Study. 258p. 1985. text ed. 22.00 (ISBN 0-86372-015-3, Pub. by Ithaca England). Evergreen Dist.

Tabatabai, Muhammad. Muhammad in the Mirror of Islam. Chittick, William, tr. from Persian. 21p. 1979. pap. 1.00 (ISBN 0-941722-18-X). Book-Dist-Ctr.

--Shi'ite Islam. Nasr, Sayyed H., tr. from Persian. 253p. 1979. pap. 4.95 (ISBN 0-941722-19-8). Book-Dist-Ctr.

Tabatabai, S. Muhammad Husayn At see Husayn at-Tabatabai, S. Muhammad & S. Saeed, Akhtar-Rizvi.

Tabataba'I, Allamah. A Shi'ite Anthology. Chittick, William C., ed. 152p. 1986. text ed. 25.00 (ISBN 0-7103-0159-6); pap. text ed. 12.95 (ISBN 0-317-40555-1). Methuen Inc.

Tabb, William K., ed. Churches in Struggle: Liberation Theologies & Social Change in North America. 331p. 1986. 27.00 (ISBN 0-85345-692-5); pap. 11.00 (ISBN 0-85345-693-3). Monthly Rev.

Tabbarah, Afif. The Spirit of Islam. 20.00x (ISBN 0-86685-029-5). Intl Bk Ctr.

Tabeling, Ernst. Mater Larum: Zum Wesen der Larenreligion. facsimile ed. LC 75-10657. (Ancient Religion & Mythology Ser.). (Ger.). 1976. Repr. of 1932 ed. 12.00x (ISBN 0-405-07265-1). Ayer Co Pubs.

Taber, Charles R. & Nida, Eugene A. La Traduction: Theorie et Methode. 1971. pap. 3.30x (ISBN 0-8267-0022-5, 51971, Pub. by United Bible). Am Bible.

Taber, Charles R., ed. The Church in Africa: Nineteen Seventy Seven. LC 78-14923. 1978. pap. 6.95 (ISBN 0-87808-161-5). William Carey Lib.

Taber, Gladys. Another Path. LC 63-17678. 1963. 12.45i (ISBN 0-397-00260-2). Har-Row.

Taber, William. The Prophetic Stream. LC 84-61291. (Orig.). 1984. pap. 2.50x (ISBN 0-87574-256-4). Pendle Hill.

Tabibi, Abdul H. Daa, Wah & Jihad. 40p. (Orig.). 1984. pap. 3.00 (ISBN 0-911119-05-1). Igram Pr.

Tablet Of London Editors. Spirituality Through the Ages. pap. 0.75 (ISBN 0-8199-0240-3, L38838). Franciscan Herald.

Tabor, James. Things Unutterable: Paul's Ascent to Paradise in Its Greco-Roman, Judaic & Early Christian Contexts. LC 86-18924. (Studies in Judaism Ser.). 166p. (Orig.). 1986. lib. bdg. 23.50 (ISBN 0-8191-5643-4, Pub. by Studies in Judaism); pap. text ed. 11.50 (ISBN 0-8191-5644-2, Pub. by Studies in Judaism). U Pr of Amer.

Tabrah, Ruth, jt. auth. see Unno, Taitetsu.

Tabrah, Ruth, ed. see Mui, Shan.

Tabrah, Ruth, ed. see Sakakibara, Tokuso, et al.

Tabrah, Ruth, tr. see Bloom, Alred.

Tache, Alexandre A. Vingt Annees De Missions Dans le Nord-Ouest De L'amerique. (Canadiana Before 1867 Ser). (Fr). Repr. of 1866 ed. 18.00 (ISBN 0-384-59425-5). Johnson Repr.

--Vingt Annees De Missions Dans le Nord-Ouest De L'amerique Par Mgr. Alex. Tache Eveque De Saint-Boniface (Montreal, 1866) (Canadiana Avant 1867: NO. 21). 1970. 16.80x (ISBN 90-2796-343-6). Mouton.

Tachibana, Shundo, pref. by. The Ethics of Buddhism. LC 74-20477. 288p. 1975. Repr. of 1926 ed. text ed. 24.50x (ISBN 0-06-496720-4). B&N Imports.

Tachikawa, Musashi, ed. see Ngor Tharttse mKhanpo bSodnams rgyamtsho.

Tackett, T. Priest & Parish in Eighteenth-Century France. 1977. 38.00 (ISBN 0-691-05243-3). Princeton U Pr.

Tackett, Timothy. Priest & Parish in Eighteenth-Century France. LC 76-29801. 368p. 1986. 19.50x (ISBN 0-691-10199-X). Princeton U Pr.

Tada, Joni E. Choices...Changes. 240p. 1986. 14.95 (ISBN 0-310-24010-7, 12018). Zondervan.

Tadmor, H. History Historiography & Interpretation: Studies in Biblical & Cuneiform Literatures. Weinfeld, M., ed. 192p. 1983. pap. text ed. 22.50 (ISBN 965-223-459-1, Pub by Magnes Pr Israel). Humanities.

Taege, Marlys. Women Through the Bible: Devotions for Women's Groups. 160p. 1987. pap. 5.95 (ISBN 0-570-04460-X, 12-3064). Concordia.

Tafoya, Alfonso. Confrontation at Calvary. (Chapbooks Ser.). 1975. pap. 1.50x (ISBN 0-914140-06-X). Carpenter Pr.

Taft, A. I., ed. The Apologye of Syr Thomas More. (EETS, OS: No. 180). Repr. of 1929 ed. 67.00 (ISBN 0-527-00177-5). Kraus Repr.

Taft, Edna. Puritan in Voodoo-Land. LC 73-174115. (Tower Bks). (Illus.). 1971. Repr. of 1938 ed. 43.00x (ISBN 0-8103-3919-6). Gale.

Taft, Robert. Beyond East & West: Problems in Liturgical Understanding. (NPM Studies in Church Music & Liturgy). 203p. 1934. pap. 11.95 (ISBN 0-912405-13-9). Pastoral Pr.

--The Liturgy of the Hours in East & West. 440p. 1986. pap. 14.95 (ISBN 0-8146-1405-1). Liturgical Pr.

Taft, Robert F., ed. The Oriental Orthodox Churches in the United States. 32p. 1986. pap. 2.95 (ISBN 1-55586-987-4). US Catholic.

Tagare, G. V., tr. Bhagavata Purana, Vol. 9. cancelled (ISBN 0-89581-480-3). Asian Human Pr.

--Bhagavata Purana, Vol. 10. cancelled (ISBN 0-89581-481-1). Asian Human Pr.

--Bhagavata Purana, Vol. 11. cancelled (ISBN 0-89581-482-X). Asian Human Pr.

--Narada Purana, Vol. 15. write for info. (ISBN 0-89581-539-7). Asian Human Pr.

--Skanda Purana. Date not set. cancelled. Asian Human Pr.

--Vayu Purana. write for info. Asian Human Pr.

Taggart, George. Bible Promises for Tiny Tots, No. 3. Coffen, Richard W., ed. 32p. (Orig.). 1987. pap. 3.95 (ISBN 0-8280-0375-0). Review & Herald.

--Bible Promises for Tiny Tots, II. Coffen, Richard W., ed. 32p. (Orig.). 1985. pap. 3.95 (ISBN 0-8280-0246-0). Review & Herald.

Tagore, Rabindranath. The Religion of Man. LC 77-27145. (Hibbert Lectures: 1930). 248p. Repr. of 1931 ed. 27.50 (ISBN 0-404-60426-9). AMS Pr.

Tagore, Rabindranath, jt. auth. see Gandhi, M. K.

Tagore, Sourindo M. The Musical Scales of the Hindus. LC 74-24225. Repr. of 1884 ed. 21.50 (ISBN 0-404-12837-8). AMS Pr.

Tagore, Sourindo M., compiled by. Hindu Music, from Various Authors. 2nd ed. LC 74-24223. 1977. Repr. of 1882 ed. 35.00 (ISBN 0-404-12835-1). AMS Pr.

Taherzadeh, Adib. Revelation of Baha'u'llah, Vol. I: Baghdad 1853-1863. (Illus.). 384p. 1974. 18.95 (ISBN 0-85398-052-7); pap. 11.95 (ISBN 0-85398-057-8). G Ronald Pub.

--The Revelation of Baha'u'llah, Vol. II: Adrianople, 1863-1868. (Illus.). 492p. 1977. 17.95 (ISBN 0-85398-070-5). G Ronald Pub.

Taherzadeh, Habib, tr. see Baha'u'llah.

Taherzaden, Ad. Revelation of Baha'u'llah Vol. III: Akka',the Early Years 1868-77. (Illus.). 544p. 19.95 (ISBN 0-85398-143-4). G Ronald Pub.

Tailang, S. B., ed. see Ballantyne & Shastri.

Tailby, John, jt. ed. see Meredith, Peter.

Taimni. Science & Occultism. 6.95 (ISBN 0-8356-7501-7). Theos Pub Hse.

--Science of Yoga. 10.95 (ISBN 0-8356-7140-2). Theos Pub Hse.

--Secret of Self-Realization. 4.50 (ISBN 0-8356-7640-4). Theos Pub Hse.

--Self-Realization Through Love. 4.75 (ISBN 0-8356-7522-X). Theos Pub Hse.

Taimni, I. K. Gayatri. 5.95 (ISBN 0-8356-7069-4). Theos Pub Hse.

--Glimpses into the Psychology of Yoga. 1973. 10.95 (ISBN 0-8356-7290-5). Theos Pub Hse.

--Man, God & the Universe. LC 74-4167. (Illus.). 447p. 1974. pap. 3.45 (ISBN 0-8356-0447-0, Quest). Theos Pub Hse.

--The Science of Yoga. LC 67-4112. pap. 6.95 (ISBN 0-8356-0023-8, Quest). Theos Pub Hse.

Tait, Vera D. Take Command. LC 80-53217. 144p. 1981. 5.95 (ISBN 0-87159-150-2). Unity School.

Taitt, Peter S. Incubus & Ideal: Ecclesiastical Figures In Chaucer & Langland. Hogg, James, ed. (Elizabethan & Renaissance Studies). 228p. (Orig.). 1975. pap. 15.00 (ISBN 3-7052-0690-7, Pub. by Salzburg Studies). Longwood Pub Group.

Tajdin, Nagib. Bibliography of Ismailism. LC 85-26960. 1986. 25.00x (ISBN 0-88206-063-5). Caravan Bks.

Takada, Koin. Spirit of Buddhism Today. Yampolsky, Philip, tr. (Illus.). 1973. 9.95 (ISBN 0-89346-095-8, Pub. by Tokuma Shoten); pap. 2.95 (ISBN 0-89346-043-5). Heian Intl.

Takahatake, Takamichi. Young Man Shinran. (SR Supplements Ser.: Vol. 18). 180p. 1987. pap. 15.00 (ISBN 0-88920-169-2, Pub. by Wilfrid Laurier Canada). Humanities.

Takakusa, Junjiro. The Essentials of Buddhist Philosophy. 236p. 1978. pap. 6.95 (ISBN 0-87728-426-1). Weiser.

Takakusu, J. Essentials of Buddhist Philosophy. 3rd ed. 1975. Repr. 8.50 (ISBN 0-8426-0826-5). Orient Bk Dist.

--Essentials of Buddhist Philosophy. 2nd ed. Chan, W. & Moore, Charles A., eds. (Illus.). Repr. of 1949 ed. text ed. 14.00x. Coronet Bks.

Takakusu, J., tr. see Tsing, I.

Takpo Tashi Namgyal. Mahamudra: The Quintessance of Mind & Meditation. Lhalungpa, Lobsang P., tr. from Tibetan. LC 85-27963. (Orig.). 1986. pap. 25.00 (ISBN 0-87773-360-0). Shambhala Pubns.

Tal, Uriel. Christians & Jews in Germany: Religion, Politics, & Ideology in the Second Reich, 1870-1914. Jacobs, Noah J., tr. from Hebrew. LC 74-21612. (Illus.). 359p. 1975. 35.00x (ISBN 0-8014-0879-2). Cornell U Pr.

Talafous, Don. Planning a Christian Wedding. 36p. 1985. pap. 1.00 (ISBN 0-8146-1407-8). Liturgical Pr.

Talberg, N. D. Istorija Kristijanskoj Tserkvi. Tr. of History of the Christian Church. 494p. 1964. pap. text ed. 20.00 (ISBN 0-317-30289-2); pap. 15.00 (ISBN 0-317-30290-6). Holy Trinity.

--Istorija Russkoi Tserkvi. Tr. of History of the Russuan Church. 927p. 1959. pap. text ed. 25.00 (ISBN 0-317-30295-7). Holy Trinity.

--K Sorokaljetiju pagubnago evlogijanskago raskola. Tr. of The Fortieth Anniversary of the Ruinous Evlogian Schism. 128p. 1966. pap. 4.00 (ISBN 0-317-30373-2). Holy Trinity.

--Russkaja Pravoslavnaja Tserkov' v Severnoj Ameriki. Tr. of The Russian Orthodox Church in North America. 224p. 1955. pap. 8.00 (ISBN 0-317-30366-X). Holy Trinity.

Talbert, Charles, ed. Perspectives on Luke-Acts. LC 78-51610. (Special Studies: No. 5). ix, 269p. 1978. pap. 10.00 (ISBN 0-932180-04-3). NABPR.

Talbert, Charles H. Acts. Hayes, John, ed. (Preaching Guides). 120p. (Orig.). 1984. pap. 6.95 (ISBN 0-8042-3231-8). John Knox.

--Literary Patterns, Theological Themes & the Genre of Luke-Acts. LC 74-78620. (Society of Biblical Literature. Monograph: No. 20). Repr. of 1974 ed. 42.00 (ISBN 0-8357-9577-2, 2017509). Bks Demand UMI.

--Reading Corinthians: A Literary & Theological Commentary on 1 and 2 Corinthians. 224p. 1987. 15.95 (ISBN 0-8245-0804-1). Crossroad NY.

--Reading Luke: A Literary & Theological Commentary on the Third Gospel. LC 82-12737. 288p. 1982. 17.95 (ISBN 0-8245-0532-8). Crossroad NY.

--Reading Luke: A Literary & Theological Commentary on the Third Gospel. 256p. 1984. pap. 10.95 (ISBN 0-8245-0668-5). Crossroad NY.

Talbert, Charles H., ed. Perspectives on First Peter. LC 86-8772. (NABPR (National Association of Baptist Professors of Religion0 Special Studies: No. 9). 151p. (Orig.). 1986. pap. 15.95 (ISBN 0-86554-198-1, MUP-M11). Mercer Univ Pr.

--Reimarus: Fragments. Fraser, Ralph S., tr. (Reprints & Translations). 1985. pap. 13.95 (ISBN 0-89130-858-X, 00-07-07). Scholars Pr Ga.

Talbert, Charles H., ed. see Tolbert, Malcolm, et al.

Talbert, Ernest W., jt. auth. see Starnes, DeWitt T.

Talbot, Alice-Mary M. Faith Healing in Late Byzantium: The Posthumous Miracles of Patriarch Athanasios I of Constaninople by Theoktistos the Stoudite. Vaporis, N. M., ed. (The Archbishop Iakovos Library of Ecclesiastical & Historical Sources Ser.). 160p. (Orig.). 1983. 17.00 (ISBN 0-916586-92-8); pap. 12.00 (ISBN 0-916586-93-6). Hellenic College Pr.

Talbot, Charles H., tr. see Borresen, Kari E.

Talbot, George. Philosophy & Unified Science. 1435p. 1982. Repr. of 1978 ed. 36.50 (ISBN 0-941524-18-3). Lotus Light.

Talbot, Gordon. A Study of the Book of Genesis. LC 81-65578. 288p. (Orig.). 1981. pap. 6.95 (ISBN 0-87509-253-5); leader's guide 2.95 (ISBN 0-87509-311-6). Chr Pubns.

Talbot, Gordon, et al. Higley Sunday School Commentary. Triplett, Loren, ed. (Illus.). 528p. (Orig.). 1985. text ed. 8.95 (ISBN 0-9614116-1-9); pap. text ed. 6.95 (ISBN 0-9614116-0-0). Higley.

Talbot, John M. The Fire of God. 144p. 1986. pap. 7.95 (ISBN 0-8245-0789-4). Crossroad NY.

--Reflections on the Gospels, 3 vols, Vol. 2. 196p. (Orig.). 1987. pap. 5.95 (ISBN 0-89283-349-1). Servant.

--Reflections on the Gospels: Daily Devotions for Radical Christian Living. 196p. (Orig.). 1986. pap. 5.95 (ISBN 0-89283-306-8). Servant.

Talbot, Louis T. God's Plan of the Ages. 1936. pap. 8.95 (ISBN 0-8028-1194-9). Eerdmans.

Talbott, Roger G., jt. auth. see Budd, Leonard H.

Talebinejad, Mohammad, tr. see Mutahhari, Morteza.

Talec, Pierre. Christ & the Sacrament Church. 144p. 1983. pap. 9.95 (ISBN 0-8164-2455-1, HarpR). Har-Row.

--Jesus & the Hunger for Things Unknown. Neugroschel, Joachim, tr. from Fr. Orig. Title: Les Choses de la Foi. 250p. 1982. 12.95 (ISBN 0-8164-0510-7, HarpR). Har-Row.

Taleghani, Sayyid M. Society & Economics in Islam. Campbell, R., tr. from Persian. LC 82-2115. (Contemporary Islamic Thought Ser.). 225p. 1983. 17.95 (ISBN 0-933782-08-X). Mizan Pr.

Talese, Gay. The Kingdom & the Power. 672p. 1981. pap. 5.95 (ISBN 0-440-14397-7). Dell.

Talib, Ali B. Abi. Peak of Eloquence-Nahjul Balagha. x ed. Jafery, Askari, tr. 558p. 1983. Repr. 10.00 (ISBN 0-941724-18-2). Islamic Seminary.

Talib, Ali I. Supplications. Chittick, William C., tr. LC 84-52746. 63p. 1985. pap. 4.95 (ISBN 0-940368-46-3). Tahrike Tarsile Quran.

Talib, Ali-Ibne-Abu. Nahjul Balagha. Jafery, Syded A., tr. from Arabic. LC 84-51778. 691p. 1984. text ed. 19.95 (ISBN 0-940368-43-9); pap. 9.00 (ISBN 0-940368-42-0). Tahrike Tarsile Quran.

Talib, Gubachana S. Bani of Sri Guru Amardas. 1979. text ed. 29.50 (ISBN 0-89684-078-6, Pub. by Sterling New Delhi). Orient Bk Dist.

Talib, Gurbachan S., tr. Sri Guru Granth Sahib in English Translation, Vol. 1. 1985. 30.00x (ISBN 0-8364-1507-8, Pub. by Punjabi U India). South Asia Bks.

Tallach, Isobel. Life of Jesus. (Orig.). 1984. pap. 1.75 (ISBN 0-85151-345-X). Banner of Truth.

Tallach, John. God Made Them Great. 144p. 1982. pap. 5.45 (ISBN 0-85151-190-2). Banner of Truth.

--They Shall Be Mine. 128p. 1981. pap. 5.45 (ISBN 0-85151-320-4). Banner of Truth.

Tallant, Robert. Voodoo in New Orleans. 248p. 1983. pap. 3.50 (ISBN 0-88289-336-X). Pelican.

--The Voodoo Queen. 314p. 1983. pap. 3.50 (ISBN 0-88289-332-7). Pelican.

Talley, Thomas J. Origins of the Liturgical Year. 300p. (Orig.). 1986. pap. 17.50 (ISBN 0-916134-75-X). Pueblo Pub Co.

Tallis, Thomas see Buck, P. C. & Fellowes, E. H.

Tallis, Thomas, et al. Thomas Tallis. Buck, P. C., ed. (Tudor Church Music Ser.: Vol. 6). 1963. Repr. of 1928 ed. write for info. (ISBN 0-8450-1856-6). Broude.

Tallmer, Margot, et al, eds. The Implications of Death & Loss for Women. (Current Thanatology Ser.). 100p. 1986. pap. 13.95 (ISBN 0-930194-40-3). Ctr Thanatology.

Tallon, Andrew. Personal Becoming: In Honor of Karl Rahner. 188p. pap. 19.95 (ISBN 0-686-65691-1). Marquette.

Talmadge, Virginia. Dear God Little Prayers to a Big God. 1981. cloth 3.25 (ISBN 0-86544-016-6). Salv Army Suppl South.

Talmage, F., ed. AJS Review, Vol. 1. 1976. 20.00x (Pub. by Assoc. for Jewish Studies). Ktav.

--AJS Review, Vol. 2. 1977. 20.00x (ISBN 0-685-55539-9, Pub. by Assoc. for Jewish Studies). Ktav.

Talmage, Frank. Disputation & Dialogue: Readings in the Jewish Christian Encounter. pap. 14.95x (ISBN 0-87068-284-9). Ktav.

Talmage, Frank, jt. ed. see Dan, Joseph.

Talmage, Frank E. David Kimhi: The Man & the Commentaries. LC 75-1747. (Harvard Judaic Monographs: No. 1). 224p. 1976. text ed. 16.50x (ISBN 0-674-19340-7). Harvard U Pr.

Talmage, James E. Articles of Faith. LC 80-22041. (Classics in Mormon Literature Edition Ser.). 537p. 1981. 9.95 (ISBN 0-87747-838-4). Deseret Bk.

--Great Apostasy. 6.95 (ISBN 0-87747-384-6). Deseret Bk.

--House of the Lord. 8.95 (ISBN 0-87747-112-6). Deseret Bk.

--Jesus the Christ. (Classics in Mormon Literature Ser.). 804p. 1982. 10.95 (ISBN 0-87747-903-8). Deseret Bk.

Talmage, Thomas. Talmage on Palestine: Series of Sermons. Davis, Moshe, ed. LC 77-70747. (America & the Holy Land Ser.). 1977. Repr. of 1890 ed. lib. bdg. 17.00x (ISBN 0-405-10293-3). Ayer Co Pubs.

Talmon, Shemaryahu, jt. ed. see Cross, Frank M.

Talon, Henri A. John Bunyan: The Man & His Works. 1978. lib. bdg. 35.00 (ISBN 0-8495-5114-5). Arden Lib.

--John Bunyan: The Man & His Works. 340p. 1980. Repr. of 1951 ed. lib. bdg. 35.00 (ISBN 0-89987-810-5). Darby Bks.

--John Bunyan: The Man & His Works. LC 76-8161. 1976. lib. bdg. 47.50 (ISBN 0-8414-8611-5). Folcroft.

Tama, M. Diogene, tr. Transactions of the Parisian Sanhedrim. (Brown Classics in Judaica Ser.). 364p. 1985. pap. text ed. 15.25 (ISBN 0-8191-4488-6). U Pr of Amer.

Tambasco, Anthony J. The Bible for Ethics: Juan Luis Segundo & First-World Ethics. LC 80-6253. 286p. (Orig.). 1981. lib. bdg. 27.50 (ISBN 0-8191-1556-8); pap. text ed. 12.75 (ISBN 0-8191-1557-6). U Pr of Amer.

--In the Days of Jesus: The Jewish Background & Unique Teaching of Jesus. LC 82-62919. 128p. (Orig.). 1983. pap. 3.95 (ISBN 0-8091-2536-6). Paulist Pr.

--What Are They Saying about Mary? (WATSA Ser.). (Orig.). 1984. pap. 4.95 (ISBN 0-8091-2626-5). Paulist Pr.

Tambiah, J. A Performative Approach to Ritual. (Radcliffe-Brown Lectures in Social Anthropology). 1978. pap. 3.75 (ISBN 0-85672-197-2, Pub. by British Acad). Longwood Pub Group.

Tambiah, S. J. Buddhism & the Spirit Cults in Northeast Thailand. LC 73-108112. (Cambridge Studies in Social Anthropology: No. 2). (Illus.). 1970. pap. 19.95 (ISBN 0-521-09958-7). Cambridge U Pr.

--World Conqueror & World Renouncer. LC 76-8290. (Cambridge Studies in Social Anthropology: No. 15). 1976. 65.00 (ISBN 0-521-21140-9); pap. 19.95 (ISBN 0-521-29290-5). Cambridge U Pr.

Tambiah, Stanley J. The Buddhist Saints of the Forest & the Cult of Amulets: A Study in Charisma, Hagiography, Sectarianism & Millenial Buddhism. LC 83-15113. (Cambridge Studies in Social Anthropology: No. 49). (Illus.). 432p. 1984. 57.50 (ISBN 0-521-25984-3); pap. 18.95 (ISBN 0-521-27787-6). Cambridge U Pr.

--Culture, Thought, & Social Action: An Anthropological Perspective. (Illus.). 432p. 1985. text ed. 30.00x (ISBN 0-674-17969-2). Harvard U Pr.

Tamby, T. Isaac. Psalm of Saiva-being. 506p. 1986. Repr. of 1925 ed. 30.00X (ISBN 0-8364-1682-1, PUb. by Abhinav India). South Asia Bks.

Tames, Richard. The Muslim World. LC 83-50694. (Religions of the World Ser.). 48p. 1983. 14.96 (ISBN 0-382-06719-3); pap. 9.25 (ISBN 0-382-06932-3). Silver.

Tamiazzo, John. Love & Be Loved: A How-To Book. 176p. 1986. pap. 7.95 (ISBN 0-87877-087-9, Greenbriar Books). Newcastle Pub.

Tamir, Nachman, ed. The Polish Jews, 1914-1939. LC 85-47709. (Illus.). 216p. 1986. 19.95 (ISBN 0-8453-4791-8, Cornwall Bks). Assoc Univ Prs.

Tamir, Vicki. Bulgaria & Her Jews: The History of a Dubious Symbiosis. LC 78-62154. (Illus.). 1979. 14.95 (ISBN 0-87203-075-X). Hermon.

Tamke, Susan S. Make a Joyful Noise Unto the Lord: Hymns As a Reflection of Victorian Social Attitudes. LC 76-51693. 209p. 1978. 12.00x (ISBN 0-8214-0371-0); pap. text ed. 5.00x (ISBN 0-8214-0382-6). Ohio U Pr.

Tan, Paul L. Encyclopedia of Seven Thousand-Seven Hundred Illustrations: Signs of the Times. 7th ed. LC 78-72973. (Illus.). 2032p. 1979. 34.95 (ISBN 0-932940-02-1). Assurance Pubs.

--The Interpretation of Prophecy. 4th ed. LC 73-85613. 1979. Repr. 8.95 (ISBN 0-932940-01-3). Assurance Pubs.

--The Interpretation of Prophecy. 1975. 8.95 (ISBN 0-88469-000-8). BMH Bks.

--Jesus Is Coming. 1982. pap. 2.95 (ISBN 0-88469-095-4). BMH Bks.

--Literal Interpretation of the Bible. LC 78-73220. 1978. pap. text ed. 2.95 (ISBN 0-932940-04-8). Assurance Pubs.

--Literal Interpretation of the Bible. 114p. 1979. pap. 3.95 (ISBN 0-88469-098-9). BMH Bks.

--The New Jerusalem. LC 78-73221. 1978. pap. text ed. 1.95 (ISBN 0-932940-05-6). Assurance Pubs.

Tanahashi, Kazuaki. Enku: Sculptor of a Hundred Thousand Buddhas. LC 81-50969. (Illus.). 176p. (Orig.). 1982. pap. 13.95 (ISBN 0-87773-212-4). Shambhala Pubns.

--Penetrating Laughter: Hakuin's Zen & Art. LC 83-43155. (Illus.). 144p. 1984. 16.95 (ISBN 0-87951-952-5); pap. 8.95 (ISBN 0-87951-280-6). Overlook Pr.

Tanenbaum, Marc H. Religious Values in an Age of Violence. (Pere Marquette Theology Lectures). 1976. 7.95 (ISBN 0-87462-508-4). Marquette.

Tanenbaum, Marc H. & Wilson, Marvin R., eds. Evangelicals & Jews in an Age of Pluralism. 272p. 1984. pap. 9.95 (ISBN 0-8010-8871-2). Baker Bk.

Tangedahl, Joanne, jt. auth. see Neill, Merrily.

Tangl, Georgine, ed. see Innocent Third, Pope.

Tangvald, Christine. I Can Talk to God. (I Am Special Bks.). (Illus.). 20p. 1985. 3.95 (ISBN 0-89191-907-4, 59071). Cook.

--Me, Myself & I. (I Am Special Bks.). (Illus.). 20p. 1985. 3.95 (ISBN 0-89191-925-2, 59253). Cook.

--My Own Special Body. (I Am Special Bks.). (Illus.). 20p. 1985. pap. 3.95 (ISBN 0-89191-903-1, 59030). Cook.

--When I Am Sick. (I Am Special Bks.). (Illus.). 20p. 1985. 3.95 (ISBN 0-89191-908-2, 59089). Cook.

Taniguchi, Ruth, tr. see Meyer, F. B.

Tanksley, Perry. Love from the Living Bible. 1976. 4.95 (ISBN 0-686-17793-2). Allgood Bks.

--These Things I've Loved. 5.95 (ISBN 0-686-21184-7). Allgood Bks.

--We're in This Thing Together. 1974. 4.50 (ISBN 0-8007-0664-1). Allgood Bks.

Tannehill, Robert C. The Narrative Unity of Luke-Acts: A Literary Interpretation Vol. 1. LC 86-45224. (The Gospel According to Luke Series). 352p. 1986. 19.95 (ISBN 0-8006-2112-3, 1-2112). Fortress.

--The Sword of His Mouth. Beardslee, William A., ed. LC 75-18948. (Semeia Studies). 236p. 1976. pap. 7.95 (ISBN 0-8006-1501-8, 1-1501). Fortress.

Tannenbaum, Leslie. Biblical Tradition in Blake's Early Prophecies: The Great Code of Art. LC 81-47158. 368p. 1982. 30.50x (ISBN 0-691-06490-3). Princeton U Pr.

Tanner, Don, jt. auth. see Swanson, James R.

Tanner, Don, ed. see Popoff, Peter.

Tanner, Florice. The Mystery Teachings in World Religions. LC 73-8887. (A Quest Book Original Ser). 160p. (Orig.). 1973. pap. 2.45 (ISBN 0-8356-0439-X, Quest). Theos Pub Hse.

Tanner, Henry. Martyrdom of Lovejoy: An Account of the Life, Trials, & Perils of Rev. Elijah P. Lovejoy. LC 68-18603. (Illus.). 1971. Repr. of 1881 ed. lib. bdg. 25.00x (ISBN 0-678-00744-6). Kelley.

Tanner, Ira J. Healing the Pain of Everyday Loss. 188p. 1980. pap. 4.95 (ISBN 0-03-057849-3, HarpR). Har-Row.

Tanner, Jerald & Tanner, Sandra. Changing World of Mormonism. LC 79-18311. 1979. 16.95 (ISBN 0-8024-1234-3). Moody.

Tanner, Paul A. Call to Righteousness. 1984. pap. 0.75 (ISBN 0-87162-404-4, D3012). Warner Pr.

Tanner, Ralph E. Transition in African Beliefs: Traditional Religion & Christian Change: A Study in Sukumaland, Tanzania, East Africa. LC 67-21411. pap. 67.50 (ISBN 0-317-26638-1, 2025117). Bks Demand UMI.

Tanner, Ralph E., jt. auth. see Reynolds, Vernon.

Tanner, Sandra, jt. auth. see Tanner, Jerald.

Tanner, William G. From Sea to Shining Sea. LC 86-9609. 1986. pap. 4.95 (ISBN 0-8054-5667-8). Broadman.

Tannery, ed. see Descartes, Rene.

Tano, Rodrigo D. Theology in the Philippine Setting: A Case Study in the Contextualization of Theology. 184p. 1981. pap. 7.50x (ISBN 0-686-32582-6, Pub. by New Day Phillipines). Cellar.

Tan Tai Wei. The Worth of Religious Truth-Claims: A Case for Religious Education. LC 81-43864. 128p. (Orig.). 1982. pap. text ed. 9.50 (ISBN 0-8191-2369-2). U Pr of Amer.

Tantaquidgeon, Gladys. Folk Medicine of the Delaware & Related Algonkian Indians. LC 73-620801. (Pennsylvania Historical & Museum Commission Anthropological Ser.: No. 3). (Illus.). 145p. 1972. 7.50 (ISBN 0-911124-70-5); pap. 4.50 (ISBN 0-911124-69-1). Pa Hist & Mus.

--A Study of Delaware Indian Medicine Practice & Folk Beliefs. LC 76-43864. (Pennsylvania Historical Commission). Repr. of 1942 ed. 18.00 (ISBN 0-404-15724-6). AMS Pr.

Tao Fong Shan Ecumenical Centre, tr. see Ting, K. H.

Tapasyananda, tr. see Shankara.

Tapasyananda, Swami. Aratrika Hymns & Ram Nam. 1979. pap. 1.50 (ISBN 0-87481-476-6). Vedanta Pr.

--Swami Ramakrishnananda: The Apostle of Sri Ramakrishna to the South. 276p. 1973. 2.50 (ISBN 0-87481-453-7). Vedanta Pr.

Tapasyananda, Swami & Nikhilananda, Swami. Sarada Devi, the Holy Mother: Her Life & Conversations. (Illus.). 12.95 (ISBN 0-87481-435-9). Vedanta Pr.

Tapasyananda, Swami, tr. see Madhava-Vidyaranya.

Tapasyananda, Swami, tr. see Puri, Vishnu.

Tapasyananda, Swami, tr. see Vyasa.

Tapia, Geraldine. The Parables of Jesus. 144p. 1987. 10.95 (ISBN 0-317-53382-7). Todd & Honeywell.

Tapley, Roberts, tr. see Febvre, Lucien P.

Tapley, William. Happily Ever after Is No Accident. Sherer, Michael L., ed. (Orig.). 1987. pap. 2.75 leaders guide (ISBN 0-89536-862-5, 7821); pap. 3.45 couples bk. (ISBN 0-89536-863-3, 7822). CSS of Ohio.

Tapp, Elizabeth, tr. see Steiner, Rudolf, et al.

Tapp, Michael, tr. see Steiner, Rudolf, et al.

Tapp, Mrs. Vernon. For Such a Time. (Illus.). 160p. 1979. pap. 3.00 (ISBN 0-89114-083-2); pap. 0.75 tchr's. guide, 15 pg. (ISBN 0-89114-084-0). Baptist Pub Hse.

Tappert, Theodore G., ed. & tr. Book of Concord: The Confessions of the Evangelical Lutheran Church. LC 59-11369. 1959. 14.95 (ISBN 0-8006-0825-9, 1-825). Fortress.

Tappert, Theodore G. & Lehmann, Helmut T., eds. Luther's Works: Table Talk, Vol. 54. Tappert, Theodore G., tr. LC 55-9893. 1967. 19.95 (ISBN 0-8006-0354-0, 1-354). Fortress.

Tappert, Theodore G., ed. & tr. see Spener, Philip J.

Tappert, Theodore G., tr. Augsburg Confession: Anniversary Edition. 64p. 1980. pap. 1.75 (ISBN 0-8006-1385-6, 1-1385). Fortress.

Tappert, Theodore G., tr. see Tappert, Theodore G. & Lehmann, Helmut T.

Tapscott, Betty. Fruit of the Spirit. 1978. pap. 4.95 (ISBN 0-917726-26-X). Hunter Bks.

--Inner Healing Through Healing of Memories. 1975. pap. 4.95 (ISBN 0-917726-29-4). Hunter Bks.

--Set Free. 1978. pap. 4.95 (ISBN 0-917726-24-3). Hunter Bks.

Taran, Leonardo, ed. see Roberts, W. Rhys.

Taranath. Taranatha's History of Buddhism in India. Chattopadhyaya, Debiprsdad & Chattopadhyaya, A., eds. 1980. Repr. of 1970 ed. 27.00x (ISBN 0-8364-1597-3, Pub. by KP Bagchi & Co.). South Asia Bks.

Taranath, Rajeeve, tr. see Alanahally, Shrikrishna.

Taraporewala, Irach J., ed. The Divine Songs of Zarathushtra. LC 74-21251. Repr. of 1951 ed. 125.00 (ISBN 0-404-12802-5). AMS Pr.

Taraval, Sigismundo. Indian Uprising in Lower California, 1734-1737. LC 79-137296. Repr. of 1931 ed. 24.00 (ISBN 0-404-06337-3). AMS Pr.

Tarazi, Paul N. First Thessalonians: A Commentary. LC 82-16952. (Orthodox Biblical Studies). 186p. (Orig.). 1982. pap. 7.95 (ISBN 0-913836-97-4). St Vladimirs.

Tarcov, Edith & Tarcov, Oscar. Illustrated Book of Jewish Knowledge. (Illus.). 1959. 6.00x (ISBN 0-87068-358-6, Pub. by Friendly Hse). Ktav.

Tarcov, Oscar, jt. auth. see Gilbert, Arthur.

Tarcov, Oscar, jt. auth. see Tarcov, Edith.

Target, C. M. The Nun in the Concentration Camp. 1974. pap. 1.60 (ISBN 0-08-017611-9). Pergamon.

Target, George. Out of This World: A Guide to the Retreat Houses of Great Britain. 1985. 35.00x (ISBN 0-900873-67-1, Pub. by Bishopsgate Pr. Ltd); pap. 21.00x (ISBN 0-900873-73-6). State Mutual Bk.

Tari, Mel. Como un Viento Recio. 208p. 1972. 3.25 (ISBN 0-88113-041-9). Edit Betania.

Tari, Mel & Dudley, Cliff. America! Jesus Is Here! LC 76-1058. 1976. 4.95 (ISBN 0-89221-021-4). New Leaf.

--Like a Mighty Wind. 171p. 1978. pap. 4.95 (ISBN 0-89221-123-7). New Leaf.

Tari, Mel & Tari, Noni. Gentle Breeze of Jesus. 125p. pap. 4.95 (ISBN 0-89221-122-9). New Leaf.

Tari, Noni, jt. auth. see Tari, Mel.

Tariq, M. A. Holy Quran Made Easy. 1968. 5.35x (ISBN 0-87902-070-9). Orientalia.

Tarneja, Sukh R. Nature, Spirituality & Science. 240p. 1980. text ed. 27.50x (ISBN 0-7069-1203-9, Pub by Vikas India). Advent NY.

Tarnor, Norman, jt. auth. see Tarnor, Pearl.

Tarnor, Pearl & Tarnor, Norman. Hebrew & Heritage, Vol. II: Siddur Track. 1982. 3.95x (ISBN 0-87441-375-3); tchr's. guide 12.50 (ISBN 0-87441-377-X). Behrman.

--Siddur Program, II to Hebrew & Heritage. (Illus.). 128p. 1982. pap. text ed. 3.95x (ISBN 0-87441-330-3). Behrman.

--Siddur Program III to Hebrew & Heritage. (Illus.). 128p. 1983. pap. text ed. 3.95x (ISBN 0-87441-359-1). Behrman.

Tarostar. Spiritual Worker's Handbook. (Illus.). 80p. (Orig.). 1985. pap. 3.95 (ISBN 0-943832-12-8). Intl Imports.

Tarrant, Christ. Life in Bible Times. 48p. (Orig.). 1986. pap. 5.95 (ISBN 0-687-21850-0). Abingdon.

Tarrant, Harold. Scepticism or Platonism: The Philosophy of the Fourth Academy. (Cambridge Classical Studies). 192p. 1985. 39.50 (ISBN 0-521-30191-2). Cambridge U Pr.

Tart, Charles T. Waking up. LC 86-11844. 300p. 1986. 17.95 (ISBN 0-87773-374-0, Pub. by New Sci Lib-Shambhala). Shambhala Pubns.

Tarthang Tulku. Dimensions of Thought: Current Explorations in Time, Space & Knowledge, 2 vols. Moon, Ralph & Randall, Steve, eds. 1980. Vol. 1. 12.95 (ISBN 0-913546-77-1); Vol. 2. 12.95 (ISBN 0-913546-78-X). Dharma Pub.

--Hidden Mind of Freedom. Derman, Sylvia, ed. 1981. pap. 6.95 (ISBN 0-89800-120-X). Dharma Pub.

Tash, Sharon. In the Potter's Hands Book. 32p. 1985. pap. 1.95 (ISBN 0-930756-96-7, 531020). Aglow Pubns.

--Kingdom Living. (Bible Study Basic Ser.). 64p. 1984. 2.95 (521018). Aglow Pubns.

Tasie, G. O. Christian Missionary Enterprise in the Niger Delta, 1864-1918. (Studies on Religion in Africa Ser.: No. 3). (Illus.). 1978. text ed. 49.95 (ISBN 90-04-05243-7). Humanities.

Task Force on World Hunger. And He Had Compassion on Them: The Christian & World Hunger. (Illus.). 1979. pap. text ed. 3.50 (ISBN 0-933140-00-2). CRC Pubns.

Tasker, G. P. Saint Paul & His Gospel. 87p. 1982. pap. 1.00 (ISBN 0-686-36256-X). Faith Pub Hse.

Tasker, R. V., ed. see Augustine, Saint.

Tasker, R. V., ed. see Moo, Douglas.

Tasker, R. V., ed. see Morris, Leon.

Tasker, Randolph V. General Epistle of James. (Tyndale Bible Commentaries). 1957. pap. 3.95 (ISBN 0-8028-1415-8). Eerdmans.

--Gospel According to St. John. (Tyndale Bible Commentaries Ser.). 1960. pap. 4.95 (ISBN 0-8028-1403-4). Eerdmans.

--Gospel According to St. Matthew. (Tyndale Bible Commentaries Ser.). 1962. pap. 5.95 (ISBN 0-8028-1400-X). Eerdmans.

--Second Epistle of Paul to the Corinthians. (Tyndale Bible Commentaries). 1958. pap. 4.95 (ISBN 0-8028-1407-7). Eerdmans.

Tassell, Paul. Pathways to Power: Keys That Open Doors. LC 83-9576. 1983. pap. 3.95 (ISBN 0-87227-093-9). Reg Baptist.

--Secrets of the Blessed Man. 1971. pap. 2.95 (ISBN 0-87227-033-5). Reg Baptist.

--Sweeter Than Honey. 1978. pap. 2.95 (ISBN 0-87227-068-8). Reg Baptist.

Tataki, A. B. Sounion: The Temple of Poseidon. (Illustrated Travel Guides Ser.). (Illus.). 1979. pap. 9.95 (ISBN 0-89241-104-X). Caratzas.

Tate, Judith. Manual for Lectors. (Orig.). 1975. 2.95 (ISBN 0-8278-0030-4, Pub. by Pflaum Pr). Peter Li.

Tatenhove, Frederick C. van see Van Tatenhove, Frederick C.

Tate-O'Brien, Judith. Welcome: Christian Parenting. 68p. (Orig.). 1980. pap. 4.00 (ISBN 0-936098-37-6); instrs.' guide 3.00 (ISBN 0-936098-36-8). Intl Marriage.

Tatford, Frederick. Daniel & His Prophecy. 1980. 9.25 (ISBN 0-86524-045-0, 2702). Klock & Klock.

Tatford, Frederick A. God's Program of the Ages. LC 67-26075. 160p. (Orig.). 1967. 4.95 (ISBN 0-8254-3800-4). Kregel.

--The Minor Prophets, 3 vols. 1214p. 1982. Set. lib. bdg. 44.95 Smythe Sewn (ISBN 0-86524-135-X, 7000). Klock & Klock.

--The Revelation. 656p. 1985. Repr. lib. bdg. 23.00 (ISBN 0-86524-186-4, 6602). Klock & Klock.

Tatham, Julie C. The Old Testament Made Easy. LC 85-90957. (Illus.). 720p. 1985. 25.00 (ISBN 0-682-40263-X). Exposition Pr FL.

--The Old Testament Made Easy. (Illus.). 540p. (Orig.). 1986. limp leatherette 20.00 (ISBN 0-9617543-0-3). J C Tatham.

Tatian. Oratorio ad Graecos & Fragments. Whittaker, Molly, ed. & tr. (Oxford Early Christian Texts). 1982. 27.50x (ISBN 0-19-826809-2). Oxford U Pr.

Tatlow, Anthony. The Mask of Evil. (European University Studies: Series 18, Comparative Literature, Vol. 12). 1977. 52.20 (ISBN 3-261-02905-6). P Lang Pubs.

Tatum, W. Barnes. In Quest of Jesus: A Guidebook. 1983. pap. 9.95 (ISBN 0-8042-0275-3). John Knox.

Tatz, Mark, tr. Buddhism & Healing: Demieville's Article "Byo" from Hobogirin. 108p. (Orig.). 1985. lib. bdg. 24.00 (ISBN 0-8191-4436-3); pap. text ed. 9.50 (ISBN 0-8191-4437-1). U Pr of Amer.

Tatz, Mark, tr. see Candragomin.

Tauber, Rhea. Rhea's World. LC 86-16989. (Paperback Ser.). 217p. 1987. pap. 7.95 (ISBN 0-8022-2499-7). Philos Lib.

Taubes, Hella. Bible Speaks, 3 vols. Bloch, Lolla, tr. (Illus.). 1974. 14.95x ea. (ISBN 0-686-76831-0). Set. Bloch.

Taubes, Hellen. The Bible Speaks By, 3 Vols. 1965. Set. 14.95. Soncino Pr.

Tauler, John. Spiritual Conferences. Colledge, Eric & Jane, M., trs. LC 78-74568. 1979. pap. 7.00 (ISBN 0-89555-082-2). TAN Bks Pubs.

Taulman, James E. Encouragers: The Sunday School Worker's Counseling Ministry. LC 85-19523. 1986. pap. 4.95 (ISBN 0-8054-3712-6). Broadman.

Taunton, Ethelred L. Thomas Wolsey: Legate & Reformer. LC 72-112819. 1970. Repr. of 1902 ed. 23.50x (ISBN 0-8046-1086-X, Pub by Kennikat). Assoc Faculty Pr.

Taussig, Hal. Dancing the New Testament: A Guide to Texts. 1977. 2.00 (ISBN 0-941500-06-3). Sharing Co.

--The Lady of the Dance: A Movement Approach to the Biblical Figures of Wisdom in Worship & Education. (Orig.). 1981. pap. 2.50 (ISBN 0-941500-24-1). Sharing Co.

--New Categories for Dancing: The Old Testament. (Orig.). 1981. pap. 2.50 (ISBN 0-941500-25-X). Sharing Co.

Taussig, Michael. Shamanism, Colonialism, & the Wild Man: A Study in Terror & Healing. LC 86-11410. (Illus.). 544p. 1987. lib. bdg. 29.95 (ISBN 0-226-79012-6). U of Chicago Pr.

Tavakoli, Amir, tr. see Bourghei, S. R., et al.

Tavard, G. H. Transiency & Permanence: The Nature of Theology According to Saint Bonaventure. 1974. Repr. of 1954 ed. 15.00 (ISBN 0-686-11588-0). Franciscan Inst.

Tavard, George. Theology for Ministry. (Theology & Life Ser.: Vol. 6). pap. 7.95 (ISBN 0-89453-337-1). M Glazier.

Tavard, George, jt. auth. see Edwards, Mark.

Tavard, George H. Holy Writ or Holy Church: The Crisis of the Protestant Reformation. LC 78-17085. 1978. Repr. of 1959 ed. lib. bdg. 22.75x (ISBN 0-313-20584-1, TAHO). Greenwood.

--Images of the Christ: An Enquiry into Christology. LC 81-40582. 134p. (Orig.). 1982. lib. bdg. 24.25 (ISBN 0-8191-2129-0); pap. text ed. 9.50 (ISBN 0-8191-2130-4). U Pr of Amer.

--Justification: An Ecumenical Study. 144p. (Orig.). 1983. pap. 7.95 (ISBN 0-8091-2549-8). Paulist Pr.

--The Vision of the Trinity. LC 80-5845. 166p. (Orig.). 1981. lib. bdg. 25.25 (ISBN 0-8191-1412-X); pap. text ed. 10.75 (ISBN 0-8191-1413-8). U Pr of Amer.

--Woman in Christian Tradition. LC 72-12637. pap. 67.30 (ISBN 0-317-26144-4, 2024373). Bks Demand UMI.

Tavard, George H., jt. auth. see Edwards, Mark.

Tavard, Georges H. Two Centuries of Ecumenism. LC 78-6449. 1978. Repr. of 1960 ed. lib. bdg. 22.50x (ISBN 0-313-20490-X, TATC). Greenwood.

Taverner, Richard, tr. see Erasmus, Desiderius.

Taves, Ann. The Household of Faith: Roman Catholic Devotions in Mid-Nineteenth Century America. LC 85-41008. 192p. 1986. text ed. 17.95x (ISBN 0-268-01082-X). U of Notre Dame Pr.

Taves, Ernest H. Trouble Enough: Joseph Smith & the Book of Mormon. LC 84-42790. (Illus.). 280p. 1984. 20.95 (ISBN 0-87975-261-0). Prometheus Bks.

Tawheedi, Mohammad S., tr. see Mutahhari, Morteza.

Tawhidi, M. Salman, ed. see Ayatollah Morteza Motahhari.

Tawney, Richard H. Religion & the Rise of Capitalism. 12.75 (ISBN 0-8446-1446-7). Peter Smith.

Taylor, A. E. The Faith of the Moralist: Gifford Lectures Delivered in the University of St. Andrews, 1926-1928, 2 vols. 1977. Repr. of 1932 ed. Set. lib. bdg. 50.00 (ISBN 0-8482-2663-1). Norwood Edns.

Taylor, A., Jr. The Life of My Years. 160p. (Orig.). 1983. pap. 9.95 (ISBN 0-687-21854-3). Abingdon.

Taylor, Alan. Prelude to Israel: An Analysis of Zionist Diplomacy, 1897-1947. rev. ed. 126p. 1970. Repr. of 1961 ed. 3.50 (ISBN 0-88728-093-5). Inst Palestine.

Taylor, Alan R. The Zionist Mind, No. 39. 1974. 6.00 (ISBN 0-88728-118-4); pap. 4.00 (ISBN 0-88728-119-2). Inst Palestine.

Taylor, Alfred. A Human Heritage. LC 74-18360. 150p. (Orig.). 1975. pap. 2.50 (ISBN 0-8356-0455-1, Quest). Theos Pub Hse.

Taylor, Alfred E. Faith of a Moralist, 2 Vols. in 1. LC 37-23815. (Gifford Lectures 1926-1928). 1968. Repr. of 1937 ed. 41.00 (ISBN 0-527-89062-6). Kraus Repr.

Taylor, Alice. How to Be a Minister's Wife & Love It. 1968. pap. 3.95 (ISBN 0-310-33131-5, 10877P). Zondervan.

Taylor, Alice H. Rescued from the Dragon. 199p. (Orig.). 1982. pap. 5.25 (ISBN 0-89367-078-2). Light & Life.

Taylor, Ariel Y. Numerology: Its Facts & Secrets. pap. 3.00 (ISBN 0-87980-109-3). Wilshire.

--Numerology Made Plain. 147p. 1973. pap. 5.95 (ISBN 0-87877-012-7, P-12). Newcastle Pub.

Taylor, Arnold C., ed. Kathavatthu, 2 vols. in one. LC 78-72450. Repr. of 1894 ed. 56.00 (ISBN 0-404-17317-9). AMS Pr.

--Patisambhidamagga, 2 vols. in one. LC 78-70108. Repr. of 1905 ed. 43.50 (ISBN 0-404-17358-6). AMS Pr.

Taylor, Barbara. From Rejection to Acceptance. 1987. text ed. 8.95 (ISBN 0-8054-5045-9). Broadman.

Taylor, Barbara B., ed. see Hopewell, James F., et al.

Taylor, Barbara D., ed. see Tharchin, Sermey G.

Taylor, Beth, jt. auth. see Heath, Lou.

Taylor, Bill. A Tale of Two Cities: The Mormons-Catholics. 1981. pap. 5.50 (ISBN 0-933046-02-2). Little Red Hen.

Taylor, Blaine. The Church's Ministry with Older Adults. 144p. 1987. pap. 10.95 (ISBN 0-687-08382-6). Abingdon.

--Gee, You Look Good. 137p. (Orig.). 1984. pap. 6.00 (ISBN 0-914527-32-0). C-Four Res.

--John Wesley: A Blueprint for Church Renewal. 221p. (Orig.). 1984. pap. 10.00 (ISBN 0-914527-19-3). C-Four Res.

Taylor, Blaine, et al. Christianity Without Morals. Cook, Jerry O., ed. 96p. (Orig.). 1982. pap. 7.00 (ISBN 0-914527-16-9). C-Four Res.

Taylor, Bonnie. Devotions for New Mothers. 128p. 1987. 10.95 (ISBN 0-8170-1081-5); pap. 6.95 (ISBN 0-8170-1115-3). Judson.

Taylor, Charles. Sayings of the Jewish Fathers, 2 Vols. in 1. rev. ed. (Library of Jewish Classics). 1969. 25.00x (ISBN 0-87068-114-1). Ktav.

Taylor, Charles H., ed. Anniversary Essays in Mediaeval History, by Students of Charles Homer Haskins: Presented on His Completion of Forty Years of Teaching. facs. ed. LC 67-30194. (Essay Index Reprint Ser). 1929. 22.00 (ISBN 0-8369-0155-X). Ayer Co Pubs.

Taylor, Charles R. Beware America! Orig. Title: A Message to the President. (Illus.). 48p. (Orig.). 1983. pap. 3.50 (ISBN 0-937682-06-3). Today Bible.

--Death of Sadat...Start of World War III. (Illus.). 96p. (Orig.). 1982. pap. 3.95 (ISBN 0-937682-05-5). Today Bible.

--Get All Excited-Jesus is Coming Soon. (Illus.). 108p. (Orig.). 1975. pap. 2.95 (ISBN 0-937682-00-4). Today Bible.

--Pretribulation Rapture & the Bible. (Illus.). 40p. (Orig.). 1980. pap. 1.50 (ISBN 0-937682-03-9). Today Bible.

--Those Who Remain. (Illus.). 104p. (Orig.). 1980. pap. 2.95 (ISBN 0-937682-02-0). Today Bible.

--When Jesus Comes. (Illus.). 76p. (Orig.). 1985. pap. 4.95 (ISBN 0-937682-08-X). Today Bible.

Taylor, Charles W. Sayings of the Jewish Fathers. 59.95 (ISBN 0-8490-0995-2). Gordon Pr.

Taylor, Dan. The Myth of Certainty. 128p. 1986. 10.95 (ISBN 0-8499-0547-8). Word Bks.

Taylor, Duncan, tr. see Block, Martin.

Taylor, Edward. Harmony of the Gospels, 4 Vols. LC 82-5452. 2688p. 1983. Set. 300.00x (ISBN 0-8201-1379-4). Schol Facsimiles.

--Upon the Types of the Old Testament. Mignon, Charles W., ed. 1988. price not set (ISBN 0-8032-3075-3). U of Nebr Pr.

Taylor, G. F. Rainbow. pap. 2.00 (ISBN 0-911866-61-2). Advocate.

--Second Coming of Jesus. 3.95 (ISBN 0-911866-63-9); pap. 2.00 (ISBN 0-911866-62-0). Advocate.

Taylor, Gardner C., jt. auth. see Edwards, O. C., Jr.

Taylor, George R. The Story of Canterbury. LC 78-63479. (Illus.). Repr. of 1912 ed. 38.50 (ISBN 0-404-16545-1). AMS Pr.

Taylor, Guillermo D. La Familia Autenticamente Cristiana. Tr. of The Authentic Christian Family. (Span.). 240p. 1983. pap. 4.50 (ISBN 0-8254-1702-3). Kregel.

Taylor, Herbert J. The Herbert J. Taylor Story. 128p. 1983. pap. 4.95 (ISBN 0-87784-836-X). Inter-Varsity.

Taylor, Horace M. Reminiscences of an Army Chaplain. LC 86-1472. Date not set. price not set. (ISBN 0-9617424-0-2). H M Taylor.

Taylor, Howard & Taylor, Mary G. Hudson Taylor's Spiritual Secret. pap. 3.95 (ISBN 0-8024-0029-9). Moody.

Taylor, Howard, jt. auth. see Stein, Jock.

Taylor, Hudson. Hudson Taylor. 2nd ed. 160p. 1987. pap. 3.50 (ISBN 0-87123-951-5). Bethany Hse.

--Union & Communion. 96p. 1971. pap. 2.95 (ISBN 0-87123-571-4, 200571). Bethany Hse.

Taylor, Hudson & Thompson, Phyllis. God's Adventurer. (Illus.). 1978. pap. 2.50 (ISBN 9971-83-777-3). OMF Bks.

Taylor, Jack. Key to Triumphant Living. LC 76-166582. 1971. 8.95 (ISBN 0-8054-5514-0). Broadman.

--Much More! LC 72-79179. 160p. 1972. 8.95 (ISBN 0-8054-5523-X). Broadman.

--One Home under God. LC 73-91609. 8.95 (ISBN 0-8054-5222-2); study guide 1.00 (ISBN 0-8054-5225-7); guide book 5.00 (ISBN 0-8054-5615-5). Broadman.

Taylor, Jack R. After the Spirit Comes. LC 73-93908. 1975. 7.95 (ISBN 0-8054-5224-9). Broadman.

--God's Miraculous Plan of Economy. LC 75-27411. 168p. 1975. 8.95 (ISBN 0-8054-5565-5). Broadman.

--God's New Creation. 1987. 8.95 (ISBN 0-8054-5046-7). Broadman.

--The Hallelujah Factor. 180p. 1983. 8.95 (ISBN 0-8054-5531-0). Broadman.

--The Key to Triumphant Living. 208p. 1986. pap. 3.50 (ISBN 0-553-26031-6). Bantam.

--La Llave para una Vida de Triunfo. Guzman, Juan P., tr. from Eng. Orig. Title: The Key to Triumphant Living. 240p. 1982. pap. 6.25 (ISBN 0-311-46095-X, Edit Mundo). Casa Bautista.

--Prayer: Life's Limitless Reach. LC 77-73984. 1977. 8.95 (ISBN 0-8054-5258-3). Broadman.

--Victory over the Devil. LC 72-96149. 128p. 1973. pap. 4.95 (ISBN 0-8054-5131-5). Broadman.

--What Every Husband Should Know. LC 81-65389. 1981. 8.95 (ISBN 0-8054-5642-2). Broadman.

Taylor, Jack R. & Hawkins, C. S. When Revival Comes. LC 80-66956. 1980. pap. 5.50 (ISBN 0-8054-6226-0). Broadman.

Taylor, Jack R., jt. auth. see Glisson, Jerry.

Taylor, James. The Andrew Project. LC 85-42826. (Illus.). 108p. (Orig.). 1985. pap. 4.95 (ISBN 0-8042-0461-6). John Knox.

--An Everyday God. 116p. (Orig.). 1983. pap. 5.95 (ISBN 0-8358-0470-4). Upper Room.

Taylor, James C., jt. auth. see Bryson, Harold T.

Taylor, Jean. Flowers in Church. 161p. 1985. pap. 10.95 (ISBN 0-8192-1361-6). Morehouse.

Taylor, Jeremy. Holy Living & Holy Dying. Hinten, Marvin D., ed. 80p. 1986. pap. 3.95 (ISBN 0-8423-1350-8). Tyndale.

--Rule & Exercises of Holy Dying: Means & Instruments of Preparing Ourselves & Others Respectively for a Blessed Death. Kastenbaum, Robert & Thirlwall, Thomas, eds. LC 76-19590. (Death & Dying Ser.). 1977. Repr. of 1819 ed. lib. bdg. 25.50x (ISBN 0-405-09585-6). Ayer Co Pubs.

--The Rule & Exercises of Holy Living. 295p. 1982. Repr. of 1982 ed. lib. bdg. 35.00 (ISBN 0-89984-468-5). Century Bookbindery.

--The Rule & Exercises of Holy Living & the Rule & Exercises of Holy Dying. LC 82-80478. (Treasures from the Spiritual Classics Ser.). 64p. 1982. pap. 2.95 (ISBN 0-8192-1309-8). Morehouse.

Taylor, John. Collected Works. 600.00 (ISBN 0-87968-899-8). Gordon Pr.

--A History of Ten Baptist Churches, of Which the Author Has Been Alternately a Member. 2nd ed. Gaustad, Edwin S., ed. LC 79-5609. (The Baptist Tradition Ser.). 1980. Repr. of 1827 ed. lib. bdg. 25.50x (ISBN 0-405-12474-0). Ayer Co Pubs.

--Icon Painting. LC 78-25925. (The Mayflower Gallery Ser.). (Illus.). 1979. 12.50 (ISBN 0-8317-4813-3, Mayflower Bks); pap. 6.95 (ISBN 0-8317-4814-1). Smith Pubs.

--The Witchcraft Delusion in Colonial Connecticut, 1647-1747. 172p. 1974. 16.95 (ISBN 0-87928-053-0). Corner Hse.

Taylor, John, ed. Believing in the Church: Doctrine Commission of the Church of England. LC 82-80254. 320p. (Orig.). 1982. Repr. of 1981 ed. 17.95 (ISBN 0-8192-1301-2). Morehouse.

Taylor, John B. Ezekiel. LC 75-98503. (Tyndale Old Testament Commentaries Ser). 1969. 12.95 (ISBN 0-87784-884-X); pap. 6.95 (ISBN 0-87784-272-8). Inter-Varsity.

--Preaching Through the Prophets. LC 84-23773. 110p. 1985. pap. 7.95 (ISBN 0-8272-2929-1). CBP.

--The World of Islam. (Orig.). 1979. pap. 3.95 (ISBN 0-377-00086-8). Friend Pr.

Taylor, John B., ed. see World Conference on Religion & Peace Staff.

Taylor, John H., tr. & annotations by. St. Augustine: The Literal Meaning of Genesis, Vol. 1. (Ancient Christian Writers Ser.: Vol. 41). 292p. 1983. 19.95 (ISBN 0-8091-0326-5). Paulist Pr.

--St. Augustine: The Literal Meaning of Genesis, Vol. 2. (Ancient Christian Writers Ser.: Vol. 42). 358p. 1983. 22.95 (ISBN 0-8091-0327-3). Paulist Pr.

Taylor, John M. Witchcraft Delusion in Colonial Connecticut, 1647-97. LC 73-165414. (American Classics in History & Social Science Ser.: No. 196). 1971. Repr. of 1908 ed. lib. bdg. 21.00 (ISBN 0-8337-4445-3). B Franklin.

Taylor, John V. Enough Is Enough: A Biblical Call for Moderation in a Consumer Oriented Societed. LC 77-72456. 1977. pap. 5.95 (ISBN 0-8066-1584-2, 10-2083). Augsburg.

--The Go-Between God: The Holy Spirit & the Christian Mission. 1979. pap. 7.95 (ISBN 0-19-520125-6). Oxford U Pr.

--The Growth of the Church in Buganda: An Attempt at Understanding. LC 78-26702. (Illus.). 1979. Repr. of 1958 ed. lib. bdg. 24.75x (ISBN 0-313-20802-6, TAGC). Greenwood.

--Weep Not for Me. 64p. 1987. pap. 3.95 (ISBN 0-89622-313-2). Twenty-Third.

--Weep Not for Me: Meditations on the Cross & the Resurrection. (Risk Book Ser.). 56p. 1986. pap. 3.50 (ISBN 2-8254-0850-6). Wrld Coun Churches.

Taylor, John W. The Coming of the Saints. rev. ed. LC 85-71651. (Illus.). 272p. 1985. pap. 10.00 (ISBN 0-934666-19-9). Artisan Sales.

--The Coming of the Saints: Imaginations & Studies in Early Church History & Tradition. 1977. lib. bdg. 59.95 (ISBN 0-8490-1647-9). Gordon Pr.

Taylor, Julia. Last, Least & Lowest. LC 78-70663. 1979. pap. 2.95 (ISBN 0-89221-058-3). New Leaf.

Taylor, Justin. As It Was Written: An Introduction to the Bible. 176p. 1987. pap. 7.95 (ISBN 0-8091-2843-8). Paulist Pr.

Taylor, Kenneth. Is Christianity Credible. pap. 0.75 (ISBN 0-87784-110-1). Inter-Varsity.

--The One-Year Bible. 1985. cloth 16.95 (ISBN 0-8423-2431-3); kivar 10.95 (ISBN 0-8423-2428-3). Tyndale.

Taylor, Kenneth, tr. The Book for Children. 640p. 1985. 9.95 (ISBN 0-8423-2145-4). Tyndale.

Taylor, Kenneth N. Almost Twelve. 1968. pap. 2.50 (ISBN 0-8423-0060-0). Tyndale.

--Bible in Pictures for Little Eyes. (Illus.). 1956. 11.95 (ISBN 0-8024-0595-9). Moody.

--La Biblia en Cuadros para Ninos. Orig. Title: The Bible in Pictures for Little Eyes. (Span.). 190p. 1956. 13.95 (ISBN 0-8254-1706-6). Kregel.

--Devotions for the Children's Hour. pap. 3.95 (ISBN 0-8024-0061-2). Moody.

--Giant Steps for Little People. 64p. 1985. 6.95 (ISBN 0-8423-1023-1). Tyndale.

--How to Grow. Expanded ed. 192p. Date not set. pap. 7.95. Oliver-Nelson.

--How to Grow: Expanded Edition. 192p. Date not set. pap. 7.95 (ISBN 0-317-47452-9). Oliver-Nelson.

--How to Grow: First Steps for New Christians. 176p. 1985. 7.95 (ISBN 0-8407-9038-4). Oliver-Nelson.

--The Living Bible Story Book. 7.95 (ISBN 0-8423-2307-4). Tyndale.

--Living Letter for the Children's Hour. LC 68-26407. (Illus.). 192p. 1968. pap. 3.95 (ISBN 0-8024-0062-0). Moody.

--Living Thoughts for the Children's Hour. LC 72-77943. (Illus.). 128p. 1972. pap. 3.95 (ISBN 0-8024-0121-X). Moody.

--Meditaciones para Ninos. Orig. Title: Devotions for the Children's Hour. (Span.). 252p. 1983. pap. 4.75 (ISBN 0-8254-1707-4). Kregel.

--What High School Students Should Know about Creation. (YA) 1983. pap. 2.50 (ISBN 0-8423-7872-3). Tyndale.

--What High School Students Should Know about Evolution. 70p. (YA) 1983. pap. 2.50 (ISBN 0-8423-7873-1). Tyndale.

Taylor, Lauren L., jt. auth. see Sutphen, Dick.

Taylor, Lelia S., jt. auth. see White, Anna.

Taylor, Lily R. The Divinity of the Roman Emperor. LC 75-7348. (Roman History Ser.). (Illus.). 1975. Repr. 29.00x (ISBN 0-405-07068-3). Ayer Co Pubs.

--The Divinity of the Roman Emperor. LC 75-31647. xv, 296p. 1975. Repr. of 1931 ed. lib. bdg. 27.50x (ISBN 0-87991-606-0). Porcupine Pr.

Taylor, Margaret. Considerations for Starting & Stretching a Sacred Dance Choir. 1978. 2.75 (ISBN 0-941500-03-9). Sharing Co.

Taylor, Margaret & Adams, Doug. Hymns in Action for Everyone Nine to Ninety Dancing Today. 90p. 1985. pap. 7.95 (ISBN 0-941500-32-2). Sharing Co.

Taylor, Margaret F. Look up & Live: Dance in Prayer & Meditation. Adams, Doug, ed. 96p. 1980. 4.95 (ISBN 0-941500-12-8). Sharing Co.

--A Time to Dance: Symbolic Movement in Worship. Adams, Doug, ed. 192p. 1980. 5.95 (ISBN 0-941500-17-9). Sharing Co.

Taylor, Mark C. Deconstructing Theology. (American Academy of Religion Studies). 176p. 1983. 12.95 (ISBN 0-8245-0533-6). Crossroad NY.

--Deconstructing Theology. LC 82-5970. (AAR Studies in Religion). 152p. 1982. 12.95 (ISBN 0-89130-582-3, 01-00-28). Scholars Pr GA.

--Erring: A Post Modern A-Theology. LC 84-88. xiv, 220p. 1987. pap. 9.95 (ISBN 0-226-79142-4). U of Chicago Pr.

--Erring: A Postmodern, A-Theology. LC 84-88. (Illus.). 232p. 1984. lib. bdg. 20.00x (ISBN 0-226-79141-6). U of Chicago Pr.

Taylor, Mark C., ed. Unfinished... Essays in Honor of Ray L. Hart. (JAAR Thematic Studies). 1981. pap. 13.50 (ISBN 0-89130-680-3, 01-24-81). Scholars Pr GA.

Taylor, Mark K. Beyond Explanation: Religious Dimensions in Cultural Anthropology. LC 85-13770. x, 262p. 1985. text ed. 24.50 (ISBN 0-86554-165-5, MUP-H155). Mercer Univ Pr.

Taylor, Mark L. God Is Love: A Study in the Theology of Karl Rahner. (AAR-Academy Ser.). 1986. 24.95 (ISBN 0-89130-925-X, 01-01-50); pap. 18.25 (ISBN 0-89130-926-8). Scholars Pr GA.

Taylor, Marvin J. Introduction to Christian Education. LC 66-11452. 412p. 1975. pap. 8.95 (ISBN 0-687-19498-9). Abingdon.

Taylor, Marvin J., ed. Changing Patterns of Religious Education. 320p. (Orig.). 1984. pap. 15.95 (ISBN 0-687-06046-X). Abingdon.

Taylor, Mary C. A History of the Foundations of Catholicism in Northern New York. LC 77-359034. (Monograph Ser.: No. 32). (Illus.). 13.50x (ISBN 0-930060-12-1). US Cath Hist.

Taylor, Mary G., jt. auth. see Taylor, Howard.

Taylor, Mendell L. Every Day with Paul. 1978. 6.95 (ISBN 0-8341-0529-2). Beacon Hill.

Taylor, Michael J. John: The Different Gospel... A Reflective Commentary. LC 83-15485. 269p. 1983. pap. 9.95 (ISBN 0-8189-0456-9). Alba.

--The Sacraments As Encasement: Jesus Is with Us. 80p. 1986. pap. 4.95 (ISBN 0-8146-1469-8). Liturgical Pr.

Taylor, Michael J., ed. A Companion to John: Readings in Johannine Theology. LC 77-7042. 1977. pap. 6.95 (ISBN 0-8189-0348-1). Alba.

--A Companion to Paul. 200p. 1975. pap. 6.95 (ISBN 0-8189-0304-X). Alba.

--The Mystery of Suffering & Death. LC 72-13294. 203p. 1973. pap. 5.95 (ISBN 0-8189-0263-9). Alba.

--The Sacraments: Readings in Contemporary Theology. LC 80-9534. 274p. (Orig.). 1981. pap. 8.95 (ISBN 0-8189-0406-2). Alba.

Taylor, Michael R., ed. see Granjon, Henry.

Taylor, Monica, ed. Progress & Problems in Moral Education. 240p. 1975. 16.00x (ISBN 0-85633-069-8, Pub. by NFER Nelson UK). Taylor & Francis.

Taylor, Myron, ed. Wartime Correspondence: Between President Roosevelt & Pope Pius 12th. (FDR & the Era of the New Deal Ser). 1975. Repr. of 1947 ed. lib. bdg. 22.50 (ISBN 0-306-70709-8). Da Capo.

Taylor, Nathaniel W. Essays, Lectures, etc. Upon Select Topics in Revealed Theology: New York 1859. Kuklick, Bruce, ed. (American Religious Thought of the 18th & 19th Centuries Ser.). 480p. 1987. lib. bdg. 65.00 (ISBN 0-8240-6960-9). Garland Pub.

--Lectures on the Moral Government of God: New York, 1859, 2 vols. Kuklick, Bruce, ed. (American Religious Thought of the 18th & 19th Centuries Ser.). 840p. 1987. lib. bdg. 110.00 (ISBN 0-8240-6961-7). Garland Pub.

--Practical Sermons: New York, 1858. Kuklick, Bruce, ed. (American Religious Thought of the 18th & 19th Centuries Ser.). 455p. 1987. lib. bdg. 60.00 (ISBN 0-8240-6959-5). Garland Pub.

Taylor, Paul. The Great Dinosaur Mystery & the Bible. (Illus.). 63p. 1987. 9.95 (ISBN 0-89051-114-4). Master Bks.

Taylor, Philip A., ed. Origins of the English Civil War: Conspiracy, Crusade, or Class Conflict. (Problems in European Civilization Ser.). 1960. pap. text ed. 5.50 (ISBN 0-669-24174-1). Heath.

Taylor, R. L. The Way of Heaven: An Introduction to the Confucian Religious Lufe. (Iconography of Religions XII Ser.: No. 3). (Illus.). xi, 37p. 1986. pap. 29.50 (ISBN 90-04-07423-6, Pub. by E J Brill). Heinman.

Taylor, Renee. Yoga... The Art of Living: The Hunza-Yoga Way to Better Living. LC 78-75329. (Illus.). 224p. 1975. pap. 4.50 (ISBN 0-87983-112-X). Keats.

Taylor, Rhena. Single & Whole. LC 85-8345. Orig. Title: Every Single Blessing. 96p. 1985. pap. 2.95 (ISBN 0-87784-510-7). Inter-Varsity.

Taylor, Richard. Ethics, Faith, & Reason. 128p. 1985. pap. text ed. 15.00 (ISBN 0-13-290552-3). P-H.

--Friends & the Racial Crisis. LC 70-129552. (Orig.). pap. 2.50x (ISBN 0-87574-172-X). Pendle Hill.

Taylor, Richard & Taylor, Willard. God, Man & Salvation. 724p. 1977. 16.95 (ISBN 0-8341-0440-7). Beacon Hill.

Taylor, Richard C., jt. ed. see Harrison, Stanley M.

Taylor, Richard K. A Peace Ministry in Practice. (YA) 1986. pap. 3.95 (ISBN 0-697-02205-6). Wm C Brown.

Taylor, Richard K., jt. auth. see Sider, Ronald J.

Taylor, Richard S. Biblical Authority & Christian Faith. 95p. (Orig.). 1980. pap. 2.95 (ISBN 0-8341-0633-7). Beacon Hill.

--The Disciplined Life. LC 62-7123. 112p. 1974. pap. 3.50 (ISBN 0-87123-098-4, 200098). Bethany Hse.

--Disciplined Life Style. LC 80-65581. 96p. 1975. pap. 2.95 (ISBN 0-87123-110-7, Dimension Bks). Bethany Hse.

--Exploring Christian Holiness, Vol. 3: The Theological Formulations. (Exploring Christian Holiness Ser.). 300p. 1985. 12.95 (ISBN 0-8341-1077-6). Beacon Hill.

--La Vida Disciplinada. 144p. 1979. 2.75 (ISBN 0-88113-341-8). Edit Betania.

Taylor, Richard S., ed. Beacon Dictionary of Theology. 560p. 1984. 29.95 (ISBN 0-8341-0811-9). Beacon Hill.

--Great Holiness Classics, Vol. 3: Leading Wesleyan Thinkers. 436p. 1985. 21.95 (ISBN 0-8341-1069-5). Beacon Hill.

Taylor, Rick. When You're the News. 112p. 1987. pap. 5.95 (ISBN 0-87403-225-3, 3185). Standard Pub.

Taylor, Robert. Bible Baseball. Date not set. pap. 2.95 (ISBN 0-8024-0211-9). Moody.

--Remembering God in Youth. 2.50 (ISBN 0-89315-238-2). Lambert Bk.

--Studies in James & Jude. 2.50 (ISBN 0-89315-293-5). Lambert Bk.

Taylor, Robert C. Building Maintenance for Churches. (Illus.). 136p. 1982. 13.95 (ISBN 0-9608714-0-3). Carrol Gate Pr.

Taylor, Robert, Jr. Elder & His Work. 7.95 (ISBN 0-89315-041-X); pap. 4.95 (ISBN 0-89315-042-8). Lambert Bk.

--Studies in First & Second Timothy. 2.50 (ISBN 0-89315-286-2). Lambert Bk.

--Studies in Titus & Philemon. 2.50 (ISBN 0-89315-287-0). Lambert Bk.

Taylor, Robert, Jr., ed. Christ in the Home. pap. 5.95 (ISBN 0-89137-314-4). Quality Pubns.

Taylor, Robert R. Sermons That Save. 1984. 10.95 (ISBN 0-317-16702-2). Firm Foun Pub.

Taylor, Robert R., Jr. Jesus Christ Hope of the Homes. 2.50 (ISBN 0-89315-131-9). Lambert Bk.

--A Review of "Shall We Splinter?". 1985. pap. 3.00 (ISBN 0-934916-08-X). Natl Christian Pr.

--Studies in First & Second Thessalonians. 1977. pap. 2.50 (ISBN 0-89315-285-4). Lambert Bk.

--Studies in First, Second Peter. pap. 2.50 (ISBN 0-89315-294-3). Lambert Bk.

--Studies in First, Second, Third John. pap. 2.50 (ISBN 0-89315-295-1). Lambert Bk.

Taylor, Rodney L. The Cultivation of Sagehood As a Religious Goal in Neo-Confucianism: A Study of Selected Writings of Kao P'an-Lung (1562-1626) LC 78-18685. 1978. pap. 10.25 (01-01-22). Scholars Pr GA.

Taylor, Rodney L., jt. auth. see Denny, Frederick M.

Taylor, Samuel W. Nightfall at Nauvoo. 1986. pap. 2.75 (ISBN 0-380-00247-7, 52696-4). Avon.

Taylor, Sharon A. The Book: That Which Has Been & That Which Shall Be, Bk. I. LC 84-91294. 74p. 1985. 7.95 (ISBN 0-533-06386-8). Vantage.

Taylor, Thomas. Against the Christians. 119p. 1980. 10.00 (ISBN 0-89005-301-4). Ares.

--Christ Revealed. LC 79-10885. 1979. Repr. of 1635 ed. 60.00x (ISBN 0-8201-1334-4). Schol Facsimiles.

--An Exposition of Titus. 1970. 20.75 (ISBN 0-86524-027-2, 5601). Klock & Klock.

--Hymns of Orpheus. Bd. with Concerning the Beautiful, Plotinus. 15.00 (ISBN 0-89314-415-0). Philos Res.

--Sallust on the Gods & the World & Other Works. 12.50 (ISBN 0-89314-401-0). Philos Res.

Taylor, Thomas, tr. see Apuleius.

Taylor, Thomas, tr. see Iamblichus.

Taylor, Thomas, tr. see Plotinus.

Taylor, Thomas, tr. see Proclus.

Taylor, Tom. New Life Principles. (Illus.). 1977. tchr's ed. 4.95 (ISBN 0-914936-26-3); wkbk. 1.10 (ISBN 0-914936-30-1). Bible Temple.

Taylor, Walter F., Jr. & Reumann, John H., eds. Augsburg Commentary on the New Testament: Ephesians, Colossians. LC 85-7479. 176p. (Orig.). 1985. kivar 8.95 (ISBN 0-8066-2165-6, 10-9030). Augsburg.

Taylor, Willard, jt. auth. see Taylor, Richard.

Taylor, Willard H. Beacon Bible Expositions: Galatians-Ephesians, Vol. 8. 228p. 1981. 8.95 (ISBN 0-8341-0734-1). Beacon Hill.

Taylor, Willard H., ed. see Airhart, Arnold E.

Taylor, Willard H., ed. see Greathouse, Willam M.

Taylor, Willard H., ed. see Martin, Sydney.

Taylor, Willard H., ed. see Purkiser, W. T.

Taylor, Willard H., ed. see Reed, Oscar F.

Taylor, Willard H., ed. see Welch, Reuben.

Taylor, Willard H., ed. see Young, Samuel.

Taylor, William M. Parables of Our Saviour. LC 74-79943. 1975. 14.95 (ISBN 0-8254-3805-5). Kregel.

Taylor, William W. & Smith, Thomas A., Sr. A History of the Chartiers Hill United Presbyterian Church of Canonsburg, Pennsylvania. 1975. write for info. (ISBN 0-87012-210-X). McClain.

Taylor-Hyler, Ariel. Numerology: Its Facts & Secrets. 1958. 8.95 (ISBN 0-910140-17-0). C & R Anthony.

Taymiya, Ibn. Public Duties in Islam: The Institution of the Hisba. Holland, Muhtar, tr. from Arabic. 159p. (Orig.). 1982. pap. 6.95x (ISBN 0-86037-113-1, Pub by Islamic Found UK). New Era Pubns MI.

Taymiyah, Ibn. A Muslim Theologian's Response to Christianity: A Translation of Ibn Taymiyya's Jawab al-Sahih li-man Baddala din al-Masih. Michel, Thomas F., tr. LC 83-15430. (Studies in Islamic Philosophy & Science). 60.00x (ISBN 0-88206-058-9). Caravan Bks.

Tazbir, Janusz. A State Without Stakes: Religious Toleration in Reformation Poland. Jordan, A. T., tr. (Library of Polish Studies: Vol. 3). text ed. 4.00 (ISBN 0-917004-05-1). Kosciuszko.

Tcherikover, Victor. Hellenistic Civilization & the Jews. Applebaum, S., tr. LC 59-8518. (Temple Bk.). 1970. pap. 9.95x (ISBN 0-689-70248-5, T22). Atheneum.

Tcherikover, Victor, tr. see Adar, Zvi.

Tcherikower, Elias, ed. Geshikhte Fun der Yidisher Arbeterbavegung, Vol. 2. LC 45-13072. (Yiddish., Illus.). 1945. 20.00 (ISBN 0-914512-18-8). Yivo Inst.

Tchividjian, Gigi. Thank You, Lord, for My Home. 1980. Repr. of 1979 ed. 3.95 (ISBN 0-89066-023-9). World Wide Pubs.

Tchividjian, Gigi & Tchividjian, Stephan. Our Search for Serenity. 168p. 1983. pap. 5.95 (ISBN 0-8007-5151-5, Power Bks). Revell.

Tchividjian, Gigi G. Sincerely. 144p. 1984. 11.95 (ISBN 0-310-44850-6, 18272). Zondervan.

Tchividjian, Stephan, jt. auth. see Tchividjian, Gigi.

Tchizhiv, P. M. Otjets Ioann Kronshtadtsky. Tr. of Father John of Kronstadt. 192p. 1958. pap. 8.00 (ISBN 0-317-29203-X). Holy Trinity.

Teaching of the Twelve Apostles. Die Lateinische Ubersetzung der Didache. 142p. Repr. of 1913 ed. 12.00 (ISBN 0-384-59780-7). Johnson Repr.

Teasdale, Wayne. Essays in Mysticism. 196p. 1982. pap. 8.95 (ISBN 0-941850-02-1). Sunday Pubns.

Teasley, D. O. The Double Cure, or Redemption Twofold. 160p. pap. 1.50 large print (ISBN 0-686-29147-6). Faith Pub Hse.

--The Holy Spirit & Other Spirits. 192p. pap. 1.75 (ISBN 0-686-29150-6). Faith Pub Hse.

--Rays of Hope. 95p. pap. 0.75 (ISBN 0-686-29137-9). Faith Pub Hse.

Tebaldus, Massimiliano. Jews, Christians & the Theory of the Soul: New Discoveries in Classical Theology. (Illus.). 138p. 1984. 88.95 (ISBN 0-89266-480-0). Am Classical Coll Pr.

Tebeau, Charlton W. Synagogue in the Central City: Temple Israel of Greater Miami 1922-1972. LC 72-85107. 5.00 (ISBN 0-87024-239-3). Rostrum Bks.

--Synagogue in the Central City: Temple Israel of Greater Miami, 1922-1972. LC 71-85107. (Illus.). 144p. 1972. 9.95 (ISBN 0-87024-239-3). U of Miami Pr.

Tec, Nechama. When Light Pierced the Darkness: Christian Rescue of Jews in Nazi-Occupied Poland. (Illus.). 320p. 1986. 19.95 (ISBN 0-19-503643-3). Oxford U Pr.

Technical Association of the Pulp & Paper Industry Staff. Nonwovens Conference, 1986: Proceedings of TAPPI, Marriott Hotel, Atlanta, GA, April 20-25, 1986. pap. 67.30 (2029189). Bks Demand UMI.

Teddlie, Tillit S. Great Christian Hymnal. 1965. 4.25 (ISBN 0-89137-600-3). Quality Pubns.

Tedeschi, John, jt. ed. see Henningsen, Gustav.

Tedlock, Barbara. Time & the Highland Maya. LC 80-54569. (Illus.). 245p. 1981. pap. 10.95x (ISBN 0-8263-0835-X). U of NM Pr.

Tedlock, Barbara, jt. ed. see Tedlock, Dennis.

Tedlock, Dennis & Tedlock, Barbara, eds. Teachings from the American Earth: Indian Religion & Philosophy. (Illus.). 304p. 1976. pap. 7.95 (ISBN 0-87140-097-9). Liveright.

Teed, Richard. Sermon on the Mount. 91p. pap. 2.75 (ISBN 0-87785-124-7). Swedenborg.

Teegarden, Kenneth L., jt. auth. see Leaders of the Christian Church Staff.

Teeguarden, Iona M. The Joy of Feeling Body-Mind: Acupressure--Jin Shin Do. LC 85-80534. (Illus.). 176p. (Orig.). 1986. pap. 13.95 (ISBN 0-87040-634-5). Japan Pubns USA.

Teeple, Howard M. The Historical Approach to the Bible. LC 81-85275. (Truth in Religion Ser.: No. 2). 323p. (Orig.). 1982. pap. 7.50 (ISBN 0-914384-02-3). Religion & Ethics.

--The Literary Origin of the Gospel of John. LC 73-87487. x, 297p. (Orig.). 1974. pap. 6.00 (ISBN 0-914384-00-7). Religion & Ethics.

--The Noah's Ark Nonsense. LC 78-53529. (Truth in Religion Ser.: No. 1). 156p. 1978. 10.00 (ISBN 0-914384-01-5). Religion & Ethics.

Teeple, John, ed. Maya Astronomy. (Classics of Anthropology Ser.). 20.00 (ISBN 0-8240-9624-X). Garland Pub.

Teertha, Swami Ananda, ed. see Rajneesh, Bhagwan Shree.

Tefler, William. The Treasure of Sao Roque. (Church Historical Society London N. S. Ser.: No. 14). Repr. of 1932 ed. 40.00 (ISBN 0-8115-3137-6). Kraus Repr.

Tegenfeldt, Herman. A Century of Growth: The Kachin Baptist Church of Burma. LC 74-4415. 540p. 1974. 10.95 (ISBN 0-87808-416-9). William Carey Lib.

Teichert, Marilyn, tr. see Bouyer, Louis.

Teichert, Marilyn, tr. see Couer de Jesus d' Elbee, Jean du.

Teichler-Zallen, Doris & Clements, Colleen D. Science & Morality: New Directions in Bioethics. LC 80-8926. 320p. 1982. 29.00x (ISBN 0-669-04406-7); pap. text ed. 12.00x (ISBN 0-669-09808-6). Lexington Bks.

Teikmanis, Arthur L. Preaching & Pastoral Care. LC 64-23551. pap. 36.00 (2026863). Bks Demand UMI.

Teilhard De Chardin, Pierre. L' Apparition de L'homme. 21.50 (ISBN 0-685-36582-4). French & Eur.

--Avenir De L'homme. 1959. 21.50 (ISBN 0-685-11021-4). French & Eur.

--Christianity & Evolution. LC 73-12926. 255p. 1974. pap. 6.95 (ISBN 0-15-617740-4, Harv). HarBraceJ.

--Comment Je Crois. 15.50 (ISBN 0-685-36585-9). French & Eur.

--Divine Milieu: An Essay on the Interior Life. pap. 6.95 (ISBN 0-06-090487-9, CN487, PL). Har-Row.

--Energie Humaine. 1962. 18.95 (ISBN 0-685-11160-1). French & Eur.

--Etre Plus. 12.50 (ISBN 0-685-36589-1). French & Eur.

--Future of Man. (Orig.). 1969. pap. 7.95 (ISBN 0-06-090496-8, CN496, PL). Har-Row.

--The Heart of Matter. Hague, Rene, tr. LC 79-24527. 276p. 1980. pap. 7.95 (ISBN 0-15-640004-9, Harv). HarBraceJ.

--Hymn of the Universe. LC 65-10375. 1969. pap. 6.95x (ISBN 0-06-131910-4, TB1910, Torch). Har-Row.

--Hymne De L'univers. 1966. 13.95 (ISBN 0-685-11240-3). French & Eur.

--Images et Paroles. 32.95 (ISBN 0-685-36592-1). French & Eur.

--Je m'explique. 13.50 (ISBN 0-685-36593-X). French & Eur.

--La Messe sur le Monde. pap. 6.25 (ISBN 0-685-36598-0). French & Eur.

--Milieu Divin. (Coll. Livre de vie). 1958. pap. 3.95 (ISBN 0-685-11395-7). French & Eur.

--Le Milieu Divin. 8.95 (ISBN 0-685-36583-2). French & Eur.

--Mon Univers. pap. 6.95 (ISBN 0-685-36599-9). French & Eur.

--On Love & Happiness. LC 83-48979. 96p. 1984. 9.45 (ISBN 0-06-068151-9, HarpR). Har-Row.

--Phenomene Humain. (Coll. Points). 1955. pap. 6.25 (ISBN 0-685-11491-0). French & Eur.

--Le Phenomene Humain. 15.95 (ISBN 0-685-36581-6). French & Eur.

--Phenomenon of Man. pap. 7.95 (ISBN 0-06-090495-X, CN495, PL). Har-Row.

--La Place de L'homme dans la Nature. 15.95 (ISBN 0-685-36584-0). French & Eur.

--Le Pretre. pap. 4.95 (ISBN 0-685-36600-6). French & Eur.

--Reflexions et Prieres dans L'espace-temps. 13.95 (ISBN 0-685-36601-4). French & Eur.

--Science et Christ. 1965. 14.50 (ISBN 0-685-11556-9). French & Eur.

--Sur L'amour. pap. 6.25 (ISBN 0-685-36602-2). French & Eur.

--Sur le Bonheur. pap. 6.25 (ISBN 0-685-36603-0). French & Eur.

Teish, Luisah. Jambalaya: The Natural Woman's Book of Personal Charms & Practical Rituals. LC 85-42793. (Illus.). 1985. 15.95 (ISBN 0-06-250860-1, HarpR). Har-Row.

Teit, James A. The Lillooet Indians. LC 73-3520. (Jesup North Pacific Expedition. Publications: No. 2, Pt. 5). Repr. of 1906 ed. 20.00 (ISBN 0-404-58121-8). AMS Pr.

--Mythology of the Thompson Indians. LC 73-3529. (Jesup North Pacific Expeditions. Publications: No. 8, Pt. 2). Repr. of 1912 ed. 27.50 (ISBN 0-404-58125-0). AMS Pr.

Teiwes, Helga. Mission San Xavier del Bac: A Photographic Essay on the Desert People & Their Church. (Illus.). 32p. 1973. pap. 3.50 (ISBN 0-8165-0423-7). U of Ariz Pr.

Teixeira, Jose. The Spanish Pilgrime, or: An Admirable Discovery of a Romish Catholike. LC 72-6033. (English Experience Ser.: No. 560). 148p. 1973. Repr. of 1625 ed. 15.00 (ISBN 90-221-0560-1). Walter J Johnson.

Tejasananda, Swami. Ramakrishna Movement: Its Ideal & Activities. (Illus.). pap. 3.95 (ISBN 0-87481-117-1). Vedanta Pr.

Tekippe, Terry J., ed. Papal Infallibility: An Application of Lonergan's Theological Method. LC 82-23837. 416p. (Orig.). 1983. lib. bdg. 34.50 (ISBN 0-8191-2995-X); pap. text ed. 17.75 o. p. (ISBN 0-8191-2996-8). U Pr of Amer.

Telang, K. T., tr. from Sanscrit. The Anugita. LC 81-50202. (Secret Doctrine Reference Ser.). 176p. 1981. Repr. of 1882 ed. 12.00 (ISBN 0-913510-40-8). Wizards.

Telford, Dr. Andrew. Miscarriage of Marriage. pap. 1.45 (ISBN 0-686-12750-1). Grace Pub Co.

Telford, Shirley. The Prince of Peace: Returns to Fulfill All Prophecy. (Illus.). 56p. (Orig.). 1984. 5.50 (ISBN 0-9600202-0-9); Audio-Video Cassette. 12.00 (ISBN 0-9613706-1-0). William & Rich.

Telford, William R. The Barren Temple & the Withered Tree. (Journal for the Study of the New Testament, Supplement Ser.: No. 1). 336p. 1980. text ed. 21.95x (ISBN 0-905774-20-5, Pub by JSOT Pr England). Eisenbrauns.

Telford, William R., ed. The Interpretation of Mark. LC 84-18708. (Issues in Religion & Theology Ser.). 176p. 1985. pap. 7.95 (ISBN 0-8006-1772-X, 1-1772). Fortress.

Teller, Woolsey. The Atheism of Astronomy: A Refutation of the Theory That the Universe Is Governed by Intelligence. LC 79-169219. (Atheist Viewpoint Ser). 126p. 1972. Repr. of 1938 ed. 13.00 (ISBN 0-405-03806-2). Ayer Co Pubs.

Teller, Woolsey & Gauvin, Marshall. Hell, A Christian Doctrine. (Illus.). 47p. pap. cancelled (ISBN 0-910309-01-9). Am Atheist.

Teller, Woosey, jt. auth. see Bales, James.

Telpaz, Gideon. Israeli Childhood Stories of the Sixties. LC 83-14202. (Brown Judaic Studies). 222p. 1983. pap. 18.00 (ISBN 0-89130-610-2, 14 00 40). Scholars Pr GA.

Telushkin, Joseph. Uncommon Sense: The World's Fullest Compendium of Wisdom. 1986. 14.95 (ISBN 0-933503-48-2). Shapolsky Pubs.

Telushkin, Joseph, jt. auth. see Prager, Dennis.

Temchin, Michael. The Witch Doctor: Memoirs of a Partisan. (Illus.). 192p. (Orig.). 1983. 16.95 (ISBN 0-8052-5046-8); pap. 10.95 (ISBN 0-8052-5047-6). Holocaust Pubns.

Temperley, Nicholas. The Music of the English Parish Church, 2 vols. LC 77-84811. (Cambridge Studies in Music). (Illus.). 1980. Vol. 1. 100.00 (ISBN 0-521-22045-9); Vol. 2. 52.50 (ISBN 0-521-22046-7). Cambridge U Pr.

--The Music of the English Parish Church, Vol. 1. LC 77-84811. (Cambridge Studies in Music). 1983. pap. 23.95 (ISBN 0-521-27457-5). Cambridge U Pr.

Tempesta, Antonio. Metamorphoseon...Ovidianarum. LC 75-27861. (Renaissance & the Gods Ser.: Vol. 19). (Illus.). 1976. Repr. of 1606 ed. lib. bdg. 88.00 (ISBN 0-8240-2067-7). Garland Pub.

Temple, Frederick. The Relations Between Religion & Science: Eight Lectures Preached Before the University of Oxford in Eighteen Eighty-Four on the Foundation of the Late Reverend John Bampton Ma. 264p. Repr. of 1884 ed. text ed. 41.40x (ISBN 0-576-29206-0, Pub. by Gregg Intl Pubs England). Gregg Intl.

Temple, Joe. Know Your Child. 1974. pap. 5.95 (ISBN 0-8010-8820-8). Baker Bk.

Temple of the People Publications Staff, ed. From the Mountain Top, 1 of 3 vols, Vol. I. 278p. 1974. Repr. of 1914 ed. 11.25 (ISBN 0-933797-00-1). Halcyon Bk.

Temple of the People Publications Staff. From the Mountain Top, Vol. 3. 144p. 1985. 11.25 (ISBN 0-933797-02-8). Halcyon Bk.

Temple of the People Publications Staff, ed. The Teachings of the Temple, 3 vols. 1985. Set. 25.00 (ISBN 0-933797-08-7); Vol. 1, 661p. 11.25 ea. (ISBN 0-933797-03-6). Vol. 2, 400p (ISBN 0-933797-04-4). Vol. 3, 400p (ISBN 0-933797-05-2) (ISBN 0-933797-05-2). Halcyon Bk.

--Temple Messages. (Illus.). 183p. 1983. 10.50 (ISBN 0-933797-07-9). Halcyon Bk.

--Theogenesis. (Illus.). 548p. 1981. 21.00 (ISBN 0-933797-06-0). Halcyon Bk.

Temple, Ruth Z. The Critic's Alchemy. (Orig.). 1953. pap. 10.95x (ISBN 0-8084-0097-5). New Coll U Pr.

Temple, Sydney. The Carmel Mission, from Founding to Rebuilding. LC 79-57168. (Illus.). 176p. 1980. pap. 5.95 (ISBN 0-913548-71-5, Valley Calif). Western Tanager.

Temple, William. Christian Faith & Life. LC 82-80474. (Treasures from the Spiritual Classics Ser.). 64p. 1982. pap. 2.95 (ISBN 0-8192-1311-X). Morehouse.

--Hope of a New World. LC 74-121507. (Essay Index Reprint Ser). 1940. 13.00 (ISBN 0-8369-1778-2). Ayer Co Pubs.

--Nature, Man & God. LC 77-27190. (Gifford Lectures Ser.: 1932-33, 1933-34). 1979. Repr. of 1935 ed. 54.50 (ISBN 0-404-60493-5). AMS Pr.

--Readings in St. John's Gospel. 391p. 1985. pap. 8.95 (ISBN 0-8192-1360-8). Morehouse.

--Religious Experience & Other Essays & Addresses. Baker, A. E., ed. 270p. 1959. 10.95 (ISBN 0-227-67579-7). Attic Pr.

Templin, J. Alton. Ideology on a Frontier: The Theological Foundation of Afrikaner Nationalism, 1652-1910. LC 83-10884. (Contributions in Intercultural & Comparative Studies: No. 11). (Illus.). xiii, 360p. 1984. lib. bdg. 35.00 (ISBN 0-313-24104-X, TIF/). Greenwood.

Temporini, Hildegard & Haase, Wolfgang, eds. Aufstieg und Niedergang der Roemischen Welt: Section 2, Principat. Incl. Vol. 13. Recht (Normen, Verbreitung, Materien) 1980. 200.00 (ISBN 3-11-008121-0); Vol. 14. Recht (Materien, Fortsetzung) 1982. 253.00 (ISBN 3-11-008122-9); Vol. 15. Recht (Methoden, Schulen, Einzelne Juristen) 1976. 184.00 (ISBN 3-11-006736-6); Vol. 16, Pt. 1. Religion (Heidentum: Romische Religion, Allgemeines) 1978. 200.00 (ISBN 3-11-006737-4); Vol. 16, Pt. 2. Religion (Heidentum: Romische Religion, Allgemeines FS) 1978. 226.00 (ISBN 3-11-007612-8); Vol. 17, Pt. 1. Religion (Heidentum: Romische Gotterkulte, Orientalische Kulte in der romischen Welt) 1981. 147.00 (ISBN 3-11-008468-6); Vol. 17, Pt. 2. Religion (Heidentum: Romische Gotterkulte, Orientalische Kulte in der romischen Welt, Fortsetzung) 1981. 190.00 (ISBN 3-11-008556-9); Vol. 17, Pt. 3. Religion (Heidentum: Romische Gotterkulte, Orientalische Kulte in der romischen Welt, Fortsetzung) 1984. 174.00 (ISBN 3-11-009521-1); Vol. 17, Pt. 4. Religion **(Heidentum: Romische Gotterkulte, Orientalische Kulte in der romishcen Welt, Fortsetzung) 1984. 205.00 (ISBN 3-11-010213-7); Vol. 19, Pt. 1. Religion (Judentum: Allgemeines, palastinensisches Judentum) 1979. 210.00 (ISBN 3-11-007968-2); Vol. 19, Pt. 2. Religion (Judentum: Allgemeines, palastinensisches Judentum FS) 1979. 160.00 (ISBN 3-11-007969-0); Vol. 21, Pt. 1. Religion (Hellinistisches Judentum in romischer Zeit): Philon & Josephus. 1984. 210.00 (ISBN 3-11-008845-2); Vol. 21, Pt. 2. Religion (Hellinistisches Judentum in romischer Zeit): Philon & Josephus (Fortsetzung) 1984. 168.00 (ISBN 3-11-009522-X); Vol. 23, Pt. 1. Religion (Vorkonstantinisches Christentum: Verhaltnis zu romischem Staat und heidnischer Religion) 1979. 205.00 (ISBN 3-11-007822-8); Vol. 23, Pt. 2. Religion (Vorkonstantinisches Christentum: Verhaltnis zu romischen Staat und heidnischer Religion) 1980. 161.00 (ISBN 3-11-008016-8). (Ger.). De Gruyter.**

--Aufstieg und Niedergang der Roemischen Welt: Section 2, Principat. Incl. Vol. 25, Pt. 1. Religion (Vorkonstantinisches Christentum: Leben und Umwelt Jesu; Neues Testament Kanonische Schriften und Apokryphen) 1982. 221.00 (ISBN 3-11-008700-6); Vol. 25, Pt. 2. Religion (Vorkonstantinisches Christentum: Leben und Umwelt Jesu; Neues Testament, Fortsetzung Kanonische Schriften und Apokryphen) 1984. 258.00 (ISBN 3-11-009523-8); Vol. 25, Pt. 3. Religion (Vorkonstantinisches Christentum: Leben und Umwelt Jesu; Neues Testament, Fortsetzung Kanonische Schriften und Apokryphen) 1985. 232.00 (ISBN 3-11-010370-2); Vol. 29, Pt. 1. Sprache und Literatur (Sprachen und Schriften) 1983. 147.00 (ISBN 3-11-009524-6); Vol. 29, Pt. 2. Sprache und Literatur (Sprachen und Schriften) (Fortsetzung) 1983. 216.00 (ISBN 3-11-009525-4); Vol. 30, Pt. 1. Sprache und Literatur (Literatur der augusteischen Zeit: Allgemeines, einzelne Autoren) 1982. 216.00 (ISBN 3-11-008469-4); Vol. 30, Pt. 2. Sprache und Literatur (Literatur der augusteischen Zeit: Allgemeines, einzelne Autoren, Fortsetzung) 1982. 147.00 (ISBN 3-11-008699-9); Vol. 30, Pt. 3. Sprache und Literatur (Literatur der augusteischen Zeit: Allgemeines, einzelne Autoren, Fortsetzung) 1983. 190.00 (ISBN 3-11-009526-2); Vol. 31, Pt. 1. Sprache und Literatur (Literatur der augusteischen Zeit: Einzelne Autoren - Vergil, Horaz, Ovid) 1980. 166.00 (ISBN 3-11-008123-7); Vol. 31, Pt. 2. Sprache und Literatur (Literatur der ausgusteischen Zeit: Einzelne Autoren, Fortsetzung Vergil, Horaz, Ovid) 1981. 155.00 (ISBN 3-11-008288-8); Vol. 31, Pt. 3. Sprache und Literatur (Literatur der ausgusteischen Zeit); Einzelne Autoren - Fortsetzung, Vergil, Horaz, Ovid. 1981. 179.00 (ISBN 3-11-008467-8); Vol. 31, Pt. 4. Sprache und Literatur (Literatur der augusteischen Zeit: Einzelne Autoren, Fortsetzung Vergil, Horaz, Ovid) 1981. 142.00 (ISBN 3-11-008555-0); Vol. 32, Pt. 1. Sprache und Literatur (Literatur der julisch-claudischen und der flavischen Zeit) 1984. 190.00 (ISBN 3-11-010363-X); Vol. 32, Pt. 2. Sprache und Literatur (Literatur der julisch-claudischen und der flavischen Zeit) (Fortsetzung) 1985. 242.00 (ISBN 3-11-010374-5); Vol. 32, Pt. 3. Sprache und Literatur (Literatur der julisch-claudischen und der flavischen Zeit) (Fortsetzung) 1985. 190.00 (ISBN 3-11-010388-5). (Ger.). De Gruyter.

Ten Boom, Corrie. Cada Nuevo Dia. Clifford, Alejandro, tr. from Eng. Tr. of Each New Day. 224p. 1983. pap. 4.50 (ISBN 0-311-40043-4, Edit Mundo). Casa Bautista.

--Each New Day. 1977. pap. 3.50 (ISBN 0-8007-8403-0, Spire Bks). Revell.

Ten Boom, Corrie & Buckingham, Jamie. Tramp for the Lord. (Illus.). 192p. 1974. pap. 6.95 (ISBN 0-8007-0769-9). Revell.

Ten Boom, Corrie, jt. auth. see Graham, Billy.

Tendzin, Osel. Buddha in the Palm of Your Hand. LC 81-84450. (Dragon Ser.). (Illus.). 120p. (Orig.). 1982. pap. 6.95 (ISBN 0-87773-223-X). Shambhala Pubns.

--Buddha in the Palm of Your Hand. 1987. pap. 8.95. Shambhala Pubns.

Tenenbaum, Joseph. Race & Reich: The Story of an Epoch. LC 76-8503. (Illus.). 1976. Repr. of 1956 ed. lib. bdg. 35.25x (ISBN 0-8371-8857-1, TERR). Greenwood.

Tengbom, Luverne, jt. auth. see Tengbom, Mildred.

Tengbom, M. Help for Families of the Terminally Ill. LC 12-2819. (Trauma Bks.: Ser. 2). 1983. pap. 2.75 ea. (ISBN 0-570-08256-0). Concordia.

Tengbom, Mildred. Devotions for a New Mother. 127p. 1983. pap. 4.95 (ISBN 0-87123-294-4). Bethany Hse.

--Does Anybody Care How I Feel? LC 81-3808. 122p. 1981. pap. 4.95 (ISBN 0-87123-142-5, 210142). Bethany Hse.

--Does It Make Any Difference What I Do? 160p. (Orig.). 1984. pap. 4.95 (ISBN 0-87123-448-3, 210448). Bethany Hse.

--I Wish I Felt Good All the Time. 160p. (Orig.). 1983. pap. 4.95 (ISBN 0-87123-281-2, 210281). Bethany Hse.

--Mealtime Prayers. LC 85-9041. 128p. (Orig.). 1985. pap. 4.95 (ISBN 0-8066-2127-3, 10-4306). Augsburg.

--September Morning: A Practical Guide for the Middle Years. Eller, David, ed. 1985. pap. 9.95 (ISBN 0-87178-776-8). Brethren.

--Sometimes I Hurt: Reflections on the Book of Job. 192p. (Orig.). 1986. pap. 7.95 (ISBN 0-570-03981-9, 12-2897). Concordia.

--Talking Together about Love & Sexuality. 160p. 1985. pap. 4.95 (ISBN 0-87123-804-7, 210804). Bethany Hse.

--Why Waste Your Illness: Let God Use It for Growth. LC 83-72113. 144p. (Orig.). 1984. pap. 6.95 (ISBN 0-8066-2057-9, 10-7182). Augsburg.

Tengbom, Mildred & Tengbom, Luverne. Bible Readings for Families. LC 80-65542. (Bible Readings Ser.). 112p. (Orig.). 1980. pap. 3.95 (ISBN 0-8066-1787-X, 10-0677). Augsburg.

Tengbom, Mildred, compiled by. Table Prayers: New Prayers, Old Favorites, Songs, & Responses. LC 77-72451. 1977. pap. 4.95 (ISBN 0-8066-1594-X, 10-6185). Augsburg.

Tengbom, Mildren. Bible Readings for Mothers. (Bible Reading Ser.). 112p. (Orig.). 1987. pap. 3.95 (ISBN 0-8066-2249-0, 10-0692). Augsburg.

Ten Grotenhuis, Elizabeth, jt. auth. see Rosenfield, John M.

Teng Ssu-Ya. Historiography of the Taiping Rebellion. LC 63-1158. (East Asian Monographs: No. 14). 1962. pap. 11.00x (ISBN 0-674-39451-8). Harvard U Pr.

Tennant, Eugenia L. American Christmases: From the Puritans to the Victorians. 1975. 10.00 (ISBN 0-682-48358-3, Banner). Exposition Pr FL.

Tennant, F. R. The Origin & Propagation of Sin: Being the Hulsean Lectures Delivered Before the University of Cambridge, 1901-2. 235p. 1982. Repr. of 1908 ed. lib. bdg. 50.00 (ISBN 0-89987-822-9). Darby Bks.

Tennen, Laura, ed. see Desai, Amrit.

Tenney, Helen. Mark's Sketch Book of Christ. 1975. spiral bound 6.45 (ISBN 0-85151-075-2). Banner of Truth.

Tenney, Merrill C. Galatians: The Charter of Christian Liberty. rev. ed. 1960. 10.95 (ISBN 0-8028-3253-9). Eerdmans.

--Handy Dictionary of the Bible. (Orig.). pap. 4.95 (ISBN 0-310-33151-X, 10898P). Zondervan.

--Handy Dictionary of the Bible. 1986. write for info. (ISBN 0-8297-0683-6). Life Pubs Intl.

--Interpreting Revelation. 1957. 15.95 (ISBN 0-8028-3254-7). Eerdmans.

--John: The Gospel of Belief. 1948. 14.95 (ISBN 0-8028-3252-0). Eerdmans.

--New Testament Survey. rev. ed. Dunnett, Walter M., rev. by. 480p. 1985. 19.95 (ISBN 0-8028-3611-9). Eerdmans.

--New Testament Times. 1965. 21.95 (ISBN 0-8028-3250-4). Eerdmans.

--Nuestro Nuevo Testamento. Orig. Title: New Testament Survey. (Span.). 492p. 1981. pap. 12.95 (ISBN 0-8254-1716-3). Kregel.

Tenney, Merrill C. & Cruden, Alexander. The Handy Bible Dictionary & Concordance. 1986. pap. 6.95 (ISBN 0-310-33271-0, 11147P). Zondervan.

Tenney, Merrill C. & Longenecker, Richard N. The Expositor's Bible Commentary, Vol. 9. 1986. 19.95 (ISBN 0-88469-195-0). BMH Bks.

Tenney, Merrill C., ed. The Zondervan Pictorial Bible Dictionary. (Illus.). 1969. 21.95 (ISBN 0-310-33160-9, 6750); indexed o.p. 23.95 (ISBN 0-310-33170-6). Zondervan.

--The Zondervan Pictorial Encyclopedia of the Bible, 5 vols. new ed. (Illus.). 1974. Set. text ed. 149.95 (ISBN 0-310-33188-9, 6700). Zondervan.

Tenney, Merrill C., ed. see Mears, Henrietta C., et al.

Tenney, Merrill C., jt. ed. see Packer, J. I.

Tennis, Diane. Is God the Only Reliable Father. LC 84-20899. 118p. (Orig.). 1985. pap. 7.95 (ISBN 0-664-24594-3). Westminster.

Tennyson, G. B. Victorian Devotional Poetry: The Tractarian Mode. LC 80-14416. 1980. text ed. 18.50x (ISBN 0-674-93586-1). Harvard U Pr.

Tennyson, Noel, illus. Christmas Carols: A Treasury of Holiday Favorites with Words & Pictures. LC 83-60412. (Illus.). 24p. 1983. 1.95 (ISBN 0-394-86125-6). Random.

Tentler, T. Sin & Confession on the Eve of the Reformation. 1977. 46.50x (ISBN 0-691-07219-1). Princeton U Pr.

Teresa. The Interior Castle or the Mansions, 2 vols. (Illus.). 325p. 1984. Set. 197.85 (ISBN 0-89266-488-6). Am Classical Coll Pr.

Teresa, Saint The Letters of St. Teresa, 4 vols. Gasquet, Cardinal, ed. 1977. Set. lib. bdg. 400.00 (ISBN 0-8490-2154-5). Gordon Pr.

Tereshchenko, Nicholas. A Look at Fourth Way Work: A System of Esoteric Exercises Based on the Work of Gurdjieff. 1987. pap. 10.00. Phanes Pr.

Teringo, J. Robert. The Land & People Jesus Knew. 250p. 1985. 24.95 (ISBN 0-87123-797-0, 230797). Bethany Hse.

Ter Linden, Nico. In the Lord's Boarding House: Stories of Caring for Others. Mitchell, Kenneth R., tr. from Dutch. 128p. (Orig.). 1985. pap. text ed. 7.95 (ISBN 0-687-18971-3). Abingdon.

Terpstra, Gerard, ed. see Hynson, Leon O.

Terrien, James S., tr. Prophecies & Revelations about the Jesuits. 143p. pap. 3.98 (ISBN 0-913452-27-0). Jesuit Bks.

Terrien, Samuel. The Elusive Presence: The Heart of Biblical Theology. LC 78-4424. 544p. 1983. pap. 12.95 (ISBN 0-06-068234-5, RD-487, HarpR). Har-Row.

--Holy Week. LC 84-18756. (Proclamation 3A Ser.). 64p. 1986. pap. 3.75 (ISBN 0-8006-4120-5). Fortress.

--Till the Heart Sings: A Biblical Theology of Manhood & Womanhood. LC 85-47731. 272p. 1985. 24.95 (ISBN 0-8006-0752-X, 1-752). Fortress.

Terrien, Sara F., tr. see Barth, Karl.

Terruwe, Anna A., jt. auth. see Baars, Conrad W.

Terry, Charles L., ed. Knowledge Without Goodness Is Dangerous: Moral Education in Boarding Schools. 2nd ed. LC 81-81105. 144p. (Orig.). 1981. pap. 6.95 (ISBN 0-939618-00-1). Phillips Exeter.

Terry, Hazelmai M., jt. auth. see Snyder, Bernadette M.

Terry, Jack. The Way to Happiness in Your Home: Bible Study on Family Living. 36p. 1982. pap. 3.50 (ISBN 0-939298-06-6). J M Prods.

Terry, John R. Powerful Points for Preaching. 150p. 1982. pap. 4.95 (ISBN 0-933704-44-5). Dawn Pr.

Terry, Lindsay. Good Morning, Lord: Devotions from Famous Hymn Stories. (Good Morning Lord Ser.). 1974. 3.95 (ISBN 0-8010-8882-8). Baker Bk.

Terry, Maury. The Ultimate Evil: An Investigation into America's Most Dangerous Satanic Cult. LC 86-29203. (Illus.). 432p. 1987. 17.95 (ISBN 0-385-23452-X, Dolp). Doubleday.

Terry, Milton S. Bible Hermeneutics. 784p. 1974. kivar 14.95 (ISBN 0-310-36831-6, 6672P). Zondervan.

Terry, Milton S., tr. from Gr. The Sibylline Oracles. new ed. LC 72-176141. Repr. of 1899 ed. 21.45 (ISBN 0-404-06362-4). AMS Pr.

Terry, Robert H. Light in the Valley: The McCurdy Mission School Story. LC 84-50388. (Illus.). 148p. (Orig.). 1984. pap. 9.95 (ISBN 0-86534-051-X). Sunstone Pr.

Terry, W. Clinton, III. Teaching Religion: The Secularization of Religion Instruction in a West German School System. LC 80-5569. 208p. 1981. pap. text ed. 12.25 (ISBN 0-8191-1367-0). U Pr of Amer.

Terstegge, Georgiana. Providence As "Idee-Maitresse" in the Works of Bossuet. LC 73-128931. (Catholic University of America. Studies in Romance Languages & Literature: No. 43). 1970. Repr. of 1948 ed. 29.00 (ISBN 0-404-50334-9). AMS Pr.

Tertullian. Apologetical Works. (Father of the Church Ser.: Vol. 10). 430p. 1950. 34.95x (ISBN 0-8132-0010-5). Cath U Pr.

--Disciplinary, Moral & Ascetial Works. (Fathers of the Church Ser: Vol. 40). 495p. 1959. 34.95x (ISBN 0-8132-0040-7). Cath U Pr.

Tertullianus, Quintus S. Opera, 2 Vols. (Lat). Repr. of 1890 ed. Set. 100.00 (ISBN 0-384-59850-1). Johnson Repr.

Terwilliger, Robert E. & Holmes, Urban T. To Be a Priest: Perspectives on Vocation & Ordination. 192p. (Orig.). 1975. pap. 4.95 (ISBN 0-8164-2592-2, 8164-2592-2, HarpR). Har-Row.

Terzian, Yervant & Bilson, Elizabeth, eds. Cosmology & Astrophysics: Essays in Honor of Thomas Gold on His 60th Birthday. (Illus.). 168p. 1982. 27.50x (ISBN 0-8014-1497-0). Cornell U Pr.

Tesniere, A. The Adoration of the Blessed Sacrament. (Illus.). 288p. 1981. Repr. of 1902 ed. lib. bdg. 35.00 (ISBN 0-89984-461-8). Century Bookbindery.

Tester, Sylvia R. The World into Which Jesus Came. LC 82-9430. (Illus.). 96p. 1982. PLB 12.95 (ISBN 0-89565-232-3, 4951, Pub. by Childs World). Standard Pub.

Tester, Sylvia R. & Miller, Marge, eds. I Read about God's Love. rev. ed. (Illus.). 128p. 1983. text ed. 7.95 (ISBN 0-87239-661-4, 2951). Standard Pub.

Testrake, John & Wimbish, Dave. Triumph over Terror on Flight 847. (Illus.). 1987. 14.95 (ISBN 0-8007-1527-6). Revell.

Tetlow, Elisabeth M. Women & Ministry in the New Testament: Called to Serve. 170p. 1985. pap. text ed. 10.75 (ISBN 0-8191-4461-4, College Theo Soc). U Pr of Amer.

Tetlow, Elisabeth M. & Tetlow, Louis M. Partners in Service: Toward a Biblical Theology of Christian Marriage. LC 83-7016. 192p. (Orig.). 1983. lib. bdg. 26.00 (ISBN 0-8191-3206-3); pap. text ed. 11.25 (ISBN 0-8191-3207-1). U Pr of Amer.

Tetlow, Louis M., jt. auth. see Tetlow, Elisabeth M.

Tettemer, John. I Was a Monk. LC 73-89888. pap. 1.25 (ISBN 0-8356-0300-8, Quest). Theos Pub Hse.

Teubal, Savina J. Sarah the Priestess: The First Matriarch of Genesis. LC 84-96. xx, 201p. 1984. 16.95 (ISBN 0-8040-0843-4, Swallow); pap. 8.95 (ISBN 0-8040-0844-2, Swallow). Ohio U Pr.

Teubner, Christian. Christmas Baking: Traditional Recipes Made Easy. (Illus.). 96p. 1985. 9.95 (ISBN 0-8120-5617-5). Barron.

Tewes, Robert E., Jr. Conflict in the Church As Seen by a Thirteen Year Old. LC 83-83650. 1983. pap. 17.95 (ISBN 0-915644-24-X). Clayton Pub Hse.

Tewinkel, Joseph M. Built upon the Cornerstone. LC 80-65148. (Illus.). 178p. (Orig.). 1980. 3.95 (ISBN 0-87509-280-2); Leader's Guide. 2.95 (ISBN 0-87509-286-1). Chr Pubns.

Tewksbury, Donald G. Founding of American Colleges & Universities Before the Civil War with Particular Reference to the Religious Influences Bearing upon the College Movement. LC 76-177718. (Columbia University. Teachers College. Contributions to Education Ser.: No. 543). Repr. of 1932 ed. 22.50 (ISBN 0-404-55543-8). AMS Pr.

--Founding of American Colleges & Universities Before the Civil War. LC 79-89246. (American Education: Its Men, Institutions & Ideas, Ser. 1). 1969. Repr. of 1932 ed. 17.00 (ISBN 0-405-01483-X). Ayer Co Pubs.

Teyler, Theodore W. Bible Basics. (Illus.). 48p. (Orig.). 1986. pap. 4.95 leader's guide (ISBN 0-933350-35-X); pap. 4.95 student manual (ISBN 0-317-46726-3). Morse Pr.

Thackeray, H. St. J. The Septuagint of Jewish Worship. (British Acadamy of London Ser.). pap. 19.00 (ISBN 0-8115-1262-2). Kraus Repr.

Thackeray, Helen & Brown, Beth. Mormon Family Cookbook. LC 82-73085. (Illus.). 180p. 1982. 12.95 (ISBN 0-87747-930-5). Deseret Bk.

Thackston, W. H., Jr., tr. see Suhrawardi, Shihabuddin Yahya.

Thackston, Wheeler, jt. auth. see Danner, Victor.

Thakar, Vimala. Life As Yoga: Discourses at Chorwad, 2 bks. Singh, Devendra, tr. 286p. 1977. 14.00 (ISBN 0-89684-242-8, Pub. by Motilal Banarsidass India); pap. 10.95 (ISBN 0-89684-241-X). Orient Bk Dist.

--Totality in Essence. 132p. 1986. pap. 7.00 (ISBN 81-208-0048-6, Pub. by Motilal Banarsidass India). Orient Bk Dist.

--Why Meditation. 82p. 1986. pap. 6.00 (ISBN 81-208-0047-8, Pub. by Motilal Banarsidass India). Orient Bk Dist.

Thakur, Shivesh C. Religion & Rational Choice. (Library of Philosophy & Religion). 132p. 1981. 29.50x (ISBN 0-389-20047-6). B&N Imports.

Thaman, Mary P. Manners & Morals of the Nineteen Twenties: A Survey of the Religious Press. LC 77-8129. 1977. Repr. of 1954 ed. lib. bdg. 22.50x (ISBN 0-8371-9679-5, THMM). Greenwood.

Thanvi, A. A. Bahishti Zewar (Heavenly Ornaments) 14.95 (ISBN 0-686-63896-4). Kazi Pubns.

ThanWi, A. A. Holy Quran: Arabic-Urdu. 22.50 (ISBN 0-686-83593-X). Kazi Pubns.

Tharchin, Sermey G. Methods of Achieving the Paths: Stages of Philosophical & Ethical Development According to the Madhyamika Svatantrika School of Buddhism. Taylor, Barbara D., ed. Tr. of Lam-thob-tsul. 59p. (Orig.). 1981. pap. 5.00 (ISBN 0-918753-02-3). Mahayana.

Tharchin, Sermey G., jt. ed. see Debate Study Group.

Tharchin, Sermey G., et al. King Udrayana & the Wheel of Life: The History & Meaning of the Buddhist Teaching of Dependent Origination. LC 84-61266. (Illus.). 248p. (Orig.). 1984. 14.50 (ISBN 0-918753-06-6); pap. 9.50 (ISBN 0-918753-05-8). Mahayana.

Tharp, Zeno C., ed. Minister's Guide for Special Occasions. Repr. 7.95 (ISBN 0-87148-553-2). Pathway Pr.

Thatcher, jt. auth. see Rogers.

Thatcher, Adrian. The Ontology of Paul Tillich. (Oxford Theological Monographs). 1978. text ed. 29.95x (ISBN 0-19-826715-0). Oxford U Pr.

Thatcher, Floyd & Thatcher, Harriett. Long Term Marriage. 1981. 5.95 (ISBN 0-8499-2963-6). Word Bks.

Thatcher, Harriett, jt. auth. see Thatcher, Floyd.

Thatcher, Martha. The Freedom of Obedience. (Christian Character Library). 1986. hdbk. 8.95 (ISBN 0-89109-541-1). NavPress.

Thayer, John. The New Thayer's Greek Lexicon. 784p. 1981. 19.95 (ISBN 0-913573-22-1). Hendrickson MA.

Thayer, Joseph, ed. Thayer's Greek-English Lexicon of the New Testament. 1984. 22.95 (ISBN 0-8010-8872-0). Baker Bk.

Thayer, Joseph H. Greek-English Lexicon of the New Testament: A Dictionary Numerically Coded to Strong's Exhaustive Concordance. (Gr. & Eng.). 1977. pap. 15.95 (ISBN 0-8010-8838-0). Baker Bk.

--Greek-English Lexicon of the New Testament. 1956. 19.95 (ISBN 0-310-36850-2, 10906); pap. 10.95 (ISBN 0-310-36851-0, 10906P). Zondervan.

--Thayer's Greek-English Lexicon of the New Testament. LC 78-67264. (Gr. & Eng.). 1978. pap. 16.95 (ISBN 0-8054-1376-6). Broadman.

Thayer, Joseph H., ed. & tr. Greek-English Lexicon of the New Testament. (Gr.). 746p. 1901. 19.95 (ISBN 0-567-01015-5, Pub. by T & T Clark Ltd UK). Fortress.

Thayer, Joseph H., tr. A Greek-English Lexicon of the New Testament. (Reference Set). Orig. Title: Grimm's Wilkes Clavis Novi Testamonti. 726p. 1982. Repr. of 1977 ed. 22.95 (ISBN 0-915134-73-X). Mott Media.

Thayer, Lee, compiled by. Ethics, Morality & the Media: Reflections of American Culture. new ed. (Humanistic Studies in the Communication Arts). 320p. 1980. 22.00x (ISBN 0-8038-1957-9, Communication Arts); pap. text ed. 15.00x (ISBN 0-8038-1958-7). Hastings.

Thayer, Nelson S. Spirituality & Pastoral Care. LC 84-48716. (Theology & Pastoral Care Ser.). 128p. 1985. pap. 7.95 (ISBN 0-8006-1734-7, 1-1734). Fortress.

Thayer, Vivian T. Religion in Public Education. LC 78-12385. 1979. Repr. of 1947 ed. lib. bdg. 22.50x (ISBN 0-313-21212-0, THRP). Greenwood.

Thee, Francis C. Julius Africanus & the Early Christian View of Magic. 549p. 1984. lib. bdg. 73.50x (ISBN 3-16-144552-X, Pub. by J C B Mohr BRD). Coronet Bks.

Theiner, Paul F., ed. see Rolle, Richard.

Theisen, Jerome. Community & Disunity: Symbols of Grace & Sin. 144p. 1985. pap. 7.50 (ISBN 0-8146-1406-X). Liturgical Pr.

Theiss, Herman C. Life with God. pap. 5.95 (ISBN 0-933350-05-8); tchrs. manual 3.00 (ISBN 0-933350-44-9). Morse Pr.

Theissen, Gerd. Biblical Faith: An Evolutionary Approach. Bowden, John, tr. LC 84-21072. 224p. 1985. pap. 8.95 (ISBN 0-8006-1842-4, 1-1842). Fortress.

--The Miracle Stories of the Early Christian Tradition. Riches, John, ed. McDonagh, Francis, tr. LC 82-48546. 416p. 1983. 29.95 (ISBN 0-8006-0700-7). Fortress.

--Psychological Aspects of Pauline Theology. Galvin, John P., tr. from Ger. LC 86-45196. 512p. 1986. 34.95 (ISBN 0-8006-0789-9). Fortress.

--The Social Setting of Pauline Christianity: Essays on Corinth. Schutz, John H., tr. LC 81-43087. 1982. 19.95 (ISBN 0-8006-0669-8). Fortress.

--Sociology of Early Palestinian Christianity. Bowden, John, tr. from Ger. LC 77-15248. Tr. of Soziologie der Jesusbewegung. 144p. 1978. pap. 5.95 (ISBN 0-8006-1330-9, 1-1330). Fortress.

Theleman. Aid to Heidelberg Catechism. 5.95 (ISBN 0-686-23483-9). Rose Pub MI.

Thelle, Notto R. Buddhism & Christianity in Japan: From Conflict to Dialogue, 1854-1899. (Illus.). 384p. 1987. text ed. 30.00x. UH Pr.

Themi. Sri Aurobindo: The Story of His Life. 95p. 1983. pap. 2.95 (ISBN 0-89071-327-8, Pub. by Sri Aurobindo Ashram India). Matagiri.

The Mother. Flowers & Their Messages. (Illus.). 308p. 1985. pap. 14.95 (ISBN 0-89071-282-4). Matagiri.

--Glimpses of the Mother's Life, Vol. 2. Das, Nilima, ed. 335p. 1980. 11.00 (ISBN 0-89071-291-3). Matagiri.

--Health & Healing in Yoga. 305p. 1982. 6.00 (ISBN 0-89071-284-0, Pub. by Sri Aurobindo Ashram India); pap. 6.00 (ISBN 0-89071-283-2). Matagiri.

--The Lesson of Life. 180p. 1985. pap. 5.25 (ISBN 0-89071-322-7, Pub. by Sri Aurobindo Ashram India). Matagiri.

The Mother, jt. auth. see Sri Aurobindo.

Theodoret. A History of the Monks of Syria. Price, R. M., tr. from Gr. (Cistercian Studies: No. 88). 1986. 26.95x (ISBN 0-87907-888-X); pap. 10.00x (ISBN 0-87907-988-6). Cistercian Pubns.

Theological Concerns of the Christian Conference of Asia Commission, ed. Minjung Theology: People As the Subjects of History. LC 83-7279. 224p. (Orig.). 1983. pap. 9.95 (ISBN 0-88344-336-8). Orbis Bks.

Theological Faculty, University of Navarre, ed. The Navarre Bible: St. Mark. 202p. 1986. 10.00 (ISBN 0-906127-92-0). Lumen Christi.

Theophane The Monk. Tales of a Magic Monastery. LC 81-9765. (Illus.). 96p. 1981. pap. 8.95 (ISBN 0-8245-0085-7). Crossroad NY.

Theophan the Recluse. Misli na Kazhdij Den' Goda. Tr. of Thoughts on Every Day of the Year. 186p. 1982. pap. 7.00 (ISBN 0-317-28912-8). Holy Trinity.

--O Pravoslavii s Predestereshenijami ot Pogreshenij Protiv Hego. Tr. of On Orthodoxy with Warning Against Apostasy from It. 202p. 1962. pap. 7.00 (ISBN 0-317-28919-5). Holy Trinity.

--Psalom 118. Tr. of Psalm 118. 496p. 22.00 (ISBN 0-317-28925-X); pap. 17.00 (ISBN 0-317-28926-8). Holy Trinity.

Theosophical Research Centre, London. Mystery of Healing. 1968. pap. 3.50 (ISBN 0-8356-0114-5, Quest). Theos Pub Hse.

Theosophy Company. Index to the Secret Doctrine. x, 172p. 1939. 6.00 (ISBN 0-938998-02-1). Theosophy.

Thera, N. Heart of Buddhist Meditation. 1973. pap. 7.95 (ISBN 0-87728-073-8). Weiser.

Thera, Nyanaponika. The Vision of Dhamma: The Buddhist Writings of Nyanaponika Thera. Bodhi, Bhikkhu, ed. 296p. (Orig.). 1986. pap. 12.50 (ISBN 0-87728-669-8). Weiser.

Theresa of Avila. The Conquest of the Perfect Love, 2 vols. (Illus.). 235p. 1986. 189.75 (ISBN 0-89266-552-1). Am Classical Coll Pr.

Thetford, William N., jt. ed. see Finegold, Julius J.

Theunissen, Michael. The Other: Studies in the Social Ontology of Husserl, Heidegger, Sartre & Buber. Macann, Christopher, tr. from Ger. LC 83-16267. (Studies in Contemporary German Social Thought). 429p. 1984. text ed. 45.00x (ISBN 0-262-20048-1). MIT Pr.

Thevenot, Xavier. Sin: A Christian View for Today. Marchand, Roger, ed. Inkel, Simone, tr. from Fr. 80p. 1984. pap. 2.95 (ISBN 0-89243-218-7). Liguori Pubns.

Thibault, Paul R. Pope Gregory XI: The Failure of Tradition. 252p. 1986. lib. bdg. 26.50 (ISBN 0-8191-5462-8); pap. text ed. 12.75 (ISBN 0-8191-5463-6). U Pr of Amer.

Thibaut, G. The Vedanta Sutras. (Sacred Bks. of the East: Vols. 34, 38). both vols. 30.00 (ISBN 0-89581-530-3); 15.00 ea. Asian Human Pr.

Thibaut, G., ed. The Vedanta Sutras. 1974. lib. bdg. 75.00 (ISBN 0-8490-1256-2). Gordon Pr.

Thibaut, G., tr. The Vendanta Sutras, 3 vols. lib. bdg. 300.00 (ISBN 0-87968-562-X). Krishna Pr.

Thieberger, Frederic. King Solomon. (Illus.). 313p. 1978. pap. 6.95 (ISBN 0-85222-200-9). Hebrew Pub.

Thiel, John E. God & World in Schleiermacher's Dialektik & Glaubenslehre, Vol. 43. (Basler und Berner Studien zur Historischen und Systematischen Theologie). xiv, 239p. 1981. pap. 28.15 (ISBN 3-261-04810-7). P Lang Pubs.

Thiele, Edwin R. The Mysterious Numbers of the Hebrew Kings. New rev. ed. 256p. 1984. pap. 11.95 (ISBN 0-310-36011-0, 10116P). Zondervan.

Thiele, Margaret. Girl Alive. LC 80-11623. (Orion Ser.). 1980. pap. 3.95 (ISBN 0-8127-0268-9). Review & Herald.

Thielicke, Helmut. Between Heaven & Earth. Doberstein, J. W., tr. from Ger. 192p. 1978. Repr. 13.95 (ISBN 0-227-67726-9). Attic Pr.

--Christ & the Meaning of Life. Doberstein, J. W., tr. from Ger. 186p. 1978. Repr. 13.95 (ISBN 0-227-67684-X). Attic Pr.

--Encounter with Spurgeon. Doberstein, J. W., tr. from Ger. 284p. 1978. Repr. 13.95 (ISBN 0-227-67655-6). Attic Pr.

--The Ethics of Sex. Doberstein, J. W., tr. from Ger. 340p. 1964. 13.95 (ISBN 0-227-67656-4). Attic Pr.

--The Evangelical Faith: The Doctrine of God & of Christ, Vol. 2. Bromiley, Geoffrey W., ed. LC 74-7010. pap. 123.30 (ISBN 0-317-30163-2, 2025345). Bks Demand UMI.

--The Evangelical Faith, Vol. 1: Prolegomena: The Relation of Theology to Modern Thought-Forms. Bromiley, Geoffrey W., tr. 420p. Date not set. 24.95 (ISBN 0-567-02354-0, Pub. by T & T Clark Ltd UK). Fortress.

--The Evangelical Faith, Vol. 2: The Doctrine of God & Christ. Bromiley, Geoffrey W., tr. 476p. Date not set. 24.95 (ISBN 0-567-02355-9, Pub. by T & T Clark Ltd UK). Fortress.

--The Evangelical Faith, Vol. 3: Theology of the Spirit. Bromiley, Geoffrey W., tr. 480p. Date not set. 24.95 (ISBN 0-8028-2344-0, Pub. by T & T Clark Ltd UK). Fortress.

--Faith the Great Adventure. LC 84-48716. 160p. 1985. pap. 8.95 (ISBN 0-8006-1833-5, 1-1833). Fortress.

--How the World Began. Doberstein, J. W., tr. from Ger. 308p. 1978. Repr. 13.95 (ISBN 0-227-67484-7). Attic Pr.

--How the World Began: Man in the First Chapters of the Bible. Doberstein, John W., tr. from Ger. LC 61-6756. 324p. 1961. pap. 6.95 (ISBN 0-8006-1894-7, 1-1894). Fortress.

--Life Can Begin Again: Sermons on the Sermon on the Mount. Doberstein, John W., tr. from Ger. LC 63-12535. 240p. 1963. pap. 5.95 (ISBN 0-8006-1934-X, 1-1934). Fortress.

--Life Can Begin Again: Sermons on the Sermon on the Mount. Doberstein, J. W., tr. from Ger. 224p. pap. 10.95 (ISBN 0-227-67854-0, Pub. by J Clarke UK). Attic Pr.

--Little Exercise for Young Theologians. (Orig.). 1962. pap. 2.95 (ISBN 0-8028-1198-1). Eerdmans.

--Man in God's World. Doberstein, J. W., tr. from Ger. 224p. 1978. Repr. 13.95 (ISBN 0-227-67709-9). Attic Pr.

--The Prayer That Spans the World. Doberstein, J. W., tr. from Ger. 160p. 1978. Repr. 13.95 (ISBN 0-227-67671-8). Attic Pr.

--Theological Ethics, 2 vols. Incl. Foundations; Politics; Vol. III. Sex. pap. 8.95 (ISBN 0-8028-1794-7). LC 78-31858. Eerdmans.

--Theological Ethics. LC 78-31858. Repr. of 1979 ed. 160.00 (2027550). Bks Demand UMI.

--The Waiting Father. Doberstein, J. W., tr. from Ger. 192p. 1978. Repr. 13.95 (ISBN 0-227-67634-3). Attic Pr.

--The Waiting Father. LC 75-12284. 192p. 1981. 5.95 (ISBN 0-06-067991-3, RD-364, HarpR). Har-Row.

Thiemann, Ronald F. Revelation & Theology: The Gospel As Narrated Promise. LC 84-40822. 208p. 1985. text ed. 23.95 (ISBN 0-268-01629-1, 85-16296). U of Notre Dame Pr.

--Revelation & Theology: The Gospel As Narrated Promise. LC 84-40822. 198p. 1987. pap. text ed. 9.95 (ISBN 0-268-01632-1, Dist. by Har-Row). U of Notre Dame Pr.

Thieme, Paul. Mitra & Aryaman. (Connecticut Academy of Arts & Sciences Transaction: Vol. 41). 1967. 18.00 (ISBN 0-208-01104-8). Shoe String.

Thien-An, Thich. Zen Philosophy, Zen Practice. LC 75-20003. (Illus.). 192p. 1975. pap. 7.95 (ISBN 0-913546-33-X). Dharma Pub.

Thien-An, Thieh. Buddhism & Zen in Vietnam: In Relation to the Development in Asia. LC 74-83391. (Illus.). 300p. 1975. 12.50 (ISBN 0-8048-1144-X). C E Tuttle.

Thierens, A. E. Astrology in Mesopotamian Culture. 1977. lib. bdg. 59.95 (ISBN 0-8490-1461-1). Gordon Pr.

Thiess, Susan, jt. auth. see Carver, Robert C.

Thiessen, Henry C. Introduction to the New Testament. 1943. 14.95 (ISBN 0-8028-3259-8). Eerdmans.

--Lectures in Systematic Theology. rev. ed. Doerksen, Vernon C., rev. by. 1981. 16.95 (ISBN 0-8028-3529-5). Eerdmans.

Thiessen, John C. Pastoring the Smaller Church. kivar 6.95 (ISBN 0-310-36901-0). Zondervan.

Thigpen, Charles, jt. auth. see Outlaw, Stanley.

Thigpen, Paul. Angels in the Air. 1986. 4.95 (ISBN 1-55513-053-4, Chariot Bks). Cook.

Thigpen, Thomas P. Come Sing God's Song. (Illus.). 1987. 7.95. Cook.

Thirlwall, Thomas, ed. see Taylor, Jeremy.

Thiroux, Jacques P. Ethics: Theory & Practice. 2nd ed. 392p. 1980. pap. text ed. write for info. (ISBN 0-02-470220-X). Macmillan.

Thiry, Joan. Creative Prayer. 1981. 9.95 (ISBN 0-89837-068-X, Pub. by Pflaum Pr). Peter Li.

--Sharing His Life. 1981. 3.75 (ISBN 0-89837-056-6, Pub. by Pflaum Pr); pap. 1.50 (ISBN 0-89837-084-1). Peter Li.

--Sharing His Love. 1981. 3.75 (ISBN 0-89837-066-3, Pub. by Pflaum Pr). Peter Li.

Thiry, Joan & Burbach, Marilyn. Confirmation Is Saying Yes to God. duplicating masterbook 12.95 (ISBN 0-89837-071-X, Pub. by Pflaum Pr). Peter Li.

--Eucharist Is for Sharing. 1977. duplicating masterbook 12.95 (ISBN 0-89837-051-5, Pub. by Pflaum Pr). Peter Li.

Thiselton, Anthony C. The Two Horizons. LC 79-14387. 1984. 12.95 (ISBN 0-8028-0006-8). Eerdmans.

Thistlethwaite, Susan B. Metaphors for the Contemporary Church. 192p. (Orig.). 1983. pap. 8.95 (ISBN 0-8298-0692-X). Pilgrim NY.

Thobaben, Robert G., jt. ed. see Piediscalzi, Nicolas.

Thoburn, Robert L. The Christian & Politics. 224p. (Orig.). 1984. pap. text ed. 4.95 (ISBN 0-317-15003-0). Thoburn Pr.

Thole, Simeon. Behind the Pine Curtain: Portraits of Peter Prep. LC 79-21013. 198p. 1979. pap. 2.50 (ISBN 0-8146-1041-2). Liturgical Pr.

Thom, Robert. New Wine Is Better. 1974. pap. 2.95 (ISBN 0-88368-036-X). Whitaker Hse.

Thom, W. T. The Struggle for Religious Freedom in Virginia: The Baptists. Repr. of 1900 ed. 13.00 (ISBN 0-384-60163-4). Johnson Repr.

Thom, William T. The Struggle for Religious Freedom in Virginia. LC 78-63877. (Johns Hopkins University. Studies in the Social Sciences. Eighteenth Ser. 1900: 10-12). Repr. of 1900 ed. 11.50 (ISBN 0-404-61133-8). AMS Pr.

Thoma, Clemens. A Christian Theology of Judaism. Croner, Helga & Frizzell, Lawrence, trs. from Ger. LC 80-82252. (Studies in Judaism & Christianity). 232p. 1980. pap. 7.95 (ISBN 0-8091-2310-X). Paulist Pr.

Thoma, Clemens & Wyschgrod, Michael, eds. Understanding Scripture: Explorations of Jewish & Christian Traditions of Interpretation. 1987. pap. 7.95 (ISBN 0-8091-2873-X). Paulist Pr.

Thomas, Abraham V. Christians in Secular India. LC 72-420. 246p. 1973. 20.00 (ISBN 0-8386-1021-8). Fairleigh Dickinson.

Thomas, Ann. God's Answer to Overeating. (Aglow Bible Study Basic Ser.). 64p. 1975. 2.95 (ISBN 0-932305-36-9, 4220-7). Aglow Pubns.

Thomas, Arthur G. Abundance Is Your Right. LC 77-76207. 1987. pap. 6.95 (ISBN 0-941992-10-1). Los Arboles Pub.

Thomas, Barbara J. Proverbs II. 56p. (Orig.). 1985. pap. 5.95 (ISBN 0-9616788-0-1). Landsberry Pr.

Thomas, Cal. Book Burning. LC 83-70319. 180p. 1983. pap. 5.95 (ISBN 0-89107-284-5, Crossway Bks). Good News.

Thomas, Charles. Christianity in Roman Britain to A. D. 500. (Illus.). 416p. 1981. 40.00x (ISBN 0-520-04392-8). U of Cal Pr.

Thomas, Curtis C., jt. auth. see Steele, David H.

Thomas, Curtis C., jt. auth. see Steele, David N.

Thomas, D. Aneurin. The Welsh Elizabethan Catholic Martyrs. 331p. 1971. text ed. 28.50 (ISBN 0-900768-97-5, Pub. by U of Wales). Humanities.

Thomas, D. Winton, ed. Documents from Old Testament Times. pap. 7.95x (ISBN 0-06-130085-3, TB85, Torch). Har-Row.

Thomas, David. Acts of the Apostles. LC 79-2543. (Kregel Bible Study Classics Ser.). 512p. 1980. 22.95 (ISBN 0-8254-3810-1). Kregel.

--Book of Job. LC 82-7767. (Bible Study Classics). 500p. 1982. 22.95 (ISBN 0-8254-3814-4). Kregel.

--Book of Proverbs, 2 Vols. in 1. LC 82-18682. (Kregel Bible Classics Ser.). 836p. 1983. 24.95 (ISBN 0-8254-3813-6). Kregel.

--Gospel of John, 2 vols. in 1. LC 79-15415. (Kregel Bible Study Classics Ser.). 846p. 1980. 24.95 (ISBN 0-8254-3809-8). Kregel.

--Sermon Notes on the Psalms. Lockyer, Herbert, ed. Tr. of The Homilist. 320p. (Orig.). Date not set. pap. 10.95 (ISBN 0-8254-3116-6). Kregel.

Thomas, David M. Christian Marriage: A Journey Together. (Message of the Sacraments Ser.: Vol. 5). 13.95 (ISBN 0-89453-395-9); pap. 9.95 (ISBN 0-89453-231-6). M Glazier.

--When God Is at Home with Your Family. LC 78-73019. (When Bk.). (Illus.). 1978. pap. 2.45 (ISBN 0-87029-146-7, 20231-7). Abbey.

Thomas, David M., ed. Family Life Ministry. LC 79-53513. (Marriage & Family Living in Depth Bk.). 1979. pap. 2.45 (ISBN 0-87029-157-2, 20243-2). Abbey.

--God, Religion, & Family Life. LC 79-53512. (Marriage & Family Living in Depth Book Ser.). 1979. pap. 2.45 (ISBN 0-87029-156-4, 20242-4). Abbey.

--Prayer in the Home. LC 81-69503. (Marriage & Family Living in Depth Bk.). 1981. pap. 2.45 (ISBN 0-87029-180-7, 20250-7). Abbey.

--Sex Education Within the Family. LC 80-69136. (Marriage & Family Living in Depth Bk.). 80p. 1980. pap. 2.45 (ISBN 0-87029-171-8, 20248-1). Abbey.

Thomas, Donald F. The Deacon in a Changing Church. LC 69-16388. 1969. pap. 4.95 (ISBN 0-8170-0414-9). Judson.

Thomas, Dylan. Child's Christmas in Wales. LC 59-13174. (Illus.). 1969. gift ed. 12.00 (ISBN 0-8112-0391-3). New Directions.

--Child's Christmas in Wales. LC 59-13174. (Illus.). 1959. pap. 3.95 (ISBN 0-8112-0203-8, NDP181). New Directions.

Thomas, E. J., tr. Early Buddhist Scriptures. lib. bdg. 79.95 (ISBN 0-87968-563-8). Krishna Pr.

Thomas, E. J., tr. from Sanskrit. The Perfection of Wisdom: The Career of the Predestined Buddhas. LC 78-12005. 1979. Repr. of 1952 ed. lib. bdg. 22.50x (ISBN 0-313-20646-5, MAPWI). Greenwood.

--The Quest of Enlightenment: A Selection of the Buddhist Scriptures. LC 78-70130. Repr. of 1950 ed. 17.50 (ISBN 0-404-17389-6). AMS Pr.

Thomas, E. J., tr. see Tripitaka.

Thomas, Edith L. The Whole World Singing. 1950. 6.95 (ISBN 0-377-30882-X); pap. 4.95 (ISBN 0-377-30881-1). Friend Pr.

Thomas, Edward. Grail Yoga. 2nd ed. LC 74-84399. (A Grail Bk). (Illus.). 128p. 1975. pap. 2.95 (ISBN 0-914896-28-8). East Ridge Pr.

Thomas, Edward J. Early Buddhist Scriptures. LC 78-70129. Repr. of 1935 ed. 31.00 (ISBN 0-404-17388-8). AMS Pr.

--The History of Buddhist Thought. 316p. 1981. pap. 17.00 (ISBN 0-89540-100-2, SB-100). Sun Pub.

Thomas, Sr. Evangeline, ed. Women's Religious History Sources. 264p. 1983. 65.00 (ISBN 0-8352-1681-0). Bowker.

Thomas, F. W., ed. see Jaini, Jagmandar L.

Thomas, Fred W. Masters of Deception. pap. 4.95 (ISBN 0-8010-8779-1). Baker Bk.

Thomas, George. Christian Indians & Indian Nationalism, 1885-1950: An Interpretation in Historical & Theological Perspectives. (IC-Studies in the Intercultural History of Christianity: Vol. 22). 271p. 1979. 28.10 (ISBN 3-8204-6399-2). P Lang Pubs.

Thomas, George F., ed. Vitality of the Christian Tradition. facsimile ed. LC 70-134143. (Essay Index Reprint Ser). Repr. of 1944 ed. 22.00 (ISBN 0-8369-2378-2). Ayer Co Pubs.

Thomas, Gordon. Desire & Denial: Celibacy & the Church. 1986. 19.95 (ISBN 0-316-84097-1). Little.

Thomas, Gordon & Morgan-Witts, Max. Averting Armageddon. LC 84-10101. 360p. 1984. 18.95 (ISBN 0-385-18985-0). Doubleday.

Thomas, Halsey M., ed. The Diary of Samuel Sewall, 1674-1729, 2 vols. (Illus.). 1254p. 1973. 30.00 (ISBN 0-374-13952-0). FS&G.

Thomas, Hilah F. & Keller, Rosemary S., eds. Women in New Worlds: Vol. 1. LC 81-7984. (Historical Perspectives on the Wesleyan Tradition Ser.). 448p. (Orig.). 1981. pap. 13.95 (ISBN 0-687-45968-0). Abingdon.

Thomas, J. D. The Biblical Doctrine of Grace. LC 76-56472. (Way of Life Ser: No. 111). (Orig.). 1977. pap. 3.95 (ISBN 0-89112-111-0, Bibl Res Pr). Abilene Christ U.

--Divorce & Remarriage. (Way of Life Ser.: No.159). 1977. pap. 3.95 (ISBN 0-89112-159-5, Bibl Res Pr). Abilene Christ U.

--Evolution & Antiquity. 2nd ed. (Way of Life Ser: No. 120). Orig. Title: Doctrine of Evolution & the Antiquity of Man. (Orig.). 1959. pap. 3.95 (ISBN 0-89112-120-X, Bibl Res Pr). Abilene Christ U.

--Facts & Faith: Reason, Science & Faith, Vol. 1. 1966. 13.95 (ISBN 0-89112-011-4, Bibl Res Pr). Abilene Christ U.

--Facts & Faith: The Bible & Faith, Vol. 2. 153p. 1980. 11.95 (ISBN 0-89112-012-2, Bibl Res Pr). Abilene Christ U.

--Heaven's Window: Sequel to We Be Brethren. LC 74-28950. 159p. 1975. 11.95 (ISBN 0-89112-002-5, Bibl Res Pr). Abilene Christ U.

--Message of the New Testament-First Corinthians. (Way of Life Ser.: No. 167). 1984. pap. 3.95 (ISBN 0-89112-167-6, Bibl Res Pr). Abilene Christ U.

--The Message of the New Testament-Romans. LC 82-70933. (Way of Life Ser.: 166). (Illus.). 108p. 1982. pap. 3.95 (ISBN 0-89112-166-8, Bibl Res Pr). Abilene Christ U.

--Second Corinthians: Message of the New Testament. (Way of Life Ser.). 60p. 1986. pap. text ed. 3.95 (ISBN 0-915547-92-9, 929). Abilene Christ U.

--Self-Study Guide to Galatians & Romans. rev. ed. (Way of Life Ser: No. 122). Orig. Title: Self-Study Guide to Romans. (Orig.). 1971. pap. text ed. 3.95 (ISBN 0-89112-122-6, Bibl Res Pr). Abilene Christ U.

--Self-Study Guide to the Corinthian Letters. (Way of Life Ser: No. 123). (Orig.). 1972. pap. text ed. 3.95 (ISBN 0-89112-123-4, Bibl Res Pr). Abilene Christ U.

--We Be Brethen. 1958. 13.95 (ISBN 0-89112-001-7, Bibl Res Pr). Abilene Christ U.

Thomas, J. D., ed. Sermons of Batsell Barrett Baxter. (Great Preachers Ser). 1960. 11.95 (ISBN 0-89112-201-X, Bibl Res Pr). Abilene Christ U.

--Sermons of Frank Pack. (Great Preachers Ser). 1963. 11.95 (ISBN 0-89112-205-2, Bibl Res Pr). Abilene Christ U.

--Sermons of George W. Bailey. (Great Preachers Ser). 1961. 11.95 (ISBN 0-89112-202-8, Bibl Res Pr). Abilene Christ U.

--Sermons of Gus Nichols. (Great Preachers Ser). 1966. 11.95 (ISBN 0-89112-209-5, Bibl Res Pr). Abilene Christ U.

--Sermons of John H. Banister. (Great Preachers Ser). 1965. 11.95 (ISBN 0-89112-208-7, Bibl Res Pr). Abilene Christ U.

--Sermons of M. Norvel Young. (Great Preachers Ser). 1963. 11.95 (ISBN 0-89112-204-4, Bibl Res Pr). Abilene Christ U.

--Sermons of William S. Banowsky. (Great Preachers Ser). 1967. 11.95 (ISBN 0-89112-211-7, Bibl Res Pr). Abilene Christ U.

Thomas, J. D., ed. see Abilene Christian University Lectureship Staff.

Thomas, J. D., ed. see Ash, Anthony L.

Thomas, J. D., ed. see Barnett, Joe R.

Thomas, J. D., ed. see Chalk, John A.

Thomas, J. D., ed. see Church of Christ Staff.

Thomas, J. D., ed. see Douglas, Robert C.

Thomas, J. D., ed. see Lemmons, Reuel.

Thomas, J. D., ed. see Limb, Akio.

Thomas, J. D., ed. see McGaughey, C. E.

Thomas, J. D., ed. see Pack, Frank & Meador, Prentice A., Jr.

Thomas, J. D., ed. see Pullias, Athens C.

Thomas, J. D., et al. Sorrow & Joy. 1963. 11.95 (ISBN 0-89112-025-4, Bibl Res Pr). Abilene Christ U.

--Spiritual Power: Great Single Sermons. LC 74-170920. 1972. 13.95 (ISBN 0-89112-026-2, Bibl Res Pr). Abilene Christ U.

Thomas, James. I Am That I Am: A Metaphysical Course on Consciousness. (Illus.). 168p. 1984. 14.95x (ISBN 0-931290-90-2); pap. 6.95x (ISBN 0-931290-91-0). Alchemy Bks.

Thomas, Jesse J. The Youniverse: Gestalt Therapy, Non-Western Religions & the Present Age. LC 77-89164. (Illus.). 1978. 8.95 (ISBN 0-930626-00-1); pap. 4.95 (ISBN 0-930626-01-X). Psych & Consul Assocs.

Thomas, Joan G. If Jesus Came to My House. (Illus.). 1951. 10.25 (ISBN 0-688-40981-4). Lothrop.

Thomas, John L. The American Catholic Family. LC 80-15221. (Illus.). xii, 471p. 1980. Repr. of 1956 ed. lib. bdg. 37.50x (ISBN 0-313-22473-0, THAC). Greenwood.

--Beginning Your Marriage, 2 vols. 1980. 4.95 (ISBN 0-915388-25-1); pap. 2.50 (ISBN 0-915388-24-3). Buckley Pubns.

Thomas, John N., tr. see Barth, Karl.

Thomas, Joseph. Universal Pronouncing Dictionary of Biography & Mythology, 2 Vols. 5th ed. LC 76-137298. Repr. of 1930 ed. Set. 225.00 (ISBN 0-404-06386-1). AMS Pr.

Thomas, Joseph R., ed. & intro. by. see Catoir, John.

Thomas, Joshua. The American Baptist Heritage in Wales, Vol. 1. 1976. 15.00 (ISBN 0-686-12332-8). Church History.

Thomas, Keith. Religion & the Decline of Magic. 716p. 1975. pap. text ed. write for info. (ISBN 0-02-420200-2, Pub. by Scribner). Macmillan.

--Religion & the Decline of Magic. 736p. 1986. pap. 17.95 (ISBN 0-684-14542-1). Scribner.

Thomas, L. R. Does the Bible Teach Millennialism. pap. 2.50 (ISBN 0-685-36796-7). Reiner.

Thomas, Latta R. Biblical Faith & the Black American. 160p. 1976. pap. 4.95 (ISBN 0-8170-0718-0). Judson.

Thomas, Leslie G. Thomas' Valedictory Sermons. 1973. 6.95 (ISBN 0-88428-021-7). Parchment Pr.

--Truth, the Millennium, & the Battle of Armageddon. 1979. pap. 2.50 (ISBN 0-89225-188-3). Gospel Advocate.

--What the Bible Teaches, 2 vols. 1962. Vol. 1. 5.95 (ISBN 0-88027-023-3). Vol. II (ISBN 0-88027-024-1). Firm Foun Pub.

Thomas, M. M. Christian Response to the Asian Revolution. 1968. pap. 1.75 (ISBN 0-377-82701-0). Friend Pr.

Thomas, Marcel, ed. The Grandes Heures of Jean, Duke of Berry. LC 75-167761. (Illus.). 192p. 1971. 80.00 (ISBN 0-8076-0613-8). Braziller.

Thomas, Mary M. Southern Methodist University: Founding & Early Years. LC 74-80248. (Illus.). 1974. 15.00 (ISBN 0-87074-138-1). SMU Press.

Thomas, Nancy. Of Deity & Bones. (Illus.). 90p. (Orig.). 1983. pap. 6.95 (ISBN 0-913342-38-6). Barclay Pr.

Thomas, Nancy, ed. & intro. by. On the Edge of a Truth. 112p. (Orig.). pap. 4.50 (ISBN 0-913342-25-4). Barclay Pr.

Thomas, Nick, tr. see Unger, Georg.

Thomas, Owen C. Attitudes Toward Other Religions: Some Christian Interpretations. LC 86-4076. 250p. (Orig.). 1986. pap. 11.50 (ISBN 0-8191-5324-9). U Pr of Amer.

--God's Activity in the World: The Contemporary Debate. LC 82-19148. (AAR Studies in Religion). 248p. 1983. pap. 8.50 (ISBN 0-89130-602-1, 01 00 31). Scholars Pr GA.

--Introduction to Theology. 2nd ed. LC 82-61890. 304p. 1983. pap. 13.95 (ISBN 0-8192-1319-5). Morehouse.

--Theological Questions: Analysis & Argument. LC 83-60658. 134p. (Orig.). 1983. pap. 8.95 (ISBN 0-8192-1328-4). Morehouse.

--William Temple's Philosophy of Religion. LC 61-4400. 1961. 10.00x (ISBN 0-8401-2330-2). A R Allenson.

Thomas, P. Hindu Religion, Customs & Manners. 6th ed. (Illus.). 144p. 1981. text ed. 35.00x (ISBN 0-86590-036-1, Pub. by Taraporevala India). Apt Bks.

--Kama Kalpa or the Hindu Ritual of Love. 14th ed. (Illus.). ix, 151p. 1981. text ed. 35.00x (ISBN 0-86590-031-0, Pub. by Taraporevala India). Apt Bks.

Thomas, Peggy. Redland Park Recorded. 240p. 1986. pap. 30.00x (ISBN 0-947939-03-2, Pub. by Elmcrest Uk). State Mutual Bk.

Thomas, R. B. You Are Gifted. (International Correspondence Program Ser.). (Orig.). 1985. pap. text ed. 6.95 (ISBN 0-87148-935-X). Pathway Pr.

Thomas, Reuen. Leaders of Thought in the Modern Church. LC 72-8559. (Essay Index Reprint Ser.). 1972. Repr. of 1892 ed. 18.00 (ISBN 0-8369-7333-X). Ayer Co Pubs.

Thomas, Robert L. & Gundry, Stanley N. A Harmony of the Gospels: New American Standard Version. 14.95x (ISBN 0-317-52392-9, HarpR). Har-Row.

Thomas, Robert L., ed. New American Standard Exhaustive Concordance of the Bible: Hebrew-Aramaic & Greek Dictionaries. LC 80-39626. 1695p. 1981. 29.95 (ISBN 0-87981-197-8, 4690-98); thumb-indexed 34.95 (ISBN 0-87981-503-5). Holman Bible Pub.

Thomas, Robert W., ed. see Athanasius.

Thomas, Roger. The Perfect Church. LC 81-14544. 96p. (Orig.). 1982. pap. 2.25 (ISBN 0-87239-479-4, 41012). Standard Pub.

--Seek First His Kingdom. 144p. 1987. pap. price not set (ISBN 0-87403-210-5, 39960). Standard Pub.

Thomas, Roger W. After the Spirit Comes. LC 77-83659. 1979. pap. 2.25 (ISBN 0-87239-194-9, 40049). Standard Pub.

--People Power. LC 80-53675. 96p. (Orig.). 1982. pap. 2.25 (ISBN 0-87239-442-5, 40096). Standard Pub.

Thomas, Roy. Planting & Growing a Fundamental Church. 1979. pap. 5.95 (ISBN 0-89265-070-2). Randall Hse.

Thomas, T. K., jt. auth. see Ariarajah, Wesley.

Thomas, Thomas A. Doctrine of the Word of God. 1972. pap. 3.50 (ISBN 0-87552-450-8). Presby & Reformed.

Thomas, Virginia & Miller, Betty. Children's Literature for All God's Children. LC 85-17169. 120p. 1986. pap. 11.95 (ISBN 0-8042-1690-8). John Knox.

Thomas, Virginia, jt. auth. see Ng, David.

Thomas, W. Griffith. Christianity Is Christ. LC 80-85341. (Shepherd Illustrated Classics Ser.). (Illus.). 200p. 1981. pap. 5.95 (ISBN 0-87983-238-X). Keats.

--Hebrews: A Devotional Commentary. 1962. pap. 4.95 (ISBN 0-8028-1552-9). Eerdmans.

--Outline Studies in Acts. 1956. pap. 10.95 (ISBN 0-8028-1570-7). Eerdmans.

--Outline Studies in Luke. LC 84-784. 408p. 1984. pap. text ed. 11.95 (ISBN 0-8254-3821-7). Kregel.

--St. Paul's Epistle to the Romans. 1946. pap. 9.95 (ISBN 0-8028-1582-0). Eerdmans.

Thomas, W. H. The Apostle John: His Life & Writings. LC 84-785. 376p. 1984. pap. 10.95 (ISBN 0-8254-3822-5). Kregel.

--The Apostle Peter: His Life & Writings. LC 84-1493. 304p. 1984. pap. 9.95 (ISBN 0-8254-3823-3). Kregel.

--Expository Sermon Outlines. 136p. 1987. pap. 5.95 (ISBN 0-8254-3830-6). Kregel.

--Genesis: A Devotional Commentary. 507p. 1988. pap. 12.95 (ISBN 0-8254-3817-9). Kregel.

--Studies in Colossians to Philemon. LC 86-7178. 192p. 1986. pap. 6.95 (ISBN 0-8254-3834-9). Kregel.

Thomas, W. H. Griffith. Through the Pentateuch Chapter by Chapter. LC 85-10076. 192p. 1985. pap. 6.95 (ISBN 0-8254-3833-0). Kregel.

Thomas, W. Ian. The Saving Life of Christ. 1961. pap. 3.95 (ISBN 0-310-33262-1, 10908S). Zondervan.

Thomas, W. W. Sunday School Outreach. 112p. 1979. 5.25 (ISBN 0-87148-787-X); pap. 4.25 (ISBN 0-87148-788-8). Pathway Pr.

Thomas a Becket. Fragments D'une Vie de Saint Thomas de Cantorbery en Vers Accouples. 25.00 (ISBN 0-384-60189-8); pap. 19.00 (ISBN 0-384-60179-0). Johnson Repr.

Thomas a Kempis. Imitation of Christ. new, rev. ed. Fitzpatrick, Clare L., ed. (Illus., Large Type). maroon, colored edges 4.95 (ISBN 0-89942-320-5, 320/00). Catholic Bk Pub.

--Imitation of Christ. 1978. plastic bdg. 3.50 (ISBN 0-8198-0533-5). Dghtrs St Paul.

--Imitation of Christ. LC 55-8729. 1955. pap. 4.50 (ISBN 0-385-02861-X, D17, Im). Doubleday.

--The Imitation of Christ. Blaiklock, E. M., tr. LC 80-54894. 228p. 1981. pap. 5.95 (ISBN 0-8407-5760-3). Nelson.

--Imitation of Christ. 1967. 5.95 (ISBN 0-88088-320-0). Peter Pauper.

--The Imitation of Christ. 20.00 (ISBN 0-8274-2557-0). R West.

--The Imitation of Christ. Rooney, John, tr. 214p. 1980. pap. 5.95 (ISBN 0-87243-097-9). Templegate.

--The Imitation of Christ. LC 82-80472. (Treasures from the Spiritual Classics Ser.). 64p. 1982. pap. 2.95 (ISBN 0-8192-1307-1). Morehouse.

--The Imitation of Christ. Helms, Hal M., ed. LC 82-61908. (Living Library Ser.). (Illus.). 280p. (Orig.). 1982. pap. 8.95 (ISBN 0-941478-07-6). Paraclete Pr.

--Imitation of Christ. Bechtel, Paul M., ed. (Moody Classics Ser.). 1984. pap. 4.50 (ISBN 0-8024-4005-3). Moody.

--The Imitation of Christ. 240p. 1983. pap. 4.95 (ISBN 0-310-38441-9, 9283P, Clarion Class). Zondervan.

--The Imitation of Christ. Zomberg, P. G., tr. LC 84-71574. Tr. of De imitatione Christi. (Lat., Illus.). 272p. 1985. 12.00 (ISBN 0-930995-00-7, 00-7). Dunstan Pr.

--Of the Imitation of Christ. (Large Print Christian Classic Ser.). 1982. 14.95 (ISBN 0-87983-288-6). Keats.

--Of the Imitation of Christ. 256p. 1981. pap. 2.95 (ISBN 0-88368-094-7). Whitaker Hse.

--Of the Imitation of Christ. Whytford, Richard & Flint, W. Russell, trs. 264p. 1983. Repr. of 1909 ed. lib. bdg. 95.00 (ISBN 0-89984-921-0). Century Bookbindery.

Thomas a Kempis & St. Therese of Lisieux. Just for Today: Selections from St. Therese of Lisieux & the Imitation of Christ. 250p. 1983. pap. 7.95 (ISBN 0-87243-121-5). Templegate.

Thomasis, Louis de see De Thomasis, Louis.

Thomasma, David C. An Apology for the Value of Human Life. LC 83-7335. 169p. 1983. pap. 18.00 (ISBN 0-87125-085-3). Cath Health.

Thomasma, Kenneth. Soun Tetoken: Nez Perce Boy. (Voyager Ser.). 144p. 1984. 8.95 (ISBN 0-8010-8874-7); pap. 5.95 (ISBN 0-8010-8873-9). Baker Bk.

Thomassin, L. Dictionnaire de Discipline Ecclesiastique, 2 vols. Migne, J. P., ed. (Troisieme et Derniere Encyclopedie Theologique Ser.: Vols. 25-26). (Fr.). 1466p. Repr. of 1856 ed. lib. bdg. 186.00x (ISBN 0-89241-306-9). Caratzas.

Thompsett, Fredrica H. Christian Feminist Perspectives on History, Theology & the Bible. 56p. (Orig.). 1986. pap. 2.50 (ISBN 0-88028-051-4). Forward Movement.

Thompson, A. Hamilton. English Monasteries. LC 78-3738. 1974. Repr. of 1913 ed. lib. bdg. 17.50 (ISBN 0-8414-8646-8). Folcroft.

Thompson, A. W. A. B. Simpson: His Life & Work. rev. ed. (Illus.). 228p. 1960. pap. 4.95 (ISBN 0-87509-044-3). Chr Pubns.

Thompson, Alden. Responsibility for Evil in the Theodicy of IV Ezra: A Study Illustrating the Significance of Form & Structure for the Meaning of the Book. LC 76-40915. (Society of Biblical Literature. Dissertation Ser.). 1977. pap. 9.95 (ISBN 0-89130-091-0, 060129). Scholars Pr GA.

Thompson, Andrew. That They May Know You. 112p. 1982. 10.55 (ISBN 0-318-00801-7). Natl Cath Educ.

Thompson, Barbara, tr. see Duby, Georges.

Thompson, Barbara R., jt. auth. see Spickard, Anderson.

Thompson, Bard. Renaissance & Reformation. (Texts & Studies in Religion). (Orig.). write for info. (ISBN 0-88946-915-6). E Mellen.

Thompson, Bard, ed. Liturgies of the Western Church. LC 80-8044. 448p. 1980. pap. 9.95 (ISBN 0-8006-1428-3, 1-1428). Fortress.

Thompson, Bard, ed. see Schaff, Philip.

Thompson, Bard, et al. Essays on the Heidelberg Catechism. LC 63-21522. 1963. pap. 5.95 (ISBN 0-8298-0325-4). Pilgrim NY.

Thompson, Bernard. Good Samaritan Faith: A Strategy for Meeting Needs in Your Community. LC 83-24805. 210p. 1984. pap. 6.95 (ISBN 0-8307-0932-0, 5418176). Regal.

Thompson, Bert. The Global, Universal, Worldwide Flood of Noah. (That You May Believe Ser.). 45p. (Orig.). 1986. pap. 1.50 (ISBN 0-932859-02-X). Apologetic Pr.

--The History of Evolutionary Thought. 192p. (Orig.). 1981. pap. 3.50 (ISBN 0-932859-10-0). Apologetic Pr.

--Non-Denominational Christianity: Is Unity Possible. 29p. (Orig.). 1984. pap. 2.00 (ISBN 0-932859-11-9). Apologetic Pr.

--The Scientific Case for Creation. (That You May Believe Ser.). 47p. (Orig.). 1985. pap. 1.50 (ISBN 0-932859-03-8). Apologetic Pr.

--Theistic Evolution. pap. 5.50 (ISBN 0-89315-300-1). Lambert Bk.

--Theistic Evolution. 235p. (Orig.). 1977. pap. 5.50 (ISBN 0-932859-08-9). Apologetic Pr.

Thompson, Bert & Jackson, Wayne. Essays in Apologetics, Vol. 1. 183p. 1984. pap. 4.50. Apologetic Pr.

--Essays in Apologetics, Vol. 2. 255p. 1986. pap. 4.95 (ISBN 0-932859-06-2). Apologetic Pr.

--The Revelation of God in Nature. (That You May Believe Ser.). 22p. (Orig.). 1985. pap. 1.50 (ISBN 0-932859-04-6). Apologetic Pr.

Thompson, Betty. A Chance to Change: Women & Men in the Church. LC 82-71832. pap. 28.00 (2029602). Bks Demand UMI.

Thompson, C. J. Hand of Destiny: The Folk-Lore & Superstition of Everyday Life. LC 70-125600. 1970. Repr. of 1932 ed. 46.00x (ISBN 0-8103-3419-4). Gale.

--The Mystery & Lore of Apparitions, with Some Account of Ghosts, Spectres, Phantoms & Boggarts in Early Times. LC 70-167225. (Illus.). 331p. 1975. Repr. of 1930 ed. 40.00x (ISBN 0-8103-3981-1). Gale.

Thompson, Carolyn, jt. auth. see Thompson, W. Oscar, Jr.

Thompson, Carroll J. The Miracle of Salvation. (Illus.). 178p. (Orig.). 1986. pap. 9.95 (ISBN 1-55630-010-7). Brentwood Comm.

Thompson, Conrad M. Mender of Broken Hearts: How Christ Gives Us Courage to Live. LC 81-52270. 128p. (Orig.). 1982. pap. 5.95 (ISBN 0-8066-1902-3, 10-4343). Augsburg.

Thompson, Craig, ed. see Erasmus.

Thompson, Craig R. Bible in English, Fifteen Twenty-Five to Sixteen Eleven. LC 59-1241. (Folger Guides to the Age of Shakespeare). 1958. pap. 3.95 (ISBN 0-918016-22-3). Folger Bks.

--The English Church in the Sixteenth Century. LC 79-65981. (Folger Guides to the Age of Shakespeare Ser.). 1979. pap. 3.95 (ISBN 0-918016-08-8). Folger Bks.

Thompson, D. D. John Wesley As a Social Reformer. facsimile ed. LC 70-164396. (Black Heritage Library Collection). Repr. of 1898 ed. 12.25 (ISBN 0-8369-8855-8). Ayer Co Pubs.

Thompson, D. E. God's Abundant Supply. (Illus., Orig.). 1984. pap. 4.95 (ISBN 0-912315-75-X). Word Aflame.

Thompson, David A. Five Steps Toward a Better Marriage. 96p. (Orig.). 1980. pap. 5.95 (ISBN 0-87123-164-6, 210164). Bethany Hse.

--A Premarital Guide for Couples & Their Counselors. 80p. 1979. pap. 4.95 (ISBN 0-87123-465-3, 210465). Bethany Hse.

--Recovering from Divorce. (Counseling Guides Ser.). 94p. (Orig.). 1982. pap. 5.95 Oversize (ISBN 0-87123-476-9, 210476). Bethany Hse.

Thompson, David L. Bible Study That Works. 72p. 1986. pap. 3.95 (ISBN 0-310-75001-6, 17024P). Zondervan.

Thompson, David M., ed. Nonconformity in the Nineteenth Century. (The Birth of Modern Britain Ser.). 1972. pap. 9.95x (ISBN 0-7100-7275-9). Methuen Inc.

Thompson, Don. Captain Noah. (Rainy Day Survival Bk.: No. 1). (Illus.). 32p. pap. 0.99 (ISBN 0-87123-696-6, 220696). Bethany Hse.

--General Joshua. (Rainy Day Survival Bk.: No. 2). 32p. pap. 0.99 (ISBN 0-87123-697-4, 220697). Bethany Hse.

Thompson, Doris V. Chart Your Own Stars. 86p. 1975. text ed. 15.00 s.p. (ISBN 0-88053-764-7). Macoy Pub.

Thompson, Dorothy, ed. see Stephens, Joseph R., et al.

Thompson, Dorothy, tr. see Roth, Joseph.

Thompson, Duane R, jt. ed. see Carter, Charles W.

Thompson, E. A. Who Was St. Patrick? LC 85-14624. (Illus.). 192p. 1986. 21.95 (ISBN 0-312-87084-1). St Martin.

Thompson, E. Margaret. The Carthusian Order in England. (Church Historical Society London N. S. Ser.: No. 3). Repr. of 1930 ed. 80.00 (ISBN 0-8115-3127-9). Kraus Repr.

Thompson, Edward H. Life & Glories of St. Joseph. LC 80-53744. 1980. pap. 7.50 (ISBN 0-89555-161-6). Tan Bks Pubs.

Thompson, Elbert. Essays on Milton. LC 72-195123. 1910. lib. bdg. 30.00 (ISBN 0-8414-8044-3). Folcroft.

Thompson, Elbert N. Controversy Between the Puritans & the Stage. LC 76-176150. Repr. of 1903 ed. 21.50 (ISBN 0-404-06396-9). AMS Pr.

--English Moral Plays. LC 70-131500. Repr. of 1910 ed. 7.00 (ISBN 0-404-06397-7). AMS Pr.

--Mysticism in Seventeenth Century English Literature. LC 78-100788. 1970. pap. text ed. 39.95x (ISBN 0-8383-0076-6). Haskell.

Thompson, Ella, jt. auth. see Thompson, R. E.

Thompson, Ernest T. Presbyterian in the South. LC 63-19121. (Presbyterian Historical Society. Publication Ser.: Vol. 13). Vol. 1. pap. 157.30 (2027295); Vol. 2. pap. 132.00; Vol. 3. pap. 159.00. Bks Demand UMI.

Thompson, Francis. The Hound of Heaven. (Illus.). 1983. 3.95 (ISBN 0-87193-157-5). Dimension Bks.

Thompson, G. H. Letters of Paul to the Ephesians, Colossians & Philemon. (Cambridge Bible Commentary on the New English Bible, New Testament Ser.). 18.95 (ISBN 0-521-04227-5); pap. 9.95x (ISBN 0-521-09410-0, 410). Cambridge U Pr.

Thompson, George N., ed. Saint Augustine on the End of the World. 55p. (Orig.). pap. text ed. 5.95 (ISBN 0-940564-15-7). Directions Pr.

Thompson, Harry. Guide to the Archives of the South Dakota Conference of the United Church of Christ. 128p. 1986. pap. 4.00 (ISBN 0-931170-31-1). Ctr Western Studies.

Thompson, Helen. Journey Toward Wholeness: A Jungian Model of Adult Spiritual Growth. LC 81-83184. 96p. (Orig.). 1982. pap. 5.95 (ISBN 0-8091-2422-X). Paulist Pr.

Thompson, Henry O., ed. The Answers Lie Below: Essays in Honor of Lawrence Edmund Toombs. LC 83-23376. (Illus.). 428p. (Orig.). 1984. lib. bdg. 32.50 (ISBN 0-8191-3745-6); pap. text ed. 17.75 (ISBN 0-8191-3746-4). U Pr of Amer.

--The Global Congress of the World's Religions. LC 82-73565. (Conference Ser.: No. 15). (Orig.). 1982. pap. text ed. write for info. (ISBN 0-932894-15-1, Pub. by New Era Bks). Paragon Hse.

--Unity in Diversity. LC 83-51715. 436p. (Orig.). 1984. pap. 12.95 (ISBN 0-932894-20-8). Rose Sharon Pr.

Thompson, Henry O., jt. ed. see Wynne, Edward J., Jr.

Thompson, Henry O., ed. see Wynne, Edward J., Jr.

Thompson, Henry P. Thomas Bray. LC 54-32504. 1954. 12.50x (ISBN 0-8401-2335-3). A R Allenson.

Thompson, J. Deuteronomy. Wiseman, D. J., ed. LC 74-14303. (Tyndale Old Testament Commentary Ser.). 320p. 1975. 12.95 (ISBN 0-87784-882-3); pap. 6.95 (ISBN 0-87784-255-8). Inter-Varsity.

Thompson, J. A. The Bible & Archaeology. wnd, rev. ed. 512p. 1981. 24.95 (ISBN 0-8028-3545-7). Eerdmans.

--Handbook of Life in Bible Times. LC 86-3046. (Illus.). 380p. 1986. 34.95 (ISBN 0-87784-949-8). Inter-Varsity.

Thompson, J. A., jt. ed. see Bratcher, R. G.

Thompson, J. Eric. Maya History & Religion. LC 72-88144. (Civilization of the American Indian Ser.: Vol. 99). 1976. Repr. of 1970 ed. 24.95 (ISBN 0-8061-0884-3). U of Okla Pr.

Thompson, James. Our Life Together. LC 77-79338. (Journey Bks.). 1977. pap. 3.50 (ISBN 0-8344-0095-2). Sweet.

--Strategy for Survival. LC 79-67274. (Journey Bks). 144p. 1980. pap. 3.50 (ISBN 0-8344-0113-4). Sweet.

Thompson, James C. Notes on the Catechism: An Outline of the Faith. 1979. pap. 4.95 (ISBN 0-8192-1249-0). Morehouse.

Thompson, James J. Fleeing the Whore of Babylon: A Modern Conversion Story. 1986. pap. 9.95 (ISBN 0-87061-130-5). Chr Classics.

Thompson, James J., Jr. Christian Classics Revisited. LC 82-84583. 163p. (Orig.). 1983. pap. 8.95 (ISBN 0-89870-028-0). Ignatius Pr.

Thompson, James J. Jr. Tried As by Fire: Southern Baptists & the Religious Controversies of the 1920's. LC 82-8056. xvi, 224p. 1982. 13.95 (ISBN 0-86554-032-2, MUP-H62). Mercer Univ Pr.

Thompson, James W. The Beginnings of Christian Philosophy: The Epistle to the Hebrews. Vawter, Bruce, ed. LC 81-12295. (Catholic Biblical Quarterly Monograph: Vol. 13). vii, 184p. 1982. 5.50x (ISBN 0-915170-12-4). Catholic Biblical.

Thompson, Jane H. Spiritual Considerations in the Preventive Treatment & Cure of Disease. 128p. 1984. cancelled (ISBN 0-85362-211-6, Oriel). Methuen Inc.

Thompson, Jean B. Bible Stories in Rhyme. 1986. text ed. 12.95 (ISBN 0-8024-0651-3). Moody.

Thompson, Jeanie. How to Enter the River. LC 84-62337. 61p. (Orig.). 1985. pap. 6.00 (ISBN 0-930100-18-2). Holy Cow.

Thompson, John & Thompson, Patti. Dance of the Broken Heart: A Family Love Story. 1986. 11.95 (ISBN 0-687-10080-1). Abingdon.

Thompson, John, ed. Theology Beyond Christendom. Essays on the Centenary of the Birth of Karl Barth, May 10, 1886. (Princeton Theological Monograph Ser.: No. 6). (Orig.). 1986. pap. 36.00 (ISBN 0-915138-85-9). Pickwick.

Thompson, John A. The Book of Jeremiah. LC 79-16510. (New International Commentary on the Old Testament Ser.). 1980. 27.95 (ISBN 0-8028-2369-6). Eerdmans.

Thompson, Juliet. Diary of Juliet Thompson. 396p. 1983. 14.95 (ISBN 0-933770-27-8). Kalimat.

Thompson, Kenneth. Beliefs & Ideologies. (Key Ideas Ser.). 150p. 1985. 19.95 (ISBN 0-85312-858-8, 9582, Pub. by Tavistock England); pap. 7.50 (ISBN 0-85312-859-6, 9583, Pub. by Tavistock England). Methuen Inc.

--Emile Durkheim. LC 81-20294. (Key Sociologists Ser.). 120p. 1982. pap. 4.95x (ISBN 0-85312-419-1, NO. 3674, Pub. by Tavistock England). Methuen Inc.

Thompson, Kenneth W. Christian Ethics & the Dilemmas of Foreign Policy. 160p. 1983. pap. text ed. 9.75 (ISBN 0-8191-3040-0). U Pr of Amer.

--Christian Ethics & the Dilemmas of Foreign Policy. LC 59-15344. pap. 30.40 (ISBN 0-8357-9098-3, 2017937). Bks Demand UMI.

Thompson, Kenneth W., ed. The Moral Imperatives of Human Rights: A World Survey. LC 79-3736. 1980. text ed. 25.00 (ISBN 0-8191-0920-7); pap. text ed. 9.75 (ISBN 0-8191-0921-5). U Pr of Amer.

Thompson, Kenneth W., ed. see Coll, Alberto R.

Thompson, Laurence G. Chinese Religion in Western Languages: A Comprehensive & Classified Bibliography of Publications in English, French, & German Through 1980. LC 84-24010. (Monograph of the Association for Asian Studies: No. XLI). 302p. 1985. HC Monograph 19.95x (ISBN 0-8165-0926-3). U of Ariz Pr.

Thompson, Leonard L. Introducing Biblical Literature: A More Fantastic Country. LC 78-6632. (Illus.). ref. ed. 28.95 (ISBN 0-13-498824-8). P-H.

Thompson, Louise S., jt. auth. see Thompson, Robert A.

Thompson, Lyle A., jt. auth. see Adams, Jay E.

Thompson, Mervin E. Starting over Single: Life & Hope after the Death of a Marriage. 160p. 1985. 10.95 (ISBN 0-933173-00-8). Prince Peace Pub.

--When Death Touches Your Life: Practical Help in Preparing for Death. 224p. 1986. 11.95 (ISBN 0-933173-02-4). Prince Peace Pub.

Thompson, Michael. Rubbish Theory: The Creation & Destruction of Value. 1979. text ed. 24.00x (ISBN 0-19-217658-7). Oxford U Pr.

Thompson, Michael E. W. Situation & Theology: Old Testament Interpretations of the Syro-Ephraimite War. (Prophets & Historians Ser.: No. 1). 1983. text ed. 25.95x (ISBN 0-907459-14-5, Pub. by Almond Pr England); pap. text ed. 12.95x (ISBN 0-907459-15-3, Pub. by Almond Pr England). Eisenbrauns.

Thompson, Mollie. Of Caesar's Household. Clanton, Charles, ed. 232p. (Orig.). 1978. pap. 4.95 (ISBN 0-912315-29-6). Word Aflame.

--When You're in You're Out. LC 86-10977. (Illus.). 192p. (Orig.). 1986. pap. 5.95 (ISBN 0-932581-50-1). Word Aflame.

Thompson, Newton, tr. see Le Roy, Alexander.

Thompson, Norma H., ed. Religious Education & Theology. LC 81-17852. 254p. 1982. pap. 12.95 (ISBN 0-89135-029-2). Religious Educ.

Thompson, Norma H. & Cole, Bruce, eds. The Future of Jewish-Christian Relations. LC 82-73896. 1982. 10.95 (ISBN 0-915744-27-9); pap. 8.95 (ISBN 0-915744-28-7). Character Res.

Thompson, Patti, jt. auth. see Thompson, John.

Thompson, Paul M. & Lillevold, Joani. The Giving Book: Creative Resources for Senior High Ministry. LC 84-47794. (Illus.). 144p. (Orig.). 1985. pap. 9.95 (ISBN 0-8042-1192-2). John Knox.

Thompson, Phyllis. Each to Her Post. 1982. pap. 3.95 (ISBN 0-340-26933-2). OMF Bks.

Thompson, Phyllis, jt. auth. see Taylor, Hudson.

Thompson, R. C. The Devils & Evil Spirits of Babylonia, 2 vols. Set. 200.00 (ISBN 0-8490-0026-2). Gordon Pr.

Thompson, R. E. & Thompson, Ella. Missionary Discipleship: The Story of R. E. & Ella Thompson. (Illus.). 42p. (Orig.). 1982. pap. 3.95 (ISBN 0-942726-00-6). Missionary Intern.

Thompson, R. W. The Footprints of the Jesuits. 1981. lib. bdg. 75.00 (ISBN 0-686-71628-0). Revisionist Pr.

Thompson, Ray. Battling with Belief. 79p. (Orig.). 1984. pap. 6.95 (ISBN 0-85819-518-6, Pub. by JBCE). ANZ Religious Pubns.

Thompson, Reginald C. The Devils & Evil Spirits of Babylonia, 2 vols. LC 73-18855. (Luzac's Semitic Text & Translation Ser.: Nos. 14-15). (Illus.). Repr. of 1904 ed. 47.50 set (ISBN 0-404-11353-2). AMS Pr.

--Semitic Magic: Its Origins & Development. LC 73-18858. Repr. of 1908 ed. 24.50 (ISBN 0-404-11361-3). AMS Pr.

Thompson, Robert. The Feasts of the Lord. pap. 5.95 (ISBN 0-89728-029-6, 645571). Omega Pubns OR.

--The Land of Promise. pap. 5.95 (ISBN 0-89728-042-3, 670209). Omega Pubns OR.

--What Comes After Pentecost. 1982. pap. 6.95 (ISBN 0-686-95485-8). Omega Pubns Or.

Thompson, Robert A. & Thompson, Louise S. Egoshell. 280p. 1986. 22.95 (ISBN 0-87975-365-X). Prometheus Bks.

Thompson, Robert E. History of the Presbyterian Churches in the U. S. (American Church History Ser). Repr. of 1895 ed. 22.00 (ISBN 0-8337-3935-2). B Franklin.

Thompson, Roy A. The Dynamic of the Printed Page in Evangelical Free Church History. LC 82-69760. (Heritage Ser.: Vol. 4). 176p. 1981. 8.95 (ISBN 0-911802-53-3). Free Church Pubns.

Thompson, Steven. The Apocalypse & Semitic Syntax. LC 84-12081. (Society for New Testament Studies Monograph: No. 52). 160p. 1985. 32.50 (ISBN 0-521-26031-0). Cambridge U Pr.

Thompson, Thomas L. The Historicity of the Patriarchal Narratives: The Quest for the Historical Abraham. LC 72-76042. (Beiheft 133 zur Zeitschrift fuer die alttestamentliche Wissenschaft). 1974. 57.00x (ISBN 3-11-004096-4). De Gruyter.

Thompson, Thomas R. Chris: A Biography of Christian C. Sanderson. LC 73-84422. (Illus.). 420p. 1973. 12.95 (ISBN 0-8059-1899-X). Dorrance.

Thompson, Virginia. Speak to Me Lord--I'm Listening. LC 78-55479. 1981. pap. 2.25 (ISBN 0-89081-117-2, 1172). Harvest Hse.

Thompson, W. Oscar, Jr. & Thompson, Carolyn. Concentric Circles of Concern. LC 81-67488. 1981. 7.95 (ISBN 0-8054-6233-3). Broadman.

Thompson, Walter R. Dialogue on Science, Psychology & God. LC 67-17638. 1967. 6.00 (ISBN 0-8022-1717-6). Philos Lib.

Thompson, William. Paul & His Message for Life's Journey. 160p. 1986. pap. 9.95 (ISBN 0-8091-2824-1). Paulist Pr.

Thompson, William D. Listening on Sunday for Sharing on Monday. 64p. 1983. pap. 3.95 (ISBN 0-317-00858-7). Judson.

--Preaching Biblically: Exegesis & Interpretation. (Abingdon Preacher's Library). (Orig.). 1981. pap. 6.95 (ISBN 0-687-33840-9). Abingdon.

Thompson, William E. Devotions for Divorcing. LC 85-42827. 96p. 1985. pap. 6.95 (ISBN 0-8042-2525-7). John Knox.

Thompson, William G. The Gospels for Whole Life. 228p. (Orig.). 1983. pap. 9.95 (ISBN 0-86683-645-4, AY8336, HarpR). Har-Row.

Thompson, William I. Evil & World Order. (World Perspectives Ser.). 1977. pap. 4.95x (ISBN 0-06-131951-1, TB1951, Torch). Har-Row.

Thompson, William M. The Jesus Debate: A Survey & Synthesis. 512p. (Orig.). 1985. pap. 12.95 (ISBN 0-8091-2666-4). Paulist Pr.

Thompson, William M., jt. ed. see Kirby, John.

Thompson-Frey, Nancy, jt. auth. see Frey, Robert S.

Thomsen, Harry. The New Religions of Japan. LC 77-13846. (Illus.). 1978. Repr. of 1963 ed. lib. bdg. 25.75x (ISBN 0-8371-9878-X, THNR). Greenwood.

Thomsen, Helen S. The Message Delivered: Leader's Guide. (Orig.). 1973. pap. 2.50x (ISBN 0-8192-4048-6). Morehouse.

--That the World May Believe: The Acts of the Apostles. 1978. pap. 2.25x (ISBN 0-8192-4085-0); tchrs guide 2.25x (ISBN 0-8192-4084-2). Morehouse.

Thomsen, Russel J. The Bible Book of Medical Wisdom. 160p. 1985. pap. 3.95 (ISBN 0-916441-26-1). Barbour & Co.

Thomson, Alexander. Tradition & Authority in Science & Theology. (Theology & Science at the Frontiers of Knowledge Ser.: Vol. 4). 160p. 1986. 17.00 (ISBN 0-7073-0452-0, Pub. by Scot Acad Pr). Longwood Pub Group.

Thomson, D. F., tr. see Erasmus, Desiderius.

Thomson, E. Roberts. Baptists & Disciples of Christ. 195p. 1948. pap. 2.95 (ISBN 0-87921-004-4). Attic Pr.

Thomson, G. T., tr. see Heppe, Heinrich.

Thomson, J. The Samaritans: Their Testimony to the Religion of Israel. 1976. lib. bdg. 59.95 (ISBN 0-8490-2564-8). Gordon Pr.

Thomson, J. A. Popes & Princes Fourteen Seventeen to Fifteen Seventeen: Politics & Polity in Late Medieval Church. (Early Modern Europe Today Ser.). 256p. 1980. text ed. 10.00 (ISBN 0-04-901027-1). Allen Unwin.

Thomson, J. A., tr. see Tredennick, Hugh.

Thomson, Judith J. Rights, Restitution, & Risk: Essays in Moral Theory. Parent, William, ed. & pref. by. (Illus.). 288p. 1986. text ed. 29.95x (ISBN 0-674-76980-5); pap. text ed. 9.95x (ISBN 0-674-76981-3). Harvard U Pr.

Thomson, Ogilvie. Walter Hilton's Mixed Life. Hogg, James, ed. (Elizabethan & Renaissance Studies). (Orig.). 1985. pap. 15.00 (ISBN 3-7052-0756-3, Pub. by Salzburg Studies). Longwood Pub Group.

Thomson, Robert W., et al, trs. see Gregory.

Thomson, S. H. The Writings of Robert Grosseteste, Bishop of Lincoln: 1235-1253. Repr. of 1940 ed. 29.00 (ISBN 0-527-89820-1). Kraus Repr.

Thomson, Thomas, ed. Accounts of the Great Chamberlains of Scotland, 3 Vols. 1817-45. Set. 250.00 (ISBN 0-404-52810-4). AMS Pr.

--Acts & Proceedings of the General Assemblies of the Kirk of Scotland, 3 Vols. LC 72-1053. 1839-45. Set. 125.00 (ISBN 0-404-52820-1). AMS Pr.

Thomson, Thomas, ed. see Calderwood, David.

Thomson, William, jt. auth. see MacIver, Kenneth.

Thomte, Reidar. Kierkegaard's Philosophy of Religion. Repr. of 1948 ed. lib. bdg. 27.50x (ISBN 0-8371-0979-5, THKI). Greenwood.

Thor, Valiant. Outwitting Tomorrow. (Illus.). 64p. (Orig.). pap. 4.50 (ISBN 0-934414-00-9, Co Pub by Intl Evang). Hover.

Thoreau, Henry D., tr. see Christy, Arthur.

Thoreau, Henry David. Henry David Thoreau: A Week on the Concord & Merrimack Rivers; Walden; The Maine Woods; Cape Cod. 1114p. 27.50. Library of America.

Thorndike, Herbert. Complete Theological Works of Herbert Thorndike, 6 Vols. in 10. LC 76-177454. (Library of Anglo-Catholic Theology: No. 17). Repr. of 1856 ed. Set. 295.00 (ISBN 0-404-52150-9). AMS Pr.

Thorndike, Ruth M. God's Everlasting Arms of Love. 1977. 6.50 (ISBN 0-682-48736-8). Exposition Pr FL.

Thorne, Leo S. Prayers from Riverside. 120p. (Orig.). 1983. pap. 5.95 (ISBN 0-8298-0643-1). Pilgrim NY.

Thorning, Joseph F. Builders of the Social Order. facs. ed. LC 68-57340. (Essay Index Reprint Ser.). 1941. 15.00 (ISBN 0-8369-0936-4). Ayer Co Pubs.

Thornsberry, Grover. God Flows Within You. 152p. pap. 7.95 (ISBN 0-942494-39-3). Coleman Pub.

Thornton, Andre & Janssen, Al. Triumph Born of Tragedy. LC 82-82812. 160p. (Orig.). 1983. pap. 4.95 (ISBN 0-89081-367-1). Harvest Hse.

Thornton, Edward E. Being Transformed: An Inner Way of Spiritual Growth. LC 83-27331. (Potentials: Guides for Productive Living Ser.: Vol. 4). 114p. (Orig.). 1984. pap. 7.95 (ISBN 0-664-24523-4). Westminster.

Thornton, Edward E., ed. A Love That Heals. LC 83-21083. 1984. pap. 3.75 (ISBN 0-8054-5105-6). Broadman.

Thornton, Francis B. Catholic Shrines in the United States & Canada. LC 78-63480. Repr. of 1954 ed. 29.50 (ISBN 0-404-16546-X). AMS Pr.

Thornton, John W., ed. Pulpit of the American Revolution: Political Sermons of the Period of 1776. LC 71-109611. (Era of the American Revolution Ser). 1970. Repr. of 1860 ed. lib. bdg. 49.50 (ISBN 0-306-71907-X). Da Capo.

Thornton, Martin. English Spirituality. 330p. 1986. 24.95 (ISBN 0-936384-38-7); pap. 11.95 (ISBN 0-936384-31-X). Cowley Pubns.

--A Joyful Heart: Meditations for Lent. LC 86-32841. 76p. 1987. pap. 6.95 (ISBN 0-936384-45-X). Cowley Pubns.

--Spiritual Direction. LC 83-73658. 145p. (Orig.). 1984. pap. 6.95 (ISBN 0-936384-17-4). Cowley Pubns.

Thornton, Mary C. The Church & Freemasonry in Brazil, 1872-1875. LC 73-2647. 287p. 1973. Repr. of 1948 ed. lib. bdg. 22.50x (ISBN 0-8371-6816-3, THCF). Greenwood.

Thorold, Algar. Six Masters in Disillusion. LC 75-113325. 1971. Repr. of 1909 ed. 21.50x (ISBN 0-8046-1364-8, Pub. by Kennikat). Assoc Faculty Pr.

Thorold, Algar, tr. from It. & see St. Catherine of Siena.

Thorold, Henry. Collins Guide to Cathedrals, Abbeys & Priories of England & Wales. (Illus.). 332p. 1987. 24.95 (ISBN 0-00-217241-0). Salem Hse Pubs.

Thorp, Margaret F. Charles Kingsley, Eighteen Nineteen to Eighteen Seventy-Five. LC 70-96170. 1969. Repr. of 1937 ed. lib. bdg. 18.50x (ISBN 0-374-97942-1, Octagon). Hippocrene Bks.

Thorp, Willard. Catholic Novelists in Defense of Their Faith, 1829-1865. 14.00 (ISBN 0-405-10862-1, 11860). Ayer Co Pubs.

Thorpe, Benjamin, tr. see Aelfric.

Thorpe, Lewis, tr. see Gregory of Tours.

Thorpe, W. H. The Origins & Rise of Ethology. 186p. 1979. 35.95 (ISBN 0-03-053251-5). Praeger.

Thorpe, William. The Examinacions of Thorpe & Oldcastell. LC 74-28889. (English Experience Ser.: No. 766). 1975. Repr. of 1530 ed. 7.00 (ISBN 90-221-0766-3). Walter J Johnson.

Thouless, R. H. An Introduction to the Psychology of Religion. 3rd ed. LC 76-184142. 160p. 1972. pap. 10.95 (ISBN 0-521-09665-0). Cambridge U Pr.

Thouless, Robert H. An Introduction to the Psychology of Religion. 286p. 1980. Repr. of 1925 ed. lib. bdg. 25.00 (ISBN 0-89987-802-4). Darby Bks.

Thrall, Homer S. A Brief History of Methodism in Texas. 304p. 1977. Repr. of 1889 ed. 9.95 (ISBN 0-87921-042-7). Attic Pr.

Thrall, Margaret E., ed. First & Second Letters of Paul to the Corinthians. (Cambridge Bible Commentary on the New English Bible, New Testament Ser.). (Orig.). 1965. pap. 10.95x (ISBN 0-521-09251-5). Cambridge U Pr.

Thrasher, Kenneth. The Complex Ministry of Rural Pastorate. 1984. pap. 5.95 (ISBN 0-89957-054-2). AMG Pubs.

Three Hundred & Fiftieth Anniversary Book Committee of Old North Church. Under the Golden Cod: A Shared History of the Old North Church & the Town of Marblehead, Massachusetts. LC 84-7821. (Illus.). 160p. 1984. 17.95 (ISBN 0-914659-05-7). Phoenix Pub.

Thrift, Minton, jt. auth. see Lee, Jesse.

Throckmorton, Burton H. Gospel Parallels: A Synopsis of the First Three Gospels. 4th ed. 1979. 10.95 (ISBN 0-8407-5150-8). Nelson.

Throop, Isabel A., ed. see Rohrer, Norman B.

Throop, P. A. Criticism of the Crusade: A Study of Public Opinion & Crusade Propaganda. 59.95 (ISBN 0-87968-968-4). Gordon Pr.

Throop, Palmer A. Criticism of the Crusade: A Study of Public Opinion & Crusade Propaganda. LC 75-26530. (Perspectives in European Hist.: No. 12). xv, 291p. 1975. Repr. of 1940 ed. lib. bdg. 27.50x (ISBN 0-87991-618-4). Porcupine Pr.

Thrower, James. Marxist-Leninist 'Scientific Atheism' & the Study of Religion & Atheism in the U. S. S. R. (Ger.). 500p. 1983. 78.00 (ISBN 90-279-3060-0). Mouton.

Thrower, James A. The Alternative Tradition: A Study of Unbelief in the Ancient World. (Religon & Society Ser.). 1979. 38.00 (ISBN 90-279-7997-9). Mouton.

Thulin, Richard L. The Caller & the Called. Sherer, Michael L, ed. (Orig.). 1986. pap. 6.25 (ISBN 0-89536-819-6, 6828). CSS of Ohio.

--The Lesser Festivals 1: Saints' Days & Special Occasions. Achtemeier, Elizabeth, et al, eds. LC 79-7377. (Proclamation 2: Aids for Interpreting the Lessons of the Church Year). 64p. (Orig.). 1980. pap. 3.75 (ISBN 0-8006-1393-7, 1-1393). Fortress.

Thulin, Richard L., jt. auth. see Furnish, Victor P.

Thunberg, Lars. Microcosm & Mediator: The Theological Anthropology of Maximus the Confessor. Allchin, A. L., rev. by. LC 80-2368. 1981. Repr. of 1965 ed. 58.00 (ISBN 0-404-18917-2). AMS Pr.

Thundy, Zacharias P., et al, eds. Religion in Dialogue: East & West Meet. 336p. (Orig.). 1985. lib. bdg. 29.75 (ISBN 0-8191-4466-5); pap. text ed. 14.75 (ISBN 0-8191-4467-3). U Pr of Amer.

Thung, Mady A. The Precarious Organisation: Sociological Explorations of the Church's Mission & Structure. (Religion & Society Ser.: No. 5). 1976. text ed. 22.00 (ISBN 0-686-22627-5). Mouton.

Thurian, Max. The Mystery of the Eucharist. 88p. (Orig.). 1984. pap. 4.95 (ISBN 0-8028-0028-9). Eerdmans.

--Our Faith: Basic Christian Belief. Chisholm, Emily, tr. from Fr. LC 82-72008. 192p. 1982. 12.95 (ISBN 0-8245-0547-6). Crossroad NY.

Thurian, Max & Wainwright, Geoffrey, eds. Baptism & Eucharist: Ecumenical Convergence in Celebration. LC 84-169338. 268p. (Orig.). 1984. pap. 11.95 (ISBN 0-8028-0005-X). Eerdmans.

Thurlnas, Chawan. Current Sufi Activity Work, Literature, Groups & Techniques. (Sufi Research Ser.). 40p. 1982. pap. 4.95 (ISBN 0-86304-004-7, Pub. by Octagon Pr England). Ins Study Human.

Thurman, Anne S., ed. see Thurman, Howard.

Thurman, Howard. The Centering Moment. LC 80-67469. 1980. pap. 6.95 (ISBN 0-913408-64-6). Friends United.

--The Creative Encounter. LC 72-12773. 155p. 1972. pap. 6.95 (ISBN 0-913408-07-7). Friends United.

--Deep Is the Hunger. LC 73-16023. 212p. 1973. pap. 6.95 (ISBN 0-913408-10-7). Friends United.

--Deep River. Bd. with The Negro Spiritual Speaks of Life & Death. LC 75-27041. 136p. 1975. pap. 5.95 (ISBN 0-913408-20-4). Friends United.

--Disciplines of the Spirit. LC 77-88388. 1977. pap. 6.95 (ISBN 0-913408-35-2). Friends United.

--For the Inward Journey: The Writings of Howard Thurman. Harding, Vincent & Thurman, Anne S., eds. LC 83-26366. 352p. 1984. 17.95 (ISBN 0-15-132656-8). HarBraceJ.

--The Growing Edge. LC 74-14866. 192p. 1974. pap. 6.95 (ISBN 0-913408-14-X). Friends United.

--Inward Journey. LC 77-70182. 1973. pap. 7.95 (ISBN 0-913408-03-4). Friends United.

--Jesus & the Disinherited. LC 81-70333. 112p. 1981. pap. 5.95 (ISBN 0-913408-77-8). Friends United.

--Meditations of the Heart. LC 76-18287. 216p. 1976. pap. 6.95 (ISBN 0-913408-25-5). Friends United.

--The Mood of Christmas. LC 85-16018. 127p. 1985. pap. 9.95 (ISBN 0-913408-90-5). Friends United.

--Mysticism & the Experience of Love. LC 61-13708. (Orig.). 1961. pap. 2.50x (ISBN 0-87574-115-0). Pendle Hill.

--The Search for Common Ground. 108p. 1986. pap. 7.95 (ISBN 0-913408-94-8). Friends United.

--Temptations of Jesus. LC 78-74718. 1979. pap. 3.95 (ISBN 0-913408-47-6). Friends United.

Thurman, Robert A., tr. from Tibetan. The Holy Teaching of Vimalakirti: Mahayana Scripture. LC 75-27197. (Institute for Advanced Study of World Religions Ser.). 176p. 1976. 20.00x (ISBN 0-271-01209-9); pap. 10.00 (ISBN 0-271-00601-3). Pa St U Pr.

Thurman, Thomas D. Acts: The Genesis of the New Testament. Evans, H. Sherwood, ed. 60p. (Orig.). 1985. pap. 2.25 (ISBN 0-9614213-0-4). Chr Restor Assn.

--The Jesus Years: A Chronological Study of the Life of Christ. LC 77-80314. (Illus.). 1977. pap. 5.95 (ISBN 0-87239-136-1, 40061). Standard Pub.

Thurmann, Joyce V. New Wineskins: A Study of the House Church Movement, Vol. 30. (IC-Studien zur Interkulturellen Geschichte). 109p. 1982. pap. 14.20 (ISBN 3-8204-7172-3). P Lang Pubs.

Thurmer, John. A Detection of the Trinity. 93p. 1986. pap. 8.75 (ISBN 0-85364-395-4, Pub. by Paternoster UK). Attic Pr.

Thurston, Herbert. The Holy Year of the Jubilee: An Account of the History & Ceremonial of the Roman Jubilee. LC 78-63481. Repr. of 1900 ed. 38.45 (ISBN 0-404-16547-8). AMS Pr.

Thurston, Mark. Discovering Your Soul's Purpose. (Illus.). 161p. (Orig.). 1984. pap. 6.95 (ISBN 0-87604-157-8). ARE Pr.

--Discovering Your Soul's Purpose. 175p. 1984. with cassettes 24.95 (ISBN 0-87604-186-1). Allen Unwin.

--Discovering Your Soul's Purpose. 1984. 24.95 (ISBN 0-87604-186-1); incl 4 cassette tapes in vinyl binder. ARE Pr.

--How to Change Attitudes & Emotions. Orig. Title: A Course in Practical Spirituality. 147p. 1986. wkbk., text, 4 cassettes 29.95 (ISBN 0-87604-181-0). ARE Pr.

Thurston, Mark, jt. auth. see Puryear, Herbert B.

Thurston, Mark A. Experiments in Practical Spirituality: Keyed to a Search for God, Book II. (Illus.). 147p. (Orig.). 1980. pap. 5.95 (ISBN 0-87604-122-5). ARE Pr.

--Visions & Prophecies for a New Age. (Illus.). 228p. 1981. pap. 6.95 (ISBN 0-87604-136-5). ARE Pr.

Thurstone, Louis L. The Measurement of Values. LC 58-11960. (Midway Reprint Ser.). pap. 82.50 (2026748). Bks Demand UMI.

Thusing, Wilhelm, jt. auth. see Rahner, Karl.

Thusing, Wilhelm, et al. The Epistle of St. Jude & the Three Epistles of St. John. McKenzie, John L., ed. LC 81-605. (New Testament for Spiritual Reading Ser.). 148p. 1981. pap. 4.95 (ISBN 0-8245-0132-2). Crossroad NY.

Thwing, Charles F. Education & Religion. facs. ed. LC 71-105044. (Essay Index Reprint Ser). 1929. 19.00 (ISBN 0-8369-1629-8). Ayer Co Pubs.

Tibawi, A. L. Islamic Education: Its Traditions & Modernization into the Arab National Systems. 256p. 1979. Repr. 60.00x (ISBN 0-317-39091-0, Pub. by Luzac & Co Ltd). State Mutual Bk.

--The Islamic Pious Foundations in Jerusalem. 163p. 1978. 20.00x (ISBN 0-317-39095-3, Pub. by Luzac & Co Ltd). State Mutual Bk.

Tibbetts, Laurene J. It's Christmas! Poems & Stories for the Holiday Season. 97p. 1981. write for info. Rector Pub.

Tibbetts, Orlando L. How to Keep Useful Church Records. 96p. 1983. pap. 3.95 (ISBN 0-317-00687-8). Judson.

--The Minister's Handbook. 224p. 1986. 9.95 (ISBN 0-8170-1088-2). Judson.

--The Work of the Church Trustee. 1979. pap. 4.95 (ISBN 0-8170-0825-X). Judson.

Tibesar, Antonine, ed. Writings of Junipero Serra, 4 vols. (Documentary Ser.). (Illus.). 1966. 60.00 (ISBN 0-88382-003-X). AAFH.

Tibi, Amin T. The Tibyan: Memoirs of Abd Allah b. Buluggin, Last Zirid Amir of Granada. Translated from the Emended Arabic Text & Provided with Introduction, Notes & Comments. (Medieval Iberian Peninsula Ser.: Vol. 5). xiii, 291p. 1986. 38.25 (ISBN 90-04-07669-7, Pub. by E J Brill). Heinman.

Tickfer, Mildred. Healing the Hurt: For Teenagers Whose Parents Are Divorced. 1985. pap. 4.50 (ISBN 0-8010-8876-3). Baker Bk.

Tickle, John. The Book of Revelation: A Catholic Interpretation of the Apocalypse. 144p. 1983. pap. 3.95 (ISBN 0-89243-195-4). Liguori Pubns.

--Discovering the Bible, Bk. 2. 96p. (Orig.). 1980. pap. 3.95 (ISBN 0-89243-133-4). Liguori Pubns.

--Discovering the Bible: 8 Simple Keys for Learning & Praying. LC 77-94872. 1978. pap. 3.95 leader's guide, Bk. 1 (ISBN 0-89243-084-2); leader's guide, bk. 2 2.95 (ISBN 0-89243-141-5). Liguori Pubns.

--Un Estudio de la Biblia. Diaz, Olimpia, Sr., tr. from Eng. 96p. 1980. pap. 1.95 (ISBN 0-89243-131-8). Liguori Pubns.

--Un Estudio de la Biblia, Libro II. Diaz, Olimpia, tr. (Span.). 96p. 1983. 3.95 (ISBN 0-89243-184-9). Liguori Pubns.

Tickle, Phyllis. Tobias & the Angels. 96p. (Orig.). 1982. pap. text ed. 2.95 (ISBN 0-918518-23-7). St Luke TN.

Tickle, Phyllis A. Final Sanity: Essays on Lent & Easter. 128p. (Orig.). 1987. pap. 6.95 (ISBN 0-8358-0545-X). Upper Room.

--What the Heart Already Knows. (Orig.). 1985. pap. 5.95 (ISBN 0-8358-0522-0). Upper Room.

Tidball, Derek. An Introduction to the Sociology of the New Testament. 1982. pap. text ed. 9.95 cancelled (ISBN 0-85364-301-6). Attic Pr.

--The Social Context of the New Testament: A Sociological Analysis. 160p. 1984. pap. 7.95 (ISBN 0-310-45391-7, 12602P). Zondervan.

Tidball, Derek J. Skillful Shepherds: An Introduction to Pastoral Theology. 1986. pap. 12.95 (ISBN 0-310-44631-7). Zondervan.

Tidwell, Charles A. Church Administration-Effective Leadership for Ministry. LC 85-6620. 1985. pap. 8.95 (ISBN 0-8054-3113-6). Broadman.

--Educational Ministry of a Church. LC 81-68922. 1982. pap. 10.95 (ISBN 0-8054-3231-0). Broadman.

Tidwell, J. B. Geografia Biblica. Pierson, Carlos C., tr. (Span., Illus.). 144p. 1982. pap. 5.50 (ISBN 0-311-15031-4). Casa Bautista.

Tieck, Johann L. Letters of Ludwig Tieck, Hitherto Unpublished, 1792-1853. Zeydel, Edwin H., et al, eds. LC 73-9682. (MLA Gen. Ser.: No. 7). 636p. 1973. Repr. of 1937 ed. 41.00 (ISBN 0-527-90100-8). Kraus Repr.

Tieck, Ludwig. The Land of Upside Down. Mandel, Oscar, tr. LC 76-50288. 123p. 1978. 17.50 (ISBN 0-8386-2061-2). Fairleigh Dickinson.

Tiede, David L. Prophecy & History in Luke-Acts. LC 79-8897. 180p. 1980. 2.00 (ISBN 0-8006-0632-9, 1-632). Fortress.

--Prophecy & History in Luke-Acts. LC 79-8897. pap. 44.00 (2029616). Bks Demand UMI.

Tiede, David L. & Kavanagh, Aidan. Pentecost 1. Achtemeier, Elizabeth, et al, eds. LC 79-7377. (Proclamation 2: Aids for Interpreting the Lessons of the Church Year, Ser. A). 64p. (Orig.). 1981. pap. 3.75 (ISBN 0-8006-4096-9, 1-4096). Fortress.

Tiede, David L., tr. see Weiser, Alfons.

Tiele, Cornelis P. Elements of the Science of Religion, 2 vols. LC 77-27226. (Gifford Lectures: 1896, 1898). Repr. of 1899 ed. Set. 55.00 (ISBN 0-404-60480-3). AMS Pr.

Tiemann, William H. & Bush, John C. The Right to Silence: Privileged Clergy Communication & the Law. 256p. (Orig.). 1983. pap. 11.95 (ISBN 0-687-36315-2). Abingdon.

Tiemeyer, Raymond, ed. see Empie, Paul C.

Tien, Chen Fu. The Current Religious Policy of People's Republic of China (January 1, 1976 to March 15, 1979) Pt. I: An Inquiry. 73p. (Orig.). 1983. pap. 12.95. Chen Fu.

Tierney, B. Origins of Papal Infallibility 1150-1350. 1972. 45.00. Heinman.

Tierney, Brian. Crisis of Church & State, Ten Fifty to Thirteen Hundred. (Orig.). 1964. pap. 6.50 (ISBN 0-13-193474-0, S102, Spec). P-H.

--Religion, Law & the Growth of Constitutional Thought, 1150-1650. LC 81-12265. 128p. 1982. 24.95 (ISBN 0-521-23495-6). Cambridge U Pr.

Tierney, Brian & Painter, Sidney. Western Europe in the Middle Ages, 300-1475. 4th ed. 1982. text ed. 24.00 (ISBN 0-394-33060-9, RanC). Random.

Tierney, Brian, et al, eds. Martin Luther - Reformer or Revolutionary? 3rd ed. (Historical Pamphlets Ser.). 1977. pap. text ed. 1.95x (ISBN 0-394-32055-7). Random.

Tierney, M. A. Dodd's Church History of England, eith Notes Additions & A Continuation, 5 Vols. 2512p. 1839. text ed. 331.20x (ISBN 0-576-78535-0, Pub. by Gregg Intl Pubs England). Gregg Intl.

Tierney, M. A., ed. see Dodd, Charles.

Tierney, Terence. Should You Become a Priest? 64p. (Orig.). (YA) 1975. pap. 1.50 (ISBN 0-89243-020-6, 29530). Liguori Pubns.

Tierney, Terence E. Annulment: Do You Have a Case? LC 78-6790. 1978. pap. 4.95 (ISBN 0-8189-0372-4). Alba.

Tietjen, John H. Which Way to Lutheran Unity? A History of Efforts to Unite the Lutherans of America. LC 66-25270. 176p. 1975. pap. text ed. 7.50 (ISBN 0-915644-01-0). Clayton Pub Hse.

Tietjen, Mary L. Holidays & Celebrations: Activities, Crafts & Stories for Children. LC 82-62416. 1983. pap. 4.95 (ISBN 0-8091-2531-5). Paulist Pr.

Tigay, Alan M., ed. see Hadassah Magazine Staff.

Tigay, Jeffrey H. Empirical Models for Biblical Criticism. LC 84-20951. 304p. 1985. 37.50 (ISBN 0-8122-7976-X). U of Pa Pr.

--You Shall Have No Other Gods: Israelite Religion in the Light of Hebrew Inscriptions. (Harvard Semitic Studies). 130p. 1987. 16.95 (ISBN 1-55540-063-9, 04-04-31). Scholars Pr GA.

Tighe, Jeanne & Szentkeresti, Karen. Rethinking Adult Religious Education: A Practical Parish Guide. 144p. (Orig.). 1986. pap. 9.95 (ISBN 0-8091-2829-2). Paulist Pr.

Til, Cornelius Van see Van Til, Cornelius.

Til, Cornelius van see Van Til, Cornelius.

Til, Cornelius van see Van Til, Cornellius.

Tilberg, Cedric W. Revolution Underway: An Aging Church in an Aging Society. LC 84-8122. 128p. 1984. pap. 5.95 (ISBN 0-8006-1817-3). Fortress.

Tilborg, Sjef van see Van Tilborg, Sjef.

Tilcomb, Shara E. Aryan Sun-Myths: The Origin of Religions. LC 78-31508. 1979. Repr. of 1889 ed. lib. bdg. 20.00 (ISBN 0-89341-323-2). Longwood Pub Group.

Tileston, Mary W. Daily Strength for Daily Needs. LC 73-80030. (Large Print Christian Classic Ser.). 1982. 14.95 (ISBN 0-87983-287-8). Keats.
--Daily Strength for Daily Needs. 1942. 7.70i (ISBN 0-316-84592-2). Little.
--Great Souls at Prayer. 366p. 1980. Repr. of 1898 ed. 9.50 (ISBN 0-227-67474-X). Attic Pr.
Tileston, Mary W., ed. Daily Strength for Daily Needs. 1959. 4.95 (ISBN 0-399-12826-3, G&D). Putnam Pub Group.
--Great Souls at Prayer. Large Print ed. 1983. 16.95 (ISBN 0-87983-343-2). Keats.
Till, Howard J. van see Van Till, Howard J.
Tillapaugh, Frank R. The Church Unleashed: Getting God's People Out Where the Needs Are. LC 82-9783. 224p. 1982. pap. 5.95 (ISBN 0-8307-0823-5, 5416300). Regal.
--Unleashing the Church. LC 82-9783. 1985. pap. 5.95 (ISBN 0-8307-1024-8, 5418433). Regal.
Tillard, J. M. The Bishop of Rome. (Theology & Life Ser.: Vol. 5). 1983. 12.95 (ISBN 0-89453-304-5); pap. 9.95 (ISBN 0-89453-298-7). M Glazier.
--Dilemmas of Modern Religious Life. (Consecrated Life Studies Ser.: Vol. 3). 1984. pap. 5.95 (ISBN 0-89453-446-7). M Glazier.
Tille, Alexander. Yule & Christmas. 1977. lib. bdg. 59.95 (ISBN 0-8490-2855-8). Gordon Pr.
Tillemont, Louis S. Le Nain De see Le Nain De Tillemont, Louis S.
Tiller, Howi. Asleep in the Light (A Musical for the Times) (Illus.). 41p. 1984. pap. text ed. 12.95 (ISBN 0-912315-79-2). Word Aflame.
Tillesley, Richard. Animadversions Upon M. Seldens History of Tithes & His Review Thereof. LC 77-7435. (English Experience Ser.: No. 896). 1977. Repr. of 1619 ed. lib. bdg. 26.50 (ISBN 90-221-0896-1). Walter J Johnson.
Tillett, Gregory. Religious Minorities in Australia. 1985. 27.95x (ISBN 0-19-554555-9). Oxford U Pr.
Tilley, Terrence. Story Theology. (Theology & Life Ser.: Vol. 12). 1985. pap. 10.95 (ISBN 0-89453-464-5). M Glazier.
Tillich, Hannah. From Place to Place: Travels with Paul Tillich, Travels Without Paul Tillich. LC 75-34490. (Illus.). 224p. 1976. 10.00 (ISBN 0-8128-1902-0). Stein & Day.
Tillich, Paul. Biblical Religion & the Search for Ultimate Reality. LC 55-5149. 1964. pap. 5.00x (ISBN 0-226-80341-4). U of Chicago Pr.
--Christianity & the Encounter of the World Religions. LC 63-7508. (Bampton Lectures in America: No. 14). pap. 26.80 (ISBN 0-317-42040-2, 2025697). Bks Demand UMI.
--The Construction of the History of Religion in Schelling's Positive Philosophy: Its Presuppositions & Principles. Nuovo, Victor, tr. 184p. 1975. 18.00 (ISBN 0-8387-1422-6). Bucknell U Pr.
--Courage to Be. (Terry Lectures Ser.). 1952. pap. 6.95 (ISBN 0-300-00241-6, Y11). Yale U Pr.
--Dynamics of Faith. pap. 6.95x (ISBN 0-06-130042-X, TB42, Torch). Har-Row.
--The Eternal Now. LC 63-17938. 1963. pap. 6.95 (ISBN 0-684-71907-X, ScribT). Scribner.
--The Future of Religions. Brauer, Jerald C., ed. LC 76-7566. 1976. Repr. of 1966 ed. lib. bdg. 22.50x (ISBN 0-8371-8861-X, TIFR). Greenwood.
--A History of Christian Thought. 1972. pap. 11.95 (ISBN 0-671-21426-8, Touchstone Bks). S&S.
--Love, Power & Justice. 1954. pap. 7.95 (ISBN 0-19-500222-9). Oxford U Pr.
--The Meaning of Health: Relation of Religion & Health. 2nd ed. 64p. 1981. 20.00 (ISBN 0-913028-87-8); pap. 7.95 (ISBN 0-913028-81-9). North Atlantic.
--My Search for Absolutes: A Credo Perspective. Anshen, Ruth N., ed. (Illus.). 1984. pap. 6.95 (ISBN 0-671-50585-8, Touchstone Bks). S&S.
--The New Being. 1955. pap. 6.95 (ISBN 0-684-71908-8, ScribT). Scribner.
--On Art & Architecture. Dillenberger, John & Dillenberger, Jane, eds. (Illus.). 272p. 1987. 14.50 (ISBN 0-8245-0829-7). Crossroad NY.
--Political Expectation. Adams, James L., ed. LC 83-10294. 208p. 1983. pap. text ed. 11.25 (ISBN 0-8191-3320-5). U Pr of Amer.
--Protestant Era. abr ed. Adams, James L., tr. 1957. pap. 7.00x (ISBN 0-226-80342-2, P19, Phoen). U of Chicago Pr.
--Shaking of the Foundations. 1948. pap. 8.95 (ISBN 0-684-71910-X, ScribT). Scribner.
--Systematic Theology, 3 vols. in 1. LC 51-2235. 950p. 1967. 49.95x (ISBN 0-226-80336-8). U of Chicago Pr.
--Systematic Theology, Vol. 1. LC 51-2235. 1973. pap. 11.00x (ISBN 0-226-80337-6, P556, Phoen). U of Chicago Pr.
--Systematic Theology, Vol. 2. LC 51-2235. xii, 188p. 1975. pap. 7.50X (ISBN 0-226-80338-4, P633, Phoen). U of Chicago Pr.
--Systematic Theology: Life & the Spirit History & the Kingdom of God, Vol. 3. LC 51-2235. 1976. pap. 11.00x (ISBN 0-226-80339-2, P706, Phoen). U of Chicago Pr.
--Theology of Culture. Kimball, Robert C., ed. 1959. pap. 8.95 (ISBN 0-19-500711-5). Oxford U Pr.
--Theology of Culture. 1983. 14.50 (ISBN 0-8446-6021-3). Peter Smith.
Tillman, Helene. Die Papstlichen Legaten in England Bis Zur Beendigung der Legation Gualas, 1218. LC 80-2208. 1981. Repr. of 1926 ed. 29.50 (ISBN 0-404-18795-1). AMS Pr.
Tillman, William A., jt. auth. see Maston, T. B.
Tillman, William M., Jr. & Gilbert, Timothy D. Christian Ethics: A Primer. LC 85-25474. 1986. pap. 5.95 (ISBN 0-8054-6128-0). Broadman.
Tillman, William M., Jr., ed. Perspectives on Applied Christianity: Essays in Honor of Thomas Buford Maston. (National Association of Baptist Professors of Religion (NABPR) Festschrift Ser.). vi, 108p. 1986. 10.50 (ISBN 0-86554-196-5, MUP-H180). Mercer Univ Pr.
Tillmann, H. Pope Innocent III. (Europe in the Middle Ages Selected Studies: Vol. 12). 374p. 1980. 64.00 (ISBN 0-444-85137-2, North-Holland). Elsevier.
Tillotson, Kathleen. Matthew Arnold & Carlyle. LC 73-16394. 1956. lib. bdg. 12.50 (ISBN 0-8414-8560-7). Folcroft.
Tillsley, Bramwell H. Life in the Spirit. 109p. (Orig.). 1986. pap. 4.95 (ISBN 0-86544-037-9). Salv Army Suppl South.
Tillyard, Eustace M. Elizabethan World Picture. 1959. pap. 3.16 (ISBN 0-394-70162-3, Vin). Random.
Tillyard, Henry J. Byzantine Music & Hymnography. LC 74-24242. Repr. of 1923 ed. 11.50 (ISBN 0-404-13116-6). AMS Pr.
Tilotta, Becky. Do You Want to Go to Heaven? 1967. 0.60 (ISBN 0-88027-106-X). Firm Foun Pub.
Tiltman, Marjorie. God's Adventurers. facs. ed. LC 68-16979. (Essay Index Reprint Ser.). 1933. 18.00 (ISBN 0-8369-0945-3). Ayer Co Pubs.
Tilton, Rafael. The Immortal Dragon of Sylene & Other Faith Tales. (Illus.). 128p. 1982. 9.95 (ISBN 0-86683-656-X, HarpR). Har-Row.
Tilton, Robert. Charting Your Course by the Dream in Your Heart. 178p. (Orig.). 1983. pap. text ed. 5.95 (ISBN 0-914307-11-8, Dist. by Harrison Hse). Word Faith.
--Charting Your Course by the Dream in Your Heart. 150p. (Orig.). 1986. pap. 5.95 (ISBN 0-89274-404-9). Harrison Hse.
--God's Laws of Success. 224p. (Orig.). 1983. pap. text ed. 7.95 (ISBN 0-914307-04-5, Dist. by Harrison Hse). Word Faith.
--God's Laws of Success. 1986. pap. 6.95 (ISBN 0-89274-405-7). Harrison Hse.
--Patience & Persistence. (Orig.). 1986. mini bk. 0.75 (ISBN 0-89274-413-8). Harrison Hse.
Timasheff, Nicholas S. Religion in Soviet Russia, Nineteen Seventeen to Nineteen Forty-Two. LC 78-23615. 1979. Repr. of 1942 ed. lib. bdg. 22.50x (ISBN 0-313-21040-3, TIRS). Greenwood.
Timayenis, Telemachus T. The Original Mr. Jacobs: Startling Expose. Grob, Gerald, ed. LC 76-46107. (Anti-Movements in America). 1977. Repr. of 1888 ed. lib. bdg. 24.50x (ISBN 0-405-09978-9). Ayer Co Pubs.
Timberlake, Henry. A True & Strange Discourse of the Travailes of Two English Pilgrimes. LC 74-80228. (English Experience Ser.: No. 699). 28p. 1974. Repr. of 1603 ed. 3.50 (ISBN 90-221-0699-3). Walter J Johnson.
Timbuktu, Adib K. What Every Christian Should Know about the Bible. 1984. 6.95 (ISBN 0-8062-2308-1). Carlton.
Timmer, John. Acts, A Study Guide. (Revelation Series for Adults). 1981. pap. text ed. 2.50 (ISBN 0-933140-20-7). CRC Pubns.
--Mark: A Study Guide. (Revelation Series for Adults). (Orig.). 1980. pap. 2.50 (ISBN 0-933140-13-4). CRC Pubns.
--They Shall Be My People. LC 83-15380. 200p. 1983. pap. 6.95 (ISBN 0-933140-82-7); pap. 5.95 leader's guide (ISBN 0-933140-83-5). CRC Pubns.
Timmerman, Joan. The Mardi Gras Syndrome: Rethinking Christian Sexuality. 144p. 1984. pap. 8.95 (ISBN 0-8245-0641-3). Crossroad NY.
Timmerman, John. A Layman Looks at the Names of Jesus. 1985. pap. 4.95 (ISBN 0-8423-2110-1). Tyndale.
Timmerman, S. F., Jr. Timmerman's Lectures on Catholicism. 1952. 3.95 (ISBN 0-88027-085-3). Firm Foun Pub.
Timmermans, Felix. The Perfect Joy of St. Francis. 280p. 1974. pap. 4.95 (ISBN 0-385-02378-2, Im). Doubleday.
Timmons, Gary. Welcome: An Adult Education Program Based on RCIA. LC 81-84388. 64p. (Orig.). 1982. pap. 4.95 (ISBN 0-8091-2429-7). Paulist Pr.
Timmons, Tim. Loneliness Is Not a Disease. (Epiphany Bks.). 1983. pap. 2.25 (ISBN 0-345-30509-4). Ballantine.
--Maximum Marriage. rev. & updated ed. 160p. pap. 5.95 (ISBN 0-8007-5106-X, Power Bks). Revell.
--Radical Christianity. 144p. 1986. pap. 4.95 (ISBN 0-89693-531-0). Victor Bks.
--Stress in the Family: How to Live Through It. LC 87-81649. 160p. (Orig.). 1982. pap. 4.95 (ISBN 0-89081-359-0). Harvest Hse.
Timmons, Tim & McAfee, Lisa. Maximum Marriage. 64p. (Orig.). 1984. pap. 4.95 (ISBN 0-915929-08-2); leader's guide 1.95 (ISBN 0-915929-17-1). Merit Bks.
Timyan, Janis, illus. A Happy Day for Ramona & Other Missionary Stories for Children. (Illus., Orig.). Date not set. pap. price not set (ISBN 0-87509-392-2). Chr Pubns.
--The Pink & Green Church & Other Missionary Stories for Children. (Illus.). Date not set. pap. price not set (ISBN 0-87509-393-0). Chr Pubns.
Tin, Maung, ed. Khudaka Patha. LC 78-70126. Repr. of 1913 ed. 18.00 (ISBN 0-404-17385-3). AMS Pr.
Tinao, D., et al, trs. see Brister, C. W.
Tindal, Matthew. Christianity As Old Creation of the Gospel. Wellek, Rene, ed. LC 75-11256. (British Philosophers & Theologians of the 17th & 18th Centuries Ser.). 1976. lib. bdg. 51.00 (ISBN 0-8240-1806-0). Garland Pub.
Tinder, Glenn. Against Fate. LC 81-50462. 173p. 1981. text ed. 16.95 (ISBN 0-268-00595-8). U of Notre Dame Pr.
Tiner, John H. Favorite Stories from Acts Word Search. 48p. 1986. pap. 2.50 (ISBN 0-87403-047-1, 2691). Standard Pub.
--Jesus the Teacher Word Search. 48p. 1986. pap. 2.50 (ISBN 0-87403-049-8, 2693). Standard Pub.
--The Seven Day Mystery. (Voyager Ser.). 176p. (Orig.). 1981. pap. 3.50 (ISBN 0-8010-8856-9). Baker Bk.
--They Followed Jesus: Word Search Puzzles. 48p. pap. 2.50 (ISBN 0-87239-586-3, 2784). Standard Pub.
--When Science Fails. (Direction Bks). 1974. pap. 2.95 (ISBN 0-8010-8823-2). Baker Bk.
--Word Search: Favorite Bible Stories from Genesis. pap. 2.70 (ISBN 0-89137-615-1). Quality Pubns.
Ting, K. H. How to Study the Bible. Tao Fong Shan Ecumenical Centre, tr. from Chinese. Tr. of Zeyang Du Shengjing. 1981. pap. 1.95 (ISBN 0-377-00122-8). Friend Pr.
Ting, K. H., et al. Chinese Christians Speak Out. (Chinese Spotlight Ser.). (Illus.). 140p. 1984. pap. 3.95 (ISBN 0-8351-1281-0). China Bks.
Tingle, Donald S. Islam & Christianity. 32p. (Orig.). 1985. pap. 0.75 (ISBN 0-87784-073-3). Inter-Varsity.
--Mormonism. rev. ed. (Viewpoints Ser.). 32p. 1987. pap. 1.95 (ISBN 0-8308-1103-6). Inter-Varsity.
Tingley, Katherine. Reincarnation. 72p. 1981. pap. 4.50 (ISBN 0-89540-111-8, SB-111). Sun Pub.
--Theosophy: The Path of the Mystic. 3rd rev ed. LC 77-82604. 1977. 8.50 (ISBN 0-911500-33-2); pap. 5.00 (ISBN 0-911500-34-0). Theos U Pr.
--The Wisdom of the Heart: Katherine Tingley Speaks. Small, W. Emmett, ed. LC 78-65338. 1978. pap. 5.75 (ISBN 0-913004-33-2). Point Loma Pub.
Tingley, Katherine, jt. auth. see De Purucker, G.
Tinker, Irene, jt. ed. see Reining, Priscilla.
Tinkham, Trudy, jt. auth. see Ogilvy, Carol.
Tinkle, William J. Heredity: A Study in Science & the Bible. LC 67-28034. 1967. 5.50 (ISBN 0-686-05046-0). St Thomas.
Tinnes, Bonnie. I Am a Woman; I Am a Person. 99p. (Orig.). 1986. pap. 4.95 (ISBN 0-9616611-0-0). Thoughts By Bonnie.
Tinsley, E. J. Gospel According to Luke. (Cambridge Bible Commentary on the New English Bible, New Testament Ser.). (Orig.). 1965. pap. 10.95x (ISBN 0-521-09252-3). Cambridge U Pr.
Tinsley, John. Tragedy: Irony & Faith. 75p. (Orig.). 1985. pap. 5.95x (ISBN 0-317-26992-5). Wyndham Hall.
Tinsley, William K. Seadog. 270p. 1986. 9.95 (ISBN 0-936637-00-5); pap. 6.95 (ISBN 0-936637-01-3). Living Stone Pubs.
Tintori, Leonetto & Meiss, Millard. The Painting of the Life of St. Francis in Assisi, with Notes on the Arena Chapel. LC 62-10308. pap. 55.50 (ISBN 0-317-10175-7, 2050842). Bks Demand UMI.
Tippett, Alan R. Introduction to Missiology. LC 86-9605. 300p. (Orig.). 1987. pap. text ed. 15.95x (ISBN 0-87808-206-9, WCL206-9). William Carey Lib.
Tippett, Donald C., ed. see Sandifer, Kevin W.
Tippett, Sir Michael. Music of the Angels. (Eulenburg Music Ser.). 1982. pap. text ed. 19.50 (ISBN 0-903873-60-5). Da Capo.
Tippit, Sammy. Fire in Your Heart: A Call to Personal Holiness. (Orig.). 1987. pap. 5.95 (ISBN 0-8024-2625-5). Moody.
Tippit, Sammy & Jenkins, Jerry. You Me He. LC 77-95030. 119p. 1978. pap. 3.95 (ISBN 0-88207-766-X). Victor Bks.
Tiptaft, William. His People. pap. 0.75 (ISBN 0-685-88377-9). Reiner.
Tipton, Steven M., jt. ed. see Douglas, Mary.
Tirabassi, Becky & Lewis, Gregg. Just One Victory. (Campus Life Bks.). (Orig.). 1987. pap. 5.95 (ISBN 0-8423-1998-0). Tyndale.
Tirard, H. M., tr. see Erman, Adolf.
Tischner, Josef. Marxism & Christianity: The Quarrel & the Dialogue in Poland. (Orig.). 1987. 9.95 (ISBN 0-87840-419-8). Georgetown U Pr.
Tisdale, John R., ed. Growing Edges in the Psychology of Religion. LC 79-20116. 350p. 1980. text ed. 24.95x (ISBN 0-88229-338-9); pap. text ed. 12.95x (ISBN 0-88229-748-1). Nelson-Hall.
Tishby, Isaiah, ed. The Wisdom of the Zohar, 3 vols. Goldstein, David, tr. (The Litman Library of Jewish Civilization). 2000p. 1986. Set. 198.00x (ISBN 0-19-710043-0). Oxford U Pr.
Tiso, Francis & Catholic Heritage Press. A Young Person's Book of Catholic Signs & Symbols. LC 81-43459. 128p. 1982. pap. 3.50 (ISBN 0-385-17951-0, Im). Doubleday.
Titchenell, Elsa-Brita. The Masks of Odin: Wisdom of the Ancient Norse. LC 85-40652. (Illus.). 316p. 1985. 15.00 (ISBN 0-911500-72-3); pap. 8.00 (ISBN 0-911500-73-1). Theos U Pr.
Titcom, Sarah E. Aryan Sun-Myths: The Origin of Religions. 1977. lib. bdg. 59.95 (ISBN 0-8490-1456-5). Gordon Pr.
Titcomb, Margaret. Native Use of Fish in Hawaii. 2nd ed. 185p. 1972. pap. 4.50 (ISBN 0-8248-0592-5). UH Pr.
Titley, E. B. Church, State, & the Control of Schooling in Ireland, 1900-1944. 232p. 1983. 27.50x (ISBN 0-7735-0394-3). McGill-Queens U Pr.
Titon, Jeff T. Powerhouse for God: Sacred Speech, Chant & Song in an Appalachian Baptist Church. (American Folklore Recordings Ser.). 26p. 1982. pap. 20.00x incl. records (ISBN 0-8078-4084-X). U of NC Pr.
Titterton, W. G. K. Chesterton. LC 73-14569. 1974. Repr. of 1947 ed. lib. bdg. 22.50 (ISBN 0-8414-8536-4). Folcroft.
--G. K. Chesterton: A Portrait. LC 72-8980. (English Biography Ser., No. 31). 1973. Repr. of 1936 ed. lib. bdg. 49.95x (ISBN 0-8383-1679-4). Haskell.
Titus, Susan. Parables for Young Teens: Twenty-Six Junior High Programs. 1986. 4.95 (ISBN 0-87403-150-8, 3412). Standard Pub.
Tiwari, J. N. Goddess Cults in Ancient India. (Illus.). 250p. 1986. 62.50x (ISBN 0-8364-1819-0, Pub. by Chanakya India). South Asia Bks.
Tiwari, K. N. Comparative Religion. 1986. 14.00 (ISBN 81-208-0293-4, Pub. by Motilal Banarsidass). South Asia Bks.
Tiwari, Kapil N. Dimensions of Renunciation in Advaita Vedanta. 1977. 12.95 (ISBN 0-89684-195-2). Orient Bk Dist.
--Dimensions of Renunciation in Advaita Vedanta. 1977. 11.00x (ISBN 0-8364-0109-3). South Asia Bks.
Tixeront, J. History of Dogmas, 3 vols. Panico, Edward J., ed. (Orig.). 1984. pap. 50.00 (ISBN 0-87061-093-7). Chr Classics.
Tjossem, Wilmer L. Quaker Sloopers: From the Fjords to the Prairies. LC 84-80195. 80p. 1984. pap. 8.95 (ISBN 0-913408-85-9). Friends United.
Tlhagale, Buti, jt. ed. see Mosala, Itumeleng.
Tlhagale, Buti, jt. ed. see Mosala, Itumeleng J.
Tobias, Henry J. Jewish Bund in Russia from Its Origins to 1905. LC 75-153820. 1972. 30.00x (ISBN 0-8047-0764-2). Stanford U Pr.
--The Jews in Oklahoma. LC 79-6723. (Newcomers to a New Land Ser.: Vol. 10). (Illus.). 96p. (Orig.). 1980. pap. 3.95 (ISBN 0-8061-1676-5). U of Okla Pr.
Tobias, Michael. After Eden: History, Ecology, & Conscience. LC 83-73257. 376p. (Orig.). 1985. pap. 14.95 (ISBN 0-932238-28-9, Pub. by Avant Bks). Slawson Comm.
Tobin, Eamon. Help for Making Difficult Decisions. 32p. 1987. pap. 1.50 (ISBN 0-89243-267-5). Liguori Pubns.
--How to Forgive Yourself & Others. 32p. 1983. pap. 1.50 (ISBN 0-89243-197-0). Liguori Pubns.
--The Sacrament of Penance: Its Past & Its Meaning for Today. 32p. (Orig.). 1984. pap. 1.50 (ISBN 0-89243-199-7). Liguori Pubns.
Tobin, John. Handel's Messiah. LC 69-13491. (Illus.). 1969. 35.00 (ISBN 0-312-35840-7). St Martin.
Tobin, Mary L. Hope Is an Open Door. LC 80-21414. (Journeys in Faith Ser). 1981. 7.95 (ISBN 0-687-17410-4). Abingdon.

Tobin, Sheldon S., et al. Enabling the Elderly: Religious Institutions Within the Community Service System. (Aging Ser.). 154p. (Orig.). 1986. 34.50x (ISBN 0-88706-334-9); pap. 10.95x (ISBN 0-88706-335-7). State U NY Pr.

Tobin, Thomas H. The Creation of Man: Philo & the History of Interpretation. Vawter, Bruce, ed. LC 82-19891. (Catholic Biblical Quarterly Monographs: No. 14). viii, 199p. (Orig.). 1983. pap. 6.00x (ISBN 0-915170-13-2). Catholic Biblical.

--Timaios of Locri, on the Nature of the World & the Soul. (Society of Biblical Literature, Texts & Translations Ser.: No. 26). 1985. 14.95 (ISBN 0-89130-767-2, 06 02 26); pap. 9.95 (ISBN 0-89130-742-7). Scholars Pr GA.

Tobin, William, ed. International Catechetical Congress: Selected Documentation: Rome, 1971. cancelled (ISBN 0-686-18988-4, V-199). US Catholic.

Todd, Colleen, jt. auth. see Schaffer, James.

Todd, Floyd & Todd, Pauline. Good Morning, Lord: Devotions for Campers. (Good Morning Lord Ser.). 1973. 3.95 (ISBN 0-8010-8792-9). Baker Bk.

Todd, H. J. Some Account of the Life & Writings of John Milton. LC 77-22935. 1826. lib. bdg. 49.50 (ISBN 0-8414-8637-9). Folcroft.

Todd, Helen, ed. see Benjamin, Elsie.

Todd, Helen, ed. see De Purucker, G.

Todd, Helen, ed. see De Purucker, G. & Tingley, Katherine.

Todd, Helen, ed. see Edge, Henry T.

Todd, Helen, ed. see Ryan, Charles J.

Todd, Helen, ed. see Van Pelt, G.

Todd, Helen, ed. see Van Pelt, Gertrude W.

Todd, Helen, ed. see Wright, Leoline L.

Todd, Helen, ed. see Wright, Leoline L., et al.

Todd, Janet M., jt. auth. see Marshall, Madeleine F.

Todd, John. Luther: A Life. 416p. 1982. 17.50x (ISBN 0-8245-0479-8). Crossroad NY.

Todd, Pauline, jt. auth. see Todd, Floyd.

Todd, Richard. The Opacity of Signs: Acts of Interpretation in George Herbert's The Temple. LC 83-36133. (Illus.). 240p. 1986. text ed. 27.00 (ISBN 0-8262-0609-3). U of Mo Pr.

Todd, Richard E., ed. Baptism. (Grace Bible Ser.). (Illus.). 16p. (Orig.). 1980. pap. 0.50 (ISBN 0-9605324-0-4). R E Todd.

Todd, Sharon. Adventures at Nameless Valley Ranch. Van Dolson, Bobbie J., ed. 96p. 1981. pap. 5.95 (ISBN 0-8280-0032-8). Review & Herald.

Todhunter, Isaac. William Whewell, D.D., Master of Trinity College, Cambridge, 2 Vols. (Sources of Science Ser.: No. 92). Repr. of 1876 ed. 68.00 (ISBN 0-384-60880-9). Johnson Repr.

Todorov, Tzvetan. Symbolism & Interpretation. Porter, Catherine, tr. from Fr. LC 82-5078. 192p. 1982. text ed. 24.95x (ISBN 0-8014-1269-2). Cornell U Pr.

Toelke, Otto W. In the Presence of God. rev. ed. LC 61-18225. 1962. 4.95 (ISBN 0-570-03019-6, 6-1152). Concordia.

Toepperwein, Emilie & Toepperwein, Fritz. The Missions of San Antonio. pap. text ed. 1.50 (ISBN 0-910722-12-9). Highland Pr.

Toepperwein, Fritz, jt. auth. see Toepperwein, Emilie.

Toews, Ed. Ministry to Single Adults. pap. 1.95 (ISBN 0-919797-48-2). Herald Pr.

Toews, J. B. The Mennonite Church in Zaire. 255p. (Orig.). 1978. pap. 3.00 (ISBN 0-919797-23-7). Kindred Pr.

Toews, J. J. The Mennonite Brethren Mission in Latin America. 255p. (Orig.). 1975. pap. 3.00 (ISBN 0-318-18905-4). Kindred Pr.

Toews, John A. A History of the Mennonite Brethren Church: Pilgrims & Pioneers. LC 74-33718. 513p. (Orig.). 1975. pap. 13.95 (ISBN 0-318-18904-6). Kindred Pr.

--People of the Way. Dueck, A. J., et al, eds. 256p. 1981. 10.95 (ISBN 0-919797-15-6); pap. 7.95 (ISBN 0-919797-16-4). Kindred Pr.

Toews, John B. Czars, Soviets & Mennonites. LC 81-71490. (Illus.). 221p. 1982. pap. 10.95 (ISBN 0-87303-064-8). Faith & Life.

--Lost Fatherland: The Story of the Mennonite Emigration from Soviet Russia, 1921-1927. LC 67-23294. (Studies in Anabaptist & Mennonite History: No. 12). pap. 65.50 (ISBN 0-317-26609-8, 2025421). Bks Demand UMI.

--With Courage to Spare. 185p. (Orig.). 1978. pap. 4.95 (ISBN 0-919797-26-1); 7.95 (ISBN 0-919797-25-3). Kindred Pr.

Toews, Paul. Pilgrims & Strangers: Essays in Mennonite Brethren History. (Perspective on Mennonite Life & Thought Ser.: Vol. 1). 183p. (Orig.). 1977. pap. 5.95 (ISBN 0-919797-36-9). Kindred Pr.

Toinet, Paul. Theological Cautions. Wrenn, Michael J., tr. 1982. 12.00 (ISBN 0-8199-0835-5). Franciscan Herald.

Tokiwa, Gishin, tr. see Hisamatsu, Shinichi.

Toksvig, Signe. Emanuel Swedenborg, Scientist & Mystic. LC 72-5447. (Biography Index Reprint Ser.). 1972. Repr. of 1948 ed. 25.00 (ISBN 0-8369-8140-5). Ayer Co Pubs.

Tola, Fernanda & Carmen, D. The Yoga Sutra of Patanjali on Concentration of Mind. 1986. 21.00 (ISBN 81-208-0258-6, Pub. by Motilal Banarsidass). South Asia Bks.

Toland, John. Christianity Not Mysterious. Wellek, Rene, ed. LC 75-11257. (The Philosophy of John Locke Ser.). 1978. lib. bdg. 46.00 (ISBN 0-8240-1807-9). Garland Pub.

--A Collection of Several Pieces, 2 vols. Wellek, Rene, ed. LC 75-11258. (British Philosophers & Theologians of the 17th & 18th Centuries: Vol. 57). 1976. Repr. of 1726 ed. Set. lib. bdg. 101.00 (ISBN 0-8240-1808-7). Garland Pub.

--The History of the Celtic Religion & Learning. LC 74-16159. 1974. Repr. lib. bdg. 40.00 (ISBN 0-8414-8553-4). Folcroft.

--Letters to Serena. Wellek, Rene, ed. LC 75-11259. (British Philosophers & Theologians of the 17th & 18th Centuries: Vol. 58). 295p. 1976. Repr. of 1704 ed. lib. bdg. 51.00 (ISBN 0-8240-1809-5). Garland Pub.

--Life of John Milton. LC 76-40068. 1761. lib. bdg. 30.00 (ISBN 0-8414-8619-0). Folcroft.

--Pantheisticon. Wellek, Rene, ed. LC 75-11260. (British Philosophers & Theologians of the 17th & 18th Centuries: Vol. 59). 1977. Repr. of 1751 ed. lib. bdg. 51.00 (ISBN 0-8240-1810-9). Garland Pub.

Tolbert, Malcolm, jt. auth. see Humphreys, Fisher.

Tolbert, Malcolm, et al. Perspectives on the New Testament: Essays in Honor of Frank Stagg. Talbert, Charles H., ed. vi, 108p. 1985. lib. bdg. 9.95x (ISBN 0-86554-152-3, MUP-H121). Mercer Univ Pr.

Tolbert, Malcolm O. Layman's Bible Book Commentary: Phillppians - Philemon, Vol. 22. LC 79-51998. 1980. 5.95 (ISBN 0-8054-1192-5). Broadman.

Tolbert, Mary A., ed. The Bible & Feminist Hermeneutics. (Semeia Ser.: No. 28). 9.95 (06 20 28). Scholars Pr GA.

Tolbert, Mary Ann. Perspectives on the Parables: An Approach to Multiple Interpretations. LC 78-54563. 144p. 1978. 9.95 (ISBN 0-8006-0527-6, 1-527). Fortress.

Toler, Thomas. Elder at the Lord's Table. 1953. pap. 3.95 (ISBN 0-8272-0800-6). CBP.

Tolkien, J. R., ed. Ancrene Wisse: English Text of the Ancrene Riwle. (Early English Text Society Ser.). 1962. 19.95x (ISBN 0-19-722249-8). Oxford U Pr.

Tolle, James M. Living Without Fear. 1977. 4.95 (ISBN 0-915378-13-2). Tolle Pubns.

Tollers, Vincent L., ed. Bibliography of Matthew Arnold, 1932-1970. 1974. 24.95x (ISBN 0-271-01113-0). Pa St U Pr.

Tollerson, Marie S. Mythology & Cosmology in the Narratives of Bernard Dadie & Birago Diop: A Structural Approach. LC 81-51668. 152p. 1985. 20.00 (ISBN 0-89410-156-0); pap. 10.00 (ISBN 0-89410-157-9). Three Continents.

Tolles, Bryant F., Jr. The John Tucker Daland House. LC 76-27382. (Historic House Booklet Ser.). 1978. 2.00 (ISBN 0-88389-065-8). Essex Inst.

Tolles, Frederick. Quakers & the Atlantic Culture. 1980. Repr. of 1960 ed. lib. bdg. 16.00x (ISBN 0-374-97949-9, Octagon). Hippocrene Bks.

Tolles, Frederick & Alderfer, Gordon E., eds. The Witness of William Penn. 1980. Repr. of 1957 ed. lib. bdg. 18.50x (ISBN 0-374-97950-2, Octagon). Hippocrene Bks.

Tolles, Frederick B. Meeting House & Counting House. (Illus.). 1963. pap. 8.95 (ISBN 0-393-00211-X, Norton Lib). Norton.

Tollett, T. O., compiled by. Best Gifts. 1971. pap. 1.00 (ISBN 0-89114-062-X). Baptist Pub Hse.

--Church Roll & Record. 1979. 11.95 (ISBN 0-89114-017-4). Baptist Pub Hse.

--Way of the Wise. 64p. 1970. pap. 1.00 (ISBN 0-89114-061-1). Baptist Pub Hse.

--We Preach Jesus. 40p. 1971. pap. 1.00 (ISBN 0-89114-063-8). Baptist Pub Hse.

Tolley, Jackie, ed. On Our Spiritual Journey: A Creative Shabbat Service. (Illus.). 74p. (Orig.). 1984. pap. 5.95 (ISBN 0-9608054-3-5). Womans Inst-Cont Jewish Ed.

Tolliver, Alice, ed. see Scoggan, Nita.

Tolliver, Gene, ed. Did Jesus Die Twice? LC 85-63545. 100p. (Orig.). 1986. pap. 3.75 (ISBN 0-937357-00-6). Substance Faith.

Tolnay, Charles Q. De see De Tolnay, Charles Q.

Tolstoy, Leo. The Kingdom of God Is Within You. Garnett, Constance, tr. from Rus. LC 84-10471. xxii, 368p. 1984. 26.95x (ISBN 0-8032-4411-8); pap. 8.50 (ISBN 0-8032-9404-2, BB 897, Bison). U of Nebr Pr.

Tom, Alan R. Teaching As a Moral Craft. LC 83-17520. 256p. 1984. pap. text ed. 12.95 (ISBN 0-582-28307-8). Longman.

Tomas, Andrew. Mirage of the Ages: A Critique of Christianity. 152p. 1983. 9.00 (ISBN 0-682-49999-4). Exposition Pr FL.

Tomasello, Andrew. Music & Ritual at Papal Avignon, 1309-1403. Buelow, George, ed. LC 83-18296. (Studies in Musicology: No. 75). 314p. 1983. 49.95 (ISBN 0-8357-1493-4). UMI Res Pr.

Tomasi, Silvano M. Piety & Power: The Role of Italian Parishes in the New York Metropolitan Area (1889-1930) LC 74-79913. 201p. 1975. 14.95x (ISBN 0-913256-16-1). Ctr Migration.

Tomback, Richard S. A Comparative Semitic Lexicon of the Phoenician & Punic Languages. LC 76-55377. (Society of Biblical Literature. Dissertation Ser.: No. 32). pap. 94.80 (ISBN 0-8357-9567-5, 2017672). Bks Demand UMI.

Tomczak, Larry. Clap Your Hands! LC 73-88241. 143p. 1973. pap. 4.95 (ISBN 0-88270-073-1). Bridge Pub.

--Divine Appointments. 168p. (Orig.). 1986. pap. 5.95 (ISBN 0-89283-261-4, Pub. by Vine Books). Servant.

--God, the Rod, & Your Child's Bod. LC 81-23507. 128p. 1982. pap. 5.95 (ISBN 0-8007-5082-9, Power Bks). Revell.

--Let's Talk about Sex: The Truth & God's Power to Live It. rev. ed. 123p. 1987. pap. 4.95 (ISBN 0-89283-353-X, Pub. by Vine Books). Servant.

--Straightforward. LC 78-59856. 1978. pap. 4.95 (ISBN 0-88270-311-0). Bridge Pub.

Tomkins, Thomas. Services, Pt. 1. Buck, P. C., ed. (Tudor Music Ser.: Vol.8). 1963. Repr. of 1928 ed. 85.00x (ISBN 0-8450-1858-2). Broude.

Tomlinson, A. J. The Last Great Conflict. 241p. 1984. Repr. of 1913 ed. 8.95 (ISBN 0-317-14173-2, 1925). White Wing Pub.

--The Last Great Conflict. (The Higher Christian Life Ser.). 219p. 1985. lib. bdg. 30.00 (ISBN 0-8240-6446-1); pap. 8.95 (ISBN 0-317-14532-0, 1925). Garland Pub.

Tomlinson, M. A. Basic Bible Beliefs. 1961. pap. 3.25 (ISBN 0-934942-01-3). White Wing Pub.

--The Glorious Church of God. 1968. pap. 3.50 (ISBN 0-934942-06-4). White Wing Pub.

--God's Church in the Plan of the Ages. 1974. pap. 2.95 (ISBN 0-934942-07-2). White Wing Pub.

--Let the Church Counsel Together. 1978. pap. 3.25 (ISBN 0-934942-10-2). White Wing Pub.

Tomlinson, Peter & Quinton, Margaret, eds. Values Across the Curriculum. LC 85-10389. 225p. 1986. 27.00x (ISBN 0-905273-75-3, Falmer Pr); pap. 15.00x (ISBN 0-905273-76-1). Taylor & Francis.

Tomoko, Terrie K. The Wonderful Story of God's Creation. 1978. plastic bdg. 2.50 (ISBN 0-8198-0375-8); pap. 1.75 (ISBN 0-8198-0376-6). Dghtrs St Paul.

Tompkins, Bert, jt. auth. see Arnold, John D.

Tompkins, Iverna. TLC Prayer Network Training Manual. Green, Shirlee & Stultz, Roberta, eds. write for info. tchr's. manual (ISBN 0-9611260-3-5). I Tompkins.

Tompkins, Iverna M. If It Please the King. 183p. (Orig.). 1983. pap. 5.00 (ISBN 0-9611260-1-9). I Tompkins.

Toms, Paul E. Winning the Battles of Life (Joshua) rev. ed. LC 86-15417. 224p. 1986. pap. 4.95 (ISBN 0-8307-1161-9, S413129). Regal.

--Winning the Battles of Life: This Land Is Your Land. LC 75-23512. 1977. pap. 2.50 (ISBN 0-8307-1161-9, S413129). Regal.

Tomval-Valtom. Soul Mates. 96p. (Orig.). 1985. pap. 5.95 (ISBN 0-9615048-0-3). St Thomas Pub.

Ton, Mary E. Las Llamas No Me Destruyeron. De Gutierrez, Edna L., tr. (Span.). 160p. 1985. pap. 4.95 (ISBN 0-311-46103-4). Casa Bautista.

Toner, Erwin J. Every Day Is a Christmas Present. 32p. 1967. pap. write for info. (ISBN 0-686-08987-1). Gonzaga U Pr.

Toner, Jules J. A Commentary on Saint Ignatius' Rules for the Discernment of Spirits: A Guide to the Principles & Practice. Ganss, George E., ed. LC 79-89606. (Original Studies Composed in English Ser.: No. 5). 352p. 1982. 14.00 (ISBN 0-912422-43-2); smyth sewn paper 11.00 (ISBN 0-912422-42-4). Inst Jesuit.

Tonge, Mildred. A Sense of Living. 1983. pap. 2.50x (ISBN 0-87574-079-0, 079). Pendle Hill.

Tonkin, John. The Church & the Secular Order in Reformation Thought. LC 73-143390. pap. 58.30 (ISBN 0-317-26653-5, 2025107). Bks Demand UMI.

Tonn, Katie. Expectations, Hopes, Dreams, Fantasies & Desires. (Uplook Ser.). 31p. 1978. pap. 0.99 (ISBN 0-8163-0346-0). Pacific Pr Pub Assn.

--Try God, You'll Like Him. (Uplook Ser.). 1975. pap. 0.99 (ISBN 0-8163-0178-6, 20340-6). Pacific Pr Pub Assn.

Tonna, Benjamin. Gospel for the Cities. Jerman, William E., tr. from It. LC 81-18807. Orig. Title: Un Vangelo per le Citta. Tr. of Un Vangelo per le Citta. 224p. (Orig.). 1982. pap. 10.95 (ISBN 0-88344-155-1). Orbis Bks.

Tonna, Benjamin, jt. auth. see Hall, Brian.

Tonna, Benjamin, jt. auth. see Hall, Brian P.

Tonothy, Ruth. Bible Crossword Puzzles. 48p. 1986. pap. 2.50 (ISBN 0-87403-050-1, 2694). Standard Pub.

Toohey, Barbara, jt. auth. see Biermann, June.

Toohey, William. Life after Birth: Spirituality for College Students. 112p. 1980. pap. 4.95 (ISBN 0-8164-2290-7, HarpR). Har-Row.

Tooke, Andrew. The Pantheon. LC 75-27880. (Renaissance & the Gods Ser.: Vol. 35). (Illus.). 1976. Repr. of 1713 ed. lib. bdg. 88.00 (ISBN 0-8240-2084-7). Garland Pub.

Tooker, Elisabeth, ed. Native North American Spirituality of the Eastern Woodlands: Sacred Myths, Dreams, Vision Speeches, Healing Formulas, Rituals & Ceremonials. LC 79-66573. (Classics of Western Spirituality Ser.). 320p. 1979. pap. 9.95 (ISBN 0-8091-2256-1). Paulist Pr.

Tool, Marc R. Essays in Social Value Theory. 1986. 35.00 (ISBN 0-87332-382-3). M E Sharpe.

Toolan, David. Facing West from California's Shores: A Jesuit's Journey in the Consciousness Movement. 352p. 1987. 19.95 (ISBN 0-8245-0805-X). Crossroad NY.

Toolan, Suzanne. Keeping Festival. 1979. pap. 4.95 (ISBN 0-89390-011-7). Resource Pubns.

Toon, Peter. The Anglican Way: Evangelical & Catholic. LC 83-60934. 96p. 1983. pap. 5.95 (ISBN 0-8192-1330-6). Morehouse.

--God's Statesman: The Life & Work of John Owen. 208p. 1971. 9.95 (ISBN 0-85364-133-1). Attic Pr.

--Heaven & Hell: A Biblical & Theological Overview. 160p. 1986. pap. 8.95 (ISBN 0-8407-5967-3). Nelson.

--J. C. Ryle: A Self-Portrait. 1975. 4.95 (ISBN 0-685-52822-7). Reiner.

--John Charles Ryle, Evangelical Bishop. 5.95 (ISBN 0-685-88379-5). Reiner.

--Justification & Sanctification. LC 83-70317. (Foundations for Faith Ser.). 160p. 1983. pap. 8.95 (ISBN 0-89107-288-8, Crossway Bks). Good News.

--Protestants & Catholics: A Guide to Understanding the Differences. 160p. (Orig.). 1984. pap. 5.95 (ISBN 0-89283-188-X). Servant.

--Your Conscience As Your Guide. LC 83-62870. 102p. (Orig.). 1984. pap. 5.95 (ISBN 0-8192-1339-X). Morehouse.

Toon, Peter & Martin, Peter, eds. Evangelical Theology, Eighteen Thirty-Three to Eighteen Fifty-Six: A Response to Tractarianism. LC 79-16701. (New Foundations Theological Library Ser.). 254p. 3.25 (ISBN 0-8042-3703-4). John Knox.

Toon, Peter, ed. see Avis, Paul D.

Toon, Peter, ed. see Carson, D. A.

Toon, Peter, jt. ed. see Martin, Ralph.

Toorn, K. van der see Van der Toorn, K.

Topel, John. The Way to Peace: Liberation Through the Bible. LC 78-9148. 208p. (Orig.). 1979. pap. 7.95 (ISBN 0-88344-704-5). Orbis Bks.

Topete, Eutimio. Recordar Es Vivir. LC 78-71069. 1978. pap. 6.00 (ISBN 0-915808-32-3). Editorial Justa.

Topp, Dale. Music in the Christian Community. LC 76-20471. Repr. of 1976 ed. 51.30 (ISBN 0-8357-9130-0, 2019340). Bks Demand UMI.

Topping, Peter W., tr. Feudal Institutions As Revealed in the Assizes of Romania. LC 80-13052. (The Crusades & Military Orders: Second Ser.). Repr. of 1949 ed. 23.50 (ISBN 0-404-17023-4). AMS Pr.

Torbet, Robert G. A History of the Baptists. rev. ed. LC 63-8225. 592p. 1973. 21.95 (ISBN 0-8170-0074-7). Judson.

Torjesen, Edward P. Fredrik Franson: Model for Worldwide Evangelism. LC 82-17892. 128p. (Orig.). 1983. pap. 4.95 (ISBN 0-87808-191-7). William Carey Lib.

Torjesen, Karen Jo. Hermeneutical Procedure & Theological Method in Origen's Exegesis. (Patristische Texts und Studien: Vol. 28). xii, 183p. 1985. 41.00x (ISBN 3-11-010202-1). De Gruyter.

Torkington, Rayner. Peter Calvay -- Hermit: A Personal Rediscovery of Prayer. LC 80-13188. 107p. (Orig.). 1980. pap. 3.95 (ISBN 0-8189-0404-6). Alba.

Tormey, John. To Love & Be Loved. 1979. pap. 1.95 (ISBN 0-89243-093-1). Liguori Pubns.

Tormey, John C. Life Beyond Death. 64p. 1981. pap. 1.50 (ISBN 0-89243-151-2). Liguori Pubns.

--Priests Are Only Human. LC 73-15083. (Illus.). 128p. 1974. pap. 1.25 (ISBN 0-8189-1114-X, Pub. by Alba Bks). Alba.

Toro, Olga L., tr. see Hynes, Kathleen.

Torpey, William G. Judicial Doctrines of Religious Rights in America. LC 78-132289. (Civil Liberties in American History Ser). 1970. Repr. of 1948 ed. lib. bdg. 42.50 (ISBN 0-306-70067-0). Da Capo.

Torrance, David W., ed. see Calvin, John.

Torrance, T. F. Reality & Evangelical Theology. LC 81-19811. 174p. 1982. pap. 8.95 (ISBN 0-664-24401-7). Westminster.

--Reality & Scientific Theology. (Theology & Science at the Frontiers of Knowledge Ser.: Vol. 1). 212p. 1985. 15.50 (ISBN 0-7073-0429-6, Pub. by Scottish Academic Pr Scotland). Longwood Pub Group.

Torrance, T. F., ed. see Barth, Karl.

Torrance, T. F., tr. see Barth, Karl.

Torrance, Thomas F. Apocalypse Today. 192p. 1960. 10.95 (ISBN 0-227-67405-7). Attic Pr.

--Calvin's Doctrine of Man. LC 77-5615. 1977. Repr. lib. bdg. 22.50x (ISBN 0-8371-9639-6, TOCD). Greenwood.

--Christian Theology & Scientific Culture. 1981. text ed. 14.95x (ISBN 0-19-520272-4). Oxford U Pr.

--Divine & Contingent Order. 1981. 29.95x (ISBN 0-19-826658-8). Oxford U Pr.

--The Ground & Grammar of Theology. LC 79-21429. 180p. 1980. 13.95x (ISBN 0-8139-0819-1). U Pr of Va.

--The Mediation of Christ. LC 83-25330. Repr. of 1984 ed. 27.00 (2027551). Bks Demand UMI.

--Space, Time & Incarnation. 1969. pap. 4.95 (ISBN 0-19-520082-9). Oxford U Pr.

--Theological Science. 1969. pap. 7.95 (ISBN 0-19-520083-7). Oxford U Pr.

Torrance, Thomas F., ed. Belief in Science & in Christian Life. 160p. 1981. pap. 12.00x (ISBN 0-905312-11-2, Pub. by Scot Acad Pr). Longwood Pub Group.

Torrance, Thomas F., ed. see Calvin, John.

Torrence, Rosemary. Mending Our Nets. 176p. 1980. 10.95 (ISBN 0-697-01757-5). Wm C Brown.

Torres, Sergio. Theology in the Americas. Eagleson, John, ed. LC 76-22545. 466p. (Orig.). 1976. 12.95 (ISBN 0-88344-479-8); pap. 12.95 (ISBN 0-88344-476-3). Orbis Bks.

Torres, Sergio & Eagleson, John, eds. The Challenge of Basic Christian Communities. Drury, John, tr. LC 81-38361. 283p. (Orig.). 1981. pap. 9.95 (ISBN 0-88344-503-4). Orbis Bks.

Torres, Sergio & Fabella, Virginia, eds. The Emergent Gospel: Theologies from the Underside of History. LC 77-22134. 303p. (Orig.). 1978. pap. 5.95 (ISBN 0-88344-113-6). Orbis Bks.

Torres, Sergio, jt. ed. see Appiah-Kubi, Kofi.

Torres, Sergio, jt. ed. see Fabella, Virginia.

Torres, Victor. El Hijo de la Calle Tenebrosa. 160p. 1975. 2.75 (ISBN 0-88113-100-8). Edit Betania.

Torrey, A. Holy Spirit: Who He Is & What He Does. 208p. 1927. 11.95 (ISBN 0-8007-0139-9). Revell.

--How to Work for Christ. 512p. 1901. 15.95 (ISBN 0-8007-0144-5). Revell.

Torrey, C. C. Composition & Date of Acts. (Harvard Theological Studies). 1916. pap. 15.00 (ISBN 0-527-01001-4). Kraus Repr.

Torrey, Charles C. Chronicler's History of Israel: Chronicles-Ezra-Nehemiah Restored to Its Original Form. 1954. 17.50x (ISBN 0-686-37866-0). Elliots Bks.

--Ezra Studies. rev. ed. 1970. 29.50x (ISBN 0-87068-014-5). Ktav.

--Jewish Foundation of Islam. rev. ed. LC 67-18817. 1968. 20.00x (ISBN 0-87068-117-6). Ktav.

--Pseudo-Ezekiel & the Original Prophecy. LC 78-63562. (Yale Oriental Ser. Researches: No. 18). Repr. of 1930 ed. 15.00 (ISBN 0-404-60288-6). AMS Pr.

Torrey, Charles C. & Spiegel, Shalom. Book of Ezekiel: Critical Studies. rev. ed. (Library of Biblical Studies). 1970. 29.50x (ISBN 0-87068-116-8). Ktav.

Torrey, Charles G. Apocalypse of John. 1958. 39.50x (ISBN 0-686-83474-7). Elliots Bks.

Torrey, Joseph, tr. see Neander, Johann A.

Torrey, R. A. The Baptism with the Holy Spirit. 96p. 1972. pap. 2.95 (ISBN 0-87123-029-1). Bethany Hse.

--Como Obtener la Plenitud del Poder. Rivas, Jose G., tr. from Eng. Orig. Title: How to Obtain Fullness of Power. (Span.). 112p. 1983. pap. 2.20 (ISBN 0-311-46083-6). Casa Bautista.

--How to Bring Men to Christ. LC 76-57111. 128p. 1977. pap. 2.95 (ISBN 0-87123-230-8, 200230). Bethany Hse.

--How to Bring Men to Christ. 128p. 1981. pap. 2.95 (ISBN 0-88368-098-X). Whitaker Hse.

--How to Find Fullness of Power. Orig. Title: How to Obtain Fullness of Power. 112p. 1971. pap. 2.95 (ISBN 0-87123-219-7, 200219). Bethany Hse.

--How to Obtain Fullness of Power. 96p. 1982. pap. text ed. 2.95 (ISBN 0-88368-116-1). Whitaker Hse.

--How to Pray. 112p. 1983. pap. text ed. 3.50 (ISBN 0-88368-133-1). Whitaker Hse.

--How to Pray. Chen, Fu H., tr. (Chinese.). 1986. pap. write for info. (ISBN 0-941598-31-4). Living Spring Pubns.

--How to Study the Bible. 155p. 1985. pap. 3.50 (ISBN 0-88368-164-1). Whitaker Hse.

--How to Succeed in the Christian Life. pap. 3.50 (ISBN 0-8024-3659-5). Moody.

--How to Succeed in the Christian Life. 128p. 1984. pap. 3.50 (ISBN 0-88368-143-9). Whitaker Hse.

--The NIV Vest Pocket Companion for Christian Workers. rev. ed. 96p. 1980. pap. 1.95 saddle-stitch (ISBN 0-310-33331-8, 12152P). Zondervan.

--The Person & the Work of the Holy Spirit. 2nd ed. 1985. pap. text ed. 7.95 (ISBN 0-310-33301-6, 10902P). Zondervan.

--Power & Peace in Prayer. (One Evening Christmas Classic Ser.). 1976. pap. 2.50 (ISBN 0-89107-019-2). Good News.

--Preguntas Practicas y Dificiles Contestadas. Orig. Title: Practical & Perplexing Questions Answered. (Span.). 128p. 1980. pap. 3.25 (ISBN 0-8254-1722-8). Kregel.

--Revival Addresses. 282p. 1974. Repr. of 1903 ed. 10.95 (ISBN 0-227-67808-7). Attic Pr.

--The Treasury of Scripture Knowledge. 784p. 1973. 21.95 (ISBN 0-8007-0324-3). Revell.

--The Treasury of Scripture Knowledge. 778p. Date not set. 17.95 (ISBN 0-917006-22-4). Hendrickson MA.

Torrey, R. A. & Davis, J. E. Como Orar. 96p. 1985. Repr. of 1984 ed. 2.00 (ISBN 0-311-40001-9). Casa Bautista.

Torrey, R. A., ed. Get Ready for Forever. 176p. 1984. pap. text ed. 3.50 (ISBN 0-88368-160-9). Whitaker Hse.

--How to Study the Bible for Greatest Profit. 1984. pap. 3.95 (ISBN 0-8010-8875-5). Baker Bk.

--How to Witness to Anyone: Guidelines for Effective Evangelism. 1985. pap. text ed. 3.50 (ISBN 0-88368-170-6). Whitaker Hse.

Torrey, Reuben A. How to Pray. (Moody Classics Ser.). 1984. pap. 3.50 (ISBN 0-8024-3709-5). Moody.

--KJV Vest Pocket Companion. pap. 1.95 (ISBN 0-310-33321-0, 12151P). Zondervan.

--Person & Work of the Holy Spirit. 1968. 7.95 (ISBN 0-310-33300-8, 10902P). Zondervan.

--Personal Work. 180p. 1956. 10.95 (ISBN 0-8007-0251-4). Revell.

--The Power of Prayer. 192p. 1971. pap. 3.95 (ISBN 0-310-33312-1, 10907P). Zondervan.

--What the Bible Teaches. 20th ed. 544p. 1984. 15.95 (ISBN 0-8007-0344-8). Revell.

Tos, John. Teachings of Old Testament. (Bible Study Commentaries Ser.). 128p. 1984. pap. 4.50 (ISBN 0-317-43392-X). Chr Lit.

Total Environmental Action, Inc. The Energy-Efficient Church. Hoffman, Douglas, ed. LC 79-10432. (Illus.). 1979. pap. 4.95 (ISBN 0-8298-0362-9). Pilgrim NY.

Toth, Max & Nielson, Greg. Pyramid Power. (Illus.). 207p. 1985. pap. 4.95 (ISBN 0-89281-106-4). Inner Tradit.

Toton, Suzanne C. World Hunger: The Responsibility of Christian Education. LC 81-16906. 224p. (Orig.). 1982. pap. 7.95 (ISBN 0-88344-716-9). Orbis Bks.

Totten, C. A. Joshua's Long Day. 1968. 5.00 (ISBN 0-685-08808-1). Destiny.

Touche, Louise De La see De La Touche, Louise M.

Touche, Louise M. De La see De La Touche, Louise M.

Touchton, Ken, jt. auth. see Knight, Walker.

Touchton, Ken, jt. auth. see Nicholas, Tim.

Toulouse, Teresa. The Art of Prophesying: New England Sermons & the Shaping of Belief. LC 86-7121. 224p. 1987. 23.00x (ISBN 0-8203-0892-7). U of Ga Pr.

Tournier, Paul. The Gift of Feeling. pap. 9.95 (ISBN 0-8042-2071-9). John Knox.

--Guilt & Grace. LC 82-11882. 224p. 1983. pap. 7.95 (ISBN 0-06-068331-7, RD416, HarpR). Har-Row.

--Learn to Grow Old. LC 72-78078. 256p. 1983. pap. 7.95 (ISBN 0-06-068361-9, RD-475, HarpR). Har-Row.

--A Listening Ear: Reflections on Christian Caring. Hudson, Paul, tr. from Fr. Tr. of Vivre a l'ecoute. 144p. 1987. pap. 7.95 (ISBN 0-8066-2266-0, 10-3900). Augsburg.

--The Meaning of Gifts. LC 63-19122. 1976. 5.95 (ISBN 0-8042-2124-3); pap. 1.25 (ISBN 0-8042-3604-6). John Knox.

--The Meaning of Persons. LC 57-9885. 244p. 1982. pap. 7.95 (ISBN 0-686-97228-7, RD 411, HarpR). Har-Row.

--The Person Reborn. LC 75-12283. 256p. 1975. (HarpR); pap. 1.95 (ISBN 0-06-068377-5, RD-327). Har-Row.

--The Strong & the Weak. LC 63-8898. 252p. 1976. pap. 6.95 (ISBN 0-664-24745-8). Westminster.

--To Understand Each Other. 6.95 (ISBN 0-8042-2235-5). John Knox.

--The Violence Within. 2nd ed. LC 78-3139. 208p. 1982. pap. 6.95 (ISBN 0-06-068295-7, RD376, HarpR). Har-Row.

--The Whole Person in a Broken World: A Biblical Remedy for Today's World. LC 81-6885. 192p. 1981. pap. 6.95 (ISBN 0-06-068312-0, HarpR, RD 360). Har-Row.

Tousley, Pershing. The Master Sculptor. LC 81-7189. 1981. pap. 10.00 (ISBN 0-8309-0316-X). Herald Hse.

Toussaint, G. C., tr. see Tsogyal, Yeshe.

Toussaint, Stanley D. Behold the King: A Study of Matthew. LC 80-13410. 1980. text ed. 16.95 (ISBN 0-930014-39-1). Multnomah.

Toussaint, Stanley D. & Dyer, Charles, eds. Essays in Honor of J. Dwight Pentecost. 1986. text ed. 15.95 (ISBN 0-8024-2381-7). Moody.

Tout, Thomas F. The Empire & the Papacy, Nine Eighteen to Twelve Seventy-Three. 8th ed. LC 80-18865. (Periods of European History: Period II). (Illus.). vii, 526p. 1980. Repr. of 1965 ed. lib. bdg. 42.50x (ISBN 0-313-22372-6, TOEP). Greenwood.

Tov, Emanual. The Book of Baruch: A Discussion of an Early Revision of the IXX of Jeremiah 29-52 & Baruch 1: 1-3: 8. LC 75-43872. (Harvard Semitic Monographs). 1976. pap. 9.75 (ISBN 0-89130-070-8, 06-02-08). Scholars Pr GA.

Tov, Emanuel. The Book of Baruch. LC 75-30775. (Society of Biblical Literature. Texts & Translation-Pseudepigrapha Ser.). 1975. pap. 9.75 (ISBN 0-89130-043-0, 060208). Scholars Pr GA.

Towler, Robert. The Need for Certainty: A Sociological Study of Conventional Religion. 180p. 1985. 22.50x (ISBN 0-7100-9973-8). Methuen Inc.

Towlson, Clifford W. Moravian & Methodist. LC 57-3559. 1957. 20.00x (ISBN 0-8401-2387-6, 8401-2387-6). A R Allenson.

Towne, Ruth W. From These Beginnings: A History of the First United Methodist Church Kirksville, Missouri. 100p. 1984. pap. 6.00 (ISBN 0-9613631-0-X). Journal Printing.

Towne, William E. Health & Wealth from Within. 157p. 1981. pap. 9.00 (ISBN 0-89540-081-2, SB-081). Sun Pub.

Towner, Jason. Forgiveness Is for Giving. pap. 5.95 (ISBN 0-310-70231-3, 14027P). Zondervan.

Towner, W. Sibley. Daniel. Mays, James L. & Miller, Patrick D., eds. LC 83-18791. (Interpretation Ser.). 228p. 1984. 16.95 (ISBN 0-8042-3122-2). John Knox.

--How God Deals with Evil. LC 76-24916. (Biblical Perspectives on Current Issues). 186p. 1976. softcover 4.95 (ISBN 0-664-24127-1). Westminster.

Townley, James, ed. see Maimonides, Moses.

Towns, Elmer. The Successful Sunday School & Teachers Guidebook. revised ed. LC 75-23009. (Illus.). 430p. 1986. pap. 10.95 (ISBN 0-88419-118-4). Creation Hse.

Towns, Elmer & Falwell, Jerry. Stepping Out on Faith. 192p. 1984. pap. 6.95 (ISBN 0-8423-6626-1). Tyndale.

Towns, Elmer L. Evangelize Thru Christian Education. LC 78-97811. 96p. 1970. pap. text ed. 4.95 (ISBN 0-910566-08-9); Perfect bdg. instr's. guide 5.95 (ISBN 0-910566-30-5). Evang Tchr.

--Say-It-Faith. 1983. pap. 5.95 (ISBN 0-8423-5825-0). Tyndale.

--What the Faith Is All About. LC 83-70235. 480p. 1983. pap. 9.95 (ISBN 0-8423-7870-7); leader's guide 2.95 (ISBN 0-8423-7869-3). Tyndale.

Towns, Elmer L. & Vaughan, John. The Complete Book of Church Growth. 1981. 14.95 (ISBN 0-8423-0408-8). Tyndale.

Towns, James E. Growing Through Grief. 1984. pap. 2.95 (ISBN 0-87162-395-1, D4000). Warner Pr.

Towns, Jim. A Family Guide to Death & Dying. 192p. (Orig.). 1987. pap. 5.95 (ISBN 0-8423-0830-X). Tyndale.

Townsend, Charles D., ed. The History of the Third Congregational Church of Middleborough, Known Today As North Congregational Church, United Church of Christ, North Middleboro, Massachusetts: Includes S. Hopkins Emery's Church History Reprinted from 1876 Edition. (Illus.). 300p. 1982. 22.50 (ISBN 0-9607906-0-8). ACETO Bookmen.

Townsend, George, ed. see Foxe, John.

Townsend, Janice M. Joy Before Us. LC 81-7198. 1982. pap. 8.00 (ISBN 0-8309-0327-5). Herald Hse.

Townsend, Jim. Colossians & Philemon: A Runaway Church & a Runaway Slave. (Bible Mastery Ser.). 144p. 1987. pap. 5.95 (ISBN 1-55513-849-7). Cook.

--Gospel Themes: Four Portraits of Christ's Life. (Bible Mastery Ser.). 144p. 1987. pap. 5.95 (ISBN 1-55513-848-9). Cook.

--Hebrews: Pilgrim's Progress or Regress? (Bible Mastery Ser.). 144p. 1987. pap. 5.95 (ISBN 1-55513-846-2). Cook.

--Old Testament Highlights: Survey of the Hebrew Scriptures. (Bible Mastery Ser.). 144p. 1987. pap. 5.95 (ISBN 1-55513-847-0). Cook.

--The Personal Bible Study. (Complete Teacher Training Meeting Ser.). 48p. 1986. tchr's ed 9.95 (ISBN 0-89191-320-3). Cook.

Townsend, John T. Midrash Tanhuma, 2 vols. 800p. 1987. price not set (ISBN 0-88125-087-2). Ktav.

Townsend, L., et al, eds. Parade of Plays I. 96p. 1986. pap. 5.95 (ISBN 0-89191-322-X). Cook.

--Parade of Plays II. 96p. 1986. pap. 5.95 (ISBN 0-89191-323-8). Cook.

--Parade of Plays III. 96p. 1987. pap. 5.95 (ISBN 0-89191-281-9). Cook.

Townsend, Leah. South Carolina Baptists: 1670-1805. LC 74-6312. (Illus.). 391p. 1978. Repr. of 1935 ed. 20.00 (ISBN 0-8063-0621-1). Genealog Pub.

Townsend, Lucy. Bible Trek-athon. (Complete Teacher Training Meeting Ser.). 48p. 1986. tchr's ed 9.95 (ISBN 0-89191-314-9). Cook.

Townsend, Meredith. Mahommed "the Great Arabian". 86p. 1981. Repr. of 1912 ed. lib. bdg. 20.00 (ISBN 0-89984-454-5). Century Bookbindery.

Townsend, Ralph. Faith, Prayer & Devotion. (Faith & the Future Ser.). 123p. 1984. cloth 24.95x (ISBN 0-631-13189-2); pap. 8.95x (ISBN 0-631-13232-5). Basil Blackwell.

Townsend, W. J. The Great Schoolmen of the Middle Ages. 1977. lib. bdg. 39.95 (ISBN 0-8490-1903-6). Gordon Pr.

Townsend, Zella. Whisperings in the Silence. 1972. pap. 2.00 (ISBN 0-87516-121-9). De Vorss.

Townshend, George. Christ & Baha'u'llah. LC 68-168. 116p. 1966. pap. 3.95 (ISBN 0-85398-005-5). G Ronald Pub.

--The Heart of the Gospel. 2nd rev. ed. 160p. (ISBN 0-85398-025-X); pap. 3.95 (ISBN 0-85398-020-9). G Ronald Pub.

--The Mission of Baha'u'llah & Other Literary Pieces. 160p. 1952. 10.95 (ISBN 0-85398-021-7). G Ronald Pub.

--The Promise of All Ages. 3rd, rev. ed. 192p. 1972. 10.95 (ISBN 0-85398-044-6); pap. 3.50 (ISBN 0-85398-006-3). G Ronald Pub.

Townsley, David & Bjork, Russell. Scripture Index to the New International Dictionary of New Testament Theology: And Index to Selected Extrabiblical Literature. Brown & Colin, eds. 208p. 1985. pap. 10.95 (ISBN 0-310-44501-9, 11315P). Zondervan.

Toy, Crawford H. A Critical & Exegetical Commentary on Proverbs. Driver, Samuel R., et al, eds. (International Critical Commentary Ser.). 592p. 1899. 24.95 (ISBN 0-567-05013-0, Pub. by T & T Clark Ltd UK). Fortress.

--Introduction to the History of Religions. LC 76-126655. Repr. of 1913 ed. 27.50 (ISBN 0-404-06498-1). AMS Pr.

Toynbee, Arnold J. Christianity & Civilization. 1983. pap. 2.50x (ISBN 0-87574-039-1, 039). Pendle Hill.

--The Islamic World since the Peace Settlement. Repr. of 1927 ed. 50.00 (ISBN 0-384-61120-6). Johnson Repr.

Toynbee, J. M. Death & Burial in the Roman World. Scullard, H. H., ed. LC 77-120603. (Aspects of Greek & Roman Life Ser). (Illus.). 336p. 1971. 35.00x (ISBN 0-8014-0593-9). Cornell U Pr.

Toynbee, Jocelyn M. The Shrine of St. Peter & the Vatican Excavations. LC 78-63482. Repr. of 1956 ed. 32.00 (ISBN 0-404-16548-6). AMS Pr.

Toyotome, M. Three Kinds of Love. pap. 0.75 (ISBN 0-87784-132-2). Inter-Varsity.

Tozer, A. H. Menace of the Religious Movie. 1974. pap. 1.00 (ISBN 0-915374-51-X, 51-X). Rapids Christian.

Tozer, A. W. The Best of A. W. Tozer. (Best Ser). 1978. pap. 3.95 (ISBN 0-8010-8845-3). Baker Bk.

--La Busqueda de Dios. Bruchez, Dardo, tr. 130p. (Orig.). 1979. pap. 2.75 (ISBN 0-87509-162-8); pap. 2.00 mass mkt. (ISBN 0-87509-159-8). Chr Pubns.

--Christ, the Eternal Son. Smith, G. B., ed. 136p. 1982. pap. 3.45 (ISBN 0-87509-230-6). Chr Pubns.

--Echoes from Eden. Smith, Gerald B., ed. LC 1-67321. (Tozer Pulpit: Vol. 8). 121p. (Orig.). 1981. 2.95 (ISBN 0-87509-227-6). Chr Pubns.

--Ese Increible Cristiano. Bruchez, Dardo, tr. from Eng. (Span.). 135p. (Orig.). 1979. pap. 2.00 (ISBN 0-87509-269-1). Chr Pubns.

--Gems from Tozer. 96p. 1979. pap. 2.45 (ISBN 0-87509-163-6). Chr Pubns.

--How to Be Filled with the Holy Spirit. 58p. pap. 1.75 (ISBN 0-87509-187-3). Chr Pubns.

--I Call It Heresy. pap. 3.45 (ISBN 0-87509-209-8). Chr Pubns.

--I Talk Back to the Devil. Smith, Gerald B., ed. Orig. Title: Tozer Pulpit, Vol. 4. Twelve Sermons on Spiritual Perfection. (Illus.). 144p. (Orig.). 1972. pap. 3.45 (ISBN 0-87509-206-3). Chr Pubns.

--Keys to the Deeper Life. 56p. 1973. pap. 1.95 (ISBN 0-310-33362-8). Zondervan.

--The Knowledge of the Holy. LC 75-12279. 128p. 1978. pap. 6.95 (ISBN 0-06-068412-7, RD 291, HarpR). Har-Row.

--The Knowledge of the Holy. LC 85-42794. 208p. 1985. pap. 12.95 large print (ISBN 0-06-068413-5, HarpR). Har-Row.
--Paths to Power. 64p. pap. 1.75 (ISBN 0-87509-190-3). Chr Pubns.
--Renewed Day by Day. Smith, Gerald B., ed. 384p. kivar binding 7.95 (ISBN 0-8007-5064-0, Power Bks). Revell.
--The Set of the Sail. Verploegh, Harry, ed. LC 86-70772. 90p. (Orig.). 1986. pap. 5.95 (ISBN 0-87509-379-5). Chr Pubns.
--That Incredible Christian. 135p. 1964. pap. 4.45; 3.45 (ISBN 0-87509-304-3). Chr Pubns.
--The Tozer Pulpit, 8 vols. Smith, Gerald B., ed. Incl. Vol. 1. Selected Quotations from the Sermons of A. W. Tozer. 158p. 1967. pap. 3.95 (ISBN 0-87509-199-7); Vol. 2. Ten Sermons on the Ministry of the Holy Spirit. 146p. 1968. pap. 3.95 (ISBN 0-87509-178-4); cloth 5.95 (ISBN 0-87509-177-6); Vol. 3. Ten Sermons from the Gospel of John. 167p. 1970. cloth 5.95 (ISBN 0-87509-201-2); Vol. 4. Twelve Sermons on Spiritual Perfection. 144p. 1972. 5.95 (ISBN 0-87509-204-7); Vol. 5. Twelve Sermons in Peter's First Epistle. 159p. 1974. 5.95 (ISBN 0-87509-207-1); Vol. 6. Twelve Messages on Well-Known & Favorite Bible Texts. 174p. 1975. 5.95 (ISBN 0-87509-210-1); Vol. 7. Twelve Sermons Relating to the Life & Ministry of the Christian Church. 1978. 5.95 (ISBN 0-87509-213-6); Vol. 8. Ten Sermons on the Voices of God Calling Man. 5.95 (ISBN 0-87509-225-X). pap. Chr Pubns.
--Treasury of A. W. Tozer. 1979. 9.95 (ISBN 0-87509-281-0); pap. 4.45 (ISBN 0-87509-176-8). Chr Pubns.
--Whatever Happened to Worship? Smith, Gerald B., ed. LC 85-71185. 128p. (Orig.). 1985. pap. 5.95 (ISBN 0-87509-367-1). Chr Pubns.
--Who Put Jesus on the Cross. 1976. pap. 3.45 (ISBN 0-87509-212-8). Chr Pubns.
--Worship: The Missing Jewel of the Evangelical Church. 30p. 1979. bklet 0.95 (ISBN 0-87509-219-5). Chr Pubns.

Tozer, A. W. & Smith, G. B. When He Is Come. Orig. Title: Tozer Pulpit, Vol. 2: Ten Sermons on the Ministry of the Holy Spirit. 146p. (Orig.). 1980. pap. 3.45 (ISBN 0-87509-221-7). Chr Pubns.

Tozer, A. W., ed. The Christian Book of Mystical Verse. 1975. Repr. 9.95 (ISBN 0-87509-381-7). Chr Pubns.

Tozer, Aiden W. Born after Midnight. pap. 4.45 (ISBN 0-87509-258-6); pap. 3.45 mass market (ISBN 0-87509-167-9). Chr Pubns.
--God Tells the Man Who Cares. Bailey, Anita, ed. 1970. 5.95 (ISBN 0-87509-184-9); pap. 4.45 (ISBN 0-87509-185-7); mass market ed. 2.95 (ISBN 0-87509-220-9). Chr Pubns.
--Let My People Go. pap. 4.45 (ISBN 0-87509-189-X). Chr Pubns.
--Man, the Dwelling Place of God. 5.95 (ISBN 0-87509-188-1); pap. 4.45 (ISBN 0-87509-165-2); mass market 2.95 (ISBN 0-87509-166-0). Chr Pubns.
--Of God & Men. pap. 4.45 (ISBN 0-87509-193-8); 2.95. Chr Pubns.
--Pursuit of God. LC 82-70768. 128p. 1982. 4.95 (ISBN 0-87509-191-1); pap. 3.95 (ISBN 0-87509-192-X); 3.25 (ISBN 0-87509-223-3); legacy ed. 5.95 (ISBN 0-87509-366-3). Chr Pubns.
--Renewed Day by Day. LC 80-69301. 380p. 12.95 (ISBN 0-87509-252-7); pap. 7.95 kivar (ISBN 0-87509-292-6). Chr Pubns.
--Root of the Righteous. 5.95 (ISBN 0-87509-194-6); pap. 4.45 (ISBN 0-87509-195-4); mass market 3.25 (ISBN 0-87509-224-1). Chr Pubns.
--Wingspread. pap. 3.95 (ISBN 0-87509-218-7). Chr Pubns.

Tozer, James R. A Shared Adventure. 1985. 5.50 (ISBN 0-89536-736-X, 5820). CSS of Ohio.

Tozer, Tom. Amazing Grace & Her Incredible Place. 1984. 4.75 (ISBN 0-89536-706-8, 4802). CSS of Ohio.
--On the Road with Jesus. 1980. 3.95 (ISBN 0-89536-415-8, 1526). CSS of Ohio.

Tozer, Tom & Dessem, Ralph E. Deck the Halls. Sherer, Michael L., ed. (Orig.). 1986. pap. 2.25 (ISBN 0-89536-827-7, 6844). CSS of Ohio.

Tozer, W. Tragedy in the Church. Smith, Gerald, ed. 1978. pap. 3.45 (ISBN 0-87509-215-2). Chr Pubns.

Trace, Arther. Christianity & the Intellectuals. 208p. (Orig.). 1983. pap. 5.95 (ISBN 0-89385-018-7). Sugden.

Tracey, David. Analogical Imagination. 496p. 1985. pap. 14.95 (ISBN 0-8245-0694-4). Crossroad NY.

Tracey, Gerard, jt. auth. see Earnest, James D.

Trachtenberg, Joshua. The Devil & the Jews: The Medieval Conception of the Jew & Its Relation to Modern Anti - Semitism. 288p. 1983. pap. 6.95 (ISBN 0-8276-0227-8, 610). Jewish Pubns.
--Jewish Magic & Superstition. LC 39-14212. (Temple Bks). 1970. pap. text ed. 6.95x (ISBN 0-689-70234-5, T15). Atheneum.

Trachtenberg, Marvin. The Campanile of Florence Cathedral: Giotto's Tower. LC 70-124532. (Illus.). 458p. 1971. 135.00 (ISBN 0-8147-8151-9). NYU Pr.

Tracy, David. Blessed Rage for Order: The New Pluralism in Theology. 1979. pap. 9.95 (ISBN 0-8164-2202-8, HarpR). Har-Row.
--Celebrating the Medieval Heritage: A Colloquy on the Thought of Aquinas & Bonaventura. 1978. pap. 8.95x (ISBN 0-226-81125-5). U of Chicago Pr.
--Plurality & Ambiguity: Religion As Test Case for Hermeneutics. 175p. 1985. 14.95 (ISBN 0-86683-983-6, 8567, HarpR). Har-Row.
--Religion in the Public Realm. 176p. 1987. 12.95 (ISBN 0-8245-0666-9). Crossroad NY.

Tracy, David & Cobb, John B., Jr. Talking about God: Doing Theology in the Context of Modern Pluralism. 144p. 1983. 6.95 (ISBN 0-8164-2458-6, HarpR). Har-Row.

Tracy, David & Lash, Nicholas. Cosmology & Theology. (Concilium 1983: Vol. 166). 128p. (Orig.). 1983. pap. 6.95 (ISBN 0-8164-2446-2, HarpR). Har-Row.

Tracy, David, jt. auth. see Grant, Robert M.

Tracy, David, jt. auth. see Happel, Stephen.

Tracy, David, jt. ed. see Eliade, Mircea.

Tracy, David, et al, eds. Towards Vatican III: The Work That Has to Be Done. 1978. 14.95x (ISBN 0-8245-0397-X); pap. 5.95 (ISBN 0-8245-0398-8). Crossroad NY.

Tracy, George E. Charged World: A Theology of Symbol. 1980. lib. bdg. 8.00 (ISBN 0-87419-054-1, U Pr of Wash); 1981 students' ed. 5.00 (ISBN 0-686-77089-7). Larlin Corp.

Tracy, James D. Luther & the Modern State in Germany. (Sixteenth Century Essays & Studies: Vol. VII). 110p. 1986. smyth sewn 25.00 (ISBN 0-940474-07-7). Sixteenth Cent.
--The Politics of Erasmus: A Pacifist Intellectual & His Political Milieu. LC 77-20697. (Erasmus Studies). 1978. 22.50x (ISBN 0-8020-5393-9). U of Toronto Pr.

Tracy, Jim. Divorce & Remarriage. (Illus.). 80p. (Orig.). 1986. pap. 9.95 (ISBN 1-55630-008-5). Brentwood Comm.

Tracy, Joseph. Great Awakening: A History of the Revival of Religion in the Time of Edwards & Whitefield. LC 72-83444. (Religion in America Ser). 1969. Repr. of 1945 ed. 21.00 (ISBN 0-405-00280-7). Ayer Co Pubs.

Tracy, Joseph, et al, eds. History of American Missions to the Heathens from Their Commencement to the Present Time. LC 35-32346. (American Studies). 1970. Repr. of 1840 ed. 45.00 (ISBN 0-384-23460-7). Johnson Repr.

Tracy, Patricia. Jonathan Edwards, Pastor: Religion & Society in Eighteenth-Century Northampton. (American Century Ser.). 288p. 1980. 14.95 (ISBN 0-8090-6195-3); pap. 5.95 (ISBN 0-8090-0149-7). Hill & Wang.

Tracy, Thomas F. God, Action & Embodiment. 208p. (Orig.). 1984. pap. 11.95 (ISBN 0-8028-1999-0). Eerdmans.

Tracy, Wesley. Beacon Small-Group Bible Studies, Micah-Obadiah: What Does the Lord Require? Wolf, Earl C., ed. 96p. (Orig.). 1985. pap. 2.50 (ISBN 0-8341-0963-8). Beacon Hill.
--When Adam Clarke Preached, People Listened. 238p. (Orig.). 1981. pap. 4.95 (ISBN 0-8341-0714-7). Beacon Hill.

Trafton, Joseph L. The Syriac Version of the Psalms of Solomon. (SBL Septuagint & Cognate Studies). 1985. 22.95 (ISBN 0-89130-910-1, 06-04-11); pap. 15.95 (ISBN 0-89130-911-X). Scholars Pr GA.

Trager, Frank N. & Koenig, William J. Burmese Sit-Tans, Seventeen Sixty-Four to Eighteen Twenty-Six: Records of Rural Life & Administration. (Association for Asian Studies Monographs: No. 36). 440p. 1979. 9.50x (ISBN 0-8165-0672-8). U of Ariz Pr.

Trager, G. L. Old Church Slavonic Kiev Fragment. (LM). 1933. pap. 16.00 (ISBN 0-527-00817-6). Kraus Repr.

Trail, W. The Literary Characteristics & Achievements of the Bible. 335p. 1983. Repr. of 1863 ed. lib. bdg. 85.00 (ISBN 0-89984-471-5). Century Bookbindery.

Traill, Robert. The Works of Robert Traill, 2 vols. 1975. Set. 28.95 (ISBN 0-85151-393-X). Vol. 1 (ISBN 0-85151-229-1). Vol. 2 (ISBN 0-85151-230-5). Banner of Truth.

Traina, Robert A. Methodical Bible Study. 1985. 12.95 (ISBN 0-317-38919-X, 17031). Zondervan.
--Methodical Bible Study. 1985. 14.95 (ISBN 0-310-31230-2). Zondervan.

Training Manual Research Division. Bible Instruction Manuals, Etc. A Bibliography. 1984. pap. text ed. 1.95 (ISBN 0-318-03127-2, Pub. by Training Manuals). Prosperity & Profits.

Tranter, John W., Jr. Images. 180p. (Orig.). 1986. pap. text ed. 3.95 (ISBN 0-88368-183-8). Whitaker Hse.

Trape, Augustine. Saint Augustine: Man, Pastor, Mystic. (Orig.). 1985. pap. 6.95 (ISBN 0-89942-172-5, 172/02). Catholic BK Pub.

Trapido, Barbara. Noah's Ark: A Novel. 264p. 1985. 16.95 (ISBN 0-531-09704-8). Watts.

Trapnell, William H. Christ & His Associates in Voltairian Polemic: An Assault on the Trinity and the Two Natures. (Stanford French & Italian Studies: Vol. 26). vi, 268p. 1982. pap. 25.00 (ISBN 0-915838-13-3). Anma Libri.

Trapp, J., ed. see Yates, Frances A.

Trapp, Jacob, ed. see Buber, Martin.

Trapp, Maria Von see Von Trapp, Maria.

Trask, Willard, tr. see Eliade, Mircea.

Trask, Willard R., tr. see Corbin, Henry.

Trask, Willard R., tr. see Eliade, Mircea.

Trattner, Ernest R. Understanding the Talmud. LC 77-27887. 1978. Repr. of 1955 ed. lib. bdg. 22.50x (ISBN 0-313-20253-2, TRUT). Greenwood.

Traub, George W., jt. auth. see Gannon, Thomas M.

Traube, Elizabeth G. Cosmology & Social Life: Ritual Exchange Among the Mambai of East Timor. (Illus.). 312p. 1987. text ed. 32.00x (ISBN 0-226-81149-2); pap. text ed. 14.95x (ISBN 0-226-81150-6). U of Chicago Pr.

Traver, Hope. Love Is for Tomorrow. 271p. 1978. pap. 3.95 (ISBN 0-930756-37-1, 531006). Aglow Pubns.

Travers, Walter. A Supplication Made to the Privy Counsel. LC 76-57419. (English Experience Ser.: No. 833). 1977. Repr. of 1591 ed. lib. bdg. 5.00 (ISBN 90-221-0833-3). Walter J Johnson.

Travis, Stephen, jt. auth. see Hughes, Gerald.

Travis, Stephen, jt. auth. see Neil, William.

Travis, Stephen H. Christ & the Judgement of God: Divine Retribution in the New Testament. 240p. Date not set. pap. 12.95 (ISBN 0-8407-5958-4). Nelson.

Traviss, Mary P. Student Moral Development in the Catholic School. 96p. 1986. 6.60 (ISBN 0-318-20565-3). Natl Cath Educ.

Travnikar, Rock. The Blessing Cup. 64p. (Orig.). 1979. pap. 2.25 (ISBN 0-912228-60-1). St Anthony Mess Pr.

Trawick, Buckner B. Bible As Literature: Old Testament & the Apocrypha. 2nd ed. 1970. pap. 5.95 (ISBN 0-06-460056-4, CO 56, B&N Bks). Har-Row.

Traylor, Ellen G. John, Son of Thunder. 1980. pap. 4.95 (ISBN 0-8423-1903-4). Tyndale.
--Noah. 256p. 1985. pap. 6.95 (ISBN 0-8423-4703-8). Tyndale.
--Song of Abraham. 1981. pap. 4.50 (ISBN 0-8423-6071-9). Tyndale.

Traylor, John H., Jr. Layman's Bible Book Commentary: One & Two Kings, Two Chronicles, Vol. 6. LC 80-67148. 1982. 5.95 (ISBN 0-8054-1176-3). Broadman.

Treadwell, William C., Jr., jt. auth. see McSwain, Larry L.

Treash, Gordon. Kant: Einzig Mogliche Beweisgrund. LC 77-86227. Tr. of The One Possible Basis for a Demonstration of the Existence of God. 1978. 20.00 (ISBN 0-913870-37-4). Abaris Bks.

Tredennick, Hugh, ed. The Ethics of Aristotle: The Nicomachean Ethics. rev ed. Thomson, J. A., tr. 1955. pap. 5.95 (ISBN 0-14-044055-0). Penguin.

Treece, Patricia. A Man for Others: Maximilian Kolbe, Saint of Auschwitz. 208p. 1986. pap. 5.95 (ISBN 0-87973-519-8, 519). Our Sunday Visitor.
--Soldier of God. 32p. 1982. pap. 1.00 (ISBN 0-913382-22-1, 111-1). Prow Bks-Franciscan.

Tregay, William. The Original Meaning of the Resurrection. 60p. (Orig.). Date not set. pap. price not set. Church Man Pub.

Tregay, William, ed. The Miracles of Jesus for the Intellectual. LC 85-63853. 128p. (Orig.). 1986. pap. text ed. write for info. (ISBN 0-936435-03-8). Church Man Pub.

Tregelles, Samuel P., tr. Gesenius' Hebrew & Chaldee Lexicon. (Reference Set). 919p. 1982. Repr. of 1979 ed. 24.95 (ISBN 0-915134-70-5). Mott Media.

Tregelles, Samuel P., tr. see Gesenius, Wilhelm.

Treinen, Sylvester. An Adventure in Prayer. 16p. (Orig.). 1983. pap. 30.00 pkg. of 100 (ISBN 0-8146-1331-4). Liturgical Pr.

Tremblay, Edward. When You Go to Tonga. (Illus.). 1954. 3.25 (ISBN 0-8198-0173-9). Dghtrs St Paul.

Tremmel, William C. Dark Side. Lambert, Herbert, ed. 160p. (Orig.). 1987. pap. 9.95 (ISBN 0-8272-0614-3). CBP.
--Religion: What Is It? 2nd ed. 1984. pap. text ed. 17.95 (ISBN 0-03-062834-2). HR&W.
--The Twenty-Seven Books That Changed the World: A Guide to Readng the New Testament. LC 80-27930. 1981. text ed. 21.95 (ISBN 0-03-052631-0, HoltC). H Holt & Co.

Trempelas, Panagiotes N. The Autocephaly of the Metropolia in America. Bebis, George S., tr. Stephanopoulos, Robert G., ed. 80p. 1974. pap. 2.50 (ISBN 0-916586-00-6). Holy Cross Orthodox.

Trench, R. C. Notes on the Miracles. (Twin Brooks Ser.). pap. 7.95 (ISBN 0-8010-8776-7). Baker Bk.
--Notes on the Parables of Our Lord. (Twin Brooks Ser). pap. 5.95 (ISBN 0-8010-8774-0). Baker Bk.

Trench, Robert C. Synonyms of the New Testament. 1950. pap. 8.95 (ISBN 0-8028-1520-0). Eerdmans.

Trenchard, Ernesto. Bosquejos de Doctrina Fundamental. (Span.). 144p. 1972. pap. 3.95 (ISBN 0-8254-1725-2). Kregel.
--Consejos para Jovenes Predicadores. (Span.). 100p. 1957. pap. 3.25 (ISBN 0-8254-1726-0). Kregel.
--Epistola a los Galatas. (Span.). 224p. 1964. 6.75 (ISBN 0-8254-1732-5); pap. 5.50 (ISBN 0-8254-1731-7). Kregel.
--Epistola a los Hebreos. (Span.). 290p. 1974. 6.95 (ISBN 0-8254-1734-1); pap. 5.75 (ISBN 0-8254-1733-3). Kregel.
--Epistola a los Romanos. (Span.). 1969. 7.95 (ISBN 0-8254-1736-8); pap. 6.95 (ISBN 0-8254-1735-X). Kregel.
--Estudios de Doctrina Biblica. (Span.). 406p. 1976. pap. 9.95 (ISBN 0-8254-1738-4). Kregel.
--Evangelio Segun Marcos. (Span.). 226p. 1957. 6.95 (ISBN 0-8254-1740-6); pap. 5.75 (ISBN 0-8254-1739-2). Kregel.
--Hechos de los Apostoles. (Span.). 686p. 1963. 13.95 (ISBN 0-8254-1742-2). Kregel.
--Introduccion a los Cuatro Evangelios. (Span.). 686p. 1961. 9.95 (ISBN 0-8254-1744-9); pap. 8.75 (ISBN 0-8254-1743-0). Kregel.
--Introduccion a los Libros de Sabiduria y Job. (Span.). 152p. 1972. 4.50 (ISBN 0-8254-1746-5); pap. 3.50 (ISBN 0-8254-1745-7). Kregel.
--Introduccion a los Libros Profeticos e Isaias. (Span.). 192p. 1974. 4.95 (ISBN 0-8254-1748-1); pap. 3.95 (ISBN 0-8254-1747-3). Kregel.
--Normas de Interpretacion Biblica. (Span.). 150p. 1958. pap. 3.95 (ISBN 0-8254-1749-X). Kregel.
--Primera Epistola a los Corintios. (Span.). 348p. 1970. 9.95 (ISBN 0-8254-1728-7); pap. 8.95 (ISBN 0-8254-1727-9). Kregel.

Trenchard, Ernesto & Wickham, Pablo. Epistola a los Efesios. (Span.). 220p. 1980. 6.75 (ISBN 0-8254-1730-9). Kregel.

Trenchard, Ernesto, jt. auth. see Martinez, Jose.

Trenchard, John & Gordon, Thomas. Cato's Letters, 4 Vols. in 2. LC 74-121105. (Civil Liberties in American History Ser). 1971. Repr. of 1775 ed. Set. lib. bdg. 125.00 (ISBN 0-306-71965-7). Da Capo.

Trenchard, Warren C. Ben Sira's View of Women: A Literary Analysis. LC 82-16755. (Brown Judaic Studies: No. 38). 352p. 1982. pap. 15.75 (ISBN 0-89130-593-9, 14-00-38). Scholars Pr GA.

Trenckner, V., ed. The Majjhima-Nikaya, 4 vols. LC 78-70099. Repr. of 1888 ed. 137.50 set (ISBN 0-404-17660-7); Vol. 1. (ISBN 0-404-17661-5); Vol. 2. (ISBN 0-404-17662-3); Vol. 3. (ISBN 0-404-17663-1); Vol. 4. (ISBN 0-404-17664-X). AMS Pr.

Trenn, Thaddeus J., ed. see Fleck, Ludwig.

Trent, John. Growing Together. 156p. 1985. pap. 5.95 (ISBN 0-89693-323-7). Victor Bks.

Trent, John, jt. auth. see Smalley, Gary.

Trent, William P. John Milton: A Short Study of His Life & Works. LC 71-177572. Repr. of 1899 ed. 12.00 (ISBN 0-404-06523-6). AMS Pr.
--John Milton: A Short Study of His Life & Work. LC 72-187004. 1899. lib. bdg. 30.00 (ISBN 0-8414-8430-9). Folcroft.

Trepp, Leo. The Complete Book of Jewish Observance. LC 79-1352. (Illus.). 1979. 16.50 (ISBN 0-87441-281-1). Behrman.
--The Complete Book of Jewish Observance. LC 79-1352. (Behrman House Book). (Illus.). 370p. 1980. 14.95 (ISBN 0-671-41797-5). Summit Bks.
--History of the Jewish Experience: Eternal Faith, Eternal People. rev. ed. LC 73-3142. Orig. Title: Eternal Faith, Eternal People: a Journey into Judaism. 296p. 1973. pap. text ed. 9.95x (ISBN 0-87441-072-X). Behrman.
--Judaism: Development & Life. 3rd ed. 384p. 1981. pap. text ed. write for info. (ISBN 0-534-00999-9). Wadsworth Pub.

Trese, Leo. The Faith Explained. rev. ed. 479p. 1984. pap. 7.95 (ISBN 971-117-042-6, Pub. by Sinag-Tala Pubs Philippines). Scepter Pubs.

Trese, Leo J. A Trilogy: More than Many Sparrows, Wisdom Shall Enter & Many Are One, 3 bks. in 1 vol. 271p. 1984. pap. 6.95 (ISBN 971-117-023-X, Pub. by Sinag-Tala Pubs Philippines). Scepter Pubs.

Trethowan, Illtyd. Process Theology & the Christian Tradition. LC 84-26240. (Studies in Historical Theology). 122p. 1985. 11.95 (ISBN 0-932506-36-4). St Bedes Pubns.

Treusch, Paul E. & Sugarman, Norman A. Tax Exempt Charitable Organizations. 2nd ed. LC 83-70067. 726p. 1983. text ed. 95.00 (ISBN 0-8318-0429-7, B429). Am Law Inst.

Trevelyan, G. M., jt. ed. see Powell, Edgar.

Trevelyan, George M. England in the Age of Wycliffe. 3rd ed. LC 78-178560. Repr. of 1900 ed. 34.50 (ISBN 0-404-56677-4). AMS Pr.

Trevelyan, Marie. Folk-Lore & Folk-Stories of Wales. (Folklore Ser). 35.00 (ISBN 0-8482-2749-2). Norwood Edns.

Trever, John C. Scrolls from Qumran Cave I: The Great Isaiah Scroll the Order of the Community, the Pesher to Habakkuk (color) 163p. 1972. text ed. 30.00x (ISBN 0-89757-002-2, Am Sch Orient Res); pap. 6.00x. Eisenbrauns.

--Scrolls from Qumran Cave I: The Great Isaiah Scroll the Order of the Community, the Pesher to Habakkuk. 82p. 1974. pap. text ed. 6.00x (ISBN 0-89757-001-4). Am Sch Orient Res.

Trevino, Alejandro. El Predicador: Platicas a Mis Estudiantes. 155p. 1984. pap. 2.95 (ISBN 0-311-42016-8). Casa Bautista.

Trevino, Alejandro, tr. see Harvey, H.

Trevino, Alejandro, tr. see Pendleton, J. M.

Trevino, Elizabeth B. De. Casilda of the Rising Moon. LC 67-10389. 224p. 1967. 3.95 (ISBN 0-374-31188-9). FS&G.

Trevisa, J. Dialogus Inter Militem et Clericum: Richard FitzRalph's Sermon. (EETS, OS Ser.: No. 167). Repr. of 1925 ed. 20.00 (ISBN 0-527-00164-3). Kraus Repr.

Trevor, Meriol. Newman's Journey. LC 84-62224. 285p. 1985. pap. 9.50 (ISBN 0-87973-627-5, 627). Our Sunday Visitor.

Trevor-Roper, Hugh R. European Witch Craze in the Sixteenth & Seventeenth Centuries & Other Essays. 1969. pap. 6.95x (ISBN 0-06-131416-1, TB1416, Torch). Har-Row.

Trexler, Richard C. The Christian at Prayer: An Illustrated Prayer Manual Attributed to Peter the Chanter. (Medieval & Renaissance Texts & Studies: Vol. 44). (Illus.). 1987. 25.00 (ISBN 0-86698-027-X). Medieval & Renaissance NY.

Tribbe, Frank C. Portrait of Jesus? The Illustrated Story of the Shroud of Turin. 176p. 1983. 19.95 (ISBN 0-8128-2904-2). Stein & Day.

Tribe, Carol. Profile of Three Theories: Erikson, Maslow, Piaget. 120p. 1982. pap. text ed. 8.95 (ISBN 0-8403-2800-1). Kendall-Hunt.

Trible, Phyllis. God & the Rhetoric of Sexuality, No. 20. LC 77-78647. (Overtures to Biblical Theology Ser.). 228p. 1978. pap. 8.95 (ISBN 0-8006-0464-4, 1-464). Fortress.

--Texts of Terror: Literary-Feminist Readings of Biblical Narratives. LC 83-48906. (Overtures to Biblical Theology Ser.). 144p. 1984. pap. 8.95 (ISBN 0-8006-1537-9, 1-1537). Fortress.

Trigg, Joseph W. Origen: The Bible & Philosophy in the Third Century Church. (Illus.). 280p. 1983. pap. 16.95 (ISBN 0-8042-0945-6). John Knox.

Trigg, Joseph W. & Sachs, William L. Of One Body: Renewal Movements in the Church. LC 86-2788. 168p. (Orig.). 1986. pap. 9.95 (ISBN 0-8042-0677-5). John Knox.

Trigger, B. G., et al. Ancient Egypt: A Social History. LC 82-22196. 450p. 1983. 57.50 (ISBN 0-521-24080-8); pap. 19.95 (ISBN 0-521-28427-9). Cambridge U Pr.

Triggs, Kathy. Charles Spurgeon. 96p. (Orig.). 1986. pap. 3.50. Bethany Hse.

Triggs, Tony D. Founders of Religion. LC 82-60697. (In Profile Ser.). 64p. PLB 13.96 (ISBN 0-382-06676-6). Silver.

Trillhaas, Wolfgang. Dogmatik. 4th ed. 543p. 1972. 24.80x (ISBN 3-11-008423-6). De Gruyter.

--Religionsphilosophie. 278p. 1972. 19.20x (ISBN 3-11-003868-4). De Gruyter.

--Schleiermachers Predigt. 2nd ed. (Theologische Bibliothek Toepelmann, Vol. 28). 1975. 20.80x (ISBN 3-11-005739-5). De Gruyter.

Trilling, Wolfgang. Conversations with Paul. 172p. 1987. 14.95 (ISBN 0-8245-0806-8). Crossroad NY.

--The Gospel According to St. Matthew, Vol. I. McKenzie, John L., ed. LC 81-605. (New Testament for Spiritual Reading Ser.). 182p. 1981. pap. 4.95 (ISBN 0-8245-0110-1). Crossroad NY.

--The Gospel According to St. Matthew, Vol. II. McKenzie, John L., ed. LC 81-605. (The New Testament for Spiritual Reading Ser.). 182p. 1981. pap. 4.95 (ISBN 0-8245-0111-X). Crossroad NY.

Trimiew, Oliver, Jr. John: The Gospel of Life. (Orig.). 1987. pap. text ed. 4.95 (ISBN 0-940955-00-8); tchr's. ed. 3.95 (ISBN 0-940955-01-6). Urban Ministries.

Trimingham, J. Spencer. Christianity among the Arabs in Pre-Islamic Times. (Arab Background Ser.). (Illus.). 1979. text ed. 30.00x (ISBN 0-582-78081-0). Longman.

--History in Two Dimensions: A Christian Interpretation of History as Being an Equation Between Time & Eternity. 1983. 11.95 (ISBN 0-533-05395-1). Vantage.

--History of Islam in West Africa. (Oxford Paperback Ser.). 1962. pap. 8.95x (ISBN 0-19-285038-5). Oxford U Pr.

--The Influence of Islam Upon Africa. 2nd ed. (Arab Background Ser.). (Illus.). 1980. text ed. 27.00x (ISBN 0-582-78499-9). Longman.

--Islam in Ethiopia. (Illus.). 299p. 1965. Repr. of 1952 ed. 29.50x (ISBN 0-7146-1731-8, F Cass Co). Biblio Dist.

Trimingham, John S. Islam in East Africa. LC 79-52567. (Islam Ser.). 1980. Repr. of 1964 ed. lib. bdg. 18.00x (ISBN 0-8369-9270-9). Ayer Co Pubs.

--Islam in West Africa. 1959. 29.95x (ISBN 0-19-826511-5). Oxford U Pr.

Trimingham, Spencer. Influence of Islam Upon Africa. 25.00x (ISBN 0-685-85423-X). Intl Bk Ctr.

Trinchard, Paul. God's Word for the Church in America. 12.95 (ISBN 0-8158-0428-8). Chris Mass.

Trine, Ralph W. In Tune with the Infinite. LC 72-125594. 1970. pap. 4.95 (ISBN 0-672-51349-8). Bobbs.

--In Tune with the Infinite. (Large Type Christian Classics Ser.). 1984. large print 10.95 (ISBN 0-87983-360-2). Keats.

Trinterud, Leonard J. Forming of an American Tradition. facs. ed. LC 78-124262. (Select Bibliographies Reprint Ser). 1949. 26.50 (ISBN 0-8369-5450-5). Ayer Co Pubs.

Tripitaka. The Quest of Enlightenment. Thomas, E. J., tr. from Sanskrit. LC 85-24863. (The Wisdom of the East Ser.). 95p. 1986. Repr. of 1950 ed. lib. bdg. 29.75x (ISBN 0-313-22185-5, TRQE). Greenwood.

Tripitaka Master Hua. Buddha Root Farm. Buddhist Text Translation Society, et al, trs. from Chinese. (Illus.). 72p. (Orig.). 1976. pap. 4.00 (ISBN 0-917512-08-1). Buddhist Text.

--The Dharma Flower Sutra; Vol. I: Introduction. Buddhist Text Translation Society, tr. from Chinese. (Illus.). 85p. (Orig.). 1977. pap. 5.00 (ISBN 0-917512-16-2). Buddhist Text.

--Flower Adornment Sutra: Names of Thus Come Ones & the Four Holy Truths, Chapters 7 & 8. Buddhist Text Translation Society, tr. from Chinese. 175p. (Orig.). 1983. pap. 8.50 (ISBN 0-88139-014-3). Buddhist Text.

--Listen to Yourself; Think Everything Over, Vol 1. Buddhist Text Translation Society Staff, tr. from Chinese. (Illus.). 153p. (Orig.). 1978. pap. 7.00 (ISBN 0-917512-24-3). Buddhist Text.

--Shuramana Mantra: A Commentary, Vol. IV. Buddhist Text Translation Society, tr. from Chinese. 140p. (Orig.). pap. 6.50 (ISBN 0-88139-022-4). Buddhist Text.

--The Shurangama Mantra: A Commentary, Vol. I. Buddhist Text Translation Society, tr. from Chinese. (Illus.). 296p. (Orig.). 1981. pap. 8.50 (ISBN 0-917512-69-3). Buddhist Text.

--Shurangama Mantra: A Commentary, Vol. II. Buddhist Text Translation Society, tr. (Illus.). 210p. (Orig.). 1982. pap. 7.50 (ISBN 0-917512-82-0). Buddhist Text.

--The Ten Dharma Realms Are Not Beyond a Single Thought. Buddhist Text Translation Society, tr. from Chinese. (Eng., Illus.). 72p. (Orig.). 1976. pap. 4.00 (ISBN 0-917512-12-X). Buddhist Text.

Tripitaka Master Hua, commentary by. The Dharani Sutra. Buddhist Text Translation Society, tr. from Chinese. (Illus.). 352p. (Orig.). 1976. pap. 12.00 (ISBN 0-917512-13-8). Buddhist Text.

--Dharma Flower Sutra, Vol. VI. Buddhist Text Translation Society, tr. from Chinese. (Illus.). 161p. (Orig.). 1980. pap. 8.00 (ISBN 0-917512-65-0). Buddhist Text.

--Dharma Flower Sutra, Vol. V. Buddhist Text Translation Society, tr. from Chinese. (Illus.). 200p. (Orig.). 1980. pap. 8.00 (ISBN 0-917512-64-2). Buddhist Text.

--Dharma Flower Sutra, Vol. IX. Buddhist Text Translation Society, tr. from Chinese. (Illus.). 270p. (Orig.). 1982. pap. 8.50 (ISBN 0-917512-85-5). Buddhist Text.

--Dharma Flower Sutra, Vol. III. Buddhist Text Translation Society, tr. from Chinese. (Illus.). 183p. (Orig.). 1979. pap. 8.00 (ISBN 0-917512-26-X). Buddhist Text.

--Dharma Flower Sutra, Vol. II. Buddhist Text Translation Society, tr. from Chinese. (Chinese., Illus.). 324p. (Orig.). 1978. pap. 9.00 (ISBN 0-917512-22-7). Buddhist Text.

--Dharma Flower Sutra, Vol. X. Buddhist Text Translation Society Staff, tr. from Chinese. 150p. (Orig.). pap. 7.50 (ISBN 0-917512-34-0). Buddhist Text.

--Flower Adornment (Avatamsaka) Sutra: Chapter 15, The Ten Dwellings. Buddhist Text Translation Society, tr. from Chinese. (Illus.). 185p. (Orig.). 1981. pap. 8.00 (ISBN 0-917512-77-4). Buddhist Text.

--Flower Adornment Sutra, Chapter 11: Pure Conduct. Buddhist Text Translation Society Staff, tr. from Chinese. (Illus.). 255p. (Orig.). 1983. pap. 9.00 (ISBN 0-917512-37-5). Buddhist Text.

--Flower Adornment Sutra, Chapter 16: Brahma Conduct. Buddhist Text Translation Society, tr. from Chinese. (Illus.). 86p. (Orig.). 1981. pap. 5.00 (ISBN 0-917512-80-4). Buddhist Text.

--Flower Adornment Sutra: Chapter 17, Merit & Virture from First Bringing Forth the Mind. Buddhist Text Translation Society, tr. from Chinese. (Illus.). 196p. (Orig.). 1982. pap. 7.00 (ISBN 0-917512-83-9). Buddhist Text.

--Flower Adornment Sutra, Chapter 24: Praises in the Tushita Heaven. Buddhist Text Translation Society, tr. from Chinese. (Illus.). 130p. (Orig.). 1982. pap. 5.00 (ISBN 0-917512-39-1). Buddhist Text.

--Flower Adornment Sutra, Chapter 26: The Ten Grounds, Part Two. Buddhist Text Translation Society, tr. from Chinese. (Illus.). 200p. (Orig.). 1981. pap. 8.00 (ISBN 0-917512-74-X). Buddhist Text.

--Flower Adornment Sutra, Chapter 39: Entering the Dharma Realm, Part IV. Buddhist Text Translation Society, tr. from Chinese. (Illus.). 280p. (Orig.). 1981. pap. 8.00 (ISBN 0-917512-76-6). Buddhist Text.

--Flower Adornment Sutra, Chapter 39: Entering the Dharma Realm, Part III. Buddhist Text Translation Society, tr. from Chinese. (Illus.). 250p. (Orig.). 1981. pap. 8.50 (ISBN 0-917512-73-1). Buddhist Text.

--Flower Adornment Sutra, Chapter 39: Entering the Dharma Realm, Part V. Buddhist Text Translation Society, tr. from Chinese. (Illus.). 310p. 1982. pap. 9.00 (ISBN 0-917512-81-2). Buddhist Text.

--Flower Adornment Sutra, Chapter 40: Universal Worthy's Conduct & Vows. Buddhist Text Translation Society, tr. from Chinese. (Illus.). 316p. (Orig.). 1982. pap. 10.00 (ISBN 0-917512-84-7). Buddhist Text.

--Flower Adornment Sutra, Chapter 5: Flower Adorned Sea of Worlds, Part 1. Buddhist Text Translation Society Staff, tr. from Chinese. (Illus.). 250p. (Orig.). 1983. pap. 8.50 (ISBN 0-917512-54-5). Buddhist Text.

--Flower Adornment Sutra, Chapter 9: Light Enlightenment. Buddhist Text Translation Society Staff, tr. from Chinese. (Illus.). 225p. (Orig.). 1983. pap. text ed. 8.50 (ISBN 0-88139-005-4). Buddhist Text.

--The Shurangama Sutra, Vol. 1. Buddhist Text Translation Society, tr. from Chinese. (Illus.). 289p. (Orig.). 1977. pap. 9.00 (ISBN 0-917512-17-0). Buddhist Text.

--The Shurangama Sutra, Vol. 2. Buddhist Text Translation Society, tr. from Chinese. (Illus.). 212p. (Orig.). 1979. pap. 8.00 (ISBN 0-917512-25-1). Buddhist Text.

--Shurangama Sutra, Vol. 6. Buddhist Text Translation Society, tr. from Chinese. (Illus.). 220p. (Orig.). 1981. pap. 8.50 (ISBN 0-917512-37-5). Buddhist Text.

--The Sixth Patriarch's Sutra: Great Master Hui Neng. Buddhist Text Translation Society Staff, tr. from Chinese. (Illus.). 235p. (Orig.). 1977. 15.00 (ISBN 0-917512-19-7); pap. 10.00 (ISBN 0-917512-33-2). Buddhist Text.

--The Sutra in Forty-Two Sections. Buddhist Text Translation Society, tr. from Chinese. (Illus.). 114p. (Orig.). 1977. pap. 5.00 (ISBN 0-917512-15-4). Buddhist Text.

--Sutra of the Past Vows of Earth Store Bodhisattva. Buddhist Text Translation Society Staff, tr. from Chinese. (Illus.). 235p. (Orig.). 1976. 16.00 (ISBN 0-915078-00-7). Buddhist Text.

Tripitaka Master Hua, commentary by see National Master Ch'ing Liang.

Triplett, Loren, ed. see Talbot, Gordon, et al.

Tripole, Martin R. The Jesus Event & Our Response. LC 79-27896. 248p. (Orig.). 1980. pap. 7.95 (ISBN 0-8189-0399-6). Alba.

Tripolitis, Antonia. The Doctrine of the Soul in the Thought of Plotinus & Origen. LC 76-16321. 1977. 6.95 (ISBN 0-87212-061-9). Libra.

--Origen: A Critical Reading. (American University Studies VII (Theology & Religion): Vol. 8). 208p. 1985. text ed. 21.55 (ISBN 0-8204-0213-3). P Lang Pubs.

Tripp, Bramwell. Big Themes in Small Portions. 121p. (Orig.). 1984. pap. 2.95 (ISBN 0-89216-054-3). Salvation Army.

Tripp, Bramwell, et al. Heritage of Holiness. 110p. 1977. pap. 3.50 (ISBN 0-89216-013-6). Salvation Army.

Tripp, Edward. Meridian Handbook of Classical Mythology. pap. 10.95 (ISBN 0-452-00785-2, Mer). NAL.

Tripp, R. P., Jr., ed. Man's Natural Powers: Essays for & About C. S. Lewis. (Orig.). 1975. pap. 5.00 (ISBN 0-905019-01-6). Soc New Lang Study.

Trisco, Robert, jt. auth. see Ellis, John T.

Trismegistos, Hermes. The Hymns of Hermes. Mead, G. R. S., tr. from Gr. 84p. (Orig.). 1985. pap. 4.00 (ISBN 0-933999-57-7). Phanes Pr.

Trismegistus, Hermes. The Divine Pymander. Randolph, J., tr. 129p. 1972. Repr. of 1889 ed. 6.00 (ISBN 0-911662-48-0). Yoga.

--The Seven Golden Chapters of Hermes. 1984. pap. 2.95 (ISBN 0-916411-82-6, Pub by Alchemical Pr). Holmes Pub.

Tristano, Richard. Black Religion in the Evangelical South. 96p. 1986. pap. 4.00x (ISBN 0-317-43431-4). Glenmary Res Ctr.

--What Southern Catholics Need to Know about Evangelical Religion. 1984. pap. 3.00x (ISBN 0-914422-14-6). Glenmary Res Ctr.

Tristram, Henry. The Living Thoughts of Cardinal Newman. 167p. 1983. Repr. of 1948 ed. lib. bdg. 25.00 (ISBN 0-8495-5218-4). Arden Lib.

Trites, A. A. The New Testament Concept of Witness. LC 76-11067. (Society for New Testament Studies Monograph: No. 31). 1977. 59.50 (ISBN 0-521-21015-1). Cambridge U Pr.

Trites, Allison A. New Testament Witness in Today's World. 144p. 1982. pap. 8.95 (ISBN 0-8170-0988-4). Judson.

Tritton, Arthur S. Islam: Belief & Practices. LC 79-2883. 200p. 1986. Repr. of 1950 ed. 20.00 (ISBN 0-8305-0051-0). Hyperion Conn.

--Muslim Theology. LC 79-2885. 218p. 1980. Repr. of 1947 ed. 22.00 (ISBN 0-8305-0052-9). Hyperion Conn.

Tritton, Frederick J. The Discipline of Prayer. 1983. pap. 2.50x (ISBN 0-87574-042-1, 042). Pendle Hill.

Trobisch, Ingrid. On Our Way Rejoicing. LC 64-20195. (Harper Jubilee Book). 256p. 1976. pap. 3.95i (ISBN 0-06-068451-8, HJ-25, HarpR). Har-Row.

--On Our Way Rejoicing. 240p. (Orig.). 1986. pap. 6.95 (ISBN 0-8423-4745-3). Tyndale.

Trobisch, Walter. The Complete Works of Walter Trobisch. 700p. 1987. 19.95 (ISBN 0-87784-524-7). Inter-Varsity.

--I Loved a Girl. LC 75-12281. 128p. 1975. pap. 6.95 (ISBN 0-06-068443-7, RD 352, HarpR). Har-Row.

--Longing for Love. LC 86-72059. Orig. Title: Living with Unfulfilled Desires. 128p. 1987. pap. 5.95 (ISBN 0-89107-417-1, Crossway Bks). Good News.

--My Journey Homeward. 140p. (Orig.). 1986. pap. 4.95 (ISBN 0-89283-299-1, Pub. by Vine Books). Servant.

--Spiritual Dryness. pap. 0.75 (ISBN 0-87784-138-1). Inter-Varsity.

Trochu, Francis. The Cure D'Ars. LC 79-112487. (Eng.). 1977. pap. 15.00 (ISBN 0-89555-020-2). TAN Bks Pubs.

Trochu, Francois. Saint Bernadette Soubirous. LC 84-51819. 432p. 1985. pap. 12.00 (ISBN 0-89555-253-1). Tan Bks Pubs.

Trocme, Andre. Jesus & the Nonviolent Revolution. Shenk, Michel, tr. from Fr. LC 73-9934. (Christian Peace Shelf Ser.). 216p. 1974. pap. 12.95 (ISBN 0-8361-3320-X). Herald Pr.

Troeger, Thomas H. New Hymns for the Lectionary: To Glorify the Maker's Name. 144p. (Music by Carol Doran). 1986. 7.95 (ISBN 0-19-385729-4). Oxford U Pr.

--Rage! Reflect. Rejoice! Praying with the Psalmists. LC 77-22755. 96p. 1977. pap. 3.95 (ISBN 0-664-24293-6). Westminster.

Troeh, M. Richard & Troeh, Marjorie. The Conferring Church. 1987. pap. 10.00 (ISBN 0-8309-0465-4). Herald Hse.

Troeh, Marjorie, jt. auth. see Troeh, M. Richard.

Troeltsch, Ernst. Protestantism & Progress: The Significance of Protestantism for the Rise of the Modern World. LC 86-45221. (Fortress Texts in Modern Theology Ser.). 112p. 1986. pap. 8.95 (ISBN 0-8006-3200-1). Fortress.

--The Social Teaching of the Christian Churches, 2 vols. Wyon, Olive, tr. LC 81-10443. 1981. Vol. 1, 446p. pap. 17.00X (ISBN 0-226-81298-7); Vol. II, 569p. pap. 17.00 (ISBN 0-226-81299-5). U of Chicago Pr.

--The Social Teaching of the Christian Churches, 2 vols. 44.00 set (ISBN 0-8446-6134-1). Peter Smith.

Troeltsch, Ernst D. Christian Thought, Its History & Application. LC 78-59047. 1985. Repr. of 1923 ed. 23.25 (ISBN 0-88355-719-3). Hyperion Conn.

Trohan, Walter, jt. auth. see Day, Donald.

Troisi, J. Tribal Religion: Religious Beliefs & Practices Among the Santals. 1979. 18.00x (ISBN 0-8364-0197-2). South Asia Bks.

Trokan, John, jt. auth. see Metz, Kenneth.

Troki, Isaac. Faith Strengthened. Mocatta, Moses, tr. from Hebrew. LC 74-136768. 320p. 1975. pap. 9.75 (ISBN 0-87203-022-9). Hermon.

Trolin, Clifford. Movement in Prayer in a Hasidic Mode. 1979. 2.50 (ISBN 0-941500-13-6). Sharing Co.

Troll, Christian W., ed. Islam in India-Studies & Commentaries: Vol. 1, The Akbar Mission & Miscellaneous Studies. 240p. 1982. text ed. 32.50x (ISBN 0-7069-1889-4, Pub. by Vikas India). Advent NY.

--Religion & Religious Education. (Islam in India: Studies & Commentaries: Vol. 2). xxi, 315p. 1985. text ed. 40.00x (ISBN 0-7069-2751-6, Pub. by Vikas India). Advent NY.

Trombley, Charles. Kicked Out of the Kingdom. 1974. pap. 2.95 (ISBN 0-88368-044-0). Whitaker Hse.

--Praise Faith in Action. (Orig.). 1976. pap. 3.95 (ISBN 0-89350-009-7). Fountain Pr.
--Released to Reign. LC 79-90266. 1979. pap. 4.95 (ISBN 0-89221-064-8). New Leaf.
Tromby, Benedetto. Storia Critico Chronologica Diplomatica del Patriarca S. Brunone e del Suo Ordine Cartusiano, 2 pts, Vol. 1. Hogg, James, ed. (Analecta Cartusiana Ser.: No. 84-1). 523p. (Orig.). 1981. pap. 50.00 (ISBN 3-7052-0131-X, Pub. by Salzburg Stiudies). Longwood Pub Group.
--Storia Critico Chronologica Diplomatica del Patriarca S. Brunone e del Suo Ordine Cartusiano, 2 pts, Vol. 3. Hogg, James, ed. (Analecta Cartusiana Ser.: No. 84-3). 522p. 1982. pap. 50.00 (ISBN 3-7052-0133-6, Pub. by Salzburg Studies). Longwood Pub Group.
--Storia Critico-Chronologica-Diplomatica del Patriarca S. Brunone E Del Suo Ordine Cartusiano, Vol. 4 (2 pts.) Hogg, James, ed. (Analecta Cartusiana Ser.: No. 84-4). 632p. (Orig.). 1982. pap. 50.00 (ISBN 3-7052-0134-4, Pub. by Salzburg Studies). Longwood Pub Group.
--Storia Critico-Chronologica-Diplomatica del Patriarca S. Brunone E. del Suo Ordine Cartusiano, 2 pts, Vol. 6. Hogg, James, ed. (Analecta Cartusiana Ser.: No. 84/6). 632p. (Orig.). 1982. pap. 50.00 (ISBN 3-7052-0136-0, Pub. by Salzburg Studies). Longwood Pub Group.
--Storia Critico-Chronologica-Diplomatica del Patriarca S. Brunone E del Suo Ordine Cartusiano, 2 pts, Vol. 7. Hogg, James, ed. (Analecta Cartusiana Ser.: No. 84/7). 637p. (Orig.). 1982. pap. 50.00 (ISBN 3-7052-0137-9, Pub. by Salzburg Studies). Longwood Pub Group.
--Storia Critico-Chronologica-Diplomatica del Patriarca S. Brunone E del Suo Ordine Carusiano, 2 pts, Vol. 8. Hogg, James, ed. (Analecta Cartusiana: No. 84-8). 574p. (Orig.). 1982. pap. 50.00 (ISBN 3-7052-0138-7, Pub. by Salzburg Studies). Longwood Pub Group.
--Storia-Critico-Chronologica-Diplomatica del Patriarca S. Brunone E. del Suo Cartusiano, 2 pts, Vol. 9. Hogg, James, ed. (Analecta Cartusiana: No. 84-9). 638p. (Orig.). 1982. pap. 50.00 (ISBN 3-7052-0139-5, Pub. by Salzburg Studies). Longwood Pub Group.
--Storia Critico-Chronologica-Diplomatica del Patriarca S. Brunone E. del Suo Ordine Cartusiano, 3 pts, Vol. 10. Hogg, James, ed. (Analecta Cartusiana Ser.: No. 84-10). 730p. (Orig.). 1982. pap. 85.00 (ISBN 3-7052-0140-9, Pub. by Salzburg Studies). Longwood Pub Group.
--Storia Critico-Chronologica-Diplomatica del Patriarca S. Brunone E. del Suo Ordine Cartusiano, Vol. 11. Hogg, James, ed. (Analecta Cartusiana Ser.: No. 84-11). 31p. (Orig.). 1981. pap. 7.50 (ISBN 3-7052-0141-7, Pub. by Salzburg Studies). Longwood Pub Group.
Tromp, Nicholas J. Primitive Conceptions of Death & the Nether World in the Old Testament. (Biblica et Orientalia: Vol. 21). 1969. pap. 18.00 (ISBN 88-7653-321-4). Loyola.
Trompf, G. W., ed. The Gospel Is Not Western: Black Theologies from Aboriginal Australia & Melanesia. LC 86-23539. (Illus.). 224p. (Orig.). 1987. pap. 17.95 (ISBN 0-88344-269-8). Orbis Bks.
Troper, Harold, jt. auth. see Abella, Irving.
Trosse, George. The Life of the Reverend Mr. George Trosse. Brink, A. W., ed. LC 73-79097. pap. 37.50 (ISBN 0-317-26445-1, 2023853). Bks Demand UMI.
Trotsky, Leon. Leon Trotsky on the Jewish Question. pap. 0.95 (ISBN 0-87348-157-7). Path Pr NY.
Trotsky, Leon, et al. Their Morals & Ours. new ed. House, ed. LC 73-82168. 96p. 1974. 14.00 (ISBN 0-87348-318-9); pap. 4.95 (ISBN 0-87348-319-7). Path Pr NY.
Trotter, E. Seventeenth Century Life in the Country Parish. 242p. 1968. Repr. of 1919 ed. 28.50x (ISBN 0-7146-1363-0, F Cass Co). Biblio Dist.
Trotter, Jesse M. Christian Wholeness: Spiritual Direction for Today. LC 81-84718. 80p. (Orig.). 1982. pap. 5.95 (ISBN 0-8192-1294-6). Morehouse.
Trotter, Mark. Grace All the Way Home. LC 81-52860. 1982. pap. 4.95 (ISBN 0-8358-0434-8). Upper Room.
Trotter, W. Five Letters on Worship & Ministry. 39p. pap. 0.60 (ISBN 0-88172-128-X). Believers Bkshelf.
Trotti, John B. The Lesser Festivals 2: Saints' Days & Special Occasions. Achtemeier, Elizabeth, et al, eds. LC 79-7377. (Proclamation 2: Aids for Interpreting Thee Lessons of the Church Year). 64p. (Orig.). 1980. pap. 3.75 (ISBN 0-8006-1394-5, 1-1394). Fortress.
Troughton, Joanna, retold by. & illus. How Rabbit Stole the Fire: A North American Indian Folk Tale. LC 85-15629. (Folk-Tales of the World Ser.). (Illus.). 28p. 1986. 10.95 (ISBN 0-87226-040-2, Bedrick Blackie). P Bedrick Bks.
Trout, Janet & Walter, Diane. Reflections of Success. 1984. pap. 5.95 (ISBN 0-912315-81-4). Word Aflame.
Troward, Thomas. Creative Process in the Individual. rev. ed. 10.95 (ISBN 0-396-02064-X). Dodd.
--Dore Lectures on Mental Science. 1909. 9.95 (ISBN 0-396-02063-1). Dodd.
--Edinburgh Lectures on Mental Science. 1909. 9.95 (ISBN 0-396-02062-3). Dodd.
Troyer, Anthony, jt. auth. see Shea, David.
Troyes, Chretien de see De Troyes, Chretien.
Tru-Faith Pub, ed. see Wagner, Clarence M.
Tru-Faith Publishers, ed. see Wagner, Clarence M.
Truch, Stephen. TM Technique & the Art of Learning. (Quality Paperback Ser: No. 329). 250p. 1977. pap. 4.95 (ISBN 0-8226-0329-2). Littlefield.
True, Michael. Homemade Social Justice: Teaching Peace & Justice in the Home. 2nd ed. 168p. 1983. pap. 5.95 (ISBN 0-89622-202-0). Twenty-Third.
--Justice Seekers Peace Makers: 32 Portraits in Courage. (Illus.). 160p. 1985. pap. 5.95 (ISBN 0-89622-212-8). Twenty Third.
Trueblood, D. E. Trustworthiness of Religious Experience. LC 78-24656. 1979. pap. 2.45 (ISBN 0-913408-45-X). Friends United.
Trueblood, D. Elton. Essays in Gratitude. LC 82-71215. 1982. 8.95 (ISBN 0-8054-6938-9). Broadman.
--People Called Quakers. LC 66-15046. 1971. pap. 9.95 (ISBN 0-913408-02-6). Friends United.
Trueblood, David E. La Iglesia un Companerismo Incendiario. Velasquez, Roger, tr. from Eng. Orig. Title: The Incendiary Fellowship. (Span.). 114p. 1981. pap. 4.75 (ISBN 0-311-17022-6, Edit Mundo). Casa Bautista.
--Philosophy of Religion. LC 75-31446. 324p. 1976. Repr. of 1957 ed. lib. bdg. 29.25x (ISBN 0-8371-8514-9, TRPHR). Greenwood.
Trueblood, Elton. Company of the Committed. LC 61-12834. 114p. (Orig.). 1980. pap. 5.95 (ISBN 0-06-068551-4, RD 317, HarpR). Har-Row.
--The Humor of Christ. LC 75-12280. 128p. 1975. pap. 4.95 (ISBN 0-06-068631-6, RD 298, HarpR). Har-Row.
--Philosophy of Religion. (Twin Brooks Ser.). 1973. 12.95 (ISBN 0-8010-8813-5). Baker Bk.
--The Prayers of Christ. LC 65-10706. Orig. Title: The Lord's Prayers. 1982. pap. 3.95 (ISBN 0-932970-24-9). Prinit Pr.
--While It Is Day. 163p. 1983. pap. write for info. (ISBN 0-932970-36-2). Yokefellow Pr.
Trueblood, Elton, ed. see Johnson, Samuel.
Truemper, David G. & Niedner, Frederick A., Jr. Keeping the Faith: A Guide to the Christian Message. LC 81-43072. 144p. 1981. pap. 6.95 (ISBN 0-8006-1608-1, 1-1608). Fortress.
Truesdale, Albert, et al, eds. A Dictionary of the Bible & Christian Doctrine in Everyday English. 200p. (Orig.). 1985. 14.95 (ISBN 0-8341-1075-X). Beacon Hill.
Truett, George W. George W. Truett Library, 4 vols. 1980. Set. pap. 34.95 (ISBN 0-8054-2237-4). Broadman.
Truit, Gloria A. Events of the Bible (Arch Bks) 1984. pap. 0.99 (59-1312). Concordia.
--Places of the Bible. 1984. pap. 0.99 (59-1313). Concordia.
Truitt. Noah & God's Promise. (Arch Bks.). 24p. (Orig.). 1985. pap. 0.99 (ISBN 0-570-06193-8, 59-1294). Concordia.
Truitt, G. A. The Ten Commandments: Learning about God's Law. LC 56-1398. (Concept Bks.: Series 4). 1983. pap. 3.95 (ISBN 0-570-08527-6). Concordia.
Truitt, Gloria. People of the New Testament: Arch Book Supplement. LC 59-1311. 1983. pap. 0.99 (ISBN 0-570-06173-3). Concordia.
--People of the Old Testament: Arch Book Supplement. LC 59-1310. 1983. pap. 0.99 (ISBN 0-570-06172-5). Concordia.
Trull, Joe E. Forty Object Sermons for Children. (Object Lesson Ser.). 96p. 1975. pap. 3.95 (ISBN 0-8010-8831-3). Baker Bk.
--Seven Last Words of the Risen Christ. (Pulpit Library). 96p. 1985. pap. 4.95 (ISBN 0-8010-8879-8). Baker Bk.
Truman, George, et al. Narrative of a Visit to the West Indies: In 1840 & 1841. facsimile ed. LC 71-38027. (Black Heritage Library Collection). Repr. of 1844 ed. 15.25 (ISBN 0-8369-8993-7). Ayer Co Pubs.
Truman, Ruth. How to Be a Liberated Christian. LC 80-27302. 160p. 1981. 8.75 (ISBN 0-687-17710-3). Abingdon.
--Spaghetti from the Chandelier: And Other Humorous Adventures of a Minister's Family. 160p. 1984. pap. 7.95 (ISBN 0-687-39146-6). Abingdon.
Trumbull, Charles. Victory in Christ. 1970. pap. 2.95 (ISBN 0-87508-533-4). Chr Lit.
Trumbull, H. Clay. The Blood Covenant. 404p. 1975. pap. 5.95 (ISBN 0-89228-029-8). Impact Bks MO.
Trungpa, Chogyam. Born in Tibet. LC 85-8174. (Illus.). 280p. 1985. pap. 9.95 (ISBN 0-87773-333-3, 74219-2). Shambhala Pubns.
--Cutting Through Spiritual Materialism. LC 73-86145. (Dragon Ser.). (Illus.). 212p. (Orig.). 1973. pap. 8.95 (ISBN 0-87773-050-4). Shambhala Pubns.
--Glimpses of Abhidharma. LC 86-31409. (Dragon Ser.). 100p. 1987. pap. 9.95 (ISBN 0-87773-282-5). Shambhala Pubns.
--Journey Without Goal: The Tantric Wisdom of the Buddha. LC 85-8175. 150p. 1985. pap. 8.95 (ISBN 0-87773-334-1, 74194-3). Shambhala Pubns.
--Meditation in Action. 74p. (Orig.). 1969. pap. 4.95 (ISBN 0-87773-000-8). Shambhala Pubns.
--The Myth of Freedom & the Way of Meditation. LC 75-40264. (Illus.). 176p. (Orig.). 1976. pap. 7.95 (ISBN 0-87773-084-9). Shambhala Pubns.
--The Rain of Wisdom. Nalanda Translation Committee, tr. from Tibetan. LC 80-51130. Tr. of Bka'-Rgyud Mgur-Mtsho. 384p. 1985. pap. 18.95 (ISBN 0-87773-345-7, 73972-8). Shambhala Pubns.
--Shambhala: The Sacred Path of the Warrior. LC 83-20401. (Illus.). 199p. 1984. pap. 7.95 (ISBN 0-87773-264-7). Shambhala Pubns.
--Shambhala: The Sacred Path of the Warriors. 176p. 1986. pap. 3.95 (ISBN 0-553-26172-X). Bantam.
Trungpa, Chogyam, jt. auth. see Guenther, Herbert V.
Trungpa, Chogyam, jt. tr. see Fremantle, Francesca.
Trungpa, Chogyam, tr. see Heruka, Tsang N.
Trunk, Isaiah. Jewish Responses to Nazi Persecution. (Illus.). 371p. Repr. 13.00 (ISBN 0-686-95071-2). ADL.
--Judenrat. LC 70-173692. 1977. pap. 8.95 (ISBN 0-8128-2170-X). Stein & Day.
Truth in History Committee. The Six Million Reconsidered. Grimstad, William N., ed. (Illus.). 1979. pap. 8.00 (ISBN 0-911038-50-7). Noontide.
Truth, Sojourner. Narrative of Sojourner Truth. LC 68-29021. (American Negro: His History & Literature Ser., No. 1). 1968. Repr. of 1878 ed. 15.00 (ISBN 0-405-01841-X). Ayer Co Pubs.
Trzeciak, Cathi. Worship: Our Gift to God. (Concept Ser.). (Illus.). 24p. 1986. pap. 3.95 saddlestitched (ISBN 0-570-08531-4, 56-1558). Concordia.
Tsakonas, Demetrios. A Man Sent by God: The Life of Patriarch Athenagoras of Constantinople. Angeloglou, George, tr. from Greek. LC 77-77699. (Illus.). 99p. 1977. pap. 3.95 (ISBN 0-916586-07-3). Holy Cross Orthodox.
Tsanoff, R. A. The Moral Ideals of Our Civilization. 1977. lib. bdg. write for info. (ISBN 0-8490-2279-7). Gordon Pr.
Tsanoff, Radoslav A. Autobiographies of Ten Religious Leaders: Alternatives in Christian Experience. LC 68-57880. 304p. 1968. 7.00 (ISBN 0-911536-34-5). Trinity U Pr.
--Moral Ideals of Our Civilization. facsimile ed. LC 70-38738. (Essay Index Reprint Ser). Repr. of 1942 ed. 36.50 (ISBN 0-8369-2675-7). Ayer Co Pubs.
Tsatsos, Ioanna. Hours on Sinai. Vaporis, N. M., ed. Demos, Jean, tr. from Gr. Orig. Title: Apo to Tetradio Mou: Hores Tou Sina. 76p. 1984. pap. text ed. 8.00 (ISBN 0-917653-00-9). Hellenic Coll Pr.
Tschan, Francis J. Saint Bernward of Hildesheim, 3 vols. Incl. His Life & Times. 242p. 1942; His Works of Art. 503p. 1951. 30.00 (ISBN 0-268-00242-8); Album of All Extant Works. 1952. 30.00 (ISBN 0-268-00240-1). (Mediaeval Studies Ser.: Vols. 6, 12, 13). U of Notre Dame Pr.
Tschan, Francis J., tr. see Helmold Priest Of Bosau.
Tseng, Chen C., tr. see Forster, Roger T. & Marston, V. Paul.
Tsering, Nawang. Buddhism in Ladakh. 112p. 1979. text ed. 9.95 (ISBN 0-89684-263-0, Pub. by Sterling India). Orient Bk Dist.
Tsevat, Matitiahu. The Meaning of Job & Other Biblical Studies: Essays on the Literature & Religion of the Hebrew Bible. 1981. 25.00x (ISBN 0-87068-714-X). Ktav.
Tsiang, Hiuen. Si-Yu-Ki, Buddhist Records of th Western World, 2 vol. in 1. Beal, Samuel, tr. 618p. Repr. of 1884 ed. 38.50x (ISBN 0-89644-454-6, Pub. by Chinese Matl Ctr). Coronet Bks.
Tsing, I. A Record of the Buddhist Religion as Practised in India & the Malay Archipelago. Takakusu, J., tr. Repr. of 1896 ed. text ed. 22.50x (ISBN 0-89644-178-4). Coronet Bks.
Tsirpanlis, C. N. Ecumenical Consensus on the Church, the Sacraments, the Minstry & Reunion. 37p. 1980. pap. 1.50 (ISBN 0-686-36333-7). EO Pr.
Tsirpanlis, Constance N. The Anthropology of Saint John of Damascus. 64p. 1980. pap. 3.00 (ISBN 0-686-36332-9). EO Pr.
--Greek Patristic Theolgy, Vol. 1: Eleven Studies in Eastern Orthodox Doctrine Spirituality. 170p. 1979. pap. 9.95 (ISBN 0-686-36327-2). EO Pr.
--The Liturgical & Mystical Theology of Nicolas Cabasilas. 2nd ed. 103p. 1979. pap. 6.99 (ISBN 0-686-36328-0). EO Pr.
--The Trinitarian & Mystical Theology of St. Symeon the New Theologian. 42p. 1981. pap. 2.00 (ISBN 0-686-36331-0). EO Pr.
Tsirpanlis, Constantine N., ed. Orthodox-Unification Dialog. 139p. (Orig.). pap. 7.95. Rose Sharon Pr.
--Orthodox-Unification Dialogue. LC 80-54586. (Conference Ser.: No. 8). (Illus.). x, 139p. (Orig.). 1981. pap. text ed. 7.95 (ISBN 0-932894-08-9, Pub. by New Era Bks). Paragon Hse.
Tsogyal, Yeshe. The Life & Liberation of Padmasambhava, 2 vols. Toussaint, G. C. & Douglas, Kenneth, trs. (Tibetan Translation Ser.). (Illus.). 1978. 60.00 set (ISBN 0-685-80849-1). Vol. I (ISBN 0-913546-18-6). Vol. II (ISBN 0-913546-20-8). Dharma Pub.
Tsu, Lao. Tao Te Ching. Wilhelm, Richard, tr. 224p. 1985. pap. 5.95 (ISBN 1-85063-011-9). Methuen Inc.
Tsukamoto, Zenryi. A History of Early Chinese Buddhism: From Its Introduction to the Death of Hui-Yuan, 2 vols. Hurvitz, Leon, tr. from Japanese. (Illus.). 648p. 1985. Boxed Set. 175.00x (ISBN 0-87011-635-5). Kodansha.
Tsung-Hsi, Huang. The Records of Ming Scholars. Ching, Julia & Fang, Chaoying, eds. LC 86-27257. 688p. 1987. text ed. 27.00x (ISBN 0-8248-1028-7). UH Pr.
Tsur, Jacob. Zionism: The Saga of a National Liberation Movement. LC 76-24801. Tr. of L'epopee Du Siosnisme. 112p. 1977. pap. text ed. 9.95x (ISBN 0-87855-631-1). Transaction Bks.
Tsybikov, G. T. The Buddist Pilgrim at the Holy Places of Tibet Based on Diaries Kept over the Years 1899-1902. 482p. Repr. of 1919 ed. text ed. 74.52x (ISBN 0-576-03102-X). Gregg Intl.
Tubesing, Donald A. & Tubesing, Nancy L. The Caring Question: You First or Me First - Choosing a Healthy Balance. LC 83-70501. 224p. (Orig.). 1983. pap. 3.95 (ISBN 0-8066-2007-2, 10-0968). Augsburg.
Tubesing, Nancy L., jt. auth. see Tubesing, Donald A.
Tucci, Giuseppe. Minor Buddhist Texts, 2 parts in 1. 1986. Repr. 28.00 (ISBN 81-208-0190-3, Pub. by Motilal Banarsidass). South Asia Bks.
Tucci, Giuseppe, ed. The Nyayanukha of Dignaga. LC 78-72427. Repr. of 1930 ed. 17.50 (ISBN 0-404-17288-1). AMS Pr.
Tucci, Giuseppe, tr. Pre-Dinnaga Buddhist Texts on Logic from Chinese Sources. 368p. 1929. Repr. text ed. 32.00 (ISBN 0-89644-478-3, Pub. by Chinese Matl Ctr). Coronet Bks.
Tuck, Donald R. The Concept of Maya in Samkara & Radhakrishnan. 1986. 17.00x (ISBN 0-8364-1375-X). South Asia Bks.
Tuck, William P. Knowing God: Religious Knowledge in the Theology of John Baillie. LC 78-52865. 1978. pap. text ed. 9.50 (ISBN 0-8191-0484-1). U Pr of Amer.
--The Way for All Seasons. 1987. 9.95 (ISBN 0-8054-1541-6). Broadman.
Tucker, Abraham. The Light of Nature Pursued, 7 vols. Wellek, Rene, ed. LC 75-11262. (British Philosophers & Theologians of the 17th & 18th Centuries: Vol. 60). 4075p. 1984. Repr. of 1805 ed. Set. lib. bdg. 355.00 (ISBN 0-8240-1811-7). Garland Pub.
Tucker, Alfred R. Eighteen Years in Uganda & East Africa. LC 77-106884. Repr. of 1911 ed. cancelled (ISBN 0-8371-3280-0, TUU&, Pub. by Negro U Pr). Greenwood.
Tucker, Austin B. Morning Meditations. 99p. 1980. pap. 2.00 (ISBN 0-89323-011-1, 450). Bible Memory.
--My Lord Knows the Way. (Illus.). 80p. (Orig.). 1982. pap. 1.50 (ISBN 0-89323-036-7). Bible Memory.
Tucker, Beverley D. Questions on the Way. 160p. (Orig.). 1987. pap. price not set (ISBN 0-88028-056-5). Forward Movement.
Tucker, Beverly. Confessions for Teens. 1985. 0.75 (ISBN 0-89274-353-0). Harrison Hse.
Tucker, Bruce. Twisting the Truth. 192p. (Orig.). 1987. pap. 5.95 (ISBN 0-87123-931-0). Bethany Hse.
Tucker, Cynthia G. A Woman's Ministry: Mary Collson's Search for Reform as a Unitarian Minister, Hull House Social Worker, & a Christian Science Practioner. (American Civilization Ser.). 222p. 1984. 27.95 (ISBN 0-87722-338-6). Temple U Pr.
Tucker, G. M., jt. auth. see Miller, J. M.

Tucker, Gene & Knight, Douglas, eds. Humanizing America's Iconic Book. LC 82-836. (SBL Biblical Scholarship in North America Ser.). 188p. 1982. 29.95 (ISBN 0-89130-654-4, 06-11-06); pap. 17.50 (ISBN 0-89130-570-X). Scholars Pr GA.

Tucker, Gene, ed. see Long, Burke O.

Tucker, Gene M. Form Criticism of the Old Testament. Rylaarsdam, J. Coert, ed. LC 72-154487. (Guides to Biblical Scholarship: Old Testament Ser.). 96p. 1971. pap. 4.50 (ISBN 0-8006-0177-7, 1-177). Fortress.

Tucker, Gene M. & Knight, Douglas A. The Hebrew Bible & Its Modern Interpreters. LC 83-49216. (SBL-The Bible & Its Modern Interpreters Ser.). 1985. 22.50 (ISBN 0-89130-671-4, 06 14 01); pap. 14.95 (ISBN 0-89130-784-2). Scholars Pr GA.

Tucker, Gene M., ed. see Klein, Ralph W.

Tucker, Gene M., jt. ed. see Knight, Douglas A.

Tucker, Gene M., ed. see Lance, H. Darrell.

Tucker, Gene M., ed. see Miller, J. Maxwell.

Tucker, Gene M., ed. see Rast, Walter E.

Tucker, Gordon, jt. ed. see Mann, Vivian B.

Tucker, Grayson L., Jr. A Church Planning Questionnaire: Manual & Discoveries from 100 Churches. 161p. (Orig.). 1983. pap. text ed. 8.50 (ISBN 0-9610706-0-9). G L Tucker.

Tucker, Helen. Then the Sun Came Up. (Orig.). 1986. pap. 7.00 (ISBN 0-915541-10-6). Star Bks Inc.

Tucker, Iva J. Paul: The Missionary. (BibLearn Ser.). (Illus.). 5.95 (ISBN 0-8054-4228-6, 4242-28). Broadman.

Tucker, James A. & Tucker, Priscilla. Glimpses of God's Love. Woolsey, Raymond H., ed. LC 83-61683. (Junior-Youth Devotional Ser.: 1984). 386p. 1983. 7.95 (ISBN 0-8280-0216-9). Review & Herald.

Tucker, Johnny, et al. Like a Meteor Across the Horizon: The Jesse B. Ferguson Story & History of the Church of Christ in Nashville. (Illus., Orig.). 1978. pap. 2.95 (ISBN 0-686-26617-X). Tucker Pubns.

Tucker, Joyce C., jt. auth. see Gray, Joan S.

Tucker, Kathleen, ed. see Haas, Dorothy.

Tucker, Louis L. Puritan Protagonist: President Thomas Clap of Yale College. xviii, 283p. 1962. 25.00x (ISBN 0-8078-0841-5). U of NC Pr.

Tucker, Lyman R., ed. see Murray, Andrew.

Tucker, Mary E. The Ecological Spirituality of Teilhard. (Teilhard Studies). 1985. pap. 2.00 (ISBN 0-89012-040-4). Anima Pubns.

Tucker, Priscilla, jt. auth. see Tucker, James A.

Tucker, Roanld D. Evangelism. (Illus.). 40p. (Orig.). 1983. pap. 2.00 (ISBN 0-933643-13-6). Grace World Outreach.

--Faith. (Illus.). 56p. 1983. pap. 2.00 (ISBN 0-933643-14-4). Grace World Outreach.

Tucker, Robert & Waitley, Denis. Winning the Innovation Game. 256p. 1986. 15.95 (ISBN 0-8007-1494-6). Revell.

Tucker, Ronald D. Healing. 57p. (Orig.). 1985. pap. 2.50 (ISBN 0-933643-27-6). Grace World Outreach.

--The Holy Spirit. (Illus.). 34p. (Orig.). 1983. pap. 1.75 (ISBN 0-933643-15-2). Grace World Outreach.

--Love Is. (Illus.). 76p. (Orig.). 1983. pap. 2.50 (ISBN 0-933643-10-1). Grace World Outreach.

--The New Creation. (Illus.). 34p. (Orig.). 1983. pap. 1.75 (ISBN 0-933643-11-X). Grace World Outreach.

--Righteousness. (Illus.). 48p. (Orig.). 1983. pap. 2.00 (ISBN 0-933643-09-8). Grace World Outreach.

--Vision. (Illus.). 24p. (Orig.). 1983. pap. 1.50 (ISBN 0-933643-12-8). Grace World Outreach.

--The Word of God. 43p. (Orig.). 1985. pap. 2.50 (ISBN 0-933643-26-8). Grace World Outreach.

Tucker, Ronald D. & Hufton, Richard A. Foundations for Christian Growth. 2nd ed. (Illus.). 322p. 1981. incl. 6 cassettes 40.00 (ISBN 0-933643-16-0). Grace World Outreach.

--Foundations for Christian Growth. 3rd ed. LC 85-81911. (Illus.). 322p. 1985. pap. 10.00 (ISBN 0-933643-25-X). Grace World Outreach.

--God's Plan for Christian Service. (Illus.). 418p. 1982. 40.00 (ISBN 0-933643-17-9). Grace World Outreach.

--God's Plan for Christian Service. 2nd ed. LC 86-81343. 300p. 1987. pap. 10.00 (ISBN 0-933643-30-6). Grace World Outreach.

Tucker, Ruth. From Jerusalem to Irian Jaya: A Biographical History of Christian Missions. 1986. pap. 14.95 (ISBN 0-310-45931-1, 12723P). Zondervan.

Tucker, T. G. Life in the Roman World of Nero & St. Paul. 1924. 45.00 (ISBN 0-8274-3984-9). R West.

Tucker, W. Leon. Studies in Ephesians. LC 83-6115. 136p. 1983. pap. 4.95 (ISBN 0-8254-3828-4). Kregel.

--Studies in Revelation. LC 80-16206. (Kregel Bible Study Classics Ser.). 400p. 1980. 14.95 (ISBN 0-8254-3826-8). Kregel.

--Studies in Romans. LC 83-6114. 112p. 1983. pap. 4.95 (ISBN 0-8254-3827-6). Kregel.

Tucker, William E., jt. auth. see McAllister, Lester G.

Tuckerman, Joseph. On the Elevation of the Poor: A Selection from His Reports As Minister at Large in Boston. LC 79-137190. (Poverty U. S. A. Historical Record Ser). 1971. Repr. of 1874 ed. 15.00 (ISBN 0-405-03128-9). Ayer Co Pubs.

Tuckett, C. M. The Revival of the Griesbach Hypothesis: An Analysis & Appraisal. LC 81-6128. (Society for New Testament Studies Monographs: No. 44). 230p. 1983. 37.50 (ISBN 0-521-23803-X). Cambridge U Pr.

Tuckett, Christopher. Nag Hammadi & the Gospel Tradition: Synoptic Tradition in the Nag Hammadi Library. 190p. 1986. 21.50 (ISBN 0-567-09364-6, Pub. by T & T Clark Ltd UK). Fortress.

Tuckett, Christopher, ed. The Messianic Secret. LC 83-5499. (Issues in Religion & Theology Ser.). 176p. 1983. pap. 7.95 (ISBN 0-8006-1767-3). Fortress.

Tuckwell, James H. Religion & Reality. LC 77-118552. 1971. Repr. of 1915 ed. 25.00x (ISBN 0-8046-1177-7, Pub. by Kennikat). Assoc Faculty Pr.

Tuckwell, W. Lycidas: A Monograph. LC 77-22476. 1911. lib. bdg. 10.00 (ISBN 0-8414-8588-7). Folcroft.

Tudor, Tasha. A Book of Christmas. (Illus.). 1979. 6.95 (ISBN 0-529-05532-5, Philomel). Putnam Pub Group.

--First Graces. LC 59-12017. (Illus.). 1955. 4.95 (ISBN 0-8098-1953-8). McKay.

--First Prayers. LC 59-9631. (Illus.). 1952. protestant ed. 4.50 (ISBN 0-8098-1952-X). McKay.

--More Prayers. LC 67-19929. (Illus.). 1967. 4.95 (ISBN 0-8098-1954-6). McKay.

--Take Joy: The Tasha Tudor Christmas Book. LC 66-10645. (Illus.). 1980. 14.95 (ISBN 0-399-20766-X, Philomel); PLB 12.99 (ISBN 0-399-61169-X). Putnam Pub Group.

Tuell, Jack M. The Organization of the United Methodist Church. rev. ed. 176p. 1985. pap. 7.95 (ISBN 0-687-29445-2). Abingdon.

Tueng, Andrew, tr. see Daughters of St. Paul.

Tugwell, Simon. The Beatitudes: Soundings in Christian Traditions. 192p. 1980. 8.95 (ISBN 0-87243-098-7). Templegate.

--Did You Receive the Spirit? rev. ed. 144p. 1982. pap. 6.95 (ISBN 0-87243-108-8). Templegate.

--Prayer in Practice. 1980. pap. 7.95 (ISBN 0-87243-099-5). Templegate.

--Prayer: Living with God. 1980. pap. 7.95 (ISBN 0-87243-100-2). Templegate.

--The Way of the Preacher. (Orig.). 1979. pap. 7.95 (ISBN 0-87243-093-6). Templegate.

--Ways of Imperfection. 252p. 1985. 12.95 (ISBN 0-87243-136-3). Templegate.

Tugwell, Simon & Hocken, Peter. New Heaven? New Earth? 1977. pap. 5.95 (ISBN 0-87243-072-3). Templegate.

Tugwell, Simon, ed. Early Dominicans, Selected Writings. (The Classics of Western Spirituality Ser.). 400p. 1982. 14.95 (ISBN 0-8091-0325-7); pap. 10.95 (ISBN 0-8091-2414-9). Paulist Pr.

Tugwell, Simon, ed. & tr. see Jordan of Saxony.

Tugwell, Simon, ed. see Lacordaire, Henry D.

Tula, Jeffries. Singleness of Purpose. LC 85-19525. (Orig.). 1986. pap. 3.25 (ISBN 0-8054-5029-7). Broadman.

Tulka, Tarthang, tr. see Nyingpo, Namkhay.

Tulku, T. Gesture of Balance: A Guide to Awareness, Self-Healing & Meditation. 170p. 1977. 25.00x (ISBN 0-317-39074-0, Pub. by Luzac & Co Ltd). State Mutual Bk.

Tulku, Tarthang. Crystal Mirror, Vol. III. (Illus.). 1974. pap. 6.95 (ISBN 0-913546-05-4). Dharma Pub.

--Crystal Mirror, Vol. V. (Illus.). 1977. pap. 12.95 (ISBN 0-913546-47-X). Dharma Pub.

--Gesture of Balance: A Guide to Awareness, Self-Healing & Meditation. LC 75-5255. (Illus.). 1976. 12.95 (ISBN 0-913546-17-8); pap. 7.95 (ISBN 0-913546-16-X). Dharma Pub.

--Kum Nye Relaxation, Vols. 1 & 2. (Nyingma Psychology Ser.). 1978. 14.95 ea. Vol. 1 (ISBN 0-913546-10-0). Vol. 2 (ISBN 0-913546-74-7). pap. 7.95 ea. Vol. 1 (ISBN 0-913546-25-9). Vol. 2 (ISBN 0-913546-75-5). Dharma Pub.

--Love of Knowledge. (Psychology Ser.). 300p. (Orig.). 1987. pap. 12.95 (ISBN 0-89800-138-2). Dharma Pub.

--Reflections of Mind: Western Psychology Meets Tibetan Buddhism. LC 75-5254. (Illus.). 1975. 14.95 (ISBN 0-913546-15-1); pap. 7.95 (ISBN 0-913546-14-3). Dharma Pub.

--Time, Space & Knowledge: A New Vision. LC 77-19224. (Illus.). 1977. 14.95 (ISBN 0-913546-08-9); pap. 10.95 (ISBN 0-913546-09-7). Dharma Pub.

Tulku, Tarthang, ed. Annals of the Nyingma Lineage, Vol. 11. (Illus.). 1977. pap. 12.00 (ISBN 0-913546-32-1). Dharma Pub.

--Nyingma Edition of the sDe-dge bKa-gyur & bsTun-gyur, 120 vols. (Tibetan Buddhist Canon). 65000p. 1981. Set. 17250.00 (ISBN 0-89800-129-3). Dharma Pub.

Tulku, Tarthang, illus. Crystal Mirror, Vol. VII. (Illus.). 450p. (Orig.). 1984. 12.95 (ISBN 0-913546-92-5). Dharma Pub.

Tull, Charles J. Father Coughlin & the New Deal. LC 65-11680. (Illus.). 1965. 10.95x (ISBN 0-8156-0043-7). Syracuse U Pr.

Tull, James E. The Atoning Gospel. LC 81-18732. 221p. 1982. 15.50 (ISBN 0-86554-029-2, MUP-H28). Mercer Univ Pr.

--A History of Southern Baptist Landmarkism in the Light of Historical Baptist Ecclesiology: Doctoral Dissertation. Gaustad, Edwin S., ed. LC 79-52578. (Baptist Tradition Ser.). 1980. lib. bdg. 64.00x (ISBN 0-405-12446-5). Ayer Co Pubs.

--Shapers of Baptist Thought. LC 84-6545. (Reprints of Scholarly Excellence Ser.: No. 8). 255p. 1984. Repr. of 1972 ed. 14.50 (ISBN 0-86554-125-6, MUP-H116). Mercer Univ Pr.

Tullis, Dawn. Teach Us to Pray. 2.25 (ISBN 0-686-13717-5). Crusade Pubs.

Tullis, Edward L. Shaping the Church from the Mind of Christ: A Study of Paul's Letter to the Philippians. LC 84-50837. 80p. (Orig.). 1984. pap. 3.95 (ISBN 0-8358-0494-1). Upper Room.

Tullis, F. LaMond. Mormonism in Mexico. (Illus.). 275p. 1987. 22.50 (ISBN 0-87421-130-1). Utah St U Pr.

Tulloch, John. Leaders of the Reformation: Luther, Calvin et al. 34.95 (ISBN 0-8490-0492-6). Gordon Pr.

Tullock, John H. The Old Testament Story. 2nd ed. (Illus.). 432p. 1987. text ed. 28.67 (ISBN 0-13-633892-5). P-H.

Tully, Dennis. Culture & Context in Sudan: The Process of Market Incorporation in Dar Masalit. (SUNY Series in Middle Eastern Studies). (Illus.). 272p. 1987. text ed. 49.50x (ISBN 0-88706-502-3); pap. 18.95x (ISBN 0-88706-504-X). State U NY Pr.

Tully, Mary J. A Family Book of Praise. (Illus.). 128p. (Orig.). 1980. pap. 5.95 (ISBN 0-8215-6542-7). Sadlier.

--No Other God. 96p. 1984. pap. 3.50 (ISBN 0-697-01942-X). Wm C Brown.

--Los Salmos. Marquez, Angelina, tr. 1986. pap. 3.95 (ISBN 0-697-02202-1). Wm C Brown.

Tully, Mary J., jt. auth. see Fearon, Mary.

Tully, Mary Jo. Blessed Be. 96p. 1982. pap. 3.50 (ISBN 0-697-01822-9). Wm C Brown.

--Church: A Faith Filled People. 96p. 1982. pap. 3.50 (ISBN 0-697-01823-7). Wm C Brown.

--Psalms: Faith Songs for the Faith-Filled. 96p. 1982. pap. 3.50 (ISBN 0-697-01824-5). Wm C Brown.

Tully, Mary Jo & Fearon, Mary. Focus on Living. (Light of Faith Ser.). (Orig.). 1981. pap. text ed. 3.85 (ISBN 0-697-01769-9); tchrs.' ed. 12.95 (ISBN 0-697-01770-2); tests 12.95 (ISBN 0-697-01830-X). Wm C Brown.

--Focus on Loving. (Light of Faith Ser.). (Orig.). 1981. pap. text ed. 3.55 (ISBN 0-697-01763-X); tchrs.' ed. 12.95 (ISBN 0-697-01764-8); tests 12.95 (ISBN 0-697-01827-X). Wm C Brown.

--Focus on Relating. (Light of Faith Ser.). (Orig.). 1981. pap. text ed. 3.90 (ISBN 0-697-01773-7); avail. tchrs.' ed. 12.95 (ISBN 0-697-01774-5); tests 12.95 (ISBN 0-697-01832-6). Wm C Brown.

Tully, Mary Jo & Hirstein, Sandra J. Focus on Believing. (Light of Faith Ser.). (Orig.). 1981. pap. text ed. 3.85 (ISBN 0-697-01767-2); tchrs.' ed. 12.95 (ISBN 0-697-01768-0); tests 12.95 (ISBN 0-697-01829-6). Wm C Brown.

--Focus on Belonging. (Light of Faith Ser.). (Orig.). 1981. pap. text ed. 3.55 (ISBN 0-697-01765-6); tchrs.' ed. 12.95 (ISBN 0-697-01766-4); tests 12.95 (ISBN 0-697-01828-8). Wm C Brown.

--Focus on Celebrating. (Light of Faith Ser.). (Orig.). 1981. pap. text ed. 3.85 (ISBN 0-697-01771-0); tchr's ed 12.95 (ISBN 0-686-69655-7); tests 12.95 (ISBN 0-697-01831-8). Wm C Brown.

Tully, Robert, jt. ed. see Clemens, Frances.

Tuma, George W. The Fourteenth Century English Mystics: A Comparative Analysis, 2 vols. Hogg, James, ed. (Elizabethan & Renaissance Studies). 400p. (Orig.). 1977. pap. 30.00 (ISBN 0-317-40144-0, Pub. by Salzburg Studies). Longwood Pub Group.

Tumins, Valerie A. & Vernadsky, George, eds. Patriarch Nikon on Church & State. 812p. 1982. 99.20 (ISBN 90-279-7676-7). Mouton.

Tumulty, Sharon A., jt. auth. see DiMauro, Joseph.

Tune, E. W., jt. auth. see Colwell, Ernest C.

Tunisi, Khayr Al see Al Tunisi, Khayr.

Tunyogi, Andrew C. Divine Struggle for Human Salvation: Biblical Convictions in Their Historical Settings. LC 78-65852. 1979. pap. text ed. 19.75 (ISBN 0-8191-0676-3). U Pr of Amer.

Turbet, Paschal. The Little Bishop. 1977. 3.50 (ISBN 0-8198-0430-4); pap. 2.50 (ISBN 0-8198-0431-2). Dghtrs St Paul.

Turell, Ebenezer. The Life & Character of the Reverend Benjamin Colman, D. D. LC 72-4539. 256p. 1972. Repr. of 1749 ed. 40.00x (ISBN 0-8201-1104-X). Schol Facsimiles.

Turitz, Evelyn, jt. auth. see Turitz, Leo.

Turitz, Leo & Turitz, Evelyn. Jews in Early Mississippi. LC 82-25093. (Illus.). 144p. (Orig.). 1983. pap. 20.00 (ISBN 0-87805-178-3). U Pr of Miss.

Turnbul, Coulson. Sema-Kanda: Threshold Memories. 254p. Date not set. pap. 15.00 (ISBN 0-89540-131-2, SB-131). Sun Pub.

Turnbull, Grace R., ed. The Essence of Plotinus: Extracts from the Six Enneads & Porphyry's Life of Plotinus. Mackenna, Stephen, tr. LC 76-40320. 1976. Repr. of 1934 ed. lib. bdg. 37.50x (ISBN 0-8371-9054-1, TUEP). Greenwood.

Turnbull, Ralph G. At the Lord's Table: Twenty Communion Meditations. (Pocket Pulpit Library). 142p. 1985. pap. 4.95 (ISBN 0-8010-8821-6). Baker Bk.

--Dargan's History of Preaching, Vol. III. 12.95 (ISBN 0-8010-8819-4). Baker Bk.

Turnbull, Ralph G., ed. Baker's Handbook of Practical Theology. 469p. 1967. 14.95 (ISBN 0-8010-8880-1). Baker Bk.

Turnbull, Ralph G., jt. ed. see Moody, Dwight L.

Turner & Rogers. The Benedictines in Britain. 1980. 12.95 (ISBN 0-8076-0992-7). Braziller.

Turner, Bryan S. Weber & Islam: A Critical Study. 1978. pap. 9.95x (ISBN 0-7100-8942-2). Methuen Inc.

Turner, Charles, ed. see Blamires, Harry, et al.

Turner, Charles W. My Favorite Reflections. pap. 1.75 (ISBN 0-88469-029-6). BMH Bks.

--Pulpit Words Translated for Pew People. pap. 4.95 (ISBN 0-88469-046-6). BMH Bks.

--Studies in Proverbs: Wise Words in a Wicked World. (Contemporary Discussion Ser.). 1977. pap. 3.50 (ISBN 0-8010-8815-1). Baker Bk.

--Wise Words in a Wicked World: Studies in Proverbs. pap. 4.95 (ISBN 0-88469-028-8). BMH Bks.

Turner, Chip R. The Church Video Answerbook. LC 85-242884. 1986. pap. 5.95 (ISBN 0-8054-3713-4). Broadman.

Turner, Dean. Commitment to Care: An Integrated Philosophy of Science, Education, & Religion. LC 77-78421. 1977. 12.50 (ISBN 0-8159-5216-3). Devin.

--Krinkle Nose: A Prayer of Thanks. LC 77-78424. 1978. 6.95 (ISBN 0-8159-6002-6). Devin.

Turner, Denys. Marxism & Christianity. LC 82-22713. 268p. 1983. text ed. 27.50x (ISBN 0-389-20351-3). B&N Imports.

Turner, Edith, jt. auth. see Turner, Victor.

Turner, Elizabeth S. Be Ye Transformed. 1969. 5.95 (ISBN 0-87159-008-5). Unity School.

--Hagase la Luz. (Span.). 320p. 1985. 5.95 (ISBN 0-317-44746-7). Unity School.

--Let There Be Light. 1954. 5.95 (ISBN 0-87159-085-9). Unity School.

Turner, F. Bernadette. God-Centered Therapy. 1968. pap. 4.95 (ISBN 0-8315-0182-0). Speller.

--Prosperity & the Healing Power of Prayer. LC 83-21276. (Illus.). 166p. 1984. pap. 6.95 (ISBN 0-13-731324-1). P-H.

Turner, G. J. & Salter, H. E., eds. The Register of St. Augustine's Abbey, Canterbury: Commonly Called the Black Book, 2 pts. (British Academy, London, Record of the Social & Economic History of England & Wales Ser.: Vol. 2). Pt. 1, Reprint of 1915 Edition. pap. 45.00 (ISBN 0-8115-1242-8); Pt. 2, Reprint of 1924 Ed. pap. 36.00 (ISBN 0-8115-1243-6). Kraus Repr.

Turner, George A. Witnesses of the Way. 176p. (Orig.). 1981. pap. 3.95 (ISBN 0-8341-0692-2). Beacon Hill.

Turner, Gladys D. & St. Clair, Mae G. One Hundred Twenty-Three Questions & Answers: From the Edgar Cayce Readings. rev. ed. 58p. 1974. pap. 3.95 (ISBN 0-87604-073-3). ARE Pr.

Turner, Harold W. From Temple to Meeting House: The Phenomenology & Theology of Sacred Space. 1979. text ed. 39.20x (ISBN 90-279-7977-4). Mouton.

--Religious Innovation in Africa: Collected Essays on New Religious Movements. 1979. lib. bdg. 32.50 (ISBN 0-8161-8303-1, Hall Reference). G K Hall.

Turner, Henry E. The Pattern of Christian Truth: A Study in the Relations Between Orthodoxy & Heresy in the Early Church. LC 77-84707. (Bampton Lectures: 1954). 1977. Repr. of 1954 ed. 47.50 (ISBN 0-404-16114-6). AMS Pr.

Turner, Henry E. & Montefiore, Hugh. Thomas & the Evangelists. LC 63-59763. (Studies in Biblical Theology: No. 35). 1962. pap. 10.00x (ISBN 0-8401-3035-X). A R Allenson.

Turner, Henry M. The Genius & Theory of Methodist Polity, or the Machinery of Methodism. LC 75-99416. xii, 318p. 1972. Repr. of 1885 ed. lib. bdg. 16.50 (ISBN 0-8411-0089-6). Metro Bks.

Turner, Iris M., ed. The Road to Reality: The Spiritual Path for Everyone. 124p. 1986. 29.00x (ISBN 0-7212-0732-4, Pub. by Regency Pr). State Mutual Bk.

Turner, J. E. Essentials in the Development of Religion: A Philosophic & Psychological Study. 1979. Repr. of 1934 ed. lib. bdg. 35.00 (ISBN 0-8482-2730-1). Norwood Edns.

--The Revelation of Deity. Repr. of 1931 ed. 20.00 (ISBN 0-527-91170-4). Kraus Repr.

Turner, J. J. Book of James. pap. 5.50 (ISBN 0-89137-548-1). Quality Pubns.

--Christ's Stamp of Approval & Other Sermonettes. 1977. pap. 2.50 (ISBN 0-89315-014-2). Lambert Bk.

--God's Way to the Top. 1983. pap. 4.25 (ISBN 0-89137-539-2). Quality Pubns.

--Growth Through Biblical Stewardship. 1986. pap. 4.50 (ISBN 0-89137-561-9). Quality Pubns.

--How to Effectively Study the Bible. pap. 2.50 (ISBN 0-686-73328-2). Lambert Bk.

--How to Turn Your Dreams into Realities. pap. 4.50 (ISBN 0-317-03774-9). Quality Pubns.

--Leadership & Church Growth. pap. 2.75 (ISBN 0-89315-137-8). Lambert Bk.

--Positive Christian Living. pap. 4.25 (ISBN 0-89137-316-0). Quality Pubns.

--Practical Sermons That Motivate. pap. 2.95 (ISBN 0-89315-211-0). Lambert Bk.

--Sermons You Should Preach. 1984. pap. 3.95 (ISBN 0-89137-547-3). Quality Pubns.

--Study of Bible Leaders. pap. 2.50 (ISBN 0-89315-290-0). Lambert Bk.

--Winning Through Positive Spiritual Attitudes. pap. 4.25 (ISBN 0-89137-318-7). Quality Pubns.

Turner, J. J. & Myers, Edwards. Doctrine of the Godhead. pap. 5.50 (ISBN 0-89137-553-8). Quality Pubns.

Turner, James. Without God, Without Creed: The Origins of Unbelief in America. LC 84-15397. (New Studies in American Intellectual & Cultural History). 336p. 1986. pap. text ed. 12.95x (ISBN 0-8018-3407-4). Johns Hopkins.

Turner, John E. Essentials in the Development of Religion. LC 70-102587. 1970. Repr. of 1934 ed. 24.50x (ISBN 0-8046-0747-8, Pub. by Kennikat). Assoc Faculty Pr.

Turner, Mary. Slaves & Missionaries: The Disintegration of Jamaican Slave Society, 1787-1834. LC 82-6983. (Blacks in the New World Ser.). (Illus.). 240p. 1982. 25.95 (ISBN 0-252-00961-4). U of Ill Pr.

Turner, Morrie. All God's Chillun Got Soul. 64p. 1980. pap. 3.95 (ISBN 0-8170-0892-6). Judson.

Turner, Nicholas. Handbook for Biblical Studies. LC 82-7111. 156p. 1982. pap. 6.95 (ISBN 0-664-24436-X). Westminster.

Turner, Nigel. Grammatical Insights into the New Testament. 208p. 1965. 15.95 (ISBN 0-567-01017-1, Pub. by T & T Clark Ltd UK). Fortress.

--Syntax, Vol. 3. (Moulton's Grammar of New Testament Greek Ser.). 438p. 1963. 21.95 (ISBN 0-567-01013-9, Pub. by T & T Clark Ltd UK). Fortress.

Turner, Philip. Sex, Money & Power: An Essay on Christian Social Ethics. LC 84-72481. 135p. (Orig.). 1985. pap. 7.95 (ISBN 0-936384-22-0). Cowley Pubns.

Turner, R. Edward. Proclaiming the Word: The Concept of Preaching in the Thought of Ellen G. White. (Andrews University Monographs, Studies in Religion: Vol. XII). x, 183p. 1980. pap. 3.95 (ISBN 0-943872-12-X). Andrews Univ Pr.

Turner, Victor. The Forest of Symbols: Aspects of Ndembu Ritual. LC 67-12308. (Illus.). 417p. 1970. pap. 12.95x (ISBN 0-8014-9101-0, CP101). Cornell U Pr.

Turner, Victor & Turner, Edith. Image & Pilgrimage in Christian Culture. LC 77-25442. (Lectures on the History of Religions Ser.). 1978. 25.00x (ISBN 0-231-04286-8). Columbia U Pr.

Turner, Wayne A. Leviticus. (Bible Commentary Ser.). 112p. 1985. pap. 2.95 (ISBN 0-8146-1372-1). Liturgical Pr.

Turner, William. A Preservative, or Triacle, Agaynst the Poyson of Pelagius. LC 78-171795. (English Experience Ser.: No. 418). 208p. 1971. Repr. of 1551 ed. 20.00 (ISBN 90-221-0418-4). Walter J Johnson.

Turner, William B. Theology - The Quintessence of Science. LC 80-82649. 306p. 1981. 17.50 (ISBN 0-8022-2375-3). Philos Lib.

Turner, William H. Pentecost & Tongues. pap. 3.50 (ISBN 0-911866-83-3). Advocate.

Turnquist, Jeanette, jt. auth. see Birkey, Verna.

Turowski, Diane, ed. see Wright, Bonnie L., et al.

Turpin, Joanne. The Healing Mysteries: A Rosary for the Sick. 25p. (Orig.). 1983. pap. text ed. 1.35 (ISBN 0-86716-018-7). St Anthony Mess Pr.

--Jesus' Journey, Our Journey: A Way of the Cross for the Sick & Shut-in. 1987. pap. 2.25. St Anthony Mess Pr.

Turrettin, Thomas. The Doctrine of Scripture: Locus 2 of Institutio Theologiae Elencticae. Beardslee, John W., III, ed. 200p. (Orig.). 1981. pap. 7.95 (ISBN 0-8010-8857-7). Baker Bk.

Turton, Mary, tr. see Godin, Andre.

Turville-Petre, E. O. Myth & Religion of the North. LC 75-5003. (Illus.). 340p. 1975. Repr. of 1964 ed. lib. bdg. 49.75x (ISBN 0-8371-7420-1, TUMR). Greenwood.

Tushita Meditation Centre, compiled by. International Buddhist Directory 1985. (A Wisdom Reference Bk.). 150p. (Orig.). 1985. pap. write for info. (ISBN 0-86171-025-8, Wisdom Bks). Great Traditions.

Tuthill, Marge. Art for Children's Liturgy: What You Need & How To Do It. LC 82-60855. 1982. pap. 4.95 (ISBN 0-8091-2478-5). Paulist Pr.

Tuttle, Anthony. With God on Our Side. 1978. pap. 2.25 (ISBN 0-89083-324-9). Zebra.

Tuttle, Daniel S. Missionary to the Mountain West: The Reminiscences of Episcopal Bishop Daniel S. Tuttle, 1866-1886. 509p. 1987. Repr. of 1906 ed. 20.00 (ISBN 0-87480-305-5). U of Utah Pr.

Tuttle, Robert G. Help Is on the Way: Overcoming Barriers to Spirit-Assisted Prayer. LC 83-80412. 128p. (Orig.). 1983. pap. 4.95 (ISBN 0-8358-0461-5). Upper Room.

--Help Me God! It's Hard to Cope. 1984. 4.95 (ISBN 0-89536-698-3, 4881). CSS of Ohio.

Tuttle, Robert G., Jr. John Wesley: His Life & Theology. 368p. 1982. pap. 9.95 (ISBN 0-310-36661-5, 11260P). Zondervan.

Tutu, Desmond M. Hope & Suffering: Sermons & Speeches. 189p. (Orig.). 1984. pap. 6.95 (ISBN 0-8028-0085-8). Eerdmans.

Tuuk, E. J., jt. auth. see Hylkema, G. W.

Tuveson, Ernest L. Imagination As a Means of Grace. LC 73-21543. 218p. 1973. Repr. of 1960 ed. 20.00x (ISBN 0-87752-173-5). Gordian.

Tvedtnes, John. The Church of the Old Testament. rev. ed. LC 80-18595. 111p. 1980. 6.95 (ISBN 0-87747-827-9). Deseret Bk.

Twain, Mark. Christian Science. 196p. 1986. 21.95 (ISBN 0-87975-316-1). Prometheus Bks.

--Concerning the Jews. LC 84-27665. 32p. (Orig.). 1985. lib. bdg. 12.90 (ISBN 0-89471-336-1); pap. 3.95 (ISBN 0-89471-335-3). Running Pr.

--Plymouth Rock & the Pilgrims: And Other Salutary Opinions. Neider, Charles, ed. LC 84-47603. 320p. 1984. 19.45i (ISBN 0-06-015353-9, HarpT). Har-Row.

--What Is Man? & Other Philosophical Writings. Baender, Paul, ed. & intro. by. LC 78-104109. (Mark Twain Works: Vol. 19). 1973. 29.00x (ISBN 0-520-01621-1). U of Cal Pr.

Tweedie, Irina. Daughter of Fire: A Diary of a Spiritual Training with a Sufi Master. Clemens, Paul M., ed. LC 86-72368. 832p. 1986. 29.95 (ISBN 0-931892-05-8); pap. 19.95 (ISBN 0-931892-04-X). B Dolphin Pub.

Tweedie, W. K., tr. see Rilliet, Albert.

Twenty-Four Magazine Editors & Burns, John. Sacred Sex. White, Thomas R., ed. LC 74-84538. (Illus.). 150p. (Orig.). 1975. pap. 1.95 (ISBN 0-914896-01-6, Strength). East Ridge Pr.

Twerski, Abraham J. Self-Discovery in Recovery. 128p. (Orig.). 1984. pap. 3.95 (ISBN 0-89486-238-3). Hazelden.

Twersky, Abraham J. Generation to Generation: Recollections of a Chassidic Legacy. 256p. 1985. 14.95 (ISBN 0-933711-17-4). Traditional Pr.

Twersky, I. Studies in Jewish Law & Philosophy. 39.50x (ISBN 0-87068-335-7). Ktav.

Twersky, Isadore. Maimonides Reader. LC 76-160818. pap. 9.95x (ISBN 0-87441-206-4). Behrman.

--Rabad of Posquieres: A Twelfth-Century Talmudist. LC 62-7192. (Semitic Ser: No. 18). 1962. 22.50x (ISBN 0-674-74550-7). Harvard U Pr.

Twersky, Isadore, jt. auth. see Maimonides, Moses.

Twersky, Isadore, ed. Danzig: Between East & West. (Harvard Judaica Texts & Studies: Vol. IV). 185p. 1984. text ed. 21.00x (ISBN 0-674-19255-9); pap. text ed. 14.00x (ISBN 0-674-19256-7). Harvard U Pr.

--Rabbi Moses Nahmanides: Explorations in His Religious & Literary Virtuosity. (Center for Jewish Studies Ser.). 110p. (Orig.). 1983. pap. text ed. 9.50x (ISBN 0-674-74560-4). Harvard U Pr.

--Studies in Medieval Jewish History & Literature. LC 79-11588. (Judaic Monographs: No. 2). 1979. text ed. 25.00x (ISBN 0-674-85192-7). Harvard U Pr.

--Studies in Medieval Jewish History & Literature, Vol. 2. (Harvard Judaic Monographs: No. V). 460p. 1985. text ed. 25.00x (ISBN 0-674-85193-5). Harvard U Ctr Jewish.

Twersky, Isadore & Septimus, Bernard, eds. Jewish Thought in the Seventeenth Century. (Harvard Judaic Texts & Studies: VI). 425p. 1986. text ed. 25.00x (ISBN 0-674-47465-1); pap. text ed. 12.50x (ISBN 0-674-47466-X). Harvard U Pr.

Twersky, Isadore, ed. see Wolfson, Harry A.

Twigg, Blanche. Penance: God's Gift for Forgiveness. (Illus.). 64p. 1974. pap. 2.50 (ISBN 0-912228-15-6). St Anthony Mess Pr.

Twining, R. H. Science and Religion-Convergence or Collision. 136p. pap. 2.95 (ISBN 0-686-12939-3). Hiawatha Bondurant.

Twitchell, Paul. Anitya. (Illus.). 1969. 5.95 (ISBN 0-914766-01-5). IWP Pub.

--Le Carnet De Notes Spiritual. 1978. pap. 3.95 (ISBN 0-914766-40-6). IWP Pub.

--Coins of Gold. 1972. 5.95 (ISBN 0-914766-02-3). IWP Pub.

--Dialogues with the Master. 1970. pap. 5.95 (ISBN 0-914766-78-3). IWP Pub.

--Drums of ECK. 1970. pap. 3.95 (ISBN 0-914766-04-X). IWP Pub.

--The ECK Vidya: The Ancient Science of Prophecy. LC 75-306773. 237p. 1972. 5.95 (ISBN 0-914766-89-9). IWP Pub.

--Eckankar: Illuminated Way Letters 1966-1971. 272p. 1975. 5.95 (ISBN 0-914766-25-2). IWP Pub.

--Eckankar: La Clave de los Mondos Secretos. 1978. pap. 5.95 (ISBN 0-88155-029-9). IWP Pub.

--L' Etranger au Bord de La Riviere. 1979. pap. 5.95 (ISBN 0-914766-42-2). IWP Pub.

--The Far Country. 1971. pap. 5.95 (ISBN 0-914766-91-0). IWP Pub.

--Der Fremde Am Fluss. 1979. pap. 5.95 (ISBN 0-914766-43-0). Iwp Pub.

--Krauter: Die Magischen Heiler. 1978. pap. 3.95 (ISBN 0-914766-39-2). IWP Pub.

--The Shariyat-Ki-Sugmad. 1971. Vol. 1 1970. kivar bdg. 7.95 (ISBN 0-914766-13-9); Vol. 2 1971. 7.95 (ISBN 0-914766-14-7). IWP Pub.

--Le Shariyat-Ki-Sugmad, Vol. 2. (Fr.). 189p. 1983. pap. 7.95 (ISBN 0-914766-72-4). IWP Pub.

--The Spiritual Notebook. LC 74-178996. 218p. 1971. pap. 5.95 (ISBN 0-914766-94-5). IWP Pub.

--Stranger by the River. 176p. 1970. pap. 5.95 (ISBN 0-914766-16-3). IWP Pub.

--The Tiger's Fang. 1979. 5.95 (ISBN 0-914766-51-1). IWP Pub.

--Way of Dharma. 1970. pap. 3.95 (ISBN 0-914766-18-X). IWP Pub.

Twitchett, Denis, jt. ed. see Wright, Arthur F.

Two Hermits. The Revelation of Bethlehem. 1985. pap. 3.50 (ISBN 0-932506-41-0). St Bedes Pubns.

Twombly, Gerald & Kennedy, Timothy. A Taste of Grace, Vol. 1. (Illus.). 182p. 1982. pap. 7.50 (ISBN 0-910219-04-4). Little People.

Twombly, Gerald H. An Analytical Survey of the Bible. pap. 5.95 (ISBN 0-88469-120-9). BMH Bks.

--Major Themes from the Minor Prophets. (Adult Study Guide Ser.). 144p. (Orig.). 1981. pap. 4.95 (ISBN 0-88469-132-2). BMH Bks.

--The Penetrating Poets. 112p. 1982. pap. 4.95 (ISBN 0-88469-151-9). BMH Bks.

Twombly, Robert C. Frank Lloyd Wright: His Life & His Architecture. 1986. pap. 19.95 (ISBN 0-471-85797-1). Wiley.

Twomey, Gerald S. When Catholics Marry Again: A Guide for the Divorced, Their Families & Those Who Minister to Them. 194p. (Orig.). 1982. pap. 7.95 (ISBN 0-86683-633-0, HarpR). Har-Row.

Twomey, Mark J. A Parade of Saints. LC 82-202387. (Illus.). 176p. 1983. 10.95 (ISBN 0-8146-1275-X). Liturgical Pr.

Twomley, Dale E. Parochiaid & the Courts. (Andrews University Monographs, Studies in Education: Vol. 2). x, 165p. 1979. 3.95 (ISBN 0-943872-51-0). Andrews Univ Pr.

Twyman, jt. tr. see McIntosk.

Twyman, Leo, tr. see Hemleben, Johannes.

Tyabji, Badi-Ud Din. The Self in Secularism. 1971. 21.50x (ISBN 0-8046-8832-X, Pub. by Kennikat). Assoc Faculty Pr.

Tyack, George S. Lore & Legend of the English Church. 1979. Repr. of 1899 ed. lib. bdg. 50.00 (ISBN 0-8495-5135-8). Arden Lib.

Tyagaraja. Spiritual Heritage of Tyagaraja. Ramanujachari, C., tr. (Sanskrit, Telegu & Eng.). 15.00 (ISBN 0-87481-440-5). Vedanta Pr.

Tyagisananda, Swami, tr. Svetasvataropanisad. (Sanskrit & Eng.). pap. 2.00 (ISBN 0-87481-418-9). Vedanta Pr.

Tyagisananda, Swami, tr. see Narada.

Tyberg, Judith M. Sanskrit Keys to the Wisdom-Religion. 180p. 1976. pap. 5.00 (ISBN 0-913004-29-4). Point Loma Pub.

Tychsen, Laurie. Too Many People? Answers & Hope for the Human Family. 46p. (Orig.). 1986. pap. 3.25 (ISBN 0-937779-03-2). Greenlawn Pr.

Tyerman, Luke. The Life & Times of the Rev. John Wesley, 3 vols. LC 72-82522. 1973. Repr. of 1872 ed. Set. lib. bdg. 89.00 (ISBN 0-8337-4710-X). B Franklin.

--The Life of the Rev. George Whitefield, 2 vols. LC 75-31102. Repr. of 1877 ed. 97.50 (ISBN 0-404-13540-4). AMS Pr.

Tygstrup, Niels & Olsson, Rolf, eds. Alcohol & Disease. (Illus.). 290p. 1985. text ed. 62.50x (ISBN 91-22-00786-5, Pub. by Almqvist & Wiksell). Coronet Bks.

Tylenda, Joseph. The Imitation of Christ: New Translation from the Original Latin Text. 1984. pap. 7.95 (ISBN 0-89453-432-7). M Glazier.

Tylenda, Joseph N. Jesuit Saints & Martyrs. 503p. 1984. 15.95 (ISBN 0-8294-0447-3). Loyola.

Tylenda, Joseph N., ed. Counsels for Jesuits: Selected Letters & Instructions of Saint Ignatius Loyola. 152p. 1985. pap. 4.95 (ISBN 0-8294-0496-1). Loyola.

--Portraits in American Sanctity. 1983. 18.00 (ISBN 0-686-45830-3). Franciscan Herald.

Tylenda, Joseph N., tr. & intro. by. A Pilgrim's Journey: The Autobiography of Ignatius of Loyola. 1985. pap. 8.95 (ISBN 0-89453-468-8). M Glazier.

Tyler, Bennet. New England Revivals, As They Existed at the Close of the Eighteenth & the Beginning of the Nineteenth Centuries Compiled Principally from Narratives First Pub. in the Conn. Evangelical Magazine Revival Library. 378p. 1980. Repr. of 1846 ed. lib. bdg. 12.95 (ISBN 0-940033-18-6). R O Roberts.

Tyler, Bennet & Bonar, Andrew. The Life & Labours of Asahel Nettleton. 1975. 10.95 (ISBN 0-85151-208-9). Banner of Truth.

Tyler, Hamilton A. Pueblo God & Myths. LC 64-11317. (The Civilization of the American Indians Ser.: Vol. 71). (Illus.). 336p. 1984. pap. 8.95 (ISBN 0-8061-1112-7). U of Okla Pr.

Tylor, Edward. Religion in Primitive Culture. (Primitive Culture - Part 2). 18.75 (ISBN 0-8446-0946-3). Peter Smith.

Tynan, Michael. Catechism For Catholics. 96p. (Orig.). 1983. pap. 5.95 (ISBN 0-87061-088-0). Chr Classics.

Tyndale, William. An Answer to Sir Thomas More's Dialogue, the Supper of the Lord After the True Meaning of John 6 & or. 11. Repr. of 1850 ed. 31.00 (ISBN 0-384-62240-2). Johnson Repr.

--A Compendious Introduccion Unto the Pistle off Paul to the Romaynes. LC 74-28890. (English Experience Ser.: No. 767). 1975. Repr. 3.50 (ISBN 90-221-0767-1). Walter J Johnson.

--Doctrinal Treatises, an Introduction to Different Portions of the Holy Scriptures. Repr. of 1848 ed. 51.00 (ISBN 0-384-62250-X). Johnson Repr.

--Expositions & Notes on Sundry Portions of the Holy Scriptures. Repr. of 1849 ed. 31.00 (ISBN 0-384-62260-7). Johnson Repr.

--Five Books of Moses Called the Pentateuch. LC 67-23739. (Centaur Classics Ser.). 791p. 1967. 32.50x (ISBN 0-8093-0259-4). S Ill U Pr.

--The Obedience of a Christen Man & How Christe Rulers Ought to Governe. LC 77-7436. (English Experience Ser.: No. 897). 1977. Repr. of 1528 ed. lib. bdg. 24.00 (ISBN 90-221-0897-X). Walter J Johnson.

Tyndale-Biscoe, J. For God Alone: The Life of George West, Bishop of Rangoon. 1985. 30.00x (ISBN 0-317-43630-9, Pub. by Amate Pr. Ltd). State Mutual Bk.

Tyrrell, Bernard J. Bernard Lonergan's Philosophy of God. LC 73-22205. pap. 54.00 (ISBN 0-317-29698-1, 2022063). Bks Demand UMI.

--Christotherapy II: A New Horizon for Counselors, Spiritual Directors & Seekers of Healing & Growth in Christ. LC 82-60597. (Orig.). 1982. 12.95 (ISBN 0-8091-0332-X); pap. 8.95 (ISBN 0-8091-2482-3). Paulist Pr.

Tyrrell, Francis M. Man: Believer & Unbeliever. LC 73-20055. 475p. (Orig.). 1974. pap. 7.95 (ISBN 0-8189-0283-3). Alba.

Tyson, John R. Charles Wesley on Sanctification: A Biographical & Theological Study. 240p. 1986. pap. 10.95 (ISBN 0-310-75131-4, 17054P). Zondervan.

Tyson, Joseph B. The Death of Jesus in Luke-Acts. 212p. 1986. text ed. 17.95 (ISBN 0-87249-461-6). U of SC Pr.

--The New Testament & Early Christianity. 480p. 1984. text ed. write for info. (ISBN 0-02-421890-1). Macmillan.

--A Study of Early Christianity. Scott, Kenneth J., ed. (Illus.). 448p. 1973. text ed. write for info. (ISBN 0-02-421900-2). Macmillan.

Tyson, Joseph B. & Longstaff, Thomas R. W. Synoptic Abstract. Baird, J. Arthur & Freedman, David Noel, eds. (The Computer Bible Ser.: Vol. XV). 1978. pap. 15.00 (ISBN 0-935106-05-7). Biblical Res Assocs.

Tyson-Flyn, Juanita, ed. see Davy, Yvonne.

Tzu, Huai-nan. Tao, the Great Luminant: Essays from Huai-Nan-Tzu. Morgan, Evan, tr. from Chinese. 301p. Repr. of 1935 ed. text ed. 24.00x (ISBN 0-89644-062-1, Pub. by Chinese Matl Ctr). Coronet Bks.

Tzu, Lao. Tao Te Ching. (Sacred Texts Ser.). Orig. Title: Chinese. viii, 88p. 1983. pap. 8.75 (ISBN 0-88695-007-4). Concord Grove.

--The Way of the Ways Tao. Maurer, Herrymon, tr. from Chinese. 108p. 1985. 10.95 (ISBN 0-8052-3985-5). Schocken.

U

Uboldi, Gian L., illus. A Book of Prayers. (Illus.). 192p. 1981. 4.95 (ISBN 0-87973-667-4, 667). Our Sunday Visitor.

UBS Committee, ed. Preliminary & Interim Report on the Hebrew Old Testament Text Project, Vols. 1-5. Incl. Vol. 1. (Pentateuch). xxxiii, 317p. 1973. pap. 4.00x (ISBN 0-8267-0008-X, 08520); Vol. 2. (Historical Bks.). xxxiv, 556p. 1976. pap. 6.60x (ISBN 0-8267-0009-8, 08521); Vol. 3. (Poetical Books). xxxiii, 620p. 1977. pap. 7.00x (ISBN 0-8267-0010-1, 08522); Vol. 4. (Prophetical Books: No. 1). xxxiii, 335p. 1979. pap. 4.50x (ISBN 0-8267-0011-X, 08523); (Prophetical Books: No. 2). xxxiii, 443p. 1980. pap. 5.00x (ISBN 0-8267-0012-8, 08559). (Eng. & Fr., Pub. by United Bible). Am Bible.

--Preliminary & Interim Report on the Hebrew Old Testament Text Project, Vol. 2. (Historical Bks.). (Eng. & Fr.). xxiv, 556p. 1976. pap. 6.60x (ISBN 0-8267-0009-8, 08521, Pub. by United Bible). Am Bible.

--Preliminary & Interim Report on the Hebrew Old Testament Text Project, Vol. 3. (Poetical Books). (Eng. & Fr.). xxxiii, 620p. 1977. pap. 7.00x (ISBN 0-8267-0010-1, 08522, Pub. by United Bible). Am Bible.

--Preliminary & Interim Report on the Hebrew Old Testament Text Project, Vol. 5. (Prophetical Bks.: No. II). (Eng. & Fr.). xxxiii, 443p. 1980. pap. 5.00x (ISBN 0-8267-0012-8, 08559, Pub. by United Bible). Am Bible.

UCC. Pilgrim Hymnal: Organist's Edition. 1981. 15.00 (ISBN 0-8298-0454-4). Pilgrim NY.

Uchill, Ida L. Pioneers, Peddlers, & Tsadikim: The Story of the Jews in Colorado. 2nd ed. LC 57-57817. 327p. 1979. pap. 9.95 (ISBN 0-9604468-0-X). Uchill.

Uchiyama, Kosho & Uchiyama, Kosho. Refining Your Life: From the Zen Kitchen to Enlightenment. Wright, Tom, tr. LC 82-20295. 136p. 1983. pap. 9.95 (ISBN 0-8348-0179-5). Weatherhill.

Ud Din Attar, Farid see Attar, Farid Ud-Din.

Udo de Haes, Daniel. The Young Child: Creative Living with Two to Four Year Olds. Blaxland de Lange, Simon & Blaxland de Lange, Paulamaria, trs. from Dutch. 90p. (Orig.). 1986. pap. 10.95 (ISBN 0-88010-169-5). Anthroposophic.

Udovitch, A. L., ed. Islamic Middle East 700-1900: Studies in Economic & Social History. LC 79-52703. (Illus.). 838p. 1981. 29.95x (ISBN 0-87850-030-8). Darwin Pr.

Udovitch, Abraham L., jt. auth. see Valensi, Lucette.

Udupa, K. N. Stress & Its Management by Yoga. 400p. 1986. 25.00X (ISBN 81-208-0000-1, Pub. by Motilal Banarsidass). South Asia Bks.

Uhl, Catherine. Gospel Lesson Plans. LC 79-65918. 136p. 1979. pap. 7.95 (ISBN 0-8091-2211-1). Paulist Pr.

Uhl, Harold J. Good News from John: Visual Messages for Children. LC 79-50094. 1979. pap. 6.95 (ISBN 0-8066-1712-8, 10-2811). Augsburg.

--The Gospel for Children: Object Messages from the Gospel of Mark. LC 75-14695. 128p. 1975. pap. 6.95 (ISBN 0-8066-1493-5, 10-2830). Augsburg.

Uhlein, Gabriele. Meditations with TM Hildegard of Bingen. LC 82-74151. (Meditations with TM). 129p. (Orig.). 1982. pap. 6.95 (ISBN 0-939680-12-2). Bear & Co.

Uhlfelder, Myra L. Life of St. Benedict: St. Gregory's Dialogues, Book 2. 1967. pap. text ed. write for info. (ISBN 0-02-422100-7). Macmillan.

Uhlfelder, Myra L., tr. see Gregory The Great.

Uhrich, Ethel. Manners in God's House. (Illus.). 1972. pap. 3.95 (ISBN 0-87239-272-4, 2586). Standard Pub.

Uhrig, Larry. Sex Positive. 160p. (Orig.). 1985. pap. 6.95 (ISBN 0-932870-82-1). Alyson Pubns.

Uitti, Karl D. Story, Myth & Celebration in Old French Narrative Poetry 1050-1200. LC 72-4048. 272p. 1973. 30.50x (ISBN 0-691-06242-0). Princeton U Pr.

Ujka, Mary. The Cross Gives Me Courage. LC 83-60743. 132p. (Orig.). 1983. pap. 5.95 (ISBN 0-87973-618-6, 618). Our Sunday Visitor.

U Kyaw Min. Buddhist Adhidhamma: Meditation & Concentration. 192p. Date not set. pap. 6.95 (ISBN 0-89346-287-X). Heian Intl.

Ulanov, Ann & Ulanov, Barry. Primary Speech: A Psychology of Prayer. LC 81-85328. 192p. 1982. 10.95 (ISBN 0-8042-1134-5). John Knox.

--Religion & the Unconscious. LC 75-16302. 288p. 1975. 13.95 (ISBN 0-664-20799-5). Westminster.

--Religion & the Unconscious. 2nd ed. LC 75-16302. 288p. 1985. pap. 14.95 (ISBN 0-664-24657-5). Westminster.

Ulanov, Ann, jt. auth. see Ulanov, Barry.

Ulanov, Ann B. Receiving Woman: Studies in the Psychology & Theology of the Feminine. LC 80-26813. 186p. 1981. pap. 9.95 (ISBN 0-664-24360-6). Westminster.

Ulanov, Barry & Ulanov, Ann. Cinderella & Her Sisters: The Envied & the Envying. LC 83-10463. 186p. 1983. pap. 9.95 (ISBN 0-664-24482-3). Westminster.

Ulanov, Barry, jt. auth. see Ulanov, Ann.

Ulanov, Barry, tr. from Lat. Prayers of St. Augustine: A Contemporary Anthology. 160p. (Orig.). 1984. pap. 7.95 (ISBN 0-86683-881-3, 7460, HarpR). Har-Row.

Ulery, Lloyd K. The Far Journey Through Life, Love & Eternity. LC 77-91280. 185p. 1978. 7.95 (ISBN 0-930984-01-3). Psychic Bks.

Ulich, Robert. History of Religious Education: Documents & Interpretations from the Judaeo-Christian Tradition. LC 68-29433. 1968. 30.00 (ISBN 0-8147-0420-4). NYU Pr.

Ullah, Mohammad Z. The Islamic Concept of God. 100p. (Orig.). 1984. 26.95x (ISBN 0-7103-0076-X, Kegan Paul). Methuen Inc.

--The Islamic Concept of God. 116p. 1985. pap. 9.95 (ISBN 0-7103-0127-8, Kegan Paul). Methuen Inc.

Ullendorff, Edward. Ethiopia & the Bible. (British Academy Ser). 1968. 29.95x (ISBN 0-19-725904-9). Oxford U Pr.

Ullian, J. S., jt. auth. see Quine, W. V.

Ullman, Joan C. Tragic Week: A Study of Anticlericalism in Spain, 1875-1912. LC 67-27082. 1968. 27.50x (ISBN 0-674-90240-8). Harvard U Pr.

Ullman, Walter. Medieval Papalism: The Political Theories of the Medieval Canonists. LC 79-1644. 1981. Repr. of 1949 ed. 21.50 (ISBN 0-88355-946-3). Hyperion Conn.

Ullmann, C. Reformers Before the Reformation in Germany & the Netherlands, 2 vols. 1977. lib. bdg. 200.00 (ISBN 0-8490-2507-9). Gordon Pr.

Ullmann, Richard K. The Dilemmas of a Reconciler. 1983. pap. 2.50x (ISBN 0-87574-131-2, 131). Pendle Hill.

Ullmann, Walter. A Short History of the Papacy in the Middle Ages. 1974. pap. 16.95x (ISBN 0-416-74970-4, NO. 2562). Methuen Inc.

Ulmer. Adam's Story. LC 59-1292. (Arch Bks.). 24p. (Orig.). 1985. pap. 0.99 (ISBN 0-570-06191-1). Concordia.

Ulmer, L. The Bible That Wouldn't Burn. LC 39-1094. 1983. pap. 3.95 (ISBN 0-570-03634-8). Concordia.

Ulmer, Louise. Bringing Bible People to Life. 1982. 2.95 (ISBN 0-89536-574-X, 0217). CSS of Ohio.

--Charity & the Great Adventure. (Orig.). 1987. pap. price not set (ISBN 0-89536-882-X, 7868). CSS of Ohio.

--Help, I'm in Trouble: True-to-Life Stories for Young Teens. LC 86-8034. (Illus.). 112p. (Orig.). 1986. pap. 3.95 (ISBN 0-8066-2215-6, 10-3008). Augsburg.

--Jesus' Twelve Disciples: Arch Bks. 1982. pap. 0.99 (ISBN 0-570-06160-1, 59-1307). Concordia.

--Samuel, the Judge. (Arch Bks.). (Illus.). 24p. 1986. pap. 0.99 saddlestitched (ISBN 0-570-06200-4, 59-1423). Concordia.

Ulrich, Eugene C., Jr. The Qumran Text of Samuel & Josephus. LC 78-15254. (Harvard Semitic Museum. Harvard Semitic Monographs: No. 19). 1978. 15.00 (ISBN 0-89130-256-5, 040019). Scholars Pr GA.

Ulrich, Robert J. The Bennett Law of 1889: Education & Politics in Wisconsin. Cordasco, Francesco, ed. LC 80-902. (American Ethnic Groups Ser.). 1981. lib. bdg. 55.00x (ISBN 0-405-13462-2). Ayer Co Pubs.

Ultee, Maarten. The Abbey of St. Germain des Pres in the Seventeenth Century. LC 81-2265. (Illus.). 224p. 1981. text ed. 24.50x (ISBN 0-300-02562-9). Yale U Pr.

Ulyat, Richard T. United in Marriage: A Guide to Premarital Counseling. 47p. 1984. pap. 3.50 (ISBN 0-86544-023-9). Salv Army Suppl South.

Umansky, Ellen J. Lily Montagu: Sermons, Addresses, Letters & Prayers. LC 85-3053. (Studies in Women & Religion: Vol. 15). (Illus.). 415p. 1985. 69.95x (ISBN 0-88946-534-7). E Mellen.

Umansky, Ellen M. Lily Montagu & the Advancement of Liberal Judaism: From Vision to Vocation. LC 83-22005. (Studies in Women & Religion: Vol. 12). 305p. 1984. 49.95x (ISBN 0-88946-537-1). E Mellen.

Umasvati. Tattvarthadhigama Sutra (A Treatise on the Essential Principles of Jainism) Jaini, J. L., ed. & intro. by. LC 73-3836. (Sacred Books of the Jainas: No. 2). Repr. of 1920 ed. 21.50 (ISBN 0-404-57702-4). AMS Pr.

Umbach, Herbert H., ed. see Donne, John.

Umbreit, Mark. Crime & Reconciliation. 144p. (Orig.). 1985. pap. 7.95 (ISBN 0-687-09885-8). Abingdon.

Umen, Samuel. Jewish Concepts & Reflections. LC 62-9774. 190p. 1962. 10.00 (ISBN 0-8022-1748-6). Philos Lib.

--Pharisaism & Jesus. LC 62-20875. 1962. 5.00 (ISBN 0-8022-1752-4). Philos Lib.

Umphrey, Don. The Meanest Man in Texas. LC 84-3383. 288p. 1984. pap. 6.95 (ISBN 0-8407-5870-7). Nelson.

Unamuno, Miguel. Tragic Sense of Life. Flitch, J. Crawford, tr. 1921. pap. 6.00 (ISBN 0-486-20257-7). Dover.

Unamuno, Miguel De see De Unamuno, Miguel.

Underdown, David. Pride's Purge: Politics in the Puritan Revolution. 440p. 1985. pap. text ed. 13.50x (ISBN 0-04-822045-0). Allen Unwin.

Underhill, Edward B. West Indies: Their Social & Religious Condition. LC 73-107525. Repr. of 1862 ed. 24.75x (ISBN 0-8371-3772-1, UWI&). Greenwood.

Underhill, Edwin B., ed. Tracts on Liberty of Conscience & Persecution. (Philosophy Monographs: No. 11). 1968. Repr. of 1846 ed. 29.50 (ISBN 0-8337-3594-2). B Franklin.

Underhill, Evelyn. Abba. LC 82-80476. (Treasures from the Spiritual Classics Ser.). 64p. 1982. pap. 2.95 (ISBN 0-8192-1313-6). Morehouse.

--The Essentials of Mysticism & Other Essays. LC 75-41277. Repr. of 1920 ed. 18.00 (ISBN 0-404-14620-1). AMS Pr.

--The Fruits of the Spirit. LC 82-80477. (Treasures from the Spiritual Classics Ser.). 64p. 1982. pap. 2.95 (ISBN 0-8192-1314-4). Morehouse.

--The House of the Soul & Concerning the Inner Life. 150p. (Orig.). 1984. pap. 6.95 (ISBN 0-86683-882-1, 7459, HarpR). Har-Row.

--Meditations Based on the Lord's Prayer. 59.95 (ISBN 0-8490-0601-5). Gordon Pr.

--Mixed Pasture. facs. ed. LC 68-8501. (Essay Index Reprint Ser). 1933. 17.00 (ISBN 0-8369-0958-5). Ayer Co Pubs.

--Mysticism. 1955. pap. 12.95 (ISBN 0-452-00840-9, Mer). NAL.

--Mystics of the Church. 260p. 1975. 13.95 (ISBN 0-227-67820-6). Attic Pr.

--Practical Mysticism. 160p. 1986. pap. 5.95 (ISBN 0-89804-143-0). Ariel OH.

--The Spiritual Life. LC 84-60646. 128p. 1984. pap. 4.95 (ISBN 0-8192-1350-0). Morehouse.

--Worship. LC 78-20499. 1983. Repr. of 1937 ed. 31.35 (ISBN 0-88355-874-2). Hyperion Conn.

--Worship. (Crossroad Paperback Ser.). (Illus.). 1982. pap. 12.95 (ISBN 0-8245-0466-6). Crossroad NY.

Underhill, Ruth M. Papago Indian Religion. LC 74-82363. (Columbia Univ. Contributions to Anthropology Ser.: Vol. 33). Repr. of 1946 ed. 37.50 (ISBN 0-404-50583-X). AMS Pr.

--Red Man's Religion: Beliefs & Practices of the Indians North of Mexico. LC 65-24985. 1972. pap. 10.00 (ISBN 0-226-84167-7, P481, Phoen). U of Chicago Pr.

Underhill, Ruth M., et al. Rainhouse & Ocean: Speeches for the Papago Year. LC 79-66733. (American Tribal Religions Ser.: Vol. 4). (Illus.). vi, 154p. 1979. pap. 12.95x (ISBN 0-89734-029-9, Pub by Mus Northern Ariz). U of Nebr Pr.

Underwood, B. E. Gifts of the Spirit. 3.95 (ISBN 0-911866-64-7); pap. 2.95 (ISBN 0-911866-65-5). Advocate.

--Spirit's Sword: God's Infallible Book. 1969. 3.95 (ISBN 0-911866-50-7); pap. 2.95 (ISBN 0-911866-91-4). Advocate.

--Spiritual Gifts-Ministries & Manifestations. pap. 6.95 (ISBN 0-911866-03-5). Advocate.

--Spiritual Gifts: Ministries & Manifestations. pap. 3.95 student wkbk. (ISBN 0-911866-04-3); pap. 6.95 tchr's. guide (ISBN 0-911866-05-1). Advocate.

Underwood, Dan. Acts. (Standard Bible Study Workbooks Ser.). 80p. 1987. wkbk. 1.95 (ISBN 0-87403-185-0, 40205). Standard Pub.

Underwood, David A. Luke. (Standard Bible Study Workbooks Ser.). 64p. 1986. pap. text ed. 1.95 (ISBN 0-87403-183-4, 40203). Standard Pub.

Underwood, Gary & Underwood, Marylyn. After First Principles. 1984. pap. 4.25 (ISBN 0-89137-710-7). Quality Pubns.

--First Principles: Topical Studies for New Converts. 1978. 4.95 (ISBN 0-89137-709-3). Quality Pubns.

Underwood, Jon. Check Your Homelife: Leader's Guide. 64p. (Orig.). pap. 2.95 (ISBN 0-87239-759-9, 39963). Standard Pub.

--Check Your Morality: Leader's Guide. 48p. (Orig.). 1984. pap. 2.95 (ISBN 0-87239-760-2, 39961). Standard Pub.

--Triumph over Temptation: Leader's Guide. 48p. (Orig.). 1984. pap. 2.95 (ISBN 0-87239-790-4, 39977). Standard Pub.

Underwood, Jon & Roadcup, David, eds. Methods for Youth Ministry. 272p. 1986. pap. 7.95 (ISBN 0-87239-991-5, 88589). Standard Pub.

Underwood, Jonathan. First Corinthians. (Standard Bible Study Workbooks Ser.). 80p. 1987. wkbk. 1.95 (ISBN 0-87403-187-7, 40207). Standard Pub.

--A History of the English Bible. LC 83-577. 96p. 1983. pap. 3.50 (ISBN 0-87239-644-4, 39974). Standard Pub.

--Matthew. (Standard Bible Study Workbooks Ser.). 64p. 1986. pap. text ed. 1.95 (ISBN 0-87403-181-8, 40201). Standard Pub.

Underwood, Kenneth W. Protestant & Catholic. LC 72-9051. (Illus.). 484p. 1973. Repr. of 1957 ed. lib. bdg. 22.50x (ISBN 0-8371-6567-9, UNPC). Greenwood.

Underwood, Marylyn, jt. auth. see Underwood, Gary.

Underwood, Ralph L. Empathy & Confrontation in Pastoral Care. LC 85-47722. (Theology & Pastoral Care Ser.). 128p. 1986. pap. 7.50 (ISBN 0-8006-1737-1). Fortress.

Underwood, Walter L. Being Human Being Hopeful. 112p. 1987. 9.95 (ISBN 0-687-02815-9). Abingdon.

--The Contemporary Twelve: The Power of Character in Today's World. 112p. (Orig.). 1984. pap. 9.50 (ISBN 0-687-09520-4). Abingdon.

Undset, Sigrid. Saga of Saints. facs. ed. Ramsden, E. C., tr. LC 68-22952. (Essay Index Reprint Ser). 1968. Repr. of 1934 ed. 20.00 (ISBN 0-8369-0959-3). Ayer Co Pubs.

--Stages on the Road. facs. ed. Chater, A. G., tr. LC 70-80404. (Essay Index Reprint Ser). 1934. 16.50 (ISBN 0-8369-1068-0). Ayer Co Pubs.

UNESCO Colloquium, 10th Anniversary of the Death of Albert Einstein & Teilhard De Charden. Science & Synthesis: An International Colloquium Organized by UNESCO on the Tenth Anniversary of the Death of Albert Einstein & Teilhard De Chardin. Crook, B. M., tr. LC 77-143044. 1971. 29.00 (ISBN 0-387-05344-1). Springer-Verlag.

Unger, Carl. Cosmic Understanding. 1982. pap. 1.95 (ISBN 0-916786-62-5). St George Bk Serv.

--The Language of the Consciousness Soul. 1983. 25.00 (ISBN 0-916786-56-0). St George Bk Serv.

--Life Forces from Anthroposophy. 1982. pap. 1.95 (ISBN 0-916786-63-3). St George Bk Serv.

--Steiner's Theosophy: Notes on the Book "Theosophy". 1982. Repr. 5.95 (ISBN 0-916786-64-1). St George Bk Serv.

Unger, Georg. Spiritual Science & the New Nature Forces: The Nuclear Dilemma. Thomas, Nick, tr. 28p. 1981. pap. 2.95 (ISBN 0-88925-063-4, Pub. by Steiner Book Centre Canada). Anthroposophic.

Unger, Merill F. Unger's Survey of the Bible. LC 81-82675. 432p. 1981. pap. 12.95 (ISBN 0-89081-298-5). Harvest Hse.

Unger, Merrill F. The Baptism & Gifts of the Holy Spirit. LC 74-2931. 192p. 1974. pap. text ed. 6.95 (ISBN 0-8024-0467-7). Moody.

--Demons in the World Today. 1980. pap. 6.95 (ISBN 0-8423-0661-7). Tyndale.

--Israel & the Aramaeans of Damascus. (BSBA Ser.). 1980. pap. 5.95 (ISBN 0-8010-9204-3). Baker Bk.

--Manual Biblico de Unger. Orig. Title: Unger's Bible Handbook. (Span.). 954p. 1976. pap. 12.95 (ISBN 0-8254-1778-3). Kregel.

--New Testament Teaching on Tongues. LC 70-165057. 1971. pap. 5.95 (ISBN 0-8254-3900-0). Kregel.

--The New Unger's Bible Handbook. rev. ed. Larson, Gary N., ed. (Illus.). 1984. 24.95 (ISBN 0-8024-9049-2). Moody.

--Nuevo Manual Biblico de Unger. Orig. Title: New Unger's Bible Handbook. (Span.). 720p. 1987. 32.95 (ISBN 0-8254-1779-1). Kregel.

--Unger's Bible Dictionary. 1961. 22.95 (ISBN 0-8024-9035-2). Moody.

--Unger's Bible Dictionary. (Affordables Ser.). (Illus.). 1200p. 13.95 (ISBN 0-8024-0418-9). Moody.

--Unger's Bible Handbook. LC 66-16224. 1966. 9.95 (ISBN 0-8024-9039-5). Moody.

--Unger's Commentary On The Old Testament: Genesis-Song of Solomon, Vol. 1. 360p. 1981. 25.95 (ISBN 0-8024-9028-X). Moody.
--Unger's Commentary on the Old Testament: Vol. 2 (Isaiah-Malachi) LC 81-2542. 1000p. 1982. 25.95 (ISBN 0-8024-9029-8). Moody.
--Unger's Concise Bible Dictionary: With Complete Pronunciation Guide to Bible Names by W. Murray Severance. 296p. 1985. pap. 7.95 (ISBN 0-8010-9208-6). Baker Bk.
Unger, Monte, jt. auth. see Irwin, James B.
Ungerer, Walter. Habakkuk: The Man with Honest Answers. (Contemporary Discussion Ser.). 80p. 1976. pap. 1.45 (ISBN 0-8010-9202-7). Baker Bk.
Ungerleider-Mayerson, Joy. Jewish Folk Art: From Biblical Days to Modern Times. 272p. 1986. 50.00 (ISBN 0-671-63007-5). Summit Bks.
Union of American Hebrew Congregations. All in My Jewish Family. (Illus.). 32p. 1984. pap. 5.00 wkbk. (ISBN 0-8074-0266-4, 103800). UAHC.
--Spiritual Resistance: Art from the Concentration Camps 1940-1945. LC 78-1169. (Illus.). 354p. 1981. 35.00 (ISBN 0-8276-0109-3, 421). Jewish Pubns.
Union Theological Seminary. Library. Alphabetical Arrangement of Main Entries from the Shelf List of the Union Theological Seminary Library, 10 Vols. 1960. Set. 1415.00 (ISBN 0-8161-0595-2, Hall Library). G K Hall.
Union Theological Seminary Library. Shelf List of the Union Theological Seminary Library (New York), 10 vols. 1960. Set. lib. bdg. 990.00 (ISBN 0-8161-0499-9, Hall Library). G K Hall.
United Pentecostal Church Int. & Hall, J. L., eds. Symposium on Oneness Pentecostalism 1986. LC 86-19024. (Orig.). pap. 7.95 (ISBN 0-932581-03-X). Word Aflame.
United Reformed Church in England & Wales-the Doctrine & Worship Committee. A Book of Services. 1980. 8.95x (ISBN 0-7152-0446-7). Outlook.
United States Catholic Conference, Conference of Catholic Bishops, Department of Education. Sharing the Light of Faith: National Catechetical Directory for Catholics of the United States. (Illus., Orig.). 1979. pap. 6.50 (ISBN 1-55586-001-X). US Catholic.
United States Trademark Association. Protection of Corporate Names: A Country by Country Survey. LC 82-4235. 1982. looseleaf 85.00 (ISBN 0-87632-404-9). Boardman.
United Synagogue, jt. auth. see Silverman, Morris.
Unity School Of Christianity. Metaphysical Bible Dictionary. 1931. 10.00 (ISBN 0-87159-098-0). Unity School.
Unity School of Christianity, ed. Works & Wonders. LC 78-68931. 1979. 5.95 (ISBN 0-87159-175-8). Unity School.
Universal House of Justice. The Baha'i World: An International Record 1954-1963, Vol. XIII. LC 27-5882. (Illus.). 1970. 27.95 (ISBN 0-87743-042-X, 233-013). Baha'i.
--The Baha'i World: An International Record 1963-1968, Vol. XIV. LC 27-5882. (Illus.). 1974. 18.95 (ISBN 0-87743-099-3, 233-014). Baha'i.
--The Baha'i World: An International Record 1968-1973, Vol. XV. (Illus.). 1976. o. s. i. 22.95 (ISBN 0-85398-059-4, 233-015). Baha'i.
--The Baha'i World: An International Record 1973-1976, Vol. XVI. (Illus.). 1979. 24.95 (ISBN 0-85398-075-6, 233-016). Baha'i.
--Bahai World: An International Record 1976-1979, Vol. XVII. (Illus.). 1981. 29.95 (ISBN 0-87743-130-2). Baha'i.
--Baha'i World: An International Record 1976-79, Vol. XVII. (Illus.). 1981. 29.95 (ISBN 0-85398-130-2). Baha'i.
--Messages from the Universal House of Justice: 1968-1973. LC 75-11795. 1976. 9.95 (ISBN 0-87743-074-6, 225-005); pap. 4.95 (ISBN 0-87743-096-9, 225-006). Baha'i.
--Wellspring of Guidance: Messages 1963-1968. rev. ed. LC 76-129996. 1976. 9.95 (ISBN 0-87743-032-2, 225-005); pap. 4.95 (ISBN 0-87743-033-0, 225-006). Baha'i.
Unknown Christian. How to Live the Victorious Life. Link, Julie, ed. 112p. 1986. pap. 2.95 (ISBN 0-310-33481-0, 6660P, Clarion Classics). Zondervan.
--The Kneeling Christian. 1979. pap. 2.95 (ISBN 0-310-33492-6, 6657P); large print kivar o.p. 6.95 (ISBN 0-310-33497-7). Zondervan.
Unno, Taitetsu & Tabrah, Ruth. Tannisho: A Shin Buddhist Classic. 73p. (Orig.). 1985. 12.50 (ISBN 0-938474-05-7); pap. 6.95 (ISBN 0-938474-04-9). Buddhist Study.
Unopolus, James J. Scriptural Signs of the Second Coming. 1979. pap. 1.50 (ISBN 0-89036-072-3). Hawkes Pub Inc.
Unrau, Ruth. Encircled: Stories of Mennonite Women. LC 86-80403. (Illus.). 352p. 1986. pap. 12.95 (ISBN 0-87303-114-8). Faith & Life.
Unruh, Fred. Questions I'd Like to Ask God. LC 80-67504. (Illus.). 64p. 1980. tchr's. guide 3.95 (ISBN 0-87303-041-9). Faith & Life.
Unstead, R. J. Monasteries. (Junior Reference Ser.). (Illus.). 1961. 10.95 (ISBN 0-7136-1043-3). Dufour.
Unsworth, Richard P., jt. auth. see Kenseth, Arnold.
Unterman, Alan. The Art & Practices of Judaism. 96p. 1985. 20.00x (ISBN 0-7062-4126-6, Pub. by Ward Lock Educ Co Ltd). State Mutual Bk.
--The Jews. (Library of Religious Beliefs & Practices). 212p. 1986. pap. text ed. 14.95 (ISBN 0-7100-0842-2). Methuen Inc.
Unterman, Isaac. The Talmud: An Analytical Guide. LC 73-148291. 351p. 1985. text ed. 17.95 (ISBN 0-8197-0189-0); pap. text ed. 10.95 (ISBN 0-8197-0005-3). Bloch.
Unwin, George, tr. see Vandenberg, Philipp.
Upadhyaya, S. C., tr. from Sanskrit. Kama Sutra of Vatsyayana. (Illus.). xvi, 270p. 1981. Repr. of 1961 ed. text ed. 45.00x (ISBN 0-86590-027-2, Pub. by Taraporevala India). Apt Bks.
Upchurch, Stanley. Arguments Against the Bible: An Expose of the Verbal Plenary Inspiration of the Bible. 10.00x (ISBN 0-686-27700-7). Freedom Univ-FSP.
Upchurch, T. Howell. How to Hear God. (Illus.). 24p. 1985. pap. text ed. 1.00 (ISBN 0-937778-09-5). Fulness Hse.
Updike, L. Wayne. Ministry to the Bereaved. 1986. pap. 6.00 (ISBN 0-8309-0450-6). Herald Hse.
Upham, C. Salem Witchcraft, 2 vols. 1022p. 1971. Repr. of 1867 ed. Set. 48.00 (ISBN 0-87928-024-7). Corner Hse.
Upham, Charles W. Salem Witchcraft, 2 Vols. LC 59-10887. (American Classics Ser.). (Illus.). 1959. 40.00 (ISBN 0-8044-1947-7). Ungar.
Upham, Edward. The Mahavansi. the Raja-Ratnacari. & the Raja-Vali, Forming the Sacred & Historical Books of Ceylon, 3 vols. LC 78-70132. Repr. of 1833 ed. 115.00 set (ISBN 0-404-17670-4). AMS Pr.
Upham, Thomas C. The Life of Faith. (The Higher Christian Life Ser.). 480p. 1985. lib. bdg. 60.00 (ISBN 0-8240-6447-X). Garland Pub.
Upjohn, Everard M. Richard Upjohn, Architect & Churchman. LC 68-26119. (Architecture & Decorative Art Ser). (Illus.). 1968. Repr. of 1939 ed. lib. bdg. 45.00 (ISBN 0-306-71043-9). Da Capo.
Uprety, Prem R. Religion & Politics in the Punjab in the 1920's. 1981. 20.00x (ISBN 0-8364-0757-1, Pub. by Sterling). South Asia Bks.
Upson, Norma S. When Someone You Love Is Dying. 192p. 1986. pap. 6.95 (ISBN 0-671-61079-1, Fireside). S&S.
Upton, Charles B. Lectures on the Bases of Religious Belief. 2nd ed. LC 77-27161. (Hibbert Lectures: 1893). Repr. of 1897 ed. 39.50 (ISBN 0-404-60411-0). AMS Pr.
Upton, Elizabeth. Secrets of a Nun: My Own Story. LC 84-14828. 264p. 1985. 16.95 (ISBN 0-688-04187-6). Morrow.
--Secrets of a Nun: My Own Story. 1987. pap. write for info. (ISBN 0-449-21127-4, Crest). Fawcett.
Upton, William H. Negro Masonry. LC 70-144696. Repr. of 1902 ed. 16.00 (ISBN 0-404-00218-8). AMS Pr.
Upward, Allen. The Divine Mystery. LC 76-27214. 384p. 1977. lib. bdg. 12.95 (ISBN 0-915520-02-8); pap. 7.95 (ISBN 0-915520-01-X). Ross-Erikson.
Urang, Gunnar. Shadows of Heaven: Religion & Fantasy in the Writing of C. S. Lewis, Charles Williams & J. R. R. Tolkien. LC 73-153998. 208p. 1971. 7.95 (ISBN 0-8298-0197-9). Pilgrim NY.
Urba, C. F., ed. see Augustinus, Aurelius.
Urban, Dieter, jt. auth. see Stiebner, Erhardt D.
Urban, Leonard. Look What They've Done to My Church. 1985. pap. 5.95 (ISBN 0-8294-0499-6). Loyola.
Urban, Linwood. A Short History of Christian Thought. LC 85-10654. 1986. text ed. 29.95x (ISBN 0-19-503716-2); pap. text ed. 10.95x (ISBN 0-19-503717-0). Oxford U Pr.
Urban, Wilbur M. The Intelligible World: Metaphysics & Value. LC 76-51208. 1977. Repr. of 1929 ed. lib. bdg. 26.75x (ISBN 0-8371-9437-7, URIW). Greenwood.
Urbano, Luis, ed. see Banes, F. Dominico.
Urberg, S. S. Introducing Old Testament Books: With an Emphasis on Their Chronological Relationship. 1979. pap. 5.95 (ISBN 0-8010-9203-5). Baker Bk.
Ureta, Floreal, tr. see Maston, T. B.
Urfer, Pamela. Coming of Age in Judea: A Play about Young Jesus. 20p. (Orig.). 1983. pap. text ed. 3.95 (ISBN 0-912801-03-4). Creat Arts Dev.
--Five Short Plays about Jesus. 26p. (Orig.). 1983. pap. text ed. 3.95 (ISBN 0-912801-02-6). Creat Arts Dev.
--The Good-Wife. 40p. (Orig.). 1983. pap. text ed. 3.95 (ISBN 0-912801-01-8). Creat Arts Dev.
--Six Short Plays about Jesus. 35p. (Orig.). pap. text ed. 3.95 (ISBN 0-912801-07-7). Creat Arts Dev.
--Two Christmas Plays. 25p. (Orig.). pap. text ed. 3.95 (ISBN 0-912801-08-5). Creat Arts Dev.
Urfer, Pamela & Jones, Judie. Self-Destructive Tendencies of Christian Women. 109p. (Orig.). 1983. pap. text ed. 7.95 (ISBN 0-912801-04-2). Creat Arts Dev.
Urofsky, Melvin, ed. Essays in American Zionism Nineteen-Seventeen to Nineteen Forty-Eight. 1979. 12.50 (ISBN 0-930832-56-6). Herzl Pr.
Urofsky, Melvin I., jt. ed. see Kaganoff, Nathan M.
Urquhart, Colin. Receive Your Healing. 312p. 1987. pap. 10.95 (ISBN 0-8245-0807-6). Crossroad NY.
Urquhart, John. Wonders of Prophecy. pap. 3.95 (ISBN 0-87509-155-5). Chr Pubns.
Urresti, Teodoro-J & Edelby, Neophytos, eds. Pastoral Reform in Church Government. LC 65-28464. (Concilium Ser.: Vol. 8). 192p. 7.95 (ISBN 0-8091-0109-2). Paulist Pr.
Urresti, Teodoro-J., jt. ed. see Edelby, Neophytos.
Urresti, Teodoro J., et al. Renewal & Reform of Canon Law. Edelby, Neophytos, ed. LC 67-30868. (Concilium Ser.: Vol. 28). 191p. 1967. 7.95 (ISBN 0-8091-0125-4). Paulist Pr.
Urrutia, Benjamin, ed. LDSF: Latter-Day Science Fiction, Vol. 2. 192p. (Orig.). 1985. pap. text ed. 4.95 (ISBN 0-9614960-0-2). Parables.
Urshan, Nathaniel A. & Becton, Cleveland M. Harvestime Pulpit Series, Vol. III. Wallace, Mary H., ed. (Illus.). 406p. (Orig.). 1985. pap. 14.95 (ISBN 0-912315-83-0). Word Aflame.
Urs von Balthasar, Hans. Does Jesus Know Us? Do We Know Him? Harrison, Graham, tr. from Ger. LC 82-84581. Orig. Title: Kennt Uns Jesus-Kennen Wir Ihn? 99p. (Orig.). 1983. pap. 6.95 (ISBN 0-89870-023-X). Ignatius Pr.
Urteaga, J. God & Children. 241p. 1965. pap. 4.95x (ISBN 0-933932-07-3). Scepter Pubs.
--Man the Saint. 218p. 1963. pap. 4.95 (ISBN 0-933932-06-5). Scepter Pubs.
Urton, Gary. At the Crossroads of the Earth & the Sky: An Andean Cosmology. (Latin American Monograph Ser.: No. 55). (Illus.). 268p. 1981. text ed. 30.00x (ISBN 0-292-70349-X). U of Tex Pr.
Urwick, Lyndall. The Golden Book of Management: A Historical Record of the Life & Work of Seventy Pioneers. Chandler, Alfred D., ed. LC 79-7557. (History of Management Thought & Practice Ser.). (Illus.). 1980. Repr. of 1956 ed. lib. bdg. 21.00x (ISBN 0-405-12343-4). Ayer Co Pubs.
Urwick, William, tr. see Cremer, Hermann.
Urwin, J. & Robinson, S. J. The Christian State after Death Before Resurrection. pap. 2.25 (ISBN 0-88172-164-6). Believers Bkshelf.
Ury, Zalman F. Bridging the Gap Between Ethical Theory & Conduct. 0.75 (ISBN 0-914131-07-9, I35). Torah Umesorah.
--The Story of Rabbi Yisroel Salanter. 3.75 (ISBN 0-914131-60-5, D54). Torah Umesorah.
Usha, Brahmacharini, ed. Ramakrishna-Vedanta Wordbook: A Brief Dictionary of Hinduism. (Orig.). pap. 3.25 (ISBN 0-87481-017-5). Vedanta Pr.
Usher, Carolyn E., jt. auth. see McClellan, Robert W.
Usher, Charles H. Prayer Life. 1967. pap. 1.50 (ISBN 0-87508-545-8). Chr Lit.
--Satan: A Defeated Foe. 1964. pap. 1.95 (ISBN 0-87508-546-6). Chr Lit.
Usher, Kerry. Heroes, Gods, & Emperors from Roman Mythology. LC 83-11085. (World Mythology Ser.). (Illus.). 132p. 1984. 15.95 (ISBN 0-8052-3880-8). Schocken.
Usher, Roland G. The Pilgrims & Their History. (Illus.). 310p. 1977. Repr. of 1918 ed. 20.00 (ISBN 0-87928-082-4). Corner Hse.
Ussani, V., ed. see Josephus, Flavius.
Ussher, Arland. The Magic People. 12.95 (ISBN 0-8159-6200-2). Devin.
Ussher, J., ed. Britannicarum Ecclesiarum Antiquitates. 788p. Date not set. Repr. of 1687 ed. text ed. 165.60x (ISBN 0-576-72233-2, Pub. by Gregg Intl Pubs England). Gregg Intl.
Usui, Shiro. A Pilgrim's Guide to Forty-Six Temples. (Illus.). 336p. (Orig.). 1986. pap. 12.50 (ISBN 0-8348-0211-2). Weatherhill.
Uthman, Ali Bin. Kashef-Al-Mahjub. 19.95 (ISBN 0-317-01606-7). Kazi Pubns.
Utley, Uldine. Why I Am a Preacher: A Plain Answer to an Oft-Repeated Question. Gifford, Carolyn D. & Dayton, Donald, eds. (Women in American Protestant Religion 1800-1930 Ser.). 152p. 1987. lib. bdg. 25.00 (ISBN 0-8240-0680-1). Garland Pub.
UUA. Hymns of the Spirit. 7.50 (ISBN 0-933840-11-X). Unitarian Univ.
Uveeler & Bronznick. Hayesod: Fundamentals of Hebrew. LC 72-86858. 16.95x (ISBN 0-87306-071-7). Feldheim.

V

V. A. February Communications, tr. see Daneel, M. L.
Vable, D. The Arya Samaj: Hindu without Hinduism. 1983. text ed. 25.00x (ISBN 0-7069-2131-3, Pub. by Vikas India). Advent NY.
Vaboulis, Peter. Byzantine Decorative Art. (Illus.). 202p. 125.00 (ISBN 0-89241-035-3). Caratzas.
Vacandard, Elphege. The Inquisition: A Critical & Historical Study of the Coercive Power of the Church. Conway, Bertrand L., tr. from Fr. LC 76-1127. 195p. 1977. Repr. of 1926 ed. lib. bdg. 20.00 (ISBN 0-915172-09-7). Richwood Pub.
Vadan, Ma Anand, ed. see Rajneesh, Bhagwan Shree.
Vadenais, Antoinette, tr. see De Saint-Martin, Louis-Claude.
Vadenais, Philip, tr. see De Saint-Martin, Louis-Claude.
Vader, John P. For the Good of Mankind: August Forel & Baha'i Faith. (Illus.). 144p. 10.95 (ISBN 0-85398-171-X); pap. 5.95 (ISBN 0-85398-172-8). G Ronald Pub.
Vagaggini, Cipriano. Canon of the Mass & Liturgical Reform. Coughlan, Peter, tr. 1967. 4.50 (ISBN 0-8189-0019-9). Alba.
Vago, Bela & Mosse, George L., eds. Jews & Non-Jews in Eastern Europe, 1918-1945. pap. 88.00 (ISBN 0-317-27256-X, 2024158). Bks Demand UMI.
Vahanian, Gabriel. The Death of God. LC 61-9962. 1961. 6.95 (ISBN 0-8076-0144-6). Braziller.
--No Other God. LC 66-28591. (Orig.). 1966. pap. 2.50 (ISBN 0-8076-0389-9). Braziller.
Vail, Harley W. When Harley Heard from Heaven. LC 82-72633. 84p. 1982. pap. 2.95 (ISBN 0-9609096-0-5). Bethel Pub Or.
Vail, James G. Science & the Business of Living. 1983. pap. 2.50x (ISBN 0-87574-070-7, 070). Pendle Hill.
Vaillancourt, Jean-Guy. Papal Power: A Study of Vatican Control Over Lay Catholic Elites. 375p. 1980. 24.95x (ISBN 0-520-03733-2). U of Cal Pr.
Vaillancourt, Raymond. Toward a Renewal of Sacramental Theology. O'Connell, Matthew, tr. from Fr. LC 79-12621. 126p. 1979. pap. 4.50 (ISBN 0-8146-1050-1). Liturgical Pr.
Vajda, Eduard M. Four Trees of Christmas. 1983. 16.75 (ISBN 0-89536-641-X, 0633). CSS of Ohio.
Vakil, AK. Three Dimensions of Hindu-Muslim Confrontation. 1982. 6.00 (ISBN 0-8364-0844-6, Pub. By Minerva India). South Asia Bks.
Valdes, Alfonso de. Dialogue of Mercury & Charon. Ricapito, Joseph V., tr. from Span. & intro. by. LC 84-48489. 224p. 1986. 25.00x (ISBN 0-253-31700-2). Ind U Pr.
Valdes, Juan de & Benedetto, Don. The Benefit of Christ. LC 84-9282. (Classics of Faith & Devotion Ser.). 1984. 10.95 (ISBN 0-88070-063-7). Multnomah.
Vale, Eugene. The Thirteenth Apostle. 352p. 1983. pap. 7.95 (ISBN 0-9609674-0-0). Jubilee Pr.
Vale, John & Hughes, Robert. Getting Even: Handling Conflict So Both Sides Win. 128p. 1987. pap. 5.95 (ISBN 0-310-35661-X). Zondervan.
Vale, Michel, tr. see Mozaffari, Mehdi.
Valency, Maurice J. Tragedies of Herod & Mariamne. LC 70-8450. Repr. of 1940 ed. 19.50 (ISBN 0-404-06750-6). AMS Pr.
Valensi, Lucette & Udovitch, Abraham L. The Last Arab Jews: The Communities of Jerba. (Social Orders: A Series of Monographs & Tracts). 180p. 1984. 36.00 (ISBN 3-7186-0135-4). Harwood Academic.
Valenti, Tony & Yonan, Grazia P. The Tony Valenti Story. LC 80-83781. 160p. (Orig.). 1981. 2.50 (ISBN 0-88243-752-6, 02-0752). Gospel Pub.
Valenti-Hilliard, Beverly & Hilliard, Richard. Come & Celebrate: More Center Celebrations. LC 85-72456. (Illus.). 184p. (Orig.). 1985. tchr's guidebook 9.95 (ISBN 0-87793-289-1). Ave Maria.
Valenti-Hilliard, Beverly, jt. auth. see Hilliard, Dick.
Valentin, Hugo. Antisemitism: Historically & Critically Examined. facsimile ed. Chater, A. G., tr. LC 79-164630. (Select Bibliographies Reprint Ser.). Repr. of 1936 ed. 22.00 (ISBN 0-8369-5914-0). Ayer Co Pubs.
Valentine, Ferdinand. Art & Technique of Prayer. (Overview Studies: No. 9). 1969. pap. 0.50x (ISBN 0-87343-049-2). Magi Bks.

Valentine, Foy. Problemas De Actualidad. Swenson, Ana M., tr. 38p. 1983. Repr. of 1981 ed. 1.50 (ISBN 0-311-46039-9). Casa Bautista.

Valentine, Foy D. & Gaustad, Edwin S., eds. A Historical Study of Southern Baptists & Race Relations 1917-1947: Doctoral Dissertation. LC 79-52579. (The Baptist Tradition Ser.). 1980. lib. bdg. 23.00x (ISBN 0-405-12447-3). Ayer Co Pubs.

Valentine, Mary H. Saints for Today's Women. 1987. 11.95 (ISBN 0-88347-210-4). Thomas More.

Valentini, Norberto & Di Meglio, Clara. Sex & the Confessional. LC 73-91861. 1975. pap. 1.95 (ISBN 0-8128-1862-8). Stein & Day.

Valenze, Deborah M. Prophetic Sons & Daughters: Female Preaching & Popular Religion in Industrial England. LC 85-42755. (Illus.). 344p. 1985. 38.50x (ISBN 0-691-05455-X). Princeton U Pr.

Valeri, Valerio. Kingship & Sacrifice: Ritual & Society in Ancient Hawaii. Wissing, Paula, tr. from Hawaiian. LC 84-23991. (Fr. & Eng., Illus.). 392p. 1985. lib. bdg. 55.00x (ISBN 0-226-84559-1); pap. text ed. 22.50x (ISBN 0-226-84560-5). U of Chicago Pr.

Valery, Nicole. Prisoner Rejoice. 238p. 1980. pap. 4.95 (ISBN 0-88264-179-4). Diane Bks.

Valery, Paul. Descartes. 133p. 1980. Repr. lib. bdg. 15.00 (ISBN 0-89984-477-4). Century Bookbindery.

Valiuddin, Mir. Love of God. (Orig.). 1979. pap. 9.95 (ISBN 0-900217-02-2, Pub. by Sufi Pub Co England). Hunter Hse.

--The Quranic Sufism. 2nd rev. ed. 1977. 16.95 (ISBN 0-89684-300-9, Pub. by Motilal Banarsidass India). Orient Bk Dist.

--The Quranic Sufism. 221p. 1981. pap. 13.25 (ISBN 0-88004-007-6). Sunwise Turn.

Valla, Mary. The Mystical Way of Life. LC 74-14058. 176p. 1975. pap. 4.95 (ISBN 0-685-52237-7). De Vorss.

--The Power of Numbers. 1972. pap. 5.95 (ISBN 0-87516-108-1). De Vorss.

Valle, Maria T. la see Brenneman, Helen G.

Valle, Rafael H. Bibliografia De Hernan Cortes. LC 75-133935. (Bibliography & Reference Ser.: No. 386). 1971. Repr. lib. bdg. 21.00 (ISBN 0-8337-3610-8). B Franklin.

Valle, Roger V., tr. see Ramm, Bernard.

Valle, Teresa La see Ralph, Margaret.

Vallee, Gerard. A Study in Anti-Gnostic Polemics: Irenaeus, Hippolytus & Epiphanius. 128p. 1981. pap. text ed. 8.95x (ISBN 0-919812-14-7, Pub. by Wilfrid Laurier Canada). Humanities.

Vallee, L. Dictionnaire du Protestantisme. Migne, J. P., ed. (Troisieme et Derniere Encyclopedie Theologique Ser.: Vol. 36). (Fr.). 692p. Repr. of 1858 ed. lib. bdg. 88.00x (ISBN 0-89241-315-8). Caratzas.

Valles, Carlos G. Living Together in a Jesuit Community. LC 84-81259. (Study Aids on Jesuit Topics: Ser. IV, No. 10). 128p. 1985. pap. 4.00 Smyth Sewn (ISBN 0-912422-66-1). Inst Jesuit.

Vallesky, David, jt. auth. see Bivens, Forest.

Valliere, Paul. Holy War & Pentecostal Peace. 176p. (Orig.). 1983. pap. 9.95 (ISBN 0-8164-2481-0, HarpR). Har-Row.

Vallotton, Annie. Priority: Jesus' Life in Sixty Drawings. (Illus.). 64p. 1969. pap. 0.95 (ISBN 0-8361-1901-0). Herald Pr.

Valmiki. Ramayana. 3rd ed. Rajagopalachari, Chakravarti, ed. & tr. from Tamil. 320p. (Orig.). 1980. pap. 4.25 (ISBN 0-934676-17-8). Greenlf Bks.

--Return to Shiva. (Sacred Texts Ser.). viii, 88p. 1983. pap. 8.75 (ISBN 0-88695-006-6). Concord Grove.

--Sundara Kandam of Srimad Valmiki Ramayana. Swami Tapasyananda, tr. from Sanskrit. 286p. 1984. 15.00 (ISBN 0-87481-527-4, Pub. by Ramakrishna Math Madras India). Vedanta Pr.

Valois, Noel. Guillaume d'Auvergne: Eveque de Paris (1228-1249), Sa vie & Ses ouvrages (Medieval Studies Ser.) (Medieval Studies Ser.). (Fr.). Repr. of 1880 ed. lib. bdg. 44.00x (ISBN 0-697-00019-2). Irvington.

Valsecchi, Ambrogio, jt. auth. see Rossi, Leandro.

Vamos, Mara S., tr. see Dorian, Emil.

Van, Kees der Ploeg see Van Os, Henk.

Van Alfen, Nicholas. Orrin Porter Rockwell, Mormon Frontier Marshall. 72p. pap. 3.95 (ISBN 0-87747-468-0). Deseret Bk.

Van Andel, Mary T., jt. auth. see Phillips, Nancy V.

Van Assendelft, Marion M. Sol Ecce Surgit Igneus: A Commentary on the Morning & Evening Hymns of Prudentius. vii, 275p. 1976. 30.00x (ISBN 90-6088-060-9, Pub. by Boumas Boekhuis Netherlands). Benjamins North AM.

Van Auken, John. Born Again... & Again & Again: How Reincarnation Occurs, Why & What It Means to You. (Illus.). 144p. 1984. 12.95 (ISBN 0-917483-00-6). Innervision.

--Born Again & Again: How Reincarnation Occurs, Why & What It Means to You! LC 84-223300. (Illus.). 144p. (Orig.). 1985. pap. 8.95 (ISBN 0-917483-02-2). Innervision.

Van Baal, T. & Van Beek, W. E. Symbols for Communication: An Introduction to the Anthropological Study of Religion. 2nd, rev. ed. (Studies of Developing Countries: No. 11). 272p. 1985. pap. 30.00 (ISBN 90-232-2074-9, Pub. by Van Gorcum Holland). Longwood Pub Group.

Van Baalen, Jan K. Chaos of Cults. 4th ed. rev. ed. 1962. 11.95 (ISBN 0-8028-3278-4). Eerdmans.

Van Baaren, T. P. Korwars & Korwar Style: Art & Ancestor Worship in North-West New Guinea. (Art in Its Context, Studies in Ethno-Aesthetics, Museum Ser.: No. 2). (Illus.). 1968. 26.75x (ISBN 0-686-21795-0). Mouton.

Van Baaren, T. P. & Driljvers, H. J., eds. Religion, Culture & Methodology: Papers of the Groningen Working-Group for the Study of Fundamental Problems & Methods of Science of Religion. 1973. text ed. 14.00x (ISBN 90-2797-249-4). Mouton.

Van Beeck, Frans J. Christ Proclaimed: Christology As Rhetoric. LC 79-66459. 632p. 1979. pap. 9.95 (ISBN 0-8091-2208-1). Paulist Pr.

--Grounded in Love: Sacramental Theology in an Ecumenical Perspective. LC 81-40117. 162p. (Orig.). 1982. lib. bdg. 26.00 (ISBN 0-8191-2040-5); pap. text ed. 11.25 (ISBN 0-8191-2041-3). U Pr of Amer.

Van Beek, W. E., jt. auth. see Van Baal, T.

Van Beek, Wil see Beek, Wil van.

Van Belzen, J. A. & Van Der Lans, J. M., eds. Proceedings of the Third Symposium on the Psychology of Religion in Europe: Current Issues in the Psychology of Religion. (Amsterdam Studies in Theology Ser.). 292p. 1986. pap. text ed. 65.00 (ISBN 90-6203-758-5, Pub. by Rodopi Holland). Humanities.

Van Bemmel, Dolores, jt. auth. see Van Bemmel, John.

Van Bemmel, John & Van Bemmel, Dolores. We Celebrate Our Marriage. (Greeting Book Line Ser.). 32p. (Orig.). 1986. pap. 1.50 (ISBN 0-89622-304-3). Twenty-Third.

Van Benschoten, A. Q., Jr. What the Bible Says about Stewardship. 96p. 1983. pap. 4.95 (ISBN 0-8170-0993-0). Judson.

Van Binsbergen, Wim M. Religious Change in Zambia: Exploratory Studies. 424p. 1984. pap. 14.95x (ISBN 0-7103-0012-3, Kegan Paul). Methuen Inc.

Van Binsbergen, Wim M. J. Religious Change in Zambia: Exploratory Studies. (Monographs from the African Studies Centre, Leiden). (Illus.). 416p. 1981. 50.00x (ISBN 0-7103-0000-X). Methuen Inc.

Van Binsbergen, Wim M. J. & Schoffeleers, J. Matthew, eds. Theoretical Explorations in African Religion. 330p. 1984. 49.95x (ISBN 0-7103-0049-2). Methuen Inc.

Van Braam Barrett, Thomas see Barrett, Thomas Van Braam.

Van Braght, Thieleman J. Martyrs' Mirror. (Illus.). 1157p. 1938. 29.95 (ISBN 0-8361-1390-X). Herald Pr.

Van Bragt, Jan see Nishitani, Keiji.

Van Breemen, Peter G. As Bread That Is Broken. 5.95 (ISBN 0-87193-052-8). Dimension Bks.

--Called by Name. 9.95 (ISBN 0-87193-094-3). Dimension Bks.

--Certain As the Dawn. pap. 6.95 (ISBN 0-87193-150-8). Dimension Bks.

Van Broeckhover, Egide see Broeckhover, Egide van.

Van Brummelen, Harro W. Telling the Next Generation: The Educational Development in North American Calvinist Christian Schools. (Illus.). 332p. (Orig.). 1986. lib. bdg. 27.50 (ISBN 0-8191-5307-9, Pub. by Inst Christ Stud); pap. text ed. 14.75 (ISBN 0-8191-5308-7). U Pr of Amer.

Van Buitenen, J. A. The Mahabharata: The Book of the Beginning, Vol. 1. LC 72-97802. (Illus.). lii, 492p. 1980. pap. 18.00x (ISBN 0-226-84663-6, P879). U of Chicago Pr.

--The Maitrayaniya Upanisad: A Critical Essay with Text, Translation & Commentary. (Disputationes Rheno-Trajectinae: No. 6). 1962. pap. 17.60x (ISBN 90-2790-032-9). Mouton.

Van Buitenen, J. A., jt. auth. see Deutsch, Eliot.

Van Buitenen, J. A., ed. The Bhagavadgita in the Mahabharata: A Bilingual Edition. LC 79-13021. 184p. 1981. lib. bdg. 19.00x (ISBN 0-226-84660-1); pap. 8.95 (ISBN 0-226-84662-8, Phoen). U of Chicago Pr.

Van Buitenen, J. A., ed. & tr. from Sanskrit. The Mahabharata. Incl. Vol. 1. Book 1: The Book of the Beginning. 1974. 32.00x (ISBN 0-226-84648-2); Vol. II. Book 2: The Book of the Assembly Hall. 1976; Book 3: The Book of the Forest. 1976. LC 72-97802. lib. bdg. 42.00x set (ISBN 0-226-84649-0). U of Chicago Pr.

Van Buitenen, J. A., ed. & tr. The Mahabharata, Vol. 2, Bks. 2 & 3. LC 75-5067. 880p. 1981. Book 2 The Book Of The Assembly Hall. 15.00x (ISBN 0-226-84664-4, Phoen). Book 3 The Book Of The Forest. U of Chicago Pr.

Van Buitenen, J. A., tr. see Dimmitt, Cornelia.

Van Buren, James & Dewett, Don. What the Bible Says about Praise & Promise. LC 80-66127. (What the Bible Says Ser.). 450p. 1980. 13.95 (ISBN 0-89900-078-9). College Pr Pub.

Van Buren, Paul M. A Christian Theology of the People Israel. (A Theology of the Jewish-Christian Reality Ser.: Pt. II). 320p. (Orig.). 1983. pap. 26.95 (ISBN 0-8164-0548-4, HarpR). Har-Row.

Van Buskirk, William R. Saviors of Mankind. LC 71-86790. (Essay Index Reprint Ser.). 1929. 32.00 (ISBN 0-8369-1432-5). Ayer Co Pubs.

Van Cauwenberg, jt. auth. see Aubert, Roger.

Vance, Mary. Monographs on Church Architecture, 2 vols. (Architecture Ser.: Bibliography A1209). 249p. 1984. Set. pap. 20.00 (ISBN 0-89028-019-3). Vance Biblios.

Vance, Norman. The Sinews of the Spirit: The Ideal of Christian Manlines in Victorian Literature & Religious Thought. 256p. 1985. 34.50 (ISBN 0-521-30387-7). Cambridge U Pr.

Vanceburg, Martha, jt. auth. see Casey, Karen.

Van Cleave, Mary E. Behold the Bride. 1986. 12.95 (ISBN 0-533-07024-4). Vantage.

Van Corstanje, Auspicius. Covenant with God's Poor. 3.95 (ISBN 0-8199-0014-1). Franciscan Herald.

--Saint Francis Prayer Book. 1978. pap. 2.50 (ISBN 0-8199-0693-X). Franciscan Herald.

Vandana. Nama Japa: Prayer of the Name in the Hindu & Christian Traditions. 1985. pap. 10.00 (ISBN 0-8364-1509-4, Pub. by Bharatiya Vidya Bhavan). South Asia Bks.

Vandana, Ma Ananda, ed. see Rajneesh, Bhagwan Shree.

Vande Kemp, Hendrika. Psychology & Theology in Western Thought, 1672-1965: A Historical & Annotated Bibliography. LC 82-49045. (Bibliographies in the History of Psychology & Psychiatry Ser.). (Orig.). 1984. lib. bdg. 75.00 (ISBN 0-527-92779-1). Kraus Intl.

Vandeman, G. Showdown in the Middle East. (Stories That Win Ser.). 1981. pap. 1.25 (ISBN 0-8163-0392-4). Pacific Pr Pub Assn.

Vandeman, George. Stuff of Survival. (Stories That Win Ser.). 1978. pap. 1.25 (ISBN 0-8163-0209-X, 19689-9). Pacific Pr Pub Assn.

--Tying Down the Sun. LC 78-61749. (Stories That Win Ser.). 1978. pap. 1.25 (ISBN 0-8163-0211-1, 20990-8). Pacific Pr Pub Assn.

Vandeman, George E. The Book That Wouldn't Go Away. (Stories That Win Ser.). 64p. 1983. pap. 1.25 (ISBN 0-8163-0537-4). Pacific Pr Pub Assn.

--Cry of a Lonely Planet. 352p. 1983. pap. 7.95 (ISBN 0-8163-0519-6). Pacific Pr Pub Assn.

--Day to Remember. LC 65-24345. (Stories That Win Ser.). 1965. pap. 1.25 (ISBN 0-8163-0096-8, 04140-0). Pacific Pr Pub Assn.

--Destination of Life. LC 66-21954. (Stories That Win Ser.). 1966. pap. 1.25 (ISBN 0-8163-0095-X, 04270-5). Pacific Pr Pub Assn.

--Hammers in the Fire. LC 79-154293. 1971. pap. 1.25 (ISBN 0-8163-0119-0, 08010-1). Pacific Pr Pub Assn.

Vandeman, Nellie. Not by Bread Alone. (Outreach Ser.). 1981. pap. 1.25 (ISBN 0-8163-0452-1). Pacific Pr Pub Assn.

Vandenberg, Philipp. The Mystery of the Oracles: World Famous Archaeologists Reveal the Best Kept Secrets of Antiquity. Unwin, George, tr. (Illus.). 288p. 1982. 14.95 (ISBN 0-02-621590-X). Macmillan.

Vandenberg, Thomas L. Study Guide for Archbishop Hunthausen's Pastoral on Matrimony. rev. ed. LC 82-62716. 59p. 1984. pap. text ed. 2.95 (ISBN 0-911905-02-2). Past & Mat Rene Ctr.

Vandenberge, Peter N. The Historical Directory of the Reformed Church in America. 1978. pap. 17.95 (ISBN 0-8028-1746-7). Eerdmans.

Vandenbergh, C. W. Sunbursts for the Spirit. LC 79-90313. (Sunbursts for the Spirit Ser.: Vol. 1). (Illus.). 56p. (Orig.). 1979. pap. 3.25 (ISBN 0-935238-02-6). Pine Row.

Van Den Bergh, S., tr. see Al-Tahafut, Tahafut.

Van Den Boogaard, Nico H. J. Autour De 1300: Etudes de Philologie et de Litterature Medievales. (Faux Titre: Vol. 21). (Fr., Illus.). 288p. 1985. pap. text ed. 45.00 (ISBN 90-6203-518-3, Pub. by Editions Rodopi). Humanities.

Vandenbosch, Amry, jt. auth. see Brookes, Edgar H.

VandenBroeck, A., tr. see Schwaller de Lubicz, R. A.

VandenBroeck, G., tr. see Schwaller de Lubicz, R. A.

Van den Broek, Silvere, ed. The Spiritual Legacy of Sister Mary of the Holy Trinity. LC 81-82830. 364p. 1981. pap. 6.00 (ISBN 0-89555-165-9). TAN Bks Pubs.

Vandenbroucke, Francis. Why Monks? LC 75-182090. (Cistercian Studies: Vol. 17). 1972. 4.00 (ISBN 0-87907-817-0). Cistercian Pub.

Vandenburg, Thomas, jt. auth. see Gallagher, Chuch.

Vanden Burgt, Robert J. The Religious Philosophy of William James. LC 80-22936. 176p. 1981. text ed. 19.95x (ISBN 0-88229-594-2); pap. text ed. 9.95x (ISBN 0-88229-767-8). Nelson-Hall.

Van Den Haag, Ernest. The Jewish Mystique. LC 76-56974. 1977. pap. 6.95 (ISBN 0-8128-2189-0). Stein & Day.

Van Den Tak, Richard. The Scientific Proof of the Existence of Reincarnation & Transmigration. (Illus.). 1981. 16.50 (ISBN 0-89962-015-9). Todd & Honeywell.

Van De Putte, Walter, tr. see Jamart, Francois.

Vander Ark, John A. Twenty-Two Landmark Years: Christian Schools International, 1943-65. 160p. 1983. pap. 9.95 (ISBN 0-8010-9291-4). Baker Bk.

VanderArk, Nelle. Devotionals for Teachers. (Ultra Bks Ser.). 80p. 1975. 5.95 (ISBN 0-8010-9263-9). Baker Bk.

Vander Ark, Nelle. Inspirations from Isaiah. (Good Morning Lord Ser.). 96p. 1980. 3.95 (ISBN 0-8010-9281-7). Baker Bk.

Vander Ark, Nelle A. Sharing from the Psalms. 64p. 1984. pap. 2.95 (ISBN 0-8010-9295-7). Baker Bk.

Van Der Bent, A. J. God So Loves the World: The Immaturity of World Christianity. LC 79-4470. 160p. (Orig.). 1979. pap. 2.98 (ISBN 0-88344-159-4). Orbis Bks.

Vanderburg, William H., ed. see Ellul, Jacques.

Vanderburgh, Frederick A., ed. Sumerian Hymns from Cuneiform Texts in the British Museum. LC 68-23118. (Columbia University. Contributions to Oriental History & Philology: No. 1). Repr. of 1908 ed. 14.00 (ISBN 0-404-50531-7). AMS Pr.

Vander Goot, Henry V. Interpreting the Bible in Theology & the Church. LC 84-9027. (Symposium Ser.: Vol. II). 128p. 1984. pap. 19.95 (ISBN 0-88946-701-3). E Mellen.

Vander Goot, Mary. Educating for Healthy Emotions: The Emotional Development of Children. 176p. (Orig.). 1987. pap. 8.95 (ISBN 0-8010-9303-1). Baker Bk.

--A Life Planning Guide for Women. 128p. 1982. pap. 9.95x (ISBN 0-88946-512-6). E Mellen.

Vanderhaar, Gerard A. Christians & Nonviolence in the Nuclear Age: Scripture, the Arms Race & You. 128p. 1982. pap. 5.95 (ISBN 0-89622-162-8). Twenty-Third.

--Enemies & How to Love Them. 128p. (Orig.). 1985. pap. 4.95 (ISBN 0-89622-241-1). Twenty Third.

Van der Heyden, A., jt. auth. see Gafni, Shlomo S.

Van Der Hoeven, Johan, jt. ed. see Hart, Hendrik.

Vanderhoof, Elisha W. Historical Sketches of Western New York. LC 71-134434. Repr. of 1907 ed. 14.00 (ISBN 0-404-08476-1). AMS Pr.

VanderKam, James C. Enoch & the Growth of an Apocalyptic Tradition. LC 83-10134. (Catholic Biblical Quarterly Monographs: No. 16). 217p. 1984. pap. 6.50 (ISBN 0-915170-15-9). Catholic Bibl Assn.

Vander Klay, Grace. Bible Activity Safari. (Pelican Activity Ser.). pap. 0.89 (ISBN 0-8010-9280-9). Baker Bk.

Vander Kolk, Justin. To Set Things Right: The Bible Speaks on Faith & Justice. 48p. 1971. pap. 1.25 (ISBN 0-377-02001-X). Friend Pr.

Van der Land, Sipke see Land, Sipke van der.

Van Der Lans, J. M., jt. ed. see Van Belzen, J. A.

Van der Leeuw. Gods in Exile. 2.75 (ISBN 0-8356-7056-2). Theos Pub Hse.

Van Der Leeuw, Gerardus. Religion in Essence & Manifestation, 2 vols. 26.50 set (ISBN 0-8446-1457-2). Peter Smith.

Van Der Leeuw, J. J. Conquest of Illusion. 1967. pap. 1.95 (ISBN 0-8356-0400-4, Quest). Theos Pub Hse.

Vanderlip, D. George. John: The Gospel of Life. 1979. pap. 5.95 (ISBN 0-8170-0826-8). Judson.

Van der Looy, H. Rule for a New Brother. 1985. pap. 4.95 (ISBN 0-87243-138-X). Templegate.

Vander Lught, Henry. There's a New Day Coming. LC 83-81267. 160p. 1983. pap. 3.95 (ISBN 0-89081-389-2, Pub. by Radio B C). Harvest Hse.

Vander Lugt, Herbert. Fifty Plus. (Direction Bks.). Orig. Title: The Art of Growing Old. 110p. 1982. pap. 2.95 (ISBN 0-8010-9288-4). Baker Bk.

--God's Plan in All the Ages: The Kingdom & Redemption from Genesis to Revelation. 208p. 1980. pap. 4.95 (ISBN 0-310-42181-0, 10227P). Zondervan.

Van der Maas, E., jt. ed. see Douglas, J. D.

Van der Maas, E., ed. see McGrath, Allister E.

Vander Meer, Charles. Quickie Quizzes from the Bible. (Quiz & Puzzles Bks.). 48p. 1976. pap. 2.50 (ISBN 0-8010-9252-3). Baker Bk.
--Quickie Quizzes No. 2. (Quiz & Puzzle Bks.). pap. 1.95 (ISBN 0-8010-9266-3). Baker Bk.
Van Der Meer, Frederik. Early Christian Art. Brown, Peter & Brown, Friedl, trs. from Ger. LC 67-25083. pap. 50.00 (ISBN 0-317-28145-3, 2024099). Bks Demand UMI.
Van Der Meer, Haye S. Women Priests in the Catholic Church? A Theological-Historical Investigation. Swidler, Leonard & Swidler, Arlene, trs. from Ger. LC 73-79480. Orig. Title: Priestertum der Frau? 230p. 1973. 12.95 (ISBN 0-87722-059-X). Temple U Pr.
Vandermey, H. Ronald, jt. ed. see Cohen, Gary.
Vandermey, Mary A. Love Is Like the Sunlight. 1985. pap. 5.95 (ISBN 0-8010-9294-9). Baker Bk.
--Sparkling Devotions for Women's Groups. 144p. 1985. pap. 4.95 (ISBN 0-8010-9300-7). Baker Bk.
Van Der Ploeg, Kees, contrib. by see Van Os, Henk.
Van Der Poel, Cornelius J. The Integration of Human Values. 5.95 (ISBN 0-87193-004-8). Dimension Bks.
--The Search for Human Values. LC 75-161445. 192p. 1973. pap. 3.95 (ISBN 0-8091-1781-9, Deus). Paulist Pr.
Vanderpool. History of New Bethel Missionary Baptist Church. 5.00x (ISBN 0-686-12400-6). Church History.
Van Der Post, Laurens. Patterns of Renewal. LC 62-15859. (Orig.). 1962. pap. 2.50x (ISBN 0-87574-121-5). Pendle Hill.
Vander Shrier, Nettie. The Golden Thread. 169p. 1983. pap. 3.95 (ISBN 0-8024-0173-2). Moody.
Vander Stelt, John C., ed. The Challenge of Marxist & Neo-Marxist Ideologies for Christian Scholarship. 280p. 1982. pap. 12.95 (ISBN 0-932914-07-1). Dordt Coll Pr.
Van der Toorn, K. Sin & Sanction in Israel & Mesopotamia: A Comparative Study. (Studia Semitica Neerlandica: No. 22). 213p. 1985. pap. 20.00 (ISBN 90-232-2166-4, Pub. by Van Gorcum Holland). Longwood Pub Group.
Van Der Veen, H. R. Jewish Characters in Eighteenth Century Fiction & Drama. 1970. 25.00x (ISBN 0-87068-076-5). Ktav.
Van Der Veer, Andrew. Bible Lessons for Juniors, 4 bks. Incl. Bk. 1. Creation Through Moses. 2.95 (ISBN 0-8010-9253-1); Bk. 2. Kings & Prophets. 2.95 (ISBN 0-8010-9251-5); Bk. 3. The Life of Christ. 2.95 (ISBN 0-8010-9257-4); Bk. 4. The Early Church. 2.95 (ISBN 0-8010-9255-8). Baker Bk.
VanderVelde, Frances. Women of the Bible. rev. ed. LC 83-19894. (Illus.). 260p. 1973. pap. 6.95 (ISBN 0-8254-3951-5). Kregel.
Vandervelde, G. Original Sin: Two Major Trends in Contemporary Roman Catholic Reinterpretation. LC 81-40000. 364p. 1982. lib. bdg. 32.50 (ISBN 0-8191-1849-4); pap. text ed. 15.75 o. p. (ISBN 0-8191-1850-8). U Pr of Amer.
Vander-Velde, Lewis G. Presbyterian Churches & the Federal Union 1861-1869. LC 32-30007. (Historical Studies: No. 33). 1932. 35.00x (ISBN 0-674-70151-8). Harvard U Pr.
Van der Veur, Paul W. Freemasonry in Indonesia from Radermacher to Soekanto, 1762-1961. LC 76-620040. (Papers in International Studies: Southeast Asia Ser.: No. 40). (Illus.). 1976. pap. 4.00x (ISBN 0-89680-026-1, 82-90413, Ohio U Ctr Intl). Ohio U Pr.
Vanderwall, Francis W. Spiritual Direction: An Invitation to Abundant Life. LC 81-83185. 128p. (Orig.). 1982. pap. 4.95 (ISBN 0-8091-2399-1). Paulist Pr.
--Water in the Wilderness: Paths of Prayer. 1985. pap. 5.95 (ISBN 0-8091-2680-X). Paulist Pr.
Van der Walt, B., ed. Calvinus Reformator: His Contribution to Theology, Church & Society. Date not set. pap. 12.50x cancelled (ISBN 0-86990-686-0). Radix Bks.
Vanderwerff, Corrine. An Arrow Returned. Woosley, Raymond H., ed. (Banner Ser.). 144p. (Orig.). 1987. pap. 6.50 (ISBN 0-8280-0364-5). Review & Herald.
Van Der Woude, A. S., ed. see Loader, J. A.
Van der Woude, A. S., ed. see Maarsingh, B.
Van Der Woude, A. S., ed. see Van Hartingsveld, L.
Van Der Woude, A. S., ed. see Van Selms, A.
Van Deursen, A. Illustrated Dictionary of Bible Manners & Customs. (Illus.). 1979. pap. 3.95 (ISBN 0-8065-0707-1). Citadel Pr.
--Illustrated Dictionary of Bible Manners & Customs. (Illus.). 1967. 6.95 (ISBN 0-8022-1762-1). Philos Lib.
Van DeVeer, Donald, jt. ed. see Regan, Tom.
Van de Walle, A. R. From Darkness to the Dawn: How Belief in the Afterlife Affects Living. Tr. of Tot het aanbreken van de dageraad. 272p. 1985. pap. text ed. 10.95 (ISBN 0-89622-272-1). Twenty-Third.
Van Dieten, Ioannes, ed. Nicetae Choniatae Historiae, 2 vols. (Corpus Fontium Historiae Byzantinae Vol. XI: Series Berolinensis). 1975. 242.00x (ISBN 3-11-004528-1). De Gruyter.
Van Dieten, Jan-Louis. Niketas Choniates: Erlaeuterungen Zu Den Reden und Briefen Nebst Einer Biographie. (Supplementa Byzantina, 2). 1971. 43.20x (ISBN 3-11-002290-7). De Gruyter.
Van Dijk, Jan, et al. Early Mesopotamian Incantations & Rituals. LC 84-13064. (Yale Oriental Ser., Babylonian Texts: Vol. 11). 200p. 1985. text ed. 35.00x (ISBN 0-300-03147-5). Yale U Pr.
Van Dolson, Bobbie J., ed. see Aaen, Bernhard.
Van Dolson, Bobbie J., ed. see Degering, Etta B.
Van Dolson, Bobbie J., ed. see Hills, Desmond B.
Van Dolson, Bobbie J., ed. see Irland, Nancy B.
Van Dolson, Bobbie J., ed. see Todd, Sharon.
Van Dolson, Bobbie J., ed. see Willis, Mary.
Van Dolson, Leo. How to Get the Most Out of Bible Study. (Harvest Ser.). 122p. 1980. pap. 5.95 (ISBN 0-8163-0360-6). Pacific Pr Pub Assn.
Van Doornik, N. Francis of Assisi: A Prophet for Our Time. 1978. 8.95 (ISBN 0-8199-0695-6). Franciscan Herald.
Van Doren, Carl. Benjamin Franklin & Jonathan Edwards. 1979. Repr. of 1920 ed. lib. bdg. 20.00 (ISBN 0-8495-5525-6). Arden Lib.
Van Doren, Mark. How Praise a World That May Not Last. 1977. pap. 6.95 handset, handbound (ISBN 0-89016-039-2). Lightning Tree.
Van Doren, W. H. Gospel of John, 2 vols. in 1. rev. ed. LC 80-8080. (Kregel Bible Study Classics Ser.). 1454p. 1981. text ed. 34.50 (ISBN 0-8254-3953-1). Kregel.
--Gospel of Luke, 2 vols. in 1. LC 80-8079. (Kregel Bible Study Classics Ser.). 1100p. 1981. 29.95 (ISBN 0-8254-3952-3). Kregel.
Van Dusen, Wilson. The Natural Depth in Man. LC 72-78055. 197p. pap. 2.50 (ISBN 0-87785-165-4). Swedenborg.
--The Presence of Other Worlds. LC 73-18684. 240p. pap. 5.95 (ISBN 0-87785-166-2). Swedenborg.
VanDyk, Wilbert M. Belonging, An Introduction to the Faith & Life of the Christian Reformed Church. LC 82-1241. (Illus.). 120p. (Orig.). 1982. pap. 4.50 (ISBN 0-933140-43-6). CRC Pubns.
Van Dyke, Henry. The Other Wise Man. 63p. (Orig.). 1984. pap. 7.95 (ISBN 0-941478-33-5). Paraclete Pr.
--The Spirit of Christmas. LC 84-19389. 64p. 1984. pap. 2.95 (ISBN 0-89783-033-4). Larlin Corp.
--The Story of the Other Wise Man. 96p. 1986. pap. 2.95 (ISBN 0-345-31882-X, Pub. by Ballantine Epiphany). Ballantine.
Van Dyke, Henry, jt. auth. see Garbee, Ed.
Van Dyke, Louis Y., jt. ed. see DeJong, James A.
Van Dyke Parunak, H., ed. Computer Tools for Ancient Texts: Proceedings of the 1980 Ann Arbor Symposium on Biblical Studies & the Computer. 1987. text ed. price not set (ISBN 0-931464-32-3). Eisenbrauns.
Van Dyne, Glen. Beacon Small-Group Bible Studies, Joshua: Never a Dull Moment. Wolf, Earl C., ed. 80p. 1986. pap. 2.50 (ISBN 0-8341-1098-9). Beacon Hill.
Van Eaton, Hugh. Run Devil Run. (Illus.). 1975. pap. 3.95 (ISBN 0-89957-513-7). AMG Pubs.
Van Eeden, Frederik. Paul's Awakening. Lake, H. S., tr. from Dutch. LC 83-81704. 96p. 1985. 6.95 (ISBN 0-86164-156-6, Pub. by Momenta Pub Ltd). Hunter Hse.
Van Eijndhoven, J., ed. Religious Education of the Deaf. (Modern Approaches to the Diagnosis & Instruction of Multi-Handicapped Children Ser.: Vol. 11). 168p. 1973. text ed. 14.75 (ISBN 90-237-4111-0, Pub. by Swets & Zeitlinger Netherlands). Hogrefe Intl.
Van Elderen, Bastiaan. The First & Second Epistle to Timothy & the Epistle to Titus. Bruce, F. F., ed. (New International Commentary on the New Testament Ser.). 256p. cancelled (ISBN 0-8028-2346-7). Eerdmans.
Van Engen. The Growth of the True Church. (Amsterdam Studies in Theology: Vol. III). 545p. 1981. pap. text ed. 55.00x (ISBN 90-6203-783-6, Pub. by Rodopi Holland). Humanities.
Van Engen, John. Rupert of Deutz. LC 82-40089. (Center for Medieval & Renaissance Studies, UCLA: Publication: No. 18). 1983. text ed. 34.50x (ISBN 0-520-04577-7). U of Cal Pr.
Van Ess, Dorothy. Pioneers in the Arab World. 1974. pap. 4.95 (ISBN 0-8028-1585-5). Eerdmans.
VanEtten, Teresa. Ways of Indian Wisdom. LC 86-5924. 96p. (Orig.). 1987. pap. 8.95 (ISBN 0-86534-090-0). Sunstone Pr.
Vanggaard, Thorkil. Phallos: A Symbol & Its History in the Male World. LC 72-80553. (Illus.). 266p. 1972. text ed. 22.50 (ISBN 0-8236-4135-X); pap. text ed. 17.95 (ISBN 0-8236-8192-0, 24135). Intl Univs Pr.
Van Gogh, Anna. Promise Me Life: Evolution & Creation As a Dynamic Unity. (Illus.). 424p. (Orig.). Date not set. PLB price not set (ISBN 0-913829-34-X); pap. price not set (ISBN 0-913829-35-8). Lucy Mary Bks.
Van Goudoever, H. D. A Contemplation about Rudolf Steiner's "Calendar of the Soul". Weber, Giselher, tr. 1984. pap. 6.95 (ISBN 0-916786-76-5). St George Bk Serv.
Van Haaften, Julia, ed. see Frith, Francis.
Van Halsema, Thea. Three Men Came to Heidelberg. (Christian Biography Ser.). 96p. 1982. pap. 3.95 (ISBN 0-8010-9289-2). Baker Bk.
Van Halsema, Thea B. This Was John Calvin. (Christian Biography Ser.). 184p. 1981. pap. 4.95 (ISBN 0-8010-9283-3). Baker Bk.
Van Harn, Roger. Galatians: A Study Guide. (Revelation Series for Adults). 1984. pap. 2.50 (ISBN 0-933140-93-2). CRC Pubns.
Van Harn, Roger E. Searchlight. rev. ed. 84p. 1980. pap. 3.25 (ISBN 0-933140-16-9). CRC Pubns.
Van Hartingsveld, L. Text & Interpretation: A Practical Commentary, Revelation. Van Der Woude, A. S., ed. (Text & Interpretation Ser.). (Dutch.). 128p. (Orig.). 1985. pap. 6.95 (ISBN 0-8028-0100-5). Eerdmans.
Van Hattenberg, Ludwig. The Conversion of the Jews. (Intimate Life of Man Library). (Illus.). 1979. 49.85 (ISBN 0-89266-191-7). Am Classical Coll Pr.
Van Heurck, Jan, tr. see Pieper, Josef & Raskop, Heinrich.
Van Hoeven, James W. Piety & Patriotism. 1976. pap. 4.95 (ISBN 0-8028-1663-0). Eerdmans.
Van Hook, John E. Systematic Philosophy: An Overview of Metaphysics Showing the Development from the Greeks to the Contemporaries with Specified Directions & Projections. (Illus.). 1979. 8.50 (ISBN 0-682-49398-8, University). Exposition Pr FL.
Van Horn, Bill. The Good Samaritan. 1983. 3.60 (ISBN 0-89536-588-X, 0730). CSS of Ohio.
--The Key to the Kingdom. 1982. 4.25 (ISBN 0-89536-555-3, 1101). CSS of Ohio.
--A Light for All People. 1981. 3.50 (ISBN 0-89536-469-7, 1215). CSS of Ohio.
--Strangers. 1983. 4.00 (ISBN 0-89536-587-1, 1926). CSS of Ohio.
Van Horn, Roger. Philippians: A Study Guide. (Revelation Series for Adults). 1983. pap. text ed. 2.50 (ISBN 0-933140-84-3). CRC Pubns.
Van Horne, John C., ed. & intro. by. Religious Philanthropy & Colonial Slavery: The American Correspondence of the Associates of Dr. Bray, 1717-1777. LC 84-2766. (Blacks in the New World Ser.). 400p. 1985. 29.95 (ISBN 0-252-01142-2). U of Ill Pr.
Vanhoye, Albert. Old Testament Priests & the New Priest. Orchard, Bernard, tr. from Fr. LC 85-2171. (Studies in Scripture: Vol. II). Tr. of Pretres anciens, pretre nouveau selon le nouveau testament. 1986. pap. 24.95 (ISBN 0-932506-38-0). St Bedes Pubns.
Vanier, Jean. Be Not Afraid. 160p. 1975. pap. 7.95 (ISBN 0-8091-1885-8). Paulist Pr.
--The Challenge of l'Arche. (Illus.). 286p. 1982. pap. 9.95 (ISBN 0-89088-072-7, HarpR). Har-Row.
--I Meet Jesus: He Tells Me "I Love You". LC 81-82109. 208p. 1982. pap. 3.95 (ISBN 0-8091-2725-3). Paulist Pr.
--I Walk with Jesus. 208p. (Orig.). 1986. pap. 7.95 (ISBN 0-8091-2786-5). Paulist Pr.
--Man & Woman He Made Them. 192p. 1985. pap. 6.95 (ISBN 0-8091-2751-2). Paulist Pr.
--Tears of Silence. 3.95 (ISBN 0-87193-011-0). Dimension Bks.
Vanier, Vean. Community & Growth: Our Pilgrimage Together. Shearer, Ann, tr. from Fr. LC 79-91603. 232p. 1979. pap. 8.95 (ISBN 0-8091-2294-4). Paulist Pr.
Van Impe, Jack. Alcohol: The Beloved Enemy. 190p. 1980. pap. 4.95 (ISBN 0-934803-07-2). J Van Impe.
--Baptism of the Holy Spirit. 45p. 1985. pap. 1.95 (ISBN 0-934803-02-1). J Van Impe.
--The Eighties, the Antichrist & Your Startling Future. 87p. 1982. pap. 1.95 (ISBN 0-934803-12-9). J Van Impe.
--Escape the Second Death. 60p. 1985. pap. 1.95 (ISBN 0-934803-38-2). J Van Impe.
--Everything You Always Wanted to Know about Prophesy. 61p. 1980. pap. 1.95 (ISBN 0-934803-11-0). J Van Impe.
--First Steps in a New Direction. 32p. 1980. pap. 0.45 (ISBN 0-934803-17-X). J Van Impe.
--God I'm Suffering, Are You Listening. 36p. 1985. pap. 1.95 (ISBN 0-934803-00-5). J Van Impe.
--Great Salvation Themes. 215p. 1984. pap. 4.95 (ISBN 0-934803-06-4). J Van Impe.
--The Happy Home: Child Rearing. 34p. 1985. pap. 1.95 (ISBN 0-934803-01-3). J Van Impe.
--Heart Disease in Christ's Body. 328p. 1984. pap. 6.95 (ISBN 0-934803-04-8). J Van Impe.
--Israel's Final Holocaust. 172p. 1979. pap. 4.95 (ISBN 0-934803-08-0). J Van Impe.
--Revelation Revealed. 282p. 1982. pap. 6.95 (ISBN 0-934803-09-9); 8-cassette set 29.95 (ISBN 0-934803-35-8). J Van Impe.
Van Impe, Rexella. Beware: Children in Peril. 40p. 1985. pap. 1.95 (ISBN 0-934803-13-7). J Van Impe.
--Hope & Fear Not. 32p. 1985. pap. 1.95 (ISBN 0-934803-14-5). J Van Impe.
--Satisfied...A Promise of Peace in a Troubled World. 142p. 1984. pap. 4.95 (ISBN 0-934803-15-3). J Van Impe.
Van Kaam, Adrian. The Art of Existential Counseling. 6.95 (ISBN 0-87193-044-7). Dimension Bks.
--The Dynamics of Spiritual Self-Direction. 24.95 (ISBN 0-87193-122-2). Dimension Bks.
--Formative Spirituality: The Formation of the Human Heart, Vol. 3. 352p. 1985. 27.50 (ISBN 0-8245-0719-3). Crossroad NY.
--Human Formation. LC 84-29241. (Formative Spirituality Ser.: Vol. 2). 271p. 1985. 24.95x (ISBN 0-8245-0578-6). Crossroad NY.
--In Search of Spiritual Identity. 14.95 (ISBN 0-87193-164-8). Dimension Bks.
--Looking for Jesus. pap. 4.95 (ISBN 0-87193-146-X); 7.95. Dimension Bks.
--Mystery of Transforming Love. 6.95 (ISBN 0-87193-182-6). Dimension Bks.
--On Being Involved. 2.95 (ISBN 0-87193-039-0). Dimension Bks.
--On Being Yourself. 6.95 (ISBN 0-87193-038-2). Dimension Bks.
--Personality Fulfillment in the Spiritual Life. 4.95 (ISBN 0-87193-043-9). Dimension Bks.
--The Roots of Christian Joy. 1985. 8.95 (ISBN 0-87193-241-5). Dimension Bks.
--Spirituality & the Gentle Life. 6.95 (ISBN 0-87193-037-4). Dimension Bks.
--The Vowed Life. 19.95 (ISBN 0-87193-040-4). Dimension Bks.
--The Woman at the Well. 6.95 (ISBN 0-87193-092-7). Dimension Bks.
Van Kaam, Adrian & Muto, Susan. Tell Me Who I Am. 4.95 (ISBN 0-87193-145-1). Dimension Bks.
Van Kaam, Adrian see Kaam, Adrian van.
Van Kaam, Adrian see Kaam, Adrian van & Muto, Susan.
Van Kaam, Adrian, et al. The Emergent Self, 4 bks. in 1. 1968. cancelled (ISBN 0-87193-165-6). Dimension Bks.
--The Participant Self, 2 vols. pap. 4.95 (ISBN 0-87193-045-5). Dimension Bks.
--The Participant Self, 2 vols. in 1. 1985. write for info. (ISBN 0-87193-160-5). Dimension Bks.
Van Kaan, Adrian see Muto, Susan A. & Kaam, Adrian Van.
Van Kamm, Adrian & Muto, Susan A. Creative Formation of Life & World. LC 82-16014. 462p. 1983. lib. bdg. 37.50 (ISBN 0-8191-2708-6); pap. text ed. 19.50 (ISBN 0-8191-2709-4). U Pr of Amer.
Van Klaveren, Pieter. The Great Deception. 160p. 1985. 12.95 (ISBN 0-8059-2997-5). Dorrance.
Van Kley, Dale. The Jansenists & the Expulsion of the Jesuits from France, 1757-1765. LC 74-26390. (Yale Historical Publication. Miscellany Ser.: No. 107). pap. 70.50 (ISBN 0-317-09445-9, 2022046). Bks Demand UMI.
Van Kluyme, Robert, ed. see Walsingham, Thomas.
Van Kluyve, Robert A., ed. see Walsingham, Thomae.
Van Kolken, Diana. Introducing the Shakers: An Explanation & Directory. (Illus.). 64p. (Orig.). 1985. pap. 3.95 (ISBN 0-911861-04-1). Gabriel's Horn.
Van Kospoth, Sylvia-Monica, tr. see Von Duerckheim, Karlfried.
Van Leeuwen, Mary S. The Sorcerer's Apprentice: A Christian Looks at the Changing Face of Psychology. 144p. (Orig.). 1982. pap. 7.95 (ISBN 0-87784-398-8). Inter-Varsity.
Van Lierde, Peter C., ed. Prayers & Devotions from Pope John Paul II. 472p. 1984. 10.95 (ISBN 0-89526-601-6). Regnery Bks.
Van Linden, Philip. The Gospel According to Mark, No. 2. Karris, Robert J., ed. LC 82-20356. (Collegeville Bible Commentary Ser.). (Illus.). 96p. 1983. pap. 2.95 (ISBN 0-8146-1302-0). Liturgical Pr.
VanLoon, Preston C., jt. auth. see McCane, Bryon R.
Van Lutsenburg Maas, Adriaan. Guest among Guests. 1987. 8.95 (ISBN 0-533-06965-3). Vantage.
Van Lysebeth, Andre. Pranayama: The Yoga of Breathing. (Unwin Paperbacks). (Illus.). 1979. pap. 6.95 (ISBN 0-04-149050-9). Allen Unwin.
--Yoga Self-Taught. Congreve, Carola, tr. from Fr. Orig. Title: J'Apprends le Yoga. (Illus.). 264p. 1973. pap. 5.95 (ISBN 0-06-463360-8, EH 360, B&N Bks). Har-Row.

Van McNeal, Henry. Beyond Fulfilment: The Spiritual Message of Henry Van McNeal, Vol. 1. 180p. (Orig.). 1986. pap. 9.95 (ISBN 0-916641-27-9). Natl Academy Songwriters.
Van Merrienboer, Edward, et al. Seeking a Just Society: An Educational Design. Incl. Elementary Edition. 42.00 (ISBN 0-318-00795-9); Secondary Edition. 42.00 (ISBN 0-318-00796-7). Total Edition. 72.00 (ISBN 0-318-00793-2); faculty unit 4.00 (ISBN 0-318-00794-0). Natl Cath Educ.
Vanmikanathan, G., tr. see Sekkizhaar.
Van Moorselaar, Corinne. Francis & the Animals. Hegener, Mark, ed. Smith, David, tr. LC 77-7391. (Dutch., Illus.). 1977. 3.50x (ISBN 0-685-81231-6). Franciscan Herald.
Vann, Vicki. The Growth of the Soul from Impiety to Ecstasy. (Illus.). 1977. pap. 3.25 (ISBN 0-87516-235-5). De Vorss.
Vannah, Joanne M. Number Sense. 1985. 4.95 (ISBN 0-8062-2451-7). Carlton.
Van Ness, Bethann & De Clemente, Elizabeth M. Historias de Toda la Biblia. (Illus.). 684p. 1979. pap. 19.95 (ISBN 0-311-03600-7). Casa Bautista.
Van Ness Goetchius, Eugene. The Language of the New Testament. 349p. 1966. text ed. write for info. (ISBN 0-02-344530-0, Pub. by Scribner). Macmillan.
Vannier, Maryhelen. Have the Time of Your Life! 1986. pap. 6.50 (ISBN 0-687-16657-8). Abingdon.
Van Nieuwenhuijze, C. A. Aspects of Islam in Post-Colonial Indonesia: Five Essays. 1958. 23.75x (ISBN 0-686-21860-4). Mouton.
Van Noord, Glenn see Hendricks, William C. & Noord, Glenn Van.
Vannorsdall, John W. Dimly Burning Wicks: Reflections on the Gospel after a Time Away. LC 81-70661. 112p. 1982. pap. 6.95 (ISBN 0-8006-1622-7, 1-1622). Fortress.
Van Note, Gene. Beacon Small-Group Bible Studies, Ephesians. 88p. (Orig.). 1981. pap. 2.50 (ISBN 0-8341-0722-8). Beacon Hill.
--Beacon Small-Group Bible Studies, Hebrews: He is Here at Last. 64p. (Orig.). 1980. pap. 2.50 (ISBN 0-8341-0623-X). Beacon Hill.
--How to Lead a Small Group Bible Study. 48p. pap. 1.75 (ISBN 0-8341-0653-1). Beacon Hill.
--Ministering to Single Adults. 109p. 1978. pap. 2.95 (ISBN 0-8341-0556-X). Beacon Hill.
--A People Called Nazarenes. 120p. 1983. pap. 2.95 (ISBN 0-8341-0894-1). Beacon Hill.
Van Nuys, Kelvin. A Holist Pilgrimage. LC 80-84738. 400p. 1981. 15.00 (ISBN 0-8022-2383-4). Philos Lib.
Van Nuys, Roscoe. Whole Man: Body Mind is Sprit. LC 77-145467. 134p. 1971. 6.95 (ISBN 0-8022-2050-9). Philos Lib.
Vano, Manolo O. God's Beloved Son. 82p. (Orig.). 1984. pap. 4.00x (ISBN 971-10-0099-7, Pub. by New Day Philippines). Cellar.
Van Oort, H. A. The Iconography of Chinese Buddhism in Traditional China, 2 pts. (Iconography of Religions Ser.: XII-5). (Illus.). 1986. Pt. 1, xii, 30p. pap. 25.50 (ISBN 90-04-07822-3, Pub. by E J Brill); Pt. 2, viii, 27p. pap. 24.75 (ISBN 90-04-07823-1). Heinman.
Van Os, Henk. Sienese Altarpieces 1215-1460 Form, Content, Function: Vol. I 1215-1344. Van Der Ploeg, Kees, contrib. by. (Mediaevalia Groningana IV: Bk. IV). (Illus.). 163p. 1984. 28.00x (ISBN 90-6088-083-8, Pub. by Boumas Boekhuis Netherlands). Benjamins North AM.
Van Oss, Adriaan C. Catholic Colonialism: A Parish History of Guatemala, 1524-1821. (Cambridge Latin American Studies: No. 57). (Illus.). 320p. 1986. 44.50 (ISBN 0-521-32072-0). Cambridge U Pr.
Van Oss, Celia, ed. see Lewis, C. S., et al.
Van Over, Raymond. Sun Songs: Creation Myths from Around the World. (Orig.). 1980. pap. 2.95 (ISBN 0-452-00730-5, Mer). NAL.
Van Pelt, Ethel. Marla. 154p. (Orig.). 1982. pap. 2.95 (ISBN 0-89084-155-1). Bob Jones Univ Pr.
Van Pelt, G. Hierarchies: The Cosmic Ladder of Life. Small, W. Emmett & Todd, Helen, eds. (Theosophical Manual: No. 9). 1975. pap. 2.00 (ISBN 0-913004-23-5). Point Loma Pub.
--Man's Divine Parentage & Destiny: The Great Rounds & Races. Small, W. Emmett & Todd, Helen, eds. (Theosophical Manual: No. 7). 64p. 1975. pap. 2.00 (ISBN 0-913004-24-3, 913004-24). Point Loma Pub.
Van Pelt, Gertrude W. The Doctrine of Karma. Small, W. Emmett & Todd, Helen, eds. (Theosophical Manual: No. 3). 64p. 1975. pap. 2.00 (ISBN 0-913004-16-2). Point Loma Pub.
Van Pelt, Nancy. The Compleat Marriage. Rev. ed. LC 78-20770. (Orion Ser). 1979. pap. 6.95 (ISBN 0-8127-0218-2). Review & Herald.
--How to Develop Your Child's Character. (Better Living Ser.). 1979. pap. 0.99 (ISBN 0-8127-0232-8). Review & Herald.
--Your Future Mate. (Outreach Ser.). 32p. 1983. pap. 0.95 (ISBN 0-8163-0531-5). Pacific Pr Pub Assn.
Van Pelt, Nancy L. The Compleat Tween. Coffen, Richard W., ed. 96p. (Orig.). 1986. pap. 5.95 (ISBN 0-8280-0288-6). Review & Herald.
--From This Day Forward: Blueprint for Family Happiness. Coffen, Richard W., ed. 128p. (Orig.). 1985. pap. 1.95 (ISBN 0-8280-0280-0). Review & Herald.
--How to Turn Minuses into Pluses. Coffen, Richard W., ed. (Better Living Ser.). 32p. (Orig.). 1985. pap. 1.25 (ISBN 0-8280-0303-3). Review & Herald.
Van Praagh, Richard. Survival: A New Approach from the Life Sciences to the Major Problem of Our Time. LC 85-80038. 208p. (Orig.). 1985. pap. 7.95 (ISBN 0-941404-35-8). Falcon Pr Az.
Van Regenmorter, John & Van Regenmorter, Sylvia. Dear God, Why Can't We Have a Baby? 1986. 6.95 (ISBN 0-8010-9301-5). Baker Bk.
Van Regenmorter, Sylvia, jt. auth. see Van Regenmorter, John.
Van Rheenen, Gailyn. Church Planting in Uganda: A Comparative Study. LC 76-20461. 1976. pap. 4.95 (ISBN 0-87808-314-6). William Carey Lib.
Van Rijckenborgh, Jan. De Sen Mascavamiento. (Span.). 1987. pap. 5.00 (ISBN 8-439827-98-9). Rosycross Pr.
--Dei Gloria Intacta. 244p. 1987. 14.50 (ISBN 0-317-52802-5). Rosycross Pr.
--Elementary Philosophy of the Modern Rosycross. 3rd ed. (Cornerstone Ser.: No. 5). Tr. of Elementaire Wijsbegeerte van het moderne Rozekruis. 207p. (Orig.). 1986. pap. 11.00 (ISBN 90-6732-004-8). Rosycross Pr.
--Ensenanza Elemental de la Rosacruz Moderna. (Span.). 1987. pap. 11.00 (ISBN 9-070196-80-8). Rosycross Pr.
--Light Over Tibet. 40p. (Orig.). 1987. pap. 1.75. Rosycross Pr.
--Mysterio de la Vide e de la Muerta. (Span.). 1987. pap. 2.00. Rosycross Pr.
--Mystery of Life & Death. Lectorium Rosicrucianum, tr. from Dutch. 50p. 1987. pap. 6.00. Rosycross Pr.
--Mystery of the Beatitudes. 104p. (Orig.). 1987. pap. 10.50. Rosycross Pr.
--Nuctemeron of Apollonius Tyana. (Dutch.). 125p. (Orig.). 1987. pap. 11.00. Rosycross Pr.
--Nueva Llamada. (Span.). 1987. pap. 1.50. Rosycross Pr.
--Secret of the Rosicrucian Brotherhood, 4 vols. Incl. Vol. 1. Call of Rosicrucian Brotherhood; Vol. 2. Confession of the Rosicrucian Brotherhood; Vol. 3. Alchemical Wedding of Christian Rosycross; Vol. 4. Alchemical Wedding of Christian Rosycross. Date not set. price not set. Rosycross Pr.
--Unmasking. 70p. 1987. pap. 3.00. Rosycross Pr.
--What Is Transfiguration? 40p. 1987. pap. 1.50. Rosycross Pr.
Van Rijckenborgh, Jan & De Petri, Catharose. Brotherhood of Shamballah. Orig. Title: De Broederschap van Shamballa. 123p. 1987. pap. 11.00 (ISBN 90-6732-008-0). Rosycross Pr.
--Fraternidade Shamballah. (Span.). 1987. pap. 11.00. Rosycross Pr.
--Lightgarment of the New Man. Tr. of Het Lichtkleed van de Niewe Mens. 100p. (Orig.). Date not set. pap. 11.00. Rosycross Pr.
--Universal Path. rev ed. (Cornerstone Ser.: No. 2). Tr. of Het Universele Pad. 99p. 1986. pap. 11.00 (ISBN 90-6732-007-2). Rosycross Pr.
Van Rijn, J. C. Living. 49p. (Orig.). 1986. pap. 7.00 (ISBN 0-9617483-0-3). What Is Pr.
--Living. 2nd ed. 130p. Date not set. pap. 8.95 (ISBN 0-9617483-1-1). What Is Pr.
Van Rijn, Rembrandt. Rembrandt: All the Etchings. LC 77-87012. (Illus.). 1977. (Pub. by Two Continents). Hippocrene Bks.
--Rembrandt Bible Drawings. LC 79-52975. (Fine Art Library). (Illus.). 64p. (Orig.). 1980. pap. 3.50 (ISBN 0-486-23878-4). Dover.
Van Rijn Rembrandt, Hermansz. Drawings of Rembrandt. Longstreet, Stephen, ed. (Master Draughtsman Ser). (Illus., Orig.). treasure trove bdg. 10.95x (ISBN 0-87505-029-8); pap. 4.95 (ISBN 0-87505-182-0). Borden.
Van Ryn, August. Acts of the Apostles. LC 61-14601. 1961. pap. 1.95 (ISBN 0-87213-883-6). Loizeaux.
--Mark: Meditations. 1957. pap. 2.25 (ISBN 0-87213-892-5). Loizeaux.
Van Rys, Janet. Walk with Praise. (Devotional Ser.). (Illus.). 200p. (Orig.). 1986. pap. 4.95 (ISBN 0-9616989-0-X). Jan Van Pubns.
Van Schooneveld, C. H., ed. see Armstrong, D., et al.
Van Scoyoc, Nancy. Women, Change, & the Church. LC 80-15739. (Into Our Third Century Ser.). 96p. (Orig.). 1980. pap. 3.95 (ISBN 0-687-45958-3). Abingdon.
Van Selms, A. Job: A Practical Commentary. Van Der Woude, A. S., ed. (Text & Interpretation Ser.). (Dutch.). 192p. (Orig.). 1985. pap. 8.95 (ISBN 0-8028-0101-3). Eerdmans.
Van Seters, John. In Search of History: Historiography in the Ancient World & the Origins of Biblical History. LC 82-48912. 416p. 1983. text ed. 35.00x (ISBN 0-300-02877-6); pap. 12.95 (ISBN 0-300-03633-7, Y-574). Yale U Pr.
Van Seters, Virginia A. Twenty-Two Object Talks for Children's Worship. (Illus.). 48p. 1986. pap. 2.95 (ISBN 0-87403-055-2, 2866). Standard Pub.
Van Siclen, Charles C., III. The Chapel of Sesostris III at Uronarti. 58p. 1982. pap. text ed. 10.00x (ISBN 0-933175-02-7). Van Siclen Bks.
--Wall Scenes from the Tomb of Amenhotep (Huy) Governor of Bahria Oasis. (Illus.). ii, 46p. 1981. pap. text ed. 11.00x (ISBN 0-933175-00-0). Van Siclen Bks.
Van Speybrouck, Edward. Father Paul of Moll. LC 79-53695. 1979. pap. 6.00 (ISBN 0-89555-122-5). TAN Bks Pubs.
Van Steenberghen, Fernand. Thomas Aquinas & Radical Aristotelianism. O'Meara, Dominic J., et al, trs. from Fr. 114p. 1980. pap. 6.95 (ISBN 0-8132-0552-2). Cath U Pr.
Vanstiphout, Herman, jt. auth. see Kinnier-Wilson, J. V.
Van Stone, Doris, jt. auth. see Lutzer, Erwin.
Vanstone, W. H. The Risk of Love. 1978. 11.95x (ISBN 0-19-520053-5). Oxford U Pr.
--The Stature of Waiting. 128p. (Orig.). 1983. pap. 8.95 (ISBN 0-8164-2478-0, HarpR). Har-Row.
Van Straalen, Alice. The Book of Holidays Around the World. (Illus.). 192p. 1986. 12.95 (ISBN 0-525-44270-7). Dutton.
Van Tatenhove, Frederick C. Ambition: Friend or Enemy? LC 84-5199. (Potentials; Guides for Productive Living Ser.: Vol. 11). 120p. 1984. pap. 7.95 (ISBN 0-664-24530-7). Westminster.
Van Til, Cornelius. Christian Apologetics. 1976. pap. 3.95 syllabus (ISBN 0-87552-477-X). Presby & Reformed.
--Christian Theistic Ethics. 1975. pap. 7.95 syllabus (ISBN 0-87552-478-8). Presby & Reformed.
--Christian Theory of Knowledge. 1969. pap. 10.95 (ISBN 0-87552-480-X). Presby & Reformed.
--Christianity & Barthianism. 1960. pap. 10.95 (ISBN 0-87552-481-8). Presby & Reformed.
--Common Grace & the Gospel. 1972. pap. 8.95 (ISBN 0-87552-482-6). Presby & Reformed.
--Defense of the Faith. 1967. pap. 6.95 (ISBN 0-87552-483-4). Presby & Reformed.
--The Doctrine of Scripture. 1967. pap. 5.50 syllabus (ISBN 0-87552-484-2). Presby & Reformed.
--An Introduction to Systematic Theology. 1974. pap. 8.95 syllabus (ISBN 0-87552-488-5). Presby & Reformed.
--My Credo. 1971. pap. 3.50 (ISBN 0-87552-490-7). Presby & Reformed.
--A Survey of Christian Epistemology. 1967. pap. 6.95 (ISBN 0-87552-495-8). Presby & Reformed.
--Why I Believe in God. 1948. pap. 0.75 (ISBN 0-87552-496-6). Presby & Reformed.
Van Til, Cornellius. Paul at Athens. 1959. pap. 0.95 (ISBN 0-87552-493-1). Presby & Reformed.
Van Tilborg, Sjef. The Sermon on the Mount As an Ideological Intervention: A Reconstruction of Meaning. 324p. 1986. 30.00 (ISBN 90-232-2243-1, Pub. by Van Gorcum Holland). Longwood Pub Group.
Van Till, Howard J. The Fourth Day: What the Bible & the Heavens Are Telling Us about the Creation. LC 85-29400. (Illus.). 286p. (Orig.). 1986. pap. 9.95 (ISBN 0-8028-0178-1). Eerdmans.
Vanuken, Sheldon. A Severe Mercy. 1979. pap. 3.95 (ISBN 0-553-25155-4). Bantam.
Van Vechten, Schuyler. The Bethlehem Star: Children's Newspaper Reports of the Life of Jesus. 1972. 4.95 (ISBN 0-8027-6097-X). Walker & Co.
Van Vuuren, Nancy. Work & Career. LC 83-12338. (Choices: Guides for Today's Woman: Vol. 2). 116p. (Orig.). 1983. pap. 6.95 (ISBN 0-664-24539-0). Westminster.
Van Wagoner, Richard S. Mormon Polygamy: A History. 275p. 1985. 19.95 (ISBN 0-941214-35-4). Signature Bks.
Van Wagoner, Richard S. & Walker, Steven C. A Book of Mormons. 468p. 1982. 14.95 (ISBN 0-941214-06-0). Signature Bks.
Van Waveren, Erlo. Pilgrimage to Rebirth. 125p. 1978. 7.95 (ISBN 0-87728-420-2); pap. 3.95. Weiser.
Van Well, Sr. Mary Stanislaus. Educational Aspects of the Missions of the Southwest. 1942. pap. 7.95 (ISBN 0-87462-438-X). Marquette.
Van Woerkom, Dorothy, jt. auth. see Christian, Mary B.
Van Wyke, Millie. You're Hired! Insights for Christian Women Who Work Outside the Home. 120p. 1983. pap. 5.95 (ISBN 0-8010-9292-2). Baker Bk.
Vanzant, Don, jt. auth. see White, Anne S.
Van Zeller, Hubert. Current of Spirituality. pap. 3.95 (ISBN 0-87243-048-0). Templegate.
--Ideas for Prayer. 1973. pap. 3.95 (ISBN 0-87243-046-4). Templegate.
--Leave Your Life Alone. 6.95 (ISBN 0-87243-043-X). Templegate.
--Letters to a Soul. 1976. 7.95 (ISBN 0-87243-067-7). Templegate.
--Other Kingdom. 3.95 (ISBN 0-87243-032-4). Templegate.
--Patterns for Prayer. 128p. 1983. pap. 5.95 (ISBN 0-87243-124-X). Templegate.
--Prayer & the Will of God. 1978. 4.95 (ISBN 0-87243-084-7). Templegate.
--Spirituality Recharted. 1985. pap. 4.95 (ISBN 0-932506-39-9). St Bedes Pubns.
--To Be in Christ. LC 81-9793. (Illus.). 112p. 1981. 9.95x (ISBN 0-8245-0086-5). Crossroad NY.
--The Trodden Road. 173p. 1982. 4.00 (ISBN 0-8198-7326-8, SP0773); pap. 3.00 (ISBN 0-8198-7327-6). Dghtrs St Paul.
Van Zijl, J. B. A Concordance to the Targum of Isaiah. LC 78-25832. (Society of Biblical Literature. Aramaic Studies: No. 3). Repr. of 1979 ed. 53.80 (ISBN 0-8357-9569-1, 2017542). Bks Demand UMI.
Van Zile, Judy. The Japanese Bon Dance in Hawaii. (Illus.). 96p. 1982. pap. 5.95 (ISBN 0-916630-27-7). Pr Pacifica.
Van Zyl, P., jt. auth. see Davies, J. G.
Vaporis, N. M, ed. Byzantine Fellowship Lectures, No. One, No. 1. (Illus.). 1974. pap. 2.95 (ISBN 0-916586-02-2). Holy Cross Orthodox.
Vaporis, N. M., intro. by see Conomos, Dimitri.
Vaporis, N. M., intro. by see Moskos, C. C., Jr. & Papajohn, J. C.
Vaporis, N. M., ed. see Patsavos, L. J. & Charles, G. J.
Vaporis, N. M., intro. by see Symeon of Thessalonike.
Vaporis, N. M., ed. see Talbot, Alice-Mary M.
Vaporis, N. M., ed. see Tsatsos, Ioanna.
Vaporis, Nomikos M. Codex Beta of the Ecumenical Patriarchate of Constantinople: Aspects of the History of the Church of Constantinople. (The Archbishop Iakovos Library of Ecclesiastical & Historical Sources). 166p. 1975. pap. 4.95 (ISBN 0-916586-03-0). Holy Cross Orthodox.
--Codex Gamma of the Ecumenical Patriarchate of Constantinople. (The Archbishop Iakovos Library of Ecclesiastical & Historical Sources Ser.). 154p. 1974. pap. 4.95 (ISBN 0-916586-01-4). Holy Cross Orthodox.
--Father Kosmas: The Apostle of the Poor. LC 77-77664. (Illus.). 164p. 1977. 7.95 (ISBN 0-916586-17-0); pap. 4.95 (ISBN 0-916586-10-3). Holy Cross Orthodox.
Vaporis, Nomikos M., ed. The Apostolos: The Acts & Letters of the Holy Apostles Read in the Orthodox Church Throughout the Year. 420p. 1980. 55.00 (ISBN 0-916586-39-1). Holy Cross Orthodox.
Vaporis, Nomikos M., pref. by. Byzantine Ecclesiastical Personalities. (Byzantine Fellowship Lectures: No. 2). 107p. 1975. pap. 2.95 (ISBN 0-916586-04-9). Holy Cross Orthodox.
Vaporis, Nomikos M., ed. The Holy Gospel. 245p. 1979. 95.00 (ISBN 0-916586-25-1). Holy Cross Orthodox.
--Mikron Euchologion: An Orthodox Prayer Book. Gelsinger, Michael, tr. from Greek. & pref. by. LC 77-77642. 288p. 1977. 18.95 (ISBN 0-916586-09-X). Holy Cross Orthodox.
--Post-Byzantine Ecclesiastical Personalities. LC 78-11037. 111p. 1978. pap. 3.95 (ISBN 0-916586-30-8). Holy Cross Orthodox.
Varacalli, Joseph A. Toward the Establishment of Liberal Catholicism in America. LC 82-23811. 326p. (Orig.). 1983. lib. bdg. 30.00 (ISBN 0-8191-2974-7); pap. text ed. 14.75 (ISBN 0-8191-2975-5). U Pr of Amer.
Varadpande, M. L. Religion & Theatre. 100p. 1982. text ed. 15.00x (ISBN 0-391-02794-8). Humanities.
Varberg, Mimi. Mischief, Messes & God's Grace. LC 53-1019. (Book Ser.). 56p. 1985. pap. 3.50 (ISBN 0-932305-34-2). Aglow Pubns.
Vardys, V. Stanley. The Catholic Church, Dissent & Nationality in Soviet Lithuania. (East European Monographs: No. 43). 336p. 1978. 30.00x (ISBN 0-914710-36-2). East Eur Quarterly.
Varela, Francisco, jt. auth. see Maurana, Humberto R.
Varenne, Jean. Yoga & the Hindu Tradition. Coltman, Derek, tr. from Fr. LC 75-19506. 1976. pap. 5.45X (ISBN 0-226-85116-8, P744, Phoen). U of Chicago Pr.
Varg, Paul A. Missionaries, Chinese & Diplomats. LC 76-30301. 1977. Repr. lib. bdg. 23.00x (ISBN 0-374-98071-3, Octagon). Hippocrene Bks.
Varga, Andrew C. Main Issues in Bioethics. LC 80-82084. 240p. (Orig.). 1984. pap. 10.95 (ISBN 0-8091-2327-4). Paulist Pr.

--On Being Human: Principles of Ethics. LC 78-51589. 160p. 1978. pap. 3.95 (ISBN 0-8091-2111-5). Paulist Pr.
Vargas, Carlos A., tr. see Cramer, Raymond L.
Vargas, Carlos A., tr. see Keller, Phillip.
Vargas, Mario. Entre Sartre y Camus. LC 81-68707. (Coleccion la Nave y el Puerto Ser.). 144p. 1981. pap. 5.50 (ISBN 0-940238-48-9). Ediciones Hura.
Vargas-Caba, Jose M., tr. see Brewer, Bartholomew F. & Furrell, Alfred W.
Vargesko, Edward B. It Happened This Way. (Orig.). 1982. pap. 2.25 (ISBN 0-937172-35-9). JLJ Pubs.
Varghese, Roy A., ed. The Intellectuals Speak Out About God. 1984. pap. 7.95 (ISBN 0-89526-827-2). Regnery Bks.
Varillon, Francois. The Humility & Suffering of God. Marans, Nelly, ed. LC 83-2724. 202p. (Orig.). 1983. pap. 8.95 (ISBN 0-8189-0448-8). Alba.
Variorum, ed. Polynj Pravoslavnyj Bogoslavskij Enciklopediceskij. 1240p. 1971. 75.00x (ISBN 0-902089-08-0). State Mutual Bk.
Varley, H. Paul, tr. from Japanese. A Chronicle of Gods & Sovereigns: Jinno Shotoki of Kitabatake Chikafusa. LC 80-10430. (Translations from Oriental Classics Ser.). 1980. 32.00x (ISBN 0-231-04940-4). Columbia U Pr.
Varma, V. P. Early Buddhism & Its Origin. 1973. text ed. 20.00x. Coronet Bks.
--The Political Philosophy of Sri Aurobindo. 2nd rev. ed. 1976. 12.50 (ISBN 0-8426-0873-7). Orient Bk Dist.
Varner, Jeanne. How to Make Children's Church Come Alive. 1979. 4.95 (ISBN 0-87148-407-2). Pathway Pr.
Varner, K. H. Prevail: A Handbook for the Overcomer. 172p. 1982. pap. 3.95 (ISBN 0-938612-06-9). Revival Press.
Varner, William. The Chariot of Israel: Exploits of the Prophet of Elijah. LC 84-80766. 1984. pap. text ed. 4.95 (ISBN 0-915540-33-9). Frnds Israel.
Vartanian, Aram. Diderot & Descartes: A Study of Scientific Naturalism in the Enlightment. LC 75-18406. (History of Ideas Series: No. 6). 336p. 1975. Repr. of 1953 ed. lib. bdg. 22.50x (ISBN 0-8371-8337-5, VADD). Greenwood.
Vasconcelos, B. Your Mass. 137p. 1961. 4.95 (ISBN 0-933932-13-8); pap. 2.50 (ISBN 0-933932-14-6). Scepter Pubs.
Vasi, Dianne. It Shouldn't Hurt to Be a Child. Coffen, Richard W., ed. (Better Living Ser.). 32p. (Orig.). 1985. pap. 0.99 (ISBN 0-8280-0310-6). Review & Herald.
Vasileios of Stavronikita. Hymn of Entry. Briere, Elizabeth, tr. from Gr. LC 84-5512. 138p. 1984. pap. text ed. 6.95 (ISBN 0-88141-026-8). St Vladimirs.
Vasquez, Guillermo H. Lo Que los Padres y Maestros Deben Saber Acerca de las Drogas. 128p. 1984. pap. 1.20 (ISBN 0-311-46080-1). Casa Bautista.
Vass, George. Understanding Karl Rahner, 2 vols. (Orig.). 1985. Vol. 1, 153 pgs. pap. 12.50 (ISBN 0-87061-115-1); Vol. 2, 200 pgs. pap. 12.50 (ISBN 0-87061-116-X); Set. pap. 25.00 (ISBN 0-317-20726-1). Chr Classics.
Vassady, Bela. Limping along: Confessions of a Pilgrim Theologian. 248p. (Orig.). 1985. pap. 13.95 (ISBN 0-8028-0095-5). Eerdmans.
Vassallo, Mario. From Lordship to Stewardship: Religion & Social Change in Malta. 1979. text ed. 22.00x (ISBN 90-279-7967-7). Mouton.
Vassilakos, Aristarchus. The Trial of Jesus Christ. Orthodox Christian Educational Society, ed. 64p. (Orig.). 1950. pap. 2.75x (ISBN 0-938366-47-5). Orthodox Chr.
Vast, Henri. Le Cardinal de Bessarion 1405-1472: Etude sun la Chretiente et la Renaissance vers le Milieu du XVe Siecle. (Fr.). 487p. Repr. of 1878 ed. lib. bdg. 57.50x. Coronet Bks.
Vasu, Srisa Chandra. A Catechism of Hindu Dharma. 2nd, rev. & enl. ed. Vidyarnava, Srisa Chandra, tr. LC 73-3829. (Sacred Books of the Hindus: No. 3). Repr. of 1919 ed. 14.50 (ISBN 0-404-57847-0). AMS Pr.
--The Daily Practice of the Hindus Containing the Morning & Midday Duties. 3rd, rev. & enl. ed. Vidyarnava, Srisa Chandra, tr. LC 73-3812. (Sacred Books of the Hindus: No. 20). Repr. of 1918 ed. 14.50 (ISBN 0-404-57820-9). AMS Pr.
--An Introduction to the Yoga Philosophy. LC 73-3806. (Scared Books of the Hindus: No. 15, Pt. 4). Repr. of 1915 ed. 14.50 (ISBN 0-404-57838-1). AMS Pr.
--Studies in the First Six Upanisads, & the Isa & Kena Upanisads with the Commentary of Sankara. Vidyarnava, Srisa Chandra, tr. LC 73-3814. (Sacred Books of the Hindus: No. 22, Pt. 1). Repr. of 1919 ed. 14.50 (ISBN 0-404-57822-5). AMS Pr.
Vasu, Srisa Chandra, tr. The Brihadaranyaka Upanisad. LC 73-3802. (Sacred Books of the Hindus: No. 14). Repr. of 1916 ed. 47.50 (ISBN 0-404-57814-4). AMS Pr.
--Chhandogya Upanisad. LC 73-3788. (Sacred Books of the Hindus: No. 3). Repr. of 1910 ed. 44.50 (ISBN 0-404-57803-9). AMS Pr.
--The Gheranda Samhita. LC 73-3804. (Sacred Books of the Hindus: 15, Pt. 2). Repr. of 1914 ed. 14.50 (ISBN 0-404-57836-5). AMS Pr.
--The Upanisads. 2nd ed. LC 73-4980. (Sacred Books of the Hindus: No. 1). Repr. of 1911 ed. 27.50 (ISBN 0-404-57801-2). AMS Pr.
--The Vedanta Sutras of Badarayana with the Commentary of Baladeva. LC 73-3790. (Sacred Books of the Hindus: Vol. 5). Repr. of 1912 ed. 57.50 (ISBN 0-404-57805-5). AMS Pr.
Vasubhandu, Bodhisattva. The Hundred Dharmas. Master Hua, Tripitaka, commentary by. Buddhist Text Translation Society, tr. from Chinese. 130p. (Orig.). 1983. pap. 6.50 (ISBN 0-88139-003-8). Buddhist Text.
Vasu-Mitra. Origin & Doctrines of Early Indian Buddhist Schools. Masuda, Jiryo, tr. LC 78-70133. Repr. of 1925 ed. 17.00 (ISBN 0-404-17403-5). AMS Pr.
Vaswani, J. P. & Mirchandani, Jyoti. Temple Flowers. 182p. 1986. text ed. 25.00x (ISBN 0-317-43153-6, Pub. by Chopmen Pubs Singapore). Advent NY.
Vaswig, William L. At Your Word, Lord. LC 81-52272. 128p. (Orig.). 1982. pap. 5.95 (ISBN 0-8066-1904-X, 10-0498). Augsburg.
--I Prayed, He Answered. LC 77-72457. 1977. pap. 5.95 (ISBN 0-8066-1589-3, 10-3189). Augsburg.
Vatai, Laszlo. Az Isten Szornyetege: Ady Iiraja. 2nd ed. LC 77-89126. (Hungarian.). 390p. 1977. 15.00 (ISBN 0-911050-45-0). Occidental.
Vath, Raymond E. & O'Neill, Daniel. Marrying for Life: A Handbook of Marriage Skills. (Illus.). 144p. (Orig.). 1982. pap. 6.95 (ISBN 0-86683-674-8, HarpR). Har-Row.
Vath, Raymond E & O'Neill, Daniel W. Marrying for Life. (Illus., Orig.). 1981. pap. 8.00 (ISBN 0-939336-00-6). Messenger Comm.
Vatican Council II, Staff. Dogmatic Constitution on the Church (Lumen Gentium) 94p. 1964. pap. 3.25 (ISBN 1-55586-000-1). US Catholic.
Vatican Council Two. Decree on Ecumenism. Stransky, Thomas, ed. (Orig.). 1965. pap. 1.95 (ISBN 0-8091-5027-1). Paulist Pr.
Vatican Secretariat for Promoting Christian Unity Staff. Sects or New Religious Movements: Pastoral Challenge. 24p. 1986. pap. 2.95 (ISBN 1-55586-100-8). US Catholic.
Vaudrey, Stephen J. How to Win Your Family to Christ. 1985. 13.95 (ISBN 0-317-18081-9); pap. 6.95 (ISBN 0-317-18082-7). P-H.
Vaughan, Alden T. & Clark, Edward W., eds. Puritans among the Indians: Accounts of Captivity & Redemption, 1676-1724. (John Harvard Library). 288p. 1986. pap. text ed. 7.95x (ISBN 0-674-73899-3, Belknap Pr). Harvard U Pr.
Vaughan, C. R. The Gifts of the Holy Spirit. 1975. 15.95 (ISBN 0-85151-222-4). Banner of Truth.
Vaughan, Charles J. Epistle to the Philippians. 318p. 1984. smythe sewn 11.50 (ISBN 0-86524-180-5, 5002). Klock & Klock.
--Studies in the Book of Acts. 620p. 1985. smythe sewn 24.95 (ISBN 0-86524-189-9, 4404). Klock & Klock.
Vaughan, Curtis. Acts-A Study Guide Commentary. 160p. (Orig.). 1974. pap. 5.95 (ISBN 0-310-33513-2, 10958P). Zondervan.
--Colossians & Philemon: A Study Guide Commentary. (Study Guide Commentary Ser.). 144p. (Orig.). 1981. pap. 4.95 (ISBN 0-310-33583-3, 10965P). Zondervan.
--Comentario Biblico Efesios. Orig. Title: Ephesians. (Port.). 1986. write for info. (ISBN 0-8297-1608-4). Life Pubs Intl.
--Ephesians: A Study Guide Commentary. (Study Guide Commentary Ser.). 1977. pap. 4.95 (ISBN 0-310-33533-7, 10962P). Zondervan.
--Ephesians (Efesios-Comemtario y Estudios) (Span.). 1986. write for info. (ISBN 0-8297-0904-5). Life Pubs Intl.
--Galatians Bible Study Commentary. 128p. 1972. pap. 4.95 (ISBN 0-310-33543-4, 10856P). Zondervan.
--James: Bible Study Commentary. pap. 4.95 (ISBN 0-310-33553-1, 10955P). Zondervan.
--One, Two, Three John. (Bible Study Commentary Ser.). 140p. 1984. pap. 4.95 (ISBN 0-310-33563-9). Zondervan.
Vaughan, Curtis & Corley, Bruce. Romans: A Study Guide Commentary. 1976. pap. 4.95 (ISBN 0-310-33573-6, 10960P). Zondervan.
Vaughan, Curtis & Gideon, Virtus E. A Greek Grammar of the New Testament. LC 78-74504. 1979. 11.95 (ISBN 0-8054-1378-2). Broadman.
Vaughan, Curtis & Lea, Thomas D. Corinthians 1: Bible Study Commentary. (Bible Study Commentary Ser.). 160p. 1983. pap. 4.95 (ISBN 0-310-44021-1, 12484P). Zondervan.
Vaughan, Curtis, jt. ed. see Drumwright, Huber L.
Vaughan, Frances. The Inward Arc: Healing & Wholeness in Psychotherapy & Spirituality. LC 85-2504. (Illus.). 238p. (Orig.). 1986. pap. 10.95 (ISBN 0-87773-324-4, 74201-X, Pub. by New Sci Lib-Shambhala). Shambhala Pubns.
Vaughan, Henry H. Welsh Proverbs with English Translations. LC 68-17945. (Eng. & Welsh.). 1969. Repr. of 1889 ed. 43.00x (ISBN 0-8103-3205-1). Gale.
Vaughan, Herbert C., tr. see Mary da Bergamo, Cajetan.
Vaughan, John, jt. auth. see Towns, Elmer L.
Vaughan, John N. The Large Church. 1985. pap. 7.95 (ISBN 0-8010-9298-1). Baker Bk.
--The World's Twenty Largest Churches. 1984. pap. 12.95 (ISBN 0-8010-9297-3). Baker Bk.
Vaughan, Judith. Sociality, Ethics, & Social Change: A Critical Appraisal of Reinhold Niebuhr's Ethics in the Light of Rosemary Radford Ruether's Works. annual LC 83-1293. 228p. (Orig.). 1983. text ed. 26.00 (ISBN 0-8191-3100-8); pap. text ed. 12.50 (ISBN 0-8191-3101-6). U Pr of Amer.
Vaughan, P. H. Meaning of Bama in the Old Testament. LC 73-89004. (Society for Old Testament Study Monographs: No. 3). (Illus.). 96p. 1974. 29.95 (ISBN 0-521-20425-9). Cambridge U Pr.
Vaughan, Richard, tr. from Lat. The Chronicles of Matthew Paris: Monastic Life in the Thirteenth Century. LC 83-40602. 286p. 1985. 25.00 (ISBN 0-312-13452-5). St Martin.
Vaughan, Richard P. Basic Skills for Christian Counselors: An Introduction for Pastoral Ministers. 192p. (Orig.). 1987. pap. 8.95 (ISBN 0-8091-2857-8). Paulist Pr.
Vaughan, Robert. The Life & Opinions of John de Wycliffe, D. D, 2 vols. 2nd ed. LC 71-178561. Repr. of 1831 ed. Set. 75.00 (ISBN 0-404-56678-2). Vol. 1 o.p (ISBN 0-404-56679-0). Vol. 2 o.p (ISBN 0-404-56680-4). AMS Pr.
Vaughan, Thomas. The Fraternity of the Rosy Cross. Waite, A. E., ed. 1983. pap. 5.95 (ISBN 0-916411-07-9, Pub. by Alchemical Pr). Holmes Pub.
Vaughan Williams, Ralph, ed. see Dearmer, Percy.
Vaughn, Joe & Klug, Ron. New Life for Men: A Book for Men & the Women Who Care about Them. LC 84-21685. 144p. 1984. pap. 4.95 (ISBN 0-8066-2114-1, 10-4642). Augsburg.
Vaughn, Lou E. Brush Arbor Birthright. LC 86-80089. (Illus.). 160p. (Orig.). 1986. pap. 3.95 (ISBN 0-88243-483-7, 02-0483). Gospel Pub.
Vaughn, Nancy R. & Sloan, Johnny W. Where Is the Rainbow? LC 84-52691. (Illus.). 144p. (Orig.). 1985. pap. 5.95 (ISBN 0-318-04447-1). Vaughn Pub KY.
Vaughn, Ruth. More Skits That Win. 1977. pap. 2.95 (ISBN 0-310-33671-6, 10942X). Zondervan.
--Skits That Win. (Orig.). (YA) 1968. pap. 2.95 (ISBN 0-310-33661-9, 10941P). Zondervan.
--To Be a Girl, to Be a Woman. 160p. 1982. 8.95 (ISBN 0-8007-1328-1). Revell.
Vaught, Carl G. The Quest for Wholeness. LC 81-18365. 224p. 1982. 44.50 (ISBN 0-87395-593-5); pap. 14.95 (ISBN 0-87395-594-3). State U NY Pr.
--The Sermon on the Mount: A Theological Interpretation. (Religious Studies). 192p. (Orig.). 1986. 34.50x (ISBN 0-88706-364-0); pap. 9.95x (ISBN 0-88706-365-9). State U NY Pr.
Vaught, Laud O. Focus on the Christian Family. 1976. pap. 3.95 (ISBN 0-87148-332-7). Pathway Pr.
--God's Plan for the World, Old Testament Survey. LC 82-62742. (Illus.). 183p. (Orig.). 1983. pap. text ed. 6.95 (ISBN 0-87148-360-2). Pathway Pr.
Vaux, Bernard Carra de see Carra de Vaux, Bernard.
Vaux, Kenneth, ed. Powers That Make Us Human: The Foundations of Medical Ethics. LC 84-28028. 152p. 1986. 16.95 (ISBN 0-252-01187-2). U of Ill Pr.
Vaux, Kenneth L., ed. see Martin, Marty E.
Vaux, R. de see De Vaux, R.
Vaux, R. de see De Vaux, R. & Milik, J. T.
Vaux, Roland de see De Vaux, Roland.
Vawter, Bruce. Advent-Christmas. LC 84-18756. (Proclamation 3A Ser.). 64p. 1986. pap. 3.75 (ISBN 0-8006-4117-5, 1-4117). Fortress.
--Amos, Hosea, Micah, with Introduction to Classical Prophecy. (Old Testament Message Ser.: Vol. 7). 1982. 12.95 (ISBN 0-89453-407-6); pap. 6.95 (ISBN 0-89453-242-1). M Glazier.
--Ezra-Nehemiah. (Bible Ser.). pap. 1.00 (ISBN 0-8091-5047-6). Paulist Pr.
--Job & Jonah: Questioning the Hidden God. LC 82-62413. 1983. pap. 4.95 (ISBN 0-8091-2524-2). Paulist Pr.
--The Path of Wisdom: Biblical Investigations. (Background Bks.: Vol. 3). 1986. pap. 12.95 (ISBN 0-89453-466-1). M Glazier.
--Sirach. (Bible Ser.). Pt. 1. pap. 1.00 (ISBN 0-8091-5138-3); Pt. 2. pap. 1.00 (ISBN 0-8091-5139-1). Paulist Pr.
Vawter, Bruce & Carl, William J., III. Easter. LC 79-7377. (Proclamation 2: Aids for Interpreting the Lessons of the Church Year, Ser. A). 64p. (Orig.). 1981. pap. 3.75 (ISBN 0-8006-4095-0, 1-4095). Fortress.
Vawter, Bruce, ed. see Osiek, Carolyn.
Vawter, Bruce, ed. see Thompson, James W.
Vawter, Bruce, ed. see Tobin, Thomas H.
Vaysse, Jean. Toward Awakening: An Approach to the Teaching of Gurdjieff. LC 79-1779. 1979. pap. 5.95i (ISBN 0-06-068860-2, RD 304, HarpR). Har-Row.
Veal, David L. Saints Galore. 160p. (Orig.). 1972. pap. 1.75 (ISBN 0-88028-009-3, 405). Forward Movement.
Veatch, Henry B. For an Ontology of Morals: A Critique of Contemporary Ethical Theory. 1971. 14.95 (ISBN 0-8101-0352-4). Northwestern U Pr.
--Rational Man: A Modern Interpretation of Aristotelian Ethics. LC 62-16161. (Midland Bks.: No. 71). 228p. 1962. pap. 8.95x (ISBN 0-253-20071-7). Ind U Pr.
Vecchio, Mary Del see Del Vecchio, Anthony & Del Vecchio, Mary.
Veccio, Anthony Del see Del Vecchio, Anthony & Del Vecchio, Mary.
Vechten, Schuyler Van see Van Vechten, Schuyler.
Vecsey, Christopher. Traditional Ojibwa Religion & Its Historical Changes. LC 83-72209. (Mem. Ser.: Vol. 152). 1983. 12.00 (ISBN 0-87169-152-3). Am Philos.
Vecsey, Christopher, ed. see Hultkrantz, Ake.
Vecsey, Joseph & Schlafly, Phyllis. Mindszenty the Man. LC 72-93906. 1972. 2.00 (ISBN 0-934640-04-1). Pere Marquette.
Veda, jt. auth. see Samskrti.
Vedant, Swami S., ed. see Rajneesh, Bhagwan S.
Vedanta Kesari Staff, ed. Paths of Meditation. 241p. 1980. pap. 3.25 (ISBN 0-87481-501-0). Vedanta Pr.
Vedas. Der Rig Veda, 4 pts. Ingalls, Daniel H., ed. LC 54-10046. (Oriental Ser: No. 33-35). Pts. 1-3. 1952 65.00x (ISBN 0-674-76965-1); Pt. 4. 1957 16.50x (ISBN 0-674-76967-8). Harvard U Pr.
Vedder, Enrique C. Breve Historia de los Bautistas Hasta 1900. Barocio, Teofilo, tr. 272p. 1985. Repr. of 1978 ed. 4.50 (ISBN 0-311-15039-X). Casa Bautista.
Vedder, H. C. History of the Baptists. 1977. lib. bdg. 59.95 (ISBN 0-8490-1988-5). Gordon Pr.
--The Reformation in Germany. 1977. lib. bdg. 59.95 (ISBN 0-8490-2506-0). Gordon Pr.
Vedder, Henry C. Baltahsar Hubmaier: The Leader of the Anabaptists. LC 79-149670. Repr. of 1905 ed. 24.50 (ISBN 0-404-06755-7). AMS Pr.
--Short History of the Baptists. 12.95 (ISBN 0-8170-0162-X). Judson.
Veen, H. R. Van Der see Van Der Veen, H. R.
Veena, Ma Prem, ed. see Rajneesh, Bhagwan Shree.
Veena, Ma Prema, ed. see Rajneesh, Bhagwan Shree.
Veenhoven, ed. Case Studies on Human Rights & Fundamental Freedoms. Incl. Vol. 1. 1975 (ISBN 90-247-1780-9); Vol. 2. 1975; Vol. 3. 1976 (ISBN 90-247-1955-0); Vol. 4. 1976; Vol. 5. 1976. lib. bdg. 52.50 ea. (Pub. by Martinus Nijhoff Netherlands). Kluwer Academic.
Veerman, David, jt. auth. see Spotts, Dwight.
Veerman, David R. Any Old Time, Bk. 6. 1986. pap. 6.95 (ISBN 0-89693-510-8). Victor Bks.
--Any Old Times, Bk. 1. 80p. 1984. pap. 6.95 (ISBN 0-88207-595-0). Victor Bks.
Veerman, David R., ed. Any Old Time, Bk. 7. 80p. 1987. pap. 5.95 (ISBN 0-89693-509-4). Victor Bks.
Vega, Pablo A. The Apparitions of Our Blessed Mother in Cuapa, Nicaragua. 1984. pap. 1.00 (ISBN 0-911988-59-9). Ami Pr.
Veilleux, Armand. Pachomian Koinonia III. Instructions, Letters & Other Writings, No. 47. (Cistercian Studies). 1983. 26.95 (ISBN 0-87907-847-2); pap. 10.00 (ISBN 0-87907-947-9). Cistercian Pubns.
Veilleux, Armand, tr. Pachomian Koinonia I: The Life of St. Pachomius. (Cistercian Studies: No. 45). (Gr.). 524p. 1981. pap. 12.95 (ISBN 0-87907-945-2). Cistercian Pubns.
Veith, Gene E., Jr. The Gift of Art. LC 83-18636. 120p. 1984. pap. 6.95 (ISBN 0-87784-813-0). Inter-Varsity.
--Reformation Spirituality: The Religion of George Herbert. LC 83-46176. 288p. 1985. 34.50 (ISBN 0-8387-5071-0). Bucknell U Pr.
Velasquez, Roger, tr. see Trueblood, David E.
Velichkovsky, Paisius. Blessed Paisius Velichkovsky: His Life & Writings. 1973. 12.00x (ISBN 0-686-05406-7). Eastern Orthodox.
Velikhov, Y., et al. The Night after: Climatic & Biological Consequences of a Nuclear War. 165p. 1985. 8.95 (ISBN 0-8285-3110-2, Pub. by Mir Pubs USSR). Imported Pubns.

Velikovsky, Immanuel. Oedipus & Akhnaton: Myth & History. LC 60-7886. 1960. 11.95 (ISBN 0-385-00529-6). Doubleday.

Velimirovic, Milos, ed. Studies in Eastern Chant, Vol. IV. 248p. 1979. pap. text ed. 10.95 (ISBN 0-913836-57-5). St Vladimirs.

Velsen, Dorothee Von see Von Velsen, Dorothee.

Venables, Edmund. Life of John Bunyan. LC 77-20805. 1977. Repr. of 1888 ed. lib. bdg. 35.00 (ISBN 0-8414-9157-7). Folcroft.

Venden, Eileen. Higher Ground. (Anch Ser.). 1984. pap. 6.95 (ISBN 0-8163-0562-5). Pacific Pr Pub Assn.

Venden, Morris. From Exodus to Advent. LC 79-22389. (Orion Ser.). 1979. pap. 5.95 (ISBN 0-8127-0255-7). Review & Herald.
--Good News & Bad News: Haru Ser. 1984. pap. 4.95 (ISBN 0-8163-0484-X). Pacific Pr Pub Assn.
--Obedience of Faith. Wheeler, Gerald, ed. LC 83-13934. 96p. (Orig.). 1984. pap. 5.95 (ISBN 0-8280-0203-7). Review & Herald.
--Return of Elijah. (Harv Ser.). 1983. pap. 4.50 (ISBN 0-8163-0453-X). Pacific Pr Pub Assn.
--To Know God: A Five-Day Plan. Woolsey, Raymond, ed. 125p. pap. 1.50 (ISBN 0-8280-0220-7). Review & Herald.
--What Jesus Said About. 1984. pap. 6.95 (ISBN 0-8163-0555-2). Pacific Pr Pub Assn.
--Your Friend the Holy Spirit. (Anchor Ser.). 80p. (Orig.). 1987. pap. 6.95 (ISBN 0-8163-0682-6). Pacific Pr Pub Assn.

Venden, Morris L. Defeated Demons. (Uplook Ser.). 16p. 1982. pap. 0.99 (ISBN 0-8163-0487-4). Pacific Pr Pub Assn.
--Salvation by Faith & Your Will. LC 78-7597. (Horizon Ser.). 1978. pap. 5.95 (ISBN 0-8127-0190-9). Review & Herald.

Venerable Louis of Granada. The Sinner's Guide. LC 84-51820. 395p. 1985. pap. 8.00 (ISBN 0-89555-254-X). Tan Bks Pubs.

Vengco, Sabino A. Juan de Cartagena, O.F.M. (1563-1618) The Mariology of His Homiliae Catholicae & Its Baroque Scripturism. (Theology Ser.). 1978. 13.00 (ISBN 0-686-27934-4). Franciscan Inst.

Veninga, Robert L. A Gift of Hope: How We Survive Our Tragedies. (Large Print Bks.). 404p. 1986. lib. bdg. 16.95 (ISBN 0-8161-4101-0, Large Print Bks). G K Hall.

Venkatacharaya, T., ed. Sriharicarita Mahakavya of Srihari Padmanabhasastrin. 11.50 (ISBN 0-8356-7322-7). Theos Pub Hse.

Venkatasubbiah, A. Vedic Studies, Vol. 2. 5.25 (ISBN 0-8356-7447-9). Theos Pub Hse.

Venkatesananda, Swami. Christ Krishna & You. 168p. (Orig.). 1983. write for info. Chiltern Yoga.
--The Enlightened Living. 2nd ed. 1978. pap. 2.95 (ISBN 0-89684-038-7, Pub. by Motilal Banarsidass India). Orient Bk Dist.

Venkatesananda, Swami, tr. from Sanskrit. The Concise Yoga Vasistha. 445p. 1984. lib. bdg. 34.50x (ISBN 0-87395-955-8); pap. 10.95 (ISBN 0-87395-954-X). State U NY Pr.

Vennen, Mark V., tr. see Goudzwaard, Bob.

Ventis, W. Larry, jt. auth. see Batson, Daniel C.

Ventura, Piero & Ceserani, Gian P. In Search of Tutankhamun. LC 85-40416. (In Search of... Ser.). (Illus.). 48p. 1985. text ed. 12.96 (ISBN 0-382-09119-1); pap. 7.75 (ISBN 0-382-09122-1). Silver.

Vera, Hernan. Professionalization & Professionalism of Catholic Priests. LC 82-6886. (University of Florida Social Sciences Monographs: No. 68). xii, 116p. 1982. pap. 7.00x (ISBN 0-8130-0713-5). U Presses Fla.

Verbit, Mervin, jt. ed. see International Center for University Teaching of Jewish Civilization Staff.

Verbitsky, F. V. Religion & Science. 1959. pap. 1.00 (ISBN 0-317-30432-1). Holy Trinity.

Verbrugge, Verlyn. Ezra-Nehemiah. (Five-on-One Ser.). 128p. (Orig.). 1986. pap. text ed. 3.95 (ISBN 0-930265-18-1); tchr's. guide 7.95 (ISBN 0-930265-19-X). CRC Pubns.

Verdesi, Elizabeth H. In But Still Out: Women in the Church. LC 75-34365. 218p. 1976. pap. 3.95 (ISBN 0-664-24788-1). Westminster.

Verdier, Paul A. Brainwashing & the Cults. 3.00 (ISBN 0-87980-357-6). Borden.

Verdiere, Eugene La see LaVerdiere, Eugene.

Verdon, Timothy G. & Dally, John, eds. Monasticism & the Arts. (Illus.). 368p. 1984. text ed. 34.95x (ISBN 0-8156-2291-0); pap. text ed. 16.95x (ISBN 0-8156-2292-9). Syracuse U Pr.

Verdu, A. The Philosophy of Buddhism: A "Totalistic" Synthesis. 264p. 1981. 34.50 (ISBN 90-247-2224-1, Pub. by Martinus Nijhoff Netherlands). Kluwer Academic.

Verdu, Alfonso. Early Buddhist Philosophy in the Light of the Four Noble Times. 241p. 1985. 24.00 (ISBN 81-208-0001-X, Pub. by Motilal Banarsidass India). Orient Bk Dist.
--Early Buddhist Philosophy in the Light of the Four Noble Truths. 220p. 1986. 22.50X (ISBN 0-317-53523-4, Pub. by Motilal Banarsidass). South Asia Bks.

Verduin, Leonard, tr. see Wenger, John C.

Vered, Ben. Why Is Hanukkah. (Illus.). 1961. pap. 2.50 (ISBN 0-914080-59-8). Shulsinger Sales.

Vergnas, Raymond Las see Las Vergnas, Raymond.

Verheijen, J. A. Het Hoogste Wezen Bij De Manggaraiers. Repr. of 1951 ed. 46.00 (ISBN 0-384-64290-X). Johnson Repr.

Verhey, Allen. The Great Reversal: Ethics & the New Testament. 288p. (Orig.). 1984. pap. 13.95 (ISBN 0-8028-0004-1). Eerdmans.
--Living the Heidelberg, the Heidelberg Catechism & the Moral Life. LC 85-31386. 120p. (Orig.). 1986. pap. text ed. 7.95 (ISBN 0-930265-21-1). CRC Pubns.

Verhey, Allen, jt. ed. see Lammers, Stephen E.

Verheyden, A. L. Anabaptism in Flanders 1530-1650. LC 61-13872. (Studies in Anabaptist & Mennonite History, No. 9). 126p. 1961. 12.95x (ISBN 0-8361-1102-8). Herald Pr.

Verheylezoon, Louis. Devotion to the Sacred Heart: Objects, Ends, Practice, Motives. LC 78-74569. 1979. pap. 8.50 (ISBN 0-89555-083-0). TAN Bks Pubs.

Verhoef, Pieter A. The Books of Haggai & Malachi. Harrison, R. K., ed. (New International Commentary on the Old Testament Ser.). 384p. 1987. 21.95 (ISBN 0-8028-2376-9). Eerdmans.

Verhovskoy, Serge S. The Light of the World. LC 82-16963. 163p. 1982. pap. 6.95 (ISBN 0-88141-004-7). St Vladimirs.

Verity, A. W. Milton's Ode on the Morning of Christ's Nativity, L'allegro, Il Penseroso, & Lycidas. LC 73-12943. 1974. Repr. of 1931 ed. lib. bdg. 22.50 (ISBN 0-8414-9150-X). Folcroft.

Verity, A. W., ed. Milton's Paradise Lost. 1974. Repr. of 1921 ed. lib. bdg. 47.50 (ISBN 0-685-45197-6). Folcroft.

Verity, A. W., ed. see Milton, John.

Verkamp, Bernard J. The Indifferent Mean: Adiaphorism in the English Reformation to 1554. LC 77-13672. (Studies in the Reformation: Vol. 1). 1977. 15.00x (ISBN 0-8214-0387-7, Co-Pub by Wayne State). Ohio U Pr.
--The Indifferent Mean: Adiaphorism in the English Reformation to 1554. Walton, Robert C. & Bebb, Philip N., eds. LC 77-13672. (Studies in the Reformation: Vol. I). 160p. 1978. text ed. 19.95x (ISBN 0-8143-1583-6). Wayne St U Pr.

Verkuyl, Johannes. Break down the Walls: Christian Cry for Racial Justice. Smedes, Lewis B., ed. LC 72-93620. pap. 41.50 (ISBN 0-317-07869-0, 2012924). Bks Demand UMI.

Vermes, G., ed. see Winter, Paul.

Vermes, G., tr. see Dupont-Sommer, A.

Vermes, Geza. The Dead Sea Scrolls: Qumran in Perspective. LC 80-2382. 240p. 1981. pap. 8.95 (ISBN 0-8006-1435-6, 1-1435). Fortress.
--Jesus & the World of Judaism. LC 83-16535. 224p. 1984. pap. 10.95 (ISBN 0-8006-1784-3, 1-1784). Fortress.
--Jesus the Jew: A Historian's Reading of the Gospels. LC 80-2381. 288p. 1981. pap. 9.95 (ISBN 0-8006-1443-7, 1-1443). Fortress.
--Scripture & Tradition in Judaism. 2nd rev. ed. (Studia Post Biblica: No. 4). 1973. text ed. 9.95x (ISBN 90-040-3626-1). Humanities.

Vermes, Geza & Neusner, Jacob, eds. Essays in Honour of Yigael Yadin. (Publications of the Oxford Centre for Postgraduate Hebrew Studies: Vol. 6). (Illus.). 618p. 1983. text ed. 45.00x (ISBN 0-86598-102-7). Allanheld.

Vermes, Geza, et al, eds. see Schurer, Emil.

Vermes, Pamela. Buber on God & the Perfect Man. Neusner, J., et al, eds. LC 80-23406. (Brown Judaic Studies). 1981. pap. 10.50 (ISBN 0-89130-427-4). Scholars Pr GA.

Vernadsky, George, jt. ed. see Tumins, Valerie A.

Vernant, Jean P. Myth & Thought Among the Greeks. 400p. 1983. 29.95x (ISBN 0-7100-9544-9). Methuen Inc.

Verner, David C. The Household of God & the Social World of the Pastoral Epistles. LC 82-25015. (Society of Biblical Literature Dissertation Ser.). 218p. 1983. pap. 13.50 (ISBN 0-89130-611-0, 06 01 71). Scholars Pr GA.

Verner, Gerald, et al. Prince of Darkness: A Witchcraft Anthology. 1978. Repr. of 1946 ed. lib. bdg. 25.00 (ISBN 0-8492-2816-6). R West.

Vernon, Glenn M. A Time to Die. 1977. 9.50 (ISBN 0-8191-0126-5). U Pr of Amer.

Vernon, Louise A. Bible Smuggler. LC 67-15994. (Illus.). 138p. 1967. pap. 4.50 (ISBN 0-8361-1557-0). Herald Pr.
--Ink on His Fingers. LC 73-171105. (Illus.). 128p. 1972. 4.95 (ISBN 0-8361-1660-7); pap. 4.50 (ISBN 0-8361-1673-9). Herald Pr.
--Key to the Prison. LC 86-11054. (Illus.). 144p. 1968. 4.50 (ISBN 0-8361-1813-8). Herald Pr.
--The King's Book. LC 80-18998. (Illus.). 128p. 1980. pap. 4.50 (ISBN 0-8361-1933-9). Herald Pr.
--Night Preacher. LC 73-94378. (Illus.). 134p. 1969. pap. 4.50 (ISBN 0-8361-1774-3). Herald Pr.

Vernon, Ruth B. Manna in the Morning. 5.75 (ISBN 0-8062-2491-6). Carlton.

Veron, J., tr. see Bullinger, Heinrich.

Veron, J., tr. see Zwingli, Ulrich.

Verploegh, Harry, compiled by. The Next Chapter after the Last. (Orig.). Date not set. pap. price not set (ISBN 0-87509-391-4). Chr Pubns.

Verploegh, Harry, ed. see Tozer, A. W.

Verrier, Jean Le see Bontier, Pierre & Le Verrier, Jean.

Verschuer, Otmar von see Von Verschuer, Otmar.

Versenyi, Laszlo. Holiness & Justice: An Interpretation of Plato's "Euthyphro". LC 81-43830. 164p. 1982. lib. bdg. 26.75 (ISBN 0-8191-2316-1); pap. text ed. 11.50 (ISBN 0-8191-2317-X). U Pr of Amer.

Versteeg, Dingman, tr. Records of the Reformed Dutch Church of New Paltz, New York. LC 77-77266. 269p. 1977. Repr. of 1896 ed. 15.00 (ISBN 0-8063-0772-2). Genealog Pub.

Versteeg, J. P. Is Adam a "Teaching Model" in the New Testament? pap. 1.75 (ISBN 0-8010-9276-0). Baker Bk.
--Is Adam a Teaching Model-in the New Testament? 1978. pap. 1.75 (ISBN 0-87552-500-8). Presby & Reformed.

Versteeg, Robert. Whose Church Is This Anyway? 1985. 6.95 (ISBN 0-89536-767-X, 5874). CSS of Ohio.

Vertot, Rene A. The History of the Knights Hospitallers of St. John of Jerusalem, 5 vols. LC 78-63372. (The Crusades & Military Orders: Second Ser.). Repr. of 1757 ed. Set. 200.00 (ISBN 0-404-17040-4). AMS Pr.

Verwer, George. Pseudo Discipleship. (YA) 1970. pap. 1.50 (ISBN 0-87508-548-2). Chr Lit.
--Veintinueve Soldados de Plomo. 112p. 1981. 2.50 (ISBN 0-88113-331-0). Edit Betania.

Very, Alice. The Lord's Prayer. 1975. 10.00 (ISBN 0-8283-1629-5). Branden Pub Co.

Vesey, A. Merry Christmas, Thomas! (Illus.). 32p. 9.95 (ISBN 0-87113-096-3). Atlantic Monthly.

Vesey, Susan. Spring Activity Book. Alexander, P., ed. (Illus.). 32p. 1987. pap. 3.95 (ISBN 0-7459-1015-7). Lion USA.

Vest, Lamar. The Church & Its Youth. (CTC Ser.). 1980. 5.25 (ISBN 0-87148-170-7); pap. 4.25 (ISBN 0-87148-171-5); instr's guide 7.95 (ISBN 0-87148-172-3). Pathway Pr.

Vestal, Kirk H. & Wallace, Arthur. The Firm Foundation of Mormonism. LC 81-80795. xii, 306p. 1981. 8.95x (ISBN 0-937892-06-8). LL Co.

Vester, Bertha H. Our Jerusalem: An American Family in the Holy City, 1881-1949. Davis, Moshe, ed. LC 77-70752. (America & the Holy Land Ser.). 1977. Repr. of 1950 ed. lib. bdg. 30.00x (ISBN 0-405-10296-8). Ayer Co Pubs.

Vetalapancavimsati. Vikram & the Vampire, or Tales of the Hindu Diety. Burton, Isadel, ed. Burton, Richard F., tr. (Illus.). 264p. Repr. of 1893 ed. text ed. 20.00x. Coronet Bks.

Vetulani, A. The Jews of Medieval Poland. 1978. lib. bdg. 59.95 (ISBN 0-685-62298-3). Revisionist Pr.

Veysey, Laurence. The Communal Experience: Anarchist & Mystical Communities in Twentieth Century America. LC 78-55045. 1978. pap. 7.95X (ISBN 0-226-85458-2, P786, Phoen). U of Chicago Pr.

Vezzosi, Antonio F. I Scrittori De'Chierici Regolari Detti Teatini. 1030p. Date not set. Repr. of 1780 ed. text ed. 165.60x (ISBN 0-576-72811-X, Pub. by Gregg Intl Pubs England). Gregg Intl.

V. Haussig, Hans. Woerterbuch der Mythologie, Vol. 2. (Ger.). 1973. 175.00 (ISBN 3-12-909820-8, M-6979). French & Eur.

Via, Dan O., Jr. The Ethics of Mark's Gospel-In the Middle of Time. LC 84-48733. 256p. 1985. 19.95 (ISBN 0-8006-0746-5, 1-746). Fortress.
--The Parables: Their Literary & Existential Dimension. LC 67-11910. 232p. 1974. pap. 6.95 (ISBN 0-8006-1392-9, 1-1392). Fortress.

Via, Dan O., Jr., ed. see Beardslee, William A.

Via, Dan O., Jr., ed. see Boers, Hendrikus.

Via, Dan O., Jr., ed. see Doty, William G.

Via, Dan O., Jr., ed. see McKnight, Edgar V.

Via, Dan O., Jr., ed. see Patte, Daniel.

Via, Dan O., Jr., ed. see Perrin, Norman.

Via, Dan O., Jr., ed. see Petersen, Norman R.

Viano, Joseph A., ed. Two Months with Mary: Short Reflections for Every Day of May & October. (Illus.). 94p. (Orig.). 1984. pap. 4.95 (ISBN 0-8189-0466-6). Alba.

Vicchio, Stephen. A Careful Disorder: Chronicles of Life & Love & Laughter. 300p. (Orig.). 1987. pap. 10.95 (ISBN 0-87061-135-6). Chr Classics.

Vichas, Robert. Annotated Handbook of Biblical Quotations, Verses, & Parables. LC 85-19346. 411p. 1985. 29.95 (ISBN 0-13-037870-4, Busn). P-H.

Vick, Edward. Speaking Well of God. LC 79-9336. (Anvil Ser.). 1979. pap. 8.95 (ISBN 0-8127-0245-X). Review & Herald.

Vick, Edward W. H. Jesus: The Man. LC 78-10253. (Anvil Ser.). 1979. pap. 6.95 (ISBN 0-8127-0220-4). Review & Herald.

Vickers, Brian, ed. Occult & Scientific Mentalities in the Renaissance. 432p. 1986. pap. 15.95 (ISBN 0-521-33836-0). Cambridge U Pr.

Vickers, Douglas. A Christian Approach to Economics & the Cultural Condition. 1982. 12.50 (ISBN 0-682-49831-9, University). Exposition Pr FL.
--Economics & Man: Prelude to a Christian Critique. 1976. pap. 6.95 (ISBN 0-934532-27-3). Presby & Reformed.
--Now That You Have Believed: An Exploration of the Life & Walk of Faith. 1981. 10.00 (ISBN 0-682-49830-0). Exposition Pr FL.

Vickers, John. John Wesley. (Ladybird Ser.). 1977. 2.50 (ISBN 0-87508-841-4). Chr Lit.

Vickers, Rod. A New Day. 47p. 1984. pap. 0.95 (ISBN 0-88144-032-9). Christian Pub.

Vickery, John B. Robert Graves & the White Goddess. LC 70-183363. Repr. of 1972 ed. 29.50 (ISBN 0-8357-9713-9, 2011899). Bks Demand UMI.

Victoria, Daizen, jt. auth. see Yokoi, Yuho.

Victoria, Ryojun, tr. see Sato, Koji.

Victorinus, Marius. Theological Treatises on the Trinity. (Fathers of the Church Ser.: Vol. 69). 357p. 1981. 29.95x (ISBN 0-8132-0069-5). Cath U Pr.

Victorinus, Saint Opera. Haussleiter, I., ed. (Corpus Scriptorum Ecclesiasticorum Latinorum Ser: Vol. 49). Repr. of 1916 ed. 40.00 (ISBN 0-384-64555-0). Johnson Repr.

Vida, Marco G. The Christiad: Latin-English Edition. Drake, Gertrude C. & Forbes, Clarence A., eds. LC 78-1430. 288p. 1978. 9.85x (ISBN 0-8093-0814-2). S Ill U Pr.

Vidich, Arthur J. & Lyman, Stanford M. American Sociology: Worldly Rejections of Religion & Their Directions. LC 84-2268. 400p. 1985. pap. 30.00x (ISBN 0-300-03037-1). Yale U Pr.

Vidler, Alec I. Church in an Age of Revolution. rev. ed. (History of the Church: Vol. 5). (Orig.). 1962. pap. 5.95 (ISBN 0-14-020506-3, Pelican). Penguin.

Vidler, Alec R. The Orb & the Cross: A Normative Study in the Relations of Church & State, with Reference to Gladstones Early Writings. LC 46-19947. 1945. text ed. 7.50x (ISBN 0-8401-2544-5). A R Allenson.

Vidler, Alexander R. The Modernist Movement in the Roman Church. 69.95 (ISBN 0-8490-0889-1). Gordon Pr.

Vidman, Ladislav. Isis und Sarapis bei den Griechen und Roemern: Epigraphische Studien zur Verbreitung und zu den Traegern des aegyptischen Kultes. (Religionsgeschichtliche Versuche und Vorarbeiten, No. 29). (Ger). 1970. 26.00x (ISBN 3-11-006392-1). De Gruyter.

Vidyalankar, Pandit S., jt. auth. see Prakash, Swami S.

Vidyaranya, Swami. Pancadasi. Swahananda, Swami, tr. (Sanskrit & Eng). 10.00 (ISBN 0-87481-429-4). Vedanta Pr.

Vidyaratna, T. & Avalon, A. Kularnava Tantra. (Sanskrit.). 1975. Repr. 25.00 (ISBN 0-8426-0966-0). Orient Bk Dist.

Vidyarnava, Srisa Chandra & Sandal, Mohan L., trs. Aitareya Upanisat, 2 pts. in 1. LC 73-3823. (Sacred Books of the Hindus: No. 30, Pts. 1-2). Repr. of 1925 ed. 14.50 (ISBN 0-404-57830-6). AMS Pr.
--The Kausitaki Upanisat. LC 73-3825. (Sacred Books of the Hindus: No. 31, Pt. 1). Repr. of 1925 ed. 14.50 (ISBN 0-404-57831-4). AMS Pr.
--The Maitri Upanisat. LC 73-3827. (Sacred Books of the Hindus: No. 31, Pt. 2). Repr. of 1926 ed. 14.50 (ISBN 0-404-57832-2). AMS Pr.

Vidyarnava, Srisa Chandra, tr. see Vasu, Srisa Chandra.

Viehmeyer, L. Allen. Tumultuous Years - Schwenkfelder Chronicles Fifteen Eighty to Seventeen Fifty: The Reports of Martin John, Jr. & Balthazar Hoffmann. 157p. (Orig.). 1980. pap. write for info. (ISBN 0-935980-00-8). Schwenkfelder Lib.

Vielhauer, Philipp. Geschichte der urchristlichen Literatur: Einleitung in das Neue Testament, die Apokryphen und die Apostolischen Vaeter. 812p. 1981. 41.00x (ISBN 3-11-007763-9). De Gruyter.

Viereck, George S. & Eldridge, Paul. My First Two Thousand Years. 1984. Repr. 25.00 (ISBN 0-911378-16-2). Sheridan.

Viereck, Peter. Inner Liberty. 1983. pap. 2.50x (ISBN 0-87574-095-2, 095). Pendle Hill.

Vierow, Duain W. On the Move with the Master: A Daily Devotional Guide on World Mission. LC 76-57679. 1977. 4.95 (ISBN 0-87808-155-0). William Carey Lib.

Viertel, John, tr. see Habermas, Jurgen.

Viertel, Joyce, ed. see Graves, William W.

Viertel, Weldon. La Biblia y Su Interpretacion. Orig. Title: The Bible & Its Interpretation. 208p. 1983. pap. 8.25 (ISBN 0-311-03670-8). Casa Bautista.

Viertel, Weldon, ed. see Graves, William W.

Viertel, Weldon E. Los Hechos de los Apostoles: Texto Programado. Tr. of Early Church Growth: a Study of the Book of Acts. (Span.). 208p. 1985. pap. write for info. (ISBN 0-311-04348-8). Casa Bautista.

--Vida y Ministerio de Cristo: Texto Programado. Zorzoli, Ruben O., tr. from Span. Tr. of The Life & Ministry of Christ. 192p. 1985. pap. text ed. write for info. (ISBN 0-311-04356-9). Casa Bautista.

Vigeveno, Henk S. Thirteen Men Who Changed the World. LC 86-3209. (Illus.). 154p. 1986. pap. 5.95 (ISBN 0-8307-1150-3, 5418817) (ISBN 0-8307-1174-0, 6102292). Regal.

Vignaux, A., jt. ed. see Jeanroy, A.

Vignoli, Tito. Myth & Science. 1976. lib. bdg. 59.95 (ISBN 0-8490-2323-8). Gordon Pr.

Vigram, George V. The Englishman's Greek Concordance of the New Testament. rev. ed. (Gr. & Eng.). 1982. pap. 29.95 (ISBN 0-8054-1388-X). Broadman.

Vijay, ed. How to Bring up a Child. (Illus.). 1985. pap. 3.50 (ISBN 0-89071-334-0, Pub. by Sri Aurobindo Ashram India). Matagiri.

Vijayaraghavacharya, V., ed. Epigraphical Glossary. (Tirupathi Devasthanam Inscription Ser.: Vol. VI, Pt. 2). 420p. 1984. Repr. of 1938 ed. lib. bdg. 65.00x (ISBN 81-7030-074-6, Pub. by Sri Satguru Pubns India). Orient Bk Dist.

Vijnanananda. The Sri Mad Devi Bhagavatam. LC 73-3819. (Sacred Books of the Hindus: No. 26, Bks. 1-12). Repr. of 1921 ed. 79.50 (ISBN 0-404-57826-8). AMS Pr.

Vijnanananda, Swami, tr. from Sanskrit. The Srimad Devi Bhagawatam, Pts. I & II. LC 75-985029. 1977. 55.00x (ISBN 0-89684-455-2). Orient Bk Dist.

Vijnananda. At the Feet of Ski Ramakrishna. 66p. 1985. pap. 1.50 (ISBN 0-87481-225-9, Pub. by Ramakrishna Math Madras India). Vedanta Pr.

Vikan, Gary. Byzantine Pilgrimage Art. (Byzantine Collection Publications Ser.: No. 5). (Illus.). 52p. 1982. pap. 4.50x (ISBN 0-88402-113-0). Dumbarton Oaks.

Vikler, Mark. Dialogue with God. LC 86-70744. 1986. pap. 5.95 (ISBN 0-88270-620-9). Bridge Pub.

Vila. To the Fountain of Christianity. pap. 3.95 (ISBN 0-935120-02-5). Christs Mission.

Vila, David, tr. see Berkhof, Louis.

Viladesau, Richard. Answering for Faith: Christ & the Human Search for Salvation. 1987. pap. 14.95. Paulist Pr.

--The Reason for Our Hope: A Introduction to Anthropology. LC 83-82019. 1984. pap. 10.95 (ISBN 0-8091-2574-9). Paulist Pr.

Vilaro, Josep, et al. Diccionario Religioso Para los Hombres De Hoy. (Span.). 260p. 1976. pap. 7.50 (ISBN 84-320-0273-9, S-50025). French & Eur.

Vilela, Ernesto S., tr. see Green, Michael.

Vilela, Ernesto S., tr. see Lewis, C. S.

Vilela, Ernesto S., tr. see Wenger, J. C.

Villafranca, Anthony L. The Theory of Sin & the Equilibrium Between the Emotional & the Rational in Man. (Illus.). 104p. 1986. 88.50 (ISBN 0-89266-568-8). Am Classical Coll Pr.

Villalobos, Fernando P., tr. see Benson, C. H.

Villalobos, Fernando P., tr. see Schultz, Samuel.

Villamette, Gaston. How to Gain the Psychological Power of Transcendental Thinking. (Illus.). 118p. 1987. 117.55 (ISBN 0-89920-147-4). Am Classical Coll Pr.

Villanueva, Emilio B., tr. from Span. Book of the True Life, Vol. I. abr. ed. Orig. Title: Libro de la Vida Verdadera. (Span., Illus.). 376p. (Orig.). 1983. text ed. 12.00 (ISBN 0-912753-00-5); pap. 6.00x (ISBN 0-912753-01-3). True Life Found.

Villard, Fanny G., ed. William Lloyd Garrison on Nonresistance Together with a Personal Sketch by His Daughter and a Tribute by Leo Tolstoi. LC 74-137556. (Peace Movement in America Ser). xii, 79p. 1972. Repr. of 1924 ed. lib. bdg. 11.95x (ISBN 0-89198-087-3). Ozer.

Villarello, Ildefonso, tr. see Dana, H. E.

Villarello, Ildefonso, tr. see Olson, Natanael.

Villari, L., tr. see Villari, Pasquale.

Villari, Linda, tr. see Villart, Pagquale.

Villari, P. Life & Times of Girolamo Savonarola. LC 68-25276. (World History Ser., No. 48). 1969. Repr. of 1888 ed. lib. bdg. 79.95x (ISBN 0-8383-0174-6). Haskell.

Villari, Pasquale. Studies, Historical & Critical. facs. ed. Villari, L., tr. LC 68-16983. (Essay Index Reprint Ser). 1968. Repr. of 1907 ed. 18.00 (ISBN 0-8369-0960-7). Ayer Co Pubs.

Villarosa, Carlantonio de Rosa see De Rosa Villarosa, Carlantonio.

Villart, Pagquale. Life & Times of Girolamo Savonarola. Villari, Linda, tr. from Ital. (Illus.). 792p. 1985. Repr. of 1888 ed. lib. bdg. 85.00 (ISBN 0-89987-906-3). Darby Bks.

Villasenor, Emma Z., tr. see Eudaly, Maria S. De.

Villasenor, Luis F., jt. auth. see Heyden, Doris.

Villa-Vicencio, Charles, ed. Between Christ & Caesar: Classic & Contemporary Texts on Church & State. 196p. (Orig.). 1986. pap. 16.95 (ISBN 0-8028-0240-0). Eerdmans.

Villa-Vicencio, Charles, jt. ed. see Boesak, Allan A.

Villa-Vicencio, Charles, jt. ed. see De Gruchy, John W.

Villehardouin, Geoffrey De see De Villehardouin, Geoffrey & De Joinville, Jean.

Villehardouin, Geoffroi De see De Villehardouin, Geoffroi.

Villehardouin, Geoffroi de see De Villehardouin, Geoffroi & Joinville.

Villehardouin, Geoffroy de see De Villehardouin, Geoffroy.

Villehardouin, Joinville. Chronicles of the Crusades. Shaw, M. R., tr. from Fr. 258p. 1985. 14.95 (ISBN 0-88029-037-4, Pub. by Dorset Pr). Hippocrene Bks.

Villey, Michel. La Croisade: Essai sur la Formation d'une Theorie Juridique. LC 78-63373. (Crusades Ser.). Repr. of 1942 ed. 30.00 (ISBN 0-404-17046-3). AMS Pr.

Villoldo, Alberto, jt. auth. see Krippner, Stanley.

Vilnay, Zev. Legends of Galilee, Jordan & Sinai. LC 73-168156. (Sacred Land Ser.: Vol. 3). (Illus.). 378p. 1978. 10.95 (ISBN 0-8276-0106-9, 419). Jewish Pubns.

--Legends of Jerusalem. LC 72-12180. (The Sacred Land Ser.: Vol. 1). (Illus.). 338p. 1973. 8.95 (ISBN 0-8276-0004-6, 323). Jewish Pubns.

Viloldo, Alberto & Krippner, Stanley. Healing States. (Illus.). 224p. 1987. pap. 8.95 (ISBN 0-671-63202-7, Fireside) (ISBN 0-671-60240-3). S&S.

Vimuktananda, Swami, tr. see Shankara.

Vince, John. Discovering Saints in Britain. (Discovering Ser.: No. 64). (Illus.). 64p. 1983. pap. 3.95 (ISBN 0-85263-449-8, Pub. by Shire Pubns England). Seven Hills Bks.

Vincellette, Arthur J. Way of Life. 160p. 1983. 7.95 (ISBN 0-89962-312-3). Todd & Honeywell.

Vincent, Hughes. Jerusalem, 2 vols. in 4. LC 78-63368. (The Crusades & Military Orders: Second Ser.). Repr. of 1926 ed. Set. 495.00 (ISBN 0-404-17060-9). AMS Pr.

Vincent, Leon H. John Heyl Vincent: A Biographical Sketch. facs. ed. LC 71-124263. (Select Bibliographies Reprint Ser). 1925. 18.00 (ISBN 0-8369-5451-3). Ayer Co Pubs.

Vincent, M. O. God, Sex & You. 192p. 1985. pap. 3.95 (ISBN 0-916441-25-3). Barbour & Co.

Vincent, M. R. Vincent's Word Studies in th New Testament, 4 vols. 2720p. 49.95 (ISBN 0-917006-30-5). Hendrickson MA.

Vincent, Marvin. Word Studies in the New Testament, 4 Vols. 1957. 49.95 (ISBN 0-8028-8083-5). Eerdmans.

Vincent, Marvin R. A Critical & Exegetical Commentary on the Philippians & Philemon. Driver, Samuel R. & Briggs, Charles A., eds. (International Critical Commentary Ser.). 248p. 1897. 22.95 (ISBN 0-567-05031-9, Pub. by T & T Clark Ltd UK). Fortress.

Vincent, Mary C. The Life of Prayer & the Way to God. LC 81-21257. (Illus.). 96p. (Orig.). 1982. pap. 3.50 (ISBN 0-932506-11-9). St Bedes Pubns.

Vincent, Stephen, ed. Omens from the Flight of Birds: The First 101 Days of Jimmy Carter. (Illus.). 1978. pap. 4.95x (ISBN 0-917672-05-4). Momos.

Vincent, Thomas. The Shorter Catechism Explained from Scripture. (Puritan Paperbacks). 282p. (Orig.). 1980. pap. 4.95 (ISBN 0-85151-314-X). Banner of Truth.

Vinck, Catherine D. A Book of Eve. 1979. text ed. 5.00 (ISBN 0-911726-40-3); stereo record & text incl. Alleluia Pr.

--Readings: "John at Patmos" & "A Book of Hours". LC 78-55341. 68p. 1978. 5.75 (ISBN 0-911726-32-2); pap. 3.75 (ISBN 0-911726-33-0). Alleluia Pr.

Vinck, Jose D. The Words of Jesus, with Key Readings from New & Old Testaments. 320p. 1977. deluxe ed. 30.00 boxed, slipcover, hand-made full morocco (ISBN 0-911726-26-8). Alleluia Pr.

--The Yes Book. 1976. pap. 3.75 (ISBN 0-685-77499-6). Franciscan Herald.

--The Yes Book: An Answer to Life (a Manual of Christian Existentialism) LC 77-190621. 200p. 1972. 12.75 (ISBN 0-911726-12-8); pap. 8.75 (ISBN 0-911726-11-X). Alleluia Pr.

Vinck, Jose D., jt. auth. see Raya, Joseph.

Vinck, Jose D., ed. see Kucharek, Casimir.

Vinck, Jose D., ed. see Raya, Joseph.

Vinck, Jose De see Raya, Joseph & Vinck, Jose D.

Vine, Aubrey R. The Nestorian Churches. LC 78-63173. (Heresies of the Early Christian & Medieval Era: Second Ser.). Repr. of 1937 ed. 31.50 (ISBN 0-404-16188-X). AMS Pr.

Vine, W. E. The Divine Sonship of Christ. 246p. 1984. smythe sewn 9.50 (ISBN 0-86524-179-1, 9520). Klock & Klock.

--The Expanded Vine's Expository Dictionary of New Testament Words. rev. ed. 1376p. 1984. pap. 14.95 (ISBN 0-87123-619-2, 230619). Bethany Hse.

--Expository Dictionary of New Testament Words. 1396p. 14.95 (ISBN 0-8007-0089-9); thumb index ed. 16.95 (ISBN 0-8007-0090-2). Revell.

--Expository Dictionary of New Testament Words. 1392p. (Orig.). 1981. pap. 12.95 (ISBN 0-310-33781-X, 6795P). Zondervan.

--An Expository Dictionary of New Testament Words. (Affordables Ser.). 1985. pap. 9.95 (ISBN 0-8024-0435-9). Moody.

--Isaiah: Prophecies, Promises, Warnings. pap. 7.95 (ISBN 0-310-33771-2, 6621P). Zondervan.

--Vines Expository Dictionary of New Testament Words. (Barbour Bks). 351p. 1985. 14.95 (ISBN 0-916441-31-8); pap. 10.95 (ISBN 0-916441-34-2). Barbour & Co.

--Vine's Expository Dictionary of Old & New Testament Words. 1568p. 1981. 19.95 (ISBN 0-8007-1282-X). Revell.

Vine, W. E. & Bruce, F. F. Vine's Expository Dictionary of Old & New Testament Words. (Reference Library Edition). 1568p. 1987. Repr. text ed. 14.95 (ISBN 0-529-06374-3). World Bible.

Vine, W. E., jt. auth. see Hogg, C. F.

Vine, William E. Vine's Expository Dictionary of New Testament Words. 1376p. Date not set. 14.95 (ISBN 0-917006-03-8). Hendrickson MA.

Vinecour, Earl. Polish Jews: The Final Chapter. LC 77-83266. (Illus.). 1977. 17.50x (ISBN 0-8147-8756-8). NYU Pr.

Vinecour, Earl & Fishman, Charles. Polish Jews: The Final Chapter. (Paperbacks Ser). (Orig.). 1977. pap. 5.95 (ISBN 0-07-067490-6). McGraw.

Viner, Jacob. Religious Thought & Economic Society: Four Chapters of an Unfinished Work. Melitz, Jacques & Winch, Donald, eds. LC 77-93857. 1978. 19.75 (ISBN 0-8223-0398-1). Duke.

Vines, Jerry. Fire in the Pulpit. LC 77-78155. 1977. 7.95 (ISBN 0-8054-5159-5). Broadman.

--A Guide to Effective Sermon Delivery. 1986. text ed. 9.95 (ISBN 0-8024-4896-8). Moody.

--A Practical Guide to Sermon Preparation. 1985. 9.95 (ISBN 0-8024-6744-X). Moody.

Viney, Donald W. Charles Hartshorne & the Existence of God. (Philosophy Ser.). 192p. 1984. 44.50 (ISBN 0-87395-907-8); pap. 14.95 (ISBN 0-87395-908-6). State U NY Pr.

Vining, Elizabeth G. Friend of Life: A Biography of Rufus M. Jones. 2nd ed. (Illus.). 347p. 1981. pap. 8.95 (ISBN 0-941308-00-6). Religious Soc Friends.

--Harnessing Pegasus: Inspiration & Meditation. 1983. pap. 2.50x (ISBN 0-87574-221-1, 221). Pendle Hill.

--A Quest There Is. 1983. pap. 2.50x (ISBN 0-87574-246-7, 246). Pendle Hill.

--William Penn: Mystic. LC 74-95891. (Orig.). 1969. pap. 2.50x (ISBN 0-87574-167-3, 167). Pendle Hill.

Vinogradoff, Paul. Villainage in England: Essays in English Medieval History. 1968. Repr. of 1892 ed. 9.00x (ISBN 0-403-00048-3). Scholarly.

Vinoi, Lawrence. God & Man: The Essential Knowledge Which Everyone, but Absolutely Everyone Ought to Possess About Human Nature & the Nature of God & How the Two Are Related. (Essential Knowledge Ser. Books). (Illus.). 1978. plastic spiral bdg. 44.75 (ISBN 0-89266-118-6). Am Classical Coll Pr.

Vinton, Jean, jt. ed. see Manning, William O.

Vinzant, Don, tr. see Alves, Rubem.

Vio, Tommaso De see De Vio, Tommaso.

Violette, Wesley La see LaViolette, Wesley.

Violi, Unicio J. Monarch Notes on the New Testament. (Orig.). pap. 4.50 (ISBN 0-671-00625-8). Monarch Pr.

Vipont, Elfrida. The Story of Quakerism. rev. ed. LC 77-71638. (Illus.). 1977. pap. 9.95 (ISBN 0-913408-31-X). Friends United.

Vireswarananda, Swami, tr. see Badarayana.

Virgo, Leslie, ed. First Aid in Pastoral Care. 220p. 1986. pap. 9.95 (ISBN 0-567-29122-7, Pub. by T & T Clark Ltd UK). Fortress.

Virkler, Henry A. Hermeneutics: Principles & Processes of Biblical Interpretation. LC 80-70530. 200p. 1981. 12.95 (ISBN 0-8010-9282-5). Baker Bk.

Virmond, Wolfgang, ed. see Schleiermacher, Friedrich D.

Vis, Jean A. We Are the Lord's. 3.50 (ISBN 0-686-23479-0). Rose Pub MI.

Vischer, Lukas, jt. ed. see Feiner, Johannes.

Viser, William C. It's OK to Be an MK. (Orig.). 1986. pap. 7.95 (ISBN 0-8054-6337-2). Broadman.

Vishnewski, Stanley. Meditations-Dorothy Day. LC 73-133570. 104p. 1970. pap. 4.95 (ISBN 0-8091-1636-7). Paulist Pr.

Vishniac, Roman. Polish Jews: A Pictorial Record. LC 65-25413. (Illus.). 1968. pap. 7.95 (ISBN 0-8052-0360-5). Schocken.

--A Vanished World. LC 83-16420. (Illus.). 192p. 1983. 65.00 (ISBN 0-374-28247-1). FS&G.

--A Vanished World. (Illus.). 192p. 1986. pap. 19.95 (ISBN 0-374-52023-2). FS&G.

Visiak, E. H. Animus Against Milton. 1945. lib. bdg. 12.50 (ISBN 0-8414-9173-9). Folcroft.

--Milton Agonistes. (Studies in Milton, No. 22). 1970. pap. 39.95x (ISBN 0-8383-0102-9). Haskell.

--Milton's Agonistes: A Metaphysical Criticism. LC 77-9361. 1922. lib. bdg. 12.50 (ISBN 0-8414-9187-9). Folcroft.

Visitation Nuns, tr. see De Sales, Francis.

Visokay, Paul, jt. auth. see Huckle, John.

Vissell, Barry & Vissell, Joyce. The Shared Heart: Relationship Initiations & Celebrations. LC 85-10981. 192p. 1985. Repr. lib. bdg. 19.95x (ISBN 0-89370-883-6). Borgo Pr.

Vissell, Joyce, jt. auth. see Vissell, Barry.

Visser, Derk. Zacharias Ursinus: The Reluctant Reformer-His Life & Times. 192p. 1983. pap. 7.95 (ISBN 0-8298-0691-1). Pilgrim NY.

Visser, Derk, ed. Controversy & Conciliation: The Reformation & the Palatinate 1559 - 1583. (Pittsburgh Theological Monographs Ser.: No. 18). (Orig.). 1986. pap. 19.95 (ISBN 0-915138-73-5). Pickwick.

Visser 't Hooft, W. A. The Fatherhood of God in an Age of Emancipation. LC 82-13403. 176p. 1983. pap. 7.95 (ISBN 0-664-24462-9). Westminster.

Vital, David. The Origins of Zionism. (Illus.). 1975. pap. 14.95x (ISBN 0-19-827439-4). Oxford U Pr.

--Zionism: The Formative Years. 1982. 34.50x (ISBN 0-19-827443-2). Oxford U Pr.

Vitale, Joseph T., jt. ed. see Cesaretti, Charles A.

Vitale, Manjushri J. Zen & the Art of Writing. 90p. (Orig.). 1984. pap. 10.95 (ISBN 0-932896-07-3). Westcliff Pubns.

Vitale, Philip H. Catholic Literary Opinion in the Nineteenth Century. 197p. 4.50 (ISBN 0-685-25451-8); pap. 2.50 (ISBN 0-685-25452-6). Auxiliary U Pr.

--Catholic Literary Opinion of the Twentieth Century. 438p. 4.50 (ISBN 0-685-25453-4). Auxiliary U Pr.

Vitalis, Orderic. The Ecclesiastical History of Orderic Vitalis, Vol. 5, Bks. 9 & 10. Chibnall, Majorie, ed. & tr. from Fr. (Oxford Medieval Texts Ser). 1975. 65.00x (ISBN 0-19-822232-7). Oxford U Pr.

--Ecclesiastical History of Orderic Vitalis, Vol. 6, Books 11, 12, 13. Chibnall, Marjorie, ed. & tr. 1978. text ed. 84.00x (ISBN 0-19-822242-4). Oxford U Pr.

Vithaldes. The Yoga System of Health & Relief from Tension. 1961. pap. 4.95 (ISBN 0-346-12500-6). Cornerstone.

Vito De, Albert see De Vito, Albert.

Vitz, Evelyn B. Continual Feast. LC 84-48629. (Illus.). 356p. 1985. 16.45i (ISBN 0-06-181897-6, HarpT). Har-Row.

Vitz, Paul C. Psychology As Religion: The Cult of Self-Worship. 192p. 1977. pap. 5.95 (ISBN 0-8028-1696-7). Eerdmans.

Vivekananda, Swami. Inspired Talks. pap. 5.50 (ISBN 0-87481-455-3). Vedanta Pr.

Vivian, Katherine, tr. see Orbeliani, Sulkhan-Saba.

Viviano, Pauline A. Genesis. (Bible Commentary Ser.). 136p. 1985. pap. 2.95 (ISBN 0-8146-1370-5). Liturgical Pr.

Vividishananda, Swami, tr. see Shivananda, Swami.

Vizkelety, ed. see Spangenberg, Wolfhart.

Vlasto, A. P. The Entry of the Slavs into Christendom: An Introduction to the Medieval History of the Slavs. LC 70-98699. pap. 113.80 (ISBN 0-317-27094-X, 2024553). Bks Demand UMI.

Vlastos, Gregory, ed. Plato Two: Ethics, Politics, & Philosophy of Art & Religion; a Collection of Critical Essays. LC 77-19103. (Modern Studies in Philosophy). 1978. text ed. 16.95 (ISBN 0-268-01530-9); pap. text ed. 8.95x (ISBN 0-268-01531-7). U of Notre Dame Pr.

Vlastos, Gregory, ed. see Bevan, Edwyn.

Vlastos, Gregory, ed. see Davidson, William L.

Vlesmas, Jerry, tr. see Makris, Kallistos.

Voarhis, B. D. Satan Exposed. 1975. pap. 2.25 (ISBN 0-87148-785-3). Pathway Pr.

Voegelin, Eric. Order & History, 4 vols. Incl. Vol. 1. Israel & Revelation. LC 56-11670. xxvi, 534p. 1956 (ISBN 0-8071-0818-9); Vol. 2. The World of the Polis. LC 57-11670. xvii, 390p. 1957 (ISBN 0-8071-0819-7); Vol. 3. Plato & Aristotle. LC 57-11670. xviii, 384p. 1957 (ISBN 0-8071-0820-0); Vol. 4. The Ecumenic Age. LC 56-11670. 1974 (ISBN 0-8071-0081-1). 19.95 ea. La State U Pr.

--Science, Politics & Gnosticism. LC 68-14367. 128p. 4.95 (ISBN 0-89526-964-3). Regnery Bks.

Voegelin, Erich. Political Religions. (TST Ser.: No. 23). 1986. 39.95x (ISBN 0-88946-767-6). E Mellen.

Voelz, James W. Fundamental Greek Grammar. 320p. 1986. 14.95 (ISBN 0-570-04226-7, 15-2185). Concordia.

Vogel, Arthur A. The Jesus Prayer for Today. LC 81-84349. 128p. (Orig.). 1982. pap. 5.95 (ISBN 0-8091-2413-0). Paulist Pr.

Vogel, Arthur A., jt. auth. see Krentz, Edgar.

Vogel, Arthur A., et al. Theology in Anglicanism. LC 84-60624. (Anglican Studies). 160p. (Orig.). 1984. pap. 8.95 (ISBN 0-8192-1344-6). Morehouse.

Vogel, Claude. The Capuchins in French Louisiana (1722-1766) LC 73-3561. (Catholic University of America. Studies in American Church History: No. 7). Repr. of 1928 ed. 20.00 (ISBN 0-404-57757-1). AMS Pr.

Vogel, Cora. Easy to Use Christmas Programs. 144p. 1986. 7.95 (ISBN 0-8010-9302-3). Baker Bk.

Vogel, Cora, jt. auth. see Hendricks, William C.

Vogel, Dan. Indian Origins & the Book of Mormon. LC 86-61016. 154p. 1986. pap. 8.95 (ISBN 0-941214-42-7). Signature Bks.

Vogel, J. P. Buddhist Art in India, Ceylon, & Java. (Illus.). 187p. 1977. Repr. of 1936 ed. text ed. 19.00x. Coronet Bks.

Vogel, Juergen. Gregor VII & Heinrich IV. 1982. 59.20 (ISBN 3-11-008959-9). De Gruyter.

Vogel, Linda J. The Religious Education of Older Adults. LC 83-21109. 217p. (Orig.). 1984. pap. 12.95 (ISBN 0-89135-040-3). Religious Educ.

Vogel, Virgil J. American Indian Medicine. LC 69-10626. (Civilization of the American Indian Ser.: Vol. 95). (Illus.). 1970. 29.95 (ISBN 0-8061-0863-0). U of Okla Pr.

Vogels, Walter. Reading & Preaching the Bible: A New Approach. (Background Bks.: Vol. 4). 1986. pap. 7.95 (ISBN 0-89453-472-6). M Glazier.

Vogelsang, Erich see Luther, Martin.

Vogelstein, Ingeborg B. Johann Sleidan's Commentaries: Vantage Point of a Second Generation Lutheran. 176p. 1987. lib. bdg. 21.75 (ISBN 0-8191-5641-8); pap. text ed. 11.50 (ISBN 0-8191-5642-6). U Pr of Amer.

Vogl, Carl. Begone Satan. 48p. 1973. pap. 1.50 (ISBN 0-89555-098-9). TAN Bks Pubs.

Vogt, Evon Z. Tortillas for the Gods: A Symbolic Analysis of Zinacanteco Rituals. 256p. 1976. 18.00x (ISBN 0-674-89554-1). Harvard U Pr.

Vogt, Evon Z., jt. auth. see Lessa, William A.

Vogue, Adalbert de. Community & Abbot in the Rule of Saint Benedict, Vol. I. Perkins, Ethel R., ed. Philippi, Charles, tr. from Fr. (Cistercian Studies). 1979. 22.95 (ISBN 0-87907-905-3). Cistercian Pubns.

Vogue, Adalbert de see De Vogue, Adalbert.

Vohn, Rick. Getting Control of Your Inner Self. 176p. 1982. pap. 2.95 (ISBN 0-8423-0999-3). Tyndale.

Voieivkov, N. N. Tserkov', Rus' i Rim. Tr. of The Church, Russia & Rome. 512p. 1983. text ed. 25.00 (ISBN 0-88465-016-2); pap. text ed. 20.00 (ISBN 0-88465-015-4). Holy Trinity.

Voigt, E. E., jt. auth. see Sellers, Ovid R.

Voigt, Tracy. Prayers of a Woman. rev. 3rd ed. 55p. 1982. Repr. of 1976 ed. spiral bdg. 4.00 (ISBN 0-686-37419-3). T Voigt.

--The Relatives. (Orig.). 1982. pap. write for info. T Voigt.

Voillaume, Rene. The Living God. 1971. 5.95 (ISBN 0-87193-169-9). Dimension Bks.

--Source of Life: The Eucharist & Christian Living. Livingstone, Dinah, tr. from Fr. 1977. pap. 2.95 (ISBN 0-914544-17-9). Living Flame Pr.

Voillaume, Rene, ed. Silent Pilgrimage to God: The Spirituality of Charles deFoucauld. Moiser, Jeremy, tr. from Fr. LC 74-32516. Orig. Title: Ce Sue Crojart Charles de Foucauld. 100p. (Orig.). 1977. pap. 4.95 (ISBN 0-88344-461-5). Orbis Bks.

Vokes, Frederick E. The Riddle of the Didache: Fact or Fiction, Heresy or Catholicism? (Church Historical Society London N. S.: No. 32). Repr. of 1938 ed. 40.00 (ISBN 0-8115-3156-2). Kraus Repr.

Volio, Maria F. Confesion de un Alma Idolatra. 152p. (Orig.). 1982. pap. 3.75 (ISBN 0-89922-218-8). Edit Caribe.

Volkman, Toby A. Feasts of Honor: Ritual & Change in the Toraja Highlands. LC 84-16123. (Illinois Studies in Anthropology). (Illus.). 234p. 1985. pap. 21.50 (ISBN 0-252-01183-X). U of Ill Pr.

Volkov, John W., tr. see Shubin, Daniel H.

Voll, John O. Islam: Continuity & Change in the Modern World. LC 82-2829. 398p. 1982. 32.00x (ISBN 0-89158-931-7); pap. text ed. 14.50x (ISBN 0-89158-983-X). Westview.

Vollert, Cyril, et al, trs. Saint Thomas, Sieger De Brabant, St. Bonaventure: On the Eternity of the World. (Medieval Philosophical Texts in Translation: No. 16). 1965. pap. 7.95 (ISBN 0-87462-216-6). Marquette.

Volney, C. F. A New Translation of Volney's Ruins, 2 vols. Feldman, Burton & Richardson, Robert D., eds. LC 78-60900. (Myth & Romanticism Ser.: Vol. 25). (Illus.). 1979. Set. lib. bdg. 160.00 (ISBN 0-8240-3574-7). Garland Pub.

Volokhonsky, Larisa, tr. see Meyendorff, John.

Voltaire. Letters Concerning the English Nation. LC 74-728. 224p. 1974. Repr. of 1926 ed. lib. bdg. 19.00 (ISBN 0-8337-4467-4). B Franklin.

--Lettres Philosophiques. Pomeau, Rene, ed. 192p. 1964. 18.95 (ISBN 0-686-55754-9). French & Eur.

--Russia under Peter the Great. Jenkins, M. F., tr. LC 81-72050. 340p. 1983. 35.00 (ISBN 0-8386-3148-7). Fairleigh Dickinson.

Voltaire, M. de see De Voltaire, M.

Volz, Carl A. Church of the Middle Ages. LC 72-99217. (Church in History Ser). 1978. pap. 4.95 (ISBN 0-570-06270-5, 12-2725). Concordia.

--Faith & Practice in the Early Church. LC 82-72654. 224p. 1983. pap. 11.95 (ISBN 0-8066-1961-9, 10-2177). Augsburg.

Volz, Fred J., ed. see Reyes, Benito F.

Volz, Hans. Die Lutherpredigten Des Johannes Mathesius. (Ger). 34.00 (ISBN 0-384-64913-0); pap. 28.00 (ISBN 0-384-64912-2). Johnson Repr.

Von Allmen, et al. Roles in the Liturgical Assembly. O'Connell, Matthew J., tr. from Fr. (Orig.). 1981. pap. 17.50 (ISBN 0-916134-44-X). Pueblo Pub Co.

Von Allmen, Jean-Jacques see Allmen, Jean-Jacques Von.

Von Arnim, Christian, tr. see Steiner, Rudolf.

Von Arx, Jeffrey P. Progress & Pessimism: Religion, Politics & History in Late Nineteenth Century Britain. (Harvard Historical Studies: No. 104). 256p. 1985. text ed. 25.00x (ISBN 0-674-71375-3). Harvard U Pr.

Von Balthasar, Hans, et al. Two Say Why. 1973. pap. 1.75 (ISBN 0-8199-0434-1). Franciscan Herald.

Von Balthasar, Hans U. Convergences: To the Source of Christian Mystery. Nelson, E. A., tr. from Ger. LC 83-81853. Orig. Title: Einfaltungen: Auf Wegen der Christlichen Einigung. 153p. (Orig.). 1984. pap. 8.95 (ISBN 0-89870-032-9). Ignatius Pr.

--Glory of the Lord, Vol. 3. 416p. cancelled (ISBN 0-8245-0699-5). Crossroad NY.

--The Glory of the Lord: A Theological Aesthetics. Riches, John, ed. Louth, Andrew, et al, trs. from Ger. LC 82-23553. (Studies in Theological Style: Clerial Styles: Vol. 2). Orig. Title: Herrlichkeit: Eine Theologische Asthetik II Facher der Stile 1: Klerikale Style. 366p. 29.95 (ISBN 0-89870-048-5). Ignatius Pr.

--The Glory of the Lord; A Theological Aesthetics: Vol. I-Seeing the Form. Fessio, Joseph & Riches, John, eds. Leiva-Merikakis, Erasmo, tr. from Ger. LC 82-23553. Tr. of Herrlickeit: Eine Theologische Asthetik, I-Schau der Gestalt. 691p. 1982. 35.00 (ISBN 0-89870-031-0). Ignatius Pr.

--Life out of Death: Meditations on the Easter Mystery. LC 84-48704. 64p. 1985. pap. 3.50 (ISBN 0-8006-1821-1, 1-1821). Fortress.

--Origen: Spirit & Fire: A Thematic Anthology of His Writings by Hans Urs von Balthasar. Daly, Robert J., tr. LC 83-14368. 416p. 1984. 34.95x (ISBN 0-8132-0591-3). Cath U Pr.

--Prayer. Harrison, Graham, tr. from Ger. LC 85-82172. Orig. Title: Das Betrachtende Gebet. 311p. 1986. pap. 10.95 (ISBN 0-89870-074-4). Ignatius Pr.

--Truth Is Symphonic: Aspects of Christian Pluralism. Harrison, Graham, tr. from Ger. Tr. of Die Warrheit Ist Symphonisch. 192p. 1987. pap. 9.95 (ISBN 0-89870-141-4). Ignatius Pr.

--The Von Balthasar Reader. Kehl, Medard & Loser, Werner, eds. Lawrence, Fred & Daly, Robert J., trs. 400p. 1982. 27.50 (ISBN 0-8245-0468-2). Crossroad NY.

Von Balthasar, Hans Urs. The Christian State of Life. McCarthy, Mary F., tr. from Ger. LC 82-84580. Tr. of Christlicher Stand. 505p. (Orig.). 1984. 24.95 (ISBN 0-89870-022-1). Ignatius Pr.

--The Heart of the World. Leiva, Erasmo, tr. from Ger. LC 79-84879. Orig. Title: Das Herz der Welt. 219p. (Orig.). 1980. pap. 9.95 (ISBN 0-89870-001-9). Ignatius Pr.

--The Threefold Garland: The World's Salvation in Mary's Prayer. Leiva-Merikakis, Erasmo, tr. from Ger. LC 81-83569. Tr. of Der Dreifache Kranz. 146p. (Orig.). 1982. pap. 7.95 (ISBN 0-89870-015-9). Ignatius Pr.

Von Balthasar, Hans Urs see Balthasar, Hans Urs Von.

Von Balthasar, Has U. The Office of Peter. Emery, Andree, tr. from German. LC 86-80787. Tr. of Der Antiromische Affekt. 368p. 1986. pap. 12.95 (ISBN 0-89870-020-5). Ignatius Pr.

Von Baravalle, Hermann. Introduction to Physics in the Waldorf Schools: The Balance Between Art & Science. 2nd ed. 1967. pap. 2.95 (ISBN 0-916786-10-2, Pub by Waldorf School Monographs). St George Bk Serv.

Von Barghahn, Barbara. Age of Gold, Age of Iron: Renaissance Spain & Symbols of Monarchy. (The Imperial Legacy of Charles V & Philip II Royal Castles, Palace-Monasteries, Princely Houses Ser.: 2 vols.). (Illus.). 1036p. 1985. Set. lib. bdg. 204.75 (ISBN 0-8191-4739-7). U Pr of Amer.

Von Bezold, Friedrich see Bezold, Friedrich.

Von Campenhausen, Hans. Ecclesiastical Authority & Spiritual Power in the Church of the First Three Centuries. Baker, J. A., tr. 1969. 25.00x (ISBN 0-8047-0665-4). Stanford U Pr.

--The Fathers of the Latin Church. Hoffmann, Manfred, tr. LC 76-75260. 1964. 32.50x (ISBN 0-8047-0685-9). Stanford U Pr.

--The Formation of the Christian Bible. Baker, J. A., tr. from Ger. LC 73-171495. 360p. 1977. pap. 10.95 (ISBN 0-8006-1263-9, 1-1263). Fortress.

Von Campenhausen, Hans see Campenhausen, Hans Von.

Von Daniken, Erich. Chariots of the Gods. 189p. 1985. 42.50 (ISBN 0-317-19961-7). Bern Porter.

--The Gods & Their Grand Design. Hemon, Michael, tr. from Ger. 1984. 18.95 (ISBN 0-399-12961-8, Putnam). Putnam Pub Group.

--Pathways to the Gods: The Stones of Kiribati. Heron, Michael, tr. from Ger. (Illus.). 288p. 1983. 16.95 (ISBN 0-399-12751-8, Putnam). Putnam Pub Group.

Von Del Chamberlain. When Stars Came Down to Earth: Cosmology of the Skidi Pawnee Indians of North America. LC 82-16390. (Ballena Press Anthropological Papers: No. 26). (Illus.). 260p. (Orig.). 1982. pap. 17.95 (ISBN 0-87919-098-1). Ballena Pr.

Von Der Mehden, Fred. Religion & Modernization in Southeast Asia. 232p. 1986. text ed. 29.95x (ISBN 0-8156-2360-7); pap. text ed. 14.95x (ISBN 0-8156-2361-5). Syracuse U Pr.

Von der Mehden, Fred R. Religion & Nationalism in Southeast Asia: Burma, Indonesia, & the Philippines. (Illus.). 272p. 1963. pap. 7.95 (ISBN 0-299-02944-1). U of Wis Pr.

Von Der Osten-Sacken, Peter. Christian-Jewish Dialogue: Theological Foundations. Kohl, Margaret, tr. from Ger. LC 85-45481. 240p. 1986. 24.95 (ISBN 0-8006-0771-6, 1-771). Fortress.

Von Dobshutz, Ernst see Dobschutz, Ernst Von.

Von Dollinger, Johann J. see Dollinger, Johann J. Von.

Von Domaszewski, Alfred. Abhandlungen Zur Romischen Religion. facsimile ed. LC 75-10633. (Ancient Religion & Mythology Ser.). (Ger., Illus.). 1976. Repr. of 1909 ed. 20.00x (ISBN 0-405-07008-X). Ayer Co Pubs.

--Die Religion Des Romischen Heeres. facsimile ed. LC 75-10634. (Ancient Religion & Mythology Ser.). (Ger., Illus.). 1976. Repr. of 1895 ed. 12.00 (ISBN 0-405-07012-8). Ayer Co Pubs.

Von Duerckheim, Karlfried. Hara: The Vital Centre of Man. Von Kospoth, Sylvia-Monica & Healey, Estelle R., trs. from Ger. (Unwin Paperbacks). 1977. pap. 6.95 (ISBN 0-04-290011-5). Allen Unwin.

Von Ende, Richard C. Church Music: An International Bibliography. LC 79-23697. 473p. 1980. lib. bdg. 30.00 (ISBN 0-8108-1271-1). Scarecrow.

--Church Music: An International Bibliography. LC 79-23697. pap. 118.30 (ISBN 0-317-52049-0, 2027497). Bks Demand UMI.

Von Eschen, Jessie M. Pot of Gold. 1983. 7.95 (ISBN 0-8062-2135-6). Carlton.

Von Franz, Marie-Louise. Patterns of Creativity Mirrored in Creation Myths. (Seminar Ser: No. 6). 250p. 1972. pap. 15.00 (ISBN 0-88214-106-6). Spring Pubns.

Von Franz, Marie-Louise, jt. auth. see Jung, Emma.

Von Funk, Franz X. Manual of Church History, 2 Vols. Cappadelta, Luigi, tr. LC 78-168077. 1910. Set. 67.50 (ISBN 0-404-02646-X). AMS Pr.

Von Furer-Haimendorf, Christoph. The Sherpas of Nepal Buddhist Highlanders. 298p. 1982. 49.00x (ISBN 0-85692-020-7, Pub. by E-W Pubns England). State Mutual Bk.

Von Furer-Haimendorf, Christoph see Nebesky-Wojkowitz, Rene De.

Von Galli, Mario. Living Our Future: St. Francis of Assisi & the Church Tomorrow. new ed. (Illus.). 239p. 1976. pap. 4.95 (ISBN 0-8199-0439-2). Franciscan Herald.

Von Gardner, Johann. Russian Church Singing: Orthodox Worship & Hymnography, Vol. I. LC 79-27480. 146p. 1980. pap. 7.95 (ISBN 0-913836-59-1). St Vladimirs.

Von Geisebrecht, Wilhel M, tr. see Gregorius, Saint.

Von Goethe, J. W. & Steiner, Rudolf. The Fairy Tale of the Green Snake & the Beautiful Lily. 2nd ed. LC 78-73644. 72p. (Orig.). 1981. pap. 3.50 (ISBN 0-89345-203-3, Steinerbks). Garber Comm.

Von Grunebaum, G. E. Muhammadam Festivals: Typical Elements of Islamic Rituals, Prayers & Pilgrimage. 144p. 1981. 20.00x (ISBN 0-7007-0087-0, Pub. by Curzon England). State Mutual Bk.

--Muhammaden Festivals: Typical Elements of Islamic Ritual, Prayer & Pilgrimage. new ed. (Illus.). 1976. text ed. 9.95x (ISBN 0-7007-0087-0). Humanities.

Von Grunebaum, Gustave E. Modern Islam: The Search for Cultural Identity. LC 83-11508. viii, 303p. 1983. Repr. of 1962 ed. lib. bdg. 39.75x (ISBN 0-313-24087-6, VGMI). Greenwood.

Von Grunebaum, Gustave E., ed. see Abel, Armand, et al.

Von Hammer-Purgstall, Joseph. History of the Assassins, Derived from Oriental Sources. Wood, Oswald C., tr. Repr. of 1835 ed. 22.50 (ISBN 0-8337-1562-3). B Franklin.

Von Harnack, Adolf. Marcion: The Gospel of the Alien God. Steely, John E. & Bierma, Lyle D., trs. from Ger. Orig. Title: Marcion, das Evangelium vom Fremden Gott. 265p. 1987. lib. bdg. 24.95 (ISBN 0-939464-16-0). Labyrinth Pr.

Von Hefele, Karl J. see Hefele, Karl J.

Von Hildebrand, Alice. Love & Selfishness. 54p. 1970. pap. 0.75 (ISBN 0-8199-0376-0). Franciscan Herald.

Von Hildebrand, Alice, jt. auth. see Von Hildebrand, Dietrich.

Von Hildebrand, Alice J. Introduction to a Philosophy of Religion. LC 79-139972. 1971. 6.95 (ISBN 0-8199-0426-0). Franciscan Herald.

Von Hildebrand, Dietrich. Encyclical Humanae Vitae: A Sign of Contradiction. (Orig.). 1969. pap. 2.00 (ISBN 0-685-10965-8). Franciscan Herald.

--Liturgy & Personality. LC 85-18388. 182p. 1986. 11.95 (ISBN 0-918477-03-4); pap. 7.95 (ISBN 0-918477-04-2). Sophia Inst Pr.

--The New Tower of Babel. LC 76-998. 1977. Repr. 5.95 (ISBN 0-8199-0600-X). Franciscan Herald.

Von Hildebrand, Dietrich & Von Hildebrand, Alice. Art of Living. 1965. 3.95 (ISBN 0-685-10959-3, L38009). Franciscan Herald.

Von Hildebrand, Dietrich see Hildebrand, Dietrich von.

Von Hilderbrand, Dietrich. Celibacy & the Crisis of Faith. 1971. 4.95 (ISBN 0-8199-0428-7). Franciscan Herald.

Von Huegel, F. The Mystical Element of Religion As Studied in Saint Catherine of Genoa & Her Friends, 2 vols. 1977. lib. bdg. 200.00 (ISBN 0-8490-2317-3). Gordon Pr.

Von Huegel, Friedrich see Hugel, Friedrich Von.

Vonk, Idalee. Thirty-Six Devotionals for Women's Groups. LC 81-52993. 112p. (Orig.). 1982. pap. 3.95 (ISBN 0-87239-493-X, 3216). Standard Pub.

Vonk, Idalee W. Elementary Activity Patterns: For Year 'Round Use. (Illus.). 48p. (Orig.). 1973. pap. 4.95 (ISBN 0-87239-323-2, 2142). Standard Pub.

--Fifty-Two Elementary Patterns. (Illus.). 48p. (Orig.). 1979. pap. 4.95 (ISBN 0-87239-340-2, 3366). Standard Pub.

Von Keitzell, F. By Many Infallible Proofs. 76p. pap. 4.95 (ISBN 0-88172-137-9). Believers Bkshelf.

Von Kietzel, F. Behold the Lamb of God. 5.95 (ISBN 0-88172-136-0). Believers Bkshelf.

Von Klemperer, Klemens. Ignaz Seipel: Christian Statesman in a Time of Crisis. LC 77-166392. 420p. 1962. 49.50 (ISBN 0-691-05197-6). Princeton U Pr.

Von Koerber, Hildegard, tr. see Lorber, Jakob.

Von Krusenstierna, Sten, ed. Services of Our Lady. 70p. 1982. pap. text ed. 2.75 (ISBN 0-918980-11-9). St Alban Pr.

Von Kuehnelt-Leddihn, Erik. The Timeless Christian. LC 73-10604. 241p. 1976. 4.50 (ISBN 0-685-77519-4). Franciscan Herald.

Von Le Fort, Gertrud. The Pope from the Ghetto: The Legend of the Family of Pier Leone. Bonacina, Conrad R., tr. 330p. 1981. Repr. of 1935 ed. lib. bdg. 15.00 (ISBN 0-89984-205-4). Century Bookbindery.

--The Song at the Scaffold. rev. ed. McMurtrey, Martin & Knopp, Robert, eds. (Illus., Orig.). 1954. pap. text ed. 3.95 (ISBN 0-910334-24-2). Cath Authors.

Von Loewenich, Walter. Luther's Theology of the Cross. Bouman, Herbert J., tr. LC 75-2845. 224p. (Orig.). 1982. pap. 10.95 (ISBN 0-8066-1490-0, 10-4233). Augsburg.

Von Loewenich, Walther. Paul: His Life & Work. 1960. text ed. 7.50x (ISBN 0-8401-1421-4). A R Allenson.
Von Loewenich, Walther see Loewenich, Walther von.
Von Murat, Leonhard, jt. auth. see Schmid, Walter.
Von Nordheim, Eckhard. Die Lehre der Alten: II Das Testament als Literaturgattung im Alten Testament und im Alten Vorderen Orient. (Arbeiten zur Literatur und Geschichte des hellenistischen Judentums Ser.: No. 18). (Ger.). xii, 184p. 1986. 25.50 (ISBN 90-04-07313-2, Pub. by E J Brill). Heinman.
Von Petzold, Gertrud. Harriet Martineau und Ihre Sittlich Religiose Weltschau. 1941. pap. 7.00 (ISBN 0-384-46100-X). Johnson Repr.
Von Rad, Gerhard. Deuteronomy: A Commentary. LC 66-23088. (Old Testament Library). 212p. 1966. 15.95 (ISBN 0-664-20734-0). Westminster.
--Genesis, a Commentary. rev ed. LC 72-6413. (Old Testament Library). 440p. 1973. 17.95 (ISBN 0-664-20957-2). Westminster.
--God at Work in Israel. Marks, John, tr. LC 79-26281. 1980. pap. 7.75 (ISBN 0-687-14960-6). Abingdon.
--The Message of the Prophets. Stalker, D. M., tr. from Ger. LC 72-183633. 288p. 1972. pap. 10.95xi (ISBN 0-06-068929-3, RD45, HarpR). Har-Row.
--Old Testament Theology, 2 vols. LC 62-7306. Vol. 1. S.D. 17.95 (ISBN 0-06-068930-7, HarpR); Vol. 2. 16.95 (ISBN 0-06-068931-5, HarpR). Har-Row.
--The Problem of the Hexateuch & Other Essays. 352p. pap. 15.95 (ISBN 0-317-31485-8, 30-1310-259). Fortress.
--Wisdom in Israel. rev. ed. Martin, James D., tr. from Ger. Orig. Title: Weisheit in Israel. 336p. 1973. 15.95 (ISBN 0-687-45757-2). Abingdon.
Von Ranke, Leopold. Ferdinand I & Maximilian II of Austria. LC 74-153627. Repr. of 1853 ed. 14.50 (ISBN 0-404-09265-9). AMS Pr.
--History of the Popes: Their Church & State, 3 vols. 1205p. 1986. Repr. of 1901 ed. lib. bdg. 150.00 (ISBN 0-8495-4730-X). Arden Lib.
Von Rohr, John. The Covenant of Grace in Puritan Thought. (American Academy of Religion Studies in Religion). 240p. 1987. 18.95 (01-00-45); pap. 13.95. Scholars Pr Ga.
Von Schiller, Friedrich. Maiden of Orleans. 2nd rev. ed. Krumpelmann, John T., tr. LC 63-62703. (North Carolina. University. Studies in the Germanic Languages & Literatures: No. 37). Repr. of 1962 ed. 18.50 (ISBN 0-404-50937-1). AMS Pr.
Von Schubert, Hans. Lazarus Spengler und Die Reformation in Nurnberg. 29.00 (ISBN 0-685-92689-3); pap. 28.00 (ISBN 0-384-54287-5). Johnson Repr.
Von Simson, Otto. The Gothic Cathedral: Origins of Gothic Architecture & the Medieval Concept of Order. LC 72-11946. (Bollingen Ser.: No. 48). (Illus.). 300p. 1973. 31.00 (ISBN 0-691-09741-0); pap. 9.50 (ISBN 0-691-01789-1). Princeton U Pr.
Von Speyr, Adrienne. The Christian State of Life. McCarthy, Mary F., tr. from Ger. LC 85-81512. Orig. Title: Christlicher Stand. 213p. (Orig.). 1986. pap. 9.95 (ISBN 0-89870-044-2). Ignatius Pr.
--The Gates of Eternal Life. Sharp, Corona, tr. from Ger. LC 82-84582. Tr. of Die Pforten des Ewigen Lebens. 140p. (Orig.). 1984. pap. 7.95 (ISBN 0-89870-025-6). Ignatius Pr.
--They Followed His Call. Leiva-Merikakis, Erasmo, tr. from Ger. LC 86-80294. Tr. of Sie Folgten Seinem Ruf. 137p. (Orig.). 1986. pap. 6.95 (ISBN 0-89870-100-7). Ignatius Pr.
--Three Women & the Lord. Harrison, Graham, tr. LC 86-80789. (Illus.). 115p. 1986. pap. 7.95 (ISBN 0-89870-059-0). Ignatius Pr.
--World of Prayer. Harrison, Graham, tr. from Ger. LC 84-80904. Tr. of Die Welt des Gebetes. 311p. (Orig.). 1985. pap. 10.95 (ISBN 0-89870-033-7). Ignatius Pr.
Von Stamwitz, Alicia. Women of Valor: The Trials & Triumphs of Seven Saints. 64p. 1986. pap. 1.95 (ISBN 0-89243-258-6). Liguori Pubns.
Von Staupitz, Johann. Tubinger Predigten. (Ger.). 34.00 (ISBN 0-384-57712-1); pap. 28.00 (ISBN 0-384-57711-3). Johnson Repr.
Von Storcksburg Staehlin, Jakob. Original Anecdotes of Peter the Great, Collected from the Conversation of Several Persons of Distinction at Petersburg & Moscow. LC 74-115587. (Russia Observed, Series I). 1970. Repr. of 1788 ed. 21.00 (ISBN 0-405-03064-9). Ayer Co Pubs.
Von Trapp, Maria. When King Was Carpenter. LC 75-46021. 142p. 1976. pap. 2.95 (ISBN 0-89221-018-4). New Leaf.
Von Velsen, Dorothee. Gegenreformation in den Furstentumern Liegnitz-Brirg-Wohlau, Ihre Vorgeschichte und Ihre Staatsrechtlichen Grundlagen. (Ger.). 34.00 (ISBN 0-384-64224-1); pap. 28.00 (ISBN 0-384-64223-3). Johnson Repr.
Von Verschuer, Otmar. Racial Biology of the Jews. (Illus.). 1984. lib. bdg. 79.95 (ISBN 0-87700-560-5). Revisionist Pr.
--Racial Biology of the Jews. 1987. lib. bdg. 75.00 (ISBN 0-8490-3945-2). Gordon Pr.
Von Wellnitz, Marcus. Christ & the Patriarchs: New Light from Apocryphal Literature & Tradition. LC 80-83035. 400p. 1980. 9.95 (ISBN 0-88290-164-8, 2045). Horizon Utah.
Von Winning, Hasso. Two Maya Monuments in Yucatan: The Palace of the Stuccoes at Acanceh & the Temple of the Owls at Chicken Itza. (Frederick Webb Hodge Publications: No. XII). (Illus.). 104p. (Orig.). 1985. pap. write for info. (ISBN 0-916561-68-2). Southwest Mus.
Von Wright, G. H. Truth, Knowledge & Modality: Philosophical Papers, Vol. III. 248p. 1985. 24.95x (ISBN 0-631-13367-4). Basil Blackwell.
Voorehoeve, H. C. & Bennett, Gordon H. El Bautismo. 2nd ed. Bautista, Sara, tr. from Eng. (La Serie Diamante). Tr. of Baptism. (Span., Illus.). 36p. 1982. pap. 0.85 (ISBN 0-942504-06-2). Overcomer Pr.
Voorhies, Alice F. Believe It or Not It's in the Bible. 38p. (Orig.). 1985. pap. 3.00 (ISBN 0-931494-77-X). Brunswick Pub.
Voorhis, H. V., compiled by. Facts for Freemasons. 258p. 1979. text ed. 9.50 (ISBN 0-88053-016-2, M-65). Macoy Pub.
Voorhis, Harold V. The Eastern Star: The Evolution from a Rite to an Order. 138p. 1986. Repr. of 1954 ed. text ed. 6.95 (ISBN 0-88053-306-4, S-300). Macoy Pub.
Voors, Tijno, jt. auth. see Schaefer, Christopher.
Vora, V., tr. see Bhagwan Shree Rajneesh.
Vorgrimler, Herbert. Understanding Karl Rahner: An Introduction to His Life & Thought. 176p. 1986. 14.95 (ISBN 0-8245-0790-8). Crossroad NY.
Vorgrimmler, jt. auth. see Rahner.
Vorobyev, Nicolai. The History & Art of the Russian Icon from the X to the XX Century. Maxym, Lucy, ed. & tr. from Rus. (Illus.). 144p. 1986. 50.00 (ISBN 0-940202-06-9). Siamese Imports.
Vorreux, Damien. First Encounter with Francis of Assisi. Schwartz, Paul & Lachance, Paul, trs. from Fr. 1979. pap. 6.95 (ISBN 0-8199-0698-0). Franciscan Herald.
Vorspan, Albert. Great Jewish Debates & Dilemmas: Perspectives on Moral Issues in Conflict in the 80's. LC 80-21057. 240p. 1980. pap. text ed. 5.95 (ISBN 0-8074-0049-1). UAHC.
Vorspan, Albert, jt. auth. see Brickner, Balfour.
Vorster, Willem S., jt. auth. see Lategan, Bernard C.
Vos, Catherine F. The Child's Story Bible. (Illus.). 432p. 1983. Repr. of 1934 ed. PLB 14.95 (ISBN 0-8028-5011-1). Eerdmans.
Vos, Geerhardus. The Kingdom of God & the Church. 1972. pap. 3.50 (ISBN 0-87552-502-4). Presby & Reformed.
--Notes on Biblical Theology. 1948. pap. 10.95 (ISBN 0-8028-1209-0). Eerdmans.
--Redemptive History & Biblical Interpretation. Gaffin, Richard B., Jr., ed. 584p. 1981. 17.50 (ISBN 0-8010-9286-8). Baker Bk.
--The Teaching of the Epistle to the Hebrews. pap. 4.95 (ISBN 0-87552-503-2). Presby & Reformed.
Vos, Howard. Archaeology in Bible Lands. LC 77-2981. (Illus.). 1977. 11.95 (ISBN 0-8024-0289-5). Moody.
Vos, Howard F. Bible Study Commentary: Ezra, Nehemiah & Esther. (Bible Study Commentary Ser.). 224p. 1987. pap. 7.95 (ISBN 0-310-33911-1). Zondervan.
--Breve Historia de la Iglesia. Orig. Title: An Introduction to Church History. (Span.). 160p. 1987. pap. 3.95 (ISBN 0-8254-1824-0). Kregel.
--Effective Bible Study. (Contemporary Evangelical Perspectives Ser.). 1956. kivar 6.95 (ISBN 0-310-33851-4, 10966P). Zondervan.
--Galatas: Una Llamada a la Libertad Cristiana (Comentarion Biblico Portavoz) Orig. Title: Galatians (Everyman's Bible Commentary) (Span.). 1981. pap. 3.50 (ISBN 0-8254-1825-9). Kregel.
--Galatians. (Everyman's Bible Commentary Ser.). 1970. pap. 5.95 (ISBN 0-8024-2048-6). Moody.
--Genesis. (Everyman's Bible Commentary Ser.). 1982. pap. 5.95 (ISBN 0-8024-2001-X). Moody.
--Genesis & Archaeology. rev. & enl. ed. 1986. pap. 6.95 (ISBN 0-310-33901-4, 11154P). Zondervan.
--An Introduction to Bible Archaeology. Rev. ed. 1983. pap. 5.95 (ISBN 0-8024-0325-5). Moody.
--An Introduction to Bible Geography. Rev. ed. 1983. pap. 6.95 (ISBN 0-8024-0326-3). Moody.
--An Introduction to Church History. (Orig.). 1984. pap. 7.95 (ISBN 0-8024-0315-8). Moody.
--Mark: A Bible Study Commentary. pap. 4.95 (ISBN 0-310-33873-5, 11044P). Zondervan.
--Matthew: A Bible Study Commentary. (Study Guide Commentary Ser.). 1979. pap. 6.95 (ISBN 0-310-33883-2, 11152P). Zondervan.
--One, Two Samuel: Bible Study Commentary. (Bible Study Commentary Ser.). 1986. pap. 5.95 (ISBN 0-310-33893-X, 11153P). Zondervan.
--Philippians: A Bible Study Commentary. (Study Guide Commentary Ser.). 96p. (Orig.). 1980. pap. 3.95 (ISBN 0-310-33863-8, 10967P). Zondervan.
Vos, Howard F., jt. auth. see Pfeiffer, Charles F.
Vos, Nelvin. Seven Days a Week: Faith in Action. LC 84-47937. 144p. 1985. pap. 5.95 (ISBN 0-8006-1658-8, 1-1658). Fortress.
Voshell, Dorothy. Whom Shall I Marry? 1979. pap. 4.50 (ISBN 0-87552-509-1). Presby & Reformed.
Vosko, Richard S. Through the Eye of a Rose Window: A Perspective on the Environment for Worship. 1981. pap. text ed. 7.95 (ISBN 0-89390-028-1). Resource Pubns.
Voskuil, Dennis. Mountains into Goldmines: Robert Schuller & the Gospel of Success. LC 83-1729. pap. 47.00 (ISBN 0-317-30165-9, 2025347). Bks Demand UMI.
Voss, Carl H. Living Religions of the World: Our Search for Meaning. (Library of Liberal Religion). 192p. 1977. pap. 6.95 (ISBN 0-87975-215-7). Prometheus Bks.
--Rabbi & Minister: The Friendship of Stephen S. Wise & John Haynes Holmes. LC 80-7453. (The Library of Liberal Religion). 384p. 1980. pap. 11.95 (ISBN 0-87975-130-4). Prometheus Bks.
Vossius, Gerardus. Theologia Gentili, 3 vols. LC 75-27872. (Renaissance & the Gods Ser.: Vol. 28). (Illus.). 1976. Repr. of 1641 ed. Set. lib. bdg. 265.00 (ISBN 0-8240-2077-4). Garland Pub.
Voth, H. R. Oraibu Marau Ceremony-Brief Miscellaneous Hopi Papers. (Chicago Field Museum of Natural History Fieldiana Anthropology Ser). 1912. 44.00 (ISBN 0-527-01871-6). Kraus Repr.
Voth, H. R., jt. auth. see Dorsey, G. A.
Voth, Norma J. Festive Breads of Easter. LC 79-23702. (Illus.). 80p. 1980. pap. 3.50 (ISBN 0-8361-1917-7). Herald Pr.
--Festive Cakes of Christmas. LC 81-2140. (Illus.). 80p. 1981. pap. 3.50 (ISBN 0-8361-1956-8). Herald Pr.
--Festive Cookies of Christmas. LC 81-18258. 104p. (Orig.). 1982. pap. 3.25 (ISBN 0-8361-1983-5). Herald Pr.
Vozdvizhensky, P. Moja pervaja Svjashchennaja Istorija, dlja detjej. Tr. of My First Sacred History, for Children. (Illus.). 101p. 1968. pap. 4.00 (ISBN 0-317-30407-0). Holy Trinity.
Voznesensky, J. Obshchjedostupnija Chtenija o Tserkovnom Peniji. Tr. of Popular Readings in Church Singing. 48p. 1969. pap. 2.00 (ISBN 0-317-30383-X). Holy Trinity.
Vrga, Djuro J. & Fahey, Frank J. Changes & Socio-Religious Conflict in an Ethnic Minority Group: The Serbian Orthodox Church in America. LC 74-31771. 1975. softcover 8.00 (ISBN 0-88247-335-2). Ragusan Pr.
Vriend, Joannes. The Blessed Virgin Mary in Medieval Drama of England. 69.95 (ISBN 0-87968-756-8). Gordon Pr.
Vriend, John, tr. see Berkhof, Hendrikus.
Vriend, John, tr. see Loader, J. A.
Vriend, John, tr. see Maarsingh, B.
Vries, Anne de see De Vries, Anne.
Vries, Dawn De see De Vries, Dawn.
Vries, James E. De see De Vries, James E.
Vries, Jan De see De Vries, Jan.
Vries, Janet M. De see DeVries, Janet M.
Vries, Vickie De, ed. see Dean, Dave.
Vrijhof, Peter H. & Waardenburg, Jacques, eds. Official & Popular Religion. (Religion & Society Ser.). 1979. text ed. 38.00x (ISBN 0-686-27030-4). Mouton.
Vryonis, Speros, Jr., jt. ed. see Hovannisian, Richard G.
Vuilleumier, Marion R. Meditations in the Mountains. 128p. (Orig.). 1983. pap. 7.75 (ISBN 0-687-24260-6). Abingdon.
Vulliamy, C. E. John Wesley. (Heroes of the Faith Ser.). 359p. 1985. Repr. 6.95 (ISBN 0-916441-14-8). Barbour & Co.
Vuuren, Nancy Van see Van Vuuren, Nancy.
Vyas, R. N. The Bhagavadgita & Jivana Yoga. 1986. 14.00x (ISBN 81-7017-203-9, Pub. by Abhinav India). South Asia Bks.
Vyasa. Bhagavata, Srimad. Tapasyananda, Swami, tr. from Sanskrit. 1983. Vol. 1, 455p. 25.00x ea. (ISBN 0-87481-516-9). Vol. 2, 492p (ISBN 0-87481-517-7). Vol. 3, 447p (ISBN 0-87481-518-5). Vol. 4 (ISBN 0-87481-519-3). Vedanta Pr.
--Mahabharata. 6th ed. Rajagopalachari, Chakravarti, ed. Rajagopalachari, Chakravarti & Rao, N. R., trs. from Tamil. 332p. 1980. pap. 5.50 (ISBN 0-934676-16-X). Greenlf Bks.
Vyvyan, John. A Case Against Jones: Study of Psychical Phenomena. 220p. 1966. 7.50 (ISBN 0-227-67683-1). Attic Pr.

W

W, Carolyn. Detaching with Love. 24p. (Orig.). 1984. pap. 0.95 (ISBN 0-89486-232-4). Hazelden.
Waagenaar, Sam. The Pope's Jews. (Illus.). 500p. 1974. 9.95 (ISBN 0-912050-49-7, Library Pr). Open Court.
Waal, Esther de see De Waal, Esther.
Waal, Esther de, jt. ed. see Allchin, A. M.
Waal, Hugo De see Faber, Heije.
Waard, J. De see De Waard, J. & Nida, E. A.
Waard, J. de see De Waard, J. & Smalley, W. A.
Waard, Jan de & Nida, Eugene A. From One Language to Another: Functional Equivalence in Bible Translation. 224p. 1986. 15.95 (ISBN 0-8407-7555-5). Nelson.
Waardenburg, Jacques. Classical Approaches to the Study of Religion: Aims, Methods & Theories of Research: Part 1: Introduction & Anthology. LC 70-152082. (Religion & Reason Ser: No. 3). 742p. 1973. pap. text ed. 47.50x (ISBN 0-686-22556-2). Mouton.
--Classical Approaches to the Study of Religion: Aims, Methods & Theories of Research, Pt. 2 Bibliography. (Religion & Reason Ser.: No. 4). 332p. 1974. text ed. 58.50 (ISBN 90-2797-971-5). Mouton.
--Reflections on the Study of Religion. (Religion & Reason Ser.: No. 15). 1978. text ed. 32.00 (ISBN 0-686-27034-7). Mouton.
Waardenburg, Jacques, jt. ed. see Vrijhof, Peter H.
Waardenburg, Jean-Jacques. L'islam Dans le Miroir De L'Occident: Comment Quelques Orientalistes Occidentaux Se Sont Penches Sur L'islam et Se Sont Forme une Image De Cette Religion. 3 ed. (Recherches Mediterraneennes: Etudes 3). 1970. 26.80x (ISBN 90-2796-304-5). Mouton.
Wace, Henry, jt. ed. see Smith, William.
Wach, Joachim. Sociology of Religion. 1944. 12.00x (ISBN 0-226-86707-2). U of Chicago Pr.
--Types of Religious Experience: Christian & Non-Christian. LC 51-9885. 275p. 1972. pap. 2.45x (ISBN 0-226-86710-2, P482, Phoen). U of Chicago Pr.
--Understanding & Believing: Essays. Kitagawa, Joseph M., ed. LC 75-31987. 204p. 1976. Repr. of 1968 ed. lib. bdg. 25.00x (ISBN 0-8371-8488-6, WAUB). Greenwood.
Wach, Joachim & Kitagawa, Joseph M. The Comparative Study of Religions. LC 58-9237. (Lectures on the History of Religions: No. 4). 1958. 30.00x (ISBN 0-231-02252-2); pap. 12.00x (ISBN 0-231-08528-1). Columbia U Pr.
Wacholder, Ben Z. The Dawn of Quran: The Sectarian Torah & the Teacher of Righteousness. 310p. 1983. 25.00 (ISBN 0-686-88437-X). Ktav.
--Eupolemus: A Study of Graeco-Judean Literature. 1974. 20.00x (ISBN 0-87820-401-6). Ktav.
Wachterhauser, Brice R., ed. Hermeneutics & Modern Philosophy. 536p. (Orig.). 1986. 49.50x (ISBN 0-88706-295-4); pap. 16.95x (ISBN 0-88706-296-2). State U NY Pr.
Wachtmeister, Constance. Reminiscences of H. P. Blavatsky. rev. new ed. LC 76-44810. 1977. pap. 3.75 (ISBN 0-8356-0488-8, Quest). Theos Pub Hse.
Waddams, Herbert M. The Swedish Church. LC 81-7021. (Illus.). viii, 70p. 1981. Repr. of 1946 ed. lib. bdg. 22.50x (ISBN 0-313-22184-7, WASW). Greenwood.
Waddell, Austine. Buddhism & Lamaism of Tibet. 1985. text ed. 40.00x (ISBN 0-86590-615-7, Pub. by Sterling Pubs India). Apt Bks.
--Tibetan Buddhism with Its Mystic Cults Symbolism & Mythology, & in Its Relation to Indian Buddhism. (Illus.). 598p. 1972. pap. 8.95 (ISBN 0-486-20130-9). Dover.
Waddell, Genny & Smith, Agnes. Linda's Song. 136p. (Orig.). 1985. pap. 5.95 (ISBN 0-89265-095-8). Randall Hse.
Waddell, Helen. Desert Fathers. 1957. pap. 7.95 (ISBN 0-472-06008-2, 8, AA). U of Mich Pr.
--Stories from Holy Writ. LC 74-25538. 280p. 1975. Repr. of 1949 ed. lib. bdg. 22.50x (ISBN 0-8371-7872-X, WAHW). Greenwood.
Waddey, John. An Album of Bible Characters. pap. 5.50 (ISBN 0-89137-542-2). Quality Pubns.
--Ecclesiastes & Song of Solomon. 1986. pap. 5.50 (ISBN 0-89137-565-1). Quality Pubns.
Waddy, Charis. The Muslim Mind. 2nd ed. LC 82-7778. (Illus.). 232p. 1983. 25.00x (ISBN 0-582-78346-1); pap. 8.95x (ISBN 0-582-78345-3). Longman.
--Women in Muslim History. LC 80-40161. (Illus.). 224p. 1980. text ed. 27.95x (ISBN 0-582-78084-5). Longman.

Wade, A. The Ten Principal Upanishads. 75.00 (ISBN 0-8490-1183-3). Gordon Pr.

Wade, David L. Prayers of Confession: Series B. (Orig.). 1987. pap. price not set (ISBN 0-89536-885-4, 7871). CSS of Ohio.

Wade, Francis C. The Catholic University & the Faith. (Aquinas Lecture Ser.). 1978. 7.95 (ISBN 0-87462-143-7). Marquette.

--John of Saint Thomas: Outlines of Formal Logic. 2nd ed. (Medieval Philosophical Texts in Translation: No. 8). 1962. pap. 7.95 (ISBN 0-87462-208-5). Marquette.

--Teaching & Morality. LC 63-17962. 1963. 2.95 (ISBN 0-8294-0080-X). Loyola.

Wade, G. W. Old Testament History. 1904. lib. bdg. 20.00 (ISBN 0-8482-9973-6). Norwood Edns.

Wade, Gladys I. Thomas Traherne. LC 73-96171. 1969. Repr. of 1944 ed. lib. bdg. 20.00x (ISBN 0-374-98113-2, Octagon). Hippocrene Bks.

Wade, John. Acts. (Standard Bible Studies). (Illus.). 288p. 1987. pap. price not set (ISBN 0-87403-165-6, 40105). Standard Pub.

Wade, John W. Dear Theophilus. 256p. 1985. pap. 4.95 (ISBN 0-87239-968-0, 41036). Standard Pub.

--God's Word B. C. LC 83-349. (Orig.). 1983. pap. 2.95 (ISBN 0-87239-667-3, 41020). Standard Pub.

Wade, John W., jt. auth. see Jacobs, J. Vernon.

Wade, Larry. Local Church Administration. (Illus.). 122p. 1978. pap. 8.95 (ISBN 0-914936-32-8). Bible Temple.

Wade, Marion E. & Kittler, Glenn D. The Lord Is My Counsel: A Businessman's Personal Experiences with the Bible. 192p. 1984. pap. 4.95 (ISBN 0-13-540658-7). P-H.

Wade, Mildred. Games for Fun. LC 77-76616. 1977. pap. 3.95 (ISBN 0-8054-7513-3). Broadman.

--Socials for All Occasions. LC 79-55492. (Orig.). 1980. pap. 4.95 (ISBN 0-8054-7518-4). Broadman.

Wade-Evans, A. W., tr. see Nennius.

Wadia, B. P. The Law of Sacrifice. (Sangam Texts). 135p. 1986. pap. 8.75 (ISBN 0-88695-023-6). Concord Grove.

Wadley, Susan S. Shakti: Power in the Conceptual Structure of Karimpur Religion. LC 76-37612. (Univ. of Chicago Studies in Anthropology Ser. in Social, Cultural, & Linguistic Anthropology: No. 2). 222p. 1975. pap. 6.00 (ISBN 0-916256-01-4). U Chi Dept Anthro.

Wadsworth, James. The English Spanish Pilgrime. LC 71-25682. (English Experience Ser.: No. 275). 96p. 1970. Repr. of 1629 ed. 11.50 (ISBN 90-221-0275-0). Walter J Johnson.

Wadsworth, Michael, ed. Ways of Reading the Bible. 232p. 1981. 28.50x (ISBN 0-389-20119-7). B&N Imports.

Wagar, W. Warren, ed. The Secular Mind: Transformations of Faith in Modern Europe. LC 81-20019. 275p. 1982. text ed. 42.50x (ISBN 0-8419-0766-8). Holmes & Meier.

Wagemaker, Herbert, Jr. Parents & Discipline. LC 80-14624. (Christian Care Bks.: Vol. 12). 120p. 1980. pap. 7.95 (ISBN 0-664-24328-2). Westminster.

Wagenknecht, Edward. Daughters of the Covenant: Portraits of Six Jewish Women. LC 83-3562. (Illus.). 200p. 1983. lib. bdg. 17.50x (ISBN 0-87023-396-3). U of Mass Pr.

Wagenseil, Joh. Chr. Tela Ignea Satanae, 2 vols. 1631p. Date not set. Repr. of 1681 ed. text ed. 207.00x (ISBN 0-576-80110-0, Pub by Gregg Intl Pubs England). Gregg Intl.

Wagenvoort, Hendrik. Studies in Roman Literature, Culture & Religion. Commager, Steele, ed. LC 77-70817. (Latin Poetry Ser.: Vol. 31). 1978. lib. bdg. 40.00 (ISBN 0-8240-2981-X). Garland Pub.

Wager, Lewis. Repentance of Mary Magdalene. LC 70-133754. (Tudor Facsimile Texts. Old English Plays: No. 36). Repr. of 1908 ed. 49.50 (ISBN 0-404-53336-1). AMS Pr.

Waggener, Florence E. The New Testament Simply Told. LC 86-90523. 160p. 1986. 11.95x (ISBN 0-9617339-0-X). Waggener Publ Co.

--Story of the Old Testament Simply Told. (Illus.). 1979. 5.50 (ISBN 0-682-49375-9). Exposition Pr FL.

Waggoner, Doreen. To Love & to Cherish. 48p. 1986. 6.95 (ISBN 0-8378-5094-0). Gibson.

Waggoner, Dorene. I Will Not Leave You Comfortless. (Illus.). 32p. 1984. 4.95 (ISBN 0-8378-2040-5). Gibson.

Waggoner, E. J. The Glad Tidings: Studies in Galatians. rev. ed. LC 72-81729. 144p. pap. 5.95 (ISBN 0-912145-06-4). MMI Pr.

Waghore, Joanne P. Images of Dharma: The Epic World of C. Rajagopalachari. 1985. 25.00x (ISBN 0-8364-1426-8, Pub. by Chanakya India). South Asia Bks.

Waghorne, Joanne Punzo, et al, eds. Gods of Flesh-Gods of Stone: The Embodiment of Divinity in India. LC 84-18543. (Orig.). 1985. pap. 12.95 (ISBN 0-89012-037-4). Anima Pubns.

Wagle, N. K., jt. ed. see Israel, Milton.

Wagler, Elizabeth. Evangelist in Chains. 8.95 (ISBN 0-318-00390-2). Rod & Staff.

Wagner, Al. Historical Records Concerning Jesus the Christ. 64p. 1984. 10.50 (ISBN 0-89962-347-6). Todd & Honeywell.

Wagner, C. P., ed. Church Growth: The State of the Art. 288p. 1986. pap. 9.95 (ISBN 0-8423-0287-5). Tyndale.

Wagner, C. Peter. Church Growth & the Whole Gospel: A Biblical Mandate. LC 81-47433. 224p. 1981. 13.00 (ISBN 0-06-068942-0, HarpR). Har-Row.

--Leading Your Church to Growth. LC 83-19272. 224p. 1984. pap. 6.95 (ISBN 0-8307-0922-3, 5418091). Regal.

--On the Crest of the Wave: Becoming a World Christian. LC 83-8616. 1983. pap. 5.95 (ISBN 0-8307-0895-2, 5418015). Regal.

--Your Church Can Be Healthy. LC 79-974. (Creative Leadership Ser.). 1979. pap. 7.50 (ISBN 0-687-46870-1). Abingdon.

--Your Church Can Grow. rev. ed. LC 84-8314. 1984. pap. 6.95 (ISBN 0-8307-0978-9, 5418284). Regal.

--Your Spiritual Gifts Can Help Your Church Grow. LC 78-53353. 272p. 1979. pap. 7.95 (ISBN 0-8307-0644-5, 5410606). Regal.

Wagner, C. Peter, jt. auth. see Christian Life Magazine Staff.

Wagner, C. Peter, jt. auth. see Dayton, Edward.

Wagner, C. Peter, jt. auth. see Waymire, Bob.

Wagner, C. Peter, et al. Unreached Peoples, Eighty-One. (Orig.). 1981. pap. 8.95 (ISBN 0-89191-331-9). Cook.

Wagner, Clarence M. The Bethlehem Mystery. (Orig.). 1981. 3.50 (ISBN 0-937498-03-3). Tru-Faith.

--Invisible & Invincible. 78p. 1982. pap. 4.00 (ISBN 0-937498-05-X). Tru-Faith.

--Profiles of Black Georgia Baptists. Bennett Brother's Printing, ed. (Illus.). 268p. 1981. pap. 12.95 (ISBN 0-686-30456-X). Tru-Faith.

--The Salt of the Earth. Tru-Faith Pub, ed. 80p. (Orig.). 1981. pap. 3.50x (ISBN 0-937498-01-7). Tru-Faith.

--The Same Jesus. Tru-Faith Publishers, ed. 72p. (Orig.). 1981. pap. 3.50x (ISBN 0-937498-00-9). Tru-Faith.

--Seeds of Faith. (Vol. 11). 100p. 1981. pap. 4.00x (ISBN 0-937498-02-5). Tru-Faith.

Wagner, Clarence M., ed. Heavens Overflow. 73p. pap. 4.00 (ISBN 0-937498-06-8). Tru-Faith.

Wagner, Donald, jt. ed. see Haddad, Hassan.

Wagner, Donald O. Church of England & Social Reform since 1854. LC 77-127438. (Columbia University. Studies in the Social Sciences: No. 325). 12.50 (ISBN 0-404-51325-5). AMS Pr.

Wagner, Doris M., ed. Missiological Abstracts. LC 84-82346. 180p. (Orig.). 1984. pap. text ed. write for info. (ISBN 0-9602638-3-7). Fuller Theol Soc.

Wagner, George. Practical Truths from Israel's Wanderings. LC 82-18706. 384p. 1983. 14.95 (ISBN 0-8254-4017-3). Kregel.

Wagner, Guenter. An Exegetical Bibliography of the New Testament: Vol. 1-Matthew & Mark. LC 83-969. (Bibliographical Tools for New Testament Studies). xviii, 668p. 1983. 35.00 (ISBN 0-86554-013-6, MUP-H26). Mercer Univ Pr.

Wagner, Gunter, ed. An Exegetical Bibliography of the New Testament, Vol. 2: Luke-Acts. xiv, 550p. 1986. 49.50 (ISBN 0-86554-140-X, MUP-H131). Mercer Univ Pr.

--An Exegetical Bibliography of the New Testament: Volume 3: John-1-2-3 John. 600p. 1987. 55.00 (ISBN 0-86554-157-4). Mercer Univ Pr.

Wagner, H. R. Rise of Fernando Cortes. (Cortes Society). 1944. 51.00 (ISBN 0-527-19733-5). Kraus Repr.

Wagner, Hans-Peter. Puritan Attitudes Towards Recreation in Early Seventeenth-Century New England, Vol. 17. (Mainzer Studien zur Internationalen Entwecklung). 273p. 1982. pap. 33.15 (ISBN 3-8204-7286-X). P Lang Pubs.

Wagner, James K. Blessed to Be a Blessing. LC 80-52615. 144p. (Orig.). 1980. pap. 5.95x (ISBN 0-8358-0410-0). Upper Room.

Wagner, James K., jt. auth. see Day, Albert E.

Wagner, Johannes, ed. Adult Baptism & the Catechumenate. LC 67-19979. (Concilium Ser.: Vol. 22). 204p. 1967. 7.95 (ISBN 0-8091-0000-2). Paulist Pr.

--Reforming the Rites of Death. LC 68-20845. (Concilium Ser.: Vol. 32). 189p. 7.95. Paulist Pr.

Wagner, Johannes, jt. ed. see Hucke, H.

Wagner, John C., jt. auth. see Sherwood, John R.

Wagner, Lilya. Heartquake. (Daybreak Ser.). 128p. 1983. pap. 4.95 (ISBN 0-8163-0510-2). Pacific Pr Pub Assn.

Wagner, Maurice. La Sensacion de Ser Alguien. Cook, David A., tr. from Eng. LC 77-16714. Tr. of The Sensation of Being Somebody. (Span.). 300p. 1977. pap. 6.50 (ISBN 0-89922-104-1). Edit Caribe.

--The Sensation of Being Somebody. 256p. 1975. 8.95 (ISBN 0-310-33970-7, 15603P). Zondervan.

Wagner, Maurice E. The Sensation of Being Somebody. 251p. 1985. pap. 8.95 (ISBN 0-310-33971-5). Zondervan.

Wagner, Melinda B. Metaphysics in Midwestern America. LC 83-2158. 241p. 1983. 20.00x (ISBN 0-8142-0346-9). Ohio St U Pr.

Wagner, Peter C. Strategies for Church Growth. 1987. 12.95 (ISBN 0-8307-1245-3, 5111756). Regal.

Wagner, Petti. Murdered Heiress, Living Witness. LC 84-80413. 211p. (Orig.). 1984. pap. 6.95 (ISBN 0-910311-09-9). Huntington Hse Inc.

Wagner, Richard. Judaism in Music. 1982. lib. bdg. 79.95 (ISBN 0-87700-354-8). Revisionist Pr.

Wagner, Richard K., jt. ed. see Sternberg, Robert J.

Wagner, Roy. Lethal Speech: Daribi Myth As Symbolic Obviation. LC 78-58049. (Symbol, Myth, & Ritual Ser). (Illus.). 272p. 1979. 27.50x (ISBN 0-8014-1193-9). Cornell U Pr.

--Symbols That Stand for Themselves. LC 85-16448. (Illus.). 1986. lib. bdg. 27.00x (ISBN 0-226-86928-8); pap. text ed. 9.95x (ISBN 0-226-86929-6). U of Chicago Pr.

Wagner, Rudolf G. Reenacting the Heavenly Vision: The Role of Religion in the Taping Rebellion. (China Research Monograph: No. 25). (Illus.). 146p. 1984. pap. 12.00x (ISBN 0-912966-60-2). IEAS.

Wagner, Stanley M., jt. auth. see Jospe, Raphael.

Wagner, Volker. Rechtssaetze in gebundener Sprache und Rechtssatzreihen im israelitischen Recht: Ein Beitrag zur Gattungsforschung. (Beiheft 127 zur Zeitschrift fuer die alttestamentliche Wissenschaft). 1972. 16.80x (ISBN 3-11-003945-1). De Gruyter.

Wagoner, R. & Goldsmith, D. Cosmic Horizons: Understanding the Universe. 250p. 1982. 22.95 (ISBN 0-7167-1417-5); pap. 12.95 (ISBN 0-7167-1418-3). W H Freeman.

Wagoner, Richard S. Van see Van Wagoner, Richard S.

Wagoner, Richard S. Van see Van Wagoner, Richard S. & Walker, Steven C.

Wahl, Jan, retold by. Runaway Jonah & Other Biblical Adventures Including Little Joseph, Singing David & Captain Noah. (Illus.). 96p. 1985. 13.95 (ISBN 0-89845-421-2). Caedmon.

Wahlberg, Rachel C. Jesus According to a Woman. LC 74-27461. 112p. 1975. pap. 4.95 (ISBN 0-8091-1861-0). Paulist Pr.

--Jesus & the Freed Woman. LC 78-61718. 176p. (Orig.). 1978. pap. 3.95 (ISBN 0-8091-2139-5). Paulist Pr.

Wahlie, Albert J. Believer's Tree of Life. Ben Menachem, Shmuel, ed. (Illus.). 105p. (Orig.). 1986. pap. 6.95x (ISBN 0-9616488-0-5). Alef Bet Comns.

Wahlie, Jim. The God Kind of Faith for Total Prosperity. 61p. 1986. pap. 3.95 (ISBN 0-88144-049-3). Christian Pub.

Wahlstrom, Eric H., tr. see Aulen, Gustaf.

Wahlstrom, Eric H., tr. see Aulen, Gustaf E.

Waibel, Paul R. Politics of Accommodation: German Social Democracy & the Catholic Church, 1945-1959. (European University Studies: No. 31, Vol. 35). 161p. 1983. pap. 23.15 (ISBN 3-8204-7270-3). P Lang Pubs.

Wailly, N. De see De Joinville, Jean.

Wainwright, Arthur. Beyond Biblical Criticism: Encountering Jesus Christ in the Scripture. LC 81-85327. 153p. 1982. pap. 4.99 (ISBN 0-8042-0007-6). John Knox.

Wainwright, Geoffrey. Doxology: The Praise of God in Worship, Doctrine & Life: A Systematic Theology. 1980. 35.00x (ISBN 0-19-520192-2); pap. 12.95 (ISBN 0-19-520433-6). Oxford U Pr.

--The Ecumenical Moment: Crisis & Opportunity for the Church. 272p. (Orig.). 1983. pap. 8.95 (ISBN 0-8028-1979-6). Eerdmans.

--Eucharist & Eschatology. 1981. 21.95x (ISBN 0-19-520248-1); pap. text ed. 8.95 (ISBN 0-19-520249-X). Oxford U Pr.

Wainwright, Geoffrey, jt. ed. see Thurian, Max.

Wainwright, William J. Mysticism. LC 81-50821. 264p. 1982. 40.00x (ISBN 0-299-08910-X). U of Wis Pr.

--Philosophy of Religion: An Annotated Bibliography of Twentieth-Century Writings in English. LC 77-83374. (Library of Humanities Reference Bks.: No. 111). lib. bdg. 83.00 (ISBN 0-8240-9849-8). Garland Pub.

Wainwright, William J., jt. ed. see Audi, Robert.

Wainwright, William J., jt. ed. see Rowe, William L.

Waite, A. E., ed. see Vaughan, Thomas.

Waite, A. E., tr. see Paracelsus.

Waite, Arthur E. Hidden Church of the Holy Graal. 710p. 1975. Repr. of 1909 ed. 12.00 (ISBN 0-911662-54-5). Yoga.

--The Holy Kabbalah. 636p. 1976. pap. 9.95 (ISBN 0-8065-0522-2). Citadel Pr.

--Holy Kabbalah: A Study of the Secret Tradition in Israel. 1960. 20.00 (ISBN 0-8216-0025-7). Univ Bks.

--Raymund Lully: Christian Mystic. 69.95 (ISBN 0-87968-100-4). Gordon Pr.

--Real History of the Rosicrucians, Vol. 20. LC 76-53632. (Spiritual Science Library). (Illus.). 456p. 1982. lib. bdg. 22.00 (ISBN 0-89345-018-9); pap. 14.00 (ISBN 0-89345-019-7). Garber Comm.

Waitley, Denis, jt. auth. see Tucker, Robert.

Waitley, Denis E. The Seeds of Greatness. 224p. 1983. 14.95 (ISBN 0-8007-1361-3); pap. 3.95 (ISBN 0-8007-8560-6). Revell.

Wajenberg, Arnold, jt. auth. see Gorecki, Danuta M.

Wake, Arthur N. Companion to Hymnbook for Christian Worship. LC 72-129621. 1970. 8.95 (ISBN 0-8272-8025-4). CBP.

Wake, C. Staniland. The Origin & Significance of the Great Pyramid. 2nd ed. LC 73-84047. (Secret Doctrine Reference Ser.). (Illus.). 170p. 1980. pap. 6.00 (ISBN 0-913510-32-7). Wizards.

Wake Forest University Law School. Law & Religion. 1985. 10.00 (ISBN 0-318-18444-3). Wake Forest Law.

Wakefield. Bible Basis for Christian Security. pap. 1.50 (ISBN 0-686-12851-6). Schmul Pub Co.

Wakefield, Gordon S., ed. The Westminster Dictionary of Christian Spirituality. LC 83-14527. 416p. 1983. 20.95 (ISBN 0-664-21396-0). Westminster.

Wakefield, John C. Artful Childmaking: Artificial Insemination in Catholic Teaching. LC 78-65765. 205p. 1978. pap. 8.95 (ISBN 0-935372-03-2). Pope john Ctr.

Wakefield, Ray M. Nibelungen Prosody. (De Proprietatibus Litterarum Ser.: No. 112). 1976. pap. 16.00x (ISBN 0-686-22366-7). Mouton.

Wakefield, Robert S., jt. auth. see Sherman, Ruth W.

Wakefield, Walter L. Heresy, Crusade, & Inquisition in Southern France, 1100-1250. 1974. 40.00x (ISBN 0-520-02380-3). U of Cal Pr.

Wakelyn, Jon L. & Miller, Randall M. Catholics in the Old South: Essays on Church & Culture. LC 83-7893. x, 262p. 1983. 15.95 (ISBN 0-86554-080-2, H74). Mercer Univ Pr.

Wakeman, Frank M. Psalms in Song for the White Cavalry. 3rd ed. (Illus.). 1979. 5.00 (ISBN 0-910840-19-9). Kingdom.

Wakeman, Henry O. Introduction to the History of the Church of England, from the Earliest Times to the Present Day. 7th ed. LC 77-137302. Repr. of 1908 ed. 32.50 (ISBN 0-404-06802-2). AMS Pr.

Wakin, Edward & Cooney, Sean. Beyond Loneliness. 112p. (Orig.). 1985. pap. 5.95 (ISBN 0-89622-248-9). Twenty-Third.

Wakin, Edward & Scheuer, Joseph F. The De-Romanization of the American Catholic Church. LC 78-10157. 1979. Repr. of 1966 ed. lib. bdg. 24.75x (ISBN 0-313-21238-4, WADE). Greenwood.

Wakin, Edward, jt. auth. see Brusselmans, Christiane.

Wakin, Edward, jt. auth. see Fahey, Charles J.

Walahfrid Strabo. Leben Des Heiligen Gallus & Des Abtes Otmar Von Sanktgallen. Potthast, A., tr. x, 86p. (Ger.). pap. 10.00 (ISBN 0-384-31951-3). Johnson Repr.

Walaskay, Paul W. And So We Came to Rome: The Political Perspectives of St. Luke. LC 82-19835. (Society for New Testament Studies Monograph: No. 49). (Illus.). 120p. 1984. 29.95 (ISBN 0-521-25116-8). Cambridge U Pr.

Walchars, John. Resurrection of Value. 176p. (Orig.). 1986. pap. 8.95 (ISBN 0-8245-0746-0). Crossroad NY.

--The Unfinished Mystery. (Orig.). 1978. pap. 5.95 (ISBN 0-8164-2184-6, HarpR). Har-Row.

--Voices on Fire: A Book of Meditations. LC 81-7767. 250p. 1981. pap. 7.95 (ISBN 0-8245-0094-6). Crossroad NY.

Walchenbach, John, jt. auth. see Battles, Ford L.

Wald, Kenneth D. Religion & Politics in the United States. LC 86-60659. 304p. 1986. 29.95 (ISBN 0-312-67058-3); pap. 10.00 (ISBN 0-312-67056-7). St Martin.

Wald, Oletta. Joy of Discovery in Bible Study. rev. ed. LC 75-22710. 96p. 1975. pap. 4.95 (ISBN 0-8066-1513-3, 10-3600). Augsburg.

--Joy of Teaching Discovery Bible Study. LC 76-3857. (Orig.). 1976. pap. 4.95 (ISBN 0-8066-1530-3, 10-3603). Augsburg.

Walden, Daniel, ed. Studies in American Jewish Literature: Isaac Bashevis Singer, 3 Vols. Incl. Vol. 1. A Mosaic of Jewish Writers; Vol. 3. Jewish Women Writers & Women in Jewish Literature; Vol. 2. From Marginality to Mainstream: A Mosaic of Jewish Writers; Vol. 4. The World of Chaim Potok. 1982. 12.95 ea. (ISBN 0-686-97287-2). State U NY Pr.

Walden, John. Bible Places: A Handbook to the Holy Land. 96p. 1984. pap. 4.95 (ISBN 0-8307-0933-9, 5018476). Regal.

Waldenfels, Hans. Absolute Nothingness: Foundations for a Buddhist-Christian Dialogue. Heisig, James W., tr. from Ger. LC 80-81442. Orig. Title: Absolutes Nichts. 224p. 1980. pap. 8.95 (ISBN 0-8091-2316-9). Paulist Pr.

Waldersee, James. Catholic Society in New South Wales 1788-1860. (Illus.). 348p. 1974. 31.00x (ISBN 0-424-06460-X, Pub. by Sydney U Pr). Intl Spec Bk.

Waldman, Marilyn Robinson, jt. ed. see McNeill, William H.

Waldman, Milton. Some English Dictators. LC 77-112820. 1970. Repr. of 1940 ed. 24.50x (ISBN 0-8046-1087-8, Pub.by Kennikat). Assoc Faculty Pr.

Waldo, Beach. Christmas Wonder: An Anthology of Verse & Song. LC 73-79038. pap. 24.00 (2026924). Bks Demand UMI.

Waldock, A. J. Paradise Lost & Its Critics. 11.50 (ISBN 0-8446-1463-7). Peter Smith.

Waldoks, Moshe, jt. auth. see Novak, William.

Waldron, John D. The Salvation Army & the Children. 135p. (Orig.). 1985. pap. 3.00 (ISBN 0-89216-060-8). Salvation Army.

--The Salvation Army & the Churches. 142p. (Orig.). 1986. pap. 3.95 (ISBN 0-89216-064-0). Salvation Army.

Waldrop, C. Sybil. Guiding Your Child Toward God. LC 84-14964. 1985. pap. 4.95 (ISBN 0-8054-5660-0). Broadman.

Waldrop, Charles T. Karl Barth's Christology: Its Basic Alexandrian Character. LC 84-20701. (Religion & Reason: Vol. 21). xvi, 265p. 1984. 52.50 (ISBN 90-279-3109-7). Mouton.

Waldrop, Claracy L. Unto Us. (Orig.). 1957. pap. 1.95 (ISBN 0-8054-9704-8). Broadman.

Waldrum, Harold J. Harold Joe Waldrum: Las Sombras de los Edificios Religiosos de Nuevo Mexico Norte. Maxon, Gayle & Hopkins, Quincie, eds. (Illus., Orig.). 1985. pap. 12.50 (ISBN 0-318-18712-4). Peters Corp NM.

--Harold Joe Waldrum: The Churches of Northern New Mexico. Maxon, Gayle & Hopkins, Quincie, eds. (Illus.). 34p. (Orig.). 1985. pap. 12.50 (ISBN 0-935037-01-2). Peters Corp NM.

Wales, H. G. Divination in Thailand: The Hope & Fears of a Southeast Asian People. 200p. 1981. 25.00x (ISBN 0-7007-0147-8, Pub. by Curzon England). State Mutual Bk.

Wales, Q. Divination in Thailand. 145p. 1983. text ed. 10.50x (ISBN 0-7007-0147-8, Pub. by Curzon Pr UK). Humanities.

Waley, Arthur, tr. The Temple, & Other Poems. LC 78-70137. Repr. of 1923 ed. 25.00 (ISBN 0-404-17407-8). AMS Pr.

Waley, Arthur, tr. see Confucius.

Waley, Arthur, tr. see Yuan, Ch'u.

Walf, Knut, jt. ed. see Huizing, Peter.

Walf, Knut, jt. ed. see Provost, James.

Walford, D. E., ed. see Cooper, A. A.

Walhout, Clarence, et al. The Responsibility of Hermeneutics. 160p. (Orig.). 1985. pap. 8.95x (ISBN 0-8028-0029-7). Eerdmans.

Walhout, Edwin. Revelation: A Study Guide. (Revelation Series for Adults). 1978. pap. text ed. 2.50 (ISBN 0-933140-07-X). CRC Pubns.

Walkenstein, Eileen. Your Inner Therapist. LC 83-19842. 128p. 1983. pap. 8.95 (ISBN 0-664-26005-5, A Bridgebooks Publication). Westminster.

Walker, Alan. Life in the Holy Spirit. LC 86-71315. 72p. 1986. pap. 3.95 (ISBN 0-88177-036-1, DR036B). Discipleship Res.

--Standing Up to Preach. LC 83-72736. 84p. (Orig.). 1983. pap. 3.95 (ISBN 0-88177-005-1, DR005B). Discipleship Res.

--Your Life Can Be Changed. LC 85-71706. 56p. (Orig.). 1985. pap. 2.95 (ISBN 0-88177-022-1, DR022B). Discipleship Res.

Walker, Barbara. The I Ching of the Goddess. LC 86-45029. (Illus.). 176p. (Orig.). 1986. pap. 12.95 (ISBN 0-06-250924-1, HarpR). Har-row.

Walker, Barbara G. The Secrets of the Tarot: Origins, History, & Symbolism. LC 84-47737. (Illus.). 256p. (Orig.). 1984. pap. 12.95 (ISBN 0-06-250927-6, CN 4102, HarpR). Har-Row.

--The Woman's Encyclopedia of Myths & Secrets. LC 83-47736. 1124p. (Orig.). 1983. 34.45 (ISBN 0-06-250926-8, HarpR); pap. 20.95 (ISBN 0-06-250925-X, CN 4066). Har-Row.

Walker, Benjamin. Gnosticism: Its History & Influence. 224p. 1984. pap. 9.95 (ISBN 0-85030-324-9). Newcastle Pub.

--Gnosticism: Its History & Influence. LC 86-34294. 320p. 1986. lib. bdg. 24.95x (ISBN 0-8095-7019-X). Borgo Pr.

--Hindu World: An Encyclopedic Survey of Hinduism, 2 vols. 1983. Set. text ed. 72.00x. Coronet Bks.

Walker, Catherine B. Bible Workbook: New Testament, Vol. 2. 1951. pap. 5.95 (ISBN 0-8024-0752-8). Moody.

--Bible Workbook: Old Testament, Vol. 1. 1943. pap. 5.95 (ISBN 0-8024-0751-X). Moody.

Walker, Clarence E. A Rock in a Weary Land: The African Methodist Episcopal Church During the Civil War & Reconstruction. LC 81-11743. 188p. 1981. 22.50x (ISBN 0-8071-0883-9). La State U Pr.

Walker, D. P. Unclean Spirits: Possession & Exorcism in France & England in the Late 16th & Early 17th Centuries. LC 80-22649. 1981. 18.95x (ISBN 0-8122-7797-X). U of Pa Pr.

Walker, David. God Is a Sea: The Dynamics of Christian Living. LC 81-8072. 144p. (Orig.). 1981. pap. 5.95 (ISBN 0-8189-0420-8). Alba.

Walker, Fintan G. The Catholic Church in the Meeting of Two Frontiers: The Southern Illinois Country (1763-1793) LC 73-3574. (Catholic University of America. Studies in American Church History: No. 19). Repr. of 1935 ed. 17.50 (ISBN 0-404-57769-5). AMS Pr.

Walker, Franklin. Irreverent Pilgrims: Melville, Browne & Mark Twain in the Holy Land. LC 74-10644. (Illus.). 246p. 1974. 16.50x (ISBN 0-295-95344-6). U of Wash Pr.

Walker, Gail. Spirits in His Parlor. LC 79-87733. (Destiny Ser.). 1980. pap. 4.95 (ISBN 0-8163-0387-8, 19499-3). Pacific Pr Pub Assn.

Walker, George A. Gatherings from Graveyards Particularly Those of London: With a Concise History of the Modes of Interment among Different Nations, from the Earliest Periods. Kastenaum, Robert, ed. LC 76-19591. (Death & Dying Ser.). 1977. Repr. of 1977 ed. lib. bdg. 25.50x (ISBN 0-405-09586-4). Ayer Co Pubs.

Walker, George L. Thomas Hooker: Preacher, Founder, Democrat. 1972. Repr. of 1891 ed. lib. bdg. 19.00 (ISBN 0-8422-8120-7). Irvington.

Walker, J. B. Walker's Comprehensive Bible Concordance. LC 76-15841. 1976. kivar 14.95 (ISBN 0-8254-4012-2). Kregel.

Walker, J. R. The Sun Dance & Other Ceremonies of the Oglala Division of the Teton Dakota. LC 76-43886. (AMNH Anthropological Papers: Vol. 16, Pt. 2). Repr. of 1917 ed. 21.50 (ISBN 0-404-15745-9). AMS Pr.

Walker, James R. Lakota Belief & Ritual. DeMallie, Raymond J. & Jahner, Elaine A., eds. LC 79-19816. (Illus.). xxx, 369p. 1980. 21.50 (ISBN 0-8032-2551-2). U of Nebr Pr.

--Lakota Myth. Jahner, Elaine A., ed. LC 83-3454. xiv, 428p. 1983. 29.95x (ISBN 0-8032-4726-5); pap. 14.95 (ISBN 0-8032-9706-8, BB 848, Bison). U of Nebr Pr.

Walker, Joe E. Money in the Church. LC 81-20583. (Into Our Third Century Ser.). (Orig.). 1982. pap. 3.95 (ISBN 0-687-27160-6). Abingdon.

Walker, John, jt. auth. see Deacon, John.

Walker, John P., ed. Dale Morgan on Early Mormonism: Correspondence & a New History. 350p. 1986. 22.95 (ISBN 0-941214-36-2). Signature Bks.

Walker, John P., ed. see Morgan, Dale L.

Walker, Joseph E., ed. Pleasure & Business in Western Pennsylvania: The Journal of Joshua Gilpin, 1809. LC 75-623536. (Illus.). 156p. 1975. 9.00 (ISBN 0-911124-78-0). Pa Hist & Mus.

Walker, K. R., ed. The Evolution-Creation Controversy Perspectives on Religion, Philosophy, Science & Education: A Handbook. (Paleontological Society Special Publications Ser.). (Illus.). 155p. pap. 6.50 (ISBN 0-931377-00-5). U of Tenn Geo.

Walker, Kenneth. Gurdjieff: A Study of His Teaching. (Unwin Paperbacks Ser.). 221p. (Orig.). 1980. pap. 5.95 (ISBN 0-04-294106-7). Allen Unwin.

--The Making of Man. 1963. 14.95 (ISBN 0-7100-2248-4). Methuen Inc.

Walker, Kenneth M. The Extra-Sensory Mind. LC 61-17460. pap. 64.00 (ISBN 0-317-10537-X, 2005153). Bks Demand UMI.

Walker, Lucille. What to Do When You Pray. LC 78-60948. 181p. 1983. pap. text ed. 6.95 (ISBN 0-87148-920-1). Pathway Pr.

Walker, Luisa J. Dynamic Evangelism. 1986. write for info. (ISBN 0-8297-0737-9). Life Pubs Intl.

Walker, Mary J. The F. Stanley Story. Lyon, Jene, ed. (Illus.). 98p. 1985. lib. bdg. 25.00 (ISBN 0-89016-082-1). Lightning Tree.

Walker, Mrs. Charles. That Ye May Abound. (Illus.). 80p. (Orig.). 1980. pap. 3.00 (ISBN 0-89114-096-4). Baptist Pub Hse.

Walker, Paul. How to Keep Your Joy. 192p. 1987. 12.95 (ISBN 0-8407-9076-7). Oliver-Nelson.

Walker, Paul L. Counseling Youth. 112p. 1967. 5.25 (ISBN 0-87148-162-6); pap. 4.25 (ISBN 0-87148-163-4). Pathway Pr.

--Faith in Action. LC 75-3504. (Illus.). 1975. pap. 1.99 (ISBN 0-87148-331-9). Pathway Pr.

--Is Christianity the Only Way? 1975. pap. 3.95 (ISBN 0-87148-429-3). Pathway Pr.

--Knowing the Future. LC 76-710. 1976. pap. 1.99 (ISBN 0-87148-477-3). Pathway Pr.

--The Ministry of the Church & Pastor. 107p. 1965. 5.25 (ISBN 0-87148-556-7); pap. 4.25 (ISBN 0-87148-557-5). Pathway Pr.

--The Ministry of Worship. LC 81-84605. 199p. (Orig.). 1981. pap. text ed. 5.95 (ISBN 0-87148-576-1). Pathway Pr.

--Understanding the Bible & Science. LC 75-25343. (Illus.). 1976. pap. 1.99 (ISBN 0-87148-878-7). Pathway Pr.

Walker, Paul L. & Conn, Charles P. Who Am I? LC 74-82934. 1974. pap. 1.99 (ISBN 0-87148-905-8). Pathway Pr.

Walker, Philip. Germinal & Zola's Philosophical & Religious Thought. (Purdue Univ. Monographs in Romance Languages: No. 14). 200p. (Orig.). pap. 28.00x (ISBN 90-272-1724-6). Benjamins North Am.

Walker, Ralph C. Kant. 1982. pap. 10.95 (ISBN 0-7100-0009-X). Methuen Inc.

Walker, Ralph C., ed. Kant on Pure Reason. (Illus.). 1982. pap. text ed. 7.95x (ISBN 0-19-875056-0). Oxford U Pr.

Walker, Ralph S. John Knox: Historia of the Reformation in Scotland. 72p. 1985. 22.00x (ISBN 0-85411-021-6, Pub. by Saltire Soc.). State Mutual Bk.

Walker, Randi J., ed. Kept by Grace: A Centennial History of First Congregational Church of Pasadena. 128p. (Orig.). 1986. text ed. 8.95 (ISBN 0-932727-10-7). Hope Pub Hse.

Walker, Raymond B. Beside Still Waters. LC 75-32601. (Illus.). 1975. 12.50 (ISBN 0-8323-0264-3). Binford-Metropolitan.

Walker, Scott. Where the Rivers Flow: Exploring the Sources of Faith Formation. 160p. 1986. 10.95 (ISBN 0-8499-0538-9, 0538-9). Word Bks.

Walker, Sheila S. Ceremonial Spirit Possession in Africa & Afro-America: Forms, Meanings & Functional Significance for Individuals & Social Groups. 179p. 1972. text ed. 37.50x (ISBN 90-040-3584-2). Humanities.

--The Religious Revolution in the Ivory Coast: The Prophet Harris & the Harris Church. LC 81-13010. (Studies in Religion). xvii, 206p. 1983. 29.95x (ISBN 0-8078-1503-9). U of NC Pr.

Walker, Shoshana. Haggadah. 104p. 1982. 24.95 (ISBN 965-220-017-4, Carta Maps & Guides Pub Isreal). Hippocrene Bks.

Walker, Steven C., jt. auth. see Van Wagoner, Richard S.

Walker, Susan, ed. Speaking of Silence: Christians & Buddhists on the Contemplative Way. 1987. pap. 14.95. Paulist Pr.

Walker, Thomas T. Jewish Views of Jesus: An Introduction & an Appreciation. LC 73-2229. (The Jewish People; History, Religion, Literature Ser.). Repr. of 1931 ed. 16.00 (ISBN 0-405-05290-1). Ayer Co Pubs.

Walker, William O., Jr., ed. see Outler, Albert C., et al.

Walker, Williston. Great Men of the Christian Church. facs. ed. LC 68-8502. (Essay Index Reprint Ser). 1908. 22.00 (ISBN 0-8369-0966-6). Ayer Co Pubs.

--A History of the Christian Church. 4th ed. 1985. text ed. write for info. (ISBN 0-02-423870-8, Pub. by Scribner). Macmillan.

--A History of the Christian Church. 3rd, rev. ed. Handy, Robert T., rev. by. 601p. 1970. text ed. write for info. (ISBN 0-02-424300-0, Pub. by Scribner). Macmillan.

--John Calvin: The Organiser of Reformed Protestantism, 1509-1564. Repr. of 1906 ed. 27.50 (ISBN 0-404-06807-3). AMS Pr.

--Ten New England Leaders. LC 76-83445. (Religion in America Ser). 1969. Repr. of 1901 ed. 28.00 (ISBN 0-405-00278-5). Ayer Co Pubs.

Walker, Williston, jt. auth. see Smyth, Norman.

Walker, Williston, ed. Creeds & Platforms of Congregationalism. LC 60-14698. 1960. 10.95 (ISBN 0-8298-0034-4). Pilgrim NY.

Walker, Winifred. All the Plants of the Bible. LC 78-22802. (Illus.). 1979. Repr. of 1957 ed. 15.95 (ISBN 0-385-14964-6). Doubleday.

Wall, Barbara, tr. see Carretto, Carlo.

Wall, Betty J. Going Through God. 277p. pap. 7.95 (ISBN 0-942494-36-9). Coleman Pub.

Wall, George B. Is God Really Good? Conversations with a Theodicist. LC 82-24854. 130p. (Orig.). 1983. pap. text ed. 9.50 (ISBN 0-8191-3032-X). U Pr of Amer.

--Looking unto Jesus. 160p. 1986. pap. 7.95 (ISBN 0-8170-1098-X). Judson.

Wall, J. C. Devils. 59.95 (ISBN 0-8490-0025-4). Gordon Pr.

Wall, James, et al. A Century of the Century. 128p. (Orig.). 1987. pap. 8.95 (ISBN 0-8028-0180-3). Eerdmans.

Wall, James M., ed. Theologians in Transition. 288p. 1981. 14.95 (ISBN 0-8245-0101-2); pap. 7.95 (ISBN 0-8245-0103-9). Crossroad NY.

Wall, James T. From the Law of Moses to the Magna Carta: Essays in Ancient & Medieval History. LC 79-66236. 1979. pap. text ed. 9.50 (ISBN 0-8191-0801-4). U Pr of Amer.

Wall, John N., ed. George Herbert: The Country Parson & the Temple. LC 81-80287. (Classics of Western Spirituality Ser.). 384p. 13.95 (ISBN 0-8091-0317-6); pap. 10.95 (ISBN 0-8091-2298-7). Paulist Pr.

Wall, John N., Jr. A New Dictionary for Episcopalians. 168p. (Orig.). 1985. pap. 7.95 (ISBN 0-86683-787-6, HarpR). Har-Row.

Wall, O. A. Eroticism in Religions of the World. (Illus.). xv, 608p. 1986. Repr. text ed. 75.00 (ISBN 81-7047-015-3, Pub. by Mayur Pubns India). Apt Bks.

Wall, Ronald E. Sermons on Prayer. (Pulpit Library). 144p. 1986. pap. 6.95 (ISBN 0-8010-9672-3). Baker Bk.

Wallace, Alston M., Jr. Guides to the Reformed Tradition: The Church. Leith, John H. & Kuykendall, John W., eds. LC 83-49052. 204p. 1984. pap. 10.95 (ISBN 0-8042-3253-9). John Knox.

Wallace, Anthony F. Religion: An Anthropological View. 1966. text ed. 16.00 (ISBN 0-394-30543-4, RanC). Random.

Wallace, Anthony F., ed. see Mooney, James.

Wallace, Archer. Religious Faith of Great Men. facs. ed. LC 67-26792. (Essay Index Reprint Ser). 1934. 17.00 (ISBN 0-8369-0968-2). Ayer Co Pubs.

Wallace, Arthur. LDS Roots in Egypt. 63p. 1981. pap. 3.50x (ISBN 0-937892-08-4). LL Co.

Wallace, Arthur, jt. auth. see Vestal, Kirk H.

Wallace, Arthur, compiled by. America's Witness for Jesus Christ. 70p. 1978. pap. 1.95x (ISBN 0-937892-04-1). LL Co.

--L. D. S. Children's Comments, Vol. 1. 60p. 1978. pap. 1.95x (ISBN 0-937892-03-3). LL Co.

Wallace, Dewey D., Jr. Puritans & Predestination: Grace in English Protestant Theology, 1525 to 1695. LC 81-11563. (Studies in Religion). xiii, 289p. 1982. 29.95x (ISBN 0-8078-1499-7). U of NC Pr.

Wallace, Doris. Lamp unto My Feet. LC 83-91018. 49p. 1985. 5.95 (ISBN 0-533-06008-7). Vantage.

Wallace, Edwin S. Jerusalem the Holy: History of Ancient Jerusalem with an Account of the Modern City & Its Conditions Political, Religious & Social. Davis, Moshe, ed. LC 77-70753. (America & the Holy Land Ser.). (Illus.). 1977. Repr. of 1898 ed. lib. bdg. 30.00x (ISBN 0-405-10298-4). Ayer Co Pubs.

Wallace, Eugene V. The History of the Reformation in Italy, 2 vols. (Illus.). 393p. 1987. Repr. of 1843 ed. Set. 189.75 (ISBN 0-89901-317-1). Found Class Reprints.

Wallace, H. A., et al. Christian Bases of World Order. facsimile ed. LC 75-134068. (Essay Index Reprint Ser). (Merrick Lectures, 1943). Repr. of 1943 ed. 19.00 (ISBN 0-8369-2490-8). Ayer Co Pubs.

Wallace, Howard N. The Eden Narrative. (Harvard Semitic Museum Monograph). 1985. 16.95 (ISBN 0-89130-838-5, 04-00-32). Scholars Pr GA.

Wallace, James. The Ministry of Lectors. 48p. 1981. softcover 1.25 (ISBN 0-8146-1229-6). Liturgical Pr.

Wallace, James A. Preaching Through the Saints. LC 82-7745. 80p. 1982. pap. 2.50 (ISBN 0-8146-1271-7). Liturgical Pr.

Wallace, James D. Heirs of the Cross. 98p. (Orig.). 1984. pap. 3.25 (ISBN 0-934942-43-9, 2022). White Wing Pub.

--Virtues & Vices. LC 77-90912. (Contemporary Philosophy Ser.). 208p. 1986. pap. 7.95x (ISBN 0-8014-9372-2). Cornell U Pr.

Wallace, Joanne. Image of Loveliness. (Illus.). 160p. 1978. pap. 5.95 (ISBN 0-8007-5134-5, Power Bks). Revell.

Wallace, Joyce. A Closer Walk. LC 82-99994. 128p. 1982. pap. 4.00 (ISBN 0-686-38098-3). Foun Christ Serv.

Wallace, Lew. Ben Hur. (Classics Ser). (YA) pap. 2.95 (ISBN 0-8049-0074-4, CL-74). Airmont.

Wallace, Mary, ed. see Adams, Jennifer K.

Wallace, Mary, ed. see Haney, Joy.

Wallace, Mary, ed. see Haney, Kenneth F.

Wallace, Mary, ed. see Herrmann, Robert A.

Wallace, Mary, ed. see Knott, Ron.

Wallace, Mary, ed. see Putnam, Joanne.

Wallace, Mary, ed. see Segraves, Daniel.

Wallace, Mary, ed. see Segraves, Judy.

Wallace, Mary, ed. see Yadon, Loren A.

Wallace, Mary, et al. Total Teaching for Today's Church. rev. ed. Orig. Title: Centers of Interest. (Illus.). 200p. (Orig.). 1985. pap. 6.95 (ISBN 0-912315-85-7). Word Aflame.

Wallace, Mary H. It's Real. (Illus.). 224p. (Orig.). 1981. pap. 5.95 (ISBN 0-912315-17-2). Word Aflame.

--My Name Is Christian Woman. LC 85-31575. (Illus., Orig.). 1982. pap. 6.95 (ISBN 0-912315-20-2). Word Aflame.

--Pioneer Pentecostal Women. (Pioneer Pentecostal Women Ser.: Vol. 1). (Illus.). 272p. (Orig.). 1983. pap. 5.95 (ISBN 0-912315-18-0). Word Aflame.

--Pioneer Pentecostal Women. LC 85-20981. (Pioneer Pentecostal Women: Vol. II). (Illus.). 288p. (Orig.). 1981. pap. 5.95 (ISBN 0-912315-19-9). Word Aflame.

--Profiles of Pentecostal Missionaries. LC 86-15919. (Illus.). 352p. (Orig.). 1986. pap. 6.95 (ISBN 0-932581-00-5). Word Aflame.

--Profiles of Pentecostal Preachers, Vol. II. LC 84-51290. (Illus.). 398p. (Orig.). 1984. pap. 6.95 (ISBN 0-912315-71-7). Word Aflame.

Wallace, Mary H., jt. auth. see Cagle, Paul R., Jr.

Wallace, Mary H., compiled by. God Answers Prayer. LC 85-22484. (Illus.). 368p. (Orig.). 1986. pap. 6.95 (ISBN 0-912315-90-3). Word Aflame.

Wallace, Mary H., ed. Harvestime Guest Pulpit Library, Vol. 1. 432p. (Orig.). 1982. pap. 6.95 (ISBN 0-912315-14-8). Word Aflame.

--Harvestime Pulpit Library: Let Them Know, Vol. 2. (Illus.). 379p. (Orig.). 1984. pap. 8.95 (ISBN 0-912315-67-9). Word Aflame.

--Profiles of Pentecostal Preachers, Vol. I. LC 84-51290. (Illus.). 281p. (Orig.). 1983. pap. 5.95 (ISBN 0-912315-63-6). Word Aflame.

Wallace, Mary H., ed. see Adams, Carl & McElhaney, Dolly.

Wallace, Mary H., ed. see Bernard, David K.

Wallace, Mary H., ed. see Fauss, O. F.

Wallace, Mary H., ed. see Foster, Fred J.

Wallace, Mary H., ed. see Freeman, Nona.

Wallace, Mary H., ed. see Gamblin, Eleanor & Morehouse, Joyce M.

Wallace, Mary H., ed. see Jackson, Sue B.

Wallace, Mary H., ed. see Martin, LaJoyce.

Wallace, Mary H., ed. see Moore, Gary.

Wallace, Mary H., ed. see Morgan, Nell & Chambers, Catherine.

Wallace, Mary H., ed. see Morley, Lewis H.

Wallace, Mary H., ed. see Patterson, Chuck.

Wallace, Mary H., ed. see Pugh, Nathanael.

Wallace, Mary H., ed. see Reeves, Kenneth V.

Wallace, Mary H., ed. see Reynolds, Ralph V.

Wallace, Mary H., ed. see Urshan, Nathaniel A. & Becton, Cleveland M.

Wallace, Mary H., ed. see Westberg, Barbara.

Wallace, Mary K., ed. see Bernard, David K.

Wallace, Ralph J. What Does He Mean by "A Little While?". (Orig.). 1981. pap. 5.95 (ISBN 0-937172-30-8). JLJ Pubs.

Wallace, Raymond P., jt. ed. see Francis, Fred O.

Wallace, Robert. Various Prospects of Mankind, Nature & Providence. LC 69-19550. 1969. Repr. of 1761 ed. 39.50x (ISBN 0-678-00491-9). Kelley.

Wallace, Robert Burns. An Introduction to the Bible As Literature. 1929. 20.00 (ISBN 0-8274-2583-X). R West.

Wallace, Robert M., tr. see Blumenberg, Hans.

Wallace, Ronald. The Atoning Death of Christ. LC 81-65758. (Foundations for Faith Ser.). 192p. (Orig.). 1981. pap. 8.95 (ISBN 0-89107-222-5, Crossway Bks). Good News.

Wallace, Ronald S. Calvin's Doctrine of the Word & Sacraments. xii, 253p. 1982. pap. 12.95 (ISBN 0-939404-02-8). Geneva Ministr.

--The Message of Daniel. LC 79-1996. (Bible Speaks Today Ser.). 1979. pap. 6.95 (ISBN 0-87784-285-X). Inter-Varsity.

Wallace, Samuel E. After Suicide. LC 73-9793. Repr. of 1973 ed. 71.30 (ISBN 0-8357-9833-X, 2012586). Bks Demand UMI.

Wallace, Tay. Ministering to the Sick. 60p. (Orig.). 1981. pap. 3.00 (ISBN 0-933643-06-3). Grace World Outreach.

--Prison Ministry Training Manual. (Illus.). 44p. (Orig.). 1981. pap. 3.00 (ISBN 0-933643-08-X). Grace World Outreach.

Wallace, William A. The Elements of Philosophy: A Compendium for Philosophers & Theologians. LC 77-1527. 1977. pap. 10.95 (ISBN 0-8189-0345-7). Alba.

Wallace-Hadrill, D. S. Christian Antioch: A Study of Early Christian Thought in the East. 240p. 1982. 37.50 (ISBN 0-521-23425-5). Cambridge U Pr.

Wallace-Hadrill, J. M. The Frankish Church. LC 83-13051. (Oxford History of the Chri). 1983. 59.95x (ISBN 0-19-826906-4). Oxford U Pr.

Wallach, Luitpold. Alcuin & Charlemagne: Studies in Carolingian History & Literature. Repr. of 1959 ed. 23.00 (ISBN 0-384-65585-8). Johnson Repr.

Wallach, Sidney, jt. auth. see Sobel, Ronald.

Wallack, F. Bradford. The Epochal Nature of Process in Whitehead's Metaphysics. LC 79-22898. 1980. 44.50x (ISBN 0-87395-404-1); pap. 16.95 (ISBN 0-87395-454-8). State U NY Pr.

Wallacker, Benjamin E. The Huai-nan-tzu, Book Eleven: Behavior, Culture, & the Cosmos. (American Oriental Ser.: Vol. 48). 1962. pap. 5.00x (ISBN 0-940490-48-X). Am Orient Soc.

Wallas, Graham. Life of Francis Place. 1898. 21.00 (ISBN 0-8337-3674-4). B Franklin.

Wallbridge, Edwin A. Demerara Martyr: Memoirs of the Reverend John Smith, Missionary to Demerara. LC 70-79812. (Illus.). Repr. of 1848 ed. 22.50x (ISBN 0-8371-1511-6, WAD&, Pub. by Negro U Pr). Greenwood.

Walle, A. R. van de see Van de Walle, A. R.

Walle, Grace, jt. auth. see O'Hara, Jim.

Wallenkampf, Arnold V. Salvation Comes from the Lord. Wheeler, Gerald, ed. LC 83-3297. 128p. (Orig.). 1983. pap. 5.95 (ISBN 0-8280-0210-X). Review & Herald.

Wallenrod, Reuben. The Literature of Modern Israel. LC 80-12709. 256p. 1980. Repr. of 1956 ed. lib. bdg. 20.00x (ISBN 0-374-98198-1, Octagon). Hippocrene Bks.

Waller, George M., ed. Puritanism in Early America. 2nd ed. (Problems in American Civilization Ser.). 1973. pap. text ed. 5.95 (ISBN 0-669-82719-3). Heath.

Waller, William C., jt. ed. see Minet, William.

Waller, William C. see Peet, Henry.

Wallerstein, Judith S. & Kelly, Joan B. Surviving the Breakup: How Children & Parents Cope with Divorce. 1982. pap. 9.95x (ISBN 0-465-08339-0, TB-5094). Basic.

Walles, Dwight, illus. Patchwork: Stories, Poems & Meditations for Mothers. (Illus.). 1987. 6.95. Cook.

Walling, Regis. When Pregnancy Is a Problem. LC 79-51280. (When Book Ser.). (Illus.). 1980. pap. 2.45 (ISBN 0-87029-152-1, 20235-8). Abbey.

Wallinga, Robert. God's Church in Today's World 1. pap. 2.25 (ISBN 0-686-14196-2). Rose Pub MI.

--God's Church in Today's World 2. pap. 2.25 (ISBN 0-686-14197-0). Rose Pub MI.

--Hand in Hand with Jesus: A New Study Guide for Today's Youth. pap. 2.25 (ISBN 0-686-14194-6); tchrs' ed. 0.75 (ISBN 0-686-14195-4). Rose Pub MI.

Wallingford, Kay, jt. auth. see Riddell, Carole.

Wallington, Nellie U. Historic Churches of America. LC 77-85628. 1977. Repr. of 1907 ed. lib. bdg. 25.00 (ISBN 0-89341-227-9). Longwood Pub Group.

Wallis, Arthur. El Ayuno Escogido por Dios. 176p. 1974. 2.95 (ISBN 0-88113-006-0). Edit Betania.

--Desafio a Triunfar. 128p. 1976. 2.50 (ISBN 0-88113-000-1). Edit Betania.

--Into Battle. 1973. pap. 2.95 (ISBN 0-87508-560-1). Chr Lit.

--Jesus of Nazareth, Who Is He. 1959. pap. 1.50 (ISBN 0-87508-558-X). Chr Lit.

--Jesus Prayed. 1966. pap. 1.50 (ISBN 0-87508-559-8). Chr Lit.

--Orad en el Espiritu. LC 82-23203. 144p. 1975. 2.75 (ISBN 0-88113-240-3). Edit Betania.

--Pray in the Spirit. 1970. pap. 2.95 (ISBN 0-87508-561-X). Chr Lit.

--The Radical Christian. 160p. 1982. pap. 5.95 (ISBN 0-8007-5081-0, Power Bks). Revell.

Wallis, Betty, jt. auth. see Wallis, Charles.

Wallis, Charles & Wallis, Betty. Our Christian Home & Family: An Illustrated Treasury of Inspirational Quotations, Poems & Prayers. LC 82-47758. (Illus.). 1982. 14.45 (ISBN 0-06-069009-7, HarpR). Har-Row.

Wallis, Charles G., et al, trs. see Pico Della Mirandola, Giovanni.

Wallis, Charles L., ed. Words of Life. 5th ed. LC 81-47850. (Illus.). 256p. 1982. 12.50 (ISBN 0-06-069239-1, HarpR). Har-Row.

Wallis, Charles L., compiled by. Treasury of Story Sermons for Children. (Charles L. Wallis Library Pulpit Helps). 290p. 1974. pap. 6.95 (ISBN 0-8010-9556-5). Baker Bk.

Wallis, E. W. Spiritualism in the Bible. 59.95 (ISBN 0-8490-1116-7). Gordon Pr.

Wallis, Jim. Agenda for Biblical People. rev. ed. LC 83-48995. 160p. 1984. pap. 6.95 (ISBN 0-06-069234-0, RD 514, HarpR). Har-Row.

--Call to Conversion: Recovering the Gospel for These Times. LC 80-8901. 208p. 1983. pap. 9.95 (ISBN 0-686-92025-2, RD414, HarpR). Har-Row.

--Peacemakers: Christian Voices from the New Abolitionist Movement. LC 82-48940. 160p. (Orig.). 1983. pap. 5.95 (ISBN 0-06-069244-8, CN-4058, HarpR). Har-Row.

Wallis, John E. A History of the Church of Blackburnshire. (Church Historical Society London, New Ser.: No. 7). Repr. of 1932 ed. 40.00 (ISBN 0-8115-3131-7). Kraus Repr.

Wallis, Louis. The Bible Is Human. LC 74-149677. Repr. of 1942 ed. 24.00 (ISBN 0-404-06814-6). AMS Pr.

Wallis, Reginald. New Boy. pap. 1.00 (ISBN 0-87213-910-7). Loizeaux.

Wallis, Roy. The Elementary Forms of the New Religious Life. LC 83-11092. (International Library of Sociology). 171p. 1984. 26.95x (ISBN 0-7100-9890-1). Methuen Inc.

--The Road to Total Freedom. LC 76-27273. 1977. 32.00x (ISBN 0-231-04200-0). Columbia U Pr.

--Salvation & Protest: Studies of Social & Religious Movements. 1979. 26.00x (ISBN 0-312-69834-8). St Martin.

Wallis, Wilson D. Culture Patterns in Christianity. 176p. 1964. 9.50x (ISBN 0-87291-053-9). Coronado Pr.

Wallis-Budge, E. A., tr. The Bandlet of Righteousness: An Ethiopian Book of the Dead. (Coptic.). 1984. pap. 3.95 (ISBN 0-916411-23-0, Near Eastern). Holmes Pub.

Wallis Budge, Ernest A., tr. see Anan Isho.

Wallraff, Charles F. Karl Jaspers: An Introduction to His Philosophy. 1970. 27.50 (ISBN 0-691-07164-0); pap. 10.50 (ISBN 0-691-01971-1). Princeton U Pr.

Walls, Francine E. The Church Library Workbook. 144p. 1980. pap. 8.95 (ISBN 0-89367-048-0). Light & Life.

Walpole, Arthur S. Early Latin Hymns. 473p. Repr. of 1922 ed. lib. bdg. 68.50X (Pub. by G Olms BRD). Coronet Bks.

Walpole, Margaret. Walking into the Morning. 48p. 1986. 6.95 (ISBN 0-8378-5093-2). Gibson.

Walpot, Peter. True Surrender & Christian Community of Goods, 1521-1578. 1957. pap. 4.00 (ISBN 0-87486-205-1). Plough.

Walrath, Douglas A. Frameworks: Patterns for Living & Believing Today. 160p. (Orig.). 1987. pap. 8.95 (ISBN 0-8298-0743-8). Pilgrim NY.

--Leading Churches Through Change. LC 79-4456. (Creative Leadership Ser.). 1979. pap. 6.95 (ISBN 0-687-21270-7). Abingdon.

--New Possibilities for Small Churches. 120p. (Orig.). 1983. pap. 7.95 (ISBN 0-8298-0668-7). Pilgrim NY.

Walsh, Albert J. Reflections on Death & Grief. 96p. 1986. 4.50 (ISBN 0-8010-9673-1). Baker Bk.

Walsh, Ann, jt. ed. see Pearson, J. D.

Walsh, Brian J. & Middleton, J. Richard. The Transforming Vision: Shaping a Christian World View. LC 84-15646. 240p. (Orig.). 1984. pap. 6.95 (ISBN 0-87784-973-0). Inter-Varsity.

Walsh, Chad. C. S. Lewis: Apostle to the Skeptics. LC 78-689. 1974. Repr. of 1949 ed. lib. bdg. 32.50 (ISBN 0-8414-9647-1). Folcroft.

--Early Christians of the Twenty-First Century. LC 78-138136. 188p. 1972. Repr. of 1950 ed. lib. bdg. 22.50x (ISBN 0-8371-5709-9, WACH). Greenwood.

--Knock & Enter. (Orig.). 1953. pap. 4.95 (ISBN 0-8192-1076-5). Morehouse.

--The Psalm of Christ: Forty Poems on the Twenty-Second Psalm. LC 82-5566. (Wheaton Literary Ser.). 74p. 1982. pap. 5.95 (ISBN 0-87788-700-4). Shaw Pubs.

Walsh, Chad, ed. The Visionary Christian: One Hundred & Thirty-One Readings from C. S. Lewis. 288p. 1984. 5.95 (ISBN 0-02-086730-1, Collier). Macmillan.

Walsh, Colin. The Grown-Up's Xmas Book. 128p. 1986. pap. 7.95 (ISBN 0-907621-44-9, Pub. by Quiller Pr England). Intl Spec Bk.

Walsh, David. Getting in Touch with Yourself-&-Your Parents. 1982. pap. 4.25 (ISBN 0-86716-009-8). St Anthony Mess Pr.

--Growing up Together: A Spiritual Perspective for Parents of Adolescents. 124p. (Orig.). 1980. pap. 2.50 (ISBN 0-912228-73-3). St Anthony Mess Pr.

--The Mysticism of Innerworldly Fulfillment: A Study of Jacob Boehme. LC 83-6554. (University of Florida Humanities Monographs: No. 53). x, 142p. (Orig.). 1983. pap. 12.50 (ISBN 0-8130-0751-8). U Presses Fla.

Walsh, Donald D., tr. see Cabestrero, Teofilo.

Walsh, Donald D., tr. see Cardenal, Ernesto.

Walsh, Donald E., tr. see Pixley, George V.

Walsh, Donaldly, tr. see Scharper, Philip & Sharper, Sally.

Walsh, Henry H. Concordat of 1801. LC 34-12835. (Columbia University. Studies in the Social Sciences: No. 387). Repr. of 1933 ed. 21.00 (ISBN 0-404-51387-5). AMS Pr.

Walsh, J. J. American Jesuits. 59.95 (ISBN 0-87968-605-7). Gordon Pr.

--Our American Cardinals. 59.95 (ISBN 0-8490-0782-8). Gordon Pr.

Walsh, J. P. The Mighty from Their Thrones: Power in the Biblical Tradition. LC 86-45198. (Overtures to Biblical Theology Ser.). 224p. 1987. pap. 12.95 (ISBN 0-8006-1546-8). Fortress.

Walsh, James, jt. auth. see Colledge, Edmund.

Walsh, James, jt. auth. see Walsh, P. G.

Walsh, James, ed. The Cloud of Unknowing. (Classics of Western Spirituality Ser.). 1981. 12.95 (ISBN 0-8091-0314-1); pap. 9.95 (ISBN 0-8091-2332-0). Paulist Pr.

--Pre-Reformation English Spirituality. LC 65-12885. 1966. 20.00 (ISBN 0-8232-0655-6). Fordham.

Walsh, James, tr. A Letter of Private Direction. 1979. pap. 5.95 (ISBN 0-87243-083-9). Templegate.

Walsh, James, tr. see Guigo II.

Walsh, James J. American Jesuits. facs. ed. LC 68-29251. (Essay Index Reprint Ser). 1934. 18.25 (ISBN 0-8369-0970-4). Ayer Co Pubs.

--Catholic Churchmen in Science, First Ser. facs. ed. LC 68-16985. (Essay Index Reprint Ser). 1906. 19.00 (ISBN 0-8369-0971-2). Ayer Co Pubs.

--Catholic Churchmen in Science, Second Ser. facs. ed. LC 67-22126. (Essay Index Reprint Ser.). 1909. 19.00 (ISBN 0-8369-1387-6). Ayer Co Pubs.

--Catholic Churchmen in Science, Third Ser. facs. ed. LC 67-22126. (Essay Index Reprint Ser). 1917. 19.00 (ISBN 0-8369-0972-0). Ayer Co Pubs.

--Our American Cardinals. facs. ed. LC 68-58815. (Essay Index Reprint Ser). 1926. 23.75 (ISBN 0-8369-1072-9). Ayer Co Pubs.

--The Popes & Science. 1977. lib. bdg. 59.95 (ISBN 0-8490-2454-4). Gordon Pr.

Walsh, James J., jt. ed. see Hyman, Arthur.

Walsh, James J., compiled by. These Splendid Priests. facs. ed. LC 68-29252. (Essay Index Reprint Ser). 1968. Repr. of 1926 ed. 17.00 (ISBN 0-8369-0973-9). Ayer Co Pubs.

--These Splendid Sisters. LC 75-128326. (Essay Index Reprint Ser). 1927. 18.00 (ISBN 0-8369-1856-8). Ayer Co Pubs.

Walsh, John. Church on Parade. LC 83-62517. 1984. pap. 7.95 (ISBN 0-89390-053-2). Resource Pubns.

--Evangelization & Justice: New Insights for Christian Ministry. LC 82-6279. 128p. (Orig.). 1982. pap. 6.95 (ISBN 0-88344-109-8). Orbis Bks.

Walsh, John & DiGiacomo, James. Going Together: The Church of Christ. (The Encounter Ser.). (Illus.). 1978. pap. text ed. 4.50 (ISBN 0-03-042771-1, HarpR); resource manual 1.95 (ISBN 0-03-042776-2). Har-Row.

Walsh, John E. Bones of St. Peter: Fascinating Account of the Search for the Apostle's Body. LC 80-2883. (Illus.). 216p. 1985. 7.95 (ISBN 0-385-15039-3, Im). Doubleday.

Walsh, Katherine. A Fourteenth-Century Scholar & Primate: Richard FitzRalph in Oxford, Avignon, & Armagh. (Illus.). 1981. 65.00x (ISBN 0-19-822637-3). Oxford U Pr.

Walsh, Katherine & Wood, Diana, eds. The Bible in the Medieval World: Essays in Memory of Beryl Smalley. (Studies in Church History: Subsidia 4). 352p. 1985. 45.00x (ISBN 0-631-14275-4). Basil Blackwell.

Walsh, Kilian, tr. Bernard of Clairvaux on the Song of Songs, Vol. I. (Cistercian Fathers Er.: No. 4). pap. 5.00 (ISBN 0-87907-104-4). Cistercian Pubns.

Walsh, Kilian & Edmonds, Irene, trs. Bernard of Clairvaux: Sermons on the Song of Songs, Vol. III. (Cistercian Fathers Ser.: No. 31). 1979. 15.95 (ISBN 0-87907-131-1); pap. 5.00 (ISBN 0-87907-931-2). Cistercian Pubns.

Walsh, Kilian, tr. see Bernard Of Clairvaux.

Walsh, Michael. An Illustrated History of the Popes: St. Peter to John Paul II. (Illus.). 256p. 1980. 19.95 (ISBN 0-312-40817-X). St Martin.

Walsh, Michael, ed. Butler's Lives of the Saints. LC 84-48781. 496p. 1985. 20.45 (ISBN 0-06-069251-0, HarpR). Har-Row.

Walsh, Michael & Davies, Brian, eds. Proclaiming Justice & Peace: Documents from John XXIII to John Paul II. 370p. 1985. 16.95 (ISBN 0-89622-239-X); pap. 12.95 (ISBN 0-89622-236-5). Twenty Third.

Walsh, Michael J. Vatican City-State. (World Bibliographical Ser.: No. 41). 105p. 1983. lib. bdg. 22.00 (ISBN 0-903450-72-0). ABC-Clio.

Walsh, P. G. & Walsh, James. Divine Providence & Human Suffering. (Message of the Fathers of the Church Ser.: Vol. 17). 1985. 15.95 (ISBN 0-89453-357-6); pap. 10.95 (ISBN 0-89453-328-2). M Glazier.

Walsh, P. G., tr. see Quasten, J.

Walsh, Roger N., jt. ed. see Shapiro, Deane H., Jr.

Walsh, Sheila. Never Give It up. 1987. pap. 6.95. Revell.

Walsh, Vincent M. Gathering the Fragments. 64p. 1980. pap. 1.00 (ISBN 0-943374-01-4). Key of David.

--A Key to Charismatic Renewal in the Catholic Church. LC 74-82238. 286p. 1974. pap. 6.00 (ISBN 0-686-32791-8). Key of David.

--Key to the Catholic Pentecostal Renewal, Vol. 2. 232p. 1985. pap. 8.00 (ISBN 0-943374-12-X). Key of David.

--The Kingdom at Hand. 340p. 1982. pap. 6.00 (ISBN 0-943374-00-6). Key of David.

--Lead My People. 104p. 1980. pap. 4.00 (ISBN 0-943374-02-2). Key of David.

--Prepare My People. 100p. (Orig.). (YA) 1986. pap. text ed. 5.00 (ISBN 0-943374-13-8). Key of David.

--Spirit of Jesus. 1984. pap. 5.00 (ISBN 0-943374-10-3). Key of David.

--Teach My People. 104p. 1983. pap. 4.00 (ISBN 0-943374-04-9). Key of David.

Walsh, W. H. Kant's Moral Theology. (Dawes Hicks Lectures on Philosophy). 1963. pap. 2.25 (ISBN 0-85672-270-7, Pub. by British Acad). Longwood Pub Group.

Walsh, Walter. Secret History of the Oxford Movement. LC 73-101915. Repr. of 1898 ed. 25.00 (ISBN 0-404-06819-7). AMS Pr.

--The Secret History of the Oxford Movement. 1977. lib. bdg. 59.95 (ISBN 0-8490-2583-4). Gordon Pr.

Walsh, William Thomas. Our Lady of Fatima. pap. 4.50 (ISBN 0-385-02869-5, D1, Im). Doubleday.

Walshe, Peter. Church Versus State in South Africa: The Case of the Christian Institute. LC 82-14533. xvi, 256p. (Orig.). 1983. 19.95 (ISBN 0-88344-097-0). Orbis Bks.

Walsingham, Thomae. De Archana Deorum. Van Kluyve, Robert A., ed. LC 67-31120. pap. 63.00 (ISBN 0-317-26876-7, 2023463). Bks Demand UMI.

Walsingham, Thomas. De Archana Deorum. Van Kluyme, Robert, ed. LC 67-31120. xxii, 227p. 1968. 24.75 (ISBN 0-8223-0183-0). Duke.

Walten, Maximilian G. & Fuller, Thomas, eds. Holy State & the Profane State, 2 Vols. LC 70-168072. Repr. of 1938 ed. 55.00 (ISBN 0-404-02637-0). AMS Pr.

Walter, Alice E. Katharine Luther, Liberated Nun. LC 81-65305. (Illus., Orig.). 1981. pap. text ed. 3.95 (ISBN 0-915644-22-3). Clayton Pub Hse.

Walter, Alicia E. Catarina Lutero, Monja Liberada. 1984. 3.50 (ISBN 0-915644-26-6). Clayton Pub Hse.

Walter, Diane, jt. auth. see Trout, Janet.

Walter, Eugen. The First Epistle to the Corinthians. McKenzie, John L., ed. LC 81-605. (New Testament for Spiritual Reading Ser.). 200p. 1981. pap. 4.95 (ISBN 0-8245-0122-5). Crossroad NY.

Walter, J. A. Need: The New Religion. LC 86-184. 173p. 1986. pap. 6.95 (ISBN 0-87784-948-X). Inter-Varsity.

Walter, James J., jt. auth. see Happel, Stephen.

Walters, Anna L., jt. auth. see Beck, Peggy V.

Walters, C. C. Monastic Archaeology in Egypt. 354p. 1974. text ed. 38.50x (ISBN 0-85668-008-7, Pub. by Aris & Phillips UK). Humanities.

Walters, Dorothy, ed. The Synergists. (Illus.). 269p. 1984. 16.95 (ISBN 0-934344-14-0, Pub. by Royal CBS). Fell.

Walters, Eva M. Christian Witness: That They Might Know Him. 1987. 7.95 (ISBN 0-533-07011-2). Vantage.

Walters, Henry B. London Churches at the Reformation: With an Account of Their Contents. (Church Historical Society London N. S. Ser.: No. 37). Repr. of 1939 ed. 95.00 (ISBN 0-8115-3160-0). Kraus Repr.

Walters, John F. Healing the Fractured Self. 122p. (Orig.). 1984. pap. 10.95 (ISBN 0-86683-883-X, HarpR). Har-Row.

Walters, Julie & De Leu, Barbara. God Is Like: Three Parables for Little Children. (Illus.). 96p. 1974. pap. 1.95 (ISBN 0-87793-073-2). Ave Maria.

Walters, Leroy, ed. Bibliography of Bioethics, Vol. 7. 375p. 1981. 55.00 (ISBN 0-02-933770-4). Free Pr.

Walters, M. History of the Church in Venezuela. 1976. lib. bdg. 59.95 (ISBN 0-8490-1991-5). Gordon Pr.

Walters, Richard P. Forgive & Be Free: Healing the Wounds of Past & Present. 144p. 1983. pap. 5.95 (ISBN 0-310-42611-1, 12339P). Zondervan.

Walters, Thomas P., jt. auth. see Haggerty, Brian A.

Walters, Thomas P., ed. Handbook for Parish Evaluation. (Orig.). 1984. pap. 10.95 (ISBN 0-8091-2587-0). Paulist Pr.

Walther, C. F. Convention Essays. Seuflow, August R., tr. (Selected Writings of C. F. W. Walther Ser.). 1981. 12.95 (ISBN 0-570-08277-3, 15-2735). Concordia.

--Editorials from Lehre und Wehre. Bouman, Herbert J., tr. (Selected Writings of C. F. W. Walther Ser.). 1981. 12.95 (ISBN 0-570-08280-3, 15-2738). Concordia.

--Selected Sermons. Bouman, Herbert J., tr. (Selected Writings of C. F. W. Walther Ser.). 1981. 12.95 (ISBN 0-570-08276-5, 15-2734). Concordia.

--Walther on the Church. Dreckamer, John M., tr. (Selected Writings of C. F. W. Walther Ser.). 1981. 12.95 (ISBN 0-570-08278-1, 15-2736). Concordia.

Walther, Carl F. Proper Distinction Between Law & Gospel. Dau, W. H., tr. 1929. 15.50 (ISBN 0-570-03248-2, 15-1601). Concordia.

Walther, James S., jt. auth. see Orr, William F.

Walther, Wiebke. Woman in Islam. (Image of Women Ser.). (Illus.). 192p. 1982. 35.00 (ISBN 0-8390-0256-4, Allanheld & Schram). Abner Schram Ltd.

Waltke, Bruce K. An Intermediate Hebrew Grammar. 1987. text ed. write for info. (ISBN 0-931464-31-5). Eisenbrauns.

Waltner, James. This We Believe. LC 68-20281. 1968. pap. 5.95 (ISBN 0-87303-845-2). Faith & Life.

Walton, A. Asklepios: The Cult of the Greek God of Medicine. 136p. 1979. 15.00 (ISBN 0-89005-277-8). Ares.

Walton, Alfred G. This I Can Believe. facs. ed. LC 79-142708. (Essay Index Reprint Ser). 1935. 18.00 (ISBN 0-8369-2207-7). Ayer Co Pubs.

Walton, Alice. The Cult of Asklepios. Repr. of 1894 ed. 15.00 (ISBN 0-384-65660-9). Johnson Repr.

Walton, Anna, ed. The Tent of Meeting Catalogue & Guide. 40p. (Orig.). 1985. 5.00 (ISBN 0-9615531-1-1). Tent Meeting.

Walton, F. A. Keys to the Kingdom. (Illus.). 80p. 1985. 8.00 (ISBN 0-682-40247-8). Exposition Pr FL.

Walton, H. Dyke. They Built with Faith: True Tales of God's Guidance in L.D.S. Chapel Building World-Wide. LC 79-89353. 125p. 1979. 5.95 (ISBN 0-88290-122-2). Horizon Utah.

Walton, John & Walton, Kim. Abraham & His Big Family. (Early Bible Foundations Ser.). (Illus.). 1986. pap. 2.95 (ISBN 1-55513-031-3, Chariot Bks). Cook.

--Daniel & the Lion's Den. (Early Foundations in the Bible Ser.). (Illus.). 1987. pap. 2.95 (ISBN 1-55513-045-3, Chariot Press). Cook.

--Daniel & the Lion's Den. (Early Foundations in the Bible Ser.). 1987. pap. 2.95. Cook.

--God & the World He Made. (Early Bible Foundations Ser.). (Illus.). 1986. pap. 2.95 (ISBN 1-55513-030-5, Chariot Bks). Cook.

--Jonah & the Big Fish. (Early Bible Foundations Ser.). (Illus.). 1986. pap. 2.95 (ISBN 1-55513-035-6, Chariot Bks). Cook.

--Moses & the Awful Plagues. (Early Bible Foundations Ser.). (Illus.). 1986. pap. 2.95 (ISBN 1-55513-041-0, Chariot Bks). Cook.

Walton, John H. Jonah: A Bible Study Commentary. 80p. (Orig.). 1982. pap. 3.95 (ISBN 0-310-36303-9, 11616P). Zondervan.

Walton, John W. Chronological & Background Charts of the Old Testament. 1977. spiral bdg. 8.95 (ISBN 0-310-36291-1, 11300P). Zondervan.

Walton, Kim, jt. auth. see Walton, John.

Walton, Lewis R. Advent! Woolsey, Raymond H., ed. 128p. (Orig.). 1986. pap. 6.95 (ISBN 0-8280-0349-1). Review & Herald.

Walton, O. F. Nadie Me Quiere. Tr. of Nobody Loves Me. (Span.). 128p. 1984. 3.25 (ISBN 0-8254-1850-X). Kregel.

Walton, Robert C. Chronological & Background Charts of Church History. 120p. 1986. pap. text ed. 8.95 (ISBN 0-310-36281-4, 11302P). Zondervan.

Walton, Robert C., ed. Bible Study Sourcebook. LC 80-26358. Vol. 1: Old Testament. pap. 54.00 (2027296); Vol. 2: New Testament. pap. 59.30. Bks Demand UMI.

Walton, Robert C., ed. see Verkamp, Bernard J.

Walton, Roy P. Names, Dates, & Numbers: A System of Numerology. 80p. 1981. pap. 5.00 (ISBN 0-89540-104-5, SB-104). Sun Pub.

Walton, Rus. Biblical Principles: Issues of Importance to Godly Christians. 370p. 1984. 4.95 (ISBN 0-317-39815-6). Plymouth Rock Found.

--FACS: Fundamentals for American Christians. 372p. 1979. pap. 4.95 (ISBN 0-942516-03-6). Plymouth Rock Found.

--One Nation under God. 240p. 1987. pap. 9.95 (ISBN 0-8407-3093-4). Nelson.

Waltz, Alan K. Images of the Future. LC 79-25028. (Into Our Third Century Ser.). (Orig.). 1980. pap. 3.95 (ISBN 0-687-18689-7). Abingdon.

--To Proclaim the Faith. 144p. 1983. pap. 3.95 (ISBN 0-687-42252-3). Abingdon.

Walvoord, John. Daniel. LC 75-123161. 1970. 17.95 (ISBN 0-8024-1752-3). Moody.

Walvoord, John & Zuck, Roy. The Bible Knowledge Commentary, Old Testament. 1985. 29.95. Victor Bks.

Walvoord, John F. The Blessed Hope & the Tribulation. (A Contemporary Evangelical Perspectives Ser.). 1976. kivar 5.95 (ISBN 0-310-34041-1, 10977P). Zondervan.

--Church in Prophecy. 6.95 (ISBN 0-310-34051-9, 10969P). Zondervan.

--Filipenses: Triunfo en Cristo (Comentario Biblico Portavoz) Orig. Title: Philippinas: Triumph in Christ (Everyman's Bible Commentary) (Span.). 1980. pap. 3.50 (ISBN 0-8254-1852-6). Kregel.

--Holy Spirit. 1958. 15.95 (ISBN 0-310-34060-8, 6388). Zondervan.

--Israel in Prophecy. 1978. pap. 4.95 (ISBN 0-310-34081-0, 10970P). Zondervan.

--Jesus Christ Our Lord. LC 70-80941. 318p. 1974. pap. 8.95 (ISBN 0-8024-4326-5). Moody.

--Nations in Prophecy. 1967. pap. 5.95 (ISBN 0-310-34101-9, 12159P). Zondervan.

--Philippians: Joy & Peace. (Everyman's Bible Commentary). 1971. pap. 5.95 (ISBN 0-8024-2050-8). Moody.

--Prophetic Trilogy: The Nations in Prophecy, the Church in Prophecy, Israel in Prophecy. pap. 15.85 (ISBN 0-310-34148-5, 17051P00687415X). Zondervan.

--Rapture Question. rev. enlarged ed. 1970. pap. 8.95 (ISBN 0-310-34151-5, 10978P). Zondervan.

--Revelation of Jesus Christ. LC 66-16227. 1966. 15.95 (ISBN 0-8024-7310-5). Moody.

--Thessalonian Epistles. 1958. pap. 4.95 (ISBN 0-310-34071-3, 6392P). Zondervan.

Walvoord, John F. & Zuck, Roy B. The Bib Sac Reader. (Orig.). 1983. pap. 8.95 (ISBN 0-8024-0459-6). Moody.

Walvoord, John F., jt. auth. see Chafer, Lewis S.

Walworth, Clarence A. The Oxford Movement in America. LC 77-150436. (Monograph Ser.: No. 30). (Illus.). 1974. Repr. of 1895 ed. 12.00x (ISBN 0-930060-10-5). US Cath Hist.

Walz, Edgar. How to Manage Your Church. 192p. 1986. pap. 8.95 (ISBN 0-570-04434-0). Concordia.

Walzer, Michael. Exodus & Revolution. LC 84-45306. 177p. 1985. 15.95 (ISBN 0-465-02164-6). Basic.

--Exodus & Revolution. LC 84-45306. 192p. 1986. pap. 6.95 (ISBN 0-465-02165-4, PL 5168). Basic.

Wamberg, Annie, jt. auth. see Wamberg, Steve.

Wamberg, Steve & Wamberg, Annie. Acting Up: A Complete Introduction to Biblical Drama for Junior High Youth Groups. (The Best of Young Teen Action Ser.). 32p. 1985. pap. 4.95 (ISBN 0-89191-379-3). Cook.

Wand, J. W. What the Church of England Stands For. LC 76-106700. 131p. 1972. Repr. of 1951 ed. lib. bdg. 22.50x (ISBN 0-8371-3382-3, WACE). Greenwood.

Wand, J. W. C. History of the Early Church from A.D. 500. 4th ed. 300p. 1975. pap. 11.95x (ISBN 0-416-18110-4, NO. 2572). Methuen Inc.

Wand, John W. The Four Great Heresies. LC 78-63174. (Heresies of the Early Christian & Medieval Era: Second Ser.). Repr. of 1955 ed. 29.00 (ISBN 0-404-16189-8). AMS Pr.

Wanefsky, Joseph. Rabbi Isaac Jacob Reines: His Life & Thought. LC 79-118314. 181p. 1970. 6.95 (ISBN 0-8022-2349-4). Philos Lib.

Wang, Robert. The Secret Temple. 1980. 15.00 (ISBN 0-87728-490-3); pap. 7.95 (ISBN 0-87728-518-7). Weiser.

Wangal, Geshe. The Door of Liberation. rev. ed. 235p. 1979. pap. 4.75 (ISBN 0-932156-01-0). Lotsawa.

Wangerin, W., Jr. O Happy Day! (Arch Bks.: No. 12). 1981. pap. 0.99 (ISBN 0-570-06093-1, 59-1211). Concordia.

Wangerin, Walter, Jr. The Baby God Promised. (Arch Bks.: No. 13). (Illus.). 32p. 1976. pap. 0.99 (ISBN 0-570-06105-9, 59-1223). Concordia.

--The Bible for Children. (Illus.). 416p. 1987. pap. 9.95 (ISBN 0-02-689000-3, Checkerboard Pr). Macmillan.

--The Bible: Its Story for Children. (Illus.). 416p. 1981. 12.95. Macmillan.

--In the Beginning...There Was No Sky. 36p. 1986. 10.95 (ISBN 0-8407-6671-8). Nelson.

--A Miniature Cathedral & Other Poems. 1987. 16.95; pap. 10.95. Har-Row.

--My First Book about Jesus. 1984. 8.95 (ISBN 0-528-82403-1). Macmillan.

--The Orphean Passages: The Drama of Faith. 305p. 1986. 16.95 (ISBN 0-06-069256-1). Har-Row.

--Ragman & Other Cries of Faith. LC 83-48980. 176p. 1984. 12.45 (ISBN 0-06-069253-7, HarpT). Har-Row.

Wang Kung-Hsing. Chinese Mind. LC 68-23336. 1968. Repr. of 1946 ed. lib. bdg. 22.50x (ISBN 0-8371-0260-X, WACM). Greenwood.

Wang-Mong, Cheng. Eight Virtues: Culture. 1987. 6.95 (ISBN 0-533-07189-5). Vantage.

Wannamaker, Bruce. God's Care Is Everywhere. LC 82-7244. (Illus.). 32p. 1982. PLB 4.95 (ISBN 0-89693-202-3). Dandelion Hse.

Wannamaker, Olin, et al, trs. see Steiner, Rudolf.

Wannamaker, Olin D., tr. see Steiner, Rudolf.

Wansbrough, Dom H. The Sunday Word: A Commentary on the Sunday Readings. 400p. 1984. pap. 14.95 (ISBN 0-225-66254-X, HarpR). Har-Row.

Wansbrough, Henry. New Testament of the New Jerusalem Bible. LC 86-11680. (Illus.). 552p. 1986. pap. 6.95 (ISBN 0-385-23706-5, Im). Doubleday.

Wansbrough, Henry, jt. auth. see Freyne, Sean.

Wansbrough, J. Quranic Studies: Sources & Methods of Scriptural Interpretations, Vol. 31. (London Oriential Ser). 1977. 55.00x (ISBN 0-19-713588-9). Oxford U Pr.

Wantland, William C. Foundations of the Faith. LC 82-61889. 176p. (Orig.). 1983. pap. 7.95 (ISBN 0-8192-1320-9). Morehouse.

Wantz, Sherman P., jt. auth. see Kelly, Clifton M.

Wapnick, Gloria & Wapnick, Kenneth. Awaken from the Dream: A Presentation of a Course in Miracles. 125p. (Orig.). 1987. pap. 10.00 (ISBN 0-933291-04-3). Foun Miracles.

Wapnick, Kenneth. The Fifty Miracle Principles of "A Course in Miracles". 153p. (Orig.). 1985. pap. 8.00 (ISBN 0-933291-02-7). Foun Miracles.

--Forgiveness & Jesus: The Meeting Place of a Course in Miracles & Christianity. 3rd ed. 340p. 1985. pap. 16.00 (ISBN 0-933291-01-9). Foun Miracles.

--Glossary: Index for "A Course in Miracles. 255p. (Orig.). 1982. 16.00. Foun Miracles.

--Glossary-Index for "A Course in Miracles". 2nd, enl. ed. 312p. 1986. text ed. 16.00 (ISBN 0-933291-03-5). Foun Miracles.

--A Talk Given on "A Course in Miracles". 2nd ed. 55p. 1985. pap. 4.00 (ISBN 0-933291-00-0). Foun Miracles.

Wapnick, Kenneth, jt. auth. see Wapnick, Gloria.

Warburton, Ernest, ed. Miscellaneous Church Music. (John Christian Bach, 1735-1782 The Collected Works Ser.). 75.00 (ISBN 0-8240-6073-3). Garland Pub.

Warburton, John. Mercies of a Covenant God. pap. 6.95 (ISBN 0-686-66520-1). Reiner.

Warburton, Thomas. Josquin Des Prez's "Missa Pange Lingua". An Edition, with Notes for Performance & Commentary. LC 76-22703. (Early Musical Masterworks--Critical Editions & Commentaries). ix, 63p. 1977. 21.00x (ISBN 0-8078-1296-X). U of NC Pr.

Warch, William A. How to Use Your Twelve Gifts from God. LC 76-41588. 112p. 1983. pap. 5.95 (ISBN 0-87516-530-3). De Vorss.

Ward, Alfred D. & Clark, John M. Goals of Economic Life. LC 72-167432. (Essay Index Reprint Ser.). Repr. of 1953 ed. 25.00 (ISBN 0-8369-2726-5). Ayer Co Pubs.

Ward, Allan L. Two Hundred & Thirty-Nine Days: Abdu'l-Baha's Journey in America. LC 79-14713. (Illus.). 1979. 10.95 (ISBN 0-87743-129-9, 332-005). Baha'i.

Ward, Alton. Ten Pennies for Jesus. (Illus.). 24p. (Orig.). 1986. pap. 3.50 (ISBN 0-570-04132-5, 56-1560). Concordia.

Ward, Barbara. World Poverty, Can It Be Solved. pap. 0.75 (ISBN 0-8199-0394-9, L39010). Franciscan Herald.

Ward, Benedicta. Miracles & the Medieval Mind: Theory, Record, & Event, 1000 to 1215. LC 81-23106. (Middle Ages Ser.). (Illus.). 300p. 1982. 29.95x (ISBN 0-8122-7836-4). U of Pa Pr.

Ward, Benedicta, tr. Prayers & Meditations of St. Anselm. (Classics Ser.). 1979. pap. 5.95 (ISBN 0-14-044278-2). Penguin.

Ward, Benedicta & Russell, Norman, trs. from Gr. The Lives of the Desert Fathers: The Historia Monachorum in Aegypto. (Cistercian Studies: No. 34). 1981. 17.95 (ISBN 0-87907-834-0); pap. 8.95 (ISBN 0-87907-934-7). Cistercian Pubns.

Ward, C. M. The Playboy Comes Home. LC 75-32603. 112p. (Orig.). 1976. pap. 1.25 (ISBN 0-88243-572-8, 02-0572). Gospel Pub.

--Sermons from Luke. 96p. (Orig.). 1983. pap. 2.25 (ISBN 0-89274-260-7). Harrison Hse.

--This Child Shall Be Lent Unto the Lord. (Illus.). 32p. 1967. pap. 0.60 12 for 6.00 (ISBN 0-88243-822-0, 02-0822). Gospel Pub.

--Two Shall Be One. (Orig.). 1986. pap. text ed. 3.95 (ISBN 0-88368-184-6). Whitaker Hse.

Ward, Carol. The Christian Sourcebook. 1986. 16.95 (ISBN 0-345-32248-7, Pub. by Ballantine Epiphany). Ballantine.

Ward, Charles A. Oracles of Nostradamus. 400p. 1981. pap. 22.00 (ISBN 0-89540-084-7, SB-084). Sun Pub.

Ward, Clarence. Mediaeval Church Vaulting. LC 72-177847. Repr. of 1915 ed. 19.50 (ISBN 0-404-06836-7). AMS Pr.

Ward, Don, ed. see Ward, Mae Y.

Ward, Duren J. The Classification of Religions. 75p. 1909. pap. 0.95 (ISBN 0-317-40432-6). Open Court.

Ward, Elaine. After My House Burned Down. 88p. (Orig.). 1982. pap. 6.95 (ISBN 0-940754-11-8). Ed Ministries.

--Be A Say a Fingerplay. 71p. (Orig.). 1982. pap. 5.95 (ISBN 0-940754-12-6). Ed Ministries.

--Being-in-Creation. 80p. (Orig.). 1983. pap. 9.95 (ISBN 0-940754-14-2). Ed Ministries.

--Feelings Grow Too! 81p. (Orig.). 1981. pap. 9.95 (ISBN 0-940754-07-X). Ed Ministries.

Ward, Elaine M. Growing with the Bible. 64p. (Orig.). 1986. pap. 6.95 (ISBN 0-940754-36-3). Ed Ministries.

--More Old Testament Stories. 65p. 1984. pap. 6.95 (ISBN 0-940754-23-1). Ed Ministries.

--Movers of Mountains. 88p. (Orig.). (YA) 1984. pap. 12.95 (ISBN 0-940754-24-X). Ed Ministries.

--Old Testament Stories: For Church & Home. 70p. (Orig.). 1984. pap. 6.95 (ISBN 0-940754-19-3). Ed Ministries.

Ward, Evangeline H., jt. auth. see Katz, Lilian G.

Ward, Frances. Keep the Fruit on the Table. 48p. 1982. pap. 1.75 (ISBN 0-88144-006-X, CPS-006). Christian Pub.

Ward, Gerald W. The Assembly House. LC 76-16903. (Historic House Booklet Ser.: No. 3). 1976. 2.00 (ISBN 0-88389-061-5). Essex Inst.

--The Peirce-Nichols House. LC 76-16904. (Historic House Booklet Ser.: No. 4). 1976. 2.00 (ISBN 0-88389-062-3). Essex Inst.

Ward, Harvey. Miracle of Prayer: Operation Esther. Floyd, Diane & Kinnaird, Judith, eds. LC 87-70021. 128p. 1987. pap. 5.95 (ISBN 0-89221-146-6). New Leaf.

Ward, Horace. Power for Living. (International Correspondence Program Ser.). (Orig.). 1986. pap. text ed. 6.95 (ISBN 0-87148-718-7). Pathway Pr.

Ward, J. Naturalism & Agnosticism: The Gifford Lectures Delivered Before the University of Aberdeen in 1896-1898, 2 Vols. in 1. 4th ed. Repr. of 1899 ed. 36.00 (ISBN 0-527-94500-5). Kraus Repr.

Ward, J. Neville. Five for Sorrow, Ten for Joy: A Consideration of the Rosary. rev. ed. LC 85-21318. xiii, 138p. 1985. pap. 6.95 (ISBN 0-936384-36-0). Cowley Pubns.

--The Following Plough: Meditations on Prayer. LC 84-71179. 128p. 1984. pap. 6.00 (ISBN 0-936384-18-2). Cowley Pubns.

--The Personal Faith of Jesus as Revealed in the Lord's Prayer. 128p. 1982. pap. 6.95 (ISBN 0-86683-678-0, HarpR). Har-Row.

--The Use of Praying. 1977. 10.95x (ISBN 0-19-520106-X); pap. 5.95 (ISBN 0-19-519959-6). Oxford U Pr.

Ward, J. S. The Hung Society: Or the Society of Heaven & Earth, 2 Vols. 1977. 35.00 (ISBN 0-89986-003-6). Oriental Bk Store.

Ward, James. Amos & Hosea. Hayes, John, ed. (Knox Preaching Guides). 96p. 1981. pap. 4.95 (ISBN 0-8042-3225-3). John Knox.

--The Realm of Ends: Or, Pluralism & Theism. LC 77-27173. (Gifford Lectures: 1907-10). Repr. of 1911 ed. 34.50 (ISBN 0-404-60464-1). AMS Pr.

Ward, James M. The Prophets. LC 81-20575. (Interpreting Biblical Texts). 160p. (Orig.). 1982. pap. 8.95 (ISBN 0-687-34370-4). Abingdon.

Ward, Kay, jt. auth. see Simons, John.

Ward, Kay, ed. see Simons, John & Ward, Kay.

Ward, Keith. Rational Theology & the Creativity of God. LC 82-81888. 256p. 1982. 17.95 (ISBN 0-8298-0618-0). Pilgrim NY.

Ward, Lynd, jt. auth. see McNeer, May.

Ward, Mae Y. The Seeking Heart: Prayer Journal of Mae Yoho Ward. Ward, Don, ed. LC 84-23836. 144p. (Orig.). 1985. pap. 7.95 (ISBN 0-8272-3420-1). CBP.

Ward, Maisie. Gilbert Keith Chesterton. LC 83-45860. 1944. 46.50 (ISBN 0-404-20280-2, PR4453). AMS Pr.

Ward, Maisie, ed. English Way: Studies in English Sanctity from St. Bede to Newman. facs. ed. LC 68-29253. (Essay Index Reprint Ser). 1968. Repr. of 1933 ed. 17.75 (ISBN 0-8369-0975-5). Ayer Co Pubs.

Ward, Marcus. Protestant Christian Churches. 1985. 13.00x (ISBN 0-7062-3597-5, Pub. by Ward Lock Educ Co Ltd). State Mutual Bk.

Ward, Margery W., ed. A Frament: The Autobiography of Mary Jane Mount Tanner. 231p. 1980. 15.00 (ISBN 0-941214-38-9). Signature Bks.

Ward, May A. Prophets of the Nineteenth Century: Carlyle, Ruskin, Tolstoi. LC 76-7949. 1978. Repr. of 1900 ed. lib. bdg. 20.00 (ISBN 0-8414-9437-1). Folcroft.

Ward, Miriam, ed. A Companion to the Bible. LC 85-15817. 419p. (Orig.). 1985. pap. 14.95 (ISBN 0-8189-0487-9). Alba.

Ward, Nathaniel. Simple Cobler of Aggawam in America. Zall, Paul M., ed. LC 69-19107. xviii, 81p. 1969. 7.50x (ISBN 0-8032-0188-5). U of Nebr Pr.

Ward, Neville. Friday Afternoon: Reflections on the Seven Last Words. 144p. 1984. pap. 5.95 (ISBN 0-86683-744-2, AY8397, HarpR). Har-Row.

Ward, Patricia A. & Stout, Martha G. Christian Women at Work. 242p. 1984. pap. 6.95 (ISBN 0-310-43701-6). Zondervan.

Ward, Rhode, tr. see Colson, Charles.

Ward, Rhode, tr. see Graham, Billy.

Ward, Rhode, tr. see Morison, Frank.

Ward, Rhode F., tr. see Galloway, Dale E.

Ward, Ruth. Devotions: A Family Affair. (Directory Bks.). 64p. 1981. pap. 2.45 (ISBN 0-8010-9632-4). Baker Bk.

Ward, Ruth M. Self Esteem: A Gift from God. 1984. pap. 7.95 (ISBN 0-8010-9664-2). Baker Bk.

Ward, Samuel, jt. auth. see Rogers, Richard.

Ward, W. History, Literature & Mythology of the Hindoos, 4 vols. 1986. Repr. of 1817 ed. text ed. 200.00x (ISBN 81-7018-240-9, Pub. by B R Pub Corp Delhi). Vol. 1: 354. Vol. 2: 505. Vol. 3: 288. Vol. 4: 344. Apt Bks.

Ward, W. Reginald. Theology, Sociology & Politics: The German Protestant Social Conscience 1890-1933. 250p. 1979. 29.90 (ISBN 3-261-04617-1). P Lang Pubs.

Ward, Wadene C. Victory Through Word Confessions. 47p. 1985. pap. 1.95 (ISBN 0-88144-040-X). Christian Pub.

Ward, Waylon O. The Bible in Counseling. 1977. pap. 12.95 (ISBN 0-8024-0623-8). Moody.

Ward, Wayne E. The Holy Spirit. (Layman's Library of Christian Doctrine). 1987. 5.95 (ISBN 0-8054-1640-4). Broadman.

Ward, Wilfred. The Life of John Henry Newman Based on His Private Journals & Correspondence, 2 vols. 1912. Repr. 50.00 (ISBN 0-8274-2889-8). R West.

Ward, Wilfrid. The Oxford Movement. (Victorian Age Ser). 20.00 (ISBN 0-8482-6908-X). Norwood Edns.

Ward, Wilfrid P. Last Lectures. facs. ed. LC 67-26793. (Essay Index Reprint Ser). 1918. 22.50 (ISBN 0-8369-0976-3). Ayer Co Pubs.

--Ten Personal Studies. LC 73-107742. (Essay Index Reprint Ser.). 1908. 21.00 (ISBN 0-8369-1584-4). Ayer Co Pubs.

--William George Ward & the Catholic Revival. LC 75-29626. Repr. of 1893 ed. 41.75 (ISBN 0-404-14042-4). AMS Pr.

--William George Ward & the Oxford Movement. LC 75-29625. Repr. of 1889 ed. 41.75 (ISBN 0-404-14043-2). AMS Pr.

Ward, William. Index of Egyptian Administrative & Religious Titles of the Middle Kingdom. 244p. 1983. text ed. 60.00x (ISBN 0-8156-6065-0, Am U Beirut). Syracuse U Pr.

Ward, William B. Toward Responsible Discipleship. LC 61-7078. (Orig.). 1961. pap. 2.50 (ISBN 0-8042-4049-3); leader's guide o.p. 1.00 (ISBN 0-8042-4050-7). John Knox.

Ward, William G. The Ideal of a Christian Church Considered in Comparison with Existing Practice. 2nd ed. LC 75-30040. Repr. of 1844 ed. 49.50 (ISBN 0-404-14044-0). AMS Pr.

Ward, William R., Jr. Faith in Action: A History of Methodism in the Empire State 1784-1984. LC 86-70533. (Illus.). 324p. (Orig.). 1986. text ed. 12.50x (ISBN 0-914960-62-8); pap. text ed. 10.00x (ISBN 0-914960-58-X). Academy Bks.

Warden, John, ed. Orpheus, the Metamorphoses of a Myth. LC 82-189058. pap. 63.50 (2026404). Bks Demand UMI.

Warder, A. K. Indian Buddhism. rev. 2nd ed. 580p. 1980. text ed. 22.00 (ISBN 0-89684-094-8, Pub. by Motilal Banarsidass India). Orient Bk Dist.

Warder, Anthony K., ed. New Paths in Buddhist Research. LC 82-83594. x, 137p. 1985. 15.95x (ISBN 0-89386-008-5); pap. 9.95 (ISBN 0-89386-009-3). Acorn NC.

Wardin, Albert W., Jr. Baptist Atlas. LC 79-52541. (Illus.). 1980. 5.50 (ISBN 0-8054-6551-0). Broadman.

Wardlaw, Don M., ed. Preaching Biblically. LC 83-1276. 174p. (Orig.). 1983. pap. 10.95 (ISBN 0-664-24478-5). Westminster.

Wardlaw, Ralph. Exposition of Ecclesiastes. 432p. 1982. lib. bdg. 16.25 Smythe Sewn (ISBN 0-86524-147-3, 2102). Klock & Klock.

Wardle, William L. The History & Religion of Israel. LC 78-11741. (The Clarendon Bible, Old Testament Ser.: Vol. I). (Illus.). 1979. Repr. of 1942 ed. lib. bdg. 24.75x (ISBN 0-313-21016-0, WAHR). Greenwood.

Wardman, Alan. Religion & Statecraft among the Romans. LC 82-47928. pap. 55.80 (2026708). Bks Demand UMI.

Ware, Ann P., ed. see Chittister, Joan, et al.

Ware, Harlan, jt. auth. see Hornaday, William H.

Ware, Henry. Memoirs of the Reverend Noah Worcester, D. D. LC 78-137557. (Peace Movement in America Ser). xii, 155p. 1972. Repr. of 1844 ed. lib. bdg. 14.95x (ISBN 0-89198-088-1). Ozer.

Ware, James R., tr. see Confucius.

Ware, K. Communion & Intercommunion. 1980. pap. 1.95 (ISBN 0-937032-20-4). Light&Life Pub Co MN.

Ware, Kallistos & Barrois, Georges. Women & the Priesthood: Essays from the Orthodox Tradition. Hopko, Thomas, ed. 190p. 1982. pap. 8.95 (ISBN 0-88141-005-5). St Vladimirs.

Ware, Kallistos see Mother Mary & Archimandrite Kallistos Ware.

Ware, Kallistos, jt. tr. see Sherrard, Philip.

Ware, Kallistos T. Orthodox Way. 196p. 1979. pap. 4.95 (ISBN 0-913836-58-3). St Vladimirs.

Ware, Kallistos T., ed. see Elchaninov, Alexander.

Ware, Sedley L. The Elizabethan Parish in Its Ecclesiastical & Financial Aspects. LC 78-63927. (Johns Hopkins University. Studies in the Social Sciences. Twenty-Sixth Ser. 1908: 7-8). Repr. of 1908 ed. 14.50 (ISBN 0-404-61177-X). AMS Pr.

Ware, Timothy. Eustratios Argenti: Study of the Greek Church under Turkish Rule. 1974. Repr. of 1964 ed. 12.50 (ISBN 0-686-10203-7). Eastern Orthodox.

--Orthodox Church. (Orig.). 1963. pap. 5.95 (ISBN 0-14-020592-6, Pelican). Penguin.

Ware, William. Julian: Scenes in Judea, 2 vols. in one. Davis, Moshe, ed. LC 77-70754. (America & the Holy Land Ser.). 1977. Repr. of 1841 ed. lib. bdg. 40.00x (ISBN 0-405-10299-2). Ayer Co Pubs.

Warenski, Marilyn. Patriarchs & Politics. (McGraw-Hill Paperbacks Ser.). 352p. 1980. pap. 6.95 (ISBN 0-07-068271-2). McGraw.

--Patriarchs & Politics. (Illus.). 1978. 10.95 (ISBN 0-07-068270-4). McGraw.

Warfield, B. B. Biblical & Theological Studies. 12.95 (ISBN 0-8010-9584-0). Baker Bk.

--Counterfeit Miracles. 1976. pap. 6.95 (ISBN 0-85151-166-X). Banner of Truth.

--Inspiration & Authority of Bible. 12.95 (ISBN 0-8010-9586-7). Baker Bk.

--Perfectionism. 12.95 (ISBN 0-8010-9587-5). Baker Bk.

--The Person & Work of Christ. 12.95 (ISBN 0-8010-9588-3). Baker Bk.

--The Works of Benjamin B. Warfield, 10 vols. 1981. Repr. of 1932 ed. 149.50 (ISBN 0-8010-9645-6). Baker Bk.

Warfield, B. B., jt. auth. see Hodge, A. A.

Warfield, Benjamin B. Biblical & Theological Studies. 1952. 12.95 (ISBN 0-87552-525-3). Presby & Reformed.

--Calvin & Augustine. 12.95 (ISBN 0-8010-9585-9). Baker Bk.

--Calvin & Augustine. 1954. 12.95 (ISBN 0-87552-526-1). Presby & Reformed.

--Inspiration & Authority of the Bible. 2nd ed. 1948. 12.95 (ISBN 0-87552-527-X). Presby & Reformed.

--Person & Work of Christ. 1950. 12.95 (ISBN 0-87552-529-6). Presby & Reformed.

--The Religious Life of Theological Students. 1983. pap. 0.95 (ISBN 0-87552-524-5). Presby & Reformed.

--Studies in Perfectionism. 1958. 12.95 (ISBN 0-87552-528-8). Presby & Reformed.

--Studies in Tertullian & Augustine. Repr. of 1930 ed. lib. bdg. 29.00x (ISBN 0-8371-4490-6, WATT). Greenwood.

Wargo, Louis G., Jr., jt. auth. see Jaberg, Gene.

Waring, E. Graham, ed. Deism & Natural Religion: A Source Book. LC 66-28139. (Milestones of Thought Ser.). pap. 4.95 (ISBN 0-8044-6968-7). Ungar.

Waring, E. Graham, ed. see Feuerbach, Ludwig.

Waring, Luther H. Political Theories of Martin Luther. LC 68-15837. 1968. Repr. of 1910 ed. 21.50x (ISBN 0-8046-0488-6, Pub. by Kennikat). Assoc Faculty Pr.

Wark, K. R. Elizabethan Recusancy in Cheshire. 1971. 30.00 (ISBN 0-7190-1154-X, Pub. by Manchester Univ Pr). Longwood Pub Group.

Warkentin, Marjorie. Ordination: A Biblical-Historical View. LC 82-8908. pap. 53.00 (ISBN 0-317-30166-7, 2025348). Bks Demand UMI.

Warkentin, Mary J. Lost, but not Forever. 1986. pap. cancelled (ISBN 0-88270-605-5). Bridge Pub.

Warkentin, Viola, jt. auth. see Whittaker, Arabelle.

Warlick, Harold C., Jr. How to Be a Minister & a Human Being. 128p. 1982. pap. 7.95 (ISBN 0-8170-0961-2). Judson.

--The Rarest of These Is Hope. 1985. 7.50 (ISBN 0-89536-743-2, 5826). CSS of Ohio.

Warmington, E. H., ed. Greek Anthology, 5vols. Incl. Vol. 1. Book 1, Christian Epigrams. Book 2 Christoclorus of Thebes in Egypt. Book 3, Cyzicene Epigrams. Book 4, Proems of the Different Anthologies. Book 5, Amatory Epigrams. Book 6, Dedicatory Epigrams (ISBN 0-674-99074-9); Vol. 2. Book 7, Sepulchral Epigrams. Book 8, Epigrams of St. Gregory the Theologian (ISBN 0-674-99075-7); Vol. 3. Book 9, Declamatory Epigrams (ISBN 0-674-99093-5); Vol. 4. Book 10, Hortatory & Admonitory Epigrams. Book 11, Convivial & Satirical Epigrams. Book 12, Strato's Musa Puerilis (ISBN 0-674-99094-3); Vol. 5. Book 13, Epigrams in Various Metres. Book 14, Arithmetical Problems, Riddles, Oracles. Book 15, Miscellanea. Book 16, Epigrams of Planudean Anthology Not in the Palatine Manuscript (ISBN 0-674-99095-1). (Loeb Classical Library: No. 67-68, 84-86). (Gr. & Eng.). 13.95x ea. Harvard U Pr.

--Scriptores Historiae Augustae, 3 vols. Magie, D., tr. (Loeb Classical Library: No. 139-140, 263). (Lat. & Eng.). 13.95x ea.; Vol. 1. (ISBN 0-674-99154-0); Vol. 2. (ISBN 0-674-99155-9); Vol. 3. (ISBN 0-674-99290-3). Harvard U Pr.

Warmington, E. H., ed. see Josephus.

Warminski, Andrzej. Readings in Interpretation: Holderlin, Hegel, Heidegger. (Theory & History of Literature Ser.: Vol. 26). 272p. (Orig.). 1987. 29.50 (ISBN 0-8166-1239-0); pap. 12.95 (ISBN 0-8166-1240-4). U of Minn Pr.

Warne, Arthur. Church & Society in Eighteenth Century England. LC 69-16764. (Illus.). 1969. 17.95x (ISBN 0-678-05642-0). Kelley.

Warner, Anna. The Melody of the Twenty-Third Psalm. pap. 1.95 (ISBN 0-685-88385-X). Reiner.

Warner, D. S. Salvation, Present, Perfect, Now or Never. 63p. pap. 0.40 (ISBN 0-686-29138-7); pap. 1.00 3 copies (ISBN 0-686-29139-5). Faith Pub Hse.

Warner, D. S. & Riggle, H. M. The Cleansing of the Sanctuary. 541p. Repr. 5.50 (ISBN 0-686-29145-X). Faith Pub Hse.

Warner, Diane. Bible Puppet Scripts for Busy Teachers. LC 81-69783. 1983. pap. 4.95 (ISBN 0-89636-076-8). Accent Bks.

Warner, Elizabeth. Heroes, Monsters & Other Worlds from Russian Mythology. LC 85-10750. (Illus.). 132p. 1986. 15.95 (ISBN 0-8052-4007-1). Schocken.

Warner, Gary. Competition. LC 79-51747. 1979. pap. 5.95 (ISBN 0-89191-074-3). Cook.

Warner, Marina. Alone of All Her Sex: The Myth & the Cult of the Virgin Mary. LC 82-40051. (Illus.). 488p. 1983. pap. 10.95 (ISBN 0-394-71155-6, Vin). Random.

--Joan of Arc: The Image of Female Heroism. LC 80-2720. (Illus.). 1981. 19.95 (ISBN 0-394-41145-5). Knopf.

--Joan of Arc: The Image of Female Heroism. LC 81-69565. (Illus.). 400p. 1982. pap. 9.95 (ISBN 0-394-75333-X, Vin). Random.

Warner, Rex. John Milton. LC 72-12371. Repr. of 1949 ed. lib. bdg. 12.50 (ISBN 0-8414-9389-8). Folcroft.

--The Stories of the Greeks. 480p. 1978. 15.00 (ISBN 0-374-27056-2); pap. 9.95 (ISBN 0-374-50728-7). FS&G.

--Vengeance of the Gods. 192p. 1955. 3.50 (ISBN 0-87013-009-9). Mich St U Pr.

Warner, Richard. Freedom, Enjoyment, & Happiness: An Essay on Moral Psychology. LC 86-19696. (Illus.). 208p. 1987. text ed. 19.95x (ISBN 0-8014-1977-8). Cornell U Pr.

Warner, Ross. Fulfillment of Book of Mormon Prophecies. 1975. pap. 4.95 (ISBN 0-89036-081-2). Hawkes Pub Inc.

Warner, Ruth, tr. see Erdozain, Placido.

Warner, Wayne E. & Warner, Wayne E. The Woman Evangelist: The Life & Times of Charismatic Evangelist Maria B. Woodworth-Etter. LC 86-11854. (Studies in Evangelicalism: No. 8). (Illus.). 354p. 1986. 32.50 (ISBN 0-8108-1912-0). Scarecrow.

Warner, Wayne E., ed. Revival! (Illus.). 163p. (Orig.). 1978. pap. 4.95 (ISBN 0-89274-303-4). Harrison Hse.

Warner, Wellman J. Wesleyan Movement in the Industrial Revolution. LC 66-24768. 1967. Repr. of 1930 ed. 8.00x (ISBN 0-8462-0960-8). Russell.

Warnke, Mike, et al. Satan-Seller. LC 79-94042. 204p. 1972. (Pub. by Logos); pap. 3.50 (ISBN 0-88270-096-0). Bridge Pub.

Warnock, G. J. Berkeley. 240p. 1983. 14.95 (ISBN 0-268-00670-9); pap. 7.95 (ISBN 0-268-00671-7). U of Notre Dame Pr.

--Object of Morality. 1971. pap. 10.95x (ISBN 0-416-29900-8, NO. 2575). Methuen Inc.

Warnock, Mary. Ethics since Nineteen Hundred. 3rd ed. 1978. pap. 4.95x (ISBN 0-19-289108-1). Oxford U Pr.

Warr, Gene. The Godly Man. 1978. pap. 3.95 (ISBN 2-01064-105-1, 40121). Word Bks.

Warr, Irma. The Godly Woman. 1978. pap. 5.95 (ISBN 2-01064-201-5, 40123). Word Bks.

Warre-Cornish, Francis. English Church in the Nineteenth Century, 2 Vols. LC 75-148325. (History of the English Church Ser.: No. 8). Repr. of 1910 ed. Set. 59.00 (ISBN 0-404-50760-3); 29.50 ea. Vol. 1 (ISBN 0-404-50758-1). Vol. 2 (ISBN 0-404-50759-X). AMS Pr.

Warren, Ann K. Anchorites & Their Patrons in Medieval England. LC 84-24091. 1985. 42.00x (ISBN 0-520-05278-1). U of Cal Pr.

Warren, Austin, jt. ed. see Stanwood, Paul.

Warren, Charles & Conder, Claude R. The Survey of Western Palestine. LC 78-63371. (The Crusades & Military Orders: Second Ser.). Repr. of 1884 ed. 41.50 (ISBN 0-404-17047-1). AMS Pr.

Warren, Erasmus. Geologia: Discourse Concerning the Earth Before the Deluge, Wherein the Form & Properties Ascribed to It. LC 77-6546. (History of Geology Ser.). (Illus.). 1978. Repr. of 1690 ed. lib. bdg. 34.50x (ISBN 0-405-10470-7). Ayer Co Pubs.

Warren, F., ed. Dance of Death. (EETS, OS: No. 181). Repr. of 1931 ed. 10.00 (ISBN 0-527-00178-3). Kraus Repr.

Warren, Frederick E. Liturgy & Ritual of the Ante-Nicene Church. 2nd rev. ed. LC 78-177851. Repr. of 1912 ed. 25.00 (ISBN 0-404-06847-2). AMS Pr.

--Liturgy & Ritual of the Celtic Church. 1987. 39.50 (ISBN 0-85115-473-5); pap. 12.50. Eastern Orthodox.

Warren, Henry C. Buddhism in Translations. LC 78-70138. Repr. of 1896 ed. 47.50 (ISBN 0-404-17408-6). AMS Pr.
--Buddhism in Translations. LC 5-17082. 1963. pap. text ed. 7.95x (ISBN 0-689-70200-0, 19). Atheneum.
Warren, Henry C., tr. Everyman's Life of the Buddha: Translated from Pali Sacred Scriptures. Westburg, John E., ed. (Comparative Literature Studies Ser). (Illus.). 138p. 1966. pap. 5.00 (ISBN 0-87423-003-9). Westburg.
Warren, Jean, compiled by. Piggyback Songs in Praise of God. (Piggyback Songs Ser.). (Illus.). 80p. (Orig.). 1986. pap. 6.95 (ISBN 0-911019-10-3). Warren Pub Hse.
Warren, Lindsey D., ed. Headed in the Direction of Heaven. 1980. pap. 2.00 (ISBN 0-934916-28-4). Natl Christian Pr.
Warren, Mary P. Lord, I'm Back Again: Story Devotions for Girls. LC 81-65651. 112p. (Orig.). 1981. pap. 3.95 (ISBN 0-8066-1887-6, 10-4098). Augsburg.
--On Our Way to Christmas: A Family Activity Book for Advent. 32p. (Orig.). 1980. pap. 4.95 (ISBN 0-8066-1784-5, 10-4768). Augsburg.
Warren, Mary P. & Mathews. Boy with a Sling. LC 65-15143. (Arch Bks: Set 2). 1965. pap. 0.99 (ISBN 0-570-06012-5, 59-1116). Concordia.
Warren, Mary P. & Rada. Little Boat That Almost Sank. LC 64-23371. (Arch Bks: Set 2). 1965. pap. 0.99 (ISBN 0-570-06010-9, 59-1111). Concordia.
Warren, Mary P. & Wind, Betty. Lame Man Who Walked Again. (Arch Bks: Set 3). 1966. laminated bdg. 0.99 (ISBN 0-570-06020-6, 59-1129). Concordia.
Warren, Max. Creo en la Gran Comision. Sipowicz, Edwin, tr. from Eng. LC 78-54272. (Serie Creo). Tr. of I Believe in the Great Commission. (Span.). 205p. 1978. pap. 5.95 (ISBN 0-89922-112-2). Edit Caribe.
--I Believe in the Great Commission. (I Believe Ser.). 1976. pap. 4.95 (ISBN 0-8028-1659-2). Eerdmans.
Warren, Mervyn A. God Made Known. Wheeler, Gerald, ed. LC 83-17677. (Illus.). 94p. (Orig.). 1983. pap. 5.95 (ISBN 0-8280-0230-4). Review & Herald.
Warren, Michael. Youth & the Future of the Church: Ministry with Youth & Young Adults. 160p. 1982. 10.95 (ISBN 0-8164-0513-1, HarpR). Har-Row.
--Youth & the Future of the Church: Ministry with Youth & Young Adults. 156p. 1985. pap. 8.95 (ISBN 0-86683-917-8, 7915, Winston-Seabury). Har-Row.
Warren, Michael, ed. Sourcebook for Modern Catechetics. LC 83-50246. 496p. (Orig.). 1983. pap. 15.95 (ISBN 0-88489-152-6). St Mary's.
Warren, Nathan B. Christmas in the Olden Time. LC 76-58002. 1977. Repr. of 1859 ed. lib. bdg. 22.50 (ISBN 0-8414-1656-7). Folcroft.
Warren, Norman. What's the Point? Reynolds, A., ed. 80p. 1987. pap. 2.50 (ISBN 0-7459-1224-9). Lion USA.
Warren, Ramona, et al. Easter Handbook. LC 85-24322. (Holiday Handbooks Ser.). (Illus.). 96p. 1986. lib. bdg. 12.95 (ISBN 0-89565-306-0). Childs World.
Warren, Richard. Answers to Life's Difficult Questions. 132p. 1985. pap. 4.95 (ISBN 0-89693-395-4). Victor Bks.
--Twelve Dynamic Bible Study Methods. 252p. 1981. pap. 7.95 (ISBN 0-88207-815-1). Victor Bks.
Warren, Rod, illus. How Do Others See You? In an LDS Ward. (Illus., Orig.). 1977. pap. 2.95 (ISBN 0-89036-101-0). Hawkes Pub Inc.
Warren, Samuel. A Compendium of Swedenborg's Theological Writings. LC 73-94196. 816p. 1974. 5.00 (ISBN 0-87785-123-9). Swedenborg.
Warren, Steve. Drat! Mythed Again: Second Thoughts on Utah. (Illus.). 183p. 1986. pap. 10.95 (ISBN 0-938117-02-5). Altair Pub UT.
Warren, Sukanya & Mellen, Francis. Gurudev: The Life of Yogi Amrit Desai. LC 82-83357. 117p. (Orig.). 1982. pap. 6.95 (ISBN 0-940258-07-2). Kripalu Pubns.
Warren, Thomas B. The Bible Only Makes Christians Only & the Only Christians. 220p. 1986. pap. 11.00 (ISBN 0-934916-09-8). Natl Christian Pr.
--Christians Only & the Only Christians. 89p. 1984. pap. 3.00 (ISBN 0-934916-05-5). Natl Christian Pr.
--Have Atheists Proved There Is No God? 1974. 8.00 (ISBN 0-934916-33-0). Natl Christian Pr.
--Keeping the Lock in Wedlock. 1980. pap. 11.00 (ISBN 0-934916-26-8). Natl Christian Pr.
--Lectures on Church Co-Operation & Orphan Homes. 1958. pap. 7.00 (ISBN 0-934916-48-9). Natl Christian Pr.
--Logic & the Bible. 1983. 11.00 (ISBN 0-934916-01-2). Natl Christian Pr.
--Marriage is for Those Who Love God & One Another. 1976. 8.00 (ISBN 0-934916-37-3). Natl Christian Pr.
--Our God: A "Sun & Shield" for Troubled Hearts. 1963. 10.00 (ISBN 0-934916-38-1). Natl Christian Pr.
--Sin, Suffering & God. 1980. pap. 15.00 (ISBN 0-934916-25-X). Natl Christian Pr.
--Three Hundred Charts You Can Use in Preaching, Teaching & Studying on Divorce & Remarriage. 1978. pap. 11.00looseleaf (ISBN 0-934916-29-2). Natl Christian Pr.
--Three Hundred Thirty-Five Crucial Questions on Christian Unity. 48p. 1984. pap. 1.50 (ISBN 0-934916-06-3). Natl Christian Pr.
--Tract: Questions on Divorce & Remarriage. 1984. 0.60 (ISBN 0-934916-04-7); dozen 6.00; hundred 40.00. Natl Christian Pr.
--When Is an Example Binding? (Biblical Hermeneutics Ser.). 1975. pap. 7.00 (ISBN 0-934916-43-8). Natl Christian Pr.
Warren, Thomas B. & Ballard, L. S. Warren-Ballard Debate. 1979. 9.00 (ISBN 0-934916-39-X). Natl Christian Pr.
Warren, Thomas B. & Barnhart, Joe. Warren-Barnhart Debate on Ethics. 1981. pap. 13.00 (ISBN 0-934916-47-0). Natl Christian Pr.
Warren, Thomas B. & Fuqua, E. C. Divorce & Remarriage: Are Non-Christians Amenable to the Law of Christ? 1977. pap. 6.00 (ISBN 0-934916-30-6). Natl Christian Pr.
Warren, Thomas B. & Matson, Wallace I. Warren-Matson Debate on the Existence of God. LC 78-64546. 1979. 14.00 (ISBN 0-934916-41-1); pap. 11.00 (ISBN 0-934916-45-4). Natl Christian Pr.
Warren, Thomas B., ed. Your Marriage Can Be Great. 1978. pap. 14.00 (ISBN 0-934916-44-6). Natl Christian Pr.
Warren, Thomas B. & Elkins, Garland, eds. The Book of Romans. 1983. 15.00 (ISBN 0-934916-03-9). Natl Christian Pr.
--The Church, the Beautiful Bride of Christ. 1980. pap. 13.00 (ISBN 0-934916-27-6). Natl Christian Pr.
--God Demands Doctrinal Preaching. 1978. pap. 9.00 (ISBN 0-934916-32-2). Natl Christian Pr.
--The Home as God Would Have It & Contemporary Attacks Against It. 1979. pap. 12.00 (ISBN 0-934916-34-9). Natl Christian Pr.
--The Living Messages of the Books of the New Testament. 1976. 13.00 (ISBN 0-934916-35-7). Natl Christian Pr.
--The Living Messages of the Books of the Old Testament. 1977. 14.00 (ISBN 0-934916-36-5). Natl Christian Pr.
--Sermon on the Mount. 1982. 15.00 (ISBN 0-934916-00-4). Natl Christian Pr.
--Some Modern Sects, Cults, Movements & World Religions. 1981. 13.00 (ISBN 0-934916-46-2). Natl Christian Pr.
Warren, Thomas B. & Flew, A. G. N., eds. Warren-Flew Debate on the Existence of God. 1977. 14.00 (ISBN 0-934916-40-3). Natl Christian Pr.
Warren, Virgil. What the Bible Says about Salvation. LC 82-73345. (What the Bible Says Ser.). 640p. 1982. 13.95 (ISBN 0-89900-088-6). College Pr Pub.
Warren, W. L. Henry II. (English Monarchs Ser.). 1973. pap. 14.95 (ISBN 0-520-03494-5, CAL367). U of Cal Pr.
Warren, William F. Universe As Pictured in Milton's Paradise Lost. LC 73-12894. 1915. lib. bdg. 15.00 (ISBN 0-8414-9418-5). Folcroft.
--Universe As Pictured in Milton's Paradise Lost: An Illustrated Study for Personal & Class Use. LC 68-59037. (Illus.). 80p. 1968. Repr. of 1915 ed. 10.00x (ISBN 0-87752-117-4). Gordian.
Warrick, Keith, et al. Catholic High School Ministry. (Illus.). 224p. 1986. loose-leaf bdg. 34.95 (ISBN 0-88489-173-9). St Mary's.
Warrier, A. G. God in Advaita. 1977. text ed. 15.00x (ISBN 0-8426-1047-2). Verry.
Warrier, A. G., tr. see Shankara.
Warrier, A. Krishna. Sakta Upanisads. 3.50 (ISBN 0-8356-7318-9). Theos Pub Hse.
Warrington, James. Short Titles of Books Relating to or Illustrating the History & Practice of Psalmody in the U. S., 1620-1820. LC 77-178095. (American Classics in History & Social Science Ser.: No. 218). 102p. 1972. Repr. of 1898 ed. lib. bdg. 19.00 (ISBN 0-8337-5357-6). B Franklin.
Warrington, John, tr. see Aristotle.
Warschauer, J. The Historical Life of Christ. 1977. lib. bdg. 69.95 (ISBN 0-8490-1960-5). Gordon Pr.
Warshaw, Thayer S. A Compact Guide to Bible Based Beliefs. LC 80-19820. 49p. (Orig.). 1981. pap. 2.25 (ISBN 0-687-09254-X). Abingdon.
Warthin, Alfred S. The Physician of the Dance of Death: A Historical Study of the Evolution of the Dance of Death Mythus in Art. Kastenbaum, Robert, ed. LC 76-19592. (Death & Dying Ser.). (Illus.). 1977. Repr. of 1931 ed. lib. bdg. 17.00x (ISBN 0-405-09587-2). Ayer Co Pubs.
Wartick, Wallace. Lessons on New Testament Evidences. 250p. 1980. pap. 4.95 (ISBN 0-89900-141-6). College Pr Pub.
--Studies in Acts, Vol. II. (Bible Student Study Guides Ser). 1978. pap. 2.95 (ISBN 0-89900-154-8). College Pr Pub.
--Studies in Acts, Vol. I. (Bible Student Study Guides Ser). 1977. pap. 2.95 (ISBN 0-89900-153-X). College Pr Pub.
--Studies in Second Corinthians. (Bible Student Study Guides Ser.). 1977. pap. 2.95 (ISBN 0-89900-155-6). College Pr Pub.
--Twenty-Six Lessons on First Corinthians. (Bible Study Guide Ser.). 176p. (Orig.). 1980. pap. 3.95 (ISBN 0-89900-168-8). College Pr Pub.
--Twenty-Six Lessons on Hebrews. LC 79-53713. (Bible Student Study Guides Ser.). 1979. pap. 3.95 (ISBN 0-89900-160-2). College Pr Pub.
--Twenty-Six Lessons on the Four Gospels. 2nd ed. (Bible Student Study Guides Ser.). 1977. pap. 9.95 (ISBN 0-89900-157-2). College Pr Pub.
Wartski, Isidore, tr. see Silbermann, A. M.
Warwick, Donald P. The Teaching of Ethics & the Social Sciences. LC 80-10154. (The Teaching of Ethics Ser.). 69p. 1980. pap. 4.00 (ISBN 0-916558-11-8). Hastings Ctr.
Washbourn, Penelope. Becoming Woman: The Quest for Spiritual Wholeness in Female Experience. LC 76-9948. 1979. pap. 7.95 (ISBN 0-06-069261-8, RD 256, HarpR). Har-Row.
Washbourn, Penelope, ed. Seasons of Woman: Song, Poetry, Ritual, Prayer, Myth, Story. LC 78-3359. (Illus.). 128p. (Orig.). 1982. pap. 7.95 (ISBN 0-06-250930-6, CN4042, HarpR). Har-Row.
Washburn, Henry B. Men of Conviction. facs. ed. LC 74-134152. (Essay Index Reprint Ser). 1931. 18.00 (ISBN 0-8369-2081-3). Ayer Co Pubs.
--Religious Motive in Philanthropy. LC 72-105047. (Essay Index Reprint Ser). 1931. 18.00 (ISBN 0-8369-1634-4). Ayer Co Pubs.
Washburn, Paul. An Unfinished Church: A Brief History of the Union of the Evangelical United Brethern Church & the Methodist Church. 176p. 14.95 (ISBN 0-687-01378-X). Abingdon.
Washington, Joseph R., Jr. Anti-Blackness in English Religion. LC 84-27334. (Texts & Studies in Religion: Vol. 19). 623p. 1985. 79.95x (ISBN 0-88946-808-7). E Mellen.
--Black Religion: The Negro & Christianity in the United States. LC 84-5659. 328p. 1984. pap. text ed. 12.75 (ISBN 0-8191-3907-6). U Pr of Amer.
--Black Sects & Cults. 190p. 1984. pap. text ed. 10.50 (ISBN 0-8191-3906-8). U Pr of Amer.
Waskow, Arthur, et al. Before There Was a Before. LC 84-11177. (Illus.). 80p. 1984. 8.95 (ISBN 0-915361-08-6, 09404-9, Dist. by Watts). Adama Pubs Inc.
Waskow, Arthur I. Seasons of Our Joy: A Handbook of Jewish Festivals. 1986. 17.95 (ISBN 0-671-61865-2). Summit Bks.
Wass, Meldon. Infinite God. pap. 2.25 (ISBN 0-8199-0052-4, L38345). Franciscan Herald.
Wasserman, Harry, jt. auth. see Bubis, Gerald B.
Wasserman, Julian N., jt. auth. see Clark, Susan L.
Wasserstein, David. The Rise & Fall of the Party-Kings: Politics & Society in Islamic Spain, 1002-1086. LC 94-16072. (Illus.). 344p. 1985. text ed. 35.00x (ISBN 0-691-05436-3). Princeton U Pr.
Wasserzug, Dr. G. Signs & Wonders. 1.95 (ISBN 0-686-12836-2). Midnight Call.
--The Terrifying Goal of the Ecumenical Movement. 1.45 (ISBN 0-937422-77-0). Midnight Call.
Watanabe, Sadao. Biblical Prints. (Illus.). 1987. deluxe ed. 100.00 (ISBN 0-8028-3635-6). Eerdmans.
Watchman, Nee. Changed into His Likeness. 1978. pap. 3.95 (ISBN 0-8423-0228-X). Tyndale.
--From Faith to Faith. Fader, Herbert L., ed. Kaung, Stephen, tr. 120p. 1984. pap. 3.50 (ISBN 0-935008-62-4). Christian Fellow Pubs.
Watchman Nee. The Messenger of the Cross. Kaung, Stephen, tr. (Orig.). 1980. pap. text ed. 3.25 (ISBN 0-935008-50-0). Christian Fellow Pubs.
--The Spirit of Wisdom & Revelation. Kaung, Stephen, tr. 1980. pap. 3.25 (ISBN 0-935008-48-9). Christian Fellow Pubs.
Waterfield, Robin, tr. see Charles, Pierre.
Waterhouse, Eric S. Modern Theories of Religion. 1977. lib. bdg. 59.95 (ISBN 0-8490-2272-X). Gordon Pr.
Waterhouse, Ruth, ed. The Triangular Clause Relationship in Aelfric's Lives of Saints & in Other Works. LC 83-5399. (American Universtiy Studies IV: English Language & Literature: Vol. 1). 119p. (Orig.). 1983. pap. text ed. 12.10 (ISBN 0-8204-0007-6). P Lang Pubs.
Waterman, Leroy. Religion Faces the World Crisis. 1943. 3.75x (ISBN 0-685-21800-7). Wahr.
--The Religion of Jesus: Christianity's Unclaimed Heritage of Prophetic Religion. LC 78-16405. 1978. Repr. of 1952 ed. lib. bdg. 22.50x (ISBN 0-313-20586-8, WARJ). Greenwood.
Waterman, Mina. Voltaire, Pascal & Human Destiny. LC 70-120676. 1970. Repr. lib. bdg. 14.50x (ISBN 0-374-98279-1, Octagon). Hippocrene Bks.
Waterman, Paul. Great Adventures of the Old Testament. (Activity Book Ser.). Vol. 1. pap. 0.99 (ISBN 0-87123-751-2, 220751); Vol. 2. pap. 0.99 (ISBN 0-87123-769-5). Bethany Hse.
Waterman, Philip F. Story of Superstition. LC 78-107770. Repr. of 1929 ed. 15.00 (ISBN 0-404-06849-9). AMS Pr.
Waters, Anna M., ed. see Roberts, Kenneth J.
Waters, Anna Marie, ed. see Roberts, Kenneth J.
Waters, Clara E. A Handbook of Legendary & Mythological Art. LC 76-27524. (Illus.). 1976. Repr. of 1876 ed. lib. bdg. 50.00 (ISBN 0-89341-037-3). Longwood Pub Group.
Waters, Ethel & Michel, Charles. His Eye Is on the Sparrow. 1972. pap. 2.95 (ISBN 0-515-06738-5). Jove Pubns.
Waters, Frank. Mexico Mystique: The Coming Sixth World of Consciousness. LC 74-18579. (Illus.). 326p. 1975. 13.95 (ISBN 0-8040-0663-6, SB). Ohio U Pr.
--Mountain Dialogues. LC 81-732. x, 237p. 1981. 16.95 (ISBN 0-8040-0361-0, SB). Ohio U Pr.
Waters, Frank, ed. see Evans-Wentz, W. Y.
Waters, Kenneth, jt. auth. see Scalf, Cherie.
Waters, Michael. The Faithful. LC 84-4796. (Illus.). 16p. 1984. pap. 4.00 (ISBN 0-918518-31-8). Raccoon Memphis.
Wathen, James F. The Great Sacrilege. LC 76-183571. 1971. pap. 5.00 (ISBN 0-89555-014-8). TAN Bks Pubs.
--Is the Order of St. John Masonic? 84p. 1973. pap. 3.50 (ISBN 0-89555-250-7). TAN Bks Pubs.
Watkin, Edward I. Poets & Mystics. facs. ed. LC 68-55862. (Essay Index Reprint Ser). 1953. 19.00 (ISBN 0-8369-0979-8). Ayer Co Pubs.
Watkin, V. E., tr. see Steiner, Rudolf.
Watkins, Dawn L. Jenny Wren. (English Skills for Christian Schools Ser.). (Illus., Orig.). 1986. pap. 4.95 (ISBN 0-89084-324-4). Bob Jones Univ Pr.
--The Medallion. (English Skills for Christian Schools Ser.). (Illus.). 223p. (Orig.). 1985. pap. 5.95 (ISBN 0-89084-282-5). Bob Jones Univ Pr.
Watkins, George. Women in Today's Church. 56p. 1984. pap. 2.25 (ISBN 0-88144-025-6). Christian Pub.
Watkins, James N. Devotional Pursuits: Truth & Trivia. 96p. (Orig.). 1986. pap. 3.95 (ISBN 0-8341-1139-X). Beacon Hill.
Watkins, Janet. Savoring the Sabbath. LC 80-83865. 80p. (Orig.). 1980. pap. 4.95 (ISBN 0-88290-165-6, 1058). Horizon Utah.
Watkins, Keith. The Feast of Joy: Ministering the Lord's Supper in the Free Tradition. LC 77-525. 1977. pap. 1.50 (ISBN 0-8272-1006-X). CBP.
--Thankful Praise. LC 86-24514. 192p. (Orig.). 1987. pap. 9.95 (ISBN 0-8272-3650-6). CBP.
Watkins, Morris. Literacy, Bible Reading & Church Growth Through the Ages. LC 78-15315. (Illus.). 1978. pap. 5.95 (ISBN 0-87808-325-1). William Carey Lib.
Watley, William D. Sermons on Special Days: Preaching Through the Year in the Black Church. 128p. 1987. pap. 6.95 (ISBN 0-8170-1089-0). Judson.
Watley, William D., jt. auth. see Proctor, Samuel D.
Watson. Divine Love Song. pap. 3.50 (ISBN 0-686-12866-4). Schmul Pub Co.
--I Believe in the Church. pap. 10.95 (ISBN 0-8028-1788-2). Eerdmans.
Watson, Burton, ed. & tr. Basic Writings of Mo Tzu, Hsun Tzu, & Han Fei Tzu. LC 67-16170. (Records of Civilization, Sources & Studies: No. 74). 1967. 20.00x (ISBN 0-231-02515-7). Columbia U Pr.
Watson, Burton, tr. see Hsun Tzu.
Watson, Burton, tr. see Ikeda, Daisaku.
Watson, Cecilia. My Sabbath Fun Book. 1983. Bk. 1. pap. 4.95 ea. Bk. 2 (ISBN 0-8163-0463-7). Pacific Pr Pub Assn.
Watson, D. J. Dedication: Nobody Said It Was Easy. 1987. pap. write for info. (ISBN 0-88469-181-0). BMH Bks.
Watson, D. Jeanene. Teresa of Calcutta. LC 84-60313. (The Sowers Ser.). 1984. 8.95 (ISBN 0-88062-013-7); pap. 4.95 (ISBN 0-88062-012-9). Mott Media.

Watson, David. Creo en la Evangelizacion. Schwieters, Elsa S., tr. from Eng. (Serie Creo). Tr. of I Believe in Evangelism. (Span.). 235p. 1979. pap. 5.95 (ISBN 0-89922-133-5). Edit Caribe.
--Grow & Flourish: A Daily Guide to Personal Renewal. Watson, Jean, ed. (General). 392p. 1983. pap. 6.95 (ISBN 0-87788-327-0). Shaw Pubs.
--The Hidden Battle: Strategies for Spiritual Victory. Rev. ed. 160p. 1985. pap. 2.95 (ISBN 0-87788-343-2). Shaw Pubs.
--How to Find God. LC 76-43125. 157p. 1976. pap. 1.95 (ISBN 0-87788-390-4). Shaw Pubs.
--I Believe in Evangelism. (I Believe Ser). 1977. pap. 5.95 (ISBN 0-8028-1687-8). Eerdmans.
--My God Is Real. LC 81-71343. 95p. 1982. pap. 4.95 (ISBN 0-89107-248-9). Good News.
--You Are My God: A Pioneer of Renewal Recounts His Pilgramage in Faith. 196p. 1984. pap. 5.95 (ISBN 0-87788-972-4). Shaw Pubs.
Watson, David & Jenkins, Simon. Jesus Then & Now. Keely, R., ed. 192p. 1987. pap. 9.95 (ISBN 0-7459-1318-0). Lion USA.
Watson, David L. Early Methodist Class Meetings. 240p. (Orig.). pap. 10.95 (ISBN 0-88170-175-0, DR017B). Discipleship Res.
Watson, E. Elaine. I Wish, I Wish. LC 82-62733. (Happy Day Bks.). (Illus.). 24p. 1983. 1.59 (ISBN 0-87239-637-1, 3557). Standard Pub.
--Jesus Loves Me All the Time. (Happy Day Bks.). (Illus.). 24p. 1984. 1.59 (ISBN 0-87239-741-6, 3711). Standard Pub.
Watson, E. W. & Blanco, Miquel A. Cuatro Dramas De Navidad. 1984. pap. 0.95 (ISBN 0-311-08224-6). Casa Bautista.
Watson, Edward W. The Church of England. LC 80-22643. (Home University Library of Modern Knowledge: No. 90). 192p. 1981. Repr. of 1961 ed. lib. bdg. 25.00x (ISBN 0-313-22683-0, WAEN). Greenwood.
Watson, Elaine. God Knows Everything. (Happy Day Bks.). (Illus.). 24p. 1986. 1.59 (ISBN 0-87403-025-0, 3485). Standard Pub.
Watson, Elizabeth. Daughters of Zion. LC 82-70600. 100p. (Orig.). 1982. pap. 8.95 (ISBN 0-913408-79-4). Friends United.
Watson, Elizabeth E. God Knows You. LC 81-50678. (A Happy Day Bks.). (Illus.). 24p. (Orig.). 1981. pap. 1.59 (ISBN 0-87239-463-8, 3596). Standard Pub.
--God Made the Sea, the Sand & Me. (Illus.). 1979. 4.95 (ISBN 0-8054-4254-5, 4242-54). Broadman.
--Sometimes I'm Small, Sometime's I'm Tall. 1984. pap. 5.99 (ISBN 0-570-04091-4, 56-1459). Concordia.
--Tell Me about Jesus. 1980. pap. 3.95 (ISBN 0-570-03484-1, 56-1705). Concordia.
--Where Are You, God? (Illus.). 1977. bds. 5.50 (ISBN 0-8054-4235-9, 4242-35). Broadman.
Watson, Elizabeth W. Gift Wrap, Please. (Orig.). 1966. pap. 1.95 (ISBN 0-8054-9710-2). Broadman.
Watson, Francis. Paul, Judaism, & the Gentiles: A Sociological Approach. (Society for New Testament Studies Monographs: No. 56). 266p. Date not set. 32.50 (ISBN 0-521-32573-0). Cambridge U Pr.
Watson, G. D. Coals of Fire. pap. 2.95 (ISBN 0-686-12857-5). Schmul Pub Co.
Watson, Harold M. Claudel's Immortal Heroes: A Choice of Deaths. LC 73-160572. 1971. 25.00 (ISBN 0-8135-0695-6). Rutgers U Pr.
Watson, Jean. Watchmaker's Daughter: The Life of Corrie Ten Boom for Young People. (Illus.). 160p. 1983. pap. 4.95 (ISBN 0-8007-5116-7, Power Bks). Revell.
Watson, Jean, ed. & compiled by see Packer, James I.
Watson, Jean, ed. see Watson, David.
Watson, Jeffrey A. Looking Beyond. 132p. 1986. pap. 4.95 (ISBN 0-89693-155-2). Victor Bks.
Watson, John. The Interpretation of Religious Experience, 2 vols. LC 77-27216. (Gifford Lectures: 1910-12). Repr. of 1912 ed. Set. 67.50 (ISBN 0-404-60510-9). AMS Pr.
--The Scot of the Eighteenth Century. LC 76-47571. 1976. Repr. of 1907 ed. lib. bdg. 39.50 (ISBN 0-8414-9459-2). Folcroft.
Watson, K., tr. see Schneeberger, Pierre-F.
Watson, Lillian E. Light from Many Lamps. 1951. 15.95 (ISBN 0-671-42300-2). S&S.
Watson, Mary A. Mary, Woman of Faith. 32p. 1986. pap. 1.50 (ISBN 0-89243-260-8). Liguori Pubns.
Watson, P. Building the Medieval Cathedrals. LC 74-19525. (Introduction to the History of Mankind). 48p. 1976. pap. 4.95 limp bdg. (ISBN 0-521-08711-2). Cambridge U Pr.
Watson, P. S., tr. see Luther, Martin.
Watson, Percy. Building the Medieval Cathedrals. LC 78-56794. (Cambridge Topic Bks). (Illus.). 1978. PLB 8.95 (ISBN 0-8225-1213-0). Lerner Pubns.
Watson, Philip S. Let God Be God: An Interpretation of the Theology of Martin Luther. LC 83-45675. Date not set. Repr. of 1947 ed. 30.00 (ISBN 0-404-19864-3). AMS Pr.
Watson, Philip S., ed. The Message of the Wesleys: A Reader of Instruction & Devotion. 270p. 1983. pap. 9.95 (ISBN 0-310-75031-8, 17027P). Zondervan.
Watson, Philip S. & Lehmann, Helmut T., eds. Luther's Works: Career of the Reformer III, Vol. 33. new ed. LC 55-9893. 1972. 19.95 (ISBN 0-8006-0333-8, 1-333). Fortress.
Watson, Philip S., jt. ed. see Rupp, E. Gordon.
Watson, Richard. An Apology for Christianity in a Series of Letters Addressed to Edward Gibbon. Wellek, Rene, ed. Bd. with An Apology for the Bible Addressed to Thomas Paine. LC 75-25132. (British Philosophers & Theologians of the 17th & 18th Centuries Ser.). 452p. 1978. lib. bdg. 51.00 (ISBN 0-8240-1765-X). Garland Pub.
Watson, Rosemary A. As the Rock Flower Blooms. 1984. pap. 4.95 (ISBN 9971-972-17-4). OMF Bks.
Watson, Stanley J. Youth Ministry in the Church. LC 78-73597. 1978. pap. 2.50 (ISBN 0-8054-3228-0, 4232-28). Broadman.
Watson, Sydney. Mark of the Beast. 256p. 1974. 5.95 (ISBN 0-8007-5199-X, Power Bks); (Spire Bks). Revell.
Watson, Thomas. All Things for Good. (Puritan Paperbacks). 128p. (Orig.). 1986. pap. 3.45 (ISBN 0-85151-478-2). Banner of Truth.
--The Beatitudes. 307p. 1981. kivar bdg. 9.95 (ISBN 0-85151-035-3). Banner of Truth.
--A Body of Divinity. 1978. pap. 9.95 (ISBN 0-85151-383-2). Banner of Truth.
--Lord's Prayer. 1978. 9.95 (ISBN 0-85151-145-7). Banner of Truth.
--The Ten Commandments. 245p. pap. 8.45 (ISBN 0-85151-146-5). Banner of Truth.
Watson, Thomas E. The Roman Catholic Hierarchy. (Studies in Populism). 1980. lib. bdg. 69.95 (ISBN 0-686-68883-X). Revisionist Pr.
Watson, Tom, Jr. How to Be Happy No Matter What. LC 77-73559. 160p. 1978. pap. 3.50 (ISBN 0-8307-0465-5, S103125). Regal.
Watson, Vera M. The Children of Ministers Tell Us. 1983. 5.95 (ISBN 0-8062-2033-3). Carlton.
Watt, Gordon. Cross in Faith & Conduct. 1965. pap. 1.95 (ISBN 0-87508-964-X). Chr Lit.
Watt, Jean M., tr. see Dermenghem, Emile.
Watt, John. The Church in Medieval Ireland, Vol. 5. (Gill History of Ireland Ser.). 1973. 18.50 (ISBN 0-7171-0562-8, Pub. by Gill & Macmillan Ireland). Irish Bk Ctr.
Watt, Leilani. Caught in the Conflict. LC 83-82700. 176p. 1984. text ed. 9.95 (ISBN 0-89081-411-2). Harvest Hse.
Watt, Montgomery. What Is Islam? 1968. 25.00x (ISBN 0-685-77133-4). Intl Bk Ctr.
Watt, Montgomery, ed. see Al-Tabari.
Watt, W. M. Faith & Practice of Al-Ghazzali. 1967. 5.75x (ISBN 0-87902-060-1). Orientalia.
--The Influence of Islam Upon Medieval Europe. 125p. 1973. pap. 10.00x (ISBN 0-85224-439-8, Pub. by Edinburgh U Pr Scotland). Columbia U Pr.
Watt, W. M., tr. see Al-Ghazzali.
Watt, W. Montgomery. Islam & Christianity Today. LC 83-10949. 157p. 1984. 19.95x (ISBN 0-7100-9766-2, Kegan Paul). Methuen Inc.
--Muhammad at Medina. 1981. Repr. of 1956 ed. 39.95x (ISBN 0-19-577307-1). Oxford U Pr.
--Muhammad: Prophet & Statesman. 1961. pap. 7.95 (ISBN 0-19-881078-4). Oxford U Pr.
--What Is Islam? 2nd ed. (Arab Background Ser.). 1979. text ed. 29.95x (ISBN 0-582-78302-X). Longman.
Wattenbach, W., ed. Die Chronik Fredegars und der Frankenkoenige, die Lebensbeschreibungen des Abtes Columban, der Bischoefe Arnulf, Leodegar und Eligius, der Koenigin Balthilde. 2nd ed. Abel, Otto, tr. (Die Geschichtschreiber der Deutschen Vorzeit Ser: Vol. 11). (Ger.). pap. 19.00 (ISBN 0-384-00104-1). Johnson Repr.
Watters, Cyril. It's Easy to Play Hymns. 1981. pap. 5.95. Music Sales.
Watters, David, ed. Markers III: The Journal of the Association for Gravestone Studies. LC 81-642903. (Illus.). 162p. (Orig.). 1985. lib. bdg. 25.25 (ISBN 0-8191-4537-8); pap. text ed. 11.50 (ISBN 0-8191-4538-6). U Pr of Amer.
Watters, Mary. History of the Church in Venezuela, 1810-1930. LC 70-137303. Repr. of 1933 ed. 22.00 (ISBN 0-404-06877-4). AMS Pr.
Watters, Thomas. On Yuan Chwang's Travels in India 629-645 A. D. LC 74-158213. Repr. of 1905 ed. Set. 45.00 (ISBN 0-404-06878-2). AMS Pr.
Watters, William R. Formula Criticism & the Poetry of the Old Testament. (Beiheft 138 zur Zeitschrift fur die Alttestamentliche Wissenschaft). 1976. 43.20x (ISBN 3-11-005730-1). De Gruyter.
Watts, jt. auth. see Null.
Watts, Alan. The Art of Contemplation. LC 72-10174. 1973. 4.95 (ISBN 0-394-70963-2). Pantheon.
--Om: Creative Meditations. LC 79-54101. 160p. 1984. pap. 6.95 (ISBN 0-89087-257-0). Celestial Arts.
--The Way of Liberation: Essays & Lectures on the Transformation of the Self. Watts, Mark & Shropshire, Rebecca, eds. LC 82-21917. 120p. 1983. pap. 8.95 (ISBN 0-8348-0181-7). Weatherhill.
Watts, Alan & Chung-Liang Huang, Al. Tao: The Watercourse Way. LC 76-4762. 1977. pap. 5.95 (ISBN 0-394-73311-8). Pantheon.
Watts, Alan, ed. see Herrigel, Eugene.
Watts, Alan W. Behold the Spirit. 288p. 1972. pap. 4.95 (ISBN 0-394-71761-9, Vin). Random.
--Beyond Theology: The Art of Godmanship. 1973. pap. 3.95 (ISBN 0-394-71923-9, Vin). Random.
--Cloud Hidden, Whereabouts Unknown: A Mountain Journal. 1965. pap. 3.95 (ISBN 0-394-71999-9, Vin). Random.
--Does It Matter. LC 72-89988. 1971. pap. 3.95 (ISBN 0-394-71665-5, Vin). Random.
--In My Own Way: An Autobiography. 1973. pap. 5.95 (ISBN 0-394-71951-4, Vin). Random.
--The Meaning of Happiness: The Quest for Freedom of the Spirit in Modern Psychology & the Wisdom of the East. 1979. pap. 6.95 (ISBN 0-06-090676-6, CN 676, PL). Har-Row.
--Myth & Ritual in Christianity. (Illus.). 1968. pap. 9.95x (ISBN 0-8070-1375-7, BP301). Beacon Pr.
--Nature, Man & Woman. LC 58-8266. 1970. pap. 3.95 (ISBN 0-394-70592-0, V592, Vin). Random.
--The Spirit of Zen: A Way of Life, Work & Art in the Far East. 1958. pap. 2.95 (ISBN 0-394-17418-6, E219, Ever). Grove.
--The Supreme Identity. 1972. pap. 4.95 (ISBN 0-394-71835-6, Vin). Random.
--This Is It. 1972. pap. 3.95 (ISBN 0-394-71904-2, Vin). Random.
--Way of Zen. 1974. pap. 4.95 (ISBN 0-394-70298-0, Vin). Random.
Watts, Alan W., ed. Patterns of Myth Series. Incl. Lord of the Four Quarters. Perry, John W; The Two Hands of God. Watts, Alan W; The Wisdom of the Serpent. Henderson, Joseph L. & Oakes, Maud.. Braziller.
Watts, Dale. Zen Sensualism: The Union of Spirituality & Sexuality. LC 86-82338. 56p. (Orig.). 1986. pap. 9.25 (ISBN 0-937497-39-8). Hart Eden Pr.
Watts, Dorothy E. Stepping Stones. Woolsey, Raymond, ed. (Morning Watch Ser.). 384p. 1987. text ed. price not set (ISBN 0-8280-0384-X). Review & Herald.
Watts, H. E. The Christian Recovery of Spain. 69.95 (ISBN 0-87968-863-7). Gordon Pr.
Watts, Issac. Logic: Or, the Right Use of Reason in the Enquiry after Truth, with a Variety of Rules to Guard Against Error, in the Affairs of Religion & Human Life as Well as the Sciences. LC 83-48579. (The Philosophy of John Locke Ser.). 365p. 1984. lib. bdg. 44.00 (ISBN 0-8240-5615-9). Garland Pub.
Watts, J. Wash. Ordination of Baptist Ministers. pap. 1.50 (ISBN 0-8054-9404-9). Broadman.
Watts, John. Isaiah Two (WBC, Vol. 25. 400p. 1987. 24.95 (ISBN 0-8499-0224-X). Word Bks.
Watts, John D. The Books of Joel, Obadiah, Jonah, Naham, Habakkuk & Zehaniah. LC 74-80355. (Cambridge Bible Commentary on the New English Bible, Old Testament Ser.). 300p. 1975. 22.95 (ISBN 0-521-20505-0); pap. 10.95 (ISBN 0-521-09870-X). Cambridge U Pr.
--Obadiah: A Critical & Exegetical Commentary. 78p. 1981. pap. 4.95x (ISBN 0-686-79148-7). Eisenbrauns.
Watts, Mark, ed. see Watts, Alan.
Watts, Mark P., jt. auth. see Hard, Larry.
Watts, Michael R. The Dissenters: From the Reformation to the French Revolution. 568p. 1986. pap. 19.95x (ISBN 0-19-822956-9). Oxford U Pr.
Watts, P. Mark. Living Through Your Separation or Divorce. Sherer, Michael L., ed. (Orig.). 1987. pap. 2.25 (ISBN 0-89536-864-1, 7823). CSS of Ohio.
Wauchope, Robert S. Buddhist Cave Temples of India. LC 78-70139. Repr. of 1933 ed. 34.50 (ISBN 0-404-17409-4). AMS Pr.
Wauck, LeRoy A., ed. see Godin, Andre.
Wauck, Mark A., tr. see Gilson, Etienne.
Waugh, Charles G., jt. ed. see Greenberg, Martin H.
Waugh, E. H., et al, eds. The Muslim Community in North America. xii, 316p. 1983. pap. 15.00x (ISBN 0-88864-034-X, Pub. by Univ of Alta Pr Canada). U of Nebr Pr.
Waugh, Margaret, ed. see Southwell, Robert.
Waugh, Teresa, tr. see Gimpel, Jean.
Waxman, Chaim I. America's Jews in Transition. 290p. 1983. 29.95 (ISBN 0-87722-321-1); pap. 12.95 (ISBN 0-87722-329-7). Temple U Pr.
Waxman, Meyer. A History of Jewish Literature, 6 vols. 50.00 set (ISBN 0-8453-8640-9, Cornwall Bks). Assoc Univ Prs.
Way, Arthur S. Letters of Paul, Hebrews & Psalms. LC 81-1092. 504p. 1981. text ed. 14.95 (ISBN 0-8254-4016-5). Kregel.
Way International Research Team, ed. Concordance to the Peshitta Version of the Aramaic New Testament. LC 85-51248. 494p. 1985. 19.95 (ISBN 0-910068-61-5). Am Christian.
Way, Nancy L. A Second Chance. 1985. 5.95 (ISBN 0-8062-2444-4). Carlton.
Way, Robert. The Garden of the Beloved. 80p. 1983. pap. 4.95 (ISBN 0-8091-2534-X). Paulist Pr.
Way, Robert, ed. The Wisdom of the English Mystics. LC 78-6435. 1978. pap. 3.75 (ISBN 0-8112-0700-5, NDP466). New Directions.
Waybill, Marjorie. God's Family Activity Book. 64p. (Orig.). 1983. pap. 3.00 (ISBN 0-8361-3336-6). Herald Pr.
--God's Justice: Activity Book. (Story Bible Ser.: Vol. 6). 88p. (Orig.). 1985. pap. 3.00 (ISBN 0-8361-3397-8). Herald Pr.
Wayland, Francis. Elements of Moral Science. Blau, Joseph L., ed. LC 63-19149. (The John Harvard Library). 1963. 27.50x (ISBN 0-674-24600-4). Harvard U Pr.
--Notes on the Principles & Practices of Baptist Churches. Gaustad, Edwin S., ed. LC 79-52610. (Baptist Tradition Ser.). 1980. Repr. of 1857 ed. lib. bdg. 27.50x (ISBN 0-405-12475-9). Ayer Co Pubs.
Wayland, Francis & Wayland, H. L. A Memoir of the Life & Labors of Francis Wayland, D. D., L. L. D. LC 76-38465. (Religion in America, Ser. 2). 818p. 1972. Repr. of 1867 ed. 52.00 (ISBN 0-405-04092-X). Ayer Co Pubs.
Wayland, H. L., jt. auth. see Wayland, Francis.
Wayland, H. Lincoln, ed. see Muller, George.
Wayland, John T. The Theological Department in Yale College, 1822-1858. Kuklick, Bruce, ed. (American Religious Thought of the 18th & 19th Centuries Ser.). 500p. 1987. lib. bdg. 70.00 (ISBN 0-8240-6962-5). Garland Pub.
Wayman, Alex. Analysis of the Sravakabhumi Manuscript. LC 61-64259. (University of California Publications in Classical Philology: Vol. 17). pap. 48.00 (ISBN 0-317-09845-4, 2021172). Bks Demand UMI.
--The Buddhist Tantras: Light on Indo-Tibetan Esotericism. LC 73-79801. (Illus.). 247p. 1973. 12.50 (ISBN 0-87728-223-4). Weiser.
--Yoga of the Guhyasamajatantra. 1977. 28.00 (ISBN 0-89684-003-4, Pub. by Motilal Banarsidass India). Orient Bk Dist.
--Yoga of the Guhyasamjatantra. 386p. 1980. pap. 7.95 (ISBN 0-87728-451-2). Weiser.
Wayman, Alex & Lessing, F. D. Introduction to the Buddhist Tantric System. 382p. 1980. pap. 7.95 (ISBN 0-87728-450-4). Weiser.
Wayman, Alex, jt. auth. see Lessing, F. D.
Wayman, Alex, tr. from Tibetan, Sanskrit. Chanting the Names of Manjusri: The Manjusri-Nama-Samgiti, Sanskrit & Tibetan Texts. LC 83-2309. 130p. 1985. 30.00 (ISBN 0-87773-316-3, 54531-1). Shambhala Pubns.
Wayman, Alex & Wayman, Hideko, trs. from Chinese. The Lion's Roar of Queen Srimala. 160p. 1974. 24.00x (ISBN 0-231-03726-0). Columbia U Pr.
Wayman, Hideko, jt. tr. see Wayman, Alex.
Waymire, Bob & Wagner, C. Peter. The Church Growth Survey Handbook. 3rd. rev. ed. 4.15 (ISBN 0-318-20599-8). Overseas Crusade.
Wayne, Jones R. Overcoming Barriers to Sunday School Growth. LC 86-23290. (Orig.). 1987. pap. 5.95 (ISBN 0-8054-3238-8). Broadman.
Waywood, Robert F. Hanging in There with Christ. 1974. 4.95 (ISBN 0-8199-0498-8). Franciscan Herald.
Waznak, Robert. Sunday after Sunday: Preaching the Homily as a Story. LC 82-62922. 128p. (Orig.). 1983. pap. 4.95 (ISBN 0-8091-2540-4). Paulist Pr.
Wead, Doug. Where Is the Lost Ark? LC 82-71755. 122p. (Orig.). 1982. pap. 2.95 (ISBN 0-87123-628-1, 200628). Bethany Hse.
Wead, Douglas. The Compassionate Touch. LC 76-62694. (Illus.). 192p. 1980. pap. 3.50 (ISBN 0-87123-021-6, 200021). Bethany Hse.
Weakland, Rembert G. All God's People: Catholic Identity after the Second Vatican Council. LC 84-61493. 216p. (Orig.). 1985. pap. 7.95 (ISBN 0-8091-2665-6). Paulist Pr.
Weakley, Clare, jt. auth. see Wesley, John.
Weakley, Clare, ed. see Wesley, John.
Weales, Gerald C. Religion in Modern English Drama. LC 75-45367. 317p. 1976. Repr. of 1961 ed. lib. bdg. 24.75x (ISBN 0-8371-8735-4, WEME). Greenwood.
Wean, Ronald. One Must Die: Six-Week Lenten Drama Series. 1986. 6.50 (ISBN 0-89536-794-7, 6812). CSS of Ohio.
Wearmouth, Robert F. Methodism & the Working-Class Movements of England 1800-1850. LC 73-139523. 1972. Repr. of 1937 ed. 29.50x (ISBN 0-678-00829-9). Kelley.

Weatherby, Harold L. Cardinal Newman in His Age: His Place in English Theology & Literature. LC 72-1347. 320p. 1973. 16.50x (ISBN 0-8265-1182-1). Vanderbilt U Pr.

Weatherby, W. J., et al. Chariots of Fire & a Christian Message for Today. LC 82-48941. (Quicksilver Bk.). 176p. (Orig.). 1983. pap. 5.95 (ISBN 0-06-069282-0, RD 455, HarpR). Har-Row.

Weatherford, W. D. American Churches & the Negro. 310p. 1957. 8.95 (ISBN 0-8158-0207-2). Chris Mass.

Weatherford De Ruiz, L. M., compiled by. La Navidad. (Span.). 192p. 1981. pap. 2.75 (ISBN 0-311-08207-6). Casa Bautista.

Weatherhead, Leslie D. Antidoto Contra la Ansiedad. 1979. pap. 2.75 (ISBN 0-8358-0414-3). Upper Room.

--The Autobiography of Jesus: What He Said about Himself. (Festival Bks.). 1980. pap. 1.95 (ISBN 0-687-02318-1). Abingdon.

--The Christian Agnostic. (Festival Books Ser.). 1979. pap. 4.50 (ISBN 0-687-06978-5). Abingdon.

--Leslie D. Weatherhead Library, 8 vols. Set in Slipcase. 17.50 (ISBN 0-687-21373-8). Abingdon.

--Life Begins at Death. (Festival Ser.). 112p. 1981. pap. 2.25 (ISBN 0-687-21806-3). Abingdon.

--The Meaning of the Cross. (Festival Ser.). 192p. 1982. pap. 2.75 (ISBN 0-687-23970-2). Abingdon.

--Prescription for Anxiety: How You Can Overcome Fear & Despair. LC 57-5284. (Festival Bks.). 1979. pap. 1.95 (ISBN 0-687-33987-1). Abingdon.

--A Private House of Prayer. (Festival Bks). 1979. pap. 2.95 (ISBN 0-687-34220-1). Abingdon.

--Time for God. (Festival Ser.). 1981. pap. 1.75 (ISBN 0-687-42113-6). Abingdon.

--The Transforming Friendship. (Festival Books). 1977. pap. 1.25 (ISBN 0-687-42510-7). Abingdon.

--The Will of God. (Festival Books). 1976. pap. 2.95 (ISBN 0-687-45600-2). Abingdon.

Weatherspool, W. W. Those Days. 1981. 5.95 (ISBN 0-8062-1835-5). Carlton.

Weaver, Bennett. Toward the Understanding of Shelley. 1967. lib. bdg. 18.50x (ISBN 0-374-98284-8, Octagon). Hippocrene Bks.

Weaver, Bertrand. His Cross in Your Life. LC 78-56766. 1978. pap. 2.25 (ISBN 0-8189-1152-2, Pub. by Alba Bks). Alba.

Weaver, Charles P. The Hermit in English Literature from the Beginnings to 1660. LC 73-515. 1973. lib. bdg. 25.00 (ISBN 0-8414-1456-4). Folcroft.

Weaver, Horace R. Getting Straight about the Bible: The Creation, Interpreting Scripture, the Apocalypse, Life on Other Planets. LC 75-2342. 160p. (Orig.). 1975. pap. 6.95 (ISBN 0-687-14138-9). Abingdon.

--International Lesson Annual, 1987-1988. 448p. 1987. pap. 7.95 (ISBN 0-687-19151-3). Abingdon.

Weaver, Horace R., ed. The International Lesson Annual, 1986-1987. 448p. (Orig.). 1986. pap. 7.95 (ISBN 0-687-19150-5). Abingdon.

Weaver, J. Denny. Becoming Anabaptist. LC 86-33650. 176p. (Orig.). 1987. pap. 14.95 (ISBN 0-8361-3434-6). Herald Pr.

Weaver, Mary J., ed. Newman & the Modernists. (Resources in Religion Ser.: Vol. 1). 232p. (Orig.). 1986. lib. bdg. 25.75 (ISBN 0-8191-4687-0, College Theo Soc); pap. text ed. 12.25 (ISBN 0-8191-4688-9). U Pr of Amer.

Webb, Barbara O. Devotions for Families: Building Blocks of Christian Life. LC 75-22162. 48p. 1976. pap. 1.95 (ISBN 0-8170-0680-X). Judson.

--Devotions for Families with Young Readers. 64p. 1985. pap. 4.95 (ISBN 0-8170-1063-7). Judson.

--Families Sharing God. 48p. 1981. pap. 3.50 (ISBN 0-8170-0900-0). Judson.

--In Christ, My Lord. 1982. pap. 4.95 (ISBN 0-570-03852-9, 12YY2807). Concordia.

--The Lord's Prayer: The Prayer Jesus Taught. (Concept Ser.). (Illus.). 24p. (Orig.). 1986. pap. 3.95 saddlestitched (ISBN 0-570-08529-2, 56-1556). Concordia.

--Now What, Lord? Bible Devotions for Girls. LC 85-22884. (Young Readers Ser.). 112p. (Orig.). 1985. pap. 3.95 (ISBN 0-8066-2182-6, 10-4680). Augsburg.

--Waiting for My Baby. 80p. 1985. 6.95 (ISBN 0-570-04219-4, 15-2180). Concordia.

Webb, Barry G. The Book of the Judges: An Integrated Reading. (JSOT Supplement Ser.: No. 46). 260p. 1987. text ed. 31.50x (ISBN 1-85075-034-3, Pub. by JSOT Pr England); pap. text ed. 14.95x (ISBN 1-85075-035-1, Pub. by JSOT Pr England). Eisenbrauns.

Webb, Benjamin, ed. see Durantis, Gulielmus.

Webb, C. J. Divine Personality & Human Life. (Gifford Lectures Delivered in the University of Aberdeen in 1918&1919, Second Course Ser.). Repr. of 1920 ed. 17.00 (ISBN 0-527-94900-0). Kraus Repr.

--God & Personality. (Gifford Lectures Delivered in the University of Aberdeen in 1918 & 1919 First Course). Repr. of 1918 ed. 17.00 (ISBN 0-527-94906-X). Kraus Repr.

--Kant's Philosophy of Religion. Repr. of 1926 ed. 18.00 (ISBN 0-527-94912-4). Kraus Repr.

--Pascal's Philosophy of Religion. Repr. of 1929 ed. 12.00 (ISBN 0-527-94918-3). Kraus Repr.

Webb, Catherine. Lives of Great Men & Women: Charles Kingsley, John Ruskin, William Morris. 1911. Repr. 25.00 (ISBN 0-8274-2976-2). R West.

Webb, Clement C. Divine Personality & Human Life: Being the Gifford Lectures Delivered in the University of Aberdeen in the Years 1918 & 1919, Second Course. facsimile ed. LC 77-37917. (Select Bibliographies Reprint Ser.). Repr. of 1920 ed. 21.00 (ISBN 0-8369-6754-2). Ayer Co Pubs.

--God & Personality: Being the Gifford Lectures Delivered in the University of Aberdeen in the Years 1918 & 1919. facsimile ed. LC 76-164632. (Select Bibliographies Reprint Ser.). Repr. of 1919 ed. 20.00 (ISBN 0-8369-5916-7). Ayer Co Pubs.

Webb, Edith B. Indian Life at the Old Missions. LC 82-23871. (Illus.). xxx, 378p. 1983. Repr. of 1952 ed. 35.00 (ISBN 0-8032-4724-9). U of Nebr Pr.

Webb, James, ed. A Quest Anthology. LC 75-36916. (Occult Ser.). 1976. Repr. of 1976 ed. 46.50x (ISBN 0-405-07971-0). Ayer Co Pubs.

Webb, Jim, et al. Effective Father Action Guide. 1979. 3.95 (ISBN 0-8423-0688-9). Tyndale.

Webb, Lance. The Art of Personal Prayer. 1977. 3.95x (ISBN 0-8358-0365-1). Upper Room.

--Disciplines for Life. 176p. pap. 7.95 (ISBN 0-8358-0539-5, ICN 602777, Dist. by Abingdon Pr). Upper Room.

--How Bad Are Your Sins? 224p. (Orig.). 1983. pap. 4.95 (ISBN 0-687-17520-8, Festival). Abingdon.

--How Good are your Virtues? 176p. (Orig.). 1983. pap. 3.95 (ISBN 0-687-17528-3, Festival). Abingdon.

--Making Love Grow: Love That Can Make Incompatibility a Myth. LC 83-80410. 176p. (Orig.). 1983. pap. 6.50 (ISBN 0-8358-0462-3). Upper Room.

--Onesimus. LC 80-21306. 374p. 1980. pap. 4.95 (ISBN 0-8407-5742-5). Nelson.

Webb, Lillian A. About My Father's Business: The Life of Elder Michaux. LC 80-24595. (Contributions in Afro-American & African Studies: No. 61). (Illus.). 232p. 1981. lib. bdg. 29.95 (ISBN 0-313-22261-4, WFB/). Greenwood.

Webb, Robert C. The Real Mormonism. LC 72-2971. Repr. of 1916 ed. 29.00 (ISBN 0-404-10736-2). AMS Pr.

Webb, Warren, jt. auth. see Collison, Kathleen.

Webb, Wheaton P. The Heart Has Its Seasons: A Sourcebook of Christmas Meditations. LC 82-3898. 96p. (Orig.). 1982. pap. 7.75 (ISBN 0-687-16800-7). Abingdon.

Webb, William P. Behind the Creed: A Plain Man's Rationale of Faith. LC 84-90201. 115p. 1985. 10.95 (ISBN 0-533-06248-9). Vantage.

Webbe, Gale D. The Shape of Growth. 110p. (Orig.). 1985. pap. 9.95 (ISBN 0-8192-1356-X). Morehouse.

Webber, Frederick R. Church Symbolism: An Explanation of the More Important Symbols of the Old & New Testament, the Primitive, the Mediaeval & the Modern Church. rev. 2nd ed. LC 79-107627. (Illus.). 1971. Repr. of 1938 ed. 56.00x (ISBN 0-8103-3349-X). Gale.

Webber, Robert. Celebrating Our Faith: Evangelism Through Worship. 1986. 10.95 (ISBN 0-06-069286-3, HarpR). Har-Row.

--The Majestic Tapestry: How the Power of Early Christian Tradition Can Enrich Contemporary Faith. 160p. 1986. 12.95 (ISBN 0-8407-5536-8). Nelson.

Webber, Robert E. The Book of Family Prayer. 288p. 1986. 17.95 (ISBN 0-8407-5479-5). Nelson.

--The Church in the World. 368p. (Orig.). 1986. pap. text ed. 11.95 (ISBN 0-310-36601-1, 12213P). Zondervan.

--Common Roots: A Call to Evangelical Maturity. 256p. 1982. pap. 7.95 (ISBN 0-310-36631-3, 12205P). Zondervan.

--Evangelicals on the Canterbury Trail: Why Evangelicals Are Attracted to the Liturgical Church. 160p. 1985. 13.95 (ISBN 0-8499-0402-1, 04021). Word Bks.

--I Believe: A Woman's Workshop on Relational Doctrine. (Woman's Workshop Ser.). 160p. 1986. pap. 3.95 (ISBN 0-310-36701-8). Zondervan.

--In Heart & Home: A Woman's Workshop on Worship. (Woman's Workshop Ser.). 112p. (Orig.). 1985. pap. 2.95 (ISBN 0-310-36681-X, 12209P). Zondervan.

--The Moral Majority: Right or Wrong. 190p. 1981. 9.95. Cornerstone.

--Secular Humanism. 144p. 1985. pap. 5.95 (ISBN 0-310-36671-2, 12208P). Zondervan.

--Worship Is a Verb. 224p. 1985. 12.95 (ISBN 0-8499-0371-8, 0371-8). Word Bks.

--Worship Old & New. 256p. 1982. 11.95 (ISBN 0-310-36650-X, 12207); pap. 9.95 (ISBN 0-310-36651-8, 12207P). Zondervan.

Webber, Roger. Evolution of Belief. 89p. 1984. 8.95 (ISBN 0-533-05475-3). Vantage.

Weber, Bill. Conquering the Kill-Joys: Positive Living in a Negative World. 160p. 1986. 12.95 (ISBN 0-8499-0439-0, 0439-0). Word Bks.

Weber, Burton J. Construction of Paradise Lost. LC 72-132483. (Literary Structures Ser.). 218p. 1971. 12.50x (ISBN 0-8093-0488-0). S Ill U Pr.

--Wedges & Wings: The Patterning of Paradise Regained. LC 74-20703. (Literary Structure Ser.). 144p. 1975. 10.00x (ISBN 0-8093-0673-5). S Ill U Pr.

Weber, C., tr. see Bratcher, Robert G. & Nida, Eugene A.

Weber, Charles E. The Holocaust: One Hundred Twenty Questions & Answers. (Illus.). 60p. (Orig.). 1983. pap. 4.00 (ISBN 0-939484-07-2). Inst Hist Rev.

Weber, Christa. Before the Moon Dies. 1984. pap. 1.50 (ISBN 9971-972-15-8). OMF Bks.

Weber, Donald A., jt. ed. see Stevens, Elliot L.

Weber, Donald R. see Stevens, Elliot L.

Weber, Francis J. California's Reluctant Prelate: The Life & Times of Thaddeus Amat. (Illus.). 1964. 6.75 (ISBN 0-87093-061-3). Dawsons.

--Readings in California Catholic History. 10.00 (ISBN 0-87026-000-6). Westernlore.

--Select Guide to California Catholic History. 12.50 (ISBN 0-87026-001-4). Westernlore.

Weber, G. P., et al, eds. Word & Worship: CCD Ed. Incl. Our Brother Jesus. pap. 2.56 (ISBN 0-02-649370-5, 64937); Jesus with Us. pap. 2.88 (ISBN 0-02-649330-6, 64933); We Follow Jesus. pap. 3.76 (ISBN 0-02-649470-1, 64947); Father, Son & Spirit Show Their Love. pap. 3.80 (ISBN 0-02-649150-8, 64915); We Break Bread in Loving Thanksgiving. 2nd ed. pap. 3.80 (ISBN 0-02-649110-9, 64941); God's Saving Word. pap. 4.36 (ISBN 0-02-649290-3, 64929); God's Saving Mystery. 2nd ed. pap. 4.36 (ISBN 0-02-649190-7, 64919); God's Saving Presence. pap. 4.36 (ISBN 0-02-649250-4, 64925). 1966-70. tchr's manual 3.36 ea.; parent's guide 2.00 (ISBN 0-02-649140-0, 64914). Benziger Pub Co.

Weber, Gerard. The Mass: Finding Its Meaning for You & Getting More Out of It. (Illus., Orig.). 1985. pap. 4.95 (ISBN 0-86716-049-7). St Anthony Mess Pr.

Weber, Gerard P., et al. Grow in God's Love. 2nd ed. 1977. 2.64 (ISBN 0-02-658200-7); tchrs. ed. 8.00 (ISBN 0-02-658210-4); family handbook 1.00 (ISBN 0-02-658250-3). Benziger Pub Co.

--We Grow in God's Family: Preparation for Confirmation. (Illus., Orig.). 1968. pap. 2.32 (ISBN 0-02-649060-9, 64906); pap. 1.50 tchr's. manual (ISBN 0-02-649070-6, 64907). Benziger Pub Co.

--Act As God's Children. 2nd ed. (The Word Is Life Ser.). 1977. 3.60 (ISBN 0-02-658300-3); tchrs. ed. 8.00 (ISBN 0-02-658310-0); family handbook 1.00 (ISBN 0-02-658350-X). Benziger Pub Co.

--Baptism & the Family. 1972. pap. 2.64 (ISBN 0-02-649000-5). Benziger Pub Co.

--Hear with God's People. 2nd ed. (The Word Is Life Ser.). 1977. 4.00 (ISBN 0-02-658600-2); tchrs. ed. 8.00 (ISBN 0-02-658610-X); family handbook 1.00 (ISBN 0-02-658650-9). Benziger Pub Co.

--Live in God's World. 2nd ed. (The Word Is Life Ser.). 1977. 2.64 (ISBN 0-02-658100-0); tchrs. ed. 8.00 (ISBN 0-02-658110-8); family handbook 1.00 (ISBN 0-02-658150-7). Benziger Pub Co.

--Think. 2nd ed. (The Word Is Life Ser.). 1979. 3.60 (ISBN 0-02-658700-9); tchrs. ed. 8.00 (ISBN 0-02-658710-6); family handbook 0.64 (ISBN 0-02-658750-5). Benziger Pub Co.

--Unite at the Lord's Table. (The Word Is Life Ser.). 4p. 1977. 3.92 (ISBN 0-02-658400-X); tchrs. ed. 8.00 (ISBN 0-02-658410-7); family handbook 1.00 (ISBN 0-02-658450-6). Benziger Pub Co.

--Believe with God's Family. 2nd ed. (The Word Is Life Ser.). 1977. 3.92 (ISBN 0-02-658500-6); tchrs. ed. 8.00 (ISBN 0-02-658510-3); family handbook 1.00 (ISBN 0-02-658550-2). Benziger Pub Co.

Weber, Giselher, tr. see Van Goudoever, H. D.

Weber, Hans R. The Militant Ministry: People & Pastors of the Early Church. LC 64-12990. (The Knubel-Miller Lectures for 1963). pap. 30.00 (2027186). Bks Demand UMI.

Weber, Hans-Reudi. Immanuel: The Coming of Jesus in Art & the Bible. (Illus.). 128p. 1984. 12.95 (ISBN 0-8028-3603-8). Eerdmans.

Weber, Hans-Ruedi. Experiments with Bible Study. LC 82-13398. 330p. 1983. pap. 12.95 (ISBN 0-664-24461-0). Westminster.

--Jesus & the Children: Biblical Resources for Study & Preaching. LC 79-87754. 1980. pap. 5.95 (ISBN 0-8042-1316-X). John Knox.

Weber, Herbert. The Parish Help Book: A Guide to Social Ministry in the Parish. LC 83-71894. 112p. 1983. pap. 3.95 (ISBN 0-87793-304-9). Ave Maria.

Weber, J. G. In Quest of the Absolute. LC 77-3596. (Cistercian Studies: No. 51). 1977. 10.95 (ISBN 0-87907-851-0); pap. 4.95 (ISBN 0-87907-951-7). Cistercian Pub.

Weber, Martin. Some Call It Heresy. Woolsey, Raymond, ed. 128p. (Orig.). 1985. pap. 6.95 (ISBN 0-8280-0248-7). Review & Herald.

Weber, Max. Ancient Judaism. Martindale, Don, ed. Gerth, Hans H., tr. LC 52-8156. 484p. 1967. pap. text ed. 12.95x (ISBN 0-02-934130-2). Free Pr.

--Protestant Ethic & the Spirit of Capitalism. rev. ed. 1977. pap. 8.95 (ISBN 0-684-16489-2, ScribT). Scribner.

--The Protestant Ethic & the Spirit of Capitalism. 1984. 15.50 (ISBN 0-8446-6118-X). Peter Smith.

--Religion of China. 1968. 14.95 (ISBN 0-02-934440-9); text ed. 14.95 (ISBN 0-02-934450-6). Free Pr.

--Sociology of Religion. Fischoff, Ephraim, tr. 1964. pap. 10.95x (ISBN 0-8070-4193-9, BP189). Beacon Pr.

Weber, Otto. Foundations of Dogmatics, Vol. 1. Guder, Darrel L., tr. 656p. 1982. 27.00 (ISBN 0-8028-3554-6). Eerdmans.

--Foundations of Dogmatics, Vol. 2. Guder, Darrell L., tr. from Ger. 736p. 1983. 27.00 (ISBN 0-8028-3564-3). Eerdmans.

Weber, Paul J. & Gilbert, Dennis A. Private Churches & Public Money: Church-Government Fiscal Relations. LC 80-1793. (Contributions to the Study of Religion: No. 1). (Illus.). xx, 260p. 1981. lib. bdg. 29.95 (ISBN 0-313-22484-6, WCM/). Greenwood.

Weber, Renee. Dialogues with Scientists & Sages: The Search for Unity in Science & Mysticism. 288p. 1986. pap. 14.95 (ISBN 0-7102-0655-0, 06550, Pub. by Routledge UK). Methuen Inc.

Weber, Steve, jt. auth. see Cook, R. Franklin.

Weber, Timothy P. Living in the Shadow of the Second Coming: American Premillennialism, 1875-1982. rev. & enl. ed. xiv, 306p. 1987. pap. 12.95 (ISBN 0-226-87732-9). U of Chicago Pr.

Webley, Simon. How to Give Away Your Money. 1979. pap. 1.95 (ISBN 0-87784-601-4). Inter-Varsity.

Weborg, John. Where Is It Written? An Introductory, Annotated Bibliography in Spirituality. 1978. 0.75 (ISBN 0-8199-0739-1). Franciscan Herald.

Webster, Brenda. Blake's Prophetic Psychology. LC 84-114638. (Illus.). 336p. 1983. 27.50x (ISBN 0-8203-0658-4). U of Ga Pr.

Webster, Dan, jt. auth. see McAllister, Dawson.

Webster, Doug, jt. auth. see Burns, Jim.

Webster, Douglas. Yes to Mission. LC 66-72166. 1966. text ed. 6.00x (ISBN 0-8401-2703-0). A R Allenson.

Webster, Ellen L., jt. ed. see Webster, John C.

Webster, Gary. Wonders of Man. LC 57-6055. 1957. 3.50 (ISBN 0-685-42655-6, Pub. by Sheed). Guild Bks.

Webster, Graham. Celtic Religion in Roman Britain. LC 86-26532. (Illus.). 176p. 1987. 30.00 (ISBN 0-389-20686-5). B&N Imports.

Webster, Hutton. Rest Days, the Christian Sunday, the Jewish Sabbath & Their Historical & Anthropological Prototypes. LC 68-58165. 1968. Repr. of 1916 ed. 48.00x (ISBN 0-8103-3342-2). Gale.

--Taboo: A Sociological Study. LC 73-4250. xii, 393p. 1973. Repr. of 1942 ed. lib. bdg. 26.00x (ISBN 0-374-98324-0, Octagon). Hippocrene Bks.

Webster, John C. & Webster, Ellen L., eds. The Church & Women in the Third World. LC 84-26967. 168p. (Orig.). 1985. pap. 11.95 (ISBN 0-664-24601-X). Westminster.

Webster, Richard A. The Cross & the Fasces: Christian Democracy and Fascism in Italy. 1960. 18.50x (ISBN 0-8047-0043-5). Stanford U Pr.

Wedderburn, A. J., jt. ed. see Logan, A. H.

Wedderspoon, A. G., ed. Religious Education, Nineteen Forty-Four to Nineteen Eighty-Four. 238p. 1968. 3.95 (ISBN 0-87921-063-X); pap. 1.95 (ISBN 0-87921-064-8). Attic Pr.

Wedderspoon, William M. God & the Procurator, Some Questions Asked. 176p. 1986. 9.95 (ISBN 0-8059-3020-5). Dorrance.

Weddle, David L. The Law As Gospel: Revival & Reform in the Theology of Charles G. Finney. LC 85-8303. (Studies in Evangelicalism: No. 6). 293p. 1985. 23.50 (ISBN 0-8108-1819-1). Scarecrow.

Weddle, Robert S. San Juan Bautista: Gateway to Spanish Texas. (Illus.). 485p. 1968. 24.50x (ISBN 0-292-73306-2). U of Tex Pr.

Wedeck, Harry E. Triumph of Satan. 160p. 1974. pap. 2.95 (ISBN 0-8065-0422-6). Citadel Pr.

Wedeck, Harry E. & Baskin, Wade. Dictionary of Pagan Religions. 324p. 1973. pap. 3.95 (ISBN 0-8065-0386-6). Citadel Pr.

Wedel, Alton. The Word Today. 1984. 5.25 (ISBN 0-89536-684-3, 4860). CSS of Ohio.

Wedel, Leonard E. Church Staff Administration: Practical Approaches. LC 78-51490. 1978. 10.95 (ISBN 0-8054-3105-5). Broadman.

Wedgewood. Meditation for Beginners. 2.50 (ISBN 0-8356-5050-2). Theos Pub Hse.

Wedgeworth, Ann. Magnificent Strangers. LC 78-67446. 128p. 1979. pap. 1.95 (ISBN 0-88243-568-X, 02-0568, Radiant Bks). Gospel Pub.

Wedgwood, Cicely V. Richelieu & the French Monarchy. 1962. pap. 4.95 (ISBN 0-02-038240-5, Collier). Macmillan.

Wedgwood, James I. The Larger Meaning of Religion. 80p. 1981. pap. text ed. 3.00 (ISBN 0-918980-10-0). St Alban Pr.

Wedmore, S. Delphine. The Woman Who Couldn't Be Stopped. LC 86-61680. (Illus.). 515p. (Orig.). 1986. pap. 10.50 (ISBN 0-9616887-0-X). Sisters Christ Charity.

Weed, John K. Wisdom of the Mystic Masters. 1968. 10.95 (ISBN 0-13-961516-4, Reward); pap. 4.95 (ISBN 0-13-961532-6). P-H.

Weed, Joseph J., jt. auth. see Bibb, Benjamin O.

Weed, Libby, jt. auth. see Weed, Michael.

Weed, Libby, ed. Read 'n Grow Picture Bible. LC 84-51093. (Illus.). 319p. 1984. 14.95 (ISBN 0-8344-0124-X, BB200C). Sweet.

Weed, Michael & Weed, Libby. Bible Handbook: A Guide for Basic Bible Learning. LC 73-91023. 1978. student's ed. 5.95 (ISBN 0-8344-0101-0). Sweet.

Weekley, James. Praise & Thanksgiving. 1986. 6.95 (ISBN 0-89536-792-0, 6810). CSS of Ohio.

--Recycled Hallelujahs. 1982. pap. 4.95 (ISBN 0-89536-532-4, 1814). CSS of Ohio.

--Tilted Haloes. (Orig.). 1987. pap. price not set (ISBN 0-89536-871-4, 7857). CSS of Ohio.

Weekley, James & Reeves, James. Beginnings. Sherer, Michael L., ed. (Orig.). 1987. pap. 3.95 (ISBN 0-89536-859-5, 7818). CSS of Ohio.

Weeks, John. Pyramids. (Cambridge Introduction to the History of Mankind Ser.). (Illus.). 1971. 5.95 (ISBN 0-521-07240-9). Cambridge U Pr.

--The Pyramids. LC 76-22457. (Cambridge Topic Bks.). (Illus.). 1977. PLB 8.95 (ISBN 0-8225-1209-2). Lerner Pubns.

Weeks, Kent R. The Classic Christian Townsite at Arminna West. (Pubns of the Penn-Yale Expedition to Egypt: No. 3). (Illus.). xv, 88p. 1967. 21.00x (ISBN 0-686-17769-X). Univ Mus of U PA.

--Classic Christian Townsite at Arminna West, Vol. 3. LC 67-26194. 1967. 25.00 (ISBN 0-686-00130-3). Penn-Yale Expedit.

Weeks, Louis. Kentucky Presbyterians. LC 83-8372. 228p. 1983. 8.95 (ISBN 0-8042-0920-0); after Sept. 1, 1983 9.95 (ISBN 0-686-46122-3). John Knox.

--To Be a Presbyterian. 96p. (Orig.). 1983. pap. 4.95 (ISBN 0-8042-1880-3). John Knox.

Weeks, Stephen B. Church & State in North Carolina. LC 78-63820. (Johns Hopkins University. Studies in the Social Sciences. Eleventh Ser. 1893: 6). Repr. of 1893 ed. 11.50 (ISBN 0-404-61082-X). AMS Pr.

--Church & State in North Carolina. pap. 9.00. Johnson Repr.

--The Religious Development in the Province of North Carolina. LC 78-63811. (Johns Hopkins University. Studies in the Social Sciences. Tenth Ser. 1892: 5-6). Repr. of 1892 ed. 11.50 (ISBN 0-404-61074-9). AMS Pr.

--Southern Quakers & Slavery: A Study in Institutional History. LC 78-64260. (Johns Hopkins University. Studies in the Social Sciences. Extra Volumes: 15). Repr. of 1896 ed. 31.00 (ISBN 0-404-61363-2). AMS Pr.

Weeks, Trisha, ed. see Paulk, Earl.

Weemhoff, Harold, jt. auth. see Henshaw, Paul.

Weems, Ann. Family Faith Stories. LC 85-13771. 142p. 1985. pap. 8.95 (ISBN 0-664-24670-2). Westminster.

--Kneeling in Bethlehem. (Illus.). 96p. (Orig.). 1987. pap. price not set (ISBN 0-664-21323-5). Westminster.

--Reaching for Rainbows: Resources for Creative Worship. LC 80-19330. 156p. 1980. pap. 8.95 (ISBN 0-664-24355-X). Westminster.

Weems, Benjamin. Reform, Rebellion & the Heavenly Way. LC 64-17267. (Association for Asian Studies Monograph: No. 15). 122p. 1964. 7.95x (ISBN 0-8165-0144-0). U of Ariz Pr.

Weems, John E., ed. A Texas Christmas, Vol. II. 130p. 1986. 19.95 (ISBN 0-939722-30-5). Pressworks.

Weems, Mason L. The Life of William Penn. LC 75-31139. Repr. of 1822 ed. 17.50 (ISBN 0-404-13613-3). AMS Pr.

--Mason Locke Weems, His Works & Ways, 3 vols. Skeel, Emily E., ed. LC 75-31140. Repr. of 1929 ed. 120.00 set (ISBN 0-404-13670-2). AMS Pr.

Weenink, Allen J. Sounds of Stillness. 1984. 3.95 (ISBN 0-89536-686-X, 4862). CSS of Ohio.

Weeramantry, C. G. Nuclear Weapons & Scientific Responsibility. 225p. 1986. 25.00 (ISBN 0-89341-542-1, Pub. by Longwood Academic). Longwood Pub Group.

Weersinghe, Sylvia. From Darkness into Light. 1980. pap. 1.95 (ISBN 0-910924-84-8). Macalester.

Wees, J. Dustin & Campbell, Michael J. Darkness Visible: The Prints of John Martin. LC 86-61656. (Illus.). 88p. (Orig.). 1986. pap. 14.95 (ISBN 0-931102-20-0). S & F Clark Art.

Weese, Wightman, ed. see Wiersbe, Warren W.

Wegener, Wilfried W., ed. see Lindemann, Emil R.

Weger, Karl-Heinz. Karl Rahner: An Introduction to His Theology. 1980. 10.95 (ISBN 0-8245-0324-4). Crossroad NY.

Weger, Karl-Heinz, jt. auth. see Rahner, Karl.

Wegman, Herman A. Christian Worship in East & West. Lathrop, Gordon, tr. from Dutch. 400p. (Orig.). 1985. pap. 19.50 (ISBN 0-916134-71-7). Pueblo Pub Co.

Wegner, Susan E. Images of the Madonna & Child by Three Tuscan Artists of the Early Seicento: Vanni, Roncalli & Manetti. LC 86-70511. (Occasional Papers: No. III). (Illus.). 42p. (Orig.). 1986. pap. 9.00 (ISBN 0-916606-10-4). Bowdoin Coll.

Wehrle, Pauline, tr. see Steiner, Rudolf.

Wei, Henry. The Guiding Light of Lao Tzu. LC 81-53011. 234p. (Orig.). 1982. 12.95 (ISBN 0-8356-0562-0, Quest); pap. 6.95 (ISBN 0-8356-0558-2, Quest). Theos Pub Hse.

Weidenschilling, J. M. Living with Luther. 1945. pap. text ed. 1.10 (ISBN 0-570-03523-6, 14-1155). Concordia.

Weidman, Judith L., ed. Christian Feminism: Visions of a New Humanity. LC 83-48462. 224p. 1984. 7.95i (ISBN 0-06-069292-8, HarpR). Har-Row.

--Women Ministers: How Women Are Redefining Traditional Roles. LC 80-8345. 192p. (Orig.). 1981. pap. 7.95 (ISBN 0-06-069291-X, RD 528, HarpR). Har-Row.

Weidman, Mavis. Junior Worker's Handbook. pap. 1.95 (ISBN 0-87509-098-2). Chr Pubns.

Weigall, Arthur. The Paganism in Our Christianity. 69.95 (ISBN 0-87968-149-7). Gordon Pr.

--Tutankhamen & Other Essays. LC 73-115210. 1971. Repr. of 1924 ed. 24.50x (ISBN 0-8046-1103-3, Pub by Kennikat). Assoc Faculty Pr.

Weigand, John. We Are the Church: The Manual. 80p. (Orig.). 1986. pap. 2.50 (ISBN 0-941850-17-X). Sunday Pubns.

Weigand, John J. We Are the Church: The Book. 128p. (Orig.). 1986. pap. 12.95 (ISBN 0-941850-16-1). Sunday Pubns.

Weigel, George. The Peace Bishops & the Arms Race: Can Religious Leadership Help in Preventing War? 54p. 1982. 2.00 (ISBN 0-318-18653-5). World Without War.

Weigel, George, Jr. Tranquillitas Ordinis: The Present Failure & Future Promise of American Catholic Thought on War & Peace. 416p. 1987. 27.50 (ISBN 0-19-504193-3). Oxford U Pr.

Weigel, James, Jr. Mythology. 210p. 1973. pap. 3.95 (ISBN 0-8220-0865-3). Cliffs.

Weigel, Van B. Ostrich Christianity: Self-Deception in Popular Christianity. LC 85-17981. 254p. (Orig.). 1986. lib. bdg. 25.75 (ISBN 0-8191-4974-8); pap. text ed. 12.75 (ISBN 0-8191-4975-6). U Pr of Amer.

Weigelt, Horst. The Schwenkfelders in Silesia. Erb, Peter C., tr. from Ger. Tr. of Spiritualistische Tradition im Protestantismus. 1985. pap. 10.00 (ISBN 0-935980-04-0). Schwenkfelder Lib.

Weigelt, Morris, ed. see Wiley, H. Orton.

Weightman, Doreen, tr. see Levi-Strauss, Claude.

Weightman, John, tr. see Levi-Strauss, Claude.

Weightman, Judith M. Making Sense of the Jonestown Suicides: A Sociological History of Peoples Temple. LC 83-21999. (Studies in Religion & Society: Vol. 7). 240p. 1984. 49.95x (ISBN 0-88946-871-0). E Mellen.

Weigle, Marta. Brothers of Light, Brothers of Blood: The Penitentes of the Southwest. 1st ed. LC 75-21188. pap. 82.00 (ISBN 0-317-27139-3, 2024680). Bks Demand UMI.

Weigle, Richard. The Glory Days: From the Life of Luther Allan Weigle. (Illus., Orig.). 1976. pap. 5.95 (ISBN 0-377-00058-2). Friend Pr.

Weihrich, F., ed. see Augustinus, Saint Aurelius.

Weil, Andrew. Health & Healing: Understanding Conventional & Alternative Medicine. 1983. 13.95 (ISBN 0-395-34430-1). HM.

--Health & Healing: Understanding Conventional & Alternative Medicine. 304p. 1985. pap. 7.95 (ISBN 0-395-37764-1). HM.

Weil, Lisl. Esther. LC 79-22543. (Illus.). 48p. 1980. 9.95 (ISBN 0-689-30761-6, Childrens Bk). Macmillan.

--Pandora's Box. LC 85-20128. (Illus.). 40p. 1986. 12.95 (ISBN 0-689-31216-4, Childrens Bk). Macmillan.

Weil, Louis. Gathered to Pray: Understanding Liturgical Prayer. LC 86-17413. (Parish Life Sourcebooks Ser.: No. 3). 148p. (Orig.). 1986. pap. 6.95 (ISBN 0-936384-35-2). Cowley Pubns.

--Sacraments & Liturgy. 116p. 1984. 24.95x (ISBN 0-631-13192-2); pap. 6.95 (ISBN 0-631-13229-5). Basil Blackwell.

Weil, Louis, jt. auth. see Price, Charles P.

Weil, Mark. The History & Decoration of the Ponte S. Angelo. LC 72-163216. (Illus.). 232p. 1974. 32.50x (ISBN 0-271-01101-7). Pa St U Pr.

Weil, Simone. A Gateway to God. LC 82-4688. 160p. 1982. pap. 6.95 (ISBN 0-8245-0534-4). Crossroad NY.

--Iliad or the Poem of Force. LC 57-6026. 1956. pap. 2.50x (ISBN 0-87574-091-X). Pendle Hill.

--Two Moral Essays: Human Personality & on Human Obligations. Repr. 2.50x (ISBN 0-686-79299-8). Pendle Hill.

--Waiting for God. pap. 5.95 (ISBN 0-06-090295-7, CN295, PL). Har-Row.

Weiland. Good News Is Better. (Anch Ser.). 1984. pap. 6.95 (ISBN 0-8163-0592-7). Pacific Pr Pub Assn.

Weilgart, W. John. AUI, Language of Space: Logos of Love, Pentecostal Peace, & Health Thru Harmony, Creation & Truth. 4th ed. (Illus.). 350p. 1979. pap. 11.95 (ISBN 0-912038-08-X). Cosmic Comm.

Weillert, Sr. Augustine. Someone Special. (Illus.). 1979. 4.95 (ISBN 0-89962-005-1). Todd & Honeywell.

Weiman, Mark. Yoga: A Bibliography. 135p. 1979. lib. bdg. 22.50 (ISBN 0-8482-7051-7). Norwood Edns.

Weimar, Peter. Untersuchungen zur Redaktionsgeschichte des Pentateuch. 1977. 34.40x (ISBN 3-11-006731-5). De Gruyter.

Wei-Ming, Tu. Humanity & Self-Cultivation Essays in Confucian Thought. 1980. text ed. 30.00 (ISBN 0-89581-600-8, Asian Humanities). Asian Human Pr.

Weinandy, Thomas. Does God Change? The Word's Becoming in the Incarnation. LC 84-26241. (Studies in Historical Theology). 1985. pap. 17.95 (ISBN 0-932506-35-6). St Bedes Pubns.

--Receiving the Promise: The Spirit's Work of Conversion. 128p. 1985. pap. 3.95 (ISBN 0-932085-01-6). Word Among Us.

Weinbach, Mendel, tr. see Malbim, Meir.

Weinbach, Sheindel. Avi Names His Price. (Illus.). 1976. 6.95 (ISBN 0-87306-119-5). Feldheim.

Weinbach, Sheindel, tr. see Gerlitz, Menaham.

Weinberg, Albert K. Manifest Destiny: A Study of Nationalist Expansionism in American History. LC 75-41293. Repr. of 1935 ed. 41.50 (ISBN 0-404-14706-2). AMS Pr.

Weinberg, David H. A Community on Trial: The Jews of Paris in the 1930's. LC 77-2999. 1977. 22.00x (ISBN 0-226-88507-0). U of Chicago Pr.

Weinberg, Florence M. The Wine & the Will: Rabelais's Bacchic Christianity. LC 78-181450. Repr. of 1972 ed. 47.30 (2027593). Bks Demand UMI.

Weinberg, Kurt. On Gide's Promethee: Private Myth & Public Mystification. LC 70-173760. (Princeton Essays in Literature Ser.). 144p. 1972. 22.50x (ISBN 0-691-06222-6). Princeton U Pr.

Weinberg, Meyer. Because They Were Jews: A History of Antisemitism. LC 86-15013. (Contributions to the Study of World History Ser.: No. 4). 300p. 1986. lib. bdg. 35.95 (ISBN 0-313-25606-3, WBJ). Greenwood.

Weinberg, Saul S. The Southeast Building, the Twin Basilicas, the Mosaic House. LC 75-25699. (Corinth Ser: Vol. 1, Pt. 5). (Illus.). 1971. Repr. of 1960 ed. 25.00x (ISBN 0-87661-015-7). Am Sch Athens.

Weinberg, Steven L., ed. see Ramtha.

Weinberg, W. How Do You Spell Chanukah? A General-Purpose Romanization of Hebrew for Speakers of English. (Bibliographica Judaica Ser: No. 5). 10.00x (ISBN 0-87820-903-4, HUC Pr). Ktav.

Weinberger, Leon J. Anthology of Hebrew Poetry in Greece, Anatolia & the Balkans. LC 75-34119. 270p. 1975. pap. 16.50 (ISBN 0-8173-8525-8). U of Ala Pr.

Weiner, David A., tr. see Schweid, ELiezer.

Weiner, Herbert. Nine & One Half Mystics. 1986. pap. 8.95 (ISBN 0-02-068160-7, Collier). Macmillan.

Weiner, Myron, jt. ed. see Banuazizi, Ali.

Weinfeld, M. Deuteronomy & the Deuteronomic School. 1972. 53.00x (ISBN 0-19-826626-X). Oxford U Pr.

Weinfeld, M., ed. see Tadmor, H.

Weingarten, Henry. A Modern Introduction to Astrology. LC 74-15939. 1974. pap. 1.95 (ISBN 0-88231-014-3). ASI Pubs Inc.

Weingartner, P., ed. see Colloquium in the Philosophy of Science Staff.

Weingreen, Jacob. Classical Hebrew Composition. 1957. 16.95x (ISBN 0-19-815423-2). Oxford U Pr.

--From Bible to Mishna: The Continuity of Tradition. LC 75-37728. 250p. 1976. text ed. 27.00x (ISBN 0-8419-0249-6). Holmes & Meier.

--An Introduction to the Critical Study of the Text of the Hebrew Bible. 1982. 8.95x (ISBN 0-19-815453-4). Oxford U Pr.

--Practical Grammar for Classical Hebrew. 2nd ed. 1959. 15.95x (ISBN 0-19-815422-4). Oxford U Pr.

Weingrod, Alex, jt. auth. see Ashkenazi, Michael.

Weinhold, Barry, jt. auth. see Hendricks, Gay.

Weinreich, ed. see Cahan, Judah L.

Weinreich, Max. Hitlers Professors. LC 47-42580. (Yiddish., Illus.). 325p. 1947. pap. 10.00x (ISBN 0-914512-26-9). Yivo Inst.

--Hitler's Professors. LC 46-5155. (Yivo English Translation Ser.). (Illus.). 291p. 1946. pap. 5.00 (ISBN 0-914512-19-6). Yivo Inst.

Weinreich, Uriel. College Yiddish; An Introduction to the Yiddish Language & to Jewish Life & Culture. 5th ed. LC 76-88208. 399p. 1979. 15.00 (ISBN 0-914512-04-8). Yivo Inst.

--Yidish Launiversitah: Hebrew Edition of "College Yiddish". Bahat, S. & Goldwasser, M., trs. (Illus.). 1977. pap. text ed. write for info. (ISBN 0-914512-35-8). Yivo Inst.

Weinreich, Uriel, ed. The Field of Yiddish: Studies in Yiddish Language, Folklore, & Literature. LC 54-12380. 317p. 1954. Repr. 12.50 (ISBN 0-936368-02-0). Lexik Hse.

Weinreich-Haste, Helen & Locke, Don. Morality in the Making: Thought, Action & the Social Context. (Developmental Psychology & Its Application Ser.). 300p. 1983. 73.95 (ISBN 0-471-10423-X, Pub. by Wiley Interscience). Wiley.

Weinrich, William C., ed. The New Testament Age: Essays in Honor of Bo Reicke, 2 vols. LC 84-713. 606p. 1984. 44.95x (ISBN 0-86554-097-7, MUP/H89). Mercer Univ Pr.

Weinsheimer, Joel C. Gadamer's Hermeneutics: A Reading of Truth & Method. LC 84-27028. 288p. 1985. 20.00x (ISBN 0-300-03320-6). Yale U Pr.

Weinstein, Brian. The Civic Tongue: Political Consequences of Language Choices. LC 82-15268. (Professional Studies in Political Communication & Policy). 213p. 1982. 22.50x (ISBN 0-582-29010-4). Longman.

Weinstein, Donald. Savonarola & Florence: Prophecy & Patriotism in the Renaissance. LC 76-113013. Repr. of 1970 ed. 102.80 (ISBN 0-8357-9511-X, 2015484). Bks Demand UMI.

Weinstein, Donald & Bell, Rudolph M. Saints & Society: The Two Worlds of Western Christendom, 1000 to 1700. LC 82-7972. (Illus.). xii, 314p. 1986. 25.00x (ISBN 0-226-89055-4); pap. 11.95 (ISBN 0-226-89056-2). U of Chicago Pr.

Weinstein, Frida S. A Hidden Childhood: A Jewish Girl's Sanctuary in a French Convent, 1942-1945. Kennedy, Barbara L., tr. 160p. 1986. pap. 6.95 (ISBN 0-8090-1529-3). Hill & Wang.

Weinstein, Jay. A Collectors' Guide to Judaica. (Illus.). 1985. 29.95 (ISBN 0-500-23440-X). Thames Hudson.

Weinstein, Michael A. Finite Perfection: Reflections on Virtue. LC 84-16215. 176p. 1985. lib. bdg. 22.50x (ISBN 0-87023-474-9); pap. 9.95 (ISBN 0-87023-475-7). U of Mass Pr.

--The Wilderness & the City: American Classical Philosophy As a Moral Quest. LC 82-4769. 176p. 1982. lib. bdg. 17.50x (ISBN 0-87023-375-0). U of Mass Pr.

Weinstein, Stanley. Buddhism under the T'ang. (Cambridge Studies in Chinese History, Literature & Institutions). 200p. 1987. 39.50 (ISBN 0-521-25585-6). Cambridge U Pr.

Weinstock, Stefan. Divus Julius. 1971. 74.00x (ISBN 0-19-814287-0). Oxford U Pr.

Weippert, Helga. Die Prosareden des Jeremiabuches. LC 72-76045. (Beiheft 132 zur Zeitschrift fuer die alttestamentliche Wissenschaft). (Ger.). 1973. 55.00x (ISBN 3-11-003867-6). De Gruyter.

Weippert, Manfred. Settlement of the Israelite Tribes in Palestine. Martin, James, tr. from Ger. LC 74-131587. (Studies in Biblical Theology, 2nd Ser.: No. 21). (Orig.). 1970. pap. 12.00x (ISBN 0-8401-3071-6). A R Allenson.

Weir, Cecil J. A Lexicon of Accadian Prayers in the Rituals of Expiation. LC 78-72774. (Ancient Mesopotamian Texts & Studies). Repr. of 1934 ed. 35.00 (ISBN 0-404-18236-4). AMS Pr.

Weir, Robert F. Ethical Issues in Death & Dying. LC 77-24707. 1977. 38.00x (ISBN 0-231-04306-6); pap. 16.00x (ISBN 0-231-04307-4). Columbia U Pr.

Weir, Robert F., ed. Ethical Issues in Death & Dying. 2nd ed. 425p. 1986. 40.00x (ISBN 0-231-06222-2); pap. 16.00x (ISBN 0-231-06223-0). Columbia U Pr.

Weir, Thomas H., ed. see Muir, William.

Weir, William & Abata, Russell M. Dealing with Depression. LC 82-84045. 144p. 1983. pap. 3.50 (ISBN 0-89243-170-9). Liguori Pubns.

Weis, Frederick L. The Colonial Clergy of Maryland, Delaware & Georgia. LC 77-93959. 104p. 1978. Repr. of 1950 ed. 10.00 (ISBN 0-8063-0800-1). Genealog Pub.

--The Life & Teaching of Ludwig Hesser: Leader & Martyr of the Anabaptists, 1500-1529. LC 83-45633. Date not set. Repr. of 1930 ed. 31.50 (ISBN 0-404-19875-9). AMS Pr.

Weisbord, Robert G. & Stein, Arthur. Bittersweet Encounter: The Afro-American & the American Jew. LC 72-127828. (Contributions in Afro-American & African Studies: No. 5). 1970. 29.95 (ISBN 0-8371-5093-0, WBS&, Pub. by Negro U Pr). Greenwood.

Weisbrot, Robert. Father Divine. LC 84-45084. (Illus.). 241p. 1984. pap. 10.95x (ISBN 0-8070-0901-6, BP684). Beacon Pr.

Weischedel, Randall, ed. see Ramtha.

Weischedel, Wilhelm, et al. Philosophische Theologie im Schatten des Nihilismus. Salaquarda, Joerg, ed. (Ger). 1971. pap. 9.60x (ISBN 3-11-001604-4). De Gruyter.

Weisel, Marion, tr. see Wiesel, Elie.

Weisenberg, David H. Jewish Way. (Illus.). 1969. 8.95 (ISBN 0-8158-0026-6). Chris Mass.

Weiser, Alfons. The Miracle of Jesus: Then & Now. Karris, Robert, ed. Tiede, David L., tr. (Herald Biblical Bklts.). 1972. pap. 1.25 (ISBN 0-8199-0519-4). Franciscan Herald.

Weiser, Artur. Psalms: A Commentary. LC 62-16760. (Old Testament Library). 842p. 1962. 29.50 (ISBN 0-664-20418-X). Westminster.

Weiser, David K. The Prose Style of John Jewel. Hogg, James, ed. (Elizabethan & Renaissance Studies). 194p. (Orig.). 1973. pap. 15.00 (ISBN 3-7052-0658-3, Pub. by Salzburg Studies). Longwood Pub Group.

Weiser, Frederick S., ed. Maryland German Church Records, Vol. 1: Christ Reformed Church, Middletown. LC 86-61245. (Maryland German Church Records Ser.). 108p. (Orig.). 1986. pap. 15.00x (ISBN 0-913281-03-4). Noodle Doosey.

--Maryland German Church Records, Vol. 2: Zion Lutheran Church, Middletown. Zahn, Charles T., tr. LC 86-62419. (Orig.). 1986. pap. 15.00x (ISBN 0-913281-04-2). Noodle-Doosey.

Weiser, Frederick S., ed. & tr. Maryland German Church Records, Vol. 3: Monocacy Lutheran Congregation & Evangelical Lutheran Church - Baptisms 1742-1779. LC 86-63901. (Orig.). 1987. pap. 20.00x (ISBN 0-913281-05-0). Noodle-Doosey.

--Maryland German Church Records, Vol. 4: Evangelical Lutheran Church Baptisms, 1780-1811, Frederick, Maryland. 150p. (Orig.). 1987. pap. 20.00x (ISBN 0-913281-06-9). Noodle Doosey.

Weiser, Frederick S., ed. Maryland German Church Records, Vol. 5: Evangelical Reformed Church 1746-1789, Frederick. Hinke, William J., tr. (Maryland German Church Records Ser.). (Orig.). 1987. pap. 20.00x (ISBN 0-913281-07-7). Noodle Doosey.

--Maryland German Church Records, Vol. 6: Evangelical Reformed Church 1790-1835, Frederick. Hinke, William J., tr. (Maryland German Church Records Ser.). (Orig.). 1987. pap. 20.00x (ISBN 0-913281-08-5). Noodle Doosey.

--Maryland German Church Records, Vol. 7: St. Mary's Lutheran Church 1783-1863, St. Mary's Reformed Church 1812-1866, & Jerusalem Lutheran Church 1799-1859. (Maryland German Church Records Ser.). (Orig.). 1987. pap. 15.00x (ISBN 0-913281-09-3). Noodle Doosey.

Weiser, Frederick S., jt. ed. see Neff, Larry M.

Weiser, Frederick S., tr. Records of Pastoral Acts at Emanual Lutheran Church (Known in the Eighteen Century as the Warwick Congregation, Near Brickerville, Elizabeth Township, Lancaster County) 1743-1799. (Sources & Documents Ser.: No. 8). 229p. 1983. pap. 15.00 (ISBN 0-911122-47-8). Penn German Soc.

Weiser, Harold. The Victorious Decision. 1983. 6.75 (ISBN 0-8062-2002-3). Carlton.

Weiser, Thomas, tr. see Barth, Karl.

Weisfeld, Israel H., ed. David the King. LC 83-62421. 290p. 20.00x (ISBN 0-8197-0493-8). Bloch.

Weisgerber, Charles A. Psychological Assessment of Candidates for a Religious Order. LC 77-91649. 1969. pap. 2.95 (ISBN 0-8294-0019-2). Loyola.

Weisheipl, James A. Friar Thomas d'Aquino: His Life, Thought, & Work. LC 83-14326. 487p. 1983. pap. 16.95 (ISBN 0-8132-0590-5). Cath U Pr.

Weisheipl, James A., ed. see St. Thomas Aquinas.

Weisheit, E. Sixty-One Worship Talks for Children. rev. ed. LC 68-20728. 1975. pap. 4.95 (ISBN 0-570-03714-X, 12-2616). Concordia.

Weisheit, Eldon. God's Love for God's Children: Story Devotion for Family Time. LC 86-3397. (Illus.). 256p. (Orig.). 1986. kivar paper 9.95 (ISBN 0-8066-2213-X, 10-2680). Augsburg.

--God's Promise for Children. LC 80-65554. (Visual Messages on Old Testament Texts, Ser. A). 128p. 1980. pap. 6.95 (ISBN 0-8066-1799-3, 10-2692). Augsburg.

--God's Promise for Children: Object Lessons on Old Testament Texts. LC 81-65656. (Series B). 128p. (Orig.). 1981. pap. 6.95 (ISBN 0-8066-1892-2, 10-2693). Augsburg.

--God's Promise for Children: Object Lessons on Old Testament Texts. LC 82-70956. (Series C). 128p. (Orig.). 1982. pap. 6.95 (ISBN 0-8066-1931-7, 10-2694). Augsburg.

--God's Word in a Child's World: Messages & Guidelines for Sharing the Gospel with Children. LC 86-3442. 128p. (Orig.). 1986. pap. 6.95 (ISBN 0-8066-2214-8, 10-2745). Augsburg.

--The Gospel for Kids: Series B. 1978. 6.75 (ISBN 0-570-03267-9, 15-2713). Concordia.

--The Gospel for Kids: Series C. 1979. 6.75 (ISBN 0-570-03279-2, 15-2723). Concordia.

--The Gospel for Little Kids. 1980. pap. 4.95 (ISBN 0-570-03811-1, 12-2920). Concordia.

--The Psalms for Children: Series B. LC 84-18562. 128p. (Orig.). 1984. pap. 6.95 (ISBN 0-8066-2096-X, 10-5304). Augsburg.

--The Psalms for Children: Series C. LC 85-11154. 128p. (Orig.). 1985. pap. 6.95 (ISBN 0-8066-2169-9, 10-5305). Augsburg.

--The Psalms for Children: Sixty Object Lessons. LC 83-70510. (Series A). 128p. (Orig.). 1983. pap. 6.95 (ISBN 0-8066-2016-1, 10-5303). Augsburg.

--Sixty-One Gospel Talks for Children: With Suggested Objects for Illustration. LC 70-96217. 1969. pap. 4.95 (ISBN 0-570-03713-1, 12-2615). Concordia.

--To the Kid in the Pew-Series A. LC 74-4548. 128p. 1974. 6.75 (ISBN 0-570-03238-5, 15-2132). Concordia.

--To the Kid in the Pew-Series B. LC 74-4548. 1975. 6.75 (ISBN 0-570-03252-0, 15-2160). Concordia.

--To the Kid in the Pew-Series C. (To the Kid in the Pew Ser.). 128p. 1976. 6.75 (ISBN 0-570-03261-X, 15-2169). Concordia.

--The Zeal of His House. LC 73-76988. 1973. 3.50 (ISBN 0-570-03516-3, 14-2020). Concordia.

Weishiet, Eldon. Gospel for Kids: Series A. 1977. 6.75 (ISBN 0-570-03265-2, 15-2711). Concordia.

Weising, Edward F. & Weising, Gwen. Singleness: An Opportunity for Growth & Fulfillment. LC 82-80197. (Radiant Life Ser.). 128p. (Orig.). 1982. pap. 2.50 (ISBN 0-88243-901-4, 02-0901); teacher's ed. 3.95 (ISBN 0-88243-196-X, 32-0196). Gospel Pub.

Weising, Gwen. Guidance-Knowing the Will of God. (Workbook Ser.). 72p. 1985. pap. 4.95 (ISBN 0-930756-99-1, 581006). Aglow Pubns.

Weising, Gwen, jt. auth. see Weising, Edward F.

Weisinger, Herbert. Agony & the Triumph: Papers on the Use & Abuse of Myth. x, 283p. 1964. 5.00 (ISBN 0-87013-081-1). Mich St U Pr.

Weisman, Richard. Witchcraft, Magic & Religion in Seventeenth Century Massachusetts. LC 83-15542. 288p. 1985. pap. text ed. 9.95x (ISBN 0-87023-494-3). U of MAss Pr.

Weiss, Anita M., ed. Islamic Reassertion in Pakistan: Islamic Laws in a Modern State. (Contemporary Issues in the Middle East Ser.). 176p. 1986. text ed. 19.95x (ISBN 0-8156-2375-5). Syracuse U Pr.

Weiss, Ann E. God & Government: The Separation of Church & State. 160p. 1982. 8.95 (ISBN 0-395-32085-2). HM.

Weiss, Avraham. Women's Prayer Groups: A Halakhic Analysis. 1987. pap. 8.95 (ISBN 0-88125-126-7). Ktav.

Weiss, Bernard, ed. see As-Said, Labib.

Weiss, David I., et al, eds. Directory of Holistic Practitioners for the Greater Boston Area. LC 87-90042. 120p. (Orig.). 1987. pap. 5.00 (ISBN 0-9618049-0-4). D I Weiss.

Weiss, Ed. The Parent, the Parish, & the Catholic School. 1986. 6.60 (ISBN 0-318-20566-1). Natl Cath Educ.

Weiss, Ellen. Things to Make & Do for Christmas. (Things to Make & Do Bks.). 1980. PLB 8.90 (ISBN 0-531-02293-5, C02); pap. 3.95 (ISBN 0-531-02145-9). Watts.

Weiss, Gerald. On Becoming Married: The Art of a Loving Marriage. LC 81-85262. 108p. (Orig.). 1982. pap. 2.95 (ISBN 0-87973-664-X, 664). Our Sunday Visitor.

Weiss, Gershon, ed. see Daud, Abraham I.

Weiss, Herold. Paul of Tarsus. 175p. (Orig.). 1986. pap. 9.95 (ISBN 0-943872-92-8). Andrews Univ Pr.

Weiss, Jess E. The Adam & Eve Fantasy. 80p. 1985. 8.00 (ISBN 0-682-40262-1). Exposition Pr FL.

Weiss, Johannes. Earliest Christianity: A History of the Period A.D. 30-150, 2 vols. Grant, F. C., ed. 24.00 set (ISBN 0-8446-0959-5). Peter Smith.

--Jesus' Proclamation of the Kingdom of God. Hiers, Richard H. & Holland, Larrimore D., eds. (Reprints & Translations). 1985. pap. 9.75 (ISBN 0-89130-859-8, 00-07-08). Scholars Pr GA.

Weiss, John. Life & Correspondence of Theodore Parker. LC 70-83446. (Religion in America, Ser. 1). 1969. Repr. of 1864 ed. 52.00 (ISBN 0-405-00279-3). Ayer Co Pubs.

--Life & Correspondence of Theodore Parker, 2 Vols. facs. ed. LC 69-16854. (Select Bibliographies Reprint Ser). 1863. 52.00 (ISBN 0-8369-5018-6). Ayer Co Pubs.

--Life & Correspondence of Theodore Parker, 2 Vols. LC 76-106987. (American Public Figures Ser). 1864. Set. lib. bdg. 95.00 (ISBN 0-306-71874-X). Da Capo.

--Life & Correspondence of Theodore Parker, Minister of the Twenty-Eighth Congregational Society, Boston. LC 74-97443. Repr. of 1864 ed. 42.00x (ISBN 0-8371-2723-8, WEQ&, Pub. by Negro U Pr). Greenwood.

Weiss, Jonathan, jt. auth. see Weiss, Paul.

Weiss, Joseph. Studies in East European Jewish Mysticism. Goldstein, David, ed. (Littman Libray of Jewish Civilazation). 1985. 29.95x (ISBN 0-19-710034-1). Oxford U Pr.

Weiss, Meir. The Story of Job's Beginning. 84p. 1983. text ed. 15.00x (ISBN 9-652-23438-9, Pub. by Magnes Pr Israel). Humanities.

Weiss, Paul. God We Seek. LC 64-13476. 267p. 1964. 10.95x (ISBN 0-8093-0133-4). S Ill U Pr.

--God We Seek. LC 72-11838. (Arcturus Books Paperbacks). 268p. 1973. pap. 7.95x (ISBN 0-8093-0628-X). S Ill U Pr.

--Man's Freedom. LC 67-23318. (Arcturus Books Paperbacks). 335p. 1967. pap. 8.95x (ISBN 0-8093-0277-2). S Ill U Pr.

--Religion & Art. (Aquinas Lecture). 1963. 7.95 (ISBN 0-87462-128-3). Marquette.

Weiss, Paul & Weiss, Jonathan. Right & Wrong: A Philosophical Dialogue Between Father & Son. LC 73-12702. (Arcturus Books Paperbacks). 222p. 1974. pap. 5.95x (ISBN 0-8093-0658-1). S Ill U Pr.

Weiss, Robert O., tr. see Schnitzler, Arthur.

Weiss, Roger, ed. see Kahan, Arcadius.

Weisser, M. My Synagogue. (Illus.). 25p. 1984. pap. text ed. 2.95x (ISBN 0-87441-386-9). Behrman.

Weisser, Thomas H. After the Way Called Heresy. (Illus.). 131p. pap. 5.95 (ISBN 0-9610710-0-1). Tom Weisser.

--Anti-Trinitarianism of Early Quakers. 39p. 2.00 (ISBN 0-317-40412-1). Tom Weisser.

--Three Persons from the Bible: Or Babylon. (Illus.). 44p. pap. 2.00 (ISBN 0-317-17477-0). Tom Weisser.

Weissinger, Muir. The Failure of Faith: An Investigation into Totalitarianism, Irrationality & Faith. LC 83-8171. 219p. 1983. 32.00 (ISBN 0-86187-284-3, Pub. by Frances Pinter). Longwood Pub Group.

Weissmann Klein, Gerda. A Passion for Sharing: The Life of Edith Rosenwald Stern. (Illus.). 448p. 1984. 18.95 (ISBN 0-940646-15-3). Rossel Bks.

Weiss-Rosmarin, T. Jewish Survival. 6.95x (ISBN 0-87068-426-4). Ktav.

Weiss-Rosmarin, T., ed. Jewish Expressions on Jesus. 14.95x (ISBN 0-87068-470-1). Ktav.

Weiss-Rosmarin, Trude. Judaism & Christianity: The Differences. 1965. pap. 4.95 (ISBN 0-8246-0044-4). Jonathan David.

Weist, Tom, jt. auth. see Henry Tall Bull.

Weitzel, Lynn. The Christmas Story Revisted. 21p. (Orig.). pap. 4.95 (ISBN 0-930161-07-6). State of the Art Ltd.

Weitzman, Kurt. The Icon: Holy Images 6th to 14th Century. LC 78-6495. (Magnificant Paperback Art Ser.). 136p. 1978. 24.95 (ISBN 0-8076-0892-0); pap. 14.95 (ISBN 0-8076-0893-9). Braziller.

Weitzmann, Kurt. Greek Mythology in Byzantine Art. LC 84-4849. (Illus.). 380p. 1984. text ed. 95.00 (ISBN 0-691-03574-1). Princeton U Pr.

--Late Antique-Early Christian Painting. LC 76-16444. (Magnificent Paperback Art Ser.). 128p. 1977. 19.95 (ISBN 0-8076-0830-0); pap. 11.95 (ISBN 0-8076-0831-9). Braziller.

--The Monastery of Saint Catherine at Mount Sinai, The Icons I: From the Sixth to the Tenth Century. LC 75-3482. 276p. 1976. 205.00x (ISBN 0-691-03543-1). Princeton U Pr.

Weitzmann, Kurt, jt. auth. see Forsyth, George H.

Weitzmann, Kurt, et al. The Icon. LC 82-47840. (Illus.). 419p. 1982. 60.00 (ISBN 0-394-52551-5). Knopf.

Weizmann, Chaim. Trial & Error: The Autobiography of Chaim Weizmann. LC 70-156215. 498p. 1972. Repr. of 1949 ed. lib. bdg. 35.00x (ISBN 0-8371-6166-5, WETE). Greenwood.

Welbers, Thomas. Banquet of the Word: Bible Study Based on the Sunday Readings. LC 86-60891. 400p. 1986. pap. 17.95 (ISBN 0-89390-073-7). Resource Pubns.

Welborn, Don. On the Subject of Tongues: From the New Testament. 56p. pap. 0.50 (ISBN 0-937396-48-6). Walterick Pubs.

Welch, A. C. Anselm & His Work. 1979. Repr. of 1901 ed. lib. bdg. 30.00 (ISBN 0-8492-2965-0). R West.

Welch, Adam C. Visions of the End: A Study in Daniel & Revelation. 260p. 1958. Repr. of 1922 ed. 10.95 (ISBN 0-227-67631-9). Attic Pr.

Welch, Claude. Protestant Thought in the Nineteenth Century, Vol. 1: 1799 to 1870. LC 72-75211. Repr. of 1972 ed. 84.00 (ISBN 0-8357-9459-8, 2013200). Bks Demand UMI.

--Protestant Thought in the Nineteenth Century: Volume 1, 1799-1870. LC 72-75211. 335p. 1986. Repr. 25.00x (ISBN 0-300-01535-6). Yale U Pr.

--Protestant Thought in the Nineteenth Century: Volume 2, 1870-1914. LC 72-75211. 328p. 1985. 25.00x (ISBN 0-300-03369-9). Yale U Pr.

Welch, Claude, jt. auth. see Dillenberger, John.

Welch, D. Don. Law & Morality. LC 86-45195. 192p. 1987. pap. text ed. 14.95 (ISBN 0-8006-1974-9, 1-1974). Fortress.

Welch, Herbert. Men of the Outposts: The Romance of the Modern Christian Movement. facs. ed. LC 69-17594. (Essay Index Reprint Ser). 1937. 16.50 (ISBN 0-8369-1162-8). Ayer Co Pubs.

Welch, Holmes. The Buddhist Revival in China: With a Section of Photos by Henri Cartier-Bresson. LC 68-15645. (Harvard East Asian Ser.: Vol. 33). pap. 80.60 (ISBN 0-317-28777-X, 2017757). Bks Demand UMI.

--Taoism: The Parting of the Way. Orig. Title: Parting of the Way. 1966. pap. 6.95 (ISBN 0-8070-5973-0, BP224). Beacon Pr.

Welch, Holmes & Seidel, Anna, eds. Facets of Taoism: Essays in Chinese Religion. LC 77-28034. 1979. 38.00x (ISBN 0-300-01695-6); pap. 8.95x (ISBN 0-300-02673-0). Yale U Pr.

Welch, Holmes H. Practice of Chinese Buddhism, 1900-1950. LC 67-13256. pap. 9.95x (ISBN 0-674-69701-4). Harvard U Pr.

Welch, Jerome A. Catholicism Today. LC 76-29584. (Illus.). 1977. 7.95 (ISBN 0-917728-01-7); pap. 6.95 (ISBN 0-917728-02-5). Jewel Pubns.

Welch, John. Spiritual Pilgrims: Carl Jung & Teresa of Avila. LC 82-80164. 208p. 1982. 8.95 (ISBN 0-8091-2454-8). Paulist Pr.

Welch, Marni & Linley, Eliza, eds. Forms for Faith: Art & Architecture for Worship. LC 86-82529. (Illus.). 24p. (Orig.). 1986. pap. 5.95 (ISBN 0-943376-36-X). Magnes Mus.

Welch, Mary L. Methods of Teaching in the Catholic School. 1986. 6.60 (ISBN 0-318-20570-X). Natl Cath Educ.

Welch, Reuben. Beacon Bible Expositions: Vol. 3, Luke. Greathouse, William M. & Taylor, Willard H., eds. 1974. 8.95 (ISBN 0-8341-0314-1). Beacon Hill.

--His Victory & Ours: The Temptations of Jesus. 78p. (Orig.). 1983. pap. 3.50 (ISBN 0-8341-0871-2). Beacon Hill.

--We Really Do Need Each Other. 112p. 1982. pap. 4.95 (ISBN 0-310-70221-6, 14012P). Zondervan.

Welch, Reuben R. Let's Listen to Jesus: Reflections on the Farewell Discourse. Allison, Joseph D., ed. 144p. (Orig.). 1985. pap. 5.95 (ISBN 0-310-75101-2, 17044P). Zondervan.

Welch, Rosa P. & Myers, Oma L. Rosa's Song: The Life & Ministry of Rosa Page Welch. LC 84-1882. 224p. 1984. pap. 8.95x (ISBN 0-8272-3210-1). CBP.

Welch, Sharon D. Communities of Resistance & Solidarity: A Feminist Theology of Liberation. LC 85-4809. 112p. (Orig.). 1985. pap. 7.95 (ISBN 0-88344-204-3). Orbis Bks.

Welch, Stuart C. & Beach, Milo C. Gods, Thrones, & Peacocks: Northern Indian Painting from Two Traditions; Fifthteenth to Nineteenth Centuries. LC 74-27422. (Asia Society Ser.). (Illus.). 1979. Repr. of 1965 ed. lib. bdg. 33.00x (ISBN 0-405-06570-1). Ayer Co Pubs.

Weld, Theodore D. Bible Against Slavery or an Inquiry into the Genius of the Mosaic System & the Teachings of the Old Testament on the Subject of Human Rights. LC 74-92447. 1970. Repr. of 1864 ed. 39.00x (ISBN 0-403-00185-4). Scholarly.

Weldon, John & Levitt, Zola. Psychic Healing. 1982. pap. 5.95 (ISBN 0-8024-6446-7). Moody.

Wellek, Rene, ed. The Divine Legation of Moses Demonstrated, 4 vols. 2nd ed. LC 75-11264. (British Philosophers & Theologians of the 17th & 18th Centuries Ser.: Vol. 62). 2259p. 1978. Set. lib. bdg. 204.00 (ISBN 0-8240-1813-3). Garland Pub.

--James Burnett Monboddo (1714-1799) Antient Metaphysics, 6 Vol., 1779-99. LC 75-11236. (British Philosophers & Theologians of the 17th & 18th Centuries Ser.). 1977. lib. bdg. 46.00 (ISBN 0-8240-1789-7). Garland Pub.

--A View of the Prinicpal Deistical Writers That Have Appeared in England in the Last & Present Century, 3 vols. LC 75-11232. (British Philosophers & Theologians of the 17th & 18th Centuries Ser.). 1348p. 1978. lib. bdg. 153.00 (ISBN 0-8240-1785-4). Garland Pub.

Wellek, Rene, ed. see Beattie, James.

Wellek, Rene, ed. see Bentley, Richard.

Wellek, Rene, ed. see Blaguy, John.

Wellek, Rene, ed. see Bolingbroke, Henry Viscount.

Wellek, Rene, ed. see Browne, Peter.

Wellek, Rene, ed. see Collier, Arthur.

Wellek, Rene, ed. see Collins, Anthony.

Wellek, Rene, ed. see Cudworth, Ralph.

Wellek, Rene, ed. see Culverwel, Nathanael.

Wellek, Rene, ed. see Digby, Sir Kenelme.

Wellek, Rene, ed. see Edward, Herbert.

Wellek, Rene, ed. see Ferguson, Adam.

Wellek, Rene, ed. see Gildon, Charles.

Wellek, Rene, ed. see Glanvill, Joseph.

Wellek, Rene, ed. see Glanville, Joseph.

Wellek, Rene, ed. see Jenyns, Soame.

Wellek, Rene, ed. see Law, Edmund.

Wellek, Rene, ed. see Mayne, Zachary.

Wellek, Rene, ed. see Middleton, Conyers.

Wellek, Rene, ed. see More, Henry.

Wellek, Rene, ed. see Norris, John.

Wellek, Rene, ed. see Paley, William.

Wellek, Rene, ed. see Price, Richard.

Wellek, Rene, ed. see Priestley, Joseph.

Wellek, Rene, ed. see Reid, Thomas.

Wellek, Rene, ed. see Sherlock, Thomas.

Wellek, Rene, ed. see Smith, John.

Wellek, Rene, ed. see Tindal, Matthew.

Wellek, Rene, ed. see Toland, John.

Wellek, Rene, ed. see Tucker, Abraham.

Wellek, Rene, ed. see Watson, Richard.

Wellek, Rene, ed. see Wollaston, William.

Wellek, Rene, ed. see Woolston, Thomas.

Weller, Alfred. Die Fruhmittelhochdeutsche Wiener Genesis. 27.00 (ISBN 0-384-66731-7); pap. 22.00 (ISBN 0-384-66730-9). Johnson Repr.

Weller, John, jt. ed. see Ranger, T. O.

Weller, Robert P. Unities & Diversities in Chinese Religion. LC 86-9085. 250p. 1986. 22.50x (ISBN 0-295-96397-2). U of Wash Pr.

Welles, Marcia L. Arachne's Tapestry: The Transformation of Myth in Seventeenth-Century Spain. (Illus.). 220p. 1986. text ed. 22.50 (ISBN 0-939980-11-8). Trinity U Pr.

Wellesz, Egon. History of Byzantine Music & Hymnography. 2nd ed. 1961. 49.95x (ISBN 0-19-816111-5). Oxford U Pr.

Wellhausen, Julius. Abriss der Geschichte Israels und Judas: Lieder der Hudhailiten. (Skizzen und Vorarbeiten, l.Heft). (Ger. & Arabic.). iv, 175p. 1985. 70.50x (ISBN 3-11-009765-6). De Gruyter.

--Medina vor dem Islam, Muhammeds Gemeindeordnung Von Medina: Seine Schriften und Die Gesandtschaften an Ihn. (Skizzen und Vorarbeiten: 4 Heft). (Ger. & Arabic.). 272p. 1985. 63.00x (ISBN 3-11-009764-8). De Gruyter.

--Prolegomena to the History of Ancient Israel. 14.25 (ISBN 0-8446-3147-7). Peter Smith.

--Prolegomena zur Altesten Geschichte des Islam: Verschiedenes (Unveraenderter Photomechanischer Nachdruck der 1. Auflage 1899) (Skizzen und Vorarbeiten: 6 Heft). (Ger.). viii, 260p. 1985. 61.00x (ISBN 3-11-002215-X). De Gruyter.

Wellington, Paul A., ed. Joseph Smith's New Translation of the Bible. LC 74-127097. 1970. 16.00 (ISBN 0-8309-0032-2). Herald Hse.

--Loneliness. 1980. pap. 4.50 (ISBN 0-8309-0287-2). Herald Hse.

--Rules & Resolutions, Nineteen Eighty. LC 74-84765. 1980. 10.00 (ISBN 0-8309-0136-1). Includes Supplements 1982, 1984 & 1986. Herald Hse.

Welliver, Dotsey. Dotsey's Diary: Her Days & Yours. (Orig.). 1979. pap. text ed. 3.95 (ISBN 0-89367-034-0). Light & Life.

--Laughing Together: The Value of Humor in Family Life. Eller, David, ed. 128p. (Orig.). 1986. pap. 6.95 (ISBN 0-87178-226-X). Brethren.

--Smudgkin Elves & Other Lame Excuses. 81p. 1981. pap. 3.95 (ISBN 0-89367-058-8). Light & Life.

Wellman, Carl. Challenge & Response: Justification in Ethics. LC 73-132478. 309p. 1971. 15.00x (ISBN 0-8093-0490-2). S Ill U Pr.

Wellman, Don, et al. Dynamics of Discipling. 210p. 1984. spiral bd. 9.95 (ISBN 0-8341-0918-2). Beacon Hill.

Wellman, Pat. Mirror, Mirror... Please Lie. 86p. (Orig.). 1984. pap. 3.50 (ISBN 0-8341-0931-X). Beacon Hill.

--You Can Bet the Ranch. 88p. (Orig.). 1986. pap. 4.50 (ISBN 0-8341-1155-1). Beacon Hill.

Wellnitz, Marcus Von see Von Wellnitz, Marcus.

Wells, Albert. As Touching the Holy. (Direction Bks.). (Orig.). 1980. pap. 2.45 (ISBN 0-8010-9637-5). Baker Bk.

Wells, Albert M., Jr., ed. Baker's Pocket Book of Religious Quotes. (Direction Bks.). 240p. 1976. pap. 2.95 (ISBN 0-8010-9575-1). Baker Bk.

Wells, Amos R. Go till You Guess Bible Games. (Quiz & Puzzle Book Ser.). 128p. (Orig.). 1980. pap. 2.95 (ISBN 0-8010-9502-6). Baker Bk.

--Treasure of Hymns. facs. ed. LC 70-128330. (Essay Index Reprint Ser). 1945. 19.50 (ISBN 0-8369-2096-1). Ayer Co Pubs.

Wells, Bruce. From Discontent: The Biography of a Mystic. (Illus.). 224p. 1985. 13.95 (ISBN 0-85398-206-6); pap. 5.95 (ISBN 0-85398-207-4). G Ronald Pub.

Wells, David F. God the Evangelist: How the Holy Spirit Works to Bring Men & Women to Faith. 144p. (Orig.). 1987. pap. 6.95 (ISBN 0-8028-0271-0). Eerdmans.

--The Person of Christ: A Biblical & Historical Analysis of the Incarnation. LC 84-70979. (Foundations for Faith Ser.). 224p. 1984. pap. 8.95 (ISBN 0-89107-315-9, Crossway Bks). Good News.

Wells, David F., ed. Reformed Theology: Essays in Its Modern Expression in America. 296p. (Orig.). 1985. pap. 19.95 (ISBN 0-8028-0096-3). Eerdmans.

Wells, Edmund. More Gospel According to Mother Goose. 159p. (Orig.). 1981. pap. 2.95 (ISBN 0-8341-0727-9). Beacon Hill.

Wells, Edmund E. Christmas Dreaming. (Orig.). pap. 1.50 (ISBN 0-686-30401-2). WOS.

--Wells of Salvation. (Orig.). pap. 2.00 (ISBN 0-686-30400-4). WOS.

Wells, G. A. Did Jesus Exist? 24.95 (ISBN 0-87975-394-3); pap. 14.95 (ISBN 0-87975-395-1). Prometheus Bks.

--The Historical Evidence for Jesus. LC 82-60381. 350p. 1982. 20.95 (ISBN 0-87975-180-0). Prometheus Bks.

Wells, Guy F. Parish Education in Colonial Virginia. LC 73-177649. Repr. of 1923 ed. 22.50 (ISBN 0-404-55138-6). AMS Pr.

--Parish Education in Colonial Virginia. LC 71-89252. (American Education: Its Men, Institutions & Ideas, Ser. 1). 1969. Repr. of 1923 ed. 11.00 (ISBN 0-405-01490-2). Ayer Co Pubs.

Wells, H. G. Crux Ansata: An Indictment of the Roman Catholic Church. LC 73-161344. (Atheist Viewpoint Ser). (Illus.). 114p. 1972. Repr. of 1944 ed. 13.00 (ISBN 0-405-03798-8). Ayer Co Pubs.

Wells, Harold G., ed. see Barth, Karl.

Wells, Henry W., jt. ed. see Loomis, Roger S.

Wells, Joel. Coping in the Eighties: Eliminating Needless Stress & Guilt. 1986. 10.95 (ISBN 0-88347-201-5); pap. 6.95 (ISBN 0-88347-202-3). Thomas More.

Wells, Kenneth E. Thai Buddhism: Its Rites & Activities. LC 77-87081. (Illus.). viii, 320p. Repr. of 1960 ed. 34.50 (ISBN 0-404-16876-0). AMS Pr.

Wells, L. The Death Brigade. LC 77-89068. 305p. 1978. pap. 10.95 (ISBN 0-89604-000-3). Holocaust Pubns.

Wells, Marian. With This Ring. LC 84-9301. 200p. (Orig.). 1984. pap. 4.95 (ISBN 0-87123-615-X, 210615). Bethany Hse.

Wells, Merle W. Anti-Mormonism in Idaho, Eighteen Seventy-Two to Ninety-Two. LC 77-89975. (Studies in Mormon History Ser.: No. 4). 1978. pap. 7.95 (ISBN 0-8425-0904-6). Brigham.

Wells, Norman. Metaphysical Disputation, XXXI, De Ento Finito, on Finite Being. cancelled. Marquette.

Wells, Norman J., tr. Francis Suarez: On the Essence of Finite Being as Such, on the Existence of the Essence & Their Distinction. (Mediaeval Philosophical Texts in Translation). 250p. 1983. pap. 24.95 (ISBN 0-87462-224-7). Marquette.

Wells, Paul R. James Barr & the Bible: Critique of a New Liberalism. 1980. pap. 12.00 (ISBN 0-87552-546-6). Presby & Reformed.

Wells, Peter S. The Emergence of an Iron Age Economy: The Mecklenburg Grave Groups from Hallstatt & Sticna: Mecklenburg Collection, Pt 3. LC 81-81958. (American School of Prehistoric Research Bulletins: No. 33). (Illus.). 256p. 1981. pap. 30.00x (ISBN 0-87365-536-2). Peabody Harvard.

Wells, Robert E. We Are Christians Because... LC 84-28762. 119p. 1985. 7.95 (ISBN 0-87747-639-X). Deseret Bk.

Wells, Ronald, jt. auth. see Mawhinney, Brian.

Wells, Ronald A. Wars of America: Christian Views. 280p. (Orig.). 1981. pap. 9.95 (ISBN 0-8028-1899-4). Eerdmans.

Wells, Ronald V. Three Christian Transcendentalists: James Marsh, Caleb Sprague Henry, Frederic Henry Hedge. LC 75-159256. xxxii, 290p. 1971. Repr. of 1943 ed. lib. bdg. 20.00x (ISBN 0-374-98345-3, Octagon). Hippocrene Bks.

Wells, Tom. Come to Me! 128p. (Orig.). 1986. pap. 3.45 (ISBN 0-85151-471-5). Banner of Truth.

--Faith the Gift of God. 156p. 1983. pap. 3.95 (ISBN 0-85151-361-1). Banner of Truth.

--Moral Basis of Faith. 28p. (Orig.). 1986. pap. 1.45 (ISBN 0-85151-469-3). Banner of Truth.

Wellwarth, George E. Modern Drama & the Death of God. LC 86-40064. 192p. 1986. text ed. 25.75x (ISBN 0-299-10850-3). U of Wis Pr.

Welsby, Paul A. The History of the Church of England, 1945-80. 1984. 29.95x (ISBN 0-19-213231-8). Oxford U Pr.

Welsch, Roger L. Omaha Tribal Myths & Tricksters Tales. LC 80-22636. x, 285p. 1981. 21.95 (ISBN 0-8040-0700-4, SB). Ohio U Pr.

Welsh, Clement. Preaching in a New Key. LC 74-5268. 192p. 1974. 5.95 (ISBN 0-8298-0273-8). Pilgrim NY.

Welsh, Evan. A Touch of Heaven Here. 96p. 1985. pap. 3.95 (ISBN 0-8423-7294-6). Tyndale.

Welter, Jean T. L' Exemplum dans la Litterature Religieuse et Didactique du Moyen Age. LC 70-178558. (Fr.). Repr. of 1927 ed. 45.00 (ISBN 0-404-56688-X). AMS Pr.

Welter, Paul. How to Help a Friend. 1983. pap. 8.95 (ISBN 0-8423-1505-5); 2.95 (ISBN 0-8423-1504-7). Tyndale.

--When Your Friend Needs You. abr. ed. (Pocket Guides Ser.). 96p. 1986. mass 1.95 (ISBN 0-8423-7998-3). Tyndale.

Weltge, Ralph, ed. Same Sex: An Appraisal of Homosexuality. LC 71-88184. 1969. pap. 3.95 (ISBN 0-8298-0118-9). Pilgrim NY.

Welwood, John. Challenge of the Heart: Love, Sex & Intimacy in Changing Times. LC 85-2461. 283p. (Orig.). 1985. pap. 9.95 (ISBN 0-87773-331-7, 74200-1). Shambhala Pubns.

Wemp, C. Sumner. Guide to Practical Pastoring. LC 82-12562. 1982. 15.95 (ISBN 0-8407-5271-7). Nelson.

Wemple, Suzanne F. Women in Frankish Society: Marriage & the Cloister, 500-900. LC 80-54051. (Illus.). 352p. 1985. pap. text ed. 18.95 (ISBN 0-8122-1209-6). U of Pa Pr.

Wendel, Francois. Calvin: Origins & Development of His Religious Thought. Mairet, Philip, tr. 384p. 1987. pap. 14.95 (ISBN 0-939464-44-6). Labyrinth Pr.

Wendell, Barrett. Cotton Mather. LC 80-23335. (American Men & Women of Letters Ser.). Orig. Title: Cotton Mather: the Puritan Priest. 328p. 1981. pap. 5.95 (ISBN 0-87754-166-3). Chelsea Hse.

--Cotton Mather: The Puritan Priest. 1978. Repr. of 1891 ed. lib. bdg. 35.00 (ISBN 0-8495-5626-0). Arden Lib.

Wendell, Belew M. Ken Prickett: Man of Joy. LC 85-6208. (Meet the Missionary Ser.). 1985. 5.50 (ISBN 0-8054-4296-0, 4242-96). Broadman.

Wendell, Leilah. The Book of Infinite Possibilities. 55p. (Orig.). 1987. pap. 4.50 (ISBN 0-89540-169-X). Sun Pub.

Wendland, E. H. Dear Mr. Missionary. 1978. pap. 4.95 (ISBN 0-8100-0035-0, 12N1714). Northwest Pub.

--Of Other Gods & Other Spirits. 1977. pap. 4.95 (ISBN 0-8100-0034-2, 12-1711). Northwest Pub.

Wendland, E. H., ed. Sermon Studies on the Gospels. (Series C). 1982. 12.95 (ISBN 0-8100-0149-7, 15NO378). Northwest Pub.

--Sermon Studies on the Old Testament. (Series B). 1984. 12.95 (ISBN 0-8100-0192-6, 15N0412). Northwest Pub.

--Sermon Texts. 1984. 9.95 (ISBN 0-8100-0186-1, 15N0409). Northwest Pub.

Wendland, Ernst H. Exodus. (People's Bible Ser.). 1984. pap. 6.95 (ISBN 0-8100-0180-2, 15N0405); study guide, 52p 1.50 (ISBN 0-938272-50-0). Northwest Pub.

--God's Mission in the New Testament. Fischer, William E., ed. (Bible Class Course Ser.). 40p. (Orig.). (YA) 1986. pap. 2.50 (ISBN 0-938272-55-1). WELS Board.

--God's Mission in the Old Testament. Fischer, William E., ed. (Bible Class Course Ser.). 40p. (Orig.). 1986. pap. text ed. 2.50 (ISBN 0-938272-54-3). WELS Board.

Wenger, Edna K. Happy Life Stories. (Illus.). 1977. 7.50 (ISBN 0-87813-912-5). Christian Light.

Wenger, J. C. Bless the Lord, O My Soul. LC 64-23575. (Illus.). 264p. 1964. 9.95 (ISBN 0-8361-1497-3). Herald Pr.

--The Book We Call the Bible. LC 79-89440. (Mennonite Faith Ser.: No. 8). 80p. 1980. pap. 1.50 (ISBN 0-8361-1908-8). Herald Pr.

--El Camino de la Paz. Casas, Arnoldo J., ed. Vilela, Ernesto S., tr. LC 79-89311. (Mennonite Faith Ser.: No. 4). (Span.). 1979. pap. 1.50x (ISBN 0-8361-1226-1). Herald Pr.

--El Camino de una Nueva Vida. Casas, Arnold J., ed. Vilela, Ernesto S., tr. LC 79-89310. (Mennonite Faith Ser.: No. 3). (Span.). 72p. 1979. pap. 1.50x (ISBN 0-8361-1224-5). Herald Pr.

--Como Surgieron los Menonitas. Casas, Arnold J., ed. Vilela, Ernesto S., tr. LC 79-89306. (Mennonite Faith Ser.: No. 1). (Span.). 72p. 1979. pap. 1.50x (ISBN 0-8361-1222-9). Herald Pr.

--Disciples of Jesus. LC 77-86343. (Mennonite Faith Ser.: No. 5). 72p. 1977. pap. 1.50 (ISBN 0-8361-1836-7). Herald Pr.

--Los Discipulos de Jesus. Casas, Arnoldo J., ed. Vilela, Ernesto S., tr. LC 79-89308. (Mennonite Faith Ser.: No. 5). (Span.). 72p. 1979. pap. 1.50x (ISBN 0-8361-1225-3). Herald Pr.

--A Faith to Live by. LC 79-89441. (Mennonite Faith Ser.: No. 9). 1980. pap. 1.50 (ISBN 0-8361-1909-6). Herald Pr.

--The Family of Faith. LC 80-84609. (Mennonite Faith Ser.: No. 10). 72p. 1981. pap. 1.50 (ISBN 0-8361-1951-7). Herald Pr.

--How Mennonites Came to Be. LC 77-86332. (Mennonite Faith Ser.: No. 1). 1977. pap. 1.50 (ISBN 0-8361-1832-4). Herald Pr.

--Introduction to Theology. LC 53-9049. 418p. 1954. pap. 12.95 (ISBN 0-8361-1791-3). Herald Pr.

--A Lay Guide to Romans. LC 82-15789. 160p. (Orig.). 1983. pap. 8.95 (ISBN 0-8361-3316-1). Herald Pr.

--El Libro Llamado la Biblia. Rindzinski, Milka, tr. from Eng. LC 84-80158. (Mennonite Faith Ser.: No. 8). 72p. (Orig.). 1984. pap. 1.50 (ISBN 0-8361-1268-7). Herald Pr.

--The Prayer Veil in Scripture & History. 31p. 1964. pap. 1.50 (ISBN 0-8361-1501-5). Herald Pr.

--Que Creen los Menonitas. Casas, Arnoldo J., ed. Vilela, Ernesto S., tr. from Eng. LC 79-89307. (Mennonite Faith Ser.: No. 2). (Span.). 72p. 1979. pap. 1.50x (ISBN 0-8361-1223-7). Herald Pr.

--The Way of Peace. LC 77-86349. (Mennonite Faith Ser.: No. 3, Christian Peace Shelf Ser). 72p. 1977. pap. text ed. 1.50 (ISBN 0-8361-1835-9). Herald Pr.

--The Way to a New Life. LC 77-86326. (Mennonite Faith Ser.: No. 2). 72p. 1977. pap. 1.50 (ISBN 0-8361-1834-0). Herald Pr.

--What Mennonites Believe, Vol. 2. LC 77-86338. 72p. 1977. pap. 1.50 (ISBN 0-8361-1833-2). Herald Pr.

Wenger, J. C., ed. They Met God: A Number of Conversion Accounts & Personal Testimonies of God's Presence & Leading in the Lives of Children. LC 64-15344. pap. 48.00 (ISBN 0-317-26611-X, 2025422). Bks Demand UMI.

Wenger, John C. God's Word Written. LC 66-24292. (Conrad Grebel Lecture Ser.). (Illus., Essays on the nature of biblical revelation, inspiration, & authority). 1966. pap. 6.95 (ISBN 0-8361-1900-2). Herald Pr.

--Mennonite Church in America. LC 66-23903. (Mennonite History Vol. 2). 384p. 1967. 14.95x (ISBN 0-8361-1179-6). Herald Pr.

Wenger, John C., ed. Complete Writings of Menno Simons: Circa 1496-1561. Verduin, Leonard, tr. LC 55-9815. 1104p. 1956. 35.00 (ISBN 0-8361-1353-5). Herald Pr.

Wenger, John P. Because God Loves. LC 76-16245. 56p. 1976. pap. 1.95 (ISBN 0-8361-1339-X). Herald Pr.

Wengrov, Charles. Hanukkah Song & Story. (Illus.). 1960. pap. 4.00 (ISBN 0-914080-29-6). Shulsinger Sales.

--Jewish Symbols. (Illus.). 1960. pap. 0.99 (ISBN 0-914080-24-5). Shulsinger Sales.

--The Story of Hanukkah. (Holiday Ser.). (Illus.). 1965. pap. 1.50 (ISBN 0-914080-52-0). Shulsinger Sales.

--The Story of Passover. (Holiday Ser.). (Illus.). 1965. pap. 1.50 (ISBN 0-914080-54-7). Shulsinger Sales.

--The Story of Purim. (Holiday Ser.). (Illus.). 1965. pap. 1.50 (ISBN 0-914080-53-9). Shulsinger Sales.

--The Story of Shavuot. (Holiday Ser.). (Illus.). 1965. pap. 1.50 (ISBN 0-914080-55-5). Shulsinger Sales.

--Tales of King Saul. (Biblical Ser.). (Illus.). 1969. 4.00 (ISBN 0-914080-21-0). Shulsinger Sales.

--Tales of Noah & the Ark. (Biblical Ser.). (Illus.). 1969. 4.00 (ISBN 0-914080-23-7). Shulsinger Sales.

--Tales of the Prophet Samuel. (Biblical Ser.). (Illus.). 1969. 4.00 (ISBN 0-914080-22-9). Shulsinger Sales.

--The Twelve Tribes of Israel. (Illus.). 1960. pap. 0.99 (ISBN 0-914080-64-4). Shulsinger Sales.

Wengrov, Charles, jt. auth. see Zaretsky, David.

Wengrov, Charles, ed. see Bunim, Irving M.

Wengrov, Charles, tr. from Hebrew. Sefer Ha'hinnuch, the Book of Education: Genesis-Exodus. (Anonymous Attributed to R. Aharon Halevi). 1978. Vol. 1. 14.95 (ISBN 0-87306-179-9). Feldheim.
Wengrov, Charles, tr. see Raz, Simcha.
Wengrov, Charles, tr. see Wildman, Joshua A.
Wengrove, Charles. The Sabbath. (Illus.). 1960. pap. 0.99 (ISBN 0-914080-65-2). Shulsinger Sales.
Wengrow, C., tr. The Hafetz Hayyim on the Siddur. 10.95 (ISBN 0-87306-996-X). Feldheim.
Wengrow, Charles, tr. see Raz, Simcha.
Wenham, Clare, ed. see Stibbs, Alan.
Wenham, David. The Jesus Tradition Outside the Gospels. (Gospel Perspectives Ser.: No. 5). 419p. 1985. text ed. 24.50x (ISBN 1-85075-006-8, Pub by JSOT Pr England); pap. text ed. 13.50x (ISBN 1-85075-007-6). Eisenbrauns.
--The Rediscovery of Jesus' Eschatological Discourse: Studies in the History of Gospel Traditions. (Gospel Perspectives Ser.: Vol. IV). 406p. 1984. text ed. 24.50x (ISBN 0-905774-72-8, Pub. by JSOT Pr England); pap. text ed. 13.50x (ISBN 0-905774-73-6, Pub. by JSOT England). Eisenbrauns.
Wenham, David & Blomberg, Craig. The Miracles of Jesus. (Gospel Perspectives Ser.: No. 6). 1986. text ed. 30.00x (ISBN 1-85075-008-4, Pub. by JSOT Pr England); pap. text ed. 14.95x (ISBN 1-85075-009-2, Pub. by JSOT Pr England). Eisenbrauns.
Wenham, David, jt. ed. see France, R. T.
Wenham, David, ed. see Stibbs, Alan.
Wenham, Gordon. The Book of Leviticus (Nicot) (New International Commentary on the Old Testament Ser.). 1979. text ed. 16.95 (ISBN 0-8028-2353-X). Eerdmans.
--Genesis I (WBC, Vol. 1. 400p. 1987. 24.95 (ISBN 0-8499-0200-2). Word Bks.
Wenham, Gordon J. Numbers. Wiseman, D. J., ed. LC 81-11806. (Tyndale Old Testament Commentaries Ser.). 240p. 1981. 12.95 (ISBN 0-87784-891-2); pap. 6.95 (ISBN 0-87784-254-X). Inter-Varsity.
Wenham, Gordon J., jt. auth. see Heth, William A.
Wenham, John. Easter Enigma: Are the Resurrection Accounts in Conflict? 176p. 1984. pap. 6.95 (ISBN 0-310-29861-X, 12448P). Zondervan.
Wenham, John W. Elements of New Testament Greek. 1966. text ed. 11.95 (ISBN 0-521-09842-4); key 4.95 (ISBN 0-521-06769-3). Cambridge U Pr.
--The Enigma of Evil: Can We Believe in the Goodness of God? 224p. (Orig.). 1985. pap. 7.95 (ISBN 0-310-29871-7, 12449P). Zondervan.
Weninger, Franz X. Die Heilige Mission, & Praktische Winke fur Missionaire. 65.00 (ISBN 0-405-10865-6, 11862). Ayer Co Pubs.
Wenley, R. M. Kant & His Philosophical Revolution. 302p. 1982. Repr. of 1910 ed. lib. bdg. 40.00 (ISBN 0-89987-894-6). Darby Bks.
--Socrates & Christ. 1977. 59.95 (ISBN 0-8490-2621-0). Gordon Pr.
Wennberg, Robert. Life in the Balance: Exploring the Abortion Controversy. 192p. (Orig.). 1985. pap. 7.95 (ISBN 0-8028-0061-0). Eerdmans.
Wensinck, A. J., tr. see Isaac The Syrian.
Wensinck, Arent J. The Muslim Creed: Its Genesis & Historical Development. 311p. 1932. Repr. text ed. 22.00x. Coronet Bks.
Wensing, Michael G. Ministering to Youth: A Guide for Parents, Teachers & Youth Workers. 120p. (Orig.). 1982. pap. 4.95 (ISBN 0-8189-0444-5). Alba.
Wentersdorf, Karl, jt. auth. see Mutschmann, Heinrich.
Wentz, Abdel R. & Lehmann, eds. Luther's Works: Word & Sacrament II, Vol. 36. LC 55-9893. 400p. 1959. 19.95 (ISBN 0-8006-0336-2, 1-336). Fortress.
Wentz, Richard E. The Contemplation of Otherness. viii, 134p. 1984. 13.90x (ISBN 0-86554-135-3, MUP-H126). Mercer Univ Pr.
--More Than You Know. 60p. (Orig.). 1983. pap. 1.25 (ISBN 0-88028-027-1). Forward Movement.
--The Saga of the American Soul. LC 80-5598. 163p. 1980. pap. text ed. 9.50 (ISBN 0-8191-1150-3). U Pr of Amer.
Wentz, W. Y. The Fairy-Faith in Celtic Countries. LC 77-12812. 1973. pap. text ed. 15.00x (ISBN 0-391-00773-4). Humanities.
Wentz, Walter Y., ed. Tibetan Yoga & Secret Doctrines: Or Seven Books of Wisdom of the Great Path. LC 78-70140. Repr. of 1935 ed. 49.50 (ISBN 0-404-17413-2). AMS Pr.
Wenzel, H., ed. see Kasawara, Kenju.
Wenzel, Siegfried. Verses in Sermons: "Fasciculus morum" & Its Middle English Poems. LC 78-55887. 1978. 20.00x (ISBN 0-910956-66-9). Medieval Acad.
Werber, Eva B. In His Presence. 2nd ed. 1970. pap. 3.25 (ISBN 0-87516-102-2). De Vorss.
--Journey with the Master. 1950. pap. 3.25 (ISBN 0-87516-103-0). De Vorss.
--Quiet Talks with the Master. 1936. pap. 3.25 (ISBN 0-87516-104-9). De Vorss.
Werblowski, R. Zwi, tr. see Scholem, Gershom.
Werblowsky, R. J., ed. see Scholem, Gershom.
Werblowsky, Raphael J. Lucifer & Prometheus: A Study of Milton's Satan. LC 79-153359. Repr. of 1952 ed. 7.50 (ISBN 0-404-06906-1). AMS Pr.
Werblowsky, Zvi & Wigoder, Geoffrey, eds. The Encyclopedia of the Jewish Religion. LC 86-10932. (Illus.). 478p. 1986. 39.95 (ISBN 0-915361-53-1, Dist. by Watts). Adama Pubs Inc.
Werman, Linda J. Draw Us Nearer to You, Lord. Sherer, Michael L., ed. (Orig.). 1987. pap. 7.25 (ISBN 0-89536-858-7, 7817). CSS of Ohio.
Wernecke, Herbert. When Loved Ones Are Called Home. (Ultra Bks Ser). pap. 1.95 (ISBN 0-8010-9513-1). Baker Bk.
Wernecke, Herbert H. Christmas Customs Around the World. LC 59-9581. 188p. 1979. pap. 7.95 (ISBN 0-664-24258-8). Westminster.
Wernecke, Herbert H., ed. Celebrating Christmas Around the World. LC 62-13232. (Illus.). 256p. 1980. pap. 5.95 (ISBN 0-664-24318-5). Westminster.
Werner, Alice. Myths & Legends of Bantu. 289p. 1968. Repr. of 1933 ed. 30.00x (ISBN 0-7146-1735-0, F Cass Co). Biblio Dist.
--Myths & Legends of the Bantu. LC 78-63237. (The Folktale). (Illus.). Repr. of 1933 ed. 34.00 (ISBN 0-404-16176-6). AMS Pr.
Werner, E. T. A Dictionary of Chinese Mythology. LC 76-27521. 1976. Repr. of 1932 ed. lib. bdg. 60.00 (ISBN 0-89341-034-9). Longwood Pub Group.
--Myths & Legends of China. LC 71-172541. (Illus.). Repr. of 1922 ed. 33.00 (ISBN 0-405-09059-5, Pub. by Blom). Ayer Co Pubs.
--Myths & Legends of China. 2nd ed. (Illus.). 453p. 1984. pap. 15.00 (ISBN 9971-947-55-2, Pub. by Graham Brash Singapore). Three Continents.
Werner, Eric. The Sacred Bridge. (Music Reprint Ser.). 1979. Repr. of 1959 ed. lib. bdg. 65.00 (ISBN 0-306-79581-7). Da Capo.
--The Sacred Bridge. 640p. 1981. 60.00x (ISBN 0-234-77352-9, Pub. by Dobson Bks England). State Mutual Bk.
--A Voice Still Heard: The Sacred Songs of the Ashkenazic Jews. LC 75-26522. 1976. 32.50 (ISBN 0-271-01167-X). Pa St U Pr.
Werner, Jayne S. Peasant Politics & Religious Sectarianism: Peasant & Priest in the Cao Dai in Viet Nam. LC 81-52078. (Monograph Ser.: No. 23). 123p. 1981. 10.50x (ISBN 0-938692-07-0). Yale U SE Asia.
Werner, Julia S. The Primitive Methodist Connexion: Its Background & Early History. LC 84-40161. (Illus.). 352p. 1985. text ed. 35.00x (ISBN 0-299-09910-5). U of Wis Pr.
Werner, Karel. Perspectives on Indian Religion. Connolly, Peter, ed. 253p. 1986. lib. bdg. 56.00 (ISBN 0-85424-021-7, Pub. by Sri Satguru Pubns India). Orient Bk Dist.
--Yoga & Indian Philosophy. 1977. 11.00 (ISBN 0-8426-0900-8, Pub. by Motilal Banarsidass India). Orient Bk Dist.
--Yoga & Indian Philosophy. 1979. 12.50x (ISBN 0-8364-0479-3). South Asia Bks.
Werner, Karl. Beda der Ehrwuerdige und Seine Zeit. new ed. 1963. Repr. of 1881 ed. 24.50 (ISBN 0-8337-3730-9). B Franklin.
--Franz Suarez und Die Scholastik Des Letzen Jahrhunderts, 2 Vols. rev. ed. 1889. 50.50 (ISBN 0-8337-3731-7). B Franklin.
--Geschichte Der Katholischen Theologie. 2nd ed. 50.00 (ISBN 0-384-66815-1). Johnson Repr.
--Heilige Thomas Von Aquino, 3 vols. rev. ed. 1963. Set. 107.00 (ISBN 0-8337-3738-4). B Franklin.
--Psychologie und Erkenntnisslehre D. Johannes Bonaventura. (Ger.). 70p. 1973. Repr. of 1876 ed. lib. bdg. 18.50 (ISBN 0-8337-3739-2). B Franklin.
Werner, Morris R. Brigham Young. LC 75-351. (The Radical Tradition in America Ser.). xvi, 478p. 1975. Repr. of 1925 ed. 32.50 (ISBN 0-88355-254-X). Hyperion Conn.
--Brigham Young. 1977. Repr. of 1925 ed. lib. bdg. 30.00 (ISBN 0-8492-2907-3). R West.
Werning, Waldo J. Christian Stewards: Confronted & Committed. LC 12-2814. 1983. pap. 8.95 (ISBN 0-570-03879-0). Concordia.
--The Radical Nature of Christianity: Church Growth Eyes Look at the Supernatural Mission of the Christian & the Church. LC 76-8359. 1976. pap. 5.85 (ISBN 0-87808-730-3, Pub. by Mandate Pr). William Carey Lib.
--Vision & Strategy for Church Growth. 2nd ed. 1983. pap. 4.50 (ISBN 0-8010-9658-8). Baker Bk.
Wersell, Thomas W. Spiritual Thoughts & Prayers. LC 74-76920. pap. 20.00 (2026829). Bks Demand UMI.
Wertenbaker, Lael T. Death of a Man. LC 73-16889. 192p. 1974. pap. 7.95x (ISBN 0-8070-2763-4, BP482). Beacon Pr.
Werth, Alvin, compiled by. Papal Pronouncements on Marriage & the Family: From Leo XIII to Pius XII (1878-1954) LC 82-6265. xxi, 189p. 1982. Repr. of 1955 ed. lib. bdg. 27.50x (ISBN 0-313-22521-4, WEPA). Greenwood.
Wertheim, S., jt. auth. see Gross, Theodore L.
Werthman, Michael S., jt. ed. see Cantor, Norman F.
Wertkin, Gerard C. The Four Seasons of Shaker Life. 1986. pap. 10.95 (ISBN 0-671-61815-6, Fireside). S&S.
Werzberger, Shmuel. Not in Heaven or Beyond the Sea: Explorations in the World of Jewish Tradition. 17.95 (ISBN 0-88125-128-3). Ktav.
Wesberry, James P. Bread in a Barren Land. LC 81-8668. 1982. pap. 4.95 (ISBN 0-8054-5103-X). Broadman.
--The Lord's Day. pap. 8.95 (ISBN 0-8054-2264-1). Broadman.
Weschcke, Carl L., ed. see Buckland, Raymond.
Weschcke, Carl L., ed. see Devine, Mary.
Weschcke, Carl L., ed. see Fitch, Ed & Renee, Janine.
Weschcke, Carl L., ed. see Godwin, David.
Weschcke, Carl L., ed. see Llewellyn Staff.
Wescott, Juanita. Magic & Music: The Language of the Gods Revealed. LC 85-71700. (Illus.). 145p. (Orig.). 1983. pap. 7.95 (ISBN 0-913407-00-3). Abbetira Pubns.
Weske, Dorothy B. Convocation of the Clergy: A Study of Antecedents & Its Rise, with Special Emphasis upon Its Growth & Activities in the Thirteenth & Fourteenth Centuries. (Church Historical Society London N. S. Ser.: No. 23). Repr. of 1937 ed. 60.00 (ISBN 0-8115-3147-3). Kraus Repr.
Wesley, et al. Christian Perfection. 6.95 (ISBN 0-686-12854-0). Schmul Pub Co.
Wesley, J. The Christian Pattern. pap. 2.75 (ISBN 0-686-12912-1). Schmul Pub Co.
Wesley, John. The Appeals to Men of Reason & Religion. Gragg, Gerald R., ed. (The Works of John Wesley: Vol. XI). (Illus.). 1975. 49.95x (ISBN 0-19-812498-8). Oxford U Pr.
--Devotions & Prayers of John Wesley. (Devotional Classics). 1977. pap. 2.95 (ISBN 0-8010-9597-2). Baker Bk.
--Explanatory Notes on the New Testament. 29.95 (ISBN 0-317-07537-3, 96510). Baker Bk.
--Explanatory Notes on the New Testament, 2 vols. 1056p. Date not set. 29.95 (ISBN 0-913573-06-X). Hendrickson MA.
--The Holy Spirit & Power. Weakley, Clare, ed. LC 77-91883. 1977. pap. 4.95 (ISBN 0-88270-262-9). Bridge Pub.
--The Nature of Revival. rev. ed. Weakley, Clare, ed. 256p. 1987. pap. 6.95 (ISBN 0-87123-925-6). Bethany Hse.
--The Nature of the Kingdom. Weakley, Clare, ed. 288p. 1986. pap. 6.95 (ISBN 0-87123-875-6, 210875). Bethany Hse.
--The New Birth. Oden, Thomas C., ed. LC 83-48460. 128p. 1984. 10.45 (ISBN 0-06-069312-6, HarpR). Har-Row.
--Sunday Services of the Methodists in North America. 144p. (Orig.). 1984. pap. 4.95 (ISBN 0-687-40632-3). Abingdon.
--Works of John Wesley, 14 vols. Set. 249.50 (ISBN 0-8010-9616-2). Baker Bk.
--The Works of John Wesley: A Collection of Hymns for the Use of the People Called Methodists, Vol. 7. Hilderbrandt, Franz & Beckerlegge, Oliver A., eds. (Oxford Edition of the Works of John Wesley Ser.). (Illus.). 1984. 86.00x (ISBN 0-19-812529-1). Oxford U Pr.
--The Works of John Wesley: Letters I, 1721-1739, Vol. 25. Baker, Frank, ed. (Oxford Edition of the Works of John Wesley Ser.). 1980. 45.00x (ISBN 0-19-812545-3). Oxford U Pr.
--The Works of John Wesley: (Letters II), 1740-1755, Vol. 26. Baker, Frank, ed. (The Oxford Edition of the Works of John Wesley Ser.). (Illus.). 1982. 45.00x (ISBN 0-19-812546-1). Oxford U Pr.
--The Works of Wesley, Vol. 3 & 4: The Journal of John Wesley. 1986. Vol. 3, 496p. 24.95 (ISBN 0-310-51290-5); Vol. 4, 544p. 24.95 (ISBN 0-310-51300-6). Zondervan.
--The Works of Wesley: Wesley's Standard Sermons, 2 vols. Sugden, E. H. & Allison, Joseph, eds. 544p. 1986. Vol. 1. 24.95 (ISBN 0-310-51270-0, 17170); Vol. 2. 24.95 (ISBN 0-310-51280-8, 17171). Zondervan.
Wesley, John & Weakley, Clare. The Nature of Spiritual Growth. rev. ed. 208p. 1986. pap. 5.95 (ISBN 0-87123-876-4). Bethany Hse.
Wesner, Maralene & Miles, E. You Are What You Choose. LC 84-3110. (Orig.). 1984. pap. 4.95 (ISBN 0-8054-5247-8). Broadman.
Wesner, Maralene & Wesner, Miles. Truth or Tradition: What Is the Gospel? LC 86-71139. 100p. 1986. pap. 4.95 (ISBN 0-936715-03-0). Diversity Okla.
--What's Your S. Q.? (Spiritual Quotient) LC 86-71133. 100p. 1986. pap. 4.95 (ISBN 0-936715-04-9). Diversity Okla.
Wesner, Maralene & Wesner, Miles E. When God Can't Answer (Divine Limitations) LC 86-70753. 100p. 1986. pap. 4.95 (ISBN 0-936715-26-X). Diversity Okla.
Wesner, Marlene & Wesner, Miles E. A Fresh Look at the Gospel. LC 82-72231. (Orig.). 1983. pap. 5.95 (ISBN 0-8054-1955-1). Broadman.
--The Living Word (God's Self-Disclosure) LC 86-70752. 164p. (Orig.). pap. cancelled (ISBN 0-936715-27-8). Diversity Okla.
Wesner, Miles, jt. auth. see Wesner, Maralene.
Wesner, MIles, jt. auth. see Wesner, Maralene.
Wesner, Miles E., jt. auth. see Wesner, Maralene.
Wesner, Miles E., jt. auth. see Wesner, Marlene.
Wesner, R. The Wesner Conjectures. LC 82-21421. 128p. 1985. pap. 4.95 (ISBN 0-88437-070-4). Psych Dimensions.
Wessel, Helen. Christian Marriage, Birth & Nature. rev. ed. LC 85-70830. 325p. Date not set. pap. cancelled (ISBN 0-933082-15-0). Bookmates Intl.
--Natural Childbirth & the Christian Family. 4th, rev. ed. LC 82-48943. (Illus.). 384p. 1985. pap. text ed. 8.95 (ISBN 0-06-069317-7, HarpR). Har-Row.
Wessel, Helen, jt. auth. see Pettit, Hermon.
Wessel, Helen S., ed. see Finney, Charles G.
Wessell, Leonard P. G.E Lessing's Theology: A Reinterpretation, a Study in the Problematic Nature of the Enlightenment. 1977. 20.00x (ISBN 90-279-7801-8). Mouton.
West, Andrew F. Alcuin & the Rise of the Christian Schools. LC 73-149674. Repr. of 1892 ed. 10.00 (ISBN 0-404-06908-8). AMS Pr.
--Alcuin & the Rise of the Christian Schools. 1892. Repr. 9.00x (ISBN 0-403-00031-9). Scholarly.
West, Anson D. A History of Methodism in Alabama. LC 83-19053. (Illus.). 840p. 1984. Repr. of 1893 ed. 30.00 (ISBN 0-87152-380-9). Reprint.
West, Cornel. Prophesy Deliverance! An Afro-American Revolutionary Christianity. LC 82-13483. 186p. 1982. pap. 11.95 (ISBN 0-664-24447-5). Westminster.
West, F. W., ed. Pahlavi Texts. (Vols. 5, 18, 24, 37, 47). 5 vols. 75.00 (ISBN 0-686-97478-6); 15.00 ea. Asian Human Pr.
West, J. K., jt. auth. see Selby, D. J.
West, James. Introduction to the Old Testament. 2nd ed. 1981. text ed. write for info. (ISBN 0-02-425920-9). Macmillan.
West, Julius. G. K. Chesterton: A Critical Study. LC 72-6120. 1973. Repr. of 1915 ed. lib. bdg. 30.00 (ISBN 0-8414-0112-8). Folcroft.
West, M. L. The Hesiodic Catalogue of Women: Its Nature, Structure & Origins. (Illus.). 1985. 24.95x (ISBN 0-19-814034-7). Oxford U Pr.
West, Marion B. Out of My Bondage. LC 76-5297. 128p. 1976. 5.50 (ISBN 0-8054-5144-7). Broadman.
West, Martin. Bishops & Prophets in a Black City: African Independent Churches in Soweto, Johannesburg. 1977. text ed. 16.50x (ISBN 0-8426-1590-3). Verry.
West, Philip. Yenching University & Sino-Western Relations, 1916-1952. (East Asian Ser.: No. 85). 1976. 18.50x (ISBN 0-674-96569-8). Harvard U Pr.
West, Rebecca. St. Augustine. 174p. 1979. Repr. of 1938 ed. lib. bdg. 22.50 (ISBN 0-89987-853-9). Darby Bks.
West, Robert H. Invisible World: A Study of Pneumatology in Elizabethan Drama. LC 74-31118. 1939. lib. bdg. 30.00 (ISBN 0-8414-9582-3). Folcroft.
West, Serene. Very Practical Meditation. LC 79-20249. 116p. (Orig.). 1981. pap. 4.95 (ISBN 0-89865-006-2, Unilaw). Donning Co.
Westberg, Barbara. Christmas Plays. Wallace, Mary H., ed. 40p. (Orig.). 1983. pap. 2.95 (ISBN 0-912315-62-8). Word Aflame.
Westberg, Barbara, jt. auth. see Smelser, Georgia.
Westberg, Granger. Ante la Perdida de un Ser Querido. Rodriguez, Jorge A., tr. 32p. 1985. Repr. of 1984 ed. 1.50 (ISBN 0-311-46081-X). Casa Bautista.
Westberg, Granger E. Good Grief. LC 78-21233. 64p. (Orig.). 1962. pap. 1.95 (ISBN 0-8006-1114-4, 1-1114); pap. 3.95 large print ed. (ISBN 0-8006-1361-9, 1-1361). Fortress.
Westburg, John E., ed. see Jowers, Lawrence V.
Westburg, John E., ed. see Warren, Henry C.
Westbury-Jones, John. Roman & Christian Imperialism. LC 78-118555. 1971. Repr. of 1939 ed. 28.00x (ISBN 0-8046-1180-7, Pub. by Kennikat). Assoc Faculty Pr.
Westcott. Numbers. 9.50 (ISBN 0-7229-5027-6). Theos Pub Hse.
Westcott, Arthur, ed. see Westcott, Brooke F.
Westcott, Brooke F. The Bible in the Church. (Canterbury Bks.). 1980. pap. 6.95 (ISBN 0-8010-9627-8). Baker Bk.
--Commentary on Epistle to the Hebrews. (Gr). 1950. 14.95 (ISBN 0-8028-3289-X). Eerdmans.

--Commentary on Gospel According to St. John. 1950. 7.95 (ISBN 0-8028-3288-1). Eerdmans.
--Commentary on the Epistles of Saint John. (Gr). 8.95 (ISBN 0-8028-3290-3). Eerdmans.
--Essays in the History of Religious Thought in the West. LC 72-8480. (Essay Index Reprint Ser.). 1972. Repr. of 1891 ed. 24.50 (ISBN 0-8369-7338-0). Ayer Co Pubs.
--The Gospel According to Saint John: The Greek Text with Introduction & Notes, 2 vols. in 1. Westcott, Arthur, ed. 877p. 1980. pap. 16.95 (ISBN 0-8010-9644-8). Baker Bk.
--St. Paul's Epistle to the Ephesians. 281p. 1983. lib. bdg. 10.50 (ISBN 0-86524-171-6, 4901). Klock & Klock.
Westcott, Frederick B. The Biblical Doctrine of Justification. 407p. 1983. lib. bdg. 15.25 (ISBN 0-86524-160-0, 8803). Klock & Klock.
--Colossians: A Letter to Asia. 1981. lib. bdg. 7.50 (ISBN 0-86524-070-1, 5102). Klock & Klock.
Westcott, W. W. Rosicrucian Thoughts on the Ever-Burning Lamps of the Ancients. 1986. pap. 2.95 (ISBN 0-916411-56-7). Sure Fire.
Westcott, W. Wynn. The Occult Power of Numbers. LC 84-21740. (Illus.). 128p. 1984. Repr. of 1984 ed. lib. bdg. 15.95x (ISBN 0-89370-675-2). Borgo Pr.
Westcott, Wayne L. Building Strength at the YMCA. LC 86-20838. (Illus.). 104p. (Orig.). 1987. pap. text ed. 8.00x (ISBN 0-87322-082-X, LWES4885). Human Kinetics.
Westcott, William W. The Chaldean Oracles Attributed to Zoroaster. pap. 5.95 (ISBN 0-916411-16-8). Sure fire.
Westcott, William W., ed. Chaldean Oracles. 1984. pap. 5.95 (ISBN 0-916411-16-8, Pub. by Alexandrian Pr). Holmes Pub.
Westcott-Wieman, Regina, jt. auth. see Wieman, Henry N.
Westenhaver, Edythe, jt. ed. see Brophy, Don.
Westerhof, Jack, jt. auth. see Hagan, Lowell.
Westerhoff, John H. & Eusden, John. The Spiritual Life: Learning East & West. 172p. 1982. 10.95 (ISBN 0-8164-0516-6, HarpR). Har-Row.
Westerhoff, John H., jt. auth. see Holmes, Urban T., III.
Westerhoff, John H., ed. A Colloquy on Christian Education. LC 72-4258. 1979. pap. 5.95 (ISBN 0-8298-0365-3). Pilgrim NY.
Westerhoff, John H., III. Building God's People in a Materialistic Society. 144p. 1983. pap. 8.95 (ISBN 0-8164-2466-7, HarpR). Har-Row.
--Inner Growth-Outer Change: An Educational Guide to Church Renewal. (Orig.). pap. 4.95 (ISBN 0-8164-2213-3, HarpR). Har-Row.
--Living the Faith Community: The Church That Makes a Difference. 1985. pap. cancelled (ISBN 0-317-18159-9). Whitaker Hse.
--Living the Faith Community: The Church That Makes a Difference. 120p. (Orig.). 1985. pap. 6.95 (ISBN 0-86683-870-8, HarpR). Har-Row.
--A Pilgrim People: Learning Through the Church Year. 128p. (Orig.). 1984. pap. 7.95 (ISBN 0-86683-884-8, 7462, HarpR). Har-Row.
--Will Our Children Have Faith? 144p. 1983. pap. 6.95 (ISBN 0-8164-2435-7, AY7452, HarpR). Har-Row.
Westerhoff, John H., III & Hughes, Caroline A. On the Threshold of God's Future. 160p. (Orig.). 1986. pap. 7.95 (ISBN 0-06-254781-X, HarpR). Har-Row.
Westerhoff, John H., III & Willimon, William H. Liturgy & Learning Through the Life Cycle. 192p. (Orig.). 1985. pap. 9.95 (ISBN 0-86683-980-1, HarpR). Har-Row.
Westerhoff, John H., III, jt. auth. see Neville, Gwen K.
Westerhoff, John H., III, ed. Values for Tomorrow's Children. LC 72-125961. 1979. pap. 5.95 (ISBN 0-8298-0377-7). Pilgrim NY.
Westerhoff, John H., III, jt. auth. see Holmes, Urban T., III.
Westerhoff, John H., 3rd. Bringing up Children in the Christian Faith. 108p. (Orig.). 1980. pap. 4.95 (ISBN 0-86683-627-6, HarpR). Har-Row.
Westerhoff, John H., 3rd, ed. A Colloquy on Christian Education. LC 72-4258. 1972. 6.95 (ISBN 0-8298-0238-X). Pilgrim NY.
Westerhoff, John H., 3rd, jt. ed. see Edwards, O. C., Jr.
Westerink, L. G., ed. Nicholas I, Patriarch of Constantinople: Miscellaneous Writings. LC 80-70736. (Dumbarton Oaks Texts: Vol. 6). 160p. 1981. 28.00x (ISBN 0-88402-089-4). Dumbarton Oaks.
Westerlund, David. African Religion in African Scholarship: A Preliminary Study of the Religious and Political Background. 104p. (Orig.). 1985. pap. 20.00x (ISBN 91-7146-344-5). Coronet Bks.
Westerman, Claus. What Does the Old Testament Say About God? new ed. Golka, F. W., ed. LC 78-52448. 1979. 8.95 (ISBN 0-8042-0190-0). John Knox.
Westermann, Claus. Blessing: In the Bible & the Life of the Church, No. 3. Brueggeman, Walter & Donahue, John R., eds. Crim, Keith, tr. from Ger. LC 78-54564. (Overtures to Biblical Theology Ser.). 144p. 1978. pap. 8.95 (ISBN 0-8006-1529-8, 1-1529). Fortress.
--Elements of Old Testament Theology. Stott, Doug, tr. LC 81-82346. Tr. of Theologie Des Alten Testaments in Grundzuegen. 249p. 1982. 20.95 (ISBN 0-8042-0191-9); pap. 15.95 (ISBN 0-8042-0193-5). John Knox.
--Genesis One-Eleven. Scullion, John J., tr. LC 82-72655. 692p. cloth 34.95 (ISBN 0-8066-1962-7, 10-2543). Augsburg.
--Genesis 12-36: A Commentary. Scullion, John J., tr. from Ger. LC 85-7449. Tr. of Genesis: Kapitel 12-36. 608p. 1985. text ed. 34.95 (ISBN 0-8066-2172-9, 10-2542). Augsburg.
--Genesis 37-50: A Commentary. Scullion, John S., tr. from Ger. LC 85-26802. 274p. 1986. 21.95 (ISBN 0-8066-2197-4, 10-2546). Augsburg.
--Handbook to the New Testament. Boyd, Robert H., ed. & tr. LC 69-14190. 1977. pap. 9.95 (ISBN 0-8066-1600-8, 10-2946). Augsburg.
--Handbook to the Old Testament. Boyd, Robert H., tr. LC 67-25362. 1967. pap. 11.95 (ISBN 0-8066-1529-X, 10-2951). Augsburg.
--Isaiah Forty to Sixty-Six: A Commentary. Stalker, David M., tr. LC 69-18647. (Old Testament Library). 446p. 1969. 19.95 (ISBN 0-664-20851-7). Westminster.
--Praise & Lament in the Psalms. rev. enl. ed. Crim, Keith & Soulen, Richard, trs. from German. LC 65-10553. 1981. 12.95 (ISBN 0-8042-1791-2); pap. 9.95 (ISBN 0-8042-1792-0). John Knox.
--The Promises to the Fathers: Studies on the Patriarchal Narratives. Green, David E., tr. from Ger. LC 79-7395. 208p. 1980. 13.95 (ISBN 0-8006-0580-2, 1-580). Fortress.
--The Promises to the Fathers: Studies on the Patriarchal Narratives. LC 79-7395. pap. 51.80 (2027191). Bks Demand UMI.
--The Psalms: Structure, Content, & Message. Gehrke, Ralph D., tr. from Ger. LC 79-54127. Tr. of Der Psalter. 136p. (Orig.). 1980. pap. 7.95 (ISBN 0-8066-1762-4, 10-5300). Augsburg.
--The Structure of the Book of Job: A Form-Critical Analysis. Muenchow, Charles A., tr. from Ger. LC 80-2379. Tr. of Der Aufbau des Buches Hiob. 160p. 1981. 14.95 (ISBN 0-8006-0651-5, 1-651). Fortress.
--The Structure of the Book of Job: A Form-Critical Analysis. LC 80-2379. pap. 40.00 (2029297). Bks Demand UMI.
--A Thousand Years & a Day. LC 62-8544. 292p. 1982. pap. 8.95 (ISBN 0-8006-1913-7, 1-1913). Fortress.
Westermann, Diedrich. Africa & Christianity. LC 74-15102. (Duff Lectures, 1935). Repr. of 1937 ed. 24.50 (ISBN 0-404-12151-9). AMS Pr.
Westermarck, Edvard A. Ethical Relativity. Repr. of 1932 ed. lib. bdg. 22.50x (ISBN 0-8371-4366-7, WEER). Greenwood.
Westermarck, Edward. The Origin & Development of the Moral Ideas, 2 vols. facsimile ed. LC 74-37359. (Select Bibliographies Reprint Ser.). Repr. of 1908 ed. Set. 81.50 (ISBN 0-8369-6706-2). Ayer Co Pubs.
--The Theory of the Moral Emotions. (Illus.). 161p. 1984. 89.75x (ISBN 0-89266-464-9). Am Classical Coll Pr.
Westermarck, Edward A. Christianity & Morals. facs. ed. LC 78-80406. (Essay Index Reprint Ser). 1939. 23.75 (ISBN 0-8369-1055-9). Ayer Co Pubs.
--The Origin & Development of the Moral Ideas, 2 vols. 2nd ed. (Landmarks in Anthropology Ser). 1621p. Repr. 115.00 (ISBN 0-384-66958-1). Johnson Repr.
Westers, Jacqueline, jt. ed. see Colina, Tessa.
Westervelt, W. D. Legends of Gods & Ghosts from Hawaiian Mythology. 1977. lib. bdg. 59.95 (ISBN 0-8490-2147-2). Gordon Pr.
Westervelt, William D., ed. Hawaiian Legends of Ghosts & Ghost-Gods. LC 63-22543. (Illus.). 1963. 7.25 (ISBN 0-8048-0238-6). C E Tuttle.
Westheimer, Karl. Humanity's Contemporary Moral Decay & the Historical Role of the Catholic Church. LC 73-76434. (Illus.). 132p. 1973. 43.40 (ISBN 0-913314-19-6). Am Classical Coll Pr.
Westin, G. & Bergsten, T., eds. Balthasar Hubmaier. (Tauferakten Kommission Ser., Vol. 9). 507p. 1962. 30.00x (ISBN 0-8361-1169-9). Herald Pr.
Westing, Harold J. Evaluate & Grow. 1984. pap. 5.95 (ISBN 0-88207-624-8). Victor Bks.
--Multiple Church-Staff Handbook. LC 85-9811. (Illus.). 208p. (Orig.). 1985. pap. 10.95 (ISBN 0-8254-4031-9). Kregel.
--Super Superintendent: A Layman's Guide to Sunday School Management. LC 80-66721. (Accent Teacher Training Ser.). 160p. (Orig.). 1980. pap. 4.95 (ISBN 0-89636-057-1). Accent Bks.
Westley, Dick. Morality & Its Beyond. 324p. (Orig.). 1984. pap. 8.95 (ISBN 0-89622-207-1). Twenty-Third.
--Redemptive Intimacy. LC 80-54810. 176p. 1981. pap. 5.95 (ISBN 0-89622-123-7). Twenty-Third.
Westley, Frances. The Complex Forms of the Religious Life: A Durkheimian View of New Religious Movements. LC 83-4579. (AAR Academy Ser.). 210p. 1983. 13.50 (ISBN 0-89130-626-9, 01 01 45). Scholars Pr GA.
Westman, Heinz. The Structure of Biblical Myths: The Ontogenesis of the Psyche. LC 83-19132. (Seminar Ser.: No. 16). v, 477p. (Orig.). 1983. pap. 18.50 (ISBN 0-88214-116-3). Spring Pubns.
Westman, Paul. Billy Graham: Reaching Out to the World. LC 81-9912. (Taking Part Ser.). (Illus.). 48p. 1981. PLB 8.95 (ISBN 0-87518-220-8). Dillon.
Westmeier, Karl-Wilhelm. Reconciling Heaven & Earth: The Transcendental Enthusiasm & Growth of an Urban Protestant Community, Bogota, Colombia. (Studies in the Intercultural History of Christianity: Vol. 41). 462p. 1986. text ed. 34.00 (ISBN 3-261-03547-1). P Lang Pubs.
Westmeyer, Nancy. Parish Life: Manual for Spiritual Leadership Formation. 1983. pap. 8.95 (ISBN 0-8091-2489-0). Paulist Pr.
Westminster Assembly. Shorter Catechism with Scripture Proofs. 0.75 (ISBN 0-85151-265-8). Banner of Truth.
Westminster Seminary Faculty Symposium. Infallible Word. Woolley, Paul, ed. pap. 9.95 (ISBN 0-87552-543-1). Presby & Reformed.
Westmoreland, Tony. In All Things I Am Not Alone. Graves, Helen, ed. 230p. 1987. 8.95 (ISBN 1-55523-059-8). Winston-Derek.
Weston, Jessie L. From Ritual to Romance. McLaughlin, Mary M., tr. 13.75 (ISBN 0-8446-3162-0). Peter Smith.
--The Legends of the Wagner Drama. LC 74-24255. Repr. of 1896 ed. 24.00 (ISBN 0-404-13132-8). AMS Pr.
--The Legends of the Wagner Drama: Studies in Mythology & Romance. LC 76-22354. 1976. Repr. of 1903 ed. lib. bdg. 35.00 (ISBN 0-89341-003-9). Longwood Pub Group.
--The Quest of the Holy Grail. LC 72-10823. (Arthurian Legend & Literature Ser., No. 1). 1973. Repr. of 1913 ed. lib. bdg. 75.00x (ISBN 0-8383-0642-X). Haskell.
Westphal, Arnold C. Bible Magic Trick Talks for Childrens Church. 1987. pap. 4.95 (ISBN 0-915398-26-5). Visual Evangels.
--Fold 'n Cut Surprise Sermonetes, No. 2. 1968. 4.95 (ISBN 0-915398-01-X). Visual Evangels.
--Fold 'n Snip Bible Bits, No. 7. 1974. 4.95 (ISBN 0-915398-06-0). Visual Evangels.
--Fold 'n Snip Story Sermonettes, No. 6. 1973. pap. 4.95 (ISBN 0-915398-05-2). Visual Evangels.
--Gospel Magic with Homemade Stuff & Things, No. 1. 1972. pap. 4.95 (ISBN 0-915398-09-5). Visual Evangels.
--Gospel Surprise Paper Tears. (No. 13). 1986. pap. 4.95 (ISBN 0-915398-25-7). Visual Evangels.
--Happy Surprise Junior Objectalks. 1978. 4.95 (ISBN 0-915398-11-7). Visual Evangels.
--Junior Surprise Sermons with Handmade Objects, 2 bks. Set. pap. 9.90 (ISBN 0-686-70924-1); No. 1. pap. 4.50 (ISBN 0-915398-18-4); No. 2. pap. 4.95 (ISBN 0-915398-19-2). Visual Evangels.
--Paper Tearing Bible Talks, No. 4. 1970. pap. 4.95 (ISBN 0-915398-03-6). Visual Evangels.
--Paper Tearing Evangels, No. 8. 1975. pap. 4.95 (ISBN 0-915398-07-9). Visual Evangels.
--Paper Tearing Gospel Illustrations, No. 3. 1969. pap. 4.95 (ISBN 0-915398-02-8). Visual Evangels.
--Paper Tearing Trick Talks, No. 1. 1967. pap. 4.95 (ISBN 0-915398-00-1). Visual Evangels.
--Surprise Paper Tearing Talks, No. 9. 1976. pap. 4.95 (ISBN 0-915398-08-7). Visual Evangels.
--Trick Paper Tears with Gospel Truth, No. 10. 1977. pap. 4.95 (ISBN 0-915398-10-9). Visual Evangels.
--Visual Evangels, 6 vols. (Orig.). 1979. pap. text ed. 4.95 ea. No. 1 (ISBN 0-915398-12-5). No. 2 (ISBN 0-915398-13-3). No. 3 (ISBN 0-915398-14-1). No. 4 (ISBN 0-915398-15-X). No. 5 (ISBN 0-915398-16-8). No. 6 (ISBN 0-915398-17-6). Visual Evangels.
--The Voyage of Life on a Paper Boat, No. 12. pap. 4.95 (ISBN 0-915398-22-2). Visual Evangels.
Westphal, Merold. God, Guilt & Death: An Existential Phenomenology of Religion. LC 83-48525. (Studies in Phenomenology & Existential Philosophy). 320p. 1987. 27.50x (ISBN 0-253-32586-2); pap. 9.95 (ISBN 0-253-32586-2). Ind U Pr.
Westphal, Merold, ed. Method & Speculation in Hegel's Phenomenology. 137p. 1982. text ed. 15.00x (ISBN 0-391-02336-5, Pub. by Harvester Pr UK). Humanities.
Westra, Rinny. The Faith of A Radical. 80p. (Orig.). 1984. pap. 8.95 (ISBN 0-86474-001-8, Pub. by Interface Press). ANZ Religious Pubns.
Westreich, Budd. The Stow Affair: Anti-Semitism in the California Legislature. (Illus.). 84p. 1981. 10.00 (ISBN 0-936300-02-7). Pr Arden Park.
Westropp, H. M. Ancient Symbol Worship: Phallic Idea. 59.95 (ISBN 0-87968-633-2). Gordon Pr.
Westropp, Hodder M. & Staniland, Wake C. Phallism in Ancient Worships: Ancient Symbol Worship. 2nd ed. (Illus.). 111p. pap. 8.95 (ISBN 0-88697-017-2). Life Science.
Westrup, J. A., ed. see Fellowes, Edmund H.
Westwood, Jennifer. Albion: A Guide to Legendary Britain. (Illus.). 448p. 1986. 18.95 (ISBN 0-88162-128-5). Salem Hse Pubs.
Wetherbee, Winthrop, ed. & tr. The Cosmographia of Bernardus Silvestris. LC 73-479. (Records of Civilization, Sources & Studies: Sources & Studies). 176p. 1973. 24.00x (ISBN 0-231-03673-6). Columbia U Pr.
Wetlesen, Jon. The Sage & the Way: Spinoza's Ethics of Freedom. (Philosophia Spinozae Perennis Ser.: No. 4). 474p. 1979. text ed. 50.00 (ISBN 90-232-1596-6, Pub. by Van Gorcum Holland). Longwood Pub Group.
--The Sage & the Way: Studies in Spinoza's Ethics of Freedom. (Philosophia Spinozae Perennis Ser.: No. 4). 1979. text ed. 55.00x (ISBN 90-232-1596-6). Humanities.
Wetmore, Gordon. Gordon Wetmore's Prayers for Boys & Girls. (Illus.). 48p. 1986. 5.95. Ideals.
Wetterer, Margaret K., jt. auth. see Reilly, Mary V.
Wetzel, Robert, compiled by. Essays on New Testament Christianity. LC 78-55881. 1978. text ed. 12.95 (ISBN 0-87239-208-2, 2856). Standard Pub.
Wetzels, Walter D., ed. Myth & Reason: A Symposium. LC 72-3096. (Germanic Languages Symposium Ser). 206p. 1973. 9.95x (ISBN 0-292-75003-X). U of Tex Pr.
Wetzl, Joseph, tr. see Frankl-Lundborg, Otto.
Wetzler, Robert & Huntington, Helen. Seasons & Symbols. LC 62-9094. (Illus., Orig.). 1962. pap. 6.95 (ISBN 0-8066-0221-X, 10-5625). Augsburg.
Wevers, John W. Ezekiel. (New Century Bible Ser). 253p. 1976. 8.95 (ISBN 0-551-00755-9). Attic Pr.
--Ezekiel. Clements, Ronald E., ed. (The New Century Bible Commentary Ser.). 243p. 1982. pap. 7.95 (ISBN 0-8028-1910-9). Eerdmans.
Wevers, John W. & Redford, D. B., eds. Essays on the Ancient Semitic World. LC 76-23038. (Toronto Semitic Texts & Studies). pap. 33.30 (2026403). Bks Demand UMI.
Wewers, Gerd S. Geheimnis und Geheimhaltung im Rabbinischen Judentum. (Religionsgeschichtliche Versuche und Vorarbeiten, Vol. 35). (Ger.). 1975. 33.60x (ISBN 3-11-005858-8). De Gruyter.
Wey, Joseph C., ed. Guillelmi de Ockham: Quodlibeta Septem, Ordinatio, Opera Theologica, Vol. 9. 1980. 50.00 (ISBN 0-686-28122-5). Franciscan Inst.
Weyland, Jack. First Day Forever & the Other Stories for LDS Youth. LC 80-82455. 120p. 1980. 7.95 (ISBN 0-88290-136-2, 2037). Horizon Utah.
--If Talent Were Pizza, You'd Be a Supreme. 1986. text ed. 8.95 (ISBN 0-87579-054-2). Deseret Bk.
Weyman, Stanley J. From the Memoirs of a Minister of France. LC 77-113694. (Short Story Index Reprint Ser.). 1895. 24.50 (ISBN 0-8369-3423-7). Ayer Co Pubs.
Weymouth, R. F. New Testament in Modern Speech. 3rd ed. LC 78-9536. 750p. 1978. kivar 14.95 (ISBN 0-8254-4025-4). Kregel.
Weymouth, Richard F. The New Testament in Modern Speech. 6th ed. 457p. 1983. 9.50 (ISBN 0-227-67550-9, Pub. by J Clarke UK). Attic Pr.
Weyna, Kathy, jt. auth. see LeFever, Marlene.
Whale, John S. Christian Doctrine. 1941. pap. 10.95 (ISBN 0-521-09642-1). Cambridge U Pr.
Whalen, James. The Spiritual Teachings of Teresa of Avila & Adrian Van Kaam: Formative Spirituality. LC 83-3628. 334p. (Orig.). 1984. lib. bdg. 27.50 (ISBN 0-8191-3864-9); pap. text ed. 15.75 (ISBN 0-8191-3865-7). U Pr of Amer.
Whalen, William J. Minority Religions in America. rev. ed. LC 81-3664. 222p. (Orig.). 1981. pap. 7.95 (ISBN 0-8189-0413-5). Alba.
--Minority Religions in America. LC 79-38979. 312p. (Orig.). 1972. pap. 7.95 (ISBN 0-8189-0239-6). Alba.
--Reaching Out to the Baptists with Heart & Mind. (Reaching Out to...Ser.). 32p. 1984. pap. 1.50 (ISBN 0-89243-209-8). Liguori Pubns.

--Reaching Out to the Episcopalians with Heart & Mind. (Reaching Out to...Ser.). 32p. 1984. pap. 1.50 (ISBN 0-89243-210-1). Liguori Pubns.
--Reaching Out to the Lutherans with Heart & Mind. (Reaching Out to...Ser.). 32p. 1984. pap. 1.50 (ISBN 0-89243-206-3). Liguori Pubns.
--Reaching Out to the Presbyterians & the Reformed with Heart & Mind. (Reaching Out to...Ser.). 32p. 1984. pap. 1.50 (ISBN 0-89243-208-X). Liguori Pubns.
--Separated Brethren. rev. ed. LC 79-83874. 1979. pap. 7.50 (ISBN 0-87973-829-4). Our Sunday Visitor.
--Strange Gods: Contemporary Religious Cults in America. LC 80-81451. 1981. pap. 4.95 (ISBN 0-87973-666-6, 666). Our Sunday Visitor.
Whaley, Joachim. Religious Toleration & Social Change in Hamburg, 1529-1819. (Cambridge Studies in Early Modern History). 290p. 1985. 49.50 (ISBN 0-521-26189-9). Cambridge U Pr.
Whaley, K. A. Basic Bible Doctrines for Victorious Living. 87p. 1981. pap. 7.95 (ISBN 0-686-35778-7). First Baptist.
--Basic Bible Doctrines for Victorious Living. 1981. pap. 7.95x (ISBN 0-686-40713-X). Freedom Univ-FSP.
Whaley, Richie. Samuel: Prophet & Judge. (BibLearn Ser.). (Illus.). 1979. 5.95 (ISBN 0-8054-4242-1, 4242-42). Broadman.
Whaling, Frank. The Rise of the Religious Significance of Rama. 392p. 1980. text ed. 10.00 (ISBN 0-8426-1758-2). Verry.
--World's Religious Traditions. 320p. (Orig.). 1986. pap. 14.95 (ISBN 0-8245-0747-9). Crossroad NY.
Whaling, Frank, ed. Contemporary Approaches to the Study of Religion, Vol. 1: The Humanities. LC 84-14807. (Religion & Reason Ser.: No. 27). 520p. 1984. 39.95x (ISBN 3-11-009834-2); Vol. 2: The Social Sciences, pgs.302. pap. 29.95 (ISBN 3-11-009836-9). Mouton.
--John & Charles Wesley: Selected Writings & Hymns. LC 81-82207. 432p. 1981. 13.95 (ISBN 0-8091-0318-4); pap. 10.95. Paulist Pr.
--The World's Religious Traditions. 320p. 1984. 22.95 (ISBN 0-567-09353-0, Pub. by T&T Clark Ltd UK). Fortress.
Wharey, James B. Study of the Sources of Bunyan's Allegories(with Special Reference to Deguileville's Pilgrimage of Man. LC 68-59038. 136p. 1968. Repr. of 1904 ed. 15.00x (ISBN 0-87752-120-4). Gordian.
Wharton, James. Easter. LC 84-18756. (Proclamation 3 A). 64p. 1987. pap. 3.75 (ISBN 0-8006-4121-3, 1-4121). Fortress.
Wharton, Janet, tr. see Hogg, James.
Wharton, Michael. Time to Stop & Think, Vol. 1. 1981. 12.00x (ISBN 0-7223-1422-1, Pub. by A H Stockwell England). State Mutual Bk.
Whately, William. A Bride-Bush, or a Wedding Sermon. LC 74-28893. (English Experience Ser.: No. 769). 1975. Repr. of 1617 ed. 5.00 (ISBN 90-221-0769-8). Walter J Johnson.
Whatmore, L. E. The Carthusians under King Henry the Eighth. Hogg, James, ed. (Analecta Cartusiana Ser.: No. 109). 227p. (Orig.). 1983. pap. 25.00 (ISBN 0-317-42558-7, Pub. by Salzburg Studies). Longwood Pub Group.
Whealon, John F. Living the Catholic Faith Today. LC 75-6801. 1975. 2.50 (ISBN 0-8198-0491-6); pap. 1.50 (ISBN 0-8198-0492-4). Dghtrs St Paul.
Wheat, Ed. Amor que no se Apaga. 1984. 4.25 (ISBN 0-88113-010-9). Edit Betania.
--How to Save Your Marriage Alone. 64p. 1983. pap. 2.50 (ISBN 0-310-42522-0, 10267P). Zondervan.
--Love Life for Every Married Couple. 288p. 1980. pap. 5.95 (ISBN 0-310-42511-5, 10266P). Zondervan.
Wheat, Ed & De Wheat, Gaye. El Placer Sexual Ordenado por Dios. 224p. 1980. 4.25 (ISBN 0-88113-320-5). Edit Betania.
Wheat, Ed & Wheat, Gaye. Intended for Pleasure. rev. ed. (Illus.). 256p. 1981. 12.95 (ISBN 0-8007-1253-6). Revell.
Wheat, Gaye, jt. auth. see Wheat, Ed.
Wheat, Gaye de see Wheat, Ed & De Wheat, Gaye.
Wheat, Leonard F. Paul Tillich's Dialectical Humanism: Unmasking the God above God. LC 74-105365. (Illus.). 287p. 1970. 26.50x (ISBN 0-8018-1161-9). Johns Hopkins.
Wheat, M. T. Progress & Intelligence of Americans: Collateral Proof of Slavery, from the First to the Eleventh Chapter of Genesis, As Founded on Organic Law. facs. ed. LC 77-83882. (Black Heritage Library Collection Ser.). 1862. 21.75 (ISBN 0-8369-8684-9). Ayer Co Pubs.
Wheatcroft, Anita L. Promises, 3 bks. (Illus.). 80p. (Orig.). 1973. Set. pap. 2.95x (ISBN 0-8192-4043-5); tchrs'. guide 4.50x (ISBN 0-8192-4044-3). Morehouse.
--Seasons & Saints. (Illus.). 112p. (Orig.). 1974. pap. text ed. 4.25x (ISBN 0-8192-4050-8); tchrs'. ed. 4.75x (ISBN 0-8192-4049-4). Morehouse.
Wheatley, L. A., tr. see Lubke, Wilhelm.
Wheatley, Melvin. Christmas Is for Celebrating. 1977. pap. 3.95 (ISBN 0-8358-0366-X). Upper Room.
Wheatley, Richard, jt. auth. see Palmer, Phoebe.
Whedon, D. D. Whedon's Commentary Revised, 2 vols. 1981. Vol. Matthew Mark. 7.65 (ISBN 0-87813-917-6); Vol. Luke John. 7.65 (ISBN 0-87813-918-4). Christian Light.
Wheeler, Barbara G., ed. see Hopewell, James F.
Wheeler, Bonnie G. Meet the Overcomers: The Story of a Special Family. (Orig.). 1984. pap. 5.95 (ISBN 0-8024-0440-5). Moody.
Wheeler, Charles, jt. auth. see Gabel, John B.
Wheeler, Charles F. Classical Mythology in the Plays, Masques, & Poems of Ben Jonson. LC 71-114234. 1970. Repr. of 1938 ed. 23.50 (ISBN 0-8046-1038-X, Pub. by Kennikat). Assoc Faculty Pr.
Wheeler, Edward L. Uplifting the Race: The Black Minister in the New South 1865-1902. 198p. (Orig.). 1986. lib. bdg. 24.75 (ISBN 0-8191-5161-0); pap. text ed. 11.75 (ISBN 0-8191-5162-9). U Pr of Amer.
Wheeler, Gerald, ed. see Anderson, Godfrey T.
Wheeler, Gerald, ed. see Byers, Carolyn.
Wheeler, Gerald, ed. see Cleveland, E. E.
Wheeler, Gerald, ed. see Coffen, Harold G.
Wheeler, Gerald, ed. see Davy, Yvonne.
Wheeler, Gerald, ed. see Doherty, Ivy D.
Wheeler, Gerald, ed. see Dudley, Roger L. & Cummings, Des, Jr.
Wheeler, Gerald, ed. see Durand, Eugene.
Wheeler, Gerald, ed. see Ferch, Arthur.
Wheeler, Gerald, ed. see Gladson, Jerry.
Wheeler, Gerald, ed. see Gordon, Paul A.
Wheeler, Gerald, ed. see Horn, Siegfried.
Wheeler, Gerald, ed. see Hyde, Gordon.
Wheeler, Gerald, ed. see Irland, Nancy B.
Wheeler, Gerald, ed. see Jarrard, Dan.
Wheeler, Gerald, ed. see Johnsson, Noelene.
Wheeler, Gerald, ed. see Kistler, Robert.
Wheeler, Gerald, ed. see Knight, George R.
Wheeler, Gerald, ed. see Kotter, Bonnie.
Wheeler, Gerald, ed. see Marcus, Sophia.
Wheeler, Gerald, ed. see Pierson, Robert H.
Wheeler, Gerald, ed. see Reece, Colleen L.
Wheeler, Gerald, ed. see Scragg, W. R.
Wheeler, Gerald, ed. see Scragg, Walter R. L.
Wheeler, Gerald, ed. see Strong, June.
Wheeler, Gerald, ed. see Venden, Morris.
Wheeler, Gerald, ed. see Wallenkampf, Arnold V.
Wheeler, Gerald, ed. see Warren, Mervyn A.
Wheeler, Gerald, ed. see Wuestefeld, Mary F.
Wheeler, Gerald W. Deluge. LC 78-8404. (Flame Ser.). 1978. pap. 0.99 (ISBN 0-8127-0191-7). Review & Herald.
Wheeler, J. M., jt. ed. see Foote, G. W.
Wheeler, Penny. The Beginning. Phillips, ed. (Daybreak Ser.). 112p. 1982. pap. 3.95 (ISBN 0-8163-0478-5). Pacific Pr Pub Assn.
Wheeler, Penny E. More Than Harps of Gold. (Outreach Ser.). 1981. pap. 1.25 (ISBN 0-8163-0424-6). Pacific Pr Pub Assn.
Wheeler, Ron. Cartoon Clip-Art for Youth Leaders. 120p. 1987. pap. price not set (ISBN 0-8010-9682-0). Baker Bk.
Wheelock, Robert D. Policies & Procedures for the Pastoral Care Department. LC 76-9660. 1977. pap. 4.00 (ISBN 0-87125-036-5). Cath Health.
Wheelwright, John. John Wheelwright: His Writings, Including His Fast-Day Sermon, 1637. 1966. 24.00 (ISBN 0-8337-3763-5). B Franklin.
--John Wheelwright's Writings, Including His Fast-Day Sermon, 1637, & His Mercurius Americanus, 1645. facs. ed. LC 70-128897. (Select Bibliographies Reprint Ser). 1876. 18.00 (ISBN 0-8369-5517-X). Ayer Co Pubs.
Wheelwright, Mary C. The Myth & Prayers of the Great Star Chant & the Myth of the Coyote Chant. (Illus.). 191p. 1987. 14.00 (ISBN 0-912586-58-3); pap. 10.00 (ISBN 0-912586-61-3). Navajo Coll Pr.
Whelan, Mariellen, jt. auth. see Duska, Ronald.
Wheless. By the Sweat of My Brow. 2.50 (ISBN 0-685-02583-7). Outlook.
Wheless, J. Forgery in Christianity. 75.00 (ISBN 0-87968-358-9). Gordon Pr.
Wherry, E. M., jt. ed. see Sales, George.
Whetstone, George. Promus & Cassandra, Pts. 1 & 2. (Tudor Facsimile Texts. Old English Plays: No. 52). Repr. of 1910 ed. 49.50 (ISBN 0-404-53352-3). AMS Pr.
Whichcote, Benjamin. Select Sermons of Benjamin Whichcote. LC 77-16025. 1977. Repr. of 1742 ed. 50.00x (ISBN 0-8201-1306-9). Schol Facsimiles.
Whicher, Olive. George Adams, Interpreter of Rudolf Steiner. 1978. pap. 8.95 (ISBN 0-904822-08-7). St George Bk Serv.
Whinfield, E. H., tr. Teachings of Rumi: The Masnavi. 1979. 15.95 (ISBN 0-900860-64-2, Pub. by Octagon Pr England). Ins Study Human.
Whipple, Edwin P. Recollections of Eminent Men with Other Papers. 397p. 1982. Repr. of 1886 ed. lib. bdg. 45.00 (ISBN 0-8495-5840-9). Arden Lib.
Whipple, Leander E. Philosophy of Mental Healing. 234p. 1981. pap. 13.50 (ISBN 0-89540-110-X, SB-110). Sun Pub.
Whipple, Maurine. Giant Joshua. Repr. 12.50 (ISBN 0-914740-17-2). Western Epics.
Whisker, James B. The Social, Political & Religious Thought of Alfred Rosenberg: An Interpretive Essay. LC 81-40652. 150p. (Orig.). 1982. lib. bdg. 25.50 (ISBN 0-8191-2023-5); pap. text ed. 9.75 (ISBN 0-8191-2024-3). U Pr of Amer.
Whiston, tr. see Josephus, Flavius.
Whiston, Charles. Instructions in the Life of Prayer. 2nd ed. 96p. 1985. pap. 1.50 (ISBN 0-88028-046-8). Forward Movement.
Whiston, Charles F., ed. see Fenelon, Francois.
Whiston, Lionel A. For Those in Love: Making Your Marriage Last a Lifetime. 128p. 1983. 10.95 (ISBN 0-687-13285-1). Abingdon.
Whiston, William. A New Theory of the Earth: Its Original, to the Consummation of All Things Wherein the Creation of the World in Six Days. Albritton, Claude C., Jr., ed. LC 77-6545. (History of Geology Ser.). 1978. lib. bdg. 37.50x (ISBN 0-405-10463-4). Ayer Co Pubs.
Whiston, William, tr. see Josephus, Flavius.
Whitacre, Rodney A. Johannine Polemic: The Role of Tradition & Theology. LC 82-5457. (SBL Dissertation Ser.). 292p. 1982. pap. 13.00 (ISBN 0-89130-579-3, 06-01-67). Scholars Pr GA.
Whitaker, Donald. The Divine Connection: Feel Better & Live Longer. LC 83-82835. 148p. (Orig.). 1983. pap. 4.95 (ISBN 0-910311-06-4). Huntington Hse Inc.
Whitaker, Lois. See & Know. 87p. (Orig.). 1980. pap. text ed. 3.95 (ISBN 0-931097-02-9). Sentinel Pub.
Whitaker, Richard W., compiled by. Eerdmans' Analytical Concordance to the Revised Standard Version. 1488p. 1987. 49.95 (ISBN 0-8028-2403-X). Eerdmans.
Whitaker, William. Disputation on Holy Scripture Against the Papists. 55.00 (ISBN 0-384-68010-0). Johnson Repr.
Whitall, Hannah & Smith, Elisabeth E. The Christian's Secret of a Happy Life: Proven Word. 192p. 1985. pap. 5.95 (ISBN 0-8499-2980-6, 2980-6). Word Bks.
Whitcomb, John. Daniel. (Everyman's Bible Commentary Ser.). (Orig.). 1985. pap. 5.95 (ISBN 0-8024-2067-2). Moody.
Whitcomb, John C. Daniel: The Coming of Christ's Kingdom. 1985. pap. 5.95 (ISBN 0-88469-165-9). BMH Bks.
--The Early Earth. 1972. pap. 6.95 (ISBN 0-8010-9679-0). Baker Bk.
--The Early Earth. pap. 4.50 (ISBN 0-88469-060-1). BMH Bks.
--Ester: El Triunfo de la Soberania de Dios (Comentario Biblico Portavoz) Orig. Title: Esther (Everyman's Bible Commentary) (Span.). 1982. pap. 4.50 (ISBN 0-8254-1866-6). Kregel.
--Esther, the Triumph of God's Sovereignty. 128p. (Orig.). 1979. pap. 4.95 (ISBN 0-88469-081-4). BMH Bks.
--Esther: Triumph of God's Sovereignty. (Everyman's Bible Commentary Ser.). 1979. pap. 5.95 (ISBN 0-8024-2016-8). Moody.
--Origin of the Solar System. (Biblical & Theological Studies). pap. 2.50 (ISBN 0-8010-9590-5). Baker Bk.
--World That Perished. pap. 5.95 (ISBN 0-8010-9537-9). Baker Bk.
--The World That Perished. pap. 4.95 (ISBN 0-88469-059-8). BMH Bks.
Whitcomb, John C. & DeYoung, Donald B. The Moon: Its Creation, Form & Significance. 7.95 (ISBN 0-88469-102-0). BMH Bks.
Whitcomb, John C. & Morris, Henry M. The Genesis Flood. pap. 8.95 (ISBN 0-8010-9501-8). Baker Bk.
--The Genesis Flood. pap. 8.95 (ISBN 0-88469-067-9). BMH Bks.
Whitcomb, John C., jt. auth. see Davis, John J.
Whitcomb, John C., Jr. Christ, Our Pattern & Plan. 1979. pap. 1.00 (ISBN 0-88469-031-8). BMH Bks.
--Darius the Mede. pap. 2.50 (ISBN 0-88469-064-4). BMH Bks.
--Does God Want Christians to Perform Miracles Today? 1979. pap. 1.00 (ISBN 0-88469-016-4). BMH Bks.
--The Origin of the Solar System. 1979. pap. 1.75 (ISBN 0-317-53170-0). BMH Bks.
--Solomon to the Exile: Studies in Kings & Chronicles. pap. 4.95 (ISBN 0-88469-054-7). BMH Bks.
Whitcomb, John C., Jr. & Morris, H. M. Genesis Flood. 1960. pap. 8.95 (ISBN 0-87552-338-2). Presby & Reformed.
Whitcomb, Paul. The Catholic Church Has the Answer. 60p. (Orig.). 1986. pap. 1.25 (ISBN 0-89555-282-5). Tan Bks Pubs.
--Confession of a Roman Catholic. 55p. 1985. pap. 1.25 (ISBN 0-89555-281-7). Tan Bks Pubs.
White, jt. auth. see Calkins.
White, Alvin D. History of the Cross Creek Presbyterian Church. 1969. 6.00 (ISBN 0-87012-040-9). McClain.
White, Andrew D. History of the Warfare of Science with Theology in Christendon, 2 Vols. Set. 26.50 (ISBN 0-8446-3170-1). Peter Smith.
White, Anna & Taylor, Lelia S. Shakerism, Its Meaning & Message. LC 73-134421. Repr. of 1904 ed. 31.50 (ISBN 0-404-08462-1). AMS Pr.
White, Anne, jt. auth. see White, Nelson.
White, Anne, jt. ed. see White, Nelson.
White, Anne S. All in All. 128p. (Orig.). 1980. pap. 2.50 (ISBN 0-9605178-0-4). Victorious Ministry.
--Healing Devotions. LC 75-5218. 138p. 1975. pap. 3.95 (ISBN 0-8192-1192-3). Morehouse.
--Trial by Fire. 108p. (Orig.). 1975. pap. 3.50 (ISBN 0-89228-045-X). Impact Bks MO.
White, Anne S. & Vanzant, Don. Study Adventure in Trial by Fire. 56p. (Orig.). 1985. pap. 1.95 (ISBN 0-89228-102-2). Impact Bks MO.
White, Arthur W. Ellen G. White Biography, Vol. 2. Woolsey, Raymond H., ed. 480p. 1986. 19.95 (ISBN 0-8280-0120-0). Review & Herald.
White, Mrs. Bob. Unto the Uttermost. (Illus.). 80p. 1977. pap. 1.00 (ISBN 0-89114-079-4). Baptist Pub Hse.
White, Charles E. The Beauty of Holiness: Phoebe Palmer As Theologian, Revivalist, Feminist, & Humanitarian. 352p. 1986. 15.95 (ISBN 0-310-46250-9). Zondervan.
White, Charles I., tr. see De Chateaubriand, Viscount.
White, Charles S., ed. The Caurasi Pad of Sri Hit Harivams: Introduction, Translation, Notes, & Edited Hindi Text. LC 76-54207. (Asian Studies at Hawaii Ser: No. 16). 212p. 1977. pap. text ed. 10.50x (ISBN 0-8248-0359-0). UH Pr.
White, D. M. Predicacion Expositiva. Estrello, Francisco E., tr. Orig. Title: The Excellence of Exposition. 160p. 1982. Repr. of 1980 ed. 3.75 (ISBN 0-311-42061-3). Casa Bautista.
White, David M. The Search for God. 448p. 1983. 24.95 (ISBN 0-02-627110-9). Macmillan.
White, Donald, ed. see Schous, Gerald P.
White, Donald R., ed. see Girdlestone, Robert B.
White, Douglas M. The Excellence of Exposition: Practical Procedure in Expository Preaching. 1977. 4.95 (ISBN 0-87213-939-5). Loizeaux.
White, E. G. From Heaven with Love. 1984. 1.50 (ISBN 0-8163-0553-6). Pacific Pr Pub Assn.
--From Splendor to Shadow. 1984. 1.50 (ISBN 0-8163-0559-5). Pacific Pr Pub Assn.
--From Trials to Triumph. 1984. 1.50 (ISBN 0-8163-0565-X). Pacific Pr Pub Assn.
White, Edward A. Science & Religion in American Thought. LC 68-54307. (Stanford University. Stanford Studies in History, Economics, & Poltical Science: No. 8). Repr. of 1952 ed. 17.50 (ISBN 0-404-50972-X). AMS Pr.
White, Ellen. The Broad Road. large print ed. 32p. 1985. pap. 5.00 (ISBN 0-914009-47-8). VHI Library.
--Forbidden Marriages & Divorce. large print ed. 27p. 1985. pap. 5.00 (ISBN 0-914009-38-9). VHI Library.
--Overeating: A Common Sin. large print ed. 52p. 1985. pap. 6.50 (ISBN 0-914009-45-1). VHI Library.
--Passions. 1985. pap. 6.00 (ISBN 0-914009-55-9). VHI Library.
--Passions among God's People. large print ed. 35p. 1985. pap. 6.00 (ISBN 0-914009-46-X). VHI Library.
--Subdue Sins. large print ed. 41p. 1985. pap. 5.50 (ISBN 0-914009-44-3). VHI Library.
White, Ellen G. The Acts of the Apostles. 633p. 1911. deluxe ed. 9.95 (ISBN 0-8163-0033-X, 01092-6). Pacific Pr Pub Assn.
--Can We Know God? (Uplook Ser.). 1970. pap. 0.99 (ISBN 0-8163-0067-4, 03035-3). Pacific Pr Pub Assn.
--Christ in His Sanctuary. LC 70-94869. (Dimension Ser.). 1969. pap. 6.95 (ISBN 0-8163-0128-X, 03254-0). Pacific Pr Pub Assn.
--Christian Experience & Teaching of Ellen G. White. 1940. deluxe ed. 10.95 (ISBN 0-8163-0126-3, 03310-0). Pacific Pr Pub Assn.
--Colporteur Ministry. 1953. 3.25 (ISBN 0-8163-0110-7, 03431-4); pap. 5.95 (ISBN 0-8163-0111-5, 03430-6). Pacific Pr Pub Assn.
--Cosmic Conflict. 640p. 1983. pap. 0.50 (ISBN 0-8280-0211-8). Pacific Pr Pub Assn.
--Counsels on Education. 1968. deluxe ed. 8.95 (ISBN 0-8163-0112-3, 03555-0). Pacific Pr Pub Assn.
--Counsels on Health & Instruction to Medical Missionary Workers. 1951. deluxe ed. 10.95 (ISBN 0-8163-0114-X, 03561-8). Pacific Pr Pub Assn.
--Counsels to Parents, Teachers & Students Regarding Christian Education. 1943. Repr. of 1913 ed. deluxe ed. 10.95 (ISBN 0-8163-0115-8, 03591-5). Pacific Pr Pub Assn.

--From Here to Forever. 436p. 1982. pap. 1.50 (ISBN 0-317-00060-8). Pacific Pr Pub Assn.
--Fundamentals of Christian Education. (CHL Ser.). 1977. 8.95 (ISBN 0-8127-0307-3). Review & Herald.
--The Great Controversy. 1950. 5.95 (ISBN 0-8163-0035-6, 07886-5); deluxe ed. 9.95 (ISBN 0-8163-0036-4, 07882-4); pap. 1.45 (ISBN 0-8163-0037-2, 07887-3). Pacific Pr Pub Assn.
--How to Get Along with Others. (Uplook Ser.). 1964. pap. 0.99 (ISBN 0-8163-0072-0, 08835-1). Pacific Pr Pub Assn.
--Impending Conflict. (Stories That Win Ser.). 1960. pap. 0.95 (ISBN 0-8163-0141-7, 09366-6). Pacific Pr Pub Assn.
--Medical Ministry. 1963. deluxe ed. 8.95 (ISBN 0-8163-0158-1, 13370-2). Pacific Pr Pub Assn.
--Message from Calvary. (Outreach Ser.). 64p. 1981. pap. 1.25 (ISBN 0-8163-0394-0). Pacific Pr Pub Assn.
--Mind, Character, & Personality: Guidelines to Mental & Spiritual Health, 2 vols. (Christian Home Library). 1978. 8.95 ea. Vol. 1 (ISBN 0-8127-0148-8). Vol. 2 (ISBN 0-8127-0149-6). Review & Herald.
--Patriarchs & Prophets. 805p. 1958. deluxe ed. 9.95 (ISBN 0-8163-0038-0, 16082-0); pap. 5.95 (ISBN 0-8163-0039-9, 16083-8). Pacific Pr Pub Assn.
--Prophets & Kings. 752p. deluxe ed. 9.95 (ISBN 0-8163-0040-2, 16642-1); pap. 5.95 (ISBN 0-8163-0041-0, 16643-9). Pacific Pr Pub Assn.
--Reflecting Christ. Woolsey, Raymond H., ed. (Devotional Ser.). 384p. 1985. 7.95 (ISBN 0-8280-0305-X). Review & Herald.
--Selected Messages, Vol. III. 1980. Christian Home Library Ed. 8.95 (ISBN 0-8280-0055-7, 19275-7); Shield Ser. Ed. 4.95 (ISBN 0-8280-0056-5, 19276-5); Special Ed. pap. 4.50 (ISBN 0-8280-0057-3, 19277-3). Review & Herald.
--Selected Messages, 3 vols. 1980. Set. pap. 11.95 (ISBN 0-8280-0059-X, 19269-0). Review & Herald.
--Steps to Christ. LC 56-7169. 134p. 1956. 6.95 (ISBN 0-8163-0045-3, 19543-8); pap. 1.25 (ISBN 0-8163-0046-1, 19547-9). Pacific Pr Pub Assn.
--Steps to Jesus. 128p. 1980. 6.95 (ISBN 0-8127-0316-2); pap. 3.25 (ISBN 0-8127-0318-9). Review & Herald.
--Testimonies for the Church, 9 vols. 1948. 5.95 ea. (ISBN 0-8163-0152-2); Set. 79.95 (ISBN 0-8163-0153-0, 20140-0). Pacific Pr Pub Assn.
--Testimonies to Ministers. 10.95 (ISBN 0-317-28268-9). Pacific pr Pub Assn.
--Thoughts from the Mount of Blessing. LC 56-7170. 172p. 1956. 6.95 (ISBN 0-8163-0047-X, 20401-6). Pacific Pr Pub Assn.
White, Ernest. The Art of Human Relations. LC 85-5953. 1985. pap. 6.95 (ISBN 0-8054-5008-4). Broadman.
White, Eugene E. Puritan Rhetoric: The Issue of Emotion in Religion. LC 76-181987. (Landmarks in Rhetoric & Public Address Ser.). 229p. 1972. 10.95x (ISBN 0-8093-0563-1). S Ill U Pr.
White, Gail. The Last Eve. LC 85-91011. 160p. 1985. 10.00 (ISBN 0-682-40244-3). Exposition Pr FL.
White, Gladyce E. Installations with Corresponding Devotionals. Crankshaw, Andrea, ed. 70p. (Orig.). Date not set. pap. 6.50 (ISBN 0-9615371-0-8). Adlen Bks.
White, H., tr. see Merle d'Aubigne, Jean H.
White, Harwood, jt. auth. see White, Stewart E.
White, Helen C. The Metaphysical Poets: A Study in Religious Experience. LC 83-45866. 1936. 39.50 (ISBN 0-404-20285-3, PR549). AMS Pr.
--Social Criticism in Popular Religious Literature of the Sixteenth-Century. 1965. lib. bdg. 20.50x (ISBN 0-374-98455-7, Octagon). Hippocrene Bks.
--The Tudor Books of Private Devotion. LC 78-21661. (Illus.). 1979. Repr. of 1951 ed. lib. bdg. 24.75x (ISBN 0-313-21063-2, WHTB). Greenwood.
--Tudor Books of Saints & Martyrs. LC 63-13741. pap. 73.00 (ISBN 0-317-07866-6, 2004164). Bks Demand UMI.
White, Hugh G. & Hauser, Walter. The Monasteries of the Wadi 'n Natrun: Metropolitan Museum of Art Egyptian Expedition Publications, 3 vols. Incl. Vol. 1. New Coptic Texts from the Monastery of Saint Macarius. (Illus.). 308p. Repr. of 1926 ed. 42.00 (ISBN 0-405-02243-3); Vol. 2. the History of the Monasteries of Nitria & of Scetis. Hauser, Walter. (Illus.). Repr. of 1932 ed. 57.50 (ISBN 0-405-02244-1); Vol. 3. Hauser, Walter. (Illus.). 480p. Repr. of 1933 ed. 57.50 (ISBN 0-405-02245-X). LC 77-168409. (Metropolitan Museum of Art Publications in Reprint). (Illus.). 1340p. 172.00 set (ISBN 0-405-02242-5). Ayer Co Pubs.
White, Hugh W. Demonism Verified & Analyzed. 69.95 (ISBN 0-8490-0016-5). Gordon Pr.
White, J. Benton. From Adam to Armageddon: A Survey of the Bible. LC 85-8921. 320p. 1985. pap. text ed. write for info. (ISBN 0-534-05111-1). Wadsworth Pub.
White, J. Manchip. Ancient Egypt: Its Culture & History. LC 75-115748. 1970. pap. 4.95 (ISBN 0-486-22548-8). Dover.
--Ancient Egypt: Its Culture & History. (Illus.). 14.50 (ISBN 0-8446-0336-8). Peter Smith.
White, James. Sketches of the Christian Life & Public Labors of William Miller. LC 70-134376. Repr. of 1875 ed. 27.50 (ISBN 0-404-08424-9). AMS Pr.
White, James A. The Founding of Cliff Haven: Early Years of the Catholic Summer School of America. LC 53-1915. (Monograph Ser.: No. 24). 1950. 7.50x (ISBN 0-930060-06-7). US Cath Hist.
White, James F. Introduction to Christian Worship. LC 79-21073. (Orig.). 1980. pap. 9.50 (ISBN 0-687-19509-8). Abingdon.
White, Jerry. The Church & the Parachurch: An Uneasy Marriage. LC 83-12125. (Critical Concern Ser.). 1983. 10.95 (ISBN 0-88070-018-1). Multnomah.
--Honesty, Morality, & Conscience. LC 78-61619. 240p. 1979. pap. 5.95 (ISBN 0-89109-431-8). NavPress.
--Making the Grade: A Guide to Excellence in College. 2nd ed. 108p. 1985. pap. 4.95 (ISBN 0-89109-447-4). NavPress.
--The Power of Commitment. (Christian Character Library). 176p. 1985. 8.95 (ISBN 0-89109-532-2). NavPress.
--Power of Commitment. Date not set. pap. price not set. NavPress.
White, Joe. How to Be a Hero to Your Teenager. 144p. (Orig.). 1985. pap. 4.95 (ISBN 0-8423-1495-4). Tyndale.
--The Kingdom of Light. 83p. 1984. pap. 2.50 (ISBN 0-88144-033-7). Christian Pub.
--Who's Number One. 144p. 1986. pap. 4.95 (ISBN 0-8423-8215-1). Tyndale.
White, John. Bible Study. 1984. pap. 0.75 (ISBN 0-87784-068-7). Inter-Varsity.
--The Book of Books. 1978. 7.50 (ISBN 0-87552-545-8). Presby & Reformed.
--Daring to Draw Near: People in Prayer. LC 77-6554. (Orig.). 1977. pap. 5.95 (ISBN 0-87784-788-6). Inter-Varsity.
--Eros Defiled: The Christian & Sexual Sin. LC 76-39711. 1977. pap. 6.95 (ISBN 0-87784-781-9). Inter-Varsity.
--Excellence in Leadership. LC 86-2938. 132p. (Orig.). 1986. pap. 5.95 (ISBN 0-87784-570-0). Inter-Varsity.
--The Fight: A Practical Handbook to Christian Living. LC 76-12297. 230p. (Orig.). 1976. pap. 6.95 (ISBN 0-87784-777-0). Inter-Varsity.
--Flirting with the World: A Challenge to Loyalty. LC 81-21491. 156p. 1982. pap. 5.95 (ISBN 0-87788-156-1). Shaw Pubs.
--Parents in Pain. LC 78-24760. 1979. pap. 7.95 (ISBN 0-87784-582-4); study guide 1.95 (ISBN 0-87784-492-5). Inter-Varsity.
--Prayer. 1984. pap. 0.75 (ISBN 0-87784-067-9). Inter-Varsity.
--The Race: Discipleship for the Long Run. LC 84-6695. 216p. 1984. pap. 5.95 (ISBN 0-87784-976-5). Inter-Varsity.
White, John & Blue, Ken. Healing the Wounded. LC 85-2358. 240p. (Orig.). 1985. 11.95 (ISBN 0-87784-939-0); pap. 6.95 (ISBN 0-87784-533-6). Inter-Varsity.
White, John B. A Study of the Language of Love in the Song of Songs & Ancient Egyptian Poetry. LC 77-13399. (Society of Biblical Literature. Dissertation Ser.: Vol. 38). 1978. pap. 10.25 (ISBN 0-89130-192-5, 060138). Scholars Pr GA.
White, John L. The Form & Function of the Body of the Greek Letter in the Non-Literary Papyri & in Paul the Apostle. LC 75-33088. (Society of Biblical Literature. Dissertation Ser.). (Illus.). 1975. pap. 9.95 (ISBN 0-89130-048-1, 060102). Scholars Pr GA.
White, John W. Arming for Armageddon. 218p. pap. 5.95 (ISBN 0-88062-109-5). Mott Media.
--The Coming World Dictator. LC 80-71003. 119p. (Orig.). 1981. pap. 2.95 (ISBN 0-87123-042-9, 200042). Bethany Hse.
--Re-Entry II. 1986. pap. 4.95 (ISBN 0-8010-9680-4). Baker Bk.
White, Jon. E., selected by see Frith, Francis.
White, Julian E., Jr., ed. see De Villehardouin, Geoffroy.
White, K. Owen. Book of Jeremiah. (New Shield Ser.). 1981. pap. 3.45 (ISBN 0-8010-9517-4). Baker Bk.
White, L. B. English Sacred Poetry of the Olden Time. Repr. of 1864 ed. 25.00 (ISBN 0-89984-136-8). Century Bookbindery.
White, L. T., Jr. Latin Monasticism in Norman Sicily. 1967. Repr. of 1938 ed. 9.00x (ISBN 0-910956-12-X). Medieval Acad.
White, Laura C., tr. Who Is Padre Pio? (Illus.). 44p. 1974. pap. 1.00 (ISBN 0-89555-101-2). TAN Bks Pubs.
White, Leland J. Christ & the Christian Movement: Jesus in the New Testament, the Creeds & Modern Theology. LC 85-11190. 296p. (Orig.). 1985. pap. 10.95 (ISBN 0-8189-0484-4). Alba.
White, Lynn, Jr. Medieval Religion & Technology: Collected Essays. LC 77-83113. (Center for Medieval & Renaissance Studies, UCLA: Publication: No. 13). 1978. pap. 11.95x (ISBN 0-520-05896-8, CAMPUS 371). U of Cal Pr.
White, M., jt. auth. see Douglas, N.
White, Marian. Bible Teaching Finger Plays. (Teaching Helps Ser). 1977. pap. 4.50 (ISBN 0-8010-9592-1). Baker Bk.
White, Mary. Growing Together: Building Your Family's Spiritual Life. 2nd ed. 144p. 1985. pap. 4.95 (ISBN 0-89109-484-9). NavPress.
White, Michael, jt. auth. see Fitzgerald, John.
White, Miles. Early Quaker Records in Virginia. LC 76-46154. 64p. 1985. pap. 5.00 (ISBN 0-317-31654-0). Genealog Pub.
White, Morton. Science & Sentiment in America: Philosophical Thought from Jonathan Edwards to John Dewey. 1972. 25.00x (ISBN 0-19-501519-3). Oxford U Pr.
--What Is & What Ought to Be Done: An Essay on Ethics & Epistemology. 1981. 14.95x (ISBN 0-19-502916-X). Oxford U Pr.
White, Morton, ed. Documents in the History of American Philosophy: From Jonathan Edward to John Dewey. 1972. pap. text ed. 13.95x (ISBN 0-19-501555-X). Oxford U Pr.
White, Morton G. Religion, Politics, & the Higher Learning: A Collection of Essays. LC 82-1013. x, 140p. 1982. Repr. of 1959 ed. lib. bdg. 22.50x (ISBN 0-313-23480-9, WHRE). Greenwood.
White, Nelson & White, Anne. Arithmancy. LC 81-84893. (Illus.). 50p. (Orig.). 1981. pap. 6.00 (ISBN 0-939856-23-9). Tech Group.
--The Complete Exorcist. LC 83-50160. (Exorcism from Scratch Ser.). (Illus.). 75p. (Orig.). 1983. pap. 15.00 (ISBN 0-939856-33-6). Tech Group.
--Index & Reference Volume to the Lemegeton of Solomon (1979 White Transcription of Sloane 2731) LC 80-52052. 75p. (Orig.). 1980. pap. 15.00 (ISBN 0-939856-07-7). Tech Group.
--Index to the Spirits Given in "Abramelin". 50p. (Orig.). 1981. pap. 8.00 (ISBN 0-939856-17-4). Tech Group.
--Selected Conjurations from the Lemegeton (& Other Sources) large type ed. LC 81-51403. 50p. (Orig.). 1981. pap. 10.00 (ISBN 0-939856-16-6). Tech Group.
--Spiritual Healing. LC 85-50745. (Illus.). 65p. (Orig.). 1985. pap. text ed. 10.00 (ISBN 0-939856-42-5). Tech Group.
--Spiritual Intimidation. LC 84-51476. 65p. (Orig.). 1984. pap. 10.00 (ISBN 0-939856-39-5). Tech Group.
White, Nelson & White, Anne, eds. Lemegeton, Clavicula Salomonis: Or the Complete Lesser Key of Solomon the King. rev ed. LC 79-91961. (Illus.). 130p. (Orig.). 1979. pap. 30.00 (ISBN 0-939856-06-9). Tech Group.
White, Nelson H. Magick & the Law: Or, How to Set-Up & Operate Your Own Occult Shop. LC 80-50273. (Magick & the Law Ser.: Vol. 5). (Illus.). 85p. (Orig.). 1982. pap. 15.00 (ISBN 0-939856-31-X). Tech Group.
White, O. Kendall, Jr. Mormon Neo-orthodoxy: A Crisis Theology. 250p. 1987. pap. 8.95 (ISBN 0-941214-52-4). Signature Bks.
White, Paul. Alias Jungle Doctor: An Autobiography. (Illus.). 236p. 1977. pap. 6.95 (ISBN 0-85364-205-2). Attic Pr.
White, Paul F. Index to the American Jewish Archives, Vols. I-X. 25.00x (ISBN 0-87820-004-5). Ktav.
White, R. E. Biblical Ethics. pap. 9.95 (ISBN 0-8042-0787-9). John Knox.
--Christian Ethics: The Historical Development. pap. 11.95 (ISBN 0-8042-0791-7). John Knox.
--A Christian Handbook to the Psalms. 224p. (Orig.). 1984. pap. 7.95 (ISBN 0-8028-0031-9). Eerdmans.
White, Reginald E. The Night He Was Betrayed: Bible Studies in Our Lord's Preparation for His Passion. LC 82-13783. pap. 35.30 (ISBN 0-317-30167-5, 2025349). Bks Demand UMI.
--Stranger of Galilee. LC 60-10096. (Pivot Family Reader Ser). 240p. 1975. pap. 2.25 (ISBN 0-87983-108-1). Keats.
White, Roger. Another Song, Another Season: Poems & Portrayals. 184p. 1979. cloth o.p. 4.00 (ISBN 0-85398-087-X); pap. 8.95 (ISBN 0-85398-088-8). G Ronald Pub.
--A Sudden Music. 200p. 12.95 (ISBN 0-85398-162-0); pap. 7.95 (ISBN 0-85398-163-9). G Ronald Pub.
White, Ronald C., Jr. & Hopkins, C. Howard. The Social Gospel: Religion & Reform in Changing America. LC 75-34745. (Illus.). 326p. 1975. 29.95 (ISBN 0-87722-083-2); pap. 9.95x (ISBN 0-87722-084-0). Temple U Pr.
White, Ronald C., Jr., et al, eds. American Christianity: A Case Approach. 208p. (Orig.). 1986. pap. text ed. 11.95 (ISBN 0-8028-0241-9). Eerdmans.
White, Ruthe. Today's Woman in Search of Freedom. 176p. (Orig.). 1985. pap. 4.95 (ISBN 0-89081-473-2). Harvest Hse.
--Touch Me Again, Lord. LC 82-84453. 136p. (Orig.). 1983. pap. 5.95 (ISBN 0-89840-038-4). Heres Life.
--What Every Pastor's Wife Should Know. 176p. (Orig.). 1986. pap. 5.95 (ISBN 0-8423-7932-0). Tyndale.
White, Sharon. The Man Who Talked With Angels. 226p. (Orig.). 1982. pap. 5.95 (ISBN 0-89221-088-5, Pub. by SonLife). New Leaf.
White, Stewart E. & White, Harwood. Across the Unknown. 336p. 1987. pap. 7.95 (ISBN 0-89804-150-3). Ariel OH.
White, Thomas. A Discoverie of Brownisme. LC 74-80226. (English Experience Ser.: No. 701). (Illus.). 30p. 1974. Repr. of 1605 ed. 5.00 (ISBN 90-221-0701-9). Walter J Johnson.
White, Thomas & O'Donnell, Desmond. Renewal of Faith. LC 74-76320. 240p. 1974. pap. 2.95 (ISBN 0-87793-068-6). Ave Maria.
White, Thomas see Field, John.
White, Thomas R., ed. see Twenty-Four Magazine Editors & Burns, John.
White, Victor. God & the Unconscious. rev. ed. LC 82-19153. (Jungian Classics Ser.: No. 4). xxxiii, 245p. 1982. pap. 15.00 (ISBN 0-88214-503-7). Spring Pubns.
White, William. John Donne Since 1900: A Bibliography of Periodical Articles. LC 77-25861. 1942. lib. bdg. 17.50 (ISBN 0-8414-9557-2). Folcroft.
White, William, Jr. Theological & Grammatical Phrasebook of the Bible. 1984. 12.95 (ISBN 0-8024-0218-6). Moody.
White, William R. Speaking in Stories: Resources for Christian Storytellers. LC 82-70954. 128p. (Orig.). 1982. pap. 6.95 (ISBN 0-8066-1929-5, 10-5886). Augsburg.
--Stories for Telling: A Treasury for Christian Storytellers. LC 85-28980. 144p. (Orig.). 1986. pap. 6.95 (10-6023). Augsburg.
White, Willie. Fifty-Two Winning Sermons. 117p. (Orig.). 1973. cancelled (ISBN 0-89900-129-7). College Pr Pub.
White, Willie W. The Greatest Work in the World. rev. ed. 1975. pap. 1.95 (ISBN 0-89900-108-4). College Pr Pub.
--What the Bible Says about Suffering. (What the Bible Says Ser.). 350p. 1984. 13.95 (ISBN 0-317-05126-1). College Pr Pub.
White Eagle. The Gentle Brother. 1968. 3.95 (ISBN 0-85487-002-4). De Vorss.
--Golden Harvest. 1958. 3.95 (ISBN 0-85487-017-2). De Vorss.
--Heal Thyself. 1962. 3.95 (ISBN 0-85487-015-6). De Vorss.
--The Living Word of St. John. new ed. 208p. 1979. pap. 13.95 (ISBN 0-85487-044-X). De Vorss.
--Morning Light. 1957. 3.95 (ISBN 0-85487-018-0). De Vorss.
--The Path of the Soul. 1959. 5.95 (ISBN 0-85487-020-2). De Vorss.
--Prayer in the New Age. 1957. 3.95 (ISBN 0-85487-041-5). De Vorss.
--Prayer in the New Age. 112p. 1984. Repr. of 1957 ed. 5.95 (ISBN 0-85487-064-4, Pub. by White Eagle Pub). De Vorss.
--The Quiet Mind. 1972. 3.95 (ISBN 0-85487-009-1). De Vorss.
--Spiritual Unfoldment One. 1942. 6.95 (ISBN 0-85487-012-1). De Vorss.
--Spiritual Unfoldment Two. 1969. 6.95 (ISBN 0-85487-001-6). De Vorss.
--Sunrise. 1958. 3.95 (ISBN 0-85487-016-4). De Vorss.
Whitefield, George. George Whitefield's Journals. 1978. 18.95 (ISBN 0-85151-147-3). Banner of Truth.
--George Whitefield's Journals. (Illus., Orig.). 1985. pap. 14.95 (ISBN 0-85151-482-0). Banner of Truth.
--Journals of George Whitefield, 1737-1741. LC 73-81363. (Illus.). 1969. Repr. of 1905 ed. 75.00x (ISBN 0-8201-1069-8). Schol Facsimiles.
--Select Sermons of George Whitefield. 200p. 1985. pap. 3.95 (ISBN 0-85151-454-5). Banner of Truth.
--The Works of Reverend G. W, 6 vols. LC 75-31107. Repr. of 1772 ed. 230.00 set (ISBN 0-404-13530-7). AMS Pr.
Whitefield, Goerge. George Whitefield's Letters: Seventeen Thirty-Four to Seventeen Forty-Two. 1976. 16.95 (ISBN 0-85151-239-9). Banner of Truth.
Whiteford-Boyle, John E. Beyond the Present Prospect. 1977. 9.95 (ISBN 0-917888-00-6). Wheat Forders.
--Graffiti on the Wall of Time: Thirty Poems Celebrating the Triumph of Western Heresy. 1983. 5.00. Wheat Forders.

--The Indra Web: The Renewal of Ancient Oriental Concepts in Modern Western Thought. 1983. 10.00. Wheat Forders.

Whiteford Boyle, John E. Primers for the Age of Innerspace - I Beyond the Present Prospect: The Impact of the Twentieth Century Revolutions in Science on the Varieties of Ethical & Religious Experience. LC 76-44888. 9.95 (ISBN 0-917888-00-6). Wheat Forders.

Whitehead, Alfred N. An Enquiry Concerning the Principles of Natural Knowledge. (Western Philosophy & Religion Ser.). 207p. 1982. pap. 5.95 (ISBN 0-486-24343-5). Dover.

--Religion in the Making. pap. 5.95 (ISBN 0-452-00723-2, Mer). NAL.

Whitehead, Evelyn & Whitehead, James. Marrying Well: Stages on the Journey of Christian Marriage. LC 81-43046. 504p. 1983. pap. 9.95 (ISBN 0-385-18829-3, Im). Doubleday.

Whitehead, Evelyn E. & Whitehead, James D. Christian Life Patterns: The Psychological Challenges & Religious Invitations of Adult Life. LC 81-43442. 288p. 1982. pap. 4.95 (ISBN 0-385-15131-4). Doubleday.

Whitehead, Evelyn E., jt. auth. see Whitehead, James D.

Whitehead, Harriet. Renunciation & Reformulation: A Study of Conversion in an American Sect. LC 86-16211. (Anthropology of Contemporary Issues Ser.). (Illus.). 304p. 1987. text ed. 32.50x (ISBN 0-8014-1849-6). Cornell U Pr.

Whitehead, Henry. Village Gods of South India. (Illus.). 175p. 1986. Repr. 15.00X (ISBN 0-8364-1709-7, Pub. by Usha). South Asia Bks.

Whitehead, James, jt. auth. see Eaton, Evelyn E.

Whitehead, James, jt. auth. see Whitehead, Evelyn.

Whitehead, James D. & Whitehead, Evelyn E. Community of Faith: Models & Strategies for Developing Christian Communities. 208p. (Orig.). 1982. pap. 9.95 (ISBN 0-86683-949-6, AY7719, HarpR). Har-Row.

--Emerging Laity: Returning Leadership to the Community of Faith. LC 85-31201. 240p. 1986. 15.95 (ISBN 0-385-23612-3). Doubleday.

--Method in Ministry: Theological Reflection & Christian Ministry. 224p. 1980. (HarpR); pap. 9.95 (ISBN 0-86683-459-1). Har-Row.

Whitehead, James D., jt. auth. see Whitehead, Evelyn E.

Whitehead, John W. Arresting Abortion: Practical Ways to Save Unborn Children. LC 84-71422. 128p. 1984. pap. 5.95 (ISBN 0-89107-314-0, Crossway Bks). Good News.

--The Freedom of Religious Expression in the Public High Schools. LC 83-72040. (Rutherford Institute Reports: No. 1). 64p. 1983. pap. 3.95 (ISBN 0-89107-295-0, Crossway Bks). Good News.

--The Stealing of America. LC 83-70320. 180p. 1983. pap. 6.95 (ISBN 0-89107-286-1, Crossway Bks). Good News.

Whitehead, K. D. Agenda for the "Sexual Revolution". Abortion, Contraception, Sex Education & Related Evils. 1981. 8.95 (ISBN 0-317-46866-9). Franciscan Herald.

--The Need for the Magisterium of the Church. (Synthesis Ser.). 1979. 0.75 (ISBN 0-8199-0747-2). Franciscan Herald.

Whitehead, K. D., jt. auth. see Likoudis, James.

Whitehead, Kenneth, tr. see Aubry, Joseph.

Whitehead, Kenneth, tr. see Messori, Vittorio.

Whitehead, Kenneth D., tr. see Guissani, Luigi.

Whitehead, O. Z. Some Baha'is to Remember. (Illus.). 304p. 14.95 (ISBN 0-85398-147-7); pap. 8.95 (ISBN 0-85398-148-5). G Ronald Pub.

--Some Early Baha'is of the West. (Illus.). 240p. 1976. 14.95 (ISBN 0-85398-065-9). G Ronald Pub.

Whitehouse, John Howard. Ruskin: Prophet of the Good Life. LC 73-16263. 1948. lib. bdg. 12.50 (ISBN 0-8414-9491-6). Folcroft.

--Ruskin the Prophet & Other Centenary Studies. LC 73-11306. 1920. lib. bdg. 25.00 (ISBN 0-8414-9368-5). Folcroft.

Whitehouse, Thomas, tr. see Hodges, Zane C.

Whitehouse, W. A. The Authority of Grace. 272p. 1981. pap. 14.95 (ISBN 0-567-09028-0, Pub. by T&T Clark Ltd UK). Fortress.

Whitelam, Keith W. The Just King: Monarchical Judicial Authority in Ancient Israel. (Journal for the Study of the Old Testament Supplement Ser.: No. 12). 1979. text ed. 19.95x (ISBN 0-905774-18-3, Pub. by JSOT Pr England). Eisenbrauns.

Whitelaw, Robert. The Gospel Millennium & Obedience to the Scripture. pap. 0.75 (ISBN 0-685-88376-0). Reiner.

Whiteley, D. E. The Theology of St. Paul. 2nd ed. 312p. 1975. pap. 14.95x (ISBN 0-631-16430-8). Basil Blackwell.

--The Theology of St. Paul. 312p. 1967. 45.00x (ISBN 0-631-15710-7). Basil Blackwell.

--Thessalonians. (New Clarendon Bible Ser). (Illus.). 1969. 8.95x (ISBN 0-19-836906-9). Oxford U Pr.

Whitelock, Dorothy & Brett, Martin. Council & Synods with Other Documents Relating to the English Church, Vol. 1: A. D. 871-1204, 2 Vols. 1981. text ed. 139.00x (ISBN 0-19-822394-3). Oxford U Pr.

Whiteman, Maxwell, jt. auth. see Wolf, Edwin, 2nd.

Whitesell, Faris D. Sixty-Five Ways to Give Evangelistic Invitations. LC 84-11269. 128p. 1984. pap. 5.95 (ISBN 0-8254-4021-1). Kregel.

Whiteside, Elena. God's Word in Culture. 233p. 1983. pap. 4.95 (ISBN 0-910068-51-8). Am Christian.

Whiteside, Elena S. The Way: Living in Love. LC 72-89132. 284p. 1972. 5.95 (ISBN 0-910068-06-2). Am Christian.

--The Way: Living in Love. LC 72-89132. Devin.

Whitfield, Stephen, ed. see Axelrad, Albert S.

Whitfield, Stephen J. Voices of Jacob, Hands of Esau: Jews in American Life & Thought. LC 83-25720. x, 322p. 1984. lib. bdg. 25.00 (ISBN 0-208-02024-1, Archon Bks). Shoe String.

Whiting, B. J. Proverbs in the Earlier English Drama. LC 70-86290. 1969. Repr. of 1938 ed. lib. bdg. 34.50x (ISBN 0-374-98513-8, Octagon). Hippocrene Bks.

Whiting, Beatrice B. Paiute Sorcery. Repr. of 1950 ed. 19.00 (ISBN 0-384-68180-8). Johnson Repr.

Whiting, Charles E. Studies in English Puritanism from the Restoration to the Revolution, 1660-1688. LC 68-56060. 1968. Repr. of 1931 ed. 37.50x (ISBN 0-678-05203-4). Kelley.

--Studies in English Puritanism from the Restoration to the Revolution, 1660-1688. (Church Historical Society London, N. S. Ser.: No. 5). Repr. of 1931 ed. 95.00 (ISBN 0-8115-3129-5). Kraus Repr.

Whitley, B. J., Jr. Sharing God's Feelings. LC 84-51661. 201p. (Orig.). 1985. pap. 9.95 (ISBN 0-9615536-0-X). Spirit Christ.

Whitley, C. F. Koheleth: His Language & Thought. (Beihefte zur Zeitschrift fuer die Alttestamentliche Wissenschaft: 148). 1979. 50.50x (ISBN 3-11-007602-0). De Gruyter.

Whitlock, Baird W., ed. The Gospel: The Life of Jesus. LC 83-40471. 160p. 1984. 11.95 (ISBN 0-8052-3875-1). Schocken.

Whitlow, Gretchen. New Bible Crossword Puzzles, No. 5. 128p. (Orig.). 1983. pap. 2.25 (ISBN 0-8007-8471-5, Spire Bks.). Revell.

Whitman, Alden, ed. American Reformers. LC 85-636. (Illus.). 944p. 1985. 75.00 (ISBN 0-8242-0705-X). Wilson.

Whitman, Cedric H. Euripides & the Full Circle of Myth. LC 74-81676. (Loeb Classical Monographs Ser). 176p. 1974. text ed. 11.00x (ISBN 0-674-26920-9). Harvard U Pr.

Whitman, Narcissa. My Journal. 2nd ed. 74p. 1985. 7.50 (ISBN 0-87770-348-5); pap. 4.95; pap. 9.95. Ye Galleon.

Whitman, Narcissa P. The Letters of Narcissa Whitman. 245p. 1986. 14.95 (ISBN 0-87770-386-8). Ye Galleon.

Whitman, Ruth. An Anthology of Modern Yiddish Poetry. LC 66-25551. 141p. 1979. pap. 4.95 (ISBN 0-686-29291-X). Workmen's Circle.

Whitman, Virginia. Excitement of Answered Prayer. (Direction Bks). pap. 3.95 (ISBN 0-8010-9617-0). Baker Bk.

Whitmarsh, Katherine. A Concordance to the Gospel of Sri Ramakrishna. LC 85-50340. 640p. (Orig.). 1985. pap. text ed. 59.95x (ISBN 0-87481-042-6). Vedanta Pr.

Whitmont, Edward C. Return of the Goddess. 288p. 1986. pap. 9.50 (ISBN 0-8334-1002-4, Freedeeds Bks). Garber Comm.

Whitmore, Bruce W. The Dawning Place: The Building of a Temple, the Forging of the North American Baha'i Community. LC 83-25852. (Illus.). xi, 331p. 1984. 24.95 (ISBN 0-87743-192-2); pap. 12.95 (ISBN 0-87743-193-0). Baha'i.

Whitmyer, Kenn, jt. auth. see Whitmyer, Margaret.

Whitmyer, Margaret & Whitmyer, Kenn. Christmas Collectibles. (Illus.). 224p. 1986. 19.95 (ISBN 0-317-52666-9). Collector Bks.

Whitney, Barry L. Evil & the Process God: The Problem of Evil in Charles Hartshorne's Thought. LC 84-25505. (Toronto Studies in Theology: Vol. 19). 247p. 1985. 49.95x (ISBN 0-88946-760-9). E Mellen.

Whitney, George G. Born to Survive, Nineteen Thirty-Six to Nineteen Forty-Six. (Illus.). 200p. 1982. pap. 12.95 (ISBN 0-916224-72-4). Banyan Bks.

Whitney, James P. Reformation Essays. (Church Historical Society London N. S. Ser.: No. 38). Repr. of 1939 ed. 40.00 (ISBN 0-8115-3161-9). Kraus Repr.

Whitney, Louise G. Burning of the Convent. LC 70-90196. (Mass Violence in America). Repr. of 1877 ed. 10.00 (ISBN 0-405-01341-8). Ayer Co Pubs.

Whitney, Norman J. Experiments in Community. 1983. pap. 2.50x (ISBN 0-87574-149-5, 149). Pendle Hill.

Whitney, Thomas R. A Defence of the American Policy As Opposed to the Encroachments of Foreign Influence, & Especially to the Interference of the Papacy in the Political Interests & Affairs of the United States. LC 75-145496. (The American Immigration Library). 372p. 1971. Repr. of 1856 ed. lib. bdg. 22.95x (ISBN 0-89198-029-6). Ozer.

Whitsett, Dan D. Does Prayer Make a Difference? (Prayers in My Life Ser.: Ser. I). 1974. pap. 1.25x (ISBN 0-8358-0312-0). Upper Room.

Whitsitt, William H. A Question in Baptist History: Whether the Anabaptists in England Practiced Immersion Before the Year 1641? Gaustad, Edwin S., ed. LC 79-52611. (The Baptist Tradition Ser.). 1980. Repr. of 1896 ed. lib. bdg. 14.00x (ISBN 0-405-12476-7). Ayer Co Pubs.

Whitson, Robley E. The Resurrection Gospel. LC 85-51481. (Illus.). 48p. (Orig.). 1985. pap. text ed. 4.95x (ISBN 0-932269-55-9). Wyndham Hall.

Whitson, Robley E., ed. The Shakers: Two Centuries of Spiritual Reflection. (Classics of Western Spirituality Ser.). 200p. 1983. 13.95 (ISBN 0-8091-0343-5); pap. 9.95 (ISBN 0-8091-2373-8). Paulist Pr.

Whitson, Skip, compiled by. Christmas One Hundred Years Ago. (Sun Historical Ser). (Illus., Orig.). 1976. pap. 3.50 (ISBN 0-89540-036-7, SB-036). Sun Pub.

Whittaker, Arabelle & Warkentin, Viola. Chol Texts on the Supernatural. (Publications in Linguistics & Related Fields Ser.: No. 13). 171p. 1965. microfiche (2) 4.00. Summer Inst Ling.

Whittaker, Colin. Great Revivals. LC 85-72333. 224p. 1986. pap. 4.50 (ISBN 0-88243-522-1, 02-0522). Gospel Pub.

Whittaker, Colin C. Seven Pentecostal Pioneers. LC 84-73310. 224p. 1985. Repr. of 1983 ed. 5.95 (ISBN 0-88243-545-0, 02-0545). Gospel Pub.

Whittaker, John H. Matters of Faith & Matter of Principle: Religious Truth Claims & Their Logic. LC 80-51940. (Trinity University Monograph Series in Religion: Vol. 6). 173p. 1981. 12.00 (ISBN 0-911536-87-6). Trinity U Pr.

Whittaker, Molly. Jews & Christians: Graeco-Roman Views. (Commentaries on Writings of the Jewish & Christian World 200 B.C. to A.D. 200: Vol. 6). 304p. 1985. 47.50 (ISBN 0-521-24251-7); pap. 18.95 (ISBN 0-521-28556-9). Cambridge U Pr.

Whittaker, Molly, ed. & tr. see Tatian.

Whittaker, R., jt. auth. see Gilbert, O.

Whittaker, Thomas. Priests, Philosophers & Prophets. LC 77-102589. 1970. Repr. of 1911 ed. 22.50x (ISBN 0-8046-0748-6, Pub. by Kennikat). Assoc Faculty Pr.

Whittaker, Violet. Puppet People Scripts. 1984. pap. 8.95 (ISBN 0-8010-9666-9). Baker Bk.

Whittemore, Carroll E., ed. Symbols of the Church. 64p. 1983. pap. 2.25 (ISBN 0-687-40786-9). Abingdon.

Whittemore, Lewis B. The Church & Secular Education. LC 78-17152. 1978. Repr. of 1960 ed. lib. bdg. 22.50 (ISBN 0-313-20540-X, WHCS). Greenwood.

Whittemore, Robert C. The Transformation of the New England Theology. (American University Studies VII-Theology & Religion: Vol. 23). 441p. 1987. text ed. 42.00 (ISBN 0-8204-0374-1). P Lang Pubs.

Whittenburg, Ruth S. Time for Everything Under the Sun. LC 79-84856. 1980. 17.50 (ISBN 0-8022-2351-6). Philos Lib.

Whittingham, William. A Briefe Discourse of the Troubles Begonne at Franckford. LC 71-38228. (English Experience Ser.: No. 492). 210p. 1972. Repr. of 1574 ed. 13.00 (ISBN 90-221-0492-3). Walter J Johnson.

Whittlesey, A. Minor Ecclesiastical, Domestic & Garden Architecture of Southern Spain. 1976. lib. bdg. 75.00 (ISBN 0-8490-2259-2). Gordon Pr.

Whitton, Joel. Life Between Life: Scientific Explorations into the Void Separating One Incarnation from the Next. LC 86-4573. 192p. 1986. 14.95 (ISBN 0-385-23274-8, Dolp). Doubleday.

Whybray, R. N. The Book of Proverbs. LC 70-171687. (New English Bible Commentaries, Old Testament). (Illus.). 192p. 1972. 24.95 (ISBN 0-521-08364-8); pap. 10.95x (ISBN 0-521-09679-0). Cambridge U Pr.

--The Intellectual Tradition in the Old Testament. LC 73-78236. (Beiheft zur Zeitschrift fuer die Alttestamentliche Wissenschaft). 1974. 44.25x (ISBN 3-11-004424-2). De Gruyter.

--Isaiah Forty to Sixty-Six. Clements, Ronald E., ed. (New Century Bible Commentary). 320p. (Orig.). 1981. pap. 8.95 (ISBN 0-8028-1884-6). Eerdmans.

--Second Isaiah. (Old Testament Guides Ser.). xiv, 84p. 1984. pap. text ed. 3.95x (ISBN 0-905774-59-0, Pub. by JSOT Pr England). Eisenbrauns.

--Thanksgiving for a Liberated Prophet: An Interpretation of Isaiah Chapter Fifty-Three. (Journal for the Study of the Old Testament Supplement Ser.: No. 4). 184p. 1978. (Pub. by JSOT Pr England); pap. text ed. 10.95 (ISBN 0-905774-04-3, Pub. by JSOT Pr England). Eisenbrauns.

Whybray, R. N., ed. Isaiah Forty to Sixty-Six. (New Century Bible Ser.). 304p. 1975. 9.95 (ISBN 0-551-00573-4). Attic Pr.

Whyte, A., ed. see Lindsay, Thomas M.

Whyte, A., ed. see Reith, George.

Whyte, A., ed. see Stalker, James.

Whyte, Alexander. Bible Characters from the New Testament, Vol. 1. LC 81-81099. (The Shepherd Illustrated Classics Ser.). (Illus.). 276p. 1982. pap. 7.95 (ISBN 0-87983-256-8). Keats.

--Bible Characters from the New Testament, Vol. 2. LC 81-81099. (The Shepherd Illustrated Classics Ser.). (Illus.). 324p. 1982. pap. 7.95 (ISBN 0-87983-257-6). Keats.

--Newman: An Appreciation. 1973. Repr. of 1901 ed. 30.00 (ISBN 0-8274-0570-7). R West.

--Whyte's Bible Characters: From the Old Testament & the New Testament. (Illus.). 1968. 24.95 (ISBN 0-310-34410-7, 11008). Zondervan.

Whyte, Florence. The Dance of Death in Spain & Catalonia. Kastenbaum, Robert, ed. LC 76-19594. (Death & Dying Ser.). 1977. Repr. of 1931 ed. lib. bdg. 19.00x (ISBN 0-405-09588-0). Ayer Co Pubs.

--The Dance of Death in Spain & Catalonia. 1977. lib. bdg. 69.95 (ISBN 0-8490-1699-1). Gordon Pr.

Whyte, H. A. Power of the Blood. 1973. pap. 3.50 (ISBN 0-88368-027-0). Whitaker Hse.

Whyte, J. H. Church & State in Modern Ireland: 1923 to 1979. 2nd ed. LC 79-55700. 491p. 1980. 32.50x (ISBN 0-389-20010-7). B&N Imports.

Whyte, John H. Catholics in Western Democracies: A Study in Political Behavior. 1981. 22.50x (ISBN 0-312-12446-5). St Martin.

Whytford, Richard, tr. see Thomas a Kempis.

Wiberg, Glen V. Called to Be His People. (Illus.). 331p. 1970. pap. text ed. 5.00 (ISBN 0-910452-16-4). Covenant.

Wiche, Donald. Religion & Truth. 295p. 1981. text ed. 44.50 (ISBN 90-279-3149-6). Mouton.

Wickens, Paul A. Christ Denied. LC 82-50585. 49p. 1982. pap. 1.25 (ISBN 0-89555-183-7). TAN Bks Pubs.

Wicker, Brian. Toward a Contemporary Christianity. 1967. 21.95 (ISBN 0-268-00282-7). U of Notre Dame Pr.

Wickes, William. Two Treatises on the Accentuation of the Old Testament. rev. ed. 1970. 35.00x (ISBN 0-87068-004-8). Ktav.

Wickham, Legg J. Breviarium Romanum a Francisco Cardinali: Quignonio Editum. 262p. Repr. of 1888 ed. text ed. 49.68x (ISBN 0-576-99727-7, Pub. by Gregg Intl Pubs England). Gregg Intl.

Wickham, Pablo. Segunda Epistola a los Corintos. (Span.). 320p. 1985. pap. 9.95 (ISBN 0-8254-1870-4). Kregel.

Wickham, Pablo, jt. auth. see Trenchard, Ernesto.

Wicks, Doug, ed. Forget the Pith Helmet: Perspectives on the Missionary Experience. (Orig.). 1984. pap. 6.95 (ISBN 0-8024-3266-2). Moody.

Wicks, Henry J. The Doctrine of God in the Jewish Apocryphal & Apocalyptic Literature. Repr. of 1915 ed. 29.00x (ISBN 0-87068-149-4). Ktav.

Wicks, Jared. Luther & His Spiritual Legacy. (Theology & Life Ser.: Vol. 7). pap. 7.95 (ISBN 0-89453-338-X). M Glazier.

Wicks, Jared, ed. Catholic Scholars Dialogue with Luther. LC 78-105429. (Orig.). 1970. pap. 3.00 (ISBN 0-8294-0181-4). Loyola.

Wicks, Jared, ed. see De Vio, Tommaso.

Wicks, Jared, ed. see Hacker, Paul.

Wicks, Jared, tr. see Hertling, Ludwig.

Wicks, Robert J. Availability, the Problem & the Gift. LC 85-62868. 144p. (Orig.). 1986. pap. 5.95 (ISBN 0-8091-2767-9). Paulist Pr.

--Christian Introspection: Self-Ministry Through Self-Understanding. LC 83-1932. 128p. 1983. pap. 7.95 (ISBN 0-8245-0583-2). Crossroad NY.

Wicks, Robert J., jt. auth. see Faricy, Robert.

Wicks, Robert J., et al. Clinical Handbook of Pastoral Counseling. 592p. (Orig.). 1985. 22.95 (ISBN 0-8091-0350-8); pap. 14.95 (ISBN 0-8091-2687-7). Paulist Pr.

Wicksteed, P. H., tr. see Goblet D'Alviella, Eugene F.

Wicksteed, Philip H. Dante & Aquinas. LC 79-153489. (Studies in Dante, No. 9). 1971. Repr. of 1913 ed. lib. bdg. 49.95x (ISBN 0-8383-1240-3). Haskell.
--The Reactions Between Dogma & Philosophy Illustrated from the Works of St. Thomas Aquinas. LC 77-27153. (Hibbert Lectures: 1916). Repr. of 1920 ed. 57.50 (ISBN 0-404-60418-8). AMS Pr.
Wicksteed, Philip H., tr. see Reville, Albert.
Wickwar, J. W. Witchcraft & the Black Art: A Book Dealing with the Psychology & Folklore of the Witches. LC 71-151817. 1971. Repr. of 1925 ed. 48.00x (ISBN 0-8103-3692-8). Gale.
Widad El Sakkakini. First among Sufis: The Life & Thought of Rabia al-Adawiyya. Safwat, Nabil, tr. from Arabic. 1982. 15.95 (ISBN 0-900860-45-6, Pub. by Octagon Pr England). Ins Study Human.
Widmer, Eric. The Russian Ecclestastical Mission in Peking During the Eighteenth Century. (East Asian Monographs: No. 69). 1976. 21.00x (ISBN 0-674-78129-5). Harvard U Pr.
Widmer, Pierre. Some People Are Throwing You Into Confusion. LC 83-82879. (Mennonite Faith Ser.: No. 14). 80p. 1984. pap. 1.50 (ISBN 0-8361-3358-7). Herald Pr.
Widoger, Geoffrey, jt. ed. see Roth, Cecil.
Widtsoe, John A., ed. Discourses of Brigham Young. 497p. 14.95 (ISBN 0-87747-066-9). Deseret Bk.
Widtsoe, Leah D., jt. auth. see Gates, Susa Y.
Widutis, Florence. The True Path. (Illus.). 1979. pap. 5.95 (ISBN 0-87516-266-5). De Vorss.
--Yours Is the Power. LC 57-9315. 1978. pap. 4.95 (ISBN 0-87516-245-2). De Vorss.
Wieand, Albert C. New Harmony of the Gospels. 1947. 15.95 (ISBN 0-8028-3299-7). Eerdmans.
Wieand, David J. Visions of Glory. 144p. (Orig.). 1980. pap. 4.95 (ISBN 0-87178-905-1). Brethren.
Wiebe, Donald, ed. see Smart, Ninian.
Wiebe, George D., tr. see Ehmann, Wilhelm.
Wiebe, Katie F. Have Cart, Will Travel. (Trailblazer Ser.). 86p. (Orig.). 1974. pap. 1.00 (ISBN 0-919797-27-X). Kindred Pr.
--Who Are the Mennonite Brethern? LC 84-82049. 107p. (Orig.). 1984. pap. 5.95 (ISBN 0-919797-31-8). Kindred Pr.
--Women among the Brethren: Stories of Fifteen Mennonite Brethren & Krimmer Mennonite Brethren Women. LC 79-54802. 197p. (Orig.). 1979. pap. 6.95 (ISBN 0-935196-00-5). Kindred Pr.
Wiebe, Paul. The Architecture of Religion: A Theoretical Essay. LC 84-8667. (Trinity University Monograph Series in Religion). 170p. 1984. text ed. 15.95 (ISBN 0-939980-07-X). Trinity U Pr.
Wiebe, Ronald W. & Rowlison, Bruce A. Let's Talk about Church Staff Relationships. 64p. 1983. pap. 3.95 (ISBN 0-938462-12-1). Green Leaf CA.
Wiedemann, Frederick. Between Two Worlds. LC 85-40773. 200p. (Orig.). 1986. pap. 6.95 (ISBN 0-8356-0602-3, Quest). Theos Pub Hse.
Wieder, Alan. Immigration, the Public School, & the 20th Century American Ethos: The Jewish Immigrant As a Case Study. 124p. (Orig.). 1985. lib. bdg. 24.00 (ISBN 0-8191-4793-1); pap. text ed. 8.75 (ISBN 0-8191-4794-X). U Pr of Amer.
Wieder, Robert. Le Docteur Johnson, Critique Litteraire (1709-1784) Essai De Biographie Psychologique. 201p. 1982. lib. bdg. 25.00 (ISBN 0-89984-528-2). Century Bookbindery.
Wieland, Robert. Eighteen Eighty-Eight Message. LC 80-10807. (Horizon Ser.). 1980. pap. 5.95 (ISBN 0-8127-0283-2). Review & Herald.
Wieland, Robert J. Gold Tried in the Fire. (Anchor Ser.). 80p. 1983. pap. 6.95 (ISBN 0-8163-0520-X). Pacific Pr Pub Assn.
--In Search of the Cross. LC 78-184590. 120p. 1986. pap. 5.95 (ISBN 0-912145-11-0). MMI Pr.
Wieman, Henry N. Creative Freedom: Vocation of Liberal Religion. Creighton, W. & Axel, Larry E., eds. LC 82-10182. 128p. (Orig.). 1982. pap. 7.95 (ISBN 0-8298-0623-7). Pilgrim NY.
--Religious Experience & Scientific Method. Repr. of 1926 ed. lib. bdg. 22.50x (ISBN 0-8371-4368-3, WIRE). Greenwood.
--Religious Experience & Scientific Method. 387p. 1971. Repr. of 1927 ed. lib. bdg. 11.95x (ISBN 0-8093-0537-2). S Ill U Pr.
--Religious Experience & Scientific Method. (Arcturus Books Paperbacks). 387p. 1971. pap. 9.95x (ISBN 0-8093-0530-5). S Ill U Pr.
Wieman, Henry N. & Meland, Bernard E. American Philosophies of Religion. 370p. 1985. Repr. of 1936 ed. lib. bdg. 75.00 (ISBN 0-89984-539-8). Century Bookbindery.
Wieman, Henry N. & Westcott-Wieman, Regina. Normative Psychology of Religion. 564p. 1986. Repr. of 1935 ed. lib. bdg. 95.00 (ISBN 0-89984-538-X). Century Bookbindery.
Wiemann, Mary, jt. auth. see Sylvester, Diane.
Wienandt, Elwyn A. Choral Music of the Church. LC 80-12943. (Music Reprint Ser.). xi, 494p. 1980. Repr. of 1965 ed. lib. bdg. 45.00 (ISBN 0-306-76002-9). Da Capo.
Wienandt, Elwyn A., ed. Opinions on Church Music: Comments & Reports from Four & a Half Centuries. LC 74-75229. 214p. 1974. 14.00 (ISBN 0-918954-12-6). Baylor Univ Pr.
Wiencke, Gustav K. & Lehman, Helmut T., eds. Luther's Works: Devotional Writings II, Vol. 43. LC 55-9893. 1968. 19.95 (ISBN 0-8006-0343-5, 1-343). Fortress.
Wiener, Aharon. The Prophet Elijah in the Development of Judaism. (Littman Library of Jewish Civilization). 250p. 1978. 24.00x (ISBN 0-19-710010-4). Oxford U Pr.
Wiener, Max. Abraham Geiger & Liberal Judaism: The Challenge of the Nineteenth Century. pap. 11.95 (ISBN 0-87820-800-3). Ktav.
Wiener, Peter F. Martin Luther: Hitler's Spiritual Ancestor. (Illus.). 92p. 1985. saddle stiched 4.00 (ISBN 0-910309-21-3). Am Atheist.
Wienpahl, Paul. The Radical Spinoza. LC 78-65448. 1979. 32.50 (ISBN 0-8147-9186-7). NYU Pr.
Wiens, A. K. & Wiens, Gertrude. Shadowed by the Great Wall: The Story of Kimmer Mennonite Brethren Missions in Inner Mongolia (1922-1949) LC 79-55686. 120p. (Orig.). 1979. pap. 3.95 (ISBN 0-935196-01-3). Kindred Pr.
Wiens, Gertrude, jt. auth. see Wiens, A. K.
Wiens, Grace. Unto You & to Your Children. (Illus.). 229p. (Orig.). 1976. pap. 5.95 (ISBN 0-912315-10-5). Word Aflame.
Wiersbe. Be Wise. 1983. 5.95 (ISBN 0-88207-384-2). Victor Bks.
Wiersbe, David & Wiersbe, Warren. Making Sense of the Ministry. 128p. (Orig.). 1983. pap. 5.95 (ISBN 0-8024-0164-3). Moody.
Wiersbe, David, jt. auth. see Wiersbe, Warren.
Wiersbe, David W., jt. auth. see Wiersbe, Warren W.
Wiersbe, W. Best of A. W. Tozer. 249p. 1979. pap. 3.95. Chr Pubns.
Wiersbe, Warren. Be Alive. 156p. 1986. pap. 5.95 (ISBN 0-89693-359-8). Victor Bks.
--Be Challenged! rev. ed. LC 82-12404. 1982. pap. 3.50 (ISBN 0-8024-1080-4). Moody.
--Be Complete. 160p. 1981. pap. 5.95 (ISBN 0-88207-257-9). Victor Bks.
--Be Loyal: Formerly Title Meet Your King. LC 79-92552. 216p. 1980. pap. 5.95 (ISBN 0-88207-799-6). Victor Bks.
--Five Secrets of Living. 1978. pap. 2.95 (ISBN 0-8423-0870-9). Tyndale.
--His Name Is Wonderful. (Livingg Studies). 160p. 1984. pap. 2.95 (ISBN 0-8423-1449-0); pap. 4.95 (ISBN 0-8423-1447-4). Tyndale.
--Live Like a King. rev. ed. (Moody Press Elective Ser.). 1983. pap. 3.95 (ISBN 0-8024-0256-9); pap. 2.50 leaders guide (ISBN 0-8024-0306-9). Moody.
--Thoughts for Men on the Move. 1970. pap. 3.50 (ISBN 0-8024-0132-5). Moody.
--Why Us? When Bad Things Happen to God's People. 160p. 1985. pap. 5.95 (ISBN 0-8007-5208-2, Power Bks). Revell.
Wiersbe, Warren & Perry, Lloyd M. The Wycliffe Handbook of Preaching & Preachers. 1984. 18.95 (ISBN 0-8024-0328-X). Moody.
Wiersbe, Warren & Wiersbe, David. Elements of Preaching. 96p. 1986. pap. 2.95 (ISBN 0-8423-0757-5). Tyndale.
Wiersbe, Warren, jt. auth. see Wiersbe, David.
Wiersbe, Warren W. A Basic Library for Bible Students. (Orig.). 1981. pap. 2.95 (ISBN 0-8010-9641-3). Baker Bk.
--Be Alert! 168p. 1984. pap. 5.95 (ISBN 0-89693-380-6). Victor Bks.
--Be Confident. 176p. 1982. pap. 5.95 (ISBN 0-88207-269-2). Victor Bks.
--Be Diligent. 156p. 1987. pap. 5.95 (ISBN 0-89693-356-3). Victor Bks.
--Be Encouraged. 156p. 1984. pap. 5.95 (ISBN 0-88207-620-5). Victor Bks.
--Be Faithful. 1981. pap. 5.95 (ISBN 0-88207-268-4). Victor Bks.
--Be Free. LC 74-33824. 160p. 1975. pap. 5.95 (ISBN 0-88207-716-3). Victor Bks.
--Be Hopeful. 1982. pap. 5.95 (ISBN 0-88207-382-6). Victor Bks.
--Be Joyful: A Practical Study of Philippians. LC 74-76328. 130p. 1974. pap. 5.95 (ISBN 0-88207-705-8). Victor Bks.
--Be Mature. LC 78-52558. 176p. 1978. pap. 5.95 (ISBN 0-88207-771-6). Victor Bks.
--Be Ready. LC 78-65555. 175p. 1979. pap. 5.95 (ISBN 0-88207-782-1). Victor Bks.
--Be Real. LC 72-77014. 190p. 1972. pap. 5.95 (ISBN 0-88207-046-0). Victor Bks.
--Be Rich. LC 76-6833. 175p. 1976. pap. 5.95 (ISBN 0-88207-730-9). Victor Bks.
--Be Right. LC 77-154327. 175p. 1977. pap. 5.95 (ISBN 0-88207-729-5). Victor Bks.
--Be Transformed. 156p. 1986. pap. 5.95 (ISBN 0-89693-352-0). Victor Bks.
--Be Victorious. 156p. 1985. pap. 5.95 (ISBN 0-89693-547-7). Victor Bks.
--Bumps Are What You Climb On. 1980. pap. 4.95 (ISBN 0-8010-9629-4). Baker Bk.
--Listen! Jesus Is Praying. 1982. pap. 4.95 (ISBN 0-8423-2167-5); leader's guide 2.95 (ISBN 0-8423-2168-3). Tyndale.
--Listening to the Giants. 1979. 14.95 (ISBN 0-8010-9618-9). Baker Bk.
--Meet Yourself in the Psalms. 192p. 1983. pap. 5.95 (ISBN 0-88207-740-6). Victor Bks.
--Real Worship. 192p. 1986. 12.95 (ISBN 0-8407-9045-7). Oliver-Nelson.
--Run with the Winners. Weese, Wightman, ed. 160p. (Orig.). 1985. pap. 4.95 (ISBN 0-8423-5798-X); study guide 2.95 (ISBN 0-8423-5799-8). Tyndale.
--The Strategy of Satan. 1979. 3.95 (ISBN 0-8423-6665-2). Tyndale.
--A Time to Be Renewed. Adair, James, ed. 400p. 1986. pap. 12.95 (ISBN 0-89693-391-1). Victor Bks.
--Victorious Christians You Should Know. 176p. 1984. pap. 4.95 (ISBN 0-8010-9667-7). Baker Bk.
--Walking with the Giants: A Minister's Guide to Good Reading & Great Preaching. LC 76-22989. 304p. 1976. 14.95 (ISBN 0-8010-9578-6). Baker Bk.
--Windows on the Parables. rev. ed. 160p. 1984. pap. 2.95 (ISBN 0-89693-710-0). Victor Bks.
Wiersbe, Warren W. & Wiersbe, David W. Comforting the Bereaved. (Orig.). 1985. pap. 5.95 (ISBN 0-8024-5293-0). Moody.
--Devotional Talks for People Who Do God's Business. 96p. 1986. pap. 5.95 (ISBN 0-8010-9675-8). Baker Bk.
Wiersbe, Warren W., jt. auth. see Sugden, Howard F.
Wiersbe, Warren W., compiled by. Classic Sermons on Faith & Doubt. LC 85-9767. (Classic Sermon Ser.). 160p. 1985. pap. 8.95 (ISBN 0-8254-4028-9). Kregel.
Wiersbe, Warren W., ed. Classic Sermons on Prayer. (Classic Sermons Ser.). (Orig.). 1987. pap. 9.95 (ISBN 0-8254-4029-7). Kregel.
Wiersbe, Warren W., compiled by. Classic Sermons on Suffering. LC 84-11260. (Classic Sermon Ser.). 204p. (Orig.). 1984. pap. text ed. 9.95 (ISBN 0-8254-4027-0). Kregel.
Wiersbe, Warren W., ed. Giant Steps. 496p. 1981. 15.95 (ISBN 0-8010-9648-0). Baker Bk.
Wiersbe, Warren W., compiled by. Treasury of the World's Great Sermons. LC 77-72366. 1977. 24.95 (ISBN 0-8254-4011-4). Kregel.
Wiersbe, Warren W., ed. see Marchant, James.
Wiersum, Beverly. The Story of Easter for Children. Kuse, James A., ed. (Illus.). 1979. pap. 2.95 (ISBN 0-89542-452-5). Ideals.
Wierwille, H. E. Uncle Harry: An Autobiography. LC 78-73348. 55p. 1978. 5.95 (ISBN 0-910068-15-1). Am Christian.
Wierwille, Victor P. Are the Dead Alive Now? LC 82-70237. 108p. 1982. 6.95 (ISBN 0-910068-40-2). Am Christian.
--The Bible Tells Me So. LC 70-176281. (Studies in Abundant Living: Vol. 1). 202p. 1971. 6.95 (ISBN 0-910068-10-0). Am Christian.
--Christians Should Be Prosperous. 31p. pap. 1.00 (ISBN 0-910068-65-8). Am Christian.
--God's Magnified Word. LC 77-87405. (Studies in Abundant Living: Vol. 4). 276p. 1977. 6.95 (ISBN 0-910068-13-5). Am Christian.
--Jesus Christ Is Not God. LC 81-66710. 180p. 1981. 6.95 (ISBN 0-910068-33-X). Am Christian.
--Jesus Christ Our Passover. LC 80-68401. 527p. 1980. 10.95 (ISBN 0-910068-30-5). Am Christian.
--Jesus Christ Our Promised Seed. LC 82-72672. 306p. 1982. 10.95 (ISBN 0-910068-42-9). Am Christian.
--Life Lines: Quotations of Victor Paul Wierwille. LC 85-52028. 136p. 1985. 5.95 (ISBN 0-910068-64-X). Am Christian.
--The New Dynamic Church. LC 70-176281. (Studies in Abundant Living: Vol. 2). 242p. 1971. 6.95 (ISBN 0-910068-03-8). Am Christian.
--Order My Steps in Thy Word. LC 70-176281. (Studies in Abundant Living: Vol. V). 300p. 1985. 6.95 (ISBN 0-910068-59-3). Am Christian.
--Receiving the Holy Spirit Today. LC 82-71185. 298p. 1983. 5.95 (ISBN 0-910068-49-6). Am Christian.
--The Word's Way. LC 70-176281. (Studies in Abundant Living: Vol. 3). 276p. 1971. 4.95 (ISBN 0-910068-04-6). Am Christian.
Wiesel, Elie. Five Biblical Portraits. LC 81-40458. 168p. 1981. 9.95 (ISBN 0-268-00957-0). U of Notre Dame Pr.
--Five Biblical Portraits. LC 81-40458. vii, 157p. 1983. pap. 4.95 (ISBN 0-268-00962-7, 85-09622). U of Notre Dame Pr.
--Four Hasidic Masters & Their Struggle Against Melancholy. LC 78-1419. (Ward-Phillips Lectures in English Language & Literature Ser: No. 9). (Illus.). 1978. 9.95 (ISBN 0-268-00944-9). U of Notre Dame Pr.
--Four Hasidic Masters & Their Struggle Against Melancholy. LC 78-1419. (Ward-Phillips Lectures in English Language & Literature: No. 9). (Illus.). 1979. pap. text ed. 4.95x (ISBN 0-268-00947-3). U of Notre Dame Pr.
--A Jew Today. Weisel, Marion, tr. from Fr. LC 79-11251. 1979. pap. 4.95 (ISBN 0-394-74057-2, Vin). Random.
--The Jews of Silence: A Personal Report on Soviet Jewry. LC 63-11041. 160p. 1987. pap. 8.95 (ISBN 0-8052-0826-7). Schocken.
--Legends of Our Time. 1980. pap. 2.50 (ISBN 0-380-00931-5, 49429, Bard). Avon.
--Messengers of God: Biblical Portraits & Legends. 224p. 1985. 16.95 (ISBN 0-671-52333-3); pap. 7.95 (ISBN 0-671-54134-X). Summit Bks.
--Somewhere a Master: Further Tales of the Hasidic Masters. 336p. 1982. 13.95 (ISBN 0-671-44170-1). Summit Bks.
--Witness for Life. 12.95 (ISBN 0-87068-766-2); pap. 7.95x (ISBN 0-87068-767-0). Ktav.
--Zalem, or the Madness of God. 171p. 1985. pap. 7.95 (ISBN 0-8052-0777-5). Schocken.
Wiesel, Elie, ed. The Golem: The Story of a Legend. Borchardt, Anne, tr. LC 83-9304. (Illus.). 105p. 1983. 12.95 (ISBN 0-671-45483-8); Special ed., signed, limited. 50.00 (ISBN 0-671-49624-7). Summit Bks.
Wiesel, Elie, pref. by. Selected & Annotated Resource List of Materials on the Holocaust. 65p. 5.00 (ISBN 0-686-74934-0). ADL.
Wiesel, Elie, et al. Dimensions of the Holocaust. 1978. 10.95 (ISBN 0-8101-0469-5); pap. 6.95x (ISBN 0-8101-0470-9). Northwestern U Pr.
Wiesenthal, Simon. Every Day Remembrance Day: A Chronicle of Jewish Martyrdom. (Illus.). 480p. 1987. 19.95 (ISBN 0-8050-0098-4). H Holt & Co.
Wiester, John. The Genesis Connection. LC 83-13409. (Illus.). 320p. 1983. 14.95 (ISBN 0-8407-5296-2). Nelson.
Wifall, Walter. Israel's Prophets: Envoys of the King. (Biblical Booklets). 1975. pap. 1.25 (ISBN 0-8199-0521-6). Franciscan Herald.
Wiggins, Arch, jt. auth. see Sandall, Robert.
Wiggins, James B., ed. Religion As Story. 218p. 1985. pap. text ed. 9.75 (ISBN 0-8191-4682-X). U Pr of Amer.
Wigginton, Peter. Popes of Vatican Council II. 329p. 1983. 15.00 (ISBN 0-8199-0828-2). Franciscan Herald.
Wigglesworth, Michael. The Diary of Michael Wigglesworth, 1653 to 1657: The Conscience of a Puritan. Morgan, Edmund, ed. 11.25 (ISBN 0-8446-0808-4). Peter Smith.
Wigglesworth, Smith. Ever Increasing Faith. rev. ed. 176p. 1971. pap. 1.95 (ISBN 0-88243-494-2, 02-0494). Gospel Pub.
--Faith That Prevails. 64p. 1966. pap. 1.75 (ISBN 0-88243-711-9, 02-0711). Gospel Pub.
Wight, Fred H. Manners & Customs of Bible Lands. 1953. 10.95 (ISBN 0-8024-5175-6). Moody.
--Usos y Costumbres de las Tierras Biblicas. Orig. Title: Manners & Customs of Bible Lands. (Span.). 336p. 1981. pap. 7.95 (ISBN 0-8254-1873-9). Kregel.
Wight, Fred H. & Gower, Ralph. The New Manners & Customs of Bible Times. rev. ed. 1986. 24.95 (ISBN 0-8024-5954-4). Moody.
Wight, Maxine C. A Story About Light. LC 79-14691. 1979. 1.99 (ISBN 0-8309-0236-8). Herald Hse.
Wightman, W. M. Saint Luke's Life of Christ. pap. 1.00x (ISBN 0-685-02586-1). Outlook.
Wigmore-Beddoes, Dennis G. Yesterday's Radicals: A Study of the Affinity Between Unitarianism & Broad Church Anglicanism in the Nineteenth Century. 182p. 1971. 19.95 (ISBN 0-227-67751-X). Attic Pr.
Wigoder, Geoffrey. Synagogues Through the Ages. LC 86-45032. (Illus.). 208p. 1986. 35.00 (ISBN 0-06-069401-7, HarpR). Har-Row.
Wigoder, Geoffrey, jt. ed. see Klenicki, Leon.
Wigoder, Geoffrey, jt. ed. see Werblowsky, Zvi.
Wigoder, Geoffrey, tr. see Abraham, B. Hayya.
Wigoder, Geoffrey, et al. The Illustrated Dictionary & Concordance of the Bible. (Illus.). 1000p. 1986. text ed. 100.00 (ISBN 0-02-916380-3). Macmillan.
Wigoder, J. Contemporary Jewry: Studies in Honor of Moshe Davis. 431p. 1984. text ed. 35.00x (ISBN 965-223-499-0, Pub. by Magnes Pr Israel). Humanities.
Wigram, George V. Englishman's Greek Concordance of the New Testament. 34.95 (ISBN 0-310-20320-1, 6258). Zondervan.
--Englishman's Greek Concordance of the New Testament. 1984. 29.95 (ISBN 0-8010-3416-7). Baker Bk.
--Englishman's Hebrew & Chaldee Concordance of the Old Testament. 39.95 (ISBN 0-310-20340-6, 6265). Zondervan.
--The Englishman's Hebrew & Chaldee Concordance of the Old Testament. (Reference Set). 1760p. 1982. Repr. of 1980 ed. 34.95 (ISBN 0-88062-105-2). Mott Media.

--New Englishmans Greek Concordance & Lexicon. 960p. 1982. 34.95 (ISBN 0-913573-23-X). Hendrickson MA.
Wigram, W. A., ed. see D'Mar Shimun, Surma.
Wigston, W. F. Bacon, Shakespeare & the Rosicrucians. 59.95 (ISBN 0-87968-694-4). Gordon Pr.
Wihl, Gary. Ruskin & the Rhetoric of Infallibility. LC 85-5310. (Yale Studies in English: No. 194). 256p. 1985. 17.50x (ISBN 0-300-03321-4). Yale U Pr.
Wijers, L. His Holiness the Fourteenth Dalai Lama of Tibet Talks to Louwrier Wijers. 192p. 1982. 29.00x (ISBN 0-317-39082-1, Pub. by Luzac & Co Ltd). State Mutual Bk.
Wijngaards, J. N. Did Christ Rule Out Women Priests? 96p. 1977. pap. 1.95 (ISBN 0-85597-204-1). Attic Pr.
Wijngaards, John. Handbook to the Gospels: A Guide to the Gospel Writings & the Life & Times of Jesus. (Illus.). 300p. 1983. pap. 8.95 (ISBN 0-89283-118-9). Servant.
--Inheriting the Master's Cloak: Creative Biblical Spirituality. LC 85-71535. 192p. (Orig.). 1985. pap. 4.95 (ISBN 0-87793-288-3). Ave Maria.
Wijngaards, John N. Experiencing Jesus. LC 81-52295. 176p. (Orig.). 1981. pap. 4.95 (ISBN 0-87793-235-2). Ave Maria.
Wijsenbeek-Wijler, H. Aristotle's Concept of Soul, Sleep, & Dreams. 260p. 1978. pap. text ed. 53.50 (Pub. by A M Hakkert). Coronet Bks.
Wikler, Madeline, jt. auth. see Groner, Judyth S.
Wikler, Madeline, jt. auth. see Saypol, Judyth.
Wikler, Madeline, jt. auth. see Saypol, Judyth R.
Wilbanks, Dana M., jt. auth. see Everding, H. Edward, Jr.
Wilber, Charles K., jt. ed. see Jameson, Kenneth P.
Wilber, Donald N. Architecture of Islamic Iran: The Il Khanid Period. Repr. of 1955 ed. lib. bdg. 36.75x (ISBN 0-8371-2504-9, WIII). Greenwood.
Wilber, Ken. A Sociable God: Toward a New Understanding of Religion. LC 84-5499. (New Science Library). 160p. 1984. pap. 8.95 (ISBN 0-87773-290-6, 72692-8). Shambhala Pubns.
--The Spectrum of Consciousness. LC 76-39690. (Illus.). 1977. 12.00 (ISBN 0-8356-0495-0). Theos Pub Hse.
--Up from Eden: A Transpersonal View of Human Evolution. LC 82-42678. (Illus.). 384p. 1983. pap. 8.95 (ISBN 0-87773-228-0). Shambhala Pubns.
Wilber, Ken, ed. Quantum Questions: Mystical Writings of the Great Physicists. LC 83-20332. (New Science Library). 200p. 1984. pap. 9.95 (ISBN 0-87773-266-3). Shambhala Pubns.
Wilberforce, Robert I. & Wilberforce, Samuel. The Life of William Wilberforce: By His Sons, 5 vols. LC 72-5506. (Black Heritage Library Collections Ser). 1972. Repr. of 1838 ed. Set. 121.00 (ISBN 0-8369-9151-6). Ayer Co Pubs.
Wilberforce, Samuel, jt. auth. see Wilberforce, Robert I.
Wilberforce, William. Real Christianity: Contrasted with the Prevailing Religious System. Houston, James M., ed. LC 82-8061. (Classics of Faith & Devotion Ser.). 1982. casebound 10.95 (ISBN 0-930014-90-1). Multnomah.
Wilbert, Johannes & Simoneau, Karin, eds. Folk Literature of the Chorote Indians. LC 85-9961. (Latin American Studies Ser.: Vol. 60). 288p. 1985. lib. bdg. 27.50x (ISBN 0-87903-060-7). UCLA Lat Am Ctr.
Wilbert, Warren N. Strategies Teaching Christian Adults. 280p. 1980. 12.95 (ISBN 0-8010-9668-5). Baker Bk.
Wilbur, C. Keith, jt. auth. see Wilbur, Ruth E.
Wilbur, Earl M. Our Unitarian Heritage: An Introduction to the History of the Unitarian Movement. LC 83-45635. Date not set. Repr. of 1925 ed. 49.50 (ISBN 0-404-19877-5). AMS Pr.
Wilbur, Earl M., tr. see Servetus, Michael.
Wilbur, James B. Spinoza's Metaphysics: Essays in Critical Appreciation. (Philosophia Spinozae Perennis Ser.: No. 1). 170p. 1976. pap. text ed. 19.00 (ISBN 90-232-1361-0, Pub. by Van Gorcum Holland). Longwood Pub Group.
Wilbur, James B., jt. ed. see Laszlo, Ervin.
Wilbur, Ken. A Sociable God. LC 82-15241. (New Press Ser.). 176p. 1982. 12.95 (ISBN 0-07-070185-7). McGraw.
Wilbur, L. Perry. How to Live Your Faith. 128p. 1984. 12.95 (ISBN 0-13-416850-X); pap. 5.95 (ISBN 0-13-416843-7). P-H.
Wilbur, Ruth E. & Wilbur, C. Keith. Bid Us God Speed: The History of the Edwards Church, Northhampton, Massachusetts 1833-1983. LC 82-22347. (Illus.). 120p. 1983. 12.95 (ISBN 0-914016-93-8). Phoenix Pub.
Wilburn, Stephen S. Kicking Those Habits. 48p. 1985. 4.95 (ISBN 0-8378-5403-2). Gibson.
--Resting in the Lord. 48p. 1985. 4.95 (ISBN 0-8378-5404-0). Gibson.
Wilcock, M. The Message of Revelation. LC 74-31845. (Bible Speaks Today Ser.). 1975. pap. 6.95 (ISBN 0-87784-293-0). Inter-Varsity.
Wilcock, Michael. Mark. 1983. pap. 4.50 (ISBN 0-87508-167-3). Chr Lit.
--The Message of Luke. Motyer, J. A. & Stott, John R., eds. LC 79-2720. (Bible Speaks Today Ser.). (Orig.). 1979. pap. 6.95 (ISBN 0-87784-291-4). Inter-Varsity.
--The Message of One & Two Chronicles. Stott, John R. & Motyer, J. A., eds. LC 86-27700. (The Bible Speaks Today Ser.). 240p. (Orig.). 1987. pap. 8.95 (ISBN 0-87784-299-X). Inter-Varsity.
Wilcox, Anne. Building Bible Study Skills. 60p. 1985. 4.95 (ISBN 0-87123-832-2); student's wkbk. 3.95 (ISBN 0-87123-821-7). Bethany Hse.
--Your God, My God: A Woman's Workshop on Ruth. (Woman's Workshop Ser.). 1985. tchr's. manual 2.95 (ISBN 0-310-44691-0, 12026P); student's manual 2.95 (ISBN 0-310-44711-9, 12027P). Zondervan.
Wilcox, Donald J. In Search of God & Self: Renaissance & Reformation Thought. (Illus.). 401p. 1987. pap. text ed. 12.95 (ISBN 0-88133-276-3). Waveland Pr.
Wilcox, John R. Taking Time Seriously: James Luther Adams. LC 78-61391. 1978. pap. text ed. 12.25 (ISBN 0-8191-0600-3). U Pr of Amer.
Wilcox, L. D. Power from on High. 1.50 (ISBN 0-686-27776-7). Schmul Pub Co.
Wilcox, Llewellyn A. Now Is the Time. rev. ed. 1966. 8.95 (ISBN 0-911080-06-6). Outdoor Pict.
Wilcox, Tamara. Bats, Cats, & Sacred Cows. LC 77-10834. (Myth, Magic & Superstition). (Illus.). 1977. PLB 14.65 (ISBN 0-8172-1026-1). Raintree Pubs.
Wilcox, Tim, jt. auth. see Anderson, Dave.
Wilcox, Tim, ed. see Anderson, Dave.
Wilczak, Paul F. When a Family Loses a Loved One. LC 81-68846. (WHEN Bk. Ser.). 96p. (Orig.). 1981. pap. 2.45 (ISBN 0-87029-179-3, 20272-1). Abbey.
Wilczak, Paul F., ed. Healing in the Family. LC 79-53515. (Marriage & Family Living in Depth Bk.). 1979. pap. 2.45 (ISBN 0-87029-158-0, 20244-0). Abbey.
--Parenting. LC 78-69758. (Marriage & Family Living in Depth Bk.). 1978. pap. 2.45 (ISBN 0-87029-138-6, 20220-0). Abbey.
--Toward the Extended Christian Family. LC 80-69137. (Marriage & Family Living in Depth Bk.). (Illus.). 80p. 1980. pap. 2.45 (ISBN 0-87029-170-X, 20247-3). Abbey.
Wild, John D. Human Freedom & Social Order: An Essay in Christian Philosophy. LC 59-14243. pap. 65.50 (ISBN 0-317-27300-0, 2023468). Bks Demand UMI.
Wild, Laura H. Geographic Influences in Old Testament Masterpieces. 182p. 1980. Repr. of 1915 ed. lib. bdg. 30.00 (ISBN 0-8414-9701-X). Folcroft.
--Geographic Influences in Old Testament Masterpieces. 1915. 27.00 (ISBN 0-8274-2396-9). R West.
--A Literary Guide to the Bible. LC 74-9861. 1976. lib. bdg. 35.00 (ISBN 0-8414-9533-5). Folcroft.
--The Romance of the English Bible. 1929. 15.00 (ISBN 0-8274-3303-4). R West.
Wild, Peter & Coss, Hal. The Saguaro Forest. LC 86-60514. (Western Horizons Ser.). (Illus.). 96p. (Orig.). 1986. pap. 11.95 (ISBN 0-87358-405-8). Northland.
Wild, Robert. His Face Shone Like the Sun: Encountering the Transfigured Christ in Scripture. LC 86-8054. 126p. (Orig.). 1986. pap. 5.95 (ISBN 0-8189-0501-8). Alba.
--The Post Charismatic Experience: The New Wave of the Spirit. 136p. (Orig.). 1984. pap. text ed. 4.50 (ISBN 0-914544-50-0). Living Flame Pr.
--Who I Will Be: Is There Joy & Suffering in God? 5.95 (ISBN 0-87193-089-7). Dimension Bks.
Wild, Robert, jt. auth. see Edwards, Richard.
Wild, Robert, ed. Journey to the Lonely Christ: The Little Mandate of Catherine de Hueck Doherty. LC 86-17388. 164p. 1987. pap. 7.95 (ISBN 0-8189-0509-3). Alba.
Wild, Robert, tr. see Blaquiere, Georgette.
Wildavsky, Aaron. The Nursing Father: Moses As a Political Leader. LC 83-1099. (Illus.). xi, 262p. 1984. text ed. 25.00 (ISBN 0-8173-0168-2); pap. text ed. 11.95 (ISBN 0-8173-0169-0). U of Ala Pr.
Wilde, Gary, ed. Acts: Powered by the Spirit. (Basic Bible Ser.). 112p. 1986. pap. 4.95 (ISBN 0-89191-519-2). Cook.
--Ephesians: Life in the Church. (Basic Bible Ser.). 112p. 1986. pap. 4.95 (ISBN 0-89191-480-3). Cook.
--Old Testament Royalty: History of a Nation. (Basic Bible Ser.). 96p. 1986. pap. 4.95 (ISBN 0-89191-481-1). Cook.
--One & Two Thessalonians: Hope of His Coming. (Basis Bible Ser.). 96p. 1986. pap. 4.95 (ISBN 0-89191-520-6). Cook.
--Philippians: Joy in the Lord. (Basic Bible Ser.). 96p. 1986. pap. 4.95 (ISBN 0-89191-482-X). Cook.
--Sermon on the Mount: Wisdom of the Kingdom. (Basic Bible Ser.). 96p. 1986. pap. 4.95 (ISBN 0-89191-521-4). Cook.
Wilde, Johannes. Michelangelo: Six Lectures by Johannes Wilde. Shearman, John & Hirst, Michael, eds. (Oxford Studies in the History of Art & Architecture). (Illus.). 1979. pap. 13.95x (ISBN 0-19-817346-6). Oxford U Pr.
Wilde, Larry. The Ultimate Official Jewish Joke Book. 192p. (Orig.). 1986. pap. 2.95 (ISBN 0-553-26227-0). Bantam.
Wilde, Robert. The Treatment of the Jews in the Christian Writers of the First Three Centuries, Vol. 81. (Patristic Studies). 255p. 1984. Repr. of 1949 ed. 38.00x (ISBN 0-939738-28-7). Zubal Inc.
Wilder, Alexander. New Platonism & Alchemy. (Secret Doctrine Reference Ser). 1975. pap. 3.00 (ISBN 0-913510-18-1). Wizards.
--The Peculiar Mystical Rites of Ancient Peoples. (Illus.). 269p. 1984. 117.85x (ISBN 0-89266-451-7). AM Classical Coll Pr.
Wilder, Amos N. Early Christian Rhetoric: The Language of the Gospel. LC 78-131949. 1971. 10.00x (ISBN 0-674-22002-1). Harvard U Pr.
--Eschatology & Ethics in the Teaching of Jesus. LC 78-16425. 1978. Repr. of 1950 ed. lib. bdg. 27.50 (ISBN 0-313-20585-X, WIEE). Greenwood.
--Jesus' Parables & the War of Myths: Essays on Imagination in the Scriptures. LC 81-43083. 176p. 1982. 3.50 (ISBN 0-8006-0668-X, 1-668). Fortress.
--Spiritual Aspects of the New Poetry. facs. ed. LC 68-16988. (Essay Index Reprint Ser). 1940. 16.25 (ISBN 0-8369-0995-X). Ayer Co Pubs.
--Theology & Modern Literature. LC 58-11556. pap. 39.30 (ISBN 0-317-10086-6, 2003002). Bks Demand UMI.
Wilder, Amos N., ed. Liberal Learning & Religion. LC 77-86072. (Essay & General Literature Index Reprint Ser). 1969. Repr. of 1951 ed. 24.50x (ISBN 0-8046-0595-5, Pub. by Kennikat). Assoc Faculty Pr.
Wilder, Franklin. The Methodist Riots: The Testing of Charles Wesley. (Illus.). 160p. 1982. 8.95 (ISBN 0-89962-236-4). Todd & Honeywell.
--The Remarkable World of John Wesley: Pioneer in Mental Health. (Illus.). 1978. 7.00 (ISBN 0-682-49129-2). Exposition Pr FL.
Wilder, Garnett M. Using Your Emotions Creatively. 80p. 1984. pap. 2.95 (ISBN 0-8170-1020-3). Judson.
Wilder, Kay W., ed. Season with Love. 288p. 1985. pap. 10.95 (ISBN 0-8341-1061-X). Beacon Hill.
Wilder-Smith, A. E. Creation of Life. LC 78-133984. 269p. 1981. pap. 8.95 (ISBN 0-89051-070-9). Master Bks.
--He Who Thinks Has to Believe. LC 81-65988. 1981. pap. 2.95 (ISBN 0-89051-073-3). Master Bks.
--He Who Thinks Has to Believe. 91p. 1982. pap. 2.95 (ISBN 0-87123-259-6, 200259). Bethany Hse.
--Why Does God Allow It? LC 80-80283. 1980. pap. 2.95 (ISBN 0-89051-060-1). Master Bks.
Wilder-Smith, A. W. Man's Origin, Man's Destiny. LC 74-28508. 320p. 1975. pap. 7.95 (ISBN 0-87123-356-8, 210356). Bethany Hse.
Wildiers, N. Max. The Theologian & His Universe: Theology & Cosmology from the Middle Ages to the Present. 320p. (Orig.). 1982. 21.95 (ISBN 0-8164-0533-6, HarpR). Har-Row.
Wilding, M. Milton's Paradise Lost. (Sydney Studies in Literature Ser.). 1969. 15.00x (ISBN 0-424-05850-2, Pub. by Sydney U Pr). Intl Spec Bk.
Wildman, Joshua A. And Let Us Say Amen. Wengrov, Charles, tr. from Hebrew. Tr. of V'imru Amen. 1978. pap. 6.95 (ISBN 0-87306-148-9). Feldheim.
Wildmon, Donald. The Home Invaders. 180p. 1985. pap. 6.95 (ISBN 0-89693-521-3). Victor Bks.
Wildridge, Thomas T. Grotesque in Church Art. LC 68-30633. 1969. Repr. of 1899 ed. 35.00x (ISBN 0-8103-3077-6). Gale.
Wildschut, William. Crow Indian Medicine Bundles. 2nd ed. Ewers, John C., ed. LC 74-33115. (Illus.). 1975. soft cover 10.00 (ISBN 0-934490-34-1). Mus Am Ind.
Wiles, G. P. Paul's Intercessory Prayers. (Society for New Testament Studies Monographs: No. 24). 360p. 1974. 59.50 (ISBN 0-521-20274-4). Cambridge U Pr.
Wiles, M. F. What Is Theology? 1977. pap. 5.95x (ISBN 0-19-289066-2). Oxford U Pr.
Wiles, Maurice. The Christian Fathers. 1982. pap. 6.95x (ISBN 0-19-520260-0). Oxford U Pr.
Wiles, Maurice & Santer, M., eds. Documents in Early Christian Thought. LC 74-31807. 304p. 1976. 42.50 (ISBN 0-521-20669-3); pap. 12.95 (ISBN 0-521-09915-3). Cambridge U Pr.
Wiles, Maurice, ed. see Lyons, J. A.
Wiles, Maurice F. Making of Christian Doctrine. 1967. 32.50 (ISBN 0-521-06803-7). Cambridge U Pr.
Wiley, Edwin. Study of the Supernatural in Three Plays of Shakespeare. LC 74-32191. 1913. lib. bdg. 15.00 (ISBN 0-8414-9382-0). Folcroft.
Wiley, H. Orton. The Epistle to the Hebrews. Weigelt, Morris, ed. 438p. 1985. text ed. 15.95 (ISBN 0-8341-0890-9). Beacon Hill.
Wiley, Margaret L. Subtle Knot: Creative Scepticism in Seventeenth-Century England. LC 68-54994. (Illus.). 1968. Repr. of 1952 ed. lib. bdg. 22.50x (ISBN 0-8371-0753-9, WISK). Greenwood.
Wiley, Peter, jt. auth. see Gottlieb, Robert.
Wilhelm, Anthony. Christ among Us: A Modern Presentation of the Catholic Faith for Adults. 4th, rev. ed. LC 84-48465. 480p. 1985. pap. 6.95 (ISBN 0-06-069417-3, HarpR). Har-Row.
Wilhelm, Richard, tr. see Tsu, Lao.
Wilhelmsen, Frederick. Hilaire Belloc: No Alienated Man. 1953. 20.00 (ISBN 0-8274-2495-7). R West.
Wilhelmsen, Frederick D. Christianity & Political Philosophy. LC 77-22754. 256p. 1978. 22.00x (ISBN 0-8203-0431-X). U of Ga Pr.
--Citizen of Rome: Reflections from the Life of a Roman Catholic. 348p. 1980. pap. 6.95 (ISBN 0-89385-005-5). Sugden.
Wilhelmsson, Lars & Wilhelmsson, Nancy. Vital Christianity Study Guide. (Religion Ser.). 64p. (Orig.). 1982. pap. 2.25 (ISBN 0-941018-08-3). Martin Pr CA.
Wilhelmsson, Nancy, jt. auth. see Wilhelmsson, Lars.
Wiliiamson, G. A., tr. see Josephus, Flavius.
Wilk, Melvin. The Jewish Presence in Eliot & Kafka. (Brown Judaic Studies). 228p. 1986. 31.95 (ISBN 0-89130-915-2, 14-00-82). Scholars Pr GA.
Wilke, Harold H. Creating the Caring Congregation: Guidelines for Ministering with the Handicapped. LC 79-28626. (Orig.). 1980. pap. 6.50 (ISBN 0-687-09815-7). Abingdon.
Wilken, Robert L. Anselm Weber, O.F.M. Missionary to the Navaho. 1955. 12.50 (ISBN 0-686-32658-X, 55-1235). St Michaels.
--The Christians As the Romans Saw Them. LC 83-12472. 240p. 1984. 22.50x (ISBN 0-300-03066-5); pap. 7.95 (ISBN 0-300-03627-2, Y-575). Yale U Pr.
--The Myth of Christian Beginnings. LC 80-11884. 218p. 1980. 17.95 (ISBN 0-268-01347-0); pap. text ed. 6.95 (ISBN 0-268-01348-9). U of Notre Dame Pr.
Wilken, Robert L., jt. auth. see Meeks, Wayne A.
Wilken, Robert L., ed. Aspects of Wisdom in Judaism & Early Christianity. LC 74-27888. (University of Notre Dame, Center for the Study of Judaism & Christianity in Antiquity: No. 1). pap. 60.00 (ISBN 0-317-26715-9, 2024365). Bks Demand UMI.
Wilkerson. Have You Felt Like Giving Up Lately? 2.50 (ISBN 0-318-18174-6). WCTU.
Wilkerson, David. The Christian Maturity Manual. rev. ed. LC 79-169590. 96p. 1977. 3.95 (ISBN 0-8307-0496-5, 5200121). Regal.
--Have You Felt Like Giving up Lately? 160p. 1980. pap. 6.95 (ISBN 0-8007-5042-X, Power Bks). Revell.
--I'm Not Mad at God. 96p. 1967. pap. 2.95 (ISBN 0-87123-245-6, 200245). Bethany Hse.
--Jesus Person Pocket Promise Book. LC 72-86208. 96p. 1979. pap. 2.50 (ISBN 0-8307-0191-5, 5007801). Regal.
--The Pocket Promise Book. gift ed. LC 72-86208. 96p. 1981. imitation leather 3.95 (ISBN 0-8307-0789-1, 5007953). Regal.
--Promesas de Jesus. (Span.). 95p. 1974. pap. 2.50 (ISBN 0-89922-027-4). Edit Caribe.
--Promises to Live by. LC 72-86208. 96p. (Orig.). 1972. pap. 2.50 (ISBN 0-8307-0197-4, 5007305). Regal.
--Racing Toward Judgment. 160p. 1976. pap. 2.50 (ISBN 0-8007-8276-3, Spire Bks). Revell.
--Sipping Saints. 128p. 1979. pap. 2.95 (ISBN 0-8007-8339-5, Spire Bks). Revell.
--Victory over Sin & Self. 80p. 1982. pap. 2.95 (ISBN 0-8007-8434-0, Spire Bks). Revell.
--Vision. (Orig.). 1984. pap. 2.95. Jove Pubns.
--The Vision. 144p. 1974. pap. 3.50 (ISBN 0-8007-8150-3, Spire Bks). Revell.
Wilkerson, David, et al. Cross & the Switchblade. 160p. pap. 2.95 (ISBN 0-8007-8009-4, Spire Bks). Revell.
Wilkerson, Don & Manuel, David. Hell-Bound. LC 78-60735. 199p. 1978. pap. 3.95 (ISBN 0-932260-03-9). Paraclete Pr.
--Ruta de Escape. Araujo, Juan S., tr. from Eng. Tr. of Hellbound. (Span.). 224p. 1986. pap. 4.75 (ISBN 0-88113-266-7). Edit Betania.

Wilkerson, Gwen & Schonauer, Betty. In His Strength. Rev. ed. LC 77-92619. 144p. 1982. pap. 4.95 (ISBN 0-8307-0825-1, 5416405). Regal.

Wilkerson, Ralph. God's Power Through Prayer. Countryman, Marsha, ed. 300p. 1985. leatherbound 19.95 (ISBN 0-937347-02-7). J Countryman Pubs.

Wilkerson, Rich. Carnal Christians: And Other Words That Don't Go Together. 175p. (Orig.). 1986. pap. 3.50 (ISBN 0-88368-188-9). Whitaker Hse.

--Hold Me While You Let Me Go. LC 82-83838. 196p. (Orig.). 1983. pap. 4.95 (ISBN 0-89081-370-1). Harvest Hse.

Wilkes, Gerald A. The Thesis of Paradise Lost. LC 76-28374. 1976. Repr. of 1961 ed. lib. bdg. 20.00 (ISBN 0-8414-9514-9). Folcroft.

Wilkes, James. The Gift of Courage. LC 81-11507. 108p. 1981. pap. 6.95 (ISBN 0-664-24394-0). Westminster.

Wilkes, John. Hernan Cortes: Conquistador in Mexico. LC 76-22436. (Cambridge Topic Bks). (Illus.). 1977. PLB 8.95 (ISBN 0-8225-1205-X). Lerner Pubns.

Wilkes, Paul, ed. Merton: By Those Who Knew Him Best. LC 84-47824. (Illus.). 160p. 1984. 13.95 (ISBN 0-06-069416-5, HarpR). Har-Row.

Wilkes, Peter. Defeating Anger & Other Dragons of the Soul. (The Dragon Slayer Ser.). 180p. 1987. pap. 5.95 (ISBN 0-87784-517-4). Inter Varsity.

Wilkie, W. E. The Cardinal Protectors of England: Rome & the Tudors Before the Reformation. LC 73-82462. 224p. 1974. 44.50 (ISBN 0-521-20332-5). Cambridge U Pr.

Wilkin, Esther. Little Prayers. (Golden Look-Look Ser.). (Illus.). 24p. 1980. pap. 1.50 (ISBN 0-307-11858-4, Golden Bks.). Western Pub.

Wilkin, Esther, ed. The Golden Treasury of Prayers for Boys & Girls. (Illus.). xx, 48p. 1975. 6.95 (ISBN 0-307-13744-9, Golden Bks). Western Pub.

Wilkins, John. Of the Principles & Duties of Natural Religion: Two Books. Repr. of 1693 ed. 35.00 (ISBN 0-384-68500-5). Johnson Repr.

Wilkins, Lewis L., tr. see Pannenberg, Wolfhart.

Wilkins, Ronald. Focus on Faith in Jesus: Parish Edition. rev. ed. 112p. 1985. pap. text ed. 5.25 (ISBN 0-697-02007-X); tchr's. ed. 12.95 (ISBN 0-697-02009-6). Wm C Brown.

--Focus on Faith in Jesus: School Edition. rev. ed. 192p. 1985. pap. text ed. 6.50 (ISBN 0-697-02006-1); tchr's. ed. 14.95 (ISBN 0-697-02008-8). Wm C Brown.

--Focus on Growth in the Church: Parish Edition. rev. ed. 128p. 1985. pap. text ed. 5.25 (ISBN 0-697-02011-8); tchr's. ed. 12.95 (ISBN 0-697-02013-4). Wm C Brown.

--Focus on Growth in the Church: School Edition. rev. ed. 224p. 1985. pap. text ed. 6.50 (ISBN 0-697-02010-X); tchr's. ed. 14.95 (ISBN 0-697-02012-6). Wm C Brown.

Wilkins, Ronald & Grover, Veronica. Achieving Social Justice: A Catholic Perspective. rev. ed. (To Live Is Christ Ser.). (YA) 1987. pap. text ed. write for info. (ISBN 0-697-02126-2); write for info. (ISBN 0-697-02127-0). Wm C Brown.

Wilkins, Ronald & Gryczka, Mary. Christian Marriage: A Sacrament of Love. (To Live Is Christ Ser.). (YA) 1986. pap. text ed. 7.25 (ISBN 0-697-02071-1); tchr's. ed. 15.95 (ISBN 0-697-02072-X); test wkbk. 14.95 (ISBN 0-697-02112-2). Wm C Brown.

Wilkins, Ronald J. Achieving Social Justice: A Christian Perspective. (To Live Is Christ Ser.). 1981. pap. text ed. 5.95 (ISBN 0-697-01775-3); tchr's manual, pap. 4.00 (ISBN 0-697-01776-1); spirit masters 10.95 (ISBN 0-697-01777-X). Wm C Brown.

--Challenge! rev. ed. (To Live Is Christ Ser.). 1983. pap. 5.25 (ISBN 0-697-01850-4); tchr's. manual 5.95 (ISBN 0-697-01851-2); tests 10.95 (ISBN 0-697-01939-X). Wm C Brown.

--Christian Faith: The Challenge of the Call. 72p. 1978. pap. 4.20 (ISBN 0-697-01684-6); tchrs.' manual 4.50 (ISBN 0-697-01688-9); spirit masters 10.95 (ISBN 0-697-01690-0). Wm C Brown.

--Christian Living: The Challenge of Response. 72p. 1978. pap. 4.20 (ISBN 0-697-01686-2); tchrs. manual 4.50 (ISBN 0-697-01689-7); spirit masters 10.95 (ISBN 0-697-01691-9). Wm C Brown.

--The Emerging Church. rev. ed. (To Live Is Christ Ser). 1981. pap. 5.95 (ISBN 0-697-01760-5); tchr's. manual 4.75 (ISBN 0-697-01761-3); activity cards 7.50 (ISBN 0-697-01899-7); stud. diaries 10.00 (ISBN 0-697-01900-4); spirit masters 9.95 (ISBN 0-697-01898-9). Wm C Brown.

--The Jesus Book: Extended Study. (To Live Is Christ Ser.). 168p. 1984. pap. 5.75 (ISBN 0-697-01917-9); tchrs. manual 5.00 (ISBN 0-697-01927-6); spirit master 10.95 (ISBN 0-697-01692-7). Wm C Brown.

--The Jesus Book: Short Ed. (To Live Is Christ Ser.). 112p. 1979. pap. 4.20 (ISBN 0-697-01695-1); tchr's manual 4.00 (ISBN 0-697-01714-1). Wm C Brown.

--Reading the New Testament. (To Live Is Christ Ser.). 160p. 1983. pap. 5.50 extended study (ISBN 0-697-01810-5); tchr's. manual 4.00 (ISBN 0-697-01811-3); spirit masters 12.95 (ISBN 0-697-01674-9); pap. 3.95 short ed. (ISBN 0-697-01673-0); tchr's. manual 3.75 (ISBN 0-697-01680-3). Wm C Brown.

--Religion in North America. (To Live Is Christ Ser.). 208p. 1984. pap. 5.75 (ISBN 0-697-01930-6); tchr's manual 4.95 (ISBN 0-697-01931-4); spirit masters 10.95 (ISBN 0-697-01735-4). Wm C Brown.

--The Religions of the World. rev. ed. (To Live Is Christ Ser.). 240p. 1984. pap. 5.95 (ISBN 0-697-01928-4); tchr's manual 5.00 (ISBN 0-697-01929-2); spirit masters 10.95 (ISBN 0-697-01730-3). Wm C Brown.

--Understanding Christian Morality. (To Live Is Christ Ser). 256p. 1982. pap. 5.75; tchr's. manual 5.00 (ISBN 0-697-01800-8); spirit masters 10.95 (ISBN 0-697-01801-6); kit 20.00 (ISBN 0-697-01675-7). Wm C Brown.

--Understanding Christian Morality: Short Edition. (To Live Is Christ Ser.). 112p. 1977. pap. 4.20 (ISBN 0-697-01661-7); tchr's. manual 6.00 (ISBN 0-697-01667-6). Wm C Brown.

--Understanding Christian Worship: School Edition. (To Live Is Christ Ser.). 216p. 1982. pap. 5.50 (ISBN 0-697-01802-4); tchr's. manual 5.00 (ISBN 0-697-01803-2); kit 32.00 (ISBN 0-697-01676-5); spirit masters 6.50 (ISBN 0-697-01902-0); poster 3.50 (ISBN 0-697-01903-9); activity cards 7.50 (ISBN 0-697-01904-7); progress in prayer 11.50 (ISBN 0-697-01905-5); prayer planning forms 3.00 (ISBN 0-697-01906-3). Wm C Brown.

--Understanding Christian Worship: Short Edition. (To Live Is Christ Ser.). 80p. 1977. pap. 3.95 (ISBN 0-697-01663-3); tchr's. ed. 6.00 (ISBN 0-697-01669-2). Wm C Brown.

--Understanding the Bible: School Edition. rev. ed. (To Live Is Christ Ser.). 212p. 1982. pap. 5.75 (ISBN 0-697-01786-9); tchr's. manual 5.00 (ISBN 0-697-01787-7); spirit masters 12.95. Wm C Brown.

--Understanding the Bible: Short Edition. (To Live Is Christ Ser.). 1977. pap. 3.95 (ISBN 0-697-01659-5); tchr's. manual 6.00 (ISBN 0-697-01665-X); spirit masters 12.95. Wm C Brown.

Wilkins, Skip & Dunn, Joseph. The Real Race. 240p. 1987. pap. 6.95 (ISBN 0-8423-5283-X). Tyndale.

Wilkins, Walter J. Science & Religious Thought: A Darwinism Case Study. Miles, Margaret R., ed. LC 86-24946. (Studies in Religion: No. 3). 224p. 1986. 39.95 (ISBN 0-8357-1778-X). UMI Res Pr.

Wilkinson, Bruce & Boa, Kenneth. Talk Thru the Bible: A Survey of a Setting & Content of Scripture. LC 83-4130. (Illus.). 469p. 1983. Repr. of 1981 ed. 14.95 (ISBN 0-8407-5286-5). Nelson.

Wilkinson, Dorcas, jt. auth. see Wilkinson, Larry.

Wilkinson, Jerry & Richardson, Jim. A Case for Radical Christianity. 1984. pap. 1.75 (ISBN 0-911739-25-4). Abbott Loop.

Wilkinson, John. Health & Healing: Studies in New Testament Principles. 220p. 1980. 15.00x (ISBN 0-905312-08-2, Pub. by Scot Acad Pr). Longwood Pub Group.

Wilkinson, Larry & Wilkinson, Dorcas. Gifts from Korea. 1983. pap. 7.00 (ISBN 0-8309-0376-3). Herald Hse.

Wilkinson, Loren, ed. Earthkeeping: Christian Stewardship of Natural Resources. 2nd ed. (Orig.). 1980. pap. 10.95 (ISBN 0-8028-1834-X). Eerdmans.

Wilkinson, Peggy O. Finding the Mystic within You. 211p. (Orig.). 1985. pap. 4.95 (ISBN 0-914544-61-6). Living Flame Pr.

Wilkinson, Theodore S. Churches at the Testing Point: A Study in Rural Michigan. (World Council of Churches Studies in Mission). 1970. pap. 3.95 (ISBN 0-377-82021-0). Friend Pr.

Wilkinson, Vernon. After the Bomb: Plight to Utopia. 154p. (Orig.). 1984. pap. 11.95 (ISBN 0-86474-003-4, Pub. by Interface Press). ANZ Religious Pubns.

Wilkinson, William. A Confutation of Certaine Articles Delivered by H. Niklaes, Unto the Familye of Love. LC 72-238. (English Experience Ser.: No. 279). 200p. 1970. Repr. of 1579 ed. 22.00 (ISBN 90-221-0279-3). Walter J Johnson.

Wilks, Karl G. Deacons: Servants of the Church Christ Built & Spiritual Gifts. LC 86-90143. (Bible Teaching on Church Government & Management Ser.). 66p. (Orig.). 1986. pap. 6.00 (ISBN 0-9616912-0-4). K G Wilks.

Wilks, Michael. The Problem of Sovereignty in the Later Middle Ages: The Papal Monarchy with Augustinus Triumphus & the Publicists. (Cambridge Studies in Medieval Life & Thought New: Vol. 9). pap. 158.30 (ISBN 0-317-09407-6, 2013890). Bks Demand UMI.

Wilks, Michael J., ed. The World of John of Salisbury. (Studies in Church History: Subsidia 3). 400p. 1985. text ed. 45.00x (ISBN 0-631-13122-1). Basil Blackwell.

Will, Herman, Jr. A Will for Peace: Peace Action in the United Methodist Church: A History. 300p. 9.95 (CS1007). General Board.

Will, James E. Must Walls Divide? The Creative Witness of the Churches in Europe. (Orig.). 1981. pap. 3.75 (ISBN 0-377-00106-6). Friend Pr.

Will, Paul J., et al. Public Education Religion Studies: An Overview. LC 80-12237. (Aids for the Study of Religion Ser.). 1981. write for info. (ISBN 0-89130-401-0); pap. 12.00 (ISBN 0-89130-402-9, 01-03-07). Scholars Pr GA.

Willard, Dallas. In Search of Guidance. LC 83-17743. 1983. 10.95 (ISBN 0-8307-0899-5, 5110807). Regal.

--The Spirit of the Disciplines: Understanding How God Changes Lives. 240p. 1986. 13.95 (ISBN 0-06-069441-6, HarpR). Har-Row.

Willard, Frances E. Woman & Temperance; or, the Work & Workers of the Woman's Christian Temperance Union. LC 74-38443. (Religion in America, Ser. 2). 654p. 1972. Repr. of 1883 ed. 38.00 (ISBN 0-405-04093-8). Ayer Co Pubs.

--Woman in the Pulpit. LC 75-34240. 1976. Repr. of 1889 ed. 15.95 (ISBN 0-89201-014-2). Zenger Pub.

Willard, Samuel. Compleat Body of Divinity. (American Studies). Repr. of 1726 ed. 62.00 (ISBN 0-384-68533-1). Johnson Repr.

Willcocks, David, jt. auth. see Jacques, Reginald.

Willcocks, David, ed. Carols for Choirs: Bk. 3, Fifty Carols. 1978. pap. text ed. 7.00 (ISBN 0-19-353570-X). Oxford U Pr.

--Carols for Christmas. (Illus.). 96p. 1983. 25.00 (ISBN 0-03-064044-X). H Holt & Co.

--Hymns for Choirs. 1976. pap. 6.00 (ISBN 0-19-353556-4). Oxford U Pr.

Willcocks, David & Ruttner, John, eds. Fifty Carols for Christmas & Advent. (Carols for Choirs, Book 2). 1970. 12.00 (ISBN 0-19-353566-1); pap. 7.00 (ISBN 0-19-353565-3). Oxford U Pr.

Willcocks, M. P. Bunyan Calling: A Voice from the Seventeenth Century. 1979. Repr. of 1943 ed. lib. bdg. 30.00 (ISBN 0-8414-9718-4). Folcroft.

--Bunyan Calling: A Voice from the Seventeenth Century. 1943. 17.50 (ISBN 0-8274-1984-8). R West.

Willcox, P. J. Modern Cosmology: A Survey in Four Lectures. LC 82-90241. (Illus.). 96p. 1982. pap. 4.50 (ISBN 0-9608436-0-4). P J Willcox.

Willcuts, Jack L. Why Friends Are Friends. 90p. (Orig.). 1984. pap. 3.95 (ISBN 0-913342-45-9). Barclay Pr.

Willeke, Bernard H. Imperial Government & Catholic Missions in China During the Years 1784-1785. (Missiology Ser). 1948. 3.50 (ISBN 0-686-11584-8). Franciscan Inst.

Willems, Boniface, jt. ed. see Schillebeeckx, Edward.

Willems, Emilio. Followers of the New Faith: Culture Change & the Rise of Protestantism in Brazil & Chile. LC 67-27517. 1967. 16.50x (ISBN 0-8265-1106-6). Vanderbilt U Pr.

Willems-Treeman, Elizabeth, tr. see Haak, B.

Willert, Albrecht. Religioese Existenz und Literarische Produktion. (Ger.). 316p. 1982. 43.70 (ISBN 3-8204-5994-4). P Lang Pubs.

Willerton, Chris. Teaching the Adult Bible Class. 2.95 (ISBN 0-89137-609-7). Quality Pubns.

Willet, Andrew. Sacrorum Emblematum Centuria Una. LC 84-5360. 1984. Repr. of 1592 ed. 35.00x (ISBN 0-8201-1395-6). Schol Facsimiles.

Willets, Walter E. Master's Book of Short Speeches. rev. ed. 65p. 1984. Repr. s.p. soft cover 2.95 (ISBN 0-88053-050-2). Macoy Pub.

Willetts, H. T., tr. see Pope John Paul II.

Willetts, Phoebe. Sharing a Vision. 116p. 1978. pap. 4.95 (ISBN 0-227-67842-7). Attic Pr.

Willetts, R. F. Cretan Cults & Festivals. LC 79-16739. 1980. Repr. of 1962 ed. lib. bdg. 32.50x (ISBN 0-313-22050-6, WICU). Greenwood.

Willey, Basil. Christianity, Past & Present. LC 78-65632. 1980. Repr. of 1952 ed. 16.50 (ISBN 0-88355-877-7). Hyperion Conn.

--Religion of Nature. LC 76-40105. 1957. lib. bdg. 12.50 (ISBN 0-8414-9506-8). Folcroft.

--Richard Crashaw. LC 76-26647. 1949. lib. bdg. 12.50 (ISBN 0-8414-9386-3). Folcroft.

--Seventeenth Century Background: Studies in the Thought of the Age in Relation to Poetry & Religion. LC 34-21849. 1942. 31.00x (ISBN 0-231-01395-7). Columbia U Pr.

Willey, Herbert L. The Bible Through the Centuries. 1929. 37.50 (ISBN 0-8274-1935-X). R West.

William Of Ockham. Predestination, God's Foreknowledge & Future Contingents. 2nd ed. Kretzmann, Norman & Adams, Marilyn M., trs. LC 82-23317. 146p. 1983. 19.50 (ISBN 0-915144-14-X); pap. text ed. 4.95x (ISBN 0-915144-13-1). Hackett Pub.

William of St. Thierry. The Mirror of Faith. Elder, E. Rozanne, ed. Davis, Thomas X., tr. from Lat. LC 78-12897. (Cistercian Fathers Ser.). (Illus.). 1979. 12.95 (ISBN 0-87907-315-2). Cistercian Pubns.

--The Nature & Dignity of Love. Elder, E. R., ed. Davis, Thomas X., tr. from Lat. (Cistercian Fathers Ser.: No. 30). Orig. Title: De natura et dignitate amoris. 1981. 13.95 (ISBN 0-87907-330-6). Cistercian Pubns.

--William of St. Thierry: Exposition on the Epistle to the Romans. Anderson, John D., ed. (Cistercian Fathers Ser.: No. 27). 1980. 17.95 (ISBN 0-87907-327-6). Cistercian Pubns.

William of Ockham. The Power of the Mind in the Philosophy of William of Ockham. (Illus.). 137p. 1986. 117.50 (ISBN 0-89920-132-6). Am Inst Psych.

William of Saint Thierry. Exposition on the Song of Songs. (Cistercian Fathers Ser.: No. 6). 171p. 7.95 (ISBN 0-87907-306-3). Cistercian Pubns.

William of St. Thierry, jt. auth. see Bernard of Clairvaux.

Williams. Essays in Process Theology. 24.95 (ISBN 0-317-46805-7); pap. 12.95 (ISBN 0-317-46806-5). Exploration Pr.

Williams, A. Lukyn. Adversus Judaeos: A Bird's-Eye View of Christian Apologiae until the Renaissance. LC 36-11257. pap. 111.50 (ISBN 0-317-29839-9, 2051943). Bks Demand UMI.

Williams, Ann. The Crusades. Reeves, Marjorie, ed. (Then & There Ser.). (Illus.). 95p. (YA) 1975. pap. text ed. 4.75 (ISBN 0-582-20441-0). Longman.

Williams, B. W. The Joke of Christianizing China. 40p. 1983. pap. 3.00 (ISBN 0-910309-13-2). Am Atheist.

Williams, Barbara. Public Relations Handbook for Your Church. 112p. 1985. pap. 5.95 (ISBN 0-8170-1050-5). Judson.

Williams, Barbara M. Freddie & the Ten Commandments. 3rd ed. 1978. 0.95 (ISBN 0-686-05835-6). Crusade Pubs.

Williams, Bernard. Ethics & the Limits of Philosophy. 248p. 1985. 17.50 (ISBN 0-674-26857-1). Harvard U Pr.

--Morality: An Introduction to Ethics. LC 70-172503. 1972. pap. 5.95x (ISBN 0-06-131632-6, TB1632, Torch). Har-Row.

Williams, Burtis. Gospel in the Feasts of Israel. 32p. 1968. pap. 0.50 (ISBN 0-89114-011-5). Baptist Pub Hse.

Williams, Carey, jt. auth. see Cranston, Sylvia.

Williams, Carole, ed. see Reid, Thomas F., et al.

Williams, Caroline, ed. see Parker, Richard B. & Sabin, Robin.

Williams, Charles. The Forgiveness of Sins. 128p. 1984. pap. 3.95 (ISBN 0-8028-0032-7). Eerdmans.

--He Came Down from Heaven. 160p. 1984. pap. 3.95 (ISBN 0-8028-0033-5). Eerdmans.

Williams, Charles, ed. see Hill, Bert H.

Williams, Charles W. A Bi-Centenary Memorial of John Bunyan Who Died A.D. 1688. LC 76-27709. 1976. Repr. of 1888 ed. lib. bdg. 17.50 (ISBN 0-8414-9510-6). Folcroft.

--Novels. Incl. War in Heaven. pap. 6.95 (ISBN 0-8028-1219-8); Many Dimensions. pap. 5.95 (ISBN 0-8028-1221-X); The Place of the Lion. pap. 7.95 (ISBN 0-8028-1222-8); Shadows of Ecstacy. pap. 4.95 (ISBN 0-8028-1223-6); Descent into Hell. pap. 6.95 (ISBN 0-8028-1220-1); Greater Trumps. pap. 6.95. 1965. Boxed set. pap. 46.95 (ISBN 0-8028-1215-5). Eerdmans.

Williams, Colin. Jerusalem: A Universal Cultural & Historical Resource. 18p. (Orig.). 1975. pap. text ed. 5.00 (ISBN 0-8191-5907-7, Pub. by Aspen Inst for Humanistic Studies). U Pr of Amer.

Williams, Colin W. John Wesley's Theology Today. LC 60-5238. 256p. 1983. pap. 9.95 (ISBN 0-687-20531-X). Abingdon.

Williams, Daniel D. Andover Liberals: A Study in American Theology. LC 79-111636. 1970. Repr. of 1941 ed. lib. bdg. 17.50x (ISBN 0-374-98584-7, Octagon). Hippocrene Bks.

--Essays in Process Theology. LeFevre, Perry, ed. LC 84-82337. 342p. 1985. text ed. 24.95x (ISBN 0-913552-25-9); pap. text ed. 12.95x (ISBN 0-913552-26-7). Exploration Pr.

--The Spirit & the Forms of Love. LC 81-40368. 316p. 1981. lib. bdg. 27.75 (ISBN 0-8191-1691-2); pap. text ed. 12.25 (ISBN 0-8191-1692-0). U Pr of Amer.

--What Present-Day Theologians Are Thinking. rev. ed. LC 78-16410. 1978. Repr. of 1959 ed. lib. bdg. 22.50x (ISBN 0-313-20587-6, WIWP). Greenwood.

Williams, Daniel D., jt. ed. see Niebuhr, H. Richard.

Williams, David. Cain & Beowulf: A Study in Secular Allegory. LC 81-94507. 114p. 1981. 25.00x (ISBN 0-8020-5519-2). U of Toronto Pr.

Williams, David R. Wilderness Lost: The Religious Origins of the American Mind. LC 85-43475. 296p. 1987. 38.50x (ISBN 0-941664-21-X). Susquehanna U Pr.

Williams, Don, jt. auth. see Maeder, Gary.

Williams, Donald. Psalms (CC, Vol. 13. 448p. 1986. 23.95 (ISBN 0-8499-0419-6). Word Bks.

Williams, Doris & Griggs, Patricia. Preparing for the Messiah. (Griggs Educational Resources Ser.). 1979. pap. 5.95 (ISBN 0-687-33920-0). Abingdon.

Williams, Dorothy, ed. see Search Institute Staff.

Williams, E. Louise, jt. auth. see Kersten, Phyllis N.

Williams, Edward, ed. see Edwards, Jonathan.

Williams, Edward J. Latin American Christian Democratic Parties. LC 67-13159. Repr. of 1967 ed. 79.00 (2027567). Bks Demand UMI.

Williams, Effie. The Man of His Counsel. 112p. pap. 1.00 (ISBN 0-686-29156-5). Faith Pub Hse.

Williams, Effie M. Just Mary. 96p. pap. 0.75 (ISBN 0-686-29124-7). Faith Pub Hse.

--Trials & Triumphs of Eva Grant. 94p. pap. 1.00 (ISBN 0-686-29173-5). Faith Pub Hse.

Williams, Ernest S. Systematic Theology, 3 vols. Incl. Vol. 1. pap. 6.95 (ISBN 0-88243-643-0, 02-0643); Vol. 2. pap. 6.95 (ISBN 0-88243-644-9, 02-0644); Vol. 3. pap. 6.95 (ISBN 0-88243-645-7, 02-0645). 1953. pap. 18.00 Set 3 vol (ISBN 0-88243-650-3, 02-0650). Gospel Pub.

--Word of Encouragement. 25p. pap. 0.40 (ISBN 0-88243-840-9, 02-0840). Gospel Pub.

Williams, Esther, jt. tr. see Nykanen, Marita.

Williams, Esther, tr. see Skhi-Igumen, John.

Williams, Ethel L. & Brown, Clifton F. Howard University Bibliography of African & Afro-American Religious Studies: With Locations in American Libraries. LC 76-5604. 1977. 50.00 (ISBN 0-8420-2080-2). Scholarly Res Inc.

Williams, F. Chenhalls. Captain Sebastian: Fifty-Two Talks to Boys & Girls. 96p. 1961. pap. 2.75 (ISBN 0-87921-007-9). Attic Pr.

Williams, Francis E. The Vailala Madness & the Destruction of Native Ceremonies in the Gulf Division. LC 75-35166. (Territory of Papua. Anthropological Report: No. 4). Repr. of 1923 ed. 20.00 (ISBN 0-404-14180-3). AMS Pr.

Williams, Gardner. Humanistic Ethics. 1951. 6.00 (ISBN 0-8022-1886-5). Philos Lib.

Williams, George. The Student's Commentary on the Holy Scriptures. LC 75-13929. 1971. 29.95 (ISBN 0-8254-4001-7). Kregel.

Williams, George, tr. Orthodox Church of the East in the Eighteenth Century. LC 73-131028. Repr. of 1868 ed. 21.00 (ISBN 0-404-06977-0). AMS Pr.

Williams, George H. American Universalism. pap. 3.50 (ISBN 0-933840-18-7). Unitarian Univ.

--The Law of Nations & the Book of Nature. Franklin, R. W., ed. LC 84-72274. (New Essays in Christian Humanism: Vol. 1). (Illus.). 60p. (Orig.). 1985. pap. 4.95x (ISBN 0-9613867-0-3). St Johns Univ Christ Hum.

--The Mind of John Paul II: Origins of His Thought & Action. LC 80-19947. 415p. 1981. 26.95 (ISBN 0-8164-0473-9, HarpR). Har-Row.

--Norman Anonymous of Eleven Hundred A.D. Toward the Identification & Evaluation of the So-Called Anonymous of York. (Harvard Theological Studies). 1951. 24.00 (ISBN 0-527-01018-9). Kraus Repr.

--Radical Reformation. LC 62-7066. (Illus.). 960p. 1962. 24.95 (ISBN 0-664-20372-8). Westminster.

Williams, George H. & Mergal, Angel M., eds. Spiritual & Anabaptist Writers. LC 57-5003. (Library of Christian Classics). 418p. 1977. pap. 11.95 (ISBN 0-664-24150-6). Westminster.

Williams, George H., ed. see Wolfson, Harry A.

Williams, George M. Freedom & Influence: The Role of Religion in American Society. 318p. 1985. write for info.; pap. write for info. (ISBN 0-915678-15-2). World Tribune Pr.

--Improving Parish Management: Working Smarter, Not Harder. 112p. pap. 9.95 (ISBN 0-89622-176-8). Twenty-Third.

Williams, George M., ed. Victory in Faith: Experiences of NSA Members. 100p. (Orig.). 1985. pap. text ed. 5.00 (ISBN 0-915678-14-4). World Tribune Pr.

Williams, George W. Image & Symbol in the Sacred Poetry of Richard Crashaw. 2nd edition ed. LC 63-12394. x, 152p. 1967. 21.95x (ISBN 0-87249-087-4). U of SC Pr.

Williams, Glanmor. Religion & Welsh Literature in the Age of the Reformation. (Sir John Rhys Memorial Lectures in Celtic Studies). 1985. pap. 4.25 (ISBN 0-85672-497-1, Pub. by British Acad). Longwood Pub Group.

--The Welsh Church from Conquest to Reformation. 612p. 1976. text ed. 28.50x (ISBN 0-7083-0651-9, Pub. by U of Wales). Humanities.

Williams, H. A. True Christianity. 1975. 5.95 (ISBN 0-87243-059-6). Templegate.

--The True Wilderness. (The Crossroad Paperback Ser.). 160p. 1982. pap. 5.95 (ISBN 0-8245-0470-4). Crossroad NY.

Williams, Harry A. True Resurrection. 192p. 1983. pap. 7.95 (ISBN 0-87243-115-0). Templegate.

Williams, Helen, jt. ed. see Abercrombie, V. T.

Williams, Herman & Greene, Ella L. Attitude Education: A Research Curriculum. LC 75-16677. 1975. pap. 3.00x (ISBN 0-915744-02-3). Character Res.

Williams, Ira, Jr. The Piano Man's Christmas & Other Stories for Christmas. 80p. (Orig.). 1986. pap. 4.95 (ISBN 0-687-30920-4). Abingdon.

Williams, J. Floyd. Christ Jesus: The God-Man. 3.95 (ISBN 0-911866-72-8). Advocate.

Williams, J. L. The Fire Inside. 1984. 6.50 (ISBN 0-89536-654-1, 0634). CSS of Ohio.

--Victor Paul Wierwille & the Way International. LC 79-22007. 1979. pap. 3.95 (ISBN 0-8024-9233-9). Moody.

Williams, James C., ed. see Fulton, Alvenia M.

Williams, James G. Gospel Against Parable: Mark's Language of Mystery. (Bible & Literature Ser.: No. 12). 246p. 1985. text ed. 24.95x (ISBN 0-907459-44-7, Pub. by Almond Pr England); pap. text ed. 10.95x (ISBN 0-907459-45-5). Eisenbrauns.

--Those Who Ponder Proverbs: Aphoristic Thinking & Biblical Literature. (Bible & Literature Ser.: No. 2). 1981. text ed. 19.95x (ISBN 0-907459-02-1, Pub. by Almond Pr England); pap. text ed. 9.95x (ISBN 0-907459-03-X, Pub. by Almond Pr England). Eisenbrauns.

--Women Recounted: Narrative Thinking & the God of Israel. (Bible & Literature Ser.: No. 6). 128p. 1982. text ed. 21.95x (ISBN 0-907459-18-8, Pub. by Almond Pr England); pap. 10.95x (ISBN 0-907459-19-6). Eisenbrauns.

Williams, Jay G. Judaism. LC 80-51551. 204p. 1981. pap. 5.50 (ISBN 0-8356-0540-X, Quest). Theos Pub Hse.

--Understanding the Old Testament. LC 74-162825. 1972. pap. 6.95 (ISBN 0-8120-0424-8). Barron.

Williams, Jerome O. Definite Decisions for New Church Members. pap. 1.25 (ISBN 0-8054-9402-2). Broadman.

Williams, Jill, jt. auth. see Williams, Pat.

Williams, John. For Every Cause? A Biblical Study of Divorce. 96p. 1982. pap. 3.25 (ISBN 0-87213-953-0). Loizeaux.

--The Holy Spirit, Lord & Life-Giver: A Biblical Introduction to the Doctrine of the Holy Spirit. LC 79-27891. 1980. 8.50 (ISBN 0-87213-950-6); pap. 5.95 (ISBN 0-87213-951-4); study guide 3.25 (ISBN 0-87213-952-2). Loizeaux.

--The Holy Table, Name & Thing, More Patiently, Properly, & Literally Used Under the New Treatment, Than That of an Altar. LC 79-84146. (English Experience Ser.: No.962). 244p. 1979. Repr. of 1637 ed. lib. bdg. 22.00 (ISBN 90-221-0962-3). Walter J Johnson.

--Living Churches: A Reconsideration of Their Basis of Life & Leadership. 144p. 1975. pap. 4.95 (ISBN 0-85364-122-6). Attic Pr.

Williams, John A., ed. & tr. The History of al-Tabari, Vol. 27: The Abbasid Revolution A. D. 743-750 - A. H.126-132) (Near Eastern Studies). 192p. 1985. 39.50 (ISBN 0-87395-884-5). State U NY Pr.

Williams, John P. Social Adjustment in Methodism. LC 76-177639. (Columbia University. Teachers College. Contributions to Education: No. 765). Repr. of 1938 ed. 22.50 (ISBN 0-404-55765-1). AMS Pr.

Williams, John R. Martin Heidegger's Philosophy of Religion. 190p. 1977. pap. text ed. 9.95x (ISBN 0-919812-03-1, Pub. by Wilfrid Laurier Canada). Humanities.

Williams, John S. The Revolutionary War & Issachar Bates. 14p. 1960. 0.50 (ISBN 0-937942-02-2). Shaker Mus.

--Shaker Religious Concept. (Illus.). 32p. 1959. pap. 2.50 (ISBN 0-937942-04-9). Shaker Mus.

Williams, Joseph J. Hebrewisms of West Africa: From Nile to Niger with the Jews. LC 67-19534. (Illus.). 1930. 20.00 (ISBN 0-8196-0194-2). Biblo.

--Voodoos & Obeahs. LC 74-11170. 1970. Repr. of 1932 ed. 23.00 (ISBN 0-404-06986-X). AMS Pr.

Williams, June A. Strategy of Service. 112p. (Orig.). 1984. pap. 5.95 (ISBN 0-310-45761-0, 12046P). Zondervan.

Williams, Kathy. The Rastafarians. 1985. 13.00x (ISBN 0-7062-4063-4, Pub. by Ward Lock Educ Co Ltd). State Mutual Bk.

Williams, Lima L. Walking in Missionary Shoes. 1986. pap. 14.95 (ISBN 0-87162-417-6, D8750). Warner Pr.

Williams, Margaret. The Society of the Sacred Heart: History of a Spirit 1800-1975. 406p. 1978. pap. 12.50 (ISBN 0-232-51395-3). Attic Pr.

Williams, Mary L. Sorrow Speaks. 1968. pap. 2.95 (ISBN 0-8272-3405-8). CBP.

Williams, Maxine. Eyes Have It. LC 62-15648. 1962. pap. 1.75 (ISBN 0-88243-495-0, 02-0495). Gospel Pub.

Williams, Mel & Brittain, Mary A. Christian Education in Family Clusters. 80p. 1982. pap. 6.95 (ISBN 0-8170-0936-1). Judson.

Williams, Melvin D. Community in a Black Pentecostal Church: An Anthropological Study. 202p. 1984. pap. 8.95x (ISBN 0-88133-049-3). Waveland Pr.

--Community in a Black Pentecostal Church: An Anthropological Study. LC 74-5108. pap. 53.50 (ISBN 0-317-42278-2, 2024332). Bks Demand UMI.

Williams, Merrill. His Spirit in You. 68p. 1982. 2.95 (ISBN 0-8341-0783-X). Beacon Hill.

Williams, Michael. American Catholics in the War: National Catholic War Council, 1917-1921. LC 74-75244. (The United States in World War 1 Ser.). x, 467p. 1974. Repr. of 1921 ed. lib. bdg. 26.95x (ISBN 0-89198-110-1). Ozer.

Williams, Michael A., ed. Charisma & Sacred Biography. (JAAR Thematic Studies). 1982. 19.50 (ISBN 0-89130-681-1, 01-24-83). Scholars Pr GA.

Williams, Michael C. St. Alban's College, Valladolid: Four Centuries of English Catholic Presence in Spain. LC 86-17787. 278p. 1986. 35.00 (ISBN 0-312-69736-8). St Martin.

Williams, Norman P. The Ideas of the Fall & of Original Sin: A Historical & Critical Study. LC 79-8125. Repr. of 1927 ed. 49.00 (ISBN 0-404-18439-1). AMS Pr.

Williams, Oliver & Houck, John, eds. Judeo-Christian Vision & the Modern Business Corporation. LC 81-40448. 336p. 1982. pap. text ed. 10.95 (ISBN 0-268-01201-6). U of Notre Dame Pr.

Williams, Oliver F. & Houck, John M. Full Value: Cases in Christian Business Ethics. LC 78-3143. 1978. pap. 8.95x S.D. (ISBN 0-06-069515-3, RD 279, HarpR). Har-Row.

Williams, Oliver F., jt. ed. see Houck, John W.

Williams, Pat & Jenkins, Jerry. The Power Within You. LC 82-24825. 180p. 1983. 12.95 (ISBN 0-664-27008-5, A Bridgebooks Publication). Westminster.

Williams, Pat & Williams, Jill. Keep the Fire Glowing: How a Loving Marriage Builds a Loving Family. 160p. 1986. 9.95 (ISBN 0-317-46133-8). Revell.

Williams, Patti. Husbands. LC 75-7477. 1976. 4.95 (ISBN 0-88270-148-7). Bridge Pub.

Williams, Paul L., ed. The Church & the Law: The Seventh Proceedings of the Fellowship of Catholic Scholars. 128p. (Orig.). 1985. pap. 6.95 (ISBN 0-937374-01-6). NE Bks.

--Historicism & Faith: The Proceedings of the Fellowship of Catholic Scholars. LC 80-117742. 1980. pap. 5.95 (ISBN 0-937374-00-8). NE Bks.

--Issues in the Wake of Vatican II: Proceedings of the Eighth Convention of the Fellowship of Catholic Scholars. 128p. (Orig.). 1985. pap. 6.95 (ISBN 0-937374-02-4). NE Bks.

Williams, Paul L., ed. see Fellowship of Catholic Scholars.

Williams, Philip L. The Heart of a Distant Forest. 1985. pap. 3.50 (ISBN 0-345-32365-3). Ballantine.

Williams, Philip W. When a Loved One Dies. LC 75-22713. 96p. 1976. pap. 5.95 (ISBN 0-8066-1520-6, 10-7056). Augsburg.

Williams, R. T. Pastor & People. pap. 2.95 (ISBN 0-686-12898-2). Schmul Pub Co.

Williams, Raymond B. A New Face of Hinduism: The Swaminarayan Religion. LC 83-7197. 256p. 1984. 37.50 (ISBN 0-521-25454-X); pap. 13.95 (ISBN 0-521-27473-7). Cambridge U Pr.

Williams, Richard E. Called & Chosen: The Story of Mother Rebecca Jackson & the Philadelphia Shakers. LC 80-25498. (ATLA Monograph Ser.: No. 17). 193p. 1981. 17.50 (ISBN 0-8108-1382-3). Scarecrow.

Williams, Robert. The Veil. 20p. 1976. pap. 3.95 (ISBN 0-89536-247-3, 2200). CSS of Ohio.

Williams, Robert R. Schleiermacher the Theologian: The Construction of the Doctrine of God. LC 77-78650. pap. 54.50 (2026892). Bks Demand UMI.

Williams, Ronald R., ed. Letters of John & James. (Cambridge Bible Commentary on the New English Bible, New Testament Ser.). (Orig.). 1965. 17.95 (ISBN 0-521-04206-2); pap. 8.95 (ISBN 0-521-09250-7, 250). Cambridge U Pr.

Williams, Rosa M., ed. Restoration: Our Philosophy Through Inspired Poems. LC 79-66586. 1980. (ISBN 0-9602366-1-9); pap. 6.50x. Sooty-Face.

Williams, Rowan. Christian Spirituality: A Theological History from the New Testament to Luther & St. John of the Cross. LC 80-82190. 193p. 1980. 10.95 (ISBN 0-8042-0660-0); pap. 8.95 (ISBN 0-8042-0508-6). John Knox.

--Christian Spirituality: A Theological History From the New Testament to Luther & St. John of the Cross. LC 80-82190. pap. 50.30 (2027154). Bks Demand UMI.

--Resurrection: Interpreting the Easter Gospel. 144p. (Orig.). 1985. pap. 5.95 (ISBN 0-8298-0727-6). Pilgrim NY.

--The Truce of God. 128p. (Orig.). 1983. pap. 3.95 (ISBN 0-8298-0660-1). Pilgrim NY.

Williams, Sally. Aunt Sally: Or, the Cross, the Way of Freedom. facs. ed. LC 75-89438. (Black Heritage Library Collection Ser.). 1858. 14.25 (ISBN 0-8369-8692-X). Ayer Co Pubs.

Williams, Sara P. National Trust Book of Christmas & Festive Day Recipes. (Illus.). 192p. 1980. 13.95 (ISBN 0-7153-8100-8). David & Charles.

Williams, Shirley & Zalaquett, Jose. The Moral Dimensions of International Conduct. Devereux, James, ed. (The Jesuit Community Lectures Ser.: 1982). 128p. (Orig.). pap. 5.95 (ISBN 0-87840-406-6). Georgetown U Pr.

Williams, Steve. The Death of a Child. 1977. 3.95 (ISBN 0-88027-005-5). Firm Foun Pub.

Williams, Terry T. Pieces of White Shell. (Illus.). 176p. 1987. pap. 8.95 (ISBN 0-8263-0969-0). U of NM Pr.

Williams, Theodore, ed. Together in Mission. 90p. (Orig.). 1983. pap. 2.00. World Evang Fellow.

--World Missions: Building Bridges or Barriers. 101p. (Orig.). 1979. pap. 2.00 (ISBN 0-936444-02-9). World Evang Fellow.

Williams, Theodore, jt. auth. see Chrysostomos, Archimandrite.

Williams, Theodore M., ed. see Chrysostomos, Archimandrite.

Williams, Thomas D., ed. A Textual Concordance of the Holy Scriptures: (Bible Passages Taken from the Douay-Rheims Bible) LC 85-52025. 848p. (Orig.). 1985. Repr. of 1908 ed. pap. 30.00 (ISBN 0-89555-286-8). Tan Bks Pubs.

Williams, Trevor. Form & Vitality in the World & God: A Christian Perspective. 1985. 29.95x (ISBN 0-19-826671-5). Oxford U Pr.

Williams, Walter L. Black Americans & the Evangelization of Africa, 1877-1900. LC 81-69830. 282p. 1982. text ed. 32.50x (ISBN 0-299-08920-7). U of Wis Pr.

Williams, Wells S. China, Chinese Philosophers & Confucianism. (Illus.). 137p. 1982. Repr. of 1883 ed. 73.45 (ISBN 0-89901-059-8). Found Class Reprints.

Williams, William H. The Garden of American Methodism: The Delmarva Peninsula, 1769-1820. (Illus.). xiv, 225p. 1984. 25.00 (ISBN 0-8420-2227-9). Scholarly Res Inc.

Williams, William J. The Miracle of Abduction. LC 84-82540. 160p. (Orig.). 1985. 12.95 (ISBN 0-930371-02-X); pap. 8.95 (ISBN 0-930371-03-8). Epistemics.

Williams, William P. A Descriptive Catalogue of Seventeenth Century Religious Literature in the Kansas State University Library. LC 67-63307. (Libraries Bibliography Ser.: No. 3). 1966. 1.50 (ISBN 0-686-20809-9). KSU.

Williams, William P., jt. ed. see Gathorne-Hardy, Robert.

Williams-Ellis, Virginia. The Baby Jesus. (Board Bks.). (Illus.). 10p. 1984. 2.95 (ISBN 0-8249-8082-4). Ideals.

--Noah's Ark. (Board Bks.). (Illus.). 10p. 1984. 2.95 (ISBN 0-8249-8079-4). Ideals.

Williamsen, Glen & Anders, Isabel. Susanna. 240p. (Orig.). 1985. pap. 3.50 (ISBN 0-8423-6691-1). Tyndale.

Williams-Forte, E., jt. ed. see Gorelick, L.

Williamson, Audrey. Love Is the Greatest. (Direction Bks). 64p. 1976. pap. 1.25 (ISBN 0-8010-9579-4). Baker Bk.

Williamson, Clark M. Has God Rejected His People? LC 81-12847. 192p. (Orig.). 1982. pap. 8.75 (ISBN 0-687-16649-7). Abingdon.

Williamson, Denise J. Bible Readings on God's Creation. (Bible Readings Ser.). 112p. (Orig.). 1987. pap. 3.95 (ISBN 0-8066-2277-6, 10-0696). Augsburg.

Williamson, G. A., tr. see Eusebeius.

Williamson, G. A., tr. see Eusebius.

Williamson, G. I. The Shorter Catechism: A Study Manual, 2 vols. Vol. 1. pap. 4.50 (ISBN 0-87552-539-3); Vol. 2. pap. 4.50 (ISBN 0-87552-540-7). Presby & Reformed.

--Understanding the Times. 1979. pap. 2.95 (ISBN 0-87552-541-5). Presby & Reformed.

--Westminster Confession of Faith. pap. 6.95 (ISBN 0-8010-9591-3). Baker Bk.

--Westminster Confession of Faith: A Study Manual. 1964. pap. 5.50 (ISBN 0-87552-538-5). Presby & Reformed.

Williamson, George C. Milton. LC 75-19089. 1975. Repr. of 1905 ed. lib. bdg. 15.00 (ISBN 0-88305-757-3). Norwood Edns.

--Milton Tercentenary: The Portraits, Prints & Writings of John Milton. LC 72-194902. 1973. lib. bdg. 18.50 (ISBN 0-8414-9743-5). Folcroft.

Williamson, George H. Secret Places of the Lion. LC 82-2374. 230p. 1983. pap. 7.95 (ISBN 0-89281-039-4, Destiny Bks). Inner Tradit.

Williamson, Gerald M. Pastor Search Committee Planbook. LC 81-68923. 1982. pap. 5.50 (ISBN 0-8054-3515-8). Broadman.

--Pastor Search Committee Primer. LC 81-68924. 1982. pap. 3.50 (ISBN 0-8054-3516-6). Broadman.

Williamson, Glen. Brother Kawabe. 1977. pap. 1.75 (ISBN 0-89367-012-X). Light & Life.

Williamson, H. G. Ezra & Nehemiah. (Old Testament Guides Ser.). 100p. 1986. pap. text ed. 4.95x (ISBN 1-85075-045-9, Pub. by JSOT Pr England). Eisenbrauns.

--Ezra-Nehemiah: Vol. 16, WBC. 1985. 22.95 (ISBN 0-8499-0215-0, 0215-0). Word Bks.

--Israel in the Book of Chronicles. LC 76-11096. 1977. 42.50 (ISBN 0-521-21305-3). Cambridge U Pr.

Williamson, Hugh Ross. Jeremy Taylor. LC 73-15705. 1902. lib. bdg. 20.00 (ISBN 0-8414-9472-X). Folcroft.

Williamson, J. J. Cataclysm Has Begun, No. 1. 20.00x (ISBN 0-317-43559-0, Pub. by Soc of Metaphysicians). State Mutual Bk.

Williamson, Jack V. Natures Religion. 6.95 (ISBN 0-8062-2425-8). Carlton.

Williamson, John. The Oak King, the Holly King, & the Unicorn: The Myths & Symbolism of the Unicorn Tapestries. LC 85-45242. (Illus.). 280p. 1987. pap. 12.95 (ISBN 0-06-096032-9, PL 6032, PL). Har-Row.

Williamson, Lamar, Jr. Mark: A Bible Commentary for Teaching & Preaching. Mays, James L. & Achtemeier, Paul J., eds. LC 82-17161. (Interpretation Ser.). 289p. 1983. 17.95 (ISBN 0-8042-3121-4). John Knox.

Williamson, Lamar, Jr., jt. auth. see Beck, Madeline H.

Williamson, Mabel. Have We No Rights? 1957. pap. 5.95 (ISBN 0-8024-3417-7). Moody.

Williamson, Nancy. Handy Helpful Household Hints. pap. cancelled (ISBN 0-89728-066-0). Omega Pubns Or.

Williamson, Nancy S. Inside & Occupied. LC 82-3139. 192p. (Orig.). 1982. pap. 9.95 (ISBN 0-8361-3304-8). Herald Pr.

--One Hundred Handy Ideas for Busy Teachers. (Teaching Helps Ser.). 1980. pap. 2.50 (ISBN 0-8010-9630-8). Baker Bk.

Williamson, Peter. How to Become the Person You Were Meant to Be. (Living As Christian Ser.). 112p. (Orig.). 1981. pap. 2.95 (ISBN 0-89283-098-0). Servant.

Williamson, Peter S., ed. see Colson, Charles, et al.

Williamson, Raymond K. An Introduction to Hegel's Philosophy of Religion. (Hegelian Studies). 376p. 1984. 49.50 (ISBN 0-87395-827-6); pap. 17.95 (ISBN 0-87395-826-8). State U NY Pr.

Williamson, Rene De Visme. Politics & Protestant Theology: An Interpretation of Tillich, Barth, Bonhoeffer, & Brunner. LC 76-20817. 1976. 20.00x (ISBN 0-8071-0193-1). La State U Pr.

Williamson, Robert W. Religion & Social Organization in Central Polynesia. Piddington, Ralph, ed. LC 75-35218. Repr. of 1937 ed. 38.00 (ISBN 0-404-14241-9). AMS Pr.

--Religious & Cosmic Beliefs of Central Polynesia, 2 vols. LC 75-35220. Repr. of 1933 ed. Set. 87.50 (ISBN 0-404-14300-8). AMS Pr.

Williamson, Tom & Bellamy, Lin. Ley Lines in Question. (Illus.). 272p. 1984. 22.50 (ISBN 0-437-19205-9, Pub. by Worlds Work). David & Charles.

Williamson, William B. Decisions in Philosophy of Religion. LC 85-42846. 407p. 1985. pap. 16.95 (ISBN 0-87975-295-5). Prometheus Bks.

Willimon, William H. The Gospel for the Person Who Has Everything. 1978. pap. 4.95 (ISBN 0-8170-0758-X). Judson.

--Integrative Preaching: The Pulpit at the Center. LC 80-39628. (Abingdon Preacher's Library). 112p. (Orig.). 1981. pap. 6.95 (ISBN 0-687-19129-7). Abingdon.

--On a Wild & Windy Mountain: And 25 other Mediations for the Christian Year. 144p. 1984. pap. 8.95 (ISBN 0-687-28846-0). Abingdon.

--Preaching & Leading Worship. LC 83-26021. (The Pastor's Handbooks Ser.: Vol. 1). 116p. (Orig.). 1984. pap. 7.95 (ISBN 0-664-24616-8). Westminster.

--Remember Who You Are: Baptism, a Model for Christian Life. LC 79-93359. (Illus.). 128p. (Orig.). 1980. pap. 4.95x (ISBN 0-8358-0399-6). Upper Room.

--The Service of God. 240p. 1983. pap. 11.50 (ISBN 0-687-38094-4). Abingdon.

--Sighing for Eden: Sin, Evil & the Christian Faith. 208p. 1985. pap. 8.95 (ISBN 0-687-38447-8). Abingdon.

--Sunday Dinner. LC 81-52215. 1981. pap. 4.50x (ISBN 0-8358-0429-1). Upper Room.

--With Glad & Generous Hearts. 176p. 1986. pap. 7.95 (ISBN 0-8358-0536-0, ICN 613183, Dist. by Abingdon Press). Upper Room.

--Word, Water, Wine, & Bread. 1980. pap. 5.95 (ISBN 0-8170-0858-6). Judson.

--Worship As Pastoral Care. rev. ed. LC 79-894. 1979. 11.95 (ISBN 0-687-46388-2). Abingdon.

Willimon, William H. & Wilson, Robert L. Preaching & Worship in the Small Church. LC 79-24529. (Creative Leadership Ser.). (Orig.). 1980. pap. 6.95 (ISBN 0-687-33820-4). Abingdon.

--Rekindling the Flame: Strategies for a Vital United Methodism. 128p. 1987. 9.95 (ISBN 0-687-35932-5). Abingdon.

Willimon, William H., jt. auth. see Westerhoff, John H., III.

Willimon, William H., ed. And the Laugh Shall be First: A Treasury of Religious Humor. 1986. pap. 12.95 (ISBN 0-687-01383-6). Abingdon.

Willims, Michael A., tr. see Dibelius, Martin.

Willing, Ora M. & Davidson, C. T. Hidden Treasures for Women. 144p. (Orig.). 1983. pap. 3.95 (ISBN 0-934942-37-4). White Wing Pub.

Willinsky, Margarete. Bischof Percy's Bearbeitung Der Volksballaden Und Kunstgedichte Seines Folio-Manuskriptes. Repr. of 1932 ed. 19.00 (ISBN 0-384-68615-X). Johnson Repr.

Willi-Plein, Ina. Vorformen der Schriftexegese innerhalb des Alten Testaments. 286p. 1971. 43.20x (ISBN 3-11-001897-7). De Gruyter.

Willis, Avery T., Jr. Indonesian Revival: Why Two Million Came to Christ. LC 77-12811. (Illus.). 1977. pap. 6.95 (ISBN 0-87808-428-2). William Carey Lib.

Willis, Elbert. Being Fully Persuaded. 1977. 1.25 (ISBN 0-89858-017-X). Fill the Gap.

--Divine Guidance. 350p. 1982. write for info. Fill the Gap.

--Faith's Explanation. 1977. 1.25 (ISBN 0-89858-007-2). Fill the Gap.

--God's Plan for Financial Prosperity. 1977. 3.00 (ISBN 0-89858-005-6). Fill the Gap.

--How Can I Be Healed. 1978. 1.25 (ISBN 0-89858-013-7). Fill the Gap.

--An Interceding Faith. 1978. 1.25 (ISBN 0-89858-018-8). Fill the Gap.

--Keys to Prosperity. 1978. 1.25 (ISBN 0-89858-016-1). Fill the Gap.

--Overcoming Discouragement. 1976. 1.25 (ISBN 0-89858-000-5). Fill the Gap.

--Overcoming Worry. 1976. 1.25 (ISBN 0-89858-001-3). Fill the Gap.

--Prayer for Guidance. 1977. 1.25 (ISBN 0-89858-012-9). Fill the Gap.

--Prayer for Patient Waiting. 1977. 1.25 (ISBN 0-89858-002-1). Fill the Gap.

--Praying the Right Way. 1977. 1.25 (ISBN 0-89858-011-0). Fill the Gap.

--Private Praise. 1977. 1.25 (ISBN 0-89858-009-9). Fill the Gap.

--Those Who Move with God. 1977. 1.25 (ISBN 0-89858-006-4). Fill the Gap.

--Victory over the Impossible. 1978. 1.25 (ISBN 0-89858-008-0). Fill the Gap.

--Who Is Responsible for Sickness. 1978. 1.25 (ISBN 0-89858-010-2). Fill the Gap.

Willis, Gladys J. The Penalty of Eve: John Milton & Divorce. LC 83-49352. (American University Studies IV (English Language & Literature): Vol. 6). 164p. (Orig.). 1985. text ed. 21.55 (ISBN 0-8204-0094-7). P Lang Pubs.

Willis, J. Armine, tr. see Marucchi, Orazio.

Willis, John R. A History of Christian Thought: From Apollinaris to Erasamus, Vol. II. 400p. 1984. 18.00 (ISBN 0-682-49973-0, University). Exposition Pr FL.

--A History of Christian Thought: From Apostolic Times to Saint Augustine. LC 76-16237. 1976. 16.00 (ISBN 0-682-48583-7, University). Exposition Pr FL.

--A History of Christian Thought: From Luther to Marx, Vol. III. LC 76-16237. 1985. 20.00 (ISBN 0-682-40256-7, University). Exposition Pr FL.

--Pleasures Forevermore: The Theology of C. S. Lewis. 157p. 1983. 12.95 (ISBN 0-8294-0446-5). Loyola.

Willis, John R., ed. Studies in West African Islamic History: The Cultivators of Islam, Vol. 1. (Illus.). 325p. 1979. 39.50x (ISBN 0-7146-1737-7, F Cass Co). Biblio Dist.

Willis, John T. Insights from the Psalms, Vol. 2. LC 73-93946. (Way of Life Ser.: No. 132). 111p. 1974. pap. 3.95 (ISBN 0-89112-132-3, Bibl Res Pr). Abilene Christ U.

--Insights from the Psalms, Vol. 3. LC 73-93946. (Way of Life Ser: No. 133). 114p. 1974. pap. 3.95 (ISBN 0-89112-133-1, Bibl Res Pr). Abilene Christ U.

--The Message of the Old Testament. Incl. Vol. I, No. 141. Adam to Moses (ISBN 0-89112-141-2); Vol. II, No. 142. Joshua to Ruth (ISBN 0-89112-142-0); Vol. III, No. 143. Samuel to Solomon (ISBN 0-89112-143-9); Vol. IV, No. 144. Rehoboam to Nehemiah (ISBN 0-89112-144-7). (Way of Life Ser.). 1977. pap. 3.95 ea. (Bibl Res Pr). Abilene Christ U.

--My Servants the Prophets, Vol. 1. LC 76-180789. (Way of Life Ser.: No. 116). 1971. pap. 3.95 (ISBN 0-89112-116-1, Bibl Res Pr). Abilene Christ U.

--My Servants the Prophets, Vol. 3. LC 76-180789. (Way of Life Ser.: No. 118). (Orig.). 1972. pap. 3.95 (ISBN 0-89112-118-8, Bibl Res Pr). Abilene Christ U.

--My Servants the Prophets, Vol. 4. (Way of Life Ser.: No. 119). 1982. pap. 3.95 (ISBN 0-89112-119-6, Bibl Res Pr). Abilene Christ U.

--The Wisdom Literature: Job, Proverbs, Ecclesiates. LC 81-69494. (Way of Life Ser.: No. 145). 1982. pap. 3.95 (ISBN 0-89112-145-5, Biblo Res Pr). Abilene Christ U.

Willis, John T., ed. The World & Literature of the Old Testament. (The Bible Study Textbook Ser.). 1979. Repr. of 1978 ed. 11.60 (ISBN 0-89900-058-4). College Pr Pub.

Willis, John T., ed. see Engnell, Ivan.

Willis, John T., tr. see Engnell, Ivan.

Willis, John Thomas. Insights from the Psalms, Vol. 1. LC 73-93946. (Way of Life Ser: No. 131). 1974. pap. text ed. 3.95 (ISBN 0-89112-131-5, Bibl Res Pr). Abilene Christ U.

Willis, Lloyd A. Archaeology in Adventist Literature, 1937-1980. (Andrews University Seminary Doctoral Dissertation Ser.: Vol. 7). x, 670p. 1984. pap. 14.95 (ISBN 0-943872-39-1). Andrews Univ Pr.

Willis, Mary. People of That Book. Van Dolson, Bobbie J., ed. 128p. 1981. pap. 4.95 (ISBN 0-8280-0033-6). Review & Herald.

Willis, Richard S. Our Church Music. LC 72-1662. Repr. of 1856 ed. 11.50 (ISBN 0-404-08336-6). AMS Pr.

Willis, Wendell L. Idol Meat in Corinth. (Society of Biblical Literature Dissertation Ser.: No. 68). 1985. 19.50 (ISBN 0-89130-764-8, 06 01 68); pap. 12.95 (ISBN 0-89130-606-4). Scholars Pr GA.

Willis, Wesley. Make Your Teaching Count! 144p. 1985. pap. 5.95 (ISBN 0-89693-324-5). Victor Bks.

Willmington, H. L. Willmington's Guide to the Bible. 1981. 29.95 (ISBN 0-8423-8804-4). Tyndale.

Willmington, Harold L. Willmington's Survey of the Old Testament. 624p. 1987. 19.95. Victor Bks.

Willmott, A. A Christian Approach to National Defense. rev. ed. 122p. 1986. pap. 20.00X (ISBN 0-7223-1968-1, Pub. by A H Stockwell England). State Mutual Bk.

Willoughby, David. What Time Is It? Clanton, Arthur L., ed. 126p. 1974. 3.95 (ISBN 0-912315-49-0). Word Aflame.

Willoughby, William C. Soul of the Bantu: A Sympathetic Study of the Magico-Religious Practices & Beliefs of the Bantu Tribes of Africa. LC 77-107526. Repr. of 1928 ed. cancelled (ISBN 0-8371-3773-X, WBA&, Pub. by Negro U Pr). Greenwood.

Wills, David W. & Newman, Richard, eds. Black Apostles at Home & Abroad: Afro-Americans & the Christian Mission from the Revolution to Reconstruction. 420p. 1982. lib. bdg. 42.00 (ISBN 0-8161-8482-8, Hall Reference). G K Hall.

Willson, Thomas B. History of the Church & State in Norway: From the 10th to the 16th Century. LC 72-145376. (Illus.). 1971. Repr. of 1903 ed. 49.00x (ISBN 0-403-01280-5). Scholarly.

Wilm, Emil C., ed. Studies in Philosophy & Theology. LC 75-3078. Repr. of 1922 ed. 17.00 (ISBN 0-404-59079-9). AMS Pr.

Wilmer, Harry A. Practical Jung: Nuts & Bolts of Jungian Psychotherapy. 250p. 1987. 17.95 (ISBN 0-933029-16-0). Chiron Pubns.

Wilmore, Gayraud S. Black & Presbyterian: The Heritage & the Hope. LC 82-23907. 142p. (Orig.). 1983. pap. 5.95 (ISBN 0-664-24440-8, Pub. by Geneva Press). Westminster.

--Black Religion & Black Radicalism: An Interpretation of the Religious History of Afro-American People. 2nd rev. & enl. ed. LC 83-8077. 320p. (Orig.). 1983. pap. 9.95 (ISBN 0-88344-032-6). Orbis Bks.

--Last Things First. LC 81-23136. (Library of Living Faith.: Vol. 3). 118p. (Orig.). 1982. pap. 5.95 (ISBN 0-664-24412-2). Westminster.

Wilmore, Gayraud S. & Cone, James H., eds. Black Theology: A Documentary History, 1966-1979. LC 79-12747. 672p. 1979. pap. 14.95 (ISBN 0-88344-042-3). Orbis Bks.

Wilmot, John. Inspired Principles of Prophetic Interpretation. pap. 10.95 (ISBN 0-686-48168-2). Reiner.

Wilmot, Laurence. Whitehead & God: Prolegomena to Theological Reconstruction. 200p. 1979. text ed. 17.25x (ISBN 0-88920-070-X, Pub. by Wilfrid Laurier Canada). Humanities.

Wilner, Herbert. The Quarterback Speaks to His God. 288p. 1987. 17.95 (ISBN 0-933529-04-X); pap. 8.95 (ISBN 0-933529-03-1). Cayuse Pr.

Wilpert, P., ed. Antike und Orient im Mittelalter: Vortraege der Koelner Mediaevistentagungen 1956-1959. 2nd ed. (Miscellanea mediaevalia, 1). 274p. 1971. 33.60x (ISBN 3-11-002395-4). De Gruyter.

Wilshire, Frances. Secrets. pap. 1.95 (ISBN 0-87516-318-1). De Vorss.

--You. pap. 3.00 (ISBN 0-87516-319-X). De Vorss.

Wilson, Arthur M. French Foreign Policy During the Administration of Cardinal Fleury: 1726-1743; a Study in Diplomacy & Commercial Development. LC 70-138193. 433p. 1972. Repr. of 1936 ed. lib. bdg. 22.50x (ISBN 0-8371-5333-6, WIFP). Greenwood.

Wilson, Bob. The Good That Lives after Them. Kings, John, ed. (Illus.). 170p. 1982. 14.50 (ISBN 0-9608192-1-5); cassette 10.00. B Wilson.

Wilson, Bruce. Can God Survive in Australia. 224p. (Orig.). 1983. pap. 7.95 (ISBN 0-86760-009-8, Pub. by Albatross Bks). ANZ Religious Pubns.

Wilson, Bryan. Contemporary Transformations of Religion. 1976. pap. text ed. 7.95x (ISBN 0-19-875045-5). Oxford U Pr.

--Religion in Sociological Perspective. 1982. pap. 7.95x (ISBN 0-19-826664-2). Oxford U Pr.

Wilson, Bryan, jt. auth. see Ikeda, Diasaku.

Wilson, Bryan, jt. ed. see Almond, Brenda.

Wilson, Bryan R. Sects & Society: A Sociological Study of Three Religious Groups in Britain. LC 78-5993. 1978. Repr. of 1961 ed. lib. bdg. 31.00x (ISBN 0-313-20439-X, WISA). Greenwood.

Wilson, C. Vincent. The Westminster Concise Handbook for the Bible. LC 79-15498. (Illus.). 112p. 1979. pap. 4.50 (ISBN 0-664-24272-3). Westminster.

Wilson, Carter, tr. see Abreu Gomez, Emilio.

Wilson, Charles A., ed. see McGill, Arthur.

Wilson, Charles H. Life & Works of Michelangelo Buonarroti. Repr. of 1876 ed. 65.00 (ISBN 0-686-19837-9). Ridgeway Bks.

Wilson, Charles R. Baptized in Blood: The Religion of the Lost Cause, 1865-1920. LC 80-126. 264p. 1980. 21.95x (ISBN 0-8203-0515-4); pap. 8.00x (ISBN 0-8203-0681-9). U of Ga Pr.

Wilson, Charles R., ed. Religion in the South. LC 85-5361. (Chancellor's Symposium Ser.). (Orig.). 1985. 15.00x (ISBN 0-87805-256-9); pap. 8.95 (ISBN 0-87805-257-7). U Pr of Miss.

Wilson, Christopher, et al. Westminster Abbey: The New Bell's Cathedral Guides. (The New Bell's Cathedral Guides). 1986. cancelled 24.95 (ISBN 0-918678-12-9). Historical Times.

Wilson, Clifford. The Passover Plot Exposed. LC 77-73814. 1977. pap. 2.95 (ISBN 0-89051-032-6). Master Bks.

--The War of the Chariots. LC 78-55211. 1978. pap. 3.95 (ISBN 0-89051-050-4). Master Bks.

Wilson, Colin. Afterlife. 288p. 1987. 16.95 (ISBN 0-385-23765-0, Dolp). Doubleday.

--Religion & the Rebel. LC 74-9134. 338p. 1974. Repr. of 1957 ed. lib. bdg. 27.50x (ISBN 0-8371-7596-8, WIRA). Greenwood.

--Religion & the Rebel. Rev. ed. 352p. 1984. pap. 9.95 (ISBN 0-88162-050-5). Salem Hse Pubs.

--The War Against Sleep: The Philosophy of Gurdjieff. 96p. 1980. pap. 6.95 (ISBN 0-85030-198-X). Weiser.

Wilson, Dan. An Opening Way. LC 61-11637. (Orig.). 1961. pap. 2.50x (ISBN 0-87574-113-4, 113). Pendle Hill.

--Promise of Deliverance. 1983. pap. 2.50x (ISBN 0-87574-060-X, 060). Pendle Hill.

Wilson, David A. Apocalypse! (Illus.). 175p. (Orig.). 1973. pap. 8.00 (ISBN 0-934852-10-3). Lorien Hse.

--The Dance of the Rites. (Illus.). 156p. (Orig.). 1983. cancelled 13.00 (ISBN 0-934852-96-0); pap. 7.00 (ISBN 0-934852-27-8). Lorien Hse.

Wilson, David B., ed. Did the Devil Make Darwin Do It? Modern Perspectives on the Creation-Evolution Controversy. (Illus.). 242p. 1983. pap. 13.95 (ISBN 0-8138-0434-5). Iowa St U Pr.

Wilson, Dora. The Self to the Self. 1983. pap. 2.50x (ISBN 0-87574-035-9, 035). Pendle Hill.

--The Totalitarian Claim of the Gospels. 1983. pap. 2.50x (ISBN 0-87574-004-9, 004A). Pendle Hill.

Wilson, Doric. A Perfect Relationship. LC 83-61708. 98p. (Orig.). 1983. pap. 5.95 (ISBN 0-933322-12-7). Sea Horse.

Wilson, Dorothy C. I Will Be a Doctor! LC 83-3862. 160p. (Orig.). 1983. pap. 7.95 (ISBN 0-687-19727-9). Abingdon.

--Ten Fingers for God: The Complete Biography of Dr. Paul Brand. LC 82-24600. 288p. 1982. pap. 5.95 (ISBN 0-8407-5834-0). Nelson.
Wilson, Earl D. The Discovered Self. LC 84-28943. 1985. pap. 4.95 (ISBN 0-87784-331-7). Inter-Varsity.
--Does God Really Love Me? LC 86-10616. 96p. (Orig.). 1986. pap. 2.95 (ISBN 0-87784-514-X). Inter-Varsity.
--Empty Nest: Life after the Kids Leave Home. (Family Ministry Ser.). 96p. 1986. pap. 19.95 (ISBN 0-89191-969-4). Cook.
--Sexual Sanity. LC 83-22753. 156p. 1984. pap. 5.95 (ISBN 0-87784-919-6). Inter-Varsity.
--The Undivided Self: Bringing Your Whole Life in Line with God's Will. LC 83-6189. 191p. (Orig.). 1983. pap. 5.95 (ISBN 0-87784-842-4). Inter-Varsity.
Wilson, Edmund. Dead Sea Scrolls 1947-1969. 1969. 22.50x (ISBN 0-19-500665-8). Oxford U Pr.
--Israel & the Dead Sea Scrolls. 416p. 1978. pap. 9.25 (ISBN 0-374-51341-4). FS&G.
Wilson, Ella M. My Testimony. 70p. 1986. pap. 6.95 (ISBN 1-55523-060-1). Winston-Derek.
Wilson, Epiphanius. Sacred Books of the East. 464p. 1986. Repr. 25.00X (ISBN 0-8364-1764-X, Pub. by Usha). South Asia Bks.
Wilson, Epiphanius, intro. by. Hebrew Literature (Comprising of Talmudic Treatises, Hebrew Melodies & the Kabbalah Unveiled) 400p. 1986. Repr. of 1901 ed. PLB 60.00 (ISBN 0-89760-658-2). Telegraph Bks.
--Hindu Literature: Comprising the Book of Good Counsels, Nala & Damayanti, Sakoontala, the Ramayan, & Poems of Toru Dutt. 467p. 1986. Repr. of 1900 ed. PLB 95.00 (ISBN 0-89760-654-X). Telegraph Bks.
Wilson, Epiphanius, ed. The Wisdom of Confucius. 15.95 (ISBN 0-89190-545-6, Pub. by Am Repr). Amereon Ltd.
Wilson, Erica. Erica Wilson's Christmas World. (Illus.). 160p. 1982. pap. 11.95 (ISBN 0-684-17651-3, ScribT); 17.95 (ISBN 0-684-16672-0). Scribner.
Wilson, Ernest C. Like a Miracle. 202p. 1971. 5.95 (ISBN 0-87159-088-3). Unity School.
--Week That Changed the World. 1968. 5.95 (ISBN 0-87159-170-7). Unity School.
Wilson, Ernest T. The Farewell Ministry of Christ: John 13-17. LC 81-316. 96p. (Orig.). 1981. pap. 2.50 (ISBN 0-87213-965-4). Loizeaux.
--The Messianic Psalms. pap. 3.95 (ISBN 0-87213-963-8). Loizeaux.
Wilson, Evan M. Jerusalem, Key to Peace. LC 70-119026. (James Terry Duce Ser.: Vol. 2). 1970. 5.95 (ISBN 0-916808-08-4). Mid East Inst.
Wilson, Everett L. Christ Died for Me. 164p. 1980. pap. 4.50 (ISBN 0-910452-45-8). Covenant.
--Jesus & the End-Time. 1977. pap. 3.95 (ISBN 0-910452-32-6). Covenant.
Wilson, Frances, ed. & tr. The Love of Krishna: The Krsnakarnamrta of Lilasuka Bilvamangala. LC 74-153426. (Haney Foundation Ser.). 448p. 1975. 24.00x (ISBN 0-8122-7655-8). U of Pa Pr.
Wilson, Frank E. Faith & Practice. rev. ed. (Orig.). 1961. pap. 7.95 (ISBN 0-8192-1082-X). Morehouse.
Wilson, Geoffrey. Ephesians. 1978. pap. 4.95 (ISBN 0-85151-263-1). Banner of Truth.
--First Corinthians. 1978. pap. 4.95 (ISBN 0-85151-277-1). Banner of Truth.
--Galatians. 1979. pap. 4.95 (ISBN 0-85151-294-1). Banner of Truth.
--Hebrews. 1976. pap. 4.95 (ISBN 0-85151-278-X). Banner of Truth.
--Romans. 254p. 1977. pap. 5.45 (ISBN 0-85151-238-0). Banner of Truth.
--Second Corinthians. 1979. pap. 4.95 (ISBN 0-85151-295-X). Banner of Truth.
Wilson, Geoffrey B. Colossians & Philemon. (Wilson's New Testament Commentaries). 111p. (Orig.). 1980. pap. 4.95 (ISBN 0-85151-313-1). Banner of Truth.
--Philippians. 109p. (Orig.). 1983. pap. 4.95 (ISBN 0-85151-363-8). Banner of Truth.
Wilson, Gerald H. The Editing of the Hebrew Psalter. (Society of Biblical Literature Disseration Ser.: No. 76). 1985. pap. 11.50 (ISBN 0-89130-728-1). Scholars Pr GA.
Wilson, Gilbert L. The Horse & the Dog in Hidatsa Culture. LC 76-43895. (AMNH Anthropological Papers: Vol. 15, Pt. 2). Repr. of 1924 ed. 23.00 (ISBN 0-404-15751-3). AMS Pr.
Wilson, Grace H. The Religious & Educational Philosophy of the Young Women's Christian Association. LC 70-177632. (Columbia University. Teachers College. Contributions to Education: No. 554). Repr. of 1933 ed. 22.50 (ISBN 0-404-55554-3). AMS Pr.
Wilson, Guy H. That Ye May Know. 2.50 (ISBN 0-910924-47-3). Macalester.
Wilson, H. H. Religion of the Hindus. 416p. 1978. Repr. of 1862 ed. 13.95x (ISBN 0-89684-135-9). Orient Bk Dist.
--The Rig-Veda Sanhita, 7 vols. Incl. Vol. I. 348p. Repr. of 1850 ed (ISBN 0-89684-125-1); Vol. II. 346p. Repr. of 1854 ed (ISBN 0-89684-126-X); Vol. III. 249p. Repr. of 1857 ed (ISBN 0-89684-127-8); Vol. IV. 179p. Repr. of 1857 ed (ISBN 0-89684-128-6); Vol. V. 314p. Repr. of 1866 ed (ISBN 0-89684-129-4); Vol VI. 443p. Repr. of 1888 ed (ISBN 0-89684-130-8); Vol. VII. 436p. Repr. of 1888 ed (ISBN 0-89684-131-6). 1977. 120.00 set (ISBN 0-686-77518-X, Pub. by Cosmo Pubns India). Orient Bk Dist.
Wilson, Herman O. & Womack, Morris M. Pillars of Faith. 6.95 (ISBN 0-8010-9540-9); pap. 4.95 (ISBN 0-8010-9538-7). Baker Bk.
Wilson, Horace M., tr. see Hall, Fitzedward.
Wilson, Ian. Exodus: The True Story. LC 85-45727. 208p. 1986. 19.45 (ISBN 0-06-250969-1, HarpR). Har-Row.
--Jesus: The Evidence. LC 84-48234. (Illus.). 208p. 1985. 17.45 (ISBN 0-06-069433-5, HarpR). Har-Row.
--The Shroud of Turin: The Burial Cloth of Jesus Christ. LC 77-81551. (Illus.). 1979. pap. 5.50 (ISBN 0-385-15042-3, Im). Doubleday.
Wilson, J. Christy. Flaming Prophet: The Story of Samuel Zwemer. LC 76-130778. (Bold Believers Ser). (Orig.). 1970. pap. 0.95 (ISBN 0-377-84201-X). Friend Pr.
Wilson, J. Christy, Jr. Today's Tentmakers. 1979. pap. 5.95 (ISBN 0-8423-7279-2). Tyndale.
Wilson, J. Kinnier. The Legend of Etana. (Assyriology Ser.). (Illus.). 150p. 1985. pap. 36.00 (ISBN 0-86516-116-X). Bolchazy-Carducci.
Wilson, J. O. Way Out Is Up. (Redwood Ser.). 1982. pap. 2.95 (ISBN 0-8163-0450-5). Pacific Pr Pub Assn.
Wilson, J. V. The Legend of Etana. 140p. 1985. pap. text ed. 44.00 (ISBN 0-85668-258-6, Pub. by Aris & Phillips UK). Humanities.
Wilson, Jean. Crusader for Christ (Billy Graham) 1973. pap. 2.50 (ISBN 0-87508-602-0). Chr Lit.
Wilson, Jim. First Steps in Meditation for Young People. pap. 2.50 (ISBN 0-227-67458-8, Pub. by J Clarke U K). Attic Pr.
--Go Preach the Kingdom Heal the Sick. 127p. 1979. pap. text ed. 2.95 (ISBN 0-227-67659-9). Attic Pr.
--Growth in Prayer. 74p. 1969. pap. 2.95 (ISBN 0-227-67475-8). Attic Pr.
--Healing Through the Power of Christ. 64p. 1969. pap. 2.50 (ISBN 0-227-67478-2). Attic Pr.
--Meditation & the Fullness of Life. 76p. 1974. pap. text ed. 2.95 (ISBN 0-227-67810-9). Attic Pr.
Wilson, John. Discipline & Moral Education: A Survey of Public Opinion & Understanding. 160p. 1981. 22.00x (ISBN 0-85633-233-X, Pub. by NFER Nelson UK). Taylor & Francis.
--Philosophy & Religion: The Logic of Religious Belief. LC 78-14000. 1979. Repr. of 1961 ed. lib. bdg. 24.75x (ISBN 0-313-20738-0, WIPH). Greenwood.
Wilson, John & Cowell, Barbara. Dialogues on Moral Education. LC 83-4433. 170p. (Orig.). 1983. pap. 10.95 (ISBN 0-89135-035-7). Religious Educ.
Wilson, John & Drakeman, Donald, eds. Church & State in American History. 2nd, rev. ed. LC 86-47513. 288p. 1986. pap. 10.95 (ISBN 0-8070-0409-X, BP 728). Beacon Pr.
Wilson, John A. Culture of Ancient Egypt. LC 56-4923. (Illus.). 1956. pap. 7.95 (ISBN 0-226-90152-1, P11, Phoen). U of Chicago Pr.
Wilson, John B. & Natale, Samuel M. Education in Religious Understanding: A Report from the Foundation for Education in Religion & Morality. LC 86-28167. 86p. 1987. lib. bdg. 19.75 (ISBN 0-8191-5948-4); pap. text ed. 9.50 (ISBN 0-8191-5949-2). U Pr of Amer.
Wilson, John D. Leslie Stephen & Matthew Arnold As Critics of Wordsworth. LC 72-2060. (English Biography Ser., No. 31). 1972. Repr. of 1939 ed. lib. bdg. 40.95x (ISBN 0-8383-1455-4). Haskell.
Wilson, John F. Public Religion in American Culture. 240p. 1981. pap. 9.95 (ISBN 0-87722-226-6). Temple U Pr.
--Public Religion in American Culture. 240p. 1979. lib. bdg. 24.95 (ISBN 0-87722-159-6). Temple U Pr.
--Religion: A Preface. (Illus.). 240p. 1982. pap. text ed. write for info. (ISBN 0-13-773192-2). P-H.
Wilson, John F. & Mulder, John M. Religion in American History: Interpretive Essays. 448p. 1978. pap. text ed. write for info. (ISBN 0-13-771980-9). P-H.
Wilson, John F., ed. Church & State in America: A Bibliographical Guide (The Colonial & Early National Periods). LC 85-31698. 447p. 1986. 49.95 (ISBN 0-313-25236-X, WNC/). Greenwood.
Wilson, John F. & Slavens, Thomas P., eds. Research Guide to Religious Studies. LC 81-22862. (Sources of Information in the Humanities Ser.). 199p. 1982. lib. bdg. 22.50x (ISBN 0-8389-0330-4). ALA.
Wilson, John F., ed. see Ramsey, Paul.
Wilson, Ken. Decision to Love: What It Means to Love Others from the Heart. (Living As a Christian Ser.). 77p. (Orig.). 1980. pap. 2.50 (ISBN 0-89283-087-5). Servant.
--God First: What It Means to Love God Above All Things. (Living As a Christian Ser.). 85p. 1980. pap. 2.50 (ISBN 0-89283-089-1). Servant.
--How to Repair the Wrong You've Done. (Living As a Christian Ser.). 80p. 1982. pap. 2.25 (ISBN 0-89283-116-2). Servant.
--Sons & Daughters of God: Our New Identity in Christ. (Living As a Christian Ser.). 80p. (Orig.). 1981. pap. 2.50 (ISBN 0-89283-097-2). Servant.
--Your Money & Your Life: Practical Guidance for Earning, Managing & Giving Money. (Living as a Christian Ser.). 96p. (Orig.). 1983. pap. 2.95 (ISBN 0-89283-171-5). Servant.
Wilson, Knox, jt. auth. see Robinson, Herbert S.
Wilson, L. R. The New Testament Church: A Divine Institution. 1970. pap. 2.7500210895x (ISBN 0-88027-035-7). Firm Foun Pub.
Wilson, Lois. Like a Mighty River. (Illus.). 125p. (Orig.). 1981. pap. 6.95 (ISBN 0-919599-01-X). Wood Lake Pr.
Wilson, Mabel P., et al. Some Early Alabama Churches. 316p. 1973. 14.95x (ISBN 0-88428-029-2). Parchment Pr.
Wilson, Marion. Adventure of Living God's Will. 48p. 1980. pap. 1.50 (ISBN 0-89114-093-X); tchr's. ed. 1.00 (ISBN 0-89114-094-8). Baptist Pub Hse.
Wilson, Marlene. How to Mobilize Church Volunteers. LC 83-70506. 160p. (Orig.). 1983. pap. 8.95 (ISBN 0-8066-2012-9, 10-3175). Augsburg.
Wilson, Martin, ed. see Rabten, Geshe.
Wilson, Marvin R., jt. ed. see Tanenbaum, Marc H.
Wilson, Mary E., jt. auth. see Miller, Kenneth R.
Wilson, Michael, jt. auth. see Wuerl, Donald.
Wilson, Michael, tr. see Steiner, Rudolf.
Wilson, Michael L. Outline of Bible History & Major Christian Movements. 1974. pap. 4.95 (ISBN 0-88027-014-4). Firm Foun Pub.
Wilson, Monica. For Men & Elders: Change in the Relations of Generations & of Men & Women Among the Nyakyusa-Ngonde People, 1875-1971. LC 77-4203. 208p. 1978. 35.00x (ISBN 0-8419-0313-1, Africana). Holmes & Meier.
Wilson, Monica H. Religion & the Transformation of Society: A Study in Social Change in Africa. LC 73-134622. (The Scott Holland Memorial Lectures: 15; 1969). pap. 43.30 (ISBN 0-317-27081-8, 2024562). Bks Demand UMI.
Wilson, Nelly. Bernard-Lazare. LC 77-82524. 1979. 47.50 (ISBN 0-521-21802-0). Cambridge U Pr.
Wilson, Ostis B. Courtship & Marriage. 12p. 1976. pap. 0.15 (ISBN 0-686-36260-8). Faith Pub Hse.
--The Plan of Salvation. 64p. pap. 0.50 (ISBN 0-686-29160-3). Faith Pub Hse.
Wilson, Otto & Barratt, Robert S. Fifty Years' Work with Girls, 1883-1933: A Story of the Florence Crittenton Homes. LC 74-1717. (Children & Youth Ser.: Vol. 12). (Illus.). 513p. 1974. Repr. of 1933 ed. 44.00x (ISBN 0-405-05992-2). Ayer Co Pubs.
Wilson, Patricia. Have You Met My Divine Uncle George? 96p. (Orig.). pap. 5.95 (ISBN 0-8358-0529-8, Dist. by Abingdon Pr). Upper Room.
Wilson, Patricia F. Who Put All These Cucumbers in My Garden? LC 83-51398. 144p. (Orig.). 1984. pap. 5.50 (ISBN 0-8358-0475-5). Upper Room.
Wilson, Peter, jt. tr. see Chittick, William.
Wilson, Peter, tr. see Nurbakhsh, Javad.
Wilson, Prue. My Father Took Me to the Circus: Religious Life from Within. 144p. 1985. pap. 5.95 (ISBN 0-87193-218-0). Dimension Bks.
Wilson, R. A., tr. see Ebeling, Gerhard.
Wilson, R. A., tr. see Soggin, J. Alberto.
Wilson, R. McL., jt. ed. see Best, Ernest.
Wilson, Richard W., et al, eds. Moral Behavior in Chinese Society. LC 81-4581. 232p. 1981. 35.95 (ISBN 0-03-056922-2). Praeger.
Wilson, Robert, jt. auth. see Carroll, Jackson.
Wilson, Robert A. Prometheus Rising. LC 83-81665. 280p. 1983. pap. 7.95 (ISBN 0-941404-19-6). Falcon Pr Az.
Wilson, Robert J., III. The Benevolent Deity: Ebenezer Gay & the Rise of Rational Religion in New England, 1669-1787. LC 83-3657. (Illus.). 320p. 1984. 26.00x (ISBN 0-8122-7891-7). U of Pa Pr.
Wilson, Robert L. Shaping the Congregation. LC 80-22228. (Into Our Third Century Ser.). 144p. (Orig.). 1981. pap. 3.95 (ISBN 0-687-38334-X). Abingdon.
Wilson, Robert L., jt. auth. see Willimon, William H.
Wilson, Robert M. The Gnostic Problem. LC 78-63175. (Heresies of the Early Christian & Medieval Era: Second Ser.). Repr. of 1958 ed. 32.00 (ISBN 0-404-16193-6). AMS Pr.
Wilson, Robert R. Prophecy & Society in Ancient Israel. LC 78-14677. 336p. 1980. 11.95 (ISBN 0-8006-1814-9, 1-1814). Fortress.
--Sociological Approaches to the Old Testament. LC 83-16607. (Guides to Biblical Scholarship). 96p. 1984. pap. 4.50 (ISBN 0-8006-0469-5, 1-469). Fortress.
Wilson, Robert S. Marcion. LC 78-63176. (Heresies of the Early Christian & Medieval Era: Second Ser.). Repr. of 1933 ed. 32.00 (ISBN 0-404-16194-4). AMS Pr.
Wilson, Roger. Relief & Reconstruction. 1983. pap. 2.50x (ISBN 0-87574-022-7, 022). Pendle Hill.
Wilson, S. G. Luke & the Law. LC 83-7263. (Society for New Testament Studies Monograph: No. 50). 200p. 1984. 29.95 (ISBN 0-521-25284-9). Cambridge U Pr.
--Modern Movements among Moslems. 1977. lib. bdg. 59.95 (ISBN 0-8490-2270-3). Gordon Pr.
--Modern Movements among Moslems. LC 74-83190. (Islam & Mideast Ser.). 1976. Repr. of 1916 ed. 33.00 (ISBN 0-8420-1753-4). Scholarly Res Inc.
Wilson, Samuel & Aeschliman, Gordon. The Hidden Half: Discovering the World of Unreached Peoples. 1984. 5.50 (ISBN 0-912552-43-3). World Vision Intl.
Wilson, Samuel & Siewert, John. Mission Handbook. 13th ed. write for info. (ISBN 0-912552-55-7). Missions Adv Res Com Ctr.
Wilson, Samuel, jt. auth. see Dayton, Ed.
Wilson, Samuel G. Bahaism & Its Claims. LC 79-131493. Repr. of 1915 ed. 22.50 (ISBN 0-404-06995-9). AMS Pr.
--Persian Life & Customs. 3rd ed. LC 76-178305. Repr. of 1900 ed. 24.50 (ISBN 0-404-06996-7). AMS Pr.
Wilson, Samuel L. The Theology of Modern Literature. LC 76-47565. 1976. Repr. of 1899 ed. lib. bdg. 40.00 (ISBN 0-8414-9484-3). Folcroft.
Wilson, Seth. Learning from Jesus. Gardner, Lynn, ed. LC 77-155407. (The Bible Study Textbook Ser.). (Illus.). 1977. 15.90 (ISBN 0-89900-056-8). College Pr Pub.
Wilson, Stanley G. With the Pilgrims to Canterbury: And the History of the Hospital of St. Thomas. LC 70-178306. Repr. of 1934 ed. 14.50 (ISBN 0-404-06997-5). AMS Pr.
Wilson, Stephen. Ideology & Experience: Anti-Semitism in France at the Time of the Dreyfus Affair. (Littman Library of Jewish Civilization). (Illus.). 832p. 1982. 37.50x (ISBN 0-19-710052-X). Oxford U Pr.
--Ideology & Experience: Antisemitism in France at the Time of the Dreyfus Affair. LC 81-65467. (Illus.). 832p. 1982. 60.00 (ISBN 0-8386-3037-5). Fairleigh Dickinson.
Wilson, Stephen, ed. Anti-Judaism in Early Christianity, Vol. 2: Separation & Polemic. (Studies in Christianity & Judaism: Vol. 2.2). 200p. 1986. pap. text ed. 18.50 (ISBN 0-88920-196-X, Pub. by Wilfrid Laurier Canada). Humanities.
--Saints & Their Cults: Studies in Religious Sociology, Folklore & History. LC 82-25296. 416p. 1984. 62.50 (ISBN 0-521-24978-3). Cambridge U Pr.
--Saints & Their Cults: Studies in Religious Sociology, Folklore & History. 447p. 1986. pap. 19.95 (ISBN 0-521-31181-0). Cambridge U Pr.
Wilson, Stephen G. The Gentiles & the Gentile Mission In Luke-Acts. LC 72-90489. (Society for New Testament Studies, Monograpn Ser.: Vol. 23). pap. 76.80 (ISBN 0-317-26365-X, 2024566). Bks Demand UMI.
Wilson, T. Ernest. Mystery Doctrines of the New Testament: God's Sacred Secrets. LC 74-78881. 128p. 1975. pap. text ed. 2.50 (ISBN 0-87213-962-X). Loizeaux.
Wilson, T. W. The Key to Lasting Joy. 192p. 1987. 12.95 (ISBN 0-8499-0534-6). Word Bks.
Wilson, Theron D. Religion for Tomorrow. LC 62-9776. 148p. 1963. 5.95 (ISBN 0-8022-1897-0). Philos Lib.
Wilson, Thomas. St. Paul & Paganism. 1977. lib. bdg. 59.95 (ISBN 0-8490-2560-5). Gordon Pr.
Wilson, Thomas W., Jr., jt. auth. see Cleveland, Harlan.
Wilson, Valerie & Hull, Shirley, eds. Preschoolers Sing & Say. 1976. wire spiral 2.50 (ISBN 0-87227-045-9). Reg Baptist.
Wilson, Walter L. Wilson's Dictionary of Bible Types. 1957. pap. 10.95 (ISBN 0-8028-1453-0). Eerdmans.
Wilson, William. New Wilson's Old Testament Word Studies: Keyed to Strong's Numbering System & to the Theological Wordbook of Old Testament. rev. ed. LC 86-7210. 584p. 1987. 27.95 (ISBN 0-8254-4030-0); prepub. 24.95 until Oct. 1987. Kregel.

--Shakespeare & Astrology, from a Student's Point of View. LC 77-178308. Repr. of 1903 ed. 16.00 (ISBN 0-404-06998-3). AMS Pr.

Wilson, William P. Croitre dans la Grace. Orig. Title: The Grace to Grow. (Fr.). 1986. write for info. (ISBN 0-8297-0745-X). Life Pubs Intl.

--Graca para Crescer. Orig. Title: The Grace to Grow. (Port.). 1986. write for info. (ISBN 0-8297-0743-3). Life Pubs Intl.

Wilson, William P. & Slattery, Kathryn. El Poder Sanador de la Gracia. Llerena, Mario, ed. Bernal, Luis, tr. from Span. Orig. Title: The Grace to Grow. 176p. 1985. pap. text ed. 2.95 (ISBN 0-8297-0744-1). Life Pubs Intl.

Wilson, William W., tr. see Deissman, Adolph.

Wilson-Kastner, Patricia. Coherence in a Fragmented World: Jonathan Edwards' Theology of the Holy Spirit. LC 78-62667. 1978. pap. text ed. 8.50 (ISBN 0-8191-0587-2). U Pr of Amer.

--Faith, Feminism & the Christ. LC 83-5688. 160p. 1983. pap. 8.95 (ISBN 0-8006-1746-0). Fortress.

Wilson-Kastner, Patricia, et al. A Lost Tradition: Women Writers of the Early Church. LC 80-6290. 210p. (Orig.). 1981. lib. bdg. 25.00 (ISBN 0-8191-1642-4); pap. text ed. 11.50 (ISBN 0-8191-1643-2). U Pr of Amer.

Wilson-Ludlam, Mae. The Power Trio. 152p. 1981. Repr. of 1976 ed. soft cover 6.95 (ISBN 0-88053-765-5). Macoy Pub.

Wilson Story, Bettie. Gospel Trailblazer: The Exciting Story of Francis Asbury. 128p. 1984. pap. 6.95 (ISBN 0-687-15652-1). Abingdon.

Wilt, Matthew R., jt. ed. see Pilley, Catherine M.

Wilterdink, Garret. Tyrant or Father? A Study of Calvin's Doctrine of God. 185p. (Orig.). 1985. pap. 9.95 (ISBN 0-932269-19-2). Wyndham Hall.

Wiltgen, Ralph M. The Rhine Flows into the Tiber: A History of Vatican II. LC 82-50583. 304p. pap. 8.00 (ISBN 0-89555-186-1). Tan Bks Pubs.

Wimber, John & Springer, Kevin. Power Evangelism. 224p. 1986. 13.45 (ISBN 0-06-069532-3). Har-Row.

Wimberly, Edward P. Pastoral Counseling & Spiritual Values: A Black Point of View. LC 81-10918. 176p. (Orig.). 1982. pap. 7.75 (ISBN 0-687-30336-2). Abingdon.

Wimberly, Edward P. & Streaty, Anne. Liberation & Human Wholeness: The Conversion Experiences of Black People in Slavery & Freedom. 144p. (Orig.). 1986. pap. 10.95 (ISBN 0-687-21698-2). Abingdon.

Wimbish, Dave, jt. auth. see Testrake, John.

Wimbush, Vincent L. Paul, the World Ascetic: Response to the World & Self-Understanding According to 1 Corinthians 7. 128p. 1987. 18.95 (ISBN 0-86554-263-5, H224). Mercer Univ Pr.

Wimmer, John R. No Pain, No Gain: Hope for Those Who Struggle. 71p. 1985. 8.95 (ISBN 0-345-32181-2, Epiphany). Ballantine.

Wimmer, Joseph F. Fasting in the New Testament. LC 81-83183. 160p. (Orig.). 1982. pap. 8.95 (ISBN 0-8091-2420-3). Paulist Pr.

Winbery, Carlton L., jt. auth. see Brooks, James A.

Winburn, Wanda. Learning to Love like Jesus. Large Type ed. (Twenty-Six Children's Church Programs Ser.). (Illus.). 112p. 1984. 7.95 (ISBN 0-87239-708-4, 3319). Standard Pub.

Winch, Donald, ed. see Viner, Jacob.

Winch, Peter. Ethics & Action. (Studies in Ethics & the Philosophy of Religion). 240p. 1972. 20.00x (ISBN 0-7100-7438-7). Methuen Inc.

Winchell, Paul. God Two Thousand: Religion Without the Bible. LC 82-71878. 329p. 1982. 20.00 (ISBN 0-9608772-0-7). April Enterp.

Wind, Betty, jt. auth. see Bergey, Alyce.

Wind, Betty, jt. auth. see Forell, Betty.

Wind, Betty, jt. auth. see Latourette, Jane.

Wind, Betty, jt. auth. see Warren, Mary P.

Wind, Edgar. Pagan Mysteries in the Renaissance. rev. ed. (Illus.). 1969. pap. 7.95 (ISBN 0-393-00475-9, Norton Lib). Norton.

--Pagan Mysteries in the Renaissance. (Illus.). 1958. 75.00x (ISBN 0-686-83672-3). Elliots Bks.

Winden, Hans-Willi. Wie Kam und Wie Kommt Es Zum Osterglauben? (Disputationes Theologicae: Vol. 12). (Ger.). 352p. 1982. 39.45 (ISBN 3-8204-5820-4). P Lang Pubs.

Winding, Eleanor. Yoga for Musicians & Other Special People. (Illus.). 68p. (Orig.). 1982. pap. 7.95 (ISBN 0-88284-193-9). Alfred Pub.

Windischmann, Friedrich, jt. ed. see Geiger, Wilhelm.

Windle, Bertram C. Science & Morals, & Other Essays. facsimile ed. LC 70-156731. (Essay Index Reprint Ser). Repr. of 1919 ed. 17.00 (ISBN 0-8369-2301-4). Ayer Co Pubs.

Windolph, F. Lyman. Selected Essays. LC 72-186116. 1972. 7.50 (ISBN 0-685-36105-5). Franklin & Marsh.

Wine, J. Floyd. A History of Calvary Church of the Brethren. LC 72-95960. (Illus.). 1972. pap. 3.95 (ISBN 0-9604350-1-8). J F Wine.

Wine, Sherwin T. Judaism Beyond God. LC 85-61942. 286p. (Orig.). 1985. pap. 13.95 (ISBN 0-912645-08-3). Soc Humanistic.

--Judaism Beyond God: A Radical New to Be Jewish. 286p. 1986. pap. 13.95 (ISBN 0-87975-363-3). Prometheus Bks.

Winebrenner, Jan. Steel in His Soul: The Dick Hillis Story. (Orig.). 1985. pap. 7.95 (ISBN 0-8024-2202-0). Moody.

Wing, R. L. Tao of Power. LC 85-10210. (Illus.). 192p. 1986. pap. 12.50 (ISBN 0-385-19637-7, Dolp). Doubleday.

Wing, Richard A. Three A. M. Meditations for the Middle of the Night. LC 21-786068. 144p. (Orig.). 1985. pap. 9.95 (ISBN 0-934849-00-5). Arthur Pub.

Wingard, Ruth. The Spoken Words of Love. 1986. 6.95 (ISBN 0-533-06768-5). Vantage.

Wingate. Tilling the Soul. 1984. pap. 9.95 (ISBN 0-317-17441-X). Aurora Press.

Wingate, F. R. Mahdiism & Egyptian Sudan. 2nd ed. (Illus.). 618p. 1968. 45.00x (ISBN 0-7146-1738-5, F Cass Co). Biblio Dist.

Wingeier, Douglas E. Working Out Your Own Beliefs: A Guide for Doing Your Own Theology. LC 79-21097. (Orig.). 1980. pap. 4.95 (ISBN 0-687-46190-1). Abingdon.

Wing-hung Lam. Chinese Theology in Construction. LC 81-15483. 320p. 1983. pap. 11.95x (ISBN 0-87808-180-1). William Carey Lib.

Wingren, Gustaf. Creation & Gospel: The New Situation of European Theology. LC 78-78183. (Toronto Studies in Theology: Vol. 2). lii, 189p. 1979. pap. 39.95x (ISBN 0-88946-994-6). E Mellen.

Wink, Walter. The Bible in Human Transformation: Towards a New Paradigm for Biblical Study. LC 73-79047. 96p. (Orig.). 1980. pap. 4.95 (ISBN 0-8006-1034-2, 1-1034). Fortress.

--Naming the Powers: The Language of Power in the New Testament. LC 83-48905. (The Power Ser.: Vol. 1). 192p. 1984. pap. 14.95 (ISBN 0-8006-1786-X, 1-1786). Fortress.

--Transforming Bible Study: A Leader's Guide. LC 80-16019. 176p. 1980. pap. 7.95 (ISBN 0-687-42499-2). Abingdon.

--Unmasking the Powers: The Invisible Forces That Determine Human Existence. LC 85-45480. 224p. 1986. pap. 12.95 (ISBN 0-8006-1902-1, 1-1902). Fortress.

Winkelmann, John P., ed. The Catholic Pharmacist: 1985. (Vol. 18). 1985. 10.00. Natl Cath Pharm.

Winkler, Gabriele. Prayer Attitude in the Eastern Church. 1978. pap. 1.45 (ISBN 0-937032-01-8). Light&Life Pub Co MN.

Winkler, Gershon. Dybbuk. (Illus.). 1981. 13.95 (ISBN 0-910818-38-X); pap. 9.95 (ISBN 0-910818-37-1). Judaica Pr.

--The Golem of Prague. (Illus.). 1980. pap. 9.95 (ISBN 0-910818-25-8). Judaica Pr.

Winkler, Jude. Great People of the Bible. (Illus.). 160p. 1985. 11.95 (ISBN 0-89942-715-4). Catholic Bk Pub.

Winkler, Kenneth D. Pilgrim of the Clear Light: The Biography of Dr. Walter Y. Evans-Wentz. Govinda A., intro. by. LC 81-70193. (Illus.). 140p. (Orig.). 1982. pap. 4.95 (ISBN 0-942058-00-3). Dawnfire.

Winkler, Marion R. Church Polity: How the Clergy Run the Church. LC 82-91145. 271p. 1983. lib. bdg. 19.95 (ISBN 0-9610344-1-6); pap. 12.95 (ISBN 0-9610344-2-4). M R Winkler.

Winks, Robin W., ed. see Butterfield, Herbert.

Winkworth, Catherine. The Choral Hymn Book for England. 59.95 (ISBN 0-87968-859-9). Gordon Pr.

Winky-Lotz, H. I Owe My Life to Jesus -- You Also? An Autobiography Charismatic. (Illus.). 210p. 1986. 10.95 (ISBN 0-936112-00-X); pap. 6.50 (ISBN 0-936112-01-8). Willyshe Pub.

Winlock, Herbert E. Bas-Reliefs from the Temple of Rameses One at Abydos, 2 vols in 1. Incl. The Temple of Rameses One at Abydos. LC 72-2519. (Metropolitan Museum of Art Publications in Reprint). (Illus.). 1972. Repr. of 1937 ed. 20.00 (ISBN 0-685-32631-4). Ayer Co Pubs.

--The Tomb of Queen Meryet-Amun at Thebes: Metropolitan Museum of Art Egyptian Expedition Publication, Vol. 6. LC 70-168415. (Metropolitan Museum of Art Publication in Reprint). (Illus.). 204p. 1972. Repr. of 1932 ed. 32.00 (ISBN 0-405-02253-0). Ayer Co Pubs.

Winlock, Herbert E., jt. auth. see Mace, Arthur C.

Winlock, Herbert E., et al. The Monastery of Epiphanius at Thebes: Metropolitan Museum of Art Egyptain Expedition Publications, Vols. 3 & 4, 2 vols. LC 72-168413. (The Metropolitan Museum of Art Publication in Reprint Ser.). 1926. 88.00 set (ISBN 0-405-02249-2). Ayer Co Pubs.

Winn, Albert C. A Sense of Mission: Guidance from the Gospel of John. LC 80-28000. 118p. 1981. pap. 6.95 (ISBN 0-664-24365-7). Westminster.

Winn, Albert C., jt. auth. see Burgess, Joseph A.

Winn, Alison. Hello God. 1985. 3.95 (ISBN 0-87162-405-2, D4310). Warner Pr.

Winn, Dick. If God Won the War, Why Isn't It Over? McFarland, Ken, ed. (Harvest Ser.). 64p. 1982. pap. 4.95 (ISBN 0-8163-0467-X). Pacific Pr Pub Assn.

Winn, Herbert E., ed. see Wycliffe, John D.

Winner, Anna K. Basic Ideas of Occult Wisdom. LC 75-116528. (Orig.). 1970. pap. 4.50 (ISBN 0-8356-0391-1, Quest). Theos Pub Hse.

Winning, Hasso von see Von Winning, Hasso.

Winold, Allen, jt. auth. see Robinson, Ray.

Winquist, Charles, ed. The Archaeology of the Imagination. (JAAR Thematic Studies). 1981. pap. 11.95 (ISBN 0-89130-679-X, 01-24-82). Scholars Pr GA.

Winquist, Charles E. The Communion of Possibility. LC 75-859. (The Religions Quest Ser: Vol. 2). 160p. 1975. pap. text ed. 6.95x (ISBN 0-914914-04-9). New Horizons.

--Epiphanies of Darkness: Deconstruction in Theology. LC 85-45479. 144p. 1986. pap. 12.95 (ISBN 0-8006-1903-X, 1-1903). Fortress.

Winsberg, Morton D. Colonia Baron Hirsch: A Jewish Agricultural Colony in Argentina. LC 64-63523. (University of Florida Social Sciences Monographs: No. 19). 1963. pap. 3.50 (ISBN 0-8130-0259-1). U Presses Fla.

Winship, George P. Cambridge Press, Sixteen Thirty-Eight to Sixteen Ninety-Two. facs. ed. LC 68-57346. (Essay Index Reprint Ser). 1945. 22.50 (ISBN 0-8369-1004-4). Ayer Co Pubs.

Winslow, Donald F. The Dynamics of Salvation: A Study in Gregory of Nazianzus. LC 79-89897. (Patristic Mongraph: No. 7). 1979. pap. 8.50 (ISBN 0-915646-06-4). Phila Patristic.

Winslow, Donald F., ed. Disciplina Nostra: Essays in Memory of Robert F. Evans. LC 79-89556. (Patristic Monograph: No. 6). (Orig.). 1979. pap. 8.50 (ISBN 0-915646-05-6). Phila Patristic.

Winslow, Miron. Memoir of Mrs. Harriet L. Winslow, Thirteen Years a Member of the American Mission in Ceylon. Gifford, Carolyn D. & Dayton, Donald, eds. (Women in American Protestant Religion 1800-1930 Ser.). 480p. 1987. lib. bdg. 70.00 (ISBN 0-8240-0684-4). Garland Pub.

Winslow, Octavius. Personal Declension & Revival of Religion in the Soul. 1978. pap. 3.95 (ISBN 0-85151-261-5). Banner of Truth.

--Work of the Holy Spirit. 223p. 1984. pap. 5.45 (ISBN 0-85151-152-X). Banner of Truth.

Winslow, Ola E. Meetinghouse Hill, Sixteen Thirty to Seventy Eighty-Three. 1972. pap. 2.95x (ISBN 0-393-00632-8, Norton Lib). Norton.

Winsnes, Andreas H. Sigrid Undset: A Study in Christian Realism. Foote, P. G., tr. LC 74-110276. (Illus.). ix, 258p. Repr. of 1953 ed. lib. bdg. 22.50x (ISBN 0-8371-4502-3, WISU). Greenwood.

Winston, Clara, tr. see Arendt, Hannah.

Winston, Clara, tr. see Hochhuth, Rolf.

Winston, Clara, tr. see Pieper, Josef.

Winston, Clara, tr. see Pieper, Josef, et al.

Winston, Clara, tr. see Schweitzer, Albert.

Winston, David. The Wisdom of Solomon. LC 78-18150. (Anchor Bible Ser.: Vol. 43). 1979. 16.00 (ISBN 0-385-01644-1, Anchor Pr). Doubleday.

Winston, David & Dillon, John. Two Treatises of Philo of Alexandria: A Commentary on De Gigantibus & Quod Deus Sit Immutabilis. LC 82-786. (Brown Judaic Studies). 416p. 1983. pap. 15.00 (ISBN 0-89130-563-7, 14 00 25). Scholars Pr GA.

Winston, David, tr. Philo of Alexandria: The Contemplative Life, Giants & Selections. LC 80-84499. (Classics of Western Spirituality Ser.). 448p. 13.95 (ISBN 0-8091-0315-X); pap. 9.95 (ISBN 0-8091-2333-9). Paulist Pr.

Winston Press Editorial Staff, ed. see Nilsen, Mary Y.

Winston Press Editorial Staff. Joy Six. rev. ed. (Joy Religious Ser.). 1979. pap. 5.87 (ISBN 0-86683-036-7, 665, HarpR); tchr's. ed. 8.95 (ISBN 0-86683-046-4). Har-Row.

Winston, Richard, tr. see Arendt, Hannah.

Winston, Richard, tr. see Hochhuth, Rolf.

Winston, Richard, tr. see Pieper, Josef.

Winston, Richard, tr. see Pieper, Josef, et al.

Winston, Richard, tr. see Schweitzer, Albert.

Winston Staff. Joy Five. rev. ed. (Joy Religion Ser.). (Illus.). 1978. pap. text ed. 5.87 (ISBN 0-86683-035-9, HarpR); tchr's. manual 8.95 (ISBN 0-03-041871-2). Har-Row.

--Joy Four. rev. ed. (Joy Religion Ser.). (Illus.). 1978. pap. text ed. 5.87 (ISBN 0-86683-034-0, HarpR); tchr's. manual 8.95 (ISBN 0-86683-044-8). Har-Row.

Winstone, Harold. Gospel for Young Christians. (Illus.). 192p. 1985. 3.95 (ISBN 0-225-27392-6, HarpR). Har-Row.

Winter, David. Believing the Bible. LC 82-62582. 116p. (Orig.). 1983. pap. 5.95 (ISBN 0-8192-1325-X). Morehouse.

--Closer Than a Brother. LC 71-181991. (Illus.). 160p. 1976. pap. 3.50 (ISBN 0-87788-129-4). Shaw Pubs.

--Faith under Fire: One Hundred Dynamic Readings from Great Men of the Early Church. LC 77-92353. (Daystar Devotional). Orig. Title: One Hundred Days in the Arena. 112p. 1981. pap. 2.95 (ISBN 0-87788-252-5). Shaw Pubs.

--Living Through Loss: God's Help in Bereavement. 96p. (Orig.). 1986. pap. 3.50 (ISBN 0-87788-507-9). Shaw Pubs.

--The Search for the Real Jesus. 160p. (Orig.). 1982. pap. 6.95 (ISBN 0-8192-1318-7). Morehouse.

--Walking into Light. 160p. 1986. pap. 3.50 (ISBN 0-87788-916-3). Shaw Pubs.

Winter, Dina S. & Richards, Theodora. Toward Freedom in Singing. 1986. pap. 4.50 (ISBN 0-916786-84-6). St George Bk Serv.

Winter, Gibson. Liberating Creation: Foundations of Religious Social Ethics. LC 81-5364. 1981. 12.95 (ISBN 0-8245-0032-6). Crossroad NY.

Winter, Jack, jt. auth. see Riggins, John.

Winter, Jakob, jt. auth. see Lazarus, M.

Winter, Michael. Society & Religion in Early Ottoman Egypt. LC 81-3042. 350p. 1981. 39.95 (ISBN 0-87855-351-7). Transaction Bks.

Winter, Michael M. Saint Peter & the Popes. LC 78-21507. 1979. Repr. of 1960 ed. lib. bdg. cancelled (ISBN 0-313-21158-2, WISP). Greenwood.

Winter, Miriam T. Why Sing? Toward a Theology of Catholic Church Music. 346p. (Orig.). 1984. pap. 11.95 (ISBN 0-912405-07-4). Pastoral Pr.

Winter, Paul. On the Trial of Jesus. 2nd ed. Burkill, T. A. & Vermes, G., eds. (Studia Judaica, Vol. 1). 1973. 31.00x (ISBN 3-11-002283-4). De Gruyter.

Winter, Ralph. Word Study New Testament & Concordance. 1978. text ed. 39.95 (ISBN 0-8423-8390-5). Tyndale.

Winter, Ralph, frwd. by. I Will Do a New Thing: The Story of the U. S. Center for World Mission. rev. ed. LC 78-66367. Orig. Title: Once More Around Jericho. 320p. 1987. pap. 4.95 (ISBN 0-87808-201-8). William Carey Lib.

Winter, Ralph D. & Hawthorne, Steven C., eds. Perspectives on the World Christian Movement: A Reader. LC 81-69924. (Illus.). 864p. (Orig.). 1981. pap. 14.95x (ISBN 0-87808-189-5). William Carey Lib.

Winter, Rebecca J. The Night Cometh: Two Wealthy Evangelicals Face the Nation. LC 77-87594. 1977. pap. 2.95 (ISBN 0-87808-429-0). William Carey Lib.

Winter, Terry. Evidence: The Truth about Christianity. rev. ed. LC 79-87769. 1979. pap. 2.25 (ISBN 0-89081-067-2, 2039). Harvest Hse.

Winter, Willard W. Studies in First & Second Samuel. LC 70-1508. (The Bible Study Textbook Ser.). 1967. 15.90 (ISBN 0-89900-011-8). College Pr Pub.

--Studies in Joshua, Judges, Ruth. (The Bible Study Textbook Ser.). (Illus.). 1969. 15.90 (ISBN 0-89900-010-X). College Pr Pub.

Winterhalter, Curt, ed. see Schneider, Reinhold.

Winterhalter, Robert. The Odes of Solomon: Original Christianity Revealed. Roche de Coppens, Peter, et al, eds. LC 85-45288. (Spiritual Perspectives Ser.). 240p. (Orig.). 1985. pap. 9.95 (ISBN 0-87542-875-4, L-875). Llewellyn Pubns.

Winternitz, M. Index. (Sacred Bks. of the East: Vol. 50). 15.00 (ISBN 0-89581-535-4). Asian Human Pr.

Winters, Mary S. Divorce Law: A Concise Guide for Clergy & Laity. 32p. (Orig.). 1986. pap. 1.95 (ISBN 0-8298-0740-3). Pilgrim NY.

Winters, Sandy & Brooks, Shirley. Flames of Power: A Study of Meditation, Candles & Special Insights. 64p. 1987. pap. 6.50 (ISBN 0-89540-164-9, SB-164). Sun Pub.

Winters, Ted & Janssen, Al. Lifer. (Living Books). 320p. 1985. pap. 3.95 (ISBN 0-8423-2142-X). Tyndale.

Winters, William, ed. Conservacion de Convertidos. (Span.). 120p. 1980. pap. 3.95 (ISBN 0-87148-182-0). Pathway Pr.

Winters, William E. Convert Conservation. 120p. pap. 4.25 (ISBN 0-87148-161-8). Pathway Pr.

Winton-Henry, Cynthia. Dancing God's People into the Year Two Thousand: A Critical Look at Dance Performance in the Church. Adams, Doug, ed. & intro. by. (Orig.). 1985. pap. 3.00 (ISBN 0-941500-36-5). Sharing Co.

--Leaps of Faith: Improvisational Dance in Worship & Education. Adams, Doug, ed. 1985. pap. 3.00 (ISBN 0-941500-33-0). Sharing Co.

Winward, Stephen F. Fruit of the Spirit. 208p. (Orig.). 1984. pap. 4.95 (ISBN 0-8028-0003-3). Eerdmans.

--Guide to the Prophets. LC 68-55819. 1976. pap. 8.95 (ISBN 0-8042-0131-5). John Knox.

Winzet, Ninian. Certane Tractatis for Reformatioun of Doctryne & Maneris in Scotland. LC 79-178311. (Maitland Club, Glasgow Publications: No. 33). Repr. of 1835 ed. 20.00 (ISBN 0-404-53001-X). AMS Pr.

Wippel, John F. Metaphysical Themes in Thomas Aquinas. LC 82-7296. (Studies in Philosophy & the History of Philosophy: Vol. 10). 294p. 1984. 31.95x (ISBN 0-8132-0578-6). Cath U Pr.

--The Metaphysical Thought of Godfrey of Fontaines: A Study in Late Thirteenth-Century Philosophy. LC 80-16900. 413p. 1981. 31.95x (ISBN 0-8132-0556-5). Cath U Pr.

Wippel, John F. & Wolter, Allen B., eds. Medieval Philosophy: From St. Augustine to Nicholas of Cusa. LC 69-10043. 1969. pap. text ed. 14.95 (ISBN 0-02-935650-4). Free Pr.

Wippler, M. Gonzalez, ed. New Revised Sixth & Seventh Books of Moses & the Magical Use of the Psalms. pap. 6.95 (ISBN 0-942272-02-1). Original Pubns.

Wirt, Sherwood & Beckstrom, Kristen. Topical Encyclopedia of Living Quotations. LC 82-4503. 290p. 1982. pap. 7.95 (ISBN 0-87123-574-9, 210574). Bethany Hse.

Wirt, Sherwood E. The Confessions of Augustine in Modern English. Link, Julie, ed. 144p. 1986. pap. 5.95 (ISBN 0-310-34641-X). Zondervan.

--Faith's Heroes. LC 78-71943. 1979. pap. 3.95 (ISBN 0-89107-162-8, Crossway Bks). Good News.

Wirt, Sherwood E., ed. Spiritual Awakening: Classic Writings of the Eighteenth Century to Inspire the Twentieth Century Reader. LC 86-70283. 256p. (Orig.). 1986. pap. 8.95 (ISBN 0-89107-394-9, Crossway Bks). Good News.

Wirth, Morand. Don Bosco & the Salesians. DeBurgh, David, tr. from Italian. LC 82-72675. Orig. Title: Don Bosco e i Salesiani. 432p. (Orig.). 1982. pap. 10.95 (ISBN 0-89944-065-7). Don Bosco Multimedia.

Wirz, Paul. Die Marind-Anim Von Hollandischsud-Neu-Guinea, 2 vols. in 1. Bolle, Kees W., ed. (Mythology Ser.). (Ger.). 1978. Repr. of 1922 ed. lib. bdg. 54.00x (ISBN 0-405-10569-X). Ayer Co Pubs.

Wise, Charles C., Jr. The Magian Gospel of Brother Yeshua. LC 79-84277. (Illus.). 306p. 1979. 11.95 (ISBN 0-917023-05-6); pap. 5.95 (ISBN 0-917023-06-4). Magian Pr.

--Mind Is It: Meditation, Prayer, Healing, & the Psychic. LC 77-82923. 191p. (Orig.). 1978. pap. 3.75 (ISBN 0-917023-02-1). Magian Pr.

--Picture Windows on the Christ. LC 78-69928. (Illus.). 354p. 1979. 11.95 (ISBN 0-917023-03-X); pap. 5.95 (ISBN 0-917023-04-8). Magian Pr.

--Thus Saith the Lord: The Autobiography of God. LC 84-60414. 293p. (Orig.). 1984. pap. 7.95 (ISBN 0-917023-07-2). Magian Pr.

Wise, Donald, rev. by see Wuest, Kenneth.

Wise, Isaac. Reminiscences. Philipson, David, ed. LC 73-2233. (The Jewish People; History, Religion, Literature Ser.). Repr. of 1901 ed. 30.00 (ISBN 0-405-05294-4). Ayer Co Pubs.

Wise, James W. Jews Are Like That. facs. ed. LC 70-84348. (Essay Index Reprint Ser). 1928. 16.75 (ISBN 0-8369-1114-8). Ayer Co Pubs.

Wise, Jennings C. see Meade, William.

Wise, John. Churches Quarrel Espoused, 1713. LC 66-10006. 1966. 35.00x (ISBN 0-8201-1052-3). Schol Facsimiles.

--Vindication of the Government of New-England Churches. Miller, Perry, ed. LC 58-5422. Repr. of 1717 ed. 30.00x (ISBN 0-8201-1246-1). Schol Facsimiles.

Wise, Louise W., tr. see Fleg, Edmond.

Wise, Louise W., tr. see Palliere, Aime.

Wise, Melvin J. Survey of the Life of Christ, 2 vols. 2.50 ea.; Vol. 1. (ISBN 0-89315-288-9); Vol. 2. (ISBN 0-89315-289-7). Lambert Bk.

Wise, Philip, jt. auth. see Humphreys, Fisher.

Wise, Robert. The Pastors' Barracks. 192p. 1986. pap. 11.95 (ISBN 0-89693-157-9). Victor Bks.

Wise, Robert, et al. The Church Divided. LC 86-71132. 1986. pap. 5.95 (ISBN 0-88270-622-5). Bridge Pub.

Wise, Robert L. Healing of the Past. 40p. 1984. 2.00 (ISBN 0-318-04134-0). Presby Renewal Pubns.

--When There Is No Miracle. LC 77-89394. 176p. 1978. pap. 4.95 (ISBN 0-8307-0582-1, 5408008); study guide o.p. 1.39 (ISBN 0-8307-0651-8, 6101518). Regal.

Wise, Stephen S., ed. see Ibn-Gabirol, Solomon B.

Wiseman, D. J. Nebuchadrezzar & Babylon. (British Academy - Schweich Lectures). (Illus.). 144p. 1986. 34.50x (ISBN 0-19-726040-3). Oxford U Pr.

Wiseman, D. J., jt. auth. see Carr, G. Lloyd.

Wiseman, D. J., jt. auth. see Harrison, R. K.

Wiseman, D. J. & Millard, A. R., eds. Essays on the Patriarchal Narratives. 1983. text ed. 17.50x (ISBN 0-931464-13-7); pap. 9.95 (ISBN 0-931464-12-9). Eisenbrauns.

Wiseman, D. J., ed. see Andersen, Francis I.

Wiseman, D. J., ed. see Baldwin, Joyce G.

Wiseman, D. J., ed. see Eaton, Michael A.

Wiseman, D. J., ed. see Kidner, Derek.

Wiseman, D. J., jt. ed. see Paterson, J. H.

Wiseman, D. J., ed. see Thompson, J.

Wiseman, D. J., ed. see Wenham, Gordon J.

Wiseman, D. J., ed. see Wiseman, P. J.

Wiseman, Lawrence. Discipling for Jesus. LC 83-70959. 1983. pap. 4.95 (ISBN 0-89900-199-8). College Pr Pub.

Wiseman, Luke H. Practical Truths From Judges. LC 85-8096. 354p. 1985. 14.95 (ISBN 0-8254-4034-3). Kregel.

Wiseman, Neil B., ed. Evangelism: One Hundred Thirty-Nine Ideas & Quotes. 110p. (Orig.). 1983. pap. 3.50 (ISBN 0-8341-0889-5). Beacon Hill.

Wiseman, P. J. Ancient Records & the Structure of Genesis. Wiseman, D. J., ed. 160p. 1985. pap. 6.95 (ISBN 0-8407-7502-4). Nelson.

Wishart, Alfred W. A History of Monks & Monasteries. 1977. lib. bdg. 59.95 (ISBN 0-8490-1980-X). Gordon Pr.

Wishnitzer, Mark, ed. see Greenberg, Louis.

Wisler, G. Clifton. A Special Gift. (Voyager Ser.). 80p. 1983. pap. 3.50 (ISBN 0-8010-9661-8). Baker Bk.

Wisley, Thomas N., jt. ed. see Kraft, Charles H.

Wisloff, Fredrik. The Evening of Life. LC 66-12386. pap. 35.00 (2027868). Bks Demand UMI.

--On Our Father's Knee: Devotions for Times of Illness. LC 72-90264. 144p. 1973. pap. 5.95 (ISBN 0-8066-1309-2, 10-4765). Augsburg.

Wismar, Adolph L. Study in Tolerance As Practiced by Muhammed & His Immediate Successors. LC 27-24455. (Columbia University. Contributions to Oriental History & Philology: No. 13). Repr. of 1927 ed. 14.00 (ISBN 0-404-50543-0). AMS Pr.

Wismer, Don. The Islamic Jesus: An Annotated Bibliography of Sources in English & French. LC 76-24737. (Reference Library of the Humanities Ser.: Vol. 58). 1977. lib. bdg. 40.00 (ISBN 0-8240-9940-0). Garland Pub.

Wisse, Frederik. The Profile Method for Classifying & Evaluating Manuscript Evidence. 140p. 1982. pap. 17.00x (ISBN 0-8028-1918-4). Eerdmans.

Wissel, Joseph. The Redemptorist on the American Missions, 3 vols. In 2. 115.00 (ISBN 0-405-10867-2). Ayer Co Pubs.

Wissing, Paula, tr. see Valeri, Valerio.

Wissler, Clark. Social Organization & Ritualistic Ceremonies of the Blackfoot Indians, 2 parts in 1 vol. LC 74-9020. (Anthropological Papers of the American Museum of Natural History: Vol. 7). (Illus.). Repr. of 1912 ed. 24.00 (ISBN 0-404-11917-4). AMS Pr.

Wissler, Clark & Duvall, D. C. Mythology of the Blackfoot Indians. LC 74-9019. (Anthropological Papers of the American Museum of Natural History: Vol. 2, Pt. 1). (Illus.). Repr. of 1909 ed. 17.00 (ISBN 0-404-11916-6). AMS Pr.

Wissowa, Georg. Gesammelte Abhandlungen Zur Romischen Religions und Stadtgeschichte. facsimile ed. LC 75-10663. (Ancient Religion & Mythology Ser.). (Ger.). 1976. Repr. of 1904 ed. 25.50x (ISBN 0-405-07279-1). Ayer Co Pubs.

Wister, Sally. Sally Wister's Journal: A True Narrative Being a Quaker Maiden's Account of Her Experiences with Officers of the Continental Army, 1777-1778. Myers, Albert C., ed. LC 73-78039. (Eyewitness Accounts of the American Revolution Ser., No. 2). 1969. Repr. of 1902 ed. 16.00 (ISBN 0-405-01169-5). Ayer Co Pubs.

Wistrich, Robert. Hitler's Apocalypse: Jews & the Nazi Legacy. 352p. 1986. 17.95 (ISBN 0-312-38819-5). St Martin.

Wistrich, Robert S. Socialism & the Jews: The Dilemmas of Assimilation in Germany & Austria-Hungary. (Littman Library of Jewish Civilization). 1982. 37.50x (ISBN 0-19-710053-8). Oxford U Pr.

Wiswedel, Wilhelm. Bilder und Fuehrergestalten Aus Dem Taeufertum: Dritter Band ein Beitrag Zur Reformationsgeschichte Des Sechszehnten Jahrhunderts. (Ger.). 231p. 1952. pap. 2.00x (ISBN 0-8361-1154-0). Herald Pr.

Wither, George. Exercises Upon the First Psalm. 1882. 29.50 (ISBN 0-8337-3836-4). B Franklin.

--Hymnes & Songs of the Church. (1623, 1881 Reprint 1967). 54.00 (ISBN 0-8337-3937-9). B Franklin.

--Preparation to the Psalter. 1884. Repr. of 1619 ed. 30.50 (ISBN 0-8337-3850-X). B Franklin.

--The Psalmes of David, 2 vols. in 1. 1967. Repr. of 1632 ed. 89.00 (ISBN 0-8337-3838-0). B Franklin.

Witherby, H. Forbes. The Gospel of Our Salvation. 254p. 1986. 9.95 (ISBN 0-8254-4026-2). Kregel.

Witherington, Ben. Women in the Ministry of Jesus: A Study of Jesus' Attitude to Women & Their Roles As Reflected in His Earthly Life. LC 83-18957. (Society for the New Testament Studies Monograph: No. 51). 210p. 1984. 29.95 (ISBN 0-521-25658-5). Cambridge U Pr.

Withers, Frederick C. Church Architecture. 1980. lib. bdg. 64.95 (ISBN 0-8490-3198-2). Gordon Pr.

Witherspoon, Jet. Acts. LC 86-25414. 192p. (Orig.). 1972. pap. 4.95 (ISBN 0-912315-34-2). Word Aflame.

Witherspoon, John. An Annotated Edition of Lectures on Moral Philosophy. Scott, Jack, ed. LC 80-24404. 213p. 1981. 27.50 (ISBN 0-87413-164-2). U Delaware Pr.

--Lectures on Moral Philosophy. Collins, Varnum L., ed. LC 75-3424. Repr. of 1912 ed. 12.00 (ISBN 0-404-59420-4). AMS Pr.

Witmer, Edith. God's Happy Family. (Jewel Bks.). 1986. pap. 1.95. Rod & Staff.

Witmer, Joseph W. & Wright, J. Robert, eds. Called to Full Unity: Documents on Anglican-Roman Catholic Relations 1966-1983. 358p. 1986. pap. 14.95 (ISBN 1-55586-937-8). US Catholic.

Witmore, Nyla. Homemaking Programs, Talks & Activities. LC 82-5626. (Illus.). 160p. (Orig.). 1982. pap. 4.95 (ISBN 0-87239-565-0, 2973). Standard Pub.

--How to Reach the Ones You Love: Help for the Family. LC 81-81849. 180p. (Orig.). 1981. pap. 5.95 (ISBN 0-89840-016-3). Campus Crusade.

Witt, James G., III. Deadly Deceptions. Fischer, William E., ed. (Illus.). 64p. (Orig.). 1987. pap. text ed. 2.95 (ISBN 0-938272-32-2); leaders guide 2.95. Wels Board.

Witt, Mason de see Carman, George.

Witt, Roselyn. W. Norman Cooper: A View of a Holy Man. LC 81-70657. 96p. 1982. 7.50 (ISBN 0-87516-492-7); pap. 4.50 (ISBN 0-87516-471-4). De Vorss.

Witt, Roy L. de see De Witt, Roy L.

Witte, Kaaren. Angels in Faded Jeans. LC 79-84795. 160p. 1979. pap. 3.95 (ISBN 0-87123-014-3, 210014). Bethany Hse.

--Great Leaps in a Single Bound. LC 82-4163. 96p. (Orig.). 1982. pap. 3.95 (ISBN 0-87123-199-9, 210199). Bethany Hse.

Witte, Nancy I., ed. Rising above Strife. pap. 4.95 (ISBN 0-89137-424-8). Quality Pubns.

Wittenback, Janet. God Makes Me His Child in Baptism. LC 85-7689. 24p. 1985. pap. 2.95 (ISBN 0-570-04126-0, 56-1537). Concordia.

Wittenmyer, Annie T. Woman's Work for Jesus. Gifford, Carolyn D. & Dayton, Donald, eds. (Women in American Protestant Religion 1800-1930 Ser.). 240p. 1987. lib. bdg. 35.00 (ISBN 0-8240-0685-2). Garland Pub.

Witter, Evelyn. How to Make Sunday School Fun for Everyone. Ronaldson, Dolores, ed. LC 82-62793. (Illus.). 80p. 1983. pap. text ed. 6.95 (ISBN 0-916260-22-4). Meriwether Pub.

Wittgenstein, Ludwig. Wittgenstein: Lectures & Conversations on Aesthetics, Psychology, & Religious Belief. Barrett, Cyril, ed. 1967. pap. 3.50 (ISBN 0-520-01354-9, CAL83). U of Cal Pr.

Wittkower, Rudolf. Allegory & the Migration of Symbols. LC 86-50689. (Illus.). 224p. 1987. pap. 14.95 (ISBN 0-500-85004-6). Thames Hudson.

--Gothic Vs. Classic: Architectural Projects in Seventeenth-Century Italy. LC 73-79607. (Illus.). 192p. 1974. 12.50 (ISBN 0-8076-0704-5); pap. 4.95 (ISBN 0-8076-0705-3). Braziller.

Wittkowski, Wolfgang. Heinrich Von Kleist: Amphithryon Materialien zur Rezeption und Interpretation. 1978. 40.40x (ISBN 3-11-006988-1). De Gruyter.

Wittlinger, Carlton O. Quest for Piety & Obedience: The Story of the Brethren in Christ. LC 77-94894. 1978. 12.95 (ISBN 0-916035-05-0). Evangel Indiana.

Wittman, Debbie D. The Birth of the Baha'i Faith. (Illus., Orig.). 1980. pap. 1.95 (ISBN 0-87743-146-9, 352-055). Baha'i.

Wittreich, Joseph A., Jr. Angel of Apocalypse: Blake's Idea of Milton. LC 74-27316. 358p. 1975. 37.50x (ISBN 0-299-06800-5). U of Wis Pr.

--Visionary Poetics: Milton's Tradition & His Legacy. LC 78-52569. (Illus.). 324p. 1979. 29.95 (ISBN 0-87328-101-2). Huntington Lib.

Wittreich, Joseph A., Jr., jt. ed. see Curran, Stuart.

Wittreich, Joseph A., Jr., ed. see Meadowcourt, Richard.

Wittreich, Joseph A., Jr., jt. ed. see Patrides, C. A.

Wittwer, Norman C., Jr. The Faithful & the Bold: The Story of the First Service of the Zion Evangelical Lutheran Church, Oldwick, New Jersey. (Illus.). 46p. 1984. 10.00x (ISBN 0-913186-10-4). Monocacy.

Witvliet, Theo. A Place in the Sun: Liberation Theology in the Third World. Bowden, John, tr. from Dutch. LC 84-27229. Tr. of Fen Plaats onder de zon Bevrijdingstheologie in de Derde Wereld. 208p. (Orig.). 1985. pap. 8.95 (ISBN 0-88344-404-6). Orbis Bks.

Witzenmann, Herbert. Beppe Assenza. (Illus.). 160p. 1979. 29.95 (ISBN 0-85440-340-X, Pub. by Steinerbooks). Anthroposophic.

Wlodyga, Ronald R. Health Secrets from the Bible. LC 79-64042. 1979. pap. 5.95 (ISBN 0-917182-12-X). Triumph Pub.

Wock, E. W. The Bible in English Literature. 69.95 (ISBN 0-87968-727-4). Gordon Pr.

Wodrow, Robert. Analecta, 4 Vols. LC 74-178318. (Maitland Club, Glasgow. Publications: No. 60). Repr. of 1843 ed. Set. 175.00 (ISBN 0-404-53051-6). AMS Pr.

--Collections Upon the Lives of the Reformers & Most Eminent Ministers of the Church of Scotland, 2 Vols. in 3 Pts. LC 70-178317. (Maitland Club, Glasgow. Publications: No. 32). Repr. of 1848 ed. Set. 105.00 (ISBN 0-404-52993-3). AMS Pr.

Wofford, Nat, ed. Showers of Blessings: Hymns for the Shower. 16p. 1986. pap. 4.95 (ISBN 0-942820-18-5). Steam Pr MA.

Wogaman, J. P. Economics & Ethics: A Christian Inquiry. LC 85-45478. 160p. 1986. pap. 9.95 (ISBN 0-8006-1904-8). Fortress.

Wogaman, J. Philip. A Christian Method of Moral Judgment. LC 76-40108. 282p. 1977. pap. 8.95 (ISBN 0-664-24134-4). Westminster.

--Faith & Fragmentation: Christianity for a New Age. LC 85-47712. 208p. 1985. pap. 10.95 (ISBN 0-8006-1864-5, 1-1864). Fortress.

--The Great Economic Debate: An Ethical Analysis. LC 77-3870. 192p. 1977. 10.95 (ISBN 0-664-20780-4); pap. 9.95 (ISBN 0-664-24141-7). Westminster.

Wogaman, J. Philip, jt. auth. see McCleary, Paul.

Wogaman, Philip J., ed. Population Crisis & Moral Responsibility. 1973. 15.00 (ISBN 0-8183-0146-5). Pub Aff Pr.

Woggon, Guillermo. Versiculos "Llave". Granberry, Nola, tr. (Libros Para Colorear). Tr. of Key Bible Verses. (Span., Illus.). 16p. 1985. pap. 1.25 (ISBN 0-311-38565-6). Casa Bautista.

Wohl, Louis De see De Wohl, Louis.

Wohlgemuth, Paul W. Rethinking Church Music. rev. ed. LC 80-85254. 112p. 1981. pap. 5.95 (ISBN 0-916642-15-1). Hope Pub.

Wohrer, Franz K. Thomas Traherne's 'The Growth of a Mystic's Mind: A Study of the Evolution & the Phenomenology of Traherne's Mystical Consciousness. Hogg, James, ed. (Elizabethan & Renaissance Studies). 207p. (Orig.). 1982. pap. 15.00 (ISBN 3-7052-0747-4, Pub. by Salzburg Studies). Longwood Pub Group.

Wojtyla, Karol. Fruitful & Responsible Love. (Orig.). 1979. pap. 2.95 (ISBN 0-8245-0310-4). Crossroad NY.

--Sign of Contradiction. 1980. pap. 3.95 (ISBN 0-686-85827-1). Crossroad NY.

Wojtyla, Cardinal Karol. The Acting Person. Potocki, Andrzej, tr. (Analecta Husserliana Ser.: No. 10). 1979. lib. bdg. 29.50 (ISBN 90-277-0969-6, Pub. by Reidel Holland); pap. 15.95 (ISBN 90-277-0985-8, Pub. by Reidel Holland). Kluwer Academic.

Wolbers, Mary J., jt. ed. see Fallon, Dennis J.

Wolcott, Carolyn & Wolcott, Leonard. We Go Forward: Stories of United Methodist Pathmakers. LC 83-73225. 72p. pap. 5.25 (ISBN 0-88177-008-6, DR008B). Discipleship Res.

Wolcott, Carolyn, jt. auth. see Arbuckle, Gwendolyne.

Wolcott, Leonard, jt. auth. see Wolcott, Carolyn.

Wold, Erling, jt. auth. see Wold, Margaret.

Wold, Margaret. The Shalom Woman. LC 75-2828. 128p. 1975. pap. 6.95 (ISBN 0-8066-1475-7, 10-5740). Augsburg.

--Women of Faith & Spirit: Profiles of Fifteen Biblical Witnesses. LC 86-28770. 128p. (Orig.). 1987. pap. 6.95 (ISBN 0-8066-2251-2, 10-7236). Augsburg.

Wold, Margaret & Wold, Erling. Bible Readings for Couples. LC 80-65541. (Bible Reading Ser.). 112p. (Orig.). 1980. pap. 3.95 (ISBN 0-317-40483-0, 10-0676). Augsburg.

Wolf, Anna W. Helping Your Child to Understand Death. rev. ed. 1973. pap. 2.30 (ISBN 0-87183-240-2). Jewish Bd Family.

Wolf, Arthur P., ed. Religion & Ritual in Chinese Society. LC 73-89863. (Studies in Chinese Society). xiv, 378p. 1974. 27.50x (ISBN 0-8047-0858-4). Stanford U Pr.

Wolf, Barbara. Journey in Faith: An Inquirer's Program. rev. ed. 144p. 1982. pap. 5.95 (ISBN 0-8164-2402-0, HarpR). Har-Row.

Wolf, Barbara & Wolf, Frederick B. Exploring Faith & Life: A Journey in Faith for Junior High - Manual for Clergy & Leaders. 64p. (Orig.). 1983. pap. 3.95 (ISBN 0-8164-2437-3, HarpR). Har-Row.

--Exploring Faith & Life: A Journey in Faith for Junior High - Manual for Sponsors. 32p. (Orig.). 1983. pap. 2.95 (ISBN 0-8164-2436-5, HarpR). Har-Row.

Wolf, Barbara B., jt. auth. see Wolf, Frederick B.

Wolf, Bob. Bible Animal Stories, Bk. 1. (Illus.). 86p. 1983. pap. 3.95 (ISBN 0-89323-044-8). Bible Memory.

--Just Like Jesus. (Illus.). 24p. (Orig.). 1982. pap. 0.75 (ISBN 0-89323-034-0). Bible Memory.

--Uncle Bob's Bible Stories. (Illus.). 108p. (Orig.). 1982. pap. 1.75 (ISBN 0-89323-028-6). Bible Memory.

Wolf, Carl J., ed. Jonathan Edwards on Evangelism. LC 81-2266. xii, 137p. 1981. Repr. of 1958 ed. lib. bdg. 22.50x (ISBN 0-8371-6588-1, EDOE). Greenwood.

Wolf, Carol. Women's Devotional Talks for Special Occasions. 64p. (Orig.). 1984. pap. 3.95 (ISBN 0-87239-745-9, 2976). Standard Pub.

Wolf, Earl, ed. see Bible, Ken.

Wolf, Earl, ed. see Carver, Frank.

Wolf, Earl C. Beacon Small-Group Bible Studies: Exodus: "Set Free". 86p. (Orig.). 1984. pap. 2.50. Beacon Hill.

--Beacon Small-Group Bible Studies, I, II & III John: Everybody Ought to Know. 80p. 1982. pap. 2.50 (ISBN 0-8341-0791-0). Beacon Hill.

--Making the Bible Yours. 13th ed. 102p. 1984. pap. 3.95 (ISBN 0-8341-0892-5). Beacon Hill.

Wolf, Earl C., ed. see Allison, Winn O.

Wolf, Earl C., ed. see Bible, Ken.

Wolf, Earl C., ed. see Bonar, Clayton.

Wolf, Earl C., ed. see Branson, Robert.

Wolf, Earl C., ed. see Carver, Frank.

Wolf, Earl C., ed. see DeMott, Harold.

Wolf, Earl C., ed. see Fairbanks, Lebron.

Wolf, Earl C., ed. see Grosse, David G.

Wolf, Earl C., ed. see Harper, A. F.

Wolf, Earl C., ed. see Miller, Stephen M.

Wolf, Earl C., ed. see Nielson, John M.

Wolf, Earl C., ed. see Shaver, Charles.

Wolf, Earl C., ed. see Simpson, Frances.

Wolf, Earl C., ed. see Stenbock, Evelyn A.

Wolf, Earl C., ed. see Strait, C. Neil.

Wolf, Earl C., ed. see Tracy, Wesley.

Wolf, Earl C., ed. see Van Dyne, Glen.

Wolf, Edwin, 2nd & Whiteman, Maxwell. History of the Jews of Philadelphia: From Colonial Times to the Age of Jackson. LC 56-7780. (Illus.). 552p. 1975. 8.50 (ISBN 0-8276-0075-5, 372). Jewish Pubns.

Wolf, Eric R., ed. Religion Power & Protest in Local Communities: The Northern Shore of the Mediterranean. LC 84-8407. (Religion & Society Ser.: No. 24). 287p. 1984. 65.00 (ISBN 3-11-009777-X). Mouton.

Wolf, Ernst. Staupitz Und Luther. (Ger). 34.00 (ISBN 0-384-69019-X); pap. 28.00 (ISBN 0-384-69018-1). Johnson Repr.

Wolf, Frederick B. Journey in Faith: Leader's Manual. 80p. (Orig.). 1982. pap. 4.95 (ISBN 0-8164-2400-4, HarpR). Har-Row.

--Journey in Faith: Things to Know. 48p. (Orig.). 1982. pap. 3.50 (ISBN 0-8164-2401-2, HarpR). Har-Row.

Wolf, Frederick B. & Wolf, Barbara B. Exploring Faith & Life: A Journey in Faith for Junior High Student's Reader. 128p. 1983. pap. 5.95 (ISBN 0-8164-2431-4, HarpR). Har-Row.

Wolf, Frederick B., jt. auth. see Wolf, Barbara.

Wolf, Hannie. Child of Two Worlds. (Illus.). 156p. 1979. 13.00 (ISBN 0-931068-02-9). Purcells.

Wolf, Hans W. Obadiah & Jonah: A Commentary. Kohl, Margaret, tr. from German. LC 86-22256. Orig. Title: Obadja, Jona. 192p. 1986. text ed. 19.95 (ISBN 0-8066-2244-X, 10-4710). Augsburg.

Wolf, Herbert. Hageo y Malaquias: Rededicacion y Renovacion. Orig. Title: Haggai & Malachi. (Span.). 1980. pap. 3.95 (ISBN 0-8254-1875-5). Kregel.

--Haggai & Malachi. (Everyman's Bible Commentary Ser.). 128p. (Orig.). 1976. pap. 5.95 (ISBN 0-8024-2037-0). Moody.

Wolf, Herbert M. Interpreting Isaiah: The Suffering & Glory of the Messiah. 272p. (Orig.). 1985. pap. 9.95 (ISBN 0-310-39061-3, 12713P). Zondervan.

Wolf, James B., ed. see Hore, Edward C.

Wolf, Jill. I Know God Loves Me. (Illus.). 24p. 1984. pap. 1.95 (ISBN 0-89954-288-3). Antioch Pub Co.

Wolf, Simon. The American Jew As Patriot, Soldier, & Citizen. LC 72-8739. (American Revolutionary Ser.). 1979. Repr. of 1895 ed. lib. bdg. 47.00x (ISBN 0-8398-2179-4). Irvington.

Wolf, William. Healers, Gurus, Spiritual Guide. LC 76-2180. 1969. pap. 6.50 (ISBN 0-933900-07-4). Foun Human Under.

Wolf, William J. An Abridgement of Maurice's Kingdom of Christ: The Original Two Volumes Abridged into One Based on the 1842 Edition Amended with an Introduction. LC 83-3516. 276p. (Orig.). 1983. lib. bdg. 28.25 (ISBN 0-8191-3150-4); pap. text ed. 13.50 (ISBN 0-8191-3151-2). U Pr of Amer.

--Lincoln's Religion. LC 70-123035. Orig. Title: Almost Chosen People. 1970. pap. 2.25 (ISBN 0-8298-0181-2). Pilgrim NY.

--Thoreau: Mystic, Prophet, Ecologist. LC 73-22368. 224p. 1974. 6.95 (ISBN 0-8298-0269-X). Pilgrim NY.

Wolf, William J., ed. Anglican Spirituality. LC 81-84717. 176p. (Orig.). 1982. pap. 9.95 (ISBN 0-8192-1297-0). Morehouse.

Wolf, William J., ed. see Maurice, Frederick D.

Wolfe, Bill, jt. auth. see Benson, Dennis C.

Wolfe, Charles E. The Seven Words from the Cross: A Commentary. 1980. pap. 4.65 (ISBN 0-89536-420-4, 1962). CSS of Ohio.

Wolfe, David L. Epistemology. Evans, C. Stephen, ed. (Contours of Christian Philosophy Ser.). 96p. 1982. pap. 5.95 (ISBN 0-87784-340-6). Inter-Varsity.

Wolfe, David L., jt. ed. see Heie, Harold.

Wolfe, Don M. Milton in the Puritan Revolution. 1963. text ed. 22.50x (ISBN 0-391-00477-8). Humanities.

Wolfe, Fred H. The Divine Pattern. LC 83-70212. 1983. pap. 5.95 (ISBN 0-8054-5244-3). Broadman.

Wolfe, Gerard R., jt. auth. see Fine, Jo Renee.

Wolfe, Hal. Through the Eye of the Dove: One Man's Journey into Reincarnation. Date not set. pap. price not set. Dearen Pub.

Wolfe, Rinna. The Singing Pope: The Story of Pope John Paul II. (Illus.). 128p. 1980. 8.95 (ISBN 0-8164-0472-0, HarpR). Har-Row.

Wolfe, Robert. Dark Star. 266p. (Orig.). 1984. 12.00 (ISBN 0-318-19328-0); pap. 6.00 (ISBN 0-318-19329-9). Memory Bks.

Wolfe, Rolland E. The Twelve Religions of the Bible. LC 82-20401. (Studies in the Bible & Early Christianity: Vol. 2). (Illus.). 440p. 1983. 69.95x (ISBN 0-88946-600-9). E Mellen.

Wolfe, S. Key to Dooyeweerd. 1978. pap. 2.95 (ISBN 0-87552-542-3). Presby & Reformed.

Wolfert, Jerry, jt. auth. see Kilinski, Kenneth.

Wolff, Hans W. Anthropology of the Old Testament. Kohl, Margaret, tr. from Ger. LC 74-21591. 304p. 1981. pap. 10.95 (ISBN 0-8006-1500-X, 1-1500). Fortress.

--Confrontations with Prophets. LC 82-48585. 80p. 1983. pap. 4.25 (ISBN 0-8006-1702-9). Fortress.

--Hosea. Hanson, Paul D., ed. Stansell, Gary, tr. from Ger. LC 70-179634. (Hermeneia: A Critical & Historical Commentary on the Bible). Orig. Title: Dodekapropheton-Hosea. 292p. 1973. 24.95 (ISBN 0-8006-6004-8, 20-6004). Fortress.

--Micah the Prophet. Gehrke, Ralph D., tr. from Ger. LC 80-2380. Tr. of Mit Micha reden: Prophetie einst und jetzt. 240p. 1981. 19.95 (ISBN 0-8006-0652-3, 1-652). Fortress.

--The Old Testament: A Guide to Its Writings. Crim, Keith R., tr. from Gr. LC 73-79010. 160p. (Orig.). 1973. pap. 4.95 (ISBN 0-8006-0169-6, 1-169). Fortress.

--Old Testment & Christian Preaching. Kohl, Margaret, tr. LC 85-45477. 112p. 1986. pap. 8.95 (ISBN 0-8006-1905-6, 1-1905). Fortress.

Wolff, Hans W., jt. auth. see Brueggemann, Walter.

Wolff, Hans W., Jr. Joel & Amos. McBride, Dean, ed. Janzen, Waldemar, tr. from Ger. LC 75-76932. (Hermeneia: a Critical & Historical Commentary on the Bible). 416p. 1977. 29.95 (ISBN 0-8006-6007-2, 20-6007). Fortress.

Wolff, Otto, ed. The Anthroposophical Approach to Medicine, Vol. 2. Karnow, G., tr. from Ger. Tr. of Das Bild des Menschen als Grundlage der Heilkunst. 1987. 40.00 (ISBN 0-88010-174-1). Anthroposophic.

Wolff, Pierre. May I Hate God? LC 78-70815. 80p. 1979. pap. 2.95 (ISBN 0-8091-2180-8). Paulist Pr.

Wolff, Richard, ed. Catholics, the State & the European Radical Right, 1919-1945. (Atlantic Studies: No. 50). write for info (ISBN 0-88033-101-1). Brooklyn Coll Pr.

Wolff, Robert L. Gains & Losses. (Victorian Fiction Ser.). Orig. Title: Faith & Doubt in Victorian England. 1977. lib. bdg. 33.00 (ISBN 0-8240-1617-3). Garland Pub.

Wolff, Robert L. see Setton, Kenneth M.

Wolff, Robert P., ed. see Kant, Immanuel.

Wolff, Robert P., et al. Critique of Pure Tolerance. LC 65-20788. 1969. pap. 7.95x (ISBN 0-8070-1559-8, BP328). Beacon Pr.

Wolff, Y, ed. A Guide to Monastic Communities in the Northeast. 1984. pap. 2.50 (ISBN 0-317-39519-X). St Bedes Pubns.

Wolfger Von Prufening. Das Leben Des Bischofs Otto Von Bamberg. xxix, 78p. (Ger.). Repr. of 1928 ed. 12.00 (ISBN 0-384-69065-3). Johnson Repr.

Wolfman, Brunetta R. Roles. LC 83-12441. (Choices: Guides for Today's Woman: Vol. 3). 118p. (Orig.). 1983. pap. 6.95 (ISBN 0-664-24542-0). Westminster.

Wolfson, Harry A. Philo: Foundations of Religious Philosophy in Judaism, Christianity & Islam, 2 vols. rev. ed. LC 47-30635. 1962. Set. 55.00x (ISBN 0-674-66450-7). Harvard U Pr.

--Philosophy of the Church Fathers: Faith, Trinity, Incarnation. 3rd rev. ed. LC 70-119077. 1970. 32.50x (ISBN 0-674-66551-1). Harvard U Pr.

--The Philosophy of the Kalam. LC 74-78718. 864p. 1976. 40.00x (ISBN 0-674-66580-5). Harvard U Pr.

--Religious Philosophy: A Group of Essays. LC 61-16696. 1961. 17.50x (ISBN 0-674-75900-1, Belknap Pr). Harvard U Pr.

--Repercussions of the Kalam in Jewish Philosophy. LC 78-9798. 1979. 18.50x (ISBN 0-674-76175-8). Harvard U Pr.

--Studies in the History of Philosophy & Religion, Vol. I. Twersky, Isadore & Williams, George H., eds. LC 72-86385. 640p. 1973. 40.00x (ISBN 0-674-84765-2). Harvard U Pr.

--Studies in the History of Philosophy & Religion, Vol. II. Twersky, Isadore & Williams, George H., eds. 1977. 40.00x (ISBN 0-674-84766-0). Harvard U Pr.

Wolfson, Ron. The Art of Jewish Living: The Sabbath Seder. (Illus.). 1985. pap. 9.95 (ISBN 0-935665-00-5); tchr's. ed 4.95 (ISBN 0-935665-01-3); cassette tape 3.00 (ISBN 0-935665-02-1). Fed Jewish Mens Clubs.

Wolfthal, Katherine, tr. see Calimani, Riccardo.

Wolheim, William, jt. auth. see Frank, Ruth S.

Wolhorn, Herman. Emmet Fox's Golden Keys to Successful Living. LC 76-62930. 1977. 10.84 (ISBN 0-06-069670-2, HarpR). Har-Row.

Wolk, jt. auth. see Bridger.

Woll, D. Bruce. Johannine Christianity in Conflict: Authority, Rank & Succession in the First Farwell Discourse. LC 81-1795. (SBL Dissertation Ser.). 1981. pap. 12.00 (ISBN 0-89130-471-1, 060160). Scholars Pr GA.

Wollaston, William. The Religion of Nature Delineated. Wellek, Rene, ed. LC 75-11267. (British Philosophers & Theologians of the 17th & 18th Centuries Ser.). 1978. Repr. of 1722 ed. lib. bdg. 51.00 (ISBN 0-8240-1816-8). Garland Pub.

--The Religion of Nature Delineated, 1724 & Related Commentaries. LC 74-1469. 1974. 45.00x (ISBN 0-8201-1127-9). Schol Facsimiles.

Wollenburg, David W. Campus Symbolism: Devotions for New Students. write for info. (ISBN 0-911770-52-6). Concordia Schl Grad Studies.

Wollheim, R. The Good Self & the Bad Self: The Moral Psychology of British Idealism & the English School of Psychoanalysis Compared. (Dawes Hicks Lectures on Philosophy). 1975. pap. 2.50 (ISBN 0-85672-278-2, Pub. by British Acad). Longwood Pub Group.

Wollman-Tsamir, Pinchas. The Graphic History of the Jewish Heritage. (Illus.). 224p. 1982. 22.50. Shengold.

Wolmarans, Theo. Blood Covenant. 175p. (Orig.). 1984. pap. text ed. 5.50 (ISBN 0-914307-26-6). Word Faith.

--Praying in the Spirit. 56p. (Orig.). 1985. 4.95 (ISBN 0-914307-50-9). Word Faith.

Wolseley, Charles. The Reasonableness of Scripture-Belief. LC 73-2618. 488p. 1973. Repr. of 1672 ed. lib. bdg. 75.00x (ISBN 0-8201-1113-9). Schol Facsimiles.

Wolseley, Roland E. Careers in Religious Communications. 264p. 1977. pap. 6.95 (ISBN 0-8361-1823-5). Herald Pr.

Wolsky, Alexander. Teilhard in Chardin's Biological Ideas. (Teilhard Studies). 1981. 2.00 (ISBN 0-89012-024-2). Anima Pubns.

Wolsted, Mabel E. Chosen Partners. 1983. 9.95 (ISBN 0-8062-1918-1). Carlton.

Wolter, Allan B. The Book of Life: An Explanation of the Rule of the Third Order Regular of Saint Francis. (Spirit & Life Ser). 1954. pap. 2.50 (ISBN 0-686-11566-X). Franciscan Inst.

--Living in God's Love. 172p. 1958. pap. 1.75 (ISBN 0-8199-0059-1, L38375). Franciscan Herald.

Wolter, Allan B., ed. Duns Scotus on the Will & Morality. 1986. 54.95 (ISBN 0-8132-0622-7). Cath U Pr.

Wolter, Allan B., jt. tr. see Alluntis, Felix.

Wolter, Allen B., jt. ed. see Wippel, John F.

Wolter, Michael. Rechtfertigung und zukuenftiges Heil. Untersuchungen zu Roemer 5, 1-11. (Beihefte zur Zeitschrift fuer die Neutestamentliche Wissenschaft: No. 43). 1978. 29.20x (ISBN 3-11-007579-2). De Gruyter.

Wolter, Michael, ed. Theologische Realenzyklopaedie: Agende-Anselm Von Cantebury, Vol. 2. (Illus.). 1978. 128.00x (ISBN 3-11-007379-X). De Gruyter.

Wolters, Clifton, tr. The Cloud of Unknowing & Other Works. (Classics Ser). 1978. pap. 3.95 (ISBN 0-14-044385-1). Penguin.

Wolters, Clifton, tr. see Rolle, Richard.

Wolterstorff, Nicholas. Reason Within the Bounds of Religion. 2nd ed. 168p. 1984. pap. 4.95 (ISBN 0-8028-1604-5). Eerdmans.

--Until Justice & Peace Embrace. 232p. (Orig.). 1983. 13.95 (ISBN 0-8028-3344-6). Eerdmans.

Wolterstorff, Nicholas, jt. ed. see Plantinga, Alvin.

Wolverton, Robert E. Outline of Classical Mythology. (Quality Paperback: No. 97). (Orig.). 1975. pap. 2.95 (ISBN 0-8226-0097-8). Littlefield.

Womack, David. Alive in Christ. LC 75-22609. (Radiant Life Ser.). 128p. 1975. pap. 2.50 (ISBN 0-88243-888-3, 02-0888, Radiant Books); teacher's ed 3.95 (ISBN 0-88243-162-5, 32-0162). Gospel Pub.

--The Wellsprings of the Pentecostal Movement. 96p. 1968. pap. 1.50 (ISBN 0-88243-628-7, 02-0628). Gospel Pub.

Womack, Edwin B. Come Follow Me: A Study Book for Acolytes. 1982. pap. 6.45 (ISBN 0-89536-536-7, 0348). CSS of Ohio.

Womack, Morris M., jt. auth. see Wilson, Herman O.

Womack, Sharon K., jt. auth. see Guthmann, Robert F., Jr.

Woman's Institute for Continuing Jewish Education. Taking the Fruit: Modern Women's Tales of the Bible. Sprague, Jane, ed. (Illus.). 61p. 1982. pap. 5.95 (ISBN 0-9608054-1-9). Womans Inst-Cont Jewish Ed.

Womens Anglow Staff. The Ministry of Prayer. (Cornerstone Ser.). 32p. 1983. pap. 2.00 (ISBN 0-930756-77-0, 533008). Aglow Pubns.

Women's League for Conservative Judaism. Welcome to the World - A Jewish Baby's Record Book. (Illus.). 40p. 1985. 12.95 (ISBN 0-936293-00-4). WLCJ.

Womer, Jan L. Morality & Ethics in Early Christianity. LC 86-45903. (Sources in Early Christian Thought Ser.). 144p. 1987. pap. 7.95 (ISBN 0-8006-1417-8). Fortress.

Wommack, Thomas, jt. auth. see Johnson, Vera.

Wonderly, Daniel E. God's Time-Records in Ancient Sediments: Evidences of Long Time Spans in Earth's History. LC 77-85681. (Illus.). 258p. (Orig.). 1977. pap. 7.00 (ISBN 0-930402-01-4). Crystal MI.

Wones, David R. Sonnets for a Christian Year. (Illus.). 80p. (Orig.). 1987. pap. 4.95 (ISBN 0-936015-06-3). Pocahontas Pr.

Wong, Ernest, tr. see Saucy, Richard L.

Wong, Mary G. Nun: A Memoir. LC 82-47656. 416p. 1983. 15.95 (ISBN 0-15-167739-5). HarBraceJ.

--Nun-A Memoir: An Intimate Account of One Women's Years in the Covent & Her Eventual Return to the World. LC 84-47611. 416p. 1984. pap. 8.95 (ISBN 0-06-091188-3, CN 1188, PL). Har-Row.

Wongmo, Karma C., ed. see Open Path.

Wong Mou-lam, tr. see Hui-neng.

Woo, Nancy E., jt. auth. see McKee, David.

Woocher, Jonathan S. Sacred Survival: The Civil Religion of American Jews. LC 85-45790. (Jewish Political & Social Studies). (Illus.). 224p. 1986. 25.00x (ISBN 0-253-35041-7). Ind U Pr.

Wood. Mind & Memory Training. 10.50 (ISBN 0-8356-5115-0). Theos Pub Hse.

--Mind & Memory Training. pap. 7.95 (ISBN 0-8356-5126-6). Theos Pub Hse.

Wood, A. Skevington. The Burning Heart: John Wesley, Evangelist. LC 78-52837. 1978. pap. 7.95 (ISBN 0-87123-043-7, 210043). Bethany Hse.

Wood, A. Skevington, et al. The Expositor's Bible Commentary, Vol. 11. 1986. 19.95 (ISBN 0-88469-197-7). BMH Bks.

Wood, Allen W. Kant's Rational Theology. LC 78-58059. 144p. 1978. 22.50x (ISBN 0-8014-1200-5). Cornell U Pr.

Wood, Allen W., tr. see Kant, Immanuel.

Wood, Andrew. Unto the Least of These: Special Education in the Church. LC 84-16077. 1984. pap. 4.95 (ISBN 0-87227-099-8). Reg Baptist.

Wood, Angela. Judaism. (World Religions Ser.). (Illus.). 72p. 1984. 16.95 (ISBN 0-7134-3656-5, Pub. by Batsford England). David & Charles.

Wood, Angela, jt. auth. see Keene, Michael.

Wood, Arthur S., ed. Daily Readings with John Wesley. 1987. pap. 4.95 (ISBN 0-87243-158-4). Templegate.

Wood, Barry. Questions Christians Ask about Prayer & Intercession. 160p. (Orig.). 1984. pap. 5.95 (ISBN 0-8007-5177-9, Power Bks). Revell.

--Questions New Christians Ask. 160p. 1979. pap. 5.95 (ISBN 0-8007-5044-6, Power Bks). Revell.

--Questions Non-Christians Ask. 160p. 1980. pap. 5.95 (ISBN 0-8007-5047-0, Power Bks). Revell.

Wood, Betty. The Healing Power of Color: How to Use Color to Improve Your Mental, Physical & Spiritual Well-Being. 112p. 1985. pap. 9.95 (ISBN 0-89281-110-2). Inner Tradit.

Wood, Bobbye & Wood, Britton. Marriage Readiness. 1984. pap. 4.95 (ISBN 0-8054-5657-0). Broadman.

Wood, Britton. Single Adults Want to Be the Church, Too. LC 77-78411. 1977. 9.50 (ISBN 0-8054-3221-3). Broadman.

Wood, Britton, jt. auth. see Wood, Bobbye.

Wood, C. T. Philip the Fair & Boniface VIII: State vs. Papacy. LC 76-23207. (European Problem Ser.). 124p. 1976. pap. 5.95 (ISBN 0-88275-454-8). Krieger.

Wood, Charles E. A Book of Tales, Being Myths of the North American Indians. 59.95 (ISBN 0-87968-770-3). Gordon Pr.

Wood, Charles M. The Formation of Christian Understanding: An Essay in Theological Hermeneutics. LC 81-5103. 126p. 1981. pap. 7.95 (ISBN 0-664-24373-8). Westminster.

--Theory & Religious Understanding: A Critique of the Hermeneutics of Joachim Wach. LC 75-26839. (American Academy of Religion. Dissertation Ser.). 1975. pap. 9.95 (ISBN 0-89130-026-0, 010112). Scholars Pr GA.

--Vision & Discernment: An Orientation in Theological Study. (Studies in Religious & Theological Scholarship). 1985. 15.95 (ISBN 0-89130-922-5, 00-08-02); pap. 11.95 (ISBN 0-89130-923-3). Scholars Pr GA.

Wood, Charles R. Outline Talks for Teens. LC 83-25543. 64p. (Orig.). 1984. pap. 2.95 (ISBN 0-8254-4024-6). Kregel.

--Sermon Outlines from Proverbs. LC 83-25569. 88p. (Orig.). 1984. pap. 3.95 (ISBN 0-8254-4023-8). Kregel.

--Sermon Outlines from the Sermon on the Mount. LC 85-23734. 64p. (Orig.). 1986. pap. 2.95 (ISBN 0-8254-4032-7). Kregel.

--Sermon Outlines on the Psalms. LC 85-23735. 64p. (Orig.). 1986. pap. 2.95 (ISBN 0-8254-4033-5). Kregel.

Wood, Charles R., ed. Evangelistic Sermon Outlines. 64p. (Orig.). 1975. pap. 2.95 (ISBN 0-8254-4004-1). Kregel.

--Revival Sermon Outlines. 64p. 1975. pap. 2.95 (ISBN 0-8254-4005-X). Kregel.

--Sermon Outlines for Funeral Services. 64p. 1970. pap. 2.95 (ISBN 0-8254-4007-6). Kregel.

--Sermon Outlines for Special Days & Occasions. 64p. 1970. pap. 2.95 (ISBN 0-8254-4006-8). Kregel.

Wood, Charles T. The Quest for Eternity: Manners & Morals in the Age of Chivalry. LC 82-40476. (Illus.). 172p. 1983. pap. 8.00x (ISBN 0-87451-259-X). U Pr of New Eng.

Wood, David. Genesis: The First Book of Revelations. 320p. 1985. 55.00x (ISBN 0-85936-180-2, Pub. by Chambers Green Ltd). State Mutual Bk.

Wood, Diana, jt. ed. see Sheils, W. J.

Wood, Diana, jt. ed. see Walsh, Katherine.

Wood, E., ed. Diccionario Zen. (Span.). 190p. 1980. pap. 13.95 (ISBN 84-7509-010-9, S-32724). French & Eur.

Wood, Edward L. John Keble: Leaders of the Church 1800-1900. Russell, George W., ed. 1909. Repr. 25.00 (ISBN 0-8274-2627-5). R West.

Wood, Eileen C. Pure Thoughts. 1985. 5.95 (ISBN 0-533-06662-X). Vantage.

Wood, Ernest. Concentration: An Approach Meditation. 6.75 (ISBN 0-8356-7337-5). Theos Pub Hse.

--Concentration: An Approach to Meditation. LC 67-2874. pap. 3.75 (ISBN 0-8356-0176-5, Quest). Theos Pub Hse.

--The Glorious Presence. LC 74-1045. pap. 2.75 (ISBN 0-8356-0446-2, Quest). Theos Pub Hse.

--An Introduction to the Science of Prayer. 2nd ed. 1980. pap. text ed. 1.95 (ISBN 0-918980-08-9). St Alban Pr.

--The Seven Rays. LC 76-4909. 191p. 1976. pap. 4.95 (ISBN 0-8356-0481-0, Quest). Theos Pub Hse.

--Seven Schools of Yoga: An Introduction. LC 72-13120. Orig. Title: The Occult Training of the Hindus. 120p. 1973. pap. 2.25 (ISBN 0-8356-0435-7, Quest). Theos Pub Hse.

--Taking Charge of Your Life. rev. ed. LC 84-40512. 136p. 1985. pap. 4.75 (ISBN 0-8356-0594-9). Theos Pub Hse.

--Zen Dictionary. LC 72-77518. 1972. pap. 5.25 (ISBN 0-8048-1060-5). C E Tuttle.

Wood, Forrest, Jr. Whiteheadian Thought as a Basis for a Philosophy of Religion. LC 86-9282. 110p. (Orig.). 1986. lib. bdg. 19.50 (ISBN 0-8191-5422-9); pap. text ed. 8.75 (ISBN 0-8191-5423-7). U Pr of Amer.

Wood, Fred M. Coming Home. LC 86-20775. (Orig.). 1987. pap. 6.95 (ISBN 0-8054-1236-0). Broadman.

--God of Grace, God of Glory. LC 81-68364. 1982. pap. 4.95 (ISBN 0-8054-1221-2). Broadman.

--Salmos: Cantos de Vida. De Gutierrez, Edna L., tr. from Span. Tr. of Psalms: Songs From Life. 160p. 1984. pap. 2.75 (ISBN 0-311-04032-2). Casa Bautista.

--The Sunnier Side of Doubt. LC 83-24020. 1984. pap. 4.95 (ISBN 0-8054-2253-6). Broadman.

Wood, Geoffrey. First Book of Kings. (Bible Ser.: No. 15). (Orig.). 1974. pap. 1.00 (ISBN 0-8091-5168-5). Paulist Pr.

--Second Book of Kings. (Bible Ser.: Vol. 16). (Orig.). 1974. pap. 1.00 (ISBN 0-8091-5169-3). Paulist Pr.

Wood, George. The Successful Life. Sekowsky, Jo Anne, ed. 64p. 1984. pap. text ed. 3.25 (ISBN 0-930756-82-7, 531017). Aglow Pubns.

Wood, George, jt. auth. see King, Pat.

Wood, George O. Living Fully: Producing Spiritual Fruit. 1985. pap. 3.95 (ISBN 0-932305-23-7, 531021). Aglow Pubns.

Wood, George O. & Krutza, William J. You Can't Beat the Beatitudes. LC 78-58721. 1978. pap. 1.25 (ISBN 0-88243-719-4, 02-0719, Radiant Bks). Gospel Pub.

Wood, Harriet H. & Brooks, Cleanth, eds. The Correspondence of Thomas Percy & John Pinkerton: The Percy Letters, Vol. 8. LC 84-2916. 160p. 1985. text ed. 25.00x (ISBN 0-300-03344-3). Yale U Pr.

Wood, Herbert G. Christianity & Civilisation. LC 73-17694. 128p. 1973. Repr. of 1943 ed. lib. bdg. 13.00x (ISBN 0-374-98713-0, Octagon). Hippocrene Bks.

--Living Issues in Religious Thought, from George Fox to Bertrand Russell. facs. ed. LC 67-22128. (Essay Index Reprint Ser). 1924. 14.25 (ISBN 0-8369-1007-9). Ayer Co Pubs.

--Living Issues in Religious Thought: From George Fox to Betrand Russell. facsimile ed. LC 67-22128. (Essay Index Reprint Ser.). 187p. 1967. Repr. of 1924 ed. lib. bdg. 13.50 (ISBN 0-8290-0489-0). Irvington.

Wood, Irving. The Bible As Literature: An Introduction. LC 79-441. (Bible Study Textbook Series). 1979. Repr. of 1914 ed. lib. bdg. 42.50 (ISBN 0-8414-9712-5). Folcroft.

Wood, Irving F. The Bible as Literature. 346p. 1980. Repr. of 1914 ed. lib. bdg. 43.50 (ISBN 0-8482-7073-8). Norwood Edns.

Wood, Irving F. & Grant, E. The Bible As Literature. 1914. Repr. 4.00 (ISBN 0-8274-3802-8). R West.

Wood, J., tr. see Barth, A.

Wood, J. G. Animals in the Bible: A Description of Their Meaning, Importance, Uses, Symbolical Value, 3 vols. (Illus.). 670p. 1986. Repr. Set. 337.45 (ISBN 0-89901-278-7). Found Class Reprints.

Wood, J. Maxwell. Witchcraft & Superstitious Record in the Southwestern District of Scotland. (Illus.). 1976. 25.00x (ISBN 0-7158-1139-8). Charles River Bks.

Wood, James D. Wisdom Literature: An Introduction. LC 67-108276. (Studies in Theology: No. 64). 1967. text ed. 8.50x (ISBN 0-8401-6064-X). A R Allenson.

Wood, James E., Jr., ed. Jewish-Christian Relations in Today's World. 164p. pap. 1.95 (ISBN 0-686-95175-1). ADL.

--Jewish-Christian Relations in Today's World. LC 74-185826. 164p. 1971. 8.95 (ISBN 0-918954-09-6); pap. 4.50 (ISBN 0-918954-10-X). Baylor Univ Pr.

--Religion & the State: Essays in Honor of Leo Pfeffer. 596p. 1985. 39.95x (ISBN 0-918954-29-0). Baylor Univ Pr.

--Religion, the State, & Education. LC 84-81477. (Institute of Church-State Studies). 151p. 1984. 10.95 (ISBN 0-918954-31-2); pap. 6.95 (ISBN 0-918954-32-0). Baylor Univ Pr.

Wood, James E., Jr., et al. Church & State in Scripture, History, & Constitutional Law. LC 59-21543. (Institute of Church-State Studies). 171p. 1985. pap. 6.95 (ISBN 0-918954-01-0). Baylor Univ Pr.

Wood, James R. Leadership in Voluntary Organizations: The Controversy Over Social Action in Protestant Churches. 155p. 1981. 17.00x (ISBN 0-8135-0920-3). Rutgers U Pr.

Wood, John, tr. see Steiner, Rudolf.

Wood, John E. Sun, Moon, & Standing Stones. (Illus.). 1978. 22.50x (ISBN 0-19-211443-3). Oxford U Pr.

Wood, John M. Witchcraft & Superstitious Record in the Southwestern District of Scotland. LC 76-25108. 1976. 40.00 (ISBN 0-8414-9530-0). Folcroft.

Wood, June S. A Workable Faith. 1975. 6.95 (ISBN 0-8022-2152-1). Philos Lib.

Wood, Laurence W. Pentecostal Grace. Burgess, Harold, ed. 1980. pap. 8.95 (ISBN 0-310-75041-5, 17028P). Zondervan.

Wood, Leon & O'Brien, David. A Survey of Israel's History. rev. ed. 416p. 1986. 19.95 (ISBN 0-310-34770-X, 6505). Zondervan.

Wood, Leon J. The Bible & Future Events. (Contemporary Evangelical Perspectives Ser.). 224p. 1973. kivar 6.95 (ISBN 0-310-34701-7, 10231P). Zondervan.

--Commentary on Daniel. 320p. 1972. 16.95 (ISBN 0-310-34710-6, 10871). Zondervan.

--Daniel: A Study Guide. 160p. 1975. pap. 6.95 (ISBN 0-310-34723-8, 10872P). Zondervan.

--Elijah: Prophet of God. 1968. 2.95 (ISBN 0-87227-020-3). Reg Baptist.

--Genesis: A Bible Study Commentary. 160p. 1975. pap. 4.95 (ISBN 0-310-34743-2, 10233P). Zondervan.

--Israel's United Monarchy. 1980. 12.95 (ISBN 0-8010-9622-7). Baker Bk.

--Prophets of Israel. LC 79-50172. 1979. 16.95 (ISBN 0-8010-9607-3). Baker Bk.

Wood, Leon U. Distressing Days of the Judges. 434p. 1982. pap. 11.95 (ISBN 0-310-34731-9, 10232P). Zondervan.

Wood, Louis A. Form & Origin of Milton's Antitrinitarian Conception. LC 72-191655. 1911. lib. bdg. 15.00 (ISBN 0-8414-0833-5). Folcroft.

Wood, Marion. Spirits, Heroes & Hunters from North American Indian Mythology. LC 81-14572. (World Mythologies Ser.). (Illus.). 156p. 1982. 16.95 (ISBN 0-8052-3792-5). Schocken.

Wood, Mike. Pilgrims' Road. 1976. pap. 2.95 (ISBN 0-89390-015-X). Resource Pubns.

Wood, Miriam. Those Happy Golden Years. 1980. 6.95 (ISBN 0-8280-0062-X, 20380-2). Review & Herald.

Wood, Nathan E. History of the First Baptist Church of Boston: Sixteen Sixty-Five to Eighteen Ninty Nine. Gaustad, Edwin S., ed. LC 79-52612. (The Baptist Tradition Ser.). (Illus.). 1980. Repr. of 1899 ed. lib. bdg. 34.50x (ISBN 0-405-12477-5). Ayer Co Pubs.

Wood, Nathan R. & Morgan, G. Campbell. The Trinity in the Universe. 2nd ed. LC 78-5483. 220p. 1984. pap. 6.95 (ISBN 0-8254-4018-1). Kregel.

Wood, Norma S., jt. auth. see Stroup, Herbert W.

Wood, Oswald C., tr. see Von Hammer-Purgstall, Joseph.

Wood, P. Moses: Founder of Preventive Medicine. 1976. lib. bdg. 59.95 (ISBN 0-8490-2285-1). Gordon Pr.

Wood, Phyllis A. This Time Count Me In. LC 80-15068. (A Hiway Book: A High Interest - Low Reading Level Book). 120p. 1980. 8.95 (ISBN 0-664-32665-X). Westminster.

Wood, Ramsey. Kalila & Dimna. 1980. 10.95 (Pub. by Octagon Pr England). Ins Study Human.

Wood, Raquel & Banerji, Ranan. Non-Christian Quakers: Their Faith & Message. Ives, Kenneth, ed. (Studies in Quakerism Ser.: No. 9). 59p. (Orig.). 1983. pap. 4.00 (ISBN 0-89670-012-7). Progresiv Pub.

Wood, Richard H. A Cyclopedic Dictionary of Ecclesiastical Terms According to the Use of the Episcopal Church. 1984. 10.95 (ISBN 0-8062-2141-0). Carlton.

Wood, Robert. A Thirty-Day Experiment in Prayer. LC 78-65160. 1978. pap. 3.75 (ISBN 0-8358-0380-5). Upper Room.

--Thirty Days Are Not Enough: More Images for Meditative Journaling. 112p. (Orig.). 1983. pap. 3.75 (ISBN 0-8358-0445-3). Upper Room.

Wood, Robert & Roy, Marie L. Day Four: A Pilgrim's Continued Journey. 64p. (Orig.). 1986. pap. 2.95 (ISBN 0-8358-0553-0). Upper Room.

Wood, Robert E. Martin Buber's Ontology: An Analysis of I & Thou. LC 73-82510. (Studies in Phenomenology & Existential Philosophy). 160p. 1969. 19.95 (ISBN 0-8101-0256-0); pap. 10.95 (ISBN 0-8101-0650-7). Northwestern U Pr.

Woodard, Bernice Stout, jt. auth. see Hughes, Ray H.

Woodberry, George. Ralph Waldo Emerson. LC 68-24947. (American Biography Ser., No. 32). 1969. Repr. of 1907 ed. lib. bdg. 49.95x (ISBN 0-8383-0262-9). Haskell.

Woodberry, George E. Great Writers. facs. ed. LC 67-30236. (Essay Index Reprint Ser). 1907. 14.50 (ISBN 0-8369-1008-7). Ayer Co Pubs.

--Ralph Waldo Emerson. 1973. lib. bdg. 12.75 (ISBN 0-8414-9790-7). Folcroft.

Woodbridge, Barry A. A Guidebook for Spiritual Friends. LC 84-51827. 96p. (Orig.). 1985. pap. 4.95 (ISBN 0-8358-0498-4). Upper Room.

Woodbridge, Charles J., jt. auth. see Lindsell, Harold.

Woodbridge, John, et al, eds. Renewing Your Mind in a Secular World. (Orig.). 1985. pap. 6.95 (ISBN 0-8024-0384-0). Moody.

Woodbridge, John D. Biblical Authority: A Critique of the Rogers-McKim Proposal. 256p. (Orig.). 1982. pap. 9.95 (ISBN 0-310-44751-8, 12647P). Zondervan.

Woodbridge, John D., jt. ed. see Carson, D. A.

Woodburn, et al. Complete Set of God's People at Work in the Parish Series, 11 bks. 1979. pap. 12.50 set (ISBN 0-570-08036-3, 12-2775). Concordia.

Woodcock, George. Thomas Merton Monk & Poet: A Critical Study. 200p. 1978. 7.95 (ISBN 0-374-27635-8); pap. 3.95 (ISBN 0-374-51487-9). FS&G.

Wooden, Kenneth, ed. The Children of Jonestown. (Paperbacks Ser.). 1980. pap. 5.95 (ISBN 0-07-071641-2). McGraw.

Wooderson, Joy, jt. auth. see Almand, Joan.

Woodeward, F. L. Some Sayings of the Buddha. 69.95 (ISBN 0-8490-2629-6). Gordon Pr.

Woodfield, Malcom, ed. R. H. Hutton, Critic & Theologian: The Writings of R. H. Hutton on Newman, Arnold, Tennyson, Wordsworth & George Eliot. 240p. 42.00 (ISBN 0-19-818564-2). Oxford U Pr.

Woodford, Susan. The Parthenon. (Cambridge Introduction to the History of Mankind Ser.). 1981. pap. 4.95 (ISBN 0-521-22629-5). Cambridge U Pr.

Woodhall, A. N., ed. see Buhlmann, Walbert.

Woodhall, Ralph, ed. see Buhlmann, Walbert.

Woodhouse, A. S. The Heavenly Muse: A Preface to Milton. Maccallum, Hugh R., ed. LC 79-185724. 1972. 35.00x (ISBN 0-8020-5247-9). U of Toronto Pr.

--Milton the Poet. LC 73-785. 1955. lib. bdg. 10.00 (ISBN 0-8414-1606-0). Folcroft.

Woodhouse, A. S., ed. & intro. by. Puritanism & Liberty: Being the Army Debates (1647-9) from the Clarke Manuscripts with Supplementary Documents. 634p. 1986. pap. 11.95x (ISBN 0-460-01057-3, Pub. by Evman England). Biblio Dist.

Woodhull, Marianna. Epic of Paradise Lost. LC 72-194899. 1907. lib. bdg. 12.50 (ISBN 0-8414-9501-7). Folcroft.

--Epic of Paradise Lost: Twelve Essays. LC 68-57833. 386p. 1968. Repr. of 1907 ed. 32.50x (ISBN 0-87752-124-7). Gordian.

Wood-Legh, Kathleen. Perpetual Chantries in Britain. LC 65-28505. pap. 93.30 (ISBN 0-317-26370-6, 2024564). Bks Demand UMI.

Woodman, Hugh M. The Ultimate Reality. LC 84-90244. 145p. 1985. 10.95 (ISBN 0-533-06292-6). Vantage.

Woodmason, Charles. Carolina Backcountry on the Eve of the Revolution: The Journal & Other Writings of Charles Woodmason, Anglican Itinerant. Hooker, Richard J., ed. (Institute of Early American History & Culture Ser.). xxxix, 305p. 1953. 25.00x (ISBN 0-8078-0643-9). U of NC Pr.

Woodroffe, John. The Garland of Letters. 18.00 (ISBN 0-89744-112-5, Pub. by Ganesh & Co. India). Auromere.

--Hymns to the Goddess - Hymn to Kali. LC 81-84749. 350p. 1982. 11.00 (ISBN 0-941524-00-0). Lotus Light.

--Introduction to Tantra Shastra. 9.00 (ISBN 0-89744-114-1, Pub. by Ganesh & Co. India). Auromere.

--Principles of Tantra, 2 vols. 1979. Set. 42.00 (ISBN 0-89744-129-X, Pub. by Ganesh & Co India). Auromere.

--Sakti & Sakta. 24.50 (ISBN 0-89744-116-8, Pub. by Ganesh & Co. India). Auromere.

--The World As Power. new ed. Bd. with Mahamaya: Power As Consciousness. Woodroffe, John & Mukhyopadhyaya, Pramatha N.. 1981. 24.00 (ISBN 0-89744-119-2, Pub. by Ganesh & Co. India). Auromere.

Woodroffe, John see Avalon, Arthur, pseud.

Woodroffe, John, tr. Great Liberation (Mahanirvana Tantra) (Sanskrit.). 28.00 (ISBN 0-89744-237-7, Pub. by Ganesh & Co. India). Auromere.

Woodroffe, John, tr. from Sanskrit. The Serpent Power (Sat-Chakra-Nirupana & Paduka-Panchaka) (Illus.). 512p. (Eng. only). 1973. 24.00 (ISBN 0-89744-117-6, Pub. by Ganesh & Co. India). Auromere.

Woodrow, Ralph. Amazing Discoveries Within the Book of Books. (Illus.). 1979. pap. 4.95 (ISBN 0-916938-04-2). R Woodrow.

--Babylon Mystery Religion: Ancient & Modern. (Illus.). 1981. 4.95 (ISBN 0-916938-00-X). R Woodrow.

--Divorce & Remarriage: What Does the Bible Really Say? LC 82-99960. (Illus.). 1982. pap. 4.95 (ISBN 0-916938-06-9). R Woodrow.

--Great Prophecies of the Bible. (Illus.). 200p. 1971. 4.95 (ISBN 0-916938-02-6). R Woodrow.

--His Truth Is Marching On! Advanced Studies on Prophecy in the Light of History. (Illus.). 1977. pap. 4.95 (ISBN 0-916938-03-4). R Woodrow.

--Noah's Flood, Joshua's Long Day, & Lucifer's Fall: What Really Happened? (Illus.). 1984. 4.95 (ISBN 0-916938-07-7). R Woodrow.

--Women's Adornment: What Does the Bible Really Say? LC 76-17711. (Illus.). 1976. pap. 3.00 (ISBN 0-916938-01-8). R Woodrow.

Woodruff, C. Eveleigh, tr. see Brewyn, William.

Woodruff, George E. From Junk to Jesus & from Crime to Christ. 1983. 6.50 (ISBN 0-8062-1862-2). Carlton.

Woodruff, Sue. Meditations with TM Mechtild of Magdeburg. LC 82-73366. (Meditations with TM Ser.). (Illus.). 132p. (Orig.). 1982. pap. 6.95 (ISBN 0-939680-06-8). Bear & Co.
Woods, B. W. Christians in Pain: Perspectives on Suffering. 176p. 1982. pap. 4.95 (ISBN 0-8010-9652-9). Baker Bk.
Woods, C. Stacey. Growth of a Work of God. LC 77-6553. 1978. pap. 4.95 (ISBN 0-87784-741-X). Inter-Varsity.
Woods, Charles A., jt. auth. see Gray, G. Franklin.
Woods, Guy N. How to Read the Greek New Testament. 5.00 (ISBN 0-89225-103-4). Gospel Advocate.
--John. 1981. 10.95 (ISBN 0-89225-261-8). Gospel Advocate.
--Questions & Answers, Vol. II. 1986. 16.95 (ISBN 0-89225-277-4). Gospel Advocate.
Woods, Guy N see Gospel Advocate.
Woods, James. The Yoga-Systems of Patanjali: The Doctrine of the Concentration of the Mind. lib. bdg. 90.00 (ISBN 0-87968-083-0). Krishna Pr.
Woods, James H. Yoga-System of Patanjali. 1977. Repr. 19.50 (ISBN 0-89684-272-X, Pub. by Motilal Banarsidass India). Orient Bk Dist.
Woods, M. A. Characters of Paradise Lost. LC 72-6863. 1908. lib. bdg. 27.50 (ISBN 0-8414-0133-0). Folcroft.
Woods, Paulette. A Teachable Spirit. 72p. 1984. pap. 3.50 (ISBN 0-8341-0904-2). Beacon Hill.
Woods, Ron. You're in Control: A Guide for Latter-Day Saint Youth. (YA) 1986. 8.95 (ISBN 0-87579-046-1). Deseret Bk.
Woods, Sylvia. Fifty Christmas Carols for All Harps: Each Arranged for Beginning & Advanced Harpers. (Sylvia Woods Multi-Level Harp Bks.). (Illus.). 96p. 1984. pap. 13.95 (ISBN 0-9602990-5-X). Woods Mus Bks Pub.
Woodsmall, Ruth F. Moslem Women Enter a New World. LC 75-180309. Repr. of 1936 ed. 31.50 (ISBN 0-404-56334-1). AMS Pr.
--Women in the Changing Islamic System. (Illus.). 432p. 1983. text ed. 60.00x (ISBN 0-86590-154-6). Apt Bks.
Woodson, Meg. I'll Get to Heaven Before You Do! 96p. 1985. pap. text ed. 6.95 (ISBN 0-687-18611-0). Abingdon.
Woodson, William. Standing for Their Faith. 1979. 8.95 (ISBN 0-317-39803-2). Gospel Advocate.
Woodward, Evelyn. Poets, Prophets & Pragmatists: A New Challenge to Religious Life. LC 86-72375. 248p. (Orig.). 1987. pap. 6.95 (ISBN 0-87793-349-9). Ave Maria.
Woodward, F. L., tr. from Pali. Buddhist Stories. LC 78-70141. Repr. of 1925 ed. 20.00 (ISBN 0-404-17414-0). AMS Pr.
Woodward, F. L., tr. see Dhammapada.
Woodward, Luther E. Relations of Religious Training & Life Patterns to the Adult Religious Life. LC 71-177627. (Columbia University. Teachers College. Contributions to Education: No. 527). Repr. of 1932 ed. 22.50 (ISBN 0-404-55527-6). AMS Pr.
Woodward, Mary A. Edgar Cayce's Story of Karma. 1984. pap. 3.50 (ISBN 0-425-07697-0, Medallion). Berkley Pub.
Woodward, Mary A., compiled by. That Ye May Heal: A Manual for Individual & Group Study of Meditation for Healing, from the Edgar Cayce Records. rev. ed. 53p. 1970. pap. 3.50 (ISBN 0-87604-075-X). ARE Pr.
Woodward, Stephen B., jt. auth. see Osborne, Grant R.
Woodward, William H., ed. Desiderius Erasmus Concerning the Aim & Method of Education. LC 64-18613. (Classics in Education Ser.). (Orig.). 1964. pap. text ed. 5.00x (ISBN 0-8077-2347-9). Tchrs Coll.
Woody, Thomas. Early Quaker Education in Pennsylvania. LC 77-177623. (Columbia University. Teachers College. Contributions to Education Ser.: No. 105). Repr. of 1920 ed. 22.50 (ISBN 0-404-55105-X). AMS Pr.
--Early Quaker Education in Pennsylvania. LC 72-89255. (American Education: Its Men, Institutions & Ideas, Ser. 1). 1969. Repr. of 1920 ed. 17.50 (ISBN 0-405-01493-7). Ayer Co Pubs.
--Quaker Education in the Colony & State of New Jersey. LC 76-89256. (American Education: Its Men, Institutions & Ideas, Ser. 1). 1969. Repr. of 1923 ed. 32.00 (ISBN 0-405-01494-5). Ayer Co Pubs.
Woodyard, David O., jt. auth. see King, Paul G.
Woofenden, William R., ed. see Dole, Anita S.
Wooff, Bertram L., tr. see Dibelius, Martin.
Woolf, Cecil & Sewell, Brocard, eds. New Quests for Corvo: A Collection of Essays. 1961. 6.95 (ISBN 0-685-09185-6); pap. 3.00 (ISBN 0-685-09186-4). Dufour.
Woolley, Davis C., ed. Encyclopedia of Southern Baptists, Vol. III. LC 58-5417. (Illus.). 1971. 19.95 (ISBN 0-8054-6511-1). Broadman.
Woolley, Paul, ed. see Westminster Seminary Faculty Symposium.
Woolman, John. The Journal of John Woolman. 256p. 1972. pap. 5.95 (ISBN 0-8065-0294-0). Citadel Pr.
--Journal of John Woolman & a Plea for the Poor. 17.00 (ISBN 0-8446-0297-3). Peter Smith.
--Worship. 1983. pap. 2.50x (ISBN 0-87574-051-0, 051). Pendle Hill.
Woolsey, Ray, ed. see Beach, Walter R. & Beach, Bert B.
Woolsey, Raymond, ed. see Jordan, Jeanne.
Woolsey, Raymond, ed. see Scragg, Walter R.
Woolsey, Raymond, ed. see Venden, Morris.
Woolsey, Raymond, ed. see Watts, Dorothy E.
Woolsey, Raymond, ed. see Weber, Martin.
Woolsey, Raymond H., ed. see Barger, R. Curtis.
Woolsey, Raymond H., ed. see Case, Charles C.
Woolsey, Raymond H., ed. see Doward, Jan S.
Woolsey, Raymond H., ed. see Dudley, Roger L.
Woolsey, Raymond H., ed. see Egbert, Elaine.
Woolsey, Raymond H., ed. see Haines, Madge.
Woolsey, Raymond H., ed. see Kistler, Robert C.
Woolsey, Raymond H., ed. see Lohne, Alf.
Woolsey, Raymond H., ed. see Morgan, Trudy J.
Woolsey, Raymond H., ed. see Odom, Martha.
Woolsey, Raymond H., ed. see Reynolds, Louis B.
Woolsey, Raymond H., ed. see Tucker, James A. & Tucker, Priscilla.
Woolsey, Raymond H., ed. see Walton, Lewis R.
Woolsey, Raymond H., ed. see White, Arthur W.
Woolsey, Raymond H., ed. see White, Ellen G.
Woolston, Thomas. Discourses on the Miracles of Our Savior. Wellek, Rene, ed. LC 75-11268. (British Philosophers & Theologians of the 17th & 18th Centuries Ser.: Vol. 67). 565p. 1979. lib. bdg. 51.00 (ISBN 0-8240-1778-1); lib. bdg. 2700.00 set of 101 vols. (ISBN 0-686-60102-5). Garland Pub.
Woolton, John. The Christian Manual: Or, of the Life & Manners of True Christians. 1851. 21.00 (ISBN 0-384-69210-9). Johnson Repr.
Woosley, Raymond H., ed. see Vanderwerff, Corrine.
Wooster, Claire, jt. auth. see Meyners, Robert.
Wooten, Bill D. & Hunt, Sonja. Talk Is Not Enough. LC 83-61814. 112p. (Orig.). 1983. pap. text ed. 4.25 (ISBN 0-87148-849-3); 7.95 (ISBN 0-87148-850-7). Pathway Pr.
Worcester. Heaven. 1967. pap. 1.25 (ISBN 0-317-03716-1). College Pr Pub.
Worcester, Vern. From God with Love. pap. cancelled (ISBN 0-89900-106-8). College Pr Pub.
Worcester, William F. The Language of Parable. LC 76-6008. 1976. pap. 4.00 (ISBN 0-87785-155-7). Swedenborg.
Worchester, J. H., Jr. David Livingstone. (Golden Oldies Ser.). 128p. 1980. pap. 3.50 (ISBN 0-8024-4782-1). Moody.
Word Ministries, Inc. Prayers That Avail Much. 110p. (Orig.). 1980. pap. 3.95 (ISBN 0-89274-116-3). Harrison Hse.
Wordsworth, Charles. Shakespeare's Knowledge & Use of the Bible. 3rd ed. LC 73-144706. Repr. of 1880 ed. 27.50 (ISBN 0-404-07039-6). AMS Pr.
Wordsworth, John. National Church of Sweden. LC 11-35349. 1911. 20.00x (ISBN 0-8401-2821-5). A R Allenson.
Worgul, George S. From Magic to Metaphor: A Validation of Christian Sacraments. 248p. 1986. pap. text ed. 11.75 (ISBN 0-8191-4983-7). U Pr of Amer.
Workman, Herbert B. Christian Thought to the Reformation. 13.75 (ISBN 0-8369-7127-2, 7961). Ayer Co Pubs.
--The Dawn of the Reformation, 2 vols. LC 77-85273. Repr. of 1902 ed. 65.00 set (ISBN 0-404-16170-7). AMS Pr.
Works, John A., Jr. Pilgrims in a Strange Land: Hausa Communities in Chad. LC 76-23138. 1976. 32.00x (ISBN 0-231-03976-X). Columbia U Pr.
Worland, Stephen T. Scholasticism & Welfare Economics. 1967. 17.95 (ISBN 0-268-00246-0). U of Notre Dame Pr.
World Book Inc. Best-Loved Bible Stories: Old Testament & New Testament, 2 vols. LC 79-55309. (Illus.). 90p. 1980. write for info. (ISBN 0-7166-2059-6). World Bk.
World Book, Inc. Christmas in Ireland. LC 84-51015. (Round the World Christmas Program Ser.). (Illus.). 80p. 1985. write for info. (ISBN 0-7166-0885-5). World Bk.
World Book, Inc. Editorial Staff. Christmas in Denmark. LC 86-50556. (Round the World Christmas Program Ser.). (Illus.). 80p. 1986. write for info. (ISBN 0-7166-0886-3). World Bk.
World Book Staff, ed. Great Myths & Legends. LC 65-25105. (Childcraft-The How & Why Library). 310p. 1984. PLB write for info. (ISBN 0-7166-0684-4). World Bk.
World Church Congregational Music Committee. Hymns of the Saints. text ed. 10.50 (ISBN 0-8309-0326-7). Herald Hse.
World Committee For The Relief Of The Victims Of German Fascism. The Reichstag Fire Trial: The Second Brown Book of the Hitler Terror. LC 68-9605. 1969. Repr. of 1934 ed. 32.50 (ISBN 0-86527-165-8). Fertig.
World Conference on Religion & Peace, 3rd Assembly. Religion in the Struggle for World Community: Unabridged Proceedings. Jack, Homer A., ed. (Orig.). 1980. pap. 6.95 (ISBN 0-935934-05-7). World Confer Rel & Peace.
World Conference on Religion & Peace Staff. Religions for Human Dignity & World Peace: Unabridged Proceedings of the World Conference on Religion & Peace, 4th. Taylor, John B. & Gebhardt, Gunther, eds. 469p. 1986. pap. write for info. (ISBN 2-88235-000-7). World Confer Rel & Peace.
World Council of Churches, Assembly (6th: 1983: Vancouver, BC) Gathered for Life: Official Report, VI Assembly, World Council of Vancouver of Churches, Vancouver, Canada, 24 July - 10 August 1983. Gill, David, ed. LC 84-141282. Repr. of 1983 ed. 91.30 (2027544). Bks Demand UMI.
World Council of Churches, Geneva. Classified Catalog of the Ecumenical Movement: First Supplement. 1981. lib. bdg. 105.00 (ISBN 0-8161-0360-7, Hall Library). G K Hall.
World Council of Churches, Geneva, Switzerland. Classified Catalog of the Ecumenical Movement, 2 vols. 1972. lib. bdg. 198.00 (ISBN 0-8161-0925-7, Hall Library). G K Hall.
World Union of Jewish Studies, ed. Eighth World Congress of Jewish Studies. 242p. 1983. pap. text ed. 25.00x (Pub. by Magnes Pr Israel). Humanities.
Worley, Robert C. A Gathering of Strangers: Understanding the Life of Your Church. rev. & updated ed. LC 83-12343. (Illus.). 122p. 1983. pap. 8.95 (ISBN 0-664-24488-2). Westminster.
Worley, Win. Annihilating the Hosts of Hell: The Battle Royal, Vol. I. 1981. 5.00 (ISBN 0-686-75479-4). HBC.
--Battling the Hosts of Hell: Diary of an Exorcist. rev. ed. 1980. pap. 5.00 (ISBN 0-9601276-1-5). HBC.
--Conquering the Hosts of Hell: An Open Triumph. 1977. pap. 5.00 (ISBN 0-685-88034-6). HBC.
--Demolishing the Hosts of Hell: Every Christian's Job. rev. ed. (Orig.). 1980. pap. 5.00 (ISBN 0-685-60693-7). HBC.
Wormald, Francis. The Miniatures in the Gospels of St. Augustine: Corpus Christi College Ms. 286. LC 54-4312. (Sandars Lectures in Bibliography Ser.: 1948). (Illus.). pap. 20.00 (ISBN 0-317-09509-9, 2051474). Bks Demand UMI.
Wormhoudt, Arthur. Diwan Hassan ibn Thabit. (Arab Translation Ser.: No. 69). 180p. (Orig.). pap. 6.50x (ISBN 0-916358-21-6). Wormhoudt.
Wormhoudt, Arthur, tr. Gospel & Qasida. (Arab Translation Ser.: No. 84). (Illus.). 180p. (Orig.). 1985. pap. 6.50x (ISBN 0-916358-36-4). Wormhoudt.
Wormhoudt, Arthur, tr. from Classical Arabic. Selections from the Quran. (Arab Translation Ser.: No. 51). 175p. 1981. pap. 6.50x (ISBN 0-916358-03-8). Wormhoudt.
Wormser, Ron, Jr., jt. auth. see Korth, Russ.
Worrall, Ambrose & Worrall, Olga. The Gift of Healing. 240p. 1985. pap. 6.95 (ISBN 0-89804-142-2). Ariel OH.
Worrall, Arthur J. Quakers in the Colonial Northeast. LC 79-63086. 248p. 1980. 20.00x (ISBN 0-87451-174-7). U Pr of New Eng.
Worrall, Olga, jt. auth. see Worrall, Ambrose.
Worrell, A. S. The Worrell New Testament. 1980. Repr. of 1904 ed. 11.95 (ISBN 0-88243-392-X, 01-0392). Gospel Pub.
Worrell, George E. How to Take the Worry Out of Witnessing. LC 76-13342. 96p. 1976. pap. 4.95 (ISBN 0-8054-5568-X, 4255-68). Broadman.
Worrell, William H. The Coptic Manuscripts in the Freer Collection. Repr. of 1923 ed. 37.00 (ISBN 0-384-38810-8). Johnson Repr.
Worsley, Peter. The Trumpet Shall Sound: A Study of Cargo Cults in Melanesia. LC 67-26995. (Illus.). 1968. pap. 8.95 (ISBN 0-8052-0156-4). Schocken.
Worsley, Peter, ed. Marx & Marxism. LC 81-6848. (Key Sociologists Ser.). 126p. 1982. pap. 4.95x (ISBN 0-85312-375-6, NO. 3675 TAVISTOCK). Methuen Inc.
Worth, B. J. Income Tax Law for Ministers & Religious Workers: 1986 Edition for 1985 Returns. 64p. 1984. pap. 4.95 (ISBN 0-8010-9671-5, 9671-5). Baker Bk.
--Income Tax Law for Ministers & Religious Workers: 1987 Edition for Preparing 1986 Returns. 96p. 1987. pap. 4.95 (ISBN 0-8010-9676-6). Baker Bk.
Worth, Grant A. Do Your Prayers Bounce off the Ceiling? LC 81-17411. 68p. 1982. 6.95 (ISBN 0-87747-895-3). Deseret Bk.
Worth, Richard. You'll Be Old Someday, Too. LC 85-29419. 128p. 1986. lib. bdg. 11.90 (ISBN 0-531-10158-4). Watts.
Worthington, Everett L., Jr. How to Help the Hurting. LC 85-23070. (Illus.). 192p. 1986. pap. 5.95 (ISBN 0-87784-388-0). Inter-Varsity.
--When Someone Asks for Help: A Practical Guide to Counseling. LC 82-81. (Illus.). 239p. (Orig.). 1982. pap. 7.95 (ISBN 0-87784-375-9). Inter-Varsity.
Worthington, Lowell. Forty-Five & Satisfied. 1983. pap. 5.50 (ISBN 0-89137-313-6). Quality Pubns.
Worthington, Vivian. A History of Yoga. 176p. 1982. pap. 8.95 (ISBN 0-7100-9258-X). Methuen Inc.
Wotschke, Theodor. Geschichte Der Reformation in Polen. (Ger). 34.00 (ISBN 0-384-69301-6); pap. 28.00 (ISBN 0-384-69300-8). Johnson Repr.
Woude, A. S. van der see Loader, J. A.
Woude, A. S. van der, ed. The World of the Bible. Woudstra, Sierd, tr. from Dutch. (Illus.). 496p. 1986. 34.95 (ISBN 0-8028-2405-6). Eerdmans.
Woude A. S. Van, Der see Van Hartingsveld, L.
Woude A. S. Van, Der see Van Selms, A.
Woudstra, Marten H. The Book of Joshua. LC 80-23413. (New International Commentary on the Old Testament). 400p. 1981. 21.95 (ISBN 0-8028-2356-4). Eerdmans.
Woudstra, Sierd, tr. see Berkhof, Hendrikus.
Woudstra, Sierd, tr. see Woude, A. S. van der.
Wouk, Herman. This Is My God. LC 79-78741. 1959. 14.95 (ISBN 0-385-02158-5). Doubleday.
--This Is My God: The Jewish Way of Life. 1986. pap. 8.95 (ISBN 0-671-62258-7, Touchstone Bks). S&S.
Woychuk, N. A. Exposicion de Segunda Timoteo. Orig. Title: Exposition of Second Timothy. (Span.). 1976. pap. 3.95 (ISBN 0-8254-1879-8). Kregel.
Wozniak, Kenneth W. & Grenz, Stanley J., eds. Christian Freedom: Essays in Honor of Vernon C. Grounds. LC 86-24584. (Illus.). 284p. (Orig.). 1987. lib. bdg. 28.50 (ISBN 0-8191-5696-5); pap. text ed. 15.75 (ISBN 0-8191-5697-3). U Pr of Amer.
Woznicki, Andrew N. Journey to the Unknown: Catholic Doctrine on Ethnicity & Migration. LC 82-83230. 105p. (Orig.). 1982. pap. text ed. 3.95 (ISBN 0-910727-01-5). Golden Phoenix.
Wray, Daniel E. Biblical Church Discipline. 25p. 1978. pap. 1.20 (ISBN 0-85151-269-0). Banner of Truth.
--The Importance of the Local Church. 15p. (Orig.). 1981. pap. 1.00 (ISBN 0-85151-330-1). Banner of Truth.
Wray, Elizabeth, et al. Ten Lives of the Buddha: Siamese Temple Paintings & Jataka Tales. LC 73-179982. (Illus.). 156p. 1972. 20.00 (ISBN 0-8348-0067-5). Weatherhill.
Wray, Robert D., jt. auth. see Chapman, Arthur G.
Wren, Malcolm, tr. see Deppermann, Klaus.
Wren, Michael, tr. see Popieluszko, Jerzy.
Wren, Thomas E. Agency & Urgency: The Origin of Moral Obligation. 169p. 1974. 9.95 (ISBN 0-913750-06-9). Precedent Pub.
Wrenn, Lawrence G. Annulments. 4th rev. ed. vi, 145p. (Orig.). 1983. pap. 4.00 (ISBN 0-943616-16-6). Canon Law Soc.
--Decisions. 2nd, rev. ed. vi, 200p. (Orig.). 1983. pap. 4.50 (ISBN 0-943616-17-4). Canon Law Soc.
Wrenn, Michael J., tr. see Carmignac, Jean.
Wrenn, Michael J., tr. see Toinet, Paul.
Wright, A. D. The Counter-Reformation: Catholic Europe & the Non-Christian World. LC 82-3210. 334p. 1984. pap. 12.95 (ISBN 0-312-17022-X). St Martin.
--Workshoes for Christ. 1979. pap. 3.75 (ISBN 0-89225-185-9). Gospel Advocate.
Wright, Arthur F. Buddhism in Chinese History. LC 59-7432. (Illus.). 1959. 13.50x (ISBN 0-8047-0546-1); pap. 6.95 (ISBN 0-8047-0548-8, SP118). Stanford U Pr.
Wright, Arthur F., ed. The Confucian Persuasion. LC 60-8561. 1960. 30.00x (ISBN 0-8047-0018-4). Stanford U Pr.
--Confucianism & Chinese Civilization. LC 75-6317. 364p. 1964. 27.50x (ISBN 0-8047-0890-8); pap. 10.95 (ISBN 0-8047-0891-6, SP138). Stanford U Pr.
Wright, Arthur F. & Twitchett, Denis, eds. Confucian Personalities. LC 62-16950. (Illus.). 1962. 30.00x (ISBN 0-8047-0044-3). Stanford U Pr.
Wright, Arthur F., jt. ed. see Nivison, David S.
Wright, B. Pueblo Cultures. (Iconography of Religions X Ser.: No. 4). (Illus.). xii, 29p. 1986. pap. 26.25 (ISBN 90-04-07106-7, Pub. by E J Brill). Heinman.
Wright, Beverly W. God Made Everything. LC 82-80029. (Happy Day Bks.). (Illus.). 24p. (Orig.). 1982. pap. 1.59 (ISBN 0-87239-537-5, 3583). Standard Pub.

Wright, Bonnie L., et al. A Prophet Crying in the Wilderness. Donohue, John & Turowski, Diane, eds. 164p. 1986. pap. 6.98 (ISBN 0-9616309-0-6). Mountain Movers.

Wright, C. D. Translations of the Gospel Back into Tongues. LC 82-17047. (SUNY Poetry Ser.). 84p. 1982. 24.50x (ISBN 0-87395-652-4) (ISBN 0-87395-685-0). State U NY Pr.

Wright, Charles & Neil, Charles, eds. The Protestant Dictionary: Containing Articles on the History, Doctrines, & Practices of the Christian Church. LC 73-155436. 1971. Repr. of 1933 ed. 65.00x (ISBN 0-8103-3388-0). Gale.

Wright, Charles H. Studies in Daniel's Prophecy. 368p. 1983. lib. bdg. 13.95 (ISBN 0-86524-162-7, 2703). Klock & Klock.

--Zechariah & His Prophecies. 1980. 24.95 (ISBN 0-86524-020-5, 3801). Klock & Klock.

Wright, Christopher. The Christian Church. (Today's World Ser.). (Illus.). 72p. 1982. 16.95 (ISBN 0-7134-4279-4, Pub. by Batsford England). David & Charles.

--Proverbs-Isaiah 39. 1983. pap. 4.95 (ISBN 0-87508-158-4). Chr Lit.

Wright, Christopher J. An Eye for an Eye: The Place of Old Testament Ethics Today. LC 83-18651. 180p. 1983. pap. 8.95 (ISBN 0-87784-821-1). Inter-Varsity.

Wright, Clifford K. Bunyan As a Man of Letters. LC 77-4072. 1977. Repr. lib. bdg. 9.50 (ISBN 0-8414-9601-3). Folcroft.

Wright, Conrad. A Stream of Light. 1975. pap. 5.75 (ISBN 0-933840-14-4). Unitarian Univ.

Wright, Conrad, ed. Three Prophets of Religious Liberalism. 1961. pap. 4.00 (ISBN 0-933840-20-9). Unitarian Univ.

Wright, David. Wisdom As a Lifestyle: Building Biblical Life-Codes. 1987. pap. 6.95 (ISBN 0-310-44311-3). Zondervan.

Wright, David & Wright, Jill. Praise with Understanding. 64p. 1983. pap. 3.50 (ISBN 0-85364-355-5, Pub. by Paternoster UK). Attic Pr.

--Thirty Hymns of the Wesleys. 65p. 1986. pap. 4.95 (ISBN 0-85364-414-4, Pub. by Paternoster UK). Attic Pr.

Wright, David F., ed. Essays in Evangelical Social Ethics. 192p. 1982. 18.95 (ISBN 0-85364-288-5); pap. text ed. 9.50 (ISBN 0-85364-290-7). Attic Pr.

--Essays in Evangelical Social Ethics. LC 82-62581. 192p. (Orig.). 1983. pap. 8.95 (ISBN 0-8192-1326-8). Morehouse.

Wright, Don. Mantle of Christ: A History of the Sydney Central Methodist Mission. (Illus.). 179p. 1985. text ed. 25.00x. U of Queensland Pr.

Wright, Dudley. Roman Catholicism & Freemasonry. 1977. lib. bdg. 69.95 (ISBN 0-8490-2531-1). Gordon Pr.

Wright, E. A. Ystoire de la Passion. Repr. of 1944 ed. 14.00 (ISBN 0-384-70484-0). Johnson Repr.

Wright, Elliott. Go Free. 128p. (Orig.). 1973. pap. 1.75 (ISBN 0-377-03011-2). Friend Pr.

--Holy Company: Christian Heros & Heroines. 1980. 12.95 (ISBN 0-02-631590-4). Macmillan.

Wright, Elliott, jt. auth. see Lynn, Robert W.

Wright, Ernest, jt. auth. see Boling, Robert G.

Wright, Ezekiel & Inesse, Daniel. God Is Gay: An Evolutionary Spiritual Work. 2nd, rev. ed. 1982. pap. 4.95 (ISBN 0-934350-01-9). Tayu Pr.

Wright, Fred. Manners & Customs of Bible Lands. (Affordables Ser.). 336p. pap. 5.50 (ISBN 0-8024-0416-2). Moody.

Wright, G. Ernest. Biblical Archaeology. rev. ed. LC 57-5020. (Illus.). 292p. 1963. 27.50 (ISBN 0-664-20420-1). Westminster.

--Isaiah. LC 59-10454. (Layman's Bible Commentary, Vol. 11). 1964. pap. 4.95 (ISBN 0-8042-3071-4). John Knox.

Wright, G. Ernest, ed. The Bible & the Ancient Near East: Essays in Honor of William Foxwell Albright. 1979. Repr. of 1961 ed. 15.00x (ISBN 0-931464-03-X). Eisenbrauns.

Wright, G. Ernest & Filson, F. V., eds. Westminster Historical Maps of Bible Lands. 24p. pap. 2.50 (ISBN 0-664-29077-9). Westminster.

Wright, G. Ernest & Filson, Floyd V., eds. Westminster Historical Atlas to the Bible. rev. ed. LC 56-9123. 130p. 1956. 18.95 (ISBN 0-664-20535-6). Westminster.

Wright, G. Ernest, jt. ed. see Miller, Samuel H.

Wright, G. H. Von see Von Wright, G. H.

Wright, Geoffrey N. Discovering Abbeys & Priories. (Discovery Ser.: No. 57). (Illus.). 1985. pap. 4.50 (ISBN 0-85263-454-4, Pub. by Shire Pubns England). Seven Hills Bks.

Wright, Gordon. In Quest of Healing. LC 83-82030. 176p. (Orig.). 1984. pap. 4.95 (ISBN 0-88243-614-7, 02-0614). Gospel Pub.

Wright, H. Norman. The Christian Use of Emotional Power. 160p. 1974. pap. 5.95 (ISBN 0-8007-5213-9, Pub. by Power Bk.). Revell.

--Improving Your Self Image. LC 83-80119. 160p. (Orig.). 1983. pap. 4.95 (ISBN 0-89081-382-5). Harvest Hse.

--The Living Marriage. (Illus.). 128p. 1975. 12.95 (ISBN 0-8007-0722-2). Revell.

--Making Peace with Your Past. 1984. 10.95 (ISBN 0-8007-1228-5). Revell.

--Marital Counseling: A Biblical Behavioral Cognitive Approach. 370p. 1981. 16.95 (ISBN 0-938786-00-8). Chr Marriage.

--Now I Know Why I'm Depressed. 1984. pap. 4.95 (ISBN 0-89081-423-6). Harvest Hse.

--The Rights & Wrongs of Anger. 176p. (Orig.). 1985. pap. 4.95 (ISBN 0-89081-457-0). Harvest Hse.

--Seasons of a Marriage. LC 82-80010. 1983. pap. 4.95 (ISBN 0-8307-0912-6, 5418058). Regal.

Wright, H. Norman & Inmon, Marvin N. Help, We're Having a Baby. LC 79-929649. 192p. 1984. pap. 5.95 (ISBN 0-8307-0997-5, 5418362). Regal.

Wright, H. Norman & Johnson, Rex. Characteristics of a Caring Home Growthbook. 80p. (Orig.). 1983. 4.95 (ISBN 0-88449-048-3, A424608). Vision Hse.

Wright, J. Eugene, Jr. Erikson: Identity & Religion. 240p. (Orig.). 1982. pap. 9.95 (ISBN 0-8164-2362-8, HarpR). Har-Row.

Wright, J. Robert, jt. ed. see Witmer, Joseph W.

Wright, J. S., jt. auth. see Burrell, M. C.

Wright, Jill, jt. auth. see Wright, David.

Wright, John. Mary Our Hope. Almagno, Stephen, pref. by. LC 84-80015. 227p. (Orig.). 1984. pap. 8.95 (ISBN 0-89870-046-9). Ignatius Pr.

--The Saints Always Belong to the Present. Almagno, Stephen, pref. by. LC 84-80016. 221p. 1984. pap. 8.95 (ISBN 0-89870-047-7). Ignatius Pr.

Wright, John W. And Then There Was One. 120p. (Orig.). 1985. pap. 4.95 (ISBN 0-8341-1057-1). Beacon Hill.

Wright, Leoline L. After Death, What? rev. ed. Small, W. Emmett & Todd, Helen, eds. (Theosophical Manual: No. 5). 96p. 1974. pap. 2.50 (ISBN 0-913004-15-4). Point Loma Pub.

--Reincarnation. LC 74-18350. pap. 3.25 (ISBN 0-8356-0453-5, Quest). Theos Pub Hse.

Wright, Leoline L., et al. Reincarnation: A Lost Chord in Modern Thought. Small, Emmett & Todd, Helen, eds. (Theosophical Manual). 122p. 1975. pap. 3.25 (ISBN 0-8356-0453-5). Point Loma Pub.

Wright, Linda R. Staying on Top When Things Go Wrong. 120p. 1983. pap. 2.95 (ISBN 0-8423-6623-7). Tyndale.

Wright, Linda R., jt. auth. see Wright, Rusty.

Wright, Louis B. Religion & Empire. 1965. lib. bdg. 18.50x (ISBN 0-374-98816-1, Octagon). Hippocrene Bks.

Wright, Ludie J. The Closing of Man's History. (Bible Prophecy Ser.: No. 1). (Illus.). 209p. (Orig.). 1986. 15.95 (ISBN 0-9617290-0-7); pap. 12.95 (ISBN 0-9617290-1-5). Hse Better Sales.

Wright, Luella M. Literary Life of the Early Friends, 1650-1725. LC 32-25426. Repr. of 1932 ed. 19.50 (ISBN 0-404-07046-9). AMS Pr.

Wright, Machaelle S. Behaving As If the God in All Life Mattered: A New Age Ecology. (Illus.). 216p. 1986. pap. cancelled (ISBN 0-913299-33-2). Stillpoint.

Wright, Sr. Mary K. God's Unfolding Plan. 2.00 (ISBN 0-87505-307-6, Pub. by Lawrence). Borden.

Wright, Norm. After You Say I Do. LC 79-66960. 80p. (Orig.). 1979. pap. 4.95 (ISBN 0-89081-205-5). Harvest Hse.

--Healing of Fears. LC 81-83238. 176p. (Orig.). 1982. pap. 4.95 (ISBN 0-89081-302-7). Harvest Hse.

Wright, Norman. Answer to Discipline. LC 76-21113. (Answer Ser.). 1976. pap. 1.95 (ISBN 0-89081-061-3, 0613). Harvest Hse.

--Answer to Divorce. LC 76-52831. (Answer Ser.). 1977. pap. 1.95 (ISBN 0-89081-033-8, 0338). Harvest Hse.

--An Answer to Loneliness. (Orig.). pap. 1.95 (ISBN 0-89081-077-X). Harvest Hse.

--An Answer to Parent-Teen Relationships. (Orig.). pap. 1.95 (ISBN 0-89081-075-3). Harvest Hse.

--An Answer to Submission & Decision Making. pap. 1.95 (ISBN 0-89081-078-8). Harvest Hse.

--Fulfilled Marriage. LC 76-21981. (Answer Ser.). 1976. pap. 1.95 (ISBN 0-89081-060-5, 0605). Harvest Hse.

--How to Have a Creative Crisis. 176p. 1986. 10.95 (ISBN 0-8499-0540-0). Word Bks.

--Living with Your Emotions: Self-Image & Depression. LC 79-83661. 1979. 7.95 (ISBN 0-89081-193-8); avail. tchr's guide. Harvest Hse.

--Self-Talk, Prayer & Imagery in Counseling (RCC) 192p. 1986. 12.95 (ISBN 0-8499-0585-0). Word Bks.

--Training Christians to Counsel. 236p. 1983. Repr. 14.95 (ISBN 0-89081-422-8). Harvest Hse.

Wright, Norman & Inmon, Marvin. Guidebook to Dating, Waiting & Choosing a Mate. LC 78-26913. 1978. pap. 4.95 (ISBN 0-89081-150-4). Harvest Hse.

--Preparing Youth for Dating, Courtship & Marriage-Teacher's Guide. LC 78-56879. (Orig.). 1978. pap. 9.95 (ISBN 0-89081-147-4); transparencies & repro masters incl. Harvest Hse.

Wright, Norman & Johnson, Rex. Building Positive Parent-Teen Relationships: Teacher's Guide. LC 78-56980. 1978. pap. 9.95 (ISBN 0-89081-148-2); transparencies & repro masters incl. Harvest Hse.

--Communication: Key to Your Teens. LC 78-61872. 1978. pap. 3.95 (ISBN 0-89081-158-X). Harvest Hse.

Wright, Norman & Roberts, Wes. Before You Say I Do: Study Manual. LC 77-94133. 1978. 4.95 (ISBN 0-89081-119-9). Harvest Hse.

Wright, Paul S. The Presbyterian Elder. rev. ed. 64p. (Orig.). 1986. pap. 4.95 saddle stapled (ISBN 0-664-24014-3). Westminster.

Wright, Ralph. Ripples of Stillness. 1978. 5.95 (ISBN 0-8198-0365-0). Dghtrs St Paul.

Wright, Robin. Sacred Rage: The Wrath of Militant Islam. 336p. 1986. pap. 7.95 (ISBN 0-671-62811-9, Touchstone Bks). S&S.

Wright, Rusty & Wright, Linda R. How to Unlock the Secrets of Love & Sex in Marriage. 144p. 1985. pap. 3.95 (ISBN 0-916441-08-3). Barbour & Co.

Wright, Sandra L. Country Handcrafts Christmas Collection. 34p. 1985. pap. 5.95 (ISBN 0-89821-069-0). Reiman Assocs.

Wright, Sara M. Brief Survey of the Bible. 1958. pap. 5.95 (ISBN 0-87213-971-9). Loizeaux.

Wright, Stafford. Psalms. (Bible Study Commentaries Ser.). 152p. 1982. pap. 4.95 (ISBN 0-317-43374-1). Chr Lit.

Wright, T. R. The Religion of Humanity: The Impact of Comtean Positivism on Victorian Britain. (Illus.). 325p. 1986. 44.50 (ISBN 0-521-30671-X). Cambridge U Pr.

Wright, Thomas. Three Chapters of Letters Relating to the Suppression of Monasteries. 37.00 (ISBN 0-384-69545-0). Johnson Repr.

Wright, Thomas, ed. Churchwardens' Accounts of the Town of Ludlow in Shropshire. (Camden Society, London. Publications, First Ser.: No. 102). Repr. of 1869 ed. 19.00 (ISBN 0-404-50202-4, A17-1267). AMS Pr.

--Early Travels in Palestine. LC 77-84863. (Bohn's Antiquarian Library). Repr. of 1848 ed. 31.50 (ISBN 0-404-50026-9). AMS Pr.

--Three Chapters of Letters Relating to the Suppression of Monasteries. LC 72-74268. (Camden Society, London. Publications First Ser.: No. 26). Repr. of 1843 ed. 37.00 (ISBN 0-404-50126-5). AMS Pr.

Wright, Toblas A., jt. ed. see Evans, Thomas G.

Wright, Tom, tr. see Uchiyama, Kosho & Uchiyama, Kosho.

Wright, W. Aldis, jt. auth. see Eastwood, J.

Wright, Wendy M., jt. ed. see Capps, Walter H.

Wright, William. An Early Christian Syrian Martyrology: The Names of Our Lords the Confessors & Victors & the Days on Which They Gained Their Crowns. pap. 5.95 (ISBN 0-317-11387-9). Eastern Orthodox.

--A Short History of Syriac Literature. LC 78-14330. 1978. Repr. of 1894 ed. lib. bdg. 42.50 (ISBN 0-8414-9709-5). Folcroft.

Wright, William, tr. A Briefe Relation of the Persecution Lately Made Against the Catholike Christians in Japonia, Taken Out of the Annuall Letters of the Soc. of Jesus. LC 75-26238. (English Experience Ser.: No. 159). 1969. Repr. of 1619 ed. 35.00 (ISBN 90-221-0159-2). Walter J Johnson.

Wright, William A. The Hexaplar Psalter, Being the Book of Psalms in Six English Versions. 395p. Repr. of 1911 ed. lib. bdg. 63.00X (Pub. by G Olms BRD). Coronet Bks.

Wrightman, Paul. Paul's Early Letters: From Hope, Through Faith, to Love. LC 83-7126. 148p. (Orig.). 1983. pap. 6.95 (ISBN 0-8189-0440-2). Alba.

--Paul's Later Letters: From Promise to Fulfillment. LC 84-11039. 238p. (Orig.). 1984. pap. 9.95 (ISBN 0-8189-0441-0). Alba.

Wringe, Colin, ed. see Sealey, John.

Writers Program, Utah. Provo, Pioneer Mormon City. LC 73-3654. (American Guide Ser.). 1942. Repr. 11.50 (ISBN 0-404-57954-X). AMS Pr.

Wroblewski, Sergius. The July Secret: The Prohetic Meaning of Fatima about Russia & the Future of the Church. (Illus.). 90p. (Orig.). 1985. pap. 4.50 (ISBN 0-913382-15-9, 105-39). Prow Bks-Franciscan.

Wrong, George M., ed. see Sagard-Theodat, Gabriel.

Wroth, Lawrence C. Parson Weems: A Biographical & Critical Study. LC 75-31143. Repr. of 1911 ed. 10.00 (ISBN 0-404-13615-X). AMS Pr.

Wroth, William. The Chapel of Our Lady of Talpa. 1979. pap. 10.00 (ISBN 0-916537-28-5, Taylor Museum). CO Springs Fine Arts.

--The Chapel of Our Lady of Talpa. LC 78-58985. (Illus.). 104p. (Orig.). 1982. pap. 8.95 (ISBN 0-295-95920-7, Pub. by Taylor Museum). U of Wash Pr.

Wu, Chao-Kwang. The International Aspect of the Missionary Movement in China. LC 75-41300. (Johns Hopkins University. Studies in Historical & Political Science: Extra Volumes; New Ser.: No. 11). Repr. of 1930 ed. 18.50 (ISBN 0-404-14708-9). AMS Pr.

Wu, John C. Beyond East & West. 388p. 1980. 5.95 (ISBN 0-89955-182-3, Pub. by Mei Ya China). Intl Spec Bk.

Wu, Kuang-ming. Chuang Tzu: World Philosopher at Play. (AAR Studies in Religion). 12.95 (ISBN 0-89130-537-8, 01-00-26). Scholars Pr GA.

Wuellner, Bernard. Summary of Scholastic Principles. LC 56-10903. 1956. 1.50 (ISBN 0-8294-0084-2). Loyola.

Wuellner, Flora S. Prayer, Stress & Our Inner Wounds. 94p. (Orig.). 1985. pap. 4.95 (ISBN 0-8358-0501-8). Upper Room.

Wuellner, Wilhelm H. & Leslie, Robert C. The Surprising Gospel: Intriguing Psychological Insights from the New Testament. 176p. (Orig.). 1983. pap. 11.95 (ISBN 0-687-40724-9). Abingdon.

Wuerffel, Stella. Two Rivers to Freedom. LC 80-66578. 385p. 1980. 11.95 (ISBN 0-915644-20-7). Clayton Pub Hse.

Wuerl, Donald & Wilson, Michael. A Visit to the Vatican for Young People. (Illus.). 1980. 3.50 (ISBN 0-8198-8002-7). Dghtrs St Paul.

Wuerl, Donald W. The Catholic Priesthood Today. 164p. 1976. 6.95 (ISBN 0-8199-0591-7). Franciscan Herald.

Wuest, Kenneth. Practical Use of the Greek New Testament. Wise, Donald, rev. by. 160p. 1982. text ed. 11.95 (ISBN 0-8024-6737-7). Moody.

Wuest, Kenneth S. Word Studies in the Greek New Testament, for the English Reader, 16 bks. Incl. Bk. 1. Golden Nuggets. pap. 4.95 (ISBN 0-8028-1242-2); Bk. 2. Bypaths. pap. 3.95 (ISBN 0-8028-1318-6); Bk. 3. Treasures. pap. 3.95 (ISBN 0-8028-1243-0); Bk. 4. Untranslatable Riches. pap. 4.95 (ISBN 0-8028-1241-4); Bk. 5. Studies in Vocabulary. pap. 3.95 (ISBN 0-8028-1240-6); Bk. 6. Great Truths to Live by. pap. 4.95 (ISBN 0-8028-1246-5); Bk. 7. Mark. pap. 5.95 (ISBN 0-8028-1230-9); Bk. 8. Romans. pap. 4.95 (ISBN 0-8028-1231-7); Bk. 9. Galatians. pap. 4.95 (ISBN 0-8028-1232-5); Bk. 10. Ephesians & Colossians. pap. 5.95 (ISBN 0-8028-1233-3); Bk. 11. Philippians. pap. 4.95 (ISBN 0-8028-1234-1); Bk. 12. The Pastoral Epistles. pap. 6.95 (ISBN 0-8028-1236-8); Bk. 13. Hebrews. pap. 6.95 (ISBN 0-8028-1235-X); Bk. 14. First Peter. pap. 4.95 (ISBN 0-8028-1237-6); Bk. 15. In These Last Days. pap. 4.95 (ISBN 0-8028-1238-4); Bk. 16. Prophetic Light in the Present Darkness. pap. 2.95 (ISBN 0-8028-1239-2). **Set. pap. 80.20 (ISBN 0-8028-1248-1); Current 4 vols. 69.95 (ISBN 0-8028-2280-0). Eerdmans.**

Wuest, Kenneth S., tr. The New Testament: An Expanded Translation. 1961. 14.95 (ISBN 0-8028-3306-3); pap. 9.95 (ISBN 0-8028-1229-5). Eerdmans.

Wuestefeld, Mary F. To Drink of His Love. Wheeler, Gerald, ed. (Banner Ser.). 128p. (Orig.). 1986. pap. 6.50 (ISBN 0-8280-0312-2). Review & Herald.

Wulf, Dick. Conozcase y Consagrese. Orig. Title: Find Yourself, Give Yourself. (Span.). 1986. write for info. (ISBN 0-8297-0688-7). Life Pubs Intl.

--De la Decouverte au Don de Soi. Orig. Title: Find Yourself, Give Yourself. (Fr.). 1986. write for info. (ISBN 0-8297-0687-9). Life Pubs Intl.

--Find Yourself, Give Yourself. LC 83-61819. 162p. 1983. pap. 5.95 (ISBN 0-89109-496-2). NavPress.

Wulf, F., et al. Ignatius of Loyola: His Personality & Spiritual Heritage, 1556-1956, Studies on the 400th Anniversary of His Death. LC 77-16677. (Modern Scholarly Studies About the Jesuits,in English Translations Ser.: No. 2). 318p. 1977. pap. 7.00 (ISBN 0-912422-22-X). Inst Jesuit.

Wulff, Donna M. Drama as Mode of Religious Realization: The Vidaghamadhava of Rupa Gosvamin. (American Academy of Religion Academy Ser.: No. 43). 280p. 1985. 14.95 (ISBN 0-89130-608-0, 01 01 43). Scholars Pr GA.

Wulff, Donna M., jt. ed. see Hawley, John S.

Wunsch, William F. Marriage: Ideals & Realizations. 155p. 1973. 1.75 (ISBN 0-87785-122-0). Swedenborg.

--An Outline of Swedenborg's Teaching. LC 74-23796. 275p. 1975. pap. 3.95 (ISBN 0-87785-151-4). Swedenborg.

Wurm, Alois. Character-Portrayals in the Ramayana of Valmiki. 1977. 30.00x (ISBN 0-686-22658-5). Intl Bk Dist.

Wurmbrand, Judy. Escape From the Grip. 126p. 1985. pap. 4.95 (ISBN 0-88264-153-0). Diane Bks.

Wurmbrand, Max & Roth, Cecil. The Jewish People: Four Thousand Years of Survival. rev. ed. (Illus.). 480p. 1987. 39.95 (ISBN 0-915361-64-7, Dist. by Watts). Adama Pubs Inc.

Wurmbrand, Richard. In God's Underground. Orig. Title: Christ in the Communist Prisons. 1973. pap. text ed. 3.95 (ISBN 0-88264-003-8). Diane Bks.

--Marx & Satan. 143p. 1986. pap. 5.95 (ISBN 0-89107-379-5, Crossway Bks). Good News.

--My Answer to the Moscow's Bible. pap. 4.95 (ISBN 0-88264-001-1). Diane Bks.

--One Hundred Prison Meditations. 1984. pap. 2.95 (ISBN 0-88270-577-6). Bridge Pub.

--Reaching Toward the Heights. 1979. pap. 7.95x (ISBN 0-88264-142-5). Diane Bks.

--Tortured for Christ. 1973. pap. 2.95 (ISBN 0-88264-001-1). Diane Bks.

--Tortured for Christ. LC 86-72054. 128p. 1987. pap. 4.95 (ISBN 0-89107-408-2, Crossway Bks). Good News.

--Victorious Faith. 1979. pap. 3.95 (ISBN 0-88264-120-4). Diane Bks.

--Where Christ is Still Tortured. 160p. 1982. pap. 3.95 (ISBN 0-88264-162-X). Diane Bks.

--Where Christ Still Suffers. Tr. of Where Christ Is Still Tortured. 1984. pap. 3.50 (ISBN 0-88270-578-4). Bridge Pub.

--With God in Solitary Confinement. 1979. pap. 4.95 (ISBN 0-88264-002-X). Diane Bks.

Wurmbrand, Sabina. The Pastor's Wife. 1979. pap. 4.95 (ISBN 0-88264-000-3). Diane Bks.

Wurth, Elmer P. Papal Documents Relating to the New China, 1937-1984. 193p. (Orig.). 1985. pap. 10.00 (ISBN 0-88344-403-8). Orbis Bks.

Wurth, G. Niebuhr. (Modern Thinkers Ser.). 1960. pap. 1.50 (ISBN 0-87552-586-5). Presby & Reformed.

Wurthwein, Ernst. The Text of the Old Testament. Rhodes, Erroll F., tr. LC 79-15492. Tr. of Text Des Alten Testaments. (Illus.). 1980. text ed. 16.95 (ISBN 0-8028-3530-9). Eerdmans.

Wurtzel, Sara, jt. auth. see Wurtzel, Yehuda.

Wurtzel, Yehuda & Wurtzel, Sara. Lights: A Fable of Hanukahkah. LC 84-18297. (Illus.). 64p. 1985. pap. 7.95 (ISBN 0-940646-56-0). Rossel Bks.

Wurzburger, Walter S. see Lamm, Norman.

Wust, Klaus. Record of Hawksbill Church 1788-1850, Page County, Virginia. 1979. pap. 5.50 (ISBN 0-917968-06-9). Shenandoah Hist.

--The Saint-Adventurers of the Virginia Frontier. LC 76-48566. (Illus.). 1977. 8.50 (ISBN 0-917968-29-8). Shenandoah Hist.

Wust, Klaus, jt. auth. see Stewart, John.

Wust, Klaus, ed. Lutheran Zion-Pine Church Record, 1786-1827-Stony Creek, Virginia, Vol. I & II. Martin, Ilse & Smith, George M., trs. from Ger. (Shenandoah Genealogical Source Bks.: Nos. 8 & 9). (Illus.). 1985. pap. 15.00 set (ISBN 0-917968-13-1). Vol. I, 49p. Vol. II, 44p. Shenandoah Hist.

Wuthnow, Robert. Experimentation in American Religion: The New Mysticisms & Their Implications for the Churches. 1978. 31.00x (ISBN 0-520-03446-5). U of Cal Pr.

Wuthnow, Robert, jt. auth. see Liebman, Robert C.

Wuthnow, Robert, ed. The Religious Dimension: New Directions in Quantitative Research. LC 79-6948. 1979. 29.95 (ISBN 0-12-766050-X). Acad Pr.

Wyatt, Janice B. Come, Let Us Welcome Jesus. 1980. pap. 3.75 (ISBN 0-89536-411-5, 0375). CSS of Ohio.

Wyatt, Margaret. My Friend Jesus. LC 86-90051. (Illus.). 20p. (Orig.). 1986. pap. 2.25 (ISBN 0-9616117-0-7). M Wyatt.

Wyckoff, D. Campbell, ed. Renewing the Sunday School & the CCD. LC 85-19419. 254p. (Orig.). 1986. pap. 14.95 (ISBN 0-89135-053-5). Religious Educ.

Wyckoff, D. Campbell & Richter, Don, eds. Religious Education Ministry with Youth. LC 81-19239. 257p. (Orig.). 1982. pap. 12.95 (ISBN 0-89135-030-6). Religious Educ.

Wycliffe, John. Apology for Lollard Doctrines, Attributed to Wycliffe. LC 80-312858. Repr. of 1842 ed. 28.00 (ISBN 0-404-50120-6). AMS Pr.

--Apology for Lollard Doctrines, Attributed to Wycliffe. 28.00 (ISBN 0-384-69838-7). Johnson Repr.

--Wyclifftte Sermons, Vol. 1. Hudson, Anne, ed. (Oxford English Texts). (Illus.). 1983. 105.00x (ISBN 0-19-812704-9). Oxford U Pr.

Wycliffe, John D. Wycliffe, Select English Writings. Winn, Herbert E., ed. LC 75-41303. Repr. of 1929 ed. 18.50 (ISBN 0-404-14635-X). AMS Pr.

Wyeth, John. Wyeth's Repository of Sacred Music, 1 & 2 pts. LC 64-18989. (Music Reprint Ser.). 148p. 1964. Repr. of 1820 ed. Pt. 1. 25.00 (ISBN 0-306-70903-1); Pt. 2. 25.00 (ISBN 0-686-85854-9). Da Capo.

Wyke, Millie Van see Van Wyke, Millie.

Wyker, Bertha P. Spanning the Decades: A Spiritual Pilgrimage. (Illus.). 224p. 1981. 8.50 (ISBN 0-682-49746-0). Exposition Pr FL.

Wylam, P. Guru Nanak. (Illus.). 1979. pap. 4.00 (ISBN 0-89744-154-0). Auromere.

Wylie, J. A. History of the Waldenses. 1985. Repr. of 1870 ed. 15.00 (ISBN 0-317-38296-9). Church History.

Wyllie, Robert W. Spiritism in Ghana: A Study of New Religious Movements. Cherry, Conrad, ed. LC 79-20486. (Studies in Religion: No. 21). 139p. 14.00 (ISBN 0-89130-355-3, 01-00-21); pap. 9.95 (ISBN 0-89130-356-1). Scholars Pr GA.

Wyly, Louise B. Fun Devotions for Kids. (Illus.). 64p. 1985. pap. 2.50 (ISBN 0-87239-891-9, 2821). Standard Pub.

--Twenty-Six Lessons for Children's Worship: Listening When God Speaks. (Illus.). 144p. 1986. 8.95 (ISBN 0-87403-057-9, 3321). Standard Pub.

Wyman, David S. The Abandonment of the Jews. LC 84-42711. 480p. 1986. pap. 8.95 (ISBN 0-394-74077-7). Pantheon.

--The Abandonment of the Jews: America & the Holocaust, 1941-1945. LC 84-42711. 450p. 1984. 6.00 (ISBN 0-394-42813-7). Pantheon.

Wyman, L. C. & Kluckhohn, Clyde. Navaho Classification of Their Song Ceremonials. LC 38-23008. (American Anthro. Association Memoirs). 1938. pap. 15.00 (ISBN 0-527-00549-5). Kraus Repr.

Wyman, L. C., jt. auth. see Kluckhohn, Clyde.

Wyman, Leland C. Blessingway. LC 66-28786. (Illus.). 660p. 1970. U of Ariz Pr.

--The Mountainway of the Navajo. LC 74-83333. 271p. 1975. 14.50x (ISBN 0-8165-0412-1). U of Ariz Pr.

Wyman, Walter E., Jr. The Concept of Glaubenslehre: Ernst Troeltsch & the Theological Heritage of Schleiermacher. LC 83-4432. (American Academy of Religion, Academy Ser.). 276p. 1983. 14.95 (ISBN 0-89130-620-X, 01 01 44). Scholars Pr GA.

Wynanda, C. What Is Love. LC 83-12729. 96p. 1984. 7.95 (ISBN 0-310-37571-1). Zondervan.

Wyndham, Lee. Thanksgiving. LC 63-13890. (Holiday Bks.). (Illus.). 1963. PLB 7.56 (ISBN 0-8116-6551-8). Garrard.

Wynkoop, Mildred B. The Theology of Love. 327p. 1972. 8.95 (ISBN 0-8341-0102-5). Beacon Hill.

Wynn, J. C. Family Therapy in Pastoral Ministry. LC 81-47840. 192p. 1982. 12.00 (ISBN 0-06-069703-2, HarpR). Har-Row.

Wynne, Edward A. Traditional Catholic Religious Orders. 224p. 1987. 24.95 (ISBN 0-88738-129-4). Transaction Bks.

Wynne, Edward J., Jr. The Implications of Carl Michalson's Theological Method for Christian Education. Thompson, Henry O., ed. LC 82-24760. (Illus.). 400p. (Orig.). 1983. lib. bdg. 31.25 (ISBN 0-8191-3021-4); pap. text ed. 15.75 (ISBN 0-8191-3022-2). U Pr of Amer.

Wynne, Edward J., Jr. & Thompson, Henry O., eds. Prayer for Today's People: Sermons on Prayer by Carl Michalson (1915-1965) LC 82-17583. 88p. (Orig.). 1983. lib. bdg. 23.50 (ISBN 0-8191-2771-X); pap. text ed. 8.75 (ISBN 0-8191-2772-8). U Pr of Amer.

Wynne-Tyson, Esme. Mithras. 1985. 50.00x (ISBN 0-900000-79-1, Pub. by Centaur Bks). State Mutual Bk.

Wynter, P., ed. see Hall, Joseph.

Wyon, Olive, tr. see Brunner, Emil.

Wyon, Olive, tr. see Goguel, Maurice.

Wyon, Olive, tr. see Troeltsch, Ernst.

Wyrtzen, Christine, jt. auth. see Bussard, Paula.

Wyrwa, Dietmar. Die Christliche Platonaneigunug in den Stromateis des Clemens von Alexandrien. (Ger.). 364p. 1983. 33.60 (ISBN 3-11-008903-3). De Gruyter.

Wyschgrod, Michael, jt. ed. see Thoma, Clemens.

Wyschogrod, Michael. The Body of Faith: Judaism As Corporeal Election. 320p. (Orig.). 1983. pap. 24.95 (ISBN 0-8164-0549-2, HarpR). Har-Row.

Wyschogrod, Michael, jt. auth. see Berger, David.

Wysinger, Voss E. The Celestial Democracy. LC 66-24014. 149p. 1966. lib. bdg. 16.95 (ISBN 0-914002-01-5); text ed. 16.95 (ISBN 0-914002-02-3); pap. text ed. 14.00 (ISBN 0-686-36904-1). Wysinger Pub.

Wyszynski, Cardinal Work. 184p. 1960. 5.95 (ISBN 0-933932-18-9). Scepter Pubs.

Y

Yaakov, Bat. The Tenth Famine: Judaism Without God. 96p. (Orig.). 1986. pap. 7.95 (ISBN 0-9617361-0-0). Bat Yaakov Pubns.

Yaconelli, Mike & Rice, Wayne. Creative Socials & Specials Events. 192p. 1986. pap. 7.95 (ISBN 0-310-35131-6, 10827P). Zondervan.

Yaconelli, Mike, jt. auth. see Burns, Jim.

Yaconelli, Mike, jt. auth. see Rice, Wayne.

Yadin, Yigael. Hazor: The Head of All Those Kingdoms, Joshua 11: 10 with a Chapter on Israelite Megiddo. 210p. 1979. 40.00x (ISBN 0-19-725925-1). State Mutual Bk.

--Message of the Scrolls. 1957. (Touchstone Bks); pap. 3.95 (ISBN 0-686-66285-7). S&S.

Yadon, Loren A. From an Acorn to an Oak. (Illus.). 89p. 1978. pap. 4.95 (ISBN 0-912315-46-6). Word Aflame.

--More Than a Dream. Wallace, Mary, ed. 128p. (Orig.). 1984. pap. 4.95 (ISBN 0-912315-66-0). Word Aflame.

Yaeger, Randolph. Renaissance New Testament, Vol. 14. 660p. 1983. 22.50 (ISBN 0-88289-859-0). Pelican.

Yaeger, Randolph O. Renaissance New Testament, Vols. 1-9. Incl. Vol. 1. 25.00 (ISBN 0-88289-957-0); Vol. 2 (ISBN 0-88289-657-1); Vol. 3 (ISBN 0-88289-357-2); Vol. 4 (ISBN 0-88289-857-4); Vol. 5 (ISBN 0-88289-257-6); Vol. 6 (ISBN 0-88289-757-8); Vol. 7. 1982. 22.50 (ISBN 0-88289-457-9); Vol. 8. 1982. 22.50 (ISBN 0-88289-358-0); Vol. 9. 1982. 22.50 (ISBN 0-88289-858-2). 590p. 1980. each 22.50 (ISBN 0-686-77622-4). Pelican.

Yahil, Leni. The Rescue of Danish Jewry. Gradel, Morris, tr. from Hebrew. (Illus.). 538p. 1983. pap. 9.95 (ISBN 0-8276-0232-4). Jewish Pubns.

Yakan, Fathi. Islamic Movement: Problems & Perspective. Al-Johani, Maneh, tr. from Arabic. pap. 5.00 (ISBN 0-89259-051-3). Am Trust Pubns.

Yale, Alfred. My Friend Paul. 1986. pap. 8.25 (ISBN 0-8309-0433-6). Herald Hse.

Yale Divinity School Faculty Members Staff & Brown, Charles R. Education for Christian Service: A Volume in Commemoration of the 100th Anniversary of the Divinity School of Yale University. 1922. 49.50x (ISBN 0-685-89749-4). Elliots Bks.

Yale, John, ed. see Swami Vivekananda.

Yamada, Abbot S., jt. auth. see Covell, Jon Carter.

Yamagata, Isoh, tr. see Ninomiya, Sontoku.

Yamaguchi, Susumu. The Mahayana Way to Buddhahood. Buddhist Books International, tr. from Japanese. LC 82-4416. 1982. 10.95x (ISBN 0-914910-11-6). Buddhist Bks.

Yamamori, Tetsunao. Church Growth in Japan. LC 74-4009. (Illus.). 184p. (Orig.). 1974. pap. 4.95 (ISBN 0-87808-412-6). William Carey Lib.

--God's New Envoys: A Bold Strategy for Penetrating "Closed Countries". (Illus.). 1987. 11.95 (ISBN 0-88070-188-9). Multnomah.

Yamamori, Tetsunao & Lawson, E. Leroy. Introducing Church Growth. LC 74-24577. (New Life Books). (Illus.). 256p. 1974. 7.95 (ISBN 0-87239-000-4, 40002). Standard Pub.

Yamauchi, Edwin. The Archaeology of New Testament Cities in Western Asia Minor. LC 80-66991. (Baker Studies in Biblical Archaeology). 160p. 1980. pap. 7.95 (ISBN 0-8010-9915-3). Baker Bk.

--Foes from the Northern Frontiers. (Baker Studies in Biblical Archaeology). 128p. (Orig.). 1982. pap. 6.95 (ISBN 0-8010-9918-8). Baker Bk.

--Harper's World of the New Testament. LC 80-8606. (Illus.). 144p. (Orig.). 1981. pap. 9.95i (ISBN 0-06-069708-3, RD349, HarpR). Har-Row.

--Stones & the Scriptures. 1981. pap. 5.95 (ISBN 0-8010-9916-1). Baker Bk.

Yamauchi, Edwin M. Las Excavaciones Y las Escrituras. 224p. 1978. 4.50 (ISBN 0-311-03658-9). Casa Bautista.

Yamori, Tetsuano, ed. see Monk, Robert C., et al.

Yampolsky, Philip, tr. see Takada, Koin.

Yampolsky, Philip B., tr. Platform Sutra of the Sixth Patriarch. LC 67-11847. (Records of Civilization, Studies & Sources: No. 76). 1967. pap. 15.00x (ISBN 0-231-08361-0). Columbia U Pr.

Yampolsky, Philip B., tr. see Hakuin.

Yance, Norman A. Religion Southern Style: Southern Baptists & Society in Historical Perspective. LC 78-61185. (Special Studies: No. 4). vi, 66p. 1978. pap. 3.95 (ISBN 0-932180-03-5). NABPR.

Yancey, Philip. True Confessions: Owning up to the Secret Everybody Knows. (Christian Essentials Ser.). 48p. (Orig.). 1987. pap. 1.95 (ISBN 0-89283-324-6). Servant.

--Where Is God When It Hurts? 1977. pap. 5.95 (ISBN 0-310-35411-0, 9992P); 2.95 (ISBN 0-310-35431-5, 9992G). Zondervan.

Yancey, Philip, jt. auth. see Brand, Paul.

Yancey, Phillip. Where Is God When It Hurts. 7.95 (ISBN 0-310-35417-X). Zondervan.

Yandell, Keith. Christianity & Philosophy. LC 83-14226. (Studies in a Christian World View: Vol. 2). 284p. 1984. pap. 12.95 (ISBN 0-8028-1964-8). Eerdmans.

Yandian, Bob. End Time Prophecy. 15p. 1983. wkbk. 3.95 (ISBN 0-914307-15-0, Dist. by Harrison Hse). Word Faith.

--Ephesians: The Maturing of the Saints. (Orig.). 1985. pap. 5.95 (ISBN 0-89274-387-5). Harrison Hse.

--Galatians: The Spirit-Controlled Life. 264p. (Orig.). 1985. pap. 6.95 (ISBN 0-89274-388-3). Harrison Hse.

--Joel: The Outpouring of God's Glory. (Commentaries for Laymen Ser.). 160p. (Orig.). 1986. pap. 5.95 (ISBN 0-89274-402-2). Harrison Hse.

--Proverbs. 1985. pap. 6.95 (ISBN 0-89274-386-7). Harrison Hse.

Yang, F. S., jt. tr. see Levy, Howard S.

Yang, Yung-Ch'Ing. China's Religious Heritage. LC 72-4542. (Essay Index Reprint Ser.). Repr. of 1943 ed. 16.00 (ISBN 0-8369-2981-0). Ayer Co Pubs.

Yang Ming, Wang. Instructions for Practical Living & Other Neo-Confucian Writings. Chan, Wing tsit, tr. from Chinese. 358p. 1985. pap. 14.00x (ISBN 0-231-06039-4). Columbia U Pr.

Yang Ming-shih. T'ai Chi Ch'uan. (Quick & Easy Ser.). (Illus.). 60p. (Orig.). 1974. pap. 3.95 (ISBN 4-07-973783-1, Pub. by Shufunmato Co Ltd Japan). C E Tuttle.

Yanich, Voyeslav. Lives of the Serbian Saints. (Illus.). 1973. 3.95 (ISBN 0-686-05412-1). Eastern Orthodox.

Yannai, Yaacov, jt. auth. see Pearlman, Moshe.

Yannaras, Christos. Freedom of Morality. Briere, Elizabeth, tr. from Gr. LC 84-9030. 272p. (Orig.). 1984. pap. text ed. 12.95 (ISBN 0-88141-028-4). St Vladimirs.

Yanoff, Morris. Where Is Joey? Lost among the Hare Krishnas. LC 81-11280. x, 260p. 1982. 15.95 (ISBN 0-8040-0414-5, Pub by Swallow). Ohio U Pr.

Yapp, Malcolm. Ibn Sina & the Muslim World. Killingray, Margaret & O'Connor, Edmund, eds. (World History Ser.). (Illus.). 1980. lib. bdg. 6.95 (ISBN 0-89908-037-5); pap. text ed. 2.45 (ISBN 0-89908-012-X). Greenhaven.

Yapp, Malcolm, ed. see Duckworth, John, et al.

Yapp, Malcolm, ed. see Painter, Desmond & Shepard, John.

Yapp, Malcolm, et al, eds. see Amey, Peter, et al.

Yapp, Malcolm, et al, eds. see Clifford, Alan.

Yapp, Malcolm, et al, eds. see Killingray, Margaret.

Yarbro, Adela, tr. see Dibelius, Martin & Conzelmann, Hans.

Yarbrough, Larry O. Not Like the Gentiles: Marriage Rules in the Letters of Paul. (SBL Dissertation Ser.). 1985. 17.95 (ISBN 0-89130-874-1, 06-01-80); pap. 11.95 (ISBN 0-89130-875-X). Scholars Pr GA.

Yarker, John. Speculative Freemasonary. 1987. pap. 3.95 (ISBN 0-916411-66-4, Pub. by Sure Fire). Holmes Pub.

Yarn, David H. The Four Gospels As One. 281p. 1982. 8.95 (ISBN 0-87747-948-8). Deseret Bk.

Yaroslavtsev, I. Zionism Stands Accused. 157p. 1985. pap. 3.95 (ISBN 0-8285-3095-5, Pub. by Progress Pubs USSR). Imported Pubns.

Yarrow, C. H. Quaker Experiences in International Conciliation. LC 78-7415. 1978. 25.00x (ISBN 0-300-02260-3). Yale U Pr.

Yarshater, Ehsan, et al, eds. see Al-Tabari.

Yaseen, Leonard C. The Jesus Connection: To Triumph over Anti-Semitism. (Illus.). 192p. 1985. pap. 9.95 (ISBN 0-8245-0718-5). Crossroad NY.

--The Jewish Connection: To Triumph over Anti-Semitism. (Illus.). 1985. pap. 9.95 (ISBN 0-317-39020-1). Crossroad NY.

Yaser, tr. see Shari'Ati, Ali.

Yasko, Bill & Yasko, Dot. Building Your Faith. 76p. (Orig.). 1984. pap. text ed. 4.95 (ISBN 0-931097-01-0). Sentinel Pub.

Yasko, Dot, jt. auth. see Yasko, Bill.

Yassif, Eli. Jewish Folklore: An Annotated Bibliography. LC 83-48282. 500p. 1985. lib. bdg. 65.00 (ISBN 0-8240-9039-X). Garland Pub.

Yatco, Nicomedes T. Jesus Christ for Today's Filipino. 124p. (Orig.). 1984. pap. 6.50x (ISBN 971-10-0053-9, Pub. by New Day Philipines). Cellar.

Yates, Elizabeth. A Book of Hours. 128p. 1985. pap. 4.95 large print ed. (ISBN 0-8027-2484-1). Walker & Co.

--Gifts of the True Love. (Illus.). 1983. pap. 2.50x (ISBN 0-87574-100-2, 100). Pendle Hill.

Yates, Frances A. Renaissance & Reform: The Italian Contribution. Trapp, J., ed. (Collected Essays Ser.: Vol. II). (Illus.). 288p. 1983. 31.50 (ISBN 0-7100-9530-9). Methuen Inc.
--The Rosicrucian Enlightenment. (Illus.). 320p. 1986. pap. 7.95 (ISBN 0-7448-0051-X, 0051W, Ark Paperbks). Methuen Inc.
Yates, Gerard F., ed. Papal Thought on the State: Excerpts from Encyclicals & Other Writings of Recent Popes. LC 58-5745. (Crofts Classics Ser.). 1958. pap. text ed. 1.25x (ISBN 0-88295-064-9). Harlan Davidson.
Yates, John W. For the Life of the Family: Family Life Action Groups or Starting & Using FLAG in Your Church. 256p. 1987. pap. 9.95. Morehouse.
Yates, K. M. Los Profetas Del Antiguo Testamento. Corona, Simon, tr. from Eng. Orig. Title: Preaching from the Prophets. (Span.). 336p. 1985. pap. 4.95 (ISBN 0-311-04026-8). Casa Bautista.
Yates, Kyle M. Essentials of Biblical Hebrew. rev. ed. Owens, J. J., ed. 1955. 13.95 (ISBN 0-06-069710-5, HarpR). Har-Row.
--Preaching from the Prophets. 1953. text ed. 12.50 (ISBN 0-8054-1502-5). Broadman.
--Psalms of Joy & Faith. 216p. 1984. pap. 7.95 (ISBN 0-913029-03-3). Stevens Bk Pr.
Yates, Kyle M. & Owens, J. J. Nociones Esenciales Del Hebreo Biblico. Daglio, S. Daniel, tr. 308p. 1984. Repr. of 1980 ed. 6.75 (ISBN 0-311-42056-7). Casa Bautista.
Yates, Martha. Financing a Sacred Dance Choir. 56p. 1981. pap. 3.00 (ISBN 0-941500-19-5). Sharing Co.
Yates, Nigel. The Anglican Revival in Victorian Portsmouth. 1981. 42.00x (ISBN 0-317-43792-5, Pub. by City of Portsmouth). State Mutual Bk.
Yatiswarananda, Swami. Adventures in Religious Life. pap. 4.50 (ISBN 0-87481-498-7). Vedanta Pr.
--Meditation & Spiritual Life. 700p. 1980. 15.00x (ISBN 0-87481-403-0). Vedanta Pr.
Yatiswarananda, Swami, tr. from Sanskrit. Universal Prayers. (Sanskrit & Eng.). 3.95 (ISBN 0-87481-443-X). Vedanta Pr.
Yazdi, Marion C. Youth in the Vanguard: Memoirs & Letters Collected by the First Baha'i Student at Berkeley & at Stanford University. LC 82-6793. (Illus.). xx, 211p. 1982. 14.95 (ISBN 0-87743-173-6, 332-089). Baha'i.
Ydur, Rudy. Key to Inerrancy. 1980. pap. 3.00 (ISBN 0-930592-05-0). Lumeli Pr.
Yeager, Randolph O. The Renaissance New Testament, Vol. 10. LC 79-28652. 660p. 1982. 22.50 (ISBN 0-88289-258-4). Pelican.
--The Renaissance New Testament, Vol. 11. 660p. 22.50 (ISBN 0-88289-758-6). Pelican.
Yeager, Robert J. The Case Statement. 1984. 4.80 (ISBN 0-318-18571-7). Natl Cath Educ.
--Resources for Development. (How to Ser.). 46p. 1986. 8.95. Natl Cath Educ.
--Volunteers. (How to Ser.). 28p. 1986. 5.65 (ISBN 0-318-20573-4). Natl Cath Educ.
Yeager, Robert J., compiled by. Directory of Development. 28p. 1986. 10.95 (ISBN 0-318-20571-8). Natl Cath Educ.
Yeakley, Flavil. Church Leadership & Organization. pap. 5.95 (ISBN 0-317-47145-7). Gospel Advocate.
Yearley, Lee H. The Ideas of Newman: Christianity & Human Religiosity. LC 77-13894. 1978. 22.50x (ISBN 0-271-00526-2). Pa St U Pr.
Yeatman, Linda. Noah's Ark. (Press-Out Model Bk.). (Illus.). 12p. 1984. 6.95 (ISBN 0-698-20598-7, Coward). Putnam Pub Group.
Yeats, W. B., tr. see Patanjali, Swami S.
Yeats, William B. & Shree, Swami. The Ten Principal Upanishads. 1975. pap. 6.95 (ISBN 0-02-071550-1, Collier). Macmillan.
Yedlicka, Leo C. Expressions of the Linguistic Area of Repentance & Remorse in Old French. LC 76-94175. (Catholic University of America Studies in Romance Languages & Literatures Ser: No. 28). 1969. Repr. of 1945 ed. 28.00 (ISBN 0-404-50328-4). AMS Pr.
Yee, Check-Hung. For My Kinsmen's Sake. 1986. 15.00 (ISBN 0-89216-066-7). Salvation Army.
Yeganeh, Nahid, jt. ed. see Tabari, Azar.
Yeivin, Israel. Introduction to the Tiberian Masorah. LC 79-24755. (Society of Biblical Literature Masoretic Studies: No. 5). pap. 14.50x (ISBN 0-89130-374-X, 06 05 05A). Scholars Pr Ga.
Yellin, David & Abrahams, Israel. Maimonides: His Life & Works. (The Judaic Studies Library: No. SHP 10). (Illus.). 240p. 1987. 12.95 (ISBN 0-87203-120-9); pap. 9.75 (ISBN 0-87203-121-7). Hermon.
Yeoman, R. S. Moneys of the Bible. (Illus.). 1982. Repr. of 1961 ed. softcover 7.00 (ISBN 0-915262-77-0). S J Durst.
Yeomans, Lilian B. The Great Physician. 80p. 1961. pap. 2.25 (ISBN 0-88243-729-1, 02-0729). Gospel Pub.
--Healing from Heaven. 145p. 1954. pap. 2.95 (ISBN 0-88243-730-5, 02-0730). Gospel Pub.
--Health & Healing. 64p. 1973. pap. 1.95 (ISBN 0-88243-732-1, 02-0732). Gospel Pub.
Ye'or, Bat. The Dhimmi: Jews & Christians under Islam. Maisel, David, et al, trs. from French. LC 84-47749. (Illus.). 444p. 1985. 25.00 (ISBN 0-8386-3233-5); pap. 9.95 (ISBN 0-8386-3262-9). Fairleigh Dickinson.
Yereance, Robert A. Strangers, All Strangers. LC 79-27016. 1981. 14.95 (ISBN 0-87949-151-5). Ashley Bks.
Yerkes, James. The Christology of Hegel. (SUNY Hegelian Studies). 240p. 1982. 49.50 (ISBN 0-87395-648-6); pap. 18.95 (ISBN 0-87395-649-4). State U NY Pr.
Yerman, Ron. Religion: Innocent or Guilty. LC 85-90019. 180p. 1985. 11.95 (ISBN 0-533-06540-2). Vantage.
Yerushalmi, Y. H. The Lisbon Massacre of 1506 & the Royal Image in the Shebet Yehuda. (Hebrew Union College Annual Supplements: Vol. 1). 12.50x (ISBN 0-87820-600-0, HUC Pr). Ktav.
Yerushalmi, Yosef H. From Spanish Court to Italian Ghetto: Isaac Cardoso, A Study in Seventeenth-Century Marranism & Jewish Apologetics. LC 76-109544. (Illus.). 548p. 1981. pap. 12.50x (ISBN 0-295-95824-3). U of Wash Pr.
--Zakhor: Jewish History & Jewish Memory. LC 82-15989. (Samuel & Althea Stroum Lectures in Jewish Studies). 162p. 1982. 17.50x (ISBN 0-295-95939-8). U of Wash Pr.
Yeshe, Lama & Rinpoche, Zopa. Wisdom Energy: Basic Buddhist Teachings. Landaw, Jonathan & Berzin, Alexander, eds. (Wisdom Basic Book: Orange Ser.). (Illus.). 151p. 1982. pap. 7.95 (ISBN 0-86171-008-8, Pub. by Wisdom Pubns). Great Traditions.
Yeshe, Lama T. Introduction to Tantra. Landaw, Jonathan, ed. (Wisdom Basic Bk. Orange). 150p. (Orig.). 1984. pap. 8.95 (ISBN 0-86171-021-5, Wisdom Pubns). Great Traditions.
Ye-Shes Rgyal-Mtshan. Mind in Buddhist Psychology: The Necklace of Clear Understanding, an Elucidation of the Workings of Mind & Mental Events. Guenther, Herbert V. & Kawamura, Leslie S., trs. from Tibetan. LC 74-24373. (Tibetan Translation Ser.: Vol. 3). (Illus.). 168p. 1975. 12.95 (ISBN 0-913546-07-0); pap. 7.95 (ISBN 0-913546-06-2). Dharma Pub.
Yeshivat Aish HaTorah Woman's Organization. Kosher for Pessach Cookbook. 1982. spiral bd. 5.95 (ISBN 0-87306-223-X). Feldheim.
Yeshurun, Avoth. The Syrian-African Rift & Other Poems. Amichai, Yehuda & Mandelbaum, Allen, eds. Schimmel, Harold, tr. LC 80-13630. (Jewish Poetry Ser.). 160p. 1980. 11.95 (ISBN 0-8276-0181-6, 464); pap. 7.95 (ISBN 0-8276-0182-4, 463). Jewish Pubns.
Yesudian, Selvarajan. Self-Reliance Through Yoga. 3rd ed. (Unwin Paperbacks). 1979. pap. 7.50 (ISBN 0-04-149054-1). Allen Unwin.
Yesudian, Selvarajan & Haich, Elisabeth. Raja Yoga. (Unwin Paperbacks). (Illus.). 1980. pap. 5.95 (ISBN 0-04-149056-8). Allen Unwin.
--Yoga & Health. (Unwin Paperbacks). (Illus.). 1978. pap. 5.95 (ISBN 0-04-149033-9). Allen Unwin.
Yeznik Koghbatsi, see Koghbatsi, Yeznik.
Yih, Miltinnie, jt. auth. see Stanley, Phyllis.
Ying-Arng, Lee. Lee's Modified Tai Chi for Health. 10.95x (ISBN 0-685-70688-5). Wehman.
Yinger, J. Milton. Anti-Semitism: A Case Study in Prejudice & Discrimination. 80p. pap. 2.50 (ISBN 0-88464-046-9). ADL.
--Scientific Study of Religion. (Illus.). 1970. text ed. write for info. (ISBN 0-02-430900-1). Macmillan.
Yinger, Milton J. Religion in the Struggle for Power: A Study in the Sociological Study of Religion. Zuckerman, Harriet & Merton, Robert K., eds. LC 79-9040. (Dissertations in Sociology Ser.). 1980. Repr. of 1946 ed. lib. bdg. 26.50x (ISBN 0-405-13007-4). Ayer Co Pubs.
Yinon, Oded & Shahak, Israel, trs. Zionist Plan for the Middle East. (Special Document: No. 1). 26p. (Orig.). 1983. pap. text ed. 2.50 (ISBN 0-937694-56-8). Assn Arab-Amer U Grads.
Yi-Pac, Mei. Motse, the Neglected Rival of Confucius. LC 73-892. (China Studies). (Illus.). xi, 222p. 1973. Repr. of 1934 ed. 20.75 (ISBN 0-88355-084-9). Hyperion Conn.
Ylvisaker, J. The Gospels. 1977. Repr. 24.95 (ISBN 0-8100-0052-0, 15N0363). Northwest Pub.
YMCA of the U. S. A. Staff. Examining Our Faith. 32p. 1980. pap. 4.95x (ISBN 0-88035-030-X). Human Kinetics.
--Y Basics: Yesterday, Today, & Tomorrow in the YMCA. LC 84-23443. 93p. 1984. pap. text ed. 5.00x (ISBN 0-931250-77-3). Human Kinetics.
YMCA of the USA. More Than a Job. 139p. 1984. 3-ring notebook 25.00x (ISBN 0-931250-76-5). Human Kinetics.
--Vital Signs of Family Life & the YMCA: Resource Notebook. (Illus.). 26p. (Orig.). 1983. pap. 19.95 3 ring Notebook (ISBN 0-88035-014-8, YMCA USA). Human Kinetics.
Yockey, James F. Mediations with Nicolas of Cusa. (Illus.). 144p. (Orig.). 1987. pap. 6.95 (ISBN 0-939680-40-8). Bear & Co.
--Meditations with Nicholas of Cusa. 1987. pap. 6.95. Bear & Co.
Yocum. The Holy Way. pap. 8.95 (ISBN 0-686-12915-6). Schmul Pub Co.
Yocum, Bruce. Prophecy. (Orig.). 1976. pap. 4.95 (ISBN 0-89283-029-8). Servant.
Yocum, Glenn E. Hymns to the Dancing Siva. 1982. 20.00x (ISBN 0-8364-0851-9). South Asia Bks.
Yoder, C. F. God's Means of Grace. 12.50 (ISBN 0-88469-111-X). BMH Bks.
Yoder, Edward. Edward: Pilgrimage of a Mind. Yoder, Ida, ed. & pref. by. (Illus.). 512p. 1985. 20.00 (ISBN 0-9614083-0-8). Yoder.
--Estudios de Doctrina Christiana: Dios. Jesucristo, el Espiritu Santo, Pt. 1. 123p. 1973. pap. 0.60x (ISBN 0-8361-1190-7). Herald Pr.
Yoder, Elizabeth, jt. auth. see Yoder, Perry.
Yoder, Elmina & Miller, Lula. Praises We Sing. 1980. 5.45 (ISBN 0-87813-515-4). Christian Light.
Yoder, Ida, ed. & pref. by see Yoder, Edward.
Yoder, John H. Christian Witness to the State. 1977. pap. 3.95 (ISBN 0-87303-165-2). Faith & Life.
--He Came Preaching Peace. LC 85-5474. 152p. (Orig.). 1985. pap. 8.95 (ISBN 0-8361-3395-1). Herald Pr.
--Nevertheless. LC 75-170197. (Christian Peace Shelf Ser.). 144p. 1972. pap. 4.95 (ISBN 0-8361-1661-5). Herald Pr.
--The Original Revolution. LC 76-181577. (Christian Peace Shelf Ser.). 208p. 1972. pap. 6.95 (ISBN 0-8361-1812-X). Herald Pr.
--The Politics of Jesus. 176p. 1972. pap. 7.95 (ISBN 0-8028-1485-9). Eerdmans.
--The Priestly Kingdom: Social Ethics As Gospel. LC 84-40358. 208p. 1986. text ed. 16.95 (ISBN 0-268-01627-5, 85-16270); pap. text ed. 8.95 (ISBN 0-268-01628-3, 85-16288). U of Notre Dame Pr.
--Taufertum Und Reformation Im Gesprach. 221p. 1969. 29.00x (ISBN 0-8361-1164-8). Herald Pr.
--When War Is Unjust: Being Honest in Just-War Thinking. LC 84-2859. 96p. (Orig.). 1984. pap. 5.95 (ISBN 0-8066-2077-3, 10-7084). Augsburg.
Yoder, John H., ed. The Legacy of Michael Sattler. LC 72-6333. (Classics of the Radical Reformation Ser., No. 1). 208p. 1973. 12.95 (ISBN 0-8361-1187-7). Herald Pr.
--Textos Encogidoes de la Reforma Radical. (Span.). 500p. (Orig.). 1984. pap. 25.00 (ISBN 0-8361-1237-7). Herald Pr.
Yoder, John H., ed. see Arnold, Ebehard.
Yoder, John H., ed. see Arnold, Eberhard.
Yoder, John H., tr. The Schleitheim Confession. 32p. 1977. pap. 1.95 (ISBN 0-8361-1831-6). Herald Pr.
Yoder, Joseph W. Rosanna of the Amish. rev. ed. 256p. 1973. pap. 3.95 (ISBN 0-8361-1714-X). Herald Pr.
Yoder, Marvin K. What We Believe about Children. LC 83-82878. (Mennonite Faith Ser.: No. 13). 72p. 1984. pap. 1.50 (ISBN 0-8361-3357-9). Herald Pr.
Yoder, Mary E. Five Little Andys. (Illus.). 1977. 2.75 (ISBN 0-87813-510-3). Christian Light.
--Story Time with Grandma. 1979. 2.50 (ISBN 0-87813-514-6). Christian Light.
Yoder, Paton. Eine Wurzel: Tennessee John Stolzfus. LC 79-26507. (Illus.). 192p. 1979. 10.50 (ISBN 0-915010-27-5). Sutter House.
Yoder, Perry. From Word to Life. LC 81-20071. (Conrad Grebel Lecture Ser.). 288p. (Orig.). 1982. pap. 14.95x (ISBN 0-8361-1249-0). Herald Pr.
Yoder, Perry & Yoder, Elizabeth. New Men-New Roles. 1977. pap. 2.00 (ISBN 0-87303-001-X). Faith & Life.
--Towards Understanding the Bible. LC 78-53649. 1978. pap. 3.95 (ISBN 0-87303-006-0). Faith & Life.
Yoder, Perry B. Shalom: The Bible's Word for Salvation, Justice & Peace. LC 86-82879. 161p. 1987. pap. 14.95 (ISBN 0-87303-120-2). Faith & Life.
Yoder, Robert A. Seeking First the Kingdom. LC 83-16618. 104p. (Orig.). 1983. pap. 4.50 (ISBN 0-8361-3349-8). Herald Pr.
Yoder, Robert S. Judgement unto Victory. 1983. 6.75 (ISBN 0-8062-1964-5). Carlton.
Yoder, Sanford C. He Gave Some Prophets: The Old Testament Prophets & Their Message. LC 64-18733. 256p. 1964. 7.95 (ISBN 0-8361-1496-5). Herald Pr.
--Poetry of the Old Testament. 426p. 1948. pap. 9.95 (ISBN 0-8361-1709-3). Herald Pr.
Yoder, Sara. Unto the Hills. 1985. 2.95 (ISBN 0-87813-523-5). Christian Light.
Yoder, Walter E., jt. ed. see Hostetler, Lester.
Yogananda, Paramahansa. Autobiography of a Yogi. LC 78-151319. (Illus.). 605p. 1974. Bengali ed. 4.00x (ISBN 0-87612-071-0); Dutch ed. 17.00x (ISBN 90-202-4016-1); German ed. 12.50x (ISBN 3-87041-015-9); Gujarati ed. 4.00x (ISBN 0-87612-072-9); Japanese ed. 11.00x (ISBN 0-87612-073-7); pap. 3.50 (ISBN 0-87612-079-6). Self Realization.
--Autobiography of a Yogi. (Illus.). 1971. pap. 9.50x British ed. (ISBN 0-09-021051-4); pap. 14.50x Danish ed. (ISBN 87-418-7082-4); pap. 11.75x French ed. (ISBN 0-87612-066-4); pap. 14.00x Greek ed. (ISBN 0-87612-069-9); pap. 6.95x Italian ed. (ISBN 0-87612-067-2); pap. 10.50x Spanish ed. (ISBN 0-87612-068-0); pap. 4.00x Hindi ed. (ISBN 0-87612-077-X); pap. 13.50x Portuguese ed. (ISBN 0-87612-081-8). Self Realization.
--Cosmic Chants. rev. 6th ed. LC 74-20347. (Illus.). 84p. 1974. flexible bdg 3.50 (ISBN 0-87612-131-8); German ed. 9.00x (ISBN 0-87612-132-6). Self Realization.
--How You Can Talk with God. 2nd ed. (Illus.). 1985. pap. 0.95 (ISBN 0-87612-160-1); pap. 2.00 French ed. (ISBN 0-87612-163-6). Self Realization.
--Law of Success. 1980. pap. 0.95 (ISBN 0-87612-150-4); pap. 1.00x Span. ed. (ISBN 0-87612-151-2); pap. 2.00 French ed. (ISBN 0-87612-152-0). Self Realization.
--Man's Eternal Quest. LC 75-17183. (Illus.). 503p. 1982. 9.95 (ISBN 0-87612-233-0); Italian ed. 10.00x (ISBN 0-87612-237-3). Self Realization.
--Man's Eternal Quest. LC 75-17183. (Illus.). 503p. 1982. pap. 5.50 (ISBN 0-87612-232-2). Self Realization.
--Metaphysical Meditations. 11th ed. LC 40-16548. 124p. 1964. pap. 1.95 (ISBN 0-87612-041-9). pap. 5.00x German ed. (ISBN 3-87041-111-2); pap. 1.25x Span. ed. (ISBN 0-87612-043-5); pap. 3.00x Italian ed. (ISBN 0-87612-046-X). Self Realization.
--Science of Religion. LC 81-52892. (Illus.). 102p. 1982. 6.00 (ISBN 0-87612-004-4); Span. ed. 1.50x (ISBN 0-87612-001-X); pap. 5.00x German ed. (ISBN 3-87041-225-9); pap. 3.50 English ed. (ISBN 0-87612-005-2). Self Realization.
--Science of Religion. (Dutch.). 1974. 6.50x (ISBN 90-202-45-465). Self Realization.
--Songs of the Soul. LC 83-60701. (Illus.). 200p. 1983. 6.50 (ISBN 0-87612-025-7). Self-Realization.
--Whispers from Eternity. 9th ed. LC 86-60584. (Illus.). 239p. 1986. 7.95 (ISBN 0-87612-103-2); pap. 3.50x Span. ed. (ISBN 0-87612-101-6); German ed. 10.00x (ISBN 3-85399-034-7). Self Realization.
--Whispers from Eternity, First Vision. 1977. 6.95 (ISBN 0-87612-102-4). Self Realization.
Yogananda, Paramahansa & Self-Realization Fellowship Editorial Staff. Sayings of Paramahansa Yogananda. LC 79-66287. (Illus.). 136p. 1980. 4.95 (ISBN 0-87612-115-6); Italian ed. 4.00x (ISBN 0-87612-113-X); German ed. 7.50x (ISBN 0-87612-114-8); Spanish ed. 2.25x (ISBN 0-87612-111-3); Icelandic ed. 9.00x (ISBN 0-87612-112-1). Self Realization.
Yogananda, Paramhansa. Second Coming of Christ, Vol. II. LC 79-50352. 1984. pap. 12.95 (ISBN 0-937134-05-8). Amrita Found.
--Songs of the Soul. LC 80-69786. 1980. pap. 9.95 (ISBN 0-937134-02-3). Amrita Found.
--Whispers from Eternity. LC 85-71375. 1978. pap. 12.95 (ISBN 0-937134-03-1). Amrita Found.
Yogeshananda, Swami. Way of the Hindu. (The Way Ser.). pap. 5.95 (ISBN 0-7175-0626-6). Dufour.
Yogeshananda, Swami, compiled by. The Visions of Sri Ramakrishna. 150p. 1974. 2.75 (ISBN 0-87481-455-3). Vedanta Pr.
Yogeswar. Textbook of Yoga. (Illus.). 574p. 1980. 24.95x (ISBN 0-940500-37-X). Asia Bk Corp.
Yogi Ramacharaka. Practical Water Cure. leatherette 3.00 (ISBN 0-911662-12-X). Yoga.
Yogi Vithaldas. Yoga System of Health. 1981. pap. 3.95 (ISBN 0-686-82888-7). Cornerstone.
Yohn, Rick. Finding Time. 1986. 6.95 (ISBN 0-8499-3058-8). Word Bks.
--Living Securely in an Unstable World: God's Solution to Man's Dilemma. LC 85-4895. (Living Theology Ser.). 1985. pap. 8.95 (ISBN 0-88070-082-3). Multnomah.
--What Every Christian Should Know about Bible Prophecy. LC 81-85895. 80p. (Orig.). 1982. pap. 3.95 (ISBN 0-89081-311-6, 3116). Harvest Hse.
--What Every Christian Should Know about God: A Study Manual. LC 76-20396. 80p. 1976. 3.95 (ISBN 0-89081-054-0). Harvest Hse.
Yokoi, Yuho & Victoria, Daizen. Zen Master Dogen: An Introduction with Selected Writings. LC 75-33200. (Illus.). 220p. 1976. 12.50 (ISBN 0-8348-0112-4); pap. 9.75 (ISBN 0-8348-0116-7). Weatherhill.

Yolton, John W. Metaphysical Analysis. LC 68-88650. pap. 58.30 (ISBN 0-317-08857-2, 2014464). Bks Demand UMI.

Yonah, Rabbeinu. Gates of Repentance, Shaarei Teshuvah. 1976. pap. 7.95 (ISBN 0-87306-112-8). Feldheim.

Yonan, Grazia P., jt. auth. see Valenti, Tony.

Yonay, Rina, jt. auth. see Yonay, Shahar.

Yonay, Shahar & Yonay, Rina. Systematic Hebrew. 1986. 12.95 (ISBN 0-9616783-0-5). S Yonay.

Yonge, Charlotte M. The Story of the Christians & Moors of Roman Spain. 1893. 30.00 (ISBN 0-89984-238-0). Century Bookbindery.

Yonge, Charlotte M., ed. see Du Boys, Albert.

Yonggi Cho, Paul. Suffering.... Why Me? LC 86-70741. 1986. pap. 3.50 (ISBN 0-88270-601-2). Bridge Pub.

Yonker, Nicolas. God, Man & the Planetary Age: Preface for a Theistic Humanism. LC 78-4233. 168p. 1978. 11.00x (ISBN 0-87071-322-1). Oreg St U Pr.

Yorgason, Blaine M. & Yorgason, Brenton G. Becoming. LC 86-70295. 176p. 1986. 9.95 (ISBN 0-87579-034-8). Deseret Bk.

--The Loftier Way. LC 85-70919. 143p. 1985. 8.95 (ISBN 0-87747-785-X). Deseret Bk.

Yorgason, Brenton G., jt. auth. see Yorgason, Blaine M.

Yorke, Malcolm. Eric Gill: Man of Flesh & Spirit. LC 81-71073. (Illus.). 304p. 1985. pap. 14.95 (ISBN 0-87663-883-3). Universe.

--Eric Gill: Man of Flesh & Sprit. LC 81-71073. (Illus.). 256p. 1982. 27.50x (ISBN 0-87663-387-4). Universe.

Yoseph. The Gilgal Theophany. 1985. 6.95 (ISBN 0-533-06448-1). Vantage.

Yoshinori, Takeuchi. The Heart of Buddhism: In Search of the Timeless Spirit of Primitive Buddhism. LC 82-23453. 192p. (Orig.). 1983. 17.50 (ISBN 0-8245-0577-8). Crossroad NY.

Yost, Frank H., jt. auth. see Johnson, Alvin W.

Youd, Pauline. Adopted for a Purpose: Bible Stories of Joseph, Moses, Samuel, & Esther. 144p. (Orig.). 1986. pap. 7.95 (ISBN 0-687-00770-4). Abingdon.

Youmans, Mary & Youmans, Roger. Testimony of Two. pap. 7.95 (ISBN 0-910924-91-0). Macalester.

Youmans, Roger, jt. auth. see Youmans, Mary.

Young, Alan. Spiritual Healing: Miracle or Mirage? LC 81-82932. 280p. (Orig.). 1982. pap. 7.95 (ISBN 0-87516-460-9). De Vorss.

Young, Alexander. Chronicles of the Pilgrim Fathers of the Colony of Plymouth, 1602-1625. LC 78-87667. (Law, Politics & History Ser). 1971. Repr. of 1841 ed. lib. bdg. 42.50 (ISBN 0-306-71760-3). Da Capo.

Young, Alexey, ed. see Chrysostomos, Archimandrite & Ambrosios, Hieromonk.

Young, Ann E. Wife Number Nineteen: The Story of a Life in Bondage, Being a Complete Expose of Mormonism, & Revealing the Sorrows, Sacrifices & Sufferings of Women in Polygamy. LC 72-2634. (American Women Ser: Images & Realities). (Illus.). 632p. 1972. Repr. of 1875 ed. 36.50 (ISBN 0-405-04488-7). Ayer Co Pubs.

Young, Barbara. Jesus Is My Very Best Friend. 1984. 4.95 (ISBN 0-570-04097-3, 56-1465). Concordia.

--This Man from Lebanon. (Illus.). (YA) 1950. 18.95 (ISBN 0-394-44848-0). Knopf.

Young, Brad. The Jewish Background to the Lord's Prayer. 54p. (Orig.). 1984. pap. 3.95 (ISBN 0-918873-02-9). Ctr Judaic-Christ Studies.

Young, C. A. Historical Documents Advocating Christian Union. (Heritage of a Movement Book Club Ser.). 376p. Repr. of 1904 ed. text ed. 10.95 (ISBN 0-89900-276-5). College Pr Pub.

Young, Carlton R., jt. auth. see Routley, Erik.

Young, Carlton R., ed. Supplement to the Book of Hymns. 160p. (Orig.). 1981. pap. 4.75 (ISBN 0-687-03757-3); pap. 6.75 accompanist ed. (ISBN 0-687-03758-1). Abingdon.

Young, Carlton R., et al, eds. Ecumenical Praise. 1977. 14.95x (ISBN 0-916642-07-0). Hope Pub.

Young, Curt. The Least of These: What Everyone Should Know About Abortion. 1984. 7.95 (ISBN 0-8024-0355-7). Moody.

Young, David P. The Speed of Love: An Exploration of Christian Faithfulness in a Technological World. 150p. (Orig.). 1986. pap. 6.95 (ISBN 0-377-00159-7). Friend Pr.

--Twenty-First Century Pioneering: A Scrapbook of the Future. (Illus., Orig.). 1986. pap. 5.95 (ISBN 0-377-00160-0). Friend Pr.

Young, David S., ed. Study War No More. (Orig.). 1981. pap. 3.95 (ISBN 0-87178-822-5). Brethren.

Young, Douglas. A Primer of Christianity & Ethics. Hunting, Constance, ed. 200p. (Orig.). (YA) 1985. pap. 12.95 (ISBN 0-913006-34-3). Puckerbrush.

Young, E. J. Daniel. (The Geneva Series of Commentaries). 320p. 13.95 (ISBN 0-85151-154-6). Banner of Truth.

--Genesis 3. 1984. pap. 4.45 (ISBN 0-85151-148-1). Banner of Truth.

--In the Beginning. 1976. pap. 3.95 (ISBN 0-85151-235-6). Banner of Truth.

Young, Edward J. Book of Isaiah, Vol. 1. 1964. 19.95 (ISBN 0-8028-2179-0). Eerdmans.

--Introduction to the Old Testament. rev ed. 1958. 14.95 (ISBN 0-8028-3310-1). Eerdmans.

--My Servants the Prophets. 1952. pap. 8.95 (ISBN 0-8028-1697-5). Eerdmans.

--Studies in Genesis One. pap. 4.95 (ISBN 0-87552-550-4). Presby & Reformed.

--Thy Word Is Truth. 1957. pap. 5.95 (ISBN 0-8028-1244-9). Eerdmans.

Young, Elizabeth & Young, Wayland. London's Churches: A Visitor's Companion. (Illus.). 252p. (Orig.). 1986. pap. 14.95 (ISBN 0-88162-212-5). Salem Hse Pubs.

Young, Fay. The Awakening. 64p. 1981. 5.00 (ISBN 0-682-49701-0). Exposition Pr FL.

Young, Frances M. Sacrificial Ideas in Greek Christian Writers. LC 78-61400. (Patristic Monograph: No. 5). 1979. pap. 10.00 (ISBN 0-915646-04-8). Phila Patristic.

Young, G. Douglas. Young's Bible Dictionary. 608p. 1984. 9.95 (ISBN 0-8423-8598-3). Tyndale.

Young, H. Edwin. David: After God's Own Heart. (Orig.). 1984. pap. 4.25 (ISBN 0-8054-1531-9). Broadman.

--The Purpose of Suffering: Knowing the God Who Comforts. LC 85-80488. 144p. (Orig.). 1985. pap. 4.95 (ISBN 0-89081-496-1). Harvest Hse.

Young, Helen. Children Won't Wait: A Parent's Prayer. 1985. gift ed. 6.95 (ISBN 0-915720-83-3). Brownlow Pub Co.

Young, Henry J. God & Human Freedom: A Festschrift in Honor of Howard Thurman. 200p. 1982. text ed. 13.95 (ISBN 0-913408-81-6). Friends United.

Young, Henry J., ed. Preaching the Gospel. LC 75-36449. pap. 23.80 (2026828). Bks Demand UMI.

Young, J. H. & Young, S. H. Terracotta Figurines from Kourion in Cyprus. (University Museum Monographs: No. 11). (Illus.). x, 260p. 1955. 16.50x (ISBN 0-934718-03-2). Univ Mus of U PA.

Young, James, jt. auth. see Hope, Marjorie.

Young, James J. Divorce Ministry & the Marriage Tribunal. LC 82-60851. 1982. pap. 5.95 (ISBN 0-8091-2477-7). Paulist Pr.

--Divorcing, Believing, Belonging. 240p. (Orig.). 1984. pap. 7.95 (ISBN 0-8091-2634-6). Paulist Pr.

--When You're Divorced & Catholic. LC 80-69090. (When Bk). 96p. 1980. pap. 2.45 (ISBN 0-87029-172-6, 20265-5). Abbey.

Young, James J., jt. auth. see Preister, Steven.

Young, Jean I., tr. see Sturluson, Snorri.

Young, John, ed. see Carson, Alexander.

Young, Josiah U. Black & African Theologies: Siblings or Distant Cousins? LC 85-32090. 240p. (Orig.). 1986. pap. 12.95 (ISBN 0-88344-252-3). Orbis Bks.

Young, Karl. The Dramatic Associations of the Easter Sepulchre. 1977. lib. bdg. 59.95 (ISBN 0-8490-1732-7). Gordon Pr.

Young, Loy, jt. auth. see Young, Robert.

Young, Mary E. & Attoe, Wayne. Places of Worship-Milwaukee. (Publications in Architecture & Urban Planning Ser.). (Illus.). viii, 112p. 1977. 10.00 (ISBN 0-938744-46-1, R77-1). U of Wis Ctr Arch Urban.

Young, Meredith L. Agartha: A Journey to the Stars. LC 84-50109. (Illus.). 340p. (Orig.). 1984. pap. 9.95 (ISBN 0-913299-01-4). Stillpoint.

Young, Mildred B. Another Will Gird You: A Message to the Society of Friends. 1983. pap. 2.50 (ISBN 0-87574-109-6, 109). Pendle Hill.

--The Candle, the Lantern, the Daylight. LC 61-15103. (Orig.). 1961. pap. 2.50x (ISBN 0-87574-116-9). Pendle Hill.

--Functional Poverty. 1983. pap. 2.50x (ISBN 0-87574-006-5, 006). Pendle Hill.

--Insured by Hope. LC 56-8831. (Orig.). pap. 2.50x (ISBN 0-87574-090-1). Pendle Hill.

--Participation in Rural Life. 1983. pap. 2.50x (ISBN 0-87574-019-7, 019). Pendle Hill.

--A Standard of Living. 1983. pap. 2.50x (ISBN 0-87574-012-X, 012). Pendle Hill.

--What Doth the Lord Require of Thee? 1983. pap. 2.50x (ISBN 0-87574-145-2, 145). Pendle Hill.

--Woolman & Blake: Prophets of Today. LC 72-170018. (Orig.). 1971. pap. 2.50x (ISBN 0-87574-177-0). Pendle Hill.

Young, Muriel. My Life as a Maine-iac. Hunting, Constance, ed. (Illus.). 150p. 1984. pap. 6.95 (ISBN 0-913006-30-0). Puckerbrush.

Young, Norman. Rebuke & Challenge: The Point of Jesus' Parables. Coffen, Richard W., ed. 96p. (Orig.). 1985. pap. 6.95 (ISBN 0-8280-0286-X). Review & Herald.

Young, Pauline V. Pilgrims of Russian-Town: The Community of Spiritual Christian Jumpers in America. LC 66-27375. (Illus.). 1967. Repr. of 1932 ed. 9.00x (ISBN 0-8462-1001-0). Russell.

Young, Percy M. Messiah, a Study in Interpretation. (Student's Music Library Ser.). 1961. 13.95 (ISBN 0-234-77215-8). Dufour.

Young, Robert. Young's Analytical Concordance to the Bible. rev. ed. 1220p. 1986. 22.95 (ISBN 0-8407-4945-7). Nelson.

--Young's Analytical Concordance to the Bible. 1216p. Date not set. 18.95 (ISBN 0-917006-29-1). Hendrickson MA.

--Young's Literal Translation of the Bible. pap. 24.95 (ISBN 0-8010-9921-8). Baker Bk.

Young, Robert & Young, Loy. Past Lives: The Key to Your Present Relationships: Introducing the Youngs' Past Life Regression Technique. Pellegrin, Mignonette, ed. LC 85-73214. (Illus.). 344p. (Orig.). 1985. pap. 19.95 (ISBN 0-936121-00-9). Draco Prod Pubns.

Young, Robert D. Religious Imagination: God's Gift to Prophets & Preachers. LC 78-26843. 176p. 1979. pap. 6.95 (ISBN 0-664-24239-1). Westminster.

Young, Robert F. Comenius in England: The Visit of Jan Amos Komensky Comenius, Czech Philosopher & Educationalist, to London in 1641-1642. LC 70-135838. (Eastern Europe Collection Ser). 1970. Repr. of 1932 ed. 12.00 (ISBN 0-405-02780-X). Ayer Co Pubs.

Young, Robert T. A Sprig of Hope. LC 79-20946. 1980. pap. 6.50 (ISBN 0-687-39260-8). Abingdon.

Young, S. H., jt. auth. see Young, J. H.

Young, Samuel. Beacon Bible Expositions, Vol. 4: John. Greathouse, William M. & Taylor, Willard H., eds. 196p. 1979. 8.95 (ISBN 0-8341-0315-X). Beacon Hill.

--Working Out What God Works in. (Harvest Ser.). 1981. pap. 4.95 (ISBN 0-8163-0440-8). Pacific Pr Pub Assn.

Young, W. J., tr. see De Guibert, Joseph.

Young, Warren C. Christian Approach to Philosophy. (Twin Brook Ser.). 1973. pap. 9.95 (ISBN 0-8010-9904-8). Baker Bk.

Young, Wayland, jt. auth. see Young, Elizabeth.

Young, William, tr. St. Ignatius's Own Story. 1980. Repr. 3.95 (ISBN 0-8294-0359-0). Loyola.

Young, William A., jt. auth. see Hauer, Christian E.

Young, William E. Moses: God's Helper. (BibLearn Ser.). (Illus.). 5.95 (ISBN 0-8054-4225-1, 4242-25). Broadman.

Young, William J., ed. see Ignatius of Loyola, Saint.

Young, William J., tr. see Dudon, Paul.

Young, Wilmer J. Visible Witness. 1983. pap. 2.50x (ISBN 0-87574-118-5, 118). Pendle Hill.

Young, Young Oon. World Religions. 1976. pap. 10.00 (ISBN 0-686-13408-7). Unification Church.

Youngblood, Ronald. Esaie, Commentaire Biblique, (Themes from Isaiah) (Fr.). 1986. write for info. (ISBN 0-8297-0607-0). Life Pubs Intl.

--Heart of the Old Testament. 1971. pap. 4.50 (ISBN 0-8010-9900-5). Baker Bk.

--How It All Began: (Genesis 1-11) LC 80-50539. (Bible Commentary for Laymen Ser.). 160p. 1980. pap. 3.50 (ISBN 0-8307-0675-5, S342103). Regal.

--Temas de Isaias. Orig. Title: Themes from Isaiah. (Span.). 1986. write for info. (ISBN 0-8297-0896-0). Life Pubs Intl.

--Themes from Isaiah. LC 83-19128. (Bible Commentary for Laymen Ser.). 1983. pap. text ed. 3.50 (ISBN 0-8307-0906-1, S373106). Regal.

Youngblood, Ronald, ed. The Genesis Debate: Persistent Questions about Creation & the Flood. 240p. 1986. pap. 12.95 (ISBN 0-8407-7517-2). Nelson.

Youngblood, Ronald & Inch, Morris, eds. The Living & Active Word of God: Studies in Honor of Samuel J. Schultz. 1983. 20.00 (ISBN 0-931464-11-0). Eisenbrauns.

Youngblood, Ronald & Kaiser, Walter C., Jr., eds. A Tribute to Gleason Archer. 1986. text ed. 15.95 (ISBN 0-8024-8780-7). Moody.

Youngblood, Ronald, ed. see Mears, Henrietta C., et al.

Youngblood, Ronald F. Exodus. (Everyman's Bible Commentary Ser.). (Orig.). 1983. pap. 5.95 (ISBN 0-8024-2002-8). Moody.

--Faith of Our Fathers. LC 75-23514. 1976. pap. 3.50 (ISBN 0-8307-0370-5, S302101). Regal.

Younger, Dory. Christmas International. 1983. pap. 3.75 (ISBN 0-89536-613-4, 0386). CSS of Ohio.

--The Nativity. 1983. pap. 3.75 (ISBN 0-89536-614-2, 1416). CSS of Ohio.

Younger, George D. From New Creation to Urban Crisis: A History of Action Training Ministries, 1962-1975. LC 86-70421. (Studies in Religion & Society). 260p. 1987. text ed. 25.95x (ISBN 0-913348-25-2). Ctr Sci Study.

Younghusband, Francis. Modern Mystics. 322p. 1970. 7.95 (ISBN 0-8216-0118-0). Univ Bks.

Younghusband, Francis E. Modern Mystics. facs. ed. LC 67-28774. (Essay Index Reprint Ser). 1935. 17.75 (ISBN 0-8369-1015-X). Ayer Co Pubs.

Youngman, Bernard R. Palestine of Jesus. (Background to the Bible Ser.: Vol. 3). pap. 8.95 (ISBN 0-7175-0418-2). Dufour.

--Patriarchs, Judges, & Kings. (Background to the Bible Ser.: Vol. 1). pap. 8.95 (ISBN 0-7175-0414-X). Dufour.

--Prophets & Rulers. (Background to the Bible Ser.: Vol. 2). pap. 8.95 (ISBN 0-7175-0416-6). Dufour.

--Spreading the Gospel. (Background to the Bible Ser.). pap. 8.95 (ISBN 0-7175-0420-4). Dufour.

Youngs, J. William T., Jr. God's Messengers: Religious Leadership in Colonial New England, 1700-1750. LC 76-8544. 192p. 1976. 19.50x (ISBN 0-8018-1799-4). Johns Hopkins.

Yount, William R. Be Opened! LC 76-2238. 240p. 1976. bds. 9.95 (ISBN 0-8054-3216-7). Broadman.

Yourgrau, Wolfgang & Breck, Allen D., eds. Cosmology, History, & Theology. LC 76-54269. (Illus.). 416p. 1977. 69.50x (ISBN 0-306-30940-8, Plenum Pr). Plenum Pub.

Yousefi, Mohammack, tr. see Bazargan, Mehdi.

Yousefi, Mohammad, tr. see Bazargan, Mehdi.

Youssef, Michael. The Leadership Style of Jesus. 168p. 1986. pap. 5.95 (ISBN 0-89693-168-4). Victor Bks.

Youth with a Mission. The Singing Word: Youth with a Mission Songbook. enl &rev. 2nd ed. (Illus.). 288p. 1974. plastic spiral bd. 5.95 (ISBN 0-87123-505-6, 280505). Bethany Hse.

Yrigoyen, Charles, Jr. & Bricker, George H, eds. Reformed & Catholic: Selected Theological Writings of Phillip Schaff. LC 79-17391. (Pittsburgh Original Texts & Translations Ser: No. 4). 1979. pap. text ed. 15.75 (ISBN 0-915138-40-9). Pickwick.

Yu, Chai-Shin. Early Buddhism & Christianity. 1981. 20.00x (ISBN 0-8364-0797-0, Pub. by Motilal Banarsidass). South Asia Bks.

Yu, David C. Guide to Chinese Religion. (Reference: Asian Phil.-Rel. Ser.). 1985. lib. bdg. 45.00 (ISBN 0-8161-7902-6). G K Hall.

Yuacharya Shri Mahaprajna. Ramblings of an Ascetic. xvi, 127p. 1979. 9.00 (ISBN 0-88065-212-8, Pub. by Messers Today & Tomorrows Printers & Publishers India). Scholarly Pubns.

Yuan, Ch'u. The Nine Songs: A Study of Shamanism in Ancient China. 2nd ed. Waley, Arthur, tr. LC 73-84228. 1973. pap. 3.95 (ISBN 0-87286-075-2). City Lights.

Yuasa, Nobuyuki, tr. from Jap. The Zen Poems of Ryokan. LC 80-8585. (Princeton Library of Asian Translations). (Illus.). 196p. 1981. 25.00x (ISBN 0-691-06466-0). Princeton U Pr.

Yuasa, Yasuo. The Body: Toward an Eastern Mind-Body Theory. Kasulis, Thomas P., ed. (Buddhist Studies). 256p. 1987. 39.50x (ISBN 0-88706-469-8); pap. 14.95 (ISBN 0-88706-468-X). State U NY Pr.

Yudkin, Leon I. Escape into Siege: A Survey of Israeli Literature Today. (Littman Library of Jewish Civilization). 1974. 18.50x (ISBN 0-19-710016-3). Oxford U Pr.

--Jewish Writing & Identity in the Twentieth Century. LC 82-827. 180p. 1982. 22.50x (ISBN 0-312-44234-3). St Martin.

Yuill, William, tr. see Kunze, Michael.

Yuki. Yuki, Temple Dog: How a California Pound Dog Became Guardian of a Japanese Buddhist Temple. (Illus.). 1986. 16.95 (ISBN 0-914910-37-X). Buddhist Bks.

Yukteswar, Swami Sri. Holy Science. LC 77-88199. (Illus.). 110p. 1984. 4.50 (ISBN 0-87612-051-6); 2nd Dutch ed. 6.50x (ISBN 90-202-4529-5); German ed. 6.00x (ISBN 3-87041-176-7); Japanese ed. 7.00x (ISBN 4-627-99950-X). Self Realization.

Yule, George, ed. Luther: Theologian for the Catholics & Protestants. 208p. 1985. pap. 12.95 (ISBN 0-567-29119-7, Pub. by T&T Clark Ltd UK). Fortress.

Yulish, Stephen M. The Search for a Civic Religion: A History of the Character Education Movement in America, Eighteen Ninety to Nineteen Thirty-Five. LC 80-5619. 318p. 1980. lib. bdg. 27.75 (ISBN 0-8191-1173-2); pap. text ed. 13.75 (ISBN 0-8191-1174-0). U Pr of Amer.

Yungblut, John. Quakerism of the Future: Mystical, Prophetic & Evangelical. LC 74-81830. (Orig.). 1974. pap. 2.50x (ISBN 0-87574-194-0). Pendle Hill.

--Seeking Light in the Darkness of the Unconscious. LC 77-71933. (Orig.). 1977. pap. 2.50x (ISBN 0-87574-211-4). Pendle Hill.

--Sex & the Human Psyche. LC 75-19951. 32p. (Orig.). 1975. pap. 2.50x (ISBN 0-87574-203-3, 203). Pendle Hill.

--Speaking As One Friend to Another. (Orig.). 1983. pap. 2.50x (ISBN 0-87574-249-1, 249). Pendle Hill.

Yungblut, John R. Discovering God Within. LC 78-21713. 198p. 1979. pap. 6.95 (ISBN 0-664-24231-6). Westminster.

Yusseff, M. A. The Dead Sea Scrolls, The Gospel of Barnabas & the New Testament. LC 85-73210. 154p. (Orig.). 1986. pap. 8.00 (ISBN 0-89259-061-0). Am Trust Pubns.

Yutang, Lin, ed. & tr. see Confucius.
Yuter, Alan J. The Holocaust in Hebrew Literature: From Genocide to Rebirth. LC 83-9973. (Judaic Studies). 152p. 1983. 18.00x (ISBN 0-8046-5322-4, Natl U). Assoc Faculty Pr.
Yuvacharya Shri Mahaprajna. Mind Beyond Mind: Perceptive Meditation, Form & Function. 186p. 1980. 9.00 (ISBN 0-88065-214-4, Pub. by Messers Today & Tomorrows Printers & Publishers India). Scholarly Pubns.
--Shraman Mahavir: His Life & Teachings. 334p. 1980. 12.00 (ISBN 0-88065-213-6, Pub. by Messers Today & Tomorows Printers & Publishers India). Scholarly Pubns.

Z

Zablocki, Benjamin. The Joyful Community: An Account of the Bruderhof, a Communal Movement Now in Its Third Generation. 1980. pap. 5.95 (ISBN 0-226-97749-8, P885, Phoen). U of Chicago Pr.
Zabriskie, Pat. Pointing the Way with Puppets. LC 81-81240. 80p. 1981. pap. 3.95 (ISBN 0-88243-574-4, 02-0574). Gospel Pub.
--The Puppet People. LC 79-53725. 80p. (Orig.). 1979. pap. 2.95 (ISBN 0-88243-753-4, 02-0753). Gospel Pub.
Zaccaria, Francesco A. Bibliotheca Ritualis, 2 vols. in 3. 1964. Repr. of 1781 ed. Set. 106.00 (ISBN 0-8337-3913-1). B Franklin.
Zaccaria, Joseph S. Facing Change: Strategies for Problem Solving in the Congregation. LC 84-18552. 112p. (Orig.). 1984. pap. 5.95 (ISBN 0-8066-2097-8, 10-2156). Augsburg.
Zacchello, Joseph. Secrets of Romanism. 232p. 1981. pap. 4.95 (ISBN 0-87213-981-6). Loizeaux.
Zacharias, Paul. Celebrate Life. LC 79-93145. 78p. pap. 1.95 (ISBN 0-87785-162-X). Swedenborg.
Zacharias, Paul B. Insights into the Beyond. LC 76-6756. pap. 1.00 (ISBN 0-87785-156-5). Swedenborg.
Zachary, Jean. The Holy Days, As Outlined in Leviticus Twenty-Three. 72p. (Orig.). 1987. pap. 3.75 (ISBN 0-9617733-0-8). Pneuma Pub.
Zacour, Norman P. see Setton, Kenneth M.
Zaehner, R. C., ed. & tr. Hindu Scriptures. 1978. 11.95x (ISBN 0-460-10944-8, Evman); pap. 5.95x (ISBN 0-460-11944-3, Evman). Biblio Dist.
Zaehner, Robert C. Hinduism. 1962. pap. 8.95 (ISBN 0-19-888012-X). Oxford U Pr.
--Mysticism: Sacred & Profane. 1957. pap. 7.95x (ISBN 0-19-500229-6). Oxford U Pr.
--The Teachings of the Magi. 1976. pap. 7.95 (ISBN 0-19-519857-3). Oxford U Pr.
Zaehner, Robert C., ed. The Bhagavad-Gita. 492p. 1969. 45.00x (ISBN 0-19-826522-0); pap. 12.95 (ISBN 0-19-501666-1). Oxford U Pr.
--Concise Encyclopedia of Living Faiths. (Illus.). (YA) pap. 16.95x (ISBN 0-8070-1151-7, BP275). Beacon Pr.
Zagat, Helen. Faith & Works. 1955. 6.95 (ISBN 0-686-24360-9). Divine Sci Fed.
Zagrebelny, P. From the Point of View of Eternity. 231p. 1978. pap. 4.45 (ISBN 0-8285-1076-8, Pub. by Progress Pubs USSR). Imported Pubns.
Zahalon, Yom-Tov B. Sefer lekarth tov: Perush le-megilat Ester, Tsfat, 1577. 31.00 (ISBN 0-405-11952-6). Ayer Co Pubs.
Zahan, Dominique. The Religion, Spirituality, & Thought of Traditional Africa. Martin, Kate E. & Martin, Lawrence M., trs. from Fr. LC 78-23525. 1979. Repr. of 1970 ed. lib. bdg. 17.00x (ISBN 0-226-97777-3). U of Chicago Pr.
--The Religion, Spirituality, & Thought of Traditional Africa. Ezra, Kate & Martin, Lawrence M., trs. vi, 180p. 1979. pap. 6.50x (ISBN 0-226-97778-1). U of Chicago Pr.
Zahavy, Tzvee. The Traditions of Eleazar Ben Azariah. LC 76-46373. (Brown University. Brown Judaic Studies: No. 2). 1977. pap. 13.50 (ISBN 0-89130-095-3, 140002). Scholars Pr GA.
Zahavy, Zev, ed. see Gordon, Harold H.
Zahirsky, Valerie G. The Conversion of Armenia. (Armenian Church Classics Ser.). (Illus.). 48p. (Orig.). 1985. pap. 5.00 (ISBN 0-934728-16-X). D O A C.
Zahl, Paul. Who Will Deliver Us? 170p. 1985. pap. 7.95 large print ed. (ISBN 0-8027-2487-6). Walker & Co.
Zahl, Paul F. Who Will Deliver Us? 96p. (Orig.). 1983. pap. 5.95 (ISBN 0-8164-2468-3, HarpR). Har-Row.
Zahler, Leah, ed. see Rinbochay, Lati, et al.
Zahn, Charles T., tr. see Weiser, Frederick S.
Zahn, Gordon. In Solitary Witness. rev. ed. 1986. pap. 10.95 (ISBN 0-87243-141-X). Templegate.
Zahn, Theodor. Introduction to the New Testament, 3 vols. 1977. 48.00 (ISBN 0-86524-119-8, 8003). Klock & Klock.
Zahorski, jt. auth. see Boyer.
Zaidi, A. M. Evolution of Muslim Political Thought in India, 6 vols. 1973. Set. text ed. 295.00x. Vol. 1, From Sayed to the Emergence of Jinnah. Vol. 2, Sectarian Nationalism & Khilafat. Vol. 3, Parting of Ways. Vol. 4, The Communal Award. Vol. 5, Demand for Pakistan. Vol. 6, Freedom at Last. Coronet Bks.
Zain, C. C. Evolution of Religion: Section 2, Lessons 133-40. (Illus.). 1976. pap. 9.95 (ISBN 0-87887-346-5). Church of Light.
Zaits, Kyrill Archpriest. Missionary Conversations with Protestant Sectarians. 49p. (Orig.). 1985. pap. 2.00 (ISBN 0-317-30291-4). Holy Trinity.
Zaitsev, Konstantine. Pastirskoje Bogoslovije, 2 Vols. Tr. of Pastoral Theology. 478p. 1960. pap. text ed. 16.00 (ISBN 0-317-30273-6). Holy Trinity.
Zakariya, M. The Virtues of Salat. 1970. 3.95x (ISBN 0-87902-193-4). Orientalia.
Zakeriyya, M. Teachings of Islam (Tablighi Nisab) Date not set. 25.00 (ISBN 0-933511-09-4). Kazi Pubns.
Zalaquett, Jose, jt. auth. see Williams, Shirley.
Zaleski, Carol. Otherworld Journeys: Accounts of Near-Death Experience in Medieval & Modern Times. 288p. 1987. 18.95 (ISBN 0-19-503915-7). Oxford U Pr.
Zall, Paul M., ed. see Ward, Nathaniel.
Zamboni, Camillo. He Speaks to You. 1966. pap. 1.25 (ISBN 0-8198-0055-4). Dghtrs St Paul.
Zamora, Lois P., ed. The Apocalyptic Vision in America: Interdisciplinary Essays on Myth & Culture. LC 81-85524. 272p. 1982. 19.95 (ISBN 0-686-82270-6). Bowling Green Univ.
Zanca, Kenneth. The Judas Within. (Illus.). 96p. (Orig.). 1978. pap. 2.95 (ISBN 0-914544-25-X). Living Flame Pr.
--Reasons for Rejoicing: Readings in Christian Hope. (Orig.). 1976. pap. 2.95 (ISBN 0-914544-12-8). Living Flame Pr.
Zandee, Jan. Death As an Enemy According to Ancient Egyptian Conceptions. Kastenbaum, Robert, ed. LC 76-19597. (Death & Dying Ser.). 1977. Repr. of 1960 ed. lib. bdg. 37.50x (ISBN 0-405-09591-0). Ayer Co Pubs.
Zander, Valentine. St. Seraphim of Sarov. LC 75-24136. Orig. Title: Seraphim of Sarov. 150p. 1975. pap. 6.95 (ISBN 0-913836-28-1). St Vladimirs.
Zandstra, Sidney. Witness of "The Vulgate," "Peshitta" & "Septuagint" to the Text of "Zephaniah". LC 72-948. (Columbia University. Contributions to Oriental History & Philology Ser.: No. 4). Repr. of 1909 ed. 12.50 (ISBN 0-404-50534-1). AMS Pr.
Zangwill, Israel. The Voice of Jerusalem. 1976. lib. bdg. 59.95 (ISBN 0-8490-2801-9). Gordon Pr.
Zannas, Eliky. Khajuraho. (Illus.). 1960. 132.00x (ISBN 0-686-21868-X). Mouton.
Zanotti, Barbara, ed. A Faith of One's Own: Explorations by Catholic Lesbians. (Feminist Ser.). 224p. (Orig.). 1986. 20.95 (ISBN 0-89594-210-0); pap. 8.95 (ISBN 0-89594-209-7). Crossing Pr.
Zanzig, Thomas. Jesus Is Lord! LC 82-62337. (Illus.). 208p. pap. 7.95 (ISBN 0-88489-149-6). St Marys.
--Jesus of History, Christ of Faith. LC 81-86361. (Illus.). 192p. (Orig.). 1981. pap. text ed. 7.20x (ISBN 0-88489-145-3); tchr's. manual 9.00 (ISBN 0-88489-146-1); spiritmasters 9.95. St Mary's.
--Sharing: A Manual for Program Directors. (Sharing Program Ser.). 214p. 1985. pap. 54.00 (ISBN 0-88489-167-4). St Mary's.
--Sharing the Christian Message: A Program Manual for Volunteer Catechists, Tenth Grade. 1977. pap. 9.95 (ISBN 0-88489-089-9); duplicating masters 6.95 (ISBN 0-88489-129-1). St Marys.
--Sharing the Christian Message: A Program Manual for Volunteer Catechists, 11th & 12th Grade. (Illus.). 1979. pap. 38.00 (ISBN 0-88489-110-0); spiritmasters 9.95 (ISBN 0-88489-130-5). St Marys.
--Sharing the Christian Message: A Program Manual for Volunteer Catechists, Ninth Grade. 1977. pap. 9.95 (ISBN 0-88489-086-4); duplicating masters 5.95 (ISBN 0-88489-128-3). St Mary's.
--Sharing 1: A Manual for Volunteer Teachers. (Sharing Program Ser.). (Illus.). 199p. 1985. pap. 18.95 (ISBN 0-88489-163-1). St Mary's.
--Sharing 4: A Manual for Volunteer Teachers. (Sharing Program Ser.). 200p. 1987. pap. 18.95 (ISBN 0-88489-166-6). St Mary's.
--Understanding Your Faith: An Introduction to Catholic Christianity for Freshmen. LC 80-50258. (Illus.). 192p. 1980. pap. text ed. 7.00x (ISBN 0-88489-115-1); tchr's guide 9.00x (ISBN 0-88489-122-4); spiritmasters 9.95 (ISBN 0-88489-131-3). St Mary's.
Zanzucchi, Annamaria. My Child & God: Religious Education in the Family. Hartman, Thomas, ed. Sczesniak, Lenny, tr. LC 78-52599. 100p. 1978. pap. 2.95 (ISBN 0-911782-31-1). New City.
Zapel, Arthur L., ed. see Gladman, Donna.
Zapel, Arthur L., ed. see Litherland, Janet.
Zapel, Arthur L., ed. see Magers, Mary A.
Zapel, Arthur L., ed. see Perrone, Stephen P. & Spata, James P.
Zapel, Arthur L., ed. see Qubein, Nido.
Zapel, Arthur L., ed. see Smith, Judy G.
Zapel, Arthur L., ed. see Sychterz, Terre.
Zapel, Michelle, tr. see Magers, Mary A.
Zappula, Robert, et al. The Modern Liturgy Planning Guide. 350p. 1987. 19.95 (ISBN 0-89390-088-5). Resource Pubns.
Zappulli, Cesare. The Power of Goodness. 1980. 3.00 (ISBN 0-8198-5800-5); pap. 2.00 (ISBN 0-8198-5801-3). Dghtrs St Paul.
Zar, Rose. In the Mouth of the Wolf. 224p. 1983. 10.95 (ISBN 0-8276-0225-1, 611). Jewish Pubns.
Zarabozo, J. M., jt. tr. see Dabas, M. S.
Zarate Salmeron, Geronimo. Relaciones. LC 66-27660. 122p. 1982. lib. bdg. 29.95x (ISBN 0-89370-728-7). Borgo Pr.
Zarathustra. The Gathas of Zarathustra. (Sacred Texts Ser.). viii, 104p. 1983. pap. 8.75 (ISBN 0-88695-011-2). Concord Grove.
Zarathustra, Frater. Magickal Qaballah. LC 86-50965. (Illus.). 75p. (Orig.). 1986. pap. 15.00 (ISBN 0-939856-63-8). Tech Group.
Zaret, David. The Heavenly Contract: Ideology & Organization in Pre-Revolutionary Puritanism. LC 84-16473. 192p. 1985. lib. bdg. 22.50x (ISBN 0-226-97882-6). U of Chicago Pr.
Zaretsky, David & Wengrov, Charles. The Stories & Parables of the Hafetz Hayyim. Orig. Title: Mishle Hafetz Hayyim. 1976. 8.95 (ISBN 0-87306-132-2). Feldheim.
Zaretsky, Irving I. & Leone, Mark P., eds. Religious Movements in Contemporary America. LC 73-39054. 900p. 1974. 71.00 (ISBN 0-691-07186-1); pap. 18.50x (ISBN 0-691-01993-2). Princeton U Pr.
Zaretsky, Tuvya. Turning to God. 32p. (Orig.). 1984. pap. 0.75 (ISBN 0-87784-064-4). Inter-Varsity.
Zarlengo, Patricia, compiled by see Brooks, Nona.
Zarnecki, George. Art of the Medieval World: Architecture, Sculpture, Painting, the Sacred Arts. 1976. 34.95 (ISBN 0-13-047514-9). P-H.
Zarqani, Mahmud-i. Abdu'l-Baha in America: Mahmud's Diary. 1978. 22.50 (ISBN 0-933770-61-8). Kalimat.
Zars, Belle, et al, eds. Education & the Threat of Nuclear War. (Reprint Ser.: No. 18). 166p. 1985. pap. 9.95x (ISBN 0-916690-20-2). Harvard Educ Rev.
Zaslavsky, Victor & Brym, Robert J. Soviet-Jewish Emigration & Soviet Nationality Policy. LC 83-3160. 172p. 1983. 22.50 (ISBN 0-312-74844-2). St Martin.
Zatko, James J., ed. Valley of Silence: Catholic Thought in Contemporary Poland. 1967. 21.95x (ISBN 0-268-00290-8). U of Notre Dame Pr.
--The Valley of Silence: Catholic Thought in Contemporary Poland. LC 67-12125. pap. 101.80 (2029313). Bks Demand UMI.
Zavel, Hubberman. God's Voice. 8.95 (ISBN 0-8062-2496-7). Carlton.
Zawodny, J. K. Nothing but Honour: The Story of the Warsaw Uprising, 1944. LC 76-51880. (Publication Ser: No. 183). (Illus.). 1978. 16.95x (ISBN 0-8179-6831-8). Hoover Inst Pr.
Zaydan, Jirji. Umayyads & Abbasids. Margoliouth, D. S., tr. from Arabic. LC 79-2889. 325p. 1982. Repr. of 1907 ed. 29.00 (ISBN 0-8305-0056-1). Hyperion Conn.
Zayed, Ismail. Zionism: The Myth & the Reality. Date not set. pap. 2.75 (ISBN 0-89259-013-0). Am Trust Pubns.
Zbozny, Frank T., ed. Annuale Mediaevale, Vol. 18. 1978. pap. text ed. 13.50x (ISBN 0-391-01220-7). Humanities.
Zebnik, Edith la see La Zebnik, Edith.
Zecha, G., ed. see Colloquium in the Philosophy of Science Staff.
Zechariah, Fendel. Anvil of Sinai. 1980. 12.95 (ISBN 0-686-76479-X). Feldheim.
Zedler, Beatrice H., ed. Saint Thomas Aquinas: On the Unity of the Intellect Against the Averroists. (Medieval Philosophical Texts in Translation: No. 19). 1968. pap. 7.95 (ISBN 0-87462-219-0). Marquette.
Zeeden, Ernest W. The Legacy of Luther: Martin Luther & the Reformation in the Estimation of the German Lutherans from Luther's Death to the Beginning of the Age of Goethe. Bethell, Ruth M., tr. from Ger. LC 83-45685. Date not set. Repr. of 1954 ed. 30.00 (ISBN 0-404-19865-1). AMS Pr.
Zehr, Paul. God Dwells with His People. LC 80-22701. 216p. 1981. pap. 7.95 (ISBN 0-8361-1939-8). Herald Pr.
Zehr, Paul M. Biblical Criticism in the Life of the Church. LC 85-24762. 112p. (Orig.). 1986. pap. 6.95 (ISBN 0-8361-3404-4). Herald Pr.
Zehr, Wilmer, jt. auth. see Campion, Michael.
Zeibig, Hartmann, ed. Urkundenbuch Des Stiftes Klosterneuburg Bis Zum Ende Des Vierzehnten Jahrhunderts. (Ger). Repr. of 1857 ed. 62.00 (ISBN 0-384-29875-3). Johnson Repr.
Zeik, Michael, ed. New Christian Communities: Origins, Style, & Survival. LC 76-181995. pap. 4.95 (ISBN 0-87957-002-4). Roth Pub.
Zeik, Michael & Siegel, Martin, eds. Root & Branch: The Jewish Christian Dialogue. LC 70-181996. pap. 4.95 (ISBN 0-87957-001-6). Roth Pub.
Zeiller, Jacques, jt. auth. see Lebreton, Jules.
Zeithlin, William & Katz, Steven, eds. Bibliotheca Hebraica Post-Mendelsohniana. LC 79-7154. (Jewish Philosophy, Mysticism & History of Ideas Ser.). 1980. Repr. of 1895 ed. lib. bdg. 45.00x (ISBN 0-405-12291-8). Ayer Co Pubs.
Zeitlin, Irving M. Ancient Judaism: Biblical Criticism from Max Weber to the Present. 328p. 1985. 29.95x (ISBN 0-7456-0059-X). Basil Blackwell.
--Ancient Judaism: Biblical Criticism from Max Weber to the Present. 328p. 1986. pap. 12.95 (ISBN 0-7456-0297-5). Basil Blackwell.
Zeitlin, Joseph. Disciples of the Wise. LC 71-121517. (Essay Index Reprint Ser). 1945. 19.00 (ISBN 0-8369-1859-2). Ayer Co Pubs.
Zeitlin, Solomon. Rise & Fall of the Judaean State, 3 vols. LC 61-11708. 1978. Vol. 3, 66-120 C. E. 534 Pgs. 12.50 (ISBN 0-686-91516-X). Jewish Pubns.
--Studies in the Early History of Judaism. Vol. 3. 49.50x (ISBN 0-87068-278-4); Vol. 4. 49.50x (ISBN 0-87068-454-X). Ktav.
--Studies in the Early History of Judaism, Vol. 1. 1973. 59.50x (ISBN 0-87068-208-3). Ktav.
--Studies in the Early History of Judaism, Vol. 2. 1973. 59.50x (ISBN 0-87068-209-1). Ktav.
--Who Crucified Jesus? 1976. pap. 6.95x (ISBN 0-8197-0013-4). Bloch.
Zeitz, James V. Spirituality & Analogia Entis According to Erich Przywara, S. J. Metaphysics & Religious Experience, the Ignation Exercises, the Balance in 'Similarity' & 'Greater Dissimilarity' According to Lateran IV. LC 82-17588. 358p. (Orig.). 1983. lib. bdg. 33.00 (ISBN 0-8191-2783-3); pap. text ed. 15.75 (ISBN 0-8191-2784-1). U Pr of Amer.
Zekowski, Arlene & Berne, Stanley. Cardinals & Saints. LC 58-11713. (Illus.). 1958. 45.00 (ISBN 0-913844-10-1). Am Canadian.
Zeldin, Mary B, jt. auth. see Cavarnos, Constatine.
Zelevansky, Paul. The Case for the Burial of Ancestors, Bk. 1. LC 80-54692. 1981. 27.00 (ISBN 0-9605610-3-X); pap. 18.00 (ISBN 0-9605610-2-1). Zartscorp.
Zeligs, Dorothy F. Psychoanalysis & the Bible: A Study in Depth of Seven Leaders. LC 73-85071. 1973. 15.95x (ISBN 0-8197-0360-5). Bloch.
Zeligs, Dorothy F., ed. Moses: A Psychodynamic Study. 384p. 1986. 39.95 (ISBN 0-89885-236-6). Human Sci Pr.
Zelle, Donald. Wind Through the Valleys. (Orig.). 1987. pap. price not set (ISBN 0-89536-876-5, 7862). CSS of Ohio.
Zeller, Dom H. van. Glimpses. 260p. 1982. 5.00 (ISBN 0-8198-3027-5, SP0185); pap. 4.00 (ISBN 0-8198-3028-3). Dghtrs St Paul.
Zeller, George W. God's Gift of Tongues: The Nature, Purpose, & Duration of Tongues As Taught in the Bible. LC 78-100. (Orig.). 1978. pap. 2.50 (ISBN 0-87213-985-9). Loizeaux.
Zeller, Hubert Van see Van Zeller, Hubert.
Zeller, Hubert van see Van Zeller, Hubert.
Zeller, Hubert Van see Van Zeller, Hubert.
Zellweger-Barth, Max. My Father-in-Law: Memories of Karl Barth. Rumscheidt, Martin, tr. from Ger. (Princeton Theological Monograph Ser.: No. 5). Tr. of Mein Schwiegervater. (Orig.). 1986. pap. 6.00 (ISBN 0-915138-84-0). Pickwick.
Zemach, Harve. The Judge: An Untrue Tale. LC 79-87209. (Illus.). 48p. 1969. 14.95 (ISBN 0-374-33960-0). FS&G.
Zeman, Jarold K. The Hussite Movement & the Reformation in Bohemia, Moravia & Slovakia, 1350-1650: A Bibliographic Study Guide. 1977. 15.00 (ISBN 0-930042-00-X). Mich Slavic Pubns.
Zembathy, J. S., jt. auth. see Mappes, T. A.
Zenkovsky, Serge A. Pan-Turkism & Islam in Russia. LC 60-5399. (Russian Research Center Studies: No. 36). 1960. 25.00x (ISBN 0-674-65350-5). Harvard U Pr.
Zenner, Walter P., jt. auth. see Deshen, Shlomo.
Zercher, Ray M., ed. see Book, Doyle C.
Zerfass, Samuel G. Souvenir Book of the Ephrata Cloister: Complete History from Its Settlement in 1728 to the Present Time. LC 72-2960. Repr. of 1921 ed. 14.25 (ISBN 0-404-10724-9). AMS Pr.

Zerin, Edward. What Catholics Should Know About Jews: And Other Christians. 1980. pap. 3.25 (ISBN 0-697-01739-7). Wm C Brown.

Zernov, Nicholas. Moscow, the Third Rome. 2nd ed. LC 76-149664. Repr. of 1938 ed. 12.50 (ISBN 0-404-07075-2). AMS Pr.

Zernov, Nicholas, compiled by. Russian Emigre Authors: A Biographical Index & Bibliography of Their Works on Theology, Religious Philosophy, Church History & Orthodox Culture, 1921-1972. 1973. lib. bdg. 23.50 (ISBN 0-8161-1005-0). G K Hall.

Zernov, Nicolas. The Russians & Their Church. 196p. 1977. pap. 6.95 (ISBN 0-913836-36-2). St Vladimirs.

Zerof, Herbert G. Finding Intimacy: The Art of Happiness in Living Together. 224p. (Orig.). 1981. pap. 6.95 (ISBN 0-86683-618-7, HarpR). Har-Row.

Zerr, Bonaventure. Psalms: A New Translation. 8.95 (ISBN 0-8091-2218-9). Paulist Pr.

Zerwick, Max. Analysis Philogica Novi Testamenti Graeci: Editio Tertia. (Scripta Pontificii Instituti Biblici,: Vol.107). (Lat.). 1966. pap. 12.00 (ISBN 88-7653-551-9). Loyola.

--The Epistle to the Ephesians. McKenzie, John L., ed. LC 81-605. (New Testament for Spiritual Reading Ser.). 181p. 1981. pap. 4.95 (ISBN 0-8245-0125-X). Crossroad NY.

--A Grammatical Analysis of Greek New Testament. (Scripta Pontificii Instituti Biblici Ser.: Vol. 1). 1974. pap. 16.00 (ISBN 88-7653-553-5). Loyola.

Zerwick, Maximilian. Biblical Greek. (Scripta Pontificci Instituti Biblica Ser.: Vol. 114). 1963. 12.00 (ISBN 88-7653-554-3). Loyola.

Zetterberg, J. Peter. Evolution Versus Creationism: The Public Education Controversy. LC 82-18795. 528p. 1983. lib. bdg. 41.00 (ISBN 0-89774-061-0). Oryx Pr.

Zeuner, Milton L. Universal Majesty. (Illus.). 80p. 1984. 6.00 (ISBN 0-682-40159-5, Chart). Exposition Pr FL.

Z'Ev ben Shimon Halevi. Kabbalah: Tradition of Hidden Knowledge. (Art & Imagination Ser.). (Illus.). 1980. pap. 10.95 (ISBN 0-500-81023-0). Thames Hudson.

Zevin, Schlomo Y. A Treasury of Chassidic Tales: On the Torah, Vol. 2. Kaploun, Uri, tr. (Art Scroll Judaica Classics Ser.). 352p. 1980. 13.95 (ISBN 0-89906-902-9); pap. 10.95 (ISBN 0-89906-903-7); gift box ed. 29.95 (ISBN 0-89906-904-5). Mesorah Pubns.

Zevin, Shlomo Y. The Festivals in Halachah, Vol. II. Kaploon, Uri, ed. Fox-Ashrei, Meir, tr. from Hebrew. (Artscroll Judica Classics Ser.). 336p. 1981. 14.95 (ISBN 0-89906-908-8); pap. 11.95 (ISBN 0-89906-909-6). Mesorah Pubns.

--A Treasury of Chassidic Tales, Vol. 1. Kaploun, Uri, tr. from Heb. (Art Scroll Judaica Classics Ser.). 320p. 1981. 13.95 (ISBN 0-89906-912-6); pap. 10.95 (ISBN 0-89906-913-4). Mesorah Pubns.

Zeydel, Edwin H., et al, eds. see Tieck, Johann L.

Zeylmans-Van-Emmichoven, F. W. The Foundation Stone. 118p. 1983. pap. 5.95 (ISBN 0-85440-399-X). Anthroposophic.

Zhenyu, Luo. Gu Mingqi Tulu. 1916. 300.00x (ISBN 0-317-44070-5, Pub. by Han-Shan Tang Ltd). State Mutual Bk.

Ziad, Kumail I. Du'A-E-Kumail. Mardi, N. Hussein, tr. from Arabic. 35p. Date not set. pap. 2.95 (ISBN 0-940368-75-7). Tahrike Tarsile Quran.

Ziavras, Charles E. The Monastery. LC 85-81279. (Illus.). 1985. 12.95 (ISBN 0-915940-05-1); pap. 4.95 (ISBN 0-915940-06-X). Ithaca Pr MA.

Ziebel, Michelle, tr. see Bernard, Helene.

Ziefle, Helmut W. Theological German. 256p. 1986. pap. 14.95 (ISBN 0-8010-9931-5). Baker Bk.

Ziegler, Edward K. Prayers for Public Worship. Eller, David, ed. 1986. pap. 3.95. Brethren.

--Simple Living. new ed. 128p. 1974. pap. 1.25 (ISBN 0-87178-791-1). Brethren.

Ziegler, Leopold. Gestaltwander der Gotter. Bolle, Kees W., ed. LC 77-79163. (Mythology Ser.). (Ger.). 1977. Repr. of 1920 ed. lib. bdg. 35.50x (ISBN 0-405-10571-1). Ayer Co Pubs.

Ziegler, Sandra. Service Project Ideas. (Ideas Ser.). (Illus.). 48p. 1977. pap. text ed. 1.95 (ISBN 0-87239-122-1, 7962). Standard Pub.

Ziegler, Sandra, et al. Our Christmas Handbook. LC 80-14587. (Illus.). 112p. (Orig.). 1980. pap. 6.50 (ISBN 0-89565-180-7). Childs World.

Ziegler, Sandy. Friends. Buerger, Jane, ed. 112p. 1980. 5.95 (ISBN 0-89565-174-2, 4931). Standard Pub.

Ziehn, Bernhard. The Doric Hymns of Mesomedes. 1979. pap. 1.75 (ISBN 0-911028-11-0). Newberry.

Zielinski, Stanislaw. Psychology & Silence. Bassuk, Daniel, ed. LC 75-7413. (Illus.). 32p. (Orig.). 1975. pap. 2.50x (ISBN 0-87574-201-7). Pendle Hill.

Zielinski, T. The Religion of Ancient Greece. x, 235p. pap. 10.00 (ISBN 0-89005-090-2). Ares.

Zielinski, Thaddeus. Religion of Ancient Greece. facsimile ed. Noyes, George R., tr. LC 76-107838. (Select Bibliographies Reprint Ser). 1926. 17.00 (ISBN 0-8369-5222-7). Ayer Co Pubs.

Ziesler, J. A. The Meaning of Righteousness in Paul: A Linguistic & Theological Enquiry. LC 75-164455. (Society for New Testament Studies, Monograph Ser.: Vol. 20). pap. 66.80 (ISBN 0-317-26359-5, 2024567). Bks Demand UMI.

Ziesler, John. Pauline Christianity. (The Oxford Bible Ser.). (Orig.). 1983. pap. 9.95 (ISBN 0-19-213247-4). Oxford U Pr.

Ziff, William B. The Rape of Palestine. LC 73-97310. (Illus.). 612p. 1975. Repr. of 1938 ed. lib. bdg. 29.25x (ISBN 0-8371-2639-8, ZIRP). Greenwood.

Ziglar, Zig. Confessions of a Happy Christian. LC 78-6729. 1978. 12.95 (ISBN 0-88289-196-0). Pelican.

--Confessions of a Happy Christian. 199p. 1982. pap. 6.95 (ISBN 0-88289-400-5). Pelican.

--Confessions of a Happy Christian. 192p. 1986. pap. 3.50 (ISBN 0-553-25551-7). Bantam.

--Nos Veremos en la Cumbre. Rev ed. Fernandez, Sergio, tr. from Eng. Orig. Title: See You at the Top. (Span., Illus.). 352p. 1985. pap. 9.95 (ISBN 0-311-46100-X). Casa Bautista.

Zijl, J. B. van see Van Zijl, J. B.

Zikmund, Barbara B. Discovering the Church. LC 82-23870. (Library of Living Faith: Vol. 9). 116p. 1983. pap. 5.95 (ISBN 0-664-24441-6). Westminster.

Zikmund, Barbara B., ed. Hidden Histories in the United Church of Christ. 192p. (Orig.). 1984. pap. 9.95 (ISBN 0-8298-0704-7). Pilgrim NY.

--Hidden Histories in the United Church of Christ, Pt. 2. 228p. (Orig.). 1987. pap. 10.95 (ISBN 0-8298-0753-5). Pilgrim NY.

Zikmund, Barbara B., jt. ed. see Manschreck, Clyde L.

Zile, Judy van see Van Zile, Judy.

Zill, Nicholas, jt. auth. see Peterson, James L.

Zilonka, Paul. Romans. (Read & Pray Ser.). 1979. 1.75 (ISBN 0-8199-0633-6). Franciscan Herald.

Zimbelman, Ernie, ed. Human Sexuality & Evangelical Christians. (Illus.). 394p. (Orig.). 1985. lib. bdg. 31.50 (ISBN 0-8191-4477-0); pap. text ed. 16.75 (ISBN 0-8191-4478-9). U Pr of Amer.

Zimmann, William C., Sr. The Legend of the Christmas Donkey. 1984. 1.95 (ISBN 0-89536-989-3, 7540). CSS of Ohio.

Zimmels, H. J. The Echo of the Nazi Holocaust in Rabbinic Literature. 25.00x (ISBN 0-87068-427-2). Ktav.

Zimmer, Allen E. God, Make Me Brave for Life. LC 81-69110. (Illus.). 128p. (Orig.). 1981. pap. 4.95 (ISBN 0-89505-057-9, 21052). Argus Comm.

Zimmer, Eric. Harmony & Discord: An Analysis of the Decline of Jewish Self-Government in Fifteenth Century Central Europe. 276p. 1970. 10.00x (ISBN 0-685-26214-6, Pub. by Yeshiva U. Pr.). Bloch.

Zimmer, Heinrich. King & the Corpse: Tales of the Soul's Conquest of Evil. Campbell, Joseph, ed. (Bollingen Ser.: Vol. 11). 1971. pap. 9.50 (ISBN 0-691-01776-X). Princeton U Pr.

Zimmer, Karl E., tr. see Steiner, Rudolf.

Zimmerli, Walther. Ezekiel I. Cross, Frank M., Jr. & Baltzer, Klaus, eds. LC 75-21540. (Hermenia: A Critical & Historical Commentary on the Bible). 558p. 1979. 39.95 (ISBN 0-8006-6008-0, 20-6008). Fortress.

--Ezekiel II. LC 72-1540. (Hermeneia-A Critical & Historical Commentary on the Bible). 576p. 1983. 39.95 (ISBN 0-8006-6010-2, 20-6010). Fortress.

--I Am Yahweh. Brueggemann, Walter, ed. Scott, Doug, tr. from German. LC 81-85326. 160p. 1982. 15.95 (ISBN 0-8042-0519-1). John Knox.

--Old Testament Theology in Outline. Green, David, tr. Tr. of Grundriss der Alttestamentlichen Theologie. 258p. 1978. pap. 12.95 (ISBN 0-567-22353-1, Pub. by T&T Clark Ltd UK). Fortress.

Zimmerman. Dictionary of Classical Mythology. (YA) pap. 4.95 (ISBN 0-553-25776-5). Bantam.

Zimmerman, Benedict, tr. see John of the Cross.

Zimmerman, Dean. Living Prophet. 1974. pap. 2.95 (ISBN 0-89036-041-3). Hawkes Pub Inc.

Zimmerman, Dean R. Evolution: A Golden Calf. 232p. (Orig.). 1976. pap. 3.95 (ISBN 0-89036-059-6). Hawkes Pub Inc.

Zimmerman, Diane, ed. Pilgrim's Progress Guides. (LifeView: a Christian Approachto Literature Studies). 1977. pap. 0.85 student guide (ISBN 0-915134-32-2); tchrs. ed. 1.50 (ISBN 0-915134-36-5). Mott Media.

Zimmerman, Diane, ed. see Lockerbie, D. Bruce.

Zimmerman, Frank. Biblical Books Translated from Arabic. 1974. 25.00x (ISBN 0-87068-252-0). Ktav.

--The Inner World of Qoehelet. 1972. 15.00x (ISBN 0-87068-181-8). Ktav.

Zimmerman, Gene. Why Do Mullet Jump? And Other Puzzles & Possibilities of God's Creation. 128p. (Orig.). 1986. pap. 6.95 (ISBN 0-935311-01-7). Post Horn Pr.

Zimmerman, Leander M. Prayers, for All People, for All Occasions. pap. 2.00 (2027877). Bks Demand UMI.

Zimmerman, Martha. Celebrate the Feasts: Of the Old Testament in Your Own Home or Church. 186p. 1981. pap. 5.95 (ISBN 0-87123-228-6). Bethany Hse.

--Should I Keep My Baby? 112p. (Orig.). 1983. pap. 3.95 (ISBN 0-87123-578-1, 210578). Bethany Hse.

Zimmerman, Moshe. Wilhelm Marr: The Patriarch of Anti-Semitism. (Studies in Jewish History). 192p. 1986. 19.95x (ISBN 0-19-504005-8). Oxford U Pr.

Zimmerman, Thomas F., et al. He Is Worthy. LC 77-92881. 64p. 1978. pap. 0.50 (ISBN 0-88243-523-X, 02-0523, Radiant Books). Gospel Pub.

Zimmerman, Thomas F., et al, eds. And He Gave Pastors. LC 78-50485. 500p. 1978. text ed. 12.95 (ISBN 0-88243-460-8, 02-0460). Gospel Pub.

Zimmermann, Friedrich. Die Agyptische Religion Nach der Darstellung der Kirchenschriftsteller und Die Agyptischen Denkmale. 15.00 (ISBN 0-384-71000-X). Johnson Repr.

Zimmermann, Gunter. Die Antwort Der Reformatoren Auf Die Zehtenfrage. (European University Studies Three: Vol. 164). 175p. 1982. 21.05 (ISBN 3-8204-5745-3). P Lang Pubs.

Zimmermann, Odo J., tr. see Gregorius I.

Zimney, Connie F. In Praise of Homemaking: Affirming the Choice to be a Mother-at-Home. LC 84-71285. 144p. (Orig.). 1984. pap. 4.95 (ISBN 0-87793-322-7). Ave Maria.

Zinberg, Israel. A History of Jewish Literature, 12 vols. 22.50x ea. (ISBN 0-685-56219-0). Ktav.

Zinberg, Norman E., ed. Alternate States of Consciousness. LC 76-46722. 1977. 14.95 (ISBN 0-02-935770-5); pap. text ed. 7.95 (ISBN 0-02-935930-9). Free Pr.

Zink, Harriet R. Emerson's Use of the Bible. 75p. 1980. Repr. of 1935 ed. lib. bdg. 15.00 (ISBN 0-8495-6206-6). Arden Lib.

--Emerson's Use of the Bible. LC 77-7882. 1977. lib. bdg. 20.00 (ISBN 0-8414-9805-9). Folcroft.

Zink, Jorg. Turn Toward Life: The Bible & Peacemaking. Rhodin, Victoria, tr. from Ger. LC 84-48709. 128p. 1985. pap. 7.95 (ISBN 0-8006-1829-7, 1-1829). Fortress.

Zink, Sidney. Concepts of Ethics. 1969. 18.95 (ISBN 0-312-16100-X). St Martin.

Zinkand, John M. Covenants: God's Claims. 120p. (Orig.). 1984. pap. 5.95 (ISBN 0-932914-10-1). Dordt Coll Pr.

Zinkewych, Osyp & Lonchyna, Taras. Martyrology of Ukrainian Churches: Vol. 1, Ukrainian Catholic Church. (Ukrainian Ser.). 839p. 1985. 29.75 (ISBN 0-914834-36-3). Smoloskyp.

Zinn, Grover A., ed. Richard of St. Victor: The Twelve Patriarchs, the Mystical Ark Book, Three of the Trinity. LC 79-83834. (Classics of Western Spirituality Ser.). 448p. 1979. 13.95 (ISBN 0-8091-0241-2); pap. 7.95 (ISBN 0-8091-2122-0). Paulist Pr.

Ziolkowski, Theodore. Fictional Transfiguration of Jesus. LC 70-39794. 536p. 1972. 34.00 (ISBN 0-691-06235-8); pap. 13.50 (ISBN 0-691-01346-2). Princeton U Pr.

Zion, Raphael Ben, tr. Anthology of Jewish Mysticism. 255p. 1984. pap. 6.95 (ISBN 0-910818-29-0). Judaica Pr.

Zipes, Jack D., jt. ed. see Rabinbach, Anson.

Zipperstein, Edward. Business Ethics in Jewish Law. 1983. 15.00 (ISBN 0-88125-005-8); pap. 9.95 (ISBN 0-88125-022-8). Ktav.

Zipperstein, Steven J. The Jews of Odessa: A Cultural History, 1794-1881. LC 84-50152. 232p. 1986. 32.50x (ISBN 0-8047-1251-4). Stanford U Pr.

Zirkoff, Boris De see Blavatsky, Helena P.

Zirkoff, Boris de see De Zirkoff, Boris.

Zitko, Howard J. New Age Tantra Yoga: The Sexual Gateway to Spiritual Fulfillment. 6th ed. LC 75-3657. 1985. pap. 7.50 (ISBN 0-941902-00-5). World Univ AZ.

Zivojinovic, Dragan. The United States & Vatican Policies, 1914-1918. LC 78-52438. 1978. 22.50x (ISBN 0-87081-112-6). Colo Assoc.

Zizola, Giancarlo. The Utopia of Pope John XXIII. Barolini, Helen, tr. from Ital. LC 79-4347. Orig. Title: L' Utopia de Papa Giovanni. 391p. (Orig.). 1979. pap. 2.49 (ISBN 0-88344-520-4). Orbis Bks.

Zizzamia, Alba I., tr. see Caliaro, Marco & Francesconi, Mario.

Zlotowitz, Bernard M. The Septuagint Translation of the Hebrew Terms in Relation to God in the Book of Jeremiah. 1981. 25.00x (ISBN 0-87068-704-2). Ktav.

Zlotowitz, Bernard M., ed. see Segal, Abraham.

Zlotowitz, Meir. Bereishis-Genesis, Vol. 5. (Art Scroll Tanach Ser.). 1980. 16.95 (ISBN 0-89906-358-6); pap. 13.95 (ISBN 0-89906-359-4). Mesorah Pubns.

--Bereishis-Genesis: Vol. 4, Vayeitzei-Vayishlach. (Art Scroll Tanach Ser.). 400p. 1979. 16.95 (ISBN 0-89906-356-X); pap. 13.95 (ISBN 0-89906-357-8). Mesorah Pubns.

--The Book of Ruth. (Art Scroll Tanach Ser.). 160p. 1976. 11.95 (ISBN 0-89906-002-1); pap. 8.95 (ISBN 0-89906-003-X). Mesorah Pubns.

--Eichah-Lamentations. (The Art Scroll Tanach Ser.). 160p. 1976. 11.95 (ISBN 0-89906-004-8); pap. 8.95 (ISBN 0-89906-005-6). Mesorah Pubns.

--The Five Megillos, 5 vols. (The Art Scroll Tanach Ser.). 928p. 1977. Boxed Set. 59.95 (ISBN 0-89906-010-2); Boxed Set. pap. 44.95 (ISBN 0-89906-011-0). Mesorah Pubns.

--Koheles-Ecclesiastes. (The Art Scroll Ser.). 224p. 1976. 11.95 (ISBN 0-89906-006-4); pap. 8.95 (ISBN 0-686-63976-6). Mesorah Pubns.

--The Megillah-the Book of Esther. (The Art Scroll Tanach Ser.). 160p. 1976. 11.95 (ISBN 0-89906-000-5); pap. 8.95 (ISBN 0-89906-001-3). Mesorah Pubns.

--Shir Hashirim-Song of Songs. (The Art Scroll Tanach Ser.). 224p. 1977. 11.95 (ISBN 0-89906-008-0); pap. 8.95 (ISBN 0-89906-009-9). Mesorah Pubns.

--Yonah-Jonah. (The Art Scroll Tanach Ser.). 160p. 1978. 11.95 (ISBN 0-89906-081-1); pap. 8.95 (ISBN 0-89906-082-X). Mesorah Pubns.

Zlotowitz, Meir, ed. see Scherman, Nosson.

Znamensky, G. A. Azbuka Pravoslavnago Vjerouchenija. Tr. of The Alphabet of the Orthodox Faith. 80p. pap. text ed. 3.00 (ISBN 0-317-29292-7). Holy Trinity.

Znoskovo-Borovsky, Mitrophan. Pravoslavije, Rimo-Katolichestvo, Protenstatizm i Sektantstvo. Tr. of Orthodoxy, Roman-Catholicism, Protenstatism & Sectarianism. 156p. 1972. pap. text ed. 5.00 (ISBN 0-317-30254-X). Holy Trinity.

Zobin, Zvi. Breakthrough to Learning Gemorah. 1987. pap. 3.95. Feldheim.

Zodhiates, Joan, ed. see Miller, J. R.

Zodhiates, Joan, ed. see Morrison, George H.

Zodhiates, Spiros. The Behavior of Belief. 1966. 19.95 (ISBN 0-89957-505-6). AMG Pubs.

--A Christian View of War & Peace. 1979. pap. 1.45 (ISBN 0-89957-509-9). AMG Pubs.

--Christianity: Not Just a Religion. (Illus.). 1979. pap. 1.75 (ISBN 0-89957-523-4). AMG Pubs.

--Getting the Most Out of Life. (I Corinthians). (Illus.). 1976. pap. 4.95 (ISBN 0-89957-515-3). AMG Pubs.

--Jesus & the Demon World. LC 82-71842. 1982. pap. 5.95 (ISBN 0-89957-556-0). AMG Pubs.

--The Labor of Love. (Trilogy Ser.: Vol. 3). (Illus.). pap. 8.95 (ISBN 0-89957-541-2). AMG Pubs.

--Life after Death!? Zodhiates, Spiros, tr. from Greek. Orig. Title: What Happens After Death? (Illus.). 1977. pap. 3.95 (ISBN 0-89957-525-0). AMG Pubs.

--The Lord's Prayer. 352p. pap. 8.95 (ISBN 0-89957-049-6). AMG Pubs.

--May I Divorce & Remarry. write for info. (ISBN 0-89957-600-1). AMG Pubs.

--The Patience of Hope. (Trilogy Ser.: Vol. 1). pap. 4.95 (ISBN 0-89957-543-9). AMG Pubs.

--The Perfect Gift. (Illus.). 1973. pap. 1.75 (ISBN 0-89957-511-0). AMG Pubs.

--The Pursuit of Happiness. 2nd ed. 665p. 1982. pap. 9.95 (ISBN 0-89957-508-0). AMG Pubs.

--Resurrection: True or False? (Illus.). 1978. pap. 3.95 (ISBN 0-89957-524-2). AMG Pubs.

--A Revolutionary Mystery. (I Corinthians). (Illus.). 1974. pap. 6.95 (ISBN 0-89957-507-2). AMG Pubs.

--A Richer Life: I Corinthians. Orig. Title: A Richer Life for You in Christ. 1972. 8.95 (ISBN 0-89957-501-3); kivar 5.95 (ISBN 0-89957-502-1). AMG Pubs.

--The Song of the Virgin. LC 82-71643. (Illus.). 1974. pap. 3.95 (ISBN 0-89957-510-2). AMG Pubs.

--To Love Is to Live. (I Corinthians). 1967. 8.95 (ISBN 0-89957-503-X). AMG Pubs.

--Tongues!? (I Corinthians Ser.). (Illus.). 1974. pap. 6.95 (ISBN 0-89957-512-9). AMG Pubs.

--Was Christ God? 1966. 7.95 (ISBN 0-89957-504-8). AMG Pubs.

--What about Divorce. 7.95 (ISBN 0-89957-574-9). AMG Pubs.

--Who Is Worth Following. 1982. pap. 4.95 (ISBN 0-89957-514-5). AMG Pubs.

--Why God Permits Accidents. LC 79-51340. 1982. pap. 2.25 (ISBN 0-89957-537-4). AMG Pubs.

--Why Pray? LC 82-71266. (Luke Trio Ser.). 1982. pap. 5.95 (ISBN 0-89957-554-4). AMG Pubs.

--The Work of Faith. (Trilogy Ser.: Vol. 2). (Illus.). pap. 6.95 (ISBN 0-89957-545-5). AMG Pubs.

--You & Public Opinion: I Corinthians. (Illus.). 1977. pap. 2.95 (ISBN 0-89957-522-6). AMG Pubs.

Zodhiates, Spiros, ed. Hebrew Greek-Key Study Bible. 59.00 (ISBN 0-89957-572-2). AMG Pubs.

--The Hebrew-Greek Key Study Bible. 1985. deluxe ed. 39.95 (ISBN 0-8010-9930-7). Baker Bk.

--Learn or Review New Testament Greek: The Answer Book. 1977. pap. 2.95 (ISBN 0-89957-519-6); wkbk. 9.95 (ISBN 0-89957-566-8); answer bk. avail. (ISBN 0-89957-567-6). AMG Pubs.

Zohar, Danah. Israel. LC 77-88352. (Countries Ser.). (Illus.). 1978. PLB 14.96 (ISBN 0-382-06146-2). Silver.

Zohary, Michael. Plants of the Bible: A Complete Handbook to all the Plants with 200 Full-Color Plates taken in the Natural Habitat. LC 82-4535. (Illus.). 224p. 1982. 17.95 (ISBN 0-521-24926-0). Cambridge U Pr.

Zohn, Harry, ed. see Kayser, Rudolf.

Zohn, Harry, tr. see Scholem, Gershom.

Zohrapian, Hovhann, ed. Astuatsashunch Matean Hin ew Nor Ktakarants. LC 84-14281. (Classical Armenian Texts Ser.). (Armenian.). 912p. 1985. Repr. of 1805 ed. 150.00 (ISBN 0-88206-054-6). Caravan Bks.

Zoller, Robert. The Lost Key to Prediction: The Arabic Parts in Astrology. 350p. 1980. pap. 8.95 (ISBN 0-89281-013-0). Inner Tradit.

Zollman, Carl. American Civil Church Law. LC 79-77996. (Columbia University. Studies in the Social Sciences: No. 181). Repr. of 1917 ed. 30.00 (ISBN 0-404-51181-3). AMS Pr.

Zom. True Yoga. 4.95 (ISBN 0-8065-0336-X). Citadel Pr.

Zomberg, P. G., tr. see Thomas a Kempis.

Zones, Jane S., ed. San Diego Women's Haggadah. rev. ed. LC 85-51376. (Illus.). 80p. 1986. pap. 7.50 (ISBN 0-9608054-5-1). Womans Inst-Cont Jewish Ed.

Zook, Mary R. Little Missionaries. 184p. (YA) 6.75 (ISBN 0-686-30764-X). Rod & Staff.

Zook, Mollie B. Dilek. 1983. 3.25 (ISBN 0-87813-521-9). Christian Light.

Zophy, Jonathan W., ed. The Holy Roman Empire: A Dictionary Handbook. LC 79-8282. (Illus.). xxvii, 551p. 1980. lib. bdg. 49.95 (ISBN 0-313-21457-3, ZHR/). Greenwood.

Zorba the Buddha Rajneesh Restaurants & Staff. Zorba the Buddha Rajneesh Cookbook. Swami Premdharma & Ma Dhyan Yogini, eds. LC 84-61260. 240p. (Orig.). 1984. pap. 4.95 (ISBN 0-918963-00-1). Rajneesh Neo-Sannyas Intl.

Zorzoli, Alicia de see Conway, Jim & Conway, Sally.

Zorzoli, Ruben O., tr. see Narramore, Clyde M.

Zorzoli, Ruben O., tr. see Viertel, Weldon E.

Zouche, Robert C. Visits to Monasteries in the Levant. LC 80-2200. Repr. of 1916 ed. 45.00 (ISBN 0-404-18989-X). AMS Pr.

Zschietzschmann, Willy, jt. auth. see Krencker, Daniel.

Zubairi, M. Yameen. The Purpose of Islam. LC 84-90999. 100p. (Orig.). 1984. pap. text ed. write for info. (ISBN 0-930895-02-9). Byron Daven Pub.

Zuber, Rene. Who Are You Monsieur Gurdjieff? Koralek, Jenny, tr. 80p. 1980. pap. 4.95 (ISBN 0-7100-0674-8). Methuen Inc.

Zubiri, Xavier. Nature, History, God. Fowler, Thomas B., Jr., tr. from Span. LC 80-1355. 441p. 1981. lib. bdg. 31.25; pap. text ed. 17.75. U Pr of Amer.

--On Essence. LC 78-68067. pap. 132.30 (2029514). Bks Demand UMI.

Zucchi, Jacopo see Baldini, Baccio.

Zuccotti, Susan. The Italians & the Holocaust: Persecution, Rescue & Survival. LC 86-47738. (Illus.). 344p. 1987. 19.95 (ISBN 0-465-03622-8). Basic.

Zucher, E. The Buddhist Conquest of China: The Spread & Adaptation of Buddhism in Early Medieval China, 2 vols. 470p. 1973. Set. text ed. 99.00x (ISBN 0-391-01961-9). Humanities.

Zuck, Lowell H. Socially Responsible Believers: Puritans, Pietists, & Unionists in the History of the United Church of Christ. 164p. (Orig.). 1987. pap. 8.95 (ISBN 0-8298-0744-6). Pilgrim NY.

Zuck, Lowell H., ed. Christianity & Revolution: Radical Christian Testimonies, 1520-1650. LC 74-25355. (Documents in Free Church History Ser.: No. 2). 324p. 1975. 29.95 (ISBN 0-87722-040-9); pap. 12.95 (ISBN 0-87722-044-1). Temple U Pr.

Zuck, Roy. Job. (Everyman's Bible Commentary Ser.). 1978. pap. 5.95 (ISBN 0-8024-2017-6). Moody.

Zuck, Roy, jt. auth. see Walvoord, John.

Zuck, Roy B. Barb, Please Wake Up! 128p. 1983. pap. 2.75 (ISBN 0-89323-042-1). Bible Memory.

--The Holy Spirit in Your Teaching. 228p. 1984. pap. 7.95 (ISBN 0-88207-622-1). Victor Bks.

Zuck, Roy B. & Getz, Gene A. Adult Education in the Church. LC 79-123154. 1970. pap. 15.95 (ISBN 0-8024-0468-5). Moody.

Zuck, Roy B., jt. auth. see Walvoord, John F.

Zuck, Roy B. & Benson, Warren S., eds. Youth Education in the Church. 1978. 13.95 (ISBN 0-8024-9844-2). Moody.

Zucker, Norman L. The Coming Crisis in Israel: Private Faith & Public Policy. 1973. pap. 7.95x (ISBN 0-262-74012-5). MIT Pr.

Zuckerman, Harriet, ed. see Birnbaum, Norman.

Zuckerman, Harriet, ed. see Goode, Erich.

Zuckerman, Harriet, ed. see Hammond, Phillip E.

Zuckerman, Harriet, ed. see Yinger, Milton J.

Zuckmayer, Carl, jt. auth. see Barth, Karl.

Zuesse, Evan. Ritual Cosmos: The Sanctification of Life in African Religions. LC 79-13454. 256p. 1985. pap. 12.95x (ISBN 0-8214-0814-3). Ohio U Pr.

Zuesse, Evan M. Ritual Cosmos: The Sanctification of Life in African Religions. LC 79-13454. x, 256p. 1980. 21.95x (ISBN 0-8214-0398-2). Ohio U Pr.

Zugibe, Frederick T. The Cross & the Shroud: A Medical Examination of the Crucifixion. (Illus.). 240p. 1987. 21.95 (ISBN 0-913729-75-2); pap. 9.95 (ISBN 0-913729-46-9). Paragon Hse.

Zuhur-U'D, A. M. M. An Examination of the Mystical Tendencies in Islam. 224p. 1973. 8.50x (ISBN 0-87902-252-3). Orientalia.

Zuker, Simon. The Unconquerable Spirit. Hirschler, Gertrude, ed. (Illus.). 160p. 1980. pap. 8.95 (ISBN 0-89906-203-2). Mesorah Pubns.

Zumkeller, Adolar. Augustine's Ideal of the Religious Life. xii, 468p. 1986. 40.00 (ISBN 0-8232-1105-3); pap. 20.00 (ISBN 0-8232-1106-1). Fordham.

Zundel, Veronica. Eerdmans' Book of Christian Classics. 125p. 1985. 12.95 (ISBN 0-8028-3612-7). Eerdmans.

Zundel, Veronica, ed. Eerdmans' Book of Famous Prayers. (Illus.). 126p. 1984. 12.95 (ISBN 0-8028-3593-7). Eerdmans.

Zunkel, C. W. Church Growth under Fire. LC 86-31814. 256p. (Orig.). 1987. pap. 8.95 (ISBN 0-317-52328-7). Herald Pr.

Zunkel, C. Wayne. Growing the Small Church: A Guide for Church Leaders. 109p. 1982. tchr's. ed. 12.95 (ISBN 0-89191-952-X). Cook.

--Growing the Small Church: A Guide for Church Members. 120p. 1984. pap. text ed. 2.95 (ISBN 0-89191-951-1). Cook.

--Strategies for Growing Your Church. 112p. 1986. pap. 12.95 (ISBN 0-89191-344-0). Cook.

Zuntz, G. The Ancestry of the Harklean New Testament. 1965. pap. 2.25 (ISBN 0-85672-677-X, Pub. by British Acad). Longwood Pub Group.

--The Text of the Epistles: A Disquisition upon the Corpus Paulinum. (Schweich Lectures on Biblical Archaeology). 306p. 1946. 8.25 (ISBN 0-85672-715-6, Pub. by British Acad). Longwood Pub Group.

Zuraw, Robert A., jt. auth. see Lewanski, Robert T.

Zurer, Rachel. A Jew Examines Christianity. LC 83-82999. 181p. (Orig.). 1985. 12.50 (ISBN 0-941752-03-8); pap. 8.50 (ISBN 0-941752-01-1). Jenna Pr.

Zuroff, E., jt. ed. see Gutman, Y.

Zusman, Evelyn, jt. auth. see Chanover, Hyman.

Zvegintzov, Catherine, compiled by. Our Mother Church, Her Worship & Offices. 1948 ed. LC 78-227697. pap. 6.50x (ISBN 0-281-00849-3). A R Allenson.

Zwack, Joseph P. Annulment-Your Chance to Remarry Within the Catholic Church: A Step-by-Step Guide Using the New Code of Canon Law. LC 83-47739. (Using the New Code of Canon Law Ser.). 144p. (Orig.). 1983. pap. 5.95 (ISBN 0-06-250990-X, BN-3004, HarpR). Har-Row.

Zwalf, Wladimir. Buddhism: Art & Faith. (Illus.). 300p. 1985. text ed. 45.00x (ISBN 0-02-934500-6). Macmillan.

Zweig, Ferdynand. Israel: The Sword & the Harp. LC 74-86291. 326p. 1970. 24.50 (ISBN 0-8386-7534-4). Fairleigh Dickinson.

Zweig, Paul. Muktananda: Selected Essays. LC 76-9994. 1977. pap. 7.95i (ISBN 0-06-069860-8, RD185, HarpR). Har-Row.

Zweig, Stefan. Erasmus. 1934. 35.00 (ISBN 0-8274-2283-0). R West.

--The Right to Heresay-Castellio Against Calvin. 2nd ed. LC 84-40514. (History & Biography Ser.). (Illus.). 300p. 1985. pap. cancelled (ISBN 0-910129-27-4). Wiener Pub Inc.

Zweigenhaft, Richard L. Who Gets to the Top? Executive Suite Discrimination in the Eighties. LC 84-70044. 48p. 1984. pap. 3.00 (ISBN 0-87495-059-7). Am Jewish Comm.

Zwerin, Raymond, jt. auth. see Friedman, Audrey M.

Zwerin, Raymond A. & Friedman, Audrey. Our Synagogue, 3 vols. (Illus.). 1974. pap. text ed. 3.50x (ISBN 0-03-012671-1). Behrman.

Zwerin, Raymond A. & Marcus, Audrey F. But This Night Is Different. (Illus.). 48p. 1981. text ed. 7.95x (ISBN 0-8074-0032-7, 102561). UAHC.

Zwerin, Raymond A., jt. auth. see Marcus, Audrey F.

Zwerin, Raymond A., jt.ed. see Marcus, Audrey F.

Zwerneman, Andrew J. In Bloody Terms: The Betrayal of the Church in Marxist Grenada. LC 85-82316. 113p. (Orig.). 1986. pap. text ed. 6.95 (ISBN 0-937779-00-8). Greenlawn Pr.

Zwetl, Austria (Cistercian Monastery) Das Stiftungen-Buch der Cistercienser-Klosters Zwetl. xvi, 736p. Repr. of 1851 ed. 62.00 (ISBN 0-384-71300-9). Johnson Repr.

Zwier, Robert. Born-Again Politics: The New Christian Right in America. (Illus.). 132p. 1982. pap. 4.95 (ISBN 0-87784-828-9). Inter-Varsity.

Zwierlein, Frederick K. Religion in the New Netherland, 1623-1664. LC 72-120851. (Civil Liberties in American History Ser.). 1971. Repr. of 1910 ed. lib. bdg. 39.50 (ISBN 0-306-71960-6). Da Capo.

Zwingli. Selected Writings. 1972. 9.95x (ISBN 0-8122-1049-2). U of Pa Pr.

Zwingli, Ulrich. The Acconmpt Rekenynge & Confession of the Faith of Huldrik Zwinglius. Cotsforde, Thomas, tr. from Latin. LC 79-84148. (The English Experience: No. 964). Orig. Title: Swinglische Bekenntuis. 156p. 1979. Repr. of 1555 ed. lib. bdg. 11.50 (ISBN 90-221-0964-X). Walter J Johnson.

--Commentary on True & False Religion. Jackson, Samuel M. & Heller, Nevin, eds. viii, 415p. 1981. pap. 15.95 (ISBN 0-939464-00-4). Labyrinth Pr.

--Early Writings, Fifteen Ten to Fifteen Twenty-Two, Vol. 1. Jackson, Samuel M., ed. Orig. Title: Latin Writings of Huldreich Zwingli. 308p. 1987. pap. 15.95 (ISBN 0-939464-42-X). Labyrinth Pr.

--A Short Pathwaye to the Ryghte & True Understanding of the Holye & Sacred Scriptures. Veron, J., tr. LC 77-7443. (English Experience Ser.: No. 901). 1977. Repr. of 1550 ed. lib. bdg. 15.00 (ISBN 90-221-0901-1). Walter J Johnson.

Zycha, I., ed. see Augustinus, Aurelius.

Zyl, P. Van see Davies, J. G. & Van Zyl, P.

Zylstra, Henry, tr. see Bavinck, Herman.

Zysk, Kenneth G. Religious Healing in the Veda. LC 84-45899. (Transaction Ser.: Vol. 75 Pt. 7). 300p. 1986. 30.00 (ISBN 0-87169-757-2). Am Philos.

Books
Title Index

A

A. B. Simpson: His Life & Work. rev. ed. A. W. Thompson. (Illus.). 228p. 1960. pap. 4.95 (ISBN 0-87509-044-3). Chr Pubns.

A. D. Nineteen Ninety-One: The Genesis of Holocaust. Henry R. Hall. (Prophetic Ser.). 375p. (Orig.). 1985. pap. 4.95 (ISBN 0-930351-01-0). Spirit Prophecy.

A Is for Apple. Elizabeth Shaver. (Illus.). 36p. 1986. pap. 2.50. Shaker Her Soc.

A. J. Muste: Pacifist & Prophet. Jo Ann Robinson. Ed. by Eleanore P. Mather. LC 81-80219. 31p. 1981. pap. 2.50x (ISBN 0-87574-235-1, 235). Pendle Hill.

A. M. Mackay: Pioneer Missionary of the Church of the Missionary Society of Uganda. A. M. Mackay. (Illus.). 485p. 1970. Repr. of 1890 ed. 35.00x (ISBN 0-7146-1874-8, F Cass Co). Biblio Dist.

A. P. A. Movement: A Sketch. Humphrey Desmond. LC 69-18772. (American Immigration Collection Ser., No. 1). 1969. Repr. of 1912 ed. 10.00 (ISBN 0-405-00519-9). Ayer Co Pubs.

A Partir del Eden. Kathryn Lindskoog. Tr. by Julio Orozco from Eng. LC 77-73843. Tr. of Up from Eden. (Span.). 144p. 1977. pap. 3.50 (ISBN 0-89922-092-4). Edit Caribe.

A. W. Tozer: A Twentieth Century Prophet. David J. Fant, Jr. LC 64-21945. (Illus.). 180p. 1964. pap. 3.95 (ISBN 0-87509-048-6). Chr Pubns.

Aamot. Luella Stroh. 320p. (Orig.). 1987. pap. 9.95 (ISBN 0-939213-02-8). Oasis Bks.

Aaron Ladner Lindsley: Founder of Alaska Missions. (Shorey Historical Ser.). 9p. pap. 2.25 (ISBN 0-8466-0050-1, S50). Shorey.

Aaron, the High Priest. Zev Paamoni. (Biblical Ser.). (Illus.). 1970. 4.00 (ISBN 0-914080-27-X). Shulsinger Sales.

Abailard's Christian Theology. Pierre Abailard. Tr. by James R. McCullum from Fr. LC 76-1128. 117p. 1976. Repr. of 1948 ed. lib. bdg. 14.50x (ISBN 0-915172-07-0). Richwood Pub.

Abandonment of Illusions: Zionist Political Attitudes Toward Palestinian Arab Nationalism, 1936-1939. Yehoyada Haim. (Relica Edition Ser.). 170p. 1983. softcover 22.50x (ISBN 0-86531-971-5). Westview.

Abandonment of the Jews. David S. Wyman. LC 84-42711. 480p. 1986. pap. 8.95 (ISBN 0-394-74077-7). Pantheon.

Abandonment of the Jews: America & the Holocaust, 1941-1945. David S. Wyman. LC 84-42711. 450p. 1984. 6.00 (ISBN 0-394-42813-7). Pantheon.

Abandonment to Divine Providence. Jean-Pierre De Caussade. LC 74-2827. 120p. 1975. pap. 3.50 (ISBN 0-385-02544-0, Im). Doubleday.

Abarbenel Al Hatorah, 3 Vols. Don I. Abarbenel. (Hebrew.). Set. 45.00 (ISBN 0-87559-078-0). Shalom.

Abba. Evelyn Underhill. LC 82-80476. (Treasures from the Spiritual Classics Ser.). 64p. 1982. pap. 2.95 (ISBN 0-8192-1313-6). Morehouse.

Abba! Father! A Personal Catechism. Gerald O'Mahoney. 160p. 1982. 10.95 (ISBN 0-8245-0546-8); pap. 5.95 (ISBN 0-8245-0519-0). Crossroad NY.

Abba Father: The Lord's Pattern for Prayer. R. Kent Hughes. LC 85-72920. 128p. 1986. pap. 5.95 (ISBN 0-89107-377-9, Crossway Bks). Good News.

ABBA: Guides to Wholeness & Holiness East & West. Ed. by John R. Sommerfeldt. (Cistercian Studies: No. 38). 1982. 22.95 (ISBN 0-87907-838-3). Cistercian Pubns.

Abbe Gregoire, 1787-1831: The Odyssey of an Egalitarian. Ruth F. Necheles. LC 75-105987. 1971. lib. bdg. 29.95 (ISBN 0-8371-3312-2, NAG/&). Greenwood.

Abbey of St. Germain des Pres in the Seventeenth Century. Maarten Ultee. LC 81-2265. (Illus.). 224p. 1981. text ed. 24.50x (ISBN 0-300-02562-9). Yale U Pr.

Abbey Psalter: The Book of Psalms Used by the Trappist Monks of Genesee Abbey. John Abbot & Eudes Bamberger. LC 81-80871. 368p. 1981. 24.95 (ISBN 0-8091-0316-8). Paulist Pr.

Abbeys & Churches of England & Wales. T. G. Bonney et al. LC 77-23529. 1977. Repr. of 1890 ed. lib. bdg. 40.00 (ISBN 0-89341-203-1). Longwood Pub Group.

Abbeys & Priories of England & Wales. Bryan Little. LC 79-213. (Illus.). 216p. 1979. text ed. 34.50x (ISBN 0-8419-0485-5). Holmes & Meier.

Abbeys & Priories of Medieval England. Colin Platt. LC 84-80387. (Illus.). xvii, 270p. 1984. 32.50 (ISBN 0-8232-1117-7); pap. 19.95 (ISBN 0-8232-1118-5). Fordham.

Abbot in Monastic Tradition. Pierre Salmon. Tr. by Claire Lavoie from Fr. LC 78-158955. (Cistercian Studies: No. 14). Tr. of Abbe' dans la Tradition Monastique. 148p. 1972. 9.95 (ISBN 0-87907-814-6). Cistercian Pubns.

Abbot Joachim of Fiore Liber De Concordia Noui Ac Veteris Testamenti. E. Randolph Daniel. LC 82-73832. 455p. 18.00 (ISBN 0-87169-738-6). Am Philos.

Abby Smith & Her Cows: With a Report of the Law Case Decided Contrary to Law. Julia E. Smith. LC 72-2622. (American Women Ser: Images & Realities). 98p. 1972. Repr. of 1877 ed. 13.00 (ISBN 0-405-04478-X). Ayer Co Pubs.

ABC Bible Characters. J. M. Stifle. 1982. pap. 3.95 (ISBN 0-570-04062-0, 56-1365). Concordia.

ABC Bible Stories. J. M. Stifle. 1982. pap. 3.95 (ISBN 0-570-04063-9, 56-1366). Concordia.

ABC Book About Christmas. J. M. Stifle. 1981. pap. 3.95 (ISBN 0-570-04053-1, 56-1714). Concordia.

ABC Book About Jesus. J. M. Stifle. 1981. pap. 3.95 (ISBN 0-570-04054-X, 56-1715). Concordia.

ABC Catechism: Ordinary Sundays & Solemnities, Vol. II. John W. Mole. LC 81-15227. 278p. 1983. 9.50 (ISBN 0-8199-0863-0). Franciscan Herald.

A.B.C. Catechism, Vol. 1: Advent to Pentecost. John W. Mole. 262p. 1980. 9.50 (ISBN 0-8199-0814-2). Franciscan Herald.

ABC for Christmas. Dick Jacobson & Bob Naujoks. 55p. (Orig.). Date not set. pap. 4.95 (ISBN 0-941988-04-X). K Q Assocs.

ABC Islamic Reader. M. A. Qazi. pap. 2.50 (ISBN 0-686-83566-2). Kazi Pubns.

ABC of Church Music. Stephen Rhys & King Palmer. LC 73-83175. 1969. 7.50 (ISBN 0-8008-0010-9, Crescendo). Taplinger.

ABC Rhymes for Young Muslims. Leila Kishta. Ed. by Hamid Quinlan. LC 83-70183. (Illus.). 32p. 1983. pap. 3.00 (ISBN 0-89259-044-0). Am Trust Pubns.

ABC's of Faith, 2 bks. Francine M. O'Connor & Kathryn Boswell. 1979. Bk. 1. pap. 1.95 (ISBN 0-89243-113-X); Bk. 2. pap. 1.95 (ISBN 0-89243-114-8). Liguori Pubns.

ABC's of Faith, Bk. 3. Francine O'Connor & Kathryn Boswell. (Illus.). 32p. (Orig.). 1980. pap. 1.95 (ISBN 0-89243-125-3). Liguori Pubns.

ABC's of Faith, Bk. 4. Francine O'Connor & Kathryn Boswell. (Illus.). 1981. pap. 1.95 (ISBN 0-89243-138-5). Liguori Pubns.

ABC'S of Faith, Bk. 5. Francine O'Connor & Kathryn Boswell. (Illus.). 32p. 1982. pap. 1.95 (ISBN 0-89243-165-2). Liguori Pubns.

ABC's of Faith, Bk. 6. Francine O'Connor & Kathryn Boswell. (Illus.). 32p. 1984. pap. 1.95 (ISBN 0-89243-214-4). Liguori Pubns.

ABC's of Financing Church & Synagogue Libraries, No. 13. Claudia Hannaford. LC 85-13286. (CSLA Guide Ser.). (Illus.). 36p. (Orig.). 1985. pap. 5.95X (ISBN 0-915324-23-7). CSLA.

ABC's of Praise. Janet Herbert. (Sparkler Bks.). (Illus.). 32p. 1986. plastic comb bdg. 2.95 (ISBN 0-89191-926-0, 59261, Chariot Bks). Cook.

ABC's of the Prophetical Scriptures. George H. Clement. pap. 2.25 (ISBN 0-685-61832-3). Reiner.

ABC'S of the Rosary. Francine M. O'Connor & Kathryn Boswell. (Illus.). 32p. 1984. pap. 1.95 (ISBN 0-89243-221-7). Liguori Pubns.

Abdu'l-Baha in America: Mahmud's Diary. Mahmud-i Zarqani. 1978. 22.50 (ISBN 0-933770-61-8). Kalimat.

Abel Being Dead, Yet Speaketh. John Norton. LC 78-8184. 1978. Repr. of 1658 ed. 30.00x (ISBN 0-8201-1310-7). Schol Facsimiles.

Abelard & the Origin & Early History of the Universities. Gabriel Compayre. LC 75-90094. (BCL Ser.: II). 1969. Repr. of 1893 ed. 11.50 (ISBN 0-404-01639-1). AMS Pr.

Abelard & the Origin & Early History of the Universities. Gabriel Compayre. 1893. 10.00x (ISBN 0-403-00009-2). Scholarly.

Abendland und Altes Testament. Herbert Schoffler. pap. 10.00 (ISBN 0-384-54210-7). Johnson Repr.

Abhandlungen zur Erinnerung an Hirsch Perez Chajes. V. Aptowitzer & A. Z. Schwarz. LC 7-7163. (Jewish Philosophy, Mysticism & History of Ideas Ser.). 1980. Repr. of 1933 ed. lib. bdg. 60.00x (ISBN 0-405-12237-3). Ayer Co Pubs.

Abhandlungen Zur Romischen Religion. facsimile ed. Alfred Von Domaszewski. LC 75-10633. (Ancient Religion & Mythology Ser.). (Ger., Illus.). 1976. Repr. of 1909 ed. 20.00x (ISBN 0-405-07008-X). Ayer Co Pubs.

Abide in Christ. Andrew Murray. 1968. 4.95 (ISBN 0-87508-371-4); pap. 2.95 (ISBN 0-87508-370-6). Chr Lit.

Abide in Christ. Andrew Murray. (Large Print Christian Classic). 192p. 1983. Repr. 14.95 (ISBN 0-87983-334-3). Keats.

Abide in Christ. Andrew Murray. 1980. pap. 2.95 (ISBN 0-88368-091-2). Whitaker Hse.

Abide in Christ. Andrew Murray. (Christian Library). 1985. Repr. text ed. 6.95 (ISBN 0-916441-10-5). Barbour & Co.

Abide in Me: A Pocket Guide to Daily Scriptural Prayer. David E. Rosage. 240p. (Orig.). 1985. pap. 3.95 (ISBN 0-89283-243-6). Servant.

Abiding in Christ. John MacArthur, Jr. (John MacArthur's Bible Studies). (Orig.). 1986. pap. 3.50 (ISBN 0-8024-5128-4). Moody.

Abiding Presence. Hugh Martin. LC 83-11337. 256p. 1984. 5.95 (ISBN 0-310-28921-1, 11337P, Clarion Class). Zondervan.

Abinadi, Man of God. Pamela Robison. (Orig.). 1981. pap. 4.00 (ISBN 0-8309-0324-0). Herald Hse.

Abingdon Bible Commentary. Ed. by Frederick Carl Eiselen et al. 1979. pap. 19.95 (ISBN 0-385-14877-1, Galilee). Doubleday.

Abingdon Bible Handbook. rev. ed. Edward P. Blair. (Illus.). 528p. 1982. pap. 23.95 (ISBN 0-687-00170-6). Abingdon.

Abingdon Clergy Income Tax Guide, 1985. 80p. (Orig.). 1986. pap. 5.95 (ISBN 0-687-00363-6). Abingdon.

Abingdon Dictionary of Living Religions. Ed. by Keith Crim et al. LC 81-1465. 864p. 1981. 17.95 (ISBN 0-687-00409-8). Abingdon.

Abingdon Manual of Installation Services. E. Jane Mall. 80p. (Orig.). 1983. pap. 4.95 (ISBN 0-687-00367-9). Abingdon.

Abingdon Marriage Manual. Perry Biddle. 208p. pap. 12.95 (ISBN 0-687-00485-3). Abingdon.

Abingdon's Strong Exhaustive Concordance of the Bible: Red Letter Edition. 1986. 26.95 (ISBN 0-687-40032-5); (thumb index) 28.95 (ISBN 0-687-40033-3). Abingdon.

Able to the Uttermost. C. H. Spurgeon. 240p. 1985. pap. 5.95. Pilgrim Pubns.

Abodah Zarah, 2 vols. 30.00 (ISBN 0-910218-77-3). Bennet Pub.

Abolition of Poverty. 8th ed. Daniel De Leon. 1969. pap. text ed. 0.50 (ISBN 0-935534-00-8). NY Labor News.

Abomination of Desolation in Biblical Eschatology. Desmond Ford. LC 79-64195. 1979. pap. text ed. 14.25 (ISBN 0-8191-0757-3). U Pr of Amer.

Abomination of Desolation: The Great Persecution. Thomas M. Carroll. 96p. 1983. pap. 5.95 (ISBN 0-87881-103-6). Mojave Bks.

Abortion: A Guide to Making Ethical Choices. Marjorie R. Maguire & Daniel C. Maguire. Ed. by Paul Jackman & Anne S. Mooney. 44p. 1983. pap. 3.00 (ISBN 0-915365-00-6). Cath Free Choice.

Abortion: A Spiritual Holocast. Walter E. Adams. 60p. (Orig.). 1986. pap. 3.95 (ISBN 0-937408-38-7). GMI Pubns Inc.

Abortion: An Annotated Indexed Bibliography. Ed. by Maureen Muldoon. LC 79-91622. (Studies in Women & Religion: Vol. 3). 148p. 1980. 49.95x (ISBN 0-88946-972-5). E Mellen.

Abortion: An Eastern Orthodox Statement. pap. 0.25 (ISBN 0-686-01293-3). Eastern Orthodox.

Abortion & the Catholic Church: Two Feminists Defend Women's Rights. Evelyn Reed & Claire Moriarty. 1973. pap. 0.35 (ISBN 0-87348-288-3). Path Pr NY.

Abortion & the Christian. John J. Davis. 128p. 1984. pap. 4.95 (ISBN 0-87552-221-1). Presby & Reformed.

Abortion & the Early Church: Christian, Jewish, & Pagan Attitudes. Michael J. Gorman. 120p. (Orig.). 1982. pap. 4.95 (ISBN 0-87784-397-X). Inter-Varsity.

Abortion & the Early Church: Christian, Jewish, & Pagan Attitudes in the Greco-Roman World. Michael J. Gorman. 4.95 (ISBN 0-8091-2511-0). Paulist Pr.

Abortion & the Meaning of Personhood. Clifford E. Bajema. (Direction Bks). 1974. pap. 1.25 (ISBN 0-8010-0672-4). Baker Bk.

Abortion & the Moral Degeneration of the American Medical Profession. Vivian De Danois. (Science of Man Library Bk). 92p. 1975. 81.50 (ISBN 0-913314-56-0). Am Classical Coll Pr.

Abortion & the Politics of Motherhood. Kristin Luker. LC 83-47849. (California Series on Social Choice & Political Economy). 350p. 1984. 25.00x (ISBN 0-520-04314-6); pap. 7.95 (ISBN 0-520-05597-7, CAL759). U of Cal Pr.

Abortion & the Sanctity of Human Life. Ed. by J. H. Channer. 160p. 1986. pap. 7.50 (ISBN 0-85364-417-9, Pub. by Paternoster UK). Attic Pr.

Abortion Bibliography for 1970. Mary K. Floyd. LC 72-78877. (Abortion Bibliography Ser.: No. 2). 120p. 1972. 7.50x (ISBN 0-87875-024-X). Whitston Pub.

Abortion Bibliography for 1971. Mary K. Floyd. LC 72-78877. (Abortion Bibliography Ser.: No. 3). 125p. 1973. 11.00x (ISBN 0-87875-030-4). Whitston Pub.

Abortion Bibliography for 1972. Mary K. Floyd. LC 72-78877. (Abortion Bibliography Ser.: No. 4). xx, 223p. 1973. 11.00x (ISBN 0-87875-044-4). Whitston Pub.

Abortion Bibliography for 1973. Mary K. Floyd. LC 72-78877. (Abortion Bibliography Ser.: No. 5). xxiii, 237p. 1974. 11.00x (ISBN 0-87875-056-8). Whitston Pub.

Abortion Bibliography for 1974. Mary K. Floyd. LC 72-78877. (Abortion Bibliography Ser.: No. 6). 1975. 15.00x (ISBN 0-87875-079-7). Whitston Pub.

Abortion Bibliography for 1976. Mary K. Floyd. LC 72-78877. (Abortion Bibliography Ser.: Vol. 7). 1978. 17.00x (ISBN 0-87875-126-2). Whitston Pub.

Abortion: Challenges Ahead. National Council of Jewish Women. (Illus.). 25p. (Orig.). 1985. pap. text ed. 5.00 (ISBN 0-941840-19-0). NCJW.

Abortion Is Murder. Dick Benjamin. 1980. pap. 1.75 (ISBN 0-911739-04-1). Abbott Loop.

Abortion Issue in the Political Process: A Briefing for Catholic Legislators. Jim Castelli et al. Ed. by Paul Jackman. 19p. pap. 3.00 (ISBN 0-915365-08-1). Cath Free Choice.

Abortion Question. Hyman Rodman et al. 250p. 1987. 25.00 (ISBN 0-231-05332-0). Columbia U Pr.

Abortion-the American Holocaust. Kent Kelly. LC 81-65240. (Illus.). 149p. (Orig.). 1981. pap. 2.95 (ISBN 0-9604138-1-2). Calvary Pr.

Abortion, the Bible, & the Christian. Donald Shoemaker. (Direction Bks). 1977. pap. text ed. 1.25 (ISBN 0-8010-8109-2). Baker Bk.

Abortion, the Bible & the Christian. Donald P. Shoemaker. 1976. 4.00 (ISBN 0-910728-15-1); pap. 1.25 (ISBN 0-910728-08-9). Hayes.

Abortion: The Catholic Debate in America. H. Lotstra. 340p. 1985. 39.50x (ISBN 0-8290-0728-8). Irvington.

Abortion: The Development of the Roman Catholic Perspective. John Connery. LC 76-51217. 1977. 12.95 (ISBN 0-8294-0257-8). Loyola.

Abortion: The Moral Issues. Ed. by Edward Batchelor, Jr. LC 82-7505. 256p. 1982. pap. 8.95 (ISBN 0-8298-0612-1). Pilgrim NY.

Abortion: Toward an Evangelical Consensus. Paul Fowler. (Critical Concern Ser.). 1987. 11.95 (ISBN 0-88070-173-0). Multnomah.

Abortion: Yes or No? John L. Grady. LC 79-53228. 32p. 1968. pap. 1.00 (ISBN 0-89555-117-9). TAN Bks Pubs.

Abortion's Second Victim. Pam Koerbel. 204p. 1986. pap. 6.95 (ISBN 0-89693-177-3). Victor Bks.

Abounding in Hope: A Family of Faith at Work through the Lutheran World Federation. Charles P. Lutz. LC 85-1216. 144p. (Orig.). 1985. pap. 5.95 (ISBN 0-8066-2158-3, 10-0123). Augsburg.

About Being a Priest. Federico Suarez. 229p. 1979. 7.00 (ISBN 0-912414-27-8). Lumen Christi.

About Bells & Bell Ringing. R. H. Jones. 1985. 11.25x (ISBN 0-317-54257-5, Pub. by J Richardson Uk). State Mutual Bk.

About Belonging. Molly Cone. (Shema Storybooks: No. 3). (Illus.). 64p. (Orig.). 1972. pap. 5.00 (ISBN 0-8074-0125-0, 101083). UAHC.

About God. Molly Cone. (Shema Storybooks: No. 4). (Illus.). 64p. 1973. pap. 5.00 (ISBN 0-8074-0126-9, 101084). UAHC.

About God's People, Bk. 4. Gladys S. Stump. (Special Ser.). 144p. 1983. pap. 7.95 (ISBN 0-8163-0461-0). Pacific Pr Pub Assn.

About Happiness. William A. Kaschmitter. 100p. 1983. pap. 5.00 (ISBN 0-912414-34-0). Lumen Christi.

About Learning. Molly Cone. (Shema Primary Ser: No. 2). (Illus., Orig.). 1972. pap. 5.00 (ISBN 0-8074-0127-7, 101082). UAHC.

About Living. Victor B. Brezik. 156p. 1980. 4.95 (ISBN 0-912414-29-4). Lumen Christi.

About Men & Women: How Your Great Story Shapes Your Destiny. Tad Guzie & Noreen M. Guzie. 176p. (Orig.). 1986. pap. 7.95 (ISBN 0-8091-2813-6). Paulist Pr.

About My Father's Business: The Life of Elder Michaux. Lillian A. Webb. LC 80-24595. (Contributions in Afro-American & African Studies: No. 61). (Illus.). 232p. 1981. lib. bdg. 29.95 (ISBN 0-313-22261-4, WFB/). Greenwood.

About People for a Special Time. Gladys S. Stump. 1981. pap. 7.95 (ISBN 0-8163-0353-3). Pacific Pr Pub Assn.

About the Beginning, Bk. 1. Gladys S. Stump. LC 78-78070. 1979. pap. 7.95 (ISBN 0-8163-0380-0, 01055-3). Pacific Pr Pub Assn.

About the Holocaust: What We Know & How We Know It. Dorothy Rabinowitz. LC 79-51801. (Illus.). 48p. 1979. pap. 1.50 (ISBN 0-87495-014-7). Am Jewish Comm.

About the Holy Spirit. Francisca J. De Valle. 120p. 5.00 (ISBN 0-912414-31-6). Lumen Christi.

About the New English Bible. G. N. Hunt. 1970. 1.25 (ISBN 0-521-07938-1). Cambridge U Pr.

About When Satan Tried to Rule, Bk. 2. Gladys S. Stump. LC 79-84610. 1980. pap. 7.95 (ISBN 0-8163-0381-9, 01056-1). Pacific Pr Pub Assn.

About Your Relation to Rudolf Steiner. Ernst Katz. (Illus.). 64p. (Orig.). 1986. pap. 6.95 (ISBN 0-9613745-0-0, 86-1955). E Katz.

Above All, Don't Wobble. Bhagwan Shree Rajneesh. Ed. by Ma Prem Maneesha. LC 83-81247. (Initiation Talks Ser.). (Illus.). 488p. (Orig.). 1976. 21.95 (ISBN 0-88050-001-8). Chidvilas Found.

Above Every Name: The Lordship of Christ & Social Systems. Ed. by Thomas E. Clarke. LC 80-82082. (Woodstock Studies). 312p. (Orig.). 1980. pap. 8.95 (ISBN 0-8091-2338-X). Paulist Pr.

Above or Within? The Supernatural in Religious Education. Ian P. Knox. LC 76-55589. 164p. (Orig.). 1977. pap. 10.95 (ISBN 0-89135-006-3). Religious Educ.

Abraham. 1979. 0.75 (ISBN 0-8198-0564-5). Dghtrs St Paul.

Abraham. Rebecca Daniel. (Our Greatest Heritage Ser.). (Illus.). 32p. 1983. wkbk. 3.95 (ISBN 0-86653-133-5, SS 802). Good Apple.

Abraham. F. B. Meyer. 1968. pap. 4.50 (ISBN 0-87508-340-4). Chr Lit.

Abraham & David: Genesis 15 & Its Meaning for Israelite Tradition. Ronald E. Clements. LC 67-8569. (Studies in Biblical Theology, 2nd Ser.: No. 5). 1967. pap. 10.00x (ISBN 0-8401-3055-4). A R Allenson.

Abraham & His Big Family. John Walton & Kim Walton. (Early Bible Foundations Ser.). (Illus.). 1986. pap. 2.95 (ISBN 1-55513-031-3, Chariot Bks). Cook.

Abraham & Isaac. Catherine Storr. LC 84-18076. (People of the Bible Ser.). (Illus.). 32p. 1985. PLB 10.65 (ISBN 0-8172-1994-3). Raintree Pubs.

Abraham & the Contemporary Mind. Silvano Arieti. LC 80-68187. 187p. 1981. 14.95 (ISBN 0-465-00005-3). Basic.

Abraham: Delay Is Not Denial. Don Anderson. (Kingfisher Ser.). 200p. 1987. pap. 6.95 (ISBN 0-87213-000-2). Loizeaux.

Abraham, Friend of God. Gordon Lindsay. (Old Testament Ser.). 1.25 (ISBN 0-89985-126-6). Christ Nations.

Abraham Galante: A Biography. Albert E. Kalderon. (Illus.). 124p. 1983. 10.00 (ISBN 0-87203-111-X). Hermon.

Abraham Geiger & Liberal Judaism: The Challenge of the Nineteenth Century. Max Wiener. pap. 11.95 (ISBN 0-87820-800-3). Ktav.

Abraham: God's Faithful Pilgrim. Ethel Barrett. LC 82-12330. (Bible Biography Ser.). 128p. (Orig.). 1982. pap. 2.50 (ISBN 0-8307-0769-7, 5810906). Regal.

Abraham Ibn Esra Als Grammatiker: Ein Beitrag zur Geschichte der Hebraischen Sprachwissenschaft. Wilhelm Bacher. Ed. by Steven Katz. LC 79-7125. (Jewish Philosophy, Mysticism & History of Ideas Ser.). 1980. Repr. of 1882 ed. lib. bdg. 16.00x (ISBN 0-405-12239-X). Ayer Co Pubs.

Abraham, Isaac, & Jacob, Servants & Prophets of God. Norman L. Heap. 1987. 12.50 (ISBN 0-533-07272-7). Vantage.

Abraham Isaac Kook: The Lights of Penitance, Lights of Holiness. the Moral Principles. Essays, Letters & Poems. Tr. by Ben Zion Bokser. LC 78-70465. (Classics of Western Spirituality Ser.). 448p. 1978. 13.95 (ISBN 0-8091-0278-1); pap. 10.95 (ISBN 0-8091-2159-X). Paulist Pr.

Abraham Joshua Heschel: Exploring His Life & Thought. John C. Merkle. 184p. 1985. 17.95x (ISBN 0-02-920970-6). Macmillan.

Abraham Lincoln & the Quakers. Daniel Bassuk. (Orig.). 1987. pap. 2.50x (ISBN 0-87574-273-4). Pendle Hill.

Abraham Lincoln the Christian. William J. Johnson. (Great American Christian Ser.). (Illus.). 1976. pap. 3.95 (ISBN 0-915134-13-6). Mott Media.

Abraham Lincoln: The Man & His Faith. G. Frederick Owen. 232p. 1981. pap. 6.95 (ISBN 0-8423-0000-7). Tyndale.

Abraham: Man of Faith. Elsie Rives. (BibLearn Ser.). (Illus.). 1976. 5.95 (ISBN 0-8054-4223-5, 4242-23). Broadman.

Abraham, Sarah & the Promised Son. Robert Mitchell. (Arch Book Ser.: No. 21). 1984. pap. 0.99 (59-1284). Concordia.

Abraham: The First Hebrew. Aaron Gerber. 180p. 1981. 12.50 (ISBN 0-89962-208-9). Todd & Honeywell.

Abraham: Twenty-Six Daily Bible Studies. David Jeremiah. (Steps to Higher Ground Ser.). 1982. pap. 1.95 (ISBN 0-86508-201-4). BCM Intl Inc.

Abraham y Jose el Patriarca: Personas Importantes de la Biblia. Tomas De La Fuente. (Span., Illus.). 76p. 1982. pap. 2.50 (ISBN 0-940048-03-5). Austin Bilingual Lang Ed.

Abraham's Test of Faith. Leslie Madison. 158p. (Orig.). 1982. pap. 3.50 (ISBN 0-89323-031-6). Bible Memory.

Abram Talked with God. (Little Learner Ser.). 24p. 1985. 5.95 (ISBN 0-570-08950-6, 56-1541). Concordia.

Abridgement of Maurice's Kingdom of Christ: The Original Two Volumes Abridged into One Based on the 1842 Edition Amended with an Introduction. William J. Wolf. LC 83-3516. 276p. (Orig.). 1983. lib. bdg. 28.25 (ISBN 0-8191-3150-4); pap. text ed. 13.50 (ISBN 0-8191-3151-2). U Pr of Amer.

Abridgement of the Secret Doctrine. Helena P. Blavatsky. Ed. by Elizabeth Preston & Christmas Humphreys. 1968. pap. 5.50 (ISBN 0-8356-0009-2, Quest). Theos Pub Hse.

Abriss der Geschichte Israels und Judas: Lieder der Hudhailiten. Julius Wellhausen. (Skizzen und Vorarbeiten, 1.Heft). (Ger. & Arabic.). iv, 175p. 1985. 70.50x (ISBN 3-11-009765-6). De Gruyter.

Absent at the Creation. Bradley Seidman. LC 83-90254. 1984. 10.95 (ISBN 0-87212-175-5). Libra.

Absolute & die Wirklichkeit in Schellings Philosophie: Mit der Erstedition einer Handschrift aus dem Berliner Schelling-Nachlass. Barbara Loer. LC 73-93164. (Quellen & Studien zur Philosophie, Vol. 7). (Illus.). viii, 288p. 1974. 53.20x (ISBN 3-11-004329-7). De Gruyter.

Absolute Nothingness: Foundations for a Buddhist-Christian Dialogue. Hans Waldenfels. Tr. by James W. Heisig from Ger. LC 80-81442. Orig. Title: Absolutes Nichts. 224p. 1980. pap. 8.95 (ISBN 0-8091-2316-9). Paulist Pr.

Absolute Primacy & Predestination of Jesus & His Virgin Mother. J. B. Carol. 1981. 7.50 (ISBN 0-8199-0848-7). Franciscan Herald.

Absolute Surrender. Andrew Murray. 1962. pap. 2.95 (ISBN 0-87508-398-6). Chr Lit.

Absolute Surrender. Andrew Murray. (Andrew Murray Ser.). pap. 3.50 (ISBN 0-8024-0560-6). Moody.

Absolute Surrender. Andrew Murray. 128p. 1981. pap. 3.50 (ISBN 0-88368-093-9). Whitaker Hse.

Absolutes in Moral Theology? Ed. by Charles E. Curran. LC 75-3988. 320p. 1976. Repr. of 1968 ed. lib. bdg. 25.00x (ISBN 0-8371-7450-3, CUMT). Greenwood.

Abulafia's Circles. Jerome Rothenberg. 1979. pap. 2.00 (ISBN 0-87924-034-2). Membrane Pr.

Abundance Is Your Right. Arthur G. Thomas. LC 77-76207. 1987. pap. 6.95 (ISBN 0-941992-10-1). Los Arboles Pub.

Abundant Life. Ray E. Baughman. 1959. pap. 3.50 (ISBN 0-8024-0047-7). Moody.

Abundant Life. Etta B. Pegues. 1971. pap. 2.75 (ISBN 0-88027-081-0). Firm Foun Pub.

Abundant Living. E. Stanley Jones. (Festival Bks.). 1976. pap. 4.25 (ISBN 0-687-00689-9). Abingdon.

Abused But Chosen. Elsie Isensce Hill & Cliff Dudley. LC 83-61439. 144p. 1983. 4.95 (ISBN 0-89221-106-7). New Leaf.

Abusing Science: The Case Against Creationism. Philip Kitcher. (Illus.). 224p. 1982. 22.50x (ISBN 0-262-11085-7); pap. 7.95 (ISBN 0-262-61037-X). MIT Pr.

Abuzar. Tr. by Sohail Bukhari. 200p. 1985. pap. 9.00 (ISBN 0-941724-35-2). Islamic Seminary.

Academic Study of Judaism: Essays & Reflections. Jacob Neusner. LC 75-5782. (Brown Judaic Studies). pap. 16.50 (14-00-35). Scholars Pr GA.

Academic Study of Judaism: Essays & Reflections I. Jacob Neusner. (Third Ser.). 20.00x (ISBN 0-87068-712-3). Ktav.

Academic Study of Religion: Proceedings. Ed. by Anne Carr. LC 74-14212. (American Academy of Religion. Section Papers). Repr. of 1974 ed. 40.50 (ISBN 0-8357-9563-2, 2017552). Bks Demand UMI.

Academic Study of Religion, 1975: Public Schools Religion-Studies. Anne Carr et al. LC 75-26653. (American Academy of Religion. Section Papers). 1975. pap. 9.95 (ISBN 0-89130-023-6, 01-09-17). Scholars Pr Ga.

Academies for Anatolia: A Study of the Rationale, Program & Impact of the Educational Institutions Sponsored by the American Board in Turkey: 1830-1980. Frank A. Stone. (Illus.). 384p. 1984. lib. bdg. 32.75 (ISBN 0-8191-4064-3). U Pr of Amer.

Academy & Community: A Study of the Jewish Identity & Involvement of Professors. Albert G. Crawford & Rela G. Monson. LC 80-68432. 40p. 1980. pap. 2.00. Am Jewish Comm.

Acarya: Sandara of Kaladi - A Story. I. S Mudugula. (Illus.). 142p. 1985. 16.00 (ISBN 0-317-46523-6, Pub. by Motilal Banarsidass India). Orient Bk Dist.

Acathist Hymn to the Name of Jesus. Joseph Raya. Ed. by Jose D. Vinck. 40p. 1983. 6.00x (ISBN 0-911726-45-4). Alleluia Pr.

Accept No Imitations: Finding a Genuine Faith in a Counterfeit World. James W. Angell. 144p. 1984. pap. 8.75 (ISBN 0-687-00692-9). Abingdon.

Acceptable Sacrifice. John Bunyan. pap. 1.75 (ISBN 0-685-88365-5). Reiner.

Acceptance. Lawrence Pote. pap. 1.50 (ISBN 0-8010-7050-3). Baker Bk.

Acceptance: Loosing the Webs of Personal Insecurity. Don Baker. LC 84-27246. 1985. pap. 6.95 (ISBN 0-88070-079-3). Multnomah.

Accidence & Word Formation, Vol. 2. James H. Moulton & Wilbert F. Howard. (Moulton's Grammar of New Testament Greek Ser.). 572p. 1929. 21.95 (ISBN 0-567-01012-0, Pub. by T & T Clark Ltd UK). Fortress.

Accidental Being: A Study in the Metaphysics of St. Thomas Aquinas. Barry F. Brown. LC 85-15653. 440p. (Orig.). 1985. lib. bdg. 32.75 (ISBN 0-8191-4886-5); pap. text ed. 19.50 (ISBN 0-8191-4887-3). U Pr of Amer.

Accidental Universe. P. C. Davies. LC 81-21592. (Illus.). 160p. 1982. 23.95 (ISBN 0-521-24212-6); pap. 11.95 (ISBN 0-521-28692-1). Cambridge U Pr.

Accompt Rekenynge & Confession of the Faith of Huldrik Zwinglius. Ulrich Zwingli. Tr. by Thomas Cotsforde from Latin. LC 79-84148. (English Experience: No. 964). Orig. Title: Swinglische Bekenntuis. 156p. 1979. Repr. of 1555 ed. lib. bdg. 11.50 (ISBN 90-221-0964-X). Walter J Johnson.

According to Luke. Frank L. Cox. 1941. pap. 2.75 (ISBN 0-88027-030-6). Firm Foun Pub.

According to Promise. C. H. Spurgeon. 106p. pap. 2.00 (ISBN 0-89323-003-0, 442). Bible Memory.

According to Promise. C. H. Spurgeon. 1979. pap. 2.50 (ISBN 0-686-26192-5). Pilgrim Pubns.

Account Book of Conrad Weiser: Berks County, Pennsylvania, 1746-1760. Ed. by Larry M. Neff & Frederick S. Weiser. LC 81-84666. (Sources & Documents of the Pennsylvania Germans Ser.: No. 6). (Illus.). 1981. 15.00 (ISBN 0-911122-43-5). Penn German Soc.

Account of the Destruction of the Jesuits. Jean D'Alembert. 59.95 (ISBN 0-87968-575-1). Gordon Pr.

Account of the Executors of Richard Bishop of London 1303, & of the Executors of Thomas Bishop of Exeter 1310. Ed. by William H. Hale & H. T. Ellacombe. 1874. 27.00 (ISBN 0-384-20950-5). Johnson Repr.

Account of the Life, Opinions, & Writings of John Milton. Thomas Keightley. LC 73-11332. 1855. Repr. lib. bdg. 49.50 (ISBN 0-8414-2222-2). Folcroft.

Account of the People Called Shakers. Thomas Brown. LC 77-17584. Repr. of 1812 ed. 27.00 (ISBN 0-404-08459-1). AMS Pr.

Account of the Tabernacle. D. W. Gooding. (Texts & Studies, New Ser.: Vol. 6). Repr. of 1959 ed. 28.00 (ISBN 0-8115-1719-5). Kraus Repr.

Accounting for Genocide: National Response & Jewish Victimization During the Holocaust. Helen Fein. LC 78-53085. (Illus.). 1979. 17.95 (ISBN 0-02-910220-0). Free Pr.

Accounting for Genocide: National Responses & Jewish Victimization During the Holocaust. Helen Fein. LC 83-24219. (Illus.). xxii, 469p. 1984. pap. 13.95 (ISBN 0-226-24034-7). U of Chicago Pr.

Accounting Principles & Reporting Practices for Churches & Church Related Organizations. 64p. 1983. pap. 21.95 (ISBN 1-55586-855-X). US Catholic.

Accounting Student Perceptions of Business & Professional Ethics. James H. Sellers & Edward E. Milam. 50p. (Orig.). 1981. pap. 4.50 (ISBN 0-938004-00-X). U MS Bus Econ.

Accounting Systems for Churches. Tom Heyd. (Administration Series for Churches). 64p. 1984. pap. 3.95 (ISBN 0-8066-2032-3, 10-0126). Augsburg.

Accounts of Religious Revivals in Many Parts of the United States from 1815 to 1818: Collected from Numerous Publications & Letters from Persons of Piety & Correct Information. Joshua Bradley. (Reival Library). 300p. lib. bdg. 11.95 (ISBN 0-940033-13-5). R O Roberts.

Accounts of the Great Chamberlains of Scotland, 3 Vols. Ed. by Thomas Thomson. 1817-45. Set. 250.00 (ISBN 0-404-52810-4). AMS Pr.

Accounts to Caesar Tiberius Concerning Jesus of Nazareth. Will Carter. 142p. (Orig.). 1986. pap. 3.99 (ISBN 0-9617190-0-1). Drame Pr.

Aceptado Por Dios. John Blanchard. 2.95 (ISBN 0-85151-406-5). Banner of Truth.

Acerca De la Religion. Vladimir I. Lenin. (Span.). 81p. 1976. pap. 1.45 (ISBN 0-8285-1359-7, Pub. by Progress Pubs USSR). Imported Pubns.

Acharya Shankara. Swami Apurvananda. 362p. 1985. pap. 7.95 (ISBN 0-87481-529-0, Pub. by Ramakrishna Math Madras India). Vedanta Pr.

Achievement of Love. Sufi M. Iqbal. Tr. by Aftab Ahmad from Arabic. 190p. 1987. pap. 9.95 (ISBN 0-915597-44-6). Amana Bks.

Achievements of Biblical Religion: A Prolegomenon to Old Testament Theology. Simon J. De Vries. LC 83-3614. 558p. (Orig.). 1983. lib. bdg. 40.75 (ISBN 0-8191-3140-7); pap. text ed. 22.25 (ISBN 0-8191-3141-5). U Pr of Amer.

Achieving. LaVell Edwards. 77p. 1985. 7.95 (ISBN 0-934126-79-8). Randall Bk Co.

Achieving Christian Maturity. Gerard Philips. 4.95 (ISBN 0-685-10957-7, L37990). Franciscan Herald.

Achieving Promises: A Spiritual Guide for the Transitions of Life. William F. Kraft. LC 81-10496. 132p. 1981. pap. 6.95 (ISBN 0-664-24384-3). Westminster.

Achieving Shared Responsibility in the American Church. Olin J. Murdick. 14p. 1977. 1.55 (ISBN 0-686-39921-8). Natl Cath Educ.

Achieving Social Justice: A Catholic Perspective. rev. ed. Ronald Wilkins & Veronica Grover. (To Live Is Christ Ser.). (YA) 1987. pap. text ed. write for info. (ISBN 0-697-02126-2); write for info. (ISBN 0-697-02127-0). Wm C Brown.

Achieving Social Justice: A Christian Perspective. Ronald J. Wilkins. (To Live Is Christ Ser.). 1981. pap. text ed. 5.95 (ISBN 0-697-01775-3); tchr's manual, pap. 4.00 (ISBN 0-697-01776-1); spirit masters 10.95 (ISBN 0-697-01777-X). Wm C Brown.

ACPA in Today's Intellectual World: Proceedings, 1983, Vol. 57. Ed. by Marc F. Griesbach & John P. Carmichael. LC 82-73233. 250p. 1984. pap. 15.00 (ISBN 0-918090-17-2). Am Cath Philo.

Acquiring Our Image of God: The Emotional Basis for Religious Education. Martin A. Lang. LC 82-62968. 160p. (Orig.). 1983. pap. 6.95 (ISBN 0-8091-2537-4). Paulist Pr.

Acres of Diamonds. Russell H. Conwell. 64p. 1975. pap. 2.50 (ISBN 0-8007-8091-4, Spire Bks). Revell.

Across a Roaring Hill: The Protestant Imagination in Modern Ireland. Ed. by Gerald Dawe & Edna Longley. 242p. 1985. 16.50 (ISBN 0-85640-334-2, Pub. by Blackstaff Pr). Longwood Pub Group.

Across the Savannas to Mecca: The Overland Pilgrimage Route from West Africa. J. S. Birks. (Illus.). 161p. 1978. 29.50x (ISBN 0-7146-6005-1, F Cass Co). Biblio Dist.

Across the Unknown. Stewart E. White & Harwood White. 336p. 1987. pap. 7.95 (ISBN 0-89804-150-3). Ariel OH.

Act & Agent: Philosophical Foundations for Moral Education & Character Development. Ed. by George F. McLean & Frederick E. Ellrod. LC 86-1619. 412p. (Orig.). 1986. lib. bdg. 34.75 (ISBN 0-8191-5281-1, Pub. by Council for Research in Values & Philosophy); pap. text ed. 17.50 (ISBN 0-8191-5282-X). U Pr of Amer.

Act & Being. Dietrich Bonhoeffer. 192p. 1983. Repr. of 1962 ed. 18.50 (ISBN 0-88254-869-7, Octagon). Hippocrene Bks.

Act As God's Children. 2nd ed. Gerard P. Weber et al. (Word Is Life Ser.). 1977. 3.60 (ISBN 0-02-658300-3); tchrs. ed. 8.00 (ISBN 0-02-658310-0); family handbook 1.00 (ISBN 0-02-658350-X). Benziger Pub Co.

Act of Marriage: The Beauty of Married Love. Tim LaHaye & Beverly LaHaye. 1976. pap. 8.95 (ISBN 0-310-27061-8, 18077P); pap. 3.95 (ISBN 0-310-27062-6, 18083P). Zondervan.

Acta Conciliorum Oecumenicorum Tomus 4, Volumen 3: Index Generalis Tomorum 1-4, Pars 1; Indices Codicum et. Rudolphus Schieffer. LC 74-79318. 579p. 1974. 136.00x (ISBN 3-11-004449-8). De Gruyter.

Actes des Colloques des Eglises Francaises et des Synodes: (Huguenot Society, Vols. 204) Ed. by Adrian C. Chamier. Bd. with Register of the Protestant Church at Guisnes. Ed. by William Minet. Repr. of 1891 ed; Registre Des Baptesmes, Mariages & Mortz. Ed. by Humphrey Marett. Repr. of 1890 ed. 93.00 (ISBN 0-8115-1643-1). Kraus Repr.

Acting for God. Kathy Jones. (Helping Hand Ser.). 48p. (YA) 1984. wkbk. 4.95 (ISBN 0-86653-236-6). Good Apple.

Acting on the Good News. John MacArthur, Jr. (John MacArthur's Bible Studies). (Orig.). 1987. pap. 3.95 (ISBN 0-8024-5348-1). Moody.

Acting Out Faith. Gordon C. Bennett. Ed. by Herbert Lambert. LC 86-6141. 160p. (Orig.). 1986. pap. 10.95 (ISBN 0-8272-0016-1). CBP.

Acting Out the Gospels. William DeAngelis. LC 81-84919. 96p. 1982. pap. 9.95 (ISBN 0-89622-136-9). Twenty-Third.

Acting Person. Cardinal Karol Wojtyla. Tr. by Andrzej Potocki. (Analecta Husserliana Ser.: No. 10). 1979. lib. bdg. 29.50 (ISBN 90-277-0969-6, Pub. by Reidel Holland); pap. 15.95 (ISBN 90-277-0985-8, Pub. by Reidel Holland). Kluwer Academic.

Acting Up: A Complete Introduction to Biblical Drama for Junior High Youth Groups. Steve Wamberg & Annie Wamberg. (Best of Young Teen Action Ser.). 32p. 1985. pap. 4.95 (ISBN 0-89191-379-3). Cook.

Action: Essay on a Critique of Life & a Science of Practice. Maurice Blondel. Tr. by Oliva Blanchette from Fr. LC 83-401133. 448p. 1984. text ed. 29.95 (ISBN 0-268-00605-9, 85-06057). U of Notre Dame Pr.

Action Rhymes: Bible Learning Through Movement. Cathy Falk. 48p. 1985. pap. 2.50 (ISBN 0-87239-920-6, 3202). Standard Pub.

Actions, Gestures & Bodily Attitudes. Carolyn Deitering. LC 80-51058. 1980. pap. 10.95 (ISBN 0-89390-021-4). Resource Pubns.

Activating the Passive Church: Diagnosis & Treatment. Lyle E. Schaller. LC 81-3460. 160p. (Orig.). 1981. pap. 6.95 (ISBN 0-687-00716-X). Abingdon.

Active Catholic. Gabriel Palau. LC 84-50405. 224p. 1984. pap. 4.00 (ISBN 0-89555-238-8). TAN Bks Pubs.

Active Life & Contemplative Life: A Study of the Concepts from Plato to the Present. Sr. M. Elizabeth Mason. Ed. by George E. Ganss. 1961. pap. 5.95 (ISBN 0-87462-418-5). Marquette.

Active Meditation: The Western Tradition. Robert R. Leichtman & Carl Japikse. LC 82-72785. 512p. 1983. 24.50 (ISBN 0-89804-040-X). Ariel OH.

Activism that Makes Sense: Congregations & Community Organization. Gregory F. Pierce. LC 83-82016. (Orig.). 1984. pap. 6.95 (ISBN 0-8091-2600-1). Paulist Pr.

Activities Du Solitaire En Chartreuse D'Apres Plus Anciens Temoins. Soeur Bruno & Barrier Osb. (Analecta Cartusiana: No. 87). 159p. 1981. pap. 25.00 (ISBN 3-7052-0144-1, Pub. by Salzburg Studies). Longwood Pub Group.

Activities of the Holy Spirit. Edmund Fortman. LC 84-13786. 199p. 1984. 12.00 (ISBN 0-8199-0881-9). Franciscan Herald.

Activities with Senior Adults. Roger L. Hauser. 1987. 7.95 (ISBN 0-8054-3901-3). Broadman.

Acts. (Erdmans Commentaries Ser.). 4.50 (ISBN 0-8010-3392-6). Baker Bk.

Acts, Vol. V. Beacon Bible Commentary Staff. 6.95 (ISBN 0-8010-0679-1). Baker Bk.

Acts. F. F. Bruce. 1983. pap. 4.95 (ISBN 0-87508-170-3). Chr Lit.

Acts. 3rd ed. Kevin Conner. 136p. 1975. 7.95 (ISBN 0-914936-16-6). Bible Temple.

Acts. Hans Conzelmann. LC 86-45203. 368p. 1987. pap. 37.95 (ISBN 0-8006-6018-8, 20-6018). Fortress.

Acts. Jerome Crowe. (New Testament Message Ser.: Vol. 8). 204p. 1980. 12.95 (ISBN 0-89453-196-4); pap. 8.95 (ISBN 0-89453-131-X). M Glazier.

Acts. H. A. Ironside. 13.95 (ISBN 0-87213-351-6). Loizeaux.

Acts. Irving L. Jensen. (Bible Self-Study Ser). 1970. pap. 3.25 (ISBN 0-8024-1044-8). Moody.

Acts. Gerhard Krodel. LC 80-2395. (Proclamation Commentaries: the New Testament Witnesses for Preaching). 128p. (Orig.). 1981. pap. 5.95 (ISBN 0-8006-0585-3, 1-585). Fortress.

Acts. Marilyn Kunz & Catherine Schell. (Neighborhood Bible Study Ser.). 1972. pap. 2.95 (ISBN 0-8423-0030-9). Tyndale.

Acts. Charles H. Talbert. Ed. by John Hayes. (Preaching Guides). 120p. (Orig.). 1984. pap. 6.95 (ISBN 0-8042-3231-8). John Knox.

Acts. Dan Underwood. (Standard Bible Study Workbooks Ser.). 80p. 1987. wkbk. 1.95 (ISBN 0-87403-185-0, 40205). Standard Pub.

Acts. John Wade. (Standard Bible Studies). (Illus.). 288p. 1987. pap. price not set (ISBN 0-87403-165-6, 40105). Standard Pub.

Acts. Jet Witherspoon. LC 86-25414. 192p. (Orig.). 1987. pap. 4.95 (ISBN 0-912315-34-2). Word Aflame.

Acts, A Study Guide. John Timmer. (Revelation Series for Adults). 1981. pap. text ed. 2.50 (ISBN 0-933140-20-7). CRC Pubns.

Acts-A Study Guide Commentary. Curtis Vaughan. 160p. (Orig.). 1974. pap. 5.95 (ISBN 0-310-33513-2, 10958P). Zondervan.

Acts, Adventures of the Early Church. Keith L. Brooks. (Teach Yourself the Bible Ser). 1961. pap. 2.75 (ISBN 0-8024-0125-2). Moody.

Acts Alive. David K. Buehring. 1986. pap. 7.95 (ISBN 0-935779-10-8). Crown Min.

Acts: An Exposition. W. A. Criswell. 948p. 1983. Repr. 19.95 (ISBN 0-310-44150-1, 11666). Zondervan.

Acts: An Inductive Study. Irving L. Jensen. 256p. 1973. pap. 7.95 (ISBN 0-8024-0138-4). Moody.

Acts & Decrees of the Synod of Jerusalem, 1672. Orthodox Eastern Church-Synod of Jerusalem. pap. 1.95 (ISBN 0-686-05637-X). Eastern Orthodox.

Acts & Letters of the Apostles. Tr. by Richmond Lattimore from Greek. 287p. 1982. 16.50 (ISBN 0-374-10082-9). FS&G.

Acts & Monuments, 8 Vols. John Foxe. Ed. by S. R. Cattley & George Townsend. LC 79-168132. Repr. of 1849 ed. Set. 400.00 (ISBN 0-404-02590-0). AMS Pr.

Acts & Proceedings of the General Assemblies of the Kirk of Scotland, 3 Vols. Ed. by Thomas Thomson. LC 72-1053. 1839-45. Set. 125.00 (ISBN 0-404-52820-1). AMS Pr.

Acts & Romans. Albert Barnes. 18.95 (ISBN 0-8010-0844-1). Baker Bk.

Acts & the History of Earliest Christianity. Martin Hengel. LC 79-8893. 160p. 1980. 9.95 (ISBN 0-8006-0630-2, 1-630); pap. 7.50 (ISBN 0-8006-1876-9, 1-1876). Fortress.

Acts, Catholic Epistles & Revelation. William Kelly. (Introductory Lecture Ser.). 580p. 6.95 (ISBN 0-88172-096-8). Believers Bkshelf.

Acts II. Thomas M. Lindsay. (Handbooks for Bible Classes & Private Students Ser.). 168p. 1885. 8.95 (ISBN 0-567-08117-6, Pub. by T & T Clark Ltd UK). Fortress.

Acts in Action, 5 vols. Gordon Lindsay. (Book of Acts Ser.). 1.25 ea. Christ Nations.

Acts in Action, Christs Great Commission. Gordon Lindsay. (Acts in Action Ser.: Vol. 1). pap. 1.25 (ISBN 0-89985-962-3). Christ Nations.

Acts in Prayer. E. W. Price. LC 74-15278. 1974. pap. 0.95 (ISBN 0-8054-9209-7). Broadman.

Acts Made Actual. rev. ed. Don DeWelt. LC 59-20263. (Bible Study Textbook Ser.). (Illus.). 1975. 14.30 (ISBN 0-89900-036-3). College Pr Pub.

Acts of Faith: A Journey to the Fringes of Jewish Identity. Dan Ross. LC 83-40468. (Illus.). 256p. 1984. pap. 8.95 (ISBN 0-8052-0759-7). Schocken.

Acts of God. George Sweeting & Donald Sweeting. (Orig.). 1986. pap. 6.95 (ISBN 0-8024-0497-9). Moody.

Acts of God & the People, 1620-1730. Peter L. Rumsey. Ed. by Margaret R. Miles. LC 86-19292. (Studies in Religion: No. 2). 182p. 1986. 39.95 (ISBN 0-8357-1761-5). UMI Res Pr.

Acts of Joanna. Anne Ortlund. 160p. 1982. 7.95 (ISBN 0-8499-0283-5). Word Bks.

Acts of the Apostles, 2 vols. in 1. J. A. Alexander. (Banner of Truth Geneva Series Commentaries). 1980. 23.95 (ISBN 0-85151-309-3). Banner of Truth.

Acts of the Apostles. Charles W. Conn. 1966. pap. 4.25 (ISBN 0-87148-010-7). Pathway Pr.

Acts of the Apostles. rev. ed. Arno C. Gaebelein. LC 61-17224. 1965. 10.95 (ISBN 0-87213-215-3). Loizeaux.

Acts of the Apostles, Vol. I. Josef Kurzinger. Ed. by John L. McKenzie. LC 81-605. (New Testament for Spiritual Reading Ser.). 227p. 1981. pap. 4.95 (ISBN 0-8245-0119-5). Crossroad NY.

Acts of the Apostles, Vol. II. Josef Kurzinger. Ed. by John L. McKenzie. LC 81-605. (New Testament for Spiritual Reading Ser.). 227p. 1981. pap. 4.95 (ISBN 0-8245-0120-9). Crossroad NY.

Acts of the Apostles. Eugene LaVerdiere. LC 79-1395. (Read & Pray Ser.). 98p. 1979. 1.75 (ISBN 0-8199-0632-8). Franciscan Herald.

Acts of the Apostles. I. Howard Marshall. (Tyndale New Testament Commentaries Ser.). (Orig.). 1980. pap. 7.95 (ISBN 0-8028-1423-9). Eerdmans.

Acts of the Apostles. G. Campbell Morgan. 560p. 1924. 17.95 (ISBN 0-8007-0000-7). Revell.

Acts of the Apostles. Ed. by Johannes Munck. LC 66-20918. (Anchor Bible Ser.: Vol. 31). 1967. 18.00 (ISBN 0-385-00914-3, Anchor Pr). Doubleday.

Acts of the Apostles. rev. ed. William Neil. Ed. by Matthew Black. (New Century Bible Commentary Ser.). 272p. 1981. pap. 9.95 (ISBN 0-8028-1904-4). Eerdmans.

Acts of the Apostles. John W. Packer. (Cambridge Bible Commentary on the New English Bible, New Testament Ser.). (Orig.). 1966. pap. 10.95 (ISBN 0-521-09383-X). Cambridge U Pr.

Acts of the Apostles. Charles Ryrie. (Everyman's Bible Commentary Ser.). 1967. pap. 5.95 (ISBN 0-8024-2044-3). Moody.

Acts of the Apostles. David Thomas. LC 79-2543. (Kregel Bible Study Classics Ser.). 512p. 1980. 22.95 (ISBN 0-8254-3810-1). Kregel.

Acts of the Apostles. August Van Ryn. LC 61-14601. 1961. pap. 1.95 (ISBN 0-87213-883-6). Loizeaux.

Acts of the Apostles. Ellen G. White. 633p. 1911. deluxe ed. 9.95 (ISBN 0-8163-0033-X, 01092-6). Pacific Pr Pub Assn.

Acts of the Apostles, No. 5. William S. Kurz & Robert J. Karris. LC 82-20872. (Collegeville Bible Commentary Ser.). (Illus.). 112p. 1983. pap. 2.95 (ISBN 0-8146-1305-5). Liturgical Pr.

Acts of the Apostles, A Commentary. Ernst Haenchen. LC 78-161218. 762p. 1971. 29.95 (ISBN 0-664-20919-X). Westminster.

Acts of the Apostles & the Letters of St. Paul. E. Ridley Lewis. (London Divinity Ser.). 160p. 1964. Repr. of 1960 ed. 3.95 (ISBN 0-227-67401-4). Attic Pr.

Acts of the Apostles: Life in Action. Roy L. Laurin. LC 85-8158. 408p. 1985. pap. 11.95 (ISBN 0-8254-3127-1). Kregel.

Acts of the Apostles (Missionary Message of the New Testament) F. Townley Lord. 119p. 1946. 2.95 (ISBN 0-87921-003-6). Attic Pr.

Acts of the Christian Martyrs. pap. 6.95 (ISBN 0-686-19380-6). Eastern Orthodox.

Acts of the Christian Martyrs: Text & Translations. Herbert Musurillo. (Oxford Early English Texts Ser). 1972. 52.00x (ISBN 0-19-826806-8). Oxford U Pr.

Acts of the Holy Spirit. A. T. Pierson. 127p. 1980. pap. 3.25 (ISBN 0-87509-274-8). Chr Pubns.

Acts of the Moscow Councils of the Years 1666 & 1667. N. Subbotin. 358p. 1893. text ed. 62.10x (ISBN 0-576-99199-6, Pub. by Gregg Intl Pubs England). Gregg Intl.

Acts of the Pagan Martyrs. Ed. by W. R. Connor. LC 78-18588. (Greek Texts & Commentaries Ser.). 1979. Repr. of 1954 ed. lib. bdg. 25.50x (ISBN 0-405-11430-3). Ayer Co Pubs.

Acts: Powered by the Spirit. Ed. by Gary Wilde. (Basic Bible Ser.). 112p. 1986. pap. 4.95 (ISBN 0-89191-519-2). Cook.

Acts Six: One to Eight, Four - The Authors Method of Composition. Earl Richard. LC 78-12926. (Society of Biblical Literature. Dissertation Ser.: No. 41). (Orig.). 1978. pap. 10.95 (ISBN 0-89130-261-1, 06-01-41). Scholars Pr GA.

Acts Story. G. Raymond Carlson. LC 78-57178. (Radiant Life Ser.). 128p. (Orig.). 1978. pap. 2.50 (ISBN 0-88243-913-8, 02-0913); tchr's. ed 3.95 (ISBN 0-88243-184-6, 32-0184). Gospel Pub.

Acts: Studies in Dynamic Christianity. William MacDonald. 5.95 (ISBN 0-937396-01-X). Walterick Pubs.

Acts: The Genesis of the New Testament. Thomas D. Thurman. Ed. by H. Sherwood Evans. 60p. (Orig.). 1985. pap. 2.25 (ISBN 0-9614213-0-4). Chr Restor Assn.

Acts Two: Thirty-Eight. Bob L. Ross. 1976. 2.25 (ISBN 0-686-09114-0). Pilgrim Pubns.

Acts 1-12: Church on the Move. Carolyn Nystrom. (Young Fisherman Bible Study Guide Ser.). 59p. 1979. tchrs. ed. 4.95 (ISBN 0-87788-126-X); student ed. 2.95 (ISBN 0-87788-125-1). Shaw Pubs.

Acts 1-12: God Moves in the Early Church. rev. ed. Chuck Christensen & Winnie Christensen. (Fisherman Bible Study Guide Ser.). 68p. 1979. saddle stitch 2.95 (ISBN 0-87788-007-7). Shaw Pubs.

Acts 13-28: Missions Accomplished. Carolyn Nystrom & Margaret Fromer. (Young Fisherman Bible Studyguide). (Illus.). 93p. 1979. tchrs. ed. 4.95 (ISBN 0-87788-011-5); student ed. 2.95 (ISBN 0-87788-010-7). Shaw Pubs.

Acts: 14 Lessons, Vol. 1. Bernice C. Jordan. (Footsteps of Faith Ser.). 1954. pap. text ed. 2.50 (ISBN 0-86508-039-9); figure text 11.45 (ISBN 0-86508-040-2). BCM Intl Inc.

Acts: 15 Lessons, Vol. 2. Bernice C. Jordan. (Footsteps of Faith Ser.). 1954. pap. text ed. 2.50 (ISBN 0-86508-041-0); figure text 11.45 (ISBN 0-86508-042-9). BCM Intl Inc.

Acvaghosa's Discourse on the Awakening of Faith in the Mahayana. Asvaghosha. Tr. by D. T. Suzuki from Chinese. 178p. 1900. Repr. text ed. 17.50x (ISBN 0-89644-475-9, Pub. by Chinese Matl Ctr). Coronet Bks.

Adam & Eve. Rebecca Daniel. (Our Greatest Heritage Ser.). (Illus.). 32p. 1983. wkbk. 3.95 (ISBN 0-86653-131-9, SS 800). Good Apple.

Adam & Eve. Gwendolyn Reed. LC 68-27712. (Illus.). 1968. PLB 11.88 (ISBN 0-688-51256-9). Lothrop.

Adam & Eve. Retold by Catherine Storr. LC 82-23060. (People of the Bible). (Illus.). 32p. 1983. PLB 10.65 (ISBN 0-8172-1981-1). Raintree Pubs.

Adam & Eve & Five Other Stories. Peter Enns & Glen Forsberg. (Stories that Live Ser.: Bk. 1). (Illus.). 24p. 1985. book & Cassette 4.95 (ISBN 0-936215-01-1). STL Intl.

Adam & Eve Fantasy. Jess E. Weiss. 80p. 1985. 8.00 (ISBN 0-682-40262-1). Exposition Pr FL.

Adam & Eve: The Spiritual Symbolism of Genesis & Exodus. S. D. Fohr. LC 86-1497. 162p. (Orig.). 1986. lib. bdg. 25.75 (ISBN 0-8191-5267-6); pap. text ed. 10.25 (ISBN 0-8191-5268-4). U Pr of Amer.

Adam & Evolution. Michael Pitman. 269p. 1986. pap. 12.95 (ISBN 0-8010-7092-9). Baker Bk.

Adam & His Family. Robert Baden. (Arch Bks.). (Illus.). 24p. 1986. pap. 0.99 saddlestitched (ISBN 0-570-06198-9, 59-1421). Concordia.

Adam Clarke's Commentary on the Entire Bible. Ed. by Adam Clarke. 29.95 (ISBN 0-8010-2321-1). Baker Bk.

Adam Davy's Five Dreams about Edward 2nd. F. J. Furnivall. Incl. Life of St. Alexius; Solomon's Book of Wisdom; St. Jeremies Fifteen Tokens Before Doomsday; Lamentacion of Souls. (EETS, OS Ser.: No. 69). Repr. of 1878 ed. 10.00 (ISBN 0-527-00068-X). Kraus Repr.

Adam, Eve & the Serpent. Elaine Pagels. 1987. 17.95 (ISBN 0-394-52140-4). Random.

Adam of Dryburgh: Six Christmas Sermons (Introduction & Translation) M. J. Hamilton. Ed. by James Hogg. (Analecta Cartusiana Ser.: No. 16). (Orig.). 1974. pap. 25.00 (ISBN 3-7052-0018-6, Pub by Salzburg Studies). Longwood Pub Group.

Adam of Witham De Quadripartito Exercitio Cellae. James Hogg. (Analecta Cartusiana Ser.: No. 98). (Orig.). 1986. pap. 25.00 (ISBN 3-7052-0169-7, Pub. by Salzburg Studies). Longwood Pub Group.

Adamic Christianity: Questions & Answers, Vol. 1. Robert E. Birdsong. 1978. pap. 3.75 (ISBN 0-917108-22-1). Sirius Bks.

Adam's Story. Ulmer. LC 59-1292. (Arch Bks.). 24p. (Orig.). 1985. pap. 0.99 (ISBN 0-570-06191-1). Concordia.

Added Dimension: The Art of Mind of Flannery O'Connor. 2nd ed. Melvin J. Friedman. LC 66-11070. xviii, 263p. 1977. pap. 9.00 (ISBN 0-8232-0711-0). Fordham.

Addicion of Salem & Byzance. Christopher Saint German. LC 73-6157. (English Experience Ser.: No. 619). 152p. 1973. Repr. of 1534 ed. 10.50 (ISBN 90-221-0619-5). Walter J Johnson.

Addict to Yearning: Inspirational Philosophy & Religion. Merle Lighton. 1952. 5.00 (ISBN 0-910892-00-8, 910892). Lighton Pubns.

Addicted to Mediocrity. Franky Schaeffer. LC 80-85325. (Illus.). 128p. 1981. pap. 5.95 (ISBN 0-89107-214-4, Crossway Bks). Good News.

Address Book of Some Assemblies of Christians (Current) 1986. pap. 5.50 (ISBN 0-937396-03-6). Walterick Pubs.

Address on the Truth, Dignity, Power & Beauty of the Principles of Peace, & on the Unchristian Character & Influence of War & the Warrior. Thomas S. Grimke. LC 72-137542. (Peace Movement in America Ser). 56p. 1972. Repr. of 1832 ed. lib. bdg. 11.95x (ISBN 0-89198-070-9). Ozer.

Addresses Delivered at the Semi-Centennial Celebration of the Dedication of the First Unitarian Church, South Natick (Massachusetts) November 20, 1878. Horatio Alger, Sr. & J. P. Sheaf, Jr. (Illus.). 41p. 1977. pap. 6.00 (ISBN 0-686-35760-4). G K Westgard.

Addresses of His Holiness Pope John Paul II to the United States Bishops During Their Ad Limina Visits: Ad Limina Addresses. 60p. 1983. pap. 4.95 (ISBN 1-55586-926-2). US Catholic.

Addresses of Pius the Twelfth to Cloistered Religious. Pope Pius Twelfth. pap. 1.25 (ISBN 0-8198-0006-6). Dghtrs St Paul.

Adept. 1983. pap. 4.95 (ISBN 0-913922-81-1). Dawn Horse Pr.

Adhan over Anatolia. M. Kazi. pap. 7.95. Am Trust Pubns.

Adhyatma Ramayana. Brahmandapurana Puranas. Tr. by Lala B. Nath. LC 73-3828. (Sacred Books of the Hindus: Extra Vol. 1). Repr. of 1913 ed. 25.00 (ISBN 0-404-57846-2). AMS Pr.

Aditi & Other Deities in the Veda. M. P. Pandit. 1979. 3.95 (ISBN 0-941524-01-9). Lotus Light.

Adjust or Self-Destruct. Craig Massey. LC 77-4088. pap. 3.50 (ISBN 0-8024-0136-8). Moody.

Administering Christian Education. Robert K. Bower. LC 64-22018. 1964. pap. 8.95 (ISBN 0-8028-1559-6). Eerdmans.

Administration of Islam in Indonesia. Deliar Noer. (Monograph Ser.). 1978. pap. 4.50 (ISBN 0-87763-002-X). Cornell Mod Indo.

Administration of Normandy Under Saint Louis. Joseph R. Strayer. LC 72-171362. Repr. of 1932 ed. 16.00 (ISBN 0-404-06297-0). AMS Pr.

Admonitions of St. Francis of Assisi. Lothar Hardick et al. Tr. by David Smith. 399p. 1983. 12.50 (ISBN 0-8199-0869-X). Franciscan Herald.

Adolescence-Its Psychology & Its Relation to Physiology, Anthropology, Sociology, Sex, Crime, Religion & Education, 2 vols. Stanley G. Hall. LC 79-89183. (American Education: Its Men, Institutions & Ideas Ser). 1970. Repr. of 1905 ed. Set. 65.00 (ISBN 0-405-01421-X); Vol. 1. 38.50 (ISBN 0-405-01422-8); Vol. 2. 35.00 (ISBN 0-405-01423-6). Ayer Co Pubs.

Adolescent, His Search for Understanding. Ed. by W. C. Bier. LC 62-17450. (Pastoral Psychology Ser.: No. 3). x, 246p. 1963. 17.50 (ISBN 0-8232-0480-4). Fordham.

Adolescent Spirituality: Pastoral Ministry for High School & College Youth. rev. ed. Charles M. Shelton. 1983. 15.00 (ISBN 0-8294-0422-8). Loyola.

Adolescent Suicidal Behavior: A Family Systems Model. Roma J. Heillig. Ed. by Peter E. Nathan. LC 83-3594. (Research in Clinical Psychology Ser.: No. 7). 170p. 1983. 37.95 (ISBN 0-8357-1390-3). Univ Microfilms.

Adolescents in Turmoil, Parents under Stress: A Pastoral Ministry Primer. Richard D. Parsons. 160p. (Orig.). 1987. pap. 7.95 (ISBN 0-8091-2855-1). Paulist Pr.

Adoniram Judson. Faith C. Bailey. (Golden Oldies Ser.). 128p. 1980. pap. 3.50 (ISBN 0-8024-0287-9). Moody.

Adoniram Judson: Following God's Plan. Fern N. Stocker. (Guessing Bks.). (Orig.). 1986. pap. 3.95 (ISBN 0-8024-4384-2). Moody.

Adoniram Judson Gordon. Earnest B. Gordon. Ed. by Donald W. Dayton. (Higher Christian Life Ser.). 386p. 1985. 55.00 (ISBN 0-8240-6421-6). Garland Pub.

Adopted & Loved Forever. Annetta E. Dellinger. (Illus.). 1987. 3.95 (ISBN 0-570-04167-8). Concordia.

Adopted Children. rev. ed. Jan De Hartog. 268p. 1987. pap. 13.95 (ISBN 0-915361-65-5, Dist. by Watts). Adama Pubs Inc.

Adopted for a Purpose: Bible Stories of Joseph, Moses, Samuel, & Esther. Pauline Youd. 144p. (Orig.). 1986. pap. 7.95 (ISBN 0-687-00770-4). Abingdon.

Adoption Book. Sheila Macmanus. (Orig.). 1984. pap. 4.95 (ISBN 0-8091-2578-1). Paulist Pr.

Adoracion y la Iglesia. (Span.). pap. 1.25 (ISBN 0-686-32316-5). Rod & Staff.

Adoration of the Blessed Sacrament. A. Tesniere. (Illus.). 288p. 1981. Repr. of 1902 ed. lib. bdg. 35.00 (ISBN 0-89984-461-8). Century Bookbindery.

Adore the Lord: Adoration Viewed Through the Old Testament. Ernest Lussier. LC 78-20783. 1979. 6.95 (ISBN 0-8189-0380-5). Alba.

Adult Baptism & the Catechumenate. Ed. by Johannes Wagner. LC 67-19979. (Concilium Ser.: Vol. 22). 204p. 1967. 7.95 (ISBN 0-8091-0000-2). Paulist Pr.

Adult Confession: Conversion in Process. Carol Cowgill. 80p. 1984. pap. 3.50 (ISBN 0-697-02030-4). Wm C Brown.

Adult Education in Church & Synagogue. Huey B. Long. LC 73-13292. (Ocassional Paper Ser.: No. 37). 1973. pap. 2.50 (ISBN 0-87060-061-3, OCP 37). Syracuse U Cont Ed.

Adult Education in the Church. Donald J. Hoekstra. LC 85-17433. 109p. (Orig.). 1985. pap. 4.95 (ISBN 0-930265-14-9). CRC Pubns.

Adult Education in the Church. Roy B. Zuck & Gene A. Getz. LC 79-123154. 1970. pap. 15.95 (ISBN 0-8024-0468-5). Moody.

Adult Education Ministry: A Parish Manual. Richard Reichert. 1986. pap. 5.95 (ISBN 0-697-02206-4). Wm C Brown.

Adult Learning & the Parish. Ed. by Neil A. Parent. 144p. 1985. pap. 6.95 (ISBN 0-697-02063-0). Wm C Brown.

Adult Ministries in the Church & the World. Lee Hart. LC 76-773. 1976. 11.00 (ISBN 0-8309-0160-4). Herald Hse.

Adults As Learners. Jack Mottweiler. (C. E. Ministries Ser.). 95p. (Orig.). 1984. pap. 3.50 (ISBN 0-89367-098-7). Light & Life.

Advaita & Visistadvaita. 2nd ed. S. M. Chari. 1976. 11.95 (ISBN 0-8426-0886-9). Orient Bk Dist.

Advaita Vedanta: A Philosophical Reconstruction. Eliot Deutsch. LC 69-19282. 1969. pap. text ed. 5.95x (ISBN 0-8248-0271-3, Eastwest Ctr). UH Pr.

Advaita Vedanta Up to Samkara & His Pupils: Encyclopedia of Indian Philosophies, Vol. 3. Ed. by Karl H. Potter. LC 77-8558. 648p. 1982. 63.00x (ISBN 0-691-07182-9). Princeton U Pr.

Advaitic Sadhana. S. S. Cohen. 1976. 8.95 (ISBN 0-8426-0989-X). Orient Bk Dist.

Advaitic Theism of the Bhagavata Purana. Daniel P. Sheridan. 1986. 14.00 (ISBN 81-208-0179-2, Pub. by Motilal Banarsidass). South Asia Bks.

Advanced Christian Training. Jean Gibson. (Orig.). 1986. pap. 7.00 (ISBN 0-937396-04-4). Walterick Pubs.

Advanced Procedure & Axioms. L. Ron Hubbard. 1951. 30.00 (ISBN 0-88404-021-6). Bridge Pubns Inc.

Advanced Procedures & Axioms. L. Ron Hubbard. 31.00 (ISBN 0-686-30782-8). Church Scient NY.

Advanced Tai Chi. A. Lum. 11.95x (ISBN 0-685-63740-9). Wehman.

Advances in Thanatology, Vol. 5, No. 2. 17.00 (ISBN 0-405-14221-8, 745). Ayer Co Pubs.

Advances in the Psychology of Religion. L. B. Brown. (International Series in Experimental Social Psychology: Vol. 11). (Illus.). 236p. 1985. 27.50 (ISBN 0-08-027948-1, Pub by PPL). Pergamon.

Advent! Lewis R. Walton. Ed. by Raymond H. Woolsey. 128p. (Orig.). 1986. pap. 6.95 (ISBN 0-8280-0349-1). Review & Herald.

Advent: A Calendar of Devotions, Nineteen Eighty-Six. Mary Lou Carney. 48p. (Orig.). 1986. pap. 30.00 (ISBN 0-687-00886-7). Abingdon.

Advent: A Calendar of Devotions, 1987. Mary L. Carney. 48p. pap. 30.00 (ISBN 0-687-00887-5). Abingdon.

Advent & Christmas Saints. Jerry Schmalenberger. 1984. 3.75 (ISBN 0-89536-685-1, 4861). CSS of Ohio.

Advent & Event. John Brokhoff. 88p. (Orig.). 1980. pap. text ed. 3.25 (ISBN 0-89536-453-0, 0147). CSS of Ohio.

Advent Begins at Home. David Polek & Rita Anderhub. 1979. pap. 1.50 (ISBN 0-89243-111-3). Liguori Pubns.

Advent Christians & the Bible. 2nd, rev. ed. Ed. by Freeman Barton. LC 84-80020. 96p. pap. 4.00 (ISBN 0-913439-03-7). Henceforth.

Advent-Christmas. Paul J. Achtemeier & J. Leland Mebust. Ed. by Elizabeth Achtemeier et al. LC 79-7377. (Proclamation 2: Aids for Interpreting the Lessons of the Church Year, Ser. B). 64p. (Orig.). 1981. pap. 3.75 (ISBN 0-8006-4060-8, 1-4060). Fortress.

Advent-Christmas. Frederick H. Borsch & Davie Napier. Ed. by Elizabeth Achtemeier et al. LC 79-7377. (Proclamation 2: Aids for Interpreting the Lessons of the Church Year, Ser. A). 64p. (Orig.). 1980. pap. 3.75 (ISBN 0-8006-4091-8, 1-4091). Fortress.

Advent-Christmas. Reginald H. Fuller. Ed. by Elizabeth Achtemeier et al. LC 79-7377. (Proclamation 2: Aids for Interpreting the Lessons of the Church Year, Ser. C). 64p. 1979. pap. 3.75 (ISBN 0-8006-4079-9, 1-4079). Fortress.

Advent-Christmas. Gerard S. Sloyan. LC 84-18756. (Proclamation 3 C Ser.). 64p. 1985. pap. 3.75 (ISBN 0-8006-4125-6). Fortress.

Advent-Christmas. Bruce Vawter. LC 84-18756. (Proclamation 3A Ser.). 64p. 1986. pap. 3.75 (ISBN 0-8006-4117-5, 1-4117). Fortress.

Advent Christmas: A Guide to the Eucharist & Hours. Kevin W. Irwin. (Liturgical Seasons Ser.). 300p. (Orig.). 1986. pap. 12.95 (ISBN 0-916134-80-6). Pueblo Pub Co.

Advent-Christmas: Series B. Walter Brueggemann. LC 84-6020. (Proclamation 3: Aids for Interpreting the Lessons of the Church Year Ser.). 64p. 1984. pap. 3.75 (ISBN 0-8006-4101-9). Fortress.

Advent Covenant Wreath. Douglas R. Behm. 16p. 1981. pap. text ed. 2.65 (ISBN 0-89536-482-4, 0102). CSS of Ohio.

Advent Day by Day in the Home. Gisela Harupa & Liselotte Nold. Tr. by Omar Kaste. LC 62-17507. 1962. pap. 2.95 (ISBN 0-8066-0209-0, 10-0160). Augsburg.

Advent Event. Herbert Skelly & Margaret Skelly. (Illus.). 32p. (Orig.). 1973. pap. 3.25 (ISBN 0-8192-1148-6); kit 13.95 (ISBN 0-8192-1283-0). Morehouse.

Advent Hope in Scripture & History. Ed. by V. Norskov Olsen et al. 272p. (Orig.). 1987. 22.95 (ISBN 0-8280-0311-4). Review & Herald.

Advent of Christ. Victor Mohr. 116p. 1985. pap. cancelled (ISBN 0-934616-16-7). Valkyrie Pub Hse.

Advent of Divine Justice. rev. ed. Shoghi Effendi. LC 84-436. x, 104p. 1984. 14.95 (ISBN 0-87743-195-7); pap. 8.95 (ISBN 0-87743-196-5). Baha'i.

Advent Recollections: Five Dramatic Monologs. Robert Morgan. 1985. 3.50 (ISBN 0-89536-764-5, 5871). CSS of Ohio.

Advent to Pentecost-A History of the Church Year. Patricia B. Buckland. 1979. pap. 4.95 (ISBN 0-8192-1251-2). Morehouse.

Advent: Twenty-Eight Ways to Celebrate the Holy in the Holiday Rush. Terrance L. Schneider. (Illus.). 37p. 1982. pap. text ed. 1.95 (ISBN 0-86716-017-9). St Anthony Mess Pr.

Adventism in America. Ed. by Gary Land. 304p. (Orig.). 1986. pap. 14.95 (ISBN 0-8028-0237-0). Eerdmans.

Adventismo Del Septimo Dia. D. M. Canright. Tr. by F. G. Correa. 1985. pap. 1.95 (ISBN 0-311-05601-6). Casa Bautista.

Adventist Evangelist's Diary. large print ed. Pearl Brians. 1985. pap. 4.00 (ISBN 0-914009-25-7). VHI Library.

Adventists & Labor Unions in the U. S. Robert Kistler. Ed. by Gerald Wheeler. LC 83-13664. (Illus.). 127p. (Orig.). 1984. pap. 9.95 (ISBN 0-8280-0221-5). Review & Herald.

Adventists in Russia. Alf Lohne. Ed. by Raymond H. Woolsey. 160p. (Orig.). 1987. pap. 9.95 (ISBN 0-8280-0373-4). Review & Herald.

Adventure in Faith. Frank S. Seilhamer. 1983. 7.95 (ISBN 0-89536-675-4, 0125). CSS of Ohio.

Adventure in Prayer. Sylvester Treinen. 16p. (Orig.). 1983. pap. 30.00 pkg. of 100 (ISBN 0-8146-1331-4). Liturgical Pr.

Adventure in Spiritual Direction: A Prophetic Pattern. Roman Ginn. (Orig.). 1979. pap. 2.95 (ISBN 0-914544-27-6). Living Flame Pr.

Adventure Inward: Christian Growth Through Personal Journal Writing. Morton T. Kelsey. LC 80-65551. 224p. (Orig.). 1980. pap. 9.95 (ISBN 0-8066-1796-9, 10-0166). Augsburg.

Adventure of Affirming: Reflections on Healing & Ministry. Anna Polocino. LC 86-8005. 111p. (Orig.). 1986. pap. 7.95 (ISBN 0-89571-030-7). Affirmation.

Adventure of Becoming One. Louis Caldwell. (Ultra Bks.). 80p. 1981. 5.95 (ISBN 0-8010-2334-3). Baker Bk.

Adventure of Giving. Bill Stafford. Ed. by Ted Griffin. 128p. (Orig.). 1985. pap. 4.95 (ISBN 0-8423-0036-8). Tyndale.

Adventure of Living God's Will. Marion Wilson. 48p. 1980. pap. 1.50 (ISBN 0-89114-093-X); tchr's. ed. 1.00 (ISBN 0-89114-094-8). Baptist Pub Hse.

Adventure of Spiritual Healing. Michael Drury. 304p. 1985. pap. 9.95 large print ed. (ISBN 0-8027-2493-0). Walker & Co.

Adventure: Putting Energy into Your Work with God. Jerry Sittser. LC 85-19695. 236p. 1985. pap. 6.95 (ISBN 0-87784-335-X). Inter-Varsity.

Adventurers: Ordinary People with Special Callings. Diane Forrest. 1984. pap. 5.95 (ISBN 0-317-13951-7). Upper Room.

Adventures & Missionary Labours in Several Countries in the Interior of Africa from 1849-1856. 2nd rev. ed. T. J. Bowen. 359p. 1968. Repr. of 1857 ed. 32.50x (ISBN 0-7146-1863-2, F Cass Co). Biblio Dist.

Adventures at Nameless Valley Ranch. Sharon Todd. Ed. by Bobbie J. Van Dolson. 96p. 1981. pap. 5.95 (ISBN 0-8280-0032-8). Review & Herald.

Adventures for the Soul. Natalie Sleeth. 139p. 1987. pap. 5.95 (ISBN 0-916642-30-5, 785). Hope Pub.

Adventures from God's Word. rev. ed. Pratricia A Burke et al. Ed. by Marge Miller. (Basic Bible Readers Ser.). (Illus.). 128p. 1983. text ed. 7.95 (ISBN 0-87239-663-0, 2953). Standard Pub.

Adventures in Church Growth. Roger L. Dudley & Des Cummings, Jr. Ed. by Gerald Wheeler. LC 83-16089. (Illus.). 160p. (Orig.). 1983. pap. 8.95 (ISBN 0-8280-0228-2). Review & Herald.

Adventures in Consciousness. Friend Stuart. 1962. pap. 6.95 (ISBN 0-912132-00-0). Dominion Pr.

Adventures in Creative Teaching. Elsiebeth McDaniel et al. 96p. 1986. pap. 6.95 (ISBN 0-89693-557-4). Victor Bks.

Adventures in God. John G. Lake. 131p. 1981. pap. 4.95 (ISBN 0-89274-206-2). Harrison Hse.

Adventures in Idealism: A Personal Record of the Life of Professor Sabsovich. facsimile ed. Katherine Sabsovich. LC 74-29520. (Modern Jewish Experience Ser.). (Illus.). 1975. Repr. of 1922 ed. 23.50x (ISBN 0-405-06745-3). Ayer Co Pubs.

Adventures in Philosophy & Religion. James B. Pratt. LC 75-3323. Repr. of 1931 ed. 16.00 (ISBN 0-404-59319-4). AMS Pr.

Adventures in Prayer. Catherine Marshall. 1980. pap. 2.25 (ISBN 0-345-27210-2). Ballantine.

Adventures in Prayer. Catherine Marshall. (Illus.). 120p. 1976. pap. 2.95 (ISBN 0-8007-8269-0, Spire Bks). Revell.

Adventures in Religious Life. Swami Yatiswarananda. pap. 4.50 (ISBN 0-87481-498-7). Vedanta Pr.

Adventures in the Land of Canaan. R. L. Berry. 128p. pap. 1.00 (ISBN 0-686-29096-8). Faith Pub Hse.

Adventures in Training the Ministry. Kenneth Mulholland. 1976. pap. 5.95 (ISBN 0-87552-340-4). Presby & Reformed.

Adventures of a Parapsychologist. Susan Blackmore. 250p. 1986. 19.95 (ISBN 0-87975-360-9). Prometheus Bks.

Adventures of a Yiddish Lecturer. Abraham Shulman. LC 79-28734. 1980. 7.95 (ISBN 0-8298-0391-2). Pilgrim NY.

Adventures of Bug & Me. Nona Freeman. Ed. by Charles Clanton. 128p. (Orig.). 1977. pap. 4.95 (ISBN 0-912315-28-8). Word Aflame.

Adventures of Eros & Psyche. I. M. Richardson. LC 82-16057. (Illus.). 32p. 1983. PLB 9.79 (ISBN 0-89375-861-2); pap. text ed. 2.50 (ISBN 0-89375-862-0). Troll Assocs.

Adventures of Gabriel in His Search for God. Charles H. Maxwell. 1933. Repr. 12.50 (ISBN 0-8274-1821-3). R West.

Adventures of Healing: How to Use New Testament Practices & Receive New Testament Results. 3rd, rev. ed. Donald W. Bartow. 204p. 1981. pap. 11.95 (ISBN 0-938736-19-1). Life Enrich.

Adventures of Huru on the Road to Baghdad. Guneli Gun. 352p. 1987. 19.95 (ISBN 0-89793-033-9). Hunter Hse.

Adventures of Jacob. Zev Paamoni. (Biblical Ser.). (Illus.). 1970. 4.00 (ISBN 0-914080-26-1). Shulsinger Sales.

Adventures of Peter & Paul. Daughters of St. Paul. (Illus.). 120p. 1984. 10.00 (ISBN 0-8198-0726-5). Dghtrs St Paul.

Adventures of Simple Shmerl. Solomon Simon. (Illus.). 1942. 4.95 (ISBN 0-87441-127-0). Behrman.

Adventures of the White Girl in Her Search for God. Charles H. Maxwell. LC 74-20648. 1974. Repr. of 1933 ed. lib. bdg. 25.00 (ISBN 0-8414-5951-7). Folcroft.

Adventures of Timoteo. Sue Fator. pap. 1.25 (ISBN 0-89985-992-5). Christ Nations.

Adventures Through the Bible. rev. ed. Dana Eynon. LC 79-1031. 176p. 1980. pap. 7.95 tchr's book (ISBN 0-87239-378-X, 3234). Standard Pub.

Adventures with God. Ed. by Harry N. Huxhold. LC 66-15551. 1966. pap. 7.95 (ISBN 0-570-03736-0, 12-2640). Concordia.

Adversary. Mark I. Bubeck. 1975. pap. 5.95 (ISBN 0-8024-0143-0). Moody.

Adversity & Grace: Studies in Recent American Literature. Ed. by Nathan A. Scott, Jr. LC 68-16717. (Essays in Divinity Ser: Vol. 4). 1968. 9.50x (ISBN 0-226-74283-0). U of Chicago Pr.

Adversus Judaeos: A Bird's-Eye View of Christian Apologiae until the Renaissance. A. Lukyn Williams. LC 36-11257. pap. 111.50 (ISBN 0-317-29839-9, 2051943). Bks Demand UMI.

Adversvs Nationes Libri Seven, Bk. 7. Afer Arnobius. (Corpus Scriptorum Ecclesiasticorum Latinorum, Vol. 4). 31.00. Johnson Repr.

Advice. Nathan of Breslov. Tr. by Avraham Greenbaum from Hebrew. LC 83-70202. Tr. of Likutey Etzot. 522p. 1983. 13.00 (ISBN 0-930213-04-1). Breslov Res Inst.

Advice from a Spiritual Friend. rev. ed. Rabten Geshe & Dhargyey Geshe. Ed. by Brian Beresford. (Wisdom Basic Book, Orange Ser.). (Illus.). 160p. 1984. pap. 8.95 (ISBN 0-86171-017-7, Wisdom Pubns). Great Traditions.

Advice to Sufferers. John Bunyan. pap. 3.25 (ISBN 0-685-19821-9). Reiner.

Aelfric's Catholic Homilies: The Second Series. Aelfric. Ed. by Malcolm Godden. (Early English Text Ser.: No. 5). (Illus.). 486p. 1979. text ed. 54.00x (ISBN 0-19-722405-9). Oxford U Pr.

Aelfric's Lives of Saints, Vol. I, Pts. I-II. (EETS OS Ser.: Vols. 76 & 82). Repr. of 1885 ed. 22.00 (ISBN 0-8115-3361-1). Kraus Repr.

Aelfric's Lives of Saints, Vol. II, Pts. III-IV. Ed. by W. W. Skeat. (EETS OS Ser.: Vols. 94 & 114). Repr. of 1900 ed. 22.00 (ISBN 0-8115-3365-4). Kraus Repr.

Aelred of Rievaulx: A Study. Aelred Squire. (Cistercian Studies Ser.: No. 50). 192p. 1981. 10.95 (ISBN 0-87907-850-2); pap. 5.00 (ISBN 0-686-85802-6). Cistercian Pubns.

Aeroplane or a Grave. Brian Peachment. 1974. pap. 1.85 (ISBN 0-08-017841-3). Pergamon.

Aeschylus' "Prometheus Bound" A Literary Commentary. D. J. Conacher. 128p. 1980. 25.00x (ISBN 0-8020-2391-6); pap. 8.50 (ISBN 0-8020-6416-7). U of Toronto Pr.

Aesthetic Dimensions of Religious Education. Gloria Durka & Joanmarie Smith. LC 78-65903. 252p. 1979. pap. 8.50 (ISBN 0-8091-2164-6). Paulist Pr.

Affair: The Case of Alfred Dreyfus. Jean-Denis Bredin. Tr. by Jeffrey Mehlman from Fr. Tr. of L'Affaire. (Illus.). 1987. pap. 12.95 (ISBN 0-8076-1175-1). Braziller.

Affirmation & Rebuke. Gordon MacDonald & Gail MacDonald. (PathFinder Pamphlets Ser.). 32p. (Orig.). 1986. pap. 1.95 (ISBN 0-87784-219-1). Inter-Varsity.

Affirmation: The Touch of Life. William Peil. LC 82-20655. (Illus.). 48p. 1983. pap. 1.95 (ISBN 0-89571-026-9). Affirmation.

Affirmations, by a Group of American Anglo-Catholics, Clerical & Lay. facs. ed. Ed. by Bernard I. Bell. LC 68-16906. (Essay Index Reprint Ser). 1938. 15.00 (ISBN 0-8369-0185-1). Ayer Co Pubs.

Affirmations of Judaism. J. H. Hertz. 338p. 1975. 9.95 (ISBN 0-900689-54-4). Soncino Pr.

Affirmative Aging: A Resource for Ministry. Compiled by The Episcopal Society for Ministry on Aging. 192p. (Orig.). 1986. pap. 8.95 (ISBN 0-86683-786-8, HarpR). Har-Row.

Affirming Life. Seymour Cohen. 350p. 1987. 20.00x (ISBN 0-88125-112-7). Ktav.

Affirming the Human & the Holy. Philomena Agudo. LC 79-1499. (Illus.). 101p. 1979. pap. 4.95 (ISBN 0-89571-006-4). Affirmation.

Affirming the Will of God. Paul Little. pap. 0.75 (ISBN 0-87784-139-X). Inter-Varsity.

Affliction. Edith Schaeffer. 256p. 1978. 10.95 (ISBN 0-8007-0926-8); 7.95 (ISBN 0-8007-5150-7). Revell.

Afghani & Abduh: Essay on Religious Unbelief & Political Activism in Modern Islam. Elie Kedourie. 97p. 1966. 28.50x (ISBN 0-7146-1989-2, F Cass Co). Biblio Dist.

Afirme Sus Valores. Charles Swindoll. Tr. by Juan Araujo from Eng. Orig. Title: Strengthening Your Grip. (Span.). 256p. 1987. pap. 4.95 (ISBN 0-88113-087-7). Edit Betania.

Africa: A Season for Hope. 1985. write for info. (ISBN 0-912552-46-8). World Vision Intl.

Africa & Christianity. Diedrich Westermann. LC 74-15102. (Duff Lectures, 1935). Repr. of 1937 ed. 24.50 (ISBN 0-404-12151-9). AMS Pr.

Africa: Apostolic Pilgrimage. Pope John Paul II. 1980. 8.00 (ISBN 0-8198-0708-7); pap. 7.00 (ISBN 0-8198-0709-5). Dghtrs St Paul.

Africa or Death. A. G. Mondini. (Illus.). 1964. 5.00 (ISBN 0-8198-0007-4). Dghtrs St Paul.

African Apostles: Ritual & Conversion in the Church of John Maranke. Bennetta Jules-Rosette. LC 75-8437. (Symbol, Myth & Ritual Ser.). (Illus.). 352p. 1975. 34.50x (ISBN 0-8014-0846-6). Cornell U Pr.

African Christian Theology: Adaptation or Incarnation? Aylward Shorter. LC 77-23325. 180p. (Orig.). 1977. 7.95 (ISBN 0-88344-002-4); pap. 4.95 (ISBN 0-88344-003-2). Orbis Bks.

African Christianity. Adrian Hastings. 12p. 1977. 9.95 (ISBN 0-8164-0336-8, AY6700, HarpR). Har-Row.

African Christianity: Patterns of Religious Continuity. Ed. by George Bond et al. LC 79-51668. (AP Studies in Anthropology Ser.). 1979. 29.95 (ISBN 0-12-113450-4). Acad Pr.

African Cosmos: An Introduction to Religion in Africa. Noel Q. King. 1985. pap. text ed. write for info (ISBN 0-534-05334-3). Wadsworth Pub.

African Cry. Jean-Marc Ela. Tr. by Robert R. Barr from Fr. LC 86-12429. Tr. of Cri de l'homme Africain. 176p. (Orig.). 1986. pap. 10.95 (ISBN 0-88344-259-0). Orbis Bks.

African Culture & the Christian Church: An Introduction to Social & Pastoral Anthropology. Aylward Shorter. LC 73-79481. pap. 60.30 (ISBN 0-317-26684-5, 2025114). Bks Demand UMI.

African Foundations of Judaism & Christianity. E. Curtis Alexander. LC 84-48679. (Alkebu-lan Historical Research Society Monograph: No. 3). 84p. (Orig.). 1985. pap. 5.95 (ISBN 0-938818-08-2). ECA Assoc.

African Godianism: A Revolutionary Religion for Mankind Through Direct Communication with God. K. O. Onyioha. 1980. 15.00 (ISBN 0-914970-31-3). Conch Mag.

African Historical Religions: A Conceptual & Ethical Foundation for Western Religions. E. Curtis Alexander. LC 83-83096. (Alkelbulan Historical Research Society Monograph Ser.: No. 2). (Illus.). 70p. 1984. pap. 4.95 (ISBN 0-938818-05-8). ECA Assoc.

African Islam. Rene A. Bravmann. LC 83-21174. (Illus.). 120p. 1984. pap. 16.95 (ISBN 0-87474-281-1, BRAIP). Smithsonian.

African Islamic Mission. Imam Alhaji Obaba Muhammadu. 38p. (Orig.). 1982. pap. 1.00 (ISBN 0-916157-04-0). African Islam Miss Pubns.

African Methodism in the South: Or Twenty-Five Years of Freedom. Wesley J. Gaines. LC 71-99379. 1969. Repr. of 1890 ed. lib. bdg. 16.00 (ISBN 0-8411-0050-0). Metro Bks.

African Mythology. Geoffrey Parrinder. LC 85-22967. (Library of the World's Myths & Legends). (Illus.). 144p. 1986. 18.95 (ISBN 0-87226-042-9). P Bedrick Bks.

African Religion in African Scholarship: A Preliminary Study of the Religious and Political Background. David Westerlund. 104p. (Orig.). 1985. pap. 20.00x (ISBN 91-7146-344-5). Coronet Bks.

African Religion Meets Islam: Religious Change in Northern Nigeria. Dean S. Gilliland. 250p. (Orig.). 1986. lib. bdg. 24.50 (ISBN 0-8191-5634-5); pap. text ed. 12.75 (ISBN 0-8191-5635-3). U Pr of Amer.

African Religions: A Symposium. Newell S. Booth. LC 73-88062. 390p. 1977. text ed. 21.50x (ISBN 0-88357-012-2). Nok Pubs.

African Religions & Philosophy. John S. Mbiti. xiv, 290p. (Orig.). 1969. pap. text ed. 13.50x (ISBN 0-435-89589-3). Heinemann Ed.

African Religions of Brazil: Toward a Sociology of the Interpenetration of Civilizations. Roger Bastide. Tr. by Helen Sebba. (Johns Hopkins Studies in Atlantic History & Culture Ser.). 1978. text ed. 45.00x (ISBN 0-8018-2056-1); pap. text ed. 14.95x (ISBN 0-8018-2130-4). Johns Hopkins.

African Religions: Symbol, Ritual & Community. Benjamin C Ray. 1976. pap. write for info. (ISBN 0-13-018622-8). P-H.

African Systems of Thought. International African Seminar - 3rd - Salisburg - Southern Rhodesia. Ed. by Meyer Fortes & Germaine Dieterlen. 1965. 42.00x (ISBN 0-19-724158-1). Oxford U Pr.

African Theology En Route: Papers from the Pan-African Conference of Third World Theologians, December 17-23, 1977, Accra, Ghana. Ed. by Kofi Appiah-Kubi & Sergio Torres. LC 78-10604. 224p. (Orig.). 1978. pap. 10.95 (ISBN 0-88344-010-5). Orbis Bks.

African Traditional Religion. 3rd ed. Geoffrey Parrinder. LC 76-22490. (Illus.). 156p. 1976. Repr. of 1976 ed. lib. bdg. 25.00x (ISBN 0-8371-3401-3, PAF&, Pub. by Negro U Pr). Greenwood.

Africana, or, the Heart of Heathen Africa, 2 Vols. Duff Macdonald. LC 70-82058. (Illus.). Repr. of 1882 ed. 14.50x (ISBN 0-8371-1523-X, MAA&, Pub. by Negro U Pr). Greenwood.

Africa's Diamonds. Yvonne Davy. Ed. by Juanita Tyson-Flyn. (Daybreak Ser.). 96p. 1983. pap. 4.95 (ISBN 0-8163-0512-9). Pacific Pr Pub Assn.

Africa's Mountain Valley; or, the Church in Regent's Town, West Africa. William A. Johnson. LC 72-3995. (Black Heritage Library Collection Ser.). Repr. of 1856 ed. 18.75 (ISBN 0-8369-9098-6). Ayer Co Pubs.

Africa's Twelve Apostles. H. Russell. 1980. 6.95 (ISBN 0-8198-0702-8); pap. 5.50 (ISBN 0-8198-0703-6). Dghtrs St Paul.

Afrikanische Religion und Weltanschauung. John S. Mbiti. Tr. by W. F. Feuser from Eng. (Ger.). xvi, 375p. 1974. 19.20 (ISBN 3-11-002498-5). De Gruyter.

Afro-American Religious History: A Documentary Witness. Ed. by Milton C. Sernett. LC 84-24686. xii, 506p. 1985. text ed. 46.50 (ISBN 0-8223-0591-7); pap. text ed. 16.95 (ISBN 0-8223-0594-1). Duke.

Afro-American Religious Music: A Bibliography & a Catalogue of Gospel Music. Compiled by Irene V. Jackson. LC 78-60527. (Illus.). 1979. lib. bdg. 35.00 (ISBN 0-313-20560-4, JGM/). Greenwood.

Afro-Caribbean Religions. Ed. by Brian Gates. 1985. 30.00x (ISBN 0-686-81323-5, Pub. by Ward Lock Educ Co Ltd). State Mutual Bk.

After a Funeral. Diana Athill. 176p. 1986. 15.95 (ISBN 0-89919-454-0). Ticknor & Fields.

After Auschwitz: Essays in Contemporary Judaism. Richard J. Rubenstein. (Orig.). 1966. pap. 10.28 scp (ISBN 0-672-61150-3). Bobbs.

After Auschwitz: Radical Theology & Contemporary Judism. Richard L. Rubenstein. 1966. pap. text ed. write for info. (ISBN 0-02-404210-2). Macmillan.

After Death-Life in God. Norman Pittenger. 96p. 1980. 4.95 (ISBN 0-8164-0108-X, HarpR). Har-Row.

After Death: The Immortality of Man. Paschal B. Randolph. 272p. 1970. write for info. (ISBN 0-932785-00-X). Philos Pub.

After Death, What? William S. Deal. 1977. 1.75 (ISBN 0-686-19329-6). Crusade Pubs.

After Death, What? Gerald C. Studer. LC 75-38074. 160p. 1976. pap. 1.95 (ISBN 0-8361-1792-1). Herald Pr.

After Death, What? rev. ed. Leoline L. Wright. Ed. by W. Emmett Small & Helen Todd. (Theosophical Manual: No. 5). 96p. 1974. pap. 2.50 (ISBN 0-913004-15-4). Point Loma Pub.

After Dionysus: An Essay on Where We Are Now. Henry Ebel. LC 70-156321. 136p. 1972. 15.00 (ISBN 0-8386-7958-7). Fairleigh Dickinson.

After Eden: History, Ecology, & Conscience. Michael Tobias. LC 83-73257. 376p. (Orig.). 1985. pap. 14.95 (ISBN 0-932238-28-9, Pub. by Avant Bks). Slawson Comm.

After Every Wedding Comes a Marriage. Florence Littauer. LC 81-80023. 208p. (Orig.). 1981. pap. 5.95 (ISBN 0-89081-289-6). Harvest Hse.

After First Principles. Gary Underwood & Marylyn Underwood. 1984. pap. 4.25 (ISBN 0-89137-710-7). Quality Pubns.

After Fundamentalism: The Future of Evangelical Theology. Bernard L. Ramm. LC 82-47792. 226p. 1984. text ed. 14.37i (ISBN 0-06-066791-5, RD 473, HarpR); pap. 9.95 (HarpR). Har-Row.

After God's Heart. Myrna Alexander. (Woman's Workshop Ser.). 160p. (Orig.). 1982. pap. 3.95p (ISBN 0-310-37141-4, 10921). Zondervan.

After Its Kind. rev. ed. Byron C. Nelson. (Illus.). 1967. pap. 5.95 (ISBN 0-87123-008-9). Bethany Hse.

After My House Burned Down. Elaine Ward. 88p. (Orig.). 1982. pap. 6.95 (ISBN 0-940754-11-8). Ed Ministries.

After Nine Hundred Years: The Background of the Schism Between the Eastern & Western Churches. Yves M. Conger. LC 78-6154. 1978. Repr. of 1959 ed. lib. bdg. 22.50x (ISBN 0-313-20493-4, COAN). Greenwood.

After One Hundred Fifty Years: The Latter-Day Saints in Sesquicentennial Perspective. Jan Shipps et al. Ed. by Thomas G. Alexander & Jessie L. Embry. (Charles Redd Monographs in Western History: No. 13). (Illus.). 207p. (Orig.). 1983. pap. 6.95 (ISBN 0-941214-08-7, Dist. by Signature Bks). C Redd Ctr.

After Revival Comes. O. S. Hawkins. LC 81-66090. 1981. pap. 4.95 (ISBN 0-8054-6231-7). Broadman.

After Suicide. John H. Hewett. LC 79-24373. (Christian Care Bks.: Vol. 4). 118p. 1980. pap. 7.95 (ISBN 0-664-24296-0). Westminster.

After Suicide. Samuel E. Wallace. LC 73-9793. Repr. of 1973 ed. 71.30 (ISBN 0-8357-9833-X, 2012586). Bks Demand UMI.

After the Adoption. Elizabeth Hormann. 1987. 8.95. Revell.

After the Bomb: Plight to Utopia. Vernon Wilkinson. 154p. (Orig.). 1984. pap. 11.95 (ISBN 0-86474-003-4, Pub. by Interface Press). ANZ Religious Pubns.

After the Reformation: Essays in Honor of J. H. Hexter. Ed. by Barbara C. Malament. LC 79-5254. 256p. 1980. 36.95x (ISBN 0-8122-7774-0). U of Pa Pr.

After the Revival-What? Robert L. Sumner. 1980. pap. 3.95 (ISBN 0-914012-22-3, Pub. by Bibl Evang Pr). Sword of Lord.

After the Sacrifice. Walter A. Henrichsen. 1979. pap. 5.95 (ISBN 0-310-37711-0, 11231P). Zondervan.

After the Spirit Comes. Jack R. Taylor. LC 73-93908. 1975. 7.95 (ISBN 0-8054-5224-9). Broadman.

After the Spirit Comes. Roger W. Thomas. LC 77-83659. 1979. pap. 2.25 (ISBN 0-87239-194-9, 40049). Standard Pub.

After the Tassel Is Moved. Louis Caldwell. (Ultra Bks Ser.). 1968. 4.95 (ISBN 0-8010-2332-7). Baker Bk.

After the Way Called Heresy. Thomas H. Weisser. (Illus.). 131p. pap. 5.95 (ISBN 0-9610710-0-1). Tom Weisser.

After We Die, What Then? George W. Meek. LC 79-90909. (Life's Energy Fields Ser.: Vol. 3). (Illus., Orig.). 1980. 8.95 (ISBN 0-935436-00-6). Metascience.

After We Die, What Then? rev. ed. George W. Meek. LC 79-909. (Illus.). 216p. 1987. pap. 8.95 (ISBN 0-89804-099-X). Ariel OH.

After You Say I Do. Norm Wright. LC 79-66960. 80p. (Orig.). 1979. pap. 4.95 (ISBN 0-89081-205-5). Harvest Hse.

Afterglow of Christ's Resurrection. Alger M. Fitch, Jr. LC 75-14692. (New Life Bks). (Illus.). 136p. 1975. pap. 3.95 (ISBN 0-87239-055-1, 40030). Standard Pub.

Afterlife. Colin Wilson. 288p. 1987. 16.95 (ISBN 0-385-23765-0, Dolp). Doubleday.

Agada: The Language of Jewish Faith. Samuel E. Karff. 15.00x (ISBN 0-87820-114-9). Ktav.

Against Dogmatism & Sectarianism. V. I. Lenin. 215p. 1978. 4.95 (ISBN 0-8285-0066-5, Pub. by Progress Pubs USSR). Imported Pubns.

Against False Union. 2nd ed. Alexander Kalomiros. Tr. by George Gabriel from Greek. (Illus., Orig.). 1979. pap. 2.50x (ISBN 0-913026-20-4). St Nectarios.

Against Fate. Glenn Tinder. LC 81-50462. 173p. 1981. text ed. 16.95 (ISBN 0-268-00595-8). U of Notre Dame Pr.

Against John Hick: An Examination of His Philosophy of Religion. Terry R. Mathis. 148p. (Orig.). 1985. lib. bdg. 22.00 (ISBN 0-8191-4512-2); pap. text ed. 9.25 (ISBN 0-8191-4513-0). U Pr of Amer.

Against Julian. St. Augustine. LC 77-81347. (Fathers of the Church Ser.: Vol. 35). 407p. 1957. 21.95x (ISBN 0-8132-0035-0). Cath U Pr.

Against Method. Paul Feyerabend. (Illus.). 1978. pap. 7.95 (ISBN 0-8052-7008-6, Pub by NLB). Schocken.

Against the Academicians. Saint Augustine. Tr. by Sr. M. Patricia Garvey. (Mediaeval Philosophical Texts in Translation). 1957. pap. 7.95 (ISBN 0-87462-202-6). Marquette.

Against the Apocalypse: Responses to Catastrophe in Modern Jewish Culture. David G. Roskies. LC 83-18663. (Illus.). 392p. 1986. pap. 9.95 (ISBN 0-674-00916-9). Harvard U Pr.

Against the Christians. Thomas Taylor. 119p. 1980. 10.00 (ISBN 0-89005-301-4). Ares.

Against the Gates of Hell. Judith Adams. 152p. pap. 2.50 (ISBN 0-87509-232-2). Chr Pubns.

Against the Manichees. Saint Serapion. Ed. by Robert P. Casey. (Harvard Theological Studies). 1931. pap. 15.00 (ISBN 0-527-01015-4). Kraus Repr.

Against the Nations: War & Survival in a Liberal Society. Stanley Hauerwas. 240p. (Orig.). 1985. 19.95 (ISBN 0-86683-957-7, AY8549, HarpR). Har-Row.

Against the Protestant Gnostics. Philip J. Lee, Jr. 288p. 1987. 18.95 (ISBN 0-19-504067-8). Oxford U Pr.

Against the Tide: An Autobiography. Adam C. Powell, Sr. Ed. by Edwin S. Gaustad. LC 79-52603. (Baptist Tradition Ser.). 1980. Repr. of 1938 ed. 27.50x (ISBN 0-405-12468-6). Ayer Co Pubs.

Against the Tide: Jewish Nonconformist Views of Israel & Zionism. Bezalel Chaim. 1979. lib. bdg. 42.95 (ISBN 0-686-24783-3). M Buber Pr.

Agape: An Ethical Analysis. Gene Outka. LC 78-88070. (Publications in Religion Ser.: No. 17). 336p. 1972. 33.00x (ISBN 0-300-01384-1); pap. 8.95x (ISBN 0-300-02122-4). Yale U Pr.

Agape & History: A Theological Essay on Historical Consciousness. Hiroshi Obayashi. LC 80-1683. 356p. (Orig.). 1981. pap. text ed. 15.25 (ISBN 0-8191-1713-7). U Pr of Amer.

Agape & the Eucharist in the Early Church: Studies in the History of Christian Love Feasts. J. F. Keating. LC 71-79511. Repr. of 1901 ed. 27.50 (ISBN 0-404-03640-6). AMS Pr.

Agartha: A Journey to the Stars. Meredith L. Young. LC 84-50109. (Illus.). 340p. (Orig.). 1984. pap. 9.95 (ISBN 0-913299-01-4). Stillpoint.

Agathiae Myrinaei Historiarum Libri quinque. Agathias. Ed. by Rudolfus Keydell. (Corpus Fontium Historiae Byzantinae Ser. Berolinensis Vol. 2). 232p. (Lat). 1967. 40.40x (ISBN 3-11-001348-7). De Gruyter.

Agathias: The Histories. Tr. by J. D. Frendo from Lat. (Corpus Fontium Historiae Byzantinae: Vol. 2a). Tr. of Agathiae Myrinaei Historiarum libri quinque. iv, 170p. 1975. 51.00x (ISBN 3-11-003357-7). De Gruyter.

Age of Abbot Desiderius: Montecassino, the Papacy & the Normans in the Eleventh & Early Twelfth Centuries. H. E. Cowdrey. 1983. 55.00x (ISBN 0-19-821939-3). Oxford U Pr.

Age of Catherine de Medici. J. E. Neale. 272p. 1978. pap. 6.50 (ISBN 0-224-60566-6, Pub. by Jonathan Cape). Salem Hse Pubs.

Age of Constantine & Julian. Diana Bowder. (Illus.). 230p. 1978. text ed. 32.50x (ISBN 0-06-490601-9, 06359). B&N Imports.

Age of Crisis: Man & World in Eighteenth Century French Thought. Lester G. Crocker. LC 59-14233. (Goucher College Ser.). Repr. of 1959 ed. 129.00 (ISBN 0-8357-9260-9, 2011983). Bks Demand UMI.

Age of Dryden. R. Garnett. 1977. Repr. of 1909 ed. lib. bdg. 17.50 (ISBN 0-8495-1902-0). Arden Lib.

Age of Dryden. facsimile ed. Richard Garnett. LC 70-164601. (Select Bibliographies Reprint Ser). Repr. of 1895 ed. 20.00 (ISBN 0-8369-5885-3). Ayer Co Pubs.

Age of Dryden. Richard Garnett. 1973. Repr. of 1895 ed. 17.50 (ISBN 0-8274-1280-0). R West.

Age of Faith. Will Durant. (Story of Civilization: Vol. 4). (Illus.). 1950. 32.95 (ISBN 0-671-01200-2). S&S.

Age of Gold, Age of Iron: Renaissance Spain & Symbols of Monarchy. Barbara Von Barghahn. (Imperial Legacy of Charles V & Philip II Royal Castles, Palace-Monasteries, Princely Houses Ser.: 2 vols.). (Illus.). 1036p. 1985. Set. lib. bdg. 204.75 (ISBN 0-8191-4739-7). U Pr of Amer.

Age of Guptas & Other Essays. R. N. Dandekar. 1982. 30.00 (ISBN 0-8364-0916-7, Pub. by Ajanta). South Asia Bks.

Age of Milton. J. Howard Masterman. 1906. Repr. lib. bdg. 15.00 (ISBN 0-8414-6453-7). Folcroft.

Age of Miracles. Morton Kelsey. LC 78-74095. 80p. 1979. pap. 2.45 (ISBN 0-87793-169-0). Ave Maria.

Age of Reformation. E. Harris Harbison. LC 76-10816. (Development of Western Civilization Ser). (Illus.). 145p. (Orig.). (YA) 1955. 5.95x (ISBN 0-8014-9844-9). Cornell U Pr.

Age of Reformation. E. Harris Harbison. LC 82-2985. (Development of Western Civilization Ser.). xiv, 145p. 1982. Repr. of 1955 ed. lib. bdg. 22.50x (ISBN 0-313-23555-4, HAAGR). Greenwood.

Age of Religious Wars, Fifteen Fifty-Nine to Seventeen Fifteen. 2nd ed. Richard S. Dunn. (Illus.). 1979. pap. text ed. 7.95x (ISBN 0-393-09021-3). Norton.

Age of Renaissance & Reformation. Charles G. Nauert, Jr. LC 81-40034. 330p. 1982. lib. bdg. 30.25 (ISBN 0-8191-1861-3); pap. text ed. 12.75 (ISBN 0-8191-1862-1). U Pr of Amer.

Age of the Cathedrals: Art & Society, 980-1420. Georges Duby. Tr. by Eleanor Levieux & Barbara Thompson. LC 80-22769. (Illus.). vi, 312p. 1981. 26.00x (ISBN 0-226-16769-0); pap. 11.95 (ISBN 0-226-16770-4). U of Chicago Pr.

Age of the Crusades. James M. Ludlow. 1977. lib. bdg. 59.95 (ISBN 0-8490-1405-0). Gordon Pr.

Age of the Fathers, 2 Vols. William Bright. LC 77-113564. Repr. of 1903 ed. Set. 85.00 (ISBN 0-404-01077-6). Vol. 1 (ISBN 0-404-01078-4). Vol. 2 (ISBN 0-404-01079-2). AMS Pr.

Age of the Gods. Christopher Dawson. LC 68-9653. (Illus., Maps, Tabs). 1971. Repr. of 1928 ed. 35.00x (ISBN 0-86527-001-5). Fertig.

Age of the Reformation. Roland H. Bainton. LC 83-25145. 192p. pap. 7.50 (ISBN 0-89874-736-8). Krieger.

Age of the Renaissance & Reformation: A Short History. J. Russell Major. LC 73-107245. (Orig.). 1970. pap. text ed. 5.50i (ISBN 0-397-47195-5). Har-Row.

Age of the World: Moses to Darwin. Francis C. Haber. LC 77-13854. 1978. Repr. of 1959 ed. lib. bdg. 22.50x (ISBN 0-8371-9898-4, HAAW). Greenwood.

Ageless Wisdom of Life. Clara M. Codd. LC 67-8630. 1967. pap. 1.75 (ISBN 0-8356-0145-5, Quest). Theos Pub Hse.

Ageless Wisdom of Life. Clara M. Codd. 4.95 (ISBN 0-8356-7329-4). Theos Pub Hse.

Agencies for Project Assistance: Sources of Support for Small Church & or Lay Sponsored Projects in Africa, Asia, Latin America & the Pacific. 2nd ed. Pierre Aubin & George Cotter. (Illus.). 330p. 1984. pap. 50.00 (ISBN 0-913671-03-7). Mission Proj Serv.

Agency & Urgency: The Origin of Moral Obligation. Thomas E. Wren. 169p. 1974. 9.95 (ISBN 0-913750-06-9). Precedent Pub.

Agenda for American Jews. Eli Ginzberg. 90p. 1964. pap. 4.50 (ISBN 0-935457-12-7). Reconstructionist Pr.

Agenda for Biblical People. rev. ed. Jim Wallis. LC 83-48995. 160p. 1984. pap. 6.95 (ISBN 0-06-069234-0, RD 514, HarpR). Har-Row.

Agenda for the "Sexual Revolution" Abortion, Contraception, Sex Education & Related Evils. K. D. Whitehead. 1981. 8.95 (ISBN 0-317-46866-9). Franciscan Herald.

Agenda for Theology. Thomas C. Oden. LC 78-19506. 1979. pap. text ed. 11.00 (ISBN 0-06-066347-2, HarpR). Har-Row.

Ages & Dispensations. Frank M. Boyd. 112p. 1955. pap. 1.50 (ISBN 0-88243-463-2, 02-0463). Gospel Pub.

Aggai, Zacharia, Malachia, Jona, Joel, Abdia. Carroll Stuhlmueller. (Bible Ser.). pap. 1.00 (ISBN 0-8091-5000-X). Paulist Pr.

Aggressive Christianity. Catherine Booth. (Writings of Catherine Booth Ser.). 1986. Repr. of 1880 ed. deluxe ed. 4.95 (ISBN 0-86544-031-X). Salvation Army.

Aging. Helen Lancaster. 1980. pap. 4.50 (ISBN 0-8309-0290-2). Herald Hse.

Aging: A Time for New Learning. David J. Maitland. LC 86-46038. 192p. (Orig.). 1987. pap. 9.95 (ISBN 0-8042-1107-8). John Knox.

Aging & the Human Spirit: A Reader in Religion & Gerontology. 2nd ed. Ed. by Carol LeFevre & Perry LeFevre. LC 84-72932. 367p. 1985. text ed. 24.95x (ISBN 0-913552-27-5); pap. text ed. 12.95x (ISBN 0-913552-28-3). Exploration Pr.

Aging in America. Bert K. Smith. LC 72-6232. 256p. 1973. pap. 5.95 (ISBN 0-8070-2769-3, BP502). Beacon Pr.

Aging Together, Serving Together: A Guide to Congregational Planning for the Aging. Fredrick J. Schenk & James V. Anderson. LC 10-185. 40p. (Orig.). 1982. pap. 3.50 (ISBN 0-8066-1963-5, 10-0185). Augsburg.

Aglow in the Kitchen. Aglow Staff. 160p. 1976. 4.95 (ISBN 0-930756-21-5, 532001). Aglow Pubns.

Aglow Prayer Diary I. Aglow Editors. 226p. 1982. 10.95 (ISBN 0-930756-70-3). Aglow Pubns.

Aglow with the Spirit: How to Receive the Baptism in the Holy Spirit. Robert C. Frost. 1965. pap. 2.95 (ISBN 0-912106-64-6). Bridge Pub.

Agni Review. Ed. by Sharon Dunn. 1985. 4.00. Agni Review.

Agni Yoga. 5th ed. (Agni Yoga Ser.). 1980. Index 12.00 (ISBN 0-933574-04-5). Agni Yoga Soc.

Agnipurana, 4 pts, Pt. III. Tr. by N. Gangadharan from Sanskirt. (Ancient Indian Tradition & Mythology: Vol. 29). 210p. 1986. 18.50 (ISBN 81-208-0174-1, Pub. by Motilal Banarsidass India). Orient Bk Dist.

Agnosticism & Theism in the Nineteenth Century. Richard A. Armstrong. 1977. lib. bdg. 59.95 (ISBN 0-8490-1406-9). Gordon Pr.

Agnosticism Is Also Faith. George G. Strem. LC 85-90970. 1986. 15.00 (ISBN 0-87212-194-1). Libra.

Agony & the Triumph: Papers on the Use & Abuse of Myth. Herbert Weisinger. x, 283p. 1964. 5.00 (ISBN 0-87013-081-1). Mich St U Pr.

Agony at Galloway: One Church's Struggle with Social Change. W. J. Cunningham. LC 79-56698. 1980. 3.95 (ISBN 0-87805-117-1). U Pr of Miss.

Agony! Can the Church Survive Without Jesus? Mary Bernard. LC 79-84343. 1979. pap. 2.95 (ISBN 0-89221-059-1). New Leaf.

Agony in the Garden. Lawrence J. Babin. LC 75-158476. 1971. deluxe ed. 3.00x (ISBN 0-912492-25-2); pap. 1.00 (ISBN 0-912492-00-7). Pyquag.

Agony of Deception. Ron Rigsbee & Dorothy Bakker. LC 83-81285. 288p. (Orig.). 1983. pap. 6.95 (ISBN 0-910311-07-2). Huntington Hse Inc.

Agony of Grief. Jewell N. Jackson. LC 85-52320. (Illus.). 96p. (Orig.). 1986. pap. 8.95 (ISBN 0-934955-02-6). Watercress Pr.

Agony of Jesus. Padre Pio. 40p. 1974. pap. 1.00 (ISBN 0-89555-097-0). TAN Bks Pubs.

Agricultural Colonization of the Zionist Organization in Palestine. Arthur Ruppin. Tr. by R. J. Feiwel from Ger. LC 75-6451. (Rise of Jewish Nationalism & the Middle East Ser). vii, 209p. 1975. Repr. of 1926 ed. 20.35 (ISBN 0-88355-337-6). Hyperion Conn.

Agricultural Mission of Churches & Land-Grant Universities: A Report of an Informal Consultation. Ed. by Dietert T. Hessel & John T. Conner. 1979. pap. text ed. 8.50x (ISBN 0-8138-0920-7). Iowa St U Pr.

Agricultural Social Gospel in America: The Gospel of the Farm. Jenkin L. Jones. Ed. & intro. by Thomas E. Graham. (Studies in American Religion: Vol. 19). 349p. 1986. lib. bdg. 59.95x (ISBN 0-88946-663-7). E Mellen.

Agyptische Abendmahlsliturgien Des Ersten Jahrtausends. Theodor Schermann. Repr. of 1912 ed. 19.00 (ISBN 0-384-53730-8). Johnson Repr.

Agyptische Religion Nach der Darstellung der Kirchenschriftsteller und Die Agyptischen Denkmale. Friedrich Zimmermann. 15.00 (ISBN 0-384-71000-X). Johnson Repr.

Agyptischen Totenstelen Als Zeugen Des Sozialen und Religiosen Lebens Ihrer Zeit. Balthasar Portner. pap. 8.00 (ISBN 0-384-47040-8). Johnson Repr.

Ah, Sweet Mystery. Mel Belanger. (Illus.). 150p. (Orig.). 1983. pap. text ed. 5.00 (ISBN 0-9608146-8-X). Western Sun Pubns.

Ah This! Bhagwan Shree Rajneesh. Ed. by Rajneesh Foundation International. LC 82-24026. (Zen Ser.). 268p. (Orig.). 1982. pap. 8.95 (ISBN 0-88050-502-8). Chidvilas Found.

Ahavat Chesed - Love Mercy: Reader. Abraham Shumsky & Adaia Shumsky. (Mah Tov Hebrew Teaching Ser.: Bk. 2). (Illus.). 1970. text ed. 5.50 (ISBN 0-8074-0175-7, 405304); tchrs'. guide 3.50 (ISBN 0-8074-0176-5, 205305); wkbk. 5.00 (ISBN 0-8074-0177-3, 405303). UAHC.

Ahavath Chesed: The Love of Kindness As Required by G-D. Chafetz Chaim, pseud. Tr. by Leonard Oschry from Hebrew. 1978. pap. 6.95 (ISBN 0-87306-167-5). Feldheim.

Ahavath Chesed: The Love of Kindness As Required by G-D. 2nd & rev. ed. Hafetz Hayyim, pseud. Tr. by Leonard Oschry from Hebrew. Orig. Title: Ahavath Hesed. 1976. 9.95 (ISBN 0-87306-110-1). Feldheim.

Ahimsa: Dynamic Compassion. Nat Altman. LC 80-51548. 150p. (Orig.). 1981. pap. 4.95 (ISBN 0-8356-0537-X, Quest). Theos Pub Hse.

Ahora Brillan las Estrellas. Paquita Berio. (Span.). 134p. (Orig.). 1981. pap. 3.75 (ISBN 0-89922-201-3). Edit Caribe.

Ahora que Creo. Robert Cook. Orig. Title: Now That I Believe. (Span.). 128p. 1984. pap. 3.25 (ISBN 0-8254-1137-8). Kregel.

Ahrimanic Deception. Rudolf Steiner. 20p. (Orig.). 1985. pap. 2.95 (ISBN 0-88010-146-6). Anthroposophic.

Aid for Churchmen, Episcopal & Orthodox. Hans H. Spoer. LC 71-79152. Repr. of 1930 ed. 12.50 (ISBN 0-404-06197-4). AMS Pr.

Aid for the Overdeveloped West. B. Goudzwaard. 1975. pap. 3.50 (ISBN 0-88906-100-9). Wedge Pub.

Aid to Heidelberg Catechism. Theleman. 5.95 (ISBN 0-686-23483-9). Rose Pub MI.

Aiding Talmud Study. 5th ed. Aryeh Carmell. (Illus.). 88p. 1987. 6.95 (ISBN 0-87306-413-5); pap. 4.95 (ISBN 0-87306-428-3). Feldheim.

AIDS, the Spiritual Dilemma. John E. Fortunato. 1987. pap. 7.95. Har-Row.

Aids to Devotions. Andrew Murray. 1961. pap. 2.95 (ISBN 0-87508-378-1). Chr Lit.

Aids to "Revelation". Watchman Nee. Tr. by Stephen Kaung. 1983. pap. 2.75 (ISBN 0-935008-60-8). Christian Fellow Pubs.

Aims of Interpretation. E. D. Hirsch, Jr. LC 75-21269. 1978. pap. 7.00x (ISBN 0-226-34241-7, P767, Phoen). U of Chicago Pr.

Ainu of Japan: The Religion, Superstitions, & General History of the Hairy Aborigines of Japan. John Batchelor. 26.00 (ISBN 0-8369-7153-1, 7985). Ayer Co Pubs.

Aishah: The Beloved of Mohammed. Nabia Abbott. LC 73-6264. (Middle East Ser.). Repr. of 1942 ed. 18.00 (ISBN 0-405-05318-5). Ayer Co Pubs.

Aitareya Brahmanam of Rigveda: Containing the Earliest Speculations of the Brahmans on the Meaning of the Sacrificial Prayers, & on the Origin, Performance & Sense of the Rites of the Vedic Religion. Ed. & tr. by Martin Haug. LC 73-3830. (Sacred Books of the Hindus: Extra Vol. 4). Repr. of 1922 ed. 27.50 (ISBN 0-404-57848-9). AMS Pr.

Aitareya Upanisat, 2 pts. in 1. Tr. by Srisa Chandra Vidyarnava & Mohan L. Sandal. LC 73-3823. (Sacred Books of the Hindus: No. 30, Pts. 1-2). Repr. of 1925 ed. 14.50 (ISBN 0-404-57830-6). AMS Pr.

Aitareyopanisad. Tr. by Swami Sarvananda. (Sanskrit & English). pap. 1.00 (ISBN 0-87481-463-4). Vedanta Pr.

Aitereya Upanishad. Tr. by Swami Gambhirananda from Sanskrit. (Upanishads with Shankara's Commentary Ser.). 75p. 1980. pap. 1.25 (ISBN 0-87481-200-3). Vedanta Pr.

AJS Review, Vol. 1. Ed. by F. Talmage. 1976. 20.00x (Pub. by Assoc. for Jewish Studies). Ktav.

AJS Review, Vol. 2. Ed. by F. Talmage. 1977. 20.00x (ISBN 0-685-55539-9, Pub. by Assoc. for Jewish Studies). Ktav.

Ajustarse o Autodestruirse. Craig Massey. Orig. Title: Adjust or Self-Destruct. (Span.). 144p. 1983. pap. 3.50 (ISBN 0-8254-1470-9). Kregel.

Akdamus. Avrohon Y. Salamon. (Art Scroll Mesorah Ser.). 160p. 1978. 11.95 (ISBN 0-89906-154-0); pap. 8.95 (ISBN 0-89906-155-9). Mesorah Pubns.

Akiba. Marcus Lehmann. Tr. by Joseph Leftwich. 7.95 (ISBN 0-87306-120-9). Feldheim.

Akiba: Scholar, Saint & Martyr. Louis Finkelstein. LC 62-12354. (Temple Bks). 1970. pap. text ed. 6.95x (ISBN 0-689-70230-2, T11). Atheneum.

Al-Dhabh. Ta Ha. 3.95 (ISBN 0-686-83897-1). Kazi Pubns.

Al Ghazali: On the Duties of Brotherhood. Tr. by Muhtar Holland. LC 76-8057. 96p. 1976. 10.00 (ISBN 0-87951-046-3); pap. 7.95 (ISBN 0-87951-083-8). Overlook Pr.

Al ibanah 'an usul addiyanah. A. H. Ali ibn Isma'il et al. Tr. by W. C. Klein. (American Oriental Ser.: Vol. 19). 1940. 18.00 (ISBN 0-527-02693-X). Kraus Repr.

Al-Islam bain Jahl 'Abna'ihi wa Ajz Ulama'ihi. Abdul Q. Audah. (Arabic.). 79p. (Orig.). 1980. pap. 1.55x (ISBN 0-939830-12-4, Pub. by IIFSO Kuwait). New Era Pubns MI.

Al-Islam, Christianity, & Freemasonry. Mustafa El-Amin. 214p. (Orig.). 1985. pap. 6.95 (ISBN 0-933821-05-0). New Mind Prod.

Al-Kafi: The Book of Divine Proof, II. Al-Kulayni Ar-Razi. Tr. by S. Muhammad Hasan-Rizvi from Arabic. LC 85-52242. 80p. (Orig.). 1985. pap. 6.00 (ISBN 0-940368-65-X). Tahrike Tarsile Quran.

Al-Kafi: The Book of Divine Proof, IV. Al-Kulayni Ar-Razi. Tr. by S. Muhammad Hasan-Rizvi from Arabic. LC 85-52242. 90p. (Orig.). 1986. pap. 12.00 (ISBN 0-940368-66-8). Tahrike Tarsile Quran.

Al-Kafi: The Book of Divine Proof, No. I. Al-Kulayni Ar-Razi. Tr. by S. Muhammad Rizvi from Arabic. LC 85-52242. 90p. (Orig.). 1985. pap. 12.00 (ISBN 0-940368-64-1). Tahrike Tarsile Quran.

Al-Kafi: The Book of Divine Proof, No. V. Al-Kulayni Ar-Razi. Tr. by S. Muhammad Rizvi from Arabic. LC 85-52242. 80p. (Orig.). 1985. pap. 12.00 (ISBN 0-940368-67-6). Tahrike Tarsile Quran.

Al-Kafi: The Book of Divine Unity. Al-Kulayni Ar-Razi. Tr. by S. Muhammad Rizvi from Arabic. LC 85-52265. 70p. (Orig.). 1985. pap. 12.00 (ISBN 0-940368-62-5). Tahrike Tarsile Quran.

Al-Kafi: The Book of Excellence of Knowledge. Al-Kulayni Ar-Razi. Tr. by S. Muhammad Rizvi from Arabic. LC 85-52264. 72p. (Orig.). 1985. pap. 12.00 (ISBN 0-940368-61-7). Tahrike Tarsile Quran.

Al-Kafi: The Book of Reason & Ignorance. Al-Kulayni Ar-Razi. Tr. by S. Muhammad Rizvi from Arabic. LC 85-52263. 72p. (Orig.). 1985. pap. 12.00 (ISBN 0-940368-63-3). Tahrike Tarsile Quran.

Al-Mizan: An Exegesis of the Qur'an, Vol. 1. S. Muhammad Husayn at-Tabatabai & Akhtar-Rizvi S. Saeed. LC 85-52243. 366p. (Orig.). 1985. pap. 30.00 (ISBN 0-940368-57-9). Tahrike Tarsile Quran.

Al-Mizan: An Exegesis of the Qur'an, Vol. 4. S. Muhammad Husayn at-Tabatabai. Tr. by S. Saeed Rizvi from Arabic. LC 85-52243. 336p. (Orig.). 1985. pap. 30.00 (ISBN 0-940368-59-5). Tahrike Tarsile Quran.

Al-Mizan: An Exegesis of the Qur'an, Vol. 5. S. Muhammad Husayn at-Tabatabai. Tr. by S. Saeed Rizvi from Arabic. LC 85-52243. 288p. (Orig.). 1985. pap. 30.00 (ISBN 0-940368-60-9). Tahrike Tarsile Quran.

Al-Mizan: En Exegesis of the Quran, Vol. 3. S. Muhammad At-Tabatabai. Tr. by S. Saeed Rizvi from Arabic. LC 85-52243. 334p. (Orig.). 1985. pap. 30.00 (ISBN 0-940368-58-7). Tahrike Tarsile Quran.

Al-Muqaddasi: Revelation of the Secrets of the Birds & Flowers. 1980. 18.95 (ISBN 0-900860-75-8). Ins Study Human.

Al-Mustaqbal li-hadha ad-Din. Sayyid Qutb. (Arabic.). 118p. (Orig.). 1978. pap. 2.35x (ISBN 0-939830-16-7, Pub. by IIFSO Kuwait). New Era Pubns MI.

Al-Niffari, Muhammad ibn'Abdi 'L-Jabbar. Ed. & tr. by A. J. Arberry. 276p. 1985. Repr. of 1978 ed. 50.00x (ISBN 0-317-39030-9, Pub. by Luzac & Co Ltd). State Mutual Bk.

Al-Qur'anal-Karim, The Holy Qur'an: Surah Al-Fatiha, Section 1 of Surah Baqarah, Ayatul Kursi, Surah Nas thru Surah Naba with Modern English Translations, & Reading Guide, Prayer modes & Qaidah, Pt. 30. Muhammad S. Haque. LC 84-63148. (Arabic & Eng., Illus.). viii, 80p. (Orig.). 1985. pap. text ed. 3.00 (ISBN 0-933057-02-4). Namuk Intl Inc.

Al Rasa'El. Molana-al-Moazam Hazrat Shah & Maghsoud Sadegh-ibn-Mohammad Angha. 146p. (Orig.). 1986. lib. bdg. 22.50 (ISBN 0-8191-5331-1); pap. text ed. 10.25 (ISBN 0-8191-5332-X). U Pr of Amer.

Al-Salat. Allama M. Asifi. 1983. pap. 4.00 (ISBN 0-941724-10-7). Islamic Seminary.

Al Who? J. Alastair Haig. LC 80-52617. 270p. (Orig.). 1980. pap. cancelled (ISBN 0-932260-05-5). Paraclete Pr.

Alabado, a Story of Old California. Paul Kocher. 1978. 6.95 (ISBN 0-8199-0689-1). Franciscan Herald.

Alabanza a la Disciplina. Richard Foster. Tr. by M. Francisco Lievano from Eng. Tr. of Celebration of Discipline. (Span.). 224p. 1986. pap. 4.95 (ISBN 0-88113-012-5). Edit Betania.

Alabanza Que Libera. Judson Cornwall. 160p. 1976. 2.75 (ISBN 0-88113-002-8). Edit Betania.

Alamo & Other Texas Missions to Remember. Nancy H. Foster. LC 84-647. (Illus.). 96p. (Orig.). 1984. pap. 9.95x (ISBN 0-88415-033-X, Lone Star Bks). Gulf Pub.

Alan of Lille: The Frontiers of Theology in the Twelfth Century. G. R. Evans. LC 83-1834. 240p. 1983. 54.50 (ISBN 0-521-24618-0). Cambridge U Pr.

Alani Priors Cantuariensis Postea Abbatis Tewkesberiensis Scripta Quae Extant. Alan of Tewkesbury. Ed. by J. A. Giles. 1966. Repr. of 1848 ed. 24.00 (ISBN 0-8337-1340-X). B Franklin.

Alaska. Paul Bills. LC 80-65307. (Illus.). 160p. (Orig.). 1980. pap. 2.50 (ISBN 0-88243-462-4, 02-0462). Gospel Pub.

Alaskan John G. Brady: Missionary, Businessman, Judge, & Governor, 1878-1918. Ted C. Hinckley. LC 81-19030. (Illus.). 415p. 1982. 40.00x (ISBN 0-8142-0336-1). Ohio St U Pr.

Alberni's India: An Account of the Religion, Philosophy, Literature, Geography, Chronology, Astronomy, Customs, Laws & Astrology of India about AD 1030, 2 vols. Al-Biruni. Tr. by Edward C. Sachau. Repr. of 1888 ed. Set. text ed. 54.00x. Coronet Bks.

Albert Camus. Carol Petersen. Tr. by Alexander Gode. LC 68-31455. (Literature & Life Ser.). 1969. 12.95 (ISBN 0-8044-2691-0). Ungar.

Albert Camus: A Biography. Herbert Lottman. LC 80-68394. (Illus.). 753p. 1981. pap. 8.95 (ISBN 0-8076-0998-6). Braziller.

Albert Schweitzer. Albert Schweitzer. Ed. by Ann Repath. Tr. by Richard Winston & Clara Winston. (Living Philosophies Ser.). (Illus.). 32p. (YA) 1985. PLB 8.95 (ISBN 0-88682-013-8). Creative Ed.

Albert Schweitzer: An International Bibliography. Nancy S. Griffith & Laura Person. 1981. lib. bdg. 47.00 (ISBN 0-8161-8531-X, Hall Reference). G K Hall.

Albert Schweitzer: Genius in the Jungle. Joseph Gollomb. (Illus.). 149p. 1949. 10.95 (ISBN 0-8149-0308-8). Vanguard.

Albert Schweitzer Jubilee Book. Ed. by A. A. Roback. LC 79-97392. (Illus.). 508p. Repr. of 1945 ed. lib. bdg. 24.50x (ISBN 0-8371-2670-3, ASJB). Greenwood.

Albert Schweitzer's Mission: Healing & Peace. Norman Cousins. 1985. 16.95 (ISBN 0-393-02238-2). Norton.

Albert the Great: Commemorative Essays. Ed. by Francis J. Kovach & Robert W. Shahan. LC 79-6713. 250p. 1980. 16.95x (ISBN 0-8061-1666-8). U of Okla Pr.

Alberuni's India. abr. ed. Ed. by Ainslie Embree. Tr. by Edward C. Sachau. 1971. pap. 2.75x (ISBN 0-393-00568-2, Norton Lib). Norton.

Albigeois. 2nd ed. Celestin Douais. LC 78-63182. (Heresies of the Early Christian & Medieval Era: Second Ser.). Repr. of 1879 ed. 64.50 (ISBN 0-404-16221-5). AMS Pr.

Albion: A Guide to Legendary Britain. Jennifer Westwood. (Illus.). 448p. 1986. 18.95 (ISBN 0-88162-128-5). Salem Hse Pubs.

Albizuri Among the Lyngams: A Brief History of the Catholic Mission Among the Lyngams on North East India. Sebastian Karotemprel. 1986. 17.50x (ISBN 0-8364-1569-8, Pub. by KL Mukhopadhyay). South Asia Bks.

Albrecht Von Eyb, Medieval Moralist. Joseph A. Hiller. LC 70-140027. (Catholic University Studies in German Ser.: No. 13). 1970. Repr. of 1939 ed. 25.00 (ISBN 0-404-50233-4). AMS Pr.

Album of Bible Characters. John Waddey. pap. 5.50 (ISBN 0-89137-542-2). Quality Pubns.

Alchemical Imagery in Bosch's "Garden of Delights". Laurinda S. Dixon. Ed. by Linda Seidel. LC 81-14673. (Studies in Fine Arts: Iconography: No. 2). 250p. 1981. 49.95 (ISBN 0-8357-1247-8). UMI Res Pr.

Alchemist to Mercury. Robert Kelly. 230p. 1981. 30.00 (ISBN 0-913028-82-7); pap. 7.95 (ISBN 0-686-69476-7). North Atlantic.

Alchemy, Ancient & Modern. H. Stanley Redgrove. (Illus.). 141p. 1980. 20.00 (ISBN 0-89005-344-8). Ares.

Alchemy of Happiness. Al-Ghazzali. 1964. 3.75x (ISBN 0-87902-055-5). Orientalia.

Alchemy of the Word: Language & the End of Theology. Carl A. Raschke. LC 79-15490. (American Academy of Religion, Studies in Religion: No. 20). 1979. 14.00 (ISBN 0-89130-319-7, 01-00-20); pap. 9.95 (ISBN 0-89130-320-0). Scholars Pr GA.

Alcohol & Disease. Ed. by Niels Tygstrup & Rolf Olsson. (Illus.). 290p. 1985. text ed. 62.50x (ISBN 91-22-00786-5, Pub. by Almqvist & Wiksell). Coronet Bks.

Alcohol & Other Drugs. 32p. (Orig.). 1982. pap. text ed. 2.90 (ISBN 0-8298-0608-3). Pilgrim NY.

Alcohol & the Bible. Howard H. Charles. LC 66-10970. 40p. 1981. pap. 1.50 (ISBN 0-8361-1941-X). Herald Pr.

Alcohol & the Jews: A Cultural Study of Drinking & Sobriety. Charles R. Snyder. LC 77-24885. (Arcturus Books Paperbacks). 240p. 1978. pap. 6.95x (ISBN 0-8093-0846-0). S Ill U Pr.

Alcohol: The Beloved Enemy. Jack Van Impe. 190p. 1980. pap. 4.95 (ISBN 0-934803-07-2). J Van Impe.

Alcohol y la Familia. P. Frank. 1981. pap. 1.50 (ISBN 0-89243-139-3). Liguori Pubns.

Alcoholic Family. Peter Steinglass et al. LC 86-47741. 320p. 1987. 22.95x (ISBN 0-465-00097-5). Basic.

Alcoholism Recovery. Billy Prasch. 60p. 1984. pap. 2.00 (ISBN 0-8198-0725-7). Dghtrs St Paul.

Alcuin & Charlemagne: Studies in Carolingian History & Literature. Luitpold Wallach. Repr. of 1959 ed. 23.00 (ISBN 0-384-65585-8). Johnson Repr.

Alcuin & the Rise of the Christian Schools. Andrew F. West. LC 73-149674. Repr. of 1892 ed. 10.00 (ISBN 0-404-06908-8). AMS Pr.

Alcuin & the Rise of the Christian Schools. Andrew F. West. 1892. Repr. 9.00x (ISBN 0-403-00031-9). Scholarly.

Alef-Bet: A Hebrew Primer. Abraham Shumsky & Adaia Shumsky. (Illus.). 1979. pap. text ed. 6.00 (ISBN 0-8074-0026-2, 405309). UAHC.

ALEF-Bet: A Primer for a Davenen Universe. Rabbi R. Shapiro. (Illus.). 70p. 1983. pap. 9.95 (ISBN 0-911511-00-8). ENR Word.

Alef-Bet of Jewish Values: Code Words of Jewish Life. Lenore Kipper & Howard Bogot. (Illus.). 64p. 1985. pap. text ed. 6.00 (ISBN 0-8074-0267-2, 101087). UAHC.

Aleph-Bet Book. Rabbi Nachman of Breslov. Tr. & intro. by Moshe Mykoff. Tr. of Sefer HaMiddot. 268p. 1986. text ed. 12.00 (ISBN 0-930213-15-7). Breslov Res Inst.

Aletheia: Spirit of Truth. 2nd ed. Aurelia G. Mace. LC 72-2989. Repr. of 1907 ed. 17.50 (ISBN 0-404-10751-6). AMS Pr.

Alexander Geddes: A Forerunner of Biblical Criticism. R. C. Fuller. (Historic Texts & Interperters Ser.: No. 3). 186p. 1985. text ed. 25.95x (ISBN 0-907459-26-9, Pub. by Almond Pr England); pap. text ed. 12.95x (ISBN 0-907459-27-7). Eisenbrauns.

Alexander Marx Jubilee Volume, 2 vols. Saul Lieberman. 1950. 35.00x (ISBN 0-685-31434-0, Pub. by Jewish Theol Seminary). KTAV.

Alexander of Lycopolis Against Manichaeism. Alexander of Lycopolis. Ed. by Ludwig Koenen. (Reprints & Translations). 1988. pap. write for info. (ISBN 0-89130-895-4, 00-07-12). Scholars Pr GA.

Alexander's Gate, Gog & Magog & the Inclosed Nations. Andrew R. Anderson. 1932. 7.50x (ISBN 0-910956-07-3). Medieval Acad.

Alexandrian Christianity. Ed. by J. E. Oulton & Henry Chadwick. LC 54-10257. (Library of Christian Classics). 472p. 1977. pap. 8.95 (ISBN 0-664-24153-0). Westminster.

Alfa & la Omega. Paul Erb. 230p. 1968. pap. 3.30x (ISBN 0-8361-1111-7). Herald Pr.

Alfred North Whitehead: The Man & His Work, Vol. 1: 1861-1910. Victor Lowe. LC 84-15467. 392p. 1985. 27.50 (ISBN 0-8018-2488-5). Johns Hopkins.

Algo Mas. Catherine Marshall. 171p. 1981. 4.75 (ISBN 0-88113-001-X). Edit Betania.

Alias Jungle Doctor: An Autobiography. Paul White. (Illus.). 236p. 1977. pap. 6.95 (ISBN 0-85364-205-2). Attic Pr.

Alien in Their Midst: Image of Jews in English Literature. Esther L. Panitz. LC 78-75183. 192p. 1981. 20.00 (ISBN 0-8386-2318-2). Fairleigh Dickinson.

Alienation in the Jewish American Novel of the Sixties. Etta K. Bothwell. LC 78-3559. 1979. pap. 10.00 (ISBN 0-8477-3191-X). U of PR Pr.

Alif Ba Ta Islamic Reader. M. A. Qazi. pap. 2.00 (ISBN 0-686-83570-0). Kazi Pubns.

Ali's Dream: The Story of Baha'u'llah. John Hatcher. (Illus.). 260p. 14.95 (ISBN 0-85398-092-6); pap. 8.95 (ISBN 0-85398-093-4). G Ronald Pub.

Alive Again! Bill Banks. 168p. (Orig.). 1977. pap. 3.95 (ISBN 0-89228-048-4). Impact Bks MO.

Alive in Christ. David Womack. LC 75-22609. (Radiant Life Ser.). 128p. 1975. pap. 2.50 (ISBN 0-88243-888-3, 02-0888, Radiant Books); teacher's ed 3.95 (ISBN 0-88243-162-5, 32-0162). Gospel Pub.

Alive in Christ: The Dynamic Process of Spiritual Formation. Maxie D. Dunnam. LC 81-20631. 160p. 1982. 8.75 (ISBN 0-687-00993-6). Abingdon.

Alive in Krishna: Living Memories of the Vedic Quest. Shri B. Birla. (Patterns of World Spirituality Ser.). 160p. 1986. pap. 8.95 (ISBN 0-913757-65-9, Pub. by New Era Bks). Paragon Hse.

Alive in the Spirit. rev. ed. Daughters of St. Paul. (Way, Truth & Life Ser.). (Illus.). 1974. text ed. 2.75 (ISBN 0-8198-0282-4); tchr's manual 6.25 (ISBN 0-8198-0283-2); activity bk. 1.50 (ISBN 0-8198-0284-0); parents' guide 01.25 (ISBN 0-8198-0285-9). Dghtrs St Paul.

Alive in the Spirit: The Church in the Acts of the Apostles. Thomas Smith. (Orig.). 1976. pap. text ed. 5.65x (ISBN 0-88489-081-3); tchr's. ed. 3.00x (ISBN 0-88489-083-X). St Marys.

Alive into the Wilderness: The Story of An Excommunicated Priest. John S. Duryea & Oso Bartlett. (Illus.). 300p. (Orig.). 1984. pap. 9.50 (ISBN 0-9606288-3-5). Coastlight Pr.

Aljeksjej Theodorovich L'vov-director Imperatorskoj pridvornoj pevcheskoj kapelli i dukhovnij kompozitor. Johann V. Gardner. Tr. of Alexei Feodorovitch Lvov-Director of the Emperors Court Capella & Composer of Sacred Music. 90p. 1970. pap. 3.00 (ISBN 0-317-30387-2). Holy Trinity.

All about Angels. C. Leslie Miller. LC 73-82096. 144p. (Orig.). 1973. pap. 3.50 (ISBN 0-8307-0467-1, 5010500). Regal.

All about Bibles. John R. Kohlenberger. (Illus.). 76p. 1985. pap. 0.95 (ISBN 0-19-526951-9). Oxford U Pr.

All about Cells. 2nd rev. ed. Ed. by James D. Craig. 32p. 1981. pap. 2.49 (ISBN 0-88151-017-3). Lay Leadership.

All about Jewish Holidays & Customs. rev. ed. Morris Epstein. 1969. pap. 7.95x (ISBN 0-87068-500-7). Ktav.

All about Love. Stirrup Associates Inc. Ed. by Cheryl M. Phillips & Bonnie C. Harvey. LC 84-50915. (Child's Paraphrase Ser.). (Illus.). 32p. 1984. pap. 1.49 (ISBN 0-937420-16-6). Stirrup Assoc.

All about Pentacost. William S. Deal. 1983. pap. 3.95 (ISBN 0-318-18716-7). Crusade Pubs.

All about Prosperity & How You Can Prosper. Cornelia Addington & Jack Addington. LC 83-73342. (Orig.). 1984. pap. 4.95 (ISBN 0-87516-533-8). De Vorss.

All about Radiation. L. Ron Hubbard. 20.00 (ISBN 0-686-30790-9). Church Scient NY.

All Are Called. Religious Education Commission. 1984. pap. 5.75 (ISBN 0-8309-0391-7). Herald Hse.

All-Around Christmas Book. Margery Cuyler. LC 82-3104. (Illus.). 96p. 1982. 11.95 (ISBN 0-03-060387-0); pap. 4.95 (ISBN 0-03-062183-6). H Holt & Co.

All Faithful People: Change & Continuity in Middletown's Religion. Theodore Caplow et al. LC 82-24759. x, 380p. 1983. 19.50 (ISBN 0-8166-1230-7). U of Minn Pr.

All for Christ: Some Twentieth Century Martyrs. Diana Dewar. 1980. pap. 8.95x (ISBN 0-19-283024-4). Oxford U Pr.

All for Jesus. Compiled by Robert Niklaus et al. LC 86-72007. (Illus.). 322p. 1986. 11.95 (ISBN 0-87509-383-3). Chr Pubns.

All for the Boss. Ruchoma Shain. 439p. 1984. 13.95 (ISBN 0-87306-346-5). Feldheim.

All Fulness Dwells. Bob Jones. 152p. 1971. 4.95 (ISBN 0-89084-002-4). Bob Jones Univ Pr.

All God's Children. Dorothy Gauchat & Arthur Lyons. 224p. 1985. pap. 2.50 (ISBN 0-345-31988-5). Ballantine.

All God's Children Got Dreams. Paul H. Hansen. (Orig.). 1980. pap. 2.95 (ISBN 0-937172-03-0). JLJ Pubs.

All God's Chillun Got Soul. Morrie Turner. 64p. 1980. pap. 3.95 (ISBN 0-8170-0892-6). Judson.

All God's People: Catholic Identity after the Second Vatican Council. Rembert G. Weakland. LC 84-61493. 216p. (Orig.). 1985. pap. 7.95 (ISBN 0-8091-2665-6). Paulist Pr.

All Good Gifts: Crafts for Christian Gift-Giving. Marilyn T. Hagans. LC 82-62924. 128p. (Orig.). 1983. pap. 5.95 (ISBN 0-8091-2543-9). Paulist Pr.

All in All. rev. ed. A. E. Knoch. 222p. 1978. pap. text ed. 4.00 (ISBN 0-910424-74-8). Concordant.

All in All. Anne S. White. 128p. (Orig.). 1980. pap. 2.50 (ISBN 0-9605178-0-4). Victorious Ministry.

All in Good Time. Donna Otto. 240p. 1985. 12.95 (ISBN 0-8407-5963-0). Nelson.

All in My Jewish Family. Union of American Hebrew Congregations. (Illus.). 32p. 1984. pap. 5.00 wkbk. (ISBN 0-8074-0266-4, 103800). UAHC.

All in the Name of Love. Glenn A. Smyly & Barbara J. Smyly. 116p. 1986. 17.95 (ISBN 0-9616707-0-3); pap. 9.95 (ISBN 0-9616707-1-1). Alivening Pubns.

All in the Name of the Bible. 2nd ed. Ed. by Hassan Haddad & Donald Wagner. 130p. 1986. pap. 7.95 (ISBN 0-915597-42-X). Amana Bks.
All Is Grace: The Spirituality of Dorothy Day. William D. Miller. LC 86-1228. 216p. 1987. 14.95 (ISBN 0-385-23429-5). Doubleday.
All Joy. Dianne Balch. LC 82-72303. 169p. 1982. pap. 5.95 (ISBN 0-86605-098-1). Here's Life.
All Knowing God: Researches into the Early Religion & Cultlure. Rattaele Pettazzoni. Ed. by Kees W. Bolle. LC 77-79150. (Mythology Ser.). (Illus.). 1978. Repr. of 1956 ed. lib. bdg. 40.00x (ISBN 0-405-10559-2). Ayer Co Pubs.
All Manner of Men. John M. Allegro. (Illus.). 186p. 1982. spiral bdg. 18.50x (ISBN 0-398-04575-5). C C Thomas.
All Men Are Brothers. M. K. Gandhi. (Modern Classics of Peace Ser). pap. 7.95 (ISBN 0-912018-15-1). World Without War.
All My Love, Kate. Trudy J. Morgan. Ed. by Raymond H. Woolsey. (Banner Ser.). 96p. (Orig.). 1986. pap. 6.50 (ISBN 0-8280-0318-1). Review & Herald.
All Nations in God's Purpose. H. Cornell Goerner. LC 78-50360. 1979. pap. 4.95 (ISBN 0-8054-6312-7). Broadman.
All Nations in God's Purpose: A Study Guide. Frank K. Means. LC 83-21073. 1984. pap. 4.25 (ISBN 0-8054-6334-8). Broadman.
All Nature Sings. Margaret Clarkson. 160p. (Orig.). 1986. pap. 5.95 (ISBN 0-8028-0225-7). Eerdmans.
All-New Super Incredible Bible Study Book on Mark. John C. Souter. 144p. (Orig.). 1985. pap. 3.95 (ISBN 0-310-45881-1, 12475P). Zondervan.
All-Occasion Craft & Gift Book. Sally Stuart. (Illus.). 96p. (Orig.). 1984. pap. 5.95 (ISBN 0-87239-709-2, 2138). Standard Pub.
All-Occasion Sermon Outlines. Eric W. Hayden. (Sermon Outline Ser.). pap. 2.50 (ISBN 0-8010-4206-2). Baker Bk.
All of Grace. C. H. Spurgeon. 1978. pap. 2.25 (ISBN 0-686-00497-3). Pilgrim Pubns.
All of Grace. C. H. Spurgeon. 144p. 1981. pap. 2.95 (ISBN 0-88368-097-1). Whitaker Hse.
All of Grace. Charles Spurgeon. Tr. by Ruth T. Chen & Peter Chou. (Chinese.). 142p. 1984. pap. write for info. (ISBN 0-941598-22-5). Living Spring Pubns.
All of Grace. Charles H. Spurgeon. (Moody Classics Ser.). 1984. pap. 3.50 (ISBN 0-8024-0001-9). Moody.
All of the Women of the Bible. Edith Deen. LC 55-8621. 1955. 18.45 (ISBN 0-06-061810-8, HarpR). Har-Row.
All Our Losses, All Our Griefs: Resources for Pastoral Care. Kenneth R. Mitchell & Herbert Anderson. LC 83-19851. 180p. (Orig.). 1983. pap. 8.95 (ISBN 0-664-24493-9). Westminster.
All Our Vows. Ruth Shamir. LC 82-61795. 1983. 11.95 (ISBN 0-88400-090-7). Shengold.
All Round Ministry. C. H. Spurgeon. 1978. pap. 7.45 (ISBN 0-85151-181-3). Banner of Truth.
All-Round Ministry. C. H. Spurgeon. 1983. pap. 4.95 (ISBN 0-686-09107-8). Pilgrim Pubns.
All Series, Bks. 1-14. Herbert Lockyer. Incl. Bk. 1. All the Apostles of the Bible. 15.95 (ISBN 0-310-28010-9, 10052); Bk. 2. All the Books & Chapters of the Bible; Bk. 3. All the Doctrines of the Bible. 15.95 (ISBN 0-310-28050-8, 10082); Bk. 4. All the Children of the Bible; Bk. 5. All the Holy Days & Holidays; Bk. 6. All the Kings & Queens of the Bible; Bk. 7. All the Men of the Bible. 15.95 (ISBN 0-310-28080-X, 10054); Bk. 8. All the Women of the Bible. 14.95 (ISBN 0-310-28150-4, 10038); Bk. 9. All the Miracles of the Bible. 16.95 (ISBN 0-310-28100-8, 10066); Bk. 10. All the Parables of the Bible. 15.95 (ISBN 0-310-28110-5, 10075); Bk. 11. All the Prayers of the Bible. 15.95 (ISBN 0-310-28120-2, 10041); Bk. 12. All the Promises of the Bible. 16.95 (ISBN 0-310-28130-X, 10074); Bk. 13. All the Trades & Occupations of the Bible; Bk. 14. All the Messianic Prophecies of the Bible. 19.95 (ISBN 0-310-28090-7, 10076). Zondervan.
All Shall Be Well: The Spirituality of Julian of Norwich for Today. Robert Llewelyn. 160p. 1985. pap. 7.95 (ISBN 0-8091-2668-0). Paulist Pr.
All Silver & No Brass: An Irish Christmas Mumming. Henry Glassie. 1983. 9.95 (ISBN 0-8122-1139-1). U of Pa Pr.
All Slave-Keepers That Keep the Innocent in Bondage, Apostates Pretending to Lay Claim to the Pure & Holy Christian Religion. Benjamin Lay. LC 72-82203. (Anti-Slavery Crusade in America Ser). 1969. Repr. of 1737 ed. 12.00 (ISBN 0-405-00642-X). Ayer Co Pubs.
All-Sufficient Christ: Studies in Paul's Letter to the Colossians. William Barclay. LC 63-18385. 142p. 1963. pap. 6.95 (ISBN 0-664-24480-7). Westminster.
All That I Have. Helene Curtis & Cliff Dudley. LC 77-81394. 1979. pap. 2.95 (ISBN 0-89221-044-3). New Leaf.
All That We Are We Give. James G. Fairfield. LC 77-14510. 192p. 1977. pap. 5.95 (ISBN 0-8361-1839-1). Herald Pr.
All the Days of Lent. Colane Recker. LC 78-73825. (Illus.). 64p. 1978. pap. 2.45 (ISBN 0-87793-168-2). Ave Maria.
All the Divine Names & Titles in the Bible. Herbert Lockyer. 352p. 1975. 15.95 (ISBN 0-310-28040-0, 10077). Zondervan.
All the Fulness of God: Essays on Orthodoxy, Ecumenism & Modern Society. Thomas Hopko. LC 82-5454. 188p. (Orig.). 1982. pap. 7.95 (ISBN 0-913836-96-6). St Vladimirs.
All the Good Gifts: On Doing Bible Stewardship. Wallace E. Fisher. LC 79-50077. 1979. pap. 5.95 (ISBN 0-8066-1702-0, 10-0227). Augsburg.
All the People & Places of the Bible. Ed. by J. I. Packer et al. LC 82-12564. 1982. pap. 6.95 (ISBN 0-8407-5819-7). Nelson.
All the Plants of the Bible. Winifred Walker. LC 78-22802. (Illus.). 1979. Repr. of 1957 ed. 15.95 (ISBN 0-385-14964-6). Doubleday.
All the Questions You Ever Wanted to Ask American Atheists with All the Answers. 2nd ed. Jon Murray & Madalyn O'Hair. 248p. (Orig.). 1986. pap. 7.00 (ISBN 0-910309-24-8). Am Atheist.
All the Seasons of Mercy. Diane Karay. LC 86-18948. 156p. (Orig.). 1987. pap. 7.95 (ISBN 0-664-24067-4). Westminster.
All These Lutherans: Three Paths Toward a New Lutheran Church. Todd Nichol. LC 86-3638. (Illus.). 128p. (Orig.). 1986. pap. 6.95 (ISBN 0-8066-2208-3, 10-0228). Augsburg.
All These Things Shall Give Thee Experience. Neal A. Maxwell. LC 79-26282. 144p. 1979. 7.95 (ISBN 0-87747-796-5). Deseret Bk.
All Things Are Possible: Humorous Interpretations of Scripture. Jere Moorman. 96p. (Orig.). 1983. pap. 3.00 (ISBN 0-915561-00-X). Crane Pubns CA.
All Things Are Possible: The Charles Cullum Lessons. Charles G. Cullum. LC 86-5819. 176p. (Orig.). 1986. pap. 7.95 (ISBN 0-937641-00-6). Stone Canyon Pr.
All Things Are Possible: The Healing & Charismatic Revivals in Modern America. David E. Harrell, Jr. LC 75-1937. (Midland Bks.: No. 221). (Illus.). 320p. 1976. 20.00x (ISBN 0-253-10090-9); pap. 8.95x (ISBN 0-253-20221-3). Ind U Pr.
All Things Are Possible Through Prayer. Charles L. Allen. 1984. pap. 2.95 (ISBN 0-515-08808-0, PV072). Jove Pubns.
All Things Are Possible Through Prayer. Charles L. Allen. o. p. 7.95 (ISBN 0-8007-0007-4); pap. 2.95 (ISBN 0-8007-8000-0, Spire Bks). Revell.
All Things Bright & Beautiful. Cheryl W. Bellville. 64p. (Orig.). 1983. pap. 7.95 (ISBN 0-86683-722-1, AY8363, HarpR). Har-Row.
All Things for Good. Thomas Watson. (Puritan Paperbacks). 128p. (Orig.). 1986. pap. 3.45 (ISBN 0-85151-478-2). Banner of Truth.
All Things in Their Time. LaWant P. Jack. pap. 5.95 (ISBN 0-89036-145-2). Hawkes Pub Inc.
All Things New. Arthur E. Bloomfield. LC 42-5300. 1959. pap. 7.95 (ISBN 0-87123-007-0); study guide 1.95 (ISBN 0-87123-520-X). Bethany Hse.
All Things New. Jessie Penn-Lewis. 1962. pap. 2.95 (ISBN 0-87508-990-9). Chr Lit.
All Things to All Men. Ralph V. Reynolds. Ed. by Mary H. Wallace. 128p. 1983. pap. 4.95 (ISBN 0-912315-01-6). Word Aflame.
All Those Mothers at the Manger. Norma Farber. LC 85-42610. (Illus.). 32p. 1985. 11.25i (ISBN 0-06-021869-X); PLB 10.89g (ISBN 0-06-021870-3). HArpJ.
All Truth is God's Truth. Arthur F. Holmes. LC 83-18411. 148p. 1983. pap. 4.95 (ISBN 0-87784-818-1). Inter-Varsity.
All Year Long. Debby Anderson. (Sparklers Ser.). 1986. comb binding 2.95 (ISBN 1-55513-043-7, Chariot Bks). Cook.
Allah or the God of the Bible: What Is the Truth? Basilea Schlink. 1984. pap. 2.50 (ISBN 0-551-01140-8, Pub. by Marshall Morgan & Scott UK). Evang Sisterhood Mary.
Alleged Discrepancies of the Bible. John W. Haley. (Direction Bks.). 1977. pap. 7.95 (ISBN 0-8010-4171-6). Baker Bk.
Alleged Discrepancies of the Bible. John W. Haley. 480p. 1984. pap. text ed. 3.95 (ISBN 0-88368-157-9). Whitaker Hse.
Allegheny Gospel Trails. Virginia Crider. (Illus.). 1971. 7.50 (ISBN 0-87813-502-2). Christian Light.
Allegoria und Anagoge bei Didymos dem Blinden von Alexandria. Wolfgang A. Bienert. (Patristische Texte und Studien Ser.: Vol. 13). xii, 188p. 1972. 23.20x (ISBN 3-11-003715-7). De Gruyter.
Allegory & the Migration of Symbols. Rudolf Wittkower. LC 86-50689. (Illus.). 224p. 1987. pap. 14.95 (ISBN 0-500-85004-6). Thames Hudson.
Allegory, Myth, & Symbol. Ed. by Morton W. Bloomfield. (Harvard English Studies: 9). 440p. 1982. text ed. 32.50x (ISBN 0-674-01640-8); pap. text ed. 10.95x (ISBN 0-674-01641-6). Harvard U Pr.
Allgemeine Kirchenordnung Fruehchristliche Liturgien und Kirchliche Ueberlieferung, 3 pts. Theodor Schermann. Repr. of 1914 ed. Set. 55.00 (ISBN 0-384-53740-5). Johnson Repr.
Allgemeine Mythologie und Ihre Ethnologischen Grundlagen. Paul Ehrenreich. Ed. by Kees W. Bolle. LC 77-79125. (Mythology Ser.). 1978. Repr. of 1915 ed. lib. bdg. 34.50x (ISBN 0-405-10536-3). Ayer Co Pubs.
Alliance of Divine Offices. Hamon L'Estrange. LC 71-172316. (Library of Anglo-Catholic Theology: No. 12). Repr. of 1846 ed. 27.50 (ISBN 0-404-52104-5). AMS Pr.
Alliluija (Liturgijnaja), 8-mi Glasov. Johann V. Gardner. Tr. of Alleluia (for Divine Liturgy) Eight Tones. 1966. pap. 3.00 (ISBN 0-317-30391-0). Holy Trinity.
Allow Divine Energy to Help You. George Snelling. 181p. pap. 4.95 (ISBN 0-934142-03-3). Vancento Pub.
Alma. Pamela Robison. 90p. 1985. pap. 5.75 (ISBN 0-8309-0409-3). Herald Hse.
Almacen de Dios: Exodo, 16 Lecciones, Vol. 2. Bernice C. Jordan. (Pasos De Fe Ser.). (Span.). pap. text ed. 2.50 tchrs'. manual (ISBN 0-86508-403-3); figuras 8.95 (ISBN 0-86508-404-1). BCM Intl Inc.
Almah: Virgin or Young Woman? George Lawlor. LC 73-76072. 1973. pap. 1.50 (ISBN 0-87227-036-X). Reg Baptist.
Almighty & the Dollar Workbook. Jim McKeever. 1980. 23.95. Omega Pubns OR.
Almost Grown: A Christian Guide for Parents of Teenagers. James Oraker & Char Meredith. LC 78-20585. 192p. 1982. pap. 6.95 (ISBN 0-06-066398-7, RD 380, HarpR). Har-Row.
Almost Twelve. Kenneth N. Taylor. 1968. pap. 2.50 (ISBN 0-8423-0060-0). Tyndale.
Alone Again. Richard Krebs. LC 77-84085. 1978. pap. 5.95 (ISBN 0-8066-1611-3, 10-0240). Augsburg.
Alone, Again! Hildreth Scott. (Uplook Ser.). 1976. pap. 0.99 (ISBN 0-8163-0251-0, 01496-9). Pacific Pr Pub Assn.
Alone of All Her Sex: The Myth & the Cult of the Virgin Mary. Marina Warner. LC 82-40051. (Illus.). 488p. 1983. pap. 10.95 (ISBN 0-394-71155-6, Vin). Random.
Alone with God: A Manual of Biblical Meditation. Campbell McAlpine. 1981. pap. 5.95 (ISBN 0-87123-000-3, 210000). Bethany Hse.
Alone with God: A Place for Your Time Together. Ron DelBene & Herb Montgomery. 120p. (Orig.). 1984. pap. 4.95 (ISBN 0-86683-856-2, 8434, HarpR). Har-Row.
Alone with Others. Stephen Batchelor. Ed. by Hannelore Rosset. LC 82-21054. (Grove Press Eastern Philosophy & Religion Ser.). 144p. 1983. pap. 5.95 (ISBN 0-394-62457-2, E843, Ever). Grove.
Alone with the Alone. George A. Maloney. LC 81-70021. (Illus.). 208p. (Orig.). 1982. pap. 4.95 (ISBN 0-87793-243-3). Ave Maria.
Along an Inner Shore: Echoes from the Gospel. Brother Leonard of Taize. 144p. (Orig.). 1986. pap. 8.95 (ISBN 0-8298-0733-0). Pilgrim NY.
Along the Rio Grande: A Pastoral Visit to Southern New Mexico in 1902. Henry Granjon. Ed. by Michael R. Taylor. Tr. by Mary W. De Lopez from Fr. LC 86-11390. (Illus.). 153p. 1986. 17.50x (ISBN 0-8263-0903-8); pap. 8.95 (ISBN 0-8263-0904-6, Co-pub. by Historical Society of New Mexico). U of NM Pr.
Along the Royal Way. Francoise De Salignac de la Mothe-Fenelon. Ed. by Hal M. Helms. LC 83-61406. (Living Library Ser.). 152p. (Orig.). 1984. pap. 5.95 (ISBN 0-941478-20-3). Paraclete Pr.
Along the Way. Donald N. Bastian. 128p. 1977. pap. 3.95 (ISBN 0-89367-008-1). Light & Life.
Along Thimblelane Trails. V. Gilbert Beers. LC 81-14197. (Muffin Family Ser.). 96p. 1981. 11.95 (ISBN 0-8024-0298-4). Moody.
Alouette. Jean Anouilh. 1963. pap. 3.95 (ISBN 0-685-10991-7, 1153). French & Eur.
Alpha & Omega: Essays on the Trinity in Honor of James A. Nichols, Jr. Ed. by Caroleen Hillriegel et al. 140p. (Orig.). 1980. pap. 4.50 (ISBN 0-913439-01-0). Henceforth.
Alpha: The Myths of Creation. Charles H. Long. LC 82-21532. (AAR-SP Classics in Religious Studies). 320p. 1982. Repr. of 1963 ed. 13.50x (ISBN 0-89130-604-8, 01-05-04). Scholars Pr GA.
Alpha thru Omega Bible Survey. Eva J. Hruska. LC 85-90314. 1985. pap. 3.95 (ISBN 0-9614616-1-6); tchr's. ed. 7.95 (ISBN 0-9614616-0-8). Eva Hruska.
Alphabet Book. Illus. by Marc Harrison. (Bible Look 'N Learn Bks.). (Illus.). 24p. 1985. bds. 3.95 (ISBN 0-8407-6685-8). Nelson.
Alphabet of God. Nora E. Larson. LC 81-66071. (Illus.). 56p. (Orig.). 1981. pap. 4.00 (ISBN 0-87516-450-1). De Vorss.
Alphabet of Grace. Frederick Buechner. LC 84-48765. 128p. 1985. 12.45 (ISBN 0-06-061173-1, HarpR). Har-Row.
Alphabetical Arrangement of Main Entries from the Shelf List of the Union Theological Seminary Library, 10 Vols. Union Theological Seminary. Library. 1960. Set. 1415.00 (ISBN 0-8161-0595-2, Hall Library). G K Hall.
Already to Harvest. Hartman Rector, Jr. 91p. 1985. 7.95 (ISBN 0-934126-67-4); pap. 4.95 (ISBN 0-934126-73-9). Randall Bk Co.
Alrightniks Row: The Making of a Professional Jew, Haunch, Paunch & Jowl. Samuel Ornitz. Ed. by Milley Gabriel. LC 85-40730. (Masterworks of Modern Jewish Writing Ser.). 320p. 1986. 18.85 (ISBN 0-910129-49-5, Distributed by Schocken Books); pap. 9.95 (ISBN 0-910129-46-0). Wiener Pub Inc.
Altar Flowers: A Bouquet of Choicest Sanskrit Hymns. Ed. by Advaita Ashrama Staff. (Eng. & Sanskrit). 1974. pap. 5.95 (ISBN 0-87481-146-5). Vedanta Pr.
Altar Guild: A Guide for the Ministry of Liturgical Preparations. S. Anita Stauffer. 64p. 1978. pap. 2.95 (ISBN 0-8006-1321-X, 1-1321). Fortress.
Altar Guild Book. Barbara Gent & Betty Sturges. LC 82-80469. (Illus.). 104p. (Orig.). 1982. pap. 5.95 (ISBN 0-8192-1305-5, 82-80469). Morehouse.
Altar Guild Handbook. Anne K. LeCroy & Marion J. Hatchett. 108p. (Orig.). 1986. pap. 4.95 (ISBN 0-86683-784-1, HarpR). Har-Row.
Altar Guild Handbook. S. Anita Stauffer. LC 85-47713. 128p. 1985. pap. 5.95 (ISBN 0-8006-1868-8, 1-1868). Fortress.
Altar Guild Manual. Edith W. Perry. (Orig.). 1945. pap. 2.95 (ISBN 0-8192-1067-6). Morehouse.
Altar Prayer Workbook A. rev. ed. Earl Albrecht. Ed. by Michael L. Sherer. 1986. 7.75 (ISBN 0-89536-812-9, 6841). CSS of Ohio.
Altar Prayer Workbook B: (Common-Luth) Earl Albrecht. 1984. 7.75 (ISBN 0-89536-688-6, 4865). CSS of Ohio.
Altar Service of the Protestant Episcopal Church. write for info. Oxford U Pr.
Altchristliche Basiliken und Lokaltraditionen in Sudjudaa. Andreas E. Mader. pap. 19.00 (ISBN 0-384-35000-3). Johnson Repr.
Alten Uebersetzungen des Neuen Testaments, die Kirchenvaeterzitate und Lektionare: Der Gegenwaertige Stand Ihrer Erforschung und Ihre Bedeutung fuer die Griechische Textgeschichte. Ed. by Kurt Aland. (Arbeiten zur neutestamentlichen Textforschung 5). xxiv, 590p. 1972. 62.40x (ISBN 3-11-004121-9). De Gruyter.
Alter Worker's Manual. 2nd ed. Jeff C. Perry. 61p. 1982. pap. 3.00 (ISBN 0-933643-07-1). Grace World Outreach.
Alter Your Life. Emmet Fox. 1950. 12.45 (ISBN 0-06-062850-2, HarpR). Har-Row.
Alternate Celebrations Catalogue. Ed. by Milo Shannon-Thornberry. LC 82-3638. (Illus.). 192p. 1982. pap. 8.95 (ISBN 0-8298-0601-6). Pilgrim NY.
Alternate States of Consciousness. Ed. by Norman E. Zinberg. LC 76-46722. 1977. 14.95 (ISBN 0-02-935770-5); pap. text ed. 7.95 (ISBN 0-02-935930-9). Free Pr.
Alternative Altars: Unconventional & Eastern Spirituality in America. Robert S. Ellwood. LC 78-15089. (Chicago History of American Religion Ser.). 1979. lib. bdg. 12.95x (ISBN 0-226-20618-1); pap. 5.50x (ISBN 0-226-20620-3). U of Chicago Pr.
Alternative Christianity. John Punshon. 1982. pap. 2.50x (ISBN 0-87574-245-9, 245). Pendle Hill.
Alternative Futures for Worship, 7 vols. Incl. Vol. 1. General Introduction. Michael A. Cowan et al. Ed. by Regis A. Duffy. 176p (ISBN 0-8146-1493-0); Vol. 2. Baptism & Confirmation. Andrew D. Thompson et al. 152p (ISBN 0-8146-1494-9); Vol. 3. The Eucharist. John H. Westerhoff, III et al. 176p (ISBN 0-8146-1495-7); Vol. 4. Reconciliation. Denis J. Woods et al. Ed. by Peter E. Fink. 160p (ISBN 0-8146-1496-5); Vol. 5. Marriage. William Roberts et al. Ed. by Bernard Cooke. 80p (ISBN 0-8146-1497-3); Vol. 6. Leadership Ministry in Community. David N. Power et al. Ed. by Michael A. Cowan. 176p (ISBN 0-8146-1498-1); Vol. 7. Anointing of the Sick. Mary F. Duffy et al. 152p (ISBN 0-8146-1499-X). 1987. Set. pap. 49.00 (ISBN 0-8146-1491-4); pap. 8.95 ea. Liturgical Pr.
Alternative Goals in Religion: Love, Freedom, Truth. George B. Burch. 1973. pap. 3.95 (ISBN 0-7735-0163-0). McGill-Queens U Pr.
Alternative Lifestyles Confront the Church. Dean W. Ferm. 144p. 1983. pap. 8.95 (ISBN 0-8164-2394-6, HarpR). Har-Row.

Alternative Readings in the Hebrew of the Books of Samuel. Otto H. Bostrom. LC 18-8964. (Augustana College Library Publication Ser.: No. 8). 60p. 1918. pap. 0.75 (ISBN 0-910182-05-1). Augustana Coll.

Alternative Tradition: A Study of Unbelief in the Ancient World. James A. Thrower. (Religon & Society Ser.). 1979. 38.00 (ISBN 90-279-7997-9). Mouton.

Alternative Views of the Bible. John Bloore. 1978. Repr. of 1925 ed. lib. bdg. 20.00 (ISBN 0-8495-0366-3). Arden Lib.

Alternative Vision: An Interpretation of Liberation Theology. Roger S. Haight. (Orig.). 1985. 10.95 (ISBN 0-8091-2679-6). Paulist Pr.

Alternatives. William L. Fischer. LC 79-67005. 1980. 5.95 (ISBN 0-87159-000-X). Unity School.

Altgermanische Religionsgeschichte: History of Ancient Germanic Religion. Richard M. Meyer. Ed. by Kees W. Bolle. LC 77-79143. (Mythology Ser.). (Ger.). 1978. Repr. of 1910 ed. lib. bdg. 49.50x (ISBN 0-405-10552-5). Ayer Co Pubs.

Altitude of Prayer. Joel S. Goldsmith. Ed. by Lorainne Sinkler. LC 74-25082. 160p. 1975. 9.45 (ISBN 0-06-063171-6, HarpR). Har-Row.

Altostniederfraenkischen Psalmenfragmente: Die Lipsius'schen Glossen & Die Altsuedmittelfraenkischen Psalmenfragmente. Ed. by William L. Van Helten. 222p. 1970. 30.00 (ISBN 0-384-22230-7). Johnson Repr.

Altspanischer Kirchenbau. A. S. Frischauer. (Studien zur spaetantiken Kunstgeschichte, Vol. 3). (Illus.). x, 100p. 1978. Repr. of 1930 ed. 58.80x (ISBN 3-11-005703-4). De Gruyter.

Alttestamentliche Namengebung in England. Arnold Meier. pap. 9.00 (ISBN 0-685-13337-0). Johnson Repr.

Alttestamentlichen Perikopen der Reihen III-VI. Karl-Heinz Hecke. (European University Studies Twenty-Three: Vol. 180). (Ger.). 203p. 1982. 24.20 (ISBN 3-8204-5759-3). P Lang Pubs.

Always Advancing. R. Daniel Reeves & Ronald Jenson. LC 83-73182. 196p. (Orig.). 1984. pap. 8.95 (ISBN 0-86605-120-1, 403188). Campus Crusade.

Always Being Reformed: The Future of Church Education. Ed. by John C. Purdy. LC 85-953. 120p. 1985. pap. 7.95 (ISBN 0-664-24655-9, A Geneva Press Publication). Westminster.

Always Growing. (Benziger Family Life Program Ser.). 8p. 1978. 3.00 (ISBN 0-02-651850-3); tchrs. ed. 4.15 (ISBN 0-02-651860-0); family handbook 1.80 (ISBN 0-02-651890-2). Benziger Pub Co.

Always with Jesus. Daughters of St. Paul. 1973. 3.95 (ISBN 0-8198-0265-4); pap. 2.95 (ISBN 0-8198-0714-1). Dghtrs St Paul.

Alzare Mis Ojos. Santiago Canclini. (Span.). 316p. 1984. pap. 7.95 (ISBN 0-311-40047-7). Casa Bautista.

Am I an Atheist or an Agnostic. Bertrand Russell. 32p. pap. cancelled (ISBN 0-911826-96-3). Am Atheist.

Am I Living A Spiritual Life? Adrian van Kaam & Susan Muto. 4.95 (ISBN 0-87193-173-7). Dimension Bks.

Am I My Brother's Keeper? facs. ed. Ananda K. Coomaraswamy. LC 67-23196. (Essay Index Reprint Ser.). 1947. 12.00 (ISBN 0-8369-0335-8). Ayer Co Pubs.

Am I Saved? Theodore Bobosh. 1984. pap. 3.45 (ISBN 0-937032-38-7). Light&Life Pub Co MN.

Am I the Only One Here with Faded Genes? Marie Chapian. (Teen Devotionals Ser.). (Illus.). 192p. 1987. pap. 5.95 (ISBN 0-87123-945-0). Bethany Hse.

Am Seguliah: A Treasured People. Eli L. Cooper. LC 82-91010. 148p. 1984. 10.00 (ISBN 0-533-05673-X). Vantage.

Amal & the Shi'a: Struggle for the Soul of Lebanon. Augustus R. Norton. (Modern Middle East Ser.: No. 13). (Illus.). 264p. 1987. text ed. 25.00x (ISBN 0-292-73039-X); pap. 10.95 (ISBN 0-292-73040-3). U of Tex Pr.

Amate Siquiera un Poco. Cecil G. Osborne. Tr. by Julio Orozco from Eng. LC 78-57808. Tr. of Art of Learning to Love Yourself. (Span.). 182p. 1978. pap. 4.95 (ISBN 0-89922-120-3). Edit Caribe.

Amazing Acts. Ivor Powell. 1987. 18.95 (ISBN 0-8254-3526-9). Kregel.

Amazing Adventures of the Jewish People. Max I. Dimont. LC 84-16806. 175p. (YA) 1984. pap. 3.95 (ISBN 0-87441-391-5). Behrman.

Amazing Body Human. Mark P. Cosgrove. 160p. 1987. pap. 7.95 (ISBN 0-8010-2517-6). Baker Bk.

Amazing Discoveries in the Words of Jesus. Gordon Lindsay. 4.50 (ISBN 0-89985-112-6). Christ Nations.

Amazing Discoveries Within the Book of Books. Ralph Woodrow. (Illus.). 1979. pap. 4.95 (ISBN 0-916938-04-2). R Woodrow.

Amazing Discovery of the Holy Ghost. Esward H. Pallenberg. (Illus.). 98p. 1984. pap. 23.75 (ISBN 0-89266-487-8). Am Classical Coll Pr.

Amazing Grace. 1978. 4.95 (ISBN 0-8378-2014-6). Gibson.

Amazing Grace & Her Incredible Place. Tom Tozer. 1984. 4.75 (ISBN 0-89536-706-8, 4802). CSS of Ohio.

Amazing Laws of Cosmic Mind Power. Joseph Murphy. 1965. pap. 4.95 (ISBN 0-13-023804-X, Reward). P-H.

Amazing Love. Corrie ten Boom. (Orig.). 1982. pap. 2.50 (ISBN 0-515-06735-0). Jove Pubns.

Amazing Love. John R. Dewitt. 160p. (Orig.). 1981. pap. text ed. 5.45 (ISBN 0-85151-328-X). Banner of Truth.

Amazing Results of Positive Thinking. Norman V. Peale. 1982. pap. 2.75 (ISBN 0-449-20304-2, Crest). Fawcett.

Amazing Secrets of Psychic Healing. Benjamin O. Bibb & Joseph J. Weed. 1976. pap. 5.95 (ISBN 0-13-023762-0). P-H.

Amazing Secrets of the Masters of the Far East. Robert Collier. pap. 6.95 (ISBN 0-912576-16-2). R Collier.

Amazing Secrets of the Mystic East. Norvell. cancelled 14.95 (ISBN 0-13-023754-X, Parker). P-H.

Amazonian Cosmos: The Sexual & Religious Symbolism of the Tukano Indians. Gerardo Reichel-Dolmatoff. Tr. by Gerardo Reichel-Dolmatoff from Span. LC 73-133491. xxiv, 290p. 1974. pap. 7.95X (ISBN 0-226-70732-6, P574, Phoen). U of Chicago Pr.

Ambassadors for Christ. John Hendee. (Ambassadors Training Program Ser.). 64p. (Orig.). 1984. pap. 2.95 trainer's manual (ISBN 0-87239-812-9, 3221); student book 2.50 (ISBN 0-87239-813-7, 3222). Standard Pub.

Ambassadors of Armstrongism. Paul N. Benware. 182p. (Orig.). 1984. pap. 5.95 (ISBN 0-87508-046-4). Chr Lit.

Ambiguity in Moral Choice. Richard A. McCormick. (Pere Marquette Theology Lectures). 1977. pap. 7.95 (ISBN 0-87462-505-X). Marquette.

Ambition: Friend or Enemy? Frederick C. Van Tatenhove. LC 84-5199. (Potentials; Guides for Productive Living Ser.: Vol. 11). 120p. 1984. pap. 7.95 (ISBN 0-664-24530-7). Westminster.

Ambrose Wathan: Silence. LC 74-188556. (Cistercian Studies: No. 22). 10.95 (ISBN 0-87907-822-7). Cistercian Pubns.

Amen, Brother Ben: A Mississippi Collection of Children's Rhymes. Marice C. Brown. LC 78-32017. 1979. pap. text ed. 5.00 (ISBN 0-87805-094-9). U Pr of Miss.

Amen-Worte Jesu: Eine Untersuchung zum Problem der Legitimation in Apokalyptischer Rede. Klaus Berger. (Beiheft 39 Zur Zeitschrift fuer Die neutestamentliche Wissenschaft Ser.). (Ger). 1970. 20.80x (ISBN 3-11-006445-6). De Gruyter.

America & Americanism. 1986. pap. 6.95 (ISBN 0-916786-82-X). St George Bk Serv.

America & Palestine: The Attitude of Official America & of the American People Toward the Rebuilding of Palestine As a Free & Democratic Jewish Commonwealth. Ed. by Reuben Fink & Davis Moshe. LC 77-70680. (America & the Holy Land Ser.). 1977. Repr. of 1944 ed. lib. bdg. 40.00x (ISBN 0-405-10245-3). Ayer Co Pubs.

America, & the American Church. Henry Caswall. LC 77-83413. (Religion in America Ser). 1969. Repr. of 1839 ed. 21.00 (ISBN 0-405-00234-3). Ayer Co Pubs.

America & the Holocaust. (American Jewish History Ser.: Vol. 70, Pt. 3). 1981. 6.00 (ISBN 0-911934-20-0). Am Jewish Hist Soc.

America & the Holocaust, Vol. I. Ed. by Sanford Pinsker & Jack Fischel. (Holocaust Studies Annual). 200p. 1984. lib. bdg. 15.00 (ISBN 0-913283-02-9). Penkevill.

America & the Holy Land Series, 72 vols. Moshe Davis. (Illus.). 1977. Repr. lib. bdg. 2212.50 (ISBN 0-405-10220-8). Ayer Co Pubs.

America Betrayed. Marlin Maddoux. Orig. Title: Humanism Exposed. 157p. 1984. pap. 5.95 (ISBN 0-910311-18-8). Huntington Hse Inc.

America: Christian or Pagan. Don R. Pegram. 1982. pap. 1.25 (ISBN 0-89265-082-6). Randall Hse.

America, Christian or Secular? Readings in American Christian History. Ed. by Jerry Herbert. LC 84-11478. (Orig.). 1984. pap. 10.95 (ISBN 0-88070-067-X). Multnomah.

America in Travail. Edgar H. Brookes. 1983. pap. 2.50x (ISBN 0-87574-159-2, 159). Pendle Hill.

America Is Too Young to Die. Leonard Ravenhill. LC 79-19229. 128p. 1979. pap. 4.95 (ISBN 0-87123-013-5, 210013). Bethany Hse.

America! Jesus Is Here! Mel Tari & Cliff Dudley. LC 76-1058. 1976. 4.95 (ISBN 0-89221-021-4). New Leaf.

America Mainline Religion: Its Changing Shape of the Religious Establishment. Wade C. Roof & William McKinney. 272p. 1987. text ed. 27.00 (ISBN 0-8135-1215-8); pap. text ed. 10.00 (ISBN 0-8135-1216-6). Rutgers U Pr.

America: Religions & Religion. Catherine L. Albanese. LC 80-21031. (Wadsworth Series in Religion Studies). 389p. 1981. pap. write for info (ISBN 0-534-00928-X). Wadsworth Pub.

America, Russia, & the Antichrist, Vol. 4. Gordon Lindsay. (Daniel Ser.). 0.95 (ISBN 0-89985-051-0). Christ Nations.

American Apocalypse: Yankee Protestants & the Civil War, 1860-1869. James H. Moorhead. LC 77-14360. 1978. 32.00x (ISBN 0-300-02152-6). Yale U Pr.

American Atheist Heritage. Joseph Lewis. Ed. by Madalyn M. O'Hair. (Illus.). 55p. 1981. pap. 4.00 (ISBN 0-911826-28-9). Am Atheist.

American Baptist Heritage in Wales, Vol. 1. Joshua Thomas. 1976. 15.00 (ISBN 0-686-12332-8). Church History.

American Book of Days. Ed. by Jane M. Hatch. LC 78-16239. 1212p. 1978. 73.00 (ISBN 0-8242-0593-6). Wilson.

American Book of Nutrition & Medical Astrology. Eileen Nauman. Ed. by Rebecca Lee. (Illus.). 304p. (Orig.). 1982. pap. 17.95 (ISBN 0-917086-28-7). A C S Pubns Inc.

American Buddhist Directory. 2nd ed. Kevin O'Neil. 116p. (Orig.). 1985. pap. 20.00 (ISBN 0-86627-012-4). Crises Res Pr.

American Buddhist Directory, 1982. Kevin O'Neil. 96p. 1982. pap. 7.00 (ISBN 0-86627-003-5). Crises Res Pr.

American Buddhist Newsletter: 1981-82, Vol. I. Ed. by Kevin R. O'Neil. 136p. (Orig.). 1982. pap. 35.00 (ISBN 0-86627-000-0). Crises Res Pr.

American Catholic: A Social Portrait. Andrew M. Greeley. LC 76-7683. (Illus.). pap. 9.95x (ISBN 0-465-09733-2, TB-5058). Basic.

American Catholic Catechism. Ed. by George Dyer. LC 75-7786. 320p. 1975. (HarpR); pap. 7.95 (ISBN 0-8164-2588-4). Har-Row.

American Catholic Crossroads: Religious-Secular Encounters in the Modern World. Walter J. Ong. LC 80-29660. xi, 160p. 1981. Repr. of 1959 ed. lib. bdg. 22.50x (ISBN 0-313-22467-6, 0NAM). Greenwood.

American Catholic Experience: A History from Colonial Times to the Present. Jay P. Dolan. LC 84-26026. 504p. 1985. 19.95 (ISBN 0-385-15206-X). Doubleday.

American Catholic Experience: A History from Colonial Times to the Present. Jay P. Dolan. 504p. 1987. pap. 10.95 (ISBN 0-385-15207-8, Im). Doubleday.

American Catholic Family. John L. Thomas. LC 80-15221. (Illus.). xii, 471p. 1980. Repr. of 1956 ed. lib. bdg. 37.50x (ISBN 0-313-22473-0, THAC). Greenwood.

American Catholic Leadership: A Decade of Turmoil, 1966-76. James H. Stewart. (Religon & Society Ser.: No. 13). 1978. pap. 13.00x (ISBN 90-279-7884-0). Mouton.

American Catholic Parish: A History from 1850 to the Present. Ed. by Jay P. Dolan. Vol. I: The Northeast, Southeast & South Central States. 19.95t; Vol. II: The Pacific States, Intermountain West & Midwest States. 19.95t (ISBN 0-8091-2854-3). Paulist Pr.

American Catholic Peace Movement, 1928-1972. Patricia F. McNeal. 32.00 (ISBN 0-405-10840-0, 11820). Ayer Co Pubs.

American Catholic People: Their Beliefs, Practices, & Values. George Gallup, Jr. & Jim Castelli. LC 86-16576. 216p. 1987. 15.95 (ISBN 0-385-23122-9). Doubleday.

American Catholic Press & the Jewish State: 1917-1959. E. Y. Feldblum. 25.00x (ISBN 0-87068-325-X). Ktav.

American Catholic Religious Thought. Ed. by Patrick Carey. 1987. pap. 12.95. Paulist Pr.

American Catholic Social Ethics: Twentieth Century Approaches. Charles E. Curran. LC 82-4829. 336p. 1982. 24.95 (ISBN 0-268-00603-2). U of Notre Dame Pr.

American Catholic Social Ethics: Twentieth-Century Approaches. Charles E. Curran. LC 82-4829. 353p. 1984. text ed. 9.95 (ISBN 0-268-00609-1, 85-06099). U of Notre Dame Pr.

American Catholic Tradition. Ed. by Jay P. Dolan. 1893.50 (ISBN 0-405-10810-9). Ayer Co Pubs.

American Catholicism. 2nd ed. John T. Ellis. Ed. by Daniel J. Boorstin. LC 69-19274. (Chicago History of American Civilization Ser.). 1969. pap. 10.00x (ISBN 0-226-20556-8, CHAC5). U of Chicago Pr.

American Catholicism & European Immigrants (1900-1924) Richard M. Linkh. LC 74-79914. vii, 200p. 1974. pap. 9.95x (ISBN 0-913256-17-X). Ctr Migration.

American Catholicism & Social Action: A Search for Social Justice, 1865-1950. Aaron I. Abell. LC 80-16876. 306p. 1980. Repr. of 1963 ed. lib. bdg. 27.50x (ISBN 0-313-22513-3, ABAC). Greenwood.

American Catholics: A History of the Roman Catholic Community in the United States. James Hennesey. 1981. pap. 10.95 (ISBN 0-19-503268-3). Oxford U Pr.

American Catholics: A History of the Roman Catholic Community in the United States. James J. Hennesey. 1981. 19.95x (ISBN 0-19-502946-1). Oxford U Pr.

American Catholics & the Social Question, 1865-1900. James E. Roohan. LC 76-6364. (Irish Americans Ser). 1976. 37.50 (ISBN 0-405-09356-X). Ayer Co Pubs.

American Catholics & Vietnam. Ed. by Thomas E. Quigley. LC 68-54102. pap. 49.30 (ISBN 0-317-07878-X, 2012814). Bks Demand UMI.

American Catholics in the War: National Catholic War Council, 1917-1921. Michael Williams. LC 74-75244. (United States in World War 1 Ser.). x, 467p. 1974. Repr. of 1921 ed. lib. bdg. 26.95x (ISBN 0-89198-110-1). Ozer.

American Catholics Since the Council: An Unauthorized Report. Andrew M. Greeley. (Illus.). 240p. (Orig.). 1985. pap. 14.95 (ISBN 0-88347-191-4). Thomas More.

American Charities & the Child of the Immigrant: Study of Typical Child Caring Institutions New York & Massachusetts-1845-1880, Vol. 6. Francis E. Lane. LC 74-1691. (Children & Youth Ser.). 188p. 1974. Repr. of 1932 ed. 18.00x (ISBN 0-405-05967-1). Ayer Co Pubs.

American Children of Krsna: Case Studies in Cultural Anthrology. Francine J. Daner. LC 75-15616. 1976. pap. text ed. 9.95 (ISBN 0-03-013546-X, HoltC). HR&W.

American Christian Bible. Thomas Jefferson. LC 82-80548. 128p. 1982. pap. 5.00 (ISBN 0-914752-14-6). Sovereign Pr.

American Christian Bible. Thomas Jefferson & Erik Holden. 128p. 1986. pap. 5.00 (ISBN 0-317-53278-2). Noontide.

American Christianity: A Case Approach. Ed. by Ronald C. White, Jr. et al. 208p. (Orig.). 1986. pap. text ed. 11.95 (ISBN 0-8028-0241-9). Eerdmans.

American Christianity: An Historical Interpretation with Representative Documents. lib. rep. ed. H. Shelton Smith et al. 1960. Vol. I. 45.00x (ISBN 0-684-15744-6, ScribT); Vol. II. 45.00x (ISBN 0-684-15745-4). Scribner.

American Christianity in Crisis. Paul K. Conkin. LC 81-80738. (Charles Edmondson Historical Lectures Ser.). 48p. (Orig.). 1981. pap. 4.50 (ISBN 0-918954-24-X). Baylor Univ Pr.

American Christmas: A Study in National Culture. James H. Barnett. LC 75-22799. (America in Two Centuries Ser.). 1976. Repr. of 1954 ed. 17.00x (ISBN 0-405-07671-1). Ayer Co Pubs.

American Christmases: From the Puritans to the Victorians. Eugenia L. Tennant. 1975. 10.00 (ISBN 0-682-48358-3, Banner). Exposition Pr FL.

American Church Politics & the Middle East. Ed. by Basheer K. Nijim. (Monograph: No. 15). 156p. (Orig.). 1982. pap. 7.50 (ISBN 0-937694-53-3). Assn Arab-Amer U Grads.

American Churches. Roger Kennedy. (Illus.). 296p. 1982. 50.00 (ISBN 0-8245-0539-5). Crossroad NY.

American Churches & the Negro. W. D. Weatherford. 310p. 1957. 8.95 (ISBN 0-8158-0207-2). Chris Mass.

American Churches: The Bulwarks of American Slavery. James G. Birney. LC 79-82174. (Anti-Slavery Crusade in America Ser). 1969. Repr. of 1842 ed. 11.00 (ISBN 0-405-00611-X). Ayer Co Pubs.

American Civil Church Law. Carl Zollman. LC 79-77996. (Columbia University. Studies in the Social Sciences: No. 181). Repr. of 1917 ed. 30.00 (ISBN 0-404-51181-3). AMS Pr.

American Civil Religion: An Assessment. Gail Gehrig. LC 81-82801. (Society for the Scientific Study of Religion Monograph: No. 3). (Orig.). 1981. pap. 5.50 (ISBN 0-932566-02-2). Soc Sci Stud Rel.

American Covenant: The Untold Story. rev. ed. Marshall E. Foster & Mary E. Swanson. (Illus.). 186p. (Orig.). 1982. limited, signed 19.95; pap. text ed. 9.95 (ISBN 0-941370-00-3). Mayflower Inst.

American Culture & Catholic Schools. Emmett McLoughlin. 288p. 1973. pap. 2.75 (ISBN 0-8065-0356-4). Citadel Pr.

American Culture & Religion. William W. Sweet. LC 72-78372. ix, 114p. 1972. Repr. of 1951 ed. lib. bdg. 19.50x (ISBN 0-8154-0421-2). Cooper Sq.

American Deaconess Movement in the Early Twentieth Century. Ed. by Carolyn D. Gifford & Donald Dayton. (Women in American Protestant Religion 1800-1930 Ser.). 288p. 1987. lib. bdg. 40.00 (ISBN 0-8240-0650-X). Garland Pub.

American Democracy & the Vatican: Population Growth & National Security. Stephen D. Mumford. LC 84-72500. 268p. (Orig.). 1984. 11.95 (ISBN 0-931779-00-6); pap. 7.95 (ISBN 0-931779-01-4). Humanist Pr.

American Denominational Organization: A Sociological View. Ed. by Ross P. Scherer. LC 80-13859. 378p. 1980. pap. 14.95x (ISBN 0-87808-173-9, Ecclesia). William Carey Lib.

American Dream Still Works. George Shinn. 1981. pap. 3.50 (ISBN 0-8423-0061-9). Tyndale.

American Education & Religion. Ed. by F. Ernest Johnson. LC 68-26192. (Essay & General Literature Index Reprint Ser). 1969. Repr. of 1952 ed. 21.50x (ISBN 0-8046-0220-4, Pub. by Kennikat). Assoc Faculty Pr.

American Essays for the Newman Centennial. Ed. by John K. Ryan & Edmond Benard. LC 47-30528. pap. 64.50 (ISBN 0-317-07851-8, 2005379). Bks Demand UMI.

American Ethical Thought. Guy W. Stroh. LC 79-891. 336p. 1979. 23.95x (ISBN 0-88229-356-7). Nelson-Hall.

American Evangelical Missionaries in France, 1945-1975. Allen V. Koop. (Illus.). 220p. (Orig.). 1986. lib. bdg. 27.00 (ISBN 0-8191-5204-8); pap. text ed. 13.50 (ISBN 0-8191-5205-6). U Pr of Amer.

American Evangelicalism: Conservative Religion & the Quandary of Modernity. James D. Hunter. LC 82-317. 166p. 1983. 27.50x (ISBN 0-8135-0960-2); pap. 9.95x (ISBN 0-8135-0985-8). Rutgers U Pr.

American Evangelicals, 1800-1900: An Anthology. William G. McLoughlin. 12.00 (ISBN 0-8446-0793-2). Peter Smith.

American Experience of God: The Spirituality of Isaac Hecker. John Farina. LC 81-80875. 240p. 1981. 11.95 (ISBN 0-8091-0321-4). Paulist Pr.

American Franciscan Missions in Central America. Leonard F. Bacigalupo. LC 80-68205. 483p. (Orig.). 1980. 19.50 (ISBN 0-933402-20-1); pap. 9.95 (ISBN 0-933402-21-X). Charisma Pr.

American Freedom & Catholic Power. Paul Blanshard. LC 84-19141. xii, 402p. 1984. Repr. of 1958 ed. lib. bdg. 47.50x (ISBN 0-313-24620-3, BLAF). Greenwood.

American Fundamentalism & Israel: The Relation of Fundamentalist Churches to Zionism & the State of Israel. Yona Malachy. 178p. 1978. pap. text ed. 10.50x (Pub. by Magnes Pr Israel). Humanities.

American Funeral: A Study in Guilt, Extravagance, & Sublimity. LeRoy E. Bowman. LC 72-14083. 181p. 1973. Repr. of 1959 ed. lib. bdg. 22.50x (ISBN 0-8371-6749-3, BOFU). Greenwood.

American Hero-Myths: A Study in the Native Religions of the Western Continent. Daniel G. Brinton. LC 15-7574. (American Studies Ser). Repr. of 1882 ed. 18.00 (ISBN 0-384-05860-4). Johnson Repr.

American History in Verse. Abridged ed. Ed. by Burton Stevenson. 494p. 1975. pap. 7.00 (ISBN 0-89084-024-5). Bob Jones Univ Pr.

American Holy Land: A History of the Archdiocese of Louisville. Clyde F. Crews. 360p. 1987. 29.95 (ISBN 0-89453-622-2). M Glazier.

American Hymns Old & New: Notes on the Hymns & Biographies of the Authors & Composers, 2 vols. Ed. by Albert Christ-Janer et al. LC 79-4630. (Illus.). 1454p. 1980. 72.00 (ISBN 0-231-05148-4). Columbia U Pr.

American Ideal of the "True Woman" As Reflected in Advice Books to Young Women. Intro. by Carolyn D. Gifford & Donald Dayton. Tr. by Carolyn Gifford. (Women in American Protestant Religion 1800-1930 Ser.). 431p. 1987. lib. bdg. 60.00 (ISBN 0-8240-0651-8). Garland Pub.

American Idol: Emerson & the "Jewish Idea". Robert J. Loewenberg. LC 84-7206. 148p. (Orig.). 1984. lib. bdg. 20.75 (ISBN 0-8191-3955-6); pap. text ed. 9.25 (ISBN 0-8191-3956-4). U Pr of Amer.

American Indian Magic: Sacred Pow Wows & Hopi Prophecies. Brad Steiger. (Illus.). 210p. 1986. 17.95 (ISBN 0-938294-19-9); pap. 9.95 (ISBN 0-938294-20-2). Global Comm.

American Indian Medicine. Virgil J. Vogel. LC 69-10626. (Civilization of the American Indian Ser.: Vol. 95). (Illus.). 1970. 29.95 (ISBN 0-8061-0863-0). U of Okla Pr.

American Indian Myth & Legends. Richard Erodes & Alfonso Ortiz. LC 84-42669. (Illus.). 504p. 1984. 19.45 (ISBN 0-394-50796-7). Pantheon.

American Indian Mythology. Alice Marriott & Carol K. Rachlin. 258p. (YA) 1972. pap. 3.50 (ISBN 0-451-62327-4, ME2327, Ment). NAL.

American Indian Prayers & Poetry. Ed. by J. Edward Sharpe. (Illus.). 32p. 1985. pap. 3.00 (ISBN 0-935741-09-7). Cherokee Pubns.

American Indians & Christian Missions: Studies in Cultural Conflict. Henry W. Bowden. LC 80-27840. (Chicago History of American Religion Ser.). 1981. 18.00x (ISBN 0-226-06811-0). U of Chicago Pr.

American Indians & Christian Missions: Studies in Cultural Conflict. Henry W. Bowden. LC 84-27840. (Chicago History of American Religion Ser). xx, 256p. 1985. pap. 7.95 (ISBN 0-226-06812-9). U of Chicago Pr.

American Inquisition: U. S. Government Agency Harassment, Religious Persecution & Abuse of Power. Conference of Scientology Ministers. 1977. pap. 7.00 (ISBN 0-915598-16-7). Church of Scient Info.

American Jesuits. J. J. Walsh. 59.95 (ISBN 0-87968-605-7). Gordon Pr.

American Jesuits. facs. ed. James J. Walsh. LC 68-29251. (Essay Index Reprint Ser). 1934. 18.25 (ISBN 0-8369-0970-4). Ayer Co Pubs.

American Jew. facs. ed. Ed. by Oscar I. Janowsky. LC 76-142647. (Essay Index Reprint Ser). 1942. 18.00 (ISBN 0-8369-2166-6). Ayer Co Pubs.

American Jew: A Study of Backgrounds. Abraham J. Feldman. LC 78-26254. 1979. Repr. of 1937 ed. lib. bdg. cancelled (ISBN 0-313-20876-X, FEAJ). Greenwood.

American Jew: A Zionistic Analysis. Ben Halpern. LC 82-16875. 192p. 1983. pap. 6.95 (ISBN 0-8052-0742-2). Schocken.

American Jew As Patriot, Soldier, & Citizen. Simon Wolf. LC 72-8739. (American Revolutionary Ser.). 1979. Repr. of 1895 ed. lib. bdg. 47.00x (ISBN 0-8398-2179-4). Irvington.

American Jew in the Civil War. Ed. by Isidore S. Meyer. Repr. of 1962 ed. 11.00 (ISBN 0-527-03218-2). Kraus Repr.

American Jewish Bibliography: Being a List of Books & Pamphlets by Jews, or Relating to Them, Printed in the United States from the Establishment of the Press in the Colonies until 1850. Abraham S. Rosenbach. (American Jewish Historical Society Publications: No. 30). (Illus.). pap. 127.30 (ISBN 0-317-09938-8, 2017816). Bks Demand UMI.

American Jewish Biographies. Murray Polner. (Illus.). 500p. 1982. 39.95x (ISBN 0-87196-462-7). Facts on File.

American Jewish Business Enterprise. (American Jewish Historical Quarterly: Vol. 66, Pt.1). 1976. 8.00 (ISBN 0-911934-03-0). Am Jewish Hist Soc.

American Jewish Community: Social Science Research & Policy Implications. Calvin Goldscheider. (Brown Judaic Studies). 183p. 1986. 27.95 (ISBN 1-55540-081-7, 14-50-03). Scholars Pr GA.

American Jewish Experience. Jonathan D. Sarna. 336p. 1986. text ed. 35.00x (ISBN 0-8419-0934-2); pap. text ed. 19.50x (ISBN 0-8419-0935-0). Holmes & Meier.

American Jewish Fertility. Calvin Goldscheider. (Brown Studies on Jews & Their Societies). 1986. text ed. 23.95 (ISBN 0-89130-919-5, 14-50-01); pap. 18.95 (ISBN 0-89130-920-9). Scholars Pr GA.

American Jewish High School Students: A National Profile. James L. Peterson & Nicholas Zill. LC 84-72249. vi, 32p. (Orig.). 1984. pap. 2.50 (ISBN 0-87495-065-1). Am Jewish Comm.

American Jewish History: A Bibliograhical Guide. Jeffrey S. Gurock. 1983. 6.95 (ISBN 0-88464-037-X). ADL.

American Jewish Landmarks: A Travel Guide & History, Vol. 1. Bernard Postal & Lionel Koppman. LC 76-27401. (Orig.). 1977. 25.00 (ISBN 0-8303-0151-8); pap. 15.00 (ISBN 0-8303-0152-6). Fleet.

American Jewish Landmarks: A Travel Guide & History, the South & Southwest, Vol. II. Bernard Postal & Lionel Koppman. LC 76-27401. 1979. 21.95 (ISBN 0-8303-0155-0); pap. 11.95 (ISBN 0-8303-0157-7). Fleet.

American Jewish Organizations & Israel. Lee O'Brien. LC 85-29117. 330p. 1985. pap. 24.95 (ISBN 0-88728-153-2). Inst Palestine.

American Jewish Woman: A Documentary History. Jacob R. Marcus. 1981. 35.00x (ISBN 0-87068-752-2). Ktav.

American Jewish Woman: 1654-1980. Ed. by Jacob R. Marcus. 1981. 15.00x (ISBN 0-87068-579-1). Ktav.

American Jewish Year Book, Vol 86. Ed. by Milton Himmelfarb & David Singer. LC 99-4040. 516p. 1986. 25.95 (ISBN 0-8276-0269-3). Am Jewish Comm.

American Jewish Year Book, 1986, Vol. 80. Date not set. price not set. Am Jewish Comm.

American Jewish Year Book, 1987. David Singer & Ruth Seldin. 1986. write for info. Am Jewish Comm.

American Jewry & the Holocaust: The American Jewish Joint Distribution Committee, 1939-1945. Yehuda Bauer. LC 80-26035. 522p. 1981. 35.00x (ISBN 0-8143-1672-7). Wayne St U Pr.

American Jewry During the Holocaust. Seymour M. Finger. 1984. pap. 14.95x (ISBN 0-9613537-3-2). Am Jewish Holo.

American Jewry During the Holocaust. Seymour M. Finger. 412p. (Orig.). 1984. pap. text ed. 17.95 (ISBN 0-8419-7506-X). Holmes & Meier.

American Jewry: The Formative Years. Bertram W. Korn. (Texts & Studies). (Hebrew.). 1971. 10.00 (ISBN 0-911934-04-9). Am Jewish Hist Soc.

American Jews. Ed. by Marshall Sklare. 352p. 1983. pap. text ed. 9.95x (ISBN 0-87441-348-6). Behrman.

American Jews & the Labor Movement. (American Jewish Historical Quarterly: Vol. 65, Pt.3). 1976. 4.00 (ISBN 0-911934-05-7). Am Jewish Hist Soc.

American Jews & the Zionist Idea. Naomi Cohen. pap. 9.95x (ISBN 0-87068-272-5). Ktav.

American Jews: Their Story. Oscar Handlin. 48p. 2.50 (ISBN 0-88464-011-6). ADL.

American Judaism. rev. ed. Nathan Glazer. LC 57-8574. (Chicago History of American Civilization Ser). 1972. 12.50x (ISBN 0-226-29839-6); pap. 7.50 (ISBN 0-226-29841-8, CHAC7). U of Chicago Pr.

American Judaism. John A. Hardon. LC 72-148264. 1971. 5.95 (ISBN 0-8294-0199-7). Loyola.

American Judaism: Adventure in Modernity. Jacob Neusner. pap. 9.95x (ISBN 0-87068-681-X). Ktav.

American Judaism: The Religion & Religious Institutions of the Jewish People in the United States. Joseph Leiser. LC 78-26230. 1979. Repr. of 1925 ed. lib. bdg. 22.50x (ISBN 0-313-20879-4, LEAJ). Greenwood.

American Liberal Disillusionment in the Wake of World War I. Stuart I. Rochester. LC 76-47613. 1977. 22.50x (ISBN 0-271-01233-1). Pa St U Pr.

American Lutheran Church, Historically, Doctrinally, & Practically Delineated in Several Discourses. Samuel S. Schmucker. LC 72-83436. (Religion in American Ser). 1969. Repr. of 1851 ed. 20.00 (ISBN 0-405-00261-0). Ayer Co Pubs.

American Majorities & Minorities: A Syllabus of United States History for Secondary Schools. Warren J. Halliburton & William L. Katz. 6.95 (ISBN 0-405-18855-2, 19424). Ayer Co Pubs.

American Meditation & Beginning Yoga. Robert L. Peck. 1976. 6.00 (ISBN 0-685-71846-8). Personal Dev Ctr.

American Mennonites & Protestant Movements. Beulah S. Hostetler. (Studies in Anabaptist & Mennonnite History). 344p. 1987. 29.95x (ISBN 0-8361-1288-1). Herald Pr.

American Messiahs by the Unofficial Observer. John F. Carter. LC 68-26232. 1968. Repr. of 1935 ed. 21.50x (ISBN 0-8046-0010-4, Pub by Kennikat). Assoc Faculty Pr.

American Methodist Pioneer: The Life & Journals of the Rev. Freeborn Garrettson 1752-1827. Ed. by Robert D. Simpson. LC 83-72532. (Illus.). 444p. 1983. text ed. 25.00 (ISBN 0-914960-49-0). Academy Bks.

American Military Movement Relating Sacred Dance. Ruth E. Neilan. Ed. & intro. by Doug Adams. (Orig.). 1985. pap. 3.00 (ISBN 0-941500-37-3). Sharing Co.

American Mirror: Social, Ethical & Religious Aspects of American Literature, 1930-1940. Halford E. Luccock. LC 75-156806. 300p. 1971. Repr. of 1940 ed. lib. bdg. 28.50x (ISBN 0-8154-0385-2). Cooper Sq.

American Missionaries among the Bulgarians: 1858-1912. Tatyana Nestorova. 160p. 1987. text ed. 20.00 (ISBN 0-88033-114-3, 218). East Eur Quarterly.

American Missionaries & Hinduism: A Study of Their Contacts from 1813-1918. Sushil M. Pathak. 294p. 1967. text ed. 20.00x. Coronet Bks.

American Missionaries in China: Papers from Harvard Seminars. Ed. by Liu Kwang-Ching. LC 66-31226. (East Asian Monographs Ser: No. 21). 1966. pap. 11.00x (ISBN 0-674-02600-4). Harvard U Pr.

American Missionary Community in China, 1895-1905. Sidney A. Forsythe. LC 70-178077. (East Asian Monographs Ser: No. 43). 1971. pap. 11.00x (ISBN 0-674-02626-8). Harvard U Pr.

American Missions in Bicentennial Perspective. Ed. by R. Pierce Beaver. LC 77-7569. 1977. pap. 10.95 (ISBN 0-87808-153-4). William Carey Lib.

American Missions in Syria. Adnan Abu-Ghazaleh. 120p. (Orig.). 1985. 16.95 (ISBN 0-915597-26-8); pap. 8.95 (ISBN 0-915597-25-X). Amana Bks.

American Modernity & Jewish Identity. Steven M. Cohen. 250p. 1983. 24.00x (ISBN 0-422-77740-4, NO.3467); pap. 9.95 (ISBN 0-422-77750-1, NO.3495). Methuen Inc.

American Montage. Celeste Loucks & Everett Hullum. Ed. by Elaine S. Furlow. (Human Touch Ser.: No. 3). (Illus.). 1976. 6.95 (ISBN 0-686-16312-5); lib. bdg. 6.95 (ISBN 0-937170-10-0). Home Mission.

American Mystical Verse. Ed. by Irene Hunter. LC 79-116407. (Granger Index Reprint Ser). 1925. 19.00 (ISBN 0-8369-6148-X). Ayer Co Pubs.

American Opinion of Roman Catholicism in the Eighteenth Century. Mary A. Ray. 456p. 1974. Repr. of 1936 ed. lib. bdg. 26.00x (ISBN 0-374-96723-7, Octagon). Hippocrene Bks.

American Peace Crusade, Eighteen Fifteen to Eighteen Sixty. Merle E. Curti. 1965. lib. bdg. 18.50x (ISBN 0-374-91976-3, Octagon). Hippocrene Bks.

American Pentecostal Movement: A Bibliographic Essay. David W. Faupel. LC 76-361994. (Occasional Bibliographic Papers of the B. L. Fisher Library: No. 2). 56p. 1972. 3.00 (ISBN 0-914368-01-X). Asbury Theological.

American Personal Religious Accounts, 1600-1980: Toward an Inner History of America's Faiths. Jon Alexander. LC 83-21950. (Studies in American Religion: Vol. 8). 518p. 1984. 69.95x (ISBN 0-88946-654-8). E Mellen.

American Philosophies of Religion. Henry N. Wieman & Bernard E. Meland. 370p. 1985. Repr. of 1936 ed. lib. bdg. 75.00 (ISBN 0-89984-539-8). Century Bookbindery.

American Piety: The Nature of Religious Commitment. Rodney Stark & Charles Y. Glock. 1968. 35.95x (ISBN 0-520-01210-0); pap. 2.65 (ISBN 0-520-01756-0, CAL197). U of Cal Pr.

American Poets & Their Theology. facs. ed. Augustus H. Strong. LC 68-26477. (Essay Index Reprint Ser). 1968. Repr. of 1916 ed. 21.50 (ISBN 0-8369-0910-0). Ayer Co Pubs.

American Political Theology: Historical Perspective & Theoretical Analysis. Charles W. Dunn. LC 84-13308. 208p. 1984. 31.95 (ISBN 0-03-071843-0); pap. 13.95 (ISBN 0-03-071844-9, B1603). Praeger.

American Pope: The Life & Times of Francis Cardinal Spellman. John Cooney. (Illus.). 448p. 1986. pap. 4.50 (ISBN 0-440-10194-8). Dell.

American Pope: The Life & Times of Francis Cardinal Spellman 1889-1967. John Cooney. LC 84-40096. (Illus.). 416p. 1984. 19.95 (ISBN 0-8129-1120-2). Times Bks.

American Prayer. Jim Morrison. 1983. pap. 8.95x (ISBN 0-915628-46-5). Zeppelin.

American Preachers of Today: Intimate Appraisals of Thirty-Two Leaders. facsimile ed. Edgar D. Jones. LC 76-156667. (Essay Index Reprint Ser). Repr. of 1933 ed. 19.00 (ISBN 0-8369-2279-4). Ayer Co Pubs.

American Presbyterians: A Pictorial History. James H. Smylie. 1985. write for info. (ISBN 0-664-24679-6). Westminster.

American Protestant Thought in the Liberal Era. Ed. by William R. Hutchison. LC 84-19614. 252p. 1985. pap. text ed. 10.75 (ISBN 0-8191-4336-7). U Pr of Amer.

American Protestant Women in World Mission. R. Pierce Beaver. LC 80-14366. Orig. Title: All Loves Excelling. Repr. of 1960 ed. 45.10 (ISBN 0-8357-9122-X, 2019317). Bks Demand UMI.

American Protestantism. Winthrop S. Hudson. LC 61-15936. (Chicago History of American Civilization Ser). 1961. pap. 4.95x (ISBN 0-226-35803-8, CHAC10). U of Chicago Pr.

American Protestantism. T. V. Parker. 1956. 7.95 (ISBN 0-8022-1264-6). Philos Lib.

American Protestantism & a Jewish State. Hertzel Fishman. LC 72-3746. (Schaver Publication Fund for Jewish Studies Ser). 250p. 1973. 24.95x (ISBN 0-8143-1481-3). Wayne St U Pr.

American Protestantism & Social Issues, 1919-1939. Robert M. Miller. LC 77-22031. 1977. Repr. of 1958 ed. lib. bdg. 26.75x (ISBN 0-8371-9777-5, MIAM). Greenwood.

American Psalmody. 2nd ed. Frank J. Metcalf. LC 68-13274. (Music Reprint Ser.). (Illus.). 1968. Repr. of 1917 ed. lib. bdg. 19.50 (ISBN 0-306-71132-X). Da Capo.

American Puritan Imagination. S. Bercovitch. LC 73-94136. 256p. 1974. 39.50 (ISBN 0-521-20392-9); pap. 14.95 (ISBN 0-521-09841-6). Cambridge U Pr.

American Puritan Imagination: Essays in Revaluation. Ed. by Sacvan Bercovitch. LC 73-94136. pap. 68.30 (2027269). Bks Demand UMI.

American Puritan Studies: An Annotated Bibliography of Dissertations, 1882-1981. Compiled by Michael S. Montgomery. LC 84-6553. (Bibliographies & Indexes in American History Ser.: No. 1). xxii, 419p. 1984. lib. bdg. 49.95 (ISBN 0-313-24237-2, MON/). Greenwood.

American Puritans: Their Prose & Poetry. Perry Miller. 1959. 21.75 (ISBN 0-8446-2596-5). Peter Smith.

American Quest for the City of God. Leland D. Baldwin. ix, 368p. 1981. 18.95x (ISBN 0-86554-016-0). Mercer Univ Pr.

American Rabbinate: A Century of Continuity & Change 1883-1983. Jacob R. Marcus & Abraham J. Peck. 300p. 1985. text ed. 20.00x (ISBN 0-88125-076-7). Ktav.

American Reform Responsa. Ed. by Walter Jacob. 561p. 1983. pap. text ed. 20.00 (ISBN 0-916694-83-6). Central Conf.

American Reformation: A Documentary History of Unitarian Christianity. Ed. by Sydney E. Ahlstrom & Jonathan S. Carey. vi, 506p. 1984. 39.50x (ISBN 0-8195-5080-9). Wesleyan U Pr.

American Reformers. Ed. by Alden Whitman. LC 85-636. (Illus.). 944p. 1985. 75.00 (ISBN 0-8242-0705-X). Wilson.

American Refugee Policy: Ethical & Religious Reflections. Ed. by Joseph M. Kitagawa. 192p. (Orig.). 1985. pap. 9.95 (ISBN 0-86683-955-0, AY8541, HarpR). Har-Row.

American Religion: A Cultural Perspective. Mary F. Bednarowski. LC 83-22895. (Illus.). 182p. 1984. pap. text ed. 17.00 (ISBN 0-13-029059-9). P-H.

American Religion & Philosophy: A Guide to Information Sources. Ed. by Ernest R. Sandeen & Frederick Hale. LC 73-17562. (American Studies Information Guide: Vol. 5). 1978. 62.00x (ISBN 0-8103-1262-X). Gale.

American Religious Empiricism. William Dean. (Religious Studies). 126p. (Orig.). 1986. 34.50x (ISBN 0-88706-280-6); pap. 10.95 (ISBN 0-88706-281-4). State U NY Pr.

American Religious Experiment: Piety & Practicality. Ed. by Clyde L. Manschreck & Barbara B. Zikmund. LC 76-7199. (Studies in Ministry & Parish Life). 128p. 1976. 13.95x (ISBN 0-913552-06-2); pap. 6.95x (ISBN 0-913552-07-0). Exploration Pr.

American Religious Groups View Foreign Policy: Trends in Rank & File Opinion, 1937-1969. Alfred O. Hero. LC 72-81335. pap. 141.00 (ISBN 0-317-26767-1, 2023400). Bks Demand UMI.

American Religious Thought: A History. William A. Clebsch. LC 73-82911. xii, 212p. 1985. pap. text ed. 10.00x (ISBN 0-226-10962-3). U of Chicago Pr.

American Saints & Seers: American-Born Religions & the Genius Behind Them. Edward Rice. LC 81-15293. (Illus.). 240p. 1982. 11.95 (ISBN 0-02-775980-6, Four Winds). Macmillan.

American Scientists & Nuclear Weapons Policy. Robert G. Gilpin, Jr. 1962. 37.00x (ISBN 0-691-07501-8). Princeton U Pr.

American Search for Soul. Robert S. Michaelsen. LC 74-82005. (Rockwell Lecture Ser.). 132p. 1975. 15.95x (ISBN 0-8071-0097-8). La State U Pr.

American Shakers: From Neo-Christianity to Presocialism. Henri Desroche. Ed. by John K. Savacool. LC 78-123537. 368p. 1971. 20.00x (ISBN 0-87023-063-8). U of Mass Pr.

American Sociology: Worldly Rejections of Religion & Their Directions. Arthur J. Vidich & Stanford M. Lyman. LC 84-2268. 400p. 1985. pap. 30.00x (ISBN 0-300-03037-1). Yale U Pr.

American State Papers Bearing on Sunday Legislation. Ed. by W. A. Blakely. LC 79-122165. (Civil Liberties in American History Ser.). 1970. Repr. of 1911 ed. lib. bdg. 95.00 (ISBN 0-306-71973-8). Da Capo.

American Strategic Theology. John A. Coleman. 10.95 (ISBN 0-8091-2469-6). Paulist Pr.

American Sunday School Union Papers, 1817-1915: A Guide to the Microfilm Edition. Ed. by Barbara A. Sokolosky. 154p. (Orig.). 1980. pap. text ed. 50.00 (ISBN 0-667-00582-X). Microfilming Corp.

American Thought from Puritanism to Pragmatism & Beyond: A Greenwood Archival Edition. 2nd ed. Isaac W. Riley. Repr. of 1923 ed. lib. bdg. 65.00x (ISBN 0-8371-2391-7, RIAT). Greenwood.

American Thought from Puritanism to Pragmatism. Woodbridge Riley. 11.75 (ISBN 0-8446-1385-1). Peter Smith.

American Tract Society Documents, Eighteen Twenty-Four to Nineteen Twenty-Five. American Tract Society Staff. LC 74-38434. (Religion in America, Ser. 2). 484p. 1972. Repr. of 1874 ed. 29.00 (ISBN 0-405-04055-5). Ayer Co Pubs.

American Transcendentalism: An Anthology of Criticism. Ed. by Brian M. Barbour. LC 72-12640. 384p. 1973. pap. 8.95x (ISBN 0-268-00494-3). U of Notre Dame Pr.

American Transcendentalists: Their Prose & Poetry. Ed. by Perry Miller. 17.25 (ISBN 0-8446-2595-7). Peter Smith.

American Universalism. George H. Williams. pap. 3.50 (ISBN 0-933840-18-7). Unitarian Univ.

American Vision of the Church: The Church in American Protestant Theology 1937-1967, Vol. 76. Thomas Riplinger. (European University Studies: Ser. 23). vi, 320p. 1977. pap. 33.95 (ISBN 3-261-02093-8). P Lang Pubs.

American Zionism & U. S. Foreign Policy, 1942-1947. Richard P. Stevens. 236p. 1970. Repr. of 1962 ed. 6.00 (ISBN 0-88728-095-1). Inst Palestine.

Americanization of the Synagogue, 1820-1870. Leon A. Jick. LC 75-18213. (Illus.). 260p. 1976. 25.00x (ISBN 0-87451-119-4). U Pr of New Eng.

American's Guide to English Parish Churches. John Betjeman. (Illus.). 1959. 20.00 (ISBN 0-8392-1004-3). Astor-Honor.

America's Aged. Dorthy M. Lochner. 0.50 (ISBN 0-911802-52-5). Free Church Pubns.

America's Attack on Itself: Truth, Faith, Ideas, Morality, & God. (Analysis Ser.: No. 16.). Date not set. 12.50 (ISBN 0-686-45487-1). Inst Analysis.

America's Family Crisis. Peter Popoff. Ed. by Don Tanner. LC 82-82843. 80p. 1982. pap. 2.00 (ISBN 0-938544-15-2). Faith Messenger.

America's Favorite Carols. Hershal Pyle. Date not set. 2.50 (ISBN 0-317-20179-4). Campus.

America's Great Revivals. Christian Life Staff. 1970. pap. 3.50 (ISBN 0-87123-003-8). Bethany Hse.

America's Jews. Marshall Sklare. 1971. pap. 9.00 (ISBN 0-394-31645-2, RanC). Random.

America's Jews in Transition. Chaim I. Waxman. 290p. 1983. 29.95 (ISBN 0-87722-321-1); pap. 12.95 (ISBN 0-87722-329-7). Temple U Pr.

America's Saints: The Rise of Mormon Power. Robert Gottlieb & Peter Wiley. LC 84-3304. 1984. 16.95 (ISBN 0-399-12924-3, Putnam). Putnam Pub Group.

America's Saints: The Rise of Mormon Power. Robert Gottlieb & Peter Wiley. LC 85-24879. 288p. 1986. pap. 5.95 (ISBN 0-15-605658-5, Harv). HarBraceJ.

America's Schools & Churches. David W. Beggs. LC 65-12279. pap. 60.30 (ISBN 0-317-28577-7, 2055190). Bks Demand UMI.

America's Thousand Bishops: From 1513 to 1974, from Abramowicz to Zuroweste. Clarence A. Liederbach. LC 73-94081. 80p. 1974. pap. 3.50 (ISBN 0-913228-09-5). R J Liederbach.

America's Twelve Great Women Leaders During the Past Hundred Years As Chosen by the Women of America. facs. ed. Ladies Home Journal & Christian Science Monitor. LC 74-90600. (Essay Index Reprint Ser). 1933. 14.00 (ISBN 0-8369-1202-0). Ayer Co Pubs.

America's Way in Church, State & Society. Joseph M. Dawson. LC 79-15522. 1980. Repr. of 1953 ed. lib. bdg. 22.50x (ISBN 0-313-22006-9, DAAW). Greenwood.

America's Witness for Jesus Christ. Compiled by Arthur Wallace. 70p. 1978. pap. 1.95x (ISBN 0-937892-04-1). LL Co.

Amigos de Dios. Sylvia Mandeville. Tr. by Edna L. Gutierrez from Eng. (Serie Apunta Con Tu Dedo). 24p. 1980. pap. 9.95 (ISBN 0-311-38532-X, Edit Mundo). Casa Bautista.

Amish. John A. Hosteter. (Illus.). 40p. 1982. pap. 1.95 (ISBN 0-8361-3317-X). Herald Pr.

Amish. Ed. by Fred L. Israel. LC 85-17516. (Let's Meet the Peoples of North America Ser.). (Illus.). 112p. 1986. lib. bdg. 15.95 (ISBN 0-87754-853-6). Chelsea Hse.

Amish Family. Phyllis R. Naylor. 12.95 (ISBN 0-8488-0109-1, Pub. by Amereon Hse). Amereon Ltd.

Amish in Switzerland & Other European Countries. Betty Miller. 1978. pap. 1.50 (ISBN 0-685-46025-8). O R Miller.

Amish Life. 2nd ed. John A. Hostetler. LC 82-83964. (Illus.). 48p. (Orig.). 1983. pap. 4.95 (ISBN 0-8361-3326-9). Herald Pr.

Amish of Canada. Orland Gingerich. LC 72-94800. 248p. 1978. pap. 4.95 (ISBN 0-8361-1856-1). Herald Pr.

Amish School. Sara E. Fisher & Rachel K. Stahl. LC 84-81142. (People's Place Booklet: No. 6). (Illus.). 96p. (Orig.). 1985. pap. 4.50 (ISBN 0-934672-17-2). Good Bks PA.

Amish Society. rev., 3rd ed. John A. Hostetler. LC 79-23823. 432p. 1980. pap. 9.95 (ISBN 0-8018-2334-X). Johns Hopkins.

Amish: Two Perceptions Two. James A. Perkins & Nelson Oestreich. (Illus.). 24p. (Orig.). 1981. pap. 4.00 (ISBN 0-936014-10-5). Dawn Valley.

Amistad Factor Decisivo. Alan L. McGinnis. Orig. Title: Friendship Factor. (Span.). 204p. 1986. pap. 5.95 (ISBN 0-311-46093-3, Edit Mundo). Casa Bautista.

Amitabha: A Story of Buddhist Theology. Paul Carus. 1977. Repr. 29.00x (ISBN 0-403-07255-7). Scholarly.

Ammar Yasir. Sadruddin Sharafuddin. Tr. by M. Fazal Haq. Orig. Title: Halif al-Makhzum. 264p. 1985. pap. 9.00 (ISBN 0-941724-40-9). Islamic Seminary.

Among Buddhas of Japan. Morgan Gibson. 1987. 10.00. White Pine.

Among My Books. James R. Lowell. LC 75-126666. 1970. 11.50 (ISBN 0-404-04039-X). AMS Pr.

Among the Believers: An Islamic Journey. V. S. Naipaul. LC 81-47503. 512p. 1981. 15.00 (ISBN 0-394-50969-2). Knopf.

Among the Dervishes. O. M. Burke. 1973. 11.95 (ISBN 0-900860-17-0, Pub. by Octagon Pr England); pap. 5.95 (ISBN 0-525-47386-6). Ins Study Human.

Among the Mormons: Historic Accounts by Contemporary Observers. Ed. by William Mulder & A. Russell Mortensen. LC 58-5825. xiv, 496p. 1973. (Bison). U of Nebr Pr.

Among the Mystics. facs. ed. William Fairweather. LC 68-20298. (Essay Index Reprint Ser.). 1936. 14.00 (ISBN 0-8369-0437-0). Ayer Co Pubs.

Among the Mystics. William Fairweather. 150p. 1936. 4.95 (ISBN 0-567-02104-1, Pub. by T & T Clark Ltd UK). Fortress.

Among the Soviet Evangelicals. Samuel J. Nesdoly. (Orig.). 1986. pap. 6.45 (ISBN 0-85151-489-8). Banner of Truth.

Amor, Asombroso Amor. Corrie ten Boom. Orig. Title: Amazing Love. 112p. 1980. pap. 2.25 (ISBN 0-311-40035-3, Edit Mundo). Casa Bautista.

Amor que no se Apaga. Ed Wheat. 1984. 4.25 (ISBN 0-88113-010-9). Edit Betania.

Amor y la Juventud. Joan Goetz. Tr. by Lidia D. Montero from Eng. Tr. of Let's Look at Love. (Illus.). 96p. 1984. pap. 2.25 (ISBN 0-311-46058-5). Casa Bautista.

Amos. A. Graeme Auld. (Old Testament Guides Ser.). 96p. 1986. pap. 3.95x (ISBN 1-85075-005-X, Pub. by JSOT Pr England). Eisenbrauns.

Amos. Richard S. Cripps. 1981. lib. bdg. 13.50 (ISBN 0-86524-081-7, 3001). Klock & Klock.

Amos: A Commentary. James L. Mays. LC 79-76885. (Old Testament Library). 176p. 1969. 15.95 (ISBN 0-664-20863-0). Westminster.

Amos among the Prophets: Composition & Theology. Robert B. Coote. LC 80-8054. 144p. 1981. pap. 5.95 (ISBN 0-8006-1400-3, 1-1400). Fortress.

Amos & Hosea. James Ward. Ed. by John Hayes. (Knox Preaching Guides). 96p. 1981. pap. 4.95 (ISBN 0-8042-3225-3). John Knox.

Amos: Bible Study Commentary. D. David Garland. 96p. 1973. pap. 4.95 (ISBN 0-310-24833-7, 9696P). Zondervan.

Amos, Hosea, Micah, Nahum, Zephaniah, Habakkuk. Carroll Stuhlmueller. (Collegeville Bible Commentary Ser.). 120p. 1986. pap. 2.95 (ISBN 0-8146-1422-1). Liturgical Pr.

Amos, Hosea, Micah, with Introduction to Classical Prophecy. Bruce Vawter. (Old Testament Message Ser.: Vol. 7). 1982. 12.95 (ISBN 0-89453-407-6); pap. 6.95 (ISBN 0-89453-242-1). M Glazier.

Amos: Israel on Trial. Whitney Kuniholm. (Fisherman Bible Studyguide). 67p. 1981. saddle stitch 2.95 (ISBN 0-87788-043-3). Shaw Pubs.

Amos (Neighborhood Bible Study) Marilyn Kunz & Catherine Schell. 1978. pap. 2.50 (ISBN 0-8423-0067-8). Tyndale.

Amos' Oracles Against the Nations. J. Barton. LC 78-67630. (Society for Old Testament Study Ser.). 1980. 22.95 (ISBN 0-521-22501-9). Cambridge U Pr.

Amos, Osee & Michae. Marcian Strange. (Bible Ser.). pap. 1.00 (ISBN 0-8091-5002-6). Paulist Pr.

Amos: The Message We Dare Not Ignore. G. Michael Cocoris. 90p. (Orig.). 1985. pap. text ed. 1.00 (ISBN 0-935729-02-X). Church Open Door.

Amostra de Salmos. Henry Morris. Orig. Title: Sampling the Psalms. (Port.). 1986. write for info. (ISBN 0-8297-0698-4). Life Pubs Intl.

Amsterdam Passover Haggadah, 1695. (Illus.). 1984. 80.00 (ISBN 0-915361-06-X, 09837-0, Dist. by Watts); leather bdg. 125.00 (09844-3). Adama Pubs Inc.

Amsterdam to Nairobi: The World Council of Churches & the Third World. Ernest W. Lefever. LC 79-2607. 126p. 1979. 10.00 (ISBN 0-89633-025-7); pap. 6.00 (ISBN 0-89633-024-9). Ethics & Public Policy.

Amsterdam to Nairobi: The World Council of Churches & the Third World. Ernest W. Lefever. 128p. 1985. pap. text ed. 7.50 (ISBN 0-8191-4484-3). U Pr of Amer.

Amy Carmichael: Let the Little Children Come. Lois H. Dick. (Orig.). 1984. pap. 3.95 (ISBN 0-8024-0433-2). Moody.

Amy Grant's Heart to Heart Bible Stories. Amy Grant et al. LC 85-62143. (Illus.). 96p. 1985. 9.95x (ISBN 0-8344-0130-4, BB500C). Sweet.

An-Nasir Li-Din Allah (1180-1225) Politik, Religion, Kultur in der Spaeten Abbasidenzeit. Angelika Hartmann. (Studien Zur Sprache, Geschichte und Kultur Des Islamischen Orients, N. F.: Vol. 8). 1975. 88.00x (ISBN 3-11-004179-0). De Gruyter.

Anabaptism & Asceticism. Kenneth R. Davis. LC 73-19593. 384p. 1974. 19.95x (ISBN 0-8361-1195-8). Herald Pr.

Anabaptism & Mission. Wilbert Shenk. LC 84-12863. (Missionary Study: No. 10). 264p. (Orig.). 1984. pap. 12.95 (ISBN 0-8361-3367-6). Herald Pr.

Anabaptism, from Its Rise at Zwickau to Its Fall at Munster. Richard Heath. LC 83-45615. Date not set. Repr. of 1895 ed. 28.00 (ISBN 0-404-19833-3). AMS Pr.

Anabaptism in Flanders 1530-1650. A. L. Verheyden. LC 61-13872. (Studies in Anabaptist & Mennonite History, No. 9). 126p. 1961. 12.95x (ISBN 0-8361-1102-8). Herald Pr.

Anabaptism in Outline: Selected Primary Sources. Walter Klaassen. 424p. 1981. pap. 12.95 (ISBN 0-8361-1241-5). Herald Pr.

Anabaptist Baptism. Rollin S. Armour. LC 66-19026. (Study in Anabaptist & Mennonite History No. 11). 1966. 16.95x (ISBN 0-8361-1178-8). Herald Pr.

Anabaptist Portraits. John A. Moore. LC 84-12769. 256p. (Orig.). 1984. pap. 9.95 (ISBN 0-8361-3361-7). Herald Pr.

Anabaptist Story. William R. Estep. 1975. pap. 7.95 (ISBN 0-8028-1594-4). Eerdmans.

Anabaptist Vision. Harold S. Bender. 1944. pap. 1.45 (ISBN 0-8361-1305-5). Herald Pr.

Anabaptists & the Sword. 2nd rev. ed. James M. Stayer. 1976. 15.00 (ISBN 0-87291-081-4). Coronado Pr.

Anabaptists & Thomas Muntzer. James M. Stayer & Werner O. Packull. 176p. 1980. pap. text ed. 13.95 (ISBN 0-8403-2235-6). Kendall-Hunt.

Anabaptists: Four Centuries Later. J. H. Kauffman & Leland Harder. LC 74-30347. 400p. 1975. 14.95x (ISBN 0-8361-1136-2); pap. 6.95 o. p. (ISBN 0-8361-1137-0). Herald Pr.

Anabaptists: Neither Catholics nor Protestants. William McGrath. pap. 1.25 (ISBN 0-686-32317-3). Rod & Staff.

Analecta, 4 Vols. Robert Wodrow. LC 74-178318. (Maitland Club, Glasgow. Publications: No. 60). Repr. of 1843 ed. Set. 175.00 (ISBN 0-404-53051-6). AMS Pr.

Analecta Byzantino-Russica. Ed. by Vasilii E. Regel. 1964. Repr. of 1891 ed. 23.50 (ISBN 0-8337-2919-5). B Franklin.

Analects. Confucius. Tr. by D. C. Lau. 1979. pap. 4.95 (ISBN 0-14-044348-7). Penguin.

Analects. Confucius. Tr. by Arthur Waley. 1966. pap. 4.95 (ISBN 0-394-70173-9, V173, Vin). Random.

Analects of Confucius. Confucius. (Illus.). 149p. 1986. 88.85 (ISBN 0-89266-538-6). Am Classical Coll Pr.

Analog of Beauty: Essays for Hans Urs von Balthasar at Eighty. Ed. by John Riches. 256p. 1986. 19.95 (ISBN 0-567-09351-4, Pub. by T & T Clark Ltd UK). Fortress.

Analogical Imagination. David Tracey. 496p. 1985. pap. 14.95 (ISBN 0-8245-0694-4). Crossroad NY.

Analogy of Religion. Joseph Butler. 30.00 (ISBN 0-8274-1862-0). R West.

Analogy of Religion. 3rd ed. Joseph Butler. 1986. lib. bdg. 25.00x (ISBN 0-935005-40-4); pap. text ed. 13.00x (ISBN 0-935005-41-2). Ibis Pub VA.

Analyse Ordinale Es Evangiles Synoptiques. Louis Frey. (Mathematiques et Sciences De L'homme: No. 11). 1972. 46.50 (ISBN 0-686-21228-2); pap. 27.20x (ISBN 0-686-21229-0). Mouton.

Analyse Structurale et Exegese Biblique. Roland Barthes et al. 128p. 1973. 17.50 (ISBN 0-686-53927-3). French & Eur.

Analysis of Coeur D'Alene Indian Myths. Gladys A. Reichard. LC 48-2411. (AFS M). Repr. of 1947 ed. 21.00 (ISBN 0-527-01093-6). Kraus Repr.

Analysis of Magic & Witchcraft: A Retrospective Introduction to the Study of Modern Metaphysics. C. W. Olliver. 244p. 1985. Repr. of 1928 ed. Set. lib. bdg. 100.00 (ISBN 0-89984-775-7). Century Bookbindery.

Analysis of Religious Belief. John R. Amberley. LC 76-161318. (Atheist Viewpoint Ser.). 745p. 1972. Repr. of 1877 ed. 41.00 (ISBN 0-405-03621-3). Ayer Co Pubs.

Analysis of Religious Belief. John R. Amberley. 59.95 (ISBN 0-87968-619-7). Gordon Pr.

Analysis of "The Institute of the Christian Religion" of John Calvin. Ford L. Battles & John Walchenbach. LC 79-57385. 1980. pap. 12.95 (ISBN 0-8010-0766-6). Baker Bk.

Analysis of the Lexicographic Resources Used by American Biblical Scholars Today. John E. Gates. LC 72-88670. (Society of Biblical Literature. Dissertation Ser.: No. 8). pap. 49.00 (ISBN 0-317-10146-3, 2017664). Bks Demand UMI.

Analysis of the Long Prayers in Old French Literature with Special Reference to the Biblical Creed Narrative Prayers. Sr. M. Pierre Koch. LC 70-94168. (Catholic University of America Studies in Romance Languages & Literatures Ser: No. 19). Repr. of 1940 ed. 24.00 (ISBN 0-404-50319-5). AMS Pr.

Analysis of the Names of Mormonism. John R. Krueger. 1979. pap. 3.00x (ISBN 0-911706-21-6). Selbstverlag.

Analysis of the Sravakabhumi Manuscript. Alex Wayman. LC 61-64259. (University of California Publications in Classical Philology: Vol. 17). pap. 48.00 (ISBN 0-317-09845-4, 2021172). Bks Demand UMI.

Analysis of Vatican Thirty. Lewis M. Barth. 1973. 20.00x (ISBN 0-87820-400-8, Pub. by Hebrew Union). Ktav.

Analysis of Zionism. L. Fry. 1982. lib. bdg. 59.00 (ISBN 0-87700-416-1). Revisionist Pr.

Analysis Philogica Novi Testamenti Graeci: Editio Tertia. Max Zerwick. (Scripta Pontificii Instituti Biblici,: Vol.107). (Lat.). 1966. pap. 12.00 (ISBN 88-7653-551-9). Loyola.

Analytical Concordance to the Revised Standard Version of the New Testament. Clinton Morrison. LC 77-26210. 800p. 1979. 45.00 (ISBN 0-664-20773-1). Westminster.

Analytical Franco-Jewish Gazetteer, 1939-1945. Soza Szajkowski. 1966. 50.00 (ISBN 0-87068-112-5). Ktav.

Analytical Greek New Testament. Ed. by Timothy Friberg & Barbara Friberg. 1000p. 1981. 24.95 (ISBN 0-8010-3496-5). Baker Bk.

Analytical Hebrew & Chaldee Lexicon. Benjamin Davidson. (Hebrew.). 27.95 (ISBN 0-310-20290-6, 6263, Pub. by Bagster). Zondervan.

Analytical Hebrew & Chaldee Lexicon. Benjamin Davidson. 784p. Date not set. 24.95 (ISBN 0-913573-03-5). Hendrickson MA.

Analytical Linguistic Concordance to the Book of Isaiah. Yehuda T. Radday. (Computer Bible Ser: Vol. II). 1975. 20.00 (ISBN 0-935106-15-4). Biblical Res Assocs.

Analytical Linguistic Key-Word-in-Context Concordance to the Book of Exodus. Yehuda Radday & Yaakov Levi. Ed. by Arthur J. Baird & David Freedman. (Computer Bible Ser.: Vol. 28). (Orig.). 1985. 45.00 (ISBN 0-935106-23-5). Biblical Res Assocs.

Analytical, Linguistic Key-Word-in-Context Concordance to the Book of Judges. Yehuda T. Radday. (Computer Bible Ser.: Vol. XI). 1977. pap. 20.00 (ISBN 0-935106-10-3). Biblical Res Assocs.

Analytical Studies in the Psalms. Arthur G. Clarke. LC 79-2518. 376p. 1979. 14.95 (ISBN 0-8254-2322-8). Kregel.

Analytical Study of the Abhidharmakosa. Sukomal Chaudhury. 1983. 18.00x (ISBN 0-8364-1017-3, Pub. by Mukhopadyaya). South Asia Bks.

Analytical Survey of the Bible. Gerald H. Twombly. pap. 5.95 (ISBN 0-88469-120-9). BMH Bks.

Analyzed Bible. Campbell G. Morgan. 256p. 1984. Isaiah I. pap. 5.95 (ISBN 0-8010-6171-7); Isaiah 2. pap. 5.95 (ISBN 0-8010-6172-5). Baker Bk.

Analyzed Bible. Campbell G. Morgan. Matthew. 6.95 (ISBN 0-8010-6159-8); Romans. pap. 5.95 (ISBN 0-8010-6149-0). Baker Bk.

Analyzed Bible: John. Campbell G. Morgan. 280p. 1984. pap. 6.95 (ISBN 0-8010-6173-3). Baker Bk.

Ananda: Where Yoga Lives. John Ball. LC 82-82100. 240p. 1982. 15.95 (ISBN 0-87972-207-X); pap. 8.95 (ISBN 0-87972-208-8). Bowling Green Univ.

Ananda: Where Yoga Lives. John Ball. (Illus.). 232p. 1982. pap. 8.95 (ISBN 0-87972-208-8). Dawn Pubns CA.

Anaphora or Great Eucharistic Prayer: An Eirenical Study in Liturgical History. Walter H. Frere. (Church Historical Society, London, New Ser.: No. 26). Repr. of 1938 ed. 50.00 (ISBN 0-8115-3150-3). Kraus Repr.

Anatomie of Popish Tyrannie. Thomas Bell. LC 74-28833. (English Experience Ser.: No. 714). 1975. Repr. of 1603 ed. 16.00 (ISBN 90-221-0714-0). Walter J Johnson.

Anatomy of a Church. 2nd ed. John MacArthur, Jr. (John MacArthur's Bible Studies). 1986. pap. 3.95 (ISBN 0-8024-5132-2). Moody.

Anatomy of a Crusade, Twelve Thirteen to Twelve Twenty-One. James M. Powell. (Middle Ages Ser.). (Illus.). 336p. 1986. text ed. 34.95x (ISBN 0-8122-8025-3). U of Pa Pr.

Anatomy of an Explosion: A Theological Analysis of the Missouri Synod Conflict. Kurt E. Marquart. 1978. pap. 3.95 (ISBN 0-8010-6049-4). Baker Bk.

Anatomy of Arminianisme. Pierre du Moulin, the Elder. LC 76-57380. (English Experience Ser.: No. 797). 1977. Repr. of 1620 ed. lib. bdg. 46.00 (ISBN 90-221-0797-3). Walter J Johnson.

Anatomy of Censorship. Jay E. Daily. (Books in Library & Information Science: Vol. 6). 424p. 1973. 50.50 (ISBN 0-8247-6065-4). Dekker.

Anatomy of Evil. Ruth N. Anshen. Orig. Title: Reality of the Devil. (Illus.). 224p. 1985. pap. 8.95 (ISBN 0-918825-15-6, Dist. by Kampmann & Co.). Moyer Bell Limited.

Anatomy of Evil. Charles W. Conn. 1984. pap. text ed. 6.95 (ISBN 0-87148-018-2). Pathway Pr.

Anatomy of God & Man. Gilbert A. Schoenbrod. (Illus.). 272p. 27.00 (ISBN 0-942494-02-4). Coleman Pub.

Anatomy of Illusion: Religious Cults & Destructive Persuasion. Thomas W. Keiser & Jacqueline L. Keiser. (Illus.). 160p. 1987. 25.25 (ISBN 0-398-05295-6). C C Thomas.

Anatomy of Lango Religion & Groups. Thomas T. Hayley. LC 74-100263. Repr. of 1947 ed. cancelled (ISBN 0-8371-2871-4, HLR&, Pub. by Negro U Pr). Greenwood.

Anatomy of the Fourth Gospel: A Study in Literary Design. R. Alan Culpepper. LC 82-16302. (Foundations & Facets Ser.). 256p. 1983. 19.95 (ISBN 0-8006-2102-6, 1-2102). Fortress.

Anatomy of the New Testament: A Guide to Its Structure & Meaning. 3rd ed. Robert A. Spivey & Moody D. Smith. 544p. 1981. text ed. write for info. (ISBN 0-02-415300-1). Macmillan.

Anatomy of the Pure & of the Impure Love. Richard Denninger. (Intimate Life of Man Library Bk.). (Illus.). 1979. 97.95 (ISBN 0-89266-177-1); spiral bdg. 37.95 (ISBN 0-685-67718-4). Am Classical Coll Pr.

Anatomy of the Sacred: An Introduction to Religion. James C. Livingston. 734p. 1987. text ed. write for info. (ISBN 0-02-371370-4). Macmillan.

Anatomy of Values: Problems of Personal & Social Choice. Charles Fried. LC 78-111483. 1970. 18.50x (ISBN 0-674-03151-2). Harvard U Pr.

Ancestor Worship in Contemporary Japan. Robert J. Smith. LC 74-82780. (Illus.). xxii, 266p. 1974. 29.50x (ISBN 0-8047-0873-8). Stanford U Pr.

Ancestry of the Harklean New Testament. G. Zuntz. 1965. pap. 2.25 (ISBN 0-85672-677-X, Pub. by British Acad). Longwood Pub Group.

Anchor of the Soul. Samuel Jardine. 1978. pap. 1.95 (ISBN 0-937396-05-2). Walterick Pubs.

Anchored in God. 2nd ed. Constantine Cavarnos. LC 75-35432. (Illus.). 230p. 1975. 10.00 (ISBN 0-914744-30-5). Inst Byzantine.

Anchorites & Their Patrons in Medieval England. Ann K. Warren. LC 84-24091. 1985. 42.00x (ISBN 0-520-05278-1). U of Cal Pr.

Anchors in Troubled Waters. Abr. ed. Batsell B. Baxter & Harold Hazelip. LC 82-50267. (Journey Adult Ser.). 126p. 1981. pap. text ed. 4.95 (ISBN 0-8344-0120-7). Sweet.

Ancienne Chartreuse du Reposoir Aujoud'hui Carmel, et les Chartruses de la Savoie. James Hogg. (Analecta Cartusiana Ser.: No. 39-2). (Illus.). 110p. (Orig.). 1979. pap. 25.00 (ISBN 3-7052-0047-X, Pub by Salzburg Studies). Longwood Pub Group.

Anciennne Chartreuse du Reposior, Aujourd'hui Carmel, et les Chartreusesde la Savoie, Introduction. James Hogg. (Analecta Cartusiana Ser.: No. 39-1). (Orig.). 1986. pap. 25.00 (ISBN 3-7052-0046-1, Pub by Salzburg Studies). Longwood Pub Group.

Ancient African Religion & the African American Church. Ulysses D. Jenkins. LC 78-65794. (Illus.). 1978. 12.95 (ISBN 0-933184-00-X); pap. 6.95 (ISBN 0-933184-01-8). Flame Intl.

Ancient American Setting for the Book of Mormon. John Sorenson. 400p. 1985. 14.95 (ISBN 0-87747-608-X). Deseret Bk.

Ancient Aramaic Prayer of Jesus. Rocco A. Errico. (Illus.). 82p. 1978. pap. 4.95 (ISBN 0-911336-69-9). Sci of Mind.

Ancient Art & Mythology. Richard P. Knight. (Most Meaningful Classics in World Culture Ser.). 1979. Repr. of 1876 ed. 69.75 (ISBN 0-89266-189-5). Am Classical Coll Pr.

Ancient Beliefs & Modern Superstitions. Martin Lings. (Unwin Paperbacks). 1980. pap. 4.50 (ISBN 0-04-200034-3). Allen Unwin.

Ancient Beliefs in the Immortality of the Soul. Clifford H. Moore. LC 63-10283. (Our Debt to Greece & Rome Ser.). 183p. 1963. Repr. of 1930 ed. 20.00x (ISBN 0-8154-0154-X). Cooper Sq.

Ancient Champions of Oneness. Rev. ed. Ed. by William B. Chalfant. (Illus.). 156p. 1982. pap. 5.95 (ISBN 0-912315-41-5). Word Aflame.

Ancient Documents & the Modern Bible. J. Paterson Smuth. 212p. 1979. Repr. of 1920 ed. lib. bdg. 40.00 (ISBN 0-8495-4885-3). Arden Lib.

Ancient Egypt: A Social History. B. G. Trigger et al. LC 82-22196. 450p. 1983. 57.50 (ISBN 0-521-24080-8); pap. 19.95 (ISBN 0-521-28427-9). Cambridge U Pr.

Ancient Egypt: Its Culture & History. J. Manchip White. LC 75-115748. 1970. pap. 4.95 (ISBN 0-486-22548-8). Dover.

Ancient Egypt: Its Culture & History. J. Manchip White. (Illus.). 14.50 (ISBN 0-8446-0336-8). Peter Smith.

Ancient Egyptian Book of the Dead. Carol Andrews. Tr. by R. O. Faulkner. (Illus.). 268p. 1985. text ed. 40.00x (ISBN 0-02-901470-0). Macmillan.

Ancient Egyptian Religion. Jaroslav Cerny. LC 78-9931. 1979. Repr. of 1957 ed. lib. bdg. 50.00x (ISBN 0-313-21104-3, CEAE). Greenwood.

Ancient Egyptian Religion: An Interpretation. Henri Frankfort. pap. 7.95x (ISBN 0-06-130077-2, TB77, Torch). Har-Row.

Ancient Egyptian Religion: An Interpretation. Henri Frankfort. 16.00 (ISBN 0-8446-2084-X). Peter Smith.

Ancient Egyptian Theology. E. A. Budge. 1985. pap. 5.95 (ISBN 0-916411-91-5). Holmes Pub.

Ancient Egyptians & the Origin of Civilization. facs. ed. Grafton E. Smith. LC 79-133534. (Select Bibliographies Reprint Ser.). 1923. 17.00 (ISBN 0-8369-5566-8). Ayer Co Pubs.

Ancient Egyptians: How They Lived & Worked. Jill Kamil. LC 76-42175. 1977. 12.95 (ISBN 0-8023-1267-5). Dufour.

Ancient Egyptians: Religious Beliefs & Practices. A. Rosalie David. (Religious Beliefs & Practices Ser.). 250p. 1982. 26.00x (ISBN 0-7100-0877-5); pap. 10.00 (ISBN 0-7100-0878-3). Methuen Inc.

Ancient Evidence for the Life of Jesus: Historical Records of His Death & Resurrection. Gary R. Habermas. 1985. pap. 6.95 (ISBN 0-8407-5919-3). Nelson.

Ancient Fathers of the Church: Translated Narratives from the Evertinos on Passions & Perfection in Christ. Archimandrite Chrysostomos. (Illus.). 118p. 1980. 7.95 (ISBN 0-916586-77-4); pap. 4.95 (ISBN 0-686-69869-X). Hellenic Coll Pr.

Ancient Greek Art & Iconography. Ed. by Warren G. Moon. LC 83-47765. (Illus.). 368p. 1983. 50.00 (ISBN 0-299-09250-X). U of Wis Pr.

Ancient Hebrew Social Life & Custom As Indicated in Law, Narrative & Metaphor. R. H. Kennett. (British Academy, London, Schweich Lectures on Biblical Archaeology Series, 1931). pap. 19.00 (ISBN 0-8115-1273-8). Kraus Repr.

Ancient Hindu Refugees: Badaga Social History 1550-1975. Ed. by Paul Hockings. (Studies in Anthropology). 1980. text ed. 39.50x (ISBN 90-279-7798-4). Mouton.

Ancient Indian Asceticism. M. G. Bhagat. LC 76-104001. 1976. 20.00 (ISBN 0-89684-476-5). Orient Bk Dist.

Ancient Indian Asceticism. M. G. Bhagat. LC 76-904001. 1976. 18.50x (ISBN 0-88386-865-2). South Asia Bks.

Ancient Indian Royal Consecration: The Rajasuya Described According to the Yajus Texts & Annotated. J. C. Heesterman. (Disputationes Rheno-Trajectinae Ser: No. 2). (Orig.). 1957. pap. text ed. 25.60x (ISBN 90-2790-028-0). Mouton.

Ancient Israel. 2nd ed. Harry M. Orlinsky. (Development of Western Civilization Ser.). (Illus.). 164p. (Orig.). 1960. pap. text ed. 5.95x (ISBN 0-8014-9849-X). Cornell U Pr.

Ancient Israel. Harry M. Orlinsky. LC 82-2937. (Development of Western Civilization Ser.). xii, 164p. 1982. Repr. of 1954 ed. lib. bdg. 24.75x (ISBN 0-313-23559-7, ORAN). Greenwood.

Ancient Israel: A New History of Israelite Society. Niels P. Lemche. (Biblical Seminar Ser.: No. 5). 250p. 1987. pap. text ed. 9.50x (ISBN 1-85075-017-3, Pub. by JSOT Pr England). Eisenbrauns.

Ancient Israel after Catastrophe: The Religious World View of the Mishnah. Jacob Neusner. LC 82-15972. 82p. 1983. pap. 8.95x (ISBN 0-8139-0980-5). U Pr of Va.

Ancient Italy & Modern Religion. Robert S. Conway. LC 77-27141. (Hibbert Lectures: 1932). Repr. of 1933 ed. 17.00 (ISBN 0-404-60428-5). AMS Pr.

Ancient Jerusalem. Selah Merrill. Ed. by Moshe Davis. LC 77-70724. (America & the Holy Land Ser.). (Illus.). 1977. Repr. of 1908 ed. lib. bdg. 40.00x (ISBN 0-405-10267-4). Ayer Co Pubs.

Ancient Jewish & Greek Consolation. C. G. Montefiore. LC 75-184052. 86p. 1973. text ed. 7.95 (ISBN 0-87677-045-6). Hartmore.

Ancient Jewish Philosophy. Israel I. Efros. 1976. pap. 5.95x (ISBN 0-8197-0014-2). Bloch.

Ancient Judaism. Max Weber. Ed. by Don Martindale. Tr. by Hans H. Gerth. LC 52-8156. 484p. 1967. pap. text ed. 12.95x (ISBN 0-02-934130-2). Free Pr.

Ancient Judaism & Modern Category Formation: "Judaism," "Midrash," "Messianism," & Canon in the Past Quarter-Century. Jacob Neusner. LC 85-30416. (Studies in Judaism Ser.). 138p. (Orig.). 1986. lib. bdg. 22.50 (ISBN 0-8191-5395-8, Pub. by Studies in Judaism); pap. text ed. 9.75 (ISBN 0-8191-5396-6). U Pr of Amer.

Ancient Judaism & the New Testament. Frederick C. Grant. LC 77-18848. 1978. Repr. of 1959 ed. lib. bdg. cancelled (ISBN 0-313-20204-4, GRAJ). Greenwood.

Ancient Judaism: Biblical Criticism from Max Weber to the Present. Irving M. Zeitlin. 328p. 1985. 29.95x (ISBN 0-7456-0059-X). Basil Blackwell.

Ancient Judaism: Debates & Disputes. Ed. by Jacob Neusner. LC 84-5532. (Brown Judaic Studies). 292p. 31.50 (ISBN 0-89130-755-9); pap. 20.95 (ISBN 0-89130-746-X, 14 00 64). Scholars Pr GA.

Ancient Judaism: Biblical Criticism from Max Weber to the Present. Irving M. Zeitlin. 328p. 1986. pap. 12.95 (ISBN 0-7456-0297-5). Basil Blackwell.

Ancient Library of Qumran & Modern Biblical Studies. Frank M. Cross. LC 76-29736. (Haskell Lectures, 1956-57). (Illus.). 1976. Repr. of 1958 ed. lib. bdg. 22.50x (ISBN 0-8371-9281-1, CRAL). Greenwood.

Ancient Liturgy of the Church of England. 3rd ed. William Maskell. LC 71-172848. Repr. of 1882 ed. 29.50 (ISBN 0-404-04196-5). AMS Pr.

Ancient Liturgy of the Church of England. William Maskell. 1977. lib. bdg. 59.95 (ISBN 0-8490-1425-5). Gordon Pr.

Ancient Maya. Rev., 4th ed. Sylvanus G. Morley & George W. Brainerd. Rev. by Robert J. Sharer. LC 81-85451. (Illus.). xx, 708p. 1983. 38.50 (ISBN 0-8047-1137-2); pap. 14.95 (ISBN 0-8047-1288-3, SP 80). Stanford U Pr.

Ancient Music in the Pines. Bhagwan Shree Rajneesh. Ed. by Ma Prem Veena. LC 78-901931. (Zen Ser.). (Illus.). 298p. (Orig.). 1977. 15.50 (ISBN 0-88050-003-4). Chidvilas Found.

Ancient Mysteries: A Sourcebook. Ed. by Marvin Meyer. LC 86-45022. (Illus.). 256p. (Orig.). 1986. 24.95 (ISBN 0-06-065577-1, HarpR); pap. 14.95 (ISBN 0-06-065576-3). Har-Row.

Ancient Mysteries Described. William Hone. LC 67-23905. (Illus.). 1969. Repr. of 1823 ed. 35.00x (ISBN 0-8103-3444-5). Gale.

Ancient Mysteries Described. William Hone. 59.95 (ISBN 0-8490-1426-3). Gordon Pr.

Ancient Myth in Modern Poetry. Lillian Feder. LC 70-154994. 1972. 38.50x (ISBN 0-691-06207-2); pap. 11.50x (ISBN 0-691-01336-5). Princeton U Pr.

Ancient Myths. Norma L. Goodrich. 256p. pap. 3.95 (ISBN 0-451-62361-4, Ment). NAL.

Ancient Myths & Biblical Faith. Foster R. McCurley. LC 82-48589. 208p. 1983. pap. 12.95 (ISBN 0-8006-1696-0, 1-1696). Fortress.

Ancient Myths: The First Science Fiction. Laurence Swinburne & Irene Swinburne. LC 77-10915. (Myth, Magic & Superstition Ser.). (Illus.). 1977. PLB 14.65 (ISBN 0-8172-1042-3). Raintree Pubs.

Ancient Myths: Their Meaning & Connection with Evolution. Rudolf Steiner. Tr. by M. Cotterell from Ger. 1978. pap. 5.95 (ISBN 0-919924-07-7). Anthroposophic.

Ancient Near East. Cyrus H. Gordon. 1965. pap. 8.95 (ISBN 0-393-00275-6, Norton Lib). Norton.

Ancient Near East in Pictures with Supplement. 2nd ed. Ed. by James B. Pritchard. Incl. Ancient Near Eastern Texts Relating to the Old Testament with Supplement. 3rd ed. Set. text ed. 60.50x ea. (ISBN 0-691-03503-2, 035032T); pictures 66.25x (032024T). 1969. deluxe ed. 68.50x ea. (ISBN 0-691-03502-4); Set. 126.75x (ISBN 0-686-66606-2). Princeton U Pr.

Ancient, Pagan & Modern Christian Symbolism. Thomas Inman. LC 77-6998. Repr. of 1884 ed. lib. bdg. 25.00 (ISBN 0-89341-301-1). Longwood Pub Group.

Ancient, Pagan & Modern Christian Symbolism. Thomas Inman. 147p. 1978. Repr. of 1884 ed. 15.95 (ISBN 0-87928-101-4). Corner Hse.

Ancient Patterns in Modern Prayer. Thomas A. Krosnicki. LC 74-172790. (Catholic University of America. Studies in Christian Antiquity Ser.). pap. 79.30 (2029516). Bks Demand UMI.

Ancient Prophets & Modern Problems. Samuel L. Brengle. 1978. pap. 3.95 (ISBN 0-86544-000-X). Salv Army Suppl South.

Ancient Quest. Swami Ramakrishnananda. 112p. pap. 1.00 (ISBN 0-87481-412-X). Vedanta Pr.

Ancient Records & the Structure of Genesis. P. J. Wiseman. Ed. by D. J. Wiseman. 160p. 1985. pap. 6.95 (ISBN 0-8407-7502-4). Nelson.

Ancient Religion & Mythology, 32 vols. Ed. by W. R. Connor. (Illus.). 1976. Set. 1039.00x (ISBN 0-405-07001-2). Ayer Co Pubs.

Ancient Roots & Modern Meanings. Jerry V. Diller. LC 77-99196. 1978. 12.50 (ISBN 0-8197-0457-1); pap. 7.95 (ISBN 0-685-27177-3). Bloch.

Ancient Sculptured Monuments of the County of Angus. Patrick Chalmers. LC 72-1052. (Bannatyne Club, Edinburgh. Publications: No. 88). Repr. of 1848 ed. 145.00 (ISBN 0-404-52818-X). AMS Pr.

Ancient Seals & the Bible. Ed. by L. Gorelick & E. Williams-Forte. (Occasional Papers on the Near East: Vol. 2, Issue 1). (Illus.). 84p. 1984. pap. 13.00x (ISBN 0-89003-045-6). Undena Pubns.

Ancient South Arabian Necropolis: Objects from the Second Campaign 1951 in the Timna Cemetery. Ray L. Cleveland. (American Foundation for the Study of Man: Vol. 4). (Illus.). 202p. 1965. 40.00x (ISBN 0-8018-0129-X). Johns Hopkins.

Ancient Symbol Worship: Phallic Idea. H. M. Westropp. 59.95 (ISBN 0-87968-633-2). Gordon Pr.

Ancient Synagogues in Palestine & Greece. E. L. Sukenik. (British Academy, London, Schweich Lectures on Biblical Archaeology Series, 1930). pap. 19.00 (ISBN 0-8115-1272-X). Kraus Repr.

Ancient Synagogues of the Iberian Peninsula. Don A. Halperin. LC 78-62577. (University of Florida Social Sciences Monographs: No. 38). (Illus.). 1969. pap. 3.50 (ISBN 0-8130-0272-9). U Presses Fla.

Ancient Synagogues Revealed. Ed. by Israel Exploration Society, Jerusalem & Lee I. Levine. LC 81-53031. (Illus.). 199p. 1982. 27.50x (ISBN 0-8143-1706-5). Wayne St U Pr.

Ancient Synagogues: The State of Research. Ed. by Joseph Gutmann. LC 81-5252. (Brown Univ. BJS Ser.). 1981. pap. 14.00 (ISBN 0-89130-467-3, 140022). Scholars Pr GA.

Ancient Teachings of the Masters. Darwin Gross. (Illus.). 45p. (Orig.). 1987. pap. 10.00 (ISBN 0-931689-06-6). SOS Pub OR.

Ancient Thoughts in Modern Perspective: A Contemporary View of the Bible. Solomon Poll. LC 68-22349. 136p. 1968. 6.95 (ISBN 0-8022-1998-5). Philos Lib.

Ancient Wisdom. 9th ed. Annie Besant. 1972. 7.95 (ISBN 0-8356-7038-4). Theos Pub Hse.

Ancient Wisdom & Modern Science. Ed. by Stanislav Grof. 360p. 1984. 39.50 (ISBN 0-87395-848-9); pap. 12.95x (ISBN 0-87395-849-7). State U NY Pr.

Ancient Wisdom Revived: A History of the Theosophical Movement. Bruce F. Campbell. LC 79-64664. 224p. 1980. 18.95x (ISBN 0-520-03968-8). U of Cal Pr.

Ancren Riwle: A Treatise on the Rules & Duties of Monastic Life. 1853. 55.00 (ISBN 0-685-13344-3). Johnson Repr.

Ancren Riwle, a Treatise on the Rules & Duties of Monastic Life from a Semi-Saxon MS. of the Thirteenth Century. Ed. by James Morton. LC 72-158250. (Camden Society, London. Publications, First Series: No. 1). Repr. of 1853 ed. 55.00 (ISBN 0-404-50157-5). AMS Pr.

Ancrene Wisse: English Text of the Ancrene Riwle. Ed. by J. R. Tolkien. (Early English Text Society Ser.). 1962. 19.95x (ISBN 0-19-722249-8). Oxford U Pr.

And a Cast of Thousands. Celeste Loucks et al. Ed. by Elaine S. Furlow. (Human Touch Photo-Text Ser.). (Illus.). 1978. 6.95 (ISBN 0-937170-11-9). Home Mission.

And a Time to Die. Mark Pelgrin. Ed. by Sheila Moon & Elizabeth Howes. LC 75-26836. 159p. 1976. pap. 2.95 (ISBN 0-8356-0305-9, Quest). Theos Pub Hse.

And Bring Them Closer to Torah: The Life & Works of Rabbi Aaron H. Blumenthal. Ed. by David R. Blumenthal. 235p. 1986. text ed. 9.95 (ISBN 0-88125-082-1). Ktav.

And Every Tongue Confess. George G. Hunter, III. LC 83-73224. 56p. (Orig.). 1983. pap. 4.50 (ISBN 0-88177-004-3, DR004B). Discipleship Res.

And God Came In: The Extraordinary Story of Joy Davidman-Her life & Marriage to C.S. Lewis. Lyle W. Dorsett. (Illus.). 192p. 1983. 14.95 (ISBN 0-02-532250-8). Macmillan.

And God Came In: The Extraordinary Story of Joy Davidman; Her Life & Marriage to C. S. Lewis. Lyle W. Dorsett. (Illus.). 192p. 1984. pap. 2.95 (ISBN 0-345-31787-4). Ballantine.

And God Created Laughter: The Bible As Divine Comedy. Conrad Hyers. LC 86-46037. 132p. (Orig.). 1987. pap. 9.95 (ISBN 0-8042-1653-3). John Knox.

And God Said... Yes! Michael L. Sherer. 1983. 5.75 (ISBN 0-89536-634-7, 0123). CSS of Ohio.

And, God, What About...? James T. Cumming & Hans G. Moll. 1980. 4.50 (ISBN 0-570-03806-5, 12-2915). Concordia.

And He Gave Pastors. Ed. by Thomas F. Zimmerman et al. LC 78-50485. 500p. 1978. text ed. 12.95 (ISBN 0-88243-460-8, 02-0460). Gospel Pub.

And He Gave Some Pastors Teachers. Ed. by James Stone. 324p. (Orig.). 1986. pap. text ed. 9.95 (ISBN 0-934942-61-7, 4052). White Wing Pub.

And He Had Compassion. William Barclay. LC 75-28099. 272p. 1976. pap. 5.95 (ISBN 0-8170-0686-9). Judson.

And He Had Compassion on Them: The Christian & World Hunger. Task Force on World Hunger. (Illus.). 1979. pap. text ed. 3.50 (ISBN 0-933140-00-2). CRC Pubns.

And He Loved Her. Carolyn Hobbs. 185p. (Orig.). 1979. pap. 1.95 (ISBN 0-89084-113-6). Bob Jones Univ Pr.

And Holy Is His Name. Robert Flynn. 1983. 5.95 (ISBN 0-87193-197-4). Dimension Bks.

And I Married the Son of a King. Sr. Mary E. Moore. 185p. 1979. pap. 6.95 (ISBN 0-8059-2688-7). Dorrance.

And It Came to Pass. Hayyim N. Bialik. 281p. 1938. 6.95 (ISBN 0-88482-887-5). Hebrew Pub.

And It Came to Pass: An Old Testament, Reader for Children. Rudolf Steiner. 1973. lib. bdg. 79.95 (ISBN 0-87968-556-5). Krishna Pr.

And It Was Good: Reflections on Beginnings. Madeleine L'Engle. LC 83-8518. 219p. 1983. 11.95 (ISBN 0-87788-046-8). Shaw Pubs.

And Jesus Said: A Handbook on the Parables of Jesus. William Barclay. LC 77-120410. 224p. 1970. pap. 7.95 (ISBN 0-664-24898-5). Westminster.

And Justice for All: New Introductory Essays in Ethics & Public Policy. Ed. by Tom Regan & Donald Van DeVeer. LC 81-23446. (Philosophy & Society Ser.). 320p. 1982. 34.00x (ISBN 0-8476-7059-7); pap. 12.50x (ISBN 0-8476-7060-0). Rowman.

And Let Us Say Amen. Joshua A. Wildman. Tr. by Charles Wengrov from Hebrew. Tr. of V'imru Amen. 1978. pap. 6.95 (ISBN 0-87306-148-9). Feldheim.

And More Celebrating the Seasons with Children. Philip E. Johnson. 120p. (Orig.). 1986. pap. 6.95 (ISBN 0-8298-0735-7). Pilgrim NY.

And Muhammad Is His Messenger: The Veneration of the Prophet in Islamic Piety. Annemarie Schimmel. LC 84-17374. (Studies in Religion). (Illus.). xii, 377p. 1985. 32.00x (ISBN 0-8078-1639-6); pap. 9.95x (ISBN 0-8078-4128-5). U of NC Pr.

And Now a Word from Our Creator. Thomas G. Savage. LC 72-1370. 1972. 5.95 (ISBN 0-8294-0213-6). Loyola.

And Now, & Here, Vol. II. Bhagwan S. Rajneesh. Ed. by Swami S. Vedant. LC 84-42798. (Early Writings & Discourses Ser.). 384p. (Orig.). 1985. pap. 4.95 (ISBN 0-88050-712-8). Chidvilas Found.

And Now, & Here, Vol. 1. Bhagwan Shree Rajneesh. Ed. by Swami Satya Mahasattva. LC 84-42798. (Early Discourses & Writings Ser.). 320p. (Orig.). 1984. pap. 4.95 (ISBN 0-88050-709-8). Chidvilas Found.

And Sarah Laughed: The Status of Woman in the Old Testament. John H. Otwell. LC 76-54671. 222p. 1977. pap. 8.95 (ISBN 0-664-24126-3). Westminster.

And Send the Sun Tomorrow: A Journal of My Father's Last Days. Maura Bremer. 1979. pap. 2.95 (ISBN 0-03-049396-X, HarpR). Har-Row.

And Signs Shall Follow. Gary D. Kinnaman. 1987. pap. 6.95 (Chosen Bks). Revell.

And So We Came to Rome: The Political Perspectives of St. Luke. Paul W. Walaskay. LC 82-19835. (Society for New Testament Studies Monograph: No. 49). (Illus.). 120p. 1984. 29.95 (ISBN 0-521-25116-8). Cambridge U Pr.

And Some Fell on Good Ground. Mary A. Sheridan. 1981. 9.95 (ISBN 0-8062-1806-1). Carlton.

And the Flowers Showered. Bhagwan Shree Rajneesh. Ed. by Swami Anand Somendra. LC 83-181344. (Zen Ser.). (Illus.). 288p. (Orig.). 1975. 16.95 (ISBN 0-88050-004-2); pap. 5.95 (ISBN 0-88050-504-4). Chidvilas Found.

And the Laugh Shall be First: A Treasury of Religious Humor. Ed. by William H. Willimon. 1986. pap. 12.95 (ISBN 0-687-01383-6). Abingdon.

And the Master Answered. Flor McCarthy. LC 84-72678. (Illus.). 96p. (Orig.). 1985. pap. 4.95 (ISBN 0-87793-279-4). Ave Maria.

And the Scroll Opened. George M. Lamsa. LC 67-23820. (Illus.). 1978. pap. 3.50 (ISBN 0-87516-274-6). De Vorss.

And the Trees Clap Their Hands: Faith, Perception & the New Physics. Virginia S. Owens. 148p. 1983. pap. 6.95 (ISBN 0-8028-1949-4). Eerdmans.

And Their Eyes Were Opened. Michael Scanlan & Ann T. Shields. 1976. pap. 3.95 (ISBN 0-89283-035-2). Servant.

And Then Comes the End. David Ewert. LC 79-28410. 216p. 1980. pap. 7.95 (ISBN 0-8361-1921-5). Herald Pr.

And Then Shall the End Come. Robert J. Pruitt. 1979. pap. 1.95 (ISBN 0-934942-20-X). White Wing Pub.

And Then the Angels Came to the First Grade Children. Marguerite Baker. 1964. pap. 1.50 (ISBN 0-685-79136-X). Summit Univ.

And Then There Was One. John W. Wright. 120p. (Orig.). 1985. pap. 4.95 (ISBN 0-8341-1057-1). Beacon Hill.

And Then There Was Peace. Dennis M. Jones. (Orig.). 1987. pap. 3.00 (ISBN 0-941992-08-X). Los Arboles Pub.

And Then There Were Three. Sara W. Shenk. LC 85-13936. 208p. (Orig.). 1985. pap. 8.95 (ISBN 0-8361-3398-6). Herald Pr.

And They All Sang Hallelujah: Plain-Folk Camp-Meeting Religion, 1800-1845. Dickson D. Bruce, Jr. LC 74-11344. (Illus.). 1974. 13.50x (ISBN 0-87049-157-1); pap. 5.95x (ISBN 0-87049-310-8). U of Tenn Pr.

And They Called Him Amos: The Story of John Amos Comenius-a Woodcut in Words. Florence H. Anastasas. LC 73-86540. 1973. 10.00 (ISBN 0-682-47814-8, University). Exposition Pr FL.

And They Felt No Shame: Christians Reclaim Their Sexuality. Joan Ohanneson. 200p. (Orig.). 1982. pap. 11.95 (ISBN 0-86683-676-4, HarpR). Har-Row.

And This Will Be a Sign. Jon L. Joyce. (Orig.). 1980. pap. 2.95 (ISBN 0-937172-05-7). JLJ Pubs.

And We Have Danced: The History of the Sacred Dance Guild, 1958-1978. Carlynn Reed. Ed. by Doug Adams. 1978. 5.95 (ISBN 0-941500-00-4). Sharing Co.

And We Mutually Pledge. Stewart M. Robinson. LC 64-17287. pap. 3.25 (ISBN 0-912806-19-2). Long Hse.

And You Visited Me. Charles W. Gusmer. (Studies in the Reformed Rites of the Catholic Church: Vol. VI). 160p. (Orig.). 1984. pap. 9.95 (ISBN 0-916134-61-X). Pueblo Pub Co.

And You Visited Me. Dennis Saylor. LC 79-88403. 1979. pap. 7.95 (ISBN 0-933350-21-X). Morse Pr.

And You, Who Do You Say I Am? 3.50 (ISBN 0-318-02212-5). Chrstphrs NY.

Anders Nygren. Thor Hall. (Makers of the Modern Theological Mind Ser.). 1978. 8.95 (ISBN 0-8499-0098-0). Word Bks.

Anders Nygren. Thor Hall. 230p. 1984. pap. text ed. 8.95 (ISBN 0-8499-3004-9, 3004-9). Word Bks.

Andover Liberals: A Study in American Theology. Daniel D. Williams. LC 79-111636. 1970. Repr. of 1941 ed. lib. bdg. 17.50x (ISBN 0-374-98584-7, Octagon). Hippocrene Bks.

Andre Gide. rev. ed. Albert J. Guerard. LC 74-88805. 1969. 20.00x (ISBN 0-674-03525-9). Harvard U Pr.

Andre Gide. Leon Pierre-Quint. Tr. by Dorothy Richardson. 1934. 30.00 (ISBN 0-8274-1865-5). R West.

Andre Gide. Vinio Rossi. LC 68-54458. (Columbia Essays on Modern Writers Ser.: No. 35). (Orig.). 1968. pap. 3.00 (ISBN 0-231-02960-8). Columbia U Pr.

Andre Gide: The Theism of an Atheist. H. J. Nersoyan. LC 69-17717. 1969. 19.95x (ISBN 0-8156-2135-3). Syracuse U Pr.

Andreae & the Formula of Concord. Robert Kolb. 1977. pap. 8.50 (ISBN 0-570-03741-7, 12-2645). Concordia.

Andrew Bonar Life & Diary. Andrew Bonar. 535p. 1984. Repr. of 1893 ed. 14.95 (ISBN 0-85151-432-4). Banner of Truth.

Andrew Law, American Psalmodist. Richard L. Crawford. (Music Ser.). (Illus.). xix, 424p. 1981. Repr. of 1968 ed. lib. bdg. 42.50 (ISBN 0-306-76090-8). Da Capo.

Andrew Murray: Apostle of Abiding Love. Leona Choy. 1978. 8.95 (ISBN 0-87508-368-4); pap. 6.95 (ISBN 0-87508-367-6). Chr Lit.

Andrew Project. James Taylor. LC 85-42826. (Illus.). 108p. (Orig.). 1985. pap. 4.95 (ISBN 0-8042-0461-6). John Knox.

Andromedans & Other Parables of Science & Faith. Denis Osborne. LC 78-18550. (Illus.). 1978. pap. 2.50 (ISBN 0-87784-600-6). Inter-Varsity.

Anesthetic Society. Donald DeMarco. 182p. (Orig.). 1982. pap. 6.95 (ISBN 0-931888-09-3). Christendom Pubns.

Anfaenge Des Erasmus: Humanismus und Devotio Moderna. Paul Mestwerdt. 34.00 (ISBN 0-384-38351-3); pap. 28.00 (ISBN 0-384-38350-5). Johnson Repr.

Anfaenge einer staendigen Inquisition in Boehmen: Ein Prager Inquisitoren-Handbuch aus der ersten Haelfte des 14 Jahrhunderts. Alexander Patschovsky. (Beitraege zur Geschichte und Quellenkunde des Mittelalters, Vol. 3). (Illus.). xviii, 319p. 1975. 39.60x (ISBN 3-11-004404-8). De Gruyter.

Anfange Des Puritanismus. Herbert Schöffler. Repr. of 1932 ed. 16.00 (ISBN 0-384-54220-4). Johnson Repr.

Angel Children: Those Who Die Before Accountability. Mary V. Hill. LC 73-75397. (Illus.). 70p. (Orig.). 1973. pap. 5.50 (ISBN 0-88290-017-X). Horizon Utah.

Angel of Apocalypse: Blake's Idea of Milton. Joseph A. Wittreich, Jr. LC 74-27316. 358p. 1975. 37.50x (ISBN 0-299-06800-5). U of Wis Pr.

Angel of Death: The Untold Story of Josef Mengele. Ed. by Yisrael Gutman & Shmuel Krakowski. 1986. 16.95 (ISBN 0-933503-62-8). Shapolsky Pubs.

Angel of His Presence. Grace L. Hill. LC 83-51594. 96p. 1984. pap. 2.50 (ISBN 0-8423-0047-3). Tyndale.

Angel of the Presence. Elise N. Morgan. (Meditation Ser.). 1922. 3.50 (ISBN 0-87516-327-0). De Vorss.

Angel Unaware. Dale E. Rogers. (Orig.). 1984. pap. 2.50 (ISBN 0-515-08952-4). Jove Pubns.

Angel with a Bushy Beard. Dudley Gardner. 1980. pap. 8.95x (ISBN 0-7152-0425-4). Outlook.

Angel World. George L. Nutting & Ruth S. Nutting. 115p. (Orig.). 1985. pap. 2.95 (ISBN 0-9612266-1-7). Numard Bks.

Angela Gods Magnet. Mary Y. Moran. (Illus.). 48p. 1987. 5.95 (ISBN 0-89962-583-5). Todd & Honeywell.

Angeles: Agentes Secretos de Dios. Billy Graham. Tr. by Juan Rojas from Eng. LC 76-20259. Tr. of Angels: God's Secret Agents. (Span.). 168p. 1976. pap. 4.95 (ISBN 0-89922-069-X). Edit Caribe.

Angels. Charles Capps. 224p. (Orig.). 1984. pap. 3.95 (ISBN 0-89274-308-5, HH-308). Harrison Hse.

Angels. Billy Graham. 1984. pap. 3.50 (ISBN 0-671-54147-1). PB.

Angels & Demons According to Lactantius. Emil Schneweis. LC 79-8121. (Satanism Ser.). 192p. Repr. of 1944 ed. 26.00 (ISBN 0-404-18433-2). AMS Pr.

Angels & Me. Carolyn Nystrom. (Children's Bible Basics Ser.). (Illus.). 1984. 4.95 (ISBN 0-8024-6017-8). Moody.

Angels & Men. Ladislaus Boros. 1976. 6.95 (ISBN 0-8245-0201-9). Crossroad NY.

Angels & Principalities. A. W. Carr. (Society for the New Testament Studies Monographs: No. 42). 240p. 1982. 32.50 (ISBN 0-521-23429-8). Cambridge U Pr.

Angels & the Other Heavenly Bodiless Powers. St. Dimitry of Rostov. pap. 0.25 (ISBN 0-686-05638-8). Eastern Orthodox.

Angels & Us. Mortimer J. Adler. 205p. 1982. 11.95 (ISBN 0-02-500550-2). Macmillan.

Angels, Angels, Angels. Landrum P. Leavell. LC 73-75627. 96p. 1973. pap. 5.95 (ISBN 0-8054-2222-6). Broadman.

Angels, Angels, Everywhere. G. Don Gilmore. LC 81-8525. 180p. 1981. 11.95 (ISBN 0-8298-0477-3); pap. 6.95 (ISBN 0-8298-0479-X). Pilgrim NY.

Angels Are My Friends. Annetta E. Dellinger. LC 85-7858. 32p. 1985. 4.95 (ISBN 0-570-04120-1, 56-1531). Concordia.

Angels Ascending & Descending. Angeln Ray. 176p. 1984. 12.95 (ISBN 0-915763-00-1). Starseed Pubns.

Angels, Elect & Evil. C. Fred Dickason. 256p. 1975. pap. 6.95 (ISBN 0-8024-0222-4). Moody.

Angels Fear: Towards an Epistemology of the Sacred. Gregory Bateson & May C. Bateson. 224p. 1987. 18.95 (ISBN 0-02-507670-1). Macmillan.

Angels: God's Messengers & Our Helpers. Lawrence G. Lovasik. (Saint Joseph Picture Bks.). (Illus.). flexible bdg. 0.95 (ISBN 0-89942-281-0, 281). Catholic Bk Pub.

Angels: God's Secret Agents. Billy Graham. 176p. 1986. 9.95 (ISBN 0-8499-0542-7, 0542-7); pap. 7.95 (ISBN 0-8499-3049-9). Word Bks.

Angels in Faded Jeans. Kaaren Witte. LC 79-84795. 160p. 1979. pap. 3.95 (ISBN 0-87123-014-3, 210014). Bethany Hse.

Angels in Religion & Art. Valentine Long. LC 77-117712. 1971. pap. 2.95 (ISBN 0-8199-0430-9). Franciscan Herald.

Angels in the Air. Paul Thigpen. 1986. 4.95 (ISBN 1-55513-053-4, Chariot Bks). Cook.

Angels in Traditional Design. Silvia Crockett. (International Design Library). (Illus.). 48p. (Orig.). 1987. pap. 3.95 (ISBN 0-88045-086-X). Stemmer Hse.

Angels: Ministers of Grace. Geddes MacGregor. (Illus.). 256p. 1987. 18.95 (ISBN 0-913729-42-6). Paragon Hse.

Angels on Assignment. Charles Hunter & Frances Hunter. 1979. pap. 4.95 (ISBN 0-917726-33-2). Hunter Bks.

Angels: Secret Agents of God & Satan. H. M. Richards, Jr. LC 80-22223. (Flame Ser.). 64p. 1980. pap. 0.99 (ISBN 0-8127-0313-8). Review & Herald.

Angels, Their Origin, Nature, Mission & Destiny. Howard A. Blazer. 64p. 1974. pap. 2.50x (ISBN 0-88428-034-9). Parchment Pr.

Angelus Silesius. Tr. by Paul Carus. 174p. 1909. 1.95 (ISBN 0-317-40418-0). Open Court.

Anger & Assertiveness in Pastoral Care. David W. Augsburger. Ed. by Howard J. Clinebell & Howard W. Stone. LC 78-14660. (Creative Pastoral Care & Counseling Ser.). 96p. 1979. pap. 0.50 (ISBN 0-8006-0562-4, 1-562). Fortress.

Angkor Wat. Michio Fujioka. LC 71-158641. (This Beautiful World Ser.: Vol. 29). (Illus.). 138p. (Orig.). 1972. pap. 4.95 (ISBN 0-87011-156-6). Kodansha.

Anglican & Puritan: The Basis of Their Opposition, 1558-1640. John F. New. 1964. 18.00x (ISBN 0-8047-0066-4). Stanford U Pr.

Anglican Church Today & Tomorrow. Michael E. Marshall. LC 83-62718. 176p. (Orig.). 1984. pap. 7.95 (ISBN 0-8192-1341-1). Morehouse.

Anglican Cycle of Prayer, Nineteen Eighty-Seven. Ed. by Charles H. Long. (Partners in Prayer Ser.). (Illus.). 128p. (Orig.). 1986. pap. 1.75 (ISBN 0-88028-053-0). Forward Movement.

Anglican Episcopate & the American Colonies. Arthur L. Cross. ix, 368p. 1964. Repr. of 1902 ed. 32.50 (ISBN 0-208-00420-3, Archon). Shoe String.

Anglican Essays. C. H. Sisson. 142p. 1983. 20.00 (ISBN 0-85635-456-2). Carcanet.

Anglican Moral Choice. Ed. by Paul Elmen. LC 82-62391. 274p. (Orig.). 1983. pap. 10.95 (ISBN 0-8192-1322-5). Morehouse.

Anglican Orders (English) The Bull of His Holiness Leo XIII, September 13, 1896, & the Answer to the Archbishops of England March 29, 1897. (Church Historical Society, London, Ser.: No. 12). pap. 16.00 (ISBN 0-317-16454-6). Kraus Repr.

Anglican Orders (Latin) The Bull of His Holiness Leo XIII, September 13, 1896, & the Answer to the Archbishops of England March 29, 1897. (Church Historical Society, London, Ser.: No. 13). Repr. of 1932 ed. 40.00 (ISBN 0-8115-3136-8). Kraus Repr.

Anglican-Orthodox Dialogue. LC 85-1766. 73p. 1986. pap. text ed. 3.95 (ISBN 0-88141-047-0). St Vladimirs.

Anglican-Orthodox Intercommunion. Bishop Raphael. pap. 0.25 (ISBN 0-686-05405-9). Eastern Orthodox.

Anglican Revival in Victorian Portsmouth. Nigel Yates. 1981. 42.00x (ISBN 0-317-43792-5, Pub. by City of Portsmouth). State Mutual Bk.

Anglican Spirituality. Ed. by William J. Wolf. LC 81-84717. 176p. (Orig.). 1982. pap. 9.95 (ISBN 0-8192-1297-0). Morehouse.

Anglican Theology & Pastoral Care. O. C. Edwards et al. Ed. by James Griffiss. 160p. (Orig.). 1985. pap. 8.95 (ISBN 0-8192-1364-0). Morehouse.

Anglican Tradition. Richard Holloway et al. Ed. by Richard Holloway. LC 83-62541. 132p. (Orig.). 1984. pap. 6.95 (ISBN 0-8192-1338-1). Morehouse.

Anglican Tradition in Eighteenth Century Verse. H. Grant Sampson. (De Proprietatibus Litterarum, Ser. Practica: No. 33). 1971. pap. text ed. 27.20x (ISBN 90-2791-907-0). Mouton.

Anglican Way: Evangelical & Catholic. Peter Toon. LC 83-60934. 96p. 1983. pap. 5.95 (ISBN 0-8192-1330-6). Morehouse.

Anglicanism. 4th ed. Stephen Neill. 1977. pap. 10.95x (ISBN 0-19-520033-0). Oxford U Pr.

Anglicanism & the Bible. Ed. by Frederick H. Borsch. LC 83-62717. (Anglican Studies). (Orig.). 1984. pap. 8.95 (ISBN 0-8192-1337-3). Morehouse.

Anglo-Catholic Revival. Sidney Ollard. 59.95 (ISBN 0-87968-634-0). Gordon Pr.

Anglo-Saxon Christian Poetry. Adriaan J. Barnouw. LC 74-20776. 1974. Repr. of 1914 ed. lib. bdg. 12.50 (ISBN 0-8414-3291-0). Folcroft.

Anglo-Saxon Church: Its History, Revenues & General Character. 4th ed. Henry Soames. LC 80-2212. Repr. of 1856 ed. 39.50 (ISBN 0-404-18786-2). AMS Pr.

Anglo-Saxon Church: Papers on History, Architecture, & Archaeology in Honor of Dr. H. M. Taylor. Ed. by L. A. Butler & R. K. Morris. (Research Report Ser.: No. 60). (Illus.). 240p. 1986. pap. 45.00x (ISBN 0-906780-54-3, Pub. by Council British Archaelogy). Humanities.

Anglo-Saxon Cross. Thomas D. Hill & Robert T. Farrell. (Yale Studies in English: Nos. 23 & 50). iv, 282p. 1976. Repr. of 1904 ed. 27.50 (ISBN 0-208-01555-8, Archon). Shoe String.

Anglo-Saxon Saints & Scholars. Eleanor S. Duckett. x, 484p. 1967. Repr. of 1947 ed. 35.00 (ISBN 0-208-00200-6, Archon). Shoe String.

Anglo-Vatican Relations, 1914-1939: Confidential Annual Reports of the British Ministers to the Holy See. Ed. by Thomas Hachey. 1972. lib. bdg. 23.00 (ISBN 0-8161-0991-5, Hall Reference). G K Hall.

Angry Catholic Women. Andrew Greeley & Mary Durkin. 1984. pap. 15.95 (ISBN 0-88347-165-5). Thomas More.

Angry Christian: How to Control & Use Your Anger. Bert Ghezzi. (Living As a Christian Ser.). 108p. (Orig.). 1980. pap. 2.95 (ISBN 0-89283-086-7). Servant.

Angry Prophet. J. C. Metcalfe. 1970. pap. 2.25 (ISBN 0-87508-909-7). Chr Lit.

Angst & the Abyss: The Hermeneutics of Nothingness. David K. Coe. (Academic Ser.). 1985. 17.95 (ISBN 0-89130-862-8, 01-01-49); pap. 11.95 (ISBN 0-89130-863-6). Scholars Pr GA.

Anguish & Joy of the Christian Life. Francois Mauriac. (Orig.). pap. 1.25x (ISBN 0-268-00005-0). U of Notre Dame Pr.

Anguish of the Jews: Twenty-Three Centuries of Antisemitism. rev. ed. Edward Flannery. LC 85-60298. 384p. 1985. pap. 12.95 (ISBN 0-8091-2702-4). Paulist Pr.

Animadversions Upon M. Seldens History of Tithes & His Review Thereof. Richard Tillesley. LC 77-7435. (English Experience Ser.: No. 896). 1977. Repr. of 1619 ed. lib. bdg. 26.50 (ISBN 90-221-0896-1). Walter J Johnson.

Animal Book. Illus. by Marc Harrison. (Bible Look-n-Learn Ser.). 1986. 3.95 (ISBN 0-8407-6708-0). Nelson.

Animal Faith & Spiritual Life: Previously Unpublished & Uncollected Writings by George Santayana with Critical Essays on His Thought. Ed. by John Lachs. LC 67-20665. (Century Philosophy Ser.). 1967. 39.50x (ISBN 0-89197-607-8). Irvington.

Animal Life in Jewish Tradition. Eli Schochet. LC 83-12015. 379p. 1983. 25.00x (ISBN 0-88125-019-8). Ktav.

Animal Sacrifice in Islam. M. I. Siddiqui. pap. 2.75 (ISBN 0-686-63893-X). Kazi Pubns.

Animal Symbolism in Ecclesiastical Architecture. E. P. Evans. 59.95 (ISBN 0-87968-638-3). Gordon Pr.

Animals. (Feelings & Growth Development Coloring Bks.). (Illus.). 0.75 (ISBN 0-8091-6542-2). Paulist Pr.

Animals, Birds & Plants of the Bible. Hilda L. Rostron. (Ladybird Ser). (Illus.). 1964. bds. 2.50 (ISBN 0-87508-830-9). Chr Lit.

Animals in the Ark. Patricia Mahany. (My Shape Bk.). (Illus.). 12p. 1984. 2.95 (ISBN 0-87239-781-5, 2721). Standard Pub.

Animals in the Bible: A Description of Their Meaning, Importance, Uses, Symbolical Value, 3 vols. J. G. Wood. (Illus.). 670p. 1986. Repr. Set. 337.45 (ISBN 0-89901-278-7). Found Class Reprints.

Animals That Show & Tell. William Coleman. LC 85-15122. 144p. 1985. pap. 4.95 (ISBN 0-87123-807-1). Bethany Hse.

Animated Hagaddah. Uri Shin'ar. Date not set. 14.95. Jonathan David.

Animated Haggadah & Story of Passover. Jacqueline Pliskin. (Illus.). 1987. pap. 7.95. Shapolsky Pubs.

Animated Megillah. Ephraim Sidon. (Animated Holydays Ser.). 54p. 1987. 14.95 (ISBN 0-8246-0324-9). Jonathan David.

Animus Against Milton. E. H. Visiak. 1945. lib. bdg. 12.50 (ISBN 0-8414-9173-9). Folcroft.

Anitya. Paul Twitchell. (Illus.). 1969. 5.95 (ISBN 0-914766-01-5). IWP Pub.

Ann H. Judson of Burma. E. R. Pitman. 1974. pap. 2.95 (ISBN 0-87508-601-2). Chr Lit.

Ann of Ava. Ethel D. Hubbard. LC 76-160921. (Biography Index Reprint Ser.). (Illus.). Repr. of 1941 ed. 17.25 (ISBN 0-8369-8084-0). Ayer Co Pubs.

Anna. Betty Barkman. 171p. (Orig.). 1985. pap. 6.65 (ISBN 0-919797-10-5). Kindred Pr.

Anna Brinton: A Study in Quaker Character. Eleanore P. Mather. LC 74-152086. (Illus., Orig.). 1971. pap. 2.50x (ISBN 0-87574-176-2). Pendle Hill.

Annales Camaldulenses Osb, 9 Vols. J. H. Mittarelli & A. Costadoni. 6787p. 1773. text ed. 745.20x (ISBN 0-576-72247-2, Pub. by Gregg Intl Pubs England). Gregg Intl.

Annales Cistercienses, 4 vols. Angel Manrique. 3196p. Date not set. Repr. of 1659 ed. text ed. 662.40x (ISBN 0-576-72863-2, Pub. by Gregg Intl Pubs England). Gregg Intl.

Annals & History of Henrico Parish, Diocese of Virginia, & St. John's P. E. Church. J. Staunton Moore. LC 78-72949. (Illus.). 578p. 1979. Repr. of 1904 ed. 25.00 (ISBN 0-8063-0829-X). Genealog Pub.

Annals of Shawnee Methodist Mission & Indian Manual Labor School. 2nd ed. Martha B. Caldwell. LC 39-28738. (Illus.). 120p. 1977. pap. 2.95 (ISBN 0-87726-005-2). Kansas St Hist.

Annals of the American Pulpit - Or, Commemorative Notices of Distinguished American Clergymen of Various Denominations, from the Early Settlement of the Country to the Close of the Year 1855, with Historical Introductions, 9 Vols. William B. Sprague. LC 75-83442. (Religion in America Ser). 1969. Repr. of 1857 ed. Set. 300.00 (ISBN 0-405-00267-X). Ayer Co Pubs.

Annals of the Early Caliphate from Original Sources. William Muir. 1977. lib. bdg. 59.95 (ISBN 0-8490-1434-4). Gordon Pr.

Annals of the Nyingma Lineage, Vol. 11. Ed. by Tarthang Tulku. (Illus.). 1977. pap. 12.00 (ISBN 0-913546-32-1). Dharma Pub.

Annals of the Reformation & Establishment of Religion & Other Various Occurrences in the Church of England, 4 vols. in 7. 2nd ed. John Strype. LC 66-20694. 1708-09. Repr. 255.00 (ISBN 0-8337-3444-X). B Franklin.

Annals of Witchcraft in New England & Elsewhere in the United States from Their First Settlement. Samuel G. Drake. LC 67-13327. 1967. Repr. of 1869 ed. 20.00 (ISBN 0-405-08466-8, Blom Pubns). Ayer Co Pubs.

Annals of Witchcraft in New England, & Elsewhere in the United States. Samuel G. Drake. LC 73-161683. (Woodward's Historical Ser.: No. 8). 306p. 1972. Repr. of 1869 ed. lib. bdg. 23.50 (ISBN 0-8337-0898-8). B Franklin.

Annals of Witchcraft in New England & Elsewhere in the United States. Samuel G. Drake. 69.95 (ISBN 0-87968-641-3). Gordon Pr.

Anne De Marquets, Poetesse Religieuse De Seizieme Siecle. Sr. M. Hilarine Seiler. LC 75-94200. (Catholic University of America. Studies in Romance Languages & Literatures: No. 4). (Fr). Repr. of 1931 ed. 21.00 (ISBN 0-404-50304-7). AMS Pr.

Anne Frank: The Diary of a Young Girl. rev. ed. Anne Frank. Tr. by B. M. Mooyaart. 312p. (YA) 1967. 16.95 (ISBN 0-385-04019-9). Doubleday.

Annie Armstrong: Dreamer in Action. Bobbie Sorrill. LC 83-70842. 1984. 8.95 (ISBN 0-8054-6333-X). Broadman.

Annie Beseant - An Autobiography. 17.50 (ISBN 0-8356-7568-8). Theos Pub Hse.

Annihilating the Hosts of Hell: The Battle Royal, Vol. I. Win Worley. 1981. 5.00 (ISBN 0-686-75479-4). HBC.

Annihilation or Salvation? Frances DiCrescenza. 1986. 8.95 (ISBN 0-8062-2505-X). Carlton.

Anniversaries to Celebrate. Verle C. Schumacher. LC 83-2228. 128p. (Orig.). 1982. pap. 7.95 (ISBN 0-8298-0628-8). Pilgrim NY.

Anniversary Essays in Mediaeval History, by Students of Charles Homer Haskins: Presented on His Completion of Forty Years of Teaching. facs. ed. Ed. by Charles H. Taylor. LC 67-30194. (Essay Index Reprint Ser). 1929. 22.00 (ISBN 0-8369-0155-X). Ayer Co Pubs.

Anno Domini Number One. Mary E. Shoemaker. (Orig.). 1981. pap. 2.95 (ISBN 0-937172-25-1). JLJ Pubs.

Annotated Bibliography of John Bunyan Studies. Compiled by Richard L. Greaves. LC 72-177693. 1972. 7.00 (ISBN 0-318-03615-0). Pitts Theolog.

Annotated Bibliography of the Work of the Canon Law Society of America 1965-1980. Richard G. Cunningham. 121p. (Orig.). 1982. pap. 4.50 (ISBN 0-943616-06-9). Canon Law Soc.

Annotated Edition of Lectures on Moral Philosophy. John Witherspoon. Ed. by Jack Scott. LC 80-24404. 213p. 1981. 27.50 (ISBN 0-87413-164-2). U Delaware Pr.

Annotated Handbook of Biblical Quotations, Verses, & Parables. Robert Vichas. LC 85-19346. 411p. 1985. 29.95 (ISBN 0-13-037870-4, Busn). P-H.

Annotated Index to the Sermons of John Donne: Index to Proper Names, Vol. II. Troy D. Reeves. Ed. by James Hogg. (Elizabethan & Renaissance Studies). 148p. (Orig.). 1980. pap. 15.00 (ISBN 0-317-40117-3, Pub by Salzburgh Studies). Longwood Pub Group.

Annotated Index to the Sermons of John Donne: Index to the Scriptures, Vol. I. Troy D. Reeves. Ed. by James Hogg. (Elizabethan & Renaissance Studies). 229p. (Orig.). 1979. pap. 15.00 (ISBN 0-317-40114-9, Pub by Salzburgh Studies). Longwood Pub Group.

Annotated Index to the Sermons of John Donne: Index to Topics, Vol. III. Troy D. Reeves. Ed. by James Hogg. (Elizabethan & Renaissance Studies). 226p. (Orig.). 1981. pap. 15.00 (ISBN 0-317-40118-1, Pub by Salzburg Studies). Longwood Pub Group.

Annotated Mahabharata Bibliography. P. Lal. 31p. 1973. 10.00 (ISBN 0-88253-306-1). Ind-US Inc.

Annotations to Richard Watson: An Apology for the Bible in a Series of Letters Addressed to Thomas Paine, 8th Edition, 1797. William Blake. Ed. by G. Ingli James. (Regency Reprints Ser.: No. III). 144p. (Orig.). 1984. pap. 9.00 (ISBN 0-906449-67-7, Pub. by UC Cardiff Pr). Longwood Pub Group.

Announcing the Reign of God: Evangelization & the Subversive Memory of Jesus. Mortimer Arias. LC 83-5696. 176p. 1984. pap. 8.95 (ISBN 0-8006-1712-6, 1-1712). Fortress.

Annual Budgeting: Developing & Using an Annual Budget Effectively. Manfred Holck, Jr. 1977. pap. 3.95 (ISBN 0-8066-1549-4, 10-0360). Augsburg.

Annual Convention Proceedings, 45th: 1983. CLSA Staff. 354p. 1984. pap. 7.00 (ISBN 0-943616-22-0). Canon Law Soc.

Annual Fund Estate Planning. Robert L. Stuhr & Jerry A. Jarc. (How to Ser.). 1984. 4.80. Natl Cath Educ.

Annual Register of the Baptist Denomination in North America to 1970. John Asplund. 1979. Repr. 10.00 (ISBN 0-317-01254-1). Church History.

Annual Review of Research: Religious Education, Vol. 1. Ed. by John H. Peatling. (Orig.). 1980. pap. 5.95 (ISBN 0-915744-23-6). Character Res.

Annual Review of Research: Religious Education, Vol. 2. Ed. by John H. Peatling. viii, 148p. (Orig.). 1981. pap. 6.95 (ISBN 0-915744-26-0). Character Res.

Annual Review of the Social Sciences of Religion, Vol. 1. Ed. by Joachim Matthes et al. 1977. pap. 23.20x (ISBN 90-279-7794-1). Mouton.

Annual Review of the Social Sciences of Religion, Vol. 3, 1979. Ed. by Joachim Matthes et al. 1979. pap. text ed. 26.00x (ISBN 0-686-27015-0). Mouton.

Annuale Mediaevale, Vol. 18. Ed. by Frank T. Zbozny. 1978. pap. text ed. 13.50x (ISBN 0-391-01220-7). Humanities.

Annulment: Do You Have a Case? Terence E. Tierney. LC 78-6790. 1978. pap. 4.95 (ISBN 0-8189-0372-4). Alba.

Annulment-Your Chance to Remarry Within the Catholic Church: A Step-by-Step Guide Using the New Code of Canon Law. Joseph P. Zwack. LC 83-47739. (Using the New Code of Canon Law Ser.). 144p. (Orig.). 1983. pap. 5.95 (ISBN 0-06-250990-X, BN-3004, HarpR). Har-Row.

Annulments. 4th rev. ed. Lawrence G. Wrenn. vi, 145p. (Orig.). 1983. pap. 4.00 (ISBN 0-943616-16-6). Canon Law Soc.

Annunciation from the Right: From Early Christian Times to the Sixteenth Century. Don Denny. LC 76-23611. (Outstanding Dissertations in the Fine Arts - 2nd Ser. - Fifteenth Century). (Illus.). 1977. Repr. of 1965 ed. lib. bdg. 55.00 (ISBN 0-8240-2683-7). Garland Pub.

Anointed to Serve: The Story of the Assemblies of God. William W. Menzies. LC 77-146707. (Illus.). 440p. 1971. 12.95 (ISBN 0-88243-465-9, 02-0465). Gospel Pub.

Anointing of the Sick. Karl Rahner. 1979. 1.50 (ISBN 0-87193-108-7). Dimension Bks.

Anointing the Sick. Maria Roccapriore. LC 80-65722. (Illus.). 144p. (Orig.). 1980. pap. 2.95 (ISBN 0-8189-1160-3, 160, Pub. by Alba Bks). Alba.

Anointing with the Spirit. Gerard Austin. (Reformed Rites of the Catholic Church Ser.: Vol. 2). 192p. (Orig.). 1985. pap. 10.95 (ISBN 0-916134-70-9). Pueblo Pub Co.

Anonymous Christ: Jesus As Savior in Modern Theology. Lee N. Snook. LC 86-14117. 192p. (Orig.). 1986. pap. 10.95 (ISBN 0-8066-2220-2, 10-0370). Augsburg.

Another Brown Bag. Jerry M. Jordan. LC 80-36849. (Illus.). 1980. pap. 6.95 (ISBN 0-8298-0406-4). Pilgrim NY.

Another Chance: How God Overrides Our Big Mistakes. Dean Merrill. 160p. (Orig.). 1981. pap. 4.95 (ISBN 0-310-35331-9, 11325P). Zondervan.

Another Day. Eugenia Price. LC 84-7697. 168p. 1984. 9.95 (ISBN 0-385-27660-5, Dial). Doubleday.

Another Generation. W. A. Davis. (Orig.). 1985. text ed. 5.25 (ISBN 0-87148-019-0); pap. 4.25 (ISBN 0-87148-020-4); instr's. guide 7.95 (ISBN 0-87148-021-2). Pathway Pr.

Another Letter of John to James. John Kater. (Illus.). 64p. (Orig.). 1982. pap. 3.95 (ISBN 0-8164-2376-8, HarpR). Har-Row.

Another Look at the Rapture. Roy Hicks. 120p. (Orig.). 1982. pap. 3.95 (ISBN 0-89274-246-1). Harrison Hse.

Another Path. Gladys Taber. LC 63-17678. 1963. 12.45i (ISBN 0-397-00260-2). Har-Row.

Another Song, Another Season: Poems & Portrayals. Roger White. 184p. 1979. cloth o.p. 4.00 (ISBN 0-85398-087-X); pap. 8.95 (ISBN 0-85398-088-8). G Ronald Pub.

Another Tassel Is Moved: Guidelines for College Graduates. Louis O. Caldwell. (Ultra Books Ser). 1970. 4.95 (ISBN 0-8010-2343-2). Baker Bk.

Another Wave of Revival. rev. ed. Frank Bartleman. Ed. by John Meyers. Orig. Title: Another Wave Rolls In. 176p. 1982. pap. text ed. 2.95 (ISBN 0-88368-111-0). Whitaker Hse.

Another Way to Live: Experiencing Intentional Community. James Best. LC 78-51384. 32p. (Orig.). 1978. pap. 2.50x (ISBN 0-87574-218-1). Pendle Hill.

Another Will Gird You: A Message to the Society of Friends. Mildred B. Young. 1983. pap. 2.50 (ISBN 0-87574-109-6, 109). Pendle Hill.

Anselm & a New Generation. G. Rosemary Evans. 1980. 32.50x (ISBN 0-19-826651-0). Oxford U Pr.

Anselm & His Work. A. C. Welch. 1979. Repr. of 1901 ed. lib. bdg. 30.00 (ISBN 0-8492-2965-0). R West.

Anselm & Talking About God. G. Rosemary Evans. 1978. 29.95x (ISBN 0-19-826647-2). Oxford U Pr.

Anselm: Fides Quaerens Intellectum. Karl Barth. Tr. by Ian W. Robertson from Ger. LC 76-10795. (Pittsburgh Reprint Ser.: No. 2). 1985. text ed. 15.00 (ISBN 0-915138-75-1). Pickwick.

Anselm of Canterbury, 4 vols. Ed. by Jasper Hopkins. Tr. by Herbert Richardson from Lat. LC 74-19840. 1919. Set. 149.95x (ISBN 0-88946-977-6). E Mellen.

Anselm of Canterbury: Vol. I, Monologion, Proslogion, Debate with Gaunilo, & a Meditation on Human Redemption. Anselm Of Canterbury. Tr. by Jasper Hopkins & Herbert Richardson. LC 74-19840. 161p. 1974. 39.95x (ISBN 0-88946-000-0). E Mellen.

Anselm of Canterbury: Vol. II, Philosophical Fragments; De Grammatico; on Truth; Freedom of Choice; the Fall of the Devil; the Harmony of the Foreknowledge, the Predestination, & the Grace of God with Free Choice. Anselm Of Canterbury. Tr. by Jasper Hopkins & Herbert Richardson. LC 74-19840. 237p. 1976. 49.95x (ISBN 0-88946-250-X). E Mellen.

Anselm of Canterbury: Vol. III, Two Letters Concerning Roscelin; the Incarnation of the Word; Why God Became a Man; the Virgin Conception & Original Sin; the Procession of the Holy Spirit; Three Letters on the Sacraments. Anselm Of Canterbury. Tr. by Jasper Hopkins & Herbert Richardson. LC 74-19840. 265p. 1976. 39.95x (ISBN 0-88946-350-6). E Mellen.

Anselm of Canterbury: Vol. IV, Hermeneutical & Textual Problems in the Complete Treatises of St. Anselm. Jasper Hopkins. LC 74-19840. 202p. 1976. 49.95x (ISBN 0-88946-551-7). E Mellen.

Anselm of Canterbury: Why God Became Man. Anselm Of Canterbury. Ed. by Jasper Hopkins & Herbert Richardson. 105p. 1980. soft cover 7.95x (ISBN 0-88946-009-4). E Mellen.

Anselm Studies: An Occasional Journal. Ed. by Marjorie Chibnall et al. 273p. (Orig.). 1983. lib. bdg. 35.00x (ISBN 0-527-03662-5). Kraus Intl.

Anselm Weber, O.F.M. Missionary to the Navaho. Robert L. Wilken. 1955. 12.50 (ISBN 0-686-32658-X, 55-1235). St Michaels.

Anselmian Explorations: Essays in Philosophical Theology. Thomas V. Morris. LC 86-40239. 264p. 1987. text ed. 28.95 (ISBN 0-268-00616-4). U of Notre Dame Pr.

Anselm's Discovery: A Re-Examination of the Ontological Proof for God's Existence. Charles Hartshorne. LC 65-20278. 349p. 1973. 23.95 (ISBN 0-87548-216-3); pap. 11.95 (ISBN 0-87548-217-1). Open Court.

Anselm's Doctrine of Freedom & The Will. G. Stanley Kane. LC 81-16939. (Texts & Studies in Religion, Vol. 10). 240p. 1982. 49.95x (ISBN 0-88946-914-8). E Mellen.

Answer for Oppression. Kenneth Hagin, Jr. 1983. pap. 0.50 mini bk. (ISBN 0-89276-717-0). Hagin Ministries.

Answer for Today, Vol. 1. Chuck Smith. 72p. (Orig.). 1980. pap. 1.95 (ISBN 0-936728-09-4). Word for Today.

Answer in Defence of the Truth Against the Apology of Private Mass. Thomas Cooper. 1850. 21.00 (ISBN 0-384-09790-1). Johnson Repr.

Answer Me. Ruth Edwards. LC 83-61453. (Illus., Orig.). 1983. pap. 7.95 (ISBN 0-89390-041-9); pap. text ed. 6.95. Resource Pubns.

Answer of Mr. R. Hooker, to a Supplication to the Privie Counsell. Richard Hooker. LC 76-57390. (English Experience Ser.: No. 807). 1977. Repr. of 1612 ed. lib. bdg. 5.00 (ISBN 90-221-0807-4). Walter J Johnson.

Answer to a Poisoned Book. Thomas More. Ed. by Stepehn Foley & Clarence H. Miller. LC 63-7949. (Complete Works of St. Thomas More Ser.: Vol. II). 544p. 1985. text ed. 60.00 (ISBN 0-300-03129-7). Yale U Pr.

Answer to Discipline. Norman Wright. LC 76-21113. (Answer Ser.). 1976. pap. 1.95 (ISBN 0-89081-061-3, 0613). Harvest Hse.

Answer to Divorce. Norman Wright. LC 76-52831. (Answer Ser.). 1977. pap. 1.95 (ISBN 0-89081-033-8, 0338). Harvest Hse.

Answer to John Martiall's Treatise of the Cross. James Calfhill. 1846. 31.00 (ISBN 0-384-07020-5). Johnson Repr.

Answer to John Robinson of Leyden by a Puritan Friend. Ed. by Champlin Burrage. (Harvard Theological Studies). 1920. pap. 15.00 (ISBN 0-527-01009-X). Kraus Repr.

Answer to Life. Paul E. Little. LC 86-72378. Orig. Title: Faith is for People. 96p. 1987. pap. 4.95 (ISBN 0-89107-429-5, Crossway Bks). Good News.

Answer to Loneliness. Norman Wright. (Orig.). pap. 1.95 (ISBN 0-89081-077-X). Harvest Hse.

Answer to Parent-Teen Relationships. Norman Wright. (Orig.). pap. 1.95 (ISBN 0-89081-075-3). Harvest Hse.

Answer to Sir Thomas More's Dialogue, the Supper of the Lord After the True Meaning of John 6 & or. 11. William Tyndale. Repr. of 1850 ed. 31.00 (ISBN 0-384-62240-2). Johnson Repr.

Answer to Submission & Decision Making. Norman Wright. pap. 1.95 (ISBN 0-89081-078-8). Harvest Hse.

Answer to the Rev. Mr. Clarkson's Essay on the Slavery & Commerce of the Human Species. facs. ed. G. Francklyn. LC 74-83963. (Black Heritage Library Collection Ser). 1789. 13.50 (ISBN 0-8369-8574-5). Ayer Co Pubs.

Answer to the Unjust Complaints of W. Best: Also an Answer to Mr. John Davenport. John Paget. LC 76-57403. (English Experience Ser.: No. 819). 1977. Repr. of 1635 ed. lib. bdg. 16.00 (ISBN 90-221-0819-8). Walter J Johnson.

Answer Will Come. Robert Russell. 91p. 1981. pap. 3.00 (ISBN 0-87516-440-4). De Vorss.

Answere Made by the Kynges Hyghnes to the Petitions of the Rebelles in Yorkshire. Henry VII. LC 77-7417. (English Experience Ser.: No. 872). 1977. Repr. of 1536 ed. lib. bdg. 3.50 (ISBN 90-221-0872-4). Walter J Johnson.

Answere to a Letter (Saint German, Christopher) LC 73-6097. (English Experience Ser.: No. 566). 1973. Repr. of 1535 ed. 8.00 (ISBN 90-221-0566-0). Walter J Johnson.

Answered Prayer. MaryAnn Berry. 28p. (Orig.). 1985. 4.95 (ISBN 0-9614947-0-0); pap. 2.50 (ISBN 0-9614947-1-9). First Love Min.

Answeres of Some Brethren of the Ministerie to the Replies Concerning the Late Covenant. LC 74-80155. (English Experience Ser.: No. 636). 1974. Repr. of 1638 ed. 18.50 (ISBN 90-221-0636-5). Walter J Johnson.

Answering Christianity's Most Puzzling Questions, Vol. 2. Richard Sisson. 240p. (Orig.). 1983. pap. 8.95 (ISBN 0-8024-5148-9). Moody.

Answering for Faith: Christ & the Human Search for Salvation. Richard Viladesau. 1987. pap. 14.95. Paulist Pr.

Answering Love's Call: Christian Love & a Life of Prayer. Stephen Doughty. LC 86-81809. 128p. (Orig.). 1986. pap. 4.95 (ISBN 0-87793-348-0). Ave Maria.

Answering the Cry. Virginia Crider. (Northland Ser.). 1976. pap. 2.50 (ISBN 0-87813-510-3). Christian Light.

Answering the Tough Ones. David Dewitt. 160p. 1980. pap. 5.95 (ISBN 0-8024-8971-0). Moody.

Answers for Parish Councillors. William J. Rademacher. LC 81-51429. 1981. pap. 6.95 (ISBN 0-89622-134-2). Twenty-Third.

Answers for Today, Vol. II. Chuck Smith. (Answers for Today Ser.). 80p. (Orig.). 1986. pap. write for info. (ISBN 0-936728-28-0). Word for Today.

Answers Lie Below: Essays in Honor of Lawrence Edmund Toombs. Ed. by Henry O. Thompson. LC 83-23376. (Illus.). 428p. (Orig.). 1984. lib. bdg. 32.50 (ISBN 0-8191-3745-6); pap. text ed. 17.75 (ISBN 0-8191-3746-4). U Pr of Amer.

Answers: Living Book Ser. Josh McDowell & Don Stewart. 256p. (Orig.). 1986. 3.95 (ISBN 0-8423-0021-X). Tyndale.

Answers of Jesus to Job. G. Campbell Morgan. (Morgan Library). 1973. pap. 3.95 (ISBN 0-8010-5917-8). Baker Bk.

Answers to Life's Difficult Questions. Richard Warren. 132p. 1985. pap. 4.95 (ISBN 0-89693-395-4). Victor Bks.

Answers to Praise. Merlin R. Carothers. 169p. (Orig.). 1972. pap. 4.95 (ISBN 0-943026-07-5). Carothers.

Answers to Prayer. Charles G. Finney. Ed. by Louis G. Parkhurst, Jr. LC 83-12253. 122p. (Orig.). 1983. pap. 3.95 (ISBN 0-87123-296-0). Bethany Hse.

Answers to Prayer. George Mueller. (Moody Classics Ser.). 1984. pap. 3.50 (ISBN 0-8024-0565-7). Moody.

Answers to Questions on the Ocean of Theosophy. Robert Crosbie. 249p. 1933. 5.00 (ISBN 0-938998-12-9). Theosophy.

Answers to the Cultist at Your Door. Robert Passantino et al. LC 80-83850. 1981. pap. 5.95 (ISBN 0-89081-275-6). Harvest Hse.

Answers to the Difficult Questions Concerning Healing. (Divine Healing & Health Ser.). 1.25 (ISBN 0-89985-025-1). Christ Nations.

Answers to the Questions Christian Women Are Asking. Bill Carmichael & Nancie Carmichael. 1984. text ed. 10.95 (ISBN 0-89081-446-5); pap. 6.95 (ISBN 0-89081-442-2). Harvest Hse.

Answers to Tough Questions. Josh McDowell & Don Stewart. 190p. (Orig.). 1980. pap. 6.95 (ISBN 0-918956-65-X). Campus Crusade.

Answers to Tough Questions Skeptics Ask About the Christian Faith. Josh McDowell & Don Stewart. LC 80-67432. 190p. 1980. pap. 6.95 (ISBN 0-918956-65-X, 402776). Campus Crusade.

Answers to Two Hundred of Life's Most Probing Questions. Pat Robertson. 1987. pap. 3.95. Bantam.

Answers to Your People Problems. John G. Kerbs. LC 68-25949. (Harvest Ser.). 1978. pap. 4.95 (ISBN 0-8163-0192-1, 01634-5). Pacific Pr Pub Assn.

Answers to Your Questions. Richard V. Lawlor. 1980. 5.00 (ISBN 0-8198-0700-1); pap. 4.00 (ISBN 0-8198-0701-X). Dghtrs St Paul.

Ante la Perdida de un Ser Querido. Granger Westberg. Tr. by Jorge A. Rodriguez. 32p. 1985. Repr. of 1984 ed. 1.50 (ISBN 0-311-46081-X). Casa Bautista.

Antes de la Ultima Batalla-Armagedon. Arthur E. Bloomfield. 192p. 1977. 3.75 (ISBN 0-88113-003-6). Edit Betania.

Anthems & Anthem Composers. Myles B. Foster. LC 76-125047. (Music Ser.). 1970. Repr. of 1901 ed. lib. bdg. 32.50 (ISBN 0-306-70012-3). Da Capo.

Anthems for Choirs Four. Ed. by Christopher Morris. 1976. pap. 8.75x (ISBN 0-19-353018-X). Oxford U Pr.

Anthems for Choirs One: Fifty Anthems for Mixed Voices. Ed. by Francis Jackson. 1973. pap. 8.75 (ISBN 0-19-353214-X). Oxford U Pr.

Anthems for Choirs Three: Twenty-Four Anthems for Sopranos & Altos, Three or More Parts. Ed. by Philip Ledger. 1973. pap. text ed. 8.75x (ISBN 0-19-353242-5). Oxford U Pr.

Anthems for Choirs Two: Twenty-Four Anthems for Sopranos & Altos, Unison & Two-Part. Ed. by Philip Ledger. 1973. pap. text ed. 8.75x (ISBN 0-19-353240-9). Oxford U Pr.

Anthems for Men's Voices, 2 vols. Peter Le Huray et al. Incl. Vol. 1. Altos, Tenors & Basses. 11.50x (ISBN 0-19-353234-4); Vol. 2. Tenors & Basses. 11.50x (ISBN 0-19-353235-2). 1965. Oxford U Pr.

Anthems for the Junior Choir, 5 bks. Ed. by W. Lawrence Curry. 1.50 ea. Westminster.

Anthenium. Ernest L. Norman. 1964. 4.95 (ISBN 0-932642-13-6). Unarius Pubns.

Anthologie Des Maitres Religieux Primirties Des XV, XVI & XVII Siecles, 6 vols. Ed. by Charles Bordes. (Music Ser.). 1981. Repr. of 1893 ed. Set. lib. bdg. 250.00 (ISBN 0-306-76089-4); Vol. 1; IV, 184 Pp. lib. bdg. 47.50 (ISBN 0-306-76114-9); Vol. 2; VIII, 194 Pp. lib. bdg. 47.50 (ISBN 0-306-76115-7); Vol. 3; IV, 184 Pp. lib. bdg. 47.50 (ISBN 0-306-76116-5); Vol. 4; IV, 190 Pp. lib. bdg. 47.50 (ISBN 0-306-76117-3); Vol. 5; II, 190 Pp. lib. bdg. 47.50 (ISBN 0-306-76118-1); Vol. 6; II, 202 Pp. lib. bdg. 47.50 (ISBN 0-306-76119-X). Da Capo.

Anthology, Nineteen Thirty-Four to Nineteen Forty-Four. facsimile ed. Jewish Frontier (Periodical) LC 76-167370. (Essay Index Reprint Ser). Repr. of 1945 ed. 31.00 (ISBN 0-8369-2459-2). Ayer Co Pubs.

Anthology of Atheism & Rationalism. Ed. by Gordon Stein. LC 80-81326. (Skeptic's Bookshelf Ser.). 354p. 1984. pap. 15.95 (ISBN 0-87975-267-X). Prometheus Bks.

Anthology of Christian Mysticism. Ed. by Paul De Jaegher. 1977. 7.95 (ISBN 0-87243-073-1). Templegate.

Anthology of Hebrew Poetry in Greece, Anatolia & the Balkans. Leon J. Weinberger. LC 75-34119. 270p. 1975. pap. 16.50 (ISBN 0-8173-8525-8). U of Ala Pr.

Anthology of Holocaust Literature. Jacob Glatstein et al. LC 68-19609. (Temple Bks). 1972. pap. text ed. 6.95x (ISBN 0-689-70343-0, T23). Atheneum.

Anthology of Jesus. James Marchant. Ed. by Warren W. Wiersbe. LC 80-25038. 382p. 1981. Repr. of 1926 ed. 11.95 (ISBN 0-8254-4015-7). Kregel.

Anthology of Jewish Mysticism. Tr. by Raphael Ben Zion from Hebrew. 5.00 (ISBN 0-686-13334-X). Yesod Pubs.

Anthology of Jewish Mysticism. Tr. by Raphael Ben Zion. 255p. 1984. pap. 6.95 (ISBN 0-910818-29-0). Judaica Pr.

Anthology of Modern Yiddish Literature. Ed. by Joseph Leftwich. LC 74-82386. (Anthology Ser: No. 1). 346p. 1974. pap. text ed. 13.60x (ISBN 90-2793-496-7). Mouton.

Anthology of Modern Yiddish Poetry. Ruth Whitman. LC 66-25551. 141p. 1979. pap. 4.95 (ISBN 0-686-29291-X). Workmen's Circle.

Anthology of the Love of God: From the Writings of Evelyn Underhill. Ed. by Lunsden Barkway & Lucy Menzies. 220p. 1981. Repr. of 1953 ed. lib. bdg. 30.00 (ISBN 0-8495-0067-2). Arden Lib.

Anthology on Armed Jewish Resistance 1939-1945, Vol. 1. Isaac Kowalski. (Illus.). 648p. 1984. Repr. 30.00x. Jewish Com Pub.

Anthology on Armed Jewish Resistance 1939-1945, Vol. 2. Isaac Kowalski. 648p. 1985. Repr. 30.00x (ISBN 0-317-46999-1). Jewish Com Pub.

Anthology on Armed Jewish Resistance 1939-1945, Vol. 3. Isaac Kowalski. 648p. 1986. Repr. 30.00x (ISBN 0-317-47002-7). Jewish Com Pub.

Anthropological Approaches to the Old Testament. Ed. by Bernhard Lang. LC 84-48723. (Issues in Religion & Theology Ser.). 176p. 1985. pap. 7.95 (ISBN 0-8006-1771-1, 1-1771). Fortress.

Anthropological Approaches to the Study of Religion. Ed. by Michael Banton. 1968. pap. 13.95 (ISBN 0-422-72510-2, NO.2068, Pub. by Tavistock England). Methuen Inc.

Anthropological Insights for Missionaries. Paul G. Hiebert. 280p. 1987. pap. 13.95 (ISBN 0-8010-4291-7). Baker Bk.

Anthropological Religion. Friedrich M. Mueller. LC 73-18822. (Gifford Lectures: 1891). 1975. Repr. of 1892 ed. 34.00 (ISBN 0-404-11428-8). AMS Pr.

Anthropological Studies of Religion: An Introductory Text. Brian Morris. (Illus.). 384p. 1987. 42.50 (ISBN 0-521-32794-6); pap. 12.95 (ISBN 0-521-33991-X). Cambridge U Pr.

Anthropology & Religion. Peter H. Buck. LC 72-121753. viii, 96p. 1970. Repr. of 1939 ed. 16.00 (ISBN 0-208-00950-7, Archon). Shoe String.

Anthropology & Religion. Peter H. Buck. 1939. 11.50x (ISBN 0-686-83471-2). Elliots Bks.

Anthropology & the Apocalypse: An Interpretation of "the Book of Revelation" in Relation to the Archaeology, Folklore & Religious Literature & Ritual of the Near East. V. Burch. 1977. lib. bdg. 59.95 (ISBN 0-8490-1437-9). Gordon Pr.

Anthropology & the Old Testament. J. W. Rogerson. (Biblical Seminar Ser.: No. 1). 128p. 1984. pap. text ed. 8.95x (ISBN 0-905774-82-5, Pub. by JSOT Pr England). Eisenbrauns.

Anthropology & the Study of Religion. Ed. by Robert L. Moore & Frank E. Reynolds. LC 83-71781. (Studies in Religion & Society). 230p. 1984. text ed. 24.95x (ISBN 0-913348-20-1); pap. text ed. 11.95 (ISBN 0-913348-21-X). Ctr Sci Study.

Anthropology in Theological Perspective. Wolfhart Pannenberg. Tr. by Matthew J. O'Connell from German. LC 84-22048. 552p. 1985. 38.95 (ISBN 0-664-21399-5). Westminster.

Anthropology of Saint John of Damascus. Constance N. Tsirpanlis. 64p. 1980. pap. 3.00 (ISBN 0-686-36332-9). EO Pr.

Anthropology of the Old Testament. Hans W. Wolff. Tr. by Margaret Kohl from Ger. LC 74-21591. 304p. 1981. pap. 10.95 (ISBN 0-8006-1500-X, 1-1500). Fortress.

Anthropomorphism & Physics. T. Percy Nunn. 1977. lib. bdg. 59.95 (ISBN 0-8490-1438-7). Gordon Pr.

Anthropos & Son of Man. Carl H. Kraeling. LC 27-23162. (Columbia University. Oriental Studies: No. 25). Repr. of 1927 ed. 18.50 (ISBN 0-404-50515-5). AMS Pr.

Anthroposophical Approach to Medicine, Vol. 1. Friedrich Husemann et al. (Illus.). 411p. 1983. 30.00 (ISBN 0-88010-031-1). Anthroposophic.

Anthroposophical Approach to Medicine, Vol. 2. Ed. by Otto Wolff. Tr. by G. Karnow from Ger. Tr. of Das Bild des Menschen als Grundlage der Heilkunst. 1987. 40.00 (ISBN 0-88010-174-1). Anthroposophic.

Anthroposophical Medicine: Spiritual Science & the Art of Healing. Victor Bott. 208p. (Orig.). 1984. pap. 8.95 (ISBN 0-7225-0958-8). Thorsons Pubs.

Anthroposophical Understanding of the Soul. F. W. Emmichoven. Tr. by Friedemann Schwarzkopf from Ger. 170p. (Orig.). 1983. pap. 8.95 (ISBN 0-88010-019-2). Anthroposophic.

Anthroposophy: An Introduction. Rudolf Steiner. Tr. by V. Compton Burnett from Ger. 130p. 1983. pap. 7.00 (ISBN 0-85440-387-6, Pub by Steinerbooks). Anthroposophic.

Anthroposophy & Christianity. Rudolf Steiner. Tr. of Christus und die menschliche Seele, Ueber den sinn deslebens, Theosophische Moral, Anthroposophie und Christentum, German. 26p. (Orig.). 1985. pap. 2.95 (ISBN 0-88010-149-0). Anthroposophic.

Anthroposophy & Russia. Andre I. Belyi. 1983. pap. 5.00 (ISBN 0-916786-69-2). St George Bk Serv.

Anthroposophy as a Healing Force. L. Francis Edmunds. 14p. pap. 2.25 (ISBN 0-88010-037-0, Pub.by Rudolf Steiner Pr). Anthroposophic.

Anti-Blackness in English Religion. Joseph R. Washington, Jr. LC 84-27334. (Texts & Studies in Religion: Vol. 19). 623p. 1985. 79.95x (ISBN 0-88946-808-7). E Mellen.

Anti-Catholicism in America, 1841-1851. Three Sermons: An Original Anthology. Ed. by Gerald Grob. (Anti-Movements in America Ser.). 1977. Repr. of 1977 ed. lib. bdg. 17.00x (ISBN 0-405-09980-0). Ayer Co Pubs.

Anti-Gentilism: Jews As Anti-Gentiles. 1984. lib. bdg. 79.95 (ISBN 0-87700-596-6). Revisionist Pr.

Anti-Judaism: A Psychohistory. Ernest A. Rappaport. LC 75-36297. 312p. 1976. 12.50 (ISBN 0-9603382-0-9). Perspective Chicago.

Anti-Judaism in Early Christianity: Vol. 1, Paul & the Gospels. Ed. by P. Richardson & D. Granskou. 240p. 1984. pap. text ed. 17.95x (ISBN 0-88920-167-6, Pub. by Wilfrid Laurier Canada). Humanities.

Anti-Judaism in Early Christianity, Vol. 2: Separation & Polemic. Ed. by Stephen Wilson. (Studies in Christianity & Judaism: Vol. 2.2). 200p. 1986. pap. text ed. 18.50 (ISBN 0-88920-196-X, Pub. by Wilfrid Laurier Canada). Humanities.

Anti-Methodist Publications Issued During the 18th Century. Richard Green. LC 71-83701. 175p. 1974. Repr. of 1902 ed. lib. bdg. 22.50 (ISBN 0-8337-1436-8). B Franklin.

Anti-Mormonism in Idaho, Eighteen Seventy-Two to Ninety-Two. Merle W. Wells. LC 77-89975. (Studies in Mormon History Ser.: No. 4). 1978. pap. 7.95 (ISBN 0-8425-0904-6). Brigham.

Anti-Semite & Jew. Jean-Paul Sartre. LC 48-9237. 1965. pap. 4.95 (ISBN 0-8052-0102-5). Schocken.

Anti-Semitic Stereotypes Without Jews: Images of the Jews in England, 1290-1700. Bernard Glassman. LC 75-16391. 218p. 1975. 22.50x (ISBN 0-8143-1545-3). Wayne St U Pr.

Anti-Semitism. Edward F. Dolan, Jr. LC 85-8820. (Illus.). 135p. 1985. PLB 11.90 (ISBN 0-531-10068-5). Watts.

Anti-Semitism: A Case Study in Prejudice & Discrimination. J. Milton Yinger. 80p. pap. 2.50 (ISBN 0-88464-046-9). ADL.

Anti-Semitism: A Modern Perspective. Caroline Arnold & Herma Silverstein. LC 84-16351. (Illus.). 224p. 1985. 10.79 (ISBN 0-671-49850-9). Messner.

Anti-Semitism: Causes & Effects of a Prejudice. Paul E. Grosser & Edwin G. Halpern. 1979. pap. 5.95 (ISBN 0-8065-0703-9). Citadel Pr.

Anti-Semitism in America. Harold E. Quinley & Charles Y. Glock. LC 78-20649. 1979. 11.95 (ISBN 0-02-925640-2). Free Pr.

Anti-Semitism in America, 1878-1939. An Original Anthology. LC 76-46110. (Anti-Movements in America). (Illus.). 1977. lib. bdg. 35.00 (ISBN 0-405-09981-9). Ayer Co Pubs.

Anti-Semitism in American History. Ed. by David A. Gerber. 440p. 1986. 29.95 (ISBN 0-252-01214-3). U of Ill Pr.

Anti-Semitism in British Society Eighteen Seventy-Six to Nineteen Thirty-Nine. Colin Holmes. LC 78-21023. 328p. 1979. text ed. 49.50x (ISBN 0-8419-0459-6). Holmes & Meier.

Anti-Semitism in the Soviet Union: Its Roots & Consequences. 664p. 1984. 35.00 (ISBN 0-88464-051-5); pap. 16.95 (ISBN 0-88464-052-3). ADL.

Anti-Semitism: Its History & Causes. Bernard Lazare. 1982. lib. bdg. 59.95 (ISBN 0-87700-426-9). Revisionist Pr.

Anti-Semitism: The Road to the Holocaust & Beyond. Charles Patterson. 160p. 1982. 11.95 (ISBN 0-8027-6470-3). Walker & Co.

Anti-Semitism Through the Ages. H. Coudenhove-Kalergi. 59.95 (ISBN 0-87968-649-9). Gordon Pr.

Anti-Slavery Manual, Being an Examination, in the Light of the Bible, & of Facts, into the Moral & Social Wrongs of American Slavery. John G. Fee. LC 74-82189. (Anti-Slavery Crusade in America Ser). 1969. Repr. of 1848 ed. 14.00 (ISBN 0-405-00627-6). Ayer Co Pubs.

Anti-Slavery, Religion & Reform. Ed. by Christine Bolt & Seymour Drescher. LC 79-41532. xi, 377p. 1980. 35.00 (ISBN 0-208-01783-6, Archon). Shoe String.

Anti-Trinitarianism of Early Quakers. Thomas H. Weisser. 39p. 2.00 (ISBN 0-317-40412-1). Tom Weisser.

Anti-Zionist Complex. Jacques Givet. Tr. by Evelyn Abel from Fr. LC 81-16693. Tr. of Israel et le Genocide Inacheve. 192p. 1982. 11.95 (ISBN 0-89961-019-6). SBS Pub.

Antichrist. Saint Hippolytus. 1979. pap. 2.95 (ISBN 0-686-26145-3). Eastern Orthodox.

Antichrist. Vincent Miceli. 14.95 (ISBN 0-8158-0395-8). Chris Mass.

Antichrist. Friedrich Nietzsche. LC 70-161338. (Atheist Viewpoint Ser). 60p. 1972. Repr. of 1930 ed. 13.00 (ISBN 0-405-03799-6). Ayer Co Pubs.

Antichrist. Arthur W. Pink. 1980. pap. 12.00 (ISBN 0-86524-000-0, 9802). Klock & Klock.

Antichrist & His Forerunner. Gordon Lindsay. (End of the Age Ser.: Vol. 2). 1.25 (ISBN 0-89985-068-5). Christ Nations.

Antichrist & Twilight of the Gods. Friedrich Nietzsche. 1974. 100.00 (ISBN 0-87968-210-8). Gordon Pr.

Antichrist in the Middle Ages: A Study of Medieval Apocalypticism, Art, & Literature. Richard K. Emmerson. LC 79-3874. (Illus.). 320p. 1981. 35.00x (ISBN 0-295-95716-6). U of Wash Pr.

Antichrist Legend: A Chapter in Christian & Jewish Folklore. Wilhelm Bousset. LC 79-8095. (Satanism Ser.). 344p. Repr. of 1896 ed. 37.50 (ISBN 0-404-18406-5). AMS Pr.

Antichrist Legend: A Chapter in Christian & Jewish Folklore. Wilhelm Bousset. 1977. lib. bdg. 59.95 (ISBN 0-8490-1439-5). Gordon Pr.

Antichrist, Orthodoxy or Heterodoxy. Archimandrite Constantine. pap. 0.25 (ISBN 0-686-11505-8). Eastern Orthodox.

Antichrist's Rise to Power. Gordon Lindsay. (End of the Age Ser.: Vol. 3). 1.25 (ISBN 0-89985-069-3). Christ Nations.

Anticlericalism: A Brief History. Jose M. Sanchez. LC 72-3504. 256p. 1973. text ed. 14.95 (ISBN 0-268-00471-4). U of Notre Dame Pr.

Anticristo y el Santuario. Thomas McCall & Zola Levitt. Orig. Title: Satan in the Sanctuary. (Span.). 128p. 1983. pap. 3.25 (ISBN 0-8254-1474-1). Kregel.

Antidote. Shragu Silverstein. 1980. pap. 3.95 (ISBN 0-87306-173-X). Feldheim.

Antidoto Contra la Ansiedad. Leslie D. Weatherhead. 1979. pap. 2.75 (ISBN 0-8358-0414-3). Upper Room.

Antifraternal Tradition in Medieval Literature. Penn R. Szittya. LC 85-43316. (Illus.). 320p. 1986. text ed. 40.00x (ISBN 0-691-06680-9). Princeton U Pr.

Antike und Orient im Mittelalter: Vortraege der Koelner Mediaevistentagungen 1956-1959. 2nd ed. Ed. by P. Wilpert. (Miscellanea mediaevalia, 1). 274p. 1971. 33.60x (ISBN 3-11-002395-4). De Gruyter.

Antikhrist. Archpriest Boris Molchanov. Tr. of Antichrist. 24p. 1976. pap. 1.00 (ISBN 0-317-29128-9). Holy Trinity.

Antinomian Controversy. Charles F. Adams. LC 74-164507. 1976. Repr. of 1892 ed. lib. bdg. 25.00 (ISBN 0-306-70290-8). Da Capo.

Antioch & Rome: New Testament Cradles of Catholic Christianity. Raymond E. Brown & John Meier. 256p. 1983. pap. 5.95 (ISBN 0-8091-2532-3). Paulist Pr.

Antiohonale Sarisburiense, 6 Vols. Walter H. Frere. 115p. 1923. text ed. 310.50 (ISBN 0-576-28701-6, Pub. by Gregg Intl Pubs England). Gregg Intl.

Antionomianism in the Colony of Massachusetts Bay, 1636-38, Including the Short Story & Documents. Ed. by Charles F. Adams. 1966. 26.00 (ISBN 0-8337-0010-3). B Franklin.

Antiphonary of Bangor. Michael Curran. 272p. 1984. 60.00x (ISBN 0-7165-0338-7, BBA 05250, Pub. by Irish Academic Pr Ireland). Biblio Dist.

Antiphons, Responsories & other Chants from the Mozarabic Rite. C. W. Brockett. (Wissenschaftliche Abhandlungen - Musicological Studies Ser.: No. 15). 300p. 1968. lib. bdg. 60.00 (ISBN 0-912024-85-2). Inst Mediaeval Mus.

Antiquitie Triumphing over Noveltie. John Favour. LC 76-171757. (English Experience Ser.: No. 325). 602p. 1971. Repr. of 1619 ed. 72.00 (ISBN 90-221-0325-0). Walter J Johnson.

Antiquities & Curiosities of the Church: Folklore & Historical Traditions About English Churches. Ed. by William Andrews. LC 77-87673. Repr. of 1897 ed. 20.00 (ISBN 0-404-16465-X). AMS Pr.

Antireligious Propaganda in the Soviet Union: A Study of Mass Persuasion. David E. Powell. LC 74-34127. 206p. 1975. pap. 8.95x (ISBN 0-262-66042-3). MIT Pr.

Antisemitic Propaganda: An Annotated Bibliography & Research. Robert Singerman. LC 81-43363. (History, Political Science, International Affairs, Area Studies). 220p. 1982. lib. bdg. 73.00 (ISBN 0-8240-9270-8, SS112). Garland Pub.

Antisemitism. Hannah Arendt. LC 66-22273. Orig. Title: Origins of Totalitarianism, Pt. 1. 136p. 1968. pap. 3.95 (ISBN 0-15-607810-4, HB131, Harv). HarBraceJ.

Antisemitism & the Foundations of Christianity. Ed. by Alan T. Davies. LC 79-65620. 276p. 1979. pap. 8.95 (ISBN 0-8091-2219-7). Paulist Pr.

Antisemitism: Historically & Critically Examined. facsimile ed. Hugo Valentin. Tr. by A. G. Chater. LC 79-164630. (Select Bibliographies Reprint Ser.). Repr. of 1936 ed. 22.00 (ISBN 0-8369-5914-0). Ayer Co Pubs.

Antisemitism in the Contemporary World. Ed. by Michael Curtis. LC 85-13919. 200p. 1985. 32.50x (ISBN 0-8133-0157-2). Westview.

Antizion. 2nd rev. ed. Compiled by William Grimstad. 1980. pap. 6.00 (ISBN 0-911038-20-5). Noontide.

Antizion: The Jewish & Zionist Question Through the Ages. William Grimstad. 1982. lib. bdg. 69.95 (ISBN 0-686-97529-4). Revisionist Pr.

Antoinette Brown Blackwell: A Biography. Elizabeth Cazden. LC 82-4986. (Illus.). 328p. 1983. 24.95 (ISBN 0-935312-00-5); pap. 9.95 (ISBN 0-935312-04-8). Feminist Pr.

Antologia de Homilias Biblicas, Vol. IV. Ed. by Hiram Almirudus. (Span.). 162p. 1981. 6.95 (ISBN 0-87148-025-5). Pathway Pr.

Antologia de Homilias Biblicas, Vol. V. Ed. by Hiram Almirudus. (Span.). 158p. 1982. 6.95 (ISBN 0-87148-026-3). Pathway Pr.

Antologia de Homilias Biblicas, Vol. VI. Ed. by Hiram Almirudus. (Span.). 158p. 1982. 6.95 (ISBN 0-87148-027-1). Pathway Pr.

Antologia de Homilias Biblicas, Vol. III. Ed. by Hiram Almirudus. (Span.). 148p. 1980. 6.95 (ISBN 0-87148-024-7). Pathway Pr.

Antologia de Homilias Biblicas, Vol. I. Ed. by Hiram Almirudus. (Span.). 159p. 1977. 6.95 (ISBN 0-87148-022-0). Pathway Pr.

Antologia de Homilias Biblicas, Vol. II. Ed. by Hiram Almirudus. (Span.). 159p. 1979. 6.95 (ISBN 0-87148-023-9). Pathway Pr.

Antonin Cyril Stojan: Apostle of Unity. Ludvik Nemec. LC 83-70817. (Illus.). 256p. 1983. pap. 11.95 (ISBN 0-89944-068-1). Don Bosco Multimedia.

Antoninus Pius. Willy Huttl. LC 75-7326. (Roman History Ser.). (Ger.). 1975. Repr. 57.00x (ISBN 0-405-07089-6). Ayer Co Pubs.

Antonio: Opera Omnia. Giovanni Campano. 608p. 1495. Repr. of 1495 ed. text ed. 99.36 (ISBN 0-576-72225-1, Pub. by Gregg Intl Pubs England). Gregg Intl.

Antwort Der Reformatoren Auf Die Zehtenfrage. Gunter Zimmermann. (European University Studies Three: Vol. 164). 175p. 1982. 21.05 (ISBN 3-8204-5745-3). P Lang Pubs.

Anugita. Tr. by K. T. Telang from Sanscrit. LC 81-50202. (Secret Doctrine Reference Ser.). 176p. 1981. Repr. of 1882 ed. 12.00 (ISBN 0-913510-40-8). Wizards.

Anvil of Sinai. Fendel Zechariah. 1980. 12.95 (ISBN 0-686-76479-X). Feldheim.

Anxious Bench: Chambersburg, PA 1844. John W. Nevin. Ed. by Bruce Kuklick. Bd. with Mystical Presence (Philadelphia, PA 1846) 56p. (American Religious Thought of the 18th & 19th Centuries Ser.). 312p. 1987. lib. bdg. 45.00 (ISBN 0-8240-6970-6). Garland Pub.

Any Miracle God Wants to Give. Danny E. Morris. 1974. pap. 1.25x (ISBN 0-8358-0314-7). Upper Room.

Any Old Time, Bk. 4. Stan Campbell. 80p. 1985. pap. 6.95 (ISBN 0-89693-640-6). Victor Bks.

Any Old Time, Bk. 5. Paul Borthwick. 80p. 1986. pap. 6.95 (ISBN 0-89693-187-0). Victor Bks.

Any Old Time, Bk. 6. David R. Veerman. 1986. pap. 6.95 (ISBN 0-89693-510-8). Victor Bks.

Any Old Time, Bk. 7. Ed. by David R. Veerman. 80p. 1987. pap. 5.95 (ISBN 0-89693-509-4). Victor Bks.

Any Old Times, Bk. 1. David R. Veerman. 80p. 1984. pap. 6.95 (ISBN 0-88207-595-0). Victor Bks.

Anybody Listening? Carol M. Floyd. 1982. 2.50 (ISBN 0-89536-572-3, 0119). CSS of Ohio.

Anybody Who Needs to Be Sure Is in Trouble. Bob Edwards. LC 82-81009. 72p. 1982. pap. 5.45 (ISBN 0-941780-11-2, Parkhurst-Little). August Hse.

Anyone Can Pray: A Guide to Methods of Christian Prayer. Graeme J. Davidson & Mary Macdonald. LC 82-62921. 208p. (Orig.). 1983. pap. 7.95 (ISBN 0-8091-2542-0). Paulist Pr.

Anyone Can Prophesy. Robert B. Hall. 1977. pap. 3.95 (ISBN 0-686-23219-4). Episcopal Ctr.

Aorist Participle of Antecedent Action. Earnell Sams, Jr. LC 81-67641. 1982. pap. write for info. (ISBN 0-940068-01-X). Doctrine Christ.

Aparokshanubhuti (Self-Realization) Shankara. Tr. by Swami Vimuktananda. (Sanskrit & Eng). pap. 2.50 (ISBN 0-87481-065-5). Vedanta Pr.

Apartheid Is a Heresy. Ed. by John W. De Gruchy & Charles Villa-Vicencio. 208p. (Orig.). 1983. pap. 5.95 (ISBN 0-8028-1972-9). Eerdmans.

Aphorismes of Christian Religion or a Verie Compendious Abridgement of M. I. Calvins Institutions Set Forth by M I Piscator. Jean Calvin. Tr. by H. Holland. LC 73-6107. (English Experience Ser.: No. 575). 1973. Repr. of 1596 ed. 26.00 (ISBN 90-221-0575-X). Walter J Johnson.

Aphorisms of Yoga. Bhagwan S. Patanjali. (Illus.). 96p. (Orig.). 1973. pap. 5.50 (ISBN 0-571-10320-0). Faber & Faber.

Aphraates & the Jews. Frank S. Gavin. LC 77-168102. (Columbia University. Contributions to Oriental History & Philology: No. 9). Repr. of 1923 ed. 12.50 (ISBN 0-404-50539-2). AMS Pr.

Apocalipsis. Ed. by Roberto A. Rivera. (Span.). 96p. 1980. pap. 3.25 (ISBN 0-87148-028-X). Pathway Pr.

Apocalipsis (Comentario Biblico Portavoz) Charles C. Ryrie. Orig. Title: Revelation (Everyman's Bible Commentary) (Span.). 128p. 1981. pap. 3.50 (ISBN 0-8254-1625-6). Kregel.

Apocalipsis de Juan: Un Comentario. George E. Ladd. Tr. by Arnoldo Canclini from Eng. LC 78-50625. Tr. of Commentary on the Revelation of John. (Span.). 269p. (Orig.). pap. 6.95 (ISBN 0-89922-111-4). Edit Caribe.

Apocalypse. Adela Y. Collins. (New Testament Message Ser.: Vol. 22). 172p. 1979. 9.95 (ISBN 0-89453-210-3); pap. 6.95 (ISBN 0-89453-145-X). M Glazier.

Apocalypse. Elizabeth S. Fiorenza. (Read & Pray Ser.). 64p. 1976. pap. 1.25 (ISBN 0-8199-0726-X). Franciscan Herald.

Apocalypse. Joseph Seiss. LC 86-27393. 536p. 1987. Repr. 24.95 (ISBN 0-8254-3754-7). Kregel.

Apocalypse! David A. Wilson. (Illus.). 175p. (Orig.). 1973. pap. 8.00 (ISBN 0-934852-10-3). Lorien Hse.

Apocalypse: A Premillennial Interpretation of the Book of Revelation. Douglas Simpson. 1975. pap. 3.95 (ISBN 0-89265-029-X). Randall Hse.

Apocalypse & Semitic Syntax. Steven Thompson. LC 84-12081. (Society for New Testament Studies Monograph: No. 52). 160p. 1985. 32.50 (ISBN 0-521-26031-0). Cambridge U Pr.

Apocalypse Attributed to St. John. Manly P. Hall. pap. 2.95 (ISBN 0-89314-810-5). Philos Res.

Apocalypse: Biblical Revelation Explained. Patrick Sena. LC 83-22299. 116p. (Orig.). 1983. pap. 6.95 (ISBN 0-8189-0454-2). Alba.

Apocalypse En Francais Au XIIIE, 2 Vols. Repr. of 1900 ed. Set. 116.00 (ISBN 0-384-04215-5). Johnson Repr.

Apocalypse Explained, 6 vols. Student ed. Emanuel Swedenborg. LC 76-46145. 12.00 ea. Vol. 1 (ISBN 0-87785-000-3). Vol. 2 (ISBN 0-87785-001-1). Vol. 3 (ISBN 0-87785-002-X). Vol. 4 (ISBN 0-87785-003-8). Vol. 5 (ISBN 0-87785-004-6). Vol. 6 (ISBN 0-87785-005-4). 72.00 set (ISBN 0-87785-006-2). Swedenborg.

Apocalypse in English Renaissance Thought & Literature. Ed. by C. A. Patrides & Joseph A. Wittreich, Jr. LC 84-71281. 452p. (Orig.). 1985. 52.00x (ISBN 0-8014-1648-5); pap. 19.95x (ISBN 0-8014-9893-7). Cornell U Pr.

Apocalypse of Elijah. Ed. by Susan T. Comstock et al. LC 79-24788. (Society of Biblical Literature Texts & Translations). 126p. 1981. pap. 14.25 (ISBN 0-89130-372-3, 06 02 19). Scholars Pr GA.

Apocalypse of History: Problems of Providence & Human Destiny. E. Lampert. 1948. 34.50x (ISBN 0-317-07646-9). Elliots Bks.

Apocalypse of John. Charles G. Torrey. 1958. 39.50x (ISBN 0-686-83474-7). Elliots Bks.

Apocalypse of St. John. 2nd ed. Rudolf Steiner. Tr. of Die Apokalypse des Johannes. 227p. 1985. pap. 12.95 (ISBN 0-88010-131-8). Anthroposophic.

Apocalypse of the Word: The Life & Message of George Fox (1624-1690) Douglas Gwyn. 240p. (Orig.). 1986. pap. 14.95 (ISBN 0-913408-91-3). Friends United.

Apocalypse Revealed, 2 vols. Emanuel Swedenborg. LC 78-5623. 1974. Vol. 1. Vol. 2. student ed. set 11.00 (ISBN 0-87785-017-8); student ed. 12.00 ea. Vol. 1 (ISBN 0-87785-015-1). Vol. 2 (ISBN 0-87785-016-X). pap. 7.00 (ISBN 0-87785-014-3). Swedenborg.

Apocalypse: The Perennial Revelation of Jesus Christ. Eugenio Corsini. Ed. by Moloney. (Good News Studies: Vol. 5). 1983. pap. 5.95 (ISBN 0-89453-310-X). M Glazier.

Apocalypse Today. Thomas F. Torrance. 192p. 1960. 10.95 (ISBN 0-227-67405-7). Attic Pr.

Apocalypse Unsealed. James M. Pryse. LC 76-41124. (Illus.). 1977. pap. 4.95 (ISBN 0-685-59031-3). Sym & Sign.

Apocalypse Unsealed. Robert F. Riggs. LC 80-81698. 328p. 1981. pap. 9.95 (ISBN 0-8022-2367-2). Philos Lib.

Apocalypse: World War III, Vol. I. L. F. Hatchell. (Illus.). 160p. 1980. pap. 3.95x (ISBN 0-940532-02-6). AOG.

Apocalypso: Revelations in Theatre. Jack Sheperd. LC 70-178680. (Orig.). pap. 2.50x (ISBN 0-87574-180-0). Pendle Hill.

Apocalyptic. Leon Morris. 88p. 1977. pap. 4.95 (ISBN 0-8028-1455-7). Eerdmans.

Apocalyptic: Ancient & Modern. D. S. Russell. LC 78-54561. 96p. 1978. pap. 4.25 (ISBN 0-8006-1342-2, 1-1342). Fortress.

Apocalyptic Book of Isaiah: A New Translation with Interpretative Key. Avraham Gileadi. Tr. by Avraham Gileadi. (Hebrew.). 207p. 1982. 10.95 (ISBN 0-910511-00-4). Hebraeus Pr.

Apocalyptic Commentary. Clyde C. Cox. 1970. 6.95 (ISBN 0-87148-011-5). Pathway Pr.

Apocalyptic Imagination. John Collins. 288p. 1984. 24.50x (ISBN 0-8245-0623-5). Crossroad NY.

Apocalyptic Messianism & Contemporary Jewish-American Poetry. R. Barbara Gitenstein. (Modern Jewish Literature & Culture Ser.). 128p. (Orig.). 1986. 39.50x (ISBN 0-88706-154-0); pap. 12.95x (ISBN 0-88706-155-9). State U NY Pr.

Apocalyptic Premise: Nuclear Arms Debated. Ed. by Ernest W. Lefever & E. Stephen Hunt. LC 82-18315. 429p. 1982. 22.00 (ISBN 0-89633-062-1); pap. 14.00 (ISBN 0-89633-063-X). Ethics & Public Policy.

Apocalyptic Spirituality. Tr. by Bernard McGinn. LC 79-90834. (Classics of Western Spirituality Ser.). 352p. 1979. 13.95 (ISBN 0-8091-0305-2); pap. 7.95 (ISBN 0-8091-2242-1). Paulist Pr.

Apocalyptic Tradition in Reformation Britain 1530-1645. Katherine R. Firth. (Historical Monographs). (Illus.). 1979. 45.00x (ISBN 0-19-821868-0). Oxford U Pr.

Apocalyptic Vision in America: Interdisciplinary Essays on Myth & Culture. Ed. by Lois P. Zamora. LC 81-85524. 272p. 1982. 19.95 (ISBN 0-686-82270-6). Bowling Green Univ.

Apocalyptic Vision of the Book of Daniel. John J. Collins. LC 77-23124. (Harvard Semitic Monograph). 1977. text ed. 11.95 (ISBN 0-89130-133-X, 040016). Scholars Pr GA.

Apocalyptic Writings. Jonathan Edwards. LC 57-2336. (Works of Jonathan Edwards: Vol. 5). (Illus.). 1977. 50.00x (ISBN 0-300-01945-9). Yale U Pr.

Apocalypticism in the Mediterranean World & the Near East: Proceedings of the International Colloquium. Ed. by David Hellholm. 889p. 1983. lib. bdg. 157.50x (ISBN 3-16-144460-4, Pub. by J C B Mohr BRD). Coronet Bks.

Apoclypse of Baruch. Intro. by R. H. Charles. 1976. Repr. of 1896 ed. 39.00x (ISBN 0-685-71069-6, Regency). Scholarly.

Apocrypha. Ed. by Edgar J. Goodspeed. 1959. pap. 5.95 (ISBN 0-394-70163-1, V163, Vin). Random.

Apocrypha & Pseudepigrapha of the Old Testament, 2 Vols. R. H. Charles et al. Vol. 1. 69.00x (ISBN 0-19-826155-1); Vol. 2. 69.00x (ISBN 0-19-826152-7). Oxford U Pr.

Apocrypha Anecdota. Ed. by M. R. James. (Texts & Studies Ser.: No. 1, Vol. 2, Pt. 3). pap. 19.00 (ISBN 0-8115-1686-5). Kraus Repr.

Apocrypha Anecdota: Second Series. Ed. by M. R. James. (Texts & Studies Ser.: No. 1, Vol. 5, Pt. 1). pap. 19.00 (ISBN 0-8115-1696-2). Kraus Repr.

Apocryphal Acts of Paul, Peter, John, Andrew, & Thomas. Bernhard Pick. 376p. 1909. 19.95 (ISBN 0-912050-60-8). Open Court.

Apocryphal Old Testament. H. F. Sparks. 990p. 1984. 44.50x (ISBN 0-19-826166-7); pap. 19.95x (ISBN 0-19-826177-2). Oxford U Pr.

Apollinarianism: An Essay on the Christology of the Early Church. Charles Raven. LC 77-84706. Repr. of 1923 ed. 38.00 (ISBN 0-404-16113-8). AMS Pr.

Apollodorus: The Library of Greek Mythology. Tr. by Keith Aldrich. 298p. 1975. 15.00x (ISBN 0-87291-072-5). Coronado Pr.

Apologetical Reply to a Book Called: An Answer to the Unjust Complaint of W.B. John Davenport. (English Experience Ser.: No. 792). 1977. Repr. of 1636 ed. lib. bdg. 35.00 (ISBN 90-221-0792-2). Walter J Johnson.

Apologetical Works. Tertullian. (Father of the Church Ser.: Vol. 10). 430p. 1950. 34.95x (ISBN 0-8132-0010-5). Cath U Pr.

Apologetics. Paul J. Glenn. LC 80-51330. 303p. 1980. pap. 6.00 (ISBN 0-89555-157-8). TAN Bks Pubs.

Apologetics: An Introduction. William L. Craig. 1984. 13.95 (ISBN 0-8024-0405-7). Moody.

Apologetics & the Biblical Christ. Avery Dulles. LC 63-22027. 88p. (Orig.). 1963. pap. 4.95 (ISBN 0-8091-1505-0). Paulist Pr.

Apologetics & the Eclipse of Mystery: Mystagogy According to Karl Rahner. James J. Bacik. LC 80-123. 192p. 1980. 15.00 (ISBN 0-268-00592-3); pap. 6.95 (ISBN 0-268-00593-1). U of Notre Dame Pr.

Apologia of Robert Keayne: The Self-Portrait of a Puritan Merchant. Bernard Bailyn. 11.25 (ISBN 0-8446-0470-4). Peter Smith.

Apologia Pro Vita Sua. John H. Newman. Ed. by A. D. Culler. LC 56-2548. (YA) 1956. pap. 6.50 (ISBN 0-395-05109-6, RivEd). HM.

Apologia Pro Vita Sua. John H. Newman. Ed. by David DeLaura. (Critical Editions Ser). 1968. pap. text ed. 11.95x (ISBN 0-393-09766-8, 9766, NortonC). Norton.

Apologie or Answer in Defence of the Church of England. John Jewel. Tr. by Ann Bacon. LC 72-38204. (English Experience Ser.: No. 470). 140p. 1972. Repr. of 1562 ed. 20.00 (ISBN 90-221-0470-2). Walter J Johnson.

Apologie or Defence of Such True Christians as Are Commonly Called Brownists. Henry Ainsworth & Francis Johnson. LC 70-25742. (English Experience Ser.: No. 217). Repr. of 1604 ed. 16.00 (ISBN 90-221-0424-9). Walter J Johnson.

Apology for Christianity in a Series of Letters Addressed to Edward Gibbon. Richard Watson. Ed. by Rene Wellek. Bd. with Apology for the Bible Addressed to Thomas Paine. LC 75-25132. (British Philosophers & Theologians of the 17th & 18th Centuries Ser.). 452p. 1978. lib. bdg. 51.00 (ISBN 0-8240-1765-X). Garland Pub.

Apology for Lollard Doctrines, Attributed to Wycliffe. John Wycliffe. LC 80-312858. Repr. of 1842 ed. 28.00 (ISBN 0-404-50120-6). AMS Pr.

Apology for Lollard Doctrines, Attributed to Wycliffe. John Wycliffe. 28.00 (ISBN 0-384-69838-7). Johnson Repr.

Apology for Perfection. Cecil F. Hirshaw. LC 64-22766. (Orig.). 1964. pap. 2.50x (ISBN 0-87574-138-X). Pendle Hill.

Apology for the Value of Human Life. David C. Thomasma. LC 83-7335. 169p. 1983. pap. 18.00 (ISBN 0-87125-085-3). Cath Health.

Apology of Appeale: Also, an Epistle to the True Hearted Nobility. Henry Burton. LC 76-57364. (English Experience Ser.: No. 782). 1977. Repr. of 1636 ed. lib. bdg. 5.00 (ISBN 90-221-0782-5). Walter J Johnson.

Apology of John the Baptist. Dennis Dallison. Ed. by Ruth Norman. 66p. (Orig.). 1982. pap. 2.50 (ISBN 0-932642-75-6). Unarius Pubns.

Apology of the Church of England. John Jewel. Ed. by John E. Booty. (Paperbacks Ser). 1978. pap. 7.90x (ISBN 0-918016-63-0). Folger Bks.

Apologye of Syr Thomas More. Ed. by A. I. Taft. (EETS, OS: No. 180). Repr. of 1929 ed. 67.00 (ISBN 0-527-00177-5). Kraus Repr.

Apolyge of Syr Thomas More. Thomas More. LC 72-221. (English Experience Ser.: No. 228). 1970. Repr. of 1533 ed. 42.00 (ISBN 90-221-0228-9). Walter J Johnson.

Apophthegmata Patrum. E. A. Budge. 150p. 1975. pap. 5.95 (ISBN 0-686-10938-4). Eastern Orthodox.

Apostasy & the Antichrist. 46p. (Orig.). 1978. pap. 2.00 (ISBN 0-317-30297-3). Holy Trinity.

Apostle. John Pollock. Orig. Title: Man Who Shook the World. 244p. 1972. pap. 7.95 (ISBN 0-88207-233-1). Victor Bks.

Apostle: A Life of Paul. John Pollock. 312p. 1985. 11.95 (ISBN 0-89693-368-7). Victor Bks.

Apostle John: His Life & Writings. W. H. Thomas. LC 84-785. 376p. 1984. pap. 10.95 (ISBN 0-8254-3822-5). Kregel.

Apostle of Culture: Emerson As Preacher & Lecturer. David Robinson. LC 81-16228. 200p. 1982. 21.00x (ISBN 0-8122-7824-0). U of Pa Pr.

Apostle of Peace: Memoir of William Ladd. John Hemmenway. LC 70-137544. 272p. 1972. Repr. of 1872 ed. lib. bdg. 20.95x (ISBN 0-89198-072-5). Ozer.

Apostle Paul: A History of the Development of the Doctrine of St. Paul. A. Sabatier. 1977. lib. bdg. 59.95 (ISBN 0-8490-1442-5). Gordon Pr.

Apostle Paul: An Introduction to His Writings & Teaching. Marion L. Soards. 1987. pap. 8.95. Paulist Pr.

Apostle Paul: Male Chauvinist or Proponent of Equality? Philip A. Cunningham. 24p. (Orig.). 1986. pap. 4.25 (ISBN 0-937997-03-X). Hi-Time Pub.

Apostle Peter & His Writing. Irene L. Johnson. 48p. (Orig.). 1983. pap. 2.50 (ISBN 0-87239-672-X, 2772). Standard Pub.

Apostle Peter: His Life & Writings. W. H. Thomas. LC 84-1493. 304p. 1984. pap. 9.95 (ISBN 0-8254-3823-3). Kregel.

Apostle to the Nations. 15.00 (ISBN 0-8198-0710-9); 14.00 (ISBN 0-8198-0711-7). Dghtrs St Paul.

Apostles. Donald Guthrie. 432p. 1981. pap. 12.95 (ISBN 0-310-25421-3, 12235P). Zondervan.

Apostle's Creed. J. I. Packer. 1983. pap. 3.95 (ISBN 0-8423-0051-1); Leader's Guide 2.95 (ISBN 0-8423-0052-X). Tyndale.

Apostles' Creed, Its Relation to Primitive Christianity. H. B. Swete. 112p. 1981. Repr. of 1905 ed. lib. bdg. 50.00 (ISBN 0-89984-447-2). Century Bookbindery.

Apostles Extraordinary: A Celebration of Saints & Sinners. Geddes MacGregor. (Illus.). 168p. (Orig.). 1986. pap. 8.95 (ISBN 0-89407-065-7). Strawberry Hill.

Apostles for Our Time: Thoughts on Apostolic Spirituality. Andre Simonet. Tr. by M. Angeline Bouchard from Fr. LC 77-8537. 1977. pap. 4.95 (ISBN 0-8189-0354-6). Alba.

Apostles: Jesus' Special Helpers. Edmon L. Rowell, Jr. (BibLearn Ser.). (Illus.). 1979. 5.95 (ISBN 0-8054-4246-4, 4242-46). Broadman.

Apostles of Christ. John D. Jones. 268p. 1982. lib. bdg. 10.00 Smythe Sewn (ISBN 0-86524-139-2, 8403). Klock & Klock.

Apostles of Denial. Edmond C. Gruss. 1970. pap. 8.95 (ISBN 0-87552-305-6). Presby & Reformed.

Apostles of Mediaeval Europe. George F. Maclear. LC 72-624. (Essay Index Reprint Ser.). Repr. of 1869 ed. 21.50 (ISBN 0-8369-2803-2). Ayer Co Pubs.

Apostles of Ramakrishna. Ed. by Swami Gambhirananda. (Illus.). 6.95x (ISBN 0-87481-098-1). Vedanta Pr.

Apostles of the Slavs. 56p. 1985. pap. 3.95 (ISBN 1-55586-972-6). US Catholic.

Apostles, Prophets & Governments. Gordon Lindsay. 1.50 (ISBN 0-89985-121-5). Christ Nations.

Apostles to the City: Biblical Strategies for Urban Missions. Roger S. Greenway. 1978. pap. 4.95 (ISBN 0-8010-3724-7). Baker Bk.

Apostolic Age. George B. Caird. (Studies in Theology). 222p. 1982. pap. 13.50 (ISBN 0-7156-1680-3, Pub. by Duckworth London). Longwood Pub Group.

Apostolic Catechism. D. Rayford Bell. LC 84-90806. 60p. 1984. 1.50 (ISBN 0-317-39381-2). D R Bell.

Apostolic Church in the New Testament. David M. Stanley. LC 65-19453. 500p. 1965. 7.95 (ISBN 0-8091-0002-9). Paulist Pr.

Apostolic Fathers. LC 47-31345. (Fathers of the Church Ser.: Vol. 1). 412p. 1947. 21.95x (ISBN 0-8132-0001-6). Cath U Pr.

Apostolic Fathers. J. B. Lightfoot. (Twin Brooks Ser). pap. 7.95 (ISBN 0-8010-5514-8). Baker Bk.

Apostolic Fathers. Ed. by J. B. Lightfoot. (Twin Brooks Ser.). 584p. 1984. pap. 15.95 (ISBN 0-8010-5627-6). Baker Bk.

Apostolic Interpretation of History: A Commentary on Acts 13: 16-41. C. A. Joachim Pillai. 1980. 9.00 (ISBN 0-682-49404-6, University). Exposition Pr FL.

Apostolic Preaching of the Cross. Leon Morris. 1956. pap. 5.95 (ISBN 0-8028-1512-X). Eerdmans.

Apostolic Regions of the United States: 1980. Bernard Quinn & John Bookser-Feister. LC 78-67012. (Illus.). 1985. pap. text ed. 4.00x (ISBN 0-914422-08-1). Glenmary Res Ctr.

Apostolic Succession. Ed. by Hans Kung. LC 68-25948. (Concilium Ser.: Vol. 34). 196p. 1968. 7.95 (ISBN 0-8091-0003-7). Paulist Pr.

Apostolic Succession in the Liberal Catholic Church. 2nd ed. Allan W. Cockerham. (Illus.). 1980. pap. text ed. 2.80 (ISBN 0-918980-09-7). St Alban Pr.

Apostolike Obedience: A Sermon. Robert Sibthorpe. LC 76-57418. (English Experience Ser.: No. 831). 1977. Repr. of 1627 ed. lib. bdg. 6.00 (ISBN 90-221-0831-7). Walter J Johnson.

Apostoliki Paradosis: The Treatise on the Apostolic Tradition of St. Hippolytus of Rome, Bishop & Martyr, Vol. 1. Ed. by Gregory Dix. (Church Historical Society, London, New Ser.: No. 24). Repr. of 1937 ed. 40.00 (ISBN 0-8115-3148-1). Kraus Repr.

Apostolos: Byzantine Epistles Lectionary. Joseph Raya & Jose D. Vinck. 550p. 1981. 87.50x (ISBN 0-911726-37-3); folded sheets 67.50x (ISBN 0-911726-38-1). Alleluia Pr.

Apostolos Makrakis--An Evaluation of Half a Century. Constantine Andronis. 369p. (Orig.). 1966. pap. 4.00x (ISBN 0-938366-33-5). Orthodox Chr.

Apostolos: The Acts & Letters of the Holy Apostles Read in the Orthodox Church Throughout the Year. Ed. by Nomikos M. Vaporis. 420p. 1980. 55.00 (ISBN 0-916586-39-1). Holy Cross Orthodox.

Apotheosis & after Life. facsimile ed. Eugenia Strong. LC 78-103668. (Select Bibliographies Reprint Ser). 1915. 33.00 (ISBN 0-8369-5168-9). Ayer Co Pubs.

Apparition de L'homme. Pierre Teilhard De Chardin. 21.50 (ISBN 0-685-36582-4). French & Eur.

Apparitions in Late Medieval & Renaissance Spain. William A. Christian, Jr. LC 80-8541. (Illus.). 304p. 1981. 34.00x (ISBN 0-691-05326-X). Princeton U Pr.

Apparitions of Our Blessed Mother in Cuapa, Nicaragua. Pablo A. Vega. 1984. pap. 1.00 (ISBN 0-911988-59-9). Ami Pr.

Apparitions of Our Lady at Medugorje: An Historical Account with Interviews. Sveosar Kraljevic. Ed. by Michael Scanlan. LC 84-5983. 217p. 1984. 9.50 (ISBN 0-8199-0878-9). Franciscan Herald.

Appeal of Adam to Lazarus in Hell. Donald R. Hitchcock. (Slavistic Printings & Reprintings Ser.: No. 302). 1979. text ed. 80.00x (ISBN 0-686-27016-9). Mouton.

Appeal to the Christian Women of the South. Angelina E. Grimke. LC 77-82195. (Anti-Slavery Crusade in America Ser). 1969. Repr. of 1836 ed. 9.50 (ISBN 0-405-00635-7). Ayer Co Pubs.

Appeals to Men of Reason & Religion. John Wesley. Ed. by Gerald R. Cragg. (Works of John Wesley: Vol. XI). (Illus.). 1975. 49.95x (ISBN 0-19-812498-8). Oxford U Pr.

Appello Caesarem: A Just Appeale from Two Unjust Informers. Richard Montagu. LC 75-38210. (English Experience Ser.: No. 475). 348p. 1972. Repr. of 1625 ed. 49.00 (ISBN 90-221-0475-3). Walter J Johnson.

Appendix with Supplementary Notes. Edmund H. Fellowes. (Tudor Church Music Ser.). 1963. Repr. of 1948 ed. 50.00x (ISBN 0-8450-1861-2). Broude.

Appetite Control for Christians. large print ed. Pearl Brians. 28p. 1985. pap. 4.50 (ISBN 0-914009-30-3). VHI Library.

Apple a Day: Treasured Selections from Apples of Gold. Jo Petty. 1979. 6.95 (ISBN 0-8378-5025-8). Gibson.

Apple Tree: Christmas Music from the Cambridge Hymnal. Ed. by David Holbrook & Elizabeth Postan. LC 76-12916. 1976. pap. 7.95 o. p. (ISBN 0-521-29116-X). Cambridge U Pr.

Apples & Ashes: Culture, Metaphor & Morality in the American Dream. Ann-Janine Morey-Gaines. LC 81-14346. (AAR Academy Ser.). 1982. 12.95 (ISBN 0-89130-535-1, 01-01-38). Scholars Pr GA.

Application of Redemption, by the Effectual Work of the Word, & the Spirit of Christ, for the Bringing Home of Lost Sinners to God. Thomas Hooker. LC 70-141111. (Research Library of Colonial Americana). 1972. Repr. of 1657 ed. 37.50 (ISBN 0-405-03324-9). Ayer Co Pubs.

Applied Christianity for Today's Christian Woman. Katheryn Price. 1978. pap. 3.50 (ISBN 0-88027-045-4). Firm Foun Pub.

Applied Science of the Soul. Eugen Rosenstock-Huessy. 40p. 1984. pap. text ed. 3.95 (ISBN 0-910727-04-X). Golden Phoenix.

Applied Yoga. Swami Jyotir Maya Nanda. (Illus.). 1971. 6.99 (ISBN 0-934664-01-3). Yoga Res Foun.

Applying for Your Church. David K. Enyart. LC 84-71852. 72p. (Orig.). pap. 2.95 (ISBN 0-89900-192-0). College Pr Pub.

Applying Moral Theories. Harris. 1985. pap. text ed. write for info. (ISBN 0-534-05898-1). Wadsworth Pub.

Applying the Gospel: Suggestions for Christian Social Action in the Local Church. new ed. William M. Pinson. LC 75-8374. 160p. 1975. pap. 5.95 (ISBN 0-8054-6306-2). Broadman.

Appointment in Jerusalem. Lydia Prince. 1975. 9.95 (ISBN 0-934920-24-9, B-26); pap. 5.95 (ISBN 0-934920-27-3, B 26A). Derek Prince.

Appraisal of the Protocols of Zion. John S. Curtiss. LC 78-63661. (Studies in Fascism: Ideology & Practice). Repr. of 1942 ed. 12.50 (ISBN 0-404-16924-4). AMS Pr.

Appreciating Marriage, Vol I. rev. ed. Patsy R. Dawson. LC 86-22746. (Marriage: A Taste of Heaven Ser.). (Illus.). 544p. 1987. pap. 12.95 (ISBN 0-938855-40-9); Set. pap. 25.90 (ISBN 0-938855-44-1). Gospel Themes Pr.

Approach to Christian Education. Ed. by Rupert E. Davies. 1956. 7.00 (ISBN 0-8022-0352-3). Philos Lib.

Approach To Reality. N. Sri Ram. 5.75 (ISBN 0-8356-7339-1). Theos Pub Hse.

Approach to the New Testament. James Moffatt. LC 77-27150. (Hibbert Lectures: 1921). Repr. of 1921 ed. 28.00 (ISBN 0-404-60420-X). AMS Pr.

Approach to the Study of the Quran. N. Jung. pap. 4.75 (ISBN 0-686-18520-X). Kazi Pubns.

Approach to the Study of the Qur'an. N. Jung. 1970. 4.75x (ISBN 0-87902-168-3). Orientalia.

Approach to the Study of the Qur'an. Nizamat Jung. 84p. (Orig.). 1981. pap. 4.50 (ISBN 0-88004-002-5). Sunwise Turn.

Approach to Understanding of Islam. Ali Shariati. Tr. by Venus Kiavantash from Persian. 26p. 1980. pap. 1.00x (ISBN 0-941722-14-7). Book-Dist-Ctr.

Approach to Vedanta. Christopher Isherwood. 1970. pap. 3.95 (ISBN 0-87481-003-5). Vedanta Pr.

Approaches Textuelles des "Memoires" de Saint-Simon. Leo Spitzer & Jules Brody. (Etudes Litteraires Francaise: No. 9). (Fr.). 107p. (Orig.). 1980. pap. 12.00 (ISBN 3-87808-888-4). Benjamins North Am.

Approaches to Ancient Judaism, Vol. IV. William S. Green. (Brown Judaic Studies). 208p. 1983. pap. 17.00 (ISBN 0-89130-673-0, 14 00 27). Scholars Pr GA.

Approaches to Ancient Judaism, Vol. V. Ed. by William S. Green. (Brown Judaic Studies: No. 32). 1985. 20.95 (ISBN 0-89130-797-4, 14 00 32); pap. 17.25 (ISBN 0-89130-798-2). Scholars Pr GA.

Approaches to Ancient Judaism II. William S. Green. LC 76-57656. (Brown Judaic Studies). 1980. 15.00 (ISBN 0-89130-447-9, 14-00-09); pap. 10.50 (ISBN 0-89130-448-7). Scholars Pr GA.

Approaches to Ancient Judaism III. Ed. by William S. Green. LC 76-57656. (Brown Judaic Studies). 220p. 1981. pap. 15.00 (ISBN 0-89130-553-X, 14 00 11). Scholars Pr GA.

Approaches to Ancient Judaism: Theory & Practice. William S. Green. LC 76-57656. 1978. pap. 16.50 (ISBN 0-89130-130-5, 14-00-01). Scholars Pr GA.

Approaches to God. Jacques Maritain. Tr. by Peter O'Reilly from Fr. LC 78-16555. 1978. Repr. of 1954 ed. lib. bdg. 32.50x (ISBN 0-313-20606-6, MATG). Greenwood.

Approaches to Group Understanding: Proceedings. Conference on Science, Philosophy & Religion in Their Relation to the Democratic Way of Life, 6th. Repr. of 1947 ed. 24.00 (ISBN 0-527-00653-X). Kraus Repr.

Approaches to Islam in Reglious Studies. Ed. by Richard C. Martin. LC 85-1099. 1985. 18.95x (ISBN 0-8165-0868-2). U of Ariz Pr.

Approaches to Judaism in Medieval Times. David R. Blumenthal. LC 83-18886. (Brown Judaic Ser.). 188p. pap. 14.95 (ISBN 0-89130-659-5, 14 00 54). Scholars Pr GA.

Approaches to Judaism in Medieval Times, Vol. II. David R. Blumenthal. (Brown Judaic Studies). 1985. 23.95 (ISBN 0-89130-848-2, 14-00-57); pap. 18.95 (ISBN 0-89130-849-0). Scholars Pr GA.

Approaches to Modern Judaism, Vol. II. Ed. by Marc L. Raphael. (Brown Judaic Studies: No. 56). 128p. 1985. 19.95 (ISBN 0-89130-793-1, 14 00 56); pap. 16.95 (ISBN 0-89130-794-X). Scholars Pr GA.

Approaches to National Unity: Proceedings. Conference on Science-Philosphy & Religion in Their Relation to the Democratic Way of Life - 5th. 1945. 70.00 (ISBN 0-527-00652-1). Kraus Repr.

Approaches to Teaching Milton's Paradise Lost. Ed. by Galbraith M. Crump. LC 85-21390. (Approaches to Teaching World Literature Ser.: No. 10). 175p. 1986. 30.00x (ISBN 0-87352-493-4); pap. text ed. 16.50x (ISBN 0-87352-494-2). Modern Lang.

Approaches to the Philosophy of Religion. facsimile ed. Ed. by Daniel J. Bronstein & Harold M. Schulweis. LC 77-93320. (Essay Index Reprint Ser). 1954. 33.00 (ISBN 0-8369-1344-2). Ayer Co Pubs.

Approaches to World Peace: Proceedings. Conference on Science-Philosophy & Religion in Their Relation to the Democratic Way of Life - 4th. 1944. 70.00 (ISBN 0-527-00651-3). Kraus Repr.

Approaches Toward Church Unity. Norman Smyth & Williston Walker. 1919. 34.50x (ISBN 0-686-37862-8). Elliots Bks.

Approaching Advent of Christ. Alexander Reese. LC 73-85374. 328p. 1975. 8.95 (ISBN 0-8254-3610-9). Kregel.

Approaching Earth. Daniel Noel. (Chrysalis Bk.). 192p. (Orig.). 1986. pap. 14.95 (ISBN 0-916349-12-8). Amity Hous Inc.

Approaching Easter. Joyce Huggett. Ed. by A. Reynolds. 96p. 1987. pap. 6.95 (ISBN 0-7459-1120-X). Lion USA.

Approaching Hoofbeats: The Four Horsemen of the Apocalypse. Billy Graham. 288p. 1985. pap. 3.95 (ISBN 0-380-69921-4). Avon.

Approaching the Gospels Together: A Leader's Guide to Group Gospels Study. Mary C. Morrison. LC 78-51385. 32p. (Orig.). 1978. pap. 2.50x (ISBN 0-87574-219-X, 219). Pendle Hill.

Approaching the Gospels Together: A Leaders' Guide to Group Gospels Study. Mary C. Morrison. (Orig.). 1987. pap. 10.95 (ISBN 0-87574-910-0). Pendle Hill.

Approaching the Sacred. Susan Muto. 4.95 (ISBN 0-87193-047-1). Dimension Bks.

Appropriate Values & Education in Developing Nations. Ed. by John Oxenham. (Illus.). 304p. 1987. 22.95 (ISBN 0-89226-050-5, Pub. by ICUS). Paragon Hse.

Appropriating Australian Folk Dances into Sacred Dance. Doug Adams. 1987. pap. 3.00 (ISBN 0-941500-45-4). Sharing Co.

Aprenda a Ser Lider. G. S. Dobbins. Tr. by S. P. Molina from Eng. Orig. Title: Learning to Lead. (Span.). 126p. 1986. pap. 2.50 (ISBN 0-311-17013-7). Casa Bautista.

Aprendamos el Plan de Dios. Bessie Dean. Tr. by Eduardo Balderas from Eng. LC 80-82256. (Books for LDS Children Ser.). Orig. Title: Let's Learn God's Plan. (Span., Illus.). 64p. (Orig.). 1980. pap. text ed. 3.95 (ISBN 0-88290-135-4). Horizon Utah.

Aprender a Vivir: Learning to Live. Keith M. Bailey. Tr. by Dorothy Bucher. (Span.). 125p. 1980. 1.50 (ISBN 0-87509-299-3). Chr Pubns.

Apres le Sacrifice. Walter Henrichsen. Orig. Title: After the Sacrifice. (Fr.). 1986. write for info. (ISBN 0-8297-0524-4). Life Pubs Intl.

April & Easter. Nancy M. Davis et al. (Davis Teaching Units Ser.: Vol. 1, No. 8). (Illus.). 45p. (Orig.). 1986. pap. 5.95 (ISBN 0-937103-10-1). DaNa Pubns.

April Ashley's Odyssey. Duncan Fallowell & April Ashley. (Illus.). 287p. 1983. 15.95 (ISBN 0-224-01849-3, Pub. by Jonathan Cape). Salem Hse Pubs.

Apuleius on the God of Socrates. Apuleius. Tr. by Thomas Taylor. (Lat.). 1984. pap. 4.95 (ISBN 0-916411-25-7, Pub. by Alexandrian Pr). Holmes Pub.

Apuntes de Sermones. Charles H. Spurgeon. Orig. Title: Spurgeon's Sermon Notes. (Span.). 432p. 1975. pap. 8.95 (ISBN 0-8254-1675-2). Kregel.

Aquarian Gospel of Jesus Christ. Levi. 1972. 7.95 (ISBN 0-87516-041-7); pap. 6.95 (ISBN 0-87516-168-5). De Vorss.

Aquinas. F. C. Copleston. 272p. 1956. pap. 5.95 (ISBN 0-14-020349-4, Pelican). Penguin.

Aquinas. Anthony Kenny. (Past Masters Ser.). 1980. pap. 4.95 (ISBN 0-19-287500-0). Oxford U Pr.

Aquinas: God & Action. David B. Burrell. LC 78-51519. 1979. text ed. 14.95x (ISBN 0-268-00588-5). U of Notre Dame Pr.

Aquinas on Being & Essence: A Translation & Interpretation. Joseph Bobik. LC 65-23516. pap. 75.50 (ISBN 0-317-26719-1, 2024364). Bks Demand UMI.

Aquinas on Nature & Grace. Ed. by A. M. Fairweather. LC 54-10259. (Library of Christian Classics). 382p. 1978. pap. 10.95 softcover (ISBN 0-664-24155-7). Westminster.

Aquinas on Politics & Ethics. St. Thomas Aquinas. Ed. by Paul e. Sigmund. (Norton Critical Edition Ser.). pap. write for info. (ISBN 0-393-95243-6). Norton.

Aquinas Reader. Ed. by Mary T. Clark. LC 72-76709. pap. 6.95 (ISBN 0-385-02505-X, Im). Doubleday.

Aquinas' Summa: An Introduction & Interpretation. Edward J. Gratsch. LC 85-15842. 305p. (Orig.). 1985. pap. 12.95 (ISBN 0-8189-0485-2). Alba.

Aquinas to Whitehead: Seven Centuries of Metaphysics of Religion. Charles Hartshorne. LC 76-5156. (Aquinas Lectures Ser.). 1976. 7.95 (ISBN 0-87462-141-0). Marquette.

Arab Heritage. Ed. by Nabih A. Faris. LC 79-2856. 279p. 1981. Repr. of 1944 ed. 30.00 (ISBN 0-8305-0030-8). Hyperion Conn.

Arab Heritage. Ed. by Nabih A. Faris. LC 84-27929. (Illus.). xii, 279p. 1985. Repr. of 1944 ed. lib. bdg. 55.00x (ISBN 0-313-23371-3, FAAH). Greenwood.

Arab Historians of the Crusades. Ed. by Francesco Gabrieli. LC 68-23783. 1978. 40.00x (ISBN 0-520-03616-6); pap. 9.95 (ISBN 0-520-05224-2, CAL 699). U of Cal Pr.

Arab-Israeli Conflict, Nineteen Forty-Five to Nineteen Seventy-One: A Bibliography. John Sherman. LC 77-83360. (Reference Library of Social Science Ser.). 1978. lib. bdg. 63.00 (ISBN 0-8240-9829-3). Garland Pub.

Arab-Jewish Unity: Testimony Before the Anglo-American Inquiry for the Ihud (Union) Judah L. Magnes & Martin Buber. LC 75-7678. (Rise of Jewish Nationalism & the Middle East Ser). 96p. 1975. Repr. of 1947 ed. 15.00 (ISBN 0-88355-348-1). Hyperion Conn.

Arab Moslems in the United States. Abdo A. Elkholy. 1966. 12.95x (ISBN 0-8084-0052-5); pap. 8.95x (ISBN 0-8084-0053-3). New Coll U Pr.

Arab Philosophy of History: Selections from the Prolegomena of Ibn Khaldun of Tunis (1332-1406) Charles Issawi. LC 86-29199. xiv, 192p. 1986. 9.95 (ISBN 0-87850-056-1). Darwin Pr.

Arab Relations in the Middle East: The Road to Realignment. Ed. by Colin Legum & Haim Shaked. LC 78-20888. (Middle Affairs Ser.: No. 1). 104p. 1978. pap. text ed. 12.50x (ISBN 0-8419-0447-2). Holmes & Meier.

Arabia & the Bible. rev. ed. James A. Montgomery. (Library of Biblical Studies). 1969. 25.00x (ISBN 0-87068-090-0). Ktav.

Arabia of the Wahhabis. Harry S. Philby. LC 73-6297. (Middle East Ser.). Repr. of 1928 ed. 33.00 (ISBN 0-405-05355-X). Ayer Co Pubs.

Arabic Alphabet & Daily Prayer. Shaikh Muhammad Sarwar. 34p. 1981. pap. 3.00 (ISBN 0-941724-07-7). Islamic Seminary.

Arabic Logic: Ibn al-Tayyib on Porphyry's "Eisagoge". Ed. & tr. by Kwame Gyekye. LC 76-4071. 1979. 49.50x (ISBN 0-87395-308-8). State U NY Pr.

Arabic Text of the Apocalypse of Baruch: Editied & Translated With a Parallel Translation of the Syriac Text. F. Leemhuis et al. viii, 154p. 1986. 32.25 (ISBN 90-04-07608-5, Pub. by E J Brill). Heinman.

Arabs & Zionism Before World War One. Neville Mandel. LC 73-78545. 1977. pap. 4.95 (ISBN 0-520-03940-8, CAL 430). U of Cal Pr.

Arachne's Tapestry: The Transformation of Myth in Seventeenth-Century Spain. Marcia L. Welles. (Illus.). 220p. 1986. text ed. 22.50 (ISBN 0-939980-11-8). Trinity U Pr.

Arakin, 1 vol. 15.00 (ISBN 0-910218-83-8). Bennet Pub.

Aram & Israel Or, Aramaeans in Syria & Mesopotamia. Emil G. Kraeling. LC 18-9797. (Columbia University. Oriental Studies: No. 13). Repr. of 1918 ed. 17.00 (ISBN 0-404-50503-1). AMS Pr.

Aramaic Approach to the Gospels & Acts. 3rd ed. Matthew Black. 1967. 32.50x (ISBN 0-19-826157-8). Oxford U Pr.

Aramaic New Testament. LC 83-71100. 524p. 1983. 24.95 (ISBN 0-910068-47-X). Am Christian.

Aramaic Proverbs of Ahiqar. James M. Lindenberger. LC 82-18000. (Near Eastern Studies). 384p. 1983. text ed. 38.00x (ISBN 0-8018-2797-3). Johns Hopkins.

Aramaic Ritual Texts from Persepolis. Raymond A. Bowman. LC 65-55148. (Oriental Institute Pubns. Ser: No. 91). 1970. 35.00x (ISBN 0-226-62194-4). U of Chicago Pr.

Aramaic Version of Jonah. 2nd ed. Etan Levine. LC 76-27614. 1979. pap. 12.75 (ISBN 0-87203-068-7). Hermon.

Aramaic Version of Lamentations. Etan Levine. LC 76-276212. 203p. 1981. pap. 14.75 (ISBN 0-87203-065-2). Hermon.

Aramaic Version of Qohelet. new ed. Etan Levine. 1979. pap. 14.75 (ISBN 0-87203-087-3). Hermon.

Ararat: A Collection of Hungarian-Jewish Short Stories. Ed. & tr. by Andrew Handler. LC 75-5244. 153p. 1978. 18.00 (ISBN 0-8386-1733-6). Fairleigh Dickinson.

Arator: The Codices. Ed. by A. P. McKinlay. 1942. 8.00x (ISBN 0-910956-18-9). Medieval Acad.

Aratrika Hymns & Ram Nam. Swami Tapasyananda. 1979. pap. 1.50 (ISBN 0-87481-476-6). Vedanta Pr.

Arbeitsbuch zum Neuen Testament. 8th ed. Hans Conzelmann & Andreas Lindemann. 474p. (Orig.). 1986. pap. 22.00x (ISBN 3-16-145007-8, Pub. by J C B Mohr BRD). Coronet Bks.

Arcadia Story. Marjorie Russell. LC 85-40651. 265p. 1985. pap. 9.95 (ISBN 0-938232-83-5, Dist. by Baker & Taylor Co.). Winston-Derek.

Arcana Coelestia (Heavenly Secrets, Vol. 1. Emanuel Swedenborg. pap. 3.95 (ISBN 0-87785-053-4). Swedenborg.

Arcana Coelestia (Heavenly Secrets) Student Edition, 12 vols. Emanuel Swedenborg. Incl. 12.00 ea. Vol. 1 (ISBN 0-87785-021-6). Vol. 2 (ISBN 0-87785-022-4). Vol. 3 (ISBN 0-87785-023-2). Vol. 4 (ISBN 0-87785-024-0). Vol. 5 (ISBN 0-87785-025-9). Vol. 6 (ISBN 0-87785-026-7); Vol. 7 (ISBN 0-87785-027-5). Vol. 8 (ISBN 0-87785-028-3). Vol. 9 (ISBN 0-87785-029-1). Vol. 10 (ISBN 0-87785-030-5). Vol. 11 (ISBN 0-87785-031-3). Vol. 12 (ISBN 0-87785-032-1). LC 63-1828. 1977. Set. 144.00 (ISBN 0-87785-033-X). Swedenborg.

Arcana of Christianity, 3 pts. in 2 vols. Thomas L. Harris. LC 72-2955. Repr. of 1867 ed. Set. 92.00 (ISBN 0-404-10720-6). AMS Pr.

Arcane Commentaries. John Stahl. 9p. 1973. pap. 2.00 (ISBN 0-318-21744-9). Evanescent Pr.

Arch Books Aloud, Sets 42 - 47. LC 59-2142. (Continued Applied Christianity Ser.). 1983. pap. 5.95 ea; two bks & cassette incl. Set no. 42 (ISBN 0-570-08091-6). Set no. 43 (ISBN 0-570-08092-4). Set no. 44 (ISBN 0-570-08093-2). Set no. 45 (ISBN 0-570-08094-0). Set no. 46 (ISBN 0-570-08095-9). Set no. 47 (ISBN 0-570-08096-7). Concordia.

Archaeological Commentary on the Bible. Gonzalo Baez-Camargo. LC 82-45473. (Illus.). 336p. 1986. pap. 9.95 (ISBN 0-385-17969-3, Galilee). Doubleday.

Archaeological Encyclopedia of the Holyland. Ed. by Avraham Negev. LC 79-92775. (Illus.). 356p. 1980. Repr. of 1974 ed. 9.95 (ISBN 0-89961-004-8). SBS Pub.

Archaeological Haggadah. Ed. by Benno Rothenberg. LC 86-1052. (Illus.). 1986. 12.95 (ISBN 0-915361-36-1, 09713-7, Dist. by Watts). Adama Pubs Inc.

Archaeological Study of Churches. Ed. by Peter Addyman & Richard Morris. LC 77-365546. (Council for British Archaeology Research Report Ser.: No. 13). (Illus.). pap. 24.00 (ISBN 0-317-09531-5, 2014021). Bks Demand UMI.

Archaeology & Bible. Jack Lewis. LC 75-20804. (Way of Life Ser: No. 113). 112p. 1975. pap. 3.95 (ISBN 0-89112-113-7, Bibl Res Pr). Abilene Christ U.

Archaeology & the Dead Sea Scrolls. 2nd & rev. ed. R. De Vaux. (Schweich Lectures on Biblical Archaeology). (Illus.). 142p. 1977. 13.50 (ISBN 0-85672-725-3, Pub. by British Acad). Longwood Pub Group.

Archaeology & the Old Testament. James B. Pritchard. LC 58-10053. pap. 69.80 (ISBN 0-317-08485-2, 2016011). Bks Demand UMI.

Archaeology, Artefacts & the Bible: The Bible Lands in Ancient Times. P. R. Moorey. (Ancient Ser.). (Illus.). 71p. (Orig.). 1969. pap. 4.50x (ISBN 0-900090-00-6, Pub. by Ashmolean Museum). State Mutual Bk.

Archaeology in Adventist Literature, 1937-1980. Lloyd A. Willis. (Andrews University Seminary Doctoral Dissertation Ser.: Vol. 7). x, 670p. 1984. pap. 14.95 (ISBN 0-943872-39-1). Andrews Univ Pr.

Archaeology in Bible Lands. Howard Vos. LC 77-2981. (Illus.). 1977. 11.95 (ISBN 0-8024-0289-5). Moody.

Archaeology in the Holy Land. 4th ed. Kathleen M. Kenyon. (Illus.). 1979. 10.95x (ISBN 0-393-01285-9). Norton.

Archaeology of New Testament Cities in Western Asia Minor. Edwin Yamauchi. LC 80-66991. (Baker Studies in Biblical Archaeology). 160p. 1980. pap. 7.95 (ISBN 0-8010-9915-3). Baker Bk.

Archaeology of Palestine. rev. ed. William F. Albright. 11.25 (ISBN 0-8446-0003-2). Peter Smith.

Archaeology of the English Church. Warwick Rodwell. (Illus.). 192p. 1981. 34.95 (ISBN 0-7134-2590-3, Pub. by Batsford England). David & Charles.

Archaeology of the Imagination. Ed. by Charles Winquist. (JAAR Thematic Studies). 1981. pap. 11.95 (ISBN 0-89130-679-X, 01-24-82). Scholars Pr GA.

Archaeology of the Jerusalem Area. W. Harold Mare. 1986. 19.95 (ISBN 0-8010-6126-1). Baker Bk.

Archaeology of the New Testament: The Mediterranean World of the Early Christian Apostles. Jack Finegan. (Illus.). 400p. 1981. 40.00x (ISBN 0-86531-064-5). Westview.

Archaic Corinthian Pottery & the Anaploga Well. D. A. Amyx & Patricia Lawrence. LC 75-4551. (Corinth Ser.: Vol. 7, Pt. 2). (Illus.). 1976. 35.00x (ISBN 0-87661-072-6, NK4647). Am Sch Athens.

Archaic Dictionary. William R. Cooper. LC 73-76018. 688p. 1969. Repr. of 1876 ed. 75.00x (ISBN 0-8103-3885-8). Gale.

Archaic Roman Religion, 2 Vols. Georges Dumezil. Tr. by Philip Krapp from Fr. LC 76-116981. 1971. Set. 45.00x (ISBN 0-226-16968-5). U of Chicago Pr.

Archaisme et Modernisme dans l'Islam Contemporain. (Economies et Societes Series V: No. 3). 1961. pap. 26.00 (ISBN 0-8115-0805-6). Kraus Repr.

Archbishop Grindal, 1519-1589: The Struggle for a Reformed Church in England. Patrick Collinson. LC 78-65474. 1979. 46.00x (ISBN 0-520-03831-2). U of Cal Pr.

Archbishop Laud Commemoration, 1895. Ed. by William E. Collins. (Bibliography & Reference Ser: No. 257). 1969. Repr. of 1895 ed. 23.50 (ISBN 0-8337-0628-4). B Franklin.

Archbishop Lefebvre & Religious Liberty. Michael Davies. 17p. 1980. pap. 1.00 (ISBN 0-89555-143-8). TAN Bks Pubs.

Archbishop Romero: Martyr of Salvador. Placido Erdozain. Tr. by John McFadden & Ruth Warner. LC 81-2007. Orig. Title: Monsenor Romero: Martis de la Iglesia Popular. (Illus.). 128p. (Orig.). 1981. pap. 4.95 (ISBN 0-88344-019-9). Orbis Bks.

Archbishop Thomas Beckett: A Character Study. M. D. Knowles. (Raleigh Lectures on History). 1970. pap. 2.25 (ISBN 0-85672-313-4, Pub. by British Acad). Longwood Pub Group.

Archeology & the Bible. John Bowden. 24p. 1982. pap. 3.00 (ISBN 0-910309-00-0). Am Atheist.

Archeology of the New Testament: The Life of Jesus & the Beginning of the Early Church. Jack Finegan. LC 69-18059. (Illus.). 1970. 60.00x (ISBN 0-691-03534-2); pap. 10.50x (ISBN 0-691-02000-0). Princeton U Pr.

Arches: The Story Behind the Scenery. David W. Johnson. LC 85-80445. (Illus.). 48p. (Orig.). 1985. pap. 4.50 (ISBN 0-88714-002-5). KC Pubns.

Archetypal Images in Greek Religion, 5 vols. Carl Kerenyi. Tr. by R. Manheim. Incl. Vol. 1. Prometheus: Archetypal Image of Human Existence. 1963; Vol. 2. Dionysos: Archetypal Image of Industructible Life. 1975; Vol. 3. Asklepios: Archetypal Image of the Physician's Existence. 1959. 37.00x (ISBN 0-691-09703-8); Vol. 4. Eleusis: Archetypal Image of Mother & Daughter. 1967; Vol. 5. Zeus & Hera-Archetypal Image of Father, Husband & Wife. Tr. by Holme. 1975. (Bollingen Ser.: Vol. 65). Princeton U Pr.

Archetypes of Conversion: The Spiritual Autobiographies of St. Augustine, John Bunyan, & Thomas Merton. Anne O. Hawkins. LC 83-46156. 192p. 1985. 25.00 (ISBN 0-8387-5079-6). Bucknell U Pr.

Architect of Unity. William J. Schmidt. 1978. cloth 14.95 (ISBN 0-377-00080-9); pap. 9.95 (ISBN 0-377-00079-5). Friend Pr.

Architects of Reform: Congregation & Community Leadership, Emanuel of San Francisco. 1849-1980. Fred Rosenbaum. LC 80-54032. 241p. 1980. 19.95 (ISBN 0-943376-14-9); pap. 9.95 (ISBN 0-943376-13-0). Magnes Mus.

Architects of Yiddishism at the Beginning of the Twentieth Century: A Study in Jewish Cultural History. Emanuel S. Goldsmith. LC 73-2894. 309p. 1976. 27.50 (ISBN 0-8386-1384-5). Fairleigh Dickinson.

Architectural Antiquities of Western India. H. Cousens. (Illus.). 1983. text ed. 34.00x. Coronet Bks.

Architecture, Classic & Early Christian. T. Roger Smith & John Slater. 1980. Repr. of 1893 ed. lib. bdg. 35.00 (ISBN 0-89341-364-X). Longwood Pub Group.

Architecture for Worship. Edward A. Sovik. LC 73-78254. (Illus.). 112p. (Orig.). 1973. pap. 5.95 (ISBN 0-8066-1320-3, 10-0425). Augsburg.

Architecture, Mysticism & Myth. William Lethaby. LC 74-25316. (Illus.). 280p. 1975. 10.00 (ISBN 0-8076-0783-5). Braziller.

Architecture of Altars & Chimneys, 2 vols. Jean Barbet. (Printed Sources of Western Art Ser.). (Fr., Illus.). 1981. pap. 35.00 slipcase (ISBN 0-915346-59-1). A Wofsy Fine Arts.

Architecture of Ancient Rome: An Account of Its Historic Development. William J. Anderson & Richard P. Spiers. LC 27-24681. 202p. 1927. Repr. 49.00x (ISBN 0-403-08618-3). Somerset Pub.

Architecture of India: Islamic. Satish Grover. (Illus.). 280p. 1981. text ed. 45.00x (ISBN 0-7069-1130-X, Pub. by Vikas India). Advent NY.

Architecture of Islamic Iran: The Il Khanid Period. Donald N. Wilber. Repr. of 1955 ed. lib. bdg. 36.75x (ISBN 0-8371-2504-9, WIII). Greenwood.

Architecture of Jeremiah, 1-20. William L. Holladay. 204p. 1976. 20.00 (ISBN 0-8387-1523-0). Bucknell U Pr.

Architecture of Religion: A Theoretical Essay. Paul Wiebe. LC 84-8667. (Trinity University Monograph Series in Religion). 170p. 1984. text ed. 15.95 (ISBN 0-939980-07-X). Trinity U Pr.

Architecture of the Islamic World: Its History & Social Meaning. Ed. by George Michell. LC 84-50341. (Illus.). 1984. 40.00f (ISBN 0-500-34076-5). Thames Hudson.

Archives from Elephantine: The Life of an Ancient Jewish Military Colony. Bezalel Porten. (Illus.). 1968. 47.50x (ISBN 0-520-01028-0). U of Cal Pr.

Archives of the Foundation of Thanatology: Social Work & Terminal Care, Vol. 9, No. 3. pap. 15.00 (ISBN 0-405-14207-2). Ayer Co Pubs.

Archives of the Foundation of Thanatology, Vol. 8: Acute Grief III: Continuum of Anticipatory Grief; Dying & Death; Acute Grief; Bereavement; Recovery from Bereavement, or Pathological Bereavement; & Lifelong Bereavement, No. 4. pap. 14.00 (ISBN 0-405-13074-0). Ayer Co Pubs.

Archives: The Light of Faith. John T. Corrigan. (Catholic Library Association Studies in Librarianship: No. 4). 1980. 4.00 (ISBN 0-87507-008-6). Cath Lib Assn.

Archivists Guide to the Catholic Church in Mexico. Virginia N. Mounce. LC 78-62226. 1979. perfect bdg. 10.95 (ISBN 0-88247-570-3). R & E Pubs.

Archko Volume. Tr. by McIntosk & Twyman. LC 74-33199. 248p. 1975. 9.95 (ISBN 0-87983-067-0). Keats.

Archpriest Avvakum: The Life Written by Himself. Ed. by Kenneth N. Brostrom. (Michigan Slavic Translations Ser.: No. 4). 1979. 20.00 (ISBN 0-930042-33-6); pap. 10.00 (ISBN 0-930042-37-9). Mich Slavic Pubns.

Archpriest Controversy, 2 Vols. Ed. by Thomas G. Law. Repr. of 1898 ed. 54.00 (ISBN 0-384-31730-8). Johnson Repr.

Arctic Mission. Jill Burrell & Maurice Burrell. 1974. 1.60 (ISBN 0-08-017621-6). Pergamon.

Are Southern Baptists "Evangelicals"? James L. Garrett, Jr. & E. Glenn Hinson. LC 82-18870. 247p. 1983. 14.95 (ISBN 0-86554-033-0, MUP-H44). Mercer Univ Pr.

Are the Dead Alive Now? Victor P. Wierwille. LC 82-70237. 108p. 1982. 6.95 (ISBN 0-910068-40-2). Am Christian.

Are There a Beginning & an End to Man's Existence? George V. Martin. 1983. 8.95 (ISBN 0-533-05562-8). Vantage.

Are These the Last Days? Robert G. Gromacki. LC 75-42165. 1975. pap. 3.50 (ISBN 0-87227-019-X). Reg Baptist.

Are You Fun to Live With? Lionel Whiston. 143p. 1985. lib. bdg. 11.95 (ISBN 0-938736-13-2); pap. 3.95 (ISBN 0-938736-14-0). Life Enrich.

Are You Listening? Henrietta Gambill. LC 84-7026. (Illus.). 32p. 1984. lib. bdg. 7.45 (ISBN 0-89693-221-4). Dandelion Hse.

Are You Listening? Henrietta Gambill. LC 85-10349. (New Values Ser.). (Illus.). 32p. 1985. PLB 7.45 (ISBN 0-89565-332-X). Childs World.

Are You Prepared? Hansi Shares How You Can Face the Future Without Fear. Maria A. Hirschmann. LC 79-90957. 64p. (Orig.). 1979. pap. 1.95 (ISBN 0-932878-06-7, HB-06). Hansi.

Are You Ready? Melba P. Palmer. 81p. (Orig.). 1984. pap. 7.95 (ISBN 0-942494-88-1). Coleman Pub.

Are You Really... Formed? F. Koenig. pap. 0.60 (ISBN 0-88172-111-5). Believers Bkshelf.

Are You Sick & Tired? Mary R. Swope. 176p. (Orig.). 1984. pap. 3.95 (ISBN 0-88368-149-8). Whitaker Hse.

Are You Spirit-Filled? David Hocking. (Orig.). pap. 5.95 (ISBN 0-89081-493-7). Harvest Hse.

Are You There God? It's Me, Margaret. Judy Blume. 156p. 1986. pap. 2.50 (ISBN 0-440-90419-6, LFL). Dell.

Are You Thinking of Becoming a Catholic? Alexander Hope. (Illus.). 90p. 1974. 47.35 (ISBN 0-913314-39-0). Am Classical Coll Pr.

Are You Weeping with Me, God? Martha B. Clark. LC 86-17194. (Orig.). 1987. pap. 5.95 (ISBN 0-8054-5436-5). Broadman.

Are You Well, Why Not? Dennis Karsten. 96p. (Orig.). 1983. pap. 2.95 (ISBN 0-88144-011-6). Christian Pub.

Are Your Meetings Held in the Life. Margaret M. Cary. 1983. pap. 2.50x (ISBN 0-87574-037-5, 037). Pendle Hill.

Arena. Ignatius Brianchianinov. Tr. by Archimandrite Lazarus Moore from Rus. 300p. (Orig.). 1982. 15.00 (ISBN 0-88465-009-X); pap. 10.00 (ISBN 0-88465-011-1). Holy Trinity.

Arena of Jerusalem. Ivan Schwebel. LC 86-3570. (Illus.). 1987. 39.95 (ISBN 0-915361-43-4, Dist. by Watts). Adama Pubs Inc.

Arguments Against the Bible: An Expose of the Verbal Plenary Inspiration of the Bible. Stanley Upchurch. 10.00x (ISBN 0-686-27700-7). Freedom Univ-FSP.

Arhats in China & Japan. Marinus W. De Visser. LC 78-70136. Repr. of 1923 ed. 27.50 (ISBN 0-404-17406-X). AMS Pr.

Arhats of Buddhism. Manly P. Hall. pap. 3.95 (ISBN 0-89314-529-7). Philos Res.

Arian Controversy. new ed. Henry M. Gwatkin. LC 77-84702. Repr. of 1903 ed. 27.50 (ISBN 0-404-16109-X). AMS Pr.

Arianism: Historical & Theological Reassessments. Ed. & intro. by Robert C. Gregg. LC 85-81654. (Patristic Monograph Ser.: No. 11). viii, 380p. 1985. pap. 12.00 (ISBN 0-915646-10-2). Phila Patristic.

Arise: A Christian Psychology of Love. Chester P. Michael & Marie C. Norrisey. 162p. (Orig.). 1981. pap. 3.95 (ISBN 0-940136-00-7). Open Door Inc.

Arise & Renew. Malcolm Cornwell. 96p. 1986. pap. 5.95 (ISBN 0-8146-1441-8). Liturgical Pr.

Arise Jerusalem: Parish Advent Program, Advent Family Handbook. Ed. by Jean M. Heisberger. LC 78-70425. 1978. pap. text ed. 1.25 (ISBN 0-8091-9179-2). Paulist Pr.

Arise, Thy Light Is Come. Robert H. DeWitt. (Orig.). 1957. pap. 1.95 (ISBN 0-8054-9703-X). Broadman.

Aristotelian Aporetic Ontology in Islamic & Christian Thinkers. Edward Booth. LC 82-22068. (Cambridge Studies in Medieval Life & Thought: No. 20). 368p. 1984. 70.00 (ISBN 0-521-25254-7). Cambridge U Pr.

Aristotle's Concept of Soul, Sleep, & Dreams. H. Wijsenbeek-Wijler. 260p. 1978. pap. text ed. 53.50 (Pub. by A M Hakkert). Coronet Bks.

Aristotle's Ethical Theory. 2nd ed. W. F. Hardie. 1981. pap. 29.95x (ISBN 0-19-824633-1). Oxford U Pr.

Arithmancy. Nelson White & Anne White. LC 81-84893. (Illus.). 50p. (Orig.). 1981. pap. 6.00 (ISBN 0-939856-23-9). Tech Group.

Arithmetic of God, Vol. 1. Ed. by Don Kistler. 187p. (Orig.). 1976. pap. 3.95x (ISBN 0-940532-00-X). AOG.

Arjuna in Meditation. Tr. by Harry Aveling. 1976. flexible cloth 8.00 (ISBN 0-89253-800-7). Ind-US Inc.

Ark & the Dove: The Beginnings of Civil & Religious Liberties in America. J. Moss Ives. LC 76-79200. (Illus.). 1969. Repr. of 1936 ed. 32.50x (ISBN 0-8154-0293-7). Cooper Sq.

Ark Book of Riddles. Myra Shofner. LC 79-57214. (Illus.). 1980. pap. 2.50 (ISBN 0-89191-250-9). Cook.

Ark Full of Animals. Tessa Colina. (Illus.). 1985. comb bdg. 4.95 (ISBN 0-317-30647-2, R2707). Standard Pub.

Armadeus Prophecy & Teaching in the New Ages, Bk. 2. Ronald G. Kaufmann. 155p. (Orig.). 1987. pap. 12.95 (ISBN 0-940539-02-0). Heridonius.

Armageddon. Gordon Lindsay. (Revelation Ser.). 1.25 (ISBN 0-89985-047-2). Christ Nations.

Armageddon: Color & Game Book. Keith A. Baumgartner & Marty Schiff. (Illus.). 28p. 1984. pap. 2.95 (ISBN 0-916343-02-2). J R Simon.

Armageddon-Dead Ahead. C. C. Cribb. LC 77-70212. pap. 2.95 (ISBN 0-932046-03-7). Manhattan Ltd NC.

Armageddon Spectre. Harold Lindsell. LC 84-72012. 142p. (Orig.). 1984. pap. 5.95 (ISBN 0-89107-329-9, Crossway Bks). Good News.

Armenian Awakening. Leon Arpee. (Works of Leon Arpee Ser.). xi, 234p. 1985. Repr. of 1909 ed. 34.00 (ISBN 0-932051-67-7, Pub. by Am Repr Serv). Am Biog Serv.

Armenian Church. Theodore E. Dowling. LC 71-131511. Repr. of 1910 ed. 16.00 (ISBN 0-404-02167-0). AMS Pr.

Armenian Church. Papken Gulleserian. Tr. by Vartapet T. Poladian. LC 70-131508. Repr. of 1939 ed. 11.50 (ISBN 0-404-02949-3). AMS Pr.

Armenian Church: Founded by Saint Gregory the Illuminator. Edward F. Fortescue. 1970. Repr. of 1872 ed. 21.50 (ISBN 0-404-02518-8). AMS Pr.

Armenian Mythology & African Mythology. Mardiros H. Ananikian. (Mythology of All Races Ser.: Vol. VII). Repr. of 1932 ed. 30.00x (ISBN 0-8154-0011-X). Cooper Sq.

Armenian Translation of Deuteronomy. Claude E. Cox. Ed. by Michael E. Stone. LC 81-5273. 1981. text ed. 16.50 (ISBN 0-89130-491-6, 21-02-02); pap. text ed. 12.00 (ISBN 0-89130-492-4). Scholars Pr GA.

Armenian Version of IV Ezra. Ed. by Michael E. Stone. LC 78-17084. 1979. 15.00 (ISBN 0-89130-287-5); pap. 10.50 (ISBN 0-89130-255-7, 210201). Scholars Pr GA.

Armenians in Rhode Island: Ancient Roots to Present Experiences. Ara A. Gelenian. Ed. by Patrick T. Conley. (Rhode Island Ethnic Heritage Ser.). (Illus.). 36p. (Orig.). 1985. pap. 2.75 (ISBN 0-917012-73-9). RI Pubns Soc.

Armies in the Sand: The Struggle for Mecca & Medina. John Sobini. (Illus.). 223p. 11.95 (ISBN 0-500-01246-6). Brown Bk.

Arming for Armageddon. John W. White. 218p. pap. 5.95 (ISBN 0-88062-109-5). Mott Media.

Arming the Protestants: The Formation of the Ulster Special Constabulary & the Royal Ulster Constabulary, 1920-1927. Michael Farrell. 274p. (Orig.). 1983. pap. 15.00 (ISBN 0-86104-705-2, Pub by Pluto Pr). Longwood Pub Group.

Arminius: A Study in the Dutch Reformation. rev. ed. Carl Bangs. Ed. by Joseph D. Allison. 384p. 1985. pap. 10.95 (ISBN 0-310-29481-9, 18368P). Zondervan.

Armonia De los Cuatro Evangelios. A. T. Robertson. Tr. by W. F. Patterson from Eng. Orig. Title: Harmony of the Four Gospels. (Span.). 259p. 1986. pap. 4.95 (ISBN 0-311-04302-X). Casa Bautista.

Armonia Familiar. Al Compton. 32p. 1981. pap. 1.30 (ISBN 0-311-46078-X). Casa Bautista.

Armonias Corales, Vol. 1. Tr. by Tony Arango. (Span.). 144p. (Orig.). 1977. pap. 4.75 (ISBN 0-89922-082-7). Edit Caribe.

Armored Gisant Before Fourteen Hundred. Judith W. Hurtig. LC 78-74368. (Outstanding Dissertations in the Fine Arts, Fourth Ser.). 1979. lib. bdg. 63.00 (ISBN 0-8240-3956-4). Garland Pub.

Armstrongism: The Worldwide Church of God Examined in the Searching Light of Scripture. Robert L. Sumner. 424p. 1974. 12.95 (ISBN 0-914012-15-0, Pub. by Bibl Evang Pr). Sword of Lord.

Arnica: The Amazing Healer. A. C. Ross. 96p. (Orig.). 1986. pap. 2.50 (ISBN 0-7225-0374-1, Dist. by Inner Traditions International). Thorsons Pubs.

Arno C. Gaebelein, Eighteen Sixty-One to Nineteen Forty-Five: Irenic Fundamentalist & Scholar. David A. Rausch. LC 83-9364. (Studies in American Religion: Vol. 10). (Illus.). 318p. 1984. 49.95x (ISBN 0-88946-652-1). E Mellen.

Arnobius of Sicca, the Case Against the Pagans, Vol. 1. Ed. by W. J. Burghardt et al. (ACW Ser.: No. 7). 372p. 1949. 13.95 (ISBN 0-8091-0248-X). Paulist Pr.

Arnobius of Sicca, the Case Against the Pagans, Vol. 2. Ed. by W. J. Burghardt et al. LC 78-62458. (ACW Ser.: No. 8). 659p. 1949. 11.95 (ISBN 0-8091-0249-8). Paulist Pr.

Arnold & God. Ruth ApRoberts. LC 82-10847. 304p. 1983. text ed. 29.00x (ISBN 0-520-04747-8). U of Cal Pr.

Arnold, Heaven's Loudest Angel. Robert Hedeman. 1982. 3.75 (ISBN 0-89536-549-9, 0103). CSS of Ohio.

Arnold Toynbee on Judaism & Zionism: A Critique. Oskar K. Rabinowitz. 372p. 1975. 17.95x (ISBN 0-8464-0149-5). Beekman Pubs.

Around Old Bethany. R. L. Berry. 83p. pap. 0.75 (ISBN 0-686-29097-6). Faith Pub Hse.

Around the Advent Wreath: Devotions for Families Using the Advent Wreath. Nancy L. Sasser. 40p. (Orig.). 1984. pap. 2.95 (ISBN 0-8066-2074-9, 23-1064). Augsburg.

Around the Wicket Gate. C. H. Spurgeon. 1973. pap. 2.50 (ISBN 0-686-09098-5). Pilgrim Pubns.

Around the World with Jesus. Dorothy Cross. 0.60 (ISBN 0-88027-102-7). Firm Foun Pub.

Around the Year with C. S. Lewis & His Friends. Ed. by Kathryn Lindskoog. 384p. 1986. 12.95 (ISBN 0-8378-5126-2). Gibson.

Around the Year with Emmet Fox. Emmet Fox. LC 58-13248. 1958. 12.45 (ISBN 0-06-062870-7, HarpR). Har-Row.

Arquitectura de los Templos Parroquiales de Puerto Rico - Architecture of Parish Churches in Puerto Rico. bilingual ed. Thomas S. Marvel & Maria L. Moreno. LC 81-10291. (Illus.). 1984. pap. 10.00 (ISBN 0-8477-2114-0). U of PR Pr.

Arrainment of the Whole Societie of Jesuites in Fraunce: Holden-the Twelfth & Thirteenth of July, 1594. Antoine Arnauld. LC 79-84084. (English Experience Ser.: No. 904). 68p. 1979. Repr. of 1594 ed. lib. bdg. 8.00 (ISBN 0-686-71069-X). Walter J Johnson.

Arranging Flowers for the Church. rev. ed. Oleta S. Moffitt. 1977. pap. 1.95 (ISBN 0-8006-1837-8, 1-1837). Fortress.

Arresting Abortion: Practical Ways to Save Unborn Children. John W. Whitehead. LC 84-71422. 128p. 1984. pap. 5.95 (ISBN 0-89107-314-0, Crossway Bks). Good News.

Arrow Returned. Corrine Vanderwerff. Ed. by Raymond H. Woosley. (Banner Ser.). 144p. (Orig.). 1987. pap. 6.50 (ISBN 0-8280-0364-5). Review & Herald.

Ars Moriendi, That Is to Saye the Craft for to Deye for the Helthe of Mannes Sowle. LC 74-80159. (English Experience Ser.: No. 639). 1974. Repr. of 1491 ed. 3.50 (ISBN 90-221-0639-X). Walter J Johnson.

Art & Architecture in Medieval France. Whitney S. Stoddard. (Icon Editions Ser.). Orig. Title: Monastery & Cathedral in Medieval France. (Illus.). 436p. 1972. pap. 14.95xi (ISBN 0-06-430022-6, IN-22, HarpT). Har-Row.

Art & Ceremony in Late Antiquity. Sabine MacCormack. (Transformation of the Classical Heritage Ser.: Vol. 1). (Illus.). 450p. 1981. 45.00x (ISBN 0-520-03779-0). U of Cal Pr.

Art & Faith. Fritz Eichenberg. (Illus., Orig.). 1952. pap. 2.50x (ISBN 0-87574-068-5). Pendle Hill.

Art & Human Consciousness. Gottfried Richter. Tr. by Margaret Frohlich & Burley Channer. (Illus.). 300p. (Orig.). 1985. 30.00 (ISBN 0-88010-108-3). Anthroposophic.

Art & Iconography of Vishnu-Narayana. Nanditha Krishna. (Illus.). xiv, 122p. 1981. text ed. 45.00x (ISBN 0-86590-025-6, Pub. by Taraporevala India). Apt Bks.

Art & Meaning: Rhetoric in Biblical Literature. D. J. Clines & D. M. Gunn. (Journal for the Study of the Old Testament, Supplement Ser.: No. 19). viii, 266p. 1982. text ed. 25.00x (ISBN 0-905774-38-8, Pub. by JSOT Pr England); pap. text ed. 13.95x (ISBN 0-905774-39-6). Eisenbrauns.

Art & Mysteries in Tombs, Mummies & Catacombs. Emmett D. Davisson. (Illus.). 1980. deluxe ed. 97.45 deluxe binding (ISBN 0-930582-63-2). Gloucester Art.

Art & Practice of Caballa Magic. Ophiel. 1977. pap. 8.95 (ISBN 0-87728-303-6). Weiser.

Art & Practices of Judaism. Alan Unterman. 96p. 1985. 20.00x (ISBN 0-7062-4126-6, Pub. by Ward Lock Educ Co Ltd). State Mutual Bk.

Art & Prudence. Mortimer J. Adler. Ed. by Garth S. Jowett. LC 77-11371. (Aspects of Film Ser.). 1978. Repr. of 1937 ed. lib. bdg. 59.50x (ISBN 0-405-11126-6). Ayer Co Pubs.

Art & Rituals: Twenty Five Hundred Years of Jainism in India. Eberhard Fischer & Jyotindra Jain. LC 78-670055. (Illus.). 1977. 20.00 (ISBN 0-89684-369-6). Orient Bk Dist.

Art & Scholasticism & the Frontiers of Poetry. Jacques Maritain. Tr. by Joseph W. Evans from Fr. LC 74-13601. 240p. 1974. pap. 6.95x (ISBN 0-268-00557-5). U of Notre Dame Pr.

Art & Science of Meditation. Ed. by L. K. Misra. 112p. 1976. pap. 3.95 (ISBN 0-89389-018-9). Himalayan Pubs.

Art & Science of Personal Magnetism. Theron Dumont. 8.00 (ISBN 0-911662-38-3). Yoga.

Art & Technique of Prayer. Ferdinand Valentine. (Overview Studies: No. 9). 1969. pap. 0.50x (ISBN 0-87343-049-2). Magi Bks.

Art & the Bible. Francis A. Schaeffer. LC 73-75891. 64p. 1973. pap. 2.95 (ISBN 0-87784-443-7). Inter-Varsity.

Art & the Changing World: Uncommon Sense in the Twentieth Century. Dorothea Blom. LC 72-80094. (Illus.). 32p. (Orig.). 1972. pap. 2.50x (ISBN 0-87574-183-5, 183). Pendle Hill.

Art & the Christian Intelligence in St. Augustine. Robert J. O'Connell. LC 78-546. 1978. 18.00x (ISBN 0-674-04675-7). Harvard U Pr.

Art & the Reformation. George G. Coulton. LC 69-15789. (Illus.). xxii, 662p. 1969. Repr. of 1928 ed. 45.00 (ISBN 0-208-00738-5, Archon). Shoe String.

Art & the Reformation in Germany. Carl C. Christensen. (Studies in the Reformation Ser.: Vol.2). (Illus.). 269p. 1981. 18.95x (ISBN 0-8214-0388-5, 82-82816, Co-Pub by Wayne State U Pr). Ohio U Pr.

Art & the Religious Experience: The Language of the Sacred. F. David Martin. LC 75-161508. (Illus.). 288p. 1972. 27.50 (ISBN 0-8387-7935-2). Bucknell U Pr.

Art & Theological Imagination. John W. Dixon, Jr. (Illus.). 1978. 12.95 (ISBN 0-8164-0397-X, HarpR). Har-Row.

Art As a Way: A Return to the Spiritual Roots. Frederick Franck. LC 81-7853. (Illus.). 160p. (Orig.). 1981. pap. 9.95 (ISBN 0-8245-0076-8). Crossroad NY.

Art as Religious Studies. Dour Adams & Diane Apostolos-Cappadona. (Illus.). 272p. (Orig.). 1987. pap. 17.95 (ISBN 0-8245-0809-2). Crossroad NY.

Art as Seen in the Light of Mystery Wisdom. 2nd ed. Rudolf Steiner. Tr. of Kunst im Lichte der Mysterienweisheit. 182p. 1984. pap. 9.95 (ISBN 0-85440-416-3, Pub. by Steinerbooks). Anthroposophic.

Art Awaiting the Saviour. Ali Shariati. Tr. by Homa Fardjadi from Persian. 23p. 1980. pap. 1.00x (ISBN 0-941722-16-3). Book Dist Ctr.

Art, Creativity & the Sacred: An Anthology in Religion & Art. Ed. by Diane Apostolos-Cappadona. (Illus.). 352p. 1983. pap. 16.95 (ISBN 0-8245-0609-X). Crossroad NY.

Art for Children's Liturgy: What You Need & How To Do It. Marge Tuthill. LC 82-60855. 1982. pap. 4.95 (ISBN 0-8091-2478-5). Paulist Pr.

Art Gregorien. 3rd ed. Amedee Gastoue. LC 77-178576. (Fr.). Repr. of 1920 ed. 21.50 (ISBN 0-404-56607-3). AMS Pr.

Art Imagery & the Mythic Process. Dorothea Blom. LC 77-91636. (Illus.). 31p. (Orig.). 1977. pap. 2.50x (ISBN 0-87574-215-7). Pendle Hill.

Art in the Mountains: Story of the Passion Play. Henry Blackburn. LC 77-94544. 1979. Repr. of 1870 ed. lib. bdg. 20.00 (ISBN 0-89341-178-7). Longwood Pub Group.

Art, Literature, Religion: Life on the Borders. Ed. by Robert Detweiler. LC 82-3319. (AAR Thermatic Studies). 208p. 1983. 22.50 (ISBN 0-89130-578-5, 01 24 92). Scholars Pr GA.

Art of Achieving Success. John D. Hawkes. 128p. 1971. pap. 2.95 (ISBN 0-89036-008-1). Hawkes Pub Inc.

Art of Being a Man. J. Allan Petersen. 1974. pap. 1.25 (ISBN 0-8423-0085-6). Tyndale.

Art of Being Human. William McNamara. pap. 3.50 (ISBN 0-385-08323-8, E45, Im). Doubleday.

Art of Biblical Narrative. Robert Alter. LC 80-68958. 208p. 1981. 14.95 (ISBN 0-465-00424-5). Basic.

Art of Biblical Narrative. Robert Alter. LC 80-68958. 195p. 1983. pap. 7.95 (ISBN 0-465-00427-X, CN-5099). Basic.

Art of Biblical Poetry. Robert Alter. LC 85-47550. 272p. 1985. 17.95 (ISBN 0-465-00430-X). Basic.

Art of Biblical Poetry. Robert Alter. LC 85-47550. 228p. 1987. pap. 8.95 (ISBN 0-465-00431-8, PL 5180). Basic.

Art of Christian Listening. Thomas N. Hart. LC 80-82810. 132p. (Orig.). 1981. pap. 4.95 (ISBN 0-8091-2345-2). Paulist Pr.

Art of Contemplation. Ramon Lull, pseud. Tr. by Allison Peers. 1976. lib. bdg. 69.95 (ISBN 0-8490-1451-4). Gordon Pr.

Art of Contemplation. Alan Watts. LC 72-10174. 1973. 4.95 (ISBN 0-394-70963-2). Pantheon.

Art of Creation. Edward Carpenter. 1978. Repr. of 1904 ed. lib. bdg. 45.00 (ISBN 0-8495-0814-2). Arden Lib.

Art of Deathlessness. V. Balaramiah. (Illus.). 128p. 1980. pap. 4.95 (ISBN 0-937698-01-6). Golden Mean.

Art of Dying. Bhagwan Shree Rajneesh. Ed. by Ma Prema Veena. LC 78-905608. (Hasidism Ser.). (Illus.). 284p. (Orig.). 1978. 14.95 (ISBN 0-88050-005-0). Chidvilas Found.

Art of Dying Well. Sr. M. Catharine O'Connor. Repr. of 1942 ed. 15.00 (ISBN 0-404-04811-0). AMS Pr.

Art of Existential Counseling. Adrian Van Kaam. 6.95 (ISBN 0-87193-044-7). Dimension Bks.

Art of Getting Along With People. Cecil G. Osborne. 192p. 1982. pap. 3.95 (ISBN 0-310-30612-4, 10477P). Zondervan.

Art of Gianlorenzo Bernini: Selected Sculpture. Michael Mezzatesta. LC 82-81080. (Illus.). 63p. (Orig.). 1982. pap. 8.50 (ISBN 0-912804-05-X). Kimbell Art.

Art of Greeting & Seating: The Church Usher's Guide. Ernest A. Clevenger, Jr. (Illus.). 16p. 1983. pap. 0.95 (ISBN 0-88428-000-4). Parchment Pr.

Art of Human Relations. Ernest White. LC 85-5953. 1985. pap. 6.95 (ISBN 0-8054-5008-4). Broadman.

Art of Inner Listening. Jesse K. Crum. LC 74-21643. (Orig.). 1975. pap. 2.25 (ISBN 0-8356-0303-2, Quest). Theos Pub Hse.

Art of Intercession. Kenneth E. Hagin. 1980. pap. 3.50 (ISBN 0-89276-503-8). Hagin Ministries.

Art of Interpretation: Selected Studies on the Interpretation of Canon Law. James A. Coriden et al. v, 79p. (Orig.). 1983. pap. 3.75 (ISBN 0-943616-18-2). Canon Law Soc.

Art of Jewish Living: The Sabbath Seder. Ron Wolfson. (Illus.). 1985. pap. 9.95 (ISBN 0-935665-00-5); tchr's. ed 4.95 (ISBN 0-935665-01-3); cassette tape 3.00 (ISBN 0-935665-02-1). Fed Jewish Mens Clubs.

Art of Learning to Love Yourself. Cecil G. Osborne. 1976. 3.95 (ISBN 0-310-30572-1, 10475P). Zondervan.

Art of Life. Edith Schaeffer. 1987. 10.95 (Crossway Bks). Good News.

Art of Listening with Love. Abraham Schmitt. (Festival Bks.). 176p. 1982. pap. 4.50 (ISBN 0-687-01836-6). Abingdon.

Art of Living, Vol. IV. Robert R. Leichtman & Carl Japikse. LC 83-703086. (Illus.). 280p. (Orig.). 1984. pap. 6.95 (ISBN 0-89804-035-3). Ariel OH.

Art of Living. Dietrich Von Hildebrand & Alice Von Hildebrand. 1965. 3.95 (ISBN 0-685-10959-3, L38009). Franciscan Herald.

Art of Meditation. Joel S. Goldsmith. LC 56-13258. 1957. 12.45 (ISBN 0-06-063150-3, HarpR). Har-Row.

Art of Mosaics. Michael Avi-Yonah. LC 72-10793. (Lerner Archaeology Ser.: Digging up the Past). (Illus.). 96p. 1975. PLB 8.95 (ISBN 0-8225-0828-1). Lerner Pubns.

Art of Parenting in a Changing Society. John F. Miller. 1979. 8.95 (ISBN 0-8199-0761-8). Franciscan Herald.

Art of Pastoral Conversation. Gaylord Noyce. LC 81-82350. 128p. 1982. pap. 3.99 (ISBN 0-8042-1131-0). John Knox.

Art of Personal Prayer. Lance Webb. 1977. 3.95x (ISBN 0-8358-0365-1). Upper Room.

Art of Personality. Inayat Khan. (Sufi Message of Hazrat Inayat Khan Ser.: Vol. 3). 256p. 1979. 14.95 (ISBN 90-6077-570-8, Pub. by Servire BV Netherlands). Hunter Hse.

Art of Prayer. Igumen Chariton. Tr. by Palmer Kadloubovsky. 288p. 1966. 26.95 (ISBN 0-571-06899-5). Faber & Faber.

Art of Prayer. Martial Lekeux. Tr. by Paul J. Oligny. LC 59-14706. pap. 78.50 (ISBN 0-317-28176-3, 2022570). Bks Demand UMI.

Art of Preaching. Alan Of Lille. Tr. by Gillian R. Evans. (Cistercian Fathers Ser.: No. 23). (Lat., Orig.). 1981. pap. 13.95 (ISBN 0-87907-923-1). Cistercian Pubns.

Art of Presence: The Poet & Paradise Lost. Arnold Stein. 1977. 30.95x (ISBN 0-520-03167-9). U of Cal Pr.

Art of Prophesying: New England Sermons & the Shaping of Belief. Teresa Toulouse. LC 86-7121. 224p. 1987. 23.00x (ISBN 0-8203-0892-7). U of Ga Pr.

Art of Real Happiness. Norman V. Peale & Smiley Blanton. 1976. pap. 2.50 (ISBN 0-449-24062-2, Crest). Fawcett.

Art of Reciting the Qur'an. Kristina Nelson. (Modern Middle East Ser.: No. 11). 271p. 1986. text ed. 25.00x (ISBN 0-292-70367-8). U of Tex Pr.

Art of Recruiting Volunteers. Mark Senter, III. 96p. 1983. pap. 9.95 (ISBN 0-88207-297-8). Victor Bks.

Art of Soul Winning. Murray W. Downey. 1957. pap. 5.95 (ISBN 0-8010-2820-5). Baker Bk.

Art of Spiritual Healing. Joel S. Goldsmith. LC 59-14532. 1959. 11.45 (ISBN 0-06-063170-8, HarpR). Har-Row.

Art of Staying Sane. facs. ed. Joseph Barth. LC 70-117757. (Essay Index Reprint Ser). 1948. 18.00 (ISBN 0-8369-1783-9). Ayer Co Pubs.

Art of Successful Praying. Gordon Lindsay. (School of Prayer Ser.). 1.25 (ISBN 0-89985-079-0). Christ Nations.

Art of Teaching Christian Doctrine. rev. ed. Johannes Hofinger. 1962. 14.95 (ISBN 0-268-00015-8). U of Notre Dame Pr.

Art of the Medieval World: Architecture, Sculpture, Painting, the Sacred Arts. George Zarnecki. 1976. 34.95 (ISBN 0-13-047514-9). P-H.

Art of the Mystic: The Master Course in Spiritual & Psychic Development. Thomas F. Kearns. Ed. by Kathy Paterson. (Illus.). 160p. (Orig.). 1986. pap. 9.95 (ISBN 0-935251-00-6). Manchurch.

Art of Thomas Merton. Ross Labrie. LC 79-1341. 188p. 1979. pap. 9.95x (ISBN 0-912646-55-1). Tex Christian.

Art of Travel by Soul: An Out of Body Experience. C. Bert Sanger. (Illus.). 150p. 1986. 15.00 (ISBN 0-9615362-0-9). Popular Pubns.

Art of Understanding Yourself. Cecil G. Osborne. 1986. pap. 4.95 (ISBN 0-310-30592-6, 10472P). Zondervan.

Art of War for the Christian Soldier. 2nd ed. Frank W. Sandford. LC 66-29707. 1966. 4.00 (ISBN 0-910840-12-1). Kingdom.

Art of Zen Gardens: A Guide to Their Creation & Enjoyment. A. K. Davidson. (Illus.). 160p. 1983. 15.95 (ISBN 0-87477-253-2); pap. 9.95 (ISBN 0-87477-254-0). J P Tarcher.

Art of Zen Sword: The History of Shim Gum Do, Pt. I. Chang S. Kim & Maria Kim. LC 85-5973. (Illus.). 144p. 1985. 19.95 (ISBN 0-9614427-0-0). Am Buddhist Shim Do.

Art Responds to the Bible. Dorothea Blom. LC 74-24006. (Illus.). 32p. (Orig.). 1974. pap. 2.50x (ISBN 0-87574-197-5). Pendle Hill.

Art, the Metaphysics of Love & Its Universal Mystical Symbols. Benjamin Constable. (Illus.). 1977. 47.25 (ISBN 0-89266-046-5). Am Classical Coll Pr.

Arte de Ensenar. C. H. Benson. Tr. by Fernando P. Villalobos from Eng. (Curso Para Maestros Cristianos: No. 5). (Span.). 128p. 1971. pap. 3.50 (ISBN 0-89922-016-9). Edit Caribe.

Artful Childmaking: Artificial Insemination in Catholic Teaching. John C. Wakefield. LC 78-65765. 205p. 1978. pap. 8.95 (ISBN 0-935372-03-2). Pope john Ctr.

Arthur Oakman's Radio Sermons, Vol. 2. Ed. by Stephen Gregson. 193p. 1984. pap. 11.00 (ISBN 0-8309-0400-X). Herald Hse.

Arthur-Peacemaker. Arthur Blessitt. LC 85-71322. (Orig.). 1986. pap. 5.00 (ISBN 0-934461-02-3, BP603). Blessitt Pub.

Articles Agreed on in the National Synode of the Reformed Churches of France. LC 76-57381. (English Experience Ser.: No. 799). 1977. Repr. of 1623 ed. lib. bdg. 5.00 (ISBN 90-221-0799-X). Walter J Johnson.

Articles Exhibited in Parliament Against William, Archbishop of Canterbury. William Laud. LC 72-212. (English Experience Ser.: No. 333). 16p. 1971. Repr. of 1640 ed. 7.00 (ISBN 90-221-0333-1). Walter J Johnson.

Articles of Faith. James E. Talmage. LC 80-22041. (Classics in Mormon Literature Edition Ser.). 537p. 1981. 9.95 (ISBN 0-87747-838-4). Deseret Bk.

Articles of Faith Learning Book. Jackie Owen & Ann Laemmlen. (Illus.). 64p. 1982. Bk. I. pap. 3.95 (ISBN 0-87747-878-3); Bk. II, 80pgs. pap. 3.95 (ISBN 0-87747-915-1); Bk. III, 80pgs. pap. 3.95 (ISBN 0-87747-922-4). Deseret Bk.

Articles of Islamic Acts. Ayatullah A. Al-Khui. Tr. by M. Fazal Haq from Arabic. 236p. 1983. pap. 6.00 (ISBN 0-941724-21-2). Islamic Seminary.

Articles to Be Inquired of, in the First Metropoliticall Visitation of the Most Reverend Father Richarde...Archbishop of Canterbury. Church of England Staff. LC 74-28851. (English Experience Ser.: No. 732). 1975. Repr. of 1605 ed. 3.50 (ISBN 90-221-0732-9). Walter J Johnson.

Artist on the Witness Stand. Fritz Eishenberg. LC 84-61828. (Orig.). 1984. pap. 2.50x (ISBN 0-87574-257-2). Pendle Hill.

Artistic & Mystical Significance of Indian & Egyptian Temples. Georg R. Nikopol. (Illus.). 187p. 1984. 137.45 (ISBN 0-86650-131-2). Gloucester Art.

Artistry & Faith in the Book of Judith. Toni Craven. LC 82-25000. (Society of Biblical Literature Dissertation Ser.). 150p. 1983. pap. 11.25 (ISBN 0-89130-612-9, 06 01 70). Scholars Pr GA.

Arts & Crafts of Hawaii: Religion. Peter Buck & Te Rangi Hiroa. (Special Publication Ser.: No. 45 (11)). (Illus.). 77p. 1957. pap. 3.00 (ISBN 0-910240-44-2). Bishop Mus.

Arts & Crafts the Year Round, 2 Vols. Ruth Sharon. (Illus.). 1965. Set. 29.00x (ISBN 0-8381-0213-1). United Syn Bk.

Arts & Inspiration: Mormon Perspectives. Ed. by Steven P. Sondrup. LC 80-21927. (Illus.). 240p. 1980. pap. 7.95 (ISBN 0-8425-1845-2). Brigham.

Arts & Practices of Christianity. P. Moore. 96p. 1985. 20.00x (ISBN 0-7062-4125-8, Pub. by Ward Lock Educ Co Ltd). State Mutual Bk.

Arts & Their Mission. Rudolf Steiner. Tr. by Monges & Moore. 125p. 1986. pap. 8.95 (ISBN 0-88010-154-7). Anthroposophic.

Arts of Orpheus. Ivan M. Linforth. LC 72-9296. (Philosophy of Plato & Aristotle Ser.). Repr. of 1941 ed. 24.50 (ISBN 0-405-04847-5). Ayer Co Pubs.

Arya Dharm: Hindu Consciousness in Nineteenth-Century Punjab. Kenneth W. Jones. LC 74-27290. 350p. 1976. 41.95x (ISBN 0-520-02919-4). U of Cal Pr.

Arya Samaj: Hindu without Hinduism. D. Vable. 1983. text ed. 25.00x (ISBN 0-7069-2131-3, Pub. by Vikas India). Advent NY.

Aryan Sun-Myths: The Origin of Religions. Shara E. Tilcomb. LC 78-31508. 1979. Repr. of 1889 ed. lib. bdg. 20.00 (ISBN 0-89341-323-2). Longwood Pub Group.

Aryan Sun-Myths: The Origin of Religions. Sarah E. Titcom. 1977. lib. bdg. 59.95 (ISBN 0-8490-1456-5). Gordon Pr.

As a Driven Leaf. Milton Steinberg. LC 75-32237. 1939. pap. 7.95x (ISBN 0-87441-074-6). Behrman.

As a Little Child. Nora E. Larson. LC 81-66072. (Illus.). 56p. (Orig.). 1981. pap. 4.00 (ISBN 0-87516-451-X). De Vorss.

As a Man Thinketh. James Allen. pap. 1.00 (ISBN 0-87516-000-X). De Vorss.

As a Man Thinketh. James Allen. 1959. 3.95 (ISBN 0-399-12829-8, G&D). Putnam Pub Group.

As a Man Thinketh. James Allen. 4.95 (ISBN 0-529-05908-8, F12); pap. 2.95 (ISBN 0-529-05906-1, D6). World Bible.

As a Man Thinketh. James Allen. 1985. 4.95 (ISBN 0-915720-20-5). Brownlow Pub Co.

As a Tree by the Waters. 1981. 9.95 (ISBN 0-87306-237-X). Feldheim.

As a Tree Grows: Reflections on Growing in the Image of Christ. W. Phillip Keller. 96p. 1985. pap. 2.95 (ISBN 0-89283-248-7, Pub. by Vine Bks). Servant.

As Angels of Light. Rose Johnson & Don Ratzlaff. LC 80-82926. (Illus.). 160p. (Orig.). 1980. pap. 4.95 (ISBN 0-937364-00-2). Kindred Pr.

As Bread That Is Broken. Peter G. Van Breemen. 5.95 (ISBN 0-87193-052-8). Dimension Bks.

As Cartuxas de Portugal. James Hogg. Ed. by James Hogg. (Analecta Cartusiana Ser.: No. 69). Tr. of Charterhouses of Portugal. (Ger. Span. & Port., Illus.). 145p. (Orig.). 1984. pap. 25.00 (ISBN 3-7052-0101-8, Pub. by Salsburg Studies). Longwood Pub Group.

As God Intended. Lynn Stephens. 1973. pap. 1.25 (ISBN 0-89114-045-X). Baptist Pub Hse.

As I Have Loved You: Challenge of Christian Ethics. James P. Hanigan. 240p. (Orig.). 1986. pap. 9.95 (ISBN 0-8091-2734-2). Paulist Pr.

As I See Religion. Harry E. Fosdick. LC 75-11835. 201p. 1975. Repr. of 1932 ed. lib. bdg. 45.00x (ISBN 0-8371-8142-9, FOAI). Greenwood.

As I Take Christ: Daily Prayer & Reflection with Paul. Dodie Gust. LC 86-72439. 136p. (Orig.). 1987. pap. 4.95 (ISBN 0-87793-352-9). Ave Maria.

As It Was Told: A Play for Christmas. Ed Irsch. 16p. (Orig.). 1980. pap. text ed. 3.75 (ISBN 0-89536-439-5, 0146). CSS of Ohio.

As It Was Written: An Introduction to the Bible. Justin Taylor. 176p. 1987. pap. 7.95 (ISBN 0-8091-2843-8). Paulist Pr.

As Once to Birth I Went, Now I Am Taken Back. Harry Brody. 1981. 2.00 (ISBN 0-936814-07-1). New Collage.

As One Who Serves: Reflections on the Pastoral Ministry of Priests in the United States. 86p. 1977. pap. 3.25 (ISBN 1-55586-549-6). US Catholic.

As the Rock Flower Blooms. Rosemary A. Watson. 1984. pap. 4.95 (ISBN 9971-972-17-4). OMF Bks.

As the Twig Is Bent: Sermons for Children. Harold Steindam. (Illus.). 128p. (Orig.). 1983. pap. 6.95 (ISBN 0-8298-0679-2). Pilgrim NY.

As Through a Veil: Mystical Poetry in Islam. Annemarie Schimmel. 359p. 1987. pap. text ed. 14.50 (ISBN 0-231-05247-2). Columbia U Pr.

As Touching the Holy. Albert Wells. (Direction Bks.). (Orig.). 1980. pap. 2.45 (ISBN 0-8010-9637-5). Baker Bk.

As We Forgive Those. Elisabeth Elliot. 16p. 1982. pap. 1.25 (ISBN 0-89107-255-1). Good News.

As We Seek God: International Reflections on Contemporary Benedictine Monasticism. Ed. by Stephanie Campbell. (Cistercian Studies Ser.: No. 70). 1983. pap. 7.95 (ISBN 0-87907-868-5). Cistercian Pubns.

As You Believe. Barbara Dewey. LC 85-7370. 208p. 1985. 18.95 (ISBN 0-933123-01-9). Bartholomew Bks.

As You Go. Waylon Bailey. LC 81-47888. 118p. (Orig.). 1981. pap. 4.00 (ISBN 0-914520-15-6). Insight Pr.

As You Recover. Douglas Elliott. 32p. 1984. pap. 1.25 (ISBN 0-8010-3414-0). Baker Bk.

As You Thinketh: Update & Revision of James Allen's Classic "As a Man Thinketh". rev. ed. James Allen. 88p. 1984. pap. 5.95 (ISBN 0-914295-03-9). Top Mtn Pub.

Ascend to Your Father: An Introduction to Marian Meditation. John A. Hammes. (Orig.). 1987. pap. 5.95 (ISBN 0-913382-36-1, 101-36). Prow Bks-Franciscan.

Ascending Cycle. George W. Russell. (Sangam Texts Ser.). 105p. (Orig.). 1983. pap. 8.75 (ISBN 0-88695-013-9). Concord Grove.

Ascension & Heavenly Priesthood of Our Lord. William Milligan. 416p. 1977. Repr. of 1894 ed. 12.50 (ISBN 0-87921-034-6). Attic Pr.

Ascension of Christ. William Milligan. 1980. 15.00 (ISBN 0-86524-061-2, 9505). Klock & Klock.

Ascent of the Mountain, Flight of the Dove: An Invitation to Religious Studies. rev. ed. Michael Novak. LC 77-20463. 1978. pap. 5.95xi (ISBN 0-06-066322-7, RD 232, HarpR). Har-Row.

Ascent to Excellence in Catholic Education: A Guide to Effective Decision-Making. Mary-Angela Harper. 278p. 1980. 9.55 (ISBN 0-318-00777-0). Natl Cath Educ.

Ascent to Harmony. Elie Bunk. 180p. 1987. 8.95 (ISBN 0-87306-407-0). Feldheim.

Ascent to Joy: Transforming Deadness of Spirit. Carol Ochs. LC 85-41019. 160p. 1986. text ed. 12.95x (ISBN 0-268-00615-6). U of Notre Dame Pr.

Ascent to the Tribes. 1956. pap. 3.95 (ISBN 0-85363-136-0). OMF Bks.

Ascetic Piety & Women's Faith: Essays in Late Ancient Christianity. Elizabeth A. Clark. (Studies in Women & Religion: Vol. 20). 1986. 69.95 (ISBN 0-88946-529-0). E Mellen.

Ascetic Piety & Women's Faith: Essays on Late Ancient Christianity. Elizabeth A. Clark. LC 86-21828. (Studies in Women & Religion: Volume 20). 448p. 1986. lib. bdg. 69.95 (ISBN 0-88946-529-0). E Mellen.

Ascetic Works of Saint Basil. Basilius. Tr. & intro. by W. K. Clarke. LC 80-2352. Repr. of 1925 ed. 47.50 (ISBN 0-404-18902-4). AMS Pr.

Ascetical Works. St. Basil. LC 50-10735. (Fathers of the Church Ser.: Vol. 9). 525p. 1950. 26.95x (ISBN 0-8132-0009-1). Cath U Pr.

Ascetical Works. St. Gregory Of Nyssa. LC 64-13360. (Fathers of the Church Ser: Vol. 58). 288p. 1967. 16.95x (ISBN 0-8132-0058-X). Cath U Pr.

Ascetics, Authority, & the Church in the Age of Jerome & Cassian. Phillip Rousseau. (Historical Monographs). 1978. 39.95x (ISBN 0-19-821870-2). Oxford U Pr.

Asclepius: A Collection & Interpretation of the Testimonies, 2 vols. in 1. facsimile ed. Emma J. Edelstein & Ludwig Edelstein. LC 75-10635. (Ancient Religion & Mythology Ser.). (Eng. & Gr.). 1976. Repr. of 1945 ed. 57.50x (ISBN 0-405-07009-8). Ayer Co Pubs.

Ascuas de Fuego. Elizabeth Bauman. Tr. by Flora Patzan. Tr. of Coals of Fire. (Span.). 128p. 1982. pap. 3.50 (ISBN 0-8361-3315-3). Herald Pr.

Aserah: Extrabiblical Evidence. Walter A. Maier, III. (Harvard Semitic Monographs). 274p. 1987. 21.95 (ISBN 1-55540-046-9, 04-00-37). Scholars Pr GA.

Ash Wednesday Supper. Giordano Bruno. Tr. by Stanley L. Jaki. Tr. of Cena de Le Ceneri. (Illus.). 174p. 1975. text ed. 19.60x (ISBN 90-2797-581-7). Mouton.

Ashes out of Hope: Fiction by Soviet-Yiddish Writers. Ed. by Irving Howe & Eliezer Greenberg. LC 76-49731. 1978. pap. 4.95 (ISBN 0-8052-0605-1). Schocken.

Ashkenazi Haggadah. David Goldstein. (Illus.). 140p. 1985. 75.00 (ISBN 0-8109-1819-6). Abrams.

Ashkenazim & Sephardim: Their Relations, Differences & Problems As Reflected in the Rabbinical Responsa. 25.00x (ISBN 0-87068-349-7). Ktav.

Ashram Observances in Action. M. K. Gandhi. 151p. 1983. pap. 1.00 (ISBN 0-934676-36-4). Greenlf Bks.

Ashtanga Yoga Primer. Baba Hari Dass. Ed. by Karuna K. Ault. LC 81-51052. (Illus.). 72p. (Orig.). 1981. pap. 4.95 (ISBN 0-918100-04-6). Sri Rama.

Asi Seremos Diferentes. Basilea Schlink. 224p. 1976. 3.75 (ISBN 0-88113-004-4). Edit Betania.

Asian Journal of Thomas Merton. Thomas Merton. Ed. by Naomi B. Stone et al. LC 71-103370. (Illus.). 448p. 1973. pap. 8.95 (ISBN 0-8112-0570-3, NDP394). New Directions.

Asian Variations in Ramayana. Ed. by K. Srinivasa Iyengar. 1986. 14.00x (ISBN 0-8364-1571-X, Pub. by National Sahitya Akademi). South Asia Bks.

Asia's Struggle for Full Humanity: Towards a Relevant Theology. Ed. by Virginia Fabella. LC 80-14923. 229p. (Orig.). 1980. pap. 8.95 (ISBN 0-88344-015-6). Orbis Bks.

Asiatic Studies: Religious & Social, 2 vols. Alfred C. Lyall. 826p. Repr. of 1882 ed. Set. text ed. 57.50x. Coronet Bks.

Asimov's Guide to the Bible: The New Testament. Isaac Asimov. 640p. 1971. pap. 8.95 (ISBN 0-380-01031-3, 60255-5). Avon.

Asimov's Guide to the Bible: The Old Testament. Isaac Asimov. 720p. 1971. pap. 10.95 (ISBN 0-380-01032-1). Avon.

Ask & It Shall Be Given. Donald T. Kauffman. 48p. 1986. 6.95 (ISBN 0-8378-5095-9). Gibson.

Ask Him Anything. Lloyd J. Ogilvie. (QP Proven-Word Ser.). 244p. 1984. pap. 7.95 (ISBN 0-8499-2982-2). Word Bks.

Ask the Bible. Ed. by R. T. Brooks. LC 83-3841. 400p. 1983. 19.95 (ISBN 0-672-52765-0). Bobbs.

Asketitcheskaya Propovjed, Tom 4. Ignatius Brianchaninov. Tr. of Ascetic Sermons. 537p. 25.00 (ISBN 0-317-28962-4); pap. 20.00 (ISBN 0-317-28963-2). Holy Trinity.

Asketitcheskije Opiti, Tom 2. Ignatius Brianchaninov. Tr. of Ascetic Experiences. 332p. 20.00 (ISBN 0-317-28949-7); pap. 15.00 (ISBN 0-317-28950-0). Holy Trinity.

Asketitcheskije Opiti, tom 3, Tom 3. Ignatius Brianchaninov. Tr. of Ascetic Experiences. 315p. 20.00 (ISBN 0-317-28957-8); pap. 15.00 (ISBN 0-317-28958-6). Holy Trinity.

Asking Questions: A Classroom Model for Teaching the Bible. D. Bruce Lockerbie. Ed. by Diane Zimmerman. LC 80-18198. (Orig.). 1980. pap. text ed. 5.95 (ISBN 0-915134-75-6). Mott Media.

Asking the Father: A Study of the Prayer of Petition. Gabriel Daly. (Ways of Prayer Ser.: Vol. 4). 1982. 8.95 (ISBN 0-89453-428-9); pap. 5.95 (ISBN 0-89453-277-4). M Glazier.

Asking the Hard Questions. Eugene B. Hines. LC 85-19528. 1986. pap. 4.95 (ISBN 0-8054-5013-0). Broadman.

Asklepios: The Cult of the Greek God of Medicine. A. Walton. 136p. 1979. 15.00 (ISBN 0-89005-277-8). Ares.

Asleep in the Light (A Musical for the Times) Howi Tiller. (Illus.). 41p. 1984. pap. text ed. 12.95 (ISBN 0-912315-79-2). Word Aflame.

Asma'ul-Husna: The 99 Beautiful Names of Allah. M. R. Bawa Muhaiyaddeen. LC 79-19619. (Illus.). 211p. 1979. pap. 4.95 (ISBN 0-914390-13-9). Fellowship Pr PA.

Asot Mishpat. Abraham Shumsky & Adaia Shumsky. (Mah Tov Hebrew Teaching Ser.: Bk. 1). (Illus.). 1969. text ed. 5.50 (ISBN 0-8074-0178-1, 405301); tchrs'. guide 3.50 (ISBN 0-8074-0179-X, 205302); wkbk. 5.00 (ISBN 0-8074-0180-3, 405300). UAHC.

Aspect of Religious & Scientific Thought. Richard H. Hutton. 766p. Repr. of 1899 ed. text ed. 49.68x (ISBN 0-576-29209-5). Gregg Intl.

Aspects of Early English Drama. Ed. by Paula Neuss. LC 83-21331. (Illus.). 176p. 1985. Repr. of 1983 ed. 42.50x (ISBN 0-389-20428-5, 07314). B&N Imports.

Aspects of Ethical Religion: Essays in Honor of Felix Adler on the Fiftieth Anniversary of His Founding of the Ethical Movement. facs. ed. Ed. by Horace J. Bridges. LC 68-29190. (Essay Index Reprint Ser). 1968. Repr. of 1926 ed. 20.00 (ISBN 0-8369-0161-4). Ayer Co Pubs.

Aspects of Ethical Religion: Essays in Honor of Felix Adler. Ed. by Horace J. Bridges. 1977. lib. bdg. 59.95 (ISBN 0-8490-1459-X). Gordon Pr.

Aspects of Human Evolution. Rudolf Steiner. Tr. by Rita Stebbing. 1986. 20.00 (ISBN 0-88010-251-9); pap. 9.95 (ISBN 0-88010-252-7). Anthroposophic.

Aspects of Islam. facsimile ed. Duncan B. Macdonald. LC 77-179530. (Select Bibliographies Reprint Ser). Repr. of 1911 ed. 25.50 (ISBN 0-8369-6659-7). Ayer Co Pubs.

Aspects of Islam in Post-Colonial Indonesia: Five Essays. C. A. Van Nieuwenhuijze. 1958. 23.75x (ISBN 0-686-21860-4). Mouton.

Aspects of Islamic Civilization As Depicted in the Original Texts. Arthur J. Arberry. LC 77-673. 1977. Repr. of 1964 ed. lib. bdg. 29.25x (ISBN 0-8371-9494-6, ARAI). Greenwood.

Aspects of Islamic Civilization as Depicted in the Original Text. Arthur J. Arberry. 1967. pap. 9.95 (ISBN 0-472-06130-5, 130, AA). U of Mich Pr.

Aspects of Jewish Belief. A. Feinsilver. 1973. pap. 5.95x (ISBN 0-87068-225-3). Ktav.

Aspects of Jewish Culture in the Middle Ages: Papers from the Eighth Annual CEMERS Conference. Ed. by Paul E. Szarmach. 230p. 10.00 (ISBN 0-87395-165-4, Pub. by SUNY Pr). Medieval & Renaissance NY.

Aspects of Jewish Culture in the Middle Ages. Ed. by Paul E. Szarmach. LC 77-29046. (Illus.). 208p. 1979. 44.50 (ISBN 0-87395-165-4). State U NY Pr.

Aspects of Pentecostal-Charismatic Origins. Vinson Synan. LC 75-2802. 1975. 6.95 (ISBN 0-88270-111-8); pap. 6.95. Bridge Pub.

Aspects of Puritan Religious Thought: Library, Vol. VI. Ed. by Sacvan Barcovitch. LC 83-12782. (Library of American Puritan Writings). 728p. 1984. Repr. 57.50 (ISBN 0-404-60806-X). AMS Pr.

Aspects of Rabbinic Theology: Major Concepts of the Talmud. Solomon Schechter. LC 61-14919. 1961. pap. 8.95 (ISBN 0-8052-0015-0). Schocken.

Aspects of Religion in the Soviet Union, 1917-1967. Ed. by Richard H. Marshall, Jr. et al. LC 70-115874. 1971. 35.00x (ISBN 0-226-50700-9). U of Chicago Pr.

Aspects of Religion in the United States of America. Isabella L. Bishop. LC 75-38438. (Religion in America, Ser. 2). 200p. 1972. Repr. of 1859 ed. 20.00 (ISBN 0-405-04059-8). Ayer Co Pubs.

Aspects of Religious Belief & Practice in Babylonia & Assyria. Morris Jastrow. LC 68-56503. Repr. of 1911 ed. 25.00 (ISBN 0-405-08667-9, Blom Pubns). Ayer Co Pubs.

Aspects of Religious Propaganda in Judaism & Early Christianity. Ed. by Elizabeth S. Fiorenza. LC 74-27890. (University of Notre Dame. Center for the Study of Judaism & Christianity in Antiquity Ser: No. 2). pap. 51.30 (2029308). Bks Demand UMI.

Aspects of the Slavic Language Question: Church Slavonic-South Slavic-West Slavic, Vol. 1. Ed. by Riccardo Picchio & Harvey Goldblatt. (Yale Russian & East European Publications Ser.: No. 4a). 416p. 1984. 35.00 (ISBN 0-936586-03-6). Slavica.

Aspects of the Slavic Language Question: Vol. 1, Church Slavonic-South Slavic-West Slavic. Ed. by Riccardo Picchio & Harvey Goldblatt. (Yale Russian & East European Publications Ser.: No. 4-a). 416p. 1984. 35.00 (ISBN 0-936586-03-6). Yale Russian.

Aspects of the Social, Political, & Economic History of the Jews in America. Rudolf Glanz. 1984. 29.50x (ISBN 0-87068-463-9). Ktav.

Aspects of Wisdom in Judaism & Early Christianity. Ed. by Robert L. Wilken. LC 74-27888. (University of Notre Dame, Center for the Study of Judaism & Christianity in Antiquity: No. 1). pap. 60.00 (ISBN 0-317-26715-9, 2024365). Bks Demand UMI.

Aspects Sociologiques du Catholicisme Americain: Vie Urbaine et Institutions Religieuses. Francois Houtart. 30.00 (ISBN 0-405-10835-4, 11841). Ayer Co Pubs.

Assassins: A Radical Sect in Islam. Bernard Lewis. 1987. pap. 8.95 (ISBN 0-19-520550-2). Oxford U Pr.

Assassins: A Study of the Cult of the Assassins in Persia and Islam. F. A. Ridley. (Islam Ser.). 1980. lib. bdg. 59.95 (ISBN 0-8490-3077-3). Gordon Pr.

Assault on Religion. Russell Kirk. LC 86-656. 126p. 1986. lib. bdg. 19.00 (ISBN 0-8191-5294-3, Pub. by Ctr for Judical Studies); pap. text ed. 8.25 (ISBN 0-8191-5295-1). U Pr of Amer.

Assault on the Bill of Rights: The Jewish Stake. LC 83-182603. 1983. 12.00. UAHC.

Assemblees Anabaptistes-Mennonites de France. J. Seguy. 1977. 64.00x (ISBN 90-279-7524-8). Mouton.

Assemblies of Al-Hariri. Amina Shah. 267p. 1980. 16.95 (ISBN 0-900860-86-3, Pub. by Octagon Pr England). Ins Study Human.

Assemblies of God: A Popular History. Edith W. Blumhofer. LC 85-70552. 160p. (Orig.). 1985. pap. 2.95 (ISBN 0-88243-469-1, 02-0469). Gospel Pub.

Assembling Together. Watchman Nee. Tr. by Stephen Kaung. (Basic Lesson Ser.: Vol. 3). 1973. 4.50 (ISBN 0-935008-01-2); pap. 3.25 (ISBN 0-935008-02-0). Christian Fellow Pubs.

Assembly House. Gerald W. Ward. LC 76-16903. (Historic House Booklet Ser.: No. 3). 1976. 2.00 (ISBN 0-88389-061-5). Essex Inst.

Assembly of the Gods: The Divine Council in Canaanite & Early Hebrew Literature. E. Theodore Mullen, Jr. LC 80-10128. (Harvard Semitic Museum Monographs: No. 24). 1980. 10.50x (ISBN 0-89130-380-4, 04 00 24). Scholars Pr GA.

Assembly of the Lord. Robert S. Paul. (Illus.). 624p. 1985. 39.95 (ISBN 0-567-09341-7, Pub. by T&T Clark Ltd UK). Fortress.

Assembly Principles. F. B. Hole. Ed. by R. P. Daniel. 40p. pap. 3.50 (ISBN 0-88172-141-7). Believers Bkshelf.

Assertive Christian. Michael Emmons & David Richardson. Ed. by Miriam Frost. 144p. (Orig.). 1981. pap. 6.95 (ISBN 0-86683-755-8, HarpR). Har-Row.

Assertiveness & the Christian. Charles E. Cerling. 140p. 1983. pap. 4.95 (ISBN 0-8423-0083-X). Tyndale.

Assignment in the Philippines: Dramatic Accounts from Jared & Marilee Barker. Marti Hefley. (Orig.). 1984. pap. 7.95 (ISBN 0-8024-0265-8). Moody.

Assimilating New Members. Lyle E. Schaller. LC 77-18037. (Creative Leadership Ser.). 1978. pap. 7.50 (ISBN 0-687-01938-9). Abingdon.

Assisi Underground. Alexander Ramati & Rufino Niccacci. 1978. 3.50 (ISBN 0-8128-8135-4). Stein & Day.

Associationalism among Baptists in America: 1707-1814. Ed. by Edwin S. Gaustad. LC 79-52577. (Baptist Tradition Ser.). 1980. lib. bdg. 22.00x (ISBN 0-405-12445-7). Ayer Co Pubs.

Associations Religieuses chez les Grecs: Thiases, Eranes, Orgeons. facsimile ed. Paul F. Foucart. LC 75-10637. (Ancient Religion & Mythology Ser.). (Fr.). 1976. Repr. of 1873 ed. 20.00x (ISBN 0-405-07014-4). Ayer Co Pubs.

Assumption of Mary. Kilian Healy. (Mary Library Ser.). 1982. pap. 5.95 (ISBN 0-89453-288-X). M Glazier.

Assumption of Our Lady. St. Dimitry of Rostov. 1976. pap. 1.50 (ISBN 0-317-30435-6). Holy Trinity.

Assur 14446: La famiglia "A". C. Saporetti. (Cybernetica Mesopotamica, Data Sets: Cuneiform Texts Ser.: Vol. 1). 140p. 1979. pap. 12.00x soft only (ISBN 0-89003-036-7). Undena Pubns.

Assurance. R. Gene Reynolds. 128p. 1982. pap. 3.95 (ISBN 0-8423-0088-0). Tyndale.

Assurance. C. H. Spurgeon. 1976. pap. 1.50 (ISBN 0-686-16842-9). Pilgrim Pubns.

Assurance & Warning. Gerald L. Borchert. (Orig.). 1987. pap. 5.95 (ISBN 0-8054-1011-2). Broadman.

Assurance of Victory. John MacArthur, Jr. (John MacArthur's Bible Studies). (Orig.). 1986. pap. 3.50 (ISBN 0-8024-5130-6). Moody.

Assyrian & Hebrew Hymns of Praise. Charles G. Cumming. LC 34-3318. (Columbia University. Oriental Studies: No. 12). Repr. of 1934 ed. 16.50 (ISBN 0-404-50502-3). AMS Pr.

Assyrian Church Customs & the Murder of Mar Shimun. Surma D'Mar Shimun. Ed. by W. A. Wigram. (Illus.). 128p. 1983. pap. 5.00 (ISBN 0-931428-02-5). Vehicle Edns.

Assyrische Beschwoerungssamlung Maalu. Gerhard Meier. LC 78-72751. (Ancient Mesopotamian Texts & Studies). Repr. of 1937 ed. 22.50 (ISBN 0-404-18194-5). AMS Pr.

Astavakra Samhita. Astavakra. Tr. by Swami Nityaswarupananda. (Sanskrit & Eng.). pap. 4.50 (ISBN 0-87481-165-1). Vedanta Pr.

Astonish Me, Yahweh! Lura J. Geiger et al. (Illus.). 106p. (Orig.). 1983. wkbk. 11.95 (ISBN 0-931055-01-6). LuraMedia.

Astonish Me, Yahweh! Leader's Guide. Lura J. Geiger. (Illus.). 101p. (Orig.). 1984. 12.95 (ISBN 0-931055-02-4). LuraMedia.

Astral Plane. Charles W. Leadbeater. 1973. 5.95 (ISBN 0-8356-7093-7). Theos Pub Hse.

Astro-Change. Aten Hati. 53p. 1981. pap. 5.00 (ISBN 0-935146-64-4). Morningland.

Astrologer's Handbook. Frances Sakoian & Louis S. Acker. LC 78-160647. (Illus.). 480p. (YA) 1973. 17.45i (ISBN 0-06-013734-7, HarpT). Har-Row.

Astrological Secrets of the Hebrew Sages: To Rule Both Day & Night. Joel C. Dobin. LC 77-8288. 256p. 1983. pap. 9.95 (ISBN 0-89281-052-1). Inner Tradit.

Astrological Works of Abraham Ibn Ezra: A Literary & Linguistic Study. Raphael Levy. (Johns Hopkins University Studies in Romance Literatures & Languages: Vol. 8). 172p. Repr. of 1927 ed. 16.00 (ISBN 0-384-32427-4). Johnson Repr.

Astrology & Religion among the Greeks & Romans. Franz Cumont. 1912. pap. 3.50 (ISBN 0-486-20581-9). Dover.

Astrology for Everyone. Evangeline Adams. LC 81-3107. 1981. pap. 5.95 (ISBN 0-396-07985-7). Dodd.

Astrology in Mesopotamian Culture. A. E. Thierens. 1977. lib. bdg. 59.95 (ISBN 0-8490-1461-1). Gordon Pr.

Astrology in the Renaissance. Eugenio Garin. Tr. by Carolyn Jackson & June Allen. Tr. of Lo Zodiaco Della Vita. 160p. 1983. 21.95 (ISBN 0-7100-9259-8). Methuen Inc.

Astrology of Accidents. Carter. 3.95 (ISBN 0-7229-5059-4). Theos Pub Hse.

Astronauta y la Lumbrera de la Noche. James B. Irwin, Jr. & W. A. Emerson. 176p. 1981. Repr. of 1978 ed. 4.25 (ISBN 0-311-01066-0). Casa Bautista.

Astronomy in the Old Testament. Giovanni Sciaparelli. 59.95 (ISBN 0-87968-673-1). Gordon Pr.

Astronomy of Milton's Paradise Lost. Thomas N. Orchard. LC 68-4178. (Studies in Milton, No. 22). (Illus.). 1969. Repr. of 1896 ed. lib. bdg. 75.00x (ISBN 0-8383-0672-1). Haskell.

Astuatsashunch Matean Hin ew Nor Ktakarants. Ed. by Hovhann Zohrapian. LC 84-14281. (Classical Armenian Texts Ser.). (Armenian.). 912p. 1985. Repr. of 1805 ed. 150.00 (ISBN 0-88206-054-6). Caravan Bks.

Asura in Early Vedic Religion. Edward W. Hale. 275p. 1986. 16.00 (ISBN 81-208-0061-3, Pub. by Motilal Banarsidass). South Asia Bks.

Asvaghosha's Discourse on the Awakening of Faith in the Mahayana. B. Asvaghosha. lib. bdg. 79.95 (ISBN 0-87968-472-0). Krishna Pr.

At All Times, in Every Age. Eusebe Menard. 1977. 4.95 (ISBN 0-8199-0663-8). Franciscan Herald.

At Camp Kee Tov: Ethics for Jewish Juniors. Helen Fine. (Illus.). text ed. 6.95 (ISBN 0-8074-0128-5, 121711). UAHC.

At Ease in Zion: A Social History of Southern Baptists, 1865-1900. Rufus B. Spain. LC 66-10367. 1967. 12.95x (ISBN 0-8265-1096-5). Vanderbilt U Pr.

At Ease under Pressure: James I, II Peter. (New Horizons Bible Study). 64p. 1982. Student's Guide 2.50 (ISBN 0-89367-073-1). Light & Life.

At Ease under Pressure: James I, II Peter. (New Horizons Bible Study). 48p. 1982. pap. 1.95 Leaders' Guide (ISBN 0-89367-072-3). Light & Life.

At Every Gate a Pearl. Shirley Boll. 1986. 3.25 (ISBN 0-87813-525-1). Christian Light.

At God's Altar. Enid M. Chadwick. Ed. by Eugenia Schuler. (Illus.). 1978. pap. 1.50x (ISBN 0-934502-00-5). Thursday Pubs.

At God's Altar: Rite One. Enid M. Chadwick. Ed. by Eugenia Schuler. (Illus.). 1978. pap. 1.50x (ISBN 0-934502-01-3). Thursday Pubs.

At Home in India. Salman Khurshid. x, 226p. 1987. text ed. 27.95 (ISBN 0-7069-3197-1, Pub. by Vikas India). Advent NY.

At Home with Jesus. Nancee Berry. (Come Unto Me Library). 1979. pap. 1.65 (ISBN 0-8127-0236-0). Review & Herald.

At Home with the Family Circus. Bil Keane. LC 72-11667. (Illus.). 64p. (Orig.). 1973. pap. 1.00 (ISBN 0-8170-0598-6). Judson.

At Liberty on Bear Creek, 1835-1985. Charles E. Boyd. 1984. 14.95; pap. 9.95. Banner Pr AL.

At Noon on Friday. Richard C. Hoefler. 1983. 3.50 (ISBN 0-89536-557-X, 0111). CSS of Ohio.

At Peace with Failure. Duane Mehl. LC 83-721141. 128p. (Orig.). 1984. pap. 5.95 (ISBN 0-8066-2058-7, 10-0472). Augsburg.

At Peace with the Unborn: A Book for Healing. Dennis Linn et al. 1.50 (ISBN 0-8091-5187-1). Paulist Pr.

At Play with Krishna: Pilgrimage Dramas from Brindavan. John S. Hawley. LC 80-8552. (Illus.). 360p. 1985. 37.00x (ISBN 0-691-06470-9); pap. 10.95x (ISBN 0-691-01419-1). Princeton U Pr.

At the Crossaroads of Faith & Reason: An Essay on Pierre Bayle. Karl C. Sandberg. LC 66-18531. pap. 33.80 (ISBN 0-317-51991-3, 2027388). Bks Demand UMI.

At the Crossroads: Essays on Ahad Ha'am. Ed. by Jacques Kornberg. (Modern Jewish History Ser.). 242p. 1983. 44.50 (ISBN 0-87395-738-5); pap. 14.95 (ISBN 0-87395-739-3). State U NY Pr.

At the Crossroads of the Earth & the Sky: An Andean Cosmology. Gary Urton. (Latin American Monograph Ser.: No. 55). (Illus.). 268p. 1981. text ed. 30.00x (ISBN 0-292-70349-X). U of Tex Pr.

At the Feet of Ski Ramakrishna. Vijnananda. 66p. 1985. pap. 1.50 (ISBN 0-87481-225-9, Pub. by Ramakrishna Math Madras India). Vedanta Pr.

At the Feet of the Master. Alcyone, pseud. 1967. 4.50 (ISBN 0-8356-0098-X). Theos Pub Hse.

At the Feet of the Master. Alcyone. 1970. pap. 1.95 (ISBN 0-8356-0196-X, Quest). Theos Pub Hse.

At the Feet of the Master. Alcyone. leatherette 3.00 (ISBN 0-911662-17-0). Yoga.

At the Feet of the Master. Alcyone. 1.75 (ISBN 0-8356-7323-5). Theos Pub Hse.

At the Gates of Spiritual Science. Rudolf Steiner. Tr. of Vor dem Tore der Theosophie. 160p. 1986. 20.00 (ISBN 0-88010-224-1); pap. 8.95 (ISBN 0-88010-135-0). Anthroposophic.

At the Head of Nations: The Rise of the Papal & Princely House of Odescalchi. Edmond De Syrmia. LC 76-44029. (Illus.). 116p. 1978. 10.00 (ISBN 0-914226-05-3). Cyclopedia.

At the Hour of Death. Karlis Osis & Erlendur Haraldsson. 1985. pap. 3.95 (ISBN 0-380-49486-8, 49486-8, Discus). Avon.

At the Lord's Table: Twenty Communion Meditations. Ralph G. Turnbull. (Pocket Pulpit Library). 142p. 1985. pap. 4.95 (ISBN 0-8010-8821-6). Baker Bk.

At the Mind's Limits: Contemplations by a Survivor on Auschwitz & Its Realities. Jean Amery. Tr. by Sidney Rosenfeld & Stella P. Rosenfeld. 128p. 1986. pap. 5.95 (ISBN 0-8052-0761-9). Schocken.

At the Mountain of God: Story & Theology in Exodus 32-34. R. W. Moberly. (Journal for the Study of the Old Testament Monograph Ser.: No. 22). 258p. 1983. text ed. 22.50x (ISBN 0-905774-44-2, Pub. by JSOT Pr England); pap. text ed. 14.95x (ISBN 0-905774-45-0, Pub. by JSOT Pr England). Eisenbrauns.

At The River I Stand. James R. Robbins. 5.95 (ISBN 0-8062-2426-6). Carlton.

At the Scent of Water. Nancy Ashcraft. 1986. pap. 4.95 (ISBN 0-87508-049-9). Chr Lit.

At the Shrine of St. Charles. E. V. Lucas. 1934. Repr. 25.00 (ISBN 0-8274-1898-1). R West.

At the Side of Our Saviour: A Walk Through the Garden of Jesus' Sufferings. First English ed. Basilea Schlink. (Illus.). 28p. (Orig.). 1982. pap. 1.50 gift edition (ISBN 3-87209-627-3). Evang Sisterhood Mary.

At the Sign of Midnight: The Concheros Dance Cult of Mexico. Martha Stone. LC 73-76303. (Illus.). 262p. 1975. pap. 7.45x (ISBN 0-8165-0507-1). U of Ariz Pr.

At the Starting Line: Beginning a New Life. Carolyn Nystrom. (Young Fisherman Bible Studyguides). 48p. 1985. pap. 2.95 student (ISBN 0-87788-053-0); pap. text ed. 4.95 Tchr's. (ISBN 0-87788-054-9). Shaw Pubs.

At the Table of the Grail: Magic & the Use of Imagination. John Matthews. 224p. (Orig.). 1984. pap. 10.95 (ISBN 0-7100-9938-X). Methuen Inc.

At Wit's End Corner. Garver. (Illus.). pap. 1.25 (ISBN 0-686-12326-3). Christs Mission.

At Your Own Pace Reference on Meditation & Wholistic Healing. Center for Self-Sufficiency, Research Division Staff. 30p. 1985. pap. text ed. 2.75 (ISBN 0-910811-71-7, Pub. by Center Self Suff). Prosperity & Profits.

At Your Word, Lord. William L. Vaswig. LC 81-52272. 128p. (Orig.). 1982. pap. 5.95 (ISBN 0-8066-1904-X, 10-0498). Augsburg.

Athanasian Creed & Its Early Commentaries. A. E. Burn. (Texts & Studies Ser.: No. 1, Vol. 4, Pt. 1). pap. 19.00 (ISBN 0-8115-1691-1). Kraus Repr.

Athanasius: The Life of Antony & the Letter to Marcellinus. Ed. by Robert C. Gregg. LC 79-56622. (Classics of Western Spirituality Ser.). 192p. 1980. 12.95 (ISBN 0-8091-0309-5); pap. 8.95 (ISBN 0-8091-2295-2). Paulist Pr.

Athar-Veda (Summary) Date not set. 5.00 (ISBN 0-938924-32-X). Sri Shirdi Sai.

Atheism & Liberation. Antonio Perez-Esclarin. Tr. by John Drury from Sp. LC 78-731. Orig. Title: Ateismo Y Liberacion. 205p. (Orig.). 1978. pap. 1.99 (ISBN 0-88344-020-2). Orbis Bks.

Atheism & Other Addresses. Joseph Lewis. LC 72-161333. (Atheist Viewpoint Ser). (Illus.). 510p. 1972. Repr. of 1960 ed. 32.00 (ISBN 0-405-03800-3). Ayer Co Pubs.

Atheism: Collected Essays, 1943-1949. Bertrand Russell. LC 71-169217. (Atheist Viewpoint Ser). 232p. 1972. Repr. of 1971 ed. 15.00 (ISBN 0-405-03808-9). Ayer Co Pubs.

Atheism In Pagan Antiquity. A. Drachman. 178p. 1977. 12.50 (ISBN 0-89005-201-8). Ares.

Atheism in Pagan Antiquity. A. B. Drachmann. 69.95 (ISBN 0-87968-675-8). Gordon Pr.

Atheism of Astronomy: A Refutation of the Theory That the Universe Is Governed by Intelligence. Woolsey Teller. LC 79-169219. (Atheist Viewpoint Ser). 126p. 1972. Repr. of 1938 ed. 13.00 (ISBN 0-405-03806-2). Ayer Co Pubs.

Atheism: The Case Against God. George H. Smith. LC 79-2726. (Skeptic's Bookshelf Ser.). 355p. 1979. pap. 10.95 (ISBN 0-87975-124-X). Prometheus Bks.

Atheismus Im Religionsunterricht. Helmut Diehl. (European University Studies Thirty-Three: Vol. 6). (Ger.). 622p. 1982. 46.30 (ISBN 3-8204-6280-5). P Lang Pubs.

Atheist Debater's Handbook. B. C. Johnson. LC 81-80487. (Skeptics Bookshelf Ser.). 134p. 1981. 14.95 (ISBN 0-87975-152-5); pap. 8.95 (ISBN 0-87975-210-6). Prometheus Bks.

Atheist Epic: Bill Murray, the Bible & the Baltimore Board of Education. Madalyn M. O'Hair. LC 71-88701. 316p. 1970. pap. 6.00 (ISBN 0-911826-01-7). Am Atheist.

Atheist Magazines: A Sampling, 1927-1970. Madalyn M. O'Hair. LC 72-171441. (Atheist Viewpoint Ser). 554p. 1972. Repr. of 1971 ed. 28.00 (ISBN 0-405-03812-7). Ayer Co Pubs.

Atheist Speaks. Madalyn O'Hair. (American Atheist Radio Series Reprints). 321p. (Orig.). 1986. pap. 6.00 (ISBN 0-910309-27-2). Am Atheist.

Atheist Truth vs. Religion's Ghosts. Robert G. Ingersoll. 57p. 1980. pap. 3.25 (ISBN 0-911826-03-3). Am Atheist.

Atheist Viewpoint, 25 bks. Ed. by Madalyn M. O'Hair. 1972. Set. 498.00 (ISBN 0-405-03620-5). Ayer Co Pubs.

Atheist Viewpoint. Ed. by Madalyn M. O'Hair. Date not set. cancelled (ISBN 0-405-03791-0, 395). Ayer Co Pubs.

Athenae Christianae. A. Mommsen. (Illus.). 177p. 1977. 12.50 (ISBN 0-89005-216-6). Ares.

Athenagoras, Embassy for the Christians, the Resurrection of the Dead. Ed. by W. J. Burghardt et al. LC 56-11421. (Ancient Christian Writers Ser.: No. 23). 193p. 1956. 10.95 (ISBN 0-8091-0036-3). Paulist Pr.

Athene. Karl Kerenyi. Tr. by Murray Stein from Ger. (Dunquin Ser.: No. 9). 106p. (Orig.). 1978. pap. 7.50 (ISBN 0-88214-209-7). Spring Pubns.

Athenian Constitution. Aristotle. Bd. with Eudemian Ethics, Bks 1-3, 7 & 8; Virtues & Vices. (Loeb Classical Library: No. 285). 13.95x (ISBN 0-674-99315-2). Harvard U Pr.

Athenian Mythology: Erichthonius & the Three Daughters of Cecrops. B. Powell. (Illus.). 90p. 1976. 15.00 (ISBN 0-89005-121-6). Ares.

Athenian Popular Religion. Jon D. Mikalson. LC 82-25616. x, 142p. 1983. 16.00x (ISBN 0-8078-1563-2). U of NC Pr.

Athenian Popular Religion. Jon D. Mikalson. LC 82-25616. xi, 142p. 1987. pap. text ed. 8.95x (ISBN 0-8078-4194-3). U of NC Pr.

Athens-Auschwitz. Errikos Sevillias. 109p. 1984. 11.95 (ISBN 0-930685-00-8). Cadmus Press.

Athletes Afire. Rick Arndt. LC 85-71182. 1985. pap. 3.50 (ISBN 0-88270-590-3). Bridge Pub.

Atid Bibliography. pap. 5.00 (ISBN 0-686-96097-1). United Syn Bk.

Atlan Revisited: The War of the Gods. George Mitrovic. LC 84-90082. 156p. 1985. 11.95 (ISBN 0-533-06152-0). Vantage.

Atlantis: The Antediluvian World. Ignatius Donnelly. lib. bdg. 100.00 (ISBN 0-87968-055-5). Krishna Pr.

Atlantis Trilogy. Blair H. Allen. 1982. pap. 1.25 (ISBN 0-917458-09-5). Kent Pubns.

Atlas & Outline of the Acts of the Apostles. Duane S. Crowther. LC 83-80528. 114p. 1983. pap. 6.95 (ISBN 0-88290-219-9). Horizon-Utah.

Atlas & Outline of the Life of Christ. Duane S. Crowther. LC 83-82414. 120p. (Orig.). 1983. pap. 6.95 (ISBN 0-88290-207-5). Horizon Utah.

Atlas Historico Westminster de la Biblia. Wright Filson. 134p. 1981. pap. 19.95 (ISBN 0-311-15030-6). Casa Bautista.

Atlas of Religious Change in America: 1952-1971. Peter L. Halvorson & William M. Newman. LC 78-67653. (Illus.). 1978. pap. 6.50 (ISBN 0-914422-09-X). Glenmary Res Ctr.

Atlas of the Bible. John Rogerson. 240p. 1985. text ed. 40.00 (ISBN 0-8407-5462-0). Nelson.

Atlas of the Bible: An Illustrated Guide to the Holy Land. Reader's Digest Editors. LC 80-53426. (Illus.). 256p. 1981. 21.95 (ISBN 0-89577-097-0, Pub. by RD Assn). Random.

Atlas of the Bible Lands. rev. ed. Harry T. Frank. LC 77-6292. (Illus.). 48p. 1984. 7.95 (ISBN 0-8437-7056-2); pap. 4.99 (ISBN 0-8437-7055-4). Hammond Inc.

Atlas of the Bible Lands. Ed. by Harry T. Frank. 1979. pap. 4.95 (ISBN 0-8054-1136-4). Broadman.

Atlas of the English Civil War. P. R. Newman. (Illus.). 144p. 1985. text ed. 35.00x (ISBN 0-02-906540-2). Macmillan.

Atlas of the Jewish World. Nicholas de Lange. (Cultiral Atlas Ser.). (Illus.). 240p. 1984. 35.00 (ISBN 0-87196-043-5). Facts on File.

Atma: Contemporary Vedic Library Series Based on the Teachings of A. C. Bhaktivedanta Swami Prabhupada. 1.50 (ISBN 0-89213-122-5). Bhaktivedanta.

Atmanushasana (Discourse to the Soul) Gunabhadra Acharya. Ed. & tr. by Rai B. Jaini. LC 73-3841. (Sacred Books of the Jainas: No. 7). Repr. of 1928 ed. 18.00 (ISBN 0-404-57707-5). AMS Pr.

Atom. Darwin Gross. 130p. (Orig.). 1984. pap. 3.95 (ISBN 0-931689-01-5). SOS Pub OR.

Atom Besieged: Extraparliamentary Dissent in France & Germany. Dorothy Nelkin & Michael Pollak. (Illus.). 256p. 1981. 30.00x (ISBN 0-262-14034-9); pap. 8.95 (ISBN 0-262-64021-X). MIT Pr.

Atomic Peace. Harold C. Gooddard. 1983. pap. 2.50x (ISBN 0-87574-057-X, 057). Pendle Hill.

Atoms, Snowflakes & God. John Hitchcock. LC 85-40842. (Illus.). 222p. 1986. pap. 6.75 (ISBN 0-8356-0604-X, Quest). Theos Pub Hse.

Atonement. Albert Barnes. LC 80-65582. 1980. pap. 7.95 (ISBN 0-87123-016-X, 210016). Bethany Hse.

Atonement. Gordon H. Clark. (Trinity Papers: No. 17). 175p. (Orig.). 1987. pap. 8.95 (ISBN 0-940931-17-6). Trinity Found.

Atonement. Leon Morris. LC 83-20649. 204p. 1984. pap. 8.95 (ISBN 0-87784-826-2). Inter-Varsity.

Atonement. John Murray. pap. 1.50 (ISBN 0-87552-342-0). Presby & Reformed.

Atonement. Arthur W. Pink. 10.95 (ISBN 0-685-19822-7). Reiner.

Atonement of George Fox. Emilia Fogelklou-Norlind. Ed. by Eleanore P. Mather. LC 75-84675. (Orig.). 1969. pap. 2.50x (ISBN 0-87574-166-5). Pendle Hill.

Atonement of the Death of Christ. H. D. McDonald. 352p. 1985. pap. 19.95 (ISBN 0-8010-6194-6). Baker Bk.

Atoning Death of Christ. Ronald Wallace. LC 81-65758. (Foundations for Faith Ser.). 192p. (Orig.). 1981. pap. 8.95 (ISBN 0-89107-222-5, Crossway Bks). Good News.

Atoning Gospel. James E. Tull. LC 81-18732. 221p. 1982. 15.50 (ISBN 0-86554-029-2, MUP-H28). Mercer Univ Pr.

Atributos de Dios. A. W. Pink. 2.95 (ISBN 0-686-12561-4). Banner of Truth.

Atrocities & Other Conditions in Concentration Camps in Germany. (Witness to the Holocaust Ser.: No. 3). 21p. 1980. 1.00. Witness Holocaust.

Attack on the Family. James Robison. 1980. pap. 2.95 (ISBN 0-8423-0092-9). Tyndale.

Attack upon "Christendom". Soren Kierkegaard. Tr. by Walter Lowrie. 1944. pap. 8.50x (ISBN 0-691-01950-9). Princeton U Pr.

Attaining Spiritual Maturity for Contemplation (According to St. John of the Cross) Venard Poslusney. (Orig.). 1973. pap. 1.50 (ISBN 0-914544-04-7). Living Flame Pr.

Attestation of Many Learned, Godly, & Famous Divines...Justifying...That the Church Government Ought to Be Always with the Peoples Free Consent. Henry Jacob. LC 74-28868. (English Experience Ser.: No. 747). 1975. Repr. of 1613 ed. 16.00 (ISBN 90-221-0747-7). Walter J Johnson.

Atthasalini, Buddhaghosa's Commentary on the Dhammasangani. Buddhaghosa. Ed. by Edward Muller. LC 78-72383. Repr. of 1897 ed. 39.50 (ISBN 0-404-17245-8). AMS Pr.

Attic Festivals of Demeter & Their Relation to the Agricultural Year. Allaire C. Brumfield. Ed. by W. R. Connor. LC 80-2643. (Monographs in Classical Studies). 1981. lib. bdg. 29.00 (ISBN 0-405-14031-2). Ayer Co Pubs.

Attitude Education: A Research Curriculum. Herman Williams & Ella L. Greene. LC 75-16677. 1975. pap. 3.00x (ISBN 0-915744-02-3). Character Res.

Attitude of the Catholic Church Toward Witchcraft & the Allied Practices of Sorcery & Magic. Sr. Antoinette M. Pratt. LC 79-8116. 144p. Repr. of 1945 ed. 22.50 (ISBN 0-404-18429-4). AMS Pr.

Attitude of the Early Christian Latin Writers Toward Pagan Literature & Learning. Gerald L. Ellspermann. 295p. 1984. Repr. of 1949 ed. 45.00x (ISBN 0-939738-26-0). Zubal Inc.

Attitudes I. Virgil Leach. 1979. pap. 4.25 (ISBN 0-89137-803-0). Quality Pubns.

Attitudes II. Virgil Leach. 1981. pap. 4.25 (ISBN 0-89137-804-9). Quality Pubns.

Attitudes of Martin Bucer Toward the Bigamy of Philip of Hesse. Hastings Eells. LC 83-45611. Date not set. Repr. of 1924 ed. 32.50 (ISBN 0-404-19829-5). AMS Pr.

Attitudes to Other Religions: Comparative Religion in Seventeenth & Eighteenth-Century Britain. David A. Pailin. LC 83-20652. 368p. 1984. 49.00 (ISBN 0-7190-1065-9, Pub. by Manchester Univ Pr). Longwood Pub Group.

Attitudes Toward Blacks among Jews: Historical Antecedents & Current Concerns. Sherman Labovitz. LC 75-5365. 1975. soft bdg. 12.00 (ISBN 0-88247-358-1). R & E Pubs.

Attitudes Toward Other Religions: Some Christian Interpretations. Owen C. Thomas. LC 86-4076. 250p. (Orig.). 1986. pap. 11.50 (ISBN 0-8191-5324-9). U Pr of Amer.

Attitudes Toward Self-Inflicted Suffering in the Middle Ages. Giles Constable. (Stephen J. Brademas Lectures Ser.). 28p. (Orig.). pap. text ed. 2.50 (ISBN 0-916586-87-1). Hellenic Coll Pr.

Attivita Artistiche & il Patrimonio Librario della Certosa di Firenze, 2 vols. Caterina Chiarelli. Ed. by James Hogg. (Analecta Cartusiana Ser.: No. 102). 491p. (Orig.). 1984. pap. 50.00 (ISBN 0-317-42557-9, Pub. by Salzburg Studies). Longwood Pub Group.

Attributes of God. (Orig.). 1987. pap. 1.95 (ISBN 0-8024-0737-4). Moody.

Attributes of God. Lewis R. Farnell. LC 77-27205. (Gifford Lectures Ser.: 1924-25). 296p. Repr. of 1925 ed. 34.50 (ISBN 0-404-60475-7). AMS Pr.

Attributes of God. Arthur W. Pink. pap. 3.95 (ISBN 0-8010-6989-0). Baker Bk.

Audience Criticism & the Historical Jesus. J. Arthur Baird. 1969. 6.50 (ISBN 0-664-20846-0). Biblical Res Assocs.

Audience with Jesus. John F. Davis. 134p. 1982. 4.00 (ISBN 0-8198-0721-4, SP0008); pap. 3.00 (ISBN 0-8198-0722-2). Dghtrs St Paul.

Audio-Visual Guide to American Holidays. Ed. by Carol A. Emmens & Harry Maglione. LC 78-6230. 284p. 1978. lib. bdg. 20.00 (ISBN 0-8108-1140-5). Scarecrow.

Audio-Visual Materials in the Church Library: How to Select, Catalog, Process, Store, Circulate & Promote. Margaret B. Korty. LC 77-74780. (Illus.). 102p. 1977. spiral bdg. 4.95 (ISBN 0-9603060-0-5). Church Lib.

Aufgaben und Ziele der Vergleichenden Mythenforschung: Tasks & Goals of Comparative Mythology. Heinrich Lessmann. Ed. by Kees W. Bolle. LC 77-79138. (Mythology Ser.). (Ger.). 1978. Repr. of 1908 ed. lib. bdg. 17.00x (ISBN 0-405-10548-7). Ayer Co Pubs.

Aufhebung der Kartause Gaming. Brunhilde Hoffman. Ed. by James Hogg. (Analecta Cartusiana Ser: No. 58). (Ger.). 120p. (Orig.). 1981. pap. 25.00 (ISBN 3-7052-0084-4, Pub. by Salzburg Studies). Longwood Pub Group.

Aufklarung Catholicism Seventeen Eighty to Eighteen Fifty: Liturgical & Other Reforms in the Catholic Aufklarung. Leonard Swidler. LC 78-2736. 1978. pap. 9.95 (ISBN 0-89130-227-1, 01-00-17). Scholars Pr GA.

Aufstieg und Niedergang der Roemischen Welt: Section 2, Principat. Ed. by Hildegard Temporini & Wolfgang Haase. Incl. Vol. 13. Recht (Normen, Verbreitung, Materien) 1980. 200.00 (ISBN 3-11-008121-0); Vol. 14. Recht (Materien, Fortsetzung) 1982. 253.00 (ISBN 3-11-008122-9); Vol. 15. Recht (Methoden, Schulen, Einzelne Juristen) 1976. 184.00 (ISBN 3-11-006736-6); Vol. 16, Pt. 1. Religion (Heidentum: Romische Religion, Allgemeines) 1978. 200.00 (ISBN 3-11-006737-4); Vol. 16, Pt. 2. Religion (Heidentum: Romische Religion, Allgemeines FS) 1978. 226.00 (ISBN 3-11-007612-8); Vol. 17, Pt. 1. Religion (Heidentum: Romische Gotterkulte, Orientalische Kulte in der romischen Welt) 1981. 147.00 (ISBN 3-11-008468-6); Vol. 17, Pt. 2. Religion (Heidentum: Romische Gotterkulte, Orientalische Kulte in der romischen Welt, Fortsetzung) 1981. 190.00 (ISBN 3-11-008556-9); Vol. 17, Pt. 3. Religion (Heidentum: Romische Gotterkulte, Orientalische Kulte in der romischen Welt, Fortsetzung) 1984. 174.00 (ISBN 3-11-009521-1); Vol. 17, Pt. 4. Religion (Heidentum: Romische **Gotterkulte, Orientalische Kulte in der romishcen Welt, Fortsetzung) 1984. 205.00 (ISBN 3-11-010213-7); Vol. 19, Pt. 1. Religion (Judentum: Allgemeines, palastinensisches Judentum) 1979. 210.00 (ISBN 3-11-007968-2); Vol. 19, Pt. 2. Religion (Judentum: Allgemeines, palastinensisches Judentum FS) 1979. 160.00 (ISBN 3-11-007969-0); Vol. 21, Pt. 1. Religion (Hellinistisches Judentum in romischer Zeit): Philon & Josephus. 1984. 210.00 (ISBN 3-11-008845-2); Vol. 21, Pt. 2. Religion (Hellinistisches Judentum in romischer Zeit): Philon & Josephus (Fortsetzung) 1984. 168.00 (ISBN 3-11-009522-X); Vol. 23, Pt. 1. Religion (Vorkonstantinisches Christentum: Verhaltnis zu romischem Staat und heidnischer Religion) 1979. 205.00 (ISBN 3-11-007822-8); Vol. 23, Pt. 2. Religion (Vorkonstantinisches Christentum: Verhaltnis zu romischen Staat und heidnischer Religion) 1980. 161.00 (ISBN 3-11-008016-8). (Ger.). De Gruyter.**

Aufstieg und Niedergang der Roemischen Welt: Section 2, Principat. Ed. by Hildegard Temporini & Wolfgang Haase. Incl. Vol. 25, Pt. 1. Religion (Vorkonstantinisches Christentum: Leben und Umwelt Jesu; Neues Testament Kanonische Schriften und Apokryphen) 1982. 221.00 (ISBN 3-11-008700-6); Vol. 25, Pt. 2. Religion (Vorkonstantinisches Christentum: Leben und Umwelt Jesu; Neues Testament, Fortsetzung Kanonische Schriften und Apokryphen) 1984. 258.00 (ISBN 3-11-009523-8); Vol. 25, Pt. 3. Religion (Vorkonstantinisches Christentum: Leben und Umwelt Jesu; Neues Testament, Fortsetzung Kanonische Schriften und Apokryphen) 1985. 232.00 (ISBN 3-11-010370-2); Vol. 29, Pt. 1. Sprache und Literatur (Sprachen und Schriften) 1983. 147.00 (ISBN 3-11-009524-6); Vol. 29, Pt. 2. Sprache und Literatur (Sprachen und Schriften) (Fortsetzung) 1983. 216.00 (ISBN 3-11-009525-4); Vol. 30, Pt. 1. Sprache und Literatur (Literatur der augusteischen Zeit: Allgemeines, einzelne Autoren) 1982. 216.00 (ISBN 3-11-008469-4); Vol. 30, Pt. 2. Sprache und Literatur (Literatur der **augusteischen Zeit: Allgemeines, einzelne Autoren, Fortsetzung) 1982. 147.00 (ISBN 3-11-008699-9); Vol. 30, Pt. 3. Sprache und Literatur (Literatur der augusteischen Zeit: Allgemeines, einzelne Autoren, Fortsetzung) 1983. 190.00 (ISBN 3-11-009526-2); Vol. 31, Pt. 1. Sprache und Literatur (Literatur der augusteischen Zeit: Einzelne Autoren - Vergil, Horaz, Ovid) 1980. 166.00 (ISBN 3-11-008123-7); Vol. 31, Pt. 2. Sprache und Literatur (Literatur der ausgusteischen Zeit: Einzelne Autoren, Fortsetzung Vergil, Horaz, Ovid) 1981. 155.00 (ISBN 3-11-008288-8); Vol. 31, Pt. 3. Sprache und Literatur (Literatur der ausgusteischen Zeit); Einzelne Autoren - Fortsetzung, Vergil, Horaz, Ovid. 1981. 179.00 (ISBN 3-11-008467-8); Vol. 31, Pt. 4. Sprache und Literatur (Literatur der augusteischen Zeit: Einzelne Autoren, Fortsetzung Vergil, Horaz, Ovid) 1981. 142.00 (ISBN 3-11-008555-0); Vol. 32, Pt. 1. Sprache und Literatur (Literatur der julisch-claudischen und der flavischen Zeit) 1984. 190.00 (ISBN 3-11-010363-X); Vol. 32, Pt. 2. Sprache und Literatur (Literatur der julisch-claudischen und der flavischen Zeit) (Fortsetzung) 1985. 242.00 (ISBN 3-11-010374-5); Vol. 32, Pt. 3. Sprache und Literatur (Literatur der julisch-claudischen und der flavischen Zeit) (Fortsetzung) 1985. 190.00 (ISBN 3-11-010388-5). (Ger.). De Gruyter.**

Augsburg & Constantinople: The Correspondence Between Patriarch Jeremiah II & the Tubingen Theologians. George Mastrantonis. 424p. 1981. 22.95 (ISBN 0-916586-81-2); pap. 14.95 (ISBN 0-916586-82-0). Hellenic Coll Pr.

Augsburg Commentary on the New Testament: Ephesians, Colossians. Ed. by Walter F. Taylor, Jr. & John H. Reumann. LC 85-7479. 176p. (Orig.). 1985. kivar 8.95 (ISBN 0-8066-2165-6, 10-9030). Augsburg.

Augsburg Commentary on the New Testament: Galatians, Philippians, Philemon. Ed. by Edgar Krentz et al. LC 85-11116. 256p. (Orig.). 1985. kivar 9.95 (ISBN 0-8066-2166-4, 10-9028). Augsburg.

Augsburg Commentary on the New Testament. John H. Elliott & R. A. Martin. LC 82-70962. 192p. (Orig.). 1982. 8.95 (ISBN 0-8066-1937-6, 10-9042). Augsburg.

Augsburg Commentary on the New Testament-Romans. Roy A. Harrisville. LC 80-65550. 246p. (Orig.). 1980. pap. 9.95 (ISBN 0-8066-8864-5, 10-9022). Augsburg.

Augsburg Commentary on the New Testament: Acts. Gerhard A. Krodel. LC 86-10796. 500p. (Orig.). 1986. pap. 19.95 (ISBN 0-8066-8884-X, 10-9046). Augsburg.

Augsburg Commentary on the New Testament-John. Robert Kysar. LC 85-26736. (Augsburg Commentaries on the New Testament Ser.). 336p. (Orig.). 1986. kivar 14.95 (ISBN 0-8066-8860-2, 10-9018). Augsburg.

Augsburg Commentary on the New Testament: Hebrews. Robert H. Smith. LC 83-72125. (Augsburg Commentary New Testament Ser.). 192p. (Orig.). 1984. pap. 8.95 kivar (ISBN 0-8066-8876-9, 10-9034). Augsburg.

Augsburg Commentary on the New Testament: 1 Timothy 2 Timothy, Titus, 2 Thessalonians. Arland J. Hultgren & Roger Aus. LC 83-72126. (Augsburg Commentary New Testament Ser.). 224p. 1984. kivar 8.95 (ISBN 0-8066-8874-2, 10-9032). Augsburg.

Augsburg Commentary on the New Testament: 1, 2, 3 John. Robert Kysar. LC 86-17416. 176p. (Orig.). 1986. pap. 9.95 Kivar (ISBN 0-8066-8862-9, 10-9044). Augsburg.

Augsburg Confession. Johann M. Reu. LC 83-45650. Date not set. Repr. of 1930 ed. 76.50 (ISBN 0-404-19859-7). AMS Pr.

Augsburg Confession: A Commentary. Ed. by Leif Grane. Tr. by John H. Rasmussen from Ger. LC 86-28832. Tr. of Confessio Augustana. 272p. (Orig.). 1987. pap. 14.95 (ISBN 0-8066-2252-0, 10-0519). Augsburg.

Augsburg Confession: A Contemporary Commentary. George W. Forell. LC 68-25798. (Orig.). 1968. pap. 6.95 (ISBN 0-8066-0815-3, 10-0518). Augsburg.

Augsburg Confession: Anniversary Edition. Tr. by Theodore G. Tappert. 64p. 1980. pap. 1.75 (ISBN 0-8006-1385-6, 1-1385). Fortress.

Augsburg Historical Atlas of Christianity in the Middle Ages & Reformation. Charles S. Anderson. LC 67-11723. 1973. pap. 9.95 (ISBN 0-8066-1317-3, 10-0521). Augsburg.

Augsburg Sermons. LC 80-65552. (Old Testament Lessons, Ser. A). 264p. 15.95 (ISBN 0-8066-1797-7, 10-0530). Augsburg.

Augsburg Sermons: Epistles. LC 77-72464. (Series A). 1977. 15.95 (ISBN 0-8066-1581-8, 10-0522). Augsburg.

Augsburg Sermons: Epistles - Series C. LC 76-3868. 228p. 1976. 15.95 (ISBN 0-8066-1523-0, 10-0524). Augsburg.

Augsburg Sermons, Epistles, Series B: Sermons on Epistle Texts from the New Lectionary & Calendar. LC 78-52205. 1978. 15.95 (ISBN 0-8066-1666-0, 10-0523). Augsburg.

Augsburg Sermons: Old Testament Lessons. LC 81-65654. (Series B). 256p. 1981. pap. 15.95 (ISBN 0-8066-1890-6, 10-0531). Augsburg.

Augsburg Sermons: Old Testament Lessons - Series C. LC 79-50092. 264p. 1979. 15.95 (ISBN 0-8066-1703-9, 10-0529). Augsburg.

Augsburg Sermons Two (Gospels - Series B) New Sermons on Gospel Texts. LC 84-72019. (Augsburg Sermon Ser.). 272p. (Orig.). 1984. kivar 15.95 (ISBN 0-8066-2095-1, 10-0534). Augsburg.

Augsburg Sermons Two Gospels: New Sermons on Gospel Texts. LC 82-70955. (Series C). 280p. (Orig.). 1982. pap. 15.95 (ISBN 0-8066-1930-9, 10-0532). Augsburg.

Augsburg Sermons, Two Gospels: New Sermons on Gospel Texts. LC 83-70509. (Series A). 280p. 1983. pap. 15.95 (ISBN 0-8066-2015-3, 10-0533). Augsburg.

Augustana - A Profession of Faith: A History of Augustana College, 1860-1935. Conrad Bergendoff. LC 76-92170. (Augustana College Library Ser.: No. 33). (Illus.). 220p. 1969. 5.95x (ISBN 0-910182-33-7). Augustana Coll.

Augustana Ministerium: A Study of the Careers of the 2504 Pastors of the Augustana Evangelical Lutheran Synod-Church 1850-1962. Conrad Bergendoff. LC 80-66400. (Augustana Historical Society Ser.: No. 28). 246p. 1980. 15.00 (ISBN 0-910184-28-3). Augustana.

Auguste Forel & the Baha'i Faith. Peter Muhlschlegel. Tr. by Helene Neri from Ger. 64p. 1979. pap. 3.50 (ISBN 0-85398-076-4). G Ronald Pub.

Augustin und der Antike Friendensgedanke. Harald Fuchs. LC 72-147669. (Library of War & Peace; Relig. & Ethical Positions on War). 1973. lib. bdg. 46.00 (ISBN 0-8240-0427-2). Garland Pub.

Augustine. Henry Chadwick. (Past Masters Ser.). 128p. 1986. 14.95x (ISBN 0-19-287535-3); pap. 4.95 (ISBN 0-19-287534-5). Oxford U Pr.

Augustine. James J. O'Donnell. LC 84-28133. (World Author Ser.). 1985. lib. bdg. 19.95 (ISBN 0-8057-6609-X, Twayne). G K Hall.

Augustine Day by Day. John Rotelle. (Orig.). 1986. pap. 4.50 (ISBN 0-89942-170-9, 170-09). Catholic BK Pub.

Augustine: Earlier Writings. Ed. by John S. Burleigh. LC 53-13043. (Library of Christian Classics). 410p. 1979. softcover 8.95 (ISBN 0-664-24162-X). Westminster.

Augustine: His Life & Thought. W. Thomas Smith. LC 79-92071. (Illus.). 190p. (Orig.). 1980. pap. 10.95 (ISBN 0-8042-0871-9). John Knox.

Augustine: Later Works. Ed. by John Burnaby. LC 55-5022. (Library of Christian Classics). 356p. 1980. pap. 11.95 (ISBN 0-664-24165-4). Westminster.

Augustine Laure, S. J., Missionary to the Yakimas. Victor Garrand. 36p. 1977. 8.00_o.s.i (ISBN 0-87770-176-8); pap. 5.95 (ISBN 0-87770-187-3). Ye Galleon.

Augustine of Hippo. Peter Brown. 463p. 1987. 22.50 (ISBN 0-88029-098-6, Pub. by Dorset Pr). Hippocrene Bks.

Augustine of Hippo: A Biography. Peter Brown. 1967. pap. 9.95 (ISBN 0-520-01411-1, CAL179). U of Cal Pr.

Augustine of Hippo: Selected Writings. Augustine of Hippo. Tr. by Mary T. Clark. (Classics of Western Spirituality Ser.). 544p. 1984. pap. 12.95 (ISBN 0-8091-2573-0). Paulist Pr.

Augustine on Evil. G. R. Evans. LC 81-21793. 220p. 1983. 34.50 (ISBN 0-521-24526-5). Cambridge U Pr.

Augustine on Prayer. rev. ed. Thomas A. Hand. (Orig.). 1986. pap. 3.95 (ISBN 0-89942-171-7, 171-04). Catholic BK Pub.

Augustine on Romans: Propositions From the Epistle to the Romans & Unfinished Commentary on the Epistle to the Romans. Paula F. Landes. LC 82-10259. (Society of Biblical Literature, Texts & Translations Ser.). 124p. 1982. pap. 12.75 (ISBN 0-89130-583-1, 06-02-23). Scholars Pr GA.

Augustine on the Body. Margaret R. Miles. LC 79-14226. (American Academy of Religion, Dissertation Ser.: No. 31). 1979. 14.00 (ISBN 0-89130-288-3, 010131); pap. 9.95 (ISBN 0-89130-289-1). Scholars Pr GA.

Augustine Treasury: Selections from the Writings of St. Augustine. Ed. by Jules Brady. 1981. 5.00 (ISBN 0-8198-0706-0); pap. 4.00 (ISBN 0-686-73823-3). Dghtrs St Paul.

Augustine: Wayward Genius. David Bently-Taylor. 1981. pap. 5.95 (ISBN 0-8010-0807-7). Baker Bk.

Augustine's Concept of Providence. Johannes Gotte. 1.00 (ISBN 0-686-23373-5). Classical Folia.

Augustine's Heritage: Readings from the Augustinian Tradition, 3 vols. Ed. by John E. Rotelle. Vol. 1. 1.50 (ISBN 0-89942-701-4, 701-04). Vol. 2 (ISBN 0-89942-702-2, 702-04). Vol. 3 (ISBN 0-89942-703-0, 703-04). Catholic Bk Pub.

Augustine's Ideal of the Religious Life. Adolar Zumkeller. xii, 468p. 1986. 40.00 (ISBN 0-8232-1105-3); pap. 20.00 (ISBN 0-8232-1106-1). Fordham.

Augustinian Concept of Auctoritas. Herbert Hohensee. 3.00 (ISBN 0-686-23374-3). Classical Folia.

Augustinian Piety & Catholic Reform: Augustine, Colet, & Erasmus. Peter I. Kaufman. LC 82-12491. 161p. 1982. text ed. 9.45 (ISBN 0-86554-047-0, MUP-H46). Mercer Univ Pr.

Augustinian Studies: Papers Read at Recent Augustinian Educational Conferences. facs. ed. Augustinian Educational Conferences Staff. LC 67-22052. (Essay Index Reprint Ser.). 1937. 16.00 (ISBN 0-8369-0163-0). Ayer Co Pubs.

AUI, Language of Space: Logos of Love, Pentecostal Peace, & Health Thru Harmony, Creation & Truth. 4th ed. W. John Weilgart. (Illus.). 350p. 1979. pap. 11.95 (ISBN 0-912038-08-X). Cosmic Comm.

Aum. (Agni Yoga Ser.). 1982. Repr. of 1959 ed. Index 12.00 (ISBN 0-933574-12-6). Agni Yoga Soc.

Aum: (Amen) Panduranga R. Malyala. Ed. by Do. (Illus.). 24p. (Orig.). 1983. pap. 2.00 (ISBN 0-938924-12-5). Sri Shirdi Sai.

Aunt Ruth's Puppet Scripts, Bk. I. Ruth Bivens. (Orig.). 1986. pap. 19.95 (ISBN 0-89265-096-6). Randall Hse.

Aunt Ruth's Puppet Scripts, Bk. IV. Ruth Bivens. (Orig.). 1987. three-ring binder & cassette 19.95 (ISBN 0-89265-122-9). Randall Hse.

Aunt Sally: Or, the Cross, the Way of Freedom. facs. ed. Sally Williams. LC 75-89438. (Black Heritage Library Collection Ser.). 1858. 14.25 (ISBN 0-8369-8692-X). Ayer Co Pubs.

Aurier's Symbolist Art Criticism & Theory. Patricia Mathews. Ed. by Donald Kuspit. LC 85-20944. (Studies in the Fine Arts: Criticism: No. 18). 130p. 1986. 49.95 (ISBN 0-8357-1686-4). UMI Res Pr.

Aurobindo, Gandhi & Roy: A Yogi, a Mahatma & a Rationalist. Niranjan Dhar. 1986. 13.50x (ISBN 0-8364-1578-7, Pub. by Minerva India). South Asia Bks.

Aurobindo's Philosophy of Brahman. Stephen H. Phillips. xii, 200p. 1986. 30.64 (ISBN 90-04-07765-0, Pub. by E J Brill). Heinman.

Aurora de la Redencion del Mundo. Erich Sauer. Orig. Title: Dawn of World Redemption. (Span.). 320p. 1967. pap. 7.95 (ISBN 0-8254-1652-3). Kregel.

Aus Altromischen Priesterbuchern. facsimile ed. Eduard Norden. LC 75-10644. (Ancient Religion & Mythology Ser.). (Ger.). 1976. Repr. of 1939 ed. 23.50x (ISBN 0-405-07019-5). Ayer Co Pubs.

Aus dem Leben der Deuschen Juden im Mittelalter. Abraham Berliner. Ed. by Steven Katz. LC 79-7127. (Jewish Philosophy, Mysticism & History of Ideas Ser.). 1980. Repr. of 1900 ed. lib. bdg. 14.00x (ISBN 0-405-12241-1). Ayer Co Pubs.

Aus Schleiermachers Leben, in Briefen, 4 vols. F. Schleiermacher. (Ger.). xxxvi, 2006p. 1974. Repr. of 1863 ed. 190.00x (ISBN 3-11-002261-3). De Gruyter.

Auschwitz - Beginning of a New Era? Reflections on the Holocaust. Ed. by E. Fleischner. 35.00x (ISBN 0-87068-499-X); pap. 16.95. Ktav.

Auschwitz Album. Text by Peter Hellman. 1987. 25.00 (ISBN 0-89604-085-2). Holocaust Pubns.

Auschwitz Myth. Wilhelm Staeglich. Ed. by Theodore J. O'Keefe. Tr. by Thomas Francis from Ger. Tr. of Auschwitz Mythos. (Illus.). 408p. 1986. 19.95 (ISBN 0-939484-23-4). Inst Hist Rev.

Austin's Topical History of Christianity. Bill R. Austin. 527p. 1983. 14.95 (ISBN 0-8423-0096-1). Tyndale.

Austria & the Papacy in the Age of Metternich: Between Conflict & Cooperation, 1809-1830. Alan J. Reinerman. LC 79-774. (Vol. 1). 254p. 1979. 27.95x (ISBN 0-8132-0548-4). Cath U Pr.

Austrian Catholics & the First Republic: Democracy, Capitalism, & the Social Order, 1918-1934. Alfred Diamant. LC 60-5745. pap. 84.30 (ISBN 0-317-09404-1, 2015226). Bks Demand UMI.

Austrian Catholics & the Social Question, 1918-1933. Alfred Diamant. LC 59-62692. (University of Florida Social Sciences Monographs: No. 2). 1959. pap. 3.50 (ISBN 0-8130-0059-9). U Presses Fla.

Austrian Monasteries, Part 1: Gottweig, Heiligenkreuz, Herzogenburg,...Seitenstetten, & Wilhering. Julian G. Plante. (Checklists of Manuscripts Microfilmed for the Hill Monastic Manuscript Library Ser.: Vol. I). iv, 52p. (Orig.). 1967. pap. 10.00 (ISBN 0-940250-26-8). Hill Monastic.

Austrian Monasteries, Part 2: Admont, Altenburg,..."Osterreichische Nationalbibliothek, Universitatsbibliothek, Wilten, Zwettl. Julian G. Plante. (Checklists of Manuscripts Microfilmed for the Hill Monastic Manuscript Library Ser.: Vol. I). viii, 296p. 1974. pap. 20.00 (ISBN 0-940250-27-6). Hill Monastic.

Authentic Christianity: A Fresh Grip on Life. Ray C. Stedman. LC 84-20536. (Authentic Christianity Bks.). 182p. 1985. pap. 6.95 (ISBN 0-88070-072-6). Multnomah.

Authentic Jesus. John R. Stott. LC 85-23831. 96p. 1986. pap. 2.95 (ISBN 0-87784-619-7). Inter-Varsity.

Authentic Records of Revival, Now in Progress in the United Kingdom. Ed. by William Reid. (Revival Library). viii, 478p. 1980. Repr. of 1860 ed. lib. bdg. 15.95 (ISBN 0-940033-17-8). R O Roberts.

Authentic Witness. C. Norman Kraus. LC 78-24012. 200p. 1981. pap. 5.95 (ISBN 0-8361-1959-2). Herald Pr.

Authentic Writings of Ignatius: A Study of Linguistic Criteria. Milton P. Brown, Jr. LC 63-19458. pap. 33.30 (ISBN 0-8357-9096-7, 2017888). Bks Demand UMI.

Authenticity. Thomas Dubay. 4.95 (ISBN 0-87193-143-5). Dimension Bks.

Authenticity & Inspiration of the Holy Scriptures. Robert Haldane. 210p. 1985. Repr. lib. bdg. 9.00 (ISBN 0-86524-182-1, 8604). Klock & Klock.

Authenticity of the Sacred Scriptures. Cornelius Hagerty. 339p. 1969. 10.00 (ISBN 0-912414-00-6). Lumen Christi.

Author As Character in the Works of Sholom Aleichem. Victoria Aarons. LC 84-22703. (Studies in Art & Religious Interpretation: Vol. 3). 192p. 1985. 39.95x (ISBN 0-88946-553-3). E Mellen.

Authoritative Word: Essays on the Nature of Scripture. Ed. by Donald K. McKim. 270p. 1983. pap. 10.95 (ISBN 0-8028-1948-6). Eerdmans.

Authority. D. Martyn Lloyd-Jones. 94p. pap. 3.45x (ISBN 0-85151-386-7). Banner of Truth.

Authority & Community: Polish Jewry in the Sixteenth Century. Nisson E. Shulman. 288p. 1986. text ed. 20.00x (ISBN 0-88125-101-1). Ktav.

Authority & Interpretation of the Bible: An Historical Approach. Jack Rogers & Donald McKim. LC 78-20584. 1979. 23.50 (ISBN 0-06-066696-X, HarpR). Har-Row.

Authority & Power in the Free Church Tradition: A Social Case Study of the American Baptist Convention. Paul M. Harrison. (Arcturus Bks.). 267p. 1971. lib. bdg. 7.00x (ISBN 0-8093-0503-8); pap. 2.45x (ISBN 0-8093-0499-6). S Ill U Pr.

Authority & Resistance in the Investiture Contest. Ian S. Robinson. LC 78-9110. 189p. 1978. text ed. 44.50x (ISBN 0-8419-0407-3). Holmes & Meier.

Authority in Islam. Mehdi Mozaffari. Tr. by Michel Vale from Fr. Tr. of Pouvoic Islamique. 156p. 1987. 39.95 (ISBN 0-87332-388-2). M E Sharpe.

Authority in Morals. Gerard Hughes. 160p. (Orig.). 1984. pap. 6.95 (ISBN 0-87840-410-4). Georgetown U Pr.

Authority in Paul & Peter: The Identification of a Pastoral Stratum in the Pauline Corpus & Peter 1. Winsome Munro. LC 81-12216. (Society of New Testament Studies: No. 45). (Illus.). 230p. 1983. 32.50 (ISBN 0-521-23694-0). Cambridge U Pr.

Authority in the Church: A Study in Changing Paradigms. T. Howland Sanks. LC 74-16565. (American Academy of Religion. Dissertation Ser.: No. 2). Repr. of 1974 ed. 37.10 (ISBN 0-8357-9564-0, 2017555). Bks Demand UMI.

Authority in the Church & the Schillebeeckx Case. Ed. by Leonard Swidler. LC 82-73005. 224p. (Orig.). 1982. pap. 9.95 (ISBN 0-8245-0543-3). Crossroad NY.

Authority in the Modern State. Harold J. Laski. LC 68-21685. 398p. 1968. Repr. of 1919 ed. 35.00 (ISBN 0-208-00460-2, Archon). Shoe String.

Authority in Three Worlds. Charles Capps. 266p. (Orig.). 1980. pap. 3.95 (ISBN 0-89274-281-X). Harrison Hse.

Authority of Grace. W. A. Whitehouse. 272p. 1981. pap. 14.95 (ISBN 0-567-09028-0, Pub. by T&T Clark Ltd UK). Fortress.

Authority of Jesus Christ. Frank E. Stranges. 12p. 1985. pap. text ed. 2.00 (ISBN 0-933470-08-8). Intl Evang.

Authority of Scripture: A Study of the Reformation & Post-Reformation Understanding of the Bible. John K. Reid. LC 79-8716. 286p. 1981. Repr. of 1962 ed. lib. bdg. 25.00x (ISBN 0-313-22191-X, REAS). Greenwood.

Authority of the Believer. J. A. MacMillan. 96p. 1981. pap. 2.25 (ISBN 0-87509-152-0). Chr Pubns.

Authority of the Bible. John R. Stott. pap. 0.75 (ISBN 0-87784-147-0). Inter-Varsity.

Authority of the Bible & the Rise of the Modern World. Henning G. Reventlow. Tr. by John Bowden from German. LC 83-48921. 688p. 1984. 42.95 (ISBN 0-8006-0288-9, 1-288). Fortress.

Authority of the Bible, Theories of Inspiration Revelation & the Canon of Scripture. Robert Gnuse. (Theological Inquirers Ser.). 160p. (Orig.). 1985. pap. 6.95 (ISBN 0-8091-2692-3). Paulist Pr.

Authority of the Old Testament. John Bright. (Twin Brooks Ser.). 272p. 1975. pap. 6.95 (ISBN 0-8010-0637-6). Baker Bk.

Authority of the Past. Sheila McDonough. LC 76-141690. (American Academy of Religion. Studies in Religion). 46p. pap. 8.95 (ISBN 0-89130-153-4, 010001). Scholars Pr GA.

Authorized Daily Prayer Book. Joseph H. Hertz. (Eng. & Hebrew.). 1948. 25.00x (ISBN 0-8197-0094-0). Bloch.

Authors of Confusion. Robert R. Gustafson. pap. 1.45 (ISBN 0-686-12743-9). Grace Pub Co.

Autobiographies of Conversion. Joseph H. Fichter. LC 87-1634. (Studies in Religion & Society: Vol. 17). 232p. 1987. 49.95 (ISBN 0-88946-857-5). E Mellen.

Autobiographies of Ten Religious Leaders: Alternatives in Christian Experience. Radoslav A. Tsanoff. LC 68-57880. 304p. 1968. 7.00 (ISBN 0-911536-34-5). Trinity U Pr.

Autobiography. Edward Gibbon. (World's Classics Ser., No. 139). 16.95 (ISBN 0-19-250139-9). Oxford U Pr.

Autobiography. Solomon Maimon. Ed. by Moses Hadas. 124p. 1985. pap. 4.95 (ISBN 0-8052-0150-5). Schocken.

Autobiography. Harriet Martineau. 962p. Repr. of 1877 ed. text ed. 62.10x (ISBN 0-576-02159-8). Gregg Intl.

Autobiography. Amanda Smith. LC 71-99407. 1969. Repr. of 1893 ed. lib. bdg. 25.00 (ISBN 0-8411-0080-2). Metro Bks.

Autobiography - Intellectual, Moral & Spiritual. Asa Mahan. LC 75-3269. Repr. of 1882 ed. 30.00 (ISBN 0-404-59257-0). AMS Pr.

Autobiography of a Shaker, & Revelation of the Apocalypse. enl. ed. Frederick W. Evans. LC 72-2986. Repr. of 1888 ed. 10.00 (ISBN 0-404-10748-6). AMS Pr.

Autobiography of a Yogi. Paramahansa Yogananda. LC 78-151319. (Illus.). 605p. 1974. Bengali ed. 4.00x (ISBN 0-87612-071-0); Dutch ed. 17.00x (ISBN 90-202-4016-1); German ed. 12.50x (ISBN 3-87041-015-9); Gujarati ed. 4.00x (ISBN 0-87612-072-9); Japanese ed. 11.00x (ISBN 0-87612-073-7); pap. 3.50 (ISBN 0-87612-079-6). Self Realization.

Autobiography of a Yogi. Paramahansa Yogananda. (Illus.). 1971. pap. 9.50x British ed. (ISBN 0-09-021051-4); pap. 14.50x Danish ed. (ISBN 87-418-7082-4); pap. 11.75x French ed. (ISBN 0-87612-066-4); pap. 14.00x Greek ed. (ISBN 0-87612-069-9); pap. 6.95x Italian ed. (ISBN 0-87612-067-2); pap. 10.50x Spanish ed. (ISBN 0-87612-068-0); pap. 4.00x Hindi ed. (ISBN 0-87612-077-X); pap. 13.50x Portuguese ed. (ISBN 0-87612-081-8). Self Realization.

Autobiography of Brook Farm. Ed. by Henry W. Sams. 15.25 (ISBN 0-8446-4056-5). Peter Smith.

Autobiography of Charles G. Finney. Charles G. Finney. Ed. by Helen S. Wessel. LC 77-2813. 1977. pap. 5.95 (ISBN 0-87123-010-0). Bethany Hse.

Autobiography of George Muller. George Muller. Ed. by H. Lincoln Wayland. (Giant Summit Books Ser.). 490p. 1981. pap. 11.95 (ISBN 0-8010-6105-9). Baker Bk.

Autobiography of George Muller. George Muller. 300p. 1984. pap. 3.50 (ISBN 0-88368-159-5). Whitaker Hse.

Autobiography of God. Lloyd J. Ogilvie. LC 78-53355. 324p. 1981. pap. 7.95 (ISBN 0-8307-0791-3, 5415106). Regal.

Autobiography of God: Leader's Guide. Margaret Parker. (Study & Grow Electives). 64p. 1985. pap. 3.95 (ISBN 0-8307-1030-2, 6102058). Regal.

Autobiography of Guibert: Abbot of Nogent-Sous-Coucy. Tr. by C. C. Bland. 1979. Repr. of 1925 ed. lib. bdg. 30.00 (ISBN 0-8482-0140-X). Norwood Edns.

Autobiography of Guibert, Abbot of Nogent-Sous-Coucy. Guibert De Nogent. Tr. by C. C. Bland from Lat. LC 79-11248. 1980. Repr. of 1926 ed. lib. bdg. 24.75x (ISBN 0-313-21460-3, GUAU). Greenwood.

Autobiography of Jesus: What He Said about Himself. Leslie D. Weatherhead. (Festival Bks.). 1980. pap. 1.95 (ISBN 0-687-02318-1). Abingdon.

Autobiography of Lydia Sexton, the Story of Her Life Through a Period of over Seventy-Five Years from 1799 to 1872: Her Early Privations, Adventures, & Reminiscences. Lydia Sexton. Ed. by Carolyn D. Gifford & Donald Dayton. (Women in American Protestant Religion 1800-1930 Ser.). 655p. 1987. lib. bdg. 95.00 (ISBN 0-8240-0673-9). Garland Pub.

Autobiography of Lyman Beecher, 2 vols. Lyman Beecher. Ed. by Barbara M. Cross. LC 61-6348. (John Harvard Library). (Illus.). 896p. 1961. Set. 55.00x (ISBN 0-674-05400-8). Harvard U Pr.

Autobiography of Malcolm X. Malcolm X. 1977. pap. 2.75 (ISBN 0-345-29420-3). Ballantine.

Autobiography of Parley P. Pratt. Parley P. Pratt. Pref. by Parley P. Pratt, Jr. LC 85-10264. (Classics in Mormon Literature Ser.). (Illus.). 475p. 1985. 14.95 (ISBN 0-87747-740-X). Deseret Bk.

Autobiography of Prayer. Albert E. Day. 1979. pap. 3.95x (ISBN 0-8358-0384-8). Upper Room.

Autobiography of St. Anthony Mary Claret. Anthony M. Claret. LC 85-51661. 227p. 1985. pap. 8.00 (ISBN 0-89555-284-1). Tan Bks Pubs.

Autobiography of St. Ignatius. Ignacio Loyola. lib. bdg. 59.95 (ISBN 0-87968-685-5). Gordon Pr.

Autobiography of St. Ignatius Loyola. Ed. by John C. Olin. 1974. pap. 6.95x (ISBN 0-06-131783-7, TB1783, Torch). Har-Row.

Autobiography of St. Ignatius Loyola, with Related Documents. St. Ignatius Loyola. Tr. by Joseph F. O'Callaghan. 16.00 (ISBN 0-8446-5240-7). Peter Smith.

Autobiography of St. John Neumann. Ed. by Alfred C. Rush. 1977. 3.50 (ISBN 0-8198-0384-7); pap. 2.50 (ISBN 0-8198-0385-5). Dghtrs St Paul.

Autobiography of Saint Therese of Lisieux: The Story of a Soul. St. Teresa of Lisieux. 1957. pap. 3.95 (ISBN 0-385-02903-9, D56, Im). Doubleday.

Autobiography of the Rev. Dr. Alexander Carlyle: Containing Memorials of Men & Events of His Time. Alexander Carlyle. Ed. by John H. Burton. LC 78-67649. Repr. of 1860 ed. 44.50 (ISBN 0-404-17179-6). AMS Pr.

Autobiography of the Rev. Luther Lee. Luther Lee. Ed. by Donald W. Dayton. (Higher Christian Life Ser.). 345p. 1985. 45.00 (ISBN 0-8240-6426-7). Garland Pub.

Autobiography: Or, the Story of My Experiments with Truth. 2nd ed. M. K. Gandhi. Tr. by Mahadev Desai from Gujarati. 432p. 1983. 8.00 (ISBN 0-934676-40-2). Greenlf Bks.

Autobiography: The Story of the Lord's Dealings with Mrs. Amanda Smith, The Colored Evangelist, Containing an Account of Her Life Work of Faith, & Her Travels in America, England, Ireland, Scotland, India & Africa, as an Independent Missionary. Amanda B. Smith. Ed. by Carolyn D. Gifford & Donald Dayton. (Women in American Protestant Religion 1800-1930 Ser.). 506p. 1987. lib. bdg. 70.00 (ISBN 0-8240-0674-7). Garland Pub.

Autocephaly of the Metropolia in America. Panagiotes N. Trempelas. Tr. by George S. Bebis. Ed. by Robert G. Stephanopoulos. 80p. 1974. pap. 2.50 (ISBN 0-916586-00-6). Holy Cross Orthodox.

Autonomy of Religious Belief: A Critical Inquiry. Ed. by Fred Crosson. LC 81-50461. (Notre Dame Studies in the Philosophy of Religion: Vol. 2). 162p. 1982. pap. text ed. 6.95 (ISBN 0-268-00601-6). U of Notre Dame Pr.

Autonomy of Religious Belief: A Critical Inquiry. Frederick J. Crosson. 160p. 1981. 14.95 (ISBN 0-268-00596-6). U of Notre Dame Pr.

Autoridad Del Creyente. 2nd ed. Kenneth E. Hagin. (Span.). 1982. pap. 1.00 (ISBN 0-89276-106-7). Hagin Ministries.

Autour De 1300: Etudes de Philologie et de Litterature Medievales. Nico H. J. Van Den Boogaard. (Faux Titre: Vol. 21). (Fr., Illus.). 288p. 1985. pap. text ed. 45.00 (ISBN 90-6203-518-3, Pub. by Editions Rodopi). Humanities.

Autumn Life: How a Surgeon Faced His Fatal Illness. Ethel Helman. 120p. (Orig.). 1986. pap. 6.95 (ISBN 0-571-13704-0). Faber & Faber.

Autumn Memoirs of St. Alphonsus Liguori. Joseph Oppitz. 96p. 1986. pap. 3.95 (ISBN 0-89243-253-5). Liguori Pubns.

Avadhuta Gita of Dattatreya. Dattatreya. Tr. by Swami Ashokananda from Sanskrit. 1978. pap. 3.95 (ISBN 0-87481-482-0). Vedanta Pr.

Avadhuta Gita: The Song of the Ever-Free. Avadhuta. Tr. by Chetanananda from Sanskrit. 138p. 1985. text ed. 3.50 (ISBN 0-87481-224-0, Pub. by Advaita Ashram India). Vedanta Pr.

Availability: Gabriel Marcel & the Phenomenology of Human Openness. Joe McCown. LC 77-22358. (American Academy of Religion. Studies in Religion: No. 14). 1978. pap. 9.95 (ISBN 0-89130-144-5, 010014). Scholars Pr GA.

Availability, the Problem & the Gift. Robert J. Wicks. LC 85-62868. 144p. (Orig.). 1986. pap. 5.95 (ISBN 0-8091-2767-9). Paulist Pr.

Available Mind. Carol R. Murphy. LC 73-94186. (Orig.). 1974. pap. 2.50x (ISBN 0-87574-193-2). Pendle Hill.

Availing Prayer. Fay C. Martin. 120p. pap. 1.00 (ISBN 0-686-29098-4). Faith Pub Hse.

Avatar. Jean Adriel. 285p. 1972. 8.95 (ISBN 0-940700-02-6); pap. 4.95 (ISBN 0-940700-01-8). Meher Baba Info.

Avatar & Incarnation. Geoffrey Parrinder. 1982. Repr. of 1970 ed. 15.95 (ISBN 0-19-520361-5). Oxford U Pr.

Avatar of Night: The Hidden Side of Sai Baba. Tal Brooke. 392p. 1982. pap. text ed. 6.95x (ISBN 0-686-91763-4, Pub. by Vikas India). Advent NY.

Avatara: The Humanization of Philosophy Through the Bhagavad Gita. Antonio T. De Nicolas. LC 76-152. 1976. 12.50 (ISBN 0-89254-001-X); pap. 8.50 (ISBN 0-89254-002-8). Nicolas-Hays.

Avenir De L'homme. Pierre Teilhard De Chardin. 1959. 21.50 (ISBN 0-685-11021-4). French & Eur.

Aventura de Morir. Nancy Karo & Alvera Mickelson. Tr. by Jose Flores from Eng. LC 77-15812. Tr. of Adventure in Dying. (Span.). 197p. 1977. pap. 4.50 (ISBN 0-89922-098-3). Edit Caribe.

Aventuras en la Oracion. Catherine Marshall. 192p. 1976. 2.95 (ISBN 0-88113-005-2). Edit Betania.

Averroes' Doctrine of Immorality: A Matter of Controversy. O. Mohammed. (Editions Ser.: No. 6). 232p. 1984. pap. text ed. 11.95x (ISBN 0-88920-178-1, Wilfrid Laurier Canada). Humanities.

Averroes's, 2 vols. in 1. Tahafut Al-Tahafut. Tr. by S. Van Den Bergh. 593p. 1985. Repr. of 1978 ed. 60.00x (ISBN 0-317-39039-2, Pub. by Luzac & Co Ltd). State Mutual Bk.

Averroes's Middle Commentary on Aristotle's Topics. Ed. by C. E. Butterworth & A. Abd Al-Magid Haridi. (American Research Center in Egypt, Publications Ser.: Vol. 4). (Arabic & Eng.). 247p. (Orig.). 1979. pap. 5.00x (ISBN 0-686-30893-X, Pub. by Am Res Ctr Egypt). Eisenbrauns.

Averting Armageddon. Gordon Thomas & Max Morgan-Witts. LC 84-10101. 360p. 1984. 18.95 (ISBN 0-385-18985-0). Doubleday.

Avesta Eschatology: Compared with the Books of Daniel & Revelations. Lawrence H. Mills. LC 74-24644. Repr. of 1908 ed. 14.00 (ISBN 0-404-12816-5). AMS Pr.

Avesta: Major Portions from the Holy Book of the Magi. Ed. by Ernestine G. Busch. LC 85-90618. 440p. (Orig.). 1985. pap. 17.50 (ISBN 0-9614750-0-5). E G Busch.

Avesta Reader. Hans Reichelt. 1968. Repr. of 1911 ed. 38.80x (ISBN 3-11-000159-4). De Gruyter.

Avesta: The Religious Books of the Parsees. Arthur H. Bleeck. lib. bdg. 79.95 (ISBN 0-87968-133-0). Krishna Pr.

Avi Names His Price. Sheindel Weinbach. (Illus.). 1976. 6.95 (ISBN 0-87306-119-5). Feldheim.

Avicenna & the Visionary Recital. Henry Corbin. Tr. by Willard R. Trask from French. (Dunquin Ser.: No. 13). 314p. 1980. pap. 14.50 (ISBN 0-88214-213-5). Spring Pubns.

Avicenna on Theology. Avicenna. Tr. by Arthur J. Arberry. LC 78-59000. 1983. Repr. of 1951 ed. 15.00 (ISBN 0-88355-676-6). Hyperion Conn.

Avicenna'a Psychology. Avicenna. Ed. by F. Rahman. LC 79-2848. 127p. 1984. Repr. of 1952 ed. 15.25 (ISBN 0-8305-0024-3). Hyperion Conn.

Avignon Papacy & the Crusades, Thirteen Five to Thirteen Seventy-Eight. Norman Housley. 450p. 1986. 55.00x (ISBN 0-19-821957-1). Oxford U Pr.

Avoth. Yitzchak Magriso. Tr. by David N. Barocas. Intro. by & Aryeh Kaplan. 400p. 15.95 (ISBN 0-940118-22-X). Maznaim.

Avrohom ben Avrohom: The Famous Historical Novel About the Ger Tzedek of Vilna. Selig Schachnowitz. (YA) 7.95 (ISBN 0-87306-134-9); pap. 5.95. Feldheim.

Avvakum et les Debuts Du Raskol. Pierre Pascal. (Etudes Sur L'histoire, L'economie et la Sociologie Des Pays Slaves Ser.: No. 8). 1969. pap. 35.60x (ISBN 90-2796-293-6). Mouton.

Avyakta Upanisad. Tr. by P. Lal from Sanskrit. 25p. 1973. 8.00 (ISBN 0-88253-272-3). Ind-US Inc.

Awaited Saviour. Muhammad B. Al Sadr. 110p. 1983. pap. text ed. 4.00 (ISBN 0-686-90398-6). Islamic Seminary.

Awake My Heart. J. Sidlow Baxter. 13.95 (ISBN 0-310-20590-5, 6729). Zondervan.

Awaken from the Dream: A Presentation of a Course in Miracles. Gloria Wapnick & Kenneth Wapnick. 125p. (Orig.). 1987. pap. 10.00 (ISBN 0-933291-04-3). Foun Miracles.

Awakened from Within: Meditations on the Christian Life. Roger of Taize. LC 86-19615. 144p. 1987. 12.95 (ISBN 0-385-23536-4). Doubleday.

Awakening. Fay Young. 64p. 1981. 5.00 (ISBN 0-682-49701-0). Exposition Pr FL.

Awakening Call. James Finley. LC 84-72094. 160p. (Orig.). 1985. pap. 4.95 (ISBN 0-87793-278-6). Ave Maria.

Awakening from the American Dream: The Human Rights Movement in the U. S. Assessed During a Crucial Decade, 1960-1970. Paul E. Kraemer. LC 73-78045. (Studies in Religion & Society Ser.). 1973. pap. 8.95x (ISBN 0-913348-09-0). Ctr Sci Study.

Awakening in Wales. Jessie Penn-Lewis. 1962. pap. 3.95 (ISBN 0-87508-991-7). Chr Lit.

Awakening of Consciousness. Carl Hulsmann. (Illus.). 192p. 1982. 18.00 (ISBN 0-86164-151-5, Pub. by Momenta Publishing Ltd. U. K.). Hunter Hse.

Awakening of Faith, Attributed to Asvaghosha. Tr. by Yoshito S. Hakeda. LC 67-13778. 128p. 1974. 24.00x (ISBN 0-231-03025-8); pap. 10.00x (ISBN 0-231-08336-X). Columbia U Pr.

Awakening of Faith in Mahayana. Kevin O'Neil. (Orig.). 1984. pap. 14.95 (ISBN 0-86627-012-4). Crises Res Pr.

Awakening of the Human Spirit. Hazrat Inayat Khan. LC 82-80091. (Collected Works of Hazyat Inayat Khan Ser.). 224p. (Orig.). 1982. pap. 8.95 (ISBN 0-930872-27-4, 1014P). Omega Pr NM.

Awakening Soul. Helen Y. Lloyd. 1984. 10.95 (ISBN 0-8062-2346-4). Carlton.

Awakening That Must Come. Lewis A. Drummond. LC 78-59239. 1979. pap. 4.50 (ISBN 0-8054-6535-9). Broadman.

Awakening the Inner Eye: Intuition in Education. Nel Noddings & Paul J. Shore. LC 83-1805. 236p. 1984. 26.95x (ISBN 0-8077-2751-2). Tchrs Coll.

Awakening to Community. Rudolf Steiner. Tr. by Marjorie Spock from Ger. LC 74-81153. 178p. 1975. 14.00 (ISBN 0-910142-61-0). Anthroposophic.

Awakenings. Mary J. Saia et al. (Education to Wonder Ser.: Pre-School Program). 1973. program director's handbook 3.50 (ISBN 0-8091-9075-3); tchr dev. handbook 3.50 (ISBN 0-8091-9074-5); tchr. guidebk. 4 yr. olds 6.95 (ISBN 0-8091-9071-0); tchr. guidebk. 5 yr. olds 6.95 (ISBN 0-8091-9072-9). parent-tchr. dev. kit 75.00 (ISBN 0-8091-9073-7); child-parent kit 4 yr. olds 5.95 (ISBN 0-8091-9077-X); child-parent kit 5 yr. olds 5.95 (ISBN 0-8091-9078-8). Paulist Pr.

Away in a Manger. (Illus.). 1987. 6.95 (ISBN 0-570-04166-X). Concordia.

Away in a Manger. Ed. by Judy Sparks. (Happy Day Bks.). (Illus.). 24p. 1985. 1.59 (ISBN 0-87239-871-4, 3671). Standard Pub.

Awesome Power of the Healing Thought. John W. Drakeford. LC 80-70915. 1981. 8.95 (ISBN 0-8054-5294-X). Broadman.

Awful Disclosures by Marcia Monk of the Hotel Dieu Nunnery of Montrial. Maria Monk & Gerald Grob. LC 76-46089. (Anti-Movements in America Ser.). 1977. lib. bdg. 29.00 (ISBN 0-405-09962-2). Ayer Co Pubs.

Axe-Age, Wolf-Age: A Selection for Children from the Norse Myths. Kevin Crossley-Holland. (Illus.). 128p. 1985. 11.95 (ISBN 0-233-97688-4). Andre Deutsch.

Axiology: The Science of Values. abbreviated ed. Archie J. Bahm. LC 84-51726. 84p. 1984. pap. 3.00 (ISBN 0-911714-14-6, World Bks). Bahm.

Axiomatics & Dogmatics. John Carnes. (Theology & Scientific Culture Ser.). 1982. 16.95x (ISBN 0-19-520377-1). Oxford U Pr.

Axioms & Logics. L. Ron Hubbard. 5.00 (ISBN 0-686-30793-3). Church Scient NY.

Axioms & Logics. L. Ron Hubbard. 1958. pap. 6.97 (ISBN 0-88404-066-6). Bridge Pubns Inc.

Axioms of Religion. Herschel H. Hobbs & E. Y. Mullins. LC 78-50799. 1978. 8.50 (ISBN 0-8054-1707-9). Broadman.

Ayatollah in the Cathedral: Reflections of a Hostage. Moorhead Kennedy. 241p. 1986. 17.95 (ISBN 0-8090-2765-8). Hill & Wang.

Ayn Keloheynu. Noah Golinkin. LC 81-51960. (Illus.). 128p. 1981. pap. 7.95x (ISBN 0-88400-076-1). Shengold.

Ayudador. Catherine Marshall. 208p. 1980. 3.25 (ISBN 0-88113-009-5). Edit Betania.

Ayuno Escogido por Dios. Arthur Wallis. 176p. 1974. 2.95 (ISBN 0-88113-006-0). Edit Betania.

Ayurveda, the Science of Self-Healing: A Practical Guide. Vasant Lad. Ed. by Malinda Elliot & Harriet Slavitz. LC 83-80620. (Illus.). 176p. (Orig.). 1984. text ed. 37.95 (ISBN 0-914955-01-2); pap. text ed. 9.95 (ISBN 0-914955-00-4). Lotus Light.

Az Isten Szornyetege: Ady Iiraja. 2nd ed. Laszlo Vatai. LC 77-89126. (Hungarian.). 390p. 1977. 15.00 (ISBN 0-911050-45-0). Occidental.

Azamra (I Will Sing) Nachman of Breslov & Nathan of Breslov. Tr. by Avraham Greenbaum from Hebrew. 64p. (Orig.). 1984. pap. 1.50 (ISBN 0-930213-11-4). Breslov Res INst.

Azbuka Pravoslavnago Vjerouchenija. G. A. Znamensky. Tr. of Alphabet of the Orthodox Faith. 80p. pap. text ed. 3.00 (ISBN 0-317-29292-7). Holy Trinity.

Aztecs: People of the Sun, Vol. 50. Alfonso Caso. Tr. by Lowell Dunham. (Civilization of the American Indian Ser.: No. 50). (Illus.). 142p. 1978. Repr. of 1958 ed. 24.95 (ISBN 0-8061-0414-7). U of Okla Pr.

Azusa Street. Frank Bartleman. LC 80-82806. 1980. pap. 5.95 (ISBN 0-88270-439-7). Bridge Pub.

B

B-I-B-L-E That's the Book for Me! Claire Lynn. (Doctrinal Series for Children: Bk. 1). (Illus.). 18p. (Orig.). 1981. pap. 1.50 (ISBN 0-89323-013-8). Bible Memory.

Baal Shem of Michelstadt. 1981. pap. 4.95 (ISBN 0-686-76481-1). Feldheim.

Bab: The Herald of the Day of Days. H. M. Balyuzi. (Illus.). 272p. 1973. 14.95 (ISBN 0-85398-048-9). G Ronald Pub.

Baba Bathra, 3 vols. 45.00 (ISBN 0-910218-73-0). Bennet Pub.

Baba Jaimal Singh: His Life & Teachings. Kirpal Singh. (Illus.). 168p. 3.00 (ISBN 0-318-03045-4). Sant Bani Ash.

Baba Mezia, 2 vols. 30.00 (ISBN 0-910218-72-2). Bennet Pub.

Babaylanism in Negros: 1896-1907. Evelyn T. Cullamar. (Illus.). 133p. (Orig.). 1986. pap. 8.50x (ISBN 971-10-0293-0, Pub. by New Day Philippines). Cellar.

Babell. Archibald Pitcairne. LC 75-174208. (Maitland Club, Glasgow. Publications Ser.: No. 6). Repr. of 1830 ed. 11.00 (ISBN 0-404-52931-3). AMS Pr.

Babi & Baha'i Religions Eighteen Forty-Four to Nineteen Forty-Four: Some Contemporary Western Accounts. Ed. by Moojan Momen. (Illus.). 608p. 29.50 (ISBN 0-85398-102-7). G Ronald Pub.

Babi & Baha'i Religions: From Messianic Sh'ism to a World Religion. Peter Smith. (Illus.). 225p. Date not set. price not set (ISBN 0-521-30128-9). Cambridge U Pr.

Babies of the Bible. Carolyn Kuykendall. (Happy Day Bks.). (Illus.). 24p. 1986. 1.59 (ISBN 0-87403-021-8, 3481). Standard Pub.

Baby Born in a Stable. A. H. Kramer-Lampher. LC 65-15145. (Arch Bks.: Set. 2). 1965. pap. 0.99 (ISBN 0-570-06013-3, 59-1118). Concordia.

Baby God Promised. Walter Wangerin, Jr. (Arch Bks.: No. 13). (Illus.). 32p. 1976. pap. 0.99 (ISBN 0-570-06105-9, 59-1223). Concordia.

Baby Jesus. Ed. by Marian Bennett. (My Shape Book Ser.). (Illus.). 10p. 1985. 2.95 (ISBN 0-87239-907-9, 2747). Standard Pub.

Baby Jesus. Illus. by Carolyn Bracken. (Tuck-A-Toy Bks.). (Illus.). 7p. 1985. 3.95 (ISBN 0-8407-6666-1). Nelson.

Baby Jesus. Kay Churchwell. LC 85-24335. (Bible-&-Me Ser.). (Illus.). 1986. 5.95 (ISBN 0-8054-4170-0). Broadman.

Baby Jesus. Mary McMillan. (Color, Cut & Paste Ser.). 48p. 1986. wkbk. 4.95 (ISBN 0-86653-369-9). Good Apple.

Baby Jesus. Hilda L. Rostron. (Ladybird Ser.). (Illus.). 1961. bds. 2.50 (ISBN 0-87508-832-5). Chr Lit.

Baby Jesus. Gladys S. Stump. (Books I Can Read Ser.). (Illus.). 1978. pap. 1.95 (ISBN 0-8127-0160-7). Review & Herald.

Baby Jesus. Virginia Williams-Ellis. (Board Bks.). (Illus.). 10p. 1984. 2.95 (ISBN 0-8249-8082-4). Ideals.

Baby Jesus ABC Storybook. Ed. by Judy Sparks. (Happy Day Bk.). (Illus.). 24p. 1979. 1.59 (ISBN 0-87239-354-2, 3624). Standard Pub.

Baby Jesus ABC's. Marian Bennett. (Little Happy Day Bks.). (Illus.). 24p. (Orig.). 1983. pap. 0.49 (ISBN 0-87239-651-7, 2121). Standard Pub.

Baby Jesus' Birthday. Nancy Irland. (Cut & Color Bks.). (Illus.). 16p. (Orig.). 1982. pap. 0.95 (ISBN 0-87239-585-5, 2389). Standard Pub.

Baby Moses. Illus. by Carol Bracken. (Tuck-A-Toy Bks.). (Illus.). 7p. 1985. 3.95 (ISBN 0-8407-6663-7). Nelson.

Baby Moses. Gladys S. Stump. (Books I Can Read Ser.). (Illus.). 1978. pap. 1.95 (ISBN 0-8127-0164-X). Review & Herald.

Baby Moses in a Basket. Patricia Mahany. (Happy Day Bible Stories Bks.). (Illus.). 24p. 1984. 1.59 (ISBN 0-87239-761-0, 3721). Standard Pub.

Babylon Mystery Religion: Ancient & Modern. Ralph Woodrow. (Illus.). 1981. 4.95 (ISBN 0-916938-00-X). R Woodrow.

Babylon: The Oldest & Most Corrupt Harlot. Charles W. Evans, Jr. 1984. 12.95 (ISBN 0-533-05914-3). Vantage.

Babylonian Genesis. 2nd ed. Alexander Heidel. LC 51-822. 1963. 6.00x (ISBN 0-226-32399-4, P133, Phoen). U of Chicago Pr.

Babylonian Hymns & Prayers. David V. Myhrman. 59.95 (ISBN 0-87968-691-X). Gordon Pr.

Babylonian Menologies & the Semitic Calendars. Stephen H. Langdon. LC 78-72744. (Ancient Mesopotamian Texts & Studies). Repr. of 1935 ed. 21.50 (ISBN 0-404-18192-9). AMS Pr.

Babylonian Planetary Omens, Enuma Anu Enlil, Tablet 50-51. Erica Reiner & D. Pingree. LC 79-67168. (Bibliotheca Mesopotamica Ser.: Vol. 2, Pt. 2). 100p. (Orig.). 1980. pap. 15.00x (ISBN 0-89003-049-9). Undena Pubns.

Babylonian Religion & Mythology. Leonard W. King. LC 73-18854. (Illus.). Repr. of 1899 ed. 18.45 (ISBN 0-404-11352-4). AMS Pr.

Babylonian Religion & Mythology. Leonard W. King. LC 77-94592. 1978. Repr. of 1899 ed. lib. bdg. 25.00 (ISBN 0-89341-311-9). Longwood Pub Group.

Babylonischen Kudurru Als Urkundenform. Franz X. Steinmetzer. Repr. of 1922 ed. 22.00 (ISBN 0-384-57850-0). Johnson Repr.

Baby's First Bible Story Book. L'Ann Carwell. (Illus.). 1979. 1.25 (ISBN 0-570-08003-7, 56-1328). Concordia.

Baby's First Book About Christmas. L'Ann Carwell. (Illus.). 1979. 1.25 (ISBN 0-570-08002-9, 56-1327). Concordia.

Baby's First Book About Creation. L'Ann Carwell. (Illus.). 1979. 1.25 (ISBN 0-570-08000-2, 56-1325). Concordia.

Baby's First Book About Jesus. L'Ann Carwell. (Illus.). 1979. 1.25 (ISBN 0-570-08001-0, 56-1326). Concordia.

Baby's First Days: Enrollment Certificate. B. J. Hoff. (Certificate Booklets Ser.). (Illus.). 16p. 1982. pap. 0.95 self-cover (ISBN 0-87239-530-8, 1182). Standard Pub.

Bach among the Theologians. Jaroslav Pelikan. LC 86-45219. 176p. 1986. 14.95 (ISBN 0-8006-0792-9, 1-792). Fortress.

Bach: Rabbi Joel Sirkes, His Life, Works & Times. Elijah Judah Schochet. 13.95 (ISBN 0-87306-031-8). Feldheim.

Back in Keith County. John Janovy, Jr. LC 83-17003. (Illus.). x, 179p. 1983. pap. 5.95 (ISBN 0-8032-7560-9, BB 875, Bison). U of Nebr Pr.

Back on Course. Gavin MacLeod et al. (Illus.). 1987. 12.95 (ISBN 0-8007-1533-0). Revell.

Back to Basics: Catholic Faith in Today's World. Pierre Riches. 176p. 1984. pap. 7.95 (ISBN 0-8245-0646-4). Crossroad NY.

Back to Basics in Church Growth. Donald McGavran & Winfield Arn. 1981. pap. 5.95 (ISBN 0-8423-0116-X). Tyndale.

Back to Eden. authorized ed. Jethro Kloss. LC 81-82411. 702p. 1984. pap. 9.95. World Wide OR.

Back to Eden: Authorized Kloss Family Edition. rev. ed. Jethro Kloss. (Illus.). 724p. 1985. pap. 3.50 (ISBN 0-940676-00-1). Back to Eden.

Back to Square One. Larry Christenson. LC 79-16413. 144p. 1979. pap. 3.95 (ISBN 0-87123-025-9, 210025). Bethany Hse.

Back to the Soil: The Jewish Farmers of Clarion, Utah, & Their World. Robert A. Goldberg. (Utah Centennial Ser.: Vol. 2). (Illus.). 208p. 1986. 19.95 (ISBN 0-87480-263-6). U of Utah Pr.

Back to the Sources: Reading the Classic Jewish Texts. Ed. by Barry Holtz. (Illus.). 416p. 1984. 19.95 (ISBN 0-671-45467-6). Summit Bks.

Background & Ceremonies of the Church of Scientology. L. Ron Hubbard. 40.00 (ISBN 0-686-30794-1). Church Scient NY.

Background & Ceremonies of the Church of Scientology of California, World Wide: From the Works of L. Ron Hubbard. 1972. 62.17 (ISBN 0-88404-054-2). Bridge Pubns Inc.

Background Information for New Testament Students. William R. Matthews, Sr. Ed. by Amos Jones, Jr. 250p. (Orig.). 1985. pap. cancelled (ISBN 0-910683-05-0). Sunday School.

Background of the Epistles. William Fairweather. 1977. 16.50 (ISBN 0-86524-118-X, 8002). Klock & Klock.

Background of the Gospels. William Fairweather. 464p. 1916. 15.95 (ISBN 0-567-02101-7, Pub. by T & T Clark Ltd UK). Fortress.

Background of the Gospels. William Fairweather. 1977. 17.00 (ISBN 0-86524-117-1, 8001). Klock & Klock.

Background to the Bible: An Introduction to Scripture Study. Richard T. Murphy. (Illus.). 1978. pap. 5.95 (ISBN 0-89283-055-7). Servant.

Background to the Gospel of St. Mark. 2nd ed. Rudolf Steiner. Tr. of Exkurse in das Gebiet des Markus-Evangeliums. 200p. 1986. pap. 10.95 (ISBN 0-88010-145-8). Anthroposophic.

Backgrounds for the Bible. M. O'Connor & David N. Freedman. 1987. text ed. 17.50x (ISBN 0-931464-30-7). Eisenbrauns.

Backgrounds of Early Christianity. Everett Ferguson. 464p. (Orig.). 1987. pap. 22.95 (ISBN 0-8028-0292-3). Eerdmans.

Backward, Christian Soldiers? Gary North. 294p. 1984. pap. 4.95 (ISBN 0-930464-01-X). Dominion Pr.

Backward Masking Unmasked: Backward Satanic Messages of Rock & Roll Exposed. Jacob Aranza. LC 83-80043. 118p. (Orig.). 1983. pap. 5.95 (ISBN 0-910311-04-8). Huntington Hse Inc.

Bacon, Shakespeare & the Rosicrucians. W. F. Wigston. 59.95 (ISBN 0-87968-694-4). Gordon Pr.

Bad News for Modern Man. Franky Schaeffer. LC 84-70082. (Illus.). 192p. (Orig.). 1984. 14.95 (ISBN 0-89107-323-X, Crossway Bks); pap. 7.95 (ISBN 0-89107-311-6). Good News.

Bad Start for Santa. Sarah Hayes. (Illus.). 12.95 (ISBN 0-87113-093-9). Atlantic Monthly.

Baedeker's Historical Palestine. Karl Baedeker. (Baedeker's Handbooks for Traveler's Ser.). (Illus.). 240p. 1985. Repr. of 1930 ed. 19.95 (ISBN 0-88254-699-6). Hippocrene Bks.

Bael Tatpauopoos und Die Kerube Des Ezechiel. Ed. by Simon K. Landersdorfer. pap. 8.00 (ISBN 0-384-31200-4). Johnson Repr.

Bag of Noodles. Wally Armbruster. (Illus.). (YA) 1973. pap. 3.95 (ISBN 0-570-03158-3, 12-2543). Concordia.

Baghdad Chronicle. Reuben Levy. LC 77-10580. (Studies in Islamic History: No. 17). (Illus.). 1978. Repr. of 1929 ed. lib. bdg. 27.50x (ISBN 0-87991-466-1). Porcupine Pr.

Bagster's Bible Handbook. Samuel Bagster. Intro. by Walter Elwell. 264p. 1983. Repr. 9.95 (ISBN 0-8007-1334-6). Revell.

Bagster's Keyword Concordance. Samuel Bagster. 96p. 1983. Repr. 5.95 (ISBN 0-8007-1335-4). Revell.

Bahai. Francis Beckwith. 64p. 1985. saddle stitched 2.95 (ISBN 0-87123-848-9). Bethany Hse.

Baha'i Faith. Phillip Hainsworth & Mary Perkins. 1985. 13.00x (ISBN 0-7062-3939-3, Pub. by Ward Lock Educ Co Ltd). State Mutual Bk.

Baha'i Faith: An Historical Bibliography. Joel Bjorling. Ed. by J. G Melton. LC 84-49294. (Reference Library of Social Science- Sects & Cults in America: Bibliographic Guides). 250p. 1985. lib. bdg. 35.00 (ISBN 0-8240-8974-X). Garland Pub.

Baha'i Faith in America: Origins, 1892-1900, Vol. 1. Robert H. Stockman. (Illus.). 225p. 1985. 24.95 (ISBN 0-87743-199-X). Baha'i.

Baha'i Faith: Its History & Teachings. William M. Miller. LC 74-8745. (Illus.). 464p. 1984. pap. 10.95 (ISBN 0-87808-137-2). William Carey Lib.

Baha'i Faith: The Emerging Global Religion. William Hatcher & James D. Martin. LC 84-42743. 224p. 1985. 14.45 (ISBN 0-06-065441-4, HarpR). Har-Row.

Baha'i Prayers. Baha'u'llah, the Bab & Abdu'l-Baha. LC 54-10901. 6.95 (ISBN 0-87743-012-8, 315-005). Baha'i.

Baha'i Prayers: A Selection of Prayers Revealed by Baha'u'llah, the Bab & Abdu'l-Baha. Bab Baha'u'llah & Abdu'l-Baha. LC 82-11502. 1985. 11.95 (ISBN 0-87743-175-2, 115-070); pap. 4.95 (ISBN 0-87743-176-0, 115-071). Baha'i.

Baha'i Proofs & A Short Sketch of the History & Lives of the Leaders of This Religion. Mirza Abul-Fadl. Tr. by Ali-Kuli Khan from Arabic. LC 83-22486. (Illus.). xi, 305p. 1983. 17.95 (ISBN 0-87743-191-4). Baha'i.

Baha'i References to Judaism, Christianity & Islam. James Heggie. 272p. 1986. 11.95. G Ronald Pub.

Baha'i World: An International Record 1954-1963, Vol. XIII. The Universal House of Justice. LC 27-5882. (Illus.). 1970. 27.95 (ISBN 0-87743-042-X, 233-013). Baha'i.

Baha'i World: An International Record 1963-1968, Vol. XIV. The Universal House of Justice. LC 27-5882. (Illus.). 1974. 18.95 (ISBN 0-87743-099-3, 233-014). Baha'i.

Baha'i World: An International Record 1968-1973, Vol. XV. The Universal House of Justice. (Illus.). 1976. o. s. i. 22.95 (ISBN 0-85398-059-4, 233-015). Baha'i.

Baha'i World: An International Record 1973-1976, Vol. XVI. The Universal House of Justice. (Illus.). 1979. 24.95 (ISBN 0-85398-075-6, 233-016). Baha'i.

Bahai World: An International Record 1976-1979, Vol. XVII. The Universal House of Justice. (Illus.). 1981. 29.95 (ISBN 0-87743-130-2). Baha'i.

Baha'i World: An International Record 1976-79, Vol. XVII. The Universal House of Justice. (Illus.). 1981. 29.95 (ISBN 0-85398-130-2). Baha'i.

Bahaism & Its Claims. Samuel G. Wilson. LC 79-131493. Repr. of 1915 ed. 22.50 (ISBN 0-404-06995-9). AMS Pr.

Baha'u'llah & the Bab Confront Modern Thinkers: Spinoza: Concerning God, Bk. 2. Ruhi M. Afnan. LC 75-109166. 188p. 1977. 10.00 (ISBN 0-8022-2197-1). Philos Lib.

Baha'u'llah & the New Era: An Introduction to the Baha'i Faith. 5th rev. ed. J. E. Esslemont. LC 80-24305. 1980. pap. 4.50 (ISBN 0-87743-160-4, 231-005). Baha'i.

Baha'u'llah & the New Era: An Introduction to the Baha'i Faith. 4th rev. ed. J. E. Esslemont. LC 79-21937. 1980. 16.95 (ISBN 0-87743-136-1, 231-004). Baha'i.

Baha'u'llah: The King of Glory. H. M. Balyuzi. (Illus.). 552p. 1980. 28.50 (ISBN 0-85398-090-X). G Ronald Pub.

Baha'u'llah: The Word Made Flesh. H. M. Balyuzi. 134p. 1963. 10.95 (ISBN 0-85398-014-4); pap. 5.95 (ISBN 0-85398-001-2). G Ronald Pub.

Bahishti Zewar (Heavenly Ornaments) A. A. Thanvi. 14.95 (ISBN 0-686-63896-4). Kazi Pubns.

Baja California & Its Missions. Tomas Robertson. (Illus.). 1978. pap. 3.95 (ISBN 0-910856-66-4). La Siesta.

Baje la Guardia! Charles R. Swindoll. Tr. by Juan S. Araujo from Eng. Tr. of Dropping Your Guard. (Span.). 176p. 1987. pap. 4.95 (ISBN 0-88113-016-8). Edit Betania.

Bajo Presion. Gene A. Getz. Tr. of When the Pressure Is On. (Span.). 1986. pap. 3.25 (ISBN 0-8297-0898-7). Life Pubs Intl.

Baker Encyclopedia of Psychology. David G. Benner. 1376p. 1985. text ed. 39.95 (ISBN 0-8010-0865-4). Baker Bk.

Baker's Bible Atlas. rev. ed. Charles F. Pfeiffer. (Illus.). 1961. Repr. 15.95 (ISBN 0-8010-6930-0). Baker Bk.

Bakers Bible Atlas Study Guide. Ray Eby. 1977. 4.95 (ISBN 0-686-25535-6); test 1.75 (ISBN 0-686-31725-4); map 1.55 (ISBN 0-686-31726-2). Rod & Staff.

Baker's Bible Study Guide. Derek Prime. (Baker's Paperback Reference Library). 296p. 1982. pap. 8.95 (ISBN 0-8010-7076-7). Baker Bk.

Baker's Concise Bible Atlas. J. Carl Laney. (Illus.). 192p. (Orig.). 1987. pap. 10.95 (ISBN 0-8010-5638-1). Baker Bk.

Baker's Concise Dictionary of Religion. Donald T. Kauffman. (Paperback Reference Library). 446p. 1985. pap. 11.95 (ISBN 0-8010-5467-2). Baker Bk.

Baker's Dictionary of Theology. Ed. by Everett F. Harrison. pap. 12.95 (ISBN 0-8010-4289-5). Baker Bk.

Baker's Handbook of Practical Theology. Ed. by Ralph G. Turnbull. 469p. 1967. 14.95 (ISBN 0-8010-8880-1). Baker Bk.

Baker's Harmony of the Gospels. Benjamin Davies. (Baker's Paperback Reference Library). 192p. 1983. pap. 6.95 (ISBN 0-8010-2928-7). Baker Bk.

Baker's Pocket Bible Concordance. (Direction Bks.). 1973. pap. 5.95 (ISBN 0-8010-0616-3). Baker Bk.

Baker's Pocket Book of Religious Quotes. Ed. by Albert M. Wells, Jr. (Direction Bks.). 240p. 1976. pap. 2.95 (ISBN 0-8010-9575-1). Baker Bk.

Baker's Pocket Treasury of Religious Verse. Compiled by Donald T. Kauffman. (Direction Bks.). 384p. 1980. pap. 4.95 (ISBN 0-8010-5417-6). Baker Bk.

Baker's Topical Bible. Roswell D. Hitchcock. 768p. 1984. pap. 11.95 (ISBN 0-8010-4284-4). Baker Bk.

Balaam Text from Deir Alla. Jo Ann Hackett. LC 83-27125. (Harvard Semitic Museum - Monograph). 160p. 1984. 11.95 (ISBN 0-89130-723-0, 04 00 31). Scholars Pr GA.

Balaam's Apocalyptic Prophecies: A Study in Reading Scripture. Calvin Seerveld. pap. 3.95 (ISBN 0-88906-110-6). Wedge Pub.

Balance: A Modern Christian Challenge. Anna Griffith. pap. 4.95 (ISBN 0-89137-425-6). Quality Pubns.

Balance, A Tried & Tested Formula for Church Growth. Ira North. 1983. pap. 5.95 (ISBN 0-89225-270-7). Gospel Advocate.

Balance in World & Man: Lucifer & Ahriman. Rudolf Steiner. pap. 2.75 (ISBN 0-919924-05-0). Anthroposophic.

Balanced Christian Life. Watchman Nee. Tr. by Stephen Koung. 1981. pap. 3.25 (ISBN 0-686-95516-1). Christian Fellow Pubs.

Balanced Church. Charles W. Conn. 1983. pap. 6.95 (ISBN 0-87148-017-4). Pathway Pr.

Balanced Church Growth. Ebbie C. Smith. LC 84-6456. 1984. pap. 5.95 (ISBN 0-8054-6246-5). Broadman.

Balancing Life's Demands: A New Perpective on Priorities. J. Grant Howard. LC 82-24581. 1983. pap. 6.95 (ISBN 0-88070-012-2); study guide 2.95 (ISBN 0-88070-033-5). Multnomah.

Balancing the Christian Life. Charles C. Ryrie. 1969. pap. 5.95 (ISBN 0-8024-0452-9). Moody.

Baldwin of Ford: Spirtual Tractates, 2 vols. Tr. & intro. by David N. Bell. 1987. Set. 50.00; Set. pap. 20.00. Vol. 1 (ISBN 0-87907-438-8, CF38). Vol. 2 (ISBN 0-87907-441-8, CF41). Cistercian Pubns.

Bales Teller Debate. James Bales & Woosey Teller. pap. 4.95 (ISBN 0-89315-018-5). Lambert Bk.

Balkan Jewish Communities: Yugoslavia, Bulgaria, Greece, & Turkey. Daniel J. Elazar & Harriet P. Friedenreich. (Illus.). 208p. (Orig.). 1984. lib. bdg. 22.00 (ISBN 0-8191-3473-2, Co-Pub. by Ctr Jewish Comm Studies); pap. text ed. 10.25 (ISBN 0-8191-3474-0). U Pr of Amer.

Ballad of God & Man: Asa Di Var. Ed. by Sohan Singh. 1984. 9.00x (ISBN 0-8364-1220-6, Pub. by Nanak Dev Univ India). South Asia Bks.

Baltahsar Hubmaier: The Leader of the Anabaptists. Henry C. Vedder. LC 79-149670. Repr. of 1905 ed. 24.50 (ISBN 0-404-06755-7). AMS Pr.

Balthasar Hubmaier. Ed. by G. Westin & T. Bergsten. (Tauferakten Kommission Ser., Vol. 9). 507p. 1962. 30.00x (ISBN 0-8361-1169-9). Herald Pr.

Baltimore Catechism, No. 1. Baltimore Plenary Council Staff. 1977. pap. 3.00 (ISBN 0-89555-010-5). TAN Bks Pubs.

Baltimore Catechism, No. 2. Baltimore Plenary Council Staff. 1977. pap. 1.75 (ISBN 0-89555-008-3). TAN Bks Pubs.

Baltimore Catechism: Cathechism of Christian Doctrine. Baltimore Plenary Council Staff. 1974. pap. 3.50 (ISBN 0-89555-007-5, 147). TAN Bks Pubs.

Ban the Bomb: A History of SANE, the Committee for a SANE Nuclear Policy, 1957-1985. Milton S. Katz. LC 85-24824. (Contributions in Political Science Ser.: No. 147). (Illus.). 230p. 1986. lib. bdg. 35.00 (ISBN 0-313-24167-8, KBB/). Greenwood.

Banaras: City of Light. Diana L. Eck. LC 81-48134. (Illus.). 1982. 25.00 (ISBN 0-394-51971-X). Knopf.

Bandits, Prophets, & Messiahs: Popular Movements at the Time of Jesus. John Hanson & Richard A. Horsley. 220p. 1985. 28.35 (ISBN 0-86683-992-5, HarpR). Har-Row.

Bandlet of Righteousness: An Ethiopian Book of the Dead. Tr. by E. A. Wallis-Budge. (Coptic.). 1984. pap. 3.95 (ISBN 0-916411-23-0, Near Eastern). Holmes Pub.

Bangor Cathedral. M. L. Clarke. 125p. 1969. text ed. 6.95x (ISBN 0-900768-23-1, Pub. by U of Wales Pr). Humanities.

Banh Chung Banh Day: The New Year's Rice Cakes. 1972. 2.50 (ISBN 0-686-10279-7). Asia Resource.

Bani of Sri Guru Amardas. Gubachana S. Talib. 1979. text ed. 29.50 (ISBN 0-89684-078-6, Pub. by Sterling New Delhi). Orient Bk Dist.

Banishing Fear from Your Life. Charles D. Bass. LC 85-23943. 168p. 1986. 14.95 (ISBN 0-385-23331-0). Doubleday.

Bankei Zen. Ed. by Yoshito S. Hakeda. Tr. by Peter Haskel. LC 83-81372. (Eastern Bks.). 240p. 1985. 27.50 (ISBN 0-394-53524-3, GP 886). Grove.

Bankei Zen. Ed. by Yoshito S. Hakeda. Tr. by Peter Haskel. LC 83-81372. (Eastern Bks.). 1985. pap. 8.95 (ISBN 0-394-62493-9, E-272, Ever). Grove.

Banner Designs for Celebrating Christians. Jane Debor & Linda Isabel. 1984. pap. 5.95 (ISBN 0-570-03931-2, 12-2865). Concordia.

Banners & Such. Adelaide Ortegel. LC 86-62616. 1986. pap. 9.95 (ISBN 0-89390-016-8). Resource Pubns.

Banquet of the Word: Bible Study Based on the Sunday Readings. Thomas Welbers. LC 86-60891. 400p. 1986. pap. 17.95 (ISBN 0-89390-073-7). Resource Pubns.

Bantu Folk Lore. Matthew L. Hewat. LC 77-129948. Repr. of 1906 ed. 22.50x (ISBN 0-8371-4992-4, HBF&, Pub. by Negro U Pr). Greenwood.

Baptism. William Freburger. 1970. pap. 0.95 (ISBN 0-8189-0425-9). Alba.

Baptism. H. A. Ironside. pap. 1.50 (ISBN 0-87213-345-1). Loizeaux.

Baptism. Ed. by Bob Korth. (Discipleship Booklets Ser.). (Illus., Orig.). 1984. pap. 0.95 (ISBN 0-87239-787-4, 1151). Standard Pub.

Baptism. Martin E. Marty. LC 77-78635. 1977. pap. 3.95 (ISBN 0-8006-1317-1, 1-1317). Fortress.

Baptism. Karen D. Merrell. 24p. pap. 4.95 (ISBN 0-87747-559-8). Deseret Bk.

Baptism. Karl Rahner. 1.50 (ISBN 0-87193-120-6). Dimension Bks.

Baptism. C. H. Spurgeon. 1976. pap. 1.50 (ISBN 0-686-18091-7). Pilgrim Pubns.

Baptism. Ed. by Richard E. Todd. (Grace Bible Ser.). (Illus.). 16p. (Orig.). 1980. pap. 0.50 (ISBN 0-9605324-0-4). R E Todd.

Baptism: A Bible Defense of Believer's Immersion. Philip Mauro. pap. 2.95 (ISBN 0-685-88367-1). Reiner.

Baptism, a Covenant. Gerald F. Mundfrom. (Illus.). 140p. (Orig.). 1985. pap. text ed. 4.00x (ISBN 0-9615494-0-8). Mercy & Truth.

Baptism & Church: A Believers' Church Vision. Ed. by Merle D. Strege. LC 85-43567. 224p. (Orig.). 1986. pap. 12.50 (ISBN 0-937021-00-8). Sagamore Bks MI.

Baptism & Eucharist: Ecumenical Convergence in Celebration. Ed. by Max Thurian & Geoffrey Wainwright. LC 84-169338. 268p. (Orig.). 1984. pap. 11.95 (ISBN 0-8028-0005-X). Eerdmans.

Baptism & Fullness: The Work of the Holy Spirit Today. John R. Stott. LC 76-21457. 1976. pap. 2.95 (ISBN 0-87784-648-0). Inter-Varsity.

Baptism & Gifts of the Holy Spirit. Merrill F. Unger. LC 74-2931. 192p. 1974. pap. text ed. 6.95 (ISBN 0-8024-0467-7). Moody.

Baptism & Restoration Movement. Bob L. Ross. 1979. pap. 1.00 (ISBN 0-686-28281-7). Pilgrim Pubns.

Baptism & Temptation of Christ: The First Day of a Medieval French Passion Play. Ed. by John R. Elliott, Jr. & Graham A. Runnalls. LC 78-6564. 1978. 24.50x (ISBN 0-300-02199-2). Yale U Pr.

Baptism & the Family. Gerard P. Weber et al. 1972. pap. 2.64 (ISBN 0-02-649000-5). Benziger Pub Co.

Baptism: Christ's Act in the Church. Lawrence H. Stookey. LC 81-17590. 208p. (Orig.). 1982. pap. 9.95 (ISBN 0-687-02364-5). Abingdon.

Baptism, Filling & Gifts of the Holy Spirit. W. A. Criswell. 192p. 1973. pap. 4.95 (ISBN 0-310-22751-8, 18351P). Zondervan.

Baptism: How Important Is It? Henry M. Morris, 3rd. LC 77-87954. 1978. pap. 1.95 (ISBN 0-916406-72-5). Accent Bks.

Baptism in the Holy Spirit. Willard Cantelon. 34p. 1951. pap. 1.00 (ISBN 0-88243-692-9, 02-0692). Gospel Pub.

Baptism in the Holy Spirit. Derek Prince. 1966. pap. 1.95 (ISBN 0-934920-07-9, B-19). Derek Prince.

Baptism in the Holy Spirit: A Re-Examination of the New Testament Teaching on the Gift of the Spirit in Relation to Pentacostalism Today. James D. Dunn. LC 77-3995. 256p. 1977. pap. 8.95 (ISBN 0-664-24140-9). Westminster.

Baptism in the New Testament. G. R. Beasley-Murray. 434p. 1973. pap. 8.95 (ISBN 0-8028-1493-X). Eerdmans.

Baptism in the New Testament. Oscar Cullmann. LC 78-6937. 84p. 1978. pap. 5.95 (ISBN 0-664-24219-7). Westminster.

Baptism: It's Mode & Subjects. Alexander Carson. Ed. by John Young. LC 80-8067. 550p. 1981. 18.95 (ISBN 0-8254-2324-4). Kregel.

Baptism of a Child. (In Envelope). Set of 10 16.95 (ISBN 0-664-29066-3). Westminster.

Baptism of Resistance-Blood & Celebration: A Road to Wholeness in the Nuclear Age. John P. Egan & Paul D. Colford. 1983. pap. 5.95 (ISBN 0-89622-164-4). Twenty-Third.

Baptism of the Holy Spirit. Jack Van Impe. 45p. 1985. pap. 1.95 (ISBN 0-934803-02-1). J Van Impe.

Baptism, Penance, Eucharist, & Confirmation. 9.95 (ISBN 0-89837-020-5, PL306, Pub. by Pflaum). Peter Li.

Baptism: The Church's Troubled Water. D. L. Norbie. 1985. pap. 1.75 (ISBN 0-937396-66-4). Walterick Pubs.

Baptism with the Holy Spirit. Perry A. Gaspard. 1983. pap. 1.00 (ISBN 0-931867-02-9). Abundant Life Pubns.

Baptism with the Holy Spirit. R. A. Torrey. 96p. 1972. pap. 2.95 (ISBN 0-87123-029-1). Bethany Hse.

Baptismal Regeneration. C. H. Spurgeon. 1979. 1.50 (ISBN 0-686-09097-7). Pilgrim Pubns.

Baptisms & Burials From the Records of Christ Church, Philadelphia, 1709-1760. Charles R. Hildeburn. LC 81-86323. 231p. 1982. Repr. of 1893 ed. 15.00 (ISBN 0-8063-0979-2). Genealog Pub.

Baptisms from Sixteen Thirty-Nine to Eighteen Hundred in the Reformed Dutch Church, New York, 2 Vols. Ed. by Thomas G. Evans & Toblas A. Wright. 1298p. 1968. Repr. of 1902 ed. 75.00 (ISBN 0-8398-0152-1). Parnassus Imprints.

Baptist Atlas. Albert W. Wardin, Jr. LC 79-52541. (Illus.). 1980. 5.50 (ISBN 0-8054-6551-0). Broadman.

Baptist Beliefs. Edgar Y. Mullins. 5.95 (ISBN 0-8170-0014-3); pap. 4.95. Judson.

Baptist Bibliography, Vols. 1-25. Edward C. Starr. Incl. Vol. 1. Authors A. 1947. 13.25x (ISBN 0-910056-00-5); Vol. 2. Authors B-Biloxi. 1952. 16.55x (ISBN 0-910056-01-3); Vol. 3. Authors Bin-Bz. 1953. 21.20x (ISBN 0-910056-02-1); Vol. 4. Authors C-Colby. 1954. 16.55x (ISBN 0-910056-03-X); Vol. 5. Authors Colchester-Cz. 1957. 13.25x (ISBN 0-910056-04-8); Vol. 6. Authors D. 1958. 13.25x (ISBN 0-910056-05-6); Vol. 7. Authors E-Flynt. 1961. 13.25x (ISBN 0-910056-06-4); Vol. 8. Authors Fo-Glazier. 1963. 16.55x (ISBN 0-910056-07-2); Vol. 9. Authors Gleason-Halko. 1964. 16.55x (ISBN 0-910056-08-0); Vol. 10. Authors Hall-Hill, Joseph. 1965. 16.55x (ISBN 0-910056-09-9); Vol. 11. Authors Hill, Kizard. 1966. 13.25x (ISBN 0-910056-10-2); Vol. 12. Authors J. 1967. 13.25x (ISBN 0-910056-11-0); Vol. 13. Authors K-Layton. 1968. 16.55x (ISBN 0-910056-12-9); Vol. 14. Authors Lea-McGuire. 1969. 16.55x (ISBN 0-910056-13-7); Vol. 15. Authors McIlvain-Merrill. 1970. 16.55x (ISBN 0-910056-14-5); Vol. 16. Authors Merrimac-Nevin. **1971. 16.55x (ISBN 0-910056-15-3); Vol. 17. Authors New-Pastors. 1972. 16.55x (ISBN 0-910056-16-1); Vol. 18. Authors Pate-Poynton. 1972. 16.55x (ISBN 0-910056-17-X); Vol. 19. Authors Pra-Rives. 1973. 16.55x (ISBN 0-910056-18-8); Vol. 20. Authors Ro-Sardis. 1974. 13.25x (ISBN 0-685-24442-3); Vol. 21. Authors Sare-Smith, S. 1974. 16.55x (ISBN 0-685-24443-1); Vol. 22. Authors Smith, T.-Steude. 1975. 16.55x (ISBN 0-685-24444-X); Vol. 23. Authors Steven-Torbet. 1976. 16.55x (ISBN 0-685-24445-8); Vol. 24. Authors Torey-Wa. 1976. 16.55x (ISBN 0-685-24446-6); Vol. 25. Authors We-Z. 1976. 21.20x (ISBN 0-910056-24-2). Set. 400.00. Am Baptist.**

Baptist Catechism. Paul K. Jewett. pap. 0.85x (ISBN 0-9602638-4-5). Fuller Theol Soc.

Baptist Church Manual. J. Newton Brown. pap. 1.25 (ISBN 0-8170-0015-1). Judson.

Baptist Church Manual. rev. ed. James M. Pendleton. 1966. Repr. of 1867 ed. 8.50 (ISBN 0-8054-2510-1). Broadman.

Baptist Confessions of Faith. William L. Lumpkin. (Illus.). 1959. 17.95 (ISBN 0-8170-0016-X). Judson.

Baptist Congregation. Stanley J. Grenz. 128p. 1985. pap. 7.95 (ISBN 0-8170-1083-1). Judson.

Baptist Convictions. Winthrop S. Hudson. pap. 1.50 (ISBN 0-8170-0295-2). Judson.

Baptist Deacon. Robert E. Naylor. 1955. 7.50 (ISBN 0-8054-3501-8). Broadman.

Baptist Distinctives: A Pattern for Service. R. Dowd Davis. 64p. (Orig.). 1986. pap. 3.95 (ISBN 0-913029-11-4). Stevens Bk Pr.

Baptist Doctrines & History. D. N. Jackson. 1974. pap. 3.50 (ISBN 0-89114-003-4). Baptist Pub Hse.

Baptist Ecclesiology: An Original Anthology. William H. Allison & W. W. Barnes. Ed. by Edwin S. Gaustad. LC 79-52582. (Baptist Tradition Ser.). 1980. lib. bdg. 21.00x (ISBN 0-405-12449-X). Ayer Co Pubs.

Baptist Heritage: Four Centuries of Baptist Witness. H. Leon McBeth. (Orig.). 1987. 24.95 (ISBN 0-8054-6569-3). Broadman.

Baptist History of the North Pacific Coast. J. C. Baker. Ed. by Edwin S. Gaustad. LC 79-52589. (Baptist Tradition Ser.). (Illus.). 1980. Repr. of 1912 ed. lib. bdg. 48.50x (ISBN 0-405-12456-2). Ayer Co Pubs.

Baptist History Sourcebook. Morgan W. Patterson. cancelled (ISBN 0-8054-6568-5). Broadman.

Baptist Life & Thought: Sixteen Hundred to Nineteen Eighty. Ed. by William Brackney. 448p. 1983. 12.95 (ISBN 0-8170-0959-0). Judson.

Baptist Manual of Polity & Practice. Norman H. Maring & Winthrop S. Hudson. 10.95 (ISBN 0-8170-0299-5). Judson.

Baptist Ministerial Directory. Ed. by George W. Lasher. 1987. 45.00. Banner Pr Al.

Baptist Missions in Nagaland. Joseph Puthenpurakal. 1984. 22.50x (ISBN 0-8364-1138-2, Pub. by Mukhopadhyaya). South Asia Bks.

Baptist Piety: The Last Will & Testimony of Obadiah Holmes. Edwin S. Gaustad. LC 79-52570. (Baptist Tradition Ser.). 1980. lib. bdg. 17.00x (ISBN 0-405-12439-2). Ayer Co Pubs.

Baptist Polity as I See It. James L. Sullivan. LC 83-70940. 1983. 9.95 (ISBN 0-8054-6575-8). Broadman.

Baptist Source Book. A. Baker. LC 66-22076. 1974. pap. 7.50 (ISBN 0-8054-6519-7). Broadman.

Baptist Succession. D. B. Ray. 1984. Repr. of 1912 ed. 22.00 (ISBN 0-317-11348-8). Church History.

Baptist Treasury. Ed. by Sydnor L. Stealey & Edwin S. Gaustad. LC 79-52607. (Baptist Tradition Ser.). 1980. Repr. of 1958 ed. lib. bdg. 27.50x (ISBN 0-405-12472-4). Ayer Co Pubs.

Baptist Way of Life. rev ed. Brooks Hays & John E. Steely. LC 81-11245. 220p. 1981. 14.95 (ISBN 0-86554-008-X, MUP-H13). Mercer Univ Pr.

Baptistery of Pisa. Christine Smith. LC 77-94715. (Outstanding Dissertations in the Fine Arts Ser.). (Illus.). 432p. 1978. lib. bdg. 53.00 (ISBN 0-8240-3249-7). Garland Pub.

Baptistry of Frejus: A Restoration Based on the Architectural & Historical Evidence. Paul A. Goettelmann. (Illus.). 75p. 1984. Repr. of 1933 ed. 25.00x (ISBN 0-939738-23-6). Zubal Inc.

Baptists. John E. Skoglund. 1967. pap. 1.50 (ISBN 0-8170-0386-X). Judson.

Baptists & Disciples of Christ. E. Roberts Thomson. 195p. 1948. pap. 2.95 (ISBN 0-87921-004-4). Attic Pr.

Baptists & Public Affairs in the Province of Canada: 1840-1867. Walter G. Pitman. Ed. by Edwin S. Gaustad. LC 79-52576. (Baptist Tradition Ser.). 1980. lib. bdg. 21.00x (ISBN 0-405-12444-9). Ayer Co Pubs.

Baptists & the American Republic. Joseph M. Dawson. Ed. by Edwin S. Gaustad. LC 79-52584. (Baptist Tradition Ser.). 1980. Repr. of 1956 ed. lib. bdg. 21.00x (ISBN 0-405-12451-1). Ayer Co Pubs.

Baptists & the American Tradition. Robert C. Newman. LC 76-7166. 1976. pap. 1.95 (ISBN 0-87227-008-4). Reg Baptist.

Baptists & the Bible. Russ Bush & Tom Nettles. LC 80-11694. 1980. pap. 10.95 (ISBN 0-8024-0474-X). Moody.

Baptists: The Bible, Church Order & the Churches. original anthology ed. Ed. by Edwin S. Gaustad. LC 79-52587. (Baptist Tradition Ser.). 1980. lib. bdg. 46.00x (ISBN 0-405-12454-6). Ayer Co Pubs.

Baptists Tradition Series, 40 bks, Vols. 1-22. Ed. by Edwin S. Gaustad. (Illus.). 1980. Repr. Set. lib. bdg. 1323.00x (ISBN 0-405-12437-6). Ayer Co Pubs.

Baptized in Blood: The Religion of the Lost Cause, 1865-1920. Charles R. Wilson. LC 80-126. 264p. 1980. 21.95x (ISBN 0-8203-0515-4); pap. 8.00x (ISBN 0-8203-0681-9). U of Ga Pr.

Baptized in the Spirit & Spiritual Gifts. Steve B. Clark. 1967. pap. 2.95 (ISBN 0-89283-033-6). Servant.

Baptized Inflation: A Critique of "Christian" Keynesian. Ian Hodge. Date not set. price not set (ISBN 0-930462-13-0). Am Bur Eco Res.

Baptizing Community: Christian Initiation & the Local Congregation. A. Theodore Eastman. 144p. (Orig.). 1982. pap. 9.95 (ISBN 0-8164-2419-5, HarpR). Har-Row.

Bar-Bat Mitzvah Planbook. Jane Lewit & Ellen R. Epstein. LC 81-48459. (Illus.). 176p. 1982. 18.95 (ISBN 0-8128-2861-5). Stein & Day.

Bar Mitzvah. Howard Greenfeld. LC 81-5104. (Illus.). 32p. 1981. 7.95 (ISBN 0-03-053861-0). H Holt & Co.

Bar Mitzvah. Stuart Schoenfeld et al. LC 85-4412. (Illus.). 192p. 1985. 50.00 (ISBN 0-385-19826-4). Doubleday.

Bar Mitzvah, Bat Mitzvah: How Jewish Boys & Girls Come of Age. Bert Metter. LC 83-23230. (Illus.). 64p. (Orig.). 1984. PLB 10.95 (ISBN 0-89919-149-5, Clarion); pap. 4.95 (ISBN 0-89919-292-0). HM.

Bar Mitzvah Book. (Illus.). 64p. 1987. 15.95 (ISBN 0-88363-088-5). H L Levin.

Bar Mitzvah Illustrated. 8th ed. Ed. by Abraham I. Katsh. LC 76-23713. (Illus.). 1976. 18.95 (ISBN 0-88400-048-6). Shengold.

Bar Mitzvah Mother's Manual. Alice K. Lanckton. (Illus.). 304p. 1986. pap. 6.95 (ISBN 0-87052-283-3). Hippocrene Bks.

Barabbas. Marie Corelli. pap. 5.95 (ISBN 0-910122-00-8). Amherst Pr.

Barabbas. Par Lagerkvist. Tr. by Alain Blair. (YA) 1955. pap. 2.95 (ISBN 0-394-70134-8, Vin). Random.

Barabudur: Esquisse d'une histoire du bouddhisme fondee sur la critique archeologique des textes, 2 vols. in 1. Paul Mus. Ed. by Kees W. Bolle. LC 77-79146. (Mythology Ser.). (Fr.). 1978. Repr. of 1935 ed. lib. bdg. 82.50x (ISBN 0-405-10555-X). Ayer Co Pubs.

Baraka: Movement of Spiritual Inner Awareness. John-Roger. 1978. pap. 5.00 (ISBN 0-914829-01-7). Baraka Bk.

Baralam & Yewasef - Baralaam & Joasaph, 3 pts. in 2 vols. Ed. by Ernest A. Budge. LC 73-18832. (Illus.). Repr. of 1923 ed. Set. 67.50 (ISBN 0-404-11300-1). AMS Pr.

Barb, Please Wake Up! Roy B. Zuck. 128p. 1983. pap. 2.75 (ISBN 0-89323-042-1). Bible Memory.

Barbarians, Christians & Muslims. Trevor Cairns. LC 69-11024. (Cambridge Introduction to the History of Mankind Ser.: Bk. 3). 1970. 8.95 (ISBN 0-521-07360-X). Cambridge U Pr.

Barbarians, Christians, & Muslims. Ed. by Trevor Cairns. LC 73-20213. (Cambridge Introduction to History Ser.). (Illus.). 104p. 1975. PLB 10.95 (ISBN 0-8225-0803-6). Lerner Pubns.

Barclay in Brief. Eleanore P. Mather. 1983. pap. 2.50x (ISBN 0-87574-028-6, 028). Pendle Hill.

Bardo Teachings: The Way of Death & Rebirth. Venerable L. Lodo. Ed. by Nancy Clark & Caroline M. Parke. LC 82-21372. (Illus.). 76p. 1982. pap. text ed. 5.95 (ISBN 0-910165-00-9). KDK Pubns.

Bards & Saints. William K. Magee. LC 76-8220. 1976. Repr. of 1906 ed. lib. bdg. 17.50 (ISBN 0-8414-3976-1). Folcroft.

Barefoot in the Palace. John T. Ball. 1985. 6.25 (ISBN 0-89536-748-3, 5854). CSS of Ohio.

Bargain & the Bridle: The General Union of the Israelites of France, 1941-1944. Cynthia J. Haft. 150p. (Orig.). 1983. pap. 14.95 (ISBN 0-914153-00-5). Dialog.

Barhebraeus' Scholia on the Old Testament Pt. 1: Genesis 2nd Samuel. Ed. by Martin Sprengling & William C. Graham. LC 32-461. (Oriental Institute Pubns. Ser: No. 13). 1931. 28.00x (ISBN 0-226-62107-3). U of Chicago Pr.

Barlaam & Iosaph. Saint John Damascene. (Loeb Classical Library: No. 34). 13.95x (ISBN 0-674-99038-2). Harvard U Pr.

Barmen Confession: Papers from the Seattle Assembly. Ed. by Hubert G. Locke. LC 86-23874. (Toronto Studies in Theology: Vol. 26). 370p. 1987. 59.95x (ISBN 0-88946-770-6). E Mellen.

Barmen Theological Declaration of 1934: Archeology of a Confessional Text, Vol. 24. Rolf Ahlers. (Toronto Studies in Theology: No. 23). 1986. 59.95 (ISBN 0-88946-768-4). E Mellen.

Barnabas Life-Style. Donald A. Atkinson. (Orig.). 1987. pap. 3.25 (ISBN 0-8054-5728-3). Broadman.

Barnes' Notes on the New Testament. Albert Barnes. LC 62-8727. 1776p. 1966. 39.95 (ISBN 0-8254-2200-0). Kregel.

Barnes' Notes on the Old & New Testaments, 14 vols. Albert Barnes. 249.50 (ISBN 0-8010-0834-4). Baker Bk.

Baron James: The Rise of the French Rothschilds. Anka Muhlstein. LC 84-40015. 224p. 1984. pap. 7.95 (ISBN 0-394-72608-1, Vin). Random.

Baroque Cartouches for Designers & Artists. Johann U. Krauss. (Pictorial Archive Ser). (Illus.). 1970. pap. 6.50 (ISBN 0-486-22222-5). Dover.

Barren Fig Tree. John Bunyan. pap. 1.25 (ISBN 0-685-19824-3). Reiner.

Barren Temple & the Withered Tree. William R. Telford. (Journal for the Study of the New Testament, Supplement Ser.: No. 1). 336p. 1980. text ed. 21.95x (ISBN 0-905774-20-5, Pub by JSOT Pr England). Eisenbrauns.

Barriers to Ecumenism: The Holy See & the World Council on Social Questions. Thomas S. Derr. LC 82-18761. 112p. (Orig.). 1983. pap. 7.95 (ISBN 0-88344-031-8). Orbis Bks.

Barth. A. D. Polman. (Modern Thinkers Ser.). pap. 2.25 (ISBN 0-87552-580-6). Presby & Reformed.

Barth-Bultmann Letters, Nineteen Twenty-Two to Nineteen Sixty-Six. Karl Barth & Rudolf Bultmann. Tr. by Geoffrey W. Bromiley. 224p. 1981. 13.95 (ISBN 0-8028-3560-0). Eerdmans.

Barthian Theology. John McConnachie. LC 72-2493. (Select Bibliography Reprint Ser). 1972. Repr. of 1933 ed. 19.00 (ISBN 0-8369-6861-1). Ayer Co Pubs.

Bartholomew De Las Casas: His Life, His Apostolate, & His Writings. Francis A. MacNutt. LC 70-172712. Repr. of 1909 ed. 32.45 (ISBN 0-404-07146-5). AMS Pr.

Bartolome de las Casas. F. A. MacNutt. 59.95 (ISBN 0-87968-708-8). Gordon Pr.

Barton W. Stone. Daniel D. Schantz. (Restoration Booklets Ser.). (Illus., Orig.). 1984. pap. 0.75 (ISBN 0-87239-775-0, 3295). Standard Pub.

Baruch Ata Befi Hataf: Illustrated Prayers & Blessings for Young Children. Illus. by Zev Lipman. (Illus.). 4.95 (ISBN 0-685-84974-0). Feldheim.

Barukh Kurzweil & Modern Hebrew Literature. James S. Diamond. LC 82-16770. (Brown Judaic Studies). 232p. 1983. pap. 18.00 (ISBN 0-89130-595-5, 14 00 39). Scholars Pr GA.

Bas-Reliefs from the Temple of Rameses One at Abydos, 2 vols in 1. Herbert E. Winlock. Incl. Temple of Rameses One at Abydos. LC 72-2519. (Metropolitan Museum of Art Publications in Reprint). (Illus.). 1972. Repr. of 1937 ed. 20.00 (ISBN 0-685-32631-4). Ayer Co Pubs.

Bases Biblicas De la Etica. J. E. Giles. 1983. Repr. of 1979 ed. 4.25 (ISBN 0-311-46028-3). Casa Bautista.

Bases de la Fe Premilenial. Charles C. Ryrie. Orig. Title: Basis of the Premillennial Faith. (Span.). 224p. 1984. pap. 3.95 (ISBN 0-8254-1626-4). Kregel.

Bases of Tantra Sadhana. Parasurama. Tr. by M. P. Pandit. (Sanskrit.). 52p. 1980. 2.00 (ISBN 0-941524-02-7). Lotus Light.

Bases of Yoga. Sri Aurobindo. 108p. 1983. pap. 3.50 (ISBN 0-89744-012-9). Auromere.

Bases of Yoga. Sri Aurobindo. 168p. 1981. pap. 2.00 (ISBN 0-89071-309-X, Pub. by Sri Aurobindo Ashram India). Matagiri.

Ba'sha'ar: Yahadus & Middos Text & Workbook. Ita Epstein. (Illus.). text ed. 4.00 (ISBN 0-914131-02-8, A10). Torah Umesorah.

Basic Beliefs. Donald E. Demaray. 1958. pap. 4.50 (ISBN 0-8010-2827-2). Baker Bk.

Basic Beliefs: A Woman's Workshop on the Christian Faith. Carolyn Nystrom. (Woman's Workshop Ser.). 124p. 1986. pap. 3.95 (ISBN 0-310-41971-9). Zondervan.

Basic Beliefs of Christians. Douglas Beyer. 64p. 1981. pap. 2.95 (ISBN 0-8170-0896-9). Judson.

Basic Beliefs: The Religious Philosophies of Mankind. Ed. by Johnson E. Fairchild. 11.50x (ISBN 0-911378-03-0). Sheridan.

Basic Bible Beliefs. M. A. Tomlinson. 1961. pap. 3.25 (ISBN 0-934942-01-3). White Wing Pub.

Basic Bible Dictionary. Velda Matthews & Ray Beard. Ed. by Bob Korth. (Illus.). 128p. (Orig.). 1984. pap. 7.95 (ISBN 0-87239-720-3, 2770). Standard Pub.

Basic Bible Doctrines. Millard F. Day. 1953. pap. 3.50 (ISBN 0-8024-0239-9). Moody.

Basic Bible Doctrines for Victorious Living. K. A. Whaley. 87p. 1981. pap. 7.95 (ISBN 0-686-35778-7). First Baptist.

Basic Bible Doctrines for Victorious Living. K. A. Whaley. 1981. pap. 7.95x (ISBN 0-686-40713-X). Freedom Univ-FSP.

Basic Bible Studies. Francis Schaeffer. 1972. pap. 2.95 (ISBN 0-8423-0103-8). Tyndale.

Basic Bible Study. Keith L. Brooks. (Teach Yourself the Bible Ser.). 1961. pap. 2.75 (ISBN 0-8024-0478-2). Moody.

Basic Bible Study. Douglas LeRoy. LC 78-65822. 72p. (Orig.). 1978. pap. text ed. 1.25 (ISBN 0-87148-699-7). Pathway Pr.

Basic Bible Study Library, 2 vols. Incl. Zondervan Pictorial Bible Dictionary. Ed. by Merrill C. Tenney. (Illus.); Matthew Henry's Commentary on the Whole Bible. Matthew Henry. Set. slip case 48.90. Zondervan.

Basic Bible Survey. Elsie Howard. LC 82-19686. 96p. (Orig.). 1983. pap. 2.95 (ISBN 0-87239-572-3, 3210). Standard Pub.

Basic Bible Truths for New Converts. Ralph O. Burns. 30p. 1978. pap. 0.60 (ISBN 0-87227-007-6). Reg Baptist.

Basic Biblical Geography. Denis Baly. LC 86-45206. 80p. 1987. pap. 4.95 (ISBN 0-8006-1922-6, 1-1922). Fortress.

Basic Bibliographic Guide for New Testament. David M. Scholer. pap. 3.95 (ISBN 0-8028-1503-0). Eerdmans.

Basic Book List for Church Libraries. 2nd rev ed. Bernard E. Deitrick. LC 77-4093. 1983. pap. 3.95x (ISBN 0-915324-10-5); pap. 3.00 members. CSLA.

Basic Buddhism. Kevin O'Neil. 41p. (Orig.). 1981. pap. 5.00 (ISBN 0-86627-006-X). Crises Res Pr.

Basic Catechism. Daughters of St Paul. 1980. 3.00 (ISBN 0-8198-0622-6); pap. 2.00 (ISBN 0-8198-0623-4). Dghtrs St Paul.

Basic Catechism Manual, Vol. I. Daughters of St. Paul. 1981. pap. 5.95 (ISBN 0-8198-1107-6). Dghtrs St Paul.

Basic Catechism Manual, Vol. II. Daughters of St. Paul. 1981. pap. 5.95 (ISBN 0-8198-1106-8). Dghtrs St Paul.

Basic Catholic Beliefs for Today: The Creed Explained. Leonard F. Badia. LC 84-14632. 170p. (Orig.). 1984. pap. 8.95 (ISBN 0-8189-0469-0). Alba.

Basic Catholic Dictionary. Daniel L. Lowery. LC 85-80600. (Orig.). 1986. pap. 3.95 (ISBN 0-89243-241-1). Liguori Pubns.

Basic Choral Concepts. Daniel Moe. 31p. 1972. pap. 4.00 (ISBN 0-8066-1216-9, 11-9080). Augsburg.

Basic Christian Doctrines. Ed. by Carl F. Henry. (Twin Brooks Ser). pap. 8.95 (ISBN 0-8010-4033-7). Baker Bk.

Basic Christian Ethics. Paul Ramsey. LC 78-56925. 424p. 1980. pap. text ed. 14.00x (ISBN 0-226-70383-5). U of Chicago Pr.

Basic Christian Faith. C. Donald Cole. LC 84-72008. 256p. (Orig.). 1985. pap. 6.95 (ISBN 0-89107-338-8, Crossway Bks). Good News.

Basic Christian Teachings. Rolf E. Aaseng. LC 81-52276. 112p. (Orig.). 1982. pap. 5.50 (ISBN 0-8066-1908-2, 10-0547). Augsburg.

Basic Christian Training. Jean Gibson. (Believer's Bible Lessons Ser.). 1980. pap. 5.95 (ISBN 0-937396-06-0). Walterick Pubs.

Basic Christianity. John R. Stott. 1957. pap. 2.95 (ISBN 0-8028-1189-2). Eerdmans.

Basic Christianity. John R. Stott. LC 58-13513. (Orig.). pap. 3.95 (ISBN 0-87784-690-1). Inter-Varsity.

Basic Communities: A Practical Guide for Renewing Neighborhood Churches. Thomas Maney. 96p. (Orig.). 1984. pap. 5.95 (ISBN 0-86683-857-0, 8411, HarpR). Har-Row.

Basic Doctrines of the Bible. A. Schuetze. 1969. pap. 2.50 (ISBN 0-8100-0016-4, 09N0921). Northwest Pub.

Basic Ecclesial Communities: The Evangelization of the Poor. Alvaro Barreiro. Tr. by Barbara Campbell from Portuguese. LC 81-16898. Orig. Title: Comunidades Eclesiais De Base E Evangelizacao Dos Pobres. 96p. (Orig.). 1982. pap. 5.95 (ISBN 0-88344-026-1). Orbis Bks.

Basic Ecclesiastical Communities. Marcello C. De Azevedo. Tr. by John Drury. 1987. write for info. (ISBN 0-87840-430-9); pap. write for info. (ISBN 0-87840-448-1). Georgetown U Pr.

Basic Encyclopedia for Youth Ministry. Dennis C. Benson & Bill Wolfe. LC 81-81967. (Illus.). 352p. 1981. 16.95 (ISBN 0-936664-04-5). Group Bks.

Basic Encyclopedia of Jewish Proverbs, Quotations, Folk Wisdom. Alcalay. 19.95 (ISBN 0-87677-153-3). Hartmore.

Basic Equities of the Palestine Problem. Simon H. Rifkind et al. Ed. by Moshe Davis. LC 77-70736. (America & the Holy Land Ser.). 1977. Repr. of 1947 ed. lib. bdg. 17.00x (ISBN 0-405-10279-8). Ayer Co Pubs.

Basic Ideas of Occult Wisdom. Anna K. Winner. LC 75-116528. (Orig.). 1970. pap. 4.50 (ISBN 0-8356-0391-1, Quest). Theos Pub Hse.

Basic Ideas of Science of Mind. Ernest Holmes. 96p. 1957. pap. 4.50 (ISBN 0-911336-23-0). Sci of Mind.

Basic Introduction to the New Testament. John R. Stott. pap. 5.95 (ISBN 0-8028-1190-6). Eerdmans.

Basic Judaism. Milton Steinberg. LC 47-30768. 1965. pap. 3.95 (ISBN 0-15-610698-1, Harv). HarBraceJ.

Basic Judaism. Milton Steinberg. 180p. 1987. 22.00 (ISBN 0-87668-975-6). Aronson.

Basic Leader Skills: Handbook for Church Leaders. Richard E. Rusbuldt. 64p. 1981. pap. 5.95 (ISBN 0-8170-0920-5). Judson.

Basic Library for Bible Students. Warren W. Wiersbe. (Orig.). 1981. pap. 2.95 (ISBN 0-8010-9641-3). Baker Bk.

Basic Luther. Martin Luther. 1984. pap. 14.95 (ISBN 0-87243-131-2). Templegate.

Basic Principles of Ayurveda. Bhagwan Dash & Lalitesh Kashyap. (Illus.). 628p. 1980. 44.95x (ISBN 0-940500-34-5). Asia Bk Corp.

Basic Principles of Biblical Counseling. Lawrence J. Crabb, Jr. 160p. 1975. 9.95 (ISBN 0-310-22560-4, 10159). Zondervan.

Basic Principles of Biblical Counseling. Lawrence J. Crabb, Jr. 1986. 9.95 (ISBN 0-88469-186-1). BMH Bks.

Basic Principles of Prayer. Perry A. Gaspard. 1984. pap. 2.00 (ISBN 0-931867-07-X). Abundant Life Pubns.

Basic Questions in Theology: Collected Essays, Vol. I. Wolfhart Pannenberg. LC 82-15984. 256p. 1983. pap. 12.95 (ISBN 0-664-24466-1). Westminster.

Basic Questions in Theology: Collected Essays, Vol. II. Wolfhart Pannenberg. LC 82-15984. 258p. 1983. pap. 12.95 (ISBN 0-664-24467-X). Westminster.

Basic Reform Judaism. William B. Silverman. LC 69-15531. 308p. 1970. 15.00 (ISBN 0-8022-2332-X). Philos Lib.

Basic Scheme for Priestly Training: Sacred Congregation for Catholic Education. 1973. pap. 0.50 (ISBN 0-8198-0251-4). Dghtrs St Paul.

Basic Skills for Christian Counselors: An Introduction for Pastoral Ministers. Richard P. Vaughan. 192p. (Orig.). 1987. pap. 8.95 (ISBN 0-8091-2857-8). Paulist Pr.

Basic Skills for Church Teachers. Donald L. Griggs. (Griggs Educational Resources Ser.). 112p. 1985. pap. 7.95 (ISBN 0-687-02488-9). Abingdon.

Basic Spiritual Metaphysics. Paul L. Peck. LC 78-61984. 1978. 14.50 (ISBN 0-87881-079-X). Mojave Bks.

Basic Teacher Skills: Handbook for Church School Teachers. Richard E. Rusbuldt. 144p. 1981. pap. 5.95 (ISBN 0-8170-0919-1). Judson.

Basic Theology. Charles C. Ryrie. 544p. 1986. 16.95 (ISBN 0-89693-814-X). Victor Bks.

Basic Theosophy. Hodson. 18.95 (ISBN 0-8356-7560-2). Theos Pub Hse.

Basic Training. Richard Kennedy. 100p. 1987. three-ring binder 12.95 (ISBN 0-89265-104-0). Randall Hse.

Basic Training: Plain Talk on the Key Truths of the Faith. R. C. Sproul. 176p. (Orig.). 1982. pap. 5.95 (ISBN 0-310-44921-9, 12371P). Zondervan.

Basic Types of Pastoral Care & Counseling. Howard Clinebell. 464p. 1984. 17.95 (ISBN 0-687-02492-7). Abingdon.

Basic United Methodist Beliefs: (An Evangelical View) Ed. by James V. Heidinger, II. 128p. 1986. pap. 4.95 (ISBN 0-917851-01-3). Forum Script.

Basic Writings of Mo Tzu, Hsun Tzu, & Han Fei Tzu. Ed. & tr. by Burton Watson. LC 67-16170. (Records of Civilization, Sources & Studies: No. 74). 1967. 20.00x (ISBN 0-231-02515-7). Columbia U Pr.
Basics of Assembly Life. G. Steidl. pap. 3.75 (ISBN 0-88172-126-3). Believers Bkshelf.
Basics of the Christian Life. rev. ed. George Sweeting. (Moody Press Electives Ser.). 1983. pap. 3.95 (ISBN 0-8024-0259-3); Leader's Guide. pap. 2.50 (ISBN 0-8024-0309-3). Moody.
Basis for Christian Ethics. John Gallagher. 240p. (Orig.). 1985. pap. 9.95 (ISBN 0-8091-2690-7). Paulist Pr.
Basis for the Peace to Come. National Study Conference of the Churches on a Just & Durable Peace 1st Ohio Wesleyan University 1942. Ed. by Francis J. McConnell. 9.75 (ISBN 0-8369-7277-5, 8076). Ayer Co Pubs.
Basis of Early Christian Theism. Lawrence T. Cole. lib. bdg. 59.95 (ISBN 0-8490-1478-6). Gordon Pr.
Basis of the Mysticism of St. Thomas Aquinas. C. Pepler. 1977. lib. bdg. 59.95 (ISBN 0-8490-1479-4). Gordon Pr.
Basis of the Premillennial Faith. Charles C. Ryrie. 1954. pap. 4.95 (ISBN 0-87213-741-4). Loizeaux.
Bastion of Faith. 3rd ed. Avraham Fishelis. 256p. 1980. 9.00 (ISBN 0-9605560-1-X). A Fishelis.
Bats, Cats, & Sacred Cows. Tamara Wilcox. LC 77-10834. (Myth, Magic & Superstition). (Illus.). 1977. PLB 14.65 (ISBN 0-8172-1026-1). Raintree Pubs.
Battle. Ed. by John Duckworth et al. (Pacesetter Ser.). 64p. 1987. tchr's. ed. 7.95. Cook.
Battle for Creation: Acts, Facts, Impacts, Vol. 2. Henry M. Morris & Duane T. Gish. LC 74-75429. (Illus.). 1976. pap. 5.95 (ISBN 0-89051-020-2). Master Bks.
Battle for Religious Liberty. Lynn Buzzard & Samuel Ericcson. (Issues & Insight Ser.). (Orig.). 1982. pap. 6.95 (ISBN 0-89191-552-4, 55525). Cook.
Battle for the Family. Tim LaHaye. (Illus.). 256p. 1981. power ed. 6.95 (ISBN 0-8007-5117-5). Revell.
Battle for the Mind. Tim LaHaye. 224p. 1980. pap. 6.95 (ISBN 0-8007-5043-8, Power Bks). Revell.
Battle for the Trinity: The Debate over Inclusive God-Language. Donald G. Bloesch. 1985. 8.95 (ISBN 0-89283-230-4, Pub. by Vine Books). Servant.
Battle for Yanga. Bv. Ben Kendrick. LC 80-20643. 127p. 1980. pap. 3.95 (ISBN 0-87227-074-2). Reg Baptist.
Battling Anorexia. Anita Haney. (Orig.). 1986. pap. 5.95 (ISBN 0-89265-111-3). Randall Hse.
Battling the Hosts of Hell: Diary of an Exorcist. rev. ed. Win Worley. 1980. pap. 5.00 (ISBN 0-9601276-1-5). HBC.
Battling with Belief. Ray Thompson. 79p. (Orig.). 1984. pap. 6.95 (ISBN 0-85819-518-6, Pub. by JBCE). ANZ Religious Pubns.
Bauls: The Spiritual Vikings. S. C. Chakravarti. 1981. 10.00x (ISBN 0-8364-0671-0, Pub. by Mukhopadhyay India). South Asia Bks.
Bautismo. 2nd ed. H. C. Voorehoeve & Gordon H. Bennett. Tr. by Sara Bautista from Eng. (Serie Diamante). Tr. of Baptism. (Span., Illus.). 36p. 1982. pap. 0.85 (ISBN 0-942504-06-2). Overcomer Pr.
Bavarian Rococo Church: Between Faith & Aestheticism. Karsten Harries. LC 82-1116. (Illus.). 304p. 1983. text ed. 42.00x (ISBN 0-300-02720-6). Yale U Pr.
Bay Area Jewish Forum Hagadah. rev. ed. Ed. by Ralph M. Kramer & Philip Schild. (Illus.). 69p. 1985. 13.95 (ISBN 0-917883-00-4). Benmir Bks.
Bay Psalm Book. Wilberforce Eames. 1978. pap. 53.95 (ISBN 0-89102-098-5, Artemis). B Franklin.
Bayonets to Lhasa. Peter Fleming. LC 73-16737. (Illus.). 1974. Repr. of 1961 ed. lib. bdg. 22.50x (ISBN 0-8371-7216-0, FLBL). Greenwood.
Be a Better Parent. Mary M. Kern. LC 79-9098. 160p. 1979. pap. 6.95 (ISBN 0-664-24271-5). Westminster.
Be a Leader People Follow. David Hocking. LC 78-67854. 192p. 1979. pap. 5.95 (ISBN 0-8307-0680-1, 5411718). Regal.
Be a New Christian All Your Life. Raymond C. Ortlund. 192p. 1983. 5.95 (ISBN 0-8007-5119-1, Power Bks). Revell.
Be A Say a Fingerplay. Elaine Ward. 71p. (Orig.). 1982. pap. 5.95 (ISBN 0-940754-12-6). Ed Ministries.
Be Alert! Warren W. Wiersbe. 168p. 1984. pap. 5.95 (ISBN 0-89693-380-6). Victor Bks.
Be Alive. Warren Wiersbe. 156p. 1986. pap. 5.95 (ISBN 0-89693-359-8). Victor Bks.
Be As You Are: The Teachings of Sri Ramana Maharshi. Ed. by David Godman. 256p. 1985. pap. 8.95 (ISBN 1-85063-006-2, Ark Paperbks). Methuen Inc.
Be Challenged! rev. ed. Warren Wiersbe. LC 82-12404. 1982. pap. 3.50 (ISBN 0-8024-1080-4). Moody.
Be Complete. Warren Wiersbe. 160p. 1981. pap. 5.95 (ISBN 0-88207-257-9). Victor Bks.
Be Confident. Warren W. Wiersbe. 176p. 1982. pap. 5.95 (ISBN 0-88207-269-2). Victor Bks.
Be Diligent. Warren W. Wiersbe. 156p. 1987. pap. 5.95 (ISBN 0-89693-356-3). Victor Bks.
Be Domes Daege (Bede's de Die Judicii) Ed. by F. R. Lumby. (EETS OS Ser.: Vol. 65). Repr. of 1876 ed. 15.00 (ISBN 0-8115-3419-7). Kraus Repr.
Be Encouraged. Warren W. Wiersbe. 156p. 1984. pap. 5.95 (ISBN 0-88207-620-5). Victor Bks.
Be Faithful. Warren W. Wiersbe. 1981. pap. 5.95 (ISBN 0-88207-268-4). Victor Bks.
Be Filled Now. Roy Hession. 1968. pap. 1.50 (ISBN 0-87508-235-1). Chr Lit.
Be Free. Warren W. Wiersbe. LC 74-33824. 160p. 1975. pap. 5.95 (ISBN 0-88207-716-3). Victor Bks.
Be Fruitful, No. 9. Robert S. Maseroni. 1983. 0.80 (ISBN 0-89536-633-9, 0237). CSS of Ohio.
Be Happy - You Are Loved! Robert H. Schuller. 224p. 1986. 15.95 (ISBN 0-8407-5517-1). Nelson.
Be-Happy Attitudes. Robert Schuller. 1985. 12.95 (ISBN 0-8499-0363-7). Word Bks.
Be-Happy Attitudes. lg. print ed. Robert Schuller. 1986. 12.95 (ISBN 0-8499-3055-3). Word Bks.
Be Holy: God's First Call to Priests Today. Ed. by Tom Forrest. Orig. Title: Call to Holiness: World Retreat for Priests. (Illus.). 132p. 1987. pap. 5.95 (ISBN 0-937779-04-0). Greenlawn Pr.
Be Hopeful. Warren W. Wiersbe. 1982. pap. 5.95 (ISBN 0-88207-382-6). Victor Bks.
Be It Ever So Humble. Daisy Hepburn. LC 83-24603. (Life with Spice Bible Study Ser.). 1984. 2.95 (ISBN 0-8307-0943-6, 6101805). Regal.
Be Joyful: A Practical Study of Philippians. Warren W. Wiersbe. LC 74-76328. 130p. 1974. pap. 5.95 (ISBN 0-88207-705-8). Victor Bks.
Be Loyal: Formerly Title Meet Your King. Warren Wiersbe. LC 79-92552. 216p. 1980. pap. 5.95 (ISBN 0-88207-799-6). Victor Bks.
Be Master of Yourself. Robert L. Backman. LC 86-2047. 227p. 1986. 9.95 (ISBN 0-87579-033-X). Deseret Bk.
Be Mature. Warren W. Wiersbe. LC 78-52558. 176p. 1978. pap. 5.95 (ISBN 0-88207-771-6). Victor Bks.
Be Mine. Daisy Hepburn. LC 83-24618. (Life with Spice Bible Study Ser.). 1984. 2.95 (ISBN 0-8307-0944-4, 6101817). Regal.
Be My Friend: The Art of Good Relationships. Patricia Sternberg. LC 83-10254. 192p. 1983. pap. 8.95 (ISBN 0-664-26007-1, A Bridgebooks Publication). Westminster.
Be My Witnesses: The Church's Mission, Message, & Messengers. Darrell L. Guder. LC 85-10129. 256p. (Orig.). 1985. pap. 10.95 (ISBN 0-8028-0051-3). Eerdmans.
Be Not Afraid. Jean Vanier. 160p. 1975. pap. 7.95 (ISBN 0-8091-1885-8). Paulist Pr.
Be Not Afraid! John Paul II Speaks Out on His Life, His Beliefs & His Inspiring Vision for Humanity. Andre Frossard & Pope John Paul II. Tr. by J. R. Foster from Fr. 252p. 1984. 13.95 (ISBN 0-312-07021-7). St Martin.
Be Not Afraid: Pope John Paul II Speaks Out on His Life, His Beliefs, & His Inspiring Vision for Humanity. Pope John Paul II & Andre Frossard. LC 85-2322. 216p. 1985. pap. 7.95 (ISBN 0-385-23151-2, Im). Doubleday.
Be Not Deceived: A Scriptural Refutation of the Adam-God Theory. Elwood G. Norris. LC 78-70362. 141p. 1978. 8.95 (ISBN 0-88290-101-X). Horizon Utah.
Be Opened! William R. Yount. LC 76-2238. 240p. 1976. bds. 9.95 (ISBN 0-8054-3216-7). Broadman.
Be Our Freedom, Lord: Responsive Prayers & Readings for Contemporary Worship. Ed. by Terry Falla. 376p. (Orig.). 1985. pap. 11.95 (ISBN 0-8028-0014-9). Eerdmans.
Be Perfect. 2nd ed. Tr. by Man Chong Fung. (Chinese.). 160p. 1982. pap. write for info (ISBN 0-941598-03-9). Living Spring Pubns.
Be Ready. Warren W. Wiersbe. LC 78-65555. 175p. 1979. pap. 5.95 (ISBN 0-88207-782-1). Victor Bks.
Be Real. Warren W. Wiersbe. LC 72-77014. 190p. 1972. pap. 5.95 (ISBN 0-88207-046-0). Victor Bks.
Be Realistic: Plan for a Miracle. Bhagwan Shree Rajneesh. Ed. by Ma Prem Maneesha. LC 78-902296. (Initiation Talks Ser.). (Illus.). 418p. (Orig.). 1977. 19.95 (ISBN 0-88050-010-7). Chidvilas Found.
Be Reconciled. Rolland Stair. 48p. 1981. softcover 0.75 (ISBN 0-8146-1233-4). Liturgical Pr.
Be Rich. Warren W. Wiersbe. LC 76-6833. 175p. 1976. pap. 5.95 (ISBN 0-88207-730-9). Victor Bks.
Be Right. Warren W. Wiersbe. LC 77-154327. 175p. 1977. pap. 5.95 (ISBN 0-88207-729-5). Victor Bks.
Be Still & Know. John A. Nimick. LC 67-11989. 1967. 7.95 (ISBN 0-8022-1222-0). Philos Lib.
Be Still & Know. Bhagwan Shree Rajneesh. Ed. by Ma Yoga Anurag. (Question & Answer Ser.). (Illus.). 364p. (Orig.). 1981. pap. 13.95 (ISBN 0-88050-511-7). Chidvilas Found.
Be Still & Know. Millie Stamm. 384p. 1981. pap. 7.95 (ISBN 0-310-32991-4, 10844P). Zondervan.
Be Still & Know: A Study in the Life of Prayer. Michael Ramsey. 128p. (Orig.). 1983. pap. 6.95 (ISBN 0-8164-2473-X, HarpR). Har-Row.
Be Still & Know That I Am God. Patricia G. Opatz. 64p. 1981. softcover 2.95 (ISBN 0-8146-1231-8). Liturgical Pr.
Be Strong & Courageous (Joshua) Leader's Guide. (New Horizons Bible Study Ser.). 47p. 1986. pap. 1.95 (ISBN 0-89367-112-6). Light & Life.
Be Strong & Courageous (Joshua) Student Guide. (New Horizons Bible Study Ser.). 64p. (Orig.). 1986. pap. 2.50 (ISBN 0-89367-111-8). Light & Life.
Be the Leader You Were Meant to Be. Leroy Eims. LC 75-5392. 132p. 1975. pap. 4.95 (ISBN 0-88207-723-6). Victor Bks.
Be Thou an Example. Gordon B. Hinckley. LC 81-15109. 144p. 1981. 7.95 (ISBN 0-87747-899-6). Deseret Bk.
Be Transformed. Warren W. Wiersbe. 156p. 1986. pap. 5.95 (ISBN 0-89693-352-0). Victor Bks.
Be Victorious. Warren W. Wiersbe. 156p. 1985. pap. 5.95 (ISBN 0-89693-547-7). Victor Bks.
Be Wise. Wiersbe. 1983. 5.95 (ISBN 0-88207-384-2). Victor Bks.
Be with Me Lord: Prayers for the Sick. Rodney J. DeMartini. LC 82-71881. 96p. (Orig.) 1982. pap. 2.95 (ISBN 0-87793-256-5). Ave Maria.
Be Ye Also Ready. Elisabeth Sayer. LC 80-82065. (Orig.). 1980. pap. text ed. 3.50 (ISBN 0-932050-07-7). New Puritan.
Be Ye Transformed. Elizabeth S. Turner. 1969. 5.95 (ISBN 0-87159-008-5). Unity School.
Be Your Best Self. Thomas S. Monson. LC 79-54782. 1979. 7.95 (ISBN 0-87747-787-6). Deseret Bk.
Be Your Own Guru. Sri S. Chakravarti. 1971. pap. 2.50 (ISBN 0-685-58384-8). Ranney Pubns.
Beacon Bible Commentary, 10 vols. 125.00 set (ISBN 0-8010-0675-9). Baker Bk.
Beacon Bible Expositions, 12 vols. Ed. by William Greathouse et al. 1984. Set. 89.95 (ISBN 0-8341-0323-0). Beacon Hill.
Beacon Bible Expositions: Galatians-Ephesians, Vol. 8. Willard H. Taylor. 228p. 1981. 8.95 (ISBN 0-8341-0734-1). Beacon Hill.
Beacon Bible Expositions: Hebrews, James, Peter, Vol. 11. W. T. Purkiser. Ed. by William M. Greathouse & Willard H. Taylor. 1974. 8.95 (ISBN 0-8341-0322-2). Beacon Hill.
Beacon Bible Expositions: Philippians, Colossians, Philemon. John A. Knight. Ed. by William H. Greathouse. 320p. 1985. 8.95 (ISBN 0-8341-0320-6). Beacon Hill.
Beacon Bible Expositions: Vol. 1, Matthew. William E. McCumber et al. (Beacon Bible Expositions Ser.). 1975. 8.95 (ISBN 0-8341-0312-5). Beacon Hill.
Beacon Bible Expositions, Vol. 10: Thessalonians, Timothy, Titus. Sydney Martin. Ed. by William M Greathouse & Willard H. Taylor. 1978. 8.95 (ISBN 0-8341-0321-4). Beacon Hill.
Beacon Bible Expositions, Vol. 12: John, Jude, Revelation. T. E. Martin. Ed. by M. Greathouse. 230p. 1983. 8.95 (ISBN 0-8341-0809-7). Beacon Hill.
Beacon Bible Expositions, Vol. 2: Mark. A. Elwood Sanner & William M. Greathouse. 1978. 8.95 (ISBN 0-8341-0313-3). Beacon Hill.
Beacon Bible Expositions: Vol. 3, Luke. Reuben Welch. Ed. by William M. Greathouse & Willard H. Taylor. 1974. 8.95 (ISBN 0-8341-0314-1). Beacon Hill.
Beacon Bible Expositions, Vol. 4: John. Samuel Young. Ed. by William M. Greathouse & Willard H. Taylor. 196p. 1979. 8.95 (ISBN 0-8341-0315-X). Beacon Hill.
Beacon Bible Expositions: Vol. 5, Acts. Arnold E. Airhart. Ed. by William M. Greathouse & Willard H. Taylor. (Beacon Bible Exposition Ser.). 1977. 8.95 (ISBN 0-8341-0316-8). Beacon Hill.
Beacon Bible Expositions: Vol. 6, Romans. Willam M. Greathouse. Ed. by Willard H. Taylor. (Beacon Bible Exposition Ser.). 1975. 8.95 (ISBN 0-8341-0317-6). Beacon Hill.
Beacon Bible Expositions: Vol. 7, Corinthians. Oscar F. Reed. Ed. by William M. Greathouse & Willard H. Taylor. 1976. 8.95 (ISBN 0-8341-0318-4). Beacon Hill.
Beacon Dictionary of Theology. Ed. by Richard S. Taylor. 560p. 1984. 29.95 (ISBN 0-8341-0811-9). Beacon Hill.
Beacon Light. Raghavan Iyer. (Sangam Texts Ser.). 124p. 1984. pap. 8.75 (ISBN 0-88695-021-X). Concord Grove.
Beacon Lights of Grace: Twelve Biographical Vignettes. facs. ed. Richard E. Day. LC 71-148210. (Biography Index Reprint Ser.). 1947. 17.00 (ISBN 0-8369-8057-3). Ayer Co Pubs.
Beacon Small-Group Bible Studies, Acts, Pt. II: The Continuing Mission of the Church. Lebron Fairbanks. Ed. by Earl C. Wolf. 90p. (Orig.). 1985. pap. 2.50 (ISBN 0-8341-0947-6). Beacon Hill.
Beacon Small-Group Bible Studies, Acts, Pt, I: The Spirit-Filled Church. Alfred F. Harper. 96p. 1982. pap. 2.50 (ISBN 0-8341-0800-3). Beacon Hill.
Beacon Small-Group Bible Studies, Daniel: Daring to Live by Faith. Harold DeMott. Ed. by Earl C. Wolf. 96p. (Orig.). 1985. pap. 2.50 (ISBN 0-8341-0962-X). Beacon Hill.
Beacon Small-Group Bible Studies, Deuteronomy: Words to Live By. Clayton Bonar. Ed. by Earl C. Wolf. 100p. (Orig.). 1986. pap. 2.50 (ISBN 0-8341-0959-X). Beacon Hill.
Beacon Small-Group Bible Studies, Ecclesiastes: "Faith or Futility?". Evelyn A. Stenbock. Ed. by Earl C. Wolf. 96p. (Orig.). 1985. pap. 2.50 (ISBN 0-8341-0964-6). Beacon Hill.
Beacon Small-Group Bible Studies, Ephesians. Gene Van Note. 88p. (Orig.). 1981. pap. 2.50 (ISBN 0-8341-0722-8). Beacon Hill.
Beacon Small-Group Bible Studies: Exodus: "Set Free". Earl C. Wolf. 86p. (Orig.). 1984. pap. 2.50. Beacon Hill.
Beacon Small-Group Bible Studies, Ezra-Nehemiah: God's Faithfulness & Man's Obedience. C. Neil Strait. Ed. by Earl C. Wolf. 96p. (Orig.). 1985. pap. 2.50 (ISBN 0-8341-0927-1). Beacon Hill.
Beacon Small-Group Bible Studies, Genesis, Pt. II: God's Hand in History. Ken Bible. Ed. by Earl C. Wolf. 96p. (Orig.). 1986. pap. 2.50 (ISBN 0-8341-0958-1). Beacon Hill.
Beacon Small-Group Bible Studies, Genesis, Pt. I: How It All Began. Robert Branson. Ed. by Earl C. Wolf. 96p. (Orig.). 1984. pap. 2.50 (ISBN 0-8341-0935-2). Beacon Hill.
Beacon Small-Group Bible Studies, Gospel of John, Pt. II: That You Might Have Life. Charles Shaver. Ed. by Earl C. Wolf. 64p. (Orig.). 1984. pap. 2.50 (ISBN 0-8341-0881-X). Beacon Hill.
Beacon Small-Group Bible Studies, Hebrews: He is Here at Last. Gene Van Note. 64p. (Orig.). 1980. pap. 2.50 (ISBN 0-8341-0623-X). Beacon Hill.
Beacon Small-Group Bible Studies: Hosea, "The Triumph of God". Hugh Gorman. 88p. (Orig.). 1984. pap. 2.50 (ISBN 0-8341-0914-X). Beacon Hill.
Beacon Small-Group Bible Studies, I & II Peter: A Faith for Testing Times. J. Grant Swank, Jr. (Beacon Small-Group Bible Studies). 80p. 1982. pap. 2.50 (ISBN 0-8341-0790-2). Beacon Hill.
Beacon Small-Group Bible Studies, I & II Samuel: David-A Man after God's Own Heart". A. F. Harper. Ed. by Earl C. Wolf. 102p. (Orig.). 1985. pap. 2.50 (ISBN 0-8341-0934-4). Beacon Hill.
Beacon Small-Group Bible Studies, I & II Timothy, Titus: Being Christian in Today's World. 72p. 1983. pap. 2.50 (ISBN 0-8341-0622-1). Beacon Hill.
Beacon Small-Group Bible Studies, I & II Thessalonians: The Distinguishing Marks of a Christian. Bill Nielson. 56p. 1982. pap. 2.50 (ISBN 0-8341-0738-4). Beacon Hill.
Beacon Small-Group Bible Studies, I Corinthians, Living As a Responsible Christian. Beacon Hill Staff. 60p. 1982. pap. 2.50 (ISBN 0-8341-0755-4). Beacon Hill.
Beacon Small-Group Bible Studies, I, II & III John: Everybody Ought to Know. Ear! C. Wolf. 80p. 1982. pap. 2.50 (ISBN 0-8341-0791-0). Beacon Hill.
Beacon Small-Group Bible Studies, II Corinthians, Galatians: Reckless Freedom, Responsible Living. Stephen M. Miller. Ed. by Earl C. Wolf. 96p. (Orig.). 1985. pap. 2.50 (ISBN 0-8341-0957-3). Beacon Hill.
Beacon Small-Group Bible Studies, Isaiah: Preparing the Way of the Lord. Robert Branson. Ed. by Earl C. Wolf. 96p. (Orig.). 1985. pap. 2.50 (ISBN 0-8341-0961-1). Beacon Hill.
Beacon Small-Group Bible Studies, James: Does God Want Faith or Obedience. A. F. Harper. 80p. (Orig.). 1980. pap. 2.50 (ISBN 0-8341-0625-6). Beacon Hill.
Beacon Small-Group Bible Studies, Job: The Trial & Triumph of Faith. David G. Grosse. Ed. by Earl C. Wolf. 88p. (Orig.). 1986. pap. 2.50 (ISBN 0-8341-1109-8). Beacon Hill.
Beacon Small-Group Bible Studies, John: That All Might Believe, Vol. 1. Charles Shaver. 68p. (Orig.). 1980. pap. 2.50 (ISBN 0-8341-0651-5). Beacon Hill.

Beacon Small-Group Bible Studies, Joshua: Never a Dull Moment. Glen Van Dyne. Ed. by Earl C. Wolf. 80p. 1986. pap. 2.50 (ISBN 0-8341-1098-9). Beacon Hill.

Beacon Small-Group Bible Studies, Luke: Good News for All of Us, Vol. 1. Jerry Hull. 72p. (Orig.). 1980. pap. 2.50 (ISBN 0-8341-0657-4). Beacon Hill.

Beacon Small-Group Bible Studies, Luke: Lessons on Discipleship, Vol. 2. Sherrill Munn. 68p. (Orig.). 1981. pap. 2.50 (ISBN 0-8341-0689-2). Beacon Hill.

Beacon Small-Group Bible Studies, Mark: Getting in on the Action. Jim Spruce. 80p. (Orig.). 1980. pap. 2.50 (ISBN 0-8341-0650-7). Beacon Hill.

Beacon Small-Group Bible Studies, Matthew, Vol. I: To Be a Disciple. Frank Carver. Ed. by Earl C. Wolf. (Beacon Small-Group Bible Study). 80p. (Orig.). 1984. pap. 2.50 (ISBN 0-8341-0870-4). Beacon Hill.

Beacon Small-Group Bible Studies, Micah-Obadiah: What Does the Lord Require? Wesley Tracy. Ed. by Earl C. Wolf. 96p. (Orig.). 1985. pap. 2.50 (ISBN 0-8341-0963-8). Beacon Hill.

Beacon Small-Group Bible Studies, Philippians, Colossians, Experiencing His Peace. LeBron Fairbanks. 100p. 1982. pap. 2.50 (ISBN 0-8341-0778-3). Beacon Hill.

Beacon Small-Group Bible Studies: Proverbs, Wisdom for Today's Challenges. Carlton D. Hansen. 80p. (Orig.). 1984. pap. 2.50 (ISBN 0-8341-0905-0). Beacon Hill.

Beacon Small-Group Bible Studies: Psalms: Keeping the Heart Aglow. Ivan A. Beals. 96p. (Orig.). 1984. pap. 2.50 (ISBN 0-8341-0885-2). Beacon Hill.

Beacon Small-Group Bible Studies, Romans: More than Conquerors. John M. Nielson. Ed. by Earl C. Wolf. 96p. (Orig.). 1984. pap. 2.50 (ISBN 0-8341-0944-1). Beacon Hill.

Beacon Small-Group Bible Studies, Ruth-Esther: Faith That Risks All. Frances Simpson. Ed. by Earl C. Wolf. 96p. (Orig.). 1984. pap. 2.50 (ISBN 0-8341-0941-7). Beacon Hill.

Beams of Illumination from the Divine Revelation. Shaykh F. Haeri. 340p. 1987. pap. 18.95 (ISBN 0-7103-0219-3, 02193, Kegan Paul). Methuen Inc.

Bearer of the Holy Spirit. 2.00 (ISBN 0-8198-1112-2). Dghtrs St Paul.

Bearing Witness: Quaker Process & a Culture of Peace. Gray Cox. LC 85-61133. 32p. (Orig.). 1985. pap. 2.50x (ISBN 0-87574-262-9). Pendle Hill.

Beast from the Bottomless Pit. Gordon Lindsay. (Revelation Ser.). 1.25 (ISBN 0-89985-043-X). Christ Nations.

Beast of Revelation Thirteen: The Number of a Man Six Threescore & Six? or Six Threescore to the Power & Six? Equals Nine? Lee Dawkins. 68p. 1982. 5.00 (ISBN 0-682-49887-4). Exposition Pr FL.

Beasts, Birds & Fish of the Bible. Nancy Peelman. LC 75-14605. (Illus.). 40p. (Orig.). 1975. pap. 4.50 (ISBN 0-8192-1197-4). Morehouse.

Beasts of the Modern Imagination: Darwin, Nietzsche, Kafka, & Lawrence. Margot Norris. LC 84-21320. 256p. 1985. text ed. 26.50x (ISBN 0-8018-3252-7). Johns Hopkins.

Beating the Break-up Habit. Dick Purnell. 128p. (Orig.). 1983. pap. 5.95 (ISBN 0-89840-059-7). Heres Life.

Beating the Church Going Blahs. Robert T. Henderson. LC 86-21338. 132p. 1986. pap. 5.95 (ISBN 0-87784-516-6). Inter Varsity.

Beating the Clock: A Guide to Maturing Successfully. Frank B. Minirth et al. (Life Enrichment Ser.). 1986. pap. 3.95 (ISBN 0-8010-6205-5). Baker Bk.

Beatitude Saints. Daniel Morris. LC 83-62423. 128p. (Orig.). 1984. pap. 4.95 (ISBN 0-87973-615-1, 615). Our Sunday Visitor.

Beatitudes. (Inspirational Library). 24p. 3.95 (ISBN 0-8326-2003-3, 3250). World Bible.

Beatitudes. C. H. Spurgeon. 1978. pap. 2.75 (ISBN 0-686-00504-X). Pilgrim Pubns.

Beatitudes. Thomas Watson. 307p. 1981. kivar bdg. 9.95 (ISBN 0-85151-035-3). Banner of Truth.

Beatitudes & the Lord's Prayer. Arthur W. Pink. 140p. 1982. pap. 4.95 (ISBN 0-8010-7073-2). Baker Bk.

Beatitudes & the Lord's Prayer for Everyman. William Barclay. LC 75-9309. 256p. 1975. pap. 7.95 (ISBN 0-06-060393-3, RD112, HarpR). Har-Row.

Beatitudes: Attitudes for a Better Future. George Drew. 63p. (Orig.). 1980. pap. 6.95 (ISBN 0-940754-03-7). Ed Ministries.

Beatitudes-Expressing the Character of Jesus. Pat King & George Wood. (Bible Study Enrichment Ser.). 64p. 1985. pap. 2.95 (ISBN 0-930756-92-4). Aglow Pubns.

Beatitudes for the Balmy: And Other Poems. Bentley Barnabas. 1985. 6.95 (ISBN 0-682-40211-7). Exposition Pr FL.

Beatitudes for Today. Joan Mitchell & Irene O'Neill. Ed. by Carl Fisher. (Illus.). 1985. dupl. masterbook 9.95 (ISBN 0-89837-102-3, Pub. by Pflaum Pr). Peter Li.

Beatitudes of Married Life. Glenn Clark. pap. 0.20 (ISBN 0-910924-02-3). Macalester.

Beatitudes: Soundings in Christian Traditions. Simon Tugwell. 192p. 1980. 8.95 (ISBN 0-87243-098-7). Templegate.

Beatitudes: To Evangelize as Jesus Did. Segundo Galilea. Tr. by Robert R. Barr from Span. LC 83-19342. Tr. of La Mision Segun Las Bienaventuranzas. 128p. (Orig.). 1984. pap. 5.95 (ISBN 0-88344-344-9). Orbis Bks.

Beautiful Attitudes Matthew 5: 3-12. Stirrup Associates Inc. Ed. by Cheryl M. Phillips & Bonnie C. Harvey. LC 84-50914. (Child's Paraphrase Ser.). (Illus.). 32p. 1984. pap. 1.49 (ISBN 0-937420-17-4). Stirrup Assoc.

Beautiful California Missions. Lee Foster. Ed. by Robert D. Shangle. LC 78-102341. (Illus.). 72p. 1986. pap. 8.95 (ISBN 0-915796-22-8). Beautiful Am.

Beautiful Garden & Other Bible Tales. Elma E. Levinger. (Illus.). 5.95 (ISBN 0-8197-0253-6). Bloch.

Beautiful Land: Palestine: Historical, Geographical & Pictorial. John Fulton. Ed. by Moshe Davis. LC 77-70694. (America & the Holy Land Ser.). (Illus.). 1977. Repr. of 1891 ed. lib. bdg. 52.00x (ISBN 0-405-10248-8). Ayer Co Pubs.

Beautiful on the Mountain. Hermon Pettit & Helen Wessel. LC 84-70118. (Illus.). 144p. 1984. 10.95 (ISBN 0-933082-03-7). Bookmates Intl.

Beautiful Poems on Jesus. facs. ed. Compiled by Basil Miller. LC 68-58826. (Granger Index Reprint Ser). 1948. 17.00 (ISBN 0-8369-6029-7). Ayer Co Pubs.

Beautiful Way of Life. Charles Lelly. 1980. 4.95 (ISBN 0-87159-010-7). Unity School.

Beautiful Ways Songs. pap. 0.30 (ISBN 0-686-29099-2). Faith Pub Hse.

Beautitudes. 20p. 1983. pap. 7.55 Dup Masters (ISBN 0-88479-037-1). Arena Lettres.

Beauty & Belief: Aesthetics & Religion in Victorian Literature. Hilary Fraser. 306p. 1986. 34.50 (ISBN 0-521-30767-8). Cambridge U Pr.

Beauty & the Best: A Handbook of Christian Loveliness. Beneth P. Jones. (Illus.). 164p. (Orig.). 1980. pap. 3.95 (ISBN 0-89084-123-3). Bob Jones Univ Pr.

Beauty & Wisdom of the Holy Qur'an. A. K. Chipa. 1971. 3.25x (ISBN 0-87902-159-4). Orientalia.

Beauty & Wisdom of the Holy Quran. A. Karim. 4.95 (ISBN 0-686-18519-6). Kazi Pubns.

Beauty-Drops. Sri Chinmoy. 51p. (Orig.). 1975. pap. 2.00 (ISBN 0-88497-224-0). Aum Pubns.

Beauty in Holiness: Studies in Jewish Ceremonial Art & Customs. Joseph Gutmann. 1970. 50.00x (ISBN 0-87068-012-9). Ktav.

Beauty of a Disciplined Life. Rebecca L. Gates. 96p. 1987. pap. 4.95 (ISBN 0-89693-248-6). Victor Bks.

Beauty of Beholding God. Darien B. Cooper. 168p. 1982. pap. 5.95 (ISBN 0-88207-350-8). Victor Bks.

Beauty of Being Prepared. James W. Robinson. 1982. 4.25 (ISBN 0-89536-548-0, 0213). CSS of Ohio.

Beauty of Caring. Lloyd J. Ogilvie. LC 80-80464. 1981. pap. 5.95 (ISBN 0-89081-244-6). Harvest Hse.

Beauty of Friendship. Lloyd J. Ogilvie. LC 80-80463. 1980. pap. 5.95 (ISBN 0-89081-243-8). Harvest Hse.

Beauty of God's Whisper. Randy Becton. 1980. pap. 4.75 (ISBN 0-89137-310-1). Quality Pubns.

Beauty of Holiness: Phoebe Palmer As Theologian, Revivalist, Feminist, & Humanitarian. Charles E. White. 352p. 1986. 15.95 (ISBN 0-310-46250-9). Zondervan.

Beauty of Love. Lloyd J. Ogilvie. LC 80-80465. (Orig.). 1980. pap. 5.95 (ISBN 0-89081-245-4). Harvest Hse.

Beauty of Sharing. Lloyd J. Ogilvie. LC 80-8880. (Orig.). 1981. pap. 5.95 (ISBN 0-89081-246-2). Harvest Hse.

Beauty of Wholeness: Program Resource for Women 1981. Ed. by Imogene Goodyear. 1980. pap. 5.00 (ISBN 0-8309-0294-5). Herald Hse.

Beauty Through Health: From the Edgar Cayce Readings. Lawrence M. Steinhart. LC 73-91501. 1974. 7.95 (ISBN 0-87795-078-4). Arbor Hse.

Because God Loves. John P. Wenger. LC 76-16245. 56p. 1976. pap. 1.95 (ISBN 0-8361-1339-X). Herald Pr.

Because of Christmas. Morcus Bach. (Illus.). 192p. 1986. pap. 8.00 (ISBN 0-940581-00-0). Fellowship Spirit.

Because of Jesus. 2nd ed. Kenneth Hagin, Jr. 1979. 1.00 (ISBN 0-89276-701-4). Hagin Ministries.

Because of Jesus. Akio Limb. Ed. by J. D. Thomas. (Twentieth Century Sermons Ser). 1972. 11.95 (ISBN 0-89112-307-5, Bibl Res Pr). Abilene Christ U.

Because They Were Jews: A History of Antisemitism. Meyer Weinberg. LC 86-15013. (Contributions to the Study of World History Ser.: No. 4). 300p. 1986. lib. bdg. 35.95 (ISBN 0-313-25606-3, WBJ). Greenwood.

Becket. Jean Anouilh. 1960. pap. 5.95 (ISBN 0-698-10031-X, Coward). Putnam Pub Group.

Becket ou, l'Honneur de Dieu. Jean Anouilh. 1973. pap. 5.50 (ISBN 0-685-11038-9, 1716). French & Eur.

Become Like Jesus. James McKeever. 408p. 1984. write for info. (ISBN 0-86694-101-0); pap. 9.95 (ISBN 0-86694-100-2). Omega Pubns OR.

Becoming. Michele McCarty. 1983. pap. 6.95 (ISBN 0-697-01856-3); program manual 10.00 (ISBN 0-697-01857-1); Journal 3.25 (ISBN 0-697-01869-5). Wm C Brown.

Becoming. Blaine M. Yorgason & Brenton G. Yorgason. LC 86-70295. 176p. 1986. 9.95 (ISBN 0-87579-034-8). Deseret Bk.

Becoming a Catholic Christian. Ed. by William J. Reedy. 198p. pap. 5.95 (ISBN 0-8215-9326-9). Sadlier.

Becoming a Christian. Harold Odor & Ruth Odor. (Illus.). 16p. 1985. 0.75 (ISBN 0-87239-901-X, 3301). Standard Pub.

Becoming a Christian. Lewis J. Sherrill & Helen H. Sherrill. 1943. pap. 1.49 (ISBN 0-8042-1548-0). John Knox.

Becoming a Christian. John R. Stott. pap. 0.75 (ISBN 0-87784-100-4). Inter-Varsity.

Becoming a Christian Person. Robert E. Lauder. 140p. (Orig.). 1985. pap. 5.95 (ISBN 0-914544-58-6). Living Flame Pr.

Becoming a Church Member. W. R. Fegan. 1979. pap. 3.50 (ISBN 0-89536-389-5, 0232). CSS of Ohio.

Becoming a Disciple of Christ: A Monk of Marmion Abbey. 5.95 (ISBN 0-87193-195-8). Dimension Bks.

Becoming a Giving Church. Herbert Mather. LC 85-72879. 64p. (Orig.). 1985. pap. 3.50 (ISBN 0-88177-023-X, DR023B). Discipleship Res.

Becoming a Minister. Thomas Oden. 256p. 1987. 17.95 (ISBN 0-8245-0825-4). Crossroad NY.

Becoming a New Person: Twelve Steps to Christian Growth. Philip St. Romain. 96p. 1984. pap. 2.95 (ISBN 0-89243-200-4). Liguori Pubns.

Becoming a Sensuous Catechist: Using the Arts in Religion Classes. Therese Boucher. (Illus.). 80p. 1984. pap. 5.95 (ISBN 0-89622-216-0). Twenty-Third.

Becoming Adult, Becoming Christian: Adult Development & Christian Faith. James W. Fowler. LC 83-48987. 144p. 1984. 14.45 (ISBN 0-06-062841-3, HarpR). Har-Row.

Becoming Anabaptist. J. Denny Weaver. LC 86-33650. 176p. (Orig.). 1987. pap. 14.95 (ISBN 0-8361-3434-6). Herald Pr.

Becoming & Being: The Doctrine of God in Charles Hartshorne & Karl Barth. Colin E. Gunton. (Theological Monographs). 1978. text ed. 39.95x (ISBN 0-19-826713-4). Oxford U Pr.

Becoming Aware of the Logos. Georg Kuhlewind. LC 85-23126. 195p. (Orig.). 1985. pap. 9.95 (ISBN 0-89281-071-8, Lindisfarne Pr). Inner Tradit.

Becoming Catholic, Even If You Happen to Be One. James J. Killgallon. LC 79-89875. 1980. pap. 4.50 (ISBN 0-914070-13-4). ACTA Found.

Becoming Christ. 4.95 (ISBN 0-87193-127-3). Dimension Bks.

Becoming Complete: Embracing Your Biblical Image. Marion Duckworth. LC 85-10465. 1985. pap. 5.95 (ISBN 0-88070-099-8). Multnomah.

Becoming Free. Charles Hummel. pap. 0.75 (ISBN 0-87784-137-3). Inter-Varsity.

Becoming God's Woman. Joyce M. Smith. 1979. pap. 2.50 (ISBN 0-8423-0130-5). Tyndale.

Becoming Human. Letty M. Russell. LC 81-23121. (Library of Living Faith: Vol. 2). 114p. 1982. pap. 5.95 (ISBN 0-664-24408-4). Westminster.

Becoming Human Together: The Pastoral anthropology of St. Paul. Jerome Murphy-O'Connor. (Good News Studies: Vol. 2). 224p. 1982. pap. 8.95 (ISBN 0-89453-075-5). M Glazier.

Becoming Jewish. Egon Mayer. 40p. (Orig.). Date not set. pap. price not set. Am Jewish Comm.

Becoming Makers of Peace. Ed. by Bruce Jones. 1987. pap. 7.00 (ISBN 0-8309-0476-X). Herald Hse.

Becoming More Like Jesus. Bert Ghezzi. LC 86-63424. 160p. 1987. pap. 5.95 (ISBN 0-87973-518-X, 518). Our Sunday Visitor.

Becoming One. Don Meredith. LC 79-12691. 1979. pap. 5.95 (ISBN 0-8407-5688-7). Nelson.

Becoming One Flesh. Denise L. Carmody & John T. Carmody. LC 84-50841. 160p. (Orig.). 1984. pap. 6.95 (ISBN 0-8358-0486-0). Upper Room.

Becoming One Flesh. Steven M. Nelson & Frank L. Starkey. 1979. pap. 2.95 (ISBN 0-89536-354-2, 0229). CSS of Ohio.

Becoming the Family of God: A Handbook for Developing Creative Relationships in the Church. Keith Huttenlocker. 128p. 1986. pap. 6.95 (ISBN 0-310-75211-6). Zondervan.

Becoming Woman: The Quest for Spiritual Wholeness in Female Experience. Penelope Washbourn. LC 76-9948. 1979. pap. 7.95 (ISBN 0-06-069261-8, RD 256, HarpR). Har-Row.

Becoming: Yourself in the Making. Calvin Miller. 1987. 10.95 (ISBN 0-8007-1522-5). Revell.

Beda der Ehrwuerdige und Seine Zeit. new ed. Karl Werner. 1963. Repr. of 1881 ed. 24.50 (ISBN 0-8337-3730-9). B Franklin.

Bede the Venerable. George H. Brown. (Twayne's English Authors Ser.). 144p. 1987. lib. bdg. 19.95 (ISBN 0-8057-6940-4, TEAS 443, Twayne). G K Hall.

Bedeutung der Wundererzaehlungen fuer die Christologie des Markusevangeliums. Dietrich-Alex Koch. (Beiheft 42 zur Zeitschrift fuer die neutestamentliche Wissenschaft Ser.). 217p. 1975. 44.40x (ISBN 3-11-004783-7). De Gruyter.

Bedside Meditations. Frank L. Cox. 1967. pap. 2.00 (ISBN 0-88027-000-4). Firm Foun Pub.

Bedtime Stories of the Saints, Bk. 2. Frank Lee. 64p. (Orig.). 1980. pap. 1.95 (ISBN 0-89243-126-1). Liguori Pubns.

Been Down So Long It Looks Like up to Me. Richard Farina. 1983. pap. 6.95 (ISBN 0-14-006536-9). Penguin.

Before Abraham Was: A Provocative Challenge to the Documentary Hypothesis. Isaac M. Kikawada & Arthur Quinn. 144p. 1985. pap. 10.95 (ISBN 0-687-02602-4). Abingdon.

Before & After My Child Died: A Collection of Parents' Experiences. Joseph Fischhoff & Noreen Brohl. 247p. (Orig.). 1981. pap. 7.95x (ISBN 0-9607956-0-X). Emmons-Fairfield Pub.

Before & After the Fall: Contrasting Modes in "Paradise Lost". Kathleen Swaim. LC 85-28925. 312p. 1986. lib. bdg. 27.50X (ISBN 0-87023-504-4). U of Mass Pr.

Before I Wake: Listening to God in Your Dreams. Abraham Schmitt. 160p. 1984. pap. 7.95 (ISBN 0-687-02605-9). Abingdon.

Before the Bible. Cyrus H. Gordon. LC 72-10828. (Essay Index Reprint Ser.). 1973. Repr. of 1962 ed. 24.00 (ISBN 0-8369-7219-8). Ayer Co Pubs.

Before the Convention: Religion & the Founders. M. Susan Power. LC 84-12004. 268p. (Orig.). 1984. lib. bdg. 26.25 (ISBN 0-8191-4133-X); pap. text ed. 13.25 (ISBN 0-8191-4134-8). U Pr of Amer.

Before the Earth Arose. J. Dobracyynski. 1981. 8.95 (ISBN 0-317-46868-5). Franciscan Herald.

Before the Ending of the Day. Norman Pittenger. 110p. 1985. pap. 5.95 (ISBN 0-8192-1365-9). Morehouse.

Before the Fury. E. Emil Herz. LC 66-18484. 1967. 7.95 (ISBN 0-8022-0710-3). Philos Lib.

Before the Last Battle-Armageddon. Arthur Bloomfield. 192p. 1976. pap. 3.95 (ISBN 0-87123-035-6). Bethany Hse.

Before the Living God. Ruth Burrows. 6.95 (ISBN 0-87193-155-9). Dimension Bks.

Before the Moon Dies. Christa Weber. 1984. pap. 1.50 (ISBN 9971-972-15-8). OMF Bks.

Before the Sabbath. Eric Hoffer. LC 78-69626. 1979. 11.45i (ISBN 0-06-011914-4, HarpT). Har-Row.

Before There Was a Before. Arthur Waskow et al. LC 84-11177. (Illus.). 80p. 1984. 8.95 (ISBN 0-915361-08-6, 09404-9, Dist. by Watts). Adama Pubs Inc.

Before We Kill & Eat You. H. B. Garlock. 1.95 (ISBN 0-89985-109-6). Christ Nations.

Before You Build Your Church. Roland A. Smith. LC 76-73134. 1979. pap. 2.50 (ISBN 0-8054-3511-5). Broadman.

Before You Cast the Second Stone. Klaus Heck. 1979. 7.95 (ISBN 0-915948-05-2); pap. 5.95 (ISBN 0-686-52664-3). Bks Distinction.

Before You Divorce. Harold Billnitzer. 1978. pap. 0.95 (ISBN 0-933350-12-0). Morse Pr.

Before You Marry. J. Allan Petersen. 1974. pap. 3.95 (ISBN 0-8423-0104-6). Tyndale.

Before You Say I Do: Study Manual. Norman Wright & Wes Roberts. LC 77-94133. 1978. 4.95 (ISBN 0-89081-119-9). Harvest Hse.

Before You Tuck Me In. William Coleman. 128p. (Orig.). 1986. pap. 4.95 (ISBN 0-87123-830-6). Bethany Hse.

Beggar at the Banquet: The Story of Dr. Woo Jun Hong. Ed. by Donald B. Sheley. LC 81-13971. (Illus.). 178p. (Orig.). pap. 5.95 (ISBN 0-88289-306-8). Pelican.

Beggars & Prayers: Adin Steinsaltz Retells the Tales of Rabbi Nahman of Bratslav. Adin Steinsaltz. LC 78-54502. 186p. 1985. pap. 6.95 (ISBN 0-465-00581-0, PL-5139). Basic.

Beggar's Greatest Wish. Alyce Bergey. (Arch Bks: No. 6). 1969. pap. 0.99 (ISBN 0-570-06040-0, 59-1155). Concordia.

Begin with Prayer: Prayers & Devotional Outlines for Church Meetings. Kenneth W. Rogahn. 112p. 1985. 6.95 (ISBN 0-570-03962-2, 15-2178). Concordia.

Beginner's Grammar of the Greek New Testament. William H. Davis. 1923. 12.45 (ISBN 0-06-061710-1, HarpR). Har-Row.

Beginners' Guide to Bible Sharing I. John Burke. 192p. 1985. pap. 8.95 (ISBN 0-697-02014-2). Wm C Brown.

Beginners' Guide to Bible Sharing II. John Burke. 240p. 1984. pap. 9.95 (ISBN 0-697-02015-0). Wm C Brown.

Beginners' Guide to Family Preparedness. Rosalie Mason. LC 77-79750. (Illus.). 160p. 1977. pap. 6.95 (ISBN 0-88290-082-X). Horizon Utah.

Beginner's Guide to Meditation. Goswami Kriyananda. 104p. (Orig.). pap. text ed. 3.95 (ISBN 0-317-43470-5). Temple Kriya Yoga.

Beginner's Guide to Zen & the Art of Windsurfing. 3rd ed. Frank Fox et al. (Illus.). 160p. 1985. pap. 6.95 (ISBN 0-934965-02-1). Amber Co Pr.

Beginners' Jewish Book of Why & What. Ian Shapolsky. (YA) 1987. 11.95. Shapolsky Pubs.

Beginner's New Testament Greek Grammar. Sakae Kubo. LC 79-64247. 1979. pap. text ed. 11.00 (ISBN 0-8191-0761-1). U Pr of Amer.

Beginner's Reader-Grammar for New Testament Greek. Ernest C. Colwell & E. W. Tune. 1965. 11.00 (ISBN 0-06-061530-3, HarpR). Har-Row.

Beginning. Penny Wheeler. Ed. by Phillips. (Daybreak Ser.). 112p. 1982. pap. 3.95 (ISBN 0-8163-0478-5). Pacific Pr Pub Assn.

Beginning a New Pastorate. Robert G. Kemper. LC 77-18055. (Creative Leadership Ser.). 1978. pap. 6.95 (ISBN 0-687-02750-0). Abingdon.

Beginning Again. Terry Hershey & Lisa McAfee. 64p. 1984. involvement guide 4.95 (ISBN 0-915929-11-2). Merit Bks.

Beginning Again: Involvement Guide. Terry Hershey. 64p. 1986. cancelled (ISBN 0-8407-3084-5). Nelson.

Beginning Again: Life after a Relationship Ends. Terry Hershey. 152p. 1986. pap. 7.95 (ISBN 0-8407-3075-6). Nelson.

Beginning & the Beyond: Papers from the Gadamer & Voegelin Conferences. Ed. by Fred Lawrence. LC 84-13940. (Boston College-Supplements to Lonergan Workshop Ser.). 1984. pap. 13.50 (ISBN 0-89130-772-9, 19 20 04). Scholars Pr GA.

Beginning & the End. Nikolai A. Berdiaev. Tr. by R. M. French from Russian. LC 76-6083. 1976. Repr. of 1952 ed. lib. bdg. 35.00x (ISBN 0-8371-8837-7, BEBE). Greenwood.

Beginning Anew. Lyle Pointer. (Christian Living Ser.). 32p. (Orig.). 1987. pap. write for info. (ISBN 0-8341-1189-6). Beacon Hill.

Beginning at the Beginning: Wittgenstein & Theological Conversation. John K. Downey. 166p. (Orig.). 1986. lib. bdg. 23.50 (ISBN 0-8191-5650-7); pap. text ed. 12.50 (ISBN 0-8191-5651-5). U Pr of Amer.

Beginning Course in Church Leadership Training for Men. Ernest Clevenger, Jr. (Illus.). 42p. 1975. 3.25 (ISBN 0-88428-036-5). Parchment Pr.

Beginning New Testament Study. Bruce Chilton. 208p. (Orig.). 1987. pap. 9.95 (ISBN 0-8028-0254-0). Eerdmans.

Beginning of the Beginning. 3rd ed. Bhagwan S. Rajneesh. Ed. by Ma P. Parimal. vi, 113p. (Orig.). 1982. pap. 2.95x (ISBN 0-7069-2123-2, Pub. by Vikas India). Advent NY.

Beginning of the End. Tim LaHaye. 1981. pap. 3.50 mass market (ISBN 0-8423-0114-3). Tyndale.

Beginning of the Middle Ages. R. W. Church. 1977. lib. bdg. 59.95 (ISBN 0-8490-1484-0). Gordon Pr.

Beginning of the Rainbow. Shona McKellar. LC 81-7954. (Illus.). 1982. 8.95g (ISBN 0-687-02770-5). Abingdon.

Beginning of the World. Neva G. Goldstein-Alpern. (Board Bks.). (Illus.). 12p. 1987. 5.95. Judaica Pr.

Beginning of the World. Masahiro Kasuya. LC 81-3582. (Illus.). 1982. 8.95g (ISBN 0-687-02765-9). Abingdon.

Beginning Old Testament Study. Ed. by John Rogerson. LC 82-20210. 164p. 1983. pap. 8.95 (ISBN 0-664-24451-3). Westminster.

Beginning Special Religious Education Programs. Kathryn Jennings. (Special Education Newsletter Ser.: Vol. 2). 1980. 4.80 (ISBN 0-686-40038-0). Natl Cath Educ.

Beginning the Christian Life. Russell Krabill. 1958. pap. 2.95 (ISBN 0-8361-1312-8); (leader's guide) 4.95 (ISBN 0-8361-1313-6). Herald Pr.

Beginning to Beginning. Siegfried. LC 84-90251. 65p. 1985. 6.95 (ISBN 0-533-06286-1). Vantage.

Beginning to Pray. Anthony Bloom. LC 70-169613. 128p. 1982. pap. 4.95 (ISBN 0-8091-1509-3). Paulist Pr.

Beginning to Pray in Old Age. Susan Coupland. LC 85-17075. (Parish Life Sourcebks.: Vol. II). xiv, 80p. 1985. pap. 6.95 (ISBN 0-936384-29-8). Cowley Pubns.

Beginning to Read the Fathers. Boniface Ramsey. 288p. (Orig.). 1985. pap. 9.95 (ISBN 0-8091-2691-5). Paulist Pr.

Beginning with Christ. H. L. Heijkoop. 6.95 (ISBN 0-88172-081-X); pap. 4.95 (ISBN 0-88172-082-8). Believers Bkshelf.

Beginning with God. James W. Sire. LC 81-14305. 128p. (Orig.). 1981. pap. 3.50 (ISBN 0-87784-369-4). Inter-Varsity.

Beginning with Mary: Women of the Gospels in Portrait. Thomas J. Carlisle. 120p. (Orig.). 1986. pap. 5.95 (ISBN 0-8028-0194-3). Eerdmans.

Beginning Your Marriage, 2 vols. John L. Thomas. 1980. 4.95 (ISBN 0-915388-25-1); pap. 2.50 (ISBN 0-915388-24-3). Buckley Pubns.

Beginnings. James Weekley & James Reeves. Ed. by Michael L. Sherer. (Orig.). 1987. pap. 3.95 (ISBN 0-89536-859-5, 7818). CSS of Ohio.

Beginnings: A Portrayal of the Creation. Spencer Marsh. LC 81-18920. (Illus.). 72p. 1982. 16.95 (ISBN 0-930014-82-0); pap. 9.95 (ISBN 0-930014-81-2). Multnomah.

Beginnings: Early American Judaica a Collection of Ten Publications in Facsimile, Illustrative of the Religious, Communal, Cultural & Political Life of American Jewry, 1761-1845. Intro. by Abraham J. Karp. LC 75-23405. (Illus.). 1975. 20.00 (ISBN 0-8276-0076-3, 376). Jewish Pubns.

Beginnings: For the Newly Married. Judith Mattison. LC 79-54114. 96p. 1980. 6.95 (ISBN 0-8066-1753-5, 10-0573). Augsburg.

Beginnings in Jewish Philosophy. Meyer Levin. LC 76-116677. (Jewish Heritage Ser). (Illus.). 192p. 1971. text ed. 5.95x (ISBN 0-87441-063-0). Behrman.

Beginnings in Ritual Studies. Ronald L. Grimes. LC 81-40521. 312p. (Orig.). 1982. lib. bdg. 32.00 (ISBN 0-8191-2210-6); pap. text ed. 14.00 (ISBN 0-8191-2211-4). U Pr of Amer.

Beginnings in the Spiritual Life. Dominic Hoffman. 1976. 5.25 (ISBN 0-8198-0387-1); pap. text ed. 4.25 (ISBN 0-8198-0388-X). Dghtrs St Paul.

Beginnings of Buddhist Art. A. Foucher. 1972. 20.00 (ISBN 0-89684-370-X). Orient Bk Dist.

Beginnings of Christian Philosophy: The Epistle to the Hebrews. James W. Thompson. Ed. by Bruce Vawter. LC 81-12295. (Catholic Biblical Quarterly Monograph: Vol. 13). vii, 184p. 1982. 5.50x (ISBN 0-915170-12-4). Catholic Biblical.

Beginnings of Christology: Together with the Lord's Supper As a Christological Problem. Willi Marxsen. LC 79-7384. pap. 31.80 (2029295). Bks Demand UMI.

Beginnings of Hindu Pantheism. Charles Lanman. 35.00 (ISBN 0-87968-719-3). Gordon Pr.

Beginnings of Quakerism. William C. Braithwaite. (Illus.). 562p. 1981. Repr. of 1923 ed. lib. bdg. 65.00 (ISBN 0-8495-0625-5). Arden Lib.

Beginnings of Religion: An Introductory & Scientific Study. Edwin O. James. 159p. 1973. Repr. of 1950 ed. lib. bdg. 22.50x (ISBN 0-8371-6706-X, JABE). Greenwood.

Beginnings of the Christian Religion: A Guide to the History & Literature of Judaism & Christianity. Meredith F. Eller. 1958. 16.95x (ISBN 0-8084-0392-3); pap. 12.95x (ISBN 0-8084-0393-1). New Coll U Pr.

Beginnings of the Church. Megan McKenna & Darryl Ducote. LC 78-71533. (Followers of the Way Ser.: Vol. 6). 1980. 22.50 (ISBN 0-8091-9547-X); cassette 7.50 (ISBN 0-8091-7671-8). Paulist Pr.

Beginnings: Preparing for Your Child's Baptism. Maxwell E. Johnson. (Pass Along Ser.). 32p. (Orig.). 1986. pap. 2.95 (ISBN 0-933350-47-3). Morse Pr.

Beginnings: The Orientation of New Teachers. Katherine Egan. 20p. 1981. 2.40 (ISBN 0-686-39892-0). Natl Cath Educ.

Beginnings: Word & Spirit in Conversion. Paul Helm. 133p. (Orig.). 1986. pap. 4.95 (ISBN 0-85151-470-7). Banner of Truth.

Begone Satan. Carl Vogl. 48p. 1973. pap. 1.50 (ISBN 0-89555-098-9). TAN Bks Pubs.

Behaving As If the God in All Life Mattered: A New Age Ecology. Machaelle S. Wright. (Illus.). 216p. 1986. pap. cancelled (ISBN 0-913299-33-2). Stillpoint.

Behavior of Belief. Spiros Zodhiates. 1966. 19.95 (ISBN 0-89957-505-6). AMG Pubs.

Behind Closed Doors: A Handbook on How to Pray. Joseph M. Champlin. 240p. (Orig.). 1984. pap. 8.95 (ISBN 0-8091-2637-0). Paulist Pr.

Behind Communism: The Jewish Background of Communism. F. L. Britton. 1982. lib. bdg. 59.95 (ISBN 0-87700-425-0). Revisionist Pr.

Behind That Wall. facs. ed. Edgar A. Peers. LC 72-90672. (Essay Index Reprint Ser). 1948. 15.00 (ISBN 0-8369-1210-1). Ayer Co Pubs.

Behind the Cosmic Curtain: The Further Writings of Swami Rudrananda. Swami Rudrananda, pseud. Ed. by John Mann. (Illus.). 176p. (Orig.). pap. 9.95x (ISBN 0-9613477-0-8). Neolog.

Behind the Creed: A Plain Man's Rationale of Faith. William P. Webb. LC 84-90201. 115p. 1985. 10.95 (ISBN 0-533-06248-9). Vantage.

Behind the Gospels. Henry J. Cadbury. LC 68-8591. (Orig.). 1968. pap. 2.50x (ISBN 0-87574-160-6). Pendle Hill.

Behind the Iron Curtain: The Story of John Visser. A. H. Barbee. 75p. 1985. pap. 2.95 (ISBN 0-89084-280-9). Bob Jones Univ Pr.

Behind the Pine Curtain: Portraits of Peter Prep. Simeon Thole. LC 79-21013. 198p. 1979. pap. 2.50 (ISBN 0-8146-1041-2). Liturgical Pr.

Behind the Scene. Douglas Reed. (Pt. 2 of Far & Wide). 1976. pap. 3.50x (ISBN 0-911038-41-8). Noontide.

Behind the Scenes with the Metaphysicians. Arthur Corey. 7.50 (ISBN 0-87516-014-X). De Vorss.

Behind the Sex of God: Toward a New Consciousness - Transcending Matriarchy & Patriarchy. Carol Ochs. LC 76-48519. 1977. pap. 8.95x (ISBN 0-8070-1113-4, Pub. by Ariadne Bks, BPA12). Beacon Pr.

Behind the Veils of Death & Sleep. Gladys Mayer. 1973. lib. bdg. 79.95 (ISBN 0-87968-541-7). Krishna Pr.

Behold a Great Image. Sharon Strassfeld & Arthur Kurzweil. LC 78-1168. (Illus.). 224p. 1978. 22.95 (ISBN 0-8276-0105-0, 417). Jewish Pubns.

Behold, He Cometh. Howard B. Rand. 1955. 5.00 (ISBN 0-685-08798-0). Destiny.

Behold His Love. Basilea Schlink. 144p. 1973. pap. 3.50 (ISBN 0-87123-039-9). Bethany Hse.

Behold I Show You a Mystery. C. W. Mabie. LC 80-82229. 150p. (Orig.). 1980. pap. 4.95 (ISBN 0-9601416-5-0). J C Print.

Behold the Beauty of the Lord: Praying with Icons. Henri J. Nouwen. LC 86-72698. (Illus.). 80p. (Orig.). 1987. spiral binding 7.95 (ISBN 0-87793-356-1). Ave Maria.

Behold the Bride. Mary E. Van Cleave. 1986. 12.95 (ISBN 0-533-07024-4). Vantage.

Behold the Flaming Sword: A Biography of John & Jesus. Harlan D. Fowler. (Illus.). 1983. 35.00 (ISBN 0-533-05059-6). Vantage.

Behold the King: A Study of Matthew. Stanley D. Toussaint. LC 80-13410. 1980. text ed. 16.95 (ISBN 0-930014-39-1). Multnomah.

Behold the Lamb. R. Kent Hughes. 180p. 1984. pap. 5.95 (ISBN 0-88207-623-X). Victor Bks.

Behold the Lamb. Ray Summers. LC 78-67924. 1979. 12.95 (ISBN 0-8054-1374-X). Broadman.

Behold the Lamb of God. F. Von Kietzel. 5.95 (ISBN 0-88172-136-0). Believers Bkshelf.

Behold the Man. R. Kent Hughes. LC 84-50144. 180p. 1984. pap. 5.95 (ISBN 0-89693-379-2). Victor Bks.

Behold the Pierced One. Joseph Ratzinger. Tr. of Schauen auf den Durchbohrten. 128p. 1986. pap. 7.95 (ISBN 0-89870-087-6). Ignatius Pr.

Behold the Sign. 12th ed. Ralph M. Lewis. LC 44-30695. 1981. 7.95 (ISBN 0-912057-16-5, G521). AMORC.

Behold the Spirit. Alan W. Watts. 288p. 1972. pap. 4.95 (ISBN 0-394-71761-9, Vin). Random.

Behold Your Christ: A Woman's Workshop on Jesus. Carolyn Nystrom. (Woman's Workshop Ser.). 128p. (Orig.). 1985. pap. 3.95 (ISBN 0-310-41981-6, 11284P). Zondervan.

Behold Your God. Agnes Sanford. 5.95 (ISBN 0-910924-35-X); pap. 4.50 (ISBN 0-910924-63-5). Macalester.

Behold Your God: A Woman's Workshop on the Attributes of God. Myrna Alexander. pap. 3.95 (ISBN 0-310-37131-7, 10916P). Zondervan.

Behold Your King. J. C. Macaulay. LC 81-22580. 256p. 1982. pap. 9.95 (ISBN 0-8024-2417-1). Moody.

Being a Christian. Washington Gladden. LC 72-4168. (Select Bibliographies Reprint Ser.). 1972. Repr. of 1876 ed. 14.00 (ISBN 0-8369-6880-8). Ayer Co Pubs.

Being a Christian. John R. Stott. pap. 0.75 (ISBN 0-87784-101-2). Inter-Varsity.

Being a Christian Friend. Kristen J. Ingram. 112p. 1985. pap. 5.95 (ISBN 0-8170-1084-X). Judson.

Being a Christian Today. Ladislaus Boros. Tr. by M. Benedict Davies. LC 79-13607. 124p. 1979. 7.95 (ISBN 0-8245-0202-7). Crossroad NY.

Being a Friend Means... Debby Anderson. (Sparkler Bks.). (Illus.). 32p. 1986. plastic comb bndg. 2.95 (ISBN 0-89191-932-5, 59329, Chariot Bks). Cook.

Being a Success at Who You Are. Andre Bustanoby. 1986. pap. 4.95 (ISBN 0-310-45381-X, 9172P). Zondervan.

Being Alive. (Benziger Family Life Program Ser.). 3p. 1978. 3.00 (ISBN 0-02-651600-4); tchrs. ed. 4.15 (ISBN 0-02-651610-1); family -handbook 1.80 (ISBN 0-02-651640-3). Benziger Pub Co.

Being & God: Introduction to the Philosophy of Being & to Natural Theology. George P. Klubertanz & Maurice R. Holloway. LC 63-15359. 1963. 39.50x (ISBN 0-89197-045-2); pap. text ed. 19.95x (ISBN 0-89197-674-4). Irvington.

Being & Having: An Existentialist Diary. Gabriel Marcel. 11.25 (ISBN 0-8446-2528-0). Peter Smith.

Being & Predication: Thomistic Interpretations. Ralph McInerny. (Studies in Philosophy & the History of Philosophy: Vol. 16). 1986. 36.95 (ISBN 0-8132-0612-X). Cath U Pr.

Being & the Messiah: The Message of St. John. Jose P. Miranda. Tr. by John Eagleson from Span. LC 77-5388. Orig. Title: Ser y el Mesias. 253p. (Orig.). 1977. 8.95x (ISBN 0-88344-027-X). Orbis Bks.

Being & Will: An Essay in Philosophical Theology. John Burbidge. LC 76-45934. pap. 40.70 (ISBN 0-8357-9484-9, 2013527). Bks Demand UMI.

Being Brothers & Sisters. Ed. by Diana Brandt. LC 83-83062. (Illus.). 115p. 1984. pap. 7.95 (ISBN 0-87303-091-5). Faith & Life.

Being, Evolution & Immortality. rev. ed. Haridas Chaudhuri. LC 74-4821. Orig. Title: Philosophy of Integralism. 224p. 1974. pap. 6.95 (ISBN 0-8356-0449-7, Quest). Theos Pub Hse.

Being Fully Persuaded. Elbert Willis. 1977. 1.25 (ISBN 0-89858-017-X). Fill the Gap.

Being Gifted, No. 1. Robert S. Maseroni. 1983. 0.80 (ISBN 0-89536-616-9, 0228). CSS of Ohio.

Being Good & Doing Good. Martin E. Marty. LC 84-47929. (Lead Bks.). 128p. 1984. pap. 4.95 (ISBN 0-8006-1603-0). Fortress.

Being Human. Edmund Hill. 304p. 1984. pap. 14.95 (ISBN 0-225-66358-9, AY8486, HarpR). Har-Row.

Being Human Being Hopeful. Walter L. Underwood. 112p. 1987. 9.95 (ISBN 0-687-02815-9). Abingdon.

Being Human: The Nature of Spiritual Experience. Ranald Macaulay & Jerram Barrs. LC 77-11365. 1978. pap. 6.95 (ISBN 0-87784-796-7). Inter-Varsity.

Being-in-Creation. Elaine Ward. 80p. (Orig.). 1983. pap. 9.95 (ISBN 0-940754-14-2). Ed Ministries.

Being in God's Family. Marian Baden. (Concordia Weekday Ser. - Gr. 3-4. Bk. 4, 2-V). 1967. pap. text ed. 2.75 (ISBN 0-570-06658-1, 22-2028); manual 5.85 (ISBN 0-686-82886-0, 22-2029). Concordia.

Being in Mission: A Resource for the Local Church & Community. Arthur O. Bauer. 1987. pap. 4.95. Friend Pr.

Being Jewish. rev. ed. Shimon Hurwitz. 1979. pap. 5.95 (ISBN 0-87306-196-9). Feldheim.

Being Jewish, Being Human: A Gift Book of Poems & Readings. Ed. by Dov P. Elkins. LC 79-88298. Date not set. pap. 16.50 (ISBN 0-918834-07-4). Growth Assoc.

Being Jewish in America: The Modern Experience. Arthur Hertzberg. LC 78-54390. 320p. 1980. pap. 7.95 (ISBN 0-8052-0654-X). Schocken.

Being Me. Grady Nutt. LC 71-145984. 1971. pap. 3.95 (ISBN 0-8054-6909-5, 4269-09). Broadman.

Being More Intense: A Study of the Prose Works of Bunyan, Swift, & Defoe. Paula R. Backscheider. LC 83-45274. (Studies in the Eighteenth Century: No. 7). 222p. 1984. 32.50 (ISBN 0-404-61473-6). AMS Pr.

Being of God: Theology & the Experience of Truth. Robert P. Scharlemann. 224p. 1981. 14.95 (ISBN 0-8164-0494-1, HarpR). Har-Row.

Being of Man & His Future Evolution. Rudolf Steiner. Tr. by Pauline Wehrle from Ger. 148p. 1981. 18.00 (ISBN 0-85440-402-3, Pub. by Steinerbooks); pap. 11.95 (ISBN 0-85440-405-8). Anthroposophic.

Being OK. Carolyn Ives. (Orig.). 1987. pap. 7.00 (ISBN 0-915541-19-X). Star Bks Inc.

Being Peace. Thich Nhat Hanh. (Illus.). 120p. (Orig.). 1987. pap. 8.50 (ISBN 0-938077-00-7). Parallax Pr.

Being Poor: A Biblical Study. Leslie Hoppe. (Theology & Life Ser.). 240p. 1987. pap. 9.95 (ISBN 0-89453-620-6). M Glazier.

Being Present to God: Letters on Prayer. Henri Caffarel. LC 83-15459. 202p. 1983. pap. 6.95 (ISBN 0-8189-0462-3). Alba.

Being Qua Being: A Theory of Identity, Existence & Predication. Panayot Butchvarov. LC 78-13812. 288p. 1979. 22.50x (ISBN 0-253-13700-4). Ind U Pr.

Being Religious in America: The Deepening Crises over Public Faith. Erling Jorstad. LC 86-3360. 128p. (Orig.). 1986. pap. 6.95 (ISBN 0-8066-2222-9, 10-0585). Augsburg.

Being Sexual...& Celibate. Keith Clark. LC 85-73158. 184p. (Orig.). 1986. pap. 4.95 (ISBN 0-87793-329-4). Ave Maria.

Being Torah. Joel L. Grishaver. LC 85-50219. (Illus.). 224p. (Orig.). 1985. pap. text ed. 7.95 (ISBN 0-933873-00-X). Torah Aura.

Being Torah Student Commentary, 2 Vols. Joel L. Grishaver. (Illus.). 72p. (Orig.). 1986. pap. text ed. 3.25 ea. Vol. 1 (ISBN 0-933873-09-3). Vol. 2 (ISBN 0-933873-10-7). Torah Aura.

Being Transformed: An Inner Way of Spiritual Growth. Edward E. Thornton. LC 83-27331. (Potentials: Guides for Productive Living Ser.: Vol. 4). 114p. (Orig.). 1984. pap. 7.95 (ISBN 0-664-24523-4). Westminster.

Beings & Their Attributes: The Teaching of the Bastian School of the Matzzila in the Classical Period. Richard M. Frank. LC 78-6957. 1978. 49.50x (ISBN 0-87395-378-9). State U NY Pr.

Beit El-Wali Temple of Ramesses Second. portfolio ed. Herbert Ricke et al. LC 67-18437. (Oriental Institute Nubian Expedition Pubns. Ser.: Vol. 1). (Illus.). 1967. 30.00x (ISBN 0-226-62365-3, OINE1). U of Chicago Pr.

Beitrage zur Geschichte der Kabbala. Adolph Jellinek. Ed. by Steven Katz. LC 79-7138. (Jewish Philosophy, Mysticism, & History of Ideas Ser.). 1980. Repr. of 1852 ed. lib. bdg. 16.00x (ISBN 0-405-12264-0). Ayer Co Pubs.

Beitrage zur Geschichte der Philosophie. Manuel Joel. Ed. by Steven Katz. LC 79-7140. (Jewish Philosophy, Mysticism & History of Ideas Ser.). 1980. Repr. of 1876 ed. lib. bdg. 51.50x (ISBN 0-405-12266-7). Ayer Co Pubs.

Beitrage zur Geschicte Agyptens unter Dem Islam, 2 vols. in 1. Carl H. Becker. LC 77-10579. (Studies in Islamic History: No. 5). 1978. Repr. of 1903 ed. lib. bdg. 25.00x (ISBN 0-87991-454-8). Porcupine Pr.

Beitrage zur Judischen Alterthumskunde, 2 vols. Leopold Low. 922p. Date not set. Repr. text ed. 149.04x (ISBN 0-576-80127-5, Pub. by Gregg Intl Pubs England). Gregg Intl.

Beitrage Zur Sektengenchichte des Mittelalter, 2 vols in 1. Johann J. Doellinger. LC 91-26634. (Social Science Ser). (Ger). 1970. Repr. of 1890 ed. Set. lib. bdg. 57.50 (ISBN 0-8337-0880-5). B Franklin.

Bekoroth, 1 vol. 18.00 (ISBN 0-910218-82-X). Bennet Pub.

Bektashi Order of Dervishes. John K. Birge. LC 77-87662. Repr. of 1937 ed. 35.00 (ISBN 0-404-16400-5). AMS Pr.

Belief & Faith: A Philosophical Tract. Josef Pieper. Tr. by Richard Winston & Clara Winston. LC 75-31841. 106p. 1976. Repr. of 1963 ed. lib. bdg. 22.50x (ISBN 0-8371-8490-8, PIBF). Greenwood.

Belief & History. Wilfred C. Smith. LC 75-50587. 138p. 1977. pap. 7.95x (ISBN 0-8139-1086-2). U Pr of Va.

Belief & Worship in Native North America. Ake Hultkrantz. Ed. by Christopher Vecsey. LC 81-18356. (Illus.). 358p. 1981. 30.00x (ISBN 0-8156-2248-1). Syracuse U Pr.

Belief, Change & Forms of Life. D. Z. Phillips. (Library of Philosophy & Religion). 144p. 1986. text ed. 29.95x (ISBN 0-391-03385-9). Humanities.

Belief in God: A Study in the Epistemology of Religion. George I. Mavrodes. LC 81-40788. 128p. 1981. pap. text ed. 7.50 (ISBN 0-8191-1816-8). U Pr of Amer.

Belief in God & Immortality, a Psychological, Anthropological & Statistical Study. J. H. Leuba. LC 17-54. Repr. of 1916 ed. 29.00 (ISBN 0-527-56600-4). Kraus Repr.

Belief in God in the Twentieth Century. John Elder. LC 82-81671. 70p. 1982. pap. 3.25 (ISBN 0-9608440-0-7). Nur Pubns.

Belief in Science & in Christian Life. Ed. by Thomas F. Torrance. 160p. 1981. pap. 12.00x (ISBN 0-905312-11-2, Pub. by Scot Acad Pr). Longwood Pub Group.

Belief That Behaves. Guy H. King. 1971. pap. 3.95 (ISBN 0-87508-271-8). Chr Lit.

Belief, Truth & Knowledge. Allen Armstrong. LC 72-83586. 240p. 1973. 42.50 (ISBN 0-521-08706-6); pap. 13.95 (ISBN 0-521-09737-1). Cambridge U Pr.

Belief Unbound. William P. Montague. LC 72-109630. (Select Bibliographies Reprint Ser). 1930. 15.00 (ISBN 0-8369-5239-1). Ayer Co Pubs.

Belief Unbound. William P. Montague. 1930. 13.50x (ISBN 0-686-83485-2). Elliots Bks.

Beliefs & Ideologies. Kenneth Thompson. (Key Ideas Ser.). 150p. 1985. 19.95 (ISBN 0-85312-858-8, 9582, Pub. by Tavistock England); pap. 7.50 (ISBN 0-85312-859-6, 9583, Pub. by Tavistock England). Methuen Inc.

Beliefs, Attitudes & Values: A Theory of Organization & Change. Milton Rokeach. LC 68-21322. (Social & Behavioral Science Ser.). 1968. 25.95x (ISBN 0-87589-013-X). Jossey-Bass.

Beliefs of United Methodist Christian. 3rd ed. Emerson Colaw. (Orig.). pap. 3.95 (ISBN 0-88177-025-6, DRO25B). Discipleship Res.

Believe! Richard M. DeVos & Charles P. Conn. 128p. 1975. pap. 2.95 (ISBN 0-8007-8267-4, Spire). Revell.

Believe It or Not It's in the Bible. Alice F. Voorhies. 38p. (Orig.). 1985. pap. 3.00 (ISBN 0-931494-77-X). Brunswick Pub.

Believe the Good News: Daily Meditations on the Lenten Masses. Emeric Lawrence. LC 82-97. 144p. 1982. pap. 5.75 (ISBN 0-8146-1256-3). Liturgical Pr.

Believe with God's Family. 2nd ed. Gerard P. Weber et al. (Word Is Life Ser.). 1977. 3.92 (ISBN 0-02-658500-6); tchrs. ed. 8.00 (ISBN 0-02-658510-3); family handbook 1.00 (ISBN 0-02-658550-2). Benziger Pub Co.

Believeing God When You Are Tempted To Doubt. Gene A. Getz. LC 83-4440. (Measure of...Ser.). 160p. 1983. pap. 5.95 (ISBN 0-8307-0881-2, 5417930). Regal.

Believer & the Powers That Are: Cases, History, & Other Data Bearing on the Relation of Religion & Government. John T. Noonan. LC 86-28440. 1987. 35.00 (ISBN 0-02-923161-2). Macmillan.

Believer's Absolute Surrender. Andrew Murray. 150p. 1985. pap. 3.95 (ISBN 0-87123-827-6). Bethany Hse.

Believers Armor. John MacArthur, Jr. (John MacArthur's Bible Studies). 1986. pap. 4.95 (ISBN 0-8024-5092-X). Moody.

Believer's Authority. 2nd ed. Kenneth E. Hagin. 1985. pap. 2.50 (ISBN 0-89276-406-6). Hagin Ministries.

Believers Baptism for Children of the Church. Marlin Jeschke. LC 82-23406. 160p. (Orig.). 1983. pap. 7.95 (ISBN 0-8361-3318-8). Herald Pr.

Believer's Bible Companion. Larry Huggins. 32p. (Orig.). 1984. pap. 1.95 (ISBN 0-89274-314-X, HH-314). Harrison Hse.

Believer's Call to Commitment. Andrew Murray. 110p. 1983. pap. 3.95 (ISBN 0-87123-289-8). Bethany Hse.

Believers' Church. Donald F. Durnbaugh. LC 85-7599. 328p. (Orig.). 1985. pap. 12.95x (ISBN 0-8361-1271-7). Herald Pr.

Believer's Daily Renewal. Andrew Murray. LC 81-6143. 125p. 1981. pap. 3.95 (ISBN 0-87123-147-6, 210147). Bethany Hse.

Believer's Full Blessing of Pentecost. Andrew Murray. 112p. 1984. pap. 3.95 (ISBN 0-87123-597-8). Bethany Hse.

Believer's Guide to Christian Maturity. A. F. Ballenger. LC 82-72493. 256p. 1982. pap. 4.95 (ISBN 0-87123-278-2, 210278). Bethany Hse.

Believer's Guidebook from Aspirin to Zoos. Lawrence O. Richards. 528p. 1983. 9.95 (ISBN 0-310-43470-X, 18163). Zondervan.

Believers Handbook. Gerard Berghoef & Lester DeKoster. LC 82-72686. 295p. 1982. 15.95 (ISBN 0-934874-03-4); pap. 8.95 (ISBN 0-934874-05-0). Chr Lib Pr.

Believer's New Covenant. Andrew Murray. LC 83-21408. 128p. 1983. pap. 3.95 (ISBN 0-87123-406-8, 210406). Bethany Hse.

Believer's New Life. Andrew Murray. LC 83-3006. 208p. 1984. pap. 3.95 (ISBN 0-87123-431-9). Bethany Hse.

Believer's Praise Book. Lawrence O. Richards. 1986. pap. 2.50 (ISBN 0-310-43512-9, 18204P). Zondervan.

Believer's Prayer Book. Lawrence O. Richards. 1986. pap. 2.50 (ISBN 0-310-43602-8, 18213P). Zondervan.

Believer's Prayer Life. rev. ed. Andrew Murray. LC 83-12254. (Andrew Murray Prayer Library). 141p. 1983. pap. 3.95 (ISBN 0-87123-277-4). Bethany Hse.

Believer's Promise Book. Lawrence O. Richards. 80p. (Orig.). 1984. pap. 2.50 (ISBN 0-310-43462-9, 18144P). Zondervan.

Believer's School of Prayer. rev. ed. Andrew Murray. LC 82-4401. 201p. 1982. pap. 3.95 (ISBN 0-87123-195-6, 210195). Bethany Hse.

Believer's Secret of Holiness. Andrew Murray. LC 84-2973. 208p. 1984. pap. 3.95 (ISBN 0-87123-432-7). Bethany Hse.

Believer's Secret of Living Like Christ. Andrew Murray. 176p. (Orig.). 1985. pap. 3.95 (ISBN 0-87123-445-9). Bethany Hse.

Believer's Secret of Obedience. Andrew Murray. LC 82-14603. (Andrew Murray Christian Maturity Library). 88p. 1982. pap. 3.95 (ISBN 0-87123-279-0, 210279). Bethany Hse.

Believer's Secret of the Abiding Presence. rev. ed. Andrew Murray et al. 144p. 1987. pap. 3.95 (ISBN 0-87123-899-3). Bethany Hse.

Believer's Secret of the Master's Indwelling. rev. ed. Andrew Murray. 192p. 1986. pap. 3.95 (ISBN 0-87123-653-2, 210653). Bethany Hse.

Believer's Secret of Waiting on God. Andrew Murray. 169p. 1986. pap. 3.95 (ISBN 0-87123-886-1). Bethany Hse.

Believer's Tree of Life. Albert J. Wahlie. Ed. by Shmuel Ben Menachem. (Illus.). 105p. (Orig.). 1986. pap. 6.95x (ISBN 0-9616488-0-5). Alef Bet Comns.

Believing. Michele McCarty. (Fullness of Life Ser.). 160p. 1980. pap. text ed. 6.95 (ISBN 0-697-01753-2); tchr's manual 8.00 (ISBN 0-697-01754-0). Wm C Brown.

Believing Bible Study. 2nd ed. Edward F. Hills. (Illus.). 258p. pap. 4.50 (ISBN 0-915923-01-7). Christian Res Pr.

Believing God for the Impossible. Bill Bright. LC 78-73565. 1979. 8.95 (ISBN 0-918956-55-2). Campus Crusade.

Believing God When You Are Tempted to Doubt: The Measure of a Christian; Studies in James I. Gene A. Getz. LC 84-27543. 160p. pap. 5.95 (ISBN 0-8307-1021-3, 5418416). Regal.

Believing in Jesus: A Popular Overview of the Catholic Faith. Leonard Foley. (Illus.). 185p. (Orig.). 1981. pap. text ed. 5.95 (ISBN 0-912228-79-2). St Anthony Mess Pr.

Believing in the Church: Doctrine Commission of the Church of England. Ed. by John Taylor. LC 82-80254. 320p. (Orig.). 1982. Repr. of 1981 ed. 17.95 (ISBN 0-8192-1301-2). Morehouse.

Believing Jew: The Selected Writings. facsimile ed. Milton Steinberg. LC 76-152215. (Essay Index Reprint Ser). Repr. of 1951 ed. 18.00 (ISBN 0-8369-2256-5). Ayer Co Pubs.

Believing the Bible. David Winter. LC 82-62582. 116p. (Orig.). 1983. pap. 5.95 (ISBN 0-8192-1325-X). Morehouse.

Believing the Impossible Before Breakfast. Bhagwan Shree Rajneesh. Ed. by Ma Prem Maneesha. LC 82-229302. (Initiation Talks Ser.). (Illus.). 266p. (Orig.). 1981. 22.95 (ISBN 0-88050-006-9). Chidvilas Found.

Believing Truth about the Church. Harold Cooper. (Illus.). 122p. 1975. pap. 3.50 (ISBN 0-89114-070-0); P. 64. tchr's ed. 1.00 (ISBN 0-89114-071-9). Baptist Pub Hse.

Bell Ringer. Robert Hathrill. 1983. 8.95 (ISBN 0-533-05631-4). Vantage.

Bell Ringer of Angel's. B. Harte. 1985. 10.00x (Pub. by J Richardson UK). State Mutual Bk.

Bell Ringing Minimus Three & Four Bell Methods. H. Lewis. 1985. 18.75x (ISBN 0-317-54263-X, Pub. by J Richardson UK). State Mutual Bk.

Belle Harris Bennett, Her Life Work. Robert W. MacDonell. Ed. by Carolyn D. Gifford & Donald Dayton. (Women in American Protestant Religion 1800-1930 Ser.). 297p. 1987. lib. bdg. 40.00 (ISBN 0-8240-0669-0). Garland Pub.

Bells & Bellringing. J. Hilton. 1977. 12.50x (ISBN 0-317-54264-8, Pub. by J Richardson UK). State Mutual Bk.

Bells in Our Lives. M. Cockett. 1985. 17.50x (ISBN 0-317-54266-4, Pub. by J Richardson UK). State Mutual Bk.

Bell's New Pantheon, 2 vols. John Bell. Ed. by Burton Feldman & Robert D. Richardson. LC 78-60919. (Myth & Romanticism Ser.: Vol. 4). 809p. 1979. Set. lib. bdg. 160.00 (ISBN 0-8240-3553-4). Garland Pub.

Bells of Haslemere Parish Church, Surrey. T. Jennings. 1985. 11.25x (ISBN 0-317-54272-9, Pub. by J Richardson UK). State Mutual Bk.

Bells of Hereford Cathedral. J. Eisel. 1985. 12.50x (ISBN 0-317-54268-0, Pub. by J Richardson UK). State Mutual Bk.

Bells of St. Mary's Twickenham. E. Morris. 1985. 11.25x (ISBN 0-317-54270-2, Pub. by J Richardson UK). State Mutual Bk.

Belonging. Leonard of Taize. 172p. 1985. pap. 7.95 (ISBN 0-8298-0565-6). Pilgrim NY.

Belonging. Michele McCarty. (Fullness of Life Ser.). (YA) 1985. pap. text ed. 7.95 (ISBN 0-697-02068-1); tchr's. ed. 10.00 (ISBN 0-697-02069-X); wkbk. 3.25 (ISBN 0-697-02070-3). Wm C Brown.

Belonging! Adventures in Church Membership. Donald N. Bastian. 1978. pap. 4.95 (ISBN 0-89367-044-8). Light & Life.

Belonging, An Introduction to the Faith & Life of the Christian Reformed Church. Wilbert M. VanDyk. LC 82-1241. (Illus.). 120p. (Orig.). 1982. pap. 4.50 (ISBN 0-933140-43-6). CRC Pubns.

Belonging: Issues of Emotional Living in an Age of Stress for Clergy & Religious. Ed. by Edwin J. Franasiak. LC 79-11482. 127p. 1979. pap. 4.95 (ISBN 0-89571-007-2). Affirmation.

Belonging: Our Need for Community in Church & Family. S. D. Gaede. LC 85-17987. 288p. (Orig.). 1985. pap. 9.95 (ISBN 0-310-36891-X, 12294P). Zondervan.

Beloved, 2 vols. Bhagwan Shree Rajneesh. Ed. by Ma Yoga Sudha. LC 78-903022. (Baul Mystics Ser.). (Illus., Orig.). 1977. Vol. I, 324 pgs. 15.95 ea. (ISBN 0-88050-007-7). Vol. II, 288 pgs. 1978. Chidvilas Found.

Beloved Adversary: Our Complex Relationship with a Loving God. W. Glyn Evans. Ed. by Julie A. Link. 96p. 1985. pap. 5.95 (ISBN 0-310-29371-5, 10462P). Zondervan.

Beloved Alcoholic: What to Do When a Family Member Drinks. Janet Ohlemacher. 128p. 1984. pap. 4.95 (ISBN 0-310-45531-6, 12480P). Zondervan.

Beloved of My Heart. Bhagwan Shree Rajneesh. Ed. by Ma Prem Maneesha. (Initiation Talks Ser.). (Illus.). 356p. (Orig.). 1978. 19.95 (ISBN 0-88050-009-3). Chidvilas Found.

Beloved Prophet: The Love Letters of Kahlil Gibran & Mary Haskell & Her Private Journal. Ed. by Virginia Hilu. 1972. 18.95 (ISBN 0-394-43298-3). Knopf.

Beloved Sufferer. Edwin Hayden. 144p. 1987. pap. 5.95 (ISBN 0-87403-236-9, 3178). Standard Pub.

Beloved Unbeliever: A Woman's Workshop. Jo Berry. (Woman's Workshop Ser.). 176p. (Orig.). 1985. leader's manual 2.95 (ISBN 0-310-42661-8, 11219P); student's manual 5.95 (ISBN 0-310-42691-X, 11220P). Zondervan.

Beloved Unbeliever: Loving Your Husband into the Faith. Jo Berry. 176p. (Orig.). 1981. pap. 5.95 (ISBN 0-310-42621-9, 11215). Zondervan.

Beloved World: The Story of God & People. Eugenia Price. (Illus.). 1979. pap. 9.95 (ISBN 0-310-31271-X, 10540P). Zondervan.

Belzec, Sobibor, Treblinka: The Operation Reinhard Death Camps. Yitzhak Arad. 1987. 29.95 (ISBN 0-253-34293-7). Ind U Pr.

Ben-Gurion Looks at the Bible. David Ben-Gurion. Tr. by Jonathan Kolatch. LC 70-167600. 320p. 1972. 12.50 (ISBN 0-8246-0127-0). Jonathan David.

Ben Hur. Lew Wallace. (Classics Ser). (YA) pap. 2.95 (ISBN 0-8049-0074-4, CL-74). Airmont.

Ben Sira & Demotic Wisdom. Jack T. Sanders. LC 82-21464. (SBL Monograph). 134p. 1983. pap. 19.50 (ISBN 0-89130-586-6). Scholars Pr GA.

Ben Sira's View of Women: A Literary Analysis. Warren C. Trenchard. LC 82-16755. (Brown Judaic Studies: No. 38). 352p. 1982. pap. 15.75 (ISBN 0-89130-593-9, 14-00-38). Scholars Pr GA.

Benedetto Da Mantova: Il Beneficio Di Cristo. Ed. by Salvatore Caponetto. LC 72-3471. (Corpus Reformatorum Italicorum & Biblioteca Ser.). (Lat. & Ital., Illus.). 558p. 1972. 40.00 (ISBN 0-87580-035-1). N Ill U Pr.

Benedict Nta Tanka's Commentary & Dramatized Ideas on Disease & Witchcraft in Our Society: A Schreber Case from Cameroon African on His Mental Illness. Alexander Boroffka. (Medical Care in Developing Countries Ser.: Vol. 7). 150p. 1980. 19.45 (ISBN 3-8204-6901-X). P Lang Pubs.

Benedicti Abbatis Petriburgenis De Vita et Miraculis S. Thomae Cantuar. Ed. by John A. Giles. Repr. of 1850 ed. 24.00 (ISBN 0-8337-1341-8). B Franklin.

Benedictine Bibliography: An Author-Subject Union List. Ed. by Oliver L. Kapsner. LC 81-20790. 832p. 1982. first suppl. 22.50 (ISBN 0-8146-1258-X). Liturgical Pr.

Benedictine Cartoons. Wm. Armstrong. (Armstrong Cartoon Ser.). (Illus., Orig.). 1973. pap. 1.00 (ISBN 0-913452-25-4). Jesuit Bks.

Benedictine Monasticism As Reflected in the Warnefrid-Hildemar Commentaries on the Rule. Sr. M. Alfred Schroll. LC 77-140026. (Columbia University. Studies in the Social Sciences: No. 478). Repr. of 1941 ed. 20.00 (ISBN 0-404-51478-2). AMS Pr.

Benedictine Way. Wulston Mork. 1987. pap. write for info. (ISBN 0-932506-48-8). St Bedes Pubns.

Benedictines in Britain. Turner & Rogers. 1980. 12.95 (ISBN 0-8076-0992-7). Braziller.

Benedictus, Saint: Abbot of Monte Cassino. Ernst A. Kock. (EETS, OS Ser.: No. 120). (Three Middle-English Versions of the Rule of St. Benet). Repr. of 1902 ed. 50.00 (ISBN 0-527-00118-X). Kraus Repr.

Benedictus, Saint, Abbot of Monte Cassino: The Rule of S. Benet. Ed. by H. Logeman. (EETS, OS Ser.: No. 90). Repr. of 1888 ed. 18.00 (ISBN 0-527-00089-2). Kraus Repr.

Benedictus: Studies in Honor of St. Benedict. (Cistercian Studies: No. 67). 8.95 (ISBN 0-87907-867-7). Cistercian Pubns.

Benefactor: Epigraphic Study of a Graeco-Roman & New Testament Semantic Field. Frederick W. Danker. LC 81-70419. 1982. 29.95x (ISBN 0-915644-23-1). Clayton Pub Hse.

Beneficent Rule of Destiny. John Jocelyn & Beredene Jocelyn. 1983. pap. 1.50 (ISBN 0-916786-73-0). St George Bk Serv.

Benefit of Christ. Juan de Valdes & Don Benedetto. LC 84-9282. (Classics of Faith & Devotion Ser.). 1984. 10.95 (ISBN 0-88070-063-7). Multnomah.

Benefit of Clergy in England in the Later Middle Ages. Leona C. Gabel. 1969. lib. bdg. 17.00x (ISBN 0-374-92964-5, Octagon). Hippocrene Bks.

Benevolent Deity: Ebenezer Gay & the Rise of Rational Religion in New England, 1669-1787. Robert J. Wilson, III. LC 83-3657. (Illus.). 320p. 1984. 26.00x (ISBN 0-8122-7891-7). U of Pa Pr.

Bengal Muslims, Eighteen Seventy-One to Nineteen Six: A Quest for Identity. Rafiuddin Ahmed. (Illus.). 1981. 34.00x (ISBN 0-19-561260-4). Oxford U Pr.

Benjamin & the Bible Donkeys. Beverly Amstutz. (Illus.). 36p. 1981. pap. 2.50x (ISBN 0-937836-03-6). Precious Res.

Benjamin Colman's "Some of the Glories of Our Lord & Saviour Jesus Christ," Exhibited in Twenty Sacramental Discourses (1928) Chester P. Sadowy. 1979. lib. bdg. 35.00 (ISBN 0-8482-6210-7). Norwood Edns.

Benjamin Franklin & Jonathan Edwards. Carl Van Doren. 1979. Repr. of 1920 ed. lib. bdg. 20.00 (ISBN 0-8495-5525-6). Arden Lib.

Benjamin Franklin & the Zealous Presbyterians. Melvin H. Buxbaum. LC 74-14932. 320p. 1974. 28.75x (ISBN 0-271-01176-9). Pa St U Pr.

Benjamin: Journey of a Jew. Ruth Abramson. (Life-Cycle Bookshelf Ser.). (Orig.). 1987. pap. 10.00 (ISBN 0-933771-02-9). Alpha Pub Co.

Benjamin, the Littlest Brother. Zev Paamoni. (Biblical Ser.). (Illus.). 1970. 4.00 (ISBN 0-914080-28-8). Shulsinger Sales.

Benjamin West: The Context of His Life's Work. John Dillenberger. LC 76-42004. (Illus.). 238p. 1977. 25.00 (ISBN 0-911536-65-5). Trinity U Pr.

Benjamin Wisner Bacon: Pioneer in American Biblical Criticism. Roy A. Harrisville. LC 76-16178. (Society of Biblical Literature. Studies in Biblical Scholarship). 1976. pap. 8.95 (ISBN 0-89130-110-0, 061102). Scholars Pr GA.

Bennett Law of 1889: Education & Politics in Wisconsin. Robert J. Ulrich. Ed. by Francesco Cordasco. LC 80-902. (American Ethnic Groups Ser.). 1981. lib. bdg. 55.00x (ISBN 0-405-13462-2). Ayer Co Pubs.

Bennett's Guide to the Bible: Graphic Aids & Outlines. Boyce M. Bennett. (Illus.). 128p. (Orig.). 1982. pap. 9.95 (ISBN 0-8164-2397-0, HarpR). Har-Row.

Benson of Cowley. Ed. by Martin L. Smith. 153p. 1983. pap. 8.00 (ISBN 0-936384-12-3). Cowley Pubns.

Bent World. Ronald Elsdon. LC 81-8261. 200p. (Orig.). 1981. pap. 4.95 (ISBN 0-87784-834-3). Inter-Varsity.

Bent World: Essays on Religion & Culture. Ed. by John R. May. LC 81-5801. (College Theology Society Annual Publications Ser.). 215p. 1979. 18.00 (ISBN 0-89130-503-3, 34 10 79). Scholars Pr GA.

Bent World: Essays on Religion & Culture. Ed. by John R. May. 224p. (Orig.). 1986. pap. 23.00 (ISBN 0-8191-5614-0, Pub. by College Theology Society). U Pr of Amer.

Bentley's Milton. John W. Mackail. LC 73-7628. 1973. lib. bdg. 15.00 (ISBN 0-8414-2343-1). Folcroft.

Beowulf & the Appositive Style. Fred C. Robinson. LC 84-11889. (Hodges Lecture Ser.). 120p. 1985. text ed. 12.95x (ISBN 0-87049-444-9); pap. 6.95x (ISBN 0-87049-531-3). U of Tenn Pr.

Beppe Assenza. Herbert Witzenmann. (Illus.). 160p. 1979. 29.95 (ISBN 0-85440-340-X, Pub. by Steinerbooks). Anthroposophic.

Bequests, Endowments, & Special Gifts. Richard H. Stough. (Orig.). 1981. pap. 1.75 (ISBN 0-937172-27-8). JLJ Pubs.

Berakoth. 18.00 (ISBN 0-910218-51-X). Bennet Pub.

Berean. John H. Noyes. LC 74-83431. (Religion in America, Ser. 1). 1969. Repr. of 1847 ed. 32.00 (ISBN 0-405-00256-4). Ayer Co Pubs.

Bereavement. Ed. by Graeme M. Griffin. (Illus.). 59p. (Orig.). 1977. pap. 5.95 (ISBN 0-85819-314-0, Pub. by JBCE). ANZ Religious Pubns.

Bereishis-Genesis, Vol. 5. Meir Zlotowitz. (Art Scroll Tanach Ser.). 1980. 16.95 (ISBN 0-89906-358-6); pap. 13.95 (ISBN 0-89906-359-4). Mesorah Pubns.

Bereishis-Genesis: Vol. 4, Vayeitzei-Vayishlach. Meir Zlotowitz. (Art Scroll Tanach Ser.). 400p. 1979. 16.95 (ISBN 0-89906-356-X); pap. 13.95 (ISBN 0-89906-357-8). Mesorah Pubns.

Berengar & the Reform of the Sacramental System. Allan J. Macdonald. 444p. 1977. Repr. of 1930 ed. lib. bdg. 30.00 (ISBN 0-915172-25-9). Richwood Pub.

Bergson et Teilhard de Chardin. Barthelemy-Madaule. 23.50 (ISBN 0-685-36604-9). French & Eur.

Berkeley. Harry M. Bracken. LC 74-15569. 176p. 1975. 19.95 (ISBN 0-312-07595-2). St Martin.

Berkeley. Alexander C. Fraser. 1899. 12.50 (ISBN 0-8274-1926-0). R West.

Berkeley. George D. Hicks. LC 68-15129. 1968. Repr. of 1932 ed. 9.00x (ISBN 0-8462-1235-8). Russell.

Berkeley. George Pitcher. (Arguments of the Philosophers Ser.). 300p. 1977. 24.95x (ISBN 0-7100-8685-7); pap. 14.95 (ISBN 0-7102-0391-8). Methuen Inc.

Berkeley. G. J. Warnock. 240p. 1983. 14.95 (ISBN 0-268-00670-9); pap. 7.95 (ISBN 0-268-00671-7). U of Notre Dame Pr.

Berkeley's Argument. C. D. Broad. LC 75-1069. (Studies in Philosophy: No. 40). 1975. lib. bdg. 22.95x (ISBN 0-8383-0113-4). Haskell.

Berkeley's Philosophical Writings. George Berkeley. Ed. by David M. Armstrong. (Orig.). 1965. pap. 5.95 (ISBN 0-02-064170-2, Collier). Macmillan.

Berkouwer's Doctrine of Election: Balance or Imbalance? Alvin L. Baker. 1981. pap. 5.95 (ISBN 0-87552-119-3). Presby & Reformed.

Bernadette: The Only Witness. John W. Lynch. 5.00 (ISBN 0-8198-1104-1); pap. 4.00 (ISBN 0-8198-1105-X). Dghtrs St Paul.

Bernard Delicieux et l'Inquisition Albigeoise, 1300-1320. Barthelemy Haureau. LC 78-63180. (Heresies of the Early Christian & Medieval Era: Second Ser.). Repr. of 1877 ed. 31.00 (ISBN 0-404-16223-1). AMS Pr.

Bernard-Lazare. Nelly Wilson. LC 77-82524. 1979. 47.50 (ISBN 0-521-21802-0). Cambridge U Pr.

Bernard Lonergan's Philosophy of God. Bernard J. Tyrrell. LC 73-22205. pap. 54.00 (ISBN 0-317-29698-1, 2022063). Bks Demand UMI.

Bernard of Clairvaux & the Cistercian Spirit. LC 76-15487. (Cistercian Studies Ser.: No. 16). (Illus.). 1976. 10.95 (ISBN 0-87907-816-2). Cistercian Pubns.

Bernard of Clairvaux: Consideration: Advice to a Pope. Tr. by John D. Anderson & Elizabeth T. Kennan. LC 75-27953. (Cistercian Fathers Ser.: No. 37). 1976. 5.00 (ISBN 0-87907-137-0). Cistercian Pubns.

Bernard of Clairvaux on the Song of Songs, Vol. II. Bernard Of Clairvaux. Tr. by Kilian Walsh. (Cistercian Fathers Ser.: No. 7). pap. 5.00 (ISBN 0-87907-707-7). Cistercian Pubns.

Bernard of Clairvaux on the Song of Songs, Vol. I. Tr. by Kilian Walsh. (Cistercian Fathers Er.: No. 4). pap. 5.00 (ISBN 0-87907-104-4). Cistercian Pubns.

Bernard of Clairvaux: Sermons I on Conversion; Lenten Sermons on the Psalm "He Who Dwells". Bernard Of Clairvaux. Tr. by Marie-Bernard Said. (Cistercian Fathers Ser.: No. 25). (Lat.). 1982. 25.95 (ISBN 0-87907-125-7); pap. 7.00 (ISBN 0-87907-925-8). Cistercian Pubns.

Bernard of Clairvaux: Sermons on the Song of Songs, Vol. IV. Bernard Of Clairvaux. Tr. by Irene Edmonds. (Cistercian Fathers Ser.: N0. 40). 1980. 15.95 (ISBN 0-87907-140-0). Cistercian Pubns.

Bernard of Clairvaux: Sermons on the Song of Songs, Vol. III. Tr. by Kilian Walsh & Irene Edmonds. (Cistercian Fathers Ser.: No. 31). 1979. 15.95 (ISBN 0-87907-131-1); pap. 5.00 (ISBN 0-87907-931-2). Cistercian Pubns.

Bernard of Clairvaux: Studies Presented to Dom Jean Leclercq. LC 73-8099. (Cistercian Studies: No. 23). 1973. 5.50 (ISBN 0-87907-823-5). Cistercian Pubns.

Bernard of Clairvaux: The Irishman. Tr. by Robert T. Mayer. LC 78-768. (Cistercian Fathers Ser.). 1978. 7.95 (ISBN 0-685-87078-2); pap. 4.00 (ISBN 0-87907-910-X). Cistercian Pubns.

Bernard of Clairvaux: The Times, the Man & His Work. Richard S. Storrs. 598p. 1981. Repr. of 1893 ed. lib. bdg. 65.00 (ISBN 0-8495-4974-4). Arden Lib.

Bernard of Clairvaux, Treatises II: The Steps of Humility & Pride, on Loving God. LC 74-7147. (Cistercian Fathers Ser.: No. 13). 1974. pap. 5.00 (ISBN 0-87907-713-1). Cistercian Pubns.

Bernard of Clairvaux, Treatises III: On Grace & Free Choice, in Praise of the New Knighthood. Tr. by Daniel O'Donovan. (Cistercian Studies Ser.: No. 3). 1977. 10.95 (ISBN 0-87907-119-2); pap. 4.95 (ISBN 0-87907-719-0). Cistercian Pubns.

Bernardus de Cura Rei Familiaris: Early Scottish Prophecies, Etc. Ed. by J. R. Lumby. (EETS OS Ser.: Vol. 42). pap. 15.00 (ISBN 0-8115-3351-4). Kraus Repr.

Beroldus, Sive Ecclesiae Ambrosianae Mediolanensis Calendarium Et Ordines Saec XII. Marco Magistretti. 294p. 1894. Repr. of 1894 ed. text ed. 66.24x (ISBN 0-576-99706-4, Pub. by Gregg Intl Pubs England). Gregg Intl.

Berrigans: A Bibliography of Published Works by Daniel, Philip, & Elizabeth Berrigan. Anne Klejment. LC 78-68214. (Garland Reference Library of Humanities: No. 154). 1979. lib. bdg. 36.00 (ISBN 0-8240-9788-2). Garland Pub.

Bertrand Russell on God & Religion. Ed. by Al Seckel. 345p. pap. 12.95 (ISBN 0-87975-323-4). Prometheus Bks.

Besa: The Life of Shenoute. Tr. & intro. by David N. Bell. (Cistercian Studies: No. 73). 1983. pap. 11.95 (ISBN 0-87907-873-1). Cistercian Pubns.

Beschneidung und Reifezeremonien Bei Naturvoelkern. Adolf E. Jensen. 1933. 19.00 (ISBN 0-384-27160-X). Johnson Repr.

Beside All Waters. J. H. Hunter. 245p. 1964. 3.95 (ISBN 0-87509-050-8). Chr Pubns.

Beside Galilee. Hector Bolitho. 206p. 1981. Repr. of 1933 ed. lib. bdg. 25.00 (ISBN 0-89987-076-7). Darby Bks.

Beside Still Waters. Hughes W. Day. 418p. 1979. 9.95 (ISBN 0-8341-0599-3). Beacon Hill.

Beside Still Waters. Raymond B Walker. LC 75-32601. (Illus.). 1975. 12.50 (ISBN 0-8323-0264-3). Binford-Metropolitan.

Beside Still Waters: Meditation Moments on the Psalms. Millie Stamm. 144p. 1983. gift edition 9.95 (ISBN 0-310-33060-2, 10743). Zondervan.

Beside the Sea of Glass: The Song of the Lamb. Daniel Berrigan. (Classic Prayer Ser.). (Illus.). 112p. 1978. pap. 2.50 (ISBN 0-8164-2174-9, HarpR). Har-Row.

Beside the Still Waters. Willa Fogle. 1979. pap. 4.00 (ISBN 0-87516-282-7). De Vorss.

Beside the Still Waters. Loretta Strahan. Ed. by Jeff Hughes. 108p. (Orig.). 1986. pap. 3.45 (ISBN 0-910653-18-6, 8101T). Archival Servs.

Best Birthday: A Christmas Entertainment for Children. G. L. Hill. 8.95 (ISBN 0-89190-404-2, Pub. by Am Repr). Amereon Ltd.

Best Black Sermons. William M. Philpot. LC 72-75358. 96p. 1972. pap. 4.95 (ISBN 0-8170-0533-1). Judson.

Best Church Plays: A Bibliography of Religious Drama. Albert Johnson. 11.25 (ISBN 0-8446-2328-8). Peter Smith.

Best Family of All. Mary E. LeBar. 32p. 1977. pap. 3.95 (ISBN 0-88207-251-X). Victor Bks.

Best Gifts. Compiled by T. O. Tollett. 1971. pap. 1.00 (ISBN 0-89114-062-X). Baptist Pub Hse.

Best Half of Life. Raymond Ortlund & Anne Ortlund. LC 76-21582. 1976. pap. 3.25 (ISBN 0-8307-0443-4, 5404193). Regal.

Best Is Yet to Be. LeRoy Patterson. 192p. (Orig.). 1986. pap. 5.95 (ISBN 0-8423-0183-6). Tyndale.

Best-Loved Bible Stories: Old Testament & New Testament, 2 vols. World Book Inc. LC 79-55309. (Illus.). 90p. 1980. write for info. (ISBN 0-7166-2059-6). World Bk.

Best-Loved Religious Poems. Compiled by James G. Lawson. 256p. 1981. 9.95 (ISBN 0-8007-0019-8). Revell.

Best of A. W. Tozer. A. W. Tozer. (Best Ser). 1978. pap. 3.95 (ISBN 0-8010-8845-3). Baker Bk.

Best of A. W. Tozer. W. Wiersbe. 249p. 1979. pap. 3.95. Chr Pubns.

Best of Alexander Maclaren. Alexander Maclaren. Ed. by Gaius G. Atkins. LC 74-179733. (Biography Index Reprint Ser). Repr. of 1949 ed. 14.00 (ISBN 0-8369-8101-4). Ayer Co Pubs.

Best of Andrew Murray. Andrew Murray. (Best Ser.). pap. 4.95 (ISBN 0-8010-6069-9). Baker Bk.

Best of C. G. Chappell. Clovis G. Chappell. (Best Ser.). 240p. 1984. pap. 5.95 (ISBN 0-8010-2500-1). Baker Bk.

Best of C. H. Spurgeon. C. H. Spurgeon. 256p. 1986. pap. 6.95 (ISBN 0-8010-8267-6). Baker Bk.

Best of Chester Swor. Chester E. Swor. LC 81-67202. 1981. pap. 6.95 (ISBN 0-8054-5293-1). Broadman.

Best of Christmas Joys. Joan W. Brown. LC 83-45165. 64p. (Orig.). 1983. pap. 2.95 (ISBN 0-385-19039-5, Galilee). Doubleday.

Best of Dwight L. Moody. Ed. by Dwight L. Moody & Ralph G. Turnbull. (Best Ser.). 1979. pap. 6.95 (ISBN 0-8010-6216-0). Baker Bk.

Best of F. B. Meyer. F. B. Meyer. 176p. 1984. pap. 5.95 (ISBN 0-8010-6179-2). Baker Bk.

Best of H. A. Ironside. H. A. Ironside. (Best Ser.). 296p. (Orig.). 1981. pap. 4.95 (ISBN 0-8010-5033-2). Baker Bk.

Best of John Calvin. John Calvin. Compiled by Samuel Dunn. (Best Ser.). 416p. 1981. pap. 5.95 (ISBN 0-8010-2467-6). Baker Bk.

Best of John Henry Jowett. John H. Jowett. Ed. by Gerald Kennedy. LC 79-179729. (Biography Index Reprint Ser.). Repr. of 1948 ed. 16.00 (ISBN 0-8369-8097-2). Ayer Co Pubs.

Best of Kripalu Yoga Quest: Handbook for Total Living. Kripalu Center for Holistic Health Staff. LC 82-84671. 101p. (Orig.). 1983. pap. 4.95 (ISBN 0-940258-08-0). Kripalu Pubns.

Best of Leader Ideabank. 110p. 1984. pap. 9.95 (ISBN 0-89191-976-7). Cook.

Best of Olomeinu Back Cover Stories: Series II - Events in the Lives of Torah Personalities. 2.75 (ISBN 0-914131-04-4, D31). Torah Umesorah.

Best of Olomeinu Back Cover Stories: Series I - Little Stories with Great Meanings. 2.75 (ISBN 0-914131-03-6, D30). Torah Umesorah.

Best of Olomeinu: Pesach & Other Stories, Bk. 5. (Illus.). 160p. 9.85 (ISBN 0-317-53889-6); pap. 7.15. Torah Umesorah.

Best of Open Windows. Compiled by Clyde Fant. LC 81-67201. 1981. 7.95 (ISBN 0-8054-5290-7). Broadman.

Best of Simpson. A. B. Simpson. Compiled by Keith M. Bailey. 1987. pap. write for info. (ISBN 0-87509-314-0). Chr Pubns.

Best of the Glow: A Fifteen Year Retrospective, Vol. 1. Ed. by Naosherwan Anzar. LC 84-23518. 208p. (Orig.). 1984. pap. 8.95 (ISBN 0-913078-54-9). Sheriar Pr.

Best of These Days. Ed. by Larry M. Correu. LC 82-13415. 132p. 1983. 8.95 (ISBN 0-664-21391-X). Westminster.

Best of This World. Michael Scully. 416p. (Orig.). 1987. lib. bdg. 32.50 (ISBN 0-8191-5605-1, Pub. by IEA); pap. text ed. 19.75 (ISBN 0-8191-5606-X). U Pr of Amer.

Best of Times: Ecclesiastes 3: 1-8. Vicki Huffman. LC 85-29087. 1986. pap. 5.95 (ISBN 0-8054-1234-4). Broadman.

Best of Times, the Worst of Times: Andrew Greeley & American Catholicism, 1950-1975. John N. Kotre. LC 78-14224. 256p. 1978. 21.95x (ISBN 0-88229-380-X). Nelson-Hall.

Best of Try This One. Ed. by Thom Schultz. (Illus.). 80p. (Orig.). 1977. pap. 5.95 (ISBN 0-936664-01-0). Group Bks.

Best of Vance Havner. Vance Havner. (Best Ser.). pap. 3.95 (ISBN 0-8010-4234-8). Baker Bk.

Best of Walter A. Maier. Paul L. Maier. 1980. pap. 7.95 (ISBN 0-570-03823-5, 12-2786). Concordia.

Best Radio Plays of 1984. (Methuen Modern Plays Ser.). 172p. 1985. 22.00 (ISBN 0-413-58430-5, 9650). Methuen Inc.

Best Sermons, Nineteen Forty-Nine to Nineteen Fifty. facsimile ed. Ed. by George P. Butler. LC 74-134065. (Essay Index Reprint Ser). Repr. of 1949 ed. 23.50 (ISBN 0-8369-2488-6). Ayer Co Pubs.

Best Sermons, 1947. facsimile ed. Ed. by George P. Butler. LC 74-134065. (Essay Index Reprint Ser). Repr. of 1947 ed. 23.50 (ISBN 0-8369-2487-8). Ayer Co Pubs.

Best That I Can Be. J. Oswald Sanders. 1976. pap. 1.95 (ISBN 9971-83-873-7). OMF Bks.

Best Things in Life. Peter Kreeft. LC 84-6697. 160p. (Orig.). 1984. pap. 6.95 (ISBN 0-87784-922-6). Inter-Varsity.

Bestiary for St. Jerome: Animal Symbolism in European Religious Art. Herbert Friedmann. LC 79-607804. (Illus.). 378p. 1980. 39.95x (ISBN 0-87474-446-6, FRBJ). Smithsonian.

Bethany. Robert M. M'Cheyne. 1974. pap. 1.65 (ISBN 0-685-52814-6). Reiner.

Bethany Parallel Commentary on the New Testament. Matthew Henry et al. 1500p. 1983. 39.95 (ISBN 0-87123-474-2). Bethany Hse.

Bethany Parallel Commentary on the Old Testament. Matthew Henry et al. 1500p. 1985. 49.95 (ISBN 0-87123-617-6). Bethany Hse.

Bethel & Aurora. Robert J. Hendricks. LC 75-134380. Repr. of 1933 ed. 26.50 (ISBN 0-404-08428-1). AMS Pr.

Bethlehem. Federick W. Faber. LC 78-66306. 1978. pap. 10.00 (ISBN 0-89555-080-6). TAN Bks Pubs.

Bethlehem Mystery. Clarence M. Wagner. (Orig.). 1981. 3.50 (ISBN 0-937498-03-3). Tru-Faith.

Bethlehem Revisited. Douglas V. Steere. LC 65-26995. (Orig.). 1965. pap. 2.50x (ISBN 0-87574-144-4, 144). Pendle Hill.

Bethlehem Star: Children's Newspaper Reports of the Life of Jesus. Schuyler Van Vechten. 1972. 4.95 (ISBN 0-8027-6097-X). Walker & Co.

Betrayal of Christ by the Churches. John M. Murry. 59.95 (ISBN 0-87968-724-X). Gordon Pr.

Betrayal of Innocence. David B. Peters. 160p. 1986. 11.95 (ISBN 0-8499-0502-8, 0502-8). Word Bks.

Betrayal of the Church: Apostasy & Renewal in the Mainline Denominations. Ed Robb & Julia Robb. LC 86-71006. 304p. (Orig.). 1986. pap. 8.95 (ISBN 0-89107-403-1, Crossway Bks). Good News.

Better Children's Sermons: 54 Visual Lessons, Dialogues, & Demonstrations. Bucky Dann. LC 83-6851. 124p. (Orig.). 1983. pap. 7.95 (ISBN 0-664-24481-5). Westminster.

Better Covenant. Francis Goode. 408p. 1986. 14.95 (ISBN 0-8254-2726-6). Kregel.

Better Covenant. Kenneth E. Hagin. 1981. pap. 0.50 mini bk. (ISBN 0-89276-251-9). Hagin Ministries.

Better Covenant. Watchman Nee. Tr. by Stephen Kaung. 1982. 4.75 (ISBN 0-935008-56-X); pap. 3.75 (ISBN 0-935008-55-1). Christian Fellow Pubs.

Better Half of Life. Jim Geddes. (Orig.). 1987. pap. 7.95 (ISBN 0-8054-5732-1). Broadman.

Better Homes & Gardens Christmas Joys to Craft & Stitch. Better Homes & Gardens Editors. (Illus.). 80p. 1985. pap. 6.95 (ISBN 0-696-01432-7). BH&G.

Better Than Gold. Ed. by Clinton T. Howell. (Illus.). 200p. 1984. 12.95 (ISBN 0-8407-5388-8). Nelson.

Better Than Rivers of Oil. Gerald Gerbrandt. LC 85-81305. (Faith & Life Bible Studies). 78p. (Orig.). pap. 4.95 (ISBN 0-87303-105-9). Faith & Life.

Better Than the Birds, Smarter Than the Bees. Helen J. Burn. LC 69-12771. (YA) pap. 21.30 (ISBN 0-8357-9000-2, 2016348). Bks Demand UMI.

Better Things from Above. J. Gregory Mantle. 1971. pap. 3.00 (ISBN 0-87509-051-6). Chr Pubns.

Better Way (Hebrews) (New Horizons Bible Study Ser.). 68p. (Orig.). pap. 2.50 student guide (ISBN 0-89367-103-7); pap. 1.95 leader's guide (ISBN 0-89367-104-5). Light & Life.

Betty Crocker's Christmas Cookbook. (Illus.). 192p. 1982. 14.95 (ISBN 0-307-09820-6, Golden Pr). Western Pub.

Between Athens & Jerusalem: Jewish Indentity in the Hellenistic Diaspora. John J. Collins. 272p. 1983. 27.50x (ISBN 0-8245-0491-7). Crossroad NY.

Between Belief & Transgression: Structuralist Essays in Religion, History & Myth. Ed. by Michel Izard & Pierre Smith. Tr. by John Leavitt. LC 81-16377. (Chicago Originals Ser.). (Illus.). 1982. lib. bdg. 20.00x (ISBN 0-226-38861-1). U of Chicago Pr.

Between Caesar & Jesus. George D. Herron. LC 75-324. (Radical Tradition in America Ser). 278p. 1975. Repr. of 1899 ed. 23.10 (ISBN 0-88355-227-2). Hyperion Conn.

Between Chaos & New Creation: Doing Theology at the Fringe. Enda McDonagh. 1987. pap. 12.95. M Glazier.

Between Christ & Caesar: Classic & Contemporary Texts on Church & State. Ed. by Charles Villa-Vicencio. 196p. (Orig.). 1986. pap. 16.95 (ISBN 0-8028-0240-0). Eerdmans.

Between Concord & Plymouth: The Transcendentalists & the Watsons. L. D. Geller. (Illus.). 1973. 6.00 (ISBN 0-685-42210-0). Thoreau Found.

Between Dying & Birth. Robert S. Bachelder. 1983. 5.95 (ISBN 0-89536-623-1, 0236). CSS of Ohio.

Between Faith & Reason: An Approach to Individual & Social Psychology. Francisco Jose Moreno. LC 76-56926. 1977. 20.00x (ISBN 0-8147-5416-3). NYU Pr.

Between God & Man. Charles J. Fitti. LC 78-50527. 49p. 1978. 10.00 (ISBN 0-8022-2225-0). Philos Lib.

Between God & Man, an Interpretation of Judaism. Abraham J. Heschel. 1965. pap. 8.95 (ISBN 0-02-914510-4). Free Pr.

Between Heaven & Earth. Helmut Thielicke. Tr. by J. W. Doberstein from Ger. 192p. 1978. Repr. 13.95 (ISBN 0-227-67726-9). Attic Pr.

Between Heaven & Hell. Peter J. Kreeft. LC 82-8975. 144p. (Orig.). 1982. pap. 5.95 (ISBN 0-87784-389-9). Inter-Varsity.

Between Honesty & Hope: Documents from & about the Church in Latin America. Peruvian Bishops' Commission for Social Action. LC 78-143185. (Maryknoll Documentation Ser.). pap. 67.80 (ISBN 0-317-26635-7, 2025116). Bks Demand UMI.

Between Jesus & Paul. Martin Hengel. LC 83-48003. 256p. 1983. pap. 14.95 (ISBN 0-8006-1720-7). Fortress.

Between Man & Man. Martin Buber. 15.25 (ISBN 0-8446-6207-0). Peter Smith.

Between Metaphysics & Protoanalysis: A Theory for Analyzing the Human Psyche. Oscar Ichazo. Ed. by John Bleibtreu. LC 82-70811. 120p. 1982. 15.95 (ISBN 0-916554-05-8); pap. 11.95 (ISBN 0-916554-06-6). Arica Inst Pr.

Between Pulpit & Pew: Folk Religion in a North Yorkshire Fishing Village. David Clark. LC 81-18166. (Illus.). 216p. 1982. 32.50 (ISBN 0-521-24071-9). Cambridge U Pr.

Between Sacred Mountains: Navajo Stories & Lessons from the Land. Ed. by Sam Bingham & Janet Bingham. LC 82-82827. (Illus.). 296p. 1982. 30.00 (ISBN 0-910675-00-7); pap. 19.95 (ISBN 0-910675-01-5). Rock Point.

Between Science & Values. Loren R. Graham. LC 81-4436. 448p. 1981. 28.00 (ISBN 0-231-05192-1); pap. 14.00x (ISBN 0-231-05193-X). Columbia U Pr.

Between the Generations. Samuel H. Dresner. pap. 1.75 (ISBN 0-87677-042-1). Hartmore.

Between the Rivers: A History of United Methodism in Iowa. John Nye. LC 86-80106. (Illus.). 350p. 1986. 12.95x (ISBN 0-9616298-0-0); pap. 10.95 (ISBN 0-9616298-1-9). IA Conf Com Arch.

Between the Sexes. Lisa S. Cahill. 160p. (Orig.). 1985. pap. 7.95 (ISBN 0-8091-2711-3). Paulist Pr.

Between the Testaments. Charles F. Pfeiffer. pap. 4.95 (ISBN 0-8010-6873-8). Baker Bk.

Between the Testaments. D. S. Russell. LC 77-74742. 176p. 1960. pap. 5.95 (ISBN 0-8006-1856-4, 1-1856). Fortress.

Between Two Gardens: Reflections on Sexuality & Religious Experience. James B. Nelson. 160p. (Orig.). 1983. pap. 8.95 (ISBN 0-8298-0681-4). Pilgrim NY.

Between Two Wars: The Story of Pope Pius XI. Robin Anderson. 1978. 7.95 (ISBN 0-8199-0687-5). Franciscan Herald.

Between Two Worlds. Frederick Wiedemann. LC 85-40773. 200p. (Orig.). 1986. pap. 6.95 (ISBN 0-8356-0602-3, Quest). Theos Pub Hse.

Between Two Worlds: An Approach to Ministry. C. R. Hill, Jr. LC 76-4276. 1976. 3.50 (ISBN 0-89937-007-1). Ctr Res Soc Chg.

Between Two Worlds: Children from the Soviet Union in Israel. Ed. by Tamar R. Horowitz. LC 86-11071. 240p. (Orig.). 1986. lib. bdg. 26.00 (ISBN 0-8191-5454-7); pap. text ed. 12.75 (ISBN 0-8191-5455-5). U Pr of Amer.

Between Us Friends. John M. Larsen. LC 83-61454. 1983. pap. 7.95 (ISBN 0-89390-050-8). Resource Pubns.

Between Walden & the Whirlwind. Jean Fleming. (Christian Character Library). 133p. 1985. hdbk. 8.95 (ISBN 0-89109-520-9). NavPress.

Between Walden & the Whirlwind. Jean M. Fleming. 133p. 1987. pap. 3.95. NavPress.

Between Yafeth & Shem: On the Relationship Between Jewish & General Philosophy. Zelev Levy. (American University Studies V-Philosophy: Vol. 21). 262p. 1986. text ed. 23.50 (ISBN 0-8204-0373-3). P Lang Pubs.

Between You & Me, God. Patricia A. Simmons. LC 74-79486. 1974. pap. 5.95 (ISBN 0-8054-4412-2, 4244-12). Broadman.

Beware America! Charles R. Taylor. Orig. Title: Message to the President. (Illus.). 48p. (Orig.). 1983. pap. 3.50 (ISBN 0-937682-06-3). Today Bible.

Beware! Be Wise. Bettie Crossan. 130p. (Orig.). 1984. pap. 2.95 (ISBN 0-87508-148-7). Chr Lit.

Beware: Children in Peril. Rexella Van Impe. 40p. 1985. pap. 1.95 (ISBN 0-934803-13-7). J Van Impe.

Beware Familiar Spirits. John Mulholland. LC 78-66328. 1938. pap. 5.95 (ISBN 0-684-16181-8). Brown Bk.

Beyond Abortion: The Origin & Future of the Secular State. Charles E. Rice. 1978. 5.25 (ISBN 0-8199-0696-4). Franciscan Herald.

Beyond All Expectations. Neil E. Jackson, Jr. (Orig.). 1987. pap. 6.95 (ISBN 0-8054-5044-0). Broadman.

Beyond Androcentrism: New Essays on Women & Religion. Ed. by Rita M. Gross. LC 77-13312. (AAR Aids for the Study of Religion: No. 6). 1981. pap. 9.95 (ISBN 0-89130-196-8, 010306). Scholars Pr GA.

Beyond Authority: How to Play to Win by the New Ethics. Clifford Kaeser. LC 82-4020. 143p. 1984. pap. 9.95 (ISBN 0-87949-222-8). Ashley Bks.

Beyond Belief. Robert N. Bellah. LC 77-109058. 1976. pap. text ed. 7.95x (ISBN 0-06-060775-0, RD129, HarpR). Har-Row.

Beyond Belief: Essays on Religion in a Post-Traditional World. Robert N. Bellah. LC 77-109058. 1970. 8.95x (ISBN 0-06-060774-2, RD-129, HarpR). Har-Row.

Beyond Belief: The American Press & the Coming of the Holocaust. Deborah Lipstadt. 336p. 19.95 (ISBN 0-02-919160-2). Free Pr.

Beyond Belief: The Christian Encounter with God. Richard Holloway. LC 81-5438. pap. 43.50 (ISBN 0-317-19824-6, 2023217). Bks Demand UMI.

Beyond Biblical Criticism: Encountering Jesus Christ in the Scripture. Arthur Wainwright. LC 81-85327. 153p. 1982. pap. 4.99 (ISBN 0-8042-0007-6). John Knox.

Beyond Birth & Death. Swami A. C. Bhaktivedanta. LC 72-84844. (Illus.). 1972. pap. 1.95 (ISBN 0-912776-41-2). Bhaktivedanta.

Beyond Broken Dreams: A Scriptural Pathway to New Life. Karen Berry. 1984. pap. 3.50 (ISBN 0-86716-034-9). St Anthony Mess Pr.

Beyond Brokenness. Louis A. Smith & Joseph R. Barndt. (Orig.). 1980. pap. 2.95 (ISBN 0-377-00100-7). Friend Pr.

Beyond Choice: The Abortion Story No One Is Telling. Don Baker. LC 85-15295. 1985. 8.95 (ISBN 0-88070-127-7). Multnomah.

Beyond Circumstances. Robert C. Jiggetts, Jr. (Illus.). 96p. (Orig.). 1986. pap. 9.95 (ISBN 1-55630-016-6). Brentwood Comm.

Beyond Companionship-Christians in Marriage. Diana S. Richmond-Garland & David E. Garland. LC 86-7767. 192p. 1986. pap. 12.95 (ISBN 0-664-24018-6). Westminster.

Beyond Conversion. Paul W. Powell. LC 77-80942. 1978. pap. 3.95 (ISBN 0-8054-5260-5). Broadman.

Beyond Coping. Bob Gliner. 273p. (Orig.). 1982. pap. 5.95x (ISBN 0-910029-01-6). Dell.

Beyond Death. C. J. Baker. 1977. 2.50 (ISBN 0-87813-953-2). Christian Light.

Beyond Death: Evidence for Life after Death. Robert Almeder. 176p. 1987. 24.50x (ISBN 0-398-05327-8). C C Thomas.

Beyond Death: The Gates of Consiousness. Stanislav Grof & Christina Grof. (Art & Imagination Ser.). (Illus.). 1980. pap. 10.95 (ISBN 0-500-81019-2). Thames Hudson.

Beyond Death's Door. Maurice Rawlings. 1979. pap. 3.50 (ISBN 0-553-25204-6). Bantam.

Beyond Despair. George Aptecker. (Illus.). 72p. 1980. 25.00 (ISBN 0-9604286-0-7). Kahn & Kahan.

Beyond Dialogue: Toward a Mutual Transformation of Christianity & Buddhism. John B. Cobb, Jr. LC 82-8389. 176p. 1982. pap. 8.95 (ISBN 0-8006-1647-2, 1-1647). Fortress.

Beyond Dilemmas. Ed. by Sceva B. Laughlin. LC 79-86035. (Essay & General Literature Index Reprint Ser). 1969. Repr. of 1937 ed. 25.50x (ISBN 0-8046-0567-X, Pub. by Kennikat). Assoc Faculty Pr.

Beyond Doubt: A Devotional Response to Questions of Faith. Cornelius Plantinga, Jr. LC 80-10647. (Illus.). 256p. (Orig.). 1980. pap. text ed. 8.95 (ISBN 0-933140-12-6); pap. text ed. 5.95 leader's guide (ISBN 0-933140-61-4). CRC Pubns.

Beyond East & West. John C. Wu. 388p. 1980. 5.95 (ISBN 0-89955-182-3, Pub. by Mei Ya China). Intl Spec Bk.

Beyond East & West: Problems in Liturgical Understanding. Robert Taft. (NPM Studies in Church Music & Liturgy). 203p. 1934. pap. 11.95 (ISBN 0-912405-13-9). Pastoral Pr.

Beyond Easy Believism. Gary Collins. 197p. 1985. pap. 8.95 (ISBN 0-8499-3025-1, 3025-1). Word Bks.

Beyond Economics: Essays on Society, Religion, & Ethics. Kenneth E. Boulding. 1970. pap. 4.95 (ISBN 0-472-06167-4, 167, AA). U of Mich Pr.

Beyond Evolution. Wilbur A. Jasson. LC 84-52700. (Illus.). 141p. 1986. 14.95 (ISBN 0-9614464-0-4); pap. 8.95 (ISBN 0-9614464-1-2). Sarasota Sci.

Beyond Existentialism & Zen: Religion in a Pluralistic World. George Rupp. 1979. 14.95x (ISBN 0-19-502462-1). Oxford U Pr.

Beyond Explanation: Religious Dimensions in Cultural Anthropology. Mark K. Taylor. LC 85-13770. x, 262p. 1985. text ed. 24.50 (ISBN 0-86554-165-5, MUP-H155). Mercer Univ Pr.

Beyond Forgiveness: The Healing Touch of Church Discipline. Don Baker. LC 84-3417. 1984. 8.95 (ISBN 0-88070-054-8). Multnomah.

Beyond Fulfilment: The Spiritual Message of Henry Van McNeal, Vol. 1. Henry Van McNeal. 180p. (Orig.). 1986. pap. 9.95 (ISBN 0-916641-27-9). Natl Academy Songwriters.

Beyond Futility. 2nd ed. David Hubbard. Tr. by Beer-Shiba Semarians. (Chinese.). 106p. 1982. pap. write for info (ISBN 0-941598-02-0). Living Spring Pubns.

Beyond God the Father: Toward a Philosophy of Women's Liberation. 2nd rev. ed. Mary Daly. LC 84-45067. 257p. 1985. 18.95x (ISBN 0-8070-1502-4); pap. 8.95 (ISBN 0-8070-1503-2, BP681). Beacon Pr.

Beyond Humiliation. J. Gregory Mantle. LC 75-6163. 256p. 1975. pap. 4.95 (ISBN 0-87123-040-2). Bethany Hse.

Beyond Hunger: A Biblical Mandate for Social Responsibility. Art Beals. LC 85-4912. (Critical Concern Ser.). 1985. 11.95 (ISBN 0-88070-098-X). Multnomah.

Beyond Identity: Finding Your Self in the Image & Character of God. Dick Keyes. 264p. (Orig.). 1984. pap. 7.95 (ISBN 0-89283-137-5). Servant.

Beyond Ideology: The Revival of Political Theory. Dante Germino. (Midway Reprint Ser.). 1976. pap. 14.00x (ISBN 0-226-28849-8). U of Chicago Pr.

Beyond Inspiration. Stephen B. Stum. 128p. 1984. 5.95 (ISBN 0-87159-011-5). Unity School.

Beyond Jesus: Reflections on the Gospel for the B-Cycle. Joseph G. Donders. LC 84-5088. 320p. (Orig.). 1984. 10.95 (ISBN 0-88344-049-0). Orbis Bks.

Beyond Knoche's Law. Keith Knoche. Ed. by Phillips. (Redwood Ser.). 96p. 1983. pap. 4.95 (ISBN 0-8163-0488-2). Pacific Pr Pub Assn.

Beyond Liberation. Carl Ellis, Jr. LC 83-18561. (Illus.). 200p. (Orig.). 1983. pap. 6.95 (ISBN 0-87784-914-5). Inter-Varsity.

Beyond Logic & Reason. Ishwar C. Puri. Ed. by Leonard Ingram. 59p. 1983. pap. 3.00 (ISBN 0-937067-00-8). Inst Study Hum Aware.

Beyond Loneliness. Edward Wakin & Sean Cooney. 112p. (Orig.). 1985. pap. 5.95 (ISBN 0-89622-248-9). Twenty-Third.

Beyond Majority Rule: Voteless Decisions in the Religious Society of Friends. Michael J. Sheeran. (Illus.). 153p. (Orig.). 1983. pap. 4.95 (ISBN 0-941308-04-9). Religious Soc Friends.

Beyond Marginality: Anglo-Jewish Literature after the Holocaust. Efraim Sicher. (Modern Jewish Literature & Culture Ser.). 224p. 1985. 44.50x (ISBN 0-87395-976-0); pap. 14.95x (ISBN 0-87395-975-2). State U NY Pr.

Beyond Marxism: Baha'i Perspectives on a New World Order. Ed. by Nader Saiedi. (Orig.). 1988. pap. 9.95 (ISBN 0-933770-59-6). Kalimat.

Beyond Me: A Christ Centered Approach to Self-Esteem. Esther Anderson & Norma Kvindlog. 160p. 1987. pap. 5.95 (ISBN 0-8423-1310-9). Tyndale.

Beyond Mechanism: The Universe in Recent Physics & Catholic Thought. Ed. by David L. Schindler. 166p. (Orig.). 1986. lib. bdg. 22.75 (ISBN 0-8191-5357-5, Pub. by Communio Intl Cth Review); pap. text ed. 10.75 (ISBN 0-8191-5358-3). U Pr of Amer.

Beyond Modernity: Reflections of a Post-Modern Catholic. George W. Ruthler. LC 86-82636. 227p. (Orig.). 1986. pap. 11.95 (ISBN 0-89870-135-X). Ignatius Pr.

Beyond Moralism. John Spong & Denise Haines. 204p. (Orig.). 1986. pap. 9.95 (ISBN 0-86683-514-8, HarpR). Har-Row.

Beyond Mysticism. James R. Horne. 158p. 1978. pap. text ed. 9.25x (ISBN 0-919812-08-2, Pub. by Wilfred Laurier Canada). Humanities.

Beyond Objectivism & Relativism: Science, Hermeneutics, & Praxis. Richard Bernstein. 320p. (Orig.). 1983. 28.95x (ISBN 0-8122-7906-9); pap. 10.95 (ISBN 0-8122-1165-0). U of Pa Pr.

Beyond Our Tribal Gods: The Maturing of Faith. Ronald Marstin. LC 79-4354. 160p. (Orig.). 1979. pap. 5.95 (ISBN 0-88344-030-X). Orbis Bks.

Beyond Politics. facsimile ed. Christopher H. Dawson. LC 74-111825. (Essay Index Reprint Ser.). 1939. 14.00 (ISBN 0-8369-1603-4). Ayer Co Pubs.

Beyond Port & Prejudice. William J. Baker. 1981. 20.00 (ISBN 0-89101-032-7). U Maine Orono.

Beyond Reason: How Miracles Can Change Your Life. Pat Robertson & William Proctor. LC 84-61470. 192p. 1984. 12.95 (ISBN 0-688-02214-6). Morrow.

Beyond Reason: How Miracles Can Change Your Life. Pat Robertson & William Proctor. (Religion Ser.). 176p. 1986. pap. 3.50 (ISBN 0-553-25415-4). Bantam.

Beyond Rejection: The Church, Homosexuality, & Hope. Don Baker. LC 85-8789. 1985. 8.95 (ISBN 0-88070-108-0). Multnomah.

Beyond Sambation: Selected Essays & Editorials, 1928-1955. A. M. Klein. Ed. by M. W. Steinberg & Usher Kaplan. (Collected Works of A. M. Klein). 1982. 35.00 (ISBN 0-8020-5566-4). U of Toronto Pr.

Beyond Seduction. Dave Hunt. 1987. pap. 7.95 (ISBN 0-89081-558-5). Harvest Hse.

Beyond Sorrow: Reflections on Death & Grief. rev. ed. Herb Montgomery & Mary Montgomery. 32p. 1985. pap. 6.95 (ISBN 0-86683-461-3, HarpR). Har-Row.

Beyond Space. Pascal P. Parente. 1977. pap. 4.50 (ISBN 0-89555-053-9). TAN Bks Pubs.

Beyond T. M. A Practical Guide to the Lost Tradition of Christian Meditation. Marilyn M. Helleberg. LC 80-82811. 144p. (Orig.). 1981. pap. 7.95 (ISBN 0-8091-2325-8). Paulist Pr.

Beyond the Basics. David DeWitt. 1983. pap. 5.95 (ISBN 0-8024-0178-3). Moody.

Beyond the Battle for the Bible. J. I. Packer. LC 80-68331. 160p. 1980. text ed. 9.95 (ISBN 0-89107-195-4, Crossway Bks). Good News.

Beyond the Battlefield. Barbara Exline. (Illus.). 78p. (Orig.). (YA) 1986. pap. 3.25 (ISBN 0-89216-063-2). Salvation Army.

Beyond the Curse: Women Called to Ministry. Aida B. Spencer. 224p. 1985. 10.95 (ISBN 0-8407-5482-5). Nelson.

Beyond the Darkness. Stella T. Mann. 1972. pap. 2.95 (ISBN 0-87516-054-9). De Vorss.

Beyond the Distant Shadows. Patricia Dunaway. 208p. (Orig.). 1984. pap. 4.95 (ISBN 0-87123-446-7). Bethany Hse.

Beyond the Facts, Acts. Pat McGeachy. (Orig.). 1973. pap. 1.95 (ISBN 0-377-03051-1). Friend Pr.

Beyond the Gates of Death: A Biblical Examination of Evidence for Life After Death. Hans Schwarz. LC 80-67805. 136p. 1981. pap. 6.95 (ISBN 0-8066-1868-X, 10-0647). Augsburg.

Beyond the Guru. Y. P. Dhawan. 227p. 1980. pap. 4.25 (ISBN 0-86578-060-9). Ind-US Inc.

Beyond the Horizon. Ed. by Charles R. Henery. 96p. (Orig.). 1986. pap. 4.30 (ISBN 0-88028-055-7). Forward Movement.

Beyond the Horizon: Being New Evidence from the Other Side of Life. Grace Rosher. 154p. 1961. 10.95 (ISBN 0-227-67412-X). Attic Pr.

Beyond the Mosque. Phil Parshall. 312p. 1985. pap. 9.95 (ISBN 0-8010-7089-9). Baker Bk.

Beyond the New Morality: The Responsibilities of Freedom. rev. ed. Germain Grisez & Russell Shaw. LC 80-18293. 240p. 1980. text ed. 14.95 (ISBN 0-268-00663-6); pap. 6.95 (ISBN 0-268-00665-2). U of Notre Dame Pr.

Beyond the New Theism: A Philosophy of Religion. Germain Grisez. LC 74-27885. 444p. 1975. text ed. 22.95x (ISBN 0-268-00567-2); pap. text ed. 8.95x (ISBN 0-268-00568-0). U of Notre Dame Pr.

Beyond the Present Prospect. John E. Whiteford-Boyle. 1977. 9.95 (ISBN 0-917888-00-6). Wheat Forders.

Beyond the "Primitive" Religions of Nonliterate Peoples. Sam Gill. (Illus.). 200p. 1982. pap. 14.95 (ISBN 0-13-076034-X). P-H.

Beyond the Rat Race. rev. ed. Arthur G. Gish. LC 73-9336. 208p. 1973. pap. 6.95 (ISBN 0-8361-1985-1). Herald Pr.

Beyond the Text: A Holistic Approach to Liturgy. Lawrence Hoffman. (Jewish Literature & Culture Ser.). 1987. 35.00 (ISBN 0-253-31199-3). Ind U Pr.

Beyond the Tomb. H. M. Riggle. 288p. 4.00 (ISBN 0-686-29100-X). Faith Pub Hse.

Beyond the Visible: The Triumph Over Yourself...Life & Emotions. Paul Molow & Doree Molow. 192p. 1981. 10.00 (ISBN 0-682-49739-8). Exposition Pr FL.

Beyond the Wall. Hank Paulson & Don Richardson. LC 81-84567. (Orig.). 1982. pap. 5.95 (ISBN 0-8307-0806-5, 5415708). Regal.

Beyond Theism: A Grammar of God-Language. Theodore W. Jennings, Jr. 1985. 29.95x (ISBN 0-19-503613-1). Oxford U Pr.

Beyond Theology: The Art of Godmanship. Alan W. Watts. 1973. pap. 3.95 (ISBN 0-394-71923-9, Vin). Random.

Beyond Time: Ideas of the Great Philosophers on Eternal Existence & Immortality. Charles J. Case. LC 85-17864. 144p. (Orig.). 1985. lib. bdg. 20.75 (ISBN 0-8191-4933-0); pap. text ed. 8.25 (ISBN 0-8191-4934-9). U Pr of Amer.

Beyond Tragedy: Essays on the Christian Interpretation of History. facsimile ed. Reinhold Niebuhr. LC 76-167397. (Essay Index Reprint Ser). Repr. of 1937 ed. 23.95 (ISBN 0-8369-2437-1). Ayer Co Pubs.

Beyond Tragedy: Essays on the Christian Interpretation of History. Reinhold Niebuhr. 1937. pap. text ed. 7.95 (ISBN 0-684-16410-8, SL38, ScribT). Scribner.

Beyond Trinity. Bernard J. Cooke. (Acquinas Lecutre). 1969. 7.95 (ISBN 0-87462-134-8). Marquette.

Beyond Within. Sri Chinmoy. 525p. 1985. pap. 10.95 (ISBN 0-88497-115-5). Aum Pubns.

Beyond Words. Sri Swam i Satchidanada. Ed. by Lester Alexander. LC 76-29896. (Illus.). 190p. 1977. pap. 5.95 (ISBN 0-03-016911-9). Integral Yoga Pubns.

Beyond Words & Thoughts. Joel Goldsmith. 6.00 (ISBN 0-8216-0041-9). Univ Bks.

Beyond Words & Thoughts. Joel S. Goldsmith. 200p. 1974. pap. 4.95 (ISBN 0-8065-0447-1). Citadel Pr.

Beyond Yiddishkeit: The Struggle for Jewish Identity in a Reform Synagogue. Frida K. Furman. (Anthropology & Judaic Studies). 152p. 1987. text ed. 29.50x (ISBN 0-88706-513-9); pap. 9.95x (ISBN 0-88706-514-7). State U NY Pr.

Bezae Codex Cantabrigiensis: Being an Exact Copy, in Ordinary Type of the Celebrated Uncial Graeco-Latin Manuscript of the Four Gospels & Acts of the Apostles. Theodore Beza. Ed. by Frederick H. Scrivener. LC 78-4144. (Pittsburgh Reprint Ser.: No. 5). 1978. pap. 19.95 (ISBN 0-915138-39-5). Pickwick.

Bezah, 1 vol. 15.00 (ISBN 0-910218-60-9). Bennet Pub.

Bhagavad Gita. Tr. by Haroutiun Saraydarian. LC 74-11759. 1974. 9.00 (ISBN 0-911794-36-0); pap. 7.00 (ISBN 0-911794-37-9). Aqua Educ.

Bhagavad Gita. Winthrop Sargeant. Ed. by Christopher Chapple. (SUNY Ser. in Cultural Perspectives). 777p. 1984. 44.50x (ISBN 0-87395-831-4); pap. 14.95x (ISBN 0-87395-830-6). State U NY Pr.

Bhagavad-Gita. Ed. by Robert C. Zaehner. 492p. 1969. 45.00x (ISBN 0-19-826522-0); pap. 12.95 (ISBN 0-19-501666-1). Oxford U Pr.

Bhagavad Gita, a Revelation. Dilipkumar Roy. 190p. 1975. 9.95 (ISBN 0-88253-698-2). Ind-US Inc.

Bhagavad Gita: A Sublime Hymn of Yoga. Guru N. Chaitanya Yati. Tr. by Nataraja Guru. 550p. 1980. text ed. 50.00x (ISBN 0-7069-1129-6, Pub. by Vikas India). Advent NY.

Bhagavad Gita: An Exegetical Commentary. Robert Minor. 1982. 38.00x (ISBN 0-8364-0817-9); text ed. 18.50x (ISBN 0-8364-0862-4). South Asia Bks.

Bhagavad-Gita: An International Bibliography of Imprints, 1785-1979. Jagdish C. Kapoor. LC 82-24253. 425p. 1983. lib. bdg. 66.00 (ISBN 0-8240-9266-X). Garland Pub.

Bhagavad Gita: An Interpretation. Mohandas K. Gandhi. Ed. by Narahari D. Parikh. 309p. (Orig.). 1984. pap. 8.00 (ISBN 0-934676-65-8). Greenlf Bks.

Bhagavad Gita: An Introduction. Georg Feuerstein. LC 82-42702. 191p. 1983. pap. 6.75 (ISBN 0-8356-0575-2, Quest). Theos Pub Hse.

Bhagavad Gita As It Is. (Illus.). 904p. 14.95 (ISBN 0-89213-123-3). Bhaktivedanta.

Bhagavad Gita in Light of Sri Aurobindo. Sri Aurobindo. Ed. by Maheshwar. 1979. 20.00 (ISBN 0-89744-902-9); pap. 15.00 (ISBN 0-89744-903-7). Auromere.

Bhagavad-Gita: Krishna's Counsel in Time of War. Tr. by Barbara S. Miller. LC 86-13725. (Illus.). 176p. 1986. 20.00x (ISBN 0-231-06468-3). Columbia U Pr.

Bhagavad-Gita: Recension with Essays. Ed. by William Q. Judge. LC 70-92964. 1977. 6.00 (ISBN 0-911500-27-8); pap. 3.50 (ISBN 0-911500-28-6). Theos U Pr.

Bhagavad Gita, Srimad Bhasya of Sri Sankaracarya. Shankara. Tr. by A. G. Warrier from Sanskrit. 652p. (Orig.). 1984. pap. 16.00x (ISBN 0-87481-526-6, Pub. by Ramakrishna Math Madras India). Vedanta Pr.

Bhagavad-Gita: The Book of Devotion Dialogue Between Krishna, Lord of Devotion, & Arjuna, Prince of India. Tr. & intro. by William Q. Judge. xviii, 133p. 1930. Repr. of 1891 ed. 3.50 (ISBN 0-938998-09-9). Theosophy.

Bhagavad Gita: The Divine Message, 2 vols. Swami Abhedananda. 25.00 set (ISBN 0-87481-625-4). Vedanta Pr.

Bhagavad Gita: The Song of God. 2nd ed. Goswami Kriyananda. (Illus.). 137p. pap. text ed. 5.95 (ISBN 0-9613099-3-8). Temple Kriya Yoga.

Bhagavad Gita: Translated with Introduction & Notes. Tr. by B. Srinivasa Murthy from Sanskrit. LC 84-82433. 150p. 1985. pap. 9.95 (ISBN 0-941910-01-6). Long Beach Pubns.

Bhagavad Gita with Commentary of Sri Sankaracharya. Sankaracharya. Tr. by Alladi M. Sastry. 1979. 16.00 (ISBN 0-89744-188-5). Auromere.

Bhagavadgeeta-Bible-Khuran (Krishna-Jesus Mohammad) Panduranga R. Malyala. Date not set. 3.99 (ISBN 0-938924-04-4). Sri Shirdi Sai.

Bhagavadgita. Pref. by M. K. Gandhi. 14.50 (ISBN 0-86516-179-8). Bolchazy-Carducci.

Bhagavadgita & Jivana Yoga. R. N. Vyas. 1986. 14.00x (ISBN 81-7017-203-9, Pub. by Abhinav India). South Asia Bks.

Bhagavadgita in the Mahabharata: A Bilingual Edition. Ed. by J. A. Van Buitenen. LC 79-13021. 184p. 1981. lib. bdg. 19.00x (ISBN 0-226-84660-1); pap. 8.95 (ISBN 0-226-84662-8, Phoen). U of Chicago Pr.

Bhagavadgitanuvada: A Study in Transcultural Translation. Winand M. Callewaert. 1984. 26.00x (ISBN 0-8364-1148-X, Pub. by Satya Bharati Pub). South Asia Bks.

Bhagavat Gita As It Is. Bhaktivedanta Swami. 6.95 (ISBN 0-89213-134-9). Bhaktivedanta.

Bhagavata Purana, Vol. 9. Tr. by G. V. Tagare. cancelled (ISBN 0-89581-480-3). Asian Human Pr.

Bhagavata Purana, Vol. 10. Tr. by G. V. Tagare. cancelled (ISBN 0-89581-481-1). Asian Human Pr.

Bhagavata Purana, Vol. 11. Tr. by G. V. Tagare. cancelled (ISBN 0-89581-482-X). Asian Human Pr.

Bhagavata Purana: Mytho-Social Study. S. S. Dange. LC 84-900334. 1984. 28.50x (ISBN 0-8364-1132-3, Pub. by Ajanta). South Asia Bks.

Bhagavata, Srimad. Vyasa. Tr. by Swami Tapasyananda from Sanskrit. 1983. Vol. 1, 455p. 25.00x ea. (ISBN 0-87481-516-9). Vol. 2, 492p (ISBN 0-87481-517-7). Vol. 3, 447p (ISBN 0-87481-518-5). Vol. 4 (ISBN 0-87481-519-3). Vedanta Pr.

Bhagavatam, Srimad: The Wisdom of God. Swami Prabhavananda. 1978. Repr. of 1943 ed. 5.95 (ISBN 0-87481-483-9). Vedanta Pr.

Bhagavatam, Srimad: The Wisdom of God. Swami Prabhavananda. 1979. pap. 5.95 (ISBN 0-87481-490-1). Vedanta Pr.

Bhagwan: The God That Failed. Hugh Milne. (Illus.). 320p. 1987. pap. 10.95 (ISBN 0-312-00106-1, Pub. by Thomas Dunne Bks). St Martin.

Bhai Vir Singh. G. S. Khosla. 1984. 15.00x (ISBN 0-8364-1230-3, Pub. by Heritage India). South Asia Bks.

Bhakti in Religions of the World: With Special Reference to Dr. Sri Bankey Behariji. 268p. 1987. text ed. 32.50x (ISBN 81-7018-371-5, Pub. by B R Pub Corp Delhi). Apt Bks.

Bhakti Ratnavali: An Anthology from the Bhagavata. Vishnu Puri. Tr. by Swami Tapasyananda from Sanskrit. 256p. 1980. pap. 5.95 (ISBN 0-87481-499-5). Vedanta Pr.

Bhakti-Ratnavali: With the Commentary of Visnu Puri. Bhagavatapurana Puranas. LC 73-3794. (Sacred Books of the Hindus: No. 7 Pt.3). Repr. of 1912 ed. 25.00 (ISBN 0-404-57835-7). AMS Pr.

Bhakti Sutras of Narada. Narada. Tr. & intro. by Nandalal Sinha. LC 73-3792. (Sacred Books of the Hindus: No. 7, Pt. 1). Repr. of 1911 ed. 17.00 (ISBN 0-404-57807-1). AMS Pr.

Bhakti Yoga. Yogi Bhikshu. 6.00 (ISBN 0-911662-21-9). Yoga.

Bhakti-Yoga: The Yoga of Love & Devotion. Swami Vivekananda. pap. 1.50 (ISBN 0-87481-157-0). Vedanta Pr.

Bhavisya Purana. write for info. Asian Human Pr.

Bi-Centenary Memorial of John Bunyan Who Died A.D. 1688. Charles W. Williams. LC 76-27709. 1976. Repr. of 1888 ed. lib. bdg. 17.50 (ISBN 0-8414-9510-6). Folcroft.

Bib Sac Reader. John F. Walvoord & Roy B. Zuck. (Orig.). 1983. pap. 8.95 (ISBN 0-8024-0459-6). Moody.

Bibel und Alter Orient: Altorientische Beitrage zum Alten Testament von Wolfram von Soden. Ed. by Hans-Peter Mueller. (Beihefte zur Zeitschrift fur die Alttestamentliche Wissenschaft Ser.: Band 162). xii, 224p. 1985. 50.50x (ISBN 3-11-010091-6). De Gruyter.

Bibeltheologisches Woerterbuch, 2 vols. 3rd ed. Johannes B. Bauer. (Ger.). 1967. Set. 150.00 (ISBN 3-222-10240-6, M-7308, Pub. by Styria). French & Eur.

Bibical Limericks. D. R. Bensen. 1986. pap. 6.95 (Pub. by Ballantine-Epiphany). Ballantine.

Bible. Ed. by John Duckworth et al. (Pacesetter Ser.). 64p. 1987. tchr's. ed. 7.95 (ISBN 0-318-21517-9). Cook.

Bible - Man's Book of Realization. Gene Sande. 1981. pap. 2.50 (ISBN 0-87613-095-3). New Age.

Bible: A Child's Playground. Roger A. Gobbel & Gertrude G. Gobbel. LC 85-45501. 192p. 1986. pap. 9.95 (ISBN 0-8006-1887-4). Fortress.

Bible: A Literary Study. John H. Gottcent. 120p. 1986. 10.50 (ISBN 0-8057-7951-5, Twayne); pap. 5.95 (ISBN 0-8057-8003-3). G K Hall.

Bible Absurdities. John Bowden. 24p. 1982. Repr. of 1968 ed. 2.50 (ISBN 0-911826-45-9, 5036). Am Atheist.

Bible Activities for Kids, No. 1. Donna L. Pape et al. (Illus.). 64p. (Orig.). 1980. pap. 1.95 (ISBN 0-87123-148-4, 210148). Bethany Hse.

Bible Activities for Kids, No. 2. Donna L. Pape & Virginia Mueller. (Illus.). 60p. (Orig.). 1980. pap. 1.95 (ISBN 0-87123-149-2, 21049). Bethany Hse.

Bible Activities for Kids, No. 3. Donna L. Pape et al. (Illus.). 63p. (Orig.). 1981. pap. 1.95 (ISBN 0-87123-172-7, 210172). Bethany Hse.

Bible Activities for Kids, No. 4. Donna L. Pape et al. (Illus.). 59p. 1981. pap. 1.95 (ISBN 0-87123-173-5, 210173). Bethany Hse.

Bible Activity Capsule. Betty DeVries. (Pelican Activity Ser.). pap. 0.89 (ISBN 0-8010-2896-5). Baker Bk.

Bible Activity Fun for Kids. Mary E. Lysne. 24p. 1983. pap. 1.50 (ISBN 0-87239-693-2, 2363). Standard Pub.

Bible Activity Safari. Grace Vander Klay. (Pelican Activity Ser.). pap. 0.89 (ISBN 0-8010-9280-9). Baker Bk.

Bible Adventures. Ruth Odor. (Flip-a-Bible-Story Bks.). (Illus.). 16p. (Orig.). 1982. pap. 3.95 (ISBN 0-87239-561-8, 2735). Standard Pub.

Bible Adventures Basic Bible Reader. Carol Ferntheil. 128p. 1985. pap. 4.95 (2757). Standard Pub.

Bible Against Slavery or an Inquiry into the Genius of the Mosaic System & the Teachings of the Old Testament on the Subject of Human Rights. Theodore D. Weld. LC 74-92447. 1970. Repr. of 1864 ed. 39.00x (ISBN 0-403-00185-4). Scholarly.

Bible Almanac: A Comprehensive Handbook of the People of the Bible & How They Lived. Ed. by James I. Packer et al. LC 79-23475. 792p. 1980. 16.95 (ISBN 0-8407-5162-1). Nelson.

Bible: An Owner's Manual, What You Need to Know Before You & Read Your Own Bible. Robert R. Hann. 160p. 1983. pap. 6.95 (ISBN 0-8091-2503-X). Paulist Pr.

Bible & American Arts & Letters. Giles Gunn. LC 83-5634. (SBL Bible in American Culture Ser.). 256p. 1983. 15.95 (ISBN 0-89130-625-0, 06 12 03). Scholars Pr GA.

Bible & American Law, Politics, & Political Rhetoric. Ed. by James T. Johnson. LC 83-16327. (Bible in American Culture Ser.: No. 4). 216p. 1985. 14.95 (ISBN 0-8006-0614-0, 1-614). Fortress.

Bible & Archaeology. wnd, rev. ed. J. A. Thompson. 512p. 1981. 24.95 (ISBN 0-8028-3545-7). Eerdmans.

Bible & Christian Life. Charles E. Cranfield. 256p. 1985. pap. 15.95 (ISBN 0-567-29125-1, Pub. by T&T Clark Ltd UK). Fortress.

Bible & Counselling. J. C. Metcalfe. 1966. pap. 2.95 (ISBN 0-87508-911-9). Chr Lit.

Bible & English Prose Style. Albert S. Cook. LC 72-192049. Repr. of 1892 ed. lib. bdg. 8.50 (ISBN 0-8414-1134-4). Folcroft.

Bible & Ethics in the Christian Life. Bruce C. Birch & Larry L. Rasmussen. LC 76-3856. 208p. 1976. pap. 8.95 (ISBN 0-8066-1524-9, 10-0702). Augsburg.

Bible & Family Relations. T. B. Maston & William A. Tillman. LC 81-67196. 1983. 8.95 (ISBN 0-8054-6124-8). Broadman.

Bible & Feminist Hermeneutics. Ed. by Mary A. Tolbert. (Semeia Ser.: No. 28). 9.95 (06 20 28). Scholars Pr GA.

Bible & Future Events. Leon J. Wood. (Contemporary Evangelical Perspectives Ser.). 224p. 1973. kivar 6.95 (ISBN 0-310-34701-7, 10231P). Zondervan.

Bible & I. E. M. Blaiklock. 128p. (Orig.). 1983. pap. 3.95 (ISBN 0-87123-298-7). Bethany Hse.

Bible & Its Painters. Bruce Bernard. LC 84-9740. (Illus.). 300p. 1984. 24.95 (ISBN 0-02-510130-7). Macmillan.

Bible & Me! Terre Sychterz. Ed. by Arthur L. Zapel. (Illus.). 40p. 1986. pap. 3.95 (ISBN 0-916260-39-9). Meriwether Pub.

Bible & Me: Writing Fun for Kids Series. Linda Priddy. (Illus.). 24p. (Orig.). 1982. pap. 1.50 (ISBN 0-87239-482-4, 2101). Standard Pub.

Bible & Mission: Biblical Foundations & Working Models for Congregational Ministry. Ed. by Wayne Stumme. LC 86-22167. (Mission in the U. S. A. Series). 208p. (Orig.). 1986. pap. 10.95 (ISBN 0-8066-2237-7, 10-0705). Augsburg.

Bible & Modern Scholarship. Frederic G. Kenyon. LC 78-9892. 1979. Repr. of 1948 ed. lib. bdg. 22.50x (ISBN 0-313-21009-8, KEBI). Greenwood.

Bible & Narrative Tradition. Ed. by Frank McConnell. 168p. 1986. 16.95x (ISBN 0-19-503698-0). Oxford U Pr.

Bible & Popular Culture in America. Ed. by Allene S. Phy. LC 83-11548. (Bible in American Culture Ser.). 1985. 15.95 (ISBN 0-89130-640-4, 06 12 02). Scholars Pr GA.

Bible & Recent Archaeology. Dame Kathleen Kenyon. LC 78-4089. (Illus.). 1979. pap. 8.95 (ISBN 0-8042-0010-6). John Knox.

Bible & Slavery: In Which the Abrahamic & Mosaic Discipline is Considered. Charles Elliott. 17.25 (ISBN 0-8369-9167-2, 9042). Ayer Co Pubs.

Bible & Social Reform. Ed. by Ernest Sandeen. LC 81-9294. (SBL The Bible In American Culture Ser.). 1982. 12.95 (ISBN 0-89130-531-9, 061206, Co-pub. by Fortress Pr). Scholars Pr GA.

Bible & Social Reform. Ed. by Ernest R. Sandeen. LC 81-71386. (Bible in American Culture Ser.). 196p. 1982. 12.95 (ISBN 0-8006-0611-6, 1-611). Fortress.

Bible & the Ancient Near East: Essays in Honor of William Foxwell Albright. Ed. by G. Ernest Wright. 1979. Repr. of 1961 ed. 15.00x (ISBN 0-931464-03-X). Eisenbrauns.

Bible & the Call of God. J. C. Metcalfe. 1970. pap. 1.95 (ISBN 0-87508-910-0). Chr Lit.

Bible & the Christian Life. Leland G. Shultz. LC 82-82701. (Radiant Life Ser.). 128p. (Orig.). 1984. pap. 2.50 (ISBN 0-88243-857-3, 02-0857); tchr's guide 3.95 (ISBN 0-88243-198-6, 32-0198). Gospel Pub.

Bible & the Common Reader. rev. ed. Mary E. Chase. 1962. pap. 4.95 (ISBN 0-02-084390-9, Collier). Macmillan.

Bible & the Faiths of Men. Vinjamuri E. Devadutt. (Orig.). 1967. pap. 1.25 (ISBN 0-377-37011-8). Friend Pr.

Bible & the Future. Anthony A. Hoekema. 1979. 24.95 (ISBN 0-8028-3516-3). Eerdmans.

Bible & the Human Mind. J. C. Metcalfe. pap. 2.95 (ISBN 0-87508-913-5). Chr Lit.

Bible & the Image: The History of Photography in the Holy Land, 1839-1899. Yeshayahu Nir. LC 84-21997. (Illus.). 1985. 39.95 (ISBN 0-8122-7981-6). U of Pa Pr.

Bible & the Message to the Men of the "New Earth". Tr. by Bertha Gonzales from Span. (Illus.). 144p. (Orig.). 1986. pap. write for info. (ISBN 0-9607590-5-0). Action Life Pubns.

Bible & the Newspaper. C. H. Spurgeon. 1973. pap. 2.50 (ISBN 0-686-09104-3). Pilgrim Pubns.

Bible & the Reader: An Introduction to Literary Criticism. Edgar V. McKnight. LC 85-4603. 176p. 1985. pap. 8.95 (ISBN 0-8006-1872-6). Fortress.

Bible & the Role of Women: A Case Study in Hermeneutics. Krister Stendahl. Ed. by John Reumann. Tr. by Emilie T. Sander. LC 66-25262. (Facet Bks). 64p. 1966. pap. 3.95 (ISBN 0-8006-3030-0, 1-3030). Fortress.

Bible & the Spirit Filled Life. J. C. Metcalfe. 1970. pap. 3.25 (ISBN 0-87508-912-7). Chr Lit.

Bible & the World & Triluminal Science. Apostolos Makrakis. Ed. by Orthodox Christian Educational Society. Tr. by Denver Cummings from Hellenic. 531p. 1950. 10.00x (ISBN 0-938366-18-1). Orthodox Chr.

Bible Animal Stories, Bk. 1. Bob Wolf. (Illus.). 86p. 1983. pap. 3.95 (ISBN 0-89323-044-8). Bible Memory.

Bible Animals. Ed. by Patricia Mahany. (Classroom Activity Bks.). (Illus., Orig.). 1984. pap. 2.95 (ISBN 0-87239-715-7, 2445). Standard Pub.

Bible Animals & the Lessons Taught by Them. Richard Newton. 1978. Repr. of 1888 ed. lib. bdg. 42.50 (ISBN 0-8492-1958-2). R West.

Bible Anonyme du Ms. Paris B. N. F. Fr, No. 763. Julia C. Szirmai. (Faux Titre Ser.: No. 22). 402p. 1985. pap. text ed. 55.00x (ISBN 90-6203-927-8, Pub. by Rodopi Holland). Humanities.

Bible Answers for King's Kids. rev. ed. Harold Hill. 224p. 1983. pap. 5.95 (ISBN 0-8007-5131-0, Power Bks). Revell.

Bible Answers to Man's Questions on Demons. Kenneth E. Hagin. 1983. pap. 1.00 (ISBN 0-89276-028-1). Hagin Ministries.

Bible As a Document of the University. Gerhard Ebeling et al. Ed. by H. D. Betz. 1981. pap. 10.00 (ISBN 0-89130-422-3, 00-03-03). Scholars Pr GA.

Bible As History. Werner Keller. (Illus.). 544p. 1974. pap. 4.95 (ISBN 0-553-25438-3). Bantam.

Bible As History. 2nd, rev. ed. Werner Keller. Ed. by Joachim Rehork. Tr. by William Neil & B. H. Rasmussen. LC 80-22218. Orig. Title: Und Die Bibel Hat Docht Recht. (Illus.). 448p. 1981. 14.95 (ISBN 0-688-03724-0). Morrow.

Bible As Literature. Kathleen E. Innes. 255p. 1980. Repr. of 1930 ed. lib. bdg. 25.00 (ISBN 0-8492-1222-7). R West.

Bible As Literature. Richard G. Moulton & A. B. Bruce. LC 78-1666. Repr. of 1899 ed. lib. bdg. 47.50 (ISBN 0-8414-6242-9). Folcroft.

Bible as Literature. Irving F. Wood. 346p. 1980. Repr. of 1914 ed. lib. bdg. 43.50 (ISBN 0-8482-7073-8). Norwood Edns.

Bible As Literature. Irving F. Wood & E. Grant. 1914. Repr. 4.00 (ISBN 0-8274-3802-8). R West.

Bible As Literature: A Selective Bibliography. John H. Gottcent. 1979. lib. bdg. 26.00 (ISBN 0-8161-8121-7, Hall Reference). G K Hall.

Bible As Literature: An Introduction. John B. Gabel & Charles Wheeler. 320p. 1986. 24.50x (ISBN 0-19-503993-9); pap. 9.95x (ISBN 0-19-503994-7). Oxford U Pr.

Bible As Literature: An Introduction. Irving Wood. LC 79-441. (Bible Study Textbook Series). 1979. Repr. of 1914 ed. lib. bdg. 42.50 (ISBN 0-8414-9712-5). Folcroft.

Bible As Literature: Old Testament & the Apocrypha. 2nd ed. Buckner B. Trawick. 1970. pap. 5.95 (ISBN 0-06-460056-4, CO 56, B&N Bks). Har-Row.

Bible As Read & Preached in the Old Synagogue, Vol. 1. rev. ed. Jacob Mann. (Library of Biblical Studies). 1970. 59.50x (ISBN 0-87068-083-8). Ktav.

Bible As the Church's Book. Phyllis A. Bird. LC 82-7049. (Library of Living Faith: Vol. 5). 118p. 1982. pap. 5.95 (ISBN 0-664-24427-0). Westminster.

Bible Atlas. Charles F. Pfeiffer. LC 60-15536. 1975. 16.95 (ISBN 0-8054-1129-1). Broadman.

Bible B. C. What Can Archaeology Prove? A. R. Millard. 1982. pap. 1.75 (ISBN 0-87552-291-2). Presby & Reformed.

Bible Babies. Ed. by Patricia Mahany. (Classroom Activity Bks.). (Illus.). 48p. (Orig.). 1984. pap. 2.95 (ISBN 0-87239-716-5, 2446). Standard Pub.

Bible Back in Our Schools. Robert O. Donovan. LC 72-80782. 80p. 1972. pap. 2.50 (ISBN 0-913748-01-3). Orovan Bks.

Bible Baseball. Robert Taylor. Date not set. pap. 2.95 (ISBN 0-8024-0211-9). Moody.

Bible BASIC: Advanced. Dianne Martin & Rachelle Heller. (Illus.). 64p. 1986. 5.95 (ISBN 0-87403-052-8, 3192). Standard Pub.

Bible BASIC: Bible Games for Personal Computers. Bernard K. Bangley. LC 83-48461. 128p. (Orig.). 1983. pap. 9.95 (ISBN 0-06-250042-2, CN 4092, HarpR). Har-Row.

Bible Basics. Theodore W. Teyler. (Illus.). 48p. (Orig.). 1986. pap. 4.95 leader's guide (ISBN 0-933350-35-X); pap. 4.95 student manual (ISBN 0-317-46726-3). Morse Pr.

Bible Basis for Christian Security. Wakefield. pap. 1.50 (ISBN 0-686-12851-6). Schmul Pub Co.

Bible Bees. Joyce Ellis & Claire Lynn. (Illus.). 36p. 1981. 1.25 (ISBN 0-89323-049-9). Bible Memory.

Bible Birthday Book. Christian Center Staff. 1983. 5.95t (ISBN 0-911346-06-6). Christianica.

Bible Bits & Relevant Rhymes. Margaret B. Korty. LC 84-71870. 117p. 1984. spiral binding 5.95 (ISBN 0-9603060-1-3). Church Lib.

Bible Book by Book: An Introduction to Bible Synthesis. G. C. Luck. 1955. pap. text ed. 3.95 (ISBN 0-8024-0045-0). Moody.

Bible Book for Today. John R. Stott. Tr. by Silas Chan. (Chinese.). 1985. pap. write for info. (ISBN 0-941598-23-3). Living Spring Pubns.

Bible Book of Lists. Joy MacKemzie & Shirley Bledsoe. 128p. 1984. pap. 5.95 (ISBN 0-310-70321-2, 14035P). Zondervan.

Bible Book of Medical Wisdom. Russel J. Thomsen. 160p. 1985. pap. 3.95 (ISBN 0-916441-26-1). Barbour & Co.

Bible Book: Resources for Reading the New Testament. Erasmus Hort. 172p. 1983. pap. 12.95x (ISBN 0-8245-0557-3). Crossroad NY.

Bible: Books of Books. Charles W. Conn. 1977. pap. 4.25 (ISBN 0-87148-102-2). Pathway Pr.

Bible Boys & Girls. Doris C. Demaree. (Bible Stories for Children Ser.). (Illus.). 1970. pap. 1.50 (ISBN 0-87162-002-2, D1443). Warner Pr.

Bible Busy Book. Marlene Speelman & Janiece Adams. 10p. 1986. 15.95 (ISBN 0-8407-6711-0). Nelson.

Bible Calculator Word Games. 1986. pap. 3.95 (ISBN 0-8010-7741-9). Baker Bk.

Bible Came from Arabia. Kamal Salibi. (Illus.). 224p. 1986. 18.95 (ISBN 0-224-02830-8, Pub. by Jonathan Cape). Salem Hse Pubs.

Bible-Centered Object Sermons for Children. C. W. Bess & Roy E. DeBand. (Object Lesson Ser.). 128p. 1985. pap. 4.95 (ISBN 0-8010-0886-7). Baker Bk.

Bible: Chain of Truth. A. Marie Miles. 168p. pap. 1.25 (ISBN 0-686-29101-8). Faith Pub Hse.

Bible Characters. Ed. by Clevenger & Hill. 1973. pap. 1.50 (ISBN 0-88428-008-X, 161). Parchment Pr.

Bible Characters. Ernest A. Clevenger, Jr. (Bible Drill Flash Cards Flipbook Ser.). 1982. pap. 4.25 (ISBN 0-88428-018-7). Parchment Pr.

Bible Characters from the New Testament, Vol. 1. Alexander Whyte. LC 81-81099. (Shepherd Illustrated Classics Ser.). (Illus.). 276p. 1982. pap. 7.95 (ISBN 0-87983-256-8). Keats.

Bible Characters from the New Testament, Vol. 2. Alexander Whyte. LC 81-81099. (Shepherd Illustrated Classics Ser.). (Illus.). 324p. 1982. pap. 7.95 (ISBN 0-87983-257-6). Keats.

Bible Children. Ed. by Patricia Mahany. (Classroom Activity Bks.). (Illus.). 48p. (Orig.). 1984. pap. 2.95 (ISBN 0-87239-717-3, 2447). Standard Pub.

Bible, Christian & Latter Day Saints. Gordon Lewis. pap. 1.25 (ISBN 0-8010-5567-9). Baker Bk.

Bible, Christian & Seventh Day Adventists. Gordon Lewis. pap. 1.25 (ISBN 0-8010-5573-3). Baker Bk.

Bible, Christians & Jehovah's Witnesses. Gordon Lewis. pap. 1.25 (ISBN 0-8010-5568-7). Baker Bk.

Bible Christmas Puzzles. William Schlegl. (Illus.). 48p. 1987. pap. 5.95 (ISBN 0-86653-409-1). Good Apple.

Bible, Church & God. 2nd ed. William McCarthy. LC 70-169211. (Atheist Viewpoint Ser). (Illus.). 736p. 1972. Repr. of 1946 ed. 41.00 (ISBN 0-405-03805-4). Ayer Co Pubs.

Bible Commentary, 10 vols. Ed. by F. C. Cook. 6803p. 1981. Repr. 195.00 (ISBN 0-8010-2431-5). Baker Bk.

Bible Communism. Oneida Community. LC 76-187475. (American Utopian Adventure Ser.). 128p. 1973. Repr. of 1853 ed. lib. bdg. 17.50x (ISBN 0-87991-015-1). Porcupine Pr.

Bible Communism: A Compilation from the Annual Reports & Other Publications of the Oneida Association & Its Branches. Oneida Community. LC 72-2978. Repr. of 1853 ed. 8.50 (ISBN 0-404-10742-7). AMS Pr.

Bible Companion. (Illus.). 1985. 17.95 (ISBN 0-687-03148-6). Abingdon.

Bible Compiled for A Blessed Life. Ed. by Grace Y. Song et al. LC 83-26389. 680p. (Orig.). 1984. pap. 4.95 (ISBN 0-916075-00-1). Intl Life Mess.

Bible Contradicts Itself. John Bowden. 36p. 1982. Repr. of 1968 ed. saddle-stitched 3.00 (ISBN 0-911826-46-7). Am Atheist.

Bible Country. Woodrow Kroll. 1982. 22.95 (ISBN 0-89636-060-1). Accent Bks.

Bible Crafts. Joyce Becker. LC 82-80820. (Illus.). 128p. 1982. 12.95 (ISBN 0-8234-0467-6); pap. 6.95 (ISBN 0-8234-0469-2). Holiday.

Bible Crossword Puzzle Book. S. K. Davis. (Quiz & Puzzle Bks). 1969. pap. 2.95 (ISBN 0-8010-2812-4). Baker Bk.

Bible Crossword Puzzles. Ruth Tonothy. 48p. 1986. pap. 2.50 (ISBN 0-87403-050-1, 2694). Standard Pub.

Bible Crosswords. Linda Krein. (Bible Baffler Ser.). 48p. 1986. wkbk. 4.95 (ISBN 0-86653-366-4). Good Apple.

Bible Cut & Tell Stories: Old & New Testaments. Jean Stangl. (Illus.). 40p. 1987. pap. 2.95 (ISBN 0-87403-154-0, 2874 (OLD TESTAMENT)); pap. 2.95 (ISBN 0-87403-155-9, 2875 (NEW TESTAMENT)). Standard Pub.

Bible Dates Itself. Arthur Earle. LC 73-88548. 1974. 12.50 (ISBN 0-9600788-1-9). A Earle.

Bible Days Are Here Again. Gordon Lindsay. pap. 4.00 (ISBN 0-89985-194-0). Christ Nations.

Bible Defence of Slavery. Josiah Priest & W. S. Brown. LC 74-92439. 1851. 79.00 (ISBN 0-403-00171-4). Scholarly.

Bible Dictionary for Young Readers. William N. McElrath. LC 65-15604. (Illus.). 1965. 9.95 (ISBN 0-8054-4404-1, 4244-04). Broadman.

Bible Difficulties & Seeming Contradictions. William F. Arndt. 1987. pap. 8.95 (ISBN 0-570-04470-7). Concordia.

Bible Digest. Charles W. Slemming. LC 68-27671. 906p. 1975. 27.95 (ISBN 0-8254-3706-7). Kregel.

Bible Digest Charts. Charles W. Slemming. LC 64-17168. 1974. pap. 12.95 (ISBN 0-8254-3701-6). Kregel.

Bible Dramas for Older Boys & Girls. Sarah W. Miller. LC 75-95409. 1970. pap. 4.95 (ISBN 0-8054-7506-0). Broadman.

Bible English: Chapters on Old & Disused Expressions. T. L. Davies. 1875. 25.00 (ISBN 0-8274-1932-5). R West.

Bible Events Quiz Book. Erma Reynolds. (Quiz & Puzzle Bks.). 96p. 1985. pap. 3.50 (ISBN 0-8010-7734-6). Baker Bk.

Bible Evidences. Ernest Clevenger, Jr. & Samuel G. Hill. (Bible Centered Studies). (Illus.). 73p. (Orig.). 1973. pap. 1.50 (ISBN 0-88428-009-8). Parchment Pr.

Bible Explorer's Guide. John Phillips. 320p. 1987. 9.95 (ISBN 0-87213-682-5). Loizeaux.

Bible: Fact, Fiction, Fantasy, Faith. H. N. Dukes. 178p. (Orig.). 1987. pap. 8.00 (ISBN 0-682-40337-7). Exposition Pr Fl.

Bible Faith Study Course. Kenneth E. Hagin. 1974. pap. 5.00 (ISBN 0-89276-080-X). Hagin Ministries.

Bible Families. Connie Sherlock. (Think 'n Check Quizzes Ser.). (Illus.). 16p. (Orig.). 1983. pap. 1.95 (ISBN 0-87239-688-6, 2792). Standard Pub.

Bible for Children. Walter Wangerin, Jr. (Illus.). 416p. 1987. pap. 9.95 (ISBN 0-02-689000-3, Checkerboard Pr). Macmillan.

Bible for Ethics: Juan Luis Segundo & First-World Ethics. Anthony J. Tambasco. LC 80-6253. 286p. (Orig.). 1981. lib. bdg. 27.50 (ISBN 0-8191-1556-8); pap. text ed. 12.75 (ISBN 0-8191-1557-6). U Pr of Amer.

Bible for Students of Literature & Art. Ed. by G. B. Harrison. LC 64-13820. 1964. pap. 8.50 (ISBN 0-385-04475-5, A394, Anch). Doubleday.

Bible for Today's Church. Robert A. Bennett & O. C. Edwards. (Church's Teaching Ser.: Vol. 2). 320p. 1979. 5.95 (ISBN 0-8164-0419-4, HarpR); pap. 4.95 (ISBN 0-8164-2215-X); users guide 1.50 (ISBN 0-8164-2222-2). Har-Row.

Bible Fun Book, No. 7. Steve Crain. (Activity Book Ser.). 32p. (Orig.). 1981. oversized saddle stitched .99 (ISBN 0-87123-766-0, 220766). Bethany Hse.

Bible Fun Book, No. 8. Steve Crain. (Activity Book Ser.). 32p. (Orig.). 1981. pap. 0.99 saddle-stitched (ISBN 0-87123-772-5, 220772). Bethany Hse.

Bible Fun Book: Puzzles, Riddles, Magic, & More. David A. Adler. (Bonim Fun-to-Do Bk.). (Illus., Orig.). 1979. pap. 3.95 (ISBN 0-88482-769-0). Hebrew Pub.

Bible Games & Activities. Ronald F. Keeler. (Game & Party Bks.). Orig. Title: Bible Game Book. 96p. 1982. pap. 2.95 (ISBN 0-8010-5436-2). Baker Bk.

Bible Games & Fun for Everyone. O'Ree. 1966. 0.60 (ISBN 0-88027-103-5). Firm Foun Pub.

Bible Games for Teams & Groups. Judene Leon. (Illus.). 64p. 1984. pap. 6.95 (ISBN 0-86683-832-5, HarpR). Har-Row.

Bible Gems. Ivor C. Powell. LC 86-27525. 172p. (Orig.). 1987. pap. 5.95 (ISBN 0-8254-3527-7). Kregel.

Bible Gems. Z. W. Swafford. 1974. pap. 0.75 (ISBN 0-89114-034-4). Baptist Pub Hse.

Bible Geography. Ed. by Clevenger & Hill. 1973. pap. 1.50 (ISBN 0-88428-003-9, 111). Parchment Pr.

Bible: God's Wonderful Book. (Teaching Bks.). (Illus.). 10p. 1968. pap. text ed. 2.95 (ISBN 0-86508-150-6). BCM Intl Inc.

Bible Guidebook. William N. McElrath. LC 72-79174. 144p. 1972. 9.95 (ISBN 0-8054-4410-6, 4244-10). Broadman.

Bible Handbook. G. W. Foote & W. P. Ball. 372p. 1983. pap. 7.00 (ISBN 0-910309-26-4). Am Atheist.

Bible Handbook, 2 vols. W. Scott. 18.00 (ISBN 0-88172-123-9). Believers Bkshelf.

Bible Handbook: A Guide for Basic Bible Learning. Michael Weed & Libby Weed. LC 73-91023. 1978. student's ed. 5.95 (ISBN 0-8344-0101-0). Sweet.

Bible Handbook: For Freethinkers & Inquiring Christians. 11th ed. Ed. by G. W. Foote & W. P. Ball. LC 71-161330. (Atheist Viewpoint Ser). 176p. 1972. Repr. of 1961 ed. 20.00 (ISBN 0-405-03797-X). Ayer Co Pubs.

Bible Handwork Ideas for Twos & Threes. Joy Averett & Donna Smith. 1983. pap. 3.25 (ISBN 0-89137-613-5). Quality Pubns.

Bible Has the Answer. Henry M Morris. pap. 8.95 (ISBN 0-8010-5905-4). Baker Bk.

Bible Has the Answer. Henry M. Morris & Martin Clark. LC 76-20206. 1976. pap. 9.95 (ISBN 0-89051-018-0). Master Bks.

Bible Hermeneutics. Milton S. Terry. 784p. 1974. kivar 14.95 (ISBN 0-310-36831-6, 6672P). Zondervan.

Bible Hero Stories. Joe Maniscalco. LC 74-28725. (Illus.). 144p. 1975. 6.95 (ISBN 0-87239-036-5, 2746). Standard Pub.

Bible Heroes. Doris C. Demaree. (Bible Stories for Children Ser.). 1970. pap. 1.50 (ISBN 0-87162-004-9, D1444). Warner Pr.

Bible Heroes. Ruth Odor. (Flip-a-Bible-Story Bks.). (Illus.). 16p. (Orig.). 1982. pap. 3.95 (ISBN 0-87239-562-6, 2736). Standard Pub.

Bible Heroes, Kings & Prophets. Mary B. Christian & Dorothy Van Woerkom. 1982. pap. 3.75 (ISBN 0-570-04066-3, 56-1718). Concordia.

Bible Highways. Ivor Powell. LC 85-8097. 192p. 1985. pap. 5.95 (ISBN 0-8254-3521-8). Kregel.

Bible History. Ed. by Richard Grunze. (WELS Lutheran Elementary Schools' Religion Curriculum Ser.). (Illus.). 556p. 1984. 11.95 (ISBN 0-938272-14-4). WELS Board.

Bible History. Ignatius Schuster. Ed. by H. J. Heck. Tr. by Philip Schumacher. (Illus.). 1974. pap. 8.00 (ISBN 0-89555-006-7). TAN Bks Pubs.

Bible History Commentary: Old Testament. Werner H. Franzmann. LC 80-53145. (Illus.). 616p. 1981. 15.95 (ISBN 0-938272-04-7). WELS Board.

Bible History: Teachers' Manual. Richard Grunze. 228p. 1985. suedene vinyl 3-ring binder 12.95 (ISBN 0-938272-15-2). WELS Board.

Bible: How to Understand & Teach It. D. P. Brooks. LC 68-14365. 1969. pap. 4.25 (ISBN 0-8054-1118-6). Broadman.

Bible Illustrated for Little Children. Ella K. Lindvall. (Illus.). 1985. text ed. 11.95 (ISBN 0-8024-0596-7). Moody.

Bible Illustration. Johann U. Krause. (Printed Sources of Western Art Ser.). (Ger., Illus.). 50p. 1981. pap. 35.00 slipcase (ISBN 0-915346-54-0). A Wofsy Fine Arts.

Bible in America: Essays in Cultural History. Ed. by Nathan O. Hatch & Mark A. Noll. LC 81-18751. 1982. 22.50x (ISBN 0-19-503099-0); pap. 6.95 (ISBN 0-19-503100-8). Oxford U Pr.

Bible in American Education. Ed. by David Barr & Nicholas Piediscalzi. LC 81-14436. (SBL The Bible in American Culture Ser.). 1982. 12.95 (ISBN 0-89130-538-6, 061205, Co-pub Fortress Pr). Scholars Pr GA.

Bible in American Law, Politics, & Political Rhetoric. Ed. by James T. Johnson. LC 83-16327. (Bible in American Culture Ser.). 1984. pap. 15.95 (ISBN 0-89130-652-8, 06 12 04). Scholars Pr GA.

Bible in Counseling. Waylon O. Ward. 1977. pap. 12.95 (ISBN 0-8024-0623-8). Moody.

Bible in Early English Literature. David C. Fowler. LC 76-7786. (Illus.). 274p. 1976. 18.95x (ISBN 0-295-95438-8). U of Wash Pr.

Bible in English Drama: An Annotated Bibliography. rev. ed. Edward D. Coleman. 1969. 25.00x (ISBN 0-87068-034-X). Ktav.

Bible in English Drama: An Annotated List of Plays. Edward D. Coleman. 1969. 6.95 (ISBN 0-87104-021-2, Co-Pub by Ktav). NY Pub Lib.

Bible in English, Fifteen Twenty-Five to Sixteen Eleven. Craig R. Thompson. LC 59-1241. (Folger Guides to the Age of Shakespeare). 1958. pap. 3.95 (ISBN 0-918016-22-3). Folger Bks.

Bible in English Literature. E. W. Wock. 69.95 (ISBN 0-87968-727-4). Gordon Pr.

Bible in Everyday Speech. L. Lyons. 1986. cancelled (ISBN 0-442-25325-7). Van Nos Reinhold.

Bible in Human Transformation: Towards a New Paradigm for Biblical Study. Walter Wink. LC 73-79047. 96p. (Orig.). 1980. pap. 4.95 (ISBN 0-8006-1034-2, 1-1034). Fortress.

Bible in Iron. 3rd ed. Henry C. Mercer. (Illus.). 356p. 1961. pap. 15.00 (ISBN 0-910302-01-4). Bucks Co Hist.

Bible in Living English: Written by an Anarchist. Tr. by Steven T. Byington. (Men & Movements in the History & Philosophy of Anarchism Ser.). 1979. lib. bdg. 59.95 (ISBN 0-686-59576-9). Revisionist Pr.

Bible in Pictures for Little Eyes. Kenneth N. Taylor. (Illus.). 1956. 11.95 (ISBN 0-8024-0595-9). Moody.

Bible in Pocket, Gun in Hand: The Story of Frontier Religion. Ross Phares. LC 64-11375. viii, 182p. 1971. pap. 5.50 (ISBN 0-8032-5725-2, BB 524, Bison). U of Nebr Pr.

Bible in Public Schools. 2nd ed. Johann B. Stallo et al. LC 67-27464. (Law, Politics & History Ser). 1967. Repr. of 1870 ed. lib. bdg. 39.50 (ISBN 0-306-70963-5). Da Capo.

Bible in Religious Education. Robert Davidson. 72p. 1980. pap. 5.00x (ISBN 0-905312-10-4, Pub. by Scot Acad Pr). Longwood Pub Group.

Bible in Scots Literature. James Moffatt. LC 73-14835. 1924. Repr. lib. bdg. 35.00 (ISBN 0-8414-6048-5). Folcroft.

Bible in Shakespeare. Carl Ackerman. 1978. lib. bdg. 18.00 (ISBN 0-8495-0134-2). Arden Lib.

Bible in Shakespeare. Carl Ackerman. lib. bdg. 15.00 (ISBN 0-8414-2954-5). Folcroft.

Bible in Shakespeare. William Burgess. 79.95 (ISBN 0-87968-728-2). Gordon Pr.

Bible in Shakespeare. William Burgess. LC 68-24900. (Studies in Shakespeare, No. 24). 1969. Repr. of 1903 ed. lib. bdg. 75.00 (ISBN 0-8383-0921-6). Haskell.

Bible in the Church. Brooke F. Westcott. (Canterbury Bks.). 1980. pap. 6.95 (ISBN 0-8010-9627-8). Baker Bk.

Bible in the Churches: How Different Christians Interpret the Scriptures. Ed. by Daniel Harrington. 1985. pap. 8.95 (ISBN 0-8091-2676-1). Paulist Pr.

Bible in the Classroom. Alan T. Dale. 96p. (Orig.). 1973. pap. 4.95 (ISBN 0-8192-1151-6). Morehouse.

Bible in the Early Middle Ages. Robert McNally. (Reprints & Translations Ser.). 1986. pap. 9.95 (ISBN 0-89130-912-8, 00-07-14). Scholars Pr GA.

Bible in the Life of the Catholic Church. Roger Mahony. 32p. (Orig.). 1983. pap. 0.50 (ISBN 0-8146-1317-9). Liturgical Pr.

Bible in the Making. Geddes MacGregor. LC 82-17499. 318p. 1983. pap. 14.50 (ISBN 0-8191-2810-4). U Pr of Amer.

Bible in the Medieval World: Essays in Memory of Beryl Smalley. Ed. by Katherine Walsh & Diana Wood. (Studies in Church History: Subsidia 4). 352p. 1985. 45.00x (ISBN 0-631-14275-4). Basil Blackwell.

Bible in the Pulpit: The Renewal of Biblical Preaching. Leander E. Keck. LC 77-12015. 1978. pap. 8.95 (ISBN 0-687-03160-5). Abingdon.

Bible in the Wesleyan Heritage. Mack B. Stokes. LC 80-23636. 96p. (Orig.). 1981. pap. 4.95 (ISBN 0-687-03100-1). Abingdon.

Bible in the Works of Thomas More, 2 vols. Germain Marc'hadour. 1098p. 1969. Set. text ed. 127.50x (Pub. by B De Graaf Netherlands). Coronet Bks.

Bible in Waverley. Nicholas Dickson. 1973. Repr. of 1884 ed. write for info. (ISBN 0-8274-1586-9). R West.

Bible in Waverley: Or, Sir Walter Scott's Use of the Sacred Scripture. Nicholas Dickson. 311p. 1980. Repr. of 1884 ed. lib. bdg. 30.00 (ISBN 0-8495-1123-2). Arden Lib.

Bible Index. Ed. by R. G. Bratcher & J. A. Thompson. 136p. 1970. pap. 2.15x (ISBN 0-8267-0005-5, 08511, Pub. by United Bible). Am Bible.

Bible Index Pocketbook. Harold Shaw Publishers. LC 81-8940. 192p. 1981. pap. 2.95 (ISBN 0-87788-077-8). Shaw Pubs.

Bible Inerrancy Primer. John Gerstner. 1981. pap. 2.50 (ISBN 0-88469-144-6). BMH Bks.

Bible Instruction Manuals, Etc. A Bibliography. Training Manual Research Division. 1984. pap. text ed. 1.95 (ISBN 0-318-03127-2, Pub. by Training Manuals). Prosperity & Profits.

Bible Is a Scientific Book. Gordon Lindsay. 1.50 (ISBN 0-89985-117-7). Christ Nations.

Bible Is Human. Louis Wallis. LC 74-149677. Repr. of 1942 ed. 24.00 (ISBN 0-404-06814-6). AMS Pr.

Bible: Its Heroes & Its Message. Marilyn Norquist. 96p. 1985. pap. 2.95 (ISBN 0-89243-227-6). Liguori Pubns.

Bible: It's Sixty Six Books in Brief. L. M. Grant. 70p. pap. 3.95 (ISBN 0-88172-160-3). Believers Bkshelf.

Bible: Its Story for Children. Walter Wangerin, Jr. (Illus.). 416p. 1981. 12.95. Macmillan.

Bible, Jesus & the Jews. Gabriel Monheim. LC 79-89891. 199p. 1980. 12.95 (ISBN 0-8022-2356-7). Philos Lib.

Bible Journeys. Dick Orr & David L. Bartlett. 80p. 1980. pap. 4.95 (ISBN 0-8170-0898-5). Judson.

Bible Keys for Today's Family. Knofel Staton. LC 83-9239. 144p. (Orig.). 1984. pap. 2.95 (ISBN 0-87239-669-X, 41024). Standard Pub.

Bible Knowledge Commentary: New Testament. 1983. 24.95 (ISBN 0-88207-812-7). Victor Bks.

Bible Knowledge Commentary, Old Testament. John Walvoord & Roy Zuck. 1985. 29.95. Victor Bks.

Bible Learn & Do: Exodus. Vivian Gunderson. (Illus.). 1981. pap. 1.25 (ISBN 0-8323-0394-1); tchr's manual 2.50 (ISBN 0-8323-0435-2). Binford-Metropolitan.

Bible Learn & Do: Genesis, Pt. I. Vivian Gunderson. (Illus.). 1979. pap. 1.25 (ISBN 0-8323-0368-2); tchr's. manual 2.50 (ISBN 0-8323-0376-3). Binford-Metropolitan.

Bible Learn & Do: Genesis, Pt. II. Vivian Gunderson. (Illus.). 1980. pap. 1.25 (ISBN 0-8323-0369-0); tchr's. manual 2.50 (ISBN 0-8323-0377-1). Binford-Metropolitan.

Bible Learn & Do: Gospel of Mark. Vivian Gunderson. (Illus.). 1982. pap. 1.25 (ISBN 0-8323-0412-3); pap. 2.50 tchr's manual (ISBN 0-8323-0439-5). Binford-Metropolitan.

Bible Learn & Do: Numbers. Vivian Gunderson. (Illus.). 1981. pap. 1.25 (ISBN 0-8323-0393-3); tchr's. manual 2.50 (ISBN 0-8323-0436-0). Binford-Metropolitan.

Bible Learn & Do: The Bible Is the Best Book, Why? Vivian Gunderson. 1985. pap. 1.25 (ISBN 0-8323-0442-5). Binford-Metropolitan.

Bible Learning Fun for Kids. Mary E. Lysne. 24p. 1983. pap. 1.50 (ISBN 0-87239-694-0, 2364). Standard Pub.

Bible Legends: An Introduction to Midrash. rev. ed. Lillian S. Freehof. Ed. by Howard Schwartz. 1987. pap. text ed. 6.95 (ISBN 0-8074-0357-1). UAHC.

Bible Legends: An Introduction to Midrash. Lillian S. Freehof. Ed. by Howard Schwartz. (YA) Date not set. pap. text ed. 6.95 (ISBN 0-8074-0357-1). UAHC.

Bible Lessons for Juniors, 4 bks. Andrew Van Der Veer. Incl. Bk. 1. Creation Through Moses. 2.95 (ISBN 0-8010-9253-1); Bk. 2. Kings & Prophets. 2.95 (ISBN 0-8010-9251-5); Bk. 3. Life of Christ. 2.95 (ISBN 0-8010-9257-4); Bk. 4. Early Church. 2.95 (ISBN 0-8010-9255-8). Baker Bk.

Bible Lessons for Little People: Revised with Learning Centers. rev. ed. Evelyn Grogg. Rev. by Sarah Eberle. LC 80-53878. 144p. 1981. pap. 7.95 (ISBN 0-87239-430-1, 3368). Standard Pub.

Bible Lessons for Youth, Bk. I. Ed. by Sherry S. DuPree & E. Myron Noble. 40p. (Orig.). 1987. pap. text ed. 2.95 (ISBN 0-9616056-4-2). Mid Atl Reg Pr.

Bible Magic Trick Talks for Childrens Church. Arnold C. Westphal. 1987. pap. 4.95 (ISBN 0-915398-26-5). Visual Evangels.

Bible Makes Sense. Walter Brueggemann. LC 76-29883. (Biblical Foundation Ser.). 1977. pap. 7.95 (ISBN 0-8042-0063-7). John Knox.

Bible Makes Sense. Walter Brueggemann. LC 76-29883. 1977. pap. 6.95 (ISBN 0-88489-087-2). St Mary's.

Bible Manners & Customs. George M. Mackie. (Illus.). 176p. 1956. (Power Bks); pap. 6.95 (ISBN 0-8007-5179-5). Revell.

Bible Manners & Customs. George M. Mackie. LC 84-230883. (Illus.). 192p. 1984. 6.95 (ISBN 0-8007-5179-5, Power Bks.). Revell.

Bible Medicine with Healing Verses. George H. Brummel. LC 83-91263. 172p. (Orig.). 1984. pap. 9.95 (ISBN 0-9613041-0-3). G Brummel Pub.

Bible Meditations for Every Day: A Guide to Living the Year in the Spirit of the Scriptures. John C. Kersten. flexible bdg. 4.95 (ISBN 0-89942-277-2, 277/04). Catholic Bk Pub.

Bible Melodies Chosen. Wayne Cargile. 1971. pap. 1.00 (ISBN 0-89012-106-5). McClain.

Bible Memory Verses. Compiled by Marian Bennett. (Little Happy Day Bks.). (Illus.). 24p. (Orig.). 1983. pap. 0.49 (ISBN 0-87239-652-5, 2122). Standard Pub.

Bible Moments with Motions. Mary A. Magers. Ed. by Arthur L. Zapel. Tr. by Michelle Zapel. (Illus.). 53p. (Orig.). 1984. pap. 3.95 (ISBN 0-916260-27-5). Meriwether Pub.

Bible Mystery Word Puzzle. U. R. King. 64p. 1986. pap. text ed. 3.00 (ISBN 0-935545-02-6). Land & Land.

Bible Myths & Their Parallels in Other Religions. T. W. Doane. 589p. spiral bdg. 12.00. Truth Seeker.

Bible, N. T. Epistles of Paul: The Pauline Epistles Contained in Ms. Ed. by Margaret J. Powell. (EETS, ES Ser.: No. 116). Repr. of 1916 ed. 35.00 (ISBN 0-527-00320-4). Kraus Repr.

Bible, Natural Science, & Evolution. Russell Maatman. (Orig.). 1980. pap. 4.95 (ISBN 0-932914-03-9). Dordt Coll Pr.

Bible, Now I Get It: A Form Criticism Handbook. Gerhard Lohfink. LC 78-1209. (Illus.). 1979. pap. 7.95 (ISBN 0-385-13432-0). Doubleday.

Bible Numbers. Marian Bennett. (Little Happy Day Bks.). (Illus.). 24p. (Orig.). 1983. pap. 0.49 (ISBN 0-87239-653-3, 2123). Standard Pub.

Bible Numerics. Oswald T. Allis. 1949. pap. 0.95 (ISBN 0-87552-100-2). Presby & Reformed.

Bible Nurture & Reader Ser. Lela Birky. 1969. write for info. (ISBN 0-686-05603-5); Span. ed. write for info.; tchr's. ed. avail. (ISBN 0-686-05604-3). Rod & Staff.

Bible Object Talks for Children. Larry Michaels. (Illus.). 48p. (Orig.). 1982. pap. 2.95 (ISBN 0-87239-532-4, 2888). Standard Pub.

Bible of the World. Ed. by R. O. Ballou et al. 1415p. 1980. pap. 5.50 (ISBN 0-380-01057-7, 17350). Avon.

Bible on Abortion. Harold O. J. Brown. 1977. 0.50 (ISBN 0-911802-43-6). Free Church Pubns.

Bible on Film: A Checklist 1897-1980. Richard H. Campbell & Michael R. Pitts. LC 81-13560. 224p. 1981. 17.50 (ISBN 0-8108-1473-0). Scarecrow.

Bible on Praise. Merlin R. Carothers. 32p. (Orig.). 1981. pap. 2.25 (ISBN 0-943026-03-2). Carothers.

Bible on the Life Hereafter. William Hendriksen. (Direction Books). 1971. pap. 6.95 (ISBN 0-8010-4022-1). Baker Bk.

Bible Only Makes Christians Only & the Only Christians. Thomas B. Warren. 220p. 1986. pap. 11.00 (ISBN 0-934916-09-8). Natl Christian Pr.

Bible Panorama. Terry Hall. 1983. text ed. 9.95 (ISBN 0-88207-273-0). Victor Bks.

Bible People Quiz Book. Erma Reynolds. (Quiz & Puzzle Books). 1979. pap. 2.95 (ISBN 0-8010-7692-7). Baker Bk.

Bible People Story-N-Puzzle Book. Ruby Maschke. 48p. (Orig.). 1983. pap. 2.50 (ISBN 0-87239-673-8, 2773). Standard Pub.

Bible Places. Velda Matthews. (Illus.). 1985. 1.95 (ISBN 0-87239-254-6, 2782). Standard Pub.

Bible Places: A Handbook to the Holy Land. John Walden. 96p. 1984. pap. 4.95 (ISBN 0-8307-0933-9, 5018476). Regal.

Bible Pop-O-Rama Books, 2 vols. Jim Roberts & Joann Scheck. Incl. The Brightest Star (ISBN 0-8066-1601-6, 10-0915); When Jesus Was a Boy (ISBN 0-8066-1602-4, 10-7064). (Illus.). 1978. laminated 1.95 ea. Augsburg.

Bible Prayer Book. Ed. by Eugene S. Geissler. LC 80-71052. 528p. (Orig.). 1981. pap. 4.95 (ISBN 0-87793-218-2). Ave Maria.

Bible Prayer Study Course. Kenneth E. Hagin. 1974. pap. 5.00 (ISBN 0-89276-081-8). Hagin Ministries.

Bible Programs & Dramas for Children. Carol Richardson. 64p. (Orig.). 1983. pap. 2.95 (ISBN 0-87239-665-7, 3350). Standard Pub.

Bible Programs & Dramas for Youth & Adults. Compiled by Judith A. Sparks. 64p. (Orig.). 1983. pap. 2.95 (ISBN 0-87239-671-1, 3351). Standard Pub.

Bible Promise Book. (Barbour Bks). 1986. bonded leather 10.95 (ISBN 0-916441-44-X); pap. 3.95 (ISBN 0-916441-43-1). Barbour & Co.

Bible Promises for Growing Christians. James Ryan. LC 84-22953. 1985. pap. 2.25 (ISBN 0-8054-5014-9). Broadman.

Bible Promises for Tiny Tots, No. 3. George Taggart. Ed. by Richard W. Coffen. 32p. (Orig.). 1987. pap. 3.95 (ISBN 0-8280-0375-0). Review & Herald.

Bible Promises for Tiny Tots, II. George Taggart. Ed. by Richard W. Coffen. 32p. (Orig.). 1985. pap. 3.95 (ISBN 0-8280-0246-0). Review & Herald.

Bible Promises, Help & Hope for Your Finances. Dick Bruso. 156p. (Orig.). 1985. pap. 2.95 (ISBN 0-89840-075-9). Heres Life.

Bible: Prose & Poetry from the Old Testament. Ed. by James F. Fullington. LC 50-9988. (Crofts Classics Ser.). 1950. pap. text ed. 4.95x (ISBN 0-88295-013-4). Harlan Davidson.

Bible Puppet Scripts for Busy Teachers. Diane Warner. LC 81-69783. 1983. pap. 4.95 (ISBN 0-89636-076-8). Accent Bks.

Bible Puzzle Book. Marcina Gay. 128p. (Orig.). 1984. pap. 2.25 (ISBN 0-8007-8487-1, Spire Bks). Revell.

Bible Puzzle Time, Friends of God. Diana Bretschneider. 16p. 1983. pap. 0.60 (ISBN 0-87239-655-X, 2303). Standard Pub.

Bible Puzzle Trails. Helen Sattler. (Pelican Activity Ser.). 32p. 1977. pap. 0.89 (ISBN 0-8010-7900-4). Baker Bk.

Bible Puzzler, No. 1. 1985. 2.95 (ISBN 0-89536-741-6, 5825). CSS of Ohio.

Bible Puzzler No. Two: Stories from Mark. 1985. 2.95 (ISBN 0-89536-768-8, 5876). CSS of Ohio.

Bible Questions Answered. William L. Pettingill. 1932. 8.95 (ISBN 0-310-31131-4, Pub. by Dunham). Zondervan.

Bible Quiz Book. Barbara Burrage. 1979. pap. 2.95 (ISBN 0-8192-1256-3). Morehouse.

Bible Quiz Book Nos. 1 & 2. 1.50 ea. No. 1 (ISBN 0-529-05715-8, BQ-1). No. 2 (ISBN 0-529-05716-6, BQ-2). World Bible.

Bible Quizzerama Puzzle Book. Barbara Burrage. 48p. (Orig.). 1981. pap. 1.95 (ISBN 0-87239-446-8, 2836). Standard Pub.

Bible Quizzes. Shirley Beegle. 1985. pap. 0.69 pocket size (ISBN 0-87239-823-4, 2813). Standard Pub.

Bible Quizzes for Everybody. Frederick Hall. (Quiz & Puzzle Bks.). 150p. 1980. pap. 3.95 (ISBN 0-8010-4032-9). Baker Bk.

Bible Quizzes for Kids. Marcina Gay. 48p. (Orig.). 1982. pap. 1.95 (ISBN 0-87239-594-4, 3136). Standard Pub.

Bible Quizzes on Bible Themes. Marjorie Collins. 48p. 1983. pap. 1.95 (ISBN 0-87239-658-4, 3138). Standard Pub.

Bible Reader's Encyclopedia & Concordance. W. Clow. (Illus.). 9.95 (ISBN 0-529-05899-5, RT1). World Bible.

Bible Reader's Guide. Adolph F. Fehlauer. 1981. 5.95 (ISBN 0-8100-0146-2, 06N0558). Northwest Pub.

Bible Readers Tool Box. Norman P. Madsen. LC 86-24523. 168p. (Orig.). 1987. pap. 7.95 (ISBN 0-8272-0214-8). CBP.

Bible Reading for Parents. Ron Klug & Lyn Klug. LC 81-52277. (Bible Readings Ser.). 112p. (Orig.). 1982. pap. 3.95 (ISBN 0-8066-1909-0, 10-0679). Augsburg.

Bible Reading for Singles. Ruth Stenerson. LC 80-65543. (Bible Reading Ser.). 112p. (Orig.). 1980. pap. 3.95 (ISBN 0-8066-1788-8, 10-0678). Augsburg.

Bible Reading for Teachers. Ruth Stenerson. LC 81-52275. (Bible Readings Ser.). 112p. (Orig.). 1982. pap. 3.95 (ISBN 0-8066-1907-4, 10-0680). Augsburg.

Bible Reading for Teenagers. Charles S. Mueller. LC 81-52274. (Bible Readings Ser.). 112p. (Orig.). 1981. pap. 3.95 (ISBN 0-8066-1906-6, 10-0681). Augsburg.

Bible Reading for the Retired. Leslie F. Brandt. LC 83-72117. 112p. (Orig.). 1984. pap. 3.95 (ISBN 0-8066-2061-7, 10-0683). Augsburg.

Bible Readings for Bible Students & for the Home & Fireside. Compiled by S. L. Speck & H. M. Riggle. 432p. 1902. 5.00 (ISBN 0-686-29102-6). Faith Pub Hse.

Bible Readings for Caregivers. Betty G. Syverson. (Bible Readings Ser.). 112p. (Orig.). 1987. pap. 3.95 (ISBN 0-8066-2276-8, 10-0695). Augsburg.

Bible Readings for Church Workers. Harry N. Huxhold. LC 84-21574. 112p. (Orig.). 1984. pap. 3.95 (ISBN 0-8066-2132-X, 10-0684). Augsburg.

Bible Readings for Couples. Margaret Wold & Erling Wold. LC 80-65541. (Bible Reading Ser.). 112p. (Orig.). 1980. pap. 3.95 (ISBN 0-317-40483-0, 10-0676). Augsburg.

Bible Readings for Families. Mildred Tengbom & Luverne Tengbom. LC 80-65542. (Bible Readings Ser.). 112p. (Orig.). 1980. pap. 3.95 (ISBN 0-8066-1787-X, 10-0677). Augsburg.

Bible Readings for Farm Living. Frederick Baltz. LC 85-7421. 112p. (Orig.). 1985. pap. 3.95 (ISBN 0-8066-2164-8, 10-0688). Augsburg.

Bible Readings for Growing Christians. Kevin E. Ruffcorn. LC 84-18424. 112p. (Orig.). 1984. pap. 3.95 (ISBN 0-8066-2131-1, 10-0685). Augsburg.

Bible Readings for Men. Steve Swanson. LC 83-72116. 112p. (Orig.). 1984. pap. 3.95 (ISBN 0-8066-2060-9, 10-0682). Augsburg.

Bible Readings for Mothers. Mildren Tengbom. (Bible Reading Ser.). 112p. (Orig.). 1987. pap. 3.95 (ISBN 0-8066-2249-0, 10-0692). Augsburg.

Bible Readings for Office Workers. Lou-Ann Good. 112p. (Orig.). 1987. pap. 3.95 (ISBN 0-8066-2250-4, 10-0693). Augsburg.

Bible Readings for Students. Ruth Stenerson. LC 85-30771. 112p. (Orig.). 1986. pap. 3.95 (ISBN 0-8066-2190-7, 10-0691). Augsburg.

Bible Readings for Troubled Times. Leslie F. Brandt. LC 84-18617. 112p. (Orig.). 1984. pap. 3.95 (ISBN 0-8066-2130-3, 10-0686). Augsburg.

Bible Readings for Women. Lyn Klug. LC 85-7508. 112p. 1985. pap. 3.95 (ISBN 0-8066-2163-X, 10-0687). Augsburg.

Bible Readings on God's Creation. Denise J. Williamson. (Bible Readings Ser.). 112p. (Orig.). 1987. pap. 3.95 (ISBN 0-8066-2277-6, 10-0696). Augsburg.

Bible Readings on Prayer. Ron Klug. LC 85-28979. 112p. (Orig.). 1986. pap. 3.95 (ISBN 0-8066-2189-3, 10-0690). Augsburg.

Bible Records, Barbour County, Ala, Vol. 1. Helen S. Foley. 80p. 1983. pap. 10.00 (ISBN 0-89308-180-9). Southern Hist Pr.

Bible Records, Barbour County, Ala, Vol. 2. Helen S. Foley. 84p. 1983. pap. 10.00 (ISBN 0-89308-181-7). Southern Hist Pr.

Bible References of John Ruskin. Ellen Gibbs & Mary Gibbs. 310p. 1973. Repr. of 1898 ed. 20.00 (ISBN 0-8274-0652-5). R West.

Bible References of John Ruskin. M. Gibbs & E. Gibbs. 59.95 (ISBN 0-87968-729-0). Gordon Pr.

Bible References of John Ruskin. John Ruskin. LC 77-13181. 1977. Repr. lib. bdg. 30.00 (ISBN 0-8414-4608-3). Folcroft.

Bible, Religion & the Public Schools. 3rd ed. Donald E. Boles. 408p. 1965. 8.95x (ISBN 0-8138-0200-8). Iowa St U Pr.

Bible Research. rev. ed. Kenneth P. Malmin. (Illus.). 149p. 1979. Repr. of 1976 ed. notebk. 11.95 (ISBN 0-914936-33-6). Bible Temple.

Bible Riddles of Birds & Beasts & Creeping Things. Lydia Regehr. (Illus.). 36p. (Orig.). 1982. pap. 1.50 (ISBN 0-89323-030-8). Bible Memory.

Bible Secret of Divine Health. Gordon Lindsay. (Divine Healing & Health Ser.). 1.25 (ISBN 0-89985-023-5). Christ Nations.

Bible Sharing: How to Grow in the Mystery of Christ. John Burke. LC 79-15006. (Orig.). 1979. pap. 5.95 (ISBN 0-8189-0386-4). Alba.

Bible Sharing Youth Retreat: Manual for Retreat Team. John Burke. 1986. pap. 4.50 (ISBN 0-697-02209-9). Wm C Brown.

Bible Smuggler. Louise A. Vernon. LC 67-15994. (Illus.). 138p. 1967. pap. 4.50 (ISBN 0-8361-1557-0). Herald Pr.

Bible Solutions to Problems of Daily Living. James Steele. 132p. 1983. 10.95 (ISBN 0-13-078022-7); pap. 4.95 (ISBN 0-13-078014-6). P-H.

Bible Speaks, 3 vols. Hella Taubes. Tr. by Lolla Bloch. (Illus.). 1974. 14.95x ea. (ISBN 0-686-76831-0). Set. Bloch.

Bible Speaks By, 3 Vols. Hellen Taubes. 1965. Set. 14.95. Soncino Pr.

Bible Speaks on Aging. Frank Stagg. LC 81-66092. 1981. softcover 6.50 (ISBN 0-8054-5292-3). Broadman.

Bible Speaks to You. Robert M. Brown. LC 84-19578. 324p. 1985. pap. 8.95 (ISBN 0-664-24597-8). Westminster.

Bible Status of Women. Lee A. Starr. Ed. by Carolyn D. Gifford & Donald Dayton. (Women in American Protestant Religion 1800-1930 Ser.). 416p. 1987. lib. bdg. 60.00 (ISBN 0-8240-0675-5). Garland Pub.

Bible Stories. William Anthony. LC 77-71655. (Illus., Orig.). pap. 5.00 (ISBN 0-912330-25-2, Dist. by Inland Bk). Jargon Soc.

Bible Stories. Charles M. Sheldon. LC 74-4817. (Illus.). 1978. pap. 4.95 (ISBN 0-448-14612-6, G&D). Putnam Pub Group.

Bible Stories Coloring Book. 48p. 1973. pap. 2.50 (ISBN 0-486-20623-8). Dover.

Bible Stories for Children. 32p. 1981. pap. 3.95 (ISBN 0-8249-8017-4). Ideals.

Bible Stories for Children. (Illus.). 20p. 1985. incl. cassette 8.95 (ISBN 0-8249-8121-9). Ideals.

Bible Stories for Everyone. Ed. by Daughters of St. Paul. 1956. 6.00 (ISBN 0-8198-0008-2); pap. 5.00 (ISBN 0-8198-0009-0). Dghtrs St Paul.

Bible Stories for Family Devotions. JoAnn Merrell. (Illus.). 80p. 1982. pap. 4.95 (ISBN 0-87123-196-4, 210196). Bethany Hse.

Bible Stories for Jewish Children, 2 vols, No. 1. Ruth Samuels. (Illus.). 1958. 7.95x (ISBN 0-87068-356-X). Ktav.

Bible Stories for Jewish Children, 2 vols, No. 2. Ruth Samuels. (Illus.). 1973. 7.95x (ISBN 0-87068-965-7). Ktav.

Bible Stories for Little Children, Bk. 1. rev. ed. Betty Hollender. (Illus.). 80p. (Orig.). 1985. pap. text ed. 6.00 (ISBN 0-8074-0309-1, 103100). UAHC.

Bible Stories for Little Children, Vol. 2. rev. ed. Betty R. Hollender. (Illus.). 80p. 1987. pap. text ed. 6.00 (ISBN 0-8074-0324-5). UAHC.

Bible Stories for the Church Year. Kristen J. Ingram. Ed. by Joseph P. Russell. LC 83-20135. 184p. (Orig.). 1986. pap. 10.95 (ISBN 0-86683-537-7, HarpR). Har-Row.

Bible Stories from the Old Testament. P. Hunt. (Illus.). 4.98 (ISBN 0-517-43909-3). Outlet Bk Co.

Bible Stories in Action for Children. Richard S. Robbins. 1981. 4.50 (ISBN 0-89536-475-1, 0209). CSS of Ohio.

Bible Stories in Rhyme. Jean B. Thompson. 1986. text ed. 12.95 (ISBN 0-8024-0651-3). Moody.

Bible Stories Reader. Robert L. Larson. 1985. 8.95 (ISBN 0-533-06749-9). Vantage.

Bible Stories to Live By. V. Gilbert Beers & Ronald A. Beers. LC 82-84616. (Illus.). 192p. 1983. 12.95 (ISBN 0-89840-044-9). Heres Life.

Bible Stories You Can't Forget No Matter How Hard You Try. Marshall Efron & Alfa B. Olsen. (Illus.). 1976. 9.95 (ISBN 0-525-26500-7, 0966-290). Dutton.

Bible Story & Color Book. Ruth Humphrey. (Illus.). 64p. (Orig.). 1982. pap. 2.95 (ISBN 0-87239-582-0, 2397). Standard Pub.

Bible Story Book: New Testament. Sarah Fletcher. LC 56-1427. (Continued Applied Christianity Ser.). 1983. 10.50 (ISBN 0-570-04080-9). Concordia.

Bible Story Book: Old Testament. Sarah Fletcher. LC 83-1801. (Continued Applied Christianity Ser.). 1983. 10.50 (ISBN 0-570-04079-5, 56-1426). Concordia.

Bible Story Favorites. Patricia Mahany. (My Shape Bk.). (Illus.). 1984. 2.95 (ISBN 0-87239-782-3, 2722). Standard Pub.

Bible Story Library. Turner Hodges. 1963. 12.95 (ISBN 0-672-23099-2, Pub. by Audel). Macmillan.

Bible, Story of a Book. 1985. pap. 3.95 (ISBN 0-89314-818-0). Philos Res.

Bible Student's Commentary: Deuteronomy. J. Ridderbos. (Bible Student's Commentary Ser.). 336p. 1984. 16.95 (ISBN 0-310-45260-0, 11760). Zondervan.

Bible Student's Commentary: Exodus. W. H. Gispen. (Bible Student's Commentary). 352p. 1982. 16.95 (ISBN 0-310-43970-1). Zondervan.

Bible Student's Commentary: Isaiah. J. Ridderbos. (Bible Student's Commentary Ser.). 528p. 1985. 24.95 (ISBN 0-310-45270-8, 11761). Zondervan.

Bible Student's Commentary: Joshua, Judges, Ruth. C. J. Goslinga. Tr. of Korte Verklaring. 544p. 1986. 24.95 (ISBN 0-310-45280-5). Zondervan.

Bible Student's Commentary: Leviticus. A. Noordtzij. (Bible Student's Commentary Ser.). 288p. 1982. 16.95 (ISBN 0-310-45090-X, 11757). Zondervan.

Bible Student's Commentary: Numbers. A. Noordtzij. (Bible Student's Commentary Ser.). 1986. 16.95 (ISBN 0-310-43980-9, 11758). Zondervan.

Bible Student's Commentary: Pentateuch Set, 5 vols. 1984. text ed. 95.75 (ISBN 0-310-45168-X, 11759). Zondervan.

Bible Student's English-Greek Concordance & Greek-English Dictionary. James Gall. (Paperback Reference Library). 376p. 1983. pap. 9.95 (ISBN 0-8010-3795-6). Baker Bk.

Bible Studies for Children. Illus. by Geoffrey Horn. Arthur Cavanaugh. LC 79-27811. (Illus.). 336p. 1980. 12.95 (ISBN 0-02-554060-2). Macmillan.

Bible Studies for Christian Discipleship. 2nd ed. Nate Krupp. 1979. Repr. 1.45 (ISBN 0-89221-052-4). New Leaf.

Bible Studies for New Christians. 2nd ed. Nate Krupp. 1979. Repr. 1.45 (ISBN 0-89221-053-2). New Leaf.

Bible Studies for Senior Citizens. Mary K. Klim. 91p. 1986. pap. 5.95x (ISBN 0-932910-59-9). Potentials Development.

Bible Studies for Soul Winners. Nate Krupp. 1979. Repr. 1.45 (ISBN 0-89221-054-0). New Leaf.

Bible Studies for Special Occasions in Youth Ministry. Compiled by Forrest W. Jackson. LC 82-70109. 1982. pap. 4.95 (ISBN 0-8054-3617-0, 4236-17). Broadman.

Bible Studies Series. Frances Easter. (Studies in Luke: Vol. 1). 1985. pap. 3.50 (ISBN 0-8309-0424-7). Herald Hse.

Bible Studies Series. Frances Easter. (Studies in Luke Ser.: Vol. II). 1985. pap. 3.50 (ISBN 0-8309-0430-1). Herald Hse.

Bible Study. Frances Easter. (Studies in Acts: vol. I). 1986. pap. 3.50 (ISBN 0-8309-0436-0). Herald Hse.

Bible Study. John White. 1984. pap. 0.75 (ISBN 0-87784-068-7). Inter-Varsity.

Bible Study Commentary: Ezra, Nehemiah & Esther. Howard F. Vos. (Bible Study Commentary Ser.). 224p. 1987. pap. 7.95 (ISBN 0-310-33911-1). Zondervan.

Bible Study for Busy Women. Ethel Herr. 160p. 1983. pap. 6.95 (ISBN 0-8024-0147-3). Moody.

Bible Study Group: An Owner's Manual. William Riley. LC 85-70362. (Illus.). 152p. 1985. pap. 7.95 (ISBN 0-87793-286-7). Ave Maria.

Bible Study in Duet. Charlie Shedd & Martha Shedd. 144p. 1984. 8.95 (ISBN 0-310-42380-5, 18360). Zondervan.

Bible Study Leadership Training. Edie Iverson et al. (Illus.). 53p. 1980. pap. 6.75 (ISBN 0-914936-46-8). Bible Temple.

Bible Study Notes, Vols. 1-3. Anita S. Dole. Ed. by William R. Woofenden. LC 76-24081. 1976-78. lib. bdg. write for info. (ISBN 0-685-92171-9). Vol 1 (ISBN 0-917426-01-0). Vol. 2 (ISBN 0-917426-02-9). Vol. 3 (ISBN 0-917426-03-7). Am New Church Sunday.

Bible Study Notes, Vol. 4. Anita S. Dole. Ed. by William R. Woofenden. LC 76-24081. 1979. write for info. (ISBN 0-917426-04-5). Am New Church Sunday.

Bible Study Notes, Vol. 5. Anita S. Dole. Ed. by William R. Woofenden. LC 76-24081. 1979. write for info (ISBN 0-917426-05-3). Am New Church Sunday.

Bible Study Notes, Vol. 6. Anita S. Dole. Ed. by William R. Woofenden. LC 76-24081. 1979. write for info (ISBN 0-917426-06-1). Am New Church Sunday.

Bible Study Puzzle Book. Thomas J. Marks. 1981. pap. 2.95 saddlewire (ISBN 0-8054-9106-6). Broadman.

Bible Study Sourcebook. Ed. by Robert C. Walton. LC 80-26358. Vol. 1: Old Testament. pap. 54.00 (2027296); Vol. 2: New Testament. pap. 59.30. Bks Demand UMI.

Bible Study That Works. David L. Thompson. 72p. 1986. pap. 3.95 (ISBN 0-310-75001-6, 17024P). Zondervan.

Bible Study Together: Making Marriage Last. Charlie Shedd & Martha Shedd. 144p. 1987. pap. 5.95 (ISBN 0-310-42381-3). Zondervan.

Bible Survey. David K. Blomgren. (Illus.). 70p. 1979. pap. 6.25 (ISBN 0-914936-39-5). Bible Temple.

Bible Survey. Ed. by Ernest Clevenger, Jr. 1973. pap. 1.50 (ISBN 0-88428-005-5, 141). Parchment Pr.

Bible Teacher Time Savers. Rebecca Daniels. (Helping Hand Ser.). 48p. 1984. wkbk. 4.95 (ISBN 0-86653-235-8). Good Apple.

Bible Teaching Finger Plays. Marian White. (Teaching Helps Ser). 1977. pap. 4.50 (ISBN 0-8010-9592-1). Baker Bk.

Bible Tells Me. Bartholomew. 1982. pap. 0.85 (ISBN 0-570-04074-4, 56-1377). Concordia.

Bible Tells Me So. Victor P Wierwille. LC 70-176281. (Studies in Abundant Living: Vol. 1). 202p. 1971. 6.95 (ISBN 0-910068-10-0). Am Christian.

Bible Tells Us So: Twelve Short Chapters on Major Themes of the Bible. R. B. Kuiper. 1978. pap. 3.45 (ISBN 0-85151-001-9). Banner of Truth.

Bible: Texts & Translations of the Bible & the Apocrypha & Their Books from the National Union Catalog, 5 vols, Vol. 5. (700 pages per volume). 1980. 113.00x (ISBN 0-7201-1575-2); Set. 456.00 (ISBN 0-7201-1567-1). Mansell.

Bible That Was Lost & Is Found. 4th ed. John Bigelow. LC 78-65549. pap. 1.95 (ISBN 0-87785-159-X). Swedenborg.

Bible That Wouldn't Burn. L. Ulmer. LC 39-1094. 1983. pap. 3.95 (ISBN 0-570-03634-8). Concordia.

Bible, the Christian & Jehovah's Witnesses. Gordon Lewis. 1966. pap. 1.25 (ISBN 0-87552-324-2). Presby & Reformed.

Bible, the Christian & Latter Day Saints. Gordon Lewis. 1966. pap. 1.25 (ISBN 0-87552-325-0). Presby & Reformed.

Bible, the Christian & Seventh Day Adventists. Gordon Lewis. 1966. pap. 1.25 (ISBN 0-87552-326-9). Presby & Reformed.

Bible, the Church, & Social Justice. Richard Schiblin. 64p. 1983. pap. 1.50 (ISBN 0-89243-187-3). Liguori Pubns.

Bible, the Quran & Science. Maurice Bucaille. Ed. by Anwer Beg. Tr. by Maurice Bucaille & Alastair D. Pannell. LC 77-90336. 253p. 1978. 11.95 (ISBN 0-89259-010-6); pap. 8.50. Am Trust Pubns.

Bible, the Supernatural & the Jews. McCandlish Phillips. LC 77-92532. 1970. pap. 8.95 (ISBN 0-87123-036-4, 210036). Bethany Hse.

Bible Through Stamps. Ord Matek. LC 73-23126. 240p. 1974. 7.50x (ISBN 0-87068-397-7). Ktav.

Bible Through the Centuries. Herbert L. Willey. 1929. 37.50 (ISBN 0-8274-1935-X). R West.

Bible Today: Historical, Social, & Literary Aspects of the Old & New Testaments. The London Times. LC 78-6130. 1978. Repr. of 1955 ed. lib. bdg. cancelled (ISBN 0-313-20449-7, TIBT). Greenwood.

Bible Translation Controversy. Wayne Jackson. (That You May Believe Ser.). 20p. (Orig.). 1985. pap. 1.50 (ISBN 0-932859-01-1). Apologetic Pr.

Bible Translations. Commission Christian Lit. 1981. pap. 0.79 (ISBN 0-8100-0132-2, 04N1212). Northwest Pub.

Bible Translations & How to Choose Between Them. Alan S. Duthie. 127p. 1986. pap. 10.95 (ISBN 0-85364-400-4, Pub. by Paternoster UK). Attic Pr.

Bible Treasures. Ivor Powell. LC 84-25090. 192p. (Orig.). 1985. pap. 5.95 (ISBN 0-8254-3518-8). Kregel.

Bible Treasures Activity Book. Betty DeVries. (Pelican Activity Ser.). pap. 0.89 (ISBN 0-8010-2895-7). Baker Bk.

Bible Trek-athon. Lucy Townsend. (Complete Teacher Training Meeting Ser.). 48p. 1986. tchr's ed 9.95 (ISBN 0-89191-314-9). Cook.

Bible Trivia. William Schlegl. (Bible Baffler Ser.). 48p. 1986. wkbk. 4.95 (ISBN 0-86653-368-0). Good Apple.

Bible Truths. A. C. Lane. pap. 0.50 (ISBN 0-88243-696-1, 02-0696). Gospel Pub.

Bible Truths. Alva J. McClain. 1981. pap. 1.25 (ISBN 0-88469-013-X). BMH Bks.

Bible Truths with Shakespearian Parallels. 6th ed. James Buchan Brown. LC 74-19106. Repr. of 1886 ed. 15.00 (ISBN 0-404-01136-5). AMS Pr.

Bible Verses in Action. Ed. by Patricia Mahany. (Stick-On Activity & Coloring Bks.). (Illus.). 16p. 1983. pap. 1.50 (ISBN 0-87239-686-X, 2366). Standard Pub.

Bible Verses in Verse. Boris Randolph. LC 80-67992. 144p. 1980. pap. 3.95 (ISBN 0-87516-424-2). De Vorss.

Bible Verses to Remember. Julianne Booth. 1982. pap. 2.95 (ISBN 0-570-04061-2, 56-1364). Concordia.

Bible Vote: Religion & the New Right. Peggy L. Shriver. LC 81-7389. 170p. 1981. pap. 5.95 (ISBN 0-8298-0465-X). Pilgrim NY.

Bible Way to Receive the Holy Spirit. Kenneth E. Hagin. 1981. pap. 0.50 mini bk. (ISBN 0-89276-255-1). Hagin Ministries.

Bible Who Am I? Patricia S. Mahany. (Stick-On Activity & Coloring Bks.). (Illus.). 16p. 1983. pap. 1.50 (ISBN 0-87239-687-8, 2367). Standard Pub.

Bible Windows. Ivor Powell. LC 85-8103. 188p. 1985. pap. 5.95 (ISBN 0-8254-3522-6). Kregel.

Bible Wisdom for Modern Living: Arranged by Subject. Ed. by David Brown. 400p. 1986. 17.95 (ISBN 0-671-62545-4). S&S.

Bible Women. Coleman Overby. 1936. pap. 2.95 (ISBN 0-88027-082-9). Firm Foun Pub.

Bible Women Speak to Us Today. Mary E. Jensen. LC 83-70507. 128p. (Orig.). 1983. pap. 5.95 (ISBN 0-8066-2013-7, 10-0708). Augsburg.

Bible Word Chain Puzzles. William C. Hendricks & Glenn Van Noord. (Quiz & Puzzle Bks.). 96p. (Orig.). 1981. pap. 2.95 (ISBN 0-8010-4238-0). Baker Bk.

Bible Word Fun. Karen Layton & Ron Layton. (Bible Baffler Ser.). 48p. 1986. wkbk. 4.95 (ISBN 0-86653-367-2). Good Apple.

Bible Word Quest. new ed. Helen Pettigrew. 96p. 1975. pap. 2.95 (ISBN 0-8010-6965-3). Baker Bk.

Bible Word Search. William C. Gordon. (Quiz & Puzzle Bks.). 112p. 1983. 2.95 (ISBN 0-8010-3679-8). Baker Bk.

Bible Work & Play, 3 vols. Joyce Fischman. (Illus., Orig.). 1966. pap. text ed. 2.50 ea. Vol. 1 o.p (102610). Vol. 2 o.p (102620). Vol. 3 (102640). UAHC.

Bible Work & Play, Vol. 1. rev. ed. Joyce Fischman. (Illus.). 80p. (Orig.). 1985. pap. text ed. 5.00 (ISBN 0-8074-0304-0). UAHC.

Bible Work & Play, Vol. 2. rev. ed. Joyce Fischman. (Illus.). 80p. 1984. wkbk. 5.00 (ISBN 0-8074-0256-7). UAHC.

Bible Workbook: New Testament, Vol. 2. Catherine B. Walker. 1951. pap. 5.95 (ISBN 0-8024-0752-8). Moody.

Bible Workbook: Old Testament, Vol. 1. Catherine B. Walker. 1943. pap. 5.95 (ISBN 0-8024-0751-X). Moody.

Bible World: Essays in Honor of Cyrus H. Gordon. Gary Rendsburg et al. 1981. 45.00x (ISBN 0-87068-758-1). Ktav.

Bible World Maps of the Old & New Testaments. Betty M. Canfield. (Illus.). 24p. (Orig.). 1983. pap. text ed. 4.95 (ISBN 0-9611756-0-5). Humble Pub Co.

Biblelearn, 24 vol. set. 1979. 129.95 (ISBN 0-8054-4257-X, 4242-57). Broadman.

Bible's Ways of Prayer. Wilfrid Harrington. 164p. (Orig.). 1981. pap. 5.95 (ISBN 0-89453-182-4, Pub. by Dominican Pubns Ireland). M Glazier.

Biblia con Notas. Ed. by Mervin Breneman. (Span.). 1696p. 1981. black imitation leather 15.95 (ISBN 0-89922-164-5); black imitation leather 19.95 (ISBN 0-89922-364-8); red imitation leather 15.95 (ISBN 0-89922-264-1); red imitation leather 19.95 (ISBN 0-89922-464-4). Edit Caribe.

Biblia, el Libro de los Libros. Ed. by Charles W. Conn. (Span.). 116p. 1979. pap. 3.95 (ISBN 0-87148-523-0). Pathway Pr.

Biblia en Cuadros para Ninos. Kenneth N. Taylor. Orig. Title: Bible in Pictures for Little Eyes. (Span.). 190p. 1956. 13.95 (ISBN 0-8254-1706-6). Kregel.

Biblia lo Dice. Ed. by Jorge Diaz & Nelly De Gonzalez. (Span., Illus.). 120p. 1986. Repr. of 1984 ed. spiral bdg. 3.95 (ISBN 0-311-11453-9). Casa Bautista.

Biblia Pauperum: Apocalypsis. Rainer Behrends et al. (Illus., LC 77-088869). 1978. boxed 500.00 (ISBN 0-87817-239-4). Hacker.

Biblia Romanceada I.I.8: The Thirteenth-Century Spanish Bible Contained in Escorial MS. I. I. 8. Ed. by Mark G. Littlefield. (Dialect Ser.: No. 4). (Illus.). xiv, 334p. 1983. inc. 10 microfiches 35.00x (ISBN 0-942260-34-1). Hispanic Seminary.

Biblia y Su Interpretacion. Weldon Viertel. Orig. Title: Bible & Its Interpretation. 208p. 1983. pap. 8.25 (ISBN 0-311-03670-8). Casa Bautista.

Biblical Advent Homilies. David Q. Liptak. 68p. (Orig.). 1986. pap. 8.95 (ISBN 0-941850-15-3). Sunday Pubns.

Biblical Affirmations of Woman. Leonard Swidler. LC 79-18886. 382p. 1979. 19.50 (ISBN 0-664-21377-4); softcover 10.95 (ISBN 0-664-24285-5). Westminster.

Biblical & Historical Background of the Jewish Holy Days. A. P. Bloch. 1978. 20.00x (ISBN 0-87068-338-1); pap. 11.95. Ktav.

Biblical & Historical Backround of Jewish Customs & Ceremonies. Abraham P. Bloch. 1979. 20.00x (ISBN 0-87068-658-5); pap. 11.95. Ktav.

Biblical & Judaic Acronyms. Lawrence Marwick. 39.00x (ISBN 0-87068-438-8). Ktav.

Biblical & Oriental Studies: Bible, Vol. 1. U. Cassuto. Tr. by Israel Abrahams from Hebrew. (Illus.). 298p. 1973. text ed. 29.95x (Pub. by Magnes Pr Israel). Humanities.

Biblical & Oriental Studies: Bible & Ancient Oriental Texts, Vol. 2. U. Cassuto. Tr. by Israel Abrahams from Hebrew. 286p. 1975. text ed. 35.00x (Pub. by Magnes Pr Israel). Humanities.

Biblical & Related Studies Related to Samuel Iwry. Ed. by Ann Kort & Scott Morschauer. xvii, 274p. 1985. text ed. 25.00x (ISBN 0-931464-23-4). Eisenbrauns.

Biblical & Talmudic Medicine. Julius Preuss. Tr. by Fred Rosner from Ger. 1978. 45.00x (ISBN 0-88482-861-1, Sandhedrin Pr). Hebrew Pub.

Biblical & Theological Reflections on the Challenge of Peace. Ed. by John Pawlikowski & Donald Senior. (Theology & Life Ser.: Vol. 10). 1984. pap. 9.95 (ISBN 0-89453-433-5). M Glazier.

Biblical & Theological Studies. B. B. Warfield. 12.95 (ISBN 0-8010-9584-0). Baker Bk.

Biblical & Theological Studies. Benjamin B. Warfield. 1952. 12.95 (ISBN 0-87552-525-3). Presby & Reformed.

Biblical Answers to Bothersome Questions. Bob Jones, III. 71p. (Orig.). 1981. pap. 2.00 (ISBN 0-89084-150-0). Bob Jones Univ Pr.

Biblical Anthropology. H. J. Astley. 1977. Repr. of 1929 ed. 32.50 (ISBN 0-685-82796-8). Sharon Hill.

Biblical Applications for Tjta. 5.95 (ISBN 0-317-15734-5). Chr Marriage.

Biblical Archaeologist Reader, No. 4. Ed. by D. N. Freedman & E. F. Campbell, Jr. (Illus.). xiii, 390p. 1983. text ed. 24.95x (ISBN 0-907459-34-X, Pub. by Almond Pr England); pap. text ed. 9.95x (ISBN 0-907459-35-8). Eisenbrauns.

Biblical Archaeology. rev. ed. G. Ernest Wright. LC 57-5020. (Illus.). 292p. 1963. 27.50 (ISBN 0-664-20420-1). Westminster.

Biblical Archaeology in Focus. Keith N. Schoville. LC 78-62914. 24.95 (ISBN 0-8010-8112-2). Baker Bk.

Biblical Attitudes on Human Sexuality. Aaron Gerber. 176p. 1982. 15.95 (ISBN 0-89962-301-8). Todd & Honeywell.

Biblical Authority: A Critique of the Rogers-McKim Proposal. John D. Woodbridge. 256p. (Orig.). 1982. pap. 9.95 (ISBN 0-310-44751-8, 12647P). Zondervan.

Biblical Authority & Christian Faith. Richard S. Taylor. 95p. (Orig.). 1980. pap. 2.95 (ISBN 0-8341-0633-7). Beacon Hill.

Biblical Authority or Biblical Tyranny? Scripture & the Christian Pilgrimage. William Countryman. LC 81-70591. 96p. 1982. pap. 6.95 (ISBN 0-8006-1630-8, 1-1630). Fortress.

Biblical Backgrounds. rev. ed. Ed. by Joseph A. Callaway & J. McKee Adams. 1966. 14.95 (ISBN 0-8054-1113-5). Broadman.

Biblical Ballads. Ed Beutner. (Illus.). 1985. 4.95 (ISBN 0-911346-09-0). Christianica.

Biblical Basis of Missions. Laura B. Barnard. 32p. 1973. pap. 1.50 (ISBN 0-89265-100-8). Randall Hse.

Biblical Basis of Modern Science. Henry M. Morris. 1984. 24.95 (ISBN 0-8010-6178-4). Baker Bk.

Biblical Beginnings: Archaeology & the Roots of Scripture. Rudolph J. Adler. LC 85-16970. (Illus.). 320p. 1985. 17.95 (ISBN 0-13-076233-4). P-H.

Biblical Beliefs. 96p. 1982. pap. text ed. 4.95 (ISBN 0-910566-10-0); Perfect bdg. instr's. guide 5.95 (ISBN 0-910566-17-8). Evang Tchr.

Biblical Books of Wisdom. James M. Efird. 96p. 1983. pap. 4.95 (ISBN 0-8170-0999-X). Judson.

Biblical Books Translated from Arabic. Frank Zimmerman. 1974. 25.00x (ISBN 0-87068-252-0). Ktav.

Biblical Bulletin Boards. Sr. Carole MacKenthun. (Helping Hand Ser.). 48p. 1984. wkbk. 4.95 (ISBN 0-86653-197-1). Good Apple.

Biblical-Catechetical Homilies for Sundays & Holy Days (A, B & C) Based on the Lectionary & Reflecting the Syllabus of the Pastoral Homiletic Plan. David Q. Liptak. LC 79-27895. 370p. (Orig.). 1980. pap. 10.95 (ISBN 0-8189-0400-3). Alba.

Biblical Christology. John Schaller. 1981. 10.95 (ISBN 0-8100-0126-8, 15N0372). Northwest Pub.

Biblical Church Discipline. Daniel E. Wray. 25p. 1978. pap. 1.20 (ISBN 0-85151-269-0). Banner of Truth.

Biblical Commentaries by Richard Rolle. Robert Boenig. Ed. by James Hogg. (Elizabethan & Renaissance Studies). (Orig.). 1984. pap. 15.00 (ISBN 0-317-40122-X, Pub. by Salzburg Studies). Longwood Pub Group.

Biblical Companions. Edward J. O'Heron. LC 78-74625. 1979. pap. 3.95 (ISBN 0-87973-647-X). Our Sunday Visitor.

Biblical Concepts for Christian Counseling: A Case for Integrating Psychology & Theology. Willia Kirwan. 240p. (Orig.). 1984. pap. 9.95 (ISBN 0-8010-5454-0). Baker Bk.

Biblical Cosmology & Modern Science. Henry Morris. 1970. pap. 4.50 (ISBN 0-87552-349-8). Presby & Reformed.

Biblical Counseling. Wim Malgo. 4.95 (ISBN 0-937422-18-5). Midnight Call.

Biblical Criteria in Modern Dance: Modern Dance As a Prophetic Form. Doug Adams & Judith Rock. 1979. 2.50 (ISBN 0-941500-01-2). Sharing Co.

Biblical Criticism in the Life of the Church. Paul M. Zehr. LC 85-24762. 112p. (Orig.). 1986. pap. 6.95 (ISBN 0-8361-3404-4). Herald Pr.

Biblical Demonology: A Treatise on Satan's Temptations. R. Gilpin. 1982. lib. bdg. 20.00 (ISBN 0-86524-093-0, 9805). Klock & Klock.

Biblical Doctrine of Creation & the Fall: Genesis 1-3. Donald MacDonald. 502p. 1984. lib. bdg. 18.95 (ISBN 0-86524-165-1, 0104). Klock & Klock.

Biblical Doctrine of God. James Bales. pap. 2.50 (ISBN 0-89315-021-5). Lambert Bk.

Biblical Doctrine of Grace. J. D. Thomas. LC 76-56472. (Way of Life Ser: No. 111). (Orig.). 1977. pap. 3.95 (ISBN 0-89112-111-0, Bibl Res Pr). Abilene Christ U.

Biblical Doctrine of Immortality. S. D. Salmond. 718p. 1984. lib. bdg. 26.95 (ISBN 0-86524-164-3, 8804). Klock & Klock.

Biblical Doctrine of Infant Baptism. Pierre Marcel. Tr. by Philip E. Hughes from Fr. 256p. 1983. pap. 11.95 (ISBN 0-227-67855-9, Pub. by J Clarke UK). Attic Pr.

Biblical Doctrine of Justification. Frederick B. Westcott. 407p. 1983. lib. bdg. 15.25 (ISBN 0-86524-160-0, 8803). Klock & Klock.

Biblical Doctrine of Man. Gordon H. Clark. (Trinity Papers: No. 7). 95p. (Orig.). 1984. pap. 5.95 (ISBN 0-940931-07-9). Trinity Found.

Biblical Doctrine of Reconciliation. James Denney. 348p. 1985. smythe sewn 14.00 (ISBN 0-86524-192-9, 8806). Klock & Klock.

Biblical Doctrine of the Atonement. John S. Lidgett. 522p. 1983. 19.50 (ISBN 0-86524-145-7, 8801). Klock & Klock.

Biblical Doctrine of the Holy Spirit. James Morgan. 510p. 1985. Repr. lib. bdg. 19.00 (ISBN 0-86524-185-6, 8805). Klock & Klock.

Biblical Doctrine of the Reign of God. John Gray. 414p. 29.95 (ISBN 0-567-09300-X, Pub. by T & T Clark Ltd UK). Fortress.

Biblical Echo: Reflection on Bible, Jews & Judaism. Ed. by Emanuel Feldman. 1986. text ed. 17.50x (ISBN 0-88125-104-6). Ktav.

Biblical Economics in Comics. Vic Lockman. (Illus.). 112p. (Orig.). 1985. pap. 6.00 (ISBN 0-936175-00-1). V Lockman.

Biblical Eldership: A Study Guide. Alexander Strauch. 100p. (Orig.). 1987. pap. price not set (ISBN 0-936083-01-8). Lewis Roth.

Biblical Eldership: An Urgent Call to Restore Biblical Church Leadership. Alexander Strauch. 425p. 1986. 12.95 (ISBN 0-936083-00-X). Lewis-Roth.

Biblical Essays. J. B. Lightfoot. (Canterbury Books Ser.). 1979. pap. 8.95 (ISBN 0-8010-5586-5). Baker Bk.

Biblical Ethics. Oswald Chambers. 1964. 2.95 (ISBN 0-87508-102-9). Chr Lit.

Biblical Ethics. Leroy Forlines. 1973. pap. 5.95 (ISBN 0-89265-014-1). Randall Hse.

Biblical Ethics. R. E. White. pap. 9.95 (ISBN 0-8042-0787-9). John Knox.

Biblical Ethics -- A Survey: A Guide to the Ethical Message of the Scriptures from Genesis Through Revelation. T. B. Maston. LC 82-6470. 320p. 1982. 13.95 (ISBN 0-86554-051-9, MUP-H32). Mercer Univ Pr.

Biblical Ethics & Social Change. Stephen C. Mott. 1982. 21.95x (ISBN 0-19-502947-X); pap. 9.95x (ISBN 0-19-502948-8). Oxford U Pr.

Biblical Exegesis: A Beginner's Handbook. John H. Hayes & Carl Holladay. LC 82-17999. 132p. 1982. pap. 7.95 (ISBN 0-8042-0030-0). John Knox.

Biblical Exegesis & Church Doctrine. Raymond E. Brown. 5.95 (ISBN 0-8091-2750-4). Paulist Pr.

Biblical Exegesis of Justin Martyr. Willis A. Shotwell. LC 66-8998. 1965. pap. 10.00x (ISBN 0-8401-2173-3). A R Allenson.

Biblical Expositor. Ed. by Carl F. Henry. 1332p. 1986. Repr. text ed. 49.95 (ISBN 0-8010-0890-5). Baker Bk.

Biblical Faith: An Evolutionary Approach. Gerd Theissen. Tr. by John Bowden. LC 84-21072. 224p. 1985. pap. 8.95 (ISBN 0-8006-1842-4, 1-1842). Fortress.

Biblical Faith & Social Ethics. E. Clinton Gardner. 1960. text ed. 23.50 scp (ISBN 0-06-042240-8, HarpC). Har-Row.

Biblical Faith & the Black American. Latta R. Thomas. 160p. 1976. pap. 4.95 (ISBN 0-8170-0718-0). Judson.

Biblical Favorites. Jim Lewis. LC 85-50948. 134p. (Orig.). 1985. pap. 7.95 (ISBN 0-942482-08-5). Unity Church Denver.

Biblical Flood & the Ice Epoch. Donald W. Patten. 1966. 9.00 (ISBN 0-686-70598-X); pap. 7.50 (ISBN 0-686-70599-8). Pacific Mer.

Biblical Foundations for Mission. Donald Senior & Carroll Stuhlmueller. LC 82-22430. 384p. (Orig.). 1983. 12.50 (ISBN 0-88344-046-6); pap. 14.95 (ISBN 0-88344-047-4). Orbis Bks.

Biblical Games: A Strategic Analysis of Stories in the Old Testament. Steven J. Brams. 1980. text ed. 22.00x (ISBN 0-262-02144-7); pap. 7.95 (ISBN 0-262-52074-5). MIT Pr.

Biblical Garden. Carol Lerner. (Illus.). 1982. 13.50 (ISBN 0-688-01071-7). Morrow.

Biblical Geography & History. Charles F. Kent. 296p. 1981. Repr. of 1911 ed. lib. bdg. 30.00 (ISBN 0-89760-431-8). Telegraph Bks.

Biblical Graphics. Roger C. Reeds. 1977. 7.95 (ISBN 0-89265-058-3); pap. 5.95 (ISBN 0-89265-042-7). Randall Hse.

Biblical Greek. Maximilian Zerwick. (Scripta Pontificci Instituti Biblica Ser.: Vol. 114). 1963. 12.00 (ISBN 88-7653-554-3). Loyola.

Biblical Guidelines for Discovering God's Kingdom. Marilyn Norquist. LC 82-81769. 64p. 1982. pap. 4.25 (ISBN 0-89243-160-1). Liguori Pubns.

Biblical Hapax Legomena in the Light of Akkadian & Ugaritic: Society of Biblical Literature, No.37. Harold R. Cohen. LC 77-13422. (Dissertation Ser.). pap. 50.30 (ISBN 0-8357-9565-9, 2017528). Bks Demand UMI.

Biblical Hebrew. Harvey E. Finley & Charles D. Isbell. 213p. 1975. pap. text ed. 13.95 (ISBN 0-8341-0350-8). Beacon Hill.

Biblical Hebrew for Beginners. 12th corr ed. Ovid R. Sellers & E. E. Voigt. 1963. pap. 3.95x (ISBN 0-8401-2163-6). A R Allenson.

Biblical Hebrew Grammar. D. Waylon Bailey & John O. Strange. LC 85-60960. 246p. 1985. 17.00 (ISBN 0-914520-23-7). Insight Pr.

Biblical Hebrew Step by Step: A Significant Breakthrough for Learning Biblical Hebrew. Menahem Mansoor. 1978. pap. 12.95 (ISBN 0-8010-6041-9); cassette 7.95 (ISBN 0-8010-6074-5). Baker Bk.

Biblical Hebrew Step by Step II: Readings from the Book of Genesis. Menahem Mansoor. 230p. (Orig.). 1984. pap. 13.95 (ISBN 0-8010-6151-2); cassette 7.95 (ISBN 0-8010-6198-9). Baker Bk.

Biblical Heritage of American Democracy. A. I. Katsh. pap. 9.95x (ISBN 0-87068-488-4). Ktav.

Biblical Hermeneutics: An Introduction. Duncan S. Ferguson. LC 85-45456. 204p. 1986. pap. 12.95 (ISBN 0-8042-0050-5). John Knox.

Biblical Hermeneutics in Jewish Moral Discourse. Ed. by Peter Haas. (Semeia Ser.: No. 34). pap. 9.95 (06 20 34). Scholars Pr GA.

Biblical Higher Criticism & the Defense of Infallibilism in 19th Century Britain. Nigel M. Cameron. (Texts & Studies in Religion: Vol. 33). 440p. 1987. text ed. 69.96 (ISBN 0-88946-821-4). E Mellen.

Biblical History As the Quest for Maturity. John S. Peale. LC 85-5067. (Symposium Ser.: Vol. 15). 120p. 1985. 39.95x (ISBN 0-88946-706-4). E Mellen.

Biblical Holy Places. Rivka Gonen. (Illus.). 192p. pap. cancelled (ISBN 0-915361-67-1). Adama Pubs Inc.

Biblical Illustrator, 23 vols. 1978. 595.00 set (ISBN 0-8010-3280-6). Baker Bk.

Biblical Images: Men & Women of the Book. Adin Steinsaltz. LC 83-46081. (Illus.). 256p. 1984. 16.95 (ISBN 0-465-00670-1). Basic.

Biblical Images: Men & Women of the Book. Adin Steinsaltz. LC 83-46081. 256p. 1985. pap. 6.95 (ISBN 0-465-00671-X, PL-5158). Basic.

Biblical Influences in Shakespeare's Great Tragedies. Peter Milward. 1987. 20.00 (ISBN 0-253-31198-5). Ind U Pr.

Biblical Inspiration. I. Howard Marshall. 128p. 1983. pap. 5.95 (ISBN 0-8028-1959-1). Eerdmans.

Biblical Interpretation & the Church: The Problem of Contextualization. Ed. by D. A. Carson. 232p. 1985. pap. 7.95 (ISBN 0-8407-7501-6). Nelson.

Biblical Interpretation in Ancient Israel. Michael Fishbane. 1985. 49.95x (ISBN 0-19-826325-2). Oxford U Pr.

Biblical Interpretation in Religious Education. Mary C. Boys. LC 80-10249. 362p. (Orig.). 1980. pap. 10.95 (ISBN 0-89135-022-5). Religious Educ.

Biblical Interpretation in the Book of Jubilees. John C. Endres. Ed. by Robert J. Karris. LC 86-6845. (Catholic Biblical Quarterly-Monograph: no. 18). 284p. (Orig.). 1987. pap. 8.50 (ISBN 0-915170-17-5). Catholic Bibl Assn.

Biblical Interpretation in the Early Church. Ed. & tr. by Karlfried Froehlich. LC 84-47922. (Sources of Early Christian Thought Ser.). 128p. 1985. pap. 7.95 (ISBN 0-8006-1414-3, 1-1414). Fortress.

Biblical Interpretation: Its History. Moises Silva. (Foundations in Hermeneutics Ser.: Vol. 1). 176p. Date not set. pap. 7.95 (ISBN 0-8407-7524-5). Nelson.

Biblical Lenten Homilies for Preaching & Meditation. rev. & exp. ed. David Q. Liptak. pap. 11.95 (ISBN 0-941850-05-6). Sunday Pubns.

Biblical Limericks, Old Testament Stories Reversed. Donald Benson. 1986. 6.95 (ISBN 0-345-33033-1). Ballantine.

Biblical Lovemaking: A Study of the Song of Solomon. Arnold G. Fruchtenbaum. 70p. 1983. pap. 3.50 (ISBN 0-914863-03-7). Ariel Pr CA.

Biblical-Medical Ethics. Franklin E. Payne, Jr. 1986. text ed. 19.95 (ISBN 0-8010-7099-6). Baker Bk.

Biblical Medical Ethics. Franklyn E. Payne, Jr. Ed. by Leonard G. Goss. 288p. 1985. write for info. (ISBN 0-88062-068-4). Mott Media.

Biblical Meditations for Advent & the Christmas Season. Carroll Stuhlmueller. LC 80-82083. (Biblical Meditations Ser.: Vol. 3). 288p. (Orig.). 1980. pap. 4.95 (ISBN 0-8091-2318-5). Paulist Pr.

Biblical Meditations for Lent. rev. ed. Carroll Stuhlmueller. LC 77-91366. 190p. 1978. pap. 4.95 (ISBN 0-8091-2089-5). Paulist Pr.

Biblical Meditations for Ordinary Time. Carroll Stuhlmeuller. 416p. (Orig.). 1984. Pt. II, Weeks 10-22. pap. 5.95 (ISBN 0-8091-2645-1); Pt. III, Weeks 23-34. pap. 5.95 (ISBN 0-8091-2648-6). Paulist Pr.

Biblical Meditations for Ordinary Time: Pt. I, Weeks 1-9. Carroll Stuhlmeuller. 320p. (Orig.). 1984. pap. 4.95 (ISBN 0-8091-2644-3). Paulist Pr.

Biblical Meditations for the Easter Season. Carroll C. Stuhmueller. LC 80-81030. 256p. 1980. pap. 4.95 (ISBN 0-8091-2283-9). Paulist Pr.

Biblical Mosaic: Changing Perspectives. Ed. by Robert M. Polzin & Eugene Rothman. LC 81-67307. (Semeia Studies). 1982. pap. 9.95 (ISBN 0-8006-1510-7, Co-Pub by Fortress Pr). Fortress.

Biblical Mysteries Revealed. Isiah L. Nottage. 1984. 9.95 (ISBN 0-8062-2315-4). Carlton.

Biblical Numerology. John J. Davis. (Orig.). 1968. pap. 4.50 (ISBN 0-8010-2813-2). Baker Bk.

Biblical Numerology. John J. Davis. pap. 4.95 (ISBN 0-88469-063-6). BMH Bks.

Biblical Origins of Modern Secular Culture. Willis B. Glover. LC 84-14868. xx, 300p. 1984. 23.95 (ISBN 0-86554-138-8, MUP-H129). Mercer Univ Pr.

Biblical Pacifism: A Peace Church Perspective. Dale W. Brown. 176p. 1985. pap. 8.95 (ISBN 0-87178-108-5). Brethren.

Biblical Pattern for Divine Healing. 1979. pap. 1.00 (ISBN 0-88469-108-X). BMH Bks.

Biblical Patterns in Modern Literature. Marion A. Fairman. LC 72-85235. 128p. 1972. 2.95 (ISBN 0-913228-04-4). Dillon-Liederbach.

Biblical Patterns in Modern Literature. Ed. by David H. Hirsch & Nehama Aschkenasy. (Brown Judiac Studies: No. 77). 252p. 1985. o.s. 21.95 (ISBN 0-89130-813-X, 14 00 77); pap. 17.95 (ISBN 0-89130-814-8). Scholars Pr GA.

Biblical Period from Abraham to Ezra: A Historical Survey. William F. Albright. pap. 4.95x (ISBN 0-06-130102-7, TB102, Torch). Har-Row.

Biblical Personalities & Archaeology. Leah Bronner. (Illus.). 216p. 1975. 7.95x (ISBN 0-685-58308-2). Bloch.

Biblical Personality Puzzlebook. Wayne T. Gise. LC 86-14720. (Orig.). 1987. pap. 2.95 (ISBN 0-8054-9112-0). Broadman.

Biblical Perspectives on Death, No. 5. Lloyd R. Bailey, Sr. Ed. by Walter Brueggemann & John R. Donahue. LC 78-145661. (Overtures to Biblical Theology Ser.). 180p. 1978. pap. 8.95 (ISBN 0-8006-1530-1, 1-1530). Fortress.

Biblical Pictures of Bread. Steven Swanson. 1985. 3.95 (ISBN 0-89536-718-1, 5802). CSS of Ohio.

Biblical Pictures of Water. Steve Swanson. 1986. 3.95 (ISBN 0-89536-784-X, 6802). CSS of Ohio.

Biblical Preaching. Haddon Robinson. LC 80-66776. 1980. 10.95 (ISBN 0-8010-7700-1). Baker Bk.

Biblical Preaching: An Expositor's Treasury. Ed. by James W. Cox. LC 83-10518. 368p. (Orig.). 1983. 19.95 (ISBN 0-664-21397-9). Westminster.

Biblical Preaching for Today's World. Lloyd M. Perry. LC 73-7471. 256p. 1973. 18.95 (ISBN 0-8024-0707-2). Moody.

Biblical Predestination. Gordon H. Clark. 1969. pap. 4.95 (ISBN 0-87552-137-1). Presby & Reformed.

Biblical Principles: Issues of Importance to Godly Christians. Rus Walton. 370p. 1984. 4.95 (ISBN 0-317-39815-6). Plymouth Rock Found.

Biblical Prints. Sadao Watanabe. (Illus.). 1987. deluxe ed. 100.00 (ISBN 0-8028-3635-6). Eerdmans.

Biblical Prose Prayer: As a Window to the Popular Religion of Ancient Israel. Moshe Greenberg. LC 83-47662. (Taubman Lectures in Jewish Studies: No. 6). 78p. 1983. 16.50x (ISBN 0-520-05011-8); pap. 3.95 (ISBN 0-520-05012-6, CAL 680). U of Cal Pr.

Biblical Psychology. Oswald Chambers. 1973. pap. 3.95 (ISBN 0-87508-099-5). Chr Lit.

Biblical Quotations. Ed. by Jennifer Speake. LC 83-1511. 208p. 1983. 17.95 (ISBN 0-87196-241-1). Facts on File.

Biblical Quotations in Middle English Literature, 2 vols. Mary W. Smyth. 105.00 (ISBN 0-87968-730-4). Gordon Pr.

Biblical Quotations in Middle English Literature Before 1350. Mary Co. Smyth. LC 74-18317. 1974. Repr. of 1910 ed. lib. bdg. 37.50 (ISBN 0-8414-7825-2). Folcroft.

Biblical Quotations in Old English Prose Writers. A. S. Cook. 59.95 (ISBN 0-87968-731-2). Gordon Pr.

Biblical Quotations in Old English Prose Writers. Albert S. Cook. LC 74-2465. 1898. lib. bdg. 40.00 (ISBN 0-8414-3552-9). Folcroft.

Biblical Quotations in Old English Prose Writers: Second Series. Albert S. Cook. LC 74-7275. 1903. lib. bdg. 40.00 (ISBN 0-686-96720-8). Folcroft.

Biblical References in Shakespeare's Tragedies. Naseeb Shaheen. LC 85-40636. 248p. 1987. 29.50x (ISBN 0-87413-293-2). U Delaware Pr.

Biblical References to Prayer. International Partners in Prayer. 15p. 1984. pap. 1.75 (ISBN 0-917593-03-0, Pub. by Intl Partners). Prosperity & Profits.

Biblical Reflections on Crises Facing the Church. Raymond E. Brown. LC 75-19861. 132p. 1975. pap. 4.95 (ISBN 0-8091-1891-2). Paulist Pr.

Biblical Religion & the Search for Ultimate Reality. Paul Tillich. LC 55-5149. 1964. pap. 5.00x (ISBN 0-226-80341-4). U of Chicago Pr.

Biblical Revelation. 2nd ed. Clark H. Pinnock. 272p. (Orig.). 1985. pap. 7.95 (ISBN 0-87552-371-4). Presby & Reformed.

Biblical Revelation & Inspiration. H. S. Bender. pap. 1.45 (ISBN 0-8361-1322-5). Herald Pr.

Biblical Semantic Logic. Arthur Gibson. 1981. 32.50 (ISBN 0-312-07796-3). St Martin.

Biblical Separation Defended. Gary G. Cohen. 1966. pap. 3.50 (ISBN 0-87552-147-9). Presby & Reformed.

Biblical Separation: The Struggle for a Pure Church. Ernest Pickering. LC 78-26840. 1979. 6.95 (ISBN 0-87227-069-6). Reg Baptist.

Biblical Standard for Evangelists. Billy Graham. LC 84-51639. 144p. 1984. pap. 5.95 (ISBN 0-89066-057-3). World Wide Pubs.

Biblical Studies in Final Things. William E. Cox. 1967. pap. 5.95 (ISBN 0-87552-152-5). Presby & Reformed.

Biblical Studies in the Light of Archaeology. Wayne Jackson. 69p. (Orig.). 1982. pap. 2.50 (ISBN 0-932859-00-3). Apologetic Pr.

Biblical Studies: Meeting Ground of Jews & Christians. Ed. by Lawrence Boadt et al. LC 80-82812. (Stimulus Bk). 232p. (Orig.). 1981. pap. 7.95 (ISBN 0-8091-2344-4). Paulist Pr.

Biblical Systematics. Leroy Forlines. 1975. 7.95 (ISBN 0-89265-025-7); pap. 4.95 (ISBN 0-89265-038-9). Randall Hse.

Biblical Text in the Making: A Study of the Kethibh-Qere. rev. ed. Robert Gordis. 1971. 29.95x (ISBN 0-87068-157-5). Ktav.

Biblical Text of Clement of Alexandria in the Four Gospels & the Acts of the Apostles. Ed. by P. M. Barnard. (Texts & Studies Ser.: No. 1, Vol. 5, Pt. 5). pap. 13.00 (ISBN 0-8115-1700-4). Kraus Repr.

Biblical Texts with Palestinian Pointing & Their Accents. E. J. Revell. LC 77-8893. (Society of Biblical Literature. Masoretic Studies). 1977. pap. 10.95 (ISBN 0-89130-141-0, 060504). Scholars Pr GA.

Biblical Themes in Religious Education. Ed. by Joseph S. Marino. LC 83-16124. 294p. (Orig.). 1983. pap. 14.95 (ISBN 0-89135-038-1). Religious Educ.

Biblical Themes in World Literature. Sol Liptzin. LC 84-19457. 316p. 1985. 20.00 (ISBN 0-88125-063-5). Ktav.

Biblical Theology of Missions. George Peters. LC 72-77952. 384p. 1972. 11.95 (ISBN 0-8024-0706-4). Moody.

Biblical Theology of the New Testament. Charles C. Ryrie. LC 59-11468. 1959. 12.95 (ISBN 0-8024-0712-9). Moody.

Biblical Trace of the Church. William G. Schell. 173p. pap. 1.50 (ISBN 0-686-29103-4). Faith Pub Hse.

Biblical Tradition in Blake's Early Prophecies: The Great Code of Art. Leslie Tannenbaum. LC 81-47158. 368p. 1982. 30.50x (ISBN 0-691-06490-3). Princeton U Pr.

Biblical View of Reality: The Bible & Christian Ethics. David N. Duke. ii, 59p. 1985. pap. text ed. 6.95x (ISBN 0-932269-05-2). Wyndham Hall.

Biblical View of Self-Esteem, Self-Love & Self-Image. Jay Adams. 1986. pap. 5.95 (ISBN 0-89081-553-4). Harvest Hse.

Biblical Words & Their Meaning: An Introduction to Lexical Semantics. Moises Silva. 1986. pap. 8.95 (ISBN 0-310-45671-1, 11630P). Zondervan.

Biblical,Evangelism in Action. Robert L. Sumner. 1966. pap. 6.50 (ISBN 0-914012-29-0, Pub. by Bibl Evang Pr). Sword of Lord.

Biblico-Theological Lexicon of New Testament Greek. Hermann Cremer. Tr. by William Urwick. (Gr.). 960p. 1895. 35.95 (ISBN 0-567-01004-X, Pub. by T & T Clark Ltd UK). Fortress.

Bibliografia De Hernan Cortes. Rafael H. Valle. LC 75-133935. (Bibliography & Reference Ser.: No. 386). 1971. Repr. lib. bdg. 21.00 (ISBN 0-8337-3610-8). B Franklin.

Bibliografica Critica Degli Studi Plotiniani: Con rassegna della loro recensioni. Bert Marien. Ed. by V. Cilento. (Classical Studies Ser.). (Ital.). Repr. of 1949 ed. lib. bdg. 47.00x (ISBN 0-697-00043-5). Irvington.

Bibliographia Catholica Americana: A List of Works by Catholic Authors & Published in the United States. Joseph Finotti. LC 74-149232. (Bibliography & Reference Ser.: No. 401). 1971. Repr. of 1872 ed. lib. bdg. 23.50 (ISBN 0-8337-1128-8). B Franklin.

Bibliographia Patristica: Internationale Patristische Bibliographie. Ed. by Wilhelm Schneemelcher. Incl. Vol. 1. Erscheinungen des Jahres 1956. xxviii, 103p. 1959. 13.80x (ISBN 3-11-001248-0); Vol. 2. Erscheinungen des Jahres 1957. xxx, 115p. 1959. 13.80 (ISBN 3-11-001249-9); Vol. 3. Erscheinungen des Jahres 1958. xxxi, 119p. 1960. 13.80x (ISBN 3-11-001250-2); Vol. 4. Erscheinungen des Jahres 1959. xxxiii, 126p. 1961. 9.20x (ISBN 3-11-001251-0); Vol. 5. Erscheinungen des Jahres 1960. xxxiii, 114p. 1962. 9.20x (ISBN 3-11-001252-9); Vol. 6. Erscheinungen des Jahres 1961. xxxiii, 98p. 1963. 9.20x (ISBN 3-11-001253-7); Vol. 7. Erscheinungen des Jahres 1962. xxxiv, 108p. 1964. 9.20x (ISBN 3-11-001254-5); Vol. 8. Erscheinungen des Jahres 1963. xxxiv, 120p. 1966. 12.00x (ISBN 3-11-001255-3); Vol. 9. Erscheinungen des Jahres 1964. xxxiv, 157p. 1967. 12.00x (ISBN 3-11-001256-1); Vol. 10. Erscheinungen Des Jahres 1965. xxxiv, 127p. 1969. 12.00x (ISBN 3-11-001257-X); Vol. 11. Erscheinungen Des Jahres 1966. 1971. 28.80x (ISBN 3-11-003531-6); Vols. 12 & **13. Erscheinungen Des Jahres 1967-68. 1975. 28.80x (ISBN 3-11-004631-8). De Gruyter.**

Bibliographia Patristica Internationale Patristische Bibliographie: Die Erscheinungen der Jahre 1969 & 1970, Vol. XIV-XV. 1977. 34.40x (ISBN 3-11-007186-X). De Gruyter.

Bibliographical Account of Catholic Bibles, Testaments & Other Portions of Scripture Translated from the Latin Vulgate. John D. Shea. 1980. lib. bdg. 49.95 (ISBN 0-8490-3114-1). Gordon Pr.

Bibliographical Essay on the History of the Society of Jesus. William V. Bangert. Ed. by George E. Ganss. LC 76-12667. (Study Aids on Jesuit Topics Ser.: No. 6). 72p. 1976. pap. 1.50 (ISBN 0-912422-16-5); Smyth Sewn. pap. 2.50 (ISBN 0-912422-21-1). Inst Jesuit.

Bibliographical Guide to New Testament Research. Ed. by R. T. France. 56p. (Orig.). 1979. pap. text ed. 3.95x (ISBN 0-905774-19-1, Pub. by JSOT Pr England). Eisenbrauns.

Bibliographical Index of Five English Mystics: Richard Rolle, Julian of Norwich, The Author of the Cloud of Unknowing, Walter Hilton, Margery Kempe. Compiled by Michael E. Sawyer. LC 73-110788. 1978. 10.00 (ISBN 0-931222-09-5). Pitts Theolog.

Bibliographie Des Mazarinades, 3 Vols. Celestin Moreau. Set. 113.00 (ISBN 0-384-40060-4); Set. pap. 95.00 (ISBN 0-384-40061-2). Johnson Repr.

Bibliographie et Iconographie De Tous les Ouvrages De Restif De la Bretonne. P. L. Jacob, pseud. 1971. Repr. of 1875 ed. lib. bdg. 32.50 (ISBN 0-8337-1817-7). B Franklin.

Bibliographie Saint-Simonienne: De 1802 au 31 December 1832. Henri Fournel. LC 70-131405. (Fr.). 130p. 1973. Repr. of 1833 ed. lib. bdg. 21.00 (ISBN 0-8337-1222-5). B Franklin.

Bibliographie zur alteuropaeischen Religionsgeschichte II, 1965-1969: Eine interdisziplinaere Auswahl von Literatur zu den Rand-und Nachfolgekulturen der Antike in Europa unter besonderer Beruecksichtigung der nichtchristlichen Religionen. Ed. by Juergen Ahrendts. LC 68-86477. (Arbeiten Zur Fruehmittelalterforschung: Vol. 5). xxvi, 591p. 1974. 59.20x (ISBN 3-11-003398-4). De Gruyter.

Bibliographie Zur alteuropaeischen Religionsgeschichte, Vol. 1: Nineteen Fifty-Four Bis Nineteen Sixty-Four Literatur zu den antiken Rand-und Nachfolgekulturen im aussermediterranen Europa unter besonderer Beruecksichtigung der nichtchristlichen Religionen. Ed. by Peter Buchholz. (Arbeitem zur Fruehmittelalterforschung, Vol. 2). (Ger). 1967. 26.80x (ISBN 3-11-000373-2). De Gruyter.

Bibliographie zur Geschichte der Judenfrage, BD 1, 1750-1848. V. Eichstadt. 278p. Date not set. Repr. of 1939 ed. text ed. 66.24x (ISBN 0-576-80137-2, Pub. by Gregg Intl Pubs England). Gregg Intl.

Bibliographie Zur Geschichte Des Kartauser-Ordens: Im Deutschen Sprachraum Und Nachbargebieten. Heribert Rossmann. Ed. by James Hogg. (Analecta Cartusiana Ser.: No. 67). (Orig.). 1987. pap. 25.00 (ISBN 3-7052-0098-4, Pub. by Salzburg Studies). Longwood Pub Group.

Bibliographie Zur Geschichte Des Karatauser-Spirit-Ualitat: Im Deutschen Sprachraum Und Nachbargebieten. Heribert Rossman. Ed. by James Hogg. (Analecta Cartusiana Ser.: No. 67). (Orig.). 1987. pap. 25.00 (ISBN 3-7052-0099-2, Pub. by Salzburg Studies). Longwood Pub Group.

Bibliographie zur Geschichte des Pietismus, Vol. 1, Die Werke Der Wuerttembergischen Pietisten des 17. Und 18. Jahrhunderts. Ed. by G. Maelzer. 415p. 1972. 41.60 (ISBN 3-11-002219-2). De Gruyter.

Bibliographie zur Geschichte und Theologie des Augustiner Eremiten Ordens bis zum Beginn der Reformation. Ed. by Egon Gindele. (Spaetmittelalter und Reformation: Texte und Untersuchungen, Vol. 1). 1977. text ed. 74.00x (ISBN 3-11-004949-X). De Gruyter.

Bibliography for the Gospel of Mark: 1954-1980. Hugh M. Humphrey. LC 81-18717. (Studies in the Bible & Early Christianity: Vol. 1). 176p. 1982. 49.95x (ISBN 0-88946-916-4). E Mellen.

Bibliography of Bioethics, Vol. 7. Ed. by Leroy Walters. 375p. 1981. 55.00 (ISBN 0-02-933770-4). Free Pr.

Bibliography of Books on Death, Bereavement, Loss & Grief, Supplement, 1935-1971. Ed. by Austin H. Kutscher & M. L. Kutscher. 170p. 1970. pap. 9.95 (ISBN 0-930194-79-9). Ctr Thanatology.

Bibliography of British Theological Literature 1850-1940. Ed. by Dikran Y. Hadidian. (Bibliographia Tripotampolitana Ser.: No. 12). (Illus.). 500p. 1985. pap. 35.00 (ISBN 0-931222-11-7). Pitts Theolog.

Bibliography of Ecclesiastical History of the French Revolution. Charles A. Gliozzo. LC 73-154506. (Bibliographia Tripotamopolitana: No. 6). 1972. 8.00x (ISBN 0-931222-05-2). Pitts Theolog.

Bibliography of French Bibles: Fifteenth & Sixteenth Century French Language Editions of the Bible. B. Chambers. 572p. (Orig.). 1983. pap. text ed. 67.50x (Pub. by Droz Switzerland). Coronet Bks.

Bibliography of George Berkeley. Thomas E. Jessop. LC 68-56592. (Bibliography & Reference Ser: No. 234). 1968. Repr. of 1934 ed. 14.50 (ISBN 0-8337-1840-1). B Franklin.

Bibliography of Greek Myth in English Poetry. Helen H. Law. LC 77-9519. 1955. lib. bdg. 15.00 (ISBN 0-8414-5827-8). Folcroft.

Bibliography of Henry Venn's Printed Writings. Compiled by Wilbert R. Shenk. (Mennonite Missionary Studies: Pt. 4). 100p. 1975. pap. 3.75x (ISBN 0-8361-1203-2). Herald Pr.

Bibliography of Ismailism. Nagib Tajdin. LC 85-26960. 1986. 25.00x (ISBN 0-88206-063-5). Caravan Bks.

Bibliography of Jewish Bibliographies. enl. 2nd ed. S. Shunami. 1969. 50.00x (ISBN 0-87068-882-0). Ktav.

Bibliography of Judaic Cultures, Nos. 749-750. Ed. by Joel M. Halpern. 1975. 8.00 (ISBN 0-686-20342-9). CPL Biblios.

Bibliography of Literature Concerning Yemenite-Jewish Music. Paul F. Marks. LC 72-90431. (Detroit Studies in Music Bibliography Ser.: No. 27). 1973. pap. 2.00 (ISBN 0-911772-57-X). Info Coord.

Bibliography of Matthew Arnold, Eighteen Ninety-Two. Thomas B. Smart. 1974. lib. bdg. 18.50 (ISBN 0-8414-7634-9). Folcroft.

Bibliography of Matthew Arnold, 1932-1970. Ed. by Vincent L. Tollers. 1974. 24.95x (ISBN 0-271-01113-0). Pa St U Pr.

Bibliography of Medieval Drama. Carl J. Stratman. LC 78-163141. 1047p. 1972. 100.00 (ISBN 0-8044-3272-4). Ungar.

Bibliography of Menno Simons. Irvin B. Horst. 157p. 1962. 45.00x (ISBN 0-8361-1104-4). Herald Pr.

Bibliography of Modern Hebrew Literature in English Translation. Yohai Goell. 132p. 1968. casebound 14.95x (ISBN 0-87855-187-5). Transaction Bks.

Bibliography of Oliver Cromwell. Wilbur C. Abbot. 1929. Repr. 65.00 (ISBN 0-8482-7261-7). Norwood Edns.

Bibliography of Published Articles on American Presbyterianism, 1901-1980. Compiled by Harold M. Parker, Jr. LC 85-7987. (Bibliographies & Indexes in Religious Studies: No. 4). xv, 261p. 1985. lib. bdg. 37.50 (ISBN 0-313-24544-4, PBP/). Greenwood.

Bibliography of Ralph Waldo Emerson. George W. Cooke. 1908. 32.00 (ISBN 0-527-19250-3). Kraus Repr.

Bibliography of Religion in the South. Charles H. Lippy. LC 85-13575. xvi, 498p. 1985. text ed. 49.95 (ISBN 0-86554-161-2, MUP-H151). Mercer Univ Pr.

Bibliography of Semiological & Structural Studies of Religion. Alfred M. Johnson. LC 79-110955. 1979. 10.00 (ISBN 0-931222-10-9). Pitts Theolog.

Bibliography of Sex Rites & Customs. Roger Goodland. LC 72-9839. Repr. of 1931 ed. 42.50 (ISBN 0-404-57445-9). AMS Pr.

Bibliography of Sex Rites & Customs. Roger Goodland. LC 77-11605. 1977. Repr. of 1931 ed. lib. bdg. 60.00 (ISBN 0-89341-193-0). Longwood Pub Group.

Bibliography of Shaker Literature, with an Introductory Study of the Writings & Publications Pertaining to Ohio Believers. John P. MacLean. 1970. Repr. of 1905 ed. 18.50 (ISBN 0-8337-2173-9). B Franklin.

Bibliography of Targum Literature, Vol. 1. B. Grossfield. 1972. 39.50x. Ktav.

Bibliography of Targum Literature: Supplement, Vol. 2. B. Grossfeld. (Bibliographica Judaica Ser: No. 8). 39.50x (ISBN 0-87820-905-0, HUC Pr). Ktav.

Bibliography of the Architecture, Arts & Crafts of Islam. 2nd ed. K. A. Creswell. 120.00 (ISBN 0-89410-306-7, Pub. by FP Van Eck Liechtenstein). Three Continents.

Bibliography of the Continental Reformation: Materials Available in English. 2nd ed. Roland H. Bainton & Eric W. Gritsch. LC 72-8216. ix, 220p. 1974. 24.50 (ISBN 0-208-01219-2, Archon). Shoe String.

Bibliography of the Cook Islands. Compiled by William Coppell & Bess Flores. 1982. cancelled. Inst Polynesian.

Bibliography of the First Editions of Books by Maurice Henry Hewlett. P. H. Muir. LC 73-14788. 1927. Repr. lib. bdg. 17.50 (ISBN 0-8414-5981-9). Folcroft.

Bibliography of the Historical Works of Dr. Creighton, Dr. Stubbs, Dr. S. R. Gardiner, & the Late Lord Acton. William A. Shaw. 1969. 17.50 (ISBN 0-8337-3242-0). B Franklin.

Bibliography of the Works of John Bunyan. Frank M. Harrison. LC 76-28174. 1932. lib. bdg. 12.50 (ISBN 0-8414-4934-1). Folcroft.

Bibliography of the Works of John Bunyan. Frank M. Harrison. 1977. lib. bdg. 59.95 (ISBN 0-8490-1502-2). Gordon Pr.

Bibliography of the Writings of Jeremy Taylor to 1700: With a Section of Tayloriana. Ed. by Robert Gathorne-Hardy & William P. Williams. LC 71-149932. 159p. 1971. 20.00 (ISBN 0-87580-023-8). N Ill U Pr.

Bibliography on Israel & Zionism. Ed. by Yona Alexander & Mordecai Chertoff. 1980. write for info. Herzl Pr.

Bibliomania in the Middle Ages. rev. ed. F. Somner Merryweather. Ed. by H. B. Copinger. LC 72-83748. Repr. of 1933 ed. 22.00 (ISBN 0-405-08787-X, Pub. by Blom). Ayer Co Pubs.

Biblioteca Espanola-Portugeza-Judaica. rev. ed. Meyer Kayserling. 1971. 35.00x (ISBN 0-87068-146-X). Ktav.

Bibliotheca Asctica Antiquo-Nova, 12 Vols. Bernhard Pez. 6600p. 1740. text ed. 414.00x (ISBN 0-576-72814-4, Pub. by Gregg Intl Pubs England). Gregg Intl.

Bibliotheca Hebraica Post-Mendelssohniana. Ed. by William Zeithlin & Steven Katz. LC 79-7154. (Jewish Philosophy, Mysticism & History of Ideas Ser.). 1980. Repr. of 1895 ed. lib. bdg. 45.00x (ISBN 0-405-12291-8). Ayer Co Pubs.

Bibliotheca Magna Rabbinica & Biblio Latino-Hebrauca. Giulio Bartolocci & Carlo Imbonati. 4440p. Date not set. Repr. of 1694 ed. text ed. 1242.00x (ISBN 0-576-72820-9, Pub. by Gregg Intl Pubs England). Gregg Intl.

Bibliotheca Ritualis, 2 vols. in 3. Francesco A. Zaccaria. 1964. Repr. of 1781 ed. Set. 106.00 (ISBN 0-8337-3913-1). B Franklin.

Bibliotheca Scholastica Instructissima: Or a Treasure of Ancient Adagies. Thomas Draxe. LC 76-57378. (English Experience Ser.: No. 796). 1977. Repr. lib. bdg. 24.00 (ISBN 90-221-0796-5). Walter J Johnson.

Bibliotheca Scriptorum Societatis Jesu. Pedro Ribadeneira. 1022p. Date not set. Repr. of 1676 ed. text ed. 207.00x (ISBN 0-576-78529-6, Pub. by Gregg Intl Pubs England). Gregg Intl.

Bibliotheca Universa Franciscana, 3 vols. Joannes A. Antonio. 1640p. Date not set. Repr. of 1733 ed. text ed. 496.80x (ISBN 0-576-72343-6, Pub. by Gregg Intl Pubs England). Gregg Intl.

Bibliotheca Wiffeniana: Bibliotheca Wiffeniana: Spanish Reformers of Two Centuries from Fifteen Twenty, 3 Vols. Eduard Boehmer. 1964. Repr. of 1904 ed. Set. 62.00 (ISBN 0-8337-0330-7). B Franklin.

Bibliotheque Des Auteurs Ecclesiastiques Du 18e Siecle, 5 vols, Ser. 4. Louis E. Dupin. 2100p. Date not set. Repr. of 1736 ed. text ed. 517.50x (ISBN 0-576-72789-X, Pub. by Gregg Intl Pubs England). Gregg Intl.

Bibliotheque Des Auteurs Separes De la Communion De L'Eglise Romaine Du 16e et 17e Siecles, 5 vols, Ser. III. Louis E. Dupin. 1910p. Date not set. Repr. of 1719 ed. text ed. 517.50x (ISBN 0-576-72788-1, Pub. by Gregg Intl Pubs England). Gregg Intl.

Bibliotheque des croisades, 4 vols. Joseph F. Michaud. LC 76-29846. (Fr.). Repr. of 1829 ed. Set. 149.50 (ISBN 0-404-15450-6). AMS Pr.

Bibliotheque liturgique, 2 vols. in 1. Charles Louis De Bourbon. Ed. by Anatole Ales. LC 72-130592. (Fr). 1970. Repr. of 1898 ed. lib. bdg. 40.50 (ISBN 0-8337-0036-7). B Franklin.

Biblisch-Talmudische Medizin. rev. ed. Julius Preuss. (Ger). 1970. 150.00 (ISBN 0-87068-121-4). Ktav.

Biblische Lehren. Von S. Speck & H. M. Riggle. 343p. 1982. pap. 4.00 (ISBN 0-686-36267-5). Faith Pub Hse.

Biblyografye Fun Artiklen Vegn Khurbn un Gvure. Josef Gar. Incl. Vol. 1. LC 67-2416. (Yad Vashem-Yivo Joint Documentary Projects Bibliographical Ser.: No.). 306p. 1966. 10.00 (ISBN 0-914512-22-6); Vol. 2. (Yad Vashem-Yivo Joint Documentary Projects Bibliographical Ser.: No. 10). 338p. 1969. 15.00 (ISBN 0-914512-10-2). Yivo Inst.

Biblyografye Fun Yidishe Bikher Vegn Khurbn un Gvure. Josef Gar & Philip Friedman. (Yad Vashem-Yivo Joint Documentary Projects Bibliographical Ser.: No. 3). (Yiddish.). 330p. 1962. 10.00 (ISBN 0-914512-12-9, HE-65-1134). Yivo Inst.

Bicentennial Festschrift for Jacob Rader Marcus. Bertram Korn. 35.00x (ISBN 0-87068-457-4). Ktav.

Bid Us God Speed: The History of the Edwards Church, Northhampton, Massachusetts 1833-1983. Ruth E. Wilbur & C. Keith Wilbur. LC 82-22347. (Illus.). 120p. 1983. 12.95 (ISBN 0-914016-93-8). Phoenix Pub.

Bien Plus Qu'un Charpentier. Josh McDowell. Ed. by Annie Cosson. Tr. by Solveng Flammanc. Orig. Title: More Than a Carpenter. 128p. 1982. pap. 1.75 (ISBN 0-8297-1248-8). Life Pubs Intl.

Big & Little in the Bible. Tina Brewer. (Happy Day Bks.). (Illus.). 1.59 (ISBN 0-87403-022-6, 3482). Standard Pub.

Big Book of Bible Crafts & Projects. Joy MacKenzie. (Illus.). 212p. (Orig.). 1981. pap. 12.95 (ISBN 0-310-70151-1, 14019P). Zondervan.

Big Book of Bible Games & Puzzles. Joy MacKenzie & Shirley Bledsoe. 192p. 1982. pap. 9.95 (ISBN 0-310-70271-2, 14029P). Zondervan.

Big Book of Jewish Humor. William Novak & Moshe Waldoks. LC 81-47234. (Illus.). 320p. 1981. pap. 14.95 (ISBN 0-06-090917-X, CN 917, PL). Har-Row.

Big Chill: How the Reagan Administration, Corporate America & Religious Conservatives Are Subverting Free Speech & the Public's Right to Know. Eve Pell. LC 83-71942. 278p. 1984. 22.50 (ISBN 0-8070-6160-3). Beacon Pr.

Big Easter Egg Hunt. Roger J. Himmel & Mary H. Manoni. LC 72-739482. (Adventures of the Lollipop Dragon Ser.). (Illus.). 1978. pap. text ed. 25.95 (ISBN 0-89290-039-3). Soc for Visual.

Big Fisherman. Lloyd C. Douglas. 1948. 15.95 (ISBN 0-395-07630-7). HM.

Big Little School: Two Hundred Years of Sunday School. Robert W. Lynn & Elliott Wright. 178p. 1980. pap. 7.75 (ISBN 0-687-03523-6). Abingdon.

Big Peanuts. Lucilda A. Newton. 1976. pap. 1.75 (ISBN 0-915374-17-X, 17-X). Rapids Christian.

Big Peanuts in Trouble. Lucilda A. Newton. 1976. pap. 1.75 (ISBN 0-915374-18-8, 18-8). Rapids Christian.

Big People, Little People. Tom Eisenman. (Family Ministry Ser.). (Illus.). 54p. 1985. pap. text ed. 19.95 (ISBN 0-89191-968-6). Cook.

Big Questions. Richard A. Kauffman. (Illus.). 128p. 1984. pap. 2.95 (ISBN 0-8361-3353-6). Herald Pr.

Big Themes in Small Portions. Bramwell Tripp. 121p. (Orig.). 1984. pap. 2.95 (ISBN 0-89216-054-3). Salvation Army.

Big Way. William Peil. 1983. 1.00 (ISBN 0-89536-952-4, 7503). CSS of Ohio.

Bigamy, Polygamy & Polyandry: A Comprehensive Bibliography. John Deer. 108p. (Orig.). 1986. pap. 11.95 (ISBN 0-940519-08-9). Res Discover Pubns.

Biggest Little Church in the World. Eugene Durand. Ed. by Gerald Wheeler. (Better Living Ser.). 32p. (Orig.). 1986. pap. 1.25 (ISBN 0-8280-0320-3). Review & Herald.

Bijak or the Complete Works of Kabir. Ahmed Shah. 1981. Repr. 16.50x (ISBN 0-89684-256-8, Pub. by Asian Pubn India). Orient Bk Dist.

Bikram's Beginning Yoga Class. new ed. Bikram Choudhury & Bonnie J. Reynolds. LC 76-29218. (Illus.). 224p. 1977. 13.50 (ISBN 0-87477-081-5); pap. 9.95 (ISBN 0-87477-082-3). J P Tarcher.

B'ikvoseihem. Vol. I, Stories 1-31. 3.50 (ISBN 0-686-33098-6, I01); Vol. II, Stories 32-72. 3.75 (ISBN 0-914131-06-0, I01A). Torah Umesorah.

Bilal Ibn Rabah. Abdul Rauf. LC 76-49691. 1977. pap. 3.95 (ISBN 0-89259-008-4). Am Trust Pubns.

Bilal in Hadith. M. A. Qazi. pap. 1.25 (ISBN 0-686-18324-X). Kazi Pubns.

Bilal: The First Muadhdhin of the Prophet of Islam. M. A. Qazi. pap. 4.50 (ISBN 0-686-18325-8). Kazi Pubns.

Bild und Lied: Archaologische Beitrage Zur Geschichte der Griechischen Heldensage. facsimile ed. Carl Robert. LC 75-10653. (Ancient Religion & Mythology Ser.). (Ger., Illus.). 1976. Repr. of 1881 ed. 20.00x (ISBN 0-405-07277-5). Ayer Co Pubs.

Bilder und Fuehrergestalten Aus Dem Taeufertum: Dritter Band ein Beitrag Zur Reformationsgeschichte Des Sechszehnten Jahrhunderts. Wilhelm Wiswedel. (Ger.). 231p. 1952. pap. 2.00x (ISBN 0-8361-1154-0). Herald Pr.

Billy Graham Christian Worker's Handbook. Billy Graham. 240p. 1982. write for info. (ISBN 0-89066-042-5); pap. 7.95. World Wide Pub.

Billy Graham: Reaching Out to the World. Paul Westman. LC 81-9912. (Taking Part Ser.). (Illus.). 48p. 1981. PLB 8.95 (ISBN 0-87518-220-8). Dillon.

Billy Graham: The Pastor's Dilemma. Erroll Hulse. pap. 2.50 (ISBN 0-685-61833-1). Reiner.

Billy Sunday. William T. Ellis. (Golden Oldies Ser.). 1959. pap. 3.95 (ISBN 0-8024-0042-6). Moody.

Billy Sunday: Baseball Preacher. Fern N. Stocker. (Preteen Biography Ser.). (Orig.). 1985. pap. text ed. 3.95 (ISBN 0-8024-0442-1). Moody.

Binding of Proteus: Perspectives on Myth & the Literary Process. Colloquium on Myth in Literature, Bucknell & Susquehanna Universities, Mar. 21-2, 1974 et al. Ed. by Marjorie W. McCune & T. Tucker Orbison. LC 76-49774. (Illus.). 352p. 1978. 28.50 (ISBN 0-8387-1708-X). Bucknell U Pr.

Bio-Bibliography of Franciscan Authors in Colonial Central America. Eleanor B. Adams. (Bibliographical Ser.). 1953. 10.00 (ISBN 0-88382-101-X). AAFH.

Bio-Spirituality: Focusing As a Way to Grow. Peter A. Campbell & Edwin M. McMahon. LC 84-21328. 1985. pap. 6.95 (ISBN 0-8294-0478-3). Loyola.

Bioethical Decision-making: Releasing Religion from the Spiritual. Barbara A. Swyhart. LC 75-13040. pap. 35.00 (2026973). Bks Demand UMI.

Bioethics. 2nd ed. Thomas Shannon. LC 76-18054. 646p. 1976. pap. 14.95 (ISBN 0-8091-1970-6). Paulist Pr.

Bioethics: A Parish Resource. William Maestri. LC 81-40822. 64p. (Orig.). 1982. lib. bdg. 22.00 (ISBN 0-8191-2171-1); pap. text ed. 7.75 (ISBN 0-8191-2172-X). U Pr of Amer.

Bioethics & Belief. John Mahoney. 128p. 1984. pap. 8.95 (ISBN 0-7220-1319-1). Chr Classics.

Bioethics & the Limits of Science. Sean O'Reilly. 176p. (Orig.). 1980. pap. 9.95 (ISBN 0-931888-02-6, Chris. Coll. Pr.). Christendom Pubns.

Biogenic Meditation: Biogenic Self-Analysis, Creative Microcosmos. Edmond B. Szekely. (Illus.). 40p. 1978. pap. 1.80 (ISBN 0-89564-051-1). IBS Intl.

Biographical Concordance of the New Testament. Madison D. Cook. 216p. 1984. pap. 8.95 (ISBN 0-87213-089-4). Loizeaux.

Biographical Dictionary of American Cult & Sect Leaders. J. Gordon Melton. LC 83-48226. (Library of Social Sciences). 534p. 1986. lib. bdg. 39.95 (ISBN 0-8240-9037-3). Garland Pub.

Biographical Dictionary of the Saints. Frederick G. Holweck. LC 68-30625. 1969. Repr. of 1924 ed. 75.00x (ISBN 0-8103-3158-6). Gale.

Biographical Encyclopedia of Kentucky: Of the Dead & Living Men of the Nineteenth Century. J. M. Armstrong Company. 1978. Repr. of 1877 ed. 42.50 (ISBN 0-89308-193-0). Southern Hist Pr.

Biographical Memoirs of Saint John Bosco, 14 vols. G. B. Lemoyne et al. Tr. by Diego Borgatello from Ital. Incl. Vol. I. lib. bdg. 14.95 (ISBN 0-89944-001-0); Vol. II. lib. bdg. 15.95 (ISBN 0-89944-002-9); Vol. III. lib. bdg. 16.95 (ISBN 0-89944-003-7); Vol. IV. lib. bdg. 19.95 (ISBN 0-89944-004-5); Vol. V. lib. bdg. 21.95 (ISBN 0-89944-005-3); Vol. VI. lib. bdg. 22.95 (ISBN 0-89944-006-1); Vol. VII. lib. bdg. 18.95 (ISBN 0-89944-007-X); Vol. VIII. lib. bdg. 15.95 (ISBN 0-89944-008-8); Vol. IX. lib. bdg. 16.95 (ISBN 0-89944-009-6); Vol. X. lib. bdg. 20.95 (ISBN 0-89944-010-X); Vol. XI. lib. bdg. 18.95 (ISBN 0-89944-011-8); Vol. XII. lib. bdg. 17.95 (ISBN 0-89944-012-6); Vol. XIII. Rev. ed. 1983. lib. bdg. 24.95 (ISBN 0-89944-013-4). LC 65-3104. Orig. Title: Memorie Biografiche di Don Giovanni Bosco. 1981. Set. lib. bdg. write for info. (ISBN 0-89944-000-2). Don Bosco Multimedia.

Biographical Memoirs of Saint John Bosco, Vol. XIV (1879-80) Eugenio Ceria. Ed. by Diego Borgatello. LC 65-3104. Tr. of Memorie Biografiche di Don Giovanni Bosco. 628p. 1985. 19.95 (ISBN 0-89944-014-2). Don Bosco Multimedia.

Biographical Process: Studies in the History & Psychology of Religion. Ed. by Frank E. Reynolds & Donald Capps. (Religion & Reason, Method & Theory in the Study & Interpretation of Religion: No. 11). 1976. text ed. 51.50x (ISBN 90-2797-522-1). Mouton.

Biographical Sketch of G. Campbell Morgan. Silas Chan. (Chinese.). 1984. pap. write for info. (ISBN 0-941598-21-7). Living Spring Pubns.

Biographical Sketches of Joseph Smith, the Prophet & His Progenitors for Many Generations. Lucy M. Smith. LC 73-83439. (Religion in America, Ser. 1). 1969. Repr. of 1853 ed. 15.00 (ISBN 0-405-00264-5). Ayer Co Pubs.

Biographical Sketches of Our Pulpit. E. R. Carter. LC 72-99355. 1969. Repr. of 1888 ed. lib. bdg. 14.00 (ISBN 0-8411-0026-8). Metro Bks.

Biographies of English Catholics in the Eighteenth Century. John Kirk. xvi, 293p. 1985. Repr. of 1901 ed. lib. bdg. 39.00 (ISBN 0-932051-45-6, Pub. by Am Repr Serv). Am Biog Serv.

Biography & Family Record of Lorenzo Snow. Eliza R. Smith. 1975. Repr. 15.00 (ISBN 0-914740-15-6). Western Epics.

Biography & Society: The Life History Approach in the Social Sciences. Ed. by Daniel Bertaux. (Sage Studies in International Sociology: Vol. 23). 308p. 1981. pap. 14.00 (ISBN 0-8039-9801-5). Sage.

Biography as Theology: How Life Stories Can Remake Today's Theology. James W. McClendon, Jr. LC 74-9715. 224p. 1974. pap. 7.75 (ISBN 0-687-03539-2). Abingdon.

Biography in Late Antiquity: A Quest for the Holy Man. Patricia Cox. LC 82-4946. (Transformation of the Classical Heritage Ser.: Vol. 5). 208p. 1983. text ed. 30.00x (ISBN 0-520-04612-9). U of Cal Pr.

Biography of Crevecoeur. Allen & Asselineau. 1987. write for info (ISBN 0-670-81345-1). Viking.

Biography of Duncan Campbell. 2.00 (ISBN 0-686-12852-4). Schmul Pub Co.

Biography of Eld. Barton Warren Stone, Written by Himself: With Additions & Reflections. Barton W. Stone. LC 79-38463. (Religion in America, Ser. 2). 476p. 1972. Repr. of 1847 ed. 27.00 (ISBN 0-405-04089-X). Ayer Co Pubs.

Biography of Jesus Christ. Robert O. Smith. 1987. 14.95 (ISBN 0-533-07232-8). Vantage.

Biography of Ralph Waldo Emerson: Set Forth As His Life Essay. Denton J. Snider. LC 77-9617. 1977. Repr. of 1921 ed. lib. bdg. 40.00 (ISBN 0-8414-7671-3). Folcroft.

Biography of the Gods. Albert E. Haydon. LC 74-37848. (Essay Index Reprint Ser.). Repr. of 1941 ed. 19.00 (ISBN 0-8369-2595-5). Ayer Co Pubs.

Biography of the Reverend Robert Finley. Isaac V. Brown. LC 73-82178. (Anti-Slavery Crusade in America Ser). 1969. Repr. of 1857 ed. 18.00 (ISBN 0-405-00617-9). Ayer Co Pubs.

Biology of Religion. Vernon Reynolds & Ralph E. Tanner. LC 82-6573. (Illus.). 321p. 1983. text ed. 31.95x (ISBN 0-582-30021-5). Longman.

Bircas Hamazon-Grace after Meals. Nosson Scherman. (Art Scroll Mesorah Ser.). 96p. 1977. 7.50 (ISBN 0-89906-152-4); pap. 5.50 (ISBN 0-89906-153-2). Mesorah Pubns.

Bird That Wouldn't Talk. (Color-a-Story Bks.). (Illus.). 1985. pap. 0.89 (ISBN 0-89191-998-8, 59980). Cook.

Birds & Scripture. Albert M. Shoemaker. (Illus.). 1984. pap. 2.50 (ISBN 0-913976-07-5). Discovery Bks.

Bird's Eye View of the Dispensation of Time. Stanley G. Lynch. 1986. 7.00 (ISBN 0-8062-2433-9). Carlton.

Birds of the Bible. Gene S. Porter. 1986. Repr. lib. bdg. 35.95x (ISBN 0-89966-529-2). Buccaneer Bks.

Birkas Hashulchan. 1980. 5.95 (ISBN 0-686-76484-6). Feldheim.

Birkat HaMazon Manual. pap. write for info. (ISBN 0-686-96116-1). United Syn Bk.

Birmingham's Rabbi: Morris Newfield & Alabama, 1895-1940. Mark Cowett. LC 85-20897. 379p. 1986. 22.50 (ISBN 0-8173-0284-0). U of Ala Pr.

Birnbaum Haggadah. Philip Birnbaum. (Illus.). 160p. 1976. 5.95 (ISBN 0-88482-908-1); pap. 3.95 (ISBN 0-88482-912-X). Hebrew Pub.

Birobidzhan Affair: A Yiddish Writer in Siberia. Israel Emiot. Tr. by Max Rosenfeld from Yiddish. LC 81-2511. 220p. 1981. 13.95 (ISBN 0-8276-0191-3, 477). Jewish Pubns.

Birth. Jacqueline Bergan & S. Marie Schwan. (Take & Receive Ser.). (Illus.). 154p. (Orig.). 1985. pap. 6.95 (ISBN 0-88489-170-4). St Mary's.

Birth & Childhood Among the Arabs. Hilma N. Granqvist. LC 72-9643. Repr. of 1947 ed. 36.00 (ISBN 0-404-57447-5). AMS Pr.

Birth & Death: Bioethical Decision-Making. Paul D. Simmons. LC 82-20160. (Biblical Perspectives on Current Issues). 270p. 1983. pap. 13.95 (ISBN 0-664-24463-7). Westminster.

Birth & Growth of Religion. George F. Moore. LC 23-13669. (Morse Lectures Ser.). 1923. text ed. 10.00x (ISBN 0-8401-1643-8). A R Allenson.

Birth & Youth of Jesus, by Mary, Mother of Jesus. David G. Samuels. 5.00 (ISBN 0-686-12714-5). New Age Min Spiritualist.

Birth Control & Morality in Nineteenth Century America: Two Discussions. Charles Knowlton & Robert D. Owen. (Family in America Ser.). 1972. cancelled (ISBN 0-405-03883-6, 13318). Ayer Co Pubs.

Birth Control in Jewish Law: Marital Relations, Contraception, & Abortion As Set Forth in the Classic Texts of Jewish Law. David M. Feldman. LC 79-16712. 1980. Repr. of 1968 ed. lib. bdg. 27.50x (ISBN 0-313-21297-X, FEBC). Greenwood.

Birth of a Kingdom: Studies in I & II Samuel & I Kings I-II. John J. Davis. pap. 5.95 (ISBN 0-88469-053-9). BMH Bks.

Birth of a Movement. David Flood & Thadee Matura. Tr. by Paul LaChance & Paul Schwartz. 168p. 1975. 6.95 (ISBN 0-8199-0567-4). Franciscan Herald.

Birth of a Reformation: Life & Labours of D. S. Warner. A. L. Byers. (Illus.). 496p. Repr. 5.50 (ISBN 0-686-29104-2). Faith Pub Hse.

Birth of Christ. H. P. Liddon & J. Orr. 1980. 15.25 (ISBN 0-86524-058-2, 9502). Klock & Klock.

Birth of God: Recovering the Mystery of Christmas. John B. Rogers. 112p. 1987. pap. 6.95 (ISBN 0-687-03554-6). Abingdon.

Birth of Jesus. Retold by Elaine Ife & Rosalind Sutton. (Now You Can Read Stories from the Bible Ser.). (Illus.). 24p. 1984. 2.50 (ISBN 0-8407-5393-4). Nelson.

Birth of Jesus. Frances T. Stewart & Charles P. Stewart. (Stick & Learn Book Ser.). (Orig.). 1985. pap. 6.95 (ISBN 0-8054-4171-9). Broadman.

Birth of Missions in America. Charles L. Chaney. LC 75-26500. 352p. 1976. pap. 7.95 (ISBN 0-87808-146-1). William Carey Lib.

Birth of Popular Heresy. Ed. by R. I. Moore. LC 75-32934. (Documents of Medieval History Ser.). 176p. 1976. 25.00 (ISBN 0-312-08190-1). St Martin.

Birth of Purgatory. Jacques Le Goff. Tr. by Arthur Goldhammer from Fr. LC 83-1108. (Illus.). 448p. 1984. 25.00 (ISBN 0-226-47082-2). U of Chicago Pr.

Birth of Purgatory. Jacques LeGoff. Tr. by Arthur Goldhammer. LC 83-1108. (Illus.). x, 430p. 1986. pap. 13.95 (ISBN 0-226-47083-0). U of Chicago Pr.

Birth of the Baha'i Faith. Debbie D. Wittman. (Illus., Orig.). 1980. pap. 1.95 (ISBN 0-87743-146-9, 352-055). Baha'i.

Birth of the Catholic Tubingen School: The Dogmatics of Johann Sebastian Drey. Wayne L. Fehr. Ed. by Carl Raschke. LC 81-14645. (American Academy of Religion, Dissertation Ser.). 1981. text ed. 14.95 (ISBN 0-89130-544-0, 01-01-37). Scholars Pr GA.
Birth of the Gods: The Origin of Primitive Beliefs. Guy E. Swanson. 1960. pap. 4.95 (ISBN 0-472-06093-7, 93, AA). U of Mich Pr.
Birth of the King. Alice Schrage. LC 80-53874. (Bible Biography Ser.). 128p. 1981. pap. 2.50 (ISBN 0-8307-0765-4, 5810507). Regal.
Birth of the Living God: A Psychoanalytic Study. Ana-Maria Rizzuto. LC 78-10475. (Illus.). 246p. 1981. pap. 8.50x (ISBN 0-226-72102-7). U of Chicago Pr.
Birth of the Messiah: A Commentary on the Infancy Narratives in Matthew & Luke. Raymond E. Brown. LC 76-56271. 1977. pap. 9.95 (ISBN 0-385-05405-X, Im). Doubleday.
Birth of the New Testament. rev. ed. C. F. Moule. LC 81-47432. 336p. 1981. pap. 9.50 (ISBN 0-06-066029-5, RD 365, HarpR). Har-Row.
Birth of the Savior. (The Inspirational Library). 24p. 3.95 (ISBN 0-8326-2004-1, 3251). World Bible.
Birth of the Synoptic Gospels. Jean Carmignac. Tr. by Michael J. Wrenn. 1986. 9.50 (ISBN 0-8199-0887-8). Franciscan Herald.
Birth of the Theotokos. Monks of New Skete Staff. (Liturgical Music Series I: Great Feasts: Vol. 3). 25p. 1986. pap. text ed. 10.00 (ISBN 0-935129-04-9). Monks of New Skete.
Birthday Blessings. William J. Freburger. (Greeting Book Line Ser.). 32p. (Orig.). 1985. pap. 1.50 (ISBN 0-89622-242-X). Twenty-Third.
Birthday Numerology. Dusty Bunker & Victoria Knowles. 240p. (Orig.). 1982. pap. 11.95 (ISBN 0-914918-39-7). Para Res.
Birthday Remembrance. Louis O. Caldwell. LC 77-7043. (Illus.). pap. 20.00 (ISBN 0-8357-9001-0, 2016349). Bks Demand UMI.
Birthday: Voices from the Heart. Date not set. price not set (ISBN 0-934383-13-8). Pride Prods.
Birthdays. rev. ed. 1973. 4.95 (ISBN 0-8066-1336-X, 10-0750). Augsburg.
Birthright! Christian, Do You Know Who You Are? David C. Needham. LC 79-90682. (Critical Concern Bks.). 293p. 1982. 10.95 (ISBN 0-930014-29-4); pap. 6.95 (ISBN 0-930014-75-8). Multnomah.
Bischof Percy's Bearbeitung Der Volksballaden Und Kunstgedichte Seines Folio-Manuskriptes. Margarete Willinsky. Repr. of 1932 ed. 19.00 (ISBN 0-384-68615-X). Johnson Repr.
Bishop & the Liturgy: Highlights of the New Ceremonial of Bishops. 104p. (Orig.). 1986. pap. 8.95 (ISBN 1-55586-996-3). US Catholic.
Bishop Barlow's Consecration & Archbishop Parker's Register: With Some New Documents. Claude Jenkins. (Church Historical Society London New Ser.: No. 17). Repr. of 1935 ed. 20.00 (ISBN 0-8115-3140-6). Kraus Repr.
Bishop Butler. W. A. Spooner. 1979. Repr. of 1901 ed. lib. bdg. 30.00 (ISBN 0-8492-8086-9). R West.
Bishop Butler & the Age of Reason. Ernest C. Mossner. LC 69-13247. 1969. Repr. of 1936 ed. 15.00 (ISBN 0-405-08807-8, Pub. by Blom). Ayer Co Pubs.
Bishop-Elect: A Study in Medieval Ecclesiastical Office. Robert L. Benson. LC 65-17130. pap. 115.00 (ISBN 0-317-07842-9, 2010535). Bks Demand UMI.
Bishop Healy: Beloved Outcaste. Albert S. Foley. LC 79-94130. (American Negro: His History & Literature, Ser. No. 3). 1970. Repr. of 1954 ed. 17.00 (ISBN 0-405-01925-4). Ayer Co Pubs.
Bishop Heber in Northern India: Selections from Heber's Journal. Ed. by M. A. Laird. LC 70-123673. (European Understanding of India Ser). (Illus.). 1971. 39.50 (ISBN 0-521-07873-3). Cambridge U Pr.
Bishop Hill Colony, a Religious Communistic Settlement in Henry County, Illinois. M. A. Mikkelsen. pap. 9.00 (ISBN 0-384-38850-7). Johnson Repr.
Bishop Hill Colony: A Religious, Communistic Settlement in Henry County, Illinois. M. A. Mikkelsen. LC 72-187466. (The American Utopian Adventure Ser.). 1973. Repr. of 1892 ed. lib. bdg. 19.50x (ISBN 0-87991-014-3). Porcupine Pr.
Bishop in the Church: Patristic Texts on the Role of the Episkopos. Agnes Cunningham. (Theology & Life Ser.: Vol. 13). 1985. pap. 3.95 (ISBN 0-89453-469-6). M Glazier.
Bishop J. G. Strossmayer: New Light on Vatican I. Ivo Sivric. 1975. 7.95 (ISBN 0-8199-0491-0). Franciscan Herald.
Bishop John B. Scalabrini: An Insight into His Spirituality. Mario Francesconi. Tr. by J. Cinquino & Vincent Monaco. LC 73-75230. (Illus.). 107p. 1973. pap. 3.00 (ISBN 0-913256-50-1). Ctr Migration.
Bishop Joseph Hall & Protestant Meditation in Seventeenth-Century England: A Study, with Texts of the Art of Divine Meditation (1606) & Occasional Meditations (1633) Frank L. Huntley. (Medieval & Renaissance Texts & Studies: 1). (Illus.). 234p. (Orig.). 1981. 15.00 (ISBN 0-86698-000-8); pap. 9.00 (ISBN 0-86698-005-9). Medieval.
Bishop Lamy's Santa Fe Cathedral. Bruce T. Ellis. LC 85-8551. (Historical Society of New Mexico Publication Ser.). (Illus.). 208p. 1985. 19.95 (ISBN 0-8263-0824-4); pap. 10.95 (ISBN 0-8263-0850-3). U of NM Pr.
Bishop of Rome. J. M. Tillard. (Theology & Life Ser.: Vol. 5). 1983. 12.95 (ISBN 0-89453-304-5); pap. 9.95 (ISBN 0-89453-298-7). M Glazier.
Bishop Percy's Folio Manuscript Ballards & Romances, 3 vols. Bishop Percy. Ed. by John W. Hales et al. LC 67-23962. 1866p. 1968. Repr. of 1868 ed. 210.00x (ISBN 0-8103-3409-7). Gale.
Bishop Pike: Ham, Heretic, or Hero. Frederick M. Morris. LC 67-28381. pap. 20.00 (ISBN 0-317-08443-7, 2012934). Bks Demand UMI.
Bishop Speaks His Mind. Earl G. Hunt. 160p. 1987. 14.95 (ISBN 0-317-54253-2). Abingdon.
Bishop Stirling of the Falklands. Frederick Macdonald. 1976. lib. bdg. 59.95 (ISBN 0-8490-1509-X). Gordon Pr.
Bishop Westcott & the Platonic Tradition. David Newsome. LC 78-409427. (Bishop Westcott Memorial Lecture Ser.: Vol. 1968). pap. 20.00 (ISBN 0-317-12985-6, 2051381). Bks Demand UMI.
Bishop Wilberforce. G. W. Daniell. 1978. Repr. of 1891 ed. lib. bdg. 20.00 (ISBN 0-8482-0607-X). Norwood Edns.
Bishop William Henry Benade: Founder & Reformer. Richard R. Gladish. (Illus.). 400p. 1983. 15.00 (ISBN 0-910557-07-1). Acad New Church.
Bishops & Nuclear Weapons: The Catholic Pastoral Letter on War & Peace. James E. Dougherty. LC 84-2994. 255p. 1984. 22.50 (ISBN 0-208-02051-9, Archon Bks). Shoe String.
Bishops & Prophets in a Black City: African Independent Churches in Soweto, Johannesburg. Martin West. 1977. text ed. 16.50x (ISBN 0-8426-1590-3). Verry.
Bishops & the Bomb: Waging Peace in a Nuclear Age. Jim Castelli. LC 82-48706. 288p. 1983. pap. 7.95 (ISBN 0-385-18760-2, IM). Doubleday.
Bishops by Ballot: An Eighteenth-Century Ecclesiastical Revolution. Frederick V. Mills, Sr. 1978. 19.95x (ISBN 0-19-502411-7). Oxford U Pr.
Bishops Extraordinary. Karl Pruter. LC 86-2284. 60p. 1985. Repr. lib. bdg. 19.95x (ISBN 0-89370-544-6). Borgo Pr.
Bitburg & Beyond. Ilya Levkov. 1986. 14.95 (ISBN 0-933503-52-0). Shapolsky Pubs.
Bits of Solace, Guidance & Consolation. Gladys E. Deck. 97p. 1984. 7.50 (ISBN 0-913382-30-2, 101-30). Prow Bks-Franciscan.
Bitter-Sweet Recollections. Barbara Brokhoff. 1983. 6.50 (ISBN 0-89536-638-X, 0238). CSS of Ohio.
Bittersweet Encounter: The Afro-American & the American Jew. Robert G. Weisbord & Arthur Stein. LC 72-127828. (Contributions in Afro-American & African Studies: No. 5). 1970. 29.95 (ISBN 0-8371-5093-0, WBS&, Pub. by Negro U Pr). Greenwood.
Bittersweet: True Stories of Decisions That Shaped Eternal Paths. Mike Berger. LC 80-81505. 124p. 1980. 6.95 (ISBN 0-88290-144-3). Horizon Utah.
Black Americans & the Evangelization of Africa, 1877-1900. Walter L. Williams. LC 81-69830. 282p. 1982. text ed. 32.50x (ISBN 0-299-08920-7). U of Wis Pr.
Black Americans & the Missionary Movement in Africa. Ed. by Sylvia M. Jacobs. LC 81-13230. (Contributions in Afro-American & African Studies: No. 66). (Illus.). xii, 255p. 1982. lib. bdg. 29.95 (ISBN 0-313-23280-6, JAA/). Greenwood.
Black & African Theologies: Siblings or Distant Cousins? Josiah U. Young. LC 85-32090. 240p. (Orig.). 1986. pap. 12.95 (ISBN 0-88344-252-3). Orbis Bks.
Black & Mennonite. Hubert L. Brown. LC 76-44043. 112p. 1976. pap. 3.95 (ISBN 0-8361-1801-4). Herald Pr.
Black & Presbyterian: The Heritage & the Hope. Gayraud S. Wilmore. LC 82-23907. 142p. (Orig.). 1983. pap. 5.95 (ISBN 0-664-24440-8, Pub. by Geneva Press). Westminster.
Black & Reformed: Apartheid, Liberation, & the Calvinist Tradition. Allan A. Boesak. LC 84-7212. 192p. (Orig.). 1984. pap. 8.95 (ISBN 0-88344-148-9). Orbis Bks.
Black Anti-Semitism & Jewish Racism. Ed. by Nat Hentoff. LC 70-89955. 1970. pap. 3.75 (ISBN 0-8052-0280-3). Schocken.
Black Apostles: Afro-American Clergy Confront the Twentieth Century. Randall K. Burkett & Richard Newman. 1978. lib. bdg. 28.50 (ISBN 0-8161-8137-3, Hall Reference). G K Hall.
Black Apostles at Home & Abroad: Afro-Americans & the Christian Mission from the Revolution to Reconstruction. Ed. by David W. Wills & Richard Newman. 420p. 1982. lib. bdg. 42.00 (ISBN 0-8161-8482-8, Hall Reference). G K Hall.
Black Baptist Secondary Schools in Virginia, 1887-1957: A Study in Black History. Lester F. Russell. LC 80-22414. 218p. 1981. 18.00 (ISBN 0-8108-1373-4). Scarecrow.
Black Bishop: Samuel Adjai Crowther. Jesse Page. LC 75-106783. (Illus.). 1979. Repr. of 1908 ed. 32.00x (ISBN 0-8371-4610-0, PBB&, Pub. by Negro U Pr). Greenwood.
Black Book. Iiya Ehrenburg & Vasily Grossman. LC 81-81519. 595p. 1980. 24.95 (ISBN 0-89604-031-3); pap. 14.95 (ISBN 0-89604-032-1). Holocaust Pubns.
Black Book of Polish Jewry: An Account of the Martyrdom of Polish Jewry Under Nazi Occupation. Ed. by Jacob Apenszlak. xvi, 343p. 1982. Repr. of 1943 ed. 27.50x (ISBN 0-86527-340-5). Fertig.
Black Church in Urban America: A Case Study in Political Economy. Ida R. Mukenge. LC 83-14593. 256p. 1984. lib. bdg. 27.50 (ISBN 0-8191-3431-7); pap. text ed. 13.50 (ISBN 0-8191-3432-5). U Pr of Amer.
Black Church Life-Styles. Emmanuel L. McCall. LC 86-17591. 1986. pap. 5.95 (ISBN 0-8054-5665-1). Broadman.
Black Episcopalians in Georgia: Strife, Struggle & Salvation. Charles L. Hoskins. (Illus.). 168p. 1980. 8.00 (ISBN 0-686-31304-6). St Matthew's.
Black Folks & Christian Liberty: Black, Christian, & Free to Be Cultural & Social. Walter A. McCray. LC 78-71258. (Black Light Fellowship Ser.). 1978. pap. 9.95 (ISBN 0-933176-01-5). Black Light Fellow.
Black Girl from Genesis to Revelations. J. E. Franklin. LC 74-30386. 1977. 9.95 (ISBN 0-88258-019-1). Howard U Pr.
Black Gods of the Metropolis, Negro Religious Cults of the Urban North. Arthur H. Fauset. LC 73-120251. 1970. Repr. lib. bdg. 16.00x (ISBN 0-374-92714-6, Octagon). Hippocrene Bks.
Black Gods of the Metropolis: Negro Religious Cults of the Urban North. Arthur H. Fauset. LC 75-133446. 1971. pap. 9.95x (ISBN 0-8122-1001-8, Pa Paperbks). U of Pa Pr.
Black Gospel, White Church. John Burgess. 128p. 1982. pap. 7.95 (ISBN 0-8164-2380-6, HarpR). Har-Row.
Black Islam: Africa's Rising Religion. Vincent Monteil. 464p. cancelled (ISBN 0-86356-114-4, Pub. by Zed Pr England); pap. cancelled (ISBN 0-86356-024-5, Pub. by Zed Pr England). Humanities.
Black Jews. James H. Boykin. LC 81-90626. iv, 98p. (Orig.). 1982. pap. 3.25x (ISBN 0-9603342-1-1). Boykin.
Black Mennonite Church in North America 1886-1986. Leroy Bechler. LC 86-25691. 192p. 1986. 17.95x (ISBN 0-8361-1287-3). Herald Pr.
Black Messiahs & Uncle Toms: Social & Literary Manipulations of a Religious Myth. Wilson J. Moses. LC 81-9645. 304p. 1982. 24.95x (ISBN 0-271-00294-8). Pa St U Pr.
Black Ministers & Laity in the Urban Church: An Analysis of Political & Social Expectations. James H. Harris. LC 86-28151. (Illus.). 146p. 1987. lib. bdg. 23.50 (ISBN 0-8191-5823-2); pap. text ed. 9.75 (ISBN 0-8191-5824-0). U Pr of Amer.
Black Pagoda. Robert Ebersole. LC 57-12929. (Illus.). 1957. 8.50 (ISBN 0-8130-0070-X). U Presses Fla.
Black Paradise: The Rastafarian Movement. Peter B. Clarke. 112p. 1986. pap. 11.95 (ISBN 0-85030-428-8). Newcastle Pub.
Black Paradise: The Rastafarian Movement. Peter B. Clarke. 176p. 1986. lib. bdg. 19.95x (ISBN 0-8095-7021-1). Borgo Pr.
Black Pastors & Churches in United Methodism. Grant S. Shockley et al. 1976. pap. 1.00 (ISBN 0-89937-005-5). Ctr Res Soc Chg.
Black Pentecostalism: Southern Religion in an Urban World. Arthur E. Paris. LC 81-16169. 192p. 1982. lib. bdg. 17.50x (ISBN 0-87023-353-X). U of Mass Pr.
Black People in the Methodist Church: Whither Thou Goest? William B. McClain. 160p. (Orig.). 1986. pap. 8.95 (ISBN 0-687-03588-0). Abingdon.
Black Pioneers in a White Denomination. Mark Morrison-Reed. LC 83-70747. 216p. 1983. pap. text ed. 9.95 (ISBN 0-8070-1601-2, BP 662). Beacon Pr.
Black Power & Black Religion: Essays & Reviews. Richard Newman. LC 86-20906. 1986. lib. bdg. 25.00 (ISBN 0-933951-03-5). Locust Hill Pr.
Black Power & White Protestants: A Christian Response to the New Negro Pluralism. Joseph C. Hough, Jr. 1968. 18.95x (ISBN 0-19-501178-3). Oxford U Pr.
Black Preaching. Henry H. Mitchell. LC 78-19508. 1979. pap. 8.95xi (ISBN 0-06-065761-8, RD297, HarpR). Har-Row.
Black Preaching: Select Sermons in the Presbyterian Tradition. Ed. by Robert T. Newbold, Jr. LC 77-4015. 180p. 1977. softcover 5.65 (ISBN 0-664-24323-1). Westminster.
Black Quakers: Brief Biographies. Kenneth Ives et al. (Studies in Quakerism: 12). (Illus.). 118p. (Orig.). 1986. pap. 8.00 (ISBN 0-89670-015-1). Progresiv Pub.
Black Rain. Masuji Ibuse. 304p. 1985. pap. 3.95 (ISBN 0-553-24988-6). Bantam.
Black Religion & Black Radicalism: An Interpretation of the Religious History of Afro-American People. 2nd rev. & enl. ed. Gayraud S. Wilmore. LC 83-8077. 320p. (Orig.). 1983. pap. 9.95 (ISBN 0-88344-032-6). Orbis Bks.
Black Religion in the Evangelical South. Richard Tristano. 96p. 1986. pap. 4.00x (ISBN 0-317-43431-4). Glenmary Res Ctr.
Black Religion: The Negro & Christianity in the United States. Joseph R. Washington, Jr. LC 84-5659. 328p. 1984. pap. text ed. 12.75 (ISBN 0-8191-3907-6). U Pr of Amer.
Black Religions in the New World. George E. Simpson. LC 78-16892. (Illus.). 1978. 40.00x (ISBN 0-231-04540-9). Columbia U Pr.
Black Robe & Buckskin. John P. Pritchett. 1960. 12.95x (ISBN 0-8084-0063-0); pap. 8.95 (ISBN 0-8084-0064-9). New Coll U Pr.
Black Sects & Cults. Joseph R. Washington, Jr. 190p. 1984. pap. text ed. 10.50 (ISBN 0-8191-3906-8). U Pr of Amer.
Black Song: The Forge & the Flame. John Lovell, Jr. (Illus.). 704p. 1986. pap. 12.95 (ISBN 0-913729-53-1). Paragon Hse.
Black Spiritual Movement: A Religious Response to Racism. Hans A. Baer. LC 83-14559. 232p. 1984. text ed. 22.95x (ISBN 0-87049-413-9); pap. 8.95x (ISBN 0-87049-515-1). U of Tenn Pr.
Black Spirituality. Walter A. McCray. 150p. (Orig.). pap. write for info. (ISBN 0-933176-04-X). Black Light Fellow.
Black Theology: A Documentary History, 1966-1979. Ed. by Gayraud S. Wilmore & James H. Cone. LC 79-12747. 672p. 1979. pap. 14.95 (ISBN 0-88344-042-3). Orbis Bks.
Black Theology & Black Power. James H. Cone. LC 70-76462. (Orig.). 1969. pap. 5.95 (ISBN 0-8164-2003-3, SP59, HarpR). Har-Row.
Black Theology As the Foundation of Three Methodist Colleges: The Educational Views & Labors of Daniel Payne, Joseph Price, Isaac Lane. Paul R. Griffin. LC 84-13070. 148p. (Orig.). 1984. lib. bdg. 20.75 (ISBN 0-8191-4160-7); pap. text ed. 9.50 (ISBN 0-8191-4161-5). U Pr of Amer.
Black Theology Exposed. Robert L. Jordan. LC 81-90503. (Illus.). 92p. 1983. 8.95 (ISBN 0-533-05215-7). Vantage.
Black Theology II: Essays on the Formation & Outreach of Contemporary Black Theology. Ed. by Calvin E. Bruce & William R. Jones. LC 75-39113. 285p. 1978. 25.00 (ISBN 0-8387-1893-0). Bucknell U Pr.
Black Theology in Dialogue. J. Deotis Roberts. LC 86-15665. 132p. (Orig.). 1987. pap. 12.95 (ISBN 0-664-24022-4). Westminster.
Black Theology of Liberation. 2nd ed. James H. Cone. LC 85-18749. 176p. 1986. pap. 9.95 (ISBN 0-88344-245-0). Orbis Bks.
Black Theology Today: Liberation & Contextualization. James D. Roberts. LC 83-17246. (Toronto Studies in Theology: Vol. 12). 218p. 1984. 49.95x (ISBN 0-88946-755-2). E Mellen.
Black Women & Religion. Marilyn Richardson. 1980. 17.50 (ISBN 0-8161-8087-3, Hall Reference). G K Hall.
Blackstone's Secrets of Magic. Harry Blackstone. pap. 3.00 (ISBN 0-87980-260-X). Wilshire.
Blackwater: Essays on Black & Southern History. Manning Marable. 1978. 12.00 (ISBN 0-89421-028-9). Challenge Pr.
Blade of Grass. Gordon De Pree & Gladis De Pree. LC 65-19504. 1971. pap. 4.95 (ISBN 0-310-23641-X). Zondervan.
Blagovjestije Khristikanskoj Slavi v Apokalipsisje. N. N. Glubokovsky. Tr. of Good News of Christian Glory in the Apocalypse. 116p. 1966. pap. 5.00 (ISBN 0-317-29139-4). Holy Trinity.
Blaiklock's Handbook to the Bible. E. M. Blaiklock. 256p. 1981. pap. 6.95 (ISBN 0-8007-5055-1, Power Bks). Revell.
Blaise Pascal. H. F. Stewart. 1973. Repr. of 1942 ed. 6.00 (ISBN 0-8274-1623-7). R West.

Blaise Pascal. Hugh F. Stewart. LC 77-16601. 1977. Repr. of 1942 ed. lib. bdg. 12.50 (ISBN 0-8414-7801-5). Folcroft.

Blaise Pascal: Das Heil Im Widerspruch. Irene Kummer. 1978. 56.80x (ISBN 3-11-007253-X). De Gruyter.

Blaise Pascal: The Life & Work of a Realist. Ernest Mortimer. 1979. Repr. of 1959 ed. lib. bdg. 25.00 (ISBN 0-8414-6341-7). Folcroft.

Blake & Novalis. Joachim J. Scholz. (European University Studies: Series 18, Comparative Literature, Vol. 19). 404p. 1978. 40.40 (ISBN 3-261-02576-X). P Lang Pubs.

Blake: Prophet Against Empire. rev. ed. David V. Erdman. LC 69-18055. 1969. pap. 17.00x (ISBN 0-691-01329-2). Princeton U Pr.

Blake's Fourfold Vision. Harold C. Goddard. LC 56-7354. (Orig.). 1956. pap. 2.50x (ISBN 0-87574-086-3). Pendle Hill.

Blake's Job: William Blake's Illustrations of the Book of Job. William Blake. Ed. by S. Foster Damon. LC 82-13585. (Illus.). 76p. 1982. pap. 8.95 (ISBN 0-87451-241-7). U Pr of New Eng.

Blake's Marriage of Heaven & Hell. Martin Nurmi. LC 72-6067. (Studies in Blake, No. 3). 1972. Repr. of 1957 ed. lib. bdg. 75.00x (ISBN 0-8383-1599-2). Haskell.

Blake's Prelude: "Poetical Sketches". Robert F. Gleckner. LC 82-47976. 216p. 1983. text ed. 20.00x (ISBN 0-8018-2850-3). Johns Hopkins.

Blake's Prophetic Psychology. Brenda Webster. LC 84-114638. (Illus.). 336p. 1983. 27.50x (ISBN 0-8203-0658-4). U of Ga Pr.

Blake's Sublime Allegory: Essays on the "Four Zoas," "Milton," & "Jerusalem". Ed. by Stuart Curran & Joseph A. Wittreich, Jr. LC 72-1377. (Illus.). 404p. 1973. 35.00x (ISBN 0-299-06180-9). U of Wis Pr.

Blaspheming Against the Holy Peoples Holy Hoax. Michael A. Hoffman, II. 1986. pap. 2.00 (ISBN 0-317-53014-3). Noontide.

Blasphemy in Massachusetts: Freedom of Conscience & the Abner Kneeland Case. Leonard Levy. LC 70-16634. 592p. 1973. lib. bdg. 65.00 (ISBN 0-306-70221-5). Da Capo.

Blast & Counterblast: Contemporary Writings on the Scottish Reformation. Ed. by I. B. Cowan. 76p. 1985. 22.00x (ISBN 0-317-39400-2, Pub. by Saltire Society). State Mutual Bk.

Blaze of Noon: A Reading of "Samson Agonistes". Anthony Low. LC 74-1484. 236p. 1974. 28.00x (ISBN 0-231-03842-9). Columbia U Pr.

Blazing Star, with an Appendix Treating of the Jewish Kabbala. William B. Greene. 1977. lib. bdg. 59.95 (ISBN 0-8490-1516-2). Gordon Pr.

Bless Me Father. Eamon Kelly. 1977. pap. 6.95 (ISBN 0-85342-489-6, Pub. by Mercier Pr Ireland). Irish Bks Media.

Bless Me, Father, for I Have Sinned: Catholics Speak Out about Confession. Quentin Donoghue & Linda Shapiro. LC 84-81332. 303p. 1984. 17.95 (ISBN 0-917657-02-0). D I Fine.

Bless Me Father, for I Have Sinned: Catholics Speak Out about Confession. Quentin Donoghue & Linda Shapiro. LC 84-81332. 303p. 1985. pap. 8.95 (ISBN 0-917657-44-6). D I Fine.

Bless My Growing: For Parents, Teachers, & Others Who Learn. Gerhard E. Frost. LC 74-77680. (Illus.). 96p. 1975. pap. 5.95 (ISBN 0-8066-1431-5, 10-0770). Augsburg.

Bless the Lord, O My Soul. J. C. Wenger. LC 64-23575. (Illus.). 264p. 1964. 9.95 (ISBN 0-8361-1497-3). Herald Pr.

Bless This Mess & Other Prayers. Jo Carr & Imogene Sorley. (Festival Books). 1976. pap. 3.25 (ISBN 0-687-03618-6). Abingdon.

Blessed among Women. Arnold Michael. 1985. pap. 8.95 (ISBN 0-87613-091-0). New Age.

Blessed & Broken: An Exploration of the Contemporary Experience of God in Eucharistic Celebration. Ralph Keifer. (Message of the Sacraments Ser.: Vol. 3). 1982. 12.95 (ISBN 0-89453-393-2); pap. 8.95 (ISBN 0-89453-267-7). M Glazier.

Blessed Are the Born Again. R. Kent Hughes. 132p. 1986. pap. 4.95 (ISBN 0-89693-369-5). Victor Bks.

Blessed are the Ignorant. Bhagwan Shree Rajneesh. Ed. by Ma Prem Maneesha. LC 83-181704. (Initiation Talks Ser.). (Illus.). 566p. (Orig.). 1979. 19.95 (ISBN 0-88050-012-3). Chidvilas Found.

Blessed Are the Persecuted: Christian Life in the Roman Empire, A.D. 64-313. Ivo Lesbaupin. Tr. by Robert R. Barr from Port. Tr. of A Bem-Aventuranca da Persecucion & La Bienaventuranza de la Persecution. 112p. (Orig.). 1987. 16.95 (ISBN 0-88344-562-X); pap. 7.95 (ISBN 0-88344-561-1). Orbis Bks.

Blessed Are the Pure in Heart: The Beatitudes. Bernard Haring. (Illus.). 1977. pap. 4.95 (ISBN 0-8245-0204-3). Crossroad NY.

Blessed Are You Who Believed. Carlo Carretto. Tr. by Barbara Wall from Ital. LC 82-22504. Tr. of Beata te Che Hai Creduto. (Illus.). 96p. (Orig.). 1983. pap. 4.95 (ISBN 0-88344-038-5). Orbis Bks.

Blessed Are Your Eyes. Bessie Beihl. pap. 1.00 (ISBN 0-87516-131-6). De Vorss.

Blessed Art Thou among Women. John H. Newman. 1985. 4.95 (ISBN 0-87193-076-5). Dimension Bks.

Blessed Assurance. William G. Johnsson. Ed. by Richard W. Coffen. 144p. (Orig.). 1985. pap. 5.95 (ISBN 0-8280-0313-0). Review & Herald.

Blessed Assurance Sermon Outlines. Russell E. Spray. (Pulpit Library). 80p. 1985. pap. 3.95 (ISBN 0-8010-8255-2). Baker Bk.

Blessed Be. Mary Jo Tully. 96p. 1982. pap. 3.50 (ISBN 0-697-01822-9). Wm C Brown.

Blessed be God, Choral Instrumental Ensemble. Betty Jacobson. pap. 20.00 (ISBN 0-317-09814-4, 2003553). Bks Demand UMI.

Blessed Be the Bond: Christian Perspectives on Marriage & Family. William J. Everett. LC 84-48712. 144p. 1985. pap. 6.95 (ISBN 0-8006-1831-9, 1-1831). Fortress.

Blessed by Illness. L. F. Mees. 248p. (Orig.). 1983. pap. 10.95 (ISBN 0-88010-054-0). Anthroposophic.

Blessed Eucharist: Our Greatest Treasure. Michael Muller. LC 79-112490. 1973. pap. 9.00 (ISBN 0-89555-040-7). TAN Bks Pubs.

Blessed Hope. George E. Ladd. 1956. pap. 6.95 (ISBN 0-8028-1111-6). Eerdmans.

Blessed Hope & the Tribulation. John F. Walvoord. (Contemporary Evangelical Perspectives Ser.). 1976. kivar 5.95 (ISBN 0-310-34041-1, 10977P). Zondervan.

Blessed Is the Ordinary. Gerhard E. Frost. (Illus.). 96p. pap. 4.95 (ISBN 0-86683-606-3, HarpR). Har-Row.

Blessed Is the Woman. Vi Jensen. Ed. by James L. Silvey. 95p. (Orig.). 1983. pap. 3.50 (ISBN 0-89114-116-2). Baptist Pub Hse.

Blessed James Salomoni. Cecelia Desmond. 1970. 2.00 (ISBN 0-8198-0000-7); pap. 1.00 (ISBN 0-8198-0001-5). Dghtrs St Paul.

Blessed John, the Wonderworker. rev. ed. Abbot Herman. Ed. by St. Herman of Alaska Brotherhood Staff. (Illus.). 350p. 1987. pap. 15.00 (ISBN 0-938635-01-8). St Herman AK.

Blessed Kateri Takakwitha: Mohawk Maiden. Daughters of St Paul. 1980. 3.75 (ISBN 0-8198-1100-9); pap. 2.25 (ISBN 0-8198-1101-7). Dghtrs St Paul.

Blessed Life. F. B. Meyer. 1979. pap. 0.95 (ISBN 0-87509-052-4). Chr Pubns.

Blessed Paisius Velichkovsky: His Life & Writings. Paisius Velichkovsky. 1973. 12.00x (ISBN 0-686-05406-7). Eastern Orthodox.

Blessed Rage for Order: The New Pluralism in Theology. David Tracy. 1979. pap. 9.95 (ISBN 0-8164-2202-8, HarpR). Har-Row.

Blessed Sacrament. Frederick W. Faber. LC 78-66302. 1978. pap. 11.00 (ISBN 0-89555-077-6). TAN Bks Pubs.

Blessed Simplicity: The Monk as Universal Archetype. Raimundo Panikkar et al. 224p. (Orig.). 1982. 17.95 (ISBN 0-8164-0531-X, HarpR). Har-Row.

Blessed to Be a Blessing. James K. Wagner. LC 80-52615. 144p. (Orig.). 1980. pap. 5.95x (ISBN 0-8358-0410-0). Upper Room.

Blessed Virgin. Clifford Stevens. LC 84-60745. 160p. 1985. pap. 6.95 (ISBN 0-87973-704-2, 704). Our Sunday Visitor.

Blessed Virgin Mary As Mediatrix in the Latin & Old French Legend Prior to the Fourteenth Century. Sr. M. Vincentine Gripkey. LC 72-94166. (Catholic University of America Studies in Romance Languages & Literatures Ser: No. 17). 1969. Repr. of 1938 ed. 26.00 (ISBN 0-404-50317-9). Ams Pr.

Blessed Virgin Mary: Excerpt from the Glories of Mary. Alphonse Liguori. 96p. 1974. pap. 3.00 (ISBN 0-89555-177-2). TAN Bks Pubs.

Blessed Virgin Mary: Her Life & Mission. Corinne Heline. (Illus.). 152p. 1986. pap. text ed. 8.95 (ISBN 0-933963-12-2). New Age Bible.

Blessed Virgin Mary in Early Christian Latin Poetry. A. B. Heyden. 59.95 (ISBN 0-87968-755-X). Gordon Pr.

Blessed Virgin Mary in Medieval Drama of England. Joannes Vriend. 69.95 (ISBN 0-87968-756-8). Gordon Pr.

Blessed Women of Islam. M. S. Siddiqui. 16.95 (ISBN 0-686-83898-X). Kazi Pubns.

Blessing & Power, Vol. 178. Ed. by David Power & Mary Collins. (Concilium Ser.). 128p. pap. 6.95 (ISBN 0-567-30058-7, Pub. by T & T Clark Ltd UK). Fortress.

Blessing Cup. Rock Travnikar. 64p. (Orig.). 1979. pap. 2.25 (ISBN 0-912228-60-1). St Anthony Mess Pr.

Blessing: Giving & Gaining Family Approval. Gary Smalley & John Trent. 224p. 1986. pap. text ed. 14.95 (ISBN 0-8407-3066-7). Nelson.

Blessing in Mosque & Mission. Larry G. Lenning. LC 80-25110. 176p. (Orig.). 1981. pap. 5.95 (ISBN 0-87808-433-9). William Carey Lib.

Blessing: In the Bible & the Life of the Church, No. 3. Claus Westermann. Ed. by Walter Brueggeman & John R. Donahue. Tr. by Keith Crim from Ger. LC 78-54564. (Overtures to Biblical Theology Ser.). 144p. 1978. pap. 8.95 (ISBN 0-8006-1529-8, 1-1529). Fortress.

Blessing Is in the Doing. Dandi Knorr. LC 83-70643. (Orig.). 1983. pap. 4.95 (ISBN 0-8054-6001-2). Broadman.

Blessing of Eliyahu: Rabbi Munk. A. Schischa. 1983. 35.00x (ISBN 0-88125-016-3). Ktav.

Blessing of Years: The Memoirs of Lawrence Cardinal Sheehan. Lawrence Sheehan. LC 82-19965. (Illus.). 314p. 1984. pap. text ed. 9.95 (ISBN 0-317-11856-0, 85-06743). U of Notre Dame Pr.

Blessings: A Reappraisal of Their Nature, Purpose, & Celebration. Thomas G. Simons. LC 80-54275. 1981. pap. 9.95 (ISBN 0-89390-026-5). Resource Pubns.

Blessings & Consecrations: A Book of Occasional Services. 64p. 1984. pap. 3.95 (ISBN 0-687-03626-7). Abingdon.

Blessings Cup: A Guide to Family Devotions for Lent. Keith M. Swenson. 32p. (Orig.). 1984. pap. 2.75 (ISBN 0-8066-2033-1, 23-1120). Augsburg.

Blessings for God's People: A Book of Blessings for All Occasions. Thomas G. Simons. LC 82-62045. 112p. (Orig.). 1983. pap. 5.95 (ISBN 0-87793-264-6). Ave Maria.

Blessings from Jehovah-Rophe: The Lord Doth Heal. Darden Powers. LC 83-90951. 173p. 1984. 11.95 (ISBN 0-533-05957-7). Vantage.

Blessings of Illness. Basilea Schlink. 1973. pap. 2.50 (ISBN 0-551-00446-0, Pub. by Marshall Morgan & Scott UK). Evang Sisterhood Mary.

Blessings of Jesus. Joy Dueland. (Illus.). 1979. 8.95 (ISBN 0-931942-02-0). Phunn Pubs.

Blessings of Obedience. Andrew Murray. Orig. Title: School of Obedience; Believer's Secret of Obedience. 107p. 1984. pap. text ed. 3.50 (ISBN 0-88368-155-2). Whitaker Hse.

Blessings of Temple Marriage. George McCune. 1974. pap. 4.95 (ISBN 0-89036-040-5). Hawkes Pub Inc.

Blessings Out of Buffetings: Studies in Second Corinthians. Alan Redpath. 256p. 1965. 11.95 (ISBN 0-8007-0026-0). Revell.

Blessings That Make Us Be: Living the Beatitudes. Susan Muto. LC 82-13102. 176p. 1982. 7.95 (ISBN 0-8245-0516-6). Crossroad NY.

Blessingway. Leland C. Wyman. LC 66-28786. (Illus.). 660p. 1970. U of Ariz Pr.

Blickiling Homilies, Pts. I-III. Ed. by R. Morris. (EETS OS Ser.: Vols. 58 & 63, 73). 1874. 28.00 (ISBN 0-8115-3354-9). Kraus Repr.

Blight or Bloom. Fernando L. Dasbach. 198p. 1981. 12.50 (ISBN 0-686-28998-6). Regenbogen-Verlag.

Blissful Life: As Realized Through the Teachings of Sri Nisargadatta Maharaj. Nisargadatta Maharaj. Compiled by Robert Powell. ix, 84p. pap. 6.95 (ISBN 0-89386-014-X). Acorn NC.

Blood Covenant. H. Clay Trumbull. 404p. 1975. pap. 5.95 (ISBN 0-89228-029-8). Impact Bks MO.

Blood Covenant. Theo Wolmarans. 175p. (Orig.). 1984. pap. text ed. 5.50 (ISBN 0-914307-26-6). Word Faith.

Blood of His Servants: The True Story of One Man's Search for His Family's Friend & Executioner. Malcolm C. MacPherson. LC 83-40089. (Illus.). 310p. 1984. 16.95 (ISBN 0-8129-1098-2). Times Bks.

Blood of Jesus. William Reid. pap. 1.50x (ISBN 0-914053-02-7). Liberty Bell Pr.

Blood of Jesus: A Foundation for Faith. Bob Lamb. 1983. pap. 1.95 (ISBN 0-910709-07-6). PTL Repro.

Blood of Kings: Dynasty & Ritual in Maya Art. Linda Scheke & Mary E. Miller. 1986. 50.00 (ISBN 0-8076-1159-X). Braziller.

Blood of Prophets. Edgar L. Masters. 59.95 (ISBN 0-87968-761-4). Gordon Pr.

Blood of the Cross. Andrew Murray. 1968. pap. 2.95 (ISBN 0-87508-374-9). Chr Lit.

Blood of the Cross. Andrew Murray. 144p. 1981. pap. 3.50 (ISBN 0-88368-103-X). Whitaker Hse.

Blood Sacrifice Complex. Edwin M. Loeb. LC 24-4020. (Amer Archaeology Association Memoirs Ser.). 1924. pap. 15.00 (ISBN 0-527-00529-0). Kraus Repr.

Blood Speaks. Larry Huggins. 128p. 1982. pap. 3.95 (ISBN 0-89274-231-3, HH-231). Harrison Hse.

Blood Witness for Unity & Peace: The Life of Max Joseph Metzger. Leonard Swidler. 3.95 (ISBN 0-87193-077-3). Dimension Bks.

Bloomsbury's Prophet: G. E. Moore & the Development of His Moral Philosophy. Tom Regan. 328p. 1986. 29.95 (ISBN 0-87722-446-3). Temple U Pr.

Bloudy Tenent, Washed, & Made White in the Bloud of the Lambe. John Cotton. LC 78-141105. (Research Library of Colonial Americana). 1972. Repr. of 1647 ed. 34.00 (ISBN 0-405-03319-2). Ayer Co Pubs.

Blow the Trumpet at the New Moon: A Sisters Today Jubilee. Ed. by Daniel Durken. LC 79-27505. xi, 480p. (Orig.). 1980. pap. 3.00 (ISBN 0-8146-1016-1). Liturgical Pr.

Blow the Trumpet in Zion. Richard Booker. LC 85-62152. 208p. (Orig.). 1985. pap. 5.95 (ISBN 0-932081-02-9). Victory Hse.

Blue-Collar Ministry. Tex Sample. 192p. 1984. pap. 9.95 (ISBN 0-8170-1029-7). Judson.

Blue Collar-Roman Collar-White Collar: U. S. Catholic Involvement in Labor Management Controversies, 1960-1980. Patrick J. Sullivan. LC 86-24593. 358p. (Orig.). 1987. lib. bdg. 26.75 (ISBN 0-8191-5704-X); pap. text ed. 16.75 (ISBN 0-8191-5705-8). U Pr of Amer.

Blue Lodge & Chapter. Edmond Ronayne. 1947. 11.00 (ISBN 0-685-19465-5). Powner.

Blue Lodge Enlightenment. 8.50 (ISBN 0-685-19466-3). Powner.

Blueprint for Building Strong Faith. Kenneth Hagin, Jr. 1980. pap. 0.50 mini bk. (ISBN 0-89276-704-9). Hagin Ministries.

Blueprint for Lent. Arley Fadness. 1983. 10.00 (ISBN 0-89536-603-7, 0219). CSS of Ohio.

Blueprint for Sainthood: A Study of the Series C Epistles for Lent. Ben Johnson. 1980. 4.25 (ISBN 0-89536-416-6, 0234). CSS of Ohio.

Blueprint for Teaching. John T. Sisemore. LC 64-12413. 1964. 8.95 (ISBN 0-8054-3405-4). Broadman.

Blueprints. Lloyd Elder. LC 84-7634. 1984. 7.50 (ISBN 0-8054-6581-2). Broadman.

Blumhardt's Battle. 1970. pap. 1.65 (ISBN 0-913926-01-9). T E Lowe.

Blush of Shame: A Few Considerations on Verbal Obscenity in the Theatre. Barrett H. Clark. 1932. pap. 1.50 (ISBN 0-910664-01-3). Gotham.

Blut, Leben und Seele, Ihr Verhaeltnis Nach Auffassung der Griechischen und Hellenistischen Antike, der Bibel und der Alten Alexandrinischen Theologen. Franz Rusche. Repr. of 1930 ed. 34.00 (ISBN 0-384-52515-6). Johnson Repr.

B'nai B'rith & the Challenge of Ethnic Leadership. Deborah D. Moore. LC 81-906. (Modern Jewish History Ser.). 292p. 1981. 18.95x (ISBN 0-87395-480-7). State U NY Pr.

Boanerges. Rendel Harris. 1978. Repr. of 1913 ed. lib. bdg. 50.00 (ISBN 0-8482-4381-1). Norwood Edns.

Boards: Purposes, Organization, Procedures. Tilman R. Smith. LC 78-62628. 64p. 1978. pap. 1.95 (ISBN 0-8361-1862-6). Herald Pr.

Bob Jones' Sermons. Bob Jones, Sr. (Illus.). 148p. 1983. pap. 3.95 (ISBN 0-89084-232-9). Bob Jones Univ Pr.

Bob Jones University Collection of Religious Art: Italian Paintings. Stephen Pepper. (Illus.). 336p. (Orig.). 1984. pap. 55.00 (ISBN 0-89084-263-9). Bob Jones Univ Pr.

Bob Pierce: This One Thing I Do. Franklinn Graham & Jeanette Lockerbie. 1983. 10.95 (ISBN 0-8499-0097-2). Word Bks.

Bobby Bagley POW. Rod Gragg. 1978. pap. 3.95 (ISBN 0-89728-022-9, 678434). Omega Pubns OR.

Bodhi Kalpa. 1978p. pap. 1.00 (ISBN 0-686-95470-X). Ananda Marga.

Bodhisattva Doctrine. Leslie S. Kawamura. 306p. 1981. pap. text ed. 11.95x (ISBN 0-919812-12-0, Pub. by Wilfrid Laurier Canada). Humanities.

Bodhisattva Doctrine in Buddhist Sanskrit Literature. Har Dayal. 1975. Repr. 22.50 (ISBN 0-89684-180-4). Orient Bk Dist.

Bodhisattva of Compassion: The Mystical Tradition of Kuan Yin. John Blofeld. LC 77-91352. (Illus.). 155p. 1978. pap. 9.95 (ISBN 0-87773-126-8, 73609-5). Shambhala Pubns.

Bodhisattvas Everywhere. Tokuso Sakakibara et al. Ed. by Ruth Tabrah. Tr. by Toshikazu Arai from Japanese. 120p. (Orig.). 1983. pap. 6.95 (ISBN 0-938474-03-0). Buddhist Study.

Bodily Healing & the Atonement. T. J. McCrossan. 1982. pap. 3.50 (ISBN 0-89276-505-4). Hagin Ministries.

Bodin & the Great God of Nature: The Moral & Religious Universe of a Judaiser. P. L. Rose. 200p. (Orig.). 1980. pap. text ed. 48.50x (Pub. by Droz Switzerland). Coronet Bks.

Bodleian Manuscript of George Herbert's Poems. George Herbert. LC 81-18454. 1984. 125.00x (ISBN 0-8201-1373-5). Schol Facsimiles.

Body: A Study in Pauline Theology. John A. Robinson. LC 77-7221. 96p. 1977. pap. 3.95 (ISBN 0-664-24149-2). Westminster.

Body Broken & Blood Shed. Luis M. Bermejo. 368p. 1987. 8.95 (ISBN 0-8294-0554-2). Loyola.

Body Building. Lyman Coleman. (Free University Ser.). (Orig.). 1981. pap. 4.95 leader's guide (ISBN 0-687-37306-9); pap. 1.25 student's bk. (ISBN 0-687-37307-7). Abingdon.

Body in Interpersonal Relations: Merleau-Ponty. Mary R. Barral. 312p. 1984. pap. text ed. 14.50 (ISBN 0-8191-3755-3). U Pr of Amer.

Body of Christ: A Reality. Watchman Nee. Tr. by Stephen Kaung. 1978. pap. 2.50 (ISBN 0-935008-13-6). Christian Fellow Pubs.

Body of Divinity. Thomas Watson. 1978. pap. 9.95 (ISBN 0-85151-383-2). Banner of Truth.

Body of Faith: Judaism As Corporeal Election. Michael Wyschogrod. 320p. (Orig.). 1983. pap. 24.95 (ISBN 0-8164-0549-2, HarpR). Har-Row.

Body, Soul & Blood: Recovering the Human in Medicine. William T. Sayers. LC 79-56194. 112p. 1980. pap. 5.95 (ISBN 0-935718-00-1). Asclepiad.

Body: Toward an Eastern Mind-Body Theory. Yasuo Yuasa. Ed. by Thomas P. Kasulis. (Buddhist Studies). 256p. 1987. 39.50x (ISBN 0-88706-469-8); pap. 14.95 (ISBN 0-88706-468-X). State U NY Pr.

Bodymind Experience in Japanese Buddhism: A Phenomenological Study of Kukai & Dogen. David E. Shaner. (Series in Buddhist Studies). 202p. 1986. 44.50x (ISBN 0-88706-061-7); pap. 14.95x (ISBN 0-88706-062-5). State U NY Pr.

Boethius. Edmund Reiss. (World Authors Ser.). 1982. lib. bdg. 19.95 (ISBN 0-8057-6519-0, Twayne). G K Hall.

Boethius: An Essay. Hugh F. Stewart. LC 74-20524. 1975. Repr. of 1891 ed. 23.50 (ISBN 0-8337-4935-8). B Franklin.

Boethius & the Liberal Arts: A Collection of Essays. Michael Masi. (Utah Studies in Literature & Linguistics: Vol. 18). 220p. 1982. pap. 27.35 (ISBN 3-261-04722-4). P Lang Pubs.

Boethius: Some Aspects of His Times & Works. Helen M. Barrett. LC 65-18789. 1965. Repr. of 1940 ed. 7.50x (ISBN 0-8462-0653-6). Russell.

Boethius: The Consolations of Music, Logic, Theology, & Philosophy. Ed. by Henry Chadwick. 1981. text ed. 47.00x (ISBN 0-19-826447-X). Oxford U Pr.

Bog Nash na Njbesi i na zjemli. Protopresbyter Michael Pomazansky. Tr. of Our God is in Heaven & on Earth. 140p. 1985. pap. 5.00 (ISBN 0-317-29087-8). Holy Trinity.

Bogojavlenije Gospodnje. Ed. by Moscow Synod. Staff. Tr. of Theophany. 194p. pap. 8.00 (ISBN 0-317-29167-X). Holy Trinity.

Bogosluzhebncje Penije Russkoj Pravoslavnoj Tserkvi: Suschnost' Sistema I Istoria: Liturgical Chant of the Russian Orthodox Church: Its Essence, Structure & History, Vol. 1. Johann v. Gardner. LC 77-77086. (Rus., Illus., Orig.). 1979. text ed. 30.00 (ISBN 0-88465-008-1); pap. text ed. 25.00 (ISBN 0-686-50014-8). Holy Trinity.

Bogosluzhebnoje Penije Russkoj Pravoslavnoj Tserkvi: Istorija, Vol. 2. Johann V. Gardner. LC 77-77086. Tr. of Liturgical Chant of the Russian Orthodox Church; History. (Illus.). 1981. text ed. 30.00 (ISBN 0-88465-010-3); pap. text ed. 25.00 (ISBN 0-317-30384-8). Holy Trinity.

Bokotola. Millard Fuller. LC 77-1277. 1978. pap. 5.95 (ISBN 0-8329-1179-8). New Century.

Bold Bearers of His Name. William N. McElrath. 1987. 12.95 (ISBN 0-8054-4339-8). Broadman.

Bold Expectations of the Gospel. Donald J. Shelby. LC 82-50943. 96p. (Orig.). 1983. pap. 3.95 (ISBN 0-8358-0454-2). Upper Room.

Bolshevism Is Jewish. A. Leese. 1982. lib. bdg. 59.95 (ISBN 0-87700-409-9). Revisionist Pr.

Bonaventure & Aquinas: Enduring Philosophers. Robert W. Shahan & Francis J. Kovach. LC 75-40963. (Illus.). 200p. 1976. pap. 8.95x (ISBN 0-8061-1349-9). U of Okla Pr.

Bonaventure, Rooted in Faith: Homilies to a Contemporary World. Saint Bonaventure. Tr. by Marigwen Schumacher from Lat. 1974. 5.95 (ISBN 0-8199-0465-1). Franciscan Herald.

Bonaventure: The Soul's Journey into God: the Tree of Life, the Life of Francis. Ed. by Ewert Cousins. LC 78-60723. (Classics of Western Spirituality). 380p. 1978. 13.95 (ISBN 0-8091-0240-4); pap. 10.95 (ISBN 0-8091-2121-2). Paulist Pr.

Boncore Di Santa Victoria Novus Liber Hymnorum Ac Orationum. Boncore Di Santa Vittoria Staff. Repr. of 1903 ed. 60.00 (ISBN 0-384-12867-X). Johnson Repr.

Bondage of the Will. Martin Luther. Tr. by J. I. Packer & O. R. Johnston. 323p. 1973. Repr. of 1957 ed. cancelled 15.95 (ISBN 0-227-67417-0). Attic Pr.

Bondage of the Will. Martin Luther. Tr. by Henry Cole. (Summit Books). 1976. pap. 6.95 (ISBN 0-8010-5570-9). Baker Bk.

Bondage of the Will. Martin Luther. Tr. by J. I. Packer & O. R. Johnston. 322p. 1970. 13.95 (ISBN 0-8007-0028-7). Revell.

Bonded in Christ's Love: Being a Member of the Church. Denise L. Carmody & John T. Carmody. 240p. (Orig.). 1986. pap. 9.95 (ISBN 0-8091-2791-1). Paulist Pr.

Bonding: Relationships in the Image of God. Donald Joy. LC 84-27121. 192p. 1985. 9.95 (ISBN 0-8499-0440-4, 0440-4). Word Bks.

Bonds of Belonging: Pathways to Discipleship for Church Members. Donald F. LaSuer & L. Ray Sells. LC 86-72150. 88p. (Orig.). 1986. pap. 5.95 (ISBN 0-88177-038-8, DR038B). Discipleship Res.

Bonds of Sisterhood: A History of the RLDS Women's Organization, 1842-1983. 170p. 1985. pap. 9.75 (ISBN 0-8309-0401-8). Herald Hse.

Bone Games: One Man's Search for the Ultimate Athletic High. Rob Schultheis. LC 84-42622. 240p. 1985. 15.95 (ISBN 0-394-53967-2). Random.

Bone of His Bone. F. J. Huegel. (Christian Classic Ser.). 96p. 1980. pap. 3.95 (ISBN 0-310-26321-2, 9955P). Zondervan.

Bones of St. Peter: Fascinating Account of the Search for the Apostle's Body. John E. Walsh. LC 80-2883. (Illus.). 216p. 1985. 7.95 (ISBN 0-385-15039-3, Im). Doubleday.

Bonhoeffer & South Africa: Theology in Dialogue. John W. DeGruchy. 128p. (Orig.). 1984. pap. 9.95 (ISBN 0-8028-0042-4). Eerdmans.

Bonhoeffer's Ethic of Discipleship: A Study in Social Psychology, Political Thought, & Religion. Kenneth E. Morris. LC 85-31949. 144p. 1986. 17.95 (ISBN 0-271-00428-2). Pa St U Pr.

Boniface of Devon: Apostle of Germany. John C. Sladden. 254p. 1980. text ed. 18.75 (ISBN 0-85364-275-3). Attic Pr.

Bonifacius: An Essay Upon the Good. Cotton Mather. Ed. by David Levin. LC 66-14448. pap. 53.80 (2014654). Bks Demand UMI.

Bonifacius: An Essay...to Do Good. Cotton Mather. LC 67-18712. 1967. Repr. of 1710 ed. 35.00x (ISBN 0-8201-1032-9). Schol Facsimiles.

Boo Hoo Bible: The Neo-American Church Catechism & Handbook. rev. ed. Arthur J. Kleps. LC 73-29356. Orig. Title: Neo-American Church Catechism. (Illus.). 218p. 1971. pap. 5.00 (ISBN 0-9600388-1-7). Neo-Am Church.

Book. Gloria Earl. 1984. 6.75 (ISBN 0-8062-1572-0). Carlton.

Book about the English Bible. Josiah H. Penniman. 1977. Repr. of 1920 ed. lib. bdg. 27.50 (ISBN 0-8492-2101-3). R West.

Book: An Introduction to the Teachings of Bhagwan Shree Rajneesh, Series III, R-Z. Bhagwan S. Rajneesh. Ed. by Rajneesh Academy Staff. LC 84-42616. (Academy Ser.). 576p. (Orig.). 1984. pap. 5.95 (ISBN 0-88050-704-7). Chidvilas Found.

Book: An Introduction to the Teachings of Bhagwan Shree Rajneesh, Series I, A-H. Bhagwan S. Rajneesh. Ed. by Rajneesh Academy Staff. LC 84-42616. (Academy Ser.). 620p. (Orig.). 1984. pap. 5.95 (ISBN 0-88050-702-0). Chidvilas Found.

Book: An Introduction to the Teachings of Bhagwan Shree Rajneesh, Series II, I-Q. Bhagwan S. Rajneesh. Ed. by Rajneesh Academy Staff. (Academy Ser.). 576p. (Orig.). 1984. pap. 5.95 (ISBN 0-88050-703-9). Chidvilas Found.

Book & Painting: Shakespeare, Milton, & the Bible. Ronald Paulson. LC 82-2769. (Hodges Lectures Ser.). (Illus.). 248p. 1982. text ed. 23.50x (ISBN 0-87049-358-2). U of Tenn Pr.

Book Burning. Cal Thomas. LC 83-70319. 180p. 1983. pap. 5.95 (ISBN 0-89107-284-5, Crossway Bks). Good News.

Book for All Seasons. Thomas More. Ed. by E. E. Reynolds. 1978. 8.95 (ISBN 0-87243-079-0). Templegate.

Book for Children. Tr. by Kenneth Taylor. 640p. 1985. 9.95 (ISBN 0-8423-2145-4). Tyndale.

Book for the Mind. Swami Muktananda. 40p. (Orig.). 1976. pap. 1.75 (ISBN 0-685-99448-1). SYDA Found.

Book for Unitarians. Parker L. Johnstone. LC 76-21519. 1977. cloth 7.95 (ISBN 0-917802-02-0). Theoscience Found.

Book I-His Birth. Rebecca Daniels. (Life of Jesus Ser.). 32p. (YA) 1984. wkbk. 3.95 (ISBN 0-86653-213-7). Good Apple.

Book II-His Boyhood. Rebecca Daniels. (Life of Jesus Ser.). 32p. (YA) 1984. wkbk. 3.95 (ISBN 0-86653-223-4). Good Apple.

Book II of Revelations for the Aquarian Age. Compiled by Easu & Gladys K. Rodehaver. 1983. pap. 7.00 (ISBN 0-930208-14-5). Mangan Bks.

Book III-Gathering His Disciples. Rebecca Daniels. (Life of Jesus Ser.). 32p. (YA) 1984. wkbk. 3.95 (ISBN 0-86653-224-2). Good Apple.

Book Introducing the E-Meter. L. Ron Hubbard. 8.75 (ISBN 0-686-30797-6). Church Scient NY.

Book IV-the Teacher. Rebecca Daniels. (Life of Jesus Ser.). 32p. (YA) 1984. wkbk. 3.95 (ISBN 0-86653-225-0). Good Apple.

Book IX-Prophacies Fulfilled. Rebecca Daniels. (Life of Jesus Ser.). 32p. (YA) 1984. wkbk. 3.95 (ISBN 0-86653-230-7). Good Apple.

Book of Acts. Walter M. Dunnett. (Shield Bible Study Ser.). 144p. (Orig.). 1981. pap. 3.95 (ISBN 0-8010-2915-5). Baker Bk.

Book of Acts. Frank Stagg. 1955. 14.50 (ISBN 0-8054-1311-1). Broadman.

Book of Acts: A Radiant Commentary on the New Testament. Stanley M. Horton. LC 80-65892. 304p. (Orig.). 1981. 10.95 (ISBN 0-88243-317-2, 02-0317). Gospel Pub.

Book of Adoration. Maimondies & Moses Hyamson. (Mishneh Torah Ser.). 330p. 1981. 11.95 (ISBN 0-87306-086-5). Feldheim.

Book of Alfred Kantor: An Artist's Journal of the Holocaust. Alfred Kantor. (Illus.). 224p. 1987. 25.00x (ISBN 0-8052-4029-2); pap. 16.95x (ISBN 0-8052-0825-9). Schocken.

Book of Angelus Silesius. Frederick Franck. LC 85-70839. 145p. 1985. pap. 10.95 (ISBN 0-939680-20-3). Bear & Co.

Book of Baruch. Emanuel Tov. LC 75-30775. (Society of Biblical Literature. Texts & Translation-Pseudepigrapha Ser.). 1975. pap. 9.75 (ISBN 0-89130-043-0, 060208). Scholars Pr GA.

Book of Baruch: A Discussion of an Early Revision of the IXX of Jeremiah 29-52 & Baruch 1: 1-3: 8. Emanual Tov. LC 75-43872. (Harvard Semitic Monographs). 1976. pap. 9.75 (ISBN 0-89130-070-8, 06-02-08). Scholars Pr GA.

Book of Beliefs. Myrtle Langley et al. Ed. by P. Alexander. 192p. 1987. pap. 12.95 (ISBN 0-85648-504-7). Lion USA.

Book of Bible History. Charles Baker. 1980. lib. bdg. 59.95 (ISBN 0-8490-3159-1). Gordon Pr.

Book of Bible Quotes. 272p. 1984. pap. 5.95 (ISBN 0-8407-5929-0). Nelson.

Book of Books. Azriel Eisenberg. 163p. 1976. pap. 9.95 (ISBN 0-900689-77-3). Soncino Pr.

Book of Books. William Kimball. LC 86-71101. 160p. (Orig.). 1986. pap. 6.95 (ISBN 0-89900-211-0). College Pr Pub.

Book of Books. John White. 1978. 7.50 (ISBN 0-87552-545-8). Presby & Reformed.

Book of Books: The Growth of the Bible. Klaus Koch. LC 69-12299. 192p. 1969. pap. 2.65 (ISBN 0-664-24840-3). Westminster.

Book of Books: The Story of the Bible Text. Azriel Eisenberg. 1976. 9.95x (ISBN 0-685-84453-6). Bloch.

Book of Catholic Authors, Fourth Series: Informal Self-Portraits of Famous Modern Catholic Writers. Ed. by Walter Romig. LC 70-179740. (Biography Index Reprint Ser.). Repr. of 1948 ed. 27.50 (ISBN 0-8369-8108-1). Ayer Co Pubs.

Book of Catholic Wisdom. Charles Dollen. LC 86-60327. 205p. (Orig.). 1986. pap. 7.95 (ISBN 0-87973-535-X, 535). Our Sunday Visitor.

Book of Celestial Images: Angelic & Godform Images in Ritual Magic. A. C. Highfield. LC 86-16209. 192p. 1986. lib. bdg. 19.95 (ISBN 0-8095-7004-1). Borgo Pr.

Book of Chanukah. Eythe Scharfstein & Sol Scharfstein. (Illus.). 1959. 5.95x (ISBN 0-87068-357-8). Ktav.

Book of Chilam Balam of Chumayel. Ed. by Ralph L. Roys. (Civilization of the American Indian Ser.: No. 87). (Illus.). 1973. pap. 19.95x (ISBN 0-8061-0735-9). U of Okla Pr.

Book of Christian Prayer. Leslie F. Brandt. LC 73-88603. 96p. (Orig.). 1974. pap. 4.95 (ISBN 0-8066-1406-4, 10-0785). Augsburg.

Book of Christian Prayer: Gift Edition. rev. ed. Leslie F. Brandt. LC 73-88603. 160p. 1980. 8.95 (ISBN 0-8066-1751-9, 10-0786). Augsburg.

Book of Christmas. Thomas K. Hervey. 1977. lib. bdg. 59.95 (ISBN 0-8490-1530-8). Gordon Pr.

Book of Christmas. Reader's Digest Editors. LC 73-84158. (Illus.). 304p. 1973. 21.95 (ISBN 0-89577-013-X, Pub. by RD Assn). Random.

Book of Christmas. Tasha Tudor. (Illus.). 1979. 6.95 (ISBN 0-529-05532-5, Philomel). Putnam Pub Group.

Book of Christmas Carols. Ideals Staff. (Illus.). 24p. 1984. pap. 2.95 (ISBN 0-8249-8072-7). Ideals.

Book of Comfort. P. B. Power. 1974. pap. 2.95 (ISBN 0-85151-203-8). Banner of Truth.

Book of Comfort. Alvin N. Rogness. LC 78-66943. 1979. kivar 7.95 (ISBN 0-8066-1677-6, 10-0795). Augsburg.

Book of Comfort: Thoughts in Late Evening. Rev. Robert Paul Mohan. LC 86-60911. 118p. (Orig.). 1986. pap. 5.95 (ISBN 0-87973-541-4, 541). Our Sunday Visitor.

Book of Common Order. Church of Scotland, Committee on Public Worship & Aids to Devotion. 1979. 8.95x (ISBN 0-7152-0391-6); leather 14.00 (ISBN 0-686-75148-5). Outlook.

Book of Common Prayer. 1928 ed. write for info. Oxford U Pr.

Book of Common Prayer. fac: ed. 1976. 15.00 (ISBN 0-8164-5088-9, HarpR). Har-Row.

Book of Common Prayer. Ed. by John Bootz. LC 75-29330. 1976. 24.95 (ISBN 0-918016-58-4). Folger Bks.

Book of Common Prayer. Joan Didion. 288p. 1983. pap. 3.95 (ISBN 0-671-49589-5). PB.

Book of Common Prayer & Administration of the Sacraments: According to the Use of the Church of England. 11.95x (ISBN 0-19-130601-0). Oxford U Pr.

Book of Common Prayer & Books Connected with Its Origin & Growth. 2nd ed. 1985. 30.00 (ISBN 0-317-13412-4). Boston Public Lib.

Book of Common Prayer with the Additions & Deviations Proposed in 1928. 10.95x (ISBN 0-19-141202-3). Oxford U Pr.

Book of Common Worship. 406p. 1978. maroon softcover 4.95 (ISBN 0-664-24331-2); green softcover 4.95 (ISBN 0-664-24332-0). Westminster.

Book of Concord: The Confessions of the Evangelical Lutheran Church. Ed. & tr. by Theodore G. Tappert. LC 59-11369. 1959. 14.95 (ISBN 0-8006-0825-9, 1-825). Fortress.

Book of Creation. Irving Friedman. 64p. 1977. pap. 2.95 (ISBN 0-87728-289-7). Weiser.

Book of Daily Thoughts & Prayers. Swami Paramananda. 1977. 9.50 (ISBN 0-911564-01-2); soft lexotone bdg. 7.50 (ISBN 0-911564-32-2). Vedanta Ctr.

Book of Daniel. R. J. Clifford. pap. 1.25 (ISBN 0-317-46870-7). Franciscan Herald.

Book of Daniel. Douglas J. Simpson. 1974. pap. 3.95 (ISBN 0-89265-023-0). Randall Hse.

Book of Daniel. W. C. Stevens. 190p. 1915. pap. 3.25 (ISBN 0-87509-061-3). Chr Pubns.

Book of Daniel: A New Translation with Introduction & Commentary. Louis F. Hartman & Alexander A. Di Lella. LC 77-82762. (Anchor Bible Ser.: Vol. 23). 1978. 18.00 (ISBN 0-385-01322-1, Anchor Pr). Doubleday.

Book of Days: A Miscellany of Popular Antiquities in Connection with the Calendar, Including Anecdote, Biography & History, Curiosities of Literature, & Oddities of Human Life & Character, 2 Vols. Ed. by Robert Chambers. LC 67-13009. (Illus.). 1967. Repr. of 1862 ed. 125.00x (ISBN 0-8103-3002-4). Gale.

Book of Delight & Other Papers. Israel Abrahams. Ed. by Steven Katz. LC 79-7124. (Jewish Philosophy, Mysticism & History of Ideas Ser.). 1980. Repr. of 1912 ed. lib. bdg. 26.50x (ISBN 0-405-12238-1). Ayer Co Pubs.

Book of Destiny. Herman B. Kramer. LC 75-13556. (Illus.). 1975. pap. 12.50 (ISBN 0-89555-046-6). TAN Bks Pubs.

Book of Devotions. Compiled by Joseph Coppolino. 68p. (Orig.). 1986. pap. 1.75 (ISBN 0-8189-0502-6). Alba.

Book of Devotions for Today's Woman. Frances Carroll. 192p. 1983. pap. 5.95 (ISBN 0-13-080028-7). P-H.

Book of Direction to the Duties of the Heart. Bahya I. Pakuda. Tr. by Menahem Mansoor et al from Arabic. (Littman Library of Jewish Civilization). 1973. 43.00x (ISBN 0-19-710020-1). Oxford U Pr.

Book of E-Meter Drills. L. Ron Hubbard. 8.75 (ISBN 0-686-30796-8). Church Scient NY.

Book of Easter. LC 76-159894. Repr. of 1911 ed. 51.00x (ISBN 0-8103-3401-1). Gale.

Book of ECK Parables, Vol. 1. Harold Klemp. (Illus.). 265p. (Orig.). 1986. pap. 8.95 (ISBN 0-88155-046-9). IWP Pub.

Book of Ecstacy. Arif of Herat. Tr. by R. S. Greenshields. 1980. 9.95 (ISBN 0-900860-74-X, Pub. by Octagon Pr England). Ins Study Human.

Book of Enoch. Tr. by Richard Lawrence. LC 80-65736. 96p. 1980. pap. 4.00 (ISBN 0-934666-06-7). Artisan Sales.

Book of Enoch: Or One Enoch. 2nd ed. Ed. & R. H. Charles. 331p. pap. 16.95 (ISBN 0-88697-009-1). Life Science.

Book of Enoch the Prophet. 2nd ed. Richard Laurence. Tr. by Richard Laurence from Old Ethiopic. LC 72-95273. (Secret Doctrine Reference Ser). 220p. 1972. Repr. of 1883 ed. 11.00 (ISBN 0-913510-01-7). Wizards.

Book of Enoch Translated from the Ethiopic. Intro. by George H. Schodde. 1982. Repr. of 1882 ed. 39.00x (ISBN 0-403-08997-2, Regency). Scholarly.

Book of Esther. Tr. by Aryeh Kaplan. 268p. 8.95 (ISBN 0-686-27543-8); pap. 6.45 (ISBN 0-940118-21-1). Maznaim.

Book of Esther. Maryn Langer. 224p. 1987. pap. 5.95 (ISBN 0-310-47841-3). Zondervan.

Book of Esther. Alexander Raleigh. 1980. 9.75 (ISBN 0-86524-037-X, 1701). Klock & Klock.

Book of Esther: Motifs, Themes & Structure. Sandra B. Berg. LC 78-32035. (SBL Dissertation Ser.). 1979. pap. 9.95 (ISBN 0-89130-279-4, 060144). Scholars Pr GA.

Book of Eve. Catherine D. Vinck. 1979. text ed. 5.00 (ISBN 0-911726-40-3); stereo record & text incl. Alleluia Pr.

Book of Exodus: A Critical, Theological Commentary. Brevard S. Childs. LC 73-23120. (Old Testament Library). 686p. 1974. 26.50 (ISBN 0-664-20985-8). Westminster.

Book of Ezekiel: Critical Studies. rev. ed. Charles C. Torrey & Shalom Spiegel. (Library of Biblical Studies). 1970. 29.50x (ISBN 0-87068-116-8). Ktav.
Book of Family Prayer. Gabe Huck. 1979. 9.95 (ISBN 0-8164-0415-1, HarpR); pap. 9.95 (ISBN 0-8164-2486-1). Har-Row.
Book of Family Prayer. Robert E. Webber. 288p. 1986. 17.95 (ISBN 0-8407-5479-5). Nelson.
Book of First Corinthians. Paul Hamar. LC 80-65305. 192p. (Orig.). 1980. 6.95 (ISBN 0-88243-316-4, 02-0316). Gospel Pub.
Book of Galatians. Robert Picirilli. 1973. pap. 3.95 (ISBN 0-89265-012-5). Randall Hse.
Book of Games: A Course in Spiritual Play. Hugh Prather. LC 80-2840. (Illus.). 192p. 1981. pap. 6.95 (ISBN 0-385-14779-1, Dolp). Doubleday.
Book of Genesis. Charles F. Pfeiffer. (Shield Bible Study). (Orig.). pap. 2.95 (ISBN 0-8010-6906-8). Baker Bk.
Book of Genesis & Part of the Book of Exodus. Dean H. Alford. 1979. 12.50 (ISBN 0-86524-001-9, 7002). Klock & Klock.
Book of God & Man. Robert Gordis. LC 65-25126. 1978. pap. 12.95x (ISBN 0-226-30410-8, P771, Phoen). U of Chicago Pr.
Book of God's Love. M. R. Bawa Muhaiyaddeen. LC 81-4503. (Illus.). 126p. 1981. 7.95 (ISBN 0-914390-19-8). Fellowship Pr PA.
Book of Gomorrah: An Eleventh-Century Treatise Against Clerical Homosexual Practices. Peter Damian. Tr. by Pierre J. Payer. 120p. 1982. pap. text ed. 10.50x (ISBN 0-88920-123-4, Pub. by Wilfrid Laurier Canada). Humanities.
Book of Gospels. Geoffrey Chapman. (Illus.). 672p. 1985. 95.00 (ISBN 0-225-66351-1, HarpR). Har-Row.
Book of Hebrew Letters. Mark Podwal. LC 78-70076. (Illus.). 64p. 1979. pap. 5.95 (ISBN 0-8276-0118-2, 435). Jewish Pubns.
Book of Holidays Around the World. Alice Van Straalen. (Illus.). 192p. 1986. 12.95 (ISBN 0-525-44270-7). Dutton.
Book of Hours. Elizabeth Yates. 128p. 1985. pap. 4.95 large print ed. (ISBN 0-8027-2484-1). Walker & Co.
Book of Hu & the Book of Tyana. John Gibson. LC 84-19096. (Illus.). 136p. 1984. 15.00 (ISBN 0-8022-2449-0). Philos Lib.
Book of Infinite Love. Louise M. De La Touche. Tr. by E. Patrick O'Connell from Fr. LC 79-90488. 1979. pap. 3.00 (ISBN 0-89555-129-2). TAN Bks Pubs.
Book of Infinite Possibilities. Leilah Wendell. 55p. (Orig.). 1987. pap. 4.50 (ISBN 0-89540-169-X). Sun Pub.
Book of Isaiah. Avraham Gileadi. 264p. 1987. 12.95 (ISBN 0-87579-076-3). Deseret Bk.
Book of Isaiah. George L. Robinson. pap. 4.50 (ISBN 0-8010-7609-9). Baker Bk.
Book of Isaiah, Vol. 1. Edward J. Young. 1964. 19.95 (ISBN 0-8028-2179-0). Eerdmans.
Book of Isaiah, Chapters 1-39. John N. Oswalt. (New International Commentary on the Old Testament Ser.). 672p. 29.95 (ISBN 0-8028-2368-8). Eerdmans.
Book of Isaiah 1. Ed. by A. J. Rosenberg. 261p. 1982. 12.95 (ISBN 0-910818-50-9). Judaica Pr.
Book of Isaiah 2. Ed. by A. J. Rosenberg. 554p. 1983. 12.95 (ISBN 0-910818-52-5). Judaica Pr.
Book of James. J. J. Turner. pap. 5.50 (ISBN 0-89137-548-1). Quality Pubns.
Book of Jeremiah. Ed. by H. Cunliffe-Jones. 1961. 8.95 (ISBN 0-02-529260-9). Macmillan.
Book of Jeremiah, Bk. II. Ed. by A. J. Rosenberg. 442p. 1985. 12.95 (ISBN 0-910818-60-6). Judaica Pr.
Book of Jeremiah. John A. Thompson. LC 79-16510. (New International Commentary on the Old Testament Ser.). 1980. 27.95 (ISBN 0-8028-2369-6). Eerdmans.
Book of Jeremiah. K. Owen White. (New Shield Ser.). 1981. pap. 3.45 (ISBN 0-8010-9517-4). Baker Bk.
Book of Jeremiah, Vol. 1. A. J. Rosenberg. (Books of the Prophet Ser.). 460p. 1985. 12.95 (ISBN 0-910818-59-2). Judaica Pr.
Book of Jeremiah: A Commentary. Solomon B. Freehof. LC 77-8259. 1977. 15.00 (ISBN 0-8074-0008-4, 381610). UAHC.
Book of Jewish Belief. Louis Jacobs. 250p. (Orig.). 1984. pap. text ed. 7.95x (ISBN 0-87441-379-6). Behrman.
Book of Jewish Books: A Readers' Guide to Judaism. Ruth S. Frank & William Wolheim. LC 86-45014. (Illus.). 272p. (Orig.). 1986. 15.95 (ISBN 0-06-063008-6, HarpR); pap. 8.95 (ISBN 0-06-063009-4, HarpR). Har-Row.
Book of Jewish Curiosities. David M. Hausdorff. LC 55-11366. 1979. pap. 5.95 (ISBN 0-8197-0466-0). Bloch.
Book of Jewish Customs. Harvey Lutske. LC 86-2362. 300p. 1986. 25.00 (ISBN 0-87668-916-0). Aronson.
Book of Jewish Ethical Concepts. Abraham P. Bloch. 1984. 20.00 (ISBN 0-88125-039-2). Ktav.
Book of Jewish Holidays. Ruth Kozodoy. Ed. by Seymour Rossel. (Illus.). 192p. (Orig.). 1981. pap. text ed. 5.95x (ISBN 0-87441-334-6); tchr's. guide with duplicating masters by Moshe Ben-Aharon 3.25x (ISBN 0-87441-367-2). Behrman.
Book of Jewish Knowledge. Nathan Ausubel. (Illus.). 1962. 23.95 (ISBN 0-517-09746-X). Crown.
Book of Jewish Lists. Ron Landau. LC 81-40500. 192p. 1982. 14.95 (ISBN 0-8128-2839-9). Stein & Day.
Book of Jewish Thoughts. Ed. by Joseph H. Hertz. 1976. Repr. 8.95 (ISBN 0-8197-0252-8). Bloch.
Book of Jewish Values. Louis Jacobs. (Limited Editions Reprints). 160p. 1984. pap. text ed. 6.95 (ISBN 0-940646-06-4, 83-21278). Rossel Bks.
Book of Job. (Modern Critical Interpretations--Ancient, Medieval, & Renaissance Ser.). 19.95 (ISBN 0-87754-913-3). Chelsea Hse.
Book of Job. Edgar C. Gibson. 266p. 1983. lib. bdg. 10.00 (ISBN 0-86524-170-8, 1801). Klock & Klock.
Book of Job. Jeanne Guyon. 1985. pap. 7.95 (ISBN 0-940232-23-5). Christian Bks.
Book of Job. N. C. Habel. LC 74-82588. (Cambridge Bible Commentary on the New English Bible, Old Testament Ser.). 250p. 1975. 27.95 (ISBN 0-521-20653-7); pap. 12.95 (ISBN 0-521-09943-9). Cambridge U Pr.
Book of Job. Wayne Jackson. pap. 5.50 (ISBN 0-89137-541-4). Quality Pubns.
Book of Job. Morris Jastrow, Jr. 1920. 40.00 (ISBN 0-8274-1953-8). R West.
Book of Job. Tr. & intro. by Stephen Mitchell. 176p. 1987. 22.50 (ISBN 0-86547-286-6); pap. 12.50 (ISBN 0-86547-270-X). N Point Pr.
Book of Job. David Thomas. LC 82-7767. (Bible Study Classics). 500p. 1982. 22.95 (ISBN 0-8254-3814-4). Kregel.
Book of Job, a Commentary. Norman C. Habel. LC 84-21580. (Old Testament Library). 586p. 1985. 39.95 (ISBN 0-664-21831-8). Westminster.
Book of Job: A New Translation According to the Traditional Hebrew Text. LC 79-25323. 88p. 1980. 7.50 (ISBN 0-8276-0172-7, 447). Jewish Pubns.
Book of Job: Commentary, New Translation & Special Studies. Robert Gordis. LC 78-2305. (Moreshet Ser.: No. 2). 1977. 45.00 (ISBN 0-87334-003-5). Ktav.
Book of Job: God's Answer to the Problem of Undeserved Suffering. Gleason L. Archer, Jr. 128p. (Orig.). 1983. pap. 5.95 (ISBN 0-8010-0190-0). Baker Bk.
Book of Jonah. Tr. by Sant Bani Ashram School Children. LC 84-50924. (Illus.). 1984. pap. 6.95 (ISBN 0-89142-044-4). Sant Bani Ash.
Book of Jonah. Peter Spier. LC 85-1676. (Illus.). 40p. 1985. 11.95 (ISBN 0-385-19334-3); PLB 11.95 (ISBN 0-385-19335-1). Doubleday.
Book of Joshua. William G. Blaikie. 416p. 1983. lib. bdg. 15.75 (ISBN 0-86524-173-2, 0601). Klock & Klock.
Book of Joshua. J. M. Miller & G. M. Tucker. (Cambridge Bible Commentary on the New English Bible, Old Testament Ser.). (Illus.). 218p. 1974. 22.95 (ISBN 0-521-08616-7); pap. 9.95 (ISBN 0-521-09777-0). Cambridge U Pr.
Book of Joshua. Ed. by A. J. Rosenberg. 350p. 1984. 12.95 (ISBN 0-910818-08-8). Judaica Pr.
Book of Joshua. Marten H. Woudstra. LC 80-23413. (New International Commentary on the Old Testament). 400p. 1981. 21.95 (ISBN 0-8028-2356-4). Eerdmans.
Book of Jubilees. Tr. by Schodde. LC 80-53467. 96p. 1980. pap. 4.00 (ISBN 0-934666-07-5). Artisan Sales.
Book of Jubilees: The Little Genesis. Ed. by R. H. Charles. 1984. Repr. of 1902 ed. 39.00x (ISBN 0-403-08996-4, Regency). Scholarly.
Book of Judges. J. D. Martin. LC 74-31797. (Cambridge Bible Commentary on the New English Bible, Old Testament Ser.). (Illus.). 272p. 1975. 24.95 (ISBN 0-521-08639-6); pap. 10.95x (ISBN 0-521-09768-1). Cambridge U Pr.
Book of Judges. Ed. by A. J. Rosenberg. 400p. 1979. 12.95 (ISBN 0-910818-17-7). Judaica Pr.
Book of Judges with Introduction & Notes. C. F. Burney. 528p. Repr. of 1920 ed. lib. bdg. 100.00 (ISBN 0-8495-0481-3). Arden Lib.
Book of Kant, Vol. 5. Richardson, J. & Co. Staff. 1983. 57.50x (ISBN 0-317-54273-7, Pub. by J Richardson UK); pap. 40.00x (ISBN 0-317-54274-5). State Mutual Bk.
Book of Kings 1. Ed. by A. J. Rosenberg. 512p. 1980. 12.95 (ISBN 0-910818-30-4). Judaica Pr.
Book of Kings 2. A. J. Rosenberg. 480p. 1980. 12.95 (ISBN 0-910818-31-2). Judaica Pr.
Book of Knowledge. Al-Ghazzali. 1970. 15.00x (ISBN 0-87902-106-3). Orientalia.
Book of Knowledge. Maimonides. Tr. by Moses Hyamson from Herbrew. (Mishneh Torah Ser.). 1981. 13.95 (ISBN 0-87306-085-7). Feldheim.
Book of Kuzari. Yehudah Halevi. (Hebrew & Eng.). 37.50 (ISBN 0-87559-077-2). Shalom.
Book of Leviticus. Samuel H. Kellogg. 1978. 21.00 (ISBN 0-86524-132-5, 0301). Klock & Klock.
Book of Leviticus: A Study Manual. Charles F. Pfeiffer. (Shield Bible Study). (Orig.). pap. 2.95 (ISBN 0-8010-6889-4). Baker Bk.
Book of Leviticus (Nicot) Gordon Wenham. (New International Commentary on the Old Testament Ser.). 1979. text ed. 16.95 (ISBN 0-8028-2353-X). Eerdmans.
Book of Lies. Aleister Crowley. LC 79-16636. (Illus.). 186p. (Orig.). 1981. pap. 8.95 (ISBN 0-87728-516-0). Weiser.
Book of Life. Roshi Jiyu-Kennett & Daizui MacPhillamy. (Illus.). 1979. pap. 9.95 (ISBN 0-930066-04-9). Shasta Abbey.
Book of Life: An Explanation of the Rule of the Third Order Regular of Saint Francis. Allan B. Wolter. (Spirit & Life Ser). 1954. pap. 2.50 (ISBN 0-686-11566-X). Franciscan Inst.
Book of Life-Sefer Hachaim. (Heb, & Eng). 18.50 (ISBN 0-87559-102-7). Shalom.
Book of Lilith. Barbara B. Koltuv. (Illus.). 142p. (Orig.). 1986. pap. 9.95 (ISBN 0-89254-014-1). Nicolas-Hays.
Book of Mag. Barbara H. Spencer. 202p. pap. 7.95 (ISBN 0-942494-40-7). Coleman Pub.
Book of Margery Kempe: A Modern Version. W. Butler-Bowdon. 1978. Repr. of 1936 ed. lib. bdg. 25.00 (ISBN 0-8482-3353-0). Norwood Edns.
Book of Mary: Devotions for October & May. Rawley Myers. LC 84-61563. 208p. (Orig.). 1984. pap. 6.50 (ISBN 0-87973-804-9, 804). Our Sunday Visitor.
Book of Mercy. Leonard Cohen. LC 84-40174. 88p. 1984. 9.95 (ISBN 0-394-53949-4, Pub. by Villard Bks). Random.
Book of Minutes: Nineteen Hundred Six to Nineteen Seventeen. (Vol. 1). 304p. 1978. 7.95 (ISBN 0-87148-103-0). Pathway Pr.
Book of Miracles: A Young Person's Guide to Jewish Spirituality. Lawrence Kushner. 96p. (Orig.). (YA) 1987. pap. text ed. 8.95 (ISBN 0-8074-0323-7). UAHC.
Book of Mirrors: Sefer Mar'ot ha-Zove'ot. Daniel Matt. LC 81-9308. (Brown Judiac Studies Ser.). 1982. pap. 22.50 (ISBN 0-89130-525-4, 14-00-30). Scholars Pr GA.
Book of Modern Jewish Etiquette: A Guide To Contemporary Manners & Religious Customs. Helen Latner. LC 86-45124. 400p. 1986. pap. 9.95 (ISBN 0-06-097054-5, PL-7054, PL). Har-Row.
Book of Mormon. Tr. by Joseph Smith, Jr. LC 66-15423. 414p. 1973. pap. 4.00 (ISBN 0-8309-0273-2). Herald Hse.
Book of Mormon: A Guide to Christian Living. Lowell L. Bennion. LC 85-16104. 138p. 1985. 8.95 (ISBN 0-87747-866-X). Deseret Bk.
Book of Mormon Activity Book: Creative Scripture Learning Experiences for Children 4-12. Sandy Halverson. (Illus.). 80p. 1982. pap. 2.95 (ISBN 0-88290-188-5, 4521). Horizon Utah.
Book of Mormon Chronology. Sidney B. Sperry. pap. 1.00 (ISBN 0-87747-408-7). Deseret Bk.
Book of Mormon Critical Text: A Tool for Scholarly Reference, 3 vols. F. A. R. M. S. Staff. LC 85-137843. (F. A. R. M. S. Critical Text Project). (Illus.). 1100p. (Orig.). 1986. Set. 55.00x (ISBN 0-934893-00-4, STF-84A); Vol. 3: Helaman - Moroni April 1987. pap. text ed. 20.00x (ISBN 0-934893-03-9). FARMS.
Book of Mormon Critical Text: A Tool for Scholarly Reference, Vol. 1, I Nephi-Words of Mormon. rev., 2nd ed. Ed. by F. A. R. M. S. Staff. (F. A. R. M. S. Critical Text Project Ser.: No. 4). (Illus.). 382p. 1986. Set of 3 Vols. 55.00 (ISBN 0-934893-07-1); pap. 20.00 (ISBN 0-934893-04-7). FARMS.
Book of Mormon Digest. John D. Hawkes. 240p. 1966. pap. 4.95 (ISBN 0-89036-010-3). Hawkes Pub Inc.
Book of Mormon: Eighteen Thirty. (Heritage Reprints Ser.). 1970. 12.00 (ISBN 0-8309-0025-X). Herald Hse.
Book of Mormon: First Edition Facsimile. Tr. by Joseph Smith, Jr. 590p. 1980. 9.99 (ISBN 0-87747-808-2). Deseret Bk.
Book of Mormon: It Begins with a Family. LC 83-73118. 270p. 1983. 8.95 (ISBN 0-87747-987-9). Deseret Bk.
Book of Mormon Puzzles & Pictures for Young Latter-Day Saints. Jean D. Crowther. LC 77-74495. (Books for LDS Children). (Illus.). 56p. 1977. pap. 4.95 (ISBN 0-88290-080-3). Horizon Utah.
Book of Mormon Study Guide. Eldin Ricks. 1976. pap. 4.95 (ISBN 0-87747-567-9). Deseret Bk.
Book of Mormons. Richard S. Van Wagoner & Steven C. Walker. 468p. 1982. 14.95 (ISBN 0-941214-06-0). Signature Bks.
Book of Myths. H. Sewell & Thomas Bulfinch. LC 42-25450. (Illus.). 128p. 1969. 11.95 (ISBN 0-02-782280-X). Macmillan.
Book of Nahum. Walter A. Maier. (Thornapple Commentaries). 392p. 1980. pap. 6.95 (ISBN 0-8010-6098-2). Baker Bk.
Book of Onias. R. C. Crossfield. LC 70-86503. 1969. 7.95 (ISBN 0-8022-2290-0). Philos Lib.
Book of Our Heritage, 3 vols. Eliyahu Kitov. Tr. by Nathan Bulman from Hebrew. Orig. Title: Sefer HaToda'ah. 1978. 32.50 (ISBN 0-87306-151-9); slipcased ed. 33.95 (ISBN 0-87306-157-8). Feldheim.
Book of Pagan Rituals, Vol. 1. Ed. by Herman Slater. 1978. pap. 9.95 (ISBN 0-87728-348-6). Weiser.
Book of Parables. Daniel Berrigan. 160p. 1977. 3.00 (ISBN 0-8164-0328-7, HarpR). Har-Row.
Book of Prayer for Junior Congregations: Sabbath & Festivals. Hyman Chanover & Evelyn Zusman. (Eng. & Hebrew.). 256p. 4.50x (ISBN 0-8381-0174-7, 10-174). United Syn Bk.
Book of Prayers. G. H. Showalter & Frank L. Cox. 1940. pap. 1.00 (ISBN 0-88027-063-2). Firm Foun Pub.
Book of Prayers. Illus. by Gian L. Uboldi. (Illus.). 192p. 1981. 4.95 (ISBN 0-87973-667-4, 667). Our Sunday Visitor.
Book of Proverbs, 2 Vols. in 1. David Thomas. LC 82-18682. (Kregel Bible Classics Ser.). 836p. 1983. 24.95 (ISBN 0-8254-3813-6). Kregel.
Book of Proverbs. R. N. Whybray. LC 70-171687. (New English Bible Commentaries, Old Testament). (Illus.). 192p. 1972. 24.95 (ISBN 0-521-08364-8); pap. 10.95x (ISBN 0-521-09679-0). Cambridge U Pr.
Book of Revelation. G. R. Beasley-Murray. (New Century Bible Commentay Ser.). 1981. pap. 7.95 (ISBN 0-8028-1885-4). Eerdmans.
Book of Revelation. Robert H. Mounce. LC 77-7664. (New International Commentary on New Testament Ser.). 1977. 16.95 (ISBN 0-8028-2348-3). Eerdmans.
Book of Revelation. Pheme Perkins. Ed. by Robert J. Karris. (Collegeville Bible Commentary Ser.: No. 11). 96p. 1983. Vol. 11. pap. 2.95 (ISBN 0-8146-1311-X). Liturgical Pr.
Book of Revelation: A Catholic Interpretation of the Apocalypse. John Tickle. 144p. 1983. pap. 3.95 (ISBN 0-89243-195-4). Liguori Pubns.
Book of Revelation Explained, Vol. 1. Patricia H. Burns. LC 82-90898. iv, 57p. 1986. pap. 9.95 (ISBN 0-9611368-0-4). B R E Pub.
Book of Revelation: Justice & Judgment. Elisabeth S. Fiorenza. LC 84-47920. 224p. 1984. pap. 11.95 (ISBN 0-8006-1793-2). Fortress.
Book of Revelation: Missionary Message of the New Testament. J. O. Barrett. 123p. 1947. Repr. 2.95 (ISBN 0-87921-005-2). Attic Pr.
Book of Revelation, Study Guide. Damon C. Dodd. 1973. pap. 2.95 (ISBN 0-89265-013-3). Randall Hse.
Book of Robert Southwell: Priest, Poet, Prisoner. Christobel M. Hood. LC 72-13696. 1972. Repr. of 1926 ed. lib. bdg. 30.00 (ISBN 0-8414-1290-1). Folcroft.
Book of Romans, 3 vols. Robert Picirilli. 1974. Set. pap. 3.50 ea.; Vol. 1. pap. (ISBN 0-89265-015-X); Vol. 2. pap. (ISBN 0-89265-016-8); Vol. 3. pap. (ISBN 0-89265-017-6). Randall Hse.
Book of Romans. Robert Picirilli. 324p. 1975. 8.95 (ISBN 0-89265-026-5). Randall Hse.
Book of Romans. Ed. by Thomas B. Warren & Garland Elkins. 1983. 15.00 (ISBN 0-934916-03-9). Natl Christian Pr.
Book of Rosicruciae, 3 Vols. R. Swinburne Clymer. 1948. Set. 27.00 (ISBN 0-686-00809-X). Philos Pub.
Book of Rosicruciae, Vol. I. R. Swinburne Clymer. 286p. 1946. 9.95 (ISBN 0-932785-03-4). Philos Pub.
Book of Runes: A Handbook for the Use of an Ancient Oracle-The Viking Runes. Ralph Blum. 1984. 22.95 (ISBN 0-312-08999-6). St Martin.
Book of Ruth. Yitzhak I. Broch. 1975. 7.95 (ISBN 0-87306-012-1); pap. 5.95. Feldheim.
Book of Ruth. Ruth H. Green. 1982. 7.00. Freedom Rel Found.
Book of Ruth. H. L. Heijkoop. 6.95 (ISBN 0-88172-086-0). Believers Bkshelf.
Book of Ruth. Meir Zlotowitz. (Art Scroll Tanach Ser.). 160p. 1976. 11.95 (ISBN 0-89906-002-1); pap. 8.95 (ISBN 0-89906-003-X). Mesorah Pubns.
Book of Sacramental Basics. Tad Guzie. LC 81-83189. 160p. (Orig.). 1982. pap. 6.95 (ISBN 0-8091-2411-4). Paulist Pr.
Book of Saints. Mary P. Hallick. 1984. pap. 5.95 (ISBN 0-937032-31-X). Light&Life Pub Co MN.

Book of Samuel 1. Ed. by A. J. Rosenberg. 525p. 1981. 12.95 (ISBN 0-910818-07-X). Judaica Pr.

Book of Samuel 2. Ed. by A. J. Rosenberg. 540p. 1982. 12.95 (ISBN 0-910818-11-8). Judaica Pr.

Book of Selected Prayers by Robert Louis Stevenson. Rev. ed. Robert Louis Stevenson. (Illus.). 99p. 1982. 47.85 (ISBN 0-89901-066-0). Found Class Reprints.

Book of Serenity. Tr. by Thomas Cleary. 464p. 1986. cancelled (ISBN 0-89281-072-6); pap. cancelled (ISBN 0-89281-074-2). Inner Tradit.

Book of Services. The United Reformed Church in England & Wales-the Doctrine & Worship Committee. 1980. 8.95x (ISBN 0-7152-0446-7). Outlook.

Book of Sufi Chivalry: Lessons to a Son of the Moment (Futuwwah) Ibn Al-Husayn al-Sulami. Tr. by Tosun Bayrak from Arabic. 1983. 8.95 (ISBN 0-89281-031-9). Inner Tradit.

Book of Sufi Healing. Shaykh Moinuddin. (Illus.). 256p. (Orig.). 1985. pap. 12.95 (ISBN 0-89281-043-2). Inner Tradit.

Book of Superstitions. Christine Chaundler. pap. 2.45 (ISBN 0-8065-0302-5). Citadel Pr.

Book of Tales, Being Myths of the North American Indians. Charles E. Wood. 59.95 (ISBN 0-87968-770-3). Gordon Pr.

Book of the Acts. Ed. by Frederick F. Bruce. (New International Commentary on the New Testament). 1954. 16.95 (ISBN 0-8028-2182-0). Eerdmans.

Book of the Book. Idries Shah. 146p. 1976. 9.95 (ISBN 0-900860-12-X, Pub. by Octagon Pr England). Ins Study Human.

Book of the Books, Vol. 1. Bhagwan S. Rajneesh. Ed. by Rajneesh Foundation International. LC 82-50462. (Buddha Ser.). 360p. (Orig.). 1982. pap. 15.95 (ISBN 0-88050-513-3). Chidvilas Found.

Book of the Books, Vol. 2. Bhagwan S. Rajneesh. Ed. by Ma P. Asha. LC 82-50462. (Buddha Ser.). 352p. (Orig.). 1983. pap. 4.95 (ISBN 0-88050-514-1). Chidvilas Found.

Book of the Books, Vol. 3. Bhagwan S. Rajneesh. Ed. by Ma P. Karima. LC 82-50462. (Buddha Ser.). 352p. (Orig.). 1984. pap. 4.95 (ISBN 0-88050-515-X). Chidvilas Found.

Book of the Books, Vol. 4. Bhagwan S. Rajneesh. Ed. by Swami P. Krishna. LC 82-50462. (Buddha Ser.). 384p. (Orig.). 1985. pap. 4.95 (ISBN 0-88050-516-8). Chidvilas Found.

Book of the Craft of Dying & Other Early English Tracts Concerning Death. Ed. by Frances M. M. Comper & Robert Kastenbaum. LC 76-19564. (Death & Dying Ser.). 1977. Repr. of 1917 ed. lib. bdg. 19.00x (ISBN 0-405-09560-0). Ayer Co Pubs.

Book of the Dead. E. A. Budge. (Illus.). 992p. 1985. pap. 9.95 (ISBN 1-85063-020-8, Ark Paperbks). Methuen Inc.

Book of the Dead. Intro. by E. A. Budge. 1977. pap. 9.95 (ISBN 0-8065-0591-5). Citadel Pr.

Book of the Dead; or, Going Forth by Day: Ideas of the Ancient Egyptians Concerning the Hereafter As Expressed in Their Own Terms. Tr. by George Allen. LC 74-10338. (Studies in Ancient Oriental Civilization Ser: No. 37). 1974. pap. text ed. 20.00x (ISBN 0-226-62410-2). U of Chicago Pr.

Book of the Foundation of St. Bartholomew's Church in London. London. St. Bartholomew's Priory. (EETS, OS Ser.: No. 163). 1923. pap. 12.00 (ISBN 0-527-00160-0). Kraus Repr.

Book of the Goddess. Carl Olsen. 264p. 1985. pap. 9.95 (ISBN 0-8245-0689-8). Crossroad NY.

Book of the Goddess, Past & Present: An Introduction to Her Religion. Ed. by Carl Olson. LC 82-23606. 275p. 1983. 14.95 (ISBN 0-8245-0566-2). Crossroad NY.

Book of the Gods & Rites & the Ancient Calendar. Fr. Diego Duran. Tr. by Fernando Horcasitas & Doris Heyden. LC 73-88147. (Civilization of the American Indian Ser.: No. 102). (Illus.). 1977. pap. 12.95 (ISBN 0-8061-1201-8). U of Okla Pr.

Book of the Judges: An Integrated Reading. Barry G. Webb. (JSOT Supplement Ser.: No. 46). 260p. 1987. text ed. 31.50x (ISBN 1-85075-034-3, Pub. by JSOT Pr England); pap. text ed. 14.95x (ISBN 1-85075-035-1, Pub. by JSOT Pr England). Eisenbrauns.

Book of the Navajo. 3rd ed. Raymond F. Locke. pap. 4.95 (ISBN 0-87687-400-6, Pub. by Mankind Pub). Borden.

Book of the Needs of the Holy Orthodox Church. G. V. Shann. LC 77-82258. 1969. Repr. of 1894 ed. 19.45 (ISBN 0-404-05951-1). AMS Pr.

Book of the New Age, Bk. 1. Haliel. 50p. (Orig.). 1985. pap. 3.00. Westgate Pr.

Book of the Popes. Tr. by Louise R. Loomis. 1965. lib. bdg. 19.50x (ISBN 0-374-95093-8, Octagon). Hippocrene Bks.

Book of the Prophet Ezekiel. K. W. Carley. LC 73-94352. (Cambridge Bible Commentary on the New English Bible Ser.). (Illus.). 340p. (Orig.). 1974. 34.50 (ISBN 0-521-08653-1); pap. 13.95 (ISBN 0-521-09755-X). Cambridge U Pr.

Book of the Prophet Isaiah. A. S. Herbert. LC 74-16997. (Cambridge Bible Commentary on the New English Bible, Old Testament Ser.). (Illus.). 250p. 1975. Bks. 1-39. pap. 12.95 (ISBN 0-521-09766-5); Bks. 40-66. 27.95 (ISBN 0-521-20721-5); pap. 12.95 (ISBN 0-521-09933-1). Cambridge U Pr.

Book of the Prophet Isaiah, 1-39. A S Herbert. L⌣ 73-79495. (Cambridge Bible Commentary on the New English Bible Ser.: NEB Old Testament). 232p. 1973. pap. 10.95. Cambridge U Pr.

Book of the Prophet Jeremiah: Chapters 1-25. E. W. Nicholson. LC 73-80477. (Cambridge Bible Commentary on the New English Bible, Old Testament Ser.). 200p. 1973. 27.95 (ISBN 0-521-08625-6); pap. 11.95 (ISBN 0-521-09769-X). Cambridge U Pr.

Book of the Prophet Jeremiah: Chapters 26-52. E. W. Nicholson. LC 74-80357. (Cambridge Bible Commentary on the New English Bible, Old Testament Ser.). 250p. 1975. 27.95 (ISBN 0-521-20497-6); pap. 12.95 (ISBN 0-521-09867-X). Cambridge U Pr.

Book of the Rosary. John Carberry. LC 83-62424. 120p. (Orig.). 1983. pap. 4.50 (ISBN 0-87973-610-0, 610). Our Sunday Visitor.

Book of the Secrets. Bhagwan S. Rajneesh. pap. 8.95 (ISBN 0-06-090564-6, CN 564, PL). Har-Row.

Book of the Secrets, Vol. IV. 2nd ed ed. Bhagwan S. Rajneesh. Ed. by Rajneesh Foundation International. LC 75-36733. (Tantra Ser.). 408p. 1982. pap. 7.95 (ISBN 0-88050-528-1). Chidvilas Found.

Book of the Secrets of Enoch. Ed. by R. H. Charles. 100p. pap. 11.95 (ISBN 0-88697-010-5). Life Science.

Book of the Secrets Two. Bhagwan S. Rajneesh. LC 75-39733. 1979. pap. 8.95 (ISBN 0-06-090668-5, CN 668, PL). Har-Row.

Book of the Secrets, Vol. V. 2nd ed. Bhagwan S. Rajneesh. Ed. by Ma Prema Veena. LC 75-36733. (Tantra Ser.). 400p. 1984. pap. 4.95 (ISBN 0-88050-529-X). Chidvilas Found.

Book of the Spiritual Life. Emilia F. Dilke. LC 70-37689. (Illus., With a memoir of the author by the Rt. Hon. Sir Charles W. Dilke). Repr. of 1905 ed. 26.00 (ISBN 0-404-56743-6). AMS Pr.

Book of the Ten Masters. Puran Singh. 1984. 6.00X (ISBN 0-8364-1159-5, Pub. by Punjabi). South Asia Bks.

Book of the True Life, Vol. I. abr. ed. Tr. by Emilio B. Villanueva from Span. Orig. Title: Libro de la Vida Verdadera. (Span., Illus.). 376p. (Orig.). 1983. text ed. 12.00 (ISBN 0-912753-00-5); pap. 6.00x (ISBN 0-912753-01-3). True Life Found.

Book of Tradition: Sefer ha-Qabbalah. Abraham I. Daud. Ed. & tr. by Gerson D. Cohen. (LLJC Ser.). 486p. 1967. Repr. of 1967 ed. 39.95x (ISBN 0-19-710019-8). Oxford U Pr.

Book of Twelve Prophets, Vol. II. A. J. Rosenberg. (Book of the Prophets Ser.). 270p. 1987. 14.95. Judaica Pr.

Book of Twelve Prophets, Vol. 1. Ed. by A. J. Rosenberg. (Books of the Prophets Ser). 465p. 1986. 14.95 (ISBN 0-910818-70-3). Judaica Pr.

Book of Uncommon Prayer. Kenneth G. Phifer. LC 82-50945. 128p. 1983. pap. 5.95 (ISBN 0-8358-0451-8). Upper Room.

Book of Universality: A Supplement to the Book of Changes. Chow Tun Yi. Tr. by F. G. Hsu from Chinese. 70p. 1979. pap. 2.00 (ISBN 0-89071-242-5). Matagiri.

Book of Unlikely Saints. Margaret T. Monro. LC 77-107727. (Essay Index Reprint Ser.). 1943. 19.00 (ISBN 0-8369-1528-3). Ayer Co Pubs.

Book of Urizen. William Blake. LC 78-58217. (Illus.). 102p. 1978. pap. 6.95 (ISBN 0-87773-131-4, 73629-X). Shambhala Pubns.

Book of Werewolves: Being an Account of Terrible Superstition. Sabine Baring-Gould. Repr. of 1865 ed. 35.00x (ISBN 0-8103-4241-3). Gale.

Book of Wisdom, Vol. I. Bhagwan S. Rajneesh. Ed. by Rajneesh Foundation International. LC 82-23142. (Buddhist Masters Ser.). 420p. (Orig.). 1983. pap. 9.95 (ISBN 0-88050-530-3). Chidvilas Found.

Book of Wisdom, Vol. 2. Bhagwan S. Rajneesh. Ed. by Swami Krishna Prabhu. LC 82-23142. (Buddhist Masters Ser.). 416p. (Orig.). 1984. pap. 5.95 (ISBN 0-88050-531-1). Chidvilas Found.

Book of Wisdom & Lies. Sulkhan-Saba Orbeliani. Tr. by Katherine Vivian. 1982. 14.95 (Pub. by Octagon Pr England). Ins Study Human.

Book of Wisdom, Song of Songs. James Reese. (Old Testament Message Ser.: Vol. 20). 12.95 (ISBN 0-89453-420-3); pap. 8.95 (ISBN 0-89453-254-5). M Glazier.

Book of Women: The Code of Maimonides, Bk. 4. Moses Maimonides. Ed. by Isaac Klein. LC 49-9495. (Judaica Ser.: No. 19). 592p. 1972. 50.00x (ISBN 0-300-01438-4). Yale U Pr.

Book of World Religions. Edward G. Parrinder. (Illus.). 1967. 12.50 (ISBN 0-7175-0443-3). Dufour.

Book on Life Beyond. Bo Yin Ra. Tr. by Bodo A. Reichenbach from Ger. LC 78-51633. 1978. pap. 5.00 (ISBN 0-915034-02-6). Kober Pr.

Book-Peddling Parson: An Account of the Life & Works of Mason Locke Weems. Lewis Leary. (Illus.). 1984. 15.95 (ISBN 0-912697-09-1). Algonquin Bks.

Book Raziel. (Heb). 7.50 (ISBN 0-87559-105-1). Shalom.

Book that Reads You. David W. Augsburger. (New Life Ser.). pap. 3.00 (ISBN 0-8361-1685-2). Herald Pr.

Book: That Which Has Been & That Which Shall Be, Bk. I. Sharon A. Taylor. LC 84-91294. 74p. 1985. 7.95 (ISBN 0-533-06386-8). Vantage.

Book That Wouldn't Go Away. George E. Vandeman. (Stories That Win Ser.). 64p. 1983. pap. 1.25 (ISBN 0-8163-0537-4). Pacific Pr Pub Assn.

Book V-The Healer. Rebecca Daniels. (Life of Jesus Ser.). 32p. (YA) wkbk. 3.95 (ISBN 0-86653-226-9). Good Apple.

Book VI-His Miracles. Rebecca Daniels. (Life of Jesus Ser.). 32p. (YA) 1984. wkbk. 3.95 (ISBN 0-86653-227-7). Good Apple.

Book VII-Parables. Rebecca Daniels. (Life of Jesus Ser.). 32p. (YA) 1984. wkbk. 3.95 (ISBN 0-86653-228-5). Good Apple.

Book VIII-More Parables. Rebecca Daniel. (Life of Jesus Ser.). 32p. (YA) 1984. wkbk. 3.95 (ISBN 0-86653-229-3). Good Apple.

Book We Call the Bible. J. C. Wenger. LC 79-89440. (Mennonite Faith Ser.: No. 8). 80p. 1980. pap. 1.50 (ISBN 0-8361-1908-8). Herald Pr.

Book: What the Black Sheep Said. Hansadutta. LC 85-5636. (Illus.). 1160p. (Orig.). 1985. pap. text ed. 9.95 (ISBN 0-933593-03-1). Hansa Pub.

Book X-His Last Days. Rebecca Daniels. (Life of Jesus Ser.). 32p. (YA) 1984. wkbk. 3.95 (ISBN 0-86653-231-5). Good Apple.

Book XI-His Last Hours. Rebecca Daniels. (Life of Jesus Ser.). 32p. (YA) 1984. wkbk. 3.95 (ISBN 0-86653-232-3). Good Apple.

Book XII-His Resurection. Rebecca Daniels. (Life of Jesus Ser.). 32p. (YA) 1984. wkbk. 3.95 (ISBN 0-86653-233-1). Good Apple.

Booke Called in Latyn Enchiridian & in Englysshe the Manuell of the Christen Knyght. Desiderius Erasmus. LC 70-25758. (English Experience Ser.: No. 156). 340p. 1969. Repr. of 1533 ed. 28.00 (ISBN 90-221-0156-8). Walter J Johnson.

Booke of Certaine Canons, Concernynge Some Parte of the Discipline of the Churche of England. Church of England Staff. LC 70-26475. (English Experience Ser.: No. 312). 1971. Repr. of 1571 ed. 7.00 (ISBN 9-0221-0312-9). Walter J Johnson.

Booke of Christian Ethicks or Moral Philosophie. William Fulbecke. LC 74-28856. (English Experience Ser.: No. 737). 1975. Repr. of 1587 ed. 6.00 (ISBN 90-221-0737-X). Walter J Johnson.

Books about the Book: A Guide to Biblical Reference Works. John R. Kohlenberger, III. 272p. 1986. pap. 10.95 (ISBN 0-310-39341-8). Zondervan.

Books & the Parchments. rev. & updated ed. Frederick F. Bruce. (Illus.). 320p. (Orig.). 13.95 (ISBN 0-8007-1214-5). Revell.

Books for Catholic Elementary Schools. Eileen Noonan. pap. 2.50 (ISBN 0-87507-024-8). Cath Lib Assn.

Books I Have Loved. Bhagwan Shree Rajneesh. Ed. by Swami Devaraj Sambuddha & Swami Devageet Mahasattva. LC 85-43070. (Biography Ser.). 288p. (Orig.). 1985. pap. 3.95 (ISBN 0-88050-716-0). Chidvilas Found.

Books of American Negro Spirituals, 2 vols. in one. Ed. by James Weldon Johnson & J. R. Johnson. LC 77-23414. 1977. Repr. of 1926 ed. text ed. 11.95 (ISBN 0-306-80074-8). Da Capo.

Books of Amos, Hosea, Micah. Ed. by Henry McKeating. (Cambridge Bible Commentary on the New English Bible, Old Testament Ser.). (Illus.). 1971. 22.95 (ISBN 0-521-08133-5); pap. 10.95 (ISBN 0-521-09647-2). Cambridge U Pr.

Books of Chronicles. Robert E. Black. (Bible Study Textbook Ser.). (Illus.). 1973. College Pr Pub.

Books of Elijah, Pts. 1 & 2. Michael E. Stone & John Strugnell. LC 79-15153. (Pseudepigrapha Ser.: No. 8). 1979. 13.50 (ISBN 0-89130-315-4, 060218); pap. 8.95 o.s. (ISBN 0-89130-316-2). Scholars Pr GA.

Books of Ezra & Nehemiah. Walter D. Adeney. 1980. 13.00 (ISBN 0-86524-050-7, 7004). Klock & Klock.

Books of Ezra & Nehemiah. R. J. Coggins. LC 75-26278. (Cambridge Bible Commentary on the New English Bible, Old Testament Ser.). (Illus.). 200p. 1976. 22.95 (ISBN 0-521-08648-5); pap. 9.95x (ISBN 0-521-09759-2). Cambridge U Pr.

Books of Ezra & Nehemiah. F. Charles Fensham. (New International Commentary on the Old Testament Ser.). 288p. 1983. 14.95 (ISBN 0-8028-2362-9). Eerdmans.

Books of Faith & Power. facs. ed. John T. McNeill. LC 75-134112. (Essay Index Reprint Ser). 1947. 18.00 (ISBN 0-8369-1996-3). Ayer Co Pubs.

Books of Haggai & Malachi. Pieter A. Verhoef. Ed. by R. K. Harrison. (New International Commentary on the Old Testament Ser.). 384p. 1987. 21.95 (ISBN 0-8028-2376-9). Eerdmans.

Books of Joel, Obadiah, Jonah, Naham, Habakkuk & Zehaniah. John D. Watts. LC 74-80355. (Cambridge Bible Commentary on the New English Bible, Old Testament Ser.). 300p. 1975. 22.95 (ISBN 0-521-20505-0); pap. 10.95 (ISBN 0-521-09870-X). Cambridge U Pr.

Books of Judith & Esther. George T. Montague. (Pamphlet Bible Ser.: Vol. 21). (Orig.). 1973. pap. 1.00 (ISBN 0-8091-5173-1). Paulist Pr.

Books of Kiu-Te in the Tibetan Buddhist Tantras. David Reigle. LC 83-60416. (Secret Doctrine Reference Ser.). (Illus.). 80p. (Orig.). 1983. pap. 5.00 (ISBN 0-913510-49-1). Wizards.

Books of Light. Robert R. Leichtman & Carl Japikse. (Illus.). 160p. (Orig.). 1986. pap. 3.95 (ISBN 0-89804-049-3). Ariel OH.

Books of Ruth & Tobit. George T. Montague. (Pamphlet Bible Ser.: Vol. 20). (Orig.). 1974. pap. 1.00 (ISBN 0-8091-5172-3). Paulist Pr.

Books of the New Testament. Julianne Booth. (Arch Book Supplement Ser.). 1981. pap. 0.99 (ISBN 0-570-06150-4, 59-1305). Concordia.

Books of the Pilgrims. Lawrence D. Geller & Peter J. Gomes. LC 74-30056. (Reference Library of the Humanities: No. 13). (Illus.). 100p. 1975. lib. bdg. 25.00 (ISBN 0-8240-1065-5). Garland Pub.

Books on Buddhism. 1986. pap. 4.95 (ISBN 0-317-46501-5). Dharma Pub.

Books That Bring Life, Vol. II. Eugene Brice. (Orig.). 1987. pap. price not set (ISBN 0-937462-05-5). Net Pr.

Books to Learn & Live by, 5 bks. Mildred Pfrimmer. Incl. Bk. 1. The ABC's of Creation; Bk. 2. The ABC's of the Flood; Bk. 3. The Aardvark in the Art; Bk. 4. Elephant in Eden; Bk. 5. The Tale of the Whale. (Little Talkers Ser.). 1977. Set. 17.50 (ISBN 0-685-80546-8). Triumph Pub.

Border Regions of Faith: An Anthology of Religion & Social Change. Ed. by Kenneth Aman. LC 86-23551. 520p. (Orig.). 1987. pap. 23.95 (ISBN 0-88344-415-1). Orbis Bks.

Borderland: A Casebook of True Supernatural Stories. W. T. Stead. LC 69-16361. 358p. 1970. 5.95 (ISBN 0-8216-0058-3). Univ Bks.

Bored Again Christian. Jere Patzer. (Quest Ser.). 16p. 1983. pap. 1.25 (ISBN 0-8163-0521-8). Pacific Pr Pub Assn.

Born after Midnight. Aiden W. Tozer. pap. 4.45 (ISBN 0-87509-258-6); pap. 3.45 mass market (ISBN 0-87509-167-9). Chr Pubns.

Born Again. Charles Colson. (Illus.). 352p. 1977. Movie ed. pap. 3.95 (ISBN 0-8007-8290-9, Spire Bks); (Spire Bks). Revell.

Born Again... & Again & Again: How Reincarnation Occurs, Why & What It Means to You. John Van Auken. (Illus.). 144p. 1984. 12.95 (ISBN 0-917483-00-6). Innervision.

Born Again & Again: How Reincarnation Occurs, Why & What It Means to You! John Van Auken. LC 84-223300. (Illus.). 144p. (Orig.). 1985. pap. 8.95 (ISBN 0-917483-02-2). Innervision.

Born Again & Growing. J. Kenneth Grider. 118p. 1982. pap. 3.50 (ISBN 0-8341-0758-9). Beacon Hill.

Born-Again Catholic. Albert Boudreau. (Illus., Orig.). 1979. pap. 4.95 (ISBN 0-914544-26-8). Living Flame Pr.

Born-Again Politics: The New Christian Right in America. Robert Zwier. (Illus.). 132p. 1982. pap. 4.95 (ISBN 0-87784-828-9). Inter-Varsity.

Born Again Radical. Don Benedict. LC 82-9100. 240p. (Orig.). 1982. pap. 7.95 (ISBN 0-8298-0371-8). Pilgrim NY.

Born Again Skeptic's Guide to the Bible. Ruth H. Green. 1979. 9.00. Freedom Rel Found.

Born Again, What Do You Mean? Charles Hunter. 1982. pap. 0.75 (ISBN 0-917726-48-0). Hunter Bks.

Born Againism: Perspectives on a Movement. Eric W. Gritsch. LC 81-70595. 112p. 1982. pap. 6.95 (ISBN 0-8006-1625-1, 1-1625). Fortress.

Born Amish. Barbara Y. Hall. (Illus.). 100p. (Orig.). 1980. pap. 6.95 (ISBN 0-9606154-0-7). Jacbar Pubns.

Born Crucified. L. E. Maxwell. (Moody Classic Ser.). 1984. pap. 3.95 (ISBN 0-8024-0038-8). Moody.

Born for Battle. 3rd ed. R. Arthur Mathews. 1980. pap. 2.95 (ISBN 0-85363-143-3). OMF Bks.

Born in the Spirit of Jesus. Richard Reichert. 84p. (Orig.). 1980. pap. text ed. 3.20 (ISBN 0-697-01725-7); tchr's manual 4.00 (ISBN 0-697-01726-5); spirit masters 10.95. Wm C Brown.

Born in the Spirit of Jesus. Richard Reichert. (YA) 1985. pap. text ed. 4.50 (ISBN 0-697-02120-3); tchr's. ed. 5.50 (ISBN 0-697-02121-1); spirit masters 10.95 (ISBN 0-697-01727-3). Wm C Brown.

Born in Tibet. Chogyam Trungpa. LC 85-8174. (Illus.). 280p. 1985. pap. 9.95 (ISBN 0-87773-333-3, 74219-2). Shambhala Pubns.

Born in Time: The Christmas Story. Mildred Cram. (Illus.). 26p. (Orig.). 1972. pap. 2.50 (ISBN 0-913270-10-5). Sunstone Pr.

Born of a Glorious Thunder: Real Life Accounts of Foreign Christian Work. Kenneth Oosterhouse et al. Tr. by Helen Kortenhoeven. 304p. (Orig.). 1986. pap. 6.95. West Indies Pub.

Born of the Spirit. Tania E. Bishop. LC 68-13394. 1968. 7.95 (ISBN 0-8022-0134-2). Philos Lib.

Born Only Once: The Miracle of Affirmation. Conrad W. Baars. 1977. pap. 4.00 (ISBN 0-8199-0700-6). Franciscan Herald.

Born to Survive, Nineteen Thirty-Six to Nineteen Forty-Six. George G. Whitney. (Illus.). 200p. 1982. pap. 12.95 (ISBN 0-916224-72-4). Banyan Bks.

Born Today, Born Yesterday: Reincarnation. Gwen Risedorf. LC 77-21406. (Myth, Magic & Superstition). (Illus.). 1977. PLB 14.65 (ISBN 0-8172-1045-8). Raintree Pubs.

Born with a Mission. Carl Adams & Dolly McElhaney. Ed. by Mary H. Wallace. (Illus.). 240p. 1981. pap. 5.95 (ISBN 0-912315-15-6). Word Aflame.

Borneo Journey into Death: Berawan Eschatology from Its Rituals. Peter Metcalf. LC 82-8460. (Symbol & Culture Ser.). (Illus.). 304p. 1982. 26.00x (ISBN 0-8122-7849-6). U of Pa Pr.

Bosnian Church: A Study of the Bosnian Church & Its Place in State & Society from the 13th to 15th Centuries. John V. Fine. (East European Monographs: No. 10). 447p. 1975. 30.00x (ISBN 0-914710-03-6). East Eur Quarterly.

Bosquejos Biblicos, Tomo III. Daniel Campderros. 96p. 1986. pap. 2.50 (ISBN 0-311-43033-3). Casa Bautista.

Bosquejos Biblicos Tomo I: Antiguo Testamento. Daniel Campderros. 96p. 1984. pap. 2.50 (ISBN 0-311-43025-2). Casa Bautista.

Bosquejos Biblicos Tomo II. Daniel Campderros. 96p. 1985. pap. 2.50 (ISBN 0-311-43026-0). Casa Bautista.

Bosquejos de Doctrina Fundamental. Ernesto Trenchard. (Span.). 144p. 1972. pap. 3.95 (ISBN 0-8254-1725-2). Kregel.

Bosquejos de Sermones Selectos. Ernesto Barocio. 144p. 1986. pap. 5.95 (ISBN 0-311-43039-2). Casa Bautista.

Bosquejos Utiles para Laicos. Roy B. Lyon. (Span., Illus.). 96p. 1985. pap. 1.95 (ISBN 0-311-42401-5). Casa Bautista.

Bossuet & Vieira. Mary C. Gotaas. LC 75-128929. (Catholic Univ. of American Studies in Romance Lang. & Lit. Ser.: No. 46). Repr. of 1953 ed. 21.00 (ISBN 0-404-50346-2). AMS Pr.

Boston Handel & Haydn Society Collection of Church Music. Ed. by Lowell Mason. LC 77-171078. (Earlier American Music Ser.: Vol. 15). 324p. 1973. Repr. of 1822 ed. lib. bdg. 37.50 (ISBN 0-306-77315-5). Da Capo.

Boston Personalist Tradition in Philosophy, Social Ethics, & Theology. Ed. by Paul Deats & Carol S. Robb. (Illus.). xiv, 295p. 1986. text ed. 28.95 (ISBN 0-86554-177-9, MUP-H167). Mercer Univ Pr.

Boston Priests, Eighteen Forty-Eight to Nineteen Ten: A Study in Social & Intellectual Change. Donna Merwick. LC 72-79309. 288p. 1973. 17.50x (ISBN 0-674-07975-2). Harvard U Pr.

Boston Revival, Eighteen Forty-Two: A Brief History of the Evangelical Churches of Boston, Together with a More Particular Account of the Revival of 1842. Martin Moore. (Revival Library). (Illus.). 148p. 1980. Repr. of 1842 ed. lib. bdg. 9.95. R O Roberts.

Boston Studies in the Philosophy of Science, Vol. 26: The Cultural Context of Medieval Learning, Proceedings. International Colloquium on Philosophy, Science, & Theology in the Middle Ages, 1st, Boston, Sept. 1973. Ed. by J. E. Murdoch & E. D. Sylla. LC 75-24997. (Synthese Library: No. 76). 566p. 1975. 68.50 (ISBN 90-277-0560-7, Pub. by Reidel Holland); pap. 39.50 (ISBN 90-277-0587-9). Kluwer Academic.

Bottom Line Catechism for Contemporary Catholics. Andrew Greeley. 304p. 1982. pap. 10.95 (ISBN 0-88347-135-3). Thomas More.

Bought & Paid For. Don Larson & Joanie Larson. 1977. 5.95 (ISBN 0-89221-038-9); pap. 2.95 (ISBN 0-89221-051-6). New Leaf.

Boulevard des Miseres: The Story of Transit Camp Westerbork. Jacob Boas. LC 85-1435. (Illus.). 174p. 1985. lib. bdg. 22.50 (ISBN 0-208-01977-4, Archon Bks). Shoe String.

Bouncing Back. Brent D. Earles. (Life Enrichment Ser.). 144p. Date not set. pap. 5.95 (ISBN 0-8010-3435-3). Baker Bk.

Bouncing Back: Finding Acceptance in the Face of Rejection. William Coleman. (Orig.). 1985. pap. 4.95 (ISBN 0-89081-455-4). Harvest Hse.

Bound for Joy. Stuart Briscoe. LC 84-17778. (Bible Commentary for Laymen Ser.). 192p. 1984. pap. 3.95 (ISBN 0-8307-1004-3, S383107). Regal.

Bound to Be Free. Ed. by James R. Hawkinson. 150p. 1975. 6.95 (ISBN 0-910452-40-7); pap. 5.45 (ISBN 0-910452-25-3). Covenant.

Boundaries of Natural Science. Rudolf Steiner. Tr. by Frederick Amrine from Ger. LC 83-9943. 144p. 1983. 14.95 (ISBN 0-88010-018-4). Anthroposophic.

Bourges Cathedral: The West Portals. Tania Bayard. LC 75-23780. (Outstanding Dissertations in the Fine Arts Ser. - Medieval). (Illus.). 1976. lib. bdg. 55.00 (ISBN 0-8240-1977-6). Garland Pub.

Bowl Judgments. Date not set. pap. 0.95 (ISBN 0-937408-11-5). GMI Pubns Inc.

Bowl of Saki. rev., 4th ed. Inayat Khan. LC 78-65653. 128p. (Orig.). 1979. pap. 4.95 (ISBN 0-900217-12-X, Pub. by Sufi Pub Co England). Hunter Hse.

Bowl of Saki Commentary. Samuel L. Lewis & Hazrat I. Khan. Ed. by Moineddin Jablonski & Saadi Klotz. 180p. (Orig.). 1981. pap. 18.00 (ISBN 0-915424-08-8). Sufi Islamia-Prophecy.

Box 44, Monrovia. Nona Freeman. Ed. by Mary H. Wallace. (Illus.). 224p. 1983. pap. 5.95 (ISBN 0-912315-09-1). Word Aflame.

Boy in the Striped Coat. Ed. by Stephanie Caffrey & Timothy Kenslea. (Rainbow Books). 1978. pap. 1.00 (ISBN 0-8192-1234-2). Morehouse.

Boy Named Jesus. Jean H. Richards. LC 77-71036. (Illus.). 1978. 3.95 (ISBN 0-8054-4415-7, 4244-15); film & cassette 19.00 (4436-38). Broadman.

Boy Who Gave His Lunch Away. Dave Hill. (Arch Bks: Set 4). 1967. laminated bdg. 0.99 (59-1138). Concordia.

Boy Who Ran Away. Irene Elmer & Mathews. LC 63-23143. (Arch Bks: Set 1). (Illus.). 1964. laminated bdg. 0.99 (ISBN 0-570-06001-X, 59-1104). Concordia.

Boy Who Saved His Family. Alyce Bergey & Betty Wind. (Arch Bks: Set 3). 1966. laminated cover 0.99 (ISBN 0-570-06017-6, 59-1126). Concordia.

Boy Who Wanted to Be a Missionary. Uta O. Ross. (Illus.). 48p. (Orig.). 1984. pap. 11.95 (ISBN 0-687-03910-X). Abingdon.

Boy with a Mission. Daughters of St. Paul. 1967. 3.00 (ISBN 0-8198-0229-8). Dghtrs St Paul.

Boy with a Sling. Mary P. Warren & Mathews. LC 65-15143. (Arch Bks: Set 2). 1965. pap. 0.99 (ISBN 0-570-06012-5, 59-1116). Concordia.

Boyd's Bible Dictionary. James P. Boyd. Orig. Title: Vest Pocket Bible Dictionary, Orig. pap. 3.75 (ISBN 0-87981-087-4). Holman Bible Pub.

Boyd's Bible Handbook. Robert T. Boyd. LC 82-81088. 800p. 1983. 26.95 (ISBN 0-89081-352-3). Harvest Hse.

Boyhood of Pope John XXIII. Anne McGravie. (Stories about Christian Heroes Ser.). (Illus.). 1979. pap. 1.95 (ISBN 0-03-049446-X, HarpR). Har-Row.

Boyhood of Ranald Bannerman. George MacDonald. Ed. by Dan Hamilton. 168p. 1987. pap. 3.95 (ISBN 0-89693-748-8). Victor Bks.

Boys Who Became Prophets. Linda C. Hardy. LC 82-2373. (Illus.). 72p. 1982. 6.95 (ISBN 0-87747-900-3). Deseret Bk.

Bradlaugh Case: Atheism, Sex, & Politics among the Late Victorians. Walter L. Arnstein. LC 83-6814. (Illus.). 384p. 1984. text ed. 30.00x; pap. text ed. 13.50x (ISBN 0-8262-0417-1). U of Mo Pr.

Bradshaw's Life of St. Werburge of Chester. H. Bradshaw. Ed. by C. Horstmann. (EETS, OS Ser.: No. 88). Repr. of 1887 ed. 20.00 (ISBN 0-527-00085-X). Kraus Repr.

Brahamism in Southeast Asia. D. Daweewarn. 322p. 1982. text ed. 40.00x (ISBN 0-391-02581-3, Pub. by Sterling India). Humanities.

Brahma-Knowledge, Philosophy of Vedanta. L. D. Barnett. 59.95 (ISBN 0-87968-780-0). Gordon Pr.

Brahma Net Sutra, Vol. II Commentary by Hui Seng, Elder Master. Tr. by Buddhist Text Translation Society. (Illus.). 210p. (Orig.). 1982. pap. 10.00 (ISBN 0-917512-88-X). Buddhist Text.

Brahma Net Sutra, Vol. 1. Commentary by Hui Seng. Tr. by Buddhist Text Translation Society. (Illus.). 312p. (Orig., Bilingual Text). 1981. pap. 10.00 (ISBN 0-917512-79-0). Buddhist Text.

Brahma Net Sutra, text only. Tr. by Buddhist Text Translation Society. 70p. (Orig.). 1982. pap. 5.00 (ISBN 0-917512-56-1). Buddhist Text.

Brahma Purana. (Ancient India Tradition & Mythology Ser.: Vol. 34). 241p. 1985. 18.50 (ISBN 0-317-46524-4, Pub. by Motilal Banarsidass India). Orient Bk Dist.

Brahma Purana, Pt. I. Ed. by J. L. Shastri. (Ancient Tradition & Mythology Ser.: Vol. 33). 240p. 1985. 18.50 (ISBN 81-208-0003-6, Pub. by Motilal Banarsidass India). Orient Bk Dist.

Brahma-Sutra Bhasya of Sankaracarya. Shankara. Tr. by Swami Gambhirananda. (Sanskrit & Eng.). 20.00 (ISBN 0-87481-066-3). Vedanta Pr.

Brahma Sutra Sri Bhasya. Swami Vireshwarananda. 1979. 10.00 (ISBN 0-87481-189-9). Vedanta Pr.

Brahma Sutra: The Philosophy of Spiritual Life. Badarayana. Tr. by S. Radhakrishnan. LC 68-21330. 1968. Repr. of 1960 ed. lib. bdg. 37.25x (ISBN 0-8371-0291-X, BABS). Greenwood.

Brahma Sutras. 2nd ed. Swami Sivanada. 1977. pap. 28.00 (ISBN 0-89684-181-2, Pub. by Motilal Banarsidass India). Orient Bk Dist.

Brahma-Sutras (Vedanta-Sutras) Badarayana. Tr. by Swami Vireswarananda. (Sanskrit & Eng.). 11.95 (ISBN 0-87481-076-0). Vedanta Pr.

Brahmanic Ritual Traditions. Baidyanath Saraswati. Ed. by S. C. Malik. LC 78-901135. (Illus.). 1977. 15.00 (ISBN 0-89684-478-1). Orient Bk Dist.

Brahmanical Gods in Burma: A Chapter of Indian Art & Iconography. Nihar-Ranjan Ray. LC 77-87020. Repr. of 1932 ed. 16.50 (ISBN 0-404-16852-3). AMS Pr.

Brahmans, Theists & Muslims of India. J. C. Oman. 1973. 24.00 (ISBN 0-89684-371-8). Orient Bk Dist.

Brahmans, Theists & Muslims of India. John C. Oman. LC 76-179231. (Illus.). Repr. of 1907 ed. 31.50 (ISBN 0-404-54858-X). AMS Pr.

Brahmin Priest of Tamil Nadu. K. Subramaniam. LC 74-13072. 183p. 1975. 19.95x (ISBN 0-470-83535-4). Halsted Pr.

Brahmins Through the Ages. R. N. Sharma. 1977. 18.00x (ISBN 0-686-22659-3). Intl Bk Dist.

Braided Streams: Esther & a Woman's Way of Growing. Marjory Z. Bankson. LC 85-50203. (Illus.). 184p. (Orig.). 1985. pap. 8.95 (ISBN 0-931055-05-9). LuraMedia.

Braided Streams: Leader's Guide. Pat Backman & Lura J. Geiger. 128p. (Orig.). 1986. pap. 12.95 spiral bound (ISBN 0-931055-09-1). LuraMedia.

Brain, the Soul, God. Judy Ball & John Danich. 174p. 1986. pap. 6.95 (ISBN 0-88144-064-7). Christian Pub.

Brainwashing & the Cults. Paul A. Verdier. 3.00 (ISBN 0-87980-357-6). Borden.

Bran the Blessed in Arthurian Romance. Helaine Newstead. LC 40-4360. Repr. of 1939 ed. 14.50 (ISBN 0-404-04687-8). AMS Pr.

Brandeis on Zionism. Louis D. Brandeis. LC 75-6425. (Rise of Jewish Nationalism & the Middle East Ser.). 156p. 1975. Repr. of 1942 ed. 17.60 (ISBN 0-88355-312-0). Hyperion Conn.

Brass Instruments in Church Services. James Ode. 1970. pap. 3.00 (ISBN 0-8066-1025-5, 11-9085). Augsburg.

Brave New People: Ethical Issues at the Commencement of Life. D. Gareth Jones. LC 85-4582. 232p. 1985. pap. 8.95 (ISBN 0-8028-0070-X). Eerdmans.

Brave New World of the Enlightenment. Louis I. Bredvold. LC 61-10987. pap. 43.00 (ISBN 0-317-08088-1, 2051585). Bks Demand UMI.

Brazil, Journey in the Light of the Eucharist. Pope John Paul II. 1980. 8.00 (ISBN 0-8198-1102-5); pap. 7.00 (ISBN 0-8198-1103-3). Dghtrs St Paul.

Brazilian Mystic: Life & Miracles of Antonio Conselheiro. R. B. Graham. 1976. lib. bdg. 59.95 (ISBN 0-87968-786-X). Gordon Pr.

Breaching the Wall: Of Separation Between Church & State, Excessive Entanglement & the IRS. pap. 4.00 (ISBN 0-915598-39-6). Church of Scient Info.

Bread & Justice: Toward a New International Economic Order. James B. McGinnis. LC 79-90224. 372p. 1979. tchrs. ed. 6.95 (ISBN 0-8091-9536-4). Paulist Pr.

Bread & the Liturgy: The Symbolism of Early Christian & Byzantine Bread Stamps. George Galavaris. LC 75-98120. pap. 63.30 (ISBN 0-317-07859-3, 2015361). Bks Demand UMI.

Bread & the Wine, No. Sixteen. Denise Ahern. (Arch Bk.). (Illus.). 1979. 0.99 (ISBN 0-570-06127-X, 59-1245). Concordia.

Bread Broken & Shared. Paul Bernier. LC 81-67539. 144p. 1981. pap. 3.95 (ISBN 0-87793-232-8). Ave Maria.

Bread Cast upon the Waters. Jeanna Merritt. 25p. (Orig.). 1985. pap. 1.25 (ISBN 0-89265-092-3). Randall Hse.

Bread for Each Day. large print ed. M. R. DeHaan & H. G. Bosch. 1979. Kivar 10.95 (ISBN 0-310-23267-8, 1257L); 13.95 (ISBN 0-310-23260-0, 9510). Zondervan.

Bread for the Eating. Kelly B. Kelly. 121p. (Orig.). 1982. pap. 3.50 (ISBN 0-914544-39-X). Living Flame Pr.

Bread for the Journey: Resources for Worship Based on the New Ecumenical Lectionary. Ruth C. Duck. LC 81-5046. 96p. 1981. pap. 4.95 (ISBN 0-8298-0423-4). Pilgrim NY.

Bread for the World. rev. ed. Arthur Simon. LC 84-238017. 219p. 1985. pap. 4.95 (ISBN 0-8091-2670-2). Paulist Pr.

Bread from My Oven. Marjorie Parker. (Quiet Time Bks). 128p. 1972. pap. 3.50 (ISBN 0-8024-0910-5). Moody.

Bread in a Barren Land. James P. Wesberry. LC 81-8668. 1982. pap. 4.95 (ISBN 0-8054-5103-X). Broadman.

Bread in the Wilderness. Thomas Merton. LC 82-23864. 180p. 1986. pap. 5.95 (ISBN 0-8006-1912-9, 1-1912). Fortress.

Bread, Meat & Raisins after the Dance. James A. Gittings. LC 77-83883. 1977. 10.00 (ISBN 0-89430-006-7). Palos Verdes.

Bread Not Stone: The Challenge of Feminist Biblical Interpretation. Elisabeth S. Fiorenza. LC 84-14669. 208p. 1986. pap. 8.95 (ISBN 0-8070-1103-7, BP 717). Beacon Pr.

Bread Not Stone: The Challenge of Feminist Biblical Interpretation. Elizabeth S. Fiorenza. LC 84-14669. 207p. 1985. 17.95 (ISBN 0-8070-1100-2). Beacon Pr.

Bread of Life. David E. Rosage. (Orig.). 1979. pap. 2.50 (ISBN 0-89283-067-0). Servant.

Bread of Life. Emma Smiley. 1972. pap. 1.00 (ISBN 0-87516-157-X). De Vorss.

Break down the Walls: Christian Cry for Racial Justice. Johannes Verkuyl. Ed. by Lewis B. Smedes. LC 72-93620. pap. 41.50 (ISBN 0-317-07869-0, 2012924). Bks Demand UMI.

Break Forth into Joy. Myrna L. Etheridge. 179p. (Orig.). 1985. pap. 5.00x (ISBN 0-937417-01-7). Etheridge Minist.

Breakfast of Champions. Levick. 1986. pap. 5.95 (ISBN 0-89225-284-7). Gospel Advocate.

Breaking Boundaries: Male-Female Friendship in Early Christian Communities. Rosemary Rader. (Theological Inquiries Ser.). 144p. 1983. pap. 6.95 (ISBN 0-8091-2506-4). Paulist Pr.

Breaking Bread: The Catholic Worker & the Origin of Catholic Radicalism in America. Mel Piehl. LC 82-10327. 233p. 1982. 24.95 (ISBN 0-87722-257-6). Temple U Pr.

Breaking Bread: The Catholic Worker & the Origin of Catholic Radicalism in America. Mel Piehl. 314p. 1984. pap. 12.95 (ISBN 0-87722-353-X). Temple U Pr.

Breaking Bread: The Table Talk of Jesus. M. Basil Pennington. LC 85-51008. 160p. 1986. 10.95 (ISBN 0-86683-489-3, HarpR). Har-Row.

Breaking Faith: The Sandinista Revolution & Its Impact on Freedom & the Christian Faith in Nicaragua. Humberto Belli. LC 85-70475. 288p. 1985. pap. 8.95 (ISBN 0-89107-359-0, Crossway Bks). Good News.

Breaking from the K. G. B. Maurice Shainberg. 1986. 15.95 (ISBN 0-933503-54-7). Shapolsky Pubs.

Breaking into Bible Games. Phyllis Hand. (Helping Hand Ser.). 48p. (YA) 1984. wkbk. 4.95 (ISBN 0-317-43001-7). Good Apple.

Breaking of Image: The Sociology of Christian Theory & Practice. David Martin. 1980. 26.00 (ISBN 0-312-09522-8). St Martin.

Breaking Silence: A Family Grows with Deafness. Ferne P. Glick & Donald R. Pellman. LC 82-6067. 208p. (Orig.). 1982. pap. 6.95 (ISBN 0-8361-3300-5). Herald Pr.

Breaking Silence Before the Lord. E. Lee Phillips. (Pulpit Library). 160p. 1986. pap. 5.95 (ISBN 0-8010-7093-7). Baker Bk.

Breaking the Devil's Hold. 1982. 1.25 (ISBN 0-89858-032-3). Fill the Gap.

Breaking up. Wayne Judd. (Uplook Ser.). 1978. pap. 0.99 (ISBN 0-8163-0194-8, 12466). Pacific Pr Pub Assn.

Breakthrough: Insights of the Great Religious Discoverers. Clifford G. Hospital. LC 85-5135. 208p. (Orig.). 1985. pap. 9.95 (ISBN 0-88344-206-X). Orbis Bks.

Breakthrough: Meister Eckhart's Creation Spirituality. Meister Eckhart. LC 80-909. 600p. 1980. pap. 10.95 (ISBN 0-385-17034-3, Im). Doubleday.

Breakthrough No. 1: Christian Assurances. Kent Fishel & Joel Deselm. 1986. pap. 2.95 (ISBN 0-310-45981-8, 12629P). Zondervan.

Breakthrough No. 2: Christian Growth. Kent Fishel & Joel Deselm. 1986. pap. 2.95 (ISBN 0-310-45971-0, 12628P). Zondervan.

Breakthrough No. 3: Christian Living. Kent Fishel & Joel Deselm. 1986. pap. 2.95 (ISBN 0-310-45941-9, 12627P). Zondervan.

Breakthrough to Creativity. Shafica Karagulla. 12.95 (ISBN 0-87516-034-4). De Vorss.

Breakthrough to Learning Gemorah. Zvi Zobin. 1987. pap. 3.95. Feldheim.

Breakthrough: Women in Religion. Betsy Smith. LC 78-3016. (Breakthrough Ser.). 1978. 7.95 (ISBN 0-8027-6286-7). Walker & Co.

Breakway: Twenty-Eight Steps to a More Reflective Life. Mark Link. LC 67553. 144p. 1980. pap. 3.25 (ISBN 0-89505-050-1). Argus Comm.

Breastplate of Faith & Love. Facs. ed. John Preston. 241p. 1979. Repr. of 1630 ed. 22.95 (ISBN 0-85151-289-5). Banner of Truth.

Breath of Life: Discovering Your Breath Prayer. Ron Delbene & Herb Montgomery. 108p. (Orig.). 1981. pap. 3.95 (ISBN 0-86683-639-X, HarpR). Har-Row.

Breath of Love. Michel Quoist. 167p. (Orig.). 1987. pap. 8.95 (ISBN 0-8245-0801-7). Crossroad NY.

Breath of the Invisible. John Redtail Freesoul. LC 86-40124. (Illus.). 226p. (Orig.). 1986. pap. 6.95 (ISBN 0-8356-0611-2). Theos Pub Hse.

Breath of the Mystic. George Maloney. 8.95 (ISBN 0-87193-058-7). Dimension Bks.

Breath, Sleep, the Heart, & Life: The Revolutionary Health Yoga of Pundit Acharya. Pundit Acharya. LC 74-24306. 190p. 1975. pap. 7.95 (ISBN 0-913922-09-9). Dawn Horse Pr.

Brecht & the Bible: A Study of Religious Nihilism & Human Weakness in Brecht's Plays. G. Ronald Murphy. LC 80-20207. (Studies in Germanic Languages & Literatures: No. 96). xi, 107p. 12.50x (ISBN 0-8078-8096-5). U of NC Pr.

Brethern, I Would Not Have You Ignorant. Henry E. Griffin, Jr. 64p. (Orig.). 1986. pap. 2.25 (ISBN 0-934942-63-3, 2262). White Wing Pub.

Brethren: Growth in Life & Thought. Ed. by F. T. Burkey. 1975. pap. 3.50x (ISBN 0-934970-00-9). Brethren Ohio.

Brethren in Colonial America. Donald F. Durnbaugh. (Illus.). 659p. (YA) 1967. 15.95 (ISBN 0-87178-110-7). Brethren.

Brethren in Industrial America. Roger E. Sappington. 512p. 1985. 24.95 (ISBN 0-87178-111-5). Brethren.

Brethren in the New Nation. Roger Sappington. (Illus.). 1976. 13.95 (ISBN 0-87178-113-1). Brethren.

Breve Historia de la Iglesia. Howard F. Vos. Orig. Title: Introduction to Church History. (Span.). 160p. 1987. pap. 3.95 (ISBN 0-8254-1824-0). Kregel.

Breve Historia de los Bautistas Hasta 1900. Enrique C. Vedder. Tr. by Teofilo Barocio. 272p. 1985. Repr. of 1978 ed. 4.50 (ISBN 0-311-15039-X). Casa Bautista.

Breviarium Romanum a Francisco Cardinali: Quignonio Editum. Legg J. Wickham. 262p. Repr. of 1888 ed. text ed. 49.68x (ISBN 0-576-99727-7, Pub. by Gregg Intl Pubs England). Gregg Intl.

Breviary Lives of the Saints, Vol. 1 Sept.- Jan., Vol. 2 Feb.-May. Frederick J. Murphy. (Lat., Illus., Orig.). 1965. Vol. 1. pap. 2.50 (ISBN 0-8198-0012-0); Vol. 2. 3.50 (ISBN 0-8198-0013-9). Dghtrs St Paul.

Breviary Lives of the Saints: A Translation into English. Frederick Murphy. 1979. pap. 1.00 (ISBN 0-8198-1108-4). Dghtrs St Paul.

Brhadaranyaka Upanisad. Tr. by P. Lal from Sanskrit. (Saffronbird Bk.). (Eng.). 117p. 1975. pap. text ed. 6.75 (ISBN 0-88253-828-4). Ind-US Inc.

Brhadaranyaka Upanishad. 2nd ed. Tr. by Swami Jagadiswarananda. (Sanskrit & Eng). 7.95 (ISBN 0-87481-415-4). Vedanta Pr.

Brhadaranyaka Upanishad. Tr. by Swami Madhavananda. (Sanskrit & Eng.). 1965. 14.00 (ISBN 0-87481-063-9). Vedanta Pr.

Brick Temples of Bengal: From the Archives of David McCutchion. Ed. by George Michell. LC 82-3872. (Illus.). 450p. 1983. 90.00x (ISBN 0-691-04010-9). Princeton U Pr.

Bride-Bush, or a Wedding Sermon. William Whately. LC 74-28893. (English Experience Ser.: No. 769). 1975. Repr. of 1617 ed. 5.00 (ISBN 90-221-0769-8). Walter J Johnson.

Bride of Christ. Paul Carus. 118p. 1908. 15.95 (ISBN 0-87548-218-X). Open Court.

Bride's Guide to a Christian Wedding. Francis A. Bowen. LC 78-73642. (Illus.). 1979. text ed. 2.95 (ISBN 0-9602830-0-5). F A Bowen.

Bridge Between the Testaments: Reappraisal of Judaism from the Exile to the Birth of Christianity. 3rd, rev. ed. Ed. by Donald E. Gowan. LC 86-9327. (Pittsburgh Theological Monographs: No. 14). 1986. text ed. 32.95 (ISBN 0-915138-88-3). Pickwick.

Bridge Between Universal Spirituality & the Physical Constitution of Man. 2nd ed. Rudolf Steiner. Tr. by Dorothy S. Osmond from Ger. 64p. (Orig.). 1979. pap. 3.95 (ISBN 0-910142-03-3). Anthroposophic.

Bridge Building. Rod Mitchell. 261p. (Orig.). 1981. pap. 21.95 (ISBN 0-85819-357-4, Pub. by JBCE). ANZ Religious Pubns.

Bridge of Dreams: The Story of Paramananda, a Modern Mystic. Sara A. Levinsky. LC 83-82698. (Illus.). 632p. (Orig.). 1984. pap. 12.95 (ISBN 0-89281-063-7, Lindisfarne Pr). Inner Tradit.

Bridge to a Better Life: An Introduction to New Thought. Lawrence Hinckley. 1978. pap. 2.25 (ISBN 0-87516-255-X). De Vorss.

Bridge to Heaven. Ruth E. Norman. 1969. 8.95 (ISBN 0-932642-10-1). Unarius Pubns.

Bridges of God. rev. ed. Donald McGavran. 1981. pap. 5.95 (ISBN 0-377-45071-5). Friend Pr.

Bridges to Islam: A Christian Perspective on Folk Islam. Phil Parshall. 120p. 1983. pap. 6.95 (ISBN 0-8010-7081-3). Baker Bk.

Bridging the Gap Between Ethical Theory & Conduct. Zalman F. Ury. 0.75 (ISBN 0-914131-07-9, I35). Torah Umesorah.

Brief & to the Point: Suggestions for Preachers. A. E. Dalton. 272p. 1973. Repr. of 1961 ed. 17.95 (ISBN 0-227-67419-7). Attic Pr.

Brief Bible Studies for Busy People. Frank L. Carroll. LC 85-3470. 144p. 1985. 13.95 (ISBN 0-13-081993-X); pap. 6.95 (ISBN 0-13-081985-9). P-H.

Brief Catechesis on Nature & Grace. Henri De Lubac. Tr. by Richard Arnandez from Fr. LC 83-82108. Tr. of Petite Catechese sur Nature et Grace. 308p. (Orig.). 1984. pap. 10.95 (ISBN 0-89870-035-3). Ignatius Pr.

Brief Catholic Dictionary for Young People. Daughters of St. Paul. 1977. pap. text ed. 1.00 (ISBN 0-8198-0389-8). Dghtrs St Paul.

Brief Counseling with Suicidal Persons. William L. Getz & David B. Allen. LC 80-8375. 288p. 1982. 29.00x (ISBN 0-669-04090-8). Lexington Bks.

Brief Fantasy History of a Himalayan. Thinley Norbu. LC 84-29754. (Orig.). Date not set. pap. 10.00 (ISBN 0-9607000-1-3). Jewel Pub Hse.

Brief History of Methodism in Texas. Homer S. Thrall. 304p. 1977. Repr. of 1889 ed. 9.95 (ISBN 0-87921-042-7). Attic Pr.

Brief History of the Church of Christ of Latter Day Saints. John Corrill. 48p. (Orig.). 1983. pap. 1.95 (ISBN 0-942284-05-4). Restoration Re.

Brief History of the Church of God Reformation Movement. John W. Smith. 1976. pap. 3.95 (ISBN 0-87162-188-6, D2350). Warner Pr.

Brief History of the Presbyterians: With a New Chapter by George Laird Hunt. 4th ed. Lefferts A. Loetscher. LC 83-21652. 224p. 1984. pap. 4.95 (ISBN 0-664-24622-2). Westminster.

Brief Life of Christ. L. Rumble. 54p. 1974. pap. 1.50 (ISBN 0-89555-096-2). TAN Bks Pubs.

Brief Review for Confirmation. Daughters of St. Paul. 1973. pap. 0.75 (ISBN 0-8198-0250-6). Dghtrs St Paul.

Brief Sketch of the Early History of the Catholic Church on the Island of New York. James R. Bayley. LC 77-359171. (Monograph Ser.: No. 29). 1973. Repr. of 1870 ed. 8.50x (ISBN 0-930060-09-1). US Cath Hist.

Brief Statement of Mennonite Doctrine. pap. 2.50 (ISBN 0-8361-1324-1). Herald Pr.

Brief Summary of the Ten Commandments. Daughters of St. Paul. 1976. pap. text ed. 1.75 (ISBN 0-8198-0386-3). Dghtrs St Paul.

Brief Survey of the Bible. Sam M. Wright. 1958. pap. 5.95 (ISBN 0-87213-971-9). Loizeaux.

Briefe & Moderate Answer to H. Burton. Peter Heylin. LC 76-57389. (English Experience Ser.: No. 806). 1977. Repr. of 1637 ed. lib. bdg. 22.00 (ISBN 90-221-0806-6). Walter J Johnson.

Briefe Apologie Against M. Sutcliffe. Thomas Cartwright. LC 78-25890. (English Experience Ser.: No. 237). 28p. 1970. Repr. of 1596 ed. 7.00 (ISBN 90-221-0237-8). Walter J Johnson.

Briefe Declaration for What Manner of Speciall Nusance Man May Have His Remedy by Assise. LC 76-38169. (English Experience Ser.: No. 446). 1972. Repr. of 1636 ed. 7.00 (ISBN 90-221-0446-X). Walter J Johnson.

Briefe des Heiligen Bonifatius. Saint Winfrid Bonifacius. pap. 23.00 (ISBN 0-384-05025-5). Johnson Repr.

Briefe Description of the Notorious Life of J. Lambe. John Lambe. LC 76-57394. (English Experience Ser.: No. 811). 1977. Repr. of 1628 ed. lib. bdg. 3.50 (ISBN 90-221-0811-2). Walter J Johnson.

Briefe Discourse of the Troubles Begonne at Franckford. William Whittinghame. LC 71-38228. (English Experience Ser.: No. 492). 210p. 1972. Repr. of 1574 ed. 13.00 (ISBN 90-221-0492-3). Walter J Johnson.

Briefe Relation of the Persecution Lately Made Against the Catholike Christians in Japonia, Taken Out of the Annuall Letters of the Soc. of Jesus. Tr. by William Wright. LC 75-26238. (English Experience Ser.: No. 159). 1969. Repr. of 1619 ed. 35.00 (ISBN 90-221-0159-2). Walter J Johnson.

Briefe Treatise Concerning the Burnynge of Bucer & Phagius at Cambridge. Martin Bucer. LC 76-57362. (English Experience Ser.: No. 780). 1977. Repr. of 1562 ed. lib. bdg. 14.00 (ISBN 90-221-0780-9). Walter J Johnson.

Brigham Young. Morris R. Werner. LC 75-351. (Radical Tradition in America Ser.). xvi, 478p. 1975. Repr. of 1925 ed. 32.50 (ISBN 0-88355-254-X). Hyperion Conn.

Brigham Young. Morris R. Werner. 1977. Repr. of 1925 ed. lib. bdg. 30.00 (ISBN 0-8492-2907-3). R West.

Brigham Young: The New York Years. Richard F. Palmer & Karl D. Butler. Ed. by Thomas G. Alexander & Howard A. Christy. (Charles Redd Monographs in Western History: No. 14). (Illus.). 106p. 1982. 9.95 (ISBN 0-941214-07-9, Dist. by Signature Bks). C Redd Ctr.

Brigham Young University: A House of Faith. Gary J. Bergera & Ronald Priddis. 513p. (Orig.). 1985. pap. 19.95 (ISBN 0-941214-34-6). Signature Bks.

Brigham's Destroying Angel. facsimile ed. Bill Hickman. LC 74-165642. (Select Bibliographies Reprint Ser). Repr. of 1904 ed. 18.00 (ISBN 0-8369-5951-5). Ayer Co Pubs.

Bright Blue. Lionel Blue. 96p. 1985. 11.95 (ISBN 0-312-09626-7). St Martin.

Bright Essence: Studies in Milton's Theology. William B. Hunter, Jr. et al. LC 74-161485. 1971. 14.95x (ISBN 0-87480-061-7). U of Utah Pr.

Bright Intervals: Prayers for Paschal People. James Bitney. 96p. 1982. pap. 5.95 (ISBN 0-86683-669-1, HarpR). Har-Row.

Bright Laughter-Warm Tears: Inspirational Thoughts for Mothers. Helen L. Marshall. 64p. 1985. pap. 3.95 (ISBN 0-8010-6195-4). Baker Bk.

Bright Legacy: Portraits of Ten Outstanding Christian Women. Ann Spangler. 196p. 1985. pap. 6.95 (ISBN 0-89283-278-9, Pub. by Vine Books). Servant.

Bright Legacy: Portraits of Ten Outstanding Christian Women. Ed. by Ann Spangler. 204p. 1983. 10.95 (ISBN 0-89283-167-7, Pub. by Vine Bks). Servant.

Bright-Shining Place. Cheryl P. Blackwood & Kathryn Slattery. (Epiphany Ser.). 240p. 1983. pap. 2.75 (ISBN 0-345-30698-8). Ballantine.

Bright Shootes of Everlastingnesse: The Seventeenth-Century Religious Lyric. Claude J. Summers & Ted-Larry Pebworth. LC 86-16132. 208p. 1987. text ed. 24.00 (ISBN 0-8262-0618-2, 83-36265). U of Mo Pr.

Bright Side of Depression. Jim Geddes. LC 85-17123. (Orig.). 1985. pap. 5.95 (ISBN 0-8054-5016-5). Broadman.

Bright Valley of Love. Edna Hong. LC 75-22723. 160p. 1985. pap. 3.95 (ISBN 0-8066-1700-4, 10-0911). Augsburg.

Brightness of His Presence: Theological Dissertation. William F. Myers. LC 82-90351. 64p. 1982. 6.95 (ISBN 0-87948-049-1). Beatty.

Brihadaranyaka Upanisad. Tr. by Srisa Chandra Vasu. LC 73-3802. (Sacred Books of the Hindus: No. 14). Repr. of 1916 ed. 47.50 (ISBN 0-404-57814-4). AMS Pr.

Brihadaranyaka Upanishad: With the Commentary of Shankaracharya. Tr. by Madhavananda. LC 83-45479. 1935. 78.50 (ISBN 0-404-20271-3, PK3521). AMS Pr.

Bring an Offering. John E. Eash. 1985. pap. 1.95 (ISBN 0-317-38498-8). Brethren.

Bring Forth Justice. Waldron Scott. LC 80-15992. 304p. 1980. pap. 11.95 (ISBN 0-8028-1848-X). Eerdmans.

Bring out the Best in Your Child. Patrick J. Jeske. 1987. pap. 4.95. Pelican.

Bringing Bible People to Life. Louise Ulmer. 1982. 2.95 (ISBN 0-89536-574-X, 0217). CSS of Ohio.

Bringing Forth in Hope: Being Creative in a Nuclear Age. Denise M. Priestley. 80p. (Orig.). 1983. pap. 4.95 (ISBN 0-8091-2551-X). Paulist Pr.

Bringing God's News to Neighbors. Carl Kromminga. 1976. pap. 4.50 (ISBN 0-87552-314-5). Presby & Reformed.

Bringing Heaven into Hell. Merlin R. Carothers. 120p. (Orig.). 1976. pap. 4.95 (ISBN 0-943026-10-5). Carothers.

Bringing up a Moral Child: A New Approach for Teaching Your Child to Be Kind, Just & Responsible. Michael Schulman & Eva Mekler. LC 84-18472. 1985. 19.95 (ISBN 0-201-16442-6); pap. 12.95 (ISBN 0-201-16443-4). Addison-Wesley.

Bringing up Children in the Christian Faith. John H. Westerhoff, 3rd. 108p. (Orig.). 1980. pap. 4.95 (ISBN 0-86683-627-6, HarpR). Har-Row.

Britain & the Vatican During the Second World War. Owen Chadwick. 350p. 1987. 39.50 (ISBN 0-521-32242-1). Cambridge U Pr.

Britain & Zion: The Fateful Entanglement. Frank Hardie & Irwin Herrman. 192p. 1980. 11.95 (ISBN 0-85640-229-X, Pub. by Blackstaff Pr). Longwood Pub Group.

Britannicarum Ecclesiarum Antiquitates. Ed. by J. Ussher. 788p. Date not set. Repr. of 1687 ed. text ed. 165.60x (ISBN 0-576-72233-2, Pub. by Gregg Intl Pubs England). Gregg Intl.

Britannien und Bibeltext. Hans Glunz. Repr. of 1930 ed. 16.00 (ISBN 0-384-18950-4). Johnson Repr.

British Baptists: An Original Anthology. H. Wheeler Robinson & Ernest A. Payne. Ed. by Edwin S. Gaustad. LC 79-52583. (Baptist Tradition Ser.). 1980. lib. bdg. 30.00x (ISBN 0-405-12450-3). Ayer Co Pubs.

British Catholic Press & the Eductional Controversy, 1847-1865. Mary G. Holland. Ed. by William H. McNeill & Peter Stanksy. (Modern European History Ser.). 400p. 1987. lib. bdg. 60.00 (ISBN 0-8240-7817-9). Garland Pub.

British Discovery of Hinduism in the 18th Century. Peter J. Marshall. 318p. 1970. text ed. 32.00x. Coronet Bks.

British Followers of Theodor Herzl: English Zionist Leaders, 1896-1904. Virginia H. Hein. Ed. by William H. McNeill & Peter Stansky. (Modern European History Ser.). 325p. 1987. lib. bdg. 50.00 (ISBN 0-8240-7815-2). Garland Pub.

British Foreign Policy, Nineteen Eighteen to Nineteen Forty-Five: A Guide to Research & Research Materials. Sidney Aster. LC 84-5339. 324p. 1984. 25.00 (ISBN 0-8420-2176-0). Scholarly Res Inc.

British Histography on the Sikh Power in the Punjab. G. Khurana. 159p. 1985. 35.00x (ISBN 0-7201-1767-4). Mansell.

British Historiography on the Sikh Power in Punjab. G. Khurana. 174p. 1985. 20.95x (ISBN 0-317-39858-X, Pub. by Allied Pubs India). Asia Bk Corp.

British Historiography on the Sikh Power in Punjab. G. Khurana. 1985. 14.50x (ISBN 0-8364-1504-3, Pub. by Allied India). South Asia Bks.

British Labour Movement & Zionism 1917-1948. Joseph Gorny. 270p. 1983. text ed. 30.00x (ISBN 0-7146-3162-0, F Cass Co). Biblio Dist.

British Moralists: Being Selections from Writers Principally of the Eighteenth Century, 2 vols. in 1. Ed. by L. A. Selby-Bigge. LC 64-20242. 1964. 74.50 (ISBN 0-672-51067-7); pap. text ed. 17.95x (ISBN 0-8290-1894-8). Irvington.

British Moralists, Sixteen Fifty to Eighteen Hundred, 2 vols. Ed. by D. D. Raphael. 1969. Set. pap. 18.95x (ISBN 0-19-875010-2). Oxford U Pr.

British Unitarians Against American Slavery, 1833-1865. Charles D. Stange. LC 82-48436. 256p. 1984. 29.50 (ISBN 0-8386-3168-1). Fairleigh Dickinson.

Brittany: Child of Joy. Anne Adams. LC 86-24477. (Orig.). 1987. pap. 7.95 (ISBN 0-8054-5038-6). Broadman.

Broad Road. large print ed. Ellen White. 32p. 1985. pap. 5.00 (ISBN 0-914009-47-8). VHI Library.

Broadman Bible Commentary, 12 vols. Ed. by Clifton J. Allen et al. Incl. Vol. 1, General Articles, Genesis-Exodus. rev. ed (ISBN 0-8054-1125-9); Vol. 2 (ISBN 0-8054-1102-X); Vol. 3 (ISBN 0-8054-1103-8); Vol. 4 (ISBN 0-8054-1104-6); Vol. 5 (ISBN 0-8054-1105-4); Vol. 6 (ISBN 0-8054-1106-2); Vol. 7 (ISBN 0-8054-1107-0); Vol. 8, General Articles, Matthew-Mark. rev. ed (ISBN 0-8054-1108-9); Vol. 9 (ISBN 0-8054-1109-7); Vol. 10 (ISBN 0-8054-1110-0); Vol. 11 (ISBN 0-8054-1111-9); Vol. 12 (ISBN 0-8054-1112-7). LC 78-93918. 1969. lib. bdg. 16.95 ea.; 195.00 set (ISBN 0-8054-1100-3). Broadman.

Broadman Church Manual. Howard Foshee. LC 72-94629. 192p. 1973. 8.95 (ISBN 0-8054-2525-X). Broadman.

Broadman Comments: April-June 1987. Donald F. Ackland et al. (Orig.). 1987. pap. 2.50 (ISBN 0-8054-1555-6). Broadman.

Broadman Comments, January-March, 1987. Donald F. Ackland. (Orig.). 1986. pap. 2.50 (ISBN 0-8054-1554-8). Broadman.

Broadman Comments: October-December, 1986. Donald F. Ackland. 1986. pap. 2.50 (ISBN 0-8054-1499-1). Broadman.

Broadman Comments, October-December 1987. Donald F. Ackland et al (Orig.). 1987. pap. 2.50 (ISBN 0-8054-1557-2). Broadman.

Broadman Comments, 1986-87. Donald F. Ackland et al. (Orig.). 1986. pap. 5.95 (ISBN 0-8054-1553-X). Broadman.

Broadman Comments, 1987-88. Donald F. Ackland. (Orig.). 1987. pap. 5.95 (ISBN 0-8054-1558-0). Broadman.

Broadman Minister's Manual. Franklin M. Segler. LC 68-26920. 1968. 9.95 (ISBN 0-8054-2307-9). Broadman.

Broken Bread & Broken Bodies: The Eucharist & World Hunger. Joseph A. Grassi. LC 84-18888. 128p. (Orig.). 1985. pap. 6.95 (ISBN 0-88344-193-4). Orbis Bks.

Broken Bread: Sermons & Poems. John W. Follette. 216p. 1957. pap. 4.95 (ISBN 0-88243-474-8, 02-0474). Gospel Pub.

Broken but Loved: Healing Through Christ's Power. George A. Maloney. LC 81-1802. 126p. (Orig.). 1981. pap. 6.95 (ISBN 0-8189-0411-9). Alba.

Broken Chains. Benjamin C. Horrell. 1972. pap. 2.95 (ISBN 0-87148-106-5). Pathway Pr.

Broken Chalice. Myron S. Augsburger. LC 70-160721. (Illus.). 1971. 7.95 (ISBN 0-8361-1651-8). Herald Pr.

Broken Churches, Broken Nation: Denominational Schism & the Coming of the American Civil War. C. C. Goen. 208p. 1985. 17.95 (ISBN 0-86554-166-3, MUP-H156). Mercer Univ Pr.

Broken Covenenant: American Civil Religion in Time of Trail. Robert N. Bellah. 1976. pap. 5.95 (ISBN 0-8164-2123-4, HarpR). Har-Row.

Broken Image. Leanne Payne. LC 81-65468. 188p. 1981. pap. 6.95 (ISBN 0-89107-215-2, Crossway Bks). Good News.

Broken Jars & Empty Cisterns: Studies in Jeremiah. Edward A. Buchanan. 32p. 1982. pap. 3.50 (ISBN 0-939298-09-0). J M Prods.

Broken Lights & Mended Lives: Theology & Common Life in the Early Church. Rowan A. Greer. LC 85-21823. 251p. 1986. 19.50x (ISBN 0-271-00422-3). Pa St U Pr.

Broken Snare. Caroline Stickly. 1975. pap. 3.75 (ISBN 0-85363-102-6). OMF Bks.

Broken Spears: The Aztec Account of the Conquest of Mexico. Miguel Leon-Portilla. (Illus.). 1962. pap. 7.95x (ISBN 0-8070-5499-2, BP230). Beacon Pr.

Bronteana: The Rev. Patrick Bronte, His Collected Works & Life. Patrick Bronte. LC 77-148320. Repr. of 1898 ed. 16.00 (ISBN 0-404-08920-8). AMS Pr.

Bronze Tables of Iguvium. James W. Poultney. (APA Philological Monographs). 37.50 (ISBN 0-89130-745-1, 40-00-18). Scholars Pr GA.

Bronzes of Kashmir. Pratapaditya Pal. LC 75-902. (Illus.). 205p. 1975. lib. bdg. 40.00 (ISBN 0-87817-158-4). Hacker.

Brother Burgess. W. J. Burgess. (Illus.). 121p. 1975. 3.50 (ISBN 0-89114-069-7); pap. 1.50 (ISBN 0-89114-068-9). Baptist Pub Hse.

Brother Jerry's Stories: Following the Inspirations of the Holy Spirit. Sunnie D. Kidd & James W. Kidd. 34p. (Orig.). 1982. pap. text ed. 3.50 (ISBN 0-910727-00-7). Golden Phoenix.

Brother Kawabe. Glen Williamson. 1977. pap. 1.75 (ISBN 0-89367-012-X). Light & Life.

Brother Mathias: Founder of the Little Brothers of the Good Shepherd. Carol N. Lovato. LC 86-62454. 288p. 1987. pap. 8.95 (ISBN 0-87973-485-X, 485). Our Sunday Visitor.

Brother of the Prophet Mohammad: The Imam Ali, 2 vols, Vol. II. Mohamad J. Chirri. LC 79-127838. 400p. 1982. 15.00 (ISBN 0-942778-00-6). Islamic Ctr.

Brother of the Third Degree. William L. Garver. 14.95 (ISBN 0-87505-089-1). Borden.

Brother Peter Ferraris. Alvin S. Manni. (Illus.). 1974. pap. 4.95 (ISBN 0-89944-027-4). Don Bosco Multimedia.

Brother Sheffey. 4.95 (ISBN 0-686-27777-5). Schmul Pub Co.

Brotherhood. (Agni Yoga Ser.). 1982. Repr. of 1962 ed. Index 12.00 (ISBN 0-933574-13-4). Agni Yoga Soc.

Brotherhood in Saffron: The Rashtriya Swayamsevak Sangh & Hindu Revivalism. Walter K. Andersen & Shridhar D. Damle. (Special Studies on South & Southeast Asia). 246p. 1987. pap. 27.50 (ISBN 0-8133-7358-1). Westview.

Brotherhood of Shamballah. Jan Van Rijckenborgh & Catharose De Petri. Orig. Title: De Broederschap van Shamballa. 123p. 1987. pap. 11.00 (ISBN 90-6732-008-0). Rosycross Pr.

Brotherhood of the Rosy Cross. Rosicrucian Foundation. 76p. 1935. 5.95 (ISBN 0-932785-06-9). Philos Pub.

Brotherhood of Thieves: Or, A True Picture of the American Church & Clergy. Stephen S. Foster. LC 79-82190. (Anti-Slavery Crusade in America Ser). 1969. Repr. of 1886 ed. 9.00 (ISBN 0-405-00628-4). Ayer Co Pubs.

Brotherhood: The Secret World of the Freemasons. Stephen Knight. LC 84-45208. 336p. 1984. 17.95 (ISBN 0-8128-2994-8). Stein & Day.

Brotherly Community, the Highest Command of Love: Two Anabaptist Documents of 1650 & 1560. Andreas Ehrenpreis & Claus Felbinger. LC 78-21065. 1979. pap. 5.00 (ISBN 0-87486-190-X). Plough.

Brothers & Sisters. Karl Konig. 96p. 1984. pap. 7.95 (ISBN 0-88010-112-1). Anthroposophic.

Brothers in Christ: The History of the Oldest Anabaptist. Fritz Blanke. Tr. by Joseph Nordenhaug. LC 61-6723. pap. 20.00 (2029246). Bks Demand UMI.

Brothers in Deed to Brothers in Need. new ed. Ed. by Clarence Hiebert. LC 74-76588. (Illus.). 486p. 1974. 29.95 (ISBN 0-87303-037-0). Faith & Life.

Brothers of Light, Brothers of Blood: The Penitentes of the Southwest. 1st ed. Marta Weigle. LC 75-21188. pap. 82.00 (ISBN 0-317-27139-3, 2024680). Bks Demand UMI.

Brothers of the Bible. James A. Auchmuty, Jr. LC 84-17510. 1985. pap. 4.50 (ISBN 0-8054-2254-4). Broadman.

Brothers of the Grape. Arnold Michael. LC 76-142525. 1972. pap. 6.95 (ISBN 0-87516-149-9). De Vorss.

Brothers of the Sled & Other Faith-Building Stories. John H. Leeper. (Orig.). 1985. pap. 4.95 (ISBN 0-8024-0622-X). Moody.

Brown Bag: A Bag Full of Sermons for Children. Jerry M. Jordan. LC 77-16813. (Illus.). 117p. 1981. pap. 6.95 (ISBN 0-8298-0411-0). Pilgrim NY.

Browning & the Christian Faith. E. Berdoe. LC 79-130244. (Studies in Browning, No. 4). 1970. Repr. of 1896 ed. lib. bdg. 39.95x (ISBN 0-8383-1134-2). Haskell.

Brownisme Turned the In-Side Out-Ward. Christopher Lawne. LC 76-6282. (English Experience Ser: No. 74). 40p. 1968. Repr. of 1613 ed. 7.00 (ISBN 90-221-0074-X). Walter J Johnson.

Brownson-Hecker Correspondence. Ed. by Joseph F. Gower & Richard M. Leliaert. LC 76-20160. 1979. text ed. 25.00x (ISBN 0-268-00656-3). U of Notre Dame Pr.

Bruchko. Olson. LC 73-81494. 1977. pap. 5.95 (ISBN 0-88419-133-8). Creation Hse.

Brujeria: A Study of Mexican American Folk-Magic. Mary Devine. Ed. by Carl L. Weschcke. LC 82-83427. (Illus.). 266p. (Orig.). 1982. pap. 7.95 (ISBN 0-87542-775-8). Llewellyn Pubns.

Brunner's Dialectic. Robert Reymond. 1967. pap. 0.75 (ISBN 0-87552-404-4). Presby & Reformed.

Brush Arbor Birthright. Lou E. Vaughn. LC 86-80089. (Illus.). 160p. (Orig.). 1986. pap. 3.95 (ISBN 0-88243-483-7, 02-0483). Gospel Pub.

Bruton's Visit of Lord Jagannath 350 Years Ago: British Beginnings in Orissa. Ed. by P. T. Nair. 1986. 14.00x (ISBN 0-8364-1610-4, Pub. by Minerva India). South Asia Bks.

Buber on God & the Perfect Man. Pamela Vermes. Ed. by J. Neusner et al. LC 80-23406. (Brown Judaic Studies). 1981. pap. 10.50 (ISBN 0-89130-427-4). Scholars Pr GA.

Buddavamsa & the Carlya-Pitaka, Pt. 1. Buddhavamsa. Ed. by Richard Morris. LC 78-72391. Repr. of 1882 ed. 17.00 (ISBN 0-404-17249-0). AMS Pr.

Buddha. Michael Carrithers. LC 83-8004. (Past Masters Ser.). 1983. 13.95x (ISBN 0-19-287590-6); pap. 4.95 (ISBN 0-19-287589-2). Oxford U Pr.

Buddha. Paul Carus. 100p. 1913. pap. 3.95 (ISBN 0-317-40410-5). Open Court.

Buddha. Nikos Kazantzakis. Tr. by Kimon Friar & Athena Dallas-Damis. LC 81-71164. 172p. (Orig.). 1983. pap. 11.95 (ISBN 0-932238-14-9, Pub. by Avant Bks.). Slawson Comm.

Buddha. Michael Pye. 148p. 1979. 18.00 (ISBN 0-7156-1302-2, Pub. by Duckworth London); pap. 8.95 (ISBN 0-7156-1387-1). Longwood Pub Group.

Buddha. F. W. Rawding. LC 74-14436. (Cambridge Introduction to the History of Mankind Ser.). (Illus.). 48p. (YA) 1975. pap. 5.95 (ISBN 0-521-20368-6). Cambridge U Pr.

Buddha. F. W. Rawding. LC 78-56789. (Cambridge Topic Bks). (Illus.). PLB 8.95 (ISBN 0-8225-1212-2). Lerner Pubns.

Buddha: A Pictorial History of His Life & Legacy. J. Auboyer. (Illus.). 272p. 1987. 40.00 (ISBN 0-8334-1000-8, Freedeeds Bks). Garber Comm.

Buddha: A Pictorial History of His Life & Legacy. Jeannine Auboyer. Tr. by Nelly Marans from Fr. LC 83-10140. (Illus.). 272p. 1983. 100.00 (ISBN 0-8245-0588-3). Crossroad NY.

Buddha & Buddhism. Arthur Lillie. LC 76-100573. 1975. 11.25x (ISBN 0-89684-372-6). Orient Bk Dist.

Buddha & Buddhism. Maurice Percheron. Tr. by Edmund Stapleton from Fr. LC 82-3471. (Overlook Spiritual Masters Ser.). (Illus.). 192p. 1982. cloth 18.95 (ISBN 0-87951-157-5). Overlook Pr.

Buddha & Buddhism. Maurice Percheron. Tr. by Edmund Stapleton from Fr. LC 82-3471. (Spiritual Masters Ser.). (Illus.). 192p. 1983. pap. 9.95 (ISBN 0-87951-193-1). Overlook Pr.

Buddha & His Doctrine. C. T. Strauss. LC 70-102584. 1970. Repr. of 1923 ed. 16.50x (ISBN 0-8046-0744-3, Pub. by Kennikat). Assoc Faculty Pr.

Buddha & His Religion. J. B. Saint-Hilaire. 59.95 (ISBN 0-87968-798-3). Gordon Pr.

Buddha & His Sayings. Hara C. Syama-Sankara. LC 78-70128. Repr. of 1914 ed. 18.00 (ISBN 0-404-17387-X). AMS Pr.

Buddha & Jesus: Conversations. Carrin Dunne. 1975. pap. 4.95 (ISBN 0-87243-057-X). Templegate.

Buddha & the Christ. B. H. Streeter. 59.95 (ISBN 0-87968-799-1). Gordon Pr.

Buddha & the Christ. Burnett H. Streeter. LC 72-102585. 1970. Repr. of 1932 ed. 29.50x (ISBN 0-8046-0745-1, Pub. by Kennikat). Assoc Faculty Pr.

Buddha & the Gospel of Buddhism. Ananda K. Coomaraswamy. (Illus.). 1975. text ed. 17.00x. Coronet Bks.

Buddha Consiousness. John-Roger. LC 76-17344. 1976. pap. 5.00 (ISBN 0-914829-03-3). Baraka Bk.

Buddha Disease. Bhagwan Shree Rajneesh. Ed. by Ma Prem Maneesha. LC 83-181256. (Initiation Talks Ser.). (Illus.). 642p. (Orig.). 1979. 21.50 (ISBN 0-88050-032-8). Chidvilas Found.

Buddha Eye: An Anthology of the Kyoto School. Frederick Franck. 256p. 1982. 14.95 (ISBN 0-8245-0410-0). Crossroad NY.

Buddha: His Life, Doctrine, Order. Oldenber. 1971. 28.00 (ISBN 0-89684-493-5). Orient Bk Dist.

Buddha: His Life, His Doctrine & His Order. Hermann Oldenberg. 59.95 (ISBN 0-87968-800-9). Gordon Pr.

Buddha in the Palm of Your Hand. Osel Tendzin. LC 81-84450. (Dragon Ser.). (Illus.). 120p. (Orig.). 1982. pap. 6.95 (ISBN 0-87773-223-X). Shambhala Pubns.

Buddha in the Palm of Your Hand. Osel Tendzin. 1987. pap. 8.95. Shambhala Pubns.

Buddha, Marx & God: Some Aspects of Religion in the Modern World. 2nd ed. Trevor Ling. 1979. 26.00 (ISBN 0-312-10679-3). St Martin.

Buddha Mimansa. Maitriya. Ed. by Maharaja Yogiraja. LC 78-70098. Repr. of 1925 ed. 23.50 (ISBN 0-404-17347-0). AMS Pr.

Buddha, Mohammed, Bacon, Whitman & Others & the Theory of Cosmic Consciousness, 2 vols. Richard M. Bucke. (Illus.). 291p. 1986. Set. 237.50 (ISBN 0-89901-269-8). Found Class Reprints.

Buddha Root Farm. Tripitaka Master Hua. Tr. by Buddhist Text Translation Society et al. (Illus.). 72p. (Orig.). 1976. pap. 4.00 (ISBN 0-917512-08-1). Buddhist Text.

Buddhacarita: Acts of Buddha. E. R. Johnston. 1978. Repr. 26.00 (ISBN 0-8426-0474-X). Orient Bk Dist.

Buddhacharita or Acts of the Buddha, 2 vols. in 1. Asvaghosa. Ed. & tr. by E. H. Johnson. Repr. of 1936 ed. text ed. 25.00x. Coronet Bks.

Buddhadatta's Manuals, 2 vols. in 1. Buddhadatta. Ed. by A. P. Buddhadatta. LC 78-72382. Repr. of 1928 ed. 47.50 (ISBN 0-404-17244-X). AMS Pr.

Buddhaghosa's Parables. Buddhaghosa. Tr. by T. Rogers from Burmese. LC 78-72384. Repr. of 1870 ed. 37.50 (ISBN 0-404-17246-6). AMS Pr.

Buddhas' Doctrine of Truth: Dhamma & Buddhist Religion As Practiced by the Holy Brotherhood in Siam. Luang Suriyabongs. Tr. by Krachang Bunnag. LC 77-87512. Repr. of 1936 ed. 14.50 (ISBN 0-404-16870-1). AMS Pr.

Buddha's Golden Path. 2nd rev. ed. Dwight Goddard. LC 78-72435. Repr. of 1931 ed. 27.00 (ISBN 0-404-17296-2). AMS Pr.

Buddha's Golden Path. Dwight Goddard. 214p. 1981. pap. 12.00 (ISBN 0-89540-074-X, SB-074). Sun Pub.

Buddha's Law among the Birds. Edward Conze. 1986. Repr. 8.00 (ISBN 81-208-0198-9, Pub. by Motilal Banarsidass). South Asia Bks.

Buddha's Lions. Abhayadatta. Tr. by James Robinson from Tibean. (Tibetan Translation Ser.). (Illus.). 1979. 19.95 (ISBN 0-913546-60-7). Dharma Pub.

Buddha's Path of Virtue. 2nd ed. Dhammapada. Tr. by F. L. Woodward. LC 78-72419. Repr. of 1929 ed. 21.50 (ISBN 0-404-17283-0). AMS Pr.

Buddha's Philosophy of Man: Early Indian Buddhist Dialogues. Ed. by Trevor Ling. 229p. 1981. pap. 5.95x (ISBN 0-460-01247-9, Evman). Biblio Dist.

Buddha's Sermon on the Mount. Manly P. Hall. pap. 2.50 (ISBN 0-89314-307-3). Philos Res.

Buddha's System of Meditation: Phase (I-VIII, 4 vols. Ayoda P. Pradhan. 1986. text ed. 150.00x (ISBN 81-207-0140-2, Pub. by Sterling Pubs India). Apt Bks.

Buddhism. Thomas Berry. LC 75-10518. 1967. pap. 5.95 (ISBN 0-89012-017-X). Anima Pubns.

Buddhism. Alexandra David-Neel. 1979. pap. 3.50 (ISBN 0-380-46185-4, 63594-1, Discus). Avon.

Buddhism. Alexandra David-Neel. LC 77-10308. 1978. 8.95 (ISBN 0-312-10680-7). St Martin.

Buddhism. Ed. by Richard A. Gard. LC 61-15499. (Great Religions of Modern Man Ser). 1976. 8.95 (ISBN 0-8076-0166-7). Braziller.

Buddhism. Christmas Humphreys. (Pelican Ser.). 256p. (Orig.). 1951. pap. 6.95 (ISBN 0-14-020228-5). Penguin.

Buddhism. Peggy Morgan. (World Religions Ser.). (Illus.). 72p. 1987. 16.95 (ISBN 0-7134-5203-X, Pub. by Batsford England). David & Charles.

Buddhism. Hans W. Schumann. Tr. by Georg Fenerstein from Ger. LC 74-6302. (Illus.). 200p. 1974. pap. 7.95 (ISBN 0-8356-0457-8). Theos Pub Hse.

Buddhism. John Snelling. (Religions of the World Ser.). (Illus.). 48p. 1986. PLB 10.90 (ISBN 0-531-18065-4, Pub. by Bookwright). Watts.

Buddhism: A Modern Perspective. Ed. by Charles S. Prebish. LC 74-300085. 346p. 1975. 24.95x (ISBN 0-271-01185-8); pap. 14.95x (ISBN 0-271-01195-5). Pa St U Pr.

Buddhism: A Select Bibliography. Satyaprakash. 1986. Repr. of 1976 ed. 28.50x (ISBN 0-8364-1828-X, Pub. by Indian Doc Serv India). South Asia Bks.

Buddhism: A Selection Bibliography. Ed. by Satyaprakash. 1977. 11.00 (ISBN 0-88386-956-X). South Asia Bks.

Buddhism: A Study of the Buddhist Norm. Carolina A. Davids. LC 78-72408. Repr. of 1912 ed. 25.00 (ISBN 0-404-17269-5). AMS Pr.

Buddhism: A Way of Life & Thought. Nancy W. Ross. LC 80-7652. (Illus.). 224p. 1980. 15.95 (ISBN 0-394-49286-2). Knopf.

Buddhism: A Way of Life & Thought. Nancy W. Ross. LC 81-40081. (Illus.). 224p. 1981. pap. 6.95 (ISBN 0-394-74754-2, Vin). Random.

Buddhism: An Introduction to the Living Spiritual Tradition. Bikshu Rinpoche. 160p. (Orig.). 1987. pap. 8.95 (ISBN 0-913757-71-3, Pub. by New Era Bks). Paragon Hse.

Buddhism & American Thinkers. Kenneth K. Inada & Nolan P. Jacobson. 182p. 1983. 39.50 (ISBN 0-87395-753-9); pap. 14.95 (ISBN 0-87395-754-7). State U NY Pr.

Buddhism & Asoka. Balkrishna G. Gokhale. LC 78-72443. Repr. of 1948 ed. 41.50 (ISBN 0-404-17298-9). AMS Pr.

Buddhism & Buddhists in China. Lewis Hodous. LC 78-72440. Repr. of 1924 ed. 17.50 (ISBN 0-404-17306-3). AMS Pr.

Buddhism & Christianity. Archibald Scott. LC 78-118547. 1970. Repr. of 1890 ed. 29.50x (ISBN 0-8046-1172-6, Pub. by Kennikat). Assoc Faculty Pr.

Buddhism & Christianity in Japan: From Conflict to Dialogue, 1854-1899. Notto R. Thelle. (Illus.). 384p. 1987. text ed. 30.00x. UH Pr.

Buddhism & Faith. Masatoshi G. Mori. LC 78-70102. Repr. of 1928 ed. 21.50 (ISBN 0-404-17353-5). AMS Pr.

Buddhism & Healing: Demieville's Article "Byo" from Hobogirin. Tr. by Mark Tatz. 108p. (Orig.). 1985. lib. bdg. 24.00 (ISBN 0-8191-4436-3); pap. text ed. 9.50 (ISBN 0-8191-4437-1). U Pr of Amer.

Buddhism & Immortality. William S. Bigelow. LC 78-72379. Repr. of 1908 ed. 16.50 (ISBN 0-404-17228-8). AMS Pr.

Buddhism & Its Christian Critics. Paul Carus. 59.95 (ISBN 0-87968-801-7). Gordon Pr.

Buddhism & Its Place in the Mental Life of Mankind. Paul Dahlke. LC 78-72403. Repr. of 1927 ed. 29.00 (ISBN 0-404-17265-2). AMS Pr.

Buddhism & Jungian Psychology. J. Marvin Spiegelman & Mokusen Miyuki. 224p. (Orig.). 1985. pap. 8.95 (ISBN 0-941404-37-4). Falcon Pr AZ.

Buddhism & Lamaism. J. B. Ellam. 1984. pap. 6.95 (ISBN 0-916411-79-6, Oriental Classics). Holmes Pub.

Buddhism & Lamaism of Tibet. Austine Waddell. 1985. text ed. 40.00x (ISBN 0-86590-615-7, Pub. by Sterling Pubs India). Apt Bks.

Buddhism & Politics in Thailand. Somboon Suksamran. 180p. (Orig.). 1982. pap. text ed. 25.00 (ISBN 9971-902-43-5, Pub. by Inst Southeast Asian Stud). Gower Pub Co.

Buddhism & Psychotherapy. Manly P. Hall. pap. 7.95 (ISBN 0-89314-394-4). Philos Res.

Buddhism & Society: A Great Tradition & Its Burmese Vicissitudes. 2nd, exp. ed. Melford E. Spiro. LC 81-18522. 530p. 1982. 40.00x (ISBN 0-520-04671-4); pap. 10.95x (ISBN 0-520-04672-2, CAMPUS 298). U of Cal Pr.

Buddhism & Society in Southeast Asia. Donald K. Swearer. LC 81-8048. (Focus on Hinduism & Buddhism Ser.). 64p. 1981. pap. 4.95x (ISBN 0-89012-023-4). Anima Pubns.

Buddhism & the Arts of Japan. Richard B. Pilgrim. LC 81-8063. (Focus on Hinduism & Buddhism Ser.). 64p. (Orig.). 1981. pap. 4.95x (ISBN 0-89012-026-9). Anima Pubns.

Buddhism & the Contemporary World: Change & Self Correction. Nolan P. Jacobson. LC 82-5909. 203p. 1982. 18.95x (ISBN 0-8093-1052-X); pap. 9.95 (ISBN 0-8093-1071-6). S Ill U Pr.

Buddhism & the Race Question. George P. Malalasekera & K. N. Jayatilleke. LC 77-18853. (Race Question in Modern Thought). 1978. Repr. of 1958 ed. lib. bdg. 22.50x (ISBN 0-313-20208-7, MABU). Greenwood.

Buddhism & the Spirit Cults in Northeast Thailand. S. J. Tambiah. LC 73-108112. (Cambridge Studies in Social Anthropology: No. 2). (Illus.). 1970. pap. 19.95 (ISBN 0-521-09958-7). Cambridge U Pr.

Buddhism & the State in Sixteenth Century Japan. Neil McMullin. LC 84-42572. (Illus.). 408p. 1984. 45.00x (ISBN 0-691-07291-4). Princeton U Pr.

Buddhism & Zen in Vietnam: In Relation to the Development in Asia. Thieh Thien-An. LC 74-83391. (Illus.). 300p. 1975. 12.50 (ISBN 0-8048-1144-X). C E Tuttle.

Buddhism: Being a Sketch of the Life & Teachings of Guatama, the Buddha. T. Rhys Davids. LC 78-72417. Repr. of 1877 ed. 28.00 (ISBN 0-404-17278-4). AMS Pr.

Buddhism, Dance & Drama. V. Subramaniam. 1985. 12.00x (ISBN 0-8364-1322-9, Pub. by Ashish India). South Asia Bks.

Buddhism for Today: A Modern Interpretation of the Threefold Lotus Sutra. Nikkyo Niwano. LC 79-22383. 476p. 1976. pap. 10.95 (ISBN 0-8348-0147-7). Weatherhill.

Buddhism: History & Diversity of a Great Tradition. Elizabeth Lyons & Heather Peters. (Illus.). 64p. 1985. pap. 8.95 (ISBN 0-934718-76-8). Univ Mus of U PA.

Buddhism: History & Diversity of a Great Tradition. Elizabeth Lyons & Heather Peters. LC 85-28817. (University of Pennsylvaina Museum Ser.). (Illus.). 64p. 1985. pap. 12.95 (ISBN 0-317-46953-3). U of Pa Pr.

Buddhism, Imperialism & War. Trevor Ling. (Illus.). 1979. text ed. 13.95x (ISBN 0-04-294105-9). Allen Unwin.

Buddhism in America. Emma M. Layman. LC 76-4566. (Illus.). 364p. 1976. pap. 13.95x (ISBN 0-88229-436-9). Nelson-Hall.

Buddhism in America: The Social Organization of an Ethnic Religious Institution. Tetsuden Kashima. LC 76-57837. (Contributions in Sociology: No. 26). (Illus.). 1977. lib. bdg. 29.95 (ISBN 0-8371-9534-9, KSO/). Greenwood.

Buddhism in China. Samuel Beal. lib. bdg. 79.95 (ISBN 0-87968-479-8). Krishna Pr.

Buddhism in China. Samuel Beal. 16.75 (ISBN 0-8369-7129-9, 7963). Ayer Co Pubs.

Buddhism in China: A Historical Survey. Kenneth Ch'en. (Studies in History of Religion: Vol. 1). 1974. pap. 13.50x (ISBN 0-691-00015-8). Princeton U Pr.

Buddhism in Chinese History. Arthur F. Wright. LC 59-7432. (Illus.). 1959. 13.50x (ISBN 0-8047-0546-1); pap. 6.95 (ISBN 0-8047-0548-8, SP118). Stanford U Pr.

Buddhism in Comparative Light. Hijime Nakamura. 1986. 15.00 (ISBN 81-208-0184-9, Pub. by Motilal Banarsidass). South Asia Bks.

Buddhism in India & Sri Lanka. J. Barthelemy Saint-Hilaire. LC 75-907912. 1975. Repr. of 1975 ed. 10.50x (ISBN 0-89684-373-4). Orient Bk Dist.

Buddhism, in Its Connection with Brahmanism & Hinduism, & in Contrast with Christianity. 2nd ed. Monier-Williams. LC 78-70101. Repr. of 1890 ed. 57.50 (ISBN 0-404-17349-7). AMS Pr.

Buddhism in Japan: With an Outline of Its Origins in India. E. Dale Saunders. LC 77-24539. 1977. Repr. of 1964 ed. lib. bdg. 25.75x (ISBN 0-8371-9746-5, SABJ). Greenwood.

Buddhism in Kerala. P. C. Alexander. LC 78-72369. Repr. of 1949 ed. 37.50 (ISBN 0-404-17216-4). AMS Pr.

Buddhism in Ladakh. Nawang Tsering. 112p. 1979. text ed. 9.95 (ISBN 0-89684-263-0, Pub. by Sterling India). Orient Bk Dist.

Buddhism in Late Ch'ing Political Thought. Sin-wai Chan. 191p. 1985. 31.50x (ISBN 0-8133-0256-0). Westview.

Buddhism in Life: The Anthropological Study of Religion & the Sinhalese Practice of Buddhism. Martin Southwold. LC 83-9890. (Themes in Social Anthropology Ser.). 232p. 1984. 36.00 (ISBN 0-7190-0971-5, Pub. by Manchester Univ Pr). Longwood Pub Group.

Buddhism in Pre-Christian Britain. Donald A. Mackenzie. 1977. lib. bdg. 59.95 (ISBN 0-8490-1558-8). Gordon Pr.

Buddhism in Sinhalese Society, 1750-1900: A Study of Religious Revival & Change. Kirsiri Malagoda. LC 74-22966. 1976. 42.00x (ISBN 0-520-02873-2). U of Cal Pr.

Buddhism in the Tibetan Tradition: A Guide. Geshe K. Gyatso. (Illus.). 144p. (Orig.). 1984. pap. 9.95 (ISBN 0-7102-0242-3). Methuen Inc.

Buddhism in the Twentieth Century. Peggy Morgan. 1985. pap. 5.95 (ISBN 0-7175-1394-7). Dufour.

Buddhism in Tibet. Emil Schlagintweit. 69.95 (ISBN 0-87968-802-5). Gordon Pr.

Buddhism in Translations. Henry C. Warren. LC 78-70138. Repr. of 1896 ed. 47.50 (ISBN 0-404-17408-6). AMS Pr.

Buddhism in Translations. Henry C. Warren. LC 5-17082. 1963. pap. text ed. 7.95x (ISBN 0-689-70200-0, 19). Atheneum.

Buddhism: Its Birth & Dispersal. rev. ed. Carolina A. Davids. LC 78-72418. Repr. of 1934 ed. 25.00 (ISBN 0-404-17268-7). AMS Pr.

Buddhism: Its Essence & Development. Edward Conze. 17.50 (ISBN 0-8446-1889-6). Peter Smith.

Buddhism: It's Essence & Development. Edward Conze. 1982. pap. 6.95x (ISBN 0-06-130058-6, TB 58, Torch). Har-Row.

Buddhism: Its Essence & Development. Edward Conze. 221p. 1975. 25.00x (ISBN 0-317-39041-4, Pub. by Luzac & Co Ltd). State Mutual Bk.

Buddhism: Japan's Cultural Identity. Stuart D. Picken. LC 81-84800. (Illus.). 80p. 1982. 19.95 (ISBN 0-87011-499-9). Kodansha.

Buddhism Made Plain: An Introduction for Christians & Jews. Antony Fernando & Leonard Swidler. LC 84-18880. 176p. (Orig.). 1985. pap. 9.95 (ISBN 0-88344-198-5). Orbis Bks.

Buddhism of Tibet & the Precious Garland. Nagarjuna & Tenzin Gyatso. 212p. 1983. pap. 12.50 (ISBN 0-04-294127-X). Allen Unwin.

Buddhism: The First Millennium. Daisaku Ikeda. Tr. by Burton Watson. LC 77-84915. 1978. 12.95x (ISBN 0-87011-321-6). Kodansha.

Buddhism: The First Millennium. Daisaku Ikeda. LC 82-80739. 172p. 1982. pap. 5.25 (ISBN 0-87011-534-0). Kodansha.

Buddhism: The Light of Asia. Kenneth K. Ch'en. LC 67-30496. 1968. pap. text ed. 5.95 (ISBN 0-8120-0272-5). Barron.

Buddhism: The Religion of Analysis. Nolan P. Jacobson. LC 66-71124. (Arcturus Books Paperbacks). 202p. 1970. pap. 7.95x (ISBN 0-8093-0463-5). S Ill U Pr.

Buddhism under the T'ang. Stanley Weinstein. (Cambridge Studies in Chinese History, Literature & Institutions). 200p. 1987. 39.50 (ISBN 0-521-25585-6). Cambridge U Pr.

Buddhist Adhidhamma: Meditation & Concentration. U Kyaw Min. 192p. Date not set. pap. 6.95 (ISBN 0-89346-287-X). Heian Intl.

Buddhist & Hindu Art in the Collection of John H. Mann. Compiled by Doanda Randall. (Illus.). 285p. (Orig.). 1981. 65.00x (ISBN 0-940492-01-6). Asian Conserv Lab.

Buddhist & Taoist Practice in Medieval Chinese Society: Buddhist & Taoist Studies II. Ed. by David W. Chappell. (Asian Studies at Hawaii: No. 34). 256p. 1987. pap. text ed. 18.00x (ISBN 0-8248-0957-2). UH Pr.

Buddhist & Taoist Studies Number One. Ed. by Michael Saso & David W. Chappell. (Asian Studies at Hawaii: No. 18). (Illus.). 174p. 1977. pap. text ed. 10.50x (ISBN 0-8248-0420-1). UH Pr.

Buddhist & Western Psychology. Ed. by Nathan Katz. LC 82-12325. 300p. (Orig.). 1983. pap. 15.00 (ISBN 0-87773-758-4, Prajna). Shambhala Pubns.

Buddhist Approach to Peace. Nikkyo Niwano. Tr. by Masuo Nezu from Japanese. (Illus.). 162p. 1977. 7.95 (ISBN 4-333-00308-3, Pub. by Kosei Publishing Co). C E Tuttle.

Buddhist Art in India. Jas Burgess. 240p. 27.00X (ISBN 0-317-52134-9, Pub. by S Chand India). State Mutual Bk.

Buddhist Art in India. Albert Grunwedel. Tr. by Agnes C. Gibson. (Ger., Illus.). 236p. Repr. of 1901 ed. text ed. 37.50x. Coronet Bks.

Buddhist Art in India, Ceylon, & Java. J. P. Vogel. (Illus.). 187p. 1977. Repr. of 1936 ed. text ed. 19.00x. Coronet Bks.

Buddhist Art of Gandhara. John Marshall. (Illus.). 1981. Repr. of 1960 ed. text ed. 30.00x. Coronet Bks.

Buddhist Bible. Ed. by Dwight Goddard. LC 72-105327. 677p. 1970. pap. 11.95 (ISBN 0-8070-5951-X, BP357). Beacon Pr.

Buddhist Birth Stories; or Jataka Tales, Vol. 1. Ed. by V. Fausboll. Tr. by Rhys T. Davids. LC 78-72443. Repr. of 1880 ed. 42.50 (ISBN 0-404-17309-8). AMS Pr.

Buddhist Catechism. Henry S. Olcott. 1971. pap. 2.75 (ISBN 0-8356-0027-0, Quest). Theos Pub Hse.

Buddhist Catechism. 44th ed. Henry S. Olcott. xv, 115p. 1983. pap. 4.95 (ISBN 0-912181-07-9). East School Pr.

Buddhist Cave Temples of India. Robert S. Wauchope. LC 78-70139. Repr. of 1933 ed. 34.50 (ISBN 0-404-17409-4). AMS Pr.

Buddhist-Christian Dialogue: Mutual Renewal & Transformation. Ed. by Paul O. Ingram & Frederick J. Streng. LC 85-24528. 1986. pap. text ed. 10.00x (ISBN 0-8248-1050-3). UH Pr.

Buddhist Conception of Spirits. 2nd rev. & enl. ed. Bimala C. Law. LC 78-72462. Repr. of 1936 ed. 21.50 (ISBN 0-404-17334-9). AMS Pr.

Buddhist Conquest of China: The Spread & Adaptation of Buddhism in Early Medieval China, 2 vols. E. Zucher. 470p. 1973. Set. text ed. 99.00x (ISBN 0-391-01961-9). Humanities.

Buddhist Dictionary. Nyanatiloka. LC 77-87508. Repr. of 1950 ed. 20.00 (ISBN 0-404-16846-9). AMS Pr.

Buddhist Education in Ceylon, & Other Essays. Ginige Jinapriya. LC 78-72901. Repr. of 1931 ed. 18.50 (ISBN 0-404-17313-6). AMS Pr.

Buddhist Faith & Sudden Enlightenment. Sung-Bae Park. LC 82-10459. 222p. 1983. 44.50x (ISBN 0-87395-673-7); pap. 12.95x (ISBN 0-87395-674-5). State U NY Pr.

Buddhist Feminine Ideal: Queen Srimala & the Tathagatagarbha American Academy of Religion. Diana Paul. LC 79-12031. (Dissertation Ser.: No. 30). 1980. o.s. 14.00 (ISBN 0-89130-284-0, 01-01-30); pap. 9.95 (ISBN 0-89130-303-0). Scholars Pr GA.

Buddhist Hand-Symbol. Aisaburo Akiyama. LC 78-72367. Repr. of 1939 ed. 22.50 (ISBN 0-404-17214-8). AMS Pr.

Buddhist Hybrid Sanscrit Reader. Ed. by Franklin Edgerton. 1953. 49.50x (ISBN 0-685-69814-9). Elliots Bks.

Buddhist I Ching. Ou-i Chih-hsu. Tr. by Thomas Cleary from Chinese. LC 86-31460. (Dragon Ser.). 290p. 1987. pap. 10.95 (ISBN 0-87773-408-9). Shambhala Pubns.

Buddhist India. Thomas W. Davids. LC 78-38349. (Select Bibliographies Reprint Ser). Repr. of 1903 ed. 28.00 (ISBN 0-8369-6766-6). Ayer Co Pubs.

Buddhist Legend of Jimutavahana. Bhatta Somadeva. LC 78-70116. Repr. of 1911 ed. 20.50 (ISBN 0-404-17373-X). AMS Pr.

Buddhist Logic, 2 Vols. T. Stcherbatsky. 1958. Repr. of 1932 ed. Set. text ed. 74.00x (ISBN 90-2790-060-4). Mouton.

Buddhist Logic, 2 vols. Theodore Stcherbatsky. 1930. pap. text ed. 8.95 ea.; Vol. 1. pap. text ed. (ISBN 0-486-20955-5); Vol. 2. pap. text ed. (ISBN 0-486-20956-3). Dover.

Buddhist Logic & Epistemology. Ed. by Evans & Matilal. 1986. lib. bdg. 59.50 (ISBN 90-277-2222-6, Pub. by Reidel Holland). Kluwer Academic.

Buddhist Mahayana Texts. E. B. Cowell & F. Max Muller. (Sacred Bks. of the East: Vol. 49). 15.00 (ISBN 0-89581-534-6). Asian Human Pr.

Buddhist Mahayana Texts. E. B. Crowell. lib. bdg. 79.95 (ISBN 0-87968-499-2). Krishna Pr.

Buddhist Meditation on China. Paul F. Schmidt. LC 84-81398. (Illus.). 74p. 1984. lib. bdg. 15.00 (ISBN 0-912998-06-7); pap. 6.00 (ISBN 0-912998-07-5). Hummingbird.

Buddhist Monastic Discipline: The Sanskrit Pratimoksa Sutras of the Mahasamghikas & Mulasarvastivadins. Charles S. Prebish. LC 74-10743. (Institute for Advanced Study of World Religions Ser.). 1975. 22.50x (ISBN 0-271-01171-8). Pa St U Pr.

Buddhist Monk, Buddhist Layman: A Study of Urban Monastic Organisation in Central Thailand. Jane Bunnag. LC 72-86420. (Cambridge Studies in Social Anthropology: No. 6). (Illus.). 230p. 1973. 34.50 (ISBN 0-521-08591-8). Cambridge U Pr.

Buddhist Monuments. Mitra. 1971. 42.50 (ISBN 0-89684-490-0). Orient Bk Dist.

Buddhist Parables. E. W. Burlingame. 59.95 (ISBN 0-87968-803-3). Gordon Pr.

Buddhist Parables. E. W. Burlingame. lib. bdg. 79.95 (ISBN 0-87968-494-1). Krishna Pr.

Buddhist Philosophy: A Historical Analysis. David J. Kalupahana. LC 75-20040. 210p. 1976. (Eastwest Ctr); pap. 4.95x (ISBN 0-8248-0392-2). UH Pr.

Buddhist Philosophy in India & Ceylon. A. B. Keith. lib. bdg. 90.00 (ISBN 0-87968-181-0). Krishna Pr.

Buddhist Philosophy of Assimilation. Alicia Matsunaga. LC 68-57058. (Illus.). 1969. 29.50 (ISBN 0-8048-0730-2). C E Tuttle.

Buddhist Philosophy of the Middle Way. Shoson Miyamoto. 1983. cancelled 9.95x (ISBN 0-914910-07-8). Buddhist Bks.

Buddhist Philosophy of Thought: Essays in Interpretation. Alexander Piatigorsky. LC 82-3987. 240p. 1984. text ed. 24.50x (ISBN 0-389-20266-5, 07084). B&N Imports.

Buddhist Philosophy of Universal Flux. S. Mookerjee. 1975. Repr. 20.00 (ISBN 0-8426-0852-4). Orient Bk Dist.

Buddhist Religion: A Historical Introduction. 3rd ed. Richard H. Robinson & Willard L. Johnson. 304p. 1982. pap. text ed. write for info (ISBN 0-534-01027-X). Wadsworth Pub.

Buddhist Revival in China: With a Section of Photos by Henri Cartier-Bresson. Holmes Welch. LC 68-15645. (Harvard East Asian Ser.: Vol. 33). pap. 80.60 (ISBN 0-317-28777-X, 2017757). Bks Demand UMI.

Buddhist Revival in India: Aspects of the Sociology of Buddhism. Trevor Ling. LC 79-20167. 1980. 26.00 (ISBN 0-312-10681-5). St Martin.

Buddhist Saints of the Forest & the Cult of Amulets: A Study in Charisma, Hagiography, Sectarianism & Millenial Buddhism. Stanley J. Tambiah. LC 83-15113. (Cambridge Studies in Social Anthropology: No. 49). (Illus.). 432p. 1984. 57.50 (ISBN 0-521-25984-3); pap. 18.95 (ISBN 0-521-27787-6). Cambridge U Pr.

Buddhist Scriptures. Tr. by Edward Conze. (Classics Ser.). (Orig.). 1959. pap. 5.95 (ISBN 0-14-044088-7). Penguin.

Buddhist Scriptures: A Bibliography. Compiled by Edward Conze & Lewis Lancaster. LC 77-83380. (Reference Library of the Humanities: Vol. 113). 161p. 1982. lib. bdg. 31.00 (ISBN 0-8240-9848-X). Garland Pub.

Buddhist Sects in India. 2nd ed. N. Dutt. 1977. 9.00x (ISBN 0-88386-971-3). South Asia Bks.

Buddhist Sects in India. Nalinaksha Dutt. 1978. (Pub. by Motilal Banarsidas India); pap. 7.50 (ISBN 0-89684-044-1). Orient Bk Dist.

Buddhist Sects of Japan: Their Histories, Philosophical Doctrines & Sanctuaries. Emile Steinilber-Oberlin. Tr. by Marc Loge. 1977. lib. bdg. 39.95 (ISBN 0-8490-1559-6). Gordon Pr.

Buddhist Sects of Japan, Their History, Philosophical Doctrines & Sanctuaries. Emile Steinilber-Oberlin. Tr. by Marc Loge. LC 78-109854. (Illus.). 303p. Repr. of 1938 ed. lib. bdg. 22.50x (ISBN 0-8371-4349-7, STBS). Greenwood.

Buddhist Sermons on Christian Texts. R. H. Blyth. 1976. pap. 2.95 (ISBN 0-89346-000-1). Heian Intl.

Buddhist Shrines in India. D. C. Ahir. (Illus.). xii, 132p. 1986. text ed. 25.00x (ISBN 81-7018-326-X, Pub. by D K Pub Corp Delhi). Apt Bks.

Buddhist Stories. facsimile ed. Paul Dahlke. Tr. by Bhikkhu Silacara. LC 71-106285. (Short Story Index Reprint Ser.). 1913. 19.00 (ISBN 0-8369-3322-2). Ayer Co Pubs.

Buddhist Stories. Tr. by F. L. Woodward from Pali. LC 78-70141. Repr. of 1925 ed. 20.00 (ISBN 0-404-17414-0). AMS Pr.

Buddhist Studies. J. W. De Jong. Ed. by Gregory Schopen. 1980. 35.00 (ISBN 0-89581-002-6). Asian Human Pr.

Buddhist Studies: Ancient & Modern. Philip Denwood & Alexander Piatigorsky. 220p. 1981. 30.00x (ISBN 0-7007-0153-2, Pub. by Curzon England). State Mutual Bk.

Buddhist Studies: Ancient & Modern. Ed. by Philip Denwood & Alexander Piatigorsky. (Collected Papers on South Asia: No. 4). (Illus.). 206p. 1983. 24.50x (ISBN 0-389-20264-9, 07082). B&N Imports.

Buddhist Studies in Honour of I. B. Horner. Ed. by L. Cousins et al. LC 74-77963. 275p. 1974. lib. bdg. 45.00 (ISBN 90-277-0473-2, Pub. by Reidel Holland). Kluwer Academic.

Buddhist Studies in Honour of Walpola Rahula. Walpola Rahula. 308p. 1981. 75.00x (ISBN 0-86092-030-5, Pub. by Fraser Bks). State Mutual Bk.

Buddhist Studies in India. R. C. Pandeya. 1975. 12.50 (ISBN 0-8426-0806-0). Orient Bk Dist.

Buddhist Studies Nineteen Thirty-Four to Nineteen Seventy-Two. Edward Conze. 512p. 1977. Repr. 20.00 (ISBN 0-686-48400-2). Wheelwright Pr.

Buddhist Suttas. Rhys Davids. lib. bdg. 79.95 (ISBN 0-87968-511-5). Krishna Pr.

Buddhist Suttas. T. W. Davids. (Sacred Bks. of the East: Vol. 11). 15.00 (ISBN 0-89581-520-6). Asian Human Pr.

Buddhist Tantras: Light on Indo-Tibetan Esotericism. Alex Wayman. LC 73-79801. (Illus.). 247p. 1973. 12.50 (ISBN 0-87728-223-4). Weiser.

Buddhist Teaching of Totality. C. C. Chang. LC 70-136965. 1971. 24.50x (ISBN 0-271-01179-3); pap. 14.95x (ISBN 0-271-01142-4). Pa St U Pr.

Buddhist Texts from Japan, 3 pts. in 1 vol. Friedrich M. Mueller. LC 73-18824. (Illus.). Repr. of 1884 ed. 34.50 (ISBN 0-404-11430-X). AMS Pr.

Buddhist Texts Through the Ages. Edward Conze et al. 322p. 1985. Repr. of 1964 ed. 20.00x (ISBN 0-317-39042-2, Pub. by Luzac & Co Ltd). State Mutual Bk.

Buddhist Thought & Asian Civilization: Essays in Honor of Herbert V. Genther on His Sixtieth Birthday. Ed. by Leslie S. Kawamura & Keith Scott. LC 77-71194. 1977. 25.00 (ISBN 0-913546-51-8). Dharma Pub.

Buddhist Thought in India. Edward Conze. 1967. pap. 8.95 (ISBN 0-472-06129-1, 129, AA). U of Mich Pr.

Buddhist Tradition: In India, China & Japan. Ed. by William T. De Bary. 448p. 1972. pap. 4.76 (ISBN 0-394-71696-5, V702, Vin). Random.

Buddhist Vision. Alex Kennedy. (Illus.). 216p. (Orig.). 1987. pap. 8.95 (ISBN 0-87728-620-5). Weiser.

Buddhist Wall-Painting of Ladakh. C. Genoud & T. Inoue. (Illus.). 116p. 1981. text ed. 75.00x (ISBN 2-88086-001-6, Pub. by Editions Olizane Holland). Humanities.

Buddhist Wisdom: The Mystery of the Self. 2nd, rev. ed. George Grimm. Ed. by M. Keller-Grimm. Tr. by Carrol Aikins from Ger. 1982. 11.50 (ISBN 0-89684-041-7, Pub. by Motilal Banarsidass India). Orient Bk Dist.

Buddhist World. Anne Bancroft. LC 84-51193. (Religions of the World Ser.). (Illus.). 48p. 1985. 9.25 (ISBN 0-382-06928-5); PLB 14.96 (ISBN 0-382-06747-9). Silver.

Buddhist Writings of Lafcadio Hearn. Ed. by Kenneth Rexroth. LC 77-2496. 312p. 1977. lib. bdg. 12.95 (ISBN 0-915520-05-2). Ross-Erikson.

Buddhist Yoga. Kanjitsu Iijima. (Illus.). 184p. 1975. pap. 8.95 (ISBN 0-87040-349-4). Japan Pubns USA.

Buddhistic Studies. Ed. by Bimala C. Law. LC 78-72463. Repr. of 1931 ed. 74.50 (ISBN 0-404-17335-7). AMS Pr.

Buddhists Find Christ: The Spiritual Quest of Thirteen Men & Women in Burma, China, Japan, Korea, Sri Lanka, Thailand, Vietnam. Compiled by Patrick O'Connor. 240p. 1975. pap. 2.25 (ISBN 0-8048-1146-6). C E Tuttle.

Buddhiyoga of the Gita & Other Essays. Anirvan. LC 84-900102. 1984. 16.00x (ISBN 0-8364-1120-X, Pub. by Biblia Impex). South Asia Bks.

Buddism. Trevor Ling. 1985. 13.00x (ISBN 0-7062-3594-0, Pub. by Ward Lock Educ Co Ltd). State Mutual Bk.

Buddism: Art & Faith. Wladimir Zwalf. (Illus.). 300p. 1985. text ed. 45.00x (ISBN 0-02-934500-6). Macmillan.

Buddist Cave Temples of India. Owen C. Kail. (Illus.). xi, 138p. 1981. text ed. 25.00x (ISBN 0-86590-043-4, Pub. by Taraporevala India). Apt Bks.

Buddist Pilgrim at the Holy Places of Tibet Based on Diaries Kept over the Years 1899-1902. G. T. Tsybikov. 482p. Repr. of 1919 ed. text ed. 74.52x (ISBN 0-576-03102-X). Gregg Intl.

Buena Familia Hace un Mundo Mejor. (Span.). 3.50 (ISBN 0-318-02210-9). Chrstphrs NY.

Bug & Nona on the Go. Nona Freeman. Ed. by Charles Clanton. LC 86-9845. 176p. (Orig.). 1979. pap. 4.95 (ISBN 0-912315-27-X). Word Aflame.

Build Your Church Through Camping. Lloyd Mattson. 48p. (Orig.). 1984. pap. 1.95 (ISBN 0-942684-06-0). Camp Guidepts.

Builder of Bridges: The Biography of Dr. Bob Jones, Sr. R. K. Johnson. (Illus.). 383p. 1982. pap. 5.95 (ISBN 0-89084-157-8). Bob Jones Univ Pr.

Builders: A Story & Study of Freemasonry. 9th printing ed. Joseph F. Newton. (Illus.). 345p. 1985. Repr. 11.95 (ISBN 0-88053-045-6). Macoy Pub.

Builders & Humanists: The Renaissance Popes As Patrons of the Arts. Raymond Marcel et al. (Illus.). 1966. pap. 8.00 (ISBN 0-914412-20-5). Inst for the Arts.

Builders of Catholic America. Albert J. Nevins. LC 85-72363. 250p. (Orig.). 1985. pap. 7.95 (ISBN 0-87973-582-1, 582). Our Sunday Visitor.

Builders of the Kingdom. Merlo Pusey. LC 81-10005. 1981. 10.95 (ISBN 0-8425-1968-8). Brigham.

Builders of the Social Order. facs. ed. Joseph F. Thorning. LC 68-57340. (Essay Index Reprint Ser.). 1941. 15.00 (ISBN 0-8369-0936-4). Ayer Co Pubs.

Building a Caring Church. Tom Lovorn & Janie Lovorn. 104p. 1986. pap. 8.95 (ISBN 0-89693-150-1). Victor Bks.

Building a Caring-Sharing Community of Believers. Elvin M. Powers. 128p. 1983. pap. 3.95 (ISBN 0-8341-0822-4). Beacon Hill.

Building a Christian Family: A Guide for Parents. Kenneth Gangel & Elizabeth Gangel. (Orig.). 1987. pap. 6.95 (ISBN 0-8024-1506-7). Moody.

Building a Christian Marriage. William E. Hulme. LC 65-22192. 1968. pap. 5.95 (ISBN 0-8066-0813-7, 10-0940). Augsburg.

Building a Christian World View, Vol. 1: God, Man, & Knowledge. Ed. by W. Andrew Hoffecker & Gary S. Smith. 368p. Date not set. 14.95 (ISBN 0-87552-281-5). Presby & Reformed.

Building a Faith to Live By: Programs for Youth (Foundation for Discipleship) Bryon R. McCane & Preston C. VanLoon. 128p. 1987. pap. 9.95 (ISBN 0-8170-1107-2). Judson.

Building a Fort in the Family Tree. Scott Noon. 1984. 3.50 (ISBN 0-89536-703-3, 4884). CSS of Ohio.

Building a Happy Marriage. Michael P. Pentar. pap. 2.95 (ISBN 0-8198-1114-9). Dghtrs St Paul.

Building a Judaica Library Collection: A/Resource Guide. Edith Lubetski & Meir Lubetski. 185p. 1983. lib. bdg. 30.00 (ISBN 0-87287-375-7). Libs Unl.

Building a Just Society. Patrick Bascio. LC 80-27238. 176p. (Orig.). 1981. pap. 5.95 (ISBN 0-88344-205-1). Orbis Bks.

Building a Love That Lasts: Outstanding Articles on Marriage from the Ensign. LC 85-16011. 192p. 1985. 8.95 (ISBN 0-87747-852-X). Deseret Bk.

Building a Meaningful Life with the Carpenter's Twenty Megatruths. Herb Miller. 108p. (Orig.). 1968. pap. write for info. (ISBN 0-937462-03-9). Net Pr.

Building a School System. Helen Praetz. 178p. 1980. 28.00x (ISBN 0-522-84213-5, Pub. by Melbourne U Pr Australia). Intl Spec Bk.

Building a Young Adult Ministry. Larry LeFeber. 1980. pap. 5.95 (ISBN 0-8170-0848-9). Judson.

Building an Effective Church School. Mary Sandell. 1986. pap. 10.00 (ISBN 0-8309-0441-7). Herald Hse.

Building an Effective Youth Ministry. Glenn E. Ludwig. LC 79-12282. (Creative Leadership Ser.). 1979. pap. 6.95 (ISBN 0-687-03992-4). Abingdon.

Building Bible Study Skills. Anne Wilcox. 60p. 1985. 4.95 (ISBN 0-87123-832-2); student's wkbk. 3.95 (ISBN 0-87123-821-7). Bethany Hse.

Building Character in the American Boy: The Boy Scouts, YMCA, & Their Forerunners, 1870-1920. David I. Macleod. LC 83-47763. 464p. 1983. text ed. 27.50x (ISBN 0-299-09400-6). U of Wis Pr.

Building Christian Character. Paul Anderson. (Trinity Teen Curriculum Ser.). 48p. 1984. Repr. student wkbk. 3.95 (ISBN 0-87123-436-X, 210436); tchr's. guide 4.95 (ISBN 0-87123-430-0). Bethany Hse.

Building Christian Commitment. Richard L. Dugan. (Trinity Bible Ser.). 107p. (Orig.). 1982. wkbk. 3.95 (ISBN 0-87123-280-4, 240280). Bethany Hse.

Building Christian Communities for Justice. Paul S. Roy. LC 81-80050. 188p. (Orig.). 1981. pap. 9.95 (ISBN 0-8091-2380-0). Paulist Pr.

Building Christian Community. Catherine Martin. 1.17 (ISBN 0-8091-9311-6). Paulist Pr.

Building Christian Community Through Small Groups. Roberta Hestenes. pap. 69.95x incl. tapes (ISBN 0-9602638-5-3). Fuller Theol Soc.

Building Christian Confidence. Eva Gibson & Steven Price. (Building Bks.). 64p. (Orig.). 1987. tchr's. guide 4.95 (ISBN 0-87123-935-3). Bethany Hse.

Building Christian Confidence. Eva Gibson & Steven Price. (Building Bks.). 76p. (Orig.). 1987. student wkbk. 3.95 (ISBN 0-87123-934-5). Bethany Hse.

Building Christian Discipline. Eileen Pollinger. 96p. (Orig.). 1986. pap. 3.95 (ISBN 0-87123-877-2); tchr's guide 4.95 (ISBN 0-87123-878-0). Bethany Hse.

Building Christian English Series. Lela Birky & Lucy Conley. 1973. write for info. (ISBN 0-686-05606-X); tchr's. ed. avail. (ISBN 0-686-05607-8). Rod & Staff.

Building Christian Relationships. Neta Jackson. 64p. 1984. pap. 3.95 (ISBN 0-87123-407-6); pap. 4.95 tchr's guide (ISBN 0-87123-429-7). Bethany Hse.

Building Christ's Body: The Dynamics of Christian Living According to St. Paul. George T. Montague. 1976. 5.50 (ISBN 0-8199-0573-9). Franciscan Herald.

Building Community in Youth Groups. Denny Rydberg. LC 85-17645. (Illus.). 177p. (Orig.). 1985. pap. 11.95 (ISBN 0-931529-06-9). Group Bks.

Building Economic Justice: The Bishops Pastoral Letter & Tools for Action. National Conference of Catholic Bishops. 112p. (Orig.). 1986. pap. 7.95 (ISBN 1-55586-122-9). US Catholic.

Building Effective Ministry: Theory & Practice in the Local Church. Ed. by Carl S. Dudley. LC 82-48411. 256p. 1983. pap. 8.95 (ISBN 0-06-062102-8, RD-418, HarpR). Har-Row.

Building Faith in Families: Using the Sacraments in Pastoral Ministry. Frank G. Dunn. 160p. (Orig.). 1987. pap. 8.95 (ISBN 0-8192-1394-2). Morehouse.

Building Family: An Act of Faith. Paul H. Connolly. LC 82-74073. 96p. 1982. pap. 4.95 (ISBN 0-87029-186-6, 20277-0). Abbey.

Building for Justice: A Guide for Social Concerns Committees. Ed. by John Bins. 1.77 (ISBN 0-8091-9309-4). Paulist Pr.

Building God's People in a Materialistic Society. John H. Westerhoff, III. 144p. 1983. pap. 8.95 (ISBN 0-8164-2466-7, HarpR). Har-Row.

Building Happy Memories & Family Traditions. Verna Birkey & Jeanette Turnquist. (Illus.). 128p. 1983. 4.95 (ISBN 0-8007-5109-4, Power Bks). Revell.

Building Jewish Ethical Character. 319p. 6.00 (ISBN 0-914131-08-7, I20). Torah Umesorah.

Building Leaders for Church Education. Kenneth O. Gangel. 1981. 21.95 (ISBN 0-8024-1592-X). Moody.

Building Maintenance for Churches. Robert C. Taylor. (Illus.). 136p. 1982. 13.95 (ISBN 0-9608714-0-3). Carrol Gate Pr.

Building of Character. rev. ed. J. R. Miller. Ed. by Joan Zodhiates. 1975. pap. 3.95 (ISBN 0-89957-516-1). AMG Pubs.

Building of the Cosmos; Or, Panchastikayasara (the Five Cosmic Constituents) Kundakunda Acharya. Ed. by A. Chakravartinayanan. LC 73-3837. (No. 3). Repr. of 1920 ed. 25.00 (ISBN 0-404-57703-2). AMS Pr.

Building of the Eighteenth Century Church. Basil Clarke. LC 66-37309. (Illus.). 1963. text ed. 20.00x (ISBN 0-8401-0404-9). A R Allenson.

Building People Through a Caring, Sharing Fellowship. Donald Bubna & Sarah Ricketts. 1982. pap. 5.95 (ISBN 0-8423-0187-9); leader's guide o. p. 2.95 (ISBN 0-8423-0188-7). Tyndale.

Building Positive Parent-Teen Relationships: Teacher's Guide. Norman Wright & Rex Johnson. LC 78-56980. 1978. pap. 9.95 (ISBN 0-89081-148-2); transparencies & repro masters incl. Harvest Hse.

Building Relationships Through Pastoral Visitation. Lyle Bradford. 64p. 1984. pap. 4.95 (ISBN 0-8170-1006-8). Judson.

Building Relationships...With God & Others. Jim Burns & Doug Webster. (Jim Burns Youth Ser.: No. 2). 64p. (Orig.). 1986. wkbk. 3.95 (ISBN 0-89081-479-1). Harvest Hse.

Building Respect, Responsibility, & Spiritual Values in Your Child. Mike Phillips. LC 81-12225. 138p. (Orig.). 1981. pap. 3.95 (ISBN 0-87123-146-8, 210146). Bethany Hse.

Building Sermons to Meet People's Needs. Harold T. Bryson & James C. Taylor. LC 78-74962. 1980. 7.95 (ISBN 0-8054-2109-2). Broadman.

Building Small Groups in the Christian Community. John Mallison. (Abridged Small Group Ser.). (Illus.). 238p. (Orig.). 1978. pap. 7.95 (ISBN 0-909202-05-2, Pub. by Renewal Pubns). ANZ Religious Pubns.

Building Stones for an Understanding of the Mystery of Golgotha. Rudolf Steiner. 240p. 1972. 10.95 (ISBN 0-85440-263-2). Anthroposophic.

Building Strength at the YMCA. Wayne L. Westcott. LC 86-20838. (Illus.). 104p. (Orig.). 1987. pap. text ed. 8.00x (ISBN 0-87322-082-X, LWES4885). Human Kinetics.

Building Stronger Families. Royce Money. LC 83-51300. 156p. 1984. pap. 5.95 (ISBN 0-88207-244-7). Victor Bks.

Building Teen Excitement: A Youth Worker's Guide. Shirley Pollock. LC 85-11256. 80p. (Orig.). 1985. pap. 8.95 (ISBN 0-687-03993-2). Abingdon.

Building the Earth. Teilhard De Chardin. 7.95 (ISBN 0-87193-078-1). Dimension Bks.

Building the Faith Community. Cora M. Dubitsky. LC 74-12632. 192p. 1975. pap. 2.95 (ISBN 0-8091-1848-3). Paulist Pr.

Building the House Church. Lois Barrett. LC 86-14324. 176p. (Orig.). 1986. pap. 8.95 (ISBN 0-8361-3415-X). Herald Pr.

Building the House: Essays on Christian Education. Ed. by James A. DeJong & Louis Y. Van Dyke. 153p. (Orig.). 1981. pap. 5.95 (ISBN 0-932914-05-5). Dordt Coll Pr.

Building the Local Church, Shared Responsibiity in Diocesan Pastoral Councils. 88p. 1984. pap. 6.95 (ISBN 1-55586-907-6). US Catholic.

Building the Medieval Cathedrals. P. Watson. LC 74-19525. (Introduction to the History of Mankind). 48p. 1976. pap. 4.95 limp bdg. (ISBN 0-521-08711-2). Cambridge U Pr.

Building the Medieval Cathedrals. Percy Watson. LC 78-56794. (Cambridge Topic Bks). (Illus.). 1978. PLB 8.95 (ISBN 0-8225-1213-0). Lerner Pubns.

Building the Word: The Dynamics of Communication & Preaching. J. Randall Nichols. LC 79-3590. 176p. 1981. 10.00 (ISBN 0-06-066109-7, HarpR). Har-Row.

Building Troyes Cathedral: The Late Gothic Campaigns. Stephen Murray. LC 85-45744. (Illus.). 272p. 1986. 47.50x (ISBN 0-253-31277-9). Ind U Pr.

Building up One Another. Gene A. Getz. LC 76-19918. 120p. 1976. pap. 4.95 (ISBN 0-88207-744-9). Victor Bks.

Building with Buses. Daniel Johnson. pap. 2.95 (ISBN 0-8010-5059-6). Baker Bk.

Building Your Bible School. Les Gleaves. 1986. 4.95 (ISBN 0-931097-10-X). Sentinel Pub.

Building Your Child's Faith. Alice Chapin. 144p. (Orig.). 1983. pap. 5.95 (ISBN 0-86605-115-5). Campus Crusade.

Building Your Christian Day School, Bk. 1: Policies & Procedures. Joy Adcock. 60p. 1985. pap. text ed. 3.95 (ISBN 0-931097-07-X). Sentinel Pub.

Building Your Christian Day School, Bk. 2: Handwork & Curriculum. Joy Adcock. 410p. 1985. pap. text ed. 14.95 (ISBN 0-931097-08-8). Sentinel Pub.

Building Your Faith. Bill Yasko & Dot Yasko. 76p. (Orig.). 1984. pap. text ed. 4.95 (ISBN 0-931097-01-0). Sentinel Pub.

Building Your Family to Last. Kari T. Malcolm. 180p. (Orig.). 1987. pap. 6.95 (ISBN 0-87784-984-6). Inter-Varsity.

Building Your Self-Image. Josh McDowell. (Living Bks.). Orig. Title: His Image...My Image. 192p. 1986. Repr. 3.95 (ISBN 0-8423-1395-8). Tyndale.

Building Your Youth Ministry. Russell Carney & Jim Moss. 1986. 4.95 (ISBN 0-931097-09-6). Sentinel Pub.

Built upon the Cornerstone. Joseph M. Tewinkel. LC 80-65148. (Illus.). 178p. (Orig.). 1980. 3.95 (ISBN 0-87509-280-2); Leader's Guide. 2.95 (ISBN 0-87509-286-1). Chr Pubns.

Bulfinch's Mythology. abr. ed. Thomas Bulfinch. Ed. by Edmund Fuller. 448p. 1959. pap. 4.50 (ISBN 0-440-30845-3, LE). Dell.

Bulfinch's Mythology, 3 vols. Thomas Bulfinch. Incl. Vol. 1. The Age of Fable. 408p. pap. 3.95 (ISBN 0-451-62444-0, ME2230); Vols 2 & 3. The Age of Chivalry & Legends of Charlemagne. 608p. pap. 3.95 (ISBN 0-451-62252-9, ME2252). (YA) pap. (Ment). NAL.

Bulfinch's Mythology. 2nd rev. ed. Thomas Bulfinch. LC 69-11314. (Illus.). 1970. 16.45i (ISBN 0-690-57260-3). T Y Crowell.

Bulgakov Photographic Bibliography. Ed. by Ellendea Proffer. 140p. 1984. 35.00 (ISBN 0-88233-812-9); pap. 15.00 (ISBN 0-88233-813-7). Ardis Pubs.

Bulgaria & Her Jews: The History of a Dubious Symbiosis. Vicki Tamir. LC 78-62154. (Illus.). 1979. 14.95 (ISBN 0-87203-075-X). Hermon.

Bulgarian Monasteries: Monuments of History, Culture & Art. Georgy Charukov. 1981. 89.00x (ISBN 0-569-08507-1, Pub. by Collets UK). State Mutual Bk.

Bull: A Religious & Secular History of Phallus Worship & Male Homosexuality. Georgia Pesek-Marous. (Illus.). 185p. (Orig.). 1984. pap. 9.95 (ISBN 0-916453-01-4). Tau Pr.

Bulletin Board Builders, No. 3. Judy Dorsett. (Illus.). 64p. 1986. 3.95 (ISBN 0-87403-020-X, 3240). Standard Pub.

Bulletin Board Designs for the Christian Classroom. Carolyn Berg. 1984. pap. 5.95 tchr's. material (ISBN 0-570-03930-4, 12-2866). Concordia.

Bulletin Board Ideas: Creative Ways to Communicate the Gospel. Sandra Sorlien. (Illus.). 40p. (Orig.). 1980. pap. 4.95 (ISBN 0-8066-1778-0, 10-0949). Augsburg.

Bulletin Board Ideas for Sunday School & Church. Virgene Coursen. 32p. 1977. pap. 3.50 (ISBN 0-687-04374-3). Abingdon.

Bulletin Boards That Communicate: Creative Ideas for the Congregation. Sandra Sorlien. 56p. (Orig.). 1984. pap. 4.95 (ISBN 0-8066-2073-0, 10-0950). Augsburg.

Bulletin Builders. Gussie Lambert. 3.95 (ISBN 0-89315-024-X). Lambert Bk.

Bulletin of Religion, ISPP Vol. 1, No. 4. M. A. Barth. 60p. 1974. Repr. 2.00 (ISBN 0-88065-050-8, Pub. by Messers Today & Tomorrow Printers & Publishers India). Scholarly Pubns.

Bultmann. H. N. Ridderbos. (Modern Thinkers Ser.). 1960. pap. 2.00 (ISBN 0-87552-581-4). Presby & Reformed.

Bultmann School of Biblical Interpretation: New Directions. James M. Robinson et al. Ed. by Robert W. Funk & Gerhard Ebeling. 1965. lib. bdg. 17.50x (ISBN 0-88307-242-4). Gannon.

Bumps Are What You Climb On. Warren W. Wiersbe. 1980. pap. 4.95 (ISBN 0-8010-9629-4). Baker Bk.

Bunker. Charles Goldstein. Tr. by Esther Malkin from Fr. LC 74-116978. (Temple Bks). 1973. pap. 3.95 (ISBN 0-689-70347-3, T27). Atheneum.

Bunyan. James A. Froude. Ed. by John Morley. LC 68-58379. (English Men of Letters). Repr. of 1888 ed. lib. bdg 12.50 (ISBN 0-404-51711-0). AMS Pr.

Bunyan. James A. Froude. LC 73-11369. 1880. lib. bdg. 12.00 (ISBN 0-8414-1985-X). Folcroft.

Bunyan As a Man of Letters. Clifford K. Wright. LC 77-4072. 1977. Repr. lib. bdg. 9.50 (ISBN 0-8414-9601-3). Folcroft.

Bunyan Calling: A Voice from the Seventeenth Century. M. P. Willcocks. 1979. Repr. of 1943 ed. lib. bdg. 30.00 (ISBN 0-8414-9718-4). Folcroft.

Bunyan Calling: A Voice from the Seventeenth Century. M. P. Willcocks. 1943. 17.50 (ISBN 0-8274-1984-8). R West.

Bunyan Pilgrim & Dreamer: John Bunyan - His Life & Work. Ernest W. Bacon. 186p. 1984. pap. 5.95 (ISBN 0-8010-0869-7). Baker Bk.

Burden Is Light. Eugenia Price. 272p. 1985. pap. 11.95 (ISBN 0-8027-2514-7). Walker & Co.

Burden is Light: The Autobiography of a Transformed Pagan. Eugenia Price. 176p. pap. 2.95 (ISBN 0-8007-8583-5, Spire Bks). Revell.

Burden of Conscience: French Jewry's Response to the Holocaust. Richard I. Cohen. (The Modern Jewish Experience Ser.). 351p. 1987. 27.50 (ISBN 0-253-31263-9). Ind U Pr.

Burial of the Dead: Rite One. Ed. by Howard Galley. 1977. pap. 0.95 (ISBN 0-8164-2152-8, HarpR). Har-Row.

Burial of the Dead: Rite Two. Ed. by Howard Galley. 1977. pap. 0.95 (ISBN 0-8164-2153-6, HarpR). Har-Row.

Burial Services: Revised & Updated. Joseph B. Bernardin. 1980. casebound 14.95 (ISBN 0-8192-1267-9). Morehouse.

Buried Alive for Christ & Other Missionary Stories. V. Ben Kendrick. LC 78-14984. 1978. pap. 3.95 (ISBN 0-87227-061-0). Reg Baptist.

Buried Cities Recovered: Explorations in Bible Lands. Frank S. De Hass. Ed. by Moshe Davis. LC 77-70774. (America & the Holy Land). (Illus.). 1977. lib. bdg. 40.00x (ISBN 0-405-10242-9). Ayer Co Pubs.

Burl Ives Bible-Time Stories, 12 bks. Set. incl. lp. 14.95 (ISBN 0-89191-299-1, 52993); Set. incl. cassette 14.95 (ISBN 0-89191-297-5, 52977). Cook.

Burma: Literature, Historiography, Scholarship, Language, Life & Buddhism. Hla Pe. 224p. 1986. pap. text ed. 17.50 (ISBN 9971-988-00-3, Pub. by Inst Southeast Asian Stud). Gower Pub Co.

Burmese Buddhist Law. E Maung. LC 77-87483. Repr. of 1937 ed. 25.00 (ISBN 0-404-16812-4). AMS Pr.

Burmese Sit-Tans, Seventeen Sixty-Four to Eighteen Twenty-Six: Records of Rural Life & Administration. Frank N. Trager & William J. Koenig. (Association for Asian Studies Monographs: No. 36). 440p. 1979. 9.50x (ISBN 0-8165-0672-8). U of Ariz Pr.

Burmese Supernaturalism. enlarged ed. Melford E. Spiro. LC 77-17280. pap. 84.00 (ISBN 0-317-42082-8, 2025708). Bks Demand UMI.

Burned Alive! Jerry Golden & Steve Lestarjette. 176p. 1987. pap. text ed. 5.95 (ISBN 0-939079-01-1). Christlife Pubs.

Burned-over District: The Social & Intellectual History of Enthusiastic Religion in Western New York, 1800-1850. Whitney R. Cross. LC 81-2636. xii, 383p. 1981. Repr. of 1950 ed. lib. bdg. 31.50x (ISBN 0-374-91932-1, Octagon). Hippocrene Bks.

Burned-over District: The Social & Intellectual History of Enthusiastic Religion in Western New York, 1800-1850. Whitney R. Cross. 400p. 1982. pap. 9.95x (ISBN 0-8014-9232-7). Cornell U Pr.

Burned to Life. Mel Kenyon & Mike Christophus. LC 76-1060. (Illus.). 1976. pap. 2.95 (ISBN 0-87123-044-5, 200044). Bethany Hse.

Burning & a Shining Light: English Spirituality in the Age of Wesley. Ed. by David L. Jeffrey. 512p. (Orig.). 1987. pap. 16.95 (ISBN 0-8028-0234-6). Eerdmans.

Burning Burning Bush. Robert O. Reddish, Jr. LC 73-85938. (Illus.). 1974. 11.95 (ISBN 0-686-05480-6). Rorge Pub Co.

Burning Bush. Stuart Y. Blanch. 1979. pap. 5.95 (ISBN 0-8192-1260-1). Morehouse.

Burning Bush. Geoffrey Spencer. LC 74-84762. 1974. pap. 6.50 (ISBN 0-8309-0129-9). Herald Hse.

Burning Cataracts of Christ. Robert M. Gautrey. 1980. Repr. of 1933 ed. lib. bdg. 30.00 (ISBN 0-8482-4193-2). Norwood Edns.

Burning Cataracts of Christ: An Evangelical Interpretation of John Mosefield's "The Ever-Lasting Mercy". R. Moffat Gautrey. LC 78-23716. 1933. lib. bdg. 20.00 (ISBN 0-8414-4483-8). Folcroft.

Burning Heart: John Wesley, Evangelist. A. Skevington Wood. LC 78-52837. 1978. pap. 7.95 (ISBN 0-87123-043-7, 210043). Bethany Hse.

Burning of the Convent. Louise G. Whitney. LC 70-90196. (Mass Violence in America). Repr. of 1877 ed. 10.00 (ISBN 0-405-01341-8). Ayer Co Pubs.

Burnout. Myron Rush. 156p. 1987. pap. 6.95 (ISBN 0-89693-242-7). Victor Bks.

Burnout in Ministry. Brooks R. Faulkner. LC 81-67752. 1981. pap. 5.95 (ISBN 0-8054-2414-8). Broadman.

Burnt Offerings: Parables for Twentieth Century Christians. E. T. Eberhart. LC 77-23158. 1977. pap. 3.95 (ISBN 0-687-04375-1). Pilgrim Hse.

Bursting of New Wineskins: Reflection on Religion & Culture at the End of Affluence. Carl A. Raschke. LC 78-16604. (Pittsburgh Theological Monographs: No. 24). 1978. 10.75 (ISBN 0-915138-34-4). Pickwick.

Bursting the Wineskins: Spiritual Odyssey of a Peacemaker. Michael Cassidy. 280p. 1983. pap. 6.95 (ISBN 0-87788-094-8). Shaw Pubs.

Bury St. Edmunds & the Urban Crisis, 1290-1539. Robert S. Gottfried. LC 81-11984. (Illus.). 324p. 1981. 34.00x (ISBN 0-691-05340-5). Princeton U Pr.

Bushido: The Soul of Japan. Inazo Nitobe. LC 77-83070. 1969. Repr. of 1905 ed. 7.25 (ISBN 0-8048-0693-4). C E Tuttle.

Business & Religion in Britain, Vol. 5. David Jeremy. (Business and History Ser.). 220p. 1987. text ed. 60.00 (ISBN 0-566-05096-X). Gower Pub Co.

Business Ethics. Edward Stevens. LC 79-91409. 248p. (Orig.). 1979. pap. 9.95 (ISBN 0-8091-2244-8). Paulist Pr.

Business Ethics in Jewish Law. Leo Jung & Aaron Levine. LC 86-22889. Date not set. 27.50x (ISBN 0-88482-918-9). Hebrew Pub.

Business Ethics in Jewish Law. Edward Zipperstein. 1983. 15.00 (ISBN 0-88125-005-8); pap. 9.95 (ISBN 0-88125-022-8). Ktav.

Business of Heaven: Daily Readings from C. S. Lewis. C. S. Lewis. 1984. pap. 7.95 (ISBN 0-15-614863-3, Harv). HarBraceJ.

Business, Religion & Ethics: Inquiry & Encounter. Ed. by Donald G. Jones. LC 82-14479. 288p. 1982. 25.00 (ISBN 0-89946-164-6); pap. text ed. 12.95 (ISBN 0-89946-166-2). Oelgeschlager.

Busqueda de Dios. A. W. Tozer. Tr. by Dardo Bruchez. 130p. (Orig.). 1979. pap. 2.75 (ISBN 0-87509-162-8); pap. 2.00 mass mkt. (ISBN 0-87509-159-8). Chr Pubns.

Bustan Al-Ukul. Nathanael Ibn Al-Fayyumi. Tr. by David Levine. LC 8-4311. (American Geographical Society. Oriental Explorations & Studies: No. 6). 20.75 (ISBN 0-404-50496-5). AMS Pr.

But for the Grace of God.... Martin. (Orig.). 1984. pap. 1.00 (ISBN 0-914733-02-8). Desert Min.

But God Has Promised. Cecil Murphey. LC 76-16283. 1976. pap. 2.95 (ISBN 0-88419-002-1). Creation Hse.

But I Didn't Want a Divorce. Andre Bustanoby. 1978. o. p. 5.95 (ISBN 0-310-22170-6, 9207P); pap. 5.95 (ISBN 0-310-22171-4). Zondervan.

But I Have Called You Friends. Mary Francis. 1974. 4.95 (ISBN 0-8199-0500-3). Franciscan Herald.

But I Never Thought He'd Die: Practical Help for Widows. Miriam B. Nye. LC 78-9644. 150p. 1978. pap. 7.95 (ISBN 0-664-24208-1). Westminster.

But Not Forsaken. Helen G. Brenneman. 1983. 3.25 (ISBN 0-87813-954-0). Christian Light.

But This Night Is Different. Raymond A. Zwerin & Audrey F. Marcus. (Illus.). 48p. 1981. text ed. 7.95x (ISBN 0-8074-0032-7, 102561). UAHC.

But Time & Chance: The Biography of Padre Martinez of Taos. Fray A. Chavez. LC 81-27. 176p. 1981. 35.00x (ISBN 0-913270-96-2); pap. 11.95 (ISBN 0-913270-95-4). Sunstone Pr.

Butler's Lives of the Saints. Ed. by Michael Walsh. LC 84-48781. 496p. 1985. 20.45 (ISBN 0-06-069251-0, HarpR). Har-Row.

Buying Time: The Foundation of the Electronic Church. Peter Elvy. (Illus.). 1987. pap. 5.95 (ISBN 0-89622-325-6). Twenty-Third.

Bwiti: An Ethnography of the Religious Imagination in Africa. James W. Fernandez. LC 81-47125. (Illus.). 708p. 1982. 97.50x (ISBN 0-691-09390-3); pap. 28.00x LPE (ISBN 0-691-10122-1). Princeton U Pr.

By Birth or by Choice. Martha D. Stahl. LC 86-33643. 136p. (Orig.). 1987. pap. 5.95 (ISBN 0-8361-3437-0). Herald Pr.

By Death Parted: The Stories of Six Widows. Intro. by Philip Jebb. 1986. pap. 5.95 (ISBN 0-932506-45-3). St Bedes Pubns.

By Faith. G. S. Steidl. 48p. pap. 3.25 (ISBN 0-88172-127-1). Believers Bkshelf.

By Faith Abraham & Sarah: Genesis 12-25. Waldemar Janzen. Ed. by Maynard Shelly. LC 86-83035. (Faith & Life Bible Studies). 70p. (Orig.). 1987. pap. 4.95 (ISBN 0-87303-108-3). Faith & Life.

By Freedom's Holy Light. Gordon Palmer. 1964. 9.95 (ISBN 0-8159-5110-8). Devin.

By God, You Can Do It. Robert G. Kirkley. 1985. 9.95 (ISBN 0-345-32266-5, Pub. by Ballantine Epiphany). Ballantine.

By His Grace. John A. Braun. 1983. pap. 7.95 (ISBN 0-8100-0161-6, 06N0560). Northwest Pub.

By His Stripes: The Doctrine of Divine Healing. Hugh P. Jeter. LC 76-20893. 224p. 1977. pap. 4.95 (ISBN 0-88243-521-3, 02-0521). Gospel Pub.

By Jupiter: Odysseys to a Giant. Eric Burgess. LC 82-4139. (Illus.). 192p. 1982. 26.50x (ISBN 0-231-05176-X). Columbia U Pr.

By Life or By Death: A Practical Commentary on Paul's Letter to the Philippians. H. Leo Eddleman. 176p. (Orig.). 1981. pap. 3.75 (ISBN 0-682-49700-2, Testament). Exposition Pr FL.

By Love Compelled. Peter M. Rinaldi. (Illus., Orig.). 1973. pap. 3.25 (ISBN 0-89944-032-0). Don Bosco Multimedia.

By Many Infallible Proofs. F. Von Keitzell. 76p. pap. 4.95 (ISBN 0-88172-137-9). Believers Bkshelf.

By My Laugh Its Jewish. 1982 ed. Nero, pseud. (Illus.). 110p. Date not set. 12.50x (ISBN 0-85303-197-5, Pub. by Vallentine Mitchell England); pap. 6.50x (ISBN 0-85303-198-3). Biblio Dist.

By One Spirit. Karl A. Olsson. (Illus.). 1962. pap. 9.95x (ISBN 0-910452-10-5). Covenant.

By Ones & By Twos: Single & Double Missionaries. Jeannie Lockerbie. LC 83-7272. (Mission Candidate Aids Ser.). 96p. 1983. pap. 4.95 (ISBN 0-87808-194-1). William Carey Lib.

By-Paths in Hebraic Bookland. Israel Abrahams. LC 77-174368. Repr. of 1920 ed. 17.00 (ISBN 0-405-08177-4, Pub. by Blom Publications). Ayer Co Pubs.

By Post to the Apostles. facs. ed. Helen Homan. LC 74-148219. (Biography Index Reprint Ser.). 1952. 20.00 (ISBN 0-8369-8066-2). Ayer Co Pubs.

By Searching. Isobel Kuhn. 1959. pap. 3.95 (ISBN 0-8024-0053-1). Moody.

By Shaker Hands. June Sprigg. (Illus.). 1975. pap. 15.95 (ISBN 0-394-73143-3). Knopf.

By the Grace of God. Nancy B. Hess. 1979. 12.50 (ISBN 0-87813-207-4). Park View.

By the Hands of Wise Men: Essays on the U. S. Constitution. Ed. by Ray C. Hillam. LC 79-13702. 1979. pap. text ed. 5.95 (ISBN 0-8425-1647-6). Brigham.

By the Holy Tetrakyts: Symbol & Reality in Man & Universe. L. Gordon Plummer. (Study Ser.: No. 9). (Illus.). 96p. (Orig.). 1982. pap. 5.75 (ISBN 0-913004-44-8). Point Loma Pub.

By the Light of His Lamp. John F. Marshall. (Spirit & Life Ser). 1967. 2.00 (ISBN 0-686-11574-0). Franciscan Inst.

By the River of No Return. Don I. Smith. LC 85-60311. (Illus.). 112p. 1985. pap. 5.95 (ISBN 0-932773-00-1). High Country Bks.

By the Sweat of My Brow. Wheless. 2.50 (ISBN 0-685-02583-7). Outlook.

By Their Blood. James Hefley & Marti Hefley. 1986. pap. 8.95 (ISBN 0-8010-4312-3). Baker Bk.

By Their Blood: Christian Martyrs of the Twentieth Century. James Hefley & Marti Hefley. LC 78-6187. 1979. pap. 7.95 (ISBN 0-915134-24-1). Mott Media.

By This Shall All Men Know. Boyce Mouton. LC 79-56541. 1980. pap. 2.95 (ISBN 0-89900-139-4). College Pr Pub.

By This Standard. Greg L. Bahnsen. 432p. 1985. pap. 4.95 (ISBN 0-930464-06-0). Dominion Pr.

By Words Alone: The Holocaust in Literature. Sidra D. Ezrahi. LC 79-56908. 1980. 19.00x (ISBN 0-226-23335-9). U of Chicago Pr.

Byttook or Crook: The Life of Peter. Jill Briscoe. 192p. 1987. 12.95 (ISBN 0-8499-0561-3). Word Bks.

Byzantine Altar Gospel. Joseph Raya & Jose D. Vinck. 350p. 1979. 87.50x (ISBN 0-911726-34-9). Alleluia Pr.

Byzantine Apocalyptic Tradition. Paul J. Alexander. Ed. by Dorothy Abrahamse. LC 82-23816. 248p. 1985. 32.50x (ISBN 0-520-04998-5). U of Cal pr.

Byzantine Churches of Istanbul: A Photographic Survey. Thomas F. Mathews. LC 75-27173. (Illus.). 425p. 1976. 60.00x (ISBN 0-271-01210-2). Pa St U Pr.

Byzantine Decorative Art. Peter Vaboulis. (Illus.). 202p. 125.00 (ISBN 0-89241-035-3). Caratzas.

Byzantine East & Latin West: Two Worlds of Christendom in Middle Ages & Renaissance. Deno J. Geankoplos. LC 76-20685. (Illus.). xii, 206p. 1976. Repr. of 1966 ed. 17.50 (ISBN 0-208-01615-5, Archon). Shoe String.

Byzantine Ecclesiastical Personalities. Pref. by Nomikos M. Vaporis. (Byzantine Fellowship Lectures: No. 2). 107p. 1975. pap. 2.95 (ISBN 0-916586-04-9). Holy Cross Orthodox.

Byzantine Fellowship Lectures, No. One, No. 1. Ed. by N M Vaporis. (Illus.). 1974. pap. 2.95 (ISBN 0-916586-02-2). Holy Cross Orthodox.

Byzantine Hymnography & Byzantine Chant. Dimitri Conomos. Intro. by N. M. Vaporis. (Nicholas E. Kulukundis Lectures in Hellenism Ser.). 56p. (Orig.). 1984. pap. text ed. 4.00 (ISBN 0-917653-04-1). Hellenic Coll Pr.

Byzantine Illumination Eleven Fifty to Twelve Fifty: The Study of a Provincial Tradition. Annemarie W. Carr. (Studies in Medieval Manuscript Illumination Chicago Visual Library: No. 47). (Illus.). 448p. 1987. lib. bdg. 85.00 text-fiche (ISBN 0-226-68863-1). U of Chicago Pr.

Byzantine Legacy in the Orthodox Church. John Meyendorff. LC 82-797. 268p. (Orig.). 1982. pap. 8.95 (ISBN 0-913836-90-7). St Vladimirs.

Byzantine Liturgy. Hans-Joachim Schulz. Tr. by Matthew J. O'Connell from Ger. (Orig.). 1986. pap. 17.50 (ISBN 0-916134-72-5). Pueblo Pub Co.

Byzantine Mosaic Decoration: Aspects of Monumental Art in Byzantium. Otto Demus. (Illus.). 162p. 1976. 25.00 (ISBN 0-89241-018-3). Caratzas.

Byzantine Music & Hymnography. Henry J. Tillyard. LC 74-24242. Repr. of 1923 ed. 11.50 (ISBN 0-404-13116-6). AMS Pr.

Byzantine Patriarchate, Four Hundred Fifty-One to Twelve Hundred Four. 2nd rev. ed. George Every. LC 78-63340. (Crusades & Military Orders: Second Ser.). Repr. of 1962 ed. 27.50 (ISBN 0-404-17015-3). AMS Pr.

Byzantine Pilgrimage Art. Gary Vikan. (Byzantine Collection Publications Ser.: No. 5). (Illus.). 52p. 1982. pap. 4.50x (ISBN 0-88402-113-0). Dumbarton Oaks.

Byzantine Sacred Art. 2nd, rev. & enl. ed. Photios Kontoglou. Compiled by & tr. by Constantine Cavarnos. LC 83-81152. (Illus.). 171p. 1985. 10.50 (ISBN 0-914744-60-7); pap. 7.95 (ISBN 0-914744-61-5). Inst Byzantine.

Byzantine Sacred Music. Constantine Cavarnos. 31p. 1981. pap. 1.00 (ISBN 0-914744-23-2). Inst Byzantine.

Byzantine Saint. Sergei Hackel. LC 83-8738. 245p. 1982. lib. bdg. 23.95x (ISBN 0-89370-081-9); pap. text ed. 15.95x (ISBN 0-7044-0451-6). Borgo Pr.

Byzantine Saint. Ed. by Sergei Hackel. (Illus.). 245p. (Orig.). 1981. pap. 6.95 (ISBN 0-7044-0451-6). St Vladimirs.

Byzantine Slav Liturgy of St. John Chrysostom, Its Origin & Evolution. Casimir Kucharek. LC 74-147735. (Illus.). 840p. 1971. 18.75 (ISBN 0-911726-06-3, BSL). Alleluia Pr.

Byzantine Text-Type & New Testament Textual Criticism. Harry A. Sturz. 320p. 1984. 18.95 (ISBN 0-8407-4958-9). Nelson.

Byzantine Theocracy. Steven Runciman. LC 76-47405. (Weil Lectures Ser.). 1977. 32.50 (ISBN 0-521-21401-7). Cambridge U Pr.

Byzantine Theology: Historical Trends & Doctrinal Themes. 2nd, rev. ed. John Meyendorff. LC 72-94167. viii, 243p. 1983. pap. 9.00 (ISBN 0-8232-0967-9). Fordham.

Byzantinische Antike: Studien auf Grund der Silbergefaesse der Ermitage. Leonid Matzulewitsch. (Archaeologische Mitteilungen aus Russischen Sammlungen, Vol. 2). (Ger., Illus.). xi, 150p. 1974. Repr. of 1929 ed. 216.00 (ISBN 3-1100-2245-1). De Gruyter.

Byzantinische Politik Zur der Zeit Kreuzzuege. Albert Gruhn. 1904. 12.50 (ISBN 0-8337-1479-1). B Franklin.

Byzantium Jewry from Justinian to the Fourth Crusade. Andrew Sharf. (Littman Library of Jewish Civilization). (Illus.). 1971. 24.00x (ISBN 0-19-710021-X). Oxford U Pr.

C

C. C. Slaughter: Rancher, Banker, Baptist. David J. Murrah. (M. K. Brown Range Life Ser.: No. 15). (Illus.). 191p. 1981. 14.95 (ISBN 0-292-71067-4). U of Tex Pr.

C. H. Spurgeon's Prayers. C. H. Spurgeon. 192p. Date not set. pap. price not set. Pilgrim Pubns.

C. S. Lewis. Joe R. Christopher. (Twayne's English Authors Ser.). 160p. 1987. lib. bdg. 16.95 (ISBN 0-8057-6944-7, TEAS 442, Twayne). G K Hall.

C. S. Lewis: A Biography. Roger L. Green & Walter Hooper. LC 75-29425. 320p. 1976. pap. 7.95 (ISBN 0-15-623205-7, Harv). HarBraceJ.

C. S. Lewis: An Annotated Checklist. J. R. Christopher & Joan K. Ostling. LC 73-76556. (Serif Ser.: No. 30). 402p. 1974. 20.00x (ISBN 0-87338-138-6). Kent St U Pr.

C. S. Lewis & the Search for Rational Religion. John Beversluis. 179p. (Orig.). 1985. pap. 9.95 (ISBN 0-8028-0046-7). Eerdmans.

C. S. Lewis: Apostle to the Skeptics. Chad Walsh. LC 78-689. 1974. Repr. of 1949 ed. lib. bdg. 32.50 (ISBN 0-8414-9647-1). Folcroft.

C. S. Lewis Had a Wife. William J. Perersen. 160p. (Orig.). 1985. pap. 2.95 (ISBN 0-8423-0202-6). Tyndale.

C. S. Lewis Through the Shadowlands. Brian Sibley. LC 86-13096. (Illus.). 160p. 1986. pap. text ed. 10.95 (ISBN 0-8007-1509-8). Revell.

C. S. Lewis's Case for the Christian Faith. Richard L. Purtill. LC 81-47435. 160p. 1985. pap. 6.68 (ISBN 0-06-066713-3, HarpR). Har-Row.

C. S. Lovett: Maranatha Man. C. S. Lovett. (Illus.). 1978. pap. 5.95 (ISBN 0-938148-02-8). Personal Christianity.

C. T. Studd. Norman P. Grubb. 1972. 7.95 (ISBN 0-87508-201-7); pap. 5.95 (ISBN 0-87508-202-5). Chr Lit.

Cabala. Bernhard Pick. LC 13-26188. 115p. 1974. pap. 4.95 (ISBN 0-87548-199-X). Open Court.

Cabalah Primer: Introduction to English-Hebrew Cabalah. Henrietta Bernstein. 192p. 1984. pap. 9.95 (ISBN 0-87516-526-5). De Vorss.

Cabalistic Keys to Prayer. Manly P. Hall. pap. 2.50 (ISBN 0-89314-308-1). Philos Res.

Cacus & Marsyas in Etrusco-Roman Legend. Jocelyn P. Small. LC 82-47614. (Princeton Monographs in Art & Archaeology: No. 45). (Illus.). 208p. 1982. 31.50x (ISBN 0-691-03562-8). Princeton U Pr.

Cada Muchacho Necesita un Modelo Vivo. Jorge A. Leon. (Span.). 96p. 1983. pap. 4.75 (ISBN 0-311-46087-9). Casa Bautista.

Cada Nuevo Dia. Corrie Ten Boom. Tr. by Alejandro Clifford from Eng. Tr. of Each New Day. 224p. 1983. pap. 4.50 (ISBN 0-311-40043-4, Edit Mundo). Casa Bautista.

Cademon's Des Angelsachsen Biblishce Dictungen, 2 Vols. K. W. Bouterwek. 393p. 1983. Repr. of 1854 ed. Set. lib. bdg. 400.00 (ISBN 0-8495-0636-0). Arden Lib.

Caer en la Grandeza. Lloyd J. Ogilvie. Tr. by M. Francisco Lievano from Eng. Orig. Title: Falling into Greatness. (Span.). 190p. 1985. pap. 4.95 (ISBN 0-8297-0702-6). Life Pubs Intl.

Caeremoniale Romanum of Agostino Patrizi Piccolomini. Agostino P. Patrizi. 310p. 1516. text ed. 66.24x (ISBN 0-576-99434-0, Pub. by Gregg Intl Pubs England). Gregg Intl.

Caesar & Christ: A History of Roman Civilization from Its Beginnings to A.D. 337. Will Durant. (Story of Civilization: Vol. 3). 1944. 29.95 (ISBN 0-671-11500-6). S&S.

Caesar Baronius: Courtier-Reformation Historian. Cyriac K. Pullapilly. 1975. 21.95x (ISBN 0-268-00501-X). U of Notre Dame Pr.

Caesar's Coin: Religion & Politics in America. Richard P. McBrien. 320p. 1987. 19.95 (ISBN 0-02-919720-1). Macmillan.

Cage. Ruth M. Sender. LC 86-8562. 252p. 1986. 13.95 (ISBN 0-02-781830-6). Macmillan.

Cain & Abel. Joyce Raub. (Arch Bks.). (Illus.). 24p. 1986. pap. 0.99 saddlestitched (ISBN 0-570-06199-7, 59-1422). Concordia.

Cain & Beowulf: A Study in Secular Allegory. David Williams. LC 81-94507. 114p. 1981. 25.00x (ISBN 0-8020-5519-2). U of Toronto Pr.

Cain, Come Home! Paul G. Bretscher. LC 76-1810. (Illus.). 144p. 1976. pap. text ed. 4.25 (ISBN 0-915644-05-3). Clayton Pub Hse.

Cain: Son of the Serpent. David M. Eichhorn. (Limited Editions Reprints). 160p. 1985. 14.95 (ISBN 0-940646-24-2); pap. 8.95 (ISBN 0-940646-19-6). Rossel Bks.

Cajetan Responds: A Reader in Reformation Controversy. Tommaso De Vio. Ed. by Jared Wicks. LC 77-22606. pap. 75.00 (2029507). Bks Demand UMI.

Calabrian Abbott: Jaochim of Fiore in the History of Thought. Bernard McGinn. 320p. 1985. 17.95 (ISBN 0-02-919550-0). Macmillan.

Calalus: A Roman Jewish Colony in America from the Time of Charlemagne Through Alfred the Great. Cyclone Covey. 190p. 1975. 10.00 (ISBN 0-533-01209-0). Vantage.

Calamities, Catastrophies, & Chaos. Peter Popoff. Ed. by Don Tanner. LC 80-69974. (Illus.). 108p. 1980. pap. 2.50 (ISBN 0-938544-01-2). Faith Messenger.

Calas Affair: Persecution, Toleration, & Heresy in Eighteenth-Century Toulouse. David D. Bien. LC 78-12393. 1979. Repr. of 1960 ed. lib. bdg. cancelled (ISBN 0-313-21206-6, BICA). Greenwood.

Calculator Word Games. 1986. pap. 3.95 (ISBN 0-8010-7742-7). Baker Bk.

Calculator Word Games. Bennie Rhodes. LC 77-8870. 1977. pap. 2.95 (ISBN 0-915134-39-X). Mott Media.

Caleb's Colt. Jill Brisco. 1986. pap. 5.95. Ideals.

Calendar of Cases of Witchcraft in Scotland, 1510-1727. Ed. by George F. Black. LC 78-137707. (New York Public Library Publications in Reprint Ser.). (Illus.). 1971. Repr. of 1938 ed. 8.00 (ISBN 0-405-01751-0). Ayer Co Pubs.

Calendar of Death: The Socio-Psychological Factors Influencing the Martyrdom of Thomas of Canterbury. Arthur F. Ide. LC 86-15455. (Medieval People: Vol. 2). (Illus.). viii, 157p. (Orig.). 1986. pap. 9.95 (ISBN 0-934667-02-0). Tangelwuld.

Calendar of Saints: The Lives of the Principal Saints of the Christian Year. James Bentley. (Illus.). 256p. 1987. 22.95 (ISBN 0-8160-1682-8). Facts on File.

Calendar of the Soul. Rudolf Steiner. Tr. by Ruth Pusch & Hans Pusch. 62p. 1982. 7.95 (ISBN 0-88010-009-5). Anthroposophic.

Calendar Question. Basil Priest Sakkas. 96p. (Orig.). 1973. pap. 4.00 (ISBN 0-317-30294-9). Holy Trinity.

Calendars & Indexes to the Letters & Papers of Edward White Benson, Archbishop of Canterbury, 1883-1896 in Lambeth Palace Library, Vol. 3. (Calenders & Indexes to Letters & Papers of Archbishops of Canterbury on Lambeth Palace Library). 252p. 1980. text ed. 52.00x (ISBN 0-7201-1615-5). Mansell.

California Connection. Bob Decard. 90p. (Orig.). 1986. pap. 6.95 (ISBN 0-9616620-1-8). Constellation Pr.

California Missions. 2nd ed. Sunset Editors. LC 79-88016. (Illus.). 320p. 1979. pap. 12.95 (ISBN 0-376-05172-8, Sunset Bks). Sunset-Lane.

California Missions: An Educational Coloring Book. Spizzirri Publishing, Inc. Staff & Linda Spizzirri. (Illus.). 32p. 1985. pap. 1.49 (ISBN 0-86545-062-5). Spizzirri.

California Missions & Their Romances. Mrs. Fremont Older. 314p. 1983. Repr. of 1938 ed. lib. bdg. 50.00 (ISBN 0-89987-620-X). Darby Bks.

California's Reluctant Prelate: The Life & Times of Thaddeus Amat. Francis J. Weber. (Illus.). 1964. 6.75 (ISBN 0-87093-061-3). Dawsons.

Caliphate & Kingship in Mediaeval Persia. Amir H. Siddiqi. LC 77-10621. (Studies in Islamic History: No. 14). 112p. 1978. Repr. of 1937 ed. lib. bdg. 17.50x (ISBN 0-87991-463-7). Porcupine Pr.

Caliphate: Its Rise, Decline & Fall. W. Muir. 624p. 1984. Repr. of 1891 ed. 90.00x (ISBN 0-317-39168-2, Pub. by Luzac & Co Ltd). State Mutual Bk.

Caliph's Design. Wyndham Lewis. (Illus.). 188p. (Orig.). 1986. 20.00 (ISBN 0-87685-665-2); pap. 9.50 (ISBN 0-87685-664-4); deluxe ed. 30.00 (ISBN 0-87685-666-0). Black Sparrow.

Call. Oral Roberts. 1982. pap. 1.25 (ISBN 0-380-01078-X, 10678). Avon.

Call Adonoi: Manual of Practical Cabalah & Gestalt Mysticism. Albert L. Schutz. LC 80-50264. (Illus.). 200p. (Orig.). 1980. 11.95 (ISBN 0-936596-01-5); pap. 8.95 (ISBN 0-936596-00-7). Quantal.

Call Me Monsignor. J. Patrick Kaye. LC 74-78032. (Illus.). 1974. pap. 5.00 (ISBN 0-87423-008-X). Westburg.

Call of God: The Theme of Vocation in the Poetry of Donne & Herbert. Robert B. Shaw. LC 81-66126. (Cowley Lectures). 123p. (Orig.). 1981. pap. 6.00 (ISBN 0-936384-04-2). Cowley Pubns.

Call of Heaven: Brother Gino, Stigmatist. Robert J. Fox. (Illus.). 206p. (Orig.). 1982. pap. 3.95 (ISBN 0-931888-06-9). Christendom Pubns.

Call of Heaven: Father Gino, Stigmatist. 2nd ed. Robert J. Fox. (Illus.). 232p. pap. 5.95 (ISBN 0-931888-22-0). Christendom Pubns.

Call of Jesus: Lessons in Becoming His Disciple. rev. ed. Martha Banks. (Bible Study: Basic Ser.). 64p. (Orig.). pap. 2.95 (ISBN 0-932305-28-8, 521009). Aglow Pubns.

Call of the Dervish. Pir Vilayat Inayat Khan. LC 81-52421. 224p. (Orig.). 1981. pap. 8.95 (ISBN 0-930872-26-6, 1013P). Omega Pr NM.

Call of the Gita. 192p. 1987. pap. 2.95 (ISBN 0-87481-537-1, Pub. by Ramakrishna Math Madras India). Vedanta Pr.

Call of the Spirit. Merritt C. Horn. 82p. (Orig.). 1984. pap. 5.95 (ISBN 0-932661-00-9). Archangel Pub.

Call of the Spirit: Conversion with Swami Akhandananda. Niramayananda. 170p. 1987. pap. text ed. 3.50 (ISBN 0-87481-538-X, Pub. by Ramakrishna Math Madras India). Vedanta Pr.

Call of the Torah, 2 vols. 1981. 24.50 (ISBN 0-87306-146-2); pap. 18.50 (ISBN 0-87306-232-9). Feldheim.

Call of the Virgin at San Damiano. Johan Osee. (Illus.). 1977. pap. 6.95 (ISBN 0-8158-0354-0). Chris Mass.

Call to America to Build Zion: An Original Anthology. Ed. by Moshe Davis. LC 77-70723. (America & the Holy Land Ser.). 1977. lib. bdg. 20.00x (ISBN 0-405-10306-9). Ayer Co Pubs.

Call to Awaken, Vol. I. Karl G. Kamper & Karen M. Carson. 269p. 1986. text ed. 15.00 (ISBN 0-9616739-1-5). Atonement Ent.

Call to Commitment. Elizabeth O'Connor. LC 63-10963. 224p. 1976. pap. 5.95 (ISBN 0-06-066330-8, RD131, HarpR). Har-Row.

Call to Commitment: Responding to the Message of Hebrews. William L. Lane. LC 85-15597. 192p. 1985. pap. 8.95 (ISBN 0-8407-5948-7). Nelson.

Call to Conscience: Jews, Judaism, & Conscientious Objection. Albert S. Axelrad. LC 85-24010. 207p. 1986. text ed. 25.00x (ISBN 0-88125-092-9); pap. 14.95x (ISBN 0-88125-081-3). Ktav.

Call to Conversion: Recovering the Gospel for These Times. Jim Wallis. LC 80-8901. 208p. 1983. pap. 9.95 (ISBN 0-686-92025-2, RD414, HarpR). Har-Row.

Call to Discipleship. Juan Carlos Ortiz & Jamie Buckingham. LC 75-7476. 1975. pap. 4.95 (ISBN 0-88270-122-3). Bridge Pub.

Call to Discipleship: A Literary Study of Mark's Gospel. Augustine Stock. (Good News Studies: Vol. 1). 1982. pap. 9.95 (ISBN 0-89453-273-1). M Glazier.

Call to Excellence. Gary Inrig. 132p. 1985. pap. 5.95 (ISBN 0-89693-523-X). Victor Bks.

Call to Faith. Rachel Henderlite. LC 55-5552. 224p. 1955. pap. 2.49 (ISBN 0-8042-3136-2). John Knox.

Call to Holiness: New Frontiers in Spirituality for Today's Religious. Renato Perino. LC 85-28621. 160p. (Orig.). 1986. pap. 7.95 (ISBN 0-8189-0475-5). ALBA.

Call to Islam. M. S. Siddiqui. pap. 2.00 (ISBN 0-686-63897-2). Kazi Pubns.

Call to Prophethood. Saida Chaudhry. (Illus.). pap. 4.00. Am Trust Pubns.

Call to Reason: An Introduction to Atheism. 3rd ed. Mary DeYoung. 1979. pap. 7.50 (ISBN 0-936128-01-1). De Young Pr.

Call to Remember. Robert E. Hooper. 1978. pap. 5.00 (ISBN 0-89225-183-2). Gospel Advocate.

Call to Righteousness. Paul A. Tanner. 1984. pap. 0.75 (ISBN 0-87162-404-4, D3012). Warner Pr.

Call to the Nations: Extracts from the Writings of Shoghi Effendi. Shoghi Effendi. LC 79-670140. 1978. 6.95 (ISBN 0-85398-068-3, 108-050); pap. 3.00 o. s. i. (ISBN 0-85398-069-1, 108-051). Baha'i.

Call to Total Consecration. James Alberione. 1974. 3.00 (ISBN 0-8198-0312-X); pap. 2.00 (ISBN 0-8198-0313-8). Dghtrs St Paul.

Call to Wholeness. Kenneth Bakken. Intro. by Morton Kelsey. LC 84-23837. 128p. (Orig.). 1985. pap. 7.95 (ISBN 0-8245-0683-9). Crossroad NY.

Called & Chosen: The Story of Mother Rebecca Jackson & the Philadelphia Shakers. Richard E. Williams. LC 80-25498. (ATLA Monograph Ser.: No. 17). 193p. 1981. 17.50 (ISBN 0-8108-1382-3). Scarecrow.

Called, Appointed, Annointed. Janny Grein. 95p. (Orig.). 1985. pap. 4.00 (ISBN 0-89274-354-9). Harrison Hse.

Called by Name. Peter G. Van Breemen. 9.95 (ISBN 0-87193-094-3). Dimension Bks.

Called by the Gospel: An Introduction of the Christian Faith. Marc Kolden. LC 82-72651. 112p. 1983. pap. 5.95 (ISBN 0-8066-1958-9, 10-0967). Augsburg.

Called to Be Faithful: Reflections on Cycle B Readings for the Sundays of Lent. Catherine Nerney. 1.95 (ISBN 0-8091-9339-6). Paulist Pr.

Called to Be Friends. Paula Ripple. LC 80-67402. 160p. (Orig.). 1980. pap. 3.95 (ISBN 0-87793-212-3). Ave Maria.

Called to Be His People. Glen V. Wiberg. (Illus.). 331p. 1970. pap. text ed. 5.00 (ISBN 0-910452-16-4). Covenant.

Called to Be Saints. Robert G. Gromacki. 1977. pap. 5.95 (ISBN 0-87227-014-9). Reg Baptist.

Called to Be Saints (I Corinthians) Robert G. Gromacki. 1977. pap. 5.95 (ISBN 0-8010-3715-8). Baker Bk.

Called to Care. Larry Pemberton. (Orig.). 1985. pap. text ed. 4.95 (ISBN 0-87148-183-9). Pathway Pr.

Called to Care. Douglas Stevens. (YA) 1985. 12.95 (ISBN 0-310-28461-9, 11366, Pub. by Youth Spec). Zondervan.

Called to Die: The Story of American Linguist Chet Bitterman, Slain by Terrorists. Steve Estes & Verna Estes. Ed. by John Sloan. 208p. pap. 6.95 (ISBN 0-310-28381-7, 12197P). Zondervan.

Called to Freedom: Liberation Theology & the Future of Christian Doctrine. Daniel L. Migliore. LC 79-21879. 128p. 1980. pap. 5.95 (ISBN 0-664-24289-8). Westminster.

Called to Full Unity: Documents on Anglican-Roman Catholic Relations 1966-1983. Ed. by Joseph W. Witmer & J. Robert Wright. 358p. 1986. pap. 14.95 (ISBN 1-55586-937-8). US Catholic.

Called to Heal: Releasing the Transforming Power of God. Ralph A. DiOrio. LC 82-45354. (Illus.). 264p. 1984. pap. 7.95 (ISBN 0-385-19704-7, Im). Doubleday.

Called to His Supper: The Biblical Eucharist. Penny Livermore. 2.95 (ISBN 0-89453-089-5). M Glazier.

Called to Holy Worldliness. Richard J. Mouw. Ed. by Mark Gibbs. LC 80-8047. (Laity Exchange). 160p. (Orig.). 1980. pap. 5.95 (ISBN 0-8006-1397-X, 1-1397). Fortress.

Called to Intimacy. George A. Maloney. LC 83-3782. 164p. 1983. pap. 6.95 (ISBN 0-8189-0452-6). Alba.

Called to Minister. Richard A. Hunt & Joan A. Hunt. LC 81-22796. (Into Our Third Century Ser.). (Orig.). 1982. pap. 3.95 (ISBN 0-687-04560-6). Abingdon.

Called to Pray. Wim Malgo. 3.95 (ISBN 0-937422-19-3). Midnight Call.

Called to Prayer: Liturgical Spirituality Today. Ed. by Lawrence Johnson. 96p. 1986. pap. 4.95 (ISBN 0-8146-1488-4). Liturgical Pr.

Called to Preach, Condemned to Survive: The Education of Clayton Sullivan. Clayton Sullivan. xiv, 237p. 1985. 19.95 (ISBN 0-86554-173-6, MUP-H163). Mercer Univ Pr.

Called to Serve: A Guidebook for Altar Servers. Albert J. Nevins. LC 81-82546. 48p. 1981. pap. 13.95 pkg. of six (ISBN 0-87973-663-1, 663). Our Sunday Visitor.

Called to Splendor. Nelson L. Price. LC 84-17506. 1984. pap. 4.95 (ISBN 0-8054-5007-6). Broadman.

Called to Teach Children. Muriel F. Blackwell. LC 82-82954. 1983. 6.95 (ISBN 0-8054-3233-7). Broadman.

Called to Teach: Ideas & Encouragement for Teachers in the Church. Kent L. Johnson. LC 83-72127. 128p. (Orig.). 1984. pap. 5.95 (ISBN 0-8066-2071-4, 10-0964). Augsburg.

Called to the Ministry. Edmund Clowney. 1976. pap. 3.50 (ISBN 0-87552-144-4). Presby & Reformed.

Called unto Holiness, Vol. 1. Timothy L. Smith. LC 62-11409. 416p. 1962. 14.95 (ISBN 0-8341-0282-X). Beacon Hill.

Called unto Holiness, Vol. 2. W. T. Purkiser. 368p. 1983. 14.95 (ISBN 0-8341-0868-2). Beacon Hill.

Caller & the Called. Richard L. Thulin. Ed. by Michael L Sherer. (Orig.). 1986. pap. 6.25 (ISBN 0-89536-819-6, 6828). CSS of Ohio.

Calling. Dan Jarrard. Ed. by Gerald Wheeler. 96p. 1987. pap. price not set (ISBN 0-8280-0382-3). Review & Herald.

Calling a Pastor to a Baptist Church. rev. ed. Allix B. James. Ed. by Amos Jones, Jr. 50p. (Orig.). 1983. pap. 4.95 (ISBN 0-910683-00-X). Sunday School.

Calling Disciples. John Colligan et al. 54p. (Orig.). 1984. 1.95 (ISBN 0-911905-22-7). Past & Mat Rene Ctr.

Calling Disciples, Mentality. John Colligan et al. LC 84-60459. (Calling Disciples Ser.: Bk. 2). 67p. (Orig.). 1984. pap. text ed. 2.95 (ISBN 0-911905-21-9). Past & Mat Rene Ctr.

Calling Disciples: Outlines. Chuck Gallagher et al. LC 84-60459. (Calling Disciples Ser.: Bk. 1). 64p. (Orig.). 1984. pap. text ed. 2.95 (ISBN 0-911905-23-5). Past & Mat Rene Ctr.

Calling for Action: An Autobiographical Enquiry. Donald Soper. LC 84-129410. (Illus.). 172p. 1985. 16.00 (ISBN 0-86051-265-7). Salem Hse Pubs.

Calm & Clear. Lama Mi-pham. LC 73-79058. (Tibetan Translation Ser., Vol. 1). (Illus.). 128p. 1973. pap. 6.95 (ISBN 0-913546-02-X). Dharma Pub.

Calm & Clear. Lama Nipham. 1985. 20.00x (ISBN 0-317-39045-7, Pub. by Luzac & Co Ltd). State Mutual Bk.

Calm Beneath the Storm: Reflections & Prayers for Young People. Donal Neary. 80p. 1984. pap. 3.95 (ISBN 0-8294-0470-8). Loyola.

Calus: Symbolic Transformation in Romanian Ritual. Gail Kligman. LC 80-21372. (Chicago Originals Ser.). (Illus.). 240p. 1981. lib. bdg. 14.00x (ISBN 0-226-44221-7). U of Chicago Pr.

Calvin. Ed. by William P. Hansen & John Haney. (World's Leaders--Past & Present Ser.). (Illus.). 112p. 1987. lib. bdg. 16.95 (ISBN 0-87754-515-4). Chelsea Hse.

Calvin. Robert N. Hunt. LC 83-45617. Date not set. Repr. of 1933 ed. 37.50 (ISBN 0-404-19835-X). AMS Pr.

Calvin. E. Stickelberger. Tr. by David Gelser. 174p. 1977. Repr. of 1959 ed. 12.95 (ISBN 0-227-67424-3). Attic Pr.

Calvin Against Himself: An Inquiry in Intellectual History. Suzanne Selinger. LC 83-21330. 238p. 1984. 29.50 (ISBN 0-208-01948-0, Archon). Shoe String.

Calvin & Augustine. Benjamin B. Warfield. 12.95 (ISBN 0-8010-9585-9). Baker Bk.

Calvin & Augustine. Benjamin B. Warfield. 1954. 12.95 (ISBN 0-87552-526-1). Presby & Reformed.

Calvin & Classical Philosophy 1977. Ed. by Charles Partee. (Studies in the History of Christian Thought: Vol. 14). 30.00 (ISBN 90-04-04839-1). Heinman.

Calvin & His Enemies: A Memoir of the Life, Character & Principles of Calvin. rev. & enl. ed. Thomas Smyth. LC 83-45632. Date not set. Repr. of 1909 ed. 28.00 (ISBN 0-404-19849-X). AMS Pr.

Calvin & Servetus: The Reformer's Share in the Trial of Michael Servetus Historically Ascertained. Albert Rilliet. Tr. by W. K. Tweedie from Fr. LC 83-45631. Date not set. Repr. of 1846 ed. 31.50 (ISBN 0-404-19848-1). AMS Pr.

Calvin & the Anabaptist Radicals. William Balke. Tr. by William Heynen. LC 81-12438. pap. 87.50 (ISBN 0-317-30132-2, 2025315). Bks Demand UMI.

Calvin & the Calvinists. Paul Helm. 84p. (Orig.). 1982. pap. 5.95 (ISBN 0-85151-344-1). Banner of Truth.

Calvin & the Reformation. James Mackinnon. LC 83-45648. Date not set. Repr. of 1936 ed. 37.50 (ISBN 0-404-19841-4). AMS Pr.

Calvin & the Reformation: Four Studies. Ed. by William P. Armstrong. (Twin Brooks Ser.). 1980. pap. 6.95 (ISBN 0-8010-2901-5). Baker Bk.

Calvin: Commentaries. Ed. by Joseph Haroutunian. LC 58-5060. (Library of Christian Classics). 410p. 1979. softcover 8.95 (ISBN 0-664-24160-3). Westminster.

Calvin in His Letters. Henry F. Henderson. 59.95 (ISBN 0-87968-810-6). Gordon Pr.

Calvin: Institutes of the Christian Religion, 2 vols. Ed. by John T. McNeill. LC 60-5379. (Library of Christian Classics). 1812p. 1960. Set. 34.95 (ISBN 0-664-22028-2). Westminster.

Calvin: Origins & Development of His Religious Thought. Francois Wendel. Tr. by Philip Mairet. 384p. 1987. pap. 14.95 (ISBN 0-939464-44-6). Labyrinth Pr.

Calvin Reader: Reflections on Living. Ed. & selected by William F. Keesecker. LC 85-15237. 144p. 1985. pap. 9.95 (ISBN 0-664-24667-2). Westminster.

Calvin: Theological Treatises. Ed. by J. K. Reid. LC 54-9956. (Library of Christian Classics). 352p. 1978. softcover 8.95 (ISBN 0-664-24156-5). Westminster.

Calvinisim & the Religious Wars. Franklin C. Palm. LC 78-80579. 1971. Repr. 24.50x (ISBN 0-86527-020-1). Fertig.

Calvinism. Arthur Dakin. LC 72-153211. 1971. Repr. of 1940 ed. 23.00x (ISBN 0-8046-1521-7, Pub. by Kennikat). Assoc Faculty Pr.

Calvinism & the Amyraut Heresy: Protestant Scholasticism & Humanism in Seventeenth-Century France. Brian G. Armstrong. LC 72-84949. (Illus.). 350p. 1969. 30.00 (ISBN 0-299-05490-X). U of Wis Pr.

Calvinism & the Capitalist Spirit: Max Weber's "Protestant Ethic". Gianfranco Poggi. LC 83-40103. 136p. 1983. lib. bdg. 13.50x (ISBN 0-87023-417-X); pap. text ed. 6.95x (ISBN 0-87023-418-8). U of Mass Pr.

Calvinism & the Religious Wars. Franklin C. Palm. LC 83-45628. Date not set. Repr. of 1932 ed. 22.50 (ISBN 0-404-19880-5). AMS Pr.

Calvinism vs. Democracy: Timothy Dwight & the Origins of American Evangelical Orthodoxy. Stephen E. Berk. LC 73-20053. xiv, 252p. 1974. 25.00 (ISBN 0-208-01419-5, Archon). Shoe String.

Calvinist Preaching & Iconoclasm in the Netherlands, 1544-1569. P. Mack Crew. LC 77-77013. (Studies in Early Modern History). 1978. 37.50 (ISBN 0-521-21739-3). Cambridge U Pr.

Calvinistic Paths Retraced. 240p. 1985. pap. 7.95 (ISBN 0-914012-25-8, Pub. by Bibl Evang Pr). Sword of Lord.

Calvinistic Temper in English Poetry. James D. Boulger. (De Proprietatibus Litterarum, Ser. Major: No. 21). 1980. text ed. 71.00x (ISBN 90-279-7575-2). Mouton.

Calvin's Commentaries, 22 vols. John Calvin. 1979. Repr. Set. 495.00 (ISBN 0-8010-2440-4). Baker Bk.

Calvin's Doctrine of Man. Thomas F. Torrance. LC 77-5615. 1977. Repr. lib. bdg. 22.50x (ISBN 0-8371-9639-6, TOCD). Greenwood.

Calvin's Doctrine of the Atonement. Robert A. Peterson. 1983. pap. 4.95 (ISBN 0-87552-369-2). Presby & Reformed.

Calvin's Doctrine of the Last Things. Heinrich Quistorp. John Knox.

Calvin's Doctrine of the Last Things. Heinrich Quistorp. Tr. by Harold Knight. LC 83-45629. Date not set. Repr. of 1955 ed. 27.50 (ISBN 0-404-19846-5). AMS Pr.

Calvin's Doctrine of the Word & Sacraments. Ronald S. Wallace. xii, 253p. 1982. pap. 12.95 (ISBN 0-939404-02-8). Geneva Ministr.

Calvin's "Doctrine of the Work of Christ". J. F. Jansen. 120p. 1956. 10.00 (ISBN 0-227-67425-1). Attic Pr.

Calvin's Letters. John Calvin. pap. 5.95 (ISBN 0-85151-323-9). Banner of Truth.

Calvin's New Testament Commentaries, 12 vols. John Calvin. Ed. by David W. Torrance & Thomas F. Torrance. Incl. Gospel According to St. John; Chapters 1-10. Tr. by T. H. Parker. 10.95 (ISBN 0-8028-2044-1); Gospel According to St. John; Chapters 11-21. Tr. by T. H. Parker. 10.95 (ISBN 0-8028-2045-X); Acts of the Apostles, Vol. 1. Tr. by W. J. McDonald. 10.95 (ISBN 0-8028-2046-8); Acts of the Apostles, Vol. 2. Tr. by John W. Fraser. 10.95 (ISBN 0-8028-2047-6); Epistle to the Romans & the Thessalonians. Tr. by R. Mackenzie. 9.95 (ISBN 0-8028-2048-4); First Epistle to the Corinthians. Tr. by John W. Fraser. 10.95 (ISBN 0-8028-2049-2); Galatians, Ephesians, Philippians, Colossians. Tr. by T. H. Parker. 10.95 (ISBN 0-8028-2051-4); Hebrews and Peter First & Second. Tr. by W. B. Johnson. 10.95 (ISBN 0-8028-2052-2); Second Corinthians, Timothy, Titus. & Philemon. T. A. Smail. 10.95 (ISBN 0-8028-2050-6); Harmony of the Gospels, 3 Vols. Tr. by T. H. Parker. 10.95 ea. (ISBN 0-685-22779-0). Vol. 1 (ISBN 0-8028-2038-7). **Vol. 2 (ISBN 0-8028-2039-5). Vol. 3 (ISBN 0-8028-2040-9). 1960. Set. 131.40 (ISBN 0-8028-2053-0). Eerdmans.**

Calvin's Old Testament Commentaries. T. H. Parker. 256p. 1986. 28.95 (ISBN 0-567-09365-4, Pub. by T & T Clark Ltd UK). Fortress.

Calvin's Selected Works: Tracts & Letters, 7 vols. John Calvin. Ed. by Henry Beveridge & Jules Bonnet. 1983. Repr. 99.95 (ISBN 0-8010-2493-5). Baker Bk.

Calvinus Reformator: His Contribution to Theology, Church & Society. Ed. by B. Van der Walt. Date not set. pap. 12.50x cancelled (ISBN 0-86990-686-0). Radix Bks.

Cambiame, Senor! Evelyn Christenson. 224p. 1980. 3.25 (ISBN 0-88113-035-4). Edit Betania.

Cambrian Biography; or Historical Notices of Celebrated Men Among the Ancient Britons. William Owen. Ed. by Burton Feldman & Robert Richardson. LC 78-60896. (Myth & Romanticism Ser.: Vol. 20). (Illus.). 1979. lib. bdg. 80.00 (ISBN 0-8240-3569-0). Garland Pub.

Cambridge History of Islam. Ed. by P. M. Holt et al. Incl. Vol. 1A. Central Islamic Lands from Pre-Islamic Times to the First World War. 67.50 (ISBN 0-521-21946-9); pap. 29.95 (ISBN 0-521-29135-6); Vol. 1B. Central Islamic Lands Since 1918. 62.50 (ISBN 0-521-21947-7); pap. 24.95 (ISBN 0-521-29136-4); Vol. 2A. The Indian Subcontinent, Southeast Asia, Africa & the Muslim West. 64.50 (ISBN 0-521-21948-5); pap. 24.95 (ISBN 0-521-29137-2); Vol. 2B. Islamic Society & Civilization. 77.50 (ISBN 0-521-21949-3); pap. 32.95 (ISBN 0-521-29138-0). 1977-78. Set. 250.00 (ISBN 0-521-22310-5); Set. pap. 90.00 (ISBN 0-521-08755-4). Cambridge U Pr.

Cambridge History of Judaism: Introduction, the Persian Period, Vol. 1. Ed. by W. D. Davies. Louis Finkelstein. LC 77-85704. 461p. 1984. 62.50 (ISBN 0-521-21880-2). Cambridge U Pr.

Cambridge History of the Bible, 3 vols. Incl. Vol. 1. From the Beginnings to Jerome. Ed. by P. R. Ackroyd & C. F. Evans. pap. 23.95 (ISBN 0-521-09973-0); Vol. 2. The West from the Fathers to the Reformation. Ed. by G. W. Lampe. 65.00 (ISBN 0-521-04255-0); pap. 23.95 (ISBN 0-521-29017-1); Vol. 3. The West from the Reformation to the Present Day. Ed. by S. L. Greenslade. 72.50 (ISBN 0-521-04254-2); pap. 21.95 (ISBN 0-521-29016-3). LC 63-24435. 57.50 ea.; Set. 155.00 (ISBN 0-521-08778-3). Set. pap. 47.50 (ISBN 0-521-29018-X). Cambridge U Pr.

Cambridge Medieval History, 9 vols. Incl. Vol. 1. Christian Roman Empire & the Foundation of the Teutonic Kingdoms. 85.50 (ISBN 0-521-04532-0); Vol. 2. Rise of the Saracens & the Foundation of the Western Empire; Vol. 3. Germany & the Western Empire. 85.00 (ISBN 0-521-04534-7); Vol. 4, Pt. 1. Byzantine Empire. 2nd ed. Ed. by J. M. Hussey & D. M. Nicol. 1966. 120.50 (ISBN 0-521-04535-5); Vol. 4, Pt. 2. Government Church & Civilization. 80.00 (ISBN 0-521-04536-3); Vol. 5. Contest of Empire & Papacy. 112.00 (ISBN 0-521-04537-1); Vol. 6. Victory of the Papacy. 112.50 (ISBN 0-521-04538-X); Vol. 7. Decline of the Empire & Papacy. 112.50 (ISBN 0-521-04539-8); Vol. 8. Close of the Middle Ages. Cambridge U Pr.

Cambridge Platonists. C. A. Patrides. (Stratford-Upon-Avon Library). 1969. 25.00x (ISBN 0-674-09125-6). Harvard U Pr.

Cambridge Platonists. Frederick J. Powicke. LC 79-151196. (Illus.). x, 219p. 1971. Repr. of 1926 ed. 23.00 (ISBN 0-208-01088-2, Archon). Shoe String.

Cambridge Platonists, a Study. Frederick J. Powicke. Repr. of 1926 ed. lib. bdg. 22.50x (ISBN 0-8371-3999-6, POPL). Greenwood.

Cambridge Press, Sixteen Thirty-Eight to Sixteen Ninety-Two. facs. ed. George P. Winship. LC 68-57346. (Essay Index Reprint Ser). 1945. 22.50 (ISBN 0-8369-1004-4). Ayer Co Pubs.

Cameos of Church History. Richard A. Boever. 64p. 1986. pap. 1.95 (ISBN 0-89243-249-7). Liguori Pubns.

Camilla. Caroline E. Miner & Edward L. Kimball. LC 80-69723. (Illus.). 1980. 8.95 (ISBN 0-87747-845-7). Deseret Bk.

Camillo Renato: Opere, Documenti E Testimonianze. Ed. by Antonio Rotondo. LC 72-3454. (Corpus Reformatorum Italicorum & Biblioteca Ser.). (Lat. & Ital., Illus.). 353p. 1968. 25.00 (ISBN 0-87580-034-3). N Ill U Pr.

Camillus: A Study of Indo-European Religion As Roman History. Georges Dumezil. Ed. by Udo Strutynski. Tr. by Annette Aronowicz et al from Fr. LC 80-36771. 250p. 1980. 24.00x (ISBN 0-520-02841-4). U of Cal Pr.

Camino de la Paz. J. C. Wenger. Ed. by Arnoldo J. Casas. Tr. by Ernesto S. Vilela. LC 79-89311. (Mennonite Faith Ser.: No. 4). (Span.). 1979. pap. 1.50x (ISBN 0-8361-1226-1). Herald Pr.

Camino de una Nueva Vida. J. C. Wenger. Ed. by Arnold J. Casas. Tr. by Ernesto S. Vilela. LC 79-89310. (Mennonite Faith Ser.: No. 3). (Span.). 72p. 1979. pap. 1.50x (ISBN 0-8361-1224-5). Herald Pr.

Camino Hacia Dios. Dwight L. Moody. Orig. Title: Way to God. (Span.). 128p. 1983. pap. 3.25 (ISBN 0-8254-1490-3). Kregel.

Camp Couselor. Lloyd Mattson. (Illus.). 192p. 1984. pap. 3.95 (ISBN 0-942684-02-8). Camp Guidepts.

Campanile of Florence Cathedral: Giotto's Tower. Marvin Trachtenberg. LC 70-124532. (Illus.). 458p. 1971. 135.00 (ISBN 0-8147-8151-9). NYU Pr.

Campbellism: Its History & Heresies. Bob L. Ross. 1981. 2.90 (ISBN 0-686-09113-2). Pilgrim Pubns.

Campus Symbolism: Devotions for New Students. David W. Wollenburg. write for info. (ISBN 0-911770-52-6). Concordia Schl Grad Studies.

Can Christians Be Educated? Morton T. Kelsey. Ed. by Harold W. Burgess. LC 77-3691. 154p. (Orig.). 1977. pap. 8.95 (ISBN 0-89135-008-X). Religious Educ.

Can Ethics Be Christian? James M. Gustafson. LC 74-11622. 1977. pap. 7.00x (ISBN 0-226-31102-3, P734, Phoen). U of Chicago Pr.

Can God Survive in Australia. Bruce Wilson. 224p. (Orig.). 1983. pap. 7.95 (ISBN 0-86760-009-8, Pub. by Albatross Bks). ANZ Religious Pubns.

Can I Talk to You? Elizabeth Skoglund. 1977. pap. 3.25 (ISBN 0-8307-0557-0, 5407508). Regal.

Can Meditation Be Done? Thomas Hora. (Discoures in Metapsychiatry Ser.). 33p. 1984. pap. 4.00 (ISBN 0-913105-09-0). PAGL Pr.

Can One Be Scientific & Yet Spiritual? Swami Budhananda. 114p. 1973. pap. 2.00 (ISBN 0-87481-145-7). Vedanta Pr.

Can Quakerism Speak to the Times? John H. Hobart. 1983. pap. 2.50x (ISBN 0-87574-078-2, 078). Pendle Hill.

Can the Pastor Do It Alone. Melvin J. Steinbron. 1987. pap. 7.95 (ISBN 0-8307-1171-6, 5418925). Regal.

Can We Know God? Ellen G. White. (Uplook Ser.). 1970. pap. 0.99 (ISBN 0-8163-0067-4, 03035-3). Pacific Pr Pub Assn.

Can We Still Call God "Father"? A Woman Looks at the Lord's Prayer Today. Celine Mangan. (Ways of Prayer Ser.: Vol. 12). 110p. 1984. pap. 4.95 (ISBN 0-89453-384-3). M Glazier.

Can We Trust Bible History? A. Pieters. 2.50 (ISBN 0-686-23481-2). Rose Pub MI.

Can We Trust the Gospels? Nigel Scotland. 54p. 1979. pap. 1.95 (ISBN 0-85364-249-4). Attic Pr.

Can You Drink This Cup? Edward Farrell. pap. 4.95 (ISBN 0-87193-179-6). Dimension Bks.

Can You Hear Me God? Vic Merrill. 96p. 1981. 6.00 (ISBN 0-682-49740-1). Exposition Pr FL.

Can You Know God's Will for Your Life? Charles R. Smith. 1979. pap. 1.00 (ISBN 0-88469-044-X). BMH Bks.

Can You Love Yourself? Jo Berry. LC 77-89395. 160p. 1978. pap. 4.95 (ISBN 0-8307-0579-1, 5407206). Regal.

Can Your Faith Fail? Charles Capps. 1978. pap. 1.75 (ISBN 0-89274-105-8). Harrison Hse.

Canaanite Myth & Hebrew Epic: Essays in the History of the Religion of Israel. Frank M. Cross. LC 72-76564. 1973. 25.00x (ISBN 0-674-09175-2). Harvard U Pr.

Canaanite Myths & Legends. John C. Gibson. (Illus.). 208p. 1978. 32.95 (ISBN 0-567-02351-6, Pub. by T & T Clark Ltd UK). Fortress.

Canada: Celebrating Our Faith. Pope John Paul II. 370p. 1985. 7.00 (ISBN 0-317-18636-1); pap. 6.00 (ISBN 0-8198-1441-5). Dghtrs St Paul.

Canada's Bishops: Sixteen Fifty-Eight to Nineteen Seventy-Five. Clarence A. Liederbach. LC 73-94082. 1976. pap. 2.95 (ISBN 0-913228-10-9). R J Liederbach.

Canadian Yiddish Writings. Ed. by Abraham Bovarsky & Lazar Sarna. LC 77-362060. pap. 37.50 (ISBN 0-317-10945-6, 2022287). Bks Demand UMI.

Canarian; or Book of the Conquest & Conversion of the Canarians, in the Year 1402, by Messire Jean de Bethencourt. Pierre Bontier & Jean Le Verrier. Ed. by Richard H. Major. LC 70-286234. (Hakluyt Society Ser.: No. 46). 300p. 1972. lib. bdg. 32.00 (ISBN 0-8337-2188-7). B Franklin.

Cancer Patient. John W. Dawson. LC 78-52192. (Religion & Medicine Ser.). 1978. pap. 5.95 (ISBN 0-8066-1662-8, 10-0960). Augsburg.

Cancer: Through the Numbers. Paul Rice & Valeta Rice. 40p. 1983. pap. 2.00 (ISBN 0-87728-568-3). Weiser.

Candi in Art & Iconography. Somnath Mukhopadhyay. 1984. 34.00x (ISBN 0-8364-1146-3, Pub. by Agam India). South Asia Bks.

Candid History of the Jesuits. Joseph McCabe. 1977. lib. bdg. 59.95 (ISBN 0-8490-1567-7). Gordon Pr.

Candid Questions Concerning Gospel Form Criticism: A Methodological Sketch of Fundamental Problematics of Form & Redaction Criticism. 2nd ed. Erhard T. Guttgemans. Tr. by William G. Doty. LC 79-10167. (Pittsburgh Theological Monographs: No. 26). 1979. pap. 15.00 (ISBN 0-915138-24-7). Pickwick.

Candidates Biblical Scoreboard. David W. Balsiger. Intro. by David W. Balsiger. (Biblical News Ser., 1986: No. 1). 1986. 2.25 (ISBN 0-89921-015-5). Biblical News Serv.

Candidates Biblical Scoreboard, 1986 California, No. 1. 1.00 (ISBN 0-89921-016-3). Biblical News Serv.

Candidates Biblical Scoreboard, 1986 California, No. 2. 1.00 (ISBN 0-89921-019-8). Biblical News Serv.

Candidates Biblical Scoreboard, 1986 California, No. 3. 1.00 (ISBN 0-89921-020-1). Biblical News Serv.

Candidates Biblical Scoreboard, 1986 National, No. 2. 2.25 (ISBN 0-89921-017-1). Biblical News Serv.

Candidates Biblical Scoreboard, 1986 National, No. 3. 2.25 (ISBN 0-89921-018-X). Biblical News Serv.

Candle in the Wind: My Thirty Years in Book Publishing. Thomas P. Coffey. 222p. 1985. pap. 5.95 (ISBN 0-87193-212-1). Dimension Bks.

Candle of the Lord. facsimile ed. William C. De Pauley. LC 75-107693. (Essay Index Reprint Ser). 1937. 16.00 (ISBN 0-8369-1496-1). Ayer Co Pubs.

Candle of the Lord. Elfrida V. Foulds. pap. 2.50x (ISBN 0-87574-248-3, 248). Pendle Hill.

Candle of the Lord: Studies in the Cambridge Platonists. William C. De Pauley. (Church Historical Society, London, New Ser.: No. 28). pap. 23.00 (ISBN 0-8115-3152-X). Kraus Repr.

Candle of Vision. AE, pseud. LC 73-17195. 1974. pap. 2.25 (ISBN 0-8356-0445-4, Quest). Theos Pub Hse.

Candle, the Lantern, the Daylight. Mildred B. Young. LC 61-15103. (Orig.). 1961. pap. 2.50x (ISBN 0-87574-116-9). Pendle Hill.

Candles in the Dark. Mae H. Ashworth. LC 83-70253. 1983. 6.95 (ISBN 0-8054-5256-7). Broadman.

Candles in the Dark. Amy Carmichael. 1982. pap. text ed. 3.50 (ISBN 0-87508-085-5). Chr Lit.

Candramaharosana Tantra. Ed. by Christopher S. George. (American Oriental Ser.: Vol. 56). 1974. pap. 15.00x (ISBN 0-940490-56-0). Am Orient Soc.

Canek, History & Legend of a Maya Hero. Emilio Abreu Gomez. Tr. by Mario L. Davila & Carter Wilson. LC 75-32674. 1979. 19.50x (ISBN 0-520-03148-2); pap. 2.95 (ISBN 0-520-03982-3, CAL 441). U of Cal Pr.

Cannibals, Witches, & Divorce: Estranging the Renaissance. Ed. by Marjorie Garber. LC 86-45472. (Selected Papers from the English Institute, 1985 New Ser.: No. 11). 256p. 1987. text ed. 19.50x (ISBN 0-8018-3405-8). Johns Hopkins.

Cannon Law for Religious: An Explanation. Joseph F. Gallen. LC 83-15883. 218p. (Orig.). 1983. pap. 9.95 (ISBN 0-8189-0461-5). Alba.

Cannon Law: History, Sources, & a Proposed Classification Scheme. Danuta M. Gorecki & Arnold Wajenberg. Date not set. price not set. Am Assn Law Libs.

Canon & Community: A Guide to Canonical Criticism. James A. Sanders. LC 83-18483. (Guides to Biblical Scholarship). 96p. 1984. pap. 4.50 (ISBN 0-8006-0468-7, 1-468). Fortress.

Canon & Connection: Intertextuality in Judaism. Jacob Neusner. (Studies in Judaism). 316p. (Orig.). 1987. lib. bdg. 27.50 (ISBN 0-8191-5796-1, Pub. by Studies in Judaism); pap. text ed. 15.75 (ISBN 0-8191-5797-X). U Pr of Amer.

Canon Law--Church Reality. Ed. by James Provost & Knut Walf. (Concilium Nineteen Eighty-Six Ser.). 120p. 1986. pap. 6.95 (ISBN 0-567-30065-X, Pub. by T & T Clark Ltd UK). Fortress.

Canon Law & the Archpriest of Hita. Henry A. Kelly. LC 82-12403. (Medieval & Renaissance Texts & Studies: Vol. 27). 204p. 1984. 16.00 (ISBN 0-86698-058-X). Medieval & Renaissance NY.

Canon Law Collection of the Library of Congress: A General Bibliography with Selective Annotations. Ed. by Dario C. Ferreira-Ibarra. LC 81-607964. (Illus.). xiv, 210p. 1981. 11.00 (ISBN 0-8444-0367-9). Lib Congress.

Canon Law in Mediaeval England: An Examination of William Lyndwood's Provinciale. Arthur Ogle. LC 78-156390. (Research & Source Works Ser.: No. 731). 1971. Repr. of 1912 ed. lib. bdg. 20.50 (ISBN 0-8337-2603-X). B Franklin.

Canon of the Mass & Liturgical Reform. Cipriano Vagaggini. Tr. by Peter Coughlan. 1967. 4.50 (ISBN 0-8189-0019-9). Alba.

Canon of the Saivagama & the Kubjika: Tantras of the Western Kaula Tradition. Mark S. Dyczkowski. (Kashmir Shaivism Ser.). 256p. 1987. text ed. 34.50x (ISBN 0-88706-494-9). State U NY Pr.

Canonical Analysis & Factor Comparison. Mark S. Levine. LC 77-75941. (University Papers: Quantitative Applications in the Social Sciences, No. 6). 62p. 1977. 6.00 (ISBN 0-8039-0655-2). Sage.

Canonization & Authority in the Western Church. Eric W. Kemp. LC 78-63467. Repr. of 1948 ed. 20.00 (ISBN 0-404-16397-1). AMS Pr.

Canonization & Authority in the Western Church. Eric W. Kemp. LC 78-20474. 1980. Repr. of 1948 ed. 20.35 (ISBN 0-88355-852-1). Hyperion Conn.

Canonization of the Synagogue Service. Lawrence A. Hoffman. LC 78-62972. (Studies in Judaism & Christianity in Antiquity: No. 4). 1979. text ed. 18.95 (ISBN 0-268-00727-6). U of Notre Dame Pr.

Canonization of the Synagogue Service. Lawrence A. Hoffman. LC 78-62972. 245p. 1986. pap. 12.95 (ISBN 0-268-00756-X). U of Notre Dame Pr.

Canons & Decrees of the Council of Trent. Tr. by H. J. Schroeder. LC 78-66132. 293p. 1978. pap. 8.00 (ISBN 0-89555-074-1). TAN Bks Pubs.

Cantate Domino: An Ecumenical Hymn Book. full music ed. 1980. 24.50x (ISBN 0-19-143371-3). Oxford U Pr.

Canterbury & Rome, Sister Churches: A Roman Catholic Monk Reflects on Reunion in Diversity. Robert Hale. 7.95 (ISBN 0-8091-2480-7). Paulist Pr.

Canterbury Cathedral. Canon D. Hill. (New Bell's Cathedral Guides Ser.). 1986. cancelled (ISBN 0-918678-13-7). Historical Times.

Canterbury Cathedral. Canon D. Ingram-Hill. (New Bell Cathedral Guides Ser.). (Illus.). 192p. (Orig.). 1987. pap. 14.95 (ISBN 0-7135-2619-X, Pub. by Automobile Assn Brit). Salem Hse Pubs.

Canterbury Cathedral. Jonathan Keates & Angelo Hornak. (Illus.). pap. 13.95 (ISBN 0-935748-17-2). Scala Books.

Cantiones Bohemicae. Ed. by Guido M. Dreves. 1886. 60.00 (ISBN 0-384-12860-2). Johnson Repr.

Cantiones et Muteti, 3 vols. Ed. by Guido M. Dreves. (Illus.). 1895-1904. 60.00 ea. (ISBN 0-384-12865-3). Johnson Repr.

Cantors. Ed. by Mary Berry. LC 78-56178. (Resources of Music Ser.). 1979. pap. 5.95 (ISBN 0-521-22149-8). Cambridge U Pr.

Canyons of Grace. Levi S. Peterson. 135p. 1982. pap. 5.95 (ISBN 0-941214-26-5, Orion). Signature Bks.

Capacitado para Orientar. Jay E. Adams. Orig. Title: Competent to Counsel. (Span.). 328p. 1981. pap. 7.95 (ISBN 0-8254-1000-2). Kregel.

Capacitese Como Lider. LeRoy Ford. Tr. by Guillermo Blair. Tr. of Developing Skills for Church Leaders. (Span.). 64p. 1986. pap. 3.75 (ISBN 0-311-17023-4, Edit Mundo). Casa Bautista.

Capacity to Love. Jack Dominian. 174p. (Orig.). 1985. text ed. 6.95 (ISBN 0-8091-2726-1). Paulist Pr.

Capitalists Without Capitalism: The Jains of India & the Quakers of the West. Balwant S. Nevaskar. LC 72-98709. (Contributions in Sociology: No. 6). 1971. lib. bdg. 29.95 (ISBN 0-8371-3297-5, NCA/). Greenwood.

Cappella Music in the Public Worksip of the Church. Everett Ferguson. LC 72-76963. (Way of Life Ser: No. 125). 1972. pap. text ed. 3.95 (ISBN 0-89112-125-0, Bibl Res Pr). Abilene Christ U.

Capsule View of the Bible. Russell Osden. 1979. pap. 1.00 (ISBN 0-88469-045-8). BMH Bks.

Captain America Complex. Robert Jewett. LC 82-73362. 220p. (Orig.). 1984. pap. 4.95 (ISBN 0-939680-15-7). Bear & Co.

Captain Mahjong. Philip Holder. 1976. pap. 2.40 (ISBN 0-85363-113-1). OMF Bks.

Captain Maxi's Secret Island. V. Gilbert Beers. (Muffin Family Ser.: No. 11). 96p. 1983. 11.95 (ISBN 0-8024-9573-7). Moody.

Captain Noah. Don Thompson. (Rainy Day Survival Bk.: No. 1). (Illus.). 32p. pap. 0.99 (ISBN 0-87123-696-6, 220696). Bethany Hse.

Captain of Our Salvation: A Study in the Patristic Exegesis of Hebrews. Rowan Greer. 325p. 1973. lib. bdg. 52.00x (Pub. by J C B Mohr BRD). Coronet Bks.

Captain Sebastian: Fifty-Two Talks to Boys & Girls. F. Chenhalls Williams. 96p. 1961. pap. 2.75 (ISBN 0-87921-007-9). Attic Pr.

Captivating Object Lessons. Wesley T. Runk. (Object Lesson Ser). 1979. pap. 3.95 (ISBN 0-8010-7671-4). Baker Bk.

Capture of Damietta. Oliverus. Tr. by John J. Gavigan. LC 78-63353. (Crusades & Military Orders: Second Ser.). Repr. of 1948 ed. 17.50 (ISBN 0-404-17026-9). AMS Pr.

Capuchins: A Contribution to the History of the Counter Reformation, 2 vols. Cuthbert. 1977. lib. bdg. 250.00 (ISBN 0-8490-1571-5). Gordon Pr.

Capuchins in French Louisiana (1722-1766) Claude Vogel. LC 73-3561. (Catholic University of America. Studies in American Church History: No. 7). Repr. of 1928 ed. 20.00 (ISBN 0-404-57757-1). AMS Pr.

Carafa Chapel, Renaissance Art in Rome. Gail Geiger. (Sixteenth Century Essays & Studies Ser.: Vol. V). (Illus.). 210p. 1985. smyth sewn 50.00x (ISBN 0-940474-05-0). Sixteenth Cent.

Caravan of Dreams. Idries Shah. 207p. 1968. 14.95 (ISBN 0-900860-14-6, Pub. by Octagon Pr England). Ins Study Human.

Card-Guide to New Testament Exegesis. Benjamin Chapman. 2.95 (ISBN 0-8010-2396-3). Baker Bk.

Card-Guide to New Testament Greek. Benjamin Chapman. 1.95 (ISBN 0-8010-2388-2). Baker Bk.

Cardanus Comforte. Girolamo Cardano. Ed. by T. Bedingfield. LC 77-6565. (English Experience Ser.: No. 82). 204p. 1969. Repr. of 1576 ed. 25.00 (ISBN 90-221-0082-0). Walter J Johnson.

Cardiac Patient. George W. Paterson. LC 78-52187. (Religion & Medicine Ser.). 1978. pap. 5.95 (ISBN 0-8066-1661-X, 10-0971). Augsburg.

Cardinal Basil Hume. Gerard Noel. (Profiles Ser.). (Illus.). 64p. 1984. 8.95 (ISBN 0-241-11204-4, Pub. by Hamish Hamilton England). David & Charles.

Cardinal de Bessarion 1405-1472: Etude sun la Chretiente et la Renaissance vers le Milieu du XVe Siecle. Henri Vast. (Fr.). 487p. Repr. of 1878 ed. lib. bdg. 57.50x. Coronet Bks.

Cardinal Manning: A Biography. Robert Gray. LC 85-10687. 366p. 1985. 29.95 (ISBN 0-312-12032-X). St Martin.

Cardinal Meaning: Essays in Comparative Hermeneutics, Buddhism & Christianity. Ed. by Michael Pye & Robert Morgan. (Religion & Reason Ser: No. 6). 203p. 1973. text ed. 23.25x (ISBN 90-2797-228-1). Mouton.

Cardinal Newman. William Barry. 1973. Repr. of 1904 ed. 20.00 (ISBN 0-8274-1797-7). R West.

Cardinal Newman. Richard H. Hutton. LC 75-30029. Repr. of 1891 ed. 21.00 (ISBN 0-404-14033-5). AMS Pr.

Cardinal Newman. J. Lewis May. 1945. Repr. lib. bdg. 20.00 (ISBN 0-8414-6605-X). Folcroft.

Cardinal Newman. Charles Sarolea. 174p. 1980. Repr. of 1908 ed. lib. bdg. 30.00 (ISBN 0-89987-759-1). Darby Bks.

Cardinal Newman in His Age: His Place in English Theology & Literature. Harold L. Weatherby. LC 72-1347. 320p. 1973. 16.50x (ISBN 0-8265-1182-1). Vanderbilt U Pr.

Cardinal Newman Prayerbook: Kindly Light. Daniel M. O'Connell. 352p. 1985. pap. 14.95 (ISBN 0-87193-220-2). Dimension Bks.

Cardinal of Lorraine & the Council of Trent: A Study in the Counter-Reformation. Henry O. Evennett. LC 83-45592. Date not set. Repr. of 1940 ed. 57.50 (ISBN 0-404-19885-6). AMS Pr.

Cardinal of Scotland - David Beaton 1494-1546. Margaret H. Sanderson. 324p. 1986. 39.95x (ISBN 0-85976-110-X, Pub. by John Donald Pub UK). Humanities.

Cardinal Protectors of England: Rome & the Tudors Before the Reformation. W. E. Wilkie. LC 73-82462. 224p. 1974. 44.50 (ISBN 0-521-20332-5). Cambridge U Pr.

Cardinal Richelieu: Power & the Pursuit of Wealth. Joseph Bergin. 352p. 1985. 30.00x (ISBN 0-300-03495-4). Yale U Pr.

Cardinal Wolsey. Mandell Creighton. 226p. 1982. Repr. of 1888 ed. lib. bdg. 35.00 (ISBN 0-8495-0878-9). Arden Lib.

Cardinals & Saints. Arlene Zekowski & Stanley Berne. LC 58-11713. (Illus.). 1958. 45.00 (ISBN 0-913844-10-1). Am Canadian.

Care & Concern of the Churches. Edwin Groenhoff. LC 81-69760. (Heritage Ser.: Vol. 8). 1984. 8.95 (ISBN 0-911802-59-2). Free Church Pubns.

Care & Counseling of the Aging. William M. Clements. Ed. by Howard J. Clinebell & Howard W. Stone. LC 78-54547. (Creative Pastoral Care & Counseling Ser). 96p. 1979. pap. 4.50 (ISBN 0-8006-0561-6, 1-561). Fortress.

Care & Counseling of Youth in the Church. Paul B. Irwin. Ed. by Howard J. Clinebell & Howard W. Stone. LC 74-26334. (Creative Pastoral Care & Counseling Ser.). 96p. 1975. pap. 4.50 (ISBN 0-8006-0552-7, 1-552). Fortress.

Care & Feeding of New Converts. 1st ed. Ed. by James D. Craig. 12p. 1981. pap. text ed. 0.49 (ISBN 0-88151-021-1). Lay Leadership.

Care & Feeding of Volunteers. Douglas W. Johnson. LC 78-8295. (Creative Leadership Ser.). 1978. pap. 7.25 (ISBN 0-687-04669-6). Abingdon.

Care & Maintenance of the Fourth Amendment: The Owner's Manual. pap. 6.00 (ISBN 0-915598-30-2). Church of Scient Info.

Care for the Dying. Richard N. Soulen. LC 74-19968. 120p. 1975. pap. 6.50 (ISBN 0-8042-1098-5). John Knox.

Care of Converts. Keith M. Baily. 95p. (Orig.). 1979. pap. 1.50 (ISBN 0-87509-156-3); leader's guide 0.75 (ISBN 0-87509-157-1). Chr Pubns.

Care of Mind-Care of Spirit: Psychiatric Dimensions of Spiritual Direction. Gerald G. May. LC 81-47840. 128p. 1982. 14.45 (ISBN 0-06-065533-X, HarpR). Har-Row.

Care of Souls in the Classic Tradition. Thomas C Oden. LC 83-48912. (Theology & Pastoral Care Ser.). pap. 7.95 (ISBN 0-8006-1729-0, 1-729). Fortress.

Careers in Religious Communications. Roland E. Wolseley. 264p. 1977. pap. 6.95 (ISBN 0-8361-1823-5). Herald Pr.

Careful Disorder: Chronicles of Life & Love & Laughter. Stephen Vicchio. 300p. (Orig.). 1987. pap. 10.95 (ISBN 0-87061-135-6). Chr Classics.

Caregiver's Handbook. Marian Cannell. 1986. 46.50 (ISBN 0-939273-00-4). Caregiving Resc.

Carelessness & Indifference. large print ed. Pearl Brians. 25p. 1985. pap. 5.00 (ISBN 0-914009-39-7). VHI Library.

C.A.R.E.S. Robert G. Bruce & Debra F. Bruce. 1984. 5.50 (ISBN 0-89536-672-X, 0393). CSS of Ohio.

Caring. rev. ed. Churches Alive, Inc. Staff. LC 81-66927. 60p. 1981. pap. text ed. 3.95 (ISBN 0-934396-23-X). Churches Alive.

Caring & Curing: Historical Essays on Health, Medicine, & the Faith Traditions. Ed. by Ronald L. Numbers & Darrel W. Amundsen. 576p. 1986. text ed. 35.00x (ISBN 0-02-919270-6). Macmillan.

Caring Church: A Guide for Lay Pastoral Care. Howard W. Stone. LC 82-48415. 116p. (Orig.). 1983. pap. 6.95 (ISBN 0-06-067695-7, RD420, HarpR). Har-Row.

Caring Community: A Design for Ministry. Christin Lore-Kelly. 1984. 12.95 (ISBN 0-8294-0423-6). Loyola.

Caring Enough Not to Forgive. David Augsburger. LC 81-80913. 160p. (Orig.). 1981. pap. 5.95 (ISBN 0-8361-1965-7). Herald Pr.

Caring Enough to Confront. rev. ed. David Augsburger. LC 73-83400. 144p. 1980. pap. 5.95 (ISBN 0-8307-0733-6, 5411602). Regal.

Caring Enough to Confront. John Richardson. LC 73-83400. (Caring Enough Ser.). 1984. pap. 3.95 (ISBN 0-8307-0990-8, 6101903). Regal.

Caring Enough to Forgive: Caring Enough to Not Forgive. David Augsburger. LC 80-50545. 176p. 1981. pap. 5.95 (ISBN 0-8307-0749-2, 5413702). Regal.

Caring Enough to Hear & Be Heard. David Augsburger. LC 82-81000. (Caring Enough Bks.). 176p. (Orig.). 1982. pap. 4.95 (ISBN 0-8361-3307-2). Herald Pr.

Caring Enough to Hear & Be Heard: Leader's Guide. Jim Larson. LC 82-403. (Caring Enough Ser.). 1984. pap. 3.95 (ISBN 0-8307-0994-0, 6101948). Regal.

Caring Father. Wilson W. Grant. LC 82-72990. (Orig.). 1983. pap. 5.95 (ISBN 0-8054-5654-6). Broadman.

Caring for Folks from Birth to Death. Ed. by James E. Hightower, Jr. LC 84-20005. 1985. pap. 6.95 (ISBN 0-8054-2415-6). Broadman.

Caring for Marriage. Denise L. Carmody. LC 85-60412. 192p. (Orig.). 1985. pap. 7.95 (ISBN 0-8091-2721-0). Paulist Pr.

Caring for Society. Robert L. Kinast. 168p. 1985. pap. 9.95 (ISBN 0-88347-197-3). Thomas More.

Caring for the Caregivers. C. W. Brister. LC 85-3793. 1985. pap. 8.95 (ISBN 0-8054-5537-X). Broadman.

Caring for the Special Child. John W. Glaser. LC 84-82551. 97p. (Orig.). 1985. pap. 6.95 (ISBN 0-934134-14-6, Leaven Pr). Sheed & Ward MO.

Caring for the World. J. Edward Carothers. (Orig.). 1978. pap. 4.95 (ISBN 0-377-00078-7). Friend Pr.

Caring for Your Aging Parent. James Kenny & Stephen Spicer. 152p. 1984. pap. 5.95 (ISBN 0-86716-037-3). St Anthony Mess Pr.

Caring: How Can We Love One Another? Morton T. Kelsey. LC 80-84659. 198p. (Orig.). 1981. pap. 8.95 (ISBN 0-8091-2366-5). Paulist Pr.

Caring in Crisis: Bible Studies for Helping People. Judith A. Shelly. LC 78-13878. 1979. pap. 4.95 (ISBN 0-87784-563-8). Inter-Varsity.

Caring Pastor: An Introduction to Pastoral Counseling in the Local Church. Charles F. Kemp. LC 85-3994. (Orig.). 1985. pap. 9.95 (ISBN 0-687-35548-6). Abingdon.

Caring Question: You First or Me First - Choosing a Healthy Balance. Donald A. Tubesing & Nancy L. Tubesing. LC 83-70501. 224p. (Orig.). 1983. pap. 3.95 (ISBN 0-8066-2007-2, 10-0968). Augsburg.

Caring Together: Faith, Hope, & Love in Your Family. Janet A. Chartier & Myron R. Chartier. LC 86-3460. 132p. (Orig.). 1986. pap. 8.95 (ISBN 0-664-24019-4). Westminster.

Carismas de Dios. Gerda Brown. (Span., Illus.). 589p. (Orig.). 1983. pap. 8.95 (ISBN 0-939868-98-9). Chr Intl Pubs.

Carl Becker's Heavenly City Revisited. Ed. by Raymond O. Rockwood. LC 68-11256. xxxii, 227p. 1968. Repr. of 1958 ed. 23.00 (ISBN 0-208-00421-1, Archon). Shoe String.

Carl F. Henry, Makers of the Modern Theological Mind. Bob Patterson. 1983. pap. 8.95 (ISBN 0-8499-2951-2). Word Bks.

Carl Jung & Soul Psychology. Ed. by E. Mark Stern. Tr. of Voices: The Art & Science of Psychotherapy. 196p. (Orig.). Repr. of 1986 ed. text ed. write for info. (ISBN 0-86656-632-5). Haworth Pr.

Carlyle & Emerson: Their Long Debate. Kenneth M. Harris. LC 77-28036. 1978. 14.00x (ISBN 0-674-09755-6). Harvard U Pr.

Carlyle & the Saint Simonians. Hill Shine. LC 71-120666. 1970. Repr. lib. bdg. 17.00x (ISBN 0-374-97360-1, Octagon). Hippocrene Bks.

Carmel Mission, from Founding to Rebuilding. Sydney Temple. LC 79-57168. (Illus.). 176p. 1980. pap. 5.95 (ISBN 0-913548-71-5, Valley Calif). Western Tanager.

Carmelite Studies II: Carmel & Psychology. John Sullivan. LC 82-1091. 320p. pap. 6.95x (ISBN 0-935216-00-6). ICS Pubns.

Carmelite Studies III: Centenary of Saint Theresa. Intro. by John Sullivan. LC 84-4498. 240p. (Orig.). 1984. pap. 6.95x (ISBN 0-935216-03-0). ICS Pubns.

Carmina Anglo-Normannica: Chasteau d'Amour, to Which Is Added La Vie de Saint-Marie Egyptienne & an English Version of the Chasteau d'Amour. Robert Grosseteste. Ed. by M. Cooke. 1852. 24.00 (ISBN 0-8337-1467-8). B. Franklin.

Carnal Christian: What Should We Think of the Carnal Christian? Ernest C. Reisinger. 75p. 1.20 (ISBN 0-85151-389-1). Banner of Truth.

Carnal Christians: And Other Words That Don't Go Together. Rich Wilkerson. 175p. (Orig.). 1986. pap. 3.50 (ISBN 0-88368-188-9). Whitaker Hse.

Carnet De Notes Spiritual. Paul Twitchell. 1978. pap. 3.95 (ISBN 0-914766-40-6). IWP Pub.

Carol Time. (Christmas Ser.). 2.95 (ISBN 0-86112-234-8, Pub. by Brimax Bks). Borden.

Carolina Backcountry on the Eve of the Revolution: The Journal & Other Writings of Charles Woodmason, Anglican Itinerant. Charles Woodmason. Ed. by Richard J. Hooker. (Institute of Early American History & Culture Ser.). xxxix, 305p. 1953. 25.00x (ISBN 0-8078-0643-9). U of NC Pr.

Carolingian Essays: Andrew W. Mellon Lectures in Early Christian Studies. Ed. by Uta-Renate Blumenthal. LC 83-14562. 249p. 1983. 25.95x (ISBN 0-8132-0579-4). Cath U Pr.

Carols & Christmas Songs: Colinde, Vol. 4. Bartok. (Rumanian Folk Music Ser). 1975. lib. bdg. 131.50 (ISBN 90-247-1737-X, Pub. by Martinus Nijhoff Netherlands). Kluwer Academic.

Carols for Choirs: Bk. 3, Fifty Carols. Ed. by David Willcocks. 1978. pap. text ed. 7.00 (ISBN 0-19-353570-X). Oxford U Pr.

Carols for Choirs: Fifty Christmas Carols, Bk. 1. Reginald Jacques & David Willcocks. (YA) 1961. 12.00 (ISBN 0-19-353221-2); pap. 7.00 (ISBN 0-19-353222-0). Oxford U Pr.

Carols for Christmas. Ed. by David Willcocks. (Illus.). 96p. 1983. 25.00 (ISBN 0-03-064044-X). H Holt & Co.
Carols for the Holidays. Hershal Pyle. Date not set. 2.25 (ISBN 0-317-20177-8). Campus.
Carols of Christmas. Rod McKuen. 1971. 3.95 (ISBN 0-394-47420-1). Random.
Carol's Story. Chip Ricks. 192p. 1981. pap. 6.95 (ISBN 0-8423-0208-5). Tyndale.
Carols, Their Origin, Music, & Connection with Mystery-Plays: A Greenwood Archival Edition. William J. Phillips. (Illus.). Repr. of 1921 ed. lib. bdg. 40.00x (ISBN 0-8371-4312-8, PHCA). Greenwood.
Carols to Sing, Clap & Play: A Companion to the Soprano Recorder Tuition Books. Heather Cox & Garth Rickard. (Illus.). 1984. pap. 4.50 (ISBN 0-918812-36-4). MMB Music.
Carpenter. Joy Haney. Ed. by Mary Wallace. LC 85-26498. (Illus.). 96p. (Orig.). 1985. pap. 5.00 (ISBN 0-912315-97-0). Word Aflame.
Carpenter's Son. Carlyle Marney. 96p. 1984. pap. 6.95 (ISBN 0-913029-02-5). Stevens Bk Pr.
Carrie-Ambassador at Large. rev. ed. Elizabeth Dean. (Illus.). 269p. 1984. pap. 4.95 (ISBN 0-930033-00-0). Christ Life Revivals.
Carrie: Heartsong Books. Carole Page. 160p. (Orig.). 1984. pap. 2.95 (ISBN 0-87123-441-6). Bethany Hse.
Carriere of Carpentras. Marianne Calmann. LC 82-48692. (Littman Library of Jewish Civilization). (Illus.). 286p. 1984. 32.50x (ISBN 0-19-710037-6). Oxford U Pr.
Carroll's First Book of Proverbs or Life Is a Fortune Cookie. Carroll Carroll. (Illus.). 80p. 1981. pap. 4.95 (ISBN 0-87786-004-1). Gold Penny.
Cartae of the Carthusian General Chapter of the Urbanist Observance During the Great Schism. James Hogg. (Analecta Cartusiana Ser.: No. 119). (Orig.). 1988. pap. 25.00 (ISBN 0-317-42562-5, Pub. by Salzburg Studies). Longwood Pub Group.
Carte Monialium De Northberwic. North Berwick Priory. Ed. by Cosmo Innes. LC 74-173799. (Bannatyne Club, Edinburgh. Publications: No. 84). Repr. of 1847 ed. 27.50 (ISBN 0-404-52809-0). AMS Pr.
Cartesian Meditations. Husserl. 1977. pap. 13.00 (ISBN 90-247-0068-X, Pub. by Martinus Nijhoff Netherlands). Kluwer Academic.
Cartesianische Meditationen und Pariser Vortrage: Photomechanischer Nachdruck. Husserl. (Husserliana Ser: No. 1). 1973. lib. bdg. 29.00 (ISBN 90-247-0214-3, Pub. by Martinus Nijhoff Netherlands). Kluwer Academic.
Carthusian Order in England. E. Margaret Thompson. (Church Historical Society London N. S. Ser.: No. 3). Repr. of 1930 ed. 80.00 (ISBN 0-8115-3127-9). Kraus Repr.
Carthusians under King Henry the Eighth. L. E. Whatmore. Ed. by James Hogg. (Analecta Cartusiana Ser.: No. 109). 227p. (Orig.). 1983. pap. 25.00 (ISBN 0-317-42558-7, Pub. by Salzburg Studies). Longwood Pub Group.
Cartoon Clip-Art for Youth Leaders. Ron Wheeler. 120p. 1987. pap. price not set (ISBN 0-8010-9682-0). Baker Bk.
Cartoons for Thinking: Issues in Ethics & Values. Joseph P. Hester & Don R. Killian. (Illus.). 1984. 9.95 (ISBN 0-89824-007-7). Trillium Pr.
Cartuja De Aniago. James Hogg. (Analecta Cartusiana Ser.: No. 94/2). 204p. (Orig.). 1980. pap. 25.00 (ISBN 3-7052-0164-6, Pub. by Salzburg Studies). Longwood Pub Group.
Cartuja De Aniago: Introduction, Vol. 1. James Hogg. (Analecta Cartusiana: No. 94/1). 1987. pap. 25.00 (ISBN 3-7052-0163-8, Pub. by Salzburg Studies). Longwood Pub Group.
Cartuja de Aula Dei. James Hogg. Ed. by James Hogg. (Analecta Cartusiana Ser.: No. 70). (Orig.). 1982. pap. 25.00 (ISBN 3-7052-0103-4, Pub. by Salzburg Studies). Longwood Pub Group.
Cartuja de el Paular. Ildefonso M. Gomez & James Hogg. Ed. by James Hogg. (Analecta Cartusiana Ser.: No. 77). 100p. (Orig.). 1982. pap. 25.00 (ISBN 3-7052-0113-1, Pub. by Salzburg Studies). Longwood Pub Group.
Cartuja de la Conception. James Hogg. Ed. by James Hogg. (Analecta Cartusiana Ser.). Tr. of Charterhouse of the Conception. (Span.). 44p. (Orig.). 1980. pap. 25.00 (ISBN 3-7052-0105-0, Pub. by Salzburg Studies). Longwood Pub Group.
Cartuja de las Fuentes. James Hogg. Ed. by James Hogg. (Anaalecta Cartusiana Ser.). Tr. of Charterhouse of las Fuentes. (Ital., Illus.). 52p. (Orig.). 1980. pap. 25.00 (ISBN 3-7052-0104-2, Pub. by Salzburg Studies). Longwood Pub Group.
Cartuja de Miraflores. James Hogg. Ed. by James Hogg. (Analecta Cartusiana Ser.: No. 79). Tr. of Charterhouse of MiraFlores. (Span., Illus., Orig.). 1979. pap. 25.00 (ISBN 3-7052-0116-6, Pub. by Salzburg Studies). Longwood Pub Group.
Cartuja de Miraflores: Introduction, Vol. 1. James Hogg. Ed. by James Hogg. (Analecta Cartusiana Ser.: No. 79). (Orig.). 1986. pap. 25.00 (ISBN 3-7052-0115-8, Pub. by Salzburg Studies). Longwood Pub Group.
Cartuja de Scala Dei: (The Charterhouse of Scala Dei) James Hogg. (Analecta Cartusiana Ser.: No. 41-3). (Span. & Eng., Illus.). 54p. (Orig.). 1980. pap. 25.00 (ISBN 3-7052-0051-8, Pub by Salzburg Studies). Longwood Pub Group.
Cartuja de Val de Cristo: (The Charterhouse of Val de Cristo) James Hogg. (Analecta Cartusiana Ser.: No. 41-5). (Span. & Eng., Illus.). 50p. (Orig.). 1979. pap. 25.00 (ISBN 3-7052-0053-4, Pub by Salzburg Studies). Longwood Pub Group.
Cartuja en Espana. Ildefonso Gomez. Ed. by James Hogg. (Analecta Cartusiana Ser.: No. 114). 499p. (Orig.). 1984. pap. 25.00 (ISBN 0-317-42560-9, Pub. by Salzburg Studies). Longwood Pub Group.
Cartujas de las Cuevas, Cazalla de la Sierra y Granada: (The Charterhouses of las Cuevas, Cazalla de la Sierra & Granada) James Hogg. (Analecta Cartusiana Ser.: No. 47-3). (Span., Illus.). 110p. (Orig.). 1979. pap. 25.00 (ISBN 3-7052-0065-8, Pub by Salzburg Studies). Longwood Pub Group.
Cartujas de Montalegre, Sant Pol de Maresme, Vallparadis, Ara Coeli y Via Coeli. James Hogg. (Analecta Cartusiana Ser.: No. 41-2). (Span., Illus.). 140p. (Orig.). 1983. pap. 25.00 (ISBN 3-7052-0050-X, Pub by Salzburg Studies). Longwood Pub Group.
Cartujos, Hoy: Una Vida Para la Vida de la Iglesia. Ed. by James Hogg. (Analecta Cartusiana Ser.: No. 81). 110p. (Orig.). 1980. pap. 25.00 (ISBN 3-7052-0118-2, Pub. by Salzburg Studies). Longwood Pub Group.
Cartulary & Terrier of the Priory of Bilsongton, Kent. Ed. by N. Neilson. (British Academy, London, Records of the Social & Economic History of England & Wales Ser.: Vol. 7). pap. 36.00 (ISBN 0-8115-1247-9). Kraus Repr.
Cartulary of Haughmond Abbey. Ed. by U. Rees. 304p. 1985. text ed. 39.95x (ISBN 0-7083-0907-0, Pub. by U of Wales). Humanities.
Cartulary of the Knights of St. John of Jerusalem in England. Ed. by Michael Gervers. (Records of Social & Economic History Ser.). 1982. 195.00x (ISBN 0-19-725996-0). Oxford U Pr.
Carved in Stone. Paul Quenon. (Illus.). 40p. 1979. pap. 2.50 (ISBN 0-87793-195-X). Ave Maria.
Carved Masonry Domes of Mediaeval Cairo. Christel Kessler. 1976. pap. 15.00x (ISBN 0-686-19945-6). Intl Learn Syst.
Caryacarya, Vol. I & II. Anandanagar. Vol. I - 37 p. pap. 2.00 (ISBN 0-686-95445-9); Vol. II - 49 p. pap. 1.00 (ISBN 0-686-99507-4). Ananda Marga.
Caryapadas: Tantric Poems of the Eighty-Four Mahasiddhas (Siddhacaryas) 2nd rev. ed. Tr. by Atindra Mojumder from Bengali. 225p. 1980. text ed. 13.95x (ISBN 0-935548-03-3). Santarasa Pubns.
Case Against Jones: Study of Psychical Phenomena. John Vyvyan. 220p. 1966. 7.50 (ISBN 0-227-67683-1). Attic Pr.
Case Against Planned Parenthood. Michael Schwartz. 200p. (Orig.). Date not set. pap. cancelled (ISBN 0-87973-539-2, 539). Our Sunday Visitor.
Case Against Religion. Marshall J. Gauvin. 500p. 10.00 (ISBN 0-318-19200-4). Truth Seeker.
Case Against Religion: A Psychotherapist's View & the Case Against Religiousity. Albert Ellis. 57p. 1985. saddle stiched 4.00 (ISBN 0-910309-18-3). Am Atheist.
Case Against TM in the Schools. John E. Patton. (Direction Bks.). 80p. 1976. pap. 1.45 (ISBN 0-8010-6957-2). Baker Bk.
Case for an Auxiliary Priesthood. Raymond Hickey. LC 81-16950. 160p. (Orig.). 1982. pap. 1.99 (ISBN 0-88344-021-0). Orbis Bks.
Case for Christianity. Colin Chapman. (Illus.). 313p. 1984. pap. 12.95 (ISBN 0-8028-1984-2). Eerdmans.
Case for Divine Healing. Bill Popejoy. LC 75-43155. 64p. 1976. pap. 0.95 (ISBN 0-88243-478-0, 02-0478). Gospel Pub.
Case for Jewish Civil Law in the Jewish State. K. Kahana. 6.25x (ISBN 0-685-01037-6). Bloch.
Case for Jewish Civil Law in the Jewish State. K. Kahana. 120p. 1960. 6.50. Soncino Pr.
Case for Radical Christianity. Jerry Wilkinson & Jim Richardson. 1984. pap. 1.75 (ISBN 0-911739-25-4). Abbott Loop.
Case for Reincarnation. Joe Fisher. 208p. 1985. pap. 3.95 (ISBN 0-553-24868-5). Bantam.
Case for Reincarnation. James D. Freeman. 320p. 1986. 5.95 (ISBN 0-87159-021-2). Unity School.
Case for the Burial of Ancestors, Bk. 1. Paul Zelevansky. LC 80-54692. 1981. 27.00 (ISBN 0-9605610-3-X); pap. 18.00 (ISBN 0-9605610-2-1). Zartscorp.
Case of Conscience. J. Guillent Perez. 370p. (Orig.). 1985. pap. 12.95 (ISBN 0-9607590-2-6). Action Life Pubns.
Case of Hotel Polski. Abraham Shulman. LC 81-81519. 240p. 1982. 16.95 (ISBN 0-89604-033-X); pap. 10.95 (ISBN 0-89604-034-8). Holocaust Pubns.
Case of John Darrell: Minister & Exorcist. Corinne H. Rickert. LC 62-62828. (University of Florida Humanities Monographs: No. 9). 1962. pap. 3.50 (ISBN 0-8130-0197-8). U Presses Fla.
Case Statement. Robert J. Yeager. 1984. 4.80 (ISBN 0-318-18571-7). Natl Cath Educ.
Case Studies in Christ & Salvation. Jack Rogers et al. LC 76-53765. 176p. 1977. pap. 7.95 (ISBN 0-664-24133-6). Westminster.
Case Studies in Missions. Frances F. Hilbert & G. Paul. 1987. pap. 7.95 (ISBN 0-8010-4308-5). Baker Bk.
Case Studies in Spirit Possession. Ed. by Vincent Crapanzano & Vivian Garrison. LC 76-26653. (Contemporary Religious Movements Ser.). pap. 118.30 (ISBN 0-317-08510-7, 2055396). Bks Demand UMI.
Case Studies of Present-Day Religions Teaching. Hugh Hartshorne & Elsa Lotz. (Educational Ser.). 1932. Repr. 15.00 (ISBN 0-8482-4454-0). Norwood Edns.
Case Studies on Human Rights & Fundamental Freedoms. Ed. by Veenhoven. Incl. Vol. 1. 1975 (ISBN 90-247-1780-9); Vol. 2. 1975; Vol. 3. 1976 (ISBN 90-247-1955-0); Vol. 4. 1976; Vol. 5. 1976. lib. bdg. 52.50 ea. (Pub. by Martinus Nijhoff Netherlands). Kluwer Academic.
Casebook for Christian Living: Value Formation for Families & Congregations. Robert A. Evans et al. pap. 6.95 (ISBN 0-8042-2032-8). John Knox.
Cases in Civil Liberties. 3rd ed. Robert F. Cushman. 1979. 18.95. P-H.
Cases in Denominational Administration: A Management Casebook for Decision-Making. Ed. by Harold R. Phillips & Robert E. Firth. vi, 314p. 1978. pap. text ed. 4.95 (ISBN 0-943872-75-8). Andrews Univ Pr.
Cases of Conscience. E. Rose. LC 74-76947. 272p. 1975. 44.50 (ISBN 0-521-20462-3). Cambridge U Pr.
Cases of Conscience: Alternatives Open to Recusants & Puritans under Elizabeth I & James I. Elliot Rose. LC 74-76947. pap. 68.50 (2027243). Bks Demand UMI.
Cash Management: Stewardship of the Church's Cash Resources. Manfred Holck, Jr. (Administration for Churches Ser.). 1978. pap. 3.95 (ISBN 0-8066-1650-4, 10-0972). Augsburg.
Casilda of the Rising Moon. Elizabeth B. De Trevino. LC 67-10389. 224p. 1967. 3.95 (ISBN 0-374-31188-9). FS&G.
Casino of Pius IV. Graham Smith. LC 76-3017. (Illus.). 1976. 44.50x (ISBN 0-691-03915-1). Princeton U Pr.
Caspar Schwenckfeld on the Person & Work of Christ. Paul A. Maier. 115p. 1959. write for info. Concordia Schl Grad Studies.
Cassadaga: An Inside Look at the South's Oldest Psychic Community with True Experiences of People Who Have Been There. Robert Harrold. (Illus.). 1979. pap. 4.95 (ISBN 0-916224-49-X). Banyan Bks.
Caste & Social Stratification Among Muslims. 2nd ed. Ed. by Imtiaz Ahmad. 1978. 16.00x (ISBN 0-8364-0050-X). South Asia Bks.
Caste in the Catholic Community in Kerala. George Koilparampil. 289p. 1986. 14.50X (Pub. by Macmillan India). South Asia Bks.
Casting Out Anger: Religion among the Taita of Kenya. Grace G. Harris. (Illus.). 193p. 1986. pap. text ed. 7.95x (ISBN 0-88133-233-X). Waveland Pr.
Casting Your Cares Upon the Lord. Kenneth E. Hagin. 1981. pap. 1.00 (ISBN 0-89276-023-0). Hagin Ministries.
Cat in the Mysteries of Religion & Magic. M. Oldfield Howey. LC 81-51289. (Illus.). 254p. 1982. Repr. of 1930 ed. 12.50 (ISBN 0-8048-1360-4). C E Tuttle.
Cataclysm Has Begun, No. 1. J. J. Williamson. 20.00x (ISBN 0-317-43559-0, Pub. by Soc of Metaphysicians). State Mutual Bk.
Catacombs & Basilicas: The Early Christians in Rome. Fabrizio Mancinelli. (Illus.). 65p. (Orig.). 1981. pap. 12.50 (ISBN 0-935748-13-X). Scala Books.
Catacombs of Rome, 2 vols. Paolo Aringhi. (Printed Sources of Western Ser.). (Lat., Illus.). 1981. pap. 120.00 slipcase (ISBN 0-915346-61-3). A Wofsy Fine Arts.
Catacombs: Rediscovered Monuments of Early Christianity. J. Stevenson. (Ancient Peoples & Places Ser.). (Illus.). 1978. 19.95 (ISBN 0-500-02091-4). Thames Hudson.
Catalog of Creative Ministries. Virgil Nelson & Lynn Nelson. 144p. 1983. pap. 9.95 (ISBN 0-8170-1017-3). Judson.
Catalog of the Friends Historical Library Book & Serial Collections, 6 vols. Swarthmore College. 1982. Set. lib. bdg. 655.00 (ISBN 0-8161-0376-3, Hall Library). G K Hall.
Catalog of the Salem Congregation Music. Ed. by Frances Cumnock. (Illus.). 682p. 31.50 (ISBN 0-8078-1398-2). Moravian Music.
Catalog of the Yiddish Collection: Harvard University College Library, 3 vols. Charles Berlin. 2100p. 1987. lib. bdg. 490.00 (ISBN 3-598-41242-8). K G Saur.
Catalogue de la Bibliotheque de l'ecole Biblique et Archeologique Francaise (Catalog of the Library of the French Biblical & Archaeological School, 13 vols. Ecole Biblique et Archeologique Francaise. Jerusalem. 1975. lib. bdg. 1405.00 (ISBN 0-8161-1154-5, Hall Library). G K Hall.
Catalogue General des Ouvrages Edites Par l'Abbe Migne. Freres Garnier. LC 71-168926. 1967. Repr. of 1885 ed. 22.50 (ISBN 0-8337-2386-3). B Franklin.
Catalogue of a Collection of 1500 Tracts by Martin Luther & His Contemporaries, 1511-1598. James L. Crawford. 1965. Repr. of 1903 ed. 32.00 (ISBN 0-8337-1001-X). B Franklin.
Catalogue of an Exhibition Commemorative of the Tercentenary of the Birth of John Milton. John Milton. Repr. of 1909 ed. lib. bdg. 20.00 (ISBN 0-8414-6620-3). Folcroft.
Catalogue of Arabic Manuscripts (Yahuda Section) in the Garrett Collection, Princeton University Library. Rudolph Mach. LC 75-2999. (Illus.). 1976. 160.00x (ISBN 0-691-03908-9). Princeton U Pr.
Catalogue of Audio & Video Testimonies of the Holocaust. Ed. by Joan Ringelheim & Esther Katz. (Occasional Papers from the Institute for Research in History Ser.: No. 5). 150p. (Orig.). Date not set. pap. 7.50 (ISBN 0-913865-04-4). Inst Res Hist.
Catalogue of Choral Music Arranged in Biblical Order. Compiled by James Laster. LC 82-16745. 269p. 1983. 27.50 (ISBN 0-8108-1592-3). Scarecrow.
Catalogue of Fancy Goods...Alfred, ME. facsimile ed. (Hands to Work Ser.: No. 1). (Illus.). 10p. 1971. pap. 0.75 (ISBN 0-915836-05-X). Shaker Pr ME.
Catalogue of Hebrew Books, 6 Vols. Harvard University Library. LC 68-22146. (Yiddish & Heb). 1968. Set. 225.00x (ISBN 0-674-10150-2). Harvard U Pr.
Catalogue of Hebrew Books: Supplement I, 3 vols. Harvard University Library. LC 68-22416. 1972. Set. 185.00x (ISBN 0-674-10173-1). Harvard U Pr.
Catalogue of Herbs, Roots, Barks, Powdered Articles, &c., Prepared in the United Society, New Gloucester, Maine. facsimile ed. (Hands to Work Ser.: No. 2). 14p. 1981. pap. 0.75 (ISBN 0-915836-06-8). Shaker Pr ME.
Catalogue of Islamic Seals & Talismans in the Ashmolean Museum. Ludvik Kalus. 1985. 45.00x (Pub. by Ashmolean Museum). State Mutual Bk.
Catalogue of Music by American Moravians, 1742-1842. Albert G. Rau & Hans T. David. LC 76-134283. Repr. of 1938 ed. 14.00 (ISBN 0-404-07206-2). AMS Pr.
Catalogue of Rembrandt's Etchings 2 Vols. in 1. 2nd ed. Arthur M. Hind. LC 67-27456. (Graphic Art Ser). 1967. Repr. of 1923 ed. lib. bdg. 65.00 (ISBN 0-306-70977-5). Da Capo.
Catalogue of the Cashel Diocesan Library. Cashel Diocesan Library, County Tipperary, Republic of Ireland Staff. 1973. 100.00 (ISBN 0-8161-1065-4, Hall Library). G K Hall.
Catalogue of the Emma B. King Library of the Shaker Museum. Compiled by Robert F. Meader. (Illus.). 63p. 1970. pap. write for info. (ISBN 0-937942-00-6). Shaker Mus.
Catalogue of the Greek Manuscripts in the Library of the Monastery of Vatopedi on Mt. Athos. Athos Monasteries Staff. (Harvard Theological Studies Ser.). 1924. 24.00 (ISBN 0-527-01011-1). Kraus Repr.
Catalogue of the Hebrew & Samaritan Manuscripts in the British Museum, Pt. 3. G. Margoliouth. 620p. 1965. Repr. of 1909 ed. 15.00 (ISBN 0-7141-0645-3, Pub. by British Lib). Longwood Pub Group.
Catalogue of the Hebrew & Samaritan Manuscripts in the British Museum: Introduction, Indexes, etc, Pt. 4. J. Leveen. 224p. 1977. Repr. of 1935 ed. 22.50 (ISBN 0-7141-0619-4, Pub. by British Lib). Longwood Pub Group.
Catalogue of the Hebrew Mss in the Jew's College, London. A. Neubauer. (Descriptive Catalogue of the Hewbrew Mss of the Montefiore Library). 274p. Repr. of 1904 ed. text ed. 74.52x (ISBN 0-576-80128-3, Pub. by Gregg Intl Pubs England). Gregg Intl.
Catalogue of the Library of the India Office: Vol. 2, Oriental Languages, Pt. 1, Sanskrit Books. Rev. ed. Prana Natha & J. B. Chaudhuri. Rev. by C. K. Napier. 3149p. 1957. Repr. of 1938 ed. 45.00 (ISBN 0-7123-0612-9, Pub. by British Lib). Longwood Pub Group.

Catalogue of the Pepys Library at Magdalene College Cambridge: Volume 5, Part 2: Modern Manuscripts, Vol. V - Pt. 2. Ed. by Robert Latham. 302p. 1981. 135.00x (ISBN 0-8476-7050-3). Rowman.

Catalogue of the Witchcraft Collection in Cornell University Library. Cornell University, Libraries Staff. LC 76-41552. 1977. lib. bdg. 120.00 (ISBN 0-527-19705-X). Kraus Intl.

Catalogue of Vocal Solos & Duets Arranged in Biblical Order. Compiled by James H. Laster. LC 84-14187. 212p. 1984. 17.50 (ISBN 0-8108-1748-9). Scarecrow.

Catalpa Bow: A Study of Shamanistic Practices in Japan. 2nd ed. Carmen Blacker. (Illus.). 382p. 1986. pap. 14.95 (ISBN 0-04-398008-2). Allen Unwin.

Catalysts of Change: Marxist versus Muslim in a Turkish Community. Arnold Leder. LC 76-29323. (Middle East Monograph: No. 1). 70p. 1976. pap. text ed. 3.95x (ISBN 0-292-71042-9, Pub. by Ctr Mid East Stud). U of Tex Pr.

Catarina Lutero, Monja Liberada. Alicia E. Walter. 1984. 3.50 (ISBN 0-915644-26-6). Clayton Pub Hse.

Catastrofe de Corinto. George E. Gardiner. Orig. Title: Corinthian Catastrophe. (Span.). 64p. 1976. pap. 2.25 (ISBN 0-8254-1254-4). Kregel.

Catastrophe of European Jewry: Antecedents, History, Reflections. Ed. by Y. Gutman & L. Rothkirchen. 25.00x (ISBN 0-87068-336-5). Ktav.

Catch the Spirit of Love. George Sweeting. 120p. 1983. pap. 4.95 (ISBN 0-88207-108-4). Victor Bks.

Catching a Glimpse of Heaven. E. M. Bounds. 150p. 1985. pap. text ed. 3.50 (ISBN 0-88368-167-6). Whitaker Hse.

Catching the Conscience. Horton M. Davies. LC 84-71181. 169p. (Orig.). 1984. pap. 7.50 (ISBN 0-936384-21-2). Cowley Pubns.

Catching the Rainbow: A Total Concept Youth Ministry. Ed. by J. David Stone. LC 81-12705. (Complete Youth Ministries Handbook: Vol. II). 256p. (Orig.). 1981. pap. 19.95 (ISBN 0-687-04730-7); leadership training kit, includes book, 2 cassettes & leader's guide 24.95 (ISBN 0-687-04731-5). Abingdon.

Catecheses Thirteen-Eighteen & Other Works, Vol. 2. St. Cyril Of Jerusalem. (Fathers of the Church Ser.: Vol. 64). 1970. 14.95x (ISBN 0-8132-0064-4). Cath U Pr.

Catechesis of the Orthodox Church. rev. ed. Apostolos Makrakis. Ed. by Orthodox Christian Educational Society. 239p. 1969. pap. text ed. 5.00x (ISBN 0-938366-14-9). Orthodox Chr.

Catechetical Helps. Edwin W. Kurth. 1981. pap. text ed. 4.95 (ISBN 0-570-03507-4, 14-1261). Concordia.

Catechetical Instruction & the Catholic Faithful. George A. Kelly. 226p. 1982. 5.95 (ISBN 0-8198-1418-0, RA0015); pap. 4.95 (ISBN 0-8198-1419-9). Dghtrs St Paul.

Catechetical Review. A. H. Lange. pap. 0.55 (ISBN 0-570-03520-1, 14-1102). Concordia.

Catechetics in Our Time: Synod of Bishops, 1977. 1978. pap. 3.50 (ISBN 1-55586-575-5, V575). US Catholic.

Catechetics in the Catholic School. Father James F. Hawker. 61p. 1986. 6.60 (ISBN 0-318-20569-6). Natl Cath Educ.

Catechism. C. H. Spurgeon. 32p. 1985. pap. 0.95. Pilgrim Pubns.

Catechism For Catholics. Michael Tynan. 96p. (Orig.). 1983. pap. 5.95 (ISBN 0-87061-088-0). Chr Classics.

Catechism for Inquirers. 4th ed. Ed. by Joseph L. Malloy. 1984. pap. 2.50 (ISBN 0-8091-5012-3). Paulist Pr.

Catechism for Young Children with Cartoon, Bk. 1. Vic Lockman. (Illus., Orig.). 1984. pap. 1.00 (ISBN 0-936175-01-X); pap. text ed. 1.00 (ISBN 0-936175-03-6). V Lockman.

Catechism Handbook. David P. Kuske. 228p. 1982. three ring binder 19.95 (ISBN 0-938272-12-8). WELS Board.

Catechism Lessons: Pupil's Book. Adolph Fehlauer. Ed. by Richard Grunze. (Illus.). 336p. 1981. 6.95 (ISBN 0-938272-09-8). WELS Board.

Catechism of Christian Doctrine. Catholic Bishops of England & Wales Staff. LC 82-50599. 72p. 1982. pap. 2.00 (ISBN 0-89555-176-4). TAN Bks Pubs.

Catechism of Eastern Greek Orthodox Church. M. Polyzoides. 96p. 4.00 (ISBN 0-686-79625-X). Divry.

Catechism of Hindu Dharma. 2nd, rev. & enl. ed. Srisa Chandra Vasu. Tr. by Srisa Chandra Vidyarnava. LC 73-3829. (Sacred Books of the Hindus: No. 3). Repr. of 1919 ed. 14.50 (ISBN 0-404-57847-0). AMS Pr.

Catechism of Mental Prayer. Joseph Simler. LC 84-51901. 69p. 1985. pap. 1.50 (ISBN 0-89555-256-6). Tan Bks Pubs.

Catechism of Modern Man. 3rd rev. ed. Ed. by Daughters of St. Paul. 1971. 7.95 (ISBN 0-8198-0015-5); pap. 6.95 (ISBN 0-8198-0016-3). Dghtrs St Paul.

Catechism of Modernism. J. B. Lemius. LC 81-52536. 160p. 1981. pap. 3.00 (ISBN 0-89555-167-5). TAN Bks Pubs.

Catechism of Positive Religion. 3rd ed. Auguste Comte. Tr. by Richard Congreve. LC 72-77053. 1973. Repr. of 1891 ed. lib. bdg. 35.00x (ISBN 0-678-00910-4). Kelley.

Catechism of the Catholic Church. Robert F. Fox. 1979. 8.95 (ISBN 0-685-94958-3). Franciscan Her.

Catechism of the Council of Trent. Council of Trent Staff. LC 82-50588. 603p. 1983. pap. 15.00 (ISBN 0-89555-185-3). TAN Bks Pubs.

Catechism of the Orthodox Church. Metropolitan Philaret Of Moscow. 1901. pap. 2.95 (ISBN 0-686-00252-0). Eastern Orthodox.

Catechism of the Visishtadwaita Philosophy. Pundit M. Bhashycharaya. Ed. by R. I. Robb. (Secret Doctrine Reference Ser.). (Orig.). 1986. pap. 4.00 (ISBN 0-913510-56-4). Wizards.

Catechism of Thomas Becon. Thomas Becon. Repr. of 1884 ed. 55.00 (ISBN 0-384-03715-1). Johnson Repr.

Catechism Written in Latin Together with the Same Catechism Translated into English. Alexander Nowell. Repr. of 1853 ed. 25.00 (ISBN 0-384-42090-7). Johnson Repr.

Catechisme, or First Instruction & Learning of Christian Religion. Alexander Nowell. LC 74-23570. 185p. 1975. Repr. of 1570 ed. lib. bdg. 30.00x (ISBN 0-8201-1143-0). Schol Facsimiles.

Catechisms or, Manner to Teach-Children the Christian Religion. Jean Calvin. LC 68-54624. (English Experience Ser.: No. 46). 168p. 1968. Repr. of 1556 ed. 14.00 (ISBN 90-221-0046-4). Walter J Johnson.

Catechist as a Minister. Carmen L. Caltagirone. LC 82-1605. 116p. (Orig.). 1982. pap. 4.95 (ISBN 0-8189-0430-5). Alba.

Catechist Formation Book. David Sork et al. LC 80-84507. 200p. (Orig.). 1981. pap. 7.95 (ISBN 0-8091-2365-7). Paulist Pr.

Catecismo Basico. (Span.). 3.00 (ISBN 0-8198-1444-X); 2.00 (ISBN 0-8198-1445-8). Dghtrs St Paul.

Catecismo Biblico y Doctrinal Para el Nuevo Creyente. Adolfo Robleto. 164p. 1985. pap. 1.95 (ISBN 0-311-09088-5). Casa Bautista.

Category Formation & the History of Religions. Robert D. Baird. (Religion & Reason Ser: No. 1). 178p. 1971. text ed. 20.50x (ISBN 90-2796-889-6). Mouton.

Category of the Aesthetic in the Philosophy of Saint Bonaventure. Emma J. Spargo. (Philosophy Ser). 1953. 8.00 (ISBN 0-686-11541-4). Franciscan Inst.

Catena of Buddhist Scriptures from the Chinese. Samuel Beal. 448p. Repr. of 1871 ed. text ed. 37.50x (ISBN 0-89644-188-1, Pub. by Chinese Matl Ctr). Coronet Bks.

Catering Service Potpourri for Centerpieces, Etc. Scentouri Staff. 16p. 1985. pap. text ed. 3.75 (ISBN 0-318-04421-8, Pub. by Scentouri). Prosperity & Profits.

Caterpillars or Butterflies. Jane McWhorter. (Illus.). 1977. pap. 4.95 (ISBN 0-89137-410-8). Quality Pubns.

Catharina, Saint, of Alexandria: The Life of St. Katherine. Ed. by E. Einenkel. (EETS, OS Ser.: No. 80). Repr. of 1884 ed. 20.00 (ISBN 0-527-00080-9). Kraus Repr.

Cathars & Reincarnation. Arthur Guirdham. LC 77-17012. (Illus.). 1978. pap. 3.75 (ISBN 0-8356-0506-X, Quest). Theos Pub Hse.

Cathechism & Guide: Navaho-English. Berard Haile. (Orig.). 1937. pap. 3.00 (ISBN 0-686-32657-1). St Michaels.

Cathedral. J. K. Huysmans. 59.95 (ISBN 0-87968-815-7). Gordon Pr.

Cathedral. Joris K. Huysmans. Ed. by C. Kegan Paul. Tr. by Clara Bell from Fr. LC 77-10270. Repr. of 1922 ed. 32.50 (ISBN 0-404-16322-X). AMS Pr.

Cathedral. David Macaulay. (Illus.). 1981. pap. 6.95 (ISBN 0-395-31668-5); prepack of 10 59.50 (ISBN 0-395-31766-5). HM.

Cathedral: A Gothic Pilgrimage. Helen H. Parkhurst. 304p. 1980. Repr. of 1936 ed. lib. bdg. 40.00 (ISBN 0-8492-2174-9). R West.

Cathedral Book. Maureen Gallagher. LC 82-60592. 1983. pap. 2.95 (ISBN 0-8091-2485-8). Paulist Pr.

Cathedral Builders. Jean Gimpel. Tr. by Teresa Waugh. LC 84-47572. (Illus.). 192p. 1984. pap. 8.95 (ISBN 0-06-091158-1, CN 1158, PL). Har-Row.

Cathedral Builders in England. Edward S. Prior. LC 77-94613. 1978. Repr. of 1905 ed. lib. bdg. 25.00 (ISBN 0-89341-247-3). Longwood Pub Group.

Cathedral Builders: The Story of a Great Masonic Guild. Lucy E. Baxter. LC 78-58191. 1978. pap. 50.00 (ISBN 0-89341-354-2). Longwood Pub Group.

Cathedral of Suitable Magnificence: St. Patrick's Cathedral, New York. Margaret Carthy. 1983. 15.00 (ISBN 0-89453-372-X); pap. 6.95 (ISBN 0-89453-373-8). M Glazier.

Cathedral on the Nile: The History of All Saints Cathedral, Cairo. Arthur Burrell. 120p. 1985. 30.00x (ISBN 0-317-43629-5, Pub. by Amate Pr. Ltd.). State Mutual Bk.

Cathedrales Abbatiales, Collegiales et Prieures Romans en France. Aubert & Goubet. 153.25 (ISBN 0-685-34010-4). French & Eur.

Cathedrales et Tresors Gothiques en France. Aubert & Goubet. 153.25 (ISBN 0-685-34011-2). French & Eur.

Cathedrals & Abbeys of England & Wales. Keith Spence & Shaun McVeigh. (Blue Guides Ser.). (Illus.). 1984. 29.95 (ISBN 0-393-01664-1); pap. 16.95 (ISBN 0-393-30071-4). Norton.

Cathedrals' Crusade. Ian Dunlop. LC 81-14431. (Illus.). 256p. 1982. 20.00 (ISBN 0-8008-1316-2). Taplinger.

Cathedrals of England. Alec Clifton-Taylor. (Illus.). 1980. pap. 8.95 (ISBN 0-500-20062-9). Thames Hudson.

Cathedrals of England: Midland, Eastern & Northern England, Vol. 2. Nikolaus Pevsner & Priscilla Metcalf. 400p. 1985. 40.00 (ISBN 0-670-80125-9). Viking.

Cathedrals of England: Southern England, Vol. 1. Nikolaus Pevsner & Priscilla Metcalf. 384p. 1985. 40.00 (ISBN 0-670-80124-0). Viking.

Cathedrals of France. rev. ed. Auguste Rodin. Tr. by Elisabeth C. Geissbuhler from Fr. (Art of the Middle Ages Ser.). Tr. of Cathedrales de France. (Illus.). 278p. 1981. 25.00 (ISBN 0-933806-07-8). Black Swan CT.

Cathedrals of Great Britain: Their History & Architecture. P. H. Ditchfield. (Illus.). 1979. Repr. of 1916 ed. lib. bdg. 45.00 (ISBN 0-8495-1112-7). Arden Lib.

Catherine II's Greek Prelate: Eugenios Voulgaris in Russia, 1771-1806. Stephen K. Batalden. (East European Monographs: No. 115). 197p. 1983. 26.00x (ISBN 0-88033-006-6). East Eur Quarterly.

Catherine Marshall Had a Husband. William J. Petersen. (Living Books Ser.). 240p. (Orig.). 1986. mass 3.95 (ISBN 0-8423-0204-2). Tyndale.

Catherine Marshall's Story Bible. Catherine Marshall. (Illus.). 216p. 1984. pap. 10.95 (ISBN 0-8245-0596-4). Crossroad NY.

Catherine Marshall's Story Bible. Catherine Marshall. 200p. 1985. pap. 9.95 (ISBN 0-380-69961-3). Avon.

Catherine of Aragon & the Sources of the English Reformation, 2 vols in 1. Albert Du Boys. Ed. by Charlotte M. Yonge. 1969. Repr. of 1881 ed. 35.50 (ISBN 0-8337-0931-3). B Franklin.

Catherine of Genoa: Purgation & Purgatory, the Spiritual Dialogue. Ed. by Serge Hughes. LC 79-88123. (Classics of Western Spirituality Ser). 190p. 1979. 12.95 (ISBN 0-8091-0285-4); pap. 8.95 (ISBN 0-8091-2207-3). Paulist Pr.

Catherine of Siena. Daughters of St. Paul. (Encounter Ser.). 1975. 3.00 (ISBN 0-8198-0395-2). Dghtrs St Paul.

Catherine of Siena: The Dialogue. Ed. by Suzanne Noffke. LC 79-56755. (Classics of Western Spirituality Ser.). 416p. 1980. 13.95 (ISBN 0-8091-0295-1); pap. 10.95 (ISBN 0-8091-2233-2). Paulist Pr.

Catholic Action in Italy: Sociology of a Sponsored Organization. Gianfranco Poggi. 1967. 25.00x (ISBN 0-8047-0292-6). Stanford U Pr.

Catholic Activism & the Industrial Worker. Neil Betten. LC 76-17280. 1976. 10.00 (ISBN 0-8130-0503-5). U Presses Fla.

Catholic Almanac, 1986. Ed. by Felician A. Foy & Rose M. Avato. LC 73-64101. 650p. (Orig.). 1985. pap. 13.95 (ISBN 0-87973-256-3, 256). Our Sunday Visitor.

Catholic Almanac 1987. Ed. by Felician A. Foy & Rose M. Avato. LC 73-64101. 600p. (Orig.). 1986. pap. 13.95 (ISBN 0-87973-257-1, 257). Our Sunday Visitor.

Catholic & Christian. Alan Schreck. 240p. (Orig.). 1984. pap. 6.95 (ISBN 0-89283-181-2). Servant.

Catholic & Christian Study Guide. Alan Schreck. 64p. (Orig.). 1985. pap. 2.95 (ISBN 0-89283-249-5). Servant.

Catholic & Manichaean Ways of Life. St. Augustine. LC 66-11337. (Fathers of the Church Ser.: Vol. 56). 128p. 1966. 14.95x (ISBN 0-8132-0056-3). Cath U Pr.

Catholic & the Jewish Approach to Sex & Their Relative Influence Upon the Cultural Character of Our Society. Watson Sharp. (Illus.). 1976. 47.75 (ISBN 0-89266-012-0). Am Classical Coll Pr.

Catholic Answers to Fundamentalists' Questions. Philip St. Romain. 64p. 1984. pap. 1.95 (ISBN 0-89243-220-9). Liguori Pubns.

Catholic Anthology: Nineteen Fourteen to Nineteen Fifteen. LC 78-64009. (Des Imagistes: Literature of the Imagist Movement). Repr. of 1915 ed. 15.00 (ISBN 0-404-17083-8). AMS Pr.

Catholic Apologetical Literature in the United States (1784-1858) Robert Gorman. LC 73-3582. (Catholic University of America. Studies in American Church History: No. 28). Repr. of 1939 ed. 23.00 (ISBN 0-404-57778-4). AMS Pr.

Catholic As Citizen. Frank Morriss. 141p. 1980. 6.95 (ISBN 0-8199-0775-8). Franciscan Herald.

Catholic Atmosphere in Marie Von Ebner Eschenbach: Its Use As a Literary Device. Sr. Rosa Doyle. LC 70-140040. (Catholic University Studies in German Ser.: No. 6). Repr. of 1936 ed. 18.00 (ISBN 0-404-50226-1). AMS Pr.

Catholic Authors: Contemporary Biographical Sketches, 1930-1947. Ed. by Matthew Hoehn. 800p. 1981. Repr. of 1947 ed. 75.00x (ISBN 0-8103-4314-2). Gale.

Catholic Authors, Crown Edition. George N. Schuster. (Illus.). (YA) 1952. pap. 3.95 (ISBN 0-910334-23-4). Cath Authors.

Catholic Baptisms in Western Pennsylvania, 1799-1828: Father Peter Helbron's Greensburg Register. Peter Helbron. LC 84-73331. 123p. 1985. Repr. of 1915 ed. 12.50 (ISBN 0-8063-1113-4). Genealog Pub.

Catholic Belief & Practice in an Ecumenical Age. Wilfred F. Dewan. (Orig.). 1966. pap. 1.95 (ISBN 0-8091-1510-7, Deus). Paulist Pr.

Catholic Beliefs, Laws, Practices: Twenty-Six Questions & Answers. Daniel L. Lowery. 64p. 1984. pap. 1.50 (ISBN 0-89243-213-6). Liguori Pubns.

Catholic Bible Study Handbook: A Popular Introduction to Studying Scripture. Jerome Kodell. 266p. (Orig.). 1985. pap. 7.95 (ISBN 0-89283-185-5). Servant.

Catholic Biblical Quarterly: Washington D.C. 1939-1968, Vols. 1-30. Set. lib. bdg. 1350.00 (ISBN 0-685-77254-3); lib. bdg. 45.00 ea. AMS Pr.

Catholic Bishops: A Memoir. John T. Ellis. 1983. pap. 6.95 (ISBN 0-89453-463-7). M Glazier.

Catholic Bishops & Nuclear War: A Critique & Analysis of the Pastoral, the Challenge of Peace. Ed. by Judith A. Dwyer. 120p. 1984. pap. 6.50 (ISBN 0-87840-409-0). Georgetown U Pr.

Catholic Book of the Mass. William Ogrodowski. LC 84-60752. 168p. 1985. pap. 6.95 (ISBN 0-87973-600-3, 600). Our Sunday Visitor.

Catholic Catechism. W. Faerber. LC 78-68498. 122p. 1978. pap. 3.00 (ISBN 0-89555-086-5, 307). TAN Bks Pubs.

Catholic Catechism. John A. Hardon. LC 73-81433. 1973. pap. 10.95 (ISBN 0-385-08045-X). Doubleday.

Catholic Catechism. Ed. by Ronald Lawler et al. 200p. (Orig.). 1986. pap. 6.50 (ISBN 0-87973-802-2, 802). Our Sunday Visitor.

Catholic Challenge to the American Economy: Reflections on the Bishops Pastoral Letter on Catholic Social Teaching & the U. S. Economy. Ed. by Thomas M. Gannon. 352p. 24.95 (ISBN 0-02-911260-5). Macmillan.

Catholic Challenge to the American Economy: Reflections on the Bishops' Pastoral Letter on Catholic Social Teaching & the U. S. Economy. Ed. by Thomas S. Gannon. 352p. 1987. pap. 14.95 (ISBN 0-02-911270-2, Collier). Macmillan.

Catholic Charismatics: Anatomy of a Modern Religious Movement. Richard J. Bord & Joseph E. Faulkner. LC 82-42782. 160p. 1983. 19.95x (ISBN 0-271-00340-5). Pa St U Pr.

Catholic Charities in the United States: History & Problems. John O'Grady. LC 71-137180. (Poverty U. S. A. Historical Record Ser). 1971. Repr. of 1930 ed. 32.00 (ISBN 0-405-03118-1). Ayer Co Pubs.

Catholic Child Care in Nineteenth Century New York: With a Correlated Summary of Public & Protestant Child Welfare. George P. Jacoby. LC 74-1686. (Children & Youth Ser.: Vol. 10). 284p. 1974. Repr. of 1941 ed. 23.90x (ISBN 0-405-05963-9). Ayer Co Pubs.

Catholic Christianity: A Guide to the Way, the Truth, & the Life. Richard Chilson. 1987. pap. 7.95. Paulist Pr.

Catholic Church. Carrie Straus. 288p. 1987. 14.95 (ISBN 0-87052-312-0). Hippocrene Bks.

Catholic Church & Art. Ralph A. Cram. 59.95 (ISBN 0-87968-817-3). Gordon Pr.

Catholic Church & the American Poor. George A. Kelly. LC 75-16293. 202p. 1976. 5.95 (ISBN 0-8189-0321-X). Alba.

Catholic Church & the Bible. Peter M. Stravinskas. LC 87-60217. 120p. (Orig.). 1987. pap. 5.95 (ISBN 0-87973-515-5). Our Sunday Visitor.

Catholic Church & the Knights of Labor. Henry J. Browne. LC 76-6326. (Irish Americans Ser). (Illus.). 1976. Repr. of 1949 ed. 32.00 (ISBN 0-405-09323-3). Ayer Co Pubs.

Catholic Church & the Negro. John T. Gillard. (Basic Afro-American Reprint Library). 1969. Repr. of 1929 ed. 19.00 (ISBN 0-384-18550-9). Johnson Repr.

Catholic Church & the Secret Societies in the United States. Fergus Macdonald. LC 46-8049. (Monograph Ser.: No. 22). 1946. 12.50x (ISBN 0-930060-04-0). US Cath Hist.

Catholic Church & the Soviet Government. Dennis J. Dunn. (East European Monographs: No. 30). 267p. 1977. 25.00x (ISBN 0-914710-23-0). East Eur Quarterly.

Catholic Church, Dissent & Nationality in Soviet Lithuania. V. Stanley Vardys. (East European Monographs: No. 43). 336p. 1978. 30.00x (ISBN 0-914710-36-2). East Eur Quarterly.

Catholic Church Has the Answer. Paul Whitcomb. 60p. (Orig.). 1986. pap. 1.25 (ISBN 0-89555-282-5). Tan Bks Pubs.

Catholic Church in Alaska. Mary G. Balcom. LC 78-97897. (Illus.). 1970. 2.50 (ISBN 0-685-47728-2). Balcom.

Catholic Church in China. L. Ladany. LC 87-23. (Perspectives on Freedom Ser.: No. 7). (Orig.). 1987. pap. 5.00 (ISBN 0-932088-12-0). Freedom Hse.

Catholic Church in Communist Poland, 1945-1985: Forty Years of Church-State Relations. Ronald C. Monticone. (East European Monographs: No. 205). 256p. 1986. 25.00 (ISBN 0-88033-102-X). East Eur Quarterly.

Catholic Church in Detroit, 1701-1888. George Pare. LC 83-67420. 733p. 1983. pap. 19.05x (ISBN 0-8143-1758-8). Wayne St U Pr.

Catholic Church in Greencastle, Putnam County, Indiana 1848-1978. Jack W. Porter & William F. Stineman. LC 78-65724. (Illus.). 1979. 14.95 (ISBN 0-9602352-0-5). St Paul the Apostle.

Catholic Church in Haiti 1704-1785: Selected Letters, Memoirs & Documents. Ed. by George Breathett. 1983. 34.95x (ISBN 0-89712-103-1). Documentary Pubns.

Catholic Church in Indiana, Seventeen Eighty-Nine to Eighteen Thirty-Four. Thomas T. McAvoy. LC 41-6425. (Columbia University. Studies in the Social Sciences: No. 471). Repr. of 1940 ed. 20.00 (ISBN 0-404-51471-5). AMS Pr.

Catholic Church in Japan: A Short History. John Laures. Repr. of 1954 ed. lib. bdg. 22.50x (ISBN 0-8371-2974-5, LACC). Greenwood.

Catholic Church in Maine. William L. Lucey. (Illus.). 372p. 1957. 7.50x (ISBN 0-686-00233-4). O'Brien.

Catholic Church in Nineteenth-Century Ireland: A Sociological Study. Desmond J. Keenan. LC 83-11941. 300p. 1984. 29.50X (ISBN 0-389-20426-9, 07312). B&N Imports.

Catholic Church in the Meeting of Two Frontiers: The Southern Illinois Country (1763-1793) Fintan G. Walker. LC 73-3574. (Catholic University of America. Studies in American Church History: No. 19). Repr. of 1935 ed. 17.50 (ISBN 0-404-57769-5). AMS Pr.

Catholic Church in World Politics. Eric O. Hanson. (Illus.). 468p. 1987. 24.95 (ISBN 0-691-07729-0). Princeton U Pr.

Catholic Church, Liturgy & Ritual: Prosarium Lemovicense. Repr. of 1889 ed. 60.00 (ISBN 0-384-07880-X). Johnson Repr.

Catholic Church on the Kentucky Frontier: 1785-1812. M. R. Mattingly. LC 73-3579. (Catholic University of America. Studies in American Church History: No. 25). Repr. of 1936 ed. 29.00 (ISBN 0-404-57775-X). AMS Pr.

Catholic Church on the Nebraska Frontier: 1854-1885. Aquinata Martin. LC 73-3580. (Catholic University of America. Studies in American Church History: No. 26). Repr. of 1937 ed. 26.00 (ISBN 0-404-57776-8). AMS Pr.

Catholic Church on the Northern Indiana Frontier, 1789-1844. William McNamara. LC 73-3567. (Catholic University of America. Studies in American Church History: No. 12). Repr. of 1931 ed. 19.00 (ISBN 0-404-57762-8). AMS Pr.

Catholic Church: Our Mission in History. Alphonsus Pluth & Carl Koch. (Illus.). 330p. (Orig.). 1985. pap. text ed. 11.00x (ISBN 0-88489-161-5); teaching manual 18.95x (ISBN 0-88489-162-3). St Mary's.

Catholic Church Records of the Pacific Northwest: Grand Ronde Register, 2 Vols. Ed. by Harriet D. Munnick & Stephen D. Beckham. (Illus.). 1987. Set. 25.00 (ISBN 0-8323-0455-7). Vol. I. Vol.II. Binford-Metropolitan.

Catholic Church Records of the Pacific Northwest: Grand Ronde Register, 2 vols. Ed. by Harriet D. Munnick & Stephan D. Beckman. (Illus.). 1987. Set. 25.00 (ISBN 0-8323-0455-7). Vol. I, (1860-1885) Vol. II, (1885-1898) Binford-Metropolitan.

Catholic Church Records of the Pacific Northwest: Oregon City, Salem & Jacksonville. Harriet D. Munnick. LC 84-70844. (Illus.). 1984. 25.00 (ISBN 0-8323-0429-8). Binford-Metropolitan.

Catholic Church Records of the Pacific Northwest: Roseburg & Portland. Compiled by Harriet D. Munnick. LC 85-63221. (Illus.). 440p. 1986. 25.00 (ISBN 0-8323-0447-6). Binford-Metropolitan.

Catholic Church Records of the Pacific Northwest: St. Louis, Gervais & Brooks. Harriet D. Munnick. LC 72-71955. (Illus.). 1982. 25.00 (ISBN 0-8323-0408-5). Binford-Metropolitan.

Catholic Church Records of the Pacific Northwest: Vancouver & Stellamaris Mission. Harriet D. Munnick. LC 72-83958. (Illus.). 1972. 25.00 (ISBN 0-8323-0375-5). Binford-Metropolitan.

Catholic Church Story. rev ed. Edward Day. LC 78-73834. (Illus.). 192p. (Orig.). 1975. pap. 3.95 (ISBN 0-89243-105-9, 65300). Liguori Pubns.

Catholic Church Story: Leader's Guide. Gary Johnson. 1978. tchr's ed 2.95 (ISBN 0-89243-092-3). Liguori Pubns.

Catholic Church, the Peace of the World & the Foreign Policy of the United States. Oswald D. Sandover. (Illus.). 117p. 1983. 99.45x (ISBN 0-86722-055-4). Inst Econ Pol.

Catholic Church Through the Ages. Martin P. Harney. LC 73-76312. 1974. 12.00 (ISBN 0-8198-0500-9); pap. 11.00 (ISBN 0-8198-0501-7). Dghtrs St Paul.

Catholic Church Today, 1920-1981. Enzo Bellini et al. Ed. & tr. by John Drury. (Illustrated History of the Church). (Illus.). 126p. 1982. 12.95 (ISBN 0-86683-160-6, HarpR). Har-Row.

Catholic Churchmen in Science, First Ser. facs. ed. James J. Walsh. LC 68-16985. (Essay Index Reprint Ser). 1906. 19.00 (ISBN 0-8369-0971-2). Ayer Co Pubs.

Catholic Churchmen in Science, Second Ser. facs. ed. James J. Walsh. LC 67-22126. (Essay Index Reprint Ser.). 1909. 19.00 (ISBN 0-8369-1387-6). Ayer Co Pubs.

Catholic Churchmen in Science. Third Ser. facs. ed. James J. Walsh. LC 67-22126. (Essay Index Reprint Ser). 1917. 19.00 (ISBN 0-8369-0972-0). Ayer Co Pubs.

Catholic Citizens in the Third Reich: Psyco-Social Principles & Moral Reasoning. Donald J. Dietrich. 385p. 1987. 39.95 (ISBN 0-88738-131-6). Transaction Bks.

Catholic Classics. Dinesh D'Souza. LC 86-61500. 168p. (Orig.). 1986. pap. 6.95 (ISBN 0-87973-545-7, 545). Our Sunday Visitor.

Catholic Colonialism: A Parish History of Guatemala, 1524-1821. Adriaan C. Van Oss. (Cambridge Latin American Studies: No. 57). (Illus.). 320p. 1986. 44.50 (ISBN 0-521-32072-0). Cambridge U Pr.

Catholic Community in the Seventeenth & Eighteenth Centuries. Patrick J. Corish. Ed. by Art Cosgrove & Elma Collins. (Helicon History of Ireland). (Illus.). 156p. 1981. 9.95 (ISBN 0-86167-064-7, Pub. by Educ Co Ireland); pap. 6.95 (ISBN 0-86167-063-9). Longwood Pub Group.

Catholic Doctrine of the Church of England. Thomas Rogers. Repr. of 1854 ed. 31.00 (ISBN 0-384-51710-2). Johnson Repr.

Catholic Education in the Western World. Ed. by James M. Lee. 1967. 17.95x (ISBN 0-268-00030-1). U of Notre Dame Pr.

Catholic Elementary School Extension Program. Arlene F. McElligott & Joseph P. McElligott. 33p. 1986. 5.30 (ISBN 0-318-20576-9). Natl Cath Educ.

Catholic Elementary Schools & Their Finances. 1980 1.50 (ISBN 0-686-39958-7); 1979 1.80 (ISBN 0-686-39959-5); 1978 1.50 (ISBN 0-686-39960-9). Natl Cath Educ.

Catholic Emancipation Crisis in Ireland, 1823-1829. James A. Reynolds. Repr. of 1954 ed. lib. bdg. 22.50x (ISBN 0-8371-3141-3, RECE). Greenwood.

Catholic Emancipation: Daniel O'Connell & the Birth of Irish Democracy. F. O'Ferrall. LC 85-14178. 350p. 1985. text ed. 38.50x (ISBN 0-391-03353-0). Humanities.

Catholic Emancipation Eighteen Twenty-Nine to Nineteen Twenty-Nine: Essays by Various Writers. facs. ed. LC 67-22084. (Essay Index Reprint Ser). 1929. 20.00 (ISBN 0-8369-0284-X). Ayer Co Pubs.

Catholic Encyclopedia. Ed. by Robert C. Broderick. 1983. pap. 14.95 (ISBN 0-87973-700-X). Our Sunday Visitor.

Catholic Encyclopedia. rev. & updated ed. Ed. by Robert C. Broderick. 612p. pap. 18.95 (ISBN 0-8407-5787-5). Nelson.

Catholic Encyclopedia. rev. ed. Ed. by Robert C. Broderick. 612p. 1987. pap. 18.95 (ISBN 0-8407-5544-9). Nelson.

Catholic Experience. Lawrence Cunningham. 270p. 1987. pap. 10.95 (ISBN 0-8245-0811-4). Crossroad NY.

Catholic Fact Book. John Deedy. 1986. 23.95 (ISBN 0-88347-186-8). Thomas More.

Catholic Faith. Robert J. Fox. LC 83-61889. 360p. (Orig.). 1983. pap. 7.95 (ISBN 0-87973-614-3, 614). Our Sunday Visitor.

Catholic Faith. Roderick Strange. 192p. 1986. 24.95 (ISBN 0-19-826685-5); pap. 8.95 (ISBN 0-19-283051-1). Oxford U Pr.

Catholic Faith & the Industrial Order. Ruth Kenyon. 1980. lib. bdg. 59.95 (ISBN 0-8490-3129-X). Gordon Pr.

Catholic Faith in a Process Perspective. Norman Pittenger. LC 81-9615. 160p. (Orig.). 1981. pap. 1.74 (ISBN 0-88344-091-1). Orbis Bks.

Catholic Faith Inventory. Kenneth Boyack et al. write for info. Paulist Pr.

Catholic Faith Today. Bennet Kelley. green, flexible bdg. 3.00 (ISBN 0-89942-243-8, 243-04). Catholic Bk Pub.

Catholic Footsteps in Old New York: A Chronicle of Catholicity in the City of New York from 1524 to 1808. William H. Bennett. LC 77-359169. (Monograph Ser.: No. 28). 1973. Repr. of 1909 ed. 10.00x (ISBN 0-930060-08-3). US Cath Hist.

Catholic Guide to the Mature Years. Charles J. Fahey & Edward Wakin. LC 84-60747. 144p. 1984. pap. 6.95 (ISBN 0-87973-603-8, 603). Our Sunday Visitor.

Catholic Heritage. Lawrence Cunningham. 240p. 1985. pap. 9.95 (ISBN 0-8245-0685-5). Crossroad NY.

Catholic Heritage: Martyrs, Ascetics, Pilgrims, Warriors, Mystics, Theologians, Artists, Humanists, Activists, Outsiders & Saints. Lawrence S. Cunningham. 256p. 1983. 14.95 (ISBN 0-8245-0592-1). Crossroad NY.

Catholic Heros & Heroines of America. John O. Murray. 35.00 (ISBN 0-87968-818-1). Gordon Pr.

Catholic Hierarchy of the United States, 1790-1922. John H. O'Donnell. LC 73-3558. (Catholic University of America. Studies in American Church History: No. 4). Repr. of 1922 ed. 28.00 (ISBN 0-404-57754-7). AMS Pr.

Catholic High School: A National Portrait. 254p. 1985. 23.75 (ISBN 0-318-04383-1). Natl Cath Educ.

Catholic High School Ministry. Keith Warrick et al. (Illus.). 224p. 1986. loose-leaf bdg. 34.95 (ISBN 0-88489-173-9). St Mary's.

Catholic High Schools & Minority Students. Andrew M. Greeley. LC 81-23131. (Illus.). 125p. 1982. 14.95 (ISBN 0-87855-452-1). Transaction Bks.

Catholic High Schools & Their Finances. 1980 3.00 (ISBN 0-686-39953-6); 1979 3.60 (ISBN 0-686-39954-4); 1978 3.00 (ISBN 0-686-39955-2). Natl Cath Educ.

Catholic High Schools: Their Impact on Low-Income Students. 254p. 1985. 26.50. Natl Cath Educ.

Catholic History of Alabama & the Floridas. facs. ed. Mary A. Carroll. LC 70-124228. (Select Bibliographies Reprint Ser). 1908. 18.00 (ISBN 0-8369-5417-3). Ayer Co Pubs.

Catholic Home Devotions. James F. Seculoff. LC 85-72535. 160p. (Orig.). 1986. pap. 5.50 (ISBN 0-87973-584-8, 584). Our Sunday Visitor.

Catholic Identity in Health Care: Principles & Practice. Orville N. Griese. 400p. (Orig.). 1987. pap. 17.95 (ISBN 0-935372-19-9). Pope John Ctr.

Catholic Immigrant Colonization Projects in the United States, 1815-1860. Mary G. Kelly. LC 74-145485. (American Immigration Library). x, 290p. 1971. Repr. of 1939 ed. lib. bdg. 17.95x (ISBN 0-89198-016-4). Ozer.

Catholic Immigrants in America. James S. Olson. 260p. 1986. 26.95x01568129x (ISBN 0-8304-1037-6). Nelson-Hall.

Catholic Imperialism & World Freedom. Avro Manhattan. LC 73-161336. (Atheist Viewpoint Ser). 528p. 1972. Repr. of 1952 ed. 29.00 (ISBN 0-405-03810-0). Ayer Co Pubs.

Catholic Indian Missions in Maine (1611-1820) Sr. Mary C. Leger. LC 73-3563. (Catholic University of America. Studies in American Church History: No. 8). Repr. of 1929 ed. 26.00 (ISBN 0-404-57758-X). AMS Pr.

Catholic Journalism. Apollinaris W. Baumgartner. LC 75-159997. (BCL Ser. I). Repr. of 1931 ed. 11.50 (ISBN 0-404-00693-0). AMS Pr.

Catholic Lawyer: 1955-1984, 1-29 vols. 696.00x (ISBN 0-686-89717-X). microfilm avail. Rothman.

Catholic Layman & Holiness. Rudolph G. Bandas. 1965. 8.95 (ISBN 0-8158-0046-0). Chris Mass.

Catholic Literary France from Verlaine to the Present Time. Sr. Mary J. Keeler. LC 76-90649. (Essay Index Reprint Ser). 1938. 19.00 (ISBN 0-8369-1219-5). Ayer Co Pubs.

Catholic Literary Opinion in the Nineteenth Century. Philip H. Vitale. 197p. 4.50 (ISBN 0-685-25451-8); pap. 2.50 (ISBN 0-685-25452-6). Auxiliary U Pr.

Catholic Literary Opinion of the Twentieth Century. Philip H. Vitale. 438p. 4.50 (ISBN 0-685-25453-4). Auxiliary U Pr.

Catholic Literary Revival. Calvert Alexander. LC 68-16288. 1968. Repr. of 1935 ed. 31.50x (ISBN 0-8046-0005-8, Pub. by Kennikat). Assoc Faculty Pr.

Catholic Loyalism in Elizabethan England. Arnold Pritchard. LC 78-10208. xiii, 243p. 1979. 22.50x (ISBN 0-8078-1345-1). U of NC Pr.

Catholic Ministries in Our Times. Ed. by George A. Kelly. 1981. 4.00 (ISBN 0-8198-1400-8); pap. 3.00 (ISBN 0-8198-1401-6). Dghtrs St Paul.

Catholic Missions in China During the Middle Ages: 1294-1368, No. 37. Paul Stanislaus Hsiang. (Studies in Sacred Theology, Second Series). 57p. 1983. Repr. of 1949 ed. 12.00x (ISBN 0-939738-32-5). Zubal Inc.

Catholic Moral Theology in Dialogue. Charles E. Curran. LC 76-14906. 1976. text ed. 18.95x (ISBN 0-268-00716-0); pap. 5.95 (ISBN 0-268-00717-9). U of Notre Dame Pr.

Catholic Movement in the Church of England. Wilfred L. Knox. 1979. Repr. of 1923 ed. lib. bdg. 30.00 (ISBN 0-8495-3029-6). Arden Lib.

Catholic Movement in the Church of England. Wilfred L. Knox. 1925. 15.00 (ISBN 0-8414-5599-6). Folcroft.

Catholic Novelists in Defense of Their Faith, 1829-1865. Willard Thorp. 14.00 (ISBN 0-405-10862-1, 11860). Ayer Co Pubs.

Catholic Orthodoxy & Anglo-Catholicism. J. J. Overbeck. LC 76-81771. Repr. of 1866 ed. 10.00 (ISBN 0-404-04839-0). AMS Pr.

Catholic Parish: Shifting Membership in a Changing Church. Thomas P. Sweetser. LC 74-84543. (Studies in Religion & Society). 1974. 15.95x (ISBN 0-913348-06-6); pap. 8.95x (ISBN 0-913348-13-9). Ctr Sci Study.

Catholic Peace Tradition. Ronald G. Musto. LC 86-12494. 464p. (Orig.). 1986. pap. 21.95 (ISBN 0-88344-263-9). Orbis Bks.

Catholic Pentecostals Today. rev. ed. Kevin Ranaghan & Dorothy Ranaghan. LC 83-70963. 196p. 1983. pap. 4.95 (ISBN 0-943780-03-9, 8039). Charismatic Ren Servs.

Catholic Periodical & Literature Index. Ed. by Natale Logan. Incl. Vol. 2 1934-38. 50.00 (ISBN 0-87507-010-8); Vol. 4. 1943-48. 50.00 (ISBN 0-87507-011-6); Vol. 10. 1959-60. 30.00 (ISBN 0-87507-012-4); Vol. 11. 1961-62; Vol. 12. 1963-64. 40.00 (ISBN 0-87507-014-0); Vol. 14. 1967-68. 40.00 (ISBN 0-87507-015-9); Vol. 15. 1969-70. 45.00 (ISBN 0-87507-016-7); Vol. 16. 1971-72. 60.00 (ISBN 0-87507-017-5); Vol. 17. 1973-1974. 55.00 (ISBN 0-87507-018-3); Vol. 18. 60.00 (ISBN 0-87507-019-1, 1975-1976); Vol. 19. 70.00 (ISBN 0-87507-020-5, 1977-1978); Vol. 21. 90.00 (ISBN 0-87507-025-6, 1981-1982). LC 70-649588. Orig. Title: Catholic Periodical Index & The Guide to Catholic Literature. Cath Lib Assn.

Catholic Periodical & Literature Index, Vol. 20. 1980. 90.00 (ISBN 0-87507-022-1). Cath Lib Assn.

Catholic Periodical & Literature Index, 1983-1984, Vol. 22. 100.00 (ISBN 0-87507-036-1). Cath Lib Assn.

Catholic Perspectives on Baptism, Eucharist & Ministry: A Study Commissioned by the Catholic Theological Society of America. Ed. by Michael A. Fahey. 240p. (Orig.). 1986. lib. bdg. 24.50 (ISBN 0-8191-5431-8, Pub. by Catholic Theological Soc of Amer); pap. text ed. 11.75 (ISBN 0-8191-5432-6). U Pr of Amer.

Catholic Pharmacist: 1985. Ed. by John P. Winkelmann. (Vol. 18). 1985. 10.00. Natl Cath Pharm.

Catholic Philosophy of History, Vol. 3. facs. ed. American Catholic Historic Association Staff. LC 67-23190. (Essay Index Reprint Ser). 1936. 16.00 (ISBN 0-8369-0285-8). Ayer Co Pubs.

Catholic Pioneers of America. John O. Murray. 35.00 (ISBN 0-87968-819-X). Gordon Pr.

Catholic Political Thought: 1789-1848. Ed. by Bela Menczer. 1962. pap. 5.95x (ISBN 0-268-00031-X). U of Notre Dame Pr.

Catholic Politics in China & Korea. Eric O. Hanson. LC 79-27206. 160p. (Orig.). 1980. pap. 2.49 (ISBN 0-88344-084-9). Orbis Bks.

Catholic Power in the Netherlands. Herman Bakvis. (Illus.). 254p. 1981. 26.50x (ISBN 0-7735-0361-7). McGill-Queens U Pr.

Catholic Prayer Book. Compiled by Michael Buckley & Tony Castle. 272p. (Orig.). 1986. pap. 6.95 (ISBN 0-89283-283-5). Servant.

Catholic Prayer Book. Robert J. Fox. LC 74-75133. 128p. 1974. pap. 3.95 (ISBN 0-87973-771-9). Our Sunday Visitor.

Catholic Prayerbook. 80p. (Compiled from Approved Sources). 1985. pap. 1.50 (ISBN 0-89555-280-9). Tan Bks Pubs.

Catholic Press Directory. James A. Doyle. 184p. 1985. pap. 25.00 (ISBN 0-686-30366-0). Cath Pr Assn.

Catholic Press Directory, 1986. Regina A. Salzmann. 208p. 1986. pap. 25.00 (ISBN 0-318-18711-6). Cath Pr Assn.

Catholic Priest & the Changing Structure of Pastoral Ministry. Philip J. Murnion. 40.00 (ISBN 0-405-10845-1, 11822). Ayer Co Pubs.

Catholic Priesthood Today. Donald W. Wuerl. 164p. 1976. 6.95 (ISBN 0-8199-0591-7). Franciscan Herald.

Catholic Prophecy. Yves DuPont. (Eng.). 1977. pap. 2.50 (ISBN 0-89555-015-6). TAN Bks Pubs.

Catholic Quakerism: A Vision for All Men. Lewis Benson. 108p. 1968. pap. text ed. 2.50 (ISBN 0-941308-03-0). Religious Soc Friends.

Catholic Rediscovery of Protestantism: A History of Ecumenical Pioneering. Paul M. Minus, Jr. LC 75-44804. 276p. 1976. pap. 6.95 (ISBN 0-8091-1944-7). Paulist Pr.

Catholic Religion. Vernon Staley. 320p. 1983. pap. 9.95 (ISBN 0-8192-1327-6). Morehouse.

Catholic Remarriage: Pastoral Issues & Preparation Models. Steven Preister & James J. Young. 224p. (Orig.). 1986. pap. 12.95 (ISBN 0-8091-2808-X). Paulist Pr.

Catholic Response. Peter M. Stravinskas. LC 84-62435. 208p. (Orig.). 1985. pap. 5.95 (ISBN 0-87973-594-5, 594). Our Sunday Visitor.

Catholic Revivalism: The American Experience, 1830-1900. Jay P. Dolan. LC 77-89755. 1979. pap. text ed. 4.95x (ISBN 0-268-00729-2). U of Notre Dame Pr.

Catholic Revivalism: The American Experience, 1830-1900. Jay P. Dolan. LC 77-89755. 1978. text ed. 19.95x (ISBN 0-268-00722-5). U of Notre Dame Pr.

Catholic Rome & Its Most Beautiful Paintings. Francesco Guicciradi. (Institute for the Promotion of the Arts Ser.). (Illus.). 1978. deluxe bdg. 75.65 (ISBN 0-930582-01-2). Gloucester Art.

Catholic Royalism in the Department of the Gard: 1814-1852. Brian Fitzpatrick. LC 82-14564. (Illus.). 224p. 1983. 49.50 (ISBN 0-521-22454-3). Cambridge U Pr.

Catholic Sacraments. Joseph Martos. (Message of the Sacraments Ser.: Vol 1). 13.95 (ISBN 0-89453-391-6); pap. 9.95 (ISBN 0-89453-227-8). M Glazier.

Catholic Scholars Dialogue with Luther. Ed. by Jared Wicks. LC 78-105429. (Orig.). 1970. pap. 3.00 (ISBN 0-8294-0181-4). Loyola.

Catholic School. 1978. pap. 1.95 (ISBN 1-55586-550-X, V550). US Catholic.

Catholic School Finance & Church-State Relations. Brother Terence McLaughlin. 81p. 1986. 6.60 (ISBN 0-318-20564-5). Natl Cath Educ.

Catholic School Principal: An Outline for Action. Theodore Drahmann. 50p. 1981. 4.80 (ISBN 0-686-39893-9). Natl Cath Educ.

Catholic Secondary Education in South-West Scotland Before 1972: Its Contributions to the Change in Status of the Catholic Community of the Area. T. A. Fitzpatrick. (Illus.). 248p. 1986. 19.00 (ISBN 0-08-032439-8, Pub. by AUP). Pergamon.

Catholic Secondary Schools & College: Reviewing the Partnership (Proceedings of the Symposium on Secondary School College Collaboration) 76p. 1986. 5.30. Natl Cath Educ.

Catholic Sex Manual for Teenagers. Charles B. Muse. (Illus.). 1980. 31.85 (ISBN 0-89266-217-4). Am Classical Coll Pr.

Catholic Sexual Ethics. Ronald Lawler et al. LC 84-62225. 360p. (Orig.). 1985. pap. text ed. 7.95 (ISBN 0-87973-805-7, 805). Our Sunday Visitor.

Catholic Shrines in the United States & Canada. Francis B. Thornton. LC 78-63480. Repr. of 1954 ed. 29.50 (ISBN 0-404-16546-X). AMS Pr.

Catholic Shrines of Europe. Gerard E. Sherry. LC 86-62664. (Illus.). 119p. 1986. pap. 5.95 (ISBN 0-87973-548-1, 548). Our Sunday Visitor.

Catholic Sisters in Transition: From the 1960's to the 1980's. Marie A. Neal. (Consecrated Life Studies Ser.: Vol. 2). 1984. pap. 7.95 (ISBN 0-89453-444-0). M Glazier.

Catholic Social Teaching on Liberation Themes. Christine E. Gudorf. LC 80-5382. 394p. 1980. lib. bdg. 29.00 (ISBN 0-8191-1080-9); pap. text ed. 15.50 (ISBN 0-8191-1081-7). U Pr of Amer.

Catholic Socialism. Francesco Nitti. 1976. lib. bdg. 69.95 (ISBN 0-8490-1586-3). Gordon Pr.

Catholic Society in New South Wales 1788-1860. James Waldersee. (Illus.). 348p. 1974. 31.00x (ISBN 0-424-06460-X, Pub. by Sydney U Pr). Intl Spec Bk.

Catholic Spirit in Modern English Literature. facs. ed. George N. Shuster. LC 67-26785. (Essay Index Reprint Ser). 1922. 20.00 (ISBN 0-8369-0878-3). Ayer Co Pubs.

Catholic Subject Headings. rev. ed. Ed. by Catherine M. Pilley & Matthew R. Wilt. 257p. 1981. pap. 25.00x (ISBN 0-87507-009-4). Cath Lib Assn.

Catholic Subjects of Elizabeth I. Adrian Horey. LC 78-312404. pap. 60.00 (ISBN 0-317-20042-9, 2023264). Bks Demand UMI.

Catholic Telephone Guide. Ed. by Miserendino Annette. 296p. 1986. 22.00 (ISBN 0-910635-54-4). Cath News Pub Co.

Catholic Thing. Rosemary Haughton. 1980. pap. 8.95 (ISBN 0-87243-116-9). Templegate.

Catholic Thinkers in the Clear: Giants of Catholic Thought from Augustine to Rahner. William A. Herr. LC 85-118829. (Basics of Christian Thought Ser.). 276p. 1985. 15.95 (ISBN 0-88347-179-5). Thomas More.

Catholic Tradition in English Literature. George Carver. 59.95 (ISBN 0-87968-820-3). Gordon Pr.

Catholic Tradition in English Literature. George Carver. 1977. Repr. lib. bdg. 25.00 (ISBN 0-8492-3819-6). R West.

Catholic Truth for Youth. Robert J. Fox. LC 78-104309. (Illus.). 448p. 1978. pap. 5.95 (ISBN 0-911988-05-X). AMI Pr.

Catholic University: A Modern Appraisal. Ed. by Neil S. McCluskey. LC 70-85353. 1970. 22.95 (ISBN 0-268-00355-6). U of Notre Dame Pr.

Catholic University & the Faith. Francis C. Wade. (Aquinas Lecture Ser.). 1978. 7.95 (ISBN 0-87462-143-7). Marquette.

Catholic Vision. Stephen Happel & David Tracy. LC 83-5687. 196p. 1984. pap. 10.95 (ISBN 0-8006-1719-3). Fortress.

Catholic Way in Education. William J. McGucken. (Request Reprint). 1962. 3.00 (ISBN 0-8294-0052-4). Loyola.

Catholic Why? Book. Andrew Greeley. 167p. 1983. 10.95 (ISBN 0-88347-154-X). Thomas More.

Catholic Youth Retreat Book: Everything You Need to Plan Prayer Experiences for a Day, an Evening, a Weekend. Mary L. Pastva. (Illus.). 87p. 1984. pap. 7.95 (ISBN 0-86716-032-2). St Anthony Mess Pr.

Catholicism. George Brantl. LC 61-15501. (Great Religions of Modern Man Ser). 1961. 8.95 (ISBN 0-8076-0162-4). Braziller.

Catholicism. John P. Dolan. LC 67-28536. (Orig.). 1968. pap. text ed. 5.95 (ISBN 0-8120-0273-3). Barron.

Catholicism, 2 vols. Richard P. McBrien. 1368p. 1980. Set. 45.00 (ISBN 0-03-056907-9, HarpR). Har-Row.

Catholicism - Hinduism: Vedantic Investigation of Raimundo Panikkar's Attempt at Bridge Building. Kana Mitra. 186p. (Orig.). 1987. lib. bdg. 23.00 (ISBN 0-8191-6157-8); pap. text ed. 11.75 (ISBN 0-8191-6158-6). U Pr of Amer.

Catholicism Against Itself, Vol. 1. O. C. Lambert. 11.95 (ISBN 0-89315-005-3). Lambert Bk.

Catholicism Against Itself, Vol. 1. abr. ed. O. C. Lambert. 1963. pap. 1.50 (ISBN 0-89315-012-6). Lambert Bk.

Catholicism Against Itself, Vol. 2. O. C. Lambert. 11.95 (ISBN 0-89315-006-1). Lambert Bk.

Catholicism & American Freedom. James M. O'Neill. LC 78-21495. 1979. Repr. of 1952 ed. lib. bdg. cancelled (ISBN 0-313-21153-1, ONCA). Greenwood.

Catholicism & Americanism: The Vision of a Conflict? Samuel O. Benedict. (Illus.). 147p. 1987. 98.85 (ISBN 0-89266-590-4). Am Classical Coll Pr.

Catholicism & English Literature. Edward Hutton. LC 76-26671. 1942. lib. bdg. 30.00 (ISBN 0-8414-4926-0). Folcroft.

Catholicism & History. Owen Chadwick. LC 77-77740. 1978. 24.95 (ISBN 0-521-21708-3). Cambridge U Pr.

Catholicism & Modernity. James Hitchcock. 250p. 1983. pap. 8.95 (ISBN 0-89283-179-0). Servant.

Catholicism & Reason. Edward J. Hayes et al. (Catholicism Catechism Ser.). 256p. (YA) 1981. pap. 5.95 (ISBN 0-913382-23-X, 103-14); tchr's manual 3.00 (ISBN 0-913382-25-6, 103-15). Prow Bks-Franciscan.

Catholicism & Scotland. Compton Mackenzie. LC 75-118486. 1971. Repr. of 1936 ed. 23.50x (ISBN 0-8046-1235-8, Pub. by Kennikat). Assoc Faculty Pr.

Catholicism & Society. Edward J. Hayes et al. (Catholicism Catechism Ser.). 1982. pap. 5.95 (ISBN 0-913382-26-4, 103-16); tchr's manual 3.00 (ISBN 0-913382-27-2, 103-17). Prow Bks-Franciscan.

Catholicism & the Mysticisms of the East. David G. Kennedy. LC 86-62211. viii, 70p. (Orig.). 1986. pap. 4.95x (ISBN 0-934995-01-X). OLW Editions.

Catholicism & the Second French Republic, 1848-1852. Ross W. Collins. 1980. lib. bdg. 27.50x (ISBN 0-374-91868-6, Octagon). Hippocrene Bks.

Catholicism Between Luther & Voltaire: A New View of the Counter-Reformation. Jean Delumeau. Tr. by Jeremy Moiser. LC 77-4005. 314p. 1977. 21.50 (ISBN 0-664-21341-3). Westminster.

Catholicism in England, Fifteen Thirty-Five to Nineteen Thirty-Five. David Mathew. 1977. lib. bdg. 59.95 (ISBN 0-8490-1587-1). Gordon Pr.

Catholicism in England: The Portraits of a Minority, Its Culture & Tradition. David Matthew. 295p. 1984. Repr. of 1948 ed. lib. bdg. 45.00 (ISBN 0-89984-946-6). Century Bookbindery.

Catholicism in Rhode Island & the Diocese of Providence, 1780-1886. Robert W. Hayman. LC 82-73128. 353p. 1982. 17.95 (ISBN 0-917012-55-0). RI Pubns Soc.

Catholicism in Rhode Island: The Formative Era. Patrick T. Conley & Matthew J. Smith. LC 76-62863. 1976. 12.50 (ISBN 0-917012-13-5). RI Pubns Soc.

Catholicism in South Florida, 1868-1968. Michael J. McNally. LC 84-7389. 334p. (Orig.). 1984. pap. 13.95 (ISBN 0-8130-0788-7). U Presses Fla.

Catholicism, Judaism & the Effort at World Domination. Victor Marx. (Illus.). 1980. 65.00 (ISBN 0-89266-216-6). Am Classical Coll Pr.

Catholicism, Protestantism & Capitalism. Amintore Fanfani. LC 78-38251. (Evolution of Capitalism Ser.). 234p. 1972. Repr. of 1935 ed. 23.50 (ISBN 0-405-04119-5). Ayer Co Pubs.

Catholicism, Protestantism, & Capitalism. Amintore Fanfani. LC 84-40363. 272p. 1984. pap. text ed. 8.95 (ISBN 0-268-00752-7, 85-07527). U of Notre Dame Pr.

Catholicism Study Edition. Richard P. McBrien. 1312p. (Orig.). 1981. pap. 24.50 (ISBN 0-86683-601-2, HarpR). Har-Row.

Catholicism Today. Jerome A. Welch. LC 76-29584. (Illus.). 1977. 7.95 (ISBN 0-917728-01-7); pap. 6.95 (ISBN 0-917728-02-5). Jewel Pubns.

Catholicism Today: A Survey of Catholic Belief & Practice. Matthew F. Kohmescher. LC 80-82085. 216p. (Orig.). 1980. pap. 4.95 (ISBN 0-8091-2335-5). Paulist Pr.

Catholicity in the Carolinas & Georgia: Leaves of Its History. Jeremiah J. O'Connell. LC 73-187371. (Illus.). 647p. 1972. Repr. of 1879 ed. 17.50 (ISBN 0-87152-099-0). Reprint.

Catholicity of Protestantism: Being a Report Presented to His Grace the Archbishop of Canterbury by a Group of Free Churchmen. Ed. by Robert N. Flew & Rupert E. Davies. LC 80-29108. 159p. 1981. Repr. of 1950 ed. lib. bdg. 22.50x (ISBN 0-313-22825-6, FLCAT). Greenwood.

Catholicity of the Church & the Structure of Catholicism. Avery Dulles. 210p. 1985. 22.50 (ISBN 0-19-826676-6). Oxford U Pr.

Catholicon. Joannes Balbus. 746p. 1460. text ed. 186.30x (ISBN 0-576-72240-5, Pub. by Greggg Intl Pubs England). Gregg Intl.

Catholics: A Celebration. A. L. Aspell. Date not set. pap. price not set (ISBN 0-940518-05-8). Guildhall Pubs.

Catholics & American Politics. Mary Hanna. LC 79-11035. 1979. text ed. 16.50x (ISBN 0-674-10325-4). Harvard U Pr.

Catholics & Broken Marriage. John Catoir. LC 78-74434. 72p. 1979. pap. 1.95 (ISBN 0-87793-176-3). Ave Maria.

Catholics & Sultans: The Church & the Ottoman Empire 1453-1923. Charles A. Frazee. LC 82-4562. 384p. 1983. 67.50 (ISBN 0-521-24676-8). Cambridge U Pr.

Catholics & the Welfare State. Peter Coman. LC 76-49523. pap. 32.00 (ISBN 0-317-08456-9, 2011288). Bks Demand UMI.

Catholics in Caroline England. Martin J. Havran. 1962. 17.50x (ISBN 0-8047-0112-1). Stanford U Pr.

Catholics in Colonial Days. Thomas P. Phelan. LC 74-145706. Repr. of 1935 ed. 40.00x (ISBN 0-8103-3685-5). Gale.

Catholics in Colonial Law. Francis X. Curran. 1963. 2.95 (ISBN 0-8294-0016-8). Loyola.

Catholics in Conversation: Seventeen Interviews with Leading American Catholics. Donald McDonald. LC 78-5695. 1978. Repr. of 1960 ed. lib. bdg. cancelled (ISBN 0-313-20486-1, MCCC). Greenwood.

Catholics in the Old South: Essays on Church & Culture. Jon L. Wakelyn & Randall M. Miller. LC 83-7893. x, 262p. 1983. 15.95 (ISBN 0-86554-080-2, H74). Mercer Univ Pr.

Catholics in the Promised Land of the Saints. James Hennessey. LC 81-80935. (Pere Marquette Lecture Ser.). 100p. 1981. 7.95 (ISBN 0-87462-536-X). Marquette.

Catholics in Western Democracies: A Study in Political Behavior. John H. Whyte. 1981. 22.50x (ISBN 0-312-12446-5). St Martin.

Catholics, Jews, & Protestants: A Study of Relationships in the United States & Canada. Claris E. Silcox. LC 78-21101. 1979. Repr. of 1934 ed. lib. bdg. 24.75x (ISBN 0-313-20882-4, SICJ). Greenwood.

Catholics, Peasants & Chewa Resistance in Nyasaland, 1889-1939. Ian Linden & Jane Linden. 1974. 38.50x (ISBN 0-520-02500-8). U of Cal Pr.

Catholics, the State & the European Radical Right, 1919-1945. Ed. by Richard Wolff. (Atlantic Studies: No. 50). write for info (ISBN 0-88033-101-1). Brooklyn Coll Pr.

Catholikes Supplication Unto the King's Majestie, for Toleration of Catholike Religion in England. Gabriel Powell. LC 76-57406. (English Experience Ser.: No. 822). 1977. lib. bdg. 6.00 (ISBN 90-221-0822-8). Walter J Johnson.

Cato's Letters, 4 Vols. in 2. John Trenchard & Thomas Gordon. LC 74-121105. (Civil Liberties in American History Ser). 1971. Repr. of 1775 ed. Set. lib. bdg. 125.00 (ISBN 0-306-71965-7). Da Capo.

Caudills: Courageous Missionaries. Tom McMinn. LC 81-70474. (Meet the Missionary Ser.). 1982. 5.50 (ISBN 0-8054-4277-4, 4242-77). Broadman.

Caught in the Conflict. Leilani Watt. LC 83-82700. 176p. 1984. text ed. 9.95 (ISBN 0-89081-411-2). Harvest Hse.

Caught in the Crossfire. Debbie Barr. 288p. (Orig.). 1985. pap. 8.95 (ISBN 0-310-28561-5, 12083P). Zondervan.

Caught in the Crossfire. Levi Keidel. LC 79-10910. 256p. 1979. pap. 7.95 (ISBN 0-8361-1888-X). Herald Pr.

Caught in the Middle. Henry Liebersat. 176p. (Orig.). 1987. pap. 8.95 (ISBN 0-8245-0822-X). Crossroad NY.

Caught in the Middle. Anne E. Schraff. (Voyager Ser.). 80p. (Orig.). (YA) 1981. pap. 2.95 (ISBN 0-8010-8200-5). Baker Bk.

Caught in the Middle: Children of Divorce. Velma T. Carter & Lynn J. Leavenworth. 176p. 1985. pap. 6.95 (ISBN 0-8170-1037-8). Judson.

Caught up into Paradise. Richard E. Eby. pap. 3.50 (ISBN 0-8007-8489-8, Spire Bks). Revell.

Caurasi Pad of Sri Hit Harivams: Introduction, Translation, Notes, & Edited Hindi Text. Ed. by Charles S. White. LC 76-54207. (Asian Studies at Hawaii Ser: No. 16). 212p. 1977. pap. text ed. 10.50x (ISBN 0-8248-0359-0). UH Pr.

Causal Body. A. E. Powell. 1972. 18.95 (ISBN 0-8356-5034-0); pap. 11.75 (ISBN 0-8356-5302-1). Theos Pub Hse.

Cause of Anti-Jewism in the United States. Irving Potter. 1982. lib. bdg. 59.95 (ISBN 0-87700-394-7). Revisionist Pr.

Cause of Our Joy. Sr. M. Francis Le Blanc. 1981. 4.00 (ISBN 0-8198-0391-X); pap. 3.00 (ISBN 0-8198-1414-8). Dghtrs St Paul.

Cause of World Unrest. Intro. by H. A. Gwynne. 1978. pap. 5.00x (ISBN 0-911038-40-X). Noontide.

Cause of World Unrest: The Jews. H. Gwynne. 1982. lib. bdg. 69.95 (ISBN 0-87700-340-8). Revisionist Pr.

Cautantowwit's House: An Indian Burial Ground on the Island of Conanicut in Narragansett Bay. William S. Simmons. LC 77-111456. (Illus.). pap. 49.50 (ISBN 0-317-41779-7, 2025642). Bks Demand UMI.

Caution: Christians under Construction. Bill Hybels. LC 77-93854. 144p. 1986. pap. 3.95 (ISBN 0-88207-759-7). Victor Bks.

Cavalier & Puritan. J. D. Mackie. 1930. Repr. 10.00 (ISBN 0-8482-5082-6). Norwood Edns.

Cave Monasteries of Byzantine Cappadocia. Lyn Rodley. (Illus.). 284p. 1986. 79.50 (ISBN 0-521-26798-6). Cambridge U Pr.

Cave Temples of India. James Burgess & James Fergusson. (Illus.). 1969. text ed. 57.50x. Coronet Bks.

Cave Temples of Maichishan. Michael Sullivan. LC 69-15829. (Illus.). 1969. 70.00x (ISBN 0-520-01448-0). U of Cal Pr.

Caves & Jungles of Hindustan. Helena P. Blavatsky. Ed. by Boris De Zirkoff. LC 74-26605. (Illus.). 750p. 1975. 18.50 (ISBN 0-8356-0219-2). Theos Pub Hse.

Cayce, Karma & Reincarnation. I. C. Sharma. LC 81-23214. 186p. 1982. pap. 5.50 (ISBN 0-8356-0563-9, Quest). Theos Pub Hse.

Cazenove Journal, 1794: A Journey Through New Jersey & Pennsylvania. Theophile Cazenove. Ed. by Rayner W. Kelsey. (Haverford Coll. Studies: No. 13). 1922. 17.50x (ISBN 0-686-17388-0). R S Barnes.

CBA Suppliers Directory, 1987. 1987. 64.95. Chr Bksellers.

CCAR Yearbook. Ed. by Elliot L. Stevens. Incl. Vol. 86. 1976. 1977. 15.00 (ISBN 0-916694-36-4); Vol. 88. 1978. Ed. by Donald R. Weber. 1979. 15.00 (ISBN 0-916694-58-5); Vol. 89. 1979. 1980. 15.00. Central Conf.

CCAR Yearbook, 1889-1891, 3 vols. (Illus.). 1951. 10.00 (ISBN 0-916694-30-5). Central Conf.

CCAR Yearbook: 1978, Vol. 88. Ed. by Elliot L. Stevens & Donald A. Weber. 1979. 15.00 (ISBN 0-916694-58-5). Central Conf.

Celebrate. Marilyn Kunz & Catherine Schell. (Neighborhood Bible Studies). 48p. (Orig.). 1984. pap. 2.95 (ISBN 0-8423-0218-2). Tyndale.

Celebrate Christmas. Kathy Jones. (Celebrate Ser.). (Illus.). 144p. 1985. wkbk. 9.95 (ISBN 0-86653-279-X). Good Apple.

Celebrate Christmas. Gail Linam. 1982. pap. 2.95 (ISBN 0-8054-9305-0, 4293-05). Broadman.

Celebrate Communion. Colleen Britton. 79p. 1984. pap. 9.95 (ISBN 0-940754-26-6). Ed Ministries.

Celebrate Easter. Gail Linam. LC 84-12692. 1985. pap. 2.95 (ISBN 0-8054-9306-9). Broadman.

Celebrate Easter. Kelly Riley. (Celebrate Ser.). (Illus.). 144p. 1987. pap. 9.95 (ISBN 0-86653-385-0). Good Apple.

Celebrate God & Country. Phyllis Hand. (Celebrate Ser.). 144p. 1987. pap. 9.95 (ISBN 0-86653-390-7). Good Apple.

Celebrate God's Mighty Deeds: Child Prayerbook. 1971. 1.95 (ISBN 0-8091-6502-3). Paulist Pr.

Celebrate Life. Paul Zacharias. LC 79-93145. 78p. pap. 1.95 (ISBN 0-87785-162-X). Swedenborg.

Celebrate! No. V. Ed. by Eugene T. Sullivan & Marilynn C. Sullivan. LC 75-24148. 1978. pap. 11.99 (ISBN 0-912696-22-2). Wilton.

Celebrate Summer! Guidebook for Families & Congregations, 2 vols. Elizabeth M. Jeep & Gabe Huck. 1973. 5.95 (ISBN 0-918208-98-X). Liturgical Conf.

Celebrate the Christian Family. Ellen Javernick. (Celebrate Ser.). (Illus.). 144p. 1987. pap. 9.95 (ISBN 0-86653-391-5, SS844). Good Apple.

Celebrate the Church. Sandy Grant. 80p. 1987. pap. 5.95 (ISBN 1-55513-826-8). Cook.

Celebrate the Feasts: Of the Old Testament in Your Own Home or Church. Martha Zimmerman. 186p. 1981. pap. 5.95 (ISBN 0-87123-228-6). Bethany Hse.

Celebrate the Seasons! Phyllis Stanley & Miltinnie Yih. 119p. (Orig.). 1986. pap. 4.95 (ISBN 0-89109-116-5). NavPress.

Celebrate-While We Wait. L. Schroeder. (Illus.). 1977. pap. 4.95 (ISBN 0-570-03052-8, 6-1177). Concordia.

Celebrate with Song. Charles Matonti. LC 81-71237. (Illus.). 144p. (Orig.). 1982. pap. 3.95 (ISBN 0-87793-245-X). Ave Maria.

Celebrating Advent in the Sanctuary. Ralph Dessem. 1983. pap. 2.50 (ISBN 0-89536-635-5, 0384). CSS of Ohio.

Celebrating Christmas. Carl Seaburg. 1983. pap. 12.00 (ISBN 0-933840-17-9). Unitarian Univ.

Celebrating Christmas Around the World. Ed. by Herbert H. Wernecke. LC 62-13232. (Illus.). 256p. 1980. pap. 5.95 (ISBN 0-664-24318-5). Westminster.

Celebrating Forgiveness. William Koplik & Joan Brady. LC 81-51994. 96p. 1981. pap. 9.95 (ISBN 0-89622-137-7). Twenty-Third.

Celebrating Life: Jewish Rites of Passage. Malka Drucker. LC 84-4684. (Illus.). 112p. 1984. reinforced bdg. 11.95 (ISBN 0-8234-0539-7). Holiday.

Celebrating Marriage: Preparing the Wedding Liturgy - A Workbook for the Engaged Couple. Ed. by Paul Covina. 1987. pap. 4.95. Pastoral Pr.

Celebrating Our Faith: Evangelism Through Worship. Robert Webber. 1986. 10.95 (ISBN 0-06-069286-3, HarpR). Har-Row.

Celebrating Our Sacraments. Mary Fearon & Sandra Hirstein. 1985. Boxed Set. 84.95 (ISBN 0-697-02066-5); program director's guide 4.95 (ISBN 0-697-02058-4); write for info. tchr's. guide & student leaflets. Wm C Brown.

Celebrating Our Wedding. Nancy L. Nehmer. 96p. 1987. text ed. 14.95 (ISBN 0-8423-0273-5). Tyndale.

Celebrating Pentecost Through Dance. Joan Huff. Ed. by Doug Adams. (Orig.). 1986. pap. 3.00 (ISBN 0-941500-41-1). Sharing Co.

Celebrating Sacraments. Joseph Stoutzenberger. Ed. by Stephan Nagel. (Illus.). 240p. (Orig.). 1984. pap. text ed. 8.25x (ISBN 0-88489-159-3); teaching manual 12.00 (ISBN 0-88489-160-7); spiritmasters 18.95. St Mary's.

Celebrating Saints. Rich Bimler. 80p. (Orig.). 1986. pap. 3.95 (ISBN 0-570-04440-5). Concordia.

Celebrating Special Days in the Church School Year. Judy G. Smith. Ed. by Arthur L. Zapel. LC 81-83441. (Illus.). 125p. (Orig.). 1981. pap. text ed. 8.95 (ISBN 0-916260-14-3). Meriwether Pub.

Celebrating the Birth of Christ. Robert Shannon & Michael Shannon. 112p. 1985. pap. 4.95 (ISBN 0-87239-916-8, 3022). Standard Pub.

Celebrating the Easter Vigil. Ed. by Berger & Hollerweger. Tr. by Matthew J. O'Connell. (Ger.). 160p. 1983. pap. 9.95 (ISBN 0-916134-56-3). Pueblo Pub Co.

Celebrating the Festivals with Children. Friedel Lenz. Tr. of Mit Kindren Feste feiern. 20p. (Orig.). 1986. pap. 3.95 (ISBN 0-88010-151-2). Anthroposophic.

Celebrating the Gift of Forgiveness. Mary Fearon & Sandra J. Hirstein. 64p. 1982. pap. 3.50 (ISBN 0-697-01792-3); program manual 6.95 (ISBN 0-697-01793-1). Wm C Brown.

Celebrating the Gift of Jesus. Mary Fearon & Sandra J. Hirstein. 64p. 1982. pap. 3.50 (ISBN 0-697-01794-X); program manual 6.95 (ISBN 0-697-01795-8). Wm C Brown.

Celebrating the Gospel. Joan Mitchell & Therese Sherlock. Ed. by Carl Fisher. (Illus.). 1985. dupl. masterbook 9.95 (ISBN 0-89837-105-8, Pub. by Pflaum Pr). Peter Li.

Celebrating the Medieval Heritage: A Colloquy on the Thought of Aquinas & Bonaventura. David Tracy. 1978. pap. 8.95x (ISBN 0-226-81125-5). U of Chicago Pr.

Celebrating the Resurrection. Robert Shannon & Michael Shannon. (Illus.). 112p. (Orig.). 1984. pap. 5.95 (ISBN 0-87239-754-8, 3021). Standard Pub.

Celebrating the Saints. Catholic Church-Sacred Congregation of Divine Worship Staff. Tr. by International Committee on English in the Liturgy, Confraternity of Christian Doctrine for the New American Bible. 1978. pap. 10.00 (ISBN 0-916134-30-X). Pueblo Pub Co.

Celebrating the Seasons with Children. Philip E. Johnson. 112p. (Orig.). 1984. pap. 6.95 (ISBN 0-8298-0723-3). Pilgrim NY.

Celebrating the Single Life. Susan A. Muto & Adrian Van Kaam. LC 81-43770. 1985. pap. 6.95 (ISBN 0-385-19915-5, Im). Doubleday.

Celebrating Your Church Anniversary. Alvin D. Johnson. LC 68-28077. 1968. pap. 3.95 (ISBN 0-8170-0408-4). Judson.

Celebration: a Sourcebook for Christian Worship. Lydia N. Niguidula. 1975. wrps. 6.50x (ISBN 0-686-18680-X). Cellar.

Celebration & Blessing of a Marriage. 1977. pap. 0.95 (ISBN 0-8164-2152-8, HarpR). Har-Row.

Celebration of Breath. Sondra Ray. LC 83-1770. 192p. 1983. pap. 8.95 (ISBN 0-89087-355-0). Celestial Arts.

Celebration of Demons: Exorcism & the Aesthetics of Healing in Sri Lanka. Bruce Kapferer. LC 81-48677. (Midland Bks: No. 304). (Illus.). 312p. 1983. 32.50x (ISBN 0-253-31326-0); pap. 18.50x (ISBN 0-253-20304-X). Ind U Pr.

Celebration of Discipline: Paths to Spiritual Growth. Richard J. Foster. LC 77-20444. 1978. 13.45 (ISBN 0-06-062831-6, HarpR). Har-Row.

Celebration of Discipline Study Guide. Richard J. Foster. LC 77-20444. 96p. (Orig.). 1983. pap. 5.95 (ISBN 0-06-062833-2, RD/390, HarpR). Har-Row.

Celebration of Holy Mass. Louis G. Hileman. 154p. 1976. pap. 2.95 (ISBN 0-912414-23-5). Lumen Christi.

Celebration of Life: With Menachem. Rolf Gompertz. LC 83-50872. 160p. 1983. velo binding 10.00 (ISBN 0-918248-06-X). Word Doctor.

Celebration of Praise: Exciting Prospects for Extraordinary Praise. Dick Eastman. pap. 4.95 (ISBN 0-8010-3420-5). Baker Bk.

Celebration of the Eucharist: The Church's Festival of Love. The Nuns of the Monastery of St. Clare, Balsbach, Germany et al. Tr. by David Smith. 1983. 6.00 (ISBN 0-8199-0866-5). Franciscan Herald.

Celebration of Womanhood. Joyce M. Smith. (New Life Bible Studies). 64p. 1985. pap. 2.95 (ISBN 0-8423-0254-9). Tyndale.

Celebrations. Gaynell Cronin & Jim Cronin. 1980. pap. 7.55 (ISBN 0-88479-031-2). Arena Lettres.

Celebrations for the Family. Tony Castle. 126p. (Orig.). 1986. pap. 5.95 (ISBN 0-89283-270-3). Servant.

Celebrations of Christmas. Ed Baldwin & Stevie Baldwin. LC 85-47331. (Family Workshop Bk.). 248p. 1985. pap. 12.95 (ISBN 0-8019-7448-8). Chilton.

Celebrations of Death. R. Huntington & P. Metcalf. LC 79-478. (Illus.). 1979. 39.50 (ISBN 0-521-22531-0); pap. 10.95x (ISBN 0-521-29540-8). Cambridge U Pr.

Celebrations of the Word for Children: Cycle A. Bernice Stadler. Ed. by Nancy Reece. 88p. (Orig.). 1986. pap. 9.95 (ISBN 0-89622-308-6). Twenty-Third.

Celebrations: Read-Aloud Holiday & Theme Book Programs. Caroline F. Bauer. LC 85-714. (Illus.). 301p. 1985. 35.00 (ISBN 0-8242-0708-4). Wilson.

Celestial Brides: A Study in Mythology & Archaeology. Octavio Alvarez. LC 77-91208. (Illus.). 1978. 30.00 (ISBN 0-9601520-0-8). H Reichner.

Celestial Cycles: The Theme of Paradise Lost in World Literature with Translations of the Major Analogues. Watson Kirkconnell. LC 67-30308. 701p. 1967. Repr. of 1952 ed. 47.50x (ISBN 0-87752-058-5). Gordian.

Celestial Democracy. Voss E. Wysinger. LC 66-24014. 149p. 1966. lib. bdg. 16.95 (ISBN 0-914002-01-5); text ed. 16.95 (ISBN 0-914002-02-3); pap. text ed. 14.00 (ISBN 0-686-36904-1). Wysinger Pub.

Celestial Gems Books, Vol. 1. rev. ed. Edna M. Coolidge. LC 73-88209. 150p. 10.00 (ISBN 0-914154-00-1). Celestial Gems.

Celestial Gems Books, Vols. 2-3. Edna M. Coolidge. LC 73-88209. (Illus.). 48p. 1972. spiral bdg. 10.00 ea. Vol. 2 (ISBN 0-914154-01-X). Celestial Gems.

Celestial Gems Books, Vol. 4. Edna M. Coolidge. LC 73-88209. 65p. 1974. spiral bdg. 10.00 (ISBN 0-914154-03-6). Celestial Gems.

Celestial Gems Books, Vols. 5-6. Edna M. Coolidge. LC 73-88209. (Illus.). 150p. 1975. 10.00 ea.; Vol. 5. (ISBN 0-914154-05-2). Celestial Gems.

Celestial Song of Creation. Annalee Skarin. 1962p. pap. 5.95 (ISBN 0-87516-090-5). De Vorss.

Celibacy & the Crisis of Faith. Dietrich Von Hilderbrand. 1971. 4.95 (ISBN 0-8199-0428-7). Franciscan Herald.

Celibacy Myth. Chuch Gallagher & Thomas Vandenburg. 144p. 1987. 12.95 (ISBN 0-8245-0814-9). Crossroad NY.

Celibacy, Prayer & Friendship: A Making-Sense-Out-of-Life Approach. Christopher Kiesling. LC 77-25084. 1978. pap. 7.95 (ISBN 0-8189-0365-1). Alba.

Celibacy Put to the Gospel Test. Pascal Foresi. 33p. 1969. pap. 1.15 (ISBN 0-911782-16-8). New City.

Celibate Loving: Encounter in Three Dimensions. Ed. by Mary A. Huddleston. (Orig.). 1984. pap. 9.95 (ISBN 0-8091-2588-9). Paulist Pr.

Cell of Self-Knowledge. Richard Of St. Victor et al. Ed. by E. G. Gardner. LC 66-25702. (Medieval Library). Repr. of 1926 ed. 17.50x (ISBN 0-8154-0188-4). Cooper Sq.

Cell of Self Knowledge: Seven Early English Mystical Treatises. Margery Kempe et al. Ed. by John Griffiths. LC 81-126. (Spiritual Classics Ser.). 128p. 1981. 8.95 (ISBN 0-8245-0082-2). Crossroad NY.

Celos Aun Del Aire Matan. Pedro C. De la Barca. Tr. by Matthew D. Stroud. LC 80-54543. (Span. & Eng., Illus.). 219p. 1981. 15.00 (ISBN 0-911536-90-6); pap. 10.00 (ISBN 0-939980-01-0). Trinity U Pr.

Celtic & Scandinavian Religions. John A. MacCulloch. LC 72-11739. 180p. 1973. Repr. of 1948 ed. lib. bdg. 22.50x (ISBN 0-8371-6705-1, MCSR). Greenwood.

Celtic Druids. Godfrey Higgins. 40.00 (ISBN 0-89314-412-6). Philos Res.

Celtic Mysteries: Art & Imagination Ser. John Sharkey. (Illus.). 1987. pap. text ed. 10.95 (ISBN 0-500-81009-5). Thames Hudson.

Celtic Myth & Arthurian Romance. Roger S. Loomis. LC 67-31638. (Arthurian Legend & Literature Ser., No. 1). 1969. Repr. of 1927 ed. lib. bdg. 75.00x (ISBN 0-8383-0586-5). Haskell.

Celtic Myth & Legend. Charles Squire. LC 74-26575. (Newcastle Mythology Library: Vol. 1). 450p. 1975. pap. 6.95 (ISBN 0-87877-030-5). Newcastle Pub.

Celtic Myth & Legend, Poetry & Romance. Charles Squire. LC 80-53343. (Newcastle Mythology Library: Vol. 1). 450p. 1980. Repr. of 1975 ed. lib. bdg. 16.95x (ISBN 0-89370-630-2). Borgo Pr.

Celtic Myth & Legend, Poetry & Romance. Charles Squire. LC 77-6985. 1977. Repr. of 1910 ed. lib. bdg. 45.00 (ISBN 0-89341-164-7). Longwood Pub Group.

Celtic Mythology. Proinsias MacCana. LC 84-45597. (Library of the World's Myths & Legends). (Illus.). 144p. 1985. 18.95 (ISBN 0-87226-002-X). P Bedrick Bks.

Celtic Mythology & Religion. Alexander McBain. LC 76-1877. 1976. Repr. of 1917 ed. lib. bdg. 28.50 (ISBN 0-8414-6043-4). Folcroft.

Celtic Mythology & Slavic Mythology. John A. MacCulloch. Bd. with Jan Machal. LC 63-19088. (Mythology of All Races Ser.: Vol. 3). (Illus.). 477p. Repr. of 1964 ed. 30.00x (ISBN 0-8154-0142-6). Cooper Sq.

Celtic Religion: In Prechristian Times. Edward Anwyl. 1977. lib. bdg. 59.95 (ISBN 0-8490-1590-1). Gordon Pr.

Celtic Religion in Roman Britain. Graham Webster. LC 86-26532. (Illus.). 176p. 1987. 30.00 (ISBN 0-389-20686-5). B&N Imports.

Celtic Researches, on the Origin, Traditions & Language, of the Ancient Britons. Edward Davies. Ed. by Burton Feldman & Robert D. Richardson. LC 78-60902. (Myth & Romanticism Ser.: Vol. 8). (Illus.). 1979. lib. bdg. 80.00 (ISBN 0-8240-3557-7). Garland Pub.

Cemetery Inscriptions from Dyer County, Tennessee. Mrs. Quintard Glass. 240p. 1978. 15.00 (ISBN 0-89308-095-0). Southern Hist Pr.

Cemetery of St. Helen-on-the-Walls, Aldwark, York. Jean D. Dawes & J. R. Magilton. (Archaeology of York Ser: Vol. 12). 132p. 1980. pap. text ed. 25.00x (ISBN 0-900312-88-2, Pub. by Coun Brit Archaeology). Humanities.

Censor Marches on. M. L. Ernst & A. Lindey. LC 73-164512. (Civil Liberties in American History Ser.). 346p. 1971. Repr. of 1940 ed. lib. bdg. 39.50 (ISBN 0-306-70295-9). Da Capo.

Censorship of the Church of Rome, 2 vols. George H. Putnam. 200.00 (ISBN 0-87968-826-2). Gordon Pr.

Censorship of the Church of Rome & Its Influence upon the Production & Distribution of Literature, 2 Vols. George H. Putnam. LC 67-12455. 1967. Repr. of 1906 ed. 55.00 (ISBN 0-405-08869-8); 27.50 ea. Vol. 1 (ISBN 0-405-08870-1). Vol. 2 (ISBN 0-405-08871-X). Ayer Co Pubs.

Censure & Judgement of Erasmus: Whyther Dyuorsemente Stondeth with the Lawe of God. Desiderius Erasmus. Tr. by N. Lesse. LC 76-38177. (English Experience Ser.: No. 452). 160p. 1972. Repr. of 1550 ed. 15.00 (ISBN 90-221-0452-4). Walter J Johnson.

Censure of Speculative Theology. G. Makdisi. 156p. 1962. 40.00x (ISBN 0-317-39046-5, Pub. by Luzac & Co Ltd). State Mutual Bk.

Census Manual. C. S. Lovett. 1961. pap. 1.00 (ISBN 0-938148-18-4). Personal Christianity.

Centenary History As Related to the Baptist General Conference of America. Adolf Olson. Ed. by Edwin S. Ganstad. LC 79-52602. (Baptist Tradition Ser.). (Illus.). 1980. Repr. of 1952 ed. lib. bdg. 55.50x (ISBN 0-405-12467-8). Ayer Co Pubs.

Center Cannot Hold: The Search for a Global Economy of Justice. Marvin M. Ellison. LC 82-23795. 330p. (Orig.). 1983. lib. bdg. 31.00 (ISBN 0-8191-2963-1); pap. text ed. 15.50 (ISBN 0-8191-2964-X). U Pr of Amer.

Centered Living: The Way of Centering Prayer. M. Basil Pennington. LC 85-27474. (Illus.). 216p. 1986. 15.95 (ISBN 0-385-23186-5). Doubleday.

Centered on Christ. Augustine Roberts. LC 79-4036. 1979. pap. 7.95 (ISBN 0-932506-03-8). St Bedes Pubns.

Centering Moment. Howard Thurman. LC 80-67469. 1980. pap. 6.95 (ISBN 0-913408-64-6). Friends United.

Centering on the Lord Jesus: The Whole Person at Prayer. George Maloney. (Ways of Prayer Ser.: Vol. 3). 1982. 8.95 (ISBN 0-89453-427-0). M Glazier.

Centering Prayer: Renewing an Ancient Christian Prayer Form. M. Basil Pennington. LC 82-45077. 256p. 1982. pap. 4.50 (ISBN 0-385-18179-5, Im). Doubleday.

Centering: Your Guide to Inner Growth. Sanders Laurie et al. 299p. 1983. 6.95 (ISBN 0-89281-050-5, Destiny Bks). Inner Tradit.

Central Asia & Tibet Towards the Holy City of Lassa, 2 Vols. Sven A. Hedin. Tr. by J. T. Bealby. LC 68-55192. (Illus.). 1968. Repr. of 1903 ed. lib. bdg. 97.50x (ISBN 0-8371-3893-0, HECA). Greenwood.

Central Conception of Buddhism. T. Stcherbatsky. 1979. Repr. 12.50 (ISBN 0-89684-183-9). Orient Bk Dist.

Central Message of the New Testament. Joachim Jeremias. LC 81-66890. pap. 23.80 (2027865). Bks Demand UMI.

Central Problem of Paradise Lost. Esmond L. Marilla. 1953. lib. bdg. 12.00 (ISBN 0-8414-6200-3). Folcroft.

Central Problem of Paradise Lost: The Fall of Man. E. L. Marilla. (Essays & Studies on English Language & Literature: Vol. 15). pap. 15.00 (ISBN 0-8115-0213-9). Kraus Repr.

Central Teaching of Christ: A Study of John 13-17. Thomas D. Bernard. 426p. 1985. Repr. lib. bdg. 16.25 (ISBN 0-86524-176-7, 9519). Klock & Klock.

Century of a Modern Church. Chandler B. Grannis et al. LC 83-4800. (Illus.). 120p. (Orig.). 1983. pap. 5.00 (ISBN 0-9610366-0-5). Union Cong Church.

Century of Excavation in Palestine. Robert A. Macalister. Ed. by Moshe Davis. LC 77-70720. (America & the Holy Land Ser.). (Illus.). 1977. Repr. of 1925 ed. lib. bdg. 32.00x (ISBN 0-405-10265-8). Ayer Co Pubs.

Century of Growth: The Kachin Baptist Church of Burma. Herman Tegenfeldt. LC 74-4415. 540p. 1974. 10.95 (ISBN 0-87808-416-9). William Carey Lib.

Century of Planting: A History of the American Friends Mission in India. E. Anna Nixon. LC 85-72070. (Illus.). 493p. (Orig.). 1985. 16.95x (ISBN 0-913342-55-6); pap. 11.95 (ISBN 0-913342-54-8). Barclay Pr.

Century of Protestant Theology. Alasdair I. Heron. LC 80-17409. 240p. 1980. pap. 9.95 (ISBN 0-664-24346-0). Westminster.

Century of the Catholic Essay. facs. ed. Ed. by Raphael H. Gross. LC 76-134087. (Essay Index Reprint Ser). 1946. 19.00 (ISBN 0-8369-2190-9). Ayer Co Pubs.

Century of the Century. James Wall et al. 128p. (Orig.). 1987. pap. 8.95 (ISBN 0-8028-0180-3). Eerdmans.

Century's Changes of Outlook. Herbert L. Samuel. LC 77-7136. (Hibbert Lectures: 1953). Repr. of 1953 ed. 11.00 (ISBN 0-404-60432-3). AMS Pr.

Ceremonial Art in the Judaic Tradition. Intro. by Abram Kanof. LC 75-126321. (Illus.). 92p. 1975. pap. 3.00 (ISBN 0-88259-078-2). NCMA.

Ceremonial Centers of the Maya. Roy C. Craven, Jr. LC 74-2016. (Illus.). 152p. 1974. 20.00 (ISBN 0-8130-0447-0). U Presses Fla.
Ceremonial Magic: A Guide to the Mechanism of Ritual. Israel Regardie. LC 86-18389. 176p. 1986. lib. bdg. 19.95x (ISBN 0-8095-7013-0). Borgo Pr.
Ceremonial Ox of India: The Mithan in Nature, Culture, & History. Frederick J. Simoons & Elizabeth S. Simoons. LC 68-9023. (Illus.). 340p. 1968. 40.00x (ISBN 0-299-04980-9). U of Wis Pr.
Ceremonial Spirit Possession in Africa & Afro-America: Forms, Meanings & Functional Significance for Individuals & Social Groups. Sheila S. Walker. 179p. 1972. text ed. 37.50x (ISBN 90-040-3584-2). Humanities.
Ceremonies, Heroines of Jericho. 3.50 (ISBN 0-685-19468-X). Powner.
Ceremonies of the Liberal Catholic Rite. 2nd ed. Irving S. Cooper. (Illus.). 225p. 1981. Repr. of 1934 ed. 16.50 (ISBN 0-935461-07-8). St Alban Pr CA.
Certain As the Dawn. Peter G. Van Breemen. pap. 6.95 (ISBN 0-87193-150-8). Dimension Bks.
Certain Days: Zionist Memoirs & Selected Papers. Julius Simon. Ed. by Evyatar Friesel. 388p. 1971. casebound 12.95x (ISBN 0-87855-183-2). Transaction Bks.
Certain Homilies Containing Profitable Admonition for This Time. Jean Calvin. LC 73-6108. (English Experience Ser.: No. 576). 120p. 1973. Repr. of 1553 ed. 8.00 (ISBN 90-221-0576-8). Walter J Johnson.
Certain Hope for Uncertain Times. Lowell Lundstrom. Orig. Title: What's Coming Next? 368p. 1984. pap. text ed. 5.95 (ISBN 0-88368-152-8). Whitaker Hse.
Certain Journey. Charles W. Conn. 152p. 1965. 4.25 (ISBN 0-87148-000-X); pap. 3.25 (ISBN 0-87148-001-8). Pathway Pr.
Certain Life: Contemporary Meditations on the Way of Christ. Herbert O'Driscoll. 96p. (Orig.). 1980. pap. 5.95 (ISBN 0-8164-2040-8, HarpR). Har-Row.
Certain Life: Contemporary Meditations on the Way of Christ. Herbert O'Driscoll. 192p. 1985. pap. 8.95 large print ed. (ISBN 0-8027-2491-4); pap. cancelled (ISBN 0-8027-7274-9). Walker & Co.
Certain People: American Jews & Their Lives Today. Charles Silberman. 1985. 19.95 (ISBN 0-671-44761-0). Summit Bks.
Certain People: American Jews & Their Lives Today. Charles E. Silberman. 464p. 1986. pap. 9.95 (ISBN 0-671-62877-1). Summit Bks.
Certain People of the Book. Maurice Samuel. 1977. pap. 7.50 (ISBN 0-8074-0082-3, 388350). UAHC.
Certain Reactions by the Atlanta Public to the Death of the Rev. Dr. Martin Luther King Jr. Fred R. Crawford et al. LC 73-85669. 1969. pap. 3.00 (ISBN 0-89937-023-3). Ctr Res Soc Chg.
Certaine Sermons or Homilies Appointed to Be Read in the Churches in the Time of Elizabeth 1st, 1547-1571, 2 vols. in 1. Church of England Staff. LC 68-17016. 1968. Repr. of 1623 ed. 50.00x (ISBN 0-8201-1008-6). Schol Facsimiles.
Certainties for Today. Lehman Strauss. 1956. pap. 3.25 (ISBN 0-87213-810-0). Loizeaux.
Certainties of Christ's Coming. J. Oswald Sanders. 128p. 1984. pap. 2.95 (ISBN 0-87788-111-1). Shaw Pubs.
Certane Tractatis for Reformatioun of Doctryne & Maneris in Scotland. Ninian Winzet. LC 79-178311. (Maitland Club, Glasgow Publications: No. 33). Repr. of 1835 ed. 20.00 (ISBN 0-404-53001-X). AMS Pr.
Certosa Di Firenze. James Hogg. Ed. by James Hogg. (Analecta Cartusiana Ser.: No. 66). Tr. of Charterhouse of Florence. (Ital., Illus.). 110p. (Orig.). 1979. pap. 25.00 (ISBN 3-7052-0097-6, Pub. by Salzburg Studies). Longwood Pub Group.
Certosa Di Firenze: Nei Suoi Rapporti con L'Architettura Certosina. Giovanni Leoncini. Ed. by James Hogg. (Analecta Cartusiana Ser.: No. 71). (Ital., Illus.). 231p. (Orig.). 1979. pap. 25.00q (ISBN 3-7052-0106-9, Pub. by Salzburg Studies). Longwood Pub Group.
Certosa Di Pesio. Giorgio Beltrutti & James Hogg. Ed. by James Hogg. (Analecta Cartusiana Ser.: No. 73). 50p. (Orig.). 1979. pap. 25.00 (ISBN 3-7052-0108-5, Pub. by Salzburg Studies). Longwood Pub Group.
Certosa di Serra San Bruno. James Hogg. (Analecta Cartusiana Ser.: No. 26-2). (Ital. & Eng., Illus.). 61p. (Orig.). 1980. pap. 25.00 (ISBN 3-7052-0027-5, Pub by Salzburg Studies). Longwood Pub Group.
Certosa di Serra San Bruno Nella Storia del Monachesimo. Maria S. Pisani. Ed. by James Hogg. (Analcecta Cartusiana Ser.: No. 26-1). (Ital.). 131p. (Orig.). 1976. pap. 25.00 (ISBN 3-7052-0026-7, Pub. by Salzburg Studies). Longwood Pub Group.
Certosa Di Trisulti Da Innocenzo III: Al Concilio Di Costanza 1204-1414. Antonietta A. Sechi. Ed. by James Hogg. (Analecta Cartusiana Ser.). (Ital.). 197p. (Orig.). 1981. pap. 25.00 (ISBN 3-7052-0109-3, Pub. by Salzburg Studies). Longwood Pub Group.
Certose D'Italia (Liguria) La Certosa di Toirano. Georgio Beltrutti. Ed. by James Hogg. (Analecta Cartusiana Ser.: No. 101). 95p. (Orig.). 1982. pap. 25.00 (ISBN 0-317-42563-3, Pub. by Salzburg Studies). Longwood Pub Group.
Cestello: A Cistercian Church of the Florentine Renaissance. Allison Luchs. LC 76-23642. (Outstanding Dissertations in the Fine Arts - 2nd Series - 15th Century). (Illus.). 1977. Repr. lib. bdg. 76.00 (ISBN 0-8240-2706-X). Garland Pub.
CFO Songs. Eva Shull & Russell Shull. 1972. pap. 2.50 (ISBN 0-910924-53-8); pap. 3.95 spiral bdg. (ISBN 0-910924-54-6). Macalester.
Chag Sameach! A Jewish Holiday Book for Children. Patricia Schaffer. (Illus.). 28p. (Orig.). 1985. pap. 4.95 (ISBN 0-935079-16-5). Tabor Sarah Bks.
Chagall & the Bible. Jean Rosensaft. (Illus.). 160p. 1987. 24.95 (ISBN 0-87663-653-9). Universe.
Chain of Jewels from James & Jude. Donald Fream. LC 71-1073. (Bible Study Textbook Ser.). (Illus.). 1965. 12.20 (ISBN 0-89900-045-2). College Pr Pub.
Chain of Tradition Series, 4 vols. Louis Jacobs. Incl. Vol. 1. Jewish Law. LC 68-27329. pap. text ed. 5.95x (ISBN 0-87441-211-0); Vol. 2. Jewish Ethics, Philosophy & Mysticism. LC 71-80005. pap. text ed. 5.95x (ISBN 0-87441-212-9); Vol. 3. Jewish Thought Today. LC 73-116679. (Illus.). 1974. pap. text ed. 5.95x (ISBN 0-87441-213-7); Vol. 4. Hasidic Thought; Vol. 5. Jewish Biblical Exegesis. LC 78-1487. (Illus.). 1974. pap. Behrman.
Chain Reaction: Changing the World from Where You Are. D. James Kennedy & T. M. Moore. LC 85-6458. 160p. 1985. 9.95 (ISBN 0-8499-0486-2, 0486-2). Word Bks.
Chains & Images of Psychological Slavery. Na'im Akbar. 76p. (Orig.). pap. 3.50 (ISBN 0-933821-00-X). New Mind Prod.
Chair for Elijah. Menke Katz. LC 85-61563. (Illus.). 104p. 1985. 9.95 (ISBN 0-912292-78-4); pap. 6.95 (ISBN 0-912292-77-6). The Smith.
Chairman's Chat-Life Lines. Ed. by A. S. Otto. 120p. 1981. vinyl 24.95 (ISBN 0-912132-11-6). Dominion Pr.
Chakras. 10th ed. Charles W. Leadbeater. 1973. 7.95 (ISBN 0-8356-7016-3). Theos Pub Hse.
Chakras. Charles W. Leadbeater. LC 73-147976. (Illus.). 148p. 1972. pap. 5.75 (ISBN 0-8356-0422-5, Quest). Theos Pub Hse.
Chakras & Esoteric Healing. Zachary F. Lansdowne. LC 84-51108. 1986. pap. 8.95 (ISBN 0-87728-584-5). Weiser.
Chakras: Energy Centers of Transformation. Harish Johari. (Illus.). 192p. 1987. pap. 14.95 (ISBN 0-89281-054-8). Inner Tradit.
Chaldean Account of Genesis. George Smith. LC 77-73714. (Secret Doctrine Reference Ser.). (Illus.). 340p. 1977. Repr. of 1876 ed. 15.00 (ISBN 0-913510-26-2). Wizards.
Chaldean Oracles. Ed. by Sapere Aude. LC 78-58111. 1978. 10.00 (ISBN 0-935214-02-X). Heptangle.
Chaldean Oracles. Ed. by William W. Westcott. 1984. pap. 5.95 (ISBN 0-916411-16-8, Pub. by Alexandrian Pr). Holmes Pub.
Chaldean Oracles Attributed to Zoroaster. William W. Westcott. pap. 5.95 (ISBN 0-916411-16-8). Sure fire.
Chalkdust: Prayer Meditations for a Teacher. Elspeth C. Murphy. 1978. 5.95 (ISBN 0-8010-6065-6). Baker Bk.
Challeging Christianity: Leader's Guide. James Aderman. Ed. by William E. Fischer. (Bible Class Course Ser.). 48p. 1986. pap. 2.95 (ISBN 0-938272-25-X). WELS Board.
Challenge. Ed. by Aryeh Carmell & Cyril Domb. 1978. 14.95 (ISBN 0-87306-174-8); pap. 9.95 (ISBN 0-87306-165-9). Feldheim.
Challenge. John W. O'Malley et al. LC 58-6622. 1958. 4.95 (ISBN 0-8294-0062-1). Loyola.
Challenge! rev. ed. Ronald J. Wilkins. (To Live Is Christ Ser.). 1983. pap. 5.25 (ISBN 0-697-01850-4); tchr's. manual 5.95 (ISBN 0-697-01851-2); tests 10.95 (ISBN 0-697-01939-X). Wm C Brown.
Challenge & Crisis in Missionary Medicine. David J. Seel. LC 79-16015. (Illus.). 1979. pap. 3.95 (ISBN 0-87808-172-0). William Carey Lib.
Challenge & Mission. Louis Bernstein. LC 82-60203. 272p. 1982. 13.95 (ISBN 0-88400-081-8). Shengold.
Challenge & Response. Frederic R. Howe. 176p. 1985. pap. text ed. 7.95 (ISBN 0-310-45071-3, 12375P). Zondervan.
Challenge & Response: Justification in Ethics. Carl Wellman. LC 73-132478. 309p. 1971. 15.00x (ISBN 0-8093-0490-2). S Ill U Pr.
Challenge & the Harvest. Franklin D. Richards. LC 82-74368. 208p. 1983. 7.95 (ISBN 0-87747-939-9). Deseret Bk.
Challenge for Discipleship. Torkom Saraydarian. LC 86-70417. 25.00 (ISBN 0-911794-50-6); pap. 20.00 (ISBN 0-911794-51-4). Aqua Educ.
Challenge, I Dare You. Lillian E. France. 1984. 5.75 (ISBN 0-8062-1803-7). Carlton.
Challenge: Life of Dominic Savio. Daniel Higgins. (Illus.). 1959. 4.25 (ISBN 0-89944-025-8). Don Bosco Multimedia.
Challenge of Basic Christian Communities. Ed. by Sergio Torres & John Eagleson. Tr. by John Drury. LC 81-38361. 283p. (Orig.). 1981. pap. 9.95 (ISBN 0-88344-503-4). Orbis Bks.
Challenge of Church Growth. Ed. by Wilbert R. Shenk. (Mennonite Missionary Studies: Pt. 1). 112p. 1973. pap. 4.95 (ISBN 0-8361-1200-8). Herald Pr.
Challenge of Fatherhood. Hugh P. Stanley. LC 82-73132. 96p. (Orig.). 1982. pap. 2.45 (ISBN 0-87029-185-8, 20279-6). Abbey.
Challenge of Jesus. John Shea. (Encore Edition Ser.). 192p. 1984. pap. 8.95 (ISBN 0-88347-169-8). Thomas More.
Challenge of l'Arche. Jean Vanier. (Illus.). 286p. 1982. pap. 9.95 (ISBN 0-89088-072-7, HarpR). Har-Row.
Challenge of Liberation Theology: A First World Response. Ed. by L. Dale Richesin. Brian Mahan. LC 81-9527. 152p. (Orig.). 1981. pap. 7.95 (ISBN 0-88344-092-X). Orbis Bks.
Challenge of Marxist & Neo-Marxist Ideologies for Christian Scholarship. Ed. by John C. Vander Stelt. 280p. 1982. pap. 12.95 (ISBN 0-932914-07-1). Dordt Coll Pr.
Challenge of Old Testament Women Two. Sara Buswell. 176p. (Orig.). 1987. pap. 5.95 (ISBN 0-8010-0932-4). Baker Bk.
Challenge of Our Age. H. Hart. LC 68-9843. 1974. pap. 3.25 (ISBN 0-686-11982-7). Wedge Pub.
Challenge of Peace: God's Promise & Our Response. National Conference of Catholic Bishops. 116p. (Orig.). 1983. pap. 1.95 (ISBN 1-555868-63-0). US Catholic.
Challenge of Religion: A Philosophical Appraisal. Thomas N. Munson. LC 85-10297. 238p. 1985. text ed. 21.00x (ISBN 0-8207-0179-3); pap. text ed. 10.00x (ISBN 0-8207-0181-5). Duquesne.
Challenge of Religion Today: Essays on the Philosophy of Religion. Ed. by John King-Farlow. LC 76-13492. 1976. pap. text ed. 6.95 (ISBN 0-88202-157-5). Watson Pub Intl.
Challenge of Schweitzer. J. Middleton Murry. LC 72-190328. Repr. of 1948 ed. lib. bdg. 20.00 (ISBN 0-8414-6171-6). Folcroft.
Challenge of Sinai. (Illus.). 1981. 12.95 (ISBN 0-686-76489-7). Feldheim.
Challenge of Single Adult Ministry. Douglas W. Johnson. 112p. 1982. pap. 5.95 (ISBN 0-8170-0939-6). Judson.
Challenge of the Aquarian Age. Robert E. Birdsong. (Aquarian Academy Monograph, Ser. A: Lecture No. 7). 1978. pap. 1.25 (ISBN 0-917108-25-6). Sirius Bks.
Challenge of the Cults. Maurice C. Burrell. (Direction Bks.). 160p. (Orig.). 1982. pap. 3.95 (ISBN 0-8010-0816-6). Baker Bk.
Challenge of the Eldership: A Handbook for the Elders of the Church. Donald J. MacNair. (Orig.). 1984. pap. text ed. 1.95 (ISBN 0-934688-12-5). Great Comm Pubns.
Challenge of the Heart: Love, Sex & Intimacy in Changing Times. John Welwood. LC 85-2461. 283p. (Orig.). 1985. pap. 9.95 (ISBN 0-87773-331-7, 74200-1). Shambhala Pubns.
Challenge of Vocation & Ministry. 5.95 (ISBN 0-8215-9874-0). Sadlier.
Challenge to Care: A Fresh Look at How Pastors & Lay Leaders Relate to the People of God. Charles Simpson. 196p. 1986. pap. 5.95 (ISBN 0-89283-269-X, Pub. by Vine Books). Servant.
Challenge to Love: Gay & Lesbian Catholics in the Church. Ed. by Robert Nugent. LC 82-19850. 256p. 1983. pap. 10.95 (ISBN 0-8245-0518-2). Crossroad NY.
Challenge to Religious Life Today: Selected Letters & Addresses--1. Pedro Arrupe. Ed. by Jerome Aixala. LC 79-87603. 310p. 1979. 7.00 (ISBN 0-912422-45-9); pap. 6.00 smyth sewn (ISBN 0-912422-44-0). Inst Jesuit.
Challenges: A Young Man's Journal for Self-Awareness & Personal Planning. Mindy Bingham et al. Ed. by Barbara Greene & Kathleen Peters. LC 84-70108. (Illus.). 240p. 1984. pap. 12.95 (ISBN 0-911655-24-7). Advocacy Pr.
Challenges in Prayer. Basil Pennington. (Ways of Prayer Ser.: Vol. 1). 1982. 8.95 (ISBN 0-89453-425-4); pap. 4.95 (ISBN 0-89453-275-8). M Glazier.
Challenges to Inerrancy: A Theological Response. Ed. by Gordon R. Lewis & Bruce Demarest. 458p. (Orig.). 1984. pap. 13.95 (ISBN 0-8024-0237-2). Moody.
Challenging Christianity: Student's Guide. James Aderman & William E. Fischer. (Bible Class Course Ser.). (Illus.). 40p. 1986. pap. 2.95 (ISBN 0-938272-24-1). WELS Board.
Challenging Gifted Students in the Catholic School. 41p. 1985. 6.00. Natl Cath Educ.
Champaklal Speaks. Champaklal. (Illus.). 275p. 1975. pap. 7.25 (ISBN 0-89071-278-6). Matagiri.
Champaklal's Treasures. Champaklal. (Illus.). 234p. 1976. pap. 5.25 (ISBN 0-89071-279-4). Matagiri.
Champion Is... Marilyn Lashbrook. (I'm Growing Up Ser.). (Illus.). 32p. 1986. casebound 3.95 (ISBN 0-87403-121-4, 3601). Standard Pub.
Champion of the Cross. Charles F. Sweet. LC 76-144692. Repr. of 1894 ed. 27.50 (ISBN 0-404-07202-X). AMS Pr.
Champion of Youth: Daniel A. Lord, S. J. Thomas F. Cavin. 1977. 6.50 (ISBN 0-8198-0398-7); pap. text ed. 5.00 (ISBN 0-8198-0399-5). Dghtrs St Paul.
Champions for God. Jerry Falwell. 132p. 1985. pap. 4.95 (ISBN 0-89693-534-5). Victor Bks.
Champions of Light. Richard C. Shipp. 118p. 1983. 7.95 (ISBN 0-934126-32-1). Randall Bk Co.
Chamulas in the World of the Sun: Time & Space in a Maya Oral Tradition. Gary Gossen. (Illus.). 382p. 1984. pap. text ed. 10.95x (ISBN 0-88133-091-4). Waveland Pr.
Chance or Design? James E. Horigan. LC 79-83605. 242p. 1979. 13.95 (ISBN 0-8022-2238-2). Philos Lib.
Chance to Change: Women & Men in the Church. Betty Thompson. LC 82-71832. pap. 28.00 (2029602). Bks Demand UMI.
Chance to Dance: Risking a Spiritually Mature Life. W. Robert McClelland. Ed. by Herbert Lambert. LC 85-18987. 128p. (Orig.). 1986. pap. 8.95 (ISBN 0-8272-0449-3). CBP.
Chance to Serve: Peer Minister's Handbook. Brian Reynolds & Northeast Center for Youth Ministry Staff. (Illus.). 75p. (Orig.). 1983. pap. 4.95 (ISBN 0-88489-154-2); pap. 9.95 leader's manual (ISBN 0-88489-153-4). St Mary's.
Chances in a Mixed Marriage. Harold Billnitzer. 1978. pap. 1.95 (ISBN 0-933350-11-2). Morse Pr.
Chandi Borobudur: A Monument of Mankind. Dr. Soekmono. (Illus.). 53p. (Co-published with Van Gorcum, Amsterdam). 1976. pap. 8.25 (ISBN 92-3-101292-4, U69, UNESCO). Bernan-Unipub.
Chandogya Upanishad. Tr. by Swami Gamshirananda from Sanskrit. 690p. 1987. 16.00 (ISBN 0-87481-416-2, Pub. by Advaita Ashram India). Vedanta Pr.
Change Agent: The Strategy of Innovative Leadership. Lyle E. Schaller. LC 77-185544. 208p. (Orig.). 1972. pap. 7.95 (ISBN 0-687-06042-7). Abingdon.
Change & Continuity in Indian Religion. J. Gonda. 1984. text ed. 30.00x. Coronet Bks.
Change Factor: The Risks & the Joys. Gary W. Kuhne. 128p. 1986. pap. 5.95 (ISBN 0-310-27251-3, 12316). Zondervan.
Change in the Path to Supersensible Knowledge. Rudolf Steiner. 22p. 1982. pap. 3.00 (ISBN 0-919924-18-2, Pub. by Steiner Book Centre Canada). Anthroposophic.
Change My Heart: Family Lenten Handbook. 1.25 (ISBN 0-8091-9173-3). Paulist Pr.
Change of Face & Pace. Warren Metz. LC 82-90982. 1983. 8.95 (ISBN 0-87212-165-8). Libra.
Change of Habit. Joanne Howe. 117p. (Orig.). 1986. 9.95 (ISBN 0-89225-290-1); pap. 6.95 (ISBN 0-89225-292-8). Gospel Advocate.
Change Your Life Through Prayer. Stella T. Mann. 1971. pap. 3.95 (ISBN 0-87516-053-0). De Vorss.
Changed by Beholding Him. Newton Conant. 1972. pap. 2.95 (ISBN 0-87508-147-9). Chr Lit.
Changed into His Likeness. Watchman Nee. 1969. 4.95 (ISBN 0-87508-411-7); pap. 3.95 (ISBN 0-87508-410-9). Chr Lit.
Changed into His Likeness. Nee Watchman. 1978. pap. 3.95 (ISBN 0-8423-0228-X). Tyndale.
Changes & Socio-Religious Conflict in an Ethnic Minority Group: The Serbian Orthodox Church in America. Djuro J. Vrga & Frank J. Fahey. LC 74-31771. 1975. softcover 8.00 (ISBN 0-88247-335-2). Ragusan Pr.
Changing Biblical Imagery & Artistic Identity in 20th Century Liturgical Dance. Doug Adams. 1984. pap. 3.00 (ISBN 0-941500-31-4). Sharing Co.
Changing Brahmans: Association & Elites among the Kanya-Kybjas of North India. R. S. Khare. LC 72-128711. (Illus.). 1970. text ed. 21.00x (ISBN 0-226-43433-8). U of Chicago Pr.
Changing Catholic College. Andrew M. Greeley. LC 67-27393. (NORC Monographs in Social Research Ser.: No. 13). 1967. 8.95x (ISBN 0-202-09011-6). NORC.

Changing Climate. Arthur Bloomfield. LC 77-80427. 128p. 1977. pap. 2.50 (ISBN 0-87123-060-7, 200060). Bethany Hse.

Changing Conceptions in Jewish Education. facsimile ed. Emanuel Gamoran. LC 74-27986. (Modern Jewish Experience Ser.). 1975. Repr. of 1924 ed. 36.50x (ISBN 0-405-06713-5). Ayer Co Pubs.

Changing Conceptions of Original Sin: A Study in American Theology since 1750. Hilary S. Smith. Ed. by Bruce Kuklick. (American Religious Thought of the 18th & 19th Centuries Ser.). 242p. 1987. lib. bdg. 35.00 (ISBN 0-8240-6954-4). Garland Pub.

Changing Contexts of Our Faith. Ed. by Letty M. Russell. LC 85-4418. 112p. 1985. pap. 4.95 (ISBN 0-8006-1862-9). Fortress.

Changing Family: Views from Theology & Social Sciences in the Light of the Apostolic Exhortation "Familiaris Consortio". Ed. by Saxton et al. 224p. 1984. 12.95 (ISBN 0-8294-0458-9). Loyola.

Changing Images of the Warrior Hero in America: A History of Popular Symbolism. Edward T. Linenthal. LC 82-22885. (Studies in American Religion: Vol. 6). 296p. 1983. 49.95 (ISBN 0-88946-921-0). E Mellen.

Changing Landscapes: Anti-Pastoral Sentiment in the English Renaissance. Peter Lindenbaum. LC 85-24546. 264p. 1986. 27.50x (ISBN 0-8203-0835-8). U of GA Pr.

Changing Male Roles in Today's World: A Christian Perspective for Men - & the Women Who Care about Them. Richard P. Olson. 160p. 1982. pap. 5.95 (ISBN 0-8170-0946-9). Judson.

Changing Mind. Vincent G. Stuart. LC 80-53447. 80p. 1981. 6.95 (ISBN 0-87773-206-X). Shambhala Pubns.

Changing of the Gods. Frank E. Manuel. LC 82-40475. 216p. 1983. 20.00x (ISBN 0-87451-254-9). U Pr of New Eng.

Changing of the Gods: Feminism & the End of Traditional Religions. Naomi R. Goldenberg. LC 78-19602. 1979. pap. 7.95 (ISBN 0-8070-1111-8, BP600). Beacon Pr.

Changing Patterns of Religious Education. Ed. by Marvin J. Taylor. 320p. (Orig.). 1984. pap. 15.95 (ISBN 0-687-06046-X). Abingdon.

Changing Perspectives in the Scientific Study of Religion. Ed. by Allan W. Eister. LC 74-2092. 370p. 1974. 25.50 (ISBN 0-471-23476-1, Pub. by Wiley). Krieger.

Changing the Seen & Shaping the Unseen. Charles Capps. 1980. pap. 1.75 (ISBN 0-89274-165-1). Harrison Hse.

Changing the Seen & Shaping the Unseen. Charles Capps. 1981. pap. 2.25 (ISBN 0-89274-220-8, HH-220). Harrison Hse.

Changing the World: An Agenda for the Churches. Vincent Cosmao. Tr. by John Drury. LC 84-5153. Tr. of Changer le monde-une tache pour l'eglise. 128p. (Orig.). 1984. pap. 7.95 (ISBN 0-88344-107-1). Orbis Bks.

Changing the World Within: The Dynamics of Personal & Spiritual Growth. Joseph A. Grassi. 128p. (Orig.). 1986. pap. 5.95 (ISBN 0-8091-2755-5). Paulist Pr.

Changing Values & Social Trends: How Do Organizations React? Presented Jointly by the Market Research Society & the American Marketing Association, June 1974, Oxford, England. American Marketing Association Staff. pap. 56.00 (ISBN 0-317-26627-6, 2011593). Bks Demand UMI.

Changing World of Mormonism. Jerald Tanner & Sandra Tanner. LC 79-18311. 1979. 16.95 (ISBN 0-8024-1234-3). Moody.

Channing: The Reluctant Radical. 2nd ed. Jack Mendelsohn. 1986. pap. 10.95 (ISBN 0-933840-28-4, Skinner Hse Bks). Unitarian Univ.

Chant & Be Happy: Based on Teachings of A. C. Bhaktivedanta Swami. (Illus.). 118p. 2.95 (ISBN 0-89213-118-7). Bhaktivedanta.

Chant the Names of God. Edward Henry. (Illus.). 260p. 1984. 20.00 (ISBN 0-916304-65-5). SDSU Press.

Chanting the Names of Manjusri: The Manjusri-Nama-Samgiti, Sanskrit & Tibetan Texts. Tr. by Alex Wayman from Tibetan, Sanskrit. LC 83-2309. 130p. 1985. 30.00 (ISBN 0-87773-316-3, 54531-1). Shambhala Pubns.

Chants for Contemplation: Shikh Text. Ed. by Raghavan Iyer. (Sacred Texts Ser.). Orig. Title: ADI Granth. 144p. (Orig.). 1984. pap. 8.75 (ISBN 0-88695-030-9). Concord Grove.

Chants from Eternity. Himalayan Institute. (Illus.). 64p. 1977. plastic comb bdg. 4.95 (ISBN 0-89389-033-2). Himalayan Pubs.

Chanukah. Howard Greenfeld. LC 76-6527. 1976. 6.95 (ISBN 0-03-015566-5). H Holt & Co.

Chanukah, Passover, Rosh Hashanah, Yom Kippur. Howard Greenfeld. 1982. boxed set 20.00 (ISBN 0-03-057626-1). H Holt & Co.

Chaos of Cults. 4th ed. rev. ed. Jan K. Van Baalen. 1962. 11.95 (ISBN 0-8028-3278-4). Eerdmans.

Chaos or Creation: Spirituality in Mid-Life. L. Patrick Carroll & Katherine M. Dyckman. 176p. 1986. pap. 8.95 (ISBN 0-8091-2832-2). Paulist Pr.

Chaos to Cosmos: Studies in Biblical Patterns of Creation. Susan Niditch. (Scholars Press Studies in the Humanities: No. 6). 1985. 13.95 (ISBN 0-89130-762-1, 00 01 06); pap. 9.25 (ISBN 0-89130-763-X). Scholars Pr GA.

Chapel Messages. L. C. Johnson. 1982. pap. 5.95 (ISBN 0-89265-081-8). Randall Hse.

Chapel of Our Lady of Talpa. William Wroth. 1979. pap. 10.00 (ISBN 0-916537-28-5, Taylor Museum). CO Springs Fine Arts.

Chapel of Our Lady of Talpa. William Wroth. LC 78-58985. (Illus.). 104p. (Orig.). 1982. pap. 8.95 (ISBN 0-295-95920-7, Pub. by Taylor Museum). U of Wash Pr.

Chapel of Sesostris III at Uronarti. Charles C. Van Siclen, III. 58p. 1982. pap. text ed. 10.00x (ISBN 0-933175-02-7). Van Siclen Bks.

Chapel Talks. C. B. Eavey. (Pocket Pulpit Library). 120p. 1981. pap. 2.95 (ISBN 0-8010-3365-9). Baker Bk.

Chaplain on Wings. Harold H. Gordon. Ed. by Zev Zahavy. LC 81-51749. (Illus.). 192p. 1981. 12.95 (ISBN 0-88400-075-3). Shengold.

Chappell's Special Day Sermons. Clovis G. Chappell. (Pocket Pulpit Library Ser.). 204p. 1983. pap. 4.50 (ISBN 0-8010-2383-1). Baker Bk.

Chapter Ceremonies & Poems. Ottillie S. Brunke. 60p. pap. text ed. 2.50 (ISBN 0-88053-305-6, S-192). Macoy Pub.

Chapter Degrees. Edmond Ronayne. 8.50 (ISBN 0-685-19469-8). Powner.

Chapter of Mediaeval History. D. H. Madden. LC 74-91048. 1969. Repr. of 1924 ed. 26.50x (ISBN 0-8046-0658-7, Pub. by Kennikat). Assoc Faculty Pr.

Chapter of Talmud. 1982. 4.50 (ISBN 0-686-76490-0). Feldheim.

Chapter of the Self. Trevor Leggett. (Illus.). 1978. 12.95 (ISBN 0-7100-8702-0). Methuen Inc.

Chapters from the Religious History of Spain Connected with the Inquisition. Henry C. Lea. LC 68-56760. (Research & Source Work Ser.: No. 245). 1967. Repr. of 1890 ed. 26.00 (ISBN 0-8337-2035-X). B Franklin.

Chapters in a Life of Paul. rev., 2nd ed. John Knox. Ed. by Douglas R. Hare. 192p. 1987. 29.95 (ISBN 0-86554-266-X, MUP/H227/P32); pap. 14.95 (ISBN 0-86554-281-3). Mercer Univ Pr.

Chapters in Early English Church History. 3rd ed. William Bright. 1897. 25.00 (ISBN 0-8337-4005-9). B Franklin.

Chapters of Coming Forth by Day, 3 vols. Book of the Dead Staff. LC 73-18833. Repr. of 1910 ed. 49.50 set (ISBN 0-404-11303-6). AMS Pr.

Chapters of Symbolism. W. Frank Shaw. 1979. Repr. of 1897 ed. lib. bdg. 45.00 (ISBN 0-8495-4902-7). Arden Lib.

Chapters of the Fathers. Samson R. Hirsch. Tr. by Gertrude Hirschler. 1979. 5.95 (ISBN 0-87306-182-9). Feldheim.

Character & the Christian Life: A Study in Theological Ethics. Stanley Hauerwas. LC 85-5873. (Monograph Series in Religion). 265p. 1985. pap. text ed. 10.95 (ISBN 0-939980-10-X). Trinity U Pr.

Character & Theological Struggle of the Church in Halmahera, Indonesia, 1941-1979. James Haire. (IC-Studies in the Intercultural History of Christianity: Vol. 26). xii, 382p. 1981. pap. 42.05 (ISBN 3-8204-5888-3). P Lang Pubs.

Character & Writings of John Milton. William Channing. 1826. lib. bdg. 8.50 (ISBN 0-8414-3465-4). Folcroft.

Character Building: A Guide for Parents & Teachers. David Isaacs. Tr. of Educacion de las Virtudes Humanas. 268p. (Orig.). 1984. write for info. (ISBN 0-906127-68-8, Pub. by Four Courts Pr Ireland); pap. 8.95 (ISBN 0-906127-67-X, Pub. by Four Courts Pr Ireland). Scepter Pubs.

Character Education & Spiritual Values in an Anxious Age. Rudolf Dreikurs. (AAI Monograph Ser.: No. 1). 1971. pap. 2.00x (ISBN 0-918560-16-0). A Adler Inst.

Character of a Quaker. Henry J. Cadbury. 1983. pap. 2.50x (ISBN 0-87574-103-7, 103). Pendle Hill.

Character of Government: An Examination of U. S. Government Agencies' Crimes. pap. 9.00 (ISBN 0-905931-10-6). Church of Scient Info.

Character of Swift's Satire: A Revised Focus. Ed. by Claude Rawson. LC 81-72062. 344p. 1983. 34.50 (ISBN 0-87413-209-6). U Delaware Pr.

Character of the Christian. rev. ed. Navigators Staff. (Design for Discipleship Ser.: Bk. 4). 49p. 1980. pap. text ed. 1.95 (ISBN 0-934396-19-1). Churches Alive.

Character-Portrayals in the Ramayana of Valmiki. Alois Wurm. 1977. 30.00x (ISBN 0-686-22658-5). Intl Bk Dist.

Character Sketches: From the Pages of Scripture, Illustrated in the World of Nature, 3 vols. LC 76-3050. (Illus.). 382p. 1976. Vol. 1. 25.00 (ISBN 0-916888-01-0); Vol. 2. 25.00 (ISBN 0-916888-02-9); Vol. 3, 1985. 30.00 (ISBN 0-916888-10-X). Inst Basic Youth.

Characteristics from the Writings of John Henry Newman. Cardinal John H. Newman. LC 76-45366. 1976. Repr. of 1875 ed. lib. bdg. 49.50 (ISBN 0-8414-5813-8). Folcroft.

Characteristics of a Caring Home Growthbook. H. Norman Wright & Rex Johnson. 80p. (Orig.). 1983. 4.95 (ISBN 0-88449-048-3, A424608). Vision Hse.

Characters & Kings: A Woman's Workshop on the History of Israel, 2 pts. Carolyn Nystrom. (Woman's Workshop Ser.). 240p. (Orig.). 1985. Part 1. pap. 2.95 (ISBN 0-310-41881-X, 11279P); Part 2. pap. 3.95 (ISBN 0-310-41871-2, 11283). Zondervan.

Characters of Paradise Lost. M. A. Woods. LC 72-6863. 1908. lib. bdg. 27.50 (ISBN 0-8414-0133-0). Folcroft.

Characters of the Reformation. facs. ed. Hilaire Belloc. LC 72-121449. (Essay Index Reprint Ser). 1936. 24.00 (ISBN 0-8369-1696-4). Ayer Co Pubs.

Charasmatic Catechism. Ernest B. Gentile. LC 76-22255. 1977. pap. 4.95 (ISBN 0-89221-025-7). New Leaf.

Charge to Keep. Bryon T. Morris. 1971. 4.00 (ISBN 0-87012-092-1). McClain.

Charged World: A Theology of Symbol. George E. Tracy. 1980. lib. bdg. 8.00 (ISBN 0-87419-054-1, U Pr of Wash); 1981 students' ed. 5.00 (ISBN 0-686-77089-7). Larlin Corp.

Chariot of Fire: A Study of William Blake In the Light of Hindu Thought. Charu S. Singh & James Hogg. (Romantic Reassessment Ser.). 194p. (Orig.). 1981. pap. 15.00 (ISBN 3-7052-0577-3, Pub. by Salzburg Studies). Longwood Pub Group.

Chariot of Fire: Religion & the Beecher Family. Marie Caskey. LC 77-5291. (Historical Publications Ser.). (Illus.). 1978. 40.00x (ISBN 0-300-02007-4). Yale U Pr.

Chariot of Israel: Exploits of the Prophet of Elijah. William Varner. LC 84-80766. 1984. pap. text ed. 4.95 (ISBN 0-915540-33-9). Frnds Israel.

Chariot of Wrath. George W. Knight. 1978. Repr. of 1942 ed. lib. bdg. 25.00 (ISBN 0-8495-3012-1). Arden Lib.

Chariot of Wrath: The Message of John Milton to Democracy at War. G. Wilson Knight. LC 72-196540. 1942. lib. bdg. 20.00 (ISBN 0-8414-5589-9). Folcroft.

Chariots of Fire & a Christian Message for Today. W. J. Weatherby et al. LC 82-48941. (Quicksilver Bk.). 176p. (Orig.). 1983. pap. 5.95 (ISBN 0-06-069282-0, RD 455, HarpR). Har-Row.

Chariots of the Gods. Erich Von Daniken. 189p. 1985. 42.50 (ISBN 0-317-19961-7). Bern Porter.

Charis: The Meaning of Grace in the New Testament. Thomas Schulz. 78p. 1971. pap. 3.95 (ISBN 0-911620-06-0). Westcott.

Charisma & Community: A Study of Religion in American Culture. Mary J. Neitz. 275p. 1987. 34.95 (ISBN 0-88738-130-8). Transaction Bks.

Charisma & Sacred Biography. Ed. by Michael A. Williams. (JAAR Thematic Studies). 1982. 19.50 (ISBN 0-89130-681-1, 01-24-83). Scholars Pr GA.

Charisma vs. Charismania. Chuck Smith. LC 82-2241. 176p. (Orig.). 1983. pap. 3.95 (ISBN 0-89081-353-1). Harvest Hse.

Charismata: God's Gift for God's People. John Koenig. LC 77-12700. (Biblical Perspectives on Current Issues). 214p. 1978. softcover 5.95 (ISBN 0-664-24176-X). Westminster.

Charismatic Gift of Tongues. Ronald E. Baxter. LC 81-17182. 162p. 1982. pap. 7.95 (ISBN 0-8254-2225-6). Kregel.

Charismatic Gifts in the Early Church. Dr. Ronald A. Kydd. 172p. 1984. pap. 4.95 (ISBN 0-913573-09-4). Hendrickson MA.

Charismatic Leader & His Followers. Martin Hengel. LC 81-9708. 124p. 1981. 10.95 (ISBN 0-8245-0137-3). Crossroad NY.

Charismatic Ministry. Gordon Lindsay. 3.25 (ISBN 0-89985-122-3). Christ Nations.

Charismatic Movement: Is There a New Pentecost? Margaret M. Poloma. (Social Movements: Past & Present Ser.). 1982. lib. bdg. 18.95 (ISBN 0-8057-9701-7, Twayne). G K Hall.

Charismatic Movement: Is There a New Pentecost? Margaret M. Poloma. (Social Movements Past & Present Ser.). 304p. 1987. pap. 9.95 (ISBN 0-8057-9721-1, Twayne). G K Hall.

Charismatic Religion in Modern Research: A Bibliography. Watson E. Mills. Ed. by David M. Scholer. LC 85-127327. (National Association of Baptist Professors of Religion Bibliographic Ser.: No. 1). viii, 178p. 1985. text ed. 14.50 (ISBN 0-86554-143-4, MUP/M010). Mercer Univ Pr.

Charismatic Renewal & You. Barbara A. Pursey. Orig. Title: Holy Spirit, the Church & You. 43p. (Orig.). 1987. pap. 2.95 (ISBN 0-934421-08-0). Presby Renewal Pubns.

Charismatic Spiritual Gifts: A Phenomenological Analysis. William J. Sneck. LC 80-8291. 312p. (Orig.). 1981. lib. bdg. 29.25 (ISBN 0-8191-1765-X); pap. text ed. 14.50 (ISBN 0-8191-1766-8). U Pr of Amer.

Charismatic Theology of St. Luke. Roger Stronstad. 96p. 1985. pap. 4.95 (ISBN 0-913573-11-6). Hendrickson MA.

Charismatica. (Illus.). 1979. 6.95 (ISBN 0-911346-03-1). Christianica.

Charismatics. John MacArthur. 1980. pap. 6.95 (ISBN 0-310-28491-0, 12645P). Zondervan.

Charisms & Charismatic Renewal: A Biblical & Theological Study. Francis A. Sullivan. 182p. 1982. pap. 8.95 (ISBN 0-89283-121-9). Servant.

Charity & the Great Adventure. Louise Ulmer. (Orig.). 1987. pap. price not set (ISBN 0-89536-882-X, 7868). CSS of Ohio.

Charity, Challenge, & Change: Religious Dimensions of the Mid-Nineteenth Century Women's Movement in Germany. Catherine M. Prelinger. LC 86-19432. (Contributions in Women's Studies Ser.: No. 75). 225p. 1987. lib. bdg. 29.95 (ISBN 0-313-25401-X, PCY). Greenwood.

Charity for the Suffering Souls. John A. Nageleisen. LC 82-83797. 375p. 1982. pap. 10.00 (ISBN 0-89555-200-0). TAN Bks Pubs.

Charity Never Faileth. Vaughn J. Featherstone. LC 80-10528. 121p. 1980. 7.95 (ISBN 0-87747-806-6). Deseret Bk.

Charlemagne's Cousins: Contemporary Lives of Adalard & Wala. Ed. by Allen Cabaniss. LC 67-26919. 1967. 14.95x (ISBN 0-8156-2115-9). Syracuse U Pr.

Charles Albert Tindley: Prince of Preachers. Ralph H. Jones. 192p. 1982. pap. 8.95 (ISBN 0-687-06325-6). Abingdon.

Charles de Lannoy: Victor of Pavia. Lucile Delano. 144p. 1983. 9.75 (ISBN 0-8158-0442-3). Chris Mass.

Charles Dickens, Resurrectionist. Andrew Sanders. LC 81-21246. 1982. 26.00 (ISBN 0-312-13014-7). St Martin.

Charles Fillmore Concordance. Charles Fillmore. 1975. 5.95 (ISBN 0-87159-015-8). Unity School.

Charles Finney. Basil Miller. 144p. 1983. pap. 2.95 (ISBN 0-88113-034-6). Edit Betania.

Charles G. Finney. Basil Miller. 144p. 1969. pap. 3.50 (ISBN 0-87123-061-5, 200061). Bethany Hse.

Charles G. Finney: An Autobiography. Charles G. Finney. 480p. 16.95 (ISBN 0-8007-0095-3). Revell.

Charles G. Finney Memorial Library, 8 vols. Charles G. Finney. 1975. Set. pap. 31.50 (ISBN 0-8254-2623-5). Kregel.

Charles Grandison Finney, Seventeen Ninety-Two to Eighteen Seventy-Five: Revivalist & Reformer. Keith J. Hardman. (Illus.). 536p. 1987. text ed. 45.00x (ISBN 0-8156-2397-6). Syracuse U Pr.

Charles Haddon Spurgeon - Autobiography: The Early Years, 1834-1860, Vol. 1. Charles H. Spurgeon. 1976. 18.95 (ISBN 0-85151-076-0). Banner of Truth.

Charles Haddon Spurgeon - Autobiography: The Full Harvest, 1861-1892, Vol. 2. Charles H. Spurgeon. 1975. 18.95 (ISBN 0-85151-182-1). Banner of Truth.

Charles Hartshorne & the Existence of God. Donald W. Viney. (Philosophy Ser.). 192p. 1984. 44.50 (ISBN 0-87395-907-8); pap. 14.95 (ISBN 0-87395-908-6). State U NY Pr.

Charles Hodge: The Way of Life & Selected Writings. Ed. by Mark A. Noll. 1987. 12.95. Paulist Pr.

Charles I & the Popish Plot. Caroline M. Hibbard. LC 81-23075. ix, 342p. 1983. 30.00x (ISBN 0-8078-1520-9). U of NC Pr.

Charles Kingsley. W. Henry Brown. LC 73-12770. 1924. lib. bdg. 17.50 (ISBN 0-8414-3231-7). Folcroft.

Charles Kingsley. James J. Ellis. 1890. Repr. 25.00 (ISBN 0-8274-3799-4). R West.

Charles Kingsley & His Ideas. Guy Kendall. LC 72-6679. (English Biography Ser., No. 31). 195p. 1972. Repr. of 1937 ed. lib. bdg. 39.95x (ISBN 0-8383-1639-5). Haskell.

Charles Kingsley & the Christian Social Movement. Charles W. Stubbs. LC 70-148310. Repr. of 1899 ed. 17.50 (ISBN 0-404-08914-3). AMS Pr.

Charles Kingsley: Christian Social Reformer. M. Kaufmann. LC 77-20677. 1892. Repr. 30.00 (ISBN 0-8492-1416-5). R West.

Charles Kingsley: Christian Socialist & Social Reformer. M. Kaufmann. 1978. Repr. of 1892 ed. lib. bdg. 25.00 (ISBN 0-8495-3010-5). Arden Lib.

Charles Kingsley, Eighteen Nineteen to Eighteen Seventy-Five. Margaret F. Thorp. LC 70-96170. 1969. Repr. of 1937 ed. lib. bdg. 18.50x (ISBN 0-374-97942-1, Octagon). Hippocrene Bks.

Charles Kingsley: His Letters & Memories of His Life, 2 Vols. Charles Kingsley. LC 74-148803. (Illus.). Repr. of 1877 ed. Set. 37.50 (ISBN 0-404-08869-4); deluxe ed. 19.00 ea. Vol. 1 (ISBN 0-404-08870-8). Vol. 2 (ISBN 0-404-08871-6). AMS Pr.

Charles Kingsley: Poet. George Seaver. LC 73-1252. 1973. lib. bdg. 10.00 (ISBN 0-8414-1540-4). Folcroft.

Charles Parish, York County, Virginia: History & Registers -- Births, 1648-1789; Deaths 1665-1787. Landon C. Bell. LC 33-27865. vi, 285p. 1984. Repr. of 1932 ed. 12.50 (ISBN 0-88490-114-9). VA State Lib.

Charles Spurgeon. W. Y. Fullerton. (Golden Oldies Ser.). 288p. 1980. pap. 4.95 (ISBN 0-8024-1236-X). Moody.

Charles Spurgeon. Kathy Triggs. 96p. (Orig.). 1986. pap. 3.50. Bethany Hse.

Charles Wesley on Sanctification: A Biographical & Theological Study. John R. Tyson. 240p. 1986. pap. 10.95 (ISBN 0-310-75131-4, 17054P). Zondervan.

Charles Williams, Poet of Theology. Glen Cavaliero. LC 82-11420. Repr. of 1983 ed. 52.30 (2027538). Bks Demand UMI.

Charlie Osburn Story: You Gotta Give It All to Jesus. Charlie Osburn & Fred Lilly. 140p. 1986. pap. 4.95 (ISBN 0-89283-287-8). Servant.

Chart Your Own Stars. Doris V. Thompson. 86p. 1975. text ed. 15.00 s.p. (ISBN 0-88053-764-7). Macoy Pub.

Chartae Of The Carthusian General Chapter, Vol. 1. James Hogg & Michael Sargent. (Analecta Catusiana Ser.: No. 100/1). 186p. (Orig.). 1983. pap. 25.00 (ISBN 3-7052-0171-9, Pub. by Salzburg Studies). Longwood Pub Group.

Chartae of the Carthusian General Chapter, Vol. 2. James Hogg & Michael Sargent. (Analecta Cartusiana Ser.: No. 100/2). 229p. (Orig.). 1983. pap. 25.00 (ISBN 3-7052-0172-7, Pub. by Salzburg Studies). Longwood Pub Group.

Chartae of the Carthusian General Chapter, Vol. 3. James Hogg & Michael Sargent. (Analecta Cartusiana Ser.: No. 100/3). 209p. (Orig.). 1984. pap. 25.00 (ISBN 3-7052-0173-5, Pub. by Salzburg Studies). Longwood Pub Group.

Chartae of the Carthusian General Chapter, Vol. 4. James Hogg & Michael Sargent. (Analecta Cartusiana Ser.: No. 100/4). 241p. (Orig.). 1984. pap. 25.00 (ISBN 0-317-42565-X, Pub. by Salzburg Studies). Longwood Pub Group.

Chartae of the Carthusian General Chapter, Vol. 5. James Hogg & Michael Sargent. (Analecta Cartusiana Ser.: No. 100/5). 229p. (Orig.). 1985. pap. 25.00 (ISBN 0-317-42566-8, Pub. by Salzburg Studies). Longwood Pub Group.

Chartae of the Carthusian General Chapter, Vol. 6. James Hogg & Michael Sargent. (Analecta Cartusiana Ser.: No. 100/6). 1985. pap. 25.00 (ISBN 0-317-42567-6, Pub. by Salzburg Studies). Longwood Pub Group.

Chartae of the Carthusian General Chapter, Vol. 7. James Hogg & Michael Sargent. (Analecta Cartusiana Ser.: No. 100/7). (Orig.). 1985. pap. 25.00 (ISBN 0-317-42569-2, Pub. by Salzburg Studies). Longwood Pub Group.

Chartae of the Carthusian General Chapter, Vol. 8. James Hogg & Michael Sargent. (Analecta Cartusiana Ser.: No. 100/8). (Orig.). 1986. pap. 25.00 (ISBN 0-317-42570-6, Pub. by Salzburg Studies). Longwood Pub Group.

Chartae of the Carthusian General Chapter, Vol. 9. James Hogg & Michael Sargent. (Analecta Cartusiana Ser.: No. 100/9). (Orig.). 1987. pap. 25.00 (ISBN 0-317-42571-4, Pub. by Salzburg Studies). Longwood Pub Group.

Charter of the Islamic Conference: The Legal & Economic Framework. Hasan Moinuddin. LC 86-802. 256p. 1986. 59.00x (ISBN 0-19-825524-1). Oxford U Pr.

Charterhouse Du Mont St. Jean Baptiste Pres de Fribourg en Brisgau, 1345-1782. Dom P. Bastin. Ed. by James Hogg. (Analecta Cartusiana Ser.: No. 76). (Orig.). 1984. pap. 25.00 (ISBN 3-7052-0112-3, Pub. by Salzburg Studies). Longwood Pub Group.

Charterhouse of Padula: Introduction. James Hogg. Ed. by James Hogg. (Analecta Cartusiana: No. 54). (Orig.). 1986. pap. 25.00 (ISBN 3-7052-0074-7, Pub. by Salzburg Studies). Longwood Pub Group.

Charterhouse of Pavia, 2 vols. James Hogg. Ed. by James Hogg. (Analecta Cartusiana Ser.: No. 52). (Orig.). 1986. pap. 50.00 (ISBN 3-7052-0072-0, Pub. by Salzburg Studies). Longwood Pub Group.

Charterhouses de Montrieux et XXX de la verne. James Hogg. Ed. by James Hogg. (Analecta Cartusiana Ser.: No. 75). (Orig.). 1986. pap. 25.00 (ISBN 3-7052-0111-5, Pub. by Salzburg Studies). Longwood Pub Group.

Charterhouses of Aragon: Introduction, Vol. 1. James Hogg. (Analecta Carusiana Ser.: No. 70-1). (Orig.). 1986. pap. 25.00 (ISBN 3-7052-0102-6, Pub. by Salzburg Studies). Longwood Pub Group.

Charterhouses of Basel, Cologne, Konz (Trier) & Roermond. James Hogg. Ed. by James Hogg. (Analecta Cartusiana Ser.: No. 62). (Orig.). 1986. pap. 25.00 (ISBN 3-7052-0090-9, Pub. by Salzburg Studies). Longwood Pub Group.

Charterhouses of Buxheim, Ittingen & la Valsainte. James Hogg. (Analecta Cartusiana Ser.: No. 38). (Illus.). 220p. (Orig.). 1977. pap. 25.00 (ISBN 3-7052-0045-3, Pub by Salzburg Studies). Longwood Pub Group.

Charterhouses of las Cuevas, Jerez de la Frontera, Cazalla & Granada: Introduction. James Hogg. (Analecta Cartusiana Ser.: No. 47-1). (Orig.). 1986. pap. 25.00 (ISBN 3-7052-0063-1, Pub by Salzburg Studies). Longwood Pub Group.

Charterhouses of Naples & Capri. James Hogg. Ed. by James Hogg. (Analecta Cartusiana Ser.: No. 57-2). (Illus.). 175p. 1978. pap. 25.00 (ISBN 3-7052-0083-6, Pub. by Salzburg Studies). Longwood Pub Group.

Charterhouses of Padula, Parma, Ferrara & Bologna. James Hogg. Ed. by James Hogg. (Analecta Cartusiana Ser.: No. 53). (Orig.). 1986. pap. 25.00 (ISBN 3-7052-0073-9, Pub. by Salzburg Studies). Longwood Pub Group.

Charterhouses of Seitz, Gairach, Freudenthal & Pletriach. James Hogg. Ed. by James Hogg. (Analecta Cartusiana Ser.: No. 56). (Orig.). 1985. pap. 25.00 (ISBN 3-7052-0081-X, Pub. by Salzburg Studies). Longwood pub Group.

Charterhouses of the Carthusian Provinces of Catalonia. James Hogg. (Analecta Cartusiana Ser.: No. 41-1). (Orig.). 1986. pap. 25.00 (ISBN 3-7052-0049-6, Pub by Salzburg Studies). Longwood Pub Group.

Charterhouses of Tuscany, 3 vols. James Hogg. Ed. by James Hogg. (Analecta Cartusiana Ser.: No. 60). (Orig.). 1986. pap. 25.00 (ISBN 3-7052-0088-7, Pub. by Salzburg Studies). Longwood Pub Group.

Charterhouses of Vedana & Schnals, With a Supplement on the Montelli & Venice. James Hogg. Ed. by James Hogg. (Analecta Cartusiana Ser.: No. 50). (Orig.). 1985. pap. 25.00 (ISBN 3-7052-0070-4, Pub. by Salzburg Studies). Longwood Pub Group.

Charterhouses of Villeneuve Les Avignon, Mougeres, Toulouse & Ste-Croix-en-Jarez. James Hogg. Ed. by James Hogg. (Analecta Cartusiana Ser.: No. 63). (Orig.). 1986. pap. 25.00 (ISBN 3-7052-0091-7, Pub. by Salzburg Studies). Longwood Pub Group.

Charters & Custumals of the Abbey of Holy Trinity, Caen. Ed. by Marjorie Chibnall. (Records of Social & Economic History Ser.). (Illus.). 1982. 37.50x (ISBN 0-19-726009-8). Oxford U Pr.

Charters & Documents Illustrating the History of the Cathedral: City & Diocese of Salisbury in the 12th & 13th Centuries. Ed. by W. D. Macray. (Rolls Ser.: No. 97). Repr. of 1891 ed. 44.00 (ISBN 0-8115-1176-6). Kraus Repr.

Charting Your Course by the Dream in Your Heart. Robert Tilton. 178p. (Orig.). 1983. pap. text ed. 5.95 (ISBN 0-914307-11-8, Dist. by Harrison Hse). Word Faith.

Charting Your Course by the Dream in Your Heart. Robert Tilton. 150p. (Orig.). 1986. pap. 5.95 (ISBN 0-89274-404-9). Harrison Hse.

Chartism & Christianity. Joseph R. Stephens et al. Ed. by Dorothy Thompson. (Chartism, Working-Class Politics in the Industrial Revolution Ser.). 132p. 1987. lib. bdg. 25.00 (ISBN 0-8240-5593-4). Garland Pub.

Chartism & the Churches. Harold U. Faulkner. LC 79-76712. (Columbia University. Studies in the Social Sciences: No. 173). Repr. of 1916 ed. 12.50 (ISBN 0-404-51173-2). AMS Pr.

Chartism & the Churches: A Study in Democracy. Harold U. Faulkner. 152p. 1970. Repr. of 1916 ed. 32.50x (ISBN 0-7146-1308-8, F Cass Co). Biblio Dist.

Chartres Cathedral. Ed. by Robert Branner. (Norton Critical Studies in Art History). (Illus.). 1969. pap. 8.95x (ISBN 0-393-09851-6, NortonC). Norton.

Chartreuse de Selignac. Augustin Devaux. Ed. by James Hogg. (Analecta Cartusiana Ser.: No. 24). (Fr.). 313p. (Orig.). 1975. pap. 25.00 (ISBN 3-7052-0024-0, Pub by Salzburg Studies). Longwood Pub Group.

Chartreuse Saint-Sauveur de Villefranche-de-Rouergue 1459-1791. Abbe L. Gilhodes. Ed. by James Hogg. (Analecta Cartusiana Ser.: No. 14). (Fr.). 236p. (Orig.). 1973. pap. 25.00 (ISBN 3-7052-0016-X, Pub by Salzburg Studies). Longwood Pub Group.

Chartruese de Lugne des Origines au Debut 14e Siecle 1172-1332. Jaquelin Legendre. Ed. by James Hogg. (Analecta Cartusiana Ser.: No. 27). (Fr., Illus.). 204p. (Orig.). 1975. pap. 25.00 (ISBN 3-7052-0028-3, Pub by Salzburg Studies). Longwood Pub Group.

Charts on Prophecy. Salem Kirban. 1982. pap. 14.92 (ISBN 0-912582-39-1). Kirban.

Chases' Calendar of Annual Events: Special Days, Weeks & Months in 1980. rev. ed. William D. Chase. LC 57-14540. (Illus., Orig.). 1979. lib. bdg. 14.95 (ISBN 0-913082-27-9); pap. 9.95 (ISBN 0-913082-26-0). Apple Tree.

Chasidic Dance. Fred Berk. (YA) 1975. pap. 5.00 (ISBN 0-8074-0083-1, 582050). UAHC.

Chassidic Insights: A Guide for the Entangled. Mattis Kantor. pap. 6.95x (ISBN 0-87068-679-8). Ktav.

Chastening of the Lord. Don Clowers. 40p. (Orig.). 1986. wkbk 4.95 (ISBN 0-914307-56-8). Word Faith.

Chastity As Autonomy: Women in the Stories of Apocryphal Acts. Virginia Burrus. (Studies in Women & Religion). 184p. 1987. text ed. 39.95 (ISBN 0-88946-526-6). E Mellen.

Chastity: Our Secret Sins. Dio Lewis. LC 73-20634. (Sex, Marriage & Society). 324p. 1974. Repr. of 1874 ed. 24.50x (ISBN 0-405-05809-8). Ayer Co Pubs.

Chastity: Who Lives It. David M. Knight. LC 85-19516. 32p. (Orig.). 1985. pap. 3.95 (ISBN 0-915488-10-8, BV4647.C5K57). Clarity Pub.

Chateaubriand et la Bible, Contribution a L'etude Des Sources Des "Martyrs". Jane Smead. 1973. Repr. of 1924 ed. 15.00 (ISBN 0-384-56347-3). Johnson Repr.

Chaterhouse of Padula: Album. James Hogg. Ed. by James Hogg. (Analecta Cartusiana Ser.: No. 54). (Illus.). 210p. (Orig.). 1978. pap. 25.00 (ISBN 3-7052-0075-5, Pub. by Salzburg Studies). Longwood Pub Group.

Chaterhouse of Rome. James Hogg. Ed. by James Hogg. (Analecta Cartusiana Ser.: No. 78). (Illus.). 55p. (Orig.). 1984. pap. 25.00 (ISBN 3-7052-0114-X, Pub. by Salzburg Studies). Longwood Pub Group.

Chaterhouses of Naples & Capri Album, Vol. 1. James Hogg. Ed. by James Hogg. (Analecta Cartusiana Ser.: No. 57-1). (Orig.). 1985. pap. 25.00 (ISBN 3-7052-0082-8, Pub. by Salzburg Studies). Longwood Pub Group.

Chats with Converts: Complete Explanation of Catholic Belief. 31st ed. M. D. Forrest. LC 78-56979. 1978. pap. 5.00 (ISBN 0-89555-069-5). TAN Bks Pubs.

Chaucer on Interpretation. J. Ferster. LC 84-23188. 194p. 1985. 29.95 (ISBN 0-521-26661-0). Cambridge U Pr.

Chaucer, Spenser, Milton: Mythopoeic Continuities & Transformations. A. Kent Hieatt. (Illus.). 336p. 1975. 25.00x (ISBN 0-7735-0228-9). McGill-Queens U Pr.

Chavurah: A Contemporary Jewish Experience. Bernard Reisman. 1977. pap. 7.50 (ISBN 0-8074-0048-3, 140050). UAHC.

Cheating. Dan Carr. (God I Need to Talk to You About...Ser.). (Illus.). 1984. pap. 0.75 (ISBN 0-570-08725-2, 56-1469). Concordia.

Cheating God. Newton Conant. 102p. 1985. pap. 3.50 (ISBN 0-317-43393-8). Chr Lit.

Check Your Chances of Success in a Mixed Marriage. Bilnitzer. pap. 1.75 (ISBN 0-686-12318-2). Christs Mission.

Check Your Commitment: Instructor. Knofel Staton. 160p. 1985. pap. 3.50 (ISBN 0-87239-828-5, 39982). Standard Pub.

Check Your Commitment: Student. Knofel Staton. 128p. 1985. pap. 2.95 (ISBN 0-87239-829-3, 39983). Standard Pub.

Check Your Discipleship. Knofel Staton. LC 81-9411. 116p. (Orig., Student's & instructor's ed. bnd. together). 1982. pap. 2.25 student ed. (ISBN 0-87239-424-7, 39991); instructor's ed. 2.50 (ISBN 0-87239-423-9, 39990). Standard Pub.

Check Your Homelife. Knofel Staton. LC 82-19600. 176p. (Orig.). 1983. pap. 4.95 (ISBN 0-87239-649-5, 39973). Standard Pub.

Check Your Homelife: Leader's Guide. Jon Underwood. 64p. (Orig.). pap. 2.95 (ISBN 0-87239-759-9, 39963). Standard Pub.

Check Your Life in Christ. Knofel Staton. 160p. pap. 2.95x (ISBN 0-89900-203-X). College Pr Pub.

Check Your Morality. Knofel Staton. LC 83-418. 194p. (Orig.). 1983. pap. 3.95 (ISBN 0-87239-630-4, 39971). Standard Pub.

Check Your Morality: Leader's Guide. Jon Underwood. 48p. (Orig.). 1984. pap. 2.95 (ISBN 0-87239-760-2, 39961). Standard Pub.

Check Your Panoply. Herman H. Rocke. 240p. 1977. pap. text ed. 4.00 (ISBN 0-910424-71-3). Concordant.

Checklist for a Perfect Wedding. rev. & expanded ed. Barbara L. Follett. LC 85-29206. (Illus.). 160p. 1986. pap. 3.95 (ISBN 0-385-23588-7). Doubleday.

Checks from God. Leila Ashton. (My Church Teaches Ser.). 32p. 1981. pap. 1.95 (ISBN 0-8127-0314-6). Review & Herald.

Cheerful Devotions to Give. Amy Bolding. (Amy Bolding Library). 96p. 1984. pap. 4.50 (ISBN 0-8010-0868-9). Baker Bk.

Cheers. David Kaplan & Marcia Phillips. (Inspirational Ser.). (Illus.). 96p. 1981. pap. 4.95 (ISBN 0-939944-04-9). M & L Sales.

Cheese & the Worms: The Cosmos of a Sixteenth-Century Miller. Carlo Genzburg. LC 79-3654. pap. 51.80 (2026706). Bks Demand UMI.

Cheiro Returns. Robert R. Leichtman. (From Heaven to Earth Ser.). (Illus.). 80p. (Orig.). 1979. pap. 3.50 (ISBN 0-89804-053-1). Ariel OH.

Cheiro's Book of Numbers. Cheiro. LC 64-11269. (Illus., Orig.). 1964. pap. 2.95 (ISBN 0-668-01170-X, 1169). Arco.

Chelkeinu. Abraham Atkin. 200p. text ed. 5.50 (ISBN 0-914131-09-5, A16). Torah Umesorah.

Chemical Evolution. S. E. Aw. LC 81-70575. 1982. pap. 9.95 (ISBN 0-89051-082-2). Master Bks.

Chemistry of the Blood. M. R. DeHaan. 160p. 1983. pap. 5.95 (ISBN 0-310-23291-0, 9282P). Zondervan.

Cheque-Book of the Book of Faith. C. H. Spurgeon. 1982. pap. 4.95 (ISBN 0-686-16836-4). Pilgrim Pubns.

Cherishing Life, Vol. 2. Buddhist Text Translation Society Staff. Tr. by Bhikshuni Heng Tao & Bhikshuni Heng Ch'ih. (Illus.). 160p. 1983. pap. 7.00 (ISBN 0-88139-015-1). Buddhist Text.

Cherokee Prayerbook. Howard Meredith & Adeline Smith. (Eng. & Cherokee.). 44p. 1981. pap. 1.50x (ISBN 0-940392-02-X). Indian U Pr OK.

Cherokee Vision of Eloh' Howard Meredith & Virginia E. Milan. Tr. by Wesley Proctor. (Eng. & Cherokee.). 37p. 1981. pap. 8.00x (ISBN 0-940392-04-6); write for info. Indian U Pr OK.

Cherokees & Missionaries, 1789-1839. William G. McLoughlin. LC 83-11759. 375p. 1984. 35.00x (ISBN 0-300-03075-4). Yale U Pr.

Cherubim. 2.25 (ISBN 0-8198-1436-9). Dghtrs St Paul.

Cherubim & Seraphim: The History of an African Independent Church. J. A. Omoyajowo. LC 78-64624. 256p. (Orig.). 1982. 21.50x (ISBN 0-88357-068-8); pap. 8.95 (ISBN 0-88357-069-6). NOK Pubs.

Chessed as an Expression of Emunah: A Schmuess. Nosson Finkel. Ed. by Joseph Kaminetsky. 0.50 (ISBN 0-914131-10-9, I30). Torah Umesorah.

Chester Beatty Biblical Papyri IV & V: A New Editioa with Text-Critical Analysis. Albert Pieterisma. LC 74-84103. 1974. 24.00 (ISBN 0-88866-016-2, 310016). Scholars Pr GA.

Chester Beatty-Papyri Zum Pentateuch. Arthur Allgeier. 12.00 (ISBN 0-384-00860-7). Johnson Repr.

Chester Mystery Cycle: Commentary & Apparatus, Vol. II. Ed. by David Mills & Robert Lumiansky. (Early English Text Society Supplementary Ser.: No. 8). 1985. 34.50x (ISBN 0-19-722408-3). Oxford U Pr.

Chester Mystery Cycle: Essays & Documents. R. M. Lumiansky & David Mills. LC 82-1838. viii, 339p. 1983. 40.00x (ISBN 0-8078-1522-5); essay "Music in the Cycle" by Richard Rastall incl. U of NC Pr.

Chester Mystery Plays. 2nd ed. Adapted by Maurice Hussey. 1975. pap. 3.50x (ISBN 0-87830-572-6). Theatre Arts.

Chester Mystery Plays. Godfrey W. Mathews. LC 77-4728. 1925. lib. bdg. 15.00 (ISBN 0-8414-6159-7). Folcroft.

Chester, N.Y. Presbyterian Church: A History. Helen R. Predmore. LC 73-89297. (Illus.). 377p. 1975. 9.45 (ISBN 0-912526-11-4). Lib Res.

Chesterton & the Edwardian Cultural Crisis. John Coates. 280p. 1984. text ed. 28.50 (ISBN 0-85958-451-8, Pub. by U of Hull UK); pap. text ed. 19.95 (ISBN 0-85958-444-5). Humanities.

Chesterton As Seen by His Contemporaries. Cyril Clemens. 1973. 69.95 (ISBN 0-87968-027-X). Gordon Pr.

Chesterton As Seen by His Contemporaries. Cyril Clemens. LC 76-92958. (English Biography Ser., No. 31). 1969. Repr. of 1938 ed. lib. bdg. 48.95x (ISBN 0-8383-0968-2). Haskell.

Chesterton, Belloc, Baring. Raymond Las Vergnas. LC 73-4884. 1938. lib. bdg. 27.00 (ISBN 0-8414-2268-0). Folcroft.

Chesterton Celebration at the University of Notre Dame. Ed. by Rufus W. Rauch. LC 85-3592. (Illus.). 96p. 1983. 9.95 (ISBN 0-268-00744-6, 83-07444). U of Notre Dame Pr.

Chesterton: Contenary Appraisal. John Sullivan. 243p. 1974. 12.50 (ISBN 0-06-496591-0). Lumen Christi.

Chetifs. Ed. by Geoffrey M. Myers et al. LC 79-2565. (Old French Crusade Cycle Ser.: Vol. V). xxxvi, 352p. 1981. text ed. 35.00 (ISBN 0-8173-0023-6). U of Ala Pr.

Cheyenne Legends of Creation. Henry Tall Bull & Tom Weist. (Indian Culture Ser.). 1972. 1.95 (ISBN 0-89992-025-X). Coun India Ed.

Chhandogya Upanisad. Tr. by Srisa Chandra Vasu. LC 73-3788. (Sacred Books of the Hindus: No. 3). Repr. of 1910 ed. 44.50 (ISBN 0-404-57803-9). AMS Pr.

Chi-Kung: The Art of Mastering the Unseen Life Force. Lily Siou. LC 75-32212. 1975. 17.50 (ISBN 0-8048-1169-5). C E Tuttle.

Chiao Hung & the Restructuring of Neo-Confucianism in the Late Ming. Edward T. Ch'ien. (Neo-Confucian Studuies). 328p. 1986. 29.00 (ISBN 0-231-06022-X). Columbia U Pr.

Chicago Churches & Synagogues. George A. Lane. iv, 236p. 1981. 25.00 (ISBN 0-8294-0373-6). Loyola.

Chicago Historical Geographic Guide. James Piety. (Illus.). 125p. (Orig.). 1983. pap. text ed. 6.80 wkbk. (ISBN 0-87563-290-4). Stipes.

Chicago Stained Glass. Erne Frueh & Florence Frueh. (Illus.). 160p. 1983. 19.95 (ISBN 0-8294-0435-X). Loyola.

Chicago's Catholics: An Evolution of an American Identity. Charles Shanabruch. LC 80-53071. (Studies in American Catholicism: Vol. 4). 288p. 1981. text ed. 22.95 (ISBN 0-268-01840-5). U of Notre Dame Pr.

Chicano Theology. Andres G. Guerrero. LC 86-23561. 192p. (Orig.). 1987. pap. 11.95 (ISBN 0-88344-407-0). Orbis Bks.

Chicanos, Catholicism & Political Ideology. Lawrence J. Mosqueda. 228p. (Orig.). 1986. lib. bdg. 24.50 (ISBN 0-8191-5318-4); pap. text ed. 12.75 (ISBN 0-8191-5319-2). U Pr of Amer.

Chichester Towers. Lewis P. Curtis. LC 66-21514. (Illus.). Repr. of 1966 ed. 32.50 (ISBN 0-8357-1319-9, 2013199). Bks Demand UMI.

Chickens, Cookies, & Cuzzin George. Katherine V. Smith. 144p. (Orig.). 1983. pap. text ed. 7.75 (ISBN 0-687-06485-6). Abingdon.

Chief of the Pilgrims: Or, the Life & Time of William Brewster. facs. ed. Ashbel Steele. LC 72-133535. (Select Bibliographies Reprint Ser). (Illus.). 1857. 23.50 (ISBN 0-8369-5567-6). Ayer Co Pubs.

Chief Promises of God. John Bale. LC 70-133635. (Tudor Facsimile Texts. Old English Plays: No. 21). Repr. of 1908 ed. 49.50 (ISBN 0-404-53321-3). AMS Pr.

Chiefe & Prycypall Articles of the Christian Faythe. Martin Luther. LC 72-6080. (English Experience Ser.: No. 84). 248p. 1969. Repr. of 1548 ed. 21.00 (ISBN 90-221-0084-7). Walter J Johnson.

Child Abuse & the Church: A New Mission. James J. Mead & Glenn M. Balch, Jr. (Illus.). 160p. 1987. pap. 9.95 (ISBN 0-937359-10-6). HDL Pubs.

Child As Quest: Method & Religious Education. J. Robert Henman. LC 83-19877. 70p. (Orig.). 1984. pap. text ed. 6.75 (ISBN 0-8191-3633-6). U Pr of Amer.

Child Dianetics. L. Ron Hubbard. 20.00 (ISBN 0-686-30781-X). Church Scient NY.

Child Dianetics. Intro. by L. Ron Hubbard. 1951. 38.59 (ISBN 0-88404-022-4). Bridge Pubns Inc.

Child of Rage. Glenn Hester & Bruce Nygren. LC 81-9490. 192p. 1981. pap. 5.95 (ISBN 0-8407-5810-3). Nelson.

Child of Satan, Child of God. Susan Atkins & Bob Slosser. LC 77-81947. 1977. (Pub. by Logos); pap. 2.95 (ISBN 0-88270-276-9). Bridge Pub.

Child of the Covenant. Michele Guinness. 160p. 1985. pap. 2.95 (ISBN 0-345-32715-2). Ballantine.

Child of the King. Ethel Mercer. (Illus.). 80p. 1987. 8.95 (ISBN 0-89962-586-X). Todd & Honeywell.

Child of Two Worlds. Hannie Wolf. (Illus.). 156p. 1979. 13.00 (ISBN 0-931068-02-9). Purcells.

Child Rearing In Today's Christian Family. Victor A. Christopherson. (Family Life Ser.). 176p. 1985. pap. 6.95 (ISBN 0-8170-1065-3). Judson.

Child Within. Mari Hanes. 1983. pap. 2.95 (ISBN 0-8423-0219-0). Tyndale.

Child Within Us Lives! William Samuel. 412p. 1986. 24.95 (ISBN 0-938747-01-0); pap. 15.95 (ISBN 0-938747-00-2). Mntn Brook Pubns.

Childbirth God's Way. 1982. 1.25 (ISBN 0-89858-027-7). Fill the Gap.

Childe Jesus: A Christmas Cantata for Mixed Voices. Joseph W. Clokey & Hazel J. Kirk. pap. 20.00 (ISBN 0-317-09646-X, 2017838). Bks Demand UMI.

Childhood Education in the Church. rev., exp. ed. Zuck Brubaber & Joanne Brubaker. 1986. text ed. 24.95 (ISBN 0-8024-1251-3). Moody.

Childhood, Marriage & the Family in the Eastern European Jewish Enlightement. David Biale. 24p. 1983. pap. 1.50 (ISBN 0-87495-049-X). Am Jewish Comm.

Childhood of Christ: As Seen by the Primitive Masters. Emile Cammaerts. 1978. Repr. of 1922 ed. lib. bdg. 20.00 (ISBN 0-8495-0766-9). Arden Lib.

Childhood of Jesus. Retold by Elaine Ife & Rosalind Sutton. (Now You Can Read Stories from the Bible Ser.). (Illus.). 24p. 1985. 2.50 (ISBN 0-8407-5394-2). Nelson.

Childless Is Not Less. Vicky Love. 144p. (Orig.). 1984. pap. 5.95 (ISBN 0-87123-449-1). Bethany Hse.

Children. Laura Lein & Lydia O'Donnell. LC 84-7543. (Choices: Guides for Today's Woman Ser.: Vol. 9). 120p. 1984. pap. 6.95 (ISBN 0-664-24550-1). Westminster.

Children & Conversion. Ed. by Clifford Ingle. LC 79-113212. 160p. 1975. pap. 4.95 (ISBN 0-8054-2514-4). Broadman.

Children & Puritanism: The Place of Children in the Life & Thought of the New England Churches, 1620-1847. Sanford Fleming. LC 70-89178. (American Education: Its Men, Institutions & Ideas Ser). 1969. Repr. of 1933 ed. 15.00 (ISBN 0-405-01416-3). Ayer Co Pubs.

Children & Quakerism. Walter J. Homan. LC 70-169387. (Family in America Ser). 180p. 1972. Repr. of 1939 ed. 14.00 (ISBN 0-405-03864-X). Ayer Co Pubs.

Children & Solitude. Elise Boulding. 1983. pap. 2.50x (ISBN 0-87574-125-8, 125). Pendle Hill.

Children As Learners. (Christian Education Ministries Ser.). 1979. pap. 3.50 (ISBN 0-89367-029-4). Light & Life.

Children As Partners in the Church. D-B Heusser & Phyllis Heusser. LC 85-9934. 64p. 1985. pap. 3.95 (ISBN 0-8170-1054-8). Judson.

Children Belong in Worship: A Guide to the Children's Sermon. W. Alan Smith. Ed. by Herbert Lambert. LC 84-5840. 128p. 1984. pap. 7.95 (ISBN 0-8272-0445-0). CBP.

Children Can Worship, Bk. 1. Shelia Souther. (Orig.). 1986. pap. 10.95 (ISBN 0-87148-185-5). Pathway Pr.

Children Can Worship, Bk. 3. Betty Call & Sheila Souther. (Orig.). 1983. pap. text ed. 10.95 (ISBN 0-87148-178-2). Pathway Pr.

Children, Children! A Ministry Without Boundries. Dorlis B. Glass. LC 86-50509. 72p. (Orig.). 1986. pap. 4.95 (ISBN 0-88177-033-7, DR033B). Discipleship Res.

Children, Go Where I Send Thee: An American Spiritual. Illus. by Kathryn E. Shoemaker. (Illus.). 32p. (Orig.). 1980. pap. 6.95 (ISBN 0-03-056673-8, HarpR). Har-Row.

Children in Amish Society: Socialization & Community Education. John A. Hostetler & Gertrude E. Huntington. LC 72-157454. (Case Studies in Education & Culture). 1971. pap. text ed. 9.95 (ISBN 0-03-077750-X, HoltC). HR&W.

Children in the New England Mind: In Death & in Life. Peter G. Slater. LC 77-7352. 248p. 1977. 27.50 (ISBN 0-208-01652-X, Archon). Shoe String.

Children in the Worshipping Community. David Ng & Virginia Thomas. LC 80-84655. (Illus.). 128p. (Orig.). 1981. pap. 7.95 (ISBN 0-8042-1688-6). John Knox.

Children Is Crying. A. Knighton Stanley. LC 78-26544. 1979. 8.95 (ISBN 0-8298-0347-5). Pilgrim NY.

Children of Abraham: Judaism, Christianity, Islam. F. E. Peters. LC 81-47941. 240p. 1983. 23.50 (ISBN 0-691-07267-1); pap. 8.50x (ISBN 0-691-02030-2). Princeton U Pr.

Children of Cottonwood: Piety & Ceremonialism in Hopi Indian Puppetry. Armin W. Geertz & Michael Lomatuway'ma. (American Tribal Religions Ser.: Vol. 12). (Illus.). viii, 412p. 1987. 24.95x (ISBN 0-8032-2127-4); pap. 14.95x (ISBN 0-8032-7021-6). U of Nebr Pr.

Children of Freedom: Black Liberation in Christian Perspective. Peter C. Hodgson. LC 74-76930. pap. 24.00 (2027866). Bks Demand UMI.

Children of God. Vardis Fisher. 1977. 12.95 (ISBN 0-918522-50-1). O L Holmes.

Children of God-Family of Love: An Annotated Bibliography. W. Douglas Pritchett. Ed. by J. Gordon Melton. LC 83-48223. (Sects & Cults in America: Bibliographical Guides Ser.). 250p. 1984. lib. bdg. 33.00 (ISBN 0-8240-9043-8). Garland Pub.

Children of Intermarriage: A Study in Pattern of Identification & Family Life. Egon Mayer. LC 83-82077. 56p. 1983. pap. 2.50 (ISBN 0-87495-055-4). Am Jewish Comm.

Children of Israel. Tamar Grand & Samuel Grand. (Illus.). 1972. text ed. 5.50 (ISBN 0-8074-0131-5, 121320); tchr's guide 2.25 (ISBN 0-8074-0132-3, 201320); fun & act bk. 4.50 (ISBN 0-8074-0133-1, 121322). UAHC.

Children of Izieu: A Human Tragedy. Serge Klarsfeld. (Illus.). 128p. 1985. pap. 9.95 (ISBN 0-8109-2307-6). Abrams.

Children of Jonestown. Ed. by Kenneth Wooden. (Paperbacks Ser.). 1980. pap. 5.95 (ISBN 0-07-071641-2). McGraw.

Children of Joy: Raising Your Own Home-Grown Christians. E. Dodson Gray & D. Dodson Gray. LC 74-80259. xviii, 258p. (Orig.). 1975. pap. 7.95 (ISBN 0-934512-03-5). Roundtable Pr.

Children of Ministers Tell Us. Vera M. Watson. 1983. 5.95 (ISBN 0-8062-2033-3). Carlton.

Children of Naples. Geoffrey Hanks. 1974. 1.60 (ISBN 0-08-017619-4). Pergamon.

Children of Noah. Ben L. Burman. 5.00 (ISBN 0-685-02658-2). Taplinger.

Children of Odin. Padraic Colum. 1920. 40.00 (ISBN 0-686-18157-3). Havertown Bks.

Children of Promise: The Case for Baptizing Infants. Geoffrey W. Bromiley. LC 79-10346. 1979. pap. 3.95 (ISBN 0-8028-1797-1). Eerdmans.

Children: Of Such Is the Kingdom of God. Ed. by Barbara Howard. LC 79-7102. 1979. pap. 8.00 (ISBN 0-8309-0243-0). Herald Hse.

Children of the Bible: Twenty-Six Exciting Stories about Children of the Bible. Cindy Baw & Paul C. Brownlow. (Illus.). 1984. 10.95 (ISBN 0-915720-19-1). Brownlow Pub Co.

Children of the Living God. Sinclair B. Ferguson. LC 86-63652. 168p. (Orig.). 1987. pap. price not set (ISBN 0-89109-137-8). NavPress.

Children of the New Testament. (Arch Book Anthology Ser.). (Illus.). 160p. 1986. 7.95 (ISBN 0-570-06206-3, 59-7000). Concordia.

Children of the Old Testament. (Arch Book Anthology Ser.). (Illus.). 152p. 1986. 7.95 (ISBN 0-570-06207-1, 59-7001). Concordia.

Children of the Rainbow: The Religions, Legends & Gods of Pre-Christian Hawaii. Leinani Melville. LC 69-17715. (Illus.). 1969. pap. 5.95 (ISBN 0-8356-0002-5, Quest). Theos Pub Hse.

Children Sing. Marguerite Cromie. 1975. pap. 1.25 (ISBN 0-8198-0390-1). Dghtrs St Paul.

Children Together. Louis Spiker. 128p. 1980. pap. 9.50 (ISBN 0-8170-0824-1). Judson.

Children Together, Vol. 2. Elizabeth W. Gale. 128p. 1982. pap. 9.95 (ISBN 0-8170-0974-4). Judson.

Children Together, Vol. 3. Ed. by Gracie R. McCay & Virginia A. Sargent. 128p. 1985. pap. 9.95 (ISBN 0-8170-1078-5). Judson.

Children We Remember. Chana B. Abells. LC 85-24876. (Illus.). 48p. 1986. 9.95 (ISBN 0-688-06371-3); PLB 10.88 (ISBN 0-688-06372-1). Greenwillow.

Children Won't Wait: A Parent's Prayer. Helen Young. 1985. gift ed. 6.95 (ISBN 0-915720-83-3). Brownlow Pub Co.

Children You Gave Us. Jacqueline Bernard. LC 72-87122. (Illus.). 1972. 8.95x (ISBN 0-8197-0356-7). Bloch.

Children's Bible. Retold by James Bentley. (Illus.). 237p. 1983. 7.95 (ISBN 0-531-03592-1). Watts.

Children's Bible Stories. Edward G. Finnegan. LC 75-18758. (Treasure House Bks). (Illus.). 256p. 1978. 7.95 (ISBN 0-8326-1803-9, 3602); deluxe ed. 8.95 (ISBN 0-686-66397-7). World Bible.

Children's Bible Stories from the Old Testament. Ruth Hannon. (Illus.). 1978. 4.95 (ISBN 0-307-13740-6, 13740, Golden Bks). Western Pub.

Children's Bible Stories Puzzle Book. Ruby Maschke. 48p. 1986. pap. 2.50 (ISBN 0-87403-046-3, 2690). Standard Pub.

Children's Bread: Divine Healing. Keith M. Bailey. LC 77-83941. 1977. kivar cover 5.95 (ISBN 0-87509-233-0). Chr Pubns.

Children's Bulletin Sundays of Easter. Barbara Reilly. 1979. pap. 7.55 (ISBN 0-88479-008-8). Arena Lettres.

Children's Christmas Woodbook. 1986. bds. 8.95 (ISBN 0-8120-5753-8). Barron.

Children's Church: A Comprehensive How-to. Doris Freese. LC 81-22426. 128p. 1982. pap. 6.95 (ISBN 0-8024-1250-5). Moody.

Children's Education in Community: The Basis of Bruderhof Education. Eberhard Arnold. Ed. by Merrill Mow. LC 76-27728. 1976. pap. 3.25 (ISBN 0-87486-164-0). Plough.

Children's Favorites: Inspirational Songs Arranged for the Piano. Carolyn S. Stevens. 40p. 1986. pap. 7.95 (ISBN 0-88290-275-X). Horizon Utah.

Children's Festivals from Many Lands. Nina Millen. 1964. pap. 4.95 (ISBN 0-377-44501-0). Friend Pr.

Children's Games from Many Lands. Nina Millen. 1965. pap. 5.95 (ISBN 0-377-45011-1). Friend Pr.

Children's God. David Heller. LC 85-24581. (Illus.). 176p. 1986. 15.95 (ISBN 0-226-32635-7). U of Chicago Pr.

Children's Guide to Islam. Allama M. Asifi. 112p. 1983. pap. 5.00 (ISBN 0-941724-11-5). Islamic Seminary.

Children's Guitar Hymnal. Steve Griffin. 32p. 1978. wkbk 1.95 (ISBN 0-89228-052-2). Impact Bks MO.

Children's Haggadah. Ed. by A. M. Silbermann. Tr. by Isidore Wartski & Arthur S. Super. (Illus.). 100p. 1972. 14.95 (ISBN 0-87306-984-6). Feldheim.

Children's Hymnary. Ed. by Arlene Hartzler & John Gaeddert. LC 67-24327. 1967. 5.95 (ISBN 0-87303-095-8). Faith & Life.

Children's Jewish Holiday Kitchen. Joan Nathan. LC 86-22016. (Illus.). 144p. 1987. plastic comb. 10.95 (ISBN 0-8052-0827-5). Schocken.

Children's Jubliee: A Bibliographical Survey of Hymnals for Infants, Youth & Sunday Schools Published in Britain & American, 1655-1900. Compiled by Samuel J. Rogal. LC 83-1661. (Illus.). xliv, 91p. 1983. lib. bdg. 35.00 (ISBN 0-313-23880-4, RCJ/). Greenwood.

Children's Literature for All God's Children. Virginia Thomas & Betty Miller. LC 85-17169. 120p. 1986. pap. 11.95 (ISBN 0-8042-1690-8). John Knox.

Children's Liturgies: Seventy-Four Eucharistic Liturgies, Prayer Services & Penance Services Designed for Primary, Middle & Junior High Children. Bernadette Kenny. LC 77-74582. 176p. 1977. pap. 9.95 (ISBN 0-8091-2030-5). Paulist Pr.

Children's Music Ministry. Connie Fortunato. 222p. 1981. pap. 6.95 (ISBN 0-89191-341-6). Cook.

Children's Object Lesson Sermons Based on the Common Lectionary Year. Jim Morentz & Doris Morentz. 112p. (Orig.). 1984. pap. 6.95 (ISBN 0-687-06499-6). Abingdon.

Children's Object Lesson Sermons Based on the New Common Lectionary: Year C. Jim Morentz & Doris Morentz. 112p. (Orig.). 1985. pap. 6.95 (ISBN 0-687-06498-8). Abingdon.

Children's Pictures of God. Ed. by V. Peter Pitts. LC 79-56298. (Illus.). 1979. pap. 3.95 (ISBN 0-915744-20-1). Character Res.

Children's Sermons for Special Occasions. Roy E. De Brand. LC 82-72228. (Orig.). 1983. pap. 3.95 (ISBN 0-8054-4927-2). Broadman.

Children's Time in Worship. Arline J. Ban. 128p. 1981. pap. 6.95 (ISBN 0-8170-0902-7). Judson.

Child's Bible. Shirley Steen & Anne Edwards. 1986. 9.95 (ISBN 0-8091-2867-5). Paulist Pr.

Child's Bible History. F. J. Knecht. Tr. by Philip Schumacher. (Illus.). 1973. pap. 2.00 (ISBN 0-89555-005-9). TAN Bks Pubs.

Child's Bible: New Testament: Rewritten for Children by Shirley Steen. LC 78-51445. 288p. 1978. pap. 4.95 (ISBN 0-8091-2118-2). Paulist Pr.

Child's Bible: Old Testament: Rewritten for Children by Anne Edwards. LC 78-51444. 384p. 1978. pap. 4.95 (ISBN 0-8091-2117-4). Paulist Pr.

Child's Book of Character Building, Bk. Two. Ron Coriell & Rebekah Coriell. 128p. 1981. 10.95 (ISBN 0-8007-1265-X). Revell.

Child's Book of Prayers. Michael Hague. LC 85-8380. (Illus.). 32p. 1985. 11.95 (ISBN 0-03-001412-3). H Holt & Co.

Child's Christmas in Wales. Dylan Thomas. LC 59-13174. (Illus.). 1969. gift ed. 12.00 (ISBN 0-8112-0391-3). New Directions.

Child's Christmas in Wales. Dylan Thomas. LC 59-13174. (Illus.). 1959. pap. 3.95 (ISBN 0-8112-0203-8, NDP181). New Directions.

Child's Dictionary of Jewish Symbols. Alex J. Goldman. (Illus.). 5.00 (ISBN 0-685-09470-7). Feldheim.

Child's First Book of Bible Stories. Wanda Hayes. LC 83-664. (Illus.). 128p. 1983. text ed. 7.95 (ISBN 0-87239-659-2, 2949). Standard Pub.

Child's Garden of Bible Stories. Arthur W. Gross. (Concordia Primary Religion Ser.). 1981. 9.95 (ISBN 0-570-03414-0, 56-1001); pap. 5.95 (ISBN 0-570-03402-7, 56-1012). Concordia.

Child's Garden of Christian Verses. Kathryn Lindskoog. LC 83-9534. 160p. 1983. 6.95 (ISBN 0-8307-0890-1, 5110603). Regal.

Child's Garden of Prayer. Ed. by Herman W. Gockel & Edward J. Saleska. (Illus.). 1981. pap. 1.50 (ISBN 0-570-03412-4, 56-1016). Concordia.

Child's Garden of Song. Theodore G. Stelzer. (Concordia Primary Religion Ser). 1949. 9.95 (ISBN 0-570-03479-5, 56-1003). Concordia.

Child's Garden of Yoga. Baba Hari Dass. Ed. by Karuna Ault. LC 80-80299. (Illus.). 108p. 1980. pap. 6.95 (ISBN 0-918100-02-X). Sri Rama.

Child's Gifts: A Twelfth Night Tale. Tomas Blanco. LC 75-46530. (Eng. & Span., Illus.). 32p. 1976. 8.95 (ISBN 0-664-32595-5). Westminster.

Child's Heart & a Child's Dreams: Growing up with Spiritual Wisdom, a Guide for Parents & Children. Sri Chinmoy. 123p. 1986. pap. text ed. write for info. (ISBN 0-88497-862-1). Aum Pubns.

Child's Introduction to the Early Prophets. Shirley Newman. LC 75-14052. (Illus.). 128p. 1975. 6.95x (ISBN 0-87441-244-7). Behrman.

Child's Introduction to Torah. Shirley Newman & Louis Newman. LC 72-2056. (Illus.). 128p. 1972. text ed. 6.95x (ISBN 0-87441-067-3). 2.25x ea., wkbk in 2 pts. Behrman.

Child's Life of Christ. Esther A. Peterson. (Illus.). 44p. 1987. 6.95 (ISBN 1-55523-045-8). Winston-Derek.

Child's Look at the Twenty-Third Psalm. W. Phillip Keller. LC 80-976. (Illus.). 96p. 1981. 8.95 (ISBN 0-385-15456-9, Galilee). Doubleday.

Child's Look at the Twenty-Third Psalm. W. Phillip Keller. LC 84-13718. (Illus.). 96p. 1985. pap. 5.95 (ISBN 0-385-15457-7, Galilee). Doubleday.

Child's Passover Haggadah. Ed. by Saul Meyzlisch. (Illus.). 76p. 1987. 9.95 (ISBN 0-915361-70-1, Dist. by Watts). Adama Pubs Inc.

Child's Picture English-Hebrew Dictionary. Ed. by Dennis Sheheen. (Children's Picture Dictionaries Ser.). (Illus.). 1987. 9.95 (ISBN 0-915361-75-2, Dist. by Watts). Adama Pubs Inc.

Child's Play. David Gamm. LC 78-51069. (Illus.). 96p. 1978. pap. 4.95 (ISBN 0-87793-150-X). Ave Maria.

Child's Shining Pathway. Louise Eavey. (Illus.). 1976. pap. 1.35 (ISBN 0-915374-08-0, 08-0). Rapids Christian.

Child's Story Bible. Catherine F. Vos. (Illus.). 432p. 1983. Repr. of 1934 ed. PLB 14.95 (ISBN 0-8028-5011-1). Eerdmans.

Child's Story of Jesus. Barbara Kanaar. (Happy Day Bks.). (Illus.). 24p. 1986. 1.59 (ISBN 0-87403-023-4, 3483). Standard Pub.

Child's Story of Saints, Past & Present. Zerlina De Santis. 1979. 1.75 (ISBN 0-8198-0567-X); pap. 1.00 (ISBN 0-8198-0568-8). Dghtrs St Paul.

Child's View of Christmas. Richard Exley & Helen Exley. (Illus.). 64p. 1981. 7.50 (ISBN 0-8298-0463-3). Pilgrim NY.

Chimaera of His Age. 146p. pap. 8.95 (ISBN 0-87907-863-4). Cistercian Pubns.

China. Jesuit Missionaries. (Illus.). 216p. 150.00 (ISBN 0-8478-5402-7). Rizzoli Intl.

China, American Catholicism, & the Missionary. Thomas A. Breslin. LC 79-27857. (Illus.). 1980. text ed. 19.75x (ISBN 0-271-00259-X). Pa St U Pr.

China & Christianity: The Missionary Movement & the Growth of Chinese Antiforeignism, 1860-1870. Paul A. Cohen. LC 63-19135. (East Asian Ser: No. 11). (Illus.). 1963. 27.50x (ISBN 0-674-11701-8). Harvard U Pr.

China & the Chinese: Their Religion, Culture, Customs, & Manufactures; The Evils Arising from the Opium Trade, 2 vols. Henry C. Sirr. 915p. Repr. of 1849 ed. Set. text ed. 38.00x (ISBN 0-89644-564-X, Pub. by Chinese Matl Ctr). Coronet Bks.

China & the Christian Impact: A Conflict of Cultures. Jacques Gernet. Tr. by Janet LLoyd. 280p. 1985. 49.50 (ISBN 0-521-26681-5); pap. 17.95 (ISBN 0-521-31319-8). Cambridge U Pr.

China Call. Leonard Bolton. LC 83-82301. 256p. 1984. pap. text ed. 4.95 (ISBN 0-88243-509-4, 02-0509). Gospel Pub.

China, Chinese Philosophers & Confucianism. Wells S. Williams. (Illus.). 137p. 1982. Repr. of 1883 ed. 73.45 (ISBN 0-89901-059-8). Found Class Reprints.

China: Christian Martyrs of the Twentieth Century. James Hefley & Marti Hefley. LC 78-6187. 1978. pap. 2.25 (ISBN 0-915134-16-0). Mott Media.

China Cry. Nora Lam & Irene B. Harrell. LC 79-63932. 120p. (Orig.). 1984. pap. 5.95 (ISBN 0-89221-110-5). New Leaf.

China: Its State & Prospects with Special Reference to the Spread of the Gospel. W. H. Medhurst. LC 72-79833. (China Library Ser.). 1972. Repr. of 1842 ed. 42.00 (ISBN 0-8420-1379-2). Scholarly Res Inc.

China of Confucius: A Critical Interpretation. Harold H. Sunoo. LC 85-7639. (Illus.). 208p. 1985. lib. bdg. 28.95 (ISBN 0-912617-00-4); pap. 12.95 (ISBN 0-912617-01-2). Heritage Res Hse.

China: The Church's Long March. David H. Adeney. LC 85-25666. (Worldview Ser.). 238p. 1985. pap. 7.95 (ISBN 0-8307-1096-5, 5418621). Regal.

China's Dirtiest Trickster: Folklore About Hsu Wen-ch'ang (1521-1593) Tr. by Howard S. Levy from Chinese. (Sino-Japanese Folklore Translations Ser.: No. 1). (Illus.). 68p. 1974. 15.00 (ISBN 0-686-05428-8). Oriental BK Store.

China's Religious Heritage. Yung-Ch'Ing Yang. LC 72-4542. (Essay Index Reprint Ser.). Repr. of 1943 ed. 16.00 (ISBN 0-8369-2981-0). Ayer Co Pubs.

Chinese Buddhism: A Volume of Sketches, Historical, Descriptive & Critical. 2nd, rev. ed. Joseph Edkins. 487p. Repr. of 1893 ed. text ed. 27.50x (Pub. by Chinese Matl Ctr). Coronet Bks.

Chinese Buddhism: Aspects of Interaction & Reinterpretation. W. Pachow. LC 80-5432. 275p. 1980. lib. bdg. 27.00 (ISBN 0-8191-1090-6). U Pr of Amer.

Chinese Buddhism at Sixes & Sevens: A Study of the First Systematization of Buddhist Thought in China. Ed. by Leon Hurvitz & Lida Shotaro. 1987. 30.00 (ISBN 0-89581-906-6). Asian Human Pr.

Chinese Buddhist Monasteries: Their Plan & Its Function As a Setting for Buddhist Monastic Life. J. Prip-Moller. (Illus.). 400p. 1983. Repr. of 1937 ed. 100.00 (ISBN 0-295-96085-X). U of Wash Pr.

Chinese Buddhist Verse. Ed. by J. L. Cranmer-Byng. Tr. by Richard H. Robinson from Chinese. LC 79-8725. 1980. Repr. of 1954 ed. lib. bdg. 18.75x (ISBN 0-313-22168-5, ROCB). Greenwood.

Chinese Christians: Elites, Middlemen, & the Church in Hong Kong. Carl T. Smith. (Illus.). 264p. 1986. 27.00x (ISBN 0-19-583973-0). Oxford U Pr.

Chinese Christians Speak Out. K. H. Ting et al. (Chinese Spotlight Ser.). (Illus.). 140p. 1984. pap. 3.95 (ISBN 0-8351-1281-0). China Bks.

Chinese Classical Work Commonly Called the Four Books, 1828. Ssu Shu. Ed. by David Collie. LC 75-122487. 1970. Repr. of 1828 ed. 50.00x (ISBN 0-8201-1079-5). Schol Facsimiles.

Chinese Divination. James Kao. pap. 26.80 (ISBN 0-317-26229-7, 2055584). Bks Demand UMI.

Chinese Folklore: Belief & Marriage. Nagao Ryuzo. (Asian Folklore & Social Life Monograph: No. 14). (Japanese.). 1938. 14.00 (ISBN 0-89986-035-4). Oriental Bk Store.

Chinese Ideas of Life & Death. Michael Loewe. 240p. 1982. China Stands Up - see attached. text ed. 25.00x (ISBN 0-04-180001-X). Allen Unwin.

Chinese Mind. Wang Kung-Hsing. LC 68-23336. 1968. Repr. of 1946 ed. lib. bdg. 22.50x (ISBN 0-8371-0260-X, WACM). Greenwood.

Chinese Monks & Nuns in a Sea of Sins: Short Stories. Tr. by Howard S. Levy & F. S. Yang. 1971. 15.00 (ISBN 0-686-01016-7). Oriental Bk Store.

Chinese Mythology. Anthony Christie. LC 85-5975. (Library of the World's Myths & Legends). (Illus.). 144p. 1985. 18.95 (ISBN 0-87226-015-1). P Bedrick Bks.

Chinese Mythology. John C. Ferguson. Bd. with Japanese Mythology. Masaharu Anesaki. LC 63-19093. (Mythology of All Races Ser.: Vol. 8). (Illus.). Repr. of 1932 ed. 30.00x (ISBN 0-8154-0068-3). Cooper Sq.

Chinese Reader's Manual: A Handbook of Biographical, Historical, Mythological, & General Literary Reference. W. E. Mayers. 70.00 (ISBN 0-87968-855-6). Gordon Pr.

Chinese Religion in Western Languages: A Comprehensive & Classified Bibliography of Publications in English, French, & German Through 1980. Laurence G. Thompson. LC 84-24010. (Monograph of the Association for Asian Studies: No. XLI). 302p. 1985. HC Monograph 19.95x (ISBN 0-8165-0926-3). U of Ariz Pr.

Chinese Religions: A Cultural Perspective. Christian Jochim. (Illus.). 224p. 1986. pap. text ed. 17.00 (ISBN 0-13-132994-4). P-H.

Chinese Spirit-Medium Cults in Singapore. Alan J. Elliott. 1981. Repr. of 1955 ed. 15.00 (ISBN 0-89986-347-7). Oriental Bk Store.

Chinese Theology in Construction. Wing-hung Lam. LC 81-15483. 320p. 1983. pap. 11.95x (ISBN 0-87808-180-1). William Carey Lib.

Chinese Tomb Pottery Figures: Catalogue of Exhibition Arranged by the Institute of Oriental Studies. Institute of Oriental Studies. 1953. pap. 22.50x (ISBN 0-317-44053-5, Pub. by Han-Shan Tang Ltd). State Mutual Bk.

Chips from a German Workshop: Volume I: Essays on the Science of Religion. Max Muller. (Reprints & Translations). 1985. pap. 13.95 (ISBN 0-89130-890-3, 00-07-10). Scholars Pr GA.

Chochmas Hamussar. A. H. Leibowitz. (Annual Fryer Memorial Lectures Ser.). 1.00 (ISBN 0-914131-11-7, 137). Torah Umesorah.

Chochmo U'Mussar, 3 vols. Salomon Breuer. 1972. Set. 24.00 (ISBN 0-87306-205-1). Feldheim.

Choice & Action: An Introduction to Ethics. Charles Reid. 1981. pap. text ed. write for info. (ISBN 0-02-399180-1). Macmillan.

Choice: Confirmation Journal. Joseph Moore. 96p. 1986. pap. text ed. 3.50 (ISBN 0-8091-9569-0). Paulist Pr.

Choice Is Always Ours. rev. ed. Ed. by Dorothy B. Phillips et al. 480p. (Orig.). 1975. pap. 3.95 (ISBN 0-8356-0302-4, Quest). Theos Pub Hse.

Choice Messages from Free Will Baptist Pulpits. Ed. by Van D. Hudson. 1976. pap. 2.50 (ISBN 0-89265-030-3). Randall Hse.

Choice Notes on Joshua to Second Kings. F. B. Meyer. LC 84-27869. (F. B. Meyer Memorial Library). 224p. 1985. pap. text ed. 8.95 (ISBN 0-8254-3241-3). Kregel.

Choice Notes on the Psalms. F. B. Meyer. LC 84-17109. (F. B. Meyer Memorial Library). 192p. 1984. pap. text ed. 7.95 (ISBN 0-8254-3242-1). Kregel.

Choicemaker. Elizabeth B. Howes & Sheila Moon. LC 76-54534. 1977. pap. 3.95 (ISBN 0-8356-0492-6, Quest). Theos Pub Hse.

Choices, Changes. Joni Eareckson-Tada. 1986. write for info. Zondervan.

Choices: Ethics & the Christian. David Brown. (Faith & the Future Ser.). 176p. 1984. pap. 24.95x (ISBN 0-631-13182-5); pap. 6.95 (ISBN 0-631-13222-8). Basil Blackwell.

Choices: Finding God's Way in Dating, Sex, Singleness & Marriage. Stacy Rinehart & Paula Rinehart. LC 82-62071. 170p. 1983. pap. 3.95 (ISBN 0-89109-494-6). NavPress.

Choices in Modern Jewish Thought. Eugene B. Borowitz. 352p. 1983. pap. text ed. 9.95x (ISBN 0-87441-343-5). Behrman.

Choices: In Pursuit of Wholeness. Cecil Paul & Jan Lanham. 88p. 1982. pap. 3.95 (ISBN 0-8341-0807-0). Beacon Hill.

Choices: Picking Your Way Through the Ethical Jungle. Sandy Larsen & Dale Larsen. (Young Fisherman Bible Studyguide). (Illus.). 61p. (Orig.). (YA) 1983. saddle-stitched student ed. 2.95 (ISBN 0-87788-113-8); tchr's. ed. 4.95 (ISBN 0-87788-114-6). Shaw Pubs.

Choices...Changes. Joni E. Tada. 240p. 1986. 14.95 (ISBN 0-310-24010-7, 12018). Zondervan.

Choirs & Choral Music. A. Mees. LC 68-25296. (Studies in Music, No. 42). 1969. Repr. of 1901 ed. lib. bdg. 49.95x (ISBN 0-8383-0308-0). Haskell.

Choirs & Choral Music. Arthur Mees. Repr. of 1901 ed. lib. bdg. 22.50 (ISBN 0-8371-1967-7, MECM). Greenwood.

Choirs of Angels in Stained Glass. (Illus.). 1985. pap. 5.95 (ISBN 0-8027-7136-X). Walker & Co.

Choix de Mazarinades, 2 Vols. Ed. by Celestin Moreau. 1853. Set. 102.00 (ISBN 0-384-40103-1); Set. pap. 90.00 (ISBN 0-685-13377-X). Johnson Repr.

Chol Texts on the Supernatural. Arabelle Whittaker & Viola Warkentin. (Publications in Linguistics & Related Fields Ser.: No. 13). 171p. 1965. microfiche (2) 4.00. Summer Inst Ling.

Choose Freedom. Michael Green. 1987. pap. 5.95 (ISBN 0-310-46361-0). Zondervan.

Choose Life. Marilyn Kunz & Catherine Schell. (Neighborhood Bible Studies). 1973. pap. 2.50 (ISBN 0-8423-0460-6). Tyndale.

Choose Life. Bernard Mandelbaum. 1972. pap. 5.95 (ISBN 0-8197-0006-1). Bloch.

Choose Life & Not Death: A Primer on Abortion, Euthanasia, & Suicide. William Maestri. LC 85-28687. 9.95 (ISBN 0-8189-0490-9). Alba.

Choose Once Again. Ed. by Julius J. Finegold & William N. Thetford. LC 76-20363. (Illus.). 112p. 1981. 6.95 (ISBN 0-89087-413-1). Celestial Arts.

Choosing a Path. Swami Rama. 200p. (Orig.). pap. 8.95 (ISBN 0-89389-077-4). Himalayan Pubs.

Choosing a Sex Ethic: A Jewish Inquiry. Eugene B. Borowitz. LC 73-79123. 1970. pap. 5.95 (ISBN 0-8052-0276-5). Schocken.

Choosing God's Way to See & Share. Beers. 1983. 12.95 (ISBN 0-88207-819-4). Victor Bks.

Choosing Is... Janet Gonter. (I'm Growing Up Ser.). (Illus.). 1986. casebound 3.95 (ISBN 0-87403-123-0, 3603). Standard Pub.

Choosing Judaism. Lydia Kukoff. (Orig.). 1981. 10.00 (ISBN 0-8074-0151-X); pap. 5.95 (ISBN 0-8074-0150-1). UAHC.

Choosing Judaism. Lydia Kukoff. 152p. (Orig.). 1983. pap. 5.95 (ISBN 0-686-88518-X, Pub. by UAHC Israel). Hippocrene Bks.

Choosing Life. Dorothee Soelle. Tr. by Margaret Kohl from Ger. LC 81-43082. Tr. of Wahlt das Leben. 128p. 1981. 9.95 (ISBN 0-8006-0667-1, 1-667). Fortress.

Choosing to Be Close: Fill Your Life with the Rewards of Relationships. Gordon McMinn & Larry Libby. LC 84-3297. 1984. pap. 5.95 (ISBN 0-88070-053-X). Multnomah.

Choosing: Which Way Do I Go? Sandy Larsen. (Bible Discovery Guide for Campers Ser.). 32p. 1985. pap. 1.50 camper (ISBN 0-87788-115-4); pap. 3.50 counselor (ISBN 0-87788-116-2). Shaw Pubs.

Choosing Your Career: The Christian's Decision Manual. Martin E. Clark. 1981. pap. 3.95 (ISBN 0-87552-205-X). Presby & Reformed.

Choosing Your Career: The Christian's Decision Manual. Martin E. Clark. 120p. (Orig.). 1983. pap. 4.95 (ISBN 0-8010-2483-8). Baker Bk.

Chop Wood, Carry Water: A Guide to Finding Spiritual Fulfillment in Everyday Life. Rick Fields et al. LC 84-23942. 304p. 1984. pap. 11.95 (ISBN 0-87477-209-5). J P Tarcher.

Choral Conducting: A Symposium. Ed. by Harold A. Decker & Julius Herford. LC 72-94347. (Illus.). 320p. 1973. 34.00 (ISBN 0-13-133355-0). P-H.

Choral Directing. Wilhelm Ehmann. Tr. by George D. Wiebe. 1968. 15.95 (ISBN 0-8066-0832-3, 11-9130). Augsburg.

Choral Experience: Literature, Materials, & Methods. Ray Robinson & Allen Winold. 1976. text ed. 25.50 scp (ISBN 0-06-161419-X, HarpC). Har-Row.

Choral Hymn Book for England. Catherine Winkworth. 59.95 (ISBN 0-87968-859-9). Gordon Pr.

Choral Music of the Church. Elwyn A. Wienandt. LC 80-12943. (Music Reprint Ser.). xi, 494p. 1980. Repr. of 1965 ed. lib. bdg. 45.00 (ISBN 0-306-76002-9). Da Capo.

Choral Settings for Six LDS Hymns. Lawrence A. Lyon. 56p. (Orig.). 1975. pap. 4.95 (ISBN 0-87747-605-5). Deseret Bk.

Chorale Harmonization in the Church Modes. Tr. by Hugo Nordon. 1974. pap. 3.75 (ISBN 0-8008-1516-5, Crescendo). Taplinger.

Chosen. rev ed. Lee Amber. LC 81-51985. 176p. 1981. pap. 3.95 (ISBN 0-88449-079-3, A424025). Vision Hse.

Chosen by God. R. C. Sproul. 1986. 10.95 (ISBN 0-8423-0282-4). Tyndale.

Chosen Children. Ed. by Muriel Dennis. 150p. 1978. 6.95 (ISBN 0-89107-154-7). Good News.

Chosen Families. Kay M. Strom. 240p. 1985. 10.95 (ISBN 0-310-33590-6, 11715). Zondervan.

Chosen For Life. Samuel C. Storms. 160p. 1987. pap. 6.95 (ISBN 0-8010-8270-6). Baker Bk.

Chosen for Riches. Bob Hendren. LC 77-25775. (Journey Bks.). 1978. 3.50 (ISBN 0-8344-0096-0). Sweet.

Chosen Partners. Mabel E. Wolsted. 1983. 9.95 (ISBN 0-8062-1918-1). Carlton.

Chosen People. Sidney L. Nyburg. Ed. by Jonathan D. Sarna. (Masterworks of Modern Jewish Writing Ser.). 382p. 1986. pap. 9.95 (ISBN 0-910129-47-9, Distr. by Schcken Books). Wiener Pub Inc.

Chosen People in America: A Study in Jewish Religious Ideology. Arnold M. Eisen. LC 82-49296. (Modern Jewish Experience Ser.). 254p. 1983. 20.00x (ISBN 0-253-31365-1). Ind U Pr.

Chosen to Salvation: Select Thoughts on the Doctrine of Election. David Nettleton. LC 83-11062. 1983. pap. 5.95 (ISBN 0-87227-094-7). Reg Baptist.

Chosen Twelve Plus One. Clarence E. Macartney. LC 80-17881. (Illus.). 124p. 1980. 39.95 (ISBN 0-930014-43-X); ltd. ed. 200.00 (ISBN 0-930014-52-9); portfolio 24.95. Multnomah.

Chosen Vessels: Portraits of Ten Outstanding Christian Men. Harry Blamires et al. Ed. by Charles Turner. 224p. (Orig.). 1985. pap. 10.95 (ISBN 0-89283-226-6, Pub. by Vine Books). Servant.

Chosen Women of the Bible. Ethel Herr. LC 75-36503. 96p. (Orig.). 1976. pap. 4.95 (ISBN 0-8024-1297-1). Moody.

Chretien Bernanos. Balthasar. 27.90 (ISBN 0-685-37226-X). French & Eur.

Chris: A Biography of Christian C. Sanderson. Thomas R. Thompson. LC 73-84422. (Illus.). 420p. 1973. 12.95 (ISBN 0-8059-1899-X). Dorrance.

Chrismon Service. James Edgar & Ellen Edgar. 20p. 1981. pap. text ed. 2.95 (ISBN 0-89536-500-6, 0341). CSS of Ohio.

Christ. Date not set. pap. 0.95 (ISBN 0-937408-14-X). GMI Pubns Inc.

Christ All in All. Philip Henry. 7.95 (ISBN 0-685-88369-8). Reiner.

Christ among Us: A Modern Presentation of the Catholic Faith for Adults. 4th, rev. ed. Anthony Wilhelm. LC 84-48465. 480p. 1985. pap. 6.95 (ISBN 0-06-069417-3, HarpR). Har-Row.

Christ & Adam: Man & Humanity in Romans Five. Karl Barth et al. Tr. by T. A. Small. 96p. 1983. Repr. of 1957 ed. lib. bdg. 12.00 (ISBN 0-88254-864-6, Octagon). Hippocrene Bks.

Christ & Apollo: The Dimensions of the Literary Imagination. William F. Lynch. 224p. 1975. pap. 5.95x (ISBN 0-268-00712-8). U of Notre Dame Pr.

Christ & Baha'u'llah. George Townshend. LC 68-168. 116p. 1966. pap. 3.95 (ISBN 0-85398-005-5). G Ronald Pub.

Christ & Caesar in Christian Missions. Ed. by Edwin L. Frizen. Wade T. Coggins. LC 79-17124. (Orig.). 1979. pap. 5.95 (ISBN 0-87808-169-0). William Carey Lib.

Christ & Culture. H. Richard Niebuhr. pap. 7.95x (ISBN 0-06-130003-9, TB3, Torch). Har-Row.

Christ & Culture. H. Richard Niebuhr. 17.00 (ISBN 0-8446-2658-9). Peter Smith.

Christ & His Associates in Voltairian Polemic: An Assault on the Trinity and the Two Natures. William H. Trapnell. (Stanford French & Italian Studies: Vol. 26). vi, 268p. 1982. pap. 25.00 (ISBN 0-915838-13-3). Anma Libri.

Christ & His Benefits: Christology & Redemption in the New Testament. Arland J. Hultgren. LC 86-45917. 288p. 1987. text ed. 24.95 (ISBN 0-8006-0861-5). Fortress.

Christ & His Church. Larry Christenson. (Trinity Bible Ser.). 160p. 1973. pap. 4.95 spiral wkbk. (ISBN 0-87123-550-1, 240550). Bethany Hse.
Christ & His Church: Teacher Guide. Sandra Hall. 96p. (Orig.). 1985. pap. 6.95 (ISBN 0-87123-801-2). Bethany Hse.
Christ & Humanity. Asheim Ivar. LC 73-10426. pap. 50.80 (2026913). Bks Demand UMI.
Christ & Krishna. J. M. Robertson. 59.95 (ISBN 0-87968-422-4). Gordon Pr.
Christ & Krishna: The Path of Pure Devotion. Kirtanananda Bhaktipada. LC 85-73024. 182p. 1986. 10.95 (ISBN 0-317-43353-9); pap. 6.95 (ISBN 0-317-43354-7). Bhaktipada Bks.
Christ & Life. Wilfrid Harrington. 160p. 1976. 7.95 (ISBN 0-8199-0571-2). Franciscan Herald.
Christ & Modernity: Christian Self-Understanding in a Technological Age. David Hawkin. (Studies in Religion: Vol. 17). 200p. 1985. pap. text ed. 12.95x (ISBN 0-88920-193-5, Pub. by Wilfrid Laurier Canada). Humanities.
Christ & Nietzsche. G. Wilson Knight. 1948. lib. bdg. 17.50 (ISBN 0-8414-5590-2). Folcroft.
Christ & Nietzsche: An Essay in Poetic Wisdom. G. Wilson Knight. 1982. 17.00 (ISBN 0-8495-3135-7). Arden Lib.
Christ & Oriental Ideals. 4th ed. Swami Paramananda. 1968. 4.50 (ISBN 0-911564-14-4). Vedanta Ctr.
Christ & Prometheus: A New Image of the Secular. William F. Lynch. LC 70-122046. 1970. 14.95 (ISBN 0-268-00431-5); pap. 4.95 (ISBN 0-268-00480-3). U of Notre Dame Pr.
Christ & Satan: A Critical Edition. Robert E. Finnegan. 169p. 1977. pap. text ed. 15.95x (ISBN 0-88920-041-6, Pub. by Wilfrid Laurier Canada); pap. text ed. 10.50 (ISBN 0-88920-040-8). Humanities.
Christ & Spirit in the New Testament. B. Lindars & S. S. Smalley. LC 72-91367. 300p. 1974. 72.50 (ISBN 0-521-20148-9). Cambridge U Pr.
Christ & the Bodhisattva. Ed. by Donald S. Lopez, Jr. & Stephen C. Rockefeller. (Buddhist Studies). 304p. (Orig.). 1987. 44.50X (ISBN 0-88706-401-9); pap. 14.95X (ISBN 0-88706-402-7). State U NY Pr.
Christ & the Catechist: The Spiritual Life of the Christian Teacher. Michael Leary. LC 86-83017. 128p. 1987. pap. 6.95 (ISBN 0-89870-139-2). Ignatius Pr.
Christ & the Christian Movement: Jesus in the New Testament, the Creeds & Modern Theology. Leland J. White. LC 85-11190. 296p. (Orig.). 1985. pap. 10.95 (ISBN 0-8189-0484-4). Alba.
Christ & the Colonel. Merrill Finley. 120p. 1987. pap. write for info. (ISBN 0-911826-51-3). Am Atheist.
Christ & the Decree: Christology & Predestination in Reformed Theology from Calvin to Perkins. Richard A. Muller. (Studies in Historical Theology: Vol. 2). 250p. 1986. lib. bdg. 30.00x (ISBN 0-939464-39-X). Labyrinth Pr.
Christ & the Eastern Soul: Oriental Consciousness & Jesus. Charles C. Hall. 1977. lib. bdg. 59.95 (ISBN 0-8490-1613-4). Gordon Pr.
Christ & the Gospels. Charles W. Conn. 109p. 1964. pap. 4.25 (ISBN 0-87148-150-2). Pathway Pr.
Christ & the Human Soul. 4th ed. Rudolf Steiner. 81p. 1984. pap. 6.50 (ISBN 0-85440-013-3, Pub. by Steinerbooks). Anthroposophic.
Christ & the Judgement of God: Divine Retribution in the New Testament. Stephen H. Travis. 240p. Date not set. pap. 12.95 (ISBN 0-8407-5958-4). Nelson.
Christ & the Meaning of Life. Helmut Thielicke. Tr. by J. W. Doberstein from Ger. 186p. 1978. Repr. 13.95 (ISBN 0-227-67684-X). Attic Pr.
Christ & the Moral Life. James M. Gustafson. 1979. 8.00x (ISBN 0-226-31109-0, P830, Phoen). U of Chicago Pr.
Christ & the Patriarchs: New Light from Apocryphal Literature & Tradition. Marcus Von Wellnitz. LC 80-83035. 400p. 1980. 9.95 (ISBN 0-88290-164-8, 2045). Horizon Utah.
Christ & the Powers. Hendrik Berkhof. LC 62-13713. 80p. 1962. pap. 5.95 (ISBN 0-8361-1820-0). Herald Pr.
Christ & the Sacrament Church. Pierre Talec. 144p. 1983. pap. 9.95 (ISBN 0-8164-2455-1, HarpR). Har-Row.
Christ & the Seasons of Marriage. John Killinger. LC 86-17411. 1987. 7.95 (ISBN 0-8054-5666-X). Broadman.
Christ & the Universe. Robert Hale. Ed. by Michael Meilach. (Theilhard de Chardin & the Universe Ser). 5.50 (ISBN 0-8199-0449-X). Franciscan Herald.
Christ & the World's Religious. Arnold D. Hunt. 124p. (Orig.). 1970. pap. 8.45 (ISBN 0-85819-003-6, Pub. by JBCE). ANZ Religious Pubns.
Christ & Time: The Primitive Christian Conception of Time & History. Oscar Cullman. 1977. lib. bdg. 59.95 (ISBN 0-8490-1614-2). Gordon Pr.
Christ & Violence. Ronald J. Sider. LC 79-9239. (Christian Peace Shelf Ser.). 104p. 1979. pap. 4.95 (ISBN 0-8361-1895-2). Herald Pr.
Christ & Your Problems. Jay E. Adams. 1976. pap. 1.25 (ISBN 0-8010-0035-1). Baker Bk.
Christ & Your Problems. Jay E. Adams. 33p. 1973. pap. 1.25 (ISBN 0-87552-011-1). Presby & Reformed.
Christ Ascended: A Study in the Significance of the Ascension of Jesus Christ in the New Testament. Brian K. Donne. 1983. pap. text ed. 7.95 (ISBN 0-85364-336-9). Attic Pr.
Christ at the Door. Earl C. Davis. LC 84-27441. 1985. pap. 5.95 (ISBN 0-8054-6249-X). Broadman.
Christ at the Round Table. E. Stanley Jones. 328p. 1981. Repr. of 1928 ed. lib. bdg. 30.00 (ISBN 0-89984-267-4). Century Bookbindery.
Christ, Avatar of Sacrificial Love. Haroutiun Saraydarian. LC 74-11760. 1974. 9.00 (ISBN 0-911794-38-7); pap. 8.00 (ISBN 0-911794-39-5). Aqua Educ.
Christ-Based Teachings. Donald Curtis. LC 75-40657. 1976. 5.95 (ISBN 0-87159-016-6). Unity School.
Christ Book: What Did He Really Say? Christopher Hills. Ed. by Norah Hills. LC 80-5865. (Illus.). 224p. 1980. gift ed. 15.95; text ed. 10.95 (ISBN 0-916438-37-6). Univ of Trees.
Christ Can Make You Fully Human. Kenneth C. Kinghorn. LC 79-10855. 1979. pap. 4.35 (ISBN 0-687-06930-0). Abingdon.
Christ-Centered Crafts for Children's Classes. Jane S. Nelson. LC 81-8711. 1981. pap. 2.50 (ISBN 0-87227-078-5). Reg Baptist.
Christ-Centered Family. Raymond T. Brock. LC 76-46036. (Radiant Life Ser.). 128p. 1977. pap. 2.50 (ISBN 0-88243-903-0, 02-0903); teacher's ed 3.95 (ISBN 0-88243-173-0, 32-0173). Gospel Pub.
Christ Child. Maud Petersham & Miska Petersham. 63p. 1931. 12.95 (ISBN 0-385-07260-0); PLB (ISBN 0-385-07319-4); pap. 5.95 (ISBN 0-385-15841-6, Zephyr). Doubleday.
Christ Church Letters. Ed. by Joseph B. Sheppard. Repr. of 1877 ed. 27.00 (ISBN 0-384-55120-3). Johnson Repr.
Christ-Church Work Book. 1987. 5.95 (240550). Bethany Hse.
Christ Consciousness. Compiled by Association for Research & Enlightenment, Readings Research Dept. (Library: Vol. 11). 277p. 1980. 10.95 (ISBN 0-87604-124-1). ARE Pr.
Christ Consciousness. 2nd, rev. ed. Norman D. Paulsen. LC 84-72066. (Illus.). 496p. (Orig.). 1985. 16.95 (ISBN 0-941848-03-5); pap. 10.95 (ISBN 0-941848-04-3). Builders Pub.
Christ Crucified. C. H. Spurgeon. 1978. pap. 0.95 (ISBN 0-686-26193-3). Pilgrim Pubns.
Christ Denied. Paul A. Wickens. LC 82-50585. 49p. 1982. pap. 1.25 (ISBN 0-89555-183-7). TAN Bks Pubs.
Christ Did Not Perish on the Cross: Christ's Body Buried Alive. Kurt Berna. (Illus.). 1975. 14.50 (ISBN 0-682-48139-4). Exposition Pr FL.
Christ Died for Me. Everett L. Wilson. 164p. 1980. pap. 4.50 (ISBN 0-910452-45-8). Covenant.
Christ Displays His Glory: Matthew Sixteen Verse Twenty Four to Seventeen Verses Thirteen. John MacArthur, Jr. (John MacArthur Bible Studies Ser.). 1987. pap. 3.50 (ISBN 0-8024-5317-1). Moody.
Christ Enthroned in Man. Cora D. Fillmore. 1981. 4.95. Unity School.
Christ, Faith & History. S. W. Sykes & J. P. Clayton. LC 70-176257. (Cambridge Studies in Christology). (Illus.). 280p. 1972. pap. text ed. 14.95 (ISBN 0-521-29325-1). Cambridge U Pr.
Christ for the World. Bertrand De Margerie. Tr. by Malachy Carroll from Fr. Tr. of Christ Pour le Monde. write for info (ISBN 0-8199-0460-0); pap. 3.95 (ISBN 0-8199-0485-6). Franciscan Herald.
Christ, God's Final Word to Man: An Exposition of the Epistle to the Hebrews. Herman A. Hoyt. pap. 4.95 (ISBN 0-88469-009-1). BMH Bks.
Christ: God's Love Gift. Joseph H. King. 3.50 (ISBN 0-911866-84-1). Advocate.
Christ Highway. Genevah D. Seivertson. LC 81-69023. 184p. 1982. pap. 7.25 (ISBN 0-87516-465-X). De Vorss.
Christ Idea. Max Kappeler. LC 79-868476. 30p. 1975. pap. 3.50 (ISBN 0-85241-079-4). Kappeler Inst Pub.
Christ in a Changing World: Toward an Ethical Christology. Tom F. Driver. LC 81-5552. 224p. 1981. 12.95 (ISBN 0-8245-0105-5). Crossroad NY.
Christ in a Pluralistic Age. John B. Cobb, Jr. LC 74-820. 286p. 1984. pap. 11.95 (ISBN 0-664-24522-6). Westminster.
Christ in a Poncho: Witnesses to the Nonviolent Struggles in Latin America. Adolfo Perez-Esquivel. Tr. by Robert R. Barr from Fr. LC 82-18760. Tr. of Le Christ au poncho, suivi de Temoignages de luttes nonviolentes en Amerique Latine. 139p. (Orig.). 1983. pap. 7.95 (ISBN 0-88344-104-7). Orbis Bks.
Christ in Catastrophe. Emil Fuchs. 1983. pap. 2.50x (ISBN 0-87574-049-9, 049). Pendle Hill.
Christ in Christian Tradition: From the Apostolic Age to Chalcedon, Vol. 1. rev. ed. Aloys Grillmeier. Tr. by John S. Bowden from Ger. LC 75-13456. 451p. 1975. 29.95 (ISBN 0-8042-0492-6). John Knox.
Christ in Colision. George E. Rice. (Harvest Ser.). 112p. 1982. pap. 4.95 (ISBN 0-8163-0473-4). Pacific Pr Pub Assn.
Christ in East & West. Ed. by Paul R. Fries & Tiran Nersoyan. 240p. 1987. 31.95 (ISBN 0-86554-267-8, MUP H-228); pap. 14.95 (ISBN 0-86554-277-5). Mercer Univ Pr.
Christ in Eastern Christian Thought. John Meyendorff. LC 75-31977. Orig. Title: Christ Dans la Theologie Byzantine. 248p. 1975. pap. 10.95 (ISBN 0-913836-27-3). St Vladimirs.
Christ in His Sanctuary. Ellen G. White. LC 70-94869. (Dimension Ser.). 1969. pap. 6.95 (ISBN 0-8163-0128-X, 03254-0). Pacific Pr Pub Assn.
Christ in India. Bede Griffiths. pap. 8.95 (ISBN 0-87243-134-7). Templegate.
Christ in Isaiah. F. B. Meyer. 1970. pap. 3.95 (ISBN 0-87508-341-2). Chr Lit.
Christ in My Life. David J. De Bargh. 1977. 4.50 (ISBN 0-8198-0396-0); pap. text ed. 3.50 (ISBN 0-8198-0397-9). Dghtrs St Paul.
Christ in Our Lives. Alfred J. Garrotto. (Orig.). 1980. pap. text ed. 4.95 (ISBN 0-03-056979-6, HarpR). Har-Row.
Christ in Relation to Lucifer & Ahriman. Rudolf Steiner. Tr. by Peter Mollenhauer. 1978. pap. 2.00 (ISBN 0-910142-77-7). Anthroposophic.
Christ in Sacred Speech: The Meaning of Liturgical Language. Gail Ramshaw-Schmidt. LC 85-45486. 144p. 1986. pap. 9.95 (ISBN 0-8006-1907-2, 1-1907). Fortress.
Christ in Shakespeare. George H. Morrison. 142p. 1981. Repr. of 1928 ed. lib. bdg. 30.00 (ISBN 0-89984-342-5). Century Bookbindery.
Christ in Shakespeare's Dramas & Sonnets. C. Ellis. 59.95 (ISBN 0-87968-860-2). Gordon Pr.
Christ in the Christian Tradition, Vol. 2, Pt. 1. Aloys Grillmeier. Tr. by Pauline Allen & John Cawte. 1987. 34.95 (ISBN 0-8042-0493-4). John Knox.
Christ in the Drama: A Study of the Influence of Christ on the Drama of England & America. facsimile ed. Fred Eastman. LC 79-167336. (Essay Index Reprints - Shaffer Lectures of Northwestern University, 1946). Repr. of 1947 ed. 15.00 (ISBN 0-8369-2647-1). Ayer Co Pubs.
Christ in the Home. Ed. by Robert Taylor, Jr. pap. 5.95 (ISBN 0-89137-314-4). Quality Pubns.
Christ in the Light of the Christian-Jewish Dialogue. John T. Pawlikowski. LC 81-83186. (Stimulus Bks.). 208p. (Orig.). 1982. pap. 7.95 (ISBN 0-8091-2416-5). Paulist Pr.
Christ in the Passover. Ceil Rosen & Moishe Rosen. LC 77-10689. 1978. pap. 4.95 (ISBN 0-8024-1392-7). Moody.
Christ in the Philippine Context. Douglas J. Elwood & Patricia L. Magdamo. 1971. newsprint 6.75 (ISBN 0-686-18694-X). Cellar.
Christ in the Poetry of Today: An Anthology from American Poets. Martha F. Crow. 1978. Repr. of 1917 ed. lib. bdg. 25.00 (ISBN 0-8495-0912-2). Arden Lib.
Christ in the Tabernacle. A. B. Simpson. LC 85-70720. 150p. 1985. 4.95 (ISBN 0-87509-361-2). Chr Pubns.
Christ in Theology: Hartford, 1851. Horace Bushnell. Ed. by Bruce Kuklick. (American Religious Thought of the 18th & 19th Centuries Ser.). 348p. 1987. lib. bdg. 50.00 (ISBN 0-8240-6965-X). Garland Pub.
Christ in Us: Reflections on Redemption. Alban Boultwood. LC 81-8371. 144p. (Orig.). 1981. pap. 5.50 (ISBN 0-8146-1234-2). Liturgical Pr.
Christ in You. 224p. 1983. pap. 5.95 (ISBN 0-87516-506-0). De Vorss.
Christ in You. Carol Eisele. (Aglow Bible Study Basic Ser.: Bk. 10). 64p. 1977. 2.95 (ISBN 0-930756-22-3, 521010). Aglow Pubns.
Christ in You. Inter-Varsity Staff. pap. 0.75 (ISBN 0-87784-175-6). Inter Varsity.
Christ in Your Life. Leslie F. Brandt. 1980. 7.50 (ISBN 0-570-03292-X, 15-2729). Concordia.
Christ Incomparable. J. Oswald Sanders. Tr. of Incomparable Christ. (Fr.). 1986. pap. 3.90 (ISBN 0-8297-1344-1). Life Pubs Intl.
Christ Is Community: The Christologies of the New Testament. Jerome H. Neyrey. (Good News Studies: Vol. 13). 1985. pap. 12.95 (ISBN 0-89453-465-3). M Glazier.
Christ Is in Our Midst: Letters from a Russian Monk. John Skhi-Igumen. Tr. by Esther Williams from Rus. LC 80-10530. 168p. (Orig.). 1980. pap. 4.95 (ISBN 0-913836-64-8). St Vladimirs.
Christ Is Passing by. Josemaria Escriva de Balaguer. LC 74-78783. 276p. (Foreign language editions avail). 1977. pap. 6.95 (ISBN 0-933932-04-9). Scepter Pubs.
Christ Jesus: The God-Man. J. Floyd Williams. 3.95 (ISBN 0-911866-72-8). Advocate.
Christ Krishna & You. Swami Venkatesananda. 168p. (Orig.). 1983. write for info. Chiltern Yoga.
Christ: Liberation of the World Today. Charles Massabki. Tr. by Sr. Eloise T. Mescall from Fr. LC 78-12998. 1979. pap. 6.95 (ISBN 0-8189-0374-0). Alba.
Christ Life. Albert B. Simpson. LC 80-69301. 96p. pap. 2.25 (ISBN 0-87509-291-8). Chr Pubns.
Christ Life from Nativity to Ascension. Geoffrey Hodson. LC 75-4169. 540p. 1975. pap. 5.50 (ISBN 0-8356-0467-5, Quest). Theos Pub Hse.
Christ Lives in Me. rev. ed. Daughters of St. Paul. (Way, Truth & Life Ser.). (Illus.). 1973. text ed. 2.00 (ISBN 0-8198-0308-1); tchr's manual 6.25 (ISBN 0-8198-0309-X); activity bk. 1.00 (ISBN 0-8198-0310-3); parent guide 1.25 (ISBN 0-8198-0311-1). Dghtrs St Paul.
Christ Lives in Me: A Pastoral Reflection on Jesus & His Meaning for Christian Life. Joseph L. Bernardin. (Illus.). 69p. (Orig.). 1985. pap. 3.95 (ISBN 0-86716-044-6). St Anthony Mess Pr.
Christ Lore. F. W. Hackwood. 59.95 (ISBN 0-87968-861-0). Gordon Pr.
Christ Lore: Being the Legends, Traditions, Myths, Symbols, Customs, & Superstitions of the Christian Church. Frederick W. Hackwood. LC 69-16064. (Illus.). 1971. Repr. of 1902 ed. 34.00x (ISBN 0-8103-3528-X). Gale.
Christ Loved the Church. William MacDonald. pap. 2.95 (ISBN 0-937396-09-5). Walterick Pubs.
Christ, Model & Reward of Religious. James Alberione. 1964. 5.00 (ISBN 0-8198-0023-6); pap. 4.00. Dghtrs St Paul.
Christ Nobody Knows: A Sentimental Vision of His Life. Gaspare Pignatelli. (Illus.). 121p. 1987. 88.85 (ISBN 0-89266-576-9). Am Classical Coll Pr.
Christ of Christmas. James M. Boice. 1983. 9.95 (ISBN 0-8024-0337-9). Moody.
Christ of Cynewulf; a Poem in Three Parts: The Advent, the Ascension, & the Last Judgement. Cynewulf. Ed. by Albert S. Cook. LC 73-178524. Repr. of 1900 ed. 32.50 (ISBN 0-404-56538-7). AMS Pr.
Christ of Cynewulf: A Poem in Three Parts, the Advent, the Ascension, & the Last Judgment. facsimile ed. Cynewulf. Ed. by Albert S. Cook. LC 74-114906. (Select Bibliographies Reprint Ser). 1900. 25.50 (ISBN 0-8369-5310-X). Ayer Co Pubs.
Christ of English Poetry. Charles W. Stubbs. LC 73-1787. 1973. lib. bdg. 25.00 (ISBN 0-8414-2621-X). Folcroft.
Christ of the Covenants. O. Palmer Robertson. 1981. pap. 9.95 (ISBN 0-87552-418-4). Presby & Reformed.
Christ of the Forty Days. Albert B. Simpson. pap. 1.25 (ISBN 0-87509-004-4). Chr Pubns.
Christ of the Gospels. rev. ed. Tr. by William F. Beck. LC 59-11068. 1959. pap. 6.95 (ISBN 0-570-03724-7, 12-2626). Concordia.
Christ of the Gospels. rev. ed. John W. Shepard. 1946. 15.95 (ISBN 0-8028-1779-3). Eerdmans.
Christ of the Mount. E. Stanley Jones. (Festival Ser.). 336p. 1981. pap. 2.45 (ISBN 0-687-06925-4). Abingdon.
Christ of Vatican Two. Daughters Of St. Paul. (St. Paul Editions). (Illus.). 1968. 2.00 (ISBN 0-8198-0024-4); pap. 1.00 (ISBN 0-8198-0025-2). Dghtrs St Paul.
Christ Our Example. Caroline Fry. 155p. 1976. pap. 3.95 (ISBN 0-685-53618-1). Reiner.
Christ, Our Pattern & Plan. John C. Whitcomb, Jr. 1979. pap. 1.00 (ISBN 0-88469-031-8). BMH Bks.
Christ Our Revelation. Jeanne Guyon. (Orig.). 1985. pap. 7.95 (ISBN 0-940232-21-9). Christian Bks.
Christ: Our Way to the Father. rev. ed. Daughters of St. Paul. (Way, Truth & Life Ser.). (Illus.). 1973. text ed. 2.00 (ISBN 0-8198-0300-6); tchrs. manual 6.25 (ISBN 0-8198-0301-4); activity bk. 1.00 (ISBN 0-8198-0302-2); parent guide 0.95 (ISBN 0-8198-0303-0). Dghtrs St Paul.
Christ Outside the Gate: Mission Beyond Christendom. Orlando Costas. LC 82-7892. 272p. (Orig.). 1982. pap. 12.95 (ISBN 0-88344-147-0). Orbis Bks.
Christ Papers, Vol. I. LC 82-90717. 150p. (Orig.). pap. 5.95 (ISBN 0-937408-22-0). GMI Pubns Inc.

Christ Precious to Those That Believe. John Fawcett. 1979. 10.00 (ISBN 0-86524-026-4, 8901). Klock & Klock.

Christ Principle & True Christianity to Be. Marie B. Hall. (Illus.). 1973. 8.50 (ISBN 0-938760-03-3). Veritat Found.

Christ Proclaimed: Christology As Rhetoric. Frans J. Van Beeck. LC 79-66459. 632p. 1979. pap. 9.95 (ISBN 0-8091-2208-1). Paulist Pr.

Christ, Resurrection Life. Valerie Owen. 268p. (Orig.). 1985. pap. text ed. 7.95 (ISBN 0-914307-32-0). Word Faith.

Christ Revealed. Thomas Taylor. LC 79-10885. 1979. Repr. of 1635 ed. 60.00x (ISBN 0-8201-1334-4). Schol Facsimiles.

Christ Revealed: The History of the Neotypological Lyric in the English Renaissance. Ira Clark. LC 82-2696. (University of Florida Humanities Monographs: No. 51). xiv, 218p. 1982. pap. 15.00x (ISBN 0-8130-0712-7). U Presses Fla.

Christ Tempted & Sympathizing. W. Kelly. 3.95 (ISBN 0-88172-091-7). Believers Bkshelf.

Christ: The Answer. Peter Sullivan. (Orig.). pap. 1.95 (ISBN 0-8198-0026-0). Dghtrs St Paul.

Christ the Center: A New Translation. new ed. Dietrich Bonhoeffer. LC 78-4747. (Harper's Ministers Paperback Library Ser.). 1978. pap. 5.95 (ISBN 0-06-060815-3, RD 285, HarpR). Har-Row.

Christ, the Crown of the Torah. Ed. by Edward E. Burgess. 220p. 1986. pap. 7.95 (ISBN 0-310-41621-3, 9942P). Zondervan.

Christ, the Divine Network: Reflections on the Gospel for the A-Cycle. Joseph G. Donders. LC 86-718. 256p. (Orig.). 1986. pap. 10.95 (ISBN 0-88344-254-X). Orbis Bks.

Christ the Educator. Clement Of Alexandria. LC 66-20313. (Fathers of the Church Ser.: Vol. 23). 309p. 1954. 16.95x (ISBN 0-8132-0023-7). Cath U Pr.

Christ the End of the Law: Romans 10-4 in Pauline Perspective. Robert Badenas. (JSoT Supplement Ser.: No. 10). 312p. 1985. text ed. 36.50x (ISBN 0-905774-93-0, Pub. by JSOT Pr England); pap. text ed. 15.95x (ISBN 0-905774-94-9). Eisenbrauns.

Christ, the Eternal Son. A. W. Tozer. Ed. by G. B. Smith. 136p. 1982. pap. 3.45 (ISBN 0-87509-230-6). Chr Pubns.

Christ: The Experience of Jesus As Lord. Edward Schillebeeckx. 928p. 1983. pap. 17.95 (ISBN 0-8245-0605-7). Crossroad NY.

Christ the Fountaine of Life, Or, Sundry Choyce Sermons on Part of the Fifth Chapter of the First Epistle of St. John. John Cotton. LC 75-141107. (Research Library of Colonial Americana). 1971. Repr. of 1651 ed. 24.50 (ISBN 0-405-03321-4). Ayer Co Pubs.

Christ: The Fullness of the Godhead, a Study in New Testament Christology. James Gunn. 256p. 1983. pap. 5.50 (ISBN 0-87213-283-8). Loizeaux.

Christ the Great Physician. Gordon Lindsay. (Divine Healing & Health Ser.). 1.25 (ISBN 0-89985-024-3). Christ Nations.

Christ the Healer. F. F. Bosworth. 241p. pap. 6.95 (ISBN 0-8007-5124-8, Power Bks). Revell.

Christ the Healer. Edward Kremers. 24p. 1911. pap. 0.95 (ISBN 0-317-40411-3). Open Court.

Christ the Placenta. David Arthur Bickimer. LC 82-24097. 239p. (Orig.). 1983. pap. 12.95 (ISBN 0-89135-034-9). Religious Educ.

Christ the Prisoner. Marion Habig. 1976. pap. 0.50 (ISBN 0-685-77502-X). Franciscan Herald.

Christ the Savior & Christ Myth. rev. ed. Prajnanananda. 7.95 (ISBN 0-87481-652-1, Pub. by Ramakrishna Math Madras India). Vedanta Pr.

Christ the Savior & Christ Myth. rev. ed. Swami Prajnanananda. 7.59. Vedanta Pr.

Christ the Sum of All Spiritual Things. Watchman Nee. Tr. by Stephen Kaung. 1973. pap. 2.50 (ISBN 0-935008-14-4). Christian Fellow Pubs.

Christ the Way: The Christology of Guerric of Igny. John Morson. (Cistercian Studies: N0.25). 1978. 11.95 (ISBN 0-87907-825-1). Cistercian Pubns.

Christ Unmasked: The Meaning of "The Life of Jesus" in German Politics. Marilyn C. Massey. LC 82-8547. (Studies in Religion Ser.). xi, 182p. 1983. 23.00x (ISBN 0-8078-1524-1). U of NC Pr.

Christ We Know. John Booty. LC 87-6779. (Illus.). 174p. 1987. pap. 9.95 (ISBN 0-936384-48-4). Cowley Pubns.

Christ Will See You Through. Richard M. Cromie. 60p. (Orig.). 1985. pap. 1.50 (ISBN 0-914733-04-4). Desert Min.

Christ Within. Lillian De Waters. 5.95 (ISBN 0-686-05717-1). L De Waters.

Christ Within. John-Roger. LC 77-70405. 1976. pap. 5.00 (ISBN 0-914829-04-1). Baraka Bk.

Christ Within Us. Ernest E. Larkin. 1984. pap. 6.95 (ISBN 0-87193-215-6). Dimension Bks.

Christ Without Myth: A Study Based on the Theology of Rudolf Bultmann. Schubert M. Ogden. LC 79-102841. 1979. pap. 8.95x (ISBN 0-87074-172-1). SMU Press.

Christ-Yoga of Peace: Proposal for a World Peace Center. Christopher Hills. 156p. 1970. 4.00 (ISBN 0-916438-01-5). Univ of Trees.

Christening of Karma. Geddes MacGregor. LC 83-40234. 200p. (Orig.). 1984. pap. 6.95 (ISBN 0-8356-0581-7, Quest). Theos Pub Hse.

Christening Pagan Mysteries: Erasmus in Pursuit of Wisdom. Marjorie O. Boyle. (Erasmus Studies). 168p. 1981. 22.50x (ISBN 0-8020-5525-7). U of Toronto Pr.

Christening: The Making of Christians. Mark Searle. LC 80-19454. (Illus.). 185p. (Orig.). 1980. pap. text ed. 6.50 (ISBN 0-8146-1183-4). Liturgical Pr.

Christentum am Roten Meer. Franz Altheim & Ruth Stiehl. Vol. 1, 1971. 153.00x (ISBN 3-11-003790-4); Vol. 2, 1973. 153.00x (ISBN 3-11-003791-2). De Gruyter.

Christenverfolgung im roemischen Reich. 2nd ed. Jacques Moreau. 119p. 1971. 9.00 (ISBN 3-1100-2456-X). De Gruyter.

Christiad: Latin-English Edition. Marco G. Vida. Ed. by Gertrude C. Drake & Clarence A. Forbes. LC 78-1430. 288p. 1978. 9.85x (ISBN 0-8093-0814-2). S Ill U Pr.

Christiada: Introduction & Text. Diego de Hojeda. Ed. by Sr. Mary H. Corcoran. LC 35-9384. (Catholic University of America. Studies in Romance Languages & Literatures: No. 11). Repr. of 1935 ed. 49.50 (ISBN 0-404-50311-X). AMS Pr.

Christian. Robert Hicks & Richard Bewes. (Understanding Bible Truth Ser.). (Orig.). 1981. pap. 0.95 (ISBN 0-89840-023-6). Heres Life.

Christian ABC Book. John Foster & June Goldsborough. (Illus.). 1982. 6.95 (ISBN 0-911346-05-8). Christianica.

Christian Adulthood. Ed. by Neil A. Parent. 125p. 1985. pap. 6.95 (ISBN 1-55586-921-1). US Catholic.

Christian Adulthood Nineteen Eighty-Seven. Ed. by Neil Parent. Date not set. pap. price not set (ISBN 1-55586-106-7). US Catholic.

Christian Adulthood 1982. Ed. by Neil A. Parent. 130p. 1982. pap. 5.95 (ISBN 1-55586-827-4). US Catholic.

Christian Adulthood 1983. Ed. by Neil A. Parent. 68p. 1983. pap. 4.95 (ISBN 1-55586-862-2). US Catholic.

Christian Adulthood 1985-1986. Ed. by Neil A. Parent. 124p. 1985. pap. 8.95 (ISBN 1-55586-965-3). US Catholic.

Christian Agnostic. Leslie D. Weatherhead. (Festival Books Ser.). 1979. pap. 4.50 (ISBN 0-687-06978-5). Abingdon.

Christian Altar in History & Today. Cyril E. Pocknee. LC 64-1983. 1962. text ed. 10.00x (ISBN 0-8401-1871-6). A R Allenson.

Christian America: Protestant Hopes & Historical Realities. 2nd & enl. ed. Robert T. Handy. 1983. 27.00x (ISBN 0-19-503386-8); pap. 10.95x (ISBN 0-19-503387-6). Oxford U Pr.

Christian Anarchy: Jesus' Primacy Over the Powers. Vernard Eller. 304p. (Orig.). 1987. pap. 13.95 (ISBN 0-8028-0227-3). Eerdmans.

Christian & Alcoholic Beverages: A Biblical Perspective. Kenneth L. Gentry, Jr. 1986. pap. 4.95 (ISBN 0-8010-3807-3). Baker Bk.

Christian & Gnostic Son of Man. Frederick H. Borsch. LC 77-131585. (Studies in Biblical Theology, 2nd Ser.: No. 14). (Orig.). 1970. pap. text ed. 10.00x (ISBN 0-8401-3064-3). A R Allenson.

Christian & Government. John MacArthur, Jr. (John MacArthur's Bible Studies). (Orig.). 1986. pap. 3.50 (ISBN 0-8024-5095-4). Moody.

Christian & Oriental Philosophy of Art. Ananda K. Coomaraswamy. 1957. pap. 3.95 (ISBN 0-486-20378-6). Dover.

Christian & Politics. Robert L. Thoburn. 224p. (Orig.). 1984. pap. text ed. 4.95 (ISBN 0-317-15003-0). Thoburn Pr.

Christian & Revolution. Melvin Gingerich. LC 68-12028. (Conrad Grebel Lecture, No. 12). 1968. 12.95 (ISBN 0-8361-1573-2). Herald Pr.

Christian & Social Drinking. Gordon L. Addington. 1984. 1.75 (ISBN 0-911802-63-0). Free Church Pubns.

Christian & the Supernatural. Morton Kelsey. LC 76-3865. 160p. (Orig.). 1976. pap. 8.95 (ISBN 0-8066-1525-7, 10-1100). Augsburg.

Christian & Warfare: The Old Testament, War & the Christian. Jacob J. Enz. (Christian Peace Shelf Ser.). 104p. 1972. pap. 2.95 (ISBN 0-8361-1684-4). Herald Pr.

Christian Antioch: A Study of Early Christian Thought in the East. D. S. Wallace-Hadrill. 240p. 1982. 37.50 (ISBN 0-521-23425-5). Cambridge U Pr.

Christian Apologetics. Norman L. Geisler. LC 76-24706. 464p. 1976. 15.95 (ISBN 0-8010-3704-2). Baker Bk.

Christian Apologetics. Cornelius Van Til. 1976. pap. 3.95 syllabus (ISBN 0-87552-477-X). Presby & Reformed.

Christian Apologetics in a World Community. William A. Dyrness. LC 82-21383. 180p. 1983. pap. 6.95 (ISBN 0-87784-399-6). Inter-Varsity.

Christian Approach to Economics & the Cultural Condition. Douglas Vickers. 1982. 12.50 (ISBN 0-682-49831-9, University). Exposition Pr FL.

Christian Approach to Education. H. W. Byrne. 1986. pap. 9.95 (ISBN 0-8010-0941-3). Baker Bk.

Christian Approach to Muslims: Reflections from West Africa. James P. Dretke. LC 79-11912. (Islamic Studies). 1979. pap. 3.95 (ISBN 0-87808-432-0). William Carey Lib.

Christian Approach to National Defense. rev. ed. A. Willmott. 122p. 1986. pap. 20.00X (ISBN 0-7223-1968-1, Pub. by A H Stockwell England). State Mutual Bk.

Christian Approach to Philosophy. Warren C. Young. (Twin Brook Ser.). 1973. pap. 9.95 (ISBN 0-8010-9904-8). Baker Bk.

Christian Approach to Successful Selling. Raymond J. Pesta. LC 81-68890. 92p. 1981. pap. 5.95 (ISBN 0-941280-00-4). Chr Acad Success.

Christian Approach to the Moslem. James T. Addison. LC 76-158227. (BCL Ser.: No. II). Repr. of 1942 ed. 24.50 (ISBN 0-404-00294-3). AMS Pr.

Christian Approaches to Learning Theory: A Symposium; Major Papers Delivered at the First Annual Conference at Trinity Christian College, November 11-12, 1983. Norman De Jong. 234p. 1985. 25.00 (ISBN 0-8191-4319-7, Pub. by Trinity Christ Coll). U Pr of Amer.

Christian Approaches to Learning Theory: A Symposium; Major Papers Delivered at Trinity Christian College, November 11-12, 1983. Norman De Jong. 234p. (Orig.). 1985. pap. 12.25 (ISBN 0-8191-4320-0, Pub. by Trinity Christ Coll). U Pr of Amer.

Christian Approaches to Learning Theory: The Nature of the Learner - Major Papers Delivered at the Second Annual Conference, Trinity Christian College, Palos Heights, Illinois, Nov. 2-3, 1984, Vol. II. Ed. by Norman DeJong. 174p. (Orig.). 1986. lib. bdg. 25.00 (ISBN 0-8191-5004-5, Pub. by Trinity Christ Coll); pap. text ed. 11.75 (ISBN 0-8191-5005-3). U Pr of Amer.

Christian Art. Charles R. Morey. (Illus.). 1958. pap. 3.95 (ISBN 0-393-00103-2, Norton Lib). Norton.

Christian Art. Charles R. Morey. (Illus.). 14.50 (ISBN 0-8446-2606-6). Peter Smith.

Christian Art in Ancient Ireland, 2 vols. in 1. Adolph R. Mahr. LC 75-11058. 1977. Repr. of 1932 ed. lib. bdg. 50.00 (ISBN 0-87817-173-8). Hacker.

Christian Art in Asia. W. A. Dyrness. 1979. pap. text ed. 11.50x (ISBN 0-391-01157-X). Humanities.

Christian Art in Italy, Spain, Holland & Germany. E. M. Healy. (Illus.). 145p. 1986. 127.45 (ISBN 0-86650-193-2). Gloucester Art.

Christian As a Consumer. Denise George. LC 83-26062. (Potentials: Guides for Productive Living Ser.,: Vol. 3). 114p. (Orig.). 1984. pap. 7.95 (ISBN 0-664-24518-8). Westminster.

Christian at Play. Robert K. Johnston. LC 83-16552. Repr. of 1983 ed. 43.50 (2027548). Bks Demand UMI.

Christian at Prayer: An Illustrated Prayer Manual Attributed to Peter the Chanter. Richard C. Trexler. (Medieval & Renaissance Texts & Studies: Vol. 44). (Illus.). 1987. 25.00 (ISBN 0-86698-027-X). Medieval & Renaissance NY.

Christian at the Crossroads. Karl Rahner. Tr. by Jeremy Moiser from Ger. 250p. 1976. 5.95 (ISBN 0-8245-0207-8). Crossroad NY.

Christian Atheist. Ken McFarland. (Uplook Ser.). 16p. 1982. pap. 0.99 (ISBN 0-8163-0500-5). Pacific Pr Pub Assn.

Christian Attitude Toward War. Loraine Boettner. 104p. 1986. pap. 3.95 (ISBN 0-87552-118-5). Presby & Reformed.

Christian Attitudes Toward War & Peace. Roland H. Bainton. LC 60-12064. 1979. pap. 7.95 (ISBN 0-687-07027-9). Abingdon.

Christian Attitudes Towards the Emperor in the Fourth Century. Kenneth M. Setton. LC 41-13567. (Columbia University. Studies in Social Sciences: No. 482). Repr. of 1941 ed. 20.00 (ISBN 0-404-51482-0). AMS Pr.

Christian Babysitter's Handbook. Sarah Fletcher. 1985. pap. 3.95 (ISBN 0-570-03948-7, 12-2881). Concordia.

Christian Baptism. A. P. Gibbs. 1982. pap. 5.00 (ISBN 0-937396-62-1). Walterick Pubs.

Christian Baptism. John Murray. 1980. pap. 3.95 (ISBN 0-87552-343-9). Presby & Reformed.

Christian Baptism, Feet Washing & the Lord's Supper. H. M. Riggle. 264p. 3.50 (ISBN 0-686-29105-0). Faith Pub Hse.

Christian Bases of World Order. facsimile ed. H. A. Wallace et al. LC 75-134068. (Essay Index Reprint Ser). (Merrick Lectures, 1943). Repr. of 1943 ed. 19.00 (ISBN 0-8369-2490-8). Ayer Co Pubs.

Christian Beliefs & Anti-Semitism. Charles Y. Glock & Rodney Stark. LC 78-31750. (Univ. of California Five-Year Study of Anti-Semitism). 1979. Repr. of 1966 ed. lib. bdg. 24.75x (ISBN 0-313-20969-3, GLCB). Greenwood.

Christian Beliefs & Teachings. John C. Meyer. LC 81-40353. 116p. (Orig.). 1981. lib. bdg. 23.50 (ISBN 0-8191-1757-9); pap. text ed. 9.50 (ISBN 0-8191-1758-7). U Pr of Amer.

Christian Believing. Urban T. Holmes, III & John H. Westerhoff. (Church's Teaching Ser.: Vol. I). 144p. 1979. 5.95 (ISBN 0-8164-0418-6, HarpR); pap. 3.95 (ISBN 0-8164-2214-1); study guide 1.50 (ISBN 0-8164-2221-4). Har-Row.

Christian Biblical Ethics. Robert J. Daly. (Orig.). 1984. pap. 9.95 (ISBN 0-8091-2592-7). Paulist Pr.

Christian Blessedness (with) Reflections upon a Late Essay Concerning Human Understanding. John Norris. Ed. by Rene Wellek. LC 75-11241. (British Philosophers & Theologians of the 17th & 18th Centuries Ser.). 1978. Repr. of 1690 ed. lib. bdg. 51.00 (ISBN 0-8240-1793-5). Garland Pub.

Christian Book of Mystical Verse. Ed. by A. W. Tozer. 1975. Repr. 9.95 (ISBN 0-87509-381-7). Chr Pubns.

Christian Book of Why. John C. McCollister. 340p. 1983. 11.95 (ISBN 0-8246-0297-8). Jonathan David.

Christian Book of Why. John C. McCollister. 360p. 1986. pap. 7.95 (ISBN 0-8246-0317-6). Jonathan David.

Christian Building: Final Report VIII, Part II. Carl H. Kraeling. LC 43-2669. 32.50 (ISBN 0-685-71744-5). J J Augustin.

Christian Call to Justice & Peace. Joseph Stoutzenberger. (Illus.). 250p. (Orig.). 1987. pap. text ed. 11.00 (ISBN 0-88489-180-1). St Mary's.

Christian Capitalism. Arthur F. Hallam. 182p. (Orig.). 1981. pap. 14.95 (ISBN 0-938770-00-4). Capitalist Pr OH.

Christian Capitalist Sermons One Thru Twenty-Six. Arthur F. Hallam. 232p. 1983. pap. 30.00 (ISBN 0-938770-02-0). Capitalist Pr OH.

Christian Care & Counseling: A Practical Guide. Roger F. Hurding. (Illus.). 128p. (Orig.). 1983. pap. 4.95 (ISBN 0-8192-1321-7). Morehouse.

Christian Caregiving: A Way of Life. Kenneth C. Haugk. LC 84-24341. (Orig.). 1984. pap. 7.95 (ISBN 0-8066-2123-0, 10-1103). Augsburg.

Christian Caregiving: A Way of Life, Leaders Guide. Kenneth Haugh & William J. McKay. LC 86-10931. 128p. (Orig.). 1986. pap. 8.95 (ISBN 0-8066-2224-5, 10-1104). Augsburg.

Christian Catalogue. McCollister. LC 77-29136. Date not set. 12.50 (ISBN 0-8246-0226-9). Jonathan David.

Christian Celebration: A Three-in-One Textbook. J. D. Chrichton. 604p. (Orig.). pap. text ed. 22.50 (ISBN 0-225-66399-6, HarpR). Har-Row.

Christian Celebration of Marriage. 32p. 1987. pap. 3.25 (ISBN 0-8006-1973-0). Fortress.

Christian Centuries: Church in a Secularized Society, Vol. 5. Roger Aubert. LC 78-53496. 820p. 1978. 22.95 (ISBN 0-8091-0244-7). Paulist Pr.

Christian Centuries, Vol. 1: First Six Hundred Years. Jean Danielou & Henri Marrou. LC 78-55069. (Illus.). 610p. 1969. 22.95 (ISBN 0-8091-0275-7). Paulist Pr.

Christian Centuries, Vol. 2: Middle Ages. David Knowles & Dimitri Obolensky. LC 63-22123. 628p. 1969. 22.95 (ISBN 0-8091-0276-5). Paulist Pr.

Christian Century in Japan: Fifteen Forty-Nine to Sixteen Fifty. C. R. Boxer. (California Library Reprint Ser: No. 51). (Illus.). 552p. 1974. Repr. of 1967 ed. 49.50x (ISBN 0-520-02702-7). U of Cal Pr.

Christian Century Reader: Representative Articles, Editorials, & Poems Selected from More Than Fifty Years of the Christian Century. Ed. by Harold E. Fey & Margaret Frakes. LC 72-331. (Essay Index Reprint Ser.). Repr. of 1962 ed. 24.50 (ISBN 0-8369-2786-9). Ayer Co Pubs.

Christian Character. Andrea Sterk & Peter Scazzero. (Lifebuilder Bible Studies). 60p. (Orig.). 1985. pap. text ed. 2.95 (ISBN 0-8308-1054-4). Inter-Varsity.

Christian Character Course. Keith L. Brooks. (Teach Yourself the Bible Ser). 1961. pap. 2.75 (ISBN 0-8024-1301-3). Moody.

Christian Charm Course. Rev. ed. Wayne Hunter & Emily Hunter. 1986. Repr. of 1967 ed. tchr's ed., 112 pp. 7.95 (ISBN 0-89081-509-7, 5097); student's wkbk., 56 pp 4.95 (ISBN 0-89081-508-9, 5089). Harvest Hse.

Christian Child Development. Iris V. Cully. LC 78-19507. 176p. 1983. pap. 6.95 (ISBN 0-06-061654-7, RD/453, HarpR). Har-Row.

Christian Child Rearing & Personality Development. Paul D. Meier. 1977. pap. 6.95 (ISBN 0-8010-6016-8). Baker Bk.

Christian Childhoods: An Anthology of Personal Memories. C. S. Lewis et al. Ed. by Celia Van Oss. 270p. 1986. 15.95 (ISBN 0-8245-0695-2); pap. cancelled (ISBN 0-8245-0696-0). Crossroad NY.

Christian Church. Christopher Wright. (Today's World Ser.). (Illus.). 72p. 1982. 16.95 (ISBN 0-7134-4279-4, Pub. by Batsford England). David & Charles.

Christian Church & Liberty. Alexander J. Carlyle. LC 68-56734. (Research & Source Works Ser.: No. 214). 1968. Repr. of 1924 ed. 14.50 (ISBN 0-8337-0476-1). B Franklin.

Christian Church & the Equal Rights Amendment. Edward M. Robbins. Ed. by Helen Graves. LC 85-40892. 80p. 1986. pap. 6.95 (ISBN 0-938232-95-9, Dist. by Baker & Taylor Co.). Winston-Derek.

Christian Church at Dura-Europos. C. Hopkins & P. V. Baur. (Illus.). 1934. pap. 39.50x (ISBN 0-686-50041-5). Elliots Bks.

Christian Church: Its Rise & Progress. H. M. Riggle. 488p. 5.00 (ISBN 0-686-29144-1). Faith Pub Hse.

Christian Church Plea. H. Eugene Johnson. LC 75-12012. (New Life Bks). 96p. 1975. pap. 2.95 (ISBN 0-87239-053-5, 40028). Standard Pub.

Christian Churches at the Crossroads. Ben Coe. LC 80-27624. 160p. (Orig.). 1980. pap. 5.95 (ISBN 0-87808-178-X). William Carey Lib.

Christian Churches in the United States, 1800-1983. Martin E. Marty. (Illus.). 126p. 1984. 12.95 (ISBN 0-86683-172-X, 1412, HarpR). Har-Row.

Christian Churches of America. rev. ed. Milton V. Backman, Jr. 288p. 1984. 17.95 (ISBN 0-684-17992-X, P656, ScribT); pap. 12.95 (ISBN 0-684-17995-4). Scribner.

Christian Churches of American Origins & Beliefs. rev. ed. Milton V. Backman, Jr. 278p. 1983. pap. text ed. write for info. (ISBN 0-02-305090-X, Pub. by Scribner). Macmillan.

Christian Classics Revisited. James J. Thompson, Jr. LC 82-84583. 163p. (Orig.). 1983. pap. 8.95 (ISBN 0-89870-028-0). Ignatius Pr.

Christian Commonwealth: Or, the Civil Policy of the Rising Kingdom of Jesus Christ. John Eliot. LC 77-141110. (Research Library of Colonial Americana). 1972. Repr. of 1659 ed. 18.00 (ISBN 0-405-03323-0). Ayer Co Pubs.

Christian Communicator's Handbook. rev. ed. Floyd A. Craig. LC 77-80946. 1977. pap. 8.95 (ISBN 0-8054-3508-5). Broadman.

Christian Compassion & Social Concern. 1.75 (ISBN 0-911802-62-2). Free Church Pubns.

Christian Confronts His Culture. Richard A. Fowler & H. Wayne House. 228p. (Orig.). 1983. pap. 7.95 (ISBN 0-8024-0232-1). Moody.

Christian Conscience. John Y. Clagett. LC 84-9824. 1984. pap. 3.95 (ISBN 0-87227-097-1). Reg Baptist.

Christian Conscience & War. John O. Nelson. 47p. 1950. pap. 1.00 (ISBN 0-8361-1547-3). Herald Pr.

Christian Considers Divorce & Remarriage. E. Earl Joiner. LC 81-70411. 1983. pap. 5.95 (ISBN 0-8054-5427-6). Broadman.

Christian Conversion in Context. Hans Kasdorf. LC 80-12871. 208p. 1980. pap. 9.95 (ISBN 0-8361-1926-6). Herald Pr.

Christian Converts & Social Protest in Meiji Japan. Irwin Scheiner. LC 74-94981. (Center for Japanese Studies). 1970. 35.00x (ISBN 0-520-01585-1). U of Cal Pr.

Christian Cornerstone Library: The Cost of Discipleship - Mere Christianity - Your God Is Too Small, 3 vols. Dietrich Bonhoeffer et al. 672p. 1987. Set. pap. 12.95 (ISBN 0-02-084440-9, Collier). Macmillan.

Christian Counseling. Gary R. Collins. 1980. pap. 13.95 (ISBN 0-8499-2889-3). Word Bks.

Christian Counselor's Casebook. Jay E. Adams. (Companion Vol. to Christian Counselor's Manual). 1976. pap. 5.95 (ISBN 0-8010-0075-0). Baker Bk.

Christian Counselor's Casebook. Jay E. Adams. 223p. 1974. pap. 7.95 (ISBN 0-87552-012-X). Presby & Reformed.

Christian Counselor's Casebook. Jay E. Adams. (Jay Adams Library). 224p. 1986. pap. 7.95 (ISBN 0-310-51161-5, 12128). Zondervan.

Christian Counselor's Handbook. Ed. by Christian Broadcasting Network Staff. 240p. 1987. pap. 8.95 (ISBN 0-8423-0255-7). Tyndale.

Christian Counselor's Manual. Jay E. Adams. 490p. 1973. 19.95 (ISBN 0-87552-013-8). Presby & Reformed.

Christian Counselor's Manual: The Practice of Nouthetic Counseling. Jay E. Adams. (Jay Adams Library). 496p. 1986. 16.95 (ISBN 0-310-51150-X, 12127). Zondervan.

Christian Counselor's New Testament. Jay E. Adams. 1977. 24.95 (ISBN 0-8010-0119-6). Baker Bk.

Christian Counselor's Pocket Guide. rev. ed. Selwyn Hughes. LC 80-65443. 96p. 1985. pap. 3.50 (ISBN 0-87123-844-6, 200047). Bethany Hse.

Christian Counselor's Wordbook. Jay E. Adams. 1981. pap. 1.95 (ISBN 0-8010-0172-2). Baker Bk.

Christian Counselor's Wordbook: A Primer of Nouthetic Counseling. Jay E. Adams. 90p. 1981. pap. 1.95 (ISBN 0-87552-069-3). Presby & Reformed.

Christian Countermoves in a Decadent Culture. Carl F. Henry. LC 86-5286. (Orig.). 1986. 9.95 (ISBN 0-88070-151-X). Multnomah.

Christian Couple. Larry Christenson & Nordis Christenson. LC 77-24085. 1977. pap. 5.95 (ISBN 0-87123-051-8); study guide 1.50 (ISBN 0-87123-046-1, 210046). Bethany Hse.

Christian Creeds. Monika Hellwig. 112p. 1973. pap. 1.95 (ISBN 0-8278-9057-5, Pub. by Pflaum Pr). Peter Li.

Christian Criticism in the Twentieth Century. Norman R. Cary. (National University Publications Literary Criticism Ser.). 1976. 17.95x (ISBN 0-8046-9104-5, Pub. by Kennikat). Assoc Faculty Pr.

Christian Cross-Cultural Communication. Ralph Robson & Jean Billings. (Mini Bible Studies). (Illus.). 1978. pap. 2.50 instructor (ISBN 0-87239-202-3, 88555); pap. 1.95 student (ISBN 0-87239-198-1, 88551). Standard Pub.

Christian Democracy in Western Europe, 1820-1953. Michael P. Fogarty. LC 73-11997. (Illus.). 448p. 1974. Repr. of 1957 ed. lib. bdg. 26.75x (ISBN 0-8371-7114-8, FOCH). Greenwood.

Christian Democracy in Western Germany. Geoffrey Pridham. LC 77-9235. 1978. 27.50x (ISBN 0-312-13396-0). St Martin.

Christian Democratic Parties of Western Europe. Ronald E. Irving. LC 78-41082. pap. 90.00 (ISBN 0-317-42290-1, 2023267). Bks Demand UMI.

Christian Devotedness. Norris A. Groves. pap. 1.95 (ISBN 0-937396-63-X). Walterick Pubs.

Christian Disciple. John E. Skinner. LC 83-21772. 92p. (Orig.). 1984. lib. bdg. 20.50 (ISBN 0-8191-3657-3); pap. text ed. 7.75 (ISBN 0-8191-3658-1). U Pr of Amer.

Christian Disciple, No. 2. Dan Caslow. 1984. pap. 1.95 (ISBN 0-8163-0497-1). Pacific Pr Pub Assn.

Christian Disciplines: Living the Way God Wants You to Live. Andrea Sterk & Peter Scazzero. (LifeBuilder Bible Studies). 64p. (Orig.). 1986. pap. 2.95 (ISBN 0-8308-1055-2). Inter-Varsity.

Christian Discourses. Soren Kierkegaard. Tr. by W. Lowrie. 1971. pap. 10.50x (ISBN 0-691-01973-8). Princeton U Pr.

Christian Doctrine. Walter T. Conner. 1940. 15.95 (ISBN 0-8054-1701-X). Broadman.

Christian Doctrine. John S. Whale. 1941. pap. 10.95 (ISBN 0-521-09642-1). Cambridge U Pr.

Christian Doctrine for the Instruction & Information of the Indians. Pedro De Cordoba. Tr. by Sterling A. Stoudemire. LC 79-121681. 1970. 7.95x (ISBN 0-87024-159-1). U of Miami Pr.

Christian Doctrine: Lectures & Sermons. J. Allen Miller. 1946. 2.50x (ISBN 0-934970-01-7). Brethren Ohio.

Christian Doctrine of Creation & Redemption. Emil Brunner. Tr. by Olive Wyon. LC 50-6821. (Dogmatic Ser.: Vol. 2). 396p. 1979. pap. 10.95 (ISBN 0-664-24248-0). Westminster.

Christian Doctrine of God. Emil Brunner. Tr. by Olive Wyon. LC 50-6821. (Dogmatics Ser.: Vol. 1). 376p. 1980. pap. 11.95 (ISBN 0-664-24304-5). Westminster.

Christian Doctrine of Man. H. Wheeler Robinson. 368p. 1958. 19.95 (ISBN 0-567-22219-5, Pub. by T & T Clark Ltd UK). Fortress.

Christian Doctrine of Slavery. George D. Armstrong. LC 69-16595. Repr. of 1857 ed. 22.50x (ISBN 0-8371-0892-6, ARC&, Pub. by Negro U Pr). Greenwood.

Christian Doctrine of the Church, Faith, & the Consummation. Emil Brunner. LC 50-6821. (Dogmatic Ser., Vol. 3). 472p. 1978. softcover o.s.i. 9.95 (ISBN 0-664-24218-9). Westminster.

Christian Doctrine: Teachings of the Christian Church. Shirley C. Guthrie, Jr. (Illus., Orig.). 1969. pap. 7.95 (ISBN 0-8042-9051-2). John Knox.

Christian Doctrine: The Faith... Once Delivered. W. Richardson. LC 82-25598. (Bible College Textbooks Ser.). 448p. (Orig.). 1983. pap. 9.95 (ISBN 0-87239-610-X, 88588). Standard Pub.

Christian Doctrines: A Compendium of Theology. James H. Pendleton. 16.95 (ISBN 0-8170-0037-2). Judson.

Christian Dogmatics, 2 vols. Ed. by Carl E. Braaten & Robert W. Jenson. LC 83-48007. 1984. Volume 1. 24.95 (ISBN 0-8006-0703-1); Volume 2. 24.95 (ISBN 0-8006-0704-X); Set. 45.95 (ISBN 0-8006-0712-0). Fortress.

Christian Dogmatics. John T Mueller. 1934. 18.95 (ISBN 0-570-03221-0, 15-1071). Concordia.

Christian Dogmatics, 4 Vols. Francis Pieper. Tr. by Theodore Engelder et al. 1950-1957. Vol. 1. 18.95 (ISBN 0-570-06712-X, 15-1001); Vol. 2. 18.95 (ISBN 0-570-06713-8, 15-1002); Vol. 3. 18.95 (ISBN 0-570-06714-6, 15-1003); Vol. 4. 25.95 (ISBN 0-570-06711-1, 15-1000); Set. 69.95 (ISBN 0-570-06715-4, 15-1852). Concordia.

Christian Education: An Introduction to Its Scope. Ed. by Douglas J. Simpson. 1979. 7.95 (ISBN 0-89265-053-2). Randall Hse.

Christian Education As Evangelism. Steve Clapp. 154p. (Orig.). 1982. pap. 9.00 (ISBN 0-914527-11-8). C-Four Res.

Christian Education Catalog. Ed. by Ruth G. Cheney. 192p. (Orig.). 1981. pap. 10.95 (ISBN 0-8164-2328-8, HarpR). Har-Row.

Christian Education Handbook. Ed. by Bruce P. Powers. LC 80-69522. 1981. pap. 9.95 (ISBN 0-8054-3229-9). Broadman.

Christian Education in China: A Study. China Educational Commission. LC 75-36223. Repr. of 1922 ed. 34.50 (ISBN 0-404-14474-8). AMS Pr.

Christian Education in Family Clusters. Mel Williams & Mary A. Brittain. 80p. 1982. pap. 6.95 (ISBN 0-8170-0936-1). Judson.

Christian Education in the Family. Susan Skoor. 1984. pap. text ed. 6.00 (ISBN 0-8309-0392-5). Herald Hse.

Christian Education in the Year Two Thousand. Marion E. Brown & Marjorie G. Prentice. 160p. 1984. pap. 5.95 (ISBN 0-8170-1055-6). Judson.

Christian Education: Its History & Philosophy. Kenneth O. Gangel & Warren S. Benson. 1983. 18.95 (ISBN 0-8024-3561-0). Moody.

Christian Education Materials for Youth & Families: Alcohol & Drugs. 54p. 1983. 6.95 (ISBN 0-89486-181-6). Hazelden.

Christian Education of Adults. Gilbert A. Peterson. 1985. text ed. 16.95 (ISBN 0-8024-0496-0). Moody.

Christian Education Thru Music. Alfred E. Lunde. LC 78-51509. (Evangelical Leadership Preparation Ser.). 80p. 1978. pap. 3.95 (ISBN 0-910566-83-6). Evang Tchr.

Christian Education: Total Task of the Church. H. D. Harrison. 28p. 1976. pap. 0.75 (ISBN 0-89265-101-6). Randall Hse.

Christian Employee. Robert Mattox. LC 77-20588. 1978. pap. 4.95 (ISBN 0-88270-263-7). Bridge Pub.

Christian Entrepreneur. Carl Kreider. LC 80-16836. (Conrad Grebel Lectures Ser.). 214p. 1980. pap. 8.95 (ISBN 0-8361-1936-3). Herald Pr.

Christian Epigraphy. Orazio Marucchi. Tr. by J. Armine Willis from It. LC 74-82057. 472p. 1975. 20.00 (ISBN 0-89005-070-8). Ares.

Christian Essays in Psychiatry. Philip Mairet. 1957. 7.95 (ISBN 0-8022-1038-4). Philos Lib.

Christian Ethic As An Economic Factor. facsimile ed. Josiah Stamp. LC 70-102256. (Select Bibliographies Reprint Ser). 1926. 17.00 (ISBN 0-8369-5141-7). Ayer Co Pubs.

Christian Ethics. J. Elliott Ross. 1951. 10.50 (ISBN 0-8159-5202-3). Devin.

Christian Ethics. Ed. by Lane A. Scott & Leon O. Hynson. (Wesleyan Theological Perspectives Ser.: Vol. III). 1983. 14.95 (ISBN 0-87162-267-X, D4852). Warner Pr.

Christian Ethics: A Primer. William M. Tillman, Jr. & Timothy D. Gilbert. LC 85-25474. 1986. pap. 5.95 (ISBN 0-8054-6128-0). Broadman.

Christian Ethics & Economics: The North South Conflict, Concilium 140. Ed. by Dietmar Mieth & Jacques Pohier. (New Concilium 1980). 128p. 1980. pap. 5.95 (ISBN 0-8164-2282-6, HarpR). Har-Row.

Christian Ethics & Imagination. Philip S. Keane. 224p. (Orig.). 1984. pap. 9.95 (ISBN 0-8091-2647-8). Paulist Pr.

Christian Ethics & Modern Problems. William R. Inge. Repr. of 1930 ed. lib. bdg. 22.50x (ISBN 0-8371-3960-0, INCE). Greenwood.

Christian Ethics & Political Action. Donald E. Messer. 176p. 1984. 8.95 (ISBN 0-8170-1018-1). Judson.

Christian Ethics & the Dilemmas of Foreign Policy. Kenneth W. Thompson. 160p. 1983. pap. text ed. 9.75 (ISBN 0-8191-3040-0). U Pr of Amer.

Christian Ethics & the Dilemmas of Foreign Policy. Kenneth W. Thompson. LC 59-15344. pap. 30.40 (ISBN 0-8357-9098-3, 2017937). Bks Demand UMI.

Christian Ethics for Black Theology. Major J. Jones. LC 74-8680. pap. cancelled (ISBN 0-317-30065-2, 2020267). Bks Demand UMI.

Christian Ethics for Today. William Barclay. LC 83-48994. 224p. 1984. pap. 7.95 (ISBN 0-06-060412-3, RD 512). Har-Row.

Christian Ethics for Today: An Evangelical Approach. Milton L. Rudnick. LC 79-53924. 1979. pap. 8.95 (ISBN 0-8010-7738-9). Baker Bk.

Christian Ethics in a Secular Arena. Josef Fuchs. Tr. by Bernard Hoose & Brian McNeil. LC 84-7964. 164p. (Orig.). 1984. pap. 9.95 (ISBN 0-87840-411-2). Georgetown U Pr.

Christian Ethics in Secular Society: An Introduction to Christian Ethics. Philip E. Hughes. 240p. 1983. 13.95 (ISBN 0-8010-4267-4). Baker Bk.

Christian Ethics in the Modern Age. Brian Hebblethwaite. LC 81-13105. 144p. 1982. pap. 6.95 (ISBN 0-664-24395-9). Westminster.

Christian Ethics-Sources of the Living Tradition. 2nd ed. Ed. by Waldo Beach & H. Richard Niebuhr. 550p. 1973. text ed. 25.00 (ISBN 0-394-34414-6). Random.

Christian Ethics: The Historical Development. R. E. White. pap. 11.95 (ISBN 0-8042-0791-7). John Knox.

Christian Evidences: Fulfilled Bible Prophecy. Alexander Keith. 456p. 1984. Repr. smythe sewn 20.00 (ISBN 0-86524-181-3, 9807). Klock & Klock.

Christian Evolution. Ursula Burton & Janice Dolley. 160p. 1984. pap. 9.95 (ISBN 0-85500-204-2). Newcastle Pub.

Christian Excellence. Jon Johnston. 1985. 9.95 (ISBN 0-8010-5215-7); pap. 6.95 (ISBN 0-8010-5195-9). Baker Bk.

Christian Experience. rev. ed. (Time of Life Learning Ser.). (Illus.). 32p. pap. 2.95 (ISBN 0-89622-246-2). Twenty-Third.

Christian Experience & Teaching of Ellen G. White. Ellen G. White. 1940. deluxe ed. 10.95 (ISBN 0-8163-0126-3, 03310-0). Pacific Pr Pub Assn.

Christian Experience of Salvation. William E. Hull. LC 84-20501. (Layman's Library of Christian Doctrine Ser.). 1987. 5.95 (ISBN 0-8054-1639-0). Broadman.

Christian Faith. Olin A. Curtis. LC 56-9279. 552p. 1971. 16.95 (ISBN 0-8254-2310-4). Kregel.

Christian Faith. Henri De Lubac. Tr. by Richard Arnandez from Fr. LC 84-80903. Orig. Title: Foi Chretienne. 353p. (Orig.). 1986. pap. 12.95 (ISBN 0-89870-053-1). Ignatius Pr.

Christian Faith. Henri De Lubac. 1986. pap. 12.95 (ISBN 0-317-52368-6, HarpR). Har-Row.

Christian Faith. rev. ed. Ed. by J. Neuner & J. Dupuis. LC 82-22700. 740p. 1983. pap. 13.95 (ISBN 0-8189-0453-4). Alba.

Christian Faith. David H. Read. LC 85-10473. 256p. 1985. pap. 9.95 (ISBN 0-8027-2515-5). Walker & Co.

Christian Faith. Friedrich Schleiermacher. Ed. by H. R. MacKintosh & J. S. Sterwart. Tr. of Christliche Glaube. 772p. 1928. 18.95 (ISBN 0-567-02239-0, Pub. by T&T Clark Ltd UK). Fortress.

Christian Faith: An Introduction to the Study of the Faith. rev. ed. Hendrikus Berkhof. Tr. by Sierd Woudstra from Dutch. 569p. 1986. 29.95 (ISBN 0-8028-3622-4). Eerdmans.

Christian Faith & Beliefs. Morris Ashcraft. LC 83-71872. 1984. 9.75 (ISBN 0-8054-1603-X). Broadman.

Christian Faith & Freedom: Proceedings. Fellowship of Catholic Scholars. Ed. by Paul L. Williams. LC 82-81072. 128p. (Orig.). 1982. pap. text ed. 4.50 (ISBN 0-686-97454-9). NE Bks.

Christian Faith & Historical Understanding. Ronald H. Nash. 176p. 1984. pap. 5.95 (ISBN 0-310-45121-3, 12379P). Zondervan.

Christian Faith & Life. William Temple. LC 82-80474. (Treasures from the Spiritual Classics Ser.). 64p. 1982. pap. 2.95 (ISBN 0-8192-1311-X). Morehouse.

Christian Faith & Natural Science. Karl Heim. 10.25 (ISBN 0-8446-0690-1). Peter Smith.

Christian Faith & Other Faiths. Stephen Neill. LC 84-19123. 304p. 1984. pap. 9.95 (ISBN 0-87784-337-6). Inter-Varsity.

Christian Faith & Public Choices: The Social Ethics of Barth, Brunner, & Bonhoeffer. Robin W. Lovin. LC 83-48922. 192p. 1984. pap. 10.95 (ISBN 0-8006-1777-0, 1-1777). Fortress.

Christian Faith & Secularism. Ed. by J. Richard Spann. LC 70-86062. (Essay & General Literature Index Reprint Ser). 1969. Repr. of 1948 ed. 28.50x (ISBN 0-8046-0589-0, Pub. by Kennikat). Assoc Faculty Pr.

Christian Faith & the Interpretation of History: A Study of St. Augustine's Philosophy of History. G. L. Keyes. LC 66-10314. xiv, 206p. 1966. 17.50x (ISBN 0-8032-0091-9). U of Nebr Pr.

Christian Faith & the Question of History. William N. Pittenger. LC 73-79353. pap. 39.00 (2026910). Bks Demand UMI.

Christian Faith & the Science of Today. J. H. Morrison. 12.50 (ISBN 0-8414-6676-9). Folcroft.
Christian Faith & War. Metropolitan Anthony Khrapovitsky. (Orig.). 1973. pap. 0.50 (ISBN 0-317-30278-7). Holy Trinity.
Christian Faith: Essays in Explanation & Defence. facsimile ed. Ed. by W. R. Matthews. LC 73-152162. (Essay Index Reprint Ser). Repr. of 1936 ed. 21.50 (ISBN 0-8369-2348-0). Ayer Co Pubs.
Christian Faith in a Religiously Plural World. Ed. by Donald G. Dawe & John B. Carman. LC 78-50927. 200p. (Orig.). 1978. pap. 7.95 (ISBN 0-88344-083-0). Orbis Bks.
Christian Faith: Introduction to Christian Thought. Dallas M. Roark. 1977. pap. 4.95 (ISBN 0-8010-7652-8). Baker Bk.
Christian Faith: The Challenge of the Call. Ronald J. Wilkins. 72p. 1978. pap. 4.20 (ISBN 0-697-01684-6); tchrs.' manual 4.50 (ISBN 0-697-01688-9); spirit masters 10.95 (ISBN 0-697-01690-0). Wm C Brown.
Christian Families in the Real World. Mitch Finley & Kathy Finley. 1984. pap. 8.95 (ISBN 0-88347-192-2). Thomas More.
Christian Family Activities for Families with Children. Wayne Rickerson. LC 82-10385. (Illus.). 96p. (Orig.). 1982. pap. 4.95 (ISBN 0-87239-569-3, 2964). Standard Pub.
Christian Family Activities for Families with Preschoolers. Wayne Rickerson. LC 82-5583. (Illus.). 96p. (Orig.). 1982. pap. 4.95 (ISBN 0-87239-568-5, 2963). Standard Pub.
Christian Family Activities for Families with Teens. Wayne Rickerson. LC 82-5833. (Illus.). 96p. (Orig.). 1982. pap. 4.95 (ISBN 0-87239-570-7, 2965). Standard Pub.
Christian Family Activities for One-Parent Families. Bobbie Reed. LC 82-5704. (Illus.). 96p. (Orig.). 1982. pap. 4.95 (ISBN 0-87239-571-5, 2966). Standard Pub.
Christian Family Almanac. Margot K. Hover & Monica E. Breidenbach. 128p. (Orig.). 1980. pap. 9.95 (ISBN 0-697-01740-0). Wm C Brown.
Christian Family Bedtime Reading Book. Ed. by Ron Klug & Lyn Klug. LC 82-70952. 128p. pap. 10.95 (ISBN 0-8066-1927-9, 10-1112). Augsburg.
Christian Family Craftbook. Burton Everist. LC 78-62064. (Illus.). 1978. pap. 5.95 (ISBN 0-8192-1239-3). Morehouse.
Christian Family Prepares for Christmas. Charles S. Mueller. 1965. laminated bdg. 3.75 (ISBN 0-570-03023-4, 6-1092). Concordia.
Christian Family Prepares for Easter. Ruth Geisler. 96p. (Orig.). 1985. pap. 6.95 (ISBN 0-570-03977-0, 12-2893). Concordia.
Christian Family Values. Thomas M. Martin. 128p. 1984. pap. 7.95 (ISBN 0-8091-2579-X). Paulist Pr.
Christian Fathers. Maurice Wiles. 1982. pap. 6.95x (ISBN 0-19-520260-0). Oxford U Pr.
Christian Feminism: Visions of a New Humanity. Ed. by Judith L. Weidman. LC 83-48462. 224p. 1984. 7.95i (ISBN 0-06-069292-8, HarpR). Har-Row.
Christian Feminist Perspectives on History, Theology & the Bible. Fredrica H. Thompsett. 56p. (Orig.). 1986. pap. 2.50 (ISBN 0-88028-051-4). Forward Movement.
Christian Folk Art: Crafts & Activities. Ann Elliott. (Illus.). 1979. pap. 4.95 (ISBN 0-8192-1250-4). Morehouse.
Christian Formation of Catholic Educators. Alfred McBride & O. Praem. 32p. 1981. 3.00 (ISBN 0-686-39896-3); member 2.25. Natl Cath Educ.
Christian Foundations: An Introduction to Faith in Our Time. Kathleen R. Fisher & Thomas N. Hart. 240p. 1986. pap. 9.95 (ISBN 0-8091-2817-9). Paulist Pr.
Christian Freedom: Essays in Honor of Vernon C. Grounds. Ed. by Kenneth W. Wozniak & Stanley J. Grenz. LC 86-24584. (Illus.). 284p. (Orig.). 1987. lib. bdg. 28.50 (ISBN 0-8191-5696-5); pap. text ed. 15.75 (ISBN 0-8191-5697-3). U Pr of Amer.
Christian Growth Series Leader's Guide. Jim Burns. 1986. 7.95 (ISBN 0-89081-555-0). Harvest Hse.
Christian Guide to Prosperity. 2nd ed. Michael Fries et al. Ed. by Diane Frank. LC 83-46178. (Illus.). 523p. 1984. pap. 9.95 (ISBN 0-9611910-5-8). Comm Res.
Christian Guide to Sexual Counseling: Recovering the Mystery & the Reality of "One Flesh". Mary A. Mayo. 288p. 1987. 16.95 (ISBN 0-310-35990-2). Zondervan.
Christian Handbook for Defending the Faith. Robert Morey. 1979. pap. 2.75 (ISBN 0-87552-336-6). Presby & Reformed.
Christian Handbook to the Psalms. R. E. White. 224p. (Orig.). 1984. pap. 7.95 (ISBN 0-8028-0031-9). Eerdmans.
Christian Harmony. Jeremiah Ingalls. (Earlier American Music Ser.: Vol. 22). 230p. 1981. Repr. of 1805 ed. lib. bdg. 29.50 (ISBN 0-306-79617-1). Da Capo.
Christian Healing. Charles Fillmore. 1909. 5.95 (ISBN 0-87159-017-4). Unity School.
Christian Healing Rediscovered. Roy Lawrence. LC 80-7470. 128p. (Orig.). 1980. pap. 3.95 (ISBN 0-87784-621-9). Inter-Varsity.
Christian Hebraists & Dutch Rabbis: Seventeenth Century Apologetics & the Study of Maimonides' Mishneh Torah. Aaron L. Katchen. (Harvard Judaic Texts & Studies: No. 3). 430p. 1985. text ed. 28.00x (ISBN 0-674-12865-6). Harvard U Ctr Jewish.
Christian Heroes of the Holocaust. Joseph J. Carr. LC 85-70538. 1985. pap. 3.50 (ISBN 0-88270-582-2). Bridge Pub.
Christian Higher Education in Changing China, 1880-1950. William P. Fenn. LC 75-43741. (Illus.). pap. 64.00 (ISBN 0-317-07969-7, 2012769). Bks Demand UMI.
Christian History & Interpretation: Studies Presented to John Knox. Ed. by William R. Farmer & C. F. Moule. LC 67-15306. pap. 116.00 (ISBN 0-317-08479-8, 2022449). Bks Demand UMI.
Christian Home. Mervin Baer. 1976. 1.95 (ISBN 0-686-11147-8). Rod & Staff.
Christian Home. pap. 4.95 (ISBN 0-88172-006-2). Believers Bkshelf.
Christian Home. Ralph Heynen. (Contemporary Discussion Ser.). (Orig.). 1974. pap. 1.25 (ISBN 0-8010-4109-0). Baker Bk.
Christian Home in Victorian America, 1840-1900. Colleen McDannell. LC 85-42947. (Religion in North America Ser.). (Illus.). 224p. 1986. 25.00x (ISBN 0-253-31376-7). Ind U Pr.
Christian Home Study Handbook 1986. Phillip G. Moormann. (Illus.). 170p. 1985. pap. 24.95 (ISBN 0-9614323-0-6). G Whitefield Pub.
Christian Hope. Brian Hebblethwaite. 248p. (Orig.). 1985. pap. 9.95 (ISBN 0-8028-0054-8). Eerdmans.
Christian Humanism, a Critique of the Secular City & Its Ideology. Thomas Molnar. 1978. 7.95 (ISBN 0-8199-0694-8). Franciscan Herald.
Christian Humanism & the Reformation: Selected Writings of Erasmus. 2nd ed. John C. Olin. LC 65-10218. (Illus.). xiv, 202p. 1975. pap. 9.00 (ISBN 0-8232-0988-1). Fordham.
Christian Humanism & the Reformation: Selected Writings with the Life of Erasmus by Beatus Rhenanus. Erasmus. Ed. by John C. Olin. 11.25 (ISBN 0-8446-2035-1). Peter Smith.
Christian Hymns Observed: When in Our Music God Is Glorified. Erik Routley. LC 82-61841. 121p. (Orig.). 1982. pap. text ed. 12.95 (ISBN 0-911009-00-0). Prestige Pubns.
Christian Iconography: A Study of Its Origins. Andre Grabar. LC 67-31114. (A. W. Mellon Lectures in the Fine Arts No. 10, Bollingen Ser: No. Xxxv). (Illus.). 432p. (Orig.). 1980. 66.00x (ISBN 0-691-09716-X); pap. 15.95x (ISBN 0-691-01830-8). Princeton U Pr.
Christian Ideals. 1970. pap. 2.85 (ISBN 0-87813-501-4). Christian Light.
Christian Identity & Theological Education. Joseph C. Hough, Jr. & John B. Cobb, Jr. (Studies in Religious & Theological Scholarship). 1985. pap. 11.95 (ISBN 0-89130-855-5, 00-08-01). Scholars Pr GA.
Christian Imagination: Essays on Literature & the Arts. Ed. by Leland Ryken. LC 80-70154. 344p. (Orig.). 1981. pap. 13.95 (ISBN 0-8010-7702-8). Baker Bk.
Christian in Complete Armour. William Gurnall. 1979. 26.95 (ISBN 0-85151-196-1). Banner of Truth.
Christian in Complete Armour: A Modernised Abridgement, Vol. 1. rev., abr. ed. William Gurnall. 320p. 1986. pap. 5.95 (ISBN 0-85151-456-1). Banner of Truth.
Christian in Wartime. Frederick H. Lynch. LC 71-147674. (Library of War & Peace; Relig. & Ethical Positions on War). 1972. lib. bdg. 46.00 (ISBN 0-8240-0431-0). Garland Pub.
Christian Indians & Indian Nationalism, 1885-1950: An Interpretation in Historical & Theological Perspectives. George Thomas. (IC-Studies in the Intercultural History of Christianity: Vol. 22). 271p. 1979. 28.10 (ISBN 3-8204-6399-2). P Lang Pubs.
Christian Initiation: A Comparative Study of the Interpretation of the Baptismal Liturgy in the Mystagogical Writing of Cyril of Jerusalem, John Chrysostom, Theodore of Mopsuetia, & Ambrose of Milan. Hugh M. Riley. LC 74-11191. (Catholic University of America Studies in Christian Antiquity: No. 17). pap. 128.80 (ISBN 0-317-27922-X, 2025126). Bks Demand UMI.
Christian Instruction, Admonition & Grace, The Christian Combat, Faith, Hope & Charity. St. Augustine. LC 66-20314. (Fathers of the Church Ser.: Vol. 2). 494p. 1950. 34.95x (ISBN 0-8132-0002-4). Cath U Pr.
Christian Introspection: Self-Ministry Through Self-Understanding. Robert J. Wicks. LC 83-1932. 128p. 1983. pap. 7.95 (ISBN 0-8245-0583-2). Crossroad NY.
Christian Island. Beram Saklatvala. LC 75-92561. (Illus.). 150p. 1970. 15.00 (ISBN 0-8386-7571-9). Fairleigh Dickinson.
Christian-Jewish Dialogue: Theological Foundations. Peter Von Der Osten-Sacken. Tr. by Margaret Kohl from Ger. LC 85-45481. 240p. 1986. 24.95 (ISBN 0-8006-0771-6, 1-771). Fortress.
Christian Job Hunter. Pam Moran. 224p. (Orig.). 1984. pap. 7.95 (ISBN 0-89283-178-2). Servant.
Christian Leader's & Speaker's Seminars. Florence Littauer. 100p. 1983. incl. lab manual & 12 cassettes 89.95 (ISBN 0-89081-369-8). Harvest Hse.
Christian Leaders of the Eighteenth Century: Includes Whitefield, Wesley, Grimshaw, Romaine, Rowlands, Berridge, Venn, Walker, Harvey, Toplady, & Fletcher. J. C. Ryle. 1978. pap. 7.45 (ISBN 0-85151-268-2). Banner of Truth.
Christian Leadership. Bruce P. Powers. LC 78-72841. 1979. 8.50 (ISBN 0-8054-3227-2). Broadman.
Christian Legal Advisor. John Eidsmoe. 1987. pap. 14.95 (ISBN 0-8010-3441-8). Baker Bk.
Christian Legends. George Every. LC 86-22242. (Library of the World's Myths & Legends). (Illus.). 144p. 1987. 18.95 (ISBN 0-87226-046-1). P Bedrick Bks.
Christian Letter of Certaine English Protestants Unto Mr. R. Hooker. Thomas Cartwright. LC 72-180. (English Experience Ser.: No. 202). 50p. 1969. Repr. of 1599 ed. 8.00 (ISBN 90-221-0202-5). Walter J Johnson.
Christian Liberty. Martin Luther. Ed. by Harold J. Grimm. Tr. by W. A. Lambert from Ger. 1943. pap. 1.50 (ISBN 0-8006-0182-3, 1-182). Fortress.
Christian Liberty. A. W. Pink. pap. 0.50 (ISBN 0-685-88370-1). Reiner.
Christian Life. Karl Barth. Ed. by Geoffrey W. Bromiley. LC 80-39942. 328p. 1981. 17.95 (ISBN 0-8028-3523-6). Eerdmans.
Christian Life. John Calvin. Ed. by John A. Leith. LC 83-48978. 112p. 1984. 10.45 (ISBN 0-06-061298-3, HarpR). Har-Row.
Christian Life. Perry Gillum. (Whole Man Whole World Bible Lessons Ser.). 151p. (Orig.). 1983. pap. 3.95 (ISBN 0-934942-46-3, 2418). White Wing Pub.
Christian Life & Worship. Gerald Ellard. 35.50 (ISBN 0-405-10819-2). Ayer Co Pubs.
Christian Life in Depth. Joseph A. Synan. 3.95 (ISBN 0-911866-60-4); pap. 2.95 (ISBN 0-911866-87-6). Advocate.
Christian Life in the Middle Ages & Other Essays. Frederick M. Powicke. LC 78-6723. (Illus.). vi, 176p. Repr. of 1935 ed. lib. bdg. 22.50x (ISBN 0-8371-9304-4, POCL). Greenwood.
Christian Life in the Primitive Church. Ernst Von Dobschutz. 1977. lib. bdg. 59.95 (ISBN 0-8490-1615-0). Gordon Pr.
Christian Life: Issues & Answers. Gary Maeder & Don Williams. LC 76-29258. 208p. 1977. pap. 3.50 (ISBN 0-8307-0470-1, 5404606). Regal.
Christian Life Patterns: The Psychological Challenges & Religious Invitations of Adult Life. Evelyn E. Whitehead & James D. Whitehead. LC 81-43442. 288p. 1982. pap. 4.95 (ISBN 0-385-15131-4). Doubleday.
Christian Living in the Home. Jay E. Adams. 1974. pap. 3.95 (ISBN 0-8010-0052-1). Baker Bk.
Christian Living in the Home. Jay E. Adams. 1972. pap. 3.95 (ISBN 0-87552-016-2). Presby & Reformed.
Christian Living: Ten Basic Virtues. Ralph F. Ranieri. 64p. 1983. pap. 1.50 (ISBN 0-89243-193-8). Liguori Pubns.
Christian Living: The Challenge of Response. Ronald J. Wilkins. 72p. 1978. pap. 4.20 (ISBN 0-697-01686-2); tchrs. manual 4.50 (ISBN 0-697-01689-7); spirit masters 10.95 (ISBN 0-697-01691-9). Wm C Brown.
Christian Looks at Himself. Anthony A. Hoekema. 1975. pap. 5.95 (ISBN 0-8028-1595-2). Eerdmans.
Christian Looks at the Jewish Question. Jacques Maritain. LC 73-2216. (Jewish People; History, Religion, Literature Ser.). Repr. of 1939 ed. 17.00 (ISBN 0-405-05280-4). Ayer Co Pubs.
Christian Love & Just War: Moral Paradox & Political Life in St. Augustine & His Modern Interpreters. William R. Stevenson, Jr. 256p. 1987. 29.95 (ISBN 0-86554-272-4, H235). Mercer Univ Pr.
Christian Love & Self-Denial: A Historical & Normative Study of Jonathan Edwards, Samuel Hopkins & American Theological Ethics. Stephen G. Post. 138p. (Orig.). 1987. lib. bdg. 22.50 (ISBN 0-8191-5261-7); pap. text ed. 8.75 (ISBN 0-8191-5262-5). U Pr of Amer.
Christian Magistrate & State Church: The Reforming Career of Johannes Brenz. James M. Estes. 208p. 1982. 30.00x (ISBN 0-8020-5589-3). U of Toronto Pr.
Christian Man. William Hamilton. LC 56-8666. (Layman's Theological Library). 94p. 1956. pap. 1.00 (ISBN 0-664-24003-8). Westminster.
Christian Manifesto. Francis A. Schaeffer. LC 81-69737. 192p. 1981. pap. 5.95 (ISBN 0-89107-233-0, Crossway Bks). Good News.
Christian Man's Promise Book. Lawrence O. Richards. 1986. pap. 2.50 (ISBN 0-310-43582-X, 18211P). Zondervan.
Christian Manual: Or, of the Life & Manners of True Christians. John Woolton. 1851. 21.00 (ISBN 0-384-69210-9). Johnson Repr.
Christian Marriage. The Office of Worship for the Presbyterian Church (U. S. A.) & the Cumberland Presbyterian Church Station. (Supplemental Liturgical Resource Ser.: 3). 120p. (Orig.). 1986. pap. 7.95 (ISBN 0-664-24033-X). Westminster.
Christian Marriage: A Journey Together. David M. Thomas. (Message of the Sacraments Ser.: Vol. 5). 13.95 (ISBN 0-89453-395-9); pap. 9.95 (ISBN 0-89453-231-6). M Glazier.
Christian Marriage: A Sacrament of Love. Ronald Wilkins & Mary Gryczka. (To Live Is Christ Ser.). (YA) 1986. pap. text ed. 7.25 (ISBN 0-697-02071-1); tchr's. ed. 15.95 (ISBN 0-697-02072-X); test wkbk. 14.95 (ISBN 0-697-02112-2). Wm C Brown.
Christian Marriage, Birth & Nature. rev. ed. Helen Wessel. LC 85-70830. 325p. Date not set. pap. cancelled (ISBN 0-933082-15-0). Bookmates Intl.
Christian Marriage Today: Growth or Breakdown? Ed. by Joseph A. Buijs. LC 85-10466. (Symposium Ser.: Vol. 16). 168p. 1985. 29.95x (ISBN 0-88946-707-2). E Mellen.
Christian Married Love. Malcolm Muggeridge et al. Ed. by Raymond Dennehy. Tr. by Sergia Englund & Erasmo Leiva. LC 81-85047. Tr. of Christlicher Stand. 132p. (Orig.). 1981. pap. 8.95 (ISBN 0-89870-008-6). Ignatius Pr.
Christian Maturity. E. Stanley Jones. (Festival Bks.). 1980. pap. 2.25 (ISBN 0-687-07453-3). Abingdon.
Christian Maturity Manual. rev. ed. David Wilkerson. LC 79-169590. 96p. 1977. 3.95 (ISBN 0-8307-0496-5, 5200121). Regal.
Christian Meditation. Edmund P. Clowney. 1979. pap. 2.50 (ISBN 0-934532-06-0). Presby & Reformed.
Christian Message for the World Today. facs. ed. E. S. Jones et al. LC 77-152163. (Essay Index Reprint Ser). 1934. 17.00 (ISBN 0-8369-2184-4). Ayer Co Pubs.
Christian Message for Today. Thomas J. Cooper & Willia S. Cooper. (Guidebook to Biblical Truth Ser.: Vol. 3). 60p. (Orig.). 1984. pap. 4.50 (ISBN 0-931429-03-X, TXU 109-949). Cooper & Cooper Pub.
Christian Method of Moral Judgment. J. Philip Wogaman. LC 76-40108. 282p. 1977. pap. 8.95 (ISBN 0-664-24134-4). Westminster.
Christian Mind. Harry Blamires. 1978. pap. 4.95 (ISBN 0-89283-049-2). Servant.
Christian Mind. Pascal. Ed. by James Houston. (Classics of Faith & Devotion Ser.). cancelled (ISBN 0-88070-159-5). Multnomah.
Christian Mindset in a Secular Society. Carl F. Henry. LC 83-25136. (Critical Concern Ser.). 1984. 9.95 (ISBN 0-88070-041-6); pap. 6.95. Multnomah.
Christian Minister. Sam E. Stone. LC 79-63601. (Bible College Textbooks Ser.). 256p. (Orig.). 1980. pap. text ed. 6.95 (ISBN 0-87239-348-8, 88580). Standard Pub.
Christian Minister's Manual. Rod Huron. (Illus.). 256p. (Orig.). 1984. skivertex 12.95 (ISBN 0-87239-753-X, 3028); sewn 19.95 (ISBN 0-87239-592-8, 3029). Standard Pub.
Christian Ministry. Charles Bridges. 1980. 13.95 (ISBN 0-85151-087-6). Banner of Truth.
Christian Ministry. J. B. Lightfoot. LC 83-62042. 120p. 1983. pap. 8.95 (ISBN 0-8192-1331-4). Morehouse.
Christian Ministry & the Fifth Step. Edward S. Sellner. 32p. 1981. pap. 1.95 (ISBN 0-89486-130-1). Hazelden.
Christian Mission: A Matter of Life. Everett L. Cattell. 160p. (Orig.). 1981. 11.95 (ISBN 0-913408-76-X); pap. 8.95 (ISBN 0-913408-68-9). Friends United.
Christian Mission & Social Justice. Samuel Escobar & John Driver. LC 78-6035. (Mennonite Missionary Study Ser.: No. 5). 112p. 1978. pap. 4.95 (ISBN 0-8361-1855-3). Herald Pr.
Christian Mission in the Modern World. John R. Stott. LC 75-21455. 128p. (Orig.). 1976. pap. 5.95 (ISBN 0-87784-485-2). Inter-Varsity.
Christian Missionaries & the Creation of Northern Rhodesia, 1880-1924. Robert I. Rotberg. 1965. 30.50x (ISBN 0-691-03009-X). Princeton U Pr.

Christian Missionary Enterprise in the Niger Delta, 1864-1918. G. O. Tasie. (Studies on Religion in Africa Ser.: No. 3). (Illus.). 1978. text ed. 49.95 (ISBN 90-04-05243-7). Humanities.

Christian Missions in Biblical Perspective. Herbert T. Kane. 14.95 (ISBN 0-8010-5370-6). Baker Bk.

Christian Missions in Nigeria, Eighteen Forty-One to Eighteen Ninety-One: The Making of a New Elite. J. F. Ajayi. 1965. 19.95 (ISBN 0-8101-0038-X). Northwestern U Pr.

Christian Moral Vision. Earl H. Brill. (Church's Teaching Ser.: Vol. 6). 254p. 1979. 5.95 (ISBN 0-8164-0423-2, HarpR); pap. 4.95 (ISBN 0-8164-2219-2). Har-Row.

Christian Morality & You: Student Text. Rev. ed. Michael Pennock & James Finley. LC 83-73085. (High School Religion Text Programs). (Illus.). 200p. 1984. pap. 5.95 (ISBN 0-87793-308-1). Ave Maria.

Christian Morality & You: Teacher Manual. Rev. ed. Michael Pennock. (High School Religion Text Program). 152p. 1984. 7.95 (ISBN 0-87793-311-1). Ave Maria.

Christian Morality: Biblical Foundations. Raymond F. Collins. LC 85-41020. 256p. 1986. 22.95 (ISBN 0-268-00758-6). U of Notre Dame Pr.

Christian Morality: Biblical Foundations. Raymond F. Collins. LC 85-41020. 258p. 1987. pap. text ed. 10.95x (ISBN 0-268-00759-4, Dist. by Har-Row). U of Notre Dame Pr.

Christian Morality, Natural, Developing, Final. Herbert H. Henson. LC 77-27189. (Gifford Lectures: 1935-36). Repr. of 1936 ed. 27.00 (ISBN 0-404-60494-3). AMS Pr.

Christian Morals. 2nd ed. T. Browne & Samuel Johnson. Ed. by S. C. Roberts. 1927. 20.00 (ISBN 0-527-12200-9). Kraus Repr.

Christian Mortalism from Tyndale to Milton. Norman T. Burns. LC 72-75406. 224p. 1972. 16.50x (ISBN 0-674-12875-3). Harvard U Pr.

Christian Mother Goose Trilogy, 3 Vols. Marjorie A. Decker. (Illus.). 336p. 1983. PLB 35.50 (ISBN 0-933724-14-4). Decker Pr Inc.

Christian Movement for Peace: Militarism & Hope. Canadian Christian Movement for Peace Staff et al. Ed. by Alyson Huntly & James Morin. 208p. 1983. pap. 29.95 (ISBN 0-697-01919-5). Wm C Brown.

Christian Music in Contemporary Witness: Historical Antecedents & Contemporary Practices. Donald P. Ellsworth. LC 79-52359. 1980. 7.95 (ISBN 0-8010-3338-1). Baker Bk.

Christian Mysticism. Harvey D. Egan. 300p. (Orig.). 1984. pap. 14.95 (ISBN 0-916134-63-6). Pueblo Pub Co.

Christian Mysticism. Harryl. Haywood. 59.95 (ISBN 0-87968-862-9). Gordon Pr.

Christian Mysticism: Psychotheology. William McNamara. LC 80-13139. 173p. 1981. 9.50 (ISBN 0-8199-0793-6). Franciscan Herald.

Christian Mysticism Today. William Johnston. LC 83-48418. 192p. 1984. 12.45i (ISBN 0-06-064202-5, HarpR). Har-Row.

Christian Mysticism Transcending Techniques: A Theological Reflection on the Empirical Testing of the Teaching of St. John of the Cross. Marilyn M. Mallory. 320p. 1977. pap. text ed. 28.00 (ISBN 90-232-1535-4, Pub. by Van Gorcum Holland). Longwood Pub Group.

Christian Myth & Ritual: A Historical Study. Edwin O. James. 11.25 (ISBN 0-8446-2307-5). Peter Smith.

Christian Neurosis. Pierre Solignac. 256p. 1982. 12.95 (ISBN 0-8245-0108-X). Crossroad NY.

Christian Non-Resistance. Adin Ballou. LC 70-121104. (Civil Liberties in American History Ser). 1970. Repr. of 1910 ed. lib. bdg. 35.00 (ISBN 0-306-71980-0). Da Capo.

Christian Non-Resistance in All Its Important Bearings, Illustrated & Defended. Adin Ballou. LC 76-137527. (Peace Movement in America Ser). 240p. 1972. Repr. of 1846 ed. lib. bdg. 18.95x (ISBN 0-89198-054-7). Ozer.

Christian Origins & Cultural Anthropology: Practical Models for Biblical Interpretation. Bruce J. Malina. 288p. 1985. pap. 24.95 (ISBN 0-8042-0241-9). John Knox.

Christian Origins & Judaism. W. D. Davies. LC 73-2192. (Jewish People; History, Religion, Literature Ser.). Repr. of 1962 ed. 22.00 (ISBN 0-405-05258-8). Ayer Co Pubs.

Christian Origins: From Messianic Movement to Christian Religion. Christopher Rowland. LC 85-70241. 448p. (Orig.). 1985. pap. 19.95 (ISBN 0-8066-2173-7, 10-1175). Augsburg.

Christian Origins in Sociological Perspective: Methods & Resources. Howard C. Kee. LC 79-26668. 204p. 1980. soft cover 9.95 (ISBN 0-664-24307-X). Westminster.

Christian Origins of Social Revolt. William D. Morris. LC 78-14133. 1979. Repr. of 1949 ed. 19.50 (ISBN 0-88355-805-X). Hyperion Conn.

Christian Orthodoxy Revisited. Michael E. Marshall. 137p. (Orig.). pap. 6.95 (ISBN 0-8192-1363-2). Morehouse.

Christian Pacifism. Michael Snow. LC 81-69724. 98p. (Orig.). 1982. pap. 6.95 (ISBN 0-913408-67-0). Friends United.

Christian Pacifism in History. Geoffrey Nuttall. pap. 1.25 (ISBN 0-912018-13-5). World Without War.

Christian Pagan: A Naturalistic Survey of Christian History. John H. Burgess. (Illus.). 1968. 7.00 (ISBN 0-912084-04-9). Mimir.

Christian Parent Burnout. Edith Lanstrom. LC 12-2979. (Continued Applied Christianity Ser.). 1983. pap. 2.95 (ISBN 0-570-03897-9). Concordia.

Christian Parenting. Ed. by Lee W. Carlson. 80p. 1984. pap. 6.95 (ISBN 0-8170-1072-6). Judson.

Christian Parenting & Child Care. William Sears. 544p. 1985. 19.95 (ISBN 0-8407-5422-1). Nelson.

Christian Parenting Handbook. Ed. by Maureen Gallagher. 2.95 (ISBN 0-8091-2262-6). Paulist Pr.

Christian Parish: Whispers of the Risen Christ. William J. Bausch. 232p. 1981. pap. 7.95 (ISBN 0-89622-146-6). Twenty-Third.

Christian Passover Celebration. Richard Blank. 1981. 2.95 (ISBN 0-89536-477-8, 0317). CSS of Ohio.

Christian Pastor. Rev. 3rd ed. Wayne E. Oates. LC 82-4933. 298p. 1982. pap. 9.95 (ISBN 0-664-24372-X). Westminster.

Christian Pattern. J. Wesley. pap. 2.75 (ISBN 0-686-12912-1). Schmul Pub Co.

Christian Pattern Book: Dozens of Creative Activities for Children. Herb Montgomery & Mary Montgomery. (Illus.). 64p. 1984. wkbk. 5.95 (ISBN 0-86683-831-7, HarpR). Har-Row.

Christian Peacemaking & International Conflict. Duane K. Friesen. LC 85-24803. 320p. (Orig.). 1986. pap. 19.95x (ISBN 0-8361-1273-3). Herald Pr.

Christian Perfection. Francois Fenelon. Ed. by Charles F. Whiston. Tr. by Mildred W. Stillman from Fr. LC 75-22545. 208p. 1976. pap. 4.95 (ISBN 0-87123-083-6, 200083). Bethany Hse.

Christian Perfection. Wesley et al. 6.95 (ISBN 0-686-12854-0). Schmul Pub Co.

Christian Perfection & American Methodism. John L. Peters. 1985. pap. 9.95 (ISBN 0-310-31241-8, 17043P). Zondervan.

Christian Periodical Index. Ed. by Barbara Nelson. 88p. 3 yr. cumulative 45.00 (ISBN 0-318-17810-9); 10.00 ea. Assn Chr Libs.

Christian Periodical Index: Annual. 1982. cancelled. Assn Chr Libs.

Christian Periodical Index: Annual & Quarterlies. 1980. cancelled. Assn Chr Libs.

Christian Periodical Index: Annual & Quarterly, 1985. 1985. 32.00 (ISBN 0-318-04217-7). Assn Chr Libs.

Christian Periodical Index: Cumulative, 1982-1984, Vol. 7. 1985. 45.00 (ISBN 0-318-04216-9). Assn Chr Libs.

Christian Periodical Index: Quarterlies, 1984. 10.00 (ISBN 0-318-01672-9). Assn Chr Libs.

Christian Periodical Index, 1976-1978. Cumulated vol. 35.00x (ISBN 0-686-37453-3). Assn Chr Libs.

Christian Periodical Index: 1979-1981, Cumulated Vol. 35.00 (ISBN 0-318-00379-1). Assn Chr Libs.

Christian Persecution & Genocide. William LeGrande. 1982. lib. bdg. 59.95 (ISBN 0-87700-392-0). Revisionist Pr.

Christian Personal Ethics. Carl F. Henry. (Twin Brooks Ser). 1977. pap. 12.95 (ISBN 0-8010-4165-1). Baker Bk.

Christian Perspectives on Controversial Issues. C. Donald Cole. 128p. (Orig.). 1983. pap. 3.50 (ISBN 0-8024-0165-1). Moody.

Christian Perspectives on Dating & Marriage. David Chadwell. 1980. pap. 4.95 (ISBN 0-89137-523-6). Quality Pubns.

Christian Perspectives on Psychology. Ed. by Richard Ruble. LC 75-15956. 147p. 1975. pap. text ed. 14.95x (ISBN 0-8422-0456-3). Irvington.

Christian Persuader. L. Ford. LC 66-22043. 160p. 1976. pap. 6.00 (ISBN 0-06-062679-8, RD/157, HarpR). Har-Row.

Christian Philosopher: A Collection of the Best Discoveries in Nature, with Religious Improvements. Cotton Mather. LC 68-29082. 1968. Repr. of 1721 ed. 45.00x (ISBN 0-8201-1033-7). Schol Facsimiles.

Christian Philosophy & Its Future. Gerard Smith. 144p. 8.95 (ISBN 0-87462-439-8). Marquette.

Christian Philosophy of Culture. D. Roper. Date not set. pap. 3.95x cancelled (ISBN 0-86990-540-6). Radix Bks.

Christian Philosophy of Education. 2nd, rev. ed. Gordon H. Clark. (Trinity Papers: No. 7). 250p. 1987. pap. 8.95 (ISBN 0-940931-20-6). Trinity Found.

Christian Philosophy of St. Augustine. Etienne Gilson. xii, 398p. 1983. Repr. of 1960 ed. lib. bdg. 35.00 (ISBN 0-88254-873-5, Octagon). Hippocrene Bks.

Christian Philosophy of St. Thomas Aquinas. Etienne Gilson. x, 502p. 1983. Repr. of 1956 ed. lib. bdg. 45.00 (ISBN 0-88254-874-3, Octagon). Hippocrene Bks.

Christian Platonists of Alexandria: Eight Lectures. Charles Bigg. LC 75-123764. Repr. of 1886 ed. 27.50 (ISBN 0-404-00799-6). AMS Pr.

Christian Poet in Paradise Lost. William G. Riggs. 1972. 30.00x (ISBN 0-520-02081-2). U of Cal Pr.

Christian Polity of John Calvin. Harro Hopfl. (Cambridge Studies in the History & Theory of Politics). 320p. 1985. pap. 14.95 (ISBN 0-521-31638-3). Cambridge U Pr.

Christian Prayer. Ladislaus Boros. 1976. 5.95 (ISBN 0-8245-0208-6). Crossroad NY.

Christian Prayer. (Two Color Sight-Saving Type, Ribbon Markers). maroon bdg., colored edges 22.50 (ISBN 0-89942-406-6, 406/10); annual guide 1.00 (ISBN 0-686-14264-0, 406G); vinyl case o.s.i. 1.95 (ISBN 0-686-14265-9, 406C). Catholic Bk Pub.

Christian Prayer Through the Centuries. Josef Jungmann. LC 78-61729. Orig. Title: Christliches Beten. 176p. 1978. pap. 3.95 (ISBN 0-8091-2167-0). Paulist Pr.

Christian Prayers & Holy Meditations. Ed. by Henry Bull. 1842. 21.00 (ISBN 0-384-06285-7). Johnson Repr.

Christian Preparation for Death. Saint Cyprian. pap. 1.50 (ISBN 0-686-25548-8). Eastern Orthodox.

Christian Primer. Louis Cassels. 112p. 1981. pap. 1.50 (ISBN 0-88028-012-3). Forward Movement.

Christian Problem: A Jewish View. Stuart E. Rosenberg. 304p. 1986. 15.95 (ISBN 0-87052-284-1). Hippocrene Bks.

Christian Protagonists for Jewish Restoration: An Original Anthology. Ed. by Moshe Davis. LC 77-70678. (America & the Holy Land Ser.). 1977. lib. bdg. 20.00x (ISBN 0-405-10221-6). Ayer Co Pubs.

Christian Psychiatry. Lawrence W. Jordan. 112p. 1984. pap. 8.95 (ISBN 0-8059-2910-X). Dorrance.

Christian Psychology. Hani R. Abdu. 288p. 1981. 11.00 (ISBN 0-682-49643-X). Exposition Pr FL.

Christian Psychology: Toward a New Synthesis. John M. McDonagh. 144p. 1982. 9.95 (ISBN 0-8245-0449-6). Crossroad NY.

Christian Readings, 6 vols. Incl. Vol. 1. Easter to 17th Sunday, Year II. red bdg. 4.00 (ISBN 0-89942-601-8, 601/04); Vol. 2. 17th Sunday to Advent, Year II. green bdg. 4.00 (ISBN 0-89942-602-6, 602/04); Vol. 3. Advent to Easter, Year I. purple bdg. 4.00 (ISBN 0-89942-603-4, 603/04); Vol. 4. Easter to 17th Sunday, Year I. tan bdg. 4.00 (ISBN 0-89942-604-2, 604/04); Vol. 5. 17th Sunday to Advent, Year I. brown bdg. 4.00 (ISBN 0-89942-605-0, 605/04); Vol. 6. Advent to Easter, Year II. blue bdg. 4.00 (ISBN 0-89942-606-9, 606/04). Catholic Bk Pub.

Christian Realism & Liberation Theology: Practical Theologies in Creative Conflict. Dennis P. McCann. LC 80-23163. 256p. (Orig.). 1981. pap. 9.95 (ISBN 0-88344-086-5). Orbis Bks.

Christian Realism & Political Problems. Reinhold Niebuhr. LC 75-128062. 1977. Repr. of 1953 ed. 19.50x (ISBN 0-678-02757-9). Kelley.

Christian Reconstruction: The American Missionary Association & Southern Blacks, 1861-1890. Joe M. Richardson. LC 85-13946. (Illus.). 352p. 1986. 30.00x (ISBN 0-8203-0816-1). U of GA Pr.

Christian Recovery of Spain. H. E. Watts. 69.95 (ISBN 0-87968-863-7). Gordon Pr.

Christian Reflections. C. S. Lewis. 1974. pap. 4.95 (ISBN 0-8028-1430-1). Eerdmans.

Christian Religion. Georg W. Hegel. Ed. by Georg Lasson. Tr. by Peter C. Hodgson from Ger. LC 79-424. (American Academy of Religion, Texts & Translation Ser.: No. 2). 1979. pap. 10.25_o.s. (ISBN 0-89130-276-X, 010202). Scholars Pr GA.

Christian Religion in the Soviet Union: A Sociological Study. Christel Lane. LC 77-801. 1978. 49.50 (ISBN 0-87395-327-4). State U NY Pr.

Christian Religious Education: Sharing Our Story & Vision. Thomas H. Groome. LC 81-47847. 320p. 1982. pap. text ed. 12.95 (ISBN 0-06-063494-4, RD 371, HarpR). Har-Row.

Christian Renaissance: With Interpretations of Dante, Shakespeare & Goethe & New Discussions of Oscar Wilde & the Gospel of Thomas. G. Wilson Knight. LC 81-40252. 366p. 1982. lib. bdg. 32.00 (ISBN 0-8191-1913-X); pap. text ed. 16.50 (ISBN 0-8191-1914-8). U Pr of Amer.

Christian Renewal: Living Beyond Burnout. Charles L. Rassieur. LC 83-26064. (Potentials: Guides for Productive Living: Vol. 5). 120p. (Orig.). 1984. pap. 7.95 (ISBN 0-664-24611-7). Westminster.

Christian Response to Domestic Violence: A Reconciliation Model for Social Workers. (Practice Monograph Ser.). 50p. 6.00 (ISBN 0-318-17617-3). N American Assn.

Christian Response to Islam. William M. Miller. 1976. pap. 4.95 (ISBN 0-87552-335-8). Presby & Reformed.

Christian Response to the Asian Revolution. M. M. Thomas. 1968. pap. 1.75 (ISBN 0-377-82701-0). Friend Pr.

Christian Response to the Sexual Revolution. David R. Mace. (Orig.). 1970. pap. 7.75 (ISBN 0-687-07570-X). Abingdon.

Christian Responsibility in a Hungry World. C. Dean Freudenberger & Paul M. Minus, Jr. LC 75-43764. 1976. pap. 3.25 (ISBN 0-687-07567-X). Abingdon.

Christian Revelation. Borden P. Bowne. LC 75-3069. Repr. of 1898 ed. 20.00 (ISBN 0-404-59068-3). AMS Pr.

Christian Revolutionary: John Milton. Hugh M. Richmond. 1974. 32.50x (ISBN 0-520-02443-5). U of Cal Pr.

Christian Ritual & the World of Shakespeare's Tragedies. Herbert R. Coursen, Jr. 441p. 1976. 32.50 (ISBN 0-8387-1518-4). Bucknell U Pr.

Christian Rosenkreutz Anthology, Vol. 10. 2nd, rev. ed. Ed. by Paul M. Allen. LC 68-13130. (Spiritual Science Library). (Illus.). 640p. 1981. Repr. of 1968 ed. lib. bdg. 65.00 (ISBN 0-89345-009-X, Steinerbks). Garber Comm.

Christian Sacraments of Initiation, Baptism, Confirmation, Eucharist. Kenan B. Osborne. 1987. pap. 12.95. Paulist Pr.

Christian Sacrifice: The Judaeo-Christian Background Before Origen. Robert J. Daly. LC 78-12004. (Studies in Christian Antiquity: Vol. 18). 587p. 1978. 26.95x (ISBN 0-8132-0530-1). Cath U Pr.

Christian Satisfaction in Aquinas: Towards a Personalist Understanding. Romanus Cessario. LC 81-43836. 390p. (Orig.). 1982. lib. bdg. 32.00 (ISBN 0-8191-2557-1); pap. text ed. 15.75 (ISBN 0-8191-2558-X). U Pr of Amer.

Christian Scholar. Adron Doran & J. E. Choate. 1985. 14.95 (ISBN 0-89225-279-0); pap. 8.95 (ISBN 0-89225-282-0). Gospel Advocate.

Christian Scholar: An Introduction to Theological Research. Gregory G. Bolich. 352p. (Orig.). 1986. lib. bdg. 30.00 (ISBN 0-8191-5135-1, Pub. by Inst Christ Stud); pap. text ed. 15.75 (ISBN 0-8191-5136-X). U Pr of Amer.

Christian Scholar in the Age of the Reformation. Elmore H. Harbison. LC 83-16511. Repr. of 1983 ed. 46.80 (2027546). Bks Demand UMI.

Christian School Finance. James W. Deuink. (Illus.). 160p. 1985. pap. 6.60 (ISBN 0-89084-304-X). Bob Jones Univ Pr.

Christian Science. Mary B. Eddy. pap. 2.00 (ISBN 0-87516-021-2). De Vorss.

Christian Science. Anthony A. Hoekema. 1974. pap. 2.95 (ISBN 0-8028-1492-1). Eerdmans.

Christian Science. Salem Kirban. LC 75-124142. (Illus.). 1974. pap. 4.95 (ISBN 0-912582-11-1). Kirban.

Christian Science. Walter Martin. 32p. 1957. pap. 2.95 (ISBN 0-87123-064-X, 210064). Bethany Hse.

Christian Science. Mark Twain. 196p. 1986. 21.95 (ISBN 0-87975-316-1). Prometheus Bks.

Christian Science & Liberty. Robert E. Merritt & Arthur Corey. LC 70-132847. 1970. 5.50 (ISBN 0-87516-060-3). De Vorss.

Christian Science, Its "Clear, Correct Teaching" & Complete Writings. 2nd ed. Herbert W. Eustace. 1037p. 1985. 16.00 (ISBN 0-9611156-0-2). Eustace CSB.

Christian Science-Kingdom or Cult? Karl Roebling. 190p. 1984. 12.95 (ISBN 0-942910-09-5). Paragon-Dynapress.

Christian Science Today: Power, Policy, Practice. Charles S. Braden. LC 58-11399. 1958. 19.95 (ISBN 0-87074-024-5). SMU Press.

Christian Science Treatment. Ann Beals. 26p. 1979. pap. 2.00 (ISBN 0-930227-06-9). Pasadena Pr.

Christian Secret of a Happy Life. Smith. 2.50 (ISBN 0-318-18169-X). WCTU.

Christian Short Story. Ruth Hobbs. 10.95 (ISBN 0-686-32320-3). Rod & Staff.

Christian Social Potential: Junior High Unit. Ernest M. Ligon. (Research Curriculum for Character Education Ser.). 1978. lesson bk. 2.00 (ISBN 0-915744-12-0); junior high unit plan 0.75 (ISBN 0-915744-14-7); junior high home assignment sheets 0.75 (ISBN 0-915744-13-9). Character Res.

Christian Social Reformers of the Nineteenth Century. facsimile ed. Ed. by Hugh Martin. LC 70-107725. (Essay Index Reprint Ser.). 1927. 18.00 (ISBN 0-8369-1526-7). Ayer Co Pubs.

Christian Social Teachings. George W. Forell. LC 71-159003. 1971. pap. 7.95 (ISBN 0-8066-1126-X, 10-1179). Augsburg.

Christian Social Thought in India, 1962-77. Shiri Godwin. (Orig.). 1983. pap. 6.00 (ISBN 0-8364-0988-4, Pub. by Christian Lit Soc India). South Asia Bks.

Christian Socialism, Eighteen Forty-Eight to Eighteen Fifty-Four. Charles E. Raven. 396p. 1968. Repr. of 1920 ed. 35.00x (F Cass Co). Biblio Dist.
Christian Socialism, Eighteen Forty-Eight to Eighteen Fifty-Four. Charles E. Raven. LC 68-56058. 1968. Repr. of 1920 ed. 35.00x (ISBN 0-678-05148-8). Kelley.
Christian Society. George D. Herron. 1969. Repr. of 1894 ed. 19.00 (ISBN 0-384-22640-X). Johnson Repr.
Christian Society & the Crusades, 1198-1229: Sources in Translation, Including the Capture of Damietta. Ed. by Edward Peters. LC 78-163385. (Middle Ages Ser). 1971. 21.00x (ISBN 0-8122-7644-2); pap. 9.95x (ISBN 0-8122-1024-7, Pa Paperbks). U of Pa Pr.
Christian Soldier. D. Martyn Lloyd-Jones. 12.95 (ISBN 0-8010-5583-0). Baker Bk.
Christian Sourcebook. Carol Ward. 1986. 16.95 (ISBN 0-345-32248-7, Pub. by Ballantine Epiphany). Ballantine.
Christian Spirituality. George A. Lane. 88p. 1984. pap. 3.95 (ISBN 0-8294-0450-3). Loyola.
Christian Spirituality. Bernard McGinn & John Meyendorf. (World Spirituality Ser.). 1985. 49.50x (ISBN 0-8245-0681-2). Crossroad NY.
Christian Spirituality. Wolfhart Pannenberg. LC 83-19662. 114p. (Orig.). 1983. pap. 8.95 (ISBN 0-664-24495-5). Westminster.
Christian Spirituality, Vol. 11. Ed. by Jill Raitt et al. (World Spirituality Ser.: Vol. 17). 528p. 1987. 49.50x (ISBN 0-8245-0765-7). Crossroad NY.
Christian Spirituality: A Theological History from the New Testament to Luther & St. John of the Cross. Rowan Williams. LC 80-82190. 193p. 1980. 10.95 (ISBN 0-8042-0660-0); pap. 8.95 (ISBN 0-8042-0508-6). John Knox.
Christian Spirituality: A Theological History From the New Testament to Luther & St. John of the Cross. Rowan Williams. LC 80-82190. pap. 50.30 (2027154). Bks Demand UMI.
Christian Spirituality for the Eighties. Claire Lowery. 96p. 1983. pap. 4.50 (ISBN 0-697-01940-3). Wm C Brown.
Christian Spirituality in the Catholic Tradition. Jordan Aumann. 336p. 1985. pap. 11.95 (ISBN 0-89870-068-X). Ignatius Pr.
Christian Standards & Convictions Without Legalism. F. Leroy Forlines. 1981. pap. 2.25 (ISBN 0-89265-074-5). Randall Hse.
Christian State: A Political Vision of Christ. George D. Herron. (American Studies). 1969. Repr. of 1894 ed. 22.00 (ISBN 0-384-22650-7). Johnson Repr.
Christian State after Death Before Resurrection. J. Urwin & S. J. Robinson. pap. 2.25 (ISBN 0-88172-164-6). Believers Bkshelf.
Christian State of Life. Hans Urs Von Balthasar. Tr. by Mary F. McCarthy from Ger. LC 82-84580. Tr. of Christlicher Stand. 505p. (Orig.). 1984. 24.95 (ISBN 0-89870-022-1). Ignatius Pr.
Christian State of Life. Adrienne Von Speyr. Tr. by Mary F. McCarthy from Ger. LC 85-81512. Orig. Title: Christlicher Stand. 213p. (Orig.). 1986. pap. 9.95 (ISBN 0-89870-044-2). Ignatius Pr.
Christian State of Matrimonye. Heinrich Bullinger. Tr. by Myles Coverdale. LC 74-80167. (English Experience Ser.: No. 646). 168p. 1974. Repr. of 1541 ed. 11.50 (ISBN 90-221-0646-2). Walter J Johnson.
Christian Stewards: Confronted & Committed. Waldo J. Werning. LC 12-2814. 1983. pap. 8.95 (ISBN 0-570-03879-0). Concordia.
Christian Story. rev. ed. Gabriel Fackre. 304p. 1985. pap. 12.95 (ISBN 0-8028-1989-3). Eerdmans.
Christian Student Dictionary. (Illus.). 862p. 1982. text ed. 15.95 (ISBN 0-89084-172-1). Bob Jones Univ Pr.
Christian Symbols & How to Use Them. Sr. Justina Knapp. LC 74-8172. (Illus.). 164p. 1975. Repr. of 1935 ed. 43.00x (ISBN 0-8103-4050-X). Gale.
Christian Symbols Handbook: Commentary & Patterns for Traditional & Contemporary Symbols. Dean L. Moe. 96p. (Orig.). 1985. pap. 9.95 (ISBN 0-8066-2153-2, 10-1180). Augsburg.
Christian System. Alexander Campbell. LC 73-83412. (Religion in America Ser). 1969. Repr. of 1871 ed. 20.00 (ISBN 0-405-00233-5). Ayer Co Pubs.
Christian, the Arts, & Truth: Regaining the Vision of Greatness. Frank E. Gaebelein. Frwd. by D. Bruce Lockerbie. LC 85-9005. (Critical Concern Bks.). 1985. 12.95 (ISBN 0-88070-114-5). Multnomah.
Christian, the Atheist, & Freedom. Joseph A. Magno & Victor S. LaMotte. LC 74-165170. 99p. 1975. 7.95 (ISBN 0-913750-08-5). Precedent Pub.
Christian Theism: A Study in Its Basic Principles. Huw P. Owen. 184p. 1984. 19.95 (ISBN 0-567-09336-0, Pub. by T&T Clark Ltd Uk). Fortress.
Christian Theistic Ethics. Cornelius Van Til. 1975. pap. 7.95 syllabus (ISBN 0-87552-478-8). Presby & Reformed.
Christian Theology. Emery Bancroft. Pref. by Ronald B. Mayers. 1976. 15.95 (ISBN 0-310-20440-2, 9141). Zondervan.
Christian Theology. rev. ed. R. R. Byrum. Ed. by Arlo F. Newell. 1982. 14.95 (ISBN 0-87162-252-1, D3051). Warner Pr.
Christian Theology, 1 vol. Ed. by Millard J. Erickson. 1986. 39.95 (ISBN 0-8010-3433-7). Baker Bk.
Christian Theology, Vol. 1. Millard J. Erickson. 432p. 1983. 19.95 (ISBN 0-8010-3391-8). Baker Bk.
Christian Theology, Vol. 2. Millard J. Erickson. 432p. 1984. 19.95 (ISBN 0-8010-3419-1). Baker Bk.
Christian Theology, Vol. 3. Millard J. Erickson. 1985. 19.95 (ISBN 0-8010-3425-6). Baker Bk.
Christian Theology: A Case Method Approach. Ed. by Robert A. Evans & Thomas D. Parker. LC 76-9963. 1976. pap. 9.95xi (ISBN 0-06-062252-0, HarpR, RD 176, HarpR). Har-Row.
Christian Theology: An Eschatological Approach, Vol. 1. Thomas Finger. 320p. 1985. text ed. 18.95 (ISBN 0-8407-7505-9). Nelson.
Christian Theology: An Introduction to Its Traditions & Tasks. rev. & enl. 2nd ed. Ed. by Peter C. Hodgson & Robert H. King. LC 84-48720. 432p. 1985. pap. 16.95 (ISBN 0-8006-1848-3, 1-1848). Fortress.
Christian Theology & Scientific Culture. Thomas F. Torrance. 1981. text ed. 14.95x (ISBN 0-19-520272-4). Oxford U Pr.
Christian Theology in Outline. William A. Brown. LC 75-41044. (BCL Ser. II). Repr. of 1906 ed. 28.00 (ISBN 0-404-14648-1). AMS Pr.
Christian Theology in Plain Language. Bruce L. Shelley. 256p. 1985. 12.95 (ISBN 0-8499-0381-5, 0381-5). Word Bks.
Christian Theology of Judaism. Clemens Thoma. Tr. by Helga Croner & Lawrence Frizzell. LC 80-82252. (Studies in Judaism & Christianity). 232p. 1980. pap. 7.95 (ISBN 0-8091-2310-X). Paulist Pr.
Christian Theology of the People Israel. Paul M. Van Buren. (Theology of the Jewish-Christian Reality Ser.: Pt. II). 320p. (Orig.). 1983. pap. 26.95 (ISBN 0-8164-0548-4, HarpR). Har-Row.
Christian Theory of Knowledge. Cornelius Van Til. 1969. pap. 10.95 (ISBN 0-87552-480-X). Presby & Reformed.
Christian Thought: From Erasmus to Berdyaev. Matthew Spinka. LC 78-11967. 1979. Repr. of 1962 ed. lib. bdg. 24.75x (ISBN 0-313-21122-1, SPCT). Greenwood.
Christian Thought, Its History & Application. Ernst D. Troeltsch. LC 78-59047. 1985. Repr. of 1923 ed. 23.25 (ISBN 0-88355-719-3). Hyperion Conn.
Christian Thought to the Reformation. Herbert B. Workman. 13.75 (ISBN 0-8369-7127-2, 7961). Ayer Co Pubs.
Christian Time Management. Kenneth A. Erickson. 128p. (Orig.). 1985. pap. 4.95 (ISBN 0-570-03972-X, 12-3007). Concordia.
Christian Tolerance: Paul's Message to the Modern Church. Robert Jewett. LC 82-13480. (Biblical Perspectives on Current Issues Ser.). 168p. 1982. pap. 9.95 (ISBN 0-664-24444-0). Westminster.
Christian Tradition, Vol. 1. Jaroslav Pelikan. LC 79-142042. 1971. pap. 12.95 (ISBN 0-226-65371-4, P644, Phoen). U of Chicago Pr.
Christian Tradition, a History of the Development of Doctrine: The Spirit of Eastern Christendom, 600-1700, Vol. 2. Jaroslav Pelikan. LC 79-142042. 1977. pap. 10.95 (ISBN 0-226-65373-0, P738, Phoen). U of Chicago Pr.
Christian Tradition: A History of the Development of Doctrine, Vol. 1: Emergence of the Catholic Tradition, 100-600. Jaroslav Pelikan. LC 79-142042. 1971. 25.00x (ISBN 0-226-65370-6). U of Chicago Pr.
Christian Tradition: A History of the Development of Doctrine Vol. III: the Growth of Medieval Theology (600-1300) Jaroslav Pelikan. LC 78-1501. 1978. 27.50x (ISBN 0-226-65374-9). U of Chicago Pr.
Christian Tradition: a History of the Development of Doctrine, Vol. 2: The Spirit of Eastern Christendom, 600-1700. Jaroslav Pelikan. LC 79-142042. xxv, 432p. 1974. 25.00x (ISBN 0-226-65372-2). U of Chicago Pr.
Christian Tradition: A History of the Development of Doctrine, Vol. 3, The Growth of Medieval Theology, 600-1300. Jaroslav Pelikan. LC 78-1501. xxviii, 336p. 1980. pap. 12.95 (ISBN 0-226-65375-7, P896). U of Chicago Pr.
Christian Tradition: A History of the Development of Doctrine, Vol. 4: Reformation of Church & Dogma (1300-1700) Jaroslav Pelikan. LC 79-142042. iii, 426p. 1985. 27.50x (ISBN 0-226-65376-5); pap. 14.95 (ISBN 0-226-65377-3). U of Chicago Pr.
Christian Trinity in History. Bertrand De Margerie. Tr. by E. J. Fortman from Fr. LC 81-8735. Tr. of Trinite Christienne dans l'histoire. 1982. cloth 29.95 (ISBN 0-932506-14-3). St Bedes Pubns.
Christian Uncertainties. Monica Furlong. LC 82-72129. xii, 124p. 1982. pap. 6.95 (ISBN 0-936384-06-9). Cowley Pubns.
Christian Understanding of God. Nels Ferre. LC 78-12234. 1979. Repr. of 1951 ed. lib. bdg. 22.50x (ISBN 0-313-21183-3, FECU). Greenwood.
Christian Understanding of the Human Person: Basic Readings. Eugene Lauer & Joel Mlecko. LC 81-8434. 160p. (Orig.). 1982. pap. 7.95 (ISBN 0-8091-2433-5). Paulist Pr.
Christian Unity: An Exposition of Ephesians 4: 1-16. D. Martyn Lloyd-Jones. 280p. 1981. 12.95 (ISBN 0-8010-5607-1). Baker Bk.
Christian Unity: Matrix for Mission. Paul A. Crow, Jr. (Orig.). 1982. pap. 4.95 (ISBN 0-377-00115-5). Friend Pr.
Christian Use of Emotional Power. H. Norman Wright. 160p. 1974. pap. 5.95 (ISBN 0-8007-5213-9, Pub. by Power Bk.). Revell.
Christian Values & Economic Life. facs. ed. John C. Bennett et al. LC 71-99624. (Essay Index Reprint Ser.). 1954. 21.50 (ISBN 0-8369-1559-3). Ayer Co Pubs.
Christian Values & the Academic Disciplines. Ed. by Floyd D. Crenshaw & John A. Flanders. 224p. (Orig.). 1985. lib. bdg. 23.25 (ISBN 0-8191-4306-5); pap. text ed. 11.75 (ISBN 0-8191-4307-3). U Pr of Amer.
Christian View of Abortion. J. Klotz. (Contemporary Theology Ser.). 1973. 3.95 (ISBN 0-570-06721-9, 12RT2560). Concordia.
Christian View of Economics. Marion Loring. 80p. 1983. 5.50 (ISBN 0-682-49903-X). Exposition Pr FL.
Christian View of Homosexuality. John W. Drakeford. LC 76-41474. 1977. pap. 3.95 (ISBN 0-8054-5620-1). Broadman.
Christian View of Justice. Mark T. Coppenger. LC 82-70867. 1983. pap. 6.95 (ISBN 0-8054-6126-4). Broadman.
Christian View of Man. H. D. McDonald. LC 81-65471. (Foundations for Faith Ser.). 160p. 1981. pap. 8.95 (ISBN 0-89107-217-9, Crossway Bks). Good News.
Christian View of Man. J. Gresham Machen. pap. 6.95 (ISBN 0-85151-112-0). Banner of Truth.
Christian View of Science & Scripture. Bernard Ramm. 1954. pap. 4.95 (ISBN 0-8028-1429-8). Eerdmans.
Christian View of the World. George J. Blewett. 1912. 49.50x (ISBN 0-685-89741-9). Elliots Bks.
Christian View of War & Peace. Spiros Zodhiates. 1979. pap. 1.45 (ISBN 0-89957-509-9). AMG Pubs.
Christian Vision: The Truth That Sets Us Free. John S. Powell. LC 83-73231. (Illus.). 155p. 1984. pap. 5.95. Argus Comm.
Christian Warfare. John Downame. LC 74-80174. (English Experience Ser.: No. 653). 674p. 1974. Repr. of 1604 ed. 67.00 (ISBN 90-221-0653-5). Walter J Johnson.
Christian Warfare: An Exposition of Ephesians 6: 10-13. D. Martyn Lloyd-Jones. 1977. Repr. of 1976 ed. 12.95 (ISBN 0-8010-5574-1). Baker Bk.
Christian Way. Maxie D. Dunnam. 112p. 1987. pap. 4.95 (ISBN 0-310-20741-X). Zondervan.
Christian Way. new ed. John W. Miller. LC 78-76622. (Christrian Peace Shelf Ser.). 104p. 1969. pap. 2.95 (ISBN 0-8361-1605-4). Herald Pr.
Christian Way in Race Relations. facs. ed. Ed. by William S. Nelson. LC 79-134121. (Essay Index Reprint Ser). 1948. 20.00 (ISBN 0-8369-2004-X). Ayer Co Pubs.
Christian Ways to Date, Go Steady, & Break up. John Butler. (Mini Bible Studies). (Illus.). 1978. pap. 2.95 (ISBN 0-87239-986-9, 39949). Standard Pub.
Christian Wedding Handbook. Kay O. Lewis. 192p. 1981. 10.95 (ISBN 0-8007-1259-5). Revell.
Christian Wedding Planner. Ruth Muzzy & R. Kent Hughes. 320p. 1984. pap. 9.95 (ISBN 0-8423-0253-0). Tyndale.
Christian Wholeness. Thomas A. Langford. LC 78-58011. 1979. pap. 3.50x (ISBN 0-8358-0383-X). Upper Room.
Christian Wholeness: Spiritual Direction for Today. Jesse M. Trotter. LC 81-84718. 80p. (Orig.). 1982. pap. 5.95 (ISBN 0-8192-1294-6). Morehouse.
Christian Witness in the Secular City. Ed. by Everett J. Morgan. LC 75-133951. (Orig.). 1970. pap. 4.00 (ISBN 0-8294-0198-9). Loyola.
Christian Witness: That They Might Know Him. Eva M. Walters. 1987. 7.95 (ISBN 0-533-07011-2). Vantage.
Christian Witness to Nominal Christians Among Roman Catholics. 38p. pap. 1.00 (ISBN 0-935120-04-1). Christs Mission.
Christian Witness to the State. John H. Yoder. 1977. pap. 3.95 (ISBN 0-87303-165-2). Faith & Life.
Christian Wives: Women Behind the Evangelists. James Schaffer & Colleen Todd. LC 87-5291. (Illus.). 168p. 1987. 12.95 (ISBN 0-385-23581-X, Dolp). Doubleday.
Christian Woman in the Working World. Martha Nelson. LC 76-127198. 141p. 1975. pap. 1.50 (ISBN 0-8054-6915-X). Broadman.
Christian Woman's Answer to Aging. Margaret Hicks. 29p. (Orig.). 1986. pap. 0.75 (ISBN 0-89274-394-8). Harrison Hse.
Christian Woman's Planner. Darien B. Cooper. 160p. (Orig.). 1986. pap. 8.95 spiral bdg. (ISBN 0-310-44621-X, 11742P). Zondervan.
Christian Woman's Promise Book. Lawrence O. Richards. 1986. pap. 2.50 (ISBN 0-310-43592-7, 18212P). Zondervan.
Christian Woman's Resource Book. Burroughs. LC 83-26063. 1987. 9.95 (A Bridgebooks Publication). Westminster.
Christian Woman's Resource Book. Melba G. Burroughs. LC 83-26063. 202p. (Orig.). 1984. pap. 9.95 (ISBN 0-664-26008-X, A Bridgebooks Publication). Westminster.
Christian Woman's Search for Self-Esteem. W. Peter Blitchington. LC 81-18963. 168p. 1983. pap. 4.95 (ISBN 0-8407-5830-8). Nelson.
Christian Women at Work. Patricia A. Ward & Martha G. Stout. 242p. 1984. pap. 6.95 (ISBN 0-310-43701-6). Zondervan.
Christian Women in a Troubled World: Madeleva Lecture 1984. Monika K. Hellwig. 60p. (Orig.). 1985. 2.95 (ISBN 0-8091-2713-X). Paulist Pr.
Christian Worker's Manual. Herbert S. Miller. pap. 4.00 (ISBN 0-87509-065-6). Chr Pubns.
Christian Workers NT: New American Standard. deluxe, brown 19.95 (ISBN 0-8024-5541-7). Moody.
Christian Working Mother's Handbook. Jayne Garrison. 144p. 1986. pap. 7.95 (ISBN 0-8423-0258-1). Tyndale.
Christian World. A. Brown. LC 83-50692. (Religions of the World Ser.). 1984. PLB 14.96 (ISBN 0-382-06721-5); 10.75 (ISBN 0-382-06929-3). Silver.
Christian World Mission: Today & Tomorrow. J. Herbert Kane. 240p. 1981. 13.95 (ISBN 0-8010-5426-5). Baker Bk.
Christian Worship. rev. ed. (Time of Life Learning Ser.). (Illus.). 32p. pap. 2.95 (ISBN 0-89622-245-4). Twenty-Third.
Christian Worship & Its Cultural Setting. Frank C. Senn. LC 82-48587. 160p. 1983. pap. 9.95 (ISBN 0-8006-1700-2, 1-1700). Fortress.
Christian Worship (Hymns) Ed. by B. Howard Mudditt. 716p. 1976. text ed. 15.00x (ISBN 0-85364-194-3). Attic Pr.
Christian Worship in East & West. Herman A. Wegman. Tr. by Gordon Lathrop from Dutch. 400p. (Orig.). 1985. pap. 19.50 (ISBN 0-916134-71-7). Pueblo Pub Co.
Christian Worship: Its Theology & Practice. Franklin Segler. LC 67-22034. 1975. pap. 8.95 (ISBN 0-8054-2309-5). Broadman.
Christian Writer's Handbook. rev. ed. Margaret J. Anderson. LC 82-48917. 288p. 1983. 9.95 (ISBN 0-06-060195-7, RD/246, HarpR). Har-Row.
Christian Year; Its Purpose & Its History. Walker Gwynne. LC 74-89269. xiv, 143p. 1972. Repr. of 1917 ed. 43.00x (ISBN 0-8103-3814-9). Gale.
Christian Year: Thoughts in Verse for the Sundays & Holidays Throughout the Year. John Keble. LC 70-167019. (Illus.). 291p. 1975. Repr. of 1896 ed. 43.00x (ISBN 0-8103-4095-X). Gale.
Christian Yogic Meditation. Swami Amaldas. (Ways of Prayer Ser.: Vol. 8). pap. 5.95 (ISBN 0-89453-368-1). M Glazier.
Christian Zen: A Way of Meditation. 2nd ed. William Johnston. LC 80-8430. (Illus.). 144p. 1981. pap. 6.95 (ISBN 0-06-064198-3, RD 343, HarpR). Har-Row.
Christianica. Christianica Center Staff. LC 74-13005. (Illus.). 1975. 5.95 (ISBN 0-911346-02-3). Christianica.
Christianity. Edwyn R. Bevan. LC 80-24452. (Home University Library of Modern Knowledge Ser.: No. 157). 255p. 1981. Repr. of 1948 ed. lib. bdg. 25.00x (ISBN 0-313-22681-4, BECY). Greenwood.
Christianity. Nancy Martin. (Religions of the World Ser.). (Illus.). 48p. 1986. PLB 10.90 (ISBN 0-531-18064-6, Pub. by Bookwright). Watts.
Christianity - Islam: Essays on Esoteric Ecumenicism. Frithjof Schuon. LC 84-52674. (Library of Traditional Wisdom). 270p. 1985. pap. 12.00 (ISBN 0-941532-05-4). Wrld Wisdom Bks.

Christianity: A Growing Experience. Jerri McCann Lucas. pap. 4.95 (ISBN 0-89137-429-9). Quality Pubns.

Christianity: A Select Bibliography. Satyaprakash. 1986. 18.50x (ISBN 0-8364-1829-8, Pub. by Indian Doc Serv India). South Asia Bks.

Christianity: A Way of Salvation. Sandra S. Frankiel. LC 84-48770. 144p. (Orig.). 1985. pap. 6.95 (ISBN 0-06-063015-9, RD 498, HarpR). Har-Row.

Christianity among the Arabs in Pre-Islamic Times. J. Spencer Trimingham. (Arab Background Ser.). (Illus.). 1979. text ed. 30.00x (ISBN 0-582-78081-0). Longman.

Christianity Among World Religions. Ed. by Hans Kung & Jurgen Moltman. (Concilium Nineteen Eighty-Six Ser.). 120p. 1986. pap. 6.95 (ISBN 0-567-30063-3, Pub. by T & T Clark Ltd UK). Fortress.

Christianity: An Introduction. Denise L. Carmody & John T. Carmody. 288p. 1982. pap. text ed. write for info (ISBN 0-534-01181-0). Wadsworth Pub.

Christianity & African Education: The Papers of a Conference at the University of Chicago. Robert P. Beaver. LC 65-25184. pap. 58.30 (ISBN 0-317-09800-4, 2012940). Bks Demand UMI.

Christianity & Anti-Christianity in Their Final Conflict. Samuel J. Andrews. 1982. lib. bdg. 15.00 (ISBN 0-86524-084-1, 9804). Klock & Klock.

Christianity & Barthianism. Cornelius Van Til. 1960. pap. 10.95 (ISBN 0-87552-481-8). Presby & Reformed.

Christianity & Capitalism: Perspectives on Religion, Liberalism, & the Economy. Ed. by Bruce Grelle & David A. Krueger. LC 85-73375. (Studies in Religion & Society Ser.). 189p. 1986. text ed. 25.95x (ISBN 0-913348-23-6); pap. 14.95x (ISBN 0-913348-24-4). Ctr Sci Study.

Christianity & Civilisation, 2 vols. in one. Heinrich E. Brunner. LC 77-27182. (Gifford Lectures: 1947-48). Repr. of 1949 ed. 35.00 (ISBN 0-404-60530-3). AMS Pr.

Christianity & Civilisation. Herbert G. Wood. LC 73-17694. 128p. 1973. Repr. of 1943 ed. lib. bdg. 13.00x (ISBN 0-374-98713-0, Octagon). Hippocrene Bks.

Christianity & Civilization. Arnold J. Toynbee. 1983. pap. 2.50x (ISBN 0-87574-039-1, 039). Pendle Hill.

Christianity & Classical Culture: A Study of Thought & Action from Augustus to Augustine. Charles N. Cochrane. 1957. pap. 10.95 (ISBN 0-19-500207-5). Oxford U Pr.

Christianity & Classical Culture: A Study of Thought & Action from Augustus to Augustine. Charles N. Cochrane. 1984. 18.00 (ISBN 0-8446-6086-8). Peter Smith.

Christianity & Culture. T. S. Eliot. Incl. The Idea of a Christian Society; Notes Towards the Definition of Culture. 202p. 1960. pap. 5.95 (ISBN 0-15-617735-8, HB32, Harv). HarBraceJ.

Christianity & Democracy. Norman De Jong. 1978. pap. 4.95 (ISBN 0-934532-08-7). Presby & Reformed.

Christianity & Democracy. Jacques Maritain. Tr. by Doris C. Anson from Fr. LC 72-6765. (Essay Index Reprint Ser). 1972. Repr. of 1944 ed. 15.00 (ISBN 0-8369-7243-0). Ayer Co Pubs.

Christianity & Democracy. Jacques Maritain. Bd. with Rights of Man & Natural Law. LC 83-80191. 1986. pap. write for info. (ISBN 0-89870-030-2). Ignatius Pr.

Christianity & Democracy & The Rights of Man & Natural Law. Jacques Maritain. LC 83-80191. 200p. 1986. pap. 12.95 (ISBN 0-89870-030-2). Ignatius Pr.

Christianity & Education: A Manifesto. Jack H. Rose. LC 86-90551. 302p. (Orig.). 1986. pap. 29.95 (ISBN 0-9617430-0-X). J H Rose.

Christianity & Evolution. Pierre Teilhard de Chardin. LC 73-12926. 255p. 1974. pap. 6.95 (ISBN 0-15-617740-4, Harv). HarBraceJ.

Christianity & Existentialism. Ed. by William Earle et al. (Studies in Phenomenology & Existential Philosophy). 1963. pap. 7.95 (ISBN 0-8101-0084-3). Northwestern U Pr.

Christianity & Humanism. Dale A. Jorgenson. LC 83-70878. 115p. (Orig.). 1983. pap. 2.95 (ISBN 0-89900-149-1). College Pr Pub.

Christianity & Islam. C. H. Becker. Tr. by H. J. Chaytor. LC 74-608. 120p. 1974. Repr. of 1909 ed. lib. bdg. 18.50 (ISBN 0-8337-4816-5). B Franklin.

Christianity & Islam in Spain, A. D. 756-1031. Charles R. Haines. LC 76-144625. Repr. of 1889 ed. 17.50 (ISBN 0-404-03024-6). AMS Pr.

Christianity & Japan: Meeting, Conflict, Hope. Stuart D. Picken. LC 82-48787. (Illus.). 80p. 1983. 18.95 (ISBN 0-87011-571-5). Kodansha.

Christianity & Judaism: The Deepening Dialogue. Ed. by Richard Rousseau. (Modern Theological Themes: Selections from the Literature Ser.: Vol. 3). (Orig.). 1983. pap. 15.00 (ISBN 0-940866-02-1). Ridge Row.

Christianity & Liberalism. J. Gresham Machen. 1923. pap. 6.95 (ISBN 0-8028-1121-3). Eerdmans.

Christianity & Life. James V. Schall. LC 79-89759. 133p. (Orig.). 1981. pap. 7.95 (ISBN 0-89870-004-3). Ignatius Pr.

Christianity & Modern Thought. Ralph H. Gabriel & Charles R. Brown. 11.00 (ISBN 0-8369-7217-1, 8016). Ayer Co Pubs.

Christianity & Morals. facs. ed. Edward A. Westermarck. LC 78-80406. (Essay Index Reprint Ser). 1939. 23.75 (ISBN 0-8369-1055-9). Ayer Co Pubs.

Christianity & Naturalism: Essays in Criticism. Robert Shafer. LC 68-26206. 1969. Repr. of 1926 ed. 25.50x (ISBN 0-8046-0413-4, Pub. by Kennikat). Assoc Faculty Pr.

Christianity & Other Faiths. Intro. by Patrick Sookhdeo. 48p. 1983. pap. 2.95 (ISBN 0-85364-363-6, Pub. by Paternoster UK). Attic Pr.

Christianity & Other Religions: Selected Readings. Ed. by John Hick & Brian Hebblethwaite. LC 80-2383. 256p. 1981. pap. 8.95 (ISBN 0-8006-1444-5, 1-1444). Fortress.

Christianity & Paganism, Three Hundred Fifty to Seven Hundred Fifty: The Conversion of Western Europe. rev. ed. Ed. by J. N. Hillgarth. LC 85-1154. (Middle Ages Ser.). 160p. 1986. lib. bdg. 25.00 (ISBN 0-8122-7993-X); pap. 10.95 (ISBN 0-8122-1213-4). U of Pa Pr.

Christianity & Philosophy. Keith Yandell. LC 83-14226. (Studies in a Christian World View: Vol. 2). 284p. 1984. pap. 12.95 (ISBN 0-8028-1964-8). Eerdmans.

Christianity & Political Philosophy. Frederick D. Wilhelmsen. LC 77-22754. 256p. 1978. 22.00x (ISBN 0-8203-0431-X). U of Ga Pr.

Christianity & Politics. James Schall. 1981. 6.95 (ISBN 0-8198-1406-7); pap. 5.95 (ISBN 0-8198-1407-5). Dghtrs St Paul.

Christianity & Politics: Catholic & Protestant Perspectives. Ed. by Carol F. Griffith. LC 81-19412. 124p. 1981. pap. 6.00 (ISBN 0-89633-050-8). Ethics & Public Policy.

Christianity & Power Politics. Reinhold Niebuhr. LC 69-12421. xi, 226p. 1969. Repr. of 1940 ed. 24.50 (ISBN 0-208-00740-7, Archon). Shoe String.

Christianity & Real Life. William E. Diehl. LC 76-7860. 128p. 1976. pap. 4.50 (ISBN 0-8006-1231-0, 1-1231). Fortress.

Christianity & Revolution: Radical Christian Testimonies, 1520-1650. Ed. by Lowell H. Zuck. LC 74-25355. (Documents in Free Church History Ser.: No. 2). 324p. 1975. 29.95 (ISBN 0-87722-040-9); pap. 12.95 (ISBN 0-87722-044-1). Temple U Pr.

Christianity & Revolution: Tomas Borge's Theology of Life. Ed. by Andrew Reding. LC 86-23788. (Illus.). 160p. (Orig.). 1987. pap. 8.95 (ISBN 0-88344-411-9). Orbis Bks.

Christianity & Scholarship. D. Kempff. Date not set. pap. 12.50x cancelled (ISBN 0-86990-687-9). Radix Bks.

Christianity & Sex Problems. 2nd ed. Hugh Northcote. LC 72-9668. Repr. of 1916 ed. 49.50 (ISBN 0-404-57486-6). AMS Pr.

Christianity & Social Problems. Lyman Abbott. LC 4-3768. Repr. of 1896 ed. 30.00 (ISBN 0-384-00074-6). Johnson Repr.

Christianity & Society. facs. ed. Nels F. Ferre. LC 78-117791. (Essay Index Reprint Ser). 1950. 19.00 (ISBN 0-8369-1924-6). Ayer Co Pubs.

Christianity & the Constitution. John Eidsmoe. 442p. 1987. pap. price not set (ISBN 0-8010-3444-2). Baker Bk.

Christianity & the Encounter of the World Religions. Paul Tillich. LC 63-7508. (Bampton Lectures in America: No. 14). pap. 26.80 (ISBN 0-317-42040-2, 2025697). Bks Demand UMI.

Christianity & the French Revolution. Alphonse Aulard. 1966. 27.50x (ISBN 0-86527-025-2). Fertig.

Christianity & the Hellenistic World. Ronald Nash. (CFUC Ser.). 1986. pap. 9.95 (ISBN 0-310-45210-4, 12383P). Zondervan.

Christianity & the Intellectuals. Arther Trace. 208p. (Orig.). 1983. pap. 5.95 (ISBN 0-89385-018-7). Sugden.

Christianity & the Machine Age. Eric Gill. 59.95 (ISBN 0-87968-864-5). Gordon Pr.

Christianity & the Narrow Way. Roy C. Jarnagin. 128p. 1982. 7.50 (ISBN 0-682-49832-7). Exposition Pr FL.

Christianity & the New Age. Christopher Dawson. LC 84-29821. 103p. 1985. 10.95 (ISBN 0-918477-02-6); pap. 7.95 (ISBN 0-918477-01-8). Sophia Inst Pr.

Christianity & the Race Problem. Joseph H. Oldham. LC 73-75534. Repr. of 1924 ed. 19.75x (ISBN 0-8371-1112-9, OLC&, Pub. by Negro U Pr). Greenwood.

Christianity & the Social Revolution. facsimile ed. Ed. by John Lewis et al. LC 79-37892. (Select Bibliographies Reprint Ser). Repr. of 1935 ed. 25.00 (ISBN 0-8369-6729-1). Ayer Co Pubs.

Christianity & the Survival of the West. Revilo P. Oliver. 1984. lib. bdg. 79.95 (ISBN 0-87700-599-0). Revisionist Pr.

Christianity & the World Order. E. R. Norman. 1979. pap. 6.95x (ISBN 0-19-283019-8). Oxford U Pr.

Christianity & Western Civilization. Carlton J. Hayes. LC 83-5680. vii, 63p. 1983. Repr. of 1954 ed. lib. bdg. 22.50x (ISBN 0-313-23962-2, HACW). Greenwood.

Christianity & World Religions. rev. ed. Norman Anderson. LC 84-115291. 192p. 1984. pap. 9.95 (ISBN 0-87784-981-1). Inter-Varsity.

Christianity As Mystical Fact. Rudolf Steiner. Tr. of Christentum als mystische Tatsache und die Mysterien des Altertums. 195p. 1986. pap. 8.95 (ISBN 0-88010-160-1). Anthroposophic.

Christianity As Mystical Fact & the Mysteries of Antiquity. Rudolf Steiner. write for info. (ISBN 0-910142-04-1). Anthroposophic.

Christianity As Old Creation of the Gospel. Matthew Tindal. Ed. by Rene Wellek. LC 75-11256. (British Philosophers & Theologians of the 17th & 18th Centuries Ser.). 1976. lib. bdg. 51.00 (ISBN 0-8240-1806-0). Garland Pub.

Christianity As Psychology: The Healing Power of the Christian Message. Morton Kelsey. LC 85-22864. 114p. (Orig.). 1986. pap. 7.95 (ISBN 0-8066-2194-X, 10-1184). Augsburg.

Christianity at Rome in the Apostolic Age. Arthur S. Barnes. LC 72-114462. (Illus.). 1971. Repr. of 1938 ed. lib. bdg. 55.00x (ISBN 0-8371-4760-3, BACR). Greenwood.

Christianity Before Christ. John G. Jackson. 238p. (Orig.). 1985. pap. 7.00 (ISBN 0-910309-20-5). Am Atheist.

Christianity Before Christ. Charles J. Stone. 1977. lib. bdg. 59.95 (ISBN 0-8490-1616-9). Gordon Pr.

Christianity Close to Life. Rita Snowden. (Crossroad Paperback Ser.). 160p. 1982. pap. 5.95 (ISBN 0-8245-0459-3). Crossroad NY.

Christianity, Communism & the Ideal Society: A Philosophical Approach to Modern Politics. James K. Feibleman. LC 75-3140. Repr. of 1937 ed. 38.00 (ISBN 0-404-59149-3). AMS Pr.

Christianity Confronts Communism. Charles McFadden. 1983. 15.00 (ISBN 0-8199-0841-X). Franciscan Herald.

Christianity Confronts Culture. Marvin Mayers. (Contemporary Evangelical Perspectives Ser.). 10.95 (ISBN 0-310-28891-6, 10230P). Zondervan.

Christianity: Faith, Love & Healing. Victoria Lidiard. LC 84-90145. 80p. 1985. 5.95 (ISBN 0-533-06204-7). Vantage.

Christianity for the Tough-Minded. Ed. & intro. by John W. Montgomery. LC 73-4842. 304p. 1973. kivar 9.95 (ISBN 0-87123-076-3, 210079). Bethany Hse.

Christianity Four Thousand Years Before Jesus. Walter A. Dawes. Ed. by Kathleen A. Dawes. (Illus.). 63p. (Orig.). 1982. pap. 4.95 (ISBN 0-938792-17-2). New Capernaum.

Christianity in a Revolutionary Age, 5 vols. Kenneth S. Latourette. 1973. Repr. of 1958 ed. Set. lib. bdg. 160.50x (ISBN 0-8371-5700-5, LACH). Greenwood.

Christianity in Action. William L. Harvey. 232p. 1954. pap. 1.95 (ISBN 0-88243-487-X, 02-0487). Gospel Pub.

Christianity in China: Early Protestant Missionary Writings. Ed. by Suzanne W. Barnett & John K. Fairbank. (Harvard Studies in American-East Asian Relations: 9). 280p. 1984. text ed. 20.00x (ISBN 0-674-12881-8). Harvard U Pr.

Christianity in Conflict: The Struggle for Christian Integrity & Freedom in Secular Culture. Charles Colson et al. Ed. by Peter S. Williamson & Kevin Perrotta. 180p. (Orig.). 1986. pap. 7.95 (ISBN 0-89283-292-4). Servant.

Christianity in Context. Francisco R. Demetrio. 134p. 1981. pap. 5.50x (ISBN 0-686-32576-1, Pub. by New Day Phillipines). Cellar.

Christianity in Crisis. Sun Myung Moon. pap. 3.00 (ISBN 0-686-13410-9). HSA Pubns.

Christianity in Culture. Charles H. Kraft. LC 78-13736. 463p. (Orig.). 1979. 14.95 (ISBN 0-88344-075-X). Orbis Bks.

Christianity in East & West. Christopher Dawson. Ed. by John J. Mulloy. 224p. 1981. pap. text ed. 5.95 (ISBN 0-89385-015-2). Sugden.

Christianity in European History. William Clebsch. 1979. pap. 8.95x (ISBN 0-19-502472-9). Oxford U Pr.

Christianity in European History: The Riddel Memorial Lectures, 1951. Herbert Butterfield. 1979. Repr. of 1952 ed. lib. bdg. 15.00 (ISBN 0-8482-3440-5). Norwood Edns.

Christianity in History. A. Azhar. 12.50 (ISBN 0-686-18580-3). Kazi Pubns.

Christianity in Human Evolution. Rudolf Steiner. 1979. pap. 2.00 (ISBN 0-88010-095-8). Anthroposophic.

Christianity in Modern Korea. Donald N. Clark. LC 86-9092. (Asian Agenda Report: No. 5). 70p. (Orig.). 1986. lib. bdg. 12.75 (ISBN 0-8191-5384-2, Pub. by the Asia Soc); pap. text ed. 4.75 (ISBN 0-8191-5385-0). U Pr of Amer.

Christianity in Roman Britain to A. D. 500. Charles Thomas. (Illus.). 416p. 1981. 40.00x (ISBN 0-520-04392-8). U of Cal Pr.

Christianity in Talmud & Midsrah. R. Travers Herford. Repr. of 1903 ed. 16.95x (ISBN 0-87068-479-5). Ktav.

Christianity in the New World: From 1500 to 1800. Martin E. Marty. LC 82-83845. (Illustrated History of the Church Ser.). (Illus.). 127p. 1984. 12.95 (ISBN 0-86683-173-8, 1411, HarpR). Har-Row.

Christianity in the Non-Western World. facs. ed. Ed. by Charles W. Forman. LC 71-117792. (Essay Index Reprint Ser). 1967. 17.00 (ISBN 0-8369-1806-1). Ayer Co Pubs.

Christianity in the People's Republic of China. G. Thompson Brown. LC 82-49018. 240p. 1983. pap. 7.25 (ISBN 0-8042-1484-0). John Knox.

Christianity in the People's Republic of China. rev., 2nd ed. G. Thompson Brown. LC 86-45554. 256p. 1986. pap. 9.95 (ISBN 0-8042-1485-9). John Knox.

Christianity in the Roman Empire. Harold Mattingly. 1967. pap. 4.95x (ISBN 0-393-00397-3, Norton Lib). Norton.

Christianity in the Southern Hemisphere: The Churches in Latin America & South Africa. Edward Norman. 1981. text ed. 38.95x (ISBN 0-19-821127-9). Oxford U Pr.

Christianity in the Twentieth Century. John A. Hardon. 1978. 5.95 (ISBN 0-8198-0356-1); pap. 2.95 (ISBN 0-8198-0357-X). Dghtrs St Paul.

Christianity in the West, Fourteen Hundred to Seventeen Hundred. John Bossy. (OPUS). 189p. 1985. 19.95x (ISBN 0-19-219174-8); pap. 7.95 (ISBN 0-19-289162-6). Oxford U Pr.

Christianity in Today's World: An Eerdmans Handbook. Ed. by Robin Keeley. (Illus.). 384p. 1985. 29.95 (ISBN 0-8028-3618-6). Eerdmans.

Christianity in Tropical Africa: A Selective Annotated Bibliography. Patrick E. Ofori. 461p. 1977. lib. bdg. 48.00 (ISBN 3-262-00002-7). Kraus Intl.

Christianity Is a Bridge. Kenna Farris. Date not set. price not set. Port Love Intl.

Christianity Is a Verb. Larry D. Powell. 1984. 5.95 (ISBN 0-89536-650-9, 0392). CSS of Ohio.

Christianity Is All Talk. Paul Kelm. Ed. by William Fischer. (Bible Class Course for Young Adults Ser.: Student's Guide). (Illus.). 44p. 1984. pap. text ed. 2.95 (ISBN 0-938272-16-0). Wels Board.

Christianity Is All Talk. Paul Kelm. Ed. by William Fischer. (Bible Class Course for Young Adults Ser.: Leader's Guide). 64p. 1984. pap. text ed. 2.95 (ISBN 0-938272-17-9). Wels Board.

Christianity Is Christ. W. Griffith Thomas. LC 80-85341. (Shepherd Illustrated Classics Ser.). (Illus.). 200p. 1981. pap. 5.95 (ISBN 0-87983-238-X). Keats.

Christianity Is for You. Milton L. Rudnick. 1961. pap. 3.25 (ISBN 0-570-03503-1, 14-1271). Concordia.

Christianity Is Jewish. Edith Schaeffer. 1977. pap. 6.95 (ISBN 0-8423-0242-5). Tyndale.

Christianity Made Simple: Belief, Vol. 1. David Hewetson & David Miller. LC 83-10866. 160p. 1983. pap. 4.95 (ISBN 0-87784-811-4). Inter-Varsity.

Christianity Makes Sense. Kenneth H. Hopp. (Lifline Ser.). 80p. 1983. pap. 5.95 (ISBN 0-8163-0522-6). Pacific Pr Pub Assn.

Christianity Meets Buddhism. Heinrich Dumoulin. Tr. by John C. Maraldo from Ger. LC 73-82783. 212p. 1974. 19.95 (ISBN 0-87548-121-3). Open Court.

Christianity: Not Just a Religion. Spiros Zodhiates. (Illus.). 1979. pap. 1.75 (ISBN 0-89957-523-4). AMG Pubs.

Christianity Not Mysterious. John Toland. Ed. by Rene Wellek. LC 75-11257. (Philosophy of John Locke Ser.). 1978. lib. bdg. 46.00 (ISBN 0-8240-1807-9). Garland Pub.

Christianity of Ignatius of Antioch. Cyril C. Richardson. LC 35-7948. Repr. of 1935 ed. 14.50 (ISBN 0-404-05297-5). AMS Pr.

Christianity, Old & New. Benjamin W. Bacon. 1914. 29.50x (ISBN 0-686-83503-4). Elliots Bks.

Christianity or the Church? St. Hilary Troitsky. 48p. (Orig.). 1985. pap. 2.00 (ISBN 0-317-30269-8). Holy Trinity.

Christianity, Past & Present. Basil Willey. LC 78-65632. 1980. Repr. of 1952 ed. 16.50 (ISBN 0-88355-877-7). Hyperion Conn.

Christianity Rediscovered. rev. ed. Vincent J. Donovan. LC 81-18992. 208p. 1982. pap. 8.95 (ISBN 0-88344-096-2). Orbis Bks.

Christianity, Social Tolerance, & Homosexuality: Gay People in Western Europe from the Beginning of the Christian Era to the Fourteenth Century. John Boswell. LC 79-11171. (Illus.). xviii, 424p. 1980. 35.00x (ISBN 0-226-06710-6); pap. 12.95 (ISBN 0-226-06711-4). U of Chicago Pr.

Christianity the Logic of Creation. Henry James, Sr. LC 72-921. (Selected Works of Henry James, Sr.: Vol. 1). 272p. 1983. Repr. of 1875 ed. 30.00 (ISBN 0-404-10081-3); Set, 10 vols. 295.00. AMS Pr.

Christianity: The True Humanism. J. I. Packer & Thomas Howard. 1985. 9.95 (ISBN 0-8499-0316-5). Word Bks.

Christianity Through Jewish Eyes. Walter Jacob. 1974. pap. 9.95x (ISBN 0-685-56220-4). Ktav.

Christianity Through the Ages. Kenneth S. Latourette. (Orig.). pap. 8.95 (ISBN 0-06-065011-7, CB1, HarpR). Har-Row.

Christianity Through the Ages. Kenneth S. Latourette. 16.75 (ISBN 0-8446-2434-9). Peter Smith.

Christianity Through the Centuries. Earle E. Cairns. 544p. 1981. 19.95 (ISBN 0-310-38360-9, 9377P). Zondervan.

Christianity Today in the U. S. S. R. Howard L. Parsons. LC 86-27320. 216p. (Orig.). 1987. pap. 6.95 (ISBN 0-7178-0651-0). Intl Pubs CO.

Christianity Unveiled. Paul H. D'Holbach. 69.95 (ISBN 0-87968-068-7). Gordon Pr.

Christianity Without Fetishes: An African Critique & Recapture of Christianity. F. Eboussi Boulaga. Tr. by Robert R. Barr from Fr. LC 84-5807. Tr. of Christianisme sans Fetiche. 256p. (Orig.). 1984. pap. 11.95 (ISBN 0-88344-432-1). Orbis Bks.

Christianity Without Morals. Blaine Taylor et al. Ed. by Jerry O. Cook. 96p. (Orig.). 1982. pap. 7.00 (ISBN 0-914527-16-9). C-Four Res.

Christianity Without the Myths. S. Farrer. 39.00x (ISBN 0-317-43636-8, Pub. by Regency pr). State Mutual Bk.

Christianity Without Ulcers. Edward Fudge. pap. 5.00 (ISBN 0-686-12686-6). E Fudge.

Christianizing the Roman Empire: A.D. 100-400. Ramsay MacMullen. LC 84-3694. 200p. 1984. 22.50x (ISBN 0-300-03216-1); pap. 7.95 (ISBN 0-300-03642-6, Y-571). Yale U Pr.

Christians. Bamber Gascoigne. (Illus.). 304p. 1986. pap. 15.95 (ISBN 0-224-02863-4, Pub. by Jonathan Cape). Salem Hse Pubs.

Christians Among Jews & Gentiles: Essays in Honor of Krister Stendahl. Ed. by George W. Nickelsburg & George W. MacRal. pap. 19.95 (ISBN 0-317-52516-6). Fortress.

Christians & Jews in Germany: Religion, Politics, & Ideology in the Second Reich, 1870-1914. Uriel Tal. Tr. by Noah J. Jacobs from Hebrew. LC 74-21612. (Illus.). 359p. 1975. 35.00x (ISBN 0-8014-0879-2). Cornell U Pr.

Christians & Jews in the Ottoman Empire: The Functioning of a Plural Society, 2 vols. Ed. by Benjamin Braude & Bernard Lewis. LC 80-11337. 1982. Set. text ed. 94.50x. Vol. 1, The Central Lands, 450p (ISBN 0-8419-0519-3). Vol. 2, The Arabic-speaking Lands, 248p (ISBN 0-8419-0520-7). Holmes & Meier.

Christians & Jews: The Eternal Bond. rev. ed. Stuart E. Rosenberg. 200p. 1985. 13.95 (ISBN 0-8044-5800-6). Ungar.

Christians & Muslims Together: An Exploration by Presbyterians. Ed. by Byron L. Haines & Frank L. Cooley. LC 87-218. 120p. (Orig.). 1987. pap. 7.95 (ISBN 0-664-24061-5). Westminster.

Christians & Nonviolence in the Nuclear Age: Scripture, the Arms Race & You. Gerard A. Vanderhaar. 128p. 1982. pap. 5.95 (ISBN 0-89622-162-8). Twenty-Third.

Christians & Prayer. Alfred J. Garrotto. (Orig.). 1980. pap. text ed. 4.95 (ISBN 0-03-056981-8, HarpR). Har-Row.

Christians & Religious Pluralism: Patterns in the Christian Theology of Religions. Alan Race. 192p. (Orig.). 1983. pap. 8.95 (ISBN 0-88344-101-2). Orbis Bks.

Christians & the American Revolution. Mark A. Noll. LC 77-23354. pap. 48.80 (ISBN 0-8357-9125-4, 2016042). Bks Demand UMI.

Christians & the Many Faces of Marxism. Wayne Stumme. LC 84-10980. 176p. (Orig.). 1984. pap. 8.95 (ISBN 0-8066-2087-0, 10-1195). Augsburg.

Christians & the Military: The Early Experience. John Helgeland & Robert J. Daly. Ed. by J. Patout Burns. LC 84-48718. 112p. 1985. pap. 5.95 (ISBN 0-8006-1836-X, 1-1836). Fortress.

Christians & the Roman Empire. Marta Sordi. Tr. by Annabel Bedini. LC 86-40081. 224p. 1986. 22.50x (ISBN 0-8061-2011-8). U of Okla Pr.

Christians & the Third World. David W. Edington. 160p. 1982. pap. text ed. 7.95 (ISBN 0-85364-286-9). Attic Pr.

Christian's Appreciation of Other Faiths. Gilbert Reid. 305p. 1921. 22.95 (ISBN 0-87548-219-8). Open Court.

Christians As Peacemakers. Henry Rust. 54p. (Orig.). 1983. pap. 5.95 (ISBN 0-940754-21-5). Ed Ministries.

Christians As the Romans Saw Them. Robert L. Wilken. LC 83-12472. 240p. 1984. 22.50x (ISBN 0-300-03066-5); pap. 7.95 (ISBN 0-300-03627-2, Y-575). Yale U Pr.

Christians at Mecca. Augustus Ralli. LC 70-118545. 1971. Repr. of 1909 ed. 27.00x (ISBN 0-8046-1170-X, Pub. by Kennikat). Assoc Faculty Pr.

Christians at Prayer. Ed. by John Gallen. LC 76-22407. 1977. text ed. 14.95x (ISBN 0-268-00718-7). U of Notre Dame Pr.

Christians at Prayer. Ed. by John Gallen. LC 76-22407. (Liturgical Studies). 1977. pap. text ed. 5.95 (ISBN 0-268-00719-5). U of Notre Dame Pr.

Christian's Attitude Toward World Religions. Ajith Fernando. 160p. (Orig.). 1987. pap. 5.95 (ISBN 0-8423-0292-1). Tyndale.

Christian's Calling. rev. ed. Donald R. Heiges. LC 84-47923. 112p. 1984. pap. 4.95 (ISBN 0-8006-1795-9). Fortress.

Christian's Daily Manna. William S. Deal. 0.95 (ISBN 0-686-13721-3). Crusade Pubs.

Christian's Everyday Problems. Leroy Brownlow. 1966. pap. 2.50 (ISBN 0-915720-39-6). Brownlow Pub Co.

Christians for Freedom: Late-Scholastic Economics. Alejandro A. Chafuen. LC 86-80784. 200p. 1986. pap. 12.95 (ISBN 0-89870-110-4). Ignatius Pr.

Christians Grieve Too. Donald Howard. 1980. pap. 1.45 (ISBN 0-85151-315-8). Banner of Truth.

Christian's Guide to Faith & Reason. Terry Miethe. 192p. (Orig.). 1987. pap. 5.95 (ISBN 0-87123-677-X). Bethany Hse.

Christians in China Before the Year 1550. A. C. Moule. 59.95 (ISBN 0-87968-865-3). Gordon Pr.

Christians in China before the Year 1550. A. C. Moule. 1972. lib. bdg. 20.00x (ISBN 0-374-95972-2, Octagon). Hippocrene Bks.

Christians in Conflict. William C. Martin. LC 72-88018. (Studies in Religion & Society Ser.). 1972. 14.95x (ISBN 0-913348-01-5); pap. 8.95x (ISBN 0-913348-10-4). Ctr Sci Study.

Christians in Families. Ross T. Bender. LC 82-6058. (Conrad Grebel Lecture Ser.). 184p. (Orig.). pap. 8.95 (ISBN 0-8361-3301-3). Herald Pr.

Christians in Pain: Perspectives on Suffering. B. W. Woods. 176p. 1982. pap. 4.95 (ISBN 0-8010-9652-9). Baker Bk.

Christians in Romans Seven. Arthur W. Pink. pap. 0.50 (ISBN 0-685-00738-3). Reiner.

Christians in Secular India. Abraham V. Thomas. LC 72-420. 246p. 1973. 20.00 (ISBN 0-8386-1021-8). Fairleigh Dickinson.

Christians in the Arab East. Robert B. Betts. LC 78-8674. 1981. 12.50 (ISBN 0-8042-0796-8). John Knox.

Christians in the Marketplace. Bill Hybels. 144p. 1982. pap. 5.95 (ISBN 0-88207-314-1). Victor Bks.

Christians in the Nicaraguan Revolution. Margaret Randall. (Illus.). 240p. (Orig.). 1984. 15.95 (ISBN 0-919573-14-2, Pub. by New Star Bks BC); pap. 7.95 (ISBN 0-919573-15-0, Pub. by New Star Bks BC). Left Bank.

Christians in the Wake of the Sexual Revolution: Recovering Our Sexual Sanity. Randy C. Alcorn. LC 85-4959. (Critical Concern Ser.). 1985. 13.95 (ISBN 0-88070-095-5). Multnomah.

Christians in Ulster, Nineteen Sixty-Eight to Nineteen Eighty. Eric Gallagher. 1982. 19.95x (ISBN 0-19-213237-7). Oxford U Pr.

Christian's Knowledge of God. W. W. Bryden. 278p. 1960. 6.95 (ISBN 0-227-67434-0). Attic Pr.

Christians Must Choose. Jan G. Linn. Ed. by Herbert Lambert. LC 85-3731. (Orig.). 1985. pap. 7.95 (ISBN 0-8272-0448-5). CBP.

Christians on the Right: The Moral Majority in Perspective. John Kater. 176p. (Orig.). 1982. pap. 8.95 (ISBN 0-8164-2379-2, HarpR). Har-Row.

Christians Only: A Study in Prejudice. Heywood Broun & George Britt. LC 73-19688. (Civil Liberties in American History Ser). 333p. 1974. Repr. of 1931 ed. lib. bdg. 39.50 (ISBN 0-306-70599-0). Da Capo.

Christians Only & the Only Christians. Thomas B. Warren. 89p. 1984. pap. 3.00 (ISBN 0-934916-05-5). Natl Christian Pr.

Christians Organizing for Political Service: A Study Guide Based on the Work of the Association for Public Justice. James W. Skillen. LC 80-66190. 113p. (Orig.). 1982. pap. 3.95 (ISBN 0-936456-01-9). Assn Public Justice.

Christians, Politics & Violent Revolution. John Davies. LC 75-42517. pap. 56.00 (ISBN 0-317-26642-X, 2025118). Bks Demand UMI.

Christians Reconciling. Alfred J. Garrotto. 96p. (Orig.). 1982. pap. 4.95 (ISBN 0-86683-170-3, HarpR). Har-Row.

Christian's Secret of a Happy Life. Hannah W. Smith. 256p. 1968. o. p. 8.95 (ISBN 0-8007-0044-9); pap. 6.95 (ISBN 0-8007-5004-7, Power Bks); pap. 3.50 (ISBN 0-8007-8007-8, Spire Bks). Revell.

Christian's Secret of a Happy Life. Hannah W. Smith. 240p. 1983. pap. text ed. 3.50 (ISBN 0-88368-132-3). Whitaker Hse.

Christian's Secret of a Happy Life. Hannah W. Smith. (Christian Library). 1985. 6.95 (ISBN 0-916441-21-0); pap. 3.95 (ISBN 0-916441-27-X). Barbour & Co.

Christian's Secret of a Happy Life. Hannah W. Smith. 224p. 1986. pap. 2.50 (ISBN 0-345-33586-4, Pub. by Ballantine Epiphany). Ballantine.

Christian's Secret of a Happy Life for Today. Catherine Jackson. 224p. 1979. pap. 5.95 (ISBN 0-8007-5061-6, Power Bks). Revell.

Christian's Secret of a Happy Life: Proven Word. Hannah Whitall & Elisabeth E. Smith. 192p. 1985. pap. 5.95 (ISBN 0-8499-2980-6, 2980-6). Word Bks.

Christians Should Be Prosperous. Victor P. Wierwille. 31p. pap. 1.00 (ISBN 0-910068-65-8). Am Christian.

Christian's Two Chief Lessons, Viz. Selfe Deniall, & Selfe Tryall. Thomas Hooker. LC 74-14112. (Research Library of Colonial Americana). 1972. Repr. of 1640 ed. 34.50 (ISBN 0-405-03325-7). Ayer Co Pubs.

Christian's Vacation & Travel Guide. Robert G. Flood. 224p. 1982. pap. 9.95 (ISBN 0-8423-0260-3). Tyndale.

Christians Will Go Through the Tribulation. Jim McKeever. LC 78-55091. (Illus.). 1978. 10.95 (ISBN 0-931608-01-5); pap. 5.95 (ISBN 0-931608-02-3). Omega Pubns OR.

Christians with Secular Power. M. Gibbs. LC 80-8048. (Laity Exchange). 144p. (Orig.). 1981. pap. 5.95 (ISBN 0-8006-1389-9, 1-1389). Fortress.

Christiansburg Montgomery County, Virginia in the Heart of the Alleghenies. Lula P. Givens. LC 80-68026. (Illus.). 256p. 1981. 12.00 (ISBN 0-9614765-1-6). Pat G Johnson.

Christiarisme en Orient. Hajjar French. 9.00x (ISBN 0-86685-172-0). Intl Bk Ctr.

Christliche Platonaneigunug in den Stromateis des Clemens von Alexandrien. Dietmar Wyrwa. (Ger.). 364p. 1983. 33.60 (ISBN 3-11-008903-3). De Gruyter.

Christliche Theologie und Philologie in der Spaetantike: Die schulwissenschaftlichen Methoden der Psalmenexegese Cassiodors. Richard Schlieben. LC 74-77213. (Arbeiten zur Kirchengeschichte, Vol. 46). (Ger.). 132p. 1974. 19.00x (ISBN 3-11-004634-2). De Gruyter.

Christlichen Sarkophage der vorkonstantinischen Zeit. Friedrich Gerke. (Studien Zur Spaetantiken Kunstgeschichte: Vol. 11). (Illus.). viii, 432p. 1978. Repr. of 1940 ed. 140.00x (ISBN 3-11-004999-6). De Gruyter.

Christmas. Barbara Cooney. LC 67-18510. (Holiday Ser.). (Illus.). 1967. PLB 12.89i (ISBN 0-690-19201-0, Crowell Jr Bks). HarpJ.

Christmas. Pauline Smith. 32p. 1985. pap. 1.50 (ISBN 0-908175-83-3, Pub. by Boolarong Pubn Australia). Intl Spec Bk.

Christmas, Vol. 47. Ed. by Randolph Haugan. LC 32-30914. 64p. 1977. 14.50 (ISBN 0-8066-8951-X, 17-0115); pap. 6.95 (ISBN 0-8066-8950-1, 17-0114). Augsburg.

Christmas: A Celebration. Ed. by John Rhodes. 1986. 15.95 (ISBN 0-571-13752-0). Faber & Faber.

Christmas: A Family Service. 1982. pap. 2.25 (ISBN 0-89536-710-6, 0363). CSS of Ohio.

Christmas: An American Annual of Christmas Literature & Art, Vol. 46. Ed. by Randolph E. Haugan. LC 32-30914. 64p. 1976. 14.50 (ISBN 0-8066-8948-X, 17-0113); pap. 6.95 (ISBN 0-8066-8947-1, 17-0112). Augsburg.

Christmas: An American Annual of Christmas Literature & Art, Vol. 48. Ed. by Randolph E. Haugan. LC 32-30914. (Illus.). 64p. 1978. 14.50 (ISBN 0-8066-8953-6, 17-0117); pap. 6.95 (ISBN 0-8066-8952-8, 17-0116). Augsburg.

Christmas: An American Annual of Christmas Literature & Art, Vol. 49. Ed. by Randolph E. Haugan. LC 32-30914. (Illus.). 64p. 1979. 14.50 (ISBN 0-8066-8955-2, 17-0119); pap. 6.95 (ISBN 0-8066-8954-4, 17-0118). Augsburg.

Christmas: An Annotated Bibliography of Analytical Scholarship. Sue Samuelson. Ed. by Alan Dundes. LC 82-48083. (Garland Folklore Bibliographies Ser.). 200p. 1982. lib. bdg. 31.00 (ISBN 0-8240-9263-5). Garland Pub.

Christmas & Christmas Lore. Thomas G. Crippen. LC 69-16067. (Illus.). 256p. 1972. Repr. of 1923 ed. 50.00x (ISBN 0-8103-3029-6). Gale.

Christmas & Christmas Lore. Thomas G. Crippen. 1976. lib. bdg. 59.95 (ISBN 0-8490-1617-7). Gordon Pr.

Christmas & Easter in the Initiatic Tradition. Omraam M. Aivanhov. (Izvor Collection: Vol. 209). (Illus.). 139p. (Orig.). pap. 4.95 (ISBN 2-85566-226-5, Pub. by Prosveta France). Prosveta USA.

Christmas Anthology of Poetry & Painting. Ed. by Vivian Campbell. LC 79-51963. (Granger Poetry Library). 1980. Repr. of 1947 ed. 27.50x (ISBN 0-89609-181-3). Roth Pub Inc.

Christmas Around the World. (Illus.). 169p. 1985. 7.98 (ISBN 1-85079-025-6, Pub. by New Orchard England). Sterling.

Christmas around the World. Emily Kelley. (On My Own Bks.). (Illus.). 48p. 1986. lib. bdg. 8.95 (ISBN 0-87614-249-8). Carolrhoda Bks.

Christmas at Home. Hasba Brinsmead. (Illus.). 52p. 1986. 12.95 (ISBN 0-207-14543-1). Salem Hse Pubs.

Christmas at Our House. Mona Conner. 64p. 1986. 14.45i (ISBN 0-06-015596-5, HarpT). Har-Row.

Christmas Baking: Traditional Recipes Made Easy. Christian Teubner. (Illus.). 96p. 1985. 9.95 (ISBN 0-8120-5617-5). Barron.

Christmas Bibliography. Leona Phillips. 1977. lib. bdg. 69.95 (ISBN 0-8490-1363-1). Gordon Pr.

Christmas Birthday Story. Margaret Laurence. LC 79-27159. (Illus.). 32p. 1980. PLB 6.99 (ISBN 0-394-94361-9). Knopf.

Christmas Blessings. 16p. 1984. pap. 1.25 (ISBN 0-89542-820-2). Ideals.

Christmas Book. (Enchanted World Ser.). (YA) 1986. lib. bdg. 22.60 (ISBN 0-8094-5262-6, Pub. by Time-Life); 16.95 (ISBN 0-8094-5261-8). Silver.

Christmas Book. Moira Eastman & Wendy Poussard. LC 80-68368. (Illus.). 40p. 1980. 5.95 (ISBN 0-87793-214-X). Ave Maria.

Christmas Book. D. B. Lewis & G. C. Hexeltine. 1977. Repr. of 1928 ed. lib. bdg. 10.00 (ISBN 0-8495-3204-3). Arden Lib.

Christmas Book. Marcia O. Martin. (Illus.). 64p. 1985. 15.95 (ISBN 0-88363-585-2). H L Levin.

Christmas Book: An Anthology for Moderns. Wyndham Lewis & Heseltine. 1977. Repr. of 1928 ed. 30.00 (ISBN 0-89984-217-8). Century Bookbindery.

Christmas Book: Christmas in the Olden Time: Its Customs & Their Origin. J. Bridgman. 1978. Repr. of 1859 ed. lib. bdg. 27.50 (ISBN 0-8492-3711-4). R West.

Christmas Caring, a Christmas Sharing. John T. Ciappetta. 32p. 1987. 6.95 (ISBN 0-89962-646-7). Todd & Honeywell.

Christmas Carol: A Playscript. Darwin R. Payne. LC 80-18827. (Illus.). 138p. 1981. pap. 4.95 net (ISBN 0-8093-0999-8). S Ill U Pr.

Christmas Carol: Retold by A. Sweaney. Charles Dickens. (Oxford Progressive English Readers Ser.). 1975. pap. text ed. 3.75x (ISBN 0-19-580724-3). Oxford U Pr.

Christmas Carol Sampler. Margaret Cusack. (Illus.). 10.95 (ISBN 0-15-217752-3, HJ). HarBraceJ.

Christmas Carols. pap. 1.50 (ISBN 0-685-22654-9). Polanie.

Christmas Carols: A Reference Guide. William E. Studwell. LC 84-48240. 320p. 1984. lib. bdg. 29.00 (ISBN 0-8240-8899-9). Garland Pub.

Christmas Carols: A Treasury of Holiday Favorites with Words & Pictures. Illus. by Noel Tennyson. LC 83-60412. (Illus.). 24p. 1983. 1.95 (ISBN 0-394-86125-6). Random.

Christmas Carols, Ancient & Modern. William Sandys. LC 76-30740. 1977. Repr. of 1833 ed. lib. bdg. 32.50 (ISBN 0-8414-7779-5). Folcroft.

Christmas Carols: Ancient & Modern. William Sandys. 69.95 (ISBN 0-87968-866-1). Gordon Pr.

Christmas Celebration. Sam Elder. LC 84-47709. (Illus.). 1984. 5.00 (ISBN 0-06-015359-8, HarpT). Har-Row.

Christmas Celebration: The Wanderer's Christmas Anthology. Ed. by Frank Morriss. LC 83-51146. 334p. 1983. 14.95 (ISBN 0-915245-00-0). Wanderer Pr.

Christmas Classics. Sue Saltkill. (Illus.). 1985. pap. 6.95 (ISBN 0-943574-32-3). That Patchwork.

Christmas Collectibles. Margaret Whitmyer & Kenn Whitmyer. (Illus.). 224p. 1986. 19.95 (ISBN 0-317-52666-9). Collector Bks.

Christmas Comes in Assorted Sizes. Marguerite Goodman. Ed. by Sylvia Ashton. LC 77-80303. 1977. 14.95 (ISBN 0-87949-111-6). Ashley Bks.
Christmas Cookbook. 64p. pap. 3.50 (ISBN 0-89542-602-1). Ideals.
Christmas Crafts. Carolyn Meyer. LC 74-2608. (Illus.). 160p. 1974. 11.70i (ISBN 0-06-024197-7). HarpJ.
Christmas Crafts for Everyone. Evelyn Coskey. LC 76-4916. (Illus.). (YA) 1976. 9.95 (ISBN 0-687-07815-6). Abingdon.
Christmas Customs & Traditions. Frank Muir. LC 77-76504. (Illus.). 1977. 7.95 (ISBN 0-8008-1552-1). Taplinger.
Christmas Customs & Traditions: Their History & Significance. Clement A. Miles. LC 76-9183. (Illus.). 1976. pap. 6.50 (ISBN 0-486-23354-5). Dover.
Christmas Customs & Traditions: Their History & Significance. Clement A. Miles. (Illus.). 15.50 (ISBN 0-8446-5484-1). Peter Smith.
Christmas Customs Around the World. Herbert H. Wernecke. LC 59-9581. 188p. 1979. pap. 7.95 (ISBN 0-664-24258-8). Westminster.
Christmas Cycle. Frederick Kemper. 1982. 6.95 (ISBN 0-570-03842-1, 12-2945). Concordia.
Christmas Day & Other Sermons. Frederick D. Maurice. 410p. 1982. Repr. of 1892 ed. lib. bdg. 50.00 (ISBN 0-89987-595-5). Darby Bks.
Christmas Decorations from Williamsburg's Folk Art Collection: Easy to Follow Instructions for Making 90 Decorations. Colonial Williamsburg Staff. LC 76-41253. (Illus.). 80p. (Orig.). 1976. pap. 4.95 (ISBN 0-87935-040-7). Williamsburg.
Christmas Drama for Youth. Sarah W. Miller. LC 76-20255. 96p. (Orig.). 1976. pap. 4.50 (ISBN 0-8054-7511-7). Broadman.
Christmas Dreaming. Edmund E. Wells. (Orig.). pap. 1.50 (ISBN 0-686-30401-2). WOS.
Christmas, Easter, Ascension & Burial Services for Knights Templar. rev. ed. Robert Macoy. 112p. 1978. pap. 4.00 (ISBN 0-88053-011-1). Macoy Pub.
Christmas Entertainments. facs. ed. Alice M. Kellogg. LC 72-139764. (Granger Index Reprint Ser). 1897. 15.00 (ISBN 0-8369-6218-4). Ayer Co Pubs.
Christmas Eve on the Big Bayou. Hasa Ortego. 1974. 3.95 (ISBN 0-87511-091-6). Claitors.
Christmas Every Friday & Other Christmas Stories. Charlie M. Simon. Ed. by Lyman B. Hagen. LC 81-65364. (Illus.). 68p. 1981. 7.95 (ISBN 0-935304-21-5). August Hse.
Christmas Feast: Poems, Sayings, Greetings, & Wishes. Edna Barth. (Illus.). 176p. 1979. 10.60 (ISBN 0-395-28965-3, Clarion). HM.
Christmas Feasts & Festivals. Lillie Patterson. LC 68-14778. (Holiday Bks.). (Illus.). 64p. 1968. PLB 7.56 (ISBN 0-8116-6562-3). Garrard.
Christmas Feasts from History. Lorna J. Sass. Ed. by Jean Atcheson. LC 81-68835. (Great American Cooking Schools Ser.). (Illus.). 84p. 1981. pap. 5.95 (ISBN 0-941034-01-1). I Chalmers.
Christmas Foundation Meeting: Beginning of a New Cosmic Age. Rudolf Grosse. Tr. by Johanna Collis from Ger. Tr. of Weihnachtstagung als Zeitenwende. 158p. (Orig.). 1984. pap. 14.00 (ISBN 0-919924-23-9, Steiner Bk Ctr). Anthroposophic.
Christmas Foundation Meeting of the Anthroposophical Society. Rudolf Steiner. Ed. by R. G. Seddon. 37p. (Orig.). 1980. pap. 3.00 (ISBN 0-88010-094-X, Pub. by Steinerbooks). Anthroposophic.
Christmas Gifts for You to Make. Susan Purdy. LC 76-10160. (Illus.). 1976. PLB 12.89 (ISBN 0-397-31695-X, Lipp Jr Bks); pap. 4.95 o. p. (ISBN 0-397-31696-8). HarpJ.
Christmas Gifts From The Kitchen Cookbook. 64p. pap. 3.50 (ISBN 0-89542-635-8). Ideals.
Christmas Greeting. 16p. 1984. pap. 1.25 (ISBN 0-89542-819-9). Ideals.
Christmas Handbook. 1986. 10.95 (ISBN 0-8120-5756-2). Barron.
Christmas Handbook, No. 3. Sharon Lee. 112p. 1985. 7.95 (ISBN 0-87239-913-3, 3043). Standard Pub.
Christmas I Remember Best. Ed. by J. Livingood et al. (Illus., Orig.). write for info. (ISBN 0-910901-00-7); pap. 5.95 (ISBN 0-910901-01-5). Deseret News.
Christmas in All the World. LC 79-50087. (Illus.). 1979. pap. 4.95 (ISBN 0-8066-1704-7, 10-11238). Augsburg.
Christmas in America. Lillie Patterson. LC 69-11077. (Holiday Bks.). (Illus.). 64p. 1969. PLB 7.56 (ISBN 0-8116-6563-1). Garrard.
Christmas in Aspen. Jill Sheeley. (Illus.). 1982. Repr. write for info (ISBN 0-9609108-0-8). Columbine Pr.
Christmas in Denmark. World Book, Inc. Editorial Staff. LC 86-50556. (Round the World Christmas Program Ser.). (Illus.). 80p. 1986. write for info. (ISBN 0-7166-0886-3). World Bk.
Christmas in Ireland. World Book, Inc. LC 84-51015. (Round the World Christmas Program Ser.). (Illus.). 80p. 1985. write for info. (ISBN 0-7166-0885-5). World Bk.
Christmas in Latin America. (Eng.). 1976. pap. 1.00 (ISBN 0-8270-4365-1). OAS.
Christmas in Legend & Story: A Book for Boys & Girls Illustrated from Famous Paintings. Compiled by Elva S. Smith & Alice I. Hazeltine. LC 72-39390. (Granger Index Reprint Ser.). Repr. of 1915 ed. 18.00 (ISBN 0-8369-6353-9). Ayer Co Pubs.
Christmas in Old New England. Irving Bell. LC 80-69858. 54p. 1981. 8.95 (ISBN 0-917780-02-7). April Hill.
Christmas in Old Santa Fe. Pedro R. Ortega. LC 73-90581. (Illus.). 1982. pap. 6.25 (ISBN 0-913270-25-3). Sunstone Pr.
Christmas in Ritual & Tradition, Christian & Pagan. Clement A. Miles. LC 68-54858. 1968. Repr. of 1912 ed. 37.00x (ISBN 0-8103-3354-6). Gale.
Christmas in Ritual & Tradition: Christian & Pagan. Clement A. Miles. 1977. lib. bdg. 59.95 (ISBN 0-8490-1618-5). Gordon Pr.
Christmas in Song, Sketch & Story: Nearly Three Hundred Christmas Songs, Hymns & Carols. John P. McCaskey. 1980. lib. bdg. 67.95 (ISBN 0-8490-3175-3). Gordon Pr.
Christmas in Texas. Ed. by V. T. Abercrombie & Helen Williams. LC 79-66212. (Illus., Orig.). 1979. pap. 7.95 (ISBN 0-933988-00-1). Brown Rabbit.
Christmas in the Air: A New Fashioned Book for An Old Fashioned Christmas. Holly Ebel. (Illus.). 96p. (Orig.). 1982. pap. 7.95 (ISBN 0-943786-00-2). HollyDay.
Christmas in the Olden Time. Nathan B. Warren. LC 76-58002. 1977. Repr. of 1859 ed. lib. bdg. 22.50 (ISBN 0-8414-1656-7). Folcroft.
Christmas in the Primary School. Redvers Brandling. (Ward Lock Educational Ser.). 1985. 29.00x (ISBN 0-7062-4068-5, Pub. by Ward Lock Educ Co Ltd). State Mutual Bk.
Christmas in the White House. Albert J. Menendez. LC 83-3629. (Illus.). 128p. 1983. 11.95 (ISBN 0-664-21392-8). Westminster.
Christmas in Vermont: Three Stories. Margaret F. Carty. LC 83-62750. (Illus.). 48p. (Orig.). 1983. pap. 2.95 (ISBN 0-933050-21-6). New Eng Pr VT.
Christmas International. Dory Younger. 1983. pap. 3.75 (ISBN 0-89536-613-4, 0386). CSS of Ohio.
Christmas Invitation. Margaret W. Jones. Ed. by Roger R. Easson. LC 85-2035. (Child's Christmas in Memphis Ser.: Vol. 3). (Illus.). 48p. 1985. 9.95 (ISBN 0-918518-42-3). St Luke TN.
Christmas Is a Time for Singing. Ruth Odor. LC 81-86706. (Happy Day Bks.). (Illus.). 24p. (Orig.). 1982. pap. 1.59 (ISBN 0-87239-535-9, 3581). Standard Pub.
Christmas Is a Time of Giving. Joan W. Anglund. LC 61-10106. (Illus.). 1961. 7.95 (ISBN 0-15-217863-5, HJ). HarBraceJ.
Christmas Is Coming. Mary Montgomery & Herb Montgomery. 40p. (Orig.). 1983. pap. text ed. 1.50 (ISBN 0-89622-197-0). Twenty-Third.
Christmas Is Coming! 1986: Holiday Projects for Children & Parents. Ed. by Linda Stewart. (Illus.). 128p. 1986. 17.95 (ISBN 0-8487-0688-9). Oxmoor Hse.
Christmas Is for Celebrating. Melvin Wheatley. 1977. pap. 3.95 (ISBN 0-8358-0366-X). Upper Room.
Christmas, Its Origin & Associations, Together with Its Historical Events & Festive Celebrations During Nineteen Centuries. William F. Dawson. LC 68-54857. 1968. Repr. of 1902 ed. 54.00x (ISBN 0-8103-3351-1). Gale.
Christmas Lover's Handbook. Lasley F. Gober. LC 85-13450. (Illus.). 256p. 1985. pap. 12.95 (ISBN 0-932620-53-1). Betterway Pubns.
Christmas Lullaby. Carlson. (Arch Bks.). 24p. 1985. pap. 0.99 (ISBN 0-570-06195-4, 59-1296). Concordia.
Christmas Mumming in Newfoundland: Essays in Anthropology, Folklore, & History. Ed. by Herbert Halpert & G. M. Story. LC 71-391290. pap. 64.50 (ISBN 0-317-42289-8, 2055819). Bks Demand UMI.
Christmas Music for Little People. Linda Clary & Larry Harms. Ed. by Richard Bradley. (Illus.). 32p. 1985. bk & cassette 9.95 (ISBN 0-89748-160-7). Bradley Pubns.
Christmas Night, O Night of Nights. Heini Arnold & Dwight Blough. 1976. pap. 1.25 (ISBN 0-87486-120-9). Plough.
Christmas Nutshell Library, 4 bks. Hilary Knight. Incl. Angels & Berries & Candy Canes (ISBN 0-06-023200-5); Christmas Stocking Story (ISBN 0-06-023205-6); Firefly in a Fir Tree (ISBN 0-06-023190-4); Night Before Christmas. LC 63-18904. 1963. Set. 9.70 (ISBN 0-06-023165-3). HarpJ.
Christmas Omnibus. Sylvia Lynd. 1932. lib. bdg. 15.00 (ISBN 0-8414-5634-8). Folcroft.
Christmas on the Prairie. Joan Anderson. LC 85-4095. (Illus.). 48p. 1985. 13.95 (ISBN 0-89919-307-2, Clarion). Ticknor & Fields.
Christmas on Trial. Norma Leary. (Orig.). 1983. pap. 2.95 (ISBN 0-937172-56-1). JLJ Pubs.
Christmas: One Hundred Seasonal Favorites. (Ultimate Ser.). 248p. 1985. 17.95 (ISBN 0-88188-157-0, 00361398). H Leonard Pub Corp.
Christmas One Hundred Years Ago. Compiled by Skip Whitson. (Sun Historical Ser). (Illus., Orig.). 1976. pap. 3.50 (ISBN 0-89540-036-7, SB-036). Sun Pub.
Christmas Ornaments, Lights & Decorations. George Johnson. (Illus.). 320p. 1986. 19.95 (ISBN 0-317-52660-X). Collector Bks.
Christmas Pageant. Nancy Steltz. (Orig.). 1987. pap. price not set (ISBN 0-89536-889-7, 7875). CSS of Ohio.
Christmas Party: A Model Book. Faith Jaques. (Illus.). 6p. 1986. 8.95 (ISBN 0-399-21393-7, Philomel). Putnam Pub Group.
Christmas Past. Robert Brenner. (Illus.). 256p. 1985. 24.95 (ISBN 0-88740-051-5). Schiffer.
Christmas Pipe: A Collector's Celebration of Pipe Smoking at Yuletide. Richard C. Hacker. LC 86-70905. (Illus.). 156p. 1986. 27.95 (ISBN 0-931253-01-2). Autumngold Pub.
Christmas Plays. Barbara Westberg. Ed. by Mary H. Wallace. 40p. (Orig.). 1983. pap. 2.95 (ISBN 0-912315-62-8). Word Aflame.
Christmas Plays for Older Children. Linda Berry. 1981. saddle wire 2.50 (ISBN 0-8054-9733-1). Broadman.
Christmas Plays From Oberufer. 3rd ed. Compiled by Karl J. Schoer. Tr. & intro. by A. C. Harwood. 64p. 1973. pap. 3.50 (ISBN 0-85440-279-9, Pub. by Steinerbooks). Anthroposophic.
Christmas Present from a Friend. Yuriko Kimura. (Illus.). 28p. 1985. Repr. 10.95 (ISBN 0-687-07817-2). Abingdon.
Christmas Program Resource Book Two. 48p. 1984. pap. 2.50 (ISBN 0-8066-2075-7, 23-1501). Augsburg.
Christmas Programs for Children. Ed. by Laurie Hoard. 48p. 1986. pap. 1.95 (ISBN 0-87239-940-0, 8601). Standard Pub.
Christmas Programs for Church Groups. Marilyn A. Smith. (Paperback Program Ser). (Orig.). 1968. pap. 3.95 (ISBN 0-8010-7910-1). Baker Bk.
Christmas Programs for the Church, No. 16. Ed. by Judy Sparks. 64p. 1983. pap. 2.95 (ISBN 0-87239-614-2, 8616). Standard Pub.
Christmas Programs for the Church, No. 19. Ed. by Laurie Hoard. 64p. 1986. pap. 2.95 (ISBN 0-87239-914-1, 8619). Standard Pub.
Christmas Puppets Plays & Art Project Puppets. Nancy Ludwig. (Stick-Out-Your-Neck Ser.). (Illus.). 32p. 1983. pap. 1.98 (ISBN 0-88724-045-3, CD-8021). Carson-Dellos.
Christmas Readiness Activities. Patti Carson & Janet Dellosa. (Stick-Out-Your-Neck Ser.). (Illus.). 32p. 1983. pap. 1.98 (ISBN 0-88724-049-6, CD-8025). Carson-Dellos.
Christmas Reading & Activity Book. Patti Carson & Janet Dellosa. (Stick-Out-Your-Neck Ser.). (Illus.). 32p. 1983. pap. 1.98 (ISBN 0-88724-038-0, CD-8029). Carson-Dellos.
Christmas Recital. (Recital Notebooks Ser.: No. 12). 1967. pap. 2.95 (ISBN 0-8256-8061-1). Music Sales.
Christmas Reflections. Mary B. Christian. 1980. pap. 3.95 (ISBN 0-570-03494-9, 56-1711). Concordia.
Christmas Remembered. Arthur R. Pitcher. 1985. pap. 5.25 (ISBN 0-86544-029-8). Salv Army Suppl South.
Christmas Revels Songbook. Compiled by John Langstaff & Nancy Langstaff. LC 85-70140. (Illus.). 128p. 1985. cancelled (ISBN 0-87923-586-1); pap. 14.95 (ISBN 0-87923-591-8). Godine.
Christmas Revisited. Robert Brenner. (Illus.). 206p. 1986. pap. 24.95 (ISBN 0-88740-067-1). Schiffer.
Christmas Search-a-Picture Puzzles. Yvette Banek. (Puzzleback Ser.). (Illus.). 64p. (Orig.). 1981. pap. 2.50 (ISBN 0-671-43365-2). Wanderer Bks.
Christmas Selections: For Readings & Recitations. facsimile ed. Compiled by Rosemond L. McNaught. LC 74-38601. (Granger Index Reprint Ser.). Repr. of 1906 ed. 12.00 (ISBN 0-8369-6333-4). Ayer Co Pubs.
Christmas Sermons. Sterling W. Sill. LC 73-86165. 184p. 1973. 8.95 (ISBN 0-87747-503-2). Deseret Bk.
Christmas Songs for Piano. Albert De Vito. 1968. pap. 2.95 (ISBN 0-934286-53-1). Kenyon.
Christmas Star Was Jesus Himself: A Theological Work Showing any Theological Value in the Miracle Side Is also Found in the Non-Miracle Side of the New Testament. 3rd ed. J. B. Patterson. LC 84-71886. 238p. 1986. pap. 7.50x (ISBN 0-9613670-2-4). Christmas Star.
Christmas Story: From the Gospels of Matthew & Luke. Marguerite Northrup. LC 65-23504. (Illus.). 1966. 8.95 (ISBN 0-87099-047-0, 139459, Pub. by Metro Mus Art). NYGS.
Christmas Story in Medieval & Renaissance Manuscripts from the Spencer Collection, the New York Public Library. Karl Kup. LC 70-98680. (Illus.). 128p. 1969. pap. 10.00 (ISBN 0-87104-053-0). NY Pub Lib.
Christmas Story in Stained Glass. (Illus.). 56p. 1985. pap. 4.95. Walker & Co.
Christmas Story Programs. Carolyn S. Peterson & Ann D. Fenton. (Illus.). 1981. 7.00 (ISBN 0-913545-01-5). Moonlight FL.
Christmas Story Revisted. Lynn Weitzel. 21p. (Orig.). pap. 4.95 (ISBN 0-930161-07-6). State of the Art Ltd.
Christmas Tales of Flanders. Jean de Bosschere & M. C. Morris. (Illus.). 7.75 (ISBN 0-8446-4516-8). Peter Smith.
Christmas Testament. Ed. & intro. by Philip Kopper. LC 82-5843. (Illus.). 144p. 1982. slipcased 25.00 (ISBN 0-941434-23-0). Stewart Tabori & Chang.
Christmas: The Annual of Christmas Literature & Arts, Vol. 51. LC 32-30914. (Illus.). 64p. 1981. pap. text ed. 6.95 (ISBN 0-8066-8958-7, 17-0122); 14.50 (ISBN 0-8066-8959-5, 17-0123). Augsburg.
Christmas: The Annual of Christmas Literature & Art, Vol. 52. LC 32-30914. (Illus.). 64p. 1982. pap. text ed. 6.95 (ISBN 0-8066-8960-9, 17-0124); 14.50 (ISBN 0-8066-8961-7, 17-0125). Augsburg.
Christmas: The Annual of Christmas Literature & Art, Vol. 54. (Illus.). 64p. 1984. 14.50 (ISBN 0-8066-8965-X, 17-0129); pap. text ed. 6.95 (ISBN 0-8066-8964-1, 17-0128). Augsburg.
Christmas: The Annual of Christmas Literature & Art, Vol. 55. Leonard Flachman. 64p. 1985. text ed. 14.50 (ISBN 0-8066-8967-6, 17-0131); pap. text ed. 6.95 (ISBN 0-8066-8966-8, 17-0130). Augsburg.
Christmas: The Annual of Christmas Literature & Art, Vol. 57. Ed. by Leonard Flachman. (Illus.). 64p. 1987. text ed. 14.50 (ISBN 0-8066-8971-4, 17-0135); pap. 6.95 (ISBN 0-8066-8970-6, 17-0134). Augsburg.
Christmas Tidings. 2nd ed. Louise Bachelder. LC 84-60961. (Illus.). 64p. 1984. Repr. of 1969 ed. 5.95 (ISBN 0-88088-088-0, 880880). Peter Pauper.
Christmas Time. (Christmas Ser.). 2.95 (ISBN 0-86112-197-X, Pub. by Brimax Bks). Borden.
Christmas Time. Gail Gibbons. LC 82-1038. (Illus.). 32p. 1982. Reinforced bdg. 12.95 (ISBN 0-8234-0453-6). Holiday.
Christmas Time. Gail Gibbons. (Illus.). 32p. 1985. pap. 5.95 (ISBN 0-8234-0575-3). Holiday.
Christmas Traditions. William M. Auld. LC 68-58167. 1968. Repr. of 1931 ed. 42.00x (ISBN 0-8103-3353-8). Gale.
Christmas Traditions. William M. Auld. 1977. lib. bdg. 59.95 (ISBN 0-8490-1619-3). Gordon Pr.
Christmas Treasury. Ed. by Jack Newcombe. LC 81-50583. (Illus.). 512p. 1982. 22.95 (ISBN 0-670-22110-4). Viking.
Christmas Treasury. Ed. by Jean L. Scrocco. LC 84-8798. (Illus.). 48p. 1985. 11.95 (ISBN 0-88101-017-0). Unicorn Pub.
Christmas Tree Book: The History of the Christmas Tree & Antique Christmas Tree Ornaments. Phillip V. Snyder. LC 76-40224. (Large Format Ser.). (Illus.). 176p. 1977. pap. 10.95 (ISBN 0-14-004518-X). Penguin.
Christmas Tree Ornaments. Lorraine Bodger. LC 84-52753. (Illus.). 168p. 1985. write for info. (ISBN 0-02-496740-8, Pub by Sedgewood Press). Macmillan.
Christmas Tree Pests Manual. Janine M. Benyus. 107p. 1983. pap. 14.00 (ISBN 0-318-11762-2, S/N 001-001-00589-4). Gov Printing Office.
Christmas Trees for Pleasure & Profit. rev. ed. Arthur G. Chapman & Robert D. Wray. 220p. 1984. pap. text ed. 14.95 (ISBN 0-8135-1074-0). Rutgers U Pr.
Christmas: Voices from the Heart. Date not set. price not set (ISBN 0-934383-10-3). Pride Prods.
Christmas Was. Roe Fowler. 88p. 1982. pap. 6.95 (ISBN 0-686-38093-2). Fig Leaf Pr.
Christmas Week at Bigler's Mill: A Sketch in Black & White. Dora F. Spratt. LC 72-2171. (Black Heritage Library Collection Ser.). Repr. of 1895 ed. 13.25 (ISBN 0-8369-9065-X). Ayer Co Pubs.
Christmas with the Poets. Illus. by Birket Foster. (Illus.). 1978. Repr. of 1851 ed. 50.00 (ISBN 0-8492-0090-3). R West.
Christmas Wonder: An Anthology of Verse & Song. Beach Waldo. LC 73-79038. pap. 24.00 (2026924). Bks Demand UMI.
Christmas Workshop for the Church Family. Trudie W. Revoir. 96p. 1982. pap. 6.95 (ISBN 0-8170-0963-9). Judson.
Christmas Wrapped in Love. Alice J. Davidson. 128p. 13.95 (ISBN 0-687-07818-0). Abingdon.
Christmas Wrappings. Philippa Kirby. LC 86-5617. (Illus.). 72p. 1986. 4.95 (ISBN 1-55584-009-4). Weidenfeld.

Christmastide: Its History, Festivities & Carols. William Sandys. 69.95 (ISBN 0-87968-867-X). Gordon Pr.

Christmen: Experience of Priesthood Today. Gerard McGinnity. 94p. 1986. pap. 7.95 (ISBN 0-87061-124-0). Chr Classics.

Christocentrism in Christian Social Ethics: A Depth Study of Eight Modern Protestants. E. Clinton Gardner. LC 82-21843. 264p. (Orig.). 1983. lib. bdg. 28.50 (ISBN 0-8191-2954-2); pap. text ed. 13.50 (ISBN 0-8191-2955-0). U Pr of Amer.

Christological Catechism: New Testament Answers. Joseph A. Fitzmyer. 160p. (Orig.). 1982. pap. 4.95 (ISBN 0-8091-2453-X). Paulist Pr.

Christological Controversy. Ed. by Richard A. Norris, Jr. & William G. Rusch. Tr. by Richard A. Norris. LC 79-8890. (Sources of Early Christian Thought). 176p. 1980. pap. 7.95 (ISBN 0-8006-1411-9, 1-1411). Fortress.

Christological Perspectives. Ed. by Robert F. Berkey & Sarah A. Edwards. 320p. 18.95 (ISBN 0-8298-0491-9); pap. 10.95 (ISBN 0-8298-0606-7). Pilgrim NY.

Christologies & Cultures: Toward a Typology of Religious Worldviews. George Rupp. (Religion & Reason Ser: No. 10). 269p. 1974. text ed. 23.75x (ISBN 90-2797-641-4). Mouton.

Christology. L. Bouyer & M. Cawley. LC 83-4420. (Word & Spirit Ser.: Vol. V). 1983. pap. 7.00 (ISBN 0-932506-28-3). St Bedes Pubns.

Christology & a Modern Pilgrimage: A Discussion with Norman Perrin. rev. ed. Ed. by Hans D. Betz. LC 79-31605. pap. 27.30 (ISBN 0-317-28877-6, 2020268). Bks Demand UMI.

Christology & Myth in the New Testament. Geraint V. Jones. LC 56-4228. 1956. A R Allenson.

Christology at the Crossroads: A Latin American Approach. Jon Sobrino. Tr. by John Drury from Span. LC 77-25025. Orig. Title: Cristologia desde America Latina. 458p. (Orig.). 1978. pap. 13.95 (ISBN 0-88344-076-8). Orbis Bks.

Christology: Basic Texts in Focus. Leopold Sabourin. LC 84-12304. 259p. (Orig.). 1984. pap. 9.95 (ISBN 0-8189-0471-2). ALBA.

Christology in Context. M. DeJonge. price not set. Westminster.

Christology in the Making: A New Testament Inquiry into the Origins of the Doctrine of the Incarnation. James D. Dunn. LC 80-16968. 462p. 1980. pap. 24.50 (ISBN 0-664-24356-8). Westminster.

Christology of Early Jewish Christianity. Richard N. Longenecker. (Twin Brooks Ser.). 178p. 1981. pap. 8.95 (ISBN 0-8010-5610-1). Baker Bk.

Christology of Hegel. James Yerkes. (SUNY Hegelian Studies). 240p. 1982. 49.50 (ISBN 0-87395-648-6); pap. 18.95 (ISBN 0-87395-649-4). State U NY Pr.

Christology of Mark's Gospel. Jack D. Kingsbury. LC 83-5576. 224p. 1983. 19.95 (ISBN 0-8006-0706-6, 1-706). Fortress.

Christology of St. Paul. S. Nowell Rostron. 1977. lib. bdg. 59.95 (ISBN 0-8490-1620-7). Gordon Pr.

Christology of the Later Fathers. Ed. by Edward R. Hardy. LC 54-9949. (Library of Christian Classics). 396p. 1977. pap. 10.95 (ISBN 0-664-24152-2). Westminster.

Christology of the New Testament. rev. ed. Oscar Cullmann. Tr. by Shirley C. Guthrie & Charles A. M. Hall. LC 59-10178. 364p. 1980. pap. 12.95 (ISBN 0-664-24351-7). Westminster.

Christology of the Old Testament. E. W. Hengstenberg. Tr. by T. K. Arnold from Ger. LC 77-129739. (Kregel Reprint Library). 716p. 1988. pap. 16.95 (ISBN 0-8254-2812-2). Kregel.

Christology: The Center & the Periphery. Ed. by Frank Flinn. 256p. 1987. 21.95 (ISBN 0-913757-75-6). Paragon Hse.

Christoph Blumhardt & His Message. R. Lejeune. LC 63-15816. 1963. 7.00 (ISBN 0-87486-200-0). Plough.

Christopher Marlowe's Use of the Bible. R. M. Cornelius. LC 84-21280. (American University Studies IV (English Language & Literature): Vol. 23). (Illus.). 335p. 1984. text ed. 32.00 (ISBN 0-8204-0193-5). P Lang Pubs.

Christopher Wren & St. Paul's Cathedral. Ronald Gray. LC 81-13696. (Cambridge Topic Bks.). (Illus.). 52p. 1982. PLB 8.95 (ISBN 0-8225-1222-X). Lerner Pubns.

Christopsychology. Morton Kelsey. 177p. 1984. pap. 9.95 (ISBN 0-8245-0630-8). Crossroad NY.

Christotherapy II: A New Horizon for Counselors, Spiritual Directors & Seekers of Healing & Growth in Christ. Bernard J. Tyrrell. LC 82-60597. (Orig.). 1982. 12.95 (ISBN 0-8091-0332-X); pap. 8.95 (ISBN 0-8091-2482-3). Paulist Pr.

Christ's Appeal for Love. Josefa Menendez. Tr. by L. Keppel from Span. 1975. pap. 4.00 (ISBN 0-89555-013-X). TAN Bks Pubs.

Christ's Cabinet. rev. ed. William McIntyre. 143p. 1982. Repr. of 1937 ed. 3.95 (ISBN 0-86544-017-4). Salv Army Suppl South.

Christ's Call to Discipleship. James M. Boice. 1986. text ed. 9.95 (ISBN 0-8024-1397-8). Moody.

Christ's Comfort for Those Who Sorrow. A. M. Coniaris. 1978. pap. 3.95 (ISBN 0-937032-00-X). Light&Life Pub Co MN.

Christ's Coming & His Kingdom. K. M. Bailey. LC 80-70733. 175p. 1981. pap. 4.95 (ISBN 0-87509-296-9); Leader's Guide. 2.95 (ISBN 0-87509-309-4). Chr Pubns.

Christ's Farewell Discourse. Ernest Lussier. LC 79-19798. 90p. (Orig.). 1980. pap. 3.95 (ISBN 0-8189-0394-5). Alba.

Christ's Incarnation-"Good Tidings of Great Joy". C. H. Spurgeon. 1978. pap. 2.50 (ISBN 0-686-00498-1). Pilgrim Pubns.

Christ's Law of Love. rev. ed. Daughters of St. Paul. (Way, Truth & Life Ser.). (Illus.). 1973. text ed. 2.50 (ISBN 0-8198-0296-4); tchrs manual 6.25 (ISBN 0-8198-0297-2); activity bk. 1.50 (ISBN 0-8198-0298-0); parent guide 1.25 (ISBN 0-8198-0299-9). Dghtrs St Paul.

Christ's Life, Our Life. John B. Coburn. LC 77-17172. 112p. 1978. 4.00 (ISBN 0-8164-0384-8, HarpR); pap. 4.95 (ISBN 0-8164-2616-3). Har-Row.

Christ's Lordship & Religious Pluralism. Ed. by Gerald H. Anderson & Thomas F. Stransky. LC 80-25406. 256p. (Orig.). 1981. pap. 8.95 (ISBN 0-88344-088-1). Orbis Bks.

Christ's Mass. Jack Kershaw. LC 74-28633. 1975. 9.95 (ISBN 0-87695-178-7). Aurora Pubs.

Christs: Meditations on Archetypal Images in Christian Theology. David L. Miller. 200p. 1981. 12.95x (ISBN 0-8164-0492-5, HarpR). Har-Row.

Christ's Object Lessons. large print ed. 1980. pap. 7.25 (ISBN 0-8280-0044-1, 03364-7). Review & Herald.

Christs Politician & Solomon's Puritan: Two Sermons. Thomas Scott. LC 73-6159. (English Experience Ser.: No. 622). 1973. Repr. of 1616 ed. 6.00 (ISBN 90-221-0622-5). Walter J Johnson.

Christ's Stamp of Approval & Other Sermonettes. J. J. Turner. 1977. pap. 2.50 (ISBN 0-89315-014-2). Lambert Bk.

Christ's Victorious Kingdom. John J. Davis. 144p. 1987. pap. 6.95 (ISBN 0-8010-2970-8). Baker Bk.

Christ's Words from the Cross. Charles H. Spurgeon. (Spurgeon Library Ser.). 120p. 1981. pap. 4.95 (ISBN 0-8010-8207-2). Baker Bk.

Christus Victor. Gustav Aulen. (Orig.). 1969. pap. 6.95 (ISBN 0-02-083400-4, Collier). Macmillan.

Christwalk. Richard Roos. 208p. (Orig.). 1985. pap. 7.95 (ISBN 0-8091-2667-2). Paulist Pr.

Chronica Jocelini De Brakelonda. Jocelin De Brakelond. LC 17-17164. (Camden Society, London. Publications, First Series: No. 13). Repr. of 1840 ed. 19.00 (ISBN 0-404-50113-3). AMS Pr.

Chronica Jocelini De Brakelonda, De Rebus Gestis Samsonis. Jocelin De Brakelonda. 1840. 19.00 (ISBN 0-384-27530-3). Johnson Repr.

Chronicle of Ahimaaz. Ahimaaz Ben Paltiel. Tr. by Marcus Salzman. LC 79-158233. (Columbia University Oriental Studies: No. 18). Repr. of 1924 ed. 15.75 (ISBN 0-404-50508-2). AMS Pr.

Chronicle of Eusebius & Greek Chronographic Tradition. Alden A. Mosshammer. LC 76-1029. 366p. 1979. 29.50 (ISBN 0-8387-1939-2). Bucknell U Pr.

Chronicle of Gods & Sovereigns: Jinno Shotoki of Kitabatake Chikafusa. Tr. by H. Paul Varley from Japanese. LC 80-10430. (Translations from Oriental Classics Ser.). 1980. 32.00x (ISBN 0-231-04940-4). Columbia U Pr.

Chronicle of the First Crusade. Foucher De Chartres. Tr. by Martha E. McGinty. LC 76-29823. Repr. of 1941 ed. 22.50 (ISBN 0-404-15417-4). AMS Pr.

Chronicle of the Hutterian Brethren, Vol. 1. Kasper Braitmichel et al. Ed. by Hutterian Brethren. (Ger. & Eng., Illus.). 900p. 1987. 36.00 (ISBN 0-87486-021-0). Plough.

Chronicle of the Lodz Ghetto, 1941-1944. Ed. by Lucjan Dobroszycki. LC 84-3614. (Illus.). 603p. 1984. 37.50x (ISBN 0-300-03208-0). Yale U Pr.

Chronicle of the Slavs. Helmold Priest Of Bosau. Tr. by Francis J. Tschan. 1967. lib. bdg. 29.00x (ISBN 0-374-98018-7, Octagon). Hippocrene Bks.

Chronicler's History. Martin Noth. (JSOT Supplement Ser.). 120p. 1987. text ed. 22.50x (ISBN 1-85075-043-2, Pub. by JSOT Pr England); pap. text ed. 9.50x (ISBN 1-85075-044-0, Pub. by JSOT Pr England). Eisenbrauns.

Chronicler's History of Israel: Chronicles-Ezra-Nehemiah Restored to Its Original Form. Charles C. Torrey. 1954. 17.50x (ISBN 0-686-37866-0). Elliots Bks.

Chronicler's Use of the Deuteronomistic History. Steven L. McKenzie. (Harvard Semitic Monograph Ser.: No. 33). 1985. 16.50 (ISBN 0-89130-828-8, 04 00 33). Scholars Pr GA.

Chronicles. Ed. by A. Cohen. 358p. 1952. 10.95 (ISBN 0-900689-37-4). Soncino Pr.

Chronicles First & Second, Vol. 10. Leslie Allan. 400p. 1987. 24.95 (ISBN 0-8499-0415-3). Word Bks.

Chronicles of a Faith Life. Elizabeth V. Baker. (Higher Christian Life Ser.). 270p. 1984. 35.00 (ISBN 0-8240-6403-8). Garland Pub.

Chronicles of Jerahmeel. rev. ed. Moses Gaster. 1971. 35.00x (ISBN 0-87068-162-1). Ktav.

Chronicles of Matthew Paris: Monastic Life in the Thirteenth Century. Tr. by Richard Vaughan from Lat. LC 83-40602. 286p. 1985. 25.00 (ISBN 0-312-13452-5). St Martin.

Chronicles of the Crusades. Gwoffrey De Lion et al. Tr. by John A. Giles & Thomas Johnes. LC 73-84862. (Bohn's Antiquarian Library Ser.). Repr. of 1848 ed. 41.50 (ISBN 0-404-50014-5). AMS Pr.

Chronicles of the Crusades. Geoffrey De Villehardouin & Jean De Joinville. Tr. by Margaret R. Shaw. (Classics Ser.). (Orig.). 1963. pap. 5.95 (ISBN 0-14-044124-7). Penguin.

Chronicles of the Crusades. Joinville Villehardouin. Tr. by M. R. Shaw from Fr. 258p. 1985. 14.95 (ISBN 0-88029-037-4, Pub. by Dorset Pr). Hippocrene Bks.

Chronicles of the Crutch. Blanchard Jerrold. 1979. Repr. of 1860 ed. lib. bdg. 40.00 (ISBN 0-8482-1394-7). Norwood Edns.

Chronicles of the Pilgrim Fathers of the Colony of Plymouth, 1602-1625. Alexander Young. LC 78-87667. (Law, Politics & History Ser). 1971. Repr. of 1841 ed. lib. bdg. 42.50 (ISBN 0-306-71760-3). Da Capo.

Chronicles One. Ed. by Jacob M. Myers. LC 65-17226. (Anchor Bible Ser.: Vol. 12). 1965. 14.00 (ISBN 0-385-01259-4, Anchor Pr). Doubleday.

Chronicles Two. Ed. by Jacob M. Myers. (Anchor Bible Ser.: Vol. 13). 1965. 14.00 (ISBN 0-385-03757-0, Anchor Pr). Doubleday.

Chronicon Angliae Petriburgense. Ed. by John A. Giles. 1966. Repr. of 1845 ed. 24.00 (ISBN 0-8337-1342-6). B Franklin.

Chronicon Ephratense: A History of the Community of Seventh Day Baptists at Ephrata, Lancaster County, Pennsylvania. Lamech. Tr. by J. Max Hark. LC 77-185946. (Research & Source Works Ser). 288p. 1972. Repr. of 1880 ed. lib. bdg. 22.50 (ISBN 0-8337-1993-9). B Franklin.

Chronicon Petroburgense. 1849. 24.00 (ISBN 0-384-08985-2). Johnson Repr.

Chronik des Bischofs Otto, Von Freising, Sechstes und Siebentes Buch. Otto Bishop of Freising. Tr. by H. Kohl. (Ger.). pap. 10.00 (ISBN 0-384-43965-9). Johnson Repr.

Chronik Des Cerbonio Besozzi: 1548-1563. Cerbonio Besozzi. 185p. pap. 23.00 (ISBN 0-384-15678-9). Johnson Repr.

Chronik Des Otto Von St. Blasien. Von St. Blasien Otto. Tr. by Horst Kohl. (Ger). pap. 10.00 (ISBN 0-384-43970-5). Johnson Repr.

Chronik Fredegars und der Frankenkoenige, die Lebensbeschreibungen des Abtes Columban, der Bischoefe Arnulf, Leodegar und Eligius, der Koenigin Balthilde. 2nd ed. Ed. by W. Wattenbach. Tr. by Otto Abel. (Geschichtschreiber der Deutschen Vorzeit Ser: Vol. 11). (Ger.). pap. 19.00 (ISBN 0-384-00104-1). Johnson Repr.

Chronique D'Enguerrand De Monstrelet, 6 Vols. Enguerrend De Monstrelet. Ed. by L. Douet D'Arcq. 1857-62. Set. 255.00 (ISBN 0-384-39781-6); Set. pap. 220.00 (ISBN 0-384-39780-8). Johnson Repr.

Chronique Du Mont-Saint-Michel 1343-1468, 2 Vols. Ed. by Simeon Luce. 1879-83. Set. 67.00 (ISBN 0-384-09010-9); Set. pap. 55.00 (ISBN 0-384-09011-7). Johnson Repr.

Chronological & Background Charts of Church History. Robert C. Walton. 120p. 1986. pap. text ed. 8.95 (ISBN 0-310-36281-4, 11302P). Zondervan.

Chronological & Background Charts of the New Testament. H. Wayne House. 160p. (Orig.). 1981. pap. 10.95 spiral bdg. (ISBN 0-310-41641-8, 11149P). Zondervan.

Chronological & Background Charts of the Old Testament. John W. Walton. 1977. spiral bdg. 8.95 (ISBN 0-310-36291-1, 11300P). Zondervan.

Chronological Aspects of the Life of Christ. Harold W. Hoehner. 1976. pap. text ed. 9.95 (ISBN 0-310-26211-9, 10841P). Zondervan.

Chronological Chart of Ancient, Modern & Biblical History. Sebastian C. Adams. 1982. Repr. of 1877 ed. educational chart 14.95 (ISBN 0-943388-04-X). South Oregon.

Chronologische Studien Zu Otfrids Evangelienbuch. Hans Bork. 27.00 (ISBN 0-685-02224-2); pap. 22.00 (ISBN 0-685-02225-0). Johnson Repr.

Chronology & Recensional Development in the Greek Text of Kings. James D. Shenkel. LC 68-21983. (Semitic Monographs: No. 1). (Illus.). 1968. text ed. 10.00x (ISBN 0-674-13050-2). Harvard U Pr.

Chronology of Paul's Life. Robert Jewett. LC 78-54553. 176p. 1979. 14.95 (ISBN 0-8006-0522-5, 1-522). Fortress.

Chronology of the Bible. 1980. lib. bdg. 49.95 (ISBN 0-8490-3140-0). Gordon Pr.

Chronology of the Public Ministry of Jesus. George Ogg. 1980. lib. bdg. 75.00 (ISBN 0-8490-3142-7). Gordon Pr.

Chrysalis: A Journey into the New Spiritual America. Mark Donicht. (Illus.). 192p. 1978. pap. 4.95 (ISBN 0-89496-011-3). Ross Bks.

Chu Hsi & Neo-Confucianism. Ed. by Wing-Tsit Chan. LC 85-24532. (Illus.). 672p. 1986. 30.00x (ISBN 0-8248-0961-0). UH Pr.

Chu Hsi & the Ta-hsueh: Neo-Confucian Reflection on the Confucian Canon. Daniel K. Gardner. (Harvard East Asian Monographs: No. 118). 300p. 1985. text ed. 20.00x (ISBN 0-674-13065-0, Pub. by Coun East Asian Stud). Harvard U Pr.

Chuang Tsu - Inner Chapters. Chuang Tsu. Ed. by Gia-Fu Feng. Tr. by Jane English. (Giant Ser.). pap. 12.95 (ISBN 0-394-71990-5, V-990, Vin). Random.

Chuang Tzu: Mystic, Moralist, & Social Reformer. 2nd rev. ed. Chuang Tzu. Tr. by Herbert A. Giles. LC 70-38059. (BCL Ser.: No. II). Repr. of 1926 ed. 44.50 (ISBN 0-404-56915-3). AMS Pr.

Chuang Tzu: World Philosopher at Play. Kuang-ming Wu. (AAR Studies in Religion). 12.95 (ISBN 0-89130-537-8, 01-00-26). Scholars Pr GA.

Chuckles & Challenges. Annetta Dellinger. 96p. 1986. pap. 4.95 (ISBN 0-8010-2960-0). Baker Bk.

Chuetas of Majorca. rev. ed. Baruch Braunstein. 1971. 25.00x (ISBN 0-87068-147-8). Ktav.

Chumash Koren. 1982. 6.95 (ISBN 0-686-76491-9). Feldheim.

Ch'un Ts'ew with the Tso Chuen, 4 vols, Vol. 4. Tr. by James Legge. (Chinese Classics Ser.). (Chinese & Eng.). 1983. Repr. of 1893 ed. 25.00x (ISBN 0-89986-356-6); 95.00x (ISBN 0-89986-352-3). Oriental Bk Store.

Church. Ernest A. Clevenger, Jr. (Bible Drill Flash Card Flipbook Ser.). 104p. 1983. pap. 4.25 (ISBN 0-88428-016-0). Parchment Pr.

Church. Ed. by Melvin E. Dieter & Daniel N. Berg. (Wesleyan Theological Perspectives Ser.: Vol. IV). 1984. 14.95 (ISBN 0-87162-406-0, D4853). Warner Pr.

Church. Thomas Halton. (Message of the Fathers of the Church Ser.: Vol. 4). 1985. 15.95 (ISBN 0-89453-344-4); pap. 10.95 (ISBN 0-89453-316-9). M Glazier.

Church. Robert Hicks & Richard Bewes. (Understanding Bible Truth Ser.). (Orig.). 1981. pap. 0.95 (ISBN 0-89840-018-X). Heres Life.

Church. Hans Kung. 600p. 1976. pap. 6.95 (ISBN 0-385-11367-6, Im). Doubleday.

Church. Wolfhart Pannenberg. Tr. by Keith Crim. LC 82-23768. 176p. 1983. pap. 10.95 (ISBN 0-664-24460-2). Westminster.

Church. Russell P. Spittler. LC 77-83982. (Radiant Life Ser.). 126p. 1977. pap. 2.50 (ISBN 0-88243-910-3, 02-0910); tchr's. ed. 3.95 (ISBN 0-88243-180-3, 32-0180). Gospel Pub.

Church, a Believing Fellowship. John H. Leith. LC 80-82192. 192p. 1981. pap. 3.95 (ISBN 0-8042-0518-3). John Knox.

Church: A Bibliography. Avery Dulles & Patrick Granfield. (Theology & Biblical Resources Ser: Vol. 1). 1985. 15.00 (ISBN 0-89453-449-1); pap. 8.95 (ISBN 0-89453-470-X). M Glazier.

Church: A Faith Filled People. Mary Jo Tully. 96p. 1982. pap. 3.50 (ISBN 0-697-01823-7). Wm C Brown.

Church Administration: A Handbook for Church Leaders. Walter H. Adams. 1979. pap. 2.95 (ISBN 0-88027-001-2). Firm Foun Pub.

Church Administration-Effective Leadership for Ministry. Charles A. Tidwell. LC 85-6620. 1985. pap. 8.95 (ISBN 0-8054-3113-6). Broadman.

Church Administration Handbook. Bruce P. Powers. LC 84-29249. 1985. pap. 9.95 (ISBN 0-8054-3112-8). Broadman.

Church Administration in the Black Perspective. Floyd Massey, Jr. & Samuel B. McKinney. LC 76-9804. 176p. 1976. pap. 7.95 (ISBN 0-8170-0710-5). Judson.

Church Advertising: A Practical Guide. Steve Dunkin. LC 81-17562. (Creative Leadership Ser.). 128p. (Orig.). 1982. pap. 6.95 (ISBN 0-687-08140-8). Abingdon.

Church After the Council: A Primer for Adults. Peter M. Stravinskas & Robert A. McBain. LC 75-4720. 113p. (Orig.). 1975. pap. 2.95 (ISBN 0-8189-0316-3). Alba.

Church & a Catholic's Conscience. Robert L. Spaeth. 96p. 1985. pap. 6.50 (ISBN 0-86683-869-4, 8456, HarpR). Har-Row.

Church & Campus: Legal Issues in Religiously Affiliated Higher Education. Philip R. Moots & Edward M. Gaffney. LC 79-14002. 1979. pap. text ed. 7.95 (ISBN 0-268-00732-2). U of Notre Dame Pr.

Church & Catechism: The Baltimore Catechism Revisited. Frederick A. Kreuziger. xiii, 126p. 1986. pap. 8.95 (ISBN 0-9616430-0-5). Reflex Bks.

Church & Community in the Diocese of Lyon: 1500-1789. Philip T. Hoffman. LC 83-23404. (Historical Publications Ser.: No. 132). 256p. 1984. text ed. 22.50x (ISBN 0-300-03141-6). Yale U Pr.

Church & Community: The Parish Church in English Life. J. H. Bettey. LC 79-14739. (Illus.). 142p. 1979. text ed. 26.50x (ISBN 0-06-490381-8, 06346). B&N Imports.

Church & Confession: Conservative Theologians in Germany, England, & America, 1815-1866. Walter H. Conser, Jr. LC 84-18990. viii, 360p. 1984. 28.95 (ISBN 0-86554-119-1, MUP/H109). Mercer Univ Pr.

Church & Culture since Vatican II: The Experience of North & Latin America. Joseph Gremillion. LC 84-40364. 350p. 1985. pap. text ed. 12.95 (ISBN 0-268-00753-5, 85-07535). U of Notre Dame Pr.

Church & Disabled Persons. Ed. by Griff Hogan. 128p. 1983. pap. 8.95 (ISBN 0-87243-123-1). Templegate.

Church & Family. J. D. Middlebrook & Larry Summers. LC 80-66326. 128p. 1980. pap. 1.95 (ISBN 0-88243-482-9, 02-0482). Gospel Pub.

Church & Freemasonry in Brazil, 1872-1875. Mary C. Thornton. LC 73-2647. 287p. 1973. Repr. of 1948 ed. lib. bdg. 22.50x (ISBN 0-8371-6816-3, THCF). Greenwood.

Church & Gnosis: A Study of Christian Thought & Speculation in the Second Century. Francis C. Burkitt. LC 77-84696. (Morse Lectures: 1931). Repr. of 1932 ed. 26.00 (ISBN 0-404-16104-9). AMS Pr.

Church & Government in the Middle Ages: Essays Presented to C. R. Cheney on His 70th Birthday. Ed. by Christopher N. Brooke et al. LC 75-41614. pap. 83.00 (2027285). Bks Demand UMI.

Church & Government in the Middle Ages. Ed. by C. Brooke et al. LC 75-41614. (Illus.). 1977. 59.50 (ISBN 0-521-21172-7). Cambridge U Pr.

Church & Healing: Papers Read at the Twentieth Summer Meeting & the Twenty-First Winter Meeting. Ed. by W. J. Sheils & Derek Baker. (Studies in Church History: Vol. 19). 400p. 1984. text ed. 45.00x (ISBN 0-631-13117-5). Basil Blackwell.

Church & Her Ideal Educational Situation. Ed. by Jesse P. Sewell. Henry E. Speck. 1933. 2.50 (ISBN 0-88027-083-7); pap. 1.50 (ISBN 0-88027-084-5). Firm Foun Pub.

Church & Its Function in Society. W. A. Hooft & J. H. Oldham. 1977. lib. bdg. 59.95 (ISBN 0-8490-1625-8). Gordon Pr.

Church & Its Order According to Scripture. Samuel Ridout. 1915. pap. 2.75 (ISBN 0-87213-711-2). Loizeaux.

Church & Its Youth. Lamar Vest. (CTC Ser.). 1980. 5.25 (ISBN 0-87148-170-7); pap. 4.25 (ISBN 0-87148-171-5); instr's guide 7.95 (ISBN 0-87148-172-3). Pathway Pr.

Church & Jesus. Francis G. Downing. LC 78-3050. (Studies in Biblical Theology, 2nd Ser.: No. 10). 1968. pap. 10.00x (ISBN 0-8401-3060-0). A R Allenson.

Church & Labour in Colombia. Kenneth N. Medhurst. LC 82-62254. 320p. 1984. 46.00 (ISBN 0-7190-0969-3, Pub. by Manchester Univ Pr). Longwood Pub Group.

Church & Law in the Balkan Peninsula during the Ottoman Rule. N. J. Pantazopoulos. (Illus.). 125p. 1983. pap. text ed. 24.00 (Pub. by A M Hakkert). Coronet Bks.

Church & Mankind. Augustin Bea. 6.50 (ISBN 0-8199-0012-5, L38112). Franciscan Herald.

Church & Mankind. Ed. by Edward Schillebeeckx. LC 65-15249. (Concilium Ser.: Vol. 1). 196p. 1965. 7.95 (ISBN 0-8091-0015-0). Paulist Pr.

Church & Manor: A Study in English Economic History. Sidney O. Addy. LC 70-107902. (Illus.). 1970. Repr. of 1913 ed. 37.50x (ISBN 0-678-00632-6). Kelley.

Church & Membership Awareness. rev. ed. Samuel Stoesz. pap. 2.95 (ISBN 0-87509-332-9). Chr Pubns.

Church & Membership Awareness. Samuel J. Stoesz. pap. 2.95 (ISBN 0-87509-066-4); leaders guide 0.95 (ISBN 0-87509-067-2). Chr Pubns.

Church & Mission in Modern Africa. Adrian Hastings. LC 67-30321. (Orig.). 1967. 25.00 (ISBN 0-8232-0770-6). Fordham.

Church & Missions Alive. Samuel J. Stoesz. 1975. pap. 2.50 (ISBN 0-87509-068-0); leaders guide 0.95 (ISBN 0-87509-069-9). Chr Pubns.

Church & Organized Movements. facs. ed. Ed. by Randolph C. Miller. LC 76-134115. (Essay Index Reprint Ser). 1946. 18.00 (ISBN 0-8369-1998-X). Ayer Co Pubs.

Church & Parliament: The Reshaping of the Church of England, 1828-1860. Olive J. Bross. LC 59-7423. pap. 30.00 (ISBN 0-317-26542-3, 2023992). Bks Demand UMI.

Church & Pastoral Records in the Archives of the United Church of Christ. Florence M. Bricker. 1982. pap. 6.00 (ISBN 0-910564-01-9). Evang & Ref.

Church & Peace. Ed. by Virgil Elizondo & Norbert Greinacher. (Concilium 1983: Vol. 164). 128p. (Orig.). 1983. pap. 6.95 (ISBN 0-8164-2444-6, HarpR). Har-Row.

Church & Persons with Handicaps. H. Oliver Ohsberg. LC 82-80342. 128p. 1982. pap. 7.95 (ISBN 0-8361-1996-7). Herald Pr.

Church & Politics: From Theology to a Case History of Zimbabwe. Edna McDonagh. LC 80-53070. 200p. 1980. text ed. 14.95 (ISBN 0-268-00734-9); pap. text ed. 5.95 (ISBN 0-268-00736-5). U of Notre Dame Pr.

Church & Politics in Chile: Challenges to Modern Catholicism. Brian H. Smith. LC 81-47951. 416p. 1982. 37.00x (ISBN 0-691-07629-4); pap. 13.50x L.P.E. (ISBN 0-691-10119-1). Princeton U Pr.

Church & Politics in Fourteenth Century England. R. M. Haines. LC 76-54062. (Studies in Medieval Life & Thought: No. 10). 1978. 49.50 (ISBN 0-521-21544-7). Cambridge U Pr.

Church & Politics Today. Ed. by George Moyser. 320p. 1985. pap. 17.95 (ISBN 0-567-29350-5, Pub. by T&T Clark Ltd Uk). Fortress.

Church & Popular Education. Herbert B. Adams. LC 78-63876. (Johns Hopkins University. Studies in the Social Sciences. Eighteenth Ser. 1900: 8-9). Repr. of 1900 ed. 11.50 (ISBN 0-404-61132-X). AMS Pr.

Church & Popular Education. Herbert B. Adams. Repr. of 1900 ed. 10.00 (ISBN 0-384-00323-0). Johnson Repr.

Church & Popular Education. Herbert B. Adams. (Works of Herbert B. Adams Ser.). 84p. 1985. Repr. of 1900 ed. lib. bdg. 29.00 (ISBN 0-318-03787-4, Pub. by Am Repr Serv). Am Biog Serv.

Church & Racial Hostility. William Radler. 282p. 1978. lib. bdg. 45.00x (Pub. by J C B Mohr BRD). Coronet Bks.

Church & Racial Hostility: A History of Interpretation of Ephesians. William Rader. 1978. 71.50x (ISBN 3-16-140112-3). Adlers Foreign Bks.

Church & Racism. Ed. by Gregory B. Baum & John Coleman. (Concilium Ser.: Vol. 151). 128p. (Orig.). 1982. pap. 6.95 (ISBN 0-8164-2382-2, HarpR). Har-Row.

Church & Residential Desegregation. Henry Clark. 1965. 16.95x (ISBN 0-8084-0076-2). New Coll U Pr.

Church & Revolution in Nicaragua. Laura O'Shaughnessy & Luis Serra. LC 82-92625. (Monographs in International Studies, Latin America Ser.: No. 11). 118p. pap. 11.00x (ISBN 0-89680-126-8, Ohio U Ctr Intl). Ohio U Pr.

Church & Revolution in Rwanda. Ian Linden & Jane Linden. LC 76-58329. 295p. 1977. text ed. 39.50x (ISBN 0-8419-0305-0, Africana). Holmes & Meier.

Church & Science. Mark J. Hurley. 167p. 1982. 6.00 (ISBN 0-8198-1420-2, MS0125); pap. 5.00 (ISBN 0-8198-1421-0). Dghtrs St Paul.

Church & Scottish Social Development, 1780-1870. Stewart Mechie. LC 75-3740. 181p. 1975. Repr. of 1960 ed. lib. bdg. 22.50x (ISBN 0-8371-8060-0, MECS). Greenwood.

Church & Secular Education. Lewis B. Whittemore. LC 78-17152. 1978. Repr. of 1960 ed. lib. bdg. 22.50 (ISBN 0-313-20540-X, WHCS). Greenwood.

Church & Slave in Perry County, Missouri, 1818-1865. Stafford Poole & Douglas J. Slawson. (Studies in American Religion: Vol. 22). (Illus.). 240p. lib. bdg. 49.95x (ISBN 0-88946-666-1). E Mellen.

Church & Slavery. Albert Barnes. LC 71-98714. Repr. of 1857 ed. 22.50 (ISBN 0-8371-2771-8, BAC&, Pub. by Negro U Pr). Greenwood.

Church & Slavery. Albert Barnes. LC 79-82416. 15.00x (ISBN 0-403-00150-1). Scholarly.

Church & Social Change in Latin America. Ed. by Henry A. Landsberger. LC 77-85355. 1970. 21.95x (ISBN 0-268-00356-4). U of Notre Dame Pr.

Church & Socialism. Sergio Arce. 200p. pap. text ed. 6.95 (ISBN 0-936123-00-1). NY Circus Pubns.

Church & Society in Catholic Europe of the Eighteenth Century. W. J. Callahan & D. Higgs. LC 78-12165. 1979. 27.95 (ISBN 0-521-22424-1). Cambridge U Pr.

Church & Society in Eighteenth Century England. Arthur Warne. LC 69-16764. (Illus.). 1969. 17.95x (ISBN 0-678-05642-0). Kelley.

Church & Society in England: Henry VIII to James I. Felicity Heal & Rosemary O'Day. LC 76-51728. vi, 206p. 1977. 23.50 (ISBN 0-208-01649-X, Archon). Shoe String.

Church & Society in the Last Centuries of Byzantium. D. M. Nicol. LC 78-72092. (Birkbeck Lectures, 1977). 1979. 32.50 (ISBN 0-521-22438-1). Cambridge U Pr.

Church & Society in the Norman Principality of Capua, 1058-1197. G. A. Loud. (Historical Monographs). (Illus.). 1985. 42.00x (ISBN 0-19-822931-3). Oxford U Pr.

Church & State from Constantine to Theodosius. Stanley L. Greenslade. LC 79-8712. 93p. 1981. Repr. of 1954 ed. lib. bdg. 22.50x (ISBN 0-313-20793-3, GRCS). Greenwood.

Church & State in America: A Bibliographical Guide (The Colonial & Early National Periods). Ed. by John F. Wilson. LC 85-31698. 447p. 1986. 49.95 (ISBN 0-313-25236-X, WNC/). Greenwood.

Church & State in American History. 2nd, rev. ed. Ed. by John Wilson & Donald Drakeman. LC 86-47513. 288p. 1986. pap. 10.95 (ISBN 0-8070-0409-X, BP 728). Beacon Pr.

Church & State in Australia, 1788-1872: A Constitutional Study of the Church of England in Australia. Ross Border. LC 64-56989. 1962. text ed. 15.00x (ISBN 0-8401-0226-7). A R Allenson.

Church & State in Early Maryland. George Petrie. LC 78-63810. (Johns Hopkins University. Studies in the Social Sciences. Tenth Ser. 1892: 4). Repr. of 1892 ed. 11.50 (ISBN 0-404-61073-0). AMS Pr.

Church & State in Early Maryland. George Petrie. 1973. pap. 9.00. Johnson Repr.

Church & State in England Since the Reformation. Norman Sykes. 1979. Repr. of 1929 ed. lib. bdg. 12.50 (ISBN 0-8482-6392-8). Norwood Edns.

Church & State in Europe. Ed. by Ernst Helmreich. LC 78-68021. (Problems in Civilization Ser.). 1979. pap. 6.95x (ISBN 0-88273-405-9). Forum Pr IL.

Church & State in France, 1300-1907. Arthur H. Galton. LC 70-185939. xxiv, 290p. 1972. Repr. of 1907 ed. lib. bdg. 21.00 (ISBN 0-8337-4124-1). B Franklin.

Church & State in Guatemala. Mary P. Holleran. LC 73-19956. 359p. 1974. Repr. of 1949 ed. lib. bdg. 23.00x (ISBN 0-374-93929-2, Octagon). Hippocrene Bks.

Church & State in Latin America: A History of Politico-Ecclesiastical Relations. rev. ed. J. Lloyd Mecham. xi, 465p. 1969. pap. 7.95x (ISBN 0-8078-4042-4). U of NC Pr.

Church & State in Massachusetts, 1691-1740. Susan M. Reed. (University of Illinois Studies in the Social Sciences: Vol. 3, No. 4). 210p. Repr. of 1914 ed. 15.00 (ISBN 0-384-50110-9). Johnson Repr.

Church & State in Mexico, 1822-1857. Wilfrid H. Callcott. 1965. lib. bdg. 27.00x (ISBN 0-374-91235-1, Octagon). Hippocrene Bks.

Church & State in Modern Ireland: 1923 to 1979. 2nd ed. J. H. Whyte. LC 79-55700. 491p. 1980. 32.50x (ISBN 0-389-20010-7). B&N Imports.

Church & State in New England. Paul E. Lauer. LC 78-63809. (Johns Hopkins University. Studies in the Social Sciences. Tenth Ser. 1892: 2-3). Repr. of 1892 ed. 11.50 (ISBN 0-404-61072-2). AMS Pr.

Church & State in North Carolina. Stephen B. Weeks. LC 78-63820. (Johns Hopkins University. Studies in the Social Sciences. Eleventh Ser. 1893: 6). Repr. of 1893 ed. 11.50 (ISBN 0-404-61082-X). AMS Pr.

Church & State in North Carolina. Stephen B. Weeks. pap. 9.00. Johnson Repr.

Church & State in Revolutionary Virginia, 1776-1787. Thomas E. Buckley. LC 77-4283. xii, 217p. 1977. 17.95x (ISBN 0-8139-0692-X). U Pr of Va.

Church & State in Scripture, History, & Constitutional Law. James E. Wood, Jr. et al. LC 59-21543. (Institute of Church-State Studies). 171p. 1985. pap. 6.95 (ISBN 0-918954-01-0). Baylor Univ Pr.

Church & State in the Middle Ages. new ed. Arthur L. Smith. 245p. 1964. 28.50x (ISBN 0-7146-1514-5, F Cass Co). Biblio Dist.

Church & State in the Social Context of Latin America. Alberto Espada-Matta. LC 85-90067. 79p. 1986. 7.95 (ISBN 0-533-06592-5). Vantage.

Church & State in the Spanish Floridas (1783-1822) Michael J. Curley. LC 73-3584. (Catholic University of America. Studies in American Church History: No. 30). Repr. of 1940 ed. 36.00 (ISBN 0-404-57780-6). AMS Pr.

Church & State in the U. S.; or, the American Idea of Religious Liberty & Its... Philip Schaff. LC 75-38462. (Religion in America, Ser. 2). 188p. 1972. Repr. of 1888 ed. 17.00 (ISBN 0-405-04083-0). Ayer Co Pubs.

Church & State in the United States. rev. ed. Anson Stokes & Leo Pfeffer. LC 73-15318. 660p. 1975. Repr. of 1964 ed. lib. bdg. 47.50x (ISBN 0-8371-7186-5, STCI). Greenwood.

Church & State in Tudor Ireland: A History of Penal Laws Against Irish Catholics 1534-1603. R. Dudley Edwards. LC 76-180608. (Illus.). xliiii, 352p. 1972. Repr. of 1935 ed. 18.00x (ISBN 0-8462-1641-8). Russell.

Church & State in Yugoslavia since Nineteen Forty-Five. Stella Alexander. LC 77-88668. (Soviet & East European Studies). 1979. 52.50 (ISBN 0-521-21942-6). Cambridge U Pr.

Church & State: The Supreme Court & the First Amendment. Philip B. Kurland. 1975. pap. 5.95x (ISBN 0-226-46402-4). U of Chicago Pr.

Church & State, Two Vols. Luigi Sturzo. (Vol. 2, O.P.). 1962. Set. pap. 11.90x (ISBN 0-268-00047-6). U of Notre Dame Pr.

Church & State Under the Tudors. Gilbert W. Child. LC 72-183695. 452p. 1974. Repr. of 1890 ed. lib. bdg. 29.50 (ISBN 0-8337-4041-5). B Franklin.

Church & Sunday School Hymnal with Supplement. Ed. by J. D. Brunk. LC 72-2053. 384p. (532 hymns & songs, & 50 german songs, words only, 1902; supplement 1911). 1902. 7.95x (ISBN 0-8361-1110-9). Herald Pr.

Church & Synagogue Libraries. Ed. by John F. Harvey. LC 80-11736. 299p. 1980. 20.00 (ISBN 0-8108-1304-1). Scarecrow.

Church & Synagogue Library Resources. 4th ed. Rachel Kohl & Dorothy Rodda. LC 75-1178. 1984. pap. 3.95x (ISBN 0-915324-08-3); pap. 3.00 members. CSLA.

Church & the Age of Reason. Gerald R. Cragg. (History of the Church: Vol. 4). (Orig.). 1961. pap. 5.95 (ISBN 0-14-020505-5, Pelican). Penguin.

Church & the Children. Ed. by Jesse P. Sewell & Henry E. Speck. 1935. 1.50 (ISBN 0-88027-104-3). Firm Foun Pub.

Church & the City: 1865-1910. Ed. by Robert D. Cross. LC 66-17273. 1967. 49.50x (ISBN 0-672-50994-6). Irvington.

Church & the Country Community. Edwin V. O'Hara. 14.00 (ISBN 0-405-10846-X, 11849). Ayer Co Pubs.

Church & the Disabled. Carl Fenn. 1985. pap. 5.00 (ISBN 0-8309-0414-X). Herald Hse.

Church & the Law: The Seventh Proceedings of the Fellowship of Catholic Scholars. Ed. by Paul L. Williams. 128p. (Orig.). 1985. pap. 6.95 (ISBN 0-937374-01-6). NE Bks.

Church & the Liberal Society. Emmet J. Hughes. 1961. pap. 1.95x (ISBN 0-268-00046-8). U of Notre Dame Pr.

Church & the Modern Nations, 1850-1920. Enzo Bellini et al. Ed. & tr. by John Drury. (Illustrated History of the Church). (Illus.). 126p. 1982. 12.95 (ISBN 0-86683-159-2, HarpR). Har-Row.

Church & the Nation: The Case for Disestablishment. Peter Cornwell. (Faith & the Future Ser.). 160p. 1984. 24.95x (ISBN 0-631-13223-6); pap. 8.95x (ISBN 0-631-13224-4). Basil Blackwell.

Church & the National Security State. Jose Comblin. LC 79-10881. 256p. (Orig.). 1979. pap. 12.95 (ISBN 0-88344-082-2). Orbis Bks.

Church & the New World Mind: The Drake Lectures for 1944. facsimile ed. W. E. Hocking et al. LC 68-57311. (Essay Index Reprint Ser). Repr. of 1944 ed. 18.00 (ISBN 0-8369-9698-4). Ayer Co Pubs.

Church & the Parachurch: An Uneasy Marriage. Jerry White. LC 83-12125. (Critical Concern Ser.). 1983. 10.95 (ISBN 0-88070-018-1). Multnomah.

Church & the Rebellion. facsimile ed. Robert L. Stanton. LC 70-168521. (Black Heritage Library Collection). Repr. of 1864 ed. 31.25 (ISBN 0-8369-8873-6). Ayer Co Pubs.

Church & the Secular Order in Reformation Thought. John Tonkin. LC 73-143390. pap. 58.30 (ISBN 0-317-26653-5, 2025107). Bks Demand UMI.

Church & the Single Person. Frances Bontrager. (Family Life Ser). 32p. (Orig.). 1969. pap. 1.00 (ISBN 0-8361-1575-9). Herald Pr.

Church & the Social Question. Franz H. Mueller. 158p. 1984. 14.95 (ISBN 0-8447-3567-1). Am Enterprise.

Church & the Society in Latin American. Ed. by Jeffrey A. Cole. 379p. 1984. pap. 12.00 (ISBN 0-317-43435-7). Tulane U Ctr Lat.

Church & the Sword. 2nd ed. G. R. Evans & C. C. Singer. LC 82-50234. 1983. pap. text ed. 5.00 (ISBN 0-932050-20-4). New Puritan.

Church & the Tribulation. Robert H. Gundry. 224p. 1973. pap. 7.95 (ISBN 0-310-25401-9, 18097P). Zondervan.

Church & the Twentieth Century. facs. ed. Ed. by George L. Harvey. LC 67-26747. (Essay Index Reprint Ser). 1936. 21.50 (ISBN 0-8369-0517-2). Ayer Co Pubs.

Church & the Urban Challenge. Walter Kloetzli. LC 61-14757. pap. 23.80 (2027195). Bks Demand UMI.

Church & the Welsh Border in the Central Middle Ages. Christopher Brooke. Ed. by D. N. Dunville & C. N. Brooke. (Studies in Celtic History). 1986. 40.00 (ISBN 0-85115-175-2, Pub. by Boydell & Bower). Longwood Pub Group.

Church & the Work, 3 vols. Watchman Nee. Tr. by Stephen Kaung. (Chinese.). 550p. 1982. 27.00 (ISBN 0-935008-57-8); pap. text ed. 15.00 (ISBN 0-935008-58-6). Christian Fellow Pubs.

Church & the Young People. Ed. by Jesse P. Sewell & Henry E. Speck. 1935. 1.50 (ISBN 0-88027-105-1). Firm Foun Pub.

Church & University in the Scottish Enlightenment: The Moderate Literati of Edinburgh. Richard B. Sher. LC 85-17911. (Illus.). 1985. text ed. 47.50x (ISBN 0-691-05445-2). Princeton U Pr.

Church & Usury. Patrick Cleary. 1979. lib. bdg. 59.95 (ISBN 0-8490-2884-1). Gordon Pr.

Church & Women in the Third World. Ed. by John C. Webster & Ellen L. Webster. LC 84-26967. 168p. (Orig.). 1985. pap. 11.95 (ISBN 0-664-24601-X). Westminster.

Church & World in the New Testament. Johannes Schneider. 59p. 1983. pap. 5.45 (ISBN 0-86554-063-2, P11). Mercer Univ Pr.

Church & World in the Plan of God: Aspects of History & Eschatology in the Thought of Pere Yves Congar. Charles MacDonald. (Regensburger Studien zur Theologie: Vol. 27). 178p. 1981. 22.75 (ISBN 3-8204-5945-6). P Lang Pubs.

Church & World Missions. Vessie D. Hargrave. 128p. 1970. 5.25 (ISBN 0-87148-152-9); pap. 4.25 (ISBN 0-87148-153-7). Pathway Pr.

Church Anthem Book: One Hundred Anthems. rev. ed. Ed. by Walford Davies & Henry G. Ley. 1959. 17.50x (ISBN 0-19-353106-2). Oxford U Pr.

Church Architecture. Henry H. Holly. 1980. lib. bdg. 75.00 (ISBN 0-8490-3141-9). Gordon Pr.

Church Architecture. Frederick C. Withers. 1980. lib. bdg. 64.95 (ISBN 0-8490-3198-2). Gordon Pr.

Church Architecture of Robert Mills. Rhodri W. Liscombe. (Illus.). 160p. 1985. 30.00 (ISBN 0-89308-542-1). Southern Hist Pr.

Church As a Sacrament of Salvation. Theodore Gakpe-Ntrsi. 112p. 1987. 9.95 (ISBN 0-89962-577-0). Todd & Honeywell.

Church As a Social Institution. David A. Moberg. 600p. 1984. pap. 18.95 (ISBN 0-8010-6168-7). Baker Bk.

Church As Communion. Ed. by James H. Provost. (Permanent Seminar Studies: No. 1). 245p. 1984. pap. 8.00 (ISBN 0-943616-23-9). Canon Law Soc.

Church As Evangelist. George E. Sweazey. LC 77-20452. 272p. 1984. pap. 7.95 (ISBN 0-06-067777-5, RD 502, HarpR). Har-Row.

Church As Mission. Ed. by James H. Provost. (Permanent Seminar Studies: No. 2). 288p. 1984. pap. 8.00 (ISBN 0-943616-24-7). Canon Law Soc.

Church at Prayer: Part One-The Liturgy. Ed. by A. G. Martimort. 264p. 1969. text ed. 17.50x (ISBN 0-7165-0511-8, Pub. by Irish Academic Pr Ireland). Biblio Dist.

Church at Prayer Part Two: The Eucharist. Ed. by A. G. Martimort. (Illus.). 250p. 1972. 17.50x (ISBN 0-7165-1107-X, BBA 01006, Pub. by Irish Academic Pr Ireland). Biblio Dist.

Church at Prayer: The Eucharist, Vol. 2. A. G. Martimort et al. Ed. by A. G. Martimort. Tr. by Matthew O'Connell from Fr. Orig. Title: L'Eglise en Priere: L'eucharistie. 286p. 1986. pap. 14.95 (ISBN 0-8146-1364-0). Liturgical Pr.

Church at Prayer: The Liturgy & Time, Vol. 4. A. G. Martimort. 304p. 1986. pap. 14.95 (ISBN 0-8146-1366-7). Liturgical Pr.

Church at the End of the Twentieth Century: The Church Before the Watching World. 2nd ed. Francis A. Schaeffer. LC 85-71893. 160p. 1985. pap. 6.95 (ISBN 0-89107-368-X, Crossway Bks). Good News.

Church at Work in the Modern World. facs. ed. Ed. by William C. Bower. LC 67-26717. (Essay Index Reprint Ser). 1935. 18.00 (ISBN 0-8369-0231-9). Ayer Co Pubs.

Church Authority & Intellectual Freedom. Christopher Derrick. LC 81-80209. 113p. (Orig.). 1981. pap. 7.95 (ISBN 0-89870-011-6). Ignatius Pr.

Church Becoming Christ's Body: The Small Church's Manual of Dances for Holy Seasons. Dane Packard. Ed. by Doug Adams. 110p. (Orig.). 1985. pap. 7.95 (ISBN 0-941500-35-7). Sharing Co.

Church Before Covenants. W. Foster. 1975. 12.50x (ISBN 0-7073-0184-X, Pub. by Scot Acad Pr). Longwood Pub Group.

Church Between Revolution & Restoration. Ed. by Hubert Jedin & John P. Dolan. (History of the Church: Vol. 7). 1980. 59.50x (ISBN 0-8245-0004-0). Crossroad NY.

Church Between Temple & Mosque: A Study of the Relationship Between the Christian Faith & Other Religions. Johan H. Bavinck. LC 66-22946. pap. 51.50 (ISBN 0-317-30133-0, 2025316). Bks Demand UMI.

Church Bible Study Handbook. Robin Maas. 208p. (Orig.). 1982. pap. 11.95 (ISBN 0-687-08146-7). Abingdon.

Church Building Sourcebook Two. Ed. by Ray Bowman. 264p. 1982. 3-ring vinyl notebook 39.95 (ISBN 0-8341-0759-7). Beacon Hill.

Church Building: The Ministry of Leadership in the Body of Christ. Jerry L. Rouse. 0.75 (ISBN 0-911802-57-6). Free Church Pubns.

Church Bulletin Bits, No. 2. Compiled By George W. Knight. 144p. (Orig.). 1980. pap. 4.50 (ISBN 0-8010-5424-9). Baker Bk.

Church Bulletin Bits 3. George W. Knight. 128p. 1987. pap. 4.95 (ISBN 0-8010-5479-6). Baker Bk.

Church Business Meeting. R. Dale Merrill. LC 68-28075. 1968. pap. 2.95 (ISBN 0-8170-0409-2). Judson.

Church Bytes Nineteen Eighty-Six. Neil B. Houk. 74p. (Orig.). 1987. pap. 7.95 (ISBN 0-9615086-5-5). Church Bytes.

Church Bytes Software Guide: For Church Administration & Finances. Neil B. Houk. 110p. (Orig.). 1986. pap. 10.95 (ISBN 0-9615086-3-9). Church Bytes.

Church Bytes: 1985. Neil B. Houk. 60p. (Orig.). 1986. pap. 5.95 (ISBN 0-9615086-1-2). Church Bytes.

Church Cannot Ordain Women to the Priesthood. David M. Malone. 1978. 0.75 (ISBN 0-8199-0724-3). Franciscan Herald.

Church, Charism, Power. Leonardo Boff. 1986. pap. 10.95 (ISBN 0-8245-0726-6). Crossroad NY.

Church Chronology: A Record of Important Events Pertaining to the History of the Church of Jesus Christ of the Latter-Day Saints (Mormons, 2 vols. Andrew Jenson. 1980. lib. bdg. 200.00 (ISBN 0-8490-3139-7). Gordon Pr.

Church: Communion, Sacrament, Communication. Robert Kress. 288p. (Orig.). 1985. pap. 9.95 (ISBN 0-8091-2663-X). Paulist Pr.

Church Computer Manual. Lowell Brown & Wes Haystead. 160p. (Orig.). 1985. pap. 12.95 (ISBN 0-8423-0271-9). Tyndale.

Church Confronts the Nazis: Barmen Then & Now. Ed. by Hubert G. Locke. (Toronto Studies in Theology: Vol. 16). 248p. 1984. 49.95x (ISBN 0-88946-762-5). E Mellen.

Church Courts & the People During the English Reformation Fifteen Twenty to Fifteen Seventy. Ralph Houlbrooke. (Oxford Historical Monographs). 1979. 36.00x (ISBN 0-19-821876-1). Oxford U Pr.

Church Covenant: Two Tracts. Richard Mather. LC 75-141115. (Research Library of Colonial Americana). 1972. Repr. of 1643 ed. 23.50 (ISBN 0-405-03329-X). Ayer Co Pubs.

Church Cyclopaedia: A Dictionary of Church Doctrine, History, Organization & Ritual, & Containing Original Articles on Special Topics, Written Expressly for This Work by Bishops, Presbyters, & Laymen. Angelo Ames Benton. LC 74-31499. 810p. 1975. Repr. of 1883 ed. 65.00x (ISBN 0-8103-4204-9). Gale.

Church Defies Modern Life. Joseph McCabe. 31p. pap. cancelled (ISBN 0-911826-75-0). Am Atheist.

Church Discipline & the Courts. Lynn R. Buzzard & Thomas Brandon. (Pressure Point Ser.). 160p. (Orig.). 1987. pap. 6.95 (ISBN 0-8423-0272-7). Tyndale.

Church Divided. Robert Wise et al. LC 86-71132. 1986. pap. 5.95 (ISBN 0-88270-622-5). Bridge Pub.

Church Divided: Catholics' Attitudes about Family Planning, Abortion, & Teenage Sexuality. Ed. by Mary J. Collins. (Bishops Watch Ser.). (Orig.). 1986. pap. 5.00 (ISBN 0-915365-12-X). Cath Free Choice.

Church Divinity, Nineteen Eighty Five. Ed. by John H. Morgan. 109p. (Orig.). 1985. pap. 10.00x (ISBN 0-932269-61-3). Wyndham Hall.

Church Doors Open Outward: A Practical Guide to Beginning Community Ministry. Dorothy Bloom. 80p. 1987. pap. 6.95 (ISBN 0-8170-1117-X). Judson.

Church Education Handbook. Kenneth O. Gangel. 300p. 1985. pap. 9.95 (ISBN 0-89693-602-3). Victor Bks.

Church Educational Ministries. LC 67-27288. 96p. 1980. pap. text ed. 4.95 (ISBN 0-910566-13-5); Perfect bdg. instr's. guide 5.95 (ISBN 0-910566-18-6). Evang Tchr.

Church Embattled: Religious Controversy in Mid-Victorian England. M. A. Crowther. LC 70-19499. (Library of Politics & Society Ser.). 272p. 1970. 29.50 (ISBN 0-208-01091-2, Archon). Shoe String.

Church Established, 180-381. Enzo Bellini et al. Ed. & tr. by John Drury. (Illustrated History of the Church). (Illus.). 126p. 12.95 (ISBN 0-03-056824-2, HarpR). Har-Row.

Church Explorer's Guide to England, Scotland, & Wales. Frank Bottomley. 1978. pap. 4.95 (ISBN 0-7182-1187-1, Pub. by Kaye & Ward). David & Charles.

Church, Falling Away & Restoration. J. W. Shepherd. 8.95 (ISBN 0-89225-065-8). Gospel Advocate.

Church Family Camps & Conferences. Elizabeth Genne & William Genne. LC 78-24395. 1979. pap. 2.95 (ISBN 0-8170-0818-7). Judson.

Church Family Gatherings. Ed. by Joe Leonard, Jr. 1978. pap. 6.95 (ISBN 0-8170-0809-8). Judson.

Church Family Ministry: Changing Loneliness to Fellowship in the Church. Susan B. Lidmus. 1985. pap. 6.95 (ISBN 0-570-03945-2, 12-2878). Concordia.

Church Fathers on the Bible. Ed. by Frank Sadowski. 1987. pap. write for info. (ISBN 0-8189-0510-7). Alba.

Church Feasts & Celebrations. Ed Curley. 1983. 9.95 (ISBN 0-89837-085-X, Pub. by Pflaum Pr). Peter Li.

Church Fellowship. Dan Caslow. 1984. pap. 1.95 (ISBN 0-8163-0499-8). Pacific Pr Pub Assn.

Church Fights: Managing Conflict in the Local Church. Paul Kittlaus & Speed Leas. LC 73-6790. 184p. 1973. pap. 9.95 (ISBN 0-664-24974-4). Westminster.

Church Finance in a Complex Economy. Manfred Holck, Jr. 138p. (Orig.). 1983. pap. 6.95 (ISBN 0-687-08156-4). Abingdon.

Church Finance Record System Manual. 7.95 (ISBN 0-8054-3103-9). Broadman.

Church Furnishing & Decoration in England & Wales. Gerald Randall. LC 80-11125. (Illus.). 240p. 1980. text ed. 42.50x (ISBN 0-8419-0602-5). Holmes & Meier.

Church Gives Thanks & Remembers. Ed. by Lawrence Johnson. 88p. 1984. pap. 4.95 (ISBN 0-8146-1355-1). Liturgical Pr.

Church Government & Ordinances. Robert E. Picirilli. 1973. pap. 0.95 (ISBN 0-89265-102-4). Randall Hse.

Church Growth - A Mighty River. Delos Miles. LC 80-67352. 1981. pap. 6.50 (ISBN 0-8054-6227-9). Broadman.

Church Growth & Group Conversion. new ed. Donald A. McGavran. LC 73-80163. 128p. 1973. pap. 3.95 (ISBN 0-87808-712-5). William Carey Lib.

Church Growth & the Whole Gospel: A Biblical Mandate. C. Peter Wagner. LC 81-47433. 224p. 1981. 13.00 (ISBN 0-06-068942-0, HarpR). Har-Row.

Church Growth Bulletin: Second Consolidated Volume (Sept. 1969 -July 1975) Ed. by Donald A. McGavran. LC 77-5192. 1977. pap. 7.95x (ISBN 0-87808-702-8). William Carey Lib.

Church Growth for Episcopalians. Robert B. Hall. 1982. pap. 4.95 (ISBN 0-686-37069-4). Episcopal Ctr.

Church Growth in Burundi. Donald W. Hohensee. LC 76-54342. 1977. pap. 4.95 (ISBN 0-87808-316-2). William Carey Lib.

Church Growth in Japan. Tetsunao Yamamori. LC 74-4009. (Illus.). 184p. (Orig.). 1974. pap. 4.95 (ISBN 0-87808-412-6). William Carey Lib.

Church Growth Manual. Juan C. Miranda. Ed. by Fernando Lamigueiro. Orig. Title: Manual De Iglecrecimiento. 192p. 1985. pap. 4.50 (ISBN 0-8297-0707-7). Life Pubs Intl.

Church Growth: Strategies That Work. Donald McGavran & George G. Hunter, III. LC 79-26962. (Creative Leadership Ser.). (Orig.). 1980. pap. 6.95 (ISBN 0-687-08160-2). Abingdon.

Church Growth Survey Handbook. 3rd. rev. ed. Bob Waymire & C. Peter Wagner. 4.15 (ISBN 0-318-20599-8). Overseas Crusade.

Church Growth That Counts. Ralph H. Elliott. 128p. 1982. pap. 5.95 (ISBN 0-8170-0943-4). Judson.

Church Growth: The State of the Art. Ed. by C. P. Wagner. 288p. 1986. pap. 9.95 (ISBN 0-8423-0287-5). Tyndale.

Church Growth Through the Sunday School. John T. Sisemore. LC 82-70870. (Orig.). 1983. pap. 6.50 (ISBN 0-8054-6237-6). Broadman.

Church Growth under Fire. C. W. Zunkel. LC 86-31814. 256p. (Orig.). 1987. pap. 8.95 (ISBN 0-317-52328-7). Herald Pr.

Church Guide for Strengthening Families: Strategies, Models, Programs, & Resources. John Larson. LC 86-7965. 128p. (Orig.). 1986. pap. 8.95 (ISBN 0-8066-2217-2, 10-1320). Augsburg.

Church Handbook: A Creative Guide for Churches. Robert Chandler et al. Ed. by Anna Marie Gardner. 224p. (Orig.). 1986. pap. text ed. 16.95 (ISBN 0-9616767-0-1). David Pub MN.

Church Heritage: A Course in Church History. General Conference Youth Department. pap. 2.50 (ISBN 0-686-82636-1). Review & Herald.

Church Histories of England. Joseph Stevenson. 59.95 (ISBN 0-87968-869-6). Gordon Pr.

Church History. Joanne L. Kepes. 1981. 9.95 (ISBN 0-89837-070-1, Pub. by Pflaum Pr). Peter Li.

Church History, Vols. 1-37. 1977. Repr. of 1932 ed. Set. lib. bdg. 1572.50 (ISBN 0-685-77256-X); lib. bdg. 42.50 ea. AMS Pr.

Church History Activity Book: Creative Learning Experiences About the Restoration for Children 4-12. Sandy Halverson. 36p. (Orig.). 1983. pap. 2.95 (ISBN 0-88290-213-X). Horizon Utah.

Church History, Early & Medieval. 2nd ed. Everett Ferguson. (Way of Life Ser: No. 106). (Orig.). 1966. pap. 3.95 (ISBN 0-89112-106-4, Bibl Res Pr). Abilene Christ U.

Church History from Nero to Constantine. C. P. Clarke. 1977. lib. bdg. 59.95 (ISBN 0-8490-1626-6). Gordon Pr.

Church History in Plain Language. Bruce Shelly. 512p. 1982. pap. 12.95 (ISBN 0-8499-2906-7). Word Bks.

Church History in the Light of the Saints. Joseph A. Dunney. LC 74-2196. (Essay Index Reprint Ser.). Repr. of 1944 ed. 25.00 (ISBN 0-518-10162-2). Ayer Co Pubs.

Church History of Britain, from the Birth of Jesus Christ Until the Year 1648, 6 Vols. Thoams Fuller. 3202p. 1845. text ed. 621.00x (ISBN 0-576-78882-1, Pub. by Gregg Intl Pubs England). Gregg Intl.

Church History of the First Three Centuries, 2 vols. Ferdinand C. Baur. Ed. by A. Menzies. 1980. lib. bdg. 199.75 (ISBN 0-8490-3146-X). Gordon Pr.

Church History, Reformation & Modern. Everett Ferguson. (Way of Life Ser: No. 107). 1967. pap. 3.95 (ISBN 0-89112-107-2, Bibl Res Pr). Abilene Christ U.

Church History: Twenty Centuries of Catholic Christianity. John C. Dwyer. 424p. (Orig.). 1985. pap. 9.95 (ISBN 0-8091-2686-9). Paulist Pr.

Church Hymnal. Ed. by S. F. Coffman. 536p. (657 hymns). 1927. 7.95x (ISBN 0-8361-1106-0). Herald Pr.

Church in a Changing Society. 508p. (Orig.). 1979. pap. text ed. 35.00x (ISBN 91-8558-207-7). Coronet Bks.

Church in a Changing Society. William E. Ramsden. LC 79-24274. (Into Our Third Century Ser.). (Orig.). 1980. pap. 4.95 (ISBN 0-687-08250-1). Abingdon.

Church in a Changing World. Purkiser. pap. 1.00 (ISBN 0-686-12910-5). Schmul Pub Co.

Church in a Democracy. Richard Kohn. Ed. by Constance McKenna. (Illus.). 23p. 1981. pap. 1.00 (ISBN 0-915365-03-0). Cath Free Choice.

Church in a Storm. Jerry Glisson & Jack R. Taylor. LC 82-74208. (Orig.). 1983. pap. 5.95 (ISBN 0-8054-5522-1). Broadman.

Church in Africa: Nineteen Seventy Seven. Ed. by Charles R. Taber. LC 78-14923. 1978. pap. 6.95 (ISBN 0-87808-161-5). William Carey Lib.

Church in an Age of Orthodoxy & Enlightenment. Robert Clouse. 1980. pap. 4.95 (ISBN 0-570-06273-X, 12-2746). Concordia.

Church in an Age of Revolution. rev. ed. Alec I. Vidler. (History of the Church: Vol. 5). (Orig.). 1962. pap. 5.95 (ISBN 0-14-020506-3, Pelican). Penguin.

Church in Brazil: The Politics of Religion. Thomas E. Bruneau. LC 81-16391. (University of Texas at Austin, Institute of Latin American Studies-Latin American Monographs: No. 56). pap. 63.30 (2026564). Bks Demand UMI.

Church in China. Carl Lawrence. 176p. (Orig.). 1985. pap. 5.95 (ISBN 0-87123-815-2). Bethany Hse.

Church in France, Eighteen Forty-Eight to Nineteen Hundred Seven. (Church Historical Society London Ser.: No. 19). pap. 31.00 (ISBN 0-8115-3142-2). Kraus Repr.

Church in France, Seventeen Eighty-Seven to Eighteen Forty-Eight. Charles S. Phillips. (Church Historical Society London Ser.: No. 19A). Repr. of 1934 ed. 40.00 (ISBN 0-8115-3143-0). Kraus Repr.

Church in God's Program. Robert L. Saucy. LC 70-175496. (Handbook of Bible Doctrine). 1972. pap. 7.95 (ISBN 0-8024-1544-X). Moody.

Church in History. John E. Booty. (Church's Teaching Ser.: Vol. 3). 320p. 1979. 5.95 (ISBN 0-8164-0420-8, HarpR); pap. 3.95 (ISBN 0-8164-2216-8); user guide 0.95 (ISBN 0-8164-2223-0). Har-Row.

Church in History. B. K. Kuiper. pap. 12.95x (ISBN 0-8028-1777-7); tchrs.' manual 6.95x (ISBN 0-8028-1314-3). Eerdmans.

Church in History Series, 6 bks. Robert Clouse et al. 1980. pap. 27.95 set (ISBN 0-570-06277-2, 12-2780). Concordia.

Church in Israel. Reed M. Holmes. (Illus.). 1983. pap. 10.00 (ISBN 0-8309-0383-6). Herald Hse.

Church in Italy in the Fifteenth Century. Denys Hay. LC 76-47409. (Birkbeck Lectures: 1971). 1977. 37.50 (ISBN 0-521-21532-3). Cambridge U Pr.

Church in Medieval Ireland, Vol. 5. John Watt. (Gill History of Ireland Ser.). 1973. 18.50 (ISBN 0-7171-0562-8, Pub. by Gill & Macmillan Ireland). Irish Bk Ctr.

Church in Mission. Wilbert R. Shenk. LC 84-81231. (Mennonite Faith Ser.: Vol. 15). 1984. pap. 1.50 (ISBN 0-8361-3377-3). Herald Pr.

Church in Mission: Sunday School Staff Training Text for 1987. William J. Martin. LC 86-80022. 128p. (Orig.). 1986. pap. 2.50 (ISBN 0-88243-803-4, 02-0803). Gospel Pub.

Church in Perspective: Standard Course for Layreaders. rev. ed. Edmund Partridge. 1976. 5.95 (ISBN 0-8192-1210-5). Morehouse.

Church in Prophecy. John F. Walvoord. 6.95 (ISBN 0-310-34051-9, 10969P). Zondervan.

Church in Revolutionary Times. Enzo Bellini et al. Ed. & tr. by John Drury. (Illustrated History of the Church). (Illus.). 126p. 1981. 12.95 (ISBN 0-86683-158-4, HarpR). Har-Row.

Church in Rome in the First Century. George Edmundson. 1976. lib. bdg. 59.95 (ISBN 0-8490-1627-4). Gordon Pr.

Church in Spain, Seventeen Thirty-Seven to Nineteen Thirty-Seven. Edgar A. Peers. 1980. lib. bdg. 44.95 (ISBN 0-8490-3149-4). Gordon Pr.

Church in the Age of Absolutism & Enlightenment. Ed. by Hubert Jedin & John P. Dolan. (History of the Church: Vol. 6). 1981. 59.50x (ISBN 0-8245-0010-5). Crossroad NY.

Church in the Age of Feudalism. Ed. by Hubert Jedin & John P. Dolan. (History of the Church: Vol. 3). 1980. 59.50x (ISBN 0-8245-0316-3). Crossroad NY.

Church in the Age of Humanism, 1300-1500. Enzo Bellini et al. Ed. & tr. by John Drury. (Illustrated History of the Church). 126p. 12.95 (ISBN 0-03-056829-3, HarpR). Har-Row.

Church in the Age of Liberalism. Ed. by Hubert Jedin & John P. Dolan. (History of the Church: Vol. 8). 1981. 59.50x (ISBN 0-8245-0011-3). Crossroad NY.

Church in the Education of the Public: Refocusing the Task of Religious Education. Jack L. Seymour & Robert T. O'Gorman. 160p. 1984. pap. 10.95 (ISBN 0-687-08252-8). Abingdon.

Church in the Industrial Age. Ed. by Hubert Jedin & John P. Dolan. (History of the Church: Vol. 9). 1981. 59.50x (ISBN 0-8245-0012-1). Crossroad NY.

Church in the Life of the Black Family. Wallace C. Smith. (Family Life Ser.). 160p. 1985. pap. 8.50 (ISBN 0-8170-1040-8). Judson.

Church in the Modern Age. Ed. by Hubert Jedin & John P. Dolan. (History of the Church: Vol. 10). 1980. 59.50x (ISBN 0-8245-0013-X). Crossroad NY.

Church in the Power of the Spirit. Juergen Moltmann. LC 76-62932. 1977. 21.45 (ISBN 0-06-065905-X, HarpR). Har-Row.

Church in the Roman Empire. Erwin R. Goodenough. LC 77-122754. 1970. Repr. of 1931 ed. lib. bdg. 23.50x (ISBN 0-8154-0337-2). Cooper Sq.

Church in the Roman Empire Before A. D. 170. W. M. Ramsay. LC 77-6997. 1977. Repr. of 1904 ed. 50.00 (ISBN 0-89341-216-3). Longwood Pub Group.

Church in the Theology of the Reformers. Paul D. Avis. Ed. by Peter Toon & Ralph Martin. LC 80-16186. (New Foundations Theological Library). 256p. 1981. 6.49 (ISBN 0-8042-3708-5); pap. 2.99 (ISBN 0-8042-3728-X). John Knox.

Church in the World. facs. ed. William R. Inge. LC 68-57324. (Essay Index Reprint Ser). 1927. 17.00 (ISBN 0-8369-0080-4). Ayer Co Pubs.

Church in the World. Robert E. Webber. 368p. (Orig.). 1986. pap. text ed. 11.95 (ISBN 0-310-36601-1, 12213P). Zondervan.

Church in Town & Countryside: Papers Read at the Seventeenth Summer Meeting & the Eighteenth Winter Meeting of the Ecclesiastical History Society. Ed. by Derek Baker. (Studies in Church History: Vol. 16). 502p. 1979. 45.00 (ISBN 0-631-11421-1). Basil Blackwell.

Church Is a Who. Bernice Hogan. LC 78-24087. (Illus.). 1979. 9.95 (ISBN 0-8272-0442-6). CBP.

Church Is One. Alexei S. Khomiakov. (Illus.). 1980. pap. 1.25x (ISBN 0-913026-23-9). St Nectarios.

Church Is You & I. Carl B. Rife & Carolyn Bishop. 1984. 1.95 (ISBN 0-89536-658-4, 0394). CSS of Ohio.

Church: Its Changing Image Through Twenty Centuries. Eric G. Jay. LC 79-92070. 1980. 12.95 (ISBN 0-8042-0877-8). John Knox.

Church: Its Changing Image Through Twenty Centuries. Eric G. Jay. LC 79-92070. pap. 120.50 (2027153). Bks Demand UMI.

Church, Kingship & Lay Investiture in England, 1089-1135. Norman F. Cantor. 1969. lib. bdg. 26.00x (ISBN 0-374-91273-4, Octagon). Hippocrene Bks.

Church Lace: Being Eight Ecclesiastical Patterns in Pillow Lace. Ed. by M. E. Milroy. (Illus.). 121p. 1981. Repr. of 1920 ed. 42.00x (ISBN 0-8103-3014-8). Gale.

Church Leaders in Primitive Times. William Lefroy. 1977. lib. bdg. 69.95 (ISBN 0-8490-1628-2). Gordon Pr.

Church Leadership & Organization. Flavil Yeakley. pap. 5.95 (ISBN 0-317-47145-7). Gospel Advocate.

Church: Learning about God's People. S. Matthews. LC 56-1396. (Concept Books Series Four). 1983. pap. 3.95 (ISBN 0-570-08525-X). Concordia.

Church Librarian's Handbook. Betty McMichael. 288p. 1984. pap. 9.95 (ISBN 0-8010-6166-0). Baker Bk.

Church Library Handbook. Rev. ed. LaVose Newton. 1987. Repr. of 1972 ed. 12.95 (ISBN 0-89081-563-1). Harvest Hse.

Church Library: Tips & Tools. Gladys E. Scheer. LC 73-10093. (Orig.). 1973. pap. 3.95 (ISBN 0-8272-0435-3). CBP.

Church Library Workbook. Francine E. Walls. 144p. 1980. pap. 8.95 (ISBN 0-89367-048-0). Light & Life.

Church Life. Gene Edwards. 132p. 1987. text ed. 8.95 (ISBN 0-940232-25-1). Christian Bks.

Church Life & Church Order During the First Four Centuries. James V. Bartlet. Ed. by Cecil J. Cadoux. 1980. lib. bdg. 59.95 (ISBN 0-8490-3147-8). Gordon Pr.

Church: Life Giving Union with Christ. John C. Krol. 1978. 7.50 (ISBN 0-8198-0525-4); pap. 5.95 (ISBN 0-8198-0526-2). Dghtrs St Paul.

Church Life in England in the Thirteenth Century. John R. Moorman. LC 76-29401. Repr. of 1945 ed. 32.50 (ISBN 0-404-15352-6). AMS Pr.

Church Life in Norway: 1800-1950. Einar Molland. Tr. by Kaasa Harris. LC 78-2711. 1978. Repr. of 1957 ed. lib. bdg. 22.50 (ISBN 0-313-20342-3, MOCL). Greenwood.

Church-Maintained in Truth: A Theological Meditation. Hans Kung. LC 81-69569. 88p. 1982. pap. 2.95 (ISBN 0-394-70816-4, Vin). Random.

Church Meetings That Matter. enl. ed. Philip A. Anderson. 128p. 1987. pap. 5.95 (ISBN 0-8298-0752-7). Pilgrim NY.

Church Members & Nontraditional Religious Groups. Glenn A. Igleheart. LC 85-4226. (Broadman Leadership Ser.). 1985. pap. 5.95 (ISBN 0-8054-6608-8). Broadman.

Church Militant & Iberian Expansion: 1440-1770. C. R. Boxer. LC 77-18386. (Johns Hopkins Symposia in Comparative History Ser.: No. 10). (Illus.). 1978. text ed. 17.50x (ISBN 0-8018-2042-1). Johns Hopkins.

Church Ministering to Adults. Jerry M. Stubblefield. LC 86-2299. (Orig.). 1986. pap. 9.95 (ISBN 0-8054-3235-3). Broadman.

Church, Ministry & Sacraments: A Critical Evaluation of the Thought of Peter Taylor Forsyth. Clifford S. Pitt. LC 82-24817. 360p. (Orig.). 1983. lib. bdg. 31.25 (ISBN 0-8191-3027-3); pap. text ed. 15.75 (ISBN 0-8191-3028-1). U Pr of Amer.

Church, Ministry, & Sacraments in the New Testament. C. K. Barrett. 112p. (Orig.). 1985. pap. 6.95 (ISBN 0-8028-1994-X). Eerdmans.

Church, Ministry & Unity: A Divine Commission. James E. Griffiss. 118p. 1984. 24.95x (ISBN 0-631-13185-X); pap. 8.95x (ISBN 0-631-13227-9). Basil Blackwell.

Church Monuments. Brian Kemp. (Shire Album Ser.: No. 149). (Illus., Orig.). 1985. pap. 3.50 (ISBN 0-85263-768-3, Pub. by Shire Pubns England). Seven Hills Bks.

Church Monuments in Romantic England. Nicholas Penny. LC 76-58912. (Studies in British Art). (Illus.). 1977. 47.00x (ISBN 0-300-02075-9). Yale U Pr.

Church Mouse: A Book with Stickers. (New Christian Thought Ser.). (Illus.). 1.95 (ISBN 0-89954-286-7). Antioch Pub Co.

Church Music: An International Bibliography. Richard C. Von Ende. LC 79-23697. 473p. 1980. lib. bdg. 30.00 (ISBN 0-8108-1271-1). Scarecrow.

Church Music: An International Bibliography. Richard C. Von Ende. LC 79-23697. pap. 118.30 (ISBN 0-317-52049-0, 2027497). Bks Demand UMI.

Church Music & Musical Life in Pennsylvania in the Eighteenth Century, 3 vols. in 4 pts. National Society of Colonial Dames of America. LC 79-38037. (Illus.). Repr. of 1926 ed. Set. 150.00 (ISBN 0-404-08090-1). AMS Pr.

Church Music & the Christian Faith. Erik Routley. LC 78-110219. 156p. 1978. pap. 7.95 (ISBN 0-916642-10-0). Agape IL.

Church Music & the Christian Faith. Erik Routley. LC 78-110219. 1979. 7.95 (ISBN 0-916642-11-9, Agape). Hope Pub.

Church Music in America. Nathaniel D. Gould. 1980. lib. bdg. 59.75 (ISBN 0-8490-3192-3). Gordon Pr.

Church Music in America, Comprising Its History & Its Peculiarities at Different Periods. Nathaniel D. Gould. LC 78-144620. Repr. of 1853 ed. 19.25 (ISBN 0-404-02888-8). AMS Pr.

Church Music in the Nineteenth Century. Arthur Hutchings. (Studies in Church Music). 1977. Repr. of 1967 ed. lib. bdg. 22.50x (ISBN 0-8371-9695-7, HUCMN). Greenwood.

Church Music of William Billings. James M. Barbour. LC 72-39000. 167p. 1972. Repr. of 1960 ed. lib. bdg. 22.50 (ISBN 0-306-70434-X). Da Capo.

Church Music of William Billings. James M. Barbour. 167p. Repr. of 1960 ed. lib. bdg. 29.00 (Pub. by Am Repr Serv). Am Biog Serv.

Church of Christ Not An Ecclesiasticism: A Letter to a Sectarian. Henry James, Sr. LC 72-922. (Selected Works of Henry James Sr.: Vol. 2). 80p. Repr. of 1854 ed. 17.00 (ISBN 0-404-10082-1). AMS Pr.

Church of England. Jan Baker. 1978. pap. 3.35 (ISBN 0-08-021408-8). Pergamon.

Church of England. Edward W. Watson. LC 80-22643. (Home University Library of Modern Knowledge: No. 90). 192p. 1981. Repr. of 1961 ed. lib. bdg. 25.00x (ISBN 0-313-22683-0, WAEN). Greenwood.

Church of England & Social Reform since 1854. Donald O. Wagner. LC 77-127438. (Columbia University. Studies in the Social Sciences: No. 325). 12.50 (ISBN 0-404-51325-5). AMS Pr.

Church of God. Louis Bouyer. Tr. by Charles U. Quinn. 1983. 25.00 (ISBN 0-686-45823-0). Franciscan Herald.

Church of God & Roman Catholic Interfaith Marriage. Bill Balzano. (Truthway Ser.). 35p. (Orig.). 1981. pap. text ed. 1.25 (ISBN 0-87148-175-8). Pathway Pr.

Church of God As Revealed in Scripture. Arlo Newell. 1983. pap. 1.95 (ISBN 0-87162-269-6, D4775). Warner Pr.

Church of God Doctrines. C. C. Carver. 180p. 1948. pap. 2.00 (ISBN 0-686-29106-9). Faith Pub Hse.

Church of God of Prophecy: History & Polity. James Stone. 1977. 12.95 (ISBN 0-934942-02-1). White Wing Pub.

Church of God of Prophecy: Pastor. R. L. Black. 1977. 4.25 (ISBN 0-934942-29-3). White Wing Pub.

Church of God Polity: With Supplement. R. H. Gause. 1958. 9.95 (ISBN 0-87148-158-8). Pathway Pr.

Church of Ireland: Ecclesiastical Reform & Revolution, 1880-1885. Donald H. Akenson. LC 76-151565. pap. 81.40 (ISBN 0-317-08435-6, 2013197). Bks Demand UMI.

Church of Jesus Begins. Norman Bull. (Bible Story & Its Background Ser.: Vol. 7). pap. 9.95 (ISBN 0-7175-0983-4). Dufour.

Church of Jesus Grows. Norman Bull. (Bible Story & Its Background Ser.: Vol. 8). pap. 9.95 (ISBN 0-7175-0454-9). Dufour.

Church of Our Fathers. Roland H. Bainton. (Illus.). 222p. 1978. pap. text ed. write for info. (ISBN 0-02-305450-6, Pub. by Scribner). Macmillan.

Church of Our Fathers. Ronald H. Bainton. 1984. 16.75 (ISBN 0-8446-6120-1). Peter Smith.

Church of Reconciliation: The Subject Matter & Problems of the Doctrine of Reconciliation. Karl Barth. Ed. by G. W. Bromiley & T. F. Torrance. Tr. by G. W. Bromiley & T. F. Torrance. (Church Dogmatics: Vol. 4, Pt. 1). 814p. 1956. 29.95 (ISBN 0-567-09041-8, Pub. by T & T Clark Ltd UK). Fortress.

Church of St. Helen, Bishopsgate, Pt. 1. Minnie Reddan & Alfred W. Clapham. LC 74-6179. (London County Council Survey of London: No. 9). Repr. of 1924 ed. 74.50 (ISBN 0-404-51659-9). AMS Pr.

Church of St. Helen on the Walls, Aldwark, York. J. R. Magilton. (Archaeology of York Ser.: Vol. 10). 64p. 1980. pap. text ed. 15.00x (ISBN 0-900312-98-X, Pub. by Coun Brit Archaeology). Humanities.

Church of Scientology Press: Volume 1, Issue 6. (Illus.). 1976. pap. 2.60 (ISBN 0-915598-13-2). Church of Scient Info.

Church of Scientology Press: Volume 1, Issue 7. (Illus.). 1977. pap. 2.60 (ISBN 0-915598-15-9). Church of Scient Info.

Church of Scientology-Religious Nature & Community Activities. (Illus.). 1976. pap. 7.00 (ISBN 0-915598-12-4). Church of Scient Info.

Church of Scientology Religious Philosophy, Religion, & Church. G. C. Oosthuizen. pap. 4.00 (ISBN 0-686-74641-4). Church of Scient Info.

Church of Stiled the Great 1881-1981: The Heart of Little Italy. LC 81-67378. (Illus.). 136p. 1982. 25.00 (ISBN 0-9607014-0-0). Church St Leo.

Church of the Brethren & the War, 1788-1914. Rufus D. Bowman. LC 75-147667. (Library of War & Peace; Relig. & Ethical Positions on War). 1972. 46.00 (ISBN 0-8240-0425-6). Garland Pub.

Church of the Brethren Yesterday & Today. Donald F. Durnbaugh. Ed. by David Eller. 192p. (Orig.). 1986. pap. 9.95 (ISBN 0-87178-151-4). Brethren.

Church of the Early Fathers. Alfred Plummer. 1892. 15.00 (ISBN 0-8414-9261-1). Folcroft.

Church of the Future: A Model for the Year 2001. Walbert Buhlmann. Tr. by Mary Groves from Ger. Tr. of Weltkirche-Neue Dimensionen-Model fur das Jahr 2001. 256p. (Orig.). 1986. pap. 10.95 (ISBN 0-88344-253-1). Orbis Bks.

Church of the Greek People. Euphrosyne Kephala. LC 77-87528. Repr. of 1930 ed. 14.50 (ISBN 0-404-16594-X). AMS Pr.

Church of the Holy Apostles. Alison Frantz. LC 76-356003. (Athenian Agora Ser: Vol. 20). (Illus.). xiii, 45p. 1972. 15.00x (ISBN 0-87661-220-6). Am Sch Athens.

Church of the Holy Sepulchre. Henry T. Duckworth. LC 78-63361. (BCL Ser.). (Illus.). Repr. of 1922 ed. 32.00 (ISBN 0-404-17014-5). AMS Pr.

Church of the Holy Sepulchre, Jerusalem. C. Couasnon. (Schweich Lectures on Biblical Archaeology). (Illus.). 62p. 1972. 10.25 (ISBN 0-85672-735-0, Pub. by British Acad). Longwood Pub Group.

Church of the Jews. Norman Bull. (Bible Story & Its Background Ser.: Vol. 4). 9.95 (ISBN 0-7175-0450-6). Dufour.

Church of the Living God. R. K. Campbell. 8.95 (ISBN 0-88172-007-0); pap. 5.95 (ISBN 0-686-13515-6). Believers Bkshelf.

Church of the Middle Ages. Carl A. Volz. LC 72-99217. (Church in History Ser). 1978. pap. 4.95 (ISBN 0-570-06270-5, 12-2725). Concordia.

Church of the New Testament. James B. North. (Restoration Booklets Ser.). (Illus., Orig.). 1984. 0.75 (ISBN 0-87239-779-3, 3299). Standard Pub.

Church of the Old Testament. rev. ed. John Tvedtnes. LC 80-18595. 111p. 1980. 6.95 (ISBN 0-87747-827-9). Deseret Bk.

Church of the Poor Devil: Reflections on a Riverboat Voyage & a Spiritual Journey. John S. Dunne. LC 83-14548. 1983. pap. text ed. 6.95 (ISBN 0-268-00746-2, 85-07469). U of Notre Dame Pr.

Church of the Renaissance & Reformation. Karl H. Dannenfeldt. LC 77-98300. (Church in History Ser). 1978. pap. 4.95 (ISBN 0-570-06271-3, 12-2726). Concordia.

Church of the Spirit. Hardy W. Steinberg. (Charismatic Bk.). 64p. 1972. pap. 0.69 (ISBN 0-88243-922-7, 02-0922). Gospel Pub.

Church Office Handbook: A Basic Guide to Keeping Order. Carol R. Shearn. 288p. pap. 12.95 (ISBN 0-8192-1391-8). Morehouse.

Church Office Handbook for Ministers. Betty Powers & E. Jane Mall. 80p. 1983. pap. 3.95 (ISBN 0-8170-1011-4). Judson.

Church Officers at Work. Glenn H. Asquith. pap. 4.95 (ISBN 0-8170-0048-8). Judson.

Church on Assignment. W. Eugene Jr. Spears. LC 84-15541. 1985. pap. 3.25 (ISBN 0-8054-5011-4). Broadman.

Church on Parade. John Walsh. LC 83-62517. 1984. pap. 7.95 (ISBN 0-89390-053-2). Resource Pubns.

Church on Purpose: Keys to Effective Church Leadership. Joe Ellis. LC 82-3175. (Illus.). 112p. (Orig.). 1982. pap. 6.95 (ISBN 0-87239-441-7, 88584). Standard Pub.

Church on Target. Joe Ellis. 128p. 1986. pap. 5.95 (ISBN 0-87403-005-6, 3019). Standard Pub.

Church Organ Method. Mildred Andrews & Pauline Riddle. 123p. 1973. pap. 15.00 (ISBN 0-8258-0050-1, 04904). Fischer Inc NY.

Church Organist. 2nd ed. Henry Coleman. 1968. 9.75 (ISBN 0-19-322100-4). Oxford U Pr.

Church Organization Development: Perspectives & Resources. H. Newton Malony. LC 86-81285. (Orig.). 1986. pap. 10.00 (ISBN 0-9609928-2-0). Integ Pr.

Church-Papal Teachings. 12.00 (ISBN 0-317-46826-X). Dghtrs St Paul.

Church: Pictures of Christ's Body. Lee Eclov. (Fisherman Bible Studyguide Ser.). 55p. 1981. saddle stitched 2.95 (ISBN 0-87788-155-3). Shaw Pubs.

Church Planning Questionnaire: Manual & Discoveries from 100 Churches. Grayson L. Tucker, Jr. 161p. (Orig.). 1983. pap. text ed. 8.50 (ISBN 0-9610706-0-9). G L Tucker.

Church Planting in America at the End of the Twentieth Century. Charles Chaney. 128p. 1982. pap. 6.95 (ISBN 0-8423-0279-4). Tyndale.

Church Planting in Uganda: A Comparative Study. Gailyn Van Rheenen. LC 76-20461. 1976. pap. 4.95 (ISBN 0-87808-314-6). William Carey Lib.

Church Planting Through Obedience Oriented Teaching. George Patterson. LC 81-285. (Illus.). 64p. (Orig.). 1981. pap. 3.95x (ISBN 0-87808-910-1). William Carey Lib.

Church Planting, Watering & Increasing in Kenya. Kenya Mission Team. Ed. by B. J. Humble. (Illus.). 130p. 1981. pap. 2.95 (ISBN 0-88027-002-0). Firm Foun Pub.

Church, Politics & Patronage in the Fifteenth Century. Ed. by R. B. Dobson. LC 84-15102. 245p. 1985. 25.00 (ISBN 0-312-13481-9). St Martin.

Church, Politics, & Society in Spain, 1750-1874. William J. Callahan. (Harvard Historical Monographs: No. 73). (Illus.). 336p. 1984. text ed. 25.00x (ISBN 0-674-13125-8). Harvard U Pr.

Church Polity: How the Clergy Run the Church. Marion R. Winkler. LC 82-91145. 271p. 1983. lib. bdg. 19.95 (ISBN 0-9610344-1-6); pap. 12.95 (ISBN 0-9610344-2-4). M R Winkler.

Church Promotion Handbook. Salem Kirban. 1963. 10.00 (ISBN 0-912582-38-3). Kirban.

Church Property, Church Finances, & Church-Related Corporations: A Canon Law Handbook. Adam J. Maida & Nicholas P. Carfardi. LC 83-20946. 1984. 28.00 (ISBN 0-87125-090-X). Cath Health.

Church Records of Killingly, Connecticut. E. D. Larned. 56p. 1984. pap. 5.95 (ISBN 0-912606-22-3). Hunterdon Hse.

Church Records of Saint Matthews Lutheran Church, Orangeburg, Co., S. C. Beginning in 1799, Giving Births, Christenings, Confirmations, Marriages, & Burials & "the Red Church", 1767-1838. Anne M. Haigler. (Illus.). 126p. 1985. 15.00 (ISBN 0-89308-563-4). Southern Hist Pr.

Church Reform of Peter the Great. James Cracraft. 1971. 27.50x (ISBN 0-8047-0747-2). Stanford U Pr.

Church Reforms in Russia, 1905-1918. Alexander Bogolepov. 59p. 1966. pap. 1.95 (ISBN 0-913836-01-X). St Vladimirs.

Church-Related Pre-School. Margaret C. Reed. 128p. 1985. pap. 7.95 (ISBN 0-687-08334-6). Abingdon.

Church Renewed: The Documents of Vatican II Reconsidered. George P. Schner. 164p. (Orig.). 1986. lib. bdg. 24.50 (ISBN 0-8191-5505-5, Pub. by Regis College Toronto CN); pap. text ed. 10.75 (ISBN 0-8191-5506-3). U Pr of Amer.

Church Roll & Record. Compiled by T. O. Tollett. 1979. 11.95 (ISBN 0-89114-017-4). Baptist Pub Hse.

Church Roots: Stories of Nine Immigrant Groups That Became the American Lutheran Church. Ed. by Charles P. Lutz. LC 85-1217. 208p. (Orig.). 1985. pap. 9.95 (ISBN 0-8066-2156-7, 10-1366). Augsburg.

Church Secretary's Handbook. Patricia M. Seraydarian. 159p. 1982. pap. 5.95 (ISBN 0-8423-0281-6). Tyndale.

Church Shall Be Free: A Glance at Eight Centuries of Church & State. Arthur E. Sutherland. LC 65-24000. pap. 15.00 (2017808). Bks Demand UMI.

Church Society & Politics. Ed. by Derek Baker. (Studies in Church History Ser.: Vol. 12). 440p. 1976. 45.00x (ISBN 0-631-16970-9). Basil Blackwell.

Church Soloists Favorites, 2 bks. Ed. by Carl Fredrickson. (Illus.). 1963. Bk. 1, High Voice, 64p. pap. 6.95 (ISBN 0-8258-0228-8, RB-65); Bk. 2, Low Voice, 85p. pap. 6.95 (ISBN 0-8258-0229-6, RB-66). Fischer Inc NY.

Church Sponsored Missions. Phillip W. Elkins. 1974. pap. 3.00 (ISBN 0-88027-003-9). Firm Foun Pub.

Church Staff Administration: Practical Approaches. Leonard E. Wedel. LC 78-51490. 1978. 10.95 (ISBN 0-8054-3105-5). Broadman.

Church Staff Support: Cultivating & Maintaining Staff Relationships. Frank H. Olsen. (Administration for Churches Ser.). 40p. (Orig.). 1982. pap. 3.95 (ISBN 0-8066-1964-3, 10-1370). Augsburg.

Church, State & Freedom, 2 vols. Leo Pfeffer. 1987. lib. bdg. 75.00 ea. Vol. 1 (ISBN 0-379-20734-6). Vol. 2 (ISBN 0-379-20735-4). Oceana.

Church, State & Jew in the Middle Ages. new ed. Robert Chazan. Ed. by Neal Kozodoy. LC 78-27221. (Library of Jewish Studies). 1979. pap. text ed. 9.95x (ISBN 0-87441-302-8). Behrman.

Church, State & Nation in Ireland, 1898-1921. David W. Miller. LC 72-95453. 1973. 49.95x (ISBN 0-8229-1108-6). U of Pittsburgh Pr.

Church, State & Opposition in U. S. S. R. Gerhard Simon. LC 73-87754. 1974. 37.95x (ISBN 0-520-02612-8). U of Cal Pr.

Church, State & Public Policy. Ed. by Jay Mechling. 1979. 12.25 (ISBN 0-8447-2159-X); pap. 5.25 (ISBN 0-8447-2160-3). Am Enterprise.

Church-State & School in Switzerland & the U. S. A Study in Comparative Constitutional Law. Walter A. Stoeckli. (European University Studies: Series 2, Law: Vol. 23). 50p. 1969. 5.85 (ISBN 3-261-00081-3). P Lang Pubs.

Church, State & Society in the Nineteenth Century. Ed. by Adolf M. Birke & Kurt Kluxen. (Prince Albert Studies: Vol. 2). 130p. 1984. lib. bdg. 24.00 (ISBN 3-598-21402-2). K G Saur.

Church, State & the Constitution. rev. ed. George Goldberg. LC 87-4566. 160p. 1987. 14.95 (ISBN 0-89526-794-2). Regnery Bks.

Church, State, & the Control of Schooling in Ireland, 1900-1944. E. B. Titley. 232p. 1983. 27.50x (ISBN 0-7735-0394-3). McGill-Queens U Pr.

Church-State Relations: An Annotated Bibliography. Albert J. Menendez. LC 75-24894. (Reference Library of Social Science: Vol. 24). 125p. 1976. lib. bdg. 25.00 (ISBN 0-8240-9956-7). Garland Pub.

Church-State Relations: Tensions & Transitions. Ed. by Thomas Robbins & Roland Robertson. 380p. 1986. 29.95 (ISBN 0-88738-108-1); pap. 14.95 (ISBN 0-88738-651-2). Transaction Bks.

Church-State Relationships in America. Gerard V. Bradley. LC 86-27149. (Contributions in Legal Studies). 1987. 29.85 (ISBN 0-313-25494-X, BYC). Greenwood.

Church Struggle in South Africa. 2nd ed. John W. De Gruchy. 300p. 1986. pap. 10.95 (ISBN 0-8028-0243-5). Eerdmans.

Church Symbolism: An Explanation of the More Important Symbols of the Old & New Testament, the Primitive, the Mediaeval & the Modern Church. rev. 2nd ed. Frederick R. Webber. LC 79-107627. (Illus.). 1971. Repr. of 1938 ed. 56.00x (ISBN 0-8103-3349-X). Gale.

Church Teaches: Documents of the Church in English Translation. St. Mary's College, Kansas, Jesuit Fathers. Ed. by John F. Clarkson et al. 1973. pap. 10.00 (ISBN 0-89555-011-3). TAN Bks Pubs.

Church Teaching & Training. William W. Graves. Ed. by Weldon Viertel & Joyce Viertel. 152p. 1982. Repr. of 1975 ed. 11.50 (ISBN 0-311-72681-X, Carib Pubns). Casa Bautista.

Church Teaching Her Young. Allan H. Jahsmann. 1967. pap. text ed. 3.75 (ISBN 0-570-06330-2, 22-1287); teacher's guide 4.50 (ISBN 0-570-06331-0, 22-1289). Concordia.

Church That Cares. Kenneth R. Miller & Mary E. Wilson. LC 85-14786. 96p. 1985. pap. 6.95 (ISBN 0-8170-1087-4). Judson.

Church That Jesus Built. R. W. Grimsley. 1969. pap. 2.75 (ISBN 0-88027-031-4). Firm Foun Pub.

Church, the Beautiful Bride of Christ. Ed. by Thomas B. Warren & Garland Elkins. 1980. pap. 13.00 (ISBN 0-934916-27-6). Natl Christian Pr.

Church, the Enemy of the Workers. Joseph McCabe. 32p. 1942. cancelled (ISBN 0-911826-74-2). Am Atheist.

Church, the Liturgy & the Soul of Man. St. Maximus the Confessor. Tr. by Dom J. Stead from Gr. LC 82-10545. 1982. pap. 6.95 (ISBN 0-932506-23-2). St Bedes Pubns.

Church, the State, & Education in Virginia. Sadie Bell. LC 78-89148. (American Education: Its Men, Institutions & Ideas Ser). 1969. Repr. of 1930 ed. 43.00 (ISBN 0-405-01385-X). Ayer Co Pubs.

Church, the State & Society in the Thought of John Paul II. J. V. Schall. 1982. 7.50 (ISBN 0-8199-0838-X). Franciscan Herald.

Church, the State & the Offender. Mennonite Church General Conference, Board of Christian Service Staff. 1963. pap. 0.50 (ISBN 0-87303-200-4). Faith & Life.

Church Then & Now: Cultivating a Sense of Tradition. William Scott & Frances M. Scott. 108p. (Orig.). 1985. pap. 3.95 (ISBN 0-934134-30-8, Leaven Pr). Sheed & Ward MO.

Church Through the Centuries. Cyril C. Richardson. LC 72-6726. Repr. of 1938 ed. 21.00 (ISBN 0-404-10645-5). AMS Pr.

Church Time for Children. Dorothy G. Johnston & Kathleen Abbas. LC 80-67855. 120p. (Orig.). 1981. 10.95 (ISBN 0-89636-056-3). Accent Bks.

Church Time for Preschoolers. Leora W. Huttar. LC 75-17368. 1975. spiral 6.95 (ISBN 0-916406-36-9). Accent Bks.

Church to Believe In: Discipleship & the Dynamics of Freedom. Avery Dulles. LC 81-17520. 208p. 1983. pap. 8.95 (ISBN 0-8245-0593-X). Crossroad NY.

Church Today. Joseph Ratzinger et al. Tr. by May Ignatius. 79p. pap. 1.25 (ISBN 0-8199-0396-5). Franciscan Herald.

Church Treasurer's Handbook. Loudell O. Ellis. LC 77-10433. 1978. 6.95 (ISBN 0-8170-0762-8). Judson.

Church Triumphant. Daniel Preston. pap. 4.95 (ISBN 0-934942-30-7). White Wing Pub.

Church Under Siege. Michael K. Smith. LC 76-12304. (Illus.). 1976. pap. 5.95 (ISBN 0-87784-855-6). Inter-Varsity.

Church Under Tension. Alcuin Coyle & Dismas Bonner. 1976. pap. 2.95 (ISBN 0-685-77495-3). Franciscan Herald.

Church Unique. Stanley J. Peters. 1987. 12.95 (ISBN 0-533-06972-6). Vantage.

Church Universal & the See of Rome: A Study of the Relations Between the Episcopate & the Papacy up to the Schism Between East & West. Henry E. Symonds. (Church Historical Society London N. S. Ser.: No. 36). pap. 60.00 (ISBN 0-8115-3159-7). Kraus Repr.

Church Unleashed: Getting God's People Out Where the Needs Are. Frank R. Tillapaugh. LC 82-9783. 224p. 1982. pap. 5.95 (ISBN 0-8307-0823-5, 5416300). Regal.

Church Usher: Servant of God. David R. Enlow. LC 80-66769. 64p. (Orig.). 1980. pap. 1.95 (ISBN 0-87509-284-5). Chr Pubns.

Church Ushering. rev. ed. Paul H. Lang. 1957. pap. 1.25 (ISBN 0-570-03522-8, 14-1141). Concordia.

Church Ushers: Embodiment of the Gospel. Kenneth M. Johnson. LC 81-21022. 64p. (Orig.). 1982. pap. 3.95 (ISBN 0-8298-0493-5). Pilgrim NY.

Church Ushers' Manual. Willis O. Garrett. 64p. pap. 2.50 (ISBN 0-8007-8456-1, Spire Bks.). Revell.

Church Versus State in South Africa: The Case of the Christian Institute. Peter Walshe. LC 82-14533. xvi, 256p. (Orig.). 1983. 19.95 (ISBN 0-88344-097-0). Orbis Bks.

Church Video Answerbook. Chip R. Turner. LC 85-242884. 1986. pap. 5.95 (ISBN 0-8054-3713-4). Broadman.

Church Views of the Mexican American. Ed. by Carlos E. Cortes. LC 73-14198. (Mexican American Ser.). (Illus.). 58p. 1974. Repr. 45.00x (ISBN 0-405-05672-9). Ayer Co Pubs.

Church Wealth in Mexico: A Study of the Juzgado de Capellanias in the Archbishopric of Mexico, 1800-1856. LC 67-18310. (Cambridge Latin American Studies: No. 2). pap. 37.30 (ISBN 0-317-26021-9, 2024431). Bks Demand UMI.

Church Will Grow by These. Robert S. Maseroni. 1983. 5.55 (ISBN 0-317-04044-8, 0060). CSS of Ohio.

Church Winning Souls. V. H. Lewis. 83p. 1983. pap. 2.95 (ISBN 0-8341-0893-3). Beacon Hill.

Church with a Human Face: New & Expanded Theology of Ministry. Edward Schillebeeckx. Tr. by John Bowden. 400p. 1985. 19.95 (ISBN 0-8245-0693-6). Crossroad NY.

Church Woodcarvings: A West Country Study. John C. Smith. LC 79-77874. (Illus.). 1969. 17.95x (ISBN 0-678-05533-5). Kelley.

Church, World, Mission. Alexander Schmemann. LC 79-27597. 227p. 1979. pap. 7.95 (ISBN 0-913836-49-4). St Vladimirs.

Church Worships. Ed. by H. Hucke & Johannes Wagner. LC 66-17730. (Concilium Ser.: Vol. 12). 196p. 1966. 7.95 (ISBN 0-8091-0020-7). Paulist Pr.

Church Year in Prayer. Jerome Neufelder. LC 84-62162. 200p. (Orig.). 1985. pap. 7.95 (ISBN 0-87973-729-8, 729). Our Sunday Visitor.

Churched & Unchurched in America: A Comparative Profile. David A. Roozen. LC 77-94682. 1978. pap. 2.00 (ISBN 0-914422-07-3). Glenmary Res Ctr.

Churches & Church Membership in the United States, 1971. Douglas W. Johnson et al. LC 73-94224. 256p. 1974. pap. 15.00x (ISBN 0-914422-01-4). Glenmary Res Ctr.

Churches & Churchgoers: Patterns of Church Growth in the British Isles since 1700. Robert Currie et al. (Illus.). 1978. 42.00x (ISBN 0-19-827218-9). Oxford U Pr.

Churches & Politics in Germany. Frederic Spotts. LC 72-11050. 419p. 1973. 25.00x (ISBN 0-8195-4059-5). Wesleyan U Pr.

Churches & Politics in Latin America. Ed. by Daniel H. Levine. LC 79-23827. (Sage Focus Editions: Vol. 14). 288p. 1980. 29.00 (ISBN 0-8039-1298-6); pap. 14.95 (ISBN 0-8039-1299-4). Sage.

Churches & States: The Religious Institution & Modernization. Ed. by Kalman H. Silvert. LC 67-22384. 224p. 1967. 7.50 (ISBN 0-910116-64-4). U Field Staff Intl.

Churches & the American Experience. Thomas A. Askew, Jr. & Peter W. Spellman. 205p. 1984. pap. 9.95 (ISBN 0-8010-0199-4). Baker Bk.

Churches & the Indian Schools, 1888-1912. Francis P. Prucha. LC 79-12220. (Illus.). xiv, 278p. 1979. 21.50x (ISBN 0-8032-3657-3). U of Nebr Pr.

Churches & the Kingdom. Julius H. Stephens. LC 78-5676. 1978. Repr. of 1959 ed. lib. bdg. cancelled (ISBN 0-313-20488-8, STCK). Greenwood.

Churches at the Testing Point: A Study in Rural Michigan. Theodore S. Wilkinson. (World Council of Churches Studies in Mission). 1970. pap. 3.95 (ISBN 0-377-82021-0). Friend Pr.

Churches in Contestation: Asian Christian Social Protest. Parig Digan. LC 83-19338. 224p. (Orig.). 1984. pap. 10.95 (ISBN 0-88344-102-0). Orbis Bks.

Churches in Cultural Captivity: A History of the Social Attitudes of Southern Baptists. John L. Eighmy. LC 70-111047. 1972. 22.50x (ISBN 0-87049-115-6). U of Tenn Pr.

Churches in Cultural Captivity: A History of the Social Attitudes of Southern Baptists. John L. Eighmy. Intro. by Samual S. Hill, Jr. LC 70-111047. pap. 67.00 (2029374). Bks Demand UMI.

Churches in English Fiction. Andrew L. Drummond. 1950. 30.00 (ISBN 0-8495-6277-5). Arden Lib.

Churches in Struggle: Liberation Theologies & Social Change in North America. Ed. by William K. Tabb. 331p. 1986. 27.00 (ISBN 0-85345-692-5); pap. 11.00 (ISBN 0-85345-693-3). Monthly Rev.

Churches Militant: The War of 1812 & American Religion. William Gribbin. LC 72-91313. pap. 55.00 (ISBN 0-317-29581-0, 2022000). Bks Demand UMI.

Churches of Eastern Christendom from Four Hundred Fifty-One A.D. to the Present Time, 2 vols. Beresford J. Kidd. 1980. Set. lib. bdg. 195.00 (ISBN 0-8490-3196-6). Gordon Pr.

Churches of Foster: A History of Religious Life in Rural Rhode Island. Margery I. Matthews et al. (Illus.). 169p. (Orig.). 1978. pap. 5.00 (ISBN 0-917012-20-8). N Foster Baptist.

Churches of God, Seventh Day: A Bibliography. Joel Bjorling. Ed. by J. Gordon Meton. LC 87-67. (Sects & Cults in America Bibliographical Guides Reference Library of Socical Sciences Ser.: Vol. 362). 250p. 1987. lib. bdg. 48.00 (ISBN 0-8240-8537-X). Garland Pub.

Churches of Portugal. Carlos De Azevedo. LC 85-50365. (Illus.). 196p. 1985. 35.00 (ISBN 0-935748-66-0). Scala Books.

Churches on the Wrong Road. Ed. by Stanley Atkins & Theodore McConnell. 270p. (Orig.). 1986. pap. 7.95 (ISBN 0-89526-803-5). Regnery Bks.

Churches Plea for Her Right. William Best. LC 76-57357. (English Experience Ser.: No. 776). 1977. Repr. of 1635 ed. lib. bdg. 10.50 (ISBN 90-221-0776-0). Walter J Johnson.

Churches Quarrel Espoused, 1713. John Wise. LC 66-10006. 1966. 35.00x (ISBN 0-8201-1052-3). Schol Facsimiles.

Churches' Response to the Holocaust. Ed. by Jack R. Fischel & Sanford Pinsker. (Holocaust Studies Annual: Vol. II). 200p. 1986. 20.00 (ISBN 0-913283-12-6). Penkevill.

Churches the Apostles Left Behind. Raymond E. Brown. 160p. (Orig.). 1984. pap. 5.95 (ISBN 0-8091-2611-7). Paulist Pr.

Churches the Victorians Forgot. Mark Chatfield. (Illus.). 1979. 15.00 (ISBN 0-903485-76-1, Pub. by Moorland Pub Co England). Eastview.

Churchill & the Jews. Michael J. Cohen. (Illus.). 408p. 1985. 25.00x (ISBN 0-7146-3254-6, F Cass Co). Biblio Dist.

Churchill Returns. Robert R. Leichtman. LC 81-66847. (From Heaven to Earth Ser.). (Illus.). 96p. (Orig.). 1981. pap. 3.50 (ISBN 0-89804-065-5). Ariel OH.

Churchmen & Philosophers: From Jonathan Edwards to John Dewey. Bruce Kuklick. LC 84-19579. 352p. 1985. 30.00 (ISBN 0-300-03269-2). Yale U Pr.

Churchmen & the Western Indians, 1820-1920. Ed. by Clyde A. Milner, II & Floyd A. O'Neil. LC 85-40477. (Illus.). 272p. 1985. 19.95 (ISBN 0-8061-1950-0). U of Okla Pr.

Church's Amazing Story. rev. ed. Ed. by Daughters of St. Paul. LC 68-59043. (Divine Master Ser., Vol. 2). 1969. 6.00 (ISBN 0-8198-0028-7); pap. 5.00 (ISBN 0-8198-0029-5); teacher's manual 8.50 (ISBN 0-8198-0030-9). Dghtrs St Paul.

Church's Confession Under Hitler. 2nd ed. Arthur C. Cochrane. LC 76-57655. (Pittsburgh Reprint Ser.: No. 4). 1977. pap. text ed. 10.75 (ISBN 0-915138-28-X). Pickwick.

Church's Desperate Need for Revival. David R. Barnhart. 163p. (Orig.). 1986. pap. 8.95 (ISBN 0-9617377-0-0). Abiding Word Pubns.

Church's Faith, Bk. I. Michael DeVito. pap. 3.95 (ISBN 0-941850-06-4). Sunday Pubns.

Church's Growing Edge: Single Adults. Ed. by Russell Claussen. 1981. pap. 4.95 (ISBN 0-8298-0429-3). Pilgrim NY.

Church's Ministry with Older Adults. Blaine Taylor. 144p. 1987. pap. 10.95 (ISBN 0-687-08382-6). Abingdon.

Church's Moral Teaching, Bk. III. Genarro P. Avento. pap. 3.95 (ISBN 0-941850-08-0). Sunday Pubns.

Church's Problem with Bible Scholars. George A. Kelly. LC 85-1507. 60p. 1985. 2.50 (ISBN 0-8199-0929-7). Franciscan Herald.

Church's Strange Bedfellows. Leslie Burbick. 1986. 6.95 (ISBN 0-8062-2408-8). Carlton.

Church's Task Under the Roman Empire. Charles Bigg. 1977. lib. bdg. 59.95 (ISBN 0-8490-1629-0). Gordon Pr.

Church's Teaching Series, 9 Vols. Urban T. Holmes, III & John H. Westerhoff, III. 1979. Set. 45.45 (ISBN 0-8164-0453-4, HarpR); Set. pap. 24.95 (ISBN 0-8164-2271-0). Har-Row.

Church's Year. Charles Alexander. (Illus.). 1950. 3.00x (ISBN 0-19-273007-X). Oxford U Pr.

Churchwardens' Accounts of the Town of Ludlow in Shropshire. Ed. by Thomas Wright. (Camden Society, London. Publications, First Ser.: No. 102). Repr. of 1869 ed. 19.00 (ISBN 0-404-50202-4, A17-1267). AMS Pr.

Churchwardens' Accounts of the Town of Ludlow in Shropshire from 1540 to the End of the Reign of Queen Elizabeth. Ludlow England Parish. Repr. of 1869 ed. 19.00 (ISBN 0-384-34130-6). Johnson Repr.

Churchyard Carvers' Art. Martin C. Johnson. 104p. 1986. 30.00x (ISBN 0-947939-00-8, Pub. by Elmcrest UK). State Mutual Bk.

Churchyard Literature. J. R. Kippax. 59.95 (ISBN 0-87968-870-X). Gordon Pr.

Churchyard Literature: A Choice Collection of American Epitaphs. John R. Kippax. 213p. 1978. Repr. of 1876 ed. 16.95 (ISBN 0-87928-087-5). Corner Hse.

Churchyards & Cemeteries. Kenneth Hudson. (Illus.). 48p. 1984. laminated boards 9.95 (ISBN 0-370-30543-4, Pub. by Bodley Head). Salem Hse Pubs.

Cicero & the State Religion. R. J. Goar. 141p. (Orig.). 1972. pap. text ed. 30.00x (Pub. by A M Hakkert). Coronet Bks.

Cicero in the Courtroom of Saint Thomas Aquinas. Edward K. Rand. (Aquinas Lecture Ser.). 1945. 7.95 (ISBN 0-87462-109-7). Marquette.

Ciencia del Alma. R. Swinburne Clymer. Tr. by Fina Aparis. (Span.). 272p. (Orig.). 1967. pap. 6.95 (ISBN 0-932785-51-4). Philos Pub.

Ciencia Retorna a Dios. J. H. Jauncey. Tr. by Ana M. Swenson. J. N. Moore. Tr. of Science Returns to God. (Span.). 110p. 1981. pap. 2.35 (ISBN 0-311-05004-2). Casa Bautista.

Cincuenta Palabras Claves de la Biblia. Julian Charley. Tr. by Jorge E. Diaz & Myriam Diaz. Orig. Title: Fifty Key Words-The Bible. (Span., Illus.). 80p. Date not set. pap. price not set (ISBN 0-311-04029-2). Casa Bautista.

Cinderella & Her Sisters: The Envied & the Envying. Barry Ulanov & Ann Ulanov. LC 83-10463. 186p. 1983. pap. 9.95 (ISBN 0-664-24482-3). Westminster.

Cinderella Syndrome: Discovering God's Plan When Your Dreams Don't Come True. Lee Ezell. 176p. (Orig.). 1985. pap. 4.95 (ISBN 0-89081-475-9). Harvest Hse.

Circle of Baal Shem Tov: Studies in Hasidism. Abraham J. Heschel. Ed. by Samuel H. Dresner. 280p. 1985. 24.95 (ISBN 0-226-32960-7). U of Chicago Pr.

Circle of Light. Shirlee Dunlap. (Illus.). 183p. (Orig.). 1982. pap. 7.95 (ISBN 0-942494-19-9). Coleman Pub.

Circle of Quiet. Madeleine L'Engle. (Crosswicks Journal Trilogy). 246p. 1977. pap. 7.95 (ISBN 0-8164-2260-5, HarpR); Three Volume Set. 19.95 (ISBN 0-8164-2617-1). Har-Row.

Circle of Unity: Baha'i Approaches to Current Social Issues. Ed. by Anthony A. Lee. 268p. (Orig.). 1984. pap. 9.95 (ISBN 0-933770-28-6). Kalimat.

Circle of Wisdom. rev ed. Helena P. Blavatsky. Ed. by Winifred A. Parley. LC 78-8790. 1978. pap. 3.25 (ISBN 0-8356-0516-7, Quest). Theos Pub Hse.

Circles. Virginia M. Malterner. (Illus.). 1977. tchrs'. manual 5.25x (ISBN 0-8192-4079-6); wkbk. 3.95x (ISBN 0-8192-4080-X); take-home cards packet 2.50x (ISBN 0-8192-4081-8). Morehouse.

Circles of God-Theology & Science from the Greeks to Copernicus. Harold P. Nebelsick. (Theology & Science at the Frontiers of Knowledge Ser.: Vol. 2). 312p. 1985. 24.00 (ISBN 0-7073-0448-2, Pub. by Scottish Academic Pr Scotland). Longwood Pub Group.

Circuit Rider Dismounts, a Social History of Southern Methodism 1865-1900. Hunter D. Farish. LC 77-87534. (American Scene Ser). 1969. Repr. of 1938 ed. 45.00 (ISBN 0-306-71450-7). Da Capo.

Circumstances & the Role of God. John Boykin. 224p. 1986. text ed. 12.95 (ISBN 0-317-46020-X). Zondervan.

Circumstances That Caused Me to Leave the Amish Church. John R. Renno. 54p. 1987. pap. 3.00 (ISBN 1-55618-021-7). Brunswick Pub.

Circumstantial Evidence. John Penter. 144p. 1981. 11.95 (ISBN 0-939762-00-5). Faraday.

Cistercian & Mendicant Monasteries in Medieval Greece. Beata K. Panagopoulos. LC 78-10769. (Illus.). 1979. lib. bdg. 24.00x (ISBN 0-226-64544-4). U of Chicago Pr.

Cistercian Finances in the Fourteenth Century. Peter King. 24.95 (ISBN 0-87907-885-5). Cistercian Pubns.

Cistercian Heritage, Vol. 4: Roche, Salley. (Orig.). 1978. pap. 16.00 (ISBN 3-7052-0263-4, Pub. by Salzburg Studies). Longwood Pub Group.

Cistercian Ideals & Reality. Ed. by John R. Sommerfeldt. LC 78-16615. (Cistercian Studies: No. 60). 1978. pap. 8.95 (ISBN 0-87907-860-X). Cistercian Pubns.

Cistercian Sign Language. Robert Barakat. LC 70-152476. (Cistercian Studies: No. 11). 1976. 14.95 (ISBN 0-87907-811-1). Cistercian Pubns.

Cistercian Spirit: A Symposium in Memory of Thomas Merton. Ed. by M. Basil Pennington. (Cistercian Studies: No. 3). xvi, 286p. 1973. Repr. of 1972 ed. 7.95 (ISBN 0-87907-803-0). Cistercian Pubns.

Cistercian Way. Andre Louf. (Cistercian Studies: No. 76). pap. 7.95 (ISBN 0-87907-976-2). Cistercian Pubns.

Cistercians & Cluniacs: The Case for Citeaux. Idung Of Prufening. Tr. by Jeremiah F. O'Sullivan & Joseph Leahey. LC 77-9289. 1977. 12.95 (ISBN 0-87907-633-X). Cistercian Pubns.

Cistercians: Ideals & Reality. Louis J. Lekai. LC 77-3692. (Illus.). 534p. 1977. 28.50x (ISBN 0-87338-201-3). Kent St. U Pr.

Cistercians in Denmark: Their Attitudes, Roles, & Functions in Medieval Society. Brian P. McGuire. (Cistercian Studies: No. 35). 1982. 35.00 (ISBN 0-87907-835-9). Cistercian Pubns.

Cistercians in the Late Middle Ages: Studies in Medieval Cistercian History. Ed. by E. Rozanne Elder et al. (Cistercian Studies: No. VI). 161p. (Orig.). 1981. pap. 8.95 (ISBN 0-87907-865-0). Cistercian Pubns.

Cities of Gods: Faith, Politics & Pluralism in Judaism, Christianity & Islam. Nigel Biggar et al. LC 85-9879. (Contributions to the Study of Religion Ser.: No. 16). 253p. 1986. lib. bdg. 39.95 (ISBN 0-313-24944-X, BCG/). Greenwood.

Citizen of Rome: Reflections from the Life of a Roman Catholic. Frederick D. Wilhelmsen. 348p. 1980. pap. 6.95 (ISBN 0-89385-005-5). Sugden.

Citizen of Two Worlds. Gordon Lindsay. 1.50 (ISBN 0-89985-000-6). Christ Nations.

Citizen Summitry. Ed. by Don Carlson & Craig K. Comstock. (Ark Reflections: No. 1). (Illus.). 396p. 1986. 11.95 (ISBN 0-934325-01-4). Ark Comm Inst.

Citizen Summitry: Keeping the Peace When It Matters Too Much to Be Left to Politicians. Ed. by Don Carlson & Craig Comstock. (Illus.). 336p. 1986. pap. 10.95 (ISBN 0-87477-406-3). J P Tarcher.

Citizens of Another Kingdom. John Balchin. 141p. 1986. pap. 4.95 (ISBN 0-89109-535-7). NavPress.

Citizens of the Cosmos: Life's Unfolding from Conception Through Death to Rebirth. Beredene Jocelyn. (Freedeeds Library). (Illus.). 198p. 1983. Repr. of 1981 ed. 14.00 (ISBN 0-89345-040-5, Freedeeds Bks). Garber Comm.

City of God, 2 Vols. Saint Augustine. Ed. by R. V. Tasker. Tr. by John Healey. 1973. Repr. of 1945 ed. 12.95x ea. (ISBN 0-686-66408-6, Evman). Vol. 1 (ISBN 0-460-00982-6). Vol. 2 (ISBN 0-460-00983-4). Biblio Dist.

City of God. St. Augustine. LC 58-5717. pap. 6.50 (ISBN 0-385-02910-1, Im). Doubleday.

City of God. St. Augustine. Ed. by David Knowles. (Classics Ser.). 1984. pap. 12.95 (ISBN 0-14-044426-2). Penguin.

City of God. St. Augustine. Tr. by Marcus Dods. LC 54-5465. 1950. 10.95 (ISBN 0-394-60397-4). Modern Lib.

City of God, Bks. 1-7. St. Augustine. LC 63-19613. (Fathers of the Church Ser.: Vol. 8). 401p. 1950. 29.95x (ISBN 0-8132-0008-3). Cath U Pr.

City of God, Bks. 8-16. St. Augustine. LC 63-19613. (Fathers of the Church Ser.: Vol. 14). 567p. 1952. 27.95x (ISBN 0-8132-0014-8). Cath U Pr.

City of God, Bks. 17-22. St. Augustine. LC 63-19613. (Fathers of the Church Ser.: Vol. 24). 461p. 1954. 27.95x (ISBN 0-8132-0024-5). Cath U Pr.

City of God Against the Pagans, 7 vols. Saint Augustine. (Loeb Classical Library: No. 411-417). 13.95x ea. Harvard U Pr.

City of God & the City of Man in Africa. Edgar H. Brookes & Amry Vandenbosch. LC 64-13998. (Illus.). 144p. 1964. 12.00x (ISBN 0-8131-1091-2). U Pr of Ky.

City of the Cosmic Dance. B. Natarajan. 193p. 1974. text ed. 15.00 (ISBN 0-86125-035-4). Apt Bks.

City of the Gods: A Study in Myth & Mortality. John S. Dunne. LC 78-2588. 1978. Repr. of 1965 ed. text ed. 7.95 (ISBN 0-268-00725-X). U of Notre Dame Pr.

City of Wisdom: A Christian View of the American University. David J. Hassel. 461p. 1983. 18.50 (ISBN 0-8294-0433-3). Loyola.

City of Zion-The Human Society in Christ, i.e., the Church Built Upon a Rock. Apostolos Makrakis. Ed. by Orthodox Christian Educational Society. Tr. by Denver Cummings from Hellenic. 109p. 1958. pap. 4.00x (ISBN 0-938366-16-5). Orthodox Chr.

City on a Mountain - Padre Pio. Pascal P. Parente. Orig. Title: Padre Pio. 154p. 1968. pap. 3.50 (ISBN 0-911988-35-1). AMI Pr.

City Scriptures: Modern Jewish Writing. Murray Baumgarten. LC 81-6879. 240p. 1982. text ed. 17.50x (ISBN 0-674-13278-5). Harvard U Pr.

Civic Tongue: Political Consequences of Language Choices. Brian Weinstein. LC 82-15268. (Professional Studies in Political Communication & Policy). 213p. 1982. 22.50x (ISBN 0-582-29010-4). Longman.

Civil Authority in Medieval Philosophy: Lombard, Aquinas & Bonaventure. Michael P. Malloy. LC 85-3210. 240p. (Orig.). 1985. lib. bdg. 26.25 (ISBN 0-8191-4582-3); pap. text ed. 12.25 (ISBN 0-8191-4583-1). U Pr of Amer.

Civil Disobedience & Political Obligation: A Study in Christian Social Ethics. James F. Childress. LC 75-158137. (Yale Publication in Religion Ser.: No. 16). pap. 66.50 (ISBN 0-317-09428-9, 2021988). Bks Demand UMI.

Civil Magistrate's Power in Matters of Religion Modestly Debated, London, 1653. Thomas Cobbett. LC 74-141104. (Research Library of Colonial Americana). 1972. Repr. of 1653 ed. 24.50 (ISBN 0-405-03318-4). Ayer Co Pubs.

Civil Religion & Moral Order: Theoretical & Historical Dimensions. Michael W. Hughey. LC 82-15429. (Contributions in Sociology Ser.: No. 43). 256p. 1983. lib. bdg. 32.95 (ISBN 0-313-23522-8, HUR/). Greenwood.

Civil Religion & Political Theology. Ed. by Leroy S. Rouner. LC 86-11242. (Boston University Studies in Philosophy & Religion: Vol. 8). 240p. 1986. text ed. 24.95x (ISBN 0-268-00757-8). U of Notre Dame Pr.

Civil Religion in Israel: Traditional Judaism & Political Culture in the Jewish State. Charles S. Liebman & Eliezer Don-Yehiya. LC 82-17427. 270p. 1983. 27.50x (ISBN 0-520-04817-2). U of Cal Pr.

Civil War Diary of Cyrus Pringle: Record of Quaker Conscience. Cyrus Pringle. LC 62-18328. Orig. Title: Record of a Quaker Conscience. (Orig.). 1962. pap. 2.50x (ISBN 0-87574-122-3, 122). Pendle Hill.

Civilian Population & the Warsaw Uprising of 1944. Joanna K. Hanson. LC 81-15545. (Illus.). 375p. 1982. 39.50 (ISBN 0-521-23421-2). Cambridge U Pr.

Civilization & Religious Values. Henry D. Major. LC 77-27137. (Hibbert Lectures: 1946). Repr. of 1948 ed. 20.00 (ISBN 0-404-60431-5). AMS Pr.

Civilization During the Middle Ages. G. B. Adams. 75.00 (ISBN 0-87968-873-4). Gordon Pr.

Civilization of Christianity. John L. McKenzie. 1986. pap. 9.95 (ISBN 0-88347-208-2). Thomas More.

Civitas: Christian Ideas of the City. Ed. by Peter S. Hawkins. (Scholars Press Studies in the Humanities). 143p. 1986. 20.95 (ISBN 0-89130-987-X, 00-01-10). Scholars Pr GA.

Claim of Reason: Wittgenstein, Skepticism, Morality, & Tragedy. Stanley Cavell. 1979. pap. 11.95 (ISBN 0-19-503195-4). Oxford U Pr.

Claim to New Roles. Page P. Miller. LC 85-2249. (ATLA Monograph Ser.: No. 22). 253p. 1985. 17.50 (ISBN 0-8108-1809-4). Scarecrow.

Claim Your Heritage. Myron C. Madden. LC 84-7315. (Potentials: Guides for Productive Living Ser.: Vol. 8). 116p. 1984. pap. 7.95 (ISBN 0-664-24531-5). Westminster.

Claiming a Frontier: Ministry & Older People. Robert W. McClellan & Carolyn E. Usher. LC 77-85413. 1977. 10.00x (ISBN 0-88474-040-4, 05741-X). Lexington Bks.

Claims in Conflict: Retrieving & Renewing the Catholic Human Rights Tradition. David Hollenbach. LC 79-84239. (Woodstock Ser.: No. 4). (Orig.). 1979. pap. 7.95 (ISBN 0-8091-2197-2). Paulist Pr.

Clairvoyant Investigations. Geoffrey Hodson. LC 84-40166. (Illus.). 160p. (Orig.). 1984. pap. 9.25 (ISBN 0-8356-0585-X). Theos Pub Hse.

Clam Lake Papers. Edward Lueders. (Festival Ser.). 160p. 1982. pap. 3.25 (ISBN 0-687-08580-2). Abingdon.

Clap Your Hands! Larry Tomczak. LC 73-88241. 143p. 1973. pap. 4.95 (ISBN 0-88270-073-1). Bridge Pub.

Clara's Story. Clara Isaacman & Joan A. Grossman. LC 84-14339. 180p. 1984. 11.95 (ISBN 0-8276-0243-X). Jewish Pubns.

Clare: Her Light & Her Song. Mary Seraphim. 44p. 1983. 18.00 (ISBN 0-8199-0870-3). Franciscan Herald.

Clarifying Jewish Values: Clarification Strategies for Jewish Groups. Dov P. Elkins. LC 77-83774. 1977. softbound 10.00 (ISBN 0-918834-02-3). Growth Assoc.

Clark Speaks from the Grave. Gordon H. Clark. (Trinity Papers: No. 12). 77p. (Orig.). 1986. pap. 3.95 (ISBN 0-940931-12-5). Trinity Found.

Clarke Papers, 4 Vols. William Clarke. Ed. by C. H. Firth. 105.00 (ISBN 0-384-09232-2); 27.00 ea. Johnson Repr.

Clarke's Christian Theology. 8.95 (ISBN 0-686-12856-7). Schmul Pub Co.

Clarke's Commentary, 3 vols. Adam Clarke. Incl. Vol. 1. Genesis-Esther (ISBN 0-687-09119-5); Vol. 2. Job-Malachi (ISBN 0-687-09120-9); Vol. 3. Matthew-Revelation (ISBN 0-687-09121-7). 1977. Set. 95.00 (ISBN 0-687-09118-7); 34.50 ea. Abingdon.

Clash by Night. Wallace Hamilton. 1983. pap. 2.50x (ISBN 0-87574-023-5, 023). Pendle Hill.

Clash of Cultures: The Norwegian Experience with Mormonism, 1842-1920. Gerald M. Haslam. LC 83-49362. (American University Studies IX (History): Vol. 7). 350p. 1984. text ed. 39.80 (ISBN 0-8204-0179-X). P Lang Pubs.

Class Devotions, 1986-1987: For Use with the 1986-1987 International Lesson Annual. Harold L. Fair. 128p. (Orig.). 1986. pap. 6.50 (ISBN 0-687-08626-4). Abingdon.

Class Devotions, 1987-1988. Harold L. Fair. 128p. 1987. pap. 6.50 (ISBN 0-687-08627-2). Abingdon.

Class Struggle & the Jewish Nation: Selected Essays in Marxist Zionism. Ber Borochov. Ed. by Mitchell Cohen. LC 83-4695. 358p. 1983. 29.95 (ISBN 0-87855-479-3). Transaction Bks.

Classic Buddhist Sculpture. Jiro Sugiyama. LC 82-80738. (Japanese Arts Library: Vol. 11). (Illus.). 200p. 1982. 25.00 (ISBN 0-87011-529-4). Kodansha.

Classic Christian Faith: Chapel Meditations Based on Luther's Small Catechism. Carlson M. Edgar. LC 59-9093. pap. 42.80 (2026912). Bks Demand UMI.

Classic Christian Townsite at Arminna West. Kent R. Weeks. (Pubns of the Penn-Yale Expedition to Egypt: No. 3). (Illus.). xv, 88p. 1967. 21.00x (ISBN 0-686-17769-X). Univ Mus of U PA.

Classic Christian Townsite at Arminna West, Vol. 3. Kent R. Weeks. LC 67-26194. 1967. 25.00 (ISBN 0-686-00130-3). Penn-Yale Expedit.

Classic Hassidic Tales. Meyer Levin. (Illus.). 10.00 (ISBN 0-8446-5216-4). Peter Smith.

Classic Hassidic Tales. Levin Meyer. 300p. 1985. 16.95 (ISBN 0-88029-035-8, Pub. by Dorset Pr). Hippocrene Bks.

Classic Myth & Legend. Ascott R. Hope-Moncrieff. LC 77-85616. 1977. Repr. of 1912 ed. lib. bdg. 45.00 (ISBN 0-89341-317-8). Longwood Pub Group.

Classic Mythology in Literature, Art, & Music. Phil Mayerson. 1971. text ed. write for info. (ISBN 0-673-15690-7). Scott F.

Classic Myths in English Literature & Art. Charles M. Gayley. LC 77-6986. 1977. Repr. of 1911 ed. lib. bdg. 45.00 (ISBN 0-89341-163-9). Longwood Pub Group.

Classic Sermons on Faith & Doubt. Compiled by Warren W. Wiersbe. LC 85-9767. (Classic Sermon Ser.). 160p. 1985. pap. 8.95 (ISBN 0-8254-4028-9). Kregel.

Classic Sermons on Prayer. Ed. by Warren W. Wiersbe. (Classic Sermons Ser.). (Orig.). 1987. pap. 9.95 (ISBN 0-8254-4029-7). Kregel.

Classic Sermons on Suffering. Compiled by Warren W. Wiersbe. LC 84-11260. (Classic Sermon Ser.). 204p. (Orig.). 1984. pap. text ed. 9.95 (ISBN 0-8254-4027-0). Kregel.

Classic Stories from the Lives of Our Prophets. Leon R. Hartshorn. LC 73-155235. 384p. 1975. 9.95 (ISBN 0-87747-438-9). Deseret Bk.

Classic Themes of Disciples Theology: Rethinking the Traditional Affirmations of the Christian Church (Disciples of Christ) Ed. by Kenneth Lawrence. LC 85-50712. 150p. 1986. text ed. 20.00x (ISBN 0-87565-024-4). Tex Christian.

Classical & Contemporary Readings in the Philosophy of Religion. 2nd ed. John Hick. LC 75-98092. (Philosophy Ser). 1969. text ed. write for info. (ISBN 0-13-135269-5). P-H.

Classical & Mediaeval Studies in Honor of Edward Kennard Rand, Presented upon the Completion of His Fortieth Year of Teaching. facs. ed. Ed. by L. W. Jones. LC 68-57312. (Essay Index Reprint Ser). 1938. 21.50 (ISBN 0-8369-0312-9). Ayer Co Pubs.

Classical Apologetics: A Rational Defense of the Christian Faith & a Critique of Presuppositional Apologetics. R. C. Sproul et al. LC 83-12372. 432p. (Orig.). 1984. pap. 12.95 (ISBN 0-310-44951-0, 12372P). Zondervan.

Classical Approaches to the Study of Religion: Aims, Methods & Theories of Research: Part 1: Introduction & Anthology. Jacques Waardenburg. LC 70-152082. (Religion & Reason Ser: No. 3). 742p. 1973. pap. text ed. 47.50x (ISBN 0-686-22556-2). Mouton.
Classical Approaches to the Study of Religion: Aims, Methods & Theories of Research, Pt. 2 Bibliography. Jacques Waardenburg. (Religion & Reason Ser.: No. 4). 332p. 1974. text ed. 58.50 (ISBN 90-2797-971-5). Mouton.
Classical Arab Islam: The Culture & Heritage of the Golden Age. Tarif Khalidi. LC 84-70416. 158p. 1985. 16.95 (ISBN 0-87850-047-2). Darwin Pr.
Classical Dictionary of Hindu Mythology & Religion, Geography, History & Literature. 11th ed. John Dowson. 26.95 (ISBN 0-7100-1302-7). Methuen Inc.
Classical Evangelical Essays in Old Testament Interpretation. Walter C. Kaiser, Jr. 1972. pap. 9.95 (ISBN 0-8010-5314-5). Baker Bk.
Classical Gods & Heroes in the National Gallery of Art. Thomas J. Sienkewicz. LC 82-23818. (Illus.). 50p. (Orig.). 1983. pap. text ed. 9.75 (ISBN 0-8191-2967-4). U Pr of Amer.
Classical Gods & Heroes: Myths As Told by the Ancient Authors. Tr. & intro. by Rhoda A. Hendricks. 1974. pap. 7.95 (ISBN 0-688-05279-7). Morrow.
Classical Hebrew Composition. Jacob Weingreen. 1957. 16.95x (ISBN 0-19-815423-2). Oxford U Pr.
Classical Hindu Mythology: A Reader in the Sanskrit Puranas. Ed. by Cornelia Dimmitt. Tr. by J. A. Van Buitenen. LC 77-92643. 388p. 1978. 34.95 (ISBN 0-87722-117-0); pap. 12.95x (ISBN 0-87722-122-7). Temple U Pr.
Classical Learning & Taoist Practices in Early Japan, with Translation of Books XVI & XX of the Engi-Shiki. Felicia G. Bock. Tr. & intro. by Felicia G. Bock. LC 82-84464. (Occasional Paper Arizona State Univ., Center for Asian Studies: No. 17). 102p. 1985. pap. 8.00 (ISBN 0-939252-13-9). ASU Ctr Asian.
Classical Literature. Center for Learning Staff. 1982. pap. text ed. 34.95 (ISBN 0-697-01884-9). Wm C Brown.
Classical Mediterranean Spirituality. Ed. by A. H. Armstrong. (World Spirituality Ser.). 499p. 1986. 49.50x (ISBN 0-8245-0764-9). Crossroad NY.
Classical Moralists: Selections Illustrating Ethics from Socrates to Martineau. Ed. by Benjamin Rand. 16.50 (ISBN 0-8446-1374-6). Peter Smith.
Classical Myth & Legend in Renaissance Dictionaries. DeWitt T. Starnes & Ernest W. Talbert. LC 73-11753. (Illus.). 517p. 1973. Repr. of 1955 ed. lib. bdg. 42.50x (ISBN 0-8371-7086-9, STCM). Greenwood.
Classical Mythology. 3rd. ed. Mark P. Morford & Robert J. Lenardon. (Illus.). 644p. 1985. pap. text ed. 19.95x (ISBN 0-582-28541-0). Longman.
Classical Mythology in the Plays, Masques, & Poems of Ben Jonson. Charles F. Wheeler. LC 71-114234. 1970. Repr. of 1938 ed. 23.50 (ISBN 0-8046-1038-X, Pub. by Kennikat). Assoc Faculty Pr.
Classical Mythology in Twentieth-Century Thought & Literature. Ed. by Wendell M. Aycock & Theodore M. Klein. (Proceedings of the Comparative Literature Symposium, Vol. XI). (Illus.). 221p. (Orig.). 1980. pap. 12.00 (ISBN 0-89672-079-9). Tex Tech Univ Pr.
Classical Mythology of Milton's English Poems. Charles G. Osgood. LC 64-8180. 198p. 1964. Repr. of 1900 ed. 17.50x (ISBN 0-87752-080-1). Gordian.
Classical Mythology of Milton's English Poems. Charles G. Osgood. LC 65-15902. (Studies in Comparative Literature, No. 35). 1969. Repr. of 1900 ed. lib. bdg. 75.00x (ISBN 0-8383-0603-9). Haskell.
Classical Mythology: The Myths of Ancient Greece & Italy. Thomas Keightley. xviii, 507p. 1976. 25.00 (ISBN 0-89005-189-5). Ares.
Classical Myths in English Literature. Daniel S. Norton & Peters Rushton. Repr. of 1952 ed. lib. bdg. 39.75x (ISBN 0-8371-2440-9, NOCM). Greenwood.
Classical Readings in Christian Apologetics: A. D. 100-1800. Ed. by L. Russ Bush. 1986. pap. 11.95 (ISBN 0-310-45641-X, 11622P). Zondervan.
Classical Theory of Relations. Constantine Cavarnos. LC 75-2659. 116p. 1975. pap. 3.75 (ISBN 0-914744-28-3). Inst Byzantine.
Classical World Bibliography of Philosophy, Religion, & Rhetoric. Walter Dolan. LC 76-52512. (Library of Humanities Reference Bks.: No. 95). 396p. 1978. lib. bdg. 51.00 (ISBN 0-8240-9878-1). Garland Pub.
Classics of Christian Missions. Ed. by Francis M. Dubose. LC 78-53147. 1979. pap. 12.95 (ISBN 0-8054-6313-5). Broadman.
Classics of Jewish Literature. Ed. by Leo Lieberman. Arthur Beringause. LC 86-8124. 432p. 1986. 24.95 (ISBN 0-8022-2092-4). Philos Lib.
Classics: Their History & Present Status in Education: A Symposium of Essays. facs. ed. Ed. by Felix M. Kirsch. LC 68-22104. (Essay Index Reprint Ser). 1928. 20.00 (ISBN 0-8369-0600-4). Ayer Co Pubs.
Classification of Jewish Immigrants & Its Implications: A Survey of Opinion. Nathan Goldberg et al. LC 45-6587. (Yivo English Translation Ser.). 154p. 1945. pap. 2.00 (ISBN 0-914512-13-7). Yivo Inst.
Classification of Religions. Duren J. Ward. 75p. 1909. pap. 0.95 (ISBN 0-317-40432-6). Open Court.
Classification of the Greek Manuscripts of the Johannine Epistles. William L. Richards. LC 77-23469. (Society of Biblical Literature. Dissertation Ser.). 1977. pap. 9.95 (ISBN 0-89130-140-2, 060135). Scholars Pr GA.
Classified Catalog of the Ecumenical Movement, 2 vols. World Council of Churches, Geneva, Switzerland. 1972. lib. bdg. 198.00 (ISBN 0-8161-0925-7, Hall Library). G K Hall.
Classified Catalog of the Ecumenical Movement: First Supplement. World Council of Churches, Geneva. 1981. lib. bdg. 105.00 (ISBN 0-8161-0360-7, Hall Library). G K Hall.
Classified Concordance, 4 vols. Eliezer Katz. Incl. Vol. 1. Torah. 415p. 1964. 30.00x (ISBN 0-8197-0382-6); Vol. 2. Early Prophets. 702p. 1967. 30.00x (ISBN 0-8197-0383-4); Vol. 3. Later Prophets. 683p. 1970. 30.00x (ISBN 0-8197-0384-2). Bloch.
Classified Concordance: To the Bible & Its Various Subjects, Vol. 4. Eliezer Katz. (Hebrew & Eng.). 1000p. 1974. 40.00x (ISBN 0-8197-0385-0). Bloch.
Classifying Church or Synagogue Library Materials. Dorothy B. Kersten. LC 77-16476. (Guide Ser.: No. 7). 1977. pap. 3.95x (ISBN 0-915324-13-X); pap. 3.00 members. CSLA.
Classroom Hanukah. Jacqueline D. Greene. (Illus.). 32p. (Orig.). 1980. pap. 3.00 (ISBN 0-938836-01-3). Pascal Pubs.
Classrooms in Crisis. Arnold Burron et al. LC 85-73068. 196p. (Orig.). 1986. pap. 7.95 (ISBN 0-89636-192-6). Accent Bks.
Classy Christmas Concert. Carol Ogilvy & Trudy Tinkham. 112p. 1986. wkbk. 8.95 (ISBN 0-86653-349-4). Good Apple.
Claude G. Montefiore on the Ancient Rabbis: The Second Generation on Reform Judaism in Britain. Joshua B. Stein. LC 77-13194. (Brown University. Brown Judaic Studies: No. 4). 85p. 1977. pap. 9.00 (ISBN 0-89130-190-9, 140004). Scholars Pr GA.
Claude Jay & Alfonso Salmeron: Two Early Jesuits. William Bangert. 1985. 15.95 (ISBN 0-8294-0459-7). Loyola.
Claudel's Immortal Heroes: A Choice of Deaths. Harold M. Watson. LC 73-160572. 1971. 25.00 (ISBN 0-8135-0695-6). Rutgers U Pr.
Claudius the God. Robert Graves. 1977. pap. 4.95 (ISBN 0-394-72537-9, Vin). Random.
Claves de Interpretacion Biblica. Thomas Fountain. 148p. 1985. pap. 4.25 (ISBN 0-311-03653-8). Casa Bautista.
Clavis Universalis: New Inquiry after Truth, Being a Demonstration of the Non-Existence or Impossibility of an External World. Arthur Collier. Ed. by Rene Wellek. LC 75-11208. (British Philosophers & Theologians of the 17th & 18th Centuries Ser.). 150p. 1978. lib. bdg. 51.00 (ISBN 0-8240-1763-3). Garland Pub.
Clean Church. W. Carl Ketcherside. 165p. 1987. pap. 3.95 (ISBN 0-938855-17-4). Gospel Themes Pr.
Clean Love in Courtship. Lawrence G. Lovasik. 1974. pap. 1.50 (ISBN 0-89555-095-4). TAN Bks Pubs.
Clean: The Meaning of Christian Baptism. William G. Johnsson. LC 80-15681. (Horizon Ser.). 96p. 1980. pap. 5.95 (ISBN 0-8127-0293-X). Review & Herald.
Cleaning Out Your Mental Closet: Transforming Negative Emotions. Chuck Cerling. 150p. 1987. pap. 9.95 (ISBN 0-87788-127-8). Shaw Pubs.
Cleansing of the Sanctuary. D. S. Warner & H. M. Riggle. 541p. Repr. 5.50 (ISBN 0-686-29145-X). Faith Pub Hse.
Clear Light of Bliss. Geshe K. Gyatso. Ed. by Jonathan Landaw. Tr. by Tenzin Norbu from Tibetan. (Wisdom Advanced Book: Blue Ser.). (Illus.). 264p. (Orig.). 1982. pap. 10.95 (ISBN 0-86171-005-3, Pub. by Wisdom Pubns). Great Traditions.
Clear Light: The Distinction Between Appearance & Reality. Lama Mipham. 1980. write for info. Dharma Pub.
Clear White Light. Subramuniya. (On the Path Ser.). (Illus.). 1979. pap. 2.00 (ISBN 0-87516-350-5). De Vorss.
Clement of Alexandria, & a Secret Gospel of Mark. Morton Smith. LC 72-148938. 1973. 30.00x (ISBN 0-674-13490-7). Harvard U Pr.
Clement's Use of Aristotle: The Aristotelian Contribution of Clement of Alexandria's Refutation of Gnosticism. Elizabeth A. Clark. LC 77-93913. (Texts & Studies in Religion: Vol. 1). vii, 192p. 1981. Repr. of 1977 ed. text ed. 49.95x (ISBN 0-88946-984-9). E Mellen.
Clergy & Clients: The Practice of Pastoral Psychotherapy. Ronald R. Lee. 1980. 10.95 (ISBN 0-8164-0115-2, HarpR). Har-Row.
Clergy Compensation & Financial Planning Workbook. Herbert L. Akin. (Illus.). 100p. 1982. wkbk. 6.95 (ISBN 0-938736-05-1). Life Enrich.
Clergy Couples in Crisis. Dean Merrill. (Leadership Library). 216p. 1985. 9.95 (ISBN 0-917463-06-4). Chr Today.
Clergy Desk Book. Manfred Holck, Jr. 288p. (Orig.). 1985. pap. 19.95 (ISBN 0-687-08656-6). Abingdon.
Clergy Malpractice. Robert W. McMenamin. LC 86-81075. 209p. 1986. lib. bdg. 27.50 (ISBN 0-89941-483-4). W S Hein.
Clergy Malpractice. H. Newton Malony. Ed. by Thomas L. Needham & Samuel Southaud. LC 85-31466. 192p. (Orig.). 1986. pap. 12.95 (ISBN 0-664-24591-9). Westminster.
Clergy Say the Dardnest Things: Or How to Speak "Clergy-ese". Walter R. Kelley. (Illus.). 200p. (Orig.). 1987. pap. text ed. write for info. (ISBN 0-937071-01-3). Pyramid Designs Pr.
Clergy System. C. Ketcherside. pap. 0.50 (ISBN 0-686-64390-9). Reiner.
Clergyman & the Psychiatrist: When to Refer. Robert L. Mason et al. LC 77-22597. 248p. 1978. 20.95x (ISBN 0-88229-260-9). Nelson-Hall.
Clerical Cartoons. 2nd ed. Wm. Armstrong. (Armstrong Cartoon Ser.). (Illus.). 48p. (Orig.). 1971. pap. 1.00 (ISBN 0-913452-02-5). Jesuit Bks.
Click in the Clock: Meditations for Junior Highs. Tom N. Emswiler. LC 81-11875. 128p. (Orig.). 1981. pap. 5.95 (ISBN 0-8298-0470-6). Pilgrim NY.
Climate of Monastic Prayer. Thomas Merton. (Cistercian Studies: No. 1). 154p. 1973. Repr. of 1969 ed. 7.95 (ISBN 0-87907-801-4). Cistercian Pubns.
Climax of the Risen Life. Jessie Penn-Lewis. 1962. pap. 2.95 (ISBN 0-87508-992-5). Chr Lit.
Climb the Highest Mountain. Mark Prophet & Elizabeth Prophet. LC 72-175101. (Illus.). 516p. 1978. pap. 16.95 (ISBN 0-916766-26-8). Summit Univ.
Climb up Through Your Valleys. Evaline Echols. 1980. 6.95 (ISBN 0-87148-174-X); pap. 5.95 (ISBN 0-87148-173-1). Pathway Pr.
Climbing Higher: Reflections on Our Spiritual Journey. David Rosage. 112p. (Orig.). 1983. pap. 4.95 (ISBN 0-89283-147-2). Servant.
Climbing on Top of Your Troubles. Berge Najarian. 1984. 6.50 (ISBN 0-8062-2283-2). Carlton.
Climbing the Rainbow. Peggy Jenkins. 92p. pap. 5.95 (ISBN 0-942494-48-2). Coleman Pub.
Clinging: The Experience of Prayer. Emilie Griffin. LC 83-48989. 96p. 1984. 11.95 (ISBN 0-06-063461-8); 11.45i. Har-Row.
Clinical Handbook of Pastoral Counseling. Robert J. Wicks et al. 592p. (Orig.). 1985. 22.95 (ISBN 0-8091-0350-8); pap. 14.95 (ISBN 0-8091-2687-7). Paulist Pr.
Clinical Pastoral Care for Hospitalized Children & Their Families. John B. Hesch. 224p. 1987. pap. 9.95 (ISBN 0-8091-2871-3). Paulist Pr.
Clinical Theology. Frank Lake. 256p. 1987. 18.95 (ISBN 0-8245-0821-1). Crossroad NY.
Clint's "Be Cheerful" Day. Patricia S. Mahany. (Happy Day Bks.). (Illus.). 24p. 1984. 1.59 (ISBN 0-87239-731-9, 3701). Standard Pub.
Clip Art-Block Prints for the Gospel of Cycles A, B, C. Helen Siegl. (Illus.). 216p. (Orig.). pap. 11.95 (ISBN 0-916134-66-0). Pueblo Pub Co.
Clip Art Features for Church Newsletters. George W. Knight. 1984. pap. 4.50 (ISBN 0-8010-5465-6). Baker Bk.
Clip-Art Features for Church Newsletters, No. 2. George W. Knight. (Illus.). 96p. 1986. pap. 4.95 (ISBN 0-8010-5471-0). Baker Bk.
Clip-Art for Feasts & Seasons. expanded ed. Gertrud M. Nelson. (Illus.). 120p. (Orig.). 1982. pap. 10.95 (ISBN 0-916134-41-5). Pueblo Pub Co.
Clip-Art Panel Cartoons for Churches 2. Howard Paris. 96p. 1987. pap. 4.95 (ISBN 0-8010-7098-8). Baker Bk.
Clip-Art Sentence Sermons for Church Publications. Compiled by George W. Knight. 96p. 1986. pap. 3.95 (ISBN 0-8010-5475-3). Baker Bk.
Clips from Tom M. Olson: Nuggets from the Writings of Tom M. Olson Provide the Only-Way to View Events. Ed. by Louise L. Dick. LC 86-90141. (One-Way Ser.: Vol. 10). 251p. (Orig.). 1986. pap. 6.95 (ISBN 0-935899-06-5). LeTourneau Pr.
Clockmaker. Gustav Meyrinck. (Orig.). 1987. pap. 3.00. Rosycross Pr.
Clocks & the Cosmos: Time in Western Life & Thought. Samuel L. Macey. LC 79-18891. (Illus.). 256p. 1980. 25.00 (ISBN 0-208-01773-9, Archon). Shoe String.
Close the Back Door. Alan F. Harre. 1984. pap. 6.50 (ISBN 0-570-03932-0, 12-2867). Concordia.
Closed: Ninety-Nine Ways to Stop Abortion. Joseph M. Scheidler. LC 85-42646. 350p. (Orig.). 1985. pap. 9.95 (ISBN 0-89107-346-9, Crossway Bks). Good News.
Closed: Ninety-Nine Ways to Stop Abortion. Joseph M. Scheidler. LC 85-61055. 350p. (Orig.). 1985. pap. 9.95 (ISBN 0-89870-075-2). Ignatius Pr.
Closeness of God. Ladislaus Boros. 1978. pap. 3.95 (ISBN 0-8245-0210-8). Crossroad NY.
Closer Look at Catholicism: A Guide for Protestants. Bob Moran. 192p. 1986. 12.95 (ISBN 0-8499-0514-1, 0514-1). Word Bks.
Closer Look at the Sacraments: A Study Guide for Catholic Adults. Joan de Merchant & Merchant Gallagher. pap. 6.95 (ISBN 0-937997-00-5). Hi Time Pub.
Closer Than a Brother. David Winter. LC 71-181991. (Illus.). 160p. 1976. pap. 3.50 (ISBN 0-87788-129-4). Shaw Pubs.
Closer Walk. Catherine Marshall. Ed. by Leonard LeSourd. 256p. 1986. 12.95 (ISBN 0-8007-9065-0). Revell.
Closer Walk. Joyce Wallace. LC 82-99994. 128p. 1982. pap. 4.00 (ISBN 0-686-38098-3). Foun Christ Serv.
Closer Walk: Reflections of John 14 Through 17 from the Edgar Cayce Readings. 74p. (Orig.). 1974. pap. 3.95 (ISBN 0-87604-078-4). ARE Pr.
Closer Walk: Spirtual Discoveries from Her Journal. Catherine Marshall. Ed. by Leonard LeSourd. 1985. 12.95 (ISBN 0-317-46132-X). Revell.
Closer Walk with God. David Mains. (Chapel Talks Ser.). 64p. 0.95 (ISBN 0-89191-264-9, 52647). Cook.
Closing of Man's History. Ludie J. Wright. (Bible Prophecy Ser.: No. 1). (Illus.). 209p. (Orig.). 1986. 15.95 (ISBN 0-9617290-0-7); pap. 12.95 (ISBN 0-9617290-1-5). Hse Better Sales.
Clothed in Christ. Michael Downey. 160p. 1987. pap. 9.95 (ISBN 0-8245-0812-2). Crossroad NY.
Clothed with the Sun. Anna Kingsford & Edward Maitland. 248p. Date not set. pap. 14.00 (ISBN 0-89540-132-0, SB 132). Sun Pub.
Clothed with the Sun: The Mystery-Tale of Jesus the Avatara. rev. ed. G. De Purucker. Ed. by Emmett Small & Helen Todd. Orig. Title: Story of Jesus. (Illus.). 56p. 1972. pap. 1.00 (ISBN 0-913004-06-5). Point Loma Pub.
Cloture of Notre-Dame & Its Role in the 14th Century Choir Program. Dorothy Gillerman. LC 76-23623. (Outstanding Dissertations in the Fine Arts - 2nd Series - Medieval). (Illus.). 292p. 1977. Repr. of 1973 ed. lib. bdg. 69.00 (ISBN 0-8240-2693-4). Garland Pub.
Cloud Hidden, Whereabouts Unknown: A Mountain Journal. Alan W. Watts. 1965. pap. 3.95 (ISBN 0-394-71999-9, Vin). Random.
Cloud of Unknowing. Ed. by Phyllis Hodgson. (Analecta Cartusiana Ser.: No. 3). (Eng.). 234p. (Orig.). 1982. pap. 25.00 (ISBN 3-7052-0003-8, Pub by Salzburg Studies). Longwood Pub Group.
Cloud of Unknowing. Ed. by James Walsh. (Classics of Western Spirituality Ser.). 1981. 12.95 (ISBN 0-8091-0314-1); pap. 9.95 (ISBN 0-8091-2332-0). Paulist Pr.
Cloud of Unknowing & Other Works. Tr. by Clifton Wolters. (Classics Ser). 1978. pap. 3.95 (ISBN 0-14-044385-1). Penguin.
Cloud of Unknowing & the Book of Privy Counselling. Ed. by William Johnston. LC 73-79737. 200p. 1973. pap. 3.50 (ISBN 0-385-03097-5, Im). Doubleday.
Clouded Witness: Initiation in the Church of England in the Mid-Victorian Period 1850-1875. Peter J. Jagger. (Pittsburgh Theological Monographs New Ser.: No. 1). vii, 221p. (Orig.). 1982. pap. 12.00 (ISBN 0-915138-51-4). Pickwick.
Clown Ministry. Floyd Shaffer & Penne Sewall. LC 84-80322. 112p. (Orig.). 1984. pap. 7.95 (ISBN 0-936664-18-5). Group Bks.
Clowning in Rome: Reflections on Solitude, Celibacy, Prayer & Contemplation. Henri J. Nouwen. LC 78-22423. (Illus.). 1979. pap. 4.95 (ISBN 0-385-15129-2, Im). Doubleday.
Clues about Jews for People Who Aren't. Sidney J. Jacobs & Betty J. Jacobs. LC 85-90337. 128p. (Orig.). 1985. pap. 8.95 (ISBN 0-933647-00-X). Jacobs Ladder Pubns.
Clues to a Successful Life. O. S. Hawkins. LC 82-71561. (Orig.). 1982. pap. 6.95 (ISBN 0-8054-5515-9). Broadman.
Clues to Creativity, Vol. 2: J-P. M. Franklin & Maryann J. Dotts. (Orig.). 1975. pap. 4.95 (ISBN 0-377-00041-8). Friend Pr.
Clues to Creativity, Vol. 3: R-Z. M. Franklin & Maryann J. Dotts. (Orig.). 1976. pap. 4.95 (ISBN 0-377-00042-6). Friend Pr.

Clues to Emerson's Mystic Verse. William S. Kennedy. (Studies in Emerson, No. 12). 1970. pap. 39.95x (ISBN 0-8383-0048-0). Haskell.

Clumsy Construction in Mark's Gospel: A Critique of Form & Redaktionsgeschichte. John C. Meagher. LC 79-66373. (Toronto Studies in Theology: Vol. 3). xii, 178p. 1979. 39.95x (ISBN 0-88946-876-1). E Mellen.

Cluniac Monasticism in the Central Middle Ages. Ed. by Noreen Hunt. x, 248p. 1971. 25.00 (ISBN 0-208-01247-8, Archon). Shoe String.

Cluny under Saint Hugh, Ten Forty-Nine to Eleven Hundred Nine. 1st ed. Noreen Hunt. LC 68-11411. pap. 60.00 (ISBN 0-317-29696-5, 2022064). Bks Demand UMI.

Co-Creation & Capitalism: John Paul II's Laborem Exercens. Ed. by John W. Houck & Oliver F. Williams. 318p. (Orig.). 1983. lib. bdg. 30.75 (ISBN 0-8191-3358-2); pap. text ed. 12.50 (ISBN 0-8191-3359-0). U Pr of Amer.

Co-Creators with God. Arthur F. McNulty. 88p. (Orig.). 1985. pap. 4.95 (ISBN 0-934134-29-4, Leaven Pr). Sheed & Ward MO.

Coaching Flag Football. John Ferrell & MaryAnn Ferrell. 56p. 1980. pap. 3.25x (ISBN 0-88035-027-X). Human Kinetics.

Coals of Fire. G. D. Watson. pap. 2.95 (ISBN 0-686-12857-5). Schmul Pub Co.

Coat of Many Colors. Behn Boruch. 1959. 3.95 (ISBN 0-88482-728-3). Hebrew Pub.

Coat of Many Colors: Jewish Subcommunities in the United States. Ed. by Abraham D. Lavender. LC 77-71865. (Contributions in Family Studies: No. 1). 1977. lib. bdg. 29.95 (ISBN 0-8371-9539-X, LCM/). Greenwood.

Coat of Many Colors: Pages from Jewish Life. Israel Shenker. LC 82-45338. 408p. 1985. 19.95 (ISBN 0-385-15811-4). Doubleday.

Cobb's Baptist Church Manual. J. E. Cobb. 193p. 1979. pap. 2.50 (ISBN 0-89114-056-5). Baptist Pub Hse.

Cochin-China: Containing Many Admirable Rarities of That Countrey. Christoforo Borri. LC 71-25710. (English Experience Ser.: No. 223). 1970. Repr. of 1633 ed. 9.50 (ISBN 90-221-0223-8). Walter J Johnson.

Cockburnspath: A Documentary History of a Border Parish. Eric Rankin. Ed. by James Bulloch. (Illus.). 166p. 1981. 16.95 (ISBN 0-567-09316-6, Pub. by T&T Clark Ltd UK). Fortress.

Code, Community, Ministry: Selected Studies for the Revised Code of Canon Law. Ed. by James H. Provost. vi, 116p. (Orig.). 1983. pap. 4.50 (ISBN 0-943616-15-8). Canon Law Soc.

Code of Canon Law: A Text & Commentary. Ed. by James A. Coriden et al. 39.95 (ISBN 0-8091-0345-1). Paulist Pr.

Code of Canon Law: A Text & Commentary, Study Edition. Ed. by James A. Coriden et al. 1184p. 1986. pap. text ed. 29.95 (ISBN 0-8091-2837-3). Paulist Pr.

Code of Canon Law in English Translation. Ed. by Canon Law Society of Great Britain, Ireland Staff. 1983. pap. 9.95 (ISBN 0-8028-1978-8). Eerdmans.

Code of Canon Law: Latin-English Edition. Tr. by Canon Law Society of America Staff. Orig. Title: Codex Iuris Canonici. xlii, 668p. (Orig.). 1983. 15.00 (ISBN 0-943616-20-4); pap. 12.00 (ISBN 0-943616-19-0). Canon Law Soc.

Code of Jewish Law: Kitzur Shulhan Arukh, 4 vols. Solomon Ganzfried. Tr. by Hyman E. Goldin. (Eng. & Hebrew.). 1961. Set. 49.50 (ISBN 0-88482-412-8). Hebrew Pub.

Code of Maimonides, Bk. 3, Treatise 8, Sanctification Of The New Moon. Moses Maimonides. Tr. by Solomon Gandz. (Judaica Ser: No. 11). 1956. 23.50x (ISBN 0-300-00476-1). Yale U Pr.

Code of Maimonides, Bks. 5-6 & 8-14. Moses Maimonides. Incl. Bk. 5. Book of Holiness. Tr. by Louis I. Rabinowitz & Philip Grossman. xxxiv, 429p. 1965. 50.00x (ISBN 0-300-00846-5); Bk. 6. Book of Asseverations. Tr. by B. D. Klien. 273p. 1962. 30.00x (ISBN 0-300-00633-0); Bk. 8. Book of Temple Service. Tr. by Mendell Lewittes. (Illus.). xxvii, 525p. 1957. 55.00x (ISBN 0-300-00717-5); Bk. 9. Book of Offerings. Tr. by Herbert Danby. xxi, 236p. 1950. 27.50x (ISBN 0-300-00398-6); Bk. 10. Book of Cleanness. Tr. by Herbert Danby. (Illus.). xiv, 645p. 1954. 60.00x (ISBN 0-300-00397-8); Bk. 11. Book of Torts. Tr. by Hyman Klein. xvii, 299p. 1954. 35.00x (ISBN 0-300-00632-2); Bk. 12. Book of Acquisition. Tr. by Isaac Klein. xv, 335p. 1951. 40.00x (ISBN 0-300-00631-4); Bk. 13. Book of Civil Laws. Tr. by Jacob J. Rabinowitz. xxiv, 345p. 1949. 45.00 (ISBN 0-300-00845-7); Bk. 14. Book of Judges. Tr. by Abraham M. Hershman. xxv, 335p. 1949. 40.00x (ISBN 0-300-00548-2). (Judaica Ser.). Yale U Pr.

Code of Maimonides - Book Three: The Book of Seasons. Moses Maimonides. Tr. by Solomon Gandz & Hyman Klein. (Judaica Ser: No. 14). 1961. 60.00x (ISBN 0-300-00475-3). Yale U Pr.

Code of the Prophets. Madeleine L. Burman. LC 84-90888. (Illus.). 100p. (Orig.). 1984. 9.95x (ISBN 0-9613283-0-4); pap. 6.95x. M L Burman.

Codeword: Catherine. Jodie Collins. 240p. (Orig.). 1984. pap. 6.95 (ISBN 0-8423-0301-4). Tyndale.

Codeword Catherine. Jodie Collins. 384p. cancelled (ISBN 0-8423-0302-2). Tyndale.

Codex Beta of the Ecumenical Patriarchate of Constantinople: Aspects of the History of the Church of Constantinople. Nomikos M. Vaporis. (Archbishop Iakovos Library of Ecclesiastical & Historical Sources). 166p. 1975. pap. 4.95 (ISBN 0-916586-03-0). Holy Cross Orthodox.

Codex Bezae: A Study of the So-Called Western Text of the New Testament. J. R. Harris. (Texts & Studies Ser.: No. 1, Vol. 2, Pt. 1). pap. 19.00 (ISBN 0-8115-1684-9). Kraus Repr.

Codex Gamma of the Ecumenical Patriarchate of Constantinople. Nomikos M. Vaporis. (Archbishop Iakovos Library of Ecclesiastical & Historical Sources Ser.). 154p. 1974. pap. 4.95 (ISBN 0-916586-01-4). Holy Cross Orthodox.

Codex Juris Ecclesiastici Anglicani, 2 Vols. Edmund Gibson. 1761. text ed. 372.60x (ISBN 0-576-99471-5, Pub. by Gregg Intl Pubs England). Gregg Intl.

Codex One of the Gospels & Its Allies. K. Lake. (Texts & Studies Ser.: No. 1, Vol. 7, Pt. 3). pap. 19.00 (ISBN 0-8115-1705-5). Kraus Repr.

Codex Rosae Crucis - DOMA. Manly P. Hall. 20.00 (ISBN 0-89314-404-5). Philos Res.

Codex Traditionum Ecclesiae Collegiatae Claustroneoburgensis Continens Donationes, Fundationes Commutationesque Hanc Ecclesiam Attinentes Ab Anno Domin: MCCLX Usque Circiter MCCLX. Ed. by Maximiliano Fischer. Repr. of 1851 ed. 23.00 (ISBN 0-384-29873-7). Johnson Repr.

Coelum Philosophorum: Or the Book of Vexations. Paracelsus. Tr. by A. E. Waite from Lat. pap. 2.95 (ISBN 0-916411-13-3, Pub. by Alchemical Pr). Holmes Pub.

Coercive Utopians. Rael Jean & Erich Issac. (Christian Activist Ser.). 1985. pap. 7.95 (ISBN 0-89526-815-9). Regnery Bks.

Coffee Talk: Sharing Christ Through Friendly Gatherings. Barbara Ball. LC 79-53980. 80p. 1980. pap. 4.95 (ISBN 0-934396-08-6). Churches Alive.

Cognitive Structures & Religious Research. W. Widick Schroeder. xiii, 211p. 1971. 7.50 (ISBN 0-87013-150-8). Mich St U Pr.

Cognitivity of Religion: Three Perspectives. J. Kellenberger. LC 84-27999. 1985. 20.00x (ISBN 0-520-05383-4). U of Cal Pr.

Cognizance. George S. Briggs. 48p. 1984. 7.95 (ISBN 0-533-06100-8). Vantage.

Coheleth & Song of Songs, with a Commentary Historical & Critical, 2 Vols. in 1. rev. ed. David C. Ginsburg. (Library of Biblical Studies Ser). 1970. 59.50x (ISBN 0-87068-059-5). Ktav.

Cohen & Troeltsch: Ethical Monotheistic Religion & Theory of Culture. Wendell S. Dietrich. (Brown Judaic Studies). 1986. text ed. 23.95 (ISBN 1-55540-017-5, 14-01-20); pap. 18.95 (ISBN 1-55540-018-3). Scholars Pr GA.

Coherence in a Fragmented World: Jonathan Edwards' Theology of the Holy Spirit. Patricia Wilson-Kastner. LC 78-62667. 1978. pap. text ed. 8.50 (ISBN 0-8191-0587-2). U Pr of Amer.

Coherence of Theism. Richard Swinburne. (Clarendon Library of Logic & Philosophy). 1977. 42.00x (ISBN 0-19-824410-X). Oxford U Pr.

Coil's Masonic Encyclopedia. Henry W. Coil. LC 60-53289. 749p. cloth w/slipcase 31.50 (ISBN 0-88053-054-5). Macoy Pub.

Coins & Christianity. Kenneth Jacob. 9.50 (ISBN 0-900652-73-X). Numismatic Fine Arts.

Coins of Gold. Paul Twitchell. 1972. 5.95 (ISBN 0-914766-02-3). IWP Pub.

Coins of the Ancient World. Ya'akov Meshorer. Ed. by Richard L. Currier. LC 72-10795. (Lerner Archaeology Ser.: Digging up the Past). (Illus.). 96p. 1975. PLB 8.95 (ISBN 0-8225-0835-4). Lerner Pubns.

Cokesbury Worship Hymnal. 288p. 1976. 4.95 (ISBN 0-687-08863-1); pap. 4.95 (ISBN 0-687-08865-8); accompanist ed. 3.95 (ISBN 0-687-08866-6). Abingdon.

Coleccion Navidena, No. 1 & 2. J. W. Blair. 1980. No. 1. pap. 1.75 (ISBN 0-311-08201-7); No. 2. pap. 1.75 (ISBN 0-311-08202-5). Casa Bautista.

Coleridge & the Pantheist Tradition. Thomas McFarland. 1969. 48.00x (ISBN 0-19-811664-0). Oxford U Pr.

Coleridge's Idealism. Claud Howard. LC 72-191125. 1924. lib. bdg. 17.50 (ISBN 0-8414-5131-1). Folcroft.

Coleridge's Religious Imagination: Three Volume Set, 3 vol. set, No. 100. Stephen Happel. (Salzburg-Romantic Reassessment). 943p. 1983. Set. pap. text ed. 80.00x (ISBN 0-391-03042-6, Pub. by Salzburg Austria). Vol.1 (ISBN 0-391-03039-6). Vol.2 (ISBN 0-391-03040-X). Vol.3 (ISBN 0-391-03041-8). Humanities.

Collaborative Approach to Personnel Relations: A Model Process for Justice in the Catholic School Community of Faith. John J. Augenstein. 191p. 1980. 2.35 (ISBN 0-686-39900-5). Natl Cath Educ.

Collage; A Resource Book for Christian Youth Groups. Jim O'Hara & Grace Walle. 86p. (Orig.). 1976. pap. 4.00 (ISBN 0-9608124-5-8). Marianist Com Ctr.

Collapse of Evolution. Scott M. Huse. 192p. 1986. pap. 7.95 (ISBN 0-8010-4310-7). Baker Bk.

Collectanea Cartusiensa, No. 1. Gaston Hocquard et al. Ed. by James Hogg. (Analecta Cartusiana Ser.: No. 82-1). (Fr., Illus.). 1980. pap. 25.00 (ISBN 3-7052-0119-0, Pub. by Salzburg Studies). Longwood Pub Group.

Collectanea Cartusiensia, No. 2. Patrick F. O'Connell. Ed. by James Hogg. (Analecta Cartusiana Ser.: No. 82-2). (Fr. & Ger.). 118p. (Orig.). 1980. pap. 25.00 (ISBN 3-7052-0120-4, Pub. by Salzburg Studies). Longwood Pub Group.

Collectanea Cartusiensia, No. 3. James Hogg & Wilhelm Brauer. Ed. by James Hogg. (Analecta Cartusiana Ser.: No. 82-3). (Lat. & Ger.). 120p. (Orig.). 1980. pap. 25.00 (ISBN 3-7052-0121-2, Pub. by Salzburg Studies). Longwood Pub Group.

Collectanea Cartusiensia, No. 4. Ed. by James Hogg. (Analecta Cartusiana Ser.: No. 82-4). (Orig.). 1985. pap. 25.00 (ISBN 3-7052-0122-0, Pub. by Salzburg Studies). Longwood Pub Group.

Collectanea Cartusiensia, No. 5. Ed. by James Hogg. (Analecta Cartusiana Ser.: No. 82-5). (Orig.). 1985. pap. 25.00 (ISBN 3-7052-0123-9, Pub. by Salzburg Studies). Longwood Pub Group.

Collectanea Cartusiensia, No. 6. James Hogg & James Hogg. (Analecta Cartusiana Ser.: No. 82-6). (Orig.). 1985. pap. 25.00 (ISBN 3-7052-0124-7, Pub. by Salzburg Studies). Longwood Pub Group.

Collectanea Cartusiensia, No. 7. Ed. by James Hogg. (Analecta Cartusiana Ser.: No. 82-7). (Orig.). 1986. pap. 25.00 (ISBN 3-7052-0125-5, Pub. by Salzburg Studies). Longwood Pub Group.

Collectanea Cartusiensia, No. 8. Ed. by James Hogg. (Analecta Cartusiana Ser.: No. 82-8). (Orig.). 1987. pap. 25.00 (ISBN 3-7052-0126-3, Pub. by Salzburg Studies). Longwood Pub Group.

Collectanea Cartusiensia, No. 9. Ed. by James Hogg. (Analecta Cartusiana Ser.: No. 82-9). (Orig.). 1987. pap. 25.00 (ISBN 3-7052-0127-1, Pub. by Salzburg Studies). Longwood Pub Group.

Collectanea Franciscana I. A. G. Little et al. 170p. 1914. text ed. 41.40x (ISBN 0-576-99205-4, Pub. by Gregg Intl Pubs England). Gregg Intl.

Collectanea Franciscana II. C. L. Kingsford. 169p. Repr. of 1922 ed. text ed. 33.12x (ISBN 0-576-99210-0, Pub. by Gregg Intl Pubs England). Gregg Intl.

Collectanea Trapezuntiana: Texts, Documents & Bibliographies of George of Trebizond. Ed. by John Monfasani. LC 83-19366. (Medieval & Renaissance Texts & Studies: Vol. 25). 896p. 1984. 60.00 (ISBN 0-86698-060-1). Medieval & Renaissance NY.

Collected Articles on Ockham. Philotheus Boehner & Eligius M. Buytaert. (Philosophy Ser). 1958. 23.00 (ISBN 0-686-11542-2). Franciscan Inst.

Collected Edition of the "Travaux Preparatoires of the European Convention on Human Rights" Vol. V Legal Committee-Ad Hoc Joint Committee-Committee of Ministers-Consultative Assembly 23 June - 28 August 1950. Ed. by Council of Europe Staff. 356p. 1979. lib. bdg. 131.60 (ISBN 90-247-1970-4). Kluwer Academic.

Collected Essays of Christopher Hill: Religion & Politics in Seventeenth-Century England, Vol. 2. Christopher Hill. LC 84-16446. 368p. 1986. lib. bdg. 27.50x (ISBN 0-87023-503-6). U of Mass Pr.

Collected Papers of Jacob Guttmann: An Original Anthology. Ed. by Steven T. Katz. LC 79-7172. (Jewish Philosophy, Mysticism & History of Ideas Ser.). 1980. lib. bdg. 40.00x (ISBN 0-405-12231-4). Ayer Co Pubs.

Collected Philosophical Papers: Ethics, Religion & Politics, Vol. 3. G. E. Anscombe. LC 81-4315. 192p. 1981. 27.50x (ISBN 0-8166-1082-7); pap. 10.95x (ISBN 0-8166-1083-5). U of Minn Pr.

Collected Works. John Taylor. 600.00 (ISBN 0-87968-899-8). Gordon Pr.

Collected Works of C. G. Jung: Psychology & Religion - West & East, No. 11. 2nd ed. Ed. by Gerard Adler et al. Tr. by R. F. Hull. (Bollingen Ser.: No. 20). 1969. 45.50 (ISBN 0-691-09772-0). Princeton U Pr.

Collected Works of G. K. Chesterton, Vol. I. G. K. Chesterton. LC 85-81511. 1986. 24.95 (ISBN 0-89870-077-9); pap. 15.95 (ISBN 0-89870-079-5). Ignatius Pr.

Collected Works of G. K. Chesterton II: The Everlasting Man, St. Francis of Assisi, St. Thomas Aquinas. G. K. Chesterton. Ed. by George Marlin. 480p. 1986. 29.95 (ISBN 0-89870-116-3); pap. 17.95 (ISBN 0-89870-117-1). Ignatius Pr.

Collected Works of G. K. Chesterton: The Illustrated London News, Vol. xxvii. G. K. Chesterton. Ed. by George Marlin. LC 85-81511. 622p. 1986. 29.95 (ISBN 0-89870-118-X); pap. 17.95 (ISBN 0-89870-119-8). Ignatius Pr.

Collected Works of Mahatma Gandhi, 90 Vols. Ed. by J. Doulatram et al. 48000p. 1983. 950.00 (ISBN 0-934676-35-6). Greenlf Bks.

Collected Works of Ramana Maharshi. Ed. by Arthur Osborne. 192p. 1970. pap. 9.95 (ISBN 0-87728-070-3). Weiser.

Collected Works of St. John of the Cross. 2nd ed. Tr. by Kieran Kavanaugh & Otilio Rodriguez. LC 78-65789. 1979. 14.95x (ISBN 0-9600876-5-6); pap. 8.95x (ISBN 0-9600876-7-2). ICS Pubns.

Collected Works of St. Teresa of Avila, Vol. 1. Tr. by Kieran Kavanaugh & Otillo Rodriquez. Incl. The Book of Her Life, Spiritual Testimonies, Soliloguies. LC 75-31305. 416p. (Orig.). 1976. 6.95x (ISBN 0-9600876-2-1). ICS Pubns.

Collected Works of St. Teresa of Avila, Vol. 2. Tr. by Kieran Kavanaugh & Otilio Rodriguez. LC 75-31305. 560p. 1980. pap. 6.95x (ISBN 0-9600876-6-4). ICS Pubns.

Collected Works of St. Teresa of Avila, Vol. 3. Tr. by Kieran Kavanaugh & Otilio Rodriguez. LC 75-31305. (Illus.). 504p. (Orig.). 1985. pap. 7.95x (ISBN 0-935216-06-5). ICS Pubns.

Collected Works of Spinoza, Vol. I. Baruch Spinoza. Ed. by Edwin Curley. LC 84-11716. (Illus.). 720p. 1985. text ed. 45.00x (ISBN 0-691-07222-1). Princeton U Pr.

Collected Writings, 35 vols. J. N. Darby. Set. 125.00 (ISBN 0-88172-055-0); 4.00 ea. Believers Bkshelf.

Collected Writings of H. P. Blavatsky, Vols. 1-11. Helena P. Blavatsky. Incl. Vol. 1. 1874-1878. rev. ed. 16.50 (ISBN 0-8356-0082-3); Vol. 2. 1879-1880 (ISBN 0-8356-0091-2); Vol. 3. 1881-1882 (ISBN 0-8356-0099-8); Vol. 4. 1882-1883 (ISBN 0-8356-0106-4); Vol. 5. 1883 (ISBN 0-8356-0117-X); Vol. 6. 1883-1884-1885 (ISBN 0-8356-0125-0); Vol. 7. 1886-1887 (ISBN 0-8356-0222-2); Vol. 8. 1887 (ISBN 0-8356-7166-6); Vol. 9. 1888 (ISBN 0-8356-0217-6); Vol. 10. 1888-1889 (ISBN 0-8356-0218-4); Vol. 11. 1889. 16.50 (ISBN 0-686-86789-0). (Illus.). 16.50 ea. Theos Pub Hse.

Collected Writings of John Murray: Claims of Truth, Vol. 1. John Murray. 374p. 1976. 22.95 (ISBN 0-85151-241-0). Banner of Truth.

Collected Writings of John Murray: Lectures in Systematic Theology, Vol. 2. John Murray. 1978. 24.95 (ISBN 0-85151-242-9). Banner of Truth.

Collected Writings of John Murray: Studies in Theology, Vol. 4. John Murray. 390p. 1983. 24.95 (ISBN 0-85151-340-9). Banner of Truth.

Collected Writings of John Murray: The Claims of Truth, 4 vols. John Murray. 1976. Set. 88.95 (ISBN 0-85151-396-4). Banner of Truth.

Collected Writings of John Murray, Vol. 3: To Serve the Living God. 24.95 (ISBN 0-85151-337-9). Banner of Truth.

Collected Writings of S. R. Hirsch, Vol. 4: Commentary on Isaiah & Additional Commentary on Psalms. 1986. 15.75 (ISBN 0-87306-950-1). Feldheim.

Collected Writings of Samson Raphael Hirsch, Vol. III: Jewish Symbolism. Ed. by Joseph Breuer Foundation. (Hirsch Heritage Ser.). Tr. of Gessamelte Schriften. 260p. 1984. 15.75 (ISBN 0-87306-924-2). Feldheim.

Collected Writings of Samson Raphael Hirsch, Vol. I: The Jewish Year, Nissan-Av. Ed. by Joseph Brever Foundation. (Hirsch Heritage). Tr. of Gessamelte Schriften. 391p. 1984. 15.75 (ISBN 0-87306-364-3). Feldheim.

Collected Writings of Samson Raphael Hirsch, Vol. 2: The Jewish Year, Elul-Adar. S. R. Hirsch. (Hirsch Heritage Ser.). 1985. 15.75 (ISBN 0-87306-951-X). Feldheim.

Collection: A Study in Paul's Strategy. Keith Nickle. LC 66-72379. (Studies in Biblical Theology: No. 48). 1966. pap. 10.00x (ISBN 0-8401-3048-1). A R Allenson.

Collection of Fifty-Five Dramatic Illustrations in Full Colours of the Cathedral Cities of Italy. Hermann Collingswood. (Masterpieces of World Architectual Library). (Illus.). 107p. 1983. Repr. of 1911 ed. 287.75 (ISBN 0-89901-081-4). Found Class Reprints.

Collection of Many Christian Experiences, Sentences, & Several Places of Scripture Improved. Clement Hall. xxv, 51p. 1961. Repr. of 1753 ed. 5.00 (ISBN 0-86526-019-2). NC Archives.

Collection of Millennial Hymns Adapted to the Present Order of the Church. Shakers. LC 72-2991. (Communal Societies in America Ser). Repr. of 1847 ed. 21.50 (ISBN 0-404-10753-2). AMS Pr.

Collection of Several Philosophical Writings, 2 vols. 2nd ed. Henry More. Ed. by Rene Wellek. LC 75-11238. (British Philosophers & Theologians of the 17th & 18th Centuries Ser.). 839p. 1978. Set. lib. bdg. 101.00 (ISBN 0-8240-1790-0). Garland Pub.

Collection of Several Pieces, 2 vols. John Toland. Ed. by Rene Wellek. LC 75-11258. (British Philosophers & Theologians of the 17th & 18th Centuries: Vol. 57). 1976. Repr. of 1726 ed. Set. lib. bdg. 101.00 (ISBN 0-8240-1808-7). Garland Pub.

Collection of the Laws & Canons of the Church of England: Theological Works, 4 Vols. John Johnson. LC 72-1032. (Library of Anglo-Catholic Theology: No. 10). Repr. of 1851 ed. Set. 115.00 (ISBN 0-404-52110-X). AMS Pr.

Collection of the Qur'an. John Burton. LC 76-27899. 1977. 49.50 (ISBN 0-521-21439-4); pap. 15.95 (ISBN 0-521-29652-8). Cambridge U Pr.

Collections of Selected Pamphlets. W. Kelly. pap. text ed. 6.95 (ISBN 0-88172-093-3). Believers Bkshelf.

Collections Upon the Lives of the Reformers & Most Eminent Ministers of the Church of Scotland, 2 Vols. in 3 Pts. Robert Wodrow. LC 70-178317. (Maitland Club, Glasgow. Publications: No. 32). Repr. of 1848 ed. Set. 105.00 (ISBN 0-404-52993-3). AMS Pr.

Collectors' Guide to Judaica. Jay Weinstein. (Illus.). 1985. 29.95 (ISBN 0-500-23440-X). Thames Hudson.

College Goes to School. facs. ed. Saint Mary's College - Holy Cross - Indiana. LC 68-58811. (Essay Index Reprint Ser). 1945. 15.00 (ISBN 0-8369-0125-8). Ayer Co Pubs.

College Yiddish; An Introduction to the Yiddish Language & to Jewish Life & Culture. 5th ed. Uriel Weinreich. LC 76-88208. 399p. 1979. 15.00 (ISBN 0-914512-04-8). Yivo Inst.

Colleges in Controversy: The Jesuit Schools in France from Revival to Suppression, 1815-1880. John W. Padberg. LC 75-78523. (Historical Studies: No. 83). 1969. text ed. 22.50x (ISBN 0-674-14160-1). Harvard U Pr.

Collegeville Bible Commentary Series, 11 Vols. Ed. by Robert J. Karris. 1983. Set. pap. 28.00. Liturgical Pr.

Collier Tracts 1698: Immorality of the English Pulpit. Bd. with Letter to A. H. Esq. Concerning the Stage. Charles Hopkins; Letter to Mr. Congreve on His Pretended Amendments; Occasional Paper. Richard Willis; Some Remarks Upon Mr. Collier's Defence of His Short View of the English Stage; Vindication of the Stage. LC 76-170453. (English Stage Ser.: Vol. 27). 1973. lib. bdg. 61.00 (ISBN 0-8240-0610-0). Garland Pub.

Collins Guide to Cathedrals, Abbeys & Priories of England & Wales. Henry Thorold. (Illus.). 332p. 1987. 24.95 (ISBN 0-00-217241-0). Salem Hse Pubs.

Colloquium of the Seven About Secrets of the Sublime. Jean Bodin. Tr. & intro. by Marion L. Daniels. LC 73-2453. 480p. 1975. 63.00x (ISBN 0-691-07193-4). Princeton U Pr.

Colloquy on Christian Education. Ed. by John H. Westerhoff. LC 72-4258. 1979. pap. 5.95 (ISBN 0-8298-0365-3). Pilgrim NY.

Colloquy on Christian Education. Ed. by John H. Westerhoff, 3rd. LC 72-4258. 1972. 6.95 (ISBN 0-8298-0238-X). Pilgrim NY.

Colloquy on New Testament Studies: A Time for Reappraisal & Fresh Approaches. Ed. by Bruce C. Corley. LC 83-8192. xiv, 370p. 1983. 21.50 (ISBN 0-86554-082-9, H54). Mercer Univ Pr.

Cologne Mani Codex. Tr. by Ron Cameron & Arthur J. Dewey. LC 79-14743. (Society of Biblical Literature Texts & Translations, 15. Early Christian Literature Ser.: No. 3). 1979. pap. 8.95 (ISBN 0-89130-312-X, 060215). Scholars Pr GA.

Colonia Baron Hirsch: A Jewish Agricultural Colony in Argentina. Morton D. Winsberg. LC 64-63523. (University of Florida Social Sciences Monographs: No. 19). 1963. pap. 3.50 (ISBN 0-8130-0259-1). U Presses Fla.

Colonial Baptists & Southern Revivals: An Original Anthology. William L. Lumpkin & Lyman Butterfield. Ed. by Edwin S. Gaustad. LC 79-52585. (Baptist Tradition Ser.). 1980. lib. bdg. 25.50x (ISBN 0-405-12452-X). Ayer Co Pubs.

Colonial Baptists: Massachusetts & Rhode Island. original anthology ed. John Clarke & William G. McLoughlin. Ed. by Edwin S. Gaustad. LC 79-52586. (Baptist Tradition Ser.). 1980. lib. bdg. 17.00x (ISBN 0-405-12453-8). Ayer Co Pubs.

Colonial Churches of Virginia, Maryland, & North Carolina. Vernon P. Davis & James S. Rawlings. 1985. pap. 25.00 (ISBN 0-87517-057-9). Dietz.

Colonial Clergy of Maryland, Delaware & Georgia. Frederick L. Weis. LC 77-93959. 104p. 1978. Repr. of 1950 ed. 10.00 (ISBN 0-8063-0800-1). Genealog Pub.

Colonial Evangelism: A Socio-Historical Study of an East African Mission at the Grassroots. T. O. Beidelman. LC 81-47771. (Midland Bks. Ser.: No. 278). (Illus.). 296p. 1982. 29.95x (ISBN 0-253-31386-4); pap. 12.50x (ISBN 0-253-20278-7). Ind U Pr.

Colonial Parson of New England. Frank S. Child. LC 74-19532. 1974. Repr. of 1896 ed. 35.00x (ISBN 0-8103-3667-7). Gale.

Colonial Williamsburg Decorates for Christmas. Libby H. Oliver et al. LC 81-10103. (Illus.). 80p. 1981. 11.95 (ISBN 0-03-060403-6). H Holt & Co.

Colonialism & After: An Algerian Jewish Community. Elizabeth Friedman. (Critical Studies in Work & Community). 288p. 1987. text ed. 34.95 (ISBN 0-89789-095-7). Bergin & Garvey.

Colonialism, Catholicism, & Contraception: A History of Birth Control in Puerto Rico. Annette B. Ramirez de Arellano & Conrad Seipp. LC 82-13646. xiv, 219p. 1983. 25.00x (ISBN 0-8078-1544-6). U of NC Pr.

Colonization & Christianity: A Popular History of the Treatment of the Natives by the Europeans in All Their Colonies. William Howitt. LC 70-76856. Repr. of 1838 ed. 22.75x (ISBN 0-8371-1162-5, HOC&, Pub. by Negro U Pr). Greenwood.

Color & the Edgar Cayce Readings. Roger Lewis. 48p. 1973. pap. 3.50 (ISBN 0-87604-068-7). Are Pr.

Color Book. Illus. by Marc Harrison. (Bible Look 'N Learn Bks.). (Illus.). 24p. 1985. bds. 3.95 (ISBN 0-8407-6687-4). Nelson.

Color Me Christian. Daisy Hepburn. LC 83-24624. (Life with Spice Bible Study Ser.). 1984. 2.95 (ISBN 0-8307-0949-5, 6101867). Regal.

Color Me Happy: It's Rosh Hashannah & Yom Kippur. Norman Geller. (Illus.). 36p. 1986. pap. 2.50 (ISBN 0-915753-10-3). N Geller Pub.

Color Me Kosher for Passover. Norman Geller. (Illus.). 23p. 1985. pap. 1.00 (ISBN 0-915753-06-5). N Geller Pub.

Color Me...Cuddly! Carolyn Owens. (Illus.). 32p. 1982. pap. 0.99 (ISBN 0-87123-695-8, 220695). Bethany Hse.

Color of God: The Concept of God in Afro-American Religious Thought. Major J. Jones. 160p. 1987. 24.95 (ISBN 0-86554-274-0, H237); pap. 14.95 (ISBN 0-86554-276-7). Mercer Univ Pr.

Color of the Air: Scenes from the Life of an American Jew, Vol. 1. John Sanford. 305p. (Orig.). 1985. 20.00 (ISBN 0-87685-644-X); pap. 12.50 (ISBN 0-87685-643-1). Black Sparrow.

Color of the Night: Reflections on the Book of Job. Gerhard E. Frost. LC 77-72458. 1977. pap. 5.95 (ISBN 0-8066-1583-4, 10-1520). Augsburg.

Colored Lady Evangelist, Being the Life, Labors, & Experiences of Mrs. Harriet A. Baker. John H. Acornley. Ed. by Carolyn G. De Swarte & Donald Dayton. (Women in American Protestant Religion Series 1800-1930). 78p. 1987. lib. bdg. 20.00 (ISBN 0-8240-0652-6). Garland Pub.

Colored Man in the Methodist Episcopal Church. facs. ed. L. M. Hagood. LC 77-149868. (Black Heritage Library Collection Ser). 1890. 19.50 (ISBN 0-8369-8631-8). Ayer Co Pubs.

Colored Man in the Methodist Episcopal Church. Lewis M. Hagood. LC 73-111577. Repr. of 1890 ed. cancelled (ISBN 0-8371-4602-X, HCM&, Pub. by Negro U Pr). Greenwood.

Coloring the Electric Church-Black Religious Broadcaster: A Selected Annotated Bibliography. Edna M. Brown & George H. Hill. 60p. 1987. 15.00X (ISBN 0-933650-31-0); pap. text ed. 7.00 (ISBN 0-933650-30-2). Daystar Co Carson.

Colors. Barbara Gregorich. Ed. by Joan Hoffman. (Get Ready! Bk.). (Illus.). 32p. 1983. pap. text ed. 1.95 (ISBN 0-938256-64-5). Sch Zone Pub Co.

Colors of Christmas. Robert A. Kramer. (Orig.). 1980. pap. 1.75 (ISBN 0-937172-07-3). JLJ Pubs.

Colors of Christmas. H. Michael Nehls. Ed. by Michael L. Sherer. (Orig.). 1986. pap. 3.95 (ISBN 0-89536-838-2, 6862). CSS of Ohio.

Colossian & Philemon Studies. H. C. G. Moule. 1981. 12.00 (ISBN 0-86524-052-3, 7106). Klock & Klock.

Colossians. rev. ed. G. Michael Cocoris. 35p. 1985. pap. 1.00 (ISBN 0-935729-05-4). Church Open Door.

Colossians. John Eadie. 1981. 10.50 (ISBN 0-86524-067-1, 5103). Klock & Klock.

Colossians. Everett Harrison. (Everyman's Bible Commentary Ser). 128p. (Orig.). 1971. pap. 5.95 (ISBN 0-8024-2051-6). Moody.

Colossians. Roy L. Laurin. 192p. 1987. pap. 9.95 (ISBN 0-8254-3135-2). Kregel.

Colossians. Handley Moule. 1975. pap. 4.95 (ISBN 0-87508-361-7). Chr Lit.

Colossians. W. R. Nicholson. LC 73-81742. 284p. 1973. 7.95 (ISBN 0-8254-3301-0); pap. 5.95 (ISBN 0-8254-3300-2). Kregel.

Colossians. Patrick V. Rogers. (New Testament Message Ser.: Vol. 15). 10.95 (ISBN 0-89453-138-7); pap. 5.95 (ISBN 0-89453-203-0). M Glazier.

Colossians, Pt. 1. rev. ed. G. Michael Cocoris. 41p. 1985. pap. text ed. 1.00 (ISBN 0-935729-04-6). Church Open Door.

Colossians: A Letter to Asia. Frederick B. Westcott. 1981. lib. bdg. 7.50 (ISBN 0-86524-070-1, 5102). Klock & Klock.

Colossians & Philemon. Keith L. Brooks. (Teach Yourself the Bible Ser.). 81p. (Orig.). 1961. pap. 2.75 (ISBN 0-8024-1525-3). Moody.

Colossians & Philemon. (Erdmans Commentaries Ser.). 3.50 (ISBN 0-8010-3393-4). Baker Bk.

Colossians & Philemon. Irving L. Jensen. (Bible Self-Study Ser.). 80p. 1973. pap. 3.25 (ISBN 0-8024-1052-9). Moody.

Colossians & Philemon. Eduard Lohse. Ed. by Helmut Koester. Tr. by William R. Poehlman & Robert J. Karris. LC 76-157550. (Hermeneia: A Critical & Historical Commentary on the Bible Ser). 256p. 1971. 22.95 (ISBN 0-8006-6001-3, 20-6001). Fortress.

Colossians & Philemon. rev. ed. Ralph P. Martin. (New Century Bible Commentary Ser.). 192p. 1981. pap. 5.95 (ISBN 0-8028-1908-7). Eerdmans.

Colossians & Philemon. Geoffrey B. Wilson. (Wilson'a New Testament Commentaries). 111p. (Orig.). 1980. pap. 4.95 (ISBN 0-85151-313-1). Banner of Truth.

Colossians & Philemon: A Runaway Church & a Runaway Slave. Jim Townsend. (Bible Mastery Ser.). 144p. 1987. pap. 5.95 (ISBN 1-55513-849-7). Cook.

Colossians & Philemon: A Study Guide Commentary. Curtis Vaughan. (Study Guide Commentary Ser.). 144p. (Orig.). 1981. pap. 4.95 (ISBN 0-310-33583-3, 10965P). Zondervan.

Colossians as Pseudepigraphy. Mark Kiley. (Biblical Seminar Ser.: No. 4). 240p. 1986. pap. text ed. 11.95x (ISBN 1-85075-024-6, Pub. by JSOT Pr England). Eisenbrauns.

Colossians: Focus on Christ. Luci Shaw. (Fisherman Bible Studyguide). 56p. 1982. saddle-stitched 2.95 (ISBN 0-87788-132-4). Shaw Pubs.

Colossians, Philemon, Ephesians. Arthur G. Patzia. LC 83-48996. (Good News Commentary Ser.). 256p. (Orig.). 1984. pap. 8.95 (ISBN 0-06-066479-7, RD 506). Har-Row.

Colossians: The Church's Lord & the Christian's Liberty. Ralph P. Martin. 192p. 1972. 8.95 (ISBN 0-85364-125-0). Attic Pr.

Colour Meditations. S. G. Ouseley. 96p. 1981. pap. 3.50 (ISBN 0-85243-062-0). Ariel OH.

Colour Terms in the Old Testament. Athalya Brenner. (Journal for the Study of the Old Testament, Supplement Ser.: No. 21). 296p. 1983. text ed. 29.95x (ISBN 0-905774-42-6, Pub. by JSOT Pr England); pap. text ed. 21.95 (ISBN 0-905774-43-4, Pub. by JSOT Pr England). Eisenbrauns.

Colporteur Ministry. Ellen G. White. 1953. 3.25 (ISBN 0-8163-0110-7, 03431-4); pap. 5.95 (ISBN 0-8163-0111-5, 03430-6). Pacific Pr Pub Assn.

Columbus Roberts: Christian Steward Extraordinary. Spright Dowell. LC 83-887. xvi, 171p. 13.95 (ISBN 0-86554-071-3, H67). Mercer Univ Pr.

Combat Faith. Hal Lindsey. 256p. (Orig.). 1986. pap. 7.95 (ISBN 0-553-34342-4). Bantam.

Combat Manual for Spiritual Warfare. (Aglow Prayer Diary: No. 2). 217p. 1983. pap. 10.95 3-ring notebook (ISBN 0-930756-81-9, 531015). Aglow Pubns.

Combat Tai Chi. A. C. Lum. 11.95x (ISBN 0-685-63750-6). Wehman.

Combined Chronology for Use with the Mahatma Letters to A. P. Sinnett & the Letters of H. P. Blavatsky to A. P. Sinnett. Margaret Conger. LC 73-92461. 1973. pap. 3.00 (ISBN 0-911500-17-0). Theos U Pr.

Combined Concordances to the Scriptures. Arthur E. Starks. 1978. 33.00 (ISBN 0-8309-0255-4). Herald Hse.

Come Alive. Frances Hunter. 1975. pap. 4.95 (ISBN 0-917726-34-0). Hunter Bks.

Come & Celebrate: More Center Celebrations. Beverly Valenti-Hilliard & Richard Hilliard. LC 85-72456. (Illus.). 184p. (Orig.). 1985. tchr's guidebook 9.95 (ISBN 0-87793-289-1). Ave Maria.

Come & Live. Tom C. McKenney. LC 84-242781. (Illus.). 167p. 1982. pap. 5.95 (ISBN 0-934527-01-6). Words Living Minis.

Come & Live. Tom C. McKenney. LC 84-242781. (Illus.). 167p. (Orig.). 1981. pap. 3.95 (ISBN 0-934527-00-8). Words Living Minis.

Come & Welcome to Jesus Christ. John Bunyan. 1974. pap. 2.50 (ISBN 0-685-52815-4). Reiner.

Come as You Are. Lois W. Johnson. LC 82-70951. 112p. (Orig.). 1982. pap. 3.95 (ISBN 0-8066-1926-0, 10-1517). Augsburg.

Come Away, My Beloved. Frances J. Roberts. 1970. 9.95 (ISBN 0-932814-01-8); pap. 6.95 (ISBN 0-932814-02-6). Kings Farspan.

Come Before Winter & Share my Hope. Charles R. Swindoll. LC 85-11590. 352p. 1985. 14.95 (ISBN 0-88070-110-2). Multnomah.

Come Celebrate: A Daily Devotional. Aglow Editors. 266p. 1984. pap. 6.95 (ISBN 0-930756-78-9, 531018). Aglow Pubns.

Come Closer to Me, God! Donald L. Deffner. 1982. pap. 4.95 (ISBN 0-570-03851-0, 12-2806). Concordia.

Come Dejar Que Dios Te Ayude. Myrtle Fillmore. Tr. of How to Let God Help You. 1984. 5.95 (ISBN 0-87159-019-0). Unity School.

Come Follow Me. Glenn Clark. 4.95 (ISBN 0-910924-04-X). Macalester.

Come Follow Me, Vol. III. Bhagwan Shree Rajneesh. Ed. by Swami Deva Paritosh. LC 80-8343. (Jesus Ser.). (Illus.). 272p. (Orig.). 1976. 12.95 (ISBN 0-88050-036-0). Chidvilas Found.

Come Follow Me, Vol. IV. Bhagwan Shree Rajneesh. Ed. by Ma Yoga Sudha. LC 80-8343. (Jesus Ser.). (Illus.). 286p. (Orig.). 1977. 12.95 (ISBN 0-88050-037-9). Chidvilas Found.

Come Follow Me, Vol. II. Bhagwan Shree Rajneesh. Ed. by Ma Satya Bharti. LC 80-8343. (Jesus Ser.). (Illus.). 316p. (Orig.). 1977. 12.95 (ISBN 0-88050-035-2). Chidvilas Found.

Come Follow Me, Vol. I. Bhagwan Shree Rajneesh. Ed. by Ma Satya Bharti. LC 80-8343. (Jesus Ser.). (Illus.). 292p. (Orig.). 1976. 12.95 (ISBN 0-88050-034-4). Chidvilas Found.

Come Follow Me. Rachael I. Scruggs. LC 80-52620. 142p. 1983. 7.95 (ISBN 0-533-04769-2). Vantage.

Come Follow Me: A Study Book for Acolytes. Edwin B. Womack. 1982. pap. 6.45 (ISBN 0-89536-536-7, 0348). CSS of Ohio.

Come Help Change Our World. Bill Bright. LC 79-53543. 1979. 8.95 (ISBN 0-918956-01-3). Campus Crusade.

Come Holy Spirit. Nevin Feather & Myrtle Collins. 1986. 4.75 (ISBN 0-89536-790-4, 6808). CSS of Ohio.

Come Holy Spirit-I Need Thee. Grace E. Gresk. 48p. 1985. 5.95 (ISBN 0-533-06177-6). Vantage.

Come, Journey with Me: A Personal Story of Conversion & Ordination. Russell C. Packard. LC 84-24356. 208p. (Orig.). 1984. pap. 8.00 (ISBN 0-89571-021-8). Affirmation.

Come, Let Us Celebrate. Francoise Darcy-Berube & John-Paul Berube. 64p. 1984. 3.95 (ISBN 0-7773-8007-2, 8514, HarpR). Har-Row.

Come Let Us Change This World. 4th ed. Abul Ala Maudoodi. Intro. by & tr. by Kaukab Siddique. 151p. 1983. pap. 2.00 (ISBN 0-942978-05-6). Am Soc Ed & Rel.

Come, Let Us Praise Him. Ed. by James R. Hawkinson. 1985. pap. 3.95 (ISBN 0-910452-57-1). Covenant.

Come, Let Us Sing a Song Unknown. Charles De Foucauld. 2.95 (ISBN 0-87193-080-3). Dimension Bks.

Come, Let Us Welcome Jesus. Janice B. Wyatt. 1980. pap. 3.75 (ISBN 0-89536-411-5, 0375). CSS of Ohio.

Come Let Us Welcome Shabbat. Judyth R. Saypol & Madeline Wikler. LC 83-25638. (Illus.). 32p. 1978. pap. 2.95 (ISBN 0-930494-04-0). Kar Ben.

Come, Let Us Worship. James R. Spruce. 118p. 1986. pap. 3.95 (ISBN 0-8341-1028-8). Beacon Hill.

Come, Let Us Worship God: A Handbook of Prayers for Leaders of Worship. David M. Currie. LC 77-6808. 132p. 1977. softcover 4.25 (ISBN 0-664-24757-1). Westminster.

Come, Lord Jesus. Mark Cambron. pap. 1.45 (ISBN 0-686-12745-5). Grace Pub Co.

Come, Lord Jesus. Watchman Nee. Tr. by Stephen Kaung. 1976. 5.50 (ISBN 0-935008-15-2); pap. 4.25 (ISBN 0-935008-16-0). Christian Fellow Pubs.

Come Mime with Me: Ten Liturgical Dramas for Children. Gail Kelley & Carol Hershberger. LC 86-62621. 100p. 1987. 11.95 (ISBN 0-89390-089-3). Resource Pubns.

Come on into My House. Judy Segraves. Ed. by Mary Wallace. (Illus.). 90p. (Orig.). 1985. pap. 4.95 (ISBN 0-912315-87-3). Word Aflame.

Come September. Cheryl Hoversten. 1984. 5.95 (ISBN 0-89536-961-3, 7512). CSS of Ohio.

Come Sing God's Song. Thomas P. Thigpen. (Illus.). 1987. 7.95. Cook.

Come Sing with Me. Margaret C. McNeil. 1971. pap. 2.95 (ISBN 0-8170-0535-8); bk. & record o.p. 5.95 (ISBN 0-685-01111-9). Judson.

Come Sit with Me Again: Sermons for Children. Don-Paul Benjamin & Ron Miner. (Illus.). 128p. (Orig.). 1987. pap. 6.95 (ISBN 0-8298-0748-9). Pilgrim NY.

Come Sit with Me: Sermons for Children. Ron Miner. LC 81-10650. (Illus.). 96p. (Orig.). 1981. pap. 5.95 (ISBN 0-8298-0469-2). Pilgrim NY.

Come Songbook. Gary L. Johnson. 1980. pap. 2.50 (ISBN 0-87123-777-6, 280777). Bethany Hse.

Come Sweet Death. rev. ed. B. Davie Napier. LC 80-27301. 64p. 1981. pap. 4.95 (ISBN 0-8298-0422-6). Pilgrim NY.

Come Sweet Death: A Quintet from Genesis. B. Davie Napier. LC 67-17793. 96p. 1975. 2 rec album 11.95 (ISBN 0-8298-0375-0). Pilgrim NY.

Come to Me! Tom Wells. 128p. (Orig.). 1986. pap. 3.45 (ISBN 0-85151-471-5). Banner of Truth.

Come to School. Jacqueline Paschos & Francoise Destang. (Rejoice Ser.). pap. 0.35 (ISBN 0-8091-6505-8). Paulist Pr.

Come to the Banquet. Ed. by Ginny Cole & Carolyn Durfey. 200p. 1983. pap. text ed. 7.00 (ISBN 0-913991-00-7). Off Christian Fellowship.

Come to the Mountain: The Comtemporary Experience of Prayer. Stan Parmisano. LC 86-70254. 96p. (Orig.). 1986. pap. 4.95 (ISBN 0-87793-337-5). Ave Maria.

Come to the Waters. Diane Head. 96p. 1985. pap. 5.95 (ISBN 0-310-25941-X, 9586P). Zondervan.

Come unto Christ. Ezra T. Benson. 136p. 1984. 8.95 (ISBN 0-87747-997-6). Deseret Bk.

Come unto Christ. Duane S. Crowther. LC 70-173393. (Scripture Guide Ser.). 240p. 1971. pap. 5.95 (ISBN 0-88290-007-2). Horizon Utah.

Come unto Me. Mildred Spires Jacobs. (Illus.). 56p. (Orig.). 1982. pap. 2.95 (ISBN 0-9609612-0-8). Enrich Enter.

Come Worship with Us: Explaining the Mass. Frank Buckley. 32p. 1987. pap. 1.95 (ISBN 0-89243-263-2). Liguori Pubns.

Come Ye Apart. J. R. Miller. 4.95 (ISBN 0-317-12209-6). AMG Pubs.

Come Ye Children. C. H. Spurgeon. 1979. pap. 2.95 (ISBN 0-686-16840-2). Pilgrim Pubns.

Comenius & the Beginnings of Educational Reform. Will S. Monroe. LC 78-135824. (Eastern Europe Collection Ser). 1970. Repr. of 1900 ed. 13.50 (ISBN 0-405-02765-6). Ayer Co Pubs.

Comenius in England: The Visit of Jan Amos Komensky Comenius, Czech Philosopher & Educationalist, to London in 1641-1642. Robert F. Young. LC 70-135838. (Eastern Europe Collection Ser). 1970. Repr. of 1932 ed. 12.00 (ISBN 0-405-02780-X). Ayer Co Pubs.

Comentario Arqueologico de la Biblia. Gonzalo Baez-Camargo. (Span.). 339p. (Orig.). 1979. pap. 7.95 (ISBN 0-89922-148-3). Edit Caribe.

Comentario Biblico Efesios. Curtis Vaughan. Orig. Title: Ephesians. (Port.). 1986. write for info. (ISBN 0-8297-1608-4). Life Pubs Intl.

Comentario Biblico Moody: Nuevo Testamento. Everett F. Harrison. Orig. Title: Wycliffe Bible Commentary: N. T. (Span.). 568p. 1965. 16.95 (ISBN 0-8254-1307-9). Kregel.

Comentario de las Epistoles Generales. (Span.). 194p. 1986. pap. 3.50 (ISBN 0-939125-31-5). Evangelical Lit.

Comentario Exegetico y Explicativo de la Biblia Tomo II. Jamieson-Fausett Brown. Tr. by Jaime C. Quarles & Lemuel C. Quarles. 382p. 1982. Repr. of 1959 ed. 15.75 (ISBN 0-311-03004-1). Casa Bautista.

Comfort & Protest. Allan A. Boesak. LC 86-28076. 120p. (Orig.). 1987. pap. 7.95 (ISBN 0-664-24602-8). Westminster.

Comfort Food: Ninety-Five Recipes to Nourish the Soul As Well As the Body. Sue Kreitzman. 96p. 1985. pap. 6.95 (ISBN 0-517-55939-0, Harmony). Crown.

Comfort for Christians. Arthur W. Pink. (Summit Bks.). 122p. 1976. pap. 2.95 (ISBN 0-8010-7062-7). Baker Bk.

Comfort for Christians. Arthur W. Pink. pap. 3.95 (ISBN 0-685-19825-1). Reiner.

Comfort for the Sick. rev. ed. B. P. Nommensen. 1976. pap. 5.00 (ISBN 0-8100-0011-3, 06N0553). Northwest Pub.

Comfort for the Sorrowing. William Goulooze. pap. 0.45 (ISBN 0-686-23474-X). Rose Pub MI.

Comfort for Those Who Mourn. Compiled by O. V. Armstrong. LC 77-17182. pap. 20.00 (ISBN 0-8357-9003-7, 2016353). Bks Demand UMI.

Comfort for Troubled Christians. J. C. Brumfield. (Moody Acorn Ser.). 1975. pap. 7.95 package of 10 (ISBN 0-8024-1400-1). Moody.

Comfort for Troubled Hearts. John MacArthur, Jr. (John MacArthur's Bible Studies). (Orig.). 1986. pap. 3.95 (ISBN 0-8024-5342-2). Moody.

Comfort: Prayers & Promises for Times of Sorrow. John M. Robertson. 1977. pap. 2.95 (ISBN 0-8423-0432-0). Tyndale.

Comfort Ye My People: Messages of Comfort for the Bereaved. Cornelius Oldenburg. (Solace Ser.). 1983. pap. 1.25 (ISBN 0-8010-6704-9). Baker Bk.

Comforter. C. H. Spurgeon. 1978. pap. 0.95 (ISBN 0-686-26194-1). Pilgrim Pubns.

Comforting the Bereaved. Warren W. Wiersbe & David W. Wiersbe. (Orig.). 1985. pap. 5.95 (ISBN 0-8024-5293-0). Moody.

Comforting Those Who Grieve. Cecil Murphey. LC 78-71052. 64p. 1979. pap. 1.00 (ISBN 0-8042-1099-3). John Knox.

Comforting Those Who Grieve: A Guide for Helping Others. Doug Manning. LC 84-48226. 112p. 1985. 10.45 (ISBN 0-06-065418-X, HarpR). Har-Row.

Comic Vision & the Christian Faith: A Celebration of Life & Laughter. Conrad Hyers. LC 81-5221. 96p. (Orig.). 1981. pap. 8.95 (ISBN 0-8298-0440-4). Pilgrim NY.

Coming Alive in the Spirit: The Spirit-led Life. Gerald Rowlands. (Basic Bible Study). Orig. Title: Holy Spirit & His Fruit. 64p. 1985. pap. 2.95 (ISBN 0-930756-90-8, 521019). Aglow Pubns.

Coming Antichrist. Walter K. Price. 240p. 1985. pap. 6.95 (ISBN 0-87213-695-7). Loizeaux.

Coming Back: The Science of Reincarnation. A. C. Bhaktivedanta. (Contemporary Vedic Library Ser.). (Illus.). 133p. 1982. 2.95 (ISBN 0-89213-114-4). Bhaktivedanta.

Coming Cataclysm: The Orthodox-Reform Rift & the Future of the Jewish People. Reuven P. Bulka. 160p. 1986. pap. 9.95 (ISBN 0-88962-275-2). Riverrun NY.

Coming Century of Peace. Mikail S. Gorbachev. Ed. by Stewart Richardson. 304p. 1986. 17.95 (ISBN 0-931933-22-6). Richardson & Steirman.

Coming Climax of History. Jim McKeever. 1983. 6.95 (ISBN 0-86694-099-5). Omega Pubns OR.

Coming Climax of History. Jim McKeever. 324p. 1983. 15.95 (ISBN 0-86694-098-7). Omega Pubns OR.

Coming Crisis in Israel: Private Faith & Public Policy. Norman L. Zucker. 1973. pap. 7.95x (ISBN 0-262-74012-5). MIT Pr.

Coming down from the Mountain. Frank A. Beattie, Jr. (Orig.). 1982. pap. 1.95 (ISBN 0-937172-38-3). JLJ Pubs.

Coming Events in Prophecy. Martin R. De Haan. 5.95 (ISBN 0-310-23301-1). Zondervan.

Coming Great Revival: Recovering the Full Evangelical Tradition. William J. Abraham. LC 84-47710. 160p. 1984. 12.45 (ISBN 0-06-060035-7, HarpR). Har-Row.

Coming Home. Catherine de Hueck Doherty. 3.95 (ISBN 0-87193-081-1). Dimension Bks.

Coming Home. Fred M. Wood. LC 86-20775. (Orig.). 1987. pap. 6.95 (ISBN 0-8054-1236-0). Broadman.

Coming Home: A Handbook for Exploring the Sanctuary Within. Betsy Caprio & Thomas Hedberg. (Illus.). 288p. (Orig.). 1986. pap. 9.95 (ISBN 0-8091-2739-3); director's manual 9.95 (ISBN 0-8091-2787-3). Paulist Pr.

Coming in Glory: Christ's Presence in the World Today. Martin Israel. 128p. 1986. pap. 7.95 (ISBN 0-8245-0785-1). Crossroad NY.

Coming into Being among the Australian Aborigines. Ashley Montagu. LC 75-41195. (Illus.). Repr. of 1937 ed. 27.45 (ISBN 0-404-14573-6). AMS Pr.

Coming Kingdom. C. C. Cribb. LC 77-70213. pap. 2.95 (ISBN 0-932046-04-5). Manhattan Ltd NC.

Coming Kingdom: Essays in American Millennialism & Eschatology. Ed. by M. Darrol Bryant & Donald W. Dayton. LC 83-82211. xii, 258p. 1984. text ed. 15.95 o. p. (ISBN 0-913757-01-2, Pub. by New Era Bks); pap. text ed. 11.95 (ISBN 0-913757-00-4, Pub. by New Era Bks). Paragon Hse.

Coming of Age in Judea: A Play about Young Jesus. Pamela Urfer. 20p. (Orig.). 1983. pap. text ed. 3.95 (ISBN 0-912801-03-4). Creat Arts Dev.

Coming of Age: Your Bar or Bat Mitzvah. Benjamin Efron & Alvan D. Rubin. LC 77-78031. (Illus.). 1977. 5.00 (ISBN 0-8074-0084-X, 142530). UAHC.

Coming of Consolation. William Sampson. (Orig.). 1986. pap. 8.95 (ISBN 0-87061-132-1). Chr Classics.

Coming of God. George R. Beasley-Murray. 64p. 1983. pap. 3.95 (ISBN 0-85364-350-4, Pub. by Paternoster UK). Attic Pr.

Coming of God. Maria Boulding. 224p. 1983. pap. text ed. 9.00 (ISBN 0-8146-1278-4). Liturgical Pr.

Coming of the Friars & Other Historic Essays. facsimile ed. Augustus Jessopp. (Select Bibliographies Reprint Ser). Repr. of 1892 ed. 21.00 (ISBN 0-8369-6696-1). Ayer Co Pubs.

Coming of the Kingdom. Herman N. Ribberbos. 1962. pap. 11.95 (ISBN 0-87552-408-7). Presby & Reformed.

Coming of the Pilgrims. E. Brooks Smith & Robert Meredith. 1964. 11.45 (ISBN 0-316-80048-1). Little.

Coming of the Russian Mennonites: An Episode in the Settling of the Last Frontier, 1874-1884. Charles H. Smith. 18.25 (ISBN 0-8369-7123-X, 7957). Ayer Co Pubs.

Coming of the Saints. rev. ed. John W. Taylor. LC 85-71651. (Illus.). 272p. 1985. pap. 10.00 (ISBN 0-934666-19-9). Artisan Sales.

Coming of the Saints: Imaginations & Studies in Early Church History & Tradition. John W. Taylor. 1977. lib. bdg. 59.95 (ISBN 0-8490-1647-9). Gordon Pr.

Coming of the Third Church: An Analysis of the Present & Future. Walbert Buhlmann. Ed. by Ralph Woodhall & A. N. Woodhall. LC 76-23237. Orig. Title: Kommt die dritte Kirche. 430p. 1977. pap. 9.95x (ISBN 0-88344-070-9). Orbis Bks.

Coming of Yahweh. Shirley M. Jones. (Illus.). 600p. 1985. 17.50 (ISBN 0-9615111-0-9). Sandbird Pub.

Coming One. Kurt E. Koch. LC 72-85597. 96p. 1974. pap. 2.95 (ISBN 0-8254-3011-9). Kregel.

Coming Out to Parents: A Two-Way Survival Guide for Lesbians & Gay Men & Their Parents. Mary V. Borhek. LC 83-3971. 224p. 1983. pap. 9.95 (ISBN 0-8298-0665-2). Pilgrim NY.

Coming Peace in the Middle East. Tim LaHaye. 208p. 1984. pap. 6.95 (ISBN 0-310-27031-6, 18341P). Zondervan.

Coming Restoration. Kenneth E. Hagin. 1985. mini bk. 0.50 (ISBN 0-89276-267-5). Hagin Ministries.

Coming Russian Invasion of Israel. Thomas S. McCall & Zola Levitt. 96p. 1976. pap. 4.95 (ISBN 0-8024-1607-1). Moody.

Coming Russian Invasion of Israel, Updated. Thoma S. McCall & Zola Levitt. 96p. 1987. pap. 4.95 (ISBN 0-8024-1624-1). Moody.

Coming to Faith in Christ. John Benton. 15p. 1977. pap. 0.80 (ISBN 0-85151-252-6). Banner of Truth.

Coming up Short in a Tall World. Kel Groseclose. (Illus.). 144p. 1984. pap. 3.95 (ISBN 0-87123-435-1). Bethany Hse.

Coming Victory. Tom Rose & Robert Metcalf. (Coronation Ser.: No. 5). 206p. (Orig.). 1980. pap. 6.95x (ISBN 0-686-28757-6). Chr Stud Ctr.

Coming World Dictator. John W. White. LC 80-71003. 119p. (Orig.). 1981. pap. 2.95 (ISBN 0-87123-042-9, 200042). Bethany Hse.

Comings of God: Meditations for the Advent Season. Richard S. Hanson. LC 81-65645. 128p. (Orig.). 1981. pap. 5.95 (ISBN 0-8066-1881-7, 10-1590). Augsburg.

Commanded to Live. Harold Kushner. LC 73-91738. 1973. 10.95x (ISBN 0-87677-154-1). Hartmore.

Commanding Power. Kenneth Hagin, Jr. 1985. pap. 0.50 (ISBN 0-317-40350-8). Hagin Ministries.

Commandments, 2 Vols. Maimonides. Set. 35.00x (ISBN 0-685-01042-2); pap. 25.00. Bloch.

Commandments & Promises of God. Bernard P. Brockbank. LC 82-23629. 667p. 1983. 15.95 (ISBN 0-87747-889-9). Deseret Bk.

Commandments for Christian Living. Douglas Beyer. 96p. 1983. pap. 5.95 (ISBN 0-8170-1008-4). Judson.

Commandments of Maimonides, 2 vols. Tr. by C. B. Chavel. 305p. 1967. 35.00 (ISBN 0-900689-71-4); pap. 25.00. Soncino Pr.

Commandments: Twenty-Eight Family Times to Respond in Love. Kathryn Fitzpatrick. (Familytime - Faithtime: A Home-Based Approach to Religious Education Ser.). (Illus.). 52p. (Orig.). 1982. pap. text ed. 3.50 (ISBN 0-86716-013-6). St Anthony Mess Pr.

Commemorative Essays Presented to Sir Ramakrishna Gopal Bhandarkar. Ramakrishna Gopala Bhanddarkar. LC 78-70111. Repr. of 1917 ed. 44.00 (ISBN 0-404-17366-7). AMS Pr.

Comment Je Crois. Pierre Teilhard De Chardin. 15.50 (ISBN 0-685-36585-9). French & Eur.

Comment Traduire la Bible. Eugene A. Nida. Tr. by J. C. Margot. 279p. 1967. pap. 4.05x (ISBN 0-8267-0024-1, 51970, Pub. by United Bible). Am Bible.

Commentaria. Johann Dobneck. 372p. 1549. text ed. 124.40x (ISBN 0-576-72201-4, Pub. by Gregg Intl Pubs England). Gregg Intl.

Commentarie upon the First & Second Chapters of Saint Paul to the Colossians. Paul Baynes. 396p. Repr. of 1635 ed. text ed. 74.52X (ISBN 0-576-99737-4, Pub. by Gregg Intl Pubs England). Gregg Intl.

Commentaries on A Course in Miracles. Tara Singh. LC 86-18350. (Orig.). 1986. 16.95 (ISBN 1-55531-015-X); pap. 12.95 (ISBN 1-55531-016-8). Life Action Pr.

Commentaries on Galatians, Philippians, Colossians & Philemon, 3 vols. J. B. Lightfoot. 1208p. 1981. 39.95 (ISBN 0-913573-02-7). Hendrickson MA.

Commentaries on Living, 3 Bks. 3 ser ed. Jiddu Krishnamurti. Ed. by D. Rajagopal. (Ser. 1, LC 67-8405; Ser. 2, LC 67-8407; Ser. 3, LC 67-8416). 1967. Ser. 1. pap. 4.75 (ISBN 0-8356-0390-3, Quest); Ser. 2. pap. 5.50 (ISBN 0-8356-0415-2); Ser. 3. pap. 5.50 (ISBN 0-8356-0402-0). Theos Pub Hse.

Commentaries on Living: 2nd Series. Ed. by D. Rajagopal. 1959. 14.95 (ISBN 0-575-00417-7, Pub. by Gollancz England). David & Charles.

Commentaries on Living: 3rd Series. Ed. by D. Rajagopal. 1961. 14.95 (ISBN 0-575-00229-8, Pub. by Gollancz England). David & Charles.

Commentaries on Romans Fifteen Thirty-Two to Fifteen Forty-Two. T. H. Parker. 250p. 1986. 25.50 (ISBN 0-567-09366-2, Pub. by T & T Clark Ltd Uk). Fortress.

Commentaries on the New Testament. Gospel Advocate. Incl. Matthew. H. Leo Boles (ISBN 0-89225-001-1); Mark. C. E. Dorris (ISBN 0-89225-002-X); Luke. H. Leo Boles (ISBN 0-89225-003-8); John. C. E. Dorris (ISBN 0-89225-004-6); Acts. H. Leo Boles (ISBN 0-89225-005-4); Romans. David Lipscomb & J. W. Shepherd (ISBN 0-89225-006-2); Corinthians I. David Lipscomb & J. W. Shepard (ISBN 0-89225-007-0); Corinthians II - Galatians. David Lipscomb & J. W. Shepherd (ISBN 0-89225-008-9); Ephesians - Colossians. J. W. Shepherd (ISBN 0-89225-009-7); Thess. I, II; Tim. I, II; Titus; Philomen. J. W. Shepherd (ISBN 0-89225-010-0); Hebrews. Robert Milligan (ISBN 0-89225-011-9); James. Guy N. Woods (ISBN 0-89225-012-7); Peter I, II; John I, II, III; Jude. Guy N. Woods (ISBN 0-89225-013-5); Revelation. John T. Hinds (ISBN 0-89225-014-3). Set. 135.00 (ISBN 0-89225-000-3); 10.95 ea. Gospel Advocate.

Commentaries on the Readings of the Lectionary: Cycles A, B, C. Robert Crotty & Gregory Manley. 1975. pap. 12.95 (ISBN 0-916134-20-2). Pueblo Pub Co.

Commentaries on the Readings of the Rites. Robert Crotty & John B. Ryan. (Orig.). 1982. pap. 12.95 (ISBN 0-916134-45-8). Pueblo Pub Co.

Commentaries on the Scriptures. Thomas Hora. 35p. 1987. pap. 4.00 (ISBN 0-913105-10-4). PAGL Pr.

Commentarius Cantabrigiensis in Epistolas Pauli e Schola Petri Abaelardi, 3 vols. Arthur Landgraf. Incl. Vol. 1. In Epistolam Ad Romanos. 223p. 1937. 17.95 (ISBN 0-268-00133-2); Vol. 2. In Epistolam Ad Corinthios Iam et Iiam, Ad Galatas et Ad Ephesios. 1223p. 1960. 17.95 (ISBN 0-268-00134-0); Vol. 3. In Epistolam ad Philippenses, ad Colossenses, ad Thessalonicenses Primam et Secundam, ed Timotheam Priman et Secundam, ad Titum et Philemonem. 447p. 1944. 17.95 (ISBN 0-268-00132-4). (Mediaeval Studies Ser.: No. 2). U of Notre Dame Pr.

Commentarius de Sacris Ecclesiae Ordinationibus. Jean Morin. 740p. Repr. of 1695 ed. text ed. 165.60 (ISBN 0-576-99716-1, Pub. by Gregg Intl Pubs England). Gregg Intl.

Commentarius de Scriptoribus Ecclesiae Antiquis Illorumque Scriptis. Casimir Oudin. 3296p. Date not set. Repr. of 1723 ed. text ed. 662.40x (ISBN 0-576-72229-4, Pub. by Gregg Intl Pubs England). Gregg Intl.

Commentarius Historicus de Disciplina in Administratione Sacramenti Poenitentiae. Jean Morin. 1020p. Repr. of 1682 ed. text ed. 248.40x (ISBN 0-576-99723-4, Pub. by Gregg Intl Pubs England). Gregg Intl.

Commentary John's Gospel, 2 vols. in 1. Frederic L. Godet. LC 78-59145. (Kregel Reprint Library). 1132p. 1980. Repr. of 1885 ed. 34.95 (ISBN 0-8254-2714-2). Kregel.

Commentary of Abraham Ibn Ezra on Hosea. Abe Lipshitz. 190p. 1987. 19.95 (ISBN 0-87203-127-6). Hermon.

Commentary of David Kimchi on Isaiah. David B. Kimchi. Ed. by Louis Finkelstein. LC 27-4417. (Columbia University. Oriental Studies: No. 19). Repr. of 1926 ed. 24.50 (ISBN 0-404-50509-0). AMS Pr.

Commentary of Ibn Ezra on Isaiah. Ibn Ezra. Tr. by Michael Friedlander. LC 66-15771. 1966. 15.00 (ISBN 0-87306-013-X). Feldheim.

Commentary of Jean-Paul Sartre's "Being & Nothingness". Joseph S. Catalano. LC 79-21234. xvi, 240p. 1985. pap. text ed. 15.00x (ISBN 0-226-09699-8). U of Chicago Pr.

Commentary of Rabbi David Kimchi on Hosea. David B. Kimchi. Ed. by Harry Cohen. LC 30-27876. (Columbia University. Oriental Studies: No. 20). Repr. of 1929 ed. 17.00 (ISBN 0-404-50510-4). AMS Pr.

Commentary of Rabbi David Kimhi on Psalms 120-150. Ed. by J. Baker & E. W. Nicholson. (Cambridge Oriental Publications Ser.: No. 22). 44.50 (ISBN 0-521-08670-1). Cambridge U Pr.

Commentary on Acts. James B. Coffman. (Firm Foundation Commentary Ser). 1976. cancelled 10.95 (ISBN 0-88027-069-1). Firm Foun Pub.

Commentary on Acts. McLaughlin. kivar 5.95 (ISBN 0-686-12858-3). Schmul Pub Co.

Commentary on "Catechesi Trandendae: The New Chsrter for Religious Education in Our Time. John Paul II. LC 80-26792. 243p. 1980. 4.50 (ISBN 0-8199-0815-0). Franciscan Herald.

Commentary on Daniel. Leon J. Wood. 320p. 1972. 16.95 (ISBN 0-310-34710-6, 10871). Zondervan.

Commentary on 'De Grammatico' The Historical-Logical Dimensions of a Dialogue of St. Anselm's. D. P. Henry. LC 73-86092. (Synthese Historical Library: No. 8). 200p. 1973. lib. bdg. 66.00 (ISBN 90-277-0382-5, Pub. by Reidel Holland). Kluwer Academic.

Commentary on Ephesians. J. Armitage Robinson. LC 78-59143. (Kregel Ltd Ed. Library). 320p. 1979. 14.95 (ISBN 0-8254-3612-5). Kregel.

Commentary on Epistle to the Hebrews. Brooke F. Westcott. (Gr). 1950. 14.95 (ISBN 0-8028-3289-X). Eerdmans.

Commentary on Exodus. James B. Coffman. 1986. 19.95 (ISBN 0-915547-49-X). Abilene Christ U.

Commentary on Exodus. J. P. Hyatt. Ed. by Ronald E. Clements. (New Century Bible Commentary Ser.). 1980. pap. 8.95 (ISBN 0-8028-1844-7). Eerdmans.

Commentary on First & Second Corinthians. F. F. Bruce. Ed. by Matthew Black. (New Century Bible Commentary Ser.). 224p. 1980. pap. 8.95 (ISBN 0-8028-1839-0). Eerdmans.

Commentary on First and Second Peter & Jude. Martin Luther. LC 82-4652. 320p. 1982. 12.95 (ISBN 0-8254-3125-5). Kregel.

Commentary on First & Second Thessalonians, I & II Timothy, Titus & Philemon. James B. Coffman. (Firm Foundation Commentary Ser.). 1978. 10.95 (ISBN 0-88027-073-X). Firm Foun Pub.

Commentary on First Corinthians. Frederic L. Godet. LC 77-79190. (Kregel Reprint Library). 928p. 1977. 29.95 (ISBN 0-8254-2716-9). Kregel.

Commentary on First Corinthians. Frederick W. Grosheide. (New International Commentary on the New Testament). 1953. 14.95 (ISBN 0-8028-2185-5). Eerdmans.

Commentary on First Peter. Robert Leighton. LC 74-165058. 512p. 16.95 (ISBN 0-8254-3103-4). Kregel.

Commentary on Galatians. Martin Luther. LC 78-59151. (Kregel Reprint Library). Orig. Title: Commentary on St. Paul's Epistle to the Galatians. 408p. 1979. 14.95 (ISBN 0-8254-3121-2). Kregel.

Commentary on Galatians, Ephesians, Phillipians, Colossians. James B. Coffman. (Firm Foundation Commentary Ser.). 1977. cancelled 10.95 (ISBN 0-88027-072-1). Firm Foun Pub.

Commentary on Genesis. James B. Coffman. 1986. 19.95 (ISBN 0-915547-48-1). Abilene Christ U.

Commentary on Genesis. W. Gunther Plaut. (Pardes Torah; Jewish Commentary on the Torah Ser.). 1974. 20.00 (ISBN 0-8074-0001-7, 381611). UAHC.

Commentary on Gospel According to St. John. Brooke F. Westcott. 1950. 7.95 (ISBN 0-8028-3288-1). Eerdmans.

Commentary on Hebrews. James B. Coffman. (Firm Foundation Commentary Ser.). 1971. cancelled 10.95 (ISBN 0-88027-074-8). Firm Foun Pub.

Commentary on Isaiah. Harry Bultema. LC 81-11795. 650p. 1981. 16.95 (ISBN 0-8254-2258-2). Kregel.

Commentary on Isaiah. Homer Hailey. 544p. 1985. 17.95 (ISBN 0-8010-4292-5). Baker Bk.

Commentary on James, First & Second; Peter, First, Second & Third, John, Jude. Burton Coffman. (Firm Foundation Commentary Ser.). 1979. cancelled 10.95 (ISBN 0-88027-075-6). Firm Foun Pub.

Commentary on James: New International Greek Testament Commentary. Peter Davids. 226p. 1982. 15.95 (ISBN 0-8028-2388-2). Eerdmans.

Commentary on Jeremiah & Lamentations. Anthony Ash. 500p. 1987. 16.95 (ISBN 0-915547-94-5). Abilene Christ U.

Commentary on Job. Samuel Cox. 562p. 1986. 18.95 (ISBN 0-8254-2328-7); pap. 14.95 (ISBN 0-8254-2330-9). Kregel.

Commentary on John. James B. Coffman. (Firm Foundation Commentary Ser.). 1974. cancelled 10.95 (ISBN 0-88027-068-3). Firm Foun Pub.

Commentary on Leviticus. Bernard J. Bamberger. Ed. by W. Gunther Plaut. (Torah: a Modern Commentary Ser.). 1979. 20.00 (ISBN 0-8074-0011-4, 3816). UAHC.

Commentary on Leviticus & Numbers. James B. Coffman. 580p. 1987. 19.95 (ISBN 0-915547-75-9). Abilene Christ U.

Commentary on Luke. James B. Coffman. (Firm Foundation Commentary Ser.). 1975. cancelled 10.95 (ISBN 0-88027-067-5). Firm Foun Pub.

Commentary on Luke. J. Norval Geldenhuys. (New International Commentary on the New Testament). 1951. 17.95 (ISBN 0-8028-2184-7). Eerdmans.

Commentary on Luke. 3rd ed. Frederic L. Godet. LC 81-18614. (Kregel Reprint Library). 586p. 1981. Repr. of 1887 ed. 24.95 (ISBN 0-8254-2720-7). Kregel.

Commentary on Luke. McLaughlin. kivar 5.95 (ISBN 0-686-12859-1). Schmul Pub Co.

Commentary on Mark. James B. Coffman. (Firm Foundation Commentary Ser.). 1975. cancelled 10.95 (ISBN 0-88027-066-7). Firm Foun Pub.

Commentary on Mark. McLaughlin. kivar 5.95 (ISBN 0-686-12860-5). Schmul Pub Co.

Commentary on Mark. Henry B. Swete. LC 77-79193. (Kregel Reprint Library). 554p. 1978. 18.95 (ISBN 0-8254-3715-6). Kregel.

Commentary on Matthew. James B. Coffman. (Firm Foundation Commentary Ser.). 1968. cancelled 10.95 (ISBN 0-88027-065-9). Firm Foun Pub.

Commentary on Matthew. McLaughlin. kivar 5.95 (ISBN 0-686-12861-3). Schmul Pub Co.

Commentary on Matthew (One) Dale Bruner. 500p. 1987. 24.95 (ISBN 0-8499-0526-5). Word Bks.

Commentary on Paul's First & Second Epistle to the Corinthians. Hermann Olshausen. 388p. 1984. 14.75 (ISBN 0-86524-184-8, 4604). Klock & Klock.

Commentary on Philippians. Ralph P. Martin. (New Century Bible Commentary Ser.). 192p. 1980. pap. 6.95 (ISBN 0-8028-1840-4). Eerdmans.

Commentary on Plotinus: Emnead. Ed. by M. J. Atkinson. (Classical & Philosophical Monographs: Vol. 1). 1983. 47.50x (ISBN 0-19-814719-8). Oxford U Pr.

Commentary on Revelation. Ethelbert W. Bullinger. LC 83-24917. 768p. 1984. 22.95 (ISBN 0-8254-2239-6). Kregel.

Commentary on Revelation. Henry B. Swete. LC 77-79192. (Kregel Reprint Library). Orig. Title: Apocalypse of John. 562p. 1979. text ed. 18.95 (ISBN 0-8254-3716-4). Kregel.

Commentary on Romans. James B. Coffman. (Firm Foundation Commentary Ser.). cancelled (ISBN 0-88027-070-5). Firm Foun Pub.

Commentary on Romans. abr. ed. C. E. Cranfield. 320p. 1985. pap. 10.95 (ISBN 0-8028-0012-2). Eerdmans.

Commentary on Romans. Frederic L. Godet. LC 77-79189. (Kregel Reprint Library). 542p. 1977. 24.95 (ISBN 0-8254-2715-0). Kregel.

Commentary on Romans. Ernst Kasemann. Tr. by Geoffrey W. Bromiley. 1978. 25.95 (ISBN 0-8028-3499-X). Eerdmans.

Commentary on Romans. McLaughlin. kivar 5.95 (ISBN 0-686-12862-1). Schmul Pub Co.

Commentary on Romans. Anders Nygren. Tr. by Carl Rasmussen. LC 49-48317. 472p. 1949. pap. 6.95 (ISBN 0-8006-1684-7, 1-1684). Fortress.

Commentary on Romans. William S. Plumer. LC 73-155251. (Kregel Reprint Library). 646p. 1971. 18.95 (ISBN 0-8254-3501-3). Kregel.

Commentary on Romans: A Classic Commentary from the Reformed Perspective. William G. Shedd. (Thornapple Commentaries Ser.). 1980. pap. 8.95 (ISBN 0-8010-8175-0). Baker Bk.

Commentary on Saint Ignatius' Rules for the Discernment of Spirits: A Guide to the Principles & Practice. Jules J. Toner. Ed. by George E. Ganss. LC 79-89606. (Original Studies Composed in English Ser.: No. 5). 352p. 1982. 14.00 (ISBN 0-912422-43-2); smyth sewn paper 11.00 (ISBN 0-912422-42-4). Inst Jesuit.

Commentary on St. John. McLaughlin. kivar 5.95 (ISBN 0-686-12863-X). Schmul Pub Co.

Commentary on St. Paul's Epistle to the Ephesians. St. Thomas Aquinas. Tr. by M. L. Lamb. LC 66-19307. (Aquinas Scripture Ser.). 1966. Vol. 2. 10.00x (ISBN 0-87343-022-0). Magi Bks.

Commentary on St. Paul's Epistle to the Galatians. St. Thomas Aquinas. Tr. by F. R. Larcher. LC 66-19306. (Aquinas Scripture Ser.). 1966. Vol. 1. 10.00x (ISBN 0-87343-021-2). Magi Bks.

Commentary on Saint Paul's Epistle to the Philippians & First Thessalonians. St. Thomas Aquinas. LC 66-19306. (Aquinas Scripture Ser.: Vol. 3). 1969. lib. bdg. 10.00x (ISBN 0-87343-047-6); pap. 6.00x (ISBN 0-87343-028-X). Magi Bks.

Commentary on Second Peter. Herman A. Hoyt. 136p. 1983. pap. 4.95 (ISBN 0-88469-153-5). BMH Bks.

Commentary on the Acts of the Apostles. Joseph Alexander. 1979. 27.50 (ISBN 0-86524-025-6, 4401). Klock & Klock.

Commentary on the American Prayer Book. Marion Hatchett. 608p. 1981. 32.50 (ISBN 0-8164-0206-X, HarpR). Har-Row.

Commentary on the Augsburg Confession. Caspar Schwenckfeld. Tr. by Fred A. Grater. 182p. 1982. pap. 5.00 (ISBN 0-935980-02-4). Schwenkfelder Lib.

Commentary on the Book of Amos. Gary Smith. 268p. 1986. 24.95 (ISBN 0-8407-5423-X). Nelson.

Commentary on the Book of Deuteronomy. P. C. Craigie. (New International Commentary of the Old Testament). 520p. 1976. 16.95 (ISBN 0-8028-2355-6). Eerdmans.

Commentary on the Book of Exodus. 2nd ed. U. Cassuto. Tr. by Israel Abrahams from Hebrew. 509p. 1974. Repr. of 1967 ed. text ed. 35.00x (ISBN 965-223-456-7, Pub. by Magnes Pr Israel). Humanities.

Commentary on the Book of Exodus. James G. Murphy. 1979. 14.50 (ISBN 0-86524-014-0, 0201). Klock & Klock.

Commentary on the Book of Genesis. James G. Murphy. xvi, 535p. 1986. Repr. of 1873 ed. lib. bdg. 27.50 (ISBN 0-89941-508-3). W S Hein.

Commentary on the Book of Mormon, 7 vols. George Reynolds & Janne M. Sjodahl. Vol. 1. 9.95 (ISBN 0-87747-039-1); Vol. 2. 9.95 (ISBN 0-87747-040-5); Vol. 3. 9.95 (ISBN 0-87747-041-3); Vol. 4. 9.95 (ISBN 0-87747-042-1); Vol. 5. 9.95 (ISBN 0-87747-043-X); Vol. 6. 9.95 (ISBN 0-87747-044-8); Vol. 7. 9.95 (ISBN 0-87747-045-6). Deseret Bk.

Commentary on the Book of Revelation of John. George E. Ladd. 1971. pap. 8.95 (ISBN 0-8028-1684-3). Eerdmans.

Commentary on the Creed of Islam. Mas'Ud Ibn Umar Al-Taftazani. LC 79-52565. (Islam Ser.). 1980. Repr. of 1950 ed. lib. bdg. 18.00x (ISBN 0-8369-9268-7). Ayer Co Pubs.

Commentary on the Dhammapada, 5 vols. in 4. Dhammapadatthakatha. Ed. by H. C. Norman. LC 78-72423. Repr. of 1915 ed. Set. 155.00 (ISBN 0-404-17620-8). AMS Pr.

Commentary on the Divine Liturgy. Nicholas Cabasilas. Tr. by J. M. Hussey & P. A. McNulty. LC 62-53410. 120p. 1977. pap. 6.95 (ISBN 0-913836-37-0). St Vladimirs.

Commentary on the Epistle of James. James Adamson. (New International Commentary on the New Testament). 480p. 1976. 13.95 (ISBN 0-8028-2377-7). Eerdmans.

Commentary on the Epistle of James. Rudolf E. Stier. 278p. 1982. lib. bdg. 10.25 Smythe Sewn (ISBN 0-86524-157-0, 5903). Klock & Klock.

Commentary on the Epistle to the Ephesians. Charles Hodge. (Thornapple Commentaries Ser.). 1980. pap. 8.95 (ISBN 0-8010-4221-6). Baker Bk.

Commentary on the Epistle to the Galatians. Martin Luther. Tr. by P. S. Watson from Ger. 573p. 1978. Repr. of 1972 ed. 15.95 (ISBN 0-227-67437-5). Attic Pr.

Commentary on the Epistle to the Hebrews, 2 vols. Franz Delitzsch. 1978. Set. 31.50 (ISBN 0-86524-110-4, 5801). Klock & Klock.

Commentary on the Epistle to the Hebrews. Philip E. Hughes. LC 82-90554. 1977. text ed. 18.95 (ISBN 0-8028-3495-7). Eerdmans.

Commentary on the Epistles of Peter & Jude. J. N. Kelly. (Thornapple Commentaries). 397p. 1981. pap. 9.95 (ISBN 0-8010-5430-3). Baker Bk.

Commentary on the Epistles of Saint John. Brooke F. Westcott. (Gr). 8.95 (ISBN 0-8028-3290-3). Eerdmans.

Commentary on the First Epistle to the Corinthians. Thomas C. Edwards. 1979. 18.00 (ISBN 0-86524-013-2, 4602). Klock & Klock.

Commentary on the Gospel of John, 2 vols. E. W. Hengstenberg. 1980. Set. 34.95 (ISBN 0-86524-047-7, 4302). Klock & Klock.

Commentary on the Gospel of John. Robert E. Obach & Albert Kirk. LC 80-84505. 272p. 1981. pap. 7.95 (ISBN 0-8091-2346-0). Paulist Pr.

Commentary on the Gospel of Luke. Robert E. Obach & Albert Kirk. 272p. (Orig.). 1986. pap. 8.95 (ISBN 0-8091-2763-6). Paulist Pr.

Commentary on the Gospel of Mark. Joseph Alexander. 1980. 16.75 (ISBN 0-86524-018-3, 4101). Klock & Klock.

Commentary on the Gospel of Mark. Terence Keegan. LC 81-82332. 224p. (Orig.). 1981. pap. 7.95 (ISBN 0-8091-2359-2). Paulist Pr.

Commentary on the Gospel of Mark. William L. Lane. (New International Commentary on the New Testament). 1973. 18.95 (ISBN 0-8028-2340-8). Eerdmans.

Commentary on the Gospel of Matthew. Albert Kirk & Robert E. Obach. LC 78-65715. 300p. 1978. pap. 8.95 (ISBN 0-8091-2173-5). Paulist Pr.

Commentary on the Gospel of St. John, Pt. 1. St. Thomas Aquinas. Ed. by James A. Weisheipl. Tr. by Fabian R. Larcher from Lat. LC 66-19306. (Aquinas Scripture Ser.: Vol. 4). (Illus.). 512p. 1980. 35.00x (ISBN 0-87343-031-X). Magi Bks.

Commentary on the Gospel of Saint Luke, 2 vols, Vol. 1. F. L. Godet. Ed. by E. W. Shalders. 448p. 1870. 13.95 (ISBN 0-567-27445-4, Pub. by T & T Clark Ltd UK). Fortress.

Commentary on the Gospel of St. Luke, 2 vols, Vol. 2. F. L. Godet. Ed. by M. D. Cusin. 472p. 1870. 13.95 (ISBN 0-567-27446-2, Pub. by T&T Clark Ltd UK). Fortress.

Commentary on the Holy Bible. John R. Dummelow. 1909. 19.95 (ISBN 0-02-533770-X). Macmillan.

Commentary on the Holy Bible, 3 vols. Matthew Henry & Thomas Scott. 1979. 59.95 (ISBN 0-8407-5163-X). Nelson.

Commentary on the Holy Bible, 3 vols. Matthew Poole. 1979. Set. 92.95 (ISBN 0-85151-211-9); 35.95 ea. Vol.1, Genesis through Job (ISBN 0-85151-054-X). Vol. 2, Psalms through Malachi (ISBN 0-85151-134-1). Vol. 3, Matthew through Revelation (ISBN 0-85151-135-X). Banner of Truth.

Commentary on the Lao Tzu by Wang Pi. Tr. by Ariane Rump & Wing-Tsit Chan. LC 79-11212. (Society for Asian & Comparative Philosophy Monograph: No. 6). 266p. 1979. pap. text ed. 8.00x (ISBN 0-8248-0677-8). UH Pr.

Commentary on the Lord's Sermon on the Mount with Seventeen Related Sermons. St. Augustine. Bd. with Related Sermons. LC 63-18827. (Fathers of the Church Ser.: Vol. 11). 382p. 1951. 21.95x (ISBN 0-8132-0011-3). Cath U Pr.

Commentary on the Maya Manuscript in the Royal Public Library of Dresden. E. Forstemann. (HU PMP). 1906. 25.00 (ISBN 0-527-01202-5). Kraus Repr.

Commentary on the Minor Prophets. Homer Hailey. 1972. 14.95 (ISBN 0-8010-4049-3). Baker Bk.

Commentary on the Minor Prophets, Vol. 1. James B. Coffman. (Firm Foundation Commentary Ser.). 360p. 1981. cancelled 8.95 (ISBN 0-88027-078-0). Firm Foun Pub.

Commentary on the Minor Prophets, Vol. 2. James B. Coffman. (Firm Foundation Commentary Ser.). 383p. 1981. cancelled 8.95 (ISBN 0-88027-079-9). Firm Foun Pub.

Commentary on the Minor Prophets, Vol. 3. James B. Coffman. (Commmentary Ser.). 322p. 1983. cancelled 10.95 (ISBN 0-88027-107-8). Firm Foun Pub.

Commentary on the New Lectionary. Gerard S. Sloyan. LC 75-22781. 444p. 1975. pap. 11.95 (ISBN 0-8091-1895-5). Paulist Pr.

Commentary on the Occasional Services. Philip H. Pfatteicher. LC 82-48542. 336p. 1983. 19.95 (ISBN 0-8006-0697-3, 1-1697). Fortress.

Commentary on the Pastoral Epistles. J. N. Kelly. (Thornapple Commentaries Ser.). 272p. 1981. pap. 7.95 (ISBN 0-8010-5428-1). Baker Bk.

Commentary on the Pearl of Great Price. George Reynolds & Janne M. Sjodahl. 9.95 (ISBN 0-87747-046-4). Deseret Bk.

Commentary on the Psalms, 2 vols. David Dickson. 1980. 32.50 (ISBN 0-86524-017-5, 1901). Klock & Klock.

Commentary on the Psalms from Primitive & Mediaeval Writers. Ed. by John M. Neale. LC 78-130990. 1976. Repr. of 1887 ed. 205.00 (ISBN 0-404-04680-0). AMS Pr.

Commentary on the Psalms of David. Apostolos Makrakis. Ed. by Orthodox Christian Educational Society. Tr. by Denver Cummings from Hellenic. 990p. 1950. 16.00x (ISBN 0-938366-19-X). Orthodox Chr.

Commentary on the Revelation of John. Leon Morris. Ed. by R. V. Tasker. (Tyndale Bible Commentaries). 1957. pap. 5.95 (ISBN 0-8028-1419-0). Eerdmans.

Commentary on the Second Epistle to the Corinthians. Philip Hughes. (New International Commentary on the New Testament). 1962. 19.95 (ISBN 0-8028-2186-3). Eerdmans.

Commentary on the Whole Bible, 6 vols. Matthew Henry. 7100p. 89.95 (ISBN 0-8007-0196-8); reference lib. ed. 74.95 (ISBN 0-8007-0968-3). Revell.

Commentary on the Whole Bible, 6 vols, Vols. 1-6. Matthew Henry. (Reference Library Edition). 7152p. 1986. Repr. Set. text ed. 59.95 (ISBN 0-529-06371-9). World Bible.

Commentary on the Whole Bible, Vol. 1: Genesis to Deuteronomy. Matthew Henry. (Reference Library Edition). 912p. 1986. Repr. text ed. 10.95 (ISBN 0-529-06365-4). World Bible.

Commentary on the Whole Bible, Vol. 2: Joshua to Esther. Matthew Henry. (Reference Library Edition). 1160p. 1986. Repr. text ed. 10.95 (ISBN 0-529-06366-2). World Bible.

Commentary on the Whole Bible, Vol. 3: Job to Song of Solomon. Matthew Henry. (Reference Library Edition). 1112p. 1986. Repr. text ed. 10.95 (ISBN 0-529-06367-0). World Bible.

Commentary on the Whole Bible, Vol. 4: Isaiah to Malachi. Matthew Henry. (Reference Library Edition). 1520p. 1986. Repr. text ed. 10.95 (ISBN 0-529-06368-9). World Bible.

Commentary on the Whole Bible, Vol. 5: Matthew to John. Matthew Henry. (Reference Library Edition). 1248p. 1986. Repr. text ed. 10.95 (ISBN 0-529-06369-7). World Bible.

Commentary on the Whole Bible, Vol. 6: Acts to Revelation. Matthew Henry. (Reference Library Edition). 1200p. 1986. Repr. text ed. 10.95 (ISBN 0-529-06370-0). World Bible.

Commentary on the Will & Testament of Abdu'l-Baha. David Hoffman. 56p. pap. 2.95 (ISBN 0-85398-158-2). G Ronald Pub.

Commentary on True & False Religion. Ulrich Zwingli. Ed. by Samuel M. Jackson & Nevin Heller. viii, 415p. 1981. pap. 15.95 (ISBN 0-939464-00-4). Labyrinth Pr.

Commentary to Mishnah Aboth. Moses Maimonides. Tr. by Arthur David. LC 68-27871. 1968. 9.95x (ISBN 0-8197-0154-8). Bloch.

Comments on Here & Hereafter. Bob Jones, Sr. Ed. by Grace W. Haight. 189p. 1942. 3.95 (ISBN 0-89084-006-7). Bob Jones Univ Pr.

Comments on the Book of Romans. L. Grant. pap. 3.95 (ISBN 0-88172-078-X). Believers Bkshelf.

Commerce of the Sacred. Jack N. Lightstone. LC 83-20180. (Brown Judaic Ser.). 234p. 1984. pap. 18.75 (ISBN 0-89130-664-1, 14 00 59). Scholars Pr GA.

Commissioned to Communicate. Harrold D. Harrison. (Sunday School Workers Training Course Ser.: No. 2). 1969. pap. 3.95 (ISBN 0-89265-003-6, Free Will Baptist Dept). Randall Hse.

Commissioned to Communicate: Teacher's Guide. Larry D. Hampton. 1978. pap. 1.50 (ISBN 0-89265-056-7). Randall Hse.

Commitment Factor. Carrol Bruce. LC 84-5005. 1984. pap. 3.95 (ISBN 0-8054-5541-8). Broadman.

Commitment on Campus: Changes in Religion & Values Over Five Decades. Dean R. Hoge. LC 74-7236. (Illus.). 240p. 1974. 10.00 (ISBN 0-664-20706-5). Westminster.

Commitment to Care: An Integrated Philosophy of Science, Education, & Religion. Dean Turner. LC 77-78421. 1977. 12.50 (ISBN 0-8159-5216-3). Devin.

Commitment to Growth: Experiencing the Fruit of the Spirit. Jim Burns & Doug Webster. 64p. (Orig.). 1985. wkbk. 3.95 (ISBN 0-89081-480-5). Harvest Hse.

Commitment to Holiness. Kenneth E. Jones. 1985. pap. 5.95 (ISBN 0-87162-413-3, D1350). Warner Pr.

Commitment to Partnership: Exploring the Theology of Marriage. Ed. by William P. Roberts. 1987. pap. 10.95. Paulist Pr.

Commitment Without Ideology. C. Daniel Batson et al. LC 72-13000. 1973. 6.95 (ISBN 0-8298-0245-2). Pilgrim NY.

Committed Church. Ed. by Laurence Bright & Simon Clements. 1966. 39.50x (ISBN 0-317-27423-6). Elliots Bks.

Committed Communities: Fresh Streams for World Missions. Charles J. Mellis. LC 76-53548. 1976. pap. 5.95 (ISBN 0-87808-426-6). William Carey Lib.

Committed Marriage. Elizabeth Achtemeier. LC 76-7611. (Biblical Perspectives on Current Issues Ser.). 224p. 1976. pap. 8.95 (ISBN 0-664-24754-7). Westminster.

Common Background of Greek & Hebrew Civilizations. Cyrus H. Gordon. (Illus.). 1965. pap. 7.95 (ISBN 0-393-00293-4, Norton Lib). Norton.

Common Catechism: A Book of Christian Faith. Ed. by Johannes Feiner & Lukas Vischer. LC 75-1070. 690p. 1975. 10.95 (ISBN 0-8245-0211-6). Crossroad NY.

Common Faith. John Dewey. (Terry Lectures Ser.). 1934. pap. 3.95x (ISBN 0-300-00069-3, Y18). Yale U Pr.

Common Faith-Uncommon People: Essays in Reconstructionist Judaism. Meir Ben-Horin. LC 71-80691. 245p. 1970. 7.50 (ISBN 0-935457-03-8). Reconstructionist Pr.

Common Grace & the Gospel. Cornelius Van Til. 1972. pap. 8.95 (ISBN 0-87552-482-6). Presby & Reformed.

Common Mystic Prayer. Gabriel Diefenbach. 1978. 2.50 (ISBN 0-8198-0527-0); pap. 1.95 (ISBN 0-8198-0528-9). Dghtrs St Paul.

Common Roots: A Call to Evangelical Maturity. Robert E. Webber. 256p. 1982. pap. 7.95 (ISBN 0-310-36631-3, 12205P). Zondervan.

Common Sense about Yoga. Swami Pavitrananda. pap. 1.25 (ISBN 0-87481-105-8). Vedanta Pr.

Common Sense & Nuclear Warfare. Bertrand Russell. LC 68-54291. Repr. of 1959 ed. 18.00 (ISBN 0-404-05465-X). AMS Pr.

Common Sense Christian Living. Edith Schaeffer. LC 83-8263. 272p. 1983. 13.95 (ISBN 0-8407-5280-6). Nelson.

Common Sense Discipline. Roger Allen & Ron Rose. LC 86-61522. 1986. 12.95 (ISBN 0-8344-0135-5, BA110H). Sweet.

Common-Sense Morality & Consequentialism. Michael Slote. (International Library of Philosophy). 160p. 1985. 24.95x (ISBN 0-7102-0309-8). Methuen Inc.

Common Sense Renewed. Robert Christian. 132p. 1986. 12.50 (ISBN 0-89279-078-4). Graphic Pub.

Commonsense about Prayer. Lewis MacLachlan. 141p. 1965. pap. 2.95 (ISBN 0-227-67653-X). Attic Pr.

Commonsense Guide to Fasting. Kenneth E. Hagin. 1981. pap. 1.50 (ISBN 0-89276-403-1). Hagin Ministries.

Commonsense Suicide: The Final Right. Doris Portwood. 142p. 1983. pap. 8.00 (ISBN 0-394-62013-5). Hemlock Soc.

Communal Experience: Anarchist & Mystical Communities in Twentieth Century America. Laurence Veysey. LC 78-55045. 1978. pap. 7.95X (ISBN 0-226-85458-2, P786, Phoen). U of Chicago Pr.

Communal Love at Oneida: A Perfectionist Vision of Authority, Property & Sexual Order. Richard De Maria. LC 78-60958. (Texts & Studies in Religion: Vol. 2). xiii, 248p. 1978. soft cover 19.95x (ISBN 0-88946-986-5). E Mellen.

Communal Love at Oneida: A Perfectionist Vision of Authority, Property & Sexual Order. 2nd. ed. Richard DeMaria. LC 78-60958. (Texts & Studies in Religion: Vol. 2). 248p. 1983. 49.95x (ISBN 0-88946-988-1). E Mellen.

Communal Pietism Among Early American Moravians. John J. Sessler. LC 70-134387. Repr. of 1933 ed. 19.50 (ISBN 0-404-08430-3). AMS Pr.

Communaute Judeo-Arameenne a Elephantine en Egypte aux VI et V Siecles avant Jesus-Christ. A. Van Hoonacker. (British Academy, London, Schweich Lectures on Biblical Archaeology Series, 1914). pap. 19.00 (ISBN 0-8115-1256-8). Kraus Repr.

Communicating. Churches Alive, Inc. Staff. LC 79-52133. (Love One Another Bible Study Ser.). (Illus.). 1979. wkbk. 3.00 (ISBN 0-934396-06-X). Churches Alive.

Communicating Christ Cross-Culturally. David J. Hesselgrave. 1978. 12.95 (ISBN 0-310-36691-7, 11157P). Zondervan.

Communicating Christ to the Cults. John T. Rogers. LC 83-4421. 1983. pap. 3.95 (ISBN 0-87227-091-2). Reg Baptist.

Communicating the Gospel. William Barclay. 1978. pap. 3.25x (ISBN 0-7152-0401-7). Outlook.

Communicating the Gospel God's Way. Charles H. Kraft. LC 80-53945. 60p. 1980. pap. 2.95x (ISBN 0-87808-742-7). William Carey Lib.

Communicating with Twentieth Century Man. Jay E. Adams. 41p. 1979. pap. 1.95 (ISBN 0-87552-008-1). Presby & Reformed.

Communication & Values. Krishan Sondhi. 1986. 22.50X (Pub. by Somaiya). South Asia Bks.

Communication in Pulpit & Parish. Merrill R. Abbey. LC 72-14329. 238p. 1980. pap. 8.50 (ISBN 0-664-24312-6). Westminster.

Communication in the Counseling Relationship. Bonnie J. Headington. LC 78-9026. 1979. cloth 16.50x (ISBN 0-910328-23-4); pap. 11.00x (ISBN 0-910328-24-2). Carroll Pr.

Communication: Key to Your Parents. Rex Johnson. LC 78-61874. 1978. pap. 3.95 (ISBN 0-89081-157-1). Harvest Hse.

Communication: Key to Your Teens. Norman Wright & Rex Johnson. LC 78-61872. 1978. pap. 3.95 (ISBN 0-89081-158-X). Harvest Hse.

Communication Skills for Ministry. John Lawyer & Neil Katz. 176p. 1983. pap. text ed. 17.95 (ISBN 0-8403-2987-3, 40371201). Kendall-Hunt.

Communicative Acts & Shared Knowledge in Natural Discourse. Marga Kreckel. LC 81-66392. 1981. 68.00 (ISBN 0-12-426180-9). Acad Pr.

Communicative Praxis & the Space of Subjectivity. Calvin O. Schrag. LC 84-48647. (Studies in Phenomenology & Existential Philosophy). 232p. 1986. 27.50x (ISBN 0-253-31383-X). Ind U Pr.

Communicator's Commentary-Acts, Vol. 5. Lloyd J. Ogilvie. (Communicator's Commentaries Ser.). 1982. 18.95 (ISBN 0-8499-0158-8). Word Bks.

Communicator's Commentary: Corinthians First; Second, Vol. 7. Kenneth L. Chafin & Lloyd J. Ogilvie. 1983. 18.95 (ISBN 0-8499-0347-5). Word Bks.

Communicator's Commentary-James First; Second, Peter, Jude, Vol. 2. Paul A. Cedar. Ed. by Lloyd J. Ogilvie. (Communicator's Commentaries Ser.). 1983. 16.95 (ISBN 0-8499-0164-2). Word Bks.

Communicator's Commentary-John, Vol. 4. Roger L. Fredrikson. Ed. by Lloyd J. Ogilvie. (Communicator's Commentaries Ser.). 1983. 18.95 (ISBN 0-8499-0157-X). Word Bks.

Communicator's Commentary-Luke, Vol. 3. Bruce Larson. Ed. by Lloyd J. Ogilvie. (Communicator's Commentaries Ser.). 1984. 18.95 (ISBN 0-8499-0156-1). Word Bks.

Communicator's Commentary-Mark, Vol. 2. David L. McKenna. Ed. by Lloyd Ogilvie. (Communicator's Commentaries Ser.). 1982. 18.95 (ISBN 0-8499-0155-3). Word Bks.

Communicators for Christ. Daughters of St. Paul. 1973. 5.00 (ISBN 0-8198-0249-2). Dghtrs St Paul.

Communio: Church & Papacy in Early Christianity. Ludwig Hertling. Tr. by Jared Wicks from Ger. LC 75-38777. (Orig.). 1972. pap. 2.95 (ISBN 0-8294-0212-8). Loyola.

Communion. Elise N. Morgan. (Meditation Ser.). 1928. 3.50 (ISBN 0-87516-328-9). De Vorss.

Communion & Intercommunion. K. Ware. 1980. pap. 1.95 (ISBN 0-937032-20-4). Light&Life Pub Co MN.

Communion Clown Circle. William R. Grimbol. 1985. 3.25 (ISBN 0-89536-734-3, 5818). CSS of Ohio.

Communion Handbook. Paul E. Cook. 96p. 1980. 5.95 (ISBN 0-8170-0877-2). Judson.

Communion Mediations. George Gritter. 80p. 1984. pap. 5.95 (ISBN 0-8010-3805-7). Baker Bk.

Communion Meditations & Outlines. Alexander Maclaren et al. (Pocket Pulpit Library). 1979. pap. 4.50 (ISBN 0-8010-6199-7). Baker Bk.

Communion Meditations & Prayers. Ed. by Robert Korth. LC 81-16668. 128p. (Orig.). 1982. pap. 4.95 (ISBN 0-87239-483-2, 3032). Standard Pub.

Communion of Love. Matthew the Poor. LC 84-10561. 234p. (Orig.). 1984. pap. text ed. 8.95 (ISBN 0-88141-036-5). St Vladimirs.

Communion of Possibility. Charles E. Winquist. LC 75-859. (Religions Quest Ser: Vol. 2). 160p. 1975. pap. text ed. 6.95x (ISBN 0-914914-04-9). New Horizons.

Communion of the Sick. 1984. pap. 1.95 (ISBN 0-8146-1368-3). Liturgical Pr.

Communion Reflections & Prayers. James L. Christensen. Ed. by Herbert Lambert. LC 84-29361. 64p. (Orig.). 1985. pap. 4.95 (ISBN 0-8272-0446-9). CBP.

Communion: The Meal That Unites? Donald Bridge & David Phypers. LC 82-62820. 192p. 1983. pap. 5.95 (ISBN 0-87788-160-X). Shaw Pubs.

Communion Thoughts & Prayers. new ed. Carlton C. Buck. LC 76-46943. 1977. 5.95 (ISBN 0-8272-0440-X). CBP.

Communion Under Both Kinds- an Ecumenical Surrender. Michael Davies. 1980. pap. 1.00 (ISBN 0-89555-141-1). TAN Bks Pubs.

Communion with God. large-type ed. the Bab Baha'u'llah & Abdu'l-Baha. 1976. pap. 1.50 (ISBN 0-87743-110-8, 315-011). Baha'i.

Communion with God. Jessie Penn-Lewis. 1962. pap. 2.95 (ISBN 0-87508-993-3). Chr Lit.

Communion with the Saints. Albert Schneider. 1983. 25.00 (ISBN 0-686-45785-4). Franciscan Herald.

Communism: A Critique & Counter Proposal. 1975. pap. 2.00 (ISBN 0-686-13413-3). Unification Church.

Communism & Christianism. William M. Brown. 252p. lib. bdg. 24.95 (ISBN 0-88286-046-1); pap. 4.00 (ISBN 0-88286-045-3). C H Kerr.

Communism & Christianity. Martin C. D'Arcy. 1957. 10.00 (ISBN 0-8159-5208-2). Devin.

Communism & the Reality of Moral Law. J. D. Bales. 1969. pap. 3.75 (ISBN 0-934532-01-X). Presby & Reformed.

Communism, Democracy, & Catholic Power. Paul Blanshard. LC 75-156175. 340p. 1972. Repr. of 1952 ed. lib. bdg. 35.00x (ISBN 0-8371-6118-5, BLCD). Greenwood.

Communism in Central Europe in the Time of the Reformation. Karl Kautsky. Tr. by J. L. Mulliken & E. G. Mulliken. LC 66-22631. 1966. Repr. of 1897 ed. 29.50x (ISBN 0-678-00193-6). Kelley.

Communism in the Bible. Jose Miranda. Tr. by Robert R. Barr from Span. LC 81-16936. Orig. Title: Comunismo En la Biblia. 96p. (Orig.). 1982. pap. 6.95 (ISBN 0-88344-014-8). Orbis Bks.

Communism with the Mask Off: The Jewish Origin of Communism. Joseph Goebbels. 1982. lib. bdg. 59.95 (ISBN 0-87700-406-4). Revisionist Pr.

Communities of Faith & Radical Discipleship. Jurgen Moltmann et al. Ed. by Carlton T. Mitchell & McLeod G. Bryan. (Luce Program on Religion & the Social Crisis Ser.). x, 130p. 1986. 16.95 (ISBN 0-86554-216-3). Mercer Univ Pr.

Communities of Resistance & Solidarity: A Feminist Theology of Liberation. Sharon D. Welch. LC 85-4809. 112p. (Orig.). 1985. pap. 7.95 (ISBN 0-88344-204-3). Orbis Bks.

Community & Abbot in the Rule of Saint Benedict, Vol. I. Adalbert de Vogue. Ed. by Ethel R. Perkins. Tr. by Charles Philippi from Fr. (Cistercian Studies). 1979. 22.95 (ISBN 0-87907-905-3). Cistercian Pubns.

Community & Commitment. John Driver. LC 76-41463. 96p. 1976. pap. 3.95 (ISBN 0-8361-1802-2). Herald Pr.

Community & Commitment: Religious Plausibility in a Liberal Protestant Church. Wade C. Roof. 278p. 1978. 28.00 (ISBN 0-444-99038-0). Elsevier.

Community & Commitment: Religious Plausibility in a Liberal Protestant Church. Wade C. Roof. LC 77-16329. 288p. pap. 10.95 (ISBN 0-8298-0669-5). Pilgrim NY.

Community & Disunity: Symbols of Grace & Sin. Jerome Theisen. 144p. 1985. pap. 7.50 (ISBN 0-8146-1406-X). Liturgical Pr.

Community & Gospel in Luke-Acts: The Social & Political Motivations of Lucan Theory. Philip S. Esler. (Society for New Testament Studies Monographs: No. 57). 224p. Date not set. price not set (ISBN 0-521-32965-5). Cambridge U Pr.

Community & Growth: Our Pilgrimage Together. Vean Vanier. Tr. by Ann Shearer from Fr. LC 79-91603. 232p. 1979. pap. 8.95 (ISBN 0-8091-2294-4). Paulist Pr.

Community & Message of Isaiah Fifty Six-Sixty Six: A Theological Commentary. Elizabeth Achtemeier. LC 81-52284. 160p. (Orig.). 1982. pap. 8.95 (ISBN 0-8066-1916-3, 10-1610). Augsburg.

Community & Polity: The Organizational Dynamics of American Jewry. Daniel J. Elazar. LC 75-8167. (Illus.). 448p. 1976. pap. 9.95 (ISBN 0-8276-0068-2, 377). Jewish Pubns.

Community & Worship. Douglas V. Steere. 1983. pap. 2.50x (ISBN 0-87574-010-3, 010). Pendle Hill.

Community Beyond Division: Chrisitan Life under South Africa's Apartheid System. Richard J. Stevens. 1984. 8.95 (ISBN 0-533-05729-9). Vantage.

Community Called Church. Juan L. Segundo. Tr. by John Drury from Span. LC 72-85795. (Theology for Artisans of a New Humanity Ser., Vol. 1). Orig. Title: Esa communidad Lleamasha Iglesia. 181p. 1973. 7.95x (ISBN 0-88344-481-X); pap. 4.95x (ISBN 0-88344-487-9). Orbis Bks.

Community in a Black Pentecostal Church: An Anthropological Study. Melvin D. Williams. 202p. 1984. pap. 8.95x (ISBN 0-88133-049-3). Waveland Pr.

Community in a Black Pentecostal Church: An Anthropological Study. Melvin D. Williams. LC 74-5108. pap. 53.50 (ISBN 0-317-42278-2, 2024332). Bks Demand UMI.

Community of Character: Toward a Constructive Christian Social Ethic. Stanley Hauerwas. LC 80-53072. 320p. 1981. pap. text ed. 7.95 (ISBN 0-268-00735-7, NDP 265). U of Notre Dame Pr.

Community of Character: Toward a Constructive Christian Social Ethic. Stanley Hauerwas. LC 80-53072. 320p. 1981. text ed. 20.00 (ISBN 0-268-00733-0). U of Notre Dame Pr.

Community of Faith: Models & Strategies for Developing Christian Communities. James D. Whitehead & Evelyn E. Whitehead. 208p. (Orig.). 1982. pap. 9.95 (ISBN 0-86683-949-6, AY7719, HarpR). Har-Row.

Community of God. Marcella Bush. (Illus.). 1975. pap. 3.75x (ISBN 0-8192-4057-5); tchr's guide 4.95x (ISBN 0-8192-4056-7). Morehouse.

Community of the Beloved Disciple. Raymond E. Brown. LC 78-65894. 204p. 1979. 5.95 (ISBN 0-8091-0274-9); pap. 4.95 (ISBN 0-8091-2174-3). Paulist Pr.

Community of the Holy Spirit: A Movement of Change in a Covent of Nuns in Puerto Rico. Julio Sanchez. 190p. (Orig.). 1984. lib. bdg. 25.25 (ISBN 0-8191-3367-1); pap. text ed. 11.75 (ISBN 0-8191-3368-X). U Pr of Amer.
Community of the King. Howard A. Snyder. LC 77-6030. (Illus.). 1977. pap. 7.95 (ISBN 0-87784-752-5). Inter-Varsity.
Community of the New Age: Studies in Mark's Gospel. Howard C. Kee. LC 83-17416. xii, 225p. 1983. 16.95 (ISBN 0-86554-100-0, MUP/H92). Mercer Univ Pr.
Community of the Spirit. Richard Reichert. 120p. 1982. pap. 3.60 (ISBN 0-697-01796-6); tchr's manual 4.00 (ISBN 0-697-01797-4); spirit masters 10.95 (ISBN 0-697-01798-2). Wm C Brown.
Community of Women & Men in the Church: A Study Program. Advisory Committee. (Orig.). 1978. pap. 1.95 (ISBN 0-377-00092-2). Friend Pr.
Community of Women & Men in the Church. Ed. by Constance F. Parvey. LC 82-71831. 288p. (Orig.). 1982. pap. 14.95 (ISBN 0-8006-1644-8, 1-1644). Fortress.
Community on Trial: The Jews of Paris in the 1930's. David H. Weinberg. LC 77-2999. 1977. 22.00x (ISBN 0-226-88507-0). U of Chicago Pr.
Community Organization in Religious Education. Hugh Hartshorne & J. Q. Miller. 1932. 49.50x (ISBN 0-686-51356-8). Elliots Bks.
Community, State & Church: Three Essays. Karl Barth. 16.75 (ISBN 0-8446-1058-5). Peter Smith.
Como Compartir Su Fe. Paul E. Little. 144p. 1985. pap. 3.95 (ISBN 0-311-13025-9). Casa Bautista.
Como Desatar Su Fe. 2nd ed. Kenneth E. Hagin. (Span.). 1982. pap. 1.00 (ISBN 0-89276-107-5). Hagin Ministries.
Como Disciplinar a Tus Hijos. Roy Lessin. 96p. 1982. 2.25 (ISBN 0-88113-032-X). Edit Betania.
Como Ensenar la Biblia. Lucien E. Coleman, Jr. Tr. by Jorge E. Diaz. Orig. Title: How to Teach the Bible. (Span.). 265p. 1985. Repr. of 1982 ed. 6.50 (ISBN 0-311-11039-8). Casa Bautista.
Como Estudiar la Biblia por Si Mismo. Tim LaHaye. 192p. 1977. 3.75 (ISBN 0-88113-042-7); 3.75 (ISBN 0-88113-033-8). Edit Betania.
Como Ganar a Tu Familia Para Cristo. Natanael Olson. Tr. by Ildefonso Villarello from Eng. 182p. 1983. pap. 1.50 (ISBN 0-311-13801-2). Casa Bautista.
Como Iniciar la Vida Cristiana. George Sweeting. Orig. Title: How to Begin the Christian Life. (Span.). 1977. pap. 3.50 (ISBN 0-8254-1697-3). Kregel.
Como Leer y Orar los Evangelios. Marilyn Norquist. Ed. by John McPhee. Tr. by Olimpia Diaz from Eng. (Handbook of the Bible Ser.). Orig. Title: Hand. 64p. 1980. pap. 1.50 (ISBN 0-89243-127-X). Liguori Pubns.
Como Llegar a Ser Vencedor. R. Escandon. (Span.). 128p. 1982. pap. 3.95 (ISBN 0-311-46092-5, Edit Mundo). Casa Bautista.
Como Mejorar Sus Relaciores Humanas. R. Lofton Hudson. Tr. by O. S. D. De Lerin. 62p. 1984. Repr. of 1982 ed. 1.75 (ISBN 0-311-46037-2). Casa Bautista.
Como Obra la Fe. Frederick Price. 111p. 1980. pap. 2.95 (ISBN 0-89274-157-0). Harrison Hse.
Como Obtener la Plenitud del Poder. R. A. Torrey. Tr. by Jose G. Rivas from Eng. Orig. Title: How to Obtain Fullness of Power. (Span.). 112p. 1983. pap. 2.20 (ISBN 0-311-46083-6). Casa Bautista.
Como Orar. R. A. Torrey & J. E. Davis. 96p. 1985. Repr. of 1984 ed. 2.00 (ISBN 0-311-40001-9). Casa Bautista.
Como Preparar Mensajes. James Braga. Orig. Title: How to Prepare Bible Messages. (Port.). 1986. write for info. (ISBN 0-8297-1609-2). Life Pubs Intl.
Como Preparar Mensajes Biblicos. James Braga. Orig. Title: How to Prepare Bible Messages. Tr. of How to Prepare Bible Messages. (Span.). 320p. 1986. pap. 9.50 (ISBN 0-8254-1072-X). Kregel.
Como Retener Su Sanidad. Kenneth E. Hagin. (Span.). 1983. pap. 0.50 mini bk. (ISBN 0-89276-159-8). Hagin Ministries.
Como Ser Encantadora (Para Alumna) Emily Hunter. Tr. by Wilma Mendoza De Mann & F. A. Mariotti. Orig. Title: Christian Charm Notebook. (Span., Illus.). 56p. 1984. pap. 2.50 teachers ed. (ISBN 0-311-46054-2); pap. 5.45 student ed., 100 pp. (ISBN 0-311-46055-0). Casa Bautista.
Como Ser Feliz. Richard W. DeHaan. Orig. Title: How to Be Happy. (Span.). 64p. 1978. pap. 2.25. Kregel.
Como Ser Feliz en el Matrimonio. Elam J. Daniels. Orig. Title: How to Be Happily Married. 96p. 1984. pap. 2.10 (ISBN 0-311-46066-6). Casa Bautista.
Como Ser un Joven Ideal (Para Alumno) Wayne Hunter & Emily Hunter. Tr. by Federico A. Mariotti. Orig. Title: Man in Demand. (Span.). 1980. pap. 6.95 student ed., 80p. (ISBN 0-311-46074-7); pap. 8.75 teacher ed. 1981 (ISBN 0-311-46075-5). Casa Bautista.
Como Surgieron los Menonitas. J. C. Wenger. Ed. by Arnold J. Casas. Tr. by Ernesto S. Vilela. LC 79-89306. (Mennonite Faith Ser.: No. 1). (Span.). 72p. 1979. pap. 1.50x (ISBN 0-8361-1222-9). Herald Pr.
Como un Viento Recio. Mel Tari. 208p. 1972. 3.25 (ISBN 0-88113-041-9). Edit Betania.
Como Vencer Tension Nerviosa. Gilbert Little. Orig. Title: Nervous Christians. 128p. (Span). 1987. pap. 3.25 (ISBN 0-8254-1443-1). Kregel.
Como Vivir en el Mundo de Hoy. T. B. Maston. Tr. by Bob Adams from Eng. Tr. of World in Travail. (Span.). 224p. Date not set. pap. price not set (ISBN 0-311-46084-4). Casa Bautista.
Como Vivir en el Plano Superior. Ruth Paxson. Orig. Title: Life on the Highest Plane. (Span.). 254p. 1984. pap. 4.95 (ISBN 0-8254-1551-9). Kregel.
Compact Bible Atlas with Gazetteer. (Illus.). 1979. pap. 4.95 (ISBN 0-8010-2432-3). Baker Bk.
Compact Guide to Bible Based Beliefs. Thayer S. Warshaw. LC 80-19820. 49p. (Orig.). 1981. pap. 2.25 (ISBN 0-687-09254-X). Abingdon.
Compact History of the Catholic Church. Alan Schreck. 192p. (Orig.). 1987. pap. 5.95 (ISBN 0-89283-328-9). Servant.
Compact Treasury of Inspiration. Compiled by Ken S. Giniger. 320p. (Orig.). 1983. pap. 3.50 (ISBN 0-515-07442-X). Jove Pubns.
Companion Dictionary of the Bible. Erwin Lueker. 192p. 1985. pap. 5.95 (ISBN 0-570-03947-9, 12-2880). Concordia.
Companion of Prayer for Daily Living. Massey H. Shepherd, Jr. LC 78-62063. 1978. pap. 3.95 kivar (ISBN 0-8192-1230-X). Morehouse.
Companion on Life's Journey: A Book of Prayers & Readings. Ed. by Bede Hubbard. 260p. 1986. pap. 9.95 (ISBN 0-8146-1550-3). Liturgical Pr.
Companion to Baptist Hymnal: 1975 Edition. William J. Reynolds. LC 75-39449. 480p. 1976. bds. 16.95 (ISBN 0-8054-6808-0). Broadman.
Companion to Hymnbook for Christian Worship. Arthur N. Wake. LC 72-129621. 1970. 8.95 (ISBN 0-8272-8025-4). CBP.
Companion to Hymns of Faith & Life. Lawrence R. Schoenhals. (Orig.). 1980. pap. 6.95 (ISBN 0-89367-040-5). Light & Life.
Companion to John: Readings in Johannine Theology. Ed. by Michael J. Taylor. LC 77-7042. 1977. pap. 6.95 (ISBN 0-8189-0348-1). Alba.
Companion to Paul. Ed. by Michael J. Taylor. 200p. 1975. pap. 6.95 (ISBN 0-8189-0304-X). Alba.
Companion to the Bible. T. W. Manson. Ed. by H. H. Rowley. 592p. 1963. 19.95x (ISBN 0-567-02197-1, Pub. by T & T Clark Ltd UK). Fortress.
Companion to the Bible. Ed. by Miriam Ward. LC 85-15817. 419p. (Orig.). 1985. pap. 14.95 (ISBN 0-8189-0487-9). Alba.
Companion to the Clams. Hugh Noonan. (Illus.). 1980. pap. 10.50 (ISBN 0-8199-0680-8). Franciscan Herald.
Companion to the Hymnal. Fred D. Gealy et al. 1970. 19.95 (ISBN 0-687-09259-0). Abingdon.
Companion to the New Scofield Reference Bible. E. Schuyler English. 1972. 6.95 (ISBN 0-19-526872-5). Oxford U Pr.
Companion to the New Testament: The New English Bible. A. E. Harvey. 858p. 1970. 49.50x (ISBN 0-19-826160-8); pap. 24.95x (ISBN 0-19-213229-6). Oxford U Pr.
Companion to the Study of St. Anselm. Jasper Hopkins. LC 72-79097. 278p. 1972. 13.95x (ISBN 0-8166-0657-9). U of Minn Pr.
Companion to the Summa, 4 vols. 1985. Set. pap. 50.00 (ISBN 0-87061-117-8). Chr Classics.
Companion to Your Study of the Book of Mormon. Dan Ludlow. LC 76-27139. 1976. 9.95 (ISBN 0-87747-610-1). Deseret Bk.
Companion to Your Study of the Doctrine & Covenants, 2 vols. Daniel H. Ludlow. LC 78-64752. 1978. Set. 17.95 (ISBN 0-87747-722-1). Deseret Bk.
Companion to Your Study of the New Testament: The Four Gospels. Daniel H. Ludlow. 454p. 1982. 9.95 (ISBN 0-87747-945-3). Deseret Bk.
Companion to Your Study of the Old Testament. Daniel H. Ludlow. LC 80-28088. 437p. 1981. 9.95 (ISBN 0-87747-853-8). Deseret Bk.
Companion Volume to the Songs We Sing. Harry Coopersmith. 1950. 3.50x (ISBN 0-8381-0210-7). United Syn Bk.
Companions of the Cave. Da'i Al-Islam. 23p. 1985. pap. 3.95 (ISBN 0-940368-55-2). Tahrike Tarsile Quran.
Companions on the Inner Way: The Art of Spiritual Guidance. Morton T. Kelsey. LC 82-23541. 250p. 1983. 17.50 (ISBN 0-8245-0585-9); pap. 9.95 (ISBN 0-8245-0560-3). Crossroad NY.
Company for Promoting & Propagation of the Gospel of Jesus Christ in New England: The Ledger for the Years 1650-1660 & the Record Book of Meetings Between 1656 & 1686. Repr. of 1920 ed. 23.50 (ISBN 0-8337-4481-X). B Franklin.
Company of Strangers: Christians & the Renewal of America's Public Life. Parker J. Palmer. 176p. 1983. pap. 7.95 (ISBN 0-8245-0601-4). Crossroad NY.
Company of the Committed. Elton Trueblood. LC 61-12834. 114p. (Orig.). 1980. pap. 5.95 (ISBN 0-06-068551-4, RD 317, HarpR). Har-Row.
Comparative Analysis of the Italians & the Jews: The Two People Who Contributed the Most to the Civilization of Mankind with Strange & Unexpected Conclusions. Maxwell Kent. (Illus.). 1977. 117.25 (ISBN 0-89266-056-2). Am Classical Coll Pr.
Comparative Analysis of the Philosophies of Erasmus & Luther. James A. Froude. (Illus.). 133p. 1981. Repr. of 1868 ed. 69.85 (ISBN 0-89901-038-5). Found Class Reprints.
Comparative Ethics in Hindu & Buddhist Traditions. Roderick Hindery. 1978. 18.95 (ISBN 0-89684-017-4, Pub. by Motilal Banarsidass India). Orient Bk Dist.
Comparative Geography of Palestine, 4 vols. Karl Ritter. 1865. Set. 65.00x (ISBN 0-403-03564-3). Scholarly.
Comparative Geography of Palestine & the Sinaitic Peninsula, 4 Vols. K. Ritter. LC 68-26367. (Reference Ser., No. 44). 1969. Repr. of 1865 ed. Set. lib. bdg. 159.95x (ISBN 0-8383-0180-0). Haskell.
Comparative Geography of Palestine & the Sinaitic Peninsula, 4 Vols. Karl Ritter. Tr. by William L. Gage. LC 69-10151. 1969. Repr. of 1866 ed. Set. lib. bdg. 71.00x (ISBN 0-8371-0638-9, RISP). Greenwood.
Comparative Midrash: The Plan & Program of Genesis Rabbah & Leviticus Rabbah. Jacob Neusner. (Brown Judaic Studies). 1986. 27.95 (ISBN 0-89130-958-6, 14-01-11); pap. 22.95 (ISBN 0-89130-959-4). Scholars Pr GA.
Comparative Mythology. Jaan Puhvel. LC 86-20882. (Illus.). 304p. 1987. text ed. 29.50x (ISBN 0-8018-3413-9). Johns Hopkins.
Comparative Mythology: An Essay. rev. ed. Friedrich Max Muller. Ed. by Richard M. Dorson. LC 77-70612. (International Folklore Ser.). 1977. Repr. of 1909 ed. lib. bdg. 22.00x (ISBN 0-405-10111-2). Ayer Co Pubs.
Comparative Philology & the Text of Job: A Study in Methodology. Lester L. Grabbe. LC 77-23489. (Society of Biblical Literature. Dissertation Ser.). 1977. pap. 9.95 (ISBN 0-89130-139-9, 060134). Scholars Pr GA.
Comparative Politics of Birth Control: Determinants of Policy Variation & Change in the Developed Nations. Marilyn J. Field. (Landmark Dissertations in Women's Studies). (Illus.). 320p. 1983. 42.95 (ISBN 0-03-069527-9). Praeger.
Comparative Religion. Frank B. Jevons. LC 76-57969. 1977. Repr. of 1913 ed. lib. bdg. 15.00 (ISBN 0-8414-5326-8). Folcroft.
Comparative Religion. Geoffrey Parrinder. LC 73-19116. 130p. 1975. Repr. of 1962 ed. lib. bdg. 45.00x (ISBN 0-8371-7301-9, PACR). Greenwood.
Comparative Religion. Ed. by Amarjit S. Sethi & Reinhard Pummer. 1979. text ed. 18.95x (ISBN 0-7069-0810-4, Pub. by Vikas India). Advent NY.
Comparative Religion. Rama Srivastava. LC 74-904268. 1974. 14.00x (ISBN 0-88386-565-3). South Asia Bks.
Comparative Religion. K. N. Tiwari. 1986. 14.00 (ISBN 81-208-0293-4, Pub. by Motilal Banarsidass). South Asia Bks.
Comparative Religion: A History. Eric J. Sharpe. LC 86-2380. 330p. 1987. 31.95 (ISBN 0-8126-9032-X); pap. 14.95 (ISBN 0-8126-9041-9). Open Court.
Comparative Religion: Its Genesis & Growth. Louis H. Jordan. Ed. by Joseph M. Kitagawa. (SP-Reprints & Translations Ser.). 1986. pap. 19.50 (ISBN 1-55540-014-0, 00 07 11). Scholars Pr GA.
Comparative Semitic Lexicon of the Phoenician & Punic Languages. Richard S. Tomback. LC 76-55377. (Society of Biblical Literature. Dissertation Ser.: No. 32). pap. 94.80 (ISBN 0-8357-9567-5, 2017672). Bks Demand UMI.
Comparative Study of Myths & Legends of Formosan Aborigines. Ho Ting-Jui. (Asian Folklore & Social Life Monograph: No. 18). 1972. 17.00 (ISBN 0-89986-020-6). Oriental Bk Store.
Comparative Study of Religions. Joachim Wach & Joseph M. Kitagawa. LC 58-9237. (Lectures on the History of Religions: No. 4). 1958. 30.00x (ISBN 0-231-02252-2); pap. 12.00x (ISBN 0-231-08528-1). Columbia U Pr.
Comparative Study of the Jaina Theories of Reality & Knowledge. Y. J. Padmarajiah. 460p. 1986. 22.00 (ISBN 81-208-0036-2, Pub. by Motilal Banarsidass India). South Asia Bks.
Comparative Study of the Religions of Today. Mohammed A. Muhiyaddin. 1984. 15.95 (ISBN 0-533-05963-1). Vantage.
Comparing Religions: A Limitative Approach. J. G Platvoet. (Religion & Reason Ser.: No. 24). xiv, 350p. 1982. 51.50x (ISBN 90-279-3170-4). Mouton.
Comparison of the Differences in the Doctrines of Faith Between the Eastern & Western Churches. Metropolitan Philaret of Moscow. Tr. by Robert Pinkerton from Rus. 1974. pap. 1.25 (ISBN 0-686-10206-1). Eastern Orthodox.
Comparison of World Religions. Henry J. Heydt. 1967. pap. 2.50 (ISBN 0-87508-241-6). Chr Lit.
Compassion: A Reflection on the Christian Life. Don McNeill et al. LC 83-45045. (Illus.). 160p. 1983. pap. 6.95 (ISBN 0-385-18957-5, Im). Doubleday.
Compassion: A Tibetan Analysis. Guy Newland. (Wisdom Advanced Book: Blue Ser.). 168p. (Orig.). 1985. pap. 12.95 (ISBN 0-318-04680-6, Wisdom Pubns). Great Traditions.
Compassion in Madhyamika Buddhism. Guy Newland. (Wisdom Advanced Book, Blue Ser.). 160p. (Orig.). 1984. pap. 10.95 (ISBN 0-86171-024-X, Wisdom Pubns). Great Traditions.
Compassion in Tibetan Buddhism. 2nd ed. Jeffrey Hopkins & Ann Klein. Ed. by Elizabeth Napper. LC 80-85453. 263p. 1980. pap. 10.95 (ISBN 0-937938-04-1). Snow Lion.
Compassion: Life Maps. Chuck Swindoll. 64p. 1984. 5.95 (ISBN 0-8499-0443-9, 0443-9). Word Bks.
Compassionate Address to the Christian Negroes in Virginia. Benjamin Fawcett. LC 72-168011. Repr. of 1756 ed. 11.50 (ISBN 0-404-00258-7). AMS Pr.
Compassionate & Free: An Asian Woman's Theology. Marianne Katoppo. (Illus.). 96p. (Orig.). 1980. pap. 4.95 (ISBN 0-88344-085-7). Orbis Bks.
Compassionate God. Choan-Seng Song. LC 81-16972. 304p. (Orig.). 1982. pap. 12.95 (ISBN 0-88344-095-4). Orbis Bks.
Compassionate Touch. Douglas Wead. LC 76-62694. (Illus.). 192p. 1980. pap. 3.50 (ISBN 0-87123-021-6, 200021). Bethany Hse.
Compassionate Visitor: Resources for Ministering to People Who Are Ill. Arthur H. Becker. LC 84-28370. 128p. (Orig.). 1985. pap. 5.95 (ISBN 0-8066-2094-3, 10-1620). Augsburg.
Compend of Luther's Theology. Ed. by Hugh T. Kerr, Jr. LC 43-16154. 276p. 1966. Westminster.
Compend of the Institutes of the Christian Religion by John Calvin. Ed. by Hugh T. Kerr, Jr. 240p. 1964. pap. 8.95 (ISBN 0-664-24557-9). Westminster.
Compendio de la Historia Cristiana. R. A. Baker. Tr. by Francisco G. Almanza. Orig. Title: Summary of Christian History. (Span.). 372p. 1985. pap. 9.50 (ISBN 0-311-15032-2). Casa Bautista.
Compendio de Teologia Cristiana. J. M. Pendleton. Tr. by Alejandro Trevino. Orig. Title: Christian Doctrines: Compendium of Theology. (Span.). 413p. 1983. pap. 5.95 (ISBN 0-311-09008-7). Casa Bautista.
Compendio Manual de la Biblia. Henry H. Halley. Tr. by C. P. Denyer. (Span., Illus.). 768p. 1985. Repr. of 1984 ed. 14.95 (ISBN 0-311-03666-X). Casa Bautista.
Compendio Manual de la Biblia. Henry H. Halley. Orig. Title: Halley's Bible Handbook. (Span.). 768p. 1955. 14.95 (ISBN 0-8254-1300-1); pap. 12.95. Kregel.
Compendious Introduccion Unto the Pistle off Paul to the Romayns. William Tyndale. LC 74-28890. (English Experience Ser.: No. 767). 1975. Repr. 3.50 (ISBN 90-221-0767-1). Walter J Johnson.
Compendium for the Study of Christian Science: No. 1, Introduction. Max Kappeler. 28p. 1951. pap. 3.50 (ISBN 0-85241-055-7). Kappeler Inst Pub.
Compendium for the Study of Christian Science: No. 10, Love. Max Kappeler. 23p. 1953. pap. 3.50 (ISBN 0-85241-064-6). Kappeler Inst Pub.
Compendium for the Study of Christian Science: No. 2, The Seven Days of Creation. Max Kappeler. 24p. 1951. pap. 3.50 (ISBN 0-85241-056-5). Kappeler Inst Pub.
Compendium for the Study of Christian Science: No. 3, The Commandments, the Beatitudes, the Lord's Prayer. Max Kappeler. 29p. 1951. pap. 3.50 (ISBN 0-85241-057-3). Kappeler Inst Pub.

Compendium for the Study of Christian Science: No. 4, Mind. Max Kappeler. 35p. 1951. pap. 3.50 (ISBN 0-85241-058-1). Kappeler Inst Pub.

Compendium for the Study of Christian Science: No. 5, Spirit. Max Kappeler. 28p. 1951. pap. 3.50 (ISBN 0-85241-059-X). Kappeler Inst Pub.

Compendium for the Study of Christian Science: No. 6, Soul. Max Kappeler. 23p. 1952. pap. 3.50 (ISBN 0-85241-060-3). Kappeler Inst Pub.

Compendium for the Study of Christian Science: No. 7, Principle. Max Kappeler. 25p. 1952. pap. 3.50 (ISBN 0-85241-061-1). Kappeler Inst Pub.

Compendium for the Study of Christian Science: No. 8, Life. Max Kappeler. 23p. 1952. pap. 3.50 (ISBN 0-85241-062-X). Kappeler Inst Pub.

Compendium for the Study of Christian Science: No. 9, Truth. Max Kappeler. 20p. 1953. pap. 3.50 (ISBN 0-85241-063-8). Kappeler Inst Pub.

Compendium of Astrology. Rose Lineman & Jan Popelka. 1984. pap. 14.95 (ISBN 0-914918-43-5). Para Res.

Compendium of Swedenborg's Theological Writings. Samuel Warren. LC 73-94196. 816p. 1974. 5.00 (ISBN 0-87785-123-9). Swedenborg.

Compendium of the Scriptures. Ed. by L. J. Lea. 1951. pap. 10.00 (ISBN 0-8309-0253-8). Herald Hse.

Competent to Counsel. Jay E. Adams. 1977. pap. 6.95 (ISBN 0-8010-0047-5). Baker Bk.

Competent to Counsel. Jay E. Adams. 309p. 1970. pap. 6.95 (ISBN 0-87552-017-0). Presby & Reformed.

Competent to Counsel: Introduction to Nouthetic Counseling. Jay E. Adams. Ed. by Michael Smith. (Jay Adams Library). 320p. 1986. 15.95 (ISBN 0-310-51140-2, 12126). Zondervan.

Competition. Gary Warner. LC 79-51747. 1979. pap. 5.95 (ISBN 0-89191-074-3). Cook.

Competitive Designs for the Cathedral of St. John the Divine in New York City. (Architecture & Decorative Art Ser.). 57p. 1982. Repr. lib. bdg. 95.00 (ISBN 0-306-76139-4). Da Capo.

Compilation of Thoughts, I Think?! Tawny DiLustre. 104p. 1985. 6.95 (ISBN 0-8059-2962-2). Dorrance.

Compilations of Litanies & Vesper Hymns. John Aitken. 25.00x (ISBN 0-87556-004-0). Saifer.

Compleat Alchemist. Steven Cordovano & Stephan M. Sechi. (Compleat Fantasy Ser.). (Illus.). 45p. 1983. pap. text ed. 7.95 (ISBN 0-9610770-0-X, 4801). Bard Games.

Compleat Body of Divinity. Samuel Willard. (American Studies). Repr. of 1726 ed. 62.00 (ISBN 0-384-68533-1). Johnson Repr.

Compleat Marriage. Rev. ed. Nancy Van Pelt. LC 78-20770. (Orion Ser). 1979. pap. 6.95 (ISBN 0-8127-0218-2). Review & Herald.

Compleat Parson: Or, a Description of Advowsons. John Doddridge. LC 73-6119. (English Experience Ser.: No. 586). 95p. 1973. Repr. of 1630 ed. 10.50 (ISBN 90-221-0586-5). Walter J Johnson.

Compleat Sermon Program for Lent. Harold Albert & James Morentz. 1982. 4.35 (ISBN 0-89536-533-2, 0347). CSS of Ohio.

Compleat Tween. Nancy L. Van Pelt. Ed. by Richard W. Coffen. 96p. (Orig.). 1986. pap. 5.95 (ISBN 0-8280-0288-6). Review & Herald.

Complete Art of Witchcraft. Sybil Leek. (Illus.). 208p. 1973. pap. 2.95 (ISBN 0-451-12714-5, AE2714, Sig). NAL.

Complete Book of Baby & Child Care. rev. & updated ed. Grace H. Ketterman. 560p. 1981. 18.95 (ISBN 0-8007-1421-0); pap. 8.95 (ISBN 0-8007-1515-2). Revell.

Complete Book of Bible Quotations. Ed. by Mark Levine & Eugene Rachlis. pap. 12.95 (ISBN 0-671-49864-9). PB.

Complete Book of Church Growth. Elmer L. Towns & John Vaughan. 1981. 14.95 (ISBN 0-8423-0408-8). Tyndale.

Complete Book of Hanukah. Kinneret Chiel. (Illus.). pap. 6.95x (ISBN 0-87068-367-5). Ktav.

Complete Book of Jewish Observance. Leo Trepp. LC 79-1352. (Illus.). 1979. 16.50 (ISBN 0-87441-281-1). Behrman.

Complete Book of Jewish Observance. Leo Trepp. LC 79-1352. (Behrman House Book). (Illus.). 370p. 1980. 14.95 (ISBN 0-671-41797-5). Summit Bks.

Complete Book of Spells, Ceremonies, & Magic. Migene Gonzalez-Wippler. (Illus.). 1977. 12.95 (ISBN 0-517-52885-1). Crown.

Complete Book of Yoga: Harmony of Body & Mind. SriAnanda. 175p. 1980. 11.95x (ISBN 0-317-12476-5, Pub. by Vision Bks India). Asia Bk Corp.

Complete Categorized Greek-English New Testament Vocabulary. David Holly. (Eng. & Gr.). 141p. 1978. 9.50 (ISBN 0-85150-119-2). Attic Pr.

Complete Categorized Greek-English New Testament Vocabulary. David Holly. (Gr. & Eng.). 1980. pap. 6.95 (ISBN 0-8010-4224-0). Baker Bk.

Complete Common-Place Book to the Holy Bible; or, a Scriptural Account of the Faith & Practices of Christians: Comprehending a Thorough Arrangement of the Various Texts of Scripture Bearing upon the Doctrines, Duties, & C., of Revealed Religion. Hugh Gaston. 1979. Repr. of 1847 ed. lib. bdg. 15.00 (ISBN 0-8482-4186-X). Norwood Edns.

Complete Concerti Grossi in Full Score. George F. Handel. 20.25 (ISBN 0-8446-5890-1). Peter Smith.

Complete Concordance to the Bible: New King James Version. LC 83-13271. 1120p. 1983. 19.95 (ISBN 0-8407-4959-7); indexed 23.95 (ISBN 0-8407-4953-8). Nelson.

Complete Concordance to the Poetical Works of John Milton. Charles D. Cleveland. LC 76-57784. 1867. lib. bdg. 38.50 (ISBN 0-8414-3459-X). Folcroft.

Complete Concordance to the Writings of Mary B. Eddy. Mary B. Eddy. 33.50 (ISBN 0-87952-092-2). First Church.

Complete Disciple. Paul W. Powell. 120p. 1982. pap. 4.95 (ISBN 0-88207-307-9). Victor Bks.

Complete English-Hebrew, Hebrew-English Dictionary, 3 vols. Reuben Alcalay. (Eng. & Hebrew.). 7180p. 1980. Repr. of 1965 ed. 69.00 set (ISBN 0-89961-017-X). Vol. 1 (ISBN 0-89961-003-X). Vol. 2 (ISBN 0-89961-007-2). Vol. 3 (ISBN 0-89961-008-0). SBS Pub.

Complete Exorcist. Nelson White & Anne White. LC 83-50160. (Exorcism from Scratch Ser.). (Illus.). 75p. (Orig.). 1983. pap. 15.00 (ISBN 0-939856-33-6). Tech Group.

Complete Family Guide to Jewish Holidays. Dalia H. Renberg. (Illus.). 256p. 1984. pap. 15.95 (ISBN 0-531-09408-1). Watts.

Complete Family Guide to Jewish Holidays. Dalia H. Renberg. LC 84-11008. (Illus.). 1985. pap. 15.95 (ISBN 0-915361-09-4, 09408-1, Dist. by Watts). Adama Pubs Inc.

Complete Green Letters. Miles J. Stanford. 368p. 1984. pap. 9.95 (ISBN 0-310-33051-3, 9480, Clarion Class). Zondervan.

Complete Guide to Asset-Based Lending. Peter S. Clarke. LC 85-9362. 314p. 1986. 69.95 (ISBN 0-13-159831-7, Busn). P-H.

Complete Guide to Making the Most of Video in Religious Settings: How to Produce, Find, Use & Distribute Video in the Church & Synagogue. Tom N. Emswiler et al. LC 85-50019. 128p. (Orig.). 1985. pap. 9.95 (ISBN 0-9606652-1-8). Wesley Found.

Complete Guide to the Christian's Budget. new ed. Michael L. Speer. LC 74-80341. 160p. 1975. pap. 3.25 (ISBN 0-8054-5227-3). Broadman.

Complete Illustrated Book of Yoga. Swami Vishnudevananda. 1981. pap. 3.50 (ISBN 0-671-44787-4). PB.

Complete Index to C. H. Spurgeon's Sermons. C. H. Spurgeon. 1980. 5.95 (ISBN 0-686-27983-2). Pilgrim Pubns.

Complete Layman's Bible Book Commentary Set, 24 vols. 1984. Set. 129.95 (ISBN 0-8054-1170-4). Broadman.

Complete Letters. St. Ambrose. LC 67-28583. (Fathers of the Church Ser.: Vol. 26). 515p. 1954. 26.95x (ISBN 0-8132-0026-1). Cath U Pr.

Complete Letters. St. Cyprian. LC 65-12906. (Fathers of the Church Ser.: Vol. 51). 352p. 1964. 19.95x (ISBN 0-8132-0051-2). Cath U Pr.

Complete Life of Christ. John F. Millar. LC 85-51584. (Illus.). 180p. (Orig.). 1986. 15.95 (ISBN 0-934943-04-4); pap. 8.95 (ISBN 0-934943-01-X). Thirteen Colonies Pr.

Complete Meditation. Steve Kravette. (Illus.). 320p. (Orig.). 1982. pap. 10.95 (ISBN 0-914918-28-1). Para Res.

Complete Poetry of John Milton. John Milton. Ed. by John T. Shawcross. LC 72-150934. 1971. pap. 8.95 (ISBN 0-385-02351-0, Anch). Doubleday.

Complete Prose Works of Matthew Arnold, 11 vols. Matthew Arnold. Ed. by R. H. Super. Incl. Vol. 1. On the Classical Tradition. 282p. 1960. 19.95x (ISBN 0-472-11651-7); Vol. 2. Democratic Education. 430p. 1962. 19.95x (ISBN 0-472-11652-5); Vol. 3. Lectures & Essays in Criticism. 586p. 1962. 19.95x (ISBN 0-472-11653-3); Vol. 4. Schools & Universities on the Continent. 446p. 1964. 19.95x (ISBN 0-472-11654-1); Vol. 5. Culture & Anarchy. 580p. 1965. 19.95x (ISBN 0-472-11655-X); Vol. 6. Dissent & Dogma. 624p. 1967. 19.95x (ISBN 0-472-11656-8); Vol. 7. God & the Bible. 604p. 1970. 19.95x (ISBN 0-472-11657-6); Vol. 8. Essays Religious & Mixed. 576p. 1972. 19.95x (ISBN 0-472-11658-4); Vol. 9. English Literature & Irish Politics. 1973. 19.95x (ISBN 0-472-11659-2); Vol. 10. Philistinism in England & America. 1974. 19.95x (ISBN 0-472-11660-6); Vol. 11. Last Word. 1976. 19.95x (ISBN 0-472-11661-4). LC 60-5018. U of Mich Pr.

Complete Purim Service. Morris Silverman & Jacob Neusner. pap. 2.95 (ISBN 0-87677-064-2). Prayer Bk.

Complete Server. Kerry J. Lanz. (Illus.). 1978. 1.95 (ISBN 0-8192-1245-8). Morehouse.

Complete Set of Commentaries, 22 vols. H. A. Ironside. 244.90 (ISBN 0-87213-350-8). Loizeaux.

Complete Set of God's People at Work in the Parish Series, 11 bks. Woodburn et al. 1979. pap. 12.50 set (ISBN 0-570-08036-3, 12-2775). Concordia.

Complete Set of Midrash Rabba: Hebrew & English, 18 vols. 395.00 (ISBN 0-87559-160-4). Shalom.

Complete Spiritual Doctrine of St. Therese of Lisieux. Francois Jamart. Tr. by Walter Van De Putte. LC 61-8203. 1977. pap. 6.95 (ISBN 0-8189-0347-3). Alba.

Complete System of Self-Healing. Stephen T. Chang. LC 86-1859. (Illus.). 224p. 1986. 17.00 (ISBN 0-942196-06-6). Tao Pub.

Complete Talmud, 64 vols. Set. 995.00 (ISBN 0-910218-50-1). Bennet Pub.

Complete Theological Works of Herbert Thorndike, 6 Vols. in 10. Herbert Thorndike. LC 76-177454. (Library of Anglo-Catholic Theology: No. 17). Repr. of 1856 ed. Set. 295.00 (ISBN 0-404-52150-9). AMS Pr.

Complete Works, 12 vols. William Beveridge. LC 72-39437. (Library of Anglo-Catholic Theology: No. 2). Repr. of 1848 ed. Set. 360.00 (ISBN 0-404-52040-5). AMS Pr.

Complete Works of Elizabeth of the Trinity: Major Spiritual Writings, Vol. 1. Tr. by Aletheia Kane from Fr. LC 84-3748. Tr. of J'ai Trouve Dieu, Oeuvres Completes. (Illus.). 208p. (Orig.). 1984. pap. 6.95x (ISBN 0-935216-01-4). ICS Pubns.

Complete Works of Francis A. Schaeffer. Francis A. Schaeffer. LC 84-72010. 2250p. 1985. (Crossway Bks); pap. 59.95 (ISBN 0-89107-331-0). Good News.

Complete Works of Josephus, 4 vols. Flavius Josephus. 39.95 set (ISBN 0-8010-5056-1). Baker Bk.

Complete Works of Josephus. Flavius Josephus. Tr. by William Whiston. LC 60-15405. 840p. (Orig.). 1974. 18.95 (ISBN 0-8254-2951-X); kivar 14.95 (ISBN 0-8254-2952-8). Kregel.

Complete Works of Lao Tzu: Tao Teh Ching & Hua Hu Ching. Hua-Ching Ni. LC 79-88745. (Illus.). 219p. (Orig.). 1979. pap. 9.50 (ISBN 0-937064-00-9). SEBT.

Complete Works of Lao Tzu: Tao Teh Ching & Hua Hu Ching. Master Ni Hua-Ching & Hua-Ching. LC 79-88745. 219p. 1979. pap. text ed. 7.50x (ISBN 0-937064-00-9). Wisdom Garden.

Complete Works of Sister Nivedita, 4 vols. Sr. Nivedita. Incl. Vol. 1. Our Master & His Message, the Master As I Saw Him, Kali the Mother, Lectures & Articles (ISBN 0-87481-112-0); Vol. 2. Web of Indian Life, an Indian Study on Love & Death, Studies from an Eastern Home, Lectures & Articles (ISBN 0-87481-113-9); Vol. 3. Indian Art, Cradle Tales of Hinduism, Religion & Dharma (ISBN 0-87481-114-7); Vol. 4. Footfalls of Indian History, Bodh-Gaya, Civic Ideal & Indian Nationality, Hints on National Education in India (ISBN 0-87481-115-5); Vol. V. Lectures & Writings (ISBN 0-87481-226-7). 60.00x set (ISBN 0-87481-216-X). Vedanta Pr.

Complete Works of Swami Abhedananda, 11 vols. Swami Abhedananda. (Illus.). Set. 125.00x (ISBN 0-87481-621-1). Vedanta Pr.

Complete Works of Swami Vivekananda, 8 Vols. Swami Vivekananda. 75.00x (ISBN 0-87481-092-2); Vol. 1. 10.95x (ISBN 0-87481-137-6); Vol. 2. 10.00x (ISBN 0-87481-138-4); Vol. 3. 10.95x (ISBN 0-87481-139-2); Vol. 4. 10.95x (ISBN 0-87481-140-6); Vol. 5. 10.95x (ISBN 0-87481-141-4); Vol. 6. 10.95x (ISBN 0-87481-142-2); Vol. 7. 10.95x (ISBN 0-87481-143-0); Vol. 8. 10.95x (ISBN 0-87481-144-9). Vedanta Pr.

Complete Works of Swami Vivekananda, 8 vols. Swami Vivekananda. pap. 55.00x (ISBN 0-87481-176-7). Vedanta Pr.

Complete Works of the Late Rev. Thomas Boston, Ettrick: Including His Memoirs, Written by Himself, 12 vols. Thomas Boston. Ed. by Samuel M'Millan. (Puritan Library). (Illus.). 1980. Repr. of 1853 ed. Set. lib. bdg. 225.00 (ISBN 0-940033-00-3). R O Roberts.

Complete Works of Walter Trobisch. Walter Trobisch. 700p. 1987. 19.95 (ISBN 0-87784-524-7). Inter-Varsity.

Complete Works of William Billings, Vol. III: The Psalm-Singer's Amusement, the Suffolk Harmony, & Independent Publications. Ed. by Karl Kroeger & Richard Crawford. (Illus.). 456p. 1986. text ed. 50.00x (ISBN 0-8139-1130-3, Pub. by American Musicological Society-Colonial Society MA). U Pr of Va.

Complete Writings. St. Justin Martyr. (Fathers of the Church Ser.: Vol. 6). 486p. 1948. 34.95 (ISBN 0-8132-0006-7). Cath U Pr.

Complete Writings. Salvian the Presbyter. (Fathers of the Church Ser.: Vol. 3). 396p. 1947. 34.95x (ISBN 0-8132-0003-2). Cath U Pr.

Complete Writings of Menno Simons: Circa 1496-1561. Ed. by John C. Wenger. Tr. by Leonard Verduin. LC 55-9815. 1104p. 1956. 35.00 (ISBN 0-8361-1353-5). Herald Pr.

Complete Yoga Book: Yoga of Breathing, Yoga of Postures, & Yoga of Meditation. James Hewitt. LC 77-15934. (Illus., Orig.). 1978. pap. 11.95 (ISBN 0-8052-0592-6). Schocken.

Complete Youth Ministries Handbook, Vol. 1. Ed. by J. David Stone. 256p. (Orig.). 1980. pap. 14.95 (ISBN 0-687-09340-6). Abingdon.

Completely Pro-Life. Evangelicals for Social Action Staff & Ronald J. Sider. 160p. (Orig.). 1987. pap. 5.95 (ISBN 0-87784-496-8). Inter-Varsity.

Completeness in Christ. Verla A. Mooth. 144p. 1984. pap. 5.95 (ISBN 0-8059-2954-1). Dorrance.

Completing the Promise. Rosalie L. Coffey & John S. Glenn. (Religious Awards for Boy Scouts Ser.). 1984. pap. 4.95x (ISBN 0-938758-17-9). MTM Pub Co.

Complex Forms of the Religious Life: A Durkheimian View of New Religious Movements. Frances Westley. LC 83-4579. (AAR Academy Ser.). 210p. 1983. 13.50 (ISBN 0-89130-626-9, 01 01 45). Scholars Pr GA.

Complex Inheritance. Ed. by James G. Moseley. LC 75-8955. (American Academy of Religion. Dissertation Ser.). ix, 169p. 1975. pap. 9.95 (ISBN 0-89130-000-7, 010104). Scholars Pr GA.

Complex Ministry of Rural Pastorate. Kenneth Thrasher. 1984. pap. 5.95 (ISBN 0-89957-054-2). AMG Pubs.

Complex Vision of Philo St. John. R. Martin Helick. LC 75-27035. 1975. 10.00 (ISBN 0-912710-07-1). Regent Graphic Serv.

Composite Portrait of Israel. Ed. by Emanuel Mark. LC 80-40889. 1981. 55.50 (ISBN 0-12-476450-9). Acad Pr.

Composition & Date of Acts. C. C. Torrey. (Harvard Theological Studies). 1916. pap. 15.00 (ISBN 0-527-01001-4). Kraus Repr.

Composition Musicale et Composition Litteraire a Propos du Chant Gregorrien. Antoine Dechevrens. 373p. 1910. Repr. lib. bdg. 62.50x (Pub. by G Olms BRD). Coronet Bks.

Composition of the Book of Isaiah in the Light of History & Archaeology. R. H. Kennett. (British Academy, London, Schweich Lectures on Biblical Archaeology Series, 1909). pap. 19.00 (ISBN 0-8115-1251-7). Kraus Repr.

Composition of the Deuteronomic History. Brian Peckham. (Harvard Semitic Museum Monographs). 1985. 13.95 (ISBN 0-89130-909-8, 04-00-35). Scholars Pr GA.

Comprehensive Bibliography of the Thanatology Literature. Ed. by Martin L. Kutscher et al. LC 75-5627. 285p. 1976. 14.00 (ISBN 0-8422-7274-7). Irvington.

Comprehensive Commentary on the Qur'an, 4 Vols. Ed. by George Sales & E. M. Wherry. LC 79-153620. Repr. of 1896 ed. Set. 145.00 (ISBN 0-404-09520-8); 27.50 ea. Vol. 1 (ISBN 0-404-09521-6). Vol. 2 (ISBN 0-404-09522-4). Vol. 3 (ISBN 0-404-09523-2). Vol. 4 (ISBN 0-404-09524-0). AMS Pr.

Comprehensive History of Jainism. Asim K. Chatterjee. 1978. 20.00x (ISBN 0-8364-0225-1). South Asia Bks.

Comprehensive History of The Church of Jesus Christ of Latter-day Saints, 6 vols plus index. B. H. Roberts. (Illus.). 1965. Vols. 1-6. 12.95 ea.; Vol. 1. (ISBN 0-8425-0299-8); Vol. 2. (ISBN 0-8425-0300-5); Vol. 3. (ISBN 0-8425-0301-3); Vol. 4. (ISBN 0-8425-0482-6); Vol. 5. (ISBN 0-8425-0304-8); Vol. 6. (ISBN 0-8425-0305-6); Index. 9.95 (ISBN 0-8425-0627-6). Brigham.

Comprehensive Index to Biblical Archaeologist, Vol. 36-45. Compiled by D. Bruce Makay. 225p. 1986. pap. 11.95 (ISBN 0-89757-008-1, Dist. by Eisenbrauns). Am Sch Orient Res.

Comprehensive Topical & Textual Lesson Commentary Index: 1922-1982. 4th ed. Ernest A. Clevenger, Jr. & Glenda W. Clevenger. 114p. 1981. pap. text ed. 6.95 (ISBN 0-88428-019-5). Parchment Pr.

Comprehensive View of Freemasonry. Henry W. Coil. (Illus.). 1985. Repr. of 1954 ed. text ed. 12.50 (ISBN 0-88053-053-7). Macoy Pub.

Compulsion of the Spirit: A Roland Allen Reader. Roland Allen. Ed. by Charles H. Long & David Paton. 160p. 1983. pap. 3.70 (ISBN 0-88028-025-5). Forward Movement.

Computer Bible Games, Bk. 2. John Conrod. LC 83-91269. 160p. (Orig.). (YA) 1984. pap. 6.95 (ISBN 0-89636-141-1). Accent Bks.

Computer Concordance to the Norum Testamentum Graece. 2nd ed. 1985. 72.00 (ISBN 3-11-010528-4). De Gruyter.

Computer Ethics: A Guide for the New Age. Douglas W. Johnson. 128p. (Orig.). 1984. pap. 6.95 (ISBN 0-87178-155-7). Brethren.

Computer Speaks: God's Message to the World. Rashad Khalifa. (Illus.). 250p. (Orig.). 1981. 9.50 (ISBN 0-934894-38-8). Islamic Prods.

Computer Tools for Ancient Texts: Proceedings of the 1980 Ann Arbor Symposium on Biblical Studies & the Computer. Ed. by H. Van Dyke Parunak. 1987. text ed. price not set (ISBN 0-931464-32-3). Eisenbrauns.

Computers in the Church: Practical Assistance in Making the Computer Decision. Richard B. Sargent & John E. Benson. (Administration Series for Churches). 112p. (Orig.). 1986. pap. 10.95 (ISBN 0-8066-2231-8, 10-1625). Augsburg.

Computers: New Opportunities for Personalized Ministry. Kenneth Bedell & Parker Rossman. 128p. 1984. pap. 4.95 (ISBN 0-8170-1039-4). Judson.

Comrades of the Trail. Colleen L. Reece. Ed. by Gerald Wheeler. (Banner Ser.). 96p. (Orig.). 1987. pap. 6.50 (ISBN 0-8280-0355-6). Review & Herald.

Comte de St. Germain. Isabel Cooper-Oakley. 15.95 (ISBN 0-7229-5146-9). Theos Pub Hse.

Comunicacion Cristiana. Alan Compton. 168p. 1985. Repr. of 1982 ed. 4.15 (ISBN 0-311-13833-0). Casa Bautista.

Comunicacion Por Medio de la Predicacion. Orlando E. Costas. (Span.). 255p. pap. 6.25 (ISBN 0-89922-021-5). Edit Caribe.

Comunidad del Rey. Howard Snyder. (Span.). 232p. (Orig.). 1983. pap. 5.50 (ISBN 0-317-00691-6). Edit Caribe.

Concatenation: Enoch's Prophecy Fulfilling! Hebrew-Christian Metaphysics Supported by Modern Science. Evolyn B. Feiring. LC 72-96989. 5.00x (ISBN 0-9603386-0-8); pap. 2.00x (ISBN 0-9603386-1-6). Rocky Mtn Bks.

Concealed Wisdom in World Mythology. Hodson. 13.50 (ISBN 0-8356-7556-4). Theos Pub Hse.

Concentration: A Guide to Mental Mastery. M. Sadhu. pap. 5.00 (ISBN 0-87980-023-2). Wilshire.

Concentration: An Approach Meditation. Ernest Wood. 6.75 (ISBN 0-8356-7337-5). Theos Pub Hse.

Concentration: An Approach to Meditation. Ernest Wood. LC 67-2874. pap. 3.75 (ISBN 0-8356-0176-5, Quest). Theos Pub Hse.

Concentration & Meditation. Christmas Humphries. 343p. 1981. pap. 18.00 (ISBN 0-89540-068-5, SD-068). Sun Pub.

Concentration & Meditation. Swami Jyotir Maya Nanda. (Illus.). 1971. 6.99 (ISBN 0-934664-03-X). Yoga Res Foun.

Concentration & Meditation. 8th ed. Swami Paramananda. 1974. pap. 3.50 (ISBN 0-911564-07-1). Vedanta Ctr.

Concentric Circles of Concern. W. Oscar Thompson, Jr. & Carolyn Thompson. LC 81-67488. 1981. 7.95 (ISBN 0-8054-6233-3). Broadman.

Concept & Empathy. Ninian Smart. Ed. by Donald Wiebe. LC 85-18957. 240p. 1986. 35.00. NYU Pr.

Concept Books Series Four, 4 bks. LC 56-1400. 1983. Set. pap. 14.50 (ISBN 0-570-08528-4). Concordia.

Concept Development & the Development of the God Concept in the Child: A Bibliography. V. Peter Pitts. LC 77-70266. 1977. pap. 2.75 (ISBN 0-915744-07-4). Character Res.

Concept of an Islamic State: An Analysis of the Ideological Controversy in Pakistan. Ishtiaq Ahmed. 266p. (Orig.). 1985. pap. text ed. 37.50x (ISBN 91-7146-458-1, Pub. by Almqvist & Wiksell). Coronet Bks.

Concept of Apokatastasis in Acts: A Study in Primitive Christian Theology. James Parker. 140p. 1981. pap. text ed. 5.95 (ISBN 0-931016-01-0). Schola Pr TX.

Concept of Belief in Islamic Theology. Toshihiko Izutsu. LC 79-52553. (Islam Ser.). 1980. Repr. of 1965 ed. lib. bdg. 20.00x (ISBN 0-8369-9261-X). Ayer Co Pubs.

Concept of Biblical Authority. Gordon H. Clark. 1979. 0.75 (ISBN 0-87552-143-6). Presby & Reformed.

Concept of Church: A Methodological Inquiry into the Use of Metaphors in Ecclesiology. Herwi Rikhof. LC 80-84751. xvi, 304p. 1981. 35.00x (ISBN 0-915762-11-0). Patmos Pr.

Concept of Comparative Philosophy. Henry Corbin. Tr. by Peter Russell from Fr. (Orig.). 1985. pap. 3.95 (ISBN 0-933999-29-1). Phanes Pr.

Concept of Consciousness. Edwin B. Holt. LC 73-2969. (Classics in Psychology Ser.). Repr. of 1914 ed. 23.50 (ISBN 0-405-05141-7). Ayer Co Pubs.

Concept of Correlation: Paul Tillich & the Possibility of a Mediating Theology. John P. Clayton. (Theologische Bibliothek Topelmann Ser.: No. 37). 427p. 1979. text ed. 44.25x (ISBN 3-11007-914-3). De Gruyter.

Concept of Cow in the Rig Veda. Doris Srinivasan. 1979. 9.95 (ISBN 0-89684-060-3, Pub. by Motilal Banarsidass India). Orient Bk Dist.

Concept of Glaubenslehre: Ernst Troeltsch & the Theological Heritage of Schleiermacher. Walter E. Wyman, Jr. LC 83-4432. (American Academy of Religion, Academy Ser.). 276p. 1983. 14.95 (ISBN 0-89130-620-X, 01 01 44). Scholars Pr GA.

Concept of God. Ronald Nash. 1983. (cep) 5.95 (ISBN 0-310-45141-8, 12381P). Zondervan.

Concept of Islam. Mahmoud Abu-Saud. Ed. by Hamid Quinlan. LC 83-70184. 147p. 1983. pap. 6.50 (ISBN 0-89259-043-2). Am Trust Pubns.

Concept of Knowledge: Indian Theories. Debabrata Sen. 1985. 24.00x (ISBN 0-8364-1398-9, Pub. by KP Bagchi India). South Asia Bks.

Concept of Love in Sidney & Spenser. Roswitha Mayr. Ed. by James Hogg. (Elizabethan & Renaissance Studies). 124p. (Orig.). 1978. pap. 15.00 (ISBN 0-317-40126-2, Pub. by Salzburg Studies). Longwood Pub Group.

Concept of Maya in Samkara & Radhakrishnan. Donald R. Tuck. 1986. 17.00x (ISBN 0-8364-1375-X). South Asia Bks.

Concept of Morals. Walter T. Stace. 11.25 (ISBN 0-8446-2990-1). Peter Smith.

Concept of Perfection in the Teachings of Kant & the Gita. B. S. Gauchhwal. 1967. 4.95 (ISBN 0-89684-186-3). Orient Bk Dist.

Concept of Purity at Quaram & in the Letters of Paul. Michael Newton. (Society of New Testament Studies Monograph: No. 53). 180p. 1985. 32.50 (ISBN 0-521-26583-5). Cambridge U Pr.

Concept of Riti & Guna in Sanskrit Poetics in Their Historical Development. P. C. Lahiri. xvi, 310p. 1974. 12.00x (ISBN 0-8364-0393-2). South Asia Bks.

Concept of State & Law in Islam. Farooq Hassan. LC 80-69038. 321p. (Orig.). 1981. lib. bdg. 29.25 (ISBN 0-8191-1426-X); pap. text ed. 13.75 (ISBN 0-8191-1427-8). U Pr of Amer.

Concept of the Guardian Spirit in North America. Ruth F. Benedict. LC 24-872. (American Anthropology Association Memoirs). 1923. 12.00 (ISBN 0-527-00528-2). Kraus Repr.

Concept of the Self in the French Enlightenment. J. A. Perkins. 162p. (Orig.). 1969. pap. text ed. 24.50x (Pub. by Droz Switzerland). Coronet Bks.

Concept of Univocity Regarding the Predication of God & Creature According to William Ockham. Matthew C. Menges. (Philosophy Ser). 1952. 8.00 (ISBN 0-686-11539-2). Franciscan Inst.

Concept of Zionist Dissent in the American Mind 1917-1941. Stuart E. Knee. 1979. 14.95 (ISBN 0-8315-0177-4). Speller.

Conception of Buddhist Nirvana. F. I. Stcherbatskoi. lib. bdg. 100.00 (ISBN 0-87968-058-X). Krishna Pr.

Conception of Buddhist Nirvana. 2nd rev. ed. Theodore Stcherbatsky. 1977. 13.95 (ISBN 0-89684-187-1). Orient Bk Dist.

Conception of Buddhist Nirvana. Theodore Stcherbatsky. 408p. 1979. pap. 6.95 (ISBN 0-87728-427-X). Weiser.

Conception of God in the Philosophy of Thomas Aquinas. Robert L. Patterson. 508p. 1977. Repr. of 1935 ed. lib. bdg. 30.00 (ISBN 0-915172-27-5). Richwood Pub.

Conception of Immortality. Josiah Royce. 1968. Repr. of 1900 ed. lib. bdg. 22.50x (ISBN 0-8371-0207-3, ROCI). Greenwood.

Conceptions of God in Ancient Egypt: The One & the Many. Tr. by Erik Hornung & John Baines. LC 82-71602. (Illus.). 296p. 1982. 29.95x (ISBN 0-8014-1223-4). Cornell U Pr.

Concepto Biblico de Justicia. Jose Gallardo. LC 86-80343. (Title from Mennonite Faith Ser.). 80p. (Orig.). 1986. pap. 1.50X (ISBN 0-8361-1285-7). Herald Pr.

Concepts in Jewish Art. Jonathan Craig. LC 84-263. (Judaic Studies). (Illus.). 165p. 1986. 24.00x (ISBN 0-8046-9355-2, 9355, Pub. by Natl U). Assoc Faculty Pr.

Concepts of Ethics. Sidney Zink. 1969. 18.95 (ISBN 0-312-16100-X). St Martin.

Concepts of Islam. M. A. Saud. pap. 6.95 (ISBN 0-317-01600-8). Kazi Pubns.

Concepts of Judaism. Isaac Breuer. Tr. by Jacob S. Levinger. 1974. 10.00 (ISBN 0-87306-058-X). Feldheim.

Concepts of Original Sin & Grace. Rudolf Steiner. Tr. by D. S. Osmond from Ger. 32p. 1973. pap. 1.95 (ISBN 0-85440-275-6, Pub. by Steinerbooks). Anthroposophic.

Concepts of Qabalah. William G. Gray. LC 82-62848. (Sangreal Sodality Ser.: Vol.3). 384p. 1984. pap. 9.95 (ISBN 0-87728-561-6). Weiser.

Concepts of Sikhism. Pritam S. Gill. 183p. 1979. 10.00x (ISBN 0-89684-379-3). Orient Bk Dist.

Concepts of Spirit & Demon: A Study in the Use of Different Languages Describing the Same Phenomena. Pamela M. Binyon. (IC-Studies in the International History of Christianity: Vol. 8). 132p. 1977. pap. 19.60 (ISBN 3-261-01787-2). P Lang Pubs.

Conceptual Approach to the Mekilta. Max Kadushin. 11.95x (ISBN 0-87334-014-0). Ktav.

Concern for the Church: Theological Investigations Vol. 20. Karl Rahner. (Theological Investigations Ser.). (Ger.). 272p. 1981. 16.95 (ISBN 0-8245-0027-X). Crossroad NY.

Concerned Women Can Make a Difference. Jane Chastain. 1987. pap. 7.95 (ISBN 0-8307-1185-6, 5418968). Regal.

Concerning Christian Unity. James E. Massey. 1979. 3.95 (ISBN 0-87162-219-X, D3070). Warner Pr.

Concerning Death: A Practical Guide for the Living. Ed. by Earl A. Grollman. LC 73-17117. 384p. 1974. pap. 9.95 (ISBN 0-8070-2765-0, BP484). Beacon Pr.

Concerning Handel: His Life & Works. William C. Smith. LC 78-59044. (Encore Music Editions). (Illus.). 1979. Repr. of 1948 ed. 27.50 (ISBN 0-88355-716-9). Hyperion Conn.

Concerning Heretics. Roland H. Bainton. 1965. Repr. lib. bdg. 27.50x (ISBN 0-374-90323-9, Octagon). Hippocrene Bks.

Concerning Our Duties to God. Apostolos Makrakis. Ed. by Orthodox Christian Educational Society. 170p. 1958. pap. text ed. 4.50x (ISBN 0-938366-13-0). Orthodox Chr.

Concerning Scandals. John Calvin. Tr. by John W. Fraser. LC 78-8675. Repr. of 1978 ed. 24.90 (ISBN 0-8357-9126-2, 2012802). Bks Demand UMI.

Concerning Spiritual Gifts. rev. ed. Donald Gee. LC 80-83784. 144p. 1972. pap. 2.95 (ISBN 0-88243-486-1, 02-0486). Gospel Pub.

Concerning Spiritual Gifts. 2nd ed. Kenneth E. Hagin. 1974. pap. 2.50 (ISBN 0-89276-072-9). Hagin Ministries.

Concerning the Eternal Predestination of God. John Calvin. Tr. by J. K. Reid. 1961. pap. 13.95 (ISBN 0-227-67438-3). Attic Pr.

Concerning the Jews. Mark Twain. LC 84-27665. 32p. (Orig.). 1985. lib. bdg. 12.90 (ISBN 0-89471-336-1); pap. 3.95 (ISBN 0-89471-335-3). Running Pr.

Concerning the Mysteries. Saint Ambrosius. 1977. pap. 1.25 (ISBN 0-686-19348-2). Eastern Orthodox.

Concerto Ecclesiae Catholicae in Anglia Adversus Calvinopapistas et Puritanos. John Bridgewater. 886p. Repr. of 1588 ed. text ed. 149.04 (ISBN 0-576-78532-6, Pub. by Gregg Intl Pubs England). Gregg Intl.

Conchita: A Mother's Diary. M. M. Philipon. Tr. by Aloysius Owen. LC 78-1929. 1978. pap. 6.95 (ISBN 0-8189-0368-6). Alba.

Concilia Scotiae, 2 Vols. Ed. by Joseph Robertson. LC 77-39875. (Bannatyne Club, Edinburgh. Publications: No. 113). Repr. of 1866 ed. 65.00 (ISBN 0-404-52866-X). AMS Pr.

Conciliator: A Reconcilement of the Apparent Contradictions in Holy Scripture. Manasseh Ben-Israel. Tr. by E. H. Lindo from Span. LC 72-83942. (Library of Judaic Studies: No. SHP 10). 688p. 1987. Repr. of 1904 ed. 23.50 (ISBN 0-87203-115-2). Hermon.

Concilium: Religion in the Eighties. Ed. by Hans Kung & Edward Schillebeeckx. (Concilium Ser.: Vols. 131-140). 128p. (Orig.). 1980. pap. 53.55 (ISBN 0-8164-2283-4, HarpR). Har-Row.

Concilium: Religion in the Eighties. Ed. by Hans Kung & Edward Schillebeeckx. (Concilium Ser.: Vols. 151-160). 128p. (Orig.). 1982. pap. 62.55 (ISBN 0-8164-2392-X, HarpR). Har-Row.

Concise Bible Dictionary. 2nd ed. Dr. Donald M. McFarlan. 208p. 1986. pap. 3.95 (ISBN 0-89622-301-9). Twenty-Third.

Concise Catholic Dictionary Shortened Titles on Reprints. R. Reynolds & Rosemary Ekstrom. 224p. 1982. pap. 3.95 (ISBN 0-89622-159-8). Twenty-Third.

Concise Church History: St. Joseph Edition. Lawerence G. Lovasik. (Orig.). 1986. pap. 5.95 (ISBN 0-89942-262-4). Catholic BK Pub.

Concise Code of Jewish Law: Daily Prayers & Religious Observances in the Life-Cycle of the Jew, Vol. 1. G. Appel. 11.95 (ISBN 0-87068-298-9). Ktav.

Concise Coptic-English Lexicon. Richard H. Smith. 81p. 1983. 10.95x (ISBN 0-8028-3581-3). Eerdmans.

Concise Dictionary of Christian Ethics. Ed. by Bernard Stoeckle. 1979. 19.50 (ISBN 0-8245-0300-7). Crossroad NY.

Concise Dictionary of Christian Theology. Millard J. Erickson. 1986. 9.95 (ISBN 0-8010-3436-1). Baker Bk.

Concise Dictionary of Greek & Roman Mythology. Michael Stapleton. LC 85-15101. (Orig.). 1986. pap. 4.95 (ISBN 0-87226-006-2). P Bedrick Bks.

Concise Dictionary of Religion. Vergilius Fern. 1956. 7.95 (ISBN 0-8022-0488-0). Philos Lib.

Concise Encyclopedia of Jewish Music. 9.95 (ISBN 0-686-76494-3). Feldheim.

Concise Encyclopedia of Living Faiths. Ed. by Robert C. Zaehner. (Illus.). (YA) pap. 16.95x (ISBN 0-8070-1151-7, BP275). Beacon Pr.

Concise Exegetical Grammar of New Testament Greek. J. Harold Greenlee. (Orig.). 1963. pap. 3.95 (ISBN 0-8028-1092-6). Eerdmans.

Concise Exegetical Grammar of New Testament Greek. 5th, rev. ed. J. Harold Greenlee. 88p. (Orig.). 1987. pap. text ed. 5.95 (ISBN 0-8028-0173-0). Eerdmans.

Concise Greek-English Dictionary of the New Testament. Barclay M. Newman. 203p. 1971. 3.25x (ISBN 3-438-06008-6, 56493, Pub. by United Bible). Am Bible.

Concise Guide to the Catholic Church. Ed. by Felician A. Foy & Rose Avato. LC 83-63170. 80p. (Orig.). 1984. pap. 6.95 (ISBN 0-87973-616-X, 616). Our Sunday Visitor.

Concise Guide to the Catholic Church, Vol. II. Ed. by Felician A. Foy & Rose M. Avato. 165p. (Orig.). 1986. pap. 6.95 (ISBN 0-87973-585-6, 585). Our Sunday Visitor.

Concise Hebrew & Aramaic Lexicon of the Old Testament. William L. Holladay. (Hebrew & Aramaic.). 1971. 27.95 (ISBN 0-8028-3413-2). Eerdmans.

Concise History of Catholicism. Marian McKenna. (Quality Paperback: No. 143). 285p. 1962. pap. 2.95 (ISBN 0-8226-0143-5). Littlefield.

Concise History of the Catholic Church. Thomas Bokenkotter. LC 78-20269. 1979. pap. 6.50 (ISBN 0-385-13015-5, Im). Doubleday.

Concise History of the Catholic Church. Alfred Lapple. (Orig.). 1985. pap. 4.95 (ISBN 0-8091-9567-4). Paulist Pr.

Concise History of the Christian World Mission. 2nd ed. J. Herbert Kane. 1978. 7.95 (ISBN 0-8010-5395-1). Baker Bk.

Concise History of the English Bible. 7th ed. Ed. by M. T. Hills & E. J. Eisenhart. 1983. pap. 3.50x (ISBN 0-8267-0326-7, 16228, Pub. by United Bible). Am Bible.

Concise History of the Kehukee Bapist Association from Its Original Rise to the Present Time. rev. ed. Lemuel Burkitt & Jesse Read. Ed. by Edwin S. Gaustad. LC 79-52591. (Baptist Tradition Ser.). 1980. Repr. of 1850 ed. lib. bdg. 28.50x (ISBN 0-405-12458-9). Ayer Co Pubs.

Concise History of the United Society of Believers Called Shakers. Charles E. Robinson. LC 75-342. (Radical Tradition in America Ser.). 134p. 1975. Repr. of 1893 ed. 16.50 (ISBN 0-88355-245-0). Hyperion Conn.

Concise Introduction to the Philosophy of Nicholas of Cusa. 3rd ed. Jasper Hopkins. LC 85-72432. xii, 194p. 1986. text ed. 20.00x (ISBN 0-938060-32-5). Banning Pr.

Concise Jewish Encyclopedia. Ed. by Cecil Roth & Geoffrey Widoger. 576p. (Orig.). 1980. pap. 8.95 (ISBN 0-452-00526-4, F526, Mer). NAL.

Concise Light on Yoga. B. K. Iyengar. LC 82-5473. (Illus.). 256p. 1982. pap. 7.95 spiral (ISBN 0-8052-0723-6). Schocken.

Concise Oxford Dictionary of Proverbs. Ed. by J. A. Simpson. (Paperback Reference Ser.). 1983. pap. 6.95 (ISBN 0-19-281880-5). Oxford U Pr.

Concise Sermon Outlines. Russell E. Spray. (Paperback Library). 72p. 1985. pap. 3.95 (ISBN 0-8010-8258-7). Baker Bk.

Concise Statement of the Principles of the Only True Church According to the Gospel of the Present Appearance of Christ...with a Letter from James Whittaker. facsimile ed. Frwd. by Bro. Theodore E. Johnson. (Mother's Work Ser.: No. 2). 14p. 1963. pap. 1.75 (ISBN 0-915836-07-6). Shaker Pr ME.

Concise Yoga Vasistha. Tr. by Swami Venkatesananda from Sanskrit. 445p. 1984. lib. bdg. 34.50x (ISBN 0-87395-955-8); pap. 10.95 (ISBN 0-87395-954-X). State U NY Pr.

Concluding Unscientific Postscript. Soren Kierkegaard. Tr. by D. F. Swenson & W. Lowrie. (American-Scandinavian Foundation). 1941. pap. 10.50x (ISBN 0-691-01960-6). Princeton U Pr.

Concordance of Selected Subjects Treated of in the Rational Psychology of Emmanuel Swedenborg. Ed. by Harold F. Pitcairn. 337p. 1960. 7.00 (ISBN 0-915221-11-X). Swedenborg Sci Assn.

Concordance of the Bible. Solomon Mendelkern. (Hebrew & Lat.). 1985. Repr. of 1896 ed. 25.00 (ISBN 0-685-81426-2). Feldheim.

Concordance of the First Targum to the Book of Esther. Bernard Grossfeld. LC 83-11550. (SBL Aramaic Studies). 186p. 1984. pap. 11.25 (ISBN 0-89130-635-8, 06 13 05). Scholars Pr GA.

Concordance of the Latin, Greek, & Italian Poems of John Milton. Ed. by L. Cooper. Repr. of 1923 ed. 18.00 (ISBN 0-527-19440-9). Kraus Repr.

Concordance of the Qur'an. Hanna E. Kassis. LC 82-40100. 1400p. 1984. 95.00x (ISBN 0-520-04327-8). U of Cal Pr.

Concordance of the Septuagint. George Morrish. 17.95 (ISBN 0-310-20300-7, 6512). Zondervan.

Concordance of the Sifrei. Binyamin Kosovsky. 75.00x (ISBN 0-685-56222-0, Pub. by Jewish Theol Seminary). Ktav.

Concordance To Juan Ruiz Libro De Buen Amor. Ed. by Rigo Mignani et al. LC 76-46390. 328p. 1977. 55.50 (ISBN 0-87395-322-3). State U NY Pr.

Concordance to Juan Ruiz's Libro De Buen Amor. Rigo Mignani & Mario A. Di Cesare. 328p. 16.00 (ISBN 0-87395-322-3, Pub. by SUNY Pr). Medieval & Renaissance NY.

Concordance to Milton's English Poetry. Ed. by William Ingram & Kathleen M. Swain. 1972. 135.00x (ISBN 0-19-811138-X). Oxford U Pr.

Concordance to Other Writings. Mary B. Eddy. 1984. 35.00 (ISBN 0-87952-089-2). First Church.

Concordance to Pascal's "Pensees". Ed. by Hugh M. Davidson & Pierre H. Dube. LC 75-16808. (Cornell Concordances Ser.). 1488p. 1975. 85.00x (ISBN 0-8014-0972-1). Cornell U Pr.

Concordance to Progress & Poverty. Helena M. McEvoy. 729p. 1959. 1.00 (ISBN 0-911312-11-0). Schalkenbach.

Concordance to Q. Richard A. Edwards. LC 75-6768. (Society of Biblical Literature. Sources for Biblical Study). iv, 186p. 1975. pap. 13.95 (ISBN 0-89130-880-6, 060307). Scholars Pr GA.

Concordance to Q. Richard A. Edwards. LC 75-6768. (Society of Biblical Literature. Sources for Biblical Study: No. 7). Repr. of 1975 ed. 36.90 (ISBN 0-8357-9568-3, 2017677). Bks Demand UMI.

Concordance to Science & Health. Mary B. Eddy. 1982. 22.50 (ISBN 0-87952-093-0). First Church.

Concordance to the Celestina. Lloyd Kasten & Jean Anderson. 1977. 12.50 (ISBN 0-87535-124-7). Hispanic Soc.

Concordance to the Christian Year. John Keble. 1871. 28.00 (ISBN 0-384-28985-1). Johnson Repr.

Concordance to the Doctrine & Covenants. John V. Bluth. 10.95 (ISBN 0-87747-048-0). Deseret Bk.

Concordance to the Good News Bible: Today's English Version. Ed. by David Robinson. 1416p. 1984. 24.95 (ISBN 0-8407-4956-2). Nelson.

Concordance to the Gospel of Sri Ramakrishna. Katherine Whitmarsh. LC 85-50340. 640p. (Orig.). 1985. pap. text ed. 59.95x (ISBN 0-87481-042-6). Vedanta Pr.

Concordance to the Hidden Words of Baha'u'llah. Jalil Mahmoudi. LC 80-21346. (Orig.). 1980. pap. 2.95 (ISBN 0-87743-148-5, 368-052). Baha'i.

Concordance to the Kitab-i-Iqan. Lee Nelson & Miriam Nelson. 350p. (Orig.). 1984. pap. 9.95 (ISBN 0-933770-29-4). Kalimat.

Concordance to the Peshitta Version of the Aramaic New Testament. Ed. by The Way International Research Team. LC 85-51248. 494p. 1985. 19.95 (ISBN 0-910068-61-5). Am Christian.

Concordance to the Poetical Works of John Milton. John Bradshaw. LC 77-13457. 1977. Repr. of 1894 ed. lib. bdg. 20.00 (ISBN 0-89341-452-2). Longwood Pub Group.

Concordance to the Poetical Works of John Milton. John Bradshaw. LC 70-144894. 412p. 1972. Repr. of 1894 ed. 27.00 (ISBN 0-403-00833-6). Scholarly.

Concordance to the Septuagint & Other Greek Versions of the Old Testament (Including the Apocryphal Books, 3 vols. in 2. Edwin Hatch & Henry A. Redpath. 1088p. 1983. Repr. of 1906 ed. Set. 75.00 (ISBN 0-8010-4270-4). Baker Bk.

Concordance to the Sermons of Bishop Zeno of Verona. Bengt M. Lofstedt & David W. Packard. (APA Philological Monographs). 1974. 37.00 (ISBN 0-89130-715-X, 40-00-32). Scholars Pr GA.

Concordance to the Targum of Isaiah. J. B. Van Zijl. LC 78-25832. (Society of Biblical Literature. Aramaic Studies: No. 3). Repr. of 1979 ed. 53.80 (ISBN 0-8357-9569-1, 2017542). Bks Demand UMI.

Concordance to the Utopia of St. Thomas More & a Frequency Word List. Ed. by Ladislaus J. Bolchazy. 388p. 1978. lib. bdg. 40.00x (ISBN 3-487-06514-2, Pub. by G Olms BRD). Coronet Bks.

Concordancia Alfabetica De la Biblia. W. H. Sloan & A. Lerin. 1024p. 1981. pap. 14.95 (ISBN 0-311-42054-0). Casa Bautista.

Concordancia Breve De la Biblia. 280p. 1985. pap. 3.50 (ISBN 0-311-42055-9, Edit Mundo). Casa Bautista.

Concordancia de las Sagradas Escrituras. Carlos Denyer. LC 74-21722. (Span.). 936p. 1969. 28.95 (ISBN 0-89922-004-5); pap. 21.95 (ISBN 0-89922-121-1). Edit Caribe.

Concordancia Tematica De la Biblia. Tr. by Carlos Branbsby from Eng. 199p. 1986. pap. 3.50 (ISBN 0-311-42043-5). Casa Bautista.

Concordant Commentary on the New Testament. rev. ed. A. E. Knoch. 407p. 1968. 10.00 (ISBN 0-910424-48-9). Concordant.

Concordant Greek Text. rev. ed. Compiled by A E. Knoch. 735p. 1975. leather bdg. o.p. 25.00 (ISBN 0-910424-32-2); 12.00 (ISBN 0-910424-31-4). Concordant.

Concordant Literal New Testament. Compiled by A. E. Knoch. 624p. 1978. pap. text ed. 5.00 (ISBN 0-910424-09-8). Concordant.

Concordant Literal New Testament with Keyword Concordance. Compiled by A. E. Knoch. 992p. 1983. text ed. 15.00 (ISBN 0-910424-14-4). Concordant.

Concordant Studies in the Book of Daniel. rev. ed. A. E. Knoch. 464p. 1968. 7.00 (ISBN 0-910424-52-7). Concordant.

Concordant Studies in the Book of Daniel. rev. ed. A. E. Knoch. 1968. pap. 4.00 (ISBN 0-910424-53-5). Concordant.

Concordat of 1801. Henry H. Walsh. LC 34-12835. (Columbia University. Studies in the Social Sciences: No. 387). Repr. of 1933 ed. 21.00 (ISBN 0-404-51387-5). AMS Pr.

Concordia Bible Dictionary. 176p. 1963. text ed. 4.95 (ISBN 0-570-03186-9, 12-2213). Concordia.

Concordia Mundi: The Career & Thought of Guillaume Postel, 1510-1581. William J. Bouwsma. LC 57-8622. (Historical Monographs Ser: No. 33). 1957. 22.50x (ISBN 0-674-15950-0). Harvard U Pr.

Concordia Primary Religion Ser. teacher's manual wkbks. 7.35 (ISBN 0-570-01520-0, 22-1206); (4 wkbks) 1.50 ea. Concordia.

Concordia Self-Study Commentary. Roehrs & Franzmann. LC 15-2721. 1979. 21.95 (ISBN 0-570-03277-6). Concordia.

Concurrences Between Dio Chrysostom's First Discourse & the New Testament. Arthur F. Hallam. 91p. (Orig.). 1985. pap. 9.95 (ISBN 0-938770-04-7). Capitalist Pr OH.

Condemned & Crucified. John MacArthur, Jr. (John MacArthur's Bible Studies). (Orig.). 1987. pap. 3.95 (ISBN 0-8024-5349-X). Moody.

Condensed Gospel of Sri Ramakrishna. M, pseud. 1979. pap. 4.95 (ISBN 0-87481-489-8). Vedanta Pr.

Condition of the Christian Philosopher. Roger Mehl. Tr. by Eva Kushner. 221p. 1963. 9.95 (ISBN 0-227-67654-8). Attic Pr.

Conduct of the Services. Ed. by Charles McClean. (Illus.). 138p. 1975. pap. 6.50 (ISBN 0-915644-04-5). Clayton Pub Hse.

Confederate Morale & Church Propaganda. James W. Silver. 1967. pap. 1.35x (ISBN 0-393-00422-8, Norton Lib). Norton.

Conference Classics. Thomas S. Monson. 59p. 1981. 4.95 (ISBN 0-87747-880-5). Deseret Bk.

Conference Classics, Vol. 2. Thomas S. Monson. 63p. 1983. 5.95 (ISBN 0-87747-957-7). Deseret Bk.

Conference Classics, Vol. 3. Thomas S. Monson. 64p. 5.95 (ISBN 0-87747-989-5). Deseret Bk.

Conference of the Birds: A Sufi Fable. Farid Ud-Din Attar. Tr. by C. S. Nott. (Clear Light Ser). (Illus.). 147p. (Orig.). 1971. pap. 6.95 (ISBN 0-87773-031-8, 73001-1). Shambhala Pubns.

Conferences for Franciscan Religious. Philotheus Boehner. (Spirit & Life Ser). 1966. 2.00 (ISBN 0-686-11571-6). Franciscan Inst.

Conferences on the Chief Decrees of the Jesuit General Congregation XXXII: A Symposium by Some of Its Members. J. Y. Calvez et al. LC 76-2977. (Study Aids on Jesuit Topics Ser.: No. 4). 173p. 1976. smyth sewn 4.50 (ISBN 0-912422-17-3); pap. 3.50 (ISBN 0-912422-13-0). Inst Jesuit.

Conferences on the Our Father. John F. Marshall. (Spirit & Life Ser). 1967. 2.00 (ISBN 0-686-11573-2). Franciscan Inst.

Conferring Church. M. Richard Troeh & Marjorie Troeh. 1987. pap. 10.00 (ISBN 0-8309-0465-4). Herald Hse.

Confesion de fe las Iglesias Menonitas. Tr. by Milka Rindzinsky from English. 32p. (Orig.). 1983. pap. 0.60x (ISBN 0-8361-1258-X). Herald Pr.

Confesion de un Alma Idolatra. Maria F. Volio. 152p. (Orig.). 1982. pap. 3.75 (ISBN 0-89922-218-8). Edit Caribe.

Confess It, Possess It: Faith's Formula? John D. Fickett. 40p. 1984. 1.95 (ISBN 0-934421-04-8). Presby Renewal Pubns.

Confessing Christ. 3rd, rev. ed. Calvin K. Cummings. (Orig.). 1977. pap. 1.45 (ISBN 0-934688-04-4). Great Comm Pubns.

Confessing Christ & Doing Politics. Mark Hatfield et al. Ed. by James Skillen. LC 80-71233. 100p. (Orig.). 1982. pap. 3.95 (ISBN 0-936456-02-7). Assn Public Justice.

Confessing One Faith: A Joint Commentary on the Augsburg Confession by Lutheran & Catholic Theologians. George W. Forell & James F. McCue. LC 80-65557. 368p. 1981. pap. 16.95 (ISBN 0-8066-1802-7, 10-1637). Augsburg.

Confession. Antony Khrapovitsky. Tr. by Christopher Birchall from Rus. LC 74-29537. 100p. (Orig.). 1975. pap. 3.00 (ISBN 0-88465-005-7). Holy Trinity.

Confession a Day Keeps the Devil Away. Frances Hunter. 1980. pap. 4.95 (ISBN 0-917726-37-5). Hunter Bks.

Confession & Forgiveness. Andrew Murray. 176p. 1984. pap. 5.95 (ISBN 0-310-29731-1, 10366P, Clarion Class). Zondervan.

Confession Can Change Your Life. David Knight. (Illus.). 64p. (Orig.). 1985. pap. text ed. 2.50 (ISBN 0-86716-041-1). St Anthony Mess Pr.

Confession, Conflict, & Community. Ed. by Richard J. Neuhaus. (Encounter Ser.: Vol. 3). 128p. (Orig.). 1986. pap. 5.95 (ISBN 0-8028-0203-6). Eerdmans.

Confession of a Catholic. Michael Novak. LC 85-20367. 232p. 1986. pap. text ed. 12.25 (ISBN 0-8191-5023-1). U Pr of Amer.

Confession of a Roman Catholic. Paul Whitcomb. 55p. 1985. pap. 1.25 (ISBN 0-89555-281-7). Tan Bks Pubs.

Confession of Dositheus. pap. 1.95 (ISBN 0-686-05640-X). Eastern Orthodox.

Confession of Faith. A. A. Hodge. 1978. 13.95 (ISBN 0-85151-275-5). Banner of Truth.

Confession of Faith Professit, & Belevit, Be the Protestantes Within the Realme of Scotland. LC 72-6029. (English Experience Ser.: No. 555). 1972. Repr. of 1561 ed. 7.00 (ISBN 90-221-0555-5). Walter J Johnson.

Confession of St. Patrick. Saint Patrick. pap. 1.95 (ISBN 0-686-25547-X). Eastern Orthodox.

Confession of Sin. John MacArthur, Jr. (John MacArthur's Bible Studies). 1986. pap. 3.50 (ISBN 0-8024-5093-8). Moody.

Confession of the Fayth of Certayne English People, Living in Exile in the Lowe Contreyes. LC 72-208. (English Experience Ser.: No. 346). 58p. Repr. of 1602 ed. 9.50 (ISBN 90-221-0346-3). Walter J Johnson.

Confession: The Road to Forgiveness. Andrew Murray. Orig. Title: Have Mercy Upon Me. 160p. 1983. pap. text ed. 3.50 (ISBN 0-88368-134-X). Whitaker Hse.

Confessional History of the Lutheran Church. James W. Richard. LC 83-45672. Date not set. Repr. of 1909 ed. 62.50 (ISBN 0-404-19861-9). AMS Pr.

Confessionary Questions: A Preparation for the Sacrament of Penitence with Text of the Office. Vladimir Glinsky. pap. 0.25 (ISBN 0-686-05391-5). Eastern Orthodox.

Confessions. Jakob Boehme. 69.95 (ISBN 0-87968-258-2). Gordon Pr.

Confessions for Kids. Harrison House Staff. (Illus.). 29p. (Orig.). 1984. pap. 0.75 (ISBN 0-89274-322-0). Harrison Hse.

Confessions for Teens. Beverly Tucker. 1985. 0.75 (ISBN 0-89274-353-0). Harrison Hse.

Confessions of a Happy Christian. Zig Ziglar. LC 78-6729. 1978. 12.95 (ISBN 0-88289-196-0). Pelican.

Confessions of a Happy Christian. Zig Ziglar. 199p. 1982. pap. 6.95 (ISBN 0-88289-400-5). Pelican.

Confessions of a Happy Christian. Zig Ziglar. 192p. 1986. pap. 3.50 (ISBN 0-553-25551-7). Bantam.

Confessions of a Jewish Cultbuster. Shea Hecht & Chaim Clorfene. Ed. by Chaya Crossen. 256p. 1985. 8.37 (ISBN 0-318-18531-8); pap. 5.97 (ISBN 0-318-18532-6). Tosefos.

Confessions of a Moonlight Writer: A Freelancer's Guide to the Church Market. James H. Cox. LC 80-70315. 97p. (Orig.). 1982. pap. 5.95 (ISBN 0-939298-00-7). J M Prods.

Confessions of a Negro Preacher. Opie Read. LC 73-18597. Repr. of 1928 ed. 21.50 (ISBN 0-404-11408-3). AMS Pr.

Confessions of a Nomad: A Devotional Guide. Carolyn S. Self & William L. Self. LC 83-61913. 168p. 1983. 1.98 (ISBN 0-931948-47-9). Peachtree Pubs.

Confessions of a Parish Priest. Andrew M. Greeley. 448p. 1986. 18.95. S&S.

Confessions of a Pentecostal. Ada N. Brownell. LC 77-92887. 112p. 1978. pap. 1.25 (ISBN 0-88243-476-4, 02-0476). Gospel Pub.

Confessions of a Preacher's Wife. Pauline Spray. 174p. (Orig.). 1986. pap. 4.95 (ISBN 0-8341-0939-5). Beacon Hill.

Confessions of a Puzzled Parson, & Other Pleas for Reality. facs. ed. Charles Fiske. LC 68-54345. (Essay Index Reprint Ser). 1968. Repr. of 1928 ed. 18.00 (ISBN 0-8369-0442-7). Ayer Co Pubs.

Confessions of a Single Father. Jim Covington. LC 82-13232. 192p. 1982. 13.95 (ISBN 0-8298-0412-9). Pilgrim NY.

Confessions of Al-Ghazzali. Al-Ghazzali. Tr. by W. M. Watt. 3.25x (ISBN 0-87902-059-8). Orientalia.

Confessions of Augustine. 2nd ed. John Gibb & William Montgomery. LC 78-66639. (Ancient Philosophy Ser.). 554p. 1980. lib. bdg. 67.00 (ISBN 0-8240-9597-9). Garland Pub.

Confessions of Augustine in Modern English. Sherwood E. Wirt. Ed. by Julie Link. 144p. 1986. pap. 5.95 (ISBN 0-310-34641-X). Zondervan.

Confessions of Jeremiah in Context: Scenes of Prophetic Drams. A. R. Diamond. (JSOT Supplement Ser.: No. 45). 250p. 1987. text ed. 29.50x (ISBN 1-85075-032-7, Pub. by JSOT Pr England); pap. text ed. 19.95x (ISBN 1-85075-033-5, Pub. by JSOT Pr England). Eisenbrauns.

Confessions of St. Augustine. abr. ed. Augustine. (Summit Books). 1977. pap. 4.95 (ISBN 0-8010-0118-8). Baker Bk.

Confessions of St. Augustine. Ed. by Paul Bechtel. LC 81-11163. 1981. 8.95 (ISBN 0-8024-1618-7). Moody.

Confessions of Saint Augustine. Saint Augustine. LC 60-13725. 6.50 (ISBN 0-385-02955-1, Im). Doubleday.

Confessions of St. Augustine: Modern English Version. Hal Helms. 304p. 1986. pap. 8.95 (ISBN 0-941478-55-6). Paraclete Pr.

Confessyon of the Fayth of the Germaynes in the Councell, 2 pts. Melanchthon. LC 76-57351. (English Experience Ser.: No. 771). 1977. Repr. of 1536 ed. Set. lib. bdg. 39.00 (ISBN 90-221-0771-X). Walter J Johnson.

Confidence in God in Times of Danger. Alex Carson. pap. 2.75 (ISBN 0-685-88371-X). Reiner.

Confident & Competent: A Challenge for the Lay Church. William Droel & Gregory Pierce. LC 86-72789. 112p. (Orig.). 1987. pap. 3.95 (ISBN 0-87793-351-0). Ave Maria.

Confident Living: Practical Psychology & the Christian Faith. Chris Schriner & Sue I. Mauck. (Illus.). 101p. (Orig.). 1982. pap. text ed. 6.00 (ISBN 0-914527-17-7). C-Four Res.

Confident Pastoral Leadership. Howard F. Sugden & Warren W. Wiersbe. (Orig.). 1977. pap. 6.95 (ISBN 0-8024-1598-9). Moody.

Confirmation. Karl Rahner. 1.50 (ISBN 0-87193-123-0). Dimension Bks.

Confirmation & the Charismata. Theodore R. Jungkuntz. LC 83-10450. 126p. (Orig.). 1983. lib. bdg. 24.00 (ISBN 0-8191-3344-2); pap. text ed. 8.75 (ISBN 0-8191-3345-0). U Pr of Amer.

Confirmation in the Church Today. Philip E. Hughes. pap. 20.00 (ISBN 0-317-08439-9, 2012949). Bks Demand UMI.

Confirmation Is Saying Yes to God. Joan Thiry & Marilyn Burbach. duplicating masterbook 12.95 (ISBN 0-89837-071-X, Pub. by Pflaum Pr). Peter Li.

Confirmation Re-Examined. Ed. by Kendig B. Cully. LC 82-81428. 144p. (Orig.). 1982. pap. 7.95 (ISBN 0-8192-1304-7). Morehouse.

Confirmation Resources. Carl B. Rife. 1982. pap. 5.25 tchr's. guide (ISBN 0-89536-537-5, 0356). CSS of Ohio.

Confirmed in Christ. Roy C. Gesch. 1983. pap. 2.25 (ISBN 0-570-03911-8, 12-2852). Concordia.

Confirming Faith. Kieran Sawyer. LC 82-71984. (Illus.). 208p. (Orig.). 1982. pap. text ed. 9.75 directors manual (ISBN 0-87793-251-4). Ave Maria.

Confirming Faith: Participant Book. Kieran Sawyer. LC 82-71984. (Illus.). 96p. (Orig.). 1982. pap. text ed. 3.75 (ISBN 0-87793-252-2). Ave Maria.

Conflict & Christianity in Northern Ireland. Brian Mawhinney & Ronald Wells. LC 75-8948. (Illus.). pap. 31.50 (ISBN 0-317-09250-2, 2012891). Bks Demand UMI.
Conflict & Context: Hermeneutics in the Americas. Ed. by Mark L. Branson & C. Rene Padilla. 304p. (Orig.). 1986. pap. 13.95 (ISBN 0-8028-0172-2). Eerdmans.
Conflict & Harmony. Andrew R. Cecil et al. (Andrew R. Cecil Lectures on Moral Values in a Free Society: Vol. III). 228p. 1982. text ed. 14.50x (ISBN 0-292-71081-X, Pub. by U of Tex. at Dallas). U of Tex Pr.
Conflict Between the Civil Power & the Clergy: Historical & Legal Essay. Emilio Portes Gil. 1976. lib. bdg. 59.95 (ISBN 0-87968-928-5). Gordon Pr.
Conflict, Holiness & Politics in the Teachings of Jesus. Marcus J. Borg. LC 84-9029. (Studies in the Bible & Early Christianity: Vol. 5). 410p. 1984. 59.95x (ISBN 0-88946-603-3). E Mellen.
Conflict in a Voluntary Association: A Case Study of a Classic Suburban Church Fight. Ed. by Perry D. LeFevre. LC 75-12388. (Studies in Ministry & Parish Life). 1975. 13.95x (ISBN 0-913552-03-8); pap. 6.95x (ISBN 0-913552-09-7). Exploration Pr.
Conflict in the Church As Seen by a Thirteen Year Old. Robert E. Tewes, Jr. LC 83-83650. 1983. pap. 17.95 (ISBN 0-915644-24-X). Clayton Pub Hse.
Conflict Ministry in the Church. Larry L. McSwain & William C. Treadwell, Jr. LC 80-67781. 1981. pap. 7.95 (ISBN 0-8054-2540-3). Broadman.
Conflict of Faith & Experience in the Psalms: A Form-Critical & Theological Study. Craig C. Broyles. (JSOT Supplement Ser.: No. 52). 200p. 1986. text ed. 27.50x (ISBN 1-85075-052-1, Pub. by JSOT Pr England); pap. text ed. 19.95x (ISBN 1-85075-053-X, Pub. by JSOT Pr England). Eisenbrauns.
Conflict of Horus & Seth - A study in Ancient Mythology from Egyptian & Classical Sources. J. G. Griffiths. 194p. 1960. text ed. 19.95x (ISBN 0-85323-071-4, Pub. by Liverpool U Pr). Humanities.
Conflict of Naturalism & Humanism. Willystine Goodsell. LC 74-176814. (Columbia University. Teachers College. Contributions to Education: No. 33). Repr. of 1910 ed. 22.50 (ISBN 0-404-55033-9). AMS Pr.
Conflict of the Ages. x ed. Arno C. Gaebelein. (Illus.). 171p. pap. 5.50 (ISBN 0-9609260-1-1). Exhorters.
Conflict of the Church & the Synagogue: A Study in the Origins of Antisemitism. James Parkes. LC 61-11472. (Temple Books). 1969. pap. text ed. 6.95x (ISBN 0-689-70151-9, T9). Atheneum.
Conflict of Traditionalism & Modernism in the Muslim Middle East: A Symposium. Carl Leiden. LC 68-59178. pap. 40.50 (ISBN 0-317-08447-X, 2000823). Bks Demand UMI.
Conflict: The Separation of the Church & State. Clayton L. Nuttall. LC 80-21267. 144p. 1980. pap. 4.95 (ISBN 0-87227-076-9, RBP5088). Reg Baptist.
Conflicting Ways of Interpreting the Bible. Ed. by Hans Kung & Jurgen Moltmann. (Concilium Ser.: Vol. 138). 128p. (Orig.). 1980. pap. 5.95 (ISBN 0-8164-2280-X, HarpR). Har-Row.
Conflicting Ways of Interpreting the Bible, Concilium 138. Ed. by Hans Kung & Jurgen Moltmann. (New Concilium 1980). 128p. 1981. pap. 5.95 (ISBN 0-8245-4771-3, HarpR). Har-Row.
Confluence of Opposites or Scientific Comparative Study of Religions. C. R. Jain. 432p. 1975. Repr. 16.00 (Pub. by Messers Today & Tomorrows Printers & Publishers India). Scholarly Pubns.
Conforming Constitutions to the New Code. Joseph F. Gallen. 58p. 1984. pap. 2.00 (ISBN 0-317-18638-8). Dghtrs St Paul.
Confrontation at Calvary. Alfonso Tafoya. (Chapbooks Ser.). 1975. pap. 1.50x (ISBN 0-914140-06-X). Carpenter Pr.
Confrontations with Prophets. Hans W. Wolff. LC 82-48585. 80p. 1983. pap. 4.25 (ISBN 0-8006-1702-9). Fortress.
Confronted by Love. Dan Baumann. LC 85-2364. (Bible Commentary for Laymen Ser.). 144p. 1985. pap. 3.95 (ISBN 0-8307-1050-7, S391101). Regal.
Confronting Casual Christianity. Charles F. Stanley. LC 85-7764. 1985. 7.95 (ISBN 0-8054-5022-X). Broadman.
Confronting Christianity: Adults & Authority. Richard Reichert. LC 78-53634. 44p. 1978. pap. 9.95 (ISBN 0-88489-102-X). St Marys.
Confronting Christianity: Faith & Religion. Richard Reichert. LC 78-53634. 44p. 1978. pap. 9.95 (ISBN 0-88489-100-3). St Marys.
Confronting Christianity: Moral Issues. Richard Reichert. LC 78-53634. 44p. 1978. pap. 9.95 (ISBN 0-88489-099-6). St Marys.
Confronting Cults, Old & New. M. Thomas Stankes. pap. 6.95 (ISBN 0-317-12202-9). AMG Pubs.
Confronting History & Holocaust: Collected Essays: 1972-1982. Jack N. Porter. LC 83-3572. (Illus.). 168p. (Orig.). 1983. lib. bdg. 26.00 (ISBN 0-8191-3107-5); pap. text ed. 11.25 (ISBN 0-8191-3108-3). U Pr of Amer.
Confronting Jesus. John Marsh. LC 84-60895. 112p. (Orig.). 1984. pap. 3.50 (ISBN 0-89109-518-7). NavPress.
Confronting Popular Cults. M. Thomas Starkes. LC 72-79177. 1972. pap. 4.25 (ISBN 0-8054-1805-9, 42-1805). Broadman.
Confronting the Cults. Gordon Lewis. pap. 6.50 (ISBN 0-8010-5560-1). Baker Bk.
Confronting the Cults. Gordon R. Lewis. 1966. pap. 6.50 (ISBN 0-87552-323-4). Presby & Reformed.
Confronting the Holocaust: The Impact of Elie Wiesel. Ed. by Alvin H. Rosenfeld & Irving Greenberg. LC 78-15821. pap. 61.80 (ISBN 0-317-27853-3, 2056054). Bks Demand UMI.
Confronting This World: Evangelicals, Fundamentalists, & Politics. Ed. by Richard J. Neuhaus & Michael Cromartie. (Orig.). 1986. text ed. 22.00 (ISBN 0-89633-107-5); pap. text ed. 14.00 (ISBN 0-89633-108-3). Ethics & Public Policy.
Confucian Analects, the Great Learning & the Doctrine of the Mean. Confucius. Ed. by James Legge. 1893. pap. 7.95 (ISBN 0-486-22746-4). Dover.
Confucian Notebook. Edward H. Kenney. LC 79-2828. 89p. 1986. Repr. of 1950 ed. 15.00 (ISBN 0-8305-0008-1). Hyperion Conn.
Confucian Personalities. Ed. by Arthur F. Wright & Denis Twitchett. LC 62-16950. (Illus.). 1962. 30.00x (ISBN 0-8047-0044-3). Stanford U Pr.
Confucian Persuasion. Ed. by Arthur F. Wright. LC 60-8561. 1960. 30.00x (ISBN 0-8047-0018-4). Stanford U Pr.
Confucian Rituals in Korea. Spencer J. Palmer. (Religions of Asia Ser.). (Illus.). 270p. 1984. 30.00 (ISBN 0-89581-457-9). Asian Human Pr.
Confucian Way: A New & Systematic Study of the Four Books. Liu F. Chen. Tr. by Shih S. Liu. 620p. 1986. text ed. 59.95 (ISBN 0-7103-0171-5). Methuen Inc.
Confucianism. Ch'u Chai & Winberg Chai. LC 73-3977. 1974. pap. text ed. 5.50 (ISBN 0-8120-0303-9). Barron.
Confucianism & Chinese Civilization. Ed. by Arthur F. Wright. LC 75-6317. 364p. 1964. 27.50x (ISBN 0-8047-0890-8); pap. 10.95 (ISBN 0-8047-0891-6, SP138). Stanford U Pr.
Confucianism & Christianity. Julia Ching. LC 77-75962. 234p. 1978. 16.95x (ISBN 0-87011-303-8). Kodansha.
Confucianism & Its Rivals. H. A. Giles. lib. bdg. 79.95 (ISBN 0-87968-520-4). Krishna Pr.
Confucianism & Its Rivals. Herbert A. Giles. LC 77-27155. (Hibbert Lectures: 1914). Repr. of 1915 ed. 30.00 (ISBN 0-404-60416-1). AMS Pr.
Confucianism & Modern China. Reginald F. Johnston. LC 79-2830. (Illus.). 272p. 1986. Repr. of 1934 ed. 24.50 (ISBN 0-8305-0007-3). Hyperion Conn.
Confucianism & Taoism. R. Douglas. 59.95 (ISBN 0-87968-930-7). Gordon Pr.
Confucianism & Tokugawa Culture. Ed. by Peter Nosco. LC 83-43086. 360p. 1984. 32.50x (ISBN 0-691-07286-8). Princeton U Pr.
Confucianism in Action. Ed. by David S. Nivison & Arthur F. Wright. LC 59-7433. 1959. 30.00x (ISBN 0-8047-0554-2). Stanford U Pr.
Confucianism: The Dynamics of Tradition. Irene Eber. 264p. 1986. text ed. 27.50x (ISBN 0-02-908780-5). Macmillan.
Confucianism vs. Marxism. T. I. Dow. 200p. 1977. pap. text ed. 12.50 (ISBN 0-8191-0183-4). U Pr of Amer.
Confucius: Ancient Chinese Philosopher. Alan L. Paley. Ed. by D. Steve Rahmas. (Outstanding Personalities Ser.: No. 59). 32p. (Orig.). 1973. lib. bdg. 3.50 incl. catalog cards (ISBN 0-87157-559-0); pap. 1.95 vinyl laminated covers (ISBN 0-87157-059-9). SamHar Pr.
Confucius & Ancient China. Theodore Rowland-Entwistle. (Life & Times Ser.). (Illus.). 64p. 1987. lib. bdg. 11.40 (ISBN 0-531-18101-4, Pub. by Bookwright Pr). Watts.
Confucius, His Life & Time. Liu Wu-Chi. LC 73-138159. 189p. 1972. Repr. of 1955 ed. lib. bdg. 22.50x (ISBN 0-8371-5616-5, LICO). Greenwood.
Confucius, the Buddha, & Christ: A History of the Gospel in Chinese. Ralph R. Covell. LC 86-8615. 304p. (Orig.). 1986. pap. 14.95 (ISBN 0-88344-267-1, CIP). Orbis Bks.
Confucius, the Man & the Myth. Herrlee G. Creel. LC 72-7816. 363p. 1973. Repr. of 1949 ed. lib. bdg. 23.00x (ISBN 0-8371-6531-8, CRCO). Greenwood.
Confucius: The Secular As Sacred. Herbert Fingarette. 160p. 1972. pap. 6.95x (ISBN 0-06-131682-2, TB1682, Torch). Har-Row.
Confusion, Call, Commitment: The Spiritual Exercises & Religious Education. Daniel J. Fitzpatrick. LC 76-3801. 178p. 1976. pap. 4.95 (ISBN 0-8189-0327-9). Alba.
Confutation of Brownisme. Richard Alison. LC 68-54608. (English Experience Ser.: No. 9). 130p. 1968. Repr. of 1590 ed. 16.00 (ISBN 90-221-0009-X). Walter J Johnson.
Confutation of Certaine Articles Delivered by H. Niklaes, Unto the Familye of Love. William Wilkinson. LC 72-238. (English Experience Ser.: No. 279). 200p. 1970. Repr. of 1579 ed. 22.00 (ISBN 90-221-0279-3). Walter J Johnson.
Confutation of the Rhemists Translation, Glosses & Annotations on the New Testament. Thomas Cartwright. LC 71-171737. (English Experience Ser.: No. 364). 830p. 1971. Repr. of 1618 ed. 114.00 (ISBN 90-221-0364-1). Walter J Johnson.
Confutation of Tyndale's Answer, 3 pts. St. Thomas More. Ed. by Louis A. Schuster et al. LC 63-7949. (Complete Works of St. Thomas More Ser.: No. 8). 1836p. 1973. Set. 155.00x (ISBN 0-300-01302-7). Yale U Pr.
Congratulations - God Believes in You. Lloyd Ogilvie. 128p. 1980. 5.95 (ISBN 0-8499-2994-6). Word Bks.
Congratulations: A Graduation Remembrance. Louis O. Caldwell. (Ultra Books). 64p. 1983. 5.95 (ISBN 0-8010-2485-4). Baker Bk.
Congratulations! You are Gifted! Jim Burns & Doug Fields. (Jim Burns Youth Ser.: No. 2). 64p. (Orig.). (YA) 1986. pap. 3.95 (ISBN 0-89081-478-3, 4783). Harvest Hse.
Congregation Shaarey Zedek: 5622-5742 1861-1981. Eli Grad & Bette Roth. LC 82-48650. (Illus.). 198p. 1982. 25.00x (ISBN 0-8143-1713-8). Wayne St U Pr.
Congregation: Stories & Structures. James F. Hopewell. Ed. by Barbara G. Wheeler. LC 86-45914. 240p. 1987. pap. 14.95 (ISBN 0-8006-1956-0). Fortress.
Congregational Dancing in Christian Worship. rev. ed. Doug Adams. 1984. 4.95 (ISBN 0-941500-02-0). Sharing Co.
Congregational House Churches. T. Ed Barlow. (Orig.). 1978. pap. 1.50 (ISBN 0-8309-0214-7). Herald Hse.
Congregational Sponsorship of Indochinese Refugees in the United States, 1979-1981: Helping Beyond Borders: A Study of Collective Altruism. Helen Fein. LC 85-45952. 168p. 1987. 26.50x (ISBN 0-8386-3279-3). Fairleigh Dickinson.
Congregationalism of the Last Three Hundred Years As Seen in Its Literature, 2 Vols. Henry M. Dexter. LC 65-58213. (Research & Source Ser.: No. 519). 1970. Repr. of 1880 ed. Set. lib. bdg. 53.00 (ISBN 0-8337-0851-1). B Franklin.
Congregationalism of the Last Three Hundred Years As Seen in Its Literature. Henry M. Dexter. 1072p. Date not set. Repr. of 1879 ed. text ed. 99.36x (Pub. by Gregg Intl Pubs England). Gregg Intl.
Congregations Alive. Donald P. Smith. LC 81-1371. 198p. 1981. pap. 10.95 (ISBN 0-664-24370-3). Westminster.
Conhecimento Espiritual. Watchman Nee. Orig. Title: Spiritual Knowledge. (Port.). 1986. write for info. (ISBN 0-8297-0781-6). Life Pubs Intl.
Conjugal Love. Student ed. Emanuel Swedenborg. LC 79-93407. 12.00 (ISBN 0-87785-054-2). Swedenborg.
Connally-Hicks Debate on Divorce & Remarriage. Andrew M. Connally & Olan Hicks. 1979. pap. 13.00 (ISBN 0-934916-31-4). Natl Christian Pr.
Connections. Steve L. Edwards. 112p. 1986. pap. 7.95x (ISBN 0-8170-1110-2). Judson.
Conoce a Jesus. Sylvia Mandeville & Lance Pierson. Tr. by Edna L. Gutierrez from Eng. (Pointing Out Bk.). 24p. 1980. pap. 9.95 (ISBN 0-311-38531-1, Edit Mundo). Casa Bautista.
Conocimiento Espiritual. Watchman Nee. Orig. Title: Spiritual Knowledge. (Span.). 1986. write for info. (ISBN 0-8297-0782-4). Life Pubs Intl.
Conozca Quienes Son. Adolfo Robleto. (Span.). 112p. 1986. pap. 3.25 (ISBN 0-311-05764-0). Casa Bautista.
Conozcamos al Alumno. C. H. Benson. Tr. by Fernando P. Villalobos from Eng. (Curso para Maestros Cristianos: No. 4). (Span.). 128p. 1972. pap. 3.50 (ISBN 0-89922-014-2). Edit Caribe.
Conozcamos Nuestro Himnario. Cecil McConnell. 144p. 1980. pap. 3.75 (ISBN 0-311-32432-0). Casa Bautista.
Conozcase y Consagrese. Dick Wulf. Orig. Title: Find Yourself, Give Yourself. (Span.). 1986. write for info. (ISBN 0-8297-0688-7). Life Pubs Intl.
Conquering Cancer. Robert W. Bermudes. 1983. 5.50 (ISBN 0-89536-619-3, 0388). CSS of Ohio.
Conquering Christ. C. Neil Strait. 56p. 1975. pap. 1.25 (ISBN 0-8341-0273-0). Beacon Hill.
Conquering Frontiers: A History of the Brethren Church. Homer A. Kent, Sr. 8.95 (ISBN 0-88469-018-0); pap. 6.95 (ISBN 0-88469-017-2). BMH Bks.
Conquering the Hosts of Hell: An Open Triumph. Win Worley. 1977. pap. 5.00 (ISBN 0-685-88034-6). HBC.
Conquering the Kill-Joys: Positive Living in a Negative World. Bill Weber. 160p. 1986. 12.95 (ISBN 0-8499-0439-0, 0439-0). Word Bks.
Conquering the Night Season. Aaron I. Jones. LC 84-17515. 1985. pap. 4.95 (ISBN 0-8054-2255-2). Broadman.
Conquerors. Leslie Hardinge. (Anchor Ser.). 112p. 1983. pap. 5.95 (ISBN 0-8163-0509-9). Pacific Pr Pub Assn.
Conquest & Crisis: Studies in Joshua, Judges & Ruth. John J. Davis. (Illus.). pap. 5.95 (ISBN 0-88469-052-0). BMH Bks.
Conquest of Illusion. J. J. Van Der Leeuw. 1967. pap. 1.95 (ISBN 0-8356-0400-4, Quest). Theos Pub Hse.
Conquest of Poverty: The Calvinist Revolt in Sixteenth-Century France. H. Heller. (Studies in Medieval & Reformation Thought: No. 35). xiv, 281p. 1986. 40.00 (ISBN 90-04-07598-4, Pub. by E J Brill). Heinman.
Conquest of Suffering. Parwez J. Saher. 1977. 12.50 (ISBN 0-89684-189-8, Pub. by Motilal Banarsidass India). Orient Bk Dist.
Conquest of the Mind. 1982. 3.50 (ISBN 0-89858-037-4). Fill the Gap.
Conquest of the Perfect Love, 2 vols. Theresa of Avila. (Illus.). 235p. 1986. 189.75 (ISBN 0-89266-552-1). Am Classical Coll Pr.
Conqueste de Constantinople. Geoffroy De Villehardouin. Ed. by Julian E. White, Jr. LC 68-16196. (Medieval French Literature Ser). (Fr., Orig.). 1968. pap. text ed. 5.95x (ISBN 0-89197-102-5). Irvington.
Conquistador. Peter Lappin. LC 69-19398. 1970. 6.95 (ISBN 0-89944-040-1). Don Bosco Multimedia.
Conrad Grebel, c. 1498-1526: The Founder of the Swiss Brethren Sometimes Called Anabaptists. Harold S. Bender. (Studies in Anabaptist & Mennonite History Ser.: No. 6). pap. 85.80 (ISBN 0-317-28810-5, 2020335). Bks Demand UMI.
Conrad Grebel: Son of Zurich (Biography) John L. Ruth. LC 75-8829. 160p. 1975. 9.95 (ISBN 0-8361-1767-0). Herald Pr.
Conscience. new ed. Ed. by John Donnelly & Leonard Lyons. LC 72-6720. 249p. (Orig.). 1973. pap. 4.95 (ISBN 0-8189-0259-0). Alba.
Conscience: A Structural Theory. M. Kroy. 244p. 1974. text ed. 49.00x (ISBN 0-7065-1462-9, Pub. by Keter Pub Jerusalem). Coronet Bks.
Conscience & Christ: Six Lectures on Christian Ethics. H. Rashdall. LC 17-2649. 1916. 26.00 (ISBN 0-527-73900-6). Kraus Repr.
Conscience & Confession. Claude Jean-Mesmy. Tr. by Carroll Malachy. LC 65-22643. 239p. 1965. 4.95 (ISBN 0-8199-0013-3, L38877). Franciscan Herald.
Conscience & Dividends: Church & the Multinationals. Thomas C. Oden. LC 85-1581. 192p. 1985. 15.00 (ISBN 0-89633-089-3); pap. 9.00 (ISBN 0-89633-090-7). Ethics & Public Policy.
Conscience & Freedom. Cormac Burke. 159p. (Orig.). 1977. pap. 4.95x (ISBN 0-933932-39-1). Scepter Pubs.
Conscience, Contract, & Social Reality: Theory & Research in Behavioral Science. Ed. by Ronald C. Johnson et al. LC 77-166108. 1972. 39.50x (ISBN 0-8290-0382-7); pap. text ed. 19.95x (ISBN 0-8290-0381-9). Irvington.
Conscience: Development & Self-Transcendence. Walter E. Conn. LC 80-24043. 230p. (Orig.). 1981. pap. 12.95 (ISBN 0-89135-025-X). Religious Educ.
Conscience Game. Daughters of St. Paul. 1966. 2.00 (ISBN 0-8198-0231-X). Dghtrs St Paul.
Conscience in Crisis. Richard K. MacMaster et al. LC 78-27530. (Studies in Anabapitst & Mennonite History: No. 20). 528p. 1979. 19.95x (ISBN 0-8361-1213-X). Herald Pr.
Conscience Is... Max Armstrong & Hylma Armstrong. (I'm Growing Up Ser.). (Illus.). 32p. 1986. casebound 3.95 (ISBN 0-87403-122-2, 3602). Standard Pub.
Conscience, Obligation & the Law: The Moral Binding Power of the Civil Law. David C. Bayne. LC 66-12757. (Jesuit Studies). 1966. 3.45 (ISBN 0-8294-0001-X). Loyola.
Conscience of a Nation. James T. Draper. LC 82-73420. 1983. pap. 7.95 (ISBN 0-8054-1530-0). Broadman.
Conscience of the Race: Sex & Religion in Irish & French Novels 1941-1973. Brian O'Rourke. 72p. 1980. 15.00x (ISBN 0-906127-22-X, BBA 03641, Pub. by Irish Academic Pr Ireland). Biblio Dist.
Conscience Plays. Claire W. Durstewitz. 1982. pap. 4.95 (ISBN 0-89536-527-8, 0340). CSS of Ohio.

Conscience Versus Law. Jeremiah Newman. 260p. 1972. 5.95 (ISBN 0-8199-0433-3). Franciscan Herald.

Conscience with the Power & Cases Thereof. William Ames. LC 74-28826. (English Experience Ser.: No. 708). 1975. Repr. of 1639 ed. 35.00 (ISBN 9-0221-0708-6). Walter J Johnson.

Conscientization & Creativity: Paulo Freire & Christian Education. Daniel S. Schipani. 224p. (Orig.). 1984. lib. bdg. 26.00 (ISBN 0-8191-3881-9); pap. text ed. 12.25 (ISBN 0-8191-3882-7). U Pr of Amer.

Conscious Contact. 24p. (Orig.). 1985. pap. 0.95 (ISBN 0-89486-323-1). Hazelden.

Conscious Exercise & the Transcendental Sun. 3rd rev. ed. Da Free John. LC 77-83388. (Illus.). 272p. 1977. o. p. (ISBN 0-913922-33-1); pap. 8.95 (ISBN 0-913922-30-7). Dawn Horse Pr.

Conscious Immortality. Roy E. Davis. 150p. 1978. pap. 2.95 (ISBN 0-87707-216-7). CSA Pr.

Conscious Union with God. Joel Goldsmith. 6.00 (ISBN 0-8216-0050-8). Univ Bks.

Conscious Union with God. Joel S. Goldsmith. 1977. pap. text ed. 5.95 (ISBN 0-8065-0578-8). Citadel Pr.

Consciousness: A Phenomenological Study of Being Conscious & Becoming Conscious. Henri Ey. Tr. by John H. Flodstrom. LC 76-26429. (Studies in Phenomenology & Existential Philosophy Ser.). (Illus.). 448p. 1978. 29.50x (ISBN 0-253-31408-9). Ind U Pr.

Consciousness & Immortality. T. Subba Row. (Sangam Texts Ser.). 96p. (Orig.). 1983. pap. 8.75 (ISBN 0-88695-012-0). Concord Grove.

Consciousness & Reality. Navickas. 1976. pap. 37.00 (ISBN 90-247-1775-2, Pub. by Martinus Nijhoff Netherlands). Kluwer Academic.

Consciousness & Self-Regulation: Advances in Research & Theory. Ed. by Gary E. Schwartz & David Shapiro. Incl. Vol. 1. 422p. 1976. 35.00x (ISBN 0-306-33601-4); Vol. 2. 470p. 1978. 35.00x (ISBN 0-306-33602-2). LC 76-8907. (Illus., Plenum Pr). Plenum Pub.

Consciousness & the Brain: A Scientific & Philosophical Inquiry. Ed. by Gordon Globus et al. LC 75-44478. (Illus.). 378p. 1976. 45.00x (ISBN 0-306-30878-9, Plenum Pr). Plenum Pub.

Consciousness & the Ultimate. John J. Gleason, Jr. LC 80-21397. 192p. (Orig.). 1981. pap. 7.75 (ISBN 0-687-09470-4). Abingdon.

Consciousness in Advaita Vedanta. William M. Indich. 1980. 14.00x (ISBN 0-8364-0607-9). South Asia Bks.

Consciousness Is What I Am. Joel S. Goldsmith. Ed. by Lorraine Sinkler. LC 76-9967. 160p. 1976. 11.45 (ISBN 0-06-063173-2, HarpR). Har-Row.

Consciousness of Christ. William G. Most. LC 80-68761. 232p. (Orig.). 1980. pap. text ed. 6.95 (ISBN 0-931888-03-4, Chr Coll Pr). Christendom Pubns.

Consciousness of Soul. John-Roger. LC 77-81388. 1977. pap. 5.00 (ISBN 0-914829-05-X). Baraka Bk.

Conscription & Conscience: A History 1916-1919. John W. Graham. LC 78-81509. 1969. Repr. of 1922 ed. 35.00x (ISBN 0-678-00507-9). Kelley.

Consecrated Woman: A Guide to the Don Bosco Volunteers. Paul P. Avallone. (Salesian Family Ser.). 27p. 1983. pap. 3.00 (ISBN 0-89944-075-4). Don Bosco Multimedia.

Consecration & the Spirit of Carmel. Mother Immaculata. LC 82-72203. (Living Meditation & Prayerbook Ser.). (Illus.). 270p. (Orig.). 1985. pap. text ed. 6.00 (ISBN 0-932406-08-4). AFC.

Consecration of Idols. Malyala Pandurangarao. (Illus.). 32p. (Orig.). 1984. pap. 2.00x (ISBN 0-938924-21-4). Sri Shirdi Sai.

Consejos a la Juventud. T. B. Maston. Tr. by H. F. Duffer, Jr. Orig. Title: Advice to Youth. (Span.). 60p. 1985. pap. 1.55 (ISBN 0-311-46005-4). Casa Bautista.

Consejos para Jovenes Predicadores. Ernesto Trenchard. (Span.). 100p. 1957. pap. 3.25 (ISBN 0-8254-1726-0). Kregel.

Consensus in Theology? A Dialogue with Hans Kung & Edward Schillebeeckx. Ed. by Leonard Swidler. LC 80-65385. 180p. 1980. 12.95 (ISBN 0-664-21379-0). Westminster.

Consequences of Sexual Freedom. J. R. Braun. 150p. (Orig.). 1980. pap. text ed. 2.95 (ISBN 0-933656-04-1). Trinity Pub Hse.

Consequences of Sin. John MacArthur, Jr. (John MacArthur's Bible Studies). 1985. pap. 3.50 (ISBN 0-8024-5109-8). Moody.

Conservacion de Convertidos. Ed. by William Winters. (Span.). 120p. 1980. pap. 3.95 (ISBN 0-87148-182-0). Pathway Pr.

Conservative Judaism: An American Religious Movement. Marshall Sklare. cancelled. Transaction Bks.

Conservative Judaism: An American Religious Movement. Marshall Sklare. (Illus.). 336p. 1985. pap. text ed. 12.75 (ISBN 0-8191-4480-0, Co-Pub. by Ctr Jewish Comm Studies). U Pr of Amer.

Conservative Judaism & Jewish Law. Ed. by S. Siegel. 20.00x (ISBN 0-87068-428-0); pap. 9.95. Ktav.

Conservative Judaism: Our Ancestors to Our Descendants. 7.95 (ISBN 0-686-96053-X); pap. 5.00 (ISBN 0-686-99689-5); tchr's. guide 3.00 (ISBN 0-686-99690-9). United Syn Bk.

Conservative Reformers: German-American Catholics & the Social Order. Philip Gleason. 1968. 22.95x (ISBN 0-268-00061-1). U of Notre Dame Pr.

Consider Christ. Daisy Hepburn. LC 83-24623. (Life with Spice Bible Study Ser.). 1984. 2.95 (ISBN 0-8307-0945-2, 6101829). Regal.

Consider Him. 2nd ed. J. Oswald Sanders. 1979. pap. 1.50 (ISBN 9971-83-778-1). OMF Bks.

Consider Jesus. Vance Havner. 104p. 1987. pap. 4.95 (ISBN 0-8010-4306-9). Baker Bk.

Consider the Grass: God Cares for You. Wesley H. Hager. (Contempo Ser.). pap. 0.95 (ISBN 0-8010-4102-3). Baker Bk.

Consider the Lilies: Flowers of the Bible. John Paterson & Katherine Paterson. LC 85-43603. (Illus.). 96p. (YA) 1986. 13.70i (ISBN 0-690-04461-5, Crowell Jr Bks); PLB 13.89 (ISBN 0-690-04463-1). HarpJ.

Consider Your Call. English Benedictine Congregation Members & Daniel Rees. (Cistercian Studies Ser.: No. 20). 447p. 1980. 17.95 (ISBN 0-87907-820-0). Cistercian Pubns.

Considerations for Starting & Stretching a Sacred Dance Choir. Margaret Taylor. 1978. 2.75 (ISBN 0-941500-03-9). Sharing Co.

Considerations on Milton's Early Reading & the Prima Stamina of His Paradise Lost. 59.95 (ISBN 0-87968-933-1). Gordon Pr.

Considerations Religieuses et Esthetiques D'un "Sturmer und Dranger". Jean-Claude Chantre. (European University Studies: No.1, Vol. 507). (Fr.). 650p. 1982. 62.10 (ISBN 3-261-04989-8). P Lang Pubs.

Considering Marriage? Margaretta Kennedy. 12p. 1982. pap. 0.15 (ISBN 0-686-36261-6). Faith Pub Hse.

Consolation of Philosophy. Boethius. Tr. by Richard H. Green. LC 62-11788. 1962. pap. 5.44 scp (ISBN 0-672-60273-3, LLA86). Bobbs.

Consolation of Philosophy. Boethius. Ed. by James J. Buchanan. LC 57-8649. (Milestones of Thought Ser.). 7.00 (ISBN 0-8044-5149-4); pap. 3.95 (ISBN 0-8044-6057-4). Ungar.

Consolation of Philosophy of Boethius. H. J. James. 1897. 25.00 (ISBN 0-8274-2093-5). R West.

Consolation of the Blessed. Elizabeth Petroff. (Illus.). 224p. 1980. 12.95 (ISBN 0-686-32835-3). Alta Gaia Bks.

Conspiracy of God: The Holy Spirit in Men. John C. Haughey. LC 73-80730. 120p. 1976. pap. 2.95 (ISBN 0-385-11558-X, Im). Doubleday.

Constant Companions: An Exhibition of Mythological Animals, Demons, & Monsters. Intro. by Dominique De Menil. (Illus.). 1964. pap. 6.00 (ISBN 0-914412-19-1). Inst for the Arts.

Constantine. Margaret Killingray. Ed. by Malcolm Yapp et al. (World History Ser.). (Illus.). 32p. 1980. lib. bdg. 6.95 (ISBN 0-89908-040-5); pap. text ed. 2.45 (ISBN 0-89908-015-4). Greenhaven.

Constantine: A Great Christian Monarch & Apostle. Paul Keresztes. (London Studies in Classical Philology Ser.). 218p. 1981. pap. text ed. 28.50x (ISBN 90-70265-03-6, Pub. by Gieben Holland). Humanities.

Constantine & Eusebius. Timothy Barnes. LC 81-4248. (Illus.). 448p. 1981. text ed. 37.50x (ISBN 0-674-16530-6). Harvard U Pr.

Constantine & Religious Liberty. Hermann Doerries. 1960. 39.50x (ISBN 0-686-51363-0). Elliots Bks.

Constantine the Great & Christianity. Christopher B. Coleman. LC 70-155636. (Columbia University Studies in the Social Sciences: No. 146). Repr. of 1914 ed. 18.50 (ISBN 0-404-51146-5). AMS Pr.

Constantine the Great & the Christian Church. N. H. Baynes. (Raleigh Lectures on History). 1977. Repr. of 1929 ed. 4.50 (ISBN 0-85672-000-3, Pub. by British Acad). Longwood Pub Group.

Constantine the Great & the Christian Church. Norman H. Baynes. 1974. lib. bdg. 59.95 (ISBN 0-87968-934-X). Gordon Pr.

Constantine the Great & the Christian Church. Norman H. Baynes. LC 74-34500. (World History Ser., No. 48). 1972. Repr. of 1930 ed. lib. bdg. 75.00x (ISBN 0-8383-0131-2). Haskell.

Constantine the Great: The Reorganization of the Empire & the Triumph of the Church. facsimile ed. John B. Firth. LC 77-152983. (Select Bibliographies Reprint Ser). Repr. of 1904 ed. 27.50 (ISBN 0-8369-5735-0). Ayer Co Pubs.

Constantine's Triumph: A Tale of the Era of the Martyrs. W. H. Spears, Jr. LC 63-19710. 1964. 3.95 (ISBN 0-9600106-1-0). Spears.

Constitution of the Islamic Republic of Iran. Tr. by Hamid Algar from Persian. 94p. 1980. 9.95 (ISBN 0-933782-07-1); pap. 4.95 (ISBN 0-933782-02-0). Mizan Pr.

Constitution of the School of Spiritual Science. 2nd ed. Rudolf Steiner. Tr. by George Adams & Joan Rudel. 78p. 1980. pap. 5.00x (ISBN 0-88010-039-7, Pub. by Anthroposophical Society London). Anthroposophic.

Constitution of the United Societies of Believers (Called Shakers) Containing Sundry Covenants & Articles of Agreement, Definitive of the Legal Grounds of the Institution. Shakers. LC 72-2992. Repr. of 1833 ed. 16.00 (ISBN 0-404-10754-0). AMS Pr.

Constitution on the Church: De Ecclesia. Gregory Baum. LC 65-17864. 192p. 1965. pap. 2.95 (ISBN 0-8091-1528-X). Paulist Pr.

Constitutional History & the Constitutions of the Church of England. Felix Makower. LC 61-2869. (Research & Source Works Ser.). Tr. of Die Verfassung der Kirche Von England. 556p. 1972. Repr. of 1895 ed. lib. bdg. 32.00 (ISBN 0-8337-2195-X). B Franklin.

Constitutional Issues in the Case of Rev. Moon: Amicus Briefs Presented to the United States Supreme Court. Ed. by Herbert Richardson. (Studies in Religion & Society: Vol. 10). 710p. 1984. 69.95x (ISBN 0-88946-873-7). E Mellen.

Constitutional Issues in the Case of Reverend Moon: Amicus Briefs Presented to the United States Supreme Court. Ed. by Herbert Richardson. 699p. 1984. pap. 19.95. Rose Sharon Pr.

Constitutional Powers of the General Conference: With a Special Application to the Subject of Slave Holding. facs. ed. William L. Harris. LC 74-146265. (Black Heritage Library Collection Ser). 1860. 12.25 (ISBN 0-8369-8740-3). Ayer Co Pubs.

Constitutional Problems in Church-State Relations: A Symposium. D. T. Mitzner et al. LC 75-155825. (Symposia on Law & Society Ser). 1971. Repr. of 1966 ed. lib. bdg. 19.50 (ISBN 0-306-70131-6). Da Capo.

Constitutions of the Order of the Pious Schools. Piarist Fathers. Ed. & tr. by Salvidor Cudinach. LC 85-60915. Tr. of Constitutiones Ordinis Scholarum Piarum. 110p. Date not set. price not set (ISBN 0-9614908-0-2). Piarist Father.

Constitutions of the Society of Jesus. St. Ignatius Of Loyola. Tr. & commentary by George E. Ganss. LC 72-108258. (Jesuit Primary Sources in English Translation Ser.: No. 1). 432p. 1970. pap. 12.00 smyth sewn (ISBN 0-912422-20-3). Inst Jesuit.

Constructing Local Theologies. Robert J. Schreiter. LC 84-14797. 240p. (Orig.). 1985. pap. 8.95 (ISBN 0-88344-108-X). Orbis Bks.

Construction of Gothic Cathedrals: A Study of Medieval Vault Erection. John Fitchen. LC 80-26291. (Illus.). 1977. pap. 12.95 (ISBN 0-226-25203-5, Phoen). U of Chicago Pr.

Construction of Junior Church School Curricula. Edna L. Acheson. LC 73-176503. Repr. of 1929 ed. 22.50 (ISBN 0-404-55331-1). AMS Pr.

Construction of Lombard & Gothic Vaults. Kingsley A. Porter. 1911. 75.00x (ISBN 0-685-69851-3). Elliots Bks.

Construction of Paradise Lost. Burton J. Weber. LC 72-132483. (Literary Structures Ser.). 218p. 1971. 12.50x (ISBN 0-8093-0488-0). S Ill U Pr.

Construction of the History of Religion in Schelling's Positive Philosophy: Its Presuppositions & Principles. Paul Tillich. Tr. by Victor Nuovo. 184p. 1975. 18.00 (ISBN 0-8387-1422-6). Bucknell U Pr.

Construction of the Wakefield Cycle. John C. Gardner. LC 74-5191. (Literary Structures Ser.). 173p. 1974. 8.95x (ISBN 0-8093-0668-9). S Ill U Pr.

Consul of God. Jeffrey Richards. 1980. 27.95x (ISBN 0-7100-0346-3). Methuen Inc.

Consultation: A Universal Lamp of Guidance. John E. Kolstoe. 208p. 1985. 13.95 (ISBN 0-85398-186-8); pap. 7.95 (ISBN 0-85398-187-6). G Ronald Pub.

Consulting the American Catholic Laity: A Decade of Dialogue. Ed. by Moira Matheison. 40p. (Orig.). 1986. pap. 2.95 (ISBN 1-55586-999-8). US Catholic.

Consummation of Human History (4) Ed. by Chung Hwan Rev. Kwak. (Home Study Course Ser.). 40p. 1980. pap. 4.00 (ISBN 0-910621-13-6). HSA Pubns.

Contacto en el Espiritu. Ralph Neighbour. Ed. by Jose L. Martinez. Tr. by Guillermo Kratzig. (Span.). 120p. 1983. pap. 2.50 (ISBN 0-311-09098-2). Casa Bautista.

Contagious Congregation: Frontiers in Evangelism & Church Growth. George Hunter, 3rd. LC 78-12322. 1979. pap. 6.95 (ISBN 0-687-09490-9). Abingdon.

Contemplating Jesus. Robert Faricy & Robert J. Wicks. 48p. (Orig.). 1986. pap. 2.95 (ISBN 0-8091-2757-1). Paulist Pr.

Contemplating Now. Monica Furlong. LC 83-70991. 128p. 1983. pap. 6.00 (ISBN 0-936384-13-1). Cowley Pubns.

Contemplatio Mortis et Immortalitatis. Henry Montagu. LC 72-218. (English Experience Ser.: No. 337). 148p. 1971. Repr. of 1631 ed. 11.50 (ISBN 90-221-0337-4). Walter J Johnson.

Contemplation. Francis K. Nemeck & Marie T. Coombs. (Ways of Prayer Ser.: Vol. 5). 151p. 1982. 8.95 (ISBN 0-89453-429-7); pap. 5.95 (ISBN 0-89453-276-6). M Glazier.

Contemplation about Rudolf Steiner's "Calendar of the Soul". H. D. Van Goudoever. Tr. by Giselher Weber. 1984. pap. 6.95 (ISBN 0-916786-76-5). St George Bk Serv.

Contemplation & Action in World Religions. Ed. by Yusuf Ibish & Ileana Marculescu. LC 78-61504. (Rothko Chapel). 1979. pap. 4.95 (ISBN 0-295-95634-8). U of Wash Pr.

Contemplation & Leisure. rev. ed. Douglas V. Steere. LC 74-30803. 32p. 1975. pap. 2.50x (ISBN 0-87574-199-1, 199). Pendle Hill.

Contemplation in a World of Action. Thomas Merton. 400p. 1973. pap. 5.50 (ISBN 0-385-02550-5, Im). Doubleday.

Contemplation of Otherness. Richard E. Wentz. viii, 134p. 1984. 13.90x (ISBN 0-86554-135-3, MUP-H126). Mercer Univ Pr.

Contemplation of Sinners. LC 75-315474. (English Experience Ser.: No. 645). 200p. 1974. Repr. of 1499 ed. 17.50 (ISBN 90-221-0645-4). Walter J Johnson.

Contemplative Community. Interdisciplinary Symposium. LC 70-184548. (Cistercian Studies: No. 21). 1972. 7.50 (ISBN 0-87907-821-9). Cistercian Pubns.

Contemplative Life. Joel S. Goldsmith. 212p. 1976. pap. 5.95 (ISBN 0-8065-0523-0). Citadel Pr.

Contemplative Life in England: Carthusians, Bridgettines, Benedictines, 2 Vols. James Hogg & Roger Ellis. Ed. by James Hogg. (Analecta Cartusiana Ser.: No. 68). (Orig.). 1985. pap. 50.00 (ISBN 3-7052-0100-X, Pub. by Salzburg Studies). Longwood Pub Group.

Contemplative Prayer. Thomas Merton. 1971. pap. 3.50 (ISBN 0-385-09219-9, Im). Doubleday.

Contemplative Prayer: A Guide for Today's Catholic. James Borst. 1979. pap. 1.50 (ISBN 0-89243-106-7). Liguori Pubns.

Contemplative Way of Prayer: Deepening Your Life with God. Robert Fancy & Lucy Rooney. 112p. (Orig.). 1986. pap. 4.95 (ISBN 0-89283-308-4). Servant.

Contemporaneity & the Chronology of Mahavira & Buddha. Muni Shri Nagraj Ji. 188p. 1975. 4.00 (ISBN 0-88065-163-6, Pub. by Messers Today & Tomorrows Printers & Publishers India). Scholarly Pubns.

Contemporaries of Erasmus: A Biographical Register of the Renaissance & Reformation, Vol. 1 (A-E) Ed. by Peter G. Bietenholz & Thomas B. Deutscher. (Illus.). 480p. 1985. 72.50x (ISBN 0-8020-2507-2). U of Toronto Pr.

Contemporary Altar Prayers, Vol. 7. Larry Hard. 1983. 5.95 (ISBN 0-89536-576-6, 0383). CSS of Ohio.

Contemporary American Literature & Religion. Halford E. Luccock. LC 73-111471. 1970. Repr. of 1934 ed. 20.50 (ISBN 0-404-00607-8). AMS Pr.

Contemporary American Literature & Religion. Halford E. Luccock. 300p. 1980. Repr. of 1934 ed. lib. bdg. 30.00 (ISBN 0-89984-324-7). Century Bookbindery.

Contemporary American Theologies: A Critical Survey. Deane W. Ferm. 192p. (Orig.). 1981. pap. 8.95 (ISBN 0-8164-2341-5, HarpR). Har-Row.

Contemporary American Theologies II: A Book of Readings. Deane W. Ferm. 214p. (Orig.). 1982. pap. 15.95 (ISBN 0-8164-2407-1, HarpR). Har-Row.

Contemporary American Theology. Ed. by Vergilius T. Ferm. LC 78-86749. (Essay Index Reprint Ser). 1933. 21.50 (ISBN 0-8369-1181-4). Ayer Co Pubs.

Contemporary & His Soul. Irwin Edman. LC 66-25907. Repr. of 1931 ed. 18.50x (ISBN 0-8046-0129-1, Pub. by Kennikat). Assoc Faculty Pr.

Contemporary Approaches to Christian Education. Jack L. Seymour & Donald E. Miller. LC 81-14899. 176p. (Orig.). 1982. pap. 8.75 (ISBN 0-687-09493-3). Abingdon.

Contemporary Approaches to the Study of Religion, Vol. 1: The Humanities. Ed. by Frank Whaling. LC 84-14807. (Religion & Reason Ser.: No. 27). 520p. 1984. 39.95x (ISBN 3-11-009834-2); Vol. 2: The Social Sciences, pgs.302. pap. 29.95 (ISBN 3-11-009836-9). Mouton.
Contemporary Biblical Interpretation for Preaching. Ronald J. Allen. 160p. 1984. pap. 5.95 (ISBN 0-8170-1002-5). Judson.
Contemporary Catholic Theology. rev. ed. John T. Carmody & Denise L. Carmody. LC 84-48213. 256p. 1985. pap. 9.95 (ISBN 0-06-061316-5, HarpR). Har-Row.
Contemporary Christian Education. Donald S. Aultman. 122p. 1968. 4.95 (ISBN 0-87148-159-6); pap. 3.95 (ISBN 0-87148-160-X). Pathway Pr.
Contemporary Christian Issues. Nene Ramientos. 71p. 1982. pap. 4.00 (ISBN 971-10-0013-X, Pub. by New Day Philippines). Cellar.
Contemporary Christian Music: Where It Came from, Where It Is, Where It Is Going. rev. ed. Paul Baker. 1985. pap. 8.95 (ISBN 0-89107-343-4, Crossway Bks). Good News.
Contemporary Christologies: A Jewish Response. Eugene B. Borowitz. LC 80-81051. 208p. (Orig.). 1980. pap. 8.95 (ISBN 0-8091-2305-3). Paulist Pr.
Contemporary Church History. Orazio M. Premoli. 1977. lib. bdg. 59.95 (ISBN 0-8490-1669-X). Gordon Pr.
Contemporary Continental Theology: An Interpretation for Anglo-Saxons. Walter M. Horton. 1979. Repr. of 1938 ed. lib. bdg. 30.00 (ISBN 0-8482-4497-4). Norwood Edns.
Contemporary Counterfeits. John J. Davis. 1979. pap. 1.25 (ISBN 0-88469-003-2). BMH Bks.
Contemporary Culture & Christianity. (Synthesis Ser). 1978. pap. 1.50 (ISBN 0-8199-0741-3). Franciscan Herald.
Contemporary Faces of Satan. Ratibor-Ray Jurjevich. 437p. 1985. 21.95 (ISBN 0-930711-00-9); pap. 14.95 (ISBN 0-317-19630-8). Ichthys Bks.
Contemporary Halakhic Problems, Vol. I. D. J. Bleich. (Library of Jewish Law & Ethics: No. 4). 20.00x (ISBN 0-87068-450-7); pap. 14.95. Ktav.
Contemporary Halakhic Problems, Vol.II. David J. Bleich. 20.00x (ISBN 0-87068-275-X); pap. 14.95. Ktav.
Contemporary Halakhic Problems, Vol. II. J. David Bleich. (Library of Jewish Law & Ethics, Volume X). 423p. 1983. 20.00x (ISBN 0-87068-451-5). Ktav.
Contemporary Hermeneutics: Hermeneutics As Method, Philosophy & Critique. Josef Bleicher. 224p. 1980. 28.00x (ISBN 0-7100-0551-2); pap. 14.00x (ISBN 0-7100-0552-0). Methuen Inc.
Contemporary Indian Philosophy. Basant K. Lal. xxi, 345p. 1986. 15.00 (ISBN 81-208-0260-8, Pub. by Motilal Banarsidass). South Asia Bks.
Contemporary Indian Philosophy. Rama S. Srivastava. 1983. text ed. 24.00x. Coronet Bks.
Contemporary Indian Short Stories, 2 vols. Ed. by Bhabani Bhattacharya. 1967. Vol. 1. 3.50 (ISBN 0-88253-409-2); Vol. 2. 3.50 (ISBN 0-88253-327-4). Ind-US Inc.
Contemporary Islam & the Challenge of History. Yvonne Y. Haddad. LC 81-8732. 272p. 1982. 49.50 (ISBN 0-87395-543-9); pap. 19.95 o. s. i. (ISBN 0-87395-544-7). State U NY Pr.
Contemporary Islamic Movements in Historical Perspective. Ira M. Lapidus. LC 83-82308. (Policy Papers in International Affairs: No. 18). viii, 76p. 1983. pap. 4.95x (ISBN 0-87725-518-0). U of Cal Intl St.
Contemporary Issues for Evangelical Christians. David L. McKenna. (Contemporary Discussion Ser). 1978. pap. 1.95 (ISBN 0-8010-6053-2). Baker Bk.
Contemporary Issues in Biomedical Ethics. Ed. by Davis et al. LC 78-71406. (Contemporary Issues in Biomedicine, Ethics, & Society Ser.). 300p. 1979. 29.50 (ISBN 0-89603-002-4). Humana.
Contemporary Jew in the Elizabethan Drama. Jacob L. Cardozo. (Research & Source Works Ser: No. 175). Repr. of 1925 ed. 15.00 (ISBN 0-8337-0466-4). B Franklin.
Contemporary Jewish Civilization. 14.50 (ISBN 0-8160-1473-6). Facts on File.
Contemporary Jewish Civilization. Ed. by International Center for University Teaching of Jewish Civilization Staff & Gideon Shimmoni. LC 85-40515. (Selected Course Outlines & Curriculum Resources Ser.). 250p. 1985. pap. text ed. 14.50x (ISBN 0-910129-28-2). Wiener Pub Inc.
Contemporary Jewish Ethics. new ed. Ed. by Menachem M. Kellner. (Sanhedrin Jewish Studies). 1978. (Sanhedrin Pr); pap. 11.95x (ISBN 0-88482-920-0, Sanhedrin Pr). Hebrew Pub.
Contemporary Jewish Ethics: A Bibliographical Survey. Compiled by S. Daniel Breslauer. LC 85-9895. (Bibliographies & Indexes in Religious Studies: No. 6). xi, 213p. 1985. lib. bdg. 37.50 (ISBN 0-313-24594-0, BCJ/). Greenwood.
Contemporary Jewish Fiction. Bernard Berenson. 1976. lib. bdg. 59.95 (ISBN 0-87968-939-0). Gordon Pr.
Contemporary Jewish Philosophies. William E. Kaufman. 290p. 1986. pap. text ed. 12.25 (ISBN 0-8191-5092-4). U Pr of Amer.
Contemporary Jewish Religious Thought. Ed. by Arthur A. Cohen & Paul Mendes-Flohr. LC 86-11856. 1986. 75.00 (ISBN 0-684-18628-4). Scribner.
Contemporary Jewry, Vol. 7. Ed. by Arnold Dashefsky. 160p. 1986. 19.95x (ISBN 0-87855-979-5). Transaction Bks.
Contemporary Jewry, Vol. 8. Ed. by Arnold Dashefsky. 160p. 1987. 19.95 (ISBN 0-88738-097-2). Transaction Bks.
Contemporary Jewry: Studies in Honor of Moshe Davis. J. Wigoder. 431p. 1984. text ed. 35.00x (ISBN 965-223-499-0, Pub. by Magnes Pr Israel). Humanities.
Contemporary Judaic Fellowship in Theory & Practice. Ed. by Jacob Neusner. 1972. 20.00x (ISBN 0-87068-187-7). Ktav.
Contemporary Judaism: Patterns of Survival. 2nd ed. Gilbert S. Rosenthal. 401p. 1986. 39.95 (ISBN 0-89885-260-9, Dist. by Independent Publishers Group); pap. 16.95 (ISBN 0-89885-277-3). Human Sci Pr.
Contemporary Logos. Richard Schain. 20p. (Orig.). 1984. pap. 2.00 (ISBN 0-9609922-2-7). Garric Pr.
Contemporary Moral Issues Facing the Orthodox Christian. S. S. Harakas. 1982. pap. 6.95 (ISBN 0-937032-24-7). Light&Life Pub Co MN.
Contemporary Muslim World: A Brief Note on Current Muslim World. A. Iqbal. 27.50 (ISBN 0-317-46090-0). Kazi Pubns.
Contemporary Object Lessons for Children's Church. Lois Edstrom. (Object Lessons Ser.). 112p. 1986. 4.50 (ISBN 0-8010-3432-9). Baker Bk.
Contemporary Options in Eschatology: A Study of the Millennium. Millard J. Erickson. LC 77-89406. 1977. 9.95 (ISBN 0-8010-3262-8). Baker Bk.
Contemporary Perspectives on Christian Marriage. Ed. by Richard Malone & John Connery. 1984. 19.95 (ISBN 0-8294-0472-4). Loyola.
Contemporary Philosophic Thought: Proceedings, 4 vols. International Philosophy Year Conferences, Brockport. Ed. by Howard E. Kiefer & Milton K. Munitz. Incl. Vol. 1. Language, Belief, & Metaphysics. LC 69-14643. 21.50x (ISBN 0-87395-151-4); Vol. 2. Mind, Science, & History. LC 69-14642. 49.50 (ISBN 0-87395-052-6); Vol. 3. Perspectives in Education, Religion, & the Arts. LC 69-14641. 33.50x (ISBN 0-87395-153-0); Vol. 4. Ethics & Social Justice. LC 69-14640. 49.50x (ISBN 0-87395-054-2). 1970. State U NY Pr.
Contemporary Philosophies of Religion. Howard A. Slaate. LC 86-13148. 252p. (Orig.). 1986. pap. text ed. 14.50 (ISBN 0-8191-5492-X). U Pr of Amer.
Contemporary Philosophy of Religion. Ed. by Stephen M. Cahn & David Shatz. 1982. pap. text ed. 9.95x (ISBN 0-19-503009-5). Oxford U Pr.
Contemporary Political Orders & Christ: Karl Barth's Christology & Political Praxis. Robert E. Hood. (Pittsburgh Theological Monographs, New Ser.: 14). (Orig.). 1985. pap. 19.90 (ISBN 0-915138-56-5). Pickwick.
Contemporary Prayers & Readings. Ed. by Sidney Greenberg. 1972. pap. 3.95 (ISBN 0-87677-050-2). Prayer BK.
Contemporary Problems of Evangelism. Wendell W. Price. LC 76-12941. 1976. 3.95 (ISBN 0-87509-070-2); pap. 2.00 (ISBN 0-87509-071-0). Chr Pubns.
Contemporary Psalms. Nelle L. Bruntz. (Illus.). 64p. 1984. 4.50 (ISBN 0-938462-13-X). Green Leaf Ca.
Contemporary Reading of the Spiritual Exercises: A Companion to St. Ignatius' Text. 2nd ed. David L. Fleming. Ed. by George E. Ganss. LC 80-81812. (Study Aids on Jesuit Topics Ser.:. No.2). 112p. 1980. pap. 3.00 (ISBN 0-912422-47-5); smyth sewn 4.00 (ISBN 0-912422-48-3). Inst Jesuit.
Contemporary Reform Response. Solomon B. Freehof. 15.00x (ISBN 0-87820-108-4, Pub. by Hebrew Union College Press). Ktav.
Contemporary Religious Poetry. Ed. by Paul Ramsey. 1987. pap. 7.95. Paulist Pr.
Contemporary Social Spirituality. Ed. by Francis X. Meehan. LC 82-2253. 133p. (Orig.). 1982. pap. 6.95 (ISBN 0-88344-022-9). Orbis Bks.
Contemporary Synagogue Art: Developments in the United States, 1945-1965. Avram Kampf. LC 65-25292. (Illus.). 1976. 15.00 (ISBN 0-8074-0085-8, 382630). UAHC.
Contemporary Theologies of Mission. Arthur F. Glasser & Donald A. McGavran. 320p. (Orig.). 1983. pap. 12.95 (ISBN 0-8010-3790-5). Baker Bk.
Contemporary Theology Series 2. Incl. Christian View of Abortion. 3.95 (ISBN 0-570-06721-9, 12-2560); Form Criticism Reexamined. 3.95 (ISBN 0-570-06722-7, 12-2561); Lord's Supper Today. 4.25 (ISBN 0-570-06723-5, 12-2562); Marxism & Christianity (ISBN 0-570-06724-3, 12-2563); Unity & Fellowship & Ecumenicity (ISBN 0-570-06725-1, 12-2564). 1973. pap. 3.50 ea. Concordia.
Contemporary Traditionalist Orthodox Thought. Chrysostomos & Hieromonk Auxentios. 80p. (Orig.). 1986. pap. 5.00 (ISBN 0-911165-07-X). Ctr Trad Orthodox.
Contemporary Transformations of Religion. Bryan Wilson. 1976. pap. text ed. 7.95x (ISBN 0-19-875045-5). Oxford U Pr.
Contemporary Trends in Studies on the Constitutions of the Society of Jesus: Annotated Bibliographical Orientations. Ignacio Iparraguirre. Ed. by George E. Ganss. Tr. by Daniel F. Meenan from Span. LC 74-77120. (Study Aids on Jesuit Topics Ser: No. 1). 96p. 1974. pap. 2.00 (ISBN 0-912422-10-6). Inst Jesuit.
Contemporary Twelve: The Power of Character in Today's World. Walter L. Underwood. 112p. (Orig.). 1984. pap. 9.50 (ISBN 0-687-09520-4). Abingdon.
Contemporary Views on the Holocaust. Ed. by Randolph L. Braham. 1983. lib. bdg. 31.50 (ISBN 0-89838-141-X). Kluwer Nijhoff.
Contemporary Wesleyan Theology, 2 vols. Ed. by Charles W. Carter & Duane R Thompson. 1200p. 1986. Set. 39.95 (ISBN 0-310-45650-9, 11626). Zondervan.
Contemporary World Theology. Harvie M. Conn. 1974. pap. 4.95 (ISBN 0-87552-149-5). Presby & Reformed.
Contemporary Worship Services. James L. Christensen. LC 75-137445. Repr. of 1971 ed. 64.00 (ISBN 0-8357-9517-9, 2011444). Bks Demand UMI.
Contemptu Mundi. Desiderius Erasmus. Tr. by Thomas Paynell. LC 67-18715. 1967. 30.00x (ISBN 0-8201-1016-7). Schol Facsimiles.
Content & Style of an Oral Literature: Clackamas Chinook Myths & Tales. Melville Jacobs. LC 58-5617. 1959. 17.50x (ISBN 0-226-38973-1). U of Chicago Pr.
Content & Taste: Religion & Myth. Ed. by Peter Davison et al. LC 77-90615. (Literary Taste, Culture & Mass Communication: Vol. 7). 338p. 1978. lib. bdg. 47.00x (ISBN 0-85964-042-6). Chadwyck-Healey.
Content of Motion Pictures. Edgar Dale. LC 77-124026. (Literature of Cinema Ser: Payne Fund Studies of Motion Pictures & Social Values). Repr. of 1935 ed. 17.00 (ISBN 0-405-01644-1). Ayer Co Pubs.
Content of Religious Instruction: A Social Science Approach. James M. Lee. LC 84-18255. 815p. (Orig.). 1985. pap. 14.95 (ISBN 0-89135-050-0). Religious Educ.
Contes. Nachman of Breslov. Tr. by Franz Regnot from Yiddish. Tr. of Sippurey Ma'asioth. (Fr.). 180p. (Orig.). 1981. pap. 7.00 (ISBN 0-930213-22-X). Breslov Res Inst.
Context for Discovery. Neal F. Fisher. LC 81-7929. (Into Our Third Century Ser.). (Orig.). 1981. pap. 4.95 (ISBN 0-687-09620-0). Abingdon.
Contexts: Absalom & Achitophel. Ed. by Robert McHenry. LC 84-24160. (Contexts Ser.: No. 3). (Illus.). xiv, 296p. 1986. lib. bdg. 29.50 (ISBN 0-208-01845-X, Archon Bks). Shoe String.
Contextualization of Theology: An Evangelical Assessment. Bruce C. E. Fleming. 1981. pap. 5.95 (ISBN 0-87808-431-2). William Carey Lib.
Continual Burnt Offering: Daily Meditations on the Word of God. H. A. Ironside. 370p. 1981. pap. 4.95 (ISBN 0-87213-353-2). Loizeaux.
Continual Feast. Evelyn B. Vitz. LC 84-48629. (Illus.). 356p. 1985. 16.45i (ISBN 0-06-181897-6, HarpT). Har-Row.
Continuation or Transformation? The Involvement of United Methodism in Social Movements & Issues. Earl D. Brewer. (Into our Third Century Ser.). 128p. (Orig.). 1982. pap. 4.95 (ISBN 0-687-09623-5). Abingdon.
Continuing Care: For the Dying Patient, Family & Staff. Ed. by Robert Debellis et al. LC 85-19165. (Foundation of Thanatology Ser.: Vol. 5). 190p. 1985. 37.95 (ISBN 0-03-000357-1, C1334). Praeger.
Continuing Conversation. Robert F. Griffin. LC 85-80352. 200p. (Orig.). 1985. pap. 7.50 (ISBN 0-87973-828-6, 828). Our Sunday Visitor.
Continuing Education: A Hedge Against Boredom in Ministry. Jerry C. Grubbs. LC 86-42931. 40p. (Orig.). 1986. pap. 4.00 (ISBN 0-937021-03-2). Sagamore Bks MI.
Continuing Formation of Priests (Growing in Wisdom, Age & Grace) 44p. 1984. pap. 2.50 (ISBN 1-55586-954-8). US Catholic.
Continuing Quest for God: Monastic Spirituality in Tradition & Transition. Ed. by William Skudlarek. LC 81-23614. x, 302p. (Orig.). 1982. pap. 8.95 (ISBN 0-8146-1235-0). Liturgical Pr.
Continuity & Change among Canadian Mennonite Brethren. Peter M. Hamm. (Social Scientific Studies in Religion: Religion & Identity). 304p. 1986. 35.00 (ISBN 0-88920-189-7, Pub. by Wilfrid Laurier Canada). Humanities.
Continuity & Change in Roman Religion. J. H. Liebeschuetz. 1979. text ed. 65.00x (ISBN 0-19-814822-4). Oxford U Pr.
Continuity of Christian Doctrine. R. P. Hanson. 112p. 1981. 9.95 (ISBN 0-8164-0504-2, HarpR). Har-Row.
Continuity of Salvation: A Study of Paul's Letter to the Romans. Theodore M. Snider. LC 84-42602. 200p. 1984. lib. bdg. 18.95x (ISBN 0-89950-126-5). McFarland & Co.
Contours of a Christian Philosophy. L. Kalsbeek. 1975. pap. 9.95x (ISBN 0-88906-000-2). Wedge Pub.
Contours of a World View. Arthur F. Holmes. Ed. by Carl F. Henry. (Studies in a Christian World View: Vol. 1). 256p. 1983. pap. 8.95 (ISBN 0-8028-1957-5). Eerdmans.
Contra Amatores Mundi of Richard Rolle of Hampole. Richard Rolle. Ed. by Paul F. Theiner. LC 68-64641. 196p. 1983. Repr. of 1968 ed. lib. bdg. 19.95x (ISBN 0-89370-791-0). Borgo Pr.
Contra Felicem De Natura Boni Epistula Secundini, Contra Secundinum, Pt. 2. Aurelius Augustinus. Bd. with De Natura Boni Epistula Secundini; Contra Secundinum. (Corpus Scriptorum Ecclesiasticorum Latinorum Ser: Vol. 25). (Lat.). Repr. of 1892 ed. unbound 50.00 (ISBN 0-384-02365-7). Johnson Repr.
Contra Gentes & De Incarnatione. Athanasius. Ed. by Robert W. Thomas. (Oxford Early Christian Texts Ser). 1971. 45.00x (ISBN 0-19-826801-7). Oxford U Pr.
Contract at Mount Horeb. Allen Mayo. LC 75-13402. (Illus.). 1977. 10.95 (ISBN 0-918268-01-X). Tex-Mex.
Contract with God. Will Eisner. 136p. 1985. signed ed. o.p. 25.00 (ISBN 0-87816-017-5); pap. 7.95 (ISBN 0-87816-018-3). Kitchen Sink.
Contradiction & Dilemma: Orestes Brownson & the American Idea. Leonard Gilhooley. LC 78-158738. xvi, 231p. 1972. 25.00 (ISBN 0-8232-0930-X). Fordham.
Contrasts in Keening: Ireland. Geraldine C. Little. LC 82-60038. 50p. (Orig.). 1982. pap. 3.50 (ISBN 0-943710-00-6). Silver App Pr.
Contre-Bible de Melville: Moby-Dick Dechiffre. Viola Sachs. 122p. 1975. pap. text ed. 13.60x (ISBN 90-2797-586-8). Mouton.
Contributing. Churches Alive, Inc. Staff. LC 79-52132. (Love One Another Bible Study Ser.). (Illus.). 1979. wkbk. 3.00 (ISBN 0-934396-05-1). Churches Alive.
Contribution of Belgium to the Catholic Church in America (1523-1857) Joseph A. Griffin. LC 73-3568. (Catholic University of America. Studies in American Church History: No. 13). Repr. of 1932 ed. 28.00 (ISBN 0-404-57763-6). AMS Pr.
Contribution of British writers Between 1560 & 1830 to the Interpretation of Revelation 13. 16-18. David Brady. 341p. 1983. lib. bdg. 60.00x (ISBN 3-16-144497-3, Pub. by J C B Mohr BRD). Coronet Bks.
Contribution of Religion to Social Work. Reinhold Niebuhr. LC 74-172444. Repr. of 1932 ed. 5.00 (ISBN 0-404-04708-4). AMS Pr.
Contribution of the Christian Churches to the Development of Western Uganda 1894-1974: Theology. Deogratias M. Byabazaire. (European University Studies: Ser. 23, Vol. 112). 198p. 1979. pap. 21.95 (ISBN 3-261-02553-0). P Lang Pubs.
Contribution to Biblical Lexicography. Israel Eitan. (Columbia University. Contributions to Oriental History & Philology: No. 10). Repr. of 1924 ed. 12.50 (ISBN 0-404-50540-6). AMS Pr.
Contributions of Black Theology to Contemporary Thought. Theodus J. Jordan. 1987. 7.95 (ISBN 0-533-06711-1). Vantage.
Contributions of Buddhism to World Civilization & Culture. Ed. by P. N. Chopra. 408p. 50.00X (ISBN 0-317-52136-5, Pub. by S Chand India). State Mutual Bk.
Contributions of Jainism to Indian Culture. R. C. Dwivedi. 1975. 12.95 (ISBN 0-8426-0953-9). Orient Bk Dist.
Contributions of Mohammedanism to the Historical Growth of Mankind & Its Future Prospects. Frank A. Dobbins. (Illus.). 103p. Repr. of 1883 ed. 97.75 (ISBN 0-89901-111-X). Found Class Reprints.

Contributions of Science to Religion. Shailer Mathews et al. LC 79-117822. (Essay Index Reprint Ser). 1924. 27.50 (ISBN 0-8369-1763-4). Ayer Co Pubs.

Contributions of the Major Philosophers into the Problem of Body Resurrection & Personal Immortality. Richard T. Reesman. (Illus.). 117p. 1981. 61.85 (ISBN 0-89920-021-4). Am Inst Psych.

Contributions of the Quakers. Elizabeth J. Gray. 1983. pap. 2.50x (ISBN 0-87574-034-0, 034). Pendle Hill.

Contributions to Islamic Economic Theory: A Study in Social Economics. Masudul A. Choudhury. LC 85-22149. 224p. 1986. 29.95 (ISBN 0-312-16881-0). St Martin.

Control & Mechanics of S. C. S. (Start, Change, Stop) L. Ron Hubbard. 1951. pap. 9.67 (ISBN 0-88404-067-4). Bridge Pubns Inc.

Control & the Mechanics of SCS. L. Ron Hubbard. 8.75 (ISBN 0-686-30792-5). Church Scient NY.

Control Your Thoughts. Mike Fick & Jim Richardson. 1983. pap. 1.75 (ISBN 0-911739-01-7). Abbott Loop.

Controversial Sholem Asch: An Introduction to His Fiction. Ben Siegel. LC 76-43446. 1976. 12.95 (ISBN 0-87972-076-X); pap. 7.95 (ISBN 0-87972-170-7). Bowling Green Univ.

Controversy & Conciliation: The Reformation & the Palatinate 1559 - 1583. Ed. by Derk Visser. (Pittsburgh Theological Monographs Ser.: No. 18). (Orig.). 1986. pap. 19.95 (ISBN 0-915138-73-5). Pickwick.

Controversy Between the Puritans & the Stage. Elbert N. Thompson. LC 76-176150. Repr. of 1903 ed. 21.50 (ISBN 0-404-06396-9). AMS Pr.

Controversy of Zion. Claude Duvernoy. LC 86-6386. 232p. 1987. pap. 6.96 (ISBN 0-89221-144-X). New Leaf.

Controversy: Roots of the Creation-Evolution Conflict. Donald E. Chittick. LC 84-22670. (Critical Concern Ser.). 1984. 13.95 (ISBN 0-88070-019-X); pap. 9.95. Multnomah.

Convention Essays. C. F. Walther. Tr. by August R. Seuflow. (Selected Writings of C. F. W. Walther Ser.). 1981. 12.95 (ISBN 0-570-08277-3, 15-2735). Concordia.

Convention of Religions in India. 215p. 1983. text ed. 27.50x (ISBN 0-86590-205-4). Apt Bks.

Convergences: To the Source of Christian Mystery. Hans U. Von Balthasar. Tr. by E. A. Nelson from Ger. LC 83-81853. Orig. Title: Einfaltungen: Auf Wegen der Christlichen Einigung. 153p. (Orig.). 1984. pap. 8.95 (ISBN 0-89870-032-9). Ignatius Pr.

Conversation on Counseling Between a Doctor & a Priest. 2nd ed. Ed. by Marcus Lefebure. 128p. pap. 6.95 (ISBN 0-317-31445-9) (ISBN 0-317-31446-7). Fortress.

Conversation with Christ. Peter T. Rohrbach. LC 82-50586. 171p. 1982. pap. 5.00 (ISBN 0-89555-180-2). TAN Bks Pubs.

Conversational Bible Studies. James A. Schacher. (Contemporary Discussion Ser). 112p. 1975. 1.65 (ISBN 0-8010-8054-1). Baker Bk.

Conversational Word of God: A Commentary on the Doctrine of St. Ignatius of Loyola Concerning Spiritual Conversation, with Four Early Jesuit Texts. Thomas H. Clancy. Frwd. by George E. Ganss. LC 78-51343. (Study Aids on Jesuit Topics: No. 8 in Ser. IV). 83p. 1978. 5.00 (ISBN 0-912422-33-5); pap. 2.50 smyth sewn (ISBN 0-912422-34-3). Inst Jesuit.

Conversations. William A. Miller. LC 80-54283. 96p. 1980. pap. 3.50 (ISBN 0-934104-04-2). Woodland.

Conversations about God from the Journal of Willis F. Cox. Willis F. Cox. LC 85-91148. (Illus., Orig.). 1985. 11.95 (ISBN 0-9610758-2-1); pap. 6.95 (ISBN 0-9610758-3-X); pap. text ed. 6.95 (ISBN 0-9610758-1-3). W F Cox.

Conversations in Umbria. Aberic Dubois. 1980. 7.95 (ISBN 0-8199-0784-7). Franciscan Herald.

Conversations on Counselling. Ed. by Marcus Lefebure. 126p. 1985. pap. 10.95 (ISBN 0-567-29120-0, Pub. by T&T Clark Ltd UK). Fortress.

Conversations: The Mother. 133p. 1973. pap. 1.75 (ISBN 0-89071-246-8). Matagiri.

Conversations with Carl Henry: Christianity for Today. Carl F. Henry et al. (Symposium Ser.: No. 18). 204p. 1986. lib. bdg. 49.95 (ISBN 0-88946-709-9). E Mellen.

Conversations with Children. James A. Jones, III. LC 85-40201. (Illus.). 96p. 1985. 7.95 (ISBN 0-938232-72-X). Winston-Derek.

Conversations with Children on the Gospels (Record of Conversations on the Gospels, Held in Mr. Alcott's School; Unfolding the Doctrine & Discipline of Human Culture, 2 vols. in 1. Ed. by A. Bronson Alcott. LC 72-4948. (Romantic Tradition in American Literature Ser.). 616p. 1972. Repr. of 1836 ed. 40.00 (ISBN 0-405-04621-9). Ayer Co Pubs.

Conversations with Christ. Mike Pictor. 73p. (Orig.). 1984. pap. 6.95 (ISBN 0-942494-84-9). Coleman Pub.

Conversations with God: A Voice That Will Drive You Sane. James M. Ryan. Ed. by Herbert Lambert. LC 84-7620. 96p. 1984. pap. 6.95 (ISBN 0-8272-0444-2). CBP.

Conversations with Monsignor Escriva de Balaguer. 210p. 1977. pap. 5.95 (ISBN 0-933932-05-7). Scepter Pubs.

Conversations with Ogotemmeli: An Introduction to Dogon Religious Ideas. Marcel Griaule. (Illus.). 1975. pap. 8.95x (ISBN 0-19-519821-2). Oxford U Pr.

Conversations with Ogotemmeli: An Introduction to Dogon Religious Ideas. Marcel Griaule. LC 65-3614. pap. 62.00 (ISBN 0-317-28624-2, 2055384). Bks Demand UMI.

Conversations with Paul. Wolfgang Trilling. 172p. 1987. 14.95 (ISBN 0-8245-0806-8). Crossroad NY.

Conversations with Sathya Sai Baba. John S. Hislop. LC 79-51262. (Illus.). 1979. pap. 5.40 (ISBN 0-9600958-5-3). Birth Day.

Conversations with the Crucified. Reid Isaac. 128p. (Orig.). 1982. pap. 6.95 (ISBN 0-8164-2417-9, HarpR). Har-Row.

Conversion & Discipleship: A Christian Foundation for Ethics & Doctrine. Stephen Happel & James J. Walter. LC 85-45499. 240p. 1986. pap. 14.95 (ISBN 0-8006-1908-0, 1-1908). Fortress.

Conversion & Experiences After Conversion. C. H. Spurgeon. 1977. pap. 1.50 (ISBN 0-686-17969-2). Pilgrim Pubns.

Conversion & the Catechumenate. Ed. by Robert Duggan. 1984. pap. 7.95 (ISBN 0-8091-2614-1). Paulist Pr.

Conversion Experience: A Biblical Study of the Blood, Water & Spirit. Gary D. Erickson. Ed. by David Bernard. (Illus.). 160p. (Orig.). 1987. pap. 5.95 (ISBN 0-932581-13-7). Word Aflame.

Conversion-Initiation & the Baptism in the Holy Spirit. Howard M. Ervin. 108p. 1985. pap. 9.95 (ISBN 0-913573-12-4). Hendrickson MA.

Conversion of Armenia. Valerie G. Zahirsky. (Armenian Church Classics Ser.). (Illus.). 48p. (Orig.). 1985. pap. 5.00 (ISBN 0-934728-16-X). D O A C.

Conversion of Constantine. Ed. by John W. Eadie. LC 76-25480. (European American Studies). 120p. 1977. pap. text ed. 5.95 (ISBN 0-88275-453-X). Krieger.

Conversion of Saint Paul: Narrative & History in Acts. Gerhard Lohfink. Ed. & tr. by Bruce J. Malina. 156p. 1976. 5.95 (ISBN 0-8199-0572-0). Franciscan Herald.

Conversion of the Jews. Ludwig Van Hattenberg. (Intimate Life of Man Library). (Illus.). 1979. 49.85 (ISBN 0-89266-191-7). Am Classical Coll Pr.

Conversion: Perspectives on Personal & Social Transformation. Walter E. Conn. LC 78-19079. 1978. pap. 10.95 (ISBN 0-8189-0368-6). Alba.

Conversion to Islam. Ed. by Nehemia Levtzion. LC 77-26771. 265p. 1979. text ed. 39.50x (ISBN 0-8419-0343-3). Holmes & Meier.

Conversion to Islam in the Medieval Period: An Essay in Quantitative History. Richard W. Bulliet. (Illus.). 158p. 1979. text ed. 16.50x (ISBN 0-674-17035-0). Harvard U Pr.

Conversion to Judaism: A History & Analysis. David M. Eichhorn. 1966. 12.50x (ISBN 0-87068-019-6). Ktav.

Conversion to Judaism: From the Biblical Period to the Present. Joseph R. Rosenbloom. 20.00x (ISBN 0-87820-113-0). Ktav.

Conversions. Ed. by Hugh T. Kerr & John M. Mulder. 288p. 1983. 12.95 (ISBN 0-8028-3587-2). Eerdmans.

Conversions. Ed. by Hugh T. Kerr & John T. Mulder. 384p. 1985. pap. 7.95 (ISBN 0-8028-0016-5). Eerdmans.

Convert Conservation. William E. Winters. 120p. pap. 4.25 (ISBN 0-87148-161-8). Pathway Pr.

Convert Looks at the Catholic Church & the World Crisis. Beryl Rodrigue. 1981. 6.50 (ISBN 0-8062-1833-9). Carlton.

Converti Paul Claudel. Guillemin. 25.95 (ISBN 0-685-37276-6). French & Eur.

Convert's Catechism of Catholic Doctrine. Peter Geiermann. 1977. pap. 2.00 (ISBN 0-89555-029-6). TAN Bks Pubs.

Converts, Dropouts, Returnees: A Study of Religious Change among Catholics. Dean R. Hoge et al. LC 81-15351. 200p. 1981. 14.95 (ISBN 0-8298-0483-8); pap. 7.95 (ISBN 0-8298-0487-0). Pilgrim NY.

Convictions That Give You Confidence. Wayne E. Oates. LC 84-5193. (Potentials: Guides for Productive Living Ser.: Vol. 10). 110p. 1984. pap. 7.95 (ISBN 0-664-24529-3). Westminster.

Convicts, Clergymen & Churches. Allan M. Grocott. 356p. 1980. 38.00x (ISBN 0-424-00072-5, Pub. by Sydney U Pr Australia). Intl Spec Bk.

Convocation Book of 1606. John Overall. LC 77-173482. (Library of Anglo-Catholic Theology: No. 15). Repr. of 1844 ed. 27.50 (ISBN 0-404-52107-X). AMS Pr.

Convocation of the Clergy: A Study of Antecedents & Its Rise, with Special Emphasis upon Its Growth & Activities in the Thirteenth & Fourteenth Centuries. Dorothy B. Weske. (Church Historical Society London N. S. Ser.: No. 23). Repr. of 1937 ed. 60.00 (ISBN 0-8115-3147-3). Kraus Repr.

Cooking for Your Children Cookbook. G. H. Donald. 17.50 (ISBN 0-87559-125-6). Shalom.

Cooking up Dreams. Kathryn Hillen. 160p. 1987. pap. 9.95 (ISBN 0-310-34551-0). Zondervan.

Cool: How a Kid Should Live. Edythe Draper. 1974. kivar 6.95 (ISBN 0-8423-0435-5). Tyndale.

Cooperation & Coercion as Methods of Social Change. Vincent D. Nicholson. 1983. pap. 2.50x (ISBN 0-87574-001-4, 001). Pendle Hill.

Cooperation & Human Values: A Study of Moral Reasoning. R. E. Ewin. 1981. 22.50 (ISBN 0-312-16956-6). St Martin.

Cooperative Ministry: Hope for Small Churches. Marshall E. Schirer & Mary A. Forehand. 96p. 1984. pap. 3.95 (ISBN 0-8170-1030-0). Judson.

Cope du Mahayana en Chine: Amsterdam, 1892. J. J. De Groot. LC 78-74288. (Oriental Religions Ser.: Vol. 15). 281p. 1980. lib. bdg. 40.00 (ISBN 0-8240-3917-3). Garland Pub.

Copenhagen Haggadah. Ed. by Chaya Benjamin. LC 86-63514. (Hebrew., Illus.). 68p. 1987. 40.00 (ISBN 0-8478-0820-3). Rizzoli Intl.

Coping. Elizabeth Skoglund. LC 79-65538. 128p. 1980. pap. 3.95 (ISBN 0-8307-0727-1, 5413109). Regal.

Coping in the Eighties: Eliminating Needless Stress & Guilt. Joel Wells. 1986. 10.95 (ISBN 0-88347-201-5); pap. 6.95 (ISBN 0-88347-202-3). Thomas More.

Coping Is Not Enough. Kendrick Strong. LC 86-23260. (Orig.). 1987. text ed. 7.95 (ISBN 0-8054-5042-4). Broadman.

Coping: Issues of Emotional Living in an Age of Stress for Clergy & Religious. Ed. by Bernard J. Bush. LC 76-362761. 83p. 1976. pap. 2.95 (ISBN 0-89571-000-5). Affirmation.

Coping: O God, I'm Struggling. Lyman Coleman. (Serendipity Ser.). (Orig.). 1981. pap. 4.95 leader's guide 64 pgs. (ISBN 0-687-37310-7); pap. 1.25 student's bk. 32 pgs. (ISBN 0-687-37311-5). Abingdon.

Coping With a Dying Relative. Derek Doyle. 1983. 30.00x (ISBN 0-86334-028-8, Pub. by Macdonald Pub UK); pap. 20.00x (ISBN 0-86334-026-1). State Mutual Bk.

Coping with a Gentle God. John Powers. 1984. pap. 6.95 (ISBN 0-89453-443-2). M Glazier.

Coping with Abuse in the Family. Wesley R. Monfalcone. LC 80-15125. (Christian Care Bks.: Vol. 10). 120p. 1980. pap. 7.95 (ISBN 0-664-24326-6). Westminster.

Coping with Being Single Again. J. Clark Hensley. LC 78-52623. 1978. 7.95 (ISBN 0-8054-5420-9). Broadman.

Coping with Clergy Burnout. G. Lloyd Rediger. 112p. 1982. pap. 5.95 (ISBN 0-8170-0956-6). Judson.

Coping with Counseling Crises. Jay E. Adams. 98p. 1976. pap. 2.95 (ISBN 0-87552-018-9). Presby & Reformed.

Coping with Death & Dying: An Interdisciplinary Approach. Ed. by John T. Chirban. 108p. 1986. lib. bdg. 22.00 (ISBN 0-8191-4984-5); pap. text ed. 8.75 (ISBN 0-8191-4985-3). U Pr of Amer.

Coping with Difficult People. Paul F. Schmidt. LC 79-27486. (Christian Care Bks.: Vol. 6). 120p. 1980. pap. 7.95 (ISBN 0-664-24299-5). Westminster.

Coping with Discouragement. Mary M. Fenocketti. 64p. 1985. pap. 1.50 (ISBN 0-89243-226-8). Liguori Pubns.

Coping with Life & Its Problems. Joyce M. Smith. 1976. pap. 2.95 (ISBN 0-8423-0434-7). Tyndale.

Coping with Physical Disability. Jan Cox-Gedmark. LC 79-28275. (Christian Care Bks.). 118p. 1980. pap. 7.95 (ISBN 0-664-24297-9). Westminster.

Coping with Stress in the Minister's Home. Robert Bailey & Mary Frances Bailey. LC 79-51135. 1979. 6.95 (ISBN 0-8054-5266-4). Broadman.

Coping with Tension. Pauline E. Spray. (Direction Bks). 136p. 1981. pap. 2.95 (ISBN 0-8010-8189-0). Baker Bk.

Coping with Widowhood. Frances C. Durland. 1979. pap. 1.50 (ISBN 0-89243-098-2). Liguori Pubns.

Coping with Your Anger: A Christian Guide. Andrew D. Lester. LC 82-24730. 114p. 1983. pap. 6.95 (ISBN 0-664-24471-8). Westminster.

Copper, Molybdenum, & Vanadium in Biological Systems: Structure & Bonding, Vol. 53. M. J. Clarke et al. (Illus.). 166p. 1983. 39.50 (ISBN 0-387-12042-4). Springer-Verlag.

Coptic Apocrypha in the Dialect of Upper Egypt. Ed. by Ernest A. Budge. LC 77-3589. (Coptic Texts: Vol. 3). (Illus.). Repr. of 1913 ed. 55.00 (ISBN 0-404-11553-5). AMS Pr.

Coptic Apocryphal Gospels. Tr. by Forbes Robinson. (Texts & Studies: No. 1, Vol. 4-Pt. 2). pap. 19.00 (ISBN 0-8115-1693-8). Kraus Repr.

Coptic Biblical Texts in the Dialect of Upper Egypt. Ed. by Ernest A. Budge. LC 77-3590. (Coptic Texts: Vol. 2). (Illus.). 1977. Repr. of 1912 ed. 45.00 (ISBN 0-404-11552-7). AMS Pr.

Coptic Homilies in the Dialect of Upper Egypt. Ed. by Ernest A. Budge. LC 77-3585. (Coptic Texts: Vol. 1). (Illus.). Repr. of 1910 ed. 50.00 (ISBN 0-404-11551-9). AMS Pr.

Coptic Manuscripts in the Freer Collection. William H. Worrell. Repr. of 1923 ed. 37.00 (ISBN 0-384-38810-8). Johnson Repr.

Coptic Martyrdoms, Etc. in the Dialect of Upper Egypt. Ed. by Ernest A. Budge. LC 77-3588. (Coptic Texts: Vol. 4). (Illus.). Repr. of 1914 ed. 60.00 (ISBN 0-404-11554-3). AMS Pr.

Coptic Morning Service for the Lord's Day. Coptic Church Staff. Tr. by John P. Crichton-Stuart. LC 72-39871. Repr. of 1908 ed. 17.25 (ISBN 0-404-01247-7). AMS Pr.

Coptic Texts Edited with Introductions & English Translations, 5 vols. Ernest A. Budge. Repr. of 1915 ed. 345.00 set (ISBN 0-404-11550-0); write for info. AMS Pr.

Copts & Moslems under British Control. Kyriakos Mikhail. LC 70-118537. 1971. Repr. of 1911 ed. 24.00x (ISBN 0-8046-1160-2, Pub. by Kennikat). Assoc Faculty Pr.

Copts in Egyptian Politics 1918 - 1952. Barbara L. Carter. 256p. 1985. 43.00 (ISBN 0-7099-3417-3, Pub. by Croom Helm Ltd). Methuen Inc.

Copy of the Letters Wherein Kyng Henry the Eyght Made Answere into a Certayn Letter of Martyn Luther. Henry VIII. LC 72-204. (English Experience Ser.: No. 322). 100p. 1971. Repr. of 1528 ed. 14.00 (ISBN 90-221-0322-6). Walter J Johnson.

Corazon de Una Madre. Jean Fleming. Tr. by Juan S. Araujo from Eng. Tr. of Mother's Heart. (Span.). 144p. 1987. pap. 4.25 (ISBN 0-88113-029-X). Edit Betania.

Cord: Twenty-Five Year Index 1950-1975. 1977. 4.00 (ISBN 0-686-19080-7). Franciscan Inst.

Coretta Scott King. Lillie Patterson. LC 76-19077. (American All Ser.). (Illus.). 96p. 1977. PLB 7.12 (ISBN 0-8116-4585-1). Garrard.

Corinthian Catastrophe. George E. Gardiner. LC 74-75106. 64p. 1975. pap. 2.95 (ISBN 0-8254-2708-8). Kregel.

Corinthian Correspondence. Russell P. Spittler. LC 75-43157. (Radiant Life Ser.). 128p. 1976. pap. 2.50 (ISBN 0-88243-892-1, 02-0892); tchr's. ed. 3.95 (ISBN 0-88243-166-8, 32-0166). Gospel Pub.

Corinthian Letters of Paul. G. Campbell Morgan. 288p. 1946. 15.95 (ISBN 0-8007-0051-1). Revell.

Corinthians, Vol. VII. Beacon Bible Commentary Staff. 6.95 (ISBN 0-8010-0681-3). Baker Bk.

Corinthians: A Commentary on the New Testament in Modern English. (J. B. Phillips New Testament Commentaries Ser). 102p. 1973. Repr. of 1972 ed. 1.50 (ISBN 0-685-29328-9). Macmillan.

Corinthians I. William F. Orr & James S. Walther. LC 75-42441. (Anchor Bible Ser.: Vol. 32). 1976. 18.00 (ISBN 0-385-02853-9). Doubleday.

Corinthians II, Vol 32A. Intro. by Victor P. Furnish. LC 83-2056. (Anchor Bible Ser.). (Illus.). 648p. 1984. 18.00 (ISBN 0-385-11199-1). Doubleday.

Corinthians One. H. A. Ironside. 12.95x (ISBN 0-87213-354-0). Loizeaux.

Corinthians One. Marilyn Kunz & Catherine Schell. (Neighborhood Bible Studies Ser.). 1974. pap. 2.50 (ISBN 0-8423-0441-X). Tyndale.

Corinthians Two. H. A. Ironside. 8.95 (ISBN 0-87213-355-9). Loizeaux.

Corinthians 1 & 2. Charles Hodge. (Geneva Commentaries Ser.). 1978. 15.95 (ISBN 0-85151-185-6). Banner of Truth.

Corinthians 1: Bible Study Commentary. Curtis Vaughan & Thomas D. Lea. (Bible Study Commentary Ser.). 160p. 1983. pap. 4.95 (ISBN 0-310-44021-1, 12484P). Zondervan.

Cornbread & Caviar. Bob Jones. (Illus.). 236p. 1985. 12.95 (ISBN 0-89084-305-8); pap. 8.95 (ISBN 0-89084-306-6). Bob Jones Univ Pr.

Cornelius VanTil: The Man & the Myth. John W. Robbins. (Trinity Papers: No. 15). 40p. (Orig.). 1986. pap. 2.45 (ISBN 0-940931-15-X). Trinity Found.

Cornerstones: Believing the Bible. Kent Fishel. 112p. 1987. pap. 4.95 (ISBN 0-310-39761-8). Zondervan.

Cornflake Crusade. Gerald Carson. LC 75-39240. (Getting & Spending: the Consumer's Dilemma). (Illus.). 1976. Repr. of 1957 ed. 25.50x (ISBN 0-405-08013-1). Ayer Co Pubs.

Cornish Ordinalia: Religion & Dramaturgy. Robert M. Longsworth. LC 67-22869. 1967. 12.50x (ISBN 0-674-17200-0). Harvard U Pr.

Corona Class Lessons. Ed. by Mark L. Prophet & Elizabeth C. Prophet. LC 83-51445. 455p. (Orig.). 1986. pap. 12.95 (ISBN 0-916766-65-9). Summit Univ.

Coronado's Friars: The Franciscans in the Coronado Expedition. Angelico Chavez. (Monograph Ser.). (Illus.). 1968. 10.00 (ISBN 0-88382-058-7). AAFH.

Corporation Sole: Cardinal Mundelein & Chicago Catholicism. Edward Kantowicz. LC 82-13420. (Notre Dame Studies in American Catholicism). 320p. 1983. text ed. 19.95 (ISBN 0-268-00738-1); pap. text ed. 9.95 (ISBN 0-268-00739-X). U of Notre Dame Pr.

Corpus Inscriptionum Judaicarum. rev. ed. Jean B. Frey. (Library of Biblical Studies). 1970. 100.00x (ISBN 0-87068-103-6). Ktav.

Corpus of the Aramaic Incantation Bowls. Charles D. Isbell. LC 75-15949. (Society of Biblical Literature. Dissertation Ser.: No. 17). pap. 40.70 (ISBN 0-317-10143-9, 2017519). Bks Demand UMI.

Corpus Vitrearum: Studies on Medieval Stained Glass. Madeline E. Caviness & Timothy Husband. (Occasional Papers: No. 1). (Illus.). 160p. 1985. 35.00 (ISBN 0-87099-391-7). Metro Mus Art.

Correct Ideas Don't Fall from the Skies: Elements for an Inductive Theology. George Casalis. Tr. by Jeanne M. Lyons & Michael John. LC 83-19374. Tr. of Idees Justes Ne Tombent Pas du Ciel. 240p. (Orig.). 1984. pap. 8.95 (ISBN 0-88344-023-7). Orbis Bks.

Correspondance avec Andre Gide: 1899-1926. Paul Claudel. 1949. pap. 7.95 (ISBN 0-686-51967-1). French & Eur.

Correspondance avec Andre Suares: 1904-1938. Paul Claudel. 1951. pap. 5.95 (ISBN 0-686-51968-X). French & Eur.

Correspondance avec Francis Jammes et Gabriel Frizeau: 1897-1938. Paul Claudel. 1952. pap. 7.95 (ISBN 0-686-51969-8). French & Eur.

Correspondence, Conferences, Documents, Vol. 1. Vincent De Paul. Tr. by Helen M. Law et al from Fr. & Lat. Ed. by Jacqueline Kilar. LC 83-63559. 675p. 1985. 28.00 (ISBN 0-317-27157-1). New City.

Correspondence of Erasmus, Letters, 1501-1514, Vol. 2. Desiderius Erasmus. Ed. by Beatrice Corrigan. LC 72-47422. (Collected Works of Erasmus: Vol. 2). (Illus.). 1975. 75.00x (ISBN 0-8020-1983-8). U of Toronto Pr.

Correspondence of Erasmus, Vol. 1: Letters 1-141: 1484-1500. Desiderius Erasmus. Ed. by Beatrice Corrigan. LC 72-97422. (Collected Works of Erasmus: Vol. 1). (Illus.). 1974. 75.00x (ISBN 0-8020-1981-1). U of Toronto Pr.

Correspondence of Erasmus, Vol. 3: Letters 298-445 (1514-1516) Mynors. Desiderius Erasmus. Tr. by R. A. Mynors & D. F. Thomson. LC 72-97422. (Collected Works of Erasmus: Vol. 3). (Illus.). 1976. 75.00x (ISBN 0-8020-2202-2). U of Toronto Pr.

Correspondence of Erasmus, Vol. 4: Letters 446-593. Desiderius Erasmus. Tr. by R. A. Mynors & D. F. Thomson. LC 72-97422. (Collected Works of Erasmus: Vol. 4). 1977. 75.00x (ISBN 0-8020-5366-1). U of Toronto Pr.

Correspondence of Erasmus, Vol. 5: Letters 594-841 (July 1517 - April 1518) Desiderius Erasmus. Tr. by R. A. Mynors & D. F. Thomson. LC 78-6904. (Collected Works of Erasmus: Vol. 5). 1979. 75.00x (ISBN 0-8020-5429-3). U of Toronto Pr.

Correspondence of Erasmus, Vol. 6: Letters 842-992 (May 1518 - June 1519) Desiderius Erasmus. Tr. by R. A. Mynors & D. F. Thomson. (Collected Works of Erasmus: Vol. 6). 1981. 75.00x (ISBN 0-8020-5500-1). U of Toronto Pr.

Correspondence of Pope Gregory VII. Pope Gregory Seventh. Tr. by E. Emerton. (Columbia University Records of Civilization Ser.). 1969. pap. 5.95x (ISBN 0-393-09859-1). Norton.

Correspondence of Thomas Percy & John Pinkerton: The Percy Letters, Vol. 8. Ed. by Harriet H. Wood & Cleanth Brooks. LC 84-2916. 160p. 1985. text ed. 25.00x (ISBN 0-300-03344-3). Yale U Pr.

Corresponding Motion: Transcendental Religion & the New America. Catherine L Albanese. LC 77-70329. 234p. 1977. 29.95 (ISBN 0-87722-098-0). Temple U Pr.

Corrie Ten Boom: Her Life, Her Faith. Carole C. Carlson. (Illus.). 224p. 1984. pap. 3.50 (ISBN 0-8007-8490-1, Spire Bks). Revell.

Cortes: The Life of the Conqueror of Mexico by His Secretary, Francisco Lopez de Gomara. Francisco Lopez de Gomara. Ed. & tr. by Lesley B. Simpson. LC 64-13474. 1964. pap. 5.95 (ISBN 0-520-00493-0, CAL 126). U of Cal Pr.

Cortinas de Humo. Jack T. Chick. (Span., Illus., Orig.). 1984. pap. 2.50 (ISBN 0-937958-20-4). Chick Pubns.

Cory Hears with His Heart. Don Goodman. LC 82-12272. (Cory Story Ser.). 32p. 1982. pap. 2.95 (ISBN 0-8307-0858-8, 5608318). Regal.

Cosas Que Hacer para Navidad. Meg Braga. (Editorial Mundo Hispano). (YA) 1981. Repr. of 1980 ed. 3.25 (ISBN 0-311-26607-X). Casa Bautista.

Cosmic Adventure: Science, Religion & the Quest for Purpose. John F. Haught. LC 83-82026. (Orig.). 1984. pap. 7.95 (ISBN 0-8091-2599-4). Paulist Pr.

Cosmic Center: The Supremacy of Christ in a Secular Wasteland. D. Bruce Lockerbie. LC 85-18741. (Critical Concern Bks.). 1986. Repr. of 1977 ed. 11.95 (ISBN 0-88070-132-3). Multnomah.

Cosmic Chants. rev. 6th ed. Paramahansa Yogananda. LC 74-20347. (Illus.). 84p. 1974. flexible bdg 3.50 (ISBN 0-87612-131-8); German ed. 9.00x (ISBN 0-87612-132-6). Self Realization.

Cosmic Christ in Origen & Teilhard de Chardin. J. A. Lyons. Ed. by Maurice Wiles. (Theological Monographs). 1982. 34.95x (ISBN 0-19-826721-5). Oxford U Pr.

Cosmic Combinations. Joan Negus. 168p. (Orig.). 1982. pap. 7.95 (ISBN 0-917086-37-6). A C S Pubns Inc.

Cosmic Conflict. Ellen G. White. 640p. 1983. pap. 0.50 (ISBN 0-8280-0211-8). Pacific Pr Pub Assn.

Cosmic Consciousness: The Highway to Wholeness. Gloria R. Rivers. Ed. by Owen Cramer. (Orig.). 1987. pap. text ed. 12.00 (ISBN 0-918341-01-9). Temple Pubns.

Cosmic Continuum. 2nd ed. Ernest L. Norman. (Illus.). 1960. 7.95 (ISBN 0-932642-17-9). Unarius Pubns.

Cosmic Genesis. Arthur Fabel. (Tielhard Studies). 1981. 2.00 (ISBN 0-89012-028-5). Anima Pubns.

Cosmic Horizons: Understanding the Universe. R. Wagoner & D. Goldsmith. 250p. 1982. 22.95 (ISBN 0-7167-1417-5); pap. 12.95 (ISBN 0-7167-1418-3). W H Freeman.

Cosmic Humanism & World Unity. new ed. Oliver Reiser. LC 73-86468. (World Institute Creative Findings Ser.). (Illus.). 286p. 1975. 49.50 (ISBN 0-677-03870-4); pap. 21.00 (ISBN 0-677-03875-5). Gordon & Breach.

Cosmic Hymns & Prayers. Satguru S. Keshavadas. (Illus.). 174p. (Orig.). 1982. pap. text ed. 10.00 (ISBN 0-942508-13-0). Vishwa.

Cosmic Meditations. Satguru S. Keshavadas. (Illus.). 22p. (Orig.). 1974. pap. 1.99 (ISBN 0-942508-08-4). Vishwa.

Cosmic Mission Fulfilled. 3rd ed. Ralph M. Lewis. LC 66-25243. 364p. 1978. 12.50 (ISBN 0-912057-22-X, G-631). AMORC.

Cosmic Moral Laws. 2nd ed. Omraam M Aivanhov. (Complete Works: Vol. 12). 294p. (Orig.). 1984. pap. 9.95 (ISBN 2-85566-112-9). Prosveta USA.

Cosmic Revelation: The Hindu Way to God. Bede Griffiths. 128p. 1983. pap. 7.95 (ISBN 0-87243-119-3). Templegate.

Cosmic Science of the Ancient Masters. 2nd ed. Hilton Hotema. 32p. 1960. pap. 8.95 (ISBN 0-88697-031-8). Life Science.

Cosmic Shakti Kundalini: The Universal Mother. Satguru S. Keshavadas. LC 76-11347. (Illus.). 112p. (Orig.). 1976. pap. 3.50 (ISBN 0-942508-04-1). Vishwa.

Cosmic Understanding. Carl Unger. 1982. pap. 1.95 (ISBN 0-916786-62-5). St George Bk Serv.

Cosmic Unfoldment: The Individualizing Process as Mirrored in the Life of Jesus. Diane K. Pike. LC 76-45344. 99p. 1976. pap. 2.00 (ISBN 0-916192-08-3). L P Pubns.

Cosmic Visions. Albert Rainey. LC 85-90309. 56p. (Orig.). 1986. pap. write for info. (ISBN 0-932971-01-6). Al Rainey Pubns.

Cosmic Womb: An Interpretation of Man's Relationship to the Infinite. Arthur W. Osborn. LC 69-17714. (Orig.). 1969. pap. 2.25 (ISBN 0-8356-0001-7, Quest). Theos Pub Hse.

Cosmic Zygote: Cosmology in the Amazon Basin. Peter G. Roe. (Illus.). 451p. 1982. 42.00x (ISBN 0-8135-0896-7). Rutgers U Pr.

Cosmogony of the Solar System. Fred Hoyle. LC 78-21286. (Illus.). 168p. 1979. 17.95x (ISBN 0-89490-023-4). Enslow Pubs.

Cosmographia of Bernardus Silvestris. Ed. & tr. by Winthrop Wetherbee. LC 73-479. (Records of Civilization, Sources & Studies: Sources & Studies). 176p. 1973. 24.00x (ISBN 0-231-03673-6). Columbia U Pr.

Cosmological Argument: A Reassessment. Bruce R. Reichenbach. (Illus.). 160p. 1972. 16.00x (ISBN 0-398-02387-5). C C Thomas.

Cosmology & Astrophysics: Essays in Honor of Thomas Gold on His 60th Birthday. Ed. by Yervant Terzian & Elizabeth Bilson. (Illus.). 168p. 1982. 27.50x (ISBN 0-8014-1497-0). Cornell U Pr.

Cosmology & Social Life: Ritual Exchange Among the Mambai of East Timor. Elizabeth G. Traube. (Illus.). 312p. 1987. text ed. 32.00x (ISBN 0-226-81149-2); pap. text ed. 14.95x (ISBN 0-226-81150-6). U of Chicago Pr.

Cosmology & Theology. David Tracy & Nicholas Lash. (Concilium 1983: Vol. 166). 128p. (Orig.). 1983. pap. 6.95 (ISBN 0-8164-2446-2, HarpR). Har-Row.

Cosmology, History, & Theology. Ed. by Wolfgang Yourgrau & Allen D. Breck. LC 76-54269. (Illus.). 416p. 1977. 69.50x (ISBN 0-306-30940-8, Plenum Pr). Plenum Pub.

Cosmotherapy of the Essenes. Edmond B. Szekely. (Illus.). 64p. 1975. pap. 3.50 (ISBN 0-89564-012-0). IBS Intl.

Cost of Authority: Manipulation & Freedom in the New Testament. Graham Shaw. LC 82-48545. 320p. 1983. pap. 16.95 (ISBN 0-8006-1707-X). Fortress.

Cost of Being Human. Corona Bamberg. 7.95 (ISBN 0-87193-128-1). Dimension Bks.

Cost of Discipleship. Dietrich Bonhoeffer. 1963. pap. 5.95 (ISBN 0-02-083850-6, Collier). Macmillan.

Cost of Discipleship. Dietrich Bonhoeffer. 1983. 14.00 (ISBN 0-8446-5960-6). Peter Smith.

Cost of Discipleship. Louis Rushmore. 1986. pap. 4.00 (ISBN 0-89137-563-5). Quality Pubns.

Cost of Something for Nothing. John P. Altgeld. 59.95 (ISBN 0-87968-948-X). Gordon Pr.

Cost of Something for Nothing. John P. Altgeld. (Illus.). 135p. Repr. of 1904 ed. 12.95 (ISBN 0-88286-152-2). C H Kerr.

Costly Grace: An Illustrated Introduction to Dietrich Bonhoeffer in His Own Words. Eberhard Bethge. LC 78-19492. (Illus.). 1979. pap. 4.95i (ISBN 0-06-060773-4, RD294, HarpR). Har-Row.

Costumes of Religious Orders of the Middle Ages. 300p. 1984. pap. 35.00 (ISBN 0-87556-491-7). Saifer.

Cotton Mather. Otho T. Beall & Richard H. Shryock. 1979. 21.00 (ISBN 0-405-10580-0). Ayer Co Pubs.

Cotton Mather. Barrett Wendell. LC 80-23335. (American Men & Women of Letters Ser.). Orig. Title: Cotton Mather: the Puritan Priest. 328p. 1981. pap. 5.95 (ISBN 0-87754-166-3). Chelsea Hse.

Cotton Mather: A Bibliography of His Works, 3 vols. Thomas J. Holmes. 1395p. 1974. Repr. Set. 70.00x (ISBN 0-89020-000-9). Crofton Pub.

Cotton Mather: A Bibliography of His Works. Thomas S. Holmes. 1940. Set. 70.00 (ISBN 0-89020-000-9); Vol. 3. Brown Bk.

Cotton Mather & American Science & Medicine: With Studies & Documents Concerning the Introduction of Innoculation or Variolation, Vol. 1. I. Bernard Cohen. 37.50 (ISBN 0-405-12520-8). Ayer Co Pubs.

Cotton Mather & American Science & Medicine: With Studies & Documents Concerning the Introduction of Inoculation or Variolation, Vol. 2. I. Bernard Cohen. 37.50 (ISBN 0-405-12521-6). Ayer Co Pubs.

Cotton Mather, the Christian Philosopher & the Classics. Winton U. Solberg. 44p. 1987. pap. write for info. (ISBN 0-912296-90-9). Am Antiquarian.

Cotton Mather: The Puritan Priest. Barrett Wendell. 1978. Repr. of 1891 ed. lib. bdg. 35.00 (ISBN 0-8495-5626-0). Arden Lib.

Cotton Mather: The Young Life of the Lord's Remembrancer, 1663-1703. David Levin. LC 78-2355. (Illus.). 1978. 25.00x (ISBN 0-674-17507-7). Harvard U Pr.

Cotton Patch Gospel: The Proclamation of Clarence Jordan. Joel P. Snider. LC 85-6224. 112p. (Orig.). 1985. lib. bdg. 22.00 (ISBN 0-8191-4680-3); pap. text ed. 9.50 (ISBN 0-8191-4681-1). U Pr of Amer.

Cotton Patch Version of Hebrews & the General Epistles. Clarence Jordan. LC 73-14856. (Cotton Patch Translations of the Bible Ser.). 1973. pap. 4.95 (ISBN 0-8329-1879-2, Assn Pr). New Century.

Cotton Patch Version of Luke & Acts. Clarence Jordan. LC 69-18840. 1969. pap. 4.95 (ISBN 0-8329-1173-9, Assn Pr). New Century.

Cotton Patch Version of Matthew & John. Clarence Jordan. LC 83-61334. 1970. pap. 4.95 (ISBN 0-8329-1062-7, Assn Pr). New Century.

Cotton Patch Version of Paul's Epistles. Clarence Jordan. LC 68-11487. 1968. pap. 4.95 (ISBN 0-8329-1041-4, Assn Pr). New Century.

Could I Be a Pastor. Marilee Schmidt. 1985. 2.95 (ISBN 0-8100-0199-3, 16N0781). Northwest Pub.

Could I Be a Teacher. Marilee Schimidt. 1985. 2.95 (ISBN 0-8100-0200-0, 16N0782). Northwest Pub.

Council & Commune: The Conciliar Movement & the Fifteenth-Century Heritage. Antony Black. LC 79-89220. x, 253p. 1979. 25.95x (ISBN 0-915762-08-0). Patmos Pr.

Council & Synods with Other Documents Relating to the English Church, Vol. 1: A. D. 871-1204, 2 Vols. Dorothy Whitelock & Martin Brett. 1981. text ed. 139.00x (ISBN 0-19-822394-3). Oxford U Pr.

Council of Florence. Joseph Gill. LC 78-63345. (Crusades & Military Orders: Second Ser.). (Illus.). 480p. Repr. of 1959 ed. 37.50 (ISBN 0-404-17016-1). AMS Pr.

Counsel & Consent. Eric W. Kemp. LC 62-3455. (Bampton Lectures). 1961. 15.00x (ISBN 0-8401-1317-X). A R Allenson.

Counseling: A Guide to Helping Others, Vol. 2. Ed. by R. Lanier Britsch & Terrance D. Olson. LC 83-72396. 335p. 1985. 9.95 (ISBN 0-87747-737-X). Deseret Bk.

Counseling & Confession. Walter J. Koehler. 1982. pap. 7.50 (ISBN 0-570-03849-9, 12-2804). Concordia.

Counseling & Health Care. Harshajan Pazhayatil. LC 76-29068. 385p. 1977. pap. 8.00 (ISBN 0-8199-0623-9). Franciscan Herald.

Counseling & the Five Points of Calvinism. Jay E. Adams. 1981. pap. 0.75 (ISBN 0-87552-072-3). Presby & Reformed.

Counseling Cross-Culturally. David J. Hesselgrave. 1984. 14.95p (ISBN 0-8010-4282-8). Baker Bk.

Counseling for Church Leaders. John W. Drakeford. LC 61-12412. 1961. 9.25 (ISBN 0-8054-2405-9). Broadman.

Counseling for Liberation. Charlotte H. Clinebell. Ed. by Howard J. Clineball & Howard W. Stone. LC 75-36447. (Creative Pastoral Care & Counseling Ser). 96p. (Orig.). 1976. pap. 4.50 (ISBN 0-8006-0555-1, 1-555). Fortress.

Counseling in Cases of Family Violence & Abuse. Grant Martin. 192p. 1987. 12.95 (ISBN 0-8499-0587-7). Word Bks.

Counseling Lesbian Women & Gay Men: A Life-Issues Approach. A. Elfin Moses & Robert O. Hawkins, Jr. 263p. 1982. pap. text ed. 19.95 (ISBN 0-675-20599-9). Merrill.

Counseling Principles for Christian Leaders. James A. Jones. 5.95 (ISBN 0-89137-534-1). Quality Pubns.

Counseling Skills for Church Leadership. Hyrum H. Huskey, Jr. 1980. pap. 6.00 (ISBN 0-8309-0295-3). Herald Hse.

Counseling the Childless Couple. William T. Bassett. LC 63-14722. (Successful Pastoral Counseling Ser.). pap. 34.80 (2026938). Bks Demand UMI.

Counseling the Depressed. Archibald Hart. 224p. 1987. 12.95 (ISBN 0-8499-0582-6). Word Bks.

Counseling the Homosexual. Bill Flatt et al. 11.00 (ISBN 0-934916-49-7). Natl Christian Pr.

Counseling with Confidence. Earl A. Goldsmith. 155p. 1984. pap. 5.95 (ISBN 0-916945-01-4). V I Pr.

Counseling with Senior Citizens. J. Paul Brown. LC 64-15217. (Successful Pastoral Counseling Ser.). pap. 36.00 (2027174). Bks Demand UMI.

Counseling with the Mind of Christ: The Dynamics of Spirituotherapy. Charles R. Solomon. 160p. 1977. pap. 5.95 (ISBN 0-8007-5049-7, Power Bks). Revell.

Counseling: With the Pastor & CPE Student in Mind. Calvin C. Green. 1984. 12.95 (ISBN 0-533-05923-2). Vantage.

Counseling Youth. new ed. Clyde M. Narramore. 128p. (Orig.). 1974. pap. 5.95 (ISBN 0-310-29891-1, 12229P). Zondervan.

Counseling Youth. Paul L. Walker. 112p. 1967. 5.25 (ISBN 0-87148-162-6); pap. 4.25 (ISBN 0-87148-163-4). Pathway Pr.

Counselling of Jesus. Duncan Buchanan. Ed. by Michael Green. LC 85-19736. (Jesus Library). 160p. 1985. pap. 6.95 (ISBN 0-87784-931-5). Inter-Varsity.

Counselor & Suicidal Crisis: Diagnosis & Intervention. John Hipple & Peter Cimbolic. 136p. 1979. 16.25x (ISBN 0-398-03872-4). C C Thomas.

Counsels for Jesuits: Selected Letters & Instructions of Saint Ignatius Loyola. Ed. by Joseph N. Tylenda. 152p. 1985. pap. 4.95 (ISBN 0-8294-0496-1). Loyola.

Counsels of Perfection: A Baha'i Guide to Mature Living. Genevieve Coy. 192p. 1979. 6.95 (ISBN 0-85398-079-9). G Ronald Pub.

Counsels on Education. Ellen G. White. 1968. deluxe ed. 8.95 (ISBN 0-8163-0112-3, 03555-0). Pacific Pr Pub Assn.

Counsels on Health & Instruction to Medical Missionary Workers. Ellen G. White. 1951. deluxe ed. 10.95 (ISBN 0-8163-0114-X, 03561-8). Pacific Pr Pub Assn.

Counsels to Parents, Teachers & Students Regarding Christian Education. Ellen G. White. 1943. Repr. of 1913 ed. deluxe ed. 10.95 (ISBN 0-8163-0115-8, 03591-5). Pacific Pr Pub Assn.

Count It All Joy. rev. ed. Buddy Harrison & Van Gale. 32p. 1981. pap. 2.50 (ISBN 0-89274-198-8). Harrison Hse.

Countdown. Dan Betzer. LC 79-53943. 112p. 1979. pap. 1.95 (ISBN 0-88243-481-0, 02-0481). Gospel Pub.

Countdown to World Disaster: Hope & Protection for the Future. Basilea Schlink. 1976. pap. 0.50 (ISBN 3-87209-620-6). Evang Sisterhood Mary.

Counter-Poyson..., to the Objections & Reproaches, Wherewith the Aunswerer to the Abstract, Would Disgrace the Holy Discipline of Christ. Dudley Fenner. LC 74-28854. (English Experience Ser.: No. 735). 1975. Repr. of 1584 ed. 10.50 (ISBN 90-221-0735-3). Walter J Johnson.

Counter-Reformation. Nicholas S. Davidson. 96p. 1987. pap. text ed. 7.95 (ISBN 0-631-14888-4). Basil Blackwell.

Counter-Reformation. A. G. Dickens. (Library of World Civilization). (Illus.). 1979. pap. 7.95x (ISBN 0-393-95086-7). Norton.

Counter-Reformation: Catholic Europe & the Non-Christian World. A. D. Wright. LC 82-3210. 334p. 1984. pap. 12.95 (ISBN 0-312-17022-X). St Martin.

Counter-Reformation, Fifteen Fifty to Sixteen Hundred. Beresford J. Kidd. LC 79-8713. 270p. 1980. Repr. of 1933 ed. lib. bdg. 24.75x (ISBN 0-313-22193-6, KICR). Greenwood.

Counterfeit Miracles. B. B. Warfield. 1976. pap. 6.95 (ISBN 0-85151-166-X). Banner of Truth.

Counterfeits at Your Door. James Bjornstad. LC 78-72864. 160p. 1979. pap. text ed. 2.95 (ISBN 0-8307-0610-0, S124254). Regal.

Counting Book. Illus. by Marc Harrison. (Bible Look 'N Learn Bks.). (Illus.). 24p. 1985. bds. 3.95 (ISBN 0-8407-6686-6). Nelson.

Counting Stars. William Coleman. LC 76-28973. 128p. 1976. 4.95 (ISBN 0-87123-055-0, 210055). Bethany Hse.

Counting the Cost: The Economics of Christian Stewardship. Robin K. Klay. 176p. (Orig.). 1986. pap. 9.95 (ISBN 0-8028-0171-4). Eerdmans.

Country Christmas Entertaining. Ed. by Jill Nickerson. LC 83-62128. 64p. 1983. pap. 5.95 (ISBN 0-89821-055-0). Reiman Assocs.

Country Handcrafts Christmas Collection. Sandra L. Wright. 34p. 1985. pap. 5.95 (ISBN 0-89821-069-0). Reiman Assocs.

Country of the Risen King: Anthology of Christian Poetry. Merle Meeter. LC 77-87993. 1978. 12.95 (ISBN 0-8010-6042-7). Baker Bk.

Country of the Spirit: Vatican City. Frank J. Korn. (Illus.). 139p. 1982. pap. 7.00 (ISBN 0-8198-1415-6, MS0214). Dghtrs St Paul.

Country Parson. Simon Goodenough. (Illus.). 192p. 1983. 19.95 (ISBN 0-7153-8238-1). David & Charles.

Country Priest in English History. A. Tindal Hart. 1959. Repr. 30.00 (ISBN 0-8274-2107-9). R West.

Country Woman's Christmas. Louisa V. Kyle. LC 83-81553. (Illus.). 80p. 1984. 10.95 (ISBN 0-938694-12-X). JCP Corp VA.

Couples Praying: A Special Intimacy. Gene O'Brien & Judith T. O'Brien. 132p. 1986. pap. 3.95 (ISBN 0-8091-2816-0). Paulist Pr.

Courage! Nachman of Breslov & Nathan of Breslov. Tr. of Meshivat Nefesh. 119p. (Orig.). 1983. pap. 3.00 (ISBN 0-930213-23-8). Breslov Res Inst.

Courage: A Book for Champions. Edwin L. Cole. 164p. (Orig.). 1985. pap. 3.95 (ISBN 0-89274-362-X). Harrison Hse.

Courage, Church! Essays in Ecclesial Spirituality. Walbert Buhlmann. Tr. by Mary Smith from Ital. LC 78-1381. Orig. Title: Corragio Chiesa! 149p. (Orig.). 1978. pap. 2.98 (ISBN 0-88344-068-7). Orbis Bks.

Courage for a Cross: Six Stories About Growing up Christian in the U. S. S. R. Lester Merlin. 1987. pap. 3.95. Friend Pr.

Courage for Dialogue: Ecumenical Issues in Inter-Religious Relationships. S. J. Samartha. LC 81-16936. 172p. (Orig.). 1982. pap. 4.48 (ISBN 0-88344-094-6). Orbis Bks.

Courage for Today-Hope for Tomorrow: A Study of the Revelation. Esther Onstad. LC 75-2829. 144p. 1975. pap. 6.95 (ISBN 0-8066-1474-9, 10-1695). Augsburg.

Courage Knows No Sex. Elaine Crovitz & Elizabeth Buford. 1978. 8.95 (ISBN 0-8158-0363-X). Chris Mass.

Courage of Carol: Pearls from Tears. Robert H. Schuller & Arvella Schuller. LC 78-65619. 1978. pap. 2.50 (ISBN 0-89081-182-2). Harvest Hse.

Courage to Be. Paul Tillich. (Terry Lectures Ser.). 1952. pap. 6.95 (ISBN 0-300-00241-6, Y11). Yale U Pr.

Courage to Be Chaste. Benedict J. Groeschel. 128p. (Orig.). 1985. pap. 4.95 (ISBN 0-8091-2705-9). Paulist Pr.

Courage to Believe. Craig Morton & Robert Burger. (Epiphany Bks.). (Illus.). 1983. pap. 2.75 (ISBN 0-345-30564-7). Ballantine.

Courage to Care: Rescuers of Jews During the Holocaust. Carol Rittner & Sondra Myers. 176p. 1986. 24.95 (ISBN 0-8147-7397-4). NYU Pr.

Courage to Change: An Introduction to the Life & Thought of Reinhold Niebuhr. June Bingham. Repr. of 1961 ed. lib. bdg. 27.50x (ISBN 0-678-02766-8). Kelley.

Courage to Cope. Marilyn Kunz & Catherine Schell. (Neighborhood Bible Studies). 48p. (Orig.). 1984. pap. 2.50 (ISBN 0-8423-0446-0). Tyndale.

Courage to Pray. 3rd ed. Anthony Bloom & George LeFebvre. Tr. by Dinah Linvingstone from Fr. 123p. (Orig.). pap. text ed. 4.95 (ISBN 0-88141-031-4). St Vladimirs.

Courage to Pray. Karl Rahner & Johann B. Metz. 112p. (Orig.). 1980. pap. 3.95 (ISBN 0-8245-2024-6). Crossroad NY.

Courageous Christians. William Coleman. LC 81-70519. (Wonderful World of the Bible Ser.). (Illus.). 1983. 9.95 (ISBN 0-89191-558-3). Cook.

Course in Miracles. LC 76-20363. 1975. Set Of 3 Vols. incl. text, tchrs' manual wkbk. 40.00 (ISBN 0-9606388-0-6). Found Inner Peace.

Course in Miracles - A Gift for All Mankind. Tara Singh. LC 86-12073. (Orig.). 1986. 12.95 (ISBN 1-55531-013-3); pap. 7.95 (ISBN 1-55531-014-1). Life Action Pr.

Course in Miracles Concordance. Barbara Findeisen. 457p. 15.00 (ISBN 0-942494-45-8). Coleman Pub.

Course in Miracless. LC 76-20363. 1985. pap. text ed. 25.00 (ISBN 0-9606388-2-2). Found Inner Peace.

Course of Lectures on the Jews: By Ministers of the Established Church in Glasgow. Ed. by Gerald Grob. LC 76-46095. (Anti-Movements in America). 1977. lib. bdg. 37.50x (ISBN 0-405-09968-1). Ayer Co Pubs.

Course of My Life. Rudolf Steiner. Tr. by Olin D. Wannamaker from Ger. Tr. of Mein Lebensgang. 400p. 1986. pap. 18.00 (ISBN 0-88010-159-8). Anthroposophic.

Course of Study Outlines for Bible Class Leaders. C. H. Dodd. 59.95 (ISBN 0-87968-954-4). Gordon Pr.

Court, Church & Castle. Margaret W. Labarge. (Illus.). 112p. 1972. pap. 3.25 (ISBN 0-88884-431-X, 56310-3, Pub. by Natl Mus Canada). U of Chicago Pr.

Court Jew: A Contribution to the History of Absolutism in Europe. Selma Stern. 316p. 1985. 29.95 (ISBN 0-88738-019-0). Transaction Bks.

Courtship & Marriage. Ostis B. Wilson. 12p. 1976. pap. 0.15 (ISBN 0-686-36260-8). Faith Pub Hse.

Covenant. Larry Christenson. (Trinity Bible Ser.). 144p. 1973. pap. 5.95 spiral wkbk. (ISBN 0-87123-551-X, 240551). Bethany Hse.

Covenant Affirmations: This We Believe. Donald C. Frisk. 196p. (Orig.). 1981. pap. 6.95 (ISBN 0-910452-48-2). Covenant.

Covenant & Creation. Piet Schoonenberg. LC 74-75119. 1969. 11.95 (ISBN 0-268-00311-4). U of Notre Dame Pr.

Covenant & Creation: A Theology of Old Testament Covenants. W. J. Dumbrell. 220p. 1986. pap. 8.95 (ISBN 0-8407-3053-5). Nelson.

Covenant & Promise: The Prophetic Understanding of the Future in Pre-Exilic Israel. John Bright. LC 76-13546. 208p. 1976. 10.00 (ISBN 0-664-20752-9). Westminster.

Covenant in the Old Testament. Michael D. Guinan. (Biblical Booklets Ser). 68p. 1975. pap. 1.25 (ISBN 0-8199-0520-8). Franciscan Herald.

Covenant Love: Reflections on the Biblical Covenant Theme. Evelyn A. Schumacher. (Orig.). 1981. pap. 2.95 (ISBN 0-914544-38-1). Living Flame Pr.

Covenant of Grace. William Hendriksen. 1978. pap. 2.95 (ISBN 0-8010-4196-1). Baker Bk.

Covenant of Grace in Puritan Thought. John Von Rohr. (American Academy of Religion Studies in Religion). 240p. 1987. 18.95 (01-00-45); pap. 13.95. Scholars Pr Ga.

Covenant of Love. Janina Babris. (Illus.). 228p. (Orig.). pap. 6.95 (ISBN 0-913382-19-1, 101-25). Prow Bks-Franciscan.

Covenant of Love: Pope John Paul II on Sexuality, Marriage & Family in the Modern World. Richard M. Hogan & John M. Levoir. LC 84-18666. 264p. 1985. 15.95 (ISBN 0-385-19540-0). Doubleday.

Covenant of Love: Pope John Paul II on Sexuality, Marriage, & Family in the Modern World. Richard M. Hogan & John M. Levoir. LC 86-4395. 264p. 1986. pap. 7.95 (ISBN 0-385-23240-3, Im). Doubleday.

Covenant of Peace. Maurice Friedman. 1983. pap. 2.50x (ISBN 0-87574-110-X, 110). Pendle Hill.

Covenant People. W. J. Cameron. 3.00 (ISBN 0-685-08801-4). Destiny.

Covenant People, Vol. 1: The First 2,000 Years of Jewish Life. Mordecai I. Soloff. LC 72-97080. (Illus.). 1973. 3.95x (ISBN 0-8246-0154-8); tchr's guide 8.95x (ISBN 0-685-30240-7); wkbk 2.95x (ISBN 0-8246-0155-6). Jonathan David.

Covenant People, Vol. 2: The Battle for Survival from Talmudic Times to the End of World War I. Mordecai I. Soloff. LC 72-97080. (Illus.). 1974. 3.95x; tchr's guide 8.95x (ISBN 0-685-47972-2); wkbk 2.95x (ISBN 0-8246-0155-6). Jonathan David.

Covenant Renewal in Religious Life: Biblical Reflections. Stephen C. Doyle. 140p. 1976. 6.95 (ISBN 0-8199-0585-2). Franciscan Herald.

Covenant Renewed. Della M. Heide. 176p. 1983. pap. 7.95 (ISBN 0-317-04516-4). Coleman Pub.

Covenant Roots: Sources & Affirmations. Ed. by Glenn P. Anderson. Tr. by Fred O. Jansson et al from Swedish. 238p. (Orig.). 1980. pap. 6.95 (ISBN 0-910452-46-6). Covenant.

Covenant Story of the Bible. rev. & enl. ed. Alexander Cambell. 256p. 1986. pap. 10.95 (ISBN 0-8298-0734-9). Pilgrim NY.

Covenant: The History of a Biblical Idea. Delbert R. Hillers. LC 69-13539. (Seminars in the History of Ideas Ser: No. 3). 206p. (Orig.). 1969. pap. 4.95x (ISBN 0-8018-1011-6). Johns Hopkins.

Covenant to Care. Louis H. Evans, Jr. 120p. 1982. pap. 4.95 (ISBN 0-88207-355-9). Victor Bks.

Covenant with God's Poor. Auspicius Van Corstanje. 3.95 (ISBN 0-8199-0014-1). Franciscan Herald.

Covenanters Monuments of Scotland. Robert W. Crone. 96p. 1984. 40.00x (ISBN 0-7212-0694-8, Pub. by Regency Pr). State Mutual Bk.

Covenants & Blessings. Andrew Murray. 176p. 1984. pap. text ed. 3.50 (ISBN 0-88368-136-6). Whitaker Hse.

Covenants: God's Claims. John M. Zinkand. 120p. (Orig.). 1984. pap. 5.95 (ISBN 0-932914-10-1). Dordt Coll Pr.

Cow in the Clinic & Other Missionary Stories from Around the World. Charles Kirkpatrick. 1977. pap. 4.95 (ISBN 0-89367-016-2). Light & Life.

Cows, Pigs, Wars, & Witches: The Riddles of Culture. Marvin Harris. 1974. pap. 2.36 (ISBN 0-394-71372-9, Vin) (ISBN 0-394-48338-3). Random.

Coyote's Pow-Wow. Hap Gilliland. (Indian Culture Ser.). 1972. 1.95 (ISBN 0-89992-022-5). Coun India Ed.

Coyoteway: A Navajo Holyway Healing Ceremonial. Karl W. Luckert. LC 78-10358. 243p. 1979. pap. 13.95 (ISBN 0-8165-0655-8). U of Ariz Pr.

CPA Exam Booklet: Intermediate Accounting. Sidney Davidson et al. 112p. 1984. pap. 10.95x (ISBN 0-03-071937-2). Dryden Pr.

Cracking the Code. LeRoy Lawson. LC 76-57045. 1977. pap. 2.25 (ISBN 0-87239-125-6, 40042). Standard Pub.

Cracow Ghetto Pharmacy. Tadeusz Pankiewicz. 1987. 16.95 (ISBN 0-89604-114-X); pap. 10.95 (ISBN 0-89604-115-8). Holocaust Pubns.

Cradle Tales of Hinduism. Sr. Nivedita. (Illus.). 329p. 1972. pap. 5.95 (ISBN 0-87481-131-7). Vedanta Pr.

Cradle, the Cross & the Crown. George Bass. Ed. by Michael L. Sherer. (Orig.). 1986. pap. 7.25 (ISBN 0-89536-817-X, 6866). CSS of Ohio.

Craft & Its Symbols. 5th printing ed. Allen E. Roberts. LC 73-89493. (Illus.). 92p. 1985. Repr. text ed. 7.50 (ISBN 0-88053-058-8). Macoy Pub.

Craft of Sermon Illustration. W. E. Sangster. (Notable Books on Preaching). 1973. pap. 7.95 (ISBN 0-8010-8214-5). Baker Bk.

Crafts for Christmas. Katherine N. Cutler & Kate C. Bogle. (Illus.). 96p. 1975. pap. 1.95 (ISBN 0-688-46663-X). Lothrop.

Crafts Handbook for Children's Church: Graded Activities for Ages 3-7. Leslea Stringer & Lea Bowman. (Teaching Help Ser.). (Orig.). 1981. pap. 8.95 (ISBN 0-8010-8197-1). Baker Bk.

Cranmer. Hilaire Belloc. LC 72-4495. (English Biography Ser., No. 31). 1972. Repr. of 1931 ed. lib. bdg. 55.95x (ISBN 0-8383-1610-7). Haskell.

Cranmer & the Reformation under Edward VI. Charles H. Smyth. Repr. of 1926 ed. lib. bdg. 22.50x (ISBN 0-8371-4025-0, SMCR). Greenwood.

Craving & Salvation: A Study in Buddhist Soteriology. Bruce Matthews. (SR Supplements). 138p. 1984. pap. text ed. 9.25x (ISBN 0-88920-147-1). Humanities.

Crazy Wisdom. Georg Feuerstein. 140p. 1987. pap. 7.95 (ISBN 0-941255-37-9). Integral Pub.

CRC Family Portrait: Sketches of Ordinary Christians in a 125-Year-Old Church. James C. Schaap. LC 82-22625. 287p. (Orig.). 1983. pap. 4.95 (ISBN 0-933140-60-6). CRC Pubns.

Creados Para Crecer. Robert Harty & Annelle Harty. Tr. by Dafne C. De Plou. (Sexo en la Vida Cristiana Ser.). (Illus.). 1985. pap. 1.50 (ISBN 0-311-46251-0). Casa Bautista.

Create! 2nd ed. Rita Foley. (Catechist Training Ser.). 1982. 3.95 (ISBN 0-8215-1230-7). Sadlier.

Create in Me: A Form of the Eucharist in a Modern Idiom. Norman C. Habel. 1978. 0.95 (ISBN 0-915644-14-2). Clayton Pub Hse.

Create in Me a Youth Ministry. Ridge Burns & Pam Campbell. 204p. 1986. pap. 11.95 (ISBN 0-89693-636-8). Victor Bks.

Create in Me: Young Adult Bible Study. Arthur G. Simmons & Beborah T. Simmons. 1985. 5.75 (ISBN 0-89536-765-3, 5872). CSS of Ohio.

Create, Two. Regina R. Barnett. 31p. (Orig.). 1979. pap. text ed. 5.95 student work pad (ISBN 0-697-01705-2); tchrs.' manual 12.95 (ISBN 0-697-01706-0). Wm C Brown.

Created for Commitment. A. Wetherell Johnson. 1982. 12.95 (ISBN 0-8423-0484-3). Tyndale.

Created in God's Image. Anthony A. Hoekema. 272p. 1986. 19.95 (ISBN 0-8028-3626-7). Eerdmans.

Created to Praise: The Language of Gerard Manley Hopkins. Margaret Ellsberg. 160p. 1987. 15.95x (ISBN 0-19-504098-8). Oxford U Pr.

Creating a Successful Christian Marriage. Cleveland McDonald. LC 74-20202. 1975. 14.95 (ISBN 0-8010-5957-7). Baker Bk.

Creating a Successful Christian Marriage. Cleveland McDonald. LC 74-20202. 1975. 10.95 (ISBN 0-87227-038-6). Reg Baptist.

Creating & Playing Games with Students. Jack Schaupp. (Orig.). 1981. pap. 6.50 (ISBN 0-687-09809-2). Abingdon.

Creating Children's Sermons: Fifty-One Visual Lessons. Bucky Dann. LC 81-10493. 132p. pap. 7.95 (ISBN 0-664-24383-5). Westminster.

Creating Closer Families: Principles of Positive Family Interaction. William G. Dyer. LC 75-20169. (Illus.). 144p. 1975. pap. 6.95 (ISBN 0-8425-0726-4). Brigham.

Creating Common Wealth. Ian Hore-Lacy. 103p. (Orig.). 1985. pap. 4.95 (ISBN 0-86760-024-1, Pub. by Albatross Bks). ANZ Religious Pubns.

Creating Contemporary Worship. Terry Dittmer. 80p. (Orig.). 1985. pap. 6.95 (ISBN 0-570-03954-1, 12-2889). Concordia.

Creating Cosmos. Barbara Dewey. LC 85-70369. 128p. 1985. 16.95 (ISBN 0-933123-00-0). Bartholomew Bks.

Creating the Caring Congregation: Guidelines for Ministering with the Handicapped. Harold H. Wilke. LC 79-28626. (Orig.). 1980. pap. 6.50 (ISBN 0-687-09815-7). Abingdon.

Creation. John G. Bennett. 1978. 5.95 (ISBN 0-900306-41-6, Pub. by Coombe Springs Pr). Claymont Comm.

Creation. Pamela Broughton. (Golden Bible Stories Ser.). (Illus.). 32p. 1985. 3.95 (ISBN 0-307-11620-4, Pub. by Golden Bks). Western Pub.

Creation. (Burl Ives Bible-Time Stories). incl. tape 4.95 (ISBN 0-89191-804-3, 98046). Cook.

Creation. Gordon Lindsay. (Old Testament Ser.). 1.25 (ISBN 0-89985-123-1). Christ Nations.

Creation. Josh McDowell & Don Stewart. LC 83-72898. (Family Handbook of Christian Knowledge Ser.). 178p. 1983. 18.95 (ISBN 0-86605-118-X). Campus Crusade.

Creation. Gordon Onslow-Ford. (Illus.). 123p. 1978. text ed. 30.00 (ISBN 0-9612760-0-2). Bishop Pine.

Creation: A Scientist's Choice. Zola Levitt. 1981. pap. 4.95 (ISBN 0-89051-074-1). Master Bks.

Creation & Discovery. Vivas L. Eliseo. LC 81-85511. 460p. 1982. pap. 4.95 (ISBN 0-89526-952-X). Regnery Bks.

Creation & Evolution: Myth or Reality? Norman D. Newell. LC 81-21767. (Convergence Ser.). 232p. 1982. 24.00x (ISBN 0-231-05348-7). Columbia U Pr.

Creation & Fall. Dietrich Bonhoeffer. Bd. with Temptation. 1965. pap. 4.95 (ISBN 0-02-083890-5). Macmillan.

Creation & Fall. Lazar Puhalo. 36p. (Orig.). 1986. pap. text ed. 4.00 (ISBN 0-913026-97-2). Synaxis Pr.

Creation & Fall: Temptation. Dietrich Bonhoeffer. 1983. 13.00 (ISBN 0-8446-5962-2). Peter Smith.

Creation & Gospel: The New Situation of European Theology. Gustaf Wingren. LC 78-78183. (Toronto Studies in Theology: Vol. 2). lii, 189p. 1979. pap. 39.95x (ISBN 0-88946-994-6). E Mellen.

Creation & Human Dynamism: A Spirituality for Life. Joseph G. Donders. 112p. (Orig.). 1985. pap. 5.95 (ISBN 0-89622-227-6). Twenty-Third.

Creation & Its Critics. H. Morris. LC 82-84483. 32p. 1982. 1.00 (ISBN 0-89051-091-1). Master Bks.

Creation & Salvation in Ancient Orphism. Larry J. Alderink. LC 81-5772. (APA American Classical Studies Ser.). 1981. pap. 10.00 (ISBN 0-89130-502-5, 400408). Scholars Pr GA.

Creation & the Character of God. Ronald Storer. 204p. 1986. 39.00X (ISBN 0-7223-1973-8, Pub. by A H Stockwell England). State Mutual BK.

Creation & the End of Days - Judaism & Scientific Cosmology: Proceedings of the 1984 Meeting of the Academy for Jewish Philosophy. Ed. by David Novak & Norbert Samuelson. LC 86-19062. 336p. (Orig.). 1986. 26.75 (ISBN 0-8191-5524-1, Pub. by Studies in Judaism); pap. text ed. 14.50 (ISBN 0-8191-5525-X, Pub. by Studies in Judaism). U Pr of Amer.

Creation & the Modern Christian. Henry M. Morris. 298p. 1985. pap. 8.95 (ISBN 0-89051-111-X). Master Bks.

Creation & the World of Science. Arthur R. Peacocke. LC 79-40267. 408p. 1985. Repr. text ed. 9.95 (ISBN 0-268-00755-1, 85-07550, Dist. by Har-Row). U of Notre Dame Pr.

Creation & the World of Science: The Bampton Lectures. A. R. Peacocke. 1979. 22.50x (ISBN 0-19-826650-2). Oxford U Pr.

Creation Book. William F. Dakenbing. LC 75-39840. (Illus.). 70p. 1976. 5.95 (ISBN 0-685-68397-4); pap. 3.95 (ISBN 0-685-68398-2). Triumph Pub.

Creation by Natural Law: Laplace's Nebular Hypothesis in American Thought. Ronald L. Numbers. LC 76-45810. 196p. 1977. 22.50x (ISBN 0-295-95439-6). U of Wash Pr.

Creation, Christ & Credibility: How & Why Mankind Has Failed to Discredit the Bible. Gerry Carroll. LC 83-72663. (Illus.). 204p. (Orig.). 1983. pap. 5.95 (ISBN 0-914569-01-5). Creat Pubns B P C M.

Creation, Christ & Culture. Ed. by Richard W. McKinney. 336p. 19.95 (ISBN 0-567-01019-8, Pub. by T & T Clark Ltd UK). Fortress.

Creation Controversy: Science or Scripture in the Schools. Dorothy Nelkin. 256p. 1982. 16.95 (ISBN 0-393-01635-8). Norton.

Creation Controversy: Science or Scripture in the Schools? Dorothy Nelkin. LC 83-45954. 242p. 1984. pap. 9.95x (ISBN 0-8070-3155-0, BP 675). Beacon Pr.

Creation-Evolution Controversy. 1976. 15.95 (ISBN 0-918112-01-X); pap. 8.95 kivar (ISBN 0-918112-02-8). Inquiry Pr.

Creation: For Kids & Other People Too. Judy Stonecipher. LC 82-62362. (Accent Discoveries Ser.). (Illus.). 64p. (Orig.). 1982. gift book 4.50 (ISBN 0-89636-095-4). Accent Bks.

Creation in Christ: Unspoken Sermons. George MacDonald. Ed. by Rolland Hein. LC 76-11282. (Wheaton Literary Ser.). 342p. 1976. pap. 8.95 (ISBN 0-87788-860-4). Shaw Pubs.

Creation in the Old Testament. Ed. by Bernhard W. Anderson. LC 83-48910. (Issues in Religion & Theology Ser.). 192p. 1984. pap. 7.95 (ISBN 0-8006-1768-1, 1-768). Fortress.

Creation Liturgy. Scott McCarthy. LC 86-43232. 150p. (Orig.). 1987. pap. 10.95 (ISBN 0-89390-105-9). Resource Pubns.

Creation Myths: Man's Introduction to the World. (Art & Imagination Ser.). (Illus.). 1977. pap. 10.95 (ISBN 0-500-81010-9). Thames Hudson.

Creation Myths of Primitive America. Jeremiah Curtin. 1980. 31.00 (ISBN 0-405-13697-8, 1710). Ayer Co Pubs.

Creation of Full Human Personality. Joseph W. Drew & W. Hague. pap. 0.75 (ISBN 0-8199-0247-0, L38115). Franciscan Herald.

Creation of Health: The Merger of Traditional Medical Diagnosis with Clairvoyant Insight. C. Norman Shealy & Caroline M. Myss. 270p. 1987. 14.95 (ISBN 0-913299-40-5). Stillpoint.

Creation of Human Ability. L. Ron Hubbard. 31.00 (ISBN 0-686-13922-4). Church Scient NY.

Creation of Human Ability: A Handbook for Scientologists. L. Ron Hubbard. 292p. 1954. 36.44 (ISBN 0-88404-011-9). Bridge Pubns Inc.

Creation of Life. A. E. Wilder-Smith. LC 78-133984. 269p. 1981. pap. 8.95 (ISBN 0-89051-070-9). Master Bks.

Creation of Man: Philo & the History of Interpretation. Thomas H. Tobin. Ed. by Bruce Vawter. LC 82-19891. (Catholic Biblical Quarterly Monographs: No. 14). viii, 199p. (Orig.). 1983. pap. 6.00x (ISBN 0-915170-13-2). Catholic Biblical.

Creation of Mythology. Marcel Detienne. Tr. by Margaret Cook. LC 85-24658. 192p. 1986. 25.00x (ISBN 0-226-14350-3); pap. 10.95x (ISBN 0-226-14348-1). U of Chicago Pr.

Creation of Sacred Literature: Composition & Redaction of the Biblical Text. Ed. by Richard E. Friedman. (U.C. Publications in Near Eastern Studies: Vol. 22). 1981. pap. 21.50x (ISBN 0-520-09637-1). U of Cal Pr.

Creation of the World According to Gersonides. Jacob Staub. LC 81-13523. (Brown Judiac Studies). 1982. pap. 20.00 (ISBN 0-89130-526-2, 14-00-24). Scholars Pr GA.

Creation of Wealth. Brian Griffiths. LC 85-5210. 160p. 1985. pap. 6.95 (ISBN 0-87784-566-2). Inter-Varsity.

Creation or Evolution-What Is the Truth? W. J. Ouweneel. 58p. pap. 3.95 (ISBN 0-88172-145-X). Believers Bkshelf.

Creation Psalms of David. D. Hayhoe. 40p. pap. 2.95 (ISBN 0-88172-148-4). Believers Bkshelf.

Creation Sings. Ed. by Ann Lodge. 1980. pap. 1.25 (ISBN 0-664-10091-0). Westminster.

Creation Story Verbatim. E. J. Gold. 278p. (Orig.). 1986. pap. 11.95 (ISBN 0-89556-047-X). Gateways Bks & Tapes.

Creation Tales from the Salish. W. H. McDonald. (Indian Culture Ser.). 1973. 1.95 (ISBN 0-89992-061-6). Coun India Ed.

Creation: The Cutting Edge-Acts, Facts, Impacts, Vol. 5. Ed. by Henry M. Morris et al. 240p. 1982. pap. 7.95 (ISBN 0-89051-088-1). Master Bks.

Creation Trilogy, 3 vols. rev. ed. Eula Allen. Incl. Vol. 1. Before the Beginning. 1966 (ISBN 0-87604-054-7); Vol. 2. River of Time. 1965 (ISBN 0-87604-055-5); Vol. 3. You Are Forever. 1966 (ISBN 0-87604-056-3). (Illus.). pap. 10.95 set (ISBN 0-87604-125-X); pap. 3.95 ea. ARE Pr.

Creation Versus Evolution--Not Really. 2nd ed. William A. Schmeling. LC 76-19997. (Illus.). 1977. pap. text ed. 5.25 (ISBN 0-915644-12-6). Clayton Pub Hse.

Creation vs. Evolution: A Comparison. Lonni R. Erickson. 30p. write for info. Scandia Pubs.

Creation vs. Evolution Handbook. Thomas F. Heinze. (Direction Books). 1973. pap. 3.50 (ISBN 0-8010-4002-7). Baker Bk.

Creational Theory of Man & of the Universe. Timothy R. McDaniel. (Illus.). 141p. 1980. deluxe ed. 88.85 (ISBN 0-89266-242-5). Am Classical Coll Pr.

Creationism on Trial: Evolution & God at Little Rock. Langdon Gilkey. LC 85-50256. 301p. (Orig.). 1985. pap. 12.95 (ISBN 0-86683-780-9, HarpR). Har-Row.

Creationism, Science, & the Law: Arkansas Case Documents & Commentaries. Marcel la Follette. LC 82-21646. 232p. (Orig.). 1983. pap. 11.95x (ISBN 0-262-62041-3). MIT Pr.

Creative Activities. Mabel Adcock & Elsie Blackwell. (Illus.). 1984. 4.95 (ISBN 0-87162-011-1, D3195). Warner Pr.

Creative Activities in Church Education. Patricia Griggs. (Griggs Educational Resources Ser.). 1980. pap. 6.95 (ISBN 0-687-09812-2). Abingdon.

Creative American Quilting Inspired by the Bible. Suzzy C. Payne & Susan A. Murwin. (Illus.). 192p. 1982. 18.95 (ISBN 0-8007-1402-4). Revell.

Creative Awakening: The Jewish Presence in Twentieth-Century American Literature, 1900-1940s-Published in Cooperation with the American Jewish Archives. Louis Harap. LC 86-14986. (Contributions in Ethnic Studies: No. 17). 216p. 1987. lib. bdg. 29.95 (ISBN 0-313-25386-2, HFI). Greenwood.

Creative Bible Learning for Adults. Monroe Marlowe & Bobbie Reed. LC 77-76206. (International Center for Learning Handbooks). 192p. 1977. pap. 3.95 (ISBN 0-8307-0480-9, 9900152). Regal.

Creative Bible Learning for Children, Grades 1-6. Barbara Bolton & Charles Smith. LC 77-74532. 208p. 1977. pap. 3.95 (ISBN 0-8307-0478-7, 9100105). Regal.

Creative Bible Learning for Early Childhood: Birth Through 5 Years. Wesley Haystead. LC 77-77030. 192p. 1977. pap. 3.95 (ISBN 0-8307-0477-9, 9000100). Regal.

Creative Bible Learning for Youth: Grades 7-12. C. Edward Reed & Bobbie Reed. LC 77-76205. 1977. pap. 3.95 (ISBN 0-8307-0479-5, 9700102). Regal.

Creative Bible Studies. Dennis C. Benson. LC 85-71044. (Illus.). 660p. (Orig.). 1985. pap. 19.95 (ISBN 0-931529-01-8). Group Bks.

Creative Bible Study. Lawrence O. Richards. 1979. pap. 5.95 (ISBN 0-310-31911-0, 10711P). Zondervan.

Creative Bible Teaching. Lawrence O. Richards. LC 74-104830. 1970. 12.95 (ISBN 0-8024-1640-3). Moody.

Creative Catechist. Janaan Manternach & Carl J. Pfeifer. (Illus.). 144p. (Orig.). 1983. pap. text ed. 6.95 (ISBN 0-89622-169-5). Twenty-Third.

Creative Christian Education: Teaching the Bible Through the Church Year. Howard Hanchey. 224p. 1986. pap. 10.95 (ISBN 0-8192-1380-2). Morehouse.

Creative Christian Home. Merla J. Sparks. pap. 1.95 (ISBN 0-8010-8050-9). Baker Bk.

Creative Classroom Communications. Winifred Currie. 126p. 1972. pap. 1.25 (ISBN 0-88243-507-8, 02-0507). Gospel Pub.

Creative Communication & Community Building. Ed. by John Roberto. LC 81-83635. (Creative Resources for Youth Ministry Ser.: Vol. 1). (Illus.). 108p. (Orig.). 1981. pap. 8.95 (ISBN 0-88489-135-6). St Mary's.

Creative Conflict in Religious Education & Church Administration. Donald E. Bossart. LC 80-12704. 284p. (Orig.). 1980. pap. 12.95 (ISBN 0-89135-048-9). Religious Educ.

Creative Counterpart. rev. & updated ed. Linda Dillow. 228p. 1986. pap. 7.95 (ISBN 0-8407-3067-5). Nelson.

Creative Couples: The Growth Factor in Marriage. Wallace Denton & Juanita H. Denton. LC 82-17439. 154p. 1983. pap. 8.95 (ISBN 0-664-24453-X). Westminster.

Creative Craft Ideas for All Ages. Ed. by Shirley Beegle. (Illus., Orig.). 1966. pap. 6.95 (ISBN 0-87239-321-6, 2795). Standard Pub.

Creative Designs with Children at Worship. A. Roger Gobbel & Phillip C. Huber. LC 80-82225. 96p. (Orig.). 1981. pap. 6.95 (ISBN 0-8042-1526-X). John Knox.

Creative Discipline. Robert A. Rausch. Ed. by Frances Brooks. 1986. pap. 5.95 (ISBN 0-939697-05-X). Graded Pr.

Creative Discussions on I Corinthians 13. Ralph Heynen. (Contemporary Discussion Ser.). 96p. 1982. pap. 2.95 (ISBN 0-8010-4260-7). Baker Bk.

Creative Drama: A Complete Source Book for Church & School. Pamela Barragar. 176p. 1987. pap. 9.95 (ISBN 0-87403-084-6, 3355). Standard Pub.

Creative Encounter. Howard Thurman. LC 72-12773. 155p. 1972. pap. 6.95 (ISBN 0-913408-07-7). Friends United.

Creative Ethers. Ronald P. Beesley. 1978. pap. 3.95 (ISBN 0-87516-268-1). De Vorss.

Creative Evolution. Henri Bergson. Tr. by Arthur Mitxhell. LC 83-19859. 460p. 1984. pap. text ed. 13.50 (ISBN 0-8191-3553-4). U Pr of Amer.

Creative Explosion: An Inquiry into the Origins of Art & Religion. John E. Pfeiffer. LC 84-72675. (Illus.). 270p. (Orig.). 1985. pap. text ed. 12.95x (ISBN 0-8014-9308-0). Cornell U Pr.

Creative Faith. T. A. Hegre. LC 80-17869. 96p. (Orig.). 1980. pap. 3.95 (ISBN 0-87123-020-8, 210020). Bethany Hse.

Creative Fidelity. Gabriel Marcel. (New Crossroad Paperback Ser.). 304p. 1982. pap. 9.95 (ISBN 0-8245-0446-1). Crossroad NY.

Creative Formation of Life & World. Adrian Van Kamm & Susan A. Muto. LC 82-16014. 462p. 1983. lib. bdg. 37.50 (ISBN 0-8191-2708-6); pap. text ed. 19.50 (ISBN 0-8191-2709-4). U Pr of Amer.

Creative Freedom: Vocation of Liberal Religion. Henry N. Wieman. Ed. by W. Creighton & Larry E. Axel. LC 82-10182. 128p. (Orig.). 1982. pap. 7.95 (ISBN 0-8298-0623-7). Pilgrim NY.

Creative Homemaker. Mary L. Bouma. LC 73-17234. 192p. 1973. pap. 3.95 (ISBN 0-87123-078-X, 200084). Bethany Hse.

Creative Homemaker. Mary L. Bouma. 3.95 (ISBN 0-87123-084-4, 200084). Bethany Hse.

Creative Hospitality As a Means of Evangelism. rev. ed. Bruce A. Rowlison. LC 81-84182. (Illus.). 144p. 1982. pap. 5.95 (ISBN 0-938462-03-2). Green Leaf CA.

Creative Ideas. Ernest Holmes. Ed. by Willis H. Kinnear. 96p. 1964. pap. 4.50 (ISBN 0-911336-00-1). Sci of Mind.

Creative Ideas for Advent. Ed. by Robert Davidson. 114p. (Orig.). 1980. pap. 9.95 (ISBN 0-940754-06-1). Ed Ministries.

Creative Ideas for Advent, Vol. 2. Robert G. Davidson. 100p. (Orig.). 1986. pap. 9.95 (ISBN 0-940754-35-5). Ed Ministries.

Creative Ideas for Christmas, 1986. Ed. by Nancy J. Fitzpatrick. (Illus.). 160p. 1986. 17.95 (ISBN 0-8487-0683-8). Oxmoor Hse.

Creative Ideas for Lent. Ed. by Robert G. Davidson. 120p. (Orig.). 1985. pap. 9.95 (ISBN 0-940754-25-8). Ed Ministries.

Creative Ideas for Small Group in the Christian Community. John Mallison. (Abridged Small Group Ser.). 250p. (Orig.). 1978. pap. 7.95 (ISBN 0-909202-06-0, Pub. by Renewal Pubns). ANZ Religious Pubns.

Creative Imagination in the Sufism of Ibn Arabi. Henry Corbin. Tr. by R. Manheim. (Bollingen Ser.: Vol. 91). 1969. 40.00 (ISBN 0-691-09852-2); pap. 12.95 (ISBN 0-691-01828-6). Princeton U Pr.

Creative Jewish Education. Ed. by Jeffrey L. Schein & Jacob J. Staub. 256p. (Orig.). 1985. pap. 7.95 (ISBN 0-940646-33-1). Rossel Bks.

Creative Kid Books, No. 1. Marlene LeFever & Kathy Weyna. 1984. pap. 1.95 (ISBN 0-89191-935-X, 59352). Cook.

Creative Kid Books, No. 2. Marlene LeFever & Kathy Weyna. 1984. pap. 1.95 (ISBN 0-89191-936-8, 59360). Cook.

Creative Learning Activities for Religious Education: A Catalog of Teaching Ideas for Church, School, & Home. Patricia Mathson. (Illus.). 192p. 1984. pap. 8.95 (ISBN 0-13-189838-8). P-H.

Creative Learning Experiences. Ed. by John Roberto. LC 81-83636. (Creative Resources for Youth Ministry Ser.: Vol. 2). (Illus.). 144p. (Orig.). 1981. pap. 8.95 (ISBN 0-88489-136-4). St Mary's.

Creative Loneliness. William E. Hulme. LC 76-27083. 112p. 1977. pap. 5.95 (ISBN 0-8066-1556-7, 10-1715). Augsburg.

Creative Mind & Success. Ernest Holmes. 1947. 10.95 (ISBN 0-396-02070-4). Dodd.

Creative Ministry. Henri J. Nouwen. LC 73-139050. 1971. pap. 3.50 (ISBN 0-385-12616-6, Im). Doubleday.

Creative Movement Ministry, Vol. I. J. David Stone. Ed. by Frances Brooks. (Orig.). 1986. pap. 5.95 (ISBN 0-939697-04-1). Graded Pr.

Creative Musician in the Church. Kent E. Schneider. 1976. pap. 8.95 (ISBN 0-89390-014-1). Resource Pubns.

Creative Parables for Christian Teachers. Christelle E. Gregory. LC 86-62626. 100p. 1987. pap. 9.95 (ISBN 0-89390-096-6). Resource Pubns.

Creative Prayer. E. Herman. 1985. pap. 2.00 (ISBN 0-88028-049-2). Forward Movement.

Creative Prayer. Joan Thiry. 1981. 9.95 (ISBN 0-89837-068-X, Pub. by Pflaum Pr). Peter Li.

Creative Preaching & Oral Writing. Richard C. Hoefler. 1978. 7.95 (ISBN 0-89536-349-6, 0342). CSS of Ohio.

Creative Preaching: Finding the Words. Elizabeth Achtemeier. LC 80-16890. (Abingdon Preacher's Library). 128p. (Orig.). 1980. pap. 6.95 (ISBN 0-687-09831-9). Abingdon.

Creative Process in the Individual. rev. ed. Thomas Troward. 10.95 (ISBN 0-396-02064-X). Dodd.

Creative Programs for the Church Year. Malcolm G. Shotwell. 96p. 1986. pap. 7.95 (ISBN 0-8170-1102-1). Judson.

Creative Projects & Worship Experiences. Ed. by John Roberto. LC 81-86367. (Creative Resources for Youth Ministry Ser.: Vol. 3). (Illus.). 80p. (Orig.). 1981. pap. 8.95 (ISBN 0-88489-137-2). St Mary's.

Creative Self-Communication. Venetia McKenzie. 1978. pap. 1.25 (ISBN 0-87516-254-1). De Vorss.

Creative Silence. Mehta. 4.75 (ISBN 0-8356-7224-7). Theos Pub Hse.

Creative Socials & Specials Events. Mike Yaconelli & Wayne Rice. 192p. 1986. pap. 7.95 (ISBN 0-310-35131-6, 10827P). Zondervan.

Creative Stewardship. Richard B. Cunningham. LC 79-973. (Creative Leadership Ser.). 1979. 6.95 (ISBN 0-687-09844-0). Abingdon.

Creative Teaching Methods. Marlene D. LeFever. 320p. 1985. pap. 14.95 (ISBN 0-89191-760-8). Cook.

Creative Touch, No. 1. Faythelma Bechtel. 1973. 5.50x (ISBN 0-87813-909-5). Christian Light.

Creative Touch, No. 2. Faythelma Bechtel. 1982. 5.50x (ISBN 0-87813-919-2). Christian Light.

Creative Tradition. Ed. by Mary Collins & David Power. (Concilium 1983: Vol. 162). 128p. (Orig.). 1983. pap. 6.95 (ISBN 0-8164-2442-X, HarpR). Har-Row.

Creative Urban Youth Ministries. Glandion Carney. 74p. 1984. pap. 6.95 (ISBN 0-89191-846-9). Cook.

Creative Visualization. Shakti Gawain. LC 79-13760. (Illus.). 158p. 1978. pap. 7.95 (ISBN 0-931432-02-2). Whatever Pub.

Creative Word: Canon as a Model for Biblical Education. Walter Brueggemann. LC 81-71387. 176p. 1982. pap. 9.95 (ISBN 0-8006-1626-X, 1-1626). Fortress.

Creative Work: Karma Yoga. Edmond B. Szekely. (Illus.). 32p. 1973. pap. 2.95 (ISBN 0-89564-066-X). IBS Intl.

Creative Worship. Faye Schwartz & David Mohr. 1982. 4.50 (ISBN 0-89536-567-7, 0376). CSS of Ohio.

Creative Worship in Youth Ministry. Dennis C. Benson. LC 85-24735. (Illus.). 249p. (Orig.). 1985. pap. 11.95 (ISBN 0-931529-05-0). Group Bks.

Creative Youth Leadership. Jan Corbett. LC 77-778950. 1977. pap. 4.95 (ISBN 0-8170-0761-X). Judson.

Creativity & God: A Challenge to Process Theology. Robert C. Neville. 192p. 1980. 12.95 (ISBN 0-8164-0120-9, HarpR). Har-Row.

Creativity & Taoism. Chang Chung-Yuan. (Illus.). 1970. pap. 6.95x (ISBN 0-06-131968-6, TB1968, Torch). Har-Row.

Creativity, Holocaust, Reconstruction: Jewish Life in Wuertemberg, Past & Present. Herman Dicker. (Illus.). 1984. 18.50 (ISBN 0-87203-118-7). Hermon.

Creativity in Preaching. J. Grant Howard. Ed. by J. Ruark. (Craft of Preaching Ser.). 112p. 1987. pap. price not set (ISBN 0-310-26251-8). Zondervan.

Creator & Creature. Frederick W. Faber. LC 78-66301. 1978. pap. 9.50 (ISBN 0-89555-076-8). TAN Bks Pubs.

Creator & Man. Warren B. Blumenthal. LC 80-5843. 139p. 1980. lib. bdg. 20.50 (ISBN 0-8191-1340-9); pap. text ed. 9.50 (ISBN 0-8191-1341-7). U Pr of Amer.

Creator & the Creature. Nona T. Princehouse. (Illus.). 96p. 1986. 9.95 (ISBN 0-89962-530-4). Todd & Honeywell.

Creator in the Courtroom "Scopes II". Norman L. Geisler. 1987. pap. 5.95 (ISBN 0-8010-3814-6). Baker Bk.

Creator of This World & the Universe. John Larimore. LC 78-54161. 1979. 13.95 (ISBN 0-87949-115-9). Ashley Bks.

Creator or Almighty Always Has an Answer. Alfreda C. Doyle. Date not set. 7.95 (Pub. by Biblio Pr GA); pap. text ed. 2.95 (ISBN 0-939476-23-1, Pub. by Biblio Pr GA). Prosperity & Profits.

Creator's World. Robert C. Carver & Susan Thiess. 1978. 4.95x (ISBN 0-8192-4082-6); parent pupil packet 4.95x (ISBN 0-8192-4083-4). Morehouse.

Crecer Contigo. Beatriz De Pons. 80p. 1978. pap. 2.50 (ISBN 0-311-40037-X). Casa Bautista.

Creche & the Cross. Hulda C. Miller. (Illus.). 73p. (Orig.). 1977. pap. 2.00 (ISBN 0-89216-014-4). Salvation Army.

Credibility of Divine Existence. Norman K. Smith. Ed. by A. J. Porteous et al. 1969. 27.50 (ISBN 0-312-17185-4). St Martin.

Credo: A Catholic Catechism. 296p. 1984. pap. 8.95 (ISBN 0-225-66343-0, HarpR). Har-Row.

Credo: A Catholic Catechism. Benedict Davies. 300p. 1985. pap. 5.95 (ISBN 0-86683-901-1, HarpR); pap. 3.95 leaders guide (ISBN 0-86683-743-4). Har-Row.

Credo: I Believe. Daria M. Sockey. Ed. by Patricia I. Puccetti. (Faith & Life Ser.). (Illus.). 132p. 1985. pap. 6.20 (ISBN 0-89870-081-7). Ignatius Pr.

Credo: I Believe: Activity Book. Patricia I. Puccetti. 46p. (Orig.). 1985. pap. 2.50 (ISBN 0-89870-082-5). Ignatius Pr.

Creed. 20p. 1980. pap. 7.55 (ISBN 0-88479-026-6). Arena Lettres.

Creed & Catechetics. 10.95 (ISBN 0-8198-1430-X); 9.50 (ISBN 0-8198-1431-8). Dghtrs St Paul.

Creed & Deed: A Series of Discourses. Felix Alder. LC 76-38430. (Religion in America Ser: 2). 254p. 1972. Repr. of 1877 ed. 17.00 (ISBN 0-405-04051-2). Ayer Co Pubs.

Creed & Drama: An Essay in Religious Drama. William M. Merchant. LC 66-23222. pap. 31.80 (2027867). Bks Demand UMI.

Creed for a Young Catholic. Richard Chilson. LC 80-2073. 128p. 1981. pap. 2.75 (ISBN 0-385-17436-5, Im). Doubleday.

Creed in the Gospels. Alfons Kemmer. Tr. by Urban Schnaus. 144p. (Orig.). 1986. pap. 7.95 (ISBN 0-8091-2830-6). Paulist Pr.

Creed of Buddha. Edmond Holmes. LC 72-9918. 260p. 1973. Repr. of 1957 ed. lib. bdg. 22.50x (ISBN 0-8371-6606-3, HOCB). Greenwood.

Creed of Half Japan: Historical Sketches of Japanese Buddhism. Arthur Lloyd. LC 78-70095. Repr. of 1912 ed. 40.50 (ISBN 0-404-17344-6). AMS Pr.

Creed of Saint Vinoba. V. Nargolkar. 320p. 1963. pap. 5.00 (ISBN 0-686-96938-3). Greenlf Bks.

Creed: Twenty-Nine Family Times to Explore Belief, 3 Vols. Kathryn Fitzpatrick. (Family Time - Faith Time: A Home-Based Approach to Religious Education Ser.). (Illus.). 70p. (Orig.). 1982. pap. text ed. 3.50 (ISBN 0-86716-012-8). St Anthony Mess Pr.

Creeds & Confessions: The Reformation & Its Modern Ecumenical Implications. Erik Routley. LC 63-3127. (Studies in Theology: No. 62). 1962. text ed. 8.50x (ISBN 0-8401-6062-3). A R Allenson.

Creeds & Platforms of Congregationalism. Ed. by Williston Walker. LC 60-14698. 1960. 10.95 (ISBN 0-8298-0034-4). Pilgrim NY.

Creeds, Councils & Christ. Gerald Bray. LC 83-26443. 220p. 1984. pap. 6.95 (ISBN 0-87784-969-2). Inter-Varsity.

Creeds in Competition: A Creative Force in American Culture. Leo Pfeffer. LC 78-2308. 1978. Repr. of 1958 ed. lib. bdg. 19.00x (ISBN 0-313-20349-0, PFCC). Greenwood.

Creeds in the Making: A Short Introduction to the History of Christian Doctrine. Alan Richardson. LC 81-43073. 128p. 1981. pap. 5.95 (ISBN 0-8006-1609-X, 1-1609). Fortress.

Creeds of Christendom, 3 vols. Philip Schaff. 1983. 75.00 (ISBN 0-8010-8232-3). Baker Bk.

Creeds of the Churches: A Reader in Christian Doctrine from the Bible to the Present. 3rd ed. Ed. by John H. Leith. LC 82-48029. 1982. pap. 10.95 (ISBN 0-8042-0526-4). John Knox.

Creeds, Society, & Human Rights: A Study in Three Cultures. Max L. Stackhouse. 320p. 1984. 19.95 (ISBN 0-8028-3599-6). Eerdmans.

Creeds to Live By, Dreams to Follow. Susan P. Schutz. LC 86-7318. (Illus.). 64p. (Orig.). 1987. pap. 4.95 (ISBN 0-88396-248-9). Blue Mtn Pr Co.

Creek (Muscogee) New Testament Concordance. Lee Chupco & Ward Coachman. 167p. 1982. spiral bdg. 12.50x (ISBN 0-940392-10-0). Indian U Pr OK.

Creek Verb. Henry O. Harwell & Delores T. Harwell. 57p. 1981. 6.00x (ISBN 0-940392-03-8). Indian U Pr OK.

Creemos en Jesucristo. Virgilio P. Elizondo. (Span.). 128p. 1982. pap. 2.95 (ISBN 0-89243-153-9). Liguori Pubns.

Cremation: Is It Christian? James W. Fraser. 1965. pap. 1.50 (ISBN 0-87213-180-7). Loizeaux.

Creo en el Espiritu Santo. Michael Green. Tr. by Ernesto S. Vilela from Eng. LC 77-164. (Serie Creo). Tr. of I Believe in the Holy Spririt. (Span.). 267p. 1977. pap. 5.95 (ISBN 0-89922-090-8). Edit Caribe.

Creo en la Evangelizacion. David Watson. Tr. by Elsa S. Schwieters from Eng. (Serie Creo). Tr. of I Believe in Evangelism. (Span.). 235p. 1979. pap. 5.95 (ISBN 0-89922-133-5). Edit Caribe.

Creo en la Gran Comision. Max Warren. Tr. by Edwin Sipowicz from Eng. LC 78-54272. (Serie Creo). Tr. of I Believe in the Great Commission. (Span.). 205p. 1978. pap. 5.95 (ISBN 0-89922-112-2). Edit Caribe.

Creo en la Resurreccion de Jesus. George E. Ladd. Tr. by Miguel Blanch from Eng. LC 77-79934. (Serie Creo). Tr. of I Believe in the Resurrection of Jesus. (Span.). 204p. 1977. pap. 5.95 (ISBN 0-89922-091-6). Edit Caribe.

Creo En la Revelacion. Leon Morris. Tr. by Miguel Blanch from Eng. (Serie Creo). Tr. of I Believe in the Revelation. (Span.). 223p. 1979. pap. 5.95 (ISBN 0-89922-140-8). Edit Caribe.

Crepusculo. Enrique Aguilar. Tr. of Twilight. 1971. 3.50 (ISBN 0-686-27937-9). Franciscan Inst.

Crescent & Star: Arab & Israeli Perspectives on the Middle East Conflict. Ed. by Yonah Alexander & Nicholas N. F. Kittrie. LC 72-5797. (AMS Studies in Modern Society: Political & Social Issues). 37.50 (ISBN 0-404-10522-X); pap. 14.00 (ISBN 0-404-10523-8). AMS Pr.

Crescent in the East: Islam in Asia Major. Ed. by Raphael Israeli. 240p. 1981. 30.00x (ISBN 0-7007-0143-5, Pub. by Curzon England). State Mutual Bk.

Cretan Cults & Festivals. R. F. Willetts. LC 79-16739. 1980. Repr. of 1962 ed. lib. bdg. 32.50x (ISBN 0-313-22050-6, WICU). Greenwood.

Crime & Immorality in the Catholic Church. Emmett McLoughlin. LC 62-7778. 1962. 4.95 (ISBN 0-910294-19-4). Brown Bk.

Crime & Reconciliation. Mark Umbreit. 144p. (Orig.). 1985. pap. 7.95 (ISBN 0-687-09885-8). Abingdon.

Crime & the Responsible Community. Ed. by John Stott & Nick Miller. LC 81-110661. (London Lectures in Contemporary Christianity: 1979). pap. 47.80 (ISBN 0-317-09298-7, 2019339). Bks Demand UMI.

Crime of Galileo. Giorgio Santillana. LC 55-7400. (Midway Reprint Ser). (Illus.). xvi, 339p. 1955. pap. 14.00x (ISBN 0-226-73481-1). U of Chicago Pr.

Crimes, Values & Religion. Ed. by James M. Day & William Laufer. 280p. 1987. text ed. 37.50 (ISBN 0-89391-411-8). Ablex Pub.

Criminal Jurisprudence of the Jews. Samuel Mendelsohn. (Studies in Jewish Jurisprudence: Vol. 6). 280p. 1986. 19.50 (ISBN 0-87203-122-5). Hermon.

Crises at the Crossroads: Ruth-Esther. (New Horizons Bible Study). 48p. (Orig.). 1982. pap. 1.95 Leader's Guide (ISBN 0-89367-074-X); student guide 2.50 (ISBN 0-89367-075-8). Light & Life.

Crises in the History of the Papacy. Joseph McCabe. 1977. lib. bdg. 59.95 (ISBN 0-8490-1684-3). Gordon Pr.

Crisis & Catharsis: The Power of the Apocalypse. Adela Y. Collins. LC 83-26084. 180p. 1984. pap. 11.95 (ISBN 0-664-24521-8). Westminster.

Crisis & Change: The Church in Latin America Today. Edward L. Cleary. LC 84-16478. 208p. (Orig.). 1985. pap. 11.95 (ISBN 0-88344-149-7). Orbis Bks.

Crisis & Covenant: The Holocaust in American Jewish Fiction. Alan L. Berger. (Series in Modern Jewish Literature & Culture). 234p. 1985. 39.50 (ISBN 0-88706-085-4); pap. 14.95 (ISBN 0-88706-086-2). State U NY Pr.

Crisis & Faith. Eliezer Berkovits. 224p. 1975. 8.95 (ISBN 0-88482-903-0, Sanhedrin Pr). Hebrew Pub.

Crisis & Leadership: Epistles of Maimonides. Ed. by David Hartman. Tr. by Abraham Halkin from Hebrew. 292p. 1985. 15.95 (ISBN 0-8276-0238-3). Jewish Pubns.

Crisis & Story: Introduction to the Old Testament. W. Lee Humphreys. LC 78-64594. (Illus.). 313p. 1979. text ed. 21.95 (ISBN 0-87484-437-1). Mayfield Pub.

Crisis Counseling. Howard W. Stone. Ed. by Howard J. Clinebell. LC 75-13047. (Creative Pastoral Care & Counseling Ser.). 96p. (Orig.). 1976. pap. 5.95 (ISBN 0-8006-0553-5, 1-553). Fortress.

Crisis in Japanese Buddhism: Case of the Otani Sect. David A. Suzuki. 285p. 1985. 19.50 (ISBN 0-914910-51-5). Buddhist Bks.

Crisis in Lutheran Theology, 2 vols. in one. John W. Montgomery. 1973. pap. 8.95 (ISBN 0-87123-050-X, 210050). Bethany Hse.

Crisis in the Christian Science Church. Ann Beals. 145p. 1978. pap. 6.95 (ISBN 0-930227-08-5). Pasadena Pr.

Crisis Ministries. Thomas C. Oden. 224p. 1985. 19.95 (ISBN 0-8245-0709-6). Crossroad NY.

Crisis of Authority: John Paul II & the American Bishops. George A. Kelly. LC 81-52143. 116p. 1982. 10.95 (ISBN 0-89526-666-0). Regnery Bks.

Crisis of Church & State, Ten Fifty to Thirteen Hundred. Brian Tierney. (Orig.). 1964. pap. 6.50 (ISBN 0-13-193474-0, S102, Spec). P-H.

Crisis of Civilization. Hilaire Belloc. LC 73-114465. 245p. 1973. Repr. of 1937 ed. lib. bdg. 22.50x (ISBN 0-8371-4761-1, BECC). Greenwood.

Crisis of Conscience: The Struggle between Loyalty to God & Loyalty to One's Religion. Raymond Franz. LC 83-62637. (Illus.). 384p. 1983. 10.95 (ISBN 0-914675-00-1); pap. 7.95 (ISBN 0-914675-03-6). Comment Pr.

Crisis of Dissent. Gerard Morrissey. 128p. (Orig.). 1985. pap. 4.95 (ISBN 0-931888-19-0). Christendom Pubns.

Crisis of European Sciences & Transcendental Phenomenology: An Introduction to Phenomenological Philosophy. Edmund Husserl. Tr. by David Carr. LC 77-82511. (Studies in Phenomenology & Existential Philosophy Ser). 1970. 28.95 (ISBN 0-8101-0255-2); pap. 11.95 (ISBN 0-8101-0458-X). Northwestern U Pr.

Crisis of Faith. Thomas Keating. LC 79-13036. 1979. pap. 4.00 (ISBN 0-932506-05-4). St Bedes Pubns.

Crisis of Possession in Voodoo. Louis B. Mars. Tr. by Kathleen Collins. LC 76-51943. 1977. 10.00 (ISBN 0-918408-07-5); pap. 4.95 (ISBN 0-918408-00-8). Reed & Cannon.

Crisis of Religious Life. Thaddee Matura. Tr. by Paul Lachance & Paul Schwartz. 1973. 4.95 (ISBN 0-8199-0453-8). Franciscan Herald.

Crisis of Truth: The Attack on Faith, Morality & Mission in the Catholic Church. Ralph Martin. 245p. 1983. pap. 6.95 (ISBN 0-89283-146-4). Servant.

Crispy Christians. Matthew Skariah. LC 85-50245. 184p. (Orig.). 1985. pap. 2.75 (ISBN 0-933495-00-5). World Prayer.

Cristianismo y Otras Religiones. E. L. Copeland. Tr. by Abdias A. Mora. Orig. Title: Christianity & World Religious. (Span., Illus.). 192p. 1981. pap. 3.50 (ISBN 0-311-05760-8, Edit Mundo). Casa Bautista.

Cristiano Frente a los Problemas Mentales. Harold I. Haas. Tr. by Sara Pais De Molina. 110p. 1977. Repr. of 1975 ed. 2.50 (ISBN 0-311-42500-3). Casa Bautista.

Cristiano Intercesor. Kenneth E. Hagin. 1985. 1.00 (ISBN 0-89276-118-0). Hagin Ministries.

Cristiano y los Problemas Eticos. Pablo Deiros. 112p. 1982. pap. 3.50 (ISBN 0-311-46064-X). Casa Bautista.

Cristification: And la Hermanidad de la Rosa Cruz. 2nd ed. R. Swinburne Clymer & George Lippard. Tr. by J. E. Bucheli. (Span.). 206p. 1980. pap. 6.95 (ISBN 0-932785-52-2). Philos Pub.

Cristo Vive en Me. (Span. & Eng.). pap. text ed. 2.00 (ISBN 0-8198-1426-1); 1.00 (ISBN 0-8198-1427-X). Dghtrs St Paul.

Cristo y el Comunismo. E. Stanley Jones. Tr. by C. T. Gattinoni from Eng. Orig. Title: Christ's Alternative to Communism. (Span.). 96p. 1981. pap. 2.10 (ISBN 0-311-05040-9, Edit Mundo). Casa Bautista.

Cristo y Su Ley de Amor. (Span. & Eng.). pap. text ed. 2.00 (ISBN 0-8198-1437-7); 1.80 (ISBN 0-8198-1438-5). Dghtrs St Paul.

Criswell's Guidebook for Pastors. W. A. Criswell. LC 79-7735. 1980. 12.95 (ISBN 0-8054-2536-5). Broadman.

Critical & Biographical Notes on Early Spanish Music. J. F. Riano. LC 79-158958. (Music Ser.). 1971. Repr. of 1887 ed. lib. bdg. 29.50 (ISBN 0-306-70193-6). Da Capo.

Critical & Exegetical Commentary on Amos & Hosea. William R. Harper. Ed. by Samuel R. Driver et al. LC 5-7893. (International Critical Commentary Ser.). 608p. 1905. 24.95 (ISBN 0-567-05018-1, Pub. by T & T Clark Ltd UK). Fortress.

Critical & Exegetical Commentary on Chronicles I & II. Edward L. Curtis & Albert A. Madsen. Ed. by Samuel R. Driver et al. LC 10-14958. (International Critical Commentary Ser.). 560p. 1910. 24.95 (ISBN 0-567-05007-6, Pub. by T & T Clark Ltd UK). Fortress.

Critical & Exegetical Commentary on Ecclesiastes. George A. Barton. Ed. by Samuel R. Driver & Alfred Plummer. LC 8-15777. (International Critical Commentary Ser.). 236p. 1912. 22.95 (ISBN 0-567-05014-9, Pub. by T & T Clark Ltd UK). Fortress.

Critical & Exegetical Commentary on Ezra & Nehemiah. Loring W. Batten. Ed. by Samuel R. Driver et al. LC 13-12806. (International Critical Commentary Ser.). 400p. 1913. 22.95 (ISBN 0-567-05008-4, Pub. by T & T Clark Ltd UK). Fortress.

Critical & Exegetical Commentary on First & Second Samuel. Henry P. Smith. Ed. by Samuel R. Driver et al. LC 99-1607. (International Critical Commentary Ser.). 462p. 1898. 22.95 (ISBN 0-567-05005-X, Pub. by T & T Clark Ltd UK). Fortress.

Critical & Exegetical Commentary on Haggai, Zechariah, Malachi & Jonah. H. G. Mitchell et al. (International Critical Commentary Ser.). 544p. 1912. 24.95 (ISBN 0-567-05020-3, Pub. by T & T Clark Ltd UK). Fortress.

Critical & Exegetical Commentary on Kings I & II. James A. Montgomery. Ed. by Samuel R. Driver et al. LC 52-8522. (International Critical Commentary Ser.). 624p. 1951. 24.95 (ISBN 0-567-05006-8, Pub. by T & T Clark Ltd UK). Fortress.

Critical & Exegetical Commentary on Micah, Zephaniah, Nahum, Habakkuk, Obadiah & Joel. John M. Smith et al. Ed. by Samuel R. Driver & Alfred Plummer. (International Critical Commentary Ser.). 560p. 1895. 24.95 (ISBN 0-567-05019-X, Pub. by T & T Clark Ltd UK). Fortress.

Critical & Exegetical Commentary on Daniel. James A. Montgomery. Ed. by Samuel R. Driver & Alfred Plummer. LC 27-14200. (International Critical Commentary Ser.). 520p. 1926. 24.95 (ISBN 0-567-05017-3, Pub. by T & T Clark Ltd UK). Fortress.

Critical & Exegetical Commentary on Deuteronomy. Samuel R. Driver. LC 2-25926. (International Critical Commentary Ser.). 556p. 1902. 24.95 (ISBN 0-567-05003-3, Pub. by T & T Clark Ltd UK). Fortress.

Critical & Exegetical Commentary on Esther. Lewis B. Paton. Ed. by Samuel R. Driver et al. LC 8-30156. (International Critical Commentary Ser.). 360p. 1908. 22.95 (ISBN 0-567-05009-2, Pub. by T & T Clark Ltd UK). Fortress.

Critical & Exegetical Commentary on Ezekiel. G. A. Cooke. Ed. by Samuel R. Driver et al. LC 38-1268. (International Critical Commentary Ser.). 608p. 1936. 24.95 (ISBN 0-567-05016-5, Pub. by T & T Clark Ltd UK). Fortress.

Critical & Exegetical Commentary on Genesis. John Skinner. Ed. by Samuel R. Driver et al. (International Critical Commentary Ser.). 640p. 1930. 24.95 (ISBN 0-567-05001-7, Pub. by T & T Clark Ltd UK). Fortress.

Critical & Exegetical Commentary on Isaiah. George B. Gray. Ed. by Samuel R. Driver et al. (International Critical Commentary Ser.). 567p. 1912. 24.95 (ISBN 0-567-05015-7, Pub. by T & T Clark Ltd UK). Fortress.

Critical & Exegetical Commentary on Job. Samuel R. Driver. Ed. by Alfred Plummer & Charles Briggs. LC 21-15647. (International Critical Commentary Ser.). 816p. 1921. 24.95 (ISBN 0-567-05010-6, Pub. by T & T Clark Ltd UK). Fortress.

Critical & Exegetical Commentary on Judges. George F. Moore. Ed. by Samuel R. Driver et al. LC 25-19368. (International Critical Commentary Ser.). 528p. 1895. 24.95 (ISBN 0-567-05004-1, Pub. by T & T Clark Ltd UK). Fortress.

Critical & Exegetical Commentary on Numbers. G. Buchanan Gray. Ed. by Samuel R. Driver & Alfred Plummer. LC 3-31887. (International Critical Commentary Ser.). 544p. 1903. 24.95 (ISBN 0-567-05002-5, Pub. by T & T Clark Ltd UK). Fortress.

Critical & Exegetical Commentary on Proverbs. Crawford H. Toy. Ed. by Samuel R. Driver et al. (International Critical Commentary Ser.). 592p. 1899. 24.95 (ISBN 0-567-05013-0, Pub. by T & T Clark Ltd UK). Fortress.

Critical & Exegetical Commentary on Psalms, 2 vols. Charles Briggs & Emile G. Briggs. Ed. by Samuel R. Driver et al. (International Critical Commentary). 24.95 ea. (Pub. by T & T Clark Ltd UK). Vol. 1, 1906, 580 pgs (ISBN 0-567-05011-4). Vol. 2, 1907, 580 pgs (ISBN 0-567-05012-2). Fortress.

Critical & Exegetical Commentary on the Acts of the Apostles, 2 vols. Paton J. Gloag. 1979. 29.95 (ISBN 0-86524-006-X, 4402). Klock & Klock.

Critical & Exegetical Commentary on the Epistles of St. Paul to the Thessalonians. James E. Frame. Ed. by Samuel R. Driver & Charles A. Briggs. (International Critical Commentary Ser.). 336p. 1912. 22.95 (ISBN 0-567-05032-7, Pub. by T & T Clark Ltd UK). Fortress.

Critical & Exegetical Commentary on the Epistle of St. James. James H. Ropes. LC 16-6543. (International Critical Commentary Ser.). 336p. 1916. 22.95 (ISBN 0-567-05035-1, Pub. by T & T Clark Ltd UK). Fortress.

Critical & Exegetical Commentary on the Epistles to the Ephesians & Colossians. T. K. Abbott. Ed. by Samuel R. Driver et al. LC 40-15742. (International Critical Commentary Ser.). 392p. 1897. 24.95 (ISBN 0-567-05030-0, Pub. by T & T Clark Ltd UK). Fortress.

Critical & Exegetical Commentary on the Epistle to the Galatians. Ernest De Witt Burton. Ed. by Samuel R. Driver & Charles A. Briggs. (International Critical Commentary Ser.). 632p. 1921. 24.95 (ISBN 0-567-05029-7, Pub. by T & T Clark Ltd UK). Fortress.

Critical & Exegetical Commentary on the Epistle to the Hebrews. James Moffatt. Ed. by Samuel R. Driver & Alfred Plummer. LC 24-21703. (International Critical Commentary Ser.). 336p. 1924. 22.95 (ISBN 0-567-05034-3, Pub. by T & T Clark Ltd UK). Fortress.

Critical & Exegetical Commentary on the Epistle to the Romans. William Sanday & Arthur C. Headlam. Ed. by Samuel R. Driver & Alfred Plummer. (International Critical Commentary Ser.). 568p. 1902. 22.95 (ISBN 0-567-05026-2, Pub. by T & T Clark Ltd UK). Fortress.

Critical & Exegetical Commentary on the Epistle to the Romans, 2 vols, Vol. 1 & 2. Charles E. Cranfield. Ed. by John A. Emerton. (International Critical Commentary Ser.). 29.95 ea. (Pub. by T & T Clark Ltd UK). Vol. I, 472 pgs., 1975 (ISBN 0-567-05040-8). Vol. II, 476 pgs., 1979 (ISBN 0-567-05041-6). Fortress.

Critical & Exegetical Commentary on the Gospel According to St. John, 2 vols. J. H. Bernard. Ed. by Samuel R. Driver & Alfred Plummer. (International Critical Commentary Ser.). 24.95 ea. (Pub. by T & T ClarK Ltd UK). Vol. I, 480p (ISBN 0-567-05024-6). Vol. II, 456p (ISBN 0-567-05025-4). Fortress.

Critical & Exegetical Commentary on the Gosped According to St. Mark. Ezra P. Gould. Ed. by Samuel R. Driver et al. (International Critical Commentary Ser.). 376p. 1896. 24.95 (ISBN 0-567-05022-X, Pub. by T & T Clark Ltd UK). Fortress.

Critical & Exegetical Commentary on the Gospel According to St. Luke. Alfred Plummer. Ed. by Samuel R. Driver & Alfred Plummer. (International Critical Commentary Ser.). 688p. 1901. 24.95 (ISBN 0-567-05023-8, Pub. by T & T Clark Ltd UK). Fortress.

Critical & Exegetical Commentary on the Johannine Epistles. A. E. Brooke. Ed. by Samuel R. Driver et al. LC 13-170. (International Critical Commentary Ser.). 336p. 1912. 24.95 (ISBN 0-567-05037-8, Pub. by T & T Clark Ltd UK). Fortress.

Critical & Exegetical Commentary on the Philippians & Philemon. Marvin R. Vincent. Ed. by Samuel R. Driver & Charles A. Briggs. (International Critical Commentary Ser.). 248p. 1897. 22.95 (ISBN 0-567-05031-9, Pub. by T & T Clark Ltd UK). Fortress.

Critical & Exegetical Commentary on The Pastoral Epistles. Walter Lock. Ed. by Samuel R. Driver et al. (International Critical Commentary Ser.). 212p. 1928. 22.95 (ISBN 0-567-05033-5, Pub. by T & T Clark Ltd UK). Fortress.

Critical & Exegetical Commentary on the Revalation of St. John, 2 vols, Vol. I. R. H. Charles. Ed. by Alfred Plummer & Charles A. Briggs. LC 21-5413. (International Critical Commentary Ser.). 568p. 1920. 24.95x (ISBN 0-567-05038-6, Pub. by T & T Clark Ltd UK). Fortress.

Critical & Exegetical Commentary on the Revalation of St. John, 2 vols, Vol. II. R. H. Charles. LC 21-5413. (International Critical Commentary Ser.). 506p. 1920. 24.95 (ISBN 0-567-05039-4, Pub. by T & T Clark Ltd UK). Fortress.

Critical & Exegetical Commentary on the Second Epistle of St. Paul to the Corinthians. Alfred Plummer. Ed. by Samuel R. Driver & Charles A. Briggs. (International Critical Commentary Ser.). 462p. 1915. 24.95 (ISBN 0-567-05028-9, Pub. by T & T Clark Ltd UK). Fortress.

Critical & Exegitical Commentary on the First Epistle of St. Paul to the Corinthians. Archibald Robertson & Alfred Plummer. Ed. by Samuel R. Driver & Charles A. Briggs. (International Critical Commentary Ser.). 496p. 1914. 24.95 (ISBN 0-567-05027-0, Pub. by T & T Clark Ltd UK). Fortress.

Critical & Exergetical Commentary on the Epistles of St. Peter & St. Jude. Charles Bigg. Ed. by Samuel R. Driver et al. (International Critical Commentary Ser.). 376p. 1902. 24.95 (ISBN 0-567-05036-X, Pub. by T & T Clark Ltd UK). Fortress.

Critical Commentary on Targum Neofiti I to Genesis. Bernard Grossfeld. Ed. by L. H. Schiffman. 75.00x (ISBN 0-87068-333-0). Ktav.

Critical Concerns in Moral Theology. Charles E. Curran. LC 83-40593. 288p. 1984. text ed. 16.95 (ISBN 0-268-00747-0, 85-07477). U of Notre Dame Pr.

Critical Concordance to I & II Corinthians. A. Q. Morton et al. (Computer Bible Ser.: Vol. XIX). 1979. pap. 30.00 (ISBN 0-935106-01-4). Biblical Res Assocs.

Critical Concordance to I, II Thessalonians. A. Q. Morton & S. Michaelson. Ed. by J. Arthur Baird & David N. Freedman. (Computer Bible: Vol XXVI). 136p. (Orig.). 1983. pap. 25.00x (ISBN 0-935106-21-9). Biblical Res Assocs.

Critical Concordance to the Acts of the Apostles. A. Q. Morton & Sidney Michaelson. (Computer Bible Ser.: Vol. VII). 1976. pap. 15.00 (ISBN 0-935106-14-6). Biblical Res Assocs.

Critical Concordance to the Epistle of Paul to the Galatians. A. Q. Morton et al. Ed. by J. Arthur Baird & David Freedman. (Computer Bible Ser.: Vol. XXI). (Orig.). 1980. pap. text ed. 20.00 (ISBN 0-935106-16-2). Biblical Res Assocs.

Critical Concordance to the Letter of Paul to the Colossians. A. Q. Morton et al. Ed. by J. Arthur Baird & David Freedman. (Computer Bible Ser.: Vol. 24). (Orig.). 1981. pap. text ed. 20.00 (ISBN 0-935106-19-7). Biblical Res Assocs.

Critical Concordance to the Letter of Paul to the Ephesians. A. Q. Morton et al. Ed. by J. Arthur Baird & David Freedman. (Computer Bible Ser.: Vol. XXII). (Orig.). 1980. pap. text ed. 20.00 (ISBN 0-935106-17-0). Biblical Res Assocs.

Critical Concordance to the Letter of Paul to the Philippians. A. Q. Morton et al. Ed. by J. Arthur Baird & David Freedman. (Computer Bible Ser.: Vol. 23). (Orig.). 1980. pap. text ed. 20.00 (ISBN 0-935106-18-9). Biblical Res Assocs.

Critical Concordance to the Letter of Paul to the Romans. A. Q. Morton & Sidney Michaelson. Ed. by J. Arthur Baird & David Noel Freedman. (Computer Bible Ser: Vol. XIII). 1977. pap. 27.50 (ISBN 0-935106-08-1). Biblical Res Assocs.

Critical Concordance to the Pastoral Epistles, I, II Timothy, Titus, Philemon. A. Q. Morton & S. Michaelson. Ed. by J. Arthur Baird & David N. Freedman. (Computer Bible Ser.: Vol. XXV). 1982. pap. 35.00 (ISBN 0-935106-20-0). Biblical Res Assocs.

Critical Edition of John Rastell's "The Pastyme of People" & " A New Book of Purgatory". John Rastell. Ed. by Albert J. Gertiz & Stephen Orgel. (Renaissance Imagination Ser.). 509p. 1985. lib. bdg. 28.00 (ISBN 0-8240-5459-8). Garland Pub.

Critical Edition of the Coptic (Bohairic) Pentateuch, Vol. 5. Melvin K. Peters. LC 83-3260. (SBL Septuagint & Cognate Studies). 126p. 1983. pap. 11.95 (ISBN 0-89130-617-X, 06 04 15). Scholars Pr GA.

Critical Edition of the Coptic (Bohairic) Pentateuch: Septuagint & Cognate Studies, Vol. 2, Exodus. Melvin K. Peters. 122p. 1986. 11.95 (ISBN 1-55540-030-2, 06-04-22); pap. 8.95 (ISBN 1-55540-031-0). Scholars Pr GA.

Critical Examination of the Belief in a Life after Death. C. J. Ducasse. 336p. 1974. pap. 39.50x spiral (ISBN 0-398-03037-5). C C Thomas.

Critical Examination of the Peshitta Version of the Book of Ezra. Charles A. Hawley. LC 24-1925. (Columbia University. Contributions to Oriental History & Philology: No. 8). Repr. of 1922 ed. 12.50 (ISBN 0-404-50538-4). AMS Pr.

Critical History & Biblical Faith: New Testament Perspectives. Ed. by Thomas J. Ryan. (Annual Publication of the College Theology Society Ser.). 242p. 1984. pap. text ed. 8.25 (ISBN 0-8191-4157-7). U Pr of Amer.

Critical Introduction to the New Testament. Reginald H. Fuller. 221p. 1979. pap. 9.95 (ISBN 0-7156-0582-8, Pub. by Duckworth London). Longwood Pub Group.

Critical Introduction to the New Testament. Arthur S. Peake. 242p. 1979. Repr. of 1909 ed. lib. bdg. 25.00 (ISBN 0-89987-009-0). Darby Bks.

Critical Introduction to the New Testament. Arthur S. Peake. 1914. lib. bdg. 25.00 (ISBN 0-8482-9974-4). Norwood Edns.

Critical Introduction to the Old Testament. G. W. Anderson. (Studies in Theology). 262p. 1979. pap. 13.50 (ISBN 0-7156-0077-X, Pub. by Duckworth London). Longwood Pub Group.

Critical Introduction to the Old Testament. George B. Gray. 1978. Repr. of 1936 ed. lib. bdg. 25.00 (ISBN 0-8495-1939-X). Arden Lib.

Critical Issues in Modern Religion. R. Johnson et al. 1973. pap. write for info. (ISBN 0-13-193979-3). P-H.

Critical Lexicon & Concordance to the English & Greek New Testament. E. W. Bullinger. 1040p. 1975. text ed. 26.95 (ISBN 0-310-20310-4, 6253P, Pub. by Bagster). Zondervan.

Critical Meaning of the Bible. Raymond E. Brown. LC 81-82333. 160p. (Orig.). 1981. pap. 5.95 (ISBN 0-8091-2406-8). Paulist Pr.

Critical Studies in Cynewulf Group. Claes Schaar. LC 67-30824. (Beowulf & the Literature of the Anglo Saxons Ser., No. 2). 1969. Repr. of 1949 ed. lib. bdg. 75.00x (ISBN 0-8383-0740-X). Haskell.

Critical Study of Adigranth. S. S. Kohli. 1976. Repr. 12.50 (ISBN 0-89684-038-7). Orient Bk Dist.

Critical Study of Hinduism. Sarasvati Chennakesvan. 1980. 12.50x (ISBN 0-8364-0614-1). South Asia Bks.

Critical Study of the Mahavastu. Bhikku T. Rahula. 1978. 24.95 (ISBN 0-89684-018-2, Pub. by Motilal Banarsidass India). Orient Bk Dist.

Critical Theory of Religion: The Frankfurt School from Universal Pragmatic to Political Theology. Rudolf J. Siebert. (Religion & Reason Ser.: Vol. 29). xvi, 722p. 1985. 112.00x (ISBN 0-89925-119-6). Mouton.

Critical Way in Religion. Duncan Howlett. LC 80-7460. (Library of Liberal Religion). 360p. 1984. pap. 14.95 (ISBN 0-87975-266-1). Prometheus Bks.

Critical Word Book of Leviticus, Numbers, Deuteronomy. Peter M. Morris & Edward James. (Computer Bible Ser.: Vol. VIII). 1975. pap. 20.00 (ISBN 0-935106-13-8). Biblical Res Assocs.

Critical Word Book of the Pentateuch. Peter M. Morris & Edward James. (Computer Bible Ser.: Vol. XVII). 1980. pap. 25.00 (ISBN 0-935106-03-0). Biblical Res Assocs.

Critical Writing by Desiderius Erasmus on the Spiritual Conditions of His Times & the Psychological Impulses Motivating the Actions of Men. Desiderius Erasmus. (Illus.). 123p. 1984. 89.45 (ISBN 0-89920-106-7). Am Inst Psych.

Criticism & Creation. Herbert Grierson. LC 73-733. 1949. lib. bdg. 17.50 (ISBN 0-8414-1603-6). Folcroft.

Criticism & Faith in Late Victorian Scotland: A. B. Davidson, William Robertson Smith & George Adam Smith. Richard A. Riesen. LC 85-5388. 490p. (Orig.). 1985. lib. bdg. 30.50 (ISBN 0-8191-4655-2); pap. text ed. 18.75 (ISBN 0-8191-4656-0). U Pr of Amer.

Criticism of Crusading, Ten Ninety-Five to Twelve Seventy-Four. Elizabeth Siberry. 1985. 37.00x (ISBN 0-19-821953-9). Oxford U Pr.

Criticism of the Crusade: A Study of Public Opinion & Crusade Propaganda. P. A. Throop. 59.95 (ISBN 0-87968-968-4). Gordon Pr.

Criticism of the Crusade: A Study of Public Opinion & Crusade Propaganda. Palmer A. Throop. LC 75-26530. (Perspectives in European Hist.: No. 12). xv, 291p. 1975. Repr. of 1940 ed. lib. bdg. 27.50x (ISBN 0-87991-618-4). Porcupine Pr.

Criticisms of Life. facsimile ed. Horace J. Bridges. LC 75-99684. (Essay Index Reprint Ser). 1915. 20.00 (ISBN 0-8369-1342-6). Ayer Co Pubs.

Criticisms on Paradise Lost. Joseph Addison. (Works of Joseph Addison Ser.). 200p. 1985. Repr. of 1892 ed. lib. bdg. 29.00 (ISBN 0-932051-91-X, Pub. by Am Repr Serv). Am Biog Serv.

Criticizing. William J. Diehm. LC 86-17372. (Christian Growth Bks). 128p. (Orig.). 1986. pap. 6.95 (ISBN 0-8066-2211-3, 10-1722). Augsburg.

Criticizing Children: A Parents Guide to Helping Children. Avi Shulman. (Dynamics of Personal Achievement Ser.). 48p. (Orig.). 1984. pap. 2.95 (ISBN 0-87306-365-1). Feldheim.

Critic's Alchemy. Ruth Z. Temple. (Orig.). 1953. pap. 10.95x (ISBN 0-8084-0097-5). New Coll U Pr.

Critique of Modernity: Theological Reflections on Contemporary Culture. Ed. by Julian N. Hartt. (Virginia Lectures on Individual & Society). 160p. 1987. text ed. 16.95x (ISBN 0-8139-1118-4). U Pr of VA.

Critique of Pure Modernity: Hegel, Heidegger, & After. David Kolb. LC 85-24510. 334p. 1987. lib. bdg. 25.00 (ISBN 0-226-45031-7). U of Chicago Pr.

Critique of Pure Reason. Immanuel Kant. 480p. 1986. Repr. of 1900 ed. lib. bdg. 75.00 (ISBN 0-8495-3103-9). Arden Lib.

Critique of Pure Tolerance. Robert P. Wolff et al. LC 65-20788. 1969. pap. 7.95x (ISBN 0-8070-1559-8, BP328). Beacon Pr.

Critique of Religion & Philosophy. Walter Kaufmann. 1979. pap. 13.50x (ISBN 0-691-02001-9). Princeton U Pr.

Critiques of Confucius in Contemporary China. Kamm Louie. LC 80-214. 210p. 1980. 27.50 (ISBN 0-312-17645-7). St Martin.

Critiques of God. Ed. by Peter Angeles. pap. 7.00 (ISBN 0-87980-349-5). Wilshire.

Croce Versus Gentile: A Dialogue on Contemporary Italian Philosophy. Patrick Romanell. LC 78-63709. (Studies in Fascism: Ideology & Practice). (Illus.). 80p. Repr. of 1947 ed. 18.00 (ISBN 0-404-16979-1). AMS Pr.

Croisade: Essai sur la Formation d'une Theorie Juridique. Michel Villey. LC 78-63373. (Crusades Ser.). Repr. of 1942 ed. 30.00 (ISBN 0-404-17046-3). AMS Pr.

Croitre dans la Grace. William P. Wilson. Orig. Title: Grace to Grow. (Fr.). 1986. write for info. (ISBN 0-8297-0745-X). Life Pubs Intl.

Cromwell's Place in History. Samuel R. Gardiner. LC 76-94270. (Select Bibliographies Reprint Ser). 1897. 15.00 (ISBN 0-8369-5044-5). Ayer Co Pubs.

Cronistoria, 5 vols. Ed. by Giselda Capetti. LC 80-68484. 400p. (Orig.). 1980. Set. pap. 40.00 (ISBN 0-89944-043-6); Vol. 1. pap. (ISBN 0-89944-044-4); Vol. 2. pap. (ISBN 0-89944-045-2); Vol. 3. pap. (ISBN 0-89944-046-0); Vol. 4. pap. (ISBN 0-89944-047-9); Vol. 5. pap. (ISBN 0-89944-048-7). Don Bosco Multimedia.

Cross. Martyn Lloyd-Jones. 192p. 1986. pap. 6.95 (ISBN 0-89107-382-5, Crossway Bks). Good News.

Cross & Beyond. Roy E. De Brand. LC 83-70374. 1984. pap. 4.95 (ISBN 0-8054-2250-1). Broadman.

Cross & Sanctification. T. A. Hegre. LC 51-7866. Orig. Title: Three Aspects of the Cross. 288p. 1960. pap. 3.95 (ISBN 0-87123-067-4, 210067). Bethany Hse.

Cross & Swastika, the Ordeal of the German Church. Arthur Frey. Tr. by J. Strathearn McNab. LC 78-63668. (Studies in Fascism: Ideology & Practice). 224p. Repr. of 1938 ed. 24.50 (ISBN 0-404-16526-5). AMS Pr.

Cross & Sword: The Political Role of Christian Missions in the Belgian Congo, 1908-1960. Marvin D. Markowitz. LC 75-170209. (Publications Ser.: No. 114). 1973. 13.50x (ISBN 0-8179-1141-3). Hoover Inst Pr.

Cross & the Bomb. 1985. pap. 29.00x (ISBN 0-317-39053-8, Pub by Mowbrays Pub Div). State Mutual Bk.

Cross & the Fasces: Christian Democracy and Fascism in Italy. Richard A. Webster. 1960. 18.50x (ISBN 0-8047-0043-5). Stanford U Pr.

Cross & the Floating Dragon: The Gospel in the Ryukyu. Edward E. Bollinger. LC 82-23540. (Illus.). 368p. 1983. pap. 10.95 (ISBN 0-87808-190-9). William Carey Lib.

Cross & the Prodigal. Kenneth Bailey. LC 72-90957. 176p. 1973. pap. 5.25 (ISBN 0-570-03139-7, 12-2523). Concordia.

Cross & the Shroud: A Medical Examination of the Crucifixion. Frederick T. Zugibe. (Illus.). 240p. 1987. 21.95 (ISBN 0-913729-75-2); pap. 9.95 (ISBN 0-913729-46-9). Paragon Hse.

Cross & the Switchblade. David Wilkerson et al. 160p. pap. 2.95 (ISBN 0-8007-8009-4, Spire Bks). Revell.

Cross & the Sword. Ed. by Jean Stern. LC 76-9415. Tr. of Cruz y la Espada. (Eng. & Span., Illus.). 144p. 1982. pap. 10.00 (ISBN 0-295-95916-9, Pub. by San Diego Museum Art). U of Wash Pr.

Cross Currents in Early Buddhism. S. N. Dube. 1981. 22.50x (ISBN 0-8364-0686-9, Pub. by Manohar India). South Asia Bks.

Cross-Currents in Seventeenth Century English Literature: The World, the Flesh & the Spirit, Their Actions & Reactions. Herbert J. Grierson. 1959. 11.25 (ISBN 0-8446-6247-X). Peter Smith.

Cross-Currents: Interaction Between Science & Faith. Colin A. Russell. 272p. 1985. pap. 10.95 (ISBN 0-8028-0163-3). Eerdmans.

Cross-Eyed Bear & Other Children's Sermons. S. Lawrence Johnson. LC 79-24765. (Orig.). 1980. pap. 6.50 (ISBN 0-687-09980-3). Abingdon.

Cross for Napoleon. Leon Cristiani. 1980. 4.00 (ISBN 0-8198-1404-0); pap. 2.00 (ISBN 0-8198-1405-9). Dghtrs St Paul.

Cross Gives Me Courage. Mary Ujka. LC 83-60743. 132p. (Orig.). 1983. pap. 5.95 (ISBN 0-87973-618-6, 618). Our Sunday Visitor.

Cross in Faith & Conduct. Gordon Watt. 1965. pap. 1.95 (ISBN 0-87508-964-X). Chr Lit.

Cross in the Life & Literature of the Anglo-Saxons. William O. Stevens. 69.95 (ISBN 0-87968-970-6). Gordon Pr.

Cross in the Sand: The Early Catholic Church in Florida, 1513-1870. Michael V. Gannon. LC 83-10498. 1965. pap. 12.00 (ISBN 0-8130-0776-3). U Presses Fla.

Cross: Its History & Symbolism. George W. Benson. LC 73-88643. 1976. Repr. of 1934 ed. lib. bdg. 25.00 (ISBN 0-87817-149-5). Hacker.

Cross: Meditations on the Last Seven Words of Christ. Morton T. Kelsey. LC 80-82086. 128p. 1980. pap. 3.95 (ISBN 0-8091-2337-1). Paulist Pr.

Cross of Christ. John R. Stott. LC 86-21293. 480p. (Orig.). 1986. Repr. 14.95 (ISBN 0-87784-998-6). Inter-Varsity.

Cross of Saint Patrick: The Catholic Unionist Tradition in Ireland. John Biggs-Davison & George Chowdharay-Best. 1985. 50.80x (ISBN 0-946041-26-1, Pub. by Kensal Pr UK). State Mutual Bk.

Cross Questions Scripture Answers. Roy H. Lanier, Jr. pap. 1.75 (ISBN 0-89137-618-6). Quality Pubns.

Cross, the Flag, & the Bomb: American Catholics Debate War & Peace, 1960-1983. William A. Au. LC 84-25290. (Contributions to the Study of Religion Ser.: No. 12). xviii, 278p. 1985. lib. bdg. 35.00 (ISBN 0-313-24754-4, AUC/). Greenwood.

Cross: Touchstone of Faith. Jessie Penn-Lewis. 1962. pap. 2.95 (ISBN 0-87508-994-1). Chr Lit.

Cross-Ways: A Book of Inspiration. Fulton J. Sheen. LC 83-45272. (Illus.). 80p. 1984. pap. 7.95 (ISBN 0-385-19205-3, Im). Doubleday.

Crosses & Culture of Ireland. Arthur K. Porter. LC 68-56480. (Illus.). 1969. Repr. of 1931 ed. 33.00 (ISBN 0-405-08860-4, Pub. by Blom). Ayer Co Pubs.

Crossing the Border (Colossians) Guy H. King. 1957. pap. 3.95 (ISBN 0-87508-274-2). Chr Lit.

Crossman Confessions & Other Essays in Politics, History & Religion. Elie Kedourie. 255p. 1985. 30.00x (ISBN 0-7201-1712-7). Mansell.

Crossroad Children's Bible. Andrew Knowles. (Illus.). 448p. 1981. 12.95 (ISBN 0-8245-0138-1); pap. 7.95 (ISBN 0-8245-0473-9). Crossroad NY.

Crossroads. Curt M. Joseph. (Orig.). 1987. pap. 4.75 (ISBN 0-89536-843-9, 7802). CSS of Ohio.

Crossroads: Essays on the Catholic Novelists. Albert Sonnenfeld. 138p. 1982. 13.95 (ISBN 0-917786-24-6). Summa Pubns.

Crossroads: Times of Decision for People of God. Herbert O'Driscoll. 96p. 1983. pap. 5.95 (ISBN 0-8164-2432-2, HarpR). Har-Row.

Crossroads to Israel 1917-1948. Christopher Sykes. LC 72-93912. (Midland Bks.: No. 165). 416p. 1973. pap. 8.95x (ISBN 0-253-20165-9). Ind U Pr.

Crow Indian Medicine Bundles. 2nd ed. William Wildschut. Ed. by John C. Ewers. LC 74-33115. (Illus.). 1975. soft cover 10.00 (ISBN 0-934490-34-1). Mus Am Ind.

Crowd Culture. facs. ed. Bernard I. Bell. LC 74-117758. (Essay Index Reprint Ser). 1952. 17.00 (ISBN 0-8369-1742-1). Ayer Co Pubs.

Crowd Is Waiting. Alan T. Dale. (Rainbow Books, Bible Story Books for Children). 1976. pap. 1.00 (ISBN 0-8192-1208-3). Morehouse.

Crown of Beauty: The Baha'i Faith & the Holy Land. Eunice Braun & Hugh E. Chance. (Illus.). 104p. 16.95 (ISBN 0-85398-139-6); pap. 11.95 (ISBN 0-85398-140-X). G Ronald Pub.

Crown of Glory: Life of J. J. Strang, Moses, of the Mormons. O. U. Riegel. 1935. 59.50x (ISBN 0-685-69857-2). Elliots Bks.

Crown of Jewels. Cora M. Groff. 144p. 1985. pap. 6.00 (ISBN 0-682-40210-9). Exposition Pr FL.

Crown of Life: A Study of Yoga. Kirpal Singh. (Illus.). xv, 255p. 1980. pap. 7.00 (ISBN 0-89142-001-2). Sant Bani Ash.

Crown of Life: A Study of Yoga. 4th ed. Kirpal Singh. LC 79-67543. (Illus.). 256p. pap. 6.95 (ISBN 0-918224-09-8). Sawan Kirpal Pubns.

Crown of Sorrow. Alban Goodier. 156p. 1982. 3.25 (ISBN 0-8198-1422-9, SP0093); pap. 2.25 (ISBN 0-8198-1423-7). Dghtrs St Paul.

Crown Them with Glory & Honor: Talks for Weddings. A. Coniaris. 1985. pap. 4.95 (ISBN 0-937032-40-9). Light&Life Pub Co MN.

Crowned Christ. F. W. Grant. pap. 4.25 (ISBN 0-88172-073-9). Believers Bkshelf.

Crowned with Glory & Honor: The Life of Rev. Lacey Kirk Williams. Ed. by L. Venchael Booth. 1978. 8.00 (ISBN 0-682-48939-5). Exposition Pr FL.

Crowning Fifty Years. Abilene Christian University Lectureship Staff. Ed. by J. D. Thomas. LC 68-21004. 1968. 9.95 (ISBN 0-89112-030-0, Bibl Res Pr). Abilene Christ U.

Crowninshield-Bentley House. A. L. Cummings & D. A. Fales, Jr. LC 76-16905. (Historic House Booklet Ser.: No. 2). 1976. 2.00 (ISBN 0-88389-060-7). Essex Inst.

Crucial Bonds: Marriage Among the Lebanese Druze. Nura S. Alamuddin & Paul D. Starr. LC 78-10465. 1980. 25.00x (ISBN 0-88206-024-4). Caravan Bks.

Crucial Experiences in the Life D. L. Moody. Paul Gericke. LC 78-7570. 72p. (Orig.). 1978. pap. 3.00 (ISBN 0-914520-12-1). Insight Pr.

Crucial Hours. William Lauterbach. 1977. pap. 5.95 (ISBN 0-8100-0050-4, 15-0358). Northwest Pub.

Crucial Issues in Philosophy. Daniel S. Robinson. 1955. 6.95 (ISBN 0-8158-0177-7). Chris Mass.

Cruciality of the Cross. Peter T. Forsyth. 104p. 1983. pap. 5.95 (ISBN 0-913029-00-9). Stevens Bk Pr.

Crucible of Europe: The Ninth & Tenth Centuries in European History. Geoffrey Barraclough. LC 75-21934. (Illus.). 180p. 1976. 36.50x (ISBN 0-520-03105-9); pap. 6.95 (ISBN 0-520-03118-0, CAL 326). U of Cal Pr.

Crucible of Redemption. Carlyle Marney. 64p. 1984. pap. text ed. 5.95 (ISBN 0-913029-04-1). Stevens Bk Pr.

Crucible of the Millennium: The Burned-Over District of New York in the 1840s. Michael Barkun. LC 86-5777. (New York State Studies). (Illus.). 240p. (Orig.). 1986. text ed. 27.50x (ISBN 0-8156-2371-2); pap. text ed. 14.95x (ISBN 0-8156-2378-X). Syracuse U Pr.

Crucified God. Jurgen Moltmann. LC 73-18694. 352p. 1974. 18.45 (ISBN 0-06-065901-7, HarpR). Har-Row.

Crucified Jesus Is No Stranger. Sebastian Moore. 1977. (HarpR); pap. 5.95 (ISBN 0-86683-891-0). Har-Row.

Crucified Life. Ed. by E. A. Adeboye. 48p. (Orig.). 1985. pap. 0.95 (ISBN 0-88144-053-1, CPS022). Christian Pub.

Crucified Ruler. Richard Jensen. (Orig.). 1987. pap. price not set (ISBN 0-89536-870-6, 7856). CSS of Ohio.

Crucifix: A Message on Christ's Sufferings. Thomas Adams. pap. 0.75 (ISBN 0-685-88372-8). Reiner.

Crucifixion in American Painting. Robert Henkes. 1978. lib. bdg. 79.95 (ISBN 0-8490-1370-4). Gordon Pr.

Crucifixion: In the Ancient World & the Folly of the Message of the Cross. Martin Hengel. Tr. by John Bowden from Ger. LC 77-78629. 118p. 1977. pap. 5.50 (ISBN 0-8006-1268-X, 1-1268). Fortress.

Crucifixion of the Jews. Franklin H. Littell. (Reprints of Scholarly Excellence: No. 12). 160p. 1986. Repr. of 1975 ed. 10.95 (ISBN 0-86554-227-9). Mercer Univ Pr.

Cruden's Compact Concordance. Alexander Cruden. 1968. 9.95 (ISBN 0-310-22910-3, 9440). Zondervan.

Cruden's Complete Concordance. Alexander Cruden. 1949. 14.95 (ISBN 0-310-22920-0, 9441). Zondervan.

Cruden's Complete Concordance. Alexander Cruden. 1976. pap. 9.95 (ISBN 0-310-22921-9, 9441P). Zondervan.

Cruden's Complete Concordance. Alexander Cruden. 796p. Date not set. 13.95 (ISBN 0-917006-31-3). Hendrickson MA.

Cruden's Concordance. Alexander Cruden. 1982. pap. 3.95 (ISBN 0-515-06741-5). Jove Pubns.

Cruden's Concordance. Alexander Cruden. Ed. by Eadie. 1982. pap. 7.95 (ISBN 0-89081-362-0). Harvest Hse.

Cruden's Concordance: Handy Reference Edition. Alexander Cruden. (Baker's Paperback Reference Library). 344p. 1982. pap. 7.95 (ISBN 0-8010-2478-1). Baker Bk.

Cruden's Handy Concordance. Alexander Cruden. pap. 3.95 (ISBN 0-310-22931-6, 6767P). Zondervan.

Cruden's Unabridged Concordance. Alexander Cruden. LC 54-11084. 17.95 (ISBN 0-8054-1123-2). Broadman.

Cruel Tragedy of My Life: The Autobiography of Peter Abelard. Peter Abelard. (Illus.). 131p. 1985. 97.45 (ISBN 0-89901-198-5). Found Class Reprints.

Crumbling Foundations: Death & Rebirth in an Age of Upheaval. Donald G. Bloesch. 160p. (Orig.). 1984. pap. text ed. 6.95 (ISBN 0-310-29821-0, 12740P). Zondervan.

Crusade & Mission. Benjamin Z. Kedar. LC 84-3403. (Illus.). 256p. 1984. text ed. 26.50x (ISBN 0-691-05424-X). Princeton U Pr.

Crusade Evangelism & the Local Church. Sterling Huston. 215p. 1984. pap. 5.95 (ISBN 0-89066-047-6). World Wide Pubs.

Crusade: Historiography & Bibliography. Aziz S. Atiya. LC 75-22640. 1976. lib. bdg. 22.50x (ISBN 0-8371-8364-2, ATTC). Greenwood.

Crusade in Spain. E. O'Duffy. 69.95 (ISBN 0-87968-972-2). Gordon Pr.

Crusade in the City: Revivalism in Nineteenth-Century Philadelphia. Marion L. Bell. (Illus.). 1978. 22.50 (ISBN 0-8387-1929-5). Bucknell U Pr.

Crusade of Brotherhood, a History of the American Missionary Association. A. F. Beard. 1909. 24.00 (ISBN 0-527-06300-2). Kraus Repr.

Crusade of Brotherhood, a History of the American Missionary Association. Augustus F. Beard. LC 76-161728. Repr. of 1909 ed. 26.50 (ISBN 0-404-00004-5). AMS Pr.

Crusade of Nicopolis. Aziz S. Atiya. LC 76-29829. (Illus.). Repr. of 1934 ed. 29.50 (ISBN 0-404-15410-7). AMS Pr.

Crusade of Richard I, 1189-92. Thomas A. Archer. LC 76-29828. Repr. of 1889 ed. 65.00 (ISBN 0-404-15408-5). AMS Pr.

Crusade of Richard Lion-Heart, by Ambroise. Morton J. Hubert & John L. La Monte. (Illus.). 1969. lib. bdg. 40.00x (ISBN 0-374-94009-6, Octagon). Hippocrene Bks.

Crusader for Christ (Billy Graham) Jean Wilson. 1973. pap. 2.50 (ISBN 0-87508-602-0). Chr Lit.

Crusader Institutions. Joshua Prawer. (Illus.). 1980. 89.00x (ISBN 0-19-822536-9). Oxford U Pr.

Crusader Manuscript Illumination at Saint-Jean D'Acre, 1275-1291. Jaroslav Folda. LC 75-2991. (Illus.). 646p. 1975. 70.50x (ISBN 0-691-03907-0). Princeton U Pr.

Crusaders. Michael R. Conroy. 1975. 19.95 (ISBN 0-915626-02-0). Yellow Jacket.

Crusaders in the East. W. B. Stevenson. 16.00x (ISBN 0-86685-035-X). Intl Bk Ctr.

Crusaders of the Jungle. J. Fred Rippy & Jean T. Nelson. LC 76-123495. 1971. Repr. of 1936 ed. 31.50x (ISBN 0-8046-1382-6, Pub. by Kennikat). Assoc Faculty Pr.

Crusades. T. A. Archer. 1894. 15.00 (ISBN 0-8482-7265-X). Norwood Edns.

Crusades. facsimile ed. Ernest Barker. LC 76-160956. (Select Bibliographies Reprint Ser). Repr. of 1923 ed. 12.00 (ISBN 0-8369-5823-3). Ayer Co Pubs.

Crusades. Konrad Bercovici. 1979. Repr. of 1929 ed. lib. bdg. 25.00 (ISBN 0-8482-3439-1). Norwood Edns.

Crusades. George W. Cox. Repr. 12.00 (ISBN 0-8482-3560-6). Norwood Edns.

Crusades. Hans E. Mayer. Tr. by John Gillingham from Ger. (Illus.). 1972. pap. text ed. 12.95x (ISBN 0-19-873016-0). Oxford U Pr.

Crusades. Ann Williams. Ed. by Marjorie Reeves. (Then & There Ser.). (Illus.). 95p. (YA) 1975. pap. text ed. 4.75 (ISBN 0-582-20441-0). Longman.

Crusades & Other Historical Essays, Presented to Dana C. Munro by His Former Students. facs. ed. Ed. by Louis J. Paetow. LC 68-14902. (Essay Index Reprint Ser). 1928. 21.50 (ISBN 0-8369-0354-4). Ayer Co Pubs.

Crusades: Idea & Reality, 1095-1274. Louise Riley-Smith & Jonathan Riley-Smith. (Documents in Medieval History). 208p. 1981. pap. text ed. 17.95 (ISBN 0-7131-6348-8). E Arnold.

Crusades: Iron Men & Saints. Harold Lamb. 368p. 1983. Repr. of 1930 ed. lib. bdg. 36.50 (ISBN 0-89987-527-0). Darby Bks.

Crusades: The Story of the Latin Kingdom of Jerusalem. Thomas A. Archer & Charles L. Kingsford. LC 76-29833. Repr. of 1900 ed. 39.50 (ISBN 0-404-15409-3). AMS Pr.

Crusades Through Arab Eyes. Amin Maalouf. 312p. 1985. 16.95 (ISBN 0-8052-4004-7). Schocken.

Crusades Through Arab Eyes. Amin Maalouf. LC 85-8367. 312p. 1987. pap. 8.95 (ISBN 0-8052-0833-X). Schocken.

Crusading Warfare, 1097-1193: A Contribution to Medieval Military History. R. C. Smail. LC 67-26956. (Cambridge Studies in Medieval Life & Thought Ser: No. 3). 1967. pap. 16.95 (ISBN 0-521-09730-4). Cambridge U Pr.

Crux Ansata: An Indictment of the Roman Catholic Church. H. G. Wells. LC 73-161344. (Atheist Viewpoint Ser). (Illus.). 114p. 1972. Repr. of 1944 ed. 13.00 (ISBN 0-405-03798-8). Ayer Co Pubs.

Crux Imperatorum Philosophia: Imperial Horizons of the Cluniac Confraternitas, 964-1109. Robert G. Heath. LC 76-56099. (Pittsburgh Theological Monographs: No. 13). 1977. pap. 10.00 (ISBN 0-915138-17-4). Pickwick.

Cry for Mercy: Prayers from the Genesee. Henri J. Nouwen. LC 80-2563. (Illus.). 175p. 1983. pap. 6.95 (ISBN 0-385-17508-6, Im). Doubleday.

Cry for the World. Lucille Oliver. 1981. pap. 3.00 (ISBN 0-8309-0307-0). Herald Hse.

Cry from the Heart: The Baha'is in Iran. William Sears. (Illus.). 224p. 1982. pap. 3.95 (ISBN 0-85398-134-5). G Ronald Pub.

Cry from the Mountain. Daniel L. Quick & Thomas A. Noton. 159p. 1986. pap. 5.95 (ISBN 0-89066-064-6). World Wide Pubs.

Cry Justice! Prayers, Meditations & Readings from South African Christians in a Time of Crisis. John W. De Gruchy. LC 86-667. (Illus.). 264p. (Orig.). 1986. pap. 6.95 (ISBN 0-88344-223-X). Orbis Bks.

Cry Justice: The Bible Speaks on Hunger & Poverty. Ronald J. Sider. LC 80-82133. 224p. 1980. pap. 3.95 (ISBN 0-8091-2308-8). Paulist Pr.

Cry of a Lonely Planet. George E. Vandeman. 352p. 1983. pap. 7.95 (ISBN 0-8163-0519-6). Pacific Pr Pub Assn.

Cry of Absence: Reflections for the Winter of the Heart. Martin E. Marty. LC 82-48416. (Illus.). 176p. 1983. 12.45 (ISBN 0-06-065434-1, HarpR). Har-Row.

Cry of Cassandra: The Resurgence of European Anti-Semitism. Simon Epstein. Tr. by Norman S. Posel from Fr. Tr. of Antisemitism Francais. 256p. 1986. 15.95 (ISBN 0-915765-13-6, Pub. by Zenith Edit); pap. 7.95 (ISBN 0-915765-14-4, Pub. by Zenith Edit). Natl Pr Inc.

Cry of the Environment: Rebuilding the Christian Creation Tradition. Ed. by Philip N. Joranson & Ken Butigan. LC 84-72254. (Illus.). 476p. (Orig.). 1984. pap. 14.95 (ISBN 0-939680-17-3). Bear & Co.

Cry of the Human Heart. Juan C. Ortiz. LC 76-24099. 1977. pap. 4.95 (ISBN 0-88419-010-2). Creation Hse.

Cry of the Northland. Virginia Crider. (Northland Ser). 1973. pap. 2.50 (ISBN 0-87813-505-7). Christian Light.

Cry of the People: Workshops for Christian Service. NFCLC. 318p. (Orig.). 1980. pap. 10.00 (ISBN 0-913605-06-9). NFCLC.

Cry Out! Inside the Terrifying World of an Abused Child. P. E. Quinn. 208p. 1984. 10.95 (ISBN 0-687-10015-1). Abingdon.

Crying for My Mother: The Intimate Life of a Clergyman. Wesley W. Nelson. 120p. 1975. pap. 4.00 (ISBN 0-910452-26-1). Covenant.

Cryptic Masonry. Jackson H. Chase. 94p. Repr. of 1981 ed. s.p. soft cover 4.75 (ISBN 0-88053-014-6). Macoy Pub.

Crystal & the Way of Light: Meditation, Contemplation & Self Liberation. Namkhai Norbu. Ed. by John Shane. (Illus.). 224p. 1986. pap. 14.95 (ISBN 0-7102-0833-2, 08332). Methuen Inc.

Crystal Chalice. rev. ed. Taj Inayat et al. (Illus.). 170p. Date not set. pap. price not set (1011P). Omega Pr NM.

Crystal Christianity: A Vital Guide to Personal Revival. Charles G. Finney. Orig. Title: Lectures to Professing Christians. 330p. 1986. pap. 3.95 (ISBN 0-88368-171-4). Whitaker Hse.

Crystal Icon. Junius Obrennen & Nopal Smith. (Illus.). vii, 200p. 1981. deluxe ed. 50.00 (ISBN 0-940578-03-4). Galahand Pr.

Crystal Mirror, Vol. III. Tarthang Tulku. (Illus.). 1974. pap. 6.95 (ISBN 0-913546-05-4). Dharma Pub.

Crystal Mirror, Vol. V. Tarthang Tulku. (Illus.). 1977. pap. 12.95 (ISBN 0-913546-47-X). Dharma Pub.

Crystal Mirror, Vol. VII. Illus. by Tarthang Tulku. (Illus.). 450p. (Orig.). 1984. 12.95 (ISBN 0-913546-92-5). Dharma Pub.

Crystal Visions: Nine Meditations for Personal & Planetary Peace. Diane Mariechild. (Feminist Ser.). (Illus.). 128p. (Orig.). 1985. 15.95 (ISBN 0-89594-183-X); pap. 6.95 (ISBN 0-89594-182-1). Crossing Pr.

Cual Es la Diferencia? William MacDonald. Orig. Title: What Is the Difference? (Span.). 112p. 1981. pap. 2.75 (ISBN 0-8254-1450-4). Kregel.

Cuando el Dinero Causa Problemas. Jose L. Martinez. (Serie de la Familia). (Span.). 96p. 1986. pap. 3.50 (ISBN 0-311-46265-0). Casa Bautista.

Cuando Jesus Nacio. (Span.). 1.25 (ISBN 0-8198-1425-3). Dghtrs St Paul.

Cuando la Familia Enfrenta Problemas. Rolando Gutierrez-Cortes. (Serie de la Familia). (Span.). 96p. 1985. pap. 3.50 (ISBN 0-311-46261-8). Casa Bautista.

Cuando la Infidelidad Asoma. Arnoldo Canclini. (Series on the Family). (Span.). 112p. (Orig.). 1986. pap. 3.50 (ISBN 0-311-46264-2). Casa Bautista.

Cuando Triunfa la Fe. Anne W. McWilliams. Tr. by Jose L. Martinez from Eng. Orig. Title: Champion of Faith: David Gomez. 152p. 1983. pap. 5.95 (ISBN 0-311-01071-7). Casa Bautista.

Cuatro Dramas De Navidad. E. W. Watson & Miquel A. Blanco. 1984. pap. 0.95 (ISBN 0-311-08224-6). Casa Bautista.

Cuchama & Sacred Mountains. W. Y. Evans-Wentz. Ed. by Frank Waters & Charles L. Adams. LC 81-8749. (Illus.). xxxii, 196p. 1982. 22.95 (ISBN 0-8040-0411-0, Pub. by Swallow). Ohio U Pr.

Cuestionamiento Etico. Kathleen Hynes. Ed. by Jan Peterson & Ada M. Isasi-Diaz. Tr. by Olga L. Toro from Eng. Tr. of Ethical Inquiry. (Span.). 16p. 1984. pap. 1.00 (ISBN 0-915365-01-4). Cath Free Choice.

Cuidado de Dios. Maria S. De Eudaly. Tr. by Emma Z. Villasenor. (Illus.). 1983. pap. 0.95 (ISBN 0-311-38555-9). Casa Bautista.

Cuidado Pastoral De la Iglesia. C. W. Brister. Tr. by D. Tinao et al. Orig. Title: Pastoral Care in the Church. (Span.). 226p. 1982. pap. 5.50 (ISBN 0-311-42040-0). Casa Bautista.

Cuidado Pastoral: Desde la Cuna Hasta la Tumba. J. A. Hightower, Jr. Tr. by Edgar Morales from Eng. Tr. of Caring for Folks from Birth to Death. (Span.). 192p. (Orig.). 1986. pap. 5.75 (ISBN 0-311-11045-2). Casa Bautista.

Cult & Controversy: The Worship of the Eucharist Outside Mass. Nathan Mitchell. Ed. by Aidan Kavanagh. (Studies in the Reformed Rites of the Catholic Church: Vol. IV). 460p. (Orig.). 1982. pap. 14.95 (ISBN 0-916134-50-4). Pueblo Pub Co.

Cult & Countercult: A Study of a Spiritual Growth Group & a Witchcraft Order. Gini G. Scott. LC 79-54057. (Contributions in Sociology: No. 38). (Illus.). 1980. lib. bdg. 29.95x (ISBN 0-313-22074-3, SCC/). Greenwood.

Cult Controversies: The Societal Response to the New Religious Movements. James A. Beckford. 336p. 1985. 39.95 (ISBN 0-422-79630-1, 9592, Pub. by Tavistock England); pap. 13.95 (ISBN 0-422-79640-9, 9593, Pub. by Tavistock England). Methuen Inc.

Cult Experience. Andrew J. Pavlos. LC 81-13175. (Contributions to the Study of Religion: No. 6). xvi, 209p. 1982. lib. bdg. 29.95 (ISBN 0-313-23164-8, PEX/). Greenwood.

Cult Experience: Responding to the New Religious Pluralism. J. Gordon Melton & Robert L. Moore. LC 82-16136. 160p. (Orig.). 1982. pap. 8.95 (ISBN 0-8298-0619-9). Pilgrim NY.

Cult Explosion. Dave Hunt. LC 80-80458. 240p. 1980. pap. 6.95 (ISBN 0-89081-241-1). Harvest Hse.

Cult, Ghetto, & State: The Persistence of the Jewish Question. Maxime Rodinson. Tr. by Jon Rothschild from Fr. 239p. (Orig.). 1984. pap. 10.95 (ISBN 0-86356-020-2, Pub. by Al Saqi UK). Evergreen Dist.

Cult of Asklepios. Alice Walton. Repr. of 1894 ed. 15.00 (ISBN 0-384-65660-9). Johnson Repr.

Cult of Jagannatha. 2nd, Rev. ed. K. C. Mishra. 1985. 28.50x (ISBN 0-317-17545-9, Pub. by Mukhopadhyaya India). South Asia Bks.

Cult of Molek: A Reassessment. George C. Heider. (JSOT Supplement Ser.: No. 43). xiv, 446p. 1986. text ed. 28.50x (ISBN 1-85075-019-X, Pub. by JSOT Pr England); pap. text ed. 13.50x (ISBN 1-85075-018-1). Eisenbrauns.

Cult of Tara: Magic & Ritual in Tibet. Stephan Beyer. LC 74-186109. (Hermeneutics: Studies in the History of Religions). (Illus.). 1974. pap. 12.95 (ISBN 0-520-03635-2, CAL 383). U of Cal Pr.

Cult of the Black Virgin. Ean Begg. (Illus.). 288p. (Orig.). 1985. pap. 11.95 (ISBN 1-85063-022-4, Ark Paperbks). Methuen Inc.

Cult of the Dead in a Chinese Village. Emily M. Ahern. LC 72-97202. (Illus.). 296p. 1973. 22.50x (ISBN 0-8047-0835-5). Stanford U Pr.

Cult of the Goddess Pattini. Gananath Obeyesekere. LC 83-5884. (Illus.). 629p. 1984. lib. bdg. 42.50x (ISBN 0-226-61602-9). U of Chicago Pr.

Cult of the Goddess: Social & Religious Change in a Hindu Temple. James J. Preston. (Illus.). 109p. 1985. pap. text ed. 6.95x (ISBN 0-88133-135-X). Waveland Pr.

Cult of the Peacock Angel: A Short Account of the Yezidi Tribes of Kurdistan. Ralph H. Empson. LC 77-87646. Repr. of 1928 ed. 21.00 (ISBN 0-404-16416-1). AMS Pr.

Cult of the Saints: Its Rise & Function in Latin Christianity. Peter Brown. LC 80-11210. xvi, 188p. 1982. pap. 7.95 (ISBN 0-226-07622-9, Phoen). U of Chicago Pr.

Cult of the Superman. Eric Bentley. Orig. Title: Century of Hero Worship. 11.50 (ISBN 0-8446-0486-0). Peter Smith.

Cult of the Virgin Mary: Psychological Origins. Michael P. Carroll. LC 85-43273. (Illus.). 325p. 1986. 25.00 (ISBN 0-691-09420-9). Princeton U Pr.

Cult Phenomenon: Its Recognition, Evaluation & Control. Kaihong. 100p. (Orig.). 1987. pap. text ed. 19.00. Kaihong.

Culte Des Heros et Ses Conditions Sociales. Stefan Czarnowski. LC 74-25745. (European Sociology Ser.). 472p. 1975. Repr. 35.50x (ISBN 0-405-06500-0). Ayer Co Pubs.

Cultivating Religious Growth Groups. Charles M. Olsen. LC 83-27328. (The Pastor's Handbook Ser.: Vol. 3). 118p. (Orig.). 1984. pap. 7.95 (ISBN 0-664-24617-6). Westminster.

Cultivating Spiritual Fruit. Robert C. Gage. 144p. (Orig.). 1986. pap. 5.25 (ISBN 0-87227-114-5). Reg Baptist.

Cultivating the Ch'i: Translated from Original Writings in the Pang Family's Secret Journal, Describing T'ai Chi Chi-Kung Exercises. Compiled by & tr. by Stuart A. Olson. (Illus.). 98p. 1986. pap. 10.95 (ISBN 0-938045-02-4). Bubbling-Well.

Cultivation of Sagehood As a Religious Goal in Neo-Confucianism: A Study of Selected Writings of Kao P'an-Lung (1562-1626) Rodney L. Taylor. LC 78-18685. 1978. pap. 10.25 (01-01-22). Scholars Pr GA.

Culto Privato di Roma Antica, 2 vols. in 1. facsimile ed. Attilio De Marchi. LC 75-10641. (Ancient Religion & Mythology Ser.). (Ital., Illus.). 1976. Repr. 40.00x (ISBN 0-405-07011-X). Ayer Co Pubs.

Cults! An Anthology of Secret Societies, Sects, & the Supernatural. Ed. by Martin H. Greenberg & Charles G. Waugh. 368p. 1983. 17.95 (ISBN 0-8253-0159-9). Beaufort Bks NY.

Cults & Creeds in Graeco-Roman Egypt. H. I. Bell. 1975. pap. 7.50 (ISBN 0-89005-088-0). Ares.

Cults, Culture & the Law: Perspectives on New Religious Movements. Ed. by Thomas Robbins et al. (American Academy of Religion Studies in Religion: No. 36). 1985. 18.95 (ISBN 0-89130-832-6, 01 00 36); pap. 13.50 (ISBN 0-89130-833-4). Scholars Pr GA.

Cults, Customs, & Superstitions of India: Being a Revised & Enlarged Edition of Indian Life, Religious & Social. John C. Oman. LC 70-179232. (Illus.). Repr. of 1908 ed. 36.00 (ISBN 0-404-54859-8). AMS Pr.

Cults: Deception or Denomination. G. Michael Cocoris. 53p. (Orig.). 1984. pap. text ed. 1.00 (ISBN 0-935729-11-9). Church Open Door.

Cults of Campania. Roy M. Peterson. LC 23-13673. (American Academy in Rome, Papers & Monographs: Vol. 1). pap. 103.30 (2026716). Bks Demand UMI.

Cults of the Greek States, 5 vols. Lewis R. Farnell. Incl. Vol. 1. Cronos, Zeus, Hera, Athena. 50.00 (ISBN 0-89241-029-9); Vol. 2. Artemis, Aphrodite. 50.00 (ISBN 0-89241-030-2); Vol. 3. Cults of the Mother of the Gods, Raeh, Cybele. 50.00 (ISBN 0-89241-031-0); Vol. 4. Poseidon, Apollo. 60.00 (ISBN 0-89241-032-9); Vol. 5. Minor Cults. 60.00 (ISBN 0-89241-033-7). (Illus.). 1977. Repr. 250.00x set (ISBN 0-89241-049-3). Caratzas.

Cults of the Sabine Territory. Elizabeth C. Evans. LC 39-25699. (American Academy in Rome. Papers & Monographs: Vol. 11). pap. 71.00 (2026727). Bks Demand UMI.

Cults: The Continuing Threat. Lowell D. Streiker. 144p. 1983. pap. 3.95 (ISBN 0-687-10069-0). Abingdon.

Cults, World Religions, & You. Kenneth Boa. 1977. pap. 6.95 (ISBN 0-88207-752-X). Victor Bks.

Cultura Artistica Nelle Certose Europee. Ed. by James Hogg. (Analecta Cartusiana Ser.: No. 115). (Orig.). 1986. pap. 25.00 (ISBN 0-317-42572-2, Pub. by Salzburg Studies). Longwood Pub Group.

Cultural Adaptation of the Liturgy. Anscar J. Chupungco. 117p. (Orig.). 1982. pap. 4.95 (ISBN 0-8091-2452-1). Paulist Pr.

Cultural Anthropology: A Christian Perspective. Stephen A. Grunlan & Marvin K. Mayers. 1979. 9.95 (ISBN 0-310-36321-7, 11280P). Zondervan.

Cultural Context of Medieval Learning: Proceedings, No.76. International Colloquium on Philosophy, Science Theology in the Middle Ages, 1st, 1973. Ed. by John E. Murdock & Edith D. Sylla. (Synthese Library: Boston Studies in the Philosophy of Science 26). ix, 540p. (Orig.). 1975. 68.50 (ISBN 90-277-0560-7, Pub. by Reidel Holland); pap. 39.50 (ISBN 90-277-0587-9, Pub. by Reidel Holland). Kluwer Academic.

Cultural Heritage of India, 5 vols. Ed. by Bhattacharyya et al. Incl. Vol. 1. Early Phases. Intro. by S. Radhakrishnan (ISBN 0-87481-560-6); Vol. 2. Itihasas, Puranas, Dharma & Other Shastras (ISBN 0-87481-561-4); Vol. 3. The Philosophies (ISBN 0-87481-562-2); Vol. 4. The Religions (ISBN 0-87481-563-0); Vol. 5: Languages & Literatures (ISBN 0-87481-564-9). (Illus.). 40.00x ea.; Set. 175.00x (ISBN 0-87481-558-4). Vedanta Pr.

Cultural Heritage of Jasna Gora. Gora Z. Rozanow. (Illus.). 1977. 14.00 (ISBN 0-912728-44-2). Newbury Bks.

Cultural History of India. Ed. by A. L. Basham. (Illus.). 1975. 29.95x (ISBN 0-19-561520-4). Oxford U Pr.

Cultural History of India During the British Period. Abdullah Yusuf Ali. LC 75-41006. Repr. of 1940 ed. 25.50 (ISBN 0-404-14723-2). AMS Pr.

Cultural History of Religion in America. James G. Moseley. LC 80-23609. (Contributions to the Study of Religion Ser.: No. 2). 216p. 1981. lib. bdg. 29.95 (ISBN 0-313-22479-X, MRA/). Greenwood.

Cultural History of Tibet. David Snellgrove & Hugh Richardson. LC 85-27861. (Illus.). 307p. 1986. pap. 12.95 (ISBN 0-87773-353-8, 74380-6, Dist. by Random). Shambhala Pubns.

Cultural Politics of Religious Change: A Study of the Sanoyea Kpelle in Liberia. Randolph Stakeman. (African Studies: Vol. 3). 264p. text ed. 49.95x (ISBN 0-88946-177-5). E Mellen.

Cultural Subversion of the Biblical Faith: Life in the 20th Century under the Sign of the Cross. James D. Smart. LC 77-22063. 126p. 1977. pap. 5.95 (ISBN 0-664-24148-4). Westminster.

Cultural Theory of Matthew Arnold. Joseph Carroll. LC 81-23996. 296p. 1982. 25.95x (ISBN 0-520-04616-1). U of Cal Pr.

Culture & Consciousness: The Social Meaning of Altered Awareness. M. D. Faber. LC 80-36683. 296p. 1981. text ed. 34.95 (ISBN 0-87705-505-X); professional 32.95. Human Sci Pr.

Culture & Context in Sudan: The Process of Market Incorporation in Dar Masalit. Dennis Tully. (SUNY Series in Middle Eastern Studies). (Illus.). 272p. 1987. text ed. 49.50x (ISBN 0-88706-502-3); pap. 18.95x (ISBN 0-88706-504-X). State U NY Pr.

Culture & Eschatology: The Iconographical Vision of Paul Evdokimov. Peter C. Phan. LC 83-48751. (American University Studies VII (Theology & Religion): Vol. 1). 345p. 1984. text ed. 36.50 (ISBN 0-8204-0040-8). P Lang Pubs.

Culture & Faith. Richard Kroner. LC 51-7837. pap. 73.50 (ISBN 0-317-09283-9, 2016993). Bks Demand UMI.

Culture & Human Values: Christian Intervention in Anthropological Perspective. Jacob A. Loewen. Ed. by William A. Smalley. LC 75-12653. (Applied Cultural Anthropology Ser.). 443p. (Orig.). 1975. pap. 10.95x (ISBN 0-87808-722-2). William Carey Lib.

Culture & Ideology. Ali Shariati. Tr. by Fathollah Marjani from Persian. 23p. 1980. pap. 1.00x (ISBN 0-941722-12-0). Book-Dist-Ctr.

Culture & Political-Military Behavior: The Hindus in Pre-Modern India. Joel Larus. 1980. 16.50x (ISBN 0-8364-0038-0). South Asia Bks.

Culture & Religion in Some of Their Relations: The Literary Theory of Culture. J. C. Shairp. 1978. Repr. of 1872 ed. lib. bdg. 30.00 (ISBN 0-8492-8044-3). R West.

Culture, Crisis & Creativity. Dane Rudhyar. LC 76-43008. (Orig.). 1977. pap. 4.25 (ISBN 0-8356-0487-X, Quest). Theos Pub Hse.

Culture in Christian Perspective: A Door to Understanding & Enjoying the Arts. Leland Ryken. LC 86-1442. 1986. 13.95 (ISBN 0-88070-115-3). Multnomah.

Culture of a Sacred Town: Sociological Study of Nathdwara. Rajendra Jindel. 233p. 1986. 12.00X (ISBN 0-8364-1672-4, Pub. by Popular Prakashan). South Asia Bks.

Culture of Ancient Egypt. John A. Wilson. LC 56-4923. (Illus.). 1956. pap. 7.95 (ISBN 0-226-90152-1, P11, Phoen). U of Chicago Pr.

Culture of Compassion: The Spirit of Polish Jewry from Hasidism to the Holocaust. Heszel Klepfisz. LC 83-13626. 265p. 1983. 25.00x (ISBN 0-88125-037-6). Ktav.

Culture of Islam. A. Iqbal. 1981. 16.50 (ISBN 0-686-97867-6). Kazi Pubns.

Culture of Unbelief: Studies & Proceedings from the First International Symposium on Belief, Held in Rome, March 22-27, 1969. Ed. by Rocco Caporale & Antonio Grumelli. LC 75-138513. 1971. 39.50x (ISBN 0-520-01856-7). U of Cal Pr.

Culture Patterns in Christianity. Wilson D. Wallis. 176p. 1964. 9.50x (ISBN 0-87291-053-9). Coronado Pr.

Culture-Protestantism: German Liberal Theology at the Turn of the Twentieth Century. George Rupp. LC 77-13763. (American Academy of Religion. Studies in Religion: No. 15). 1977. pap. 8.95 (ISBN 0-89130-197-6, 010015). Scholars Pr GA.

Culture, Thought, & Social Action: An Anthropological Perspective. Stanley J. Tambiah. (Illus.). 432p. 1985. text ed. 30.00x (ISBN 0-674-17969-2). Harvard U Pr.

Cultures of Prehistoric Egypt, 2 vols. in 1. Elise J. Baumgartel. LC 80-24186. (Illus.). xxiii, 286p. 1981. Repr. of 1955 ed. lib. bdg. 60.00x (ISBN 0-313-22524-9, BACU). Greenwood.

Cumbres De Inspiracion. Mrs. Charles E. Cowman. Tr. by Adolfo Robleto. 1982. pap. 4.25 (ISBN 0-311-40026-4). Casa Bautista.

Cuneiform Parallels to the Old Testament. Ed. by Robert W. Rogers. 1977. lib. bdg. 69.95 (ISBN 0-8490-1695-9). Gordon Pr.

Cunning of History: The Holocaust & the American Future. Richard Rubenstein. price not set (ISBN 0-8446-5860-X). Peter Smith.

Cunning of Modern Religious Thought. David S. Pacini. LC 86-45201. 192p. 1986. 16.95 (ISBN 0-8006-0786-4, 1-786). Fortress.

Cuomo vs. O'Connor: Did a Catholic Politician Make an Anti-Catholic Appeal? Ellen McCormack. LC 85-71482. 100p. (Orig.). 1985. pap. 5.95 (ISBN 0-934117-00-4). Dolores Pr.

Cup & the Waterfall: The Adventure of Living in the Present Moment. John Killinger. LC 82-61421. 1983. pap. 4.95 (ISBN 0-8091-2515-3). Paulist Pr.

Cup of Destiny: The Quest for the Grail. Trevor Ravenscroft. LC 82-60160. 194p. 1982. pap. 6.95 (ISBN 0-87728-546-2). Weiser.

Cup of Sugar, Neighbor. Jeanette Lockerbie. (Quiet Time Bks.). 128p. 1974. pap. 3.50 (ISBN 0-8024-1681-0). Moody.

Cup of Tea. 2nd ed ed. Bhagwan S. Rajneesh. Ed. by Swami Anand Somendra. LC 83-43215. (Early Discourses & Writings Ser.). 272p. 1983. pap. 4.95 (ISBN 0-88050-538-9). Chidvilas Found.

Cup of Wonder: Communion Meditations. Lloyde J. Ogilvie. 142p. 1985. pap. 5.95 (ISBN 0-8010-6710-3). Baker Bk.

Cup Running Over. James Robinson. (Orig.). 1987. pap. price not set (ISBN 0-89536-873-0, 7859). CSS of Ohio.

Cupid & Psyche. Apuleius. Ed. by M. G. Balme & J. H. Morwood. (Illus.). 1976. pap. 6.95x (ISBN 0-19-912047-1). Oxford U Pr.

Cupid & Psyche. Walter Pater. (Illus.). 48p. 1977. 9.95 (ISBN 0-571-11115-7). Faber & Faber.

Cups Running Over. Judy Miller. 1973. cancelled 5.95 (ISBN 0-88027-096-9). Firm Foun Pub.

Cups Running Over. Judy Miller. 1985. pap. 5.95 (ISBN 0-89225-278-2). Gospel Advocate.

Curacion Cristiana. Charles Fillmore. LC 84-52152. Tr. of Christian Healing. (Span.). 160p. 5.95 (ISBN 0-87159-020-4). Unity School.

Curative Eurythmy. Rudolf Steiner. 132p. 1984. pap. 9.95 (ISBN 0-85440-398-1, Pub. by Steinerbooks). Anthroposophic.

Cure D'Ars. Francis Trochu. LC 79-112487. (Eng.). 1977. pap. 15.00 (ISBN 0-89555-020-2). TAN Bks Pubs.

Cure of Mind, Cure of Soul: Depth Psychology & Pastoral Care. Josef Goldbrunner. 1962. pap. 2.50x (ISBN 0-268-00067-0). U of Notre Dame Pr.

Curia & Cortes in Leon & Castille, Ten Seventy-Two to Twelve Ninety-Five. Evelyn S. Procter. LC 79-51750. (Cambridge Iberian & Latin American Studies). (Illus.). 350p. 1980. 44.50 (ISBN 0-521-22639-2). Cambridge U Pr.

Curiosities of Puritan Nomenclature. C. W. Bardsley. (International Library of Names). 252p. Repr. of 1880 ed. text ed. cancelled (ISBN 0-8290-1239-7). Irvington.

Curious Cases: A Collection of American & English Decisions Selected for Their Readability. B. A. Milburn. (Illus.). xvi, 441p. 1985. Repr. of 1902 ed. lib. bdg. 37.50x (ISBN 0-8377-0819-2). Rothman.

Curious Lore of Precious Stones. George Kunz. (Illus.). 14.50 (ISBN 0-8446-0173-X). Peter Smith.

Curious Lore of Precious Stones. George F. Kunz. 1970. pap. 7.95 (ISBN 0-486-22227-6). Dover.

Curious Myths of the Middle Ages. S. Baring-Gould. (Works of S. Baring-Gould Ser.). 254p. 1985. Repr. of 1867 ed. lib. bdg. 29.00 (ISBN 0-932051-19-7, Pub. by Am Repr Serv). Am Biog Serv.

Curious Myths of the Middle Ages. Sabine Baring-Gould. 69.95 (ISBN 0-87968-261-2). Gordon Pr.

Curious Myths of the Middle Ages. Sabine Baring-Gould. 1976. Repr. of 1867 ed. 69.00x (ISBN 0-403-06309-4, Regency). Scholarly.

Current Concerns of Anthropologists & Missionaries. Ed. & intro. by Karl Franklin. LC 86-81558. (International Museum of Cultures Ser.: No. 22). 174p. (Orig.). 1987. pap. text ed. 14.00 (ISBN 0-88312-176-X); microfiche (3) 6.00 (ISBN 0-88312-259-6). Summer Inst Ling.

Current Issues in Catholic Higer Education: Trends in Enrollment & Finances 1978-1982, Vol. 4, No. 1. 32p. 1983. 6.00 (ISBN 0-318-00780-0). Natl Cath Educ.

Current Issues in Catholic Higher Education: Facing the Future, Vol.3, No. 2. 31p. 1983. 3.60 (ISBN 0-318-00779-7). Natl Cath Educ.

Current Issues in Catholic Higher Education: Sponsorship-Partnership & 1984 Annual Meeting Papers, Vol. 4. (No. 2). 6.00 (ISBN 0-318-03688-6). Natl Cath Educ.

Current Issues in Catholic Higher Education. Incl. Vol. 1, No. 1. Registration-Draft-National Service. 40p. 1980. 2.40 (ISBN 0-686-39990-0); Vol. 1, No. 2. Peace & Justice. 40p. 1981. 2.40 (ISBN 0-686-39991-9); Vol. 2, No. 1. 50p. 1981. 2.40 (ISBN 0-686-39994-3); Vol. 2, No. 2. Campus as Context. 48p. 1982. 2.40 (ISBN 0-686-39995-1); Vol. 3, No. 1. 40p. 1982. 3.60. Natl Cath Educ.

Current Issues in Catholic Higher Education. Incl. Vol. 1, No. 1. Registration-Draft-National Service. 40p. 1980. 2.40 (ISBN 0-318-20581-5); Vol. 1, No. 2. Peace & Justice Education. 40p. 1981. 2.40 (ISBN 0-318-20582-3); Vol. 2, No. 1. Purposes & Leadership. 50p. 1981. 2.40 (ISBN 0-318-20583-1); Vol. 2, No. 2. Campus As Context. 48p. 1982. 2.40 (ISBN 0-318-20584-X); Vol. 3, No. 1. Report on Graduate Education. 40p. 1982. 3.60 (ISBN 0-318-20585-8); Vol. 3, No. 2. Facing the Future. 31p. 1983. 3.60 (ISBN 0-318-20586-6); Vol. 4, No. 1. Trends in Enrollment & Finance, 1978-82. 32p. 1983. 6.00 (ISBN 0-318-20587-4); Vol. 4, No. 2. Sponsorship-Partnership & 1984 Annual Meeting Papers. 47p. 1984. 6.00 (ISBN 0-318-20588-2); Vol. 5, No. 1. International Perspectives. 36p. 1984. 6.00 (ISBN 0-318-20589-0); Vol. 5, No. 2. Tradition in a Changed Context. 32p. 1985. 6.00 (ISBN 0-318-20590-4); Vol. 6, No. 1. Beyond Basketball. 38p. 1985. 6.00 (ISBN 0-318-20591-2); Vol. 6, No. 2. Town & Gown. 40p. 1986. 6.50 (ISBN 0-318-20592-0). Set. **37.00 (ISBN 0-318-20580-7). Natl Cath Educ.**

Current of Spirituality. Hubert Van Zeller. pap. 3.95 (ISBN 0-87243-048-0). Templegate.

Current Reform Responsa. Solomon B. Freehof. 1969. 15.00x (ISBN 0-87820-102-5, Pub. by Hebrew Union). Ktav.

Current Religious Policy of People's Republic of China (January 1, 1976 to March 15, 1979) Pt. I: An Inquiry. Chen Fu Tien. 73p. (Orig.). 1983. pap. 12.95. Chen Fu.

Current Sufi Activity Work, Literature, Groups & Techniques. Chawan Thurlnas. (Sufi Research Ser.). 40p. 1982. pap. 4.95 (ISBN 0-86304-004-7, Pub. by Octagon Pr England). Ins Study Human.

Curriculum in the Catholic School. Brother Robert J. Kealey. 61p. 1986. 6.60 (ISBN 0-318-20568-8). Natl Cath Educ.

Curriculum of Religious Education. George H. Betts. (Educational Ser.). 1924. Repr. 30.00 (ISBN 0-8482-7352-4). Norwood Edns.

Curriculum of Religious Education. William C. Bower. (Educational Ser.). 1930. Repr. 30.00 (ISBN 0-8482-7353-2). Norwood Edns.

Cursillo: Anatomy of a Movement: The Experience of Spiritual Renewal. Marcene Marcoux. 299p. 1982. 16.95x (ISBN 0-931186-00-5). Lambeth Pr.

Curso Biblico por Correspondencia, Vol. III. 538p. 1975. pap. 15.95 (ISBN 0-87148-179-0). Pathway Pr.

Curtain of Time. Paul R. Cagle, Jr. & Mary H. Wallace. (Illus., Orig.). 1984. pap. 6.95 (ISBN 0-912315-76-8). Word Aflame.

Curtain Time: Plays, Readings, Sketches, Cantatas, & Poems for Jewish Programs. Compiled by Zara Shakow. 1985. pap. 9.95 (ISBN 0-8246-0310-9). Jonathan David.

Curve of Fate: From Man-Ape to the Man-God. J. Lonsdale Bryans. 1977. lib. bdg. 59.95 (ISBN 0-8490-1696-7). Gordon Pr.

Custom & Myth. 2nd rev. ed. Andrew Lang. LC 68-59267. Repr. of 1885 ed. 11.00 (ISBN 0-404-03817-4). AMS Pr.

Custom & Myth. Andrew Lang. (Illus.). 1977. Repr. of 1885 ed. 14.95x (ISBN 0-85409-969-7). Charles River Bks.

Custom Clip Art for Churches, Vol. 2. Jack Hamm. 48p. (Orig.). 1985. pap. 9.95 (ISBN 0-933545-00-2). Knight Media.

Customs & Cultures: Anthropology for Christian Missions. 2nd ed. Eugene A. Nida. LC 54-8976. (Applied Cultural Anthropology Ser.). 306p. 1975. Repr. of 1954 ed. 7.95x (ISBN 0-87808-723-0). William Carey Lib.

Cut & Color Patterns for Young Children. rev. ed. Rosemary W. Edwards. (Illus.). 112p. 1985. pap. 4.95 (ISBN 0-912315-93-8). Word Aflame.

Cutting Edge, Vol. 2. David A. Clemens. LC 79-52420. (Steps to Maturity Ser.). 1975. student's manual 15.95x (ISBN 0-86508-003-8); tchr's. manual 17.95x (ISBN 0-86508-004-6). BCM Intl Inc.

Cutting Through Spiritual Materialism. Chogyam Trungpa. LC 73-86145. (Dragon Ser.). (Illus.). 212p. (Orig.). 1973. pap. 8.95 (ISBN 0-87773-050-4). Shambhala Pubns.

Cycle of Day & Night, Where One Proceeds along the Path of the Primordial Yoga: A Basic Text on the Practice of Dzog Chen. Namkhai Norbu. 80p. Date not set. 8.50 (ISBN 0-931892-09-0). B Dolphin Pub.

Cycle of Day & Night: Where One Proceeds Along the Path of the Primordial Yoga; A Basic Tibetan Text on the Practice of Dzogchen. Namkhai Norbu. Ed. & tr. by John Reynolds. (Illus.). 128p. 1987. pap. 9.95 (ISBN 0-88268-040-4). Station Hill Pr.

Cycle of the Jewish Year. 1982. 6.00 (ISBN 0-686-76502-8). Feldheim.

Cyclical Time & Ismaili Gnosis. Henry Corbin. (Islamic Texts & Contexts Ser.). 193p. 1983. 24.95x (ISBN 0-7103-0047-6, Kegan Paul); pap. 13.95 (ISBN 0-7103-0048-4). Methuen Inc.

Cyclopaedia of Biblical, Theological, & Ecclesiastical Literature: Cyclopaedia of Biblical Literature, Vol. 1-10. John McClintock & James Strong. 250.00 (ISBN 0-405-00020-0, 11917). Ayer Co Pubs.

Cyclopedia of Biblical, Theological, & Ecclesiastical Literature, 12 vols. John McClintock & James Strong. 12400p. 1981. text ed. 395.00 (ISBN 0-8010-6123-7). Baker Bk.

Cyclopedic Dictionary of Ecclesiastical Terms According to the Use of the Episcopal Church. Richard H. Wood. 1984. 10.95 (ISBN 0-8062-2141-0). Carlton.

Cylinder Seals, A Documentary Essay on the Art & Religion of the Ancient Near East. Henri Frankfort. 427p. Repr. of 1939 ed. text ed. 74.52x (ISBN 0-576-19456-5). Gregg Intl.

Cynewulf & His Poetry. Kenneth Sisam. LC 75-1103. Repr. of 1933 ed. lib. bdg. 12.50 (ISBN 0-8414-7838-4). Folcroft.

Cynewulf & the Cynewulf Canon. S. K. Das. 59.95 (ISBN 0-87968-987-0). Gordon Pr.

Cynewulf & the Cynewulf Canon. Das Satyendra Kimar. LC 73-17006. 1942. lib. bdg. 27.50 (ISBN 0-8414-7701-9). Folcroft.

Cynewulf: Structure, Style, & Theme in His Poetry. Earl R. Anderson. LC 81-65464. 248p. 1983. 32.50 (ISBN 0-8386-3091-X). Fairleigh Dickinson.

Cynewulf's Poems. Tr. by C. W. Kennedy. 11.25 (ISBN 0-8446-1143-3). Peter Smith.

Cynewulfs Wortshatz. Richard Simons. 1899. 65.00 (ISBN 0-8274-2126-5). R West.

Cypress in the Courtyard. Bhagwan Shree Rajneesh. Ed. by Ma Prem Maneesha. LC 83-181284. (Initiation Talks Ser.). (Illus.). 466p. (Orig.). 1978. 18.95 (ISBN 0-88050-039-5). Chidvilas Found.

Cyprian & the Bible: A Study of Third-Century Exegesis. Michael A. Fahey. 701p. 1971. lib. bdg. 65.00 (Pub. by J C B Mohr BRD). Coronet Bks.

Cyprian: The Churchman. John A. Faulkner. 1977. lib. bdg. 59.95 (ISBN 0-8490-1698-3). Gordon Pr.

Cyrus Adler: Selected Letters. Ed. by Ira Robinson. 1000p. 1985. 2 vols. boxed 50.00 (ISBN 0-8276-0224-3). Jewish Pubns.

Czars, Soviets & Mennonites. John B. Toews. LC 81-71490. (Illus.). 221p. 1982. pap. 10.95 (ISBN 0-87303-064-8). Faith & Life.

D

D. L. Moody. Faith C. Bailey. (Golden Oldies Ser.). 1959. pap. 3.50 (ISBN 0-8024-0039-6). Moody.

D. L. Moody: God's Salesman. Sandy Dengler. (Preteen Biography Ser.). (Orig.). 1986. pap. 3.50 (ISBN 0-8024-1786-8). Moody.

Daa, Wah & Jihad. Abdul H. Tabibi. 40p. (Orig.). 1984. pap. 3.00 (ISBN 0-911119-05-1). Igram Pr.

Daat Tevnoth: The Knowing Heart. Mosche Chaim Luzzatto. Tr. by Shraga Silverstein from Hebrew. (Torah Classics Library). 357p. 1982. 12.95 (ISBN 0-87306-194-2); pap. 9.95 (ISBN 0-87306-345-7). Feldheim.

Dabney Discussions, Vol. 1. Robert L. Dabney. 728p. 1982. Repr. of 1891 ed. 19.95 (ISBN 0-85151-348-4). Banner of Truth.

Dabney Discussions, Vol. 2. Robert L. Dabney. (Religious Ser.). 684p. 1982. Repr. of 1891 ed. 19.95 (ISBN 0-85151-349-2). Banner of Truth.

Dabney Discussions, Vol. 3. Robert L. Dabney. (Religious Ser.). 493p. 1982. Repr. of 1892 ed. 17.95 (ISBN 0-85151-350-6). Banner of Truth.

Dachau. LC 79-51047. (Witness to the Holocaust Ser.: No. 2). 67p. 1982. 2.75. Witness Holocaust.

Daddy's Letter. Keith Neely. (Color & Learn Bks.). (Orig.). pap. 2.25 (ISBN 0-8024-0502-9). Moody.

Dads Are Special, Too. J. David Purdy. 96p. 1985. pap. 3.95 (ISBN 0-8423-0503-3). Tyndale.

Daemonologie, in Forme of a Dialogue. James First King Of England. (English Experience Ser.: No. 94). 1969. Repr. of 1597 ed. 13.00 (ISBN 90-221-0094-4). Walter J Johnson.

Dag Hammarskjold's Fortress White Book: An Analysis of Markings. Gustaf Aulen. LC 75-84608. pap. 40.50 (2026974). Bks Demand UMI.

Daily Bread Cookbook. LC 82-83956. 1975. pap. 6.95 (ISBN 0-916035-00-X, BE-141). Evangel Indiana.

Daily Bread, Nineteen Eighty-Six. Ed. by Imogene Goodyear. 1985. pap. 7.50 (ISBN 0-8309-0407-7). Herald Hse.

Daily Bread, 1987. Ed. by Imogene Goodyear. 1986. pap. 8.00 (ISBN 0-8309-0435-2). Herald Hse.

Daily Christian Living. William S. Deal. LC 62-22195. 1962. pap. 0.95 (ISBN 0-686-05840-2). Crusade Pubs.

Daily Compounding Savings Certificate Tables: Five Percent to Ten Percent. Financial Publishing Co. Staff. 319p. 1982. pap. write for info. (ISBN 0-87600-582-2). Finan Pub.

Daily Cycle of Services of the Orthodox Church: An Historical Synopsis. Father Benedict. 30p. (Orig.). 1986. pap. 4.95x (ISBN 0-936649-09-7, TX 1-781-934). St Anthony Orthodox.

Daily Devotional Bible Commentary, 4 vols. LC 76-46492. 1982. Repr. of 1974 ed. 39.95 (ISBN 0-8054-1228-X). Broadman.

Daily Devotional Bible Commentary: Genesis--Job, Vol. 1. LC 79-46492. 1982. Repr. of 1974 ed. 10.95 (ISBN 0-8054-1224-7). Broadman.

Daily Devotional Bible Commentary: Matthew--Acts, Vol. 3. LC 76-46441. 1982. Repr. of 1974 ed. 10.95 (ISBN 0-8054-1226-3). Broadman.

Daily Devotional Bible Commentary: Psalms--Malachi, Vol. 2. LC 76-46493. 1982. Repr. of 1974 ed. 10.95 (ISBN 0-8054-1225-5). Broadman.

Daily Devotional Bible Commentary: Romans--Revelation, Vol. 4. LC 76-46442. 1982. Repr. of 1974 ed. 10.95 (ISBN 0-8054-1227-1). Broadman.

Daily Devotions for Newlyweds. Davis Cooper. LC 81-67204. 1983. 8.95 (ISBN 0-8054-5646-5). Broadman.

Daily Devotions from the Christian's Secret of a Happy Life. Hannah W. Smith. Ed. by Robert C. Hill. 288p. (Orig.). 1984. pap. 5.95 (ISBN 0-8007-5139-6, Power Bks). Revell.

Daily Discipline of Worship. Torkom Saraydarian. 1986. pap. 1.00 (ISBN 0-911794-52-2). Aqua Educ.

Daily Guide to a Better Marriage. Donald Moore. 32p. 1984. pap. 0.75 (ISBN 0-88144-021-3). Christian Pub.

Daily Help. Charles H. Spurgeon. 1959. 4.95 (ISBN 0-399-12825-5, G&D). Putnam Pub Group.

Daily Homilies, 3 Vols. S. Joseph Krempa. Incl. Vol. 1. Ordinary Time (Year One) 242p. 1985 (ISBN 0-8189-0480-1); Vol. 2. Ordinary Time (Year Two) 253p. 1985 (ISBN 0-8189-0481-X); Vol. 3. Seasonal & Sanctoral Cycle: Advent, Christmas, Lent & Easter & all Obligatory Memorials. 217p. 1985 (ISBN 0-8189-0479-8). 1985. pap. 7.50 ea.; Set. pap. 19.95 (ISBN 0-8189-0483-6). Alba.

Daily Journal of Oneida Community, 5 vols. in 1. LC 74-32539. (American Utopian Adventure Ser.). (Illus., Vols. 1-3, bd. with the O.C. daily, vols. 4-5). 1975. Repr. of 1868 ed. lib. bdg. 95.00x (ISBN 0-87991-032-1). Porcupine Pr.

Daily Lectionary. Ed. by James E. Barrett. 70p. 1982. 2.45 (ISBN 0-942466-02-0). Hymnary Pr.

Daily Lectionary: A Weekly Guide for Daily Bible Readings, the Sundays After Pentecost Year One. Joseph P. Russell. (Daily Lectionary Ser.). 136p. (Orig.). 1987. pap. 3.25 (ISBN 0-88028-060-3). Forward Movement.

Daily Lectionary: Scripture Readings for Every Day Based on the New Common Lectionary. W. Douglas Mills. 144p. (Orig.). 1986. pap. 6.95 (ISBN 0-8358-0517-4). Upper Room.

Daily Lectionary-Year 1: Advent-Easter. Joseph Russell. (Orig.). 1986. pap. 2.50 (ISBN 0-88028-057-3). Forward Movement.

Daily Lenten Meditations for Orthodox Christians. Emily Harakas. 1983. pap. 2.95 (ISBN 0-937032-27-1). Light&Life Pub Co MN.

Daily Life in the Time of Jesus. Henri Daniel-Rops. Tr. by Patrick O'Brian from Fr. (Illus.). 518p. 1981. pap. 8.95 (ISBN 0-89283-085-9). Servant.

Daily Life of Early Christians. John G. Davies. LC 75-91757. Repr. of 1953 ed. lib. bdg. 22.50x (ISBN 0-8371-2413-1, DAEC). Greenwood.

Daily Light. Samuel Bagster. 1985. Repr. of 1975 ed. 6.95 (ISBN 0-916441-09-1). Barbour & Co.

Daily Light. deluxe ed. 384p. 1985. 12.95 (ISBN 0-8407-5480-9). Nelson.

Daily Light from the New American Standard Bible. Ed. by Vivian Stensland. 416p. 1975. 9.95 (ISBN 0-8024-1740-X). Moody.

Daily Light on the Daily Path. 9.95 (ISBN 0-310-23060-8, 18011); pap. 5.95 (ISBN 0-310-23061-6, 18012P). Zondervan.

Daily Light on the Daily Path. large print ed. 384p. 1975. kivar 9.95 (ISBN 0-310-23067-5, 18011L). Zondervan.

Daily Light on the Daily Path: From the New International Version. large print ed. 384p. 1983. pap. 9.95 (ISBN 0-310-23117-5, 18027L). Zondervan.

Daily Light on the Daily Path (NIV) 384p. 1981. 9.95 (ISBN 0-310-23110-8, 18027); pap. 5.95 (ISBN 0-310-23111-6). Zondervan.

Daily Living. Compiled by Association for Research & Enlightenment, Readings Research Dept. (Library: Vol. 12). 241p. 1981. 10.95 (ISBN 0-87604-133-0). ARE Pr.

Daily Look at Jesus, No. 1-2. Mary L. Miles. (Pre-Teen Books Ser.). 1970. No. 2. Moody.

Daily Meditations, 4 vols. Compiled by Edith M. Beyerle. 120p. Vol. 2. pap. 0.50 (ISBN 0-87509-075-3); Vol. 3. pap. 0.50 (ISBN 0-87509-076-1); Vol. 4. pap. 0.50 (ISBN 0-87509-077-X). Chr Pubns.

Daily Meditations. 3.95 (ISBN 0-8198-1812-7); 2.95 (ISBN 0-8198-2315-5). Dghtrs St Paul.

Daily Meditations for Prayer. Ed. by Charles Cook. Gift Ed. 9.95 (ISBN 0-89107-160-1). Good News.

Daily Miracle. Harold E. Dye. (Orig.). 1986. pap. 3.25 (ISBN 0-8054-5026-2). Broadman.

Daily Power Thoughts. Robert Schuller. 384p. 1984. pap. 3.95 (ISBN 0-515-08164-7). Jove Pubns.

Daily Power Thoughts. Robert H. Schuller. LC 77-68012. 1978. 9.95 (ISBN 0-89081-131-8); pap. 6.95 (ISBN 0-89081-123-7). Harvest Hse.

Daily Practice of the Hindus Containing the Morning & Midday Duties. 3rd, rev. & enl. ed. Srisa Chandra Vasu. Tr. by Srisa Chandra Vidyarnava. LC 73-3812. (Sacred Books of the Hindus: No. 20). Repr. of 1918 ed. 14.50 (ISBN 0-404-57820-9). AMS Pr.

Daily Prayer in the Early Church: A Study of the Origins & Early Development of the Divine Office. Paul F. Bradshaw. 1982. 26.00x (ISBN 0-19-520394-1); pap. 9.95x (ISBN 0-19-520395-X). Oxford U Pr.

Daily Prayers. Pandurangarao Malyala. (Illus., Orig.). 1984. pap. 2.00 (ISBN 0-938924-24-9). Sri Shirdi Sai.

Daily Readings from Prayers & Praises in the Celtic Tradition. Ed. by A. M. Allchin & Esther de Waal. 1987. pap. 4.95 (ISBN 0-87243-151-7). Templegate.

Daily Readings from the Cloud of Unknowing. Ed. by Robert Llewelyn. (Daily Readings Ser.). 1986. pap. 4.95 (ISBN 0-87243-149-5). Templegate.

Daily Readings with Brother Lawrence. Brother Lawrence. Ed. by Robert Llewelyn. (Daily Readings Ser.). 1986. pap. 4.95 (ISBN 0-87243-144-4). Templegate.

Daily Readings with Jean-Pierre de Caussade. Jean Pierre De Caussode. Ed. by Robert LLewelyn. (Daily Readings Ser.). 1986. pap. 4.95 (ISBN 0-87243-145-2). Templegate.

Daily Readings with John Wesley. Ed. by Arthur S. Wood. 1987. pap. 4.95 (ISBN 0-87243-158-4). Templegate.

Daily Readings with Julian of Norwich, 2 vols. Julian of Norwich. Ed. by Robert LLewelyn. (Daily Reading Ser.). 1986. pap. 4.95 ea. Vol. 1 (ISBN 0-87243-142-8). Vol. 2 (ISBN 0-87243-143-6). Templegate.

Daily Readings with Martin Luther. Ed. by James Atkinson. 1987. pap. 4.95 (ISBN 0-87243-157-6). Templegate.

Daily Readings with St. Augustine. Ed. by Maura See. 1987. pap. 4.95 (ISBN 0-87243-152-5). Templegate.

Daily Readings with St. Francis de Sales. St. Francis de Sales. Ed. by Robert LLewelyn. (Daily Readings Ser.). 1986. pap. 4.95 (ISBN 0-87243-147-9). Templegate.

Daily Readings with St. John of the Cross. St. John of the Cross. Ed. by Robert Llewelyn. (Daily Readings Ser.). 1986. pap. 4.95 (ISBN 0-87243-148-7). Templegate.

Daily Readings with St. Teresa of Avila. St. Teresa of Avila. Ed. by Robert LLewelyn. (Daily Readings Ser.). 1986. pap. 4.95 (ISBN 0-87243-146-0). Templegate.

Daily Readings with St. Therese of Lisieux. Ed. by Michael Hollings. 1987. pap. 4.95 (ISBN 0-87243-154-1). Templegate.

Daily Readings with William Law. Ed. by Robert Llewelyn & Edward Moss. 1987. pap. 4.95 (ISBN 0-87243-153-3). Templegate.

Daily Sacrifice: Daily Meditations on the Word of God. H. A. Ironside. 370p. 1982. pap. 4.95 (ISBN 0-87213-356-7). Loizeaux.

Daily Secrets of Christian Living. Andrew Murray. LC 77-17187. 400p. 1978. pap. 7.95 (ISBN 0-87123-500-5, 210500). Bethany Hse.

Daily Strength for Daily Needs. Mary W. Tileston. LC 73-80030. (Large Print Christian Classic Ser.). 1982. 14.95 (ISBN 0-87983-287-8). Keats.

Daily Strength for Daily Needs. Mary W. Tileston. 1942. 7.70i (ISBN 0-316-84592-2). Little.

Daily Strength for Daily Needs. Ed. by Mary W. Tileston. 1959. 4.95 (ISBN 0-399-12826-3, G&D). Putnam Pub Group.

Daily Thoughts-Disciples. Oswald Chambers. 1983. pap. 5.95 (ISBN 0-87508-143-6). Chr Lit.

Daily Thoughts for Disciples. Oswald Chambers. 1976. 10.95 (ISBN 0-310-22400-4). Zondervan.

Daily Thoughts for Disciples. Oswald Chambers. 208p. 1985. 8.95 (ISBN 0-310-30470-9). Zondervan.

Daily Thoughts on Bible Characters. 2nd ed. Harry Foster. Tr. by Living Spring Publications Staff. (Chinese.). 1982. write for info. (ISBN 0-941598-99-3); pap. write for info (ISBN 0-941598-00-4). Living Spring Pubns.

Daily Thoughts on Holiness. Andrew Murray. 1977. 6.95 (ISBN 0-87508-369-2). Chr Lit.

Daily Thoughts on Living Free. Neva Coyle. LC 82-4495. 174p. (Orig.). 1982. pap. 4.95 (ISBN 0-87123-286-3, 210286). Bethany Hse.

Daily Walk with God. Herman W. Gockel. 1982. 15.95 (ISBN 0-570-03298-9, 15-2171); pap. 10.95 (ISBN 0-570-03855-3, 12YY2810). Concordia.

Daily We Follow Him: Learning Discipleship from Peter. M. Basil Pennington. LC 86-20157. 160p. 1987. pap. 4.95 (ISBN 0-385-23535-6, Im). Doubleday.

Daily We Touch Him: Practical Religious Experiences. M. Basil Pennington. LC 76-20836. 1977. pap. 3.50 (ISBN 0-385-14802-X, Im). Doubleday.

Daily Wings. J. Sidlow Baxter. 384p. 1983. pap. 10.95 (ISBN 0-310-20751-7). Zondervan.

Daily with the King. W. Glyn Evans. LC 79-21970. 1979. pap. 5.95 (ISBN 0-8024-1739-6). Moody.

Dakshinamurti Stotra. Sri Sankaracharya. Tr. by Alladi M. Sastri. 1979. 12.00 (ISBN 0-89744-189-3). Auromere.

Dale Morgan on Early Mormonism: Correspondence & a New History. Dale L. Morgan. Ed. by John P. Walker. LC 86-60251. 414p. 1986. 20.95 (ISBN 0-941214-36-2). Signature Bks.

Dale Morgan on Early Mormonism: Correspondence & a New History. Ed. by John P. Walker. 350p. 1986. 22.95 (ISBN 0-941214-36-2). Signature Bks.

Dale Oldham Memorial Trilogy. Dale Oldham. 1984. Set. pap. 3.95 (ISBN 0-317-38180-6, D5042). Giants along My Path (ISBN 0-87162-162-2, D3784). How to Grow Spiritually (ISBN 0-87162-142-8, D5043). Living Close to God (ISBN 0-87162-013-8, D5304). Warner Pr.

Damascus Chronicle of the Crusades. Ibn Al-Qalanisi. Tr. by H. A. Gibb. LC 78-63342. (Crusades & Military Orders: Second Ser.). Repr. of 1967 ed. 32.50 (ISBN 0-404-17019-6). AMS Pr.

Damascus Covenant: An Interpretation of the "Damascus Document". Philip R. Davies. (Journal for the Study of the Old Testament, Supplement Ser.: No. 25). 267p. 1983. text ed. 28.00x (ISBN 0-905774-50-7, Pub. by JSOT Pr England); pap. text ed. 18.50x (ISBN 0-905774-51-5, Pub. by JSOT Pr England). Eisenbrauns.

Damien & the Island of Sickness: A Story About Damien. new ed. Kenneth Christopher. (Stories About Christian Heroes Ser.). (Illus.). 1979. pap. 1.95 (ISBN 0-86683-768-X, HarpR). Har-Row.

Damien of Molokai, Eighteen Forty to Eighteen Eighty-Nine. Irene Caudwell. 1979. Repr. of 1932 ed. lib. bdg. 20.00 (ISBN 0-8492-4041-7). R West.

Damien the Leper. John Farrow. 1954. pap. 3.95 (ISBN 0-385-02918-7, D3, Im). Doubleday.

Damien, the Leper Priest. Anne E. Neimark. LC 80-15141. 160p. 1980. 11.25 (ISBN 0-688-22246-3); PLB 11.88 (ISBN 0-688-32246-8). Morrow.

Damnation & Deviance: The Protestant Ethic & the Spirit of Failure. Mordechai Rotenberg. LC 77-18432. 1978. 12.95 (ISBN 0-02-927490-7). Free Pr.

Damned Through the Church. John W. Montgomery. 96p. 1970. 2.95 (ISBN 0-87123-090-9, 200090). Bethany Hse.

Damodar & the Pioneers of the Theosophical Movement. Sven Eek. 19.95 (ISBN 0-8356-7003-1). Theos Pub Hse.

Dance & Song Rituals of Six Nations Reserve, Ontario. Gertrude P. Kurath. (Illus.). 205p. 1968. pap. text ed. 5.50x (ISBN 0-660-02066-1, 56320-0, Pub. by Natl Mus Canada). U of Chicago Pr.

Dance & the Christian Faith. Martin Blogg. (Illus.). 283p. 1987. pap. 17.95 (ISBN 0-340-35173-X, Pub. by Hodder & Stoughton UK). David & Charles.

Dance, Children, Dance. Jim Rayburn, III. 192p. 1984. 9.95 (ISBN 0-8423-0515-7). Tyndale.

Dance in Hebrew Poetry. Olaf Hoeckmann. Ed. by Doug Adams. 1987. pap. 3.00 (ISBN 0-941500-44-6). Sharing Co.

Dance of Being: Man's Labyrinthe Rhythms, the Natural Ground of the Human. Leonard C. Feldstein. LC 77-75799. xvi, 302p. 1979. 30.00 (ISBN 0-8232-1032-4). Fordham.

Dance of Death. Ed. by F. Warren. (EETS, OS: No. 181). Repr. of 1931 ed. 10.00 (ISBN 0-527-00178-3). Kraus Repr.

Dance of Death & the Macabre Spirit in European Literature. L. P. Kurtz. 79.95 (ISBN 0-87968-188-8). Gordon Pr.

Dance of Death in Spain & Catalonia. Florence Whyte. Ed. by Robert Kastenbaum. LC 76-19594. (Death & Dying Ser.). 1977. Repr. of 1931 ed. lib. bdg. 19.00x (ISBN 0-405-09588-0). Ayer Co Pubs.

Dance of Death in Spain & Catalonia. Florence Whyte. 1977. lib. bdg. 69.95 (ISBN 0-8490-1699-1). Gordon Pr.

Dance of Life. Dorothy Buck. (Patterns of World Spirituality Ser.). 160p. (Orig.). 1987. pap. 8.95 (ISBN 0-913757-52-7, Pub. by New Era Bks). Paragon Hse.

Dance of Love: My Life with Meher Baba. Margaret Craske. LC 80-53859. 180p. (Orig.). 1980. pap. 6.95 (ISBN 0-913078-40-9). Sheriar Pr.

Dance of the Broken Heart: A Family Love Story. John Thompson & Patti Thompson. 1986. 11.95 (ISBN 0-687-10080-1). Abingdon.

Dance of the Dialectic: A Dramatic Dialogue Presenting Hegel's Philosophy of Religion. Edward Beach. LC 78-63255. pap. text ed. 6.75 (ISBN 0-8191-0615-1). U Pr of Amer.

Dance of the Rites. David A. Wilson. (Illus.). 156p. (Orig.). 1983. cancelled 13.00 (ISBN 0-934852-96-0); pap. 7.00 (ISBN 0-934852-27-8). Lorien Hse.

Dance with God. W. Norman Cooper. LC 81-69932. 128p. (Orig.). 1982. 7.50 (ISBN 0-87516-491-9); pap. 4.50 (ISBN 0-87516-468-4). De Vorss.

Dance Your Way to God. Bhagwan Shree Rajneesh. Ed. by Ma Prem Maneesha. LC 78-907936. (Initiation Talks Ser.). (Illus.). 384p. (Orig.). 1978. 19.95 (ISBN 0-88050-041-7). Chidvilas Found.

Dancing Christmas Carols. Ed. by Doug Adams. LC 78-63292. 1978. pap. 7.95 (ISBN 0-89390-006-0). Resource Pubns.

Dancing Festivals of the Church Year. Constance Fisher. Ed. by Doug Adams. (Illus.). 120p. (Orig.). 1986. pap. 8.95 (ISBN 0-941500-42-X). Sharing Co.

Dancing God's People into the Year Two Thousand: A Critical Look at Dance Performance in the Church. Cynthia Winton-Henry. Ed. & intro. by Doug Adams. (Orig.). 1985. pap. 3.00 (ISBN 0-941500-36-5). Sharing Co.

Dancing Madly Backwards: A Journey into God. Paul Marechal. (Crossroad Paperback Ser.). 128p. 1982. pap. 5.95 (ISBN 0-8245-0408-9). Crossroad NY.

Dancing Siva in Early South Indian Art. D. Barrett. (Mortimer Wheeler Archaeological Lectures). 1976. pap. 2.50 (ISBN 0-85672-354-1, Pub. by British Acad). Longwood Pub Group.

Dancing the New Testament: A Guide to Texts. Hal Taussig. 1977. 2.00 (ISBN 0-941500-06-3). Sharing Co.

Dancing the Old Testament: Christian Celebrations of Israelite Heritage for Worship & Education. Constance L. Fisher. Ed. by Doug Adams. (Illus.). 1980. pap. 5.95 (ISBN 0-941500-07-1). Sharing Co.

Dancing Through Pentecost: Dance Language for Worship from Pentecost to Thanksgiving. Marian B. MacLeod. Ed. by Doug Adams. (Orig.). 1981. pap. 3.00 (ISBN 0-941500-23-3). Sharing Co.

Dancing to Zion: How to Harvest Joy on the Road to Heaven. Judson Edwards. Ed. by John Sloan. 180p. 1986. pap. 5.95 avail. (ISBN 0-310-34511-1, 12066P). Zondervan.

Dancing with Early Christians. Constance Fisher & Doug Adams. (Illus.). 176p. 1983. pap. 6.95 (ISBN 0-941500-30-6). Sharing Co.

Dang Dang Doko Dang. Bhagwan Shree Rajneesh. Ed. by Ma Prem Veena. LC 77-907636. (Zen Ser.). (Illus.). 290p. (Orig.). 1977. 14.50 (ISBN 0-88050-042-5). Chidvilas Found.

Danger at Your Door. Gordon McLean. LC 83-70954. 183p. 1984. pap. 5.95 (ISBN 0-89107-296-9). Good News.

Danger Lines in the Deeper Life. A. B. Simpson. 133p. 1966. pap. 2.00 (ISBN 0-87509-007-9). Chr Pubns.

Danger of Self-Love. Paul Brownback. LC 82-12543. 1982. pap. 5.95 (ISBN 0-8024-2068-0). Moody.

Dangerous Journey: Symbolic Aspects of Boys' Initiation Among the Wagenia of Kisangani, Zaire. Andre Droogers. (Change & Continuity in Africa Ser.). 1979. pap. text ed. 23.60x (ISBN 90-279-3357-X). Mouton.

Dangerous Positions & Proceedings. Richard Bancroft. LC 74-38147. (English Experience Ser.: No. 427). 192p. 1972. Repr. of 1593 ed. 28.50 (ISBN 90-221-0427-3). Walter J Johnson.

Dangers of Growing up in a Christian Home. Donald E. Sloath. 224p. 1986. pap. 8.95 (ISBN 0-8407-3064-0). Nelson.

Daniel. Joyce G. Baldwin. Ed. by D. J. Wiseman. LC 78-18547. (Tyndale Old Testament Commentary Ser.). 1978. 12.95 (ISBN 0-87784-961-7); pap. 6.95 (ISBN 0-87784-273-6). Inter-Varsity.

Daniel. Albert Barnes. 16.95 (ISBN 0-8010-0841-7). Baker Bk.

Daniel. Ethel Barrett. LC 79-65230. (Bible Biography Ser.). 128p. 1979. pap. 1.95 (ISBN 0-8307-0761-1, 5810306). Regal.

Daniel. Raymond E. Brown. (Bible Ser.). pap. 1.00 (ISBN 0-8091-5024-7). Paulist Pr.

Daniel. John Calvin. Ed. by Thomas Myers. (Geneva Commentary Ser.). 816p. 1986. Repr. of 1853 ed. 19.95 (ISBN 0-85151-092-2). Banner of Truth.

Daniel. rev. ed. G. Michael Cocoris. 150p. 1985. pap. text ed. 3.00 (ISBN 0-935729-06-2). Church Open Door.

Daniel. (Burl Ives Bible-Time Stories). incl. tape 4.95 (ISBN 0-89191-800-0, 98004). Cook.

Daniel. Rebecca Daniel. (Our Greatest Heritage Ser.). (Illus.). 32p. 1983. wkbk. 3.95 (ISBN 0-86653-140-8, SS 809). Good Apple.

Daniel. P. R. Davies. (Old Testament Guides Ser.). 133p. 1985. pap. text ed. 3.95x (ISBN 1-85075-002-5, Pub. by JSOT Pr England). Eisenbrauns.

Daniel. John G. Gammie. (Preaching Guides Ser.). 116p. 1983. pap. 5.95 (ISBN 0-8042-3224-5). John Knox.

Daniel. Hersh Goldwurm. (Art Scroll Tanach Ser.). 352p. 1979. 16.95 (ISBN 0-89906-079-X); pap. 13.95 (ISBN 0-89906-080-3). Mesorah Pubns.

Daniel. John C. Jeske. (People's Bible Ser.). 1985. pap. 6.50 (ISBN 0-8100-0197-7, 15N0407); study guide, 32p 1.50 (ISBN 0-938272-52-7). Northwest Pub.

Daniel. Ezra Nehemiah. Ed. by A. Cohen. 278p. 1951. 10.95 (ISBN 0-900689-36-6). Soncino Pr.

Daniel. D. S. Russell. LC 81-1777. (Daily Study Bible - Old Testament Ser.). 244p. 1981. 12.95 (ISBN 0-664-21800-8); pap. 6.95 (ISBN 0-664-24567-6). Westminster.

Daniel. W. Sibley Towner. Ed. by James L. Mays & Patrick D. Miller. LC 83-18791. (Interpretation Ser.). 228p. 1984. 16.95 (ISBN 0-8042-3122-2). John Knox.

Daniel. John Walvoord. LC 75-123161. 1970. 17.95 (ISBN 0-8024-1752-3). Moody.

Daniel. John Whitcomb. (Everyman's Bible Commentary Ser.). (Orig.). 1985. pap. 5.95 (ISBN 0-8024-2067-2). Moody.

Daniel. E. J. Young. (Geneva Series of Commentaries). 320p. 13.95 (ISBN 0-85151-154-6). Banner of Truth.

Daniel, a Commentary. Norman W. Porteous. LC 65-21071. (Old Testament Library). 174p. 1965. 14.95 (ISBN 0-664-20663-8). Westminster.

Daniel: A Study Guide. Leon J. Wood. 160p. 1975. pap. 6.95 (ISBN 0-310-34723-8, 10872P). Zondervan.

Daniel & His Prophecy. Frederick Tatford. 1980. 9.25 (ISBN 0-86524-045-0, 2702). Klock & Klock.

Daniel & the Lions. Heidi Petach. (Happy Day Bible Stories Bks.). (Illus.). 24p. 1984. 1.59 (ISBN 0-87239-762-9, 3722). Standard Pub.

Daniel & the Lions & Five Other Stories. Peter Enns & Glen Forsberg. (Stories that Live Ser.: Bk. 4). (Illus.). 24p. 1985. book & cassette 4.95 (ISBN 0-936215-04-6). STL Intl.

Daniel & the Lion's Den. Illus. by Hanna-Barbera. (Greatest Adventure: Ser.Stories from the Bible.). (Illus., Orig.). Date not set. 5.95 (ISBN 0-687-15746-3). Abingdon.

Daniel & the Lion's Den. John Walton & Kim Walton. (Early Foundations in the Bible Ser.). (Illus.). 1987. pap. 2.95 (ISBN 1-55513-045-3, Chariot Press). Cook.

Daniel & the Lion's Den. John Walton & Kim Walton. (Early Foundations in the Bible Ser.). 1987. pap. 2.95. Cook.

Daniel & the Revelation. F. V. Rowland. 1984. 11.95 (ISBN 0-533-05996-8). Vantage.

Daniel & the Silver Flute: An Old Hassidic Tale. Retold by Gerald C. Ruthen. (Illus.). 32p. 11.95. United Synagogue.

Daniel, Esther, & Jeremiah: The Additions. Carey A. Moore. LC 76-42376. (Anchor Bible Ser.: Vol. 44). (Illus.). 1977. 16.00 (ISBN 0-385-04702-9, Anchor Pr). Doubleday.

Daniel: Faithful Captive. Lou Heath. (Biblearn Ser.). (Illus.). 1977. bds. 5.95 (ISBN 0-8054-4231-6, 4242-31). Broadman.

Daniel in the Lion's Den. Penny Frank. Ed. by P. Alexander. (Lion Story Bible Ser.). 24p. 1987. 2.95 (ISBN 0-85648-752-X). Lion USA.

Daniel in the Lions' Den. Adapted by Belinda Hollyer. LC 84-50453. (Bible Stories Ser.). (Illus.). 24p. 1984. 6.96 (ISBN 0-382-06939-0); PLB 5.96 (ISBN 0-382-06939-0). Silver.

Daniel in the Lions' Den. Jane Latourette & Mathews. (Arch Bks.: Set 3). 1966. laminated bdg. 0.99 (ISBN 0-570-06018-4, 59-1127). Concordia.

Daniel: Living Courageously. J. Allen Blair. LC 70-140898. 1971. pap. 4.95 (ISBN 0-87213-044-4). Loizeaux.

Daniel, One-Two Maccabees, with Excursus on Apocalyptic Genre. John Collins. (Old Testament Message Ser.: Vol. 15). 1982. 15.95 (ISBN 0-89453-415-7); pap. 12.95 (ISBN 0-89453-250-2). M Glazier.

Daniel: Prophecies. Lehman Strauss. LC 70-85293. Orig. Title: Prophecies of Daniel. 1969. 9.95 (ISBN 0-87213-812-7). Loizeaux.

Daniel Rowland & the Great Evangelical Awakening in Wales. Eifion Evans. 383p. 1985. 22.95 (ISBN 0-85151-446-4). Banner of Truth.

Daniel: Spiritual Living in a Secular World. Douglas Connelly. (LifeBuilder Bible Studies). 64p. (Orig.). 1986. pap. 2.95 (ISBN 0-8308-1031-5). Inter-Varsity.

Daniel: The Coming of Christ's Kingdom. John C. Whitcomb. 1985. pap. 5.95 (ISBN 0-88469-165-9). BMH Bks.

Daniel the Dog. Jane Hammond. (God's Animals Story Bks.). 1983. pap. 1.50 (ISBN 0-87162-287-4, D5601). Warner Pr.

Daniel, the Kingdom of the Lord. Charles L. Feinberg. 1984. 9.95 (ISBN 0-88469-157-8). BMH Bks.

Daniel the Prophet. M. R. DeHaan. 340p. 1983. pap. 8.95 (ISBN 0-310-23321-6). Zondervan.

Daniel the Prophet. H. A. Ironside. with chart 9.95 (ISBN 0-87213-357-5); chart only 0.15. Loizeaux.

Daniel the Prophet. Edward B. Pusey. 1978. 19.50 (ISBN 0-86524-103-1, 2701). Klock & Klock.

Daniel: With an Introduction to Apocalyptic Literature. John J. Collins. Ed. by Rolf Knierim et al. (Forms of the Old Testament Literature Ser.: Vol. XX). 160p. (Orig.). 1984. pap. 12.95 (ISBN 0-8028-0020-3). Eerdmans.

Daniel y el Reino Mesianico. Evis L. Carballosa. Orig. Title: Daniel & the Messianic Kingdom. 320p. 1979. pap. 7.95 (ISBN 0-8254-1101-7). Kregel.

Daniel's Prophecy of the Seventy Weeks. Alva J. McClain. pap. 3.95 (ISBN 0-88469-076-8). BMH Bks.

Daniel's Prophecy of the Seventy Weeks. Alva J. McClain. pap. 3.95 (ISBN 0-310-29011-2, 10177P). Zondervan.

Dante & Aquinas. Philip H. Wicksteed. LC 79-153489. (Studies in Dante, No. 9). 1971. Repr. of 1913 ed. lib. bdg. 49.95x (ISBN 0-8383-1240-3). Haskell.

Dante & Milton. C. H. Herford. 1924. lib. bdg. 10.00 (ISBN 0-8414-5044-7). Folcroft.

Dante & Other Waning Classics. Albert Mordell. LC 68-8219. 1969. Repr. of 1915 ed. 18.50x (ISBN 0-8046-0322-7, Pub. by Kennikat). Assoc Faculty Pr.

Dante & the Mystics: A Study of the Mystical Aspect of the Divina Commedia. E. G. Gardner. LC 68-24952. (Studies in Italian Literature, No. 46). 1969. Repr. of 1913 ed. lib. bdg. 49.95x (ISBN 0-8383-0271-8). Haskell.

Dante's Conception of Justice. Allan H. Gilbert. LC 76-166199. (BCL Ser.: I). Repr. of 1925 ed. 15.00 (ISBN 0-404-02757-1). AMS Pr.

Dante's Paradiso & the Limitations of Modern Criticism. R. Kirkpatrick. LC 77-80839. 1978. 39.50 (ISBN 0-521-21785-7). Cambridge U Pr.

Danzig: Between East & West. Ed. by Isadore Twersky. (Harvard Judaica Texts & Studies: Vol. IV). 185p. 1984. text ed. 21.00x (ISBN 0-674-19255-9); pap. text ed. 14.00x (ISBN 0-674-19256-7). Harvard U Pr.

Dare to Be Christian: Developing a Social Conscience. Bernard Haring. 160p. 1983. pap. 4.25 (ISBN 0-89243-180-6). Liguori Pubns.

Dare to Be Different. Fred Hartley. 128p. 1980. pap. 5.95 (ISBN 0-8007-5041-1, Power Bks). Revell.

Dare to Be Different, Dare to Be Christian. Charles Colson. 48p. 1986. pap. 1.95 (ISBN 0-89693-159-5). Victor Bks.

Dare to Believe. May Rowland. 1961. 5.95 (ISBN 0-87159-024-7). Unity School.

Dare to Believe: Addresses, Sermons, Interviews, 1981-1984. Jean-Marie Lustiger. Tr. by Nelly Marana. 260p. 1986. 14.95 (ISBN 0-8245-0778-9). Crossroad NY.

Dare to Discipline. James Dobson. 1973. pap. 6.95 (ISBN 0-8423-0631-5). Tyndale.

Dare to Discipline. James Dobson. 1977. pap. 3.50 mass (ISBN 0-8423-0635-8). Tyndale.

Dare to Live Free. Hoyt E. Stone. 132p. 1984. pap. 4.95 (ISBN 0-88207-617-5). Victor Bks.

Dare to Prosper. Catherine Ponder. LC 82-74520. 80p. 1983. pap. 3.00 (ISBN 0-87516-511-7). De Vorss.

Dargan's History of Preaching, Vol. III. Ralph G. Turnbull. 12.95 (ISBN 0-8010-8819-4). Baker Bk.

Daring to Draw Near: People in Prayer. John White. LC 77-6554. (Orig.). 1977. pap. 5.95 (ISBN 0-87784-788-6). Inter-Varsity.

Darius the Mede. John C. Whitcomb, Jr. pap. 2.50 (ISBN 0-88469-064-4). BMH Bks.

Dark Ages: Essays Illustrating the State of Religion & Literature in the Ninth, Tenth, Eleventh & Twelfth Centuries, 2 vols. S. R. Maitland. LC 68-8242. 1969. Repr. of 1889 ed. 40.00 (ISBN 0-8046-0297-2, Pub. by Kennikat). Assoc Faculty Pr.

Dark Angels of Light. David A. Lewis. LC 84-61915. 100p. (Orig.). 1985. pap. 5.95 (ISBN 0-89221-117-2). New Leaf.

Dark Horse: The Story of a Winner. John Fischer. LC 83-11411. 100p. 1983. pap. 3.95 (ISBN 0-88070-016-5). Multnomah.

Dark Interval: Towards a Theology of Story. John D. Crossan. 1975. pap. cancelled (ISBN 0-913592-52-8). Argus Comm.

Dark Intimacy: Hope for Those in Difficult Prayer Experiences. David J. Hassel. 176p. (Orig.). 1986. pap. 8.95 (ISBN 0-8091-2818-7). Paulist Pr.

Dark Lord: Cult Images & the Hare Krishnas in America. Larry D. Shinn. 204p. (Orig.). 1987. pap. 16.95 (ISBN 0-664-24170-0). Westminster.

Dark Night, Brilliant Star. Eileen E. Lantry. (Daybreak Ser.). 112p. 1981. pap. 2.89 (ISBN 0-8163-0397-5). Pacific Pr Pub Assn.

Dark Night of the Soul. Manly P. Hall. pap. 2.50 (ISBN 0-89314-311-1). Philos Res.

Dark Night of the Soul. John of the Cross. Tr. by Benedict Zimmerman. 246p. 1974. pap. 10.95 (ISBN 0-227-67807-9). Attic Pr.
Dark Night of the Soul. St. John of the Cross. 1959. pap. 3.95 (ISBN 0-385-02930-6, D78, Im). Doubleday.
Dark Prophets of Hope. Jean Kellogg. LC 75-5697. 1975. pap. 5.95 (ISBN 0-8294-0243-8). Loyola.
Dark Side. William C. Tremmel. Ed. by Herbert Lambert. 160p. (Orig.). 1987. pap. 9.95 (ISBN 0-8272-0614-3). CBP.
Dark Side of the Millennium: The Problem of Evil in Revelation 20: 1-10. Arthur H. Lewis. 96p. (Orig.). 1980. pap. 3.95 (ISBN 0-8010-5596-2). Baker Bk.
Dark Star. Robert Wolfe. 266p. (Orig.). 1984. 12.00 (ISBN 0-318-19328-0); pap. 6.00 (ISBN 0-318-19329-9). Memory Bks.
Darkeinu Aleph & Bais: In One Volume. Abraham Atkin. pap. text ed. 3.50 (ISBN 0-686-33046-3, A13). Torah Umesorah.
Darkeinu Daled. Abraham Atkin. text ed. 3.75 (ISBN 0-914131-13-3, A15). Torah Umesorah.
Darkeinu Gimel. Abraham Atkins. text ed. 3.50 (ISBN 0-686-33046-3, A14). Torah Umesorah.
Darkened Sky: Nineteenth-Century American Novelists & Religion. John T. Frederick. LC 69-14811. pap. 72.50 (ISBN 0-317-29688-4, 2022068). Bks Demand UMI.
Darkening Valley. Dale Aukerman. 1981. pap. 8.95 (ISBN 0-8164-2295-8, HarpR). Har-Row.
Darkest Day. William Grimbol. 1986. 1.75 (ISBN 0-89536-789-0, 6807). CSS of Ohio.
Darkness & Daylight: Or, Lights & Shadows of New York Life: A Pictorial Record of Personal Experiences by Day & Night in the Great Metropolis with Hundreds of Thrilling Anecdotes & Incidents. Helen Campbell. LC 76-81511. 1969. Repr. of 1895 ed. 48.00x (ISBN 0-8103-3566-2). Gale.
Darkness & Light: An Exposition of Ephesians 4 17-5 17. D. Martyn Lloyd-Jones. 408p. 1983. Repr. of 1965 ed. 12.95 (ISBN 0-8010-5617-9). Baker Bk.
Darkness Discovered (Satans Stratagems) Giacomo Aconcio. LC 78-9490. 1978. Repr. of 1651 ed. 45.00x (ISBN 0-8201-1313-1). Schol Facsimiles.
Darkness in the Marketplace. Thomas H. Green. LC 81-67559. 128p. (Orig.). 1981. pap. 3.95 (ISBN 0-87793-230-1). Ave Maria.
Darkness of God: Theology after Hiroshima. James Garrison. LC 83-1415. pap. 62.00 (ISBN 0-317-30139-X, 2025322). Bks Demand UMI.
Darkness or Light. Kurt E. Koch. 80p. 1981. pap. 2.95 (ISBN 0-8254-3048-8). Kregel.
Darkness over Tibet. Theodore Illion. 192p. 1983. pap. 6.95 (ISBN 0-912181-03-6). East School Pr.
Darkness Visible: The Prints of John Martin. J. Dustin Wees & Michael J. Campbell. LC 86-61656. (Illus.). 88p. (Orig.). 1986. pap. 14.95 (ISBN 0-931102-20-0). S & F Clark Art.
Darkwater: Voices from Within the Veil. W. E. B. Dubois. LC 70-91785. Repr. of 1920 ed. 12.50 (ISBN 0-404-00151-3). AMS Pr.
Darrow-Lewis Debate on the Theory of Non-Resistance to Evil. Clarence Darrow & Arthur Lewis. 26p. 1987. pap. write for info. (ISBN 0-911826-48-3). Am Atheist.
Darsan: Seeing the Divine Image in India. 2nd, enl. ed. Diana L. Eck. 97p. 1985. pap. 5.95 (ISBN 0-89012-042-0). Anima Pubns.
Daruma: The Founder of Zen in Japanese Art & Popular Culture. H. Neill McFarland. LC 87-45214. (Illus.). 120p. 1987. 22.50 (ISBN 0-87011-817-X). Kodansha.
Darwin & the Modern World View. John C. Greene. LC 61-15489. (Rockwell Lectures Ser.). 152p. 1973. pap. text ed. 6.95x (ISBN 0-8071-0062-5). La State U Pr.
Darwin Was Wrong: A Study in Probabilities. I. L. Cohen. Ed. by G. Murphy. LC 84-22613. (Illus.). 225p. 1985. 16.95 (ISBN 0-910891-02-8). New Research.
Darwinism & Divinity: Essays on Evolution & Religious Belief. Ed. by John Durant. 224p. 1986. pap. text ed. 14.95 (ISBN 0-631-15101-X). Basil Blackwell.
Darwinism in Texas. Compiled by Thomas Glick. LC 72-185614. (Illus.). 38p. 1972. 7.00 (ISBN 0-87959-032-7). U of Tex H Ransom Ctr.
Darwin's Forgotten Defenders: The Encounter Between Evangelical Theology & Evolutionary Thought. David N. Livingstone. 144p. (Orig.). 1987. pap. 9.95 (ISBN 0-8028-0260-5). Eerdmans.
Dasavaikalika Sutra. K. C. Lalwani. 1973. 8.95 (ISBN 0-89684-192-8). Orient Bk Dist.
Dating & Relating. Cherie Scalf & Kenneth Waters. 160p. 1982. pap. 7.95 (ISBN 0-8499-2890-7). Word Bks.
Dating & Waiting: A Chrisitan View of Love, Sex, & Dating. Les Christie. LC 83-1232. (Illus.). 80p. (Orig.). 1983. pap. 2.95 (ISBN 0-87239-643-6, 39972). Standard Pub.
Dating Etiquette for Christian Teens. MaryAnn L. Diorio. (Illus.). 48p. (Orig.). 1984. pap. 3.95 (ISBN 0-930037-00-6). Daystar Comm.
Dating: Guidelines from the Bible. Scott Kirby. 1979. pap. 2.95 (ISBN 0-8010-5400-1). Baker Bk.
Dating: Making Your Own Choices. Karen Dockrey. LC 86-30985. (Orig.). (YA) 1987. pap. 4.95 (ISBN 0-8054-5345-8). Broadman.
Dating, Marriage, Sex & Divorce. R. P. Daniel. 75p. pap. 3.95 (ISBN 0-88172-147-6). Believers Bkshelf.
Dating Maze. Brent D. Earles. pap. 3.95 (ISBN 0-8010-3424-8). Baker Bk.
Dating, Sex & Friendship. Joyce Huggett. LC 85-19734. 204p. 1985. pap. 5.95 (ISBN 0-87784-406-2). Inter-Varsity.
Dating Tips. Nathanael Pugh. Ed. by Mary H. Wallace. (Illus.). 120p. 1983. pap. 4.95 (ISBN 0-912315-00-8). Word Aflame.
Dating Your Mate. Rick Bundschuh & Dave Gilbert. 144p. (Orig.). 1987. pap. 4.95 (ISBN 0-89081-598-4). Harvest Hse.
Daughter of Destiny. Jamie Buckingham. LC 76-12034. 1976. (Pub. by Logos); pap. 2.95 pocket ed. (ISBN 0-88270-318-8). Bridge Pub.
Daughter of Earth: A Roman Myth. Gerald McDermott. LC 82-23585. (Illus.). 32p. 1984. 15.00 (ISBN 0-385-29294-5). Delacorte.
Daughter of Fire: A Diary of a Spiritual Training with a Sufi Master. Irina Tweedie. Ed. by Paul M. Clemens. LC 86-72368. 832p. 1986. 29.95 (ISBN 0-931892-05-8); pap. 19.95 (ISBN 0-931892-04-X). B Dolphin Pub.
Daughter of Israel: Laws of Family Purity. Kalman Kahana. Tr. by Leonard Oschry. 6.95 (ISBN 0-87306-092-X). Feldheim.
Daughter of the Sanctuary. Carol Hopper. 111p. (Orig.). 1984. pap. 3.95 (ISBN 0-88144-022-1, CPS023). Christian Pub.
Daughter Zion. Joseph Ratzinger. Tr. by John M. McDermott from Ger. LC 82-84579. Orig. Title: Tochter Zion. 83p. (Orig.). 1983. pap. 5.95 (ISBN 0-89870-026-4). Ignatius Pr.
Daughters of Chutzpah: Humorous Verse on the Jewish Woman. Mollee Kruger. LC 82-71394. (Illus.). 112p. (Orig.). 1983. pap. 5.00 (ISBN 0-9602036-7-2). Biblio NY.
Daughters of Jerusalem. Marla J. Sevidge. LC 87-7437. 176p. (Orig.). 1987. pap. 9.95 (ISBN 0-8361-3440-0). Herald Pr.
Daughters of St. Paul: 50 Years of Service in the U. S. A., 1932-1982. Daughters of St. Paul. (Illus.). 295p. 1982. 15.00 (ISBN 0-8198-1805-4, MS0133). Dghtrs St Paul.
Daughters of the Covenant: Portraits of Six Jewish Women. Edward Wagenknecht. LC 83-3562. (Illus.). 200p. 1983. lib. bdg. 17.50x (ISBN 0-87023-396-3). U of Mass Pr.
Daughters of the Puritans: A Group of Brief Biographies. facs. ed. Seth C. Beach. LC 67-22054. (Essay Index Reprint Ser). 1905. 19.00 (ISBN 0-8369-0180-0). Ayer Co Pubs.
Daughters of the Sphinx Ritual. 3.50 (ISBN 0-685-19471-X). Powner.
Daughters of Zion. Elizabeth Watson. LC 82-70600. 100p. (Orig.). 1982. pap. 8.95 (ISBN 0-913408-79-4). Friends United.
D'Aulaires' Book of Greek Myths. Ingri D'Aulaire & Edgar P. D'Aulaire. LC 62-15877. (Illus.). 1962. 17.95a (ISBN 0-385-01583-6); PLB o. p. (ISBN 0-385-07108-6); pap. 10.95 (ISBN 0-385-15787-8). Doubleday.
David. Rebecca Daniel. (Our Greatest Heritage Ser.). (Illus.). 1983. wkbk. 3.95 (ISBN 0-86653-138-6, SS 807). Good Apple.
David. Daughters of St. Paul. 0.75 (ISBN 0-8198-1800-3). Dghtrs St Paul.
David. (Burl Ives Bible-Time Stories). incl. tape 4.95 (ISBN 0-89191-803-5, 98038). Cook.
David. F. B. Meyer. 1970. pap. 4.50 (ISBN 0-87508-342-0). Chr Lit.
David: After God's Own Heart. H. Edwin Young. (Orig.). 1984. pap. 4.25 (ISBN 0-8054-1531-9). Broadman.
David & Bathsheba. Roberta Dorr. 1982. pap. 4.95 (ISBN 0-8423-0618-8). Tyndale.
David & Goliath. Ruth F. Brin. (Foreign Lands Bks). (Illus.). 32p. 1977. PLB 5.95 (ISBN 0-8225-0365-4). Lerner Pubns.
David & Goliath. Retold by Pamela Broughton. LC 85-81161. (Golden Bible Stories). (Illus.). 32p. 1986. 3.95 (ISBN 0-307-11625-5, Pub. by Golden Bks). Western Pub.
David & Goliath. (Read, Show & Tell Ser.). (Eng. & Span., Illus.). 1977. Eng. Ed. pap. 2.25 (ISBN 0-8326-2602-3, 3620). Span. Ed (5620). World Bible.
David & Goliath. Illus. by Tomie DePaola. (Bible Story Cutout Bks.). (Illus., Orig.). 1984. 32 pages 12.95, (ISBN 0-86683-820-1, 8452, HarpR); pap. 5.95, 40 pages (ISBN 0-86683-700-0, 8469). Har-Row.
David & Goliath. Illus. by Hanna-Barbera. (Greatest Adventure Ser.Stories from the Bible). (Illus., Orig.). 1986. 5.95 (ISBN 0-687-15741-2). Abingdon.
David & Goliath. Belinda Hollyer. LC 84-50452. (Bible Stories Ser.). (Illus.). 24p. 1984. 5.45 (ISBN 0-382-06940-4); PLB 6.96 (ISBN 0-382-06791-6). Silver.
David & Goliath. Retold by Elaine Ife & Rosalind Sutton. (Now You Can Read Stories from the Bible Ser.). (Illus.). 24p. 1985. 2.50 (ISBN 0-8407-5392-6). Nelson.
David & Goliath. Laurent Lalo. LC 83-24975. (Illus.). 24p. 1985. 4.95 (ISBN 0-88070-044-0). Multnomah.
David & Goliath. Catherine Storr. LC 84-18138. (People of the Bible Ser.). (Illus.). 32p. 1985. PLB 10.65 (ISBN 0-8172-1995-1). Raintree Pubs.
David & Goliath & Five Other Stories. Peter Enns & Glen Forsberg. (Stories that Live Ser.: Bk. 3). (Illus.). 24p. 1985. book & Cassette 4.95 (ISBN 0-936215-03-8). STL Intl.
David & His Mighty Men. facs. ed. R. O. Corvin. LC 74-136646. (Biography Index Reprint Ser.). 1950. 17.00 (ISBN 0-8369-8041-7). Ayer Co Pubs.
David & I Talk to God. Campbell Murphy. 1983. pap. 2.95 each (ISBN 0-686-45018-3). Cook.
David & Jonathan. Alyce Bergey. (Arch Bks.). (Illus.). 24p. 1987. pap. 00.99 (ISBN 0-570-09006-7, 59-01434). Concordia.
David & Jonathan. Retold by Elaine Ife & Rosalind Sutton. (Now You Can Read Stories from the Bible Ser.). (Illus.). 24p. 1985. 2.50 (ISBN 0-8407-5448-5). Nelson.
David Brainerd's Personal Testimony. David Brainerd. (Summit Bks.). pap. 3.95 (ISBN 0-8010-8159-9). Baker Bk.
David Comes into the Kingdom. Gordon Lindsay. (Old Testament Ser.). 1.25 (ISBN 0-89985-142-8). Christ Nations.
David Friedrich Strauss & His Critics: The Life of Jesus Debate in Early Nineteenth-Century German Journals. Edwina Lawler. (American University Studies VII - Theology & Religion: Vol. 16). 170p. 1986. text ed. 21.95 (ISBN 0-8204-0290-7). P Lang Pubs.
David I: The Time of Saul's Tyranny. W. Phillip Keller. 256p. 1985. 10.95 (ISBN 0-8499-0470-6, 0470-6). Word Bks.
David II: The Shepherd King. W. Phillip Keller. 224p. 1986. 11.95 (ISBN 0-8499-0559-1). Word Bks.
David Kimhi: The Man & the Commentaries. Frank E. Talmage. LC 75-1747. (Harvard Judaic Monographs: No. 1). 224p. 1976. text ed. 16.50x (ISBN 0-674-19340-7). Harvard U Pr.
David, King of Israel. Frederick W. Krummacher. 548p. 1983. lib. bdg. 20.50 (ISBN 0-86524-142-2, 8404). Klock & Klock.
David Livingstone. W. W. Blackie. (Heroes of the Faith Ser.). 1986. 6.95 (ISBN 0-916441-48-2). Barbour & Co.
David Livingstone. J. H. Worchester, Jr. (Golden Oldies Ser.). 128p. 1980. pap. 3.50 (ISBN 0-8024-4782-1). Moody.
David Livingstone: Glorifying God, Not Himself. Fern N. Stocker. (Guessing Bks.). (Orig.). 1986. pap. 3.95 (ISBN 0-8024-4758-9). Moody.
David Livingstone, Missionary to Africa. Alice Bostrom. (Children's Missionary Library: Bk. 7). (Illus.). 32p. (Orig.). 1982. pap. 1.50 (ISBN 0-89323-027-8). Bible Memory.
David: Man after God's Own Heart, 2 vols. Robbie Castleman. (Fisherman Bible Studyguide). 1981. saddle stitched 2.95 ea. Vol. 1, 70p (ISBN 0-87788-164-2). Vol. 2, 63p (ISBN 0-87788-165-0). Shaw Pubs.
David Matthew Kennedy: Banker, Statesman, Churchman. Martin Hickman. 1987. 14.95 (ISBN 0-87579-093-3). Deseret Bk.
David O. McKay: Apostle to the World, Prophet of God. Francis M. Gibbons. LC 86-4564. (Illus.). 455p. 1986. 13.95 (ISBN 0-87579-036-4). Deseret Bk.
David: Psalm Twenty-Four. Illus. by Joyce Alexander & Dorsey Alexander. (Illus., Calligraphy & Illus.). 1970. pap. 5.00 (ISBN 0-912020-17-2). Turtles Quill.
David Reaping the Whirlwind. Gordon Lindsay. (Old Testament Ser.). 1.25 (ISBN 0-89985-143-6). Christ Nations.
David: Shepherd, Musician, & King. Lee Hollaway. (BibLearn Ser.). (Illus.). 1977. bds. 5.95 (ISBN 0-8054-4230-8, 4242-30). Broadman.
David the Anointed: Leader's Guide. (Orig.). 1984. pap. text ed. 3.95 (ISBN 0-934688-10-9). Great Comm Pubns.
David, the Chosen King: A Traditio-Historical Approach to the 2nd Book of Samuel. R. A. Carlson. 304p. (Orig.). 1964. pap. text ed. 23.50x. Coronet Bks.
David: The Giant-Slayer. Ethel Barrett. LC 82-80009. (Bible Biography Ser.). 128p. 1982. pap. 2.50 (ISBN 0-8307-0770-0, 5811007). Regal.
David the King. Ed. by Israel H. Weisfeld. LC 83-62421. 290p. 20.00x (ISBN 0-8197-0493-8). Bloch.
David, the Man after God's Own Heart. G. Andre. (Let's Discuss It Ser.). pap. 2.50 (ISBN 0-88172-134-4). Believers Bkshelf.
David, the Shepherd. Marian Bennett. (Happy Day Bible Stories Bks.). (Illus.). 24p. 1984. 1.59 (ISBN 0-87239-763-7, 3723). Standard Pub.
David, the Story of a King. Lillie Patterson. (Illus.). 96p. 1985. PLB 7.95 (ISBN 0-687-10280-4). Abingdon.
David's Faithfulness. N. R. Day. 85p. (Orig.). 1979. pap. 6.95 (ISBN 0-940754-02-9). Ed Ministries.
David's Seder. Norman Geller. (Illus.). 16p. 1983. pap. 4.95 (ISBN 0-915753-01-4). N Geller Pub.
David's Truth: In Israel's Imagination & Memory. Walter Brueggemann. LC 85-47717. 128p. 1985. pap. 5.95 (ISBN 0-8006-1865-3). Fortress.
Davidsburg Church Baptisms 1785-1845 New Market, Virginia. John Stewart & Klaus Wust. Tr. by John Stewart from Virginia German. 44p. 1983. pap. 6.75 (ISBN 0-917968-10-7). Shenandoah Hist.
Davis Dictionary of the Bible. Davis. 24.95 (ISBN 0-8054-1124-0). Broadman.
Davis Dictionary of the Bible. John D. Davis. 1954. 24.95 (ISBN 0-8010-2805-1). Baker Bk.
Davva-Samgaha (Dravya-Samgaha) Devendra Gani. Ed. & intro. by Sarat C. Goshal. LC 73-3835. Repr. of 1917 ed. 27.50 (ISBN 0-404-57701-6). AMS Pr.
Dawn of a Consecration. Thomas Dubay. 1964. 4.00 (ISBN 0-8198-0034-1). Dghtrs St Paul.
Dawn of a New Religious Era. Paul Carus. 131p. 1916. 1.95 (ISBN 0-317-40419-9). Open Court.
Dawn of Apocalyptic: The Historical & Sociological Roots of Jewish Apocalyptic Eschatology. rev. ed. Paul D. Hanson. LC 79-17099. 464p. 1979. 16.95 (ISBN 0-8006-0285-4, 1-285); pap. 12.95 (ISBN 0-8006-1809-2). Fortress.
Dawn of Christianity. Robert H. Bogue. 1985. 15.00 (ISBN 0-533-06545-3). Vantage.
Dawn of Day. Friedrich Nietzsche. 1974. 100.00 (ISBN 0-87968-204-3). Gordon Pr.
Dawn of Modern Thought: Descartes, Spinoza, Leibniz, with Introductory Note by W. D. Ross. Sydney H. Mellone. LC 72-85001. 124p. 1973. Repr. of 1930 ed. 10.00x (ISBN 0-8462-1686-8). Russell.
Dawn of Quran: The Sectarian Torah & the Teacher of Righteousness. Ben Z. Wacholder. 310p. 1983. 25.00 (ISBN 0-686-88437-X). Ktav.
Dawn of Tantra. Herbert V. Guenther & Chogyam Trungpa. LC 74-10250. (Illus.). 92p. pap. 6.95 (ISBN 0-87773-059-8). Shambhala Pubns.
Dawn of the Reformation, 2 vols. Herbert B. Workman. LC 77-85273. Repr. of 1902 ed. 65.00 set (ISBN 0-404-16170-7). AMS Pr.
Dawn of the Reformation: Essays in Late Medieval & Early Reformation Thought. Heiko A. Oberman. 352p. 1986. pap. 26.95 (ISBN 0-567-09371-9, Pub. by T & T Clark Ltd UK). Fortress.
Dawn Without Darkness. Anthony Padovano. LC 82-45117. (Illus.). 272p. 1982. pap. 4.95 (ISBN 0-385-18183-3, Im). Doubleday.
Dawning Place: The Building of a Temple, the Forging of the North American Baha'i Community. Bruce W. Whitmore. LC 83-25852. (Illus.). xi, 331p. 1984. 24.95 (ISBN 0-87743-192-2); pap. 12.95 (ISBN 0-87743-193-0). Baha'i.
Dawoodi Bohras: An Anthropological Perspective. Shibani Roy. (Illus.). xv, 191p. 1984. text ed. 27.50x (ISBN 0-86590-324-7, Pub. by B R Publishing Corp). Apt Bks.
Day by Day. 365p. (Orig.). 1986. pap. 5.95 (ISBN 0-86683-536-9, HarpR). Har-Row.
Day by Day: Daily Meditations for Young Adults. (Hazelden Meditation Ser.). 1986. 5.95 (ISBN 0-317-46280-6). Har-Row.
Day by Day: Daily Meditations for Young Adults. (Hazelden Bks.). scp 5.95t (ISBN 0-317-46482-5). Har-Row.
Day by Day: The Notre Dame Prayerbook for Students. Thomas McNally & William Storey. (Illus.). 208p. 1975. pap. 2.95 (ISBN 0-87793-100-3). Ave Maria.
Day by Day Through Advent: Reflections, Prayers, Practices. Daniel L. Lowery. 80p. 1984. pap. 1.95 (ISBN 0-89243-216-0). Liguori Pubns.
Day by Day Through Lent: Reflections, Prayers, Practices. Daniel L. Lowery. 160p. 1983. pap. 3.95 (ISBN 0-89243-194-6). Liguori Pubns.
Day by Day We Magnify Thee. Martin Luther. LC 82-2481. 448p. 1982. pap. 10.95 (ISBN 0-8006-1637-5, 1-1637). Fortress.
Day-by-Day with Billy Graham. Compiled by Joan W. Brown. 1976. pap. 5.95 (ISBN 0-89066-000-X). World Wide Pubs.
Day by Day with God. Francoise Darey-Bembe & John P. Bembe. 1982. 4.95 (ISBN 0-8215-9908-9). Sadlier.

Day by Day with Jesus. Rudolph F. Norden. 400p. (Orig.). 1985. pap. 10.95 (ISBN 0-570-03971-1, 12-3006). Concordia.

Day by Day with John. Donald F. Ackland. LC 81-67374. 1982. pap. 4.95 (ISBN 0-8054-5187-0). Broadman.

Day by Day with Mary. Ed. by Patrick R. Moran. LC 83-60101. 204p. 1983. pap. 6.95 (ISBN 0-87973-613-5, 613). Our Sunday Visitor.

Day by Day: With My Daily Visitor. Ed. by Patrick R. Moran. LC 79-92536. 200p. (Orig.). 1980. pap. 5.95 (ISBN 0-87973-530-9, 530). Our Sunday Visitor.

Day by Day With Pope John Paul II. Pope John Paul II. 1982. pap. 6.95 (ISBN 0-8091-2458-0). Paulist Pr.

Day by Day with the Master. Donald P. Ackland. LC 83-70209. 1985. pap. 5.95 (ISBN 0-8054-5196-X). Broadman.

Day by Day with the Prophets. Donald F. Ackland. LC 82-82950. 1983. pap. 4.95 (ISBN 0-8054-5193-5). Broadman.

Day by Day with the Saints. Patrick R. Moran. 214p. (Orig.). 1985. pap. 7.95 (ISBN 0-87973-714-X, 714). Our Sunday Visitor.

Day by Day: With Vance Havner. Vance Havner. 272p. 1984. pap. 5.95 (ISBN 0-8010-4279-8). Baker Bk.

Day Christ Died. Jim Bishop. LC 57-6125. 1978. pap. 4.95 (ISBN 0-06-060786-6, HJ 38, HarpR). Har-Row.

Day Christ Was Born. Jim Bishop. LC 60-13444. 1978. pap. 2.95i (ISBN 0-06-060785-8, HJ 37, HarpR). Har-Row.

Day Dawn in Africa: Or Progress of the Protestant Episcopal Mission at Cape Palmas, West Africa. Anna M. Scott. LC 69-18659. (Illus.). Repr. of 1858 ed. cancelled (ISBN 0-8371-5091-4, SCD&, Pub. by Negro U Pr). Greenwood.

Day Dawns in Fire: America's Quest for Meaning. Abbey R. Merrill. LC 75-36439. pap. 32.00. Bks Demand UMI.

Day Four: A Pilgrim's Continued Journey. Robert Wood & Marie L. Roy. 64p. (Orig.). 1986. pap. 2.95 (ISBN 0-8358-0553-0). Upper Room.

Day Full of Grace. Richard Bansemer. Ed. by Michael Sherer. (Orig.). 1987. pap. 5.95 (ISBN 0-89536-854-4, 7813). CSS of Ohio.

Day God Made It Rain. Loyal Kolbrek. (Arch Books Series Fourteen). 1977. pap. 0.99 (ISBN 0-570-06108-3, 59-1226). Concordia.

Day in the Life of a Director of Religious Education. 36p. 1977. 3.60. Natl Cath Educ.

Day in the Life of a DRE. 36p. 1977. 3.60 (ISBN 0-318-20612-9). Natl Cath Educ.

Day in Thy Courts. Dorothy Ranaghan. LC 84-70866. 144p. (Orig.). 1984. pap. 4.95 (ISBN 0-943780-05-5, 8055). Charismatic Ren Servs.

Day Israel Dies! Salem Kirban. (Illus.). 1975. pap. 2.95 (ISBN 0-912582-21-9). Kirban.

Day Japan Bombed Pearl Harbor & Other Stories. Leslie W. Hedley. 148p. 1984. pap. 7.95 (ISBN 0-933515-03-0). Exile Pr.

Day Jesus Died. Stanley Paregien. 1970. 3.00 (ISBN 0-88027-004-7). Firm Foun Pub.

Day of Brahma. Sri Donato. Ed. by Morningland Publications, Inc. (Illus.). 377p. 1981. pap. 10.00 (ISBN 0-935146-20-2). Morningland.

Day of Humiliation: Times of Affliction & Disaster. Cotton Mather. LC 68-24211. 1970. 55.00x (ISBN 0-8201-1067-1). Schol Facsimiles.

Day of Joy. (Hebrew & Eng.). 7.50 (ISBN 0-87559-103-5). Shalom.

Day of Redemption. Douglas Orbaker & Robert A. Blake. Ed. by Michael L. Sherer. (Orig.). 1987. pap. 2.25 (ISBN 0-89536-848-X, 7807). CSS of Ohio.

Day School Directory. 7.00 (ISBN 0-914131-15-X, E30). Torah Umesorah.

Day the Dollar Dies: Biblical Prophecy of a New World System in the End Times. Willard Cantelon. LC 72-94186. 190p. 1973. (Haven Bks); pap. 2.95 (ISBN 0-88270-170-3). Bridge Pub.

Day the Lion Roars. Jamin Denslow. Ed. by Helen Graves. LC 86-40284. 286p. (Orig.). 1987. pap. 8.95 (ISBN 1-55523-029-6). Winston-Derek.

Day the Little Children Came. A. Jennings. (Arch Bks.). 1984. pap. 0.99 (ISBN 0-570-06092-3, 59-1210). Concordia.

Day They Padlocked the Church. H. Edward Rowe. LC 83-80608. 86p. (Orig.). 1983. pap. 3.50 (ISBN 0-910311-05-6). Huntington Hse Inc.

Day to Remember. George E. Vandeman. LC 65-24345. (Stories That Win Ser.). 1965. pap. 1.25 (ISBN 0-8163-0096-8, 04140-0). Pacific Pr Pub Assn.

Day with Charles Kingsley. Maurice Clare. Repr. 10.00 (ISBN 0-8274-2148-6). R West.

Day with Yoga. Elisabeth Haich. pap. 3.95 (ISBN 0-943358-12-4). Aurora Press.

Daybreak. Jack Hayford. 112p. (Orig.). 1987. mass 2.95, (ISBN 0-8423-0524-6). Tyndale.

Daybreak Below the Border. Vera F. Barnes. 1975. Repr. 2.50 (ISBN 0-87509-078-8). Chr Pubns.

Daybreak in Livingstonia: The Story of the Livingstonia Mission, British Central Africa. rev. ed. James W. Jack. LC 79-77204. (Illus.). Repr. of 1900 ed. cancelled (ISBN 0-8371-1308-3, JAL&, Pub. by Negro U Pr). Greenwood.

Daybreak: Thoughts on the Prejudices of Morality. Friedrich Nietzsche. Tr. by R. J. Hollingdale. LC 81-18017. (Texts in German Philosophy). 220p. 1982. 22.95 (ISBN 0-521-24396-3); pap. 9.95 (ISBN 0-521-28662-X). Cambridge U Pr.

Daybreak: Walking Daily in Christ's Presence. Jack W. Hayford. LC 84-80749. (Orig.). 1984. pap. 2.95 (ISBN 0-916847-05-5). Living Way.

Daykeeper: The Life & Discource of As Ixtil Dviner. Benjamin N. Colby & Lore M. Colby. (Illus.). 352p. 1981. text ed. 27.50x (ISBN 0-674-19409-8). Harvard U Pr.

Days Multiplied. Leonard H. Budd. 1984. 4.00 (ISBN 0-89536-666-5, 0424). CSS of Ohio.

Days of Awe: A Treasury of Tradition, Legends & Learned Commentaries Concerning Rosh Hashanah, Yom Kippur & the Days Between. Y. Agnon. LC 48-8316. 1965. pap. 8.95 (ISBN 0-8052-0100-9). Schocken.

Days of Glory, Seasons of Night. rev. ed. Marilee P. Dunker. 176p. 1984. pap. text ed. 6.95 (ISBN 0-310-45501-4, 12040P). Zondervan.

Days of Heaven on Earth. rev. ed. Albert B. Simpson. LC 84-70154. 369p. 1984. pap. 7.95 (ISBN 0-87509-346-9). Chr Pubns.

Days of Noah. M. R. De Haan. 5.95 (ISBN 0-310-23331-3, 9512P). Zondervan.

Days of Praise. Robert C. Broderick. 1977. 5.50 (ISBN 0-8199-0653-0). Franciscan Herald.

Days of Praise. Henry M. Morris. (Illus.). 388p. (Orig.). 1986. pap. 9.95 (ISBN 0-89051-116-0). Master Bks.

Days of the Martyrs. C. Bernard Ruffin. LC 85-60517. 200p. (Orig.). 1985. pap. 7.95 (ISBN 0-87973-595-3, 595). Our Sunday Visitor.

Days Remembered. Alma Barkman. (Illus.). 96p. 1983. pap. 8.95 (ISBN 0-8024-0188-0). Moody.

Dayspring of Youth. (Illus.). 357p. 1985. 12.00 (ISBN 0-911662-67-7). Yoga.

Daytime Prayer from the Liturgy of the Hours. 521p. pap. 6.95 (ISBN 1-55586-577-1, V-577). US Catholic.

Dazzling Darkness: An Anthology of Western Mysticism. Ed. by Patrick Grant. (Orig.). 1985. pap. 9.95 (ISBN 0-8028-0088-2). Eerdmans.

De Archana Deorum. Thomae Walsingham. Ed. by Robert A. Van Kluyve. LC 67-31120. pap. 63.00 (ISBN 0-317-26876-7, 2023463). Bks Demand UMI.

De Archana Deorum. Thomas Walsingham. Ed. by Robert Van Kluyme. LC 67-31120. xxii, 227p. 1968. 24.75 (ISBN 0-8223-0183-0). Duke.

De Arte Cabbalistica. Johann Reuchlin. Tr. by Martin Goodman. LC 77-86231. (Bilingual Editions of Classics in Philosophy & Science Ser.: No. 1). 1983. 20.00 (ISBN 0-913870-56-0). Abaris Bks.

De Authoritate Summi Pontificis. Cristoforo Marcello. 304p. Repr. of 1521 ed. text ed. 66.24x (ISBN 0-576-99483-9, Pub. by Gregg Intl Pubs England). Gregg Intl.

De Catholicis Seu Patriarchis Chaldaeorum et Nestorianorum Commentarius: De Unione et Communione Ecclesiastica. Joseph A. Assamani. 410p. Repr. of 1775 ed. text ed. 82.80x (ISBN 0-576-99702-1, Pub. by Gregg Intl Pubs England). Gregg Intl.

De Civitate Dei Liber 22: Sec. 5, 2 pts, Pts. 1 & 2. Saint Aurelius Augustinus. (Corpus Scriptorum Ecclesiasticorum Latinorum Ser: Vol. 40). Repr. of 1899 ed. 50.00 ea. (ISBN 0-384-02370-3). Johnson Repr.

De Consensu Evangelistarum Librer4, Bk. 4. Saint Aurelius Augustinus. Ed. by F. Weihrich. (Corpus Scriptorum Ecclesiasticorum Latinorum Ser: Vol. 43). 40.00 (ISBN 0-384-02480-7). Johnson Repr.

De Eternidad a Eternidad. Erich Sauer. Orig. Title: From Eternity to Eternity. (Span.). 1977. pap. 4.95 (ISBN 0-8254-1653-1). Kregel.

De Fide et Symbolo, De Fide et Operibus, De Agone Christiano, Pt. 3. Saint Aurelius Augustinus. (Corpus Scriptorum Ecclesiasticorum Latinorum Ser: Vol. 41). 65.00 (ISBN 0-384-02385-1). Johnson Repr.

De Genesi ad Litteram Libri Duodecim Eiusdem Libri Capitula, Pt. 1. Saint Aurelius Augustinus. (Corpus Scriptorum Ecclesiasticorum Latinorum Ser: Vol. 28). 50.00 (ISBN 0-384-02485-8). Johnson Repr.

De Institutis Coenobiorum et De Octo Principalium Remediis Liber Xii: De Incarnatione Domini Contra Nestorium Liber Vii, Bk. 12. Joannes Cassianus. (Corpus Scriptorum Ecclesiasticorum Latinorum Ser: Vol. 17). (Cat). 1888. 50.00 (ISBN 0-384-07850-8). Johnson Repr.

De la Angoisse a la Foi. Martyn D. Lloyd-Jones. Tr. of From Fear to Faith. (Fr.). 1986. pap. 1.70 (ISBN 0-8297-0694-1). Life Pubs Intl.

De la Conqueste de Constantinoble. Geoffroi De Villehardouin. Ed. by Paulin Paris. 1965. 39.00 (ISBN 0-685-92799-7); pap. 33.00 (ISBN 0-384-64581-X). Johnson Repr.

De la Decouverte au Don de Soi. Dick Wulf. Orig. Title: Find Yourself, Give Yourself. (Fr.). 1986. write for info. (ISBN 0-8297-0687-9). Life Pubs Intl.

De la Grace et de l'Humanite de Jesus. 2nd ed. Jacques Maritain. 156p. 1967. 8.95 (ISBN 0-686-56347-6). French & Eur.

De la Salle: A Pioneer of Modern Education. W. J. Battersby. 236p. 1981. Repr. of 1949 ed. lib. bdg. 40.00 (ISBN 0-89987-065-1). Darby Bks.

De Lapsis & de Eeciesiae Catholicae Unitate. Cyprian. Ed. by Maurice Benevot. (Oxford Early Christian Texts Ser.). 1971. 32.50x (ISBN 0-19-826804-1). Oxford U Pr.

De l'Eglise du Christ. Jacques Maritain. 430p. 1970. 15.95 (ISBN 0-686-56348-4). French & Eur.

De Liturgia Romani Pontificis in Solemni Celebratione Missarum, 3 vols. D. Georgi. 1822p. Repr. of 1731 ed. text ed. 372.60 (ISBN 0-576-99174-0, Pub. by Gregg Intl Pubs England). Gregg Intl.

De Natura et Gratia. Domingo De Soto. 612p. Repr. of 1549 ed. text ed. 99.36 (ISBN 0-576-99423-5, Pub. by Gregg Intl Pubs England). Gregg Intl.

De Padres a Hijos Acerca del Sexo. Wilson W. Grant. Tr. by Maria T. La Valle et al from Eng. (Sexo en la Vida Cristiana Ser.). (Span., Illus.). 192p. 1982. pap. 3.95 (ISBN 0-311-46255-3). Casa Bautista.

De Paroecia Domui Religiosae Commissa. Francis J. Muller. 1956. 3.50 (ISBN 0-686-11580-5). Franciscan Inst.

De Pascal a Chateaubriand: Les Defenseurs Francais de Christianisme de 1670 a 1802. Albert Monod. LC 70-170954. (Philosophy Monographs Ser: No. 78). 1916. 32.50 (ISBN 0-8337-4283-3). B Franklin.

De Peccatorum Meritis et Remissione et de Baptismo Parvulorum, Ad Marcellinum Liber Tres, Bk. 3. Aurelius Augustinus. Ed. by C. F. Urba & I. Zycha. (Corpus Scriptorum Ecclesiasticorum Latinorum Ser: Vol. 60). 50.00 (ISBN 0-384-02490-4). Johnson Repr.

De Perfectione Ivstitiae Hominis, De Gestis Pelagii, De Gratia Christi et De Peccato Originali Liber Duo. Aurelius Augustinus. (Corpus Scriptorum Ecclesiasticorum Latinorum Ser: Vol. 42). Repr. of 1902 ed. 50.00 (ISBN 0-384-02495-5). Johnson Repr.

De Profectione Ludovici VII in Orientem: The Journey of Louis the Seventh to the East. Odo of Deuil. Ed. & tr. by Virginia G. Berry. 1965. pap. 6.95x (ISBN 0-393-09662-9). Norton.

De Reductione Artium Ad Theologiam. Sr. Emma T. Healy. (Works of Saint Bonaventure Ser). (Translated). 1955. 4.50 (ISBN 0-686-11590-2). Franciscan Inst.

De-Romanization of the American Catholic Church. Edward Wakin & Joseph F. Scheuer. LC 78-10157. 1979. Repr. of 1966 ed. lib. bdg. 24.75x (ISBN 0-313-21238-4, WADE). Greenwood.

De Romanorum Precationibus. facsimile ed. Georgius Appel. LC 75-10628. (Ancient Religion & Mythology Ser.). 1976. Repr. of 1909 ed. 18.00x (ISBN 0-405-07004-7). Ayer Co Pubs.

De Sapientia Veterum, Repr. Of 1609 Ed. Francis Bacon. Bd. with Wisedome of the Ancients. Tr. by Arthur Gorges. Repr. of 1619 ed. LC 75-27863. (Renaissance & the Gods Ser.: Vol. 20). (Illus.). 1976. lib. bdg. 88.00 (ISBN 0-8240-2068-5). Garland Pub.

De Sen Mascavamiento. Jan Van Rijckenborgh. (Span.). 1987. pap. 5.00 (ISBN 8-439827-98-9). Rosycross Pr.

De Summo Pontifice. Reginald Pole. 330p. Repr. of 1569 ed. text ed. 62.10 (ISBN 0-576-99123-6, Pub. by Gregg Intl Pubs England). Gregg Intl.

De Utilitate Credendi, Pt. 1. Aurelius Augustinus. Bd. with De Duabus Animabus; Contra Fortunatem; Contra Adimantum. (Corpus Scriptorum Ecclesiasticorum Latinorum Ser: Vol. 25). Repr. of 1891 ed. 50.00 (ISBN 0-384-02364-9). Johnson Repr.

Deacon & His Ministry. Richard L. Dresselhaus. LC 77-73518. 1977. pap. 2.25, 2.00 for 6 or more (ISBN 0-88243-493-4, 02-0493). Gospel Pub.

Deacon & the Jewess: Adventures in Heresy. Samuel Meyer. LC 80-84734. 208p. 1982. 10.00 (ISBN 0-8022-2379-6). Philos Lib.

Deacon at Work. Frederick A. Agar. 1923. 4.95 (ISBN 0-8170-0783-0). Judson.

Deacon in a Changing Church. Donald F. Thomas. LC 69-16388. 1969. pap. 4.95 (ISBN 0-8170-0414-9). Judson.

Deacon in the Church. Edward P. Echlin. LC 75-158571. 1971. 4.95 (ISBN 0-8189-0213-2). Alba.

Deacon in the Liturgy. Ormonde Plater. (Illus.). 60p. (Orig.). 1981. pap. 6.00 (ISBN 0-9605798-0-X). Natl Ctr Diaconate.

Deacons & Their Ministry. Waldo Hiebert & Herb Kopp. (Orig.). 1981. pap. 1.95 (ISBN 0-937364-02-9). Kindred Pr.

Deacon's Handbook. Gerard Berghoef & Lester DeKoster. 269p. 15.95 (ISBN 0-934874-01-8). Chr Lib Pr.

Deacons: Permanent or Passing? Kenneth Kleiber & Deacon H. Lemire. 70p. 1982. 6.95 (ISBN 0-911519-02-5). Richelieu Court.

Deacons: Servants of the Church Christ Built & Spiritual Gifts. Karl G. Wilks. LC 86-90143. (Bible Teaching on Church Government & Management Ser.). 66p. (Orig.). 1986. pap. 6.00 (ISBN 0-9616912-0-4). K G Wilks.

Deacon's Upholding the Pastor's Arms. Alfred J. Smith. 96p. 1983. pap. 4.00 (ISBN 0-686-46044-8). Prog Bapt Pub.

Dead Are with Us. Rudolf Steiner. Tr. by D. S. Osmond from Ger. 32p. 1973. pap. 2.95 (ISBN 0-85440-274-8, Pub. by Steinerbooks). Anthroposophic.

Dead Martyrs & Living Heroes. Denis Curtis et al. LC 83-61651. 260p. 13.95 (ISBN 0-88400-097-4). Shengold.

Dead Sea Community: Its Origin & Teachings. Kurt Schubert. Tr. by John W. Doberstein. LC 73-15245. 178p. 1974. Repr. of 1959 ed. lib. bdg. 22.50x (ISBN 0-8371-7169-5, SCDS). Greenwood.

Dead Sea Scriptures. 2nd ed. Theodor H. Gaster. LC 76-2840. 1976. pap. 7.95 (ISBN 0-385-08859-0, Anchor Pr). Doubleday.

Dead Sea Scrolls. J. M. Allegro. 1956. pap. 4.95 (ISBN 0-14-020376-1, Pelican). Penguin.

Dead Sea Scrolls. 2nd ed. Menahem Mansoor. 300p. 1983. pap. 8.95 (ISBN 0-8010-6152-0). Baker Bk.

Dead Sea Scrolls: A New Historical Approach. Cecil Roth. 1966. pap. 3.95x (ISBN 0-393-00303-5, Norton Lib). Norton.

Dead Sea Scrolls & Primitive Christianity. Jean Danielou. Tr. by Salvator Attanasio from Fr. LC 78-21516. 1979. Repr. of 1958 ed. lib. bdg. 22.50x (ISBN 0-313-21144-2, DADE). Greenwood.

Dead Sea Scrolls & the Bible. rev. & enl. ed. Charles F. Pfeiffer. (Baker Studies in Biblical Archaeology). (Illus.). 1969. pap. 5.95 (ISBN 0-8010-6898-3). Baker Bk.

Dead Sea Scrolls & the Christian Myth. John Allegro. LC 83-63566. (Illus.). 248p. 1984. 19.95 (ISBN 0-87975-241-6). Prometheus Bks.

Dead Sea Scrolls & the New Testament. William S. LaSor. 280p. 1972. pap. 5.95 (ISBN 0-8028-1114-0). Eerdmans.

Dead Sea Scrolls: Major Publications & Tools for Study. Joseph A. Fitzmyer. LC 75-5987. (Society of Biblical Literature. Sources for Biblical Study Ser.). xiv, 171p. 1975. pap. 10.50 (ISBN 0-88414-053-9, 060308). Scholars Pr GA.

Dead Sea Scrolls: Qumran in Perspective. Geza Vermes. LC 80-2382. 240p. 1981. pap. 8.95 (ISBN 0-8006-1435-6, 1-1435). Fortress.

Dead Sea Scrolls, The Gospel of Barnabas & the New Testament. M. A. Yusseff. LC 85-73210. 154p. (Orig.). 1986. pap. 8.00 (ISBN 0-89259-061-0). Am Trust Pubns.

Dead Sea Scrolls 1947-1969. Edmund Wilson. 1969. 22.50x (ISBN 0-19-500665-8). Oxford U Pr.

Dead Years: Surviving the Holocaust. Joseph Schupack. LC 86-81286. 1987. 16.95 (ISBN 0-89604-066-6); pap. 10.95 (ISBN 0-89604-067-4). Holocaust Pubns.

Deadly Deceptions. James G. Witt, III. Ed. by William E. Fischer. (Illus.). 64p. (Orig.). 1987. pap. text ed. 2.95 (ISBN 0-938272-32-2); leaders guide 2.95. Wels Board.

Deadly Sins & Saving Virtues. Donald Capps. LC 85-45912. 176p. 1987. pap. text ed. 10.95 (ISBN 0-8006-1948-X, 1-1948). Fortress.

Deadly Words. Jeanne Favret-Saada. Tr. by Catherine Cullen from Fr. LC 79-41607. (Illus.). 1981. o. p. 57.50 (ISBN 0-521-22317-2); pap. text ed. 15.95 o. p. (ISBN 0-521-29787-7). Cambridge U Pr.

Deafening Silence: American Jewish Leaders & the Holocaust, 1933-1945. Rafael Medoff. 1986. 14.95 (ISBN 0-933503-63-6). Shapolsky Pubs.

Dealing Creatively with Death: A Manual of Death Education & Simple Burial. 10th ed. Ernest Morgan. 1984. pap. 6.50. Continent Assn Funeral.

Dealing with Conflict. E. Leonard Gillingham. LC 81-20662. 144p. 1982. 8.75 (ISBN 0-687-10329-0). Abingdon.

Dealing with Depression. William Weir & Russell M. Abata. LC 82-84045. 144p. 1983. pap. 3.50 (ISBN 0-89243-170-9). Liguori Pubns.

Dealing with Difficult People. Charles J. Keating. LC 83-82018. 224p. 1984. pap. 7.95 (ISBN 0-8091-2596-X). Paulist Pr.

Dealing with Divorce. Roger Paige. 1979. pap. 4.50 (ISBN 0-8309-0240-6). Herald Hse.

Dealing with the Devil. Daniel Cohen. LC 79-14692. (Illus.). 1979. 11.95 (ISBN 0-396-07700-5). Dodd.

Dealing with the Devil. C. S. Lovett. 1967. pap. 5.45 (ISBN 0-938148-05-2). Personal Christianity.

Dean Bond of Swarthmore, a Quaker Humanist. Emily C. Johnson. 25.00 (ISBN 0-932062-92-X). Sharon Hill.

Dean's Administrative Manual, 2 pts. 180p. Set. 12.00 (ISBN 0-914131-16-8, C20). Torah Umesorah.

Dear Bishop: Memoirs of the Author Concerning the History of the Blue Army. John M. Haffert. (Illus.). 352p. 1981. 8.95 (ISBN 0-911988-44-0); pap. 5.95 (ISBN 0-911988-42-4). AMI Pr.

Dear Brothers & Sisters in Christ: Five Letters of Comfort. Basilea Schlink. 1978. pap. 0.95 (ISBN 3-87209-622-2). Evang Sisterhood Mary.

Dear Children. Hattie Larlham. LC 82-25842. 152p. 1983. 9.95 (ISBN 0-8361-3325-0). Herald Pr.

Dear Daughter: Letters from Eve & Other Women of the Bible. Colleen I. Hartsoe. LC 81-80627. 1981. pap. 4.95 (ISBN 0-8192-1288-1). Morehouse.

Dear Ellen: Two Mormon Women & Their Letters. Ed. by S. George Ellsworth. 92p. 1974. 12.00 (ISBN 0-941214-33-8). Signature Bks.

Dear Father: A Message of Love to Priests. Catherine D. Doherty. LC 78-31389. 1979. pap. 3.50 (ISBN 0-8189-0377-5). Alba.

Dear Father in Heaven. rev. ed. R. Schlesselman & L. Ahrens. (Illus.). 1977. pap. 2.25 (ISBN 0-570-03469-8, 56-1301). Concordia.

Dear Friend, I Love You. Mary-Katherine MacDougall. 176p. (Orig.). 1986. pap. 9.95 (ISBN 0-87707-226-4). Now Comns.

Dear Georgia. Beulah F. Stevens. LC 78-13546. 1979. pap. 0.75 (ISBN 0-8127-0204-2). Review & Herald.

Dear Gift of Life: A Man's Encounter with Death. Bradford Smith. LC 65-24496. (Orig.). 1965. pap. 2.50x (ISBN 0-87574-142-8). Pendle Hill.

Dear God. (First Prayer Ser.). 2.95 (ISBN 0-86112-218-6, Pub. by Brimax Bks). Borden.

Dear God, Bless Our Food. Annie Fitzgerald. LC 84-71372. (Dear God Bks.). 16p. (Orig.). 1984. pap. 1.50 (ISBN 0-8066-2108-7, 10-1859). Augsburg.

Dear God, Good Morning. Annie Fitzgerald. LC 84-71377. (Dear God Bks.). 16p. (Orig.). 1984. pap. 1.50 (ISBN 0-8066-2104-4, 10-1860). Augsburg.

Dear God, Good Night. Annie Fitzgerald. LC 84-71374. (Dear God Bks.). 16p. 1984. pap. 1.50 (ISBN 0-8066-2105-2, 10-1861). Augsburg.

Dear God, I Have This Terrible Problem: A Housewife's Secret Letters. Bernadet M. Snyder. 96p. 1983. pap. 2.95 (ISBN 0-89243-188-1). Liguori Pubns.

Dear God, I Just Love Birthdays. Annie Fitzgerald. LC 84-71371. (Dear God Bks.). 16p. (Orig.). 1984. pap. 1.50 (ISBN 0-8066-2107-9, 10-1862). Augsburg.

Dear God, Is Justice Still With You? Alexander Shaanan. (Illus.). 144p. 1983. 8.95 (ISBN 0-89962-306-9). Todd & Honeywell.

Dear God, Let's Play. Annie Fitzgerald. LC 83-70495. 16p. (Orig.). 1983. pap. 1.50 (ISBN 0-8066-2001-3, 10-1852). Augsburg.

Dear God Little Prayers to a Big God. Virginia Talmadge. 1981. cloth 3.25 (ISBN 0-86544-016-6). Salv Army Suppl South.

Dear God, Pourquoi? Why Did You Born Me in Texas. John H. Hill. LC 84-91310. 167p. 1985. 10.95 (ISBN 0-533-06400-7). Vantage.

Dear God, Thanks for Friends. Annie Fitzgerald. LC 84-71873. (Dear God Bks.). 16p. (Orig.). 1984. pap. 1.50 (ISBN 0-8066-2109-5, 10-1863). Augsburg.

Dear God, Thanks for Making Me. Annie Fitzgerald. LC 83-71368. (Dear God Bks.). 16p. (Orig.). 1984. pap. 1.50 (ISBN 0-8066-2106-0, 10-1864). Augsburg.

Dear God, Thanks for Thinking up Love. Annie Fitzgerald. LC 83-70499. 16p. 1983. pap. 1.50 (ISBN 0-8066-2005-6, 10-1853). Augsburg.

Dear God, Thanks for Your Help. Annie Fitzgerald. LC 83-70496. 16p. 1983. pap. 1.50 (ISBN 0-8066-2002-1, 10-1854). Augsburg.

Dear God, We Just Love Christmas. Annie Fitzgerald. LC 83-70494. 16p. (Orig.). 1983. pap. 1.50 (ISBN 0-8066-2000-5, 10-1855). Augsburg.

Dear God, Where Do You Live? Annie Fitzgerald. LC 83-70497. 16p. 1983. pap. 1.50 (ISBN 0-8066-2003-X, 10-1856). Augsburg.

Dear God, Why Can't We Have a Baby? John Van Regenmorter & Sylvia Van Regenmorter. 1986. 6.95 (ISBN 0-8010-9301-5). Baker Bk.

Dear God, Your World Is Wonderful. Annie Fitzgerald. LC 83-70498. 16p. 1983. pap. 1.50 (ISBN 0-8066-2004-8, 10-1857). Augsburg.

Dear Jesus, Love Sandy. Sandra Drescher. 112p. 1982. pap. 3.95 (ISBN 0-310-44841-7, 18235P); gift ed. o. p. cancelled 7.95 (ISBN 0-310-44840-9). Zondervan.

Dear Laddie. John Cordner. LC 86-71593. 300p. (Orig.). 1987. pap. 4.50 (ISBN 0-9617224-0-1). J Cordner.

Dear Mr. Missionary. E. H. Wendland. 1978. pap. 4.95 (ISBN 0-8100-0035-0, 12N1714). Northwest Pub.

Dear Mommy, Please Don't Kill Me. Adalu Justus. 14p. 1986. pap. 2.50 (ISBN 0-937109-01-0). Silo Pubs.

Dear Moses: Letters to Saints & Other Prominent People. Lois Donahue. LC 84-60743. (Illus.). 104p. 1984. pap. 4.95 (ISBN 0-87973-699-2, 699). Our Sunday Visitor.

Dear Theophilus. John W. Wade. 256p. 1985. pap. 4.95 (ISBN 0-87239-968-0, 41036). Standard Pub.

Dear Tim. Charles De Santo. LC 81-23744. 200p. (Orig.). 1982. pap. 7.95 (ISBN 0-8361-1991-6). Herald Pr.

Dear Unborn Child. Denise George & Timothy George. LC 83-71714. 1984. pap. 4.95 (ISBN 0-8054-5658-9). Broadman.

Dear World: Don't Spin So Fast, I'm Having Trouble Hanging On. Joan W. Anderson. LC 82-73131. 160p. 1982. pap. 4.95 (ISBN 0-87029-188-2, 20280-4). Abbey.

Death. C. H. Spurgeon. 1978. pap. 1.95 (ISBN 0-686-23024-8). Pilgrim Pubns.

Death & After. Annie Besant. 1972. 2.95 (ISBN 0-8356-7039-2). Theos Pub Hse.

Death & After. Manly P. Hall. 2.50 (ISBN 0-89314-312-X). Philos Res.

Death & After-Life in the Theologies of Karl Barth & John Hick: A Comparative Study. Keith R. Schmitt. (Amsterdam Studies in Theology Ser.: Vol. 5). 230p. 1985. pap. 32.50x (ISBN 90-6203-528-0, Pub. by Rodopi Holland). Humanities.

Death & After: What Will Really Happen? Hubert J. Richards. (What Really Happened? Ser.). 1987. pap. 5.95 (ISBN 0-89622-288-8). Twenty-Third.

Death & Afterwards. H. A. Ironside. pap. 1.50 (ISBN 0-87213-346-X). Loizeaux.

Death & Beyond in the Eastern Perspective. new ed. Jung Y. Lee. LC 73-85065. 112p. 1974. 24.50x (ISBN 0-677-05010-0). Gordon & Breach.

Death & Birth of Judaism: The Impact of Christianity, Secularism & the Holocaust on Jewish Faith. Jacob Neusner. LC 86-47733. 352p. 1987. 21.95 (ISBN 0-465-01577-8). Basic.

Death & Burial in Christian Antiquity. Alfred C. Rush. 59.59 (ISBN 0-8490-0009-2). Gordon Pr.

Death & Burial in the Roman World. J. M. Toynbee. Ed. by H. H. Scullard. LC 77-120603. (Aspects of Greek & Roman Life Ser). (Illus.). 336p. 1971. 35.00x (ISBN 0-8014-0593-9). Cornell U Pr.

Death & Dying. Dick Hill. 4.25 (ISBN 0-89137-532-5). Quality Pubns.

Death & Dying. 2nd, rev. ed. Ed. by Janelle Rohr. (Opposing Viewpoints Ser.). (Illus.). 1987. 12.95 (ISBN 0-317-53944-2); pap. 6.95. Greenhaven.

Death & Eastern Thought: Understanding Death in Eastern Religions & Philosophies. Ed. by Frederick H. Holck. LC 74-10650. pap. 49.10 (ISBN 0-8357-9004-5, 2015656). Bks Demand UMI.

Death & Eternal Life. John H. Hick. LC 76-9965. 496p. 1980. pap. text ed. 11.95 (ISBN 0-06-063904-0, RD 332, HarpR). Har-Row.

Death & Grief: Selected Readings for the Medical Student. Ed. by David Peretz et al. 270p. 1977. pap. 6.95 (ISBN 0-930194-82-9). Ctr Thanatology.

Death & Immortality in the Religions of the World. Paul Badham & Linda Badham. 256p. 1987. 22.95 (ISBN 0-913757-54-3, Pub. by New Era Bks); pap. 12.95 (ISBN 0-913757-67-5, Pub. by New Era Bks). Paragon Hse.

Death & Life: An American Theology. Arthur McGill. Ed. by Charles A. Wilson & Per M. Anderson. LC 86-45215. 112p. 1987. pap. 7.95 (ISBN 0-8006-1927-7, 1-1927). Fortress.

Death & Reincarnation. Swami Jyotir Maya Nanda. (Illus.). 1970. 6.99 (ISBN 0-934664-04-8). Yoga Res Foun.

Death & Reincarnation: Eternity's Voyage. Sri Chinmoy. LC 74-81308. (Illus.). 143p. (Orig.). 1974. pap. 3.95 (ISBN 0-88497-038-8). Aum Pubns.

Death & Resurrection in Guatemala. Fernando Bermudez. Tr. by Robert R. Barr from Span. LC 85-48305. Tr. of Cristo Muere y Resucita en Guatemala. 96p. (Orig.). 1986. pap. 7.95 (ISBN 0-88344-268-X). Orbis Bks.

Death & Resurrection of Christ. Gordon Lindsay. (Life of Christ Ser.: Vol. 3). (Span.). 1.50 (ISBN 0-89985-983-6). Christ Nations.

Death & the Afterlife. Robert A. Morey. 250p. 1984. pap. 11.95 (ISBN 0-87123-433-5). Bethany Hse.

Death & the Afterlife in Pre-Columbian America: A Conference at Dumbarton Oaks, October 27, 1973. Ed. by Elizabeth P. Benson. LC 74-22694. (Illus.). 196p. 1975. 15.00x (ISBN 0-88402-062-2). Dumbarton Oaks.

Death & the Christian Answer. Mary E. Lyman. 1983. pap. 2.50x (ISBN 0-87574-107-X, 107). Pendle Hill.

Death & the Hereafter. Gordon Lindsay. (Sorcery & Spirit World Ser.). 1.25 (ISBN 0-89985-096-0). Christ Nations.

Death & the Regeneration of Life. Ed. by Maurice Bloch & Jonathan Parry. LC 82-9467. 256p. 1982. 34.50 (ISBN 0-521-24875-2); pap. 11.95 (ISBN 0-521-27037-5). Cambridge U Pr.

Death As a Speculative Theme in Religious, Scientific, & Social Thought: An Original Anthology. Ed. by Robert Kastenbaum. LC 76-19566. (Death & Dying Ser.). 1977. Repr. of 1976 ed. lib. bdg. 29.00x (ISBN 0-405-09562-7). Ayer Co Pubs.

Death As an Enemy According to Ancient Egyptian Conceptions. Jan Zandee. Ed. by Robert Kastenbaum. LC 76-19597. (Death & Dying Ser.). 1977. Repr. of 1960 ed. lib. bdg. 37.50x (ISBN 0-405-09591-0). Ayer Co Pubs.

Death Book: Terrors, Consolations, Contradictions & Paradoxes. Joseph A. Amato. 1985. 13.95 (ISBN 0-9614119-1-0, Co-Pub Ellis Press). V Amati.

Death Brigade. L. Wells. LC 77-89068. 305p. 1978. pap. 10.95 (ISBN 0-89604-000-3). Holocaust Pubns.

Death by Bread Alone: Texts & Reflections on Religious Experience. Dorothee Soelle. Tr. by David L. Scheidt from Ger. LC 77-78643. 168p. 1978. 2.00 (ISBN 0-8006-0514-4, 1-514). Fortress.

Death Camp Treblinka. Ed. by Alexander Donat. LC 79-53471. (Illus.). 320p. (Orig.). 1979. 16.95 (ISBN 0-89604-008-9); pap. 12.95 (ISBN 0-89604-009-7). Holocaust Pubns.

Death Cheaters. Gordon Lindsay. (Sorcery & Spirit World Ser.). 1.25 (ISBN 0-89985-081-2). Christ Nations.

Death Christ Died. Robert P. Lightner. LC 67-30992. 1975. pap. 3.25 (ISBN 0-87227-012-2). Reg Baptist.

Death Comes Dancing: Celebrating Life with Bhagwan Shree Rajneesh. Ma Satya Bharti. 200p. 1981. pap. 9.95 (ISBN 0-7100-0705-1). Methuen Inc.

Death: Confronting the Reality. William E. Phipps. LC 86-45405. 204p. (Orig.). 1987. pap. 11.95 (ISBN 0-8042-0487-X). John Knox.

Death Customs: An Analytical Study of Burial Rites. Effie Bendann. 1971. 37.00x (ISBN 0-8103-3733-9). Gale.

Death Customs: An Analytical Study of Burial Rites. Effie Bendann. 59.95 (ISBN 0-8490-0010-6). Gordon Pr.

Death-Dying. Ed. by Bruno Leone et al. (Opposing Viewpoints SOURCES Ser.). 375p. 1984. text ed. 39.95 (ISBN 0-89908-515-6). Greenhaven.

Death, Dying & Grief: A Bibliography. Robert F. Guthmann, Jr. & Sharon K. Womack. LC 77-82084. 1978. pap. text ed. 5.50 (ISBN 0-918626-01-3, Pied Publications). Word Serv.

Death-Dying, 1985 Annual. Ed. by Bruno Leone et al. (Opposing Viewpoints SOURCES Ser.). 115p. 1985. pap. text ed. 9.95 (ISBN 0-89908-511-3). Greenhaven.

Death Education: Attitudes of Teachers, School Board Members & Clergy. Beverly F. Croskery. LC 78-68458. 1979. perfect bdg. 9.95 (ISBN 0-88247-559-2). R & E Pubs.

Death: Graduation to Glory. C. S. Lovett. 1974. pap. 4.25 (ISBN 0-938148-20-6). Personal Christianity.

Death, Grief & Bereavement: A Bibliography, 1845-1975. Robert Fulton. Ed. by Robert Kastenbaum. LC 76-19572. (Death and Dying Ser.). 1976. PLB 27.50 (ISBN 0-405-09570-8). Ayer Co Pubs.

Death, Grief & Friendship in the Eighteenth Century: Edward Gibbon & Lord Sheffield. Marvin Stern. 1985. pap. 11.95 (ISBN 0-930194-35-7). Ctr Thanatology.

Death, Grief, & Mourning. Geoffrey Gorer. Ed. by Robert Kastenbaum. LC 76-19573. (Death & Dying Ser.). (Illus.). 1977. Repr. of 1965 ed. lib. bdg. 24.50x (ISBN 0-405-09571-6). Ayer Co Pubs.

Death in the Nursery: The Secret Crime of Infanticide. James Manney & John Blattner. 224p. (Orig.). 1984. pap. 6.95 (ISBN 0-89283-192-8). Servant.

Death, Intermediate State & Rebirth in Tibetan Buddhism. Lati Rinbochay & Jeffrey Hopkins. LC 80-80130. 86p. 1980. lib. bdg. cancelled (ISBN 0-937938-01-7); pap. 6.95 (ISBN 0-937938-00-9). Snow Lion.

Death into Life: A Conversation. F. J. Sheed. 1977. pap. 1.95 (ISBN 0-88479-005-3). Arena Lettres.

Death Is, & Approaches to the Edge. William J. Higginson. (Xtras Ser.: No. 9). 48p. (Orig.). 1981. pap. 2.50 (ISBN 0-89120-019-3). From Here.

Death of a Child. Steve Williams. 1977. 3.95 (ISBN 0-88027-005-5). Firm Foun Pub.

Death of a Christian: The Rite of Funerals. Richard Rutherford. (Studies in the Reformed Rites of the Catholic Church: Vol. 7). 1980. pap. 9.95 (ISBN 0-916134-40-7). Pueblo Pub Co.

Death of a Guru. Rev. ed. Rabindranath R. Maharaj & Dave Hunt. LC 84-81212. 208p. 1986. pap. 5.95 (ISBN 0-89081-434-1). Harvest Hse.

Death of a Man. Lael T. Wertenbaker. LC 73-16889. 192p. 1974. pap. 7.95x (ISBN 0-8070-2763-4, BP482). Beacon Pr.

Death of an American: The Killing of John Singer. David Fleisher & David M. Freedman. (Illus.). 248p. 1983. 15.95 (ISBN 0-8264-0231-3). Crossroad NY.

Death of Christ. James Denney. LC 81-81100. (Shephard Illustrated Classics Ser.). (Illus.). 372p. 1981. pap. 6.95 (ISBN 0-87983-258-4). Keats.

Death of Christ. James Denny. 1982. lib. bdg. 12.50 (ISBN 0-86524-090-6, 9507). Klock & Klock.

Death of Christian Culture. John Senior. 1978. 12.95 (ISBN 0-87000-416-6). Educator Pubns.

Death of Death. John Owen. 1983. pap. 7.95 (ISBN 0-85151-382-4). Banner of Truth.

Death of God. Gabriel Vahanian. LC 61-9962. 1961. 6.95 (ISBN 0-8076-0144-6). Braziller.

Death of Gurdjieff in the Foothills of Georgia: Secret Papers of an American Work Group. Jan Cox. 316p. 1980. 9.00 (ISBN 0-936380-03-9). Chan Shal Imi.

Death of Jesus. Joel Carmichael. 296p. (Orig.). 1982. pap. 8.95 (ISBN 0-8180-0826-1). Horizon.

Death of Jesus in Luke-Acts. Joseph B. Tyson. 212p. 1986. text ed. 17.95 (ISBN 0-87249-461-6). U of SC Pr.

Death of Plato, the Aftermath. Ronald Christensen. vii, 120p. 1983. lib. bdg. 8.95 (ISBN 0-938876-18-X). Entropy Ltd.

Death of Sadat...Start of World War III. Charles R. Taylor. (Illus.). 96p. (Orig.). 1982. pap. 3.95 (ISBN 0-937682-05-5). Today Bible.

Death of the Old & the Birth of the New: Framework of the Book of Numbers & the Pentateuch. Dennis T. Olson. (Brown Judaic Ser.). 1985. 29.95 (ISBN 0-89130-885-7, 14-00-71); pap. 22.95 (ISBN 0-89130-886-5). Scholars Pr Ga.

Death of the Prophet. Jason Leen. LC 79-18719. (Illus.). 1979. 11.95 (ISBN 0-87961-094-8); pap. 5.95 (ISBN 0-87961-093-X). Naturegraph.

Death of the Soul. William Barrett. LC 82-45317. 192p. 1986. 16.95 (ISBN 0-385-15965-X, Anchor Pr). Doubleday.

Death of the Third Nature. Robert J. Pruitt. 1975. pap. 1.95 (ISBN 0-934942-04-8). White Wing Pub.

Death, Property, & the Ancestors: A Study of the Mortuary Customs of the LoDagaa of West Africa. Jack Goody. (Illus.). 1962. 32.50x (ISBN 0-8047-0068-0). Stanford U Pr.

Death, Resurrection, Immortality. Joseph E. Kirk. 111p. 1977. 4.00 (ISBN 0-910424-66-7); pap. 3.00 (ISBN 0-910424-67-5). Concordant.

Death Rites. Date not set. pap. price not set (ISBN 0-938924-18-4). Sri Shirdi Sai.

Death: The Causes & Phenomena with Special Reference to Immortality. Hereward Carrington. Ed. by Robert Kastenbaum. LC 76-19563. (Death & Dying Ser.). 1977. lib. bdg. 27.50 (ISBN 0-405-09559-7). Ayer Co Pubs.

Death to Rebirth. Manly P. Hall. pap. 4.95 (ISBN 0-89314-395-2). Philos Res.

Death Train. Luba K. Gurdus. LC 78-54657. (Illus.). 1979. 12.95 (ISBN 0-8052-5005-0, Pub. by Holocaust Library). Schocken.

Death Train. Luba K. Gurdus. LC 78-54657. (Illus.). 165p. (Orig.). 1978. 12.95 (ISBN 0-89604-005-4). Holocaust Pubns.

Death Was His Koan: The Samurai Zen of Suzuki Shosan. Winston King. 1986. 40.00 (ISBN 0-89581-998-8). Asian Human Pr.

Deathday of Socrates: Living, Dying & Immortality-The Theater of Ideas in Plato's "Phaedo". Jerome Eckstein. 1981. 17.95 (ISBN 0-914366-19-X); pap. 12.95 (ISBN 0-914366-20-3). Vanguard.

Deathly Trivia from the Bible. Niles Auldtomes. (Odd Books for Odd Moments Ser.: No. 6). (Illus.). 120p. (Orig.). 1986. pap. 5.95 (ISBN 0-930937-34-1). Winds World Pr.

Death's an End & a Beginning Without. B. M. Billon. 1981. 15.00x (ISBN 0-7223-1388-8, Pub. by A H Stockwell England). State Mutual Bk.

Debate on Slavery: Is Slavery in Itself Sinful & the Relation Between Master & Slave a Sinful Relation. Jonathan Blanchard & N. L. Rice. LC 72-82175. (Anti-Slavery Crusade in America Ser.). 1969. Repr. of 1846 ed. 21.00 (ISBN 0-405-00614-4). Ayer Co Pubs.

Debate on the English Reformation. Rosemary O'Day. 217p. 1986. text ed. 29.95 (ISBN 0-416-72670-4, 9794); pap. text ed. 9.95 (ISBN 0-416-72680-1, 9802). Methuen Inc.

Deborah. new ed. Margit S. Heppenstall. LC 67-19497. (Crown Ser.). 1977. pap. 4.95 (ISBN 0-8127-0169-0). Review & Herald.

Debra the Donkey. Jane Hammond. (God's Animals Story Bks.). 1983. pap. 1.50 (ISBN 0-87162-288-2, D5602). Warner Pr.

Decade of Creation: Acts-Facts-Impacts, Vol. 4. Morris & Rohrer. LC 80-67426. 320p. 1980. pap. 7.95 (ISBN 0-89051-069-5). Master Bks.

Decadence of Judaism in Our Time. Moshe Menuhin. 1981. lib. bdg. 59.95 (ISBN 0-686-73181-6). Revisionist Pr.

Decades of Henry Bullinger, Minister of the Church of Zurich, 4 vols. Henry Bullinger. 1849-1851. Set. 144.00 (ISBN 0-384-06315-2). Johnson Repr.

Decalogue & the Gospel. Sotirios D. Philaretos. Ed. by Orthodox Christian Educational Society. Tr. by D. Cummings from Hellenic. 62p. (Orig.). 1957. pap. 2.00x (ISBN 0-938366-43-2). Orthodox Chr.

December Decorations: A Holiday How-to Book. Peggy Parish. LC 75-14285. (Illus.). 64p. 1975. 9.95 (ISBN 0-02-769920-X). Macmillan.

December Twenty-Fifth: The Joy of Christmas Past. Phillip V. Snyder. (Illus.). 346p. 1985. 17.95 (ISBN 0-396-08588-1). Dodd.

Decide for Yourself: A Theological Workbook. Gordon R. Lewis. LC 71-116046. (Orig.). 1970. pap. 7.95 (ISBN 0-87784-633-2). Inter-Varsity.

Decide to Live. William A. Charland, Jr. LC 79-9563. 156p. 1979. pap. 6.95 (ISBN 0-664-24277-4). Westminster.

Decide to Love. Anthony L. Ash. LC 80-80294. (Journey Bks.). 140p. (Orig.). 1980. pap. 3.50 (ISBN 0-8344-0116-9). Sweet.

Decide to Love. Gary Smalley et al. 64p. (Orig.). 1985. tchr's. manual 19.95 (ISBN 0-310-44861-1, 18249P); student's manual 2.95 (ISBN 0-310-44331-8, 18253P). Zondervan.

Deciding for Yourself Youth Manual. James Cisek & Anthea George. (Illus.). 60p. (Orig.). 1985. pap. 5.95 (ISBN 0-9604510-1-3). Life Skills.

Deciding to Grow. Evertt W. Huffard. 1983. pap. 3.95 (ISBN 0-89137-540-6). Quality Pubns.

Decision Making & the Bible. H. Edward Everding, Jr. & Dana M. Wilbanks. LC 75-11656. 160p. 1975. pap. 5.95 (ISBN 0-8170-0668-0). Judson.

Decision Making & the Will of God. Garry Friesen & J. Robin Maxson. LC 80-24592. (Critical Concern Bks.). 1981. 13.95 (ISBN 0-930014-47-2). Multnomah.

Decision Making & the Will of God: A Biblical Alternative to the Traditional View. Garry Friesen & J. Robin Maxson. LC 80-24592. (Critical Concern Ser.). 252p. 1983. pap. 9.95 (ISBN 0-88070-024-6); study guide 2.95 (ISBN 0-88070-021-1). Multnomah.

Decision Making & the Will of God: A Biblical Alternative to the Traditional View. expanded ed. Garry Friesen & J. Robin Maxson. (Critical Concern Bks.). pap. cancelled (ISBN 0-88070-100-5). Multnomah.

Decision Making in the Church: A Biblical Model. Luke T. Johnson. LC 82-17675. 112p. 1983. pap. 6.95 (ISBN 0-8006-1694-4). Fortress.

Decision to Love: What It Means to Love Others from the Heart. Ken Wilson. (Living As a Christian Ser.). 77p. (Orig.). 1980. pap. 2.50 (ISBN 0-89283-087-5). Servant.

Decisions. Sherlie Rowe. Vol. 1. pap. 3.95 (ISBN 0-89137-806-5); Vol. 2. pap. 3.95 (ISBN 0-89137-807-3). Quality Pubns.

Decisions. 2nd, rev. ed. Lawrence G. Wrenn. vi, 200p. (Orig.). 1983. pap. 4.50 (ISBN 0-943616-17-4). Canon Law Soc.

Decisions: A Study of Christian Ethics. Jack Roeda. LC 80-189628. (Orig.). 1980. pap. text ed. 4.50 (ISBN 0-933140-14-2); tchr's. manual 5.95 (ISBN 0-933140-15-0). CRC Pubns.

Decisions by Consensus: A Study of the Quaker Method. Glenn Bartoo. (Studies in Quakerism: No. 4). 48p. (Orig.). 1978. pap. 2.00 (ISBN 0-89670-003-8). Progresiv Pub.

Decisions in Philosophy of Religion. William B. Williamson. LC 85-42846. 407p. 1985. pap. 16.95 (ISBN 0-87975-295-5). Prometheus Bks.

Decisiveness of the Christ-Event & the Universality of Christianity in a World of Religious Plurality. Origen V. Jathanna. (IC-Studies in the Intercultural History of Christianity: Vol. 29). 583p. 1982. pap. 51.60 (ISBN 3-261-04974-X). P Lang Pubs.

Deck the Halls. Tom Tozer & Ralph E. Dessem. Ed. by Michael L. Sherer. (Orig.). 1986. pap. 2.25 (ISBN 0-89536-827-7, 6844). CSS of Ohio.

Declaration of a Heretic. Jeremy Rifkin. 150p. 1985. 19.95 (ISBN 0-7102-0709-3); pap. 7.95 (ISBN 0-7102-0710-7). Methuen Inc.

Decline & Fall of Israel & Judah. Gordon Lindsay. (Old Testament Ser.). 1.25 (ISBN 0-89985-153-3). Christ Nations.

Decline & Fall of the Hebrew Kingdoms. T. H. Robinson. LC 74-137284. Repr. of 1926 ed. 21.50 (ISBN 0-404-05376-9). AMS Pr.

Decline & Revival of the Social Gospel: Social & Political Liberalism in American Protestant Churches, 1920-1940. 2nd ed. Paul A. Carter. LC 70-122413. xxvi, 265p. 1971. Repr. of 1956 ed. 27.50 (ISBN 0-208-01083-1, Archon). Shoe String.

Decline of the Medieval Church, 2 vols. Alexander C. Flick. (Bibliography & Reference Ser.: No. 133). 1968. Repr. of 1930 ed. Set. 48.00 (ISBN 0-8337-1158-X). B Franklin.

Decline of U. S. Religious Faith: 1912 - 1984 & the Effect of Education & Intelligence on Such Faith. Burnham P. Beckwith. 1985. 9.00x (ISBN 0-9603262-4-3). Beckwith.

Decoding the Rabbis: A Thirteenth-Century Commentary on the Aggadah. Marc Saperstein. LC 80-13166. (Judaic Monographs: No. 3). 298p. 1980. text ed. 20.00x (ISBN 0-674-19445-4). Harvard U Pr.

Decolonizing Theology: A Caribbean Perspective. Noel L. Erskine. LC 80-21784. 144p. (Orig.). 1981. pap. 6.95 (ISBN 0-88344-087-3). Orbis Bks.

Deconstructing Theology. Mark C. Taylor. (American Academy of Religion Studies). 176p. 1983. 12.95 (ISBN 0-8245-0533-6). Crossroad NY.

Deconstructing Theology. Mark C. Taylor. LC 82-5970. (AAR Studies in Religion). 152p. 1982. 12.95 (ISBN 0-89130-582-3, 01-00-28). Scholars Pr GA.

Deconstruction & Theology. Thomas Altizer et al. 176p. 1982. 14.95 (ISBN 0-8245-0475-5); pap. 8.95 (ISBN 0-8245-0412-7). Crossroad NY.

Decorated Jewish Ossuaries. P. Figueras. (Documenta et Monumenta Orientis Antiqui Ser.: No. 20). (Illus.). 119p. 1983. text ed. 39.95x (ISBN 90-04-06579-2, Pub. by EJ Brill Holland). Humanities.

Decorated Letter. Ed. by J. J. Alexander. LC 78-6487. (Magnificent Paperback Ser.). 1978. 22.95 (ISBN 0-8076-0894-7); pap. 12.95 (ISBN 0-8076-0895-5). Braziller.

Decorating Christmas Trees. W. Eugene Burkhart, Jr. (Illus.). 64p. (Orig.). 1985. pap. 8.95 (ISBN 0-9615199-0-8). Burkharts.

Decorations for Forty-Four Parish Celebrations: Enhancing Worship Experiences Tastefully & Simply. Bernadette M. Snyder & Hazelmai M. Terry. (Illus., Orig.). 1982. pap. 9.95 (ISBN 0-89622-167-9). Twenty-Third.

Decree on Ecumenism. Vatican Council Two. Ed. by Thomas Stransky. (Orig.). 1965. pap. 1.95 (ISBN 0-8091-5027-1). Paulist Pr.

Dedication: Nobody Said It Was Easy. D. J. Watson. 1987. pap. write for info. (ISBN 0-88469-181-0). BMH Bks.

Dedication Services for Every Occasion. Compiled by Manfred Holck, Jr. 96p. 1984. pap. 5.95 (ISBN 0-8170-1033-5). Judson.

Deed of Christ & the Opposing Spiritual Powers Lucifer, Ahriman, Mephistopheles, Asuras. Rudolf Steiner. 2.75 (ISBN 0-919924-02-6, Pub by Steiner Book Centre Canada). Anthroposophic.

Deeds & Rules in Christian Ethics. Paul Ramsey. LC 83-10257. 256p. 1983. pap. text ed. 13.25 (ISBN 0-8191-3355-8). U Pr of Amer.

Deeds of God in Rddhipur. Ed. by Anne Feldhaus. LC 83-21949. 1984. 27.00x (ISBN 0-19-503438-4). Oxford U Pr.

Deeds of the Righteous. Beth Jacob Hebrew Teachers College Staff. (Illus.). 160p. 6.95 (ISBN 0-934390-00-2). B J Hebrew Tchrs.

Deep Is the Hunger. Howard Thurman. LC 73-16023. 212p. 1973. pap. 6.95 (ISBN 0-913408-10-7). Friends United.

Deep River. Howard Thurman. Bd. with Negro Spiritual Speaks of Life & Death. LC 75-27041. 136p. 1975. pap. 5.95 (ISBN 0-913408-20-4). Friends United.

Deep South: Memory & Observation. Erskine Caldwell. LC 80-16013. (Brown Thrasher Bks.). 270p. 1980. pap. 6.95 (ISBN 0-8203-0525-1). U of Ga Pr.

Deep Things of God. Norman P. Grubb. 1970. pap. 4.95 (ISBN 0-87508-209-2). Chr Lit.

Deeper Christian Life. Andrew Murray. Ed. by Lyman R. Tucker. 112p. 1986. pap. 5.95 (ISBN 0-310-29791-5, 10365P). Zondervan.

Deeper Experiences of Famous Christians. James G. Lawson. 1981. pap. 2.95 (ISBN 0-87162-069-3, D3349). Warner Pr.

Deeper Faith. Carol Murphy. 1983. pap. 2.50x (ISBN 0-87574-099-5, 099). Pendle Hill.

Deeper Faith: An Exposition of the Canons of Dort. Gordon H. Girod. 1978. pap. 1.95 (ISBN 0-8010-3725-5). Baker Bk.

Deeper Kind of Truth: Biblical Tales for Life & Prayer. Elizabeth M. Reis. 112p. (Orig.). 1987. pap. 5.95 (ISBN 0-8091-2858-6). Paulist Pr.

Deeper Life: A Meditation on Christian Mysticism. Louis Dupre. 128p. (Orig.). 1981. pap. 4.95 (ISBN 0-8245-0007-5). Crossroad NY.

Deeper Man. John G. Bennett. LC 84-73170. 254p. 1985. 8.95 (ISBN 0-934254-07-9). Claymont Comm.

Deeper Meaning of Economic Life: Critical Essays on the U. S. Bishops' Pastoral Letter on the Economy. R. Bruce Douglass et al. (Studies in Ethics). Orig. Title: Forging a New Public Philosophy. 296p. 1987. 19.95 (ISBN 0-87840-440-6); pap. 12.95 (ISBN 0-87840-441-4). Georgetown U Pr.

Deeper Secrets in Human History in the Light of the Gospel of St. Matthew. 2nd ed. Rudolf Steiner. Tr. of Die tieferen Geheimmnisse des Menschheitswerdens im Lichte der Evangelien. 60p. 1985. pap. 6.95 (ISBN 0-88010-132-6). Anthroposophic.

Deeper Things. Hames. pap. 2.95 (ISBN 0-686-12864-8). Schmul Pub Co.

Deesses Latines et Mythes Vediques. Georges Dumezil. Ed. by Kees W. Bolle. LC 77-79121. (Mythology Ser.). (Fr.). 1978. Repr. of 1956 ed. lib. bdg. 17.00x (ISBN 0-405-10533-9). Ayer Co Pubs.

Defeated Demons. Morris L. Venden. (Uplook Ser.). 16p. 1982. pap. 0.99 (ISBN 0-8163-0487-4). Pacific Pr Pub Assn.

Defeating Anger & Other Dragons of the Soul. Peter Wilkes. (Dragon Slayer Ser.). 180p. 1987. pap. 5.95 (ISBN 0-87784-517-4). Inter Varsity.

Defence of the American Policy As Opposed to the Encroachments of Foreign Influence, & Especially to the Interference of the Papacy in the Political Interests & Affairs of the United States. Thomas R. Whitney. LC 75-145496. (American Immigration Library). 372p. 1971. Repr. of 1856 ed. lib. bdg. 22.95x (ISBN 0-89198-029-6). Ozer.

Defence of the Gospel in the New Testament. rev. ed. F. F. Bruce. LC 77-2282. 1977. pap. 4.95 (ISBN 0-8028-1024-1). Eerdmans.

Defence of the Short View off the Profaneness & Immorality of the English Stage. Jeremy Collier. LC 72-170444. (English Stage Ser.: Vol. 30). 1973. lib. bdg. 61.00 (ISBN 0-8240-0613-5). Garland Pub.

Defence of the Sincere & True Translations of the Holy Scriptures into the English Tongue. William Fulke. Repr. of 1843 ed. 51.00 (ISBN 0-384-17230-X). Johnson Repr.

Defences of the Upper Roman Enclosure. Michael J. Jones. (Archaeology of Lincoln Ser.: Vol. 7). 62p. 1980. pap. text ed. 25.00x (ISBN 0-906780-00-4, Pub. by Coun Brit Archaeology). Humanities.

Defender of the Church of England: A Biography of R. R. Williams, Bishop of Leicester. John S. Peart-Binns. 172p. 1984. 30.00x (ISBN 0-317-43628-7, Pub. by Amate Pr. Ltd.). State Mutual Bk.

Defender of the Race: James Theodore Holly, Black Nationalist Bishop. David M. Dean. 150p. 1979. 16.95x (ISBN 0-931186-02-1). Lambeth Pr.

Defenders of the Faith: Religion & Politics from Pilgrim Fathers to Ronald Reagan. Wilbur Edel. LC 87-2367. 280p. 1987. lib. bdg. 38.95 (ISBN 0-275-92662-1, C2662). Praeger.

Defending "A Christian Country" Churchmen & Society in New South Wales in the 1880's & After. Walter Phillips. (Illus.). 332p. 1982. text ed. 39.95 (ISBN 0-7022-1539-2). U of Queensland Pr.

Defending the Blind Man. large print ed. Pearl Brians. 1985. pap. 4.00 (ISBN 0-914009-28-1). VHI Library.

Defending the Papacy. Gerard Morrissey. 96p. (Orig.). 1984. pap. 4.95 (ISBN 0-931888-15-8). Christendom Pubns.

Defense of Biblical Infallibility. Clark Pinnock. pap. 1.75 (ISBN 0-8010-6863-0). Baker Bk.

Defense of Biblical Infallibility. Clark H. Pinnock. 1967. pap. 1.75 (ISBN 0-87552-350-1). Presby & Reformed.

Defense of God. Ed. by John Roth & Fredrick E. Sontag. LC 84-25592. (God Ser.). 196p. (Orig.). 1985. text ed. 21.95 (ISBN 0-913757-26-8, Pub. by New Era Bks); pap. text ed. 12.95 (ISBN 0-913757-27-6, Pub. by New Era Bks). Paragon Hse.

Defense of the Faith. Cornelius Van Til. 1967. pap. 6.95 (ISBN 0-87552-483-4). Presby & Reformed.

Defense of Women's Rights to Ordination in the Methodist Episcopal Church. Ed. by Carolyn G. De Swarte & Donald Dayton. (Women in American Protestant Religion Series 1800-1930). 230p. 1987. lib. bdg. 35.00 (ISBN 0-8240-0654-2). Garland Pub.

Defensio Ecclesiae Anglicanae. Richard Crakanthorp. LC 72-1027. (Library of Anglo-Catholic Theology: No. 6). Repr. of 1847 ed. 27.50 (ISBN 0-404-52087-1). AMS Pr.

Deference of Iudiciall Astrologie: In Answer to a Treatise Lately Published by M. John Chamber. Christopher Heydon. LC 77-7407. (English Experience Ser.: No. 873). 1977. Repr. of 1603 ed. lib. bdg. 58.00 (ISBN 90-221-0873-2). Walter J Johnson.

Defining America: Christian Critique of the American Dream. Robert Benne & Philip Hefener. LC 73-89062. pap. 40.00 (2026941). Bks Demand UMI.

Definite Decisions for New Church Members. Jerome O. Williams. pap. 1.25 (ISBN 0-8054-9402-2). Broadman.

Definition of Good. Alfred C. Ewing. LC 78-59021. 1979. Repr. of 1947 ed. 20.25 (ISBN 0-88355-695-2). Hyperion Conn.

Defoe & Casuistry. G. A. Starr. LC 75-113010. 1971. 25.50x (ISBN 0-691-06192-0). Princeton U Pr.

Dei Gloria Intacta. Jan Van Rijckenborgh. 244p. 1987. 14.50 (ISBN 0-317-52802-5). Rosycross Pr.

Deidad de Cristo. Evis L. Carballosa. Orig. Title: Deity of Christ. (Span.). 168p. 1982. pap. 3.50 (ISBN 0-8254-1102-5). Kregel.

Deification of Man. Georgios I. Mantzaridis. Tr. by Liadain Sherrard from Gr. 136p. (Orig.). 1984. pap. text ed. 7.95 (ISBN 0-88141-027-6). St Vladimirs.

Deification of Man: Its Methods & Stages According to the Yoga Vasistha Including a Translation of the Essence of Vasistha's Teachings. B. L. Atreya. 116p. 1980. pap. 4.50 (ISBN 0-935548-02-5). Santarasa Pubns.

Deism & Natural Religion: A Source Book. Ed. by E. Graham Waring. LC 66-28139. (Milestones of Thought Ser.). pap. 4.95 (ISBN 0-8044-6968-7). Ungar.

Deist's Manual; or a Rational Enquiry into the Christian Religion. Charles Gildon. Ed. by Rene Wellek. LC 75-11220. (British Philosophers & Theologians of the 17th & 18th Centuries Ser.: Vol. 23). 1976. Repr. of 1705 ed. lib. bdg. 51.00 (ISBN 0-8240-1774-9). Garland Pub.

Deity & Morality-with Regard to the Naturalistic Fallacy. Burton F. Porter. LC 68-16017. 1968. text ed. 7.95x (ISBN 0-04-100012-9). Humanities.

Del Odio al Amor. Francisco Ordonez. 1983. pap. 1.50 (ISBN 0-311-08223-8). Casa Bautista.

Delhi Diary: Daily Talks at Prayer Meetings, 1947-1948. M. K. Gandhi. 426p. 1982. 7.50 (ISBN 0-934676-56-9). Greenlf Bks.

Delicate Balance: Church, State & the Schools. Martha M. McCarthy. LC 83-60797. 184p. 1983. pap. 6.00 (ISBN 0-87367-427-8). Phi Delta Kappa.

Delightful Discipline. Louis R. Goodgame. Date not set. pap. 3.00 (ISBN 0-8010-3815-4). Baker Bk.

Delinquent Saints: Disciplinary Action in the Early Congregational Churches of Massachusetts. Emil Oberholzer, Jr. LC 70-76660. (Columbia University. Studies in the Social Sciences: No. 590). Repr. of 1956 ed. 14.50 (ISBN 0-404-51590-8). AMS Pr.

Deliver Us from Evil: The Prayer of Our Lord. John B. Coburn. 96p. 1976. pap. 4.95 (ISBN 0-8164-2124-2, HarpR). Har-Row.

Deliver Us from the Evil One. Robert G. Bayley. 36p. 1987. pap. 2.95 (ISBN 0-934421-09-9). Presby Renewal Pubns.

Deliverance from Evil Spirits: A Weapon for Spiritual Warfare. Michael Scanlan & Randall J. Cirner. 125p. (Orig.). 1980. pap. 4.95 (ISBN 0-89283-091-3). Servant.

Deliverance from the Bondage of Fear. Bob Buess. 1972. pap. 2.50 (ISBN 0-934244-03-0). Sweeter Than Honey.

Deliverance Prayer: Experiential, Psychological & Theological Approaches. Ed. by Matthew Linn & Dennis Linn. LC 81-82334. 256p. (Orig.). 1981. pap. 6.95 (ISBN 0-8091-2385-1). Paulist Pr.

Delivering the Male: Out of the Tough-Guy Trap into a Better Marriage. Clayton C. Barbeau. 120p. (Orig.). 1982. pap. 6.95 (ISBN 0-86683-642-X, HarpR). Har-Row.

Della Contemplazione. Guigo Du Pont. Ed. by James Hogg. Tr. & intro. by Emilio Piovesan. (Analecta Cartusiana Ser.: No. 45). (Ital. & Lat.). 123p. (Orig.). 1979. pap. 25.00 (ISBN 3-7052-0061-5, Pub by Salzburg Studies). Longwood Pub Group.

Delphic Oracle: Its Early History, Influence & Fall. T. Dempsey. LC 69-13234. Repr. of 1918 ed. 15.00 (ISBN 0-405-08442-0). Ayer Co Pubs.

Deluge. Gerald W. Wheeler. LC 78-8404. (Flame Ser.). 1978. pap. 0.99 (ISBN 0-8127-0191-7). Review & Herald.

Deluge Story in Stone. Byron C. Nelson. (Illus.). 1968. Repr. of 1931 ed. 5.95 (ISBN 0-87123-095-X, 210095). Bethany Hse.

Deluxe Haggadah. Tr. by Abraham Regelson. 1961. velour bound 30.00 (ISBN 0-914080-34-2). Shulsinger Sales.

Deluxe Story of Easter for Children. Beverly Charette. (Illus.). 48p. 1985. 5.95 (ISBN 0-8249-8076-X). Ideals.

Demaundes of Holy Scripture, with Answers to the Same. Thomas Becon. LC 79-84087. (English Experience Ser.: No.907). 116p. 1979. Repr. of 1577 ed. lib. bdg. 9.00 (ISBN 90-221-0907-0). Walter J Johnson.

Demerara Martyr: Memoirs of the Reverend John Smith, Missionary to Demerara. Edwin A. Wallbridge. LC 70-79812. (Illus.). Repr. of 1848 ed. 22.50x (ISBN 0-8371-1511-6, WAD&, Pub. by Negro U Pr). Greenwood.

Demeter & Persephone in Ancient Corinth. Nancy Bookidis & Ronald Stroud. (Corinth Notes Ser.: No. 2). (Illus.). 32p. (Orig.). 1987. pap. 3.00. Am Sch Athens.

Democracy & Mediating Structures: A Theological Inquiry. Ed. by Michael Novak. 1980. 13.25 (ISBN 0-8447-2175-1); pap. 7.25 (ISBN 0-8447-2176-X). Am Enterprise.

Democracy & Mission Education in Korea. James E. Fisher. LC 70-176773. (Columbia University. Teachers College. Contributions to Education Ser.: No. 306). Repr. of 1928 ed. 22.50 (ISBN 0-404-55306-0). AMS Pr.

Democracy & Religion: Gladstone & the Liberal Party, 1867-1876. J. P. Parry. (Cambridge Studies in the History & Theory of Politics). 520p. 1986. 59.50 (ISBN 0-521-30948-4). Cambridge U Pr.

Democracy & the Islamic State. A. H. Siddiqui. 2.50 (ISBN 0-686-83892-0). Kazi Pubns.

Democratic Manifesto: The Impact of Dynamic Christianity Upon Public Life & Government. Samuel E. Stumpf. LC 54-4773. 1954. 7.95x (ISBN 0-8265-1039-6). Vanderbilt U Pr.

Demolishing the Hosts of Hell: Every Christian's Job. rev. ed. Win Worley. (Orig.). 1980. pap. 5.00 (ISBN 0-685-60693-7). HBC.

Demon of Discord: Tensions in the Catholic Church of Victoria, 1853-1864. Margaret M. Pawsey. (Illus.). 200p. 1983. 25.00x (ISBN 0-522-84249-6, Pub. by Melbourne U Pr). Intl Spec Bk.

Demon Possession. John W. Montgomery. LC 75-19313. 1976. pap. 9.95 (ISBN 0-87123-102-6, 210102). Bethany Hse.

Demoniality. Ludovico M. Sinistrari. LC 72-83751. Repr. of 1927 ed. lib. bdg. 22.00 (ISBN 0-405-08976-7, Pub. by Blom). Ayer Co Pubs.

Demonic: A Selected Theological Study: An Examination into the Theology of Edwin Lewis, Karl Barth, & Paul Tillich. Vernon Mallow. LC 83-1143. 192p. (Orig.). 1983. lib. bdg. 26.00 (ISBN 0-8191-3069-9); pap. text ed. 11.50 (ISBN 0-8191-3070-2). U Pr of Amer.

Demonic Imagination: Style & Theme in French Romantic Poetry. John P. Houston. LC 69-15051. xi, 177p. 20.00x (ISBN 0-8071-0306-3). La State U Pr.

Demonism Verified & Analyzed. Hugh W. White. 69.95 (ISBN 0-8490-0016-5). Gordon Pr.

Demonology & Devil-Lore, 2 vols. Moncure D. Conway. Set. 250.00 (ISBN 0-8490-0017-3). Gordon Pr.

Demonology & Witchcraft. Walter Scott. 1970. 7.95 (ISBN 0-8065-0213-4). Citadel Pr.

Demonology of the Early Christian World. Everett Ferguson. LC 84-16681. (Symposium Ser.: Vol. 12). 190p. 1984. 19.95 (ISBN 0-88946-703-X). E Mellen.

Demons & How to Deal With Them. 2nd ed. Kenneth E. Hagin. 1983. pap. 1.00 (ISBN 0-89276-026-5). Hagin Ministries.

Demons At Your Doorstep. Peter Popoff. Ed. by Don Tanner. LC 82-82842. (Illus.). 56p. 1982. pap. 1.50 (ISBN 0-938544-13-6). Faith Messenger.

Demons, Demons, Demons. John P. Newport. LC 78-189503. 1977. pap. 3.95 (ISBN 0-8054-5577-9). Broadman.

Demons, Doubters & Dead Men. Joyce M. Smith. (Good Life Bible Studies Book). 64p. (Orig.). 1986. 2.95wkbk. (ISBN 0-8423-0542-4). Tyndale.

Demons, Exorcism & the Evangelical. John J. Davis. 1979. pap. 1.00 (ISBN 0-88469-043-1). BMH Bks.

Demons in the World Today. Merrill F. Unger. 1980. pap. 6.95 (ISBN 0-8423-0661-7). Tyndale.

Demons, Yes - but Thank God for Good Angels. Lehman Strauss. LC 75-38804. 1976. pap. 2.95 (ISBN 0-87213-831-3). Loizeaux.

Demonstrating God's Power. Walter J. Cummins. LC 85-50446. 276p. 1985. 6.95 (ISBN 0-910068-60-7). Am Christian.

Denial: A Play for Lent. Clinton R. Morey. 1980. 3.95 (ISBN 0-89536-412-3, 0420). CSS of Ohio.

Denial of Death. Ernest Becker. LC 73-1860. 1973. 19.95 (ISBN 0-02-902150-2); pap. 8.95 (ISBN 0-02-902380-7). Free Pr.

Denominational Policies in the Support & Supervision of Higher Education. Paul M. Limbert. LC 75-176994. (Columbia University. Teachers College. Contributions to Education: No. 378). Repr. of 1929 ed. 22.50 (ISBN 0-404-55378-8). AMS Pr.

Denys the Carthusian: Commentator on Boethius's De Consolatione Philosophiae. Raymond Macken. Ed. by James Hogg. (Analecta Cartusiana Ser.: No. 118). 94p. (Orig.). 1984. pap. 25.00 (ISBN 0-317-42573-0, Pub. by Salzburg Studies). Longwood Pub Group.

Deo: Studien Zur Literaturkritik und Thelogie des Buches Jona, des Gespraechs zwischen Abraham und Jahiwe in Gen. 18, 22ff. Ludwig Schmidt. (Beiheft 143 zur Zeitschrift Fuer die Alttestamentliche Wissenschaft Ser.). 1976. 41.60x (ISBN 3-11-006618-1). De Gruyter.

Departing Glory: Eight Jeremiads of Increase Mather. Increase Mather. LC 86-31349. 1987. 50.00x (ISBN 0-8201-1415-4). Schol Facsimiles.

Depopulation Arranged, Convicted & Condemned by the Lawes of God & Man. Robert Powell. LC 76-57407. (English Experience Ser.: No. 823). 1977. Repr. of 1636 ed. lib. bdg. 16.00 (ISBN 90-221-0823-6). Walter J Johnson.

Deportation of the Jews to the East: Settin, 1940 to Hungary 1944. John Mendelsohn. LC 81-80316. (Holocaust Ser.). 256p. 1982. lib. bdg. 61.00 (ISBN 0-8240-4882-2). Garland Pub.

Depressed Christian. Gerald F. Mundfrom. 115p. (Orig.). 1983. 2.50 (ISBN 0-318-19335-3). Mercy & Truth.

Depression & Its Remedy. Wim Malgo. 1980. 2.95 (ISBN 0-937422-03-7). Midnight Call.

Depression: Finding Hope & Meaning in Life's Darkest Shadow. Don Baker & Emery Nester. LC 82-24609. (Critical Concern Ser.). 1983. 10.95 (ISBN 0-88070-011-4). Multnomah.

Deprived, the Disabled & the Fullness of Life. Ed. by Flavian Dougherty. 1984. pap. 4.95 (ISBN 0-89453-442-4). M Glazier.

Depth Psychology & Vocation: A Psycho-Social Perspective. Luigi M. Rulla. LC 70-146938. 1971. 28.00 (ISBN 88-7652-374-X). Loyola.

Deputy. Rolf Hochhuth. Tr. by Richard Winston & Clara Winston. 1963. pap. 7.95 (ISBN 0-394-17125-X, B154, BC). Grove.

Derech HaShem: The Way of G-D. Moshe C. Luzatto. Tr. by Aryeh Kaplan from Hebrew. 1978. 12.95 (ISBN 0-87306-136-5); pap. 9.95. Feldheim.

Derek Emunah: The Path of Faith. Abraham Bibago. 204p. 1521. text ed. 49.68x (ISBN 0-576-80102-X, Pub. by Gregg Intl Pubs England). Gregg Intl.

Dermis Probe. Idries Shah. 191p. 1980. 15.95 (ISBN 0-900860-83-9, Pub. by Octagon Pr England). Ins Study Human.

Derrida on the Mend. Robert R. Magliola. LC 82-62779. 256p. 1984. 18.00 (ISBN 0-911198-69-5). Purdue U Pr.

Dervish Virtues. Muzaffer Ozak. 192p. (Orig.). 1987. pap. 9.00 (ISBN 0-939660-22-9). Threshold VT.

Derwood, Inc. Jeri Massi. (English Skills for Christian Schools Ser.). 288p. (Orig.). 1986. pap. 5.95 (ISBN 0-89084-323-6). Bob Jones Univ Pr.

Desafio a Triunfar. Arthur Wallis. 128p. 1976. 2.50 (ISBN 0-88113-000-1). Edit Betania.

Desafio del Liderazgo. Ted W. Engstrom. Tr. by Adriana P. De Bedoian from Eng. Tr. of Your Gift of Administration. (Span.). 128p. 1987. pap. 3.25 (ISBN 0-88113-058-3). Edit Betania.

Desatir. Tr. by Mulla Firuz Bin Kaus from Mahabhadian. LC 73-84045. (Secret Doctrine Reference Ser.). 208p. 1980. pap. 9.00 (ISBN 0-913510-33-5). Wizards.

Descartes. facs. ed. John P. Mahaffy. LC 71-94277. (Select Bibliographies Reprint Ser.). 1902. 19.00 (ISBN 0-8369-5051-8). Ayer Co Pubs.

Descartes. Paul Valery. 133p. 1980. Repr. lib. bdg. 15.00 (ISBN 0-89984-477-4). Century Bookbindery.

Descartes Against the Skeptics. E. M. Curley. LC 77-14366. 1978. 17.50x (ISBN 0-674-19826-3). Harvard U Pr.

Descartes & the Modern Mind. Albert G. Balz. xiv, 492p. 1967. Repr. of 1952 ed. 37.50 (ISBN 0-208-00023-2, Archon). Shoe String.

Descartes' Conversation with Burman. Ed. & tr. by John Cottingham. 1974. 11.95x (ISBN 0-19-824671-4). Oxford U Pr.

Descartes: His Moral Philosophy & Psychology. John J. Blom. LC 78-55241. 1978. 35.00 (ISBN 0-8147-0999-0). NYU Pr.

Descent from Heaven: Images of Dew in Greek Poetry & Religion. Deborah Boedeker. (American Philological Association, American Classical Studies: No. 13). 154p. 1985. pap. 11.95 (ISBN 0-89130-807-5, 40 04 13). Scholars Pr GA.

Descent from the Cross: Its Relation to the Extra-Liturgical Depositio Drama. Elizabeth C. Parker. LC 77-94713. (Outstanding Dissertations in the Fine Arts Ser.). 1978. lib. bdg. 41.00 (ISBN 0-8240-3245-4). Garland Pub.

Descent into Hell: A Study of the Radical Reversal of the Christain Consciousness. Thomas J. Altizer. 222p. 1979. pap. 6.95 (ISBN 0-8164-1194-8, HarpR). Har-Row.

Description of the Clergy in Rural Russia: The Memoir of a Nineteenth Century Parish Priest. I. S. Belliustin. Ed. by Gregory L. Freeze. LC 85-47699. (Illus.). 224p. 1985. text ed. 29.95x (ISBN 0-8014-1796-1); pap. text ed. 9.95x (ISBN 0-8014-9335-8). Cornell U Pr.

Descriptive Catalogue of Seventeenth Century Religious Literature in the Kansas State University Library. William P. Williams. LC 67-63307. (Libraries Bibliography Ser.: No. 3). 1966. 1.50 (ISBN 0-686-20809-9). KSU.

Descubramos Como Orar. Hope McDonald. Tr. by F. G. Coleman from Eng. Tr. of Discovering How to Pray. (Span.). 128p. 1982. pap. 3.20 (ISBN 0-311-40040-X). Casa Bautista.

Descubre Tu Poder Interno. Charles Filmore. LC 81-69933. Orig. Title: Discover the Power Within You. (Eng.). 448p. 1983. 5.95 (ISBN 0-87159-026-3). Unity School.

Desecration of Christ. Richard Egenter. 1967. 4.50 (ISBN 0-8199-0018-4, L38133). Franciscan Herald.

Desert a City. Derwas J. Chitty. 222p. 1977. pap. 8.95 (ISBN 0-913836-45-1). St Vladimirs.

Desert & the City: An Interpretation of the History of Christian Spirituality. Thomas M. Gannon & George W. Traub. 338p. 1984. 8.95 (ISBN 0-8294-0452-X). Loyola.

Desert Blooms: A Personal Adventure in Growing Old Creatively. Sarah-Patton Boyle. 208p. (Orig.). 1983. pap. 7.95 (ISBN 0-687-10484-X). Abingdon.

Desert Fathers. Helen Waddell. 1957. pap. 7.95 (ISBN 0-472-06008-2, 8, AA). U of Mich Pr.

Desert in the City. Carlo Carretto. (Crossroad Paperback Ser.). 112p. 1982. pap. 4.95 (ISBN 0-8245-0423-2). Crossroad NY.

Desert Is Fertile. Dom H. Camara. 1976. pap. 1.50 (ISBN 0-89129-060-5). Jove Pubns.

Desert Notes: Reflections in the Eye of a Raven. Barry H. Lopez. LC 76-6099. (Illus.). 96p. 1976. 6.95 (ISBN 0-8362-0661-4). Andrews McMeel Parker.

Desert of the Exodus: Journeys on Foot in the Wilderness of the Forty Years Wanderings, 2 vols. in one. Edward H. Palmer. Ed. by Moshe Davis. (America & the Holy Land Ser.). (Illus.). lib. bdg. 51.00x (ISBN 0-405-10276-3). Ayer Co Pubs.

Desert Place. Adolfo Quezada. (Illus.). 96p. (Orig.). 1982. pap. 2.95 (ISBN 0-914544-40-3). Living Flame Pr.

Desert Wisdom: Sayings from the Desert Fathers. Yushi Nomura. LC 82-45488. (Illus.). 128p. 1982. 14.95 (ISBN 0-385-18078-0). Doubleday.

Desert Wisdom: Sayings from the Desert Fathers. Yushi Nomura. LC 82-45488. (Illus.). 128p. 1984. pap. 8.95 (ISBN 0-385-18079-9, Im). Doubleday.

Desiderius Erasmus Concerning the Aim & Method of Education. Ed. by William H. Woodward. LC 64-18613. (Classics in Education Ser.). (Orig.). 1964. pap. text ed. 5.00x (ISBN 0-8077-2347-9). Tchrs Coll.

Desiderius Erasmus of Rotterdam. Ephraim Emerton. 1900. 35.00 (ISBN 0-8274-2167-2). R West.

Design for Church Growth. Charles L. Chaney & Ron S. Lewis. LC 77-87364. 1978. pap. 6.95 (ISBN 0-8054-6218-X). Broadman.

Design for Discipleship, 6 bks. rev. ed. Navigators Staff. 1980. pap. text ed. 9.35 (ISBN 0-934396-15-9). Churches Alive.

Design for Discipleship. J. Dwight Pentecost. 1977. pap. 4.95 (ISBN 0-310-30861-5, 17011P). Zondervan.

Design for Kingship: The Deuteronomistic Narrative Technique in 1 Kings 3: 4-15. Helen A. Kenik. LC 82-21054. (SBL Dissertation Ser.). 258p. 1983. pap. 13.50 (ISBN 0-89130-605-6, 06 01 69). Scholars Pr GA.

Design for Living: The Sermon on the Mount. John A. Ishee. 36p. 1982. pap. 3.50 (ISBN 0-939298-07-4). J M Prods.

Design for Preaching. H. Grady Davis. LC 58-5749. (Orig.). 1958. 9.95 (ISBN 0-8006-0806-2, 1-806). Fortress.

Design for Teaching & Training: A Self-Study Guide to Lesson Planning. Ford LeRoy. LC 77-87249. (Illus.). 1978. pap. 12.95 (ISBN 0-8054-3422-4). Broadman.

Designed by God: A Woman's Workshop on Wholeness. Kirkie Morrissey. (Woman's Workshop Ser.). 160p. (Orig.). 1985. pap. 3.95 (ISBN 0-310-45011-X, 16246P). Zondervan.

Designed for Destiny. Jerry H. Combee & Cline E. Hall. 112p. 1985. 4.95 (ISBN 0-8423-0619-6). Tyndale.

Designed for Holiness: God's Plan to Shape & Use You for His Kingdom. rev. ed. Peter Gillquist. 210p. 1986. pap. 5.95 (ISBN 0-89283-286-X). Servant.

Designing the Sermon: Order & Movement in Preaching. James E. Massey. LC 80-17920. (Abingdon Preacher's Library). 128p. (Orig.). 1980. pap. 6.95 (ISBN 0-687-10490-4). Abingdon.

Designs for a Just Society. James Alberione. (Divine Master Ser.). 1976. 6.00 (ISBN 0-8198-0400-2); pap. 5.00 (ISBN 0-8198-0401-0); wkbk 0.60 (ISBN 0-8198-0402-9). Dghtrs St Paul.

Desir et la Reflexion Dans la Philosophie De Spinoza. R. Misrahi. (Publications Gramma Ser.). 382p. 1972. pap. 30.25x (ISBN 0-677-50815-8). Gordon & Breach.

Desire & Denial: Celibacy & the Church. Gordon Thomas. 1986. 19.95 (ISBN 0-316-84097-1). Little.

Desire & Fulfillment. Hugh Shearman. 1.75 (ISBN 0-8356-7054-6). Theos Pub Hse.

Desire of the Righteous Granted. John Bunyan. 1974. pap. 1.75 (ISBN 0-685-52816-2). Reiner.

Desiring God: Meditations of a Christian Hedonist. John Piper. (Critical Concern Ser.). 1987. 12.95 (ISBN 0-88070-169-2). Multnomah.

Desolate City: Revolution in the Catholic Church. Anne R. Muggeridge. 256p. 1986. 16.95 (ISBN 0-06-066038-4, HarpR). Har-Row.

Destin De la Pensee et, la Mort De Dieu, Selon Heidegger. Laffoucriere. (Phaenomenologica Ser: No. 24). 1968. lib. bdg. 29.00 (ISBN 90-247-0255-0, Pub. by Martinus Nijhoff Netherlands). Kluwer Academic.

Destination of Life. George E. Vandeman. LC 66-21954. (Stories That Win Ser.). 1966. pap. 1.25 (ISBN 0-8163-0095-X, 04270-5). Pacific Pr Pub Assn.

Destined for Glory: The Meaning of Suffering. Margaret Clarkson. 144p. 1983. pap. 4.95 (ISBN 0-8028-1953-2). Eerdmans.

Destined for Royalty: A Brahmin Priest's Search for Truth. Lorry Lutz. LC 85-22681. 152p. (Orig.). 1986. pap. 5.95 (ISBN 0-87808-202-6, WCL202-6). William Carey Lib.

Destined for the Cross. Paul E. Billheimer. 1982. pap. 3.95 (ISBN 0-8423-0604-8). Tyndale.

Destined for the Throne. Paul E. Billheimer. LC 83-15151. 140p. (Orig.). 1983. pap. 4.95 (ISBN 0-87123-309-6, 210309). Bethany Hse.

Destined for the Throne. Paul E. Billheimer. 1983. pap. 4.95 (ISBN 0-87508-040-5). Chr Lit.

Destined to Mature. Gerald Derstine. 144p. (Orig.). 1984. pap. 3.50 (ISBN 0-88368-147-1). Whitaker Hse.

Destined to Overcome. Paul E. Billheimer. 123p. 1982. pap. 4.95 (ISBN 0-87123-287-1, 210287). Bethany Hse.

Destiny of a King. Georges Dumezil. Tr. by Alf Hiltebeitel. 1973. 15.00x (ISBN 0-226-16975-8). U of Chicago Pr.

Destiny of Man. Nikolai Berdiaev. Tr. by Natalie Duddington. LC 78-14100. 1987. Repr. of 1954 ed. 26.50 (ISBN 0-88355-775-4). Hyperion Conn.

Destiny of the Soul: Critical History of the Doctrine of a Future Life, 2 Vols. 10th ed. William R. Alger. LC 68-19263. 1968. Repr. of 1880 ed. Set. lib. bdg. 43.25x (ISBN 0-8371-0003-8, ALDS). Greenwood.

Destiny of the Warrior. Georges Dumezil. Tr. by Alf Hiltebeitel. LC 75-113254. 184p. 1971. pap. write for info. (ISBN 0-226-16971-5). U of Chicago Pr.

Destruction of Death. Nelson L. Price. LC 82-72464. 1983. 4.50 (ISBN 0-8054-1528-9). Broadman.

Destruction of the European Jews, 3 vols. rev. ed. Raul Hilberg. LC 84-18369. 1312p. 1985. Boxed Set. text ed. 159.50x (ISBN 0-8419-0832-X); pap. 14.95 student ed. (ISBN 0-8419-0910-5). Holmes & Meier.

Destructive Conception of God in Kant's "Philosophy of Man". Douglas P. Somerset. (Illus.). 129p. 1982. 73.45 (ISBN 0-89266-355-3). Am Classical Coll Pr.

Detaching with Love. Carolyn W. 24p. (Orig.). 1984. pap. 0.95 (ISBN 0-89486-232-4). Hazelden.

Detection of the Trinity. John Thurmer. 93p. 1986. pap. 8.75 (ISBN 0-85364-395-4, Pub. by Paternoster UK). Attic Pr.

Determination of Death: Theological, Medical, Ethical & Legal Issues. Albert S. Moraczewski & J. Stuart Showalter. LC 82-1127. 32p. (Orig.). 1982. pap. 3.00 (ISBN 0-87125-072-1). Cath Health.

Determinations of the Most Famous Universities of Italy & France. LC 72-189. (English Experience Ser.: No. 329). 308p. Repr. of 1531 ed. 22.00 (ISBN 90-221-0329-3). Walter J Johnson.

Determined! Benjamin Balshone. 1984. 15.95 (ISBN 0-8197-0494-6). Bloch.

Deus Destroyed: The Image of Christianity in Early Modern Japan. George Elison. LC 72-97833. (East Asian Ser: No. 72). 704p. 1974. 40.00x (ISBN 0-674-19961-8). Harvard U Pr.

Deuterocanonical Books (Paraphrase) Albert J. Nevins. 1976. pap. 1.25 (ISBN 0-87973-721-2). Our Sunday Visitor.

Deuteronomic History. Terence E. Fretheim. Ed. by Lloyd R. Bailey & Victory P. Furnish. 160p. (Orig.). 1983. pap. 9.95 (ISBN 0-687-10497-1). Abingdon.

Deuteronomio: El Evangelio del Amor (Comentario Biblico Portavoz) Samuel J. Schultz. Orig. Title: Deuteronomy (Everyman's Bible Commentary) (Span.). 122p. 1979. pap. 3.50 (ISBN 0-8254-1658-2). Kregel.

Deuteronomistic History. Martin Noth. (Journal for the Study of the Old Testament, Supplement Ser.: No. 15). 1981. text ed. 20.95x (ISBN 0-905774-25-6, Pub. by JSOT Pr England); pap. text ed. 10.95x (ISBN 0-905774-30-2, Pub. by JSOT Pr England). Eisenbrauns.

Deuteronomistische Pentateuchredaktion in Exodus 3-17. Werner Fuss. (Beiheft 126 zur Zeitschrift fuer die alttestamentliche Wissenschaft). xii, 406p. 1972. 48.40x (ISBN 3-11-003854-4). De Gruyter.

Deuteronomy. John Cummings. 1982. lib. bdg. 16.00 (ISBN 0-86524-085-X, 0501). Klock & Klock.

Deuteronomy. Charles R. Erdman. 96p. 1982. pap. 3.50 (ISBN 0-8010-3379-9). Baker Bk.

Deuteronomy. George S. Glanzman. Pt. 1. pap. 1.00 (ISBN 0-8091-5028-X); Pt. 2. pap. 1.00 (ISBN 0-8091-5029-8). Paulist Pr.

Deuteronomy. Louis Goldberg. (Bible Study Commentary Ser.). 208p. 1986. pap. 7.95 (ISBN 0-310-20201-9, 11412P). Zondervan.

Deuteronomy. Leslie J. Hoppe. (Bible Commentary Ser.). 104p. 1985. pap. 2.95 (ISBN 0-8146-1374-8). Liturgical Pr.

Deuteronomy. A. D. Mayes. (New Century Bible Ser.). 352p. 1979. 15.95 (ISBN 0-551-00804-0). Attic Pr.

Deuteronomy. A. D. Mayes. Ed. by Ronald E. Clements. (New Century Bible Commentary Ser.). (Orig.). 1981. pap. 9.95 (ISBN 0-8028-1882-X). Eerdmans.

Deuteronomy. Bruce Oberst. LC 70-1070. (Bible Study Textbook Ser.). 1968. 14.30 (ISBN 0-89900-009-6). College Pr Pub.

Deuteronomy. David F. Payne. LC 85-13653. (Daily Study Bible - Old Testament). 210p. 1985. 14.95 (ISBN 0-664-21832-6); pap. 7.95 (ISBN 0-664-24580-3). Westminster.

Deuteronomy. Anthony Phillips. LC 73-77172. (Cambridge Bible Commentary on the New English Bible, Old Testament Ser.). (Illus.). 224p. 1973. pap. 29.95 (ISBN 0-521-08636-1); pap. 12.95 (ISBN 0-521-09772-X). Cambridge U Pr.

Deuteronomy. Samuel Schultz. (Everyman Bible Commentary Ser). 128p. (Orig.). 1971. pap. 5.95 (ISBN 0-8024-2005-2). Moody.

Deuteronomy. J. Thompson. Ed. by D. J. Wiseman. LC 74-14303. (Tyndale Old Testament Commentary Ser.). 320p. 1975. 12.95 (ISBN 0-87784-882-3); pap. 6.95 (ISBN 0-87784-255-8). Inter-Varsity.

Deuteronomy: A Commentary. Gerhard Von Rad. LC 66-23088. (Old Testament Library). 212p. 1966. 15.95 (ISBN 0-664-20734-0). Westminster.

Deuteronomy: A Favored Book of Jesus. Bernard N. Schneider. pap. 5.95 (ISBN 0-88469-051-2). BMH Bks.

Deuteronomy & City Life: A Form Criticism of Texts with the Word City ('ir) in Deuteronomy 4: 41 -26: 19. Don C. Benjamin. LC 83-3609. (Illus.). 366p. (Orig.). 1983. lib. bdg. 31.25 (ISBN 0-8191-3138-5); pap. text ed. 15.75 (ISBN 0-8191-3139-3). U Pr of Amer.

Deuteronomy & the Deuteronomic School. M. Weinfeld. 1972. 53.00x (ISBN 0-19-826626-X). Oxford U Pr.

Deuteronomy, Joshua. Edward P. Blair. LC 59-10454. (Layman's Bible Commentary Ser: Vol. 5). 1964. pap. 4.95 (ISBN 0-8042-3065-X). John Knox.

Deuteronomy: The Torah. W. Gunther Plaut. (Modern Commentary Ser.). 528p. 1983. 20.00 (ISBN 0-8074-0045-9). UAHC.

Deuteronomy, with Excursus on Covenant & Law. Richard Clifford. (Old Testament Message Ser.: Vol. 4). 1982. 12.95 (ISBN 0-89453-404-1); pap. 7.95 (ISBN 0-89453-239-1). M Glazier.

Deux Pieces Imparfaites sur la Grace et le Concile de Trente, Extraites du M. S. de l'Abbe Perier. Blaise Pascal & Louis Lafuma. 76p. 1947. 5.95 (ISBN 0-686-54845-0). French & Eur.

Deux Redactions Du Roman Des Sept Sages De Rome. 1876. 28.00 (ISBN 0-384-54933-0); pap. 22.00 (ISBN 0-384-54923-3). Johnson Repr.

Devachanic Plane. Leadbeater. 5.50 (ISBN 0-8356-7075-9). Theos Pub Hse.

Devas & Men. South Ctr. of Theos. 8.95 (ISBN 0-8356-7518-1). Theos Pub Hse.

Devata (an Essay on Indian Mythology), by a Recluse of Vindhyachala. LC 73-3811. (Sacred Books of the Hindus: No. 19). Repr. of 1917 ed. 29.00 (ISBN 0-404-57819-5). AMS Pr.

Developing a Child's Spiritual Growth: Through Sight, Sound, Taste, Touch & Smell. Judy G. Smith. 80p. (Orig.). 1983. pap. 8.75 (ISBN 0-687-10499-8). Abingdon.

Developing Artistic & Perceptual Awareness: Art Practice in the Elementary Classroom. 5th. ed. Don Herberholz & Kay Alexander. 128p. 1985. pap. write for info. (ISBN 0-697-03221-3). Wm C Brown.

Developing Christian Education in a Smaller Church. Carolyn C. Brown. LC 81-17563. (Griggs Educational Resources Ser.). 96p. (Orig.). 1982. pap. 7.75 (ISBN 0-687-10508-0). Abingdon.

Developing Dynamic Stewardship: Fifteen Sermons on Commitment & Giving. Raymond B. Knudsen. LC 78-7846. 1978. pap. 5.50 (ISBN 0-687-10500-5). Abingdon.

Developing Faith. Kieran Sawyer. LC 78-72942. (Illus.). 152p. 1978. pap. text ed. 5.95 (ISBN 0-87793-164-X). Ave Maria.

Developing Faith in Your Confession. Charles Capps. 1986. mini bk. 0.75 (ISBN 0-89274-412-X). Harrison Hse.

Developing Leaders for Youth Ministry. David Ng. 64p. 1984. pap. 5.95 (ISBN 0-8170-1032-7). Judson.

Developing Leadership in the Teaching Church. Jan Chartier. 112p. 1985. pap. 5.95 (ISBN 0-8170-1067-X). Judson.

Developing Performance Excellence in Catholic Educational Policymaking: A Handbook of Training Programs. Mary-Angela Harper. 82p. 1982. 6.00 (ISBN 0-686-39917-X). Natl Cath Educ.

Developing Spiritually & Professionally. William M. Moremen. LC 84-5194. (Pastor's Handbooks: Vol. 5). 120p. 1984. pap. 7.95 (ISBN 0-664-24604-4). Westminster.

Development & Decline of Chinese Cosmology. John B. Henderson. LC 84-4000. (Neo-Confucian Studies). 280p. 1984. 36.00 (ISBN 0-231-05772-5); pap. cancelled (ISBN 0-231-05773-3). Columbia U Pr.

Development & Public Relations for the Catholic School. Jerry A. Jarc. 65p. 1986. 6.60 (ISBN 0-318-20562-9). Natl Cath Educ.

Development & Stress in Navajo Religion. Guy H. Cooper. 126p. (Orig.). 1984. pap. text ed. 20.00x (ISBN 91-7146-337-2). Coronet Bks.

Development from Kant to Hegel. Andrew Seth. 1975. lib. bdg. 49.95 (ISBN 0-8490-0020-3). Gordon Pr.

Development from Kant to Hegel, with Chapters on the Philosophy of Religion. Andrew Seth. Ed. by Lewis W. Beck. LC 75-32044. (Philosophy of Immanuel Kant Ser.: Vol. 7). 1976. Repr. of 1882 ed. lib. bdg. 24.00 (ISBN 0-8240-2331-5). Garland Pub.

Development in Total Catholic Education. 1985. 4.80 (ISBN 0-318-20606-4). Natl Cath Educ.

Development of Berkeley's Philosophy. George A. Johnston. LC 65-17903. 1965. Repr. of 1923 ed. 10.00x (ISBN 0-8462-0686-2). Russell.

Development of Buddhism in England. Christmas Humphreys. LC 78-72442. Repr. of 1937 ed. 17.50 (ISBN 0-404-17308-X). AMS Pr.

Development of Buddhist Ethics. G. S. Misra. 1984. text ed. 14.00x. Coronet Bks.

Development of Buddhist Iconography in Eastern India. Mallar Ghosh. (Illus.). 1980. text ed. 44.00x. Coronet Bks.

Development of Christian Doctrine: Some Historical Prolegomena. Jaroslav Pelikan. LC 69-14864. (St. Thomas More Lectures Ser.: No. 3). 174p. 1969. 18.50x (ISBN 0-300-01082-6). Yale U Pr.

Development of Consciousness: A Confluent Theory of Values. Brian Hall. LC 75-34843. 288p. 1976. 9.95 (ISBN 0-8091-0201-3); pap. 8.95 (ISBN 0-8091-1894-7). Paulist Pr.

Development of English Theology in the Later Nineteenth Century. L. Elliott-Binns. LC 72-122411. ix, 137p. 1971. Repr. of 1952 ed. 17.50 (ISBN 0-208-01045-9, Archon). Shoe String.

Development of Hindu Iconography. 3rd ed. J. N. Banerjee. (Illus.). 1974. text ed. 36.00x. Coronet Bks.

Development of Hindu Polity & Political Theories. Narayan C. Bandyopadhyaya. 1980. text ed. 28.50x. Coronet Bks.

Development of Islamic State & Society. M. M. Siddiqui. 1986. 22.50 (ISBN 0-317-46088-9). Kazi Pubns.

Development of Methodism in the Old Southwest: 1783-1824. Walter B. Posey. LC 73-18408. (Perspectives in American History Ser.: No. 19). (Illus.). 1974. Repr. of 1933 ed. lib. bdg. 22.50x (ISBN 0-87991-339-8). Porcupine Pr.

Development of Moral Reasoning: Practical Approaches. Ed. by Donald B. Cochrane & Michael Manley-Casimir. LC 80-17141. 352p. 1980. 44.95 (ISBN 0-03-056209-0). Praeger.

Development of Muslim Jurisprudence & Constitutional Theory. D. B. MacDonald. 1964. 29.00 (ISBN 0-87902-173-X). Orientalia.

Development of Muslim Theology, Jurisprudence & Constitutional Theory. Duncan B. Macdonald. LC 65-18818. 1965. Repr. of 1903 ed. 14.00 (ISBN 0-89684-381-5). Orient Bk Dist.

Development of Neo-Confucian Thought. Carsun Chang. LC 77-8338. 1977. Repr. of 1957 ed. lib. bdg. 26.75x (ISBN 0-8371-9693-0, CHDN). Greenwood.

Development of Neo-Confucian Thought, Vol. 1. Carsun Chang. 1957. pap. 10.95x (ISBN 0-8084-0105-X); 14.95x (ISBN 0-8084-0104-1). New Coll U Pr.

Development of Religion & Thought in Ancient Egypt. James H. Breasted. LC 58-7111. 406p. 1972. pap. 12.95x (ISBN 0-8122-1045-X, Pa Paperbks). U of Pa Pr.

Development of Religion in Japan. George W. Knox. LC 78-72456. Repr. of 1907 ed. 27.00 (ISBN 0-404-17325-X). AMS Pr.

Development of Religious Liberty in Connecticut. facs. ed. M. Louise Greene. LC 79-126235. (Select Bibliographies Reprint Ser). 1905. 26.50 (ISBN 0-8369-5461-0). Ayer Co Pubs.

Development of Religious Liberty in Connecticut. M. Louise Greene. LC 74-99858. (Civil Liberties in American History Ser). 1970. Repr. of 1905 ed. lib. bdg. 59.50 (ISBN 0-306-71861-8). Da Capo.

Development of Religious Toleration in England, 4 vols. W. K. Jordan. Incl. Vol. 1. From the Beginning of the English Reformation to the Death of Queen Elizabeth (ISBN 0-8446-1251-0); Vol. 2. From the Accession of James One to the Convention of the Long Parliament; Vol. 3. From the Convention of the Long Parliament to the Restoration (ISBN 0-8446-1253-7); Vol. 4. Attainment of the Theory & Accommodations in Thought & Institutions (ISBN 0-8446-1254-5). 1932. 16.50 ea. Peter Smith.

Development of Spiritual Healing. Inayat Khan. LC 85-22358. 112p. 1985. Repr. lib. bdg. 19.95x (ISBN 0-89370-582-9). Borgo Pr.

Development of Spiritual Healing. 3rd ed. Inayat Khan. LC 78-65080. 112p. pap. 4.95 (ISBN 0-900217-15-4, Pub. by Sufi Pub Co England). Hunter Hse.

Development of the Christian Science Idea & Practice. Max Kappeler. LC 73-178890. 78p. 1970. pap. 6.50 (ISBN 0-85241-092-1). Kappeler Inst Pub.

Development of the Logical Method in Ancient China. Shih Hu. lib. bdg. 79.95 (ISBN 0-87968-524-7). Krishna Pr.

Developments in Buddhist Thought: Canadian Contributions to Buddhist Studies. Ed. by Roy C. Amore. 196p. 1979. pap. text ed. 9.95x (ISBN 0-919812-11-2, Pub. by Wilfred Laurier Canada). Humanities.

Devi & the Spouse Goddess: Women, Sexuality & Marriage in India. Lynn E. Gatwood. LC 85-61077. 206p. 1985. 18.00 (ISBN 0-913215-01-5). Riverdale Co.

Devi Bhagavata. Date not set. cancelled. Asian Human Pr.

Devi-Mahatmyam (the Chandi) Tr. by Swami Jagadiswarananda. (Sanskrit & Eng). pap. 3.25 (ISBN 0-87481-426-X). Vedanta Pr.

Deviance & Moral Boundaries: Witchcraft, the Occult, Science Fiction, Deviant Sciences & Scientists. Nachman Ben-Yehuda. LC 85-1167. x, 260p. 1985. 25.00x (ISBN 0-226-04335-5). U of Chicago Pr.

Devil Ain't What He Used to Be. Hilton Sutton. 78p. (Orig.). 1982. pap. 2.25 (ISBN 0-89274-255-0). Harrison Hse.

Devil & Karen Kingston: The Incredible Three-Day Exorcism That Brought Miraculous Deliverance to a Totally Demonized Young Girl. Robert W. Pelton. LC 76-12148. (Illus.). 1976. 7.50 (ISBN 0-916620-10-7). Portals Pr.

Devil & the Jews: The Medieval Conception of the Jew & Its Relation to Modern Anti - Semitism. Joshua Trachtenberg. 288p. 1983. pap. 6.95 (ISBN 0-8276-0227-8, 610). Jewish Pubns.

Devil at Baptism: Ritual, Theology, & Drama. Henry A. Kelly. LC 85-404. 304p. 1985. text ed. 29.95x (ISBN 0-8014-1806-2). Cornell U Pr.

Devil: Does He Exist & What Does He Do? Delaporte. 212p. 1982. pap. 4.00 (ISBN 0-89555-173-X). TAN Bks Pubs.

Devil: His Origin, Greatness & Decline. F. P. Cobbe. 59.95 (ISBN 0-8490-0022-X). Gordon Pr.

Devil in Britain & America. J. Ashton. 75.00 (ISBN 0-87968-450-X). Gordon Pr.

Devil in Britain & America. John Ashton. LC 80-19692. 363p. 1980. Repr. of 1972 ed. lib. bdg. 19.95x (ISBN 0-89370-608-6). Borgo Pr.

Devil in Legend & Literature. Maximilian Rudwin. LC 73-85284. (Illus.). 365p. 1973. 22.95 (ISBN 0-87548-247-3); pap. 9.95 (ISBN 0-87548-248-1). Open Court.

Devil in Legend & Literature. Maximilian J. Rudwin. LC 71-111780. (Illus.). Repr. of 1931 ed. 14.50 (ISBN 0-404-05451-X). AMS Pr.

Devil in Massachusetts: A Modern Enquiry into the Salem Witch Trials. Marion L. Starkey. LC 49-10395. 1969. pap. 5.95 (ISBN 0-385-03509-8, Anch). Doubleday.

Devil in Massachusetts: A Modern Inquiry into the Salem Witch Trials. Marion L. Starkey. 15.00 (ISBN 0-8446-2996-0). Peter Smith.

Devil: Perceptions of Evil from Antiquity to Primitive Christianity. Jeffrey B. Russell. LC 77-3126. (Illus.). 288p. 1977. 27.50x (ISBN 0-8014-0938-1). Cornell U Pr.

Devil Take the Youngest. Winkie Pratney. Ed. by Bill Keith. 300p. (Orig.). 1985. pap. 6.95 (ISBN 0-910311-29-3). Huntington Hse Inc.

Devil, You Can't Steal What's Mine. Frances Hunter. 1982. pap. 0.75 (ISBN 0-917726-42-1). Hunter Bks.

Devils. J. C. Wall. 59.95 (ISBN 0-8490-0025-4). Gordon Pr.

Devils & Evil Spirits of Babylonia, 2 vols. R. C. Thompson. Set. 200.00 (ISBN 0-8490-0026-2). Gordon Pr.

Devils & Evil Spirits of Babylonia, 2 vols. Reginald C. Thompson. LC 73-18855. (Luzac's Semitic Text & Translation Ser.: Nos. 14-15). (Illus.). Repr. of 1904 ed. 47.50 set (ISBN 0-404-11353-2). AMS Pr.

Devil's Children: Tales of Demons & Exorcists. Ed. by Michel Parry. LC 74-21721. 212p. 1975. 7.95 (ISBN 0-8008-2188-2). Taplinger.

Devil's Classroom. David E. Staley. 1984. 7.95 (ISBN 0-89536-972-9, 7532). CSS of Ohio.

Devil's Disciples. Jeff Godwin. (Illus.). 352p. (Orig.). 1986. pap. 7.95 (ISBN 0-937958-23-9). Chick Pubns.

Devil's Empire. C. C. Cribb. LC 77-70211. pap. 2.95 (ISBN 0-932046-02-9). Manhattan Ltd NC.

Devil's Island. Brian Peachment. 1974. pap. 1.60 (ISBN 0-08-017613-5). Pergamon.

Devl. Suzanne Ironbiter. 125p. (Orig.). 1987. pap. 6.95 (ISBN 0-938999-02-8). Yuganta Pr.

Devotion for Every Day. J. David Lang. (Illus.). pap. cancelled (ISBN 0-87239-230-9, 2099). Standard Pub.

Devotion to the Blessed Virgin Mary. Pope Paul the Sixth. 1974. pap. 0.35 (ISBN 0-8198-0295-6). Dghtrs St Paul.

Devotion to the Holy Spirit in American Catholicism. Ed. by Joseph P. Chinnici. LC 85-60956. (Sources of American Spirituality Ser.: Vol. 3). 256p. 1985. 12.95 (ISBN 0-8091-0366-4). Paulist Pr.

Devotion to the Infant Jesus of Prague. 32p. 1975. pap. 0.40 (ISBN 0-89555-106-3). TAN Bks Pubs.

Devotion to the Sacred Heart: Objects, Ends, Practice, Motives. Louis Verheylezoon. LC 78-74569. 1979. pap. 8.50 (ISBN 0-89555-083-0). TAN Bks Pubs.

Devotional Bible Studies. F. E. Marsh. LC 79-2548. 304p. 1980. 10.95 (ISBN 0-8254-3230-8). Kregel.

Devotional Commentary on Exodus. F. B. Meyer. LC 78-9530. 476p. 1978. pap. 12.95 (ISBN 0-8254-3244-8). Kregel.

Devotional Commentary on Philippians. F. B. Meyer. LC 78-59146. 1978. pap. 7.95 (ISBN 0-8254-3227-8). Kregel.

Devotional Dramas for a Mission Witness. Sarah H. Miller. 1967. pap. 1.95 (ISBN 0-8054-9716-1). Broadman.

Devotional Dramas for Christmas. Miller. LC 72-79175. 1.95 (ISBN 0-8054-7510-9). Broadman.

Devotional Dramas for Easter. Sarah W. Miller. (Orig.). 1967. pap. 1.95 (ISBN 0-8054-9715-3). Broadman.

Devotional Dramas for the Christian Life. Sarah W. Miller. (Orig.). 1968. pap. 1.95 (ISBN 0-8054-9717-X). Broadman.

Devotional Guide to the Gospels: Three Hundred Sixty-Six Meditations. John Killinger. 588p. 1984. Repr. 14.95 (ISBN 0-8499-3008-1, 3008-1). Word Bks.

Devotional Interpretation of Familiar Hymns. facsimile ed. Earl E. Brock. LC 72-93319. (Essay Index Reprint Ser.). 1947. 14.00 (ISBN 0-8369-1395-7). Ayer Co Pubs.

Devotional Life in the Wesleyan Tradition. Steve Harper. 80p. (Orig.). 1983. pap. 3.95 (ISBN 0-8358-0467-4). Upper Room.

Devotional Poems of Mirabai. Tr. by Shreeprakash Kurl. (Writers Workshop Saffronbird Ser.). 87p. 1975. 15.00 (ISBN 0-88253-722-9); pap. 6.75 (ISBN 0-89253-539-3). Ind-US Inc.

Devotional Pursuits: Truth & Trivia. James N. Watkins. 96p. (Orig.). 1986. pap. 3.95 (ISBN 0-8341-1139-X). Beacon Hill.

Devotional Resource Guide: Selecting the Best in Classic & Contemporary Christian Literature. Joseph D. Allison. 176p. 1986. pap. 8.95 (ISBN 0-8407-5950-9). Nelson.

Devotional Talks for People Who Do God's Business. Warren W. Wiersbe & David W. Wiersbe. 96p. 1986. pap. 5.95 (ISBN 0-8010-9675-8). Baker Bk.

Devotional Talks on Christian Commitment. Timothy E. Moody. (Devotional Resources for Adults Ser.). 96p. 1986. 4.95 (ISBN 0-8010-6203-9). Baker Bk.

Devotional Warm-ups for Church Choirs. Kenneth W. Osbeck. LC 85-17222. 96p. (Orig.). 1985. pap. 2.95 (ISBN 0-8254-3421-1); pap. 29.00 dozen (ISBN 0-8254-3423-8). Kregel.

Devotional Writings of Phoebe Palmer. Phoebe Palmer. Ed. by Donald W. Dayton. (Higher Christian Life Ser.). 640p. 1985. 80.00 (ISBN 0-8240-6431-3). Garland Pub.

Devotional Writings of Robert Pearsall Smith & Hannah Whitall Smith. Ed. by Donald W. Dayton. (Higher Christian Life Ser.). 477p. 1985. lib. bdg. 60.00 (ISBN 0-8240-6444-5). Garland Pub.

Devotionals for Nurses. Rhonda S. Lapp. (Ultra Bks.). 4.95 (ISBN 0-8010-5539-3). Baker Bk.

Devotionals for Teachers. Nelle VanderArk. (Ultra Bks Ser.). 80p. 1975. 5.95 (ISBN 0-8010-9263-9). Baker Bk.

Devotions: A Family Affair. Ruth Ward. (Directory Bks.). 64p. 1981. pap. 2.45 (ISBN 0-8010-9632-4). Baker Bk.

Devotions & Prayers in Honor of St. Joseph. Jerome F. Coniker. (Living Meditation & Prayer Bklt. Library). (Illus.). 34p. (Orig.). 1978. pap. text ed. 2.50 (ISBN 0-932406-04-1). AFC.

Devotions & Prayers of John Wesley. John Wesley. (Devotional Classics). 1977. pap. 2.95 (ISBN 0-8010-9597-2). Baker Bk.

Devotions & Prayers of Martin Luther: 52 One-Page Meditations & Prayers on the Psalms. Martin Luther. 1978. pap. 2.95 (ISBN 0-8010-5582-2). Baker Bk.

Devotions for a Deeper Life. Oswald Chambers. Ed. by Glenn D. Black. 320p. 1986. 10.95 (ISBN 0-310-38710-8, 17070). Zondervan.

Devotions for a New Mother. Mildred Tengbom. 127p. 1983. pap. 4.95 (ISBN 0-87123-294-4). Bethany Hse.

Devotions for Boys & Girls. Compiled by Hester Monsma. (Devotions for Daily Living Ser.). 30p. 1982. pap. 1.50 (ISBN 0-8010-2924-4). Baker Bk.

Devotions for Church School Teachers. Richard Andersen. LC 76-2158. 64p. 1976. pap. 2.25 (ISBN 0-570-03722-0, 12-2624). Concordia.

Devotions for Dieters. Charlie Shedd. 1983. 8.95 (ISBN 0-8499-0330-0). Word Bks.

Devotions for Divorcing. William E. Thompson. LC 85-42827. 96p. 1985. pap. 6.95 (ISBN 0-8042-2525-7). John Knox.

Devotions for Early Teens, 4 vols. Ruth I. Johnson. 1960-74. Vol. 1. pap. 2.95 (ISBN 0-8024-2181-4); Vol. 3. pap. 2.95 (ISBN 0-8024-2183-0). Moody.

Devotions for Families: Building Blocks of Christian Life. Barbara O. Webb. LC 75-22162. 48p. 1976. pap. 1.95 (ISBN 0-8170-0680-X). Judson.

Devotions for Families with Young Readers. Barbara O. Webb. 64p. 1985. pap. 4.95 (ISBN 0-8170-1063-7). Judson.

Devotions for Graduates. Hester Monsma. 25p. 1984. pap. 1.50 (ISBN 0-8010-2939-2). Baker Bk.

Devotions for Growing Christians. David R. Reid. 256p. (Orig.). 1986. pap. 4.95 (ISBN 0-87213-701-5). Loizeaux.

Devotions for Laymen...by a Layman. Russell E. Aven. LC 81-67751. 1982. pap. 6.50 (ISBN 0-8054-5185-4). Broadman.

Devotions for Lifting Your Heart. Hester Monsma. 30p. 1984. pap. 1.25 (ISBN 0-8010-2940-6). Baker Bk.

Devotions for Men. Hester Monsma. 30p. 1984. pap. 1.25 (ISBN 0-8010-2941-4). Baker Bk.

Devotions for Mothers. Hester Monsma. 30p. 1984. pap. 1.25 (ISBN 0-8010-2942-2). Baker Bk.

Devotions for New Mothers. Bonnie Taylor. 128p. 1987. 10.95 (ISBN 0-8170-1081-5); pap. 6.95 (ISBN 0-8170-1115-3). Judson.

Devotions for New Parents. Alfred M. Buls. (Orig.). (YA) 1972. pap. 1.50 (ISBN 0-570-03675-5, 74-1010). Concordia.

Devotions for New Parents. Peg Roberts. 85p. 1984. 4.95 (ISBN 0-8010-7727-3). Baker Bk.

Devotions for the Children's Hour. Kenneth N. Taylor. pap. 3.95 (ISBN 0-8024-0061-2). Moody.

Devotions for Those God Loves. Hester Monsma. 30p. 1984. pap. 1.25 (ISBN 0-8010-2943-0). Baker Bk.

Devotions for Those Who Are Recovering. Compiled by Hester Monsma. (Devotions for Daily Living Ser.). 30p. 1982. pap. 1.25 (ISBN 0-8010-2919-8). Baker Bk.

Devotions for Those Who Sorrow. Hester Monsma. 30p. 1984. pap. 1.25 (ISBN 0-8010-2944-9). Baker Bk.

Devotions for Today's Teens. Compiled by Hester M...sma. (Devotions for Daily Living Ser.). 30p. 1982. pap. 1.25 (ISBN 0-8010-2923-6). Baker Bk.

Devotions for Travelers. Murphey. 1.95 (ISBN 0-318-18171-1). WCTU.

Devotions for Your Preschool Classroom. Sue Richterkessing. 1983. pap. 4.95 (ISBN 0-570-03913-4, 12-2854). Concordia.

Devotions from a Stamp Album. David McCarthy. 104p. 1983. pap. 4.95 (ISBN 0-8010-6156-3). Baker Bk.

Devotions of Hope. Richard C. Eyer. 1984. 1.95 (ISBN 0-89536-653-3, 0418). CSS of Ohio.

Devotions upon Emergent Occasions. John Donne. Bd. with Death's Duel. 1959. pap. 7.95 (ISBN 0-472-06030-9, 30, AA). U of Mich Pr.

Devotions upon Emergent Occasions. John Donne. Ed. by Anthony Raspa. LC 76-361973. pap. 62.00 (ISBN 0-317-26281-5, 2024263). Bks Demand UMI.

Devotions with a Difference. Stephen Bly & Janet Bly. LC 82-8304. 128p. 1982. pap. 5.95 (ISBN 0-8024-1789-2). Moody.

Devout Humanism as a Style. Cecilian Streebing. LC 70-128930. (Catholic University. Romance Literature: No. 50). Repr. of 1954 ed. 23.80 (ISBN 0-404-50350-0). AMS Pr.

Dewey. Gordon H. Clark. (Modern Thinkers Ser.). 1960. pap. 2.00 (ISBN 0-87552-582-2). Presby & Reformed.

Deyadharma: Studies in Memory of Dr. D. C. Sircar. Ed. by Gouriswar Bhattacharya. (Illus.). 276p. 1986. lib. bdg. 75.00x (ISBN 81-7030-021-5, Pub. by Sri Satguru Pubns India). Orient Bk Dist.

Dhammapada. Gautama Buddha. Tr. by Irving Babbitt. LC 64-23655. Tr. of Path of Truth. 1965. pap. 5.95 (ISBN 0-8112-0004-3, NDP188). New Directions.

Dhammapada. ix, 139p. 1955. 3.00 (ISBN 0-938998-16-1). Cunningham Pr.

Dhammapada. (Life Companion Library). 116p. (Orig.). 1983. pap. 5.95 (ISBN 0-89744-016-1). Auromere.

Dhammapada. Tr. by Eknath Easwaran from Pali. 1986. 13.95 (ISBN 0-915132-38-9); pap. 6.95 (ISBN 0-915132-37-0). Nilgiri Pr.

Dhammapada: Anonymous Translation with Explanatory Notes & a Short Essay on Buddha's Thought. ix, 139p. 3.00 (ISBN 0-938998-16-1). Theosophy.

Dhammapada, Wisdom of the Buddha. Tr. by Harischandra Kaviratna. LC 80-52031. 1980. 12.50 (ISBN 0-911500-39-1); pap. 7.50 (ISBN 0-911500-40-5). Theos U Pr.

Dharam Shastra: Hindu Religious Codes, 6 vols. Incl. Vol. I. 267p. 1978 (ISBN 0-89684-137-5); Vol. II. 230p. 1979 (ISBN 0-89684-138-3); Vol. III. 309p. 1979 (ISBN 0-89684-139-1); Vol. IV. 187p. 1979 (ISBN 0-89684-140-5); Vol. V. 438p. 1979 (ISBN 0-89684-141-3); Vol. VI. 222p. 1979 (ISBN 0-89684-142-1). Repr. of 1908 ed. 100.00 set (ISBN 0-686-77519-8, Pub. by Cosmo Pubns India). Orient Bk Dist.

Dharani Sutra. Commentary by Tripitaka Master Hua. Tr. by Buddhist Text Translation Society. (Illus.). 352p. (Orig.). 1976. pap. 12.00 (ISBN 0-917512-13-8). Buddhist Text.

Dharma. Besant. 3.25 (ISBN 0-8356-7116-X). Theos Pub Hse.

Dharma & Development. rev. ed. Joanna Macy. LC 85-256. (KP Monograph: No. 2). 119p. 1985. pap. 8.75 (ISBN 0-931816-53-X). Kumarian Pr.

Dharma Flower Sutra, Vol. VI. Commentary by Tripitaka Master Hua. Tr. by Buddhist Text Translation Society. (Illus.). 161p. (Orig.). 1980. pap. 8.00 (ISBN 0-917512-65-0). Buddhist Text.

Dharma Flower Sutra, Vol. V. Commentary by Tripitaka Master Hua. Tr. by Buddhist Text Translation Society. (Illus.). 200p. (Orig.). 1980. pap. 8.00 (ISBN 0-917512-64-2). Buddhist Text.

Dharma Flower Sutra, Vol. IX. Commentary by Tripitaka Master Hua. Tr. by Buddhist Text Translation Society. (Illus.). 270p. (Orig.). 1982. pap. 8.50 (ISBN 0-917512-85-5). Buddhist Text.

Dharma Flower Sutra, Vol. III. Commentary by Tripitaka Master Hua. Tr. by Buddhist Text Translation Society. (Illus.). 183p. (Orig.). 1979. pap. 8.00 (ISBN 0-917512-26-X). Buddhist Text.

Dharma Flower Sutra, Vol. II. Commentary by Tripitaka Master Hua. Tr. by Buddhist Text Translation Society. (Chinese., Illus.). 324p. (Orig.). 1978. pap. 9.00 (ISBN 0-917512-22-7). Buddhist Text.

Dharma Flower Sutra, Vol. X. Commentary by Tripitaka Master Hua. Tr. by Buddhist Text Translation Society Staff. 150p. (Orig.). pap. 7.50 (ISBN 0-917512-34-0). Buddhist Text.

Dharma Flower Sutra; Vol. I: Introduction. Tripitaka Master Hua. Tr. by Buddhist Text Translation Society. (Illus.). 85p. (Orig.). 1977. pap. 5.00 (ISBN 0-917512-16-2). Buddhist Text.

Dharma Flower Sutra, Vol. IV. Commentary by Tripitaka Master Hua. Tr. by Buddhist Text Translation Society. (Illus.). 371p. (Orig.). 1980. pap. 9.00 (ISBN 0-917512-62-6). Buddhist Text.

Dharma Flower Sutra, Vol. VII. Commentary by Tripitaka Master Hua. Tr. by Buddhist Text Translation Society. (Illus.). 250p. (Orig.). 1980. pap. 8.50 (ISBN 0-917512-93-6). Buddhist Text.

Dharma Flower Sutra, Vol. VIII. Commentary by Tripitaka Master Hua. Tr. by Buddhist Text Translation Society. (Illus.). 160p. (Orig.). 1980. pap. 8.00 (ISBN 0-917512-71-5). Buddhist Text.

Dharma for All. 264p. 1987. pap. 3.50 (Pub. by Ramakrishna Math Madras India). Vedanta Pr.

Dharma in Hindu Ethics. Austin Creel. 1978. 11.00x (ISBN 0-88386-999-3). South Asia Bks.

Dharma; or, the Religious Enlightenment; an Exposition of Buddhism. 5th rev. & enl. ed. Paul Carus. LC 78-72393. Repr. of 1907 ed. 24.00 (ISBN 0-404-17253-9). AMS Pr.

Dharma-Samgraha, an Ancient Collection of Buddhist Technical Terms. Kenju Kasawara. Ed. by F. Max Muller & H. Wenzel. LC 78-72425. Repr. of 1885 ed. 17.50 (ISBN 0-404-17286-5). AMS Pr.

Dharma: That Benefits All Beings Impartially Like the Light of the Sun & Moon. Kalu Rinpoche. 256p. (Orig.). 1986. 34.50x (ISBN 0-88706-156-7); pap. 10.95x (ISBN 0-88706-157-5). State U NY Pr.

Dhatu Katha Pakarana & Its Commentary. Ed. by Edmund R. Gooneratne. LC 78-72426. Repr. of 1892 ed. 21.50 (ISBN 0-404-17287-3). AMS Pr.

Dhimmi: Jews & Christians under Islam. Bat Ye'or. Tr. by David Maisel et al from French. LC 84-47749. (Illus.). 444p. 1985. 25.00 (ISBN 0-8386-3233-5); pap. 9.95 (ISBN 0-8386-3262-9). Fairleigh Dickinson.

Dhyana. M. P. Pandit. 1979. pap. 1.95 (ISBN 0-941524-03-5). Lotus Light.

Dia-Tras-Dia Con Billy Graham. Compiled by Joan W. Brown. Orig. Title: Day by Day with Billy Graham. 192p. 1982. Repr. of 1978 ed. 3.95 (ISBN 0-311-40039-6, Edit Mundo). Casa Bautista.

Diabetes Control & the Kosher Diet. Ada P. Kahn. LC 84-51535. 180p. 1985. pap. 9.95x (ISBN 0-930121-00-7). Wordscope Inc.

Diabolic Root: A Study of Peyotism, the New Indian Religion, Among the Delawares. Vincenzo Petrullo. 185p. 1975. Repr. of 1934 ed. lib. bdg. 18.00x (ISBN 0-374-96411-4, Octagon). Hippocrene Bks.

Diabolology: The Person & Kingdom of Satan. Edward H. Jewett. 1977. lib. bdg. 59.95 (ISBN 0-8490-1715-7). Gordon Pr.

Diaconado Permanente en los Estados Unidos: Directivas para Su Formacion y Ministerio. (Span.). 56p. 1986. pap. 4.95 (ISBN 1-55586-131-8). US Catholic.

Diaconal Reader: Selected Articles from the Diaconal Quarterly. 112p. 1985. pap. 4.95 (ISBN 1-55586-939-4). US Catholic.

Diaconate: A Full & Equal Order. James M. Barnett. 256p. (Orig.). 1981. pap. 9.95 (ISBN 0-8164-2331-8, HarpR). Har-Row.

Diagram & List of Goshen Presbyterian Church Pews, 1796. Orange County Genealogical Society. 1986. pap. text ed. 0.50 (ISBN 0-937135-02-X). Orange County Genealog.

Diagrams for Living: The Bible Unveiled. Emmet Fox. LC 69-10475. 1968. 12.45 (ISBN 0-06-062851-0, HarpR). Har-Row.

Dial-A-Prayer. Richard H. Stough. (Orig.). 1983. pap. 4.50 (ISBN 0-937172-44-8). JLJ Pubs.

Dial-a-Word from the Bible. Gordon DeYoung. (Quiz & Puzzle Bks). 1977. pap. 0.95 (ISBN 0-8010-2862-0). Baker Bk.

Dial 911: Peaceful Christians & Urban Violence. Dave Jackson. LC 81-2541. 160p. 1981. pap. 5.95 (ISBN 0-8361-1952-5). Herald Pr.

Dialect of the "Life of Saint Katherine" A Linguistic Study of the Phonology & Inflections. H. M. Logan. (Janua Linguarum Ser. Practica: No. 130). 1973. pap. text ed. 34.40x (ISBN 0-686-22600-3). Mouton.

Dialectic in Practical Religion. Edmund R. Leach. (Cambridge Papers in Social Anthropology: No. 5). 34.50 (ISBN 0-521-05525-3). Cambridge U Pr.

Dialectic of Biblical Critique: Interpretation & Existence. Brayton Polka. LC 84-26216. 192p. 1986. 25.00 (ISBN 0-312-19874-4). St Martin.

Dialectic of Enlightenment. Max Horkheimer & Theodor W. Adorno. Tr. by John Cumming from Ger. LC 77-167870. 1975. pap. 9.95x (ISBN 0-8264-0093-0, Continuum). Continuum.

Dialectical Method of Thinking. Edmond B. Szekely. (Illus.). 40p. 1973. pap. 2.95 (ISBN 0-89564-063-5). IBS Intl.

Dialectics of Creation: Patterns of Birth & Regeneration in "Paradise Lost". Michael Lieb. LC 71-76047. 272p. 1970. 17.50x (ISBN 0-87023-049-2). U of Mass Pr.

Dialogicall Discourses of Spirits & Devils, Declaring Their Proper Essence. John Deacon & John Walker. LC 76-57377. (English Experience Ser.: No. 795). 1977. Repr. of 1601 ed. lib. bdg. 37.00 (ISBN 90-221-0795-7). Walter J Johnson.

Dialogue Between Bergson, Aristotle, & Philologos. 3rd. enl. ed. Constantine Cavarnos. 100p. 1986. pap. 4.95 (ISBN 0-914744-77-1). Inst Byzantine.

Dialogue Between Theology & Psychology. Ed. by Peter Homans. LC 68-16698. (Essays in Divinity Ser: Vol. 3). 1968. 25.00x (ISBN 0-226-35110-6). U of Chicago Pr.

Dialogue Concerning Heresies: Complete Works of St. Thomas More, Vol. 6, Pts. 1 & 2. Ed. by St. Thomas More et al. LC 63-7949. (Illus.). 910p. 1981. Set. text ed. 87.00x (ISBN 0-300-02211-5). Yale U Pr.

Dialogue Des Carmelites. Georges Bernanos. 1960. 13.50 (ISBN 0-685-11136-9). French & Eur.

Dialogue Des Carmelites. Georges Bernanos. (Coll. Le Livre de Vie). pap. 3.95 (ISBN 0-685-37216-2). French & Eur.

Dialogue of Comfort Against Tribulation. St. Thomas More. (Complete Works of St. Thomas More Ser.: No. 12). 1976. 77.00x (ISBN 0-300-01609-3). Yale U Pr.

Dialogue of Mercury & Charon. Alfonso de Valdes. Tr. & intro. by Joseph V. Ricapito. LC 84-48489. 224p. 1986. 25.00x (ISBN 0-253-31700-2). Ind U Pr.

Dialogue of Religions. Ninian Smart. LC 79-8730. (Library of Philosophy & Theology). 142p. 1981. Repr. of 1960 ed. lib. bdg. 22.50x (ISBN 0-313-22187-1, SMDR). Greenwood.

Dialogue of St. Catherine of Siena. St. Catherine of Siena. Tr. & intro. by Algar Thorold. 1976. pap. 6.00 (ISBN 0-89555-037-7). TAN Bks Pubs.

Dialogue of the Immortality of the Soul. Plato. LC 73-161797. Repr. of 1713 ed. 20.00 (ISBN 0-404-54134-8). AMS Pr.

Dialogue on Diversity: A New Agenda for Women. Ed. by Barbarba Peters & Victoria Samuels. 88p. 1978. pap. 1.95 (ISBN 0-87495-003-1). Am Jewish Comm.

Dialogue on G. E. Moore's Ethical Philosophy: Together with an Account of Three Talks with Moore on Diverse Philosophical Questions. Constantine Cavarnos. LC 79-65479. 1979. 5.95 (ISBN 0-914744-43-7); pap. 2.95 (ISBN 0-914744-44-5). Inst Byzantine.

Dialogue on Personal Identity & Immortality. John R. Perry. LC 78-52943. 60p. 1978. lib. bdg. 15.00 (ISBN 0-915144-91-3); pap. text ed. 2.95 (ISBN 0-915144-53-0). Hackett Pub.

Dialogue on Science, Psychology & God. Walter R. Thompson. LC 67-17638. 1967. 6.00 (ISBN 0-8022-1717-6). Philos Lib.

Dialogue on the Soul. Aelred Of Rievaulx. (Cistercian Fathers Ser.: No. 22). Orig. Title: De Anima. 1981. 10.95 (ISBN 0-87907-222-9). Cistercian Pubns.

Dialogue: The Key to Understanding Other Religions. Donald K. Swearer. LC 77-3964. (Biblical Perspectives on Current Issues). 172p. 1977. soft cover 4.95 (ISBN 0-664-24138-7). Westminster.

Dialogue with C. G. Jung. Richard I. Evans. LC 81-15371. 256p. 1981. 36.95 (ISBN 0-03-059927-X). Praeger.

Dialogue with Christ. Torkom Saraydarian. LC 77-86722. 1979. pap. 4.00 (ISBN 0-911794-42-5). Aqua Educ.

Dialogue with Deviance: The Hasidic Ethic & the Theory of Social Contraction. Mordechai Rotenberg. LC 81-13309. 224p. 1983. text ed. 27.50 (ISBN 0-89727-031-2). ISHI PA.

Dialogue with Erik Erikson: And Reactions from Ernest Jones. Richard I. Evans. LC 81-15379. 188p. 1981. 33.95 (ISBN 0-03-059923-7). Praeger.

Dialogue with God. Mark Vikler. LC 86-70744. 1986. pap. 5.95 (ISBN 0-88270-620-9). Bridge Pub.

Dialogue with the Other: Martin Buber & the Quaker Experience. Janet E. Schroeder. LC 73-92486. 32p. (Orig.). 1973. pap. 2.50x (ISBN 0-87574-192-4). Pendle Hill.

Dialogues. St. Gregory The Great. (Fathers of the Church Ser.: Vol. 39). 287p. 1959. 29.95x (ISBN 0-8132-0039-3). Cath U Pr.

Dialogues & Ideologues. Thomas Molnar. 1977. Repr. of 1964 ed. 6.95 (ISBN 0-8199-0679-4). Franciscan Herald.

Dialogues Concerning Natural Religion. David Hume. Ed. by Norman K. Smith. 1947. pap. 8.40 scp (ISBN 0-672-60404-3, LLA174). Bobbs.

Dialogues Concerning Natural Religion. David Hume. Ed. by Richard H. Popkin. LC 79-25349. 132p. 1980. lib. bdg. 15.00 (ISBN 0-915144-46-8); pap. text ed. 2.95 (ISBN 0-915144-45-X). Hackett Pub.

Dialogues Concerning Natural Religion. David Hume. Ed. by Henry D. Aiken. (Library of Classics Ser: No. 5). pap. text ed. 5.95x (ISBN 0-02-846180-0). Hafner.

Dialogues Concerning Natural Religion: Text & Critical Essays. David Hume. Ed. by Nelson Pike. LC 77-132933. (Text & Critical Essays Ser). (Orig.). 1970. pap. write for info. (ISBN 0-02-358440-8, TC6). Macmillan.

Dialogues in Metapsychiatry. Thomas Hora. LC 77-8268. 238p. 16.00x (ISBN 0-913105-16-3). PAGL Pr.

Dialogues of G. de Purucker, 3 vols. G. De Purucker. Ed. by Arthur L. Conger. LC 79-65630. 1948. Set. 25.00 (ISBN 0-911500-59-6). Theos U Pr.

Dialogues on A Course in Miracles. Tara Singh. LC 86-82912. (Orig.). 1987. 19.95 (ISBN 1-55531-130-X); pap. 14.95 (ISBN 1-55531-131-8). Life Action Pr.

Dialogues on Moral Education. John Wilson & Barbara Cowell. LC 83-4433. 170p. (Orig.). 1983. pap. 10.95 (ISBN 0-89135-035-7). Religious Educ.

Dialogues on Morality & Religion. Jakob F. Fries. Ed. by D. Z. Phillips et al. LC 82-13787. (Values & Philosophical Inquiry Ser.). (Illus.). 268p. 1982. text ed. 28.95x (ISBN 0-389-20326-2). B&N Imports.

Dialogues with God. Frances J. Roberts. 1968. 6.95 (ISBN 0-932814-07-7); pap. 4.95 (ISBN 0-932814-08-5). Kings Farspan.

Dialogues with God: Sonnet Psalms on the Significance of Being Human. Benito F. Reyes. LC 78-244706. 139p. 1969. pap. 7.50 (ISBN 0-939375-37-0). World Univ Amer.

Dialogues with Myself: Personal Essays on Mormon Experience. Eugene England. 205p. (Orig.). 1984. pap. 7.50 (ISBN 0-941214-21-4, Orion). Signature Bks.

Dialogues with Scientists & Sages: The Search for Unity in Science & Mysticism. Renee Weber. 288p. 1986. pap. 14.95 (ISBN 0-7102-0655-0, 06550, Pub. by Routledge UK). Methuen Inc.

Dialogues with the Master. Paul Twitchell. 1970. pap. 5.95 (ISBN 0-914766-78-3). IWP Pub.

Dialogus Inter Militem et Clericum: Richard FitzRalph's Sermon. J. Trevisa. (EETS, OS Ser.: No. 167). Repr. of 1925 ed. 20.00 (ISBN 0-527-00164-3). Kraus Repr.

Diamond Heart, Bk. 1: Elements of the Real in Man. A. H. Almaas. 280p. (Orig.). 1987. pap. 10.00 (ISBN 0-936713-01-1). Almaas Pubns.

Diamond in the Darkness. Veni Raj. (Illus.). 32p. 1984. pap. 3.50 (ISBN 0-85398-161-2). G Ronald Pub.

Diamond Sutra. Gautama Buddha. (Sacred Texts Ser.). viii, 72p. 1983. pap. 8.75 (ISBN 0-88695-004-X). Concord Grove.

Diamond Sutra. Kevin O'Neil. 1978. pap. 5.00 (ISBN 0-86627-004-3). Crises Res Pr.

Diamond Sutra. Bhagwan Shree Rajneesh. Ed. by Ma Yoga Pratima. LC 82-185071. (Buddha Ser.). (Illus.). 492p. (Orig.). 1979. 19.50 (ISBN 0-88050-043-3). Chidvilas Found.

Diamond Sutra & the Sutra of Hui Neng. Tr. by A. F. Price & Mou-Lam. (Clear Light Ser.). 190p. 1969. pap. 7.95 (ISBN 0-87773-005-9). Shambhala Pubns.

Diamonds Everywhere: Appreciating God's Gifts. Ernest A. Fitzgerald. 112p. (Orig.). 1983. pap. 7.75 (ISBN 0-687-10734-2). Abingdon.

Diamonds From Daniel. William G. Heslop. LC 76-12082. (W. G. Heslop Bible Study Aids Ser.). 184p. 1976. pap. text ed. 4.50 (ISBN 0-8254-2833-5). Kregel.

Diamonds in Daniel. Heslop. pap. 2.95 (ISBN 0-686-12865-6). Schmul Pub Co.

Diamonds in the Rough. Charles E. Cravey. 64p. (Orig.). 1986. pap. 4.00 (ISBN 0-938645-00-5). Upper Rm Pub.

Dianetic Information Group. pap. 4.00 (ISBN 0-686-74640-6). Church of Scient Info.

Dianetica: la Ciencia Moderna De Salud Mental. spanish ed. L. Ron Hubbard. 1976. pap. 3.95 (ISBN 0-88404-086-0). Bridge Pubns Inc.

Dianetics. L. Ron Hubbard. 1977. pap. 2.00 (ISBN 0-685-76384-6). Church of Scient Info.

Dianetics & Scientology Technical Dictionary. L. Ron Hubbard. 50.00 (ISBN 0-686-30803-4). Church Scient NY.

Dianetics & Scientology Technical Dictionary. L. Ron Hubbard. 1975. 79.32 (ISBN 0-88404-037-2). Bridge Pubns Inc.

Dianetics: Evolution of a Science. L. Ron Hubbard. 20.00 (ISBN 0-686-30777-1). Church Scient NY.

Dianetics Fifty-Five. L. Ron Hubbard. 20.00 (ISBN 0-686-13920-8). Church Scient NY.

Dianetics Fifty-Five. L. Ron Hubbard. 168p. 1955. 36.44 (ISBN 0-88404-003-8). Bridge Pubns Inc.

Dianetics: The Evolution of a Science. L. Ron Hubbard. 110p. 1950. 21.44 (ISBN 0-88404-017-8). Bridge Pubns Inc.

Dianetics: The Modern Science of Mental Health. L. Ron Hubbard. 20.00 (ISBN 0-686-30776-3). Church Scient NY.

Dianetics: The Modern Science of Mental Health. L. Ron Hubbard. 483p. 1950. 32.16 (ISBN 0-88404-000-3). Bridge Pubns Inc.

Dianetics, the Original Thesis. L. Ron Hubbard. 20.00 (ISBN 0-686-13917-8). Church Scient NY.

Dianetics: The Original Thesis. L. Ron Hubbard. 157p. 1951. 21.44 (ISBN 0-88404-002-X). Bridge Pubns Inc.

Dianetics Today. L. Ron Hubbard. 76.00 (ISBN 0-686-30802-6). Church Scient NY.

Dianetics Today. L. Ron Hubbard. 1975. 120.04 (ISBN 0-88404-036-4). Bridge Pubns Inc.

Diaries of the Popish Plot. Ed. by Douglas Greene. LC 77-938. 1977. 50.00x (ISBN 0-8201-1288-7). Schol Facsimilies.

Diaries of Theodor Herzl. Theodor Herzl. Ed. by Lowenthal. 16.50 (ISBN 0-8446-2247-8). Peter Smith.

Diario de Oraciones Privada. John Baillie. pap. 2.75 (ISBN 0-8358-0412-7). Upper Room.

Diary. Thomas Cartwright. 1843. 19.00 (ISBN 0-384-07815-X). Johnson Repr.

Diary. James Melville. LC 70-172723. (Bannatyne Club, Edinburgh. Publications: No. 34). Repr. of 1829 ed. 32.50 (ISBN 0-404-52740-X). AMS Pr.

Diary of a Country Priest: Thomas More Books to Live Ser. Georges Bernanos. Tr. by Pamela Morris. (Fr.). 1983. 14.95 (ISBN 0-88347-155-8). Thomas More.

Diary of a Drug Fiend. Aleister Crowley. 1973. lib. bdg. 79.95 (ISBN 0-87968-110-1). Krishna Pr.

Diary of a Russian Priest. 2nd ed. Alexander Elchaninov. Ed. by Kallistos T. Ware. LC 82-16795. (Illus.). 225p. (Orig.). 1982. pap. 8.95 (ISBN 0-88141-000-4). St Vladimirs.

Diary of a Young Girl. Anne Frank. LC 58-11474. 1958. o.s. 5.95 (ISBN 0-394-60451-2). Modern Lib.

Diary of a Zen Nun. Nan Shin. LC 85-27576. (Illus.). 192p. 1986. 15.95 (ISBN 0-525-24408-5, 01549-460). Dutton.

Diary of an Old Soul. George MacDonald. LC 65-12143. 132p. 1965. pap. 6.95 (ISBN 0-8066-1503-6, 10-1895). Augsburg.

Diary of an Oxford Methodist: Benjamin Ingham, 1733-34. Ed. by Richard P. Heitzenrater. xvi, 304p. 1985. 37.50 (ISBN 0-8223-0595-X). Duke.

Diary of Brigham Young, 1857. Ed. by Everett L. Cooley. 105p. 1980. 17.50 (ISBN 0-941214-37-0). Signature Bks.

Diary of Daily Prayer. J. Barrie Shepherd. LC 74-14176. 136p. (Orig.). 1975. pap. 5.95 (ISBN 0-8066-1459-5, 10-1900). Augsburg.

Diary of David Zeisberger: A Missionary Among the Indians of Ohio, 2 vols. Ed. by Eugene F. Bliss. LC 73-108557. 1972. Repr. of 1885 ed. 59.00x (ISBN 0-403-00253-2). Scholarly.

Diary of Dr. Thomas Cartwright, Bishop of Chester October 1687. Thomas Cartwright. (Camden Society, London. Publications. First Ser.: No. 22). Repr. of 1843 ed. 19.00 (ISBN 0-404-50122-2). AMS Pr.

Diary of Fire. Igino Giordani. Tr. of Diario di Fuoco. 127p. (Orig.). 1982. pap. 3.95 (ISBN 0-911782-41-9). New City.

Diary of Isaac Backus, 3 vols. Isaac Backus. Ed. by William G. McLoughlin. LC 76-12018. (Illus.). 1834p. 1979. Set. 120.00x (ISBN 0-87057-148-6). U Pr of New Eng.

Diary of Juliet Thompson. Juliet Thompson. 396p. 1983. 14.95 (ISBN 0-933770-27-8). Kalimat.

Diary of Kenneth Macrae. Ed. by Iain H. Murray. (Illus.). 535p. 1980. 19.95 (ISBN 0-85151-297-6). Banner of Truth.

Diary of Michael Wigglesworth, 1653 to 1657: The Conscience of a Puritan. Michael Wigglesworth. Ed. by Edmund Morgan. 11.25 (ISBN 0-8446-0808-4). Peter Smith.

Diary of Personal Prayer. Julie J. McDonald. Ed. & illus. by Joan Liffring-Zug. (Illus.). 96p. (Orig.). 1986. pap. 9.95. Penfield.

Diary of Prayer: Daily Meditations on the Parables of Jesus. J. Barrie Shepherd. LC 80-27037. 132p. 1981. pap. 5.95 (ISBN 0-664-24352-5). Westminster.

Diary of Private Prayer. John Baillie. 136p. 1978. 8.95 (ISBN 0-684-30997-1, ScribT). Scribner.

Diary of Private Prayer. John Baillie. 1979. pap. 3.95 (ISBN 0-684-16323-3, ScribT). Scribner.

Diary of Readings. John Baillie. 400p. 1986. pap. 4.95 (ISBN 0-02-048360-0, Collier). Macmillan.

Diary of Rev. William Bentley: 1784-1819, 4 vols. William Bentley. 72.00 (ISBN 0-8446-1071-2). Set. Peter Smith.

Diary of Richard L. Burtsell, Priest of New York the Early Years, 1865-1868. Richard L. Burtsell & Nelson J. Callahan. 37.50 (ISBN 0-405-10813-3). Ayer Co Pubs.

Diary of Samuel Sewall, 1674-1729, 2 vols. Ed. by Halsey M. Thomas. (Illus.). 1254p. 1973. 30.00 (ISBN 0-374-13952-0). FS&G.

Diary of Soren Kierkegaard. Soren Kierkegaard. Ed. by Peter P. Rohde. 1971. pap. 2.75 (ISBN 0-8065-0251-7). Citadel Pr.

Diary of William Pynchon of Salem. William Pynchon. Ed. by Fitch E. Oliver. LC 75-31131. Repr. of 1890 ed. 28.50 (ISBN 0-404-13608-7). AMS Pr.

Dias Sin Gloria. Jose R. Estrada. (Span.). 64p. 1982. pap. 1.95 (ISBN 0-311-08213-0, Edit Mundo). Casa Bautista.

Diaspora. Ed. by Etan Levine. LC 82-6723. 350p. 1983. 20.00 (ISBN 0-87668-601-3). Aronson.

Diaspora: An Inquiry into the Contemporary Jewish World. Howard M. Sachar. LC 84-48190. 480p. 1985. 27.00i (ISBN 0-06-015403-9, HarpT). Har-Row.

Diaspora: An Inquiry into the Contemporary Jewish World. Howard M. Sachar. LC 84-48190. (Illus.). 539p. 1986. pap. 10.95 (ISBN 0-06-091347-9, PL-1347, PL). Har-Row.

Diaspora: Exile & the Contemporary Jewish Condition. Ed. by Etan Levine. 363p. 1986. 18.95 (ISBN 0-933503-50-4). Shapolsky Pubs.

Dicccionario De las Religiones Prerromanas De Hispania. Jose M. Blazquez. (Span.). 192p. 1975. pap. 9.95 (ISBN 84-7090-071-4, S-50058). French & Eur.

Diccionario Biblico Arqueologico. Tr. by Roberto Gama from Eng. Ed. by Charles F. Pfeiffer. Tr. of Biblical World - A Dictionary of Biblical Archaelolgy. (Span.). 768p. 1982. 29.95 (ISBN 0-311-03667-8). Casa Bautista.

Diccionario Biblico Manual. Heinz Obermayer. (Span.). 352p. 1975. pap. 7.95 (ISBN 84-7263-094-3, S-50212). French & Eur.

Diccionario de Demonologia. 3rd ed. Frederick Koning. (Span.). 1978. pap. 2.95 (ISBN 0-686-57362-5, S-50155). French & Eur.

Diccionario De la Biblia. 7th ed. Herbert Haag. (Span.). 1080p. 1977. 50.00 (ISBN 84-254-0077-5, S-50196). French & Eur.

Diccionario de la Mitologia Clasica. C. Falcon et al. (Span.). 633p. 1980. pap. 25.00 (ISBN 84-206-1961-2, S-32723). French & Eur.

Diccionario de la Mitologia Mundial. (Span.). 383p. 1971. 12.25 (ISBN 84-7166-165-9, S-12258). French & Eur.

Diccionario de la Santa Biblia. W. W. Rand. (Span., Illus.). 768p. 1969. pap. 15.50 (ISBN 0-89922-003-7). Edit Caribe.

Diccionario De las Religiones. Konig. (Span.). 816p. 1977. 37.50 (ISBN 84-254-0358-8, S-50201). French & Eur.

Diccionario de los Papas. Juan Dacio. (Span.). 37.50 (ISBN 84-233-0112-5, S-50110). French & Eur.

Diccionario De los Santos De Cada Dia. Dom P. Rouillard. (Span.). 472p. 1966. 15.75 (ISBN 84-281-0062-4, S-50020). French & Eur.

Diccionario de Mitologia. Henri Aubert. (Span.). 238p. 1961. 14.95 (ISBN 0-686-56710-2, S-33055). French & Eur.

Diccionario de Mitologia. Homero Lelama. (Span.). 364p. 1974. 44.95 (ISBN 0-686-56670-X, S-33075). French & Eur.

Diccionario de Moral Cristiana. 2nd ed. Karl Hoermann. (Span.). 704p. 1978. pap. 35.95 (ISBN 84-254-0966-7, S-50192). French & Eur.

Diccionario De Moral Cristiana. 2nd ed. Karl Hoermann. (Span.). 704p. 1978. 41.95 (ISBN 84-254-0967-5, S-50193). French & Eur.

Diccionario de Religiones Comparadas, 2 vols. S. G. F. Brandon. (Span.). 1553p. 1975. Set. 49.95 (ISBN 8-4705-7188-5). French & Eur.

Diccionario De Teologia. 4th ed. Louis Bouyer. (Span.). 672p. 1977. 25.50 (ISBN 84-254-0377-4, S-14671). French & Eur.

Diccionario De Teologia Biblica. 2nd ed. Bauer. (Span.). 582p. 1976. 38.95 (ISBN 84-254-0360-X, S-50203). French & Eur.

Diccionario de Teologia Contemporanea. Bernard Ramm. Tr. by Roger V. Valle. 143p. 1984. pap. 3.75 (ISBN 0-311-09064-8). Casa Bautista.

Diccionario del Cristianismo. La. Brosse. (Span.). 1104p. 1976. 53.95 (ISBN 84-254-0777-X, S-50202). French & Eur.

Diccionario del Hogar Catolico. (Span.). 1180p. 1962. 17.95 (ISBN 84-261-0075-9, S-12259). French & Eur.

Diccionario Enciclopedico de la Masoneria. (Span.). 40.95 (ISBN 0-686-56654-8, S-14860). French & Eur.

Diccionario Enciclopedico De Teologia Moral. 3rd ed. Leandro Rossi & Ambrogio Valsecchi. (Span.). 1488p. 1978. 38.95 (ISBN 84-285-0468-7, S-50077); pap. 32.95 (ISBN 84-285-0467-9, S-50078). French & Eur.

Diccionario Enciclopedico De Teologia Moral: Suplemento. Leandro Rossi & Ambrogio Valsecchi. (Span.). 256p. 1978. 13.95 (ISBN 84-285-0709-0, S-50079). French & Eur.

Diccionario Ilustrado de la Biblia. Ed. by Wilton M. Nelson. (Span., Illus.). 735p. 1974. 29.95 (ISBN 0-89922-033-9); pap. 21.95 (ISBN 0-89922-099-1). Edit Caribe.

Diccionario Mitologico. A. Gavalda. (Span.). 900p. 29.95 (ISBN 0-686-92532-7, S-37663). French & Eur.

Diccionario Mitologico. C. Gaytan. (Span.). 3.75 (ISBN 0-686-56651-3, S-25775). French & Eur.

Diccionario Religioso Para los Hombres De Hoy. Josep Vilaro et al. (Span.). 260p. 1976. pap. 7.50 (ISBN 84-320-0273-9, S-50025). French & Eur.

Diccionario Teologico del Antiguo Testamento, 4 vols. G. Johannes Botterweck. (Span.). 1116p. 1978. Set. pns (S-50106). French & Eur.

Diccionario Teologico Manual del Antiguo Testamento, 2 vols. Ernst Jenni. (Span.). 642p. 1978. Set. 75.00 (S-50105). French & Eur.

Diccionario Zen. Ed. by E. Wood. (Span.). 190p. 1980. pap. 13.95 (ISBN 84-7509-010-9, S-32724). French & Eur.

Dick Gregory's Bible Tales. Dick Gregory. 1978. pap. 2.95 (ISBN 0-06-080445-9, P 445, PL). Har-Row.

Dictionario Biblico Buckland. Ed. by Vera Balthazar & Joao Batista. Orig. Title: Buckland Bible Dictionary. (Illus.). 453p. text ed. 6.50 (ISBN 0-8297-0836-7); pap. 4.50 (ISBN 0-686-97837-4). Life Pubs Intl.

Dictionary & Glossary of the Koran. John Penrice. (Arabic & Eng.). 20.00x (ISBN 0-86685-088-0). Intl Bk Ctr.

Dictionary & Glossary of the Koran. John Penrice. 180p. 1985. 15.00x (ISBN 0-7007-0001-3, Pub. by Curzon Pr England). Humanities.

Dictionary & Glossary of the Koran, with Copious Grammatical References & Explanations of the Text. J. Penrice. 176p. 1978. text ed. 26.00. Coronet Bks.

Dictionary & Glossary of the Koran, with Copious Grammatical References & Explanations. John Penrice. LC 70-90039. (Arabic.). 1969. Repr. of 1873 ed. 20.00 (ISBN 0-8196-0252-3). Biblo.

Dictionary & Glossary of the Koran with Grammatical References & Explanations. John Penrice. 1980. lib. bdg. 55.00 (ISBN 0-8490-3123-0). Gordon Pr.

Dictionary & Thesaurus of the Hebrew Language, 8 Vols. Ed. by Eliezer Ben-Yehuda. Set. 150.00 (ISBN 0-498-07038-7, Yoseloff); lea. bd. set o.p. 250.00 (ISBN 0-498-08915-0). A S Barnes.

Dictionary Catalog of Jewish Collection, 14 Vols. New York Public Library, Research Libraries. 1960. Set. 1240.00 (ISBN 0-8161-0409-3, Pub. by Hall Library). G K Hall.

Dictionary Catalog of the Jewish Collection, First Supplement, 8 vols. New York Public Library, Research Libraries. 5424p. 1975. Set. lib. bdg. 875.00 (ISBN 0-8161-0773-4, Hall Library). G K Hall.

Dictionary Catalogue of the Byzantine Collection of the Dumbarton Oaks Research Library, 12 vols. Harvard University Dumbarton Oaks Research Library. 1975. Set. lib. bdg. 1390.00 (ISBN 0-8161-1150-2, Hall Library). G K Hall.

Dictionary Catalogue of the Library of the Pontifical Institute of Medieval Studies, 5 vols. Pontifical Institute of Medieval Studies, Ontario. 1972. Set. lib. bdg. 505.00 (ISBN 0-8161-0970-2, Hall Library). G K Hall.

Dictionary-Handbook to Hymns for the Living Church. Donald P. Hustad & George H Shorney, Jr. LC 77-75916. 1978. 14.95 (ISBN 0-916642-09-7). Hope Pub.

Dictionary Hebrew Verbs. Moses Debahy. (Hebrew & Arabic.). 1974. 15.00x (ISBN 0-86685-123-2). Intl Bk Ctr.

Dictionary of American Catholic Biography. John J. Delaney. LC 83-25524. 624p. 1984. 24.95 (ISBN 0-385-17878-6). Doubleday.

Dictionary of American Religious Biography. Henry W. Bowden. Ed. by Edwin S. Gaustad. LC 76-5258. (Orig.). 1976. lib. bdg. 45.00 (ISBN 0-8371-8906-3, BAR/). Greenwood.

Dictionary of Basic Bible Truths. Larry Richards. 528p. 1987. pap. 14.95 (ISBN 0-310-43521-8). Zondervan.

Dictionary of Bible. John Mackenzie. 1967. pap. 14.95 (ISBN 0-02-087720-X, Collier). Macmillan.

Dictionary of Bible. John Mackenzie. 1965. 29.95 (ISBN 0-02-583470-3). Macmillan.

Dictionary of Bible & Religion. Ed. by William H. Gentz. (Illus.). 1152p. 1986. 26.95 (ISBN 0-687-10757-1). Abingdon.

Dictionary of Bible Imagery. Ed. by Alice S. Sechrist. LC 79-63409. 1972. 3.95 (ISBN 0-87785-118-2). Swedenborg.

Dictionary of Buddhism. T. O. Ling. LC 72-37231. 244p. 1972. 7.95 (ISBN 0-684-12763-6, ScribT). Scribner.

Dictionary of Buddhism. Trevor Ling. 1985. 15.00x (ISBN 0-8364-1436-5, Pub. by KP Bagchi India). South Asia Bks.

Dictionary of Chinese Mythology. E. T. Werner. LC 76-27521. 1976. Repr. of 1932 ed. lib. bdg. 60.00 (ISBN 0-89341-034-9). Longwood Pub Group.

Dictionary of Christian Antiquities: Being a Continuation of the Dictionary of the Bible, 2 Vols. Ed. by William Smith & Samuel Cheetham. LC 17-21174. (LM). (Illus.). 1968. Repr. of 1880 ed. Set. 148.00 (ISBN 0-527-84150-1). Kraus Repr.

Dictionary of Christian Biography, Literature, Sects & Doctrines: Being a Continuation of the Dictionary of the Bible, 4 Vols. Ed. by William Smith & Henry Wace. LC 12-3122. 1968. Repr. of 1877 ed. Set. 375.00 (ISBN 0-527-84200-1). Kraus Repr.

Dictionary of Christian Ethics. Ed. by John Macquarrie. LC 67-17412. 378p. 1967. 18.95 (ISBN 0-664-20646-8). Westminster.

Dictionary of Christian Lore & Legend. J. C. Metford. LC 82-50815. (Illus.). 272p. 1983. 24.95f (ISBN 0-500-11020-4). Thames Hudson.

Dictionary of Christian Theology. Peter Angeles. LC 79-2988. 336p. 1985. 17.45 (ISBN 0-06-060237-6, HarpR). Har-Row.

Dictionary of Classical Mythology. Pierre Grimal. 580p. 1985. 34.95x (ISBN 0-631-13209-0). Basil Blackwell.

Dictionary of Classical Mythology. Zimmerman. (YA) pap. 4.95 (ISBN 0-553-25776-5). Bantam.

Dictionary of Classical Mythology: Symbols, Attributes, & Associations. Robert E. Bell. LC 81-19141. 390p. 1982. 30.00 (ISBN 0-87436-305-5). ABC Clio.

Dictionary of Comparative Religions. S. G. Brandon. LC 76-11390. 1970. lib. bdg. 55.00 (ISBN 0-684-15561-3, ScribT). Scribner.

Dictionary of Doctrinal Terms. Fisher Humphreys & Philip Wise. LC 81-86635. (Orig.). 1983. pap. 4.95 (ISBN 0-8054-1141-0). Broadman.

Dictionary of Ecclesiastical Terms. J. A. Bumpus. 75.00 (ISBN 0-8490-0034-3). Gordon Pr.

Dictionary of Ecclesiastical Terms: Being a History & Explanation of Certain Terms Used in Architecture, Ecclesiology, Liturgiology, Music, Ritual, Cathedral, Constitution, Etc. John S. Bumpus. LC 68-30653. 1969. Repr. of 1910 ed. 35.00x (ISBN 0-8103-3321-X). Gale.

Dictionary of Esoteric Words. Ann Cattell. (Orig.). 1967. pap. 1.75 (ISBN 0-8065-0175-8, C205). Citadel Pr.

Dictionary of Hindu Architecture. P. K. Acharya. 1981. text ed. 58.50x. Coronet Bks.

Dictionary of Hymnology, 2 vols. John Julian. LC 83-8373. 1786p. 1985. Repr. of 1907 ed. 120.00 (ISBN 0-8254-2960-9). Kregel.

Dictionary of Hymnology: Origin & History of Christian Hymns, 4 vols. Ed. by J. Julian. 1977. Set. lib. bdg. 600.00 (ISBN 0-8490-1719-X). Gordon Pr.

Dictionary of Indian Mythology. V. S. Naravane. 350p. Date not set. text ed. price not set (ISBN 0-7069-2463-0, Vikas India). Advent NY.

Dictionary of Islam. Hughes. 45.00 (ISBN 0-686-18366-5). Kazi Pubns.

Dictionary of Islam, 2 vols. Thomas P. Hughes. 1980. Set. lib. bdg. 199.95 (ISBN 0-8490-3121-4). Gordon Pr.

Dictionary of Islam. Thomas P. Hughes. (Illus.). 750p. 1977. Repr. of 1885 ed. 48.00x (ISBN 0-89684-103-0, Pub. by Cosmo Pubns India). Orient Bk Dist.

Dictionary of Islam. Thomas P. Hughes. 1976. Repr. 37.50x (ISBN 0-8364-0395-9). South Asia Bks.

Dictionary of Islam: A Cyclopedia of the Muhammadan Religion. Thomas P. Hughes. (Reprints in History). (Illus.). 750p. lib. bdg. 34.00 (ISBN 0-697-00053-2). Irvington.

Dictionary of Judaism. Dagobert D. Runes. 236p. 1981. 5.95 (ISBN 0-8065-0787-X). Citadel Pr.

Dictionary of Latin & Greek Theological Terms. Richard A. Muller. 1985. 14.95 (ISBN 0-8010-6185-7). Baker Bk.

Dictionary of Miracles, 2 vols. E. Cobham Brewer. (Illus.). 337p. 1986. Repr. of 1882 ed. Set. 217.50 (ISBN 0-89901-263-9). Found Class Reprints.

Dictionary of Miracles. Ebenezer Brewer. 75.00 (ISBN 0-8490-0040-8). Gordon Pr.

Dictionary of Miracles, Imitative, Realistic, & Dogmatic. E. Cobham Brewer. LC 66-29783. 1966. Repr. of 1885 ed. 50.00x (ISBN 0-8103-3000-8). Gale.

Dictionary of Muslim Philosophy. M. Saeeed. 14.50 (ISBN 0-686-18370-3). Kazi Pubns.

Dictionary of Mysticism. Frank Gaynor. 211p. 1973. pap. 2.45 (ISBN 0-8065-0172-3). Citadel Pr.

Dictionary of Mythology, Folklore & Symbols, 3 Vols. Gertrude Jobes. LC 61-860. 1759p. 1961. Vols. 1 & 2. 70.00 (ISBN 0-8108-0034-9); Vol. 3 index, 482 pgs. 35.00 (ISBN 0-8108-1697-0). Scarecrow.

Dictionary of Non-Christian Religions. Geoffrey Parrinder. LC 73-4781. (Illus.). 320p. 1973. 10.95 (ISBN 0-664-20981-5). Westminster.

Dictionary of Non-Christian Religions. Geoffrey Parrinder. 19.95 (ISBN 0-7175-0972-9). Dufour.

Dictionary of Old Testament Words for English Readers. Aaron Pick. LC 76-16230. 602p. 1977. kivar 14.95 (ISBN 0-8254-3511-0). Kregel.

Dictionary of Pagan Religions. Harry E. Wedeck & Wade Baskin. 324p. 1973. pap. 3.95 (ISBN 0-8065-0386-6). Citadel Pr.

Dictionary of Philosophy & Religion: Eastern & Western Thought. William L. Reese. text ed. 29.95x 648p. 1980 (ISBN 0-391-00688-6); pap. text ed. 19.95x 644p. 1981 (ISBN 0-391-00941-9). Humanities.

Dictionary of Proverbs. Petros D. Baz. (Orig.). pap. 1.85 (ISBN 0-685-19399-3, 108, WL). Citadel Pr.

Dictionary of Religion & Ethics. Ed. by Shailer Mathews & Gerald B. Smith. LC 70-145713. 1971. Repr. of 1921 ed. 51.00x (ISBN 0-8103-3196-9). Gale.

Dictionary of Saints. John J. Delaney. LC 79-7783. (Illus.). 648p. 1980. 24.95 (ISBN 0-385-13594-7). Doubleday.

Dictionary of Satanism. Wade Baskin. 1972. pap. 3.95 (ISBN 0-8065-0292-4). Citadel Pr.

Dictionary of Scripture Proper Names of the Old & New Testaments. J. B. Jackson. 1909. pap. 3.95 (ISBN 0-87213-410-5). Loizeaux.

Dictionary of Sects, Heresies, Ecclesiastical Parties & Schools of Religious Thought. John H. Blunt. LC 74-9653. 1974. Repr. of 1874 ed. 75.00x (ISBN 0-8103-3751-7). Gale.

Dictionary of Sri Aurobindo's Yoga. Sri Aurobindo. Ed. by Sri M. Pandit. 1979. Repr. of 1966 ed. 7.95 (ISBN 0-941524-04-3). Lotus Light.

Dictionary of Superstitions. Sophie Lasne & Andre P. Gaultier. LC 84-11717. 304p. 1984. 20.95 (ISBN 0-13-210881-X); pap. 10.95 (ISBN 0-13-210873-9). P-H.

Dictionary of Superstitions & Mythology. Biren Bonnerjea. LC 69-17755. 1969. Repr. of 1927 ed. 43.00x (ISBN 0-8103-3572-7). Gale.

Dictionary of the Bible. Ed. by James Hastings. 1963. lib. bdg. 55.00x (ISBN 0-684-15556-7, ScribT). Scribner.

Dictionary of the Bible & Christian Doctrine in Everyday English. Ed. by Albert Truesdale et al. 200p. (Orig.). 1985. 14.95 (ISBN 0-8341-1075-X). Beacon Hill.

Dictionary of the Gathic Language. Lawrence H. Mills. LC 74-21253. (Gaelic.). Repr. of 1913 ed. 57.50 (ISBN 0-404-12804-1). AMS Pr.

Dictionary of the Jewish-Christian Dialogue. Ed. by Leon Klenicki & Geoffrey Wigoder. (Stimulus Book, Studies in Judaism & Christianity). (Orig.). 1984. pap. 7.95 (ISBN 0-8091-2590-0). Paulist Pr.

Dictionary of the Liturgy. Jovian Lang. 1986. 8.00 (ISBN 0-89942-273-X). Catholic BK Pub.

Dictionary of the New Testament. Xavier Leon-Dufour. LC 79-3004. 464p. 1983. pap. 12.95 (ISBN 0-06-065242-X, RD-486, HarpR). Har-Row.

Dictionary of Theology. Karl Rahner. 548p. 1985. pap. 17.50 (ISBN 0-8245-0691-X). Crossroad NY.

Dictionary of Women in Church History. Mary L. Hammack. LC 84-14710. 1984. 11.95 (ISBN 0-8024-0332-8). Moody.

Dictionary of World Mythology. Arthur Cotterell. (Illus.). 256p. 1982. pap. 8.95 (ISBN 0-399-50619-5, Perigee). Putnam Pub Group.

Dictionnaire Alphabetique, Theorique et Pratique de Droit Civil Ecclesiastique, 2 vols. Andre. Ed. by J. P. Migne. (Troisieme et Derniere Encyclopedie Theologique Ser.: Vols. 64-65). (Fr.). 1332p. Repr. of 1873 ed. lib. bdg. 170.00x (ISBN 0-89241-328-X). Caratzas.

Dictionnaire Archeologique de la Bible. Ed. by Abraham Negev. (Fr.). 350p. 1970. 47.50 (ISBN 0-686-57094-4, M-6117). French & Eur.

Dictionnaire Biblique. Joseph Dheilly. (Fr.). 1284p. 1964. 22.50 (ISBN 0-686-57092-8, M-6114). French & Eur.

Dictionnaire d'Anecdotes Chretiennes. P. Jouhanneaud. Ed. by J. P. Migne. (Nouvelle Encyclopedie Theologique Ser.: Vol. 10). (Fr.). 610p. Repr. of 1857 ed. lib. bdg. 78.00x (ISBN 0-89241-260-7). Caratzas.

Dictionnaire d'Antiphilosophisme ou Refutation des Erreurs du 18e Siecle. E. Grosse. Ed. by J. P. Migne. (Troisieme et Derniere Encyclopedie Theologique Ser.: Vol. 18). (Fr.). 770p. Repr. of 1856 ed. lib. bdg. 97.50x (ISBN 0-89241-301-8). Caratzas.

Dictionnaire d'Archeologie Chretienne et de Liturgie, 28 vols. Dom H. Leclercq & Henri Marron. (Fr.). 1903. Set. 1995.00 (ISBN 0-686-57001-4, M-6342). French & Eur.

Dictionnaire d'Archeologie Sacree, 2 vols. J. J. Bourasse. Ed. by J. P. Migne. (Nouvelle Encyclopedie Theologique Ser.: Vols. 11-12). (Fr.). 1236p. Repr. of 1852 ed. lib. bdg. 157.00x (ISBN 0-89241-261-5). Caratzas.

Dictionnaire d'Ascetisme, 2 vols. J. C. Gainet. Ed. by J. P. Migne. (Nouvelle Encyclopedie Theologique Ser.: Vols. 45-46). (Fr.). 1520p. Repr. of 1854 ed. lib. bdg. 192.50x (ISBN 0-89241-284-4). Caratzas.

Dictionnaire de Bibliographie Catholique, Presentant l'Indication et les Titres Complets de tous les Ouvrages qui Ontetes Publies dans les Trois Lanques Grecque, Latine et Francaise... Suivi d'un Dictionnaire de Bibliologie par G. Brunet (the Last 2 Vols., 6 vols. F M. Perennes. Ed. by J. P. Migne. (Troisieme et Derniere Encyclopedie Theologique Ser.: Vols. 39-44). (Fr.). 4001p. Repr. of 1866 ed. lib. bdg. 510.00x (ISBN 0-89241-318-2). Caratzas.

Dictionnaire de Biographie Chretienne, 3 vols. F. X. Defeller & F. Perennes. Ed. by J. P. Migne. (Nouvelle Encyclopedie Theologique Ser.: Vols. 1-3). (Fr.). 2352p. Repr. of 1851 ed. lib. bdg. 298.00x (ISBN 0-89241-254-2). Caratzas.

Dictionnaire de Cas de Conscience ou Decisions, 2 vols. J. Pontas. Ed. by J. P. Migne. (Encyclopedie Theologique Ser.: Vols. 18-19). (Fr.). 1326p. Repr. of 1847 ed. lib. bdg. 169.00x (ISBN 0-89241-238-0). Caratzas.

Dictionnaire de Discipline Ecclesiastique, 2 vols. L. Thomassin. Ed. by J. P. Migne. (Troisieme et Derniere Encyclopedie Theologique Ser.: Vols. 25-26). (Fr.). 1466p. Repr. of 1856 ed. lib. bdg. 186.00x (ISBN 0-89241-306-9). Caratzas.

Dictionnaire de Droit Canonique, 7 vols. R. Naz. (Fr.). 1965. Set. 695.00 (ISBN 0-686-57057-X, M-6423). French & Eur.

Dictionnaire de Geographie Sacree et Ecclesiastique, 3 vols. L. Benoist De Matougues. Ed. by J. P. Migne. (Encyclopedie Theologique Ser.: Vols. 28-30). (Fr.). 1886p. Repr. of 1854 ed. lib. bdg. 240.50x (ISBN 0-89241-241-0). Caratzas.

Dictionnaire de la Foi Chretienne, 2 vols. Ed. by Antonir Marie Henry & Olivier De LaBrosse. (Fr.). 792p. 1968. pap. 47.50 (ISBN 0-686-56818-4, M-6596). French & Eur.

Dictionnaire de la Franc-Maconnerie et des Francs-Macons. Allec Mellor. (Fr.). 400p. 1971. 27.50 (ISBN 0-686-57043-X, M-6403). French & Eur.

Dictionnaire de la Litterature Chretienne, Vol. 7. A. L. Constant. Ed. by J. P. Migne. (Nouvelle Encyclopedie Theologique Ser.). (Fr.). 626p. Repr. of 1851 ed. lib. bdg. 80.00x (ISBN 0-89241-257-7). Caratzas.

Dictionnaire de la Mythologie Grecque et Romaine. 5th ed. Pierre Grimal. (Fr.). 612p. 1969. 59.95 (ISBN 0-686-57316-1, M-6299). French & Eur.

Dictionnaire de la Tradition Pontificale, Patristique et Conciliaire, 2 vols. J. C. Poussin & J. C. Garnier. Ed. by J. P. Migne. (Troisieme et Derniere Encyclopedie Theologique Ser.: Vol. 12-13). (Fr.). 1464p. Repr. of 1855 ed. lib. bdg. 186.00x (ISBN 0-89241-296-8). Caratzas.

Dictionnaire de Lecons et Exemples de Litterature Chretienne en Prose et en Verse, 2 vols. F. Perennes. Ed. by J. P. Migne. (Troisieme et Derniere Encyclopedie Theologique Ser.: Vols. 61-62). (Fr.). 1510p. Repr. of 1864 ed. lib. bdg. 191.50x (ISBN 0-89241-326-3). Caratzas.

Dictionnaire de l'Histoire Universelle de l'Eglise, 6 vols. L. F. Guerin. Ed. by J. P. Migne. (Troisieme et Derniere Encyclopedie Theologique Ser.: Vols. 51-56). (Fr.). 4187p. Repr. of 1873 ed. lib. bdg. 532.50x (ISBN 0-89241-322-0). Caratzas.

Dictionnaire de Mystique Chretienne. Ed. by J. P. Migne. (Troisieme et Derniere Encyclopedie Theologique Ser.: Vol. 35). (Fr.). 784p. Date not set. Repr. of 1858 ed. lib. bdg. 99.50x (ISBN 0-89241-314-X). Caratzas.

Dictionnaire de Mythologie. Ed. by J. P. Migne. (Troisieme et Derniere Encyclopedie Theologique Ser.: Vol. 10). (Fr.). 760p. Repr. of 1855 ed. lib. bdg. 96.50x (ISBN 0-89241-294-1). Caratzas.

Dictionnaire de Noels et de Cantiques. F. Perennes. Ed. by J. P. Migne. (Troisieme et Derniere Encyclopedie Theologique Ser.: Vol. 63). (Fr.). 720p. Repr. of 1867 ed. lib. bdg. 91.50x (ISBN 0-89241-327-1). Caratzas.

Dictionnaire de Patrologie, 4 vols. in 5. A. Sevestre. Ed. by J. P. Migne. (Nouvelle Encyclopedie Theologique Ser.: Vols. 20-23b). (Fr.). 3830p. Repr. of 1859 ed. lib. bdg. 485.00x (ISBN 0-89241-267-4). Caratzas.

Dictionnaire de Philosophie Catholique, 3 vols. L. F. Jehan. Ed. by J. P. Migne. (Troisieme et Derniere Encyclopedie Theologique Ser.: Vols. 48-50). (Fr.). 2047p. Repr. of 1864 ed. lib. bdg. 260.00x (ISBN 0-89241-321-2). Caratzas.

Dictionnaire de Philosophie et de Theologie Scolastiques, 2 vols. F. Morin. Ed. by J. P. Migne. (Troisieme et Derniere Encyclopedie Theologique Ser.: Vols. 21-22). (Fr.). 1496p. Repr. of 1865 ed. lib. bdg. 190.00x (ISBN 0-89241-304-2). Caratzas.

Dictionnaire de Proverbes & Dictons. Robert. 45.00 (ISBN 0-317-45633-4). French & Eur.

Dictionnaire de Spiritualite, 12 vols. Andre Rayez. (Fr.). 1970. Set. 1195.00 (ISBN 0-686-57101-0, M-6125). French & Eur.

Dictionnaire de Statistique Religieuse. L. Des Mas-Latrie. Ed. by J. P. Migne. (Nouvelle Encyclopedie Theologique Ser.: Vol. 9). (Fr.). 538p. Repr. of 1851 ed. lib. bdg. 69.00x (ISBN 0-89241-259-3). Caratzas.

Dictionnaire de Theologie Catholigue. E. Amanne. (Fr.). Set. pap. 1995.00 (ISBN 0-686-56893-1, M-6003). French & Eur.

Dictionnaire de Theologie Catholique, Tables Generales: De Raison a Stolz, 3 vols. Bernard Loth & Albert Michel. (Fr.). 256p. 1970. Set. 295.00 (ISBN 0-686-57021-9, M-6379). French & Eur.

Dictionnaire de Theologie Morale, 2 vols. Pierrot. Ed. by J. P. Migne. (Encyclopedie Theologique Ser.: Vols. 31-32). (Fr.). 1486p. Repr. of 1849 ed. lib. bdg. 188.50x (ISBN 0-89241-242-9). Caratzas.

Dictionnaire de Theologique Dogmatique, Liturgique, Canonique et Disciplinaire, 3 vols. in 4. N. S. Bergier. Ed. by J. P. Migne. (Encyclopedie Theologique Ser.: Vols. 33-35). (Fr.). 2681p. Repr. of 1851 ed. lib. bdg. 341.00x (ISBN 0-89241-243-7). Caratzas.

Dictionnaire d'Economic Charitable, 4 vols. F. Martin-Doisy. Ed. by J. P. Migne. (Troisieme et Derniere Encyclopedie Theologique Ser.: Vols. 5-8). (Fr.). 3616p. Repr. of 1857 ed. lib. bdg. 456.00x (ISBN 0-89241-292-5). Caratzas.

Dictionnaire d'Eloquence Sacree, Vol. 6. J. C. Nadal. Ed. by J. P. Migne. (Nouvelle Encyclopedie Theologique Ser.). (Fr.). 650p. Repr. of 1851 ed. lib. bdg. 83.00x (ISBN 0-89241-256-9). Caratzas.

Dictionnaire d'Epigraphie Chretienne, 2 vols. J. J. Bourasse. Ed. by J. P. Migne. (Nouvelle Encyclopedie Theologique Ser.: Vols. 30-31). (Fr.). 1262p. Repr. of 1852 ed. lib. bdg. 161.00x (ISBN 0-89241-273-9). Caratzas.

Dictionnaire des Abbayes et Monasteres ou Histoire Des Establissements Religieux. M. De Montrond. Ed. by J. P. Migne. (Troisieme et Derniere Encyclopedie Theologique Ser.: Vol. 16). (Fr.). 614p. Repr. of 1856 ed. lib. bdg. 81.00x (ISBN 0-89241-299-2). Caratzas.

Dictionnaire des Apocryphes, 2 vols. G. Brunet. Ed. by J. P. Migne. (Troisieme et Derniere Encyclopedie Theologique Ser.: Vols. 23-24). (Fr.). 1310p. Repr. of 1858 ed. lib. bdg. 167.50x (ISBN 0-89241-305-0). Caratzas.

Dictionnaire des Apologistes Involontaires, 2 vols. C. F. Cheve. Ed. by J. P. Migne. (Nouvelle Encyclopedie Theologique Ser.: Vols. 38-39). (Fr.). 1494p. Repr. of 1853 ed. lib. bdg. 189.50x (ISBN 0-89241-279-8). Caratzas.

Dictionnaire des Bienfaits et Beautes du Christianisme. C. F. Cheve. Ed. by J. P. Migne. (Troisieme et Derniere Encyclopedie Theologique Ser.: Vol. 9). (Fr.). 732p. Repr. of 1856 ed. lib. bdg. 95.00x (ISBN 0-89241-293-3). Caratzas.

Dictionnaire des Cardinaux. C. Berton. Ed. by J. P. Migne. (Troisieme et Derniere Encyclopedie Theologique Ser.: Vol. 31). (Fr.). 912p. Repr. of 1857 ed. lib. bdg. 115.00x (ISBN 0-89241-310-7). Caratzas.

Dictionnaire des Cardinaux. C. Berton. 912p. Date not set. Repr. of 1866 ed. text ed. 186.30x (ISBN 0-576-78521-0, Pub. by Gregg Intl Pubs England). Gregg Intl.

Dictionnaire des Cathedrales de France. Michel Florisoone. (Fr.). 256p. 1971. pap. 6.95 (ISBN 0-686-56834-6, M-6612). French & Eur.

Dictionnaire des Controverses Historiques. L. F. Jehan. Ed. by J. P. Migne. (Troisieme et Derniere Encyclopedie Theologique Ser.: Vol. 66). (Fr.). 698p. Repr. of 1866 ed. lib. bdg. 90.00x (ISBN 0-89241-329-8). Caratzas.

Dictionnaire des Conversions. C. F. Cheve. Ed. by J. P. Migne. (Nouvelle Encyclopedie Theologique Ser.: Vol. 33). (Fr.). 836p. Repr. of 1852 ed. lib. bdg. 106.00x (ISBN 0-89241-275-5). Caratzas.

Dictionnaire des Droits et de la Raison. C. P. LeNoir. Ed. by J. P. Migne. (Troisieme et Derniere Encyclopedie Theologique Ser.: Vol. 57). (Fr.). 952p. Repr. of 1860 ed. lib. bdg. 120.00x (ISBN 0-89241-323-9). Caratzas.

Dictionnaire des Eglises de France, 5 tomes. Incl. Tome I. Histoire Generale des Eglises de France; Tome II. Region Centre et Sud-Est; Tome III. Region Sud-Ouest; Tome IV. Region ouest de Paris, Paris et ses environs, Bretagne, Normandie; Tome V. Nord, Est, Belgique, Luxembourg, Suisse. 91.95 ea. French & Eur.

Dictionnaire des Erreurs Sociales. A. Jouffroy. Ed. by J. P. Migne. (Nouvelle Encyclopedie Theologique Ser.: Vol. 19). (Fr.). 664p. Repr. of 1852 ed. lib. bdg. 84.50x (ISBN 0-89241-266-6). Caratzas.

Dictionnaire des Facultes Intellectuelles et Affectives de l'ame ou l'on Traite des Passions, des Vertus, des Vices, des Defauts. F. A. Poujol. Ed. by J. P. Migne. (Encyclopedie Theologique Ser.: Vol. 39). (Fr.). 560p. Repr. of 1849 ed. lib. bdg. 72.00x (ISBN 0-89241-245-3). Caratzas.

Dictionnaire des Harmonies de la Raison et de la Foi. C. P. LeNoir. Ed. by J. P. Migne. (Troisieme et Derniere Encyclopedie Theologique Ser.: Vol. 19). (Fr.). 876p. Repr. of 1856 ed. lib. bdg. 110.50x (ISBN 0-89241-302-6). Caratzas.

Dictionnaire des Heresies des Erreurs et des Schismes, 2 vols. F. A. Pluquet. Ed. by J. P. Migne. (Encyclopedie Theologique Ser.: Vols. 11-12). (Fr.). 1374p. Repr. of 1847 ed. lib. bdg. 175.00x (ISBN 0-89241-235-6). Caratzas.

Dictionnaire Des Heresies Meridionales. Rene Nelli. (Fr.). 384p. 18.50 (ISBN 0-686-56886-9, F-21110). French & Eur.

Dictionnaire des Legendes du Christianisme. J. Douhet. Ed. by J. P. Migne. (Troisieme et Derniere Encyclopedie Theologique Ser.: Vol. 14). (Fr.). 764p. Repr. of 1855 ed. lib. bdg. 97.50x (ISBN 0-89241-297-6). Caratzas.

Dictionnaire des Missions Catholiques, 2 vols. Lacroix & E. De Djunkovskoy. Ed. by J. P. Migne. (Troisieme et Derniere Encyclopedie Theologique Ser.: Vols. 59-60). (Fr.). 1545p. Repr. of 1864 ed. lib. bdg. 197.50x (ISBN 0-89241-325-5). Caratzas.

Dictionnaire des Mots d'Esprit. Jean Delacour. (Fr.). 352p. 1976. pap. 15.95 (ISBN 0-686-56849-4, M-6627). French & Eur.

Dictionnaire des Mysteres. J. Douhet. Ed. by J. P. Migne. (Nouvelle Encyclopedie Theologique Ser.: Vol. 43). (Fr.). 788p. Repr. of 1854 ed. lib. bdg. 100.00x (ISBN 0-89241-282-8). Caratzas.

Dictionnaire des Noms Propres de la Bible. (Fr.). 536p. 1978. 59.95 (ISBN 0-686-56850-8, M-6628). French & Eur.

Dictionnaire des Objections Populaires contre le Dogme, la Morale, la Discipline et L'histoire de Eglise Catholique. C. Pinard. Ed. by J. P. Migne. (Troisieme et Derniere Encyclopedie Theologique Ser.: Vol. 33). (Fr.). 756p. Repr. of 1858 ed. lib. bdg. 96.50x (ISBN 0-89241-312-3). Caratzas.

Dictionnaire des Origines du Christianisme. L. F. Jehan. Ed. by J. P. Migne. (Troisieme et Derniere Encyclopedie Theologique Ser.: Vol. 15). (Fr.). 630p. Repr. of 1856 ed. lib. bdg. 81.00x (ISBN 0-89241-298-4). Caratzas.

Dictionnaire des Papes. Hans Kuhner. (Fr.). pap. 6.95 (ISBN 0-686-56856-7, M-6634). French & Eur.

Dictionnaire des Papes ou Histoire Complete des tous les Souvenirs Pontifes. C. F. Cheve. Ed. by J. P. Migne. (Troisieme et Derniere Encyclopedie Theologique Ser.: Vol. 32). (Fr.). 706p. Repr. of 1857 ed. lib. bdg. 90.00x (ISBN 0-89241-311-5). Caratzas.

Dictionnaire des Prenoms et des Saints. Pierre Pierrard. (Fr.). 224p. 1975. pap. 6.95 (ISBN 0-686-56861-3, M-6639). French & Eur.

Dictionnaire des Propheties et des Miracles, 2 vols. A. F. Lecanu. Ed. by J. P. Migne. (Nouvelle Encyclopedie Theologique Ser.: Vols. 24-25). (Fr.). 1246p. Repr. of 1852 ed. lib. bdg. 159.00x (ISBN 0-89241-268-2). Caratzas.

Dictionnaire d'Esthetique Chretienne ou Theorie du Beau dans l'Art Chretien. E. G. Jouve. Ed. by J. P. Migne. (Troisieme et Derniere Encyclopedie Theologique Ser.: Vol. 17). (Fr.). 646p. Repr. of 1856 ed. lib. bdg. 82.50x (ISBN 0-89241-300-X). Caratzas.

Dictionnaire d'Histoire et du Geographie Ecclesiastiques, 16 vols. Roger Aubert & Van Cauwenberg. (Fr.). Set. pap. 1795.00 (ISBN 0-686-56903-2, M-6014). French & Eur.

Dictionnaire Dogmatique, Historique, Ascetique et Pratique, des Indulgences des Confreries et Associations Catholiques. P. Jouhanneaud. Ed. by J. P. Migne. (Nouvelle Encyclopedie Theologique Ser.: Vol. 27). (Fr.). 686p. Repr. of 1852 ed. lib. bdg. 87.50x (ISBN 0-89241-270-4). Caratzas.

Dictionnaire Dogmatique, Moral, Historique, Canonique, Liturgique et Disciplinaire des Decrets des Diverse Congregations Romaines. V. D. Boissonet. Ed. by J. P. Migne. (Nouvelle Encyclopedie Theologique Ser.: Vol. 26). (Fr.). 646p. Repr. of 1852 ed. lib. bdg. 82.50x (ISBN 0-89241-269-0). Caratzas.

Dictionnaire du Nouveau Testament. Xavier Leon-Dufour. (Fr.). 1975. 29.95 (ISBN 0-686-57011-1, M-6352). French & Eur.

Dictionnaire du Parallele entre Diverses Doctrines Philosophiques et Religieuses. C. Berton. Ed. by J. P. Migne. (Troisieme et Derniere Encycolpedie Theologique Ser.: Vol. 38). (Fr.). 698p. Repr. of 1858 ed. lib. bdg. 90.00x (ISBN 0-89241-317-4). Caratzas.

Dictionnaire du Protestantisme. L. Vallee. Ed. by J. P. Migne. (Troisieme et Derniere Encyclopedie Theologique Ser.: Vol. 36). (Fr.). 692p. Repr. of 1858 ed. lib. bdg. 88.00x (ISBN 0-89241-315-8). Caratzas.

Dictionnaire Francais-Hebreu. Marc M. Cohn. (Fr. & Hebrew.). 760p. 1966. 27.50 (ISBN 0-686-56955-5, M-6077). French & Eur.

Dictionnaire General et Complet des Persecutions, 2 vols. P. Belouino. Ed. by J. P. Migne. (Nouvelle Encyclopedie Theologique Ser.: Vols. 4-5). (Fr.). 1468p. Repr. of 1851 ed. lib. bdg. 186.50x (ISBN 0-89241-255-0). Caratzas.

Dictionnaire Geographique, Historique, Descriptif, Archeologique des Pelegrinages, 2 vols. L. De Sivry. Ed. by J. P. Migne. (Encyclopedie Theologique Ser.: Vols. 43-44). (Fr.). 1328p. Repr. of 1851 ed. lib. bdg. 169.00x (ISBN 0-89241-248-8). Caratzas.

Dictionnaire Grec-Francais du Nouveau Testament. Maurice Carrez & Francois Morel. (Fr.-Gr.). 276p. 37.50 (ISBN 0-686-56940-7, M-6062). French & Eur.

Dictionnaire Hagiographique, 2 vols. L. M. Petin. Ed. by J. P. Migne. (Encyclopedie Theologique Ser.: Vols. 40-41). (Fr.). 1580p. Repr. of 1850 ed. lib. bdg. 240.00x (ISBN 0-89241-246-1). Caratzas.

Dictionnaire Historique, Archeologique, Philologique, Chronologique Geographique et Literal de la Bible, 4 vols. A. Calmet. Ed. by J. P. Migne. (Encyclopedie Theologique First Ser.: Vols. 1-4). (Fr.). 2602p. Repr. of 1846 ed. lib. bdg. 332.50x (ISBN 0-89241-231-3). Caratzas.

Dictionnaire Historique, Geographique et Biographique des Croisades. G. E. D'Ault-Dumesnil. Ed. by J. P. Migne. (Nouvelle Encyclopedie Theologique Ser.: Vol. 18). (Fr.). 619p. Repr. of 1852 ed. lib. bdg. 79.00x (ISBN 0-89241-265-8). Caratzas.

Dictionnaire Iconographique des Figures Legendes et Actes des Saints. L. J. Guenebault. Ed. by J. P. Migne. (Encyclopedie Theologique Ser.: Vol. 45). (Fr.). 716p. Repr. of 1850 ed. lib. bdg. 91.00x (ISBN 0-89241-249-6). Caratzas.

Dictionnaire les Antiquites Bibligues. L. F. Saulcy. Ed. by J. P. Migne. (Troisieme et Derniere Encyclopedie Theologique Ser.: Vol. 45). (Fr.). 516p. Repr. of 1859 ed. lib. bdg. 66.50x (ISBN 0-89241-319-0). Caratzas.

Dictionnaire Liturgique, Historique, et Theorique de Plain Chante de Musique Religieuse. J. L. D'Ortigue. Ed. by J. P. Migne. (Nouvelle Encyclopedie Theologique Ser.: Vol. 29). (Fr.). 782p. Date not set. Repr. of 1860 ed. lib. bdg. 99.00x (ISBN 0-89241-272-0). Caratzas.

Dictionnaire Liturgique, Historique et Theorique de Plainchant et de Musique d'Eglise. M. J. D'Ortigue. LC 79-155353. (Music Ser). (Fr.). 1971. Repr. of 1854 ed. lib. bdg. 110.00 (ISBN 0-306-70165-0). Da Capo.

Dictionnaire Raisonne de Diplomatie Chretienne, Vol. 47. M. Quantin. Ed. by J. P. Migne. (Encyclopedie Theologique Ser.). (Fr.). 578p. Repr. of 1846 ed. lib. bdg. 74.00x (ISBN 0-89241-251-8). Caratzas.

Dictionnaire Raisonne de Droit et de Jurisprudence en Matiere Civile Ecclesiastique, 3 vols. J. H. Prompsault. Ed. by J. P. Migne. (Encyclopedie Theologique Ser.: Vols. 36-38). (Fr.). 1948p. Repr. of 1849 ed. lib. bdg. 248.00x (ISBN 0-89241-244-5). Caratzas.

Dictionnaire Raisonne Des Superstitions et Des Croyances Populaires. Pierre Canavaggio. (Fr.). 247p. 1977. pap. 19.95 (ISBN 0-686-56937-7, M-6059). French & Eur.

Dictionnaire Universel de Philologie Sacree... Suivi du Dictionnaire de Lanque Sainte... par Louis de Wolzoque, 3 vols. in 4. Hure. Ed. by J. P. Migne. (Encyclopedie Theologique Ser.: Vols. 5-7). (Fr.). 2426p. Repr. of 1846 ed. lib. bdg. 309.50x (ISBN 0-89241-232-1). Caratzas.

Dictionnaire Universel et Complet des Conciles, 2 vols. A. C. Peltier. Ed. by J. P. Migne. (Encyclopedie Theologique Ser.: Vols. 13-14). (Fr.). 1378p. Repr. of 1846 ed. lib. bdg. 175.00x (ISBN 0-89241-236-4). Caratzas.

Dictionnaire Universel, Historique et Comparatif des Toutes les Religions du Monde, 4 vols. F. M. Bertrand. Ed. by J. P. Migne. (Encyclopedie Theologique Ser.: Vols. 24-27). (Fr.). 2588p. Repr. of 1851 ed. lib. bdg. 329.50x (ISBN 0-89241-240-2). Caratzas.

Dictionnaires des Ordres Religieux ou Historie des Ordres Monastiques, Religieux et Militaires, 4 vols. P. Helyot. Ed. by J. P. Migne. (Encyclopedie Theologique Ser.: Vols. 20-23). (Fr.). 2724p. Repr. of 1859 ed. lib. bdg. 347.50x (ISBN 0-89241-239-9). Caratzas.

Dictionnaires des Preuves de la Divinite de Jesus Christ. Ed. by J. P. Migne. (Troisieme et Derniere Encyclopedie Theologique Ser.: Vol. 37). (Fr.). 516p. Repr. of 1858 ed. lib. bdg. 66.50x (ISBN 0-89241-316-6). Caratzas.

Dictionnaires Heraldique. C. De Grandmaison. Ed. by J. P. Migne. (Nouvelle Encyclopedie Theologique Ser.: Vol. 13). (Fr.). 688p. Repr. of 1852 ed. lib. bdg. 90.00x (ISBN 0-89241-262-3). Caratzas.

Dictionnaires Sciences Occultes. (Fr.). 416p. 1976. pap. 19.95 (ISBN 0-686-57104-5, M-6130). French & Eur.

Did Christ Die for All? George E. Failing. 1980. 1.25 (ISBN 0-937296-02-3, 222-B). Presence Inc.

Did Christ Die Only for the Elect? Charles R. Smith. 1979. pap. 1.00 (ISBN 0-88469-025-3). BMH Bks.

Did Christ Rule Out Women Priests? J. N. Wijngaards. 96p. 1977. pap. 1.95 (ISBN 0-85597-204-1). Attic Pr.

Did Jesus Die Twice? Ed. by Gene Tolliver. LC 85-63545. 100p. (Orig.). 1986. pap. 3.75 (ISBN 0-937357-00-6). Substance Faith.

Did Jesus Exist? G. A. Wells. 24.95 (ISBN 0-87975-394-3); pap. 14.95 (ISBN 0-87975-395-1). Prometheus Bks.

Did Jesus Go to Church? And Fifty-One Other Children's Sermons. Graham R. Hodges. LC 81-20585. 128p. (Orig.). 1982. pap. 5.95 (ISBN 0-687-10762-8). Abingdon.

Did Jesus Know He Was God? Francois Dreyfus. Date not set. price not set (ISBN 0-8199-0899-1). Franciscan Herald.

Did Jesus Know What He Was Talking About? Ralph H. Peterson. 112p. 1982. 6.95 (ISBN 0-8187-0045-9). Am Developing.

Did Jesus Rise from the Dead? Gary Habermas & Anthony Flew. 1987. 14.95 (HarpR). Har-Row.

Did Politics Influence Jesus? Gordon Lindsay. 86p. (Orig.). 1982. pap. 2.50 (ISBN 0-89985-113-4, 1002). Christ Nations.

Did the Devil Make Darwin Do It? Modern Perspectives on the Creation-Evolution Controversy. Ed. by David B. Wilson. (Illus.). 242p. 1983. pap. 13.95 (ISBN 0-8138-0434-5). Iowa St U Pr.

Did the Mathers Disagree about the Salem Witchcraft Trials? Proceedings of the American Antiquarian Society. David Levin. 19p. 1985. pap. 3.95 (ISBN 0-912296-77-1, Dist. by U Pr of Va). Am Antiquarian.

Did the Virgin Mary Live & Die in England. 1986. 49.00x (Pub. by Megiddo Pr Cardiff). State Mutual Bk.

Did You Receive the Spirit? rev. ed. Simon Tugwell. 144p. 1982. pap. 6.95 (ISBN 0-87243-108-8). Templegate.

Didache, the Epistle of Barnabas, the Epistle & Martyrdom of St. Polycarp, the Fragments of Papias, the Epistle of Diognetus. Ed. by W. J. Burghardt et al. LC 78-62453. (ACW Ser.: No. 6). 241p. 1948. 13.95 (ISBN 0-8091-0247-1). Paulist Pr.

Diderot & Descartes: A Study of Scientific Naturalism in the Enlightment. Aram Vartanian. LC 75-18406. (History of Ideas Series: No. 6). 336p. 1975. Repr. of 1953 ed. lib. bdg. 22.50x (ISBN 0-8371-8337-5, VADD). Greenwood.

Diet Alternative. Diane Hampton. Orig. Title: Scriptural Eating Patterns. 144p. (Orig.). 1984. pap. 3.95 (ISBN 0-88368-148-X). Whitaker Hse.

Diet Signs: Follow Your Horoscope to a Slimmer You. Joanne H. Lemieux. LC 82-16251. 1982. pap. 6.95 (ISBN 0-87491-491-4). Acropolis.

Dietrich Bonhoeffer. Ederhard Bethge. LC 70-10975. 1977. pap. 19.95 (ISBN 0-06-060771-8, RD 165, HarpR). Har-Row.

Dietrich Bonhoeffer. Dallas M. Roark. Ed. by Bob E. Patterson. LC 72-76439. (Makers of the Modern Theological Mind Ser.). 140p. 1972. 8.95 (ISBN 0-87680-253-6, 80253). Word Bks.

Dietrich Bonhoeffer on Christian Community & Common Sense. Thomas I. Day. LC 83-25900. (Toronto Studies in Theology: Vol. 11). 248p. 1983. 49.95x (ISBN 0-88946-752-8). E Mellen.

Dieu et la Permission du Mal. 3rd ed. Jacques Maritain. 116p. 1963. 8.95 (ISBN 0-686-56349-2). French & Eur.

Dieux D'hommes: Dictionnaire Des Messianismes & Millenarismes De L'ere Chretienne. Henri Desroche et al. 1969. 30.40x (ISBN 90-2796-415-7). Mouton.

Diez Pasos a la Vida. Edith Schaeffer. Tr. by David Powell from Eng. Orig. Title: Lifelines. (Span.). 192p. 1987. pap. 4.95 (ISBN 0-88113-251-9). Edit Betania.

Diferencias Personales? Enfrentelas con Amor. David Augsburger. Tr. by Alfonso Olmedo from Eng. Tr. of Caring Enough to Confront. 176p. 1985. pap. 5.95 (ISBN 0-311-46098-4, Edit Mundo). Casa Bautista.

Difference Jesus Makes. Robert Kress. (Synthesis Ser.). 1981. 1.25 (ISBN 0-8199-0372-8). Franciscan Herald.

Differences of the Churches of the Seperation Containing a Description of the Leitourgie & Ministerie of the Visible Church. John Smyth. LC 73-6161. (English Experience Ser.: No. 624). 32p. 1973. Repr. of 1608 ed. 5.00 (ISBN 90-221-0624-1). Walter J Johnson.

Different Call: Women's Ministries in the Episcopal Church. Mary S. Donovan. 216p. (Orig.). 1986. text ed. 19.95 (ISBN 0-8192-1396-9). Morehouse.

Different Is Not the Same As Wrong. B. C. Denim. 1982. pap. 1.95 (ISBN 0-570-08408-3, 39-1083). Concordia.

Different Kind of Gentleman: Parish Clergy As Professional Men in Early & Mid-Victorian England. Brian Heeney. LC 76-17329. (Studies in British History & Culture: Vol. 5). (Illus.). xii, 169p. 1976. 21.50 (ISBN 0-208-01605-8, Archon). Shoe String.

Different Kinds of Prayer. Perry A. Gaspard. 88p. 1984. pap. text ed. 3.00 (ISBN 0-931867-08-8). Abundant Life Pubns.

Different Theologies, Common Responsibilities. Ed. by Claude Geffre et al. (Concilium Ser.: Vol. 171). 116p. 1984. pap. 6.95 (ISBN 0-567-30051-X, Pub. by T & T Clark Ltd Uk). Fortress.

Different Ways to Pray. Naomi S. Nye. LC 79-5470. 1980. pap. 6.95 (ISBN 0-932576-04-4). Breitenbush Bks.

Differentiated Supervision for Catholic Schools. Allan A. Glathorn & Carmel R. Shields. 72p. 1983. 5.75 (ISBN 0-318-00781-9). Natl Cath Educ.

Difficult Beginnings: Three Works on the Bodhisattva Path. Candragomin. Tr. by Mark Tatz. LC 83-2317. Tr. of Sanskrit. 121p. 1985. 22.50 (ISBN 0-87773-317-1, 54530-3). Shambhala Pubns.

Difficult Passages in the Gospels. Robert H. Stein. 139p. 1984. pap. 6.95 (ISBN 0-8010-8249-8). Baker Bk.

Difficult Questions About the Bible Answered. Gordon Lindsay. 1.25 (ISBN 0-89985-114-2). Christ Nations.

Difficult Sayings in the Gospels: Jesus's Use of Overstatement & Hyperbole. Robert H. Stein. 96p. pap. 4.95 (ISBN 0-8010-8262-5). Baker Bk.

Difficult Sayings of Jesus. William Neil. 1977. pap. 2.95 (ISBN 0-8028-1668-1). Eerdmans.

Difficult Years of Survival. Fouad Guirguis. LC 83-90921. 89p. 1985. 7.95 (ISBN 0-533-05937-2). Vantage.

Difficulties in Mental Prayer. Eugene D. Boylan. 128p. 1984. pap. 5.95 (ISBN 0-87061-105-4). Chr Classics.

Diffusion of the Reformation in Southwestern Germany, 1518-1534. Manfred Hannemann. LC 75-14120. (Research Papers Ser.: No. 167). (Illus.). 1975. pap. 10.00 (ISBN 0-89065-074-8). U Chicago Dept Geog.

Digase la Verdad. William Backus & Marie Chaplan. 1983. 3.75 (ISBN 0-88113-049-4). Edit Betania.

Digest & Index of the Minutes of General Synod, 1958-1977. Mildred Schuppert. pap. 10.95 (ISBN 0-8028-1774-2). Eerdmans.

Digest of Moohammudan Law, 2 Vols. N. B. Baillie. 1965. 65.50x (ISBN 0-87902-048-2). Orientalia.

Digest of the Divine Law. Howard B. Rand. 1943. 8.00 (ISBN 0-685-08802-2). Destiny.

Digging Diamonds Daily. C. C. Cribb. LC 77-70215. Set. (ISBN 0-932046-09-6); Vol. 1. 12.95 (ISBN 0-932046-07-X); Vol. 2. 12.95 (ISBN 0-932046-08-8). Manhattan Ltd NC.

Digno es el Cordero. Ray Summers. Tr. by Alfredo Lerin from Eng. Orig. Title: Worthy is the Lamb. (Span.). 287p. 1981. pap. 4.95 (ISBN 0-311-04305-4). Casa Bautista.

Dilek. Mollie B. Zook. 1983. 3.25 (ISBN 0-87813-521-9). Christian Light.

Dilemma of Contemporary Theology Prefigured in Luther, Pascal, Kierkegaard, Nietzsche. Per Lonning. LC 78-16470. 1978. Repr. of 1962 ed. lib. bdg. cancelled (ISBN 0-313-20596-5, LODC). Greenwood.

Dilemma of Israel. Harry B. Ellis. 1970. pap. 5.25 (ISBN 0-8447-1041-5). Am Enterprise.

Dilemma of Religious Knowledge. Charles A. Bennett. LC 71-85986. (Essay & General Literature Index Reprint Ser). 1969. pap. text ed. 15.95x (ISBN 0-8046-0538-6, Pub. by Kennikat). Assoc Faculty Pr.

Dilemmas of a Reconciler. Richard K. Ullmann. 1983. pap. 2.50x (ISBN 0-87574-131-2, 131). Pendle Hill.

Dilemmas of Contemporary Religion. David Martin. LC 78-17704. 1978. 20.00x (ISBN 0-312-21055-8). St Martin.

Dilemmas of Modern Religious Life. J. M. Tillard. (Consecrated Life Studies Ser.: Vol. 3). 1984. pap. 5.95 (ISBN 0-89453-446-7). M Glazier.

Dilemmas of Tomorrow's World. Franz Bockle & Theo. Beemer. LC 78-86974. (Concilium Ser.: No. 45). 188p. 1965. 7.95 (ISBN 0-8091-0030-4). Paulist Pr.

Diligence. Dennis Burke. 96p. (Orig.). 1983. pap. 2.50 (ISBN 0-89274-307-7, HH307). Harrison Hse.

Dimensions of Belief & Unbelief. John R. Connolly. LC 80-67241. 373p. 1981. lib. bdg. 30.50 (ISBN 0-8191-1389-1); pap. text ed. 15.75 (ISBN 0-8191-1390-5). U Pr of Amer.

Dimensions of Faith. James A. Mohler. LC 69-13120. (Orig.). 1969. pap. 2.80 (ISBN 0-8294-0100-8). Loyola.

Dimensions of Job: A Study & Selected Readings. Nahum N. Glatzer. LC 69-11936. 320p. 1973. pap. 7.95 (ISBN 0-8052-0378-8). Schocken.

Dimensions of Moral Creativity: Paradigms, Principles, & Ideals. A. S. Cua. LC 77-16169. 1978. 22.50x (ISBN 0-271-00540-8). Pa St U Pr.

Dimensions of Moral Education. Robert E. Carter. 254p. 1984. pap. 11.95 (ISBN 0-8020-6540-6). U of Toronto Pr.

Dimensions of Orthodox Judaism. Ed. by Rueven P. Bulka. LC 83-260. 471p. 1983. 25.00x (ISBN 0-87068-894-4). Ktav.

Dimensions of Pilgrimage: An Anthropoligical Appraisal (Based on the Transactions of a World Symposium of Pilgrimage) Ed. by Makhan Jha. (Illus.). xvi, 180p. 1986. text ed. 45.00x (ISBN 81-210-0007-6, Pub. by Inter India Pubns N Delhi). Apt Bks.

Dimensions of Renunciation in Advaita Vedanta. Kapil N. Tiwari. 1977. 12.95 (ISBN 0-89684-195-2). Orient Bk Dist.

Dimensions of Renunciation in Advaita Vedanta. Kapil N. Tiwari. 1977. 11.00x (ISBN 0-8364-0109-3). South Asia Bks.

Dimensions of Spiritual Education. Norman Dowsett & Sita R. Jayaswal. (Integral Education Ser.: No.4). (Illus.). 91p. 1975. pap. 2.50 (ISBN 0-89071-216-6). Matagiri.

Dimensions of the Holocaust. Elie Wiesel et al. 1978. 10.95 (ISBN 0-8101-0469-5); pap. 6.95x (ISBN 0-8101-0470-9). Northwestern U Pr.

Dimensions of the Holocaust: A Series of Lectures Presented at Northwestern University & Coordinated by the Department of History. 64p. 3.50 (ISBN 0-88464-091-4). ADL.

Dimensions of the Priesthood. new ed. Ed. by Daughters of St. Paul. 1973. 5.75 (ISBN 0-8198-0253-0); pap. 4.50 (ISBN 0-8198-0254-9). Dghtrs St Paul.

Dimensions of Thought: Current Explorations in Time, Space & Knowledge, 2 vols. Tarthang Tulku. Ed. by Ralph Moon & Steve Randall. 1980. Vol. 1. 12.95 (ISBN 0-913546-77-1); Vol. 2. 12.95 (ISBN 0-913546-78-X). Dharma Pub.

Dimly Burning Wicks: Reflections on the Gospel after a Time Away. John W. Vannorsdall. LC 81-70661. 112p. 1982. pap. 6.95 (ISBN 0-8006-1622-7, 1-1622). Fortress.

Dinamica de Adiestrar Discipulos. Gary W. Kuhne. 160p. 1980. 2.95 (ISBN 0-88113-040-0). Edit Betania.

Dinamicas de la Escuela Dominical. Ed. by Wilfredo Calderon. (Span.). 108p. 1973. pap. 3.25 (ISBN 0-87148-255-X). Pathway Pr.

Diocesans Tryall. Paul Baynes. 102p. Repr. of 1621 ed. text ed. 33.12x (ISBN 0-576-99736-6, Pub. by Gregg Intl Pubs England). Gregg Intl.

Dionysiac Mysteries of the Hellenistic & Roman Age. facsimile ed. Martin P. Nilsson. LC 75-10643. (Ancient Religion & Mythology Ser.). (Illus.). 1976. Repr. of 1957 ed. 13.00x (ISBN 0-405-07261-9). Ayer Co Pubs.

Dionysian Aesthetics: The Role of Destruction in Creation as Reflected in the Life & Works of Friedrich Nietzsche. Adrian Del Caro. (European University Studies: Series 20, Philosophy: Vol. 69). 157p. 1980. 20.65 (ISBN 3-8204-6819-6). P Lang Pubs.

Dionysius of Halicarnassus, on Literary Composition & Dionysius of Halicarnassus: The Three Literary Letters (EP. AD Ammaeum I, EP. AD Popeium, EP. AD Ammaeum II, 2 vols. W. Rhys Roberts. Ed. by Leonardo Taran. (Ancient Greek Literature Ser.). 616p. 1987. lib. bdg. 90.00 (ISBN 0-8240-7766-0). Garland Pub.

Dionysius the Pseudo-Areopagite: The Ecclesiastical Hierarchy. Tr. by Thomas L. Campbell from Gr. LC 81-40140. 236p. (Orig.). 1981. lib. bdg. 27.50 (ISBN 0-8191-1798-6); pap. text ed. 12.50 (ISBN 0-8191-1799-4). U Pr of Amer.

Dionysius Von Alexandrien Zur Frage Des Originismus. Wolfgang Bienert. (Patristische Texte und Studien, 21). 1978. 35.20x (ISBN 3-11-007442-7). De Gruyter.

Dionysus: Myth & Cult. Walter F. Otto. Tr. by Robert B. Palmer from Ger. LC 86-13742. (Dunquin Ser.: No. 14). xxi, 243p. 1981. pap. 13.00 (ISBN 0-88214-214-3). Spring Pubns.

Dios de Nuestros Libertadores. Luis Salem. LC 77-165. (Span., Illus.). 172p. (Orig.). 1977. pap. 3.25 (ISBN 0-89922-093-2). Edit Caribe.

Dios, el Atomo, y el Universo. James Reid. Tr. by Julio Orozco from Eng. LC 76-55491. Tr. of God, the Atom & the Universe. (Span.). 240p. (Orig.). 1977. pap. 5.95 (ISBN 0-89922-083-5). Edit Caribe.

Dios Padre Envia a Su Hijo. (Span. & Eng.). pap. text ed. 2.00 (ISBN 0-8198-1806-2); 1.00 (ISBN 0-8198-1807-0). Dghtrs St Paul.

Dios, Tu y la Escuela. Tiago Lima. Tr. by Alfredo Diaz. (Dios, Tu y La Vida). 32p. (Orig.). 1974. pap. 0.95 (ISBN 0-311-46200-6). Casa Bautista.

Dios, Tu y Tu Familia. Tr. by Betty M. De Poor. (Dios, Tu y la Vida). Orig. Title: Deus, Voce E Sua Familia. 1981. Repr. of 1978 ed. 0.95 (ISBN 0-311-46202-2). Casa Bautista.

Dios y Sus Ayudantes. A. M. Cutts. (Span., Illus.). 48p. 1981. pap. 1.25 (ISBN 0-311-38548-6). Casa Bautista.

Diplomacy & Dogmatism: Bernardino de Mendoza & the French Catholic League. DeLamar Jensen. LC 63-20769. (Illus.). 1964. 22.50x (ISBN 0-674-20800-5). Harvard U Pr.

Diplomacy in Islam. A. Iqbal. 14.95 (ISBN 0-686-18588-9). Kazi Pubns.

Diplomatarium of the Crusader Kingdom of Valencia: The Registered Charters of Its Conqueror, Jaume I, 1257-1276. Volume I: Society & Documentation in Crusader Valencia. Robert I. Burns. LC 84-17828. (Illus.). 288p. 1985. text ed. 40.00x (ISBN 0-691-05435-5). Princeton U Pr.

Direct Bible Discovery. Ronald W. Leigh. LC 81-67203. 1982. pap. 7.95 (ISBN 0-8054-1139-9). Broadman.

Direct Healing. Paul Ellsworth. LC 83-3920. 1983. lib. bdg. 15.95x (ISBN 0-89370-658-2). Borgo Pr.

Direct Healing. Paul Ellsworth. 1982. pap. 5.95 (ISBN 0-87877-058-5). Newcastle Pub.

Directions: A Look at the Paths of Life. Walter R. Scragg. LC 77-78101. (Horizon Ser.). 1977. pap. 5.95 (ISBN 0-8127-0136-4). Review & Herald.

Directions for Justice-Peace Education in the Catholic Elementary School. Justice Peace Education Council & Sister Loretta Carey. 44p. 1985. 4.80 (ISBN 0-318-20608-0). Natl Cath Educ.

Directions in Biblical Hebrew Poetry. Elaine R. Follis. (JSOT Supplement Ser.: No. 40). 340p. 1986. text ed. 33.50x (ISBN 1-85075-013-0, Pub. by JSOT Pr England); pap. text ed. 15.95x (ISBN 1-85075-012-2). Eisenbrauns.

Directions in Catholic Social Ethics. Charles E. Curran. LC 84-28079. 304p. (Orig.). 1985. pap. text ed. 8.95 (ISBN 0-268-00853-1, 85-08533). U of Notre Dame Pr.

Directions in Fundamental Moral Theology. Charles E. Curran. LC 85-2543. 304p. 1985. pap. text ed. 8.95x (ISBN 0-268-00854-X, 85-08541, Dist. by Har-Row). U of Notre Dame Pr.

Directions, Please. Kenneth D. Barney. LC 82-82080. 128p. (Orig.). 1983. pap. 2.50 (ISBN 0-88243-856-5, 02-0856); tchr's. ed. 3.95 (ISBN 0-88243-197-8, 32-0197). Gospel Pub.

Directives for the Mutual Relations Between Bishops & Religions in the Church. pap. cancelled (ISBN 0-686-15367-7, V-591). US Catholic.

Directives to Lay Apostles: Eighty-Six Pronouncements. Pope Pius Twelfth. Ed. by Monks Of Solesmes. 1964. 4.00 (ISBN 0-8198-0035-X); pap. 3.00 (ISBN 0-8198-0036-8). Dghtrs St Paul.

Directory Alabama Churches of Christ, 1976. Ernest Clevenger, Jr. (Illus.). 1976. pap. 2.00 (ISBN 0-88428-039-X). Parchment Pr.

Directory-Department of Chief Administrators of Catholic Education. 75p. 3.60 (ISBN 0-686-39967-6). Natl Cath Educ.

Directory: North American Protestant Schools & Professors of Mission. Ed. by MARC. 220p. pap. 6.60 (ISBN 0-912552-37-9). Missions Adv Res Com Ctr.

Directory of Autocephalous Anglican, Catholic, & Orthodox Bishops. 3rd ed. Karl Pruter. LC 86-34289. 53p. 1986. lib. bdg. 19.95x (ISBN 0-89370-528-4). Borgo Pr.

Directory of Catholic Schools & Colleges. 64p. 1982. 25.00x (ISBN 0-317-43550-7, Pub. by Truman & Knightley). State Mutual BK.

Directory of Development. (How To Ser.). 28p. 1986. 10.95. Natl Cath Educ.

Directory of Development. Compiled by Robert J. Yeager. 28p. 1986. 10.95 (ISBN 0-318-20571-8). Natl Cath Educ.

Directory of Holistic Practitioners for the Greater Boston Area. Ed. by David I. Weiss et al. LC 87-90042. 120p. (Orig.). 1987. pap. 5.00 (ISBN 0-9618049-0-4). D I Weiss.

Directory of Jewish Archival Institutions. Philip P. Mason. LC 75-15504. 72p. 1975. pap. text ed. 7.95x (ISBN 0-8143-1547-X). Wayne St U Pr.

Directory of Lay Ministry Training Programs. 1986. pap. 9.95 (ISBN 1-55586-109-1). US Catholic.

Directory of Religious Bodies in the United States. James G. Melton & James V. Geisendorfer. (Reference Library of the Humanities: Vol. 91). (LC 76-052700). 1977. lib. bdg. 40.00 (ISBN 0-8240-9882-X). Garland Pub.

Directory of Women Religious in the United States. Ed. by Magdalen O'Hara. 1985. 65.00 (ISBN 0-89453-528-5). M Glazier.

Dirty Hands, Pure Hearts. Michael Mills. 1985. 4.50 (ISBN 0-89536-724-6, 5808). CSS of Ohio.

Disappearance of God: Five Nineteenth Century Writers. J. Hillis Miller. 392p. 1976. text ed. 22.50x (ISBN 0-674-21101-4, Belknap Pr). Harvard U Pr.

Disappointed: Millerism & Millenarianism in the Nineteenth Century. Ed. by Ronald L. Numbers & Jonathan M. Butler. (Religion in North America Ser.). 1987. 29.95 (ISBN 0-253-34299-6). Ind U Pr.

Disarmament Catalogue. Ed. by Murray Polner. LC 82-13226. (Illus.). 224p. (Orig.). 1982. pap. 12.95 (ISBN 0-8298-0627-X). Pilgrim NY.

Disarming the Heart, Toward a Vow of Non-Violence. John Dear. 144p. (Orig.). 1987. pap. 6.95 (ISBN 0-8091-2842-X). Paulist Pr.

Disaster & Deliverance. Larry Armstrong. LC 79-88400. 1979. pap. 3.75 (ISBN 0-933350-22-8). Morse Pr.

Disaster & the Millennium. Michael Barkun. LC 86-5979. 256p. 1986. pap. text ed. 12.95x (ISBN 0-8156-2392-5). Syracuse U Pr.

Discerning Christian. K. Neill Foster. 104p. (Orig.). 1982. 6.95 (ISBN 0-87509-312-4); pap. 3.95 (ISBN 0-87509-316-7). Chr Pubns.

Discerning the Body. R. L. Black. 98p. (Orig.). 1984. pap. 3.95 (ISBN 0-934942-42-0, 1264). White Wing Pub.

Discerning the Mystery: An Essay on the Nature of Theology. Andrew Louth. 1983. text ed. 32.00x (ISBN 0-19-826657-X). Oxford U Pr.

Discernment: A Study in Ecstasy & Evil. Morton Kelsey. LC 78-58958. 168p. 1978. pap. 7.95 (ISBN 0-8091-2157-3). Paulist Pr.

Discernment: Seeking God in Every Situation. Chris Aridas. 120p. (Orig.). 1981. pap. 3.50 (ISBN 0-914544-37-3). Living Flame Pr.

Disciple. Juan C. Ortiz. LC 74-29650. 144p. 1975. pap. 4.95 (ISBN 0-88419-145-1). Creation Hse.

Disciple & the Master: St. Bonaventure's Sermons on St. Francis of Assisi. Eric Doyle. 220p. 1983. 15.00 (ISBN 0-8199-0842-8). Franciscan Herald.

Disciple-Maker Workbook. Albert L. Kurz. 1981. pap. 10.95 (ISBN 0-8024-2217-9). Moody.

Disciple of Christ. Vaughn J. Featherstone. LC 84-71706. 100p. 7.95 (ISBN 0-87747-910-0). Deseret Bk.

Discipled to Christ. Stephen Kaung. Ed. by Herbert L. Fader. 1976. pap. 2.25 (ISBN 0-935008-17-9). Christian Fellow Pubs.

Discipled to Christ. Stephen Kaung. Tr. by Lily Hsu from Eng. (Chinese.). 1984. pap. write for info. (ISBN 0-941598-13-6). Living Spring Pubns.

Discipler's Manual. new ed. F. E. Marsh. LC 79-2550. 412p. 1980. 12.95 (ISBN 0-8254-3231-6). Kregel.

Disciples & Discipleship: Studies in the Gospel According to Mark. Ernest Best. 272p. 1986. 19.95 (ISBN 0-567-09369-7, Pub. by T & T Clark Ltd UK). Fortress.

Disciples & Prophets. F. J. Moloney. 240p. 1981. 12.95 (ISBN 0-8245-0049-0). Crossroad NY.

Disciples Are Made-Not Born. Walter A. Henrichsen. LC 74-79162. 160p. 1974. pap. 4.50 (ISBN 0-88207-706-6). Victor Bks.

Disciples of Christ. John-Roger. 1976. pap. 5.00 (ISBN 0-914829-07-6). Baraka Bk.

Disciples of Christ Story-N-Puzzle Book. Ruby Maschke. 48p. (Orig.). 1983. pap. 2.50 (ISBN 0-87239-675-4, 2775). Standard Pub.

Disciples of Destruction. Charles W. Sutherland. 325p. 1986. 22.95 (ISBN 0-87975-349-8). Prometheus Bks.

Disciples of Jesus. J. C. Wenger. LC 77-86343. (Mennonite Faith Ser.: No. 5). 72p. 1977. pap. 1.50 (ISBN 0-8361-1836-7). Herald Pr.

Disciples of Jesus, Beginner-Primary Teacher. Carol E. Miller. 1984. pap. 1.75 (ISBN 0-915374-47-1). Rapids Christian.

Disciples of Jesus Junior-Junior High Teacher. 1984. pap. 2.25 (ISBN 0-915374-48-X). Rapids Christian.

Disciples of the Wise. Joseph Zeitlin. LC 71-121517. (Essay Index Reprint Ser). 1945. 19.00 (ISBN 0-8369-1859-2). Ayer Co Pubs.

Disciples' Prayer. John MacArthur, Jr. (John MacArthur's Bible Studies). (Orig.). 1986. pap. 4.95 (ISBN 0-8024-5129-2). Moody.

Disciple's Profile of Jesus. William R. Cannon. LC 75-2956. 1975. 2.95x (ISBN 0-8358-0322-8). Upper Room.

Discipleship. Harold Hazelip. LC 77-89541. (Twentieth Century Sermons Ser.). 1977. 11.95 (ISBN 0-89112-309-1, Bibl Res Pr). Abilene Christ U.

Discipleship. G. Campbell Morgan. (Morgan Library). 1973. pap. 3.45 (ISBN 0-8010-5920-8). Baker Bk.

Discipleship for High School Teens. Len Kageler & Daryl Dale. 76p. 1984. wkbk. 5.25 (ISBN 0-87509-351-5). Chr Pubns.

Discipleship: Helping Other Christians Grow. Allen Hadidian. 1987. pap. 6.95 (ISBN 0-8024-3362-6). Moody.

Discipleship in the New Testament. Ed. by Fernando F. Segovia. LC 85-47730. 240p. 1985. pap. 16.95 (ISBN 0-8006-1873-4, 1-1873). Fortress.

Discipleship Pro & Con. Bob Buess. 1975. pap. 2.50 (ISBN 0-934244-06-5). Sweeter Than Honey.

Discipleship: The Growing Christians Lifestyle. Jim & Martha Reapsome. (Fisherman Bible Studyguide). 64p. 1984. pap. 2.95 (ISBN 0-87788-175-8). Shaw Pubs.

Discipleship: The Price & the Prize. Jack Mayhall. 156p. 1984. pap. 5.95 (ISBN 0-88207-110-6). Victor Bks.

Disciplina en el Hogar. Clyde M. Narramore. Tr. by Ruben O. Zorzoli from Eng. 32p. 1985. Repr. of 1982 ed. 1.50 (ISBN 0-311-46051-8). Casa Bautista.

Disciplina Nostra: Essays in Memory of Robert F. Evans. Ed. by Donald F. Winslow. LC 79-89556. (Patristic Monograph: No. 6). (Orig.). 1979. pap. 8.50 (ISBN 0-915646-05-6). Phila Patristic.

Disciplinary, Moral & Ascetial Works. Tertullian. (Fathers of the Church Ser: Vol. 40). 495p. 1959. 34.95x (ISBN 0-8132-0040-7). Cath U Pr.

Discipline. Gordon Addington. 0.75 (ISBN 0-911802-51-7). Free Church Pubns.

Discipline & Discovery. rev. ed. Albert E. Day. 1977. pap. 4.95x (ISBN 0-8358-0354-6). Upper Room.

Discipline & Moral Education: A Survey of Public Opinion & Understanding. John Wilson. 160p. 1981. 22.00x (ISBN 0-85633-233-X, Pub. by NFER Nelson UK). Taylor & Francis.

Discipline for Non-Violence. Richard B. Gregg. 1983. pap. 2.50x (ISBN 0-87574-011-1, 011). Pendle Hill.

Discipline of Love. Martin Israel. 128p. (Orig.). 1986. pap. 8.95 (ISBN 0-8245-0739-8). Crossroad NY.

Discipline of Prayer. Frederick J. Tritton. 1983. pap. 2.50x (ISBN 0-87574-042-1, 042). Pendle Hill.

Discipline of Transcendence, 4 vols. Bhagwan Shree Rajneesh. Ed. by Ma Ananda Vandana & Ma Yoga Pratima. LC 78-906087. (Buddha Ser.). (Illus., Orig.). 1978. Vol. I, 324 pgs. 16.50 ea. (ISBN 0-88050-045-X). Vol. II, 348 pgs (ISBN 0-88050-046-8). Vol. III, 320 pgs (ISBN 0-88050-047-6). Vol. IV, 376 pgs (ISBN 0-88050-048-4). Chidvilas Found.

Discipline That Can't Fail. Arnold H. Burron. 1986. pap. 4.95 (ISBN 0-8010-0940-5). Baker Bk.

Discipline: The Canonical Buddhism of the Vinayapataka. John C. Holt. 1983. 16.00x (ISBN 0-8364-0951-5). South Asia Bks.

Discipline: The Glad Surrender. Elisabeth Elliot. 1985. pap. 5.95 (ISBN 0-8007-5195-7, Power Bks). Revell.

Discipline Them, Love Them. Betty N. Chase. 112p. 1982. wkbk. 6.95 (ISBN 0-89191-359-9). Cook.

Disciplined Life. Richard S. Taylor. LC 62-7123. 112p. 1974. pap. 3.50 (ISBN 0-87123-098-4, 200098). Bethany Hse.

Disciplined Life Style. Richard S. Taylor. LC 80-65581. 96p. 1975. pap. 2.95 (ISBN 0-87123-110-7, Dimension Bks). Bethany Hse.

Disciplines for Life. Lance Webb. 176p. pap. 7.95 (ISBN 0-8358-0539-5, ICN 602777, Dist. by Abingdon Pr). Upper Room.

Disciplines in Transformation: A Guide to Theology & the Behavioral Sciences. William W. Everett & T. J. Bachmeyer. LC 78-68570. 1979. pap. text ed. 11.75 (ISBN 0-8191-0692-5). U Pr of Amer.

Disciplines of a Disciple. John Bertolucci. 136p. (Orig.). 1985. pap. 4.95 (ISBN 0-89283-240-1). Servant.

Disciplines of Faith. Jim Obelkevich & Lyndal Roper. 512p. 1987. 55.00 (ISBN 0-7102-0750-6, Pub. by Routledge UK); pap. 25.00 (ISBN 0-7102-0993-2). Methuen Inc.

Disciplines of the Beautiful Woman. Gift ed. Anne Ortland. 131p. 1986. Repr. 9.95 (ISBN 0-8499-0551-6). Word Bks.

Disciplines of the Beautiful Woman. Anne Ortlund. (QP Proven-Word Ser.). 132p. 1984. pap. 5.95 (ISBN 0-8499-2983-0). Word Bks.

Disciplines of the Christian Life. Eric Liddell. 160p. (Orig.). 1985. pap. 6.95 (ISBN 0-687-10810-1). Abingdon.

Disciplines of the Heart. Anne Ortland. 1987. 12.95. Word Bks.

Disciplines of the Holy Quest. 4th ed. Flower A. Newhouse. LC 59-15553. (Illus.). 1959. 10.50 (ISBN 0-910378-05-3). Christward.

Disciplines of the Inner Life. Bob Benson & Michael Benson. 380p. 1985. 18.95 (ISBN 0-8499-0468-4, 0468-4). Word Bks.

Disciplines of the Spirit. Howard Thurman. LC 77-88388. 1977. pap. 6.95 (ISBN 0-913408-35-2). Friends United.

Discipling & Developing. Malcolm C. Fry. (Sunday School Workers Training Course Ser.: No. 4). 1971. pap. 3.95 (ISBN 0-89265-006-0, Free Will Baptist Dept). Randall Hse.

Discipling & Developing: Teachers Guide. Malcolm C. Fry. 1979. pap. 1.50 (ISBN 0-89265-062-1). Randall Hse.

Discipling for Jesus. Lawrence Wiseman. LC 83-70959. 1983. pap. 4.95 (ISBN 0-89900-199-8). College Pr Pub.

Discipling New Christians with the Spiritual T. E. A. M. Veteran Season. John Hendee. (Spiritual T.E.A.M Ser.). 64p. 1986. pap. 2.95 wkbk. (ISBN 0-87403-153-2, 3246). Standard Pub.

Discipling New Christians with the Spiritual T. E. A. M. Rookie Season. John Hendee. (Spiritual T.E.A.M. Ser.). 64p. 1986. pap. 2.95 wkbk. (ISBN 0-87403-152-4, 3245). Standard Pub.

Discipling New Christians with the Spiritual T. E. A. M. Coach's Manual. John Hendee. (Spiritual T.E.A.M. Ser.). 136p. 1986. pap. 5.95 (ISBN 0-87403-151-6, 3244). Standard Pub.

Discipling One to One. Michael Basler. (Pathfinder Pamphlets Ser.). 32p. (Orig.). 1986. pap. 1.95 (ISBN 0-87784-217-5). Inter-Varsity.

Discipling the Brother. rev. ed. Marlin Jeschke. LC 72-2052. 190p. 1979. pap. 2.95 (ISBN 0-8361-1897-9). Herald Pr.

Discipling the Children of Black America: A Discussion of Christian Black Education for Black Youth. Walter A. McCray. 50p. (Orig.). pap. write for info. (ISBN 0-933176-02-3). Black Light Fellow.

Discipling the City. Roger S. Greenway. LC 78-67165. 1979. pap. 9.95 (ISBN 0-8010-3727-1). Baker Bk.

Discipulado de Timoteo. William J. Petersen. Orig. Title: Discipling of Timothy. (Port.). 1986. write for info. (ISBN 0-8297-0685-2). Life Pubs Intl.

Discipulado Del Joven una Guia de Estudio. Dawson McAllister & Dan Webster. (Span.). 80p. 1986. pap. 4.50 (ISBN 0-311-12324-4, Edit Mundo). Casa Bautista.

Discipulo. Juan C. Ortiz. 192p. 1978. 3.75 (ISBN 0-88113-065-6). Edit Betania.

Discipulos de Jesus. J. C. Wenger. Ed. by Arnoldo J. Casas. Tr. by Ernesto S. Vilela. LC 79-89308. (Mennonite Faith Ser.: No. 5). (Span.). 72p. 1979. pap. 1.50x (ISBN 0-8361-1225-3). Herald Pr.

Disclosure Concerning the Nature of Man, 1694. James Lowde. LC 75-11233. (British Philosophers & Theologians in the 17th & 18th Century Ser.). 271p. 1979. lib. bdg. 51.00 (ISBN 0-8240-1786-2). Garland Pub.

Disclosure on Free-Thinking. Anthony Collins. LC 75-11209. (British Philosophers & Theologians of the 17th & 18th Centuries Ser.). 395p. 1976. lib. bdg. 51.00 (ISBN 0-8240-1764-1). Garland Pub.

Discorso Sopra la Mascherata Della Genealogia Delg'Iddei, Repr. Of 1565 Ed. Baccio Baldini. Bd. with Discorso Sopra Li Dei De'Gentili. Jacopo Zucchi. Repr. of 1602 ed. LC 75-27852. (Renaissance & the Gods Ser.: Vol. 10). (Illus.). 1976. lib. bdg. 88.00 (ISBN 0-8240-2059-6). Garland Pub.

Discours de la Religion des Anciens Romains Illustre. Guillaume Du Choul. LC 75-27851. (Renaissance & the Gods Ser.: Vol. 9). (Illus.). 1976. Repr. of 1556 ed. lib. bdg. 88.00 (ISBN 0-8240-2058-8). Garland Pub.

Discours de la Servitude Volontaire ou le Contr'un. Michel de Montaigne & Etienne de La Boetie. 90p. 1947. 12.50 (ISBN 0-686-54775-6). French & Eur.

Discourse About the State of True Happinesse. Robert Bolton. LC 79-84089. (English Experience Ser.: No. 909). 184p. 1979. Repr. of 1611 ed. lib. bdg. 14.00 (ISBN 90-221-0909-7). Walter J Johnson.

Discourse Between Two Souls. Jacob Boehme. pap. 3.95 (ISBN 0-916411-89-3). Sure Fire.

Discourse Conteyning the Life & Death of John Calvin. Theodore De Beze. LC 77-38153. (English Experience Ser.: No. 433). 80p. 1972. Repr. of 1564 ed. 11.50 (ISBN 90-221-0433-8). Walter J Johnson.

Discourse of Matters Pertaining to Religion. Theodore Parker. LC 72-4968. (Romantic Tradition in American Literature Ser.). 510p. 1972. Repr. of 1842 ed. 35.00 (ISBN 0-405-04639-1). Ayer Co Pubs.

Discourse of the Subtill Practises of Devilles by Witches & Sorcerers. George Gifford. LC 77-6745. (English Experience Ser.: No. 871). 1977. Repr. of 1587 ed. lib. bdg. 8.00 (ISBN 90-221-0871-6). Walter J Johnson.

Discourse on the Grounds & Reasons of the Christian Religion. Anthony Collins. Ed. by Rene Wellek. LC 75-11212. (British Philosophers & Theologians of the 17th & 18th Centuries: Vol. 15). 1976. Repr. of 1724 ed. lib. bdg. 51.00 (ISBN 0-8240-1766-8). Garland Pub.

Discourse on the Latest Form of Infidelity. Andrews Norton. LC 71-122660. 1971. Repr. of 1839 ed. 18.00x (ISBN 0-8046-1309-5, Pub. by Kennikat). Assoc Faculty Pr.

Discourse on the Tranfiguration. St. Gregory & David Balfour. LC 85-13299. 170p. 1985. Repr. lib. bdg. 19.95x (ISBN 0-89370-862-3). Borgo Pr.

Discourse Preached in the Center Church. facsimile ed. Leonard Bacon. LC 78-168507. (Black Heritage Library Collection). Repr. of 1828 ed. 11.50 (ISBN 0-8369-8861-2). Ayer Co Pubs.

Discourses Against Judaizing Christains. John Chrysostom. (Fathers of the Church Ser.: Vol. 68). 286p. 1979. 29.95x (ISBN 0-8132-0068-7). Cath U Pr.

Discourses of Brigham Young. Ed. by John A. Widtsoe. 497p. 14.95 (ISBN 0-87747-066-9). Deseret Bk.

Discourses of the Fall: A Study of Pascal's Pensees. Sara E. Melzer. LC 85-24519. 128p. 1986. text ed. 22.95x (ISBN 0-520-05540-3). U of Cal Pr.

Discourses of the Prophet Joseph Smith. Alma P. Burton. LC 77-23977. 399p. 9.95 (ISBN 0-87747-067-7). Deseret Bk.

Discourses on Siva. Michael W. Meister. LC 83-12529. (Illus.). 568p. 1985. 75.00 (ISBN 0-8122-7909-3). U of Pa Pr.

Discourses on the Christian Spirit & Life: With an Introduction. 2nd ed. Cyrus A. Bartol. LC 72-4951. (Romantic Tradition in American Literature Ser.). 418p. 1972. Repr. of 1850 ed. 30.00 (ISBN 0-405-04622-7). Ayer Co Pubs.

Discourses on the Gita. M. K. Gandhi. 73p. (Orig.). 1983. pap. 1.50 (ISBN 0-934676-55-0). Greenlf Bks.

Discourses on the Miracles of Our Savior. Thomas Woolston. Ed. by Rene Wellek. LC 75-11268. (British Philosophers & Theologians of the 17th & 18th Centuries Ser.: Vol. 67). 565p. 1979. lib. bdg. 51.00 (ISBN 0-8240-1778-1); lib. bdg. 2700.00 set of 101 vols. (ISBN 0-686-60102-5). Garland Pub.

Discover a New Beginning. Renee Gelfond. LC 83-20079. (Illus.). 100p. (Orig.). 1983. pap. 6.95 (ISBN 0-914789-00-7). Serenity Hse.

Discover a Richer Life. Ernest Holmes. Ed. by Willis H. Kinnear. 96p. 1961. pap. 4.50 (ISBN 0-911336-27-3). Sci of Mind.

Discover Freedom. Robert H. Schuller. (Orig.). 1978. pap. 1.25 (ISBN 0-89081-155-5). Harvest Hse.

Discover How Tou Can Turn Activity into Energy. Robert H. Schuller. (Orig.). 1978. pap. 1.25 (ISBN 0-89081-135-0). Harvest Hse.

Discover Joy: Studies in Philippians. James T. Draper, Jr. 1983. pap. 4.95 (ISBN 0-8423-0606-4); leader's guide 2.95 (ISBN 0-8423-0607-2). Tyndale.

Discover Life. Laurence Martin. LC 75-18373. 80p. 1975. pap. 1.95 (ISBN 0-8361-1779-4). Herald Pr.

Discover Self-Love. Robert H. Schuller. (Orig.). 1978. pap. 1.25 (ISBN 0-89081-134-2). Harvest Hse.

Discover the Power Within You. Eric Butterworth. LC 68-17583. 1968. 13.45 (ISBN 0-06-061266-5, HarpR). Har-Row.

Discover Your Possibilities. Robert H. Schuller. (Orig.). 1980. pap. 3.95 (ISBN 0-89081-214-4). Harvest Hse.

Discover Yourself. rev ed. Paul Brunton. LC 83-60832. 244p. 1983. pap. 7.95 (ISBN 0-87728-592-6). Weiser.

Discovered Self. Earl D. Wilson. LC 84-28943. 1985. pap. 4.95 (ISBN 0-87784-331-7). Inter-Varsity.

Discoverie of Brownisme. Thomas White. LC 74-80226. (English Experience Ser.: No. 701). (Illus.). 30p. 1974. Repr. of 1605 ed. 5.00 (ISBN 90-221-0701-9). Walter J Johnson.

Discoveries. Dan Harless. 1982. pap. 4.95 (ISBN 0-89225-207-3). Gospel Advocate.

Discoveries in the Judaean Desert: Qumran Grotte 4-11, Vol. 6. R. De Vaux & J. T. Milik. (Illus.). 1977. text ed. 52.00x (ISBN 0-19-826317-1). Oxford U Pr.

Discoveries of the Hidden Things of God. Erma Mestinsek & Minnie G. Mestinsek. 64p. 1980. 12.50 (ISBN 0-682-49635-9). Exposition Pr FL.

Discovering Abbeys & Priories. Geoffrey N. Wright. (Discovery Ser.: No. 57). (Illus.). 1985. pap. 4.50 (ISBN 0-85263-454-4, Pub. by Shire Pubns England). Seven Hills Bks.

Discovering Cathedrals. 5th. ed. David Pepin. (Discovering Ser.: No. 112). (Illus.). 1985. pap. 4.95 (ISBN 0-85263-718-7, Pub. by Shire Pubns England). Seven Hills Bks.

Discovering Christmas Customs & Folklore: A Guide to Seasonal Rites. Margaret Baker. 3.25 (ISBN 0-913714-56-9). Legacy Bks.

Discovering Christmas Customs & Folklore. Margaret Baker. (Discovering Ser.: No. 32). (Illus.). 56p. (Orig.). 1985. pap. 3.50 (ISBN 0-85263-173-1, Pub. by Shire Pubns England). Seven Hills Bks.

Discovering Church Architecture. Mark Child. (Discovering Ser.: No. 214). (Illus., Orig.). 1984. pap. 3.50 (ISBN 0-85263-328-9, Pub. by Shire Pubns England). Seven Hills Bks.

Discovering Church Furniture. Christopher Howkins. (Discovering Ser.: No. 69). (Illus.). 80p. 1983. pap. 3.50 (ISBN 0-85263-496-X, Pub. by Shire Pubns England). Seven Hills Bks.

Discovering Churches. John Harries. (Discovering Ser.: No. 137). 1984. pap. 4.50 (ISBN 0-85263-471-4, Pub. by Shire Pubns England). Seven Hills Bks.

Discovering Churchyards. Mark Child. (Discovering Ser.: No. 268). (Illus.). 80p. 1983. pap. 3.50 (ISBN 0-85263-603-2, Pub. by Shire Pubns England). Seven Hills Bks.

Discovering Discipleship: A Resource for Home Bible Studies. Thomas A. Smith. LC 80-54073. (Illus.). 64p. (Orig.). 1981. pap. 2.75 (ISBN 0-87239-438-7, 88570). Standard Pub.

Discovering English Churches: A Beginner's Guide to the Story of the Parish Church from Before the Conquest to the Gothic Revival. Richard Foster. (Illus.). 1982. 30.00x (ISBN 0-19-520366-6). Oxford U Pr.

Discovering God Within. John R. Yungblut. LC 78-21713. 198p. 1979. pap. 6.95 (ISBN 0-664-24231-6). Westminster.

Discovering God's Presence. Robert F. Morneau. LC 80-18590. 188p. (Orig.). 1980. pap. 3.95 (ISBN 0-8146-1197-4). Liturgical Pr.

Discovering God's Will. Sinclair B. Ferguson. 125p. (Orig.). 1981. pap. 3.95 (ISBN 0-85151-334-4). Banner of Truth.

Discovering God's Will in Your Life. Lloyd J. Ogilvie. (Orig.). 1985. pap. 4.95 (ISBN 0-89081-468-6). Harvest Hse.

Discovering How to Pray. Hope MacDonald. 160p. 1976. pap. 2.95 (ISBN 0-310-28512-7, 10050P). Zondervan.

Discovering Jesus. Gordon Moyes. (Illus.). 160p. (Orig.). 1984. pap. 9.95 (ISBN 0-86760-005-5, Pub. by Albatross Bks). ANZ Religious Pubns.

Discovering Mormon Trails. Stanley B. Kimball. LC 79-53092. (Illus.). 1979. pap. 4.95 (ISBN 0-87747-756-6). Deseret Bk.

Discovering My Gifts for Service. rev. ed. Knofel Staton. 48p. 1984. 2.50 (ISBN 0-87239-810-2, 39978). Standard Pub.

Discovering My Gifts for Service: Leader's Guide. rev. ed. Steve Hancock. 48p. 1984. pap. 2.95 (ISBN 0-87239-811-0, 39979). Standard Pub.

Discovering Our Family Covenants. Danny Morris. LC 81-51299. 1981. pap. 2.95x (ISBN 0-8358-0419-4). Upper Room.

Discovering Our Gifts. Thomas D. DeVries. 1.50 (ISBN 0-8091-9328-0). Paulist Pr.

Discovering Philosophy. Nina E. Crosby & Elizabeth H. Marten. (Illus.). 72p. (Orig.). 1980. pap. 5.95 (ISBN 0-914634-81-X). DOK Pubs.

Discovering Saints in Britain. John Vince. (Discovering Ser.: No. 64). (Illus.). 64p. 1983. pap. 3.95 (ISBN 0-85263-449-8, Pub. by Shire Pubns England). Seven Hills Bks.

Discovering Shrines & Holy Places. David Pepin. (Discovering Ser.: No. 254). (Illus.). 80p. (Orig.). 1983. pap. 3.95 (ISBN 0-85263-514-1, Pub. by Shire Pubns England). Seven Hills Bks.

Discovering the Bible. Ed. by Tim Dowley. (Illus.). 144p. 1986. 14.95 (ISBN 0-8028-3624-0). Eerdmans.

Discovering the Bible, Bk. 2. John Tickle. 96p. (Orig.). 1980. pap. 3.95 (ISBN 0-89243-133-4). Liguori Pubns.

Discovering the Bible: 8 Simple Keys for Learning & Praying. John Tickle. LC 77-94872. 1978. pap. 3.95 leader's guide, Bk. 1 (ISBN 0-89243-084-2); leader's guide, bk. 2 2.95 (ISBN 0-89243-141-5). Liguori Pubns.

Discovering the Biblical World. rev. ed. Harry T. Frank. LC 74-7044. (Illus.). 228p. 1977. 19.95 (ISBN 0-8437-3624-0). Hammond Inc.

Discovering the Biblical World. rev. ed. Harry T. Frank & James F. Strange. (Illus.). 288p. 1987. pap. 14.95 (ISBN 0-8437-3626-7). Hammond Inc.

Discovering the Church. Barbara B. Zikmund. LC 82-23870. (Library of Living Faith: Vol. 9). 116p. 1983. pap. 5.95 (ISBN 0-664-24441-6). Westminster.

Discovering the Depths. William P. Clemmons. LC 75-22507. 140p. 1976. pap. 7.95 (ISBN 0-8054-5562-0). Broadman.

Discovering the Fullness of Worship. Paul E. Engle. (Illus.). 129p. (Orig.). 1978. pap. 4.95 (ISBN 0-934688-01-X). Great Comm Pubns.

Discovering the Needs & Interests of Young People. Denham Grierson et al. (Youth Work Guides Ser.). (Illus.). 88p. (Orig.). 1977. pap. 8.95 (ISBN 0-85819-177-6, Pub. by JBCE). ANZ Religious Pubns.

Discovering the Old Testament. John E. Eggleton. 306p. 1980. pap. text ed. 7.95 (ISBN 0-933656-07-6). Trinity Pub Hse.

Discovering the Word of God. Dean Guest. 64p. (Orig.). 1980. pap. 1.95 (ISBN 0-89841-011-8). Zoe Pubns.

Discovering Your Soul's Purpose. Mark Thurston. (Illus.). 161p. (Orig.). 1984. pap. 6.95 (ISBN 0-87604-157-8). ARE Pr.

Discovering Your Soul's Purpose. Mark Thurston. 175p. 1984. with cassettes 24.95 (ISBN 0-87604-186-1). Allen Unwin.

Discovering Your Soul's Purpose. Mark Thurston. 1984. 24.95 (ISBN 0-87604-186-1); incl 4 cassette tapes in vinyl binder. ARE Pr.

Discovering Your Spiritual Gifts: A Personal Inventory Method. Kenneth C. Kinghorn. 1981. pap. 2.95 (ISBN 0-310-75061-X, 17029P). Zondervan.

Discovery Class Leader's Guide. 4th ed. LC 83-71852. (Illus.). 82p. 1983. pap. text ed. 7.95 (ISBN 0-934396-38-8). Churches Alive.

Discovery II. Campus Crusade for Christ Staff. 1980. pap. 2.95 saddlestitched (ISBN 0-918956-63-3). Campus Crusade.

Discovery of a Dead Sea Scroll: It's Importance in the History of Jesus Research. James H. Charlesworth. 41p. 1985. pap. 6.00 (ISBN 0-318-18993-3, 85-1). Intl Ctr Arid & Semi-Arid.

Discovery of Genesis. C. H. Kang & Ethel Nelson. 1979. pap. 4.95 (ISBN 0-570-03792-1, 12-2755). Concordia.

Discovery of the Essene Gospel of Peace: The Essenes & the Vatican. Edmond B. Szekely. (Illus.). 96p. 1977. pap. 4.80 (ISBN 0-89564-004-X). IBS Intl.

Discovery of the Great Subtiltie & Wonderful Wisdom of the Italians. LC 74-80221. (English Experience Ser.: No. 656). 1974. Repr. of 1591 ed. 10.50 (ISBN 90-221-0656-X). Walter J Johnson.

Discovery of the Lost Art Treasures of California's First Mission. James L. Nolan. Ed. by Richard F. Pourade. LC 78-73173. (Illus.). 128p. 1978. 20.00 (ISBN 0-913938-20-3). Copley Bks.

Discovery of the Tomb of Tutankhamen. Howard Carter & A. C. Mace. LC 77-71042. (Illus.). 382p. 1977. pap. 6.50 (ISBN 0-486-23500-9). Dover.

Discursos a Mis Estudiantes. Carlos M. Spurgeon. 352p. 1981. pap. 5.75 (ISBN 0-311-42006-0). Casa Bautista.

Discussion: Is the Roman Catholic Religion Inimical to Civil or Religious Liberty? Is the Presbyterian Religion Inimical to Civil or Religious Liberty? John Hughes & John Breckinridge. LC 76-122167. (Civil Liberties in American History Ser). 1970. Repr. of 1836 ed. lib. bdg. 75.00 (ISBN 0-306-71979-7). Da Capo.

Discussions, 3 vols. Robert L. Dabney. 1982. 51.95 (ISBN 0-85151-395-6). Banner of Truth.

Discussions in History & Theology. George P. Fisher. Ed. by Bruce Kuklick. (American Religious Thought of the 18th & 19th Centuries Ser.). 565p. 1987. lib. bdg. 75.00 (ISBN 0-8240-6963-3). Garland Pub.

Discussions with Teachers. Rudolf Steiner. Tr. by Helen Fox from Ger. 166p. 1983. pap. 11.00 (ISBN 0-85440-404-X, Pub by Steinerbooks). Anthroposophic.

Disease, Pain & Sacrifice: Toward a Psychology of Suffering. David Bakan. 1971. pap. 3.95x (ISBN 0-8070-2971-8, BP394). Beacon Pr.

Disease: The Cause & Cure. Holly Lynn. 32p. pap. 3.00 (ISBN 0-942494-67-9). Coleman Pub.

Disestablishment in Ireland & Wales. Philip Bell. LC 73-488607. (Church Historical Society Ser.: No. 90). 1969. pap. 21.50x (ISBN 0-8401-5090-3). A R Allenson.

Disfrute Su Biblia. Irving Jensen. Orig. Title: Enjoy Your Bible. (Span.). 1981. pap. 3.50 (ISBN 0-8254-1350-8). Kregel.

Disinformation: The Manufacture of Consent. Alternative Museun Staff. LC 85-70365. (Illus.). 64p. (Orig.). 1985. pap. text ed. 8.00 (ISBN 0-932075-01-0). Alternative Mus.

Disobedient Spirits & Christian Baptism: Study of First Peter, III-19 & Its Context. Bo I. Reicke. LC 79-8117. 288p. 1984. Repr. of 1946 ed. 41.50 (ISBN 0-404-18430-8). AMS Pr.

Dispensacionalismo, Hoy. Charles C. Ryrie. Orig. Title: Dispensationalism Today. (Span.). 256p. 1974. pap. 4.75 (ISBN 0-8254-1627-2). Kregel.

Dispensationalism Today. Charles C. Ryrie. LC 65-14611. 211p. 1973. pap. 6.95 (ISBN 0-8024-2256-X). Moody.
Displaying & Exhibiting Your Church's History. Bill Sumners. Ed. by Charles W. Deweese. (Resource Kit for Your Church's History Ser.). 1984. 0.50 (ISBN 0-939804-22-0). Hist Comm S Baptist.
Dispossessed: Homelessness in America. George Grant. LC 86-71355. 256p. 1986. pap. 8.95 (ISBN 0-89107-411-2, Crossways Bks). Good News.
Disputation & Dialogue: Readings in the Jewish Christian Encounter. Frank Talmage. pap. 14.95x (ISBN 0-87068-284-9). Ktav.
Disputation at Barcelona. Tr. by C. B. Chavel. 48p. 1983. pap. 2.95 (ISBN 0-88328-025-6). Shilo Pub Hse.
Disputation at Barcelona, Nachmanides(Ramban) With Introduction & Commentaries. Tr. by B. Haskelevich from Hebrew. Tr. of Vikkuakh Hazamban. (Rus.). (1982) 6.00 (ISBN 0-938666-03-7); pap. 3.75 (1981) (ISBN 0-938666-00-2). CHAMAH Pubs.
Disputation on Holy Scripture Against the Papists. William Whitaker. 55.00 (ISBN 0-384-68010-0). Johnson Repr.
Disputed Questions. Thomas Merton. 297p. 1960. 12.50 (ISBN 0-374-14061-8). FS&G.
Disputed Questions: On Being a Christian. Rosemary R. Ruether. LC 81-12718. (Journeys in Faith Ser.). 144p. 1982. 9.95 (ISBN 0-687-10950-7). Abingdon.
Disquisitions Relating to Matter & Spirit. Joseph Priestley. LC 74-26285. (History, Philosophy & Sociology of Science Ser). 1975. Repr. 27.00x (ISBN 0-405-06612-0). Ayer Co Pubs.
Dissent & Reform in the Early Middle Ages. Jeffrey B. Russell. LC 78-63178. (Heresies of the Early Christian & Medieval Era: Second Ser.). 344p. Repr. of 1965 ed. 36.00 (ISBN 0-404-16196-0). AMS Pr.
Dissent in American Religion. Edwin S. Gaustad. (Chicago History of American Religion Ser). 1973. 12.95x (ISBN 0-226-28436-0). U of Chicago Pr.
Dissent in American Religion. Edwin S. Gaustad. LC 73-77131. xii, 184p. 1975. pap. 3.95x (ISBN 0-226-28437-9, P637, Phoen). U of Chicago Pr.
Dissenter in the Baptist Southland: Fifty Years in the Career of William Wallace Finlator. G. McLeod Bryan. (Illus.). xi, 198p. 1985. 17.95 (ISBN 0-86554-176-0, MUP-H166). Mercer Univ Pr.
Dissenter in Zion: From the Writings of Judah L. Magnes. Ed. by Arthur A. Goren. (Illus.). 576p. 1982. text ed. 32.50X (ISBN 0-674-21283-5). Harvard U Pr.
Dissenters: From the Reformation to the French Revolution. Michael R. Watts. 568p. 1986. pap. 19.95x (ISBN 0-19-822956-9). Oxford U Pr.
Dissertation Concerning Liberty & Necessity. Jonathan Edwards. LC 73-21786. 1974. Repr. of 1797 ed. lib. bdg. 22.50 (ISBN 0-8337-1003-6). B Franklin.
Dissertation on Musical Taste. Thomas Hastings. LC 68-16237. (Music Ser.). 228p. 1974. Repr. of 1822 ed. lib. bdg. 35.00 (ISBN 0-306-71085-4). Da Capo.
Dissertation on Musical Taste. Thomas Hastings. LC 6-18360. (American Studies). 1968. Repr. of 1853 ed. 24.00 (ISBN 0-384-21750-8). Johnson Repr.
Dissertations in American Biography Series, 38 bks. Ed. by Richard B. Morris et al. 1982. write for info. Ayer Co Pubs.
Dissolution of Eastern European Jewry: An Analysis of the Six Million Myth. Walter N. Sanning. 1983. lib. bdg. 79.95 (ISBN 0-87700-463-3). Revisionist Pr.
Dissolution of Eastern European Jewry. Walter N. Sanning. (Illus.). 239p. 1986. pap. 8.00 (ISBN 0-317-53010-0). Noontide.
Dissolving Depression & Finding Peace. Richard J. Green. pap. 2.50 (ISBN 0-87516-278-9). De Vorss.
Distinctive Protestant & Catholic Themes Reconsidered. Ernst Kasemann et al. Ed. by Robert W. Funk & Gerhard Ebeling. 1967. lib. bdg. 17.50x (ISBN 0-88307-161-4). Gannon.
Distinctive Qualities of the Catholic School. Father Edwin J. McDermott. 78p. 1986. 6.60 (ISBN 0-318-20560-2). Natl Cath Educ.
Distinctives: Yesterday & Today. Peter A. Judd & Clifford A. Cole. 168p. 1983. pap. 10.50 (ISBN 0-8309-0378-X). Herald Hse.
Distinguer Pour Unir: Les Degres du Savoir. 8th ed. Jacques Maritain. 946p. 1959. 32.50 (ISBN 0-686-56350-6). French & Eur.
Distintivos de la Iglesia de Dios. Ed. by Ray H. Hughes. (Span.). 116p. 1970. pap. 5.95 (ISBN 0-87148-256-8). Pathway Pr.
Distressing Days of the Judges. Leon U. Wood. 434p. 1982. pap. 11.95 (ISBN 0-310-34731-9, 10232P). Zondervan.
Distribution of Catholic Priests in the United States: 1971. Bernard Quinn. 1975. pap. 3.50x (ISBN 0-914422-04-9). Glenmary Res Ctr.
Disturbed Peace: Selected Writings of an Irish Catholic Homosexual. Brian R. McNaught. LC 81-67627. 125p. (Orig.). 1981. pap. 5.95 (ISBN 0-940680-00-9). Dignity Inc.
Divergent Paths of the Restoration. Steven L. Shields. 282p. 1982. 12.95 (ISBN 0-941214-48-6). Signature Bks.
Divergent Paths of the Restoration: A History of the Latter Day Saint Movement. 3rd, rev., enlarged ed. Steven L. Shields. LC 81-86304. (Illus.). 282p. 1982. 12.95 (ISBN 0-942284-00-3). Restoration Re.
Divergent Paths of the Restoration: 1984 Supplement. Steven Shields. (Orig.). Date not set. pap. cancelled (ISBN 0-942284-02-X). Restoration Re.
Diversity & Communion. Yves Congar. Tr. of Diversities et Communion. 240p. 1985. pap. text ed. 9.95 (ISBN 0-89622-275-6). Twenty-Third.
Diversity & Unity in the New Testament Picture of Christ. J. D. McCaughney. (Lectures in Biblical Studies: No. III). 1969. pap. 2.00x (ISBN 0-85564-016-2, Pub. by U of W Austral Pr). Intl Spec Bk.
Diversity in Faith-Unity in Christ. Shirley C. Gutherie, Jr. LC 86-9157. 144p. (Orig.). 1986. pap. 10.95 (ISBN 0-664-24013-5). Westminster.
Diversity in Holiness. facs. ed. Robert H. Steuart. LC 67-28770. (Essay Index Reprint Ser). 1937. 17.00 (ISBN 0-8369-0906-2). Ayer Co Pubs.
Diversity in Unity: The Development & Expansion of the Cherubim & Seraphim Church in Nigeria. Akin Omoyajowo. LC 83-21706. 126p. (Orig.). 1984. lib. bdg. 22.00 (ISBN 0-8191-3655-7). U Pr of Amer.
Diversity of Moral Thinking. Neil Cooper. (CLLP Ser.). (Illus.). 1981. text ed. 45.00x (ISBN 0-19-824423-1). Oxford U Pr.
Diversity of Scripture: Trajectories in the Confessional Heritage. Paul D. Hanson. LC 81-43079. (Overtures to Biblical Theology Ser.: No. 11). 1982. pap. 8.95 (ISBN 0-8006-1535-2, 1-1535). Fortress.
Dives & Pauper, Vol. I, Pt. 2. Ed. by Priscilla H. Barnum. (Early English Text Society Original Ser.). (Illus.). 1980. 32.50x (ISBN 0-19-722282-X). Oxford U Pr.
Dives & Pauper (1493) LC 73-17391. 1973. Repr. of 1493 ed. lib. bdg. 90.00x (ISBN 0-8201-1111-2). Schol Facsimiles.
Divided Flame: Wesleyans & the Charismatic Renewal. Howard A. Snyder & Daniel V. Runyon. Ed. by James Ruark. 128p. 1986. pap. 6.95 (ISBN 0-310-75181-0, 17082P). Zondervan.
Divided Mind of Protestant America, 1880-1930. Ferenc M. Szasz. LC 81-7597. 216p. 1982. text ed. 19.95 (ISBN 0-8173-0080-5). U of Ala Pr.
Divided People of God. Ogbu Kalu. LC 74-81853. 1978. 13.95x (ISBN 0-88357-048-3); pap. 4.95 (ISBN 0-88357-070-X). NOK Pubs.
Divided We Fall. James E. Smith. LC 79-67439. 96p. (Orig.). 1980. pap. 2.25 (ISBN 0-87239-381-X, 40086). Standard Pub.
Divided We Stand: Institutional Religion As a Reflection of Pluralism & Integration in America. Arthur L. Anderson. LC 78-61582. 1978. pap. text ed. 9.95 (ISBN 0-8403-1935-5). Kendall-Hunt.
Divination in Thailand. Q. Wales. 145p. 1983. text ed. 10.50x (ISBN 0-7007-0147-8, Pub. by Curzon Pr UK). Humanities.
Divination in Thailand: The Hope & Fears of a Southeast Asian People. H. G. Wales. 200p. 1981. 25.00x (ISBN 0-7007-0147-8, Pub. by Curzon England). State Mutual Bk.
Divine Analogy: A Study of the Creation Motif in Blake & Coleridge. Warren Stevenson. Ed. by James Hogg. (Romantic Reassessment Ser.). 403p. (Orig.). 1972. pap. 15.00 (ISBN 0-317-40044-4, Pub. by Salzburg Studies). Longwood Pub Group.
Divine & Contingent Order. Thomas F. Torrance. 1981. 29.95x (ISBN 0-19-826658-8). Oxford U Pr.
Divine & Sacred Catechism. Apostolos Makrakis. Ed. by Orthodox Christian Educational Society. 224p. 1946. 5.50x (ISBN 0-938366-15-7). Orthodox Chr.
Divine Appointments. Larry Tomczak. 168p. (Orig.). 1986. pap. 5.95 (ISBN 0-89283-261-4, Pub. by Vine Books). Servant.
Divine Art of Living. Compiled by Mabel H. Paine & Betty J. Fisher. 272p. 1986. pap. 9.95 (ISBN 0-87743-194-9). Baha'i.
Divine Breakthrough. George Snelling. 92p. 1981. pap. 2.95 (ISBN 0-934142-01-7). Vancento Pub.
Divine Church. John P. Brooks. Ed. by Donald W. Dayton. (Higher Christian Life Ser.). 283p. 1985. 35.00 (ISBN 0-8240-6408-9). Garland Pub.
Divine Command Morality: Historical & Contemporary Readings. Janine M. Idziak. LC 79-91621. (Texts & Studies in Religion: Vol. 5). 348p. 1980. 49.95x (ISBN 0-88946-969-5). E Mellen.
Divine Commands & Moral Requirements. Philip L. Quinn. (Clarendon Library of Logic & Philosophy). 1978. text ed. 36.00x (ISBN 0-19-824413-4). Oxford U Pr.
Divine Commands & Morality. Ed. by Paul Helm. (Readings in Philosophy Ser.). 1981. pap. 9.95x (ISBN 0-19-875049-8). Oxford U Pr.
Divine Communication: Word & Sacrament in Biblical, Historical & Contemporary Perspective. Hans Schwarz. LC 84-48732. 176p. 1985. pap. 10.95 (ISBN 0-8006-1846-7, 1-1846). Fortress.
Divine Community: Trinity, Church, & Ethics in Reformation Theologies. John R. Loeschen. (Sixteenth Century Essays & Studies Ser.: Vol. I). 238p. 1981. 25.00x (ISBN 0-940474-01-8). Sixteenth Cent.
Divine Connection: Feel Better & Live Longer. Donald Whitaker. LC 83-82835. 148p. (Orig.). 1983. pap. 4.95 (ISBN 0-910311-06-4). Huntington Hse Inc.
Divine Consort: Radha & the Goddesses of India. Ed. by John S. Hawley & Donna M. Wulff. LC 86-47759. (Illus.). 432p. 1987. pap. 11.95 (ISBN 0-8070-1303-X, BP-734). Beacon Pr.
Divine Courtship: A History of Our Salvation. Jeffrey Mirus. 183p. 1977. 7.95 (ISBN 0-931888-13-1). Christendom Pubns.
Divine Covenants: God's Seven Covenant Engagements with Man. Arthur W. Pink. 317p. 1984. pap. 7.95 (ISBN 0-8010-7082-1). Baker Bk.
Divine Discontent: The Life of Nathan S. S. Beman. Owen Peterson. (Illus.). xvii, 224p. 1985. text ed. 21.95 (ISBN 0-86554-170-1, MUP-H160). Mercer Univ Pr.
Divine Drama in History & Liturgy: Essays Presented to Horton Davies on His Retirement from Princeton University. Ed. by John E. Booty. (Pittsburgh Theological Monographs: New Ser. 10). 1984. pap. 16.50 (ISBN 0-915138-67-0). Pickwick.
Divine Emblems. Albert B. Simpson. pap. 2.95 (ISBN 0-87509-009-5). Chr Pubns.
Divine Epic. Frank Morris. LC 72-96118. 539p. 1973. pap. 5.00 (ISBN 0-913382-18-3, 101-18). Prow Bks-Franciscan.
Divine Favors Granted to St. Joseph. Pere Binet. LC 82-50590. 176p. 1983. pap. 3.00 (ISBN 0-89555-187-X). TAN Bks Pubs.
Divine Feminine: The Biblical Imagery of God As Female. Virginia R. Mollenkott. 128p. 1984. pap. 8.95 (ISBN 0-8245-0669-3). Crossroad NY.
Divine Footprints. Eugene P. Kauffeld. 1983. pap. 9.95 (ISBN 0-8100-0148-9, 15N0382). Northwest Pub.
Divine Guidance. Elbert Willis. 350p. 1982. write for info. Fill the Gap.
Divine Guidance: That Voice Behind You. Charles G. Coleman. LC 77-6796. 1977. pap. 2.50 (ISBN 0-87213-087-8). Loizeaux.
Divine Healing. Andrew Murray. 1962. pap. 3.50 (ISBN 0-87508-375-7). Chr Lit.
Divine Healing. Andrew Murray. 160p. 1982. pap. text ed. 3.50 (ISBN 0-88368-112-9). Whitaker Hse.
Divine Healing. Arthur W. Pink. pap. 0.75 (ISBN 0-685-00742-1). Reiner.
Divine Healing of Mind & Body. Murdo MacDonald-Bayne. 215p. 1983. pap. 8.75 (ISBN 0-85243-035-3). Ariel OH.
Divine Healing Today. Richard Mayhue. 1983. pap. 6.95 (ISBN 0-8024-0453-7). Moody.
Divine Healing Today. Richard Mayhue. 1983. pap. 6.96 (ISBN 0-88469-154-3). BMH Bks.
Divine Healing Under the Searchlight. Samuel Fisk. LC 78-15083. 1978. pap. 2.25 (ISBN 0-87227-057-2). Reg Baptist.
Divine Helmsman: Studies on God's Control of Human Events. James L. Crenshaw & Samuel Sandmel. 1979. 35.00x (ISBN 0-87068-700-X). Ktav.
Divine Hierarchy: Popular Hinduism in Central India. Lawrence A. Babb. LC 75-61693. (Illus.). 266p. 1975. 27.50x (ISBN 0-231-03882-8). Columbia U Pr.
Divine-Human Encounter. Emil Brunner. Tr. by Amandus W. Loos from Ger. 207p. 1980. Repr. of 1943 ed. lib. bdg. 24.75x (ISBN 0-313-22398-X, BRDH). Greenwood.
Divine Humanness. Aarne Siirala. Tr. by T. A. Kantonen. LC 70-99460. pap. 48.00 (2026964). Bks Demand UMI.
Divine Impartiality: Paul & a Theological Axiom. Jouette M. Bassler. Ed. by William Baird. LC 81-1367. (Society of Biblical Literature Dissertation Ser.). 1981. pap. text ed. 13.50 (ISBN 0-89130-475-4, 0-06-01-59). Scholars Pr GA.
Divine Impassibility: An Essay in Philosophical Theology. Richard E. Creel. 300p. 1985. 39.50 (ISBN 0-521-30317-6). Cambridge U Pr.
Divine Imperative. Emil Brunner. LC 47-2443. 728p. 1979. softcover 9.95 (ISBN 0-664-24246-4). Westminster.
Divine Initiative & Human Response in Ezekiel. Paul Joyce. (JSOT Supplement Ser.: No. 51). 200p. 1987. text ed. 30.00x (ISBN 1-85075-041-6, Pub. by JSOT Pr England); pap. text ed. 14.95x (ISBN 1-85075-042-4, Pub. by JSOT Pr England). Eisenbrauns.
Divine Inspiration of Holy Scripture. William J. Abraham. 1981. 32.00x (ISBN 0-19-826659-6). Oxford U Pr.
Divine Inspiration of the Bible. L. Gaussen. LC 75-155249. (Kregel Reprint Library). 382p. 1971. 12.95 (ISBN 0-8254-2707-X). Kregel.
Divine Inspiration of the Bible. Arthur W. Pink. pap. 4.50 (ISBN 0-685-19827-8). Reiner.
Divine Institutes, Bks. 1-7. Lactantius. LC 64-18669. (Fathers of the Church Ser: Vol. 49). 495p. 1964. 29.95x (ISBN 0-8132-0049-0). Cath U Pr.
Divine Intimacy, Vol. III. Gabriel. 1983. 12.95 (ISBN 0-87193-203-2). Dimension Bks.
Divine Intimacy, Vol. II. Gabriel. 1983. 12.95 (ISBN 0-87193-201-6). Dimension Bks.
Divine Intimacy, Vol. IV. Gabriel. 12.95 (ISBN 0-87193-204-0). Dimension Bks.
Divine Intimacy, Vol. 1. Gabriel. 12.95 (ISBN 0-87193-194-X). Dimension Bks.
Divine Intimacy: A Celebration of Prayer and the Joy of Christian Life, 4 vols. 2nd ed. Gabriel of St. Mary Magdalen. LC 86-83132. (Orig.). 1987. pap. 12.95 ea. Vol. 1, 285 p (ISBN 0-89870-142-2). Vol. 2, 285 p (ISBN 0-89870-143-0). Vol. 3, 285 p (ISBN 0-89870-144-9). Vol. 4, 285 p (ISBN 0-89870-145-7). Ignatius Pr.
Divine Legation of Moses Demonstrated, 4 vols. 2nd ed. Ed. by Rene Wellek. LC 75-11264. (British Philosophers & Theologians of the 17th & 18th Centuries Ser.: Vol. 62). 2259p. 1978. Set. lib. bdg. 204.00 (ISBN 0-8240-1813-3). Garland Pub.
Divine Light Invocation. Swami S. Radha. 54p. 1982. pap. 5.00 (ISBN 0-931454-08-5). Timeless Bks.
Divine Liturgy. Ed. by David Drillock & John Erickson. 368p. 1982. text ed. 30.00 (ISBN 0-913836-95-8); pap. 20.00 (ISBN 0-913836-93-1). St Vladimirs.
Divine Liturgy of St. Basil the Great. Tr. by Ernest T. Abdel-Massih et al from Coptic. 257p. 1982. pap. 7.00 (ISBN 0-932098-19-3). St Mark Coptic Orthodox.
Divine Liturgy of the Great Church with Melodies for Congregational Sin. Paul N. Harrilchak. (Illus.). x, 221p. (Orig.). 1984. 15.00x (ISBN 0-930055-00-4). Holy Trinity Ortho.
Divine Love & Wisdom. Emanuel Swedenborg. LC 75-37094. student ed. 12.00 (ISBN 0-87785-056-9). Swedenborg.
Divine Love & Wisdom. Emanuel Swedenborg. Tr. by George Dole. LC 85-50918. 1986. pap. 6.95 (ISBN 0-87785-129-8). Swedenborg.
Divine Love Song. Watson. pap. 3.50 (ISBN 0-686-12866-4). Schmul Pub Co.
Divine Luminous Wisdom That Dispels the Darkness God-Man Man-God. rev. ed. M. R. Bawa Muhaiyaddeen. (Illus.). 288p. 1977. pap. 6.95 (ISBN 0-914390-11-2). Fellowship Pr PA.
Divine Madman: The Sublime Life & Songs of Drukpa Kunley. Tr. by Kieth Dowman. (Illus.). 180p. 1982. pap. 8.95 (ISBN 0-913922-75-7). Dawn Horse Pr.
Divine Man or Magician? Celsus & Origin on Jesus. Eugene V. Gallagher. (SBL Dissertation Ser.). 1982. pap. 13.50 (ISBN 0-89130-542-4, 06 01 64). Scholars Pr GA.
Divine Meditations (Sixteen Forty) Ed. by Henry Colman. 1979. 27.50x (ISBN 0-300-02305-7). Yale U Pr.
Divine Melody. Bhagwan Shree Rajneesh. Ed. by Ma Deva Bhasha. LC 83-174697. (Kabir Ser.). (Illus.). 284p. (Orig.). 1978. 16.50 (ISBN 0-88050-049-2). Chidvilas Found.
Divine Milieu: An Essay on the Interior Life. Pierre Teilhard De Chardin. pap. 6.95 (ISBN 0-06-090487-9, CN487, PL). Har-Row.
Divine Mother: A Trinitarian Theology of the Holy Spirit. Donald L. Gelpi. LC 84-11921. 260p. (Orig.). 1984. lib. bdg. 27.25 (ISBN 0-8191-4034-1); pap. text ed. 12.50 (ISBN 0-8191-4035-X). U Pr of Amer.
Divine Mystery. J. Reader. 79p. pap. 4.95 (ISBN 0-88172-117-4). Believers Bkshelf.
Divine Mystery. Allen Upward. LC 76-27214. 384p. 1977. lib. bdg. 12.95 (ISBN 0-915520-02-8); pap. 7.95 (ISBN 0-915520-01-X). Ross-Erikson.
Divine Name & Presence: The Memra. Robert Hayward. LC 81-10928. (Publications of the Oxford Centre for Postgraduate Hebrew Study). 208p. 1981. 25.50x (ISBN 0-86598-067-5). Allanheld.
Divine Nectar. 2nd rev. ed. Swami Sivananda. 1976. pap. 14.00 (ISBN 0-89684-196-0). Orient Bk Dist.

Divine Omniscience & Human Freedom: Thomas Aquinas & Charles Hartshorne. John C. Moskop. LC 84-1172. xviii, 105p. 1984. 14.95 (ISBN 0-86554-123-X, MUP/H102). Mercer Univ Pr.

Divine Omniscience & Omnipotence in Medieval Philosophy. Ed. by Tamar Rudavsky. 1984. lib. bdg. 54.00 (ISBN 90-277-1750-8, Pub. by Reidel Holland). Kluwer Academic.

Divine Pattern. Fred H. Wolfe. LC 83-70212. 1983. pap. 5.95 (ISBN 0-8054-5244-3). Broadman.

Divine Perceptions. pap. 14.95 (ISBN 0-937134-09-0). Amrita Found.

Divine Personality & Human Life. C. J. Webb. (Gifford Lectures Delivered in the University of Aberdeen in 1918&1919, Second Course Ser.). Repr. of 1920 ed. 17.00 (ISBN 0-527-94900-0). Kraus Repr.

Divine Personality & Human Life: Being the Gifford Lectures Delivered in the University of Aberdeen in the Years 1918 & 1919, Second Course. facsimile ed. Clement C. Webb. LC 77-37917. (Select Bibliographies Reprint Ser.). Repr. of 1920 ed. 21.00 (ISBN 0-8369-6754-2). Ayer Co Pubs.

Divine Physical Healing, Past & Present. 272p. pap. 2.50 (ISBN 0-686-29107-7). Faith Pub Hse.

Divine Plan. Glenn Clark. pap. 0.50 (ISBN 0-910924-05-8). Macalester.

Divine Plan: Commentary on the Secret Doctrine. 3rd ed. Geoffrey Barborka. 1972. 19.95 (ISBN 0-8356-7167-4). Theos Pub Hse.

Divine Player: A Study of Krishna Lila. David R. Kinsley. 1978. 17.95 (ISBN 0-89684-019-0, Pub. by Motilal Barnarsidass India). Orient Bk Dist.

Divine Player: A Study of Krishna Lila. David R. Kinsley. 1979. 22.00x (ISBN 0-89684-019-0). South Asia Bks.

Divine Power: A Study of Karl Barth & Charles Hartshorne. Sheila G. Davaney. LC 85-45502. (Harvard Dissertions in Religion Ser.). 224p. 1986. pap. 16.95 (ISBN 0-8006-7072-8, 1-7072). Fortress.

Divine Principle. 1977. write for info.; pap. write for info. Rose Sharon Pr.

Divine Principle. 2nd rev. ed. Sun M. Moon. 536p. 1973. 10.95 (ISBN 0-910621-05-5). HSA Pubns.

Divine Principle. 2nd rev. ed. Sun M. Moon. 536p. 1973. pap. 7.95 (ISBN 0-910621-04-7). HSA Pubns.

Divine Principle. 5th rev. ed. Sun M. Moon. 536p. 1977. pap. 5.95 (ISBN 0-910621-03-9). HSA Pubns.

Divine Principles of Gathering. R. K. Campbell. 40p. pap. 0.45 (ISBN 0-88172-015-1). Believers Bkshelf.

Divine Providence. Emanuel Swedenborg. LC 74-30441. 1974. trade ed. o.p. 10.00 (ISBN 0-87785-060-7); student ed. 12.00 (ISBN 0-87785-059-3); pap. 3.95 (ISBN 0-87785-061-5). Swedenborg.

Divine Providence & Human Suffering. P. G. Walsh & James Walsh. (Message of the Fathers of the Church Ser.: Vol. 17). 1985. 15.95 (ISBN 0-89453-357-6); pap. 10.95 (ISBN 0-89453-328-2). M Glazier.

Divine Providence in the England of Shakespeare's Histories. Henry A. Kelly. LC 75-111485. 1970. 22.50x (ISBN 0-674-21292-4). Harvard U Pr.

Divine Pymander. Hermes Trismegistus. Tr. by J. Randolph. 129p. 1972. Repr. of 1889 ed. 6.00 (ISBN 0-911662-48-0). Yoga.

Divine Relativity: A Social Conception of God. Charles Hartshorne. LC 48-7802. (Terry Lectures Ser.). 184p. 1982. pap. 7.95x (ISBN 0-300-02880-6, Y-430). Yale U Pr.

Divine Revelation. Paul Helm. LC 82-72325. (Foundations for Faith Ser.). 144p. (Orig.). 1982. pap. 8.95 (ISBN 0-89107-258-6, Crossway Bks). Good News.

Divine Revelation & the Limits of Historical Criticism. William J. Abraham. 1982. 29.95x (ISBN 0-19-826665-0). Oxford U Pr.

Divine Revelation in Pali Buddhism. Peter Masefield. 216p. 1986. 27.95 (ISBN 0-04-294132-6). Allen Unwin.

Divine Right & Original of the Civil Magistrate from God. Edward Gee. LC 75-31092. Repr. of 1658 ed. 30.00 (ISBN 0-404-13510-2). AMS Pr.

Divine Right of Kings. John N. Figgis. 14.00 (ISBN 0-8446-0621-9). Peter Smith.

Divine Romance. Ed. by Gene Edwards. 1984. 10.95 (ISBN 0-940232-24-3); pap. 7.95. Christian Bks.

Divine Runner. Earl Paulk. LC 78-71967. 142p. (Orig.). 1978. pap. 3.25 (ISBN 0-917595-00-9). K-Dimension.

Divine Science & the Science of God: A Reformulation of Thomas Aquinas. Victor Preller. LC 66-21838. pap. 72.80 (ISBN 0-317-08468-2, 2010543). Bks Demand UMI.

Divine Science: Its Principle & Practice. Compiled by Fannie B. James. 1957. pap. 7.50 (ISBN 0-686-24361-7). Divine Sci Fed.

Divine Songs of Zarathushtra. Ed. by Irach J. Taraporewala. LC 74-21251. Repr. of 1951 ed. 125.00 (ISBN 0-404-12802-5). AMS Pr.

Divine Sonship of Christ. W. E. Vine. 246p. 1984. smythe sewn 9.50 (ISBN 0-86524-179-1, 9520). Klock & Klock.

Divine Sovereignty & Human Freedom. Samuel Fisk. LC 73-81550. 1973. pap. 5.95 (ISBN 0-87213-166-1). Loizeaux.

Divine Sovereignty & Human Responsibility: Biblical Perspectives in Tension. D. A. Carson. Ed. by Peter Toon & Ralph Martin. LC 79-27589. (New Foundations Theological Library). 228p. 1981. 12.95 (ISBN 0-8042-3707-7); pap. 11.95 (ISBN 0-8042-3727-1). John Knox.

Divine Struggle for Human Salvation: Biblical Convictions in Their Historical Settings. Andrew C Tunyogi. LC 78-65852. 1979. pap. text ed. 19.75 (ISBN 0-8191-0676-3). U Pr of Amer.

Divine Substance. G. C. Stead. (Illus.). 1966. 49.50x (ISBN 0-19-826630-8). Oxford U Pr.

Divine Therapy: Pearls of Wisdom from the Bahai Writings. Annamarie Honnald. 1986. 14.95 (ISBN 0-85398-236-8); pap. 6.95 (ISBN 0-85398-237-6). G Ronald Pub.

Divine Trinity. Norman Pittenger. LC 76-55002. 1977. 5.95 (ISBN 0-8298-0330-0). Pilgrim NY.

Divine Unity of Scripture. Adolph Saphir. LC 84-9642. (Adolph Saphir Study Ser.). 376p. 1984. pap. 10.95 (ISBN 0-8254-3747-4). Kregel.

Divine Vision. Ed. by Vivian De Sola Pinto. LC 68-24905. (Studies in Blake, No. 3). 1973. Repr. of 1957 ed. lib. bdg. 75.00x (ISBN 0-8383-0790-6). Haskell.

Divine Wisdom & Awareness of a Spiritual & True Religious Life. Charles Lee. 1986. 6.95 (ISBN 0-533-06748-0). Vantage.

Divine Word & Prophetic Word in Early Islam: A Reconsideration of the Sources, with Special Reference to the Divine Saying or Hadith Qudsi. William A. Graham. (Religion & Society Ser.). 1977. text ed. 37.50x (ISBN 90-279-7612-0). Mouton.

Divine Yes. E. Stanley Jones. 1976. pap. 1.50 (ISBN 0-89129-154-7). Jove Pubns.

Diving Deep & Surfacing: Women Writers on Spiritual Quest. 2nd, rev. ed. Carol Christ. LC 86-70552. 157p. 1986. pap. 8.95 (ISBN 0-8070-6351-7, BP 722). Beacon Pr.

Divining Hand. Christopher Bird. 1985. pap. 15.00 (ISBN 0-87613-090-2). New Age.

Divinity & Experience: The Religion of the Dinka. Godfrey Lienhardt. 1961. 45.00x (ISBN 0-19-823119-9). Oxford U Pr.

Divinity of Krishna. S. J. Seth. 1984. text ed. 14.00x. Coronet Bks.

Divinity of Our Lord. Henry P. Liddon. 1978. 20.50 (ISBN 0-86524-130-9, 9801). Klock & Klock.

Divinity of the Roman Emperor. Lily R. Taylor. LC 75-7348. (Roman History Ser.). (Illus.). 1975. Repr. 29.00x (ISBN 0-405-07068-3). Ayer Co Pubs.

Divinity of the Roman Emperor. Lily R. Taylor. LC 75-31647. xv, 296p. 1975. Repr. of 1931 ed. lib. bdg. 27.50x (ISBN 0-87991-606-0). Porcupine Pr.

Divinsis Catholicae Ecclesiae Officiis et Mysteriis. Melchior Hittorpius. 796p. Repr. of 1610 ed. text ed. 207.00 (ISBN 0-576-99170-8, Pub. by Gregg Intl Pubs England). Gregg Intl.

Divorce, a Christian Dilemma. Norma Martin & Zola Levitt. LC 76-45939. 168p. 1977. pap. 1.95 (ISBN 0-8361-1808-1). Herald Pr.

Divorce & Beyond. Harry J. Ashenhurst. 1984. pap. 7.75 (ISBN 0-8309-0385-2). Herald Hse.

Divorce & Marriage. James H. Feeney. 1980. pap. 1.75 (ISBN 0-911739-06-8). Abbott Loop.

Divorce & Remarriage. Guy Duty. LC 96-2485. 160p. 1983. 8.95 (ISBN 0-87123-097-6, 230097). Bethany Hse.

Divorce & Remarriage. Theodore Mackin. (Marriage in the Catholic Church Ser.: Vol. II). 688p. (Orig.). 1984. pap. 19.95 (ISBN 0-8091-2585-4). Paulist Pr.

Divorce & Remarriage. Ken Stewart. 141p. (Orig.). 1984. pap. 4.95 (ISBN 0-89274-343-3). Harrison Hse.

Divorce & Remarriage. J. D. Thomas. (Way of Life Ser.: No.159). 1977. pap. 3.95 (ISBN 0-89112-159-5, Bibl Res Pr). Abilene Christ U.

Divorce & Remarriage. Jim Tracy. (Illus.). 80p. (Orig.). 1986. pap. 9.95 (ISBN 1-55630-008-5). Brentwood Comm.

Divorce & Remarriage: A Perspective for Counseling. John R. Martin. LC 73-18038. 144p. 1974. pap. 6.95 (ISBN 0-8361-1328-4). Herald Pr.

Divorce & Remarriage: Are Non-Christians Amenable to the Law of Christ? Thomas B. Warren & E. C. Fuqua. 1977. pap. 6.00 (ISBN 0-934916-30-6). Natl Christian Pr.

Divorce & Remarriage in the Church. Stanley A. Ellisen. 1977. pap. 5.95 (ISBN 0-310-35561-3, 11256P). Zondervan.

Divorce & Remarriage: What Does the Bible Really Say? Ralph Woodrow. LC 82-99960. (Illus.). 1982. pap. 4.95 (ISBN 0-916938-06-9). R Woodrow.

Divorce & Second Marriage: Facing the Challenge. Kevin T. Kelly. 112p. 1983. pap. 6.95 (ISBN 0-8164-2471-3, HarpR). Har-Row.

Divorce & the Faithful Church. G. Edwin Bontrager. LC 78-4671. 224p. 1978. 12.95 (ISBN 0-8361-1850-2); pap. 8.95 (ISBN 0-8361-1851-0). Herald Pr.

Divorce & the Jewish Child. Thomas J. Cottle. 28p. 1981. pap. 2.50 (ISBN 0-87495-034-1). Am Jewish Comm.

Divorce in Jewish Law & Life. Irwin H. Haut. (Studies in Jewish Jurisprudence Ser.: Vol. 5). 160p. 1983. 12.50 (ISBN 0-87203-110-1); pap. 9.75 (ISBN 0-87203-114-4). Hermon.

Divorce in the Parsonage. Mary La G. Bouma. LC 79-16157. 160p. 1979. pap. 3.95 (ISBN 0-87123-109-3, 210109). Bethany Hse.

Divorce Is Not the Answer. Marilyn Hickey. LC 75-32006. 1979. pap. 4.95 (ISBN 0-89221-009-5). New Leaf.

Divorce: Its Causes & Consequences in Hindu Society. S. Pothen. 320p. 1986. text ed. 35.00x (ISBN 0-7069-2932-2, Pub. by Vikas India). Advent NY.

Divorce Law: A Concise Guide for Clergy & Laity. Mary S. Winters. 32p. (Orig.). 1986. pap. 1.95 (ISBN 0-8298-0740-3). Pilgrim NY.

Divorce: Making It a Growth Experience. Joyce Baca. LC 85-13067. 136p. 1985. 8.95 (ISBN 0-87747-835-X). Deseret Bk.

Divorce Ministry & the Marriage Tribunal. James J. Young. LC 82-60851. 1982. pap. 5.95 (ISBN 0-8091-2477-7). Paulist Pr.

Divorce Myth. J. Carl Laney. LC 81-7690. 152p. 1981. 8.95 (ISBN 0-87123-144-1, 230144). Bethany Hse.

Divorce Myth. J. Carl Laney. pap. 5.95 (ISBN 0-87123-892-6, 210892). Bethany Hse.

Divorce of Catherine of Aragon. 2nd ed. James A. Froude. LC 68-58379. Repr. of 1891 ed. 31.50 (ISBN 0-404-02626-5). AMS Pr.

Divorce: Prevention or Survival. William V. Arnold et al. LC 77-22066. 128p. 1977. pap. 5.95 (ISBN 0-664-24142-5). Westminster.

Divorce-The Pain & the Healing: Personal Mediations When Marriage Ends. Judith Mattison. LC 85-11140. 96p. (Orig.). 1985. pap. 5.95 (ISBN 0-8066-2128-1, 10-1905). Augsburg.

Divorced & Christian. Alice S. Peppler. LC 74-4505. 96p. 1974. pap. 3.75 (ISBN 0-570-03189-3, 12-2591). Concordia.

Divorced Christian. Charles Cerling. 1984. 9.95 (ISBN 0-8010-2495-1); pap. 5.95 (ISBN 0-8010-2486-2). Baker Bk.

Divorced Parent & the Jewish Community. Nathalie Friedman & Theresa F. Rogers. LC 85-61859. 58p. (Orig.). 1985. pap. 5.00 (ISBN 0-87495-074-0). Am Jewish Comm.

Divorcing, Believing, Belonging. James J. Young. 240p. (Orig.). 1984. pap. 7.95 (ISBN 0-8091-2634-6). Paulist Pr.

Divorcing Christian. Lewis Rambo. 96p. (Orig.). 1983. pap. 5.25 (ISBN 0-687-10994-9). Abingdon.

Divorcio y Nuevo Matrimonio. Guy Duty. 176p. 1975. 2.95 (ISBN 0-88113-060-5). Edit Betania.

Divrei Rabboseinu. (Hebrew.). 1.00 (ISBN 0-914131-17-6, E01). Torah Umesorah.

Divrei Y'mei Yisroel: In Hebrew. Chaim D. Rabinowitz. text ed. 10.00 (ISBN 0-914131-18-4, A80). Torah Umesorah.

Divus Julius. Stefan Weinstock. 1971. 74.00x (ISBN 0-19-814287-0). Oxford U Pr.

Divyatattva of Raghunandana Bhattacarya: Ordeals in Classical Hindu Law. Richard W. Lariviere. 1982. 22.00x (ISBN 0-8364-0854-3, Pub. by Manohar India). South Asia Bks.

Diwan Hassan ibn Thabit. Arthur Wormhoudt. (Arab Translation Ser.: No. 69). 180p. (Orig.). pap. 6.50x (ISBN 0-916358-21-6). Wormhoudt.

Dix-Huit Ans Chez Les Sauvages: Voyages Et Missions De Monseigneur Henry Faraud. Henri J. Faraud. Repr. of 1866 ed. 28.00 (ISBN 0-384-15135-3). Johnson Repr.

Dix-Huit Ans Chez les Sauvages: Voyages et Missions De Mgr. Henry Faraud Paris-Bruxelles 1866. Henri J. Faraud. (Canadiana Avant 1867: No.12). 1966. 26.00x (ISBN 90-2796-329-0). Mouton.

Dizionario Di Mitologia Egizia, 3 vols. R. V. Lanzone. (Ital.). 1312p. 1974. 400.00x (ISBN 90-272-0931-6, 0932-4, 0933-2). Benjamins North Am.

Dizzionario Di Mitologia Egizia, Vol. 4. R. V. Lanzone. xv, 205p. 1975. Repr. of 1881 ed. 80.00x (ISBN 90-272-0934-0). Benjamins North Am.

Do All to the Glory of God. Watchman Nee. Tr. by Stephen Kaung. (Basic Lesson Ser.: Vol. 5). 1974. 5.50 (ISBN 0-935008-03-9); pap. 4.25 (ISBN 0-935008-04-7). Christian Fellow Pubs.

Do from the Octave of Man Number Four: The Awakening & Crisis, Vol. 1. Andrew J. Da Silva. Ed. by Olivera Sajkovic. LC 85-71128. 128p. 1985. 12.00 (ISBN 0-9614941-0-7). Borderline NY.

Do I Need a Flood? Barbara King. 3.00 (ISBN 0-317-46971-1). CSA Pr.

Do It! Six Steps to Happiness. Winston K. Pendleton. Ed. by Herbert Lambert. LC 86-6112. 96p. (Orig.). 1986. pap. 5.95 (ISBN 0-8272-0613-5). CBP.

Do It Yourself Hebrew & Greek. 2nd ed. Edward W. Goodrick. LC 79-25463. 1980. pap. text ed. 9.95 (ISBN 0-930014-35-9); with cassette 14.95 (ISBN 0-930014-42-1). Multnomah.

Do It Yourself Hebrew & Greek: Everybody's Guide to the Language Tools. Edward W. Goodrick. 256p. (Orig.). 1980. pap. 11.95 (ISBN 0-310-41741-4, 6245P). Zondervan.

Do Kamo: La Personne et le Mythe Dans le Monde Melanesien. Maurice Leenhardt. Ed. by Kees W. Bolle. LC 77-79137. (Mythology Ser.). (Fr.). 1978. Repr. of 1971 ed. lib. bdg. 24.50x (ISBN 0-405-10547-9). Ayer Co Pubs.

Do Miracles Exist? Jan De Vries. 176p. 1986. 39.75x (ISBN 1-85158-029-8, Pub. by Mainstream Scotland); pap. 24.75x (ISBN 1-85158-030-1). State Mutual Bk.

Do This in Memory of Me. Thomas A. Dunne. LC 81-67927. (Illus.). 237p. (Orig.). 1981. pap. text ed. 4.95x (ISBN 0-89944-056-8); tchr's manual 2.95x (ISBN 0-89944-057-6). Don Bosco Multimedia.

Do We Hear the Song of This Joy? Meditations on the Acts of the Apostles. Elisabeth Schmidt. Tr. by Allen Hackett from Fr. 120p. (Orig.). 1983. pap. 6.95 (ISBN 0-8298-0680-6). Pilgrim NY.

Do We Know the Others? Hans Kung. LC 66-20895. (Concilium Ser.: Vol. 14). 196p. 1966. 7.95 (ISBN 0-8091-0033-9). Paulist Pr.

Do What You Love, the Money Will Follow. Marsha Sinetar. 1987. pap. 9.95. Paulist Pr.

Do You Feel Alone in the Spirit? Ruth Sanford. 1978. pap. 1.95 (ISBN 0-89283-056-5). Servant.

Do You Hear What You're Thinking? Jerry A. Schmidt. 1983. pap. 5.95 (ISBN 0-88207-381-8). Victor Bks.

Do You Know What Anything Is? Da F. John. LC 84-70215. 1984. pap. 8.95 (ISBN 0-913922-87-0). Dawn Horse Pr.

Do You Know Where Your Children Are? John Benton. 160p. 1983. pap. 2.95 (ISBN 0-8007-8480-4). Revell.

Do You Mean Me, Lord? The Call to the Ordained Ministry. Robert G. Cox. LC 85-8785. 116p. 1985. pap. 8.95 (ISBN 0-664-24668-0). Westminster.

Do You See What I See? Jae Jah Noh. LC 77-5255. (Orig.). 1977. pap. 3.95 (ISBN 0-8356-0499-3, Quest). Theos Pub Hse.

Do You Think It Snows In Heaven? Sally A. Schwing. Ed. by Helen Graves. 213p. 1987. 12.95 (ISBN 1-55523-049-0). Winston-Derek.

Do You Want to Go to Heaven? Becky Tilotta. 1967. 0.60 (ISBN 0-88027-106-X). Firm Foun Pub.

Do Your Prayers Bounce off the Ceiling? Grant A. Worth. LC 81-17411. 68p. 1982. 6.95 (ISBN 0-87747-895-3). Deseret Bk.

Dobrotoljubije tom Five, Vol. 5. Tr. of Philokalia. 343p. 20.00 (ISBN 0-317-28890-3); pap. 15.00 (ISBN 0-317-28891-1). Holy Trinity.

Dobrotoljubije Tom Four. Tr. of Philokalia. 451p. 25.00 (ISBN 0-317-28889-X); pap. 20.00 (ISBN 0-317-37275-0). Holy Trinity.

Dobrotoljubije, Tom Pjatij: Philokalia, Vol. 5. Ed. by St. Nicodemos the Hagiorite. Tr. by Theophan Govoroff from Greek. (Rus.). 350p. (Orig.). 1966. 20.00x (ISBN 0-88465-030-8); pap. 15.00x (ISBN 0-88465-029-4). Holy Trinity.

Dobrotoljubije, Tom Tchetvjortij: Philokalia, Vol. 4. Ed. by St. Nicodemos the Hagiorite. Tr. by Theofan Govoroff from Greek. (Rus.). 495p. (Orig.). 1965. 25.00x (ISBN 0-88465-027-8); pap. 20.00x (ISBN 0-88465-028-6). Holy Trinity.

Docteur Johnson, Critique Litteraire (1709-1784) Essai De Biographie Psychologique. Robert Wieder. 201p. 1982. lib. bdg. 25.00 (ISBN 0-89984-528-2). Century Bookbindery.

Dr. & Mrs. Fix-It: The Story of Frank & Bessie Beck. Natalie Barber. LC 79-130776. (Bold Believers Ser). (Orig.). 1969. pap. 0.95 (ISBN 0-377-84181-1). Friend Pr.

Dr. Cullis & His Work. W. H. Daniels. Ed. by Donald W. Dayton. (Higher Christian Life Ser.). 364p. 1985. 45.00 (ISBN 0-8240-6410-0). Garland Pub.

Dr. Edward McGlynn. Sylvester L. Malone. 17.00 (ISBN 0-405-10841-9, 11847). Ayer Co Pubs.

Dr. Frau. Grace Kaiser. LC 86-81059. 168p. 1986. 14.95 (ISBN 0-934672-34-2). Good Bks PA.

Doctor Ironside's Bible. H. A. Ironside. (Illus.). pap. 4.25 (ISBN 0-87213-393-1). Loizeaux.

Doctor Johnson's Prayers. Samuel Johnson. LC 76-25954. 1976. Repr. of 1947 ed. lib. bdg. 17.50 (ISBN 0-8414-8580-1). Folcroft.

Dr. Johnson's Prayers. Samuel Johnson. Ed. by Elton Trueblood. 88p. 1980. pap. 2.50 (ISBN 0-932970-17-6). Prinit Pr.

Doctor Luther. Gustav Freytag. Tr. by G. C. Reimer. LC 83-45642. Date not set. Repr. of 1916 ed. 27.50 (ISBN 0-404-19851-1). AMS Pr.

Dr. Sa'eed of Iran: Kurdish Physician to Princes & Peasants, Nobles & Nomads. Jay M. Rasooli & Cady H. Allen. LC 57-13245. (Illus.). 192p. 1983. pap. 6.95 (ISBN 0-87808-743-5). William Carey Lib.

Doctor Watson: Prolegomena to the Study of a Biographical Problem. S. C. Roberts. LC 73-16388. lib. bdg. 10.00 (ISBN 0-8414-7268-8). Folcroft.

Dr. Who Never Gave up, Ida Scudder. Carolyn Scott. (Stories of Faith & Fame Ser.). (YA) 1975. pap. 2.95 (ISBN 0-87508-607-1). Chr Lit.

Doctrina Cristiana. T. Conner. Tr. by Adolfo Robleto. Orig. Title: Christian Doctrine. (Span.). 408p. 1981. pap. 7.50 (ISBN 0-311-09012-5). Casa Bautista.

Doctrina de la Trinidad. Eberhard Jungel. Tr. by Arnoldo Canclini from Eng. Tr. of Doctrine of the Trinity. (Span.). 152p. 1980. pap. 4.50 (ISBN 0-89922-153-X). Edit Caribe.

Doctrinal Distinctives of Asbury. pap. 2.95 (ISBN 0-686-12867-2). Schmul Pub Co.

Doctrinal Theology of the Evangelical Lutheran Church. Heinrich Schmid. LC 66-13052. 1961. 25.95 (ISBN 0-8066-0107-8, 10-1930). Augsburg.

Doctrinal Treatises, an Introduction to Different Portions of the Holy Scriptures. William Tyndale. Repr. of 1848 ed. 51.00 (ISBN 0-384-62250-X). Johnson Repr.

Doctrinas Claves. Edwin H. Palmer. 2.95 (ISBN 0-85151-407-3). Banner of Truth.

Doctrine & Administration of the Church. rev. ed. Paul R. Jackson. LC 68-28699. 1980. pap. 3.95 (ISBN 0-87227-072-6). Reg Baptist.

Doctrine & Covenants. Reorganized Church of Jesus Christ of Latter Day Saints, Board of Publication Staff. LC 78-134922. 1978. 14.00 (ISBN 0-8309-0204-X). Herald Hse.

Doctrine & Covenants & Pearl of Great Price Digest. John D. Hawkes. 1977. pap. text ed. 4.95 (ISBN 0-89036-100-2). Hawkes Pub Inc.

Doctrine & Covenants Commentary. Hyrum M. Smith & Janne M. Sjodahl. 14.95 (ISBN 0-87747-070-7). Deseret Bk.

Doctrine & Covenants of the Church of Jesus Christ of Latter-Day Saints: Containing the Revelations Given to Joseph Smith, Jun, the Prophet, for the Building up of the Kingdom of God in the Last Days. Joseph Smith. Ed. by Orson Pratt. LC 69-14082. 1971. Repr. of 1880 ed. lib. bdg. 29.75x (ISBN 0-8371-4101-X, SMCC). Greenwood.

Doctrine & Covenants: Our Modern Scripture. rev. ed. Richard O. Cowan. LC 78-19190. (Illus.). 1978. pap. 7.95 (ISBN 0-8425-1316-7). Brigham.

Doctrine & Practice of Yoga. A. P. Mukerji. 6.00 (ISBN 0-911662-23-5). Yoga.

Doctrine & Word: Theology in the Pulpit. Mark Ellingsen. LC 82-21311. pap. 51.00 (2027152). Bks Demand UMI.

Doctrine of Baptism. Edmund Schlink. Tr. by Herbert Bouman from Ger. LC 78-159794. 256p. 1972. pap. 10.95 (ISBN 0-570-03726-3, 12-2628). Concordia.

Doctrine of Creation: The Creator & His Creature. Karl Barth. Ed. by G. W. Bromiley & T. F. Torrance. Tr. by G. W. Bromiley & T. F. Torrance. (Church Dogmatics Ser.: Vol. 3, Pt. 3). 560p. 29.95 (ISBN 0-567-09033-7, Pub. by T & T Clark Ltd UK). Fortress.

Doctrine of Creation: The Work of Creation. Karl Barth. Ed. by G. W. Bromiley & T. F. Torrance. Tr. by G. W. Bromiley & T. F. Torrance. (Church Dogmatics Ser.: Vol. 3, Pt. 1). 440p. 1958. 29.95 (ISBN 0-567-09031-0, Pub. by T & T Clark Ltd UK). Fortress.

Doctrine of Endless Punishment. W. G. Shedd. 1980. 8.25 (ISBN 0-86524-019-1, 9803). Klock & Klock.

Doctrine of Faith. Nestor Beck. 1987. pap. 15.95 (ISBN 0-570-04469-3). Concordia.

Doctrine of God. Herman Bavinck. (Twin Brooks Ser.). 1977. pap. 13.95 (ISBN 0-8010-0723-2). Baker Bk.

Doctrine of God. Herman Bavinck. Tr. by W. Hendricksen. (Student's Reformed Theological Library Ser.). 1977. 16.95 (ISBN 0-85151-255-0). Banner of Truth.

Doctrine of God. Christopher B. Kaiser. LC 82-72324. (Foundations for Faith Ser.). 160p. 1982. pap. 8.95 (ISBN 0-89107-259-4, Crossway Bks). Good News.

Doctrine of God in the Jewish Apocryphal & Apocalyptic Literature. Henry J. Wicks. Repr. of 1915 ed. 29.00x (ISBN 0-87068-149-4). Ktav.

Doctrine of God: The Election of God, The Command of God. Karl Barth. Ed. by T. F. Torrance & G. W. Bromiley. Tr. by G. W. Bromiley & T. F. Torrance. (Church Dogmatics Ser.: Vol. 2, Pt. 2). 820p. 1957. 29.95 (ISBN 0-567-09022-1, Pub. by T & T Clark Ltd UK). Fortress.

Doctrine of God: The Knowledge of God. Karl Barth. Ed. by G. W. Bromiley & T. F. Torrance. Tr. by G. W. Bromiley & T. F. Torrance. (Church Dogmatics Ser.: Vol. 2, Pt. 1). 710p. 1957. text ed. 29.95 (ISBN 0-567-09021-3, Pub. by T & T Clark Ltd UK). Fortress.

Doctrine of Justification. James Buchanan. 514p. 1985. Repr. of 1867 ed. 15.95 (ISBN 0-85151-440-5). Banner of Truth.

Doctrine of Karma. Swami Abhedananda. 5.95 (ISBN 0-87481-608-4). Vedanta Pr.

Doctrine of Karma. Gertrude W. Van Pelt. Ed. by W. Emmett Small & Helen Todd. (Theosophical Manual: No. 3). 64p. 1975. pap. 2.00 (ISBN 0-913004-16-2). Point Loma Pub.

Doctrine of Last Things. Robert E. Picirilli. 29p. 1973. pap. 0.95 (ISBN 0-89265-103-2). Randall Hse.

Doctrine of Law & Grace Unfolded. John Bunyan. 1974. pap. 2.95 (ISBN 0-685-52817-0). Reiner.

Doctrine of Liberation in Indian Religion. Muni Shivkumar. 1984. text ed. 14.00x (ISBN 0-89563-286-1). Coronet Bks.

Doctrine of Perseverance. 2nd ed. F. Leroy Forlines. 24p. 1987. pap. price not set. Randall Hse.

Doctrine of Prajna-Paramita As Exposed in the Abhisamayalamkara of Maitreya. E. Obermiller. 153p. 1984. Repr. of 1932 ed. lib. bdg. 19.50x (ISBN 0-88181-002-9). Canon Pubns.

Doctrine of Reconciliation: Jesus Christ the Servant as Lord. Karl Barth. Ed. by G. W. Bromiley & T. F. Torrance. Tr. by G. W. Bromiley & T. F. Torrance. 882p. 1958. 26.95x (ISBN 0-567-09042-6, Pub. by T & T Clark Ltd UK). Fortress.

Doctrine of Reconciliation: Jesus Christ the True Witness. Karl Barth. Ed. by G. W. Bromiley & T. F. Torrance. Tr. by G. W. Bromiley & T. F. Torrance. 496p. 1961. 29.95 (ISBN 0-567-09043-4, Pub. by T & T Clark Ltd UK). Fortress.

Doctrine of Reconciliation: Jesus Christ the True Witness. Karl Barth. Ed. by G. W. Bromiley & T. F. Torrance. Tr. by G. W. Bromiley from Ger. (Church Dogmatics Ser.: Vol. 4, Pt. 3, 2nd Half). 492p. 1962. 29.95 (ISBN 0-567-09044-2, Pub. by T & T Clark Ltd UK). Fortress.

Doctrine of Reconciliation: The Christian Life. Karl Barth. Ed. by G. W. Bromiley & T. F. Torrance. Tr. by G. W. Bromiley from Ger. (Church Dogmatics Ser.: Vol. 4, Pt. 4). 240p. 1969. 19.95 (ISBN 0-567-09045-0, Pub. by T & T Clark Ltd UK). Fortress.

Doctrine of Reprobation in the Christian Reformed Church. Harry R. Boer. LC 83-1602. Repr. of 1983 ed. 23.50 (2027537). Bks Demand UMI.

Doctrine of St. John Damascene on the Procession of the Holy Spirit. N. Bogorodskii. LC 80-2351. Tr. of Uchenie Sv. Ioann Damaskina Ob' Iskhozhdenii Sv. Dukha. Repr. of 1879 ed. 28.50 (ISBN 0-404-18903-2). AMS Pr.

Doctrine of Salvation. Charles Horne. 1984. pap. 5.95 (ISBN 0-8024-0424-3). Moody.

Doctrine of Scripture. Cornelius Van Til. 1967. pap. 5.50 syllabus (ISBN 0-87552-484-2). Presby & Reformed.

Doctrine of Scripture: Locus 2 of Institutio Theologiae Elencticae. Thomas Turrettin. Ed. by John W. Beardslee, III. 200p. (Orig.). 1981. pap. 7.95 (ISBN 0-8010-8857-7). Baker Bk.

Doctrine of the Atonement in the Theology of Wolfhart Panneberg. Herbert Neie. (Theologische Bibliothek Toepelmann: Vol. 36). 1978. 40.00x (ISBN 3-11-007506-7). De Gruyter.

Doctrine of the Bhagavad Gita: Sangam Texts Ser. Bhavani Shankar. Ed. by Raghavan Iyer. 131p. (Orig.). 1984. pap. 8.75 (ISBN 0-88695-031-7). Concord Grove.

Doctrine of the Buddha. 2nd ed. G. Grimm. 1984. Repr. 32.00 (ISBN 0-8426-0489-8). Orient Bk Dist.

Doctrine of the Godhead. J. J. Turner & Edwards Myers. pap. 5.50 (ISBN 0-89137-553-8). Quality Pubns.

Doctrine of the Heart. Besant. 1.95 (ISBN 0-8356-7189-5). Theos Pub Hse.

Doctrine of the Holy Spirit. Hendrikus Berkhof. LC 64-16279. 1976. pap. 6.95 (ISBN 0-8042-0551-5). John Knox.

Doctrine of the Holy Spirit. George Smeaton. 1980. 15.95 (ISBN 0-85151-187-2). Banner of Truth.

Doctrine of the Jainas. Walther Schubring. Tr. by Wolfgang Buerlen. 1978. Repr. 15.00 (ISBN 0-89684-005-0, Pub. by Motilal Banarsidass India). Orient Bk Dist.

Doctrine of the New Testament in Ten Great Subjects. G. W. Lane. 127p. 1964. pap. 1.95 (ISBN 0-87148-250-9). Pathway Pr.

Doctrine of the Person of Jesus Christ. H. R. Mackintosh. 560p. 1913. pap. 15.95 (ISBN 0-567-27218-4, Pub. by T&T Clark Ltd UK). Fortress.

Doctrine of the Soul in the Thought of Plotinus & Origen. Antonia Tripolitis. LC 76-16321. 1977. 6.95 (ISBN 0-87212-061-9). Libra.

Doctrine of the Sufis. A. J. Arberry. 12.95 (ISBN 0-686-18608-7). Kazi Pubns.

Doctrine of the Sufis. A. J. Arberry. 1966. 12.95x (ISBN 0-87902-195-0). Orientalia.

Doctrine of the Sufis. Arthur J. Arberry. LC 76-58075. 1977. pap. 13.95 (ISBN 0-521-29218-2). Cambridge U Pr.

Doctrine of the Sufis. Muhammed Kalabadhi. Tr. by Arthur J. Arberry from Arabic. LC 75-41003. Repr. of 1935 ed. 18.00 (ISBN 0-404-14637-6). AMS Pr.

Doctrine of the Word of God. Thomas A. Thomas. 1972. pap. 3.50 (ISBN 0-87552-450-8). Presby & Reformed.

Doctrine of the Word of God: Prolegomena to Church Dogmatics. Karl Barth. Ed. by G. W. Bromiley & T. F. Torrance. Tr. by G. W. Bromiley & T. F. Torrance. (Church Dogmatics Ser.: Vol. 1, Pt. 1). 528p. 29.95 (ISBN 0-567-09013-2, Pub. by T & T Clark Ltd UK). Fortress.

Doctrine of the Word of God: The Revelation of God, Holy Scripture, the Proclamation of the Church. Karl Barth. Ed. by G. W. Bromiley & T. F. Torrance. (Church Dogmatics Ser.: Vol. 1. Pt. 2). 924p. 1956. 29.95 (ISBN 0-567-09012-4, Pub. by T & T Clark Ltd UK). Fortress.

Doctrine of Virtue: Metaphysic of Morals, Pt. II. Immanuel Kant. (Works in Contin. Philos. Ser.). 1971. 10.95x (ISBN 0-8122-1025-5). U of Pa Pr.

Doctrine on Divine Healing. Earnell Sams, Jr. (Orig.). 1982. pap. write for info. (ISBN 0-940068-02-8). Doctrine Christ.

Doctrines from the Beloved Disciple: Outlined Gospel of John. Harold Cooper. 137p. 1972. pap. 1.00 (ISBN 0-89114-054-9). Baptist Pub Hse.

Doctrines of the Bible. Daniel Kaufman. 639p. 1928. 12.95 (ISBN 0-8361-1358-6). Herald Pr.

Doctrines of the Christian Religion. William W. Stevens. LC 77-83282. 1977. pap. 10.95 (ISBN 0-8054-1706-0). Broadman.

Document of Vatican 11. Austin P. Flannery. 1975. pap. 7.95 (ISBN 0-8028-1623-1). Eerdmans.

Documentary History of Religion in America, Vol. 1. Ed. by Edwin Gaustad. 1982. pap. 19.95 (ISBN 0-8028-1871-4). Eerdmans.

Documentary History of Religion in America Since 1865, Vol. 2. Edwin S. Gaustad. (Illus.). 640p. 1983. pap. 19.95 (ISBN 0-8028-1874-9). Eerdmans.

Documentary History of the Anti-Cult Movement. David Bromley & Anson Shupe. LC 84-25560. (Studies in American Religion: Vol. 13). 420p. 1985. 69.95x_cancelled (ISBN 0-88946-656-4). E Mellen.

Documentary History of the Struggle for Religious Liberty in Virginia. Charles F. James. LC 70-121101. (Civil Liberties in American History Ser). 1971. Repr. of 1900 ed. lib. bdg. 37.50 (ISBN 0-306-71977-0). Da Capo.

Documentary Reports on Early American Catholicism. Philip Gleason. 17.00 (ISBN 0-405-10833-8, 11825). Ayer Co Pubs.

Documents & Facts Illustrating the Origin of the Mission to Japan. Aaron H. Palmer. LC 72-82105. (Japan Library Ser.). 1973. Repr. of 1857 ed. lib. bdg. 11.00 (ISBN 0-8420-1399-7). Scholarly Res Inc.

Documents Concerning Baptism & Church Membership: A Controversy Among North Carolina Baptists. G. McLeod Bryan et al. LC 76-45687. (Special Studies Ser.: No. 1). vii, 81p. 1977. pap. 2.00 (ISBN 0-932180-00-0). NABPR.

Documents for the Study of the Gospels. David R. Cartlidge & David L. Dungan. LC 79-21341. 300p. (Orig.). 1980. 16.95 (ISBN 0-8006-0640-X, 1-640); pap. 10.95 (ISBN - 08006-1640-5, 1-1640). Fortress.

Documents from Old Testament Times. Ed. by D. Winton Thomas. pap. 7.95x (ISBN 0-06-130085-3, TB85, Torch). Har-Row.

Documents from the Temple Archives of Nippur Dated in the Reigns of Cassite Rulers with Incomplete Dates. A. T. Clay. (Publications of the Babylonian Section, Ser. A: Vol. 15). (Illus.). xii, 68p. 1906. soft bound 12.00x (ISBN 0-686-11914-2). Univ Mus of U PA.

Documents from the Temple Arhcives of Nippur Dated in the Reigns of Cassite Rulers. Albert T. Clay. LC 13-1106. (University of Pennsylvania, The Museum, Publications of the Babylonian Section: Vol. 2, No. 2). pap. 27.00 (ISBN 0-317-28572-6, 2052022). Bks Demand UMI.

Documents Illustrating Papal Authority, A.D. 96-454. Ed. by Edward Giles. LC 78-59023. 1979. Repr. of 1952 ed. 28.00 (ISBN 0-88355-696-0). Hyperion Conn.

Documents Illustrating the History of St. Paul's Cathedral. London - St. Paul'S Cathedral. Ed. by W. S. Simpson. 1880. 27.00 (ISBN 0-384-55530-6). Johnson Repr.

Documents Illustrative of English Church History. Compiled by Henry Gee & William J. Hardy. LC 83-45580. Date not set. Repr. of 1896 ed. 62.50 (ISBN 0-404-19898-8). AMS Pr.

Documents Illustrative of the Continental Reformation. Ed. by Beresford J. Kidd. LC 83-45663. Date not set. Repr. of 1911 ed. 64.50 (ISBN 0-404-19813-9). AMS Pr.

Documents in Early Christian Thought. Ed. by Maurice Wiles & M. Santer. LC 74-31807. 304p. 1976. 42.50 (ISBN 0-521-20669-3); pap. 12.95 (ISBN 0-521-09915-3). Cambridge U Pr.

Documents in the History of American Philosophy: From Jonathan Edward to John Dewey. Ed. by Morton White. 1972. pap. text ed. 13.95x (ISBN 0-19-501555-X). Oxford U Pr.

Documents Inedits Pour Servir a l'Histoire Du Christianisme En Orient, 2 Vols. Antoine Rabbath. LC 72-174293. Repr. of 1911 ed. Set. lib. bdg. 95.00 (ISBN 0-404-05202-9). AMS Pr.

Documents of American Catholic History, 3 vols. Ed. by John T. Ellis. LC 86-80801. 1200p. 1987. Set. 65.00; 25.00 ea. Vol. 1: 1494-1865 (ISBN 0-89453-611-7). Vol. 2: 1866-1966 (ISBN 0-89453-612-5). Vol. 3: 1967-1986 (ISBN 0-89453-588-9). M Glazier.

Documents of Jewish Sectaries, 2 Vols. in 1. rev. ed. Solomon Schecter. (Library of Biblical Studies Ser). (Illus.). 1970. 35.00 (ISBN 0-87068-016-1). Ktav.

Documents of the Christian Church. 2nd ed. Ed. by Henry Bettenson. 1970. pap. 8.95 (ISBN 0-19-501293-3). Oxford U Pr.

Documents of the Thirty-First & Thirty-Second General Congregations of the Society of Jesus: An English Translation of the Official Latin Texts of the General Congregations & of the Accompanying Papal Documents. Ed. by John W. Padberg. LC 77-70881. (Jesuit Primary Sources in English Translation: No. 2). 608p. 1977. pap. 6.00 smyth sewn (ISBN 0-912422-26-2). Inst Jesuit.

Documents of the Thirty-Third General Congregation of the Society of Jesus: An English Translation of the Official Latin Texts. Ed. by Donald R. Campion & Albert C. Louapre. LC 84-80080. 116p. pap. 3.00 (ISBN 0-912422-64-5). Inst Jesuit.

Documents of Vatican II. Ed. by Walter M. Abbott. pap. cancelled (ISBN 0-686-19062-9, EC-101). US Catholic.

Documents of Vatican II with Notes & Comments by Catholic, Protestant & Orthodox Authorities. Ed. by Walter M. Abbott. LC 82-80350. 794p. 1974. pap. 8.95 (ISBN 0-8329-1115-1, Assn Pr). New Century.

Documents on the Liturgy, 1963-1979: Conciliar, Papal & Curial Texts. International Committee on English in the Liturgy. Ed. by Thomas C. O'Brien. LC 82-83580. 1496p. 1983. text ed. 49.95 (ISBN 0-8146-1281-4). Liturgical Pr.

Documents Relatifs aux Rapports du Clerge avec la Royaute de 1682 a 1789, 2 vols. in 1. Leon Mention. (Fr.). 461p. Repr. of 1893 ed. lib. bdg. 67.50x. Coronet Bks.

Documents Relating to the Foundation & Antiquities of the Collegiate Church of Middleham in the County of York. Ed. by William L. Atthill. LC 70-161702. (Camden Society, London. Publications, First Ser.: No. 38). Repr. of 1847 ed. 19.00 (ISBN 0-404-50138-9). AMS Pr.

Documents Relating to the Foundation & Antiquities of the Collegiate Church of Middleham, County of York. Ed. by William L. Atthill. (Camden Society Ser.: Vol. 38). 19.00 (ISBN 0-384-02270-7). Johnson Repr.

Documents Relating to the Proceedings Against William Prynne, in 1634 & 1637. Ed. by Samuel R. Gardiner. Repr. of 1877 ed. 27.00 (ISBN 0-384-17635-6). Johnson Repr.

Dodd's Church History of England, eith Notes Additions & A Continuation, 5 Vols. M. A. Tierney. 2512p. 1839. text ed. 331.20x (ISBN 0-576-78535-0, Pub. by Gregg Intl Pubs England). Gregg Intl.

Dodd's Church History of England, 1500-1688, 5 Vols. Charles Dodd. Ed. by M. A. Tierney. LC 75-119152. Repr. of 1843 ed. Set. 262.00 (ISBN 0-404-02150-6); 52.50 ea. Vol. 1 (ISBN 0-404-02151-4). Vol. 2 (ISBN 0-404-02152-2). Vol. 3 (ISBN 0-404-02153-0). Vol. 4 (ISBN 0-404-02154-9). Vol. 5 (ISBN 0-404-02155-7). AMS Pr.

Doers of the Word. John V. Apczynski. LC 76-51640. (American Academy of Religion. Dissertation Ser.). 1977. pap. 10.50 (ISBN 0-89130-128-3, 010118). Scholars Pr GA.

Does Anybody Care How I Feel? Mildred Tengbom. LC 81-3808. 122p. 1981. pap. 4.95 (ISBN 0-87123-142-5, 210142). Bethany Hse.

Does Death Really Exist? Swami Muktananda. LC 81-50161. 64p. 1983. pap. 3.95 (ISBN 0-914602-56-X). SYDA Found.

Does God Answer Prayer? Peter Baelz. (Illus.). 122p. (Orig.). 1983. pap. 6.95 (ISBN 0-87243-117-7). Templegate.

Does God Change? The Word's Becoming in the Incarnation. Thomas Weinandy. LC 84-26241. (Studies in Historical Theology). 1985. pap. 17.95 (ISBN 0-932506-35-6). St Bedes Pubns.

Does God Condemn Those Who Never Hear the Gospel? C. S. Lovett. 1963. pap. 2.95 (ISBN 0-938148-19-2). Personal Christianity.

Does God Exist? Sebastian Faure. lib. bdg. 59.95 (ISBN 0-8490-0054-8). Gordon Pr.

Does God Exist? An Answer for Today. Hans Kung. LC 81-40072. 864p. 1981. pap. 10.95 (ISBN 0-394-74737-2, Vin). Random.

Does God Give Interviews? Carolyn Hall. 56p. 1985. 7.95 (ISBN 0-533-06644-1). Vantage.

Does God Have a Body? Rosalyn Kendrick. 1979. pap. 4.95 (ISBN 0-8192-1257-1). Morehouse.

Does God Have a Nature? Alvin Plantinga. LC 80-6585. (Aquinas Lecture Ser.). 1980. 7.95 (ISBN 0-87462-145-3). Marquette.

Does God Really Love Me? Earl D. Wilson. LC 86-10616. 96p. (Orig.). 1986. pap. 2.95 (ISBN 0-87784-514-X). Inter-Varsity.

Does God Want Christians to Perform Miracles Today? John C. Whitcomb, Jr. 1979. pap. 1.00 (ISBN 0-88469-016-4). BMH Bks.

Does Inspiration Demand Inerrancy? Stewart Custer. 1968. pap. 3.50 (ISBN 0-934532-07-9). Presby & Reformed.

Does It Make Any Difference What I Do? Mildred Tengbom. 160p. (Orig.). 1984. pap. 4.95 (ISBN 0-87123-448-3, 210448). Bethany Hse.

Does It Matter. Alan W. Watts. LC 72-89988. 1971. pap. 3.95 (ISBN 0-394-71665-5, Vin). Random.

Does Jesus Know Us? Do We Know Him? Hans Urs von Balthasar. Tr. by Graham Harrison from Ger. LC 82-84581. Orig. Title: Kennt Uns Jesus-Kennen Wir Ihn? 99p. (Orig.). 1983. pap. 6.95 (ISBN 0-89870-023-X). Ignatius Pr.

Does Prayer Make a Difference? Dan D. Whitsett. (Prayers in My Life Ser.: Ser. I). 1974. pap. 1.25x (ISBN 0-8358-0312-0). Upper Room.

Does Suffering Make Sense? Russell Shaw. LC 86-62613. 180p. (Orig.). 1987. pap. 4.95 (ISBN 0-87973-834-0). Our Sunday Visitor.

Does the Bible Contradict Itself. Swetmon. 1985. pap. 3.95 (ISBN 0-89225-276-6). Gospel Advocate.

Does the Bible Teach Millennialism. L. R. Thomas. pap. 2.50 (ISBN 0-685-36796-7). Reiner.

Does the Gospel Make Sense Today? Michael Scrogin. 128p. 1983. pap. 7.95 (ISBN 0-8170-0967-1). Judson.

Dogen Kigen - Mystical Realist. Hee-Jin Kim. LC 74-33725. (Association for Asian Studies Monograph: No. 29). 384p. 1975. pap. 8.95x (ISBN 0-8165-0513-6). U of Ariz Pr.

Dogen Studies. Ed. by William R. LaFleur. LC 85-16427. (Studies in East Asian Buddhism Ser.: No. 2). 288p. 1985. pap. text ed. 19.00x (ISBN 0-8248-1011-2). UH Pr.

Dogma, 6 vols. Michael Schmaus. Incl. Vol. 1. God in Revelation (ISBN 0-87061-098-8); Vol. 2. God & Creation (ISBN 0-87061-099-6); Vol. 3. God & His Christ (ISBN 0-87061-100-3); Vol. 4. Church (ISBN 0-87061-101-1); Vol. 5. Church As Sacrament (ISBN 0-87061-102-X); Vol. 6. Justification & the Last Things (ISBN 0-87061-103-8). 1984. Set. pap. 60.00 (ISBN 0-87061-095-3); pap. 10.00 ea. Chr Classics.

Dogma & Compulsion. Theodor Reik. LC 72-9369. 332p. 1973. Repr. of 1951 ed. lib. bdg. 45.00x (ISBN 0-8371-6577-6, REDC). Greenwood.

Dogma & Preaching. Joseph C. Ratzinger. Tr. by Matthew J. O'Connell. 1983. 9.95 (ISBN 0-8199-0819-3). Franciscan Herald.

Dogma in Medieval Jewish Thought: From Maimonides to Abravanel. Menachem Kellner. (Littman Library of Jewish Civilization). 350p. 1987. 45.00 (ISBN 0-19-710044-9). Oxford U Pr.

Dogmat o Svjatejshej Evkharistii. Metropolitan Stefan Yavorsky. Tr. of Dogma of the Holy Eucharist. 32p. pap. 1.00 (ISBN 0-317-28973-X). Holy Trinity.

Dogmat Tserkvi v Sovrjemjennom Mire. George Grabbe. Tr. of Dogma of the Church in the Modern World. 1975. pap. 1.50 (ISBN 0-317-30381-3). Holy Trinity.

Dogmatic & Mystical Theology of Donne. I. Husain. LC 70-119088. (Studies in Philosophy, No. 40). 1970. Repr. of 1938 ed. lib. bdg. 39.95x (ISBN 0-8383-1084-2). Haskell.

Dogmatic & Mystical Theology of John Donne. Itra Husain. LC 75-43972. 1938. lib. bdg. 17.50 (ISBN 0-8414-4747-0). Folcroft.

Dogmatic & Mystical Theology of John Donne. Itrat Husain. Repr. of 1938 ed. lib. bdg. 22.50x (ISBN 0-8371-4243-1, HUJD). Greenwood.

Dogmatic & Polemical Works. St. Jerome. (Fathers of the Church Ser: Vol. 53). 405p. 1965. 21.95x (ISBN 0-8132-0053-9). Cath U Pr.

Dogmatic Canons & Decrees of the Council of Trent, Vatican Council I, Plus the Decree on the Immaculate Conception & the Syllabus of Errors. Devin-Adair Staff. LC 79-112469. (Eng.). 1977. pap. 5.00 (ISBN 0-89555-018-0). TAN Bks Pubs.

Dogmatic Constitution on the Church (Lumen Gentium) Vatican Council II, Staff. 94p. 1964. pap. 3.25 (ISBN 1-55586-000-1). US Catholic.

Dogmatic Theology for the Laity. Mattias Premm. 1977. pap. 12.00 (ISBN 0-89555-022-9). TAN Bks Pubs.

Dogmatics in Outline. Karl Barth. pap. 5.95x (ISBN 0-06-130056-X, TB56, Torch). Har-Row.

Dogmatik. 4th ed. Wolfgang Trillhaas. 543p. 1972. 24.80x (ISBN 3-11-008423-6). De Gruyter.

Dogsled Apostles. facs. ed. Alma H. Savage. LC 68-55857. (Essay Index Reprint Ser). 1942. 18.00 (ISBN 0-8369-0851-1). Ayer Co Pubs.

Doing Evil to Achieve Good: Moral Choice in Conflict Situations. Ed. by Richard A. McCormick & Paul Ramsey. LC 78-11316. 1978. 11.95 (ISBN 0-8294-0285-3). Loyola.

Doing Evil to Achieve Good: Moral Choice in Conflict Situations. Ed. by Richard A. McCormick & Paul Ramsey. 274p. 1985. pap. text ed. 11.75 (ISBN 0-8191-4586-6). U Pr of Amer.

Doing Right Makes Me Happy. Cara L. Phillips. Ed. by Patricia Mahany. LC 82-80028. (Happy Day Bks.). (Illus.). 24p. (Orig.). 1982. pap. 1.59 (ISBN 0-87239-536-7, 3582). Standard Pub.

Doing Something by Doing Nothing. Thomas Peterson. 1985. 6.25 (ISBN 0-89536-747-5, 5853). CSS of Ohio.

Doing the Truth in Charity: Statements of Popes Paul VI, John Paul I, John Paul II & the Secretariat for Promoting Christian Unity. Ed. by Thomas F. Stransky & John B. Sheerin. LC 81-85384. 400p. (Orig.). 1982. 12.95 (ISBN 0-8091-2398-3). Paulist Pr.

Doing the Truth: The Quest for Moral Theology. Edna McDonagh. LC 79-63361. 223p. 1980. pap. text ed. 6.95 (ISBN 0-268-00845-0). U of Notre Dame Pr.

Doing the Truth: The Quest for Moral Theology. Edna McDonagh. LC 79-63361. 1979. text ed. 14.95x (ISBN 0-268-00844-2). U of Notre Dame Pr.

Doing Theology in a Divided World. Ed. by Virginia Fabella & Sergio Torres. LC 84-14712. 224p. (Orig.). 1985. pap. 11.95 (ISBN 0-88344-197-7). Orbis Bks.

Doing Theology in a Revolutionary Situation. Jose M. Bonino. Ed. by William H. Lazareth. LC 74-80424. 208p. 1975. pap. 5.95 (ISBN 0-8006-1451-8, 1-1451). Fortress.

Doing Time in the Pulpit. Eugene L. Lowry. 112p. (Orig.). pap. 6.95 (ISBN 0-687-11034-3). Abingdon.

Doing Your Part When You'd Rather Let God Do It All: The Measure of a Christian Based on James 2-5. Gene A. Getz. LC 84-17749. 1985. pap. 5.95 (ISBN 0-8307-1002-7, 5418395). Regal.

Dojo: Magic & Exorcism in Modern Japan. Winston Davis. LC 79-64219. (Illus.). xx, 324p. 1980. 27.50x (ISBN 0-8047-1053-8); pap. 9.95 (ISBN 0-8047-1131-3, SP-7). Stanford U Pr.

Dolorous Passion of Our Lord Jesus Christ. Anne C. Emmerich. 1980. lib. bdg. 64.95 (ISBN 0-8490-3100-1). Gordon Pr.

Dolorous Passion of Our Lord Jesus Christ. Anne C. Emmerich. LC 83-70406. 382p. 1983. pap. 10.00 (ISBN 0-89555-210-8). TAN Bks Pubs.

Domesday Book: A Reassessment. Ed. by Peter Sawyer. 224p. 1985. 49.95 (ISBN 0-7131-6440-9). E Arnold.

Domesday of Saint Paul of the Year Twelve Twenty-Two. London-St. Paul'S Cathedral. Repr. of 1858 ed. 37.00 (ISBN 0-384-33475-X). Johnson Repr.

Domestic Correspondance of Dominique-Marie Varlet: Bishop of Babylon 1678-1742. B. Guy. (Studies in the History of Christian Thought: No. 36). ix, 150p. 1986. 22.00 (ISBN 90-04-07671-9, Pub. by E J Brill). Heinman.

Domesticating the Clergy: The Inception of the Reformation in Strasbourg 1522-1524. William S. Stafford. LC 76-15567. (American Academy of Religion, Dissertation Ser.). 1976. pap. 9.95 (ISBN 0-89130-109-7, 010117). Scholars Pr GA.

Dominance & Defiance: A Study of Marital Instability in an Islamic African Society. R. Cohen. (Anthropological Studies: No. 6). 1971. pap. 6.00 (ISBN 0-686-36563-1). Am Anthro Assn.

Dominic Savio: Teenage Saint. Peter Lappin. LC 54-11044. 1982. 2.75 (ISBN 0-89944-034-7, D Bosco Pubns); pap. 1.25 (ISBN 0-89944-033-9). Don Bosco Multimedia.

Dominican Mission Frontier of Lower California. Peveril Meigs. pap. 25.00 (ISBN 0-384-38005-0). Johnson Repr.

Dominion Covenant: Genesis. Gary North. 1982. 14.95 (ISBN 0-930464-03-6). Inst Christian.

Don Bosco & the Death of Charles. Pietro Stella. Tr. by John Drury from Italian. (Don Bosco in the History of Catholic Religious Thought & Practice Ser.). 56p. (Orig.). 1985. pap. 5.95 (ISBN 0-89944-080-0). Don Bosco Multimedia.

Don Bosco & the Salesians. Morand Wirth. Tr. by David DeBurgh from Italian. LC 82-72675. Orig. Title: Don Bosco e i Salesiani. 432p. (Orig.). 1982. pap. 10.95 (ISBN 0-89944-065-7). Don Bosco Multimedia.

Don Bosco & the Spiritual Life. Francis Desramaut. Tr. by Roger M. Luna from Fr. LC 79-52674. (Orig.). 1979. pap. text ed. 10.95 (ISBN 0-89944-022-3). Don Bosco Multimedia.

Don Bosco: Life & Work. Pietro Stella. Tr. by John Drury from Italian. (Don Bosco in the History of Catholic Religious Thought & Practice Ser.). Tr. of Don Bosco Nella Storia della Religiosita Cattolica: Vita e Opere. 336p. (Orig.). 1985. 24.95 (ISBN 0-89944-081-9). Don Bosco Multimedia.

Don Bosco the Catechist. Gian C. Isoardi. Tr. by Wallace L. Cornell from Ital. 89p. 1981. pap. 4.75 (ISBN 0-89944-053-3). Don Bosco Multimedia.

Don Bosco's Lay Religious: Essays on the Salesian Brother, Pt. 1. Enzo Bianco. Tr. by Peter Swain. LC 84-72160. 75p. pap. 3.00 (ISBN 0-89944-078-9). Don Bosco Multimedia.

Don Bosco's Lay Religious: Profiles in Courage, Pt. 2. Enzo Bianco. Tr. by Peter Swain. 101p. pap. 3.00 (ISBN 0-89944-079-7). Don Bosco Multimedia.

Don del Espiritu Santo. Ed. by T. L. Lowery. (Span.). 80p. 1978. pap. 2.25 (ISBN 0-87148-307-6). Pathway Pr.

Don Juan, Mescalito & Modern Magic: The Mythology of Inner Space. Nevill Drury. 256p. 1985. pap. 8.95 (ISBN 1-85063-015-1, Ark Paperbks). Methuen Inc.

Dona Gracia of the House of Nasi. Cecil Roth. LC 77-92984. 208p. 1978. pap. 4.95 (ISBN 0-8276-0099-2, 415). Jewish Pubns.

Donald Orrs: Missionary Duet. Lee Hollaway. LC 82-732666. (Meet the Missionary Ser.). 1983. 5.50 (ISBN 0-8054-4283-9, 4242-83). Broadman.

Donatist Church: A Movement of Protest in Roman North Africa. W. H. Frend. 384p. 1985. 42.00x (ISBN 0-19-826408-9). Oxford U Pr.

Donde Estan los Muertes? Gavin Hamilton & David Fernandez. Orig. Title: Where Are the Dead? (Span.). 64p. 1983. pap. 2.25 (ISBN 0-8254-1301-X). Kregel.

Dones del Espiritu. Ed. by Hiram Almirudus. (Span.). 88p. 1978. pap. 2.75 (ISBN 0-87148-520-6). Pathway Pr.

Dones Del Ministerio. Kenneth E. Hagin. 1983. study guide 10.00 (ISBN 0-89276-192-X). Hagin Ministries.

Donkey Who Served the King. Joyce Coe. (Arch Bk. Ser.: No. 15). (Illus.). 1978. 0.99 (ISBN 0-570-06120-2, 59-1238). Concordia.

Donkey's Tale. Margaret Gray. (Illus.). 32p. 1984. casebound 3.95 (ISBN 0-8307-0963-0, 5111209). Regal.

Donne, a Spirit in Conflict. Evelyn Hardy. LC 72-187484. 1942. lib. bdg. 35.00 (ISBN 0-8414-4993-7). Folcroft.

Donne at Sermons: A Christian Existential World. Gale H. Carrithers. LC 74-171183. 1972. 49.50 (ISBN 0-87395-122-0). State U NY Pr.

Donne, Milton, & the End of Humanist Rhetoric. Thomas O. Sloane. LC 83-24315. 1985. 38.50x (ISBN 0-520-05212-9). U of Cal Pr.

Don't Be a Puppet on a String. Bob Donahue & Marilyn Donahue. 1983. pap. 3.95 (ISBN 0-8423-0610-2). Tyndale.

Don't Bite My Finger, Look Where I Am Pointing. Bhagwan Shree Rajneesh. Ed. by Ma Prem Maneesha. LC 82-21602. (Initiation Talks Ser.). 232p. (Orig.). 1982. pap. 14.95 (ISBN 0-88050-550-8). Chidvilas Found.

Don't Blame God. Kenneth E. Hagin. 1979. pap. 0.50 mini bk. (ISBN 0-89276-056-7). Hagin Ministries.

Don't Blame It All on Adam. J. W. Jepson. 144p. 1984. pap. 4.95 (ISBN 0-87123-437-8, 210437). Bethany Hse.

Don't Cry for Anna. Mary Erickson. LC 85-10975. (Jesus, the Wonder Worker Ser.). 48p. 1985. pap. 3.95 (ISBN 0-89191-683-0, 56838, Chariot Bks). Cook.

Don't Drop the Sugar Bowl in the Sink! Birdie L. Etchison. LC 84-80057. 144p. 1984. pap. 4.50 (ISBN 0-88243-485-3, 02-0485). Gospel Pub.

Don't Fence Me In: An American Teenager in the Holocaust. 8th ed. Barry Spanjaard. Ed. by Bunnie J. Spanjaard. LC 81-68713. (Illus.). 224p. (Orig.). 1981. pap. 8.95 (ISBN 0-9607008-0-3). B & B Pub CA.

Don't Give Me That Stuff about the Birds & the Bees. Shirley Jones. LC 82-24610. (Outreach Ser.). 32p. 1983. pap. 0.99 (ISBN 0-8163-0518-8). Pacific Pr Pub Assn.

Don't Go Overseas until You've Read This Book. Neil Gallagher. LC 77-2643. 128p. 1977. pap. 5.95 (ISBN 0-87123-105-0, 210105). Bethany Hse.

Don't Just Do Something, Sit There. Bhagwan Shree Rajneesh. Ed. by Ma Prem Maneesha. (Initiation Talks Ser.). (Illus.). 370p. (Orig.). 1980. 25.50 (ISBN 0-88050-052-2). Chidvilas Found.

Don't Let Go! An Exposition of Hebrews. George M. Bowman. 170p. 1982. pap. 4.95 (ISBN 0-87552-121-5). Presby & Reformed.

Don't Let the Goats Eat the Loquat Trees. Thomas Hale, Jr. 304p. pap. 9.95 (ISBN 0-310-21301-0, 18318P). Zondervan.

Don't Let Your Conscience Be Your Guide. C. Ellis Nelson. LC 77-94430. 120p. 1978. pap. 2.95 (ISBN 0-8091-2099-2). Paulist Pr.

Don't Let Yourself Be Upset by the Sutra: Rather Upset the Sutra Yourself. Bhagwan Shree Rajneesh. Ed. by Swami Krishna Prabhu. LC 85-43054. (Initiation Talks Ser.). 560p. (Orig.). 1985. pap. 5.95 (ISBN 0-88050-584-2). Chidvilas Found.

Don't Limit God. Charles Hunter & Frances Hunter. 1976. pap. 4.95 (ISBN 0-917726-04-9). Hunter Bks.

Don't Look Before You Leap. Bhagwan Shree Rajneesh. Ed. by Rajneesh Foundation International. LC 83-3282. (Initiation Talks Ser.). 480p. (Orig.). 1983. pap. 4.95 (ISBN 0-88050-554-0). Chidvilas Found.

Don't Miss Your Miracle. Vance Havner. 74p. 1984. pap. 4.95 (ISBN 0-8010-4280-1). Baker Bk.

Don't Park Behind a Truck & Other Chapel Talks. Welsley W. Nelson. 40p. 1982. pap. 2.95 (ISBN 0-910452-51-2). Covenant.

Don't Teach! Let Me Learn about World War II, Adventure, Dreams & Superstition. Nina E. Crosby & Elizabeth H. Marten. (Don't Teach! Let Me Learn Ser.). (Illus.). 72p. (Orig.). 1984. 5.95 (ISBN 0-88047-044-5, 8411). DOK Pubs.

Don't Waste Your Sorrows. Paul Billheimer. 1977. pap. 4.95 (ISBN 0-87508-007-3). Chr Lit.

Don't Waste Your Sorrows. Paul E. Billheimer. LC 83-15821. 144p. (Orig.). 1983. pap. 4.95 (ISBN 0-87123-310-X, 210310). Bethany Hse.

Don't You Belong to Me? Monk of New Clairvaux. LC 79-88985. 180p. 1979. pap. 7.95 (ISBN 0-8091-2217-0). Paulist Pr.

Don't You Know? Haven't You Heard? R. Curtis Barger. Ed. by Raymond H. Woolsey. (Banner Ser.). 128p. (Orig.). 1985. pap. 5.95 (ISBN 0-8280-0278-9). Review & Herald.

Donum Gentilicium: New Testament Studies in Honor of David Daube. Ed. by E Bammel & C. K. Barrett. 1978. 59.00x (ISBN 0-19-826629-4). Oxford U Pr.

Doom & Warning All Men to the Judgement. Stephen Batman. LC 84-1441. 1984. Repr. of 1581 ed. 60.00x (ISBN 0-8201-1393-X). Schol Facsimiles.

Doom of the Dictators. Delber H. Elliot. LC 59-14581. pap. 23.00 (ISBN 0-317-07875-5, 2012820). Bks Demand UMI.

Doomsday Cult: A Study of Conversion, Proselytization, & Maintenance of Faith. enl. ed. John Lofland. LC 77-23028. 1981. 29.00 (ISBN 0-8290-1111-0); pap. text ed. 12.95x (ISBN 0-8290-0095-X). Irvington.

Doomsday or Deterence? On the Antinuclear Issue. Agnes Heller & Ferenc Feher. 192p. 1986. 35.00 (ISBN 0-87332-368-8); pap. 12.95 (ISBN 0-87332-369-6). M E Sharpe.

Door Ajar: Facing Death Without Fear. Josephine M. Benton. LC 65-16442. 1979. pap. 4.45 (ISBN 0-8298-0366-1). Pilgrim NY.

Door in the Wall: Story of Medieval London. Marguerite DeAngeli. LC 64-7025. (Illus.). 111p. 10.95a (ISBN 0-385-07283-X). Doubleday.

Door of Hope: A Century of the Baha'i Faith in the Holy Land. David S. Ruhe. 254p. 19.95 (ISBN 0-85398-149-3); pap. 13.50 (ISBN 0-85398-150-7). G Ronald Pub.

Door of Liberation. rev. ed. Geshe Wangal. 235p. 1979. pap. 4.75 (ISBN 0-932156-01-0). Lotsawa.

Doors of Perception. Aldous Huxley. Bd. with Heaven & Hell. pap. 5.95 (ISBN 0-06-090007-5, CN7, PL). Har-Row.

Doors of Perception. Aldous Huxley. 1970. pap. 3.95 (ISBN 0-06-080171-9, P171, PL). Har-Row.

Doors to the Sacred: A Historical Introduction to Sacraments in the Catholic Church. Joseph Martos. LC 82-45148. 552p. 1982. pap. 10.95 (ISBN 0-385-18180-9, Im). Doubleday.

Doorway Papers: Flood; Local or Global, Vol. 9. Arthur C. Custance. 312p. 1985. pap. text ed. 9.95 (ISBN 0-310-23041-1, 10667P). Zondervan.

Doorway to Meditation. Avery Brooke. 1976. pap. 6.95 (ISBN 0-8164-0903-X, HarpR). Har-Row.

Doorway to Silence: The Contemplative Use of the Rosary. Robert Llewelyn. 96p. (Orig.). 1987. pap. 5.95 (ISBN 0-8091-2900-0). Paulist Pr.

Doorways to Christian Growth. Jacqueline McMakin & Rhoda Nary. 300p. 1984. pap. 9.95 (ISBN 0-86683-818-X, HarpR). Har-Row.

Doorways to Discipleship. Winkie Pratney. LC 77-80008. 272p. 1977. pap. 5.95 (ISBN 0-87123-106-9, 210106). Bethany Hse.

Dorcas Sews for Others. Alberta P. Miller. (Arch Book Ser.: No. 21). pap. 0.99 (59-1285). Concordia.

Dore Bible Illustrations. Gustave Dore. (Illus.). 256p. 1974. pap. 8.95 (ISBN 0-486-23004-X). Dover.

Dore Lectures on Mental Science. Thomas Troward. 1909. 9.95 (ISBN 0-396-02063-1). Dodd.

Dori: The Life & Times of Theodor Herzl in Budapest, 1860-1878. Andrew Handler. LC 82-8509. (Judaic Studies). (Illus.). 176p. 1983. text ed. 16.95 (ISBN 0-8173-0125-9). U of Ala Pr.

Doric Hymns of Mesomedes. Bernhard Ziehn. 1979. pap. 1.75 (ISBN 0-911028-11-0). Newberry.

Dorie: The Girl Nobody Loved. Erwin Lutzer & Doris Van Stone. 1981. pap. 5.95 (ISBN 0-8024-2275-6). Moody.

Dormition of the Theotokos. Monks of New Skete Staff. Tr. by Reverend Laurence Mancuso. (Liturgical Music Series I: Great Feasts: Vol. 2). 40p. (Orig.). 1986. pap. text ed. 12.00 (ISBN 0-935129-03-0). Monks of New Skete.

Dorotheos of Gaza: Discourses & Sayings. Dorotheus Of Gaza. LC 77-4295. (Cistercian Studies Ser: No. 33). 1977. 7.00 (ISBN 0-87907-933-9). Cistercian Pubns.

Dorothy Day: A Biography. William D. Miller. LC 81-47428. (Illus.). 1984. pap. 10.95 (ISBN 0-06-065749-9, RD 501, HarpR). Har-Row.

Dorozhnij Posokh. V. Nikiforoff-Volgin. Tr. of Staff for the Road. 188p. 1971. pap. 6.00 (ISBN 0-317-30421-6). Holy Trinity.

Do's & Do Nots in Islam. A. R. Shad. Tr. of Al-Halal wal-Haram. 15.95 (ISBN 0-317-01588-5). Kazi Pubns.

Do's & Don'ts for an Overnight Stay in the Lion's Den. Ken Stewart. 31p. write for info. (ISBN 0-89274-043-4). Harrison Hse.

Dos Naturalezas del Creyente. 2nd ed. Guillermo Collingwood. Ed. by Gordon H. Bennett. Tr. by Sara Bautista from Eng. (Serie Diamante). Tr. of Believer's Two Natures. (Span., Illus.). 52p. 1982. pap. 0.85 (ISBN 0-942504-03-8). Overcomer Pr.

Doscientas Anecdotas e Ilustraciones. Dwight L. Moody. Orig. Title: Two Hundred Anecdotes & Illustrations. (Span.). 1983. pap. 3.25 (ISBN 0-8254-1491-1). Kregel.

Dossier Disease: The Truth About Government Agency False Files. pap. 6.00 (ISBN 0-915598-27-2). Church of Scient Info.

Dossier on the Ascension. Serapis Bey. 212p. 1979. pap. 5.95 (ISBN 0-916766-21-7). Summit Univ.

Dostoevsky. Andre P. Gide. LC 78-14443. 1979. Repr. of 1961 ed. lib. bdg. 22.50x (ISBN 0-313-21178-7, GIDO). Greenwood.

Dostoevsky & the Catholic Church. Denis Dirscherl. 179p. 1986. 12.95 (ISBN 0-8294-0502-X). Loyola.

Dostoevsky: His Life & Work. Ronald Hingley. 1978. 5.95 (ISBN 0-684-15916-3, ScribT); encore ed. 5.95 (ISBN 0-684-17232-1). Scribner.

Dostoevsky: His Life & Work. Konstantin Mochulsky. Tr. by Michael A. Minihan. 1967. pap. 14.50x (ISBN 0-691-01299-7). Princeton U Pr.

Dostoevsky in Russian & World Theatre. Vladimir Seduro. 1977. 17.50 (ISBN 0-8158-0347-8). Chris Mass.

Dostojino Jest', 8-mi glasov, znamennago rospjeva. Johann V. Gardner. Tr. of It is Truly Meet, Eight Tones, Znamenny Chant. 1967. pap. 3.00 (ISBN 0-317-30397-X). Holy Trinity.

Dostoyevsky & the Jews. David I. Goldstein. (University of Texas Press Slavic Ser.: No. 3). 256p. 1981. 20.00x (ISBN 0-292-71528-5). U of Tex Pr.

Dotsey's Diary: Her Days & Yours. Dotsey Welliver. (Orig.). 1979. pap. text ed. 3.95 (ISBN 0-89367-034-0). Light & Life.

Double Agent. Chris Panos. 1986. pap. 6.95 (ISBN 0-910311-43-9). Huntington Hse Inc.

Double Counterpoint & Canon. E. Prout. LC 68-25300. (Studies in Music, No. 42). 1969. Repr. of 1893 ed. lib. bdg. 48.95x (ISBN 0-8383-0312-9). Haskell.

Double Counterpoint & Canon. Ebenezer Prout. Repr. of 1893 ed. lib. bdg. 22.50x (ISBN 0-8371-2265-1, PRDC). Greenwood.

Double Cross. Denixe L. Carmody. 192p. (Orig.). 1986. pap. 10.95 (ISBN 0-8245-0736-3). Crossroad NY.

Double Cure, or Redemption Twofold. D. O. Teasley. 160p. pap. 1.50 large print (ISBN 0-686-29147-6). Faith Pub Hse.

Double Dying: Reflections on Holocaust Literature. Alvin H. Rosenfeld. LC 79-3006. 224p. 1980. 17.50x (ISBN 0-253-13337-8). Ind U Pr.

Double Image: Mutations of Christian Mythology in the Works of Four French Catholic Writers of Today & Yesterday. Rayner Heppenstall. LC 72-93063. 1969. Repr. of 1947 ed. 23.00 (ISBN 0-8046-0676-5, Pub. by Kennikat). Assoc Faculty Pr.

Double Mind. Don J. Kenyon. 95p. 1981. pap. 2.25 (ISBN 0-87509-288-8). Chr Pubns.

Double Yoke. Lillian E. Hansen. (Illus.). 268p. 1979. pap. 2.95 (ISBN 0-89216-020-9). Salvation Army.

Doubleday Christmas Treasury. Jane Olliver. LC 86-6297. 128p. 1986. 14.95 (ISBN 0-385-23409-0). Doubleday.

Doubleday Illustrated Children's Bible. Sandol Stoddard. LC 82-45340. (Illus.). 384p. 1984. deluxe ed. 22.95 (ISBN 0-385-18541-3). Doubleday.

Doubleday Illustrated Children's Bible. Sandol Stoddard. LC 82-45340. (Illus.). 384p. 1983. 14.95 (ISBN 0-385-18521-9). Doubleday.

Doubling Your Ability Through God. Michael Landsman. 58p. 1982. pap. 2.25 (ISBN 0-89274-266-6). Harrison Hse.

Doubt & Religious Commitment: The Role of the Will in Newman's Thought. M. Jamie Ferreira. 1980. 29.95x (ISBN 0-19-826654-5). Oxford U Pr.

Doubt: The Enemy of Faith. Ken Stewart. 32p. (Orig.). 1984. pap. 1.95 (ISBN 0-89274-034-5). Harrison Hse.

Doubting Conscience: Donne & the Poetry of Moral Argument. Dwight Cathcart. LC 74-78985. 1975. 10.00x (ISBN 0-472-08198-5). U of Mich Pr.

Doubting Thomas. Yvonne Patterson. (Arch Book Ser.: No. 18). 1981. pap. 0.99 (ISBN 0-570-06144-X, 59-1261). Concordia.

Doubt's Boundless Sea. Don C. Allen. 1979. 25.50 (ISBN 0-405-10577-0). Ayer Co Pubs.

Doubts, Loneliness & Rejection. Catherine D. Doherty. LC 81-19115. (Illus.). 93p. 1982. pap. 4.50 (ISBN 0-8189-0419-4). Alba.

Doug: Man & Missionary. Doug Abrahams. 1983. pap. 3.95 (ISBN 0-85363-151-4). OMF Bks.

Dove Songs. 88p. 1983. 1.95 (ISBN 0-934421-07-2). Presby Renewal Pubns.

Down among the Dead Men. Brian Peachment. 1974. pap. 1.60 (ISBN 0-08-017615-1). Pergamon.

Down-East Spirituals & Others: Three Hundred Songs Supplementary to the Author's "Spiritual Folk-Songs of Early America". Ed. by George P. Jackson. LC 74-34317. (Music Reprint Ser.). (Illus.). 296p. 1975. Repr. of 1943 ed. lib. bdg. 35.00 (ISBN 0-306-70666-0). Da Capo.

Down Gospel Byways: Eighteen Stories of People Who Met Jesus. Mary T. Donze. 80p. 1984. pap. 2.95 (ISBN 0-89243-198-9). Liguori Pubns.

Down Side of Up. Marian Greenberg. LC 86-80657. (Illus.). 264p. 1986. pap. 8.95 (ISBN 0-941404-40-4). Falcon Pr AZ.

Down to Earth: Studies in Christianity & Culture. 2nd ed. John R. Stott & Robert Coote. (Orig.). 1980. pap. 9.95 (ISBN 0-8028-1827-7). Eerdmans.

Downfall of the Dervishes. Ernest N. Bennett. LC 71-79818. (Illus.). Repr. of 1899 ed. 22.50x (ISBN 0-8371-1545-0, BEB&). Greenwood.

DownGrade Controversy. C. H. Spurgeon. 1978. pap. 2.75 (ISBN 0-686-00493-0). Pilgrim Pubns.

Downward Ascent. Edna Hong. LC 78-66942. 1979. pap. 5.95 (ISBN 0-8066-1679-2, 10-1955). Augsburg.

Doxology: The Praise of God in Worship, Doctrine & Life: A Systematic Theology. Geoffrey Wainwright. 1980. 35.00x (ISBN 0-19-520192-2); pap. 12.95 (ISBN 0-19-520433-6). Oxford U Pr.

Drachenkampfe: Untersuchungen Sagenkunde, Vol. 1-pt. 1. Ernst Siecke. Ed. by Kees W. Bolle. LC 77-79155. (Mythology Ser.). (Ger.). 1978. Repr. of 1907 ed. lib. bdg. 14.00x (ISBN 0-405-10564-9). Ayer Co Pubs.

Dragon Bound: Revelation Speaks to Our Times. Ernest L. Stoffel. 120p. (Orig.). 1981. pap. 5.25 (ISBN 0-8042-0227-3). John Knox.

Dragons, Gods & Spirits from Chinese Mythology. Tao T. Saunders. (World Mythologies Ser.). (Illus.). 132p. 1983. 16.95 (ISBN 0-8052-3799-2). Schocken.

Dragons of Rizvania. Carol Handy. (Illus.). 64p. 1984. 8.95 (ISBN 0-85398-192-2). G Ronald Pub.

Drama & Liturgy. Oscar Cargill. LC 73-86272. 1969. Repr. of 1930 ed. lib. bdg. 17.00x (ISBN 0-374-91292-0, Octagon). Hippocrene Bks.

Drama & Religion in the English Mystery Plays: A Re-Evaluation. Eleanor Prosser. 1961. 18.50x (ISBN 0-8047-0060-5). Stanford U Pr.

Drama Anthology. Ed. by Michael L. Sherer. (Orig.). 1987. pap. price not set (ISBN 0-89536-890-0, 7876). CSS of Ohio.

Drama as Mode of Religious Realization: The Vidaghamadhava of Rupa Gosvamin. Donna M. Wulff. (American Academy of Religion Academy Ser.: No. 43). 280p. 1985. 14.95 (ISBN 0-89130-608-0, 01 01 43). Scholars Pr GA.

Drama in the Church: Planning & Staging Dramatic Productions. Bev Johnson. 80p. 1983. pap. 8.95 (ISBN 0-8066-2027-7, 10-1976). Augsburg.

Drama of Christianity: An Interpretation of the Book of Revelation. S. L. Morris. 152p. 1982. pap. 4.95 (ISBN 0-8010-6136-9). Baker Bk.

Drama of Decision: Baptism in the New Testament. Oscar S. Brooks. 280p. 1986. 11.95 (ISBN 0-913573-40-X). Hendrickson MA.

Drama of Dissent: The Radical Poetics of Nonconformity, 1380-1590. Ritchie D. Kendall. LC 86-1289. (Studies in Religion). 286p. 1986. 27.50x (ISBN 0-8078-1700-7). U of NC Pr.

Drama of Incarnation. 4th ed. Flower A. Newhouse. 1948. 7.50 (ISBN 0-910378-04-5). Christward.

Drama Through the Church Year. Judy G. Smith. Ed. by Arthur L. Zapel. LC 84-61476. 164p. (Orig.). 1984. pap. 7.95 (ISBN 0-916260-26-7). Meriwether Pub.

Dramas De Navidad. Ed Garbee & Henry Van Dyke. Tr. by Soledad G. Prince & Guillermo Castellon. 1981. pap. 1.50 (ISBN 0-311-08214-9). Casa Bautista.

Dramas Navidenos para Jovenes y Adultos. (Span.). 64p. 1985. pap. 2.25 (ISBN 0-311-08227-0). Casa Bautista.

Dramas Navidenos para Ninos. 32p. (Orig.). 1985. pap. 1.25 (ISBN 0-311-08226-2). Casa Bautista.

Dramatic Associations of the Easter Sepulchre. Karl Young. 1977. lib. bdg. 59.95 (ISBN 0-8490-1732-7). Gordon Pr.

Dramatic Elements in American Indian Ceremonials. Virginia S. Heath. (American History & Americana Ser., No. 47). 1970. pap. 22.95x (ISBN 0-8383-0093-6). Haskell.

Dramatic Monologue Preaching. Alton H. McEachern. LC 82-82953. 1984. pap. 4.50 (ISBN 0-8054-2111-4). Broadman.

Dramatic Programs for Christmas. Cecil McGee. LC 74-93917. 1970. pap. 4.95 (ISBN 0-8054-7507-9). Broadman.

Dramatic Providence in Macbeth: A Study of Shakespeare's Tragic Theme of Humanity & Grace, with a Supplementary Essay on King Lear. George R. Ellict. LC 70-90501. Repr. of 1960 ed. lib. bdg. 27.50x (ISBN 0-8371-3091-3, ELMA). Greenwood.

Dramatic Uses of Biblical Allusions in Marlowe & Shakespeare. James H. Sims. LC 66-64917. (University of Florida Humanities Monographs: No. 24). 1966. pap. 3.50 (ISBN 0-8130-0206-0). U Presses Fla.

Dramatics for Creative Teaching. Samuel J. Citron. (Illus.). 1961. 9.50x (ISBN 0-8381-0212-3). United Syn Bk.

Dramatizaciones Infantiles Para Dias Especiales. Norma H. C. De Deiros. 96p. 1985. pap. 2.50 (ISBN 0-311-07606-8). Casa Bautista.

Dramatized New Testament. 1987. 34.95 (280006). Bethany Hse.

Drames liturgiques du moyen age, texte et musique. Ed. by Edmond De Coussemaker. (Fr., Lat., Illus.). 370p. 1964. Repr. of 1860 ed. 57.50x (ISBN 0-8450-1004-2). Broude.

Drat! Mythed Again: Second Thoughts on Utah. Steve Warren. (Illus.). 183p. 1986. pap. 10.95 (ISBN 0-938117-02-5). Altair Pub UT.

Draughts of Remembrance. Ann R. Colton. 177p. 1959. 8.95 (ISBN 0-917187-09-1). A R C Pub.

Dravidian Element in Indian Culture. G. Slater. (Illus.). 192p. 1986. Repr. 14.00X (ISBN 0-8364-1706-2, Pub. by Manohar India). South Asia Bks.

Draw Near the Cross: Lenten Devotions for Children & Those Who Love Them. Ellen Skatrud-Mickelson. 48p. (Orig.). 1985. pap. 2.95 (ISBN 0-8066-2200-8, 23-1604). Augsburg.

Draw Us Nearer to You, Lord. Linda J. Werman. Ed. by Michael L. Sherer. (Orig.). 1987. pap. 7.25 (ISBN 0-89536-858-7, 7817). CSS of Ohio.

Drawing down the Moon: Witches, Druids, Goddess-Worshippers, & Other Pagans in America Today. rev. & enl. ed. Margot Adler. LC 86-70551. 608p. 1987. pap. 14.95 (ISBN 0-8070-3253-0, BP 723). Beacon Pr.

Drawing Near Him with Confidence. Daughters of St. Paul. 1976. 3.95 (ISBN 0-8198-0403-7); pap. 2.95 (ISBN 0-8198-0404-5). Dghtrs St Paul.

Drawing Near Him with Confidence. Ed. by Daughters of St. Paul. (Chinese.). 1978. 3.95 (ISBN 0-8198-1801-1); pap. 2.95 (ISBN 0-8198-1802-X). Dghtrs St Paul.

Drawing Near with Daily Bible Readings & Prayer. Kenneth Boa & Max Anders. 1987. 16.95. Nelson.

Drawings by Old Masters at Christ Church, Oxford, 2 vols. James B. Shaw. (Illus.). 1976. 150.00x (ISBN 0-19-817323-7). Oxford U Pr.

Drawings: Eighty-First Exhibition by Artists of Chicago & Vicinity. Ed. by Lyn Delliquadri. 32p. (Orig.). 1985. pap. 6.95 (ISBN 0-86559-071-0). Art Inst Chi.

Drawings of Rembrandt, 2 Vols. Rembrandt. Ed. by Seymour Slive. (Illus.). pap. 12.50 ea.; Vol. 1. pap. (ISBN 0-486-21485-0); Vol. 2. pap. (ISBN 0-486-21486-9). Dover.

Drawings of Rembrandt. Hermansz Van Rijn Rembrandt. Ed. by Stephen Longstreet. (Master Draughtsman Ser). (Illus., Orig.). treasure trove bdg. 10.95x (ISBN 0-87505-029-8); pap. 4.95 (ISBN 0-87505-182-0). Borden.

DRE Reader: A Sourcebook in Education & Ministry. Ed. by Maria Harris. LC 80-52059. 192p. (Orig.). 1980. pap. 6.95 (ISBN 0-88489-124-0). St Marys.

Dreaded Gom-Boo: Or the Imaginary Desease That Religion Seeks to Cure. Da Free John. LC 83-70401. 400p. (Orig.). 1983. pap. 9.95 (ISBN 0-913922-74-9). Dawn Horse Pr.

Dream. Keith Miller. 128p. 1985. 8.95 (ISBN 0-8499-0462-5, 0462-5). Word Bks.

Dream by the River. rev. ed. William B. Faherty. (Illus.). 1981. Repr. of 1973 ed. 4.95 (ISBN 0-933150-21-0). River City MO.

Dream Incarnate. C. William Mensendiek. (Illus.). 136p. 1987. text ed. 12.95 (ISBN 0-8298-0715-2). Pilgrim NY.

Dream Lives On. Muriel F. Blackwell. LC 82-73865. 1984. 6.95 (ISBN 0-8054-4808-X, 4248-08). Broadman.

Dream of Christian Socialism: An Essay on its European Origins. Bernard Murchland. 74p. 1982. pap. 4.25 (ISBN 0-8447-3470-5). Am Enterprise.

Dream of Ravan. (Institute of World Culture Ser.). 99p. pap. 8.75 (ISBN 0-88695-015-5). Concord Grove.

Dream of Spring. Margaret C. Nickel. 256p. 1987. 12.95 (ISBN 0-89962-589-4). Todd & Honeywell.

Dream of Zorel. Jakob Lorber. Tr. by Violet Ozols from Ger. 124p. 1985. pap. cancelled (ISBN 0-934616-17-5). Valkyrie Pub Hse.

Dream That Never Dies: Boris de Zirkoff Speaks Out on Theosophy. Boris De Zirkoff. Ed. by W. Emmett Small. (Illus.). 242p. 1983. pap. 11.50 lexitone (ISBN 0-913004-45-6). Point Loma Pub.

Dream Your Way to Success. Nell Kennedy. LC 79-93290. 1980. pap. 4.95 (ISBN 0-88270-407-9). Bridge Pub.

Dreamcatcher: The Life of John Neihardt. Marion M. Brown & Jane K. Leech. 144p. (Orig.). 1983. pap. 6.95 (ISBN 0-687-11174-9). Abingdon.

Dreamers of Dreams: The Rise & Fall of 19th Century Idealism. Holbrook Jackson. LC 78-15808. 1978. Repr. of 1948 ed. lib. bdg. 35.00 (ISBN 0-8414-5410-8). Folcroft.

Dreaming & Achieving the Impossible. Aril Edvardsen & Madalene Harris. 1984. pap. 5.95 (ISBN 0-88419-192-3). Creation Hse.

Dreams & Spiritual Growth: A Christian Approach to Dreamwork. Louis M. Savary et al. LC 84-60566. 241p. pap. 9.95 (ISBN 0-8091-2629-X). Paulist Pr.

Dreams & Visions. Leigh Pope. 96p. (Orig.). 1982. pap. 7.95 (ISBN 0-85819-339-6, Pub. by JBCE). ANZ Religious Pubns.

Dreams for a Quiet Night. Ernest Pate. LC 83-73639. 80p. (Orig.). 1984. pap. 4.95 (ISBN 0-87516-535-4). De Vorss.

Dreams: God's Forgotten Language. John A. Sanford. (Crossroad Paperback Ser.). 224p. 1982. pap. 9.95 (ISBN 0-8245-0456-9). Crossroad NY.

Dreams, Illusion, & Other Realities. Wendy D. O'Flaherty. LC 83-17944. (Illus.). xvi, 366p. 1986. pap. 13.95 (ISBN 0-226-61855-2). U of Chicago Pr.

Dreams, Visions & Prophecies of Don Bosco. Eugene Brown. LC 86-13533. 344p. 1986. lib. bdg. 13.95 (ISBN 0-89944-085-1); pap. 9.95 (ISBN 0-89944-086-X). Don Bosco Multimedia.

Drevne-Russkii Dukhovnik: Izsledovnatie Po Istorii Tserkovnago Byta. S. Smirnov. 870p. Repr. of 1914 ed. text ed. 74.52 (ISBN 0-576-99178-3, Pub. by Gregg Intl Pubs England). Gregg Intl.

Drg-Drsya-Viveka. Tr. by Swami Nikhilananda. (Sanskrit & Eng.). pap. 1.50 (ISBN 0-87481-402-2). Vedanta Pr.

Drifted Astray: Returning the Church to Witness & Ministry. Ira Gallaway. 160p. (Orig.). 1983. pap. 6.95 (ISBN 0-687-11186-2). Abingdon.

Drink from the Deeper Wells. Stanley E. Sayers. 7.50 (ISBN 0-89225-079-8). Gospel Advocate.

Drinking at the Sources. Jacques Doukhan. 1981. 7.95 (ISBN 0-8163-0407-6). Pacific Pr Pub Assn.

Drinking Problem. John E. Keller. Ed. by William E. Hulme. LC 75-133036. (Pocket Counsel Bks.). 56p. 1971. pap. 2.50 (ISBN 0-8006-0155-6, 1-155). Fortress.

Droodles Ten Commandments Storybook. Ray Cioni & Sally Cioni. (Droodles Adventure Ser.). (Illus.). 64p. 1983. text ed. 8.95 (ISBN 0-89191-636-9). Cook.

Dropping Your Guard. Charles A. Swindoll. 1986. deluxe ed. 9.95 (ISBN 0-8499-3850-3). Word Bks.

Dropping Your Guard. Charles R. Swindoll. 224p. 1987. pap. 3.50 (ISBN 0-553-26324-2). Bantam.

Drudgerie Divine: The Rhetoric of God & Man in George Herbert. Edmund Miller. Ed. by James Hogg. (Elizabethan & Renaissance Studies). 250p. (Orig.). 1979. pap. 15.00 (ISBN 0-317-40130-0, Pub by Salzburg Studies). Longwood Pub Group.

Drug Abuse Education. Russell N. Cassel. 1970. 8.95 (ISBN 0-8158-0245-5). Chris Mass.

Druids. Thomas D. Kendrick. (Illus.). 227p. 1966. Repr. of 1927 ed. 32.50x (ISBN 0-7146-1485-8, BHA-01485, F Cass Co). Biblio Dist.

Druids: Magicians of the West. Ward Rutherford. 176p. 1984. pap. 7.95 (ISBN 0-85030-346-X). Newcastle Pub.

Druids: Magicians of the West. Ward Rutherford. LC 86-18803. 176p. 1986. lib. bdg. 19.95x (ISBN 0-8095-7007-6). Borgo Pr.

Drum & the Hoe: Life & Lore of the Haitian People. Harold Courlander. (California Library Reprint: No. 31). (Illus.). 436p. 1981. 40.00x (ISBN 0-520-02364-1); pap. 10.95 (ISBN 0-520-05449-0, CAL 731). U of Cal Pr.

Drums of ECK. Paul Twitchell. 1970. pap. 3.95 (ISBN 0-914766-04-X). IWP Pub.

Druze Faith. Sami N. Makarim. LC 73-19819. 1974. 25.00x (ISBN 0-88206-003-1). Caravan Bks.

Druzes & the Maronites Under the Turkish Rule from 1840 to 1860. Charles H. Churchill. LC 73-6273. (Middle East Ser.). Repr. of 1862 ed. 20.00 (ISBN 0-405-05329-0). Ayer Co Pubs.

Dry Bones. Stuart Briscoe. 168p. 1985. pap. 5.95 (ISBN 0-89693-522-1). Victor Bks.

Dry Bones Can Live Again. Robert E. Coleman. pap. 4.95 (ISBN 0-8007-5154-X, Power Bks). Revell.

Dry Those Tears. Robert A. Russell. 133p. 1975. pap. 4.95 (ISBN 0-87516-203-7). De Vorss.

Du Culte Des Dieux Fetiches, Ou Parallele de l'Ancienne Religion de l'Egypte Avec la Religion Actuelle de Nigrittie. Charles De Brosses. 286p. Repr. of 1760 ed. text ed. 62.10 (ISBN 0-576-12101-0, Pub. by Gregg Intl Pubs England). Gregg Intl.

Du'A-E-Kumail. Kumail I. Ziad. Tr. by N. Hussein Mardi from Arabic. 35p. Date not set. pap. 2.95 (ISBN 0-940368-75-7). Tahrike Tarsile Quran.

DU'A, on Wings of Prayer. rev. ed. Ruth Moffet. Ed. by Keven Brown. 96p. 1984. 11.95 (ISBN 0-87961-142-1); pap. 5.95 (ISBN 0-87961-143-X). Naturegraph.

Dual Ministry. M. Thomas Starkes. 1986. pap. 3.95 (ISBN 0-937931-01-2). Global TN.

Dualism. Herbert L. Beierle. 1979. 10.00 (ISBN 0-940480-06-9). U of Healing.

Duality of Human Existence: Isolation & Communion in Western Man. David Bakan. (Illus.). 1971. pap. 4.95x (ISBN 0-8070-2969-6, BP395). Beacon Pr.

DuBose Reader. William P. DuBose. Ed. by Donald S. Armentrout. LC 84-51878. 256p. 1984. pap. 10.95 (ISBN 0-918769-06-X). Univ South.

Dubuque District - A History: The United Methodist Church. Lyle Johnston. (Illus.). 128p. (Orig.). 1979. pap. 2.95 (ISBN 0-9616365-1-3). Grt Plains Emporium.

Ducrue's Account of Expulsion of the Jesuits from Lower California. Ernest Burrus. 1967. pap. 20.00 (ISBN 88-7041-502-3). Jesuit Hist.

Dukes & Poets of Ferrara: A Story in the Poetry, Religion & Politics of Fifteenth & Early Sixteenth Centuries. Edmund G. Gardner. LC 78-145033. xiv, 578p. 1972. Repr. of 1904 ed. 39.00x (ISBN 0-403-00776-3). Scholarly.

Dukhovnija Posjevi. Gregory Diachenko. Tr. of Spiritual Sowing. (Illus.). 475p. 1977. 20.00 (ISBN 0-317-30414-3); pap. 15.00 (ISBN 0-317-30415-1). Holy Trinity.

Dulcimer Hymn Book. Bud Ford & Donna Ford. 72p. 1979. wkbk 4.95 (ISBN 0-89228-054-9). Impact Bks MO.

Duncan's Masonic Ritual & Monitor. new ed. Malcolm C. Duncan. 288p. 1976. 10.95 (ISBN 0-679-50979-8); pap. 5.95. McKay.

Duns Scotus on the Will & Morality. Ed. by Allan B. Wolter. 1986. 54.95 (ISBN 0-8132-0622-7). Cath U Pr.

Duns Scotus: The Basic Principles of His Philosophy. Efrem Bettoni. Ed. by Berbardine Bonansea. LC 78-14031. 1979. Repr. of 1961 ed. lib. bdg. 35.00x (ISBN 0-313-21142-6, BEDS). Greenwood.

Dupolytheisme Romain: Considere dans ses rapports avec la philosophie grecque et la religion chertienne. Constant De Rebecque & Henri Benjamin. Ed. by Kees W. Bolle. LC 77-79118. (Mythology Ser.). (Fr.). 1978. Repr. of 1833 ed. lib. bdg. 59.50 (ISBN 0-405-10530-4). Ayer Co Pubs.

Durga Stotra. Sri Aurobindo. 31p. (Orig.). 1982. pap. 5.00 (ISBN 0-89744-235-0). Auromere.

Durham Book: Being the First Draft of the Revision of the Book of Common Prayer in 1661. Church of England Staff. Ed. by G. J. Cuming. LC 79-12674. 1979. Repr. of 1961 ed. lib. bdg. cancelled (ISBN 0-313-21481-6, CEBC). Greenwood.

During My Conversion. large print ed. Pearl Brians. 44p. 1984. pap. 8.00 (ISBN 0-914009-11-7). VHI Library.

Durkheim on Religion. Ed. by W. S. Pickering. 1983. pap. 10.95x (ISBN 0-7100-9074-9). Methuen Inc.

Durkheim's Sociology of Religion: Themes & Theories. W. S. Pickering. 576p. 1984. 45.00x (ISBN 0-7100-9298-9). Methuen Inc.

Dushepoljeznija Pouchjenija. St. Dorotheos of Gaza. Tr. of Spiritual Teachings. (Rus.). 300p. (Orig.). 1970. 15.00x (ISBN 0-88465-035-9); pap. 10.00x (ISBN 0-88465-036-7). Holy Trinity.

Dustmop Devotionals. Katharine W. Parrish. (Orig.). 1986. pap. 7.00 (ISBN 0-915541-09-2). Star Bks Inc.

Dutch Anabaptists: Stone Lectures Delivered at Princeton Theological Seminary, 1918-1919. Ed. by Henry E. Dosker. LC 83-45610. Date not set. Repr. of 1921 ed. 36.50 (ISBN 0-404-19828-7). AMS Pr.

Dutch Calvinism in Modern America: A History of a Conservative Subculture. James D. Bratt. (Illus.). 368p. (Orig.). 1984. pap. 13.95 (ISBN 0-8028-0009-2). Eerdmans.

Dutch Dissenters: A Critical Companion to Their History & Ideas with a Bibliographical Survey of Recent Research Pertaining to the Early Reformation in the Netherlands. I. B. Horst. (Kerhistorische Bijdragen Ser.: No. 13). vii, 233p. 1986. 39.25 (ISBN 90-04-07454-6, Pub. by E J Brill). Heinman.

Dutch Oracle. John Booker. (Illus.). 224p. 1981. pap. 5.95 (ISBN 0-931116-01-5). Ralston-Pilot.

Dutch Puritanism. Keith Sprunger. (Studies in the History of Christian Thought: Vol. 31). 485p. 1982. text ed. 90.00x (ISBN 90-04-06793-0, Pub. by E J Brill Holland). Humanities.

Dutch Reformed Church in the American Colonies. DeJong. LC 78-17216. 1978. pap. 8.95 (ISBN 0-8028-1741-6). Eerdmans.

Duties Beyond Borders: On the Limits & Possibilities of Ethical International Politics. Stanley Hoffmann. LC 81-2401. 288p. 1981. 22.00x (ISBN 0-8156-0167-0); pap. 10.95x (ISBN 0-8156-0168-9). Syracuse U Pr.

Duties of Parents & Children to One Another. St. John Chrysostom. pap. 0.25 (ISBN 0-686-17310-4). Eastern Orthodox.

Duties of Parish Priests in the Russian Orthodox Church. Tr. by R. W. Blackmore. Repr. of 1845 ed. 15.00 (ISBN 0-686-01291-7). Eastern Orthodox.

Duties of the Heart, Chovoth Halevovoth, 2 vols. 1978. Set. pap. 11.95 (ISBN 0-87306-161-6). Feldheim.

Duty or Pleasure? A New Appraisal of Christian Ethics. Albert Ple. 208p. 1986. 22.95 (ISBN 0-913729-24-8); pap. 12.95 (ISBN 0-913729-25-6). Paragon Hse.

Dwell in Peace. Ronald C. Arnett. 156p. (Orig.). 1980. pap. 7.95 (ISBN 0-87178-199-9). Brethren.

Dweller on Two Planets. Phylos. LC 80-8896. (Harper's Library of Spiritual Wisdom). 424p. 1981. pap. 10.95 (ISBN 0-06-066565-3, CN 4010, HarpR). Har-Row.

Dweller on Two Planets, or the Dividing of the Way, Vol. 12. Phylos the Thibetan. As told to Frederick S. Oliver. LC 73-94420. (Spiritual Science Library). (Illus.). 432p. 1983. lib. bdg. 18.00 (ISBN 0-89345-039-1). Garber Comm.

Dwellers on the Nile: The Life, History, Religion, & Literature of the Ancient Egyptians. E. Wallis Budge. (Illus.). 326p. 1977. pap. 5.95 (ISBN 0-486-23501-7). Dover.

Dwelling in Scullerland. Larry W. Gates. LC 85-40200. 105p. (Orig.). 1985. pap. text ed. 8.95 (ISBN 0-938232-68-1). Winston-Derek.

Dyaloge Descrybyng the Orygynall Ground of These Lutheran Saccyons, That Is, Faccyons. William Barlow. LC 74-80161. (English Experience Ser.: No. 641). 200p. 1974. Repr. of 1531 ed. 13.00 (ISBN 90-221-0641-1). Walter J Johnson.

Dyaloge of Syr T. More...Wherein Be Treatyd Dyvers Maters, As of the Veneration & Worshyp of Ymagys. Sir Thomas More. LC 74-28873. (English Experience Ser.: No. 752). 1975. Repr. of 1529 ed. 26.50 (ISBN 90-221-0752-3). Walter J Johnson.

Dybbuk. Gershon Winkler. (Illus.). 1981. 13.95 (ISBN 0-910818-38-X); pap. 9.95 (ISBN 0-910818-37-1). Judaica Pr.

Dying, Death & Grief. Madelon Brunson. 1978. pap. 4.50 (ISBN 0-8309-0223-6). Herald Hse.

Dying, Death, & Grief: A Critically Annotated Bibliography & Source Book of Thanatology & Terminal Care. M. A. Simpson. LC 78-27273. 300p. 1979. 35.00x (ISBN 0-306-40147-9, Plenum Pr). Plenum Pub.

Dying for a Drink: What You Should Know about Alcoholism. Anderson Spickard & Barbara R. Thompson. 192p. 1985. 11.95 (ISBN 0-8499-0467-6, 0467-6). Word Bks.

Dying to Live. rev. ed. J. R. Miller. Ed. by Joan Zodhiates. LC 79-51337. Orig. Title: Making the Most of Life. (Illus.). 147p. 1980. pap. 3.95 (ISBN 0-89957-045-3). AMG Pubs.

Dying to Live. Jessie Penn-Lewis. 1962. pap. 2.25 (ISBN 0-87508-995-X). Chr Lit.

Dynamic & Inspirational Sermons for Today. Ralph L. Greene. 128p. 1980. 7.95 (ISBN 0-89962-021-3). Todd & Honeywell.

Dynamic Aspects of Inspiration. Sunnie D. Kidd & James W. Kidd. 38p. (Orig.). 1982. pap. text ed. 3.50 (ISBN 0-910727-02-3). Golden Phoenix.

Dynamic Bible Teaching with Overhead Transparencies. Terry Hall. 80p. 1985. pap. 9.95 (ISBN 0-89191-584-2). Cook.

Dynamic Character of Christian Culture: Essays on Dawsonian Themes. Ed. by Peter J. Cataldo. 242p. (Orig.). 1984. lib. bdg. 26.00 (ISBN 0-8191-3959-9, Soc Christ Cult); pap. text ed. 11.75 (ISBN 0-8191-3960-2). U Pr of Amer.

Dynamic Children's Sermons. Donald R. Brewer. (Orig.). 1984. pap. 3.95 (ISBN 0-937172-58-8). JLJ Pubs.

Dynamic Christian Fellowship. rev. ed. LeRoy J. Day. (Orig.). pap. 2.95 (ISBN 0-8170-0226-X). Judson.

Dynamic Classroom. Billie C. Davis. LC 86-83084. (Sunday School Staff Training Text for 1988). 144p. (Orig.). 1987. pap. 2.95 (ISBN 0-88243-798-4). Gospel Pub.

Dynamic Difference: How the Holy Spirit Can Add an Exciting New Dimension to Your Life. David Petts. LC 77-91483. 64p. 1978. pap. 0.95 (ISBN 0-88243-484-5, 02-0484, Radiant Bks). Gospel Pub.

Dynamic Discipleship. Kenneth C. Kinghorn. 160p. 1975. pap. 4.95 (ISBN 0-8010-5357-9). Baker Bk.

Dynamic Discipleship. Paul W. Powell. LC 84-11388. 1984. pap. 5.95 (ISBN 0-8054-5004-1). Broadman.

Dynamic Evangelism. Luisa J. Walker. 1986. write for info. (ISBN 0-8297-0737-9). Life Pubs Intl.

Dynamic Fingertip Devotions. Amy Bolding. (Paperback Program Ser). 1977. pap. 3.95 (ISBN 0-8010-0708-9). Baker Bk.

Dynamic Idealism. Alfred H. Lloyd. LC 75-3243. Repr. of 1898 ed. 17.00 (ISBN 0-404-59233-3). AMS Pr.

Dynamic Judaism: The Essential Writings of Mordecai M. Kaplan. Mordecai M. Kaplan. Ed. by Emanuel S. Goldsmith & Mel Scult. LC 85-2391. 256p. (Orig.). 1985. text ed. 22.00x (ISBN 0-8052-3997-9); pap. 12.95 (ISBN 0-8052-0786-4). Schocken.

Dynamic Laws of Healing. Catherine Ponder. 1972. pap. 6.95 (ISBN 0-87516-156-1). De Vorss.

Dynamic of the Printed Page in Evangelical Free Church History. Roy A. Thompson. LC 82-69760. (Heritage Ser.: Vol. 4). 176p. 1981. 8.95 (ISBN 0-911802-53-3). Free Church Pubns.

Dynamic Personal Bible Study: Principles of Inductive Bible Study Based on the Life of Abraham. Cyril J. Barber. LC 81-8443. 1981. pap. 4.95 (ISBN 0-87213-023-1). Loizeaux.

Dynamic Praying for Exciting Results. Russ Johnston & Maureen Rank. 1982. pap. 3.95 (ISBN 0-8423-0611-0); pap. 2.95 leader's guide (ISBN 0-8423-0612-9). Tyndale.

Dynamic Preaching. Chevis F. Horne. LC 82-70871. (Orig.). 1983. pap. 6.95 (ISBN 0-8054-2110-6). Broadman.

Dynamic Psychology of Early Buddhism. Rune Johansson. (Scandinavian Institute of Asian Studies Monographs: No. 37). (Illus.). 1979. pap. text ed. 15.00x (ISBN 0-7007-0114-1). Humanities.

Dynamic Religious Movements: Case Studies of Rapidly Growing Religious Movement Around the World. Ed. by David J. Hesselgrave. 1978. 9.95 (ISBN 0-8010-4130-9). Baker Bk.

Dynamic Stillness: A Practice Guide to Kundalini Yoga. Swami Chetanananda. 208p. 1987. pap. 9.95 (ISBN 0-915801-06-X). Rudra Pr.

Dynamic Thought. limited ed. Henry T. Hamblin. 8.00 (ISBN 0-911662-22-7). Yoga.

Dynamic Transcendence: The Correlation of Confessional Heritage & Contemporary Experience in Biblical Model of Divine Activity. Paul D. Hanson. LC 78-54552. pap. 27.30 (2026940). Bks Demand UMI.

Dynamic Truths for the Spirit-Filled Life. C. S. Lovett. 1973. pap. 5.95 (ISBN 0-938148-13-3). Personal Christianity.

Dynamic Voice of Vatican II. Ed. by Marina E. Ruffolo. 1977. 4.50 (ISBN 0-8198-0405-3); pap. 2.95 (ISBN 0-8198-0406-1). Dghtrs St Paul.

Dynamic Way of Meditation. Dhiravamsa. 160p. 1983. pap. 8.95 (ISBN 0-85500-163-1). Newcastle Pub.

Dynamic Word: New Testament Insights for Contemporary Christians. Karl P. Donfried. LC 80-8905. 244p. 1981. 12.95 (ISBN 0-06-061945-7, HarpR). Har-Row.

Dynamics for Living. Charles Fillmore. 1967. 5.95 (ISBN 0-87159-025-5). Unity School.

Dynamics of a City Church. Joseph H. Fichter. 26.50 (ISBN 0-405-10829-X, 11836). Ayer Co Pubs.

Dynamics of Christian Discipleship. Hollis L. Green. 112p. 1962. 5.25 (ISBN 0-87148-251-7); pap. 4.25 (ISBN 0-87148-252-5). Pathway Pr.

Dynamics of Christian Living for Women. Sue Burnham. LC 81-67598. 50p. (Orig.). (YA) 1981. pap. 2.95 (ISBN 0-940386-00-3). Dynamics Chr Liv.

Dynamics of Church Growth. Ron Jenson & Jim Stevens. 280p. 1981. pap. 8.95 (ISBN 0-8010-5161-4). Baker Bk.

Dynamics of Discipleship Training. Gary W. Kuhne. 1977. pap. 5.95 (ISBN 0-310-26961-X, 12311P). Zondervan.

Dynamics of Discipling. Don Wellman et al. 210p. 1984. spiral bd. 9.95 (ISBN 0-8341-0918-2). Beacon Hill.

Dynamics of Evangelism. Dean Fetterhoff. pap. 1.00 (ISBN 0-88469-019-9). BMH Bks.

Dynamics of Faith. Paul Tillich. pap. 6.95x (ISBN 0-06-130042-X, TB42, Torch). Har-Row.

Dynamics of Human Rights in United States Foreign Policy. Ed. by Natalie K. Hevener. LC 79-66435. 375p. 1981. pap. 14.95x. Transaction Bks.

Dynamics of Hutterite Society: An Analytical Approach. Karl A. Peter. 250p. 1986. 27.50x (ISBN 0-88864-108-7, Univ of Atla Pr Canada); pap. 16.95x (ISBN 0-88864-109-5). U of Nebr Pr.

Dynamics of Intimacy with God. Donald G. Mostrom. 158p. 1983. pap. 5.95 (ISBN 0-8423-1701-5). Tyndale.

Dynamics of Personal Follow-up. Gary W. Kuhne. 192p. 1976. pap. 5.95 (ISBN 0-310-26951-2, 12310P). Zondervan.

Dynamics of Religion: Meaning & Change in Religious Traditions. Peter Slater. LC 78-4426. 1978. pap. 6.95x (ISBN 0-685-53934-2, RD 280, HarpR). Har-Row.

Dynamics of Salvation: A Study in Gregory of Nazianzus. Donald F. Winslow. LC 79-89897. (Patristic Mongraph: No. 7). 1979. pap. 8.50 (ISBN 0-915646-06-4). Phila Patristic.

Dynamics of Spiritual Gifts. William McRae. 144p. 1983. pap. 4.95 (ISBN 0-310-29091-0). Zondervan.

Dynamics of Spiritual Gifts. William J. McRae. 160p. 1976. pap. 2.95 (ISBN 0-310-29092-9). Zondervan.

Dynamics of Spiritual Life. Richard Lovelace. LC 78-24757. 1979. pap. 11.95 (ISBN 0-87784-626-X). Inter-Varsity.

Dynamics of Spiritual Self-Direction. Adrian Van Kaam. 24.95 (ISBN 0-87193-122-2). Dimension Bks.

Dynamics of the Lower Self. John-Roger. LC 77-70406. 1976. pap. 5.00 (ISBN 0-914829-10-6). Baraka Bk.

Dynamics of the Psychic World: Comments by H. P. Blavatsky on Magic, Mediumship, Psychism, & the Powers of the Spirit. Helena P. Blavatsky. LC 72-78193. 150p. (Orig.). 1972. pap. 1.95 (ISBN 0-8356-0429-2, Quest). Theos Pub Hse.
Dynamics of Yoga, Vol. I. M. P. Pandit. 182p. 1979. 9.95 (ISBN 0-941524-05-1). Lotus Light.
Dynamics of Yoga, Vol. II. M. P. Pandit. 1979. 9.95 (ISBN 0-941524-06-X). Lotus Light.
Dynamics of Yoga, Vol. III. M. P. Pandit. 164p. 1980. 10.95 (ISBN 0-941524-07-8). Lotus Light.
Dynamism of Biblical Tradition. Ed. by Pierre Benoit et al. LC 67-15983. (Concilium Ser.: Vol. 20). 226p. 1967. 7.95 (ISBN 0-8091-0035-5). Paulist Pr.
Dzog Chen & Zen. Namkhai Norbu. Ed. by Kennard Lipman. Tr. by Namkhai Norbu from Ital. (Illus.). 52p. (Orig.). 1987. pap. 5.00 (ISBN 0-931892-08-2). B Dolphin Pub.

E

E. A. Gordon - Pioneer in East-West Religious Understanding. Manly P. Hall. pap. 2.50 (ISBN 0-89314-377-4). Philos Res.
E Ele Concedeu Uns Para Mestres. D. V. Hurst. (Portuguese Bks.). Tr. of And He Gave Teachers. 1979. 2.40 (ISBN 0-8297-0838-3). Life Pubs Intl.
E. K.'s Commentary on the Shepheards Calender. Peter S. Cornelius. Ed. by James Hogg. (Elizabethan & Renaissance Studies). 111p. (Orig.). 1974. pap. 15.00 (ISBN 3-7052-0679-6, Pub. by Salzburg Studies). Longwood Pub Group.
E. M. E. T. T. A Step-by-Step Guide to Emotional Maturity Established Through Torah. Miriam Adahan. 1987. 14.95 (ISBN 0-87306-410-0). Feldheim.
E-Meter Essentials. L. Ron Hubbard. 8.75 (ISBN 0-686-30795-X). Church Scient NY.
E. T. Christmas: Two Nativity Dramas. Edward S. Long. 1985. 3.25 (ISBN 0-89536-763-7, 5870). CSS of Ohio.
E. Y. Mullins Lectures on Preaching with Reference to the Aristotelian Triad. Don M. Aycock. LC 79-6080. 113p. 1980. text ed. 20.50 (ISBN 0-8191-0981-9); pap. text ed. 9.25 (ISBN 0-8191-0982-7). U Pr of Amer.
Each Day a New Beginning. 400p. (Orig.). 1985. pap. 5.95 (ISBN 0-86683-501-6, HarpR). Har-Row.
Each New Day. Corrie T. Boom. (Christian Library). 1985. Repr. of 1980 ed. 6.95 (ISBN 0-916441-20-2). Barbour & Co.
Each New Day. Corrie Ten Boom. 1977. pap. 3.50 (ISBN 0-8007-8403-0, Spire Bks). Revell.
Each One a Minister. Bill Carter. LC 86-71722. 72p. (Orig.). 1986. pap. 4.95 (ISBN 0-88177-037-X, DR037B). Discipleship Res.
Each to Her Post. Phyllis Thompson. 1982. pap. 3.95 (ISBN 0-340-26933-2). OMF Bks.
Eadwine's Canterbury Psalter from Ms of Trinity College. Ed. by F. Harsley. (EETS, OS Ser.: No. 92). Repr. of 1889 ed. 50.00 (ISBN 0-527-00091-4). Kraus Repr.
Eagle & the Butterfly. Mary Moline. (Illus.). 57p. (Orig.). 1986. pap. 8.00 (ISBN 0-913444-10-3). Rumbleseat.
Eagle's Chase: The Agony of Success. John A. Leahy. LC 85-21644. (Illus.). 192p. 1986. 13.95 (ISBN 0-88280-114-7). ETC Pubns.
Earl Nightingale's Greatest Discovery: The Strangest Secret...Revisited. Earl Nightingale. (PMA Ser.). 1987. 17.95 (ISBN 0-396-08928-3). Dodd.
Earliest Christianity: A History of the Period A.D. 30-150, 2 vols. Johannes Weiss. Ed. by F. C. Grant. 24.00 set (ISBN 0-8446-0959-5). Peter Smith.
Earliest Life of Gregory the Great. Ed. by Bertram Colgrave. 192p. 1985. 37.50 (ISBN 0-521-30924-7); pap. 12.95 (ISBN 0-521-31384-8). Cambridge U Pr.
Earliest Saint's Lives Written in England. Bertram Colgrave. 1978. Repr. of 1958 ed. lib. bdg. 12.50 (ISBN 0-8495-0739-1). Arden Lib.
Earliest Saints Lives Written in England. Bertram Colgrave. LC 72-193175. 1958. lib. bdg. 12.50 (ISBN 0-8414-2353-9). Folcroft.
Earliest Sources for the Life of Jesus. F. Crawford Burkitt. 1977. lib. bdg. 59.95 (ISBN 0-8490-1736-X). Gordon Pr.
Early Abbasid Caliphate: A Political History. Hugh Kennedy. 238p. 1981. 28.50x (ISBN 0-389-20018-2, 06791). B&N Imports.
Early Adventist Educators. Ed. by George R. Knight. LC 83-71043. (Illus.). xvi, 250p. 1983. 12.95 (ISBN 0-943872-60-X). Andrews Univ Pr.
Early American Christianity. Bill J. Leonard. LC 83-71489. 1984. pap. 10.95 (ISBN 0-8054-6578-2). Broadman.
Early Anabaptists. 2nd, rev. ed. Eberhard Arnold. Ed. by Hutterian Brethren. LC 84-14259. Tr. of History of the Baptizers Movement. (Ger.). 64p. 1984. pap. 4.00 (ISBN 0-87486-192-6). Plough.
Early Arianism: A View of Salvation. Robert C. Gregg & Dennis E. Groh. LC 79-7379. 224p. 1981. 5.00 (ISBN 0-8006-0576-4, 1-576). Fortress.
Early Baptist Church West of the Mississippi: Calvary at Bayou Chicot; A History & Transcript of the Early Records. Jane McManus. 1986. 30.00. Banner Pr AL.
Early Bible Illustrations: A Short Study Based on Some Fifteenth & Early Sixteenth Century Printed Texts. James Strachan. LC 58-571. pap. 44.80 (ISBN 0-317-10120-X, 2050748). Bks Demand UMI.
Early Biblical Interpretation. James L. Kugel & Rowan A. Greer. LC 85-26397. (Library of Early Christianity: Vol. 3). 214p. 1986. 16.95 (ISBN 0-664-21907-1). Westminster.
Early Buddhism & Christianity. Yu Chai-Shin. xv, 241p. 1986. Repr. 17.50 (ISBN 81-208-0050-8, Pub. by Motilal Banarsidass). South Asia Bks.
Early Buddhism & Christianity. Chai-Shin Yu. 1981. 20.00x (ISBN 0-8364-0797-0, Pub. by Motilal Banarsidass). South Asia Bks.
Early Buddhism & Its Origin. V. P. Varma. 1973. text ed. 20.00x. Coronet Bks.
Early Buddhist Mythology. J. R. Halder. 1977. 15.00x (ISBN 0-88386-998-5). South Asia Bks.
Early Buddhist Philosophy in the Light of the Four Noble Times. Alfonso Verdu. 241p. 1985. 24.00 (ISBN 81-208-0001-X, Pub. by Motilal Banarsidass India). Orient Bk Dist.
Early Buddhist Philosophy in the Light of the Four Noble Truths. Alfonso Verdu. 220p. 1986. 22.50X (ISBN 0-317-53523-4, Pub. by Motilal Banarsidass). South Asia Bks.
Early Buddhist Rock Temples. Vidya Dehejia. LC 75-158835. (Studies in Ancient Art & Archaeology Ser.). (Illus.). 193p. 1972. 42.50x (ISBN 0-8014-0651-X). Cornell U Pr.
Early Buddhist Scriptures. Tr. by E. J. Thomas. lib. bdg. 79.95 (ISBN 0-87968-563-8). Krishna Pr.
Early Buddhist Scriptures. Edward J. Thomas. LC 78-70129. Repr. of 1935 ed. 31.00 (ISBN 0-404-17388-8). AMS Pr.
Early Buddhist Theory of Knowledge. K. Jayatilleke. 1981. 22.00x (ISBN 0-8364-0795-4, Pub. by Motilal Banarsidass). South Asia Bks.
Early Burials from the Agora Cemeteries. Sara A. Immerwahr. (Excavations of the Athenian Agora Picture Bks.: No. 13). (Illus.). 1973. pap. 3.00x (ISBN 0-87661-613-9). Am Sch Athens.
Early Catholic Americana. Wilfrid Parsons. LC 77-91536. 1977. Repr. of 1939 ed. lib. bdg. 25.00 (ISBN 0-89341-469-7). Longwood Pub Group.
Early Child Care in Israel. Rapaport et al. (International Monograph on Early Child Care). 212p. 1976. 38.50 (ISBN 0-677-05270-7). Gordon & Breach.
Early Christian & Byzantine Architecture. William Macdonald. LC 62-7531. (Great Ages of World Architecture Ser). 128p. 1963. 7.95 (ISBN 0-8076-0176-4); pap. 7.95 (ISBN 0-8076-0338-4). Braziller.
Early Christian & Byzantine Art. John Beckwith. (Pelican History of Art Ser.). 1980. pap. 18.95 (ISBN 0-14-056133-1, Pelican). Penguin.
Early Christian & Byzantine Political Philosophy: Origins & Background, 2 vols. Francis Dvornik. LC 67-4089. (Dumbarton Oaks Studies: Vol. 9). 975p. 1966. 50.00x (ISBN 0-88402-016-9). Dumbarton Oaks.
Early Christian Art. Frederik Van Der Meer. Tr. by Peter Brown & Friedl Brown. LC 67-25083. pap. 50.00 (ISBN 0-317-28145-3, 2024099). Bks Demand UMI.
Early Christian Art in Ireland. Margaret Stokes. LC 70-39211. (Select Bibliobraphies Reprint Ser.). Repr. of 1911 ed. 23.50 (ISBN 0-8369-6813-1). Ayer Co Pubs.
Early Christian Attitude to War: A Contribution to the History of Christian Ethics. C. John Cadoux. 304p. 1982. pap. 9.95 (ISBN 0-8164-2416-0, HarpR). Har-Row.
Early Christian Attitude Toward War. C. John Cadoux. 69.95 (ISBN 0-87968-198-5). Gordon Pr.
Early Christian Biographies: Lives of St. Cyprian, St. Ambrose, St. Augustine, St. Anthony, St. Paul the first Hermit, St. Hilarion, Malchus, St. Epiphanius. LC 64-19949. (Fathers of the Church Ser: Vol. 15). 407p. 1952. 21.95x (ISBN 0-8132-0015-6). Cath U Pr.
Early Christian Books. William J. Ferrar. 1919. Repr. 20.00 (ISBN 0-8274-2211-3). R West.
Early Christian Books: A Short Introduction to Christian Literature to the Middle of the Second Century. William J. Ferrar. 1979. Repr. of 1919 ed. lib. bdg. 20.00 (ISBN 0-8495-1637-4). Arden Lib.
Early Christian Church. J. G. Davies. (Twin Brooks Ser.). 1980. pap. 9.95 (ISBN 0-8010-2906-6). Baker Bk.
Early Christian Church. John G. Davies. LC 75-3989. (Illus.). 314p. 1976. Repr. of 1965 ed. lib. bdg. 24.00x (ISBN 0-8371-7696-4, DAECC). Greenwood.
Early Christian Creeds. 3rd ed. J. N. Kelly. 446p. 1981. text ed. 16.95 (ISBN 0-582-49219-X). Longman.
Early Christian Doctrines. rev. ed. J. N. Kelly. LC 58-12933. 1978. pap. 10.95xi (ISBN 0-06-064334-X, RD 233, HarpR). Har-Row.
Early Christian Epoch. Compiled by Association for Research & Enlightenment, Readings Research Dept. (Library: Vol. 6). (Illus.). 593p. 1976. 10.95 (ISBN 0-87604-089-X). ARE Pr.
Early Christian Fathers. Ed. by Cyril C. Richardson. (Library of Christian Classics: Vol. 1). 1970. pap. 9.95 (ISBN 0-02-088980-1, Collier). Macmillan.
Early Christian Fathers: A Selection from the Writings of the Fathers from St. Clement of Rome to St. Athanasius. Tr. by Henry Bettenson. 1969. pap. 9.95x (ISBN 0-19-283009-0). Oxford U Pr.
Early Christian Interpretations of History. Robert L. Milburn. LC 79-21671. 1980. Repr. of 1954 ed. lib. bdg. 22.50x (ISBN 0-313-22157-X, MIEA). Greenwood.
Early Christian Irish Art. rev. ed. Francoise Henry. (Illus.). 128p. 1979. pap. 6.95 (ISBN 0-85342-462-4, Pub. by Mercier Pr Ireland). Irish Bks Media.
Early Christian Life As Reflected in Its Literature. Donald W. Riddle. 256p. 1981. Repr. of 1936 ed. lib. bdg. 40.00 (ISBN 0-8495-4646-X). Arden Lib.
Early Christian Rhetoric: The Language of the Gospel. Amos N. Wilder. LC 78-131949. 1971. 10.00x (ISBN 0-674-22002-1). Harvard U Pr.
Early Christian Spirituality. Ed. by Charles Kannengiesser. Tr. by Pamela Bright from Lat. & Gr. LC 86-45226. (Sources of Early Christian Thought). 144p. 1986. pap. 7.95 (ISBN 0-8006-1416-X). Fortress.
Early Christian Syrian Martyrology: The Names of Our Lords the Confessors & Victors & the Days on Which They Gained Their Crowns. William Wright. pap. 5.95 (ISBN 0-317-11387-9). Eastern Orthodox.
Early Christian Thoughts & the Classical Tradition: Studies in Justin, Clement & Origan. Henry Chadwick. 182p. 1984. pap. text ed. 13.95x (ISBN 0-19-826673-1). Oxford U Pr.
Early Christian, Viking & Romanesque Art. U. O'Meadhra. (Illus.). 260p. (Orig.). 1979. pap. text ed. 30.00x (ISBN 91-22-00270-7, Pub. by Almqvist & Wiksell). Coronet Bks.
Early Christian Worship. Oscar Cullmann. LC 78-6636. 126p. 1978. pap. 6.95 (ISBN 0-664-24220-0). Westminster.
Early Christian Writings. Apostolic Fathers. Tr. by Maxwell Staniforth. (Gr.). 320p. 1986. 16.95 (ISBN 0-88029-074-9, Pub. by Dorset). Hippocrene Bks.
Early Christian Writings: The Apostolic Fathers. Tr. by Maxwell Staniforth. (Classics Ser.). 240p. 1968. pap. 5.95 (ISBN 0-14-044197-2). Penguin.
Early Christian Writings: The Apostolic Fathers. Tr. by Maxwell Staniforth. 208p. 1987. 5.95 (ISBN 0-14-044475-0). Penguin.
Early Christianity. Roland H. Bainton. LC 83-25150. 188p. 1984. pap. text ed. 7.50 (ISBN 0-89874-735-X). Krieger.
Early Christianity. S. B. Slack. 94p. 1914. 0.95 (ISBN 0-317-40436-9). Open Court.
Early Christianity & Greek Paideia. Werner Jaeger. 160p. 1985. pap. text ed. 5.95x (ISBN 0-674-22052-8, Belknap Pr). Harvard U Pr.
Early Christianity Outside the Roman Empire: Two Lectures Delivered at Trinity College, Dublin. Francis C. Burkitt. LC 82-45806. 1983. Repr. of 1899 ed. 18.00 (ISBN 0-404-62375-1). AMS Pr.
Early Christians: After the Death of the Apostles. Eberhard Arnold. LC 70-115839. (Illus.). 1970. 13.00 (ISBN 0-87486-110-1). Plough.
Early Christians in Rome. H. D. Spence-Jones. 1977. lib. bdg. 56.95 (ISBN 0-8490-1737-8). Gordon Pr.
Early Christians: Life in the First Years of the Church, an Illustrated Documentary. John Drane. LC 81-47835. (Illus.). 144p. (Orig.). 1982. pap. 9.95 (ISBN 0-06-062067-6, RD 378, HarpR). Har-Row.
Early Christians of the Twenty-First Century. Chad Walsh. LC 78-138136. 188p. 1972. Repr. of 1950 ed. lib. bdg. 22.50x (ISBN 0-8371-5709-9, WACH). Greenwood.
Early Christians Speak. Everett Ferguson. LC 81-68871. 258p. 1981. pap. text ed. 9.95 (ISBN 0-89112-044-0, Bibl Res Pr). Abilene Christ U.
Early Christians: Workers for Jesus. Marsha Barrett. (BibLearn Ser.). (Illus.). 1979. 5.95 (ISBN 0-8054-4247-2, 4242-47). Broadman.
Early Church. Gene Edwards. 1974. pap. text ed. 5.95 (ISBN 0-940232-02-2). Christian Bks.
Early Church. W. H. Frend. LC 81-43085. 1982. pap. 11.95 (ISBN 0-8006-1615-4). Fortress.
Early Church & the State. Agnes Cunningham. LC 81-70666. (Sources of Early Christian Thought Ser.). 128p. 1982. pap. 7.95 (ISBN 0-8006-1413-5, 1-1413). Fortress.
Early Church Art in Northern Europe. Josef Strzygowski. LC 77-73725. (Illus.). 1980. Repr. of 1928 ed. lib. bdg. 30.00 (ISBN 0-87817-246-7). Hacker.
Early Church History to A. D. 313, 2 vols. Henry M. Gwatkin. 1977. lib. bdg. 200.00 (ISBN 0-8490-1738-6). Gordon Pr.
Early Church History to A.D. 313, 2 Vols. Henry M. Gwatkin. LC 77-168216. Repr. of 1909 ed. 52.50 (ISBN 0-404-02966-3). AMS Pr.
Early Church in Eastern England. Margaret Gallyon. 1979. 30.00x (ISBN 0-900963-19-0, Pub. by Terence Dalton England). State Mutual Bk.
Early Church in the Middle East. E. A. Moore. 55p. 1985. 19.00x (ISBN 0-317-39058-9, Pub. by Luzac & Co Ltd). State Mutual Bk.
Early Church, Pelican History of the Church, Vol. 1. Henry Chadwick. (Orig.). 1968. pap. 5.95 (ISBN 0-14-020502-0, Pelican). Penguin.
Early Churches in Palestine. J. W. Crowfoot. (British Academy, London, Schweich Lectures on Biblical Archaeology Series, 1937). pap. 28.00 (ISBN 0-8115-1279-7). Kraus Repr.
Early Churches of Constantinople: Architecture & Liturgy. Thomas F. Mathews. LC 78-111972. (Illus.). 1971. 29.95x (ISBN 0-271-00108-9). Pa St U Pr.
Early Churches of Washington State. Esther Pearson. LC 79-57216. (Illus.). 182p. 1980. 27.50 (ISBN 0-295-95713-1). U of Wash Pr.
Early Colonial Religious Drama in Mexico: From Tzompantli to Golgotha. Marilyn E. Raviez. LC 77-76157. pap. 68.30 (2029506). Bks Demand UMI.
Early Days at the Mission San Juan Bautista. Isaac L. Mylar. (Illus.). 208p. 1986. pap. 9.95 (ISBN 0-317-44751-3). Panorama West.
Early Days of Christian Socialism in America. James Dombrowski. 1966. lib. bdg. 19.50x (ISBN 0-374-92223-3, Octagon). Hippocrene Bks.
Early Deism in France. C. J. Betts. 1984. lib. bdg. 53.50 (ISBN 90-247-2923-8, Pub. by Martinus Nijhoff Netherlands). Kluwer Academic.
Early Development of Mohammedanism. David S. Margoliouth. LC 77-27156. (Hibbert Lectures: 1913). Repr. of 1914 ed. 22.50 (ISBN 0-404-60415-3). AMS Pr.
Early Development of the Hermeneutic of Karl Barth. David P. Henry. (Dissertation Ser.: No. 5). ix, 215p. pap. 18.95 (ISBN 0-86554-130-2). NABPR.
Early Development of the Hermeneutic of Karl Barth As Evidenced by His Appropriation of Romans Chapter Five, Twelve to Twenty-One. David P. Henry. ix, 275p. 1985. 18.95 (ISBN 0-86554-130-2, MUP/P16). Mercer Univ Pr.
Early Dominicans, Selected Writings. Ed. by Simon Tugwell. (Classics of Western Spirituality Ser.). 400p. 1982. 14.95 (ISBN 0-8091-0325-7); pap. 10.95 (ISBN 0-8091-2414-9). Paulist Pr.
Early Dominicans: Studies in 13th-Century Dominican History. Ralph F. Bennett. LC 71-139903. 1971. Repr. of 1937 ed. 12.00x (ISBN 0-8462-1531-4). Russell.
Early Earth. John C. Whitcomb. 1972. pap. 6.95 (ISBN 0-8010-9679-0). Baker Bk.
Early Earth. John C. Whitcomb. pap. 4.50 (ISBN 0-88469-060-1). BMH Bks.
Early English Baptists, 2 vols. B. Evans. (Illus.). 1977. Repr. of 1862 ed. Vol. 1, 298 pp. 9.50 (ISBN 0-87921-041-9); Vol. 2, 362 pp. 9.50 (ISBN 0-87921-045-1). Attic Pr.
Early English Carols. Richard L. Greene. LC 76-161945. 461p. 1935. Repr. 79.00x (ISBN 0-403-01342-9). Scholarly.
Early English Carols. 2nd ed. Ed. by Richard L. Greene. 1977. 129.00x (ISBN 0-19-812715-4). Oxford U Pr.
Early English Christian Poetry. Charles W. Kennedy. 1977. lib. bdg. 59.95 (ISBN 0-8490-1739-4). Gordon Pr.
Early English Christian Poetry. Tr. by Charles W. Kennedy. 1963. pap. 5.95 (ISBN 0-19-500246-6). Oxford U Pr.
Early English Homilies, from the Twelfth Century Ms. Part I. (EETS, OS Ser.: No. 152). Repr. of 1917 ed. 16.00 (ISBN 0-527-00148-1). Kraus Repr.
Early English Lyric & Franciscan Spirituality. David L. Jeffrey. LC 74-78478. (Illus.). xvi, 306p. 1975. 24.50x (ISBN 0-8032-0845-6). U of Nebr Pr.

Early Fathers from the Philokalia. E. Kadloubowsky. Tr. by G. E. Palmer. 454p. 1954. 18.95 (ISBN 0-571-03794-1). Faber & Faber.

Early Fathers on War & Military Service. Louis J. Swift. (Message of the Fathers of the Church Ser.: Vol. 19). 1984. 15.95 (ISBN 0-89453-359-2); pap. 9.95 (ISBN 0-89453-330-4). M Glazier.

Early Field Notes from the All-American Revival Church. Richard Grossinger. 1973. pap. 3.50 (ISBN 0-913028-19-3). North Atlantic.

Early Gravestone Art in Georgia & South Carolina. Diana W. Combs. LC 85-1129. (Illus.). 256p. 1986. 35.00x (ISBN 0-8203-0788-2). U of Ga Pr.

Early Greek Concept of the Soul. Jan Bremmer. LC 82-47583. 190p. 1983. 23.00x (ISBN 0-691-03131-2). Princeton U Pr.

Early Growth of Christianity & the History of the First Christians. Edward Gibbon. (Illus.). 177p. 1986. 137.45 (ISBN 0-89266-557-2). Am Classical Coll Pr.

Early Hadith Literature. M. M. Azami. LC 77-90341. 1978. 10.50 (ISBN 0-89259-012-2). Am Trust Pubns.

Early Hebrew Manuscripts in Facsimile, Vol. 7. Munich Mekhilta. Ed. by Martin Edelmann & Menahem Schmelzer. 220p. 1980. 450.00x (ISBN 0-8018-2464-8); pap. 410.00x (ISBN 0-8018-2465-6). Johns Hopkins.

Early History of a Purpose Machine. Tom Mooney. 1976. 5.95 (ISBN 0-9601240-1-2); pap. 2.95 (ISBN 0-9601240-2-0). Mooney.

Early History of Divine Science. Louise Brooks. 1963. 5.95 (ISBN 0-686-24363-3). Divine Sci Fed.

Early History of Free Will Baptists, Vol. 1. William F. Davidson. (Free Will Baptist History Ser.). 1974. 7.95 (ISBN 0-89265-037-0); pap. 4.95 (ISBN 0-89265-022-2). Randall Hse.

Early History of Islam. Sayyid S. Husayn. 360p. 1984. pap. 7.50 (ISBN 0-941724-25-5). Islamic Seminary.

Early History of Israel. Roland De Vaux. LC 78-1883. 914p. 1978. Westminster.

Early History of Syria & Palestine. Lewis B. Paton. LC 79-2878. (Illus.). 302p. 1981. Repr. of 1901 ed. 28.50 (ISBN 0-8305-0046-4). Hyperion Conn.

Early History of the Church at Canterbury. Nicholas Brooks. (Studies in the Early History of Britain). 237p. 1983. text ed. 60.00x (ISBN 0-7185-1182-4, Leicester). Humanities.

Early History of the Disciples in the Western Reserve, Ohio; with Biographical Sketches of the Principal Agents in Their Religious Movement. Amos S. Hayden. LC 76-38449. (Religion in America, Ser. 2). 480p. 1972. Repr. of 1875 ed. 32.00 (ISBN 0-405-04068-7). Ayer Co Pubs.

Early History of the Vaisnava Faith & Movement in Bengal from Sanskrit & Bengal Sources. Sushil K. De. 700p. 1986. 54.00X (ISBN 0-8364-1642-2, Pub. by Mukhopadhyay). South Asia Bks.

Early History of Zionism in America: Proceedings. Papers Presented at the Conference, Convened by the American Jewish Historical Society & the Theodor Herzl Foundation in New York City, December 26-27,1955. LC 77-70725. (America & the Holy Land Ser.). 1977. Repr. of 1958 ed. lib. bdg. 26.50x (ISBN 0-405-10268-2). Ayer Co Pubs.

Early in the Morning. Woodrow M. Kroll. 128p. 1986. 4.95 (ISBN 0-87213-474-1). Loizeaux.

Early Irish Church: From the Beginnings to the Two Doves. 2nd ed. Paul R. Lonigan. (Illus.). 100p. 1986. pap. 15.99x (ISBN 0-9614753-1-5). Celt Heritage Pr.

Early Irish Myths & Sagas. Jeffrey Gantz. (Pengiun Classic Ser.). 1982. pap. 4.95 (ISBN 0-14-044397-5). Penguin.

Early Irish Myths & Sagas. Jeffrey Gantz. 250p. 1985. 14.95 (ISBN 0-88029-038-2, Pub. by Dorset Pr). Hippocrene Bks.

Early Islamic Conquests. Fred M. Donner. LC 80-8544. (Princeton Studies on the Near East). (Illus.). 328p. 1981. 19.95x (ISBN 0-691-10182-5). Princeton U Pr.

Early Jewish Hermeneutic in Palestine. Daniel Patte. LC 75-22225. (Society of Biblical Literature. Dissertation Ser.: No. 22). Repr. of 1975 ed. 89.50 (ISBN 0-8357-9570-5, 2017666). Bks Demand UMI.

Early Judaism & Its Modern Interpreters. Ed. by Robert A. Kraft et al. (SBL Bible & Its Modern Interpreters Ser.). 1986. 24.95 (ISBN 0-89130-669-2, 06-14-02); pap. 19.95 (ISBN 0-89130-884-9). Scholars Pr GA.

Early Judaism & Its Modern Interpreters. Ed. by George W. Nickelsburg & Robert A. Kraft. LC 85-45491. (The Bible & its Modern Interpreters Ser.). 544p. 1986. 24.95 (ISBN 0-8006-0722-8). Fortress.

Early Kabbalah. Ed. by Joseph Dan & Ronald C. Kiener. (Classics of Western Spirituality Ser.: Vol. 51). 224p. 1986. 13.95 (ISBN 0-8091-0373-7); pap. 10.95 (ISBN 0-8091-2769-5). Paulist Pr.

Early Latin Hymnaries. James Mearns. 127p. Repr. of 1913 ed. lib. bdg. 38.50X (Pub. by G Olms BRD). Coronet Bks.

Early Latin Hymns. Arthur S. Walpole. 473p. Repr. of 1922 ed. lib. bdg. 68.50X (Pub. by G Olms BRD). Coronet Bks.

Early Latin Theology. S. L. Greenslade. LC 56-5229. (Library of Christian Classics). 412p. 1978. pap. 8.95 (ISBN 0-664-24154-9). Westminster.

Early Life of David. Gordon Lindsay. (Old Testament Ser.). 1.25 (ISBN 0-89985-141-X). Christ Nations.

Early Liturgy, to the Time of Gregory the Great. Josef A. Jungmann. Tr. by Francis A. Brunner. (Liturgical Studies: No. 7). 1959. 10.95 (ISBN 0-268-00083-2). U of Notre Dame Pr.

Early Lives of Milton. Ed. by Helen Darbishire. LC 77-144967. (Illus.). 1971. Repr. of 1932 ed. 49.00x (ISBN 0-403-00935-9). Scholarly.

Early Madhyamika in India & China. Richard H. Robinson. 1976. Repr. 18.50 (ISBN 0-8426-0904-0). Orient Bk Dist.

Early Madhyamika in India & China. Richard H. Robinson. 346p. 1978. pap. 6.95 (ISBN 0-87728-433-4). Weiser.

Early Medieval Philosophy Four Eighty to Eleven Fifty: An Introduction. John Marenbon. 224p. 1983. 19.95x (ISBN 0-7100-9405-1). Methuen Inc.

Early Mesopotamian Incantations & Rituals. Jan Van Dijk et al. LC 84-13064. (Yale Oriental Ser., Babylonian Texts: Vol. 11). 200p. 1985. text ed. 35.00x (ISBN 0-300-03147-5). Yale U Pr.

Early Methodist Class Meetings. David L. Watson. 240p. (Orig.). pap. 10.95 (ISBN 0-88170-175-0, DR017B). Discipleship Res.

Early Methodist under Persecution. Barr. pap. 4.95 (ISBN 0-686-23582-7). Schmul Pub Co.

Early Missionary Preaching: A Study of Luke's Report in Acts 13. C. A. Joachim Pillai. 1979. 8.00 (ISBN 0-682-49403-8, University). Exposition Pr FL.

Early Monastic Buddhism. Nalinaksha Dutt. 1981. Repr. of 1971 ed. 12.50x (ISBN 0-8364-0815-2, Pub. by Mukhopadhyay). South Asia Bks.

Early Monastic Rules: The Rules of the Fathers & the Regula Orientalis. Tr. by Ivan Havener et al. LC 82-51. 88p. (Orig.). 1982. pap. 5.95 (ISBN 0-8146-1251-2). Liturgical Pr.

Early Monastic Schools of Ireland, Their Missionaries, Saints & Scholars. William G. Hanson. 1927. 18.00 (ISBN 0-8337-4580-8). B Franklin.

Early Mormon Settlements in Nevada: Humpherys. 1981. 12.50 (ISBN 0-686-92671-4). Byzantine Pr.

Early Mormonism & the Magic World View. D. Michael Quinn. 250p. 1987. 14.95 (ISBN 0-941214-46-X). Signature Bks.

Early Muslim Architecture: Umayyads, Early 'Abbasids, & Tulunids, 2 vols. in 3 pts. K. A. Creswell. LC 75-11057. 1978. Repr. of 1932 ed. lib. bdg. 375.00 (ISBN 0-87817-176-2). Hacker.

Early Muslim Dogma. M. Cook. 256p. 1981. 54.50 (ISBN 0-521-23379-8). Cambridge U Pr.

Early Mystic of Baghdad: A Study of the Life & Teaching of Harith B. Asad al-Muhasibi, A.D. 781-A.D. 857. Margaret Smith. LC 76-180379. Repr. of 1935 ed. 16.50 (ISBN 0-404-56324-4). AMS Pr.

Early New England Catechisms. Wilberforce Eames. 1898. 16.00 (ISBN 0-8337-0989-5). B Franklin.

Early New England Catechisms. Wilberforce Eames. LC 68-31081. 1969. Repr. of 1898 ed. 35.00x (ISBN 0-8103-3478-X). Gale.

Early New England Gravestone Rubbings. Edmund V. Gillon, Jr. (Illus., Orig.). 1966. pap. 7.95 (ISBN 0-486-21380-3). Dover.

Early New England Psalmody: An Historical Appreciation, 1620-1820. Hamilton C. MacDougall. LC 79-87398. (Music Reprint Ser.). 1969. Repr. of 1940 ed. lib. bdg. 29.50 (ISBN 0-306-71542-2). Da Capo.

Early Nonconformity, 1566-1800: A Catalogue of Books in Dr. Williams' Library, London, 3 pts. Dr. Williams' Library, London. Incl. Pt. 1. Author Catalogue, 5 vols. Set. 495.00 (ISBN 0-8161-0797-1); Pt. 2. Subject Catalogue, 5 vols. Set. 495.00 (ISBN 0-8161-0174-4); Pt. 3. Chronological Catalogue, 2 vols. Set. 198.00 (ISBN 0-8161-0173-6). 1968 (Hall Library). G K Hall.

Early Occupants of the Office of Organist & Master of the Choristers of the Cathedral Church of Christ & the Blessed Virgin Mary, Worcester. Ivor A. Atkins. LC 74-27329. Repr. of 1913 ed. 24.50 (ISBN 0-404-12855-6). AMS Pr.

Early Persecutions of the Christians. Leon H. Canfield. LC 68-54259. (Columbia University Studies in the Social Sciences: No. 136). Repr. of 1913 ed. 14.50 (ISBN 0-404-51136-8). AMS Pr.

Early Pilgrimage. May Maxwell. 45p. pap. 2.95 (ISBN 0-85398-004-7). G Ronald Pub.

Early Poetry of Israel in Its Physical & Social Origins. George A. Smith. (British Academy, London, Schweich Lectures on Biblical Archaeology Series, 1910). pap. 19.00 (ISBN 0-8115-1252-5). Kraus Repr.

Early Popularity of Milton's Minor Poems. George Sherburn. LC 73-14758. 1974. Repr. of 1919 ed. lib. bdg. 8.50 (ISBN 0-8414-7647-0). Folcroft.

Early Presbyterianism in Maryland. James W. McIlvain. Bd. with Study of History in Germany & France. Paul Fredericq. Tr. by Henrietta Leonard from Fr. (Johns Hopkins University Studies in Historical & Political Science, 8: No. 5,6). Repr. of 1890 ed. 15.00 (ISBN 0-384-16755-1). Johnson Repr.

Early Quaker Education in Pennsylvania. Thomas Woody. LC 77-177623. (Columbia University. Teachers College. Contributions to Education Ser.: No. 105). Repr. of 1920 ed. 22.50 (ISBN 0-404-55105-X). AMS Pr.

Early Quaker Education in Pennsylvania. Thomas Woody. LC 72-89255. (American Education: Its Men, Institutions & Ideas, Ser. 1). 1969. Repr. of 1920 ed. 17.50 (ISBN 0-405-01493-7). Ayer Co Pubs.

Early Quaker Records in Virginia. Miles White. LC 76-46154. 64p. 1985. pap. 5.00 (ISBN 0-317-31654-0). Genealog Pub.

Early Records of the St. James Episcopal Church of Goshen, New York: Baptisms, Marriages, & Funerals, 1799-1911. Ed. by Orange County Genealogical Committee Members & Gretchen A. Hovemeyer. 140p. (Orig.). 1985. pap. 20.00 (ISBN 0-9604116-4-X). Orange County Genealog.

Early Reformation English Polemics. David Birch. Ed. by James Hogg. (Elizabethan & Renaissance Studies). 181p. (Orig.). 1983. pap. 15.00 (ISBN 0-317-40131-9, Pub by Salzburg Studies). Longwood Pub Group.

Early Russian Painting 11th to Early 13th Centuries: Mosaics, Frescoes & Icons. Ed. by Collet's Holdings, Ltd. Staff. 308p. 1982. 125.00x (ISBN 0-317-39496-7, Pub. by Collets UK). State Mutual Bk.

Early Samkhya. E. H. Johnston. 1974. Repr. 5.95 (ISBN 0-8426-0684-X). Orient Bk Dist.

Early Sermons of Luther & Their Relation to the Pre-Reformation Sermon. Elmer C. Kiessling. LC 75-171064. Repr. of 1935 ed. 21.50 (ISBN 0-404-03669-4). AMS Pr.

Early Slavonic Psalter from Rus' Vol. 1: Phoreproduction. Ed. by Mosha Altbauer & Horace G. Lunt. LC 78-59967. (Harvard Ukrainian Research Institute, Sources & Documents Ser.). 1979. text ed. 15.00x (ISBN 0-674-22310-1). Harvard U Pr.

Early Stained Glass of Canterbury Cathedral: 1175-1220. Madeline H. Caviness. (Illus.). 1978. text ed. 68.50x (ISBN 0-691-03927-5). Princeton U Pr.

Early Stone Temples of Orissa. Vidya Dehejia. LC 78-54434. (Illus.). 217p. 1979. 37.75 (ISBN 0-89089-092-7). Carolina Acad Pr.

Early Syriac Theology: With Special Reference to the Maronite Tradition. Seely J. Beggiani. LC 83-3658. 172p. (Orig.). 1983. lib. bdg. 26.00 (ISBN 0-8191-3152-0); pap. text ed. 10.75 (ISBN 0-8191-3153-9). U Pr of Amer.

Early Temples of the Mormons: The Architecture of the Millennial Kingdom in the American West. Laurel B. Andrew. LC 77-23971. (Illus.). 1978. 29.50 (ISBN 0-87395-358-4). State U NY Pr.

Early Theological Writings. G. W. Hegel. Tr. by T. M. Knox & R. Kroner. (Works in Continental Philosophy Ser). 1971. pap. 12.95x (ISBN 0-8122-1022-0, Pa. Paperbacks). U of Pa Pr.

Early Thunder. Jean Fritz. LC 67-24217. (Illus.). 1967. 9.95 (ISBN 0-698-20036-5, Coward). Putnam Pub Group.

Early Travels in Palestine. Ed. by Thomas Wright. LC 77-84863. (Bohn's Antiquarian Library). Repr. of 1848 ed. 31.50 (ISBN 0-404-50026-9). AMS Pr.

Early Versions of the New Testament. Bruce Metzger. 1977. 24.95x (ISBN 0-19-826170-5). Oxford U Pr.

Early Will I Seek Thee. Eugenia Price. 160p. pap. 2.95 (ISBN 0-8007-8584-3, Spire Bks). Revell.

Early Will I Seek Thee: Journal of a Heart That Longed & Found. Eugenia Price. LC 82-22179. 188p. 1983. pap. 6.95 (ISBN 0-385-27864-0, Dial). Doubleday.

Early Works of Thomas Becon, Chaplain to Archbishop Cranmer. Thomas Becon. Repr. of 1843 ed. 41.00 (ISBN 0-384-03725-9). Johnson Repr.

Early Writings, Fifteen Ten to Fifteen Twenty-Two, Vol. 1. Ulrich Zwingli. Ed. by Samuel M. Jackson. Orig. Title: Latin Writings of Huldreich Zwingli. 308p. 1987. pap. 15.95 (ISBN 0-939464-42-X). Labyrinth Pr.

Early Writings of John Hooper. John Hooper. 1843. 51.00 (ISBN 0-384-24210-3). Johnson Repr.

Early Writings of Krishnamurti, 2 Vols. J. Krishnamurti. 1974. lib. bdg. 250.00 (ISBN 0-87968-533-6). Krishna Pr.

Early Years of Isaac Thomas Hecker (1819-1844) Vincent F. Holden. LC 73-3583. (Catholic University of America. Studies in American Church History: No. 29). Repr. of 1939 ed. 29.00 (ISBN 0-404-57779-2). AMS Pr.

Early Years of John Calvin: A Fragment, 1509-1536. Thomas McCrie. LC 83-45622. Date not set. Repr. of 1880 ed. 28.00 (ISBN 0-404-19840-6). AMS Pr.

Early Zoroastrianism. James H. Moulton. 1976. lib. bdg. 59.95 (ISBN 0-8490-1743-2). Gordon Pr.

Early Zoroastrianism: Lectures Delivered at Oxford & in London, February to May, 1912. James H. Moulton. LC 77-27517. (Hibbert Lectures Ser.). Repr. of 1913 ed. 37.00 (ISBN 0-404-60414-5). AMS Pr.

Earnest Man; or the Character & Labors of Adoniram Judson. D. C. Conant. 1978. Repr. of 1856 ed. lib. bdg. 20.00 (ISBN 0-8492-3943-5). R West.

Earning Your Wings. William Coleman. 144p. 1984. pap. 4.95 (ISBN 0-87123-311-8, 210311). Bethany Hse.

Ears to Hear. Tilly H. Gandy. 1984. 6.95 (ISBN 0-8062-2293-X). Carlton.

Ears to Hear, Eyes to See. Don Bouldin. (Orig.). 1987. pap. 6.95 (ISBN 0-8054-3002-4). Broadman.

Ears to Hear: Hearts to Praise. Marie McIntyre. (Greeting Book Line Ser.). (Illus.). 48p. (Orig.). 1985. pap. 1.50 (ISBN 0-89622-210-1). Twenty-Third.

Earth & Altar: The Community of Prayer in a Self-Bound Society. Eugene H. Paterson. 180p. (Orig.). 1985. pap. 5.95 (ISBN 0-8091-2732-6). Paulist Pr.

Earth-Bound Journey & Heaven-Bound Journey. 2.00 (ISBN 0-685-61408-5). Aum Pubns.

Earth is Round. Margaret Epp. 228p. (Orig.). pap. 4.00 (ISBN 0-919797-00-8). Kindred Pr.

Earth Is the Lord's: The Inner World of the Jew in Eastern Europe. Abraham J. Heschel. 109p. 1978. 8.95 (ISBN 0-374-14613-6); pap. 5.95. FS&G.

Earth Spirit: Its Ways, Shrines & Mysteries. John Mitchell. 1976. pap. 5.95 (ISBN 0-380-01154-9, 26880). Avon.

Earth, the Stars, & the Bible. Paul M. Steidl. 1979. pap. 5.95 (ISBN 0-87552-430-3). Presby & Reformed.

Earth, the Temple, & the Gods. Scully. LC 79-12717. 1979. pap. 16.95x (ISBN 0-300-02397-9, Y-346). Yale U Pr.

Earthkeeping: Christian Stewardship of Natural Resources. 2nd ed. Ed. by Loren Wilkinson. (Orig.). 1980. pap. 10.95 (ISBN 0-8028-1834-X). Eerdmans.

Earthly & Cosmic Man. Rudolf Steiner. Ed. by Bernard J. Garber. LC 85-80915. (Spiritual Science Library: Vol. 27). 176p. 1986. lib. bdg. 14.00 (ISBN 0-89345-055-3, Spiritual Sci Lib). Garber Comm.

Earthquake. Harold Richards. LC 79-13559. (Flame Ser.). 1979. pap. 0.99 (ISBN 0-8127-0240-9). Review & Herald.

Earthquakes & Endtimes. Vincent Montane. (Orig.). pap. cancelled (ISBN 0-88070-155-2). Multnomah.

Earth's Cry Meets Heaven's Smile, Bk. 2. Sri Chinmoy. 145p. (Orig.). 1975. Bk. 2. pap. 3.00 (ISBN 0-88497-143-0). Aum Pubns.

Earth's Final Hours. Kirk Davies. 330p. (Orig.). 1982. pap. 9.95 (ISBN 0-9609174-0-3). Pacific Inst.

Earth's Greatest Day. E. L. Austin. 96p. (Orig.). 1980. pap. 3.95 (ISBN 0-8010-0163-3). Baker Bk.

Earthy Mysticism: Contemplation & the Life of Passionate Presence. William McNamara. LC 82-33554. 128p. 1983. pap. 6.95 (ISBN 0-8245-0562-X). Crossroad NY.

Ease of Being. 2nd ed. Jean Klein. xiii, 110p. 1986. pap. 8.50 (ISBN 0-89386-015-8). Acorn NC.

East & West: Ancient Wisdom & Modern Science. Stanislav Grof. (Broadside Ser.). 30p. 1985. pap. 2.95 (ISBN 0-931191-00-9). Rob Briggs.

East & West: Conflict or Cooperation. facs. ed. Ed. by Basil J. Mathews. LC 67-26764. (Essay Index Reprint Ser). 1936. 14.25 (ISBN 0-8369-0694-2). Ayer Co Pubs.

East European Jewish Experience in America: A Century of Memories, 1882-1982. Ed. by Uri D. Herscher. LC 83-6416. (Monographs of the American Jewish Archives: No. 9). 192p. 1983. 15.75x (ISBN 0-87820-011-8). Ktav.

East in the Light of the West: The Children of Lucifer & the Brothers of Christ & Antique Drama in 5 Acts, Vol. 28. Rudolf Steiner & Edward Schure. Ed. by Bernard J. Garber. LC 85-80914. (Spiritual Science Library Ser.: Vol. 28). 384p. 1986. lib. bdg. 21.00 (ISBN 0-89345-056-1, Spiritual Sci Lib). Garber Comm.

East of Byzantium: Syria & Armenia in the Formative Period. Ed. by Nina Garsoian & Thomas Mathews. LC 82-9665. (Dumbarton Oaks Symposium). (Illus.). 266p. 1982. 35.00x (ISBN 0-88402-104-1). Dumbarton Oaks.

East West Understanding of Man. V. Narayan Reddy. 320p. 1985. text ed. 40.00x (ISBN 0-86590-704-8, Pub. by B R Pub Corp India). Apt Bks.

East Wind. Maria Z Linke & Ruth Hunt. 1978. pap. 2.50 (ISBN 0-310-27852-X). Zondervan.

Eastbound Ecumenicism: A Collection of Essays on the World Council of Churches & Eastern Europe. Hans Helby. LC 86-9137. 154p. (Orig.). 1986. lib. bdg. 24.50 (ISBN 0-8191-5400-8, Pub. by Interuniversity Inst for Missiological & Ecumenical Res); pap. text ed. 12.25 (ISBN 0-8191-5401-6). U Pr of Amer.

Easter. (Illus.). 64p. 1984. 19.95 (ISBN 0-86683-826-0, 8465, HarpR); pap. 9.95 (ISBN 0-86683-811-2, 8343). Har-Row.

Easter. Aileen Fisher. LC 67-23666. (Holiday Ser.). (Illus.). 1968. PLB 12.89 (ISBN 0-690-25236-6, Crowell Jr Bks). HarpJ.

Easter. F. Wellford Hobbie. LC 84-18756. (Proclamation Three C Ser.). 64p. 1986. pap. 3.75 (ISBN 0-8006-4129-9, 1-4129). Fortress.

Easter. Edgar Krentz. LC 84-18756. (Proclamation 3, Ser. B). 64p. 1985. pap. 3.75 (ISBN 0-8006-4105-1, 1-4105). Fortress.

Easter. Edgar Krentz & Arthur A. Vogel. Ed. by Elizabeth Achtemeier et al. LC 79-7377. (Proclamation 2: Aids for Interpreting the Lessons of the Church Year, Ser. C). 64p. 1980. pap. 3.75 (ISBN 0-8006-4080-2, 1-4080). Fortress.

Easter. George W. MacRae & Charles P. Price. LC 79-7377. 64p. 1982. pap. 3.75 (ISBN 0-8006-4087-X, 1-4087). Fortress.

Easter. Lillie Patterson. LC 66-10150. (Holiday Bks.). (Illus.). 1966. PLB 7.56 (ISBN 0-8116-6559-3). Garrard.

Easter. Bruce Vawter & William J. Carl, III. LC 79-7377. (Proclamation 2: Aids for Interpreting the Lessons of the Church Year, Ser. A). 64p. (Orig.). 1981. pap. 3.75 (ISBN 0-8006-4095-0, 1-4095). Fortress.

Easter. James Wharton. LC 84-18756. (Proclamation 3 A). 64p. 1987. pap. 3.75 (ISBN 0-8006-4121-3, 1-4121). Fortress.

Easter: A Promise Kept. Mary E. Shoemaker. (Orig.). 1981. pap. 1.75 (ISBN 0-937172-19-7). JLJ Pubs.

Easter Activity Book. Sarah S. Dietz. (Stick-Out-Your Neck Ser.). (Illus.). 32p. 1984. pap. 1.98 (ISBN 0-88724-067-4, CD-8051). Carson-Dellos.

Easter & Other Spring Holidays. Gilda Berger. (First Bks.). (Illus.). 72p. 1983. PLB 9.90 (ISBN 0-531-04547-1). Watts.

Easter Bunny Book: A Celebration of the Easter Season. Leona W. Hunter. LC 85-23216. (Illus.). 96p. (Orig.). 1986. pap. 8.95 (ISBN 0-915590-84-0). Main Street.

Easter Chimes: Stories for Easter & the Spring. Ed. by Wilhelmina Harper. (Illus.). 1967. 8.95 (ISBN 0-525-29037-0). Dutton.

Easter Enigma: Are the Resurrection Accounts in Conflict? John Wenham. 176p. 1984. pap. 6.95 (ISBN 0-310-29861-X, 12448P). Zondervan.

Easter Fun. Judith H. Corwin. LC 84-9122. (Messner Holiday Library). (Illus.). 64p. 1984. PLB 9.29 (ISBN 0-671-50798-2); pap. 5.95 (ISBN 0-671-53108-5). Messner.

Easter Gospels: The Resurrection of Jesus According to the Four Evangelists. Robert H. Smith. LC 83-70518. 272p. (Orig.). 1983. pap. 15.95 (ISBN 0-8066-2024-2, 10-1988). Augsburg.

Easter Handbook. Ramona Warren et al. LC 85-24322. (Holiday Handbooks Ser.). (Illus.). 96p. 1986. lib. bdg. 12.95 (ISBN 0-89565-306-0). Childs World.

Easter in Durham: Bishop Jenkins & the Resurrection of Jesus. Murray J. Harris. 32p. 1986. pap. 1.95 (ISBN 0-85364-419-5, Pub. by Paternoster UK). Attic Pr.

Easter Is a Time. Daniel R. Seagren. (Contempo Ser.). pap. 0.95 (ISBN 0-8010-8140-8). Baker Bk.

Easter Is Coming: Lenten Celebrations for the Family. Mary Montgomery & Herb Montgomery. (Illus.). 120p. (Orig.). 1982. pap. 7.95 (ISBN 0-86683-609-8, HarpR). Har-Row.

Easter Joy. Jane Lawrence. 1983. 0.50 (ISBN 0-89536-594-4, 0501). CSS of Ohio.

Easter Moment. John S. Spong. 176p. 1980. 9.95 (ISBN 0-8164-0133-0, HarpR). Har-Row.

Easter Passage: The RCIA Experience. Mary P. Ellebracht. 204p. 1983. pap. 11.95 (ISBN 0-86683-693-4, HarpR). Har-Row.

Easter People. Robert Beringer. 1984. 4.75 (ISBN 0-89536-682-7, 4858). CSS of Ohio.

Easter People: Family Devotional Activities for Lent & Easter. Debbie T. O'Neal. 32p. (Orig.). 1986. pap. 3.95 (ISBN 0-8066-2255-5, 10-1990). Augsburg.

Easter People, Grade 1: Welcome. Ed. by Susan Stochl et al. (Easter People Ser.). 1977. pap. text ed. 3.34 (ISBN 0-03-020356-2, 161, HarpR); tchr's. ed. 7.60 (ISBN 0-03-020366-X, 163); activity pack 3.90 (ISBN 0-03-020371-6, 162); parent bk. 2.25 (ISBN 0-03-020361-9, 164). Har-Row.

Easter People, Grade 2: Belong. Ed. by Susan Stochl et al. (Easter People Ser). 1977. pap. text ed. 3.34 (ISBN 0-03-020376-7, 165, HarpR); tchr's. ed. 7.60 (ISBN 0-03-020386-4, 167); activity pack 3.90 (ISBN 0-03-020391-0, 166); parent bk. 2.25 (ISBN 0-03-020381-3, 168). Har-Row.

Easter People, Grade 3: Journey. Ed. by Susan Stochl et al. (Easter People Ser.). (Illus.). 1977. pap. text ed. 3.34 (ISBN 0-03-020396-1, 169, HarpR); tchr's. ed. 7.60 (ISBN 0-03-020406-2, 171); parent wkbk. 2.25 (ISBN 0-03-020401-1, 172); activity pack 3.90 (ISBN 0-03-020411-9, 170). Har-Row.

Easter People, Grade 4: Remember. Ed. by Susan Stochl et al. (Easter People Ser). (Illus.). 1978. pap. text ed. 4.75 (ISBN 0-03-042801-7, HarpR); tchr's. manual 7.60 (ISBN 0-03-042796-7); activity pack 3.90 (ISBN 0-03-042911-0); parent book 2.25 (ISBN 0-03-042791-6). Har-Row.

Easter People, Grade 5: Gather. Ed. by Susan Stochl. (Easter People Ser.). (Illus.). 1979. pap. text ed. 5.65 (ISBN 0-03-050761-8, HarpR); tchr's manual 7.60 (ISBN 0-03-050771-5); wkbk. 3.90 (ISBN 0-03-050776-6); parent bk. 2.25 (ISBN 0-03-050766-9). Har-Row.

Easter Plays. Jon L. Joyce. (Orig.). 1983. pap. 2.95 (ISBN 0-937172-48-0). JLJ Pubs.

Easter Preschool-K Practice. Patti Carson & Janet Dellosa. (Stick-Out-Your-Neck Ser.). (Illus.). 32p. 1984. pap. 1.98 (ISBN 0-88724-017-8, CD-8032). Carson-Dellos.

Easter Primary Reading & Art Activities. Patti Carson & Janet Dellosa. (Stick-Out-Your-Neck Ser.). (Illus.). 32p. 1984. pap. 1.98 (ISBN 0-88724-027-5, CD-8042). Carson-Dellos.

Easter Programs for the Church, No. 8. Compiled by Laurie Hoard. 64p. (Orig.). 1984. pap. 2.95 (ISBN 0-87239-767-X, 8720). Standard Pub.

Easter Programs for the Church, No. 9. Compiled by Laurie Hoard. 64p. 1985. pap. 2.95 (ISBN 0-87239-845-5, 8721). Standard Pub.

Easter Programs for the Church, No. 10. Compiled by Laurie Hoard. 64p. 1986. pap. 2.95 (ISBN 0-87403-082-X, 8722). Standard Pub.

Easter Programs for the Church, No. 11. Compiled by Pat Fittro. (Illus.). 64p. 1987. pap. 3.50 (ISBN 0-87403-283-0, 8723). Standard Pub.

Easter Sermons of Gregory of Nyssa: A Translation & Commentary. Andreas Spira & Christoph Klock. LC 81-84108. (Patristic Monograph Ser.: No. 9). 384p. 1981. pap. 11.00 (ISBN 0-915646-08-0). Phila Patristic.

Easter: Voices from the Heart. Date not set. price not set (ISBN 0-934383-15-4). Pride Prods.

Easter Women. Carol Greene. (Arch Bks.). (Illus.). 24p. 1987. pap. 0.99 (ISBN 0-570-09003-2, 59-1432). Concordia.

Eastern Church in the Western World. William C. Emhardt. LC 74-131039. Repr. of 1928 ed. 15.75 (ISBN 0-404-02329-0). AMS Pr.

Eastern Churches Review, Vols. I-X, 1966-1978. Ed. by Barbara Fry et al. 2000p. 1985. pap. text ed. 80.00x (ISBN 0-89370-095-9). Borgo Pr.

Eastern Churches Review: An Index to Volumes One Through Ten, 1966-1978. Boden Clarke & Mary Burgess. LC 80-2550. (Borgo Reference Library: Vol. 6). 96p. 1987. lib. bdg. 19.95x (ISBN 0-89370-812-7); pap. text ed. 9.95x (ISBN 0-89370-912-3). Borgo Pr.

Eastern Light for the Western Mind. 3.95 (ISBN 0-87847-014-X). Aum Pubns.

Eastern Monachism: An Account of the Origin, Laws, Discipline, Sacred Writings, Mysterious Rites, Religious Ceremonies, & Present Circumstances, of the Order of Mendicants Founded by Gotama Budha. Robert S. Hardy. LC 78-72438. Repr. of 1850 ed. 40.00 (ISBN 0-404-17304-7). AMS Pr.

Eastern Orthodox Mission Theology Today. James J. Stamoolis. LC 85-15596. 208p. (Orig.). 1986. pap. 18.95 (ISBN 0-88344-215-9). Orbis Bks.

Eastern Orthodox Response to Evangelical Claims. P. O. O'Callaghan. 1984. pap. 2.95 (ISBN 0-937032-35-2). Light&Life Pub Co MN.

Eastern Orthodox Saints. Sabine Baring-Gould. pap. 0.95 (ISBN 0-686-01292-5). Eastern Orthodox.

Eastern Orthodoxy: A Way of Life. A. M. Coniaris. 1966. pap. 6.95 (ISBN 0-937032-14-X). Light&Life Pub Co MN.

Eastern Paths & the Christian Way. Paul Clasper. LC 80-13730. 128p. (Orig.). 1980. pap. 5.95 (ISBN 0-88344-100-4). Orbis Bks.

Eastern Politics of the Vatican, 1917-1979. Hansjakob Stehle. Tr. by Sandra Smith from Ger. LC 80-15236. Orig. Title: Ostpolitik Des Vatikans, 1917-1975. (Illus.). 1981. 28.95x (ISBN 0-8214-0367-2); pap. 14.95 (ISBN 0-8214-0564-0). Ohio U Pr.

Eastern Portal of the North Transept at Chartres: Christological Rather Than Mariological. Roger J. Adams. (Kultstatten der Gallisch-frankischen Kirche Vol.2). 190p. 1982. pap. 27.90 (ISBN 3-8204-6902-8). P Lang Pubs.

Eastern Religions. Elizabeth Seeger. LC 73-10206. (Illus.). 1973. 14.70 (ISBN 0-690-25342-7, Crowell Jr Bks). HarpJ.

Eastern Religions & Western Thought. 2nd ed. S. Radhakrishnan. 1975. pap. text ed. 10.95x (ISBN 0-19-560604-3). Oxford U Pr.

Eastern Schism. Steven Runciman. LC 78-63367. (Crusades & Military Orders: Second Ser.). 200p. Repr. of 1956 ed. 24.50 (ISBN 0-404-16247-9). AMS Pr.

Eastern Spirituality in America: Selected Writings. Ed. by Rober S. Ellwood. (Sources of American Spirituality Ser.). 256p. 1987. pap. 16.95 (ISBN 0-8091-0388-5). Paulist Pr.

Eastern Star. Bell. 8.95x (ISBN 0-685-21937-2). Wehman.

Eastern Star Ritual. F. A. Bell. 5.50 (ISBN 0-685-19473-6). Powner.

Eastern Star: The Evolution from a Rite to an Order. Harold V. Voorhis. 138p. 1986. Repr. of 1954 ed. text ed. 6.95 (ISBN 0-88053-306-4, S-300). Macoy Pub.

Eastern View of Jesus Christ. write for info. Birth Day.

Eastern Wisdom & Western Thought: A Comparative Study in the Modern Philosophy of Religion. P. J. Saher. LC 72-441621. pap. 73.50 (ISBN 0-317-09011-9, 2012165). Bks Demand UMI.

Easy Bible Object Talks. Larry Michaels. (Illus.). 48p. 1985. pap. 2.95 (ISBN 0-87239-846-3, 2886). Standard Pub.

Easy Bible Quizzes for All Ages. rev. ed. Shirley Beegle. 1983. pap. 1.95 (ISBN 0-87239-657-6, 3137). Standard Pub.

Easy Death: Talks & Essays on the Inherent & Ultimate Transcendence of Death & Everything Else. Da Free John. 450p. pap. 10.95 (ISBN 0-913922-57-9). Dawn Horse Pr.

Easy Devotions to Give. Amy Bolding. (Paperback Program Ser.). 96p. (Orig.). 1981. pap. 3.95 (ISBN 0-8010-0794-1). Baker Bk.

Easy Does It: Yoga for Older People. Alice Christensen & David Rankin. LC 78-4755. (Illus.). 1979. spiral bdg. 11.95 (ISBN 0-06-250145-3, RD 289, HarpR). Har-Row.

Easy Essays. Peter Moran. 1977. pap. 6.95 (ISBN 0-8199-0681-6). Franciscan Herald.

Easy Hebrew (Iurit Kallah) Mordecai Lewittes. 5.95 (ISBN 0-88482-682-1). Hebrew Pub.

Easy History of the Prophet of Islam. Nadvi. pap. 3.95 (ISBN 0-686-18309-6). Kazi Pubns.

Easy Journey to Other Planets. Swami A. C. Bhaktivedanta. LC 70-118080. (Illus.). 1970. pap. 1.95 (ISBN 0-912776-10-2). Bhaktivedanta.

Easy Object Stories. Luther S. Cross. 114p. 1984. pap. 3.95 (ISBN 0-8010-2502-8). Baker Bk.

Easy-to-Make Christmas & Holiday Lightcatchers: With Full-Size Template for 66 Stained Glass Projects. Ed Sibbett, Jr. 64p. 1984. pap. 4.50 (ISBN 0-486-24706-6). Dover.

Easy-to-Make Christmas Crafts. Judith Conaway. LC 85-16475. (Illus.). 48p. 1986. PLB 9.49 (ISBN 0-8167-0674-3); pap. text ed. 1.95 (ISBN 0-8167-0675-1). Troll Assocs.

Easy-to-Make Felt Ornaments for Christmas & Other Occasions. Betty Deems. LC 76-18405. (Dover Needlework Ser). (Illus.). 32p. (Orig.). 1976. pap. 3.50 (ISBN 0-486-23389-8). Dover.

Easy to Use Christmas Programs. Cora Vogel. 144p. 1986. 7.95 (ISBN 0-8010-9302-3). Baker Bk.

Easy-to-Use Object Lessons. Sheryl Bruinsma. (Object Lesson Ser.). 96p. (Orig.). 1983. pap. 3.95 (ISBN 0-8010-0832-8). Baker Bk.

Easy-to-Use Sermon Outlines. Russell E. Spray. (Sermon Outline Ser.). 1978. pap. 2.45 (ISBN 0-8010-8143-2). Baker Bk.

Eating Gorilla Comes in Peace. Da Free John. LC 75-24582. 1979. 12.95 (ISBN 0-913922-19-6). Dawn Horse Pr.

Ecce Homo. John R. Seeley. 1970. Repr. of 1908 ed. 12.95x (ISBN 0-460-00305-4, Evman). Biblio Dist.

Eccentric Preachers. C. H. Spurgeon. 1978. pap. 3.25 (ISBN 0-686-00496-5). Pilgrim Pubns.

Ecclesial Reflection: An Anatomy of Theological Method. Edward Farley. LC 81-43088. 1982. 29.95 (ISBN 0-8006-0670-1). Fortress.

Ecclesiam Suam. Pope Paul Sixth. pap. 0.50 (ISBN 0-8091-5035-2). Paulist Pr.

Ecclesiastes. Charles Bridges. 319p. 1981. Repr. 12.95 (ISBN 0-85151-322-0). Banner of Truth.

Ecclesiastes. Michael A. Eaton. Ed. by D. J. Wiseman. (Tyndale Old Testament Commentary Ser.). 1983. 12.95 (ISBN 0-87784-963-3); pap. 6.95 (ISBN 0-87784-267-1). Inter-Varsity.

Ecclesiastes. J. A. Loader. Ed. by A. S. Van Der Woude. Tr. by John Vriend from Dutch. (Text & Interpretation Commentary Ser.). 120p. (Orig.). 1986. pap. 6.95 (ISBN 0-8028-0102-1). Eerdmans.

Ecclesiastes. James M. MacDonald. 1982. lib. bdg. 15.50 (ISBN 0-86524-091-4, 2101). Klock & Klock.

Ecclesiastes & Canticle of Canticles. Roland E. Murphy. (Bible Ser.). pap. 1.00 (ISBN 0-8091-5036-0). Paulist Pr.

Ecclesiastes & Song of Solomon. John Waddey. 1986. pap. 5.50 (ISBN 0-89137-565-1). Quality Pubns.

Ecclesiastes & the Song of Solomon. Robert Davidson. LC 86-15659. (Daily Study Bible - Old Testament Ser.). 168p. 1986. 14.95 (ISBN 0-664-21838-5); pap. 7.95 (ISBN 0-664-24589-7). Westminster.

Ecclesiastes & the Song of Solomon. Irving L. Jensen. (Bible Self Study Guide Ser.). 1974. pap. 3.25 (ISBN 0-8024-1021-9). Moody.

Ecclesiastes: Bible Study Commentary. Louis Goldberg. 1986. pap. 4.95 (ISBN 0-310-41823-2, 18199P). Zondervan.

Ecclesiastes: God's Wisdom for Evangelism. Dee Brestin. (Fisherman Bible Studyguide Ser.). 93p. 1980. saddle stitch 2.95 (ISBN 0-87788-212-6). Shaw Pubs.

Ecclesiastes in A. S. L. - Chapter Three, Verses 1-4: Written in Sutton Sign Writing. David McKee & Nancy E. Woo. text ed. 3.00x. Ctr Sutton Movement.

Ecclesiastes; Song of Solomon. R. J. Kidwell & Don DeWelt. LC 78-301088. (Bible Study Textbook Ser.). 1977. 14.30 (ISBN 0-89900-019-3). College Pr Pub.

Ecclesiastes: The Mid-Life Crisis. Don Anderson. (Kingfisher Ser.). 268p. (Orig.). 1987. pap. 7.95 (ISBN 0-87213-001-0). Loizeaux.

Ecclesiastes: Total Life. Walter C. Kaiser, Jr. (Everyman's Bible Commentary Ser.). 1979. pap. 5.95 (ISBN 0-8024-2022-2). Moody.

Ecclesiastical Admininstration in Medieval England: The Anglo-Saxons to the Reformation. Robert E. Rodes, Jr. LC 73-22584. 1977. text ed. 19.95x (ISBN 0-268-00903-1). U of Notre Dame Pr.

Ecclesiastical Art in Germany During the Middle Ages. Wilhelm Lubke. Tr. by L. A. Wheatley from Ger. LC 78-16244. 1978. Repr. of 1877 ed. lib. bdg. 35.00 (ISBN 0-89341-359-3). Longwood Pub Group.

Ecclesiastical Authority & Spiritual Power in the Church of the First Three Centuries. Hans Von Campenhausen. Tr. by J. A. Baker. 1969. 25.00x (ISBN 0-8047-0665-4). Stanford U Pr.

Ecclesiastical Cartoons. 2nd ed. Wm. Armstrong. (Armstrong Cartoon Ser.). (Illus.). 48p. (Orig.). 1972. pap. 1.00 (ISBN 0-913452-08-4). Jesuit Bks.

Ecclesiastical Censure at the End of the Fifteenth Century. William K. Gotwald. LC 78-64124. (Johns Hopkins University. Studies in the Social Sciences. Forty-Fifth Ser. 1927: 3). Repr. of 1927 ed. 13.50 (ISBN 0-404-61238-5). AMS Pr.

Ecclesiastical Documents. Ed. by Joseph Hunter. 1840. 19.00 (ISBN 0-384-24935-3). Johnson Repr.

Ecclesiastical History. Eusebius. (Twin Brooks Ser). pap. 11.95 (ISBN 0-8010-3306-3). Baker Bk.

Ecclesiastical History, 2 Vols. Eusebius Pamphili. (Loeb Classical Library: No. 153, 265). 13.95x ea. Vol. 1 (ISBN 0-674-99169-9). Vol. 2 (ISBN 0-674-99293-8). Harvard U Pr.

Ecclesiastical History, Bks. 6-10. Eusebius Pamphili. (Fathers of the Church Ser: Vol. 29). 325p. 1955. 17.95x (ISBN 0-8132-0029-6). Cath U Pr.

Ecclesiastical History: Books 1-5. Eusebius Pamphili. LC 65-27501. (Fathers of the Church Ser: Vol. 19). 347p. 1953. 18.95x (ISBN 0-8132-0019-9). Cath U Pr.

Ecclesiastical History of England. Bede the Venerable. Ed. by John A. Giles. LC 78-136367. (Bohn's Antiquarian Lib.). (Illus.). Repr. of 1849 ed. 42.50 (ISBN 0-404-50001-3). AMS Pr.

Ecclesiastical History of England & Normandy, 4 Vols. Ordericus Vitalis. Tr. by T. Forrester. LC 68-57872. (Bohn's Antiquarian Library Ser). Repr. of 1856 ed. Set. 115.00 (ISBN 0-404-50040-4). AMS Pr.

Ecclesiastical History of Orderic Vitalis, Vol. 1. Ed. by Marjorie Chibnall. (Oxford Medieval Texts Ser.). (Illus.). 1981. 98.00x (ISBN 0-19-822243-2). Oxford U Pr.

Ecclesiastical History of Orderic Vitalis, Vol. 5, Bks. 9 & 10. Orderic Vitalis. Ed. & tr. by Majorie Chibnall. (Oxford Medieval Texts Ser). 1975. 65.00x (ISBN 0-19-822232-7). Oxford U Pr.

Ecclesiastical History of Orderic Vitalis, Vol. 6, Books 11, 12, 13. Orderic Vitalis. Ed. & tr. by Marjorie Chibnall. 1978. text ed. 84.00x (ISBN 0-19-822242-4). Oxford U Pr.

Ecclesiastical History of the English People. Bede the Venerable. Ed. by Bertram Colgrave & R. A. Minors. (Oxford Medieval Texts Ser). 1969. 87.00x (ISBN 0-19-822202-5). Oxford U Pr.

Ecclesiastical History of the English People. Bede the Venerable. Ed. by Philip Hereford. Tr. by Thomas Stapleton from Latin. 1983. Repr. of 1935 ed. lib. bdg. 45.00 (ISBN 0-89760-062-2). Telegraph Bks.

Ecclesiastical History of the English Nation & Other Writings. Bede the Venerable. Tr. by John Stevens. 1978. Repr. of 1910 ed. 12.95x (ISBN 0-460-00479-4, Evman). Biblio Dist.

Ecclesiastical Office & the Primacy of Rome: An Evaluation of Recent Theological Discussion of First Clement. John Fuellenbach. LC 79-17574. (Catholic University of America. Studies in Christian Antiquity Ser.: No. 20). pap. 72.00 (2029502). Bks Demand UMI.

Ecclesiastical Polity, Bk. 8. Richard Hooker. LC 77-170046. Repr. of 1931 ed. 24.00 (ISBN 0-404-03329-6). AMS Pr.

Ecclesiastical Researches. Robert Robinson. 1984. Repr. of 1792 ed. 37.00 (ISBN 0-317-11349-6). Church History.

Ecclesiasticus: Or, the Wisdom of Jesus Son of Sirach. Ed. by John G. Snaith. LC 73-82459. (Cambridge Bible Commentary on the New English Bible, Old Testament Ser.). 180p. 1974. 32.50 (ISBN 0-521-08657-4); pap. 10.95 (ISBN 0-521-09775-4). Cambridge U Pr.

Ecclesiogenesis: The Base Communities Reinvent the Church. Leonardo Boff. Tr. by Robert R. Barr from Port. LC 85-15600. 128p. (Orig.). 1986. pap. 9.95 (ISBN 0-88344-214-0). Orbis Bks.

Ecclesiology of Vatican II. Bonaventure Kloppenburg. 1974. 6.95 (ISBN 0-8199-0484-8). Franciscan Herald.

Ecclesiology of Yves Congar: Foundational Themes. Timothy I. MacDonald. LC 83-19882. 346p. (Orig.). 1984. lib. bdg. 28.75 (ISBN 0-8191-3644-1); pap. text ed. 14.75 (ISBN 0-8191-3645-X). U Pr of Amer.

Echo is of God. Barbara Sadtler. 96p. (Orig.). 1986. pap. 1.90 (ISBN 0-88028-052-2). Forward Movement.

Echo of the Nazi Holocaust in Rabbinic Literature. H. J. Zimmels. 25.00x (ISBN 0-87068-427-2). Ktav.

Echoes from Beautiful Feet. Mrs. Edwin Peters. (Illus.). 168p. 1975. pap. 1.95 (ISBN 0-89114-073-5). Baptist Pub Hse.

Echoes from Eden. A. W. Tozer. Ed. by Gerald B. Smith. LC 1-67321. (Tozer Pulpit: Vol. 8). 121p. (Orig.). 1981. 2.95 (ISBN 0-87509-227-6). Chr Pubns.

Echoes from the Hills. Winnie Corley. 1981. lib. bdg. 14.95x (ISBN 0-934188-06-8). Evans Pubns.

Echoes of Pauline Concepts in the Speech at Antioch. Paul E. Deterding. (Concordia Student Journal Monograph Ser.: No. 1). (Illus.). 50p. (Orig.). 1980. pap. 2.50 (ISBN 0-911770-51-8). Concordia Schl Grad Studies.

Echoes of the General Holiness Assembly. Ed. by S. B. Shaw. (Higher Christian Life Ser.). 345p. 1985. lib. bdg. 45.00 (ISBN 0-8240-6442-9). Garland Pub.

Echoes of the New Creation. Albert B. Simpson. pap. 1.25 (ISBN 0-87509-010-9). Chr Pubns.

Echoes of Thunder. Harry L. Green. LC 80-66322. 167p. 1980. 10.95 (ISBN 0-936958-00-6); pap. 5.95 (ISBN 0-936958-01-4). Emerald Hse.

Echoes of Voidness. Geshe Rabten. Ed. by Stephen Batchelor. (Intermediate Book: White Ser.). (Illus.). 148p. (Orig.). 1983. pap. 8.95 (ISBN 0-86171-010-X, Pub. by Wisdom Pubns). Great Traditions.

ECK Vidya: The Ancient Science of Prophecy. Paul Twitchell. LC 75-306773. 237p. 1972. 5.95 (ISBN 0-914766-89-9). IWP Pub.

Eckankar: Illuminated Way Letters 1966-1971. Paul Twitchell. 272p. 1975. 5.95 (ISBN 0-914766-25-2). IWP Pub.

Eckankar: La Clave de los Mondos Secretos. Paul Twitchell. 1978. pap. 5.95 (ISBN 0-88155-029-9). IWP Pub.

Eckerd. Jack Eckerd & Charles P. Conn. (Illus.). 1987. 12.95 (ISBN 0-8007-1532-2). Revell.

Eclipse of Biblical Narrative: A Study in Eighteenth & Nineteenth-Century Hermeneutics. Hans W. Frei. LC 73-86893. 384p. 1974. pap. 10.95x (ISBN 0-300-02602-1). Yale U Pr.

Eclipse of Christianity in Asia. Lawrence E. Browne. 1967. Repr. 27.50x (ISBN 0-86527-049-X). Fertig.

Eclipse of God: Studies in the Relation Between Religion & Philosophy. Martin Buber. 1979. pap. text ed. 7.95x (ISBN 0-391-00902-8). Humanities.

Eclipse of Man & Nature: Spiritual Anthroposophy. Philip Sherrard. 160p. (Orig.). Date not set. pap. 8.95 (Lindisfarne Pr). Inner Tradit.

Eclipse of Reason. Max Horkheimer. LC 73-17887. 1973. pap. 12.95x (ISBN 0-8264-0009-4, Continuum). Continuum.

Eclipse of the Abbasid Caliphate, 7 vols. Miskawayh et al. Tr. by H. F. Amedroz & D. S. Margoliouth. Repr. of 1920 ed. lib. bdg. 500.00. Caratzas.

Eclipse of the Historical Jesus. Henry J. Cadbury. LC 64-12998. (Orig.). 1964. 2.50x (ISBN 0-87574-133-9, 133). Pendle Hill.

Ecole des Psaumes. Lloyd J. Ogilvie. Ed. by Annie L. Cosson. Tr. by Marie-Andre Rousseau. Tr. of Falling into Greatness. (Fr.). 208p. 1985. pap. 3.50 (ISBN 0-8297-0700-X). Life Pubs Intl.

Ecological Spirituality of Teilhard. Mary E. Tucker. (Teilhard Studies). 1985. pap. 2.00 (ISBN 0-89012-040-4). Anima Pubns.

Ecology & Religion: Toward a New Christian Theology of Nature. John Carmody. LC 82-62412. 1983. pap. 6.95 (ISBN 0-8091-2526-9). Paulist Pr.

Economic & Social Origins of Gnosticism. Henry A. Green. (SBL Dissertation). 1985. 26.95 (ISBN 0-89130-842-3, 06-01-77); pap. 17.95 (ISBN 0-89130-843-1). Scholars Pr GA.

Economic Causes of the Reformation in England. Oscar A. Marti. LC 83-45586. Date not set. Repr. of 1929 ed. 32.50 (ISBN 0-404-19904-6). AMS Pr.

Economic Conditions of the Jews in Russia. facsimile ed. Isaac M. Rubinow. LC 74-29519. (Modern Jewish Experience Ser.). 1975. Repr. of 1907 ed. 15.00x (ISBN 0-405-06744-5). Ayer Co Pubs.

Economic History of the California Missions. Robert R. Archibald. (Monograph). 1977. 25.00 (ISBN 0-88382-063-3). AAFH.

Economic History of the Jews in England. Harold Pollins. (Littman Library of Jewish Civilization). 1983. 37.50x (ISBN 0-19-710048-1). Oxford U Pr.

Economic Indicators & the GPID: An Attempt to Bring Economics Back into the Church Without Losing the Faith. 27p. 1980. pap. 5.00 (ISBN 92-808-0134-1, TUNU068, UNU). Bernan-Unipub.

Economic Justice for All: Pastoral Letter in Catholic Social Teaching & U. S. Economy. National Conference of Catholic Bishops. 192p. 1986. pap. 2.95 (ISBN 1-55586-101-6). US Catholic.

Economic Justice for All: Study Guide, the American Bishops' Pastoral on Social Teaching & the U. S. Economy. Joan M. Maliszewski et al. 48p. (Orig.). 1987. pap. 1.95 (ISBN 0-8091-5201-0). Paulist Pr.

Economic Morals of the Jesuits. James Broderick. LC 76-38248. (Evolution of Capitalism Ser.). 168p. 1972. Repr. of 1934 ed. 12.00 (ISBN 0-405-04113-6). Ayer Co Pubs.

Economic Order & Religion. Frank H. Knight & Thornton W. Merriam. LC 78-31760. 1979. Repr. of 1945 ed. lib. bdg. 24.75x (ISBN 0-313-20970-7, KNEO). Greenwood.

Economic Principles of Confucius & His School, 2 vols. Huan-Chang Chen. lib. bdg. 250.00 set (ISBN 0-87968-080-6). Krishna Pr.

Economic Rights & Human Development. Canadian Christian Movement for Peace Staff. (People Living for Justice Ser.). 240p. 1984. pap. 29.95 (ISBN 0-697-01932-2). Wm C Brown.

Economic Role of Jews in Medieval Poland: The Contribution of Yitzhak Schipper. Jacob Litman. (Illus.). 320p. (Orig.). 1985. lib. bdg. 29.50 (ISBN 0-8191-4244-1); pap. text ed. 15.25 (ISBN 0-8191-4245-X). U Pr of Amer.

Economic Security in Islam. M. I. Siddiqui. 1981. 19.95 (ISBN 0-686-97853-6). Kazi Pubns.

Economics & Ethics: A Christian Inquiry. J. P. Wogaman. LC 85-45478. 160p. 1986. pap. 9.95 (ISBN 0-8006-1904-8). Fortress.

Economics & Man: Prelude to a Christian Critique. Douglas Vickers. 1976. pap. 6.95 (ISBN 0-934532-27-3). Presby & Reformed.

Economics & the Christian Mind. Arnold F. McKee. 1987. 10.95 (ISBN 0-533-07175-5). Vantage.

Economics of Sainthood: Religious Change among the Rimrock Navajos. Kendall Blanchard. LC 75-10141. (Illus.). 244p. 1976. 22.50 (ISBN 0-8386-1770-0). Fairleigh Dickinson.

Economics: Principles & Policy from a Christian Perspective. 2nd ed. Tom Rose. LC 85-72235. (Illus.). 380p. 1985. text ed. 18.95 (ISBN 0-9612198-5-8); instrs' manual 7.00 (ISBN 0-9612198-1-5). A E P.

Ecritures Manicheennes. Prosper Alfaric. (Reprints & Translations). Date not set. Vol. 1, Vue Generale. pap. price not set (ISBN 0-89130-896-2, 00-07-13). Vol. 2, Etude Analythique. Scholars Pr GA.

Ecstacy of Angus. Liam O'Flaherty. 64p. 1978. Repr. of 1931 ed. 10.95 (ISBN 0-905473-18-3, Pub. by Wolfhound Pr Ireland). Irish Bks Media.

Ecstasy: A Study of Some Secular & Religious Experiences. Marghanita Laski. LC 68-55635. (Illus.). 1968. Repr. of 1962 ed. bds. 27.50x (ISBN 0-8371-0529-3, LAEC). Greenwood.

Ecstasy: Shamanism in Korea. Alan C. Covell. LC 83-81487. (Illus.). 107p. 1983. 19.50x (ISBN 0-930878-33-7). Hollym Intl.

Ecstasy: The Forgotten Language. Bhagwan Shree Rajneesh. Ed. by Swami Prem Chinmaya. LC 83-179587. (Kabir Ser.). (Illus.). 332p. (Orig.). 1978. 16.50 (ISBN 0-88050-055-7). Chidvilas Found.

Ecstatic Confessions: The Heart of Mysticism. Martin Buber. Ed. by Paul Mendes-Flor. LC 84-48212. 224p. 1985. 16.45 (ISBN 0-06-061154-5, HarpR). Har-Row.

Ecumenical Century: 1900-1965. Horton Davies. (Worship & Theology in England Ser.: Vol. 5). 1965. 39.50x (ISBN 0-691-07145-4). Princeton U Pr.

Ecumenical Consensus on the Church, the Sacraments, the Minstry & Reunion. C. N. Tsirpanlis. 37p. 1980. pap. 1.50 (ISBN 0-686-36333-7). EO Pr.

Ecumenical Councils. William P. DuBose. 1977. lib. bdg. 59.95 (ISBN 0-8490-1751-3). Gordon Pr.

Ecumenical Creeds & Reformed Confessions. 1979. pap. text ed. 3.75 (ISBN 0-933140-02-9). CRC Pubns.

Ecumenical Dialogue at Harvard, the Roman Catholic-Protestant Colloquium. Ed. by Samuel H. Miller & G. Ernest Wright. LC 64-19583. 1964. 25.00x (ISBN 0-674-23700-5, Belknap Pr). Harvard U Pr.

Ecumenical Documents of the Faith: The Creed of Nicea; Three Epistles of Cyril; The Tome of Leo; The Chalcedonian Definition. 4th ed. Ed. by T. Herbert Bindley. LC 79-8708. viii, 246p. 1980. Repr. of 1950 ed. lib. bdg. 24.75x (ISBN 0-313-22197-9, BIOD). Greenwood.

Ecumenical Lectionary. Larry A. Sansoucie. 111p. (Orig.). 1986. pap. 9.95 (ISBN 0-937505-04-8). Glyndwr Resc.

Ecumenical Moment: Crisis & Opportunity for the Church. Geoffrey Wainwright. 272p. (Orig.). 1983. pap. 8.95 (ISBN 0-8028-1979-6). Eerdmans.

Ecumenical Perspective & the Modernization of Jewish Religion: A Study in the Relationship Between Theology & Myth. S. Daniel Breslauer. 1978. pap. 9.00 (ISBN 0-89130-236-0, 140005). Scholars Pr GA.

Ecumenical Praise. Ed. by Carlton R. Young et al. 1977. 14.95x (ISBN 0-916642-07-0). Hope Pub.

Ecumenical Services of Prayer: Consultation on Common Texts. James M. Schellman. 80p. 1983. pap. 1.95 (ISBN 0-8091-5180-4). Paulist Pr.

Ecumenical World of Orthodox Civilization: Russia & Orthodoxy, Vol. 3. Ed. by Andrew Blane. (Slavistic Printings & Reprintings Ser: No. 260). 1974. text ed. 44.80x (ISBN 90-2792-610-7). Mouton.

Ecumenism: A Movement Toward Church Unity. William G. Rusch. LC 84-48707. 96p. 1985. pap. 6.95 (ISBN 0-8006-1847-5, 1-1847). Fortress.

Ecumenism & the Reformed Church. Herman Harmelink. 1969. pap. 3.95 (ISBN 0-8028-1281-3). Eerdmans.

Ecumenism in the Age of the Reformation: The Colloquy of Poissy. Donald Nugent. LC 73-80026. (Historical Studies: No. 89). 296p. 1974. text ed. 20.00x (ISBN 0-674-23725-0). Harvard U Pr.

Ecumenism: Striving for Unity amid Diversity. Mark D. Lowrey. 272p. (Orig.). 1985. pap. text ed. 9.95 (ISBN 0-89622-274-8). Twenty-Third.

Ed Taylor: Father of Migrant Missions. Lou Heath. LC 81-70911. (Meet the Missionary Ser.). 1982. 5.50 (ISBN 0-8054-4278-2, 4242-78). Broadman.

Edda I: The Divine Mythology of the North, 2: The Heroic Mythology of the North, 2 Vols. in 1. Lucy W. Faraday. (Popular Studies in Mythology, Romance & Folklore: Nos. 12 & 13). Repr. of 1902 ed. 11.00 (ISBN 0-404-53512-7). AMS Pr.

Eddic Mythology. John A. MacCulloch. LC 63-19087. (Mythology of All Races Ser.: Vol. 2). (Illus.). Repr. of 1932 ed. 30.00x (ISBN 0-8154-0143-4). Cooper Sq.

Eden in Winter. Harry E. Chase. LC 78-71941. 1978. write for info. (ISBN 0-9601662-2-X). C Schneider.

Eden Narrative. Howard N. Wallace. (Harvard Semitic Museum Monograph). 1985. 16.95 (ISBN 0-89130-838-5, 04-00-32). Scholars Pr GA.

Edgar Cayce & the Born Again Christian. Lynn E. Sparrow. 237p. (Orig.). 1985. pap. 6.95 (ISBN 0-87604-158-6). ARE Pr.

Edgar Cayce on Prophecy. Mary E. Carter. 208p. 1968. pap. 3.50 (ISBN 0-446-32712-3). Warner Bks.

Edgar Cayce Reader. Ed. by Hugh L. Cayce. 192p. 1969. pap. 3.50 (ISBN 0-446-32561-9). Warner Bks.

Edgar Cayce Returns. Robert R. Leichtman. (From Heaven to Earth Ser.). (Illus.). 112p. (Orig.). 1978. pap. 3.50 (ISBN 0-89804-052-3). Ariel OH.

Edgar Cayce's Story of Attitudes & Emotions. Ed. by Jeffrey Furst. 1983. pap. 3.50 (ISBN 0-425-08194-X). Berkley Pub.

Edgar Cayce's Story of Jesus. Ed. by Jeffrey Furst. 1984. pap. 3.95 (ISBN 0-425-09534-7, Medallion). Berkley Pub.

Edgar Cayce's Story of Karma. Mary A. Woodward. 1984. pap. 3.50 (ISBN 0-425-07697-0, Medallion). Berkley Pub.

Edge. Howard E. Ferguson. (Illus.). 340p. 1983. text ed. 29.95x (ISBN 0-9611180-0-8). H E Ferguson.

Edge of Contingency: French Catholic Reaction to Scientific Change from Darwin to Duhem. Harry W. Paul. LC 78-11168. 1979. 15.00 (ISBN 0-8130-0582-5). U Presses Fla.

Edge of Greatness: A Portrait of American Jewry in the Early National Period. Ira Rosewaike. (Illus.). 1985. 25.00 (ISBN 0-87820-013-4, Pub. by Am Jewish Archives). Ktav.

Edge of Paradise: Fifty Years in the Pulpit. William R. Pankey. 1972. 7.00 (ISBN 0-87012-111-1). McClain.

Edinburgh Lectures on Mental Science. Thomas Troward. 1909. 9.95 (ISBN 0-396-02062-3). Dodd.

Edith Stein: Life in a Jewish Family. Tr. by Josephine Koeppel from Ger. LC 84-25164. (Illus.). 576p. (Orig.). 1986. pap. 10.95x (ISBN 0-935216-04-9). ICS Pubns.

Editing of the Hebrew Psalter. Gerald H. Wilson. (Society of Biblical Literature Disseration Ser.: No. 76). 1985. pap. 11.50 (ISBN 0-89130-728-1). Scholars Pr GA.

Edition of the Judica Me Deus of Richard Rolle. John P. Daly. Ed. by James Hogg. (Elizabethan & Renaissance Studies). (Orig.). 1984. pap. 15.00 (ISBN 0-317-40134-3, Pub by Salzburg Studies). Longwood Pub Group.

Editorial Wild Oats: Edward Ward Carmack & Tennessee Politics. William R. Majors. LC 84-10870. xx, 194p. 1984. 17.50 (ISBN 0-86554-133-7, MUP/H124). Mercer Univ Pr.

Editorially Speaking. O. W. Polen. 1975. pap. 2.25 (ISBN 0-87148-300-9). Pathway Pr.

Editorially Speaking, Vol. 2. O. W. Polen. 58p. 1980. pap. 2.25 (ISBN 0-87148-296-7). Pathway Pr.

Editorials from Lehre und Wehre. C. F. Walther. Tr. by Herbert J. Bouman. (Selected Writings of C. F. W. Walther Ser.). 1981. 12.95 (ISBN 0-570-08280-3, 15-2738). Concordia.

Edmond Jabes: Un Judaisme Apres Dieu. Miryam Laifer. (American University Studies II: Romance Languages & Literature: Vol. 39). 165p. 1986. pap. 33.70 (ISBN 0-8204-0283-4). P Lang Pubs.

Edmund Spenser. Ed. by Harold Bloom. (Modern Critical Views-Medieval & Renaissance Ser.). 1986. 29.50 (ISBN 0-87754-672-X). Chelsea Hse.

Eduardo el Curandero: The Words of a Peruvian Healer. Eduardo Caleron et al. (Illus.). 200p. 1982. 20.00 (ISBN 0-913028-94-0); pap. 7.95 (ISBN 0-913028-95-9). North Atlantic.

Educating for Healthy Emotions: The Emotional Development of Children. Mary Vander Goot. 176p. (Orig.). 1987. pap. 8.95 (ISBN 0-8010-9303-1). Baker Bk.

Educating the New Jewish Woman: A Dynamic Approach. Irene Fine. LC 85-51215. 80p. (Orig.). 1985. pap. 8.95 (ISBN 0-9608054-4-3). Womans Inst-Cont Jewish Ed.

Education. Ed. by Monks of Solesmes. 1960. 8.50 (ISBN 0-8198-2300-7). Dghtrs St Paul.

Education. Swami Vivekananda. pap. 1.95 (ISBN 0-87481-451-0). Vedanta Pr.

Education & Religion. facs. ed. Charles F. Thwing. LC 71-105044. (Essay Index Reprint Ser). 1929. 19.00 (ISBN 0-8369-1629-8). Ayer Co Pubs.

Education & the Signficance of Life. J. Krishnamurti. LC 53-10971. 128p. 1981. pap. 6.95 (ISBN 0-06-064876-7, RD 356, HarpR). Har-Row.

Education & the Threat of Nuclear War. Ed. by Belle Zars et al. (Reprint Ser.: No. 18). 166p. 1985. pap. 9.95x (ISBN 0-916690-20-2). Harvard Educ Rev.

Education As an Art, Vol. 13. Rudolf Steiner et al. Ed. by Paul M. Allen. Tr. by Michael Tapp & Elizabeth Tapp. LC 73-130816. (Spiritual Science Library). 128p. (Orig.). 1981. lib. bdg. 11.00 (ISBN 0-89345-024-3); pap. 6.00 (ISBN 0-89345-202-5, Steinerbks). Garber Comm.

Education, Christianity & the State. J. Gresham Machen. Ed. & intro. by John W. Robbins. (Trinity Papers: No. 19). 150p. (Orig.). 1987. pap. 5.95 (ISBN 0-940931-19-2). Trinity Found.

Education for Christian Living: Strategies for Nurture Based on Biblical & Historical Foundations. Ed. by Marvin L. Roloff. LC 86-28756. 224p. (Orig.). 1986. pap. 12.95 (ISBN 0-8066-2238-5, 10-2003). Augsburg.

Education for Christian Service: A Volume in Commemoration of the 100th Anniversary of the Divinity School of Yale University. Yale Divinity School Faculty Members Staff & Charles R. Brown. 1922. 49.50x (ISBN 0-685-89749-4). Elliots Bks.

Education for Continuity & Change: A New Model for Christian Religious Education. Mary E. Moore. 224p. (Orig.). 1983. pap. 10.95 (ISBN 0-687-11523-X). Abingdon.

Education for Freedom: The Philosophy of Education of Jacques Maritain. Jean-Louis Allard. Tr. by Ralph C. Nelson. 130p. 1982. pap. text ed. 8.95 (ISBN 0-268-00909-0). U of Notre Dame Pr.

Education for Peace: Testimonies from World Religions. Ed. by Haim Gordon & Leonard Grob. LC 86-31083. 224p. (Orig.). 1987. pap. 14.95 (ISBN 0-88344-359-7). Orbis Bks.

Education for Spiritual Growth. Iris V. Cully. LC 83-48464. 192p. 1984. 14.45 (ISBN 0-06-061655-5, HarpR). Har-Row.

Education for the Real World. Henry M. Morris. LC 77-78017. 1977. pap. 8.95 (ISBN 0-89051-093-8). Master Bks.

Education for Values. Ed. by David C. McClelland. 220p. 1982. 29.50x (ISBN 0-8290-0090-9). Irvington.

Education, Human Nature & Peace: A Scientific Look at Religion. rev. ed. Lillian Maki. 192p. 1985. 8.50 (ISBN 0-9617372-0-4). Maryatta Co.

Education in Human Development. 400p. 1987. pap. 12.95 (ISBN 0-89800-134-X). Dharma Pub.

Education in Human Sexuality for Christians, Guidelines for Discussion & Planning. 118p. 1981. pap. 8.50 (ISBN 1-55586-691-3). US Catholic.

Education in Religious Understanding: A Report from the Foundation for Education in Religion & Morality. John B. Wilson & Samuel M. Natale. LC 86-28167. 86p. 1987. lib. bdg. 19.75 (ISBN 0-8191-5948-4); pap. text ed. 9.50 (ISBN 0-8191-5949-2). U Pr of Amer.

Education Ministry in the Congregation: Eight Ways We Learn from One Another. Norma J. Everist. LC 83-70515. 240p. (Orig.). 1983. pap. 11.95 (ISBN 0-8066-2021-8, 10-2006). Augsburg.

Education of a Black Muslim. Ibrahim Shalaby. 1980. pap. 1.25 (ISBN 0-686-32639-3). Impresora Sahuaro.

Education of Catholic Americans. Andrew M. Greeley & Peter H. Rossi. LC 66-10867. (NORC Monographs in Social Research Ser.: No. 6). 1966. 8.95x (ISBN 0-202-09003-5). NORC.

Education of Christ. William M. Ramsay. LC 80-84438. (Shepherd Illustrated Classics Ser.). (Illus.). 168p. 1981. pap. 5.95 (ISBN 0-87983-236-3). Keats.

Education of Desire: Plato & the Philosophy of Religion. Michel Despland. 400p. 1985. 25.00 (ISBN 0-8020-6524-4). U of Toronto Pr.

Education of Negro Ministers. William A. Daniel. LC 77-78581. Repr. of 1925 ed. cancelled (ISBN 0-8371-1410-1, DNM&, Pub. by Negro U Pr). Greenwood.

Education of Primitive People. Albert D. Helser. LC 75-97403. Repr. of 1934 ed. cancelled (ISBN 0-8371-2651-7, HPP&, Pub. by Negro U Pr). Greenwood.

Education of the Child. 2nd ed. Tr. of Die Erziehung des Kindes vom Gesichtspunkee. 50p. 1985. pap. 5.95 (ISBN 0-88010-133-4). Anthroposophic.

Education, Religion, & the Supreme Court. Ed. by Richard C. McMillan. LC 78-74196. (Special Studies: No. 6). iv, 129p. 1979. pap. 8.95 (ISBN 0-932180-05-1). NABPR.

Educational Aspects of the Legislation of the Councils of Baltimore, 1829-1884. Bernard J. Meiring. 25.50 (ISBN 0-405-10844-3, 11821). Ayer Co Pubs.

Educational Aspects of the Missions of the Southwest. Sr. Mary Stanislaus Van Well. 1942. pap. 7.95 (ISBN 0-87462-438-X). Marquette.

Educational Ministry of a Church. Charles A. Tidwell. LC 81-68922. 1982. pap. 10.95 (ISBN 0-8054-3231-0). Broadman.

Educational Philosophy of Martin Buber. Adir Cohen. LC 81-68074. 350p. 1983. 32.50 (ISBN 0-8386-3098-7). Fairleigh Dickinson.

Educational Philosophy of Saint John Bosco. John A. Morrison. LC 79-54817. 258p. (Orig.). 1979. pap. 8.95 (ISBN 0-89944-050-9). Don Bosco Multimedia.

Educational Thought, Vol. 1. Jal J. Nanavaty. 1973. pap. 10.00 (ISBN 0-89744-150-8, Pub. by Joshi & Lockhande India). Auromere.

Educational Thought & Influence of Matthew Arnold. William F. Connell. LC 74-109305. 1971. Repr. of 1950 ed. lib. bdg. 22.50x (ISBN 0-8371-3580-X, COMA). Greenwood.

Edward Gibbon & His Age. Edmund Blunden. 1978. Repr. of 1935 ed. lib. bdg. 12.50 (ISBN 0-8495-0448-1). Arden Lib.

Edward Gibbon & His Age. Edmund C. Blunden. LC 74-14702. 1974. Repr. of 1935 ed. lib. bdg. 7.50 (ISBN 0-8414-3287-2). Folcroft.

Edward Granville Browne & the Baha'i Faith. H. M. Balyuzi. (Illus.). 152p. 1970. 14.95 (ISBN 0-85398-023-3). G Ronald Pub.

Edward Hicks, Primitive Quaker. Eleanore P. Mather. LC 75-110287. (Illus., Orig.). 1970. pap. 2.50x (ISBN 0-87574-170-3, 170). Pendle Hill.

Edward Hicks: His Peaceable Kingdoms & Other Paintings. Eleanore P. Mather & Dorothy C. Miller. LC 81-71405. (Illus.). 224p. 1983. 40.00 (ISBN 0-87413-208-8). U Delaware Pr.

Edward Hicks, Painter of the Peaceable Kingdom. Alice E. Ford. LC 52-13392. (Illus.). 1973. Repr. of 1952 ed. 63.00 (ISBN 0-527-30400-X). Kraus Repr.

Edward: Pilgrimage of a Mind. Edward Yoder. Ed. & pref. by Ida Yoder. (Illus.). 512p. 1985. 20.00 (ISBN 0-9614083-0-8). Yoder.

Edward Schillebeeckx: In Search of the Kingdom of God. John Bowden. 160p. 1983. pap. 8.95 (ISBN 0-8245-0610-3). Crossroad NY.

Edward Taylor's "Church Records" & Related Sermons. Ed. by Thomas M. Davis & Virginia L. Davis. (American Literary Manuscripts Ser.). 1981. lib. bdg. 36.50 (ISBN 0-8057-9650-9, Twayne). G K Hall.

Edwin Diller Starbuck: Pioneer in the Psychology of Religion. Howard J. Booth. LC 80-5731. 304p. 1981. pap. text ed. 15.50 (ISBN 0-8191-1703-X). U Pr of Amer.

Eerdmans' Analytical Concordance to the Revised Standard Version. Compiled by Richard W. Whitaker. 1488p. 1987. 49.95 (ISBN 0-8028-2403-X). Eerdmans.

Eerdmans' Book of Christian Classics. Veronica Zundel. 125p. 1985. 12.95 (ISBN 0-8028-3612-7). Eerdmans.

Eerdmans Book of Christian Poetry. Ed. by Pat Alexander. 128p. 1981. 12.95 (ISBN 0-8028-3555-4). Eerdmans.

Eerdmans' Book of Famous Prayers. Ed. by Veronica Zundel. (Illus.). 126p. 1984. 12.95 (ISBN 0-8028-3593-7). Eerdmans.

Eerdmans' Concise Bible Encyclopedia. Ed. by Pat Alexander. LC 80-19885. (Illus.). 256p. (Orig.). 1981. pap. 8.95 (ISBN 0-8028-1876-5). Eerdmans.

Eerdmans' Concise Bible Handbook. Ed. by David Alexander & Pat Alexander. LC 80-20131. (Illus.). 384p. (Orig.). 1981. pap. 9.95 (ISBN 0-8028-1875-7). Eerdmans.

Eerdmans' Family Encyclopedia of the Bible. Ed. by Patricia Alexander. (Illus.). 1978. 18.95 (ISBN 0-8028-3517-1). Eerdmans.

Eerdmans' Handbook to Christian Belief. Robin Keely. (Illus.). 480p. 1982. 24.95 (ISBN 0-8028-3577-5). Eerdmans.

Eerdmans' Handbook to Christianity in America. Ed. by Mark A. Noll et al. LC 83-1656. (Illus.). 544p. 1983. 24.95 (ISBN 0-8028-3582-1). Eerdmans.

Eerdmans' Handbook to the Bible. rev. ed. Ed. by David Alexander & Pat Alexander. (Illus.). 680p. 1983. 24.95 (ISBN 0-8028-3486-8). Eerdmans.

Eerdmans' Handbook to the History of Christianity. Tim Dowley. LC 77-5616. 1977. 24.95 (ISBN 0-8028-3450-7). Eerdmans.

Eerdmans' Handbook to the World's Religions. (Illus.). 1982. 21.95 (ISBN 0-8028-3563-5). Eerdmans.

Efesios: La Gloria de la Iglesia (Comentario Biblico Portavoz) Homer Kent, Jr. Orig. Title: Ephesians: The Glory of the Church (Everyman's Bible Commentary) (Span.). 144p. 1981. pap. 3.95 (ISBN 0-8254-1405-9). Kregel.

Efesios y Filemon. Marilyn Kunz & Catherine Schell. Tr. by Julio Orozco from Eng. LC 77-83811. (Encuentros Biblicos Ser.). Tr. of Ephesians & Philemon. (Span.). 55p. 1977. pap. 1.25 (ISBN 0-89922-095-9). Edit Caribe.

Effective Bible Study. Howard F. Vos. (Contemporary Evangelical Perspectives Ser.). 1956. kivar 6.95 (ISBN 0-310-33851-4, 10966P). Zondervan.

Effective Biblical Counseling. Crabb, Jr. & J. Lawrence. 1986. 9.95 (ISBN 0-88469-187-X). BMH Bks.

Effective Biblical Counseling: A Model for Helping Caring Christians Become Capable Counselors. Lawrence J. Crabb, Jr. 1977. 10.95 (ISBN 0-310-22570-1, 10173). Zondervan.

Effective Catholic Schools: An Exploration-Executive Summary. 104p. 1984. 21.60 (ISBN 0-318-03689-4). Natl Cath Educ.

Effective Christian Ministry. Ronald W. Leigh. 256p. 1984. pap. 6.95 (ISBN 0-8423-0733-8); leader's guide 2.95 (ISBN 0-8423-0734-6). Tyndale.

Effective Christian School Management. 2nd ed. James W. Deuink & Carl D. Herbster. (Illus.). 291p. 1986. pap. 8.95 (ISBN 0-89084-319-8). Bob Jones Univ Pr.

Effective Church Councils: Leadership Styles & Decision Making in the Church. Paul Fransen. (Administration Series for Churches). 56p. (Orig.). 1985. pap. 3.95 (ISBN 0-8066-2198-2, 10-2023). Augsburg.

Effective Church Planning. Lyle E. Schaller. LC 78-26462. 1979. 6.95 (ISBN 0-687-11530-2). Abingdon.

Effective Communication. David S. Bishop. LC 76-58043. 1977. 5.25 (ISBN 0-87148-285-1); pap. text ed. 4.25 (ISBN 0-87148-286-X). Pathway Pr.

Effective Communications Instructor's Manual. Joseph Laing & Grant McClung. 1977. pap. 5.25 (ISBN 0-87148-289-4). Pathway Pr.

Effective Encouragement. Charlotte Adelsperger. (Illus.). 64p. 1986. pap. 2.95 (ISBN 0-87403-077-3, 3197). Standard Pub.

Effective Faith. J. Oswald Sanders. Orig. Title: Mighty Faith. 1980. pap. 1.00 (ISBN 9971-83-833-8). OMF Bks.

Effective Father. Gordon MacDonald. 1977. pap. 6.95 (ISBN 0-8423-0680-3). Tyndale.

Effective Father Action Guide. Jim Webb et al. 1979. 3.95 (ISBN 0-8423-0688-9). Tyndale.

Effective Invitation. R. Alan Streett. 1984. pap. 6.95 (ISBN 0-8007-5170-1, Power Bks). Revell.

Effective Jewish Parenting. Miriam Levi. 1986. 10.95 (ISBN 0-87306-405-4). Feldheim.

Effective Leadership for Today's Church. Arthur M. Adams. LC 77-27547. 202p. 1978. pap. 6.95 (ISBN 0-664-24196-4). Westminster.

Effective Methods of Church Growth. Andy Anderson. LC 85-6620. 1985. pap. 5.95 (ISBN 0-8054-3237-X). Broadman.

Effective Minister. Michael E. Cavanagh. 160p. (Orig.). 1986. 14.95 (ISBN 0-06-254210-9, HarpR). Har-Row.

Effective Missionary. Rulon G. Craven. LC 82-1471. 106p. 1982. 6.95 (ISBN 0-87747-898-8). Deseret Bk.

Effective Mormon Families. William G. Dyer & Phillip R. Kunz. 1986. text ed. 9.95 (ISBN 0-87579-059-3). Deseret Bk.

Effective Pastor. Zenas J. Bicket. LC 74-80729. 185p. 1973. 3.95 (ISBN 0-88243-512-4, 02-0512). Gospel Pub.

Effective Pastor: A Practical Guide to the Ministry. Robert C. Anderson. 1985. 15.95 (ISBN 0-8024-6359-2). Moody.

Effective Prayer. Ernest Holmes. Ed. by Willis H. Kinnear. 52p. 1966. pap. 4.50 (ISBN 0-911336-02-8). Sci of Mind.

Effective Prayer. J. Oswald Sanders. pap. write for info. (ISBN 0-8024-0781-1). Moody.

Effective Prayer. J. Oswald Sanders. 1961. pap. 1.00 (ISBN 9971-83-818-4). OMF Bks.

Effective Prayer. R. C. Sproul. 96p. 1984. 2.50 (ISBN 0-8423-0735-4). Tyndale.

Effective Prayer Life. Chuck Smith. LC 78-27511. 96p. 1980. pap. 1.95 (ISBN 0-936728-03-5). Word for Today.

Effective Preaching: A Manual for Students & Pastors. Deane A. Kemper. LC 84-20880. 142p. (Orig.). 1985. pap. 10.95 (ISBN 0-664-24595-1). Westminster.

Effective Urban Church Ministry. G. Willis Bennett. LC 83-70370. 1983. pap. 5.95 (ISBN 0-8054-5526-4). Broadman.

Effectual Prayer. Frances W. Foulks. 1979. 5.95 (ISBN 0-87159-031-X). Unity School.

Efrain Rios Montt - Servant or Dictator? The Real Story of Guatemala's Controversial "Born Again" President. Joseph Anfuso & David Sczepanski. LC 84-7553. pap. 5.95 (ISBN 0-88449-110-2, A424705). Vision Hse.

Egeria, Diary of a Pilgrimage. Ed. by W. J. Burghardt et al. LC 70-119159. (ACW Ser.: No. 38). 292p. 1970. 14.95 (ISBN 0-8091-0029-0). Paulist Pr.

Egermeier's Bible Story Book. 5th ed. Elsie E. Egermeier. LC 68-23397. (Illus.). 1969. 14.95 (ISBN 0-87162-006-5, D2005); deluxe ed. 15.95 (ISBN 0-87162-007-3, D2006); pap. 8.95 (ISBN 0-87162-229-7, D2008). Warner Pr.

Egermeier's Favorite Bible Stories. Elsie E. Egermeier. 1965. 7.95 (ISBN 0-87162-014-6, D3695). Warner Pr.

Egermeier's Picture-Story Life of Jesus. Elsie E. Egermeier. (Illus.). 1969. 7.95 (ISBN 0-87162-008-1, D2015). Warner Pr.

Eglise Byzantine De 527 a 847. Jules Pargoire. 1971. Repr. of 1905 ed. lib. bdg. 26.00 (ISBN 0-8337-2672-2). B Franklin.

Eglise et l'Orient au moyen age: Les croisades. 2nd ed. Louis Brehier. LC 76-29834. (Fr.). Repr. of 1907 ed. 39.50 (ISBN 0-404-15413-1). AMS Pr.

Eglise Latine et le Protestantisme, Au Point De Vue De l'Eglise d'Orient. Aleksiei S. Khomiakov. LC 80-2362. Repr. of 1872 ed. 49.00 (ISBN 0-404-18908-3). AMS Pr.

Ego in Faith: Martin Luther & the Origins of Anthropocentric Religion. Paul Hacker. Ed. by Jared Wicks. LC 70-85506. (Das Ich Im Glauben Bei Martin Luther). 1971. 6.50 (ISBN 0-8199-0406-6). Franciscan Herald.

Ego: Revealer-Concealer, a Key to Yoga. Frank R. Podgorski. (Illus.). 306p. 1985. lib. bdg. 27.50 (ISBN 0-8191-4345-6); pap. text ed. 14.50 (ISBN 0-8191-4346-4). U Pr of Amer.

Egoshell. Robert A. Thompson & Louise S. Thompson. 280p. 1986. 22.95 (ISBN 0-87975-365-X). Prometheus Bks.

Egypt & Bible History: From Earliest Times to 1000 B.C. Charles F. Aling. (Baker Studies in Biblical Archaeology). 144p. (Orig.). 1981. pap. 5.95 (ISBN 0-8010-0174-9). Baker Bk.

Egypt & Negro Africa: Study in Divine Kingship. Charles G. Seligman. LC 74-15088. (Frazer Lecture: 1933). (Illus.). Repr. of 1934 ed. 21.50 (ISBN 0-404-12138-1). AMS Pr.

Egypt & Nuclear Technology: The Peace Divident. Ed. by G. H. Schuler. (Significant Issues Ser.: Vol. V, No. 9). 24p. (Orig.). 1983. pap. text ed. 6.95 (ISBN 0-8191-5924-7, Pub. by CSIS). U Pr of Amer.

Egypt & Palestine: A Millennium of Association (868-1948) Ed. by Amnon Cohen & Gabriel Baer. LC 84-16109. 400p. 1985. 32.50 (ISBN 0-312-23927-0). St Martin.

Egypt & the Holy Land in Historic Photographs. Francis Frith. Selected by Jon. E. White. 16.50 (ISBN 0-8446-5887-1). Peter Smith.

Egypt & the Holy Land in Historic Photographs: Seventy-Seven Views. Francis Frith. Ed. by Julia Van Haaften. 112p. 1981. pap. 7.95 (ISBN 0-486-24048-7). Dover.

Egyptian Background of Hebrew History. Charles Kent. (Illus.). 133p. 1982. Repr. of 1908 ed. 73.45 (ISBN 0-89901-068-7). Found Class Reprints.

Egyptian Book of the Dead: The Papyrus of Ani in the British Museum. E. A. Wallis Budge. 1967. pap. 8.95 (ISBN 0-486-21866-X). Dover.

Egyptian Book of the Dead: The Papyrus of Ani. E. A. Budge. 16.25 (ISBN 0-8446-1764-4). Peter Smith.

Egyptian Gods. Alan W. Shorter. (Mythology Library: Vol. 5). 300p. 1985. pap. 7.95 (ISBN 0-87877-082-8). Newcastle Pub.

Egyptian Gods: A Handbook. A. W. Shorter. 1978. pap. 7.50 (ISBN 0-7100-0982-8). Methuen Inc.

Egyptian Gods: A Handbook. Alan W. Shorter. LC 85-26911. (Newcastle Mythology Library: Vol. 5). 300p. 1985. Repr. lib. bdg. 17.95x (ISBN 0-89370-682-5). Borgo Pr.

Egyptian Heaven & Hell. E. A. Budge. 1980. lib. bdg. 59.95 (ISBN 0-8490-3203-2). Gordon Pr.

Egyptian Heaven & Hell, 3 vols. Ernest A. Budge. LC 73-18844. (Illus.). Repr. of 1906 ed. Set. 57.50 (ISBN 0-404-11326-5). AMS Pr.

Egyptian Heaven & Hell. Ernest A. Budge. (Illus.). 200p. 1974. lib. bdg. 16.95 (ISBN 0-87548-311-9); pap. 5.95 (ISBN 0-87548-298-8). Open Court.

Egyptian Heritage: Based on the Edgar Cayce Readings. Mark Lehner. 136p. 1974. pap. 5.95 (ISBN 0-87604-071-7). ARE Pr.

Egyptian Ideas of the Future Life. Ernest A. Budge. LC 73-18839. Repr. of 1899 ed. 14.00 (ISBN 0-404-11330-3). AMS Pr.

Egyptian Magic. E. Wallis Budge. 1971. pap. 4.00 (ISBN 0-486-22681-6). Dover.

Egyptian Magic. Wallis Budge. 1978. pap. 3.95 (ISBN 0-8065-0629-6). Citadel Pr.

Egyptian Miracle: The Wisdom of the Temple. R. A. Schwaller de Lubicz. Tr. by A. VandenBroeck & G. VandenBroeck. (Illus.). 320p. 1985. 14.95 (ISBN 0-89281-008-4). Inner Tradit.

Egyptian Mummy: Secrets & Science. Stuart Fleming et al. (University Museum Handbook Ser.: No. 1). (Illus.). x, 93p. (Orig.). 1980. pap. 10.00x (ISBN 0-934718-38-5). Univ Mus of U Pa.

Egyptian Mysteries: New Light on Ancient Spiritual Knowledge. Lucie Lamy. Ed. by Jill Purce. LC 81-66806. (Illustrated Library of Sacred Imagination Ser.). (Illus.). 96p. 1981. pap. 9.95 (ISBN 0-8245-0055-5). Crossroad NY.

Egyptian Myth & Legend. Donald A. Mackenzie. LC 76-27520. (Illus.). 1976. Repr. of 1907 ed. lib. bdg. 40.00 (ISBN 0-89341-033-0). Longwood Pub Group.

Egyptian Myth & Legend. Donald A. MacKenzie. 454p. 1984. pap. cancelled (ISBN 0-89341-487-5). Longwood Pub Group.

Egyptian Mythology. rev. ed. Veronica Ions. LC 83-71478. (Library of the World's Myths & Legends). (Illus.). 144p. 1983. 18.95 (ISBN 0-911745-07-6). P Bedrick Bks.

Egyptian Mythology. Veronica Ions. (Library of the World's Myths & Legends). (Illus.). 144p. PLB 16.95 (ISBN 0-317-31011-9). Creative Ed.

Egyptian Mythology & Indochinese Mythology. W. Max Muller. Bd. with James G. Scott. LC 63-19097. (Mythology of All Races Ser.: Vol. 12). (Illus.). Repr. of 1932 ed. 30.00x (ISBN 0-8154-0160-4). Cooper Sq.

Egyptian Myths & Mysteries. Rudolf Steiner. Tr. by Norman Macbeth from Ger. 1971. 15.00 (ISBN 0-910142-09-2); pap. 7.95 (ISBN 0-910142-10-6). Anthroposophic.

Egyptian Religion. E. Wallis Budge. (Illus.). 1979. pap. 6.95 (ISBN 0-7100-0134-7). Methuen Inc.

Egyptian Religion. Siegfried Morenz. LC 73-8407. 395p. 1973. 39.95x (ISBN 0-8014-0782-6). Cornell U Pr.

Egyptian Religious Poetry. Margaret A. Murray. Ed. by J. L. Cranmer-Byng. LC 79-8714. (Wisdom of the East Ser.). 120p. 1980. Repr. of 1949 ed. lib. bdg. 22.50x (ISBN 0-313-21012-8, MUER). Greenwood.

Egyptian Revival. James S. Curl. (Illus.). 256p. 1982. 50.00 (ISBN 0-04-724001-6). Allen Unwin.

Egyptian Revival: Its Sources, Monuments, & Meaning (1808-1858) Richard G. Carrott. LC 76-24579. (Illus.). 1978. 44.50x (ISBN 0-520-03324-8). U of Cal Pr.

Egyptian Temple: A Lexicographical Study. Patricia Spencer. 300p. 1984. 50.00x (ISBN 0-7103-0065-4, Kegan Paul). Methuen Inc.

Egyptian Temples. Margaret A. Murray. LC 75-41203. Repr. of 1931 ed. 27.50 (ISBN 0-404-14719-4). AMS Pr.

Ehe. (Ger.). pap. 2.55 (ISBN 0-686-32321-1). Rod & Staff.

Eichah-Lamentations. Meir Zlotowitz. (Art Scroll Tanach Ser.). 160p. 1976. 11.95 (ISBN 0-89906-004-8); pap. 8.95 (ISBN 0-89906-005-6). Mesorah Pubns.

Eichmann in Jerusalem: A Report of the Banality of Evil. rev ed. Hannah Arendt. 1977. pap. 6.95 (ISBN 0-14-004450-7). Penguin.

Eiffel Tower & Other Mythologies. Roland Barthes. Tr. by Richard Howard from Fr. 152p. 1979. 9.95 (ISBN 0-8090-4115-4); pap. 5.25 (ISBN 0-8090-1391-6). Hill & Wang.

Eight Boyle Lectures on Atheism. Richard Bentley. Ed. by Rene Wellek. LC 75-11196. (British Philosophers & Theologians of the 17th & 18th Centuries Ser.: Vol. 3). 1976. Repr. of 1692 ed. lib. bdg. 51.00 (ISBN 0-8240-1752-8). Garland Pub.

Eight Chapters of Maimonides on Ethics. Moses Ben Maimon. (Columbia University. Oriental Studies: No. 7). Repr. of 1912 ed. 24.50 (ISBN 0-404-50497-3). AMS Pr.

Eight Decisive Books of Antiquity. Frederick R. Hoare. LC 73-99638. (Essay Index Reprint Ser). 1952. 19.50 (ISBN 0-8369-1414-7). Ayer Co Pubs.

Eight Favorite Anthems. Evan Stephens. 1972. pap. 1.95 (ISBN 0-87747-350-1). Deseret Bk.

Eight Jewish Philosophers. 1982. 12.95 (ISBN 0-686-76505-2). Feldheim.

Eight Keys to Spiritual & Physical Health. 96p. 1982. pap. 3.95 (ISBN 0-89221-092-3, Pub. by SonLife). New Leaf.

Eight Keys to Success. Jim Bakker. LC 79-92249. 128p. 1980. pap. 2.50 (ISBN 0-89221-071-0). New Leaf.

Eight Laws of Health. Joe Maniscalco. 1985. pap. 3.95 (ISBN 0-8163-0568-4). Pacific Pr Pub Assn.

Eight Lectures on Yoga. Aleister Crowley. 1972. pap. 5.95 (ISBN 0-87728-122-X). Weiser.

Eight Lectures on Yoga. Aleister Crowley. 80p. 1985. pap. 5.95 (ISBN 0-941404-36-6). Falcon Pr AZ.

Eight Lives: A Study of the Hindu-Muslim Encounter. Rajmohan Gandhi. 320p. 1986. 39.50x (ISBN 0-88706-196-6); pap. 14.95x (ISBN 0-88706-197-4). State U NY Pr.

Eight Minor Prophets: A Linguistic Concordance. Francis I. Andersen & A. Dean Forbes. (Computer Bible Ser.: Vol. X). 1976. pap. 25.00 (ISBN 0-935106-11-1). Biblical Res Assocs.

Eight Nights: A Chanukah Counting Book. Jane Bearman. Ed. by Daniel B. Syme. LC 78-60781. (Illus.). 1979. pap. 4.50 (ISBN 0-8074-0025-4, 102562). UAHC.

Eight Sacred Horizons: The Religious Imagination East & West. Vernon Ruland. 240p. 1985. 19.95x (ISBN 0-317-18117-3). MacMillan.

Eight Sculptors. Douglas G. Schultz. LC 79-50457. (Illus.). 1979. pap. 6.50 (ISBN 0-914782-25-8). Buffalo Acad.

Eight Stages of Christian Growth: Human Development in Psycho-Spiritual Terms. Philip A. Captain. (Illus.). 240p. 1984. pap. 6.95 (ISBN 0-13-246661-9). P-H.

Eight Thousand Years of Wisdom: Conversations with Taoist Master Ni, Hua Ching, Bk. 1. Ni Hua Ching. LC 83-51082. 248p. (Orig.). 1983. pap. text ed. 12.50 (ISBN 0-937064-07-6). SEBT.

Eight Thousand Years of Wisdom: Conversations with Taoist Master Ni, Hua Ching, Bk. 2. Ni Hua Ching. LC 83-51082. 248p. (Orig.). 1983. pap. text ed. 12.50 (ISBN 0-937064-08-4). SEBT.

Eight, Tulpengasse: A Church Blossom's in Vienna. Margaret Epp. 276p. (Orig.). 1978. pap. 4.95 (ISBN 0-919797-01-6, Dist. by Herald Pr.). Kindred Pr.

Eight Virtues: Culture. Cheng Wang-Mong. 1987. 6.95 (ISBN 0-533-07189-5). Vantage.

Eight Years in Kaffraria, 1882-1890. Alan G. Gibson. LC 79-82052. (Illus.). Repr. of 1891 ed. cancelled (ISBN 0-8371-1573-6, GIK&, Pub. by Negro U Pr). Greenwood.

Eighteen Eighty-Eight Message. Robert Wieland. LC 80-10807. (Horizon Ser.). 1980. pap. 5.95 (ISBN 0-8127-0283-2). Review & Herald.

Eighteen Thirty-Eight Mormon War in Missouri. Stephen C. LeSueur. LC 86-16090. 256p. 1987. text ed. 24.00 (ISBN 0-8262-0626-3, 83-36349). U of Mo Pr.

Eighteen Years in Uganda & East Africa. Alfred R. Tucker. LC 77-106884. Repr. of 1911 ed. cancelled (ISBN 0-8371-3280-0, TUU&, Pub. by Negro U Pr). Greenwood.

Eighteenth Century Creche. Hanns Swarzenski. LC 66-25450. (Illus.). 1966. pap. 2.00 (ISBN 0-87846-142-6, Pub. by Mus Fine Arts Boston). C E Tuttle.

Eighth Century Prophets: Amos, Hosea, Isaiah, Micah. Bernhard W. Anderson. Ed. by Foster R. McCurley. LC 78-54545. (Proclamation Commentaries: the Old Testament Witnesses for Preaching). 128p. 1978. pap. 5.95 (ISBN 0-8006-0595-0, 1-595). Fortress.

Eighth, Ninth & Tenth Books of Moses. H. Gamache. 4.95x (ISBN 0-685-21888-0). Wehman.

Eighth World Congress of Jewish Studies. Ed. by World Union of Jewish Studies. 242p. 1983. pap. text ed. 25.00x (Pub. by Magnes Pr Israel). Humanities.

Eighties, the Antichrist & Your Startling Future. Jack Van Impe. 87p. 1982. pap. 1.95 (ISBN 0-934803-12-9). J Van Impe.

Eighty Seven Immortals. 1982. limited 900.00 (ISBN 0-384-14045-9). Johnson Repr.

Eighty Talks for Orthodox Young People. A. M. Coniaris. 1975. pap. 4.95 (ISBN 0-937032-16-6). Light&Life Pub Co MN.

Eighty-Three Different Questions. St. Augustine. LC 81-2546. (Fathers of the Church Ser.: Vol. 70). 257p. 1982. 29.95x (ISBN 0-8132-0070-9). Cath U Pr.

Ein Leben Fur Den Herrn. Erich Ratzlaff. 171p. (Orig.). 1985. pap. 6.75 (ISBN 0-919797-37-7). Kindred Pr.

Eine Wurzel: Tennessee John Stolzfus. Paton Yoder. LC 79-26507. (Illus.). 192p. 1979. 10.50 (ISBN 0-915010-27-5). Sutter House.

Einfluss Bernhards von Clairvaux auf Gottfried von Strassburg. Karl Allgaier. (European University Studies Ser.: No. 1, Vol. 641). (Ger.). 185p. 1983. 24.20 (ISBN 3-8204-7541-9). P Lang Pubs.

Einfuehrung in das Alte Testament: Dritte, Erweiterte Auflage. Werner H. Schmidt. (Ger.). x, 394p. 1985. 19.20x (ISBN 3-11-010403-2). De Gruyter.

Einfuehrung in die Mischna. Chanoch Albeck. (Studia Judaica, 6). 493p. 1971. 33.60x (ISBN 3-11-006429-4). De Gruyter.

Einleitung in die Drei Ersten Evangelien. Walter Schmithals. 512p. 1985. 23.20x (ISBN 3-11-010263-3). De Gruyter.

Einleitung Zu Den Werken Des Dom Georgius Schwengel. Wilhelm Brauer. Ed. by James Hogg. (Analecta Cartusiana Ser.: No. 90). 27p. (Orig.). 1982. pap. 25.00 (ISBN 3-7052-0147-6, Pub. by Salzburg Studies). Longwood Pub Group.

Einsatzgruppen or Murder Commandos. John Mendelsohn. LC 81-80318. (Holocaust Ser.). 256p. 1982. lib. bdg. 61.00 (ISBN 0-8240-4884-9). Garland Pub.

Einsatzgruppen Reports: Selections from the Official Dispatches of the Nazi Death Squads' Campaign Against the Jews. Compiled by Yitzhak Arad. 1986. 15.95 (ISBN 0-89604-057-7); pap. 10.95 (ISBN 0-89604-058-5). Holocaust Pubns.

Einstein & Christ: A New Approach to the Defence of Christian Religion. Ralph Mitchell. (Theology & Science at the Frontiers of Knowledge Ser.: Vol. 5). 256p. 1986. 21.95 (ISBN 0-7073-0453-9, Pub. by Scot Acad Pr). Longwood Pub Group.

Einstein Syndrome: Corporate Anti-Semitism in America Today. Stephen L. Slavin & Mary A. Pradt. LC 81-43767. (Illus., Orig.). 1982. lib. bdg. 26.25 (ISBN 0-8191-2370-6); pap. text ed. 11.25 (ISBN 0-8191-2371-4). U Pr of Amer.

Einstein Was Wrong: Or the Scroll Theory of Cosmology & of Matter. Reginald T. Chelvam. LC 82-71689. (Illus.). 268p. (Orig.). 1982. pap. 19.95 (ISBN 0-943796-00-8). Penso Pubns.

Either-Or, 2 Vols. Soren Kierkegaard. Tr. by W. Lowrie. 1944. Vol 1. pap. 7.95 (ISBN 0-691-01976-2); Vol. 2. pap. 7.95x (ISBN 0-691-01977-0). Princeton U Pr.

Either Way, I Win: A Guide for Growth in the Power of Prayer. Lois W. Johnson. LC 79-50078. 1979. pap. 4.95 (ISBN 0-8066-1706-3, 10-2040). Augsburg.

El Shaddai. Kenneth E. Hagin. 1980. pap. 1.50 (ISBN 0-89276-401-5). Hagin Ministries.

El Shaddai. Vicki Jamison-Peterson. 191p. 1983. pap. 4.95 (ISBN 0-88144-055-8). Christian Pub.

Elbert Hubbard Notebook. rev ed. Ed. by Orlando R. Petrocelli. 192p. 1980. Repr. 10.00 (ISBN 0-89433-144-2). Petrocelli.

Elder & His Work. Robert Taylor, Jr. 7.95 (ISBN 0-89315-041-X); pap. 4.95 (ISBN 0-89315-042-8). Lambert Bk.

Elder at the Lord's Table. Thomas Toler. 1953. pap. 3.95 (ISBN 0-8272-0800-6). CBP.

Elder Joseph of Optina. Holy Transfiguration Monastery Staff. LC 82-81456. 312p. (Orig.). 1985. pap. 10.50x (ISBN 0-913026-53-0). St Nectarios.

Elder Northfield's Home; or, Sacrificed on the Mormon Altar. facsimile ed. Jennie B. Switzer. LC 71-164576. (American Fiction Reprint Ser). Repr. of 1882 ed. 25.50 (ISBN 0-8369-7053-5). Ayer Co Pubs.

Elders Handbook. Gerard Berghoef & Lester DeKoster. LC 79-54143. 303p. 1979. 15.95 (ISBN 0-934874-00-X). Chr Lib Pr.

Elders of the Church. Lawrence Eyres. 1975. pap. 2.50 (ISBN 0-87552-258-0). Presby & Reformed.

Elders, Shades, & Women: Ceremonial Change in Lango, Uganda. Richard T. Curley. LC 70-634788. 1973. 32.50x (ISBN 0-520-02149-5). U of Cal Pr.

Eldership of the Churches of Christ. H. Leo Boles. 1978. pap. 1.50 (ISBN 0-89225-179-4). Gospel Advocate.

Elect in the Son: A Study of the Doctrine of Election. Robert Shank. LC 74-114957. 256p. 1970. 7.95 (ISBN 0-911620-02-8). Westcott.

Electing Our Own Bishops. Ed. by Peter Huizing & Knut Walf. (Concilium Ser.: Vol. 137). 128p. (Orig.). 1980. pap. 5.95 (ISBN 0-8164-2279-6, HarpR). Har-Row.

Election. C. H. Spurgeon. 1978. pap. 1.50 (ISBN 0-686-00503-1). Pilgrim Pubns.

Election & Predestination. Paul K. Jewett. 184p. (Orig.). 1985. pap. 8.95 (ISBN 0-8028-0090-4). Eerdmans.

Electric Woman. Marabel Morgan. 224p. 1985. 11.95 (ISBN 0-8499-0497-8, 0497-8). Word Bks.

Electric Woman. Marabel Morgan. 1986. 3.95 (ISBN 0-8499-4175-X). Word Bks.

Electronic Giant: A Critique of the Telecommunications Revolution from a Christian Perspective. Stewart M. Hoover. LC 81-6083. pap. 42.80 (2029383). Bks Demand UMI.

Elegant & Learned Discourse on the Light of Nature, 1652: Nathanael Culverwel (1618-1651) Nathanael Culverwel. Ed. by Rene Wellek. Bd. with Spiritual Opticks. LC 75-11215. (British Philosophers & Theologians of the 17th & 18th Centuries Ser.). 456p. 1978. lib. bdg. 51.00 (ISBN 0-8240-1769-2). Garland Pub.

Elegant Composition Concerning Relief Adversity. Tr. by William M. Brinner. LC 49-9495. (Judaica Ser.: No. 20). 1977. 26.50x (ISBN 0-300-01952-1). Yale U Pr.

Elegant Sayings. Nagarjuna & Sakya Pandit. LC 77-23433. (Tibetan Translation Ser.: Vol. 8). 1977. 10.95 (ISBN 0-913546-12-7); pap. 6.95 (ISBN 0-913546-13-5). Dharma Pub.

Element of Islamic Studies. Allama S. Rizvi. Ed. by Maulana Anwarali. Tr. by Saeed A. Rizvi. LC 84-52745. 60p. 1984. pap. 3.95 (ISBN 0-940368-44-7). Tahrike Tarsile Quran.

Element of Love. Clare McCausland. Ed. by Mobium Corporation & K. Ineman. (Illus.). 140p. (Orig.). 1981. pap. 10.00 (ISBN 0-9607400-0-7). Children's Memorial.

Elemental Theology. Emery Bancroft & Ronald B. Mayers. 1977. 15.95 (ISBN 0-310-20460-7, 9146). Zondervan.

Elementary Activity Patterns: For Year 'Round Use. Idalee W. Vonk. (Illus.). 48p. (Orig.). 1973. pap. 4.95 (ISBN 0-87239-323-2, 2142). Standard Pub.

Elementary Christian Metaphysics. Joseph Owens. LC 84-23888. 399p. 1985. pap. text ed. 12.95 (ISBN 0-268-00916-3, 85-09168, Dist. by Harper & Row). U of Notre Dame Pr.

Elementary Forms of the New Religious Life. Roy Wallis. LC 83-11092. (International Library of Sociology). 171p. 1984. 26.95x (ISBN 0-7100-9890-1). Methuen Inc.

Elementary Forms of the Religious Life. Emile Durkheim. Tr. by Joseph W. Swain. 1965. pap. text ed. 14.95 (ISBN 0-02-908010-X). Free Pr.

Elementary Forms of the Religious Life. 2nd ed. Emile Durkheim. Tr. by Joseph W. Swain. LC 76-369730. pap. 117.80 (ISBN 0-317-20057-7, 2023276). Bks Demand UMI.

Elementary Philosophy of the Modern Rosycross. 3rd ed. Jan Van Rijckenborgh. (Cornerstone Ser.: No. 5). Tr. of Elementaire Wijsbegeerte van het moderne Rozekruis. 207p. (Orig.). 1986. pap. 11.00 (ISBN 90-6732-004-8). Rosycross Pr.

Elementary School Finance Manual. 126p. 1984. 12.00 (ISBN 0-318-03690-8). Natl Cath Educ.

Elementary Teacher Survival Kit. Robert Klausmeier. 80p. 1986. tchr's ed 9.95 (ISBN 0-89191-363-7). Cook.

Elementary Teachings of Islam. A. A. Siddiqui. pap. 4.50 (ISBN 0-686-18397-5). Kazi Pubns.

Elementary Teachings of Islam. Muhammad A. Siddiqui. Date not set. 1.75 (ISBN 0-89259-022-X). Am Trust Pubns.

Elements of Ancient Indian Psychology. B. Kuppuswamy. 305p. 1986. text ed. 30.00x (ISBN 0-7069-2620-X, Pub. by Vikas India); pap. text ed. 10.95x (ISBN 0-7069-2620-X, Pub. by Vikas India). Advent NY.

Elements of Brahmanism in the Transcendentalism of Emerson. Leyla Goren. LC 80-2534. Repr. of 1959 ed. 18.50 (ISBN 0-404-19260-2). AMS Pr.

Elements of Buddhist Iconography. Ananda K. Coomaraswamy. (Illus.). 1979. text ed. 23.00x. Coronet Bks.

Elements of Christian Philosophy. Etienne H. Gilson. LC 78-10231. 1978. Repr. of 1960 ed. lib. bdg. 35.00 (ISBN 0-313-20734-8, GIEL). Greenwood.

Elements of Hebrew by an Inductive Method. William R. Harper. LC 59-7625. (Midway Reprint Ser). 204p. 1974. pap. 9.00x (ISBN 0-226-31681-5). U of Chicago Pr.

Elements of Homiletic. O. C. Edwards, Jr. LC 84-157333. 110p. (Orig.). 1982. pap. 7.95 (ISBN 0-916134-55-5). Pueblo Pub CO.

Elements of Law-the Formative Years: Being a Comprehensive Summary of American Civil Jurisprudence. Francis Hilliard. LC 78-37979. (American Law Ser.). 372p. 1972. Repr. of 1835 ed. 22.00 (ISBN 0-405-04022-9). Ayer Co Pubs.

Elements of Moral Science, 2 vols. James Beattie. Ed. by Rene Wellek. LC 75-11195. (British Philosophers & Theologians of the 17th & 18th Centuries: Vol. 2). 1976. Repr. of 1793 ed. Set. lib. bdg. 101.00 (ISBN 0-8240-1751-X); lib. bdg. write for info. Garland Pub.

Elements of Moral Science. Francis Wayland. Ed. by Joseph L. Blau. LC 63-19149. (John Harvard Library). 1963. 27.50x (ISBN 0-674-24600-4). Harvard U Pr.

Elements of New Testament Greek. John W. Wenham. 1966. text ed. 11.95 (ISBN 0-521-09842-4); key 4.95 (ISBN 0-521-06769-3). Cambridge U Pr.

Elements of Old Testament Theology. Claus Westermann. Tr. by Doug Stott. LC 81-82346. Tr. of Theologie Des Alten Testaments in Grundzuegen. 249p. 1982. 20.95 (ISBN 0-8042-0191-9); pap. 15.95 (ISBN 0-8042-0193-5). John Knox.

Elements of Philosophy: A Compendium for Philosophers & Theologians. William A. Wallace. LC 77-1527. 1977. pap. 10.95 (ISBN 0-8189-0345-7). Alba.

Elements of Preaching. Warren Wiersbe & David Wiersbe. 96p. 1986. pap. 2.95 (ISBN 0-8423-0757-5). Tyndale.

Elements of Rite. Aidan Kavanaugh. LC 84-158728. 110p. (Orig.). 1982. pap. 7.95 (ISBN 0-916134-54-7). Pueblo Pub CO.

Elements of the Jewish Muhammadan Calendars. Sherrard B. Burnaby. 1976. lib. bdg. 59.95 (ISBN 0-8490-1757-2). Gordon Pr.

Elements of the Science of Religion, 2 vols. Cornelis P. Tiele. LC 77-27226. (Gifford Lectures: 1896, 1898). Repr. of 1899 ed. Set. 55.00 (ISBN 0-404-60480-3). AMS Pr.

Elements of Worship. Judson Cornwall. LC 85-61459. 1985. pap. 5.95 (ISBN 0-88270-594-6). Bridge Pub.

Elene of Cynewulf. Lucius H. Holt. LC 75-11897. (Yale Studies in English Ser: Vol. 21). 1904. lib. bdg. 12.50 (ISBN 0-8414-4851-5). Folcroft.

Elene of Cynewulf. Ed. by Lucius H. Holt. 1904. 20.00 (ISBN 0-8274-2235-0). R West.

Elephant in the Dark. Idries Shah. 76p. 1982. 9.95 (ISBN 0-900860-36-7, Pub. by Octagon Pr England). Ins Study Human.

Eleusis und die Orphische Dichtung Athens in Vorhellenistischer Zeit. Fritz Graf. (Religionsgeschichtliche Versuche und Vorarbeiten, Vol. 33). xii, 224p. 1974. 33.60x (ISBN 3-11-004498-6). De Gruyter.

Eleven Great Cantatas in Full Vocal & Instrumental Score. Johann Sebastian Bach. Date not set. 16.50 (ISBN 0-8446-5459-0). Peter Smith.

Eleven Old English Rogationtide Homilies. Ed. by Joyce Bazire & James E. Cross. LC 83-107819. (Toronto Old English Ser.: No. 7). pap. 35.80 (2056127). Bks Demand UMI.

Eleven Religions & Their Proverbial Lore: A Comparative Study. Selwyn G. Champion. 1979. Repr. of 1945 ed. lib. bdg. 30.00 (ISBN 0-8492-3856-0). R West.

Eleven Religions & Their Proverbial Lore: A Comparative Study. Selwyn G. Champion. 340p. 1985. Repr. of 1945 ed. lib. bdg. 75.00 (ISBN 0-8492-4102-2). R West.

Eleven Surahs Explained. A. S. Hashim. (Islamics Books for Children: Bk. 3). pap. 4.95 (ISBN 0-686-18412-2); pap. 45.00 entire ser. (ISBN 0-686-18413-0). Kazi Pubns.

Eleventh-Century Background of Citeaux. Bede K. Lackener. LC 70-152484. (Cistercian Studies: No. 8). xxii, 305p. 1972. 7.50 (ISBN 0-87907-808-1). Cistercian Pubns.

Eleventh-Century Buddhist Logic of 'Exists' Ratnakirti's Ksanabhangasiddih Vyatirekatmika. Ed. by A. C. McDermott. (Foundations of Language Supplementary Ser: No. 11). 88p. 1969. 18.50 (ISBN 90-277-0081-8, Pub. by Reidel Holland). Kluwer Academic.

Elfreth Book of Letters. ltd. ed. Susan W. Hodge. (Illus.). 320p. (Orig.). 1985. text ed. 50.00 leather & Bucksam (ISBN 0-8122-7982-4); pap. 9.95 (ISBN 0-8122-1208-8). U of Pa Pr.

Elias Hicks: Quaker Liberal. Bliss Forbush. LC 56-6250. pap. 95.80 (ISBN 0-317-08431-3, 2050181). Bks Demand UMI.

Eliezer Ben-Yehuda: The Father of Modern Hebrew. Malka Drucker. LC 86-15213. (Jewish Biography Ser.). (Illus.). 128p. 1987. 13.95 (ISBN 0-525-67184-6, 01354-410). Lodestar Bks.

Elijah. F. B. Meyer. 1972. pap. 4.50 (ISBN 0-87508-343-9). Chr Lit.

Elijah. William H. Stephens. 1979. pap. 3.95 (ISBN 0-8423-4023-8). Tyndale.

Elijah & the Great Drought. Illus. by Graham Round. (Illus.). 16p. 1982. pap. 0.99 (ISBN 0-86683-662-4, AY8239, HarpR). Har-Row.

Elijah: Brave Prophet. Angeline J. Entz. (BibLearn Ser.). (Illus.). 1978. 5.95 (ISBN 0-8054-4244-8, 4242-44). Broadman.

Elijah: Messenger of God. Adapted by Diana Craig. LC 84-51683. (Bible Stories Ser.). (Illus.). 24p. 1984. 5.45 (ISBN 0-382-06943-9); PLB 6.96 (ISBN 0-382-06794-0). Silver.

Elijah: Obedience in a Threatening World. Robbie Castleman. (Fisherman Bible Studyguide Ser.). 64p. (Orig.). 1986. pap. 2.95 (ISBN 0-87788-218-5). Shaw Pubs.

Elijah: Prophet of God. Leon J. Wood. 1968. 2.95 (ISBN 0-87227-020-3). Reg Baptist.

Elijah: Prophet of Power. Phillip Keller. 160p. 1980. 8.95 (ISBN 0-8499-0266-5). Word Bks.

Elijah Task. John Sandford & Paula Sandford. LC 77-82331. 252p. (Orig.). 1986. pap. 5.95 (ISBN 0-932081-11-8). Victory Hse.

Elijah: The Man Who Did Not Die. Gordon Lindsay. (Old Testament Ser.). 1.25 (ISBN 0-89985-149-5). Christ Nations.

Elijah: The Whirlwind Prophet. Gordon Lindsay. (Old Testament Ser.). 1.25 (ISBN 0-89985-148-7). Christ Nations.

Elijah: Yahweh Is My God. G. Avery Lee. (Orig.). 1987. pap. 5.50 (ISBN 0-8054-1539-4). Broadman.

Eliminate Your SDBS: Self-Defeating Behaviors. Jonathan M. Chamberlain. LC 77-27634. (Illus.). 1978. pap. 7.95 (ISBN 0-8425-0998-4). Brigham.

Elisha Principle. Mark Chironna. 54p. (Orig.). 1985. pap. 2.95 (ISBN 0-938612-11-5). Revival Press.

Elisha-Prophet of the Supernatural. Gordon Lindsay. (Old Testament Ser.). 1.25 (ISBN 0-89985-151-7). Christ Nations.

Elisha-The Man Who Received the Double Portion. Gordon Lindsay. (Old Testament Ser.). 1.25 (ISBN 0-89985-150-9). Christ Nations.

Elisha's Room. Gladys S. Stump. (Books I Can Read). (Illus.). 1978. pap. 1.95 (ISBN 0-8127-0162-3). Review & Herald.

Elixir of Enlightenment. A. H. Almaas. LC 84-50159. 64p. (Orig.). 1984. pap. 3.95 (ISBN 0-87728-613-2). Weiser.

Elizabeth Ann Seton - A Self-Portrait: A Study of Her Spirituality. Marie Celeste. LC 85-72765. (Illus.). 305p. 1986. 18.95 (ISBN 0-913382-33-7, 101-33). Prow Bks-Franciscan.

Elizabeth Bayley Seton. Annabelle M. Melville. 1976. pap. 2.25 (ISBN 0-515-09682-2). Jove Pubns.

Elizabeth Bayley Seton. Annabelle M. Melville. 1976. lib. bdg. 25.00x (ISBN 0-684-14735-1, ScribT). Scribner.

Elizabeth Demonology. T. A. Spalding. 1880. lib. bdg. 27.50 (ISBN 0-8414-1620-6). Folcroft.

Elizabeth One & the Puritans. William Haller. LC 64-7541. 1965. pap. 3.95 (ISBN 0-918016-24-X). Folger Bks.

Elizabeth Seton: Selected Writings, Vol. 5. Ed. by Elin M. Kelly. (Sources of American Spirituality Ser.). 384p. 1986. 16.95 (ISBN 0-8091-0382-6). Paulist Pr.

Elizabethan Clergy & the Settlement of Religion, 1558-64. Henry Gee. LC 83-45581. Date not set. Repr. of 1898 ed. 39.50 (ISBN 0-404-19899-6). AMS Pr.

Elizabethan Parish in Its Ecclesiastical & Financial Aspects. Sedley L. Ware. LC 78-63927. (Johns Hopkins University. Studies in the Social Sciences. Twenty-Sixth Ser. 1908: 7-8). Repr. of 1908 ed. 14.50 (ISBN 0-404-61177-X). AMS Pr.

Elizabethan Puritan Movement. Patrick Collinson. (Library Reprints Ser.). 528p. 1982. 60.00x (ISBN 0-416-34000-8, NO. 3701). Methuen Inc.

Elizabethan Recusancy in Cheshire. K. R. Wark. 1971. 30.00 (ISBN 0-7190-1154-X, Pub. by Manchester Univ Pr). Longwood Pub Group.

Elizabethan Sermon. Alan F. Herr. LC 77-75996. 1969. Repr. of 1940 ed. lib. bdg. 16.50x (ISBN 0-374-93838-5, Octagon). Hippocrene Bks.

Elizabethan World Picture. Eustace M. Tillyard. 1959. pap. 3.16 (ISBN 0-394-70162-3, Vin). Random.

Elizabeth's Christmas Story. Vivian H. Dede. LC 59-1430. (Arch Bks.). (Illus.). 24p. 1987. pap. 0.99 (ISBN 0-570-09002-4, 59/1430). Concordia.

Ellen G. White & the Jews: An Interpretative Analysis of Her Writings & Their Significance for Our Time. Jacques Doukhan. Ed. by Adar Publications. LC 85-70340. 35p. (Orig.). 1985. pap. 1.75x (ISBN 0-916169-01-4). Adar Pubns.

Ellen G. White Biography, Vol. 2. Arthur W. White. Ed. by Raymond H. Woolsey. 480p. 1986. 19.95 (ISBN 0-8280-0120-0). Review & Herald.

Ellen G. White: Co-Founder of the Seventh-Day Adventist Church. Roy E. Graham. (American University Studies VII: Theology & Religion: Vol 12). 506p. 1985. text ed. 41.00 (ISBN 0-8204-0255-9). P Lang Pubs.

Ellen G. White: Prophet of Destiny. Rene Noorbergen. LC 70-190456. 363p. 1970. text ed. 6.95 (ISBN 0-87983-014-X); pap. 2.50 (ISBN 0-87983-077-8); spanish version 1.95 (ISBN 0-87983-076-X). MMI Pr.

Ellicott's Commentaries, Critical & Grammatical on the Epistles of Saint Paul, 2 vol. Charles Ellicott. 1986. Repr. of 1879 ed. lib. bdg. 45.00 (ISBN 0-89941-506-7). W S Hein.

Eloquence & Ignorance in Augustine's "On the Nature & Origin of the Soul". Mary Preus. (AAR Academy Ser.). 1986. 19.95 (ISBN 0-89130-927-6, 01-01-51); pap. 15.25 (ISBN 0-89130-928-4). Scholars Pr Ga.

Elsass Eins, Stadt Strassburg: 1522-32. Ed. by Manfred Krebs & H. G. Rott. (Tauferakten Kommission Ser., Vol. 7). 599p. (Ger). 1959. 35.00x (ISBN 0-8361-1167-2). Herald Pr.

Elsass Zwei, Stadt Strassburg: 1533-35. Ed. by Manfred Krebs & H. G. Rott. (Tauferakten Kommission Ser., Vol. 8). 555p. (Ger). 1959. 35.00x (ISBN 0-8361-1168-0). Herald Pr.

Else Von Hollander. Eberhard Arnold et al. LC 72-96191. 1973. 4.50 (ISBN 0-87486-111-X). Plough.

Elusive Mr. Wesley, Vol. II. Richard P. Heitzenrather. 224p. (Orig.). 1984. pap. 9.75 (ISBN 0-687-11555-8). Abingdon.

Elusive Mr. Wesley: John Wesley His Own Biographer. Richard P. Heitzenrater. LC 83-25882. 220p. 1984. pap. 9.75 (ISBN 0-687-11554-X); Set. pap. 19.50 (ISBN 0-687-11556-6). Abingdon.

Elusive Presence: The Heart of Biblical Theology. Samuel Terrien. LC 78-4424. 544p. 1983. pap. 12.95 (ISBN 0-06-068234-5, RD-487, HarpR). Har-Row.

Elysium. Ernest L. Norman. (Illus.). 1956. 4.95 (ISBN 0-932642-14-4). Unarius Pubns.

Emancipation, Assimilation & Stereotype: The Image of the Jew in German & Austrian Drama (1800-1850) Charlene A. Lea. (Modern German Studies: Vol. 2). viii, 171p. (Orig.). 1978. pap. 18.00x (ISBN 3-416-01420-0, Pub. by Bouvier Verlag W Germany). Benjamins North Am.

Emancipation of the Jews in Britain: The Question of Admission of the Jews to Parliament, 1828-1860. Michail Salbstein. (Littman Library of Jewish Civilization). 1982. 24.95x (ISBN 0-19-710050-3). Oxford U Pr.

Emanuel Swedenborg, Scientist & Mystic. Signe Toksvig. LC 72-5447. (Biography Index Reprint Ser.). 1972. Repr. of 1948 ed. 25.00 (ISBN 0-8369-8140-5). Ayer Co Pubs.

Emanuel Swedenborg: Universal Human & Soul Body Interaction. Emanuel Swedenborg. (Classic of Western Spirituality Ser.). 258p. 1984. 12.95 (ISBN 0-8091-0344-3); pap. 9.95 (ISBN 0-8091-2554-4). Paulist Pr.

Emanuel Swedenborg's Journal of Dreams. Emanuel Swedenborg. LC 86-70341. 1986. pap. 8.95 (ISBN 0-87785-133-6). Swedenborg.

Emblemata: Supplement der Erstausgabe. Ed. by Arthur Henkel. Albrecht Schoene. (Ger.). 400p. 1976. 65.00 (ISBN 0-317-02568-6). Interbk Inc.

Emblems of the Holy Spirit. F. E. Marsh. LC 63-11465. 268p. 1974. pap. 9.95 (ISBN 0-8254-3222-7). Kregel.

Embodied in Love: The Sacramental Spirituality of Sexual Intimacy. Charles A. Gallagher & George A. Maloney. 176p. (Orig.). 1983. pap. 9.95 (ISBN 0-686-46141-X). Crossroad NY.

Embodiment: An Approach to Sexuality & Christian Theology. James B. Nelson. LC 78-55589. 1979. pap. 11.95 (ISBN 0-8066-1701-2, 10-2071). Augsburg.

Embodiment: An Approach to Sexuality & Christian Theology. James B. Nelson. 296p. 1978. 9.95 (ISBN 0-8298-0349-1). Pilgrim NY.

Embrace of the Soul: Reflections on the Song of Songs. Charles Rich. LC 83-23066. 1984. pap. 3.50 (ISBN 0-932506-31-3). St Bedes Pubns.

Embrace Tiger, Return to Mountain: The Essence of T'ai Chi. Al C. Huang. LC 73-80134. (Illus.). 185p. 1973. 10.00 (ISBN 0-911226-12-5); pap. 6.50 (ISBN 0-911226-13-3). Real People.

Embracing Heaven & Earth: A Personal Odyssey. Hal Stone. LC 84-72044. 179p. 1985. pap. 8.95 (ISBN 0-87516-547-8). De Vorss.

Embracing the Exile: Healing Journeys of Gay Christians. John Fortunato. 156p. (Orig.). 1984. pap. 7.95 (ISBN 0-8164-2637-6, 6338, HarpR). Har-Row.

Embroidery in Religion & Ceremonial. Beryl Dean. (Illus.). 288p. 1985. pap. 16.50 (ISBN 0-7134-3325-6). Branford.

Emergence from Chaos. Stuart Holroyd. LC 73-167356. (Essay Index Reprint Ser.). Repr. of 1957 ed. 18.00 (ISBN 0-8369-2695-1). Ayer Co Pubs.

Emergence of an Iron Age Economy: The Mecklenburg Grave Groups from Hallstatt & Sticna: Mecklenburg Collection, Pt 3. Peter S. Wells. LC 81-81958. (American School of Prehistoric Research Bulletins: No. 33). (Illus.). 256p. 1981. pap. 30.00x (ISBN 0-87365-536-2). Peabody Harvard.

Emergence of Christian Science in American Religious Life. Stephen Gottschalk. LC 72-85530. 1974. 20.95 (ISBN 0-520-02308-0); pap. 4.95 (ISBN 0-520-03718-9, CAL 398). U of Cal Pr.

Emergence of Contemporary Judaism: A Survey of Judaism from the 7th to the 17th Centuries, Vol. 2. LC 77-831. (Pittsburgh Theological Monographs: No. 12). 1977. Set. pap. text ed. 15.25 (ISBN 0-915138-14-X). Pickwick.

Emergence of Contemporary Judaism: From Medievalism to Proto-Modernity in the 16th & 17th Century, Vol. 3. Phillip Sigal. (Pittsburgh Theological Monographs New Ser.: No. 17). 1986. pap. text ed. 31.90 (ISBN 0-915138-57-3). Pickwick.

Emergence of Contemporary Judaism: The Foundation of Judaism from Biblical Origins to the Sixth Century A. D, Vol. 1, Pts. 1 & 2. Phillip Sigal. Incl. Pt. 1. From the Origins to the Separation of Christianity. (Pittsburgh Theological Monographs: No. 29). pap. text ed. 22.25 (ISBN 0-915138-30-1); Pt. 2. Rabbinic Judaism. (Pittsburgh Theological Monographs: No. 29a). pap. text ed. 20.25 (ISBN 0-915138-46-8). 1980. pap. text ed. 39.75 set (ISBN 0-915138-46-8). Pickwick.

Emergence of Hebrew Biblical Pointing, Vol. 1. Bruno Chiesa. (Judentum v. Umwelt Ser.: Vol. 1). 92p. 1979. pap. 17.70 (ISBN 3-8204-6419-0). P Lang Pubs.

Emergence of Israel in Canaan. Baruch Halpern. LC 82-24030. (Society of Biblical Literature Monographic Ser.: No. 29). 352p. 1984. 36.75 (ISBN 0-89130-649-8, 06 00 29); pap. 24.50 (ISBN 0-89130-609-9). Scholars Pr GA.

Emergence of Liberal Catholicism in America. Robert A. Cross. LC 58-5593. 1958. 25.00x (ISBN 0-674-24800-7). Harvard U Pr.

Emergence of Roman Catholic Medical Ethics in North America: An Historical-Methodological-Bibliographical Study. David F. Kelly. LC 79-66372. (Texts & Studies in Religion: Vol. 3). xi, 534p. 1982. Repr. 79.95x (ISBN 0-88946-877-X). E Mellen.

Emergence of the Jewish Problem, 1878-1939. James W. Parkes. Repr. of 1946 ed. lib. bdg. 22.50x (ISBN 0-8371-2794-7, PJPR). Greenwood.

Emergence: The Rebirth of the Sacred. David Spangler. LC 83-7626. 160p. (Orig.). 1984. pap. 10.95 (ISBN 0-385-29311-9, Delta). Dell.

Emergency Radiology of the Acutely Ill or Injured Child. 2nd ed. Leonard Swischuk. (Illus.). 656p. 1985. text ed. 78.50 (ISBN 0-683-08049-0). Williams & Wilkins.

Emergent Church. Johann B. Metz. 160p. 1986. pap. 9.95 (ISBN 0-8245-0729-0). Crossroad NY.

Emergent Church: The Future of Christianity in a Post-Bourgeois World. Johann B. Metz. 160p. 1981. 10.95 (ISBN 0-8245-0036-9). Crossroad NY.

Emergent Gospel: Theologies from the Underside of History. Ed. by Sergio Torres & Virginia Fabella. LC 77-22134. 303p. (Orig.). 1978. pap. 5.95 (ISBN 0-88344-113-6). Orbis Bks.

Emergent Self, 4 bks. in 1. Adrian Van Kaam et al. 1968. cancelled (ISBN 0-87193-165-6). Dimension Bks.

Emerging Christian Woman. S. Faria et al. 292p. 1986. 8.50x (ISBN 0-8364-1810-7, Pub. by Macmillan India). South Asia Bks.

Emerging Church. rev. ed. Ronald J. Wilkins. (To Live Is Christ Ser). 1981. pap. 5.95 (ISBN 0-697-01760-5); tchr's. manual 4.75 (ISBN 0-697-01761-3); activity cards 7.50 (ISBN 0-697-01899-7); stud. diaries 10.00 (ISBN 0-697-01900-4); spirit masters 9.95 (ISBN 0-697-01898-9). Wm C Brown.

Emerging Laity: Returning Leadership to the Community of Faith. James D. Whitehead & Evelyn E. Whitehead. LC 85-31201. 240p. 1986. 15.95 (ISBN 0-385-23612-3). Doubleday.

Emerging New Class of Experts: Implications for Church & Society. Barbara Hargrove. 160p. (Orig.). 1986. pap. 8.95 (ISBN 0-8298-0578-8). Pilgrim NY.

Emerging Order: God in the Age of Scarcity. Jeremy Rifkin & Ted Howard. (Epiphany Bks.). 1983. pap. 2.95 (ISBN 0-345-30464-0). Ballantine.

Emerging Role of Deacons. Charles W. Deweese. LC 79-50337. 1980. pap. 3.75 (ISBN 0-8054-3512-3). Broadman.

Emerson. George H. Perris. 1973. Repr. of 1910 ed. 25.00 (ISBN 0-8274-0995-8). R West.

Emerson. A Lecture. Thomas F. Husband. LC 77-23227. 1977. Repr. of 1892 ed. lib. bdg. 8.50 (ISBN 0-8414-4947-3). Folcroft.

Emerson & His Philosophy. J. Arthur Hill. LC 72-192678. 1919. lib. bdg. 15.00 (ISBN 0-8414-0783-5). Folcroft.

Emerson & Others. Van Wyck Brooks. LC 73-3132. 250p. 1973. Repr. lib. bdg. 20.50x (ISBN 0-374-90998-9, Octagon). Hippocrene Bks.

Emerson & Vedanta. 2nd ed. Swami Paramananda. 1985. pap. 3.50 (ISBN 0-911564-13-6). Vedanta Ctr.

Emerson As Mythmaker. J. Russell Reaver. LC 54-8431. 1954. pap. 4.00 (ISBN 0-8130-0195-1). U Presses Fla.

Emerson, Haber & Dorsen's Political & Civil Rights in the United States, Vol. 2. 4th ed. Norman Dorsen & Sylvia Law. 1979. text ed. 34.00 student ed. (ISBN 0-316-19049-7); lawyers ed. 55.00 (ISBN 0-316-23627-6). Little.

Emerson: His Life & Writings. January Searle, pseud. LC 76-40142. 1973. lib. bdg. 10.00 (ISBN 0-8414-7813-9). Folcroft.

Emerson on the Soul. Jonathan Bishop. LC 80-2527. Repr. of 1964 ed. 29.50 (ISBN 0-404-19251-3). AMS Pr.

Emerson, the Enraptured Yankee. Regis Michaud. Tr. by George Boas. LC 74-5374. Repr. of 1930 ed. 30.00 (ISBN 0-404-11538-1). AMS Pr.

Emerson Today. Bliss Perry. LC 69-19220. 140p. 1969. Repr. of 1931 ed. 18.00 (ISBN 0-208-00798-9, Archon). Shoe String.

Emerson, Whitman, & the American Muse. Jerome Loving. LC 82-1868. xii, 220p. 1982. 22.00 (ISBN 0-8078-1523-3). U of NC Pr.

Emerson's Optics: Biographical Process & the Dawn of Religious Leadership. Richard A. Hutch. 380p. (Orig.). 1983. lib. bdg. 34.25 (ISBN 0-8191-3005-2); pap. text ed. 17.75 (ISBN 0-8191-3006-0). U Pr of Amer.

Emerson's Use of the Bible. Harriet R. Zink. 75p. 1980. Repr. of 1935 ed. lib. bdg. 15.00 (ISBN 0-8495-6206-6). Arden Lib.

Emerson's Use of the Bible. Harriet R. Zink. LC 77-7882. 1977. lib. bdg. 20.00 (ISBN 0-8414-9805-9). Folcroft.

Emigrants at Worship: One Hundred & Twenty-Five Years of Chisago Lake Methodism. Ed. by Robert Porter. (Illus.). 85p. (Orig.). 1983. pap. 8.75 (ISBN 0-933565-02-X). Porter Pub Co.

Emil Brunner. J. Edward Humphrey. Ed. by Bob E. Patterson. LC 75-36186. (Maker's of the Modern Theological Mind Ser.). 1976. 8.95 (ISBN 0-87680-453-9). Word Bks.

Emil Brunner. J. Edward Humphrey. 183p. 1984. pap. text ed. 8.95 (ISBN 0-8499-3006-5, 3006-5). Word Bks.

Emile Durkheim. Kenneth Thompson. LC 81-20294. (Key Sociologists Ser.). 120p. 1982. pap. 4.95x (ISBN 0-85312-419-1, NO. 3674, Pub. by Tavistock England). Methuen Inc.

Emily Post on Weddings. Elizabeth L. Post. LC 86-12094. (Illus.). 192p. (Orig.). 1987. pap. 2.95 (ISBN 0-06-080812-8, P 812, PL). Har-Row.

Emily's Tiger. Penny Pollock. (Orig.). 1984. pap. 1.95 (ISBN 0-8091-6554-6). Paulist Pr.

Eminent Baha'is in the Time of Baha'u'llah. H. M. Balyazi. (Illus.). 400p. 1986. 28.50 (ISBN 0-85398-151-5); pap. 15.95 (ISBN 0-85398-152-3). G Ronald Pub.

Eminent Hebrew Christians of the Nineteenth Century: Brief Biographical Sketches. Ed. by David A. Rausch. LC 83-22013. (Texts & Studies in Religion: Vol. 17). 184p. lib. bdg. 39.95x (ISBN 0-88946-806-0). E Mellen.

Eminent Victorians. Lytton Strachey. 354p. 1969. pap. 6.95 (ISBN 0-15-628697-1, Harv). HarBraceJ.

Emirs & Evangelicals. Ian Linden. 1986. 29.50x (ISBN 0-7146-3146-9, BHA-03146, F Cass Co). Biblio Dist.

Emissaries: The Overseas Work of the American YWCA, 1895-1970. Nancy Boyd. (Illus.). 412p. 16.95 (ISBN 0-9614878-0-1). Woman's Pr.

Emma Bailey Seeks Truth. Mabel Hale. 24p. 1982. pap. 0.25 (ISBN 0-686-36258-6); pap. 1.00 5 copies (ISBN 0-686-37283-2). Faith Pub Hse.

Emma Smith: Elect Lady. Margaret W. Gibson. LC 54-7910. 1954. pap. 8.00 (ISBN 0-8309-0256-2). Herald Hse.

Emmanuel Factor. Nelson L. Price. 1987. 8.95 (ISBN 0-8054-5050-5). Broadman.

Emmanuel, God with Us: Studies in Matthew. Harold H. Etling. pap. 4.95 (ISBN 0-88469-107-1). BMH Bks.

Emmet Fox's Golden Keys to Successful Living. Herman Wolhorn. LC 76-62930. 1977. 10.84 (ISBN 0-06-069670-2, HarpR). Har-Row.

Emory Studies on the Holocaust. Ed. by David R. Blumenthal. LC 84-52494. 178p. (Orig.). 1985. pap. 5.00 (ISBN 0-912313-01-3). Witness Holocaust.

Emotional Development & Spiritual Growth. Timothy J. Gannon. pap. 0.75 (ISBN 0-8199-0386-8, L38135). Franciscan Herald.

Emotions. Rochelle S. Albin. LC 83-10187. (Choices: Guides for Today's Woman: Vol. 1). 120p. 1983. pap. 6.95 (ISBN 0-664-24540-4). Westminster.

Emotions As Resources: A Biblical & Pastoral Perspective. Bert Ghezzi & Mark Kinzer. 110p. 1983. pap. 6.95 (ISBN 0-89283-158-8). Servant.

Emotions: Can You Trust Them? James Dobson. LC 79-91703. 144p. 1980. text ed. 7.95 (ISBN 0-8307-0730-1, 5109108). Regal.

Emotions: Can You Trust Them? Leader's Guide. Alex Chisholm & Sarah Chisholm. 48p. 1984. pap. 3.95 (ISBN 0-8307-0992-4, 6101926). Regal.

Emotions in God's World. Beverly Beckmann. 24p. 1986. 5.95 (ISBN 0-570-04149-X). Concordia.

Emotive Image: Jesuit Poetics in the English Renaissance. Anthony Raspa. LC 83-502. 173p. 1983. 19.50x (ISBN 0-912646-65-9). Tex Christian.

Empathy & Confrontation in Pastoral Care. Ralph L. Underwood. LC 85-47722. (Theology & Pastoral Care Ser.). 128p. 1986. pap. 7.50 (ISBN 0-8006-1737-1). Fortress.

Empire & the Papacy, Nine Eighteen to Twelve Seventy-Three. 8th ed. Thomas F. Tout. LC 80-18865. (Periods of European History: Period II). (Illus.). vii, 526p. 1980. Repr. of 1965 ed. lib. bdg. 42.50x (ISBN 0-313-22372-6, TOEP). Greenwood.

Empire of Reason: How Europe Imagined & America Realized the Enlightenment. Henry S. Commager. 1984. 17.25 (ISBN 0-8446-6088-4). Peter Smith.

Empirical Argument for God in Late British Thought. P. A. Bertocci. Repr. of 1938 ed. 36.00 (ISBN 0-527-07300-8). Kraus Repr.

Empirical Models for Biblical Criticism. Jeffrey H. Tigay. LC 84-20951. 304p. 1985. 37.50 (ISBN 0-8122-7976-X). U of Pa Pr.

Empirical Philosophies of Religion. James A. Martin. LC 78-111850. (Essay Index Reprint Ser.). 1945. 17.00 (ISBN 0-8369-1618-2). Ayer Co Pubs.

Empirical Theology of Henry Nelson Weiman. Bretall. 1981. pap. 6.95 (ISBN 0-8298-0485-4). Pilgrim NY.

Employed Wife. Lenore Buth. 176p. (Orig.). 1986. pap. 5.95 (ISBN 0-570-04436-7). Concordia.

Empowered by the Spirit: Campus Ministry Faces the Future. National Conference of Catholic Bishops. 56p. 1986. pap. 2.95 (ISBN 1-55586-981-5). US Catholic.

Empowered People. Teresa Pirola. 48p. (Orig.). 1985. pap. text ed. 1.95 (ISBN 0-911905-26-X). Past & Mat Rene Ctr.

Empowered to Care. Pastoral Care Office. 1980. pap. 9.00 (ISBN 0-8309-0291-0). Herald Hse.

Empowered to Serve: Acts one Verses one to two Verses Thirteen. John MacArthur, Jr. (John Mac Arthur Bible Studies Ser.). 1987. pap. 3.95 (ISBN 0-8024-5314-7). Moody.

Empowering Hope. Josephs G. Donders. 112p. (Orig.). 1986. pap. 5.95 (ISBN 0-89622-281-0). Twenty-Third.

Empowering the Catholic Teacher. John Podgorski. 1987. pap. write for info. (ISBN 0-697-02242-0). Wm C Brown.

Empowerment: Skills for Parish Social Action. Harry Fagan. LC 79-52106. 64p. 1979. pap. 4.95 (ISBN 0-8091-2210-3). Paulist Pr.

Emptiness Yoga. Jeffrey Hopkins. LC 86-6484. 504p. 1987. 35.00 (ISBN 0-937938-36-X); pap. 19.95 (ISBN 0-937938-31-9). Snow Lion.

Empty Cross of Jesus. Michael Green. LC 84-19312. (Jesus Library). 224p. 1984. pap. 7.95 (ISBN 0-87784-930-7). Inter-Varsity.

Empty Logic: Madhyamika Buddhism from Chinese Sources. Hsueh-li Cheng. LC 83-13246. 220p. 1984. 17.95 (ISBN 0-8022-2442-3). Philos Lib.

Empty Nest: Life after the Kids Leave Home. Earl D. Wilson. (Family Ministry Ser.). 96p. 1986. pap. 19.95 (ISBN 0-89191-969-4). Cook.

Empty Sleeves. Philip Rushing. LC 83-11322. 224p. (Orig.). 1984. 9.95 (ISBN 0-310-28820-7, 11322). Zondervan.

En Busca del Ser. Swami Muktananda. LC 81-50917. 140p. 1981. pap. 4.95 (ISBN 0-914602-71-3). SYDA Found.

En Compania de un Siddha. Swami Muktananda. LC 81-84263. 1981. pap. 5.95. SYDA Found.

En El. Kenneth E. Hagin. (Span.). 1983. pap. 0.50 mini bk. (ISBN 0-89276-152-0). Hagin Ministries.

En Espiritu y en Verdad. Robert Fisher. (Span., Orig.). pap. text ed. 5.95 (ISBN 0-87148-313-0). Pathway Pr.

En las Huellas de los Heroes: 14 Lecciones, Tomo 4. Bernice C. Jordan. (Pasos De Fe Ser.). (Span.). pap. text ed. 2.50 (ISBN 0-86508-407-6); figuras 8.95 (ISBN 0-86508-408-4). BCM Intl Inc.

Enabling the Elderly: Religious Institutions Within the Community Service System. Sheldon S. Tobin et al. (Aging Ser.). 154p. (Orig.). 1986. 34.50x (ISBN 0-88706-334-9); pap. 10.95x (ISBN 0-88706-335-7). State U NY Pr.

Enchanted World: Fabled Lands. 1986. 16.95 (ISBN 0-8094-5253-7); lib. bdg. 22.60 (ISBN 0-8094-5254-5). Time-Life.

Enchanted World: Fall of Camelot. 1986. 16.95 (ISBN 0-8094-5257-X); lib. bdg. 22.60 (ISBN 0-8094-5258-8). Time-Life.

Enchanted World: Seekers & Saviors. 1986. 16.95 (ISBN 0-8094-5249-9); lib. bdg. 22.60 (ISBN 0-8094-5250-2). Time-Life.

Enchanted World: Water Spirits. 1985. 16.95 (ISBN 0-8094-5245-6); lib. bdg. 22.60 (ISBN 0-8094-5246-4). Time-Life.

Enchantments of Judaism: Rites of Transformation from Birth Through Death. Jacob Neusner. LC 87-47507. 192p. 1987. 15.95 (ISBN 0-465-01964-1). Basic.

Enchiridion Militis Christiani. Erasmus. Ed. by Anne M. O'Donnell. (Early English Text Society Ser.). (Illus.). 1981. text ed. 47.00x (ISBN 0-19-722284-6). Oxford U Pr.

Enchiridion of Commonplaces of John Eck. John Eck. (Twin Brooks Ser.). pap. 9.95 (ISBN 0-8010-3352-7). Baker Bk.

Enchiridion of Erasmus. Erasmus. Tr. by Raymond Himelick. 16.50 (ISBN 0-8446-0614-6). Peter Smith.

Enchiridion of Indulgences. rev. ed. maroon cloth 5.00 (ISBN 0-89942-555-0, 555/22). Catholic Bk Pub.

Enchiridion on Faith, Hope & Love. Saint Augustine. Ed. by Henry Paolucci. 177p. 1961. pap. 4.95 (ISBN 0-89526-938-4). Regnery Bks.

Enciclopedia de Citas Morales y Religiosas. (Span.). 456p. 1976. 18.95 (ISBN 84-7228-251-1, S-50575). French & Eur.

Enciclopedia de Historias Biblicas. Jenny Robertson. Tr. by Maria T. LaValle. Tr. of Encyclopedia of Bible Stories. (Span., Illus.). 272p. 1984. 12.95 (ISBN 0-311-03671-6). Casa Bautista.

Enciclopedia de Poesia Evangelica. 3rd ed. (Span.). 365p. 1978. pap. 12.25 (ISBN 84-7228-037-3, S-50573). French & Eur.

Encircled: Stories of Mennonite Women. Ruth Unrau. LC 86-80403. (Illus.). 352p. 1986. pap. 12.95 (ISBN 0-87303-114-8). Faith & Life.

Encounter. Anita P. Robb. (Illus.). 153p. (Orig.). 1982. pap. 3.95 (ISBN 0-89216-048-9). Salvation Army.

Encounter of the Faiths. George W. Carpenter. (Orig.). 1967. pap. 1.75 (ISBN 0-377-37001-0). Friend Pr.

Encounter Through Questioning Paul: A Fresh Approach to the Apostle's Life & Letters. William E. Phipps. LC 82-17580. (Illus.). 114p. (Orig.). 1983. lib. bdg. 24.25 (ISBN 0-8191-2785-X); pap. text ed. 9.50 (ISBN 0-8191-2786-8). U Pr of Amer.

Encounter with an Angry God. Carobeth Laird. 1977. pap. 2.25 (ISBN 0-345-28464-X). Ballantine.

Encounter with Darkness. John A. MacMillan. LC 80-67656. 116p. 2.25 (ISBN 0-87509-287-X). Chr Pubns.

Encounter with Emancipation: The German Jews in the United States, 1830 to 1914. Naomi Cohen. (Illus.). 407p. 1984. 25.95 (ISBN 0-8276-0236-7). Jewish Pubns.

Encounter with Erikson: Historical Interpretation & Religious Biography. Donald Capps et al. LC 76-44434. (American Academy of Religion, Formative Contemporary Thinkers Ser.: No. 2). 1977. pap. 13.50 (010402). Scholars Pr GA.

Encounter with God. Duncan Forrester et al. 192p. 1983. pap. 13.95 (ISBN 0-567-29346-7, Pub. by T&T Clark Ltd UK). Fortress.

Encounter with God: A Theology of Christian Experience. Morton Kelsey. 48p. 1972. pap. 8.95 (ISBN 0-87123-123-9, 210123); study guide 1.25 (ISBN 0-87123-506-4, 210506). Bethany Hse.

Encounter with Silence: Reflections from the Quaker Tradition. John Punshon. 156p. (Orig.). 1987. pap. 6.95 (ISBN 0-913408-96-4). Friends United.

Encounter with Spurgeon. Helmut Thielicke. Tr. by J. W. Doberstein from Ger. 284p. 1978. Repr. 13.95 (ISBN 0-227-67655-6). Attic Pr.

Encounter with the Holy Spirit. Ed. by George R. Brunk. LC 72-2053. 240p. 1972. pap. 5.95 (ISBN 0-8361-1693-3). Herald Pr.

Encounter with Zen: Writings on Poetry & Zen. Lucien Stryk. LC 81-9611. x, 259p. 1982. 26.95x (ISBN 0-8040-0405-6, Pub. by Swallow); pap. 10.95 (ISBN 0-8040-0406-4, Pub. by Swallow). Ohio U Pr.

Encountering Evil: Live Options in Theodicy. Ed. by Stephen T. Davis. LC 80-84647. 1981. pap. 9.95 (ISBN 0-8042-0517-5). John Knox.

Encountering Marx: Bonds & Barriers between Christians & Marxists. Jan M. Lochman. Tr. by Edwin H. Robertson. LC 76-55827. pap. 39.00 (2026917). Bks Demand UMI.

Encountering the Holocaust: An Interdisciplinary Survey. Byron Sherwin & Susan Ament. LC 79-9126. 500p. 1979. 22.50 (ISBN 0-88482-936-7). Impact Pr IL.

Encountering the Lord in Daily Life. David E. Rosage. 160p. (Orig.). 1983. pap. 4.50 (ISBN 0-914544-45-4). Living Flame Pr.

Encounters Between Judaism & Modern Philosophy: A Preface to Future Jewish Thought. Emil L. Fackenheim. LC 80-16437. 288p. 1980. pap. 7.95 (ISBN 0-8052-0656-6). Schocken.

Encounters in World Religions. Geoffrey Parrinder. 224p. 1987. 15.95 (ISBN 0-8245-0826-2). Crossroad NY.

Encounters in Yoga & Zen. Trevor Leggett. 1982. pap. 9.95 (ISBN 0-7100-9241-5). Methuen Inc.

Encounters: Poetic Meditations on the Old Testament. J. Barrie Shepherd. LC 82-22422. 176p. (Orig.). 1983. pap. 8.95 (ISBN 0-8298-0637-7). Pilgrim NY.

Encounters with Art. Dorothea Blom. 1983. pap. 2.50x (ISBN 0-87574-128-2, 128). Pendle Hill.

Encounters with Christ: An Introduction to the Sacraments. William P. Roberts. 256p. (Orig.). 1985. pap. 8.95 (ISBN 0-8091-2707-5). Paulist Pr.

Encounters with Eternity. Ed. by Christopher J. Johnson & Marsha G. McGee. LC 85-17045. (Paperback Ser.). 352p. 1986. 19.95 (ISBN 0-8022-2493-8); pap. 12.95 (ISBN 0-8022-2508-X). Philos Lib.

Encounters with Israeli Authors. Esther Fuchs. LC 82-62086. (Illus.). 95p. 1983. pap. 7.50 (ISBN 0-916288-14-5). Micah Pubns.

Encounters with the Antichrist. Paul Dilsaver. 4.00 (ISBN 0-317-52034-2). Jelm Mtn.

Encounters with the Jewish People. Chaim Raphael. LC 79-14424. 1979. pap. text ed. 6.95x (ISBN 0-87441-282-X). Behrman.

Encounters with the Lord of the Universe. Ravindra Svarupa dasa. Ed. by Jayadvaita Swami & Dravida dasa. 130p. 1985. pap. text ed. 3.50 (ISBN 0-911233-20-2). Gita Nagari.

Encounters with Transcendence: Confessions of a Religious Philosopher. Scott Crom. (Orig.). 1986. 2.50 (ISBN 0-87574-267-X). Pendle Hill.

Encouragement. Crabb, Jr. & J. Lawrence. 1986. 9.95 (ISBN 0-88469-199-3). BMH Bks.

Encouragement. George Douma. pap. 0.45 (ISBN 0-686-23477-4). Rose Pub MI.

Encouragement: The Key to Caring. Lawrence J. Crabb, Jr. & Dan B. Allender. 144p. 1984. 9.95 (ISBN 0-310-22590-6, 10182). Zondervan.

Encouragers: The Sunday School Worker's Counseling Ministry. James E. Taulman. LC 85-19523. 1986. pap. 4.95 (ISBN 0-8054-3712-6). Broadman.

Encouraging New Christians. Michael Griffiths. pap. 0.75 (ISBN 0-87784-106-3). Inter-Varsity.

Encouraging One Another. Gene A. Getz. 1981. pap. 5.95 (ISBN 0-88207-256-0). Victor Bks.

Encrucijadas. Leon Jaworski & Dick Schneider. 1982. 3.95 (ISBN 0-88113-082-6). Edit Betania.

Encuentro con Jesus. Robert E. Adams. (Illus.). 80p. 1977. pap. 1.50 (ISBN 0-311-04657-6). Casa Bautista.

Encyclical Epistle of the One Holy Catholic & Apistolic Church: Being a Reply to the Epistle of Pius IX to the Easterns. pap. 2.50 (ISBN 0-686-05641-8). Eastern Orthodox.

Encyclical Humanae Vitae: A Sign of Contradiction. Dietrich Von Hildebrand. (Orig.). 1969. pap. 2.00 (ISBN 0-685-10965-8). Franciscan Herald.

Encyclical Letter of St. Mark of Ephesus. Saint Mark Of Ephesus. pap. 0.50 (ISBN 0-686-16366-4). Eastern Orthodox.

Encyclical on World Good Will. El Morya. 1963. 1.50 (ISBN 0-685-79130-0). Summit Univ.

Encyclopaedia of Indian Culture, V-Z, Vol. 5. R. N. Saletore. 324p. 1985. text ed. 50.00x (ISBN 0-391-02978-9, Pub. by Sterling India). Humanities.

Encyclopaedia of Religions. Maurice A. Canney. LC 75-123370. 1970. Repr. of 1921 ed. 53.00 (ISBN 0-8103-3856-4). Gale.

Encyclopaedia of Seerah I-IV. A. Rahman. 55.00 ea. (ISBN 0-317-46105-2). Kazi Pubns.

Encyclopedia Biblica, 4 vols. Ed. by T. K. Cheyne & J. S. Black. 1977. lib. bdg. 425.95 (ISBN 0-8490-1764-5). Gordon Pr.

Encyclopedia for Today's Christian Woman. Compiled by Cecil B. Murphey. (Encyclopedias Ser.). 512p. 1984. 16.95 (ISBN 0-8007-1393-1). Revell.

Encyclopedia of American Religions. 2nd ed. Ed. by J. Gordon Melton. 1200p. 1986. 165.00x (ISBN 0-8103-2133-5). Gale.

Encyclopedia of Bible Animals. Peter France et al. (Illus.). 168p. 1986. 26.95 (ISBN 0-7099-3737-7). Salem Hse Pubs.

Encyclopedia of Bible Difficulties. Gleason L. Archer. 352p. 1982. 19.95 (ISBN 0-310-43570-6, 112252). Zondervan.

Encyclopedia of Biblical Interpretation, 9 vols. M. M. Kasher. Set. 35.00 ea. (ISBN 0-87068-315-2). Ktav.

Encyclopedia of Biblical Prophecy. J. Barton Payne. 784p. 1980. pap. 18.95 (ISBN 0-8010-7051-1). Baker Bk.

Encyclopedia of Biblical Theology: The Concise Sacramentum Verbi. J. B. Bauer. 1172p. 1981. 39.50x (ISBN 0-8245-0042-3). Crossroad NY.

Encyclopedia of Christian Marriage. 414p. 1983. 16.95 (ISBN 0-8007-1376-1). Revell.

Encyclopedia of Christian Parenting. 540p. 1982. 16.95 (ISBN 0-8007-1276-5). Revell.

Encyclopedia of Death. large type ed. J. R. Francis. (Illus.). pap. 7.00 (ISBN 0-910122-47-4). Amherst Pr.

Encyclopedia of Hindu Architecture. P. K. Acharya. (Illus.). 1979. text ed. 38.50x. Coronet Bks.

Encyclopedia of Indian Temple Architecture: South India, Lower Dravidadesa, 300 B.C.-A.D. 1326, 2 pts, Vol. 1. Ed. by Michael W. Meister. LC 82-50173. (Illus.). 736p. 1982. Set. 84.00x (ISBN 0-8122-7840-2). U of Pa Pr.

Encyclopedia of Indian Temple Architecture, Vol. 1, Part II: South India: Upper Dravidadesa. Ed. by Michael W. Meister & M. A. Dhaky. (Illus.). 736p. 1982. Set. text ed. 84.00x. U of Pa Pr.

Encyclopedia of Islam. E. J. Brill. 1983. text ed. write for info. (ISBN 0-02-903770-0). Macmillan.

Encyclopedia of Islam, 4 vols. Ed. by B. Lewis et al. Incl. Vol. 1. A-B: Fasc. 1-22. Ed. by H. A. Gibb et al. 1960. text ed. 185.75x (ISBN 90-040-0530-7); Vol. 2. C-G: Fasc. 23-40. Ed. by B. Lewis et al. 1965; Vol. 3. H-Iram: Fasc. 41-60. 1969. text ed. 226.25x (ISBN 90-040-3275-4); Vols. 4 & 5. I-Ram &K-Ha: Fasc. 61-78. 1978. text ed. 275.50. Humanities.

Encyclopedia of Jewish History. Ed. by Joseph Alpher. (Illus.). 288p. 1986. 35.00x (ISBN 0-8160-1220-2). Facts on File.

Encyclopedia of Jewish History: Events & Eras of the Jewish People. Ed. by Joseph Alpher. Tr. by Haya Amir. LC 85-23941. (Illus.). 285p. 1985. 35.00. Facts on File.

Encyclopedia of Jewish Humor. Ed. by Henry D. Spalding. LC 68-21429. 1978. 16.95 (ISBN 0-8246-0021-5). Jonathan David.

Encyclopedia of Jewish Institutions: United States & Canada. Ed. by Oded Rosen. 512p. 1983. 55.00 (ISBN 0-913185-00-0). Mosadot Pubns.

Encyclopedia of Methodism, 2 vols. Matthew Simpson. 1977. lib. bdg. 250.00 (ISBN 0-8490-1766-1). Gordon Pr.

Encyclopedia of Missions: Descriptive, Historical, Biographical, Statistical. 2nd ed. Ed. by Henry Otis Dwight et al. LC 74-31438. 851p. 1975. Repr. of 1904 ed. 80.00x (ISBN 0-8103-3325-2). Gale.

Encyclopedia of Morals. Ed. by Vergilius Ferm. LC 70-90504. Repr. of 1956 ed. lib. bdg. 40.00x (ISBN 0-8371-2138-8, FEEM). Greenwood.

Encyclopedia of Mysticism & Mystery Religions. John Ferguson. (Crossroad Paperback Ser.). (Illus.). 228p. 1982. pap. 9.95 (ISBN 0-8245-0429-1). Crossroad NY.

Encyclopedia of Mysticism & the Occult. Nevill Drury. LC 84-48215. (Illus.). 544p. (Orig.). 1985. 24.45 (ISBN 0-06-062093-5, HarpR); pap. 12.95 (ISBN 0-06-062094-3). Har-Row.

Encyclopedia of Numbers: Their Essence of Meaning. L. Stebbing. 1973. lib. bdg. 79.95 (ISBN 0-87968-553-0). Krishna Pr.

Encyclopedia of Religion, 16 vols. Ed. by Mircea Eliade. 8000p. 1986. Set. reference 1100.00x (ISBN 0-02-909480-1). Macmillan.

Encyclopedia of Religion. Vergilius Ferm. LC 75-36508. 844p. 1976. Repr. of 1945 ed. lib. bdg. 55.00x (ISBN 0-8371-8638-2, FEEOR). Greenwood.

Encyclopedia of Religion. Ed. by Vergilius Ferm. LC 62-18535. 86p. 1962. 19.95 (ISBN 0-8022-0490-2). Philos Lib.

Encyclopedia of Religion & Ethics, 12 vols. Ed. by James Hastings. 1926. Set. 599.95 (ISBN 0-567-06514-6, Pub. by T&T Clark Ltd Uk). Fortress.

Encyclopedia of Religion in the South. Ed. by Samuel S. Hill. LC 84-8957. viii, 878p. 1984. 60.00 (ISBN 0-86554-117-5, MUP/H97). Mercer Univ Pr.

Encyclopedia of Religious Quotations. Ed. by Frank S. Mead. 540p. 1985. 16.95 (ISBN 0-8007-1410-5). Revell.

Encyclopedia of Seven Thousand-Seven Hundred Illustrations: Signs of the Times. 7th ed. Paul L. Tan. LC 78-72973. (Illus.). 2032p. 1979. 34.95 (ISBN 0-932940-02-1). Assurance Pubs.

Encyclopedia of Southern Baptists, Vols. I & II. Ed. by Norman W. Cox. LC 58-5417. (Illus.). 1958. 39.95 (ISBN 0-8054-6501-4). Broadman.

Encyclopedia of Southern Baptists, Vol. IV. Ed. by Lynn May. LC 81-66989. 1982. 19.95 (ISBN 0-8054-6556-1). Broadman.

Encyclopedia of Southern Baptists, Vol. III. Ed. by Davis C. Woolley. LC 58-5417. (Illus.). 1971. 19.95 (ISBN 0-8054-6511-1). Broadman.

Encyclopedia of Southern Baptists: Index to Vols. I-IV. Ed. by Lynn May. 1982. pap. 1.75 (ISBN 0-8054-6562-6). Broadman.

Encyclopedia of Superstitions. Edwin Radford & Mona A. Radford. Repr. of 1949 ed. lib. bdg. 45.00x (ISBN 0-8371-2115-9, RASU). Greenwood.

Encyclopedia of the Jewish Religion. Ed. by Zvi Werblowsky & Geoffrey Wigoder. LC 86-10932. (Illus.). 478p. 1986. 39.95 (ISBN 0-915361-53-1, Dist. by Watts). Adama Pubs Inc.

Encyclopedia of the Upanishads. N. S. Subrahmanian. 564p. 1986. text ed. 50.00x (ISBN 0-86590-771-4, Pub. by Sterling Pubs India). Apt Bks.

Encyclopedia of Theology: The Concise Sacramentum Mundi. rev., abr. ed. Ed. by Karl Rahner. LC 82-7285. 1536p. 1975. 49.50x (ISBN 0-8245-0303-1). Crossroad NY.

Encyclopedia of Torah Thoughts. Charles B. Chavel. Orig. Title: Rabeinu Bachya Ben Asher "Kad Hakemach". 734p. 1980. 19.50 (ISBN 0-88328-016-7); pap. 14.50 (ISBN 0-88328-017-5). Shilo Pub Hse.

Encyclopedia of Unbelief, 2 vols. LC 85-43327. 819p. 1985. Set. 99.95 (ISBN 0-87975-307-2). Prometheus Bks.

Encyclopedia Talmudica, 3 vols. 25.00 ea. Vol. I (ISBN 0-87306-209-4). Vol. II (ISBN 0-87306-210-8). Vol. III (ISBN 0-87306-211-6). Feldheim.

Encyclopedia Yiddishanica. Endel Markowitz. LC 79-89973. (Illus.). 450p. 1980. 19.95 (ISBN 0-933910-02-9); pap. write for info. (ISBN 0-933910-04-5). Haymark.

Encyclopedic Dictionary of Religion, 3 vols. Paul K. Meagher et al. LC 78-62029. 3815p. 1979. 69.95 (ISBN 0-9602572-3-3). Cath U Pr.

Encyclopedie de l'Esoterisme, 1: Mythologies. Jacques d' Ares. (Fr.). 232p. 1975. pap. 19.95 (ISBN 0-686-56898-2, M-6008). French & Eur.

Encyclopedie De l'Esoterismelrisme, 2: Religions Non Chretiennes. Jacques D'ares. Jacques d' Ares. (Fr.). 244p. 1975. pap. 19.95 (ISBN 0-686-56899-0, M-6009). French & Eur.

Encyclopedie Des Musiques Sacrees, 3 vols. Jacques Porte. (Fr.). 1978. Set. 95.00 (ISBN 0-686-57145-2, M-6202). French & Eur.

Encyclopedie Theologique, 168 vols. in 171. Ed. by J. P. Migne. (Fr., Illus.). 119060p. Repr. of 1873 ed. Set. lib. bdg. 14,177.48 (ISBN 0-89241-230-5). Caratzas.

Encyclopedist of the Dark Ages, Isidore of Seville. Ernest Brehaut. (Columbia University. Studies in History, Economics, & Public Law: Vol. 48, No. 1). 1967. Repr. of 1912 ed. 21.50 (ISBN 0-8337-0361-7). B Franklin.

End of Christendom. Malcolm Muggeridge. 1980. pap. 2.95 (ISBN 0-8028-1837-4). Eerdmans.

End of False Religion-When? Gerald S. Sage. LC 87-80323. (Illus.). 192p. (Orig.). 1987. pap. 9.95 (ISBN 0-941813-00-2). Elite Pubs.

End of Strife. Ed. by David M. Loades. 233p. 1984. 17.95 (ISBN 0-567-09347-6, PUb. by T&T Clark Ltd UK). Fortress.

End of the Ages Has Come: An Early Interpretation of the Passion & Resurrection of Jesus. Dale C. Allison, Jr. LC 85-47732. 208p. 1985. 19.95 (ISBN 0-8006-0753-8, 1-753). Fortress.

End of the Ancient World, Three Hundred Eighty-One to Six Hundred. Enzo Bellini et al. Ed. & tr. by John Drury. (Illustrated History of the Church). (Illus.). 126p. 1982. 12.95 (ISBN 0-03-056826-9, HarpR). Har-Row.

End of the Days. Arthur E. Bloomfield. LC 51-9505. 288p. 1961. 8.95 (ISBN 0-87123-122-0, 210122). Bethany Hse.

End of the Historical Critical Method. Gerhard Maier. 1977. pap. 6.25 (ISBN 0-570-03752-2, 12-2656). Concordia.

End of the Line? The Development of Christian Theology in the Last Two Centuries. John H. Kent. LC 82-7263. 144p. 1982. pap. 6.95 (ISBN 0-8006-1652-9, 1-1652). Fortress.

End of the Religious Life. Robert Faricy. 96p. 1983. pap. 6.95 (ISBN 0-86683-690-X, HarpR). Har-Row.

End of the Rope. rev. ed. Claud C. Crawford. LC 85-90684. 96p. 1985. pap. 6.95 (ISBN 0-933697-00-7). Claud Crawford.

End of 'The World' facs. ed. Ed. by James W. Barrett. LC 72-117866. (Select Bibliographies Reprint Ser). 1931. 24.50 (ISBN 0-8369-5319-3). Ayer Co Pubs.

End of the World: A Catholic View. Robert F. Baldwin. LC 83-63166. 192p. 1984. pap. 5.95 (ISBN 0-87973-608-9, 608). Our Sunday Visitor.

End of the World, A.D. 2133. Lucio B. Silvestre. LC 83-90813. 233p. 1985. 12.95 (ISBN 0-533-05822-8). Vantage.

End Time-God's Glory. John W. Hartsaw. 112p. 1982. 6.50 (ISBN 0-682-49848-3). Exposition Pr FL.

End Time Prophecy. Bob Yandian. 15p. 1983. wkbk. 3.95 (ISBN 0-914307-15-0, Dist. by Harrison Hse). Word Faith.

End Times. Herman A. Hoyt. pap. 6.95 (ISBN 0-88469-077-6). BMH Bks.

End-Times: Rapture, Antichrist, Mellennium. James M. Efird. 96p. (Orig.). 1986. pap. 5.95 (ISBN 0-687-11787-9). Abingdon.

Endless Line of Splendor. Earle E. Cairns. 352p. 1986. text ed. 14.95 (ISBN 0-8423-0770-2). Tyndale.

Endpapers: Political Essay. Breyten Breybach. 1986. 16.95 (ISBN 0-374-14829-5). FS&G.

Enduring Significance of Emerson's Divinity School Address. John H. Holmes. LC 73-9537. 1938. Repr. lib. bdg. 8.50 (ISBN 0-8414-2073-4). Folcroft.

Enduring to the End: Jehovah's Witnesses & Bible Doctrine. John Hartog. 200p. 1987. pap. write for info. (ISBN 0-87227-118-8). Reg Baptist.

Enemies & How to Love Them. Gerard A. Vanderhaar. 128p. (Orig.). 1985. pap. 4.95 (ISBN 0-89622-241-1). Twenty Third.

Enemies of God: The Witch-Hunt in Scotland. Christina Larner. LC 81-47605. 256p. 1981. text ed. 25.00x (ISBN 0-8018-2699-3). Johns Hopkins.

Enemy Disguised: Unmasking the Illusion of Meaningful Death. Robert L. Gram. 224p. 1985. 10.95 (ISBN 0-8407-5942-8). Nelson.

Enemy Guest. Vivian D. Gunderson. 1964. pap. 1.75 (ISBN 0-915374-11-0, 11-0). Rapids Christian.

Enemy Within the Gate. John McKee. LC 74-80023. 1974. 10.00 (ISBN 0-912414-16-2). Lumen Christi.

Energie Humaine. Pierre Teilhard De Chardin. 1962. 18.95 (ISBN 0-685-11160-1). French & Eur.

Energizing Your Faith. N. Raymond Day. 56p. (Orig.). 1985. pap. 5.95 (ISBN 0-940754-28-2). Ed Ministries.

Energizing Your Faith. Jerry Savelle. 64p. 1984. pap. 2.25 (ISBN 0-89274-285-2, HH-285). Harrison Hse.

Energy Ecstasy & Your Seven Vital Shakras. Bernard Gunther. LC 83-8822. 200p. 1983. lib. bdg. 21.95x (ISBN 0-89370-666-3). Borgo Pr.

Energy-Efficient Church. Total Environmental Action, Inc. Ed. by Douglas Hoffman. LC 79-10432. (Illus.). 1979. pap. 4.95 (ISBN 0-8298-0362-9). Pilgrim NY.

Energy Ethics: A Christian Response. Ed. by Dieter T. Hessel. (Orig.). 1979. pap. 4.25 (ISBN 0-377-00094-9). Friend Pr.

Energy, Prayer & Relaxation. Israel Regardie. LC 82-83292. 80p. 1982. pap. 5.95 (ISBN 0-941404-02-1). Falcon Pr Az.

Enfolded by Christ: An Encouragement to Pray. Michael Hollings. Orig. Title: Day by Day. 128p. 1976. pap. 2.95 (ISBN 0-914544-10-1). Living Flame Pr.

Enfolded in Love: Daily Readings with Julian of Norwich. Julian of Norwich. Tr. by Julian Shrine Members Staff. 96p. (Orig.). 1981. pap. 4.95 (ISBN 0-8164-2318-0, HarpR). Har-Row.

Engaged. William L. Coleman. 1980. pap. 5.95 (ISBN 0-8423-0693-5). Tyndale.

Engaging the Aging in Ministry. Elmer Otte. 1981. pap. 7.95 (ISBN 0-9602938-5-X). Retirement Res.

Engaging the Aging in Ministry. Elmer Otte & Mark Bergmann. LC 12-2798. 1981. pap. 6.95 (ISBN 0-570-03833-2). Concordia.

England Against the Papacy: 1858-1861. C. T. McIntire. LC 82-9405. (Illus.). 280p. 1983. 44.50 (ISBN 0-521-24237-1). Cambridge U Pr.

England & Germany: Studies in Theological Diplomacy. Ed. by S. W. Sykes. (IC-Studies in the Intercultural History of Christianity: Vol. 25). 170p. 1981. pap. 22.15 (ISBN 3-8204-5854-9). P Lang Pubs.

England & Holland of the Pilgrims. Henry M. Dexter & Morton Dexter. LC 77-90433. (Illus.). 673p. 1978. Repr. of 1906 ed. 28.50 (ISBN 0-8063-0794-3). Genealog Pub.

England, Before & after Wesley: The Evangelical Revival & Social Reform. John W. Bready. LC 72-139906. (Illus.). 463p. 1971. Repr. of 1938 ed. 17.00x (ISBN 0-8462-1533-0). Russell.

England in the Age of Wycliffe. 3rd ed. George M. Trevelyan. LC 78-178560. Repr. of 1900 ed. 34.50 (ISBN 0-404-56677-4). AMS Pr.

England und Die Schmalkaldener, 1535-1540. Friedrich Pruser. 34.00 (ISBN 0-384-48058-6); pap. 28.00 (ISBN 0-384-48057-8). Johnson Repr.

England: Unity God's Gift. 3.50 (ISBN 0-8198-2302-3); 2.50 (ISBN 0-8198-2307-4). Dghtrs St Paul.

Englands & Scotlands Happiness in Being Reduced to Unitie of Religion. John Gordon. LC 75-38190. (English Experience Ser.: No. 461). 50p. 1972. Repr. of 1604 ed. 7.00 (ISBN 90-221-0461-3). Walter J Johnson.

England's Earliest Protestants, 1520-1535. William A. Clebsch. LC 80-15226. (Yale Publications in Religion: No. 11). xvi, 358p. 1980. Repr. of 1964 ed. lib. bdg. 22.50x (ISBN 0-313-22420-X, CLEE). Greenwood.

English Abbey: Its Life & Work in the Middle Ages. Frederick H. Crossley. LC 82-25127. (Illus.). xiv, 114p. 1983. Repr. of 1935 ed. lib. bdg. 45.00x (ISBN 0-313-23849-9, CRFE). Greenwood.

English Baptist Literature on Religious Liberty to Sixteen Eighty Nine: Doctoral Dissertation. H. Leon McBeth. Ed. by Edwin S. Gaustad. LC 79-52575. (Baptist Tradition Ser.). 1980. lib. bdg. 39.00x (ISBN 0-405-12443-0). Ayer Co Pubs.

English Benedictines, Fifteen Forty to Sixteen Eighty-Eight: From Reformation to Revolution. David Lunn. (Illus.). 282p. 1980. 28.50x (ISBN 0-06-494411-5). B&N Imports.

English Bible as Literature. Charles A. Dinsmore. 1931. Repr. 30.00 (ISBN 0-8274-3832-X). R West.

English Biography. Vivan De Sola Pinto. 1973. lib. bdg. 10.00 (ISBN 0-8414-9259-X). Folcroft.

English Cabalah, 2 vols, Vol. 1. William Eisen. (Illus.). 608p. 1980. text ed. 16.95 (ISBN 0-87516-390-4). De Vorss.

English Cabalah Volume 2: The Mysteries of Phi. William Eisen. LC 79-57053. (Agashan Teachings Ser.). 652p. 1982. 26.95 (ISBN 0-87516-459-5). De Vorss.

English Carol. Erik Routley. LC 73-9129. (Illus.). 272p. 1973. Repr. of 1959 ed. lib. bdg. 22.50x (ISBN 0-8371-6989-5, ROEC). Greenwood.

English Cathedral Music. 5th, rev. ed. Edmund H. Fellowes. Ed. by J. A. Westrup. LC 80-24400. (Illus.). xi, 283p. 1981. Repr. of 1973 ed. lib. bdg. 27.50x (ISBN 0-313-22643-1, FEEC). Greenwood.

English Cathedrals. F. Bono. 1976. lib. bdg. 234.95 (ISBN 0-8490-1771-8). Gordon Pr.

English Cathedrals. Patrick Cormack. (Illus.). 1984. 14.95 (ISBN 0-517-55409-7, Harmony). Crown.

English Catholic Books, 1641-1700. Thomas H. Clancy. LC 74-704. 158p. 1974. pap. 8.00 (ISBN 0-8294-0231-4). Loyola.

English Catholic Church in the Nineteenth Century. Edward Norman. 1984. pap. 13.95x (ISBN 0-19-822955-0). Oxford U Pr.

English Catholic Community, 1570-1850. John Bossy. (Illus.). 1976. 39.95x (ISBN 0-19-519847-6); pap. 5.95x (ISBN 0-19-285148-9). Oxford U Pr.

English Catholic Enlightenment: John Lingard & the Cisalpine Movement, 1780 to 1850. Joseph P. Chinnici. LC 79-20250. (Illus.). xiv, 262p. 1980. 24.95x (ISBN 0-915762-10-2). Patmos Pr.

English Catholic Modernism: Maude Petre's Way of Faith. Clyde Crews. LC 83-50747. 156p. 1984. text ed. 16.95x (ISBN 0-268-00912-0, 85-09127). U of Notre Dame Pr.

English Catholic Poets, Chaucer to Dryden. facs. ed. Elbridge Colby. LC 67-28733. (Essay Index Reprint Ser.). 1936. 18.00 (ISBN 0-8369-0321-8). Ayer Co Pubs.

English Catholics in the Reign of Queen Elizabeth: A Study of Their Politics, Civil Life & Government. John H. Pollen. 1971. Repr. of 1920 ed. lib. bdg. 24.50 (ISBN 0-8337-2798-2). B Franklin.

English Chantries: The Road to Dissolution. Alan Kreider. LC 78-12453. (Harvard Historical Studies: No. 97). 1979. 22.50x (ISBN 0-674-25560-7). Harvard U Pr.

English Christmas: The Traditions, the Observances, the Festivities. Celia McInnes. LC 86-7553. (Illus.). 104p. 1986. 14.95 (ISBN 0-8050-0043-7). H Holt & Co.

English Church. G. K. Bell. 10.00 (ISBN 0-8414-1634-6). Folcroft.

English Church & Its Bishops, 1700-1800, 2 Vols. Charles J. Abbey. LC 77-130230. Repr. of 1887 ed. Set. 74.50 (ISBN 0-404-00290-0). AMS Pr.

English Church & the Papacy in the Middle Ages. Lawrence. LC 65-12529. 265p. 1984. pap. 10.00 (ISBN 0-8232-0646-7). Fordham.

English Church Brasses from the 13th to the 17th Century, a Manual for Antiquaries, Archaeologists & Collectors. Ernest R. Suffling. LC 73-126133. (Illus.). 456p. 1970. Repr. of 1910 ed. 22.50 (ISBN 0-8063-0437-5). Genealog Pub.

English Church Composers: The Great Musicians. facsimile ed. William A. Barrett. LC 70-102224. (Select Bibliographies Reprint Ser). 1882. 19.00 (ISBN 0-8369-5109-3). Ayer Co Pubs.

English Church from Its Foundation to the Norman Conquest, 597-1066. William Hunt. LC 2-21442. (History of the English Church: No. 1). Repr. of 1899 ed. 29.50 (ISBN 0-404-50751-4). AMS Pr.

English Church from the Accession of Charles First to the Death of Anne, 1625-1714. William H. Hutton. LC 4-4381. (History of the English Church Ser.: No. 6). Repr. of 1903 ed. 29.50 (ISBN 0-404-50756-5). AMS Pr.

English Church from the Accession of George First to the End of the Eighteenth Century, 1714-1800. John H. Overton & Frederic Relton. (History of the English Church Ser.: No. 7). Repr. of 1906 ed. 29.50 (ISBN 0-404-50757-3). AMS Pr.

English Church from the Norman Conquest to the Accession of Edward First, 1066-1272. William R. Stephens. LC 2-21443. (History of the English Church Ser.: No. 2). Repr. of 1901 ed. 29.50 (ISBN 0-404-50752-2). AMS Pr.

English Church History: From the Death of Archbishop Parker to the Death of King Charles I. Alfred Plummer. 1977. lib. bdg. 59.95 (ISBN 0-8490-1772-6). Gordon Pr.

English Church in the Fourteenth & Fifteenth Centuries, 1272-1486. William W. Capes. LC 2-21441. (History of the English Church: No. 3). Repr. of 1900 ed. 29.50 (ISBN 0-404-50753-0). AMS Pr.

English Church in the Fourteenth Century. W. A. Pantin. (Medieval Academy Reprints for Teaching Ser.). 1980. pap. 6.50 (ISBN 0-8020-6411-6). U of Toronto Pr.

English Church in the Nineteenth Century, 2 Vols. Francis Warre-Cornish. LC 75-148325. (History of the English Church Ser.: No. 8). Repr. of 1910 ed. Set. 59.00 (ISBN 0-404-50760-3); 29.50 ea. Vol. 1 (ISBN 0-404-50758-1). Vol. 2 (ISBN 0-404-50759-X). AMS Pr.

English Church in the Nineteenth Century (1800-1833) John H. Overton. (Victorian Age Ser.). 1894. Repr. 35.00 (ISBN 0-8482-5454-6). Norwood Edns.

English Church in the Reigns of Elizabeth & James First, 1558-1625. Walter H. Frere. (History of the English Church: No. 5). Repr. of 1904 ed. 29.50 (ISBN 0-404-50755-7). AMS Pr.

English Church in the Reigns of Elizabeth & James I: 1558-1625. Walter H. Frere. 1977. lib. bdg. 59.95 (ISBN 0-8490-1773-4). Gordon Pr.

English Church in the Sixteenth Century, from the Accession of Henry Eighth to the Death of Mary, 1509-1558. James Gairdner. LC 72-168089. (History of the English Church Ser.: No. 4). Repr. of 1902 ed. 29.50 (ISBN 0-404-50754-9). AMS Pr.

English Church in the Sixteenth Century. Craig R. Thompson. LC 79-65981. (Folger Guides to the Age of Shakespeare Ser.). 1979. pap. 3.95 (ISBN 0-918016-08-8). Folger Bks.

English Church Members' Responses to Women Clergy: A Sociological Analysis. Edward C. Lehman, Jr. LC 86-28547. (Studies in Religion & Society). 224p. 1987. text ed. 49.95 (ISBN 0-88946-858-3). E Mellen.

English Church Monuments. Brian Kemp. 240p. 1980. 45.00 (ISBN 0-7134-1735-8, Pub. by Batsford England). David & Charles.

English Church, Ten Sixty-Six to Eleven Fifty-Four: A History of the Anglo-Norman Church. Frank Barlow. (Illus.). 1979. text ed. 40.00x (ISBN 0-582-50236-5). Longman.

English Churches in a Secular Society: Lambeth, 1870-1930. Jeffrey Cox. (Illus.). 1982. 45.00x (ISBN 0-19-503019-2). Oxford U Pr.
English Congregational Hymns in the Eighteenth Century. Madeleine F. Marshall & Janet M. Todd. LC 82-40176. 192p. 1982. 16.00x (ISBN 0-8131-1470-5). U Pr of Ky.
English Connection: The Puritan Roots of Seventh-Day Adventist Belief. Bryan W. Ball. 252p. 1981. text ed. 17.50 (ISBN 0-227-67844-3). Attic Pr.
English Country Churches. Derry Brabbs. 160p. 1985. 25.00 (ISBN 0-670-80736-2). Viking.
English Dictionary Supplement to the Concordance to the Peshitta Version Of the Aramaic New Testament. 59p. 1985. 2.95 (ISBN 0-910068-67-4). Am Christian.
English Domestic or Homiletic Tragedy: 1575-1642. Henry H. Adams. LC 65-16225. Repr. of 1943 ed. 17.00 (ISBN 0-405-08178-2, Pub. by Blom). Ayer Co Pubs.
English Ecclesiastical Tenants-in-Chief & Knight Service, Especially in the Thirteenth & Fourteenth Centuries. Helena M. Chew. LC 80-2310. Repr. of 1932 ed. 37.50 (ISBN 0-404-18558-4). AMS Pr.
English Episcopal Acta: Canterbury, 1193-1205, 2 vols, Vols. I & II. Ed. by C. R. Cheney & Bridgette A. Jones. (Episcopal Acta). 1984. Set. 165.00x (ISBN 0-19-726022-5). Oxford U Pr.
English Episcopal Acta I: Lincoln 1067-1185. David M. Smith. (English Episcopal Acta Ser.). (Illus.). 312p. 1980. 67.50 (ISBN 0-85672-645-1, Pub. by British Acad). Longwood Pub Group.
English Free Churches. 2nd. ed. Horton Davies. LC 85-7684. vii, 208p. 1985. Repr. of 1963 ed. lib. bdg. 37.50x (ISBN 0-313-20838-7, DAEF). Greenwood.
English Hymn. Louis Benson. (Music Reprint Ser.). 624p. 1985. Repr. of 1915 ed. 65.00 (ISBN 0-306-76261-7). Da Capo.
English Hymnal. 1933. 20.00x (ISBN 0-19-231111-5); words only o.p. 9.95x (ISBN 0-19-231108-5). Oxford U Pr.
English Hymns & Ballads. Peter Haworth. 1927. lib. bdg. 16.50 (ISBN 0-8414-4975-9). Folcroft.
English Hymns: Their Authors & History. Samuel W. Duffield. 1980. Repr. of 1886 ed. lib. bdg. 60.00 (ISBN 0-89341-441-7). Longwood Pub Group.
English Jewry under Angevin Kings. Henry G. Richardson. LC 83-18539. ix, 313p. 1983. Repr. of 1960 ed. lib. bdg. 35.00x (ISBN 0-313-24247-X, RIEJ). Greenwood.
English Mediaeval Monasteries, 1066-1540. Roy Midmer. LC 79-53097. 394p. 1980. 27.00x (ISBN 0-8203-0488-3). U of Ga Pr.
English Messiahs: Studies of Six English Religious Pretenders, 1656-1927. Ronald Matthews. LC 76-172553. Repr. of 1936 ed. 12.75 (ISBN 0-405-18187-6, Pub. by Blom). Ayer Co Pubs.
English Metrical Homilies from Manuscripts of the Fourteenth Century. Ed. by John Small. LC 79-178504. Repr. of 1862 ed. 22.50 (ISBN 0-404-56674-X). AMS Pr.
English Miracle Plays & Moralities. E. Hamilton Moore. LC 77-100517. Repr. of 1907 ed. 17.25 (ISBN 0-404-00598-5). AMS Pr.
English Missionaries in Sweden & Finland. (Church Historical Society, London, Ser.: No. 27). Repr. of 1937 ed. 55.00 (ISBN 0-8115-3151-1). Kraus Repr.
English Missionaries in Sweden & Finland. Charles J. Oppermann. LC 38-16784. (Church Historical Society Ser.: No. 26). 1937. 17.50x (ISBN 0-281-00240-1). A R Allenson.
English Monasteries. A. Hamilton Thompson. LC 78-3738. 1974. Repr. of 1913 ed. lib. bdg. 17.50 (ISBN 0-8414-8646-8). Folcroft.
English Monastic Life. fascimile ed. Francis A. Gasquet. LC 77-157336. (Select Bibliographies Reprint Ser.). Repr. of 1904 ed. 32.00 (ISBN 0-8369-5796-2). Ayer Co Pubs.
English Monastic Life. Francis A. Gasquet. LC 76-118470. 1971. Repr. of 1904 ed. 29.50x (ISBN 0-8046-1219-6, Pub. by Kennikat). Assoc Faculty Pr.
English Moral Plays. Elbert N. Thompson. LC 70-131500. Repr. of 1910 ed. 7.00 (ISBN 0-404-06397-7). AMS Pr.
English Moralities from the Point of View of Allegory. W. Roy MacKenzie. LC 68-54172. (Studies in Drama, No. 39). 1969. Repr. of 1914 ed. lib. bdg. 49.95x (ISBN 0-8383-0592-X). Haskell.
English Moralities from the Point of View of Allegory. William R. Mackenzie. LC 66-29466. 278p. 1966. Repr. of 1914 ed. 25.00x (ISBN 0-87752-066-6). Gordian.
English Moralities from the Point of View of Allegory. William R. MacKenzie. (Harvard Studies in English). Repr. of 1914 ed. 23.00 (ISBN 0-384-34880-7). Johnson Repr.
English Morality & Related Drama: A Bibliographical Survey. Peter J. Houle. LC 70-38714. xviii, 195p. 1972. 26.00 (ISBN 0-208-01264-8, Archon). Shoe String.
English Mystics. Geraldine E. Hodgson. LC 73-13663. 1973. lib. bdg. 25.00 (ISBN 0-8414-4756-X). Folcroft.
English Mystics. Geraldine E. Hodgson. 1977. lib. bdg. 59.95 (ISBN 0-8490-1777-7). Gordon Pr.
English Mystics. G. E. Hollingworth. 1973. lib. bdg. 15.00 (ISBN 0-8414-5096-X). Folcroft.
English Mystics of the Fourteenth Century. Thomas W. Coleman. LC 74-109723. 1971. Repr. of 1938 ed. lib. bdg. 22.50x (ISBN 0-8371-4213-X, COEM). Greenwood.
English Myths & Traditions. Henry Bett. (Illus.). 144p. 1980. Repr. of 1952 ed. lib. bdg. 17.50 (ISBN 0-8414-2921-9). Folcroft.
English Omnibus of Sources: St. Francis of Assisi. new ed. Ed. by Marion A. Habig. 1977. 30.00 (ISBN 0-8199-0658-1). Franciscan Herald.
English Parish Church. J. Charles Cox. (Illus.). 1977. Repr. of 1914 ed. 25.00x (ISBN 0-7158-1174-6). Charles River Bks.
English Parish Church. Gerald Randall. 192p. 1982. 35.00 (ISBN 0-8419-6402-5). Holmes & Meier.
English Penitential Discipline & Anglo-Saxon Law in Their Joint Influence. Thomas P. Oakley. LC 71-82243. (Columbia University. Studies in the Social Sciences: No. 242). Repr. of 1923 ed. 20.00 (ISBN 0-404-51242-9). AMS Pr.
English Political Thought, Sixteen Hundred Three to Sixteen Forty-Four. John W. Allen. x, 525p. 1967. Repr. of 1938 ed. 37.50 (ISBN 0-208-00144-1, Archon). Shoe String.
English Praise: A Supplement to the English Hymnal, Full Music Edition. 1975. pap. 5.95x (ISBN 0-19-231126-3). Oxford U Pr.
English Primers, Fifteen Twenty-Nine to Fifteen Forty-Five: Their Publication & Connection with the English Bible & the Reformation in England. Charles C. Butterworth. 1970. lib. bdg. 26.00x (ISBN 0-374-91131-2, Octagon). Hippocrene Bks.
English Protestants Plea. Richard Broughton. LC 76-57380. (English Experience Ser.: No. 798). 1977. Repr. of 1621 ed. lib. bdg. 9.50 (ISBN 90-221-0798-1). Walter J Johnson.
English Pulpit Oratory from Andrews to Tillotson: A Study of Its Literary Aspects. Mitchell W. Fraser. 516p. 1982. Repr. of 1932 ed. lib. bdg. 85.00 (ISBN 0-89760-564-0). Telegraph Bks.
English Puritanisme & Other Works. William Bradshaw. 326p. text ed. 62.10 (ISBN 0-576-99738-2, Pub. by Gregg Intl Pub England). Gregg Intl.
English Puritans. John Brown. 1978. Repr. of 1910 ed. lib. bdg. 20.00 (ISBN 0-8495-0434-1). Arden Lib.
English Puritans. John Brown. LC 73-12821. 1910. lib. bdg. 22.50 (ISBN 0-8414-3235-X). Folcroft.
English Quakers & the First Industrial Revolution: A Study of the Quaker Community in Four Industrial Counties; York, Warwick, & Gloucester, 1750-1830. David H. Pratt. LC 84-46009. (British Economic History Ser.). 236p. 1985. lib. bdg. 28.00 (ISBN 0-8240-6689-8). Garland Pub.
English Reformation. Arthur G. Dickens. LC 64-22987. (Fabric of British History Ser). 1968. pap. 8.95 (ISBN 0-8052-0177-7). Schocken.
English Register of Oseney Abbey: Parts 1 & 2. Oseney Abbey. (EETS, OS Ser.: No. 133, 144). 1907-1913. Repr. of 1907 ed. 22.00 (ISBN 0-527-00130-9). Kraus Repr.
English Religious Drama. Katharine L. Bates. 1975. Repr. of 1911 ed. 30.00 (ISBN 0-8274-4103-7). R West.
English Religious Drama of the Middle Ages. Hardin Craig. LC 78-6893. 1978. Repr. of 1968 ed. lib. bdg. 37.50x (ISBN 0-313-20496-9, CRER). Greenwood.
English Religious Life in the Eighth Century. Thomas Allison. LC 75-106708. Repr. of 1929 ed. lib. bdg. 22.50x (ISBN 0-8371-3438-2, ALRL). Greenwood.
English Religious Life in the Eighth Century As Illustrated by Contemporary Letters. Thomas Allison. LC 70-136409. Repr. of 1929 ed. 9.00 (ISBN 0-404-00348-6). AMS Pr.
English Religious Tradition: Sketches of Its Influence on Church, State & Society. Norman Sykes. LC 78-59045. 1986. Repr. of 1953 ed. 15.00 (ISBN 0-88355-717-7). Hyperion Conn.
English Religious Verse. G. Lacey May. 1937. lib. bdg. 8.50 (ISBN 0-8414-6604-1). Folcroft.
English Sabbath: A Study of Doctrine & Practice from the Reformation to the Civil War. Kenneth L. Parker. (Illus.). 224p. Date not set. price not set (ISBN 0-521-30535-7). Cambridge U Pr.
English Sacred Lyrics. 1978. Repr. of 1884 ed. lib. bdg. 30.00 (ISBN 0-8492-0061-X). R West.
English Sacred Poetry of the Olden Time. L. B. White. Repr. of 1864 ed. 25.00 (ISBN 0-89984-136-8). Century Bookbindery.
English Sermons of John Foxe. John Foxe. LC 77-29100. 1978. Repr. of 1578 ed. 60.00x (ISBN 0-8201-1267-4). Schol Facsimiles.
English Spanish Pilgrime. James Wadsworth. LC 71-25682. (English Experience Ser.: No. 275). 96p. 1970. Repr. of 1629 ed. 11.50 (ISBN 90-221-0275-0). Walter J Johnson.
English Spirit. 2nd ed. D. Faulkner Jones. 235p. 1982. 13.95 (ISBN 0-85440-388-4, Pub. by Steinerbooks); pap. 9.95 (ISBN 0-85440-389-2). Anthroposophic.
English Spirituality. Martin Thornton. 330p. 1986. 24.95 (ISBN 0-936384-38-7); pap. 11.95 (ISBN 0-936384-31-X). Cowley Pubns.
English Treasury of Religious Prose. J. Lewis May. 1977. Repr. of 1932 ed. 15.00 (ISBN 0-89984-062-0). Century Bookbindery.
English View of American Quakerism: The Journal of Walter Robson 1842-1929 Written During the Fall of 1877, While Traveling Among American Friends. Walter Robson. Ed. by Edwin B. Bronner. LC 71-107345. (American Philosophical Society Memoirs Ser.: Vol. 79). pap. 43.80 (ISBN 0-317-27898-3, 2025135). Bks Demand UMI.
English Way: Studies in English Sanctity from St. Bede to Newman. facs. ed. Ed. by Maisie Ward. LC 68-29253. (Essay Index Reprint Ser). 1968. Repr. of 1933 ed. 17.75 (ISBN 0-8369-0975-5). Ayer Co Pubs.
English Workbook for Christian Students. Merle Meeter et al. 1980. pap. 5.95x (ISBN 0-89051-066-0); tchr.'s guide 2.95x (ISBN 0-686-85807-7). Master Bks.
English Works of Raja Ramohun Roy. R. Rammohun Roy. Ed. by Jogendra C. Ghose. LC 75-41220. Repr. of 1906 ed. 49.50 (ISBN 0-404-14738-0). AMS Pr.
Englishe Romayne Lyfe. Anthony Munday. LC 76-38213. (English Experience Ser.: No. 478). 84p. 1972. Repr. of 1582 ed. 6.00 (ISBN 90-221-0478-8). Walter J Johnson.
Englishman's Greek Concordance of the New Testament. rev. ed. George V. Wigram. (Gr. & Eng.). 1982. pap. 29.95 (ISBN 0-8054-1388-X). Broadman.
Englishman's Greek Concordance of the New Testament. George V. Wigram. 34.95 (ISBN 0-310-20320-1, 6258). Zondervan.
Englishman's Greek Concordance of the New Testament. George V. Wigram. 1984. 29.95 (ISBN 0-8010-3416-7). Baker Bk.
Englishman's Hebrew & Chaldee Concordance of the Old Testament. (Hebrew & Eng.). 1980. pap. 35.95 (ISBN 0-8054-1387-1). Broadman.
Englishman's Hebrew & Chaldee Concordance of the Old Testament. George V. Wigram. 39.95 (ISBN 0-310-20340-6, 6265). Zondervan.
Englishman's Hebrew & Chaldee Concordance of the Old Testament. George V. Wigram. (Reference Set). 1760p. 1982. Repr. of 1980 ed. 34.95 (ISBN 0-88062-105-2). Mott Media.
Engrammes of the Universe: Extra-Cerebral Memory, Reincarnation & Demonic Possession. J. M. Sanchez-Perez. 1980. 8.50 (ISBN 0-682-49474-7). Exposition Pr FL.
Enigma of Evil: Can We Believe in the Goodness of God? John W. Wenham. 224p. (Orig.). 1985. pap. 7.95 (ISBN 0-310-29871-7, 12449P). Zondervan.
Enigma of God & Man's Proclivity to Evil. Dwane K. Martell. (Institute for Religious Research Library). (Illus.). 77p. 1983. 47.75 (ISBN 0-89920-049-4). Am Inst Psych.
Enigmas of Life. William R. Greg. LC 72-323. (Essay Index Reprint Ser.). Repr. of 1879 ed. 21.00 (ISBN 0-8369-2794-X). Ayer Co Pubs.
Enjoy! Virginia K. Leih. 124p. 1983. pap. 3.95 (ISBN 0-8341-0814-3). Beacon Hill.
Enjoy the Lord. John T. Catoir. 1979. pap. 2.95 (ISBN 0-88479-023-1). Arena Lettres.
Enjoy the Lord. 3.50 (ISBN 0-318-02213-3). Chrstphrs NY.
Enjoy Your Bible. Irving L. Jensen. 1969. pap. 5.95 (ISBN 0-8024-2347-7). Moody.
Enjoy Your Quiet Time. Wilberta L. Chinn & Gregory R. Owyang. 52p. 1986. wkbk. 3.00 (ISBN 0-937673-01-3). Peacock Ent LA.
Enjoying Intimacy with God. J. Oswald Sanders. LC 80-21398. 218p. 1980. pap. 5.95 (ISBN 0-8024-2346-9). Moody.
Enjoying the Harvest: Reflections for Your Mature Years. Donald Mackinnon. 48p. 1983. pap. 1.50 (ISBN 0-89243-196-2). Liguori Pubns.
Enjoying the Proverbs. William MacDonald. 1982. pap. 4.00 (ISBN 0-937396-23-0). Walterick Pubs.
Enjoying the Psalms, 2 vols. William MacDonald. 1977. pap. 7.00 ea. Vol. 1 (ISBN 0-937396-34-6). Vol. 2 (ISBN 0-937396-35-4). Walterick Pubs.
Enjoyment of Scripture: The Law, the Prophets, & the Writings. Samuel Sandmel. (Illus.). 1972. pap. 8.95 (ISBN 0-19-501783-8). Oxford U Pr.
Enku: Sculptor of a Hundred Thousand Buddhas. Kazuaki Tanahashi. LC 81-50969. (Illus.). 176p. (Orig.). 1982. pap. 13.95 (ISBN 0-87773-212-4). Shambhala Pubns.
Enlightened Living. 2nd ed. Swami Venkatesananda. 1978. pap. 2.95 (ISBN 0-89684-038-7, Pub. by Motilal Banarsidass India). Orient Bk Dist.
Enlightened Society. John L. Hill. LC 86-40403. 278p. (Orig.). 1987. pap. 7.95 (ISBN 0-8356-0615-5). Theos Pub Hse.
Enlightenment: An Interpretation-the Rise of Modern Paganism, Vol. 1. Peter Gay. 1977. pap. 10.95x (ISBN 0-393-00870-3, N870, Norton Lib). Norton.
Enlightenment & the Transformation of Man. Da F. John. LC 83-72730. 1983. pap. 7.95 (ISBN 0-913922-83-8). Dawn Horse Pr.
Enlightenment of the Whole Body. Da Free John. LC 77-94504. 600p. 1978. pap. 14.95 (ISBN 0-913922-35-8). Dawn Horse Pr.
Ennin's Diary: The Record of a Pilgrimage to China in Search of the Law. Tr. by Edwin O. Reischauer. LC 55-5553. (Illus.). pap. 119.50 (ISBN 0-8357-9521-7, 2012366). Bks Demand UMI.
Enoch & Noah, Patriarchs of the Deluge. Gordon Lindsay. (Old Testament Ser.). 1.25 (ISBN 0-89985-125-8). Christ Nations.
Enoch & the Growth of an Apocalyptic Tradition. James C. VanderKam. LC 83-10134. (Catholic Biblical Quarterly Monographs: No. 16). 217p. 1984. pap. 6.50 (ISBN 0-915170-15-9). Catholic Bibl Assn.
Enoch the Prophet. Hugh Nibley. 1986. text ed. 15.95 (ISBN 0-87579-047-X). Deseret Bk.
Enoch Three, or the Hebrew Book of Enoch. rev. ed. Hugo Odeberg. (Library of Biblical Studies). 1970. 39.50x (ISBN 0-87068-093-5). Ktav.
Enomiya: Zen Meditation for Christians. H. M. Lassalle. Tr. by John C. Maraldo. 187p. 1974. 16.95 (ISBN 0-87548-151-5). Open Court.
Enosh & His Generation: Pre-Israelite Hero & History in Post-Biblical Interpretation. Steven D. Fraade. LC 83-27137. (Society of Biblical Literature-Monograph Ser.). 1984. 29.95 (ISBN 0-89130-724-9, 06 00 30); pap. 19.95 (ISBN 0-89130-725-7). Scholars Pr GA.
Enough Is Enough: A Biblical Call for Moderation in a Consumer Oriented Societed. John V. Taylor. LC 77-72456. 1977. pap. 5.95 (ISBN 0-8066-1584-2, 10-2083). Augsburg.
Enough of Christmas. Harriet Faust. (Orig.). 1980. pap. 2.95 (ISBN 0-937172-08-1). JLJ Pubs.
Enquiries Concerning Human Understanding & Concerning the Principles of Morals. 3rd ed. David Hume. Ed. by P. H. Nidditch. 1975. pap. text ed. 10.95x (ISBN 0-19-824536-X). Oxford U Pr.
Enquiries into Religion & Culture. facs. ed. Christopher H. Dawson. LC 68-29200. (Essay Index Reprint Ser.). 1933. 24.50 (ISBN 0-8369-0367-6). Ayer Co Pubs.
Enquiry Concerning the Principles of Morals. 2nd ed. David Hume. 200p. 1966. 15.95 (ISBN 0-87548-017-9); pap. 4.95 (ISBN 0-87548-018-7). Open Court.
Enquiry Concerning the Principles of Morals. David Hume. Ed. by J. B. Schneewind. LC 82-11679. (HPC Philosophical Classics Ser.). 132p. 1983. lib. bdg. 15.00 (ISBN 0-915145-46-4); pap. text ed. 3.45 (ISBN 0-915145-45-6). Hackett Pub.
Enquiry Concerning the Principles of Natural Knowledge. Alfred N. Whitehead. (Western Philosophy & Religion Ser.). 207p. 1982. pap. 5.95 (ISBN 0-486-24343-5). Dover.
Enquiry into Moral Notions. John Laird. LC 76-114045. Repr. of 1936 ed. 22.50 (ISBN 0-404-03802-6). AMS Pr.
Enquiry into the Ideas of Space & Time. Edmund Law. Ed. by Rene Wellek. LC 75-11230. (British Philosophers & Theologians of the 17th & 18th Century: Vol. 31). 1976. Repr. of 1734 ed. lib. bdg. 51.00 (ISBN 0-8240-1783-8). Garland Pub.
Enquiry into the Origin of Honour & the Usefullness of Christianity in War. Bernard Mandeville. 240p. 1971. Repr. of 1732 ed. 32.50x (ISBN 0-7146-2314-8, F Cass Co). Biblio Dist.
Enriching Your Marriage. Ed. by Robert Heyer. 2.45 (ISBN 0-8091-2261-8). Paulist Pr.
Enriching Your Marriage: A Tune-up for Partners in Love. Clark Swain. LC 80-84568. 250p. 1982. 9.95 (ISBN 0-88290-171-0, 2015). Horizon Utah.
Enrollment in the School of Discipleship. Catherine Nerney. 1.50 (ISBN 0-8091-9331-0). Paulist Pr.

Ensayo Sobre el Catolicismo, el Liberalismo y el Socialismo & Donoso Cortes, 2 vols. in one. Juan D. Cortes & Edmund Schramm. Ed. by J. P. Mayer. LC 78-67342. (European Political Thought Ser.). (Span. & Ger.). 1979. Repr. of 1935 ed. lib. bdg. 39.00x (ISBN 0-405-11687-X). Ayer Co Pubs.

Ensenanza Elemental de la Rosacruz Moderna. Jan Van Rijckenborgh. (Span.). 1987. pap. 11.00 (ISBN 9-070196-80-8). Rosycross Pr.

Ensenanzas, Disciplina y Gobierna de la Iglesia de Dios. (Span.). 137p. 1980. pap. 3.95 (ISBN 0-87148-304-1). Pathway Pr.

Ensign to the Nations: A History of the LDS Church from 1846 to 1972. Russell R. Rich. LC 72-91730. (Illus.). 680p. 1972. pap. 9.95 (ISBN 0-8425-0671-3). Brigham.

Entendamos. Walter A. Henrichsen. Tr. by David A. Cook from Eng. Tr. of Understand. (Span.). 112p. 1979. pap. 2.95 (ISBN 0-89922-131-9). Edit Caribe.

Enter the Crocus. Halford E. Luccock. Ed. by Charles S. Hartman. LC 79-22592. 1980. 3.50 (ISBN 0-8298-0386-6). Pilgrim NY.

Entering & Leaving Vocation: Intrapsychic Dynamics. Luigi M. Rulla. 1976. 20.00 (ISBN 88-7652-407-X). Loyola.

Entering God's Rest: Hebrew Three Through Four. John MacArthur, Jr. (John MacArthur Bible Studies). 1987. pap. 3.50 (ISBN 0-8024-5316-3). Moody.

Entering His Presence. Don McMinn. LC 86-70743. 1986. pap. 5.95 (ISBN 0-88270-608-X). Bridge Pub.

Entering the Diamond Way: My Path among the Lamas. Ole Nydahl. Ed. by Carol A. Aronoff & Paul M. Clemens. LC 85-73182. (Illus.). 256p. (Orig.). 1985. pap. 12.95 (ISBN 0-931892-03-1). B Dolphin Pub.

Enterprise in Education: The Story of the Work of the Established Church in the Education of the People Prior to 1870. Henry J. Burgess. LC 59-1586. 1958. text ed. 15.00x (ISBN 0-8401-0289-5). A R Allenson.

Entertaining Angels: A Guide to Heaven or Atheists & True Believers. F. Forester Church. 1987. 13.95. Har-Row.

Entertaining Satan: Witchcraft & the Culture of Early New England. John P. Demos. LC 81-22463. 558p. 1982. 29.95x (ISBN 0-19-503131-8); pap. 12.95 (ISBN 0-19-503378-7). Oxford U Pr.

Enthroned Christian. F. J. Huegel. 1967. pap. 2.95 (ISBN 0-87508-905-4). Chr Lit.

Enthronement of the Sacred Heart. Francis Larkin. 1978. 6.95 (ISBN 0-8198-0529-7); pap. 4.95 (ISBN 0-8198-0530-0). Dghtrs St Paul.

Enthusiasm. Ronald A. Knox. 630p. 1983. pap. 14.95 (ISBN 0-87061-080-5). Chr Classics.

Enthusiasm Makes the Difference. Norman V. Peale. 1978. pap. 2.50 (ISBN 0-449-23698-6, Crest). Fawcett.

Entire Devotion to God. Phobe Palmer. 2.95 (ISBN 0-686-27774-0). Schmul Pub Co.

Entirely for God. Elizabeth Isichei. (Cistercian Studies: No. 43). 132p. 1980. pap. 11.95 (ISBN 0-87907-943-6). Cistercian Pubns.

Entombment of Christ: French Sculptures of the Fifteenth & Sixteenth Centuries. William H. Forsyth. LC 70-99523. (Illus., Pub. for the Metropolitan Museum of Art). 1970. 22.50x (ISBN 0-674-25775-8). Harvard U Pr.

Entrance to the Tree of Life of Rabbi Isaac Luria. Yehuda Ashlag. Ed. by Philip S. Berg. 1977. 13.95 (ISBN 0-943688-05-1); pap. 10.95 (ISBN 0-943688-35-3). Res Ctr Kabbalah.

Entrance to the Zohar. Yehuda Ashlag. Ed. by Philip S. Berg. 1974. 12.95 (ISBN 0-943688-04-3); 10.95 (ISBN 0-943688-34-5). Res Ctr Kabbalah.

Entre Sartre y Camus. Mario Vargas. LC 81-68707. (Coleccion la Nave y el Puerto Ser.). 144p. 1981. pap. 5.50 (ISBN 0-940238-48-9). Ediciones Hura.

Entrega Absoluta. Andrew Murray. 192p. 1981. 2.95 (ISBN 0-88113-079-6). Edit Betania.

Entretiens Sur L'homme et le Diable. Ed. by Max Milner. (Decades Du Centre Culturel International De Cerisy-la Salle, Nouvelle Ser.: No. 1). 1965. pap. 14.00x (ISBN 90-2796-012-7). Mouton.

Entretiens Sur Paul Claudel: Decades Du Centre Culturel International De Cerisy-la-Salle. Ed. by Georges Cattaui & Jacques Madaule. (Nouvelle Series: No. 11). 1968. pap. 14.00x (ISBN 90-2796-249-9). Mouton.

Entry into the Inconceivable: An Introduction to Hua-yen Buddhism. Thomas Cleary. LC 83-3613. 227p. 1983. text ed. 16.95x (ISBN 0-8248-0824-X). UH Pr.

Entry of the Slavs into Christendom: An Introduction to the Medieval History of the Slavs. A. P. Vlasto. LC 70-98699. pap. 113.80 (ISBN 0-317-27094-X, 2024553). Bks Demand UMI.

Entry of the Theotokos. Monks of New Skete Staff. Tr. by Reverend Laurence Mancuso from Gr. & Church Slavonic. (Liturgical Music Series I: Great Feasts: Vol. 5). 40p. 1986. pap. text ed. 12.00 (ISBN 0-935129-06-5). Monks of New Skete.

Entscheidungen in Kirchensachen Seit 1946, Vol. 13. 1978. 79.20 (ISBN 3-11-007625-X). De Gruyter.

Entstehung der Geschichtsschreibung Im Alten Israel. Hannelis Schulte. (Beiheft 128 zur Zeitschrift fuer die altestamentliche Wissenschaft). 1972. 36.40x (ISBN 3-11-003960-5). De Gruyter.

Envia Senor Tu Espiritu. (Span.). 3.00 (ISBN 0-8198-2302-3); 2.00 (ISBN 0-8198-2303-1). Dghtrs St Paul.

Enviame a Mi: Aventuras de los esposos Davis, fundadores de la C. B. P. Olivia S. De Lerin. 64p. 1980. pap. 1.75 (ISBN 0-311-01062-8). Casa Bautista.

Environment & Art in Catholic Worship. 100p. 1978. pap. 7.95 (ISBN 1-55586-563-1, V563). US Catholic.

Environment of Early Christianity. S. Angus. 1977. lib. bdg. 59.95 (ISBN 0-8490-1778-5). Gordon Pr.

Environment of Early Christianity. facsimile ed. Samuel Angus. LC 75-157322. (Select Bibliographies Reprint Ser). Repr. of 1915 ed. 17.00 (ISBN 0-8369-5781-4). Ayer Co Pubs.

Ephemeris Nineteen Fifty to Nineteen Seventy-Five. A. LeRoi Simmons. (Illus.). 375p. 1977. 14.00 (ISBN 0-9605126-1-6). Aquarian Bk Pubs.

Ephesiana. Irwin J. Habeck. 1985. 7.95 (ISBN 0-8100-0171-3, 15N0404). Northwest Pub.

Ephesians. Noel Brooks. pap. 5.95 (ISBN 0-911866-02-7). Advocate.

Ephesians. Gordon H. Clark. (Trinity Papers: No. 11). 225p. (Orig.). 1985. pap. 8.95 (ISBN 0-940931-11-7). Trinity Found.

Ephesians. G. Michael Cocoris. (Orig.). Date not set. pap. text ed. price not set (ISBN 0-935729-37-2). Church Open Door.

Ephesians. (Erdmans Commentaries Ser.). 3.50 (ISBN 0-8010-3396-9). Baker Bk.

Ephesians. Irving L. Jensen. (Bible Self-Study Ser.). 1973. pap. 3.25 (ISBN 0-8024-1049-9). Moody.

Ephesians. Andrew T. Le Peau & Phyllis J. Le Peau. (Lifefuilder Bible Studies). 60p. (Orig.). 1985. pap. text ed. 2.95 (ISBN 0-8308-1012-9). Inter-Varsity.

Ephesians. John F. MacArthur, Jr. 1986. 14.95 (ISBN 0-88469-171-3). BMH Bks.

Ephesians. John MacArthur, Jr. (MacArthur New Testament Commentary Ser.). 1986. text ed. 14.95 (ISBN 0-8024-2358-2). Moody.

Ephesians. F. B. Meyer. 1968. pap. 4.50 (ISBN 0-87508-344-7). Chr Lit.

Ephesians. C. Leslie Mitton. Ed. by Matthew Black. (New Century Bible Commentary Ser.). 256p. 1981. pap. 6.95 (ISBN 0-8028-1907-9). Eerdmans.

Ephesians. Handley Moule. 1975. pap. 4.95 (ISBN 0-87508-363-3). Chr Lit.

Ephesians. Lionel Swain. (New Testament Message Ser.: Vol. 13). 10.95 (ISBN 0-89453-201-4); pap. 5.95 (ISBN 0-89453-136-0). M Glazier.

Ephesians. Geoffrey Wilson. 1978. pap. 4.95 (ISBN 0-85151-263-1). Banner of Truth.

Ephesians: A Study Guide. Francis Breisch. (Revelation Series for Adults). 1976. pap. text ed. 2.50 (ISBN 0-317-39618-8). CRC Pubns.

Ephesians: A Study Guide Commentary. Curtis Vaughan. (Study Guide Commentary Ser.). 1977. pap. 4.95 (ISBN 0-310-33533-7, 10962P). Zondervan.

Ephesians & Philemon. Marilyn Kunz & Catherine Schell. (Neighborhood Bible Studies). 1973. pap. 2.95 (ISBN 0-8423-0695-1). Tyndale.

Ephesians, Baptism & Pentecost: An Inquiry into the Structure & Purpose of the Epistle to the Ephesians. John C. Kirby. 1968. 12.50x (ISBN 0-7735-0051-0). McGill-Queens U Pr.

Ephesians (Efesios-Comemtario y Estudios) Curtis Vaughan. (Span.). 1986. write for info. (ISBN 0-8297-0904-5). Life Pubs Intl.

Ephesians for the Family: A Daily Devotional Commentary. Duane Spencer. 336p. 1984. 12.95 (ISBN 0-8059-2942-8). Dorrance.

Ephesians: Galatians. H. A. Ironside. 11.95 (ISBN 0-87213-397-4). Loizeaux.

Ephesians, II Colossians, Thessalonians: Pastoral Epistles. J. Paul Sampley et al. LC 77-78652. (Proclamation Commentaries: the New Testament Witness for Preaching). 128p. 1978. pap. 4.95 (ISBN 0-8006-0589-6, 1-589). Fortress.

Ephesians: Life in the Church. Ed. by Gary Wilde. (Basic Bible Ser.). 112p. 1986. pap. 4.95 (ISBN 0-89191-480-3). Cook.

Ephesians: Living in God's Household. Robert Baylis. LC 76-43523. (Fisherman Bible Studyguide). 45p. 1976. saddle stitched 2.95 (ISBN 0-87788-223-1). Shaw Pubs.

Ephesians: Pattern for Christian Living. Ray Summers. LC 73-87069. pap. 4.25 (ISBN 0-8054-1345-6). Broadman.

Ephesians-Philemon. Albert Barnes. 15.95 (ISBN 0-8010-0847-6). Baker Bk.

Ephesians, Philippians, Colassians. Mary A. Getty. (Read & Pray Ser.). 1980. pap. 1.95 (ISBN 0-8199-0636-0). Franciscan Herald.

Ephesians, the Epistle of Christian Maturity. Keith L. Brooks. (Teach Yourself the Bible Ser.). 1944. pap. 2.75 (ISBN 0-8024-2333-7). Moody.

Ephesians, the Glory of the Church. Homer A. Kent, Jr. pap. 5.95 (ISBN 0-88469-078-4). BMH Bks.

Ephesians: The Glory of the Church. Homer Kent, Jr. (Everyman's Bible Commentary Ser.). 1971. pap. 5.95 (ISBN 0-8024-2049-4). Moody.

Ephesians: The Maturing of the Saints. Bob Yandian. (Orig.). 1985. pap. 5.95 (ISBN 0-89274-387-5). Harrison Hse.

Ephesians: The Mystery Within. Richard A. Hufton. 126p. (Orig.). 1984. pap. 3.50 (ISBN 0-933643-04-7). Grace World Outreach.

Ephesians-Thessalonians. Ian Cundy. 1981. pap. 4.95 (ISBN 0-87508-173-8). Chr Lit.

Epic Beautiful: An English Verse Rendering of the Sundara Kanda of the Ramayana of Valmiki. K. Srinivasa Iyengar. 1986. 12.50x (ISBN 0-8364-1545-0, Pub. by National Sahitya Akademi). South Asia Bks.

Epic God-Talk: Paradise Lost & the Grammar of Religious Language. Thomas F. Merrill. LC 85-29385. 140p. 1986. lib. bdg. 18.95x (ISBN 0-89950-194-X). McFarland & Co.

Epic Mythology. rev. ed. E. Washburn Hopkins. LC 76-75358. 1968. Repr. of 1915 ed. 18.00 (ISBN 0-8196-0228-0). Biblo.

Epic Mythology. E. Washburn Hopkins. 1974. Repr. 14.00 (ISBN 0-8426-0560-6). Orient Bk Dist.

Epic of Paradise Lost. Marianna Woodhull. LC 72-194899. 1907. lib. bdg. 12.50 (ISBN 0-8414-9501-7). Folcroft.

Epic of Paradise Lost: Twelve Essays. Marianna Woodhull. LC 68-57833. 386p. 1968. Repr. of 1907 ed. 32.50x (ISBN 0-87752-124-7). Gordian.

Epic of Survival: The Story of Anti-Semitism. Samuel Glassman. LC 80-69018. 400p. 20.00x (ISBN 0-8197-0481-4). Bloch.

Epic of the Fall of Man. S. Humphreys Gurteen. LC 65-15879. (Studies in Comparative Literature, No. 35). 1969. Repr. of 1896 ed. lib. bdg. 75.00x (ISBN 0-8383-0561-X). Haskell.

Epic of Unitarianism. David Parke. 1957. pap. 3.50 (ISBN 0-933840-05-5). Unitarian Univ.

Epic of United Methodist Preaching: A Profile in American Social History. Merrill R. Abbey. 216p. (Orig.). 1983. lib. bdg. 26.75 (ISBN 0-8191-3691-3); pap. text ed. 12.25 (ISBN 0-8191-3692-1). U Pr of Amer.

Epics, Hymns, Omens & Other Texts. Albert T. Clay. LC 78-63519. (Babylonian Records in the Library of J. Pierpont Morgan: 4). Repr. of 1923 ed. 30.00 (ISBN 0-404-60124-3). AMS Pr.

Epicurus's Morals. Epicurus. Tr. by John Digby. LC 74-158299. Tr. of Morale d'Epicure. Repr. of 1712 ed. 28.00 (ISBN 0-404-54114-3). AMS Pr.

Epigones: A Study of the Theology of the Synod of Dort, with Special Reference to Giovanni Diodati. William A. McComish. (Princeton Theological Monograph Ser.: No. 13). (Orig.). 1987. pap. price not set (ISBN 0-915138-62-X). Pickwick.

Epigraphic Survey - Reliefs & Inscriptions at Karnak, 3 vols. Incl. Vol. 1. Ramses the Third's Temple Within the Great Inclosure of Amon, Part One. Harold H. Nelson. (Oriental Institute Pubns. Ser: No. 25). 1936. 60.00x (ISBN 0-226-62121-9); Vol. 2. Ramses the Third's Temple Within the Inclosure of Amon, Part Two, & Ramses the Third's Temple in the Precinct of Mut. (Oriental Institute Pubns. Ser: No. 35). 1936. 60.00x (ISBN 0-226-62132-4); Vol. 3. The Bubastic Portal. George R. Hughes. (Oriental Institute Pubns. Ser: No. 74). 1954. 50.00x (ISBN 0-226-62175-8). LC 36-11240. U of Chicago Pr.

Epigraphical Glossary. Ed. by V. Vijayaraghavacharya. (Tirupathi Devasthanam Inscription Ser.: Vol. VI, Pt. 2). 420p. 1984. Repr. of 1938 ed. lib. bdg. 65.00x (ISBN 81-7030-074-6, Pub. by Sri Satguru Pubns India). Orient Bk Dist.

Epiphanies of Darkness: Deconstruction in Theology. Charles E. Winquist. LC 85-45479. 144p. 1986. pap. 12.95 (ISBN 0-8006-1903-X, 1-1903). Fortress.

Epiphany. Joseph A. Burgess & Albert C. Winn. Ed. by Elizabeth Achtemeier et al. LC 79-7377. (Proclamation 2: Aids for Interpreting the Lessons of the Church Year, Series A). 64p. (Orig.). 1980. pap. 3.75 (ISBN 0-8006-4092-6, 1-4092). Fortress.

Epiphany. David Buttrick. LC 84-18756. (Proclamation 3 C Ser.). 64p. 1985. pap. 3.75 (ISBN 0-8006-4126-4). Fortress.

Epiphany. Charles Carlston. Ed. by Elizabeth Achtemeier. LC 84-6012. (Proclamation 3: Aids for Interpreting the Lessons of the Church Year Series B). 64p. 1984. pap. 3.75 (ISBN 0-8006-4102-7). Fortress.

Epiphany. Marianne H. Micks. LC 84-18756. (Proclamation 3A Ser.). 64p. 1986. pap. 3.75 (ISBN 0-8006-4118-3). Fortress.

Epiphany. Richard I. Pervo & William J. Carl, III. Ed. by Elizabeth Achtemeier et al. LC 79-7377. (Proclamation 2: Aids for Interpreting the Lessons of the Church Year, Series C). 64p. 1979. pap. 3.75 (ISBN 0-8006-4085-3, 1-4085). Fortress.

Epiphany. Ernest W. Saunders & Fred B. Craddock. Ed. by Elizabeth Achtemeier et al. LC 79-7377. (Proclamation 2: Aids for Interpreting the Lessons of the Church Year, Series B). 64p. 1981. pap. 3.75 (ISBN 0-8006-4069-1, 1-4069). Fortress.

Episcopacy & the Royal Supremacy in the Church of England in the XVI Century. Ebenezer T. Davies. LC 78-13202. 1978. Repr. of 1950 ed. lib. bdg. 24.75x (ISBN 0-313-20626-0, DAER). Greenwood.

Episcopal Church Annual. LC 46-33254. 1987. 22.50 (ISBN 0-8192-3015-4). Morehouse.

Episcopal Church in Alaska: A Catalog of Photographs from the Archives & Historical Collections of the Episcopal Church. William E. Simeone. (Alaska Historical Commission Studies in History: No. 19). 152p. (Orig.). 1981. pap. text ed. 8.00 (ISBN 0-943712-08-4); microfiche 4.50 (ISBN 0-943712-07-6). Alaska Hist.

Episcopal Church in the United States, 1800-1840: A Study in Church Life. William W. Manross. LC 38-38020. (Columbia University. Studies in the Social Sciences: No. 441). Repr. of 1938 ed. 21.00 (ISBN 0-404-51441-3). AMS Pr.

Episcopal Church: Its Message for Today. rev ed. George P. Atwater. 1978. pap. 4.95 (ISBN 0-8192-1244-X). Morehouse.

Episcopal Church Welcomes You: An Introduction to Its History, Worship & Mission. rev. ed. William B. Gray & Betty Gray. LC 73-17898. 168p. 1974. (HarpR); pap. 3.95 (ISBN 0-8164-2087-4). Har-Row.

Episcopal Church's History: 1945-1985. David E. Sumner. 1987. 24.95. Morehouse.

Episcopal Leadership Role in United Methodism. Roy H. Short. 224p. 1985. text ed. 9.95 (ISBN 0-687-11965-0). Abingdon.

Episcopal Vision-American Reality: High Church Theology & Social Thought in Evangelical America. Robert B. Mullin. 1986. 20.00 (ISBN 0-300-03487-3). Yale U Pr.

Episcopal Visitation of Monasteries in the Thirteenth Century. 2nd, rev. ed. Christopher R. Cheney. xxxi, 192p. 1983. lib. bdg. 25.00x (ISBN 0-87991-638-9). Porcupine Pr.

Episcopal Way. Carl G. Carlozzi. 1977. pap. text ed. 4.95x (ISBN 0-8192-4073-7); tchrs ed. 4.95x (ISBN 0-8192-4074-5). Morehouse.

Episcopate in the Kingdom of Leon in the Twelfth Century. R. A. Fletcher. (Historical Monographs). (Illus.). 1978. 42.00x (ISBN 0-19-821869-9). Oxford U Pr.

Episcopi Vagantes & the Anglican Church. Henry R. Brandreth. 80p. Date not set. lib. bdg. 19.95x (ISBN 0-89370-558-6). Borgo Pr.

Episode in the Struggle for Religious Freedom. Austin P. Evans. LC 74-130618. Repr. of 1924 ed. 19.00 (ISBN 0-404-02357-6). AMS Pr.

Epistemology. David L. Wolfe. Ed. by C. Stephen Evans. (Contours of Christian Philosophy Ser.). 96p. 1982. pap. 5.95 (ISBN 0-87784-340-6). Inter-Varsity.

Epistemology of Dvaita Vedanta. P. Nagaraja Rao. 6.50 (ISBN 0-8356-7442-8). Theos Pub Hse.

Epistle of Comfort. Robert Southwell. Ed. by Margaret Waugh. LC 66-22384. 1966. 3.95 (ISBN 0-8294-0072-9). Loyola.

Epistle of James. D. Edmond Hiebert. LC 78-23925. 1979. 13.95 (ISBN 0-8024-2357-4). Moody.

Epistle of James. Sophie Laws. LC 80-8349. (Harper's New Testament Commentaries Ser.). 288p. 1981. 16.00 (ISBN 0-06-064918-6, HarpR). Har-Row.

Epistle of Paul to the Churches of Galatia. Herman N. Ridderbos. (New International Commentary on the New Testament Ser.). 1953. 12.95 (ISBN 0-8028-2191-X). Eerdmans.

Epistle of Paul to the Galatians. Alan Cole. (Tyndale Bible Commentaries). 1964. pap. 4.95 (ISBN 0-8028-1408-5). Eerdmans.

Epistle of Paul to the Galatians. J. Koehler. Tr. by E. E. Sauer. 1957. 2.95 (ISBN 0-8100-0038-5, 15N0315). Northwest Pub.

Epistle of Paul to the Philippians. Ralph P. Martin. (Tyndale Bible Commentaries). 1960. pap. 4.95 (ISBN 0-8028-1410-7). Eerdmans.

Epistle of Paul to the Romans. John Murray. (New International Commentary on the New Testament). 1960. 19.95 (ISBN 0-8028-2286-X). Eerdmans.

Epistle of Saint James. Joseph B. Mayor. 1977. 20.25 (ISBN 0-86524-971-7, 5902). Klock & Klock.

Epistle of St. Jude & the Three Epistles of St. John. Wilhelm Thusing et al. Ed. by John L. McKenzie. LC 81-605. (New Testament for Spiritual Reading Ser.). 148p. 1981. pap. 4.95 (ISBN 0-8245-0132-2). Crossroad NY.

Epistle on the Possibility of Conjunction with the Active Intellect by Ibn Rushd with the Commentary of Moses Narboni. Kalman P. Bland. LC 81-20788. 314p. 1982. 35.00x (ISBN 0-87334-005-1). Ktav.

Epistle on the Possibility of Conjunction with the Active Intellect. Ibn Rushd. Ed. & tr. by Kalman P. Bland. (Moreshet Ser: No. 7). 35.00x (ISBN 0-87334-005-1). Ktav.

Epistle to Philemon. S. Cox & A. H. Drysdale. 246p. 1982. lib. bdg. 9.25 Smythe Sewn (ISBN 0-86524-134-1, 7108). Klock & Klock.

Epistle to the Colossians: A Study Manual. Charles N. Pickell. (Shield Bible Study Ser). (Orig.). 1965. pap. 1.00 (ISBN 0-8010-6942-4). Baker Bk.

Epistle to the Ephesians. F. F. Bruce. 144p. 1962. 10.95 (ISBN 0-8007-0083-X). Revell.

Epistle to the Ephesians. Max Zerwick. Ed. by John L. McKenzie. LC 81-605. (New Testament for Spiritual Reading Ser.). 181p. 1981. pap. 4.95 (ISBN 0-8245-0125-X). Crossroad NY.

Epistle to the Galatians. C. F. Hogg & W. E. Vine. 360p. (Orig.). pap. cancelled (ISBN 0-8254-2858-0). Kregel.

Epistle to the Galatians. Gerhard Schneider. Ed. by John L. McKenzie. LC 81-605. (New Testament for Spiritual Reading Ser.). 142p. 1981. pap. 4.95 (ISBN 0-8245-0124-1). Crossroad NY.

Epistle to the Hebrews. A. B. Bruce. 1980. 17.25 (ISBN 0-86524-028-0, 5802). Klock & Klock.

Epistle to the Hebrews. Ed. by Frederick F. Bruce. (New International Commentary on the New Testament Ser.). 1964. 19.95 (ISBN 0-8028-2183-9). Eerdmans.

Epistle to the Hebrews. Milton Crowson. 1974. pap. 4.95 (ISBN 0-89265-021-4). Randall Hse.

Epistle to the Hebrews. Thomas C. Edwards. 394p. 1982. lib. bdg. 13.00 Smythe Sewn (ISBN 0-86524-154-6, 5803). Klock & Klock.

Epistle to the Hebrews. W. Kelly. 272p. pap. 8.50 (ISBN 0-88172-155-7). Believers Bkshelf.

Epistle to the Hebrews. Homer A. Kent, Jr. 1972. pap. 8.95 (ISBN 0-8010-5458-3). Baker Bk.

Epistle to the Hebrews. Homer A. Kent, Jr. pap. 11.95 (ISBN 0-88469-069-5). BMH Bks.

Epistle to the Hebrews. Charles F. Pfeiffer. (Everyman's Bible Commentary Ser.). (Orig.). 1968. pap. 5.95 (ISBN 0-8024-2058-3). Moody.

Epistle to the Hebrews, 2 vols. in 1. Adolph Saphir. LC 83-4390. 924p. 1983. 21.95 (ISBN 0-8254-3728-8). Kregel.

Epistle to the Hebrews. H. Orton Wiley. Ed. by Morris Weigelt. 438p. 1985. text ed. 15.95 (ISBN 0-8341-0890-9). Beacon Hill.

Epistle to the Hebrews: An Introduction & Commentary. Donald Guthrie. (Tyndale New Testament Commentaries: Vol. 15). 288p. 1983. pap. 5.95 (ISBN 0-8028-1427-1). Eerdmans.

Epistle to the Hebrews & the Epistle of St. James. F. J. Schierse. Ed. by John L. McKenzie. LC 81-605. (New Testament for Spiritual Reading Ser.). 246p. 1981. pap. 4.95 (ISBN 0-8245-0130-6). Crossroad NY.

Epistle to the Learned Nobility of England: Touching Translating the Bible. Hugh Broughton. LC 77-6862. (English Experience Ser.: No. 855). 1977. Repr. of 1597 ed. lib. bdg. 7.00 (ISBN 90-221-0855-4). Walter J Johnson.

Epistle to the Philippians. Charles J. Vaughan. 318p. 1984. smythe sewn 11.50 (ISBN 0-86524-180-5, 5002). Klock & Klock.

Epistle to the Phillipians & the Epistle to the Colossians. Joachim Gnilka & Franz Mussner. Ed. by John L. McKenzie. LC 81-605. (New Testament for Spiritual Reading Ser.). 180p. 1981. pap. 4.95 (ISBN 0-8245-0126-8). Crossroad NY.

Epistle to the Romans. Barnabas M. Ahern. 1979. 1.75 (ISBN 0-8199-0629-8). Franciscan Herald.

Epistle to the Romans. Charles K. Barrett. LC 57-12722. 1958. 17.95 (ISBN 0-06-060550-2, HarpR). Har-Row.

Epistle to the Romans. 6th ed. Karl Barth. Tr. by Edwyn C. Hoskyns. 1968. pap. 12.95 (ISBN 0-19-500294-6). Oxford U Pr.

Epistle to the Son of the Wolf. rev. ed. Baha'u'llah. Tr. by Shoghi Effendi. LC 53-18798. 1976. 12.95 (ISBN 0-87743-048-9, 103-001). Baha'i.

Epistle to the Thessalonians. C. F. Hogg & W. E. Vine. (Orig.). pap. cancelled (ISBN 0-8254-2859-9). Kregel.

Epistles in the Light of Christian Science. Max Kappeler. LC 72-200094. 253p. 1962. 14.00 (ISBN 0-85241-042-5). Kappeler Inst Pub.

Epistles Now. Leslie F. Brandt. LC 75-38711. (Illus.). 176p. 1976. 8.50 (ISBN 0-570-03258-X, 15-2166). Concordia.

Epistles of James, Peter & Jude. Ed. by Bo I. Reicke. LC 63-8221. (Anchor Bible Ser.: Vol. 37). 1964. 14.00 (ISBN 0-385-01374-4, Anchor Pr). Doubleday.

Epistles of John. James M. Boice. 224p. 1983. pap. 7.95 (ISBN 0-310-21531-5, 10421). Zondervan.

Epistles of John. Raymond E. Brown. LC 81-43380. (Anchor Bible Ser.: Vol. 30). 840p. 1982. 20.00 (ISBN 0-385-05686-9). Doubleday.

Epistles of John. F. F. Bruce. LC 78-22069. 1978. pap. 5.95 (ISBN 0-8028-1783-1). Eerdmans.

Epistles of John. Donald Burdick. (Everyman's Bible Commentary Ser.). 1970. pap. 5.95 (ISBN 0-8024-2062-1). Moody.

Epistles of John. J. Morgan & S. Cox. 612p. 1982. lib. bdg. 22.95 Smythe Sewn (ISBN 0-86524-133-3, 6202). Klock & Klock.

Epistles of John. John R. Stott. (Tyndale Bible Commentaries). Orig. Title: Johannine Epistles. 1964. pap. 4.95 (ISBN 0-8028-1418-2). Eerdmans.

Epistles of John. Lehman Strauss. LC 62-17542. 1962. pap. 3.95 (ISBN 0-87213-821-6). Loizeaux.

Epistles of John & Jude. Irving L. Jenson. (Bible Self-Study Ser.). 128p. (Orig.). 1971. pap. 3.25 (ISBN 0-8024-1062-6). Moody.

Epistles of John: Living Confidently. Allen J. Blair. LC 82-15196. pap. 4.95 (ISBN 0-87213-028-2). Loizeaux.

Epistles of Paul & Rudolf Steiner's Philosophy of Freedom. Frederick Hiebel. 1979. pap. 4.95 (ISBN 0-916786-41-2). St George Bk Serv.

Epistles of Paul: Hebrews. (Banner of Truth Geneva Series Commentaries). 1978. 24.95 (ISBN 0-85151-271-2). Banner of Truth.

Epistles of Paul in Modern English: A Paraphrase. St. Paul. Tr. by George B. Stevens from Gr. 1980. Repr. of 1898 ed. 10.95 (ISBN 0-939464-03-9). Labyrinth Pr.

Epistles of Paul in Modern English: A Paraphrase. George B. Stevens. viii, 331p. 1980. Repr. of 1898 ed. 10.95 (ISBN 0-940033-26-7). R O Roberts.

Epistles of Paul the Apostle to the Colossians & to Philemon. Charles F. Moule. (Cambridge Greek Testament Ser.). 1959. text ed. 32.50 (ISBN 0-521-04252-6); pap. text ed. 10.95 (ISBN 0-521-09236-1). Cambridge U Pr.

Epistles of Paul the Apostle to the Thessalonians. G. G. Findlay. (Thornapple Commentaries Ser.). 319p. 1982. pap. 9.95 (ISBN 0-8010-3503-1). Baker Bk.

Epistles of Paul the Apostle to the Thessalonians. C. F. Hogg & W. E. Vine. 5.95 (ISBN 0-89315-040-1). Lambert Bk.

Epistles of Paul to the Colossians & to Philemon. Herbert M. Carson. (Tyndale Bible Commentaries). 1960. pap. 3.95 (ISBN 0-8028-1411-5). Eerdmans.

Epistles of Paul to the Corinthians. Arthur P. Stanley. 1981. 20.95 (ISBN 0-86524-051-5, 7105). Klock & Klock.

Epistles of Paul to the Philippians. Jacobus J. Muller. (New International Commentary on the New Testament). 1985. 12.95 (ISBN 0-8028-2188-X). Eerdmans.

Epistles of Peter. Edgar C. James. (Teach Yourself the Bible Ser.). 1964. pap. 2.75 (ISBN 0-8024-2355-8). Moody.

Epistles of St. Clement of Rome & St. Ignatius of Antioch. Ed. by Quasten & Plumpe. Tr. by James A. Kleist. (Ancient Christian Writers Ser.: No. 1). 1946. 12.95 (ISBN 0-8091-0038-X). Paulist Pr.

Epistles of St. Ignatius. Saint Ignatius. Tr. by J. D. Lightfoot. pap. 1.25 (ISBN 0-686-25549-6). Eastern Orthodox.

Epistles of Saint John. Alfred Plummer. (Thornapple Commentaries Ser.). 302p. 1980. pap. 7.95 (ISBN 0-8010-7058-9). Baker Bk.

Epistles of the Blessed Hope: First & Second Thessalonians. Raymond E. Gingrich. 1986. pap. 5.95 (ISBN 0-88469-176-4). BMH Bks.

Epistles to the Colossians, to Philemon, & to the Ephesians. F. F. Bruce. (New International Commentary on the New Testament Ser.). 464p. 1984. 18.95 (ISBN 0-8028-2401-3). Eerdmans.

Epistles to the Romans. Karl Kertlege. Ed. by John L. McKenzie. LC 81-605. (New Testament for Spiritual Reading Ser.). 144p. 1981. pap. 4.95 (ISBN 0-8245-0121-7). Crossroad NY.

Epistola a los Efesios. Ernesto Trenchard & Pablo Wickham. (Span.). 220p. 1980. 6.75 (ISBN 0-8254-1730-9). Kregel.

Epistola a los Galatas. Ernesto Trenchard. (Span.). 224p. 1964. 6.75 (ISBN 0-8254-1732-5); pap. 5.50 (ISBN 0-8254-1731-7). Kregel.

Epistola a los Hebreos. Ernesto Trenchard. (Span.). 290p. 1974. 6.95 (ISBN 0-8254-1734-1); pap. 5.75 (ISBN 0-8254-1733-3). Kregel.

Epistola a los Hebreos (Comentario Biblico Portavoz) Charles R. Pfeiffer. Orig. Title: Epistle to the Hebrews (Everyman's Bible Commentary) (Span.). 128p. 1981. pap. 3.50 (ISBN 0-8254-1564-0). Kregel.

Epistola a los Romanos. Ernesto Trenchard. (Span.). 1969. 7.95 (ISBN 0-8254-1736-8); pap. 6.95 (ISBN 0-8254-1735-X). Kregel.

Epistolae Romanorum Pontificum. Pierre Coustant. 942p. Repr. of 1721 ed. text ed. 207.00x (ISBN 0-576-99106-6, Pub. by Gregg Intl Pubs England). Gregg Intl.

Epistolae Tigurinae De Rebus Potissimum Ad Ecclesiae Anglicanae Reformationem Pertinentibus Conscriptae. 1848. 41.00 (ISBN 0-384-14505-1). Johnson Repr.

Epistolae Vagantes of Pope Gregory Seven. Pope Gregory VII. Ed. by H. E. Cowdrey. (Oxford Medieval Texts). (Eng. & Lat.). 1972. 42.00x (ISBN 0-19-822220-3). Oxford U Pr.

Epistolario de Juan Ignacio Molina. Ronan & Hanisch. (Span.). 1980. 11.60 (ISBN 0-8294-0360-4). Loyola.

Epistolas De Pablo Tomo III. L. Bonnet & A. Schroeder. Tr. by A. Cativiela from Fr. (Comentario del Nuevo Testamento). 538p. 1986. pap. 14.95 (ISBN 0-311-03052-1). Casa Bautista.

Epithets in the Rgveda. Jan Gonda. (D. R. T. Ser: No. 3). 1959. pap. text ed. 29.60x (ISBN 90-2790-030-2). Mouton.

Epitomes for the Structural Interpretation of the Christian Science Textbook. Max Kappeler. LC 82-82377. 120p. 1982. write for info. (ISBN 0-942958-06-3). Kappeler Inst Pub.

Epoch of Miracles: Oral Literature of the Yucatec Maya. Tr. by Allan F. Burns. (Texas Pan American Ser.). (Illus.). 282p. 1983. text ed. 24.50x (ISBN 0-292-72037-8). U of Tex Pr.

Epoch of Negro Baptists & the Foreign Mission Board. Edward A. Freeman. Ed. by Edwin S. Gaustad. LC 79-52593. (Baptist Tradition Ser.). 1980. Repr. of 1953 ed. lib. bdg. 26.50x (ISBN 0-405-12460-0). Ayer Co Pubs.

Epochal Nature of Process in Whitehead's Metaphysics. F. Bradford Wallack. LC 79-22898. 1980. 44.50x (ISBN 0-87395-404-1); pap. 16.95 (ISBN 0-87395-454-8). State U NY Pr.

Epochs in Buddhist History; the Haskell Lectures, 1921. Kenneth J. Saunders. LC 78-70118. Repr. of 1924 ed. 32.00 (ISBN 0-404-17375-6). AMS Pr.

Epokha Apostasii. Archpriest Boris Molchanov. Tr. of Epoch of Apostasy. 24p. 1976. pap. 1.00 (ISBN 0-317-29125-4). Holy Trinity.

Epoxy Epistles: Letters That Stick. Thomas D. Peterson. Ed. by Michael L. Sherer. (Orig.). 1987. pap. 3.95 (ISBN 0-89536-868-4, 7827). CSS of Ohio.

Equal Circles: Baha'i Views of Women & Men. Ed. by Peggy Caton. (Orig.). 1987. pap. 9.95 (ISBN 0-933770-60-X). Kalimat.

Equality & Submission in Marriage. John C. Howell. LC 78-67292. 1979. 8.50 (ISBN 0-8054-5632-5). Broadman.

Equality & the Religious Traditions of Asia. Ed. by R. Siriwardena. 300p. 1987. 29.95 (ISBN 0-312-00401-X). St Martin.

Equality, Moral Incentives, & the Market. Joseph H. Carens. LC 80-36774. (Illus.). 264p. 1981. lib. bdg. 19.00x (ISBN 0-226-09269-0). U of Chicago Pr.

Equals Before God: Seminarians as Humanistic Professionals. Sherryl Kleinman. LC 83-24208. 160p. 1984. lib. bdg. 15.00x (ISBN 0-226-43999-2). U of Chicago Pr.

Equilibrio en la Vida Cristiana. Charles C. Ryrie. Orig. Title: Balancing the Christian Life. (Span.). 208p. 1983. pap. 5.95 (ISBN 0-8254-1628-0). Kregel.

Equinox: Sex & Religion, Vol. 5. Aleister Crowley & Marcelo Motta. (No. 4). 1981. 44.00 (ISBN 0-933454-04-X, Pub. by Thelema Pub). O T O.

Equipped for Good Work: A Guide for Pastors. Joe H. Cothen. LC 80-37964. 336p. 1981. 14.95 (ISBN 0-88289-271-1). Pelican.

Equipping Adults Through Bible Study. Neal McBride. 32p. 1977. pap. 1.50 (ISBN 0-8307-0505-8, 9970118). Regal.

Equipping for Ministry. John M. Palmer. LC 85-80220. 88p. (Orig.). 1985. pap. cancelled (ISBN 0-88243-802-6, 02-0802). Gospel Pub.

Equipping God's People. Gary T. Evans & Richard E. Hayes. (Church's Teaching Ser.: Introductory). 80p. 1979. pap. 1.25 (ISBN 0-86683-896-1, HarpR). Har-Row.

Equipping of Disciples. Ed. by John Hendrix & Lloyd Householder. LC 76-29803. 1977. bds. 9.95 (ISBN 0-8054-3218-3). Broadman.

Era de las Tinieblas. Justo L. Gonzalez. (Y Hasta Lo Ultimo de la Tierra: una Historia Ilustrada del Cristianismo Ser.: Tomo III). (Span., Illus.). 199p. (Orig.). 1978. pap. 5.95 (ISBN 0-89922-128-9). Edit Caribe.

Era de los Altos Ideales. Justo L. Gonzalez. (Y Hasta Lo Ultimo de la Tierra: una Historia Ilustrada Del Cristianismo Ser.: Tomo IV). (Span., Illus.). 197p. (Orig.). 1979. pap. 5.95 (ISBN 0-89922-135-1). Edit Caribe.

Era de los Conquistadores. Justo L. Gonzalez. (Y Hasta Lo Ultimo de la Tierra: una Historia Ilustrada del Cristianismo: Tomo VII). (Span., Illus.). 218p. (Orig.). 1981. pap. 5.95 (ISBN 0-89922-162-9). Edit Caribe.

Era de los Dogmas y las Dudas. Justo L. Gonzalez. (Y hasta lo ultimo de la tierra Ser.: Tomo No. 8). (Illus.). 224p. (Orig.). 1983. pap. 5.95 (ISBN 0-89922-171-8). Edit Caribe.

Era de los Gigantes. Justo L. Gonzalez. (Y Hasta Lo Ultimo de la Tierra: una Historia Ilustrada del Cristianismo Ser.: Tomo II). (Span., Illus.). 184p. (Orig.). 1978. pap. 5.95 (ISBN 0-89922-117-3). Edit Caribe.

Era de los Martires. Justo L. Gonzalez. (Y Hasta Lo Ultimo de la Tierra: una Historia Ilustrada del Cristianismo Ser.: Tomo I). (Span., Illus.). 189p. (Orig.). 1978. pap. 5.95 (ISBN 0-89922-109-2). Edit Caribe.

Era de los Reformadores. Justo L. Gonzalez. (Y Hasta Lo Ultimo de la Tierra: una Historia Ilustrada del Cristianismo Ser.: Tomo VI). (Span., Illus.). 219p. (Orig.). 1980. pap. 5.95 (ISBN 0-89922-154-8). Edit Caribe.

Era de los Suenos Frustrados. Justo L. Gonzalez. (Y Hasta Lo Ultimo de la Tierra: una Historia Ilustrada del Cristianismo Ser.: Tomo V). (Span., Illus.). 182p. (Orig.). 1979. pap. 5.95 (ISBN 0-89922-139-4). Edit Caribe.

Era of A. J. Tomlinson. Daniel Preston. 206p. (Orig.). 1984. pap. 6.95 (ISBN 0-934942-41-2, 1925). White Wing Pub.

Era of the Protestant Revolution. Frederic Seebohm. LC 77-147114. Repr. of 1903 ed. 7.50 (ISBN 0-404-05695-4). AMS Pr.

Era of the Protestant Revolution. Frederic Seebohm. 1902. 25.00 (ISBN 0-8495-6274-0). Arden Lib.

Era of the Second Temple. Sidney B. Hoenig. LC 74-79271. Orig. Title: Korot Am Olam. 480p. 1974. 11.95 (ISBN 0-88400-009-5). Shengold.

Erasmus. Ernest F. Capey. 1902. 25.00 (ISBN 0-8274-2284-9). R West.

Erasmus. Ed. by Richard L. DeMolen. LC 73-89992. (Documents of Modern History Ser.). 208p. 1974. 18.95 (ISBN 0-312-25795-3). St Martin.

Erasmus. Richard C. Jebb. (Select Bibliographies Reprint Ser). 1890. 12.00 (ISBN 0-8369-5289-8). Ayer Co Pubs.

Erasmus. Stefan Zweig. 1934. 35.00 (ISBN 0-8274-2283-0). R West.

Erasmus: A Play on Words. James D. Barber. LC 81-40002. 80p. (Orig.). 1982. lib. bdg. 23.50 (ISBN 0-8191-1868-0); pap. text ed. 5.75 (ISBN 0-8191-1869-9). U Pr of Amer.

Erasmus & Luther: Their Attitude to Toleration. Robert H. Murray. LC 83-45659. (Zodiac Club Ser.). Date not set. Repr. of 1920 ed. 57.50 (ISBN 0-404-19809-0). AMS Pr.

Erasmus & the Age of Reformation: With a Selection from the Letters of Erasmus. Johan Huizinga. LC 84-42547. (Illus.). 312p. 1984. text ed. 32.50x (ISBN 0-691-05421-5); pap. 8.95 (ISBN 0-691-00801-9). Princeton U Pr.

Erasmus & the Jews. Shimon Markish. Tr. by Anthony Olcott from Rus. LC 85-16454. 1986. lib. bdg. 25.00x (ISBN 0-226-50590-1). U of Chicago Pr.

Erasmus & the New Testament: The Mind of a Christian Humanist. Albert Rabil. LC 71-184768. (Trinity University Monograph Series in Religion: Vol. 1). pap. 51.50 (ISBN 0-317-08044-X, 2022565). Bks Demand UMI.

Erasmus & the Seamless Coat of Jesus. Tr. by Raymond Himelick. LC 70-151515. 232p. 1971. 6.25 (ISBN 0-911198-29-6). Purdue U Pr.

Erasmus of Christendom. Roland Bainton. (Crossroad Paperback Ser.). 320p. 1982. pap. 12.95 (ISBN 0-8245-0415-1). Crossroad NY.

Erasmus of Christendom. Roland H. Bainton. LC 68-27788. (Illus.). 1969. 20.00 (ISBN 0-684-15380-7, ScribT). Scribner.

Erasmus of Rotterdam. E. Emerton. 59.95 (ISBN 0-8490-0122-6). Gordon Pr.

Erasmus of Rotterdam: A Quincentennial Symposium. Ed. by Richard L. DeMolen. LC 76-125264. 151p. 1971. text ed. 29.00x (ISBN 0-8290-0170-0). Irvington.

Erasmus on His Times: A Shortened Version of the Adages of Erasmus. Desiderius Erasmus. Ed. by Margaret M. Phillips. 1967. pap. 9.95 (ISBN 0-521-09413-5). Cambridge U Pr.

Erasmus on Language & Method in Theology. Marjorie O. Boyle. LC 77-2606. (Erasmus Studies: No. 2). pap. 70.30 (ISBN 0-317-26938-0, 2023596). Bks Demand UMI.

Erasmus' Services to Learning. P. S. Allen. 1974. lib. bdg. 59.95 (ISBN 0-8490-0123-4). Gordon Pr.

Erasmus' Services to Learning. P. S. Allen. (Studies in Philosophy: No. 40). 1972. pap. 39.95x (ISBN 0-8383-0111-8). Haskell.

Erasmus the Reformer: A Study in Restatement. Ed. by Leonard E. Elliott-Binns. LC 83-45655. Date not set. Repr. of 1923 ed. 24.50 (ISBN 0-404-19805-8). AMS Pr.

Erasmus Von Rotterdam und Seine Welt. Robert Stupperich. 1977. 19.20x (ISBN 3-11-007085-5). De Gruyter.

Erbadistan ud Nirangistan: Facsimile Edition of the Manuscript TD. Ed. by Firoze M. Kotwal & James W. Boyd. (Harvard Iranian Ser.: No. 3). 152p. 1981. text ed. 16.00x (ISBN 0-674-26040-6). Harvard U Pr.

Erdman's Commentary on New Testament, 17 vols. (Erdmans Commentaries Ser.). 65.00 (ISBN 0-8010-3409-4). Baker Bk.

Eres Tu, Senor? Loren Cunningham & Janice Rogers. Tr. by Juan S. Araujo from Eng. Tr. of Is That Really You, God? (Span.). 176p. 1986. pap. 3.50 (ISBN 0-88113-061-3). Edit Betania.

Eretici Italiani in Moravia, Polonia, Transilvania (1558-1611) Domenico Caccamo. LC 72-3474. (Corpus Reformatorum Italicorum & Biblioteca Ser.). (Lat. & Ital., Illus.). 286p. 1970. pap. 17.50 (ISBN 0-87580-511-6). N Ill U Pr.

Eric Gill: Further Thoughts by an Apprentice. David Kindersley. (Illus.). 60p. 1982. pap. 14.00 (ISBN 0-913720-35-6). Beil.

Eric Gill: Man of Flesh & Spirit. Malcolm Yorke. LC 81-71073. (Illus.). 304p. 1985. pap. 14.95 (ISBN 0-87663-883-3). Universe.

Eric Gill: Man of Flesh & Sprit. Malcolm Yorke. LC 81-71073. (Illus.). 256p. 1982. 27.50x (ISBN 0-87663-387-4). Universe.

Eric Voegelin's Thought: A Critical Appraisal. Ed. by Ellis Sandoz. LC 81-43591. xv, 208p. 1982. 24.75 (ISBN 0-8223-0465-1). Duke.

Erica Wilson's Christmas World. Erica Wilson. (Illus.). 160p. 1982. pap. 11.95 (ISBN 0-684-17651-3, ScribT); 17.95 (ISBN 0-684-16672-0). Scribner.

Erikson: Identity & Religion. J. Eugene Wright, Jr. 240p. (Orig.). 1982. pap. 9.95 (ISBN 0-8164-2362-8, HarpR). Har-Row.

Ernest Renan. William Barry. 1905. Repr. 25.00 (ISBN 0-8274-3825-7). R West.

Ernest Renan. Richard M. Chadbourne. LC 67-25197. (Twayne's World Authors Ser.). 1968. lib. bdg. 17.95 (ISBN 0-8057-2754-X). Irvington.

Ernest Renan in Memoriam. Mountstuart Grant Duff. 1893. Repr. 25.00 (ISBN 0-8274-2285-7). R West.

Ernst Troeltsch: Writings on Theology & Religion. Ed. by Robert Morgan & Michael Pye. LC 77-79596. 1977. 9.95 (ISBN 0-8042-0554-X). John Knox.

Ernsthafte Christenpflicht. 251p. 1924. 5.95x (ISBN 0-8361-1141-9). Herald Pr.

Eros & Evil: The Sexual Psychopathology of Witchcraft. R. E. Masters. LC 79-8114. Repr. of 1962 ed. 36.50 (ISBN 0-404-18427-8). AMS Pr.

Eros & Psyche: Studies in Plato, Plotinus & Origen. LC 66-627. (Phoenix Supplementary Ser.: No. 6). pap. 63.50 (ISBN 0-317-08094-6, 2019201). Bks Demand UMI.

Eros Defiled: The Christian & Sexual Sin. John White. LC 76-39711. 1977. pap. 6.95 (ISBN 0-87784-781-9). Inter-Varsity.

Erotic Communications: Studies in Sex, Sin & Censorship. new ed. George N. Gordon. (Humanistic Studies in the Communication Arts). (Illus.). 352p. 1980. 21.00x (ISBN 0-8038-1959-5, Communication Arts); pap. 13.00x (ISBN 0-8038-1960-9). Hastings.

Erotic Sculpture of India: A Socio-Cultural Study. Devangana Desai. (Illus.). 290p. 1984. text ed. 55.00x. Coronet Bks.

Erotic Spirituality: The Integrative Tradition from Leone Ebreo to John Donne. T. Anthony Perry. 208p. 1980. 15.75 (ISBN 0-8173-0024-4). U of Ala Pr.

Eroticism in Religions of the World. O. A. Wall. (Illus.). xv, 608p. 1986. Repr. text ed. 75.00 (ISBN 81-7047-015-3, Pub. by Mayur Pubns India). Apt Bks.

Errand into the Wilderness. Perry G. Miller. LC 56-11285. 1956. 15.00x (ISBN 0-674-26151-8, Belknap Pr); pap. 6.95x (ISBN 0-674-26155-0). Harvard U Pr.

Errand to the World: American Protestant Thought & Foreign Missions. William R. Hutchinson. 216p. 1987. lib. bdg. 24.95x (ISBN 0-226-36257-4). U of Chicago Pr.

Erring: A Post Modern A-Theology. Mark C. Taylor. LC 84-88. xiv, 220p. 1987. pap. 9.95 (ISBN 0-226-79142-4). U of Chicago Pr.

Erring: A Postmodern, A-Theology. Mark C. Taylor. LC 84-88. (Illus.). 232p. 1984. lib. bdg. 20.00x (ISBN 0-226-79141-6). U of Chicago Pr.

Erste Buch der Tora Genesis. Benno Jacob. (Ger.). 1934. 100.00 (ISBN 0-87068-247-4). Ktav.

Erubin, 3 vols. 45.00 (ISBN 0-910218-54-4). Bennet Pub.

Erwin Ramsdell Goodenough: A Personal Pilgrimage. Robert S. Eccles. (SBL-Biblical Scholarship in North America). 1985. 22.95 (ISBN 0-89130-907-1, 01-11-11); pap. 16.95 (ISBN 0-89130-908-X). Scholars Pr GA.

Es Will Abend Werden. William Lauterbach. Ed. by Mentor Kujath. 1978. pap. 2.25 (ISBN 0-8100-0101-2, 26-0511). Northwest Pub.

Esaie, Commentaire Biblique, (Themes from Isaiah) Ronald Youngblood. (Fr.). 1986. write for info. (ISBN 0-8297-0607-0). Life Pubs Intl.

Escape from Auschwitz. Erich Kulka. (Illus.). 192p. (Orig.). 1986. 27.95 (ISBN 0-89789-088-4); pap. 12.95 (ISBN 0-89789-089-2). Bergin & Garvey.

Escape from Evil. Ernest Becker. LC 75-12059. 1976. pap. 8.95 (ISBN 0-02-902450-1). Free Pr.

Escape from Jesus: One Man's Search for a Meaningful Judaism. Shlomoh Sherman. 1983. 14.95 (ISBN 0-915474-03-4). Effective Learn.

Escape from the Coming Tribulation. Guy Duty. LC 75-17979. 160p. (Orig.). 1975. pap. 4.95 (ISBN 0-87123-131-X, 210131). Bethany Hse.

Escape From the Grip. Judy Wurmbrand. 126p. 1985. pap. 4.95 (ISBN 0-88264-153-0). Diane Bks.

Escape into Siege: A Survey of Israeli Literature Today. Leon I. Yudkin. (Littman Library of Jewish Civilization). 1974. 18.50x (ISBN 0-19-710016-3). Oxford U Pr.

Escape the Drug Scene. LaDean Griffin. pap. 3.95 (ISBN 0-89036-141-X). Hawkes Pub Inc.

Escape the Second Death. Jack Van Impe. 60p. 1985. pap. 1.95 (ISBN 0-934803-38-2). J Van Impe.

Escape to Egypt. (Color-a-Story Bks.). (Illus.). 1985. pap. 0.89 (ISBN 0-89191-946-5, 59469). Cook.

Escaping Collusion. Richard Aschwanden & Maria Aschwanden. 90p. (Orig.). 1983. pap. 4.20x (ISBN 0-913071-01-3). Rama Pub Co.

Eschatologic & Jenseitserwartung Im Hellenistischen Diasporajudentum. Ulrich Fischer. (Beiheft 44 Zur Zeitschrift Fuer Die Alttestamentliche Wissenschaft). 1978. 29.20x (ISBN 3-11-007595-4). De Gruyter.

Eschatology. Joseph Pohle. LC 72-109823. 1971. Repr. of 1917 ed. lib. bdg. 22.50x (ISBN 0-8371-4314-4, POES). Greenwood.

Eschatology & Ethics in the Teaching of Jesus. Amos N. Wilder. LC 78-16425. 1978. Repr. of 1950 ed. lib. bdg. 27.50 (ISBN 0-313-20585-X, WIEE). Greenwood.

Eschatology Handbook: The Bible Speaks to Us about Endtimes. Val J. Sauer, Jr. (Illus.). 180p. (Orig.). 1981. pap. 3.99 (ISBN 0-8042-0066-1). John Knox.

Eschatology in Maimonidean Thought: Messianism, Resurrection, & the World to Come-Jacob I. Jacob I. Dienstag. LC 82-17303. cxx, 281p. 1982. 59.50x (ISBN 0-87068-706-9). Ktav.

Eschatology in the Old Testament. Donald E. Gowan. LC 85-4550. 160p. 1985. pap. 9.95 (ISBN 0-8006-1906-4, 1-1906). Fortress.

Eschatology of Victory. J. M. Kik. 1971. pap. 8.95 (ISBN 0-87552-313-7). Presby & Reformed.

Escogidos en Cristo. Jose Martinez & Ernesto Trenchard. Tr. of Chosen in Christ. (Span.). 320p. 1987. pap. 9.95 (ISBN 0-8254-1737-6). Kregel.

Escucha a los Animales. William L. Coleman. 144p. 1981. 3.25 (ISBN 0-88113-063-X). Edit Betania.

Escuela de la Obediencia. Andrew Murray. Orig. Title: School of Obedience. (Span.). 128p. 1984. pap. 3.25 (ISBN 0-317-14852-4). Kregel.

Escuela Dominical en Accion. C. H. Benson. Tr. by Fernando P. Villalobos from Eng. (Curso Para Maestros Cristianos: No. 6). (Span.). 122p. 1972. pap. 3.50 (ISBN 0-89922-018-5); instructor's manual 1.50 (ISBN 0-89922-019-3). Edit Caribe.

Ese Increible Cristiano. A. W. Tozer. Tr. by Dardo Bruchez from Eng. (Span.). 135p. (Orig.). 1979. pap. 2.00 (ISBN 0-87509-269-1). Chr Pubns.

Esoteric Buddhism. Sinnett. 11.25 (ISBN 0-8356-5230-0). Theos Pub Hse.

Esoteric Buddhism. 5th ed. A. P. Sinnett. LC 73-76091. (Secret Doctrine Reference Ser.). 240p. 1981. pap. 8.00 (ISBN 0-913510-45-9). Wizards.

Esoteric Buddhist Painting: Japanese Arts Library, Vol. 15. Hisatoyo Ishida. LC 86-40437. (Japanese Arts Library). (Illus.). 210p. 1987. 29.95 (ISBN 0-87011-767-X). Kodansha.

Esoteric Christianity. Annie Besant. 59.95 (ISBN 0-8490-0124-2). Gordon Pr.

Esoteric Christianity. 8th ed. Annie Besant. 1966. 7.00 (ISBN 0-8356-7052-X). Theos Pub Hse.

Esoteric Christianity & the Mission of Christian Rosenkreutz. 2nd ed. Rudolf Steiner. Tr. by Pauline Wehrle from Ger. 200p. 1984. pap. 9.95 (ISBN 0-88440-413-7, Pub. by Steinerbooks). Anthroposophic.

Esoteric Keys to the Christian Scriptures. rev. 2nd ed. Henry T. Edge. Ed. by W. Emmett Small & Helen Todd. Bd. with Universal Mystery-Language of Myth & Symbol. Orig. Title: Universal Mystery-Language & Its Interpretations. Orig. Title: Theosophical Light on the Christian Bible. 1973. pap. 3.00 (ISBN 0-913004-12-X, 913004-12). Point Loma Pub.

Esoteric Orders & Their Work. Ed. by Dion Fortune. 144p. 1983. pap. 7.95 (ISBN 0-85030-310-9). Newcastle Pub.

Esoteric Teachings of the Tibetan Tantra. C. A. Muses. 319p. 1982. pap. 8.95 (ISBN 0-87728-307-9). Weiser.

Esoteric Writings. Subba T. Row. 17.95 (ISBN 0-8356-7544-0). Theos Pub Hse.

Esoteric Writings of H. P. Blavatsky. Helena P. Blavatsky. LC 79-6547. (Illus.). 500p. (Orig.). 1980. pap. 8.75 (ISBN 0-8356-0535-3, Quest). Theos Pub Hse.

Esotericism of the Popol Vuh. Raphael Girard. LC 78-74712. (Illus.). 1979. 14.00 (ISBN 0-911500-13-8); pap. 8.50 (ISBN 0-911500-14-6). Theos U Pr.

Esoterism as Principle & as Way. Frithjof Schuon. 240p. 1981. pap. 7.50 (ISBN 0-900588-23-3). Wrld Wisdom Bks.

Especially for Grandparents. Michael Campion & Wilmer Zehr. (When Was the Last Time Ser.). (Illus.). 112p. (Orig.). 1980. pap. 5.95 (ISBN 0-87123-141-7, 210141). Bethany Hse.

Especially for Husbands. Michael Campion & Wilmer Zehr. (When Was the Last Time Ser.). (Illus.). 112p. 1978. pap. 5.95 (ISBN 0-87123-136-0, 210136). Bethany Hse.

Especially for Parents. Michael Campion & Wilmer Zehr. (When Was the Last Time Ser.). (Illus.). 112p. 1978. pap. 5.95 (ISBN 0-87123-137-9, 210137). Bethany Hse.

Especially for the Single Woman. Yvonne K. Pratt. 1980. pap. 2.25 (ISBN 0-87148-295-9). Pathway Pr.

Esperanza: Zacarias-El Probeta de Esperanza. F. B. Meyer. Orig. Title: Prophet of Hope - Zechariah. (Span.). 1986. write for info. (ISBN 0-8297-0895-2). Life Pubs Intl.

Espiritu Santo. Billy Graham. Tr. by A. Edwin Sipowicz from Eng. Orig. Title: Holy Spirit. (Span.). 252p. 1981. pap. 6.25 (ISBN 0-311-09096-6). Casa Bautista.

Espiritu Santo. Charles C. Ryrie. Orig. Title: Holy Spirit. (Span.). 192p. 1978. pap. 3.95 (ISBN 0-8254-1629-9). Kregel.

Espiritu Santo en la Experiencia del Cristiano. J. D. Crane. Tr. by Olivia De Lerin. Orig. Title: Christian's Esperience of the Holy Spirit. Tr. of Christian Experience of the Holy Spirit. 128p. 1982. Repr. of 1979 ed. 5.95 (ISBN 0-311-09093-1). Casa Bautista.

Esposa Virtuosa. Linda Dillow. 160p. 1981. 2.95 (ISBN 0-88113-064-8). Edit Betania.

Esprit du Jeu Chez les Azteques. Christian Duverger. (Civilisations et Societes Ser.: No. 59). (Illus.). 1978. pap. 26.00 (ISBN 90-279-7664-3). Mouton.

Essai sur les rapports du pouvoir politique et du pouvoir religieux chez Montesquieu. Jean Carayon. LC 75-168919. (Fr.). 1973. Repr. of 1903 ed. lib. bdg. 15.00 (ISBN 0-8337-4024-5). B Franklin.

Essai Sur L'Histoire et la Geographie de la Palestine, D'Apres les Autres Sources Rabbiniques. Premiere Partie, Hisoire Depuis Cyrun Jusqu' a Adrien. Joseph Derenbourg. 490p. Repr. of 1867 ed. text ed. 99.36x (ISBN 0-576-80155-0). Gregg Intl.

Essai Sur l'Idee de Dieu et les Preuves de Son Existence Chez Descartes. Alexandre Koyre. Ed. by Willis Doney. (Philosophy of Descartes Ser.). (Fr.). 250p. 1987. lib. bdg. 40.00 (ISBN 0-8240-4665-X). Garland Pub.

Essais, 4 vols. Michel de Montaigne & Etienne de La Boetie. 1974. Set. 500.00 (ISBN 0-686-54776-4). French & Eur.

Essay in Aid of a Grammar of Assent. John H. Newman. LC 78-51523. 1979. text ed. 18.95 (ISBN 0-268-00999-6, NDP-214); pap. text ed. 9.95 (ISBN 0-268-01000-5). U of Notre Dame Pr.

Essay in Aid of a Grammar of Assent. John H. Newman. Ed. & intro. by Ian Ker. 480p. 1985. 59.95x (ISBN 0-19-812751-0). Oxford U Pr.

Essay in the Development of Fifth & Sixth Century Indian Thought. Radhika Herzberger. 1986. lib. bdg. 64.00 (ISBN 90-277-2250-1, Pub. by Reidel Holland). Kluwer Academic.

Essay on Catholicism, Authority & Order Considered in Their Fundamental Principles. Juan Donoso Cortes. Tr. by Madeleine V. Goddard. LC 78-59018. 1979. Repr. of 1925 ed. 28.00 (ISBN 0-88355-692-8). Hyperion Conn.

Essay on the Life, the Writings, & the Doctrine of the Anabaptist, Hans Denk. Gustave G. Roehrich. Tr. by Claude R. Foster et al from Fr. & Ger. LC 83-10295. 54p. (Orig.). 1983. pap. text ed. 5.50 (ISBN 0-8191-3347-7). U Pr of Amer.

Essay on the Myth of the Rbhus. Felix Neve. Tr. by G. V. Davanc from Fr. 370p. 1985. 42.50 (ISBN 81-202-0150-7, Pub. by Ajanta). South Asia Bks.

Essay on the Nature & Conduct of the Passions & Affections, 1742. 3rd ed. Francis Hutcheson. LC 76-81361. (History of Psychology Ser.). 1969. Repr. of 1742 ed. 50.00x (ISBN 0-8201-1058-2). Schol Facsimiles.

Essay on the Origin of Evil. William King. Bd. with Dissertations Concerning the Fundamental Principle & Immediate Criterion of Virtue. LC 75-11228. (British Philosophers & Theologians of the 17th & 18th Centuries Ser.). 391p. 1978. lib. bdg. 51.00 (ISBN 0-8240-1782-X). Garland Pub.

Essay on the Origin of the South Indian Temples. Venkata Ramanayyan. (Illus.). 92p. 1986. Repr. 15.00X (ISBN 0-8364-1725-9, Pub. by Manohar India). South Asia Bks.

Essay on the Slavery & Commerce of the Human Species. facs. ed. Thomas Clarkson. LC 73-93417. (Black Heritage Library Collection Ser). 1786. 15.50 (ISBN 0-8369-8542-7). Ayer Co Pubs.

Essay on Theological Method. Gordon D. Kaufman. LC 75-31656. (American Academy of Religion. Studies in Religion: No. 11). 1975. pap. 10.25 (010011). Scholars Pr GA.

Essay on Transcendentalism. Charles M. Ellis. LC 70-91761. Repr. of 1954 ed. lib. bdg. 22.50x (ISBN 0-8371-3092-1, ELTR). Greenwood.

Essay upon Reason & the Nature of Spirits. Richard Burthogge. LC 75-11204. (British Philosophers & Theologians of the 17th & 18th Centuries: Vol. 10). 1976. Repr. of 1694 ed. lib. bdg. 51.00 (ISBN 0-8240-1759-5). Garland Pub.

Essays. William Godwin. LC 77-23245. 1977. Repr. of 1873 ed. lib. bdg. 35.00 (ISBN 0-8414-4502-8). Folcroft.

Essays. Henry Slonimsky. 10.00x (ISBN 0-87068-884-7). Ktav.

Essays & Addresses on the Philosophy of Religion. Friedrich Von Hugel. LC 72-9828. 308p. 1974. Repr. of 1921 ed. lib. bdg. 29.50x (ISBN 0-8371-6219-X, HUPR). Greenwood.

Essays & Colours of Good & Evil. Francis Bacon. LC 72-56. (Select Bibliographies Reprint Ser.). 1972. Repr. of 1862 ed. 20.25 (ISBN 0-8369-9951-7). Ayer Co Pubs.

Essays & Criticisms: Containing Letters on the Christian Religion, The Philosophy of History, The Ignorant Philosopher, & the Chinese Catechism. M. De Voltaire. 120p. 1983. Repr. of 1982 ed. lib. bdg. 65.00 (ISBN 0-89987-878-4). Darby Bks.

Essays & Pamphlets on Antislavery. LC 68-55924. 1833-1898. Repr. 19.75x (ISBN 0-8371-1795-X, ESP&, Pub. by Negro U Pr). Greenwood.

Essays & Reviews: New York, 1879. Charles Hodge. Ed. by Bruce Kuklick. (American Religious Thought of the 18th & 19th Centuries Ser.). 633p. 1987. lib. bdg. 85.00 (ISBN 0-8240-6966-8). Garland Pub.

Essays & Reviews: Tendencies of Religious Thought in England. Mark Pattison. Ed. by Benjamin Jowett. 434p. 1982. Repr. of 1861 ed. lib. bdg. 75.00 (ISBN 0-89987-040-6). Darby Bks.

Essays & Sketches. John H. Newman. Ed. by Charles F. Harrold. Repr. of 1948 ed. lib. bdg. 41.00x (ISBN 0-8371-2842-0, NEER). Greenwood.

Essays & Sketches: Oberlin, 1904-1934. facsimile ed. Kemper Fullerton. LC 70-156644. (Essay Index Reprint Ser). Repr. of 1938 ed. 17.00 (ISBN 0-8369-2361-8). Ayer Co Pubs.

Essays, Catholic & Critical. facs. ed. Ed. by Edward G. Selwyn. LC 75-142695. (Essay Index Reprint Ser). 1926. 24.50 (ISBN 0-8369-2075-9). Ayer Co Pubs.

Essays Chiefly on Questions of Church & State from 1850 to 1870. Arthur P. Stanley. 656p. Repr. of 1870 ed. text ed. 74.52x (ISBN 0-576-02173-3). Gregg Intl.

Essays in American History. Henry Ferguson. LC 68-26266. 1969. Repr. of 1894 ed. 21.50x (ISBN 0-8046-0144-5, Pub. by Kennikat). Assoc Faculty Pr.

Essays in American Jewish History, in Honor of Jacob Rader Marcus. 35.00x (ISBN 0-87068-459-0). Ktav.

Essays in American Theology: The Life & Thought of Harris Franklin Rall. W. J. McCutcheon. LC 72-190198. 350p. 1972. 15.00 (ISBN 0-8022-2085-1). Philos Lib.

Essays in American Zionism Nineteen-Seventeen to Nineteen Forty-Eight. Ed. by Melvin Urofsky. 1979. 12.50 (ISBN 0-930832-56-6). Herzl Pr.

Essays in Apologetics, Vol. 1. Bert Thompson & Wayne Jackson. 183p. 1984. pap. 4.50. Apologetic Pr.

Essays in Apologetics, Vol. 2. Bert Thompson & Wayne Jackson. 255p. 1986. pap. 4.95 (ISBN 0-932859-06-2). Apologetic Pr.

Essays in Biblical & Jewish Culture & Bible Translation. Harry M. Orlinsky. 1973. 25.00x (ISBN 0-87068-218-0). Ktav.

Essays in Christian Philosophy. facs. ed. Leonard Hodgson. LC 69-17577. (Essay Index Reprint Ser). 1930. 14.00 (ISBN 0-8369-0079-0). Ayer Co Pubs.

Essays in Evangelical Social Ethics. Ed. by David F. Wright. 192p. 1982. 18.95 (ISBN 0-85364-288-5); pap. text ed. 9.50 (ISBN 0-85364-290-7). Attic Pr.

Essays in Evangelical Social Ethics. Ed. by David F. Wright. LC 82-62581. 192p. (Orig.). 1983. pap. 8.95 (ISBN 0-8192-1326-8). Morehouse.

Essays in Gratitude. D. Elton Trueblood. LC 82-71215. 1982. 8.95 (ISBN 0-8054-6938-9). Broadman.

Essays in History, Written Between the Years 1896-1912. facs. ed. Pope Pius Eleventh. LC 67-26771. (Essay Index Reprint Ser.). 1934. 17.00 (ISBN 0-8369-0791-4). Ayer Co Pubs.

Essays in Honor of J. Dwight Pentecost. Ed. by Stanley D. Toussaint & Charles Dyer. 1986. text ed. 15.95 (ISBN 0-8024-2381-7). Moody.

Essays in Honor of Karl Kerenyi. Ed. by Edgar C. Polome. (Journal of Indo-European Studies Monographs: No. 4). (Illus.). 144p. (Orig.). 1984. pap. 30.00x (ISBN 0-941694-20-8). Inst Study Man.

Essays in Honour of Yigael Yadin. Ed. by Geza Vermes & Jacob Neusner. (Publications of the Oxford Centre for Postgraduate Hebrew Studies: Vol. 6). (Illus.). 618p. 1983. text ed. 45.00x (ISBN 0-86598-102-7). Allanheld.

Essays in Humanism. Albert Einstein. 130p. 1983. pap. 4.95 (ISBN 0-8022-2417-2). Philos Lib.

Essays in Idleness: The Tsurezuregusa of Kenko. Tr. by Donald Keene. LC 67-23566. (Records of Civilization Sources & Studies & Translations of the Oriental Classics Ser.). (Illus.). 213p. 1967. pap. 12.50x (ISBN 0-231-08308-4). Columbia U Pr.

Essays in Jewish Biography. Alexander Marx. (Brown Classics in Judaica Ser.). 322p. 1986. pap. text ed. 14.25 (ISBN 0-8191-5022-3). U Pr of Amer.

Essays in Jewish Intellectual History. Alexander Altmann. LC 80-54471. 336p. 1981. 30.00x (ISBN 0-87451-192-5). U Pr of New Eng.

Essays in Jewish Social & Economic History. Arcadius Kahan. Ed. by Roger Weiss. LC 86-1427. xx, 208p. 1986. lib. bdg. 27.50x (ISBN 0-226-42240-2). U of Chicago Pr.

Essays in Medieval Life & Thought. John H. Mundy et al. LC 65-25472. 1955. 18.00 (ISBN 0-8196-0159-4). Biblo.

Essays in Modern Jewish History: A Tribute to Ben Halpern. Ed. by Frances Malino & Phyllis C. Albert. LC 80-70585. 500p. 1981. 27.50 (ISBN 0-8386-3095-2). Fairleigh Dickinson.

Essays in Moral Philosophy. Ed. by A. I. Melden. LC 58-10483. 288p. 1966. 15.00x (ISBN 0-295-73774-3); pap. 4.95x (ISBN 0-295-74049-3, WP20). U of Wash Pr.

Essays in Mysticism. Wayne Teasdale. 196p. 1982. pap. 8.95 (ISBN 0-941850-02-1). Sunday Pubns.

Essays in New Testament Interpretation. Charles F. Moule. LC 81-10141. (Illus.). 260p. 1982. 42.50 (ISBN 0-521-23783-1). Cambridge U Pr.

Essays in Phenomenological Theology. Ed. by Steven W. Laycock & James G. Hart. 204p. (Orig.). 1986. 44.50x (ISBN 0-88706-164-8); pap. 14.95x (ISBN 0-88706-165-6). State U NY Pr.

Essays in Philosophical Analysis. Nicholas Rescher. LC 82-45160. (Illus.). 438p. 1982. pap. text ed. 17.75 (ISBN 0-8191-2459-1). U Pr of Amer.

Essays in Process Theology. Williams. 24.95 (ISBN 0-317-46805-7); pap. 12.95 (ISBN 0-317-46806-5). Exploration Pr.

Essays in Process Theology. Daniel D. Williams. Ed. by Perry LeFevre. LC 84-82337. 342p. 1985. text ed. 24.95x (ISBN 0-913552-25-9); pap. text ed. 12.95x (ISBN 0-913552-26-7). Exploration Pr.

Essays in Puritanism: Jonathan Edwards, John Winthrop, Margaret Fuller, Walt Whitman, John Wesley. Andrew Macphail. LC 68-26205. 1969. Repr. of 1905 ed. 22.50x (ISBN 0-8046-0286-7, Pub. by Kennikat). Assoc Faculty Pr.

Essays in Reconstruction. Ed. by Ralph D. Russell. LC 68-15835. 1968. Repr. of 1946 ed. 21.50x (ISBN 0-8046-0398-7, Pub. by Kennikat). Assoc Faculty Pr.

Essays in Religion & Morality. William James. LC 81-7040. (Illus.). 376p. text ed. 25.00x (ISBN 0-674-26735-4). Harvard U Pr.

Essays in Social Value Theory. Marc R. Tool. 1986. 35.00 (ISBN 0-87332-382-3). M E Sharpe.

Essays in the History of Religious Thought in the West. Brooke F. Westcott. LC 72-8480. (Essay Index Reprint Ser.). 1972. Repr. of 1891 ed. 24.50 (ISBN 0-8369-7338-0). Ayer Co Pubs.

Essays in Thomism. Ed. by Robert E. Brennan. LC 72-1149. (Essay Index Reprint Ser.). Repr. of 1942 ed. 27.50 (ISBN 0-8369-2834-2). Ayer Co Pubs.

Essays in Zen Buddhism. D. T. Suzuki. 1961. pap. 5.95 (ISBN 0-394-17230-2, E309, Ever). Grove.

Essays, Lectures, etc. Upon Select Topics in Revealed Theology: New York 1859. Nathaniel W. Taylor. Ed. by Bruce Kuklick. (American Religious Thought of the 18th & 19th Centuries Ser.). 480p. 1987. lib. bdg. 65.00 (ISBN 0-8240-6960-9). Garland Pub.

Essays, Moral & Divine. Sir William Anstruther. LC 74-170474. (English Stage Ser.: Vol. 40). 1973. lib. bdg. 61.00 (ISBN 0-8240-0623-2). Garland Pub.

Essays of a Catholic. facs. ed. Hilaire Belloc. LC 67-26713. (Essay Index Reprint Ser.). 1931. 18.00 (ISBN 0-8369-0188-6). Ayer Co Pubs.

Essays of an Atheist Activist. Ed. by Jon G. Murray. 67p. (Orig.). 1981. pap. 3.25 (ISBN 0-911826-02-5). Am Atheist.

Essays on a Science of Mythology: The Myths of the Divine Child & the Mysteries of Eleusis. rev. ed. Carl G. Jung & Carl Kerenyi. (Bollingen Ser.: Vol. 22). 1963. pap. 6.95 (ISBN 0-691-01756-5). Princeton U Pr.

Essays on American Atheism, Vol. I. Jon G. Murray. 350p. (Orig.). 1986. pap. 8.00 (ISBN 0-910309-28-0). Am Atheist.

Essays on American Atheism, Vol. II. Jon G. Murray. 300p. (Orig.). 1986. pap. 8.00 (ISBN 0-910309-29-9). Am Atheist.

Essays on Apostolic Themes. Paul Elbert. 252p. 1985. 14.95 (ISBN 0-913573-14-0). Hendrickson MA.

Essays on Berkeley: A Tercentennial Celebration. Ed. by J. Foster & H. Robinson. 1985. 38.00x (ISBN 0-19-824734-6). Oxford U Pr.

Essays on Biblical Interpretation. Paul Ricoeur. Ed. by Lewis S. Mudge. LC 80-8052. 192p. (Orig.). 1980. pap. 8.95 (ISBN 0-8006-1407-0, 1-1407). Fortress.

Essays on Biblical Preaching. Jay E. Adams. (Jay Adams Library). 160p. 1986. pap. 7.95 (ISBN 0-310-51041-4, 12116P). Zondervan.

Essays on Camus' Exile & the Kingdom. Judith D. Suther. LC 80-36800. (Romance Monographs: No. 41). 329p. 1982. 30.00x (ISBN 84-499-4725-1). Romance.

Essays on Catholic Education in the U. S. facsimile ed. Ed. by Roy J. Deferrari. LC 71-90629. (Essay Index Reprint Ser.). 566p. Repr. of 1942 ed. lib. bdg. 32.00 (ISBN 0-8290-0814-4). Irvington.

Essays on Catholic Life. facs. ed. Thomas O'Hagan. LC 67-22106. (Essay Index Reprint Ser). 1916. 17.00 (ISBN 0-8369-1333-7). Ayer Co Pubs.

Essays on Christianity & Political Philosophy. Ed. by George W. Carey & James V. Schall. (ISI Roots of Western Culture Ser.). 144p. (Orig.). 1985. 24.00 (ISBN 0-8191-4275-1, Co-pub. by Intercollegiate Studies); pap. text ed. 8.75 (ISBN 0-8191-4276-X). U Pr of Amer.

Essays on Church & State. Lord Acton. 12.00 (ISBN 0-8446-1505-6). Peter Smith.

Essays on Counseling. Jay E. Adams. (Jay Adams Library). 288p. 1986. pap. 9.95 (ISBN 0-310-51171-2, 1219P). Zondervan.

Essays on Ethics, Religion & Society. John S. Mill. Ed. by J. M. Robson. (Collected Works of John Stuart Hill Ser.: Vol. 10). pap. 160.00 (ISBN 0-317-41695-2, 2055827). Bks Demand UMI.

Essays On Foundation of Astrology. C. E. Carter. 9.95 (ISBN 0-8356-5506-7). Theos Pub Hse.

Essays on Foundation of Astrology. C. E. Carter. pap. 5.95 (ISBN 0-8356-5503-2). Theos Pub Hse.

Essays on Freedom & Power. Acton. 13.25 (ISBN 0-8446-0000-8). Peter Smith.

Essays on History, Literature & Religion of Ancient India, 2 vols. H. T. Colebrooke. 1024p. Repr. of 1873 ed. text ed. 57.50x. Coronet Bks.

Essays on Human Rights: Contemporary Issues & Jewish Perspectives. Ed. by David Sidorsky et al. LC 78-1170. 416p. 1978. 12.00 (ISBN 0-8276-0107-7, 420). Jewish Pubns.

Essays on Indo-Aryan Mythology. Narayan Aiyangar. 656p. 1986. Repr. 34.00X (ISBN 0-8364-1712-7, Pub. by Manohar India). South Asia Bks.

Essays on Islamic Philosophy & Science. Ed. by George F. Hourani. LC 74-13493. 1974. 49.50 (ISBN 0-87395-224-3). State U Ny Pr.

Essays on Jewish Folklore & Comparative Literature. Alexander Scheiber. (Illus.). 456p. 1985. 55.00x (ISBN 963-05-3944-6, Pub. by Akademiai Kiado Hungary). Humanities.

Essays on Jewish Life & Thought. Ed. by Joseph L. Blau. LC 57-11757. 458p. 1959. 31.00x (ISBN 0-231-02171-2). Columbia U Pr.

Essays on John. C. K. Barrett. LC 82-2759. 176p. 1982. 18.95 (ISBN 0-664-21389-8). Westminster.

Essays on Jung & the Study of Religion. Ed. by Luther H. Martin & James Goss. LC 85-17865. 214p. (Orig.). 1986. lib. bdg. 29.50 (ISBN 0-8191-4923-3); pap. text ed. 12.75 (ISBN 0-8191-4924-1). U Pr of Amer.

Essays on Knowledge & Justification. Ed. by George S. Pappas & Marshall Swain. LC 77-10299. (Illus.). 384p. 1978. 42.50x (ISBN 0-8014-1086-X); pap. 10.95x (ISBN 0-8014-9865-1). Cornell U Pr.

Essays on Liturgiology & Church History. John M. Neale. LC 70-173070. Repr. of 1863 ed. 32.50 (ISBN 0-404-04667-3). AMS Pr.

Essays on Maimonides. Ed. by Salo W. Baron. LC 79-160004. Repr. of 1941 ed. 24.50 (ISBN 0-404-00658-2). AMS Pr.

Essays on Milton. W. J. Courthope. 1908. lib. bdg. 10.00 (ISBN 0-8414-3599-5). Folcroft.

Essays on Milton. Elbert Thompson. LC 72-195123. 1910. lib. bdg. 30.00 (ISBN 0-8414-8044-3). Folcroft.

Essays on New Testament Christianity. Compiled by Robert Wetzel. LC 78-55881. 1978. text ed. 12.95 (ISBN 0-87239-208-2, 2856). Standard Pub.

Essays on Old Testament Ethics: J. P. Hyatt in Memoriam. J. L. Crenshaw & Willis Crenshaw. 1974. 35.00x (ISBN 0-87068-233-4). Ktav.

Essays on Paul. C. K. Barrett. LC 82-2764. 180p. 1982. 18.95 (ISBN 0-664-21390-1). Westminster.

Essays on Puritans & Puritanism. Leon Howard. Ed. by James Barbour & Thomas Quirk. LC 85-28878. 221p. 1986. 19.95 (ISBN 0-8263-0877-5). U of NM Pr.

Essays on Reason, Will, Creativity, & Time: Studies in the Philosophy of Friedrich Nietzsche. Bernard D. Ouden. LC 82-45042. 124p. (Orig.). 1982. PLB 23.75 o. p. (ISBN 0-8191-2449-4); pap. text ed. 9.50 (ISBN 0-8191-2450-8). U Pr of Amer.

Essays on Religion. facs. ed. Arthur Clutton-Brock. LC 79-84302. (Essay Index Reprint Ser). 1926. 14.50 (ISBN 0-8369-1078-8). Ayer Co Pubs.

Essays on Religion & the Ancient World. Arthur D. Nock. Ed. by Zeph Stewart. 1164p. 1986. Set. 98.00x (ISBN 0-19-814282-X). Oxford U Pr.

Essays on Russian Folklore & Mythology. Felix J. Oinas. (Illus.). 183p. (Orig.). 1985. pap. 12.95 (ISBN 0-89357-148-2). Slavica.

Essays on Several Important Subjects in Philosophy & Religion. Joseph Glanvill. Repr. of 1676 ed. 32.00 (ISBN 0-384-18880-X). Johnson Repr.

Essays on Some of the First Principles of Metaphysicks, Ethicks, & Theology. Asa Burton. LC 73-4839. (History of Psychology Ser.). 432p. 1973. Repr. of 1824 ed. lib. bdg. 60.00x (ISBN 0-8201-1114-7). Schol Facsimiles.

Essays on Some of the Modern Guides to English Thought in Matters of Faith. Richard H. Hutton. LC 72-8580. (Essay Index Reprint Ser.). 1972. Repr. of 1887 ed. 23.50 (ISBN 0-8369-7319-4). Ayer Co Pubs.

Essays on the Active Powers of Man. Thomas Reid. Ed. by Rene Wellek. LC 75-11251. (British Philosophers & Theologians of the 17th & 18th Centuries: Vol. 50). 1977. Repr. of 1788 ed. lib. bdg. 51.00 (ISBN 0-8240-1802-8). Garland Pub.

Essays on the Ancient Semitic World. Ed. by John W. Wevers & D. B. Redford. LC 76-23038. (Toronto Semitic Texts & Studies). pap. 33.30 (2026403). Bks Demand UMI.

Essays on the Gita. Sri Aurobindo. 1979. 20.00 (ISBN 0-89744-907-X); lib. bdg. 30.00 (ISBN 0-89744-906-1); pap. 16.00 (ISBN 0-89744-908-8). Auromere.

Essays on the Gita. Sri Aurobindo. 588p. 1983. 12.50 (ISBN 0-89071-297-2, Pub. by Sri Aurobindo Ashram India); pap. 8.75 (ISBN 0-89071-296-4, Pub. by Sri Aurobindo Ashram India). Matagiri.

Essays on the Gita. Sri Aurobindo. 1976. 12.50 (ISBN 0-89071-231-X). Matagiri.

Essays on the Gita. Sri Aurobindo. 1976. pap. 8.75 (ISBN 0-89071-222-0). Matagiri.

Essays on the Gita. Sri Aurobindo. (Life Companion Library). 763p. 1983. 21.95 (ISBN 0-89744-006-4). Auromere.

Essays on the Heidelberg Catechism. Bard Thompson et al. LC 63-21522. 1963. pap. 5.95 (ISBN 0-8298-0325-4). Pilgrim NY.

Essays on the Latin Orient. William Miller. LC 78-63360. (Crusades & Military Orders: Second Ser.). Repr. of 1921 ed. 54.50 (ISBN 0-404-17024-2). AMS Pr.

Essays on the Life of Muhammad. S. A. Khan. 1968. 27.00x (ISBN 0-87902-172-1). Orientalia.

Essays on the Lord's Supper. Oscar Cullmann & Franz J. Leenhardt. LC 58-8979. 1958. pap. 4.95 (ISBN 0-8042-3748-4). John Knox.

Essays on the Monteverdi Mass & Vespers of 1610. Jeffrey Kurtzman. LC 78-66039. (Rice University Studies: Vol. 64, No.4). (Illus.). 182p. 1979. pap. 10.00x (ISBN 0-89263-238-0). Rice Univ.

Essays on the Moral Concepts. R. M. Hare. LC 70-187322. (New Studies in Practical Philosophy). 150p. 1972. 18.50x (ISBN 0-520-02231-9). U of Cal Pr.

Essays on the Patriarchal Narratives. Ed. by D. J. Wiseman & A. R. Millard. 1983. text ed. 17.50x (ISBN 0-931464-13-7); pap. 9.95 (ISBN 0-931464-12-9). Eisenbrauns.

Essays on the Semitic Background of the New Testament. Joseph A. Fitzmyer. LC 74-83874. (Society of Biblical Literature. Sources for Biblical Study). 1974. pap. 13.50 (060305). Scholars Pr GA.

Essays on the Sermon on the Mount. Hans D. Betz. LC 84-47910. 192p. 1984. 24.95 (ISBN 0-8006-0726-0). Fortress.

Essays on War & Peace: Bible & Early Church. Ed. by Willard M. Swartley. (Occasional Papers Ser.: No. 9). 154p. 1986. pap. text ed. 6.50 (ISBN 0-936273-09-7). Inst Mennonite.

Essays on Zionism & the Contemporary Jewish Condition. Ed. by Nathan Rotenstreich. 1981. write for info. Herzl Pr.

Essence. A. H. Almaas. LC 85-51109. (Illus.). 208p. (Orig.). 1986. pap. 10.95 (ISBN 0-87728-627-2). Weiser.

Essence & the Vocation of Man. David B. Gilmore. (Illus.). 123p. 1980. deluxe ed. 57.50 (ISBN 0-89920-009-5). Am Inst Psych.

Essence-Christian Faith. Martin A. Larson. 273p. 10.95 (ISBN 0-318-19483-X). Truth Seeker.

Essence of All Religions. Benito F. Reyes. 25p. 1983. pap. 3.00 (ISBN 0-939375-14-1). World Univ Amer.

Essence of Bhagavad Gita & Bible. Satguru S. Keshavadas. LC 80-50446. (Illus.). 303p. 1982. pap. 30.00 (ISBN 0-942508-00-9); pap. 15.00 (ISBN 0-942508-01-7). Vishwa.

Essence of Buddhism. 3rd rev. & enl. ed. Pokala Lakshmi Narasu. LC 78-72459. Repr. of 1948 ed. 32.50 (ISBN 0-404-17327-6). AMS Pr.

Essence of Buddhism with an Introduction by Anagarika H. Dharmmapals. P. Lakshmi Narasu. 212p. 1986. Repr. of 1907 ed. 15.00X (ISBN 0-8364-1748-8, Pub. by Manohar India). South Asia Bks.

Essence of Chinese Wisdom. B. Brown. (Illus.). 227p. 1986. 117.50 (ISBN 0-89901-279-5). Found Class Reprints.

Essence of Christianity. Ludwig Feuerbach. pap. 7.95x (ISBN 0-06-130011-X, TB11, Torch). Har-Row.

Essence of Christianity. Ludwig Feuerbach. Tr. by George Eliot. 1958. 18.25 (ISBN 0-8446-2055-6). Peter Smith.

Essence of Christianity. Ludwig Feuerbach. Ed. by E. Graham Waring & F. W. Strothmann. LC 57-8650. (Milestones of Thought Ser.). 1975. pap. 3.45 (ISBN 0-8044-6145-7). Ungar.

Essence of Christianity. Michael Schmaus. 288p. 1966. pap. 2.50 (ISBN 0-933932-16-2). Scepter Pubs.

Essence of Faith. Albert Schweitzer. pap. 0.95 (ISBN 0-685-19400-0, 127, WL). Citadel Pr.

Essence of Faith in Islam. A. D. Ajijola. pap. 12.50 (ISBN 0-686-63898-0). Kazi Pubns.

Essence of Judaism. rev. ed. Leo Baeck. LC 61-8992. 1961. pap. 8.50 (ISBN 0-8052-0006-1). Schocken.

Essence of Orthodox Inconography. Constantine D. Kalokyris. Tr. by Peter A. Chamberas from Greek. (Illus.). 129p. 1971. pap. 9.95 (ISBN 0-917651-12-X). Holy Cross Orthodox.

Essence of Plotinus: Extracts from the Six Enneads & Porphyry's Life of Plotinus. Ed. by Grace R. Turnbull. Tr. by Stephen Mackenna. LC 76-40320. 1976. Repr. of 1934 ed. lib. bdg. 37.50x (ISBN 0-8371-9054-1, TUEP). Greenwood.

Essence of Rastafari Nationalism & Black Economic Development. Trevor C. Myers. 1986. 10.00 (ISBN 0-533-06629-8). Vantage.

Essence of Religion. Borden P. Bowne. LC 75-3070. Repr. of 1910 ed. 34.50 (ISBN 0-404-59069-1). AMS Pr.

Essence of Religion. Arthur Schopenhauer. (Illus.). 109p. 1985. 98.85 (ISBN 0-89266-505-X). Am Classical Coll Pr.

Essence of Sufism. R. A. Nicholson. 1984. pap. 3.95 (ISBN 0-916411-49-4, Near Eastern). Holmes Pub.

Essence of the Cabalah. William Eisen. (Illus.). 480p. 1984. 22.95 (ISBN 0-87516-524-9). De Vorss.

Essence of the Catholic Approach to Education. Claudio O. Mittelstaadt. (Illus.). 134p. 1982. 59.15 (ISBN 0-89266-356-1). Am Classical Coll Pr.

Essence of Yoga. Georg Feuerstein. LC 75-42897. 1976. pap. 3.95 (ISBN 0-394-17902-1, E671, Ever). Grove.

Essene Book of Asha: Journey to the Cosmic Ocean. Edmond B. Szekely. (Illus.). 140p. 1976. pap. 7.50 (ISBN 0-89564-008-2). IBS Intl.

Essene Book of Creation. Edmond B. Szekely. (Illus.). 86p. 1975. pap. 4.50 (ISBN 0-89564-005-8). IBS Intl.

Essene Book of Days 1987. Danaan Parry. 400p. (Orig.). 1986. pap. 12.95 (ISBN 0-913319-02-3). Sunstone Pubns.

Essene Christ. Upton C. Ewing. LC 61-10608. (Illus.). 456p. 1977. pap. 12.95 (ISBN 0-8022-0461-9). Philos Lib.

Essene Christ. Upton C. Ewing. 438p. pap. 12.95 (ISBN 0-317-07627-2). Edenite.

Essene-Christian Faith. Martin A. Larson. LC 79-83606. 297p. 1980. 10.95 (ISBN 0-8022-2241-2). Philos Lib.

Essene Christian Faith. Martin A. Larson. 273p. 1986. 12.00 (ISBN 0-317-53276-6). Noontide.

Essene-Christian Faith. Martin A. Larson. 273p. 10.95. Truth Seeker.

Essene Code of Life. Edmond B. Szekely. (Illus.). 44p. 1978. pap. 3.50 (ISBN 0-89564-013-9). IBS Intl.

Essene Communions with the Infinite. Edmond B. Szekely. (Illus.). 64p. 1979. pap. 3.95 (ISBN 0-89564-009-0). IBS Intl.

Essene Gospel of Peace, Bk. 1. Edmond B. Szekely. (Illus.). 72p. 1981. pap. 1.00 (ISBN 0-89564-000-7). IBS Intl.

Essene Gospel of Peace, Bk. 2. Edmond B. Szekely. (Illus.). 132p. 1981. pap. 5.80 (ISBN 0-89564-001-5). IBS Intl.

Essene Gospel of Peace, Bk. 3: Lost Scrolls of the Essene Brotherhood. Edmond B. Szekely. (Illus.). 144p. 1981. pap. 5.60 (ISBN 0-89564-002-3). IBS Intl.

Essene Gospel of Peace, Bk. 4: Teachings of the Elect. Edmond B. Szekely. (Illus.). 40p. 1981. pap. 4.50 (ISBN 0-89564-003-1). IBS Intl.

Essene Humane Gospel of Jesus. Frank J. Muccie, Jr. 174p. pap. 4.95 (ISBN 0-938520-02-4). Edenite.

Essene Jesus. Edmond B. Szekely. (Illus.). 72p. 1977. pap. 4.50 (ISBN 0-89564-007-4). IBS Intl.

Essene Origins of Christianity. Edmond B. Szekely. (Illus.). 184p. 1981. pap. 8.50 (ISBN 0-89564-015-5). IBS Intl.

Essene Science of Fasting & the Art of Sobriety. Edmond B. Szekely. (Illus.). 48p. 1981. pap. 3.50 (ISBN 0-89564-011-2). IBS Intl.

Essene Science of Life. Edmond B. Szekely. (Illus.). 64p. 1976. pap. 3.50 (ISBN 0-89564-010-4). IBS Intl.

Essene Teachings of Zarathurstra. Edmond B. Szekely. (Illus.). 32p. 1974. pap. 2.95 (ISBN 0-89564-016-3). IBS Intl.

Essene Way: Biogenic Living. Edmond B. Szekely. (Illus.). 200p. 1981. pap. 8.80 (ISBN 0-89564-019-8). IBS Intl.

Essene Way: World Pictures & Cosmic Symbols. Edmond B. Szekely. (Illus.). 40p. 1978. pap. 1.80 (ISBN 0-89564-050-3). IBS Intl.

Essene Writings from Qumran. A. Dupont-Sommer. Tr. by G. Vermes. 13.50 (ISBN 0-8446-2012-2). Peter Smith.

Essenes & Their Ancient Mysteries. Robert G. Chaney. (Adventures in Esoteric Learning Ser.). 1968. pap. 4.25 (ISBN 0-918936-14-4). Astara.

Essenes, by Josephus & His Contemporaries. Edmond B. Szekely. (Illus.). 32p. 1981. pap. 2.95 (ISBN 0-89564-014-7). IBS Intl.

Essenes: The Elect of Israel & the Priests of Artemis. Allen H. Jones. (Illus.). 146p. (Orig.). 1985. lib. bdg. 23.50 (ISBN 0-8191-4744-3); pap. text ed. 9.50 (ISBN 0-8191-4745-1). U Pr of Amer.

Essential Augustine. Saint Augustine. Commentary by Vernon J. Bourke. 274p. 1973. 15.00 (ISBN 0-915144-08-5); pap. text ed. 4.95 (ISBN 0-915144-07-7). Hackett Pub.

Essential Catholicism. Tr. by Thomas Bokenkotter. LC 84-13631. 432p. 1985. 19.95 (ISBN 0-385-18357-7). Doubleday.

Essential Catholicism: Dynamics of Faith & Belief. Thomas Bokenkotter. LC 86-4390. 456p. 1986. pap. 9.95 (ISBN 0-385-23243-8, Im). Doubleday.

Essential Christianity. Walter Martin. 1985. pap. 4.95 (ISBN 0-8307-1029-9, 5418458). Regal.

Essential Nectar. Geshe Rabten. Ed. by Martin Wilson. (Wisdom Basic Book, Orange Ser.). 304p. (Orig.). 1984. pap. 11.95 (ISBN 0-86171-013-4, Wisdom Pubns). Great Traditions.

Essential Plotinus: Representative Treatises from The Enneads. Tr. by Elmer O'Brien. 236p. 1975. lib. bdg. 15.00 (ISBN 0-915144-10-7); pap. 4.95 (ISBN 0-915144-09-3). Hackett Pub.

Essential Reinhold Niebuhr: Selected Essays & Addresses. Ed. by Robert M. Brown. LC 85-22798. 272p. 1986. 19.95 (ISBN 0-300-03464-4). Yale U Pr.

Essential Rudolf Steiner. Ed. by Robert A. McDermott. LC 82-48934. 320p. 1983. pap. 10.95 (ISBN 0-06-065345-0, RD-399, HarpR). Har-Row.

Essential Swedenborg. Sig Synnestvedt. LC 76-57901. 3.95 (ISBN 0-87785-116-6); pap. 2.95 (ISBN 0-87785-152-2). Swedenborg.

Essential Talmud. Adin Steinsaltz. LC 75-36384. 1982. pap. 8.95 (ISBN 0-465-02063-1, CN-5112). Basic.

Essential Writings of Frithjof Schuon. Ed. by Seyyed H. Nast. (Roots of Wisdom Bk). 512p. 1986. 34.95 (ISBN 0-916349-05-5). Amity Hous Inc.

Essentials in the Development of Religion: A Philosophic & Psychological Study. J. E. Turner. 1979. Repr. of 1934 ed. lib. bdg. 35.00 (ISBN 0-8482-2730-1). Norwood Edns.

Essentials in the Development of Religion. John E. Turner. LC 70-102587. 1970. Repr. of 1934 ed. 24.50x (ISBN 0-8046-0747-8, Pub. by Kennikat). Assoc Faculty Pr.

Essentials of Basic Youth Ministry. Spencer Nordyke & Cyndy Nordyke. 49p. (Orig.). 1984. wkbk. 4.95 (ISBN 0-914307-21-5). Word Faith.

Essentials of Biblical Hebrew. rev. ed. Kyle M. Yates. Ed. by J. J. Owens. 1955. 13.95 (ISBN 0-06-069710-5, HarpR). Har-Row.

Essentials of Buddhist Philosophy. Junjiro Takakusa. 236p. 1978. pap. 6.95 (ISBN 0-87728-426-1). Weiser.

Essentials of Buddhist Philosophy. 3rd ed. J. Takakusu. 1975. Repr. 8.50 (ISBN 0-8426-0826-5). Orient Bk Dist.

Essentials of Buddhist Philosophy. 2nd ed. J. Takakusu. Ed. by W. Chan & Charles A. Moore. (Illus.). Repr. of 1949 ed. text ed. 14.00x. Coronet Bks.

Essentials of Christian Relationship. Michael Palandro & Steve Lestarjette. 56p. 1987. pap. text ed. 2.95 (ISBN 0-939079-00-3). Christlife Pubs.

Essentials of Discipleship. Francis M. Cosgrove. LC 79-93015. 192p. 1980. pap. 5.95 (ISBN 0-89109-442-3). NavPress.

Essentials of Hinduism, Jainism & Buddhism. A. N. Dwivedi. 148p. 1979. 12.00 (ISBN 0-88065-083-4, Pub. by Messers Today & Tomorrows Printers & Publishers India). Scholarly Pubns.

Essentials of Islam. A. Rahman. pap. 4.95 (ISBN 0-686-67786-2). Kazi Pubns.

Essentials of Leadership & Other Papers in Moral & Religious Education. Herman H. Horne. LC 76-117808. (Essay Index Reprint Ser). 1931. 14.00 (ISBN 0-8369-1660-3). Ayer Co Pubs.

Essentials of Mysticism & Other Essays. Evelyn Underhill. LC 75-41277. Repr. of 1920 ed. 18.00 (ISBN 0-404-14620-1). AMS Pr.

Essentials of New Life. Francis M. Cosgrove. LC 78-54949. (Illus.). 180p. (Orig.). 1978. pap. 5.95 (ISBN 0-89109-427-X). NavPress.

Essentials of New Testament: Greek. P. G. Bell. 1983. pap. 9.95 Wkbk. (ISBN 0-89957-569-2); answer bk. for wkbk. 4.95 (ISBN 0-89957-570-6); answers for essentials 2.95. AMG Pubs.

Essentials of New Testament Greek. Ray Summers. 1950. text ed. 11.95 (ISBN 0-8054-1309-X). Broadman.

Essentials of Oneness Theology. David Bernard. (Illus.). 32p. (Orig.). 1985. pap. 2.25 (ISBN 0-912315-89-X). Word Aflame.

Essentials of Our faith: What Christians Believe. Jo Anne Sekowsky. (Basic Bible Study Ser.). (Orig.). 1987. pap. 2.95 (ISBN 0-932305-37-7, 521023). Aglow Pubns.

Essentials of Prayer. E. M. Bounds. (Direction Bks Ser.). 1979. pap. 3.95 (ISBN 0-8010-0756-9). Baker Bk.

Essentials of Religious Life Today. Peter Stravinskas. (Orig.). pap. price not set (ISBN 0-913382-34-5, 101-34). Prow Bks-Franciscan.

Essentials of the Christian Life. R. K. Campbell. 46p. pap. 0.50 (ISBN 0-88172-008-9). Believers Bkshelf.

Essentials of the Shramanera Vinaya & Rules of Deportment: A General Explanation. Commentary by Great Master Lyan Chr. Tr. by Buddhist Text Translation Society Staff. (Eng., Illus.). 112p. (Orig.). 1975. pap. 5.00 (ISBN 0-917512-04-9). Buddhist Text.

Essentials of Theism. Denis J. Hawkins. LC 72-9373. 151p. 1973. Repr. of 1949 ed. lib. bdg. 22.50x (ISBN 0-8371-6579-2, HAET). Greenwood.

Essentials of Wesleyan Theology: A Contemporary Affirmation. Paul Mickey. 160p. 1980. pap. 5.95 (ISBN 0-310-39151-2, 9312P). Zondervan.

Essentials of Zen Buddhism. Tr. by O'Hyun Park. 143p. 1985. pap. 4.95 (ISBN 0-317-20880-2). CSA Pr.

Essentials of Zen Buddhism. Daisetz T. Suzuki. Ed. & intro. by Bernard Phillips. LC 61-5041. 544p. 1973. Repr. of 1962 ed. lib. bdg. 45.00x (ISBN 0-8371-6649-7, SUEZ). Greenwood.

Establishing Values. Joan Almand & Joy Wooderson. LC 76-17147. 1976. pap. 1.99 (ISBN 0-87148-283-5). Pathway Pr.

Establishment Clause: Religion & the First Amendment. Leonard W. Levy. LC 86-5417. 1986. 16.95 (ISBN 0-02-918750-8). Macmillan.

Establishment of Christianity & the Proscription of Paganism. Maude A. Huttman. LC 15-703. (Columbia University. Studies in the Social Sciences: No. 147). Repr. of 1914 ed. 18.50 (ISBN 0-404-51147-3). AMS Pr.

Establishment of Human Antiquity (Monograph) Ed. by Donald K. Grayson. LC 82-11571. 280p. 1983. 29.50 (ISBN 0-12-297250-3). Acad Pr.

Establishment of the English Church in Continental American Colonies. Elizabeth H. Davidson. (Duke University. Trinity College Historical Society. Historical Papers: No. 20). Repr. of 1936 ed. 24.50 (ISBN 0-404-51770-6). AMS Pr.

Estat Present De L'eglise & De la Colonie Francoise Dans la Nouvelle France Par M. L'eveque De Quebec. Jean B. Saint-Vallier. (Canadiana Avant 1867: No. 20). 1967. 18.40x (ISBN 90-2796-332-0). Mouton.

Estate Planning: A Workbook for Christians. Richard D. Bailey. LC 81-14907. 96p. (Orig.). 1982. pap. 7.75 (ISBN 0-687-12004-7). Abingdon.

Estates of Grace: The Architectural Heritage of Religious Structures in Rye, N. Y. Barbara C. Abrams. Intro. by Susan A. Morison. (Illus.). 20p. (Orig.). 1986. pap. text ed. 4.00 (ISBN 0-9615327-1-8). Rye Hist Soc.

Estatura de Uma Mulher. Gene Getz. Ed. by Jaoa Batista. Tr. by Ruth V. Ferreira. (Port.). 144p. 1981. pap. 1.60 (ISBN 0-8297-1075-2). Life Pubs Intl.

Este Es el Tiempo para la Fe. Martha Smock. Tr. of Now Is the Time for Faith. 1984. 5.95 (ISBN 0-87159-033-6). Unity School.

Esteeming. Churches Alive, Inc. Staff. LC 79-52130. (Love One Another Bible Study Ser.). (Illus.). 1979. wkbk. 3.00 (ISBN 0-934396-03-5). Churches Alive.

Ester: El Triunfo de la Soberania de Dios (Comentario Biblico Portavoz) John C. Whitcomb. Orig. Title: Esther (Everyman's Bible Commentary) (Span.). 1982. pap. 4.50 (ISBN 0-8254-1866-6). Kregel.

Estetica Gregoriana. Paolo A. Ferretti. LC 77-5498. (Music Reprint Ser.). 1977. Repr. of 1934 ed. lib. bdg. 45.00 (ISBN 0-306-77414-3). Da Capo.

Esther. Marlee Alex. (Outstanding Women of the Bible Ser.). (Illus.). 32p. 1987. 8.95 (ISBN 0-8028-5016-2). Eerdmans.

Esther. Joyce G. Baldwin. Ed. by D. J. Wiseman. LC 84-15670. (Tyndale Old Testament Commentaries Ser.). 122p. 1984. 12.95 (ISBN 0-87784-964-1); pap. 6.95 (ISBN 0-87784-262-0). Inter-Varsity.

Esther. (Burl Ives Bible-Time Stories). incl. tape 4.95 (ISBN 0-89191-802-7, 98020). Cook.

Esther. Ed. by Carey A. Moore. LC 75-140615. (Anchor Bible Ser.: Vol. 7B). 14.00 (ISBN 0-385-00472-9, Anchor Pr). Doubleday.

Esther. Lisl Weil. LC 79-22543. (Illus.). 48p. 1980. 9.95 (ISBN 0-689-30761-6, Childrens Bk). Macmillan.

Esther: A Play. Gilbert S. Aberg. LC 69-17410. (Illus.). 163p. 1969. 4.50 (ISBN 0-87601-001-X). Carnation.

Esther, a Woman of Courage. Joyce M. Smith. 1981. pap. 2.95 (ISBN 0-8423-0729-X). Tyndale.

Esther: Joshua, Ezra, Nehemiah. H. A. Ironside. 11.95 (ISBN 0-87213-396-6). Loizeaux.

Esther, Judith, Tobit, Jonah, Ruth. John Craghan. (Old Testament Message Ser.: Vol. 16). 1982. 12.95 (ISBN 0-89453-416-5); pap. 8.95 (ISBN 0-89453-249-9). M Glazier.

Esther, Queen of Persia. Claire Lynn. 63p. 1981. pap. 1.50 (ISBN 0-89323-019-7). Bible Memory.

Esther Scroll: Its Genesis, Growth, & Meaning. David J. Clines. (JSOT Supplement Ser.: No. 30). 260p. 1984. text ed. 29.50x (ISBN 0-905774-66-3, Pub. by JSOT Pr England); pap. text ed. 13.50x (ISBN 0-905774-67-1, Pub. by JSOT Pr England). Eisenbrauns.

Esther: The Romance of Providence. J. Vernon McGee. LC 81-22362. 140p. 1982. pap. 4.95 (ISBN 0-8407-5796-4). Nelson.

Esther: The Star & the Sceptre. Gini Andrews. 288p. 1981. pap. 7.95 (ISBN 0-310-20181-0, 10859). Zondervan.

Esther, the Triumph of God's Sovereignty. John C. Whitcomb. 128p. (Orig.). 1979. pap. 4.95 (ISBN 0-88469-081-4). BMH Bks.

Esther: Triumph of God's Sovereignty. John C. Whitcomb. (Everyman's Bible Commentary Ser.). 1979. pap. 5.95 (ISBN 0-8024-2016-8). Moody.

Esto Creemos. Ed. by James L. Slay. (Span.). 156p. 1963. pap. 4.95 (ISBN 0-87148-309-2). Pathway Pr.

Esto Creemos Curzo de Doctrina Biblica Para Ninos. James L. Slay. (Span., Orig.). pap. 1.00 (ISBN 0-87148-311-4). Pathway Pr.

Esto Creemos los Bautistas. James E. Giles. 111p. 1981. pap. 2.50 (ISBN 0-311-09091-5). Casa Bautista.

Esto Es Ser Hombre: Conversaciones Francas Con los Hombres y Sus Esposas. James Dobson. Tr. by Francisco Almanza from Eng. Orig. Title: Straight Talk to Men & Wives. 240p. 1986. pap. 7.50 (ISBN 0-311-46096-8, Edit Mundo). Casa Bautista.

Estoy Creciendo Estoy Cambiando. David Edens. Tr. by Dafne C. Du Plou. (Sexo en la Vida Cristiana Ser). (Illus.). 1985. pap. 1.75 (ISBN 0-311-46252-9). Casa Bautista.

Estructura Mitica del Popol Vuh. Alfonso Rodriguez. LC 84-81886. (Coleccion Polymita Ser.). (Span.). 108p. (Orig.). 1985. pap. 10.00 (ISBN 0-89729-360-6). Ediciones.

Estudio Biblico para Exhortador. (Span.). 33p. 1975. pap. 0.95 (ISBN 0-87148-305-X). Pathway Pr.

Estudio Biblico para Licenciado. (Span.). 43p. 1975. pap. 1.25 (ISBN 0-87148-310-6). Pathway Pr.

Estudio de la Biblia. John Tickle. Tr. by Olimpia Diaz, Sr. from Eng. 96p. 1980. pap. 1.95 (ISBN 0-89243-131-8). Liguori Pubns.

Estudio de la Biblia, Libro II. John Tickle. Tr. by Olimpia Diaz. (Span.). 96p. 1983. 3.95 (ISBN 0-89243-184-9). Liguori Pubns.

Estudios de Doctrina Biblica. Ernesto Trenchard. (Span.). 406p. 1976. pap. 9.95 (ISBN 0-8254-1738-4). Kregel.

Estudios de Doctrina Christiana: Dios. Jesucristo, el Espiritu Santo, Pt. 1. Edward Yoder. 123p. 1973. pap. 0.60x (ISBN 0-8361-1190-7). Herald Pr.

Estudios en el Nuevo Testamento. A. T. Robertson. Tr. by Sara A. Hale from Eng. Orig. Title: Studies in the New Testament. (Span.). 224p. 1983. pap. 3.50 (ISBN 0-311-03629-5). Casa Bautista.

Estudios sobre el Antiguo Testamento. R. Sampey. 226p. 1983. pap. 3.50 (ISBN 0-311-03627-9). Casa Bautista.

Eternal Answers for an Anxious Age. Robert P. Mohan. LC 85-60518. 140p. (Orig.). 1985. pap. 6.95 (ISBN 0-87973-592-9, 592). Our Sunday Visitor.

Eternal Christ: Sonnet Prayer for the Second Coming. Benito F. Reyes. 18p. 1977. pap. 5.50 (ISBN 0-939375-00-1). World Univ Amer.

Eternal Church. Bill Hanon. 398p. (Orig.). 1981. 12.95 (ISBN 0-939868-01-6); pap. 8.95 (ISBN 0-939868-00-8). Chr Intl Pubs.

Eternal Companion: Brahmananda, His Life & Teachings. 3rd ed. Swami Prabhavananda. LC 72-113256. 1960. pap. 7.95 (ISBN 0-87481-024-8). Vedanta Pr.

Eternal Echo of Easter: A Choral Drama. Esther Russ. 1980. 4.50 (ISBN 0-89536-423-9, 0515). CSS of Ohio.

Eternal Fruits of Knowledge. 3rd ed. Cecil A. Poole. LC 76-352583. 162p. 1978. 6.95 (ISBN 0-912057-27-0, G524). AMORC.

Eternal Grit: Up-to-Heaven Insights & Down-to-Earth Wisdom. McKay Allphin. LC 78-70363. 138p. 1978. 7.95 (ISBN 0-88290-102-8). Horizon Utah.

Eternal Hope. Heinrich E. Brunner. Tr. by Harold Knight. LC 72-6930. 232p. 1973. Repr. of 1954 ed. lib. bdg. 22.50x (ISBN 0-8371-6508-3, BREH). Greenwood.

Eternal Judgment. Derek Prince. (Foundation Ser.: Bk. VII). 1965-66. pap. 2.95 (ISBN 0-934920-06-0, B-16). Derek Prince.

Eternal Life: Life after Death as a Medical, Philosophical, & Theological Problem. Hans Kung. Tr. by Edward Quinn. LC 82-45112. 271p. 1984. 15.95 (ISBN 0-385-18207-4). Doubleday.

Eternal Life: Life after Death As a Medical, Philosophical, & Theological Program. Hans Kung. LC 82-45112. 288p. 1985. 9.95 (ISBN 0-385-19910-4, Im). Doubleday.

Eternal Life: Why We Believe. L. Harold DeWolf. LC 79-21670. 112p. 1980. pap. 6.95 (ISBN 0-664-24288-X). Westminster.

Eternal Light. Rohit Mehta. 1961. 8.95 (ISBN 0-8356-7004-X). Theos Pub Hse.

Eternal Love. Boyd K. Packer. LC 73-88635. 22p. 1973. 1.50 (ISBN 0-87747-514-8). Deseret Bk.

Eternal Message of Muhammad. Abd-Al-Rahman Azzam. 1964. 9.50 (ISBN 0-8159-5401-8). Devin.

Eternal Now. Paul Tillich. LC 63-17938. 1963. pap. 6.95 (ISBN 0-684-71907-X, ScribT). Scribner.

Eternal Ones of the Dream: Myth & Ritual, Dreams & Fantasies-Their Role in the Lives of Primitive Man. Geza Roheim. 1970. pap. text ed. 19.95 (ISBN 0-8236-8044-4, 021760). Intl Univs Pr.

Eternal People. Elias Charry & Abraham Segal. (Illus.). 448p. 7.50x (ISBN 0-8381-0206-9, 10-206). United Syn Bk.

Eternal Punishment. Arthur W. Pink. pap. 0.75 (ISBN 0-685-00734-0). Reiner.

Eternal Security Is Conditional. Carlos E. Portillo. LC 85-52117. 150p. (Orig.). 1987. pap. write for info. (ISBN 0-937365-03-3). WCP Pubns.

Eternal Security Obtained after Completing a Faithful Course. Joe Chatham. 1978. pap. 1.50 (ISBN 0-934942-05-6). White Wing Pub.
Eternal Security of the Believer. H. A. Ironside. pap. 1.50 (ISBN 0-87213-347-8). Loizeaux.
Eternal Sonship: A Refutation According to Adam Clarke. David Campbell. (Illus.). 95p. (Orig.). 1977. pap. 1.95 (ISBN 0-912315-44-X). Word Aflame.
Eternal Spirit: His Person & Powers. C. C. Crawford. (Bible Study Textbook Ser.). 1973. 14.30 (ISBN 0-89900-050-9). College Pr Pub.
Eternal Thoughts from Christ the Teacher, 2 Vols. Richard J. Cushing. 1962. 3.50 ea. Vol. 1 (ISBN 0-8198-0606-4). Vol. 2 (ISBN 0-8198-0607-2). Dghtrs St Paul.
Eternal Torah: A Commentary Integrating All the Prophets into the Books of Kings, Bk. 3. David Lieberman. 600p. 1986. 25.00x (ISBN 0-9609840-2-X). Twin Pines Pr.
Eternal Torah: A Commentary upon the Books of Joshua-Judges-Smauel One, Samuel Two, Pt. 2. David Liberman. 360p. 1983. 20.00 (ISBN 0-9609840-1-1). Twin Pines Pr.
Eternal Torah: A Commentary upon Torah Pentateuch Consolidating the Scholarship Throughout Hebrew Literature, Pt. 1. David Lieberman. 570p. 1986. Repr. of 1979 ed. 25.00 (ISBN 0-9609840-0-3). Twin Pines Pr.
Eternal Truths of Life. Robson. 4.75 (ISBN 0-8356-7030-9). Theos Pub Hse.
Eternal Wisdom. 10.00 (ISBN 0-8198-2310-4); 8.00 (ISBN 0-8198-2311-2). Dghtrs St Paul.
Eternal Word & Changing Worlds: Theology, Anthropology & Mission in Trialogue. Harvie M. Conn. 336p. 1984. pap. 10.95 (ISBN 0-310-45321-6, 11647P). Zondervan.
Eternal Yes. Karl Rahner. 1.50 (ISBN 0-87193-119-6). Dimension Bks.
Eternal You. Carroll Simcox. 112p. (Orig.). 1986. pap. 7.95 (ISBN 0-8245-0745-2). Crossroad NY.
Eternity's Breadth. Sri Chinmoy. 116p. 1975. pap. 5.00 (ISBN 0-88497-235-6). Aum Pubns.
Eternity's Silence-Heart. Sri Chinmoy. 200p. (Orig.). 1974. pap. 3.00 (ISBN 0-88497-106-6). Aum Pubns.
Ethel Barrett Tells Favorite Bible Stories, Vol.3. Ethel Barrett. LC 77-93051. (Bible Biography Ser.). 128p. 1978. pap. 3.95 (ISBN 0-8307-0615-1, 5605806). Regal.
Etheric Double. Powell. 12.50 (ISBN 0-8356-5068-5). Theos Pub Hse.
Etheric Double. Arthur E. Powell. (Illus.). 1969. pap. 3.95 (ISBN 0-8356-0075-0, Quest). Theos Pub Hse.
Etheric Heliang. Ed. by Society of Metaphysicians Staff. 12.00x (ISBN 0-317-43573-6, Pub. by Soc of Metaphysicians). State Mutual Bk.
Etherisation of the Blood: The Entry of the Etheric Christ into the Evolution of the Earth. 4th ed. Rudolf Steiner. Tr. by Arnold Freeman & D. S. Osmond. 42p. 1985. pap. 3.95 (ISBN 0-85440-248-9, Pub. by Steinerbooks). Anthroposophic.
Ethic of the Christian Life. T. B. Maston. Ed. by Gayle Hogg. (Religious Education Ser.). 152p. 1982. kivar 10.75 (ISBN 0-311-72605-4). Casa Bautista.
Ethica Dialectica. Howard P. Kainz. x, 145p. 1980. lib. bdg. 34.00 (ISBN 90-247-2078-8, Pub. by Martinus Nijhoff Netherlands). Kluwer Academic.
Ethica Thomistica: The Moral Philosophy of Thomas Aquinas. Ralph McInerny. LC 78-62029. 129p. 1982. pap. 7.95 (ISBN 0-8132-0561-1). Cath U Pr.
Ethical & Scientific Issues Posed by Human Uses of Molecular Genetics, Vol. 265. Ed. by Marc Lappe & Robert S. Morison. (Annals of the New York Academy of Sciences). 208p. 1976. 26.00x (ISBN 0-89072-019-3). NY Acad Sci.
Ethical Arguments for Analysis. 2nd ed. Robert J. Baum. LC 76-1952. 1976. pap. text ed. 19.95 (ISBN 0-03-089646-0, HoltC). HR&W.
Ethical Arguments for Analysis: Brief Edition. 2nd ed. Robert J. Baum. LC 78-10770. 1979. pap. text ed. 15.95 (ISBN 0-03-045011-X, HoltC). HR&W.
Ethical Behavior in Early Childhood Education. Lilian G. Katz & Evangeline H. Ward. LC 78-57538. 26p. 1978. pap. text ed. 2.00 (ISBN 0-912674-61-X, NAEYC #112). Natl Assn Child Ed.
Ethical Choice: A Case Study Approach. R. N. Beck & J. B. Orr. LC 70-122282. 1970. pap. text ed. 10.95 (ISBN 0-02-902060-3). Free Pr.
Ethical Confrontation in Counseling. John C. Hoffman. LC 78-11799. 1979. lib. bdg. 10.50x (ISBN 0-226-34785-0). U of Chicago Pr.
Ethical Dilemmas in Social Service. Frederic G. Reamer. LC 81-18071. 304p. 1982. 22.50x (ISBN 0-231-05188-3). Columbia U Pr.
Ethical Edge of Christian Theology: Forty Years of Communitarian Personalism. Walter G. Muelder. LC 83-21935. (Toronto Studies in Theology: Vol. 13). 435p. 1984. 69.95x (ISBN 0-88946-754-4). E Mellen.
Ethical ESP. Ann R. Colton. LC 78-149600. 367p. 1971. 11.50 (ISBN 0-917187-03-2). A R C Pub.
Ethical in the Jewish & American Heritage. S. Greenberg. (Moreshet Ser: No. 4). 25.00x (ISBN 0-87334-002-7, Pub. by Jewish Theol Seminary). Ktav.
Ethical Inquiry. Kathleen Hynes. Ed. by Constance McKenna & Karen Johnson. 16p. 1981. pap. 1.00 (ISBN 0-915365-07-3). Cath Free Choice.
Ethical Issues in Death & Dying. Thom Beauchamp & Seymour Perlin. 1978. pap. write for info. (ISBN 0-13-290114-5). P-H.
Ethical Issues in Death & Dying. Robert F. Weir. LC 77-24707. 1977. 38.00x (ISBN 0-231-04306-6); pap. 16.00x (ISBN 0-231-04307-4). Columbia U Pr.
Ethical Issues in Death & Dying. 2nd ed. Ed. by Robert F. Weir. 425p. 1986. 40.00x (ISBN 0-231-06222-2); pap. 16.00x (ISBN 0-231-06223-0). Columbia U Pr.
Ethical Issues in Human Genetics: Genetic Counseling & the Use of Genetic Knowledge. Ed. by Bruce Hilton et al. LC 72-93443. 468p. 1973. 35.00x (ISBN 0-306-30715-4, Plenum Pr). Plenum Pub.
Ethical Issues in Psychosurgery. John Kleinig. (Studies in Applied Philosophy: No. 1). (Illus.). 176p. 1985. text ed. 19.95x (ISBN 0-04-170032-5); pap. text ed. 7.95x (ISBN 0-04-170033-3). Allen Unwin.
Ethical Issues in Suicide. Margaret P. Battin. 250p. 1982. write for info. (ISBN 0-13-290155-2). P-H.
Ethical Mysticism in the Society of Friends. Howard Brinton. LC 67-31429. (Orig.). 1983. pap. 2.50x (ISBN 0-87574-156-8). Pendle Hill.
Ethical Naturalism & the Modern World-View. Elie M. Adams. LC 73-3019. 229p. 1973. Repr. of 1960 ed. lib. bdg. 45.00 (ISBN 0-8371-6820-1, ADEN). Greenwood.
Ethical Patterns in Early Christian Thought. E. Osborn. LC 75-10040. 288p. 1976. 39.50 (ISBN 0-521-20835-1). Cambridge U Pr.
Ethical Patterns in Early Christian Thought. Eric F. Osborn. LC 75-10040. pap. 65.50 (2026351). Bks Demand UMI.
Ethical Philosophy of the Gita. P. N. Srinivasachari. 2.00 (ISBN 0-87481-454-5). Vedanta Pr.
Ethical Principles for Social Policy. Ed. by John Howie. LC 82-5801. 176p. 1982. 16.95x (ISBN 0-8093-1063-5). S Ill U Pr.
Ethical Problem: Three Lectures on Ethics As a Science. 2nd enl ed. Paul Carus. LC 75-3103. Repr. of 1899 ed. 25.50 (ISBN 0-404-59100-0). AMS Pr.
Ethical Relativity. Edvard A. Westermarck. Repr. of 1932 ed. lib. bdg. 22.50x (ISBN 0-8371-4366-7, WEER). Greenwood.
Ethical Religion of Zoroaster. Miles M. Dawson. LC 73-90100. (BCL Ser. I). Repr. of 1931 ed. 22.50 (ISBN 0-404-01999-4). AMS Pr.
Ethical Responsibility: Bonhoeffer's Legacy to the Churches. Ed. by Geffrey B. Kelly & John D. Godsey. LC 81-18823. (Toronto Studies in Theology: Vol. 6). 352p. 1982. 59.95x (ISBN 0-88946-960-1). E Mellen.
Ethical Teaching of Hugo of Trimberg. Leo Behrendt. LC 77-140042. (Catholic University of America. Studies in German: No. 1). Repr. of 1926 ed. 18.00 (ISBN 0-404-50221-0). AMS Pr.
Ethical Teachings in the Latin Hymns of Medieval England. Ruth E. Messenger. LC 30-20975. (Columbia University. Studies in the Social Sciences: No. 321). Repr. of 1930 ed. 18.50 (ISBN 0-404-51321-2). AMS Pr.
Ethical Theories: A Book of Readings with Revisions. 2nd ed. A. I. Melden. 1967. text ed. write for info. (ISBN 0-13-290122-6). P-H.
Ethical Treatises of Berachya, Son of Rabbi Natronai Ha-Nakdan. Berachya. LC 73-2187. (Jewish People; History, Religion, Literature Ser.). Repr. of 1902 ed. 37.50 (ISBN 0-405-05253-7). Ayer Co Pubs.
Ethical Viewpoint of Islam. A. A. Maududi. pap. 1.00 (ISBN 0-686-18492-0). Kazi Pubns.
Ethical Wills: A Jewish Tradition. Ed. by Jack Riemer & Nathaniel Stampfer. LC 82-19160. 192p. 1983. 16.95 (ISBN 0-8052-3839-5). Schocken.
Ethical Wisdom East &-or West. Ed. by George F. McLean. LC 78-106891. (Proceedings of the American Catholic Philosophical Association: Vol. 51). 1977. pap. 15.00 (ISBN 0-918090-11-3). Am Cath Philo.
Ethical Writings of Maimonides. Maimonides. (Philosophy & Religion Ser.). 182p. (Orig.). 1983. pap. 4.50 (ISBN 0-486-24522-5). Dover.
Ethics. Peter Abelard. Ed. by D. E. Luscombe. (Oxford Medieval Texts Ser). 1971. 54.00X (ISBN 0-19-822217-3). Oxford U Pr.
Ethics. Aristotle. Tr. by John Warrington. 1975. Repr. of 1963 ed. 12.95x (ISBN 0-460-00547-2, Evman). Biblio Dist.
Ethics. Karl Barth. 1981. 34.95 (ISBN 0-8164-0484-4, HarpR). Har-Row.
Ethics. Alfred C. Ewing. 1965. pap. text ed. 9.95 (ISBN 0-02-910030-5). Free Pr.
Ethics. 2nd ed. William K. Frankena. (Foundations of Philosophy Ser.). 144p. 1973. pap. text ed. write for info. (ISBN 0-13-290478-0). P-H.
Ethics. George E. Moore. 1967. pap. 5.95x (ISBN 0-19-500354-3). Oxford U Pr.
Ethics. Wolfhart Pannenberg. Tr. by Keith Crim from Ger. LC 81-13051. Orig. Title: Ethik und Ekklesiologie. 222p. 1981. pap. 10.95 (ISBN 0-664-24392-4). Westminster.
Ethics. Frank C. Sharp. LC 75-3365. Repr. of 1928 ed. 45.50 (ISBN 0-404-59362-3). AMS Pr.
Ethics, Vol. 1 (incl. 1979 & 1981 Supplement) Ed. by Eleanor C. Goldstein. (Social Issues Resources Ser.). 1982. 70.00 (ISBN 0-89777-026-9). Soc Issues.
Ethics: A Short Introduction. Robert G. Olson. 1977. pap. text ed. 6.50 (ISBN 0-394-32033-6, RanC). Random.
Ethics: Alternatives & Issues. Norman Geisler. 256p. 1971. 14.95 (ISBN 0-310-24930-9, 18079). Zondervan.
Ethics & Action. Peter Winch. (Studies in Ethics & the Philosophy of Religion). 240p. 1972. 20.00x (ISBN 0-7100-7438-7). Methuen Inc.
Ethics & Anthropology. Michael A. Rynkiewich & James P. Spradley. LC 81-3698. 198p. 1981. Repr. of 1976 ed. lib. bdg. 14.50 (ISBN 0-89874-349-4). Krieger.
Ethics & Bigness: Proceedings. Conference on Science-Philosophy & Religion in Their Religion to the Democratic Way of Life, New York. 1962. 41.00 (ISBN 0-527-00664-5). Kraus Repr.
Ethics & Defence: Power & Responsibility in the Nuclear Age. Ed. by Howard Davis. 224p. 1987. text ed. 39.95 (ISBN 0-631-15174-5); pap. text ed. 19.95 (ISBN 0-631-15175-3). Basil Blackwell.
Ethics & Economics: An Islamic Synthesis. Syed N. H. Naqvi. 176p. (Orig.). 1981. 17.25x (ISBN 0-86037-079-8, Pub by Islamic Found UK); pap. 9.95x (ISBN 0-86037-080-1). New Era Pubns MI.
Ethics & European Security. Ed. by Barrie Paskins. 192p. 1986. 28.95x (ISBN 0-86569-146-0). Auburn Hse.
Ethics & Human Action in Early Stoicism. Brad Inwood. (Illus.). 1985. 32.00x (ISBN 0-19-824739-7). Oxford U Pr.
Ethics & Language. Charles Stevenson. LC 75-41263. Repr. of 1944 ed. 22.50 (ISBN 0-404-14806-9). AMS Pr.
Ethics & Morals in Business. Samuel M. Natale. LC 83-3200. 183p. 1983. text ed. 19.95 (ISBN 0-89135-036-5, Pub. by REP Bks). Religious Educ.
Ethics & Nuclear Arms: European & American Perspectives. Edward R. Norman & Raymond English. LC 85-10304. 1985. pap. 7.00 (ISBN 0-89633-095-8). Ethics & Public Policy.
Ethics & on the Improvement of the Understanding. B. De Spinoza. 1974. 7.95x (ISBN 0-02-852650-3). Hafner.
Ethics & Other Knowledge: Proceedings, Vol. 31. American Catholic Philosophical Association Staff. 1957. 18.00 (ISBN 0-384-14760-7). Johnson Repr.
Ethics & Other Liabilities. Harry Stein. 160p. 1982. 10.95 (ISBN 0-312-26557-3). St Martin.
Ethics & Other Liabilities: Trying to Live Right in an Amoral World. Harry Stein. 176p. 1983. pap. 4.95 (ISBN 0-312-26544-1). St Martin.
Ethics & Population Limitation. Daniel Callahan. LC 78-155736. 45p. (Orig.). 1971. pap. text ed. 3.95 (ISBN 0-87834-002-5). Population Coun.
Ethics & Public Policy: Introduction to Ethics. Ed. by Tom L. Beauchamp & Terry P. Pinkard. (Illus.). 416p. 1983. pap. write for info. (ISBN 0-13-290957-X). P-H.
Ethics & Selected Letters. Baruch Spinoza. Intro. by Seymour Feldman. Tr. by Samuel Shirley from Lat. & Heb. LC 81-7199. 268p. 1982. lib. bdg. 19.50 (ISBN 0-915145-18-9); pap. text ed. 4.95 (ISBN 0-915145-19-7). Hackett Pub.
Ethics & Social Justice. Ed. by Howard E. Kiefer & Milton K. Munitz. (Contemporary Philosophic Thought: Vol. 4). 1970. 49.50 (ISBN 0-87395-054-2). State U NY Pr.
Ethics & Society: A Marxist Interpretation of Value. Milton Fisk. LC 79-3513. 1980. 20.00x (ISBN 0-8147-2564-3). NYU Pr.
Ethics & the Christian. R. C. Sproul. 94p. 1983. pap. 2.95 (ISBN 0-8423-0775-3). Tyndale.
Ethics & the Limits of Philosophy. Bernard Williams. 248p. 1985. 17.50 (ISBN 0-674-26857-1). Harvard U Pr.
Ethics & the New Medicine. Harmon L. Smith. LC 76-124756. Repr. of 1970 ed. 43.50 (ISBN 0-8357-9005-3, 2016356). Bks Demand UMI.
Ethics & the New Testament. Houlden. 1977. pap. 6.95 (ISBN 0-19-519958-8). Oxford U Pr.
Ethics & the Search for Values. Ed. by Luis E. Navia & Eugene Kelly. LC 80-82123. 530p. 1980. pap. text ed. 17.95 (ISBN 0-87975-139-8). Prometheus Bks.
Ethics & the Urban Ethos: An Essay in Social Theory & Theological Reconstruction. Max Stackhouse. LC 77-179155. 240p. 1974. pap. 4.95x (ISBN 0-8070-1137-1, BP479). Beacon Pr.
Ethics & Theology from the Other Side: Sounds of Moral Struggle. Enoch H. Oglesby. LC 79-62897. 1979. pap. text ed. 11.50 (ISBN 0-8191-0706-9). U Pr of Amer.
Ethics, Faith, & Reason. Richard Taylor. 128p. 1985. pap. text ed. 15.00 (ISBN 0-13-290552-3). P-H.
Ethics for an Industrial Age: A Christian Inquiry. Victor Obenhaus. LC 73-15317. 338p. 1975. Repr. of 1965 ed. lib. bdg. 22.50x (ISBN 0-8371-7189-X, OBIA). Greenwood.
Ethics for the Affluent. Peter L. Danner. LC 80-5528. 424p. 1980. lib. bdg. 31.25 (ISBN 0-8191-1163-5); pap. text ed. 15.25 (ISBN 0-8191-1164-3). U Pr of Amer.
Ethics for the Professions: A Christian Perspective. Darrell Reeck. LC 81-52282. 176p. (Orig.). 1982. pap. 11.95 (ISBN 0-8066-1914-7, 10-2088). Augsburg.
Ethics from a Theocentric Perspective: Theology & Ethics, Vol. 1. James M. Gustafson. LC 81-11603. 284p. 1981. 27.50x (ISBN 0-226-31110-4). U of Chicago Pr.
Ethics from a Theocentric Perspective: Theology & Ethics, Vol. 1. James M. Gustafson. LC 81-11603. xiv, 346p. 1983. pap. 12.00x (ISBN 0-226-31111-2). U of Chicago Pr.
Ethics from a Theocentric Perspective, Vol. 2: Ethics & Theology. James M. Gustafson. LC 81-11603. 370p. 1984. lib. bdg. 25.00x (ISBN 0-226-31112-0). U of Chicago Pr.
Ethics from Sinai, 3 vols. Bunim. 1964. Set. 32.95 set (ISBN 0-87306-002-4); Set. pap. 19.95 set (ISBN 0-87306-003-2). Feldheim.
Ethics: Fundamental Principles of Moral Philosophy. John F. Fitzgibbon. LC 83-1178. 92p. (Orig.). 1983. lib. bdg. 22.25 (ISBN 0-8191-3064-8); pap. text ed. 8.75 (ISBN 0-8191-3065-6). U Pr of Amer.
Ethics in a Business Society. Marquis W. Childs & Douglass Cater. LC 73-7073. 191p. 1973. Repr. of 1954 ed. lib. bdg. 22.50x (ISBN 0-8371-6905-4, CHBS). Greenwood.
Ethics in a Christian Context. Paul L. Lehmann. LC 78-31749. 1979. Repr. of 1963 ed. lib. bdg. 27.50x (ISBN 0-313-20971-5, LEEC). Greenwood.
Ethics in a Christian Context. Paul L. Lehmann. LC 63-11545. 1976. pap. 4.95x (ISBN 0-06-065231-4, RD 192, HarpR). Har-Row.
Ethics in Government. Peter A. French. 176p. 1983. pap. write for info. (ISBN 0-13-290908-1). P-H.
Ethics in Hard Times. Ed. by Arthur L. Caplan & Daniel Callahan. LC 81-17728. (Hastings Center Series in Ethics). 312p. 1981. text ed. 29.50 (ISBN 0-306-40790-6, Plenum Pr). Plenum Pub.
Ethics in Islam. Ed. by R. Hovannisian. (Giorgio Levi Della Vida Biennial Conference Ser.: Vol. 9). 150p. 1984. pap. 20.50x (ISBN 0-89003-182-7). Undena Pubns.
Ethics in Perspective: A Reader. 3rd ed. Ed. by Paula R. Struhl & Karsten J. Struhl. 1980. pap. text ed. 13.00 (ISBN 0-394-32354-8, RanC). Random.
Ethics in the Undergraduate Curriculum. Bernard Rosen & Arthur L. Caplan. LC 80-12351. (Teaching of Ethics Ser.). 67p. 1980. pap. 4.00 (ISBN 0-916558-13-4). Hastings Ctr.
Ethics: Inventing Right & Wrong. J. L. Mackie. 1977. pap. 6.95 (ISBN 0-14-021957-9, Pelican). Penguin.
Ethics, Living or Dead? Joseph Amato. xii, 132p. 1982. 10.50 (ISBN 0-9614119-0-2, Co-Pub Portals Press). V Amati.
Ethics, Morality, & Mores. Royal Purcell. 177p. (Orig.). 1986. pap. 9.95 (ISBN 0-933189-01-X). Purcell Pub.
Ethics, Morality & the Media: Reflections of American Culture. new ed. Compiled by Lee Thayer. (Humanistic Studies in the Communication Arts). 320p. 1980. 22.00x (ISBN 0-8038-1957-9, Communication Arts); pap. text ed. 15.00x (ISBN 0-8038-1958-7). Hastings.
Ethics of Al-Ghazali. Mohammad A. Quasem. LC 78-15259. (Monographs in Islamic Religion & Theology). 1978. 35.00x (ISBN 0-88206-021-X). Caravan Bks.
Ethics of al-Ghazali: A Composite Ethics in Islam. Muhammad A. Quasem. 1975. 17.85 (ISBN 0-686-18952-3); pap. 9.00 (ISBN 0-686-18953-1). Quasem.
Ethics of Aristotle: The Nicomachean Ethics. rev ed. Ed. by Hugh Tredennick. Tr. by J. A. Thomson. 1955. pap. 5.95 (ISBN 0-14-044055-0). Penguin.
Ethics of Belief. James Livingston. LC 74-18616. (American Academy of Religion. Studies in Religion). 1974. pap. 7.50 (ISBN 0-88420-121-X, 010009). Scholars Pr GA.

Ethics of Belief Debate. Gerald McCarthy. (AAR Studies in Religion). 1986. 20.95 (ISBN 0-89130-892-X, 01-00-41); pap. 15.95 (ISBN 0-89130-893-8). Scholars Pr GA.

Ethics of Buddhism. Pref. by Shundo Tachibana. LC 74-20477. 288p. 1975. Repr. of 1926 ed. text ed. 24.50x (ISBN 0-06-496720-4). B&N Imports.

Ethics of Comparative Religion. Henry McDonald. LC 84-17370. 102p. (Orig.). 1985. lib. bdg. 19.75 (ISBN 0-8191-4304-9); pap. text ed. 7.75 (ISBN 0-8191-4305-7). U Pr of Amer.

Ethics of Decision: An Introduction to Christian Ethics. George W. Forell. LC 55-7767. 176p. 1955. pap. 4.50 (ISBN 0-8006-1770-3, 1-1770). Fortress.

Ethics of G. E. Moore & David Hume: The Treatise as a Response to Moore's Refutation of Ethical Naturalism. Richard J. Soghoian. LC 79-88306. 1979. pap. text ed. 9.50 (ISBN 0-8191-0774-3). U Pr of Amer.

Ethics of Gita. G. W. Kaveeshwar. 1971. 8.50 (ISBN 0-89684-203-7). Orient Bk Dist.

Ethics of Liberation: The Liberation of Liberation, Vol. 172. Ed. by Dietmar Mieth & Jacques Pohier. (Concilium Ser.). 128p. 1984. pap. 6.95 (ISBN 0-567-30052-8, Pub. by T & T Clark Ltd UK). Fortress.

Ethics of Mark's Gospel-In the Middle of Time. Dan O. Via, Jr. LC 84-48733. 256p. 1985. 19.95 (ISBN 0-8006-0746-5, 1-746). Fortress.

Ethics of Martin Luther. Paul Althaus. Tr. by Robert C. Schultz from Ger. LC 72-164552. 192p. 1972. pap. 8.95 (ISBN 0-8006-1709-6, 1-1709). Fortress.

Ethics of Martin Luther King Jr. Ervin Smith. LC 81-18976. (Studies in American Religion: Vol. 2). 226p. 1982. 49.95x (ISBN 0-88946-974-1). E Mellen.

Ethics of Persuasive Preaching. Raymond W. McLaughlin. 1978. 9.95 (ISBN 0-8010-6051-6). Baker Bk.

Ethics of Sex. Helmut Thielicke. Tr. by J. W. Doberstein from Ger. 340p. 1964. 13.95 (ISBN 0-227-67656-4). Attic Pr.

Ethics of Social Holiness: A Way of Living for God's Global Nation. Alan Kreider. 1987. 14.95 (ISBN 0-310-38390-0). Zondervan.

Ethics of Socrates. M. M. Dawson. LC 74-30274. (Studies in Philosophy, No. 40). 1974. lib. bdg. 75.00x (ISBN 0-8383-2042-2). Haskell.

Ethics of Spinoza. Baruch Spinoza. 1976. pap. 4.95 (ISBN 0-8065-0536-2). Citadel Pr.

Ethics of the Fathers. Philip Blackman. 166p. 1980. pap. 4.95 (ISBN 0-910818-15-0). Judaica Pr.

Ethics of the New Testament. Wolfgang Schrage. Tr. by David E. Green. LC 86-45922. 384p. 1987. pap. 29.95 (ISBN 0-8006-0835-6, 1-835). Fortress.

Ethics of the Old Testament. W. S. Bruce. 1909. 17.95 (ISBN 0-567-02058-4, Pub. by T & T Clark Ltd UK). Fortress.

Ethics of the Talmud. 2nd ed. Aryeh Kaplan. 336p. 1981. pap. 2.95 (ISBN 0-940118-31-9). Maznaim.

Ethics of the Talmud: Sayings of the Fathers. Ed. by R. Travers Herford. LC 62-13138. 1962. pap. 6.25 (ISBN 0-8052-0023-1). Schocken.

Ethics of United States Foreign Relations. Erwin D. Canham. LC 66-14031. 101p. 1966. 6.00x (ISBN 0-8262-0044-3). U of Mo Pr.

Ethics of World Religions. Arnold D. Hunt & Robert B. Crotty. (Illus.). 1978. lib. bdg. 11.95 (ISBN 0-912616-74-1); pap. 6.95 (ISBN 0-912616-73-3). Greenhaven.

Ethics on a Catholic University Campus. Thomas F. McMahon et al. Ed. by James D. Barry. 1981. pap. 5.95 (ISBN 0-8294-0369-8). Loyola.

Ethics since Nineteen Hundred. 3rd ed. Mary Warnock. 1978. pap. 4.95x (ISBN 0-19-289108-1). Oxford U Pr.

Ethics: Systematic Theology. James W. McClendon, Jr. 400p. 1986. 22.95 (ISBN 0-687-12015-2). Abingdon.

Ethics Teaching in Higher Education. Ed. by Daniel Callahan & Sissela Bok. LC 80-24002. (Hastings Center Monograph Ser.). 332p. 1980. 29.50x (ISBN 0-306-40522-9). Plenum Pub.

Ethics: The Science of Oughtness. Archie J. Bahm. LC 80-66406. 260p. 1980. 15.00 (ISBN 0-911714-12-X). Bahm.

Ethics: Theory & Practice. 2nd ed. Jacques P. Thiroux. 392p. 1980. pap. text ed. write for info. (ISBN 0-02-470220-X). Macmillan.

Ethics, Value, & Reality: Selected Papers of Aurel Kolnai. Aurel Kolnai. LC 77-83145. 280p. 1978. 25.00 (ISBN 0-915144-39-5); pap. text ed. 15.00 cancelled (ISBN 0-915144-40-9). Hackett Pub.

Ethics, Vol. 1: Basic Elements & Methodology in an Ethical Theology. Trutz Rendtorff. Tr. by Keith Crimm. LC 85-45484. 208p. 1986. 19.95 (ISBN 0-8006-0767-8, 1-767). Fortress.

Ethics Without God. Kai Nielsen. (Skeptic's Bookshelf Ser.). 112p. 1973. pap. 9.95 (ISBN 0-87975-019-7). Prometheus Bks.

Ethik der Griechen. facsimile ed. Eduard Schwartz. Ed. by Will Richter. LC 75-13293. (History of Ideas in Ancient Greece Ser.). (Ger.). 1976. Repr. of 1951 ed. 17.00x (ISBN 0-405-07337-2). Ayer Co Pubs.

Ethiopia & the Bible. Edward Ullendorff. (British Academy Ser). 1968. 29.95x (ISBN 0-19-725904-9). Oxford U Pr.

Ethiopia: Her Gloom & Glory. David Christy. LC 73-75550. Repr. of 1857 ed. 22.50x (ISBN 0-8371-1016-5, CHR&, Pub. by Negro U Pr). Greenwood.

Ethiopian Jews & Israel. Michael Ashkenazi & Alex Weingrod. 188p. 1987. 24.95 (ISBN 0-88738-133-2). Transaction Bks.

Ethiopian Jews: Photographs & Letters. Arlene Kushner. 1986. pap. 9.95 (ISBN 0-933503-47-4). Shapolsky Pubs.

Ethiopian Magic Scrolls. Jacques Mercier. Tr. by Ursule Molinaro from Fr. LC 78-9330. (Illus.). 1979. 24.95 (ISBN 0-8076-0896-3); pap. 12.95 (ISBN 0-8076-0897-1). Braziller.

Ethiopian Orthodox Church. Jon Bonk. LC 84-10547. (ATLA Bibliography Ser.: No. 11). 132p. 1984. 15.00 (ISBN 0-8108-1710-1). Scarecrow.

Ethiopian Tattoo Shop. Edward Hays. LC 83-82276. (Illus.). 184p. (Orig.). 1983. pap. 7.95 (ISBN 0-939516-06-3). Forest Peace.

Ethiopic Book of Enoch, 2 vols. Ed. by M. A. Knibb. 1978. 84.00x set (ISBN 0-19-826163-2). Oxford U Pr.

Ethnic & Social Background of the Franciscan Friars in Seventeenth Century Mexico. Francisco Morales. (Monograph Ser.). 1973. 20.00 (ISBN 0-88382-060-9). AAFH.

Ethnic Education: The Impact of Mennonite Schooling. Donald B. Kraybill. LC 77-81022. 1977. soft bdg. 11.95 (ISBN 0-88247-480-4). R & E Pubs.

Ethnic Identity & Marital Conflict: Jews, Italians & WASPs. Joel Crohn. LC 86-70084. 44p. (Orig.). 1986. pap. 2.50 (ISBN 0-87495-078-3). Am Jewish Comm.

Ethnic Identity & Religion: Tradition & Change in Liverpool Jewry. N. Kokosalakis. LC 82-13609. (Illus.). 276p. 1983. lib. bdg. 29.75 (ISBN 0-8191-2732-9); pap. text ed. 13.25 (ISBN 0-8191-2733-7). U Pr of Amer.

Ethnic Integration in Israel: A Comparative Study of Moroccan Brothers Who Settled in France & in Israel. Michael Inbar & Chaim Adler. LC 76-27933. (Illus.). 120p. 1977. lib. bdg. 16.95 (ISBN 0-87855-204-9). Transaction Bks.

Ethnic Realities & the Church: Lessons from India. Donald A. McGavran. LC 78-11517. (Illus.). 1979. pap. 8.95 (ISBN 0-87808-168-2). William Carey Lib.

Ethnik des Judenthums, 2 vols. M. Lazarus & Jakob Winter. LC 79-7146. (Jewish Philosophy, Mysticism & History of Ideas Ser.). 1980. Repr. of 1911 ed. Set. lib. bdg. 80.00x (ISBN 0-405-12276-4). Ayer Co Pubs.

Etica Cristiana del Amor. Norman Geisler. Tr. by Arnoldo Canclini from Eng. LC 77-15813. Tr. of Christian Ethic of Love. (Span.). 126p. 1977. pap. 3.95 (ISBN 0-89922-103-3). Edit Caribe.

Etica de la Vida Cristiana Sus Principios Basicos. T. B. Maston. Tr. by Floreal Ureta from English. (Span.). 200p. 1981. pap. 6.50 (ISBN 0-311-46076-3). Casa Bautista.

Etica Para la Era Atomica. facsimile ed. Ana M. O'Neill. 10.00 (ISBN 0-8477-2815-3); pap. 9.00 (ISBN 0-8477-2807-2). U of PR Pr.

Etranger au Bord de La Riviere. Paul Twitchell. 1979. pap. 5.95 (ISBN 0-914766-42-2). IWP Pub.

Etre Plus. Pierre Teilhard De Chardin. 12.50 (ISBN 0-685-36589-1). French & Eur.

Etude des Religions dans les Ecoles: L'experience Americaine, Anglaise et Canadienne. F. Ouellett. (SR Editions Ser.: No. 7). (Fr.). 666p. 1985. pap. text ed. 20.50x (ISBN 0-88920-183-8, Pub. by Wilfrid Laurier Canada). Humanities.

Etude Sur les Epistres Morales D'Honore D'Urfe. Sr. M. Lucien Goudard. LC 70-94204. (Catholic University of America Studies in Romance Languages & Literatures Ser: No. 8). (Fr). Repr. of 1933 ed. 21.00 (ISBN 0-404-50308-X). AMS Pr.

Etudes De Sociologie Religieuse: Studies in Religious Sociology, 2 vols. in one. Gabriel Le Bras. LC 74-25763. (European Sociology Ser.). 824p. 1975. Repr. 59.50x (ISBN 0-405-06517-5). Ayer Co Pubs.

Etudes Historiques et Critiques sur la Philosophie de Pascal, 3 tomes. Baudin. Incl. Tome I. Pascal et Descartes. 11.95 (ISBN 0-685-34021-X); Tome II. Pascal, les Libertins et les Jansenites. 22.50 (ISBN 0-685-34022-8); Tome III. Pascal et la Casuistique. 11.50 (ISBN 0-685-34023-6). (Coll. Etre et Penser). French & Eur.

Etudes sur Descartes, 2 tomes. Laberthonniere. Set. 29.90 (ISBN 0-685-34226-3). French & Eur.

Etz Chaim: Hebrew Text, 2 vols. condensed ed. Yehuda Ashlag. 40.00 (ISBN 0-943688-18-3). Res Ctr Kabbalah.

Eucharist. Chiara Lubich. LC 77-82230. 93p. 1977. pap. 2.50 (ISBN 0-911782-30-3). New City.

Eucharist. Karl Rahner. 1970. 1.50 (ISBN 0-87193-106-0). Dimension Bks.

Eucharist & Eschatology. Geoffrey Wainwright. 1981. 21.95x (ISBN 0-19-520248-1); pap. text ed. 8.95 (ISBN 0-19-520249-X). Oxford U Pr.

Eucharist & Human Liberation. Tissa Balasuriya. LC 78-9160. 184p. (Orig.). 1979. pap. 6.95 (ISBN 0-88344-118-7). Orbis Bks.

Eucharist & Offering. Kenneth W. Stevenson. 300p. (Orig.). 1986. pap. 17.50 (ISBN 0-916134-77-6). Pueblo Pub Co.

Eucharist & the Hunger of the World. Monika Hellwig. LC 76-18050. 100p. 1976. pap. 3.95 (ISBN 0-8091-1958-7). Paulist Pr.

Eucharist: God's Gift of Love. Sr. Marlene Brokamp & Sr. Marilyn Brokamp. (Illus.). 28p. (Orig.). 1976. pap. 1.95 (ISBN 0-912228-25-3). St Anthony Mess Pr.

Eucharist in Bible & Lithurgy: The Moorhouse Lectures 1975. G. D. Kilpatrick. LC 83-14315. 130p. 1984. 32.50 (ISBN 0-521-24675-X). Cambridge U Pr.

Eucharist Is for Sharing. Joan Thiry & Marilyn Burbach. 1977. duplicating masterbook 12.95 (ISBN 0-89837-051-5, Pub. by Pflaum Pr). Peter Li.

Eucharist Makes Us One. Mary Fearon & Sandra J. Hirstein. 1983. box set 84.95 (ISBN 0-697-01843-1); program dir. guide 4.95 (ISBN 0-697-01844-X); tchr's. manual, pre-school to junior levels 3.25 (ISBN 0-697-01845-8); write for info. student leaflets; attendance certificates 6.95 (ISBN 0-697-01973-X). Wm C Brown.

Eucharist of the Early Christians. Willy Rordorf et al. Tr. by Matthew J. O'Connell from Fr. 1978. pap. 9.95 (ISBN 0-916134-33-4). Pueblo Pub Co.

Eucharist: Our Communal Celebration. Marie McIntyre. LC 76-25620. (Illus., Orig.). 1978. pap. 2.95 (ISBN 0-89622-077-X). Twenty-Third.

Eucharist: The Bread of Life. Ernest Lussier. LC 77-3035. 248p. 1979. pap. 3.95 (ISBN 0-8189-0349-X). Alba.

Eucharist: Theology & Spirituality of the Eucharist Prayer. Louis Bouyer. Tr. by Charles U. Quinn. LC 68-17064. 1968. pap. 13.95 (ISBN 0-268-00498-6). U of Notre Dame Pr.

Eucharist Yesterday & Today. Basil Pennington. 224p. 1984. 10.95 (ISBN 0-8245-0602-2). Crossroad NY.

Eucharist: Yesterday & Today. Basil Pennington. 148p. pap. 6.95 (ISBN 0-8245-0690-1). Crossroad NY.

Eucharistic Controversy of the Eleventh Century Against the Background of Pre-Scholastic Theology. Charles E. Sheedy. LC 78-63179. (Heresies of the Early Christian & Medieval Era: Second Ser.). Repr. of 1947 ed. 30.00 (ISBN 0-404-16197-9). AMS Pr.

Eucharistic Devotion: New Meanings for a Timeless Tradition. Bernard Haring. 48p. 1987. pap. 1.95 (ISBN 0-89243-261-6). Liguori Pubns.

Eucharistic Manual for Children. Eileen Garrison & Gayle Albanese. LC 84-60217. (Illus.). 28p. (Orig.). 1984. pap. 3.95 (ISBN 0-8192-1343-8). Morehouse.

Eucharistic Prayers of the Roman Catholic Church. Enrico Mazza. Tr. by Matthew J. O'Connell from Ital. 380p. (Orig.). 1986. pap. 19.50 (ISBN 0-916134-78-4). Pueblo Pub Co.

Eucharistic Presence & Conversion in Late Thirteenth Century Franciscan Thought. David Burr. LC 83-73283. (Transactions Ser.: Vol. 74 Pt. 3). 113p. 1984. 12.00 (ISBN 0-87169-743-2). Am Philos.

Eucharistic Teaching of William Ockham. Gabriel Buescher. (Theology Ser). 1974. Repr. of 1950 ed. 10.00 (ISBN 0-686-11585-6). Franciscan Inst.

Eucharistic Theology of Theodore Beza: Development of the Reformed Doctrine. Jill Raitt. LC 74-188907. (American Academy of Religion. Studies in Religion). 1972. pap. 9.95 (ISBN 0-89130-156-9, 010004). Scholars Pr GA.

Eucharistic Words of Jesus. Joachim Jeremias. Tr. by Norman Perrin from Ger. LC 77-78633. 280p. 1977. pap. 12.95 (ISBN 0-8006-1319-8, 1-1319). Fortress.

Euchology: A Manual of Prayers of the Holy Orthodox Church. G. V. Shann. LC 75-82260. 1969. Repr. of 1891 ed. 32.50 (ISBN 0-404-05952-X). AMS Pr.

Eugen Rosenstock-Huessy: Studies in His Life & Thought. M. Darrol Bryant & Hans R. Huessy. LC 86-28469. (Toronto Studies in Theology: Vol. 28). 280p. 1987. text ed. 49.95x (ISBN 0-88946-772-2). E Mellen.

Eulogies. Jean D'Alembert. 59.95 (ISBN 0-8490-0137-4). Gordon Pr.

Eupolemus: A Study of Graeco-Judean Literature. Ben Z. Wacholder. 1974. 20.00x (ISBN 0-87820-401-6). Ktav.

Euripides & the Full Circle of Myth. Cedric H. Whitman. LC 74-81676. (Loeb Classical Monographs Ser). 176p. 1974. text ed. 11.00x (ISBN 0-674-26920-9). Harvard U Pr.

Europe & the Middle East. Albert Hourani. LC 78-59452. 1980. 33.00x (ISBN 0-520-03742-1). U of Cal Pr.

Europe Blossoms. Sri Chinmoy. 1000p. (Orig.). 1974. pap. 15.00 (ISBN 0-88497-077-9). Aum Pubns.

Europe in the Middle Ages. 3rd ed. Robert S. Hoyt & Stanley Chodorow. (Illus.). 707p. 1976. text ed. 25.95 (ISBN 0-15-524712-3, HC). HarBraceJ.

European Drama of the Early Middle Ages. Richard Axton. LC 74-24680. 1975. 19.95x (ISBN 0-8229-3301-2). U of Pittsburgh Pr.

European Immigrants & the Catholic Church in Connecticut: 1870-1920. Dolores Liptak. 1987. 17.50 (ISBN 0-913256-79-X); pap. text ed. 12.95 (ISBN 0-913256-80-3). Ctr Migration.

European Jewry & the First Crusade. Robert Chazan. 1987. 37.50. U of Cal Pr.

European Jewry in the Age of Mercantilism, 1550-1750. Jonathan L. Israel. 1985. 34.50x (ISBN 0-19-821928-8). Oxford U Pr.

European Origins of the Brethren. Donald F. Durnbaugh. 463p. 1958. 13.95 (ISBN 0-87178-256-1). Brethren.

European Seventh-Day Adventists Mission in the Middle East 1879-1939. Ed. by Baldur Pfeiffer. (European University Studies: Ser. 23, Vol. 161). 124p. 1981. pap. 16.45 (ISBN 3-8204-5918-9). P Lang Pubs.

European Thought in the Eighteenth Century: From Montesquieu to Lessing. Paul Hazard. 16.50 (ISBN 0-8446-2226-5). Peter Smith.

European Witch Craze in the Sixteenth & Seventeenth Centuries & Other Essays. Hugh R. Trevor-Roper. 1969. pap. 6.95x (ISBN 0-06-131416-1, TB1416, Torch). Har-Row.

European Witch Trials: Their Foundations in Popular & Learned Culture, 1300-1500. Richard Kieckhefer. 1976. 34.00x (ISBN 0-520-02967-4). U of Cal Pr.

Europe's Inner Demons: An Enquiry Inspired by the Great Witch-Hunt. Norman Cohn. 1977. pap. 8.95 (ISBN 0-452-00761-5, Mer). NAL.

Eurythmy. Marjorie Spock. (Illus.). 148p. (Orig.). 1980. 15.95 (ISBN 0-88010-023-0); pap. 9.95 (ISBN 0-910142-88-2). Anthroposophic.

Eusebius As Church Historian. Robert M. Grant. 1980. 36.00x (ISBN 0-19-826441-0). Oxford U Pr.

Eusebius of Caesarea & the Arian Crisis. Colm Luibheid. 136p. 1981. 22.50x (ISBN 0-7165-2277-2, BBA 03636, Pub. by Irish Academic Pr Ireland). Biblio Dist.

Eustratios Argenti: Study of the Greek Church under Turkish Rule. Timothy Ware. 1974. Repr. of 1964 ed. 12.50 (ISBN 0-686-10203-7). Eastern Orthodox.

Euthaliana, Studies of Euthalius: Codex H of the Pauline Epistles & the Armenian Version. J. A. Robinson. (Texts & Studies Ser.: No. 1, Vol. 3, Pt. 3). pap. 19.00 (ISBN 0-8115-1690-3). Kraus Repr.

Euthanasia & Religion: A Survey of the Attitudes of World Religions to the Right-to-Die. Gerald A. Larue. LC 84-62806. 155p. 1985. pap. 10.00 (ISBN 0-394-62078-X). Hemlock Soc.

Euthanasia & the Newborn: Conflicts Regarding Saving Lives. Richard C. McMillan et al. LC 86-33835. (Philosophy & Medicine Ser.: Vol. 24). 1987. 39.50 (ISBN 9-02-772299-4). Kluwer Academic.

Eva: A Novel of the Holocaust. Meyer Levin. LC 79-14440. 1979. pap. text ed. 5.95x (ISBN 0-87441-283-8). Behrman.

Evagrius Ponticus. Praktikos. Tr. by John E. Bamberger from Gr. & Syriac. LC 76-152483. (Cistercian Studies: No. 4). xciv, 88p. 1970. pap. 4.00 (ISBN 0-87907-804-9). Cistercian Pubns.

Evaluate & Grow. Harold J. Westing. 1984. pap. 5.95 (ISBN 0-88207-624-8). Victor Bks.

Evaluating Moral Development. Ed. by Lisa Kuhmerker et al. LC 80-68348. (Orig.). 1980. 9.95 (ISBN 0-915744-24-4); pap. 6.95 (ISBN 0-915744-21-X). Character Res.

Evaluating the Charismatic Movement: A Theology & Biblical Appraisal. Robert H. Culpepper. 192p. 1987. pap. text ed. 6.95 (ISBN 0-913029-17-3). Stevens Bk Pr.

Evaluating Versions of the New Testament. Everett W. Fowler. LC 80-81607. (Illus.). 80p. (Orig.). 1981. pap. 2.95 (ISBN 0-937136-03-4). Maranatha Baptist.

Evangel Reader. Charles W. Conn. 1958. 3.25 (ISBN 0-87148-275-4). Pathway Pr.

Evangel Sermons. Wade H. Horton. LC 76-57860. 1977. pap. 3.95 (ISBN 0-87148-287-8). Pathway Pr.

Evangelical Agenda: Nineteen Eighty-Four & Beyond. Ed. by Graham, Billy, Center Staff. LC 79-15889. 1979. pap. 5.95 (ISBN 0-87808-171-2). William Carey Lib.

Evangelical Alliance for the United States of America, 1847-1900: Ecumenism, Identity & the Religion of the Republic. Phillip D. Jordan. LC 82-24953. (Studies in American Religion: Vol. 7). 288p. 1983. 49.95x (ISBN 0-88946-650-5). E Mellen.

Evangelical & Oxford Movements. Elisabeth Jay. LC 82-9605. (Cambridge English Prose Texts Ser.). 232p. 1983. 34.50 (ISBN 0-521-24403-X); pap. 13.95 (ISBN 0-521-28669-7). Cambridge U Pr.

Evangelical Catechism. LC 82-70953. 416p. (Orig.). 1982. pap. 5.95 (ISBN 0-8066-1928-7, 10-2099). Augsburg.

Evangelical Christology: Ecumenic & Historic. Bernard Ramm. 224p. 1985. 14.95 (ISBN 0-8407-7518-0). Nelson.

Evangelical Dictionary of Theology. Walter A. Elwell. LC 84-71575. 1984. 29.95 (ISBN 0-8010-3413-2). Baker Bk.

Evangelical Ethics: Issues Facing the Church Today. John J. Davis. 304p. 1985. 13.95 (ISBN 0-87552-222-X). Presby & Reformed.

Evangelical Faith: The Doctrine of God & of Christ, Vol. 2. Helmut Thielicke. Ed. by Geoffrey W. Bromiley. LC 74-7010. pap. 123.30 (ISBN 0-317-30163-2, 2025345). Bks Demand UMI.

Evangelical Faith, Vol. 1: Prolegomena: The Relation of Theology to Modern Thought-Forms. Helmut Thielicke. Tr. by Geoffrey W. Bromiley. 420p. Date not set. 24.95 (ISBN 0-567-02354-0, Pub. by T & T Clark Ltd UK). Fortress.

Evangelical Faith, Vol. 2: The Doctrine of God & Christ. Helmut Thielicke. Tr. by Geoffrey W. Bromiley. 476p. Date not set. 24.95 (ISBN 0-567-02355-9, Pub. by T & T Clark Ltd UK). Fortress.

Evangelical Faith, Vol. 3: Theology of the Spirit. Helmut Thielicke. Tr. by Geoffrey W. Bromiley. 480p. Date not set. 24.95 (ISBN 0-8028-2344-0, Pub. by T & T Clark Ltd UK). Fortress.

Evangelical Idolatry. Don W. Hillis. (Illus.). 95p. (Orig.). 1983. pap. 2.75 (ISBN 0-89323-040-5). Bible Memory.

Evangelical Ministry in Ethiopia: The Ethiopian Evangelical Church Mekana Yesus. Johnny Bakke. (Studia Missionalia Upsaliensia). 96p. 1987. text ed. price not set (ISBN 0-391-03544-4, Pub. by Solum Verlag). Humanities.

Evangelical Perfection: An Historical Examination of the Concept in the Early Franciscan Sources. Duane Lapsanski. (Theology Ser.). 1977. 15.00 (ISBN 0-686-27933-6). Franciscan Inst.

Evangelical Perspectives: Toward a Biblical Balance. Ronald B. Mayers. LC 86-28966. 204p. (Orig.). 1987. lib. bdg. 24.50 (ISBN 0-8191-6062-8); pap. text ed. 12.75 (ISBN 0-8191-6063-6). U Pr of Amer.

Evangelical Preaching: An Anthology of Sermons. Charles Simeon. Ed. by James M. Houston. LC 85-28389. (Classics of Faith & Devotion Ser.). 1986. 12.95 (ISBN 0-88070-120-X); pap. 9.95. Multnomah.

Evangelical Precepts of the Revelation. Clyde C. Cox. 1972. 5.95 (ISBN 0-87148-278-9). Pathway Pr.

Evangelical-Roman Catholic Dialogue on Mission, 1977-1984. Ed. by John R. Stott & Basil Meeking. 80p. (Orig.). 1986. pap. 4.95 (ISBN 0-8028-0184-6). Eerdmans.

Evangelical S. S. Commentary, 1985-1986. Ed. by James Humbertson. text ed. 7.95 (ISBN 0-87148-312-2). Pathway Pr.

Evangelical Succession. Ed. by D. N. Samuel. 144p. 1979. pap. 5.95 (ISBN 0-227-67834-6). Attic Pr.

Evangelical Sunday School Lesson Commentary, 1976. Ed. by James E. Humbertson. 396p. 1976. 2.25 (ISBN 0-87148-281-9). Pathway Pr.

Evangelical Sunday School Lesson Commentary, 1982-1983. Ed. by Jame E. Humbertson. (YA) 1982. 3.65 (ISBN 0-87148-298-3). Pathway Pr.

Evangelical Sunday School Lesson Commentary 1980-1981. Ed. by James E. Humbertson. 448p. 3.50 (ISBN 0-87148-294-0). Pathway Pr.

Evangelical Sunday School Lesson Commentary, 1981-1982. Ed. by James E. Humbertson. 448p. text ed. 3.65 (ISBN 0-87148-297-5). Pathway Pr.

Evangelical Sunday School Lesson Commentary: 1983-1984. Ed. by James E. Humbertson. 1983. text ed. 7.95 (ISBN 0-87148-301-7). Pathway Pr.

Evangelical Sunday School Lesson Commentary 1984-1985. Ed. by James E. Humbertson. 424p. 1984. 4.00 (ISBN 0-87148-302-5). Pathway Pr.

Evangelical Terrorism: Censorship, Jerry Falwell, Pat Robertson & the Seamy Side of Christian Fundamentalism. Arthur F. Ide. LC 86-22013. xxxi, 195p. 1986. pap. 12.95 (ISBN 0-938659-01-4). Scholars Bks.

Evangelical Theology. A. A. Hodge. 1976. pap. 6.95 (ISBN 0-85151-236-4). Banner of Truth.

Evangelical Theology. Robert P. Lightner. 1984. 15.95 (ISBN 0-8010-5628-4). Baker Bk.

Evangelical Theology: An Introduction. Karl Barth. Tr. by Grover Foley. LC 79-16735. Tr. of Einfuhrung in Die Evangelische Theologie. 1979. pap. 9.95 (ISBN 0-8028-1819-6). Eerdmans.

Evangelical Theology, Eighteen Thirty-Three to Eighteen Fifty-Six: A Response to Tractarianism. Ed. by Peter Toon & Peter Martin. LC 79-16701. (New Foundations Theological Library Ser.). 254p. 3.25 (ISBN 0-8042-3703-4). John Knox.

Evangelical Tradition in America. Ed. by Leonard I. Sweet. LC 84-6723. x, 320p. 1984. 25.95 (ISBN 0-86554-092-6, MUP/H84). Mercer Univ Pr.

Evangelical-Unification Dialogue. Ed. by Richard Quebedeaux & Rodney Sawatsky. LC 79-89421. (Conference Ser.: No. 3). 374p. (Orig.). 1979. pap. text ed. 7.95 (ISBN 0-932894-02-X, Pub. by New Era Bks). Paragon Hse.

Evangelical Witness in South Africa: An Evangelical Critique of Evangelical Theology & Practice. South African Evangelicals. 46p. (Orig.). 1987. pap. 3.95 (ISBN 0-8028-0291-5). Eerdmans.

Evangelicalism & Anabaptism. Ed. by C. Norman Kraus. LC 79-12663. 192p. 1979. pap. 5.95 (ISBN 0-8361-1892-8). Herald Pr.

Evangelicalism & Modern America. Ed. by George Marsden. 212p. (Orig.). 1984. pap. 8.95 (ISBN 0-8028-1993-1). Eerdmans.

Evangelicalism: The Coming Generation. James D. Hunter. LC 86-16022. (Illus.). 320p. 1987. lib. bdg. 19.95 (ISBN 0-226-36082-2). U of Chicago Pr.

Evangelicals & Development: Toward a Theology of Social Change. Ed. by Ronald J. Sider. LC 82-6970. (Contemporary Issues in Social Ethics Ser.). 122p. 1982. pap. 6.95 (ISBN 0-664-24445-9). Westminster.

Evangelicals & Jews in an Age of Pluralism. Ed. by Marc H. Tanenbaum & Marvin R. Wilson. 272p. 1984. pap. 9.95 (ISBN 0-8010-8871-2). Baker Bk.

Evangelicals & the Bishops' Pastoral Letter. Ed. by Dean C. Curry. LC 84-4005. 254p. (Orig.). 1984. pap. 10.95 (ISBN 0-8028-1985-0). Eerdmans.

Evangelicals at an Impasse: Biblical Authority in Practice. Robert K. Johnston. pap. 3.99 (ISBN 0-8042-2038-7). John Knox.

Evangelical's Guidebook to the Holy Land. Wayne Dehoney. LC 73-85698. pap. 9.95 (ISBN 0-8054-5701-1). Broadman.

Evangelicals in America: Who They Are, What They Believe. Ronald H. Nash. 128p. 1987. pap. 7.95 (ISBN 0-687-12177-9). Abingdon.

Evangelicals in the White House: The Cultural Maturation of Born-Again Christianity, 1960-1981. Erling Jorstad. LC 81-9674. (Studies in American Religion: Vol. 4). 171p. 1981. 39.95x (ISBN 0-88946-982-2). E Mellen.

Evangelicals on the Canterbury Trail: Why Evangelicals Are Attracted to the Liturgical Church. Robert E. Webber. 160p. 1985. 13.95 (ISBN 0-8499-0402-1, 04021). Word Bks.

Evangelicals United: Ecumenical Stirrings in Pre-Victorian Britain, 1795-1830. Roger H. Martin. LC 82-10784. (Studies in Evangelicalism: No. 4). 244p. 1983. 19.00 (ISBN 0-8108-1586-9). Scarecrow.

Evangelicos, los Catolicos y la Virgen Maria, Los. Stephen Benko. Tr. by Alfonso Olmedo from Eng. Orig. Title: Protestants, Catholics & Mary. 1985. pap. 6.95 (ISBN 0-311-05041-7). Casa Bautista.

Evangelife: A Guide to Life-Style Evangelism. Dan R. Crawford. LC 84-1805. 1984. pap. 4.95 (ISBN 0-8054-6247-3). Broadman.

Evangelio Bajo Sito: Un Estudio Sobre la Fe y las Obras. Zane C. Hodges. Tr. by Thomas Whitehouse. 128p. (Orig.). 1985. pap. 4.95 (ISBN 0-9607576-4-3). Redencion Viva.

Evangelio Cuadruple: Fourfold Gospel, Spanish. A. B. Simpson. Tr. by Dorothy Bucher from Eng. 96p. 1981. pap. 2.00 (ISBN 0-87509-268-3). Chr Pubns.

Evangelio Segun Marcos. Ernesto Trenchard. (Span.). 226p. 1957. 6.95 (ISBN 0-8254-1740-6); pap. 5.75 (ISBN 0-8254-1739-2). Kregel.

Evangeliorum Libri Quattuor. C. Vettius Juvencus. (Corpus Scriptorum Ecclesiasticorum Latinorum Ser: Vol. 24). 1891. 30.00 (ISBN 0-384-28270-9). Johnson Repr.

Evangelios-Para que vino Jesus? 14 Lecciones, Tomo 2. Bernice C. Jordan. (Pasos De Fe Ser.). (Span.). pap. text ed. 2.50 (ISBN 0-86508-411-4); figuras 8.95 (ISBN 0-86508-412-2). BCM Intl Inc.

Evangelios-Quien es Jesus? 14 Lecciones, Tomo 1. Bernice C. Jordan. (Pasos De Fe Ser.). (Span.). pap. text ed. 2.50 (ISBN 0-86508-409-2); figuras 8.95 (ISBN 0-86508-410-6). BCM Intl Inc.

Evangelische Religionspaedagogik. Helmuth Kittel. (Ger). 1970. 23.20x (ISBN 3-11-002654-6). De Gruyter.

Evangelisches Staatslexikon. 2nd rev. ed. H. Kunst. (Ger.). 1975. 125.00 (ISBN 3-7831-0463-7, M-7373, Pub. by Kreuz Vlg.). French & Eur.

Evangelism. Rebecca Pippert & Ruth Siemens. (Lifebuilder Bible Studies). 64p. (Orig.). 1985. pap. text ed. 2.95 (ISBN 0-8308-1050-1). Inter-Varsity.

Evangelism. Roanld D. Tucker. (Illus.). 40p. (Orig.). 1983. pap. 2.00 (ISBN 0-933643-13-6). Grace World Outreach.

Evangelism: A Biblical Approach. G. Michael Cocoris. (Orig.). 1984. pap. 6.95 (ISBN 0-8024-2396-5). Moody.

Evangelism & Social Involvement. Delos Miles. LC 86-2660. 1986. 9.95 (ISBN 0-8054-6248-1). Broadman.

Evangelism & the Sovereignty of God. James I. Packer. LC 67-28875. 1961. pap. 3.95 (ISBN 0-87784-680-4). Inter-Varsity.

Evangelism & Your Church. C. J. Miller. 1980. pap. 2.95 (ISBN 0-87552-290-4). Presby & Reformed.

Evangelism As a Lifestyle. Jim Petersen. LC 80-83874. 144p. 1980. pap. 5.95 (ISBN 0-89109-475-X). NavPress.

Evangelism As Discipling. Myon S. Augsburger. LC 82-83387. (Mennonite Faith Ser.: Vol. 12). 80p. 1983. pap. 1.50 (ISBN 0-8361-3322-6). Herald Pr.

Evangelism: Christ's Imperative Commission. rev. ed. Landrum P. Leavell & Harold Bryson. LC 78-59983. 1979. 10.95 (ISBN 0-8054-2534-9). Broadman.

Evangelism: Doing Justice & Preaching Grace. Harvie Conn. 112p. (Orig.). 1982. pap. 4.95 (ISBN 0-310-45311-9, 11646P). Zondervan.

Evangelism: Every Member, Every Day. James Bales. pap. 2.50 (ISBN 0-89315-038-X). Lambert Bk.

Evangelism for Our Generation. Jim Petersen. 216p. 1985. pap. 5.95 (ISBN 0-89109-476-8). NavPress.

Evangelism in My Parish. Howard Harper. 1972. pap. 3.00 (ISBN 0-686-14947-5). Episcopal Ctr.

Evangelism in Perspective. Robert E. Coleman. LC 75-31306. 3.95 (ISBN 0-87509-080-X); pap. 2.00 (ISBN 0-87509-081-8). Chr Pubns.

Evangelism in the Early Church. Michael Green. 1970. pap. 7.95 (ISBN 0-8028-1612-6). Eerdmans.

Evangelism Ministry of the Local Church. Walter R. Pettitt. 119p. 1969. 5.25 (ISBN 0-87148-276-2); pap. 4.25 (ISBN 0-87148-277-0). Pathway Pr.

Evangelism: Now & Then. Michael Green. 150p. 1982. pap. 3.50 (ISBN 0-87784-394-5). Inter-Varsity.

Evangelism on Purpose. Richard E. Rusbuldt. 48p. 1980. pap. 2.95 (ISBN 0-8170-0894-2). Judson.

Evangelism: One Hundred Thirty-Nine Ideas & Quotes. Ed. by Neil B. Wiseman. 110p. (Orig.). 1983. pap. 3.50 (ISBN 0-8341-0889-5). Beacon Hill.

Evangelism Primer: Practical Principles for Congregations. Ben C. Johnson. LC 82-49021. 120p. 1983. pap. 5.95 (ISBN 0-8042-2039-5). John Knox.

Evangelism: The Church on Fire! Robert L. Sumner. 220p. 1960. 3.25 (ISBN 0-87398-211-8, Pub. by Bibl Evang Pr). Sword of Lord.

Evangelism: The Ministry of the Church. Ed. by Richard Hughes & Joseph A. Serig. 1981. pap. 12.00 (ISBN 0-8309-0304-6). Herald Hse.

Evangelism: The Unfinished Task. Robert J. Strand. LC 81-80303. (Workers Training Ser.). 128p. (Orig.). 1981. pap. 2.25 (ISBN 0-88243-513-2, 02-0513). Gospel Pub.

Evangelismo en Accion. Le Roy. Tr. by Carlos C. Pierson. 144p. 1979. 4.95 (ISBN 0-311-13831-4). Casa Bautista.

Evangelism's open Secrets. 2nd ed. Herbert Miller. LC 77-23468. 112p. 1985. pap. 6.95 (ISBN 0-8272-0805-7). CBP.

Evangelist in Chains. Elizabeth Wagler. 8.95 (ISBN 0-318-00390-2). Rod & Staff.

Evangelistic Embellishments: How to Make Hymns & Gospel Songs Come Alive. Duane Shinn & Diane Hoffman. 1980. spiral bdg. 49.95 (ISBN 0-912732-49-0). Duane Shinn.

Evangelistic Growth in Acts One & Two. D. Wade Armstrong. LC 83-70375. (Orig.). 1983. pap. 4.95 (ISBN 0-8054-6242-2). Broadman.

Evangelistic Sermon Outlines. Billy Apostolon. (Sermon Outline Ser.). pap. 2.50 (ISBN 0-8010-0144-7). Baker Bk.

Evangelistic Sermon Outlines. Ed. by Charles R. Wood. 64p. (Orig.). 1975. pap. 2.95 (ISBN 0-8254-4004-1). Kregel.

Evangelistic Sermons. D. Martyn Lloyd-Jones. 294p. (Orig.). 1983. pap. 9.45 (ISBN 0-85151-362-X). Banner of Truth.

Evangelists Speak. Jon L. Joyce. (Orig.). 1983. pap. 2.95 (ISBN 0-937172-50-2). JLJ Pubs.

Evangelizacion y Discipulado. Myron S. Augsburger. Tr. by Milka Rindzinski from Eng. LC 84-80159. (Mennonite Faith Ser.: No. 12). 72p. (Orig.). 1984. pap. 1.50x (ISBN 0-8361-1267-9). Herald Pr.

Evangelization. Lisa Holash. 80p. 1984. pap. 3.50 (ISBN 0-697-01868-7). Wm C Brown.

Evangelization & Justice: New Insights for Christian Ministry. John Walsh. LC 82-6279. 128p. (Orig.). 1982. pap. 6.95 (ISBN 0-88344-109-8). Orbis Bks.

Evangelization, Dialogue & Development. Ed. by Mariasusai Dhavamony. (Documenta Missionalia Ser.: No. 5). 1972. pap. 20.00 (ISBN 0-8294-0323-X, Pub. by Gregorian U Pr). Loyola.

Evangelization in the American Context. Ed. by David B. Burrell & Franzita Kane. LC 76-22403. 1976. pap. 2.95x (ISBN 0-268-00902-3). U of Notre Dame Pr.

Evangelization in the World Today. Ed. by Norbert Greinacher. (Concilium Ser.: Vol. 114). 1979. pap. 6.95 (ISBN 0-8245-0274-4). Crossroad NY.

Evangelization: Mission & Ministry for Catholic Educators. 25p. 1979. 3.60. Natl Cath Educ.

Evangelization of the Roman Empire: Identity & Adaptability. E. Glenn Hinson. LC 81-11266. viii, 332p. 1981. 22.00 (ISBN 0-86554-244-9, MUP-P36). Mercer Univ Pr.

Evangelization of the World in This Generation. John R. Mott. LC 76-38457. (Religion in America, Ser. 2). 258p. 1972. Repr. of 1900 ed. 17.00 (ISBN 0-405-04078-4). Ayer Co Pubs.

Evangelize Thru Christian Education. Elmer L. Towns. LC 78-97811. 96p. 1970. pap. text ed. 4.95 (ISBN 0-910566-08-9); Perfect bdg. instr's. guide 5.95 (ISBN 0-910566-30-5). Evang Tchr.

Evangelized America. facsimile ed. Grover C. Loud. LC 70-169770. (Select Bibliographies Reprint Ser). Repr. of 1928 ed. 27.50 (ISBN 0-8369-5990-6). Ayer Co Pubs.

Evangelizers. Kenneth J. Roberts. Ed. by Anna M. Waters. (Illus.). 100p. (Orig.). 1984. pap. text ed. 3.50 (ISBN 0-9610984-2-2). PAX Tapes.

Evangelizing Adults. Glen C. Smith. 404p. (Orig.). 1985. pap. 12.95 (ISBN 0-8423-0793-1). Tyndale.

Evangelizing Neopagan North America. Alfred C. Krass. LC 81-23768. (Mennonite Missionary Study Ser.: No. 9). 256p. (Orig.). 1982. pap. 9.95 (ISBN 0-8361-1989-4). Herald Pr.

Evangelizing the American Jew. Eichhorn. LC 77-28975. 1978. 12.50 (ISBN 0-8246-0225-0). Jonathan David.

Evangelizing the Hard-to-Reach. Robert D. Dale. LC 85-24262. (Broadman Leadership Ser.). 1986. pap. 4.95 (ISBN 0-8054-6251-1). Broadman.

Evangelizing Youth. Glenn C. Smith. 352p. (Orig.). 1985. pap. 12.95 (ISBN 0-8423-0791-5). Tyndale.

Evangical-Unification Dialog. Ed. by Richard Quebedeaux & Rodney Sawatsky. LC 79-89421. 374p. (Orig.). pap. 7.95. Rose Sharon Pr.

Evangile du Royaume. George E. Ladd. Ed. by Annie L. Cosson. Tr. by Marie-Therese Martin. Tr. of Gospel of the Kingdom. (Fr.). 192p. 1985. pap. text ed. 2.25 (ISBN 0-8297-1012-4). Life Pubs Intl.

Eve & after: Old Testament Woman in Portrait. Thomas J. Carlisle. 160p. (Orig.). 1984. pap. 5.95 (ISBN 0-8028-1970-2). Eerdmans.

Eve of the Reformation. Francis A. Gasquet. LC 75-118522. 1971. Repr. of 1900 ed. 35.00x (ISBN 0-8046-1144-0, Pub. by Kennikat). Assoc Faculty Pr.

Eve: The History of an Idea. J. A. Phillips. LC 83-48424. (Illus.). 192p. 1984. 12.45 (ISBN 0-06-066552-1, HarpR). Har-Row.

Eve: The History of an Idea. John A. Phillips. LC 83-48424. (Illus.). 224p. 1985. pap. 7.95 (ISBN 0-06-250670-6, HarpR). Har-Row.

Evelyn Underhill: Eighteen Seventy-Five to Nineteen Forty-One: An Introduction to Her Life & Writing. Christopher Armstrong. LC 75-33401. Repr. of 1976 ed. 81.80 (ISBN 0-8357-9127-0, 2012859). Bks Demand UMI.

Even As I Am. Neal A. Maxwell. 128p. 1982. 8.95 (ISBN 0-87747-943-7). Deseret Bk.

Evening by Evening. C. H. Spurgeon. 368p. 1984. pap. text ed. 3.95 (ISBN 0-88368-154-4). Whitaker Hse.

Evening Light Songs. 512p. 6.00 (ISBN 0-686-29108-5). Faith Pub Hse.

Evening of Life. Fredrik Wisloff. LC 66-12386. pap. 35.00 (2027868). Bks Demand UMI.

Evening Service for Yom Kippur. large type ed. Morris Silverman. 17.50 (ISBN 0-87677-073-1). Prayer Bk.

Evening Sun. Joseph Folliet. 183p. 1983. 12.50 (ISBN 0-8199-0817-7). Franciscan Herald.

Evenings for Parish Ministers: Leader's Guide. John Colligan & Kathleen Colligan. LC 84-60266. 53p. (Orig.). 1984. pap. text ed. 2.95 (ISBN 0-911905-20-0); wkbk. 1.95 (ISBN 0-911905-16-2). Past & Mat Rene Ctr.

Evenings of Joy & Inspiration for Parish Leaders. Sherry Gibbons et al. LC 83-62197. 64p. (Orig.). 1983. pap. text ed. 2.95 (ISBN 0-911905-08-1). Past & Mat Rene Ctr.

Events & Their Afterlife: The Dialectics of Christian Typology in the Bible & Dante. Alan Charity. 300p. Date not set. pap. price not set (ISBN 0-521-34923-0). Cambridge U Pr.

Events of the Bible (Arch Bks) Gloria A. Truit. 1984. pap. 0.99 (59-1312). Concordia.

Events, Reference, & Logical Form. Richard M. Martin. LC 77-24685. pap. 67.80 (2029492). Bks Demand UMI.

Ever Increasing Faith. rev. ed. Smith Wigglesworth. 176p. 1971. pap. 1.95 (ISBN 0-88243-494-2, 02-0494). Gospel Pub.

Ever since Sinai. Irving M. Bunim. Ed. by Charles Wengrov. 1978. 13.95 (ISBN 0-87306-138-1). Feldheim.

Ever since Sinai. 3rd ed. Jakob J. Petuchowski. LC 79-64324. 1979. pap. text ed. 5.95 (ISBN 0-930038-11-8). Arbit.

Everest-Aspiration. Sri Chinmoy. 1979. pap. 4.95 (ISBN 0-88497-460-X). Aum Pubns.

Everflowing Streams. Michael Bausch & Ruth Duck. LC 81-701. 96p. (Orig.). 1981. pap. 4.95 (ISBN 0-8298-0428-5). Pilgrim NY.

Evergrowing, Evergreen. Jill Briscoe. 96p. 1986. pap. 4.95 (ISBN 0-89693-255-9). Victor Bks.

Everlasting Gospel. A. L. Morton. 1978. Repr. of 1958 ed. lib. bdg. 15.00 (ISBN 0-8495-3736-3). Arden Lib.

Everlasting Gospel. A. L. Morton. (Studies in Blake, No. 3). 1958. pap. 39.95x (ISBN 0-8383-0098-7). Haskell.

Everlasting Life: Towards a Theology of the Future Life. Edmund J. Fortman. LC 85-30720. 369p. (Orig.). 1986. pap. 9.95 (ISBN 0-8189-0495-X). Alba.

Everlasting Love: A Devotional Commentary on the Gospel of John. John G. Mitchell. LC 82-22285. 1982. 13.95 (ISBN 0-88070-005-X). Multnomah.

Everlasting Man. G. K. Chesterton. 320p. 1981. Repr. of 1925 ed. lib. bdg. 37.00 (ISBN 0-8495-0855-X). Arden Lib.

Everlasting Man. G. K. Chesterton. 344p. 1981. Repr. of 1926 ed. lib. bdg. 20.00 (ISBN 0-89984-115-5). Century Bookbindery.

Everlasting Man. G. K. Chesterton. 280p. 1974. pap. 4.50 (ISBN 0-385-07198-1, Im). Doubleday.

Everlasting Man. G. K. Chesterton. LC 72-11233. 344p. 1974. Repr. of 1925 ed. lib. bdg. 22.50x (ISBN 0-8371-6636-5, CEVM). Greenwood.

Everlasting Now. George A. Maloney. LC 79-57550. 224p. (Orig.). 1980. pap. 3.95 (ISBN 0-87793-201-8). Ave Maria.

Every Bush Is Burning: A Spirituality for Today. 2nd ed. Joan Puls. 112p. 1986. pap. 5.95 (ISBN 0-89622-280-2). Twenty-Third.

Every Cloud Has One. William F. Davis. 1985. 7.95 (ISBN 0-8062-2477-0). Carlton.

Every Day Bible Commentary. C. H. Irwin. Orig. Title: Irwin's Bible Commentary. 582p. 1983. pap. 8.95 (ISBN 0-310-26531-2, 9906P). Zondervan.

Every Day Is a Christmas Present. Erwin J. Toner. 32p. 1967. pap. write for info. (ISBN 0-686-08987-1). Gonzaga U Pr.

Every Day Remembrance Day: A Chronicle of Jewish Martyrdom. Simon Wiesenthal. (Illus.). 480p. 1987. 19.95 (ISBN 0-8050-0098-4). H Holt & Co.

Every Day with Andrew Murray. rev. ed. Andrew Murray. Tr. of God's Best Secret. 208p. 1986. pap. 3.95 (ISBN 0-89283-302-5, Pub. by Vine Books). Servant.

Every Day with Jesus. George Duncan. 288p. 1984. pap. 6.95 (ISBN 0-89066-059-X). World Wide Pubs.

Every Day with Paul. Mendell L. Taylor. 1978. 6.95 (ISBN 0-8341-0529-2). Beacon Hill.

Every Day with Saint Francis de Sales. Augustine Archenti & Arnold Petrini. Ed. by Francis Klauder. Tr. by W. L. Cornell from Italian. LC 85-72838. Tr. of Buon Giorno. (Illus.). 390p. (Orig.). 1985. pap. 11.95 (ISBN 0-89944-082-7). Don Bosco Multimedia.

Every Friday Night. Norma Simon. (Festival Series of Picture Story Booxs). (Illus.). plastic cover 4.50 (ISBN 0-8381-0708-7). United Syn Bk.

Every Knee Shall Bow. Joan W. Brown. 194p. 1984. pap. 5.95 (ISBN 0-89066-054-9). World Wide Pubs.

Every Man My Brother. Frances Sweeney. 1976. 4.00 (ISBN 0-8198-0410-X); pap. 3.00 (ISBN 0-8198-0411-8). Dghtrs St Paul.

Every Member Evangelism for Today. rev. ed. Roy J. Fish. LC 75-12289. 128p. 1976. pap. 6.95 (ISBN 0-06-061551-6, RD125, HarpR). Har-Row.

Every Need Supplied: Mutual Aid & Christian Community in Free Churches, 1525-1675. Ed. by Donald F. Durnbaugh. LC 73-94279. (Documents in Free Church History Ser.: No. 1). (Illus.). 258p. 1974. 19.95 (ISBN 0-87722-031-X). Temple U Pr.

Every Single Day. Jim Smoke. 256p. 1983. 6.95 (ISBN 0-8007-5120-5, Power Bks). Revell.

Every Woman Can. Janie D'Addio. Ed. by Terri Cox. (Illus.). 112p. 1983. pap. 9.95 (ISBN 0-914759-00-0). Preferred Pr.

Every Woman Has a Ministry. Regina Lambert. LC 79-84321. (Illus.). 1979. pap. 2.95 (ISBN 0-89221-062-1). New Leaf.

Every Woman's Privilege: Taking Responsibility for Your Spiritual Growth. Joy Gage. (Touch of Grace Ser.). 1986. pap. 6.95 (ISBN 0-88070-177-3). Multnomah.

Everybody Can Know. Edith Schaeffer. 1978. 8.95 (ISBN 0-8423-0786-9). Tyndale.

Everybody Is Your Teacher. Jerry Fankhauser. 58p. 1986. pap. 7.00 (ISBN 0-9617006-2-9). J Fankhauser.

Everybody Needs a Friend: A Young Christian Book for Girls. Barbara DeGrote-Sorensen. LC 86-32152. 112p. (Orig.). 1987. pap. 4.95 (ISBN 0-8066-2247-4, 10-2120). Augsburg.

Everybody Needs the Body. Sandy Larsen. 1984. pap. 3.95 (ISBN 0-88207-594-2). Victor Bks.

Everybody Ought to Go to Learning Centers. Linda Burba. (Teaching Helps Ser.). 80p. 1981. pap. 2.95 (ISBN 0-8010-0811-5). Baker Bk.

Everybody, Shout Hallelujah! Elspeth Murphy. (David & I Talk to God Ser.). (Illus.). 24p. 1981. pap. 2.50 (ISBN 0-89191-369-6, 53694). Cook.

Everybody Steals from God: Communication as Worship. Edward Fischer. LC 77-3711. 1977. text ed. 10.95x (ISBN 0-268-00904-X). U of Notre Dame Pr.

Everybody's Guide to Paradise. I. K. Berger. 204p. 1986. pap. 29.00x (ISBN 0-7212-0776-6, Pub. by Regency Pr). State Mutual Bk.

Everybody's Pope: The Life of John 23rd. Sergius C. Lorit. LC 67-15775. 1966. pap. 2.95 (ISBN 0-911782-06-0). New City.

Everyday Bible Dictionary. Francis N. Peloubet. 816p. 1967. 14.95 (ISBN 0-310-30850-X, 10551). Zondervan.

Everyday Evangelism. Tom Eisenman. 180p. (Orig.). 1987. pap. 5.95 (ISBN 0-87784-997-8). Inter-Varsity.

Everyday Evangelist. Duncan McIntosh. 64p. 1984. pap. 2.95 (ISBN 0-8170-1042-4). Judson.

Everyday Fight, 2 vols. A. A. Kamal. Set. pap. 18.00 (ISBN 0-686-63899-9). Kazi Pubns.

Everyday God. James Taylor. 116p. (Orig.). 1983. pap. 5.95 (ISBN 0-8358-0470-4). Upper Room.

Everyday Issues Related to Justice & Other Gospel Values. Robert J. Kealey. 80p. 1984. 4.80 (ISBN 0-318-17779-X). Natl Cath Educ.

Everyday Life in New Testament Times. A. C. Bouquet. (Hudson River Editions). (Illus.). 1953. lib. rep. ed. 20.00 (ISBN 0-684-14833-1, ScribT). Scribner.

Everyday Life in Old Testament Times. E. W. Heaton. LC 76-29288. (Illus.). 1977. lib. rep. ed. 17.50H (ISBN 0-684-14836-6). Scribner.

Everyday Prayer. Ronald Jasper et al. 1978. pap. 5.95 (ISBN 0-916134-34-2). Pueblo Pub Co.

Everyday Prayer Book with the Order of Mass. Ed. by Dermot Hurley. 208p. 1984. pap. 1.95 (ISBN 0-225-66273-6, HarpR). Har-Row.

Everyday Prayers. William Barclay. LC 60-5326. 160p. 1981. pap. 6.95 (ISBN 0-06-060411-5, RD 361, HarpR). Har-Row.

Everyday Prayers for Everyday People. Bernadette M. Snyder. LC 83-63165. 132p. 1984. pap. 4.95 (ISBN 0-87973-604-6, 604). Our Sunday Visitor.

Everyday Yoga. Lyn Marshall. LC 83-24177. (Illus.). 96p. (Orig.). 1984. pap. 6.95 (ISBN 0-8069-7864-3). Sterling.

Everyman & Medieval Miracle Plays. Ed. by A. C. Cawley. 10.95x (ISBN 0-460-10381-4, Evman). Biblio Dist.

Everyman's Challenge. Daughters of St. Paul. LC 73-89938. 1974. 5.00 (ISBN 0-8198-0294-8). Dghtrs St Paul.

Everyman's Dictionary of Non-Classical Mythology. rev. ed. Egerton Sykes. (Everyman's Reference Library). (Illus.). 298p. 1977. Repr. of 1968 ed. 13.50x (ISBN 0-460-03010-8, Pub. by J. M. Dent England). Biblio Dist.

Everyman's Gospel: Studies in Romans. John A. Ishee. 34p. (Orig.). 1983. pap. 3.50 (ISBN 0-939298-19-8). J M Prods.

Everyman's Life of the Buddha: Translated from Pali Sacred Scriptures. Tr. by Henry C. Warren. Ed. by John E. Westburg. (Comparative Literature Studies Ser). (Illus.). 138p. 1966. pap. 5.00 (ISBN 0-87423-003-9). Westburg.

Everyman's Struggle for Peace. Horace Alexander. 1983. pap. 2.50x (ISBN 0-87574-074-X, 074). Pendle Hill.

Everyman's Talmud. Abraham Cohen. LC 75-10750. 446p. 1975. pap. 11.25 (ISBN 0-8052-0497-0). Schocken.

Everyone a Minister. O. E. Feucht. 160p. pap. 2.95 (ISBN 0-570-03184-2, 12-2587). Concordia.

Everyone in the Bible. William P. Barker. 384p. 1966. 15.95 (ISBN 0-8007-0084-8). Revell.

Everyone Is Right. Roland Peterson. 352p. (Orig.). 1986. pap. 12.95 (ISBN 0-87516-565-6). De Vorss.

Everyone Needs Someone: Poems of Love & Friendship. Helen S. Rice. 80p. 1973. 8.95 (ISBN 0-8007-0966-7). Revell.

Everyone's Guide to Theosophy. Harry Benjamin. 1969. 8.50 (ISBN 0-8356-5079-0). Theos Pub Hse.

Everything & the Nothing. Meher Baba. 1976. 70p. 4.95, (ISBN 0-913078-49-2, Pub. by R J Mistry India); pap. 2.95, 115p. (ISBN 0-913078-48-4). Sheriar Pr.

Everything Is Politics but Politics Is Not Everything. H. M. Kuitert. Tr. by John Bowden from Dutch. 208p. (Orig.). 1986. pap. 8.95 (ISBN 0-8028-0235-4). Eerdmans.

Everything Jesus Taught. Herbert Lockyer. LC 83-48431. 576p. 1984. pap. 6.95 (ISBN 0-06-065259-4, RD 503, HarpR). Har-Row.

Everything Necessary: God's Provisions for the Holy Life. Luke Keefer, Jr. 1984. Teacher ed. 64p. 3.95 (ISBN 0-916035-11-5); Student ed. 160p. 4.95 (ISBN 0-916035-12-3). Evangel Indiana.

Everything You Always Wanted to Know about Prophesy. Jack Van Impe. 61p. 1980. pap. 1.95 (ISBN 0-934803-11-0). J Van Impe.

Everything You Ever Wanted to Know About Heaven-But Never Dreamed of Asking. Peter J. Kreeft. LC 82-47747. 160p. (Orig.). 1982. pap. 7.95 (ISBN 0-06-064777-9, RD/413, HarpR). Har-Row.

Everything You Need for Children's Worship: Except Children. pap. cancelled (ISBN 0-912228-50-4). St Anthony Mess Pr.

Everything You Need to Grow a Messianic Synagogue. Phillip E. Goble. LC 74-28017. (Illus., Orig.). 1974. pap. 3.95 (ISBN 0-87808-421-5). William Carey Lib.

Everything You Need to Grow a Messianic Yeshiva. Ed. by Phillip E. Goble. LC 81-1032. 312p. (Orig.). 1981. pap. 10.95 (ISBN 0-87808-181-X). William Carey Lib.

Everything You Need to Know for a Cassette Ministry. Viggo B. Sogaard. LC 74-20915. 224p. 1975. pap. 7.95 (ISBN 0-87123-125-5, 210125). Bethany Hse.

Eve's Journey: Feminine Images In Hebraic Literary Tradition. Nehama Aschkenasy. LC 85-29427. 176p. 1986. text ed. 29.95 (ISBN 0-8122-8033-4); pap. 15.95. U of Pa Pr.

Eve's Version: One Hundred Fifty Women of the Bible Speak Through Modern Poets. (Illus.). 1983. 13.95. Paramount TX.

Evidence for Jesus. James D. Dunn. LC 85-22540. 128p. (Orig.). 1986. pap. 8.95 (ISBN 0-664-24698-2). Westminster.

Evidence for Jesus. R. T. France. Ed. by Michael Green. LC 86-20927. (Jesus Library). 144p. 1986. pap. 6.95 (ISBN 0-87784-986-2). Inter-Varsity.

Evidence for Joy. Josh McDowell & Dale Bellis. 192p. 1986. pap. 3.50 (ISBN 0-553-26153-3). Bantam.

Evidence for Our Faith. 3rd ed. Joseph H. Cavanaugh. 1959. 8.00x (ISBN 0-268-00092-1). U. of Notre Dame Pr.

Evidence for the Resurrection. J. N. Anderson. pap. 0.75 (ISBN 0-87784-124-1). Inter-Varsity.

Evidence for Visions of the Virgin Mary. Kevin McClure. (Illus.). 158p. (Orig.). 1984. pap. 5.95 (ISBN 0-85030-351-6, Pub. by Aquarian Pr England). Sterling.

Evidence Growth Guide, Vol. 1: Explaining Misconceptions about Christianity. Josh McDowell & Dale Bellis. (Truth Alive Ser.). 80p. (Orig.). 1981. 4.95 (ISBN 0-86605-018-3). Campus Crusade.

Evidence Growth Guide, Vol. 2: Uniqueness of the Bible. Josh McDowell & Dale Bellis. 80p. (Orig.). 1981. 4.95 (ISBN 0-86605-019-1). Campus Crusade.

Evidence Growth Guide, Vol. 3: Trustworthiness of the Bible. Josh McDowell & Dale Bellis. (Truth Alive Ser.: Pt. III). 120p. (Orig.). 1983. pap. 4.95 (ISBN 0-86605-020-5). Campus Crusade.

Evidence of Conflation in Mark? A Study in the Synoptic Problem. Thomas R. Longstaff. LC 76-40001. (Society of Biblical Literature. Dissertation Ser.: No. 28). (Illus.). 1977. pap. 9.95 (ISBN 0-89130-086-4, 060128). Scholars Pr GA.

Evidence of Satan in the Modern World. Leon Christiani. 1975. pap. 1.50 (ISBN 0-380-00413-5, 25122). Avon.

Evidence of Satan in the Modern World. Leon Cristiani. Tr. by Cynthia Rowland from Fr. (Eng.). 1977. pap. 5.50 (ISBN 0-89555-032-6). TAN Bks Pubs.

Evidence of the Authenticity, Inspiration & Canonical Authority of the Holy Scriptures. Archibald Alexander. (Works of Reverend Archibald Alexander). 308p. Repr. of 1842 ed. lib. bdg. 39.00 (ISBN 0-932051-73-1, Pub. by Am Repr Serv). Am Biog Serv.

Evidence on Religious Bona Fides & Status of the Church of Scientology. 1974. pap. 8.00 (ISBN 0-915598-02-7). Church of Scient Info.

Evidence That Demands a Verdict. rev. ed. Josh McDowell. LC 78-75041. 1979. pap. 7.95 (ISBN 0-918956-46-3). Campus Crusade.

Evidence: The Truth about Christianity. rev. ed. Terry Winter. LC 79-87769. 1979. pap. 2.25 (ISBN 0-89081-067-2, 2039). Harvest Hse.

Evidences of Romantic Treatment of Religious Elements in Late Eighteenth Century Minor Poetry, 1771-1800. Mary E. Horning. LC 72-3719. (English Literature Ser., No. 33). 1972. Repr. of 1932 ed. lib. bdg. 29.95x (ISBN 0-8383-1542-9). Haskell.

Evidences of the Authenticity, Inspiration, & Canonical Authority of the Holy Scriptures. Archibald Alexander. LC 70-38431. (Religion in America, Ser. 2). 314p. 1972. Repr. of 1836 ed. 23.50 (ISBN 0-405-04052-0). Ayer Co Pubs.

Evil & a Good God. Bruce Reichenbach. LC 82-71120. xviii, 198p. 1982. 22.50 (ISBN 0-8232-1080-4); pap. 9.00 (ISBN 0-8232-1081-2). Fordham.

Evil & Danger of Stage Plays. Arthur Bedford. LC 72-170479. (English Stage Ser.: Vol. 43). lib. bdg. 61.00 (ISBN 0-8240-0626-7). Garland Pub.

Evil & Evolution. Richard W. Kropf. LC 81-72041. 224p. 1983. 27.50 (ISBN 0-8386-3157-6). Fairleigh Dickinson.

Evil & Suffering. Roger Kite. 1985. 19.00x (ISBN 0-7062-3911-3, Pub. by Ward Lock Educ Co Ltd). State Mutual Bk.

Evil & the Christian Faith. facsimile ed. Nels F. Ferre. LC 71-134075. (Essay Index Reprints - Reason & the Christian Faith Ser.: Vol. 2). Repr. of 1947 ed. 18.00 (ISBN 0-8369-2393-6). Ayer Co Pubs.

Evil & the Christian God. Michael L. Peterson. LC 82-70465. 176p. (Orig.). 1982. pap. 7.95 (ISBN 0-8010-7070-8). Baker Bk.

Evil & the God of Love. rev. ed. John H. Hick. LC 76-62953. 1977. pap. 6.95 (ISBN 0-06-063902-4, RD219, HarpR). Har-Row.

Evil & the Morality of Ged. Harold M. Schulweis. (Hebrew Union College Jewish Perspectives Ser.: No. 3). 1984. 15.00 (ISBN 0-87820-502-0). Hebrew Union Coll Pr.

Evil & the Process God: The Problem of Evil in Charles Hartshorne's Thought. Barry L. Whitney. LC 84-25505. (Toronto Studies in Theology: Vol. 19). 247p. 1985. 49.95x (ISBN 0-88946-760-9). E Mellen.

Evil & the Unconscious. Walter Lowe. LC 82-19147. (AAR Studies in Religion Ser.). 142p. 1983. 16.50 (ISBN 0-89130-600-5, 01 00 30). Scholars Pr GA.

Evil & World Order. William I. Thompson. (World Perspectives Ser.). 1977. pap. 4.95x (ISBN 0-06-131951-1, TB1951, Torch). Har-Row.

Evil Eye. Ed. by Clarence Maloney. LC 76-16861. (Illus.). 334p. 1976. 30.00 (ISBN 0-231-04006-7); pap. 14.50. Columbia U Pr.

Evil Eye: An Account of This Ancient & Widespread Superstition. Frederick T. Elworthy. (Illus.). 1986. pap. 7.95 (ISBN 0-517-55971-4, Julian). Crown.

Evil Side of Good. Carlos E. Portillo. LC 85-52117. 200p. (Orig.). Date not set. pap. price not set (ISBN 0-937365-04-1). WCP Pubns.

Evil: The Shadow Side of Reality. John A. Sanford. 176p. 1981. 10.95 (ISBN 0-8245-0037-7); pap. 9.95 (ISBN 0-8245-0526-3). Crossroad NY.

Evocation de Junipero Serra, Foundateur de la Californie. Charles J. Piette. (Fr., Illus.). 1946. 5.00 (ISBN 0-88382-251-2); pap. 5.00 (ISBN 0-88382-250-4). AAFH.

Evolution. Leroy Forlines. 1973. pap. 0.95 (ISBN 0-89265-105-9). Randall Hse.

Evolution. Philip Mauro. pap. 2.25 (ISBN 0-685-88374-4). Reiner.

Evolution: A Golden Calf. Dean R. Zimmerman. 232p. (Orig.). 1976. pap. 3.95 (ISBN 0-89036-059-6). Hawkes Pub Inc.

Evolution & Antiquity. 2nd ed. J. D. Thomas. (Way of Life Ser: No. 120). Orig. Title: Doctrine of Evolution & the Antiquity of Man. (Orig.). 1959. pap. 3.95 (ISBN 0-89112-120-X, Bibl Res Pr). Abilene Christ U.

Evolution & Christian Faith. Bolton Davidheiser. 1969. pap. 10.95 (ISBN 0-87552-251-3). Presby & Reformed.

Evolution & Creation. Ed. by Ernan McMullin. LC 84-40818. (University of Notre Dame Studies in the Philosophy of Religion: Vol. 4). 307p. 1987. pap. 12.95 (ISBN 0-268-00918-X). U of Notre Dame Pr.

Evolution & Creation: A Catholic Understanding. Rev. William Kramer. LC 86-60907. 168p. (Orig.). 1986. pap. 6.95 (ISBN 0-87973-511-2, 511). Our Sunday Visitor.

Evolution & Ethics, & Other Essays. Thomas H. Huxley. LC 70-8391. 334p. 1897. Repr. 49.00x (ISBN 0-403-00041-6). Scholarly.

Evolution & Guilt. Juan L. Segundo. Tr. by John Drury from Span. LC 73-89054. (Theology for Artisans of a New Humanity Ser: Vol. 5). Orig. Title: Evolucion y Culpa. 154p. (Orig.). 1974. 7.95 (ISBN 0-88344-485-2). Orbis Bks.

Evolution & Revelation. Willard O. Davis. 6.95 (ISBN 0-88027-097-7). Firm Foun Pub.

Evolution & the Authority of the Bible. Nigel Cameron. 128p. 1983. pap. 6.95 (ISBN 0-85364-326-1, Pub. by Paternoster UK). Attic Pr.

Evolution & the Inward Light. Howard H. Brinton. LC 77-137101. (Orig.). 1970. pap. 2.50x (ISBN 0-87574-173-8). Pendle Hill.

Evolution & the Modern Christian. Henry M. Morris. pap. 3.95 (ISBN 0-8010-5881-3). Baker Bk.

Evolution & the Modern Christian. Henry M. Morris. 1967. pap. 2.95 (ISBN 0-87552-337-4). Presby & Reformed.

Evolution & the Word of God. P. J. Bart-Williams. LC 83-91501. 87p. 1985. 8.95 (ISBN 0-533-06080-X). Vantage.

Evolution As a Religion: Strange Hopes & Stranger Fears. Mary Midgley. 192p. 1986. text ed. 33.00 (ISBN 0-416-39650-X, 9512); pap. text ed. 12.95 (ISBN 0-416-39660-7, 9513). Methuen Inc.

Evolution-Creation Controversy Perspectives on Religion, Philosophy, Science & Education: A Handbook. Ed. by K. R. Walker. (Paleontological Society Special Publications Ser.). (Illus.). 155p. pap. 6.50 (ISBN 0-931377-00-5). U of Tenn Geo.

Evolution Hoax Exposed. A. N. Field. 1971. pap. 3.00 (ISBN 0-89555-049-0). TAN Bks Pubs.

Evolution in Science & Religion. Robert A. Millikan. 1979. Repr. of 1929 ed. lib. bdg. 17.50 (ISBN 0-8495-3846-7). Arden Lib.

Evolution in Science & Religion. Robert A. Millikan. 1935. 15.50x (ISBN 0-686-51381-9). Elliots Bks.

Evolution in Science & Religion. Robert A Millikan. LC 72-85283. 104p. 1973. Repr. of 1927 ed. 21.50x (ISBN 0-8046-1702-3, Pub. by Kennikat). Assoc Faculty Pr.

Evolution: Its Nature Its Evidences, - Its Relation to Religious Thought. 2nd ed. Joseph Le Conte. 1897. 29.00 (ISBN 0-527-55700-5). Kraus Repr.

Evolution: Material or Spiritual? 25p. 1986. 3.50 (ISBN 0-942958-08-X). Kappeler Inst Pub.

Evolution of a Mystery Play: Le Sacrifice d'Abraham. Barbara Craig. 329p. 1983. 24.00 (ISBN 0-917786-30-0). Summa Pubns.

Evolution of Ancient Buddhism. A. M. Floyer. 59.95 (ISBN 0-8490-0143-9). Gordon Pr.

Evolution of Belief. Roger Webber. 89p. 1984. 8.95 (ISBN 0-533-05475-3). Vantage.

Evolution of Buddhist Architecture in Japan. Alexander C. Soper. LC 76-26054. (Illus.). 1978. Repr. of 1942 ed. lib. bdg. 75.00 (ISBN 0-87817-196-7). Hacker.

Evolution of Christian Thought. T. A. Burkill. LC 76-127775. 518p. 1971. 29.50x (ISBN 0-8014-0581-5). Cornell U Pr.

Evolution of Christianity. Lyman Abbott. (American Studies Ser.). Repr. of 1892 ed. 24.00 (ISBN 0-384-00075-4). Johnson Repr.

Evolution of Christianity. Lyman Abbott. vi, 258p. 1985. Repr. of 1919 ed. 34.00 (ISBN 0-318-04538-9, Pub. by Am Repr Serv). Am Biog Serv.

Evolution of Christianity Leading to Christianity Without the Myths. S. Farrer. 1986. 40.00x (ISBN 0-7212-0740-5, Pub. by Regency Pr). State Mutual Bk.

Evolution of Christology. Thor Hall. LC 81-14838. 128p. (Orig.). 1982. pap. 6.50 (ISBN 0-687-12190-6). Abingdon.

Evolution of Consciousness: A Contemporary Mythic Journey into the Roots of Global Awareness. Kishore Gandhi. (Patterns of World Spirituality Ser.). 272p. 1986. pap. 11.95 (ISBN 0-913757-50-0, Pub. by New Era Bks). Paragon Hse.

Evolution of Darwin's Religious Views. Frank B. Brown. (Special Studies: No. 10). 72p. pap. text ed. 7.95 (ISBN 0-86554-239-2, MUP/M12). NABPR.

Evolution of Dutch Catholicism, Nineteen Fifty-Eight to Nineteen Seventy-Four. John A. Coleman. LC 74-22958. 1979. 42.50x (ISBN 0-520-02885-6). U of Cal Pr.

Evolution of Ethics. Ed. by E. Hershey Sneath. 1927. 49.50x (ISBN 0-685-69867-X). Elliots Bks.

Evolution of Hindu Ethical Ideals. S. Cromwell Crawford. (Asian Studies at Hawaii: No. 28). 197p. 1982. pap. text ed. 14.00x (ISBN 0-8248-0782-0). UH Pr.

Evolution of Hindu Sects. S. Chattopadhyaya. 1970. text ed. 18.00x. Coronet Bks.

Evolution of Human Thought. Edmond B. Szekely. (Illus.). 44p. 1971. pap. 2.50 (ISBN 0-89564-062-7). IBS Intl.

Evolution of Immortality. S. D. McConnell. 1978. Repr. of 1901 ed. lib. bdg. 25.00 (ISBN 0-8495-3508-5). Arden Lib.

Evolution of Integral Consciousness. Haridas Chaudhuri. LC 77-4219. 1977. pap. 4.25 (ISBN 0-8356-0494-2, Quest). Theos Pub Hse.

Evolution of Jewish Thought. Jacob B. Agus. LC 73-2185. (Jewish People; History, Religion, Literature Ser.). Repr. of 1959 ed. 30.00 (ISBN 0-405-05251-0). Ayer Co Pubs.

Evolution of Muslim Political Thought in India, 6 vols. A. M. Zaidi. 1973. Set. text ed. 295.00x. Vol. 1, From Sayed to the Emergence of Jinnah. Vol. 2, Sectarian Nationalism & Khilafat. Vol. 3, Parting of Ways. Vol. 4, The Communal Award. Vol. 5, Demand for Pakistan. Vol. 6, Freedom at Last. Coronet Bks.

Evolution of Religion, 2 Vols. in 1. Edward Caird. LC 1-17697. (Gifford Lectures 1890-1892). 1968. Repr. of 1893 ed. 46.00 (ISBN 0-527-14120-8). Kraus Repr.

Evolution of Religion: Section 2, Lessons 133-40. C. C. Zain. (Illus.). 1976. pap. 9.95 (ISBN 0-87887-346-5). Church of Light.

Evolution of the Buddha Image. Benjamin Rowland, Jr. LC 74-27420. (Asia Society Ser.). (Illus.). 1979. Repr. of 1963 ed. lib. bdg. 31.00x (ISBN 0-405-06568-X). Ayer Co Pubs.

Evolution of the Carthusian Statutes from the Consuetudines Guigonis to the Teria Compilatio, 2 Vols. James Hogg. (Analecta Cartusiana: No. 99). (Orig.). 1988. pap. 50.00 (ISBN 3-7052-0170-0, Pub. by Salzburg Studies). Longwood Pub Group.

Evolution of the Earth & the Influence of the Stars. Rudolf Steiner. Tr. by Gladys Hahn from Ger. Tr. of Schoepfung der Welt und des Menschen Erdenleben und Sternenwirken. (Illus.). 200p. 1987. 20.00 (ISBN 0-88010-181-4); pap. 10.95 (ISBN 0-88010-180-6). Anthroposophic.

Evolution of the Human Mind: The Passage from Self to Cosmic Consciousness. Maurice R. Burke. (Physic Research Library Bks.). (Illus.). 137p. 1981. Repr. of 1905 ed. 69.85 (ISBN 0-89901-033-4). Found Class Reprints.

Evolution of the Idea of God. Grant Allen. 1977. lib. bdg. 59.95 (ISBN 0-8490-1796-3). Gordon Pr.

Evolution of the Option for the Poor in France, 1880-1965. Mary T. Moser. (Illus.). 216p. (Orig.). 1985. lib. bdg. 24.00 (ISBN 0-8191-4814-8); pap. text ed. 11.75 (ISBN 0-8191-4815-6). U Pr of Amer.

Evolution of the Sikh Community: Five Essays. W. H. McLeod. 1976. 22.00x (ISBN 0-19-826529-8). Oxford U Pr.

Evolution of the Soul. Richard Swinburne. 320p. 1986. 45.00x (ISBN 0-19-824915-2). Oxford U Pr.

Evolution of Theology in the Greek Philosophers, 2 Vols in 1. Edward Caird. LC 4-16272. (Gifford Lectures 1900-1902). 1968. Repr. of 1904 ed. 46.00 (ISBN 0-527-14130-5). Kraus Repr.

Evolution of Theology in the Greek Philosophers, the Gifford Lectures, 1900-1902, 2 Vols. Edward Caird. 1968. 39.00x (ISBN 0-403-00116-1). Scholarly.

Evolution-The Incredible Hoax. Gordon Lindsay. 1.50 (ISBN 0-89985-115-0). Christ Nations.

Evolution Toward Divinity. Beatrice Bruteau. LC 73-16198. 260p. 1974. 10.00 (ISBN 0-8356-0216-8). Theos Pub Hse.

Evolution Versus Creationism: The Public Education Controversy. J. Peter Zetterberg. LC 82-18795. 528p. 1983. lib. bdg. 41.00 (ISBN 0-89774-061-0). Oryx Pr.

Evolution: When Fact Became Fiction. Ricki Pavlu. LC 86-13144. (Illus.). 184p. (Orig.). 1986. pap. 6.95 (ISBN 0-932581-51-X). Word Aflame.

Evolution: Who & What Is Man. Henry T. Edge. Ed. by W. Emmett Small & Helen Todd. (Theosophical Manual: No. 6). 78p. 1975. pap. 2.00 (ISBN 0-913004-22-7, 913004-22). Point Loma Pub.

Evolutionary Potential of Quakerism. Kenneth E. Boulding. 1983. pap. 2.50x (ISBN 0-87574-136-3, 136). Pendle Hill.

Evolving Church. Donal Flanagan. 1966. 4.95 (ISBN 0-8189-0047-4). Alba.

Evolving Church & the Sacrament of Penance. Ladislas Orsy. 1974. 6.95 (ISBN 0-87193-072-2). Dimension Bks.

Evolving World & Theology. Ed. by Johannes B. Metz. LC 67-25695. (Concilium Ser.: Vol. 26). 91p. 1967. 7.95 (ISBN 0-8091-0042-8). Paulist Pr.

Ex-Nuns: Women Who Have Left the Convent. Gerelyn Hollingsworth. LC 84-43207. 136p. 1985. lib. bdg. 16.95x (ISBN 0-89950-156-7). McFarland & Co.

Exagoge of Ezekiel. Howard Jacobson. LC 82-4410. 240p. 1983. 49.50 (ISBN 0-521-24580-X). Cambridge U Pr.

Exalt His Name: A Christmas Program. Muriel Browne. 1984. pap. 0.95 (ISBN 0-8024-3551-3). Moody.

Exaltation of the Holy Cross. Monks of New Skete Staff. Tr. by Reverend Laurence Mancuso from Gr. & Church Slavonic. (Liturgical Music Series I: Great Feasts: Vol. 4). 60p. 1986. pap. text ed. 15.00 (ISBN 0-935129-05-7). Monks of New Skete.

Exalted Faith. Abraham I. Daud. Ed. by Gershon Weiss. Tr. by Norbert Samuelson. LC 83-49341. (Hebrew.). 408p. 1986. 75.00x (ISBN 0-8386-3185-1). Fairleigh Dickinson.

Examinacions of Thorpe & Oldcastell. William Thorpe. LC 74-28889. (English Experience Ser.: No. 766). 1975. Repr. of 1530 ed. 7.00 (ISBN 90-221-0766-3). Walter J Johnson.

Examination of Dispensationalism. William E. Cox. 1963. pap. 2.75 (ISBN 0-87552-153-3). Presby & Reformed.

Examination of Dr. Reid's Inquiry into the Human Mind. Joseph Priestley. Ed. by Rene Wellek. LC 75-11249. (British Philosophers & Theologians of the 17th & 18th Centuries Ser.). 1978. Repr. of 1774 ed. lib. bdg. 51.00 (ISBN 0-8240-1800-1). Garland Pub.

Examination of T. Cartwrights Late Apologie. Matthew Sutcliffe. LC 72-7837. (English Experience Ser.: No. 558). 120p. 1973. Repr. of 1596 ed. 13.00 (ISBN 90-221-0558-X). Walter J Johnson.

Examination of the Council of Trent. Martin Chemnitz. Tr. by Fred Kramer from Lat. LC 79-143693. 1971. 29.95 (ISBN 0-570-03213-X, 15-2113). Concordia.

Examination of the Council of Trent: Part II. Martin Chemnitz. 1979. 29.95 (ISBN 0-570-03272-5, 15-2717). Concordia.

Examination of the Mystical Tendencies in Islam. A. M. M. Zuhur-U'D. 224p. 1973. 8.50x (ISBN 0-87902-252-3). Orientalia.

Examined Life. Carol Murphy. 1983. pap. 2.50x (ISBN 0-87574-085-5, 085). Pendle Hill.

Examining Our Faith. YMCA of the U. S. A. Staff. 32p. 1980. pap. 4.95x (ISBN 0-88035-030-X). Human Kinetics.

Examining the Claims of Jesus. Dee Brestin. (Core Study in the Fisherman Bible Studyguides). 48p. 1985. pap. 2.95 (ISBN 0-87788-246-0). Shaw Pubs.

Example of Jesus. Michael Griffiths. LC 84-6739. (Jesus Library). 180p. 1985. pap. 6.95 (ISBN 0-87784-929-3). Inter-Varsity.

Example of Jesus Christ: Imago Christi. James Stalker. LC 80-82322. (Shepherd Illustrated Classics Ser.). (Orig.). 1980. pap. 5.95 (ISBN 0-87983-231-2). Keats.

Examples of Gregorian Chant & Other Sacred Music of the 16th Century. Compiled by G. F. Soderlund & Samuel H. Scott. LC 70-129090. (Orig.). 1971. 27.95 (ISBN 0-13-293753-0). P-H.

Excavaciones Y las Escrituras. Edwin M. Yamauchi. 224p. 1978. 4.50 (ISBN 0-311-03658-9). Casa Bautista.

Excavating Kirjath-Sepher's Ten Cities. Melvin G. Kyle. 19.00 (ISBN 0-405-10262-3, 14452). Ayer Co Pubs.

Excavations at Kerma, Pts. I-V. G. A. Reisner. Ed. by E. A. Hooton & Natica I. Bates. (Harvard African Studies: Vol. 5). Pts. I-III. lib. bdg. 118.00set (ISBN 0-527-01028-6); Pts. IV-V. lib. bdg. 69.00 set (ISBN 0-527-01029-4). Kraus Repr.

Excavations at Mission San Antonio, 1976-1978. Ed. by Robert L. Hoover & Julia G. Costello. (Monographs: No. XXVI). (Illus.). 221p. 1985. pap. 16.00 (ISBN 0-917956-48-6). UCLA Arch.

Excavations at New Testament Jericho & Khirbet en-Nitla. James L. Kelso & Dimitri Baramki. (Annual of the American Schools of Oriental Research: Vols. 29 & 30). 60p. 1955. text ed. 10.00x (ISBN 0-89757-030-8, Am Sch Orient Res). Eisenbrauns.

Excavations at Nippur. McGuire Gibson. LC 75-9054. (Oriental Institute Communications Ser.: No. 22). 1976. pap. 15.00x (ISBN 0-226-62339-4). U of Chicago Pr.

Excavations at Nippur: Twelfth Season. McGuire Gibson et al. LC 78-59117. (Oriental Institute Communications Ser.: No. 23). (Illus.). 1978. pap. 22.00x (ISBN 0-918986-22-2). Oriental Inst.

Exceedingly Growing Faith. Kenneth E. Hagin. 1983. pap. 3.50 (ISBN 0-89276-506-2). Hagin Ministries.

Excellence. Ed. by T. H. Bell et al. LC 84-71872. 140p. 1984. 8.95 (ISBN 0-87747-776-0). Deseret Bk.

Excellence in Leadership. John White. LC 86-2938. 132p. (Orig.). 1986. pap. 5.95 (ISBN 0-87784-570-0). Inter-Varsity.

Excellence in Ministry. Ed. by Michael L. Sherer. (Orig.). 1987. pap. 8.75 (ISBN 0-89536-866-8, 7825). CSS of Ohio.

Excellence in Teaching with the Seven Laws: A Contemporary Abridgment of Gregory's Seven Laws of Teaching. Carl Shafer. 80p. 1985. pap. 4.95 (ISBN 0-8010-8261-7). Baker Bk.

Excellence of Exposition: Practical Procedure in Expository Preaching. Douglas M. White. 1977. 4.95 (ISBN 0-87213-939-5). Loizeaux.

Excellency & Nobleness of the True Religion. John Smith the Platonist. 1984. pap. 4.95 (ISBN 0-916411-35-4, Pub by Alexandrian Pr). Holmes Pub.

Except the Lord. Joyce Cary. LC 85-10601. (Second Trilogy Ser.: Bk. 2). 288p. 1985. pap. 7.95 (ISBN 0-8112-0965-2, NDP607). New Directions.

Exceptional Child: A Guidebook for Churches & Community Agencies. Ed. by James L. Paul. LC 82-16914. 176p. text ed. 22.00x (ISBN 0-8156-2287-2); pap. text ed. 12.95x (ISBN 0-8156-2288-0). Syracuse U Pr.

Excitement of Answered Prayer. Virginia Whitman. (Direction Bks). pap. 3.95 (ISBN 0-8010-9617-0). Baker Bk.

Exciting Adventures. Doris C. Demaree. (Bible Stories for Children Ser.). 1974. pap. 1.50 (ISBN 0-87162-235-1, D1445). Warner Pr.

Exciting Christian Life: Bible Study on Christian Growth. Lucien E. Coleman. 36p. 1982. pap. 3.50 (ISBN 0-939298-11-2). J M Prods.

Exclusiveness & Tolerance. Jacob Katz. 208p. 1983. pap. 7.95x (ISBN 0-87441-365-6). Behrman.

Exclusiveness & Tolerance: Studies in Jewish-Gentile Relations in Medieval & Modern Times. Jacob Katz. LC 80-12181. (Scripta Judaica: No. III). xv, 200p. 1980. Repr. of 1961 ed. lib. bdg. 24.75x (ISBN 0-313-22387-4, KAEX). Greenwood.

Executive I Ching: The Business Oracle. Michael Colmer. 176p. 1987. 17.95 (ISBN 0-7137-1934-6, Pub. by Blandford Pr England). Sterling.

Exegesis at Qumran: Four Q Florilegium in Its Jewish Context. George J. Brooke. (JSOT Supplement Ser.: No. 29). 370p. 1984. text ed. 28.50x (ISBN 0-905774-76-0, Pub. by JSOT Pr England); pap. text ed. 13.50x (ISBN 0-905774-77-9, Pub. by JSOT Pr England). Eisenbrauns.

Exegesis: Problems of Method & Exercises in Reading. Ed. by Francois Bovon & Gregoire Rouiller. Tr. by Donald G Miller from Fr. LC 78-27622. (Pittsburgh Theological Monographs: No. 21). Orig. Title: Exegesis; Problemes de Methode et Exercices de Lecture. 1978. pap. 15.00 (ISBN 0-915138-25-5). Pickwick.

Exegetic Homilies. St. Basil. LC 63-12483. (Father of the Church Ser.: Vol. 46). 378p. 1963. 19.95x (ISBN 0-8132-0046-6). Cath U Pr.

Exegetical Bibliography of the New Testament: Vol. 1-Matthew & Mark. Guenter Wagner. LC 83-969. (Bibliographical Tools for New Testament Studies). xviii, 668p. 1983. 35.00 (ISBN 0-86554-013-6, MUP-H26). Mercer Univ Pr.

Exegetical Bibliography of the New Testament, Vol. 2: Luke-Acts. Ed. by Gunter Wagner. xiv, 550p. 1986. 49.50 (ISBN 0-86554-140-X, MUP-H131). Mercer Univ Pr.

Exegetical Bibliography of the New Testament: Volume 3: John-1-2-3 John. Ed. by Gunter Wagner. 600p. 1987. 55.00 (ISBN 0-86554-157-4). Mercer Univ Pr.

Exegetical Commentary on The Gospel According To Matthew. Alfred Plummer. (Thornapple Commentaries Ser.). 497p. 1982. pap. 12.95 (ISBN 0-8010-7078-3). Baker Bk.

Exegetical Fallacies. D. A. Carson. 1984. text ed. 7.95p (ISBN 0-8010-2499-4). Baker Bk.

Exegetical Grammar of the Greek New Testament. William D. Chamberlain. 1979. pap. 7.95 (ISBN 0-8010-2438-2). Baker Bk.

Exempla of the Rabbis. rev. ed. Moses Gaster. 1968. 25.00x (ISBN 0-87068-055-2). Ktav.

Exempla or Illustrative Stories from the Sermones: Vulgares off Jacques de Vitry. Thomas F. Crane. (Folk-Lore Society, London, Ser.: Vol. 26). 240p. pap. 35.00 (ISBN 0-8115-0512-X). Kraus Repr.

Exempla, or Illustrative Stories from the Sermones Vulgares of Jacques De Vitry. Jacobus De Vitriaco. Ed. by Thomas F. Crane. 1971. Repr. of 1890 ed. lib. bdg. 23.50 (ISBN 0-8337-0715-9). B Franklin.

Exemplum dans la Litterature Religieuse et Didactique du Moyen Age. Jean T. Welter. LC 70-178558. (Fr.). Repr. of 1927 ed. 45.00 (ISBN 0-404-56688-X). AMS Pr.

Exercice de la Piete. Jerry Bridges. Ed. by Annie L. Cosson. Tr. by Monique Claeys. Tr. of Practice of Godliness. (Fr.). 240p. 1985. pap. text ed. 2.50 (ISBN 0-8297-1458-8). Life Pubs Intl.

Exercise of Church Leadership. Charles Moore. 1976. pap. 2.75 (ISBN 0-88027-032-2). Firm Foun Pub.

Exercise Without Movement. Swami Rama. (Illus.). 88p. (Orig.). pap. 5.95 (ISBN 0-89389-089-8). Himalayan Pubs.

Exercises in Religious Understanding. David B. Burrell. LC 74-12566. pap. 63.30 (ISBN 0-317-26713-2, 2024366). Bks Demand UMI.

Exercises Upon the First Psalm. George Wither. 1882. 29.50 (ISBN 0-8337-3836-4). B Franklin.

Exhaustive Concordance of the Book of Mormon, Doctrine & Covenants & Pearl of Great Peace. R. Gary Shapiro. Orig. Title: Triple Concordance. 1977. 17.95 (ISBN 0-89036-085-5). Hawkes Pub Inc.

Exhaustive Outline of the Entire Bible. Christopher A. Anacker. LC 81-90358. (Orig.). 1981. 10.95 (ISBN 0-9607942-5-5); lib. bdg. 12.95 (ISBN 0-9607942-7-1); pap. 8.95 (ISBN 0-9607942-0-4). Ref Guide Bks.

Exhibition of Judaica & Hebraica. Compiled by Eisig Silberschlag. (Illus.). 26p. 1973. pap. 3.50 (ISBN 0-87959-034-3). U of Tex H Ransom Ctr.

Exhibitions of the Rosicrucian Salon. Ed. by Theodore Reff. (Modern Art in Paris 1855 to 1900 Ser.). 354p. 1981. lib. bdg. 53.00 (ISBN 0-8240-4730-3). Garland Pub.

Exhortation to Styre All Englyshe Men to the Defense of Theyr Countreye. Richard Morison. LC 79-38211. (English Experience Ser.: No. 476). 64p. 1972. Repr. of 1539 ed. 9.50 (ISBN 90-221-0476-1). Walter J Johnson.

Exhortation to the Diligent Studye of Scripture. Desiderius Erasmus. Tr. by W. Roy. LC 72-5983. (English Experience Ser.: No. 510). 156p. 1973. Repr. of 1529 ed. 11.50 (ISBN 90-221-0510-5). Walter J Johnson.

Exhortation to Unity & Peace. John Bunyan. pap. 0.95 (ISBN 0-685-00744-8). Reiner.

Exile & Biblical Narrative: The Formation of the Deuteronomistic & Priestly Works. Richard E. Friedman. LC 80-28836. 1981. 12.00 (ISBN 0-89130-457-6, 04 00 22). Scholars Pr GA.

Exile & Restoration: A Study of Hebrew Thought of the Sixth Century B. C. Peter R. Ackroyd. LC 68-27689. (Old Testament Library). 302p. 1968. 14.95 (ISBN 0-664-20843-6). Westminster.

Exile & Return: The Struggle for a Jewish Homeland. Martin Gilbert. (Illus.). 364p. 1978. 12.95 (ISBN 0-397-01249-7). Brown Bk.

Exile in the Fatherland: Martin Niemoller's Letters from Moabit Prison. Martin Niemoller. Ed. by Hubert G. Locke. Tr. by Ernst Kaemke. 212p. (Orig.). 1986. pap. 9.95 (ISBN 0-8028-0188-9). Eerdmans.

Exile of the Soul. Roy Mitchell. Ed. by John L. Davenport. LC 83-62528. 338p. 1984. 18.95 (ISBN 0-87975-232-7); pap. 9.95 (ISBN 0-87975-233-5). Prometheus Bks.

Exile of the Word: From the Silence of the Bible to the Silence of Auschwitz. Andre Neher. LC 80-12612. 224p. 1980. 17.95 (ISBN 0-8276-0176-X, 465). Jewish Pubns.

Exiles from History. David McCalden. (Illus.). 40p. (Orig.). 1982. pap. 5.00 (ISBN 0-910607-00-1). Truth Missions.

Exiles in Babylon. Larry Kuenning. LC 77-85708. 1978. pap. 2.25 (ISBN 0-930682-00-9). Friends Truth.

Existence. John G. Bennett. 1977. 4.50 (ISBN 0-900306-40-8, Pub. by Coombe Springs Pr). Claymont Comm.

Existence & Attributes of God, 2 vols. Stephen Charnock. 1979. Repr. 29.95 set (ISBN 0-8010-2437-4). Baker Bk.

Existence & Nature of God. Ed. by Alfred J. Freddoso. LC 83-47521. (Notre Dame Studies in Philosophy of Religion). 190p. 1984. 16.95x (ISBN 0-268-00910-4, 85-09119); pap. text ed. 9.95x (ISBN 0-268-00911-2). U of Notre Dame Pr.

Existence, Being & God: An Introduction to the Philosophical Theology of John Mcquarrie. Eugene T. Long. LC 84-16566. 144p. 1985. 17.95 (ISBN 0-913729-02-7); pap. 10.95 (ISBN 0-913729-08-6). Paragon Hse.

Existence of God. John H. Hick. 305p. 1964. pap. 4.95 (ISBN 0-02-085450-1, Collier). Macmillan.

Existence of God. Ed. by George F. McLean. LC 73-161203. (Proceedings of the American Catholic Philosophical Association: Vol. 46). 1972. pap. 15.00 (ISBN 0-918090-06-7). Am Cath Philo.

Existence of God. Richard Swinburne. 1979. 42.00x (ISBN 0-19-824611-0); pap. 10.95x (ISBN 0-19-824778-8). Oxford U Pr.

Existence of the Soul. F. R. Ansari. pap. 1.00 (ISBN 0-686-18460-2). Kazi Pubns.

Existential Christian, No. 1. James Park. (Existential Freedom Ser. No. 1). 1970. pap. 1.00x (ISBN 0-89231-001-4). Existential Bks.

Existential Christian, No. 2. James Park. (Existential Freedom Ser.: No. 2). 1971. pap. 5.00x (ISBN 0-89231-002-2). Existential Bks.

Existential Interpretation of Paul's Letters to the Romans. James Park. LC 83-8852. 1983. pap. 4.00x (ISBN 0-89231-200-9). Existential Bks.

Existentialism. Patricia F. Sanborn. 192p. 1984. text ed. 22.00x (ISBN 0-8290-1015-7); pap. text ed. 9.95x (ISBN 0-8290-1016-5). Irvington.

Existentialism & Its Implications for Counseling. M. E. Fontes. pap. 0.75 (ISBN 0-8199-0382-5, L38138). Franciscan Herald.

Existentialism & Thomism. Joseph C. Mihalich. (Orig.). pap. 0.95 (ISBN 0-685-19401-9, 77, WL). Citadel Pr.

Existentialism & Thomism. Joseph C. Mihalich. (Quality Paperback: No. 170). 91p. 1969. pap. 3.95 (ISBN 0-8226-0170-2). Littlefield.

Existentialism, Religion & Death. Walter Kaufmann. 1976. pap. 4.95 (ISBN 0-452-00648-1, F648, Mer). NAL.

Existentialism: The Philosophy of Despair & the Quest for Hope. C. Stephen Evans. LC 83-11198. (Orig.). 1984. pap. 6.95 (ISBN 0-310-43741-5, 11198P). Zondervan.

Existentialism: With or Without God. Francis J. Lescoe. LC 74-1427. 1976. pap. 10.95 (ISBN 0-8189-0340-6). Alba.

Existentialist Theology: A Comparison of Heidegger & Bultmann. John Macquarrie. LC 79-4604. 1979. Repr. of 1955 ed. lib. bdg. 22.50x (ISBN 0-313-20795-X, MAAE). Greenwood.

Existentialist Theology of Paul Tillich. Bernard Martin. 1963. 14.95x (ISBN 0-8084-0399-0); pap. 10.95x (ISBN 0-8084-0400-8). New Coll U Pr.

Exit Here Please: Puzzles, Games & Mazes about the Book of Exodus. Zoe S. LeCours. (Illus.). 64p. (Orig.). 1986. pap. 4.95 (ISBN 0-934661-01-4, 7078). Lions Head Pr.

Exodus. George Bush. 1981. 22.50 (ISBN 0-86524-097-3, 0202). Klock & Klock.

Exodus. Miriam Chaikin. LC 85-27361. (Illus.). 32p. 1987. reinforced bdg. 14.95 (ISBN 0-8234-0607-5). Holiday.

Exodus. E. E. Cleveland. Ed. by Gerald Wheeler. 1985. write for info. (ISBN 0-8280-0299-1). Review & Herald.

Exodus. John F. Craghan. (Bible Commentary Ser.). 112p. 1985. pap. 2.95 (ISBN 0-8146-1371-3). Liturgical Pr.

Exodus. H. L. Ellison. LC 81-12917. (Daily Study Bible Old Testament Ser.). 216p. 1982. 12.95 (ISBN 0-664-21803-2); pap. 7.95 (ISBN 0-664-24570-6). Westminster.

Exodus. F. B. Huey, Jr. (Bible Study Commentary Ser.). 1977. pap. 4.95 (ISBN 0-310-36053-6, 11021P). Zondervan.

Exodus. Irving L. Jensen. (Bible Self-Study Ser.). 1970. pap. 3.25 (ISBN 0-8024-1002-2). Moody.

Exodus. Max Kappeler. LC 82-80905. (Bible in the Light of Christian Science Ser.: Vol. II). 90p. (Orig.). 1982. pap. 6.00 (ISBN 0-942958-01-2). Kappeler Inst Pub.

Exodus. Craig J. Lovik. (Arch Bks.). (Illus.). 24p. 1987. pap. 0.99 (ISBN 0-570-09001-6, 59-1429). Concordia.

Exodus. Roland E. Murphy. (Bible Ser.). Pt. 1. pap. 1.00 (ISBN 0-8091-5043-3); Pt. 2. pap. 1.00 (ISBN 0-8091-5044-1). Paulist Pr.

Exodus. B. Davie Napier. LC 59-10454. (Layman's Bible Commentary Ser: Vol. 3). 1963. write for info. (ISBN 0-8042-3003-X); pap. 4.95 (ISBN 0-8042-3063-3). John Knox.

Exodus. Ernst H. Wendland. (People's Bible Ser.). 1984. pap. 6.95 (ISBN 0-8100-0180-2, 15N0405); study guide, 52p 1.50 (ISBN 0-938272-50-0). Northwest Pub.

Exodus. Ronald F. Youngblood. (Everyman's Bible Commentary Ser.). (Orig.). 1983. pap. 5.95 (ISBN 0-8024-2002-8). Moody.

Exodus, a Commentary. Martin Noth. LC 62-7940. (Old Testament Library). 284p. 1962. 17.95 (ISBN 0-664-20370-1). Westminster.

Exodus: A Hermeneutics of Freedom. J. Severino Croatto. LC 80-26148. 112p. (Orig.). 1981. pap. 4.95 (ISBN 0-88344-111-X). Orbis Bks.

Exodus: A Modern Commentary. W. Gunther Plaut. (Torah Commentary Ser.). 571p. 1983. 20.00 (ISBN 0-8074-0040-8, 381606). UAHC.

Exodus & Daniel. Ed. by Francis A. Blackburn. LC 76-144440. (Belles Lettres Ser., Section I: No. 6). Repr. of 1907 ed. 16.50 (ISBN 0-404-53607-7). AMS Pr.

Exodus & Revolution. Michael Walzer. LC 84-45306. 177p. 1985. 15.95 (ISBN 0-465-02164-6). Basic.

Exodus & Revolution. Michael Walzer. LC 84-45306. 192p. 1986. pap. 6.95 (ISBN 0-465-02165-4, PL 5168). Basic.

Exodus: Cambridge Bible Commentary on the New English Bible. Ed. by R. E. Clements. (Old Testament Ser.). 1972. 32.50 (ISBN 0-521-08218-8); pap. 10.95 (ISBN 0-521-09656-1). Cambridge U Pr.

Exodus: (CC, Vol. 2. Maxie Dunnam. 320p. 1987. 18.95 (ISBN 0-8499-0407-2). Word Bks.

Exodus-Esther. Albert Barnes. 24.95 (ISBN 0-8010-0836-0). Baker Bk.

Exodus-Exodus, Cabalistic Bible: Part I, Slavery & the Coming of Moses. Albert L. Schutz. (Orig.). 1984. pap. 6.95 (ISBN 0-936596-10-4). Quantal.

Exodus, Leviticus, Numbers, with Excursus on Feasts, Ritual, Typology. Rita Burns. (Old Testament Message Ser.: Vol. 3). 15.95 (ISBN 0-89453-403-3); pap. 9.95 (ISBN 0-89453-238-3). M Glazier.

Exodus Pattern in the Bible. David Daube. LC 78-9920. 1979. Repr. of 1963 ed. lib. bdg. 24.75 (ISBN 0-313-21190-6, DAEX). Greenwood.

Exodus Scroll from Qumran: 4QpaleoExodm & the Samaritan Tradition. Judith E. Sanderson. (Harvard Semitic Studies). 378p. 1986. 20.95 (ISBN 1-55540-036-1, 04-04-30). Scholars Pr GA.

Exodus: The True Story. Ian Wilson. LC 85-45727. 208p. 1986. 19.45 (ISBN 0-06-250969-1, HarpR). Har-Row.

Exodus: Tyndale Old Testament Commentary. R. Alan Cole. LC 72-97952. 243p. 1973. 12.95 (ISBN 0-87784-865-3); pap. 6.95 (ISBN 0-87784-252-3). Inter-Varsity.

Exodus (WBC, Vol. 3. John Durham. 448p. 1986. 25.95 (ISBN 0-8499-0202-9). Word Bks.

Exon, Biography of a Governor. Duane Hutchinson. (Illus.). 243p. (Orig.). 1973. 5.95 (ISBN 0-934988-01-3); pap. 2.95 (ISBN 0-934988-02-1). Foun Bks.

Exorcising the Trouble Makers: Magic, Science, & Culture. Francis L. Hsu. LC 83-5522. (Contributions to the Study of Religion Ser.: No. 11). (Illus.). xvi, 164p. 1983. lib. bdg. 29.95 (ISBN 0-313-23780-8, HET/). Greenwood.

Exorcism Through the Ages. Elmo Nauman, Jr. (Illus.). 256p. 1974. pap. 3.95 (ISBN 0-8065-0450-1). Citadel Pr.

Exorzismus Im Altchristlichen Taufritual. Franz J. Dolger. 1909. pap. 15.00 (ISBN 0-384-12090-3). Johnson Repr.

Exoteric & Esoteric Christianity. Rudolf Steiner. 17p. 1983. pap. 3.00 (ISBN 0-919924-20-4). Anthroposophic.

Expanded Ministry to Adults: Program Guidelines. Dorsey Brause. 1979. pap. 3.50 (ISBN 0-89367-030-8). Light & Life.

Expanded Ministry to Youth: Program Guidelines. David Markell. (C. E. Ministries Ser.). 1977. pap. 3.50 (ISBN 0-89367-021-9). Light & Life.

Expanded Mission of "Old First" Churches. Raymond J. Bakke & Samuel K. Roberts. 128p. 1986. pap. 8.95 (ISBN 0-8170-1100-5). Judson.

Expanded Panorama Bible Study Course. Alfred T. Eade. (Illus.). 192p. 12.95 (ISBN 0-8007-0086-4). Revell.

Expanded Search for God: Pts. 1 & 2. Compiled by Association for Research & Enlightenment, Readings Research Dept. (Library: Vol.16 & 17). Pt. 1 499pgs. 11/1983. 12.95 (ISBN 0-87604-153-5); Pt. 2 662pgs. 12/1983. 14.95 (ISBN 0-87604-154-3). ARE Pr.

Expanded Vine's Expository Dictionary of New Testament Words. rev. ed. W. E. Vine. 1376p. 1984. pap. 14.95 (ISBN 0-87123-619-2, 230619). Bethany Hse.

Expanding Church. Spencer W. Palmer. LC 78-26082. 1979. 6.95 (ISBN 0-87747-732-9). Deseret Bk.

Expanding Circle: Ethics & Sociobiology. Peter Singer. 190p. 1981. 10.95 (ISBN 0-374-15112-1). FS&G.

Expanding Horizons. James A. Long. LC 65-24093. 1965. pap. 3.50 (ISBN 0-911500-75-8). Theos U Pr.

Expanding Outlines of the New Testament Books. Harvey Childress. 5.95 (ISBN 0-89137-536-8). Quality Pubns.

Expanding Role of the Yeshiva Educator. 1.50 (ISBN 0-914131-19-2, C26). Torah Umesorah.

Expanding Your Church School Program: Planning Elective Classes for Adults. David W. Andersen & Wendell Brooker. 88p. 1983. pap. 3.95 (ISBN 0-8170-1009-2). Judson.

Expansion of Christianity. D. R. De Lacey. (Discovering the Bible Ser.). pap. 8.95 (ISBN 0-7175-1163-4). Dufour.

Expansion of Christianity in the First Three Centuries, 2 vols. Adolf Harnack. Tr. by James Moffatt. LC 72-4163. (Select Bibliographies Reprint Ser.). 1972. Repr. of 1905 ed. Set. 64.00 (ISBN 0-8369-6882-4). Ayer Co Pubs.

Expansion of Christianity in the First Three Centuries, Vol. I. Adolf Harnack. Ed. by James Moffatt. LC 72-4163. 494p. Repr. of 1904 ed. 56.00 (ISBN 0-8290-0530-7). Irvington.

Expansion of God. Leslie G. Howard. LC 81-4521. 464p. (Orig.). 1981. pap. 3.74 (ISBN 0-88344-121-7). Orbis Bks.

Expect a Miracle. Dale E. Galloway. 1982. pap. 4.95 (ISBN 0-8423-0822-9). Tyndale.

Expectant Creativity: The Action of Hope in Christian Ethics. Vincent J. Genovesi. LC 81-43807. 172p. (Orig.). 1982. lib. bdg. 27.75 (ISBN 0-8191-2407-9); pap. text ed. 11.50 (ISBN 0-8191-2408-7). U Pr of Amer.

Expectation of the Poor: Latin American Base Ecclesial Communities in Protestant Perspective. Guillermo Cook. LC 85-5131. 256p. (Orig.). 1985. pap. 13.95 (ISBN 0-88344-209-4). Orbis Bks.

Expectations, Hopes, Dreams, Fantasies & Desires. Katie Tonn. (Uplook Ser.). 31p. 1978. pap. 0.99 (ISBN 0-8163-0346-0). Pacific Pr Pub Assn.

Expeditions to Prussia & the Holy Land Made by Henry Earl of Derby. Richard Kyngeston. Ed. by L. T. Smith. 1965. Repr. of 1894 ed. 27.00 (ISBN 0-384-30775-2). Johnson Repr.

Expelling Demons. Derek Prince. 1969. pap. 0.25 (ISBN 0-934920-18-4, B70). Derek Prince.

Experience & Faith. William Horden. LC 82-72653. 160p. 1983. pap. 9.95 (ISBN 0-8066-1960-0, 10-2133). Augsburg.

Experience & God. John E. Smith. 1968. 11.95x (ISBN 0-19-501207-0). Oxford U Pr.

Experience & God. John E. Smith. LC 68-18566. 1974. pap. 6.95 (ISBN 0-19-501847-8). Oxford U Pr.

Experience & Language of Grace. Roger Haight. LC 79-84403. 192p. 1979. pap. 7.95 (ISBN 0-8091-2200-6). Paulist Pr.

Experience, Explanation & Faith: An Introduction to the Philosophy of Religion. Anthony O'Hear. LC 83-15957. 266p. (Orig.). 1984. pap. 10.95 (ISBN 0-7100-9768-9). Methuen Inc.

Experience of Celibacy. Keith Clark. LC 81-69747. (Illus.). 176p. (Orig.). 1982. pap. 4.95 (ISBN 0-87793-240-9). Ave Maria.

Experience of Death: The Moral Problem of Suicide. Paul-Louis Landsberg. Ed. by Robert Kastenaum. LC 76-19579. (Death & Dying Ser.). 1977. Repr. of 1953 ed. lib. bdg. 19.00x (ISBN 0-405-09576-7). Ayer Co Pubs.

Experience of God: An Invitation to Do Theology. Dermot A. Lane. LC 81-80873. 96p. (Orig.). 1981. pap. 4.95 (ISBN 0-8091-2394-0). Paulist Pr.

Experience of Insight: A Simple & Direct Guide to Buddhist Meditation. Joseph Goldstein. LC 82-42682. 185p. (Orig.). 1983. pap. 7.95 (ISBN 0-87773-226-4). Shambhala Pubns.

Experience of Insight: A Simple & Direct Guide to Buddhist Meditation. Joseph Goldstein. 1987. pap. 9.95. Shambhala Pubns.

Experience of Lent with the Risen Christ. Catherine Nerney. 1.95 (ISBN 0-8091-9308-6). Paulist Pr.

Experience of Life in the Spirit. Jean LaPlace. Tr. by John R. Mooney. 220p. 1977. 6.95 (ISBN 0-8199-0594-1). Franciscan Herald.

Experience of No-Self: A Contemplative Journey. Bernadette Roberts. LC 84-5500. 204p. 1984. pap. 9.95 (ISBN 0-87773-289-2, 72693-6). Shambhala Pubns.

Experience of Nothingness. Michael Novak. 1971. pap. 5.95x (ISBN 0-06-131938-4, TB 1938, Torch). Har-Row.

Experience of Praying. Sean Caulfield. LC 79-92428. 88p. 1980. 3.95 (ISBN 0-8091-2358-4). Paulist Pr.

Experience of Religious Diversity. John Hick & Hasan Askari. 242p. 1985. text ed. 39.95 (ISBN 0-566-05020-X). Gower Pub Co.

Experience of the Christmas Foundation Meeting, 1923. Arvia M. Ege. 14p. 1981. pap. 2.50 (ISBN 0-932776-03-5). Adonis Pr.

Experience with the Supernatural in Early Christian Times. Shirley J. Case. LC 75-174851. Repr. of 1929 ed. 26.50 (ISBN 0-405-08345-9, Blom Pubns). Ayer Co Pubs.

Experience Worketh Hope. A. J. Gossip. (Scholar As Preacher Ser.). 208p. 1945. 10.95 (ISBN 0-567-04423-8, Pub. by T & T Clark Ltd UK). Fortress.

Experiences Facing Death. Mary Austin. Ed. by Robert Kastenbaum. LC 76-19557. (Death and Dying Ser.). 1977. Repr. of 1931 ed. lib. bdg. 23.50x (ISBN 0-405-09553-8). Ayer Co Pubs.

Experiences in Spiritualism with Mr. D. D. Home. Viscount Adare. LC 75-36824. (Occult Ser.). 1976. Repr. of 1870 ed. 16.00x (ISBN 0-405-07937-0). Ayer Co Pubs.

Experiences of God. Jurgen Moltmann. Tr. by Margaret Kohl from Ger. LC 80-8046. 96p. 1980. pap. 4.25 (ISBN 0-8006-1406-2, 1-1406). Fortress.

Experiences with God & His Messengers: The Key to God's Kingdom. Hendrik Th. Lilipaly. 1980. 6.00 (ISBN 0-682-49506-9). Exposition Pr FL.

Experiencing Comprehensive Education: A Study of Bishop McGregor School. Robert G. Burgess. 288p. 1983. 24.00 (ISBN 0-416-35150-6, NO. 4037); pap. 11.95 (ISBN 0-416-35160-3, NO. 4038). Methuen Inc.

Experiencing Fullness in Christian Living: Studies in Colossians. Roger Ferguson. 36p. 1982. pap. 3.50 (ISBN 0-939298-08-2). J M Prods.

Experiencing God All Ways & Every Day. J. Norman King. 160p. (Orig.). 1982. pap. 7.95 (ISBN 0-86683-632-2, HarpR). Har-Row.

Experiencing God: Theology as Spirituality. Kenneth Leech. LC 84-48237. 352p. 1985. 20.45 (ISBN 0-06-065226-8, HarpR). Har-Row.

Experiencing God Through Prayer. Madame Guyon. (Experiencing the Depths of Jesus Christ Ser.). 176p. 1984. pap. text ed. 3.50 (ISBN 0-88368-153-6). Whitaker Hse.

Experiencing Jesus. John N. Wijngaards. LC 81-52295. 176p. (Orig.). 1981. pap. 4.95 (ISBN 0-87793-235-2). Ave Maria.

Experiencing Jewish Boston. Brigite S. Grossman. LC 80-85316. (Illus.). 54p. (Orig.). 1981. pap. 3.50 (ISBN 0-9605624-0-0). Jewish Comm Ctr.

Experiencing More with Less. Meredith S. Dregni. LC 83-80954. 88p. (Orig.). 1983. pap. 4.95 (ISBN 0-8361-3334-X). Herald Pr.

Experiencing Reincarnation. James S. Perkins. LC 77-5249. (Illus.). 1977. pap. 4.95 (ISBN 0-8356-0500-0, Quest). Theos Pub Hse.

Experiencing Siva: Encounters with a Hindu Diety. Ed. by Fred Clothey & J. Bruce Long. 1983. 24.00x (ISBN 0-8364-1041-6). South Asia Bks.

Experiencing the Depths of Jesus Christ. 3rd ed. Jeanne M. Guyon. Ed. by Gene Edwards. 1975. pap. 5.95 (ISBN 0-940232-00-6). Christian Bks.

Experiencing the Good News: The New Testament as Communication. James M. Reese. (Good News Studies Ser.: Vol. 10). 1984. pap. 9.95 (ISBN 0-89453-448-3). M Glazier.

Experientiae Spirituales, 6 Vols. 2nd ed. Emanuel Swedenborg. Ed. by John D. Odhner. (Lat.). 3600p. 1982. Set. 270.00 (ISBN 0-910557-00-4). Acad New Church.

Experiment in Practical Christianity: Leader's Guide. rev. ed. John Carr & Adrienne Carr. 96p. 1985. manual 6.95 (ISBN 0-88177-028-0, DRO28B). Discipleship Res.

Experiment in Practical Christianity: Participant's Guide. John Carr & Adrienne Carr. 104p. (Orig.). 1985. pap. 6.95 (ISBN 0-88177-027-2, DRO27B). Discipleship Res.

Experiment of Life: Science & Religion. Ed. by F. Kenneth Hare. 192p. 1983. 25.00x (ISBN 0-8020-2486-6); pap. 9.95 (ISBN 0-8020-6506-6). U of Toronto Pr.

Experiment with a Life. Howard E. Collier. (Orig.). 1953. pap. 2.500784485x (ISBN 0-87574-069-3). Pendle Hill.

Experimental Preaching. Ed. by John Killinger. LC 72-8419. Repr. of 1973 ed. 33.30 (ISBN 0-8357-9006-1, 2009067). Bks Demand UMI.

Experimentation in American Religion: The New Mysticisms & Their Implications for the Churches. Robert Wuthnow. 1978. 31.00x (ISBN 0-520-03446-5). U of Cal Pr.

Experimenting with Truth: The Fusion of Religion with Technology Needed for Humanity's Survival. Rustrum Roy. (Hibbert Lectures: 1979). (Illus.). 228p. 1981. 32.00 (ISBN 0-08-025820-4); pap. 10.00 (ISBN 0-08-025819-0). Pergamon.

Experiments in Community. Norman J. Whitney. 1983. pap. 2.50x (ISBN 0-87574-149-5, 149). Pendle Hill.

Experiments in Living: A Study of the Nature & Foundation of Ethics or Morals in the Light of Recent Work in Social Anthropology. Alexander Macbeath. LC 77-27180. (Gifford Lectures: 1948-49). Repr. of 1952 ed. 28.00 (ISBN 0-404-60503-6). AMS Pr.

Experiments in Practical Spirituality: Keyed to a Search for God, Book II. Mark A. Thurston. (Illus.). 147p. (Orig.). 1980. pap. 5.95 (ISBN 0-87604-122-5). ARE Pr.

Experiments in Prayer. Betsy Caprio. (Illus.). 192p. 1973. pap. 5.95 (ISBN 0-87793-054-6). Ave Maria.

Experiments with Bible Study. Hans-Ruedi Weber. LC 82-13398. 330p. 1983. pap. 12.95 (ISBN 0-664-24461-0). Westminster.

Explaining Death to Children. Ed. by Earl A. Grollman. LC 67-4891. 1969. pap. 8.95 (ISBN 0-8070-2385-X, BP317). Beacon Pr.

Explaining Salvation to Children. 8th ed. Marjorie Soderholm. 1979. pap. 1.50 (ISBN 0-911802-13-4). Free Church Pubns.

Explaining Unificatiion Thought. Sang H. Lee. LC 80-54858. 356p. pap. 10.95 (ISBN 0-9606480-0-3). Rose Sharon Pr.

Explaining Unification Thought. Sang H. Lee. LC 80-54858. 356p. (Orig.). 1981. pap. 9.95 (ISBN 0-9606480-0-3). HSA Pubns.

Explanation of Dr. Martin Luther's Small Catechism. 265p. 1982. write for info. (ISBN 0-89279-043-1). Board Pub Evang.

Explanation of the Baltimore Catechism. Thomas L. Kinkead. LC 78-74571. (Baltimore Catechism Ser.: No. 4). 1978. pap. text ed. 8.50 (ISBN 0-89555-085-7). TAN Bks Pubs.

Explanatory Notes & Remarks on Milton's Paradise Lost. Jonathan Richardson & Jonathan Richardson, Jr. LC 77-174317. Repr. of 1734 ed. 37.50 (ISBN 0-404-05298-3). AMS Pr.

Explanatory Notes on the New Testament. John Wesley. 29.95 (ISBN 0-317-07537-3, 96510). Baker Bk.

Explanatory Notes on the New Testament, 2 vols. John Wesley. 1056p. Date not set. 29.95 (ISBN 0-913573-06-X). Hendrickson MA.

Exploding Church. Frederick Franck. pap. 2.95 (ISBN 0-440-52432-6). Dell.

Exploding the Myths That Could Destroy America. Erwin W. Lutzer. (Orig.). 1986. pap. 6.95 (ISBN 0-8024-5692-8). Moody.

Exploits of the Incomparable Mulla Nasrudin. Ed. by Idries Shah. 1983. Repr. of 1968 ed. 14.95 (ISBN 0-86304-022-5, Pub. by Octagon Pr England). Ins Study Human.

Exploration into God. John A. Robinson. LC 67-26529. 1967. 4.95 (ISBN 0-8047-0322-1). Stanford U Pr.

Exploration into Insight. J. Krishnamurti. LC 79-6651. 192p. (Orig.). 1980. pap. 7.95 (ISBN 0-06-064811-2, RD 326, HarpR). Har-Row.

Exploration of the Inner World: A Study of Mental Disorder and Religious Experience. Anton T. Boisen. 1971. pap. 12.95x (ISBN 0-8122-1020-4, Pa Paperbks). U of Pa Pr.

Explorations at Sodom: Story of Ancient Sodom in the Light of Modern Research. Melvin G. Kyle. Ed. by Moshe Davis. LC 77-70715. (America & the Holy Land Ser.). (Illus.). 1977. Repr. of 1928 ed. lib. bdg. 12.00x (ISBN 0-405-10304-2). Ayer Co Pubs.

Explore the Book. J. Sidlow Baxter. 36.95 (ISBN 0-310-20620-0, 6729). Zondervan.

Explore the Word! Henry Morris, 3rd. LC 78-55611. 1978. pap. 7.95 (ISBN 0-89051-047-4). Master Bks.

Explorer of Realms of Art, Life, & Thought: A Survey of the Works of Philosopher & Theologian Constantine Cavarnos. John E. Rexine. LC 85-81278. (Illus.). 184p. 1985. 9.00 (ISBN 0-914744-69-0, 85-81278); pap. 6.00 (ISBN 0-914744-70-4). Inst Byzantine.

Exploring Acts, Vol. 1. John Phillips. (Exploring Ser.). (Orig.). 1986. pap. 11.95 (ISBN 0-8024-2435-X). Moody.

Exploring Buddhism. Christmas Humphreys. LC 74-12206. 188p. (Orig.). 1975. pap. 2.50 (ISBN 0-8356-0454-3, Quest). Theos Pub Hse.

Exploring Christian Education. A. E Sanner & A. F. Harper. 504p. 1978. 15.95 (ISBN 0-8341-0494-6). Beacon Hill.

Exploring Christian Holiness: The Historical Development, Vol. 2. Paul M. Bassett & William M. Greathouse. (Exploring Christian Holiness Ser.). 250p. 1984. 15.95 (ISBN 0-8341-0926-3). Beacon Hill.

Exploring Christian Holiness, Vol. I: The Biblical Foundations, 3 Vols. W. T. Purkiser. (Exploring Christian Holiness Ser.). 280p. 1983. 10.95 (ISBN 0-8341-0843-7). Beacon Hill.

Exploring Christian Holiness, Vol. 3: The Theological Formulations. Richard S. Taylor. (Exploring Christian Holiness Ser.). 300p. 1985. 12.95 (ISBN 0-8341-1077-6). Beacon Hill.

Exploring Christian Theology. Ronnie Littlejohn. 542p. (Orig.). 1985. lib. bdg. 37.25 (ISBN 0-8191-4459-2); pap. text ed. 19.75 (ISBN 0-8191-4460-6). U Pr of Amer.

Exploring Christianity: An Introduction. Robert C. Monk & Joseph Stamey. (Illus.). 256p. 1984. text ed. write for info. (ISBN 0-13-296385-X). P-H.

Exploring Church Growth. Wilbert R. Shenk. 336p. 1983. pap. 10.95 (ISBN 0-8028-1962-1). Eerdmans.

Exploring Churches. Paul Clowney & Tessa Clowney. LC 82-210857. pap. 23.50 (ISBN 0-317-30134-9, 2025317). Bks Demand UMI.

Exploring Exodus. Wilbur Fields. LC 78-301089. (Bible Study Textbook Ser.). (Illus.). 1977. 18.95 (ISBN 0-89900-006-1). College Pr Pub.

Exploring Exodus: The Heritage of Biblical Israel. Nahum M. Sarna. LC 85-18445. 288p. 1987. pap. 8.95 (ISBN 0-8052-0830-5). Schocken.

Exploring Faith & Life: A Journey in Faith for Junior High - Manual for Clergy & Leaders. Barbara Wolf & Frederick B. Wolf. 64p. (Orig.). 1983. pap. 3.95 (ISBN 0-8164-2437-3, HarpR). Har-Row.

Exploring Faith & Life: A Journey in Faith for Junior High - Manual for Sponsors. Barbara Wolf & Frederick B. Wolf. 32p. (Orig.). 1983. pap. 2.95 (ISBN 0-8164-2436-5, HarpR). Har-Row.

Exploring Faith & Life: A Journey in Faith for Junior High Student's Reader. Frederick B. Wolf & Barbara B. Wolf. 128p. 1983. pap. 5.95 (ISBN 0-8164-2431-4, HarpR). Har-Row.

Exploring Genesis. John Phillips. LC 80-23685. 582p. 1980. pap. 9.95 (ISBN 0-8024-2430-9). Moody.

Exploring God's Web of Life. Timothy L. Barnett & Steven R. Flora. 80p. 1982. pap. 5.25 (ISBN 0-942684-01-X). Camp Guidepts.

Exploring God's Word: A Guide to John's Gospel. Donald Guthrie. 232p. (Orig.). pap. 7.95 (ISBN 0-8028-0256-7). Eerdmans.

Exploring God's World: A Guide to Ephesians, Philippians, & Colossians. Donald Guthrie. 224p. (Orig.). 1985. pap. 6.95 (ISBN 0-8028-0084-X). Eerdmans.

Exploring Hebrews. John Phillips. LC 76-39908. 1977. pap. 9.95 (ISBN 0-8024-2431-7). Moody.

Exploring India's Sacred Art: Selected Writings of Stella Kramrisch. Ed. by Barbara S. Miller. LC 82-60302. (Illus., Orig.). 1983. 57.95x (ISBN 0-8122-7856-9); pap. 21.00x (ISBN 0-8122-1134-0). U of Pa Pr.

Exploring Jewish History. Shirley Stern. 1978. pap. 8.95x (ISBN 0-87068-651-8). Ktav.

Exploring Judaism: A Reconstructionist Approach. Rebecca T. Alpert & Jacob J. Staub. 108p. 1985. 11.95 (ISBN 0-935457-01-1); pap. 5.95 (ISBN 0-935457-00-3). Reconstructionist Pr.

Exploring Mysticism: A Methodological Essay. Frits Staal. LC 74-76391. (Center for South & Southeast Asia Studies). 1975. 42.00x (ISBN 0-520-02726-4); pap. 4.95 (ISBN 0-520-03119-9, CAL 313). U of Cal Pr.

Exploring Our Living Past. Laura Simms & Ruth Kozodoy. Ed. by Jules Harlow. (Our Living Past Ser). (Illus.). 1978. pap. 6.95x (ISBN 0-87441-309-5). Behrman.

Exploring Religious Meaning. 2nd ed. Robert Monk et al. (Illus.). 1980. text ed. write for info. (ISBN 0-13-297515-7). P-H.

Exploring Religious Meaning. 3rd ed. Robert C. Monk et al. Ed. by Bert Affleck & Tetsuano Yamori. (Illus.). 416p. 1987. pap. text ed. write for info. (ISBN 0-13-297524-6). P-H.

Exploring Revelation. John Phillips. LC 74-15330. 288p. 1974. pap. 9.95 (ISBN 0-8024-2432-5). Moody.

Exploring Revelation. rev. ed. John Phillips. (Exploring Ser.). 1987. pap. 11.95 (ISBN 0-8024-2497-X). Moody.

Exploring Romans. John Phillips. 250p. 1971. pap. 9.95 (ISBN 0-8024-2433-3). Moody.

Exploring Romans. rev. ed. John Phillips. (Exploring Ser.). 1987. pap. 11.95 (ISBN 0-8024-2429-5). Moody.

Exploring Spiritual Direction. Alan Jones. 160p. 1982. (HarpR); pap. 7.95 (ISBN 0-8164-2483-7). Har-Row.

Exploring the Bible. rev. ed. (Time of Life Learning Ser.). (Illus.). 32p. 1985. pap. 2.95 (ISBN 0-89622-243-8). Twenty-Third.

Exploring the Bible with Children. Dorothy J. Furnish. LC 74-34486. 176p. 1975. pap. 6.95 (ISBN 0-687-12426-3). Abingdon.

Exploring the California Missions: Activity Cards. Carol O. Martin. Ed. by Malcolm Margolin. (Illus.). 94p. (Orig.). 1984. pap. 7.95 (ISBN 0-318-18397-8). Bay Area CA.

Exploring the Faith We Share. Ed. by Charles V. LaFontaine & Glenn C. Stone. LC 79-92856. 144p. 1980. pap. 3.50 (ISBN 0-8091-2301-0). Paulist Pr.

Exploring the Future. John Phillips. LC 82-557. 400p. 1983. 14.95 (ISBN 0-8407-5275-X). Nelson.

Exploring the New Testament. John Carmody et al. (Illus.). 448p. 1986. text ed. 31.00 (ISBN 0-13-297276-X). P-H.

Exploring the New Testament. Rachel Henderlite. (Orig.). 1946. pap. 5.95 (ISBN 0-8042-0240-0). John Knox.

Exploring the Old Testament. Rachel Henderlite. (Orig.). 1945. pap. 5.95 (ISBN 0-8042-0120-X). John Knox.

Exploring the Philosophy of Religion. D. Stewart. (Illus.). 1980. pap. text ed. write for info. (ISBN 0-13-297366-9). P-H.

Exploring the Psalms. Erik Routley. LC 74-20674. 170p. 1975. pap. 3.95 (ISBN 0-664-24999-X). Westminster.

Exploring the Psalms, Vol. 3. John Philips. 318p. 1986. 14.95 (ISBN 0-87213-686-8). Loizeaux.

Exploring the Psalms, Vol. 4. John Phillips. 1987. 14.95 (ISBN 0-87213-687-6). Loizeaux.

Exploring the Psalms, Vol. 5. John Phillips. 1987. 14.95 (ISBN 0-87213-688-4). Loizeaux.

Exploring the Psalms: Vol. II, 42-72. John Phillips. 288p. 1986. 14.95 (ISBN 0-87213-685-X). Loizeaux.

Exploring the Psalms: Volume 1 (Psalms 1-41) John Phillips. 318p. 1985. 14.95 (ISBN 0-87213-684-1). Loizeaux.

Exploring the Scriptures. John Phillips. 1965. pap. 9.95 (ISBN 0-8024-2434-1). Moody.

Exploring the Song of Solomon. John Phillips. 157p. 1984. pap. 6.95 (ISBN 0-87213-683-3). Loizeaux.

Exploring the World of the Jew. John Phillips. LC 81-16844. 288p. 1982. pap. 9.95 (ISBN 0-8024-2411-2). Moody.

Exploring Truths Through. Louise Ebner. pap. 3.95 (ISBN 0-89957-602-8). AMG Pubs.

Exploring Unification Theology. Ed. by Darrol Bryant & Susan Hodges. LC 78-63274. 168p. (Orig.). 1978. pap. 7.95. Rose Sharon Pr.

Exploring Unification Theology. 2nd ed. Ed. by M. Darrol Bryant & Susan Hodges. LC 78-63274. (Conference Ser.: No. 1). 168p. 1978. pap. text ed. 7.95x (ISBN 0-932894-00-3, Pub. by New Era Bks). Paragon Hse.

Exploring Unification Theology. Ed. by Susan Hodges & M. Darrol Bryant. LC 78-51957. 226p. 1978. write for info. E Mellen.

Exploring Worship: Practical Guide to Praise & Worship. Bob Sorge. 304p. (Orig.). 1987. pap. 5.95 (ISBN 0-936369-04-3). Son-Rise Pubns.

Exploring Your Family Story. Douglas Purnell. (Illus.). 156p. (Orig.). 1983. pap. 9.95 (ISBN 0-85819-415-5, Pub. by JBCE). ANZ Religious Pubns.

Exposicion de Segunda Timoteo. N. A. Woychuk. Orig. Title: Exposition of Second Timothy. (Span.). 1976. pap. 3.95 (ISBN 0-8254-1879-8). Kregel.

Exposing Demon's Work. 1982. 1.25 (ISBN 0-89858-034-X). Fill the Gap.

Exposing False Spiritual Leaders. John MacArthur, Jr. (John MacArthur's Bible Studies). (Orig.). 1986. pap. 3.95 (ISBN 0-8024-5345-7). Moody.

Exposing the Devil's Work. 1982. 1.25 (ISBN 0-89858-033-1). Fill the Gap.

Exposition of Colossians. Jean Daille. 698p. 1983. lib. bdg. 24.95 (ISBN 0-86524-141-4, 5104). Klock & Klock.

Exposition of Daniel. Herbert C. Leupold. 1969. 13.95 (ISBN 0-8010-5531-8). Baker Bk.

Exposition of Ecclesiastes. Herbert C. Leupold. 1966. 12.95 (ISBN 0-8010-5505-9). Baker Bk.

Exposition of Ecclesiastes. Ralph Wardlaw. 432p. 1982. lib. bdg. 16.25 Smythe Sewn (ISBN 0-86524-147-3, 2102). Klock & Klock.

Exposition of Ephesians: Lessons in Grace & Godliness. R. Pattison & H. Moule. 390p. 1983. lib. bdg. 14.75 Smythe Sewn (ISBN 0-86524-153-8, 4902). Klock & Klock.

Exposition of First Corinthians Thirteen. John D. Jones. 253p. 1982. lib. bdg. 9.50 Smythe Sewn (ISBN 0-86524-144-9, 4603). Klock & Klock.

Exposition of Genesis, 2 Vols. Herbert C. Leupold. Vol. 1. 15.95 (ISBN 0-8010-5549-0); Vol. 2. 15.95 (ISBN 0-8010-5522-9). Baker Bk.

Exposition of Hebrews. Arthur W. Pink. 1954. 29.95 (ISBN 0-8010-6857-6). Baker Bk.

Exposition of Isaiah, 1 vol. ed. Herbert C. Leupold. 1977. 22.95 (ISBN 0-8010-5577-6). Baker Bk.

Exposition of Paul's Epistle to the Philippians. John Hutchinson. 328p. 1985. smythe sewn 13.00 (ISBN 0-86524-190-2, 5003). Klock & Klock.

Exposition of Proverbs, 2 vols. in 1. George Lawson. LC 80-8070. (Kregel Timeless Classics Ser.). 904p. 1981. 27.50 (ISBN 0-8254-3123-9). Kregel.

Exposition of Psalm 119. C. Bridges. 504p. 1986. 16.95 (ISBN 0-8254-2257-4). Kregel.

Exposition of Psalms. Herbert C. Leupold. 1970. 24.95 (ISBN 0-8010-5521-0). Baker Bk.

Exposition of St. Paul's Epistles. Richard Sibbes. (Works of Sibbes: Vol. 5). 1978. Repr. 16.95 (ISBN 0-85151-246-1). Banner of Truth.

Exposition of the Book of Isaiah. William Kelly. 1979. 15.25 (ISBN 0-86524-003-5, 2301). Klock & Klock.

Exposition of the Books of Chronicles. William H. Bennett. 467p. 1983. lib. bdg. 17.50 (ISBN 0-86524-169-4, 1401). Klock & Klock.

Exposition of the Doctrines of Grace. C. H. Spurgeon. 1975. 1.50 (ISBN 0-686-09096-9). Pilgrim Pubns.

Exposition of the Epistle of Jude. Thomas Manton. 375p. 14.00 (ISBN 0-86524-172-4, 6501). Klock & Klock.

Exposition of the Epistles of James & John. Simon J. Kistemaker. 1986. 18.95 (ISBN 0-8010-5469-9). Baker Bk.

Exposition of the Epistles of John. W. Kelly. 6.25 (ISBN 0-88172-100-X). Believers Bkshelf.

Exposition of the Gospel of John, 4 Vols. in 1. Arthur W. Pink. 1945. 29.95 (ISBN 0-310-31180-2, 10566). Zondervan.

Exposition of the Gospel of Luke. W. Kelly. 6.25 (ISBN 0-88172-102-6). Believers Bkshelf.

Exposition of the Gospel of Mark. W. Kelly. 5.50 (ISBN 0-88172-103-4). Believers Bkshelf.

Exposition of the Gospels, 2 vol. Philip Doddridge. 1986. Set. 37.50 (ISBN 0-8254-2456-9). Vol. I, 472pgs. Vol. II, 492pgs. Kregel.

Exposition of the Parables. Benjamin Keach. LC 73-85297. (Kregel Reprint Library). 918p. 1988. 29.95 (ISBN 0-8254-3016-X). Kregel.

Exposition of the Pilgrim's Progress, with Illustrative Quotations from Bunyan's Minor Works. Robert Stevevson. LC 77-24243. 1977. Repr. of 1912 ed. lib. bdg. 27.50 (ISBN 0-8414-7933-X). Folcroft.

Exposition of the Revelation of Jesus Christ. Walter Scott. LC 79-88736. 1979. Repr. 16.95 (ISBN 0-8254-3731-8). Kregel.

Exposition of the Whole Bible. G. Campbell Morgan. 544p. 1959. 17.95 (ISBN 0-8007-0088-0). Revell.

Exposition of Titus. Thomas Taylor. 1970. 20.75 (ISBN 0-86524-027-2, 5601). Klock & Klock.

Exposition of Zechariah. Herbert C. Leupold. 1965. 9.95 (ISBN 0-8010-5512-1). Baker Bk.

Exposition on the Sermon on the Mount. Arthur W. Pink. 9.95 (ISBN 0-8010-7075-9). Baker Bk.

Exposition on the Song of Songs. William of Saint Thierry. (Cistercian Fathers Ser.: No. 6). 171p. 7.95 (ISBN 0-87907-306-3). Cistercian Pubns.

Expositions & Notes on Sundry Portions of the Holy Scriptures. William Tyndale. Repr. of 1849 ed. 31.00 (ISBN 0-384-62260-7). Johnson Repr.

Expositions of Bible Doctrines, 10 vols. in four. Donald C. Barnhouse. (Bible Study). 1952-64. Set. 49.95 (ISBN 0-8028-3014-5). Eerdmans.

Expositions of Holy Scripture, 17 vols. Alexander MacLaren. 12830p. 1975. Repr. Set. 295.00 (ISBN 0-8010-5967-4). Baker Bk.

Expositions of the Epistles of Peter & Jude: New Testament Commentary. Simon J. Kistemaker. 1987. text ed. 19.95 (ISBN 0-8010-5484-2). Baker Bk.

Expositor (Atthasalini, 2 vols. in 1. rev. ed. Buddhaghosa. Tr. by Maung Tin. Rev. by Carolina A. Davis. LC 78-72385. Repr. of 1920 ed. 49.50 (ISBN 0-404-17247-4). AMS Pr.

Expositor's Bible Commentary, Vol. I. 1986. cloth 29.95 (ISBN 0-88469-189-6). BMH Bks.

Expositor's Bible Commentary, 5 vols. Frank E. Gaebelein. 1979. Set. 107.75 (ISBN 0-310-36568-6, 11183). Zondervan.

Expositor's Bible Commentary, Vol. 1. Ed. by Frank E. Gaebelein. (Introductory Actilces). 1979. 22.95 (ISBN 0-310-36430-2, 11170). Zondervan.

Expositor's Bible Commentary, Vol. 6. Ed. by Frank E. Gaebelein. 1986. text ed. 29.95 (ISBN 0-88469-182-9). BMH Bks.

Expositor's Bible Commentary, Vol. 7. Archer, Jr. et al. 1986. 24.95 (ISBN 0-88469-194-2). BMH Bks.

Expositor's Bible Commentary, Vol. 8. D. A. Carson et al. 1986. 29.95 (ISBN 0-88469-188-8). BMH Bks.

Expositor's Bible Commentary, Vol. 9. Ed. by Frank E. Gaebelein. (John & Acts). 464p. 1980. 19.95 (ISBN 0-310-36510-4, 11178). Zondervan.

Expositor's Bible Commentary, Vol. 9. Merrill C. Tenney & Richard N. Longenecker. 1986. 19.95 (ISBN 0-88469-195-0). BMH Bks.

Expositor's Bible Commentary, Vol. 10. Everett F. Harrison et al. 1986. 19.95 (ISBN 0-88469-196-9). BMH Bks.

Expositor's Bible Commentary, Vol. 11. A. Skevington Wood et al. 1986. 19.95 (ISBN 0-88469-197-7). BMH Bks.

Expositor's Bible Commentary, Vol. 12. Ed. by Frank E. Gaebelein. (Hebrews - Revelation). 624p. 1981. 19.95 (ISBN 0-310-36540-6, 11181). Zondervan.

Expositor's Bible Commentary, Vol. 12. Leon Morris et al. 1986. cloth 19.95 (ISBN 0-88469-198-5). BMH Bks.

Expositor's Bible Commentary: Daniel & the Minor Prophets, Vol. 7. Ed. by Frank E. Gaebelein. 752p. 1985. text ed. 24.95 (ISBN 0-310-36490-6, 11176). Zondervan.

Expositor's Bible Commentary: Isaiah, Jeremiah, Lamentations, Ezekiel, Vol. 6. Ed. by Frank E. Gaebelein. 1088p. 1986. 29.95 (ISBN 0-310-36480-9, 11175). Zondervan.

Expositors' Bible Commentary: Matthew, Mark, Luke, Vol. 8. Ed. by Frank E. Gaebelein. LC 83-11177. 1056p. (Orig.). 1984. 29.95 (ISBN 0-310-36500-7, 11177). Zondervan.

Expositor's Bible Commentary, (Romans - Galatians, Vol. 10. Ed. by Frank E. Gaebelein. 600p. 1976. 19.95 (ISBN 0-310-36520-1, 11179). Zondervan.

Expositor's Bible Commentary Vol. 11 (Ephesians-Philemon) Ed. by Frank E. Gaebelein. 1978. 19.95 (ISBN 0-310-36530-9, 11180). Zondervan.

Expositor's Bible Commentary, Vol. 4: Kings-Job. Ed. by Frank E. Gaebelein. (Expositor's Bible Commentary Ser.). 1987. 29.95 (ISBN 0-310-36460-4). Zondervan.

Expositor's Greek New Testament, 5 Vols. Ed. by W. Robertson Nicoll. 1952. Set. 60.00 (ISBN 0-8028-2108-1). Eerdmans.

Expository & Exegetical Studies. F. J. Hort & A. F. Hort. 1980. 29.50 (ISBN 0-86524-021-3, 7103). Klock & Klock.

Expository Dictionary of Bible Words. Lawrence O. Richards. 596p. 1985. 24.95 (ISBN 0-310-39000-1, 18300). Zondervan.

Expository Dictionary of New Testament Words. W. E. Vine. 1396p. 14.95 (ISBN 0-8007-0089-9); thumb index ed. 16.95 (ISBN 0-8007-0090-2). Revell.

Expository Dictionary of New Testament Words. W. E. Vine. 1392p. (Orig.). 1981. pap. 12.95 (ISBN 0-310-33781-X, 6795P). Zondervan.

Expository Dictionary of New Testament Words. W. E. Vine. (Affordables Ser.). 1985. pap. 9.95 (ISBN 0-8024-0435-9). Moody.

Expository Outlines from Romans. Croft M. Pentz. (Sermon Outline Ser.). 48p. (Orig.). 1980. pap. 2.50 (ISBN 0-8010-7057-0). Baker Bk.

Expository Outlines on Ephesians. Edward Fudge. 2.00 (ISBN 0-686-12688-2). E Fudge.

Expository Outlines on Hebrews. Croft M. Pentz. (Sermon Outline Ser.). pap. 1.95 (ISBN 0-8010-7045-7). Baker Bk.

Expository Preaching. Robert Shannon & J. Michael Shannon. 128p. (Orig.). 1982. pap. 5.95 (ISBN 0-87239-605-3, 3020). Standard Pub.

Expository Preaching & Teaching-Hebrews. Owen Crouch. LC 83-71985. 454p. (Orig.). 1983. pap. 9.95 (ISBN 0-89900-197-1). College Pr Pub.

Expository Preaching Without Notes Plus Sermons Preached Without Notes. Charles W. Koller. 1962. 10.95 (ISBN 0-8010-5301-3). Baker Bk.

Expository Sermon Outlines. W. H. Thomas. 136p. 1987. pap. 5.95 (ISBN 0-8254-3830-6). Kregel.

Expository Sermon Outlines to Saints & Sinners. Roy A. Suggs. 1981. pap. 2.75 (ISBN 0-934942-24-2). White Wing Pub.

Expository Sermons on Revelation, 5 Vols. in 1. W. A. Criswell. 1961-66. 24.95 (ISBN 0-310-22840-9, 9442). Zondervan.

Expository Sermons on the Book of Daniel. W. A. Criswell. 19.95 (ISBN 0-310-22800-X, 9461). Zondervan.

Expository Sermons on the Book of Ezekiel. W. A. Criswell. 272p. 1987. 12.95 (ISBN 0-310-23010-1, 18352). Zondervan.

Expository Thoughts on the Gospels, 3 vols. J. C. Ryle. Incl. St. Matthew. 426p. 1974. Repr. 9.95 (ISBN 0-227-67697-1); St. Mark. 384p. 1973. Repr. 9.95 (ISBN 0-227-67698-X); St. Luke. 540p. Repr. of 1983 ed. 19.95 (ISBN 0-227-67877-X); St. John. write for info. (ISBN 0-227-67453-7); Vol. 2. 9.95 (ISBN 0-227-67454-5); Matthew-Mark. 380p. Repr. of 1983 ed. 19.95 (ISBN 0-227-67874-5). Set. 65.00 (ISBN 0-227-67874-5). Attic Pr.

Expression de la Passion Interieure dans le Style de Bernanos Romancier. Pierre Maubrey. LC 70-94195. (Catholic University of America Studies in Romance Languages & Literatures Ser: No. 59). (Fr). Repr. of 1959 ed. 25.00 (ISBN 0-404-50359-4). AMS Pr.

Expressions of Religious Thought & Feeling in the Chansons De Geste. Sr. Marianna Gildea. LC 75-94172. (Catholic University of America Studies in Romance Languages & Literatures Ser: No. 25). 1969. Repr. of 1943 ed. 30.00 (ISBN 0-404-50325-X). AMS Pr.

Expressions of the Linguistic Area of Repentance & Remorse in Old French. Leo C. Yedlicka. LC 76-94175. (Catholic University of America Studies in Romance Languages & Literatures Ser: No. 28). 1969. Repr. of 1945 ed. 28.00 (ISBN 0-404-50328-4). AMS Pr.

Extended Catholic Family: Rediscovering Our Catholic Identity Through Intimate Relationships with Fellow Catholics. John Colligan et al. LC 83-62198. 110p. (Orig.). 1983. pap. text ed. 4.95 (ISBN 0-911905-06-5). Past & Mat Rene Ctr.

Extinction of the Christian Churches in North Africa. Leonard R. Holme. 1969. 20.50 (ISBN 0-8337-1724-3). B Franklin.

Extra Dimension. Roland B. Gittelsohn. 228p. 1983. pap. 7.95 (ISBN 0-8074-0170-6, 168500). UAHC.

Extra-Sensory Mind. Kenneth M. Walker. LC 61-17460. pap. 64.00 (ISBN 0-317-10537-X, 2005153). Bks Demand UMI.

Extramural Sanctuary of Demeter & Persephone at Cyrene, Libya, Final Reports: Volume II: The East Greek, Island, & Laconian Pottery. Gerald P. Schous. Ed. by Donald White. (University Museum Monograph: No. 56). (Illus.). xxi, 121p. 1986. 45.00 (ISBN 0-934718-55-5). Univ Mus of U PA.

Extraordinary Synod Nineteen Eighty-Five: An Evaluation. Ed. by Giuseppe Albergio & James Provost. (Concilium Nineteen Eighty-Six Ser.). 120p. 1986. pap. 6.95 (ISBN 0-567-30068-4, Pub. by T & T Clark Ltd UK). Fortress.

Extraordinary Synod Nineteen Eighty-Five. 2.50 (ISBN 0-8198-2315-5). Dghtrs St Paul.

Exuberant Years: A Guide for Junior High Leaders. Ginny W. Holderness. LC 75-13458. 128p. 1976. pap. 7.95 (ISBN 0-8042-1225-2). John Knox.

Eydie Mae: How I Conquered Cancer Naturally. Chris Loeffler & Eydie M. Hunsberger. pap. 2.95 (ISBN 0-932638-01-5). Prod Hse.

Eye for an Eye: The Place of Old Testament Ethics Today. Christopher J. Wright. LC 83-18651. 180p. 1983. pap. 8.95 (ISBN 0-87784-821-1). Inter-Varsity.

Eye of the Storm. Joseph P. Bishop. 128p. (Orig.). 1983. pap. 3.95 (ISBN 0-87123-263-4, 210263). Bethany Hse.

Eye of the Storm. Noreen Riols. 176p. 1985. pap. 2.95 (ISBN 0-345-32716-0). Ballantine.

Eye Opening Bible Studies. Sandy Larsen. (Bible Discovery Guide for Campers Ser.). 32p. 1986. pap. 1.95 (ISBN 0-87788-247-9). Shaw Pubs.

Eyes Are Sunlight: A Journey Through Grief. Shirley Koers. LC 86-82036. 200p. (Orig.). 1986. pap. 4.95 (ISBN 0-87793-345-6). Ave Maria.

Eyes Have It. Maxine Williams. LC 62-15648. 1962. pap. 1.75 (ISBN 0-88243-495-0, 02-0495). Gospel Pub.

Eyes of Jehovah: Life of James A. Harding. Lloyd C. Sears. 8.50 (ISBN 0-89225-089-5). Gospel Advocate.

Eyes of Light. Henri Le Saux. 1983. 12.95 (ISBN 0-87193-202-4). Dimension Bks.

Eyes to Behold. Michael Gaydos. LC 73-77531. 1982. pap. 4.95 (ISBN 0-89221-069-9). New Leaf.

Eyes to See, Ears to Heart: A Study Guide to the Theme "Peoples & Churches of the U. S. S. R.". Intro. by Betty J. Bailey. 1987. pap. 5.95. Friend Pr.

Eyewitness Accounts of the Restoration. Milton V. Backman, Jr. 1986. Repr. of 1983 ed. 10.95 (ISBN 0-87579-027-5). Deseret Bk.

Eyewitnesses to American Jewish History: East European Immigration 1881-1920, Pt. 3. Ed. by Azriel Eisenberg et al. (Illus.). 1978. pap. 5.00 (ISBN 0-8074-0017-3, 144061); tchrs'. guide 5.00 (ISBN 0-8074-0021-1, 204063). UAHC.

Eyewitnesses to American Jewish History: 1492-1793, Pt. 1. Ed. by Azriel Eisenberg et al. 1976. pap. 5.00 (ISBN 0-686-77106-0, 144060); tchrs'. guide 5.00 (ISBN 0-8074-0019-X, 204061). UAHC.

Eyewitnesses to American Jewish History, Pt. 4: The American Jew 1915 to 1969. Azriel Eisenberg. 1979. 6.00 (ISBN 0-8074-0018-1, 044062). UAHC.

Eyewitnesses to American Jewish History: The German Immigration 1800-1875, Pt. 2. Ed. by Azriel Eisenberg et al. (Illus.). 1977. pap. 5.00 (ISBN 0-8074-0016-5, 144059); tchrs'. guide 5.00 (ISBN 0-8074-0020-3, 204062). UAHC.

Ezechiel. Edward F. Siegman. (Bible Ser.). pap. 1.00 ea.; Pt. 1. pap. (ISBN 0-8091-5045-X); Pt. 2. pap. (ISBN 0-8091-5046-8). Paulist Pr.

Ezechiel und Deuterojesaja: Beruehrungen in der Heilserwartung der beiden grossen Exilspropheten. Dieter Baltzer. (Beiheft 121 Zur Zeitschrift fuer die alttestamentliche Wissenschaft Ser.). 1971. 28.40x (ISBN 3-11-001756-3). De Gruyter.

Ezekiel. Ralph Alexander. (Everyman's Bible Commentary Ser). 160p. (Orig.). 1976. pap. 5.95 (ISBN 0-8024-2026-5). Moody.

Ezekiel. A. Cohen. 350p. 1950. 10.95 (ISBN 0-900689-30-7). Soncino Pr.

Ezekiel. Peter C. Craigie. LC 83-7044. (Daily Study Bible-Old Testament). 332p. 1983. 14.95 (ISBN 0-664-21807-5); pap. 7.95 (ISBN 0-664-24574-9). Westminster.

Ezekiel. Paul P. Enns. (Bible Study Commentary Ser.). 224p. 1986. pap. 7.95 (ISBN 0-310-44071-8). Zondervan.

Ezekiel. Arno C. Gaebelein. LC 72-88419. 9.95 (ISBN 0-87213-217-X). Loizeaux.

Ezekiel. H. A. Ironside. 9.95 (ISBN 0-87213-359-1). Loizeaux.

Ezekiel. James E. Smith. (Bible Study Textbook Ser.). 1979. 14.30 (ISBN 0-89900-024-X). College Pr Pub.

Ezekiel. John B. Taylor. LC 75-98503. (Tyndale Old Testament Commentaries Ser). 1969. 12.95 (ISBN 0-87784-884-X); pap. 6.95 (ISBN 0-87784-272-8). Inter-Varsity.

Ezekiel. John W. Wevers. (New Century Bible Ser). 253p. 1976. 8.95 (ISBN 0-551-00755-9). Attic Pr.

Ezekiel. John W. Wevers. Ed. by Ronald E. Clements. (The New Century Bible Commentary Ser.). 243p. 1982. pap. 7.95 (ISBN 0-8028-1910-9). Eerdmans.

Ezekiel: A Commentary. Walther Eichrodt. LC 71-117646. (Old Testament Library). 608p. 1970. 18.95 (ISBN 0-664-20872-X). Westminster.

Ezekiel: A Commentary. Solomon B. Freehof. 1979. 15.00 (ISBN 0-8074-0033-5, 380010). UAHC.

Ezekiel Among the Prophets: A Study of Ezekiel's Place in Prophetic Tradition. Keith W. Carley. (Studies in Biblical Theology, 2nd Ser.: No. 31). 1975. pap. text ed. 10.00x (ISBN 0-8401-3081-3). A R Allenson.

Ezekiel & Daniel. Irving L. Jensen. (Bible Self Study Ser.). 1970. pap. 2.95 (ISBN 0-8024-1026-X). Moody.

Ezekiel, Daniel. Toni Craven. (Collegeville Bible Commentary Ser.). 144p. 1986. pap. 2.95 (ISBN 0-8146-1423-X). Liturgical Pr.

Ezekiel, Daniel. Carl G. Howie. LC 59-10454. (Layman's Bible Commentary, Vol. 13). 1961. pap. 4.95 (ISBN 0-8042-3073-0). John Knox.

Ezekiel I. Walther Zimmerli. Ed. by Frank M. Cross, Jr. & Klaus Baltzer. LC 75-21540. (Hermenia: A Critical & Historical Commentary on the Bible). 558p. 1979. 39.95 (ISBN 0-8006-6008-0, 20-6008). Fortress.

Ezekiel II. Walther Zimmerli. LC 72-1540. (Hermeneia-A Critical & Historical Commentary on the Bible). 576p. 1983. 39.95 (ISBN 0-8006-6010-2, 20-6010). Fortress.

Ezekiel: Prophet of Jehovah's Glory. Edward Fudge. 1.00 (ISBN 0-686-12692-0). E Fudge.

Ezekiel, Second Isaiah. James L. Mays. Ed. by Foster R. McCurley. LC 77-15239. (Proclamation Commentaries, The Old Testament Witnesses for Preaching). 96p. (Orig.). 1978. pap. 4.95 (ISBN 0-8006-0592-6, 1-592). Fortress.

Ezekiel: (WBC, Vol. 28. William Brownlee. 384p. 1986. 22.95 (ISBN 0-8499-0227-4). Word Bks.

Ezekiel: With Excursus on Old Testament Priesthood. Aelred Cody. (Old Testament Message Ser.: Vol. 11). 1984. 12.95 (ISBN 0-89453-411-4); pap. 9.95 (ISBN 0-89453-245-6). M Glazier.

Ezekiel, 1-20: A New Translation with Introduction & Commentary. Moshe Greenberg. LC 77-12855. (Anchor Bible Ser.: Vol. 22). (Illus.). 408p. 1983. 16.00 (ISBN 0-385-00954-2, Anchor Pr). Doubleday.

Ezequiel (Comentario Biblico Portavoz) Ralph Alexander. Orig. Title: Ezekiel (Everyman's Bible Commentary) (Span.). 128p. 1979. pap. 4.50 (ISBN 0-8254-1002-9). Kregel.

Ezourvedam: A French Veda of the Eighteenth Century. Ed. by Ludo Rocher. LC 84-6308. (University of Pennsylvania Studies on Southeast Asia: No. 1). 250p. 1984. 34.00x (ISBN 0-915027-05-4); pap. 16.00 (ISBN 0-915027-06-2). Benjamins North Am.

Ezra & Nehemiah. Derek Kidner. Ed. by D. J. Wiseman. (Tyndale Old Testament Commentaries Ser.). 1979. text ed. 12.95 (ISBN 0-87784-962-5); pap. 6.95 (ISBN 0-87784-261-2). Inter-Varsity.

Ezra & Nehemiah. Ed. by Jacob M. Myers. LC 65-23788. (Anchor Bible Ser.: Vol. 14). 1965. 16.00 (ISBN 0-385-04695-2, Anchor Pr). Doubleday.

Ezra & Nehemiah. H. G. Williamson. (Old Testament Guides Ser.). 100p. 1986. pap. text ed. 4.95x (ISBN 1-85075-045-9, Pub. by JSOT Pr England). Eisenbrauns.

Ezra & Nehemiah & the Return from Babylon. Gordon Lindsay. (Old Testament Ser.). 1.25 (ISBN 0-89985-154-1). Christ Nations.

Ezra-Job. Balmer H. Kelly. LC 59-10454. (Layman's Bible Commentary, Vol. 8). 1962. 4.95 (ISBN 0-8042-3008-0); pap. 3.95 (ISBN 0-8042-3068-4). John Knox.

Ezra-Job. P. Southwell. 1983. pap. 4.95 (ISBN 0-87508-156-8). Chr Lit.

Ezra: Joshua, Nehemiah & Esther. H. A. Ironside. 11.95 (ISBN 0-87213-396-6). Loizeaux.

Ezra Nehemiah. Rita Burns. (Bible Commentary Ser.). 96p. 1985. pap. 2.95 (ISBN 0-8146-1418-3). Liturgical Pr.

Ezra, Nehemiah. J. Carl Laney. (Everyman's Bible Commentary Ser.). (Orig.). 1982. pap. 5.95 (ISBN 0-8024-2014-1). Moody.

Ezra-Nehemiah. Bruce Vawter. (Bible Ser.). pap. 1.00 (ISBN 0-8091-5047-6). Paulist Pr.

Ezra-Nehemiah. Verlyn Verbrugge. (Five-on-One Ser.). 128p. (Orig.). 1986. pap. text ed. 3.95 (ISBN 0-930265-18-1); tchr's. guide 7.95 (ISBN 0-930265-19-X). CRC Pubns.

Ezra, Nehemiah & Esther. L. H. Brockington. (New Century Bible Ser). 262p. 1969. text ed. 9.50 (ISBN 0-551-00530-0). Attic Pr.

Ezra, Nehemiah & Esther. Irving L. Jensen. (Bible Self-Study Ser.). 1970. pap. 3.25 (ISBN 0-8024-1015-4). Moody.

Ezra, Nehemiah, & Esther. J. G. McConville. LC 84-25825. (Daily Study Bible-Old Testament Ser.). 210p. 1985. 14.95 (ISBN 0-664-21814-8); pap. 7.95 (ISBN 0-664-24583-8). Westminster.

Ezra, Nehemiah, Esther. D. J. Clines. Ed. by Ronald Clements et al. (New Century Bible Commentary Ser.). 384p. 1984. pap. 8.95 (ISBN 0-8028-0017-3). Eerdmans.

Ezra-Nehemiah-Esther. Ruben M. Ratzlaff & Paul T. Butler. (Bible Study Textbook Ser.). 1979. 14.30 (ISBN 0-89900-014-2). College Pr Pub.

Ezra-Nehemiah: Vol. 16, WBC. H. G. Williamson. 1985. 22.95 (ISBN 0-8499-0215-0, 0215-0). Word Bks.

Ezra of Galilee. T. R. Hollingsworth. 80p. (Orig.). 1987. pap. text ed. 6.95 (ISBN 0-9617668-0-8). Hollybridge Pubns.

Ezra Stiles Gannett: Unitarian Minister in Boston, 1824-1871. William C. Gannett. 1979. Repr. of 1875 ed. lib. bdg. 30.00 (ISBN 0-8492-4932-5). R West.

Ezra Studies. rev. ed. Charles C. Torrey. 1970. 29.50x (ISBN 0-87068-014-5). Ktav.

F

F. B. Meyer Bible Commentary. F. B. Meyer. 1979. cloth 15.95 (ISBN 0-8423-4250-8). Tyndale.

F. O. Matthiessen: Christian Socialist As Critic. Frederick C. Stern. LC 80-29013. xv, 281p. 1981. 27.50x (ISBN 0-8078-1478-4). U of NC Pr.

F. Stanley Story. Mary J. Walker. Ed. by Jene Lyon. (Illus.). 98p. 1985. lib. bdg. 25.00 (ISBN 0-89016-082-1). Lightning Tree.

F. W. Maitland. G. R. Elton. LC 85-40439. 128p. 1985. 15.00x (ISBN 0-300-03528-4). Yale U Pr.

F. W. Maitland. S. F. Milson. (Master-Mind Lectures (Henriette Hertz Trust)). 1980. pap. 3.75 (ISBN 0-85672-241-3, Pub. by British Acad). Longwood Pub Group.

Faber Book of Carols & Christmas Songs. Ed. by Eric Roseberry. 118p. 1983. 8.95 (ISBN 0-571-09249-7); pap. 6.95 (ISBN 0-571-13189-1). Faber & Faber.

Faber Book of Christmas Stories. Ed. by Sara Corrin & Stephen Corrin. LC 84-13552. (Illus.). 150p. 1984. 9.95 (ISBN 0-571-13348-7). Faber & Faber.

Faber Book of Christmas Stories. Ed. by Sara Corrin & Stephen Corrin. 9.95 (ISBN 0-317-31393-2). Faber & Faber.

Faber Book of Greek Legends. Ed. by Kathleen Lines. 268p. 1973. 13.95 (ISBN 0-571-09830-4). Faber & Faber.

Fabiola. 7.00 (ISBN 0-8198-2606-5); 6.00 (ISBN 0-8198-2607-3). Dghtrs St Paul.

Fabric Applique for Worship: Patterns & Guide for Sewing Banners, Vestments, & Paraments. Rebecca Jerde. LC 83-133006. 80p. 1983. pap. 8.95 (ISBN 0-8066-1965-1, 10-2153). Augsburg.

Fabric of Dreams, Dream Lore & Dream Interpretation, Ancient & Modern. Katherine T. Craig. Repr. of 1918 ed. 20.00 (ISBN 0-89987-048-1). Darby Bks.

Fabricantes de Dioses. Ed Decker & Dave Hunt. Tr. by Adriana Powell from Eng. Tr. of Godmakers. (Span.). 240p. 1987. pap. 4.95 (ISBN 0-88113-088-5). Edit Betania.

Facade of Saint-Gilles-du-Gard: Its Influence on French Sculpture. Whitney S. Stoddard. LC 72-3696. (Illus.). 341p. 1973. pap. 17.50 (ISBN 0-8195-6068-5). Wesleyan U Pr.

Face of Christ in the Old Testament. Georges A. Barrois. 172p. 1974. pap. 6.95 (ISBN 0-913836-22-2). St Vladimirs.

Face of Faith. George Kranzler. 1972. 15.00x (ISBN 0-685-38401-2). Ktav.

Face of God. Meher Baba. (Illus.). 28p. pap. 1.75 (ISBN 0-913078-00-X). Sheriar Pr.

Face of Silence: A Biography of Rama Krishna. Dhan G. Mukherji. LC 85-22355. 264p. 1985. Repr. lib. bdg. 19.95x (ISBN 0-89370-584-5). Borgo Pr.

Face of the Saints. Wilhelm Schamoni. Tr. by Anne Fremantle. LC 70-38328. (Biography Index Reprint Ser). Repr. of 1947 ed. 26.50 (ISBN 0-8369-8128-6). Ayer Co Pubs.

Face of Truth: A Study of Meaning & Metaphysics in the Vedantic Theology of Ramanuja. Julius J. Lipner. 224p. 1986. 44.50x (ISBN 0-88706-038-2); pap. 18.95x (ISBN 0-88706-039-0). State U NY Pr.

Face the Light. Gerard T. Bradley. LC 82-99822. 89p. 1983. 8.95 (ISBN 0-533-05448-6). Vantage.

Face up with a Miracle. Don Basham. 190p. 1971. pap. 2.95 (ISBN 0-88368-002-5). Whitaker Hse.

Faces. Ed. by Andre Midgett. (Campus Life Bks.). (Illus.). 160p. (Orig.). 1987. pap. 5.95 (ISBN 0-8423-0826-1). Tyndale.

Faces & Facets: A Workbook for the Liturgical Celebrant. George F. Simons. LC 77-78972. 1977. pap. 3.95 (ISBN 0-914070-11-8). ACTA Found.

Faces of Courage. Daughters of St. Paul. (Illus.). 1974. 5.00 (ISBN 0-8198-0292-1); pap. 4.00 (ISBN 0-8198-0293-X). Dghtrs St Paul.

Faces of God. Gordon DePree & Gladis DePree. LC 80-14384. 128p. 1980. pap. 5.95 (ISBN 0-664-24350-9). Westminster.

Faces of God. James D. Hamilton. 100p. 1985. pap. 3.95 (ISBN 0-8341-0940-9). Beacon Hill.

Faces of Jesus: Latin American Christologies. Ed. by Jose Miguez-Bonino. Tr. by Robert R. Barr from Span. LC 83-19375. Tr. of Jesus ni Vencido ni Monarca Celestial. 192p. 1984. pap. 10.95 (ISBN 0-88344-129-2). Orbis Bks.

Facets of Medieval Judaism: Proceedings. American Academy for Jewish Research Staff. (Jewish People; History, Religion, Literature Ser.). 19.00 (ISBN 0-405-05262-6). Ayer Co Pubs.

Facets of Spirituality: Dialogues & Discourses of Swami Krishnananda. Ed. by Krishnananda & S. Bhagyalakshmi. 1986. 22.00X (ISBN 81-208-0087-7, Pub. by Motilal Banarsidass). South Asia Bks.

Facets of Taoism: Essays in Chinese Religion. Ed. by Holmes Welch & Anna Seidel. LC 77-28034. 1979. 38.00x (ISBN 0-300-01695-6); pap. 8.95x (ISBN 0-300-02673-0). Yale U Pr.

Facing a Catastrophic Illness with Hope. 20p. (Orig.). 1986. pap. 0.85 (ISBN 0-89486-344-4). Hazelden.

Facing & Fulfilling the Later Years. Elsie M. Andrews. LC 68-16318. (Orig.). 1968. pap. 2.50x (ISBN 0-87574-157-6). Pendle Hill.

Facing Change: Strategies for Problem Solving in the Congregation. Joseph S. Zaccaria. LC 84-18552. 112p. (Orig.). 1984. pap. 5.95 (ISBN 0-8066-2097-8, 10-2156). Augsburg.

Facing Death & Grief. George Marshall. LC 80-84402. (Library of Liberal Religion Ser.). 200p. 1981. 18.95 (ISBN 0-87975-140-1); pap. 11.95 (ISBN 0-87975-169-X). Prometheus Bks.

Facing Death & Loss. Elizabeth Ogg. LC 85-51126. 106p. 1985. pap. 19.00 (ISBN 0-87762-423-2). Technomic.

Facing Karma. Rudolf Steiner. 1977. 2.00 (ISBN 0-910142-64-5). Anthroposophic.

Facing the Enlightenment & Pietism: Archibald Alexander & the Founding of Princeton Theological Seminary. Lefferts A. Loetscher. LC 82-11995. (Contributions to the Study of Religion Ser.: No. 8). x, 303p. 1983. lib. bdg. 35.00 (ISBN 0-313-23677-1, LOE/). Greenwood.

Facing the Final Foe. James E. Carter. LC 85-19517. 1986. pap. 2.25 (ISBN 0-8054-5433-0). Broadman.

Facing the Holocaust. Ed. by Gila Ramras-Rauch & Joseph Michman-Melkman. 1986. 16.95 (ISBN 0-8276-0253-7). Jewish Pubns.

Facing the Issues, No. 1. William J. Krutza & Philip P. Dicicco. (Contemporary Discussion Ser.). 1969. pap. 3.50 (ISBN 0-8010-5325-0). Baker Bk.

Facing the Issues, No. 2. William J. Krutza & Philip P. Dicicco. (Contemporary Discussion Ser.). pap. 3.50 (ISBN 0-8010-5326-9). Baker Bk.

Facing the Issues, No. 3. William J. Krutza & Philip P. Dicicco. (Contemporary Discussion Ser.). (Orig.). 1970. pap. 3.50 (ISBN 0-8010-5300-5). Baker Bk.

Facing the Issues, No. 4. William J. Krutza & Philip P. DiCicco. (Contemporary Discussion Ser.). (Orig.). 1971. pap. 3.50 (ISBN 0-8010-5310-2). Baker Bk.

Facing the Nuclear Heresy. G. Clarke Chapman. Ed. by David Eller. 224p. (Orig.). 1986. pap. 9.95 (ISBN 0-87178-225-1). Brethren.

Facing the Twentieth Century. James M. King. Ed. by Gerald Grob. LC 76-46085. (Anti-Movements in America Ser.). (Illus.). 1977. Repr. of 1899 ed. lib. bdg. 54.00x (ISBN 0-405-09958-4). Ayer Co Pubs.

Facing West from California's Shores: A Jesuit's Journey in the Consciousness Movement. David Toolan. 352p. 1987. 19.95 (ISBN 0-8245-0805-X). Crossroad NY.

Facing Your Feelings: How to Get Your Emotions to Work for You. Bert Ghezzi. (Living as a Christian Ser.). 112p. 1983. pap. 2.95 (ISBN 0-89283-133-2). Servant.

Facing Your Nation. William J. Krutza & Philip P. DiCicco. (Contemporary Discussion Ser.). 1975. pap. 1.95 (ISBN 0-8010-5372-2). Baker Bk.

Facing Yourself in the Bible: Studies in Human Personalities from the Bible. William J. Krutza. (Contemporary Discussion Ser.). 128p. 1976. pap. 1.25 (ISBN 0-8010-5369-2). Baker Bk.

FACS: Fundamentals for American Christians. Rus Walton. 372p. 1979. pap. 4.95 (ISBN 0-942516-03-6). Plymouth Rock Found.

Facsimile of Some Leaves in Saxon Handwriting on Saint Swidhun. John Earle. 1861. lib. bdg. 35.00 (ISBN 0-8414-3989-3). Folcroft.

Fact & Faith in the Kerygma of Today. Paul Althaus. Tr. by David Cairas. 89p. 1978. Repr. of 1959 ed. lib. bdg. cancelled (ISBN 0-313-20446-2, ALFA). Greenwood.

Faction & Conversion in a Plural Society: Religious Alignments in the Hindu Kush. Robert L. Canfield. (Anthropological Papers: No. 50). 1973. 3.00x (ISBN 0-932206-48-4). U Mich Mus Anthro.

Factors Related to Sunday School Growth & Decline in the Eastern Synod of the Reformed Church in the U. S. Nevin C. Harner. LC 71-176839. (Columbia University. Teachers College. Contributions to Education Ser.: No. 479). Repr. of 1931 ed. 22.50 (ISBN 0-404-55479-2). AMS Pr.

Facts about Lutherans. Albert P. Stauderman. 32p. 1959. pap. 0.95, 10 for 5.50 (ISBN 0-8006-1832-7, 1-1832). Fortress.

Facts About Your Feelings: What Every Christian Woman Should Know. Therese Cirner. 142p. 1982. pap. 4.95 (ISBN 0-89283-103-0). Servant.

Facts & Faith: Reason, Science & Faith, Vol. 1. J. D. Thomas. 1966. 13.95 (ISBN 0-89112-011-4, Bibl Res Pr). Abilene Christ U.

Facts & Faith: The Bible & Faith, Vol. 2. J. D. Thomas. 153p. 1980. 11.95 (ISBN 0-89112-012-2, Bibl Res Pr). Abilene Christ U.

Facts, Baptist History: Sixteen Hundred to Nineteen Eighty. Kevin Sandifer. Ed. by Lydia Bryan & Rowland Gill. LC 83-80441. (Illus.). 144p. (Orig.). 1983. pap. 6.50 (ISBN 0-910653-01-1). Archival Servs.

Facts for Freemasons. Compiled by H. V. Voorhis. 258p. 1979. text ed. 9.50 (ISBN 0-88053-016-2, M-65). Macoy Pub.

Facts from Acts. Gussie Lambert. 1.50 (ISBN 0-89315-056-8). Lambert Bk.

Facts on File Dictionary of Classical, Biblical, & Literary Allusions. Abraham H. Lass et al. 240p. 1987. 18.95 (ISBN 0-8160-1267-9). Facts on File.

Facts on File Dictionary of Religions. Ed. by John R. Hinnells. LC 83-20834. 560p. 1984. 24.95x (ISBN 0-87196-862-2). Facts On File.

Fads & Quackery in Healing. Morris Fishbein. LC 75-23708. Repr. of 1932 ed. 45.00 (ISBN 0-404-13260-X). AMS Pr.

Failing Forward. Ted Roberts. 1985. pap. 4.95 (ISBN 0-89081-432-5). Harvest Hse.

Failure of Faith: An Investigation into Totalitarianism, Irrationality & Faith. Muir Weissinger. LC 83-8171. 219p. 1983. 32.00 (ISBN 0-86187-284-3, Pub. by Frances Pinter). Longwood Pub Group.

Failure: The Back Door to Success. Erwin Lutzer. LC 75-16177. 1977. pap. 3.50 (ISBN 0-8024-2516-X). Moody.

Fair-Spoken & Persuading: An Interpretation of Second Isaiah. Richard J. Clifford. (Theological Inquiries Ser.). (Orig.). 1984. pap. 8.95. Paulist Pr.

Faire & Easie Way to Heaven: Covenant Theology & Antinomianism in Early Massachusetts. William K. Stoever. LC 77-14851. 251p. 1978. 22.00x (ISBN 0-8195-5024-8). Wesleyan U Pr.

Fairest Girlhood. Margaret E. Sangster. 224p. 1987. pap. 5.95 (ISBN 0-310-34471-9). Zondervan.

Fairy-Faith in Celtic Countries. W. Y. Wentz. LC 77-12812. 1973. pap. text ed. 15.00x (ISBN 0-391-00773-4). Humanities.

Fairy Mythology of Shakespeare. Alfred T. Nutt. LC 71-139169. (Popular Studies in Mythology, Romance & Folklore: No. 6). Repr. of 1900 ed. 5.50 (ISBN 0-404-53506-2). AMS Pr.

Fairy Tale of the Green Snake & the Beautiful Lily. 2nd ed. J. W. Von Goethe & Rudolf Steiner. LC 78-73644. 72p. (Orig.). 1981. pap. 3.50 (ISBN 0-89345-203-3, Steinerbks). Garber Comm.

Faith. Ed. by Leo Jung. 212p. 1968. 8.50 (ISBN 0-900689-01-3). Soncino Pr.

Faith. Ed. by Spencer W. Kimball et al. LC 83-72343. 119p. 1983. 8.95 (ISBN 0-87747-980-1). Deseret Bk.

Faith. Carole MacKenthun & Paulinus Dwyer. (Fruit of the Spirit Ser.). (Illus.). 48p. 1986. wkbk. 4.95 (ISBN 0-86653-361-3). Good Apple.

Faith. Roanld D. Tucker. (Illus.). 56p. 1983. pap. 2.00 (ISBN 0-933643-14-4). Grace World Outreach.

Faith: A Thirty-One-Day Experiment. Dick Purnell. 60p. (Orig.). 1985. pap. 2.95 (ISBN 0-89840-076-7). Heres Life.

Faith Abroad. John D. Davies. (Faith & the Future Ser.). 163p. 1984. 24.95x (ISBN 0-631-13183-3); pap. 8.95x (ISBN 0-631-13221-X). Basil Blackwell.

Faith According to St. John of the Cross. Pope John Paul II. Tr. by Jordan Aumann. LC 80-82265. Orig. Title: Doctrina de Fide apud S. Joannem a Cruce. 276p. (Orig.). 1981. pap. 13.95 (ISBN 0-89870-010-8). Ignatius Pr.

Faith Active in Love. George W. Forell. LC 15-5702. 1954. kivar 7.95 (ISBN 0-8066-0186-8, 10-2165). Augsburg.

Faith After the Holocaust. Eliezer Berkovits. 1973. pap. 7.95x (ISBN 0-87068-193-1). Ktav.

Faith & Belief. Wilfred C. Smith. LC 78-63601. 1979. 35.50x (ISBN 0-691-07232-9). Princeton U Pr.

Faith & Belief. Wilfred C. Smith. 360p. 1987. pap. 12.50 (ISBN 0-691-02040-X). Princeton U Pr.

Faith & Certitude. Thomas Dubay. LC 84-80910. 266p. (Orig.). 1985. pap. 9.95 (ISBN 0-89870-054-X). Ignatius Pr.

Faith & Courage. 1986. 6.95 (ISBN 0-87306-258-2). Feldheim.

Faith & Crisis in the Stages of Life. James F. Cobble. 128p. 1985. pap. 6.95 (ISBN 0-913573-17-5). Hendrickson MA.

Faith & Culture. Bernard E. Meland. (Arcturus Books Paperbacks). 176p. 1972. lib. bdg. 7.00x (ISBN 0-8093-0591-7); pap. 2.45x (ISBN 0-8093-0571-2). S Ill U Pr.

Faith & Culture: A Multicultural Catechetical Resource. Contrib. by Michael Falvan et al. 96p. (Orig.). 1987. pap. 5.95 (ISBN 1-55586-994-7). US Catholic.

Faith & Doctrines of the Early Church. G. M. Bowers. LC 78-60521. 1978. pap. 4.95 (ISBN 0-917182-09-X). Triumph Pub.

Faith & Doubt. Norman Lamm. 1986. 11.95x (ISBN 0-87068-138-9). Ktav.

Faith & Doubt in Victorian Britain. Elisabeth Jay. (Context & Commentary Ser.). (Illus.). 152p. 1986. text ed. 29.95 (ISBN 0-333-37658-7, Pub. by Macmillan Pubs UK); pap. text ed. 9.95 (ISBN 0-333-37659-5). Humanities.

Faith & Doubt of Holocaust Survivors. Reeve R. Brenner. LC 79-6764. 1980. 12.95 (ISBN 0-02-904420-0). Free Pr.

Faith & Doubt: The Unfolding of Newman's Thought on Certainty. William R. Fey. LC 75-38101. xxii, 229p. 1976. 22.95x (ISBN 0-915762-02-1). Patmos Pr.

Faith & Doubt Today. Philip St. Romain. LC 85-82033. 128p. (Orig.). 1986. pap. 3.25 (ISBN 0-89243-245-4). Liguori Pubns.

Faith & Ethics. Vincent MacNamara. 216p. (Orig.). 1985. 17.95 (ISBN 0-87840-426-0); pap. 10.95 (ISBN 0-87840-414-7). Georgetown U Pr.

Faith & Ethics: The Theology of H. Richard Niebuhr. Paul Ramsey. 11.25 (ISBN 0-8446-2778-X). Peter Smith.

Faith & Families. Ed. by Lindell Sawyers. 208p. (Orig.). 1986. pap. 12.95 (ISBN 0-664-24038-0). Westminster.

Faith & Fatherland. Anthony Kuzniewski. 183p. 1980. text ed. 16.95 (ISBN 0-268-00948-1). U of Notre Dame Pr.

Faith & Ferment: An Interdisciplinary Study of Christian Beliefs & Practices. Ed. by Robert S. Bilheimer. LC 83-70512. 352p. (Orig.). 1983. pap. 15.95 (ISBN 0-8066-2018-8, 10-2168). Augsburg.

Faith & Ferment: An Interdisciplinary Study of Christian Beliefs & Practices. Joan D. Chittister & Martin E. Marty. Ed. by Robert S. Bilheimer. 352p. 1983. pap. 15.95 (ISBN 0-8146-1289-X). Liturgical Pr.

Faith & Fiction: Creative Process in Greene & Mauriac. Philip Stratford. 1964. pap. 9.95x (ISBN 0-268-00379-3). U of Notre Dame Pr.

Faith & Fragmentation: Christianity for a New Age. J. Philip Wogaman. LC 85-47712. 208p. 1985. pap. 10.95 (ISBN 0-8006-1864-5, 1-1864). Fortress.

Faith & Fratricide: The Theological Roots of Anti-Semitism. Rosemary Ruether. 1974. pap. 8.95 (ISBN 0-8164-2263-X, HarpR). Har-Row.

Faith & Freedom: A Study of Western Society. W. Barbara Jackson. LC 72-8239. 308p. 1974. Repr. of 1954 ed. lib. bdg. 22.50x (ISBN 0-8371-6542-3, JAFF). Greenwood.

Faith & Fulfillment: Christians & the Return to the Promised Land. Michael J. Pragai. (Illus.). 326p. 1985. 24.00x (ISBN 0-85303-210-6, Vallentine Mitchell England); pap. 12.50x (ISBN 0-85303-211-4). Biblio Dist.

Faith & History: A Comparison of Christian & Modern Views of History. Reinhold Niebuhr. (Lib. Rep. Ed.). 1949. 25.00 (ISBN 0-684-15318-1, ScribT). Scribner.

Faith & History in the Old Testament. R. A. MacKenzie. LC 63-10585. 1963. 8.95 (ISBN 0-8166-0297-2). U of Minn Pr.

Faith & Its Psychology. William R. Inge. LC 10-654. (Studies in Theology Ser.: No. 12). 1909. text ed. 8.50x (ISBN 0-8401-6012-7). A R Allenson.

Faith & Justice. Margaret Betz. LC 80-50259. 176p. 1980. pap. text ed. 5.00x (ISBN 0-88489-114-3); tchr's guide 9.00x (ISBN 0-88489-121-6). St Mary's.

Faith & Justice. Ed. by Walter Krolikowski. 174p. 1982. pap. text ed. 6.95 (ISBN 0-8294-0397-3). Loyola.

Faith & Knowledge: The Reflective Philosophy of Subjectivity. G. W. Hegel. Ed. by H. S. Harris & Walter Cerf. Tr. by H. S. Harris & Walter. Cerf. LC 76-10250. 1977. 39.50 (ISBN 0-87395-338-X). State U NY Pr.

Faith & Learning: Christian Faith & Higher Education in Twentieth Century America. Alexander Miller. LC 77-23142. 1977. Repr. of 1960 ed. lib. bdg. 22.50x (ISBN 0-8371-9458-X, MIFL). Greenwood.

Faith & Ministry. Karl Rahner. (Theological Investigations Ser.: Vol. 19). 352p. 1983. 24.50x (ISBN 0-8245-0572-7). Crossroad NY.

Faith & Morals. Ed. by Lynchburg College Faculty Staff. LC 81-71948. (Classical Selections on Great Issues, Symposium Readings Ser.: Vol. 4). 472p. 1982. lib. bdg. 24.00 (ISBN 0-8191-2301-3); pap. text ed. 9.25 (ISBN 0-8191-2302-1). U Pr of Amer.

Faith & Philosophy. David Patterson. LC 81-43469. 162p. (Orig.). 1982. pap. text ed. 10.50 (ISBN 0-8191-2651-9). U Pr of Amer.

Faith & Philosophy: New York, 1877. Henry B. Smith. Ed. by Bruce Kuklick. (American Religious Thought of the 18th & 19th Centuries Ser.). 496p. 1987. lib. bdg. 70.00 (ISBN 0-8240-6967-6). Garland Pub.

Faith & Piety in Early Judaism: Texts & Documents. George W. Nickelsburg & Michael E. Stone. LC 82-71830. 272p. 1983. 19.95 (ISBN 0-8006-0679-5). Fortress.

Faith & Power: The Politics of Islam. Edward Mortimer. (Illus.). 425p. 1982. 6.36 (ISBN 0-394-71173-4). Random.

Faith & Practice. rev. ed. Frank E. Wilson. (Orig.). 1961. pap. 7.95 (ISBN 0-8192-1082-X). Morehouse.

Faith & Practice in the Early Church. Carl A. Volz. LC 82-72654. 224p. 1983. pap. 11.95 (ISBN 0-8066-1961-9, 10-2177). Augsburg.

Faith & Practice of Al-Ghazzali. W. M. Watt. 1967. 5.75x (ISBN 0-87902-060-1). Orientalia.

Faith & Practice of the Quakers. Rufus M. Jones. 181p. 1980. pap. 3.95 (ISBN 0-913408-57-3). Friends United.

Faith & Prayer. H. M. Richards, Jr. (Uplook Ser.). 32p. 1971. pap. 0.79 (ISBN 0-8163-0071-2, 06010-3). Pacific Pr Pub Assn.

Faith & Rationality: Reason & Belief in God. Ed. by Alvin Plantinga & Nicholas Wolterstorff. LC 83-14843. 336p. 1984. 24.95x (ISBN 0-268-00964-3, 85-09648); pap. text ed. 11.95x (ISBN 0-268-00965-1, 85-09655). U of Notre Dame Pr.

Faith & Reality. Wolfhart Pannenberg. LC 77-682. 148p. 1977. softcover 6.50 (ISBN 0-664-24755-5). Westminster.

Faith & Reason. facsimile ed. Nels F. Ferre. LC 78-142626. (Essay Index Reprints - Reason & the Christian Faith Ser.: Vol. 1). Repr. of 1946 ed. 19.00 (ISBN 0-8369-2392-8). Ayer Co Pubs.

Faith & Reason. Anthony Kenny. LC 82-22187. (Bampton Lectures in America Ser.). 100p. 1983. 21.50 (ISBN 0-231-05488-2). Columbia U Pr.

Faith & Reason. Richard Swinburne. 1981. pap. 10.95X (ISBN 0-19-824725-7). Oxford U Pr.

Faith & Reason: Essays in the Religious & Scientific Imagination. Frederick Plotkin. LC 72-97937. 1970. 6.00 (ISBN 0-8022-2322-2). Philos Lib.

Faith & Reason in Kierkegaard. F. Russell Sullivan. LC 78-60695. 1978. pap. text ed. 9.50 (ISBN 0-8191-0559-7). U Pr of Amer.

Faith & Reason: Some Baha'i Perspectives. Ed. by Peter Smith & Anthony A. Lee. (Orig.). 1987. pap. 9.95 (ISBN 0-933770-56-1). Kalimat.

Faith & Saving Faith. Gordon H. Clark. (Trinity Papers: No. 5). 118p. (Orig.). 1983. pap. 5.95 (ISBN 0-940931-05-2). Trinity Found.

Faith & Sexism: Guidelines for Religious Educators. Marianne Sawicki. 112p. 1979. pap. 4.95 (ISBN 0-8164-0105-5, HarpR). Har-Row.

Faith & the Future. Walter Kasper. LC 82-12720. 192p. 1982. 12.95 (ISBN 0-8245-0504-2). Crossroad NY.

Faith & the Life at Reason. J. King-Farlow & W. N. Christensen. LC 72-83376. 253p. 1973. lib. bdg. 36.00 (ISBN 90-277-0275-6, Pub. by Reidel Holland). Kluwer Academic.

Faith & the Sources of Faith: The Sixth Convention of the Fellowship of Catholic Scholars. Fellowship of Catholic Scholars. Ed. by Paul L. Williams. 120p. (Orig.). 1985. pap. 5.95 (ISBN 0-937374-00-8). NE Bks.

Faith & the World of Politics. Johannes B. Metz. LC 68-31786. (Concilium Ser.: Vol. 36). 191p. 7.95 (ISBN 0-8091-0046-0). Paulist Pr.

Faith & Understanding. Rudolf Bultmann. Ed. by Robert W. Funk. Tr. by Louise P. Smith. LC 86-45901. 352p. 1987. pap. 12.95 (ISBN 0-8006-3202-8). Fortress.

Faith & Violence: Christian Teaching & Christian Practice. Thomas Merton. 1968. pap. 6.95 (ISBN 0-268-00094-8). U of Notre Dame Pr.

Faith & Works. Helen Zagat. 1955. 6.95 (ISBN 0-686-24360-9). Divine Sci Fed.

Faith & Works: Cranmer & Hooker on Justification. Ed. & intro. by Philip E. Hughes. 128p. (Orig.). 1982. pap. 7.95 (ISBN 0-8192-1315-2). Morehouse.

Faith Applied. Jean Daujat. 1963. 5.95x (ISBN 0-933932-22-7). Scepter Pubs.

Faith at Work. Dorothy Martin. (Peggy Ser.: No. 9). 1985. pap. 3.50 (ISBN 0-8024-8309-7). Moody.

Faith, Authenticity, & Morality. Donald Evans. 1980. 30.00x (ISBN 0-8020-5424-2). U of Toronto Pr.

Faith Brokers: Professional Christians & Their Un-Godly Gains. Walley Metts. 1986. pap. 5.95 (ISBN 0-937931-00-4). Global TN.

Faith Builder. 2.95 (ISBN 0-686-12914-8). Schmul Pub Co.

Faith: Conversations with Contemporary Theologians. Ed. by Teofilo Cabestrero. Tr. by Donald D. Walsh from Span. LC 80-1431. Orig. Title: Coversationes sobre la fe. 192p. (Orig.). 1980. pap. 3.98 (ISBN 0-88344-126-8). Orbis Bks.

Faith Crisis. Ronald Dunn. Tr. by Lorna Y. Chao. (Chinese.). 1985. pap. write for info. (ISBN 0-941598-30-6). Living Spring Pubns.

Faith, Culture & the Dual System: A Comparative Study of Church & County Schools. Bernadette O'Keefe. 200p. 1986. 27.00x (ISBN 1-85000-110-3, Falmer Pr); pap. 15.00x (ISBN 1-85000-111-1, Falmer Pr). Taylor & Francis.

Faith Despite the KGB. Hermann Hartfield. 248p. 1980. pap. 5.95 (ISBN 0-88264-156-5). Diane Bks.

Faith Development & Fowler. Ed. by Craig Dykstra & Sharon Parks. 322p. (Orig.). 1986. pap. 14.95 (ISBN 0-89135-056-X). Religious Educ.

Faith Development & Pastoral Care. James W. Fowler. LC 86-45904. 128p. 1987. pap. 7.95 (ISBN 0-8006-1739-8). Fortress.

Faith Development in the Adult Life Cycle. 1983. 10.95 (ISBN 0-8215-9899-6). Sadlier.

Faith Development: The Lifelong Process. Charles O. Bradshaw. (Complete Teacher Training Meeting Ser.). 48p. 1985. pap. text ed. 9.95 (ISBN 0-89191-761-6). Cook.

Faith Encounters Ideology: Christian Discernment & Social Change. Douglas Elwood. xvi, 318p. (Orig.). 1985. pap. 16.00 (ISBN 971-10-0201-9, Pub. by New Day Philippines). Cellar.

Faith Enough to Finish. Jill Briscoe. 108p. 1987. pap. 4.95 (ISBN 0-89693-238-9). Victor Bks.

Faith Establishes the Law. C. Thomas Rhyne. Ed. by Howard Kee. LC 81-1794. (Society of Biblical Literature Dissertation Ser.). 1981. pap. 13.50 (ISBN 0-89130-483-5, 06-01-55). Scholars Pr GA.

Faith Explained. rev. ed. Leo Trese. 479p. 1984. pap. 7.95 (ISBN 971-117-042-6, Pub. by Sinag-Tala Pubs Philippines). Scepter Pubs.

Faith, Facts & Feelings. 3rd ed. William S. Deal. 1978. pap. 0.95 (ISBN 0-686-05527-6). Crusade Pubs.

Faith, Fancies & Fetish or Yoruba Paganism. Stephen S. Farrow. LC 76-98718. (Illus.). Repr. of 1926 ed. 22.50x (ISBN 0-8371-2759-9, FFF&, Pub. by Negro U Pr). Greenwood.

Faith, Feminism & the Christ. Patricia Wilson-Kastner. LC 83-5688. 160p. 1983. pap. 8.95 (ISBN 0-8006-1746-0). Fortress.

Faith Food for Autumn. 2nd ed. Kenneth E. Hagin. (Illus.). 1978. pap. 1.95 (ISBN 0-89276-040-0). Hagin Ministries.

Faith Food for Spring. 2nd ed. Kenneth E. Hagin. (Illus.). 1978. pap. 1.95 (ISBN 0-89276-042-7). Hagin Ministries.

Faith Food for Summer. 2nd ed. Kenneth E. Hagin. (Illus.). 1978. pap. 1.95 (ISBN 0-89276-043-5). Hagin Ministries.

Faith Food for Winter. 2nd ed. Kenneth E. Hagin. (Illus.). 1977. pap. 1.95 (ISBN 0-89276-041-9). Hagin Ministries.

Faith, Foolishness, or Presumption. Frederick K. Price. 160p. (Orig.). 1979. pap. 4.95 (ISBN 0-89274-103-1). Harrison Hse.

Faith for a New Day. Lamar Cope. Ed. by Herbert Lambert. 128p. (Orig.). 1986. pap. 8.95 (ISBN 0-8272-1013-2). CBP.

Faith for All Generations. Robert Flood. LC 86-70628. Orig. Title: Up with America. 96p. 1986. pap. 4.95 (ISBN 0-89636-214-0). Accent Bks.

Faith for Moderns. 2nd rev. ed. Robert Gordis. LC 76-136424. 1971. pap. 8.95x (ISBN 0-8197-0001-0, 10001). Bloch.

Faith for the Nations. Charles W. Forman. LC 57-9601. (Layman's Theological Library). 1957. pap. 1.00 (ISBN 0-664-24007-0). Westminster.

Faith for the Older Years: Making the Most of Life's Second Half. Paul B. Maves. LC 85-13466. 192p. (Orig.). 1986. pap. 9.95 (ISBN 0-8066-2195-8, 10-2181). Augsburg.

Faith for the Second Mile. Winfred Moore. LC 86-9535. 1986. 8.95 (ISBN 0-8054-5726-7). Broadman.

Faith for the 1980s. J. R. Paterson. 3.95x (ISBN 0-7152-0433-5). Outlook.

Faith for Today. E. Flesseman-Van Leer. Tr. by John E. Steely. LC 79-56514. (Special Studies Ser.: No. 7). vii, 148p. 1980. pap. 6.95 (ISBN 0-932180-06-X). NABPR.

Faith for Today. J. D. O'Donnell. LC 65-29130. (Sunday School Workers Training Course Ser.: No. 5). 1974. pap. 3.95 (ISBN 0-89265-000-1). Randall Hse.

Faith for Today: A Brief Outline of Christian Thought. William D. Streng. LC 75-2843. 48p. (Orig.). 1975. pap. 2.95 (ISBN 0-8066-1488-9, 10-2180). Augsburg.

Faith for Today: Teacher's Guide. Herman Hersey. 1980. pap. 1.50 (ISBN 0-89265-067-2). Randall Hse.

Faith-Hardy Christian: How to Face the Challenges of Life with Confidence. Gary L. Harbaugh. LC 86-7966. (Christian Growth Ser.). 128p. 1986. pap. 6.95 (ISBN 0-8066-2212-1, 10-2184). Augsburg.

Faith Healing & Speaking in Tongues. H. L. Heijkoop. 40p. pap. 2.95 (ISBN 0-88172-083-6). Believers Bkshelf.

Faith Healing in Late Byzantium: The Posthumous Miracles of Patriarch Athanasios I of Constaninople by Theoktistos the Stoudite. Alice-Mary M. Talbot. Ed. by N. M. Vaporis. (The Archbishop Iakovos Library of Ecclesiastical & Historical Sources Ser.). 160p. (Orig.). 1983. 17.00 (ISBN 0-916586-92-8); pap. 12.00 (ISBN 0-916586-93-6). Hellenic College Pr.

Faith, Hope & Charity in Primitive Religion. R. R. Marett. LC 72-80150. Repr. of 1932 ed. 22.00 (ISBN 0-405-08780-2, Pub. by Blom). Ayer Co Pubs.

Faith, Hope & Charity in Primitive Religion. Robert R. Marett. LC 77-27193. (Gifford Lectures: 1931-32). Repr. of 1932 ed. 15.00 (ISBN 0-404-60487-0). AMS Pr.

Faith, Hope & Love. Allen. 5.95 (ISBN 0-318-18178-9). WCTU.

Faith, Hope, & Love. Charles L. Allen. 192p. 1982. pap. 5.95 (ISBN 0-8007-5096-9, Power Bks). Revell.

Faith, Hope & Love: Learning about I Corinthians 13. D. S. Roberts. LC 56-1397. (Concept Books Series Four). 1983. pap. 3.95 (ISBN 0-570-08526-8). Concordia.

Faith, Hope, No Charity: An Inside Look at the Born Again Movement in Canada & the United States. Judith Haiven. (Illus.). 221p. 1984. lib. bdg. 14.95 (ISBN 0-919573-32-0); pap. 7.95 (ISBN 0-919573-33-9). Left Bank.

Faith in a Nuclear Age. Duane Beachey. LC 82-11785. (Christian Peace Shelf Ser.). 136p. (Orig.). 1983. pap. 6.95 (ISBN 0-8361-3308-0). Herald Pr.

Faith in Action. Paul L. Walker. LC 75-3504. (Illus.). 1975. pap. 1.99 (ISBN 0-87148-331-9). Pathway Pr.

Faith in Action: A History of Methodism in the Empire State 1784-1984. William R. Ward, Jr. LC 86-70533. (Illus.). 324p. (Orig.). 1986. text ed. 12.50x (ISBN 0-914960-62-8); pap. text ed. 10.00x (ISBN 0-914960-58-X). Academy Bks.

Faith in Christ & the Worship of Christ. Ed. by Leo Scheffczyk. Tr. by Graham Harrison from Ger. LC 85-82174. Orig. Title: Christusglaube und Christusverehrung. 216p. (Orig.). 1986. pap. 9.95 (ISBN 0-89870-057-4). Ignatius Pr.

Faith in Conflict. Owen L. Christian. 192p. 1986. 12.50 (ISBN 0-89962-519-3). Todd & Honeywell.

Faith in Fiction: The Emergence of Religious Literature in America. David S. Reynolds. LC 80-20885. 304p. 1981. text ed. 25.00x (ISBN 0-674-29172-7). Harvard U Pr.

Faith in Focus: A Compact Introduction to Christian Theology. J. Edward Barrett. LC 81-40167. 130p. (Orig.). 1982. lib. bdg. 24.25 (ISBN 0-8191-1878-8); pap. text ed. 9.50 (ISBN 0-8191-1879-6). U Pr of Amer.

Faith in God & Full Speed Ahead: Fe en Dios y Adelante. Grant La Farge. LC 84-23948. (Illus.). 160p. (Orig.). 1985. pap. 14.95 (ISBN 0-86534-050-1). Sunstone Pr.

Faith in History & Society: Toward a Practical Fundamental Theology. Johann B. Metz. 1979. 12.95 (ISBN 0-8245-0305-8). Crossroad NY.

Faith in Jesus Christ. John Coventry. 54p. 1982. pap. 3.95 (ISBN 0-86683-620-9, HarpR). Har-Row.

Faith in Paradise. Maggie Bunson. 1977. 8.00 (ISBN 0-8198-0414-2). Dghtrs St Paul.

Faith in the Furnace. Elizabeth Y. Anderson. LC 84-72818. (Illus.). 1985. 10.00 (ISBN 0-9614002-0-X). E Y Anderson.

Faith in the Word: The Fourth Gospel. George W. MacRae. (Biblical Booklets Ser). 1975. pap. 1.25 (ISBN 0-8199-0515-1). Franciscan Herald.

Faith Is. Pamela Reeve. 1970. pap. 4.95 (ISBN 0-930014-05-7). Multnomah.

Faith is Friendship. Josef Heinzmann. 146p. 1983. pap. 6.95 (ISBN 0-8189-0451-8). Alba.

Faith Is Not a Feeling. Ney Bailey. LC 78-60077. 1979. pap. 4.95 (ISBN 0-918956-45-5). Campus Crusade.

Faith is Power. 2nd ed. Swami Paramananda. Orig. Title: Faith as Constructive Force. 1961. 4.50 (ISBN 0-911564-09-8). Vedanta Ctr.

Faith Is Sort of Like This. James E. Boyd. (Illus.). 64p. (Orig.). 1986. pap. 9.95 (ISBN 1-55630-012-3). Brentwood Comm.

Faith Is the Victory. Mae Fry. (Orig.). 1986. pap. 1.95 (ISBN 0-89265-098-2). Randall Hse.

Faith is the Victory. Buell H. Kazee. 1983. pap. 4.95 (ISBN 0-8423-0844-X). Tyndale.

Faith It or Fake It? Fritz Ridenour. LC 73-120783. 176p. 1978. pap. 3.50 (ISBN 0-8307-0441-8, S114186). Regal.

Faith: Key to the Heart of God. John H. Hampsch & Clint Kelly. LC 84-62433. (Keyhole Ser.: No. 1). 102p. (Orig.). 1985. pap. 6.95 (ISBN 0-9613575-1-7). Perf Pr.

Faith Leads to Salvation: The Truths of the Nicene Creed. Zygmunt V. Szarnicki. 137p. (Orig.). 1984. pap. 9.95 (ISBN 0-939332-08-6). J Pohl Assocs.

Faith of a Modern Man. Louis Evely. 1.95 (ISBN 0-317-06468-1). Dimension Bks.

Faith of a Moralist, 2 Vols. in 1. Alfred E. Taylor. LC 37-23815. (Gifford Lectures 1926-1928). 1968. Repr. of 1937 ed. 41.00 (ISBN 0-527-89062-6). Kraus Repr.

Faith of a People: The Life of a Basic Christian Community in El Salvador. Pablo Galdamez. Tr. by Robert R. Barr from Span. LC 85-30981. Tr. of La Fe de un Pueblo: Historia de una Comunidad Cristiana en El Salvador. 112p. (Orig.). 1986. pap. 7.95 (ISBN 0-88344-270-1). Orbis Bks.

Faith of A Radical. Rinny Westra. 80p. (Orig.). 1984. pap. 8.95 (ISBN 0-86474-001-8, Pub. by Interface Press). ANZ Religious Pubns.

Faith of a Surgeon: Belief & Experience in the Life of Arthur Rendle Short. Ed. by W. M. Capper & D. Johnson. 160p. 1976. pap. 5.95 (ISBN 0-85364-198-6). Attic Pr.

Faith of America. Ed. by Mordecai M. Kaplan et al. LC 51-14109. 328p. 1951. pap. 4.95 (ISBN 0-935457-33-X). Reconstructionist Pr.

Faith of An Ex-Agnostic. Carol Murphy. 1983. pap. 2.50x (ISBN 0-87574-046-4, 046). Pendle Hill.

Faith Of Australians. Hans Mol. (Studies In Society: No. 25). 220p. 1985. text ed. 27.50x (ISBN 0-86861-628-1); pap. text ed. 12.50x (ISBN 0-86861-636-2). Allen Unwin.

Faith of Catholics: An Introduction. rev. ed. Richard Chilson. LC 72-81229. 320p. 1975. pap. 4.95 (ISBN 0-8091-1873-4, Deus). Paulist Pr.

Faith of Christians. Denis Baly & Royal W. Rhodes. LC 84-47914. 256p. 1984. pap. 14.95 (ISBN 0-8006-1790-8). Fortress.

Faith of Islam. Imam Mohamad Jawad Chirri. 24p. Date not set. pap. 3.00 (ISBN 0-317-52358-9). Islamic Ctr.

Faith of Jesus Christ. Richard B. Hays. LC 82-10660. (SBL Dissertation Ser.). 316p. 1983. pap. 15.00 (ISBN 0-89130-589-0, 06 01 56). Scholars Pr GA.

Faith of John Dryden: Change & Continuity. G. Douglas Atkins. LC 80-12890. 208p. 1980. 19.00x (ISBN 0-8131-1401-2). U Pr of Ky.

Faith of Judaism. Isadore Epstein. 418p. 1954. pap. 8.75 (ISBN 0-900689-13-7). Soncino Pr.

Faith of Judaism. Isidore Epstein. pap. 8.75x (ISBN 0-900689-13-7). Bloch.

Faith of Little Waddle Duck: Love Conquers Fear. Jerry N. Martin. 1985. 5.95 (ISBN 0-8062-2483-5). Carlton.

Faith of Millions. rev. ed. John A. O'Brien. LC 74-82119. 416p. 1974. pap. 6.50 (ISBN 0-87973-830-8). Our Sunday Visitor.

Faith of Modernism. Shailer Mathews. LC 71-108117. Repr. of 1924 ed. 17.50 (ISBN 0-404-04266-X). AMS Pr.

Faith of One's Own: Explorations by Catholic Lesbians. Ed. by Barbara Zanotti. (Feminist Ser.). 224p. (Orig.). 1986. 20.95 (ISBN 0-89594-210-0); pap. 8.95 (ISBN 0-89594-209-7). Crossing Pr.

Faith of Other Men. Wilfred C. Smith. 144p. 1972. pap. 6.95x (ISBN 0-06-131658-X, TB1658, Torch). Har-Row.

Faith of Our Fathers. Cardinal Gibbons. LC 80-51331. 352p. 1980. pap. 9.00 (ISBN 0-89555-158-6). Tan Bks Pubs.

Faith of Our Fathers. Ronald F. Youngblood. LC 75-23514. 1976. pap. 3.50 (ISBN 0-8307-0370-5, S302101). Regal.

Faith of Our Own. Roger Lovette. LC 75-27086. 144p. 1976. 6.95 (ISBN 0-8298-0299-1). Pilgrim NY.

Faith of Ours Fathers: Being a Plain Exposition & Vindication of the Church Founded by Our Lord Jesus Christ. James Gibbons. 33.00 (ISBN 0-405-10832-X, 11839). Ayer Co Pubs.

Faith of People of God. John Macquarrie. 191p. 1972. pap. text ed. write for info. (ISBN 0-02-374520-7, Pub. by Scribner). Macmillan.

Faith of Reason. Charles Frankel. LC 71-86277. 1969. Repr. of 1948 ed. lib. bdg. 17.00x (ISBN 0-374-92850-9, Octagon). Hippocrene Bks.

Faith of Secular Jews. S. L. Goodman. (Library of Judaic Learning). 25.00x (ISBN 0-87068-489-2); pap. 11.95. Ktav.

Faith of Shi'a Islam. Muhammad Al-Muzaffar. LC 83-50153. 80p. pap. 4.00 (ISBN 0-940368-26-9). Tahrike Tarsile Quran.

Faith of Shi'a Islam. Muhammed R. Al-Muzaffar. 89p. (Orig.). 1986. pap. text ed. 8.95 (ISBN 0-7103-0157-X). Methuen Inc.

Faith of Shi'ia Islam. Muhammad Rida Al-Muzaffar. 89p. 1982. 20.00x (ISBN 0-317-39062-7, Pub. by Luzac & Co Ltd). State Mutual Bk.

Faith of the Christian Church. rev. ed. Gustaf Aulen. Tr. by Eric H. Wahlstrom from Swedish. LC 61-5302. 416p. 1973. pap. 8.95 (ISBN 0-8006-1655-3, 1-1655). Fortress.

Faith of the Church. James A. Pike & W. Norman Pittenger. 224p. (Orig.). 1951. pap. 1.00 (ISBN 0-8164-2019-X, SP3, HarpR). Har-Row.

Faith of the Fathers: Science, Religion, & Reform in the Development of Early American Sociology. William H. Swatos, Jr. vi, 102p. 1985. pap. text ed. 6.95x (ISBN 0-932269-11-7). Wyndham Hall.

Faith of the Moralist: Gifford Lectures Delivered in the University of St. Andrews, 1926-1928, 2 vols. A. E. Taylor. 1977. Repr. of 1932 ed. Set. lib. bdg. 50.00 (ISBN 0-8482-2663-1). Norwood Edns.

Faith of the Old Testament: A History. Werner H. Schmidt. Tr. by John Sturdy. LC 82-21780. 312p. (Orig.). 1983. 25.00 (ISBN 0-664-21826-1); pap. 12.95 (ISBN 0-664-24456-4). Westminster.

Faith of the People of God: A Lay Theology. John Macquarrie. LC 72-1224. 188p. 1973. pap. 7.95 (ISBN 0-684-13060-2, ScribT). Scribner.

Faith on Trial: Studies in Psalm 73. D. Martyn Lloyd-Jones. 128p. 1982. pap. 4.50 (ISBN 0-8010-5618-7). Baker Bk.

Faith Once Delivered. Ed. by Clarence DeLoach, Jr. (Illus.). 170p. 1974. 6.95 (ISBN 0-88428-033-0). Parchment Pr.

Faith: Once for All Delivered unto the Saints. Louis Bauman. pap. 2.95 (ISBN 0-88469-026-1). BMH Bks.

Faith Passages & Patterns. Thomas A. Droege. LC 82-48544. (Lead Bks.). 128p. 1983. pap. 4.95 (ISBN 0-8006-1602-2, 1-1602). Fortress.

Faith Plus - Search for the Holy Life. J. D. Harvey. 1976. pap. 1.75 (ISBN 0-89367-002-2). Light & Life.

Faith, Prayer & Devotion. Ralph Townsend. (Faith & the Future Ser.). 123p. 1984. cloth 24.95x (ISBN 0-631-13189-2); pap. 8.95x (ISBN 0-631-13232-5). Basil Blackwell.

Faith Precedes the Miracle. Spencer W. Kimball. 9.95 (ISBN 0-87747-490-7). Deseret Bk.

Faith Prints: Youth Devotions for Every Day of the Year. Steve Swanson et al. LC 85-13466. 224p. (Orig.). 1985. pap. 4.95 (ISBN 0-8066-2178-8, 10-2189). Augsburg.

Faith Questions: Seeking God's Answers to Our Toughest Questions. Ed. by Kevin Miller. (Senior High Pacesetter Ser.). 64p. 1986. pap. 7.95 (ISBN 0-89191-329-7). Cook.

Faith, Reason & Civilization: An Essay in Historical Analysis. facsimile ed. Harold J. Laski. LC 74-167375. (Essay Index Reprint Ser). Repr. of 1944 ed. 15.00 (ISBN 0-8369-2662-5). Ayer Co Pubs.

Faith, Reason & the Plague in Seventeenth-Century Tuscany. Carlo M. Cipolla. Tr. by Muriel Kittel from Ital. LC 79-2479. (Illus.). 140p. 1980. 17.50x (ISBN 0-8014-1230-7). Cornell U Pr.

Faith, Reason, & the Plague in Seventeenth-Century Tuscany. Carlo M. Cipolla. 128p. 1981. pap. 4.95 (ISBN 0-393-00045-1). Norton.

Faith Refined by Fire. David Schroeder. LC 85-80428. (Faith & Life Bible Studies). 143p. (Orig.). 1985. pap. 4.95 (ISBN 0-87303-103-2). Faith & Life.

Faith: Reflections on Experience, Theology & Fiction. Kent D. Smith. 114p. (Orig.). 1984. lib. bdg. 22.00 (ISBN 0-8191-3634-4); pap. text ed. 9.25 (ISBN 0-8191-3635-2). U Pr of Amer.

Faith, Science, & the Future. Paul Abrecht. LC 79-7035. pap. 60.00 (2026942). Bks Demand UMI.

Faith Seeking Understanding: Essays Theological & Critical. Robert E. Cushman. LC 80-69402. xvi, 373p. 1981. 30.25 (ISBN 0-8223-0444-9). Duke.

Faith-Sharing. H. Eddie Fox & George E. Morris. 144p. 1987. pap. 7.95 (ISBN 0-310-38381-1). Zondervan.

Faith Sharing: Dynamic Christian Witnessing By Invitation. George E. Morris & H. E. Fox. LC 86-71913. 176p. (Orig.). 1986. pap. 6.95 ea. (ISBN 0-88177-039-6, DR039B). Discipleship Res.

Faith, Skepticism & Evidence: An Essay in Religious Epistemology. Stephen Davis. 233p. 1978. 20.00 (ISBN 0-8387-2039-0). Bucknell U Pr.

Faith Speaks. T. L. Osborn. 1982. pap. 2.95 (ISBN 0-89274-226-7, HH-226). Harrison Hse.

Faith Strengthened. Isaac Troki. Tr. by Moses Mocatta from Hebrew. LC 74-136768. 320p. 1975. pap. 9.75 (ISBN 0-87203-022-9). Hermon.

Faith Takes Back What the Devil's Stolen. Kenneth Hagin, Jr. 1982. pap. 0.50 mini bk (ISBN 0-89276-709-X). Hagin Ministries.

Faith That Does Justice: Examining the Christian Sources for Social Change. John C. Haughey. LC 77-74578. 312p. (Orig.). 1977. pap. 8.95 (ISBN 0-8091-2026-7). Paulist Pr.

Faith That Enquires. Henry Jones. LC 77-27211. (Gifford Lectures: 1920-21). Repr. of 1922 ed. 20.00 (ISBN 0-404-60466-8). AMS Pr.

Faith That Goes Further: Facing the Contradictions of Life. Ed Dayton. LC 84-14693. 1984. pap. 5.95 (ISBN 0-88070-062-9). Multnomah.

Faith That Heals. Fenwicke L. Holmes. 100p. 1986. pap. 6.00 (ISBN 0-89540-124-X, SB 124). Sun Pub.

Faith That Makes a Difference. John W. Bachman. LC 83-70508. 128p. (Orig.). 1983. pap. 6.95 (ISBN 0-8066-2014-5, 10-2193). Augsburg.

Faith That Prevails. Smith Wigglesworth. 64p. 1966. pap. 1.75 (ISBN 0-88243-711-9, 02-0711). Gospel Pub.

Faith That Works. Homer A. Kent, Jr. 1986. pap. 7.95 (ISBN 0-88469-180-2). BMH Bks.

Faith That Works: Eleven Studies in James. Andrew T. LePeau & Phyllis J. LePeau. 72p. (Orig.). 1980. pap. 2.25 (ISBN 0-87784-365-1). Inter Varsity.

Faith that Works: Studies in James. James T. Draper, Jr. 1983. pap. 5.95 (ISBN 0-8423-0872-5); Leader's Guide 2.95 (ISBN 0-8423-0873-3). Tyndale.

Faith That Works: Studies in the Epistle of James. Homer A. Kent, Jr. 1986. pap. 7.95 (ISBN 0-8010-5476-1). Baker Bk.

Faith that Works: Study of the Book of James. George Sweeting. 1983. pap. 3.95 (ISBN 0-8024-0276-3). Moody.

Faith the Gift of God. Tom Wells. 156p. 1983. pap. 3.95 (ISBN 0-85151-361-1). Banner of Truth.

Faith the Great Adventure. Helmut Thielicke. LC 84-48716. 160p. 1985. pap. 8.95 (ISBN 0-8006-1833-5, 1-1833). Fortress.

Faith, the Ultimate Power. Donald L. Lackey. LC 81-52786. 144p. (Orig.). 1981. pap. 4.95x (ISBN 0-941116-00-X, 711A). Univ Pubns.

Faith to Change the World. Lester Sumrall. 173p. (Orig.). 1983. pap. 4.95 (ISBN 0-89274-306-9, HH-306). Harrison Hse.

Faith to Grow by. Ed. by Lloyd H. Knox. 1977. pap. 2.95 (ISBN 0-89367-009-X). Light & Life.

Faith to Keep. Charles P. Conn. LC 77-70783. pap. 1.99 (ISBN 0-87148-016-6). Pathway Pr.

Faith to Know. Barbie Engstrom. LC 77-94207. (Christian Guidebook Ser.). (Illus., Orig.). Date not set. pap. 10.50 (ISBN 0-932210-01-5). Kurios Found.

Faith to Live by. Kenneth D. Barney. LC 76-27929. (Radiant Life Ser.). 128p. 1977. pap. 2.50 (ISBN 0-88243-899-9, 02-0899); teacher's ed. 3.95 (ISBN 0-88243-171-4, 32-0171). Gospel Pub.

Faith to Live by. Derek Prince. 1977. pap. 5.95 (ISBN 0-934920-25-7, B-29). Derek Prince.

Faith to Live by. J. C. Wenger. LC 79-89441. (Mennonite Faith Ser.: No. 9). 1980. pap. 1.50 (ISBN 0-8361-1909-6). Herald Pr.

Faith to Move Mountains: Reflections on the Gospels of the Lectionary (A, B, C,) Mieczyslaw Malinski. LC 82-61194. 144p. 1982. 5.95 (ISBN 0-8245-0509-3). Crossroad NY.

Faith to See: Reflections & Photographs. Barbie Engstrom. LC 74-25540. (Illus.). 64p. 1979. pap. 3.00 (ISBN 0-932210-00-7). Kurios Found.

Faith under Fire: Biblical Interpretations of Suffering. Danile J. Simundson. LC 79-54119. 158p. 1980. pap. 7.95 (ISBN 0-8066-1756-X, 10-2195). Augsburg.

Faith under Fire: One Hundred Dynamic Readings from Great Men of the Early Church. David Winter. LC 77-92353. (Daystar Devotional). Orig. Title: One Hundred Days in the Arena. 112p. 1981. pap. 2.95 (ISBN 0-87788-252-5). Shaw Pubs.

Faith under Scrutiny. Tibor Horvath. LC 75-1179. 343p. 1975. pap. text ed. 5.95 (ISBN 0-8190-0073-6). Loyola.

Faith: Voices from the Heart. William J. Crockett. 15p. Date not set. pap. 3.00 (ISBN 0-934383-31-6). Pride Prods.

Faith vs. Fear. Don Godwin & Vi Godwin. 257p. 1986. pap. 7.95 (ISBN 0-317-52284-1). Christian Pub.

Faith We Affirm. Ronald E. Osborn. LC 79-21079. 1979. pap. 3.50 (ISBN 0-8272-1009-4). CBP.

Faith We Confess: An Ecumenical Dogmatics. Jan M. Lochman. Tr. by David Lewis. LC 83-48908. 288p. 1984. 19.95 (ISBN 0-8006-0723-6, 1-723). Fortress.

Faith We Hold: Archbishop Paul. Tr. by Marita Nykanen & Esther Williams. LC 80-10404. 96p. 1980. pap. 4.95 (ISBN 0-913836-63-X). St Vladimirs.

Faith We Hold: The Living Witness of Luther & the Augsburg Confession. James A. Nestingen. LC 83-70516. 96p. (Orig.). 1983. pap. 5.95 (ISBN 0-8066-2022-6, 10-2200). Augsburg.

Faith We Live By. Daughters Of St. Paul. LC 68-59044. (Divine Master Ser., Vol. 3). (Illus.). 1969. 7.50 (ISBN 0-8198-0039-2); pap. 6.00 (ISBN 0-8198-0040-6); discussion & project manual 0.60 (ISBN 0-8198-0041-4). Dghtrs St Paul.

Faith We Sing. S. Paul Schilling. LC 82-21749. 262p. 1983. pap. 14.95 (ISBN 0-664-24434-3). Westminster.

Faith Within the Hills. Mary E. Repass. (Heritage Group Ser.). (Illus.). 1873. text ed. 15.00 (ISBN 0-940502-03-8). Foxhound Ent.

Faith Within You: The Essence & Meaning of the Christian Faith. John Akehurst. 141p. (Orig.). 1984. pap. 10.95 (ISBN 0-85819-469-4, Pub. by JBCE). ANZ Religious Pubns.

Faith Without Fantasy. Robert M. McMillan. LC 80-66541. 1981. 4.50 (ISBN 0-8054-5285-0). Broadman.

Faith Without Prejudice: Rebuilding Christian Attitudes Toward Judaism. Eugene Fisher. LC 77-83550. 196p. 1977. pap. 3.95 (ISBN 0-8091-2064-X). Paulist Pr.

Faith Worketh by Love. Kenneth Hagin, Jr. 1979. pap. 0.50 mini bk. (ISBN 0-89276-703-0). Hagin Ministries.

Faith Workout. Bill Myers. (Illus.). 144p. 1986. 3.95 (ISBN 0-89693-265-6). Victor Bks.

Faithful. Michael Waters. LC 84-4796. (Illus.). 16p. 1984. pap. 4.00 (ISBN 0-918518-31-8). Raccoon Memphis.

Faithful Account of the Religion & Manners of the Mahometans. Joseph Pitts. 284p. Repr. of 1738 ed. text ed. 62.10x (ISBN 0-576-03333-2). Gregg Intl.

Faithful & the Bold: The Story of the First Service of the Zion Evangelical Lutheran Church, Oldwick, New Jersey. Norman C. Wittwer, Jr. (Illus.). 46p. 1984. 10.00x (ISBN 0-913186-10-4). Monocacy.

Faithful Church: Issues in the History of Catechesis. Ed. by O. C. Edwards, Jr. & John H. Westerhoff, 3rd. LC 80-81099. 320p. (Orig.). 1981. pap. 14.95 (ISBN 0-8192-1278-4). Morehouse.

Faithful City: A Biblical Study. Richard J. Skiba. 68p. 1976. 1.25 (ISBN 0-8199-0704-9). Franciscan Herald.

Faithful Followers. Judy Hartweg. (Helping Hand Ser.). 48p. 1984. wkbk. 4.95 (ISBN 0-86653-237-4). Good Apple.

Faithful Friendship. Dorothy Devers. 1980. 2.40 (ISBN 0-88028-011-5). Forward Movement.

Faithful Mohawks. John W. Lydekker. LC 68-18362. (Empire State Historical Publications Ser.: No. 50). (Illus.). 1968. Repr. of 1938 ed. 27.50 (ISBN 0-87198-050-9). Friedman.

Faithful of Christ: The New Canon Law for the Laity. J. M. Huels. 1983. 5.50 (ISBN 0-8199-0873-8). Franciscan Herald.

Faithful Rebels. Israel Levine. LC 76-118533. 1971. Repr. of 1936 ed. 22.00x (ISBN 0-8046-1156-4, Pub. by Kennikat). Assoc Faculty Pr.

Faithful Sayings in the Pastoral Letters. George W. Knight, III. (Baker Biblical Monographs). 1979. pap. 6.95 (ISBN 0-8010-5402-8). Baker Bk.

Faithful Shepherd: A History of the New England Ministry in the Seventeenth Century. David D. Hall. 320p. 1974. pap. 3.45x (ISBN 0-393-00719-7, Norton Lib). Norton.

Faithful Shepherd: A History of the New England Ministry in the Seventeenth Century. David D. Hall. LC 72-81326. (Institute for Early American History & Culture Ser.). xvi, 301p. 1972. 27.50x (ISBN 0-8078-1193-9). U of NC Pr.

Faithful Witness. James McLeish. LC 85-4300. 276p. (Orig.). 1985. pap. 6.95 (ISBN 0-87784-531-X). Inter-Varsity.

Faithfulness. Ed Dufresne. 57p. 1981. pap. 0.75 (ISBN 0-89274-378-6). Harrison Hse.

Faithfulness in Action: Loyalty in Biblical Perspective. Katharine D. Sakenfeld. LC 84-18738. (Overtures to Biblical Theology Ser.). 176p. 1985. pap. 8.95 (ISBN 0-8006-1540-9, 1-1540). Fortress.

Faithfulness of Faith. C. E. Colton. LC 85-9845. 1985. pap. 4.95 (ISBN 0-8054-1534-3). Broadman.

Faithfulness: The Crowbar of God. Buddy Bell. 47p. 1986. pap. 2.95 (ISBN 0-89274-350-6). Christian Pub.

Faithfulness to the Gospel. Pope John Paul II. Compiled by Daughters of St. Paul. 335p. 1982. 4.50 (ISBN 0-8198-2614-6, EP0482); pap. 3.50 (ISBN 0-8198-2615-4). Dghtrs St Paul.

Faithing Oak. Robert Raines. 128p. 1984. pap. 6.95 (ISBN 0-8245-0636-7). Crossroad NY.

Faithing Oak: Meditations from the Mountain. Robert A. Raines. LC 82-12720. 128p. 1982. 9.95 (ISBN 0-8245-0485-2). Crossroad NY.

Faiths & Festivals. Martin Palmer. (Ward Lock Educational Ser.). 25.00x (ISBN 0-7062-4293-9, Pub. by Ward Lock Educ Co Ltd). State Mutual Bk.

Faiths & Folklore of the British Isles, 2 Vols. William C. Hazlitt. LC 64-18758. 1905. Set. 44.00 (ISBN 0-405-08604-0, Blom Pubns); 22.00 ea. Vol. 1 (ISBN 0-405-08605-9). Vol. 2 (ISBN 0-405-08606-7). Ayer Co Pubs.

Faith's Answer: The Mystery of Jesus. Vittorio Messori. Ed. by Eugene Brown. Tr. by Kenneth Whitehead from Ital. LC 86-13509. Tr. of Ipotesi su Jesu. 312p. (Orig.). 1986. lib. bdg. 16.95 (ISBN 0-89944-083-5); pap. 12.95 (ISBN 0-89944-084-3). Don Bosco Multimedia.

Faith's Checkbook. Charles H. Spurgeon. pap. 3.95 (ISBN 0-8024-0014-0). Moody.

Faith's Cooperating Powers. 1979. 1.25 (ISBN 0-89858-028-5). Fill the Gap.

Faith's Definition. 1981. 1.25 (ISBN 0-89858-019-6). Fill the Gap.

Faith's Destroyers. 1981. 1.25 (ISBN 0-89858-020-X). Fill the Gap.

Faith's Explanation. Elbert Willis. 1977. 1.25 (ISBN 0-89858-007-2). Fill the Gap.

Faith's Framework: The Structure of New Testament Theology. Donald Robinson. 152p. 1986. pap. 9.95 (ISBN 0-85364-317-2, Pub. by Paternoster UK). Attic Pr.

Faith's Heroes. Sherwood E. Wirt. LC 78-71943. 1979. pap. 3.95 (ISBN 0-89107-162-8, Crossway Bks). Good News.

Faiths Men Live by. facsimile ed. John C. Archer. LC 79-156606. (Essay Index Reprint Ser). Repr. of 1934 ed. 25.50 (ISBN 0-8369-2266-2). Ayer Co Pubs.

Faith's Prayer Sequence. 1979. 1.25 (ISBN 0-89858-029-3). Fill the Gap.

Faith's Steadfastness. 1981. 1.25 (ISBN 0-89858-021-8). Fill the Gap.

Faithsong: A New Look at the Ministry of Music. Thomas L. Are. LC 81-4789. 96p. 1981. pap. 6.95 (ISBN 0-664-24375-4). Westminster.

Fakers: Exploding the Myths of the Supernatural. Danny Korem & Paul Meier. LC 80-23180. (Illus.). 1981. pap. 4.95 (ISBN 0-8010-5435-4). Baker Bk.

Fakhruddin Iraqi: Divine Flashes. Tr. by William Chittick & Peter Wilson. 1982. 12.95 (ISBN 0-8091-0329-X); pap. 7.95 (ISBN 0-8091-2372-X). Paulist Pr.

Falasha Anthology. Tr. by Wolf Leslau. (Judaica Ser.: No. 6). (Illus.). 1951. 26.00x (ISBN 0-300-00681-0). Yale U Pr.

Falasha No More: An Ethiopian Jewish Child Comes Home. Arlene Kushner. (Illus.). 58p. 1986. 9.95 (ISBN 0-933503-43-1). Shapolsky Pubs.

Falashas. David Kessler. (Illus.). 205p. 1985. pap. 7.95 (ISBN 0-8052-0791-0). Schocken.

Falcon & the Dove: The Story of Laura Vicuna. Peter Lappin. (Illus.). 180p. (YA) 1985. pap. 4.95 (ISBN 0-89944-067-3). Don Bosco Multimedia.

Fall of Christianity. Gerrit J. Heering. LC 77-147670. (Library of War & Peace; Relig. & Ethical Positions on War). 1973. lib. bdg. 46.00 (ISBN 0-8240-0428-0). Garland Pub.

Fall of Man (2) Ed. by Chung Hwan Kwak. (Home Study Course Ser.). 60p. (Orig.). 1980. pap. 4.00 (ISBN 0-910621-11-X). HSA Pubns.

Fallacies of Unbelief. Arlie J. Hoover. LC 75-36313. (Way of Life Ser: No. 128). 94p. 1976. pap. 3.95 (ISBN 0-89112-128-5, Bibl Res Pr). Abilene Christ U.

Fallen Angel: Hell's Angel to Heaven's Saint. Barry Mayson & Tony Marco. LC 81-43539. (Illus.). 312p. 1982. 15.95 (ISBN 0-385-17934-0); pap. write for info. (ISBN 0-385-19626-1). Doubleday.

Fallen Angels in Jewish & Christian & Mohammedan Literature. Leo Jung. 1926. 25.00x (ISBN 0-87068-236-9). Ktav.

Fallen Images: Experiencing Divorce in the Ministry. Keith Madsen. 128p. 1985. pap. 5.95 (ISBN 0-8170-1076-9). Judson.

Fallible Forms & Symbols: Discourses on Method in a Theology of Culture. Bernard E. Meland. LC 76-7868. pap. 56.50 (2026957). Bks Demand UMI.

Falling Apart or Coming Together: How You Can Experience the Faithfulness of God. Lois W. Johnson. LC 83-72112. 128p. (Orig.). 1984. pap. 5.95 (ISBN 0-8066-2056-0, 10-2208). Augsburg.

Falling in Love with the Lord. Ron Bridges. 1987. price not set (ISBN 0-89109-143-2). NavPress.

Falling into Greatness. Lloyd J. Oglivie. LC 84-1946. 224p. 1984. 11.95 (ISBN 0-8407-5326-8). Nelson.

False Christs, False Prophets. Gordon Lindsay. (Prophecy Ser.). 1.95 (ISBN 0-89985-054-5). Christ Nations.

False Faces of the Iroquois. William N. Fenton. (Illus.). 1987. 75.00. U of Okla Pr.

False Gods of Our Time. Norm Geisler. (Orig.). 1985. pap. 5.95 (ISBN 0-89081-494-5). Harvest Hse.

False Messiahs: Prophets of the Millennium. Jack Gratus. LC 75-29890. 284p. 1976. 10.95 (ISBN 0-8008-2588-8). Taplinger.

Falsos Testigos De Jehova. D. S. Fernandez. 46p. 1985. pap. 1.25 (ISBN 0-311-06351-9). Casa Bautista.

Familia Autenticamente Cristiana. Guillermo D. Taylor. Tr. of Authentic Christian Family. (Span.). 240p. 1983. pap. 4.50 (ISBN 0-8254-1702-3). Kregel.

Familia Cristiana. Larry Christenson. 238p. 1972. 3.95 (ISBN 0-88113-080-X). Edit Betania.

Familia del Cirujano. David Hernandez & Carole G. Page. 272p. 1982. 3.50 (ISBN 0-88113-090-7). Edit Betania.

Familia Sujeta al Espiritu. Berverly LaHaye & Tim LaHaye. 208p. 1980. 3.75 (ISBN 0-88113-085-0). Edit Betania.

Familiar Mysteries: The Truth in Myth. Shirley Lowry. LC 80-27792. (Illus.). 1981. 25.00x (ISBN 0-19-502925-9). Oxford U Pr.

Familias Conviven Mejor con Amor. Howard Hendricks. 48p. 1979. 1.65 (ISBN 0-88113-095-8). Edit Betania.

Families & Religions: Conflict & Change in Modern Society. Ed. by William V. D'Antonio & Joan Aldous. 320p. 1983. 29.00 (ISBN 0-8039-2075-X); pap. 14.50 (ISBN 0-8039-2468-2). Sage.

Families & the Prospect of Nuclear Attack-Holocaust. Ed. by Teresa Marciano & Marvin B. Sussman. LC 86-18320. (Marriage & Family Review Ser.: Vol. 10, No. 2). 1986. pap. 22.95 (ISBN 0-86656-374-1). Haworth Pr.

Families: Black & Catholic, Catholic & Black, Readings, Resources & Family Activities. Ed. by Thea Bowman, Sr. 160p. 1985. pap. 14.95 (ISBN 1-55586-890-8). US Catholic.

Families Can Be Happy. Betty J. Grams. LC 81-82420. 128p. (Orig.). 1981. pap. 2.50 (ISBN 0-88243-759-3, 02-0759); tchr's ed 3.95 (ISBN 0-88243-334-2, 02-0334). Gospel Pub.

Families Sharing God. Barbara O. Webb. 48p. 1981. pap. 3.50 (ISBN 0-8170-0900-0). Judson.

Families, the Economy & the Church: A Book of Readings & Discussion Guide. Paul Schervish et al. Ed. by Frederick Brigham & Steven Preister. 144p. (Orig.). 1987. pap. 5.95 (ISBN 1-55586-136-9). US Catholic.

Family. Ed. by John Duckworth et al. (Pacesetter Ser.). 64p. 1987. tchr's. ed. 7.95. Cook.

Family. John MacArthur. 1982. pap. 5.95 (ISBN 0-8024-2524-0). Moody.

Family. Ed. by Hayyim Schneid. LC 73-11760. (Popular Judaica Library). (Illus.). 120p. 1974. pap. 3.95 (ISBN 0-8276-0029-1, 341). Jewish Pubns.

Family: A Church Challenge for the 80's. Dolores Curran. (Orig.). 1980. pap. 3.50 (ISBN 0-86683-640-3, HarpR). Har-Row.

Family Adventures. Bruce Clanton. LC 80-51060. 1980. pap. 4.95 (ISBN 0-89390-018-4). Resource Pubns.

Family Altar. rev. ed. Harry N. Huxhold. 1964. 12.95 (ISBN 0-570-03071-4, 6-1085). Concordia.

Family & Pastoral Care. Herbert Anderson. Ed. by Don S. Browning. LC 83-48914. (Theology & Pastoral Care Ser.). 128p. pap. 7.95 (ISBN 0-8006-1728-2, 1-1728). Fortress.

Family & the Church. Robert Fisher. LC 77-99163. 1978. 5.25 (ISBN 0-87148-334-3); pap. 4.25 (ISBN 0-87148-335-1). Pathway Pr.

Family & the Unification Church. Ed. by Gene G. James. LC 83-80638. (Conference Ser.: No. 17). 1983. 14.95 (ISBN 0-932894-19-4, Pub. by New Era Bks); pap. text ed. 10.95 (ISBN 0-932894-17-8). Paragon Hse.

Family & the Unification Church. Ed. by Gene G. James. LC 83-80638. 269p. (Orig.). 1983. 15.95; pap. 11.95. Rose Sharon Pr.

Family As a Way into the Future. Elise Boulding. 1983. pap. 2.50x (ISBN 0-87574-222-X, 222). Pendle Hill.

Family Awakening in Body, Mind, & Spirit. Jim Morningstar. 60p. 1984. pap. 6.00 (ISBN 0-9604856-1-9). Transform Inc.

Family Bible Encyclopedia, 2 vols. Alvera Mickelsen & Berkley Mickelsen. Incl. Volume I (A-K (ISBN 0-89191-100-6); Volume II (L-Z (ISBN 0-89191-127-8). LC 78-55384. (Illus.). 1978. 9.95 ea.; Set. 12.95 (ISBN 0-89191-201-0). Cook.

Family Bible Holy Scriptures Commentary, 2 vols. Alexander Harkovy. Set. 62.50 (ISBN 0-317-30501-8). Shalom.

Family Book of Bible Stories. John B. Donovan. 120p. 1986. pap. 8.95 (ISBN 0-8192-1381-0). Morehouse.

Family Book of Christmas Songs & Stories. Jim Charlton & Jason Shulman. (Illus.). 208p. 1986. pap. 9.95 (ISBN 0-399-51276-4, Perigee). Putnam Pub Group.

Family Book of Praise. Mary J. Tully. (Illus.). 128p. (Orig.). 1980. pap. 5.95 (ISBN 0-8215-6542-7). Sadlier.

Family: Center of Love. 6.00 (ISBN 0-8198-2608-1); 5.00 (ISBN 0-8198-2609-X). Dghtrs St Paul.

Family Christmas Tree Book. Tomie De Paola. LC 80-12081. (Illus.). 32p. 1980. reinforced bdg. 11.95 (ISBN 0-8234-0416-1). Holiday.

Family Circle Christmas Treasury. Ed. by Family Cirle & Ceri Hadda. 1986. 19.95 (ISBN 0-933585-02-0). Family Circle Bks.

Family Connections: A History of Italian & Jewish Immigrant Lives in Providence, Rhode Island, 1900-1940. Judith E. Smith. (SUNY Series in American Social History). 256p. 1985. 44.50 (ISBN 0-87395-964-7); pap. 16.95 (ISBN 0-87395-965-5). State U NY Pr.

Family Covenant: Leaders Manual. Janet Kobobel. 35p. 1984. tchr's ed. 10.95 (ISBN 0-89191-892-2). Cook.

Family Covenant: Students Manual. Dennis B. Guernsey. 113p. 1984. pap. text ed. 3.95 (ISBN 0-89191-843-4). Cook.

Family Devotions Idea Book. Evelyn Blitchington. LC 82-4252. 139p. (Orig.). 1982. pap. 4.95 (ISBN 0-87123-254-5, 210254). Bethany Hse.

Family Enrichment Book. Carol Anway. 1979. pap. 8.00 (ISBN 0-8309-0247-3). Herald Hse.

Family Enrichment with Family Clusters. Margaret M. Sawin. 1979. pap. 6.95 (ISBN 0-8170-0830-6). Judson.

Family Evening Activity Devotions. Ron Brusius & Margaret Noettl. pap. 4.95 (ISBN 0-570-03803-0, 12-2912). Concordia.

Family Faith Stories. Ann Weems. LC 85-13771. 142p. 1985. pap. 8.95 (ISBN 0-664-24670-2). Westminster.

Family Fare. Paul Martin. 79p. 1976. pap. 1.25 (ISBN 0-8341-0403-2). Beacon Hill.

Family Fare: Christian Activities for Every Season of the Year. Darlene McRoberts. LC 81-65642. (Illus.). 80p. (Orig.). 1981. pap. 5.95 (ISBN 0-8066-1878-7, 10-2247). Augsburg.

Family First. Kenneth O. Gangel. pap. 3.50 (ISBN 0-88469-106-3). BMH Bks.

Family Forum. Jay Kesler. 1984. 12.95 (ISBN 0-88207-820-8). Victor Bks.

Family Foundations. Paul Meier & Richard Meier. 96p. (Orig.). 1981. 8.95 (ISBN 0-8010-6117-2). Baker Bk.

Family Fun Times: Activities That Bind Marriages, Build Families, & Develop Christian Leaders. Wayne Rickerson. 80p. Date not set. pap. 7.95 (ISBN 0-87403-207-5, 3187). Standard Pub.

Family Guide to Death & Dying. Jim Towns. 192p. (Orig.). 1987. pap. 5.95 (ISBN 0-8423-0830-X). Tyndale.

Family Guide to the Bible: A Concordance & Reference Companion to the King James Version. Reader's Digest Editors. LC 84-13261. (Illus.). 832p. 1984. 24.50 (ISBN 0-89577-192-6, Pub. by RD Assn). Random.

Family Haggadah. Tr. by Nosson Scherman. (Artscroll Mesorah Ser.). 96p. (Orig.). 1981. pap. 2.75 (ISBN 0-89906-178-8). Mesorah Pubns.

Family Haggadah. Shoshana Silberman. 1987. pap. 3.95; Songs for a Family Seder. cassette 6.95. Kar Ben.

Family Hope for the World. Pontifical Council for the Family. 71p. pap. 3.50 (ISBN 0-317-46615-1). New City.

Family Idea Book: Praying & Playing Together. Matilda Nordtvedt. (Orig.). 1984. pap. 5.95 (ISBN 0-8024-0436-7). Moody.

Family Ideas for Prayers. Jan Hartley. (Together with God Ser.). (Illus.). 80p. (Orig.). 1984. pap. 5.95 (ISBN 0-85819-495-3, Pub. by JBCE). ANZ Religious Pubns.

Family Journey into Joy. C. S. Cowles. 168p. 1982. pap. 3.95 (ISBN 0-8341-0803-8). Beacon Hill.

Family, Kinship, & Marriage among the Muslims. Ed. by Imtiaz Ahmad. LC 77-74484. 1977. 18.50x (ISBN 0-88386-757-5). South Asia Bks.

Family Laws of Islam. M. I. Siddiqui. Date not set. 22.00. Kazi Pubns.

Family Life Education Program Idea Guide. National Council of Jewish Women. (Illus.). 37p. 1985. pap. text ed. 3.00 (ISBN 0-941840-21-2). NCJW.

Family Life in Islam. Khurshid Ahmad. 38p. (Orig.). 1974. pap. 2.25x (ISBN 0-86037-016-X, Pub by Islamic Found UK). New Era Pubns MI.

Family Life Ministry. Ed. by David M. Thomas. LC 79-53513. (Marriage & Family Living in Depth Bk.). 1979. pap. 2.45 (ISBN 0-87029-157-2, 20243-2). Abbey.

Family Life of Ralph Josselin: An Essay in Historical Anthropology. Alan Macfarlane. (Illus.). 1977. pap. 7.95 (ISBN 0-393-00849-5, Norton Lib). Norton.

Family Matters. John Catoir. Ed. & intro. by Joseph R. Thomas. 180p. (Orig.). 1984. pap. 5.00 (ISBN 0-317-46547-3). Chrstphrs NY.

Family Ministry. Gloria Durka & Joanmarie Smith. 216p. (Orig.). 1980. pap. 7.95 (ISBN 0-86683-762-0, HarpR). Har-Row.

Family Ministry: Family Life Through the Church. Charles M. Sell. 272p. 15.95 (ISBN 0-310-42580-8, 12335). Zondervan.

Family Nights: Advent-Christmas. Terry Reilly & Mimi Reilly. 1977. pap. 1.45 (ISBN 0-87029-135-1, 20161-6). Abbey.

Family Nights: Lent-Easter. Terry Reilly & Mimi Reilly. 1977. pap. 1.45 (ISBN 0-87029-130-0, 20158-2). Abbey.

Family Nights: Summer-Vacation. Terry Reilly & Mimi Reilly. 1977. pap. 1.45 (ISBN 0-87029-134-3, 20160-8). Abbey.

Family of Faith. Karl A. Olsson. 157p. 1975. cloth 5.45 (ISBN 0-910452-24-5). Covenant.

Family of Faith. J. C. Wenger. LC 80-84609. (Mennonite Faith Ser.: No. 10). 72p. 1981. pap. 1.50 (ISBN 0-8361-1951-7). Herald Pr.

Family of God: The Meaning of Church Membership. LeRoy Lawson. LC 80-53497. 64p. (Orig.). 1981. pap. 1.50 (ISBN 0-87239-432-8, 39970). Standard Pub.

Family of Love. Alastair Hamilton. 185p. 1981. text ed. 29.95 (ISBN 0-227-67845-1). Attic Pr.

Family Passover. Anne Rosen et al. LC 79-89298. 64p. 1980. 6.95 (ISBN 0-8276-0169-7, 452). Jewish Pubns.

Family Planning Dilemma Revisited. John Q. Quesnell. (Synthesis Ser.). 64p. 1975. pap. 1.75 (ISBN 0-8199-0364-7). Franciscan Herald.

Family Planning: How To Decide What's Best for You. Peter DeJong & William Smit. 208p. 1987. pap. 6.95 (ISBN 0-310-37961-X). Zondervan.

Family Pocket Promise Book. Larry Christenson. LC 83-72175. 128p. (Orig.). 1983. pap. 2.95 (ISBN 0-87123-303-7, 200303). Bethany Hse.

Family Prayer. rev. ed. Dolores Curran. 136p. (Orig.). 1983. pap. text ed. 5.95 (ISBN 0-86716-014-4). St Anthony Mess Pr.

Family Prayers. Frank Colquhoun. 80p. 1984. pap. 1.35 (ISBN 0-88028-040-9). Forward Movement.

Family Prayers. Ron Klug & Lyn Klug. LC 79-50081. 1979. pap. 4.95 (ISBN 0-8066-1708-X, 10-2258). Augsburg.

Family Protection Scoreboard, Special Edition on South Africa, No. 1. Ed. & intro. by David W. Balsiger. 56p. 1987. 2.95 (ISBN 0-89921-021-X). Biblical News Serv.

Family Relationships. Chuck Smith. 48p. (Orig.). 1980. pap. 0.95 (ISBN 0-936728-04-3). Word for Today.

Family Renewal in the Home. Thomas McGuiness. LC 83-63006. 83p. (Orig.). 1984. pap. text ed. 4.95 (ISBN 0-911905-17-0). Past & Mat Rene Ctr.

Family Rituals. Compiled by Charla Honea. LC 81-52861. (Illus., Orig.). 1981. pap. 3.95x (ISBN 0-8358-0433-X). Upper Room.

Family Secrets: What You Need to Know to Build a Strong Christian Family. Gladys Hunt. 98p. 1985. pap. 3.95 (ISBN 0-89283-233-9, Pub. by Vine Books). Servant.

Family Seder. rev. ed. Alfred J. Kolatch. LC 67-17778. (Illus.). 1972. pap. 3.95 (ISBN 0-8246-0132-7). Jonathan David.

Family Structure in Islam. Hammudah Abdalati. LC 77-79635. 1976. 10.95 (ISBN 0-89259-004-1); pap. 8.50. Am Trust Pubns.

Family Symphony. Virginia Clawson. LC 84-17524. 1984. 7.95 (ISBN 0-8054-5661-9). Broadman.

Family Takes a Child. Nancy B. Barcus. 96p. 1983. pap. 5.95 (ISBN 0-8170-0998-1). Judson.

Family That Wanted a Home. Stephanie Caffrey & Timothy Kenslea. (Rainbow Books (Bible Story Books for Children)). (Orig.). 1978. pap. 1.00 (ISBN 0-8192-1235-0). Morehouse.

Family Therapy in Pastoral Ministry. J. C. Wynn. LC 81-47840. 192p. 1982. 12.00 (ISBN 0-06-069703-2, HarpR). Har-Row.

Family Time, Faith Time, 3 Vols. Kathryn Fitzpatrick. (Illus.). 307p. (Orig.). 1982. Set. pap. text ed. 8.95 (ISBN 0-86716-030-6). St Anthony Mess Pr.

Family Today & Tomorrow: The Church Addresses Her Future. Ed. by Donald G. McCarthy. 291p. 1985. pap. 17.95 (ISBN 0-935372-17-2). Pope John Ctr.

Family Worship Through the Year. Kristen J. Ingram. 80p. 1984. pap. 5.95 (ISBN 0-8170-1052-1). Judson.

Famine in China & the Missionary: Timothy Richard As Relief Administrator & Advocate of National Reform, 1876-1884. Paul R. Bohr. LC 72-75828. (East Asian Monographs Ser: No. 48). (Illus.). 1972. pap. 11.00x (ISBN 0-674-29425-4). Harvard U Pr.

Famous Caves & Catacombs. facsimile ed. William H. Adams. LC 70-37773. (Essay Index Reprint Ser). Repr. of 1886 ed. 23.00 (ISBN 0-8369-2577-7). Ayer Co Pubs.

Famous Couples of the Bible. Brian L. Harbour. LC 78-60053. 1979. pap. 4.95 (ISBN 0-8054-5630-9). Broadman.

Famous Couples of the Bible. Richard Strauss. 1982. pap. 4.95 (ISBN 0-8423-0836-9); pap. 2.95 leader's guide (ISBN 0-8423-0837-7). Tyndale.

Famous Couples of the Bible. Richard L. Strauss. Tr. by Ruth T. Chen. (Chinese.). 1985. pap. write for info. (ISBN 0-941598-29-2). Living Spring Pubns.

Famous Curses. Daniel Cohen. (Illus.). pap. 1.95 (ISBN 0-671-41867-X). Archway.

Famous Curses. Daniel Cohen. LC 79-52039. (High Interest-Low Vocabulary Ser.). (Illus.). 1979. 8.95 (ISBN 0-396-07712-9). Dodd.

Famous Druids: A Survey of Three Centuries of English Literature in the Druids. A. L. Owen. LC 78-13614. (Illus.). 1979. Repr. of 1962 ed. lib. bdg. 22.50x (ISBN 0-313-20629-5, OWFD). Greenwood.

Famous Ex-Priests. Emmett McLoughlin. LC 68-18759. 1968. 4.95 (ISBN 0-8184-0030-7). Lyle Stuart.

Famous Hymns & Their Authors. F. A. Jones. 59.95 (ISBN 0-8490-0154-4). Gordon Pr.

Famous Mather Byles: Noted Boston Tory Preacher, Poet, & Wit 1707-1788. facsimile ed. Arthur W. Eaton. LC 74-165626. (Select Bibliographies Reprint Ser). Repr. of 1914 ed. 33.00 (ISBN 0-8369-5933-7). Ayer Co Pubs.

Famous Mather Byles, the Noted Boston Tory Preacher, Poet, & Wit. facsimile ed. Arthur W. Eaton. LC 72-8697. (American Revolutionary Ser.). Repr. of 1914 ed. lib. bdg. 19.00x (ISBN 0-8398-0458-X). Irvington.

Famous Parents of the Bible. Brian L. Harbour. LC 82-73079. 1983. pap. 4.95 (ISBN 0-8054-5655-4). Broadman.

Famous Singles of the Bible. Brian L. Harbour. LC 79-56309. 1980. pap. 4.95 (ISBN 0-8054-5640-6). Broadman.

Fan the Flame: Living Out Your First Love for Christ. Joseph M. Stowell. (Orig.). 1986. pap. 5.95 (ISBN 0-8024-2528-3). Moody.

Fanaticism. Josef Rudin. LC 69-14813. (Ger). 1969. Repr. of 1965 ed. 17.95 (ISBN 0-268-00318-1). U of Notre Dame Pr.

Fanaticism, Intolerance & Islam. K. Ahmed. pap. 1.00 (ISBN 0-686-18491-2). Kazi Pubns.

Fanfare: A Celebration of Belief. Nancy Spiegelberg & Dorothy Purdy. LC 80-25519. (Illus., Orig.). 1981. pap. 6.95 (ISBN 0-930014-56-1). Multnomah.

Fanny Crosby. Bernard Ruffin. (Heroes of the Faith Ser.). 1985. Repr. of 1976 ed. 6.95 (ISBN 0-916441-16-4). Barbour & Co.

Fanny Crosby's Story. S. Trevena Jackson. (Christian Biography Ser.). 198p. 1981. pap. 3.95 (ISBN 0-8010-5127-4). Baker Bk.

Fanny J. Crosby: Autobiography of Fanny J Crosby. Fanny J. Crosby. (Christian Biography Ser.). 254p. 1986. Repr. of 1906 ed. 7.95 (ISBN 0-8010-2509-5). Baker Bk.

Fantasia & Psychoanalysis & the Unconscious. D. H. Lawrence. 1978. pap. 6.95 (ISBN 0-14-003303-3). Penguin.

Fantasy Explosion. Bob Maddux. Ed. by Mary Beckwith. LC 86-21938. 168p. (Orig.). pap. 5.95 (ISBN 0-8307-1163-5, 5418886). Regal.

Fantasy of Human Rights. Patrick J. O'Mahoney. 192p. 1978. pap. 4.95 (ISBN 0-85597-256-4). Attic Pr.

Far above Rubies. H. W. Darst. 128p. (Orig.). 1982. pap. 2.50 (ISBN 0-89114-110-3). Baptist Pub Hse.

Far Beyond the Stars. Bhagwan Shree Rajneesh. Ed. by Ma Prem Maneesha. LC 82-229145. (Initiation Talks Ser.). (Illus.). 306p. (Orig.). 1980. 20.95 (ISBN 0-88050-059-X). Chidvilas Found.

Far Country. Paul Twitchell. 1971. pap. 5.95 (ISBN 0-914766-91-0). IWP Pub.

Far East Journey of Peace & Brotherhood. Pope John Paul II. write for info. Dghtrs St Paul.

Far Journey Through Life, Love & Eternity. Lloyd K. Ulery. LC 77-91280. 185p. 1978. 7.95 (ISBN 0-930984-01-3). Psychic Bks.

Far Out Ideas for Young Groups. Wayne Rice & Mike Yaconelli. 96p. 1975. pap. 6.95 (ISBN 0-310-34941-9, 10797P). Zondervan.

Far Shore. Mitchell Ginsberg. 100p. 1984. 21.00x (ISBN 0-7212-0577-1, Pub. by Regency Pr). State Mutual Bk.

Far West Record. Ed. by Donald Q. Cannon & Lyndon W. Cook. LC 82-23476. 318p. 1983. 10.95 (ISBN 0-87747-901-1). Deseret Bk.

Farewell Discourse & the Final Prayer of Jesus: An Exposition of John 14-17. D. A. Carson. LC 80-68769. 196p. 1981. 9.95 (ISBN 0-8010-2460-9). Baker Bk.

Farewell Ministry of Christ: John 13-17. Ernest T. Wilson. LC 81-316. 96p. (Orig.). 1981. pap. 2.50 (ISBN 0-87213-965-4). Loizeaux.

Farewell to Fear. Nelson L. Price. (Orig.). 1983. pap. 5.95 (ISBN 0-8054-5533-7). Broadman.

Farm Sermons. C. H. Spurgeon. 328p. Date not set. pap. write for info. Pilgrim Pubns.

Farming the Lord's Land: Christian Perspectives on American Agriculture. Charles P. Lutz. LC 80-80285. 208p. (Orig.). 1980. pap. 8.95 (ISBN 0-8066-1785-3, 10-2264). Augsburg.

Farnese Hours. Webster Smith. LC 76-4041. (Library of Illuminated Manuscripts). (Illus.). 168p. 1976. slipcase 45.00 (ISBN 0-8076-0856-4). Braziller.

Farthing in Her Hand: Stewardship for Women. Ed. by Helen Alderfer. LC 64-23376. 226p. 1964. pap. 4.95 (ISBN 0-8361-1515-5). Herald Pr.

Fasciculi Zizaniorium Magistri Johannis Wyclif Cum Tritico. Thomas Netter. Ed. by Walter W. Shirley. (Rolls Ser.: No. 5). Repr. of 1858 ed. 60.00 (ISBN 0-8115-1006-9). Kraus Repr.

Fascinante Mundo de la Biblia. Nelson B. Keyes. Orig. Title: Story of the Bible World. (Span., Illus.). 216p. 1980. 20.95 (ISBN 0-311-03664-3, Edit Mundo); pap. 16.95 (ISBN 0-311-03665-1, Edit Mundo). Casa Bautista.

Fascinating Facts about the Spirit of Prophecy. Phyllis C. Bailey. 64p. pap. 2.95 (ISBN 0-317-01322-X). Review & Herald.

Fascination of Faith. Albert A. Dickson. Ed. by Gerald Keith. 268p. (Orig.). 1980. pap. 4.95x (ISBN 0-9604080-0-2). Gloria Pubs.

Fascination of Old Testament Story. W. Graham Scroggie. Date not set. 7.95 (ISBN 0-8254-3726-1). Kregel.

Fassungen der Alexius-Legende. Margarete Rosler. Repr. of 1905 ed. 25.00 (ISBN 0-384-51670-X). Johnson Repr.

Fast & Feast: Food in Medieval Society. Bridget Ann Henisch. LC 76-15677. (Illus.). 1977. pap. 12.50x (ISBN 0-271-00424-X). Pa St U Pr.

Fastened on God: A Practical Catechtical Program for Teenagers. Joseph Moore. 88p. (Orig.). 1984. pap. 4.95 (ISBN 0-8091-9566-6). Paulist Pr.

Fasti Romani: The Civil & Literary Chronology of Rome & Constantinople from the Death of Augustus to the Death of Justin the 2nd, 2 Vols. Henry F. Clinton. 1965. Repr. of 1850 ed. Set. 105.50 (ISBN 0-8337-0602-0). B Franklin.

Fasting. Ignatius Brianchaninov. pap. 0.25 (ISBN 0-686-05642-6). Eastern Orthodox.

Fasting. Romara Chatham. LC 85-73212. 1986. pap. cancelled (ISBN 0-88270-604-7). Bridge pub.

Fasting. Jerry Falwell. 1981. pap. 2.50 (ISBN 0-8423-0849-0). Tyndale.

Fasting. D. Smith. 1973. 3.95 (ISBN 0-87508-516-4); pap. 2.95 (ISBN 0-87508-515-6). Chr Lit.

Fasting: A Reference. International Partners in Prayer. 25p. Date not set. pap. text ed. 2.00 (ISBN 0-917593-07-3, Pub. by Intl Partners). Prosperity & Profits.

Fasting Changed My Life. Andy Anderson. LC 77-82404. 1977. pap. 3.95 (ISBN 0-8054-5259-1). Broadman.

Fasting in the New Testament. Joseph F. Wimmer. LC 81-83183. 160p. (Orig.). 1982. pap. 8.95 (ISBN 0-8091-2420-3). Paulist Pr.

Fasting Primer. 2nd & rev. ed. Alvenia M. Fulton. Ed. by James C. Williams. LC 78-60661. 1978. pap. 5.95 (ISBN 0-931564-04-2). JBR Pub.

Fasting Rediscovered: A Guide to Health & Wholeness for Your Body-Spirit. Thomas Ryan. LC 80-81581. 160p. (Orig.). 1981. pap. 6.95 (ISBN 0-8091-2323-1). Paulist Pr.

Fasting: The Ultimate Diet. Allan Cott. 160p. 1986. pap. 3.50 (ISBN 0-553-25967-9). Bantam.

Fatalism in the Works of Thomas Hardy. Albert P. Elliott. LC 74-10791. 1972. lib. bdg. 17.50 (ISBN 0-8414-3950-8). Folcroft.

Fate of King Saul. D. M. Gunn. (Journal for the Study of the Old Testament, Supplement Ser.: No. 14). 1980. text ed. 18.95x (ISBN 0-905774-24-8, Pub. by JSOT Pr England); pap. text ed. 10.95 (ISBN 0-905774-63-9). Eisenbrauns.

Fate of the Dead: A Study in Folk-Eschatology in the West Country After the Reformation. Theo Brown. (Folklore Society Mistletoe Ser.). 118p. 1979. 26.50x (ISBN 0-8476-6214-4). Rowman.

Fateful Mission. Meir Bar-Am. 180p. 1986. 9.95 (ISBN 0-87306-420-8); pap. 6.95 (ISBN 0-87306-421-6). Feldheim.

Fateful Months: Essays on the Emergence of the Final Solution, 1941-1942. Christopher R. Browning. LC 84-9089. (Illus.). 100p. 1985. text ed. 24.95x (ISBN 0-8419-0967-9). Holmes & Meier.

Father & Son. Darrell Sifford. LC 82-11063. 270p. 1982. 9.95 (ISBN 0-664-27004-2, A Bridgebooks Publication). Westminster.

Father & Son. Sri Chinmoy. 100p. (Orig.). 1975. pap. 2.00 (ISBN 0-88497-119-8). Aum Pubns.

Father & Sons Shall Be One, Vol. 1. Don Kistler. 141p. (Orig.). 1978. pap. 3.50x (ISBN 0-940532-01-8). AOG.

Father Bombo's Pilgrimage to Mecca, 1770. Hugh H. Brackenridge & Philip Freneau. Ed. by Michael D. Bell. LC 75-5391. (Illus.). 129p. 1975. 10.00 (ISBN 0-87811-020-8). Princeton Lib.

Father Clark: Or, The Pioneer Preacher. John M. Peck. 285p. 1986. pap. text ed. 6.95x (ISBN 0-8290-1901-4). Irvington.

Father Coughlin & the New Deal. Charles J. Tull. LC 65-11680. (Illus.). 1965. 10.95x (ISBN 0-8156-0043-7). Syracuse U Pr.

Father Damien of Molokai. Daughters of St Paul. 1979. pap. 0.95 (ISBN 0-8198-0640-4). Dghtrs St Paul.

Father Divine. Robert Weisbrot. LC 84-45084. (Illus.). 241p. 1984. pap. 10.95x (ISBN 0-8070-0901-6, BP684). Beacon Pr.

Father Eusebio Francisco Kino & His Missions of the Pimeria Alta: The Side Altars, Bk. I. Erni Cabat. Ed. by Charles W. Polzer. Tr. by Carmen V. Prezelski. LC 82-50219. (Illus.). 36p. (Orig.). 1982. pap. 5.00 (ISBN 0-915076-06-3). SW Mission.

Father Eusebio Francisco Kino & His Missions of the Pimeria Alta: Bk. II, The Main Altars, Book II. Erni Cabat & Charles W. Polzer. Tr. by Carmen V. Prezelski. LC 82-50219. (Illus.). 36p. (Orig.). 1983. pap. 5.00 (ISBN 0-915076-08-X). SW Mission.

Father Eusebio Francisco Kino & His Missions of the Pimeria Alta: Facing the Missions, Bk. II. Erni Cabat & Charles W. Polzer. Tr. by Carmen V. Prezelski. LC 82-50219. (Illus.). 36p. 1983. pap. 5.00 (ISBN 0-915076-09-8). SW Mission.

Father Garces: The Maverick Priest. Peter R. Odens. (Illus.). 1980. pap. 3.50 (ISBN 0-9609484-3-0). P R Odens.

Father, Give Us Another Chance. Edmond B. Szekely. (Illus.). 62p. 1969. pap. 6.80 (ISBN 0-89564-071-6). IBS Intl.

Father Has Come. Fernando L. Dasbach. 113p. 1981. 10.00 (ISBN 0-686-28999-4). Regenbogen-Verlag.

Father Henson's Story of His Own Life. Josiah Henson. 212p. 1973. Repr. of 1855 ed. 16.95 (ISBN 0-87928-037-9). Corner Hse.

Father Henson's Story of His Own Life. Josiah Henson. LC 70-99381. (Illus.). vii, 212p. 1972. Repr. of 1858 ed. lib. bdg. 12.50 (ISBN 0-8411-0052-7). Metro Bks.

Father Henson's Story of His Own Life. Josiah Henson. (Illus.). 224p. 1986. pap. text ed. 6.95x (ISBN 0-8290-1902-2). Irvington.

Father Is Very Fond of Me. Edward Farrell. 6.95 (ISBN 0-87193-029-3). Dimension Bks.

Father John of Kronstadt: A Life. Alexander Semenoff-Tian-Chansky. 160p. 1979. pap. 7.95 (ISBN 0-913836-56-7). St Vladimirs.

Father Junipero Serra, the Traveling Missionary. Linda Lyngheim et al. LC 85-82131. (Illus.). 64p. 1986. 12.95 (ISBN 0-915369-01-X). Langtry Pubns.

Father Kosmas: The Apostle of the Poor. Nomikos M. Vaporis. LC 77-77664. (Illus.). 164p. 1977. 7.95 (ISBN 0-916586-17-0); pap. 4.95 (ISBN 0-916586-10-3). Holy Cross Orthodox.

Father McGuire's New, Modern Catechism Know, Love, & Serve: The Holy Father, Our God-Given Supreme Teacher. Michael A. McGuire. LC 73-158919. (Know, Love, & Serve Catechisms Ser.). (Illus.). 222p. 1973. pap. 11.00 (ISBN 0-913382-43-4, 103-5). Prow Bks-Franciscan.

Father McGuire's New, Modern Catechism Know, Love, & Serve, Bk. 1. Michael A. McGuire. LC 73-158919. (Know, Love & Serve Catechisms). (Illus.). 58p. 1971. pap. 5.25 (ISBN 0-913382-39-6, 103-1). Prow Bks-Franciscan.

Father McGuire's New, Modern Catechism Know, Love, & Serve: Preparing for First Holy Communion, BK. 2. Michael A. McGuire. LC 73-158919. (Know, Love, & Serve Catechisms Ser.). (Illus.). 90p. 1971. pap. 6.50 (ISBN 0-913382-40-X, 103-2). Prow Bks-Franciscan.

Father McGuire's New, Modern Catechism Know, Love, & Serve, Bk. 3. Michael A. McGuire. LC 73-158919. (Know, Love, & Serve Catechisms Ser.). (Illus.). 175p. 1972. pap. 9.50 (ISBN 0-913382-41-8, 103-3). Prow Bks-Franciscan.

Father McGuire's New, Modern Catechism Know, Love, & Serve, Bk. 4. Michael A. McGuire. LC 73-158919. (Know, Love, & Serve Catechisms Ser.). (Illus.). 192p. 1973. pap. 10.00 (ISBN 0-913382-42-6, 103-4). Prow Bks-Franciscan.

Father Meroto. Jorge Narvaez. 160p. pap. text ed. 6.95 (ISBN 0-936123-03-6). NY Circus Pubns.

Father of Comfort. Basilea Schlink. 128p. 1971. pap. 3.50 (ISBN 0-87123-156-5, 200156). Bethany Hse.

Father Paul of Moll. Edward Van Speybrouck. LC 79-53695. 1979. pap. 6.00 (ISBN 0-89555-122-5). TAN Bks Pubs.

Father Smith Instructs Jackson. rev. ed. Ed. by Albert J. Nevins. LC 75-628. 278p. 1975. pap. 6.50 (ISBN 0-87973-864-2). Our Sunday Visitor.

Father, the Son & the Holy Spirit: An Investigation of the Origin & Meaning of the Triadic Phrase in Matt 28: 19b. Jane Schaberg. LC 81-14466. (SBL Dissertation Ser.). 1982. pap. 18.00 (ISBN 0-89130-543-2, 060161). Scholars Pr GA.

Father the Son the Holy Spirit. Katy Moyer. 1983. pap. 1.25 (ISBN 0-910709-18-1). PTL Repro.

Father Theobald Matthew: Apostle of Temperance. Moira Lysaght. 48p. 1984. 3.00 (ISBN 0-912414-42-1). Lumen Christi.

Father Tom of the Artic. Louis L. Renner. LC 85-71951. (Illus.). 176p. (Orig.). 24.95 (ISBN 0-8323-0445-X); pap. 10.95 (ISBN 0-8323-0443-3). Binford-Metropolitan.

Father Who Dwelleth Within. Benjamin. 1979. pap. 2.50 (ISBN 0-87516-293-2). De Vorss.

Fathercare: What It Means to Be Gods Child. Charles P. Conn. 128p. 1984. pap. 2.95 (ISBN 0-425-08460-4); pap. 3.95 (ISBN 0-8128-8184-2). Berkley Pub.

Fatherhood of God & the Victorian Family: The Social Gospel in America. Janet F. Fishburn. LC 81-43090. 220p. 1982. 4.95 (ISBN 0-8006-0671-X). Fortress.

Fatherhood of God in an Age of Emancipation. W. A. Visser 't Hooft. LC 82-13403. 176p. 1983. pap. 7.95 (ISBN 0-664-24462-9). Westminster.

Fathering: Fact or Fable? Ed. by Edward V. Stein. LC 76-56840. Repr. of 1977 ed. 47.50 (ISBN 0-8357-9007-X, 2016357). Bks Demand UMI.

Fathers: A Fresh Start for the Christian Family. Robert Iatesta. 238p. (Orig.). 1980. pap. 5.95 (ISBN 0-89283-083-2). Servant.

Fathers According to Rabbi Nathan. Tr. by Jacob Neusner. (Brown Judaic Studies). 274p. 1986. 41.95 (ISBN 1-55540-051-5, 14-01-14). Scholars Pr GA.

Fathers According to Rabbi Nathan Goldin. Tr. by Moses Maimonides & Judah. (Judaica Ser.: No. 10). 1955. 26.50x (ISBN 0-300-00497-4). Yale U Pr.

Fathers Are Special. Ed. by William H. Preston. LC 76-39715. (Illus.). 1977. 8.95 (ISBN 0-8054-5622-8, 4256-22). Broadman.

Father's Day: Father with His European Children. Sri Chinmoy. 54p. (Orig.). 1976. pap. 2.00 (ISBN 0-88497-297-6). Aum Pubns.

Father's Day: Voices from the Heart. Date not set. price not set (ISBN 0-934383-14-6). Pride Prods.

Father's Mantle: The Legacy of Gustav Niebuhr. William G. Chrystal. LC 81-21108. 160p. (Orig.). 1982. pap. 7.95 (ISBN 0-8298-0494-3). Pilgrim NY.

Fathers of Jesus: A Study of the Lineage of the Christian Doctrine & Tradition, 2 vols. Keningale Cook. 1977. lib. bdg. 250.00 (ISBN 0-8490-1807-2). Gordon Pr.

Fathers of the Church. 4.00 (ISBN 0-317-46836-7); 3.00 (ISBN 0-8198-2612-X). Dghtrs St Paul.

Fathers of the Latin Church. Hans Von Campenhausen. Tr. by Manfred Hoffmann. LC 76-75260. 1964. 32.50x (ISBN 0-8047-0685-9). Stanford U Pr.

Father's Son. James O'Connor. 324p. 1984. 7.00 (ISBN 0-8198-2621-9); pap. 6.00 (ISBN 0-8198-2622-7). Dghtrs St Paul.

Fathers Talking: An Anthology. Ed. & tr. by Aelred Squire. (Studies: No. 93). 1986. 12.95 (ISBN 0-87907-893-6); pap. 6.95 (ISBN 0-87907-993-2). Cistercian Pubns.

Fatigue: Satan's Secret Weapon against Women. Elizabeth R. Handford & Joy R. Martin. 23p. (Orig.). 1986. pap. 1.00 (ISBN 0-912623-03-9). Joyful Woman.

Fatima: Cove of Wonders. Alphonse Cappa. 1980. 4.50 (ISBN 0-8198-0569-6); pap. 3.25 (ISBN 0-8198-0570-X). Dghtrs St Paul.

Fatima from the Beginning. John Di Marchi. (Illus.). 1980. pap. 5.95 (ISBN 0-911218-16-5). Ravengate Pr.

Fatima Is Fatima. Ali Shariati. Tr. by Laleh Bakhtiar from Arabic. LC 81-52831. 226p. 1982. pap. 4.95 (ISBN 0-940368-09-9). Tahrike Tarsile Quran.

Fatima Secret. Emmett Culligan. 1975. pap. 1.50 (ISBN 0-89555-052-0). TAN Bks Pubs.

Fatima: The Great Sign. Francis Johnston. 152p. 1980. 4.95 (ISBN 0-911988-37-8). AMI Pr.

Fatima: The Great Sign. Francis Johnston. LC 80-54423. 1980. Repr. of 1979 ed. 5.00 (ISBN 0-89555-163-2). Tan Bks Pubs.

Fatima Today. Robert J. Fox. (Illus.). 263p. (Orig.). pap. 6.95 (ISBN 0-931888-11-5). Christendom Pubns.

Fauna & Flora of the Bible. 2nd ed. 224p. 1980. pap. 4.50x (ISBN 0-8267-0021-7, 08513, Pub. by United Bible). Am Bible.

Fausset's Bible Dictionary. A. R. Fausset. (Illus.). 1970. 9.95 (ISBN 0-310-24311-4, 9616P). Zondervan.

Faustus Socinus. David M. Cory. LC 83-45606. Date not set. Repr. of 1932 ed. 28.50 (ISBN 0-404-19874-0). AMS Pr.

Favor the Road to Success. Bob Buess. 1982. pap. 2.50 (ISBN 0-934244-17-0). Sweeter Than Honey.

Favorable Year of the Lord: A Study of Jubilary Theology in the Gospel of Luke. Robert B. Sloan. 213p. (Orig.). 1977. pap. 6.95 (ISBN 0-931016-02-9). Schola Pr TX.

Favorite Bible Stories. G. L. LeFevre. (Bible Quiz 'N Tattletotals Ser.). 16p. (Orig.). 1982. pap. 0.98 (ISBN 0-87239-578-2, 2805). Standard Pub.

Favorite Bible Stories. Ed. by Patricia Mahany. (Classroom Activity Bks.). (Illus.). 48p. (Orig.). 1984. pap. 2.95 (ISBN 0-87239-718-1, 2448). Standard Pub.

Favorite Bible Stories, Vol. 1. 1.95 (ISBN 0-89954-378-2). Antioch Pub Co.

Favorite Bible Stories & Verses. Mary A. Jones. 112p. 1986. 9.95 (ISBN 0-02-689034-8). Macmillan.

Favorite Bible Verses. Shirley Beegle. (Double Trouble Puzzles Ser.). (Illus.). 48p. 1987. pap. 2.50 (ISBN 0-87403-325-X, 2765). Standard Pub.

Favorite Christmas Carols. Ed. by Charles J. Cofone. (Illus.). 64p. 1975. pap. 3.50 (ISBN 0-486-20445-6). Dover.

Favorite Christmas Stories. Ed. by Frances Cavanah. 1948. 5.95 (ISBN 0-448-02376-8, G&D). Putnam Pub Group.

Favorite Christmas Stories. Laura M. Hawkes. 64p. 1973. pap. 2.50 (ISBN 0-89036-015-4). Hawkes Pub Inc.

Favorite Family Recipes. Mary E. Showalter. 128p. 1972. pap. 2.95 (ISBN 0-8361-1682-8). Herald Pr.

Favorite Hymns for Senior Adults. LC 77-80939. 1977. pap. 4.95 (ISBN 0-8054-3303-1). Broadman.

Favorite Men of the Bible. R. Blaine Detrick. Ed. by Michael L. Sherer. (Orig.). 1987. pap. 7.25 (ISBN 0-89536-855-2, 7814). CSS of Ohio.

Favorite Novenas & Prayers. Norma C. Cassidy. LC 72-91456. 144p. 1972. pap. 3.95 (ISBN 0-8091-1761-4, Deus). Paulist Pr.

Favorite Old Testament Passages: A Popular Commentary for Today. Douglas Stuart. LC 85-5148. 130p. 1985. pap. 8.95 (ISBN 0-664-24676-1). Westminster.

Favorite Poems of Faith & Comfort. Barbara M. Olds. 1977. Repr. of 1947 ed. 25.00 (ISBN 0-89984-077-9). Century Bookbindery.

Favorite Stories from Acts Word Search. John H. Tiner. 48p. 1986. pap. 2.50 (ISBN 0-87403-047-1, 2691). Standard Pub.

Favorite Stories from the Bible. Ed. by S. E. Frost, Jr. 176p. 1986. pap. 2.95 (ISBN 0-345-33125-7, Pub. by Ballantine Epiphany). Ballantine.

Favorite Stories of Jesus. Mary A. Jones. LC 81-50278. (Rand McNally "Favorite" Ser.). (Illus.). 112p. 1981. 9.95 (ISBN 0-02-689035-6). Macmillan.

Fe Es. Pamela Reeve. Orig. Title: Faith Is. (Span.). 50p. 1983. spiral bd 4.95 (ISBN 0-930014-96-0). Multnomah.

Fe, Lo Que Es. 2nd ed. Kenneth E. Hagin. (Span.). 1982. pap. 1.00 (ISBN 0-89276-102-4). Hagin Ministries.

Fe Obra Por El Amor. Kenneth Hagin, Jr. (Span.). 1983. pap. 0.50 mini bk. (ISBN 0-89276-173-3). Hagin Ministries.

Fe y Cultura: Manual de Direccion. Maria De la Cruz Aymes & Francis J. Buckley. 112p. (Orig.). 1986. pap. 8.95 (ISBN 0-8091-2749-0); apuntes 5.95; leader's manual 8.95 (ISBN 0-8091-2748-2). Paulist Pr.

Fear & Trembling-Repetition, 2 vols. in 1. Soren Kierkegaard. Ed. by Howard V. Hong & Edna H. Hong. Tr. by Howard V. Hong & Edna H. Hong. LC 82-9006. (Kierkegaard's Writings Ser.: No. VI). 420p. 1983. 37.00 (ISBN 0-691-07237-X); pap. 7.95 (ISBN 0-691-02026-4). Princeton U Pr.

Fear & Worry: Our Common Enemies. Jean Kirkpatrick. 14p. 1982. pap. 1.50 (ISBN 0-686-19760-7). WFS.

Fear at Work: Job Blackmail, Labor & the Environment. Richard Kazis & Richard L. Grossman. LC 82-9829. 306p. (Orig.). 1982. pap. 10.95 (ISBN 0-8298-0600-8). Pilgrim NY.

Fear Factor. Jim McFadden. (Living As a Christian Ser.). (Orig.). 1983. pap. 3.95 (ISBN 0-89283-159-6). Servant.

Fear Free Faith Filled. Marilyn Hickey. 176p. 1982. pap. 3.50 (ISBN 0-89274-259-3). Harrison Hse.

Fear: Issues of Emotional Living in an Age of Stress for Clergy & Religious. J. William Huber et al. Ed. by Marie Kraus. LC 86-3533. 141p. 1986. pap. 8.00 (ISBN 0-89571-028-5). Affirmation.

Fear, Love, & Worship. C. FitzSimons Allison. pap. 4.95 (ISBN 0-8164-2020-3, SP17, HarpR). Har-Row.

Fear Not, I Am with You. National Association of Catholic Chaplains. 1970. pap. 0.75 (ISBN 0-685-22552-6). Alba.

Fear Not Warrior: A Study of Pericopes in the Hebrew Scriptures. Edgar W. Conrad. (Brown Judaic Studies). 1985. 30.95 (ISBN 0-89130-864-4, 14-06-75); pap. 25.95 (ISBN 0-89130-865-2). Scholars Pr GA.

Fear of God. John Bunyan. pap. 3.95 (ISBN 0-685-19828-6). Reiner.

Fear of the Dead in Primitive Religion. J. G. Frazel. LC 66-15215. 1933. 10.00 (ISBN 0-8196-0167-5). Biblo.

Fear of the Dead in Primitive Religion, 3 vols. in one. James G. Frazer. Ed. by Robert Kastenaum. LC 76-19571. (Death & Dying Ser.). 1977. Repr. of 1936 ed. lib. bdg. 57.50x (ISBN 0-405-09566-X). Ayer Co Pubs.

Fearfully & Wonderfully Made. Paul Brand & Philip Yancey. (Illus.). 224p. 1980. 11.95 (ISBN 0-310-35450-1, 10241). Zondervan.

Fearing No Evil. Myrna L. Etheridge. (Illus.). 119p. (Orig.). 1984. pap. 5.00x (ISBN 0-937417-00-9). Etheridge Minist.

Fearing No Evil: One Woman's Life of Tragedy & Victory. Myrna L. Goehri Ethridge. (Illus.). 108p. (Orig.). 1984. pap. 5.95 (ISBN 0-941018-12-1). Martin Pr CA.

Fear's Answer: A Case History in Nouthetic Counseling. Martha G. DeBardeleben. 1981. pap. 3.75 (ISBN 0-87552-236-X). Presby & Reformed.

Feast for Advent. 2nd ed. Delia Smith. 96p. 1985. pap. 4.95 (ISBN 0-89622-219-5). Twenty-Third.

Feast for Lent. Delia Smith. 96p. pap. 3.95 (ISBN 0-89622-220-9). Twenty-Third.

Feast of Faith. Joseph Ratzinger. Tr. by Graham Harrison from Ger. LC 85-82175. Orig. Title: Das Fest des Glaubens. 175p. (Orig.). 1986. pap. 8.95 (ISBN 0-89870-056-6). Ignatius Pr.

Feast of Fools: A Theological Essay on Festivity & Fantasy. Harvey Cox. LC 75-75914. (William Belden Noble Lectures Ser). 1969. 15.00x (ISBN 0-674-29525-0). Harvard U Pr.

Feast of Joy: Ministering the Lord's Supper in the Free Tradition. Keith Watkins. LC 77-525. 1977. pap. 1.50 (ISBN 0-8272-1006-X). CBP.

Feast of Love. Mary G. Durkin. 248p. 1984. 9.95 (ISBN 0-8294-0443-0). Loyola.

Feasting & Social Oscillation: A Working Paper on Religion & Society in Upland Southeast Asia. A. Thomas Kirsch. 57p. 1973. 5.00 (ISBN 0-87727-092-9, DP 92). Cornell SE Asia.

Feasting & Social Oscillation: A Working Paper on Religion & Society in Upland Southeast Asia. A. Thomas Kirsch. LC 74-168308. (Cornell University, Southeast Asia Program, Data Paper: No. 92). pap. 20.00 (ISBN 0-317-29889-5, 2021843). Bks Demand UMI.

Feasting & Social Oscillation: A Working Paper on Religion & Society in Upland Southeast Asia, No. 92. Thomas Kirsch. 67p. 1984. 5.00 (ISBN 0-317-11683-5). Cornell SE Asia.

Feasting Upon the Word. Dennis J. Packard & Sandra Packard. LC 81-12446. 242p. 7.95 (ISBN 0-87747-879-1). Deseret Bk.

Feasts of Honor: Ritual & Change in the Toraja Highlands. Toby A. Volkman. LC 84-16123. (Illinois Studies in Anthropology). (Illus.). 234p. 1985. pap. 21.50 (ISBN 0-252-01183-X). U of Ill Pr.

Feasts of Israel. Victor Buksbazen. 1976. pap. 2.95 (ISBN 0-87508-043-X). Chr Lit.

Feasts of Israel. Kevin J. Conner. (Illus.). 122p. 1980. pap. 7.95 (ISBN 0-914936-42-5). Bible Temple.

Feasts of Jehovah. John Ritchie. LC 82-182. 80p. 1982. pap. 3.95 (ISBN 0-8254-3613-3). Kregel.

Feasts of the Lord. Robert Thompson. pap. 5.95 (ISBN 0-89728-029-6, 645571). Omega Pubns OR.

Feathers for Arrows. C. H. Spurgeon. 1973. pap. 3.25 (ISBN 0-686-09105-1). Pilgrim Pubns.

Feathers on the Moor. facs. ed. Archibald Alexander. LC 67-22050. (Essay Index Reprint Ser). 1928. 17.00 (ISBN 0-8369-0145-2). Ayer Co Pubs.

Fecundity Figures: Egyptian Personification & the Iconology of a Genre. J. Baines. (Illus.). 200p. 1983. 60.00 (ISBN 0-85668-087-7, Pub. by Aris & Phillips UK). Humanities.

Fecundity Figures: Egyptian Personification & the Iconology of a Genre. John Baines. (Egyptology Ser.). (Illus.). 400p. (Orig.). 1985. pap. 59.00 (ISBN 0-86516-122-4). Bolchazy-Carducci.

Federal Government & the Nonprofit Sector: The Impact of the 1981 Tax Act on Individual Charitable Giving. Charles T. Clotfelter & Lester M. Salamon. LC 82-113321. cancelled. Urban Inst.

Feed My Sheep. D. Coffey Parker. (Illus.). 1983. 3.00. Harlo Pr.

Feed My Sheep. Alfred E. Pontious. 26p. pap. text ed. 1.95 (ISBN 0-940227-01-0). Liberation Pub.

Feed My Sheep. John H. Schaal. 1972. pap. 1.95 (ISBN 0-8010-7958-6). Baker Bk.

Feed My Sheep: Sermons on Contemporary Issues in Pastoral Care. Ed. by Gregory J. Johanson. 6.95. Paulist Pr.

Feeding Fire. John B. Coburn. LC 80-81103. 62p. 1980. 8.95 (ISBN 0-8192-1281-4). Morehouse.

Feeding the Sheep. Benjamin S. Baker. LC 85-15139. 1985. pap. 5.95 (ISBN 0-8054-2544-6). Broadman.

Feeling & Healing Your Emotions. Conrad W. Baars. LC 79-53629. 1979. pap. 5.95 (ISBN 0-88270-384-6, Pub. by Logos). Bridge Pub.

Feeling Good about Yourself. Herman C. Ahrens, Jr. (Orig.). 1983. pap. 1.25 (ISBN 0-8298-0644-X). Pilgrim NY.

Feelings Grow Too! Elaine Ward. 81p. (Orig.). 1981. pap. 9.95 (ISBN 0-940754-07-X). Ed Ministries.

Feelings Women Rarely Share. Judy Reamer. Ed. by Donna Arthur. 150p. (Orig.). 1987. pap. text ed. 3.50 (ISBN 0-88368-186-2). Whitaker Hse.

Feet-on-the-Ground Theology: Pastoral Ministry in Western Brazil. Clodovis Boff. Tr. by Phillip Berryman from Port. 288p. (Orig.). 1987. 19.95 (ISBN 0-88344-579-4); pap. 8.95 (ISBN 0-88344-554-9). Orbis Bks.

Fellowship. Guy H. King. 1972. pap. 3.95 (ISBN 0-87508-279-3). Chr Lit.

Fellowship: A Devotional Study of the Epistles of John. John G. Mitchell. LC 84-193801. (Orig.). 1974. pap. text ed. 6.95 (ISBN 0-930014-06-5). Multnomah.

Fellowship of Love, the Heritage of First Baptist Church of Blanchard, Louisiana. Kevin W. Sandifer. Ed. by Donald C. Tippett. (Illus.). 1986. lib. bdg. 2.50 (ISBN 0-910653-02-X). Archival Servs.

Fellowship of the Holy Spirit. Kenneth D. Barney. LC 77-70475. 96p. 1977. pap. 1.25 (ISBN 0-88243-515-9, 02-0515). Gospel Pub.

Fellowship with the Word of Life: Studies in I, II, III John. Raymond E. Gingrich. pap. 4.95 (ISBN 0-88469-042-3). BMH Bks.

Female & Catholic: A Journal of Mind & Heart. Marie McIntyre. 80p. (Orig.). 1986. pap. 3.95 (ISBN 0-89622-307-8). Twenty-Third.

Female Experience & the Nature of the Divine. Judith Ochshorn. LC 81-47012. pap. 71.50 (2056237). Bks Demand UMI.

Female Fault & Fulfilment in Gnosticism. Jorunn J. Buckley. LC 85-29020. (Studies in Religion). xvi, 180p. 1986. 32.50x (ISBN 0-8078-1696-5). U of NC Pr.

Female Preacher: Memoir of Salome Lincoln, Afterwards the Wife of Elder Junia S. Mowry. Almond H. Davis. LC 72-2599. (American Women Ser.: Images & Realities). (Illus.). 168p. 1972. Repr. of 1843 ed. 13.50 (ISBN 0-405-04489-5). Ayer Co Pubs.

Feminine Aspects of Divinity. Erminie H. Lantero. LC 73-84214. 36p. (Orig.). 1973. pap. 2.50x (ISBN 0-87574-191-6). Pendle Hill.

Feminine Free & Faithful. Ronda Chervin. LC 86-80785. 143p. 1986. pap. 7.95 (ISBN 0-89870-103-1). Ignatius Pr.

Feminine Spirituality in America: From Sarah Edwards to Martha Graham. Amanda Porterfield. 248p. 1980. 29.95 (ISBN 0-87722-175-8). Temple U Pr.

Feminism & Christianity: A Two-Way Reflection. Denise L. Carmody. LC 82-1709. 192p. (Orig.). 1982. pap. 9.95 (ISBN 0-687-12914-1). Abingdon.

Feminist Interpretation of the Bible. Ed. by Letty M. Russell. LC 84-17342. 166p. (Orig.). 1985. pap. 10.95 (ISBN 0-664-24639-7). Westminster.

Feminist Mystic & Other Essays on Women & Spirituality. Mary E. Giles. 208p. 1982. pap. 8.95 (ISBN 0-8245-0432-1). Crossroad NY.

Feminist Perspectives on Biblical Scholarship. Ed. by Adela Collins. (Society of Bliblical Literature Centennial Biblical Scholarship in North America Ser.: No. 10). 152p. 13.95_o.s. (ISBN 0-89130-774-5, 06 11 10); pap. 9.50 (ISBN 0-89130-773-7). Scholars Pr GA.

Fenelon. James H. Davis, Jr. (World Authors Ser.). 1979. lib. bdg. 15.95 (ISBN 0-8057-6384-8, Twayne). G K Hall.

Fenelon's Spiritual Letters. Fenelon. Ed. by Gene Edwards. 139p. pap. 5.95 (ISBN 0-940232-09-X). Christian Bks.

Feodor Dostoevsky. William J. Leatherbarrow. (World Authors Ser.). 15.95 (ISBN 0-8057-6480-1, Twayne). G K Hall.

Ferdinand & Isabella. Melveena McKendrick. LC 68-14974. (Horizon Caravel Bks.). 1544p. (YA) 1968. PLB 15.89 (ISBN 0-06-024165-9). HarpJ.

Ferdinand I & Maximilian II of Austria. Leopold Von Ranke. LC 74-153627. Repr. of 1853 ed. 14.50 (ISBN 0-404-09265-9). AMS Pr.

Fernando Gallego & the Retablo of Ciudad Rodrigo. R. M. Quinn. LC 60-15915. (Span. & Eng., Illus.). 117p. 1961. 8.50x (ISBN 0-8165-0034-7). U of Ariz Pr.

Ferrerii Historia Abbatum De Kynlos. Giovanni Ferrerio. LC 78-168018. (Bannatyne Club, Edinburgh. Publications: No. 63). Repr. of 1839 ed. 15.00 (ISBN 0-404-52774-4). AMS Pr.

Festal Menaion. Tr. by Mother Mary & Archimandrite Kallistos Ware. 248p. 1977. pap. 10.95 (ISBN 0-571-11137-8). Faber & Faber.

Festbrevier und Kirchenjahr der Syrischen Jakobiten. Anton Baumstark. Repr. of 1910 ed. 22.00 (ISBN 0-384-03575-2). Johnson Repr.

Festival! An Experiment in Living. Gladis DePree. 208p. 1985. 12.95 (ISBN 0-310-44110-2, 9488). Zondervan.

Festival & Their Meaning. Rudolf Steiner. 399p. 1981. 21.00 (ISBN 0-85440-370-1, Pub. by Steinerbooks); pap. 15.00 (ISBN 0-85440-380-9). Anthroposophic.

Festival of Asian Christmas Music: Christmas Music from Hongkong, India, Indonesia, Malaysia, Philippines & Taiwan. Ed. by Loh. (Asian Inst. for Liturgy & Music Anthems Ser: No. 2). 68p. (Orig.). 1984. pap. 8.50x (ISBN 971-10-0228-0, Pub. by New Day Philippines). Cellar.

Festival of Holiday Songs. Hershal Pyle. Date not set. pap. 2.95 (ISBN 0-317-20180-8). Campus.

Festival of Hope. Pontifical Council for the Laity. 179p. pap. 6.00 (ISBN 0-317-46617-8). New City.

Festival of Lights. James M. Bloom & Michael L. Sherer. (Orig.). 1986. pap. 2.25 (ISBN 0-89536-833-1, 6847). CSS of Ohio.

Festival Prayerbook. Ed. by Eugene Kohn. LC 57-13301. 547p. 1958. 10.00 (ISBN 0-935457-28-3). Reconstructionist Pr.

Festivals & Ceremonies of the Roman Republic. H. H. Scullard. LC 80-70447. (Aspects of Greek & Roman Life Ser.). (Illus.). 288p. 1981. 32.50x (ISBN 0-8014-1402-4). Cornell U Pr.

Festivals & Commemorations: Handbook to the Calendar in Lutheran Book of Worship. Philip H. Pfatteicher. LC 79-54129. 336p. 24.95 (ISBN 0-8066-1757-8, 10-2295). Augsburg.

Festivals in Halachah, Vol. II. Shlomo Y. Zevin. Ed. by Uri Kaploon. Tr. by Meir Fox-Ashrei from Hebrew. (Artscroll Judica Classics Ser.). 336p. 1981. 14.95 (ISBN 0-89906-908-8); pap. 11.95 (ISBN 0-89906-909-6). Mesorah Pubns.

Festivals of Attica: An Archaeological Commentary. Erika Simon. LC 81-70160. 160p. 1983. text ed. 26.50x (ISBN 0-299-09180-5). U of Wis Pr.

Festivals of the Athenians. H. W. Parke. LC 76-12819. (Aspects of Greek & Roman Life Ser.). (Illus.). 288p. 1986. pap. text ed. 8.95x (ISBN 0-8014-9440-0). Cornell U Pr.

Festivals of the Jewish Year: A Modern Interpretation & Guide. Theodor H. Gaster. 1971. pap. 7.95 (ISBN 0-688-06008-0). Morrow.

Festive Breads of Easter. Norma J. Voth. LC 79-23702. (Illus.). 80p. 1980. pap. 3.50 (ISBN 0-8361-1917-7). Herald Pr.

Festive Cakes of Christmas. Norma J. Voth. LC 81-2140. (Illus.). 80p. 1981. pap. 3.50 (ISBN 0-8361-1956-8). Herald Pr.

Festive Cookies of Christmas. Norma J. Voth. LC 81-18258. 104p. (Orig.). 1982. pap. 3.25 (ISBN 0-8361-1983-5). Herald Pr.

Festschrift Adolf Schwarz zum Siebzigsten Geburtstage. Ed. by Samuel Krauss & Steven Katz. LC 79-7162. (Jewish Philosophy, Mysticism & History of Ideas Ser.). (Illus.). 1980. Repr. of 1917 ed. lib. bdg. 57.50x (ISBN 0-405-12275-6). Ayer Co Pubs.

Festschrift Seventy-Five Jahrigen Bestehen Des Judich-Theologischen Seminars, 2 vols. Stiftung Fraenckelscher. Ed. by Steven Katz. LC 79-7159. (Jewish Philosophy, Mysticism & History of Ideas Ser.). 1980. Repr. of 1929 ed. Set. lib. bdg. 80.00x (ISBN 0-405-12243-8). Ayer Co Pubs.

Festschrift Siebzigsten Geburtstage Jakob Guttmanns. Gesellschaft zur Forderung der Wissenschaft des Judentums. Ed. by Steven Katz. LC 79-7155. (Jewish Philosophy, Mysticism & History of Ideas Ser.). 1980. Repr. of 1915 ed. lib. bdg. 25.50x (ISBN 0-405-12253-5). Ayer Co Pubs.

Festschrift zu Ehren des Dr. A. Harkavy. Ed. by D. Gunzburg et al. LC 79-7160. (Jewish Philosophy, Mysticism & History of Ideas Ser.). 1980. Repr. of 1908 ed. lib. bdg. 60.00x (ISBN 0-405-12259-4). Ayer Co Pubs.

Festschrift zu Israel Lewy's Siebzigstem Geburtstag. M. Brann & I. Elbogen. Ed. by Steven Katz. LC 79-7157. (Jewish Philosophy, Mysticism & the History of Ideas Ser.). (Ger. & Hebrew.). 1980. Repr. of 1911 ed. lib. bdg. 51.50x (ISBN 0-405-12242-X). Ayer Co Pubs.

Festschrift zum Siebzigsten Geburtstage A. Berliner's. Ed. by A. Freiman et al. LC 79-7165. (Jewish Philosophy, Mysticism & History of Ideas Ser.). 1980. Repr. of 1903 ed. lib. bdg. 45.00x (ISBN 0-405-12252-7). Ayer Co Pubs.

Festschriftum, 3 vols. Simon Eppenstein et al. Ed. by Steven Katz. LC 79-7161. (Jewish Philosophy, Mysticism & History of Ideas Ser.). 1980. Repr. of 1914 ed. Set. lib. bdg. 69.00x (ISBN 0-405-12247-0); lib. bdg. 23.00x ea. Vol. 1 (ISBN 0-405-12248-9). Vol. 2 (ISBN 0-405-12249-7). Vol. 3 (ISBN 0-405-12304-3). Ayer Co Pubs.

Fetishism in West Africa: Forty Years' Observation of Native Customs & Superstitions. Robert H. Nassau. LC 69-18995. (Illus.). Repr. of 1904 ed. 22.50x (ISBN 0-8371-0977-9, NAF&, Pub. by Negro U Pr). Greenwood.

Feudal Documents from the Abbey of Bury St. Edmunds. Ed. by D. C. Douglas. (British Academy, London, Records of the Social & Economic History of England & Wales: Vol. 8). pap. 45.00 (ISBN 0-8115-1248-7). Kraus Repr.

Feudal Institutions As Revealed in the Assizes of Romania. Tr. by Peter W. Topping. LC 80-13052. (Crusades & Military Orders: Second Ser.). Repr. of 1949 ed. 23.50 (ISBN 0-404-17023-4). AMS Pr.

Few Minutes with Jesus. Joslyn W. Moldstad. 1984. pap. 5.95 (ISBN 0-8100-0189-6, 06N0565). Northwest Pub.

Few Summer Ceremonials at the Tusayon Pueblos: Natal Ceremonies of the Hopi Indians,& a Report on the Present Condition of a Ruin in Arizona Called Casa Grande. Jesse W. Fewkes & John G. Owens. LC 76-21217. (Journal of American Ethnology & Archaeology: Vol. 2). 1977. Repr. of 1892 ed. 30.00 (ISBN 0-404-58042-4). AMS Pr.

Few Summer Ceremonials at Zuni Pueblo: Zuni Melodies, Reconnaissance of Ruins in or Near the Zuni Reservation. Jessie W. Fewkes & Benjamin I. Gilman. LC 76-21216. (Journal of American Ethnology & Archaeology: Vol. 1). Repr. of 1891 ed. 25.00 (ISBN 0-404-58041-6). AMS Pr.

Fichier Augustinien, 4 vols. Institut Des Etudes Augustiniennes, Paris. (Augustine Bibliography). 1972. Set. 355.00 (ISBN 0-8161-0947-8, Hall Library). G K Hall.

Fichier Augustinien, First Supplement. Institut des Etudes Augustiniennes, Paris. 1981. lib. bdg. 125.00 (ISBN 0-8161-0365-8, Hall Library). G K Hall.

Fichte's Critique of All Revelation. J. G. Fichte. Tr. by G. D. Green. LC 77-77756. 1978. 34.50 (ISBN 0-521-21707-5). Cambridge U Pr.

Fiction with a Parochial Purpose: Social Uses of American Catholic Literarture, 1884-1900. Paul R. Messbarger. 1971. 11.95 (ISBN 0-87270-017-8). U of Notre Dame Pr.

Fictional Transfiguration of Jesus. Theodore Ziolkowski. LC 70-39794. 536p. 1972. 34.00 (ISBN 0-691-06235-8); pap. 13.50 (ISBN 0-691-01346-2). Princeton U Pr.

Fidel & Religion: Castro Talks on Revolution & Religion with Frei Betto. Fidel Castro & Frei Betto. 1987. 19.95 (ISBN 0-671-64114-X). S&S.

Fidelity: Issues of Emotional Living in an Age of Stress for Clergy & Religious. Sean D. Sammon et al. Ed. by Joseph L. Hart. LC 81-533. 148p. (Orig.). 1981. pap. 5.00 (ISBN 0-89571-011-0). Affirmation.

Field of Diamonds. Compiled by Joe Johnson. LC 73-87067. 12.95 (ISBN 0-8054-5133-1). Broadman.

Field of Yiddish: Studies in Yiddish Language, Folklore, & Literature. Ed. by Uriel Weinreich. LC 54-12380. 317p. 1954. Repr. 12.50 (ISBN 0-936368-02-0). Lexik Hse.

Fields of Offerings: Studies in Honor of Raphael Patai. Ed. by Victor D. Sanua. LC 82-21072. (Illus.). 352p. 1983. 28.50 (ISBN 0-8386-3171-1). Fairleigh Dickinson.

Fiery Chariots. Edmond B. Szekely. (Illus.). 96p. 1971. pap. 4.80 (ISBN 0-89564-017-1). IBS Intl.

Fiery World. Incl. (Agni Yoga Ser.: Vol. I). 1982. Repr. of 1969 ed. Index 12.00 (ISBN 0-933574-09-6); (Vol. II). 1978. Repr. of 1946 ed. softcover 12.00 (ISBN 0-933574-10-X); (Agni Yoga Ser.: Vol. III). 1980. Repr. of 1948 ed. flexible cover. 12.00 (ISBN 0-933574-11-8). Agni Yoga Soc.

Fiestas of San Juan Nuevo: Ceremonial Art from Michoacan, Mexico. Linda Bahm et al. LC 83-42809. (Illus.). 70p. 1983. pap. 12.50 (ISBN 0-912535-00-8). Max Mus.

Fifteen Fun-Filled Programs for Adults. Elizabeth Crisci. (Illus.). 112p. 1986. pap. 4.95 (ISBN 0-87403-078-1, 3198). Standard Pub.

Fifteen Years in the Senior Order of Shakers: A Narration of Facts, Concerning That Singular People. Hervey Elkins. LC 72-2984. Repr. of 1853 ed. 16.00 (ISBN 0-404-10746-X). AMS Pr.

Fifteenth Century Bibles. Wendell Prime. LC 77-85626. 1977. Repr. of 1888 ed. lib. bdg. 15.00 (ISBN 0-89341-320-8). Longwood Pub Group.

Fifteenth Century Courtesy Book & Two Franciscan Rules: EETS OS Ser, Vol. 148. Repr. of 1914 ed. 15.00 (ISBN 0-8115-3372-7). Kraus Repr.

Fifteenth-Century English Prayers & Meditations: A Bibliography of Manuscripts Preserved at the British Museum Library. Peter Revell. LC 75-6579. (Reference Library of Humanities: Vol. 19). 150p. 1975. lib. bdg. 28.00 (ISBN 0-8240-1098-1). Garland Pub.

Fifteenth Century Guidebook to the Principal Churches of Rome. William Brewyn. Tr. by C. Eveleigh Woodruff. LC 78-63451. (Crusades & Military Orders: Second Ser.). Repr. of 1933 ed. 17.00 (ISBN 0-404-16374-2). AMS Pr.

Fifth Gospel. Rudolf Steiner. Tr. by C. Davy & D. S. Osmond. Tr. of Aus der Akkasha Forschung: Das Fuenfte Evangelium. 168p. 1985. pap. 9.95 (ISBN 0-85440-520-8, Pub. by Steinerbooks). Anthroposophic.

Fifth Gospel: The Experience of Black Christian Values. Joseph G. Healey. LC 80-25033. (Illus.). 220p. (Orig.). 1981. pap. 3.98 (ISBN 0-88344-013-X). Orbis Bks.

Fifth Horseman of the Apocalypse. Jesse M. Hendley. LC 85-19795. 236p. (Orig.). 1985. pap. 10.95 (ISBN 0-8254-2849-1). Kregel.

Fifth Pillar: The Story of a Pilgrimage to Mecca & Medina. Saida M. Khalifa. 1977. 7.50 (ISBN 0-682-48772-4). Exposition Pr FL.

Fifth Sun: Aztec Gods, Aztec World. Burr C. Brundage. (Texas Pan American Ser.). (Illus.). 283p. 1979. pap. 8.95 (ISBN 0-292-72438-1). U of Tex Pr.

Fifth Week. John O'Malley. LC 75-43583. 1976. 2.95 (ISBN 0-8294-0248-9). Loyola.

Fiftieth Anniversary Issue: Kingston Lake Woman's Baptist Educational & Missionary Convention of Horry County, South Carolina. rev. ed. Bulletin Committee Staff. Ed. by Etrulia P. Dozier. (Illus.). 80p. (Orig.). 1985. pap. text ed. 5.00 (ISBN 0-9615271-2-9). Positive Images.

Fifty Carols for Christmas & Advent. Ed. by David Willcocks & John Ruttner. (Carols for Choirs, Book 2). 1970. 12.00 (ISBN 0-19-353566-1); pap. 7.00 (ISBN 0-19-353565-3). Oxford U Pr.

Fifty Christmas Carols for All Harps: Each Arranged for Beginning & Advanced Harpers. Sylvia Woods. (Sylvia Woods Multi-Level Harp Bks.). (Illus.). 96p. 1984. pap. 13.95 (ISBN 0-9602990-5-X). Woods Mus Bks Pub.

Fifty-Five Hundred Questions & Answers on the Holy Bible. 192p. 1974. pap. 3.95 (ISBN 0-310-24361-0, 9666P). Zondervan.

Fifty-Four Crafts with Easy Patterns. Loretta Reese. LC 78-62788. (Illus.). 1979. pap. 4.95 (ISBN 0-87239-175-2, 2134). Standard Pub.

Fifty Freedom-Boats to One Golden Shore, Pt. 1. Sri Chinmoy. 93p. (Orig.). 1974. pap. 3.00 (ISBN 0-88497-087-6). Aum Pubns.

Fifty Freedom-Boats to One Golden Shore, Pt. 2. Sri Chinmoy. 108p. 1974. pap. 3.00 (ISBN 0-88497-101-5). Aum Pubns.

Fifty Freedom-Boats to One Golden Shore, Pt. 3. Sri Chinmoy. 94p. 1974. pap. 3.00 (ISBN 0-88497-071-X). Aum Pubns.

Fifty Freedom-Boats to One Golden Shore, Pt. 4. Sri Chinmoy. 112p. (Orig.). 1974. pap. text ed. 3.00 (ISBN 0-88497-073-6). Aum Pubns.

Fifty Freedom-Boats to One Golden Shore, Pt. 5. Sri Chinmoy. 68p. (Orig.). 1975. pap. 2.00 (ISBN 0-88497-229-1). Aum Pubns.

Fifty Funeral Homilies. Charles H. Doyle. 110p. 1984. pap. 10.00 spiral bdg. (ISBN 0-87061-094-5). Chr Classics.

Fifty letije Arkjierejskgo Sluzhenie Mitropolita Anastasia. Tr. of Fifty Anniversary of Episcopal Service of Metropolitan Anastassy. 259p. 1956. pap. 10.00 (ISBN 0-317-29032-0). Holy Trinity.

Fifty Meditations. Kosuke Koyama. LC 77-7026. (Illus.). 191p. (Orig.). 1979. pap. 6.95 (ISBN 0-88344-134-9). Orbis Bks.

Fifty Miracle Principles of "A Course in Miracles". Kenneth Wapnick. 153p. (Orig.). 1985. pap. 8.00 (ISBN 0-933291-02-7). Foun Miracles.

Fifty Object Lessons. Donald J. Poganski. 1967. 4.50 (ISBN 0-570-03172-9, 12-2282). Concordia.

Fifty Plus. Herbert Vander Lugt. (Direction Bks.). Orig. Title: Art of Growing Old. 110p. 1982. pap. 2.95 (ISBN 0-8010-9288-4). Baker Bk.

Fifty Questions Most Frequently Asked about the Second Coming. Wim Malgo. 3.95 (ISBN 0-937422-04-5). Midnight Call.

Fifty Spiritual Homilies. Saint Macarius. 1974. Repr. of 1921 ed. 17.50 (ISBN 0-686-10200-2). Eastern Orthodox.

Fifty-Two Children's Programs. Ed. by Mary R. Pearson. 224p. (Orig.). 1985. pap. 14.95 (ISBN 0-89636-189-6). Accent Bks.

Fifty-Two Elementary Patterns. Idalee W. Vonk. (Illus.). 48p. (Orig.). 1979. pap. 4.95 (ISBN 0-87239-340-2, 3366). Standard Pub.

Fifty-Two Middler-Junior Crafts. Jacqueline Rowland. 48p. (Orig.). 1984. pap. 2.95 (ISBN 0-87239-727-0, 2107). Standard Pub.

Fifty-Two Nursery Patterns. Marie H. Frost. (Illus.). 48p. (Orig.). 1979. pap. 4.95 (ISBN 0-87239-341-0, 42046). Standard Pub.

Fifty-Two Preschool Crafts. Joanna Hart. 48p. (Orig.). 1984. pap. 2.95 (ISBN 0-87239-725-4, 2105). Standard Pub.

Fifty-Two Primary Crafts. Marie H. Frost. 48p. (Orig.). 1984. pap. 2.95 (ISBN 0-87239-726-2, 2106). Standard Pub.

Fifty-Two Sundays of Worship for Children, Bk. 2. Emily Moore. 1972. 6.95 (ISBN 0-8341-0253-6). Beacon Hill.

Fifty-Two Teen Crafts. Susan Russell. 48p. (Orig.). 1984. pap. 2.95 (ISBN 0-87239-728-9, 2108). Standard Pub.

Fifty-Two Visual Ideas for Opening Assemblies, 3 vols. Ed. by Christian Publications, Inc. Staff. 2.25 ea. Vol. 1 (ISBN 0-87509-271-3). Vol. 2 (ISBN 0-87509-272-1). Vol. 3 (ISBN 0-87509-273-X). Chr Pubns.

Fifty-Two Visualized Talks for Children's Church. Georgia Smelser & Barbara Westberg. (Illus., Orig.). 1981. pap. 4.50 tchr's ed (ISBN 0-912315-13-X). Word Aflame.

Fifty-Two Winning Sermons. Willie White. 117p. (Orig.). 1973. cancelled (ISBN 0-89900-129-7). College Pr Pub.

Fifty Worship Talks for Children. Daniel J. Behnke. 1982. pap. 5.56 (ISBN 0-570-03850-2, 12-2805). Concordia.

Fifty Years among the Baptists. David Benedict. Repr. of 1860 ed. 13.00 (ISBN 0-317-38297-7). Church History.

Fifty Years in the "Church" of Rome. abr. ed. Charles Chiniquy. 366p. 1985. pap. 7.95 (ISBN 0-937958-21-2). Chick Pubns.

Fifty Years in Western Africa. Alfred Barrow. LC 79-92739. Repr. of 1900 ed. cancelled (ISBN 0-8371-2193-0, BAW&, Pub. by Negro U Pr). Greenwood.

Fifty Years' Work with Girls, 1883-1933: A Story of the Florence Crittenton Homes. Otto Wilson & Robert S. Barratt. LC 74-1717. (Children & Youth Ser.: Vol. 12). (Illus.). 513p. 1974. Repr. of 1933 ed. 44.00x (ISBN 0-405-05992-2). Ayer Co Pubs.

Figh Al Sunnah. Sayyed Sabiq. Ed. by Hamid Quilan. Tr. by Movel Y. Izzidien from Arabic. LC 82-70450. 1700p. (Orig.). 1983. text ed. 30.00 (ISBN 0-89259-033-5); pap. 20.00 (ISBN 0-686-81828-8). Am Trust Pubns.

Fight: A Practical Handbook to Christian Living. John White. LC 76-12297. 230p. (Orig.). 1976. pap. 6.95 (ISBN 0-87784-777-0). Inter-Varsity.

Fight for Peace, 2 vols. Devere Allen. LC 74-147439. (Library of War & Peace; Histories of the Organized Peace Movement). 1972. Set. lib. bdg. 92.00 (ISBN 0-8240-0228-8); lib. bdg. 38.00 ea. Garland Pub.

Fight with Rome. Justin D. Fulton. LC 76-46077. (Anti-Movements in America). 1977. Repr. of 1889 ed. lib. bdg. 30.00x (ISBN 0-405-09950-9). Ayer Co Pubs.

Fighting Back. rev. ed. Rocky Bleier & Terry O'Neil. LC 75-12865. (Illus.). 240p. 1980. 14.95 (ISBN 0-8128-2767-8). Stein & Day.

Fighting Back. Rocky Bleier & Terry O'Neil. (Illus.). 288p. 1976. pap. 2.75 (ISBN 0-446-95704-6). Warner Bks.

Fighting Back: Lithuanian Jewry's Armed Resistance to the Nazis. Dov Levin. 325p. 1985. text ed. 49.50x (ISBN 0-8419-0831-1). Holmes & Meier.

Fighting for Life. Melinda Delahoyde. 96p. (Orig.). 1984. pap. 3.95 (ISBN 0-89283-138-3). Servant.

Fighting Giants: Joshua-Solomon 14 Lessons, Vol. 3. Bernice C. Jordan. (Footsteps of Faith Ser.). 1957. pap. text ed. 2.50 (ISBN 0-86508-031-3); figures text 11.45 (ISBN 0-86508-032-1). BCM Intl Inc.

Figures in Our Catholic History. George E. Ryan. 1979. 4.00 (ISBN 0-8198-0608-0); pap. 2.50 (ISBN 0-8198-0609-9). Dghtrs St Paul.

Figures of Speech Used in the Bible. E. W. Bullinger. 24.95 (ISBN 0-8010-0559-0). Baker Bk.

Figures of the True. Amy Carmichael. 1968. pap. 1.50 (ISBN 0-87508-065-0). Chr Lit.

Figures or Types of the Old Testament. Samuel Mather. 1969. Repr. of 1705 ed. 34.00 (ISBN 0-384-35880-2). Johnson Repr.

Fiji Revisited: A Columbian Father's Memories of Twenty-Eight Years in the Islands. Edward Fischer. LC 81-5365. (Illus.). 1981. 10.95 (ISBN 0-8245-0097-0). Crossroad NY.

File Folder Learning Centers. Donna Skinner. LC 81-84001. 160p. (Orig.). 1982. pap. 7.95 (ISBN 0-87239-492-1, 3071). Standard Pub.

Filiality, the Human Source, Vol. 1. Buddhist Text Translation Society Staff. 132p. 1983. pap. 7.00 (ISBN 0-88139-006-2). Buddhist Text.

Filiality, the Human Source, Vol. 2. Buddhist Text Translation Society Staff. 120p. (Orig.). 1983. pap. 7.00 (ISBN 0-88139-020-8). Buddhist Text.

Filipenses: Triunfo en Cristo (Comentario Biblico Portavoz) John F. Walvoord. Orig. Title: Philippinas: Triumph in Christ (Everyman's Bible Commentary) (Span.). 1980. pap. 3.50 (ISBN 0-8254-1852-6). Kregel.

Filipenses: Un Comentario Exegetico y Practico. Evis L. Carballosa. Orig. Title: Phillippians: Commentary. (Span.). 140p. 1973. pap. 1.95 (ISBN 0-8254-1105-X). Kregel.

Filipino Lippi's Strozzi Chapel in Santa Maria Novella. J. Russell Sale. Ed. by Sydney J. Freedberg. LC 78-74376. (Outstanding Dissertations in the Fine Arts Ser.). (Illus.). 1979. lib. bdg. 57.00 (ISBN 0-8240-3963-7). Garland Pub.

Filippo Brunelleschi: The Cupola of Santa Maria del Fiore. Howard Saalman. Ed. by John Harris & Alastair Laing. (Studies in Architecture: No. XX). (Illus.). 420p. 1986. 95.00 (ISBN 0-302-02784-X, Pub. by Zwemmer Bks UK). Sotheby Pubns.

Filled with the Spirit-Then What? R. Mabel Francis. 1974. 2.50 (ISBN 0-87509-082-6). Chr Pubns.

Filling Your Loving Cup. Rev. ed. Kay Kuzma. LC 83-60606. 1983. pap. 5.95 (ISBN 0-910529-02-7). Parent Scene.

Filosofia del Fuego. R. Swinburne Clymer. Tr. by Hector V. Morel. Tr. of Philosophy of Fire. (Span.). 190p. (Orig.). 1980. pap. 5.95 (ISBN 0-932785-54-9). Philos Pub.

Final Chapter. S. Maxwell Coder. 318p. 1984. pap. 7.95 (ISBN 0-8423-0866-0). Tyndale.

Final Countdown. Charles C. Ryrie. 120p. 1982. pap. 4.95 (ISBN 0-88207-347-8). Victor Bks.

Final Curtain. John H. Bratt. (Contemporary Discussion Ser.). 1978. pap. 1.95 (ISBN 0-8010-0748-8). Baker Bk.

Final Gift: A New Way of the Cross. Basil Arbour. (Illus.). 64p. 1981. pap. 2.95 (ISBN 0-86683-647-0, HarpR). Har-Row.

Final Journey: The Fate of the Jews in Nazi Europe. Martin Gilbert. (Illus.). 1980. 12.50 (ISBN 0-8317-3325-X, Mayflower Bks). Smith Pubs.

Final Prophet. Harold D. Lyons. Ed. by Helen Graves. LC 86-40282. 288p. 1987. 12.95 (ISBN 1-55523-037-7). Winston-Derek.

Final Sanity: Essays on Lent & Easter. Phyllis A. Tickle. 128p. (Orig.). 1987. pap. 6.95 (ISBN 0-8358-0545-X). Upper Room.

Final Solution & the German Foreign Office. Christopher R. Browning. LC 78-8996. 276p. 1978. text ed. 35.00x (ISBN 0-8419-0403-0). Holmes & Meier.

Final Solution in the Extermination Camps & the Aftermath. J. Mendelsohn. LC 81-80320. (Holocaust Ser.). 250p. 1982. lib. bdg. 61.00 (ISBN 0-8240-4886-5). Garland Pub.

Final Solution: The Attempt to Exterminate the Jews of Europe 1939-45. Gerald Reitlinger. 622p. 1987. Repr. of 1953 ed. 40.00 (ISBN 0-87668-951-9). Aronson.

Final Solution to the Jewish Question: Mass-Murder or Hoax? Ludwig Rosenthal. (Illus.). 145p. (Orig.). 1984. pap. 9.95 (ISBN 0-318-04673-3). Magnes Mus.

Final Steps in Christian Maturity. Jeanne Guyon. 1985. pap. 6.95 (ISBN 0-940232-22-7). Christian Bks.

Finale. Calvin Miller. LC 78-70810. (Illus.). 1979. pap. 5.95 (ISBN 0-87784-627-8). Inter-Varsity.

Finality & Intelligence. Leszek Figurski. LC 78-62252. 1978. pap. text ed. 11.25 (ISBN 0-8191-0565-1). U Pr of Amer.

Finality of Faith, & Christianity Among the World Religions. Nels F. Ferre. LC 78-11979. 1979. Repr. of 1963 ed. lib. bdg. 22.50x (ISBN 0-313-21182-5, FEFF). Greenwood.

Finality of Prophethood. A. M. Dehlvi. pap. 1.25 (ISBN 0-686-18424-6). Kazi Pubns.

Finally, Family Devotions That Work. Terry Hall. (Orig.). 1986. pap. 5.95 (ISBN 0-8024-2538-0). Moody.

Financial & Commercial Policy under Cromwellian Protectorate. 2nd ed. Maurice Ashley. 190p. 1962. Repr. of 1934 ed. 28.50x (ISBN 0-7146-1265-0, BHA 01265, F Cass Co). Biblio Dist.

Financial Guidance. Jim McKeever. 400p. 1980. 10.95 (ISBN 0-931608-09-0); pap. 7.95 (ISBN 0-931608-10-4). Omega Pubns OR.

Financial Management for Clergy. David L. Northcutt. 192p. 1984. pap. 6.95 (ISBN 0-8010-6740-5). Baker Bk.

Financial Planning Workbook. Larry Burkett. LC 82-7877. (Christian Financial Concepts Ser.). 1982. pap. 6.95 (ISBN 0-8024-2546-1). Moody.

Financial Relations of the Papacy with England to 1327. W. E. Lunt. 1967. Repr. of 1939 ed. 20.00X (ISBN 0-910956-13-8). Medieval Acad.

Financial Relations of the Papacy with England, 1327-1534. W. E. Lunt. 1962. 25.00X (ISBN 0-910956-48-0). Medieval Acad.

Financing a Sacred Dance Choir. Martha Yates. 56p. 1981. pap. 3.00 (ISBN 0-941500-19-5). Sharing Co.

Find & Use Your Inner Power. Emmet Fox. 1941. 11.60 (ISBN 0-06-062890-1, HarpR). Har-Row.

Find & Use Your Spiritual Gifts. John E. Packo. LC 80-69967. 117p. (Orig.). 1980. pap. 2.95 (ISBN 0-87509-293-4); Leader's Guide. 2.95 (ISBN 0-87509-294-2). Chr Pubns.

Find Yourself, Give Yourself. Dick Wulf. LC 83-61819. 162p. 1983. pap. 5.95 (ISBN 0-89109-496-2). NavPress.

Finders Keepers: Introducing Your Friends to Christ & Helping Them Grow. Dee Brestin. LC 83-8522. 180p. 1985. 8.95 (ISBN 0-87788-265-7); pap. 5.95 (ISBN 0-87788-267-3). Shaw Pubs.

Findhorn Garden. Findhorn Community. 1976. pap. 10.95 (ISBN 0-06-090520-4, CN520, PL). Har-Row.

Finding a Pastor: The Search Committee Handbook. Theodore A. McConnell. 72p. (Orig.). 1985. pap. 4.95 (ISBN 0-86683-493-1, HarpR). Har-Row.

Finding a Way to Follow. William V. Coleman. 1977. pap. 4.95 (ISBN 0-8192-1227-X). Morehouse.

Finding Deep Joy. Robert Ellwood. LC 84-40167. 156p. (Orig.). 1984. pap. 4.50 (ISBN 0-8356-0586-8). Theos Pub Hse.

Finding Eternal Treasures. Cheryl B. Johns. (International Correspondence Program Ser.). (Orig.). 1985. pap. text ed. 6.95 (ISBN 0-87148-340-8). Pathway Pr.

Finding Faith in the Headlines. James L. Merrell. Ed. by Herbert Lambert. LC 85-481. (Orig.). 1985. pap. 7.95 (ISBN 0-8272-1012-4). CBP.

Finding Fulfillment in the Manse. Margaret M. Damp. 115p. 1978. pap. 2.95 (ISBN 0-8341-0544-6). Beacon Hill.

Finding God. Rifat Sonsino & Daniel B. Syme. 1986. 7.95 (ISBN 0-8074-0312-1, 571200). UAHC.

Finding God among Us. 2nd ed. Donald Gray. LC 77-89322. 1977. pap. 3.95 (ISBN 0-88489-090-2). St Mary's.

Finding God in Everyday Life. Kevin Coughlin. LC 80-84506. 64p. (Orig.). 1981. pap. 2.95 (ISBN 0-8091-2351-7). Paulist Pr.

Finding God in the Space Age. Thomas A. Bolten. 1987. 14.95 (ISBN 0-533-06954-8). Vantage.

Finding Grace at the Center. rev. ed. Thomas Keating et al. LC 78-10514. 1979. 2.50 (ISBN 0-932506-20-8); pap. 2.50 (ISBN 0-932506-00-3). St Bedes Pubns.

Finding Hope Again: A Pastor's Guide to Counseling Depressed Persons. Roy W. Fairchild. LC 79-2988. 160p. 1980. 9.45 (ISBN 0-06-062325-X, HarpR). Har-Row.

Finding Intimacy: The Art of Happiness in Living Together. Herbert G. Zerof. 224p. (Orig.). 1981. pap. 6.95 (ISBN 0-86683-618-7, HarpR). Har-Row.

Finding Jesus: Living Through Lent with John's Gospel. Gerald O'Collins. 64p. 1984. pap. 3.95 (ISBN 0-8091-2565-X). Paulist Pr.

Finding Peace in Pain. Yvonne C. Hebert. 108p. (Orig.). 1984. pap. text ed. 3.50 (ISBN 0-914544-53-5). Living Flame Pr.

Finding the Freedom of Self-Control. William Backus. 176p. (Orig.). 1987. pap. 5.95 (ISBN 0-87123-676-1). Bethany Hse.

Finding the Mystic within You. Peggy O. Wilkinson. 211p. (Orig.). 1985. pap. 4.95 (ISBN 0-914544-61-6). Living Flame Pr.

Finding the Quiet Mind. Robert Ellwood. LC 83-615. 155p. (Orig.). 1983. pap. 4.50 (ISBN 0-8356-0576-0, Quest). Theos Pub Hse.

Finding the Treasure Within You. Jim Lewis. LC 81-70339. 128p. 1982. pap. 4.75 (ISBN 0-87516-469-2). De Vorss.

Finding Time. Rick Yohn. 1986. 6.95 (ISBN 0-8499-3058-8). Word Bks.

Finding Your Life Partner. William J. Diehm. 128p. 1984. pap. 4.95 (ISBN 0-8170-1028-9). Judson.

Finding Your Place after Divorce: How Women Can Find Healing. Carole S. Streeter. 144p. 1986. pap. 5.95 (ISBN 0-310-41691-4, 10816P). Zondervan.

Finding Your Place in the Body of Christ. Dick Benjamin. 1980. pap. text ed. 3.95 (ISBN 0-911739-07-6). Abbott Loop.

Finding Your Self. new ed. Norman W. Cooper. 96p. 1974. pap. 4.50 (ISBN 0-87516-183-9). De Vorss.

Finding Your Way Through the Bible. Paul B. Maves & Mary C. Maves. (Orig.). 1971. pap. 3.50 (ISBN 0-687-13049-2). Abingdon.

Fine Art of Friendship. Ted W. Engstrom & Robert C. Larson. 176p. 1985. 9.95 (ISBN 0-8407-5419-1). Nelson.

Fine Art of Meditation. Subramuniya. pap. 1.00 (ISBN 0-87516-356-4). De Vorss.

Fine Arts in Islamic Civilisation. M. A. S. Beg. 7.95 (ISBN 0-686-83581-6). Kazi Pubns.

Finest of Fulness. Ed. by Ras Robinson. 192p. 1979. pap. 4.00 (ISBN 0-937778-00-1). Fulness Hse.

Finger of God: Religious Thought & Themes in Literature from Chaucer to Kafka. Hilda L. Schmerling. 1977. lib. bdg. 69.95 (ISBN 0-8490-1358-5). Gordon Pr.

Finger of God: Sermons on Faith & Socio-Political Responsibility. Allan Boesak. Tr. by Peter Randall from Afrikaans. LC 81-16943. Tr. of Vinger Van God. 112p. (Orig.). 1982. pap. 5.95 (ISBN 0-88344-135-7). Orbis Bks.

Fingerplay Friends. Audrey O. Leighton. 128p. 1984. pap. 5.95 (ISBN 0-8170-1051-3). Judson.

Fingertip Devotions. Amy Bolding. 1970. 3.95 (ISBN 0-8010-0798-4). Baker Bk.
Finished Kingdom. Lillian De Waters. 5.95 (ISBN 0-686-05716-3). L De Waters.
Finite & Infinite: A Philosophical Essay. Austin Farrer. 312p. (Orig.). 1979. pap. 8.95 (ISBN 0-8164-2001-7, HarpR). Har-Row.
Finite Perfection: Reflections on Virtue. Michael A. Weinstein. LC 84-16215. 176p. 1985. lib. bdg. 22.50x (ISBN 0-87023-474-9); pap. 9.95 (ISBN 0-87023-475-7). U of Mass Pr.
Finland & the Holocaust: The Finnish Experience. Hannu Rautkallio. 1987. 20.95 (ISBN 0-89604-120-4); pap. 13.95 (ISBN 0-89604-121-2). Holocaust Pubns.
Finlay & Julia Graham: Missionary Partners. Johnnie Human. LC 86-4148. (Meet the Missionary Ser.). 1986. 5.50 (ISBN 0-8054-4327-4). Broadman.
Finney Lives On. V. Raymond Edman. 256p. 1970. pap. 4.95 (ISBN 0-87123-150-6, 210150). Bethany Hse.
Finney on Revival. Charles G. Finney. Ed. by E. E. Shelhamer. 128p. 1974. pap. 3.50 (ISBN 0-87123-151-4, 200151). Bethany Hse.
Finney's Systematic Theology. Charles G. Finney. LC 76-3500. Orig. Title: Finney's Lectures on Systematic Theology. 448p. 1976. pap. 9.95 (ISBN 0-87123-153-0, 210153). Bethany Hse.
Finno-Ugric, Siberian Mythology. Uno Holmberg. (Mythology of All Races Ser: Vol. Iv). (Illus.). Repr. of 1932 ed. 30.00x (ISBN 0-8154-0116-7). Cooper Sq.
Fionn Mac Cumhaill: Celtic Myth in English Literature. James MacKillop. LC 85-22116. (Irish Studies). 256p. (Orig.). 1986. pap. text ed. 35.00x (ISBN 0-8156-2344-5); pap. 15.00x (ISBN 0-8156-2353-4). Syracuse U Pr.
Fiqh us-Sunnah Purification & Prayer, Vol. 1. Tr. by M. S. Dabas & J. M. Zarabozo. LC 85-73207. 205p. 1986. Repr. of 1985 ed. text ed. 15.00 (ISBN 0-89259-060-2). Am Trust Pubns.
Fire & Sword in Shansi: The Story of the Martyrdom of Foreigners & Chinese Christians. E. H. Edwards. LC 74-111738. (American Imperialism: Viewpoints of United States Foreign Policy, 1898-1941). 1970. Repr. of 1903 ed. 21.00 (ISBN 0-405-02014-7). Ayer Co Pubs.
Fire & the Rose Are One. Sebastian Moore. 176p. 1980. 9.95 (ISBN 0-8164-0468-2, HarpR). Har-Row.
Fire & the Spirits: Cherokee Law From Clan to Court. Rennard Strickland. LC 74-15903. (Illus.). 260p. 1982. pap. 10.95 (ISBN 0-8061-1619-6). U of Okla Pr.
Fire Gospel. Da Free John. 224p. (Orig.). 1982. pap. 8.95 (ISBN 0-913922-73-0). Dawn Horse Pr.
Fire in His Bones. Benson Idahosa. (Orig.). 1986. pap. 4.95 (ISBN 0-89274-429-4). Harrison Hse.
Fire in My Bones: Reflection on Faith. C. Robert Mesle. 1984. pap. 14.00 (ISBN 0-8309-0387-9). Herald Hse.
Fire in the Brand: An Introduction to the Creative Work & Theology of John Wesley. Howard A. Slaatte. LC 83-16721. 158p. 1983. pap. text ed. 11.25 (ISBN 0-8191-3552-6). U Pr of Amer.
Fire in the Pulpit. Jerry Vines. LC 77-78155. 1977. 7.95 (ISBN 0-8054-5159-5). Broadman.
Fire in Their Eyes: Spiritual Mentors for the Christian Life. Gregory M. Smith. 1984. pap. 4.95 (ISBN 0-8091-2620-6). Paulist Pr.
Fire in Your Heart: A Call to Personal Holiness. Sammy Tippit. (Orig.). 1987. pap. 5.95 (ISBN 0-8024-2625-5). Moody.
Fire Inside. J. L. Williams. 1984. 6.50 (ISBN 0-89536-654-1, 0634). CSS of Ohio.
Fire Next Time. James Baldwin. 1985. pap. 3.95 (ISBN 0-440-32542-0, LE). Dell.
Fire of Contemplation: A Guide for Interior Souls. Thomas Philippe. Tr. by Verda C. Doran from Fr. LC 81-8099. 128p. (Orig.). 1981. pap. 4.95 (ISBN 0-8189-0414-3). Alba.
Fire of God. John M. Talbot. 144p. 1986. pap. 7.95 (ISBN 0-8245-0789-4). Crossroad NY.
Fire of Love. Richard Rolle. Tr. by Clifton Wolters. (Classics Ser.). 192p. 1972. pap. 4.95 (ISBN 0-14-044256-1). Penguin.
Fire of Love & the Mending of Life. Richard Rolle. Ed. by Francis M. Comper. Tr. by Richard Misyn. 1920. Repr. 25.00 (ISBN 0-8274-2346-2). R West.
Fire of Sinai. Aaron Soloveitchik. (Annual Fryer Memorial Lecture Ser.). 1.00 (ISBN 0-914131-20-6, I32). Torah Umesorah.
Fire of Truth. Richard A. Spencer. LC 82-71218. (Orig.). 1982. pap. 6.95 (ISBN 0-8054-2248-X). Broadman.
Fire of Your Life: A Solitude Shared. Maggie Ross. LC 82-61420. 128p. 1983. pap. 6.95 (ISBN 0-8091-2513-7). Paulist Pr.
Fire on the Earth. Paul H. Furfey. 17.00 (ISBN 0-405-10830-3, 11837). Ayer Co Pubs.
Fire on the Earth. Ralph Martin. 1975. pap. 2.95 (ISBN 0-89283-021-2). Servant.
Fire over the Holy Land. Gordon Lindsay. 1.25 (ISBN 0-89985-185-1). Christ Nations.
Fire That Consumes: A Biblical & Historical Study of Final Punishment. Edward W. Fudge. 1983. 19.95 (ISBN 0-89890-018-2). Providential Pr.
Fire upon the Earth. 4.95 (ISBN 0-87193-142-7). Dimension Bks.
Fire Without Fuel. B. Hari Dass. Ed. by Ma Renu & A. Dass Tabachnick. LC 86-60051. (Illus.). 200p. (Orig.). 1986. 35.00 (ISBN 0-918100-09-7); pap. 12.95 (ISBN 0-918100-08-9). Sri Rama.
Fireflames. Oswald Mtshali. (Illus.). 72p. (Orig.). 1983. pap. 6.95 (ISBN 0-88208-501-8). Lawrence Hill.
Fireseeds of Spiritual Awakening. Dan Hayes. 144p. 1983. pap. 5.95 (ISBN 0-86605-130-9). Campus Crusade.
Firm Foundation of Mormonism. Kirk H. Vestal & Arthur Wallace. LC 81-80795. xii, 306p. 1981. 8.95x (ISBN 0-937892-06-8). LL Co.
Firmicus Maternus, the Error of the Pagan Religions. Ed. by W. J. Burghardt et al. (Ancient Christian Writers Ser.: No. 37). 1970. 11.95 (ISBN 0-8091-0039-8). Paulist Pr.
First Age of Christianity & the Church. John J. Dollinger. 1977. lib. bdg. 59.95 (ISBN 0-8490-1840-4). Gordon Pr.
First Aid in Pastoral Care. Ed. by Leslie Virgo. 220p. 1986. pap. 9.95 (ISBN 0-567-29122-7, Pub. by T & T Clark Ltd UK). Fortress.
First Album for Church Organists. Ed. by Robert Cundick. (Illus.). 64p. 1967. pap. 7.95 (ISBN 0-8258-0227-X, 0-4655). Fischer Inc NY.
First Amendment: The Legacy of George Mason. Robert A. Rutland. LC 85-2958. (Illus.). 208p. 1985. 15.00 (ISBN 0-913969-05-2, Pub. by G Mason U Pr). U Pr of Amer.
First American Catholic Missionary Congress: Proceedings of the American Catholic Missionary, 1st, Chicago, 1908. American Catholic Missionary Staff. 51.00 (ISBN 0-405-10837-0, 11844). Ayer Co Pubs.
First American Peace Movement. Incl. War Inconsistent with the Religion of Jesus Christ. David L. Dodge; Lawfulness of War for Christians Examined. James Mott; Solemn Review of the Custom of War. Noah Worcester. LC 73-147428. (Library of War & Peace; Proposals for Peace: a History). 1973. lib. bdg. 46.00 (ISBN 0-8240-0220-2). Garland Pub.
First among Sufis: The Life & Thought of Rabia al-Adawiyya. Widad El Sakkakini. Tr. by Nabil Safwat from Arabic. 1982. 15.95 (ISBN 0-900860-45-6, Pub. by Octagon Pr England). Ins Study Human.
First & Second Book of the Chronicles. R. J. Coggins. LC 75-17117. (Cambridge Bible Commentary on the New English Bible, Old Testament Ser.). (Illus.). 256p. 1976. 39.50 (ISBN 0-521-08647-7); pap. 16.95x (ISBN 0-521-09758-4). Cambridge U Pr.
First & Second Books of Chronicles. Alice Laffey. (Bible Commentary Ser.). 96p. 1985. pap. 2.95 (ISBN 0-8146-1417-5). Liturgical Pr.
First & Second Books of Discipline: Together with Some Acts of the General Assemblies. Church of Scotland Staff. LC 77-7433. (English Experience Ser.: No. 893). 1977. Repr. of 1621 ed. lib. bdg. 6.00 (ISBN 90-221-0893-7). Walter J Johnson.
First & Second Books of Esdras: Cambridge Bible Commentary on the New English Bible. R. J. Coggins & M. A. Knibb. LC 78-16420. (Old Testament Ser.). 1979. pap. 15.95 (ISBN 0-521-09757-6). Cambridge U Pr.
First & Second Books of the Maccabees: Cambridge Bible Commentary on the New English Bible. Ed. by J. R. Bartlett. LC 72-87436. (Old Testament Ser.). (Orig.). 1973. 42.50 (ISBN 0-521-08658-2); pap. 15.95 (ISBN 0-521-09749-5). Cambridge U Pr.
First & Second Chronicles. J. G. McConville. LC 84-2371. (Daily Study Bible-Old Testament Ser.). 280p. 1984. 14.95 (ISBN 0-664-21811-3); pap. 7.95 (ISBN 0-664-24578-1). Westminster.
First & Second Chronicles. John Sailhamer. (Everyman's Bible Commentary Ser.). (Orig.). 1983. pap. 5.95 (ISBN 0-8024-2012-5). Moody.
First & Second Corinthians. L. M. Grant. 194p. pap. 7.25 (ISBN 0-88172-154-9). Believers Bkshelf.
First & Second Corinthians. Ed. by John Hayes. William Baird. (Knox Preaching Guides Ser.). pap. 4.95 (ISBN 0-8042-3239-3). John Knox.
First & Second Epistle to the Thessalonians. Heinz Schurmann et al. Ed. by John L. McKenzie. LC 81-605. (New Testament for Spiritual Reading Ser.). 168p. 1981. pap. 4.95 (ISBN 0-8245-0127-6). Crossroad NY.
First & Second Epistle to Timothy & the Epistle to Titus. Bastiaan Van Elderen. Ed. by F. F. Bruce. (New International Commentary on the New Testament Ser.). 256p. cancelled (ISBN 0-8028-2346-7). Eerdmans.
First & Second Epistles of St. Peter. Bernedikt Schwank. Ed. by John T. McKenzie. LC 81-605. (New Testament for Spiritual Reading Ser.). 192p. 1981. pap. 4.95 (ISBN 0-8245-0131-4). Crossroad NY.
First & Second Epistles to the Thessalonians. Leon Morris. (New International Commentary of the New Testament). 1959. 14.95 (ISBN 0-8028-2187-1). Eerdmans.
First & Second Kings. A. Graeme Auld. LC 86-15658. (Daily Study Bible - Old Testament Ser.). 266p. 1986. 15.95 (ISBN 0-664-21836-9); pap. 8.95 (ISBN 0-664-24585-4). Westminster.
First & Second Kings. Alice Laffey. (Bible Commentary Ser.). 112p. 1985. pap. text ed. 2.95 (ISBN 0-8146-1416-7). Liturgical Pr.
First & Second Kings. Richard I. McNeely. (Everyman's Bible Commentary Ser.). 1978. pap. 5.95 (ISBN 0-8024-2011-7). Moody.
First & Second Kings. James E. Smith. LC 78-300507. (Bible Study Textbook Ser.). (Illus.). 1975. 17.50 (ISBN 0-89900-012-6). College Pr Pub.
First & Second Kings, a Commentary. rev. ed. 2nd ed. John Gray. LC 73-134271. (Old Testament Library). (Illus.). 826p. 1978. 27.50 (ISBN 0-664-20898-3). Westminster.
First & Second Letters of Paul to the Corinthians. Ed. by Margaret E. Thrall. (Cambridge Bible Commentary on the New English Bible, New Testament Ser.). (Orig.). 1965. pap. 10.95x (ISBN 0-521-09251-5). Cambridge U Pr.
First & Second Maccabees. Alphonse Spilly. (Bible Commentary Ser.). 136p. 1985. pap. 2.95 (ISBN 0-8146-1419-1). Liturgical Pr.
First & Second Peter. Louis Barbieri. (Everyman's Bible Commentary Ser.). 1977. pap. 5.95 (ISBN 0-8024-2061-3). Moody.
First & Second Peter. Gordon H. Clark. 1980. pap. 5.95 (ISBN 0-87552-167-3). Presby & Reformed.
First & Second Peter. Irving L. Jensen. (Bible Self-Study Ser.). 1971. pap. 3.25 (ISBN 0-8024-1060-X). Moody.
First & Second Peter. Alexander Nisbet. (Geneva Series Commentaries). 14.95 (ISBN 0-85151-338-7). Banner of Truth.
First & Second Peter. Donald Senior. (New Testament Message Ser.: Vol. 20). 10.95 (ISBN 0-89453-208-1); pap. 6.95 (ISBN 0-89453-143-3). M Glazier.
First & Second Samuel. Paula Bowes. (Bible Commentary Ser.). 128p. 1985. pap. text ed. 2.95 (ISBN 0-8146-1415-9). Liturgical Pr.
First & Second Samuel. Irving L. Jensen. (Bible Self-Study Ser.). 1970. pap. 3.25 (ISBN 0-8024-1009-X). Moody.
First & Second Samuel. Max Kappeler. Tr. by Rory Larson from Ger. LC 82-80904. (Bible in the Light of Christian Science Ser.: Vol. IV). Orig. Title: Die Wissenschaft der Bibel. Tr. of Das Buch 1 und 2 Samuel. 200p. 1985. 12.00 (ISBN 0-942958-10-1). Kappeler Inst Pub.
First & Second Samuel. J. Carl Laney. (Everyman's Bible Commentary Ser.). 1982. pap. 5.95 (ISBN 0-8024-2010-9). Moody.
First & Second Samuel. David F. Payne. LC 82-16009. (Daily Study Bible-Old Testament). 292p. 1982. 12.95 (ISBN 0-664-21806-7); pap. 6.95 (ISBN 0-664-24573-0). Westminster.
First & Second Samuel, A Commentary. Hans W. Hertzberg. LC 65-10074. (Old Testament Library). 416p. 1965. 22.95 (ISBN 0-664-20541-0). Westminster.
First & Second Samuel, First & Second Kings, with Excursus on Davidic Dynasty & Holy City Zion. Charles Conroy. (Old Testament Message Ser.: Vol. 6). 12.95 (ISBN 0-89453-406-8); pap. 8.95 (ISBN 0-89453-241-3). M Glazier.
First & Second Thessalonians. Keith L. Brooks. (Teach Yourself the Bible Ser). 1961. pap. 2.75 (ISBN 0-8024-2645-X). Moody.
First & Second Thessalonians. L. M. Grant. 46p. pap. 2.95 (ISBN 0-88172-079-8). Believers Bkshelf.
First & Second Thessalonians. Irving L. Jensen. (Bible Self-Study Ser.). 112p. 1974. pap. 3.25 (ISBN 0-8024-1053-7). Moody.
First & Second Thessalonians. I. Howard Marshall. (New Century Bible Commentary Ser.). 240p. 1983. pap. 6.95 (ISBN 0-8028-1946-X). Eerdmans.
First & Second Thessalonians. rev. ed. Leon Morris. Ed. by R. V. Tasker. (Tyndale New Testament Commentaries Ser.). 160p. 1984. pap. 4.95 (ISBN 0-8028-0034-3). Eerdmans.
First & Second Thessalonians. James M. Reese. (New Testament Message Ser.: Vol. 16). 130p. 1980. 10.95 (ISBN 0-89453-204-9); pap. 5.95 (ISBN 0-89453-139-5). M Glazier.
First & Second Thessalonians. Charles C. Ryrie. (Everyman's Bible Commentary Ser.). 1968. pap. 5.95 (ISBN 0-8024-2052-4). Moody.
First & Second Thessalonians: A Good News Commentary. Earl Palmer. LC 82-48409. (Good News Commentary Ser.). 128p. (Orig.). 1983. pap. 6.95 (ISBN 0-06-066455-X, RD426, HarpR). Har-Row.
First & Second Thessalonians, First & Second Timothy, Titus, Philemon: A Daily Dialogue. Whitney Kuniholm. (Personal Bible Studyguide Ser.). 120p. (Orig.). 1986. pap. 5.95 (ISBN 0-87788-809-4). Shaw Pubs.
First & Second Thessolonians. Gordon H. Clark. (Trinity Papers: No. 14). 152p. (Orig.). 1986. pap. 5.95 (ISBN 0-940931-14-1). Trinity Found.
First & Second Timothy & Titus. Irving L. Jensen. (Bible Self-Study Ser.). 1973. pap. 3.25 (ISBN 0-8024-1054-5). Moody.
First & Second Timothy & Titus: Letters to Two Young Men. Calvin W. Becker. (Teach Yourself the Bible Ser.). 1961. pap. 2.75 (ISBN 0-8024-2646-8). Moody.
First & Second Timothy, Titus. Luke T. Johnson. Ed. by John H. Hayes. LC 86-45403. (Preaching Guides). 132p. (Orig.). 1987. pap. 7.95 (ISBN 0-8042-3242-3). John Knox.
First & Third Crusades. Jon Nichol. (Resource Units: Middle Ages, 1066-1485 Ser.). (Illus.). 24p. 1974. pap. text ed. 12.95 10 copies & tchr's guide (ISBN 0-582-39377-9). Longman.
First Baron Herbert of Cherbury. Herbert Edward. Ed. by Rene Wellek. (British Philosophers & Theologians of the 17th & 18th Centuries Ser.). 1979. 51.00 (ISBN 0-8240-1779-X). Garland Pub.
First Bible Lessons: A Course for Two and Three-Year-Olds. rev. ed. Jean Baxendale. LC 81-53021. (Illus.). 144p. 1982. pap. 7.95 (ISBN 0-87239-486-7, 3369). Standard Pub.
First Book of Christian Doctrine. rev. ed. G. W. Hylkema & E. J. Tuuk. (YA) pap. 2.95 (ISBN 0-8028-8012-6). Eerdmans.
First Book of Chronicles. John A. Grindel. (Bible Ser.: No. 17). (Orig.). 1974. pap. 1.00 (ISBN 0-8091-5170-7). Paulist Pr.
First Book of Daily Readings. D. Martyn Lloyd-Jones. 1970. pap. 6.95 (ISBN 0-8028-1354-2). Eerdmans.
First Book of Irish Myths & Legends. Eoin Neeson. 128p. 1982. pap. 5.95 (ISBN 0-85342-130-7, Pub. by Mercier Pr Ireland). Irish Bks Media.
First Book of Jewish Holidays. Sophia Cedarbaum. LC 85-105348. (Illus.). 80p. 1984. pap. text ed. 6.00 (ISBN 0-8074-0274-5, 301500). UAHC.
First Book of Jewish Holidays. Robert Garvey. (Illus.). 1954. pap. 4.50x (ISBN 0-87068-362-4). Ktav.
First Book of Kings. Ed. by J. Robinson. LC 72-80592. (Cambridge Bible Commentary on the New English Bible, Old Testament Ser.). (Illus.). 228p. 1972. pap. 12.95 (ISBN 0-521-09734-7). Cambridge U Pr.
First Book of Kings. Geoffrey Wood. (Bible Ser.: No. 15). (Orig.). 1974. pap. 1.00 (ISBN 0-8091-5168-5). Paulist Pr.
First Book of Maccabees. Intro. by H. A. Fischel. 124p. 1985. pap. 4.95 (ISBN 0-8052-0793-7). Schocken.
First Book of Maccabees. Neil J. McEleney. (Bible Ser.: No. 22). (Orig.). 1974. pap. 1.00 (ISBN 0-8091-5166-9). Paulist Pr.
First Book of Records of the First Church in Pepperrellborough: Now Saco, Maine. 78p. 1985. pap. 7.75 (ISBN 0-935207-25-2). DanBury Hse Bks.
First Book of Samuel. William G. Blaikie. 440p. 1983. lib. bdg. 16.50 (ISBN 0-86524-174-0, 0901). Klock & Klock.
First Book of Samuel. Frederic L. Moriarty. (Bible Ser.). 1971. pap. 1.00 (ISBN 0-8091-5135-9). Paulist Pr.
First Book of Samuel: Cambridge Bible Commentary on the New English Bible. Peter R. Ackroyd. LC 77-128636. (Old Testament Ser.). (Illus.). 1971. 27.95 (ISBN 0-521-07965-9); pap. 9.95x (ISBN 0-521-09635-9). Cambridge U Pr.
First Book of the Lamb. Peter C. Stone. 110p. 1987. 15.00 (ISBN 0-934469-01-6). Gabriel Pr CA.
First Century: Church of God Reformation Movement, 2 vols. Ed. by Barry L. Callen. 1977. Set. 19.95 set. Vol. I (ISBN 0-87162-200-9, D1386). Vol. II (ISBN 0-87162-220-3, D1387). Warner Pr.
First-Century Judaism in Crisis: Yohanan ben Zakkai & the Renaissance of Torah. X ed. Jacob Neusner. 1982. 14.95x (ISBN 0-87068-728-X). Ktav.
First-Century Slavery & the Interpretation of I Corinthians 7: 21. S. Scott Bartchy. LC 73-83723. (Society of Biblical Literature. Dissertation Ser.). 1973. pap. 12.00 (ISBN 0-89130-220-4, 060111). Scholars Pr GA.
First Chanukah. Charles E. Bloch. LC 56-12405. (Illus.). 1957. pap. 2.25 (ISBN 0-8197-0450-4). Bloch.

First Christian Histories: Eusebius, Socrates, Sozomen, Theodoret, & Evagrius. 2nd, rev. ed. Glenn F. Chesnut. xiv, 296p. 1986. 34.95 (ISBN 0-86554-164-7, MUP/H154); pap. 19.95 (ISBN 0-86554-203-1, MUP-P22). Mercer Univ Pr.

First Christian Theology Studies in Romans. Herman A. Hoyt. pap. 4.95 (ISBN 0-88469-038-5). BMH Bks.

First Christians: An Illustrated History of the Church. Enzo Bellini et al. Ed. & tr. by John Drury. (Illus.). 126p. 1980. 12.95 (ISBN 0-03-056823-4, HarpR). Har-Row.

First Christians: Pentecost & the Spread of Christianity. Paul L. Maier. LC 75-36751. (Illus.). 160p. 1976. 11.00 (ISBN 0-06-065399-X, HarpR). Har-Row.

First Christians: Their Beginnings, Writings, & Beliefs. Eduard Lohse. LC 82-7454. 128p. (Orig.). 1983. pap. 6.95 (ISBN 0-8006-1646-4, 1-1646). Fortress.

First Christmas. (Read, Show & Tell Ser.). (Eng. & Span., Illus.). 1977. Eng. ed. 2.52 (ISBN 0-8326-2603-1, 3621); Span. ed. 2.95 (ISBN 0-685-52280-6, 5621). World Bible.

First Christmas. (Color-a-Story Bks.). (Illus.). 1985. pap. 0.89 (ISBN 0-89191-958-9, 59584). Cook.

First Christmas. (Christmas Ser.). 2.95 (ISBN 0-86112-198-8, Pub. by Brimax Bks). Borden.

First Christmas. David Galusha. LC 81-82147. (Illus.). 32p. 1981. wkbk. 3.95 (ISBN 0-87973-662-3, 662). Our Sunday Visitor.

First Christmas Dinner. Julian Lee Rayford. (Illus.). 35p. 1947. 7.50 (ISBN 0-940882-03-5). Haunted Bk Shop.

First Christmas, First Easter, First Christians, 3 Bks. Paul L. Maier. (Illus.). 128p. 1982. Boxed Set. pap. 11.00 ea. (ISBN 0-06-065395-7, RD 381, HarpR). Har-Row.

First Christmas: The True & Unfamiliar Story in Words & Pictures. Paul L. Maier. LC 76-163162. (Illus.). 1971. 10.45i (ISBN 0-06-065396-5, HarpR). Har-Row.

First Christmas Tree. Van Henry Dyke. 76p. 1984. 2.95 (ISBN 0-89783-034-2). Larlin Corp.

First Christmas: What Really Happened? Hubert J. Richards. (What Really Happened? Ser.). 128p. 1986. pap. 5.95 (ISBN 0-89622-289-6). Twenty-Third.

First Church of Christ, Scientist, & Miscellany. Mary B. Eddy. German Ed. pap. 8.50 (ISBN 0-87952-155-4). First Church.

First Church of Christ, Scientist & Miscellany. Mary B. Eddy. 1982. pap. 4.50 (ISBN 0-87952-041-8). First Church.

First Colored Baptist Church in North America. James M. Simms. LC 70-82074. (Illus.). Repr. of 1888 ed. 22.50x (ISBN 0-8371-1561-2, SIC&, Pub. by Negro U Pr). Greenwood.

First Corinthians. Keith L. Brooks. (Teach Yourself the Bible Ser.). 1964. pap. 2.75 (ISBN 0-8024-2649-2). Moody.

First Corinthians. Hans Conzelmann. Ed. by George W. MacRae. Tr. by James W. Leitch from Ger. LC 73-88360. (Hermeneia: a Critical & Historical Commentary on the Bible). 352p. 1975. 25.95x (ISBN 0-8006-6005-6, 20-6005). Fortress.

First Corinthians. (Erdmans Commentaries Ser.). 3.95 (ISBN 0-8010-3394-2). Baker Bk.

First Corinthians. Robert B. Hughes. (Everyman's Bible Commentary Ser.). (Orig.). 1985. pap. 5.95 (ISBN 0-8024-0447-2). Moody.

First Corinthians. Irving L. Jensen. (Bible Self-Study). 98p. 1972. pap. 3.25 (ISBN 0-8024-1046-4). Moody.

First Corinthians. Roy L. Laurin. Orig. Title: First Corinthians: Where Life Matures. 336p. 1987. pap. 10.95 (ISBN 0-8254-3132-8). Kregel.

First Corinthians. John MacArthur, Jr. 1984. 14.95 (ISBN 0-88469-161-6). BMH Bks.

First Corinthians. Jerome Murphy-O'Connor. (New Testament Message Ser.: Vol. 10). 172p. 1980. 12.95 (ISBN 0-89453-198-0); pap. 7.95 (ISBN 0-89453-133-6). M Glazier.

First Corinthians. Carolyn A. Osiek. (Read & Pray Ser.). 1980. 1.75 (ISBN 0-8199-0634-4). Franciscan Herald.

First Corinthians. Knofel Staton. (Standard Bible Studies). (Illus.). 272p. 1987. pap. price not set (ISBN 0-87403-167-2, 40107). Standard Pub.

First Corinthians. Jonathan Underwood. (Standard Bible Study Workbooks Ser.). 80p. 1987. wkbk. 1.95 (ISBN 0-87403-187-7, 40207). Standard Pub.

First Corinthians. Geoffrey Wilson. 1978. pap. 4.95 (ISBN 0-85151-277-1). Banner of Truth.

First Corinthians: A Translation with Notes. Paul R. Caudill. LC 82-71220. 1983. 4.95 (ISBN 0-8054-1391-X). Broadman.

First Corinthians: An Introduction & Study Guide. John J. Kilgallen. (Illus.). 128p. (Orig.). 1987. pap. 5.95 (ISBN 0-8091-2847-0). Paulist Pr.

First Corinthians, Galatians. Albert Barnes. 18.95 (ISBN 0-8010-0846-8). Baker Bk.

First Corinthians-Galatians. Gordon Bridger. (Bible Study Commentaries Ser.). 95p. 1985. pap. 4.95 (ISBN 0-317-43383-0). Chr Lit.

First Corinthians: Living Wisely. J. Allen Blair. LC 68-58844. 1969. pap. 5.50 (ISBN 0-87213-057-6). Loizeaux.

First Corinthians: MacArthur New Testament Commentary. John MacArthur, Jr. 1984. 14.95 (ISBN 0-8024-0754-4). Moody.

First Corinthians, Second Corinthians, No. 7. Mary A. Getty & Robert J. Karris. (Collegeville Bible Commentary Ser.). 128p. 1983. pap. 2.95 (ISBN 0-8146-1307-1). Liturgical Pr.

First Crusade: Accounts of Eye-Witnesses & Participants. A. C. Krey. 11.75 (ISBN 0-8446-1272-3). Peter Smith.

First Crusade & the Idea of Crusading. Jonathan R. Smith. LC 86-1608. (Middle Ages Ser.). 224p. 1986. text ed. 29.95x (ISBN 0-8122-8026-1). U of Pa Pr.

First Crusade: The Chronicle of Fulcher of Chartres & Other Source Materials. Ed. by Edward Peters. LC 74-163384. (Middle Ages Ser.). 1971. 21.00x (ISBN 0-8122-7643-4); pap. text ed. 9.95x (ISBN 0-8122-1017-4, Pa Paperbks). U of Pa Pr.

First Day Forever & the Other Stories for LDS Youth. Jack Weyland. LC 80-82455. 120p. 1980. 7.95 (ISBN 0-88290-136-2, 2037). Horizon Utah.

First Day of Eternity: Resurrection Now. Ed. by George A. Maloney. 128p. 1982. 8.95 (ISBN 0-8245-0445-3). Crossroad NY.

First Day of the New Creation: The Resurrection & the Christian Faith. Veselin Kesich. LC 81-21516. 206p. 1982. pap. 7.95 (ISBN 0-913836-78-8). St Vladimirs.

First Dynasty of Islam: The Umayyad Caliphate A.D. 661-750. G. R. Hawting. 160p. 1986. text ed. 24.95x (ISBN 0-8093-1324-3). S Ill U Pr.

First Easter: Retold by Catherine Storr. Illus. by Chris Molan. (People of the Bible Ser.). (Illus.). 32p. 1984. 10.65 (ISBN 0-8172-1987-0, Raintree Childrens Books Belitha Press Ltd. - London). Raintree Pubs.

First Easter: What Really Happened? Hubert J. Richards. (What Really Happened? Ser.). 144p. 1986. pap. 5.95 (ISBN 0-89622-282-9). Twenty-Third.

First Encounter with Francis of Assisi. Damien Vorreux. Tr. by Paul Schwartz & Paul Lachance. 1979. pap. 6.95 (ISBN 0-8199-0698-0). Franciscan Herald.

First Epistle of John. Robert S. Candlish. LC 79-14801. (Kregel Bible Study Classics Ser.). 602p. 1979. 22.95 (ISBN 0-8254-2320-1). Kregel.

First Epistle of John. John J. Lias. 1982. lib. bdg. 15.75 (ISBN 0-86524-092-2, 6201). Klock & Klock.

First Epistle of Paul to the Corinthians. Leon Morris. (Tyndale New Testament Commentary). 1958. pap. 5.95 (ISBN 0-8028-1406-9). Eerdmans.

First Epistle of Peter. Alan M. Stibbs. (Tyndale Bible Commentaries). 1959. 4.95 (ISBN 0-8028-1416-6). Eerdmans.

First Epistle of St. Peter. 2nd ed. Edward G. Selwyn. (Thornapple Commentaries Ser.). 517p. 1981. pap. 10.95 (ISBN 0-8010-8199-8). Baker Bk.

First Epistle to the Corinthians. Charles K. Barrett. LC 68-17594. (New Testament Commentaries Ser., Vol. 9). 1968. 18.00 (ISBN 0-06-060551-0, HarpR). Har-Row.

First Epistle to the Corinthians. Gordon D. Fee. Ed. by F. F. Bruce. (New International Commentary on the New Testament Ser.). 736p. 1987. pap. 27.95 (ISBN 0-8028-2288-6). Eerdmans.

First Epistle to the Corinthians. Eugen Walter. Ed. by John L. McKenzie. LC 81-605. (New Testament for Spiritual Reading Ser.). 200p. 1981. pap. 4.95 (ISBN 0-8245-0122-5). Crossroad NY.

First Epistle to Timothy. Henry P. Liddon. 1978. 6.00 (ISBN 0-86524-109-0, 5401). Klock & Klock.

First Epistle to Timothy & the Second Epistle to Timothy. Josef Reuss. Ed. by John L. McKenzie. LC 81-605. (New Testament for Spiritual Reading Ser.). 171p. 1981. pap. 4.95 (ISBN 0-8245-0128-4). Crossroad NY.

First Essene. Edmond B. Szekely. (Illus.). 240p. 1981. pap. 9.50 (ISBN 0-89564-018-X). IBS Intl.

First Establishment of the Faith in New France, 2 Vols. Chretien Le Clercq. LC 77-172312. Repr. of 1881 ed. Set. 67.50 (ISBN 0-404-03914-6). Vol. 1 (ISBN 0-404-03915-4). Vol. 2 (ISBN 0-404-03916-2). AMS Pr.

First Fast. Barbara Cohen. (Illus.). 32p. 1987. 7.95 (ISBN 0-8074-0354-7). UAHC.

First Fifty Years. David Filbeck. LC 80-65966. 336p. 1980. pap. cancelled (ISBN 0-89900-060-6). College Pr Pub.

First Franciscans & the Gospel. Duane V. Lapsanski. 1976. 6.95 (ISBN 0-8199-0568-2). Franciscan Herald.

First Freedoms: The Establishment of Freedom of Religion in America. Thomas J. Curry. 288p. 1986. text ed. 24.95x (ISBN 0-19-503661-1). Oxford U Pr.

First Genesis: A New Case for Creation. William F. Dankenbring. LC 75-10841. (Illus.). 408p. 1975. 8.95 (ISBN 0-685-54180-0). Triumph Pub.

First Genesis: The Saga of Creation Versus Evolution. new ed. William F. Dankenbring. LC 79-65131. (Illus.). 1979. 12.00 (ISBN 0-917182-14-6). Triumph Pub.

First Glance at Adrienne Von Speyr. Hans Urs Von Balthasar. Tr. by Antje Lawry & Sergia Englund. LC 79-84879. Orig. Title: Erster Blick Auf Adrienne Von Speyr. 249p. (Orig.). 1981. pap. 9.95 (ISBN 0-89870-003-5). Ignatius Pr.

First Graces. Tasha Tudor. LC 59-12017. (Illus.). 1955. 4.95 (ISBN 0-8098-1953-8). McKay.

First Guide to the Universe. Myring. (Let's Find Out About Ser.). 1982. 10.95 (ISBN 0-86020-611-4, Usborne-Hayes). EDC.

First Haggadah. Shulamit Kustanowitz & Ronnie Foont. LC 98-11598. (Illus.). 64p. 1980. 6.95 (ISBN 0-88482-766-6). Hebrew Pub.

First Human Right: A Pro-Life Primer. Catherine Odell & William Odell. LC 82-61466. 1983. pap. 4.95 (ISBN 0-87973-620-8, 620). Our Sunday Visitor.

First I Say the Shema. Molly Cone. (Shema Primary Ser: No. 1). (Illus., Orig.). 1971. pap. text ed. 5.00 (ISBN 0-8074-0134-X, 101081). UAHC.

First Impressions: From the Diary of Althea Austin. Althea Austin. 1984. 6.95 (ISBN 0-533-05806-6). Vantage.

First Jesuit. rev. ed. Mary Purcell. 225p. 1981. 10.00 (ISBN 0-8294-0371-X). Loyola.

First John. Roy L. Laurin. LC 86-27394. Orig. Title: Epistle of John: Life at its Best. 200p. 1987. pap. 8.95 (ISBN 0-8254-3136-0). Kregel.

First John-Revelation. Julian P. Love. LC 59-10454. (Layman's Bible Commentary, Vol. 25). pap. 4.95 (ISBN 0-8042-3085-4). John Knox.

First Kings. G. H. Jones. (New Century Bible Commentary Ser.). 384p. 1984. pap. 8.95 (ISBN 0-8028-0019-X). Eerdmans.

First Kings & Chronicles. Ed. by Irving L. Jensen. (Bible Self-Study Ser.). (Illus.). 1968. pap. 3.25 (ISBN 0-8024-1011-1). Moody.

First Kings, Second Chronicles. Alan Millard. (Bible Study Commentaries Ser.). 126p. 1985. pap. 4.95 (ISBN 0-317-43372-5). Chr Lit.

First Ladies of the Restoration. Frances H. Mulliken. 1985. pap. 6.50 (ISBN 0-8309-0419-0). Herald Hse.

First Lambeth Conference. Alan M. Stephenson. LC 67-95915. (Church Historical Society Ser.: No. 88). 1967. 22.50x (ISBN 0-8401-5088-1). A R Allenson.

First Liberty: Religion & the American Republic. William L. Miller. LC 85-40342. 416p. 1986. 24.95 (ISBN 0-394-53476-X). Knopf.

First Light. Ann G. O'Barr. LC 83-70211. (Orig.). 1984. pap. 5.95 (ISBN 0-8054-7305-X). Broadman.

First Mishna & the Controversies of the Tannaim. David Hoffmann. Tr. by Paul Forchheimer from German. Incl. Highest Court in the City of Sanctuary. LC 77-98683. 1977. 12.50 (ISBN 0-87203-072-5). Hermon.

First Mornings with God. Inter-Varsity Staff. pap. 0.75 (ISBN 0-87784-134-9). Inter-Varsity.

First Noel. Illus. by Janina Domanska. LC 85-27084. (Illus.). 24p. 1986. 11.75 (ISBN 0-688-04324-0); PLB 11.88 (ISBN 0-688-04325-9). Greenwillow.

First of All Persons: A New Look at Men-Women Relationships. Elizabeth S. Genne & William H. Genne. (Orig.). 1973. pap. 1.95 (ISBN 0-377-03041-4). Friend Pr.

First Parish: A Pastor's Survival Manual. J. Keith Cook. LC 83-6940. 154p. (Orig.). 1983. pap. 8.95 (ISBN 0-664-24442-4). Westminster.

First Person. Lehman Strauss. LC 67-20931. 1967. 7.95 (ISBN 0-87213-815-1). Loizeaux.

First Person Singular. Genevieve Caldwell. 180p. 1986. 10.95 (ISBN 0-8407-3072-1). Nelson.

First Peter, 2 vols. John Brown. 1980. 32.95 (ISBN 0-85151-204-6); Vol. 1, 577 Pp. (ISBN 0-85151-205-4); Vol. 2, 640 Pp. (ISBN 0-85151-206-2). Banner of Truth.

First Prayers. Helen Gompertz. (Illus.). 32p. 1983. 5.95 (ISBN 0-8170-1013-0). Judson.

First Prayers. Illus. by Anna M. Magagna. LC 82-60742. (Illus.). 64p. 1983. 8.95 (ISBN 0-02-762120-0). Macmillan.

First Prayers. Tasha Tudor. LC 59-9631. (Illus.). 1952. protestant ed. 4.50 (ISBN 0-8098-1952-X). McKay.

First Prayers for Young Catholics. Maureen Curley. (Children of the Kingdom Activities Ser.). 1978. 9.95 (ISBN 0-89837-008-6, Pub. by Pflaum Pr). Peter Li.

First Prelude. Francis J. Smith. (Illus.). 64p. 1981. pap. 5.95 (ISBN 0-8294-0387-6). Loyola.

First Principle. Bhagwan Shree Rajneesh. Ed. by Swami Prem Chinmaya. LC 83-179587. (Zen Ser.). (Illus.). 386p. (Orig.). 1979. 17.95 (ISBN 0-88050-061-1). Chidvilas Found.

First Principles: Topical Studies for New Converts. Gary Underwood & Marylyn Underwood. 1978. 4.95 (ISBN 0-89137-709-3). Quality Pubns.

First, Second Kings & First, Second Chronicles. Robert C. Dentan. LC 59-10454. (Layman's Bible Commentary Ser., Vol. 7). 1964. pap. 4.95 (ISBN 0-8042-3067-6). John Knox.

First Seven Days. Norman Geller. (Illus.). 32p. 1983. pap. 6.95 (ISBN 0-915753-00-6). N Geller Pub.

First Steps. Timothy Roland. 1984. pap. 1.95 (ISBN 0-88207-450-4). Victor Bks.

First Steps in a New Direction. Jack Van Impe. 32p. 1980. pap. 0.45 (ISBN 0-934803-17-X). J Van Impe.

First Steps in Faith. Ed. by Clayton Pepper. pap. 2.25 (ISBN 0-89137-206-7). Quality Pubns.

First Steps in Meditation for Young People. Jim Wilson. pap. 2.50 (ISBN 0-227-67458-8, Pub. by J Clarke U K). Attic Pr.

First Steps in Prayer. Kermit Olsen. pap. 2.50 (ISBN 0-910924-49-X). Macalester.

First Steps in Ritual: Safe, Effective Techniques for Experiencing the Inner Worlds. Dolores Ashcroft-Nowicki. 96p. 1983. pap. 6.95 (ISBN 0-85030-314-1). Newcastle Pub.

First Steps in Ritual: Safe, Effective Techniques for Experiencing the Inner Worlds. Dolores Ashcroft-Nowicki. LC 86-18829. 176p. 1986. lib. bdg. 19.95x (ISBN 0-8095-7010-6). Borgo Pr.

First Swallows. Leon Rubinstein. LC 83-45138. (Illus.). 216p. 1986. 14.50 (ISBN 0-8453-4758-6, Cornwall Bks). Assoc Univ Prs.

First Targum to Esther. Bernard Grossfeld. (Aramaic & Eng., Illus.). xiv, 224p. 1983. pap. 19.50 (ISBN 0-87203-112-8). Hermon.

First Ten Annual Reports 1871-1880, Young Women's Christian Association, New York, 1871-1880. Ed. by David J. Rothman & Sheila M. Rothman. (Women & Children First Ser.). 375p. 1986. lib. bdg. 45.00 (ISBN 0-8240-7682-6). Garland Pub.

First Theologians. Charles W. Lowry. 200p. (Orig.). 1986. pap. 7.95 (ISBN 0-89526-804-3). Regnery Bks.

First Thessalonians: A Commentary. Paul N. Tarazi. LC 82-16952. (Orthodox Biblical Studies). 186p. (Orig.). 1982. pap. 7.95 (ISBN 0-913836-97-4). St Vladimirs.

First Thessalonians-Philemon. Holmes Rolston. LC 59-10454. (Layman's Bible Commentary Ser: Vol. 23). pap. 4.95 (ISBN 0-8042-3083-8). John Knox.

First Thessalonians, Philippians, Philemon, Second Thessalonians, Colossians, Ephesians, No. 8. Ivan Havener & Robert J. Karris. (Collegeville Bible Commentary Ser.). (Illus.). 112p. 1983. pap. 2.95 (ISBN 0-8146-1308-X). Liturgical Pr.

First Things: An Inquiry into the First Principles of Morals & Justice. Hadley Arkes. LC 85-43267. 480p. 1986. text ed. 45.00 (ISBN 0-691-07702-9); pap. 9.95 (ISBN 0-691-02247-X). Princeton U Pr.

First Things First. Palms. 1983. 5.95 (ISBN 0-88207-290-0). Victor Bks.

First Things First. 2nd rev. ed. Keith H. Parks. 32p. 1981. pap. 2.49 (ISBN 0-88151-012-2). Lay Leadership.

First Things First: The Ten Commandments in the 20th Century. Frederick Catherwood. LC 81-51. 160p. 1981. pap. 5.95 (ISBN 0-87784-472-0). Inter Varsity.

First Thousand Words in Hebrew. Amery & Haron. (First Thousand Words Ser.). (Illus.). 62p. 1985. PLB 10.95 (ISBN 0-86020-863-X, Pub. by Usborne). EDC.

First Three Years of School: A Survivor's Guide. Cliff Schimmels. 160p. (Orig.). 1984. pap. 5.95 (ISBN 0-8007-5175-2, Power Bks). Revell.

First Timothy. D. Edmond Hiebert. (Everyman's Bible Commentary Ser.). 1967. pap. 5.95 (ISBN 0-8024-2054-0). Moody.

First Timothy, Second Timothy, Titus, James, First Peter, Second Peter, Jude, No. 9. Jerome H. Neyrey. Ed. by Robert J. Karris. (Collegeville Bible Commentary Ser.). 112p. 1983. pap. 2.95 (ISBN 0-8146-1309-8). Liturgical Pr.

First Tome or Volume of the Paraphrase of Erasmus Upon the Newe Testamente. Desiderius Erasmus. LC 75-23361. 1350p. 1975. Repr. of 1548 ed. lib. bdg. 100.00x (ISBN 0-8201-1159-7). Schol Facsimiles.

First Twelve Meditations: On Black American Philosophy & Theology - A Study into the Meaning of Genesis & the African Concept of the Great Past & African Time Concepts As Spiritual & Two Dimensional. Patrique Hunttmiller. 150p. Date not set. pap. 6.95 (ISBN 0-318-20332-4). Scojtia Renee.

First Two Partes of the Acts or Unchaste Examples of the Englyshe Votaryes. John Bale. LC 79-84086. (English Experience Ser.: No. 906). 540p. 1979. Repr. of 1560 ed. lib. bdg. 40.00 (ISBN 90-221-0906-2). Walter J Johnson.

First Two Stuarts & the Puritan Revolution: 1603-1660. Samuel R. Gardiner. 1977. Repr. of 1891 ed. lib. bdg. 25.00 (ISBN 0-8495-1911-X). Arden Lib.

First Two Thousand Years. W. Cleon Skousen. 1953. 8.95 (ISBN 0-88494-029-2). Bookcraft Inc.

First Two Years of Marriage: Foundations for a Life Together. Thomas Hart & Kathleen Hart. 144p. (Orig.). 1983. pap. 5.95 (ISBN 0-8091-2553-6). Paulist Pr.

First Urban Christians: The Social World of the Apostle Paul. Wayne A. Meeks. LC 82-8447. (Illus.). 296p. 1982. 30.00x (ISBN 0-300-02876-8). Yale U Pr.

First Urban Christians: The Social World of the Apostle Paul. Wayne A. Meeks. LC 82-8447. 312p. 1984. pap. 9.95 (ISBN 0-300-03244-7, Y-503). Yale U Pr.

First We Have Coffee. Margaret Jensen. LC 83-48412. 144p. (Orig.). 1983. pap. 5.95 (ISBN 0-89840-050-3). Heres Life.

First Year: Incorporating New Members. Suzanne G. Braden. (Pathways to Church Growth Ser.). 80p. (Orig.). Date not set. pap. 5.95 (ISBN 0-88177-046-9, DR046B). Discipleship Res.

First Year of Life: A Curriculum for Parenting Information. Nina R. Lief. 362p. 21.95 (ISBN 0-686-86720-3). Sadlier.

First Years Together. Ruth Sanford. 140p. (Orig.). 1983. pap. 5.95 (ISBN 0-89283-134-0). Servant.

First Zen Reader. Trevor P. Leggett. LC 60-12739. (Illus.). 1960. pap. 6.95 (ISBN 0-8048-0180-0). C E Tuttle.

Fiscal System of Islam. A. I. Qureshi. 1981. 10.50 (ISBN 0-686-97866-8). Kazi Pubns.

Fish in the Sea is Not Thirsty. Bhagwan Shree Rajneesh. Ed. by Ma Yoga Anurag. LC 82-244585. (Kabir Ser.). (Illus.). 524p. (Orig.). 1980. 22.95 (ISBN 0-88050-062-X). Chidvilas Found.

Fishermen's Surprise. Alyce Bergey. (Arch Bks: Set 4). 1967. laminated cover 0.99 (ISBN 0-570-06028-1, 59-1139). Concordia.

Fishers of Men. Glenn Clark. pap. 1.95 (ISBN 0-910924-62-7). Macalester.

Fishers of Men. 3rd rev. ed. Keith H. Parks. 196p. 1981. pap. text ed. 17.00 (ISBN 0-88151-014-9). Lay Leadership.

Fishers of Men: Group Leader Guide. 3rd rev. ed. James D. Craig. 116p. 1981. 4.00 (ISBN 0-88151-016-5). Lay Leadership.

Fishers of Men: Home Study Guide. 3rd rev. ed. Keith h. Parks. 64p. 1981. 8.00 (ISBN 0-88151-015-7). Lay Leadership.

Fishers of Men or Founders of Empire: The Wycliffe Bible Translators in Latin America. David Stoll. (Illus.). 352p. 1983. 29.50x (ISBN 0-86232-111-5, Pub. by Zed Pr England); pap. 10.75 (ISBN 0-86232-112-3, Pub. by Zed Pr England). Humanities.

Fishing on the Asphalt. Herbert Miller. LC 83-10006. 208p. (Orig.). 1983. pap. 8.95 (ISBN 0-8272-1011-6). CBP.

Fishy Story. 1.75 (ISBN 0-8198-0197-6). Dghtrs St Paul.

Fit for the King. Bill Martin. Ed. by Glenda Haynes. (Illus.). 384p. (Orig.). (YA) pap. 11.50 (ISBN 0-89114-154-5). Baptist Pub Hse.

Fitness & Faith. Paul Brynteson & Donna Brynteson. 224p. 1985. pap. 7.95 (ISBN 0-8407-5920-7). Nelson.

Fitzpatrick's Boston, 1846-1866: John Bernard Fitzpatrick, Third Bishop of Boston. Thomas H. O'Connor. LC 83-23806. 308p. 1984. text ed. 22.95x (ISBN 0-930350-56-1). NE U Pr.

Five Biblical Portraits. Elie Wiesel. LC 81-40458. 168p. 1981. 9.95 (ISBN 0-268-00957-0). U of Notre Dame Pr.

Five Biblical Portraits. Elie Wiesel. LC 81-40458. vii, 157p. 1983. pap. 4.95 (ISBN 0-268-00962-7, 85-09622). U of Notre Dame Pr.

Five Books of Moses. Oswald T. Allis. 1977. pap. 5.95 (ISBN 0-8010-0108-0). Baker Bk.

Five Books of Moses. Oswald T. Allis. 1949. pap. 7.95 (ISBN 0-87552-102-9). Presby & Reformed.

Five Books of Moses Called the Pentateuch. William Tyndale. LC 67-23739. (Centaur Classics Ser.). 791p. 1967. 32.50x (ISBN 0-8093-0259-4). S Ill U Pr.

Five Cries of Youth. Merton P. Strommen. LC 73-18690. 192p. 1974. pap. 8.95 (ISBN 0-06-067748-1, RD224, HarpR). Har-Row.

Five Daily Prayers. Imam Mohamad Jawad Chirri. 24p. Date not set. pap. 3.00 (ISBN 0-317-52360-0). Islamic Ctr.

Five Deans. facsimile ed. Sidney Dark. LC 71-93332. (Essay Index Reprint Ser.). 1928. 18.00 (ISBN 0-8369-1285-3). Ayer Co Pubs.

Five Deans: John Colet, John Donne, Jonathan Swift, Arthur Penrhyn Stanley & William Ralph Inge. Sidney Dark. LC 70-86011. (Essay & General Literature Index Reprint Ser.). 1969. Repr. of 1928 ed. 22.50x (ISBN 0-8046-0555-6, Pub. by Kennikat). Assoc Faculty Pr.

Five Divorces of a Healthy Marriage. Harold Straughn. Ed. by Herbert Lambert. LC 85-29923. 160p. (Orig.). 1986. pap. 10.95 (ISBN 0-8272-2318-8). CBP.

Five Dollar Convention. Helen L. Snyder. (Orig.). 1982. pap. 2.95 (ISBN 0-937172-31-6). JLJ Pubs.

Five English Reformers. rev. ed. J. C. Ryle. 156p. (Orig.). 1981. pap. text ed. 3.95 (ISBN 0-85151-138-4). Banner of Truth.

Five Evangelical Leaders. Christopher Catherwood. 240p. 1985. pap. 7.95 (ISBN 0-87788-274-6); 12.95 (ISBN 0-87788-257-6). Shaw Pubs.

Five for Sorrow, Ten for Joy: A Consideration of the Rosary. rev. ed. J. Neville Ward. LC 85-21318. xiii, 138p. 1985. pap. 6.95 (ISBN 0-936384-36-0). Cowley Pubns.

Five Foreigners in Japan. facs. ed. Herbert H. Gowen. LC 67-28735. (Essay Index Reprint Ser). 1936. 20.00 (ISBN 0-8369-0491-5). Ayer Co Pubs.

Five Gifts from God. 1979. 1.75 (ISBN 0-8198-0616-1); pap. 1.00 (ISBN 0-8198-0617-X). Dghtrs St Paul.

Five Gospels: An Account of How the Good News Came to Be. John C. Meagher. 324p. 1983. 24.50 (ISBN 0-86683-731-0, HarpR); pap. 11.95 (ISBN 0-86683-691-8). Har-Row.

Five Great Healers Speak Here. Ed. by Nancy Gardner & Esmond Gardner. LC 82-50164. (Illus.). 138p. (Orig.). 1982. pap. 6.25 (ISBN 0-8356-0567-1, Quest). Theos Pub Hse.

Five Great Mantrams of the New Age. Torkom Saraydarian. LC 73-39431. 1975. pap. 2.00 (ISBN 0-911794-19-0). Aqua Educ.

Five Great Oxford Leaders: Keble, Newman, Pusey, Liddon & Church. Augustas B. Donaldson. 1978. Repr. of 1900 ed. lib. bdg. 35.00 (ISBN 0-8495-1036-8). Arden Lib.

Five Hindrances to Growth in Grace. Kenneth E. Hagin. 1981. pap. 0.50 mini bk (ISBN 0-89276-253-5). Hagin Ministries.

Five Hundred & Fifty Books on Buddhism: Translations, Studies, General Readings. (Nyingma Reference Ser.). 95p. pap. 4.95 (ISBN 0-913546-97-6). Dharma Pub.

Five Hundred Bible Study Outlines. F. E. Marsh. LC 79-2549. 382p. 1985. pap. 10.95 (ISBN 0-8254-3248-0). Kregel.

Five Hundred Children's Sermon Outlines. John Ritchie. LC 86-27396. 128p. 1987. pap. 4.95 (ISBN 0-8254-3623-0). Kregel.

Five Hundred Eight Answers to Bible Questions. M. R. DeHaan. 1979. pap. 7.95 (ISBN 0-310-23341-0, 9495P). Zondervan.

Five Hundred Evangelistic Sermon Outlines. John Ritchie. LC 86-27200. 128p. 1987. pap. 4.95 (ISBN 0-8254-3619-2). Kregel.

Five Hundred Gospel Sermon Illustrations. John Ritchie. LC 86-27201. 152p. 1987. pap. 5.95 (ISBN 0-8254-3620-6). Kregel.

Five Hundred Gospel Sermon Outlines. John Ritchie. LC 86-27760. 128p. 1987. pap. 4.95 (ISBN 0-8254-3621-4). Kregel.

Five Hundred Sermon Outlines on Basic Bible Truths. John Ritchie. LC 86-27541. 128p. 1987. pap. 4.95 (ISBN 0-8254-3618-4). Kregel.

Five Hundred Sermon Outlines on the Christian Life. John Ritchie. LC 86-27759. 120p. 1987. pap. 4.95 (ISBN 0-8254-3622-2). Kregel.

Five in Search of Wisdom. abr. ed. John M. Oesterreicher. Orig. Title: Walls Are Crumbling: Seven Jewish Philosophers Discover Christ. 1967. pap. 2.25x (ISBN 0-268-00100-6). U of Notre Dame Pr.

Five Instructions on the Sacraments. St. Cyril, Bishop of Jerusalem. 1974. pap. 1.25 (ISBN 0-686-10197-9). Eastern Orthodox.

Five Letters on Worship & Ministry. W. Trotter. 39p. pap. 0.60 (ISBN 0-88172-128-X). Believers Bkshelf.

Five Little Andys. Mary E. Yoder. (Illus.). 1977. 2.75 (ISBN 0-87813-510-3). Christian Light.

Five Loaves & Two Fishes: New Life Through Inner Healing. Phoebe Cranor. 1987. pap. 4.95. Paulist Pr.

Five Megillos, 5 vols. Meir Zlotowitz. (Art Scroll Tanach Ser.). 928p. 1977. Boxed Set. 59.95 (ISBN 0-89906-010-2); Boxed Set. pap. 44.95 (ISBN 0-89906-011-0). Mesorah Pubns.

Five Megilloth. Ed. by Bydr A. Cohen. 252p. 1946. 10.95 (ISBN 0-900689-35-8). Soncino Pr.

Five Metaphysical Poets: Donne, Herbert, Vaughan, Crashaw, Marvell. Joan Bennett. 1964. 32.50 (ISBN 0-521-04156-2); pap. 9.95 (ISBN 0-521-09238-8). Cambridge U Pr.

Five Minutes a Day. Robert E. Speer. LC 43-16427. 384p. 1977. softcover 3.95 (ISBN 0-664-24139-5). Westminster.

Five Minutes with God, No. 2. Jane Sorenson. (Illus.). 64p. 1985. pap. 2.50 (ISBN 0-87239-894-3, 2824). Standard Pub.

Five Mountains: The Rinzai Zen Monastic Institution in Medieval Japan. Martin Collcutt. (Harvard East Asian Monograph: Vol. 85). (Illus.). 450p. 1980. 27.50x (ISBN 0-674-30497-7). Harvard U Pr.

Five Points of Calvinism. Jack Seaton. 1979. pap. 1.20 (ISBN 0-85151-264-X). Banner of Truth.

Five Points of Calvinism. David H. Steele & Thomas C. Curtis. 1963. pap. 2.50 (ISBN 0-87552-444-3). Presby & Reformed.

Five Points of Calvinism. David N. Steele & Curtis C. Thomas. (Biblical & Theological Studies). pap. 2.50 (ISBN 0-8010-7919-5). Baker Bk.

Five Points of Calvinism: A Study Guide. Edwin H. Palmer. 1972. pap. 4.95 (ISBN 0-8010-6926-2). Baker Bk.

Five Polyphonic Masses. Heirich Isaac. Ed. by Louise Cuyler. LC 56-7145. pap. 38.50 (ISBN 0-317-09652-4, 2051077). Bks Demand UMI.

Five Religions in the Twentieth Century. W. Owen Cole. LC 81-68724. (Illus.). 256p. 1981. pap. 11.95 (ISBN 0-8023-1272-1). Dufour.

Five Scrolls. Ed. by Herbert Bronstein & Albert Friedlander. 324p. 1984. 19.95 (ISBN 0-916694-80-1); deluxe ed. 60.00 (ISBN 0-916694-81-X); special ltd. ed., leatherbound 675.00 (ISBN 0-916694-82-8). Central Conf.

Five Secrets of Living. Warren Wiersbe. 1978. pap. 2.95 (ISBN 0-8423-0870-9). Tyndale.

Five Sermons. Joseph Butler. Ed. by Stephen Darwall. LC 83-12577. (HPC Philosophical Classics Ser.). 86p. 1983. pap. text ed. 3.45 (ISBN 0-915145-61-8). Hackett Pub.

Five Shaping Forces: Using Organizational Dynamics to Do More with Less. Merton P. Strommen. 104p. 1982. 9.60 (ISBN 0-686-39889-0). Natl Cath Educ.

Five Short Plays about Jesus. Pamela Urfer. 26p. (Orig.). 1983. pap. text ed. 3.95 (ISBN 0-912801-02-6). Creat Arts Dev.

Five Silent Years of Corrie Ten Boom. Pamela Rosewell. Ed. by David Hazzard. 192p. 1986. pap. 6.95 (ISBN 0-310-61121-0, 13228P). Zondervan.

Five Smooth Stones for Pastoral Work. Eugene H. Peterson. LC 79-87751. 1980. pap. 9.95 (ISBN 0-8042-1103-5). John Knox.

Five Stages of Greek Religion. Gilbert Murray. LC 76-27675. 1976. Repr. of 1925 ed. lib. bdg. 22.50x (ISBN 0-8371-9080-0, MUFS). Greenwood.

Five Stages of Greek Religion: Studies Based on a Course of Lectures Delivered in April 1912 at Columbia University. Gilbert Murray. LC 75-41202. Repr. of 1925 ed. 12.50 (ISBN 0-404-14577-9). AMS Pr.

Five Steps to Freedom. R. David Stevens. 60p. 1980. pap. 2.25 (ISBN 0-87516-400-5). De Vorss.

Five Steps Toward a Better Marriage. David A. Thompson. 96p. (Orig.). 1980. pap. 5.95 (ISBN 0-87123-164-6, 210164). Bethany Hse.

Five Types of Ethical Theory. 8th ed. C. D. Broad. (International Library of Philosophy & Scientific Method). 1930. text ed. 35.00x (ISBN 0-7100-3080-0). Humanities.

Five Ways: St. Thomas Aquinas' Proofs of God's Existence. Anthony Kenny. LC 80-10416. 140p. 1980. pap. text ed. 4.95 (ISBN 0-268-00952-X). U. of Notre Dame Pr.

Five Years of Theosophy. 575p. 1981. Repr. of 1885 ed. 14.00 (ISBN 0-938998-21-8). Theosophy.

Five Years of Theosophy: Mystical, Philosophical, Theosophical, Historical & Scientific Essay. G. R. Mead. LC 75-36850. (Occult Ser.). 1976. Repr. of 1894 ed. 30.00x (ISBN 0-405-07966-4). Ayer Co Pubs.

Fivesquare City. James Dougherty. 178p. 1980. 15.95 (ISBN 0-268-00946-5). U. of Notre Dame Pr.

Flame. William Sears & Robert Quigley. 144p. 1972. 7.95 (ISBN 0-85398-031-4); pap. 3.50 (ISBN 0-85398-030-6). G Ronald Pub.

Flame & the Candle. Amelia Bishop. (Orig.). 1987. 7.50 (ISBN 0-8054-5033-5). Broadman.

Flame & the Light: Meanings in Vedanta & Buddhism. Hugh A. Fausset. LC 69-10089. Repr. of 1969 ed. lib. bdg. 22.50x (ISBN 0-8371-0996-5, FAVB). Greenwood.

Flame & the Light: Vedanta & Buddhism. H. L'Anson Fausset. 59.95 (ISBN 0-8490-0173-0). Gordon Pr.

Flame in the Night. Daughters of St. Paul. 1967. 3.00 (ISBN 0-8198-0234-4); pap. 2.00 (ISBN 0-8198-2610-3). Dghtrs St Paul.

Flame of Beauty, Culture, Love, Joy. Torkom Saraydarian. LC 80-67681. 1980. pap. 10.00 (ISBN 0-911794-02-6). Aqua Educ.

Flame of Fire. J. H. Hunter. 5.00 (ISBN 0-685-20860-5). Univ Place.

Flame of Fire: The Story of Troy Annual Conference. Charles D. Schwartz & Ouida D. Schwartz. LC 82-70624. (Illus.). 376p. (Orig.). 1982. pap. text ed. 15.00x (ISBN 0-914960-38-5). Academy Bks.

Flame-Waves, Pt. 1. Sri Chinmoy. 52p. (Orig.). 1975. pap. 2.00 (ISBN 0-88497-213-5). Aum Pubns.

Flame-Waves, Pt. 2. Sri Chinmoy. 47p. (Orig.). 1975. pap. 2.00 (ISBN 0-88497-214-3). Aum Pubns.

Flame-Waves, Pt. 3. Sri Chinmoy. 47p. (Orig.). 1975. pap. 2.00 (ISBN 0-88497-215-1). Aum Pubns.

Flame-Waves, Pt. 4. Sri Chinmoy. 53p. (Orig.). 1975. pap. 2.00 (ISBN 0-88497-216-X). Aum Pubns.

Flame-Waves, Pt. 5. Sri Chinmoy. 50p. (Orig.). 1975. pap. 2.00 (ISBN 0-88497-217-8). Aum Pubns.

Flames of Fire: Biographical Accounts of Pentecost Through the Centuries. Rhonda R. Pruitt. (Orig.). pap. text ed. write for info. Faith Print.

Flames of Power: A Study of Meditation, Candles & Special Insights. Sandy Winters & Shirley Brooks. 64p. 1987. pap. 6.50 (ISBN 0-89540-164-9, SB-164). Sun Pub.

Flames of Rome. Paul L. Maier. (Living Bks.). 640p. 1987. pap. 4.95 (ISBN 0-8423-0903-9). Tyndale.

Flames of the Spirit. Ruth C. Duck. (Orig.). 1985. pap. 6.95 (ISBN 0-8298-0537-0). Pilgrim NY.

Flaming Center: A Theology of the Christian Mission. Carl E. Braaten. LC 76-62605. pap. 44.00 (2026958). Bks Demand UMI.

Flaming Prophet: The Story of Samuel Zwemer. J. Christy Wilson. LC 76-130778. (Bold Believers Ser). (Orig.). 1970. pap. 0.95 (ISBN 0-377-84201-X). Friend Pr.

Flannery O'Connor. Dorothy T. McFarland. LC 74-78443. (Literature and Life Ser.). 141p. 1976. 14.95x (ISBN 0-8044-2609-0). Ungar.

Flannery O'Connor & Caroline Gordon: A Reference Guide. Robert Golden & Mary C. Sullivan. 1977. lib. bdg. 28.50 (ISBN 0-8161-7845-3, Hall Reference). G K Hall.

Flannery O'Connor: Voice of the Peacock. 2nd ed. Kathleen Feeley. LC 76-163958. xviii, 198p. 1982. pap. 9.00 (ISBN 0-8232-1093-6). Fordham.

Flannery O'Connor's Religion of the Grotesque. Marshall B. Gentry. LC 85-20267. 216p. 1986. 22.50x (ISBN 0-87805-285-2). U Pr of Miss.

Flat in Bliss. Carol Flint. 1980. 2.00 (ISBN 0-936814-06-3). New Collage.

Flaxman, Blake, Coleridge, & Other Men of Genius Influenced by Swedenborg. H. N. Morris. 1973. Repr. of 1915 ed. lib. bdg. 20.00 (ISBN 0-8414-1515-3). Folcroft.

Fleeing the Whore of Babylon: A Modern Conversion Story. James J. Thompson. 1986. pap. 9.95 (ISBN 0-87061-130-5). Chr Classics.

Flesh of My Flesh. Una Kroll. 112p. 1975. pap. 6.50 (ISBN 0-232-51336-8). Attic Pr.

Fletcher's Complete Works, 4 vols. 59.95 (ISBN 0-686-12868-0). Schmul Pub Co.

Flight from Authority: Religion, Morality & the Quest for Autonomy. Jeffrey Stout. LC 81-2340. (Revisions Ser.: Vol. 1). 307p. 1987. pap. text ed. 12.95x (ISBN 0-268-00971-6, Dist. by Har-Row). U of Notre Dame Pr.

Flight of the Lucky Lady. Don S. Midlam. (Illus.). 1954. 8.95 (ISBN 0-8323-0091-8). Binford-Metropolitan.

Flight of the Seventh Moon: The Teaching of the Shields. Lynn V. Andrews. LC 83-48414. (Illus.). 208p. 1984. 13.45 (ISBN 0-06-250027-9, HarpR). Har-Row.

Flight of the Wild Gander. Joseph Campbell. LC 70-183820. 256p. 1972. pap. 7.50 (ISBN 0-89526-914-7). Regnery Bks.

Flights: Readings in Magic, Mysticism, Fantasy & Myth. David A. Leeming. 388p. (Orig.). 1974. pap. text ed. 11.95 (ISBN 0-15-527556-9, HC). HarBraceJ.

Flirting with the World: A Challenge to Loyalty. John White. LC 81-21491. 156p. 1982. pap. 5.95 (ISBN 0-87788-156-1). Shaw Pubs.

Flood. 2nd ed. Alfred M. Rehwinkel. (Orig.). (YA) 1951-1957. pap. 9.95 (ISBN 0-570-03183-4, 12-2103). Concordia.

Florentine Codex, General History of the Things of New Spain, 13 bks. Bernardino de Sahagun. Tr. by Arthur J. Anderson & Charles E. Dibble. Incl. Introductory Volume: Introductions, Sahagun's Prologues & Interpolations, General Bibliography, General Indices. 1982. 35.00x (ISBN 0-87480-165-6); Bk. 1. Gods. rev., 2nd ed. 1970. 17.50 (ISBN 0-87480-000-5); Bk. 2. Ceremonies. rev., 2nd ed. 1981. 40.00x (ISBN 0-87480-194-X); Bk. 3. Origins of the Gods. rev., 2nd ed. 1979. 17.50x (ISBN 0-87480-002-1); Bks. 4 & 5. Soothsayers, the Omens. Repr. of 1979 ed. 40.00x (ISBN 0-87480-003-X); Bk. 6. Rhetoric & Moral Philosophy. 1976. 40.00x (ISBN 0-87480-010-2); Bk. 7. Sun, Moon & Stars, & the Binding of the Years. Repr. of 1977 ed. 17.50 (ISBN 0-87480-004-8); Bk. 8. Kings & Lords. Repr. of 1979 ed. 20.00x (ISBN 0-87480-005-6); Bk. 9. Merchants. Repr. of 1976 ed. 20.00x (ISBN 0-87480-006-4); Bk. 10. People. Repr. of 1974 ed. 30.00x (ISBN 0-87480-007-2); Bk. 11. Earthly Things. Repr. of 1975 ed. 45.00x (ISBN 0-87480-008-0); Bk. 12. Conquest of Mexico. **rev., 2nd ed. 1975. 27.50x (ISBN 0-87480-096-X). 1982. Set. 350.00x (ISBN 0-87480-082-X). U of Utah Pr.**

Flow of Religious Instruction: A Social-Science Approach. James M. Lee. LC 74-29824. (Illus.). 379p. (Orig.). 1975. pap. 14.95 (ISBN 0-89135-003-9). Religious Educ.

Flower Adornment (Avatamsaka) Sutra: Chapter 15, The Ten Dwellings. Commentary by Tripitaka Master Hua. Tr. by Buddhist Text Translation Society. (Illus.). 185p. (Orig.). 1981. pap. 8.00 (ISBN 0-917512-77-4). Buddhist Text.

Flower Adornment (Avatamsaka) Sutra: Chapter 26, The Ten Grounds, Pt. One. Commentary by Tripitaka Master Hua. Tr. by Buddhist Text Translation Society. (Illus.). 234p. (Orig.). 1980. pap. 7.00 (ISBN 0-917512-87-1). Buddhist Text.

Flower Adornment Sutra, Chapter 11: Pure Conduct. Commentary by Tripitaka Master Hua. Tr. by Buddhist Text Translation Society Staff. (Illus.). 255p. (Orig.). 1983. pap. 9.00 (ISBN 0-917512-37-5). Buddhist Text.

Flower Adornment Sutra, Chapter 16: Brahma Conduct. Commentary by Tripitaka Master Hua. Tr. by Buddhist Text Translation Society. (Illus.). 86p. (Orig.). 1981. pap. 5.00 (ISBN 0-917512-80-4). Buddhist Text.

Flower Adornment Sutra: Chapter 17, Merit & Virture from First Bringing Forth the Mind. Commentary by Tripitaka Master Hua. Tr. by Buddhist Text Translation Society. (Illus.). 196p. (Orig.). 1982. pap. 7.00 (ISBN 0-917512-83-9). Buddhist Text.

Flower Adornment Sutra, Chapter 22: The Ten Inexhaustible Treasuries Commentary by Tripitka Master Hua. Tr. by Buddhist Text Translation Society Staff. (Illus.). 184p. (Orig.). 1983. pap. 7.00 (ISBN 0-917512-38-3). Buddhist Text.

Flower Adornment Sutra, Chapter 24: Praises in the Tushita Heaven. Commentary by Tripitaka Master Hua. Tr. by Buddhist Text Translation Society. (Illus.). 130p. (Orig.). 1982. pap. 5.00 (ISBN 0-917512-39-1). Buddhist Text.

Flower Adornment Sutra, Chapter 26: The Ten Grounds, Part Two. Commentary by Tripitaka Master Hua. Tr. by Buddhist Text Translation Society. (Illus.). 200p. (Orig.). 1981. pap. 8.00 (ISBN 0-917512-74-X). Buddhist Text.

Flower Adornment Sutra, Chapter 36: Universal Worthy's Conduct. Tr. by Buddhist Text Translation Society Staff. (Illus.). 75p. (Orig.). 1983. pap. 5.00 (ISBN 0-88139-011-9). Buddhist Text.

Flower Adornment Sutra, Chapter 39: Entering the Dharma Realm, Part VII. Tr. by Buddhist Text Translation Society Staff. 160p. (Orig.). 1983. pap. 9.00 (ISBN 0-88139-050-X). Buddhist Text.

Flower Adornment Sutra, Chapter 39: Entering the Dharma Realm, Part VI. Tr. by Buddhist Text Translation Society Staff. (Illus.). 320p. (Orig.). 1982. pap. 9.00 (ISBN 0-917512-48-0). Buddhist Text.

Flower Adornment Sutra, Chapter 39: Entering the Dharma Realm Part VIII. Commentary by Tripitaka Master Hua. Tr. by Buddhist Text Translation Society. 228p. (Orig.). 1984. pap. 8.50 (ISBN 0-88139-055-0). Buddhist Text.

Flower Adornment Sutra, Chapter 39: Entering the Dharma Realm., Part I. Commentary by Tripitaka Master Hua. Tr. by Buddhist Text Translation Society. (Illus.). 284p. (Orig.). 1980. pap. 8.50 (ISBN 0-917512-68-5). Buddhist Text.

Flower Adornment Sutra, Chapter 39: Entering the Dharma Realm, Part II. Commentary by Tripitaka Master Hua. Tr. by Buddhist Text Translation Society. (Illus.). 312p. (Orig.). 1980. pap. 8.50 (ISBN 0-917512-70-7). Buddhist Text.

Flower Adornment Sutra, Chapter 39: Entering the Dharma Realm, Part IV. Commentary by Tripitaka Master Hua. Tr. by Buddhist Text Translation Society. (Illus.). 280p. (Orig.). 1981. pap. 8.00 (ISBN 0-917512-76-6). Buddhist Text.

Flower Adornment Sutra, Chapter 39: Entering the Dharma Realm, Part III. Commentary by Tripitaka Master Hua. Tr. by Buddhist Text Translation Society. (Illus.). 250p. (Orig.). 1981. pap. 8.50 (ISBN 0-917512-73-1). Buddhist Text.

Flower Adornment Sutra, Chapter 39: Entering the Dharma Realm, Part V. Commentary by Tripitaka Master Hua. Tr. by Buddhist Text Translation Society. (Illus.). 310p. 1982. pap. 9.00 (ISBN 0-917512-81-2). Buddhist Text.

Flower Adornment Sutra, Chapter 40: Universal Worthy's Conduct & Vows. Commentary by Tripitaka Master Hua. Tr. by Buddhist Text Translation Society. (Illus.). 316p. (Orig.). 1982. pap. 10.00 (ISBN 0-917512-84-7). Buddhist Text.

Flower Adornment Sutra, Chapter 5: Flower Adorned Sea of Worlds, Part 1. Commentary by Tripitaka Master Hua. Tr. by Buddhist Text Translation Society Staff. (Illus.). 250p. (Orig.). 1983. pap. 8.50 (ISBN 0-917512-54-5). Buddhist Text.

Flower Adornment Sutra, Chapter 9: Light Enlightenment. Commentary by Tripitaka Master Hua. Tr. by Buddhist Text Translation Society Staff. (Illus.). 225p. (Orig.). 1983. pap. text ed. 8.50 (ISBN 0-88139-005-4). Buddhist Text.

Flower Adornment Sutra: Names of Thus Come Ones & the Four Holy Truths, Chapters 7 & 8. Tripitaka Master Hua. Tr. by Buddhist Text Translation Society. 175p. (Orig.). 1983. pap. 8.50 (ISBN 0-88139-014-3). Buddhist Text.

Flower Adornment Sutra Preface. Bilingual ed. National Master Ch'ing Liang. Commentary by Tripitaka Master Hua. Tr. by Buddhist Text Translation Society. (Illus.). 244p. (Orig.). 1980. pap. 7.00 (ISBN 0-917512-28-6). Buddhist Text.

Flower Adornment Sutra Prologue: Vol. I, The First Door. National Master Ch'ing Liang. Commentary by Tripitaka Master Hua. Tr. by Buddhist Text Translation Society. (Illus.). 252p. (Orig.). 1981. pap. 10.00 (ISBN 0-917512-66-9). Buddhist Text.

Flower Adornment Sutra Prologue: Vol. II, The Second Door, Part I. National Master Ch'ing Liang. Commentary by Tripitaka Master Hua. Tr. by Buddhist Text Translation Society. (Illus.). 280p. (Orig.). 1981. pap. 10.00 (ISBN 0-917512-73-1). Buddhist Text.

Flower Adornment Sutra Prologue: Vol. III: The Second Door, Part II. National Master Ch'ing Liang. Commentary by Tripitaka Master Hua. Tr. by Buddhist Text Translation Society Staff. (Illus.). 220p. (Orig.). 1983. pap. 10.00 (ISBN 0-917512-98-7). Buddhist Text.

Flower Adornment Sutra Prologue, Vol. IV: The Second Door, Part III. National Master Ch'ing Liang. Tr. by Buddhist Text Translation Society. 170p. (Orig.). 1983. pap. 8.00 (ISBN 0-88139-009-7). Buddhist Text.

Flower Essences & Vibrational Healing. 2nd ed. Gurudas. 314p. 1985. pap. 12.95 (ISBN 0-914732-09-9). Bro Life Inc.

Flower-Flames. Sri Chinmoy. 208p. 1985. pap. 10.00 (ISBN 0-88497-829-X). Aum Pubns.

Flower of Chinese Buddhism. Daisaku Ikeda. (Illus.). 216p. 1986. 19.95 (ISBN 0-8348-0208-2). Weatherhill.

Flower Ornament Scripture: A Translation of the Avatamsaka Sutra, Vol. 1. Tr. by Thomas Cleary. LC 83-2370. 703p. 1984. 40.00 (ISBN 0-87773-767-3, 53690-8). Shambhala Pubns.

Flowering Tree. Gladys V. Jones. 316p. 1984. pap. 8.95 (ISBN 0-87516-527-3). De Vorss.

Flowers & Fruits of the Bible. John Chancellor. LC 81-69042. (Illus.). 64p. 1982. 14.95 (ISBN 0-8253-0085-1). Beaufort Bks NY.

Flowers & Their Messages. rev. ed. 308p. Date not set. pap. 32.50 (ISBN 0-89744-990-8, Pub. by Sri Aurobindo Ashram Trust India). Auromere.

Flowers & Their Messages. The Mother. (Illus.). 308p. 1985. pap. 14.95 (ISBN 0-89071-282-4). Matagiri.

Flowers in Church. Jean Taylor. 161p. 1985. pap. 10.95 (ISBN 0-8192-1361-6). Morehouse.

Flowres of Sion: To Which Is Adjoyned His Cypresse Grove. William Drummond. LC 73-6124. (English Experience Ser.: No. 590). 80p. 1973. Repr. of 1623 ed. 8.00 (ISBN 90-221-0590-3). Walter J Johnson.

Fluctuations Du Produit De la Dime: Conjoncture Decimale et Domaniale De la Fin Dumoyen Age Au XV11le Siecle. Joseph Goy. (Cahiers Des Etudes Rurales: No. 3). 1972. pap. 34.40x (ISBN 90-2797-000-9). Mouton.

Flurry of Angels: Angels in Literature. Dorsey Alexander & Joyce Alexander. (Illus.). 1986. pap. 5.00. Turtles Quill.

Flying High Against the Sky: If God Has It I Want It! C. C. Cribb. LC 79-84881. Date not set. pap. 2.95 (ISBN 0-932046-16-9). Manhattan Ltd NC.

Fo-Kuang Ssu: Literary Evidences & Buddhist Images. Marylin M. Rhie. LC 76-23690. (Outstanding Dissertations in the Fine Arts - Far Eastern). (Illus.). 1977. Repr. of 1970 ed. lib. bdg. 55.00 (ISBN 0-8240-2721-3). Garland Pub.

Fo-sho-hing-tsan-king. Samuel Beal. (Sacred Books of the East: Vol. 19). 15.00 (ISBN 0-89581-523-0). Asian Human Pr.

Focolare: After Thirty Years: Insights into the Life of the Focolare Movement. Sergius C. Lorit & Nuzzo Grimaldi. LC 76-18456. (Illus.). 268p. 1976. pap. 4.50 (ISBN 0-911782-27-3). New City.

Focus for Evangelism: The Evangelical Implications of Ministry. Dennis Orsen. 48p. (Orig.). 1985. pap. 3.95 (ISBN 0-8066-2199-0, 23-1601). Augsburg.

Focus on Believing. Mary Jo Tully & Sandra J. Hirstein. (Light of Faith Ser.). (Orig.). 1981. pap. text ed. 3.85 (ISBN 0-697-01767-2); tchrs.' ed. 12.95 (ISBN 0-697-01768-0); tests 12.95 (ISBN 0-697-01829-6). Wm C Brown.

Focus on Belonging. Mary Jo Tully & Sandra J. Hirstein. (Light of Faith Ser.). (Orig.). 1981. pap. text ed. 3.55 (ISBN 0-697-01765-6); tchrs.' ed. 12.95 (ISBN 0-697-01766-4); tests 12.95 (ISBN 0-697-01828-8). Wm C Brown.

Focus on Buddhism. Ed. by Robert A. McDermott. LC 81-8084. (Focus on Hinduism & Buddhism Ser.). 160p. 1981. text ed. 14.50 (ISBN 0-89012-020-X); pap. 7.95 (ISBN 0-89012-021-8). Anima Pubns.

Focus on Celebrating. Mary Jo Tully & Sandra J. Hirstein. (Light of Faith Ser.). (Orig.). 1981. pap. text ed. 3.85 (ISBN 0-697-01771-0); tchr's ed 12.95 (ISBN 0-686-69655-7); tests 12.95 (ISBN 0-697-01831-8). Wm C Brown.

Focus on Faith in Jesus: Parish Edition. rev. ed. Ronald Wilkins. 112p. 1985. pap. text ed. 5.25 (ISBN 0-697-02007-X); tchr's. ed. 12.95 (ISBN 0-697-02009-6). Wm C Brown.

Focus on Faith in Jesus: School Edition. rev. ed. Ronald Wilkins. 192p. 1985. pap. text ed. 6.50 (ISBN 0-697-02006-1); tchr's. ed. 14.95 (ISBN 0-697-02008-8). Wm C Brown.

Focus on Growth in the Church. rev. ed. Joel R. Gordon. (To Live in Christ Ser.). 1980. pap. write for info. (ISBN 0-697-01724-9); instrs.' manual avail. (ISBN 0-697-01722-2). Wm C Brown.

Focus on Growth in the Church: Parish Edition. rev. ed. Ronald Wilkins. 128p. 1985. pap. text ed. 5.25 (ISBN 0-697-02011-8); tchr's. ed. 12.95 (ISBN 0-697-02013-4). Wm C Brown.

Focus on Growth in the Church: School Edition. rev. ed. Ronald Wilkins. 224p. 1985. pap. text ed. 6.50 (ISBN 0-697-02010-X); tchr's. ed. 14.95 (ISBN 0-697-02012-6). Wm C Brown.

Focus on Hinduism: Audio Visual Resources for Teaching Religion. 2nd, enl. ed. Ed. by Robert A. McDermott. Kenneth W. Morgan & Daniel Smith. LC 81-8085. (Focus on Hinduism & Buddhism Ser.). 160p. 1981. text ed. 14.50 (ISBN 0-89012-018-8); pap. text ed. 7.95 (ISBN 0-89012-019-6). Anima Pubns.

Focus on Living. Mary Jo Tully & Mary Fearon. (Light of Faith Ser.). (Orig.). 1981. pap. text ed. 3.85 (ISBN 0-697-01769-9); tchrs.' ed. 12.95 (ISBN 0-697-01770-2); tests 12.95 (ISBN 0-697-01830-X). Wm C Brown.

Focus on Loving. Mary Jo Tully & Mary Fearon. (Light of Faith Ser.). (Orig.). 1981. pap. text ed. 3.55 (ISBN 0-697-01763-X); tchrs.' ed. 12.95 (ISBN 0-697-01764-8); tests 12.95 (ISBN 0-697-01827-X). Wm C Brown.

Focus on Relating. Mary Jo Tully & Mary Fearon. (Light of Faith Ser.). (Orig.). 1981. pap. text ed. 3.90 (ISBN 0-697-01773-7); avail. tchrs.' ed. 12.95 (ISBN 0-697-01774-5); tests 12.95 (ISBN 0-697-01832-6). Wm C Brown.

Focus on the Christian Family. Laud O. Vaught. 1976. pap. 3.95 (ISBN 0-87148-332-7). Pathway Pr.

Focus on the Jewish Family: A Selected Annotated Bibliography, 1970-1982. David Singer. 32p. 1984. pap. 2.00 (ISBN 0-87495-058-9). Am Jewish Comm.

Focus on Watergate: An Examination of the Moral Dilemma of Watergate in the Light of Civil Religion. H. Dale Crockett. LC 81-16952. 126p. 1982. 10.95 (ISBN 0-86554-017-9, MUP-H17). Mercer Univ Pr.

Focused Life. Edward L. Hayes. 96p. 1986. 4.95 (ISBN 0-8010-4297-6). Baker Bk.

Foes from the Northern Frontiers. Edwin Yamauchi. (Baker Studies in Biblical Archaeology). 128p. (Orig.). 1982. pap. 6.95 (ISBN 0-8010-9918-8). Baker Bk.

Fold 'n Cut Surprise Sermonetes, No. 2. Arnold C. Westphal. 1968. 4.95 (ISBN 0-915398-01-X). Visual Evangels.

Fold 'n Snip Bible Bits, No. 7. Arnold C. Westphal. 1974. 4.95 (ISBN 0-915398-06-0). Visual Evangels.

Fold 'n Snip Story Sermonettes, No. 6. Arnold C. Westphal. 1973. pap. 4.95 (ISBN 0-915398-05-2). Visual Evangels.

Folded Lies: Bribery, Crusades, & Reforms. W. Michael Reisman. LC 78-3207. 1979. 12.95 (ISBN 0-02-926280-1). Free Pr.

Folio. R. A. Cram. 1932. 22.00 (ISBN 0-527-01687-X). Kraus Repr.

Folk Beliefs of the Southern Negro. Newbell N. Puckett. LC 68-55780. (Criminology, Law Enforcement, & Social Problems Ser.: No. 22). (Illus.). 1968. Repr. of 1926 ed. 18.00x (ISBN 0-87585-022-7). Patterson Smith.

Folk Buddhist Religion: Dissenting Sects in Late Traditional China. Daniel L. Overmyer. (Harvard East Asian Ser.: No.83). 256p. 1976. 15.00x (ISBN 0-674-30705-4). Harvard U Pr.

Folk Culture of Tibet. Norbu Chophel. 105p. 1986. Repr. 7.50X (ISBN 0-8364-1676-7, Pub. by Manohar India). South Asia Bks.

Folk-Element in Hindu Culture: A Contribution to Socio-Religious Studies in Hindu Folk Institutions. Benoy K. Sarkar. LC 72-907790. 332p. 1972. Repr. of 1917 ed. 24.00 (ISBN 0-89684-387-4). Orient Bk Dist.

Folk Elements in Burmese Buddhism. U. Htin Aung. LC 77-29231. 1978. Repr. of 1962 ed. lib. bdg. 22.50x (ISBN 0-313-20275-3, HTFE). Greenwood.

Folk Literature of the Chorote Indians. Ed. by Johannes Wilbert & Karin Simoneau. LC 85-9961. (Latin American Studies Ser.: Vol. 60). 288p. 1985. lib. bdg. 27.50x (ISBN 0-87903-060-7). UCLA Lat Am Ctr.

Folk Literature of the Kurdistani Jews: An Anthology. Ed. by Yona Sabar. LC 81-43605. (Judaica Ser.: No. 23). 320p. 1982. 35.00x (ISBN 0-300-02698-6). Yale U Pr.

Folk-Literature of the Sephardic Jews, Vol. 1. The Judeo-Spanish Ballad Chapbooks of Yacob Abraham Yona. Samuel G. Armistead & Joseph H. Silverman. LC 71-78565. 1971. 60.00x (ISBN 0-520-01648-3). U of Cal Pr.

Folk-Lore & Folk-Stories of Wales. Marie Trevelyan. (Folklore Ser). 35.00 (ISBN 0-8482-2749-2). Norwood Edns.

Folk-Lore of the Holy Land: Moslem, Christian & Jewish. James E. Hanauer. LC 77-22030. 1977. Repr. of 1935 ed. lib. bdg. 25.00 (ISBN 0-8414-4955-4). Folcroft.

Folk Medicine of the Delaware & Related Algonkian Indians. Gladys Tantaquidgeon. LC 73-620801. (Pennsylvania Historical & Museum Commission Anthropological Ser.: No. 3). (Illus.). 145p. 1972. 7.50 (ISBN 0-911124-70-5); pap. 4.50 (ISBN 0-911124-69-1). Pa Hist & Mus.

Folk of Christendom. Arthur Garrett. LC 79-92433. 500p. 1981. 49.95 (ISBN 0-8022-2363-X). Philos Lib.

Folk Religion & Spiritual Belief in Modernizing Japan. 23p. 1979. pap. 5.00 (ISBN 92-808-0108-2, TUNU078, UNU). Bernan-Unipub.

Folk Religion in Japan: Continuity & Change. Ichiro Hori. Ed. by Joseph M. Kitagawa & Alan L. Miller. LC 67-30128. (Midway Reprint Ser.). xvi, 278p. 1983. pap. text ed. 15.00x (ISBN 0-226-35335-4). U of Chicago Pr.

Folklore & Myth in the Mabinogion. W. J. Gruffydd. LC 75-34083. 1958. lib. bdg. 15.00 (ISBN 0-8414-4522-2). Folcroft.

Folklore of the Holy Land. James E. Hanauer. 280p. 1980. Repr. of 1935 ed. lib. bdg. 35.00 (ISBN 0-8492-5272-5). R West.

Folklore of the Jews. Angelo S. Rappoport. LC 71-167125. Repr. of 1937 ed. 40.00x (ISBN 0-8103-3864-5). Gale.

Folklore of Wells. Rustom P. Masani. LC 77-11936. 1977. Repr. lib. bdg. 32.00 (ISBN 0-8414-6216-X). Folcroft.

Folktale in the Old Testament. Hermann Gunkel. (Historic Texts & Interpreters Ser.: No. 5). 224p. 1985. text ed. 24.95x (ISBN 1-85075-031-9, Pub. by Almond Pr England); pap. text ed. 10.95x (ISBN 1-85075-030-0). Eisenbrauns.

Folktales of Israel. Ed. by Dov Noy. Tr. by Gene Baharav. LC 63-16721. (Folktales of the World Ser). 1963. 14.00x (ISBN 0-226-59719-9); pap. 7.95x (ISBN 0-226-59720-2, FW8). U of Chicago Pr.

Follow ME. William K. Cumming. 6.95 (ISBN 0-917920-01-5); pap. 1.95 (ISBN 0-917920-00-7). Mustardseed.

Follow Me! Charles Hunter. 1975. pap. 4.95 (ISBN 0-917726-35-9). Hunter Bks.

Follow Me: A Pocket Guide to Daily Scriptural Prayer. David E. Rosage. 240p. 1982. pap. 3.95 (ISBN 0-89283-168-5). Servant.

Follow Me: A Study of the Life of Christ. Maria A. Hirschmann & Betty Pershing. LC 79-84331. (Bible Study & Sharing Ser.: No. 2). 224p. (Orig.). 1979. pap. 4.95 (ISBN 0-932878-01-6, HB/01). Hansi.

Follow the Gleam. Wayne Arnason. 1980. pap. 3.50 (ISBN 0-933840-07-1). Unitarian Univ.

Follow the Leader. Dan Schmidt. 144p. 1986. pap. 3.95 (ISBN 0-89693-629-5). Victor Bks.

Follow the Moon: A Journey Through the Jewish Year. Yaffa Ganz. 1984. 8.95 (ISBN 0-87306-369-4). Feldheim.

Follow the Year: A Family Celebration of Christian Holidays. Mala Powers. LC 85-42791. (Illus.). 128p. 1985. 14.45 (ISBN 0-06-066693-5, HarpR). Har-Row.

Followers in the Way. Henry F. Mackay. LC 71-93359. (Essay Index Reprint Ser). 1934. 17.00 (ISBN 0-8369-1304-3). Ayer Co Pubs.

Followers of God. Doris C. Demaree. (Bible Stories for Children Ser.). 1974. pap. 1.50 (ISBN 0-87162-236-X, D1446). Warner Pr.

Followers of the Cross. Harry N. Huxhold. LC 85-22823. 80p. (Orig.). 1985. pap. 4.95 (ISBN 0-8066-2184-2, 10-2346). Augsburg.

Followers of the New Faith: Culture Change & the Rise of Protestantism in Brazil & Chile. Emilio Willems. LC 67-27517. 1967. 16.50x (ISBN 0-8265-1106-6). Vanderbilt U Pr.

Following. Gary Sivewright. 32p. 1986. pap. 1.50 (ISBN 0-8341-1127-6). Beacon Hill.

Following Christ. Joseph DiCarlo, Jr. (Faith & Life Ser.). (Illus.). 142p. (Orig.). 1985. pap. 6.20 (ISBN 0-89870-065-5). Ignatius Pr.

Following Christ: A Handbook of Catholic Moral Teaching. Daniel Lowery. LC 82-84373. 160p. 1983. pap. 3.50 (ISBN 0-89243-173-3). Liguori Pubns.

Following Christ: Activity Book. Mary E. Podhaizer. Ed. by Patricia I. Puccetti. (Faith & Life Ser.). 41p. (Orig.). 1985. pap. 2.50 (ISBN 0-89870-066-3). Ignatius Pr.

Following Christ in a Consumer Society: The Spirituality of Cultural Resistance. John F. Kavanaugh. LC 81-38359. 192p. (Orig.). 1981. pap. 6.95 (ISBN 0-88344-090-3). Orbis Bks.

Following Christ: Prayers from Imitation of Christ. Ronald Klug. LC 80-25260. (Illus.). 63p. 1981. pap. 3.95 (ISBN 0-570-03826-X, 12-2791). Concordia.

Following God's Trailblazers: Kings & Prophets 14 Lessons, Vol. 4. (Footsteps of Faith Ser.). 1958. pap. text ed. 2.50 (ISBN 0-86508-033-X); figures text 11.45 (ISBN 0-86508-034-8). BCM Intl Inc.

Following Jesus. Linda Corbin. Ed. by Pat Dys. (Studies for Kids Ser.: Pt. 1). (Illus.). 48p. 1985. 2.95 (ISBN 0-87239-903-6, 3303). Standard Pub.

Following Jesus. Linda Corbin & Pat Dys. (Studies for Kids Ser.: Pt. 2). (Illus.). 48p. 1985. 2.95 (ISBN 0-87239-904-4, 3304). Standard Pub.

Following Jesus. Segundo Galilea. Tr. by Helen Phillips from Span. LC 80-24802. Orig. Title: Seguimiento de Cristo. 128p. (Orig.). 1981. pap. 6.95 (ISBN 0-88344-136-5). Orbis Bks.

Following Jesus. St. Clair. 1983. 4.95 (ISBN 0-88207-301-X). Victor Bks.

Following Jesus: A Guide to the Gospels. Robert Karris. (Biblical Ser.). 1973. pap. 1.25 (ISBN 0-8199-0514-3). Franciscan Herald.

Following Jesus: A Woman's Workshop on Luke. Evelyn Bence. (Woman's Workshop Ser.). 112p. 1986. pap. 3.95 (ISBN 0-310-44781-X, 11314P). Zondervan.

Following Jesus: Discipleship in the Gospel of Mark. E. A. Best. (Journal for the Study of the New Testament, Supplement Ser.: No. 4). 283p. 1981. text ed. 25.95 (ISBN 0-905774-28-0, Pub. by JSOT Pr England); pap. text ed. 12.50x (ISBN 0-905774-29-9, Pub. by JSOT Pr England). Eisenbrauns.

Following Jesus: The Book of Acts, Pt. 1. Linda Corbin & Pat Dys. (Illus.). 48p. 1986. wkbk. 2.95 (ISBN 0-87403-053-6, 3197). Standard Pub.

Following Jesus: The Book of Acts, Pt. 2. Linda Corbin & Pat Dys. (Illus.). 48p. 1986. wkbk. 2.95 (ISBN 0-87403-054-4, 3308). Standard Pub.

Following Plough: Meditations on Prayer. J. Neville Ward. LC 84-71179. 128p. 1984. pap. 6.00 (ISBN 0-936384-18-2). Cowley Pubns.

Following the Way: The Setting of John's Gospel. Bruce E. Schein. LC 79-54121. 224p. 1980. 14.95 (ISBN 0-8066-1758-6, 10-2348). Augsburg.

Foochow Missionaries, 1847-1880. Ellsworth C. Carlson. LC 72-97832. (East Asian Monographs Ser: No. 51). 1973. pap. 20.00x (ISBN 0-674-30735-6). Harvard U Pr.

Food Consciousness for Spiritual Development. Jacques De Langre. LC 80-84993. (Illus., Orig.). 1986. pap. 6.00 (ISBN 0-916508-05-6). Happiness Pr.

Food-Energy & the Major Faiths. Ed. by Joseph Gremillion. LC 77-17975. 302p. (Orig.). 1978. pap. 2.49 (ISBN 0-88344-138-1). Orbis Bks.

Food for Lambs. C. E. Orr. 168p. pap. 1.50 (ISBN 0-686-29109-3). Faith Pub Hse.

Food for Life. Peter Lee et al. LC 77-27693. 1978. pap. 3.95 (ISBN 0-87784-489-5). Inter-Varsity.

Food for Temple & Table. Gayle Griffin. 1981. spiral bdg. 9.95 (ISBN 0-89323-018-9). Bible Memory.

Food for the Spirit: Vegetarianism & the World Religions. Steven Rosen. Ed. by Joshua M. Greene. (Illus.). 144p. (Orig.). 1987. 9.95 (ISBN 0-89647-022-9); pap. 6.95 (ISBN 0-89647-021-0). Bala Bks.

Food for Thought. Hazelden Foundation Staff. 400p. (Orig.). 1985. pap. 5.95 (ISBN 0-86683-503-2, HarpR). Har-Row.

Food for Thought: Daily Meditations for Overeaters. (Hazelden Meditation Ser.). 1986. 6.50 (ISBN 0-317-46275-X). Har-Row.

Food for Thought: Daily Meditations for Overeaters. (Hazelden Bks.). scp 6.50t (ISBN 0-317-46482-5). Har-Row.

Food for Thought from God's Kettle. V. Gladys Shutt. 1982. 8.95 (ISBN 0-533-05178-9). Vantage.

Food for Tomorrow. C. Dean Freudenberger. LC 83-72119. 176p. 1984. pap. 9.95 (ISBN 0-8066-2063-3, 10-2333). Augsburg.

Food from Afar. Ed. by Dana Gustafson. spiral 3.95 (ISBN 0-686-12747-1). Grace Pub Co.

Food of Angels. Carl K. Barniak. 96p. (Orig.). 1984. pap. 4.95 (ISBN 0-9613803-0-6). Barniak Pubns.

Food, Sex & Pollution: A New Guinea Religion. Anna S. Meigs. 195p. 1984. text ed. 22.50 (ISBN 0-8135-0968-8). Rutgers U Pr.

Fool of God. Louis Cochran. (Heritage of a Movement Book Club Ser.). 416p. Repr. of 1958 ed. 11.95 (ISBN 0-89900-275-7). College Pr Pub.

Fool of God: The Mystical Verse of Baba Tahir. Tr. by E. Heron-Allen. 1979. 12.95 (ISBN 0-900860-70-7, Pub. by Octagon England). Ins Study Human.

Foolishness of God. Kenneth Adams. 1981. pap. 5.95 (ISBN 0-87508-036-7). Chr Lit.

Foolishness of God. Siegbert W. Becker. 1982. 8.95 (ISBN 0-8100-0155-1, 15N0383). Northwest Pub.

Foolishness to the Greeks. Lesslie Newbigin. 176p. (Orig.). 1986. pap. 7.95 (ISBN 0-8028-0176-5). Eerdmans.

Fool's Crow. Thomas E. Mails. 1980. pap. 3.50 (ISBN 0-380-52175-X, 52175-X, Discus). Avon.

Fool's Paradise. Hansadutta. LC 85-5839. (Illus.). 190p. (Orig.). 1985. pap. 5.95 (ISBN 0-933593-05-8). Hansa Pub.

Foot of the Cross: The Sorrows of Mary. Frederick W. Faber. LC 78-66303. 1978. pap. 10.00 (ISBN 0-89555-078-4). TAN Bks Pubs.

Footholds: Understanding the Shifting Family & Sexual Tensions in Our Culture. Philip Slater. LC 77-12124. 1978. 13.95x (ISBN 0-8070-4160-2). Beacon Pr.

Footprints: An Affirmation of Faith. (Illus.). 24p. (Orig.). 1984. pap. 1.95 (ISBN 0-89954-285-9). Antioch Pub Co.

Footprints: Following Jesus for Junior Highers. Ed. by Bruce Oldham. 170p. (Orig.). 1983. pap. 4.50 (ISBN 0-8341-0863-1). Beacon Hill.

Footprints in the Snow: A Pictorial Biography of the Founder of Opus Dei, Josemaria Escriva. Dennis M. Helming. (Illus.). 80p. (Orig.). 1986. pap. write for info. (ISBN 0-933932-50-2). Scepter Pubs.

Footprints of Gautama the Buddha. Marie B. Byles. LC 68-5855. (Illus.). 1967. pap. 5.95 (ISBN 0-8356-0399-7, Quest). Theos Pub Hse.

Footprints of Jesus' Twelve in Early Christian Traditions: A Study in the Meaning of Religious Symbolism. Heinz O. Guenther. LC 84-48032. (American University Studies VII (Theology & Religion): Vol. 7). 156p. 1984. text ed. 20.90 (ISBN 0-8204-0164-1). P Lang Pubs.

Footprints of the Buddha. Mary Baskett. LC 80-80133. (Illus.). 125p. (Orig.). 1980. pap. 8.95 (ISBN 0-87633-034-0). Phila Mus Art.

Footprints of the Jesuits. R. W. Thompson. 1981. lib. bdg. 75.00 (ISBN 0-686-71628-0). Revisionist Pr.

Footprints on the Sands of China. Grace C. Story. pap. 2.25 (ISBN 0-686-13722-1). Crusade Pubs.

Footprints: Walking Through the Passages of Life. Howard Hendricks & Jeanne Hendricks. LC 80-25868. (Illus.). 96p. 1981. pap. 5.95 (ISBN 0-930014-55-3). Multnomah.

Footsteps along the Path. rev. ed. Paul L. Peck. (Spiritual Metaphysics: Freeways to Divine Awareness Ser.). 164p. (Orig.). 1982. pap. 7.95 (ISBN 0-941600-01-7). Harmony Pr.

Footsteps in the Sea: A Biography of Archbishop Athenagoras Cavadas. George Poulos. (Illus.). 186p. 1979. 7.95 (ISBN 0-916586-36-7); pap. 10.95 (ISBN 0-916586-35-9). Holy Cross Orthodox.

Footsteps of St. Peter. John R. MacDuff. 648p. 1982. lib. bdg. 24.25 Smythe Sewn (ISBN 0-86524-149-X, 8406). Klock & Klock.

Footsteps of the Messiah: A Study of the Sequence of Prophetic Events. Arnold G. Fruchtenbaum. (Illus.). 468p. 1982. 20.00 (ISBN 0-914863-02-9). Ariel Pr CA.

Footsteps of the Mystical Child. Master Ni. 180p. 1986. pap. text ed. 9.50 (ISBN 0-937064-11-4). SEBT.

Footsteps to God: Six Basic Bible Truth Lessons. Bernice Jordan. (Illus.). 1970. pap. text ed. 6.50 (ISBN 0-86508-025-9). BCM Intl Inc.

For a Special Friend. Tina Iannaci. (Greeting Book Line Ser.). 24p. (Orig.). 1986. pap. 1.50 (ISBN 0-89622-303-5). Twenty-Third.

For a World Like Ours: Studies in I Corinthians. James L. Boyer. pap. 4.95 (ISBN 0-88469-057-1). BMH Bks.

For All Mankind: A New Approach to the Old Testament. Stuart Blanch. pap. 4.95 (ISBN 0-19-520025-X). Oxford U Pr.

For All Seasons. Charles H. Numrich. 43p. 1981. pap. text ed. 6.25 (ISBN 0-89536-490-5, 0600). CSS of Ohio.

For All the Saints: Changing Perceptions of Martyrdom & Sainthood in the Lutheran Reformation. Robert Kolb. (Illus.). 192p. 1987. 29.95 (ISBN 0-86554-270-8, H233). Mercer Univ Pr.

For an Ontology of Morals: A Critique of Contemporary Ethical Theory. Henry B. Veatch. 1971. 14.95 (ISBN 0-8101-0352-4). Northwestern U Pr.

For Better & for Ever: Sponsor Couple Program for Christian Marriage Preparation. Robert Ruhnke. 1981. pap. 3.95 (ISBN 0-89243-143-1); dialogue packet wkbk. 3.75 (ISBN 0-89243-144-X). Liguori Pubns.

For Better, for Worse. James T. Burtchaell. 160p. (Orig.). 1985. pap. 5.95 (ISBN 0-8091-2664-8). Paulist Pr.

For Better or for Best. Gary Smalley & Steve Scott. 160p. 1982. pap. 5.95 (ISBN 0-310-44871-9, 18246P). Zondervan.

For Christ's Sake. Tom Harpur. LC 86-47866. 118p. 1987. 17.95 (ISBN 0-8070-1012-X); pap. 8.95 (ISBN 0-8070-1013-8, BP 756). Beacon Pr.

For Conscience' Sake. Solomon Stucky. LC 83-98283. 240p. (Orig.). pap. 9.95 (ISBN 0-8361-3333-1). Herald Pr.

For Creation's Sake: Preaching, Ecology, & Justice. Ed. by Dieter T. Hessel. LC 85-816. 144p. 1985. pap. 8.95 (ISBN 0-664-24637-0, A Geneva Press Publication). Westminster.

For Every Cause? A Biblical Study of Divorce. John Williams. 96p. 1982. pap. 3.25 (ISBN 0-87213-953-0). Loizeaux.

For Every Idle Silence: A Congressman Speaks Out. Henry J. Hyde. 140p. (Orig.). 1985. pap. 6.95 (ISBN 0-89283-282-7). Servant.

For Example... Richard Andersen & Donald Deffner. 1978. pap. 7.95 (ISBN 0-570-03766-2, 12-2701). Concordia.

For Families Only. J. Allan Petersen. 1981. pap. 2.95 (ISBN 0-8423-0879-2). Tyndale.

For God Alone: The Life of George West, Bishop of Rangoon. J. Tyndale-Biscoe. 1985. 30.00x (ISBN 0-317-43630-9, Pub. by Amate Pr. Ltd). State Mutual Bk.

For God & Clarity: New Essays in Honor of Austin Farrer. Ed. by Jeffrey C. Eaton. Ann Loades. (Pittsburgh Theological Monographs New Series: No. 4). 206p. 1983. pap. 12.00 (ISBN 0-915138-52-2). Pickwick.

For God & the King. Henry Burton. LC 76-57365. (English Experience Ser.: No. 783). 1977. lib. bdg. 17.50 (ISBN 90-221-0783-3). Walter J Johnson.

For God & the People. Walter Rauschenbusch. LC 77-8615. 1977. lib. bdg. 22.00 (ISBN 0-8414-7332-3). Folcroft.

For Grandparents: Wonders & Worries. Myron C. Madden & Mary B. Madden. LC 80-12778. (Christian Care Bks.: Vol, 9). 118p. 1980. pap. 7.95 (ISBN 0-664-24325-8). Westminster.

For He Delights in Me. Glenna Oldham. 1982. gift, padded cover 9.95 (ISBN 0-87162-260-2, D1017). Warner Pr.

For Heaven's Sake. Peter Kreeft. 192p. 1986. 12.95 (ISBN 0-8407-5494-9). Nelson.

For Inner Peace & Strength. Don Costello. 1978. 4.00 (ISBN 0-8198-0380-4); pap. 3.00 (ISBN 0-8198-0381-2). Dghtrs St Paul.

For Madmen Only: Price of Admission: Your Mind. Bhagwan Shree Rajneesh. Ed. by Ma Prem Maneesha. LC 83-186152. (Initiation Talks Ser.). (Illus.). 616p. (Orig.). 1979. 19.50 (ISBN 0-88050-063-8). Chidvilas Found.

For Max Weinreich on His Seventieth Birthday: Studies in Jewish Language, Literature & Society. Ed. by L. S. Dawidowicz et al. 1964. 66.00x (ISBN 0-686-22430-2). Mouton.

For Members Only: A Guide to Responsible Church Membership. Tom Carter. 1986. pap. write for info. (ISBN 0-88270-614-4). Bridge Pub.

For Men & Elders: Change in the Relations of Generations & of Men & Women Among the Nyakyusa-Ngonde People, 1875-1971. Monica Wilson. LC 77-4203. 208p. 1978. 35.00x (ISBN 0-8419-0313-1, Africana). Holmes & Meier.

For Men Only. J. Allan Petersen. 1982. pap. 3.95 (ISBN 0-8423-0892-X). Tyndale.

For My Kinsmen's Sake. Check-Hung Yee. 1986. 15.00 (ISBN 0-89216-066-7). Salvation Army.

For My People: Black Theology & the Black Church. James H. Cone. LC 84-5195. (Bishop Henry McNeal Turner Studies in North America Black Religion: Vol. 1). 288p. (Orig.). 1984. pap. 9.95 (ISBN 0-88344-106-3). Orbis Bks.

For My Sins, He Died. Jon L. Joyce. (Orig.). 1981. pap. 3.25 (ISBN 0-937172-20-0). JLJ Pubs.

For People Just Like Us. Robert Mueller. Ed. by Michael L. Sherer. (Orig.). 1986. pap. 3.75 (ISBN 0-89536-834-X, 6848). CSS of Ohio.

For Preachers Only. J. T. Pugh. LC 86-10976. 192p. (Orig.). 1971. pap. 5.95 (ISBN 0-912315-35-0). Word Aflame.

For Real People Only. Sandy Larsen. 96p. 1986. pap. 1.95 student bk. (ISBN 0-89693-516-7); tchr's. ed. 11.95 (ISBN 0-89693-513-2). Victor Bks.

For Righteousness' Sake: Contemporary Moral Philosophies. A. Roy Eckardt. 1987. 29.95 (ISBN 0-253-32241-3). Ind U Pr.

For Seekers of God: Spiritual Talks of Mahapurush Swami Shivananda. Swami Shivananda. Tr. by Swami Vividishananda & Swami Gambhirananda. 186p. 1972. 10.00 (ISBN 0-87481-169-4); pap. 7.50 (ISBN 0-87481-130-9). Vedanta Pr.

For Self-Examination & Judge for Yourself. Soren Kierkegaard. (American-Scandinavian Foundation Ser.). 1944. pap. 8.50x (ISBN 0-691-01952-5). Princeton U Pr.

For Singles Only. Janet Fix & Zola Levitt. 128p. 1978. pap. 5.95 (ISBN 0-8007-5034-9, Power Bks). Revell.

For Such a Time. Mrs. Vernon Tapp. (Illus.). 160p. 1979. pap. 3.00 (ISBN 0-89114-083-2); pap. 0.75 tchr's. guide, 15 pg. (ISBN 0-89114-084-0). Baptist Pub Hse.

For Teens Only: Straight Talk about Parents - Life - Love. Jim Auer. 64p. 1985. pap. 1.95 (ISBN 0-89243-228-4). Liguori Pubns.

For the Children's Sake: Foundations of Education for Home & School. Susan S. Macaulay. LC 83-72043. 192p. 1984. pap. 6.95 (ISBN 0-89107-290-X, Crossway Bks). Good News.

For the Good of Mankind: August Forel & Baha'i Faith. John P. Vader. (Illus.). 144p. 10.95 (ISBN 0-85398-171-X); pap. 5.95 (ISBN 0-85398-172-8). G Ronald Pub.

For the Greater Glory: A Church Needlepoint Handbook. Mary P. Olsen. (Illus.). 192p. 1980. 17.50 (ISBN 0-8164-0476-3, HarpR). Har-Row.

For the Health of Body & Soul. Stanley S. Harakas. 48p. (Orig.). 1980. pap. 1.95 (ISBN 0-916586-42-1). Hellenic Coll Pr.

For the Inward Journey: The Writings of Howard Thurman. Howard Thurman. Intro. by Vincent Harding & Anne S. Thurman. LC 83-26366. 352p. 1984. 17.95 (ISBN 0-15-132656-8). HarBraceJ.

For the Life of the Family: Family Life Action Groups or Starting & Using FLAG in Your Church. John W. Yates. 256p. 1987. pap. 9.95. Morehouse.

For the Life of the World: Sacraments & Orthodoxy. Alexander Schmemann. 151p. 1973. pap. 5.95 (ISBN 0-913836-08-7). St Vladimirs.

For the Love of Children. Ulrich Schaffer. LC 79-2984. 128p. (Orig.). 1980. pap. 3.95i (ISBN 0-06-067084-3, RD 310, HarpR). Har-Row.

For the Love of God. Janet Dailey. (Nightingale Paperbacks Ser.). 1984. pap. 9.95 (ISBN 0-8161-3697-1, Large Print Bks). G K Hall.

For the Next Nine Months: Meditations for Expectant Mothers. Melodie M. Davis. 256p. 1983. pap. 3.95 (ISBN 0-310-45542-1, 12477P). Zondervan.

For the Reputation of Truth: Politics, Religion, & Conflict Among the Pennsylvanian Quakers, 1750-1800. Richard Rauman. LC 79-143626. pap. 70.00 (ISBN 0-317-39712-5, 2025828). Bks Demand UMI.

For the Sake of Divine Truth: 1974 Visit of Four Brothers to Central Europe. Jacob Kleinsasser et al. LC 74-23787. 1974. pap. 1.20 (ISBN 0-87486-146-2). Plough.

For the Sake of Heaven. Martin Buber. Tr. by Ludwig Lewisohn. LC 77-97311. Repr. of 1953 ed. lib. bdg. 60.50x (ISBN 0-8371-2592-8, BUSH). Greenwood.

For the Sake of Heaven: A Chronicle. Martin Buber. Tr. by Ludwig Lewisohn. LC 58-8531. (Temple Bks.). 1969. pap. 9.95 (ISBN 0-689-70026-1, T2). Atheneum.

For the Sake of Simple Folk: Popular Propaganda for the German Reformation. R. W. Scribner. (Cambridge Studies in Oral & Literate Culture: No. 2). (Illus.). 350p. 1981. Cambridge U Pr.

For the Sake of the Kingdom. Anglican Consultative Council Staff. 72p. (Orig.). 1986. pap. 2.25 (ISBN 0-88028-054-9). Forward Movement.

For the Umpteenth Time. Roger Bothwell. (Outreach Ser.). 16p. 1983. pap. 0.95 (ISBN 0-8163-0538-2). Pacific Pr Pub Assn.

For the Vietnamese Buddhists. Paul Mariah. Man-Root.
For They Shall Be Comforted. Clea M. Burton & Alma P. Burton. 5.95 (ISBN 0-87747-091-X). Deseret Bk.
For Those in Love: Making Your Marriage Last a Lifetime. Lionel A. Whiston. 128p. 1983. 10.95 (ISBN 0-687-13285-1). Abingdon.
For Those Who Hurt. Charles R. Swindoll. LC 77-4594. (Illus.). 1977. pap. 3.95 (ISBN 0-930014-13-8). Multnomah.
For Thou Art with Me: A Manual of Mourning. David Stavsky. 1965. pap. 1.50 (ISBN 0-87306-093-8). Feldheim.
For unto Us a Child Is Born. Emma C. Hopkins. pap. 1.00 (ISBN 0-87516-322-X). De Vorss.
For Whom the Rabbi Speaks. Joseph R. Narot. pap. 1.65 (ISBN 0-686-15800-8). Rostrum Bks.
For Women Only. Evelyn Petersen & J. Allan Petersen. pap. 7.95, 1974 (ISBN 0-8423-0896-2); pap. 3.95 1982 (ISBN 0-8423-0897-0). Tyndale.
For Young Souls. Eleanor Curtiss. 1941. pap. 1.95 (ISBN 0-87516-303-3). De Vorss.
Forbidden Door. Jeanne Norweb. LC 82-84552. (Illus.). 216p. 1985. pap. 5.95 (ISBN 0-89191-937-6, 59378, Chariot Bks). Cook.
Forbidden Fruits: Taboos & Tabooism in Culture. Ray B. Browne. LC 84-71938. 192p. 1984. 21.95 (ISBN 0-317-14769-2); pap. 9.95 (ISBN 0-87972-256-8). Bowling Green Univ.
Forbidden Marriages & Divorce. large print ed. Ellen White. 27p. 1985. pap. 5.00 (ISBN 0-914009-38-9). VHI Library.
Forbidden Mysteries of Enoch. Elizabeth C. Prophet. LC 82-62445. (Illus.). 504p. 1983. pap. 12.95 (ISBN 0-916766-60-8). Summit Univ.
Force of the Feminine: Women, Men & the Church. Ed. by Margaret A. Franklin. 232p. 1986. text ed. 29.95x (ISBN 0-86861-930-2); pap. text ed. 12.95x (ISBN 0-86861-914-0). Allen Unwin.
Force of Tradition: A Case Study of Women Priests in Sweden. Brita Stendahl. LC 84-48713. (Illus.). 208p. 1985. pap. 14.95 (ISBN 0-8006-1808-4, 1-1808). Fortress.
Force of Truth. Thomas Scott. 1984. pap. 3.45 (ISBN 0-85151-425-1). Banner of Truth.
Forced Conversions of Croatians to the Serbian Faith in History. Ivo Omrcanin. 92p. (Orig.). 1985. pap. 6.00 (ISBN 0-9613814-1-8). Samizdat.
Forced Options. Roger L. Shinn. 272p. 1985. pap. 10.95 (ISBN 0-8298-0552-4). Pilgrim NY.
Forced Options: Social Decisions for the 21st Century. Roger L. Shinn. LC 82-47755. (Religious Perspective Ser.). 256p. 1982. 16.30 (ISBN 0-06-067282-X, HarpR). Har-Row.
Forced Termination. Brooks R. Faulkner. LC 86-6122. (Orig.). 1986. pap. 4.95 (ISBN 0-8054-5435-7). Broadman.
Forces of Prejudice in Oregon, Nineteen Twenty to Nineteen Twenty-Five. Lawrence J. Saalfeld. LC 84-14599. (Oregon Catholic History Ser.). (Orig.). 1984. pap. 8.95 (ISBN 0-9613644-0-8). Archdiocesan.
Foreign Conspiracy Against the Liberties of the United States: The Numbers of Brutus. Samuel F. Morse. LC 76-46090. (Anti-Movements in America Ser.). 1977. lib. bdg. 18.00 (ISBN 0-405-09963-0). Ayer Co Pubs.
Foreign Countries: A Gateway to the Interpretation & Development of Certain Symbols of Freemasonry. Ed. by Carl H. Claudy. 160p. 1971. Repr. of 1925 ed. text ed. 6.00 (ISBN 0-88053-039-1, M-88). Macoy Pub.
Foreign Protestant Communities in Sixteenth-Century London. Andrew Pettegree. (Historical Monographs). 280p. 1987. 49.50 (ISBN 0-19-822938-0). Oxford U Pr.
Foreign Words in the Old Testament: Their Origin & Terminology. M. Ellenbogen. 190p. 1972. 50.00x (ISBN 0-317-39068-6, Pub. by Luzac & Co Ltd). State Mutual Bk.
Foremothers: Women of the Bible. Janice Nunnally-Cox. 192p. (Orig.). 1981. pap. 6.95 (ISBN 0-8164-2329-6, HarpR). Har-Row.
Forerunner of the Charismatic Movement. Arnold Dallimore. (Orig.). 1983. pap. 7.95 (ISBN 0-8024-0286-0). Moody.
Forerunners & Rivals of Christianity, 2 vols. in 1. Francis Legge. 19.00 (ISBN 0-8446-1280-4). Peter Smith.
Forerunners of Saint Francis & Other Studies. Ellen S. Davison. Ed. by Gertrude R. Richards. LC 77-85270. Repr. of 1927 ed. 49.50 (ISBN 0-404-16120-0). AMS Pr.
Forerunners of the Reformation: The Shape of Late Medieval Thought, Illustrated by Key Documents: Heiko A. Oberman. Tr. by Paul L. Nyhus. LC 81-66518. pap. 86.80 (2027871). Bks Demand UMI.
Foresight: Ten Major Trends That Will Dramatically Affect the Future of Christians & the Church. Howard A. Snyder & Daniel V. Runyon. 176p. 1986. 12.95 (ISBN 0-8407-5531-7). Nelson.
Forest Folklore, Mythology & Romance. A. Porteous. 1977. lib. bdg. 59.95 (ISBN 0-8490-1858-7). Gordon Pr.
Forest Monks of Sri Lanka: An Anthropological & Historical Study. Michael Carrithers. (Illus.). 1983. 34.50x (ISBN 0-19-561389-9). Oxford U Pr.
Forest of Symbols: Aspects of Ndembu Ritual. Victor Turner. LC 67-12308. (Illus.). 417p. 1970. pap. 12.95x (ISBN 0-8014-9101-0, CP101). Cornell U Pr.
Foretaste of the Feast to Come: Devotions on Holy Communion. Philip H. Pfatteicher. (Illus.). 64p. (Orig.). 1987. kivar paper 3.95 (ISBN 0-8066-2283-0, 10-2357). Augsburg.
Forever, Amen. Earl C. Davis. LC 81-67199. 1982. pap. 4.50 (ISBN 0-8054-1953-5). Broadman.
Forever Beginning: Exploration of the Faith for New Believers. Donald J. Shelby. 160p. (Orig.). 1987. pap. 5.95 (ISBN 0-8358-0557-3). Upper Room.
Forever Fit: Aerobic Dance & Exercise for the Latter-day Saint Woman. Michele W. Herrscher. LC 85-13637. (Illus.). 120p. 1985. pap. 12.95 (ISBN 0-87747-768-X). Deseret Bk.
Forever My Love. Margaret Hardisty. LC 74-32644. 1979. pap. 3.25 (ISBN 0-89081-140-7, 1407). Harvest Hse.
Forgery in Christianity. J. Wheless. 75.00 (ISBN 0-87968-358-9). Gordon Pr.
Forget the Pith Helmet: Perspectives on the Missionary Experience. Ed. by Doug Wicks. (Orig.). 1984. pap. 6.95 (ISBN 0-8024-3266-2). Moody.
Forging of an American Jew: The Life & Times of Judge Julian W. Mack. Harry Barnard. 1974. 7.95 (ISBN 0-685-52984-3). Herzl Pr.
Forgive & Be Free: Healing the Wounds of Past & Present. Richard P. Walters. 144p. 1983. pap. 5.95 (ISBN 0-310-42611-1, 12339P). Zondervan.
Forgive, Forget & Be Free. rev. ed. Jeanette Lockerbie. 160p. 1984. pap. 5.95 (ISBN 0-89840-068-6). Heres Life.
Forgive Me, Lord, I Goofed! Terry Helwig. (Orig.). 1986. pap. 3.25 (ISBN 0-8054-5035-1). Broadman.
Forgiveness. Ed. by Casiano Floristan & Christian DuQuoc. (Concilium Nineteen Eighty-Six Ser.). 120p. 1986. pap. 6.95 (ISBN 0-567-30064-1, Pub. by T & T Clark Ltd UK). Fortress.
Forgiveness. Thomas Hora. (Discourses in Metapsychiatry Ser.). 48p. 1983. pap. 4.00 (ISBN 0-913105-05-8). PAGL Pr.
Forgiveness: A Guide for Prayer. Jacqueline Bergan & S. Marie Schwan. (Take & Receive Ser.). 200p. (Orig.). 1985. pap. 6.95 (ISBN 0-88489-169-0). St Mary's.
Forgiveness-A Two-Way Street. JoAnne Sekowsky. LC 53-3011. (Cornerstone Ser.). 40p. 1985. pap. 2.75 (ISBN 0-930756-95-9). Aglow Pubns.
Forgiveness & Atonement. H. D. McDonald. 1984. 5.95p (ISBN 0-8010-6165-2). Baker Bk.
Forgiveness & Jesus: The Meeting Place of a Course in Miracles & Christianity. 3rd ed. Kenneth Wapnick. 340p. 1985. pap. 16.00 (ISBN 0-933291-01-9). Foun Miracles.
Forgiveness Is a Work As Well As a Grace. Edna Hong. LC 84-6470. 128p. (Orig.). 1984. pap. 5.95 (ISBN 0-8066-2081-1, 10-2356). Augsburg.
Forgiveness Is for Giving. Jason Towner. pap. 5.95 (ISBN 0-310-70231-3, 14027P). Zondervan.
Forgiveness: No Guilt, No Grudges. Sandy Larsen & Dale Larsen. (Young Fisherman Bible Studyguides). (Illus.). 80p. 1984. pap. 2.95 student ed. (ISBN 0-87788-277-0); tchr's. ed. 4.95 (ISBN 0-87788-278-9). Shaw Pubs.
Forgiveness of Sins. Charles Williams. 128p. 1984. pap. 3.95 (ISBN 0-8028-0032-7). Eerdmans.
Forgiving. Churches Alive, Inc. Staff. LC 79-52128. (Love One Another Bible Study Ser.). (Illus.). 1979. wkbk. 3.00 (ISBN 0-934396-01-9). Churches Alive.
Forgiving. Georg Kuhlewind. Tr. by Maria St. Goar from Ger. Ed. by John Miller. (Illus.). 24p. (Orig.). 1985. pap. 3.50 (ISBN 0-932776-09-4). Adonis Pr.
Forgiving Family: First Steps to Reconciliation. Carol Luebering. 84p. (Orig.). 1983. pap. text ed. 2.50 (ISBN 0-86716-027-6). St Anthony Mess Pr.
Forgiving God in an Unforgiving World. Ron L. Davis. 1984. pap. 5.95 (ISBN 0-89081-431-7). Harvest Hse.
Forgiving: Lightening Your Load. Sandy Larsen. (Bible Discovery Guide). 32p. 1985. pap. 1.50 campers (ISBN 0-87788-279-7); pap. 3.50 counselor (ISBN 0-87788-280-0). Shaw Pubs.
Forgiving the Unforgivable. Elizabeth R. Handford. ("Joyful Living" Ser.). 31p. (Orig.). 1985. pap. 1.50 (ISBN 0-912623-02-0). Joyful Woman.
Forgiving Yourself. Bernard Bangley. 96p. (Orig.). 1986. pap. 4.95 (ISBN 0-87788-281-9). Shaw Pubs.
Forgotten Factors. Roy Hession. 1976. pap. 2.95 (ISBN 0-87508-234-3). Chr Lit.
Forgotten Heritage: A Lineage of Great Baptist Preaching. Thomas R. McKibbens, Jr. (Orig.). 1986. 27.95 (ISBN 0-86554-179-5, MUP-H169); pap. 18.95 (ISBN 0-86554-186-8, MUP-P18). Mercer Univ Pr.
Forgotten Is the Name. Paul Perkins. 1985. 7.95 (ISBN 0-89536-938-9, 7556). CSS of Ohio.
Forgotten Man's Almanac: Rations of Common Sense from William Graham Sumner. William G. Sumner. Ed. by A. G. Keller. LC 70-141268. 1971. Repr. of 1943 ed. lib. bdg. 22.50x (ISBN 0-8371-5828-1, SUFM). Greenwood.
Forgotten Miracles of the Bible. Gordon Lindsay. (Miracles in the Bible Ser.: Vol. 6). 0.95 (ISBN 0-89985-183-5). Christ Nations.
Forgotten Religions. facs. ed. Ed. by Vergilius T. Ferm. LC 70-128240. (Essay Index Reprint Ser). 1950. 22.00 (ISBN 0-8369-1922-X). Ayer Co Pubs.
Forgotten Symbols of God: Five Essays Reprinted from Konsthistorisk Tidskrift. Patrik Reutersward. (Stockholm Studies in History of Art: No. 35). (Illus.). 152p. (Orig.). 1986. pap. text ed. 22.00x (Pub. by SPN Yugoslavia). Coronet Bks.
Forgotten Teachings of Jesus. Stephen Finlan. (Illus.). 49p. (Orig.). 1984. pap. 3.00 perfect bound (ISBN 0-9614275-0-7). Spiritual.
Forgotten Teachings of Jesus. rev. ed. Stephen Finlan. (Illus.). 46p. 1985. pap. 4.50 (ISBN 0-9615301-1-1). Dilman Pr.
Forgotten Truth: The Primordial Tradition. Huston Smith. 1977. pap. 6.95x (ISBN 0-06-132054-4, TB 2054, Torch). Har-Row.
Forgotten Truths. Robert Anderson. LC 80-17526. (Sir Robert Anderson Library). 166p. 1980. pap. 4.50 (ISBN 0-8254-2130-6). Kregel.
Forgotten Victim: A History of the Civilian. Richard S. Hartigan. 173p. 1982. 16.95x (ISBN 0-913750-19-0). Transaction Bks.
Forgotton Surgeon. Iain H. Murray. 1978. pap. 5.45 (ISBN 0-85151-156-2). Banner of Truth.
Fork in the Road: Young Adult Decisions. Charles R. Kishpaugh & Kathy B. Finnell. 72p. (Orig.). 1986. pap. 3.75 (ISBN 0-88177-042-6, DR042B). Discipleship Res.
Form-Analysis & Exegesis: A Fresh Approach to the Interpretation of Mishnah. Jacob Neusner. 224p. 1981. 22.50 (ISBN 0-8166-0984-5); pap. 9.95x (ISBN 0-8166-0985-3). U of Minn Pr.
Form & Function of the Body of the Greek Letter in the Non-Literary Papyri & in Paul the Apostle. John L. White. LC 75-33088. (Society of Biblical Literature. Dissertation Ser.). (Illus.). 1975. pap. 9.95 (ISBN 0-89130-048-1, 060102). Scholars Pr GA.
Form & Meaning: Studies in Literary Techniques in the Book of Jonah. Jonathan Magonet. (Bible & Literature Ser.: No. 8). vi, 184p. 1983. pap. text ed. 10.95x (ISBN 0-907459-25-0, Pub. by Almond Pr England). Eisenbrauns.
Form & Origin of Milton's Antitrinitarian Conception. Louis A. Wood. LC 72-191655. 1911. lib. bdg. 15.00 (ISBN 0-8414-0833-5). Folcroft.
Form & Spirit. John H. Badley. LC 77-113347. (Essay & General Literature Index Reprint Ser). 1971. Repr. of 1951 ed. 19.50x (ISBN 0-8046-1398-2, Pub. by Kennikat). Assoc Faculty Pr.
Form & Vitality in the World & God: A Christian Perspective. Trevor Williams. 1985. 29.95x (ISBN 0-19-826671-5). Oxford U Pr.
Form Criticism of the Old Testament. Gene M. Tucker. Ed. by J. Coert Rylaarsdam. LC 72-154487. (Guides to Biblical Scholarship: Old Testament Ser.). 96p. 1971. pap. 4.50 (ISBN 0-8006-0177-7, 1-177). Fortress.
Form of Christian Policy Gathered Out of French. Tr. by Geoffrey Fenton. 504p. Repr. of 1574 ed. 50.00 (ISBN 0-384-15483-2). Johnson Repr.
Formalism in Ethics & Non-Formal Ethics of Values: A New Attempt Toward the Foundation of an Ethical Personalism. Max Scheler. Tr. by Manfred S. Frings & Roger L. Funk. LC 72-97416. (Studies in Phenomenology & Existential Philosophy). Orig. Title: Formalismus der Ethik und die Materiale Wertethik. 750p. 1973. text ed. 29.95 (ISBN 0-8101-0415-6); 14.95 (ISBN 0-8101-0620-5). Northwestern U Pr.
Formation of Christian Europe: An Illustrated History of the Church. Enzo Bellini et al. Ed. & tr. by John Drury. (Illus.). 126p. 1980. text ed. 12.95 (ISBN 0-03-056827-7, HarpR). Har-Row.
Formation of Christian Understanding: An Essay in Theological Hermeneutics. Charles M. Wood. LC 81-5103. 126p. 1981. pap. 7.95 (ISBN 0-664-24373-8). Westminster.
Formation of Faith. Bernard Cooke. LC 65-27619. (Pastoral Ser). 1965. pap. 2.00 (ISBN 0-8294-0014-1). Loyola.
Formation of Isaiah 40-55. Roy F. Melugin. (Beiheft 141 Zur Zeitschrift fuer die Altestamentliche Wissenschaft). 1976. text ed. 42.00 (ISBN 3-11-005820-0). De Gruyter.
Formation of Q: Trajectories in Ancient Wisdom Collections. John S. Kloppenborg. LC 86-45225. 416p. 1987. 39.95 (ISBN 0-8006-3101-3). Fortress.
Formation of Social Policy in the Catholic & Jewish Tradition. new ed. Ed. by Eugene J. Fisher & Daniel F. Polish. LC 80-50268. 208p. text ed. 17.95 (ISBN 0-268-00953-8); pap. text ed. 8.95 (ISBN 0-268-00951-1). U of Notre Dame Pr.
Formation of the Christian Bible. Hans Von Campenhausen. Tr. by J. A. Baker from Ger. LC 73-171495. 360p. 1977. pap. 10.95 (ISBN 0-8006-1263-9, 1-1263). Fortress.
Formation of the Lutheran Church in America. Johannes Knudsen. LC 77-15235. pap. 31.50 (2026956). Bks Demand UMI.
Formation of the New Testament. Edward Lohse. Tr. by M. Eugene Boring. LC 80-27032. 256p. (Orig.). 1981. pap. 9.95 (ISBN 0-687-13294-0). Abingdon.
Formation of the New Testament Canon: An Ecumenical Approach. William R. Farmer & Denis Farkasfalvy. LC 82-62417. (Theological Inquiries Ser.). 1983. pap. 8.95 (ISBN 0-8091-2495-5). Paulist Pr.
Formation of the Old Testament. J. Becker. 1.25 (ISBN 0-8199-0513-5). Franciscan Herald.
Formation of the Resurrection Narratives. Reginald H. Fuller. LC 79-8885. 240p. 1980. pap. 7.95 (ISBN 0-8006-1378-3, 1-1378). Fortress.
Formation of the State in Ancient Israel: A Survey of Models & Theories. Frank S. Frick. (Social World of Biblical Antiquity Ser.). 219p. 1985. text ed. 24.95x (ISBN 0-907459-51-X, Pub. by Almond Pr England); pap. text ed. 10.95 (ISBN 0-907459-52-8). Eisenbrauns.
Formation of the United Church of Christ (U. S. A.) Compiled by Hanns P. Keiling. Ed. by Ford L. Battles. LC 79-25049. (Bibliographia Tripotamopolitana: No.2). 1970. 7.00x (ISBN 0-931222-01-X). Pitts Theolog.
Formation of Thomas Fuller's Holy & Profane States. Walter E. Houghton, Jr. (Harvard Studies in English: Vol. 19). 1969. Repr. of 1938 ed. 23.00 (ISBN 0-384-24390-8). Johnson Repr.
Formative Judaism. Jacob Neusner. LC 82-16746. (Brown Judaic Studies). 182p. 1982. pap. 13.50 (ISBN 0-89130-594-7, 14 00 37). Scholars Pr GA.
Formative Judaism - Religious Historical & Literary Studies: Fourth Series - Problems of Classification & Composition. Jacob Neusner. (Brown Judaic Studies: No. 76). 222p. 1984. 24.95 (ISBN 0-89130-782-6, 14 00 76); pap. 16.95 (ISBN 0-89130-783-4). Scholars Pr GA.
Formative Judaism II. Jacob Neusner. LC 82-25072. (Brown Judiac Studies). 198p. 1983. pap. 13.50 (ISBN 0-89130-614-5, 14 00 41). Scholars Pr GA.
Formative Judaism: Religious, Historical, & Literary Studies. Jacob Neusner. (Brown Judaic Studies). (Fifth Series Revisioning the Written Records of a Nascent Religion). 1985. 29.95 (ISBN 0-89130-850-4, 14-00-91); pap. 21.95 (ISBN 0-89130-851-2). Scholars Pr Ga.
Formative Judaism: Religious, Historical & Literary Studies-Third Series. Jacob Neusner. LC 83-8662. (Brown Judaic Studies). 212p. 1983. pap. 15.00 (ISBN 0-89130-633-1, 14 00 46). Scholars Pr GA.
Formative Spirituality: Fundamental Formation, Vol. I. Adrian V. Kaam. LC 82-22079. (Formative Spirituality Ser.). 320p. 1983. 24.50x (ISBN 0-8245-0544-1). Crossroad NY.
Formative Spirituality: The Formation of the Human Heart, Vol. 3. Adrian Van Kaam. 352p. 1985. 27.50 (ISBN 0-8245-0719-3). Crossroad NY.
Formative Years of the Missionary College of Santa Cruz of Queretaro: 1683-1733. Michael McCloskey. (Monograph Ser.). 1955. 10.00 (ISBN 0-88382-051-X). AAFH.
Forme of Christian Pollicie. Geoffrey Fenton. LC 78-38180. (English Experience Ser.: No. 454). 424p. 1972. Repr. of 1574 ed. 42.00 (ISBN 90-221-0454-0). Walter J Johnson.
Formed by His Word: Patterns of Scriptural Prayer. Malcolm Cornwell. (Orig.). 1978. pap. 2.95 (ISBN 0-914544-20-9). Living Flame Pr.
Forming of an American Tradition. facs. ed. Leonard J. Trinterud. LC 78-124262. (Select Bibliographies Reprint Ser). 1949. 26.50 (ISBN 0-8369-5450-5). Ayer Co Pubs.
Forms & Techniques of Altruistic & Spiritual Growth: A Symposium. P. A. Sorokin. Repr. of 1954 ed. 28.00 (ISBN 0-527-84810-7). Kraus Repr.

Forms for Faith: Art & Architecture for Worship. Ed. by Marni Welch & Eliza Linley. LC 86-82529. (Illus.). 24p. (Orig.). 1986. pap. 5.95 (ISBN 0-943376-36-X). Magnes Mus.

Forms of Man: The Buddhist Vision of Thawan Duchanee. Commentary by Russell Marcus. (Illus.). 1974. pap. 15.00 (ISBN 0-8048-1234-9). C E Tuttle.

Formula Criticism & the Poetry of the Old Testament. William R. Watters. (Beiheft 138 zur Zeitschrift fur die Alttestamentliche Wissenschaft). 1976. 43.20x (ISBN 3-11-005730-1). De Gruyter.

Formulas for Family Living. G. Michael Cocoris. 46p. (Orig.). 1983. pap. text ed. 1.00 (ISBN 0-935729-28-3). Church Open Door.

Formulas for Transformation: A Mantram Handbook. Eknath Easwaran. 264p. 1977. 15.00 (ISBN 0-915132-41-9); pap. 8.00. Nilgiri Pr.

Formulators of the Formula of Concord. Theodore R. Jungkuntz. 1977. pap. 8.50 (ISBN 0-570-03740-9, 12-2644). Concordia.

Fort Supply: Brigham Young's Green River Experiment. Fred R. Gowans & Eugene E. Campbell. 1976. pap. 2.95 (ISBN 0-8425-0248-3). Brigham.

Fortieth Anniversary: Voices from the Heart. Date not set. price not set (ISBN 0-934383-12-X). Pride Prods.

Fortify Your Faith. Wayne Jackson. 74p. (Orig.). 1974. pap. text ed. 2.50 (ISBN 0-932859-09-7). Apologetic Pr.

Fortress for Well-Being: Baha'i Teachings on Marriage. (Comprehensive Deepening Program Ser.: Gift Ed.). 1974. 12.95 (ISBN 0-87743-093-4, 364-010). Baha'i.

Fortress of Faith. 3rd ed. R. K. Johnson. (Illus.). 456p. 1984. pap. 7.95 (ISBN 0-89084-252-3). Bob Jones Univ Pr.

Fortunate Fall of Sir Gawain: The Typology of Sir Gawain & the Green Knight. Victor Y. Haines. LC 80-5847. (Illus.). 240p. (Orig.). 1982. PLB 29.00 (ISBN 0-8191-2437-0); pap. text ed. 12.75 (ISBN 0-8191-2438-9). U Pr of Amer.

Fortune Cookie Christmas. Carole Marsh. (Illus.). 50p. (Orig.). 1986. pap. 9.95 (ISBN 0-935326-53-7). Gallopade Pub Group.

Fortune-Philosophy. Sri Chinmoy. 69p. (Orig.). 1974. pap. 2.00 (ISBN 0-88497-138-4). Aum Pubns.

Fortunes of Inquiry. N. Jardine. (Clarendon Library of Logic & Philosophy). 204p. 36.00 (ISBN 0-19-824929-2). Oxford U Pr.

Forty Ahadith: Asqalani. A. N. Busool. 1981. 4.50 (ISBN 0-686-97860-9). Kazi Pubns.

Forty Devotions That Work with Youth. Ed. by Geraldine Anderson. (Youth Work Guide Ser.). (Illus.). 60p. (Orig.). 1983. pap. 7.45 (ISBN 0-85819-414-7, Pub. by JBCE). ANZ Religious Pubns.

Forty-Eight Hours More or Less: A Retreat Resource. Kathleen Collison & Warren Webb. 111p. (Orig.). pap. 11.00 (ISBN 0-941988-03-1). K Q Assocs.

Forty-Five & Satisfied. Lowell Worthington. 1983. pap. 5.50 (ISBN 0-89137-313-6). Quality Pubns.

Forty-Four Hours to Change Your Life: Marriage Encounter. Henry P. Durkin. (Orig.). pap. write for info (ISBN 0-515-09442-0). Jove Pubns.

Forty-Nine & Holding. Richard K. Smith. LC 75-11179. (Illus.). 1975. 10.00 (ISBN 0-89430-023-7). Palos Verdes.

Forty-Niner in Utah with the Stansbury Exploration of Great Salt Lake: Letters & Journal of John Hudson, 1848-50. Ed. by Brigham D. Madsen. 227p. 1981. 22.50 (ISBN 0-941214-39-7). Signature Bks.

Forty Object Lessons. Donald J. Poganski. LC 72-86233. 160p. 1973. pap. 4.50 (ISBN 0-570-03148-6, 12-2283). Concordia.

Forty Object Sermons for Children. Joe E. Trull. (Object Lesson Ser.). 96p. 1975. pap. 3.95 (ISBN 0-8010-8831-3). Baker Bk.

Forty-Seven Object Lessons for Youth Programs. H. W. Connelly. (Object Lesson Ser). (YA) 1964. pap. 3.95 (ISBN 0-8010-2314-9). Baker Bk.

Forty Signs of the Soon Coming of Christ. Gordon Lindsay. (Prophecy Ser.). 1.95 (ISBN 0-89985-055-3). Christ Nations.

Forty Ways to Fortify Your Faith. James R. Bjorge. LC 83-72115. 128p. (Orig.). 1984. pap. 5.95 (ISBN 0-8066-2059-5, 10-2358). Augsburg.

Forty Ways to Say I Love You. James R. Bjorge. LC 78-52179. 1978. pap. 5.95 (ISBN 0-8066-1654-7, 10-2360). Augsburg.

Forty Ways to Say Thank You, Lord. James R. Bjorge. LC 80-67802. 96p. (Orig.). 1981. pap. 5.95 (ISBN 0-8066-1864-7, 102361). Augsburg.

Forty Ways to Teach Your Child Values. Paul Lewis. 224p. 1985. pap. 6.95 (ISBN 0-8423-0920-9). Tyndale.

Forty Years in the Mormon Church: Why I Left It. R. C. Evans. 1976. Repr. of 1920 ed. 6.95 (ISBN 0-89315-054-1). Lambert Bk.

Fossils, Flood & Fire. Harold W. Clark. (Illus.). 1968. 8.95 (ISBN 0-911080-16-3). Outdoor Pict.

Fostering Discipline & Discipleship Within the Catholic Educational Community. 70p. 1985. 34.30 (ISBN 0-318-18579-2). Natl Cath Educ.

Found God's Will. John Macarthur, Jr. 1977. pap. 1.95 (ISBN 0-88207-503-9). Victor Bks.

Foundation & Orders of Sannerz & the Rhon Bruderhof: Introductory History: The Basis for Our Orders, Vol. 1. Eberhard Arnold. LC 76-5856. 1976. pap. 2.50 (ISBN 0-87486-162-4). Plough.

Foundation & Structure of Sartrean Ethics. Thomas C. Anderson. LC 79-11762. x, 186p. 1979. 22.50x (ISBN 0-7006-0191-0). U Pr of KS.

Foundation Course Folder III: Greek Religion. Cambridge School Classics Project Foundation Course Staff. 1974. 13.95x (ISBN 0-521-08724-4). Cambridge U Pr.

Foundation for a New Consciousness. John Caris. LC 86-20201. (Illus.). 136p. (Orig.). 1987. pap. 8.95 (ISBN 0-9607320-1-2). Westgate Hse.

Foundation for Faith. Derek Prince. (Foundation Ser.: Bk. I). 1965-66. pap. 2.95 (ISBN 0-934920-00-1, B-10). Derek Prince.

Foundation for Missions. M. Thomas Starkes. LC 80-67460. 1981. pap. 5.50 (ISBN 0-8054-6325-9). Broadman.

Foundation Guide for Religious Grant Seekers. 2nd, rev., updated ed. Francis J. Butler & Catherine E. Farrell. LC 84-10593. (Handbook Ser.). 150p. 1984. pap. 11.95 (ISBN 0-89130-756-7, 00 15 02). Scholars Pr GA.

Foundation Guide for Religious Grant Seekers. Ed. by Peter S. Robinson. LC 79-19006. (Scholars Press Handbooks in Humanities Ser.: No. 1). 1979. 10.50 (ISBN 0-89130-339-1, 001501); pap. 9.95 (ISBN 0-89130-340-5). Scholars Pr GA.

Foundation of Articles of Faith. N. A. Faris. 9.50 (ISBN 0-686-18607-9). Kazi Pubns.

Foundation of British East Africa. John W. Gregory. LC 78-88412. Repr. of 1901 ed. cancelled (ISBN 0-8371-1727-5, GRB&, Pub. by Negro U Pr). Greenwood.

Foundation of Japanese Buddhism: The Aristocratic Age, Vol. I. Daigan Matsunaga & Alicia Matsunaga. LC 74-83654. 1974. 14.95x (ISBN 0-914910-25-6); pap. 8.50x (ISBN 0-914910-26-4). Buddhist Bks.

Foundation of Japanese Buddhism: The Mass Movement, Vol. 2. Alicia Matsunaga & Daigan Matsunaga. LC 74-83654. 1976. 16.95x (ISBN 0-914910-27-2); pap. 9.50 (ISBN 0-914910-28-0). Buddhist Bks.

Foundation of Moral Goodness, 2 vols. in 1. John Blaguy. Ed. by Rene Wellek. LC 75-11194. (British Philosophers & Theologians of the 17th & 18th Centuries Ser.: Vol. 1). 1976. Repr. of 1729 ed. lib. bdg. 51.00 (ISBN 0-8240-1750-1). Garland Pub.

Foundation of Philosophy-a Refutation of Skepticism, the True Jesus Christ, the Science of God & Man; the God of the Christians. Apostolos Makrakis. Ed. by Orthodox Christian Educational Society. Tr. by Anthony Lekatsos & Denver Cummings. 395p. 1955. 7.50x (ISBN 0-938366-07-6). Orthodox Chr.

Foundation Stone. Rudolf Steiner. 72p. 1979. pap. 5.50x (ISBN 0-85440-346-9, Pub. by Steinerbooks). Anthroposophic.

Foundation Stone. F. W. Zeylmans-Van-Emmichoven. 118p. 1983. pap. 5.95 (ISBN 0-85440-399-X). Anthroposophic.

Foundation Stone Meditation by Rudolf Steiner. Daisy Aldan. 1981. pap. 2.00 (ISBN 0-916786-53-6). St George Bk Serv.

Foundational Theology: Jesus & the Church. Francis S. Fiorenza. 320p. 1984. 22.50 (ISBN 0-8245-0494-1). Crossroad NY.

Foundational Theology: Jesus & the Church. rev. ed. Francis S. Fiorenza. 352p. 1985. pap. 14.95 (ISBN 0-8245-0706-1). Crossroad NY.

Foundations: A Statement of Christian Belief in Terms of Modern Thought by 70 Oxford Men. facs. ed. Burnett H. Streeter. (Essay Index Reprint Ser.). 1912. 20.50 (ISBN 0-8369-2189-5). Ayer Co Pubs.

Foundations & Practice of Adult Religious Education. John L. Elias. LC 81-19327. 312p. 1982. 18.50 (ISBN 0-89874-339-7). Krieger.

Foundations for a Practical Theology of Ministry. James N. Poling & Donald E. Miller. 192p. 1985. pap. 9.95 (ISBN 0-687-13340-8). Abingdon.

Foundations for Christian Growth. 2nd ed. Ronald D. Tucker & Richard A. Hufton. (Illus.). 322p. 1981. incl. 6 cassettes 40.00 (ISBN 0-933643-16-0). Grace World Outreach.

Foundations for Christian Growth. 3rd ed. Ronald D. Tucker & Richard A. Hufton. LC 85-81911. (Illus.). 322p. 1985. pap. 10.00 (ISBN 0-933643-25-X). Grace World Outreach.

Foundations for Faith. rev. ed. Navigators Staff. (Design for Discipleship Ser.: Bk. 5). 1980. pap. text ed. 1.95 (ISBN 0-934396-20-5). Churches Alive.

Foundations for Living. Jim Richardson. LC 82-74215. 1983. pap. 9.95 (ISBN 0-911739-13-0). Abbott Loop.

Foundations for Purposeful Church Administration. Alvin J. Lindgren. LC 65-16459. 1965. 13.95 (ISBN 0-687-13339-4). Abingdon.

Foundations for Social Theology: Praxis, Process & Salvation. Dermot A. Lane. (Orig.). 1984. pap. 7.95 (ISBN 0-8091-2622-2). Paulist Pr.

Foundations for the Teaching Church. Grant W. Hanson. 96p. 1986. pap. 5.95 (ISBN 0-8170-1096-3). Judson.

Foundations of Belief. Leslie Dewart. LC 69-17777. 1970. pap. 4.95 (ISBN 0-8164-2549-3, HarpR). Har-Row.

Foundations of Biblical Faith. James T. Draper, Jr. LC 78-67001. 1979. 8.95 (ISBN 0-8054-1951-9). Broadman.

Foundations of Biblical Inerrancy. David R. Nicholas. pap. 2.50 (ISBN 0-88469-104-7). BMH Bks.

Foundations of Buddhism. Helena Roerich. 1971. Repr. index 8.00 (ISBN 0-686-79661-6). Agni Yoga Soc.

Foundations of Christian Doctrine. Kevin J. Conner. 313p. 1979. pap. 14.95 (ISBN 0-914936-38-7). Bible Temple.

Foundations of Christian Faith: An Introduction to the Idea of Christianity. Karl Rahner. LC 82-4663. 492p. 1982. pap. 16.95 (ISBN 0-8245-0523-9). Crossroad NY.

Foundations of Christianity. Karl Kautsky. Tr. by Jacob W. Hartmann from Ger. LC 72-81774. 512p. 1972. pap. 15.00 (ISBN 0-85345-262-8, PB-2628). Monthly Rev.

Foundations of Christianity. Karl Kautsky. Tr. by Jacob W. Hartmann from Ger. LC 72-81774. Repr. of 1972 ed. 120.00 (ISBN 0-8357-9441-5, 2016442). Bks Demand UMI.

Foundations of Dogmatics, Vol. 1. Otto Weber. Tr. by Darrel L. Guder. 656p. 1982. 27.00 (ISBN 0-8028-3554-6). Eerdmans.

Foundations of Dogmatics, Vol. 2. Otto Weber. Tr. by Darrell L. Guder from Ger. 736p. 1983. 27.00 (ISBN 0-8028-3564-3). Eerdmans.

Foundations of Evangelical Theology: A Contextualized Approach. John J. Davis. 232p. 1984. pap. 9.95 (ISBN 0-8010-2937-6). Baker Bk.

Foundations of Faith. F. R. Ansari. pap. 1.50 (ISBN 0-686-18472-6). Kazi Pubns.

Foundations of Faith & Morals. Bronislaw Malinowski. LC 74-20949. 1974. Repr. of 1936 ed. lib. bdg. 20.50 (ISBN 0-8414-5965-7). Folcroft.

Foundations of Jewish Life: Three Studies. Israel Abrahams & Adolf Buchler. LC 73-2197. (Jewish People; History, Religion, Literature Ser.). 38.50 (ISBN 0-405-05263-4). Ayer Co Pubs.

Foundations of Mennonite Brethren Missions. George W. Peters. LC 83-72078. 262p. (Orig.). 1984. pap. 12.95 (ISBN 0-318-18902-X). Kindred Pr.

Foundations of Moral Philosophy, Vol. 2. John G. Bennett. (Dramatic Universe Ser.). 12.95 (ISBN 0-900306-42-4, Pub. by Coombe Springs Pr). Claymont Comm.

Foundations of Natural Philosophy, Vol. 1. John G. Bennett. (Dramatic Universe Ser.). 29.95 (ISBN 0-900306-39-4, Pub. by Coombe Springs Pr). Claymont Comm.

Foundations of New Testament Christology. Reginald H. Fuller. 1965. lib. bdg. 25.00x (ISBN 0-684-15532-X, ScribT); pap. 1.50 (ISBN 0-684-15537-0, SL772, ScribT). Scribner.

Foundations of Religious Literacy. John Apczynski. LC 83-4453. (College Theology Society Annual Publications Ser.). 188p. 1983. pap. 10.50 (ISBN 0-89130-621-8, 34 10 82). Scholars Pr GA.

Foundations of Religious Literacy. Ed. by John V. Apczynski. 186p. 1986. pap. text ed. 12.00 (ISBN 0-8191-5617-5, Pub. by College Theology Society). U Pr of Amer.

Foundations of Religious Tolerance. Jay Newman. 192p. 1982. 27.50x (ISBN 0-8020-5591-5); pap. 9.95 (ISBN 0-8020-6507-4). U of Toronto Pr.

Foundations of the Articles of Faith. Al-Ghazzali. 1969. 7.50x (ISBN 0-87902-058-X). Orientalia.

Foundations of the Christian Faith. 2nd ed. James M. Boice. 782p. 24.95 (ISBN 0-87784-991-9). Inter-Varsity.

Foundations of the Christian Missions in the British, French & Spanish West Indies. James Latimer. 1984. 10.95 (ISBN 0-533-05875-9). Vantage.

Foundations of the Faith. William C. Wantland. LC 82-61889. 176p. (Orig.). 1983. pap. 7.95 (ISBN 0-8192-1320-9). Morehouse.

Foundations of the Metaphysics of Morals. Immanuel Kant. Tr. by Lewis W. Beck. Bd. with What Is Enlightenment. LC 59-11679. 1959. pap. 4.79 scp (ISBN 0-672-60312-8, LLA113). Bobbs.

Foundations of the Metaphysics of Morals: Text & Critical Essays. Immanuel Kant. Ed. by Robert P. Wolff. LC 68-9841. (Text & Critical Essays Ser.). 1969. pap. 10.28 scp (ISBN 0-672-61114-7, TC1). Bobbs.

Foundations of the Seventh-Day Adventist Message & Mission. P. Gerard Damsteegt. LC 76-56799. pap. 91.00 (ISBN 0-317-30135-7, 2025318). Bks Demand UMI.

Foundations of Theology. Gerald O'Collins. LC 70-153756. 1971. pap. 3.95 (ISBN 0-8294-0201-2). Loyola.

Foundations of Tibetan Mysticism. L. Anagarika Govinda. (Illus.). 331p. 1969. pap. 7.95 (ISBN 0-87728-064-9). Weiser.

Foundations of Truth. Mary E. Fields. LC 80-67931. 275p. 1980. 10.00 (ISBN 0-87516-423-4). De Vorss.

Foundations of Unity. Ser. One. 4.50 (ISBN 0-87159-038-7); Ser. Two. 8.50 (ISBN 0-87159-039-5). Unity School.

Foundations of World Organization: A Political & Cultural Appraisal: Proceeding. Conference on Science-Philosophy & Religion in Their Relation to the Democratic Way of Life, 11th. 37.00 (ISBN 0-527-00658-0). Kraus Repr.

Founded on a Rock: A History of the Catholic Church. Louis De Wohl. LC 81-6557. 248p. 1981. Repr. lib. bdg. 23.50x (ISBN 0-313-23168-0, DEF0). Greenwood.

Founded Upon a Rock. Dale Edwards. 1977. pap. 3.95 (ISBN 0-89265-043-5). Randall Hse.

Founder of Christianity. C. H. Dodd. 1970. pap. 5.95 (ISBN 0-02-084640-1, Collier). Macmillan.

Founder of Torah Umesorah. Joseph Kaminetsky & Alexander Gross. pap. 1.00 (ISBN 0-914131-21-4, E-23). Torah Umesorah.

Founders of Christian Movements. Ed. by Philip H. Lotz. LC 71-111843. (Essay Index Reprint Ser). 1941. 17.00 (ISBN 0-8369-1672-7). Ayer Co Pubs.

Founders of Great Religions: Being Personal Sketches of Famous Leaders. Millart Burrows. LC 72-13272. (Essay Index Reprint Ser.). Repr. of 1931 ed. 16.75 (ISBN 0-8369-8148-0). Ayer Co Pubs.

Founders of Religion. Tony D. Triggs. LC 82-60697. (In Profile Ser.). 64p. PLB 13.96 (ISBN 0-382-06676-6). Silver.

Founders of the Jews. Norman Bull. (Bible Story & Its Background Ser.: Vol. 1). pap. 9.95 (ISBN 0-7175-0977-X). Dufour.

Founders of the Middle Ages. Edward K. Rand. 1928. pap. 7.95 (ISBN 0-486-20369-7). Dover.

Founding Fathers: The Puritans in England & America. John Adair. 314p. 1982. 24.95x (ISBN 0-460-04421-4, Pub. by J M Dent England). Biblio Dist.

Founding of American Colleges & Universities Before the Civil War with Particular Reference to the Religious Influences Bearing upon the College Movement. Donald G. Tewksbury. LC 76-177718. (Columbia University. Teachers College. Contributions to Education Ser.: No. 543). Repr. of 1932 ed. 22.50 (ISBN 0-404-55543-8). AMS Pr.

Founding of American Colleges & Universities Before the Civil War. Donald G. Tewksbury. LC 79-89246. (American Education: Its Men, Institutions & Ideas, Ser. 1). 1969. Repr. of 1932 ed. 17.00 (ISBN 0-405-01483-X). Ayer Co Pubs.

Founding of Christendom. Warren H. Carroll. (History of Christendom Ser.: Vol. 1). 605p. 1985. 24.95 (ISBN 0-931888-21-2); pap. 12.95 (ISBN 0-931888-21-2). Christendom Pubns.

Founding of Cliff Haven: Early Years of the Catholic Summer School of America. James A. White. LC 53-1915. (Monograph Ser.: No. 24). 1950. 7.50x (ISBN 0-930060-06-7). US Cath Hist.

Founding of Faith. Maggie Bunson. 1977. 6.00 (ISBN 0-8198-0412-6); pap. 5.00 (ISBN 0-8198-0413-4). Dghtrs St Paul.

Founding the Life Divine. Morwenna Donnelly. 176p. 1976. Repr. of 1976 ed. write for info. Auromere.

Founding the Life Divine: An Introduction to the Integral Yoga of Sri Aurobindo. Morwenna Donnelly. LC 74-2430. 250p. 1976. pap. 7.95 (ISBN 0-913922-13-7). Dawn Horse Pr.

Foundlings on the Frontier: Racial & Religious Conflict in Arizona Territory, 1904-1905. A. Blake Brophy. LC 79-187824. (Southwest Chronicles). 129p. 1972. pap. 3.95 (ISBN 0-8165-0319-2). U of Ariz Pr.

Fountain of Life. Solomon I. Gabirol. pap. 1.45 (ISBN 0-685-19402-7, 104, WL). Citadel Pr.

Four Anthems. Adrian Batten. Ed. by David Evans. LC 68-65217. (Penn State Music Series, No. 17). 232p. pap. 3.25x (ISBN 0-271-09117-7). Pa St U Pr.

Four Cardinal Virtues. Josef Pieper. 1966. pap. 5.95 (ISBN 0-268-00103-0). U of Notre Dame Pr.

Four Centuries of Witch-Belief. R. Trevor Davies. LC 74-180026. Repr. of 1947 ed. 27.50 (ISBN 0-405-08437-4). Ayer Co Pubs.

Four Concepts of the Spiritual Structure of Creation. Peter D. Francuch. LC 82-62630. 119p. 1983. pap. 3.95 (ISBN 0-939386-05-4). TMH Pub.

Four Doctrines. Emanuel Swedenborg. LC 67-1465. 1971. student ed. 12.00 (ISBN 0-87785-063-1); pap. 2.95 (ISBN 0-87785-064-X). Swedenborg.

Four Early Bibles in Pilgrim Hall. Charles C. Forman. (Pilgrim Society Notes: No. 9). 1959. 1.00 (ISBN 0-940628-17-1). Pilgrim Soc.

Four Earthen Vessels. Urie Bender. 320p. 1982. pap. 9.95x (ISBN 0-8361-1246-6). Herald Pr.

Four Existentialist Theologians. Ed. by Will Herberg. LC 75-17472. 346p. 1975. Repr. of 1958 ed. lib. bdg. 29.75x (ISBN 0-8371-8303-0, HEFE). Greenwood.

Four Faces of Asia: A Summary Report on the Asian Bishops' Meeting, Manila 1971. Vitaliano R. Gorospe. 1971. wrps. 3.00x (ISBN 0-686-09496-4). Cellar.

Four Faces of Siva. Robert J. Casey. 1929. 25.00 (ISBN 0-8482-3565-7). Norwood Edns.

Four-Fold Gospel. rev. ed. Albert B. Simpson. 1984. pap. 4.95 (ISBN 0-87509-347-7). Chr Pubns.

Four-Fold Health. Harriette Curtiss & F. Homer. 1936. 4.95 (ISBN 0-87516-304-1). De Vorss.

Four Gospels. Boyce Blackwelder. 1980. 9.95 (ISBN 0-87162-221-1, D3768). Warner Pr.

Four Gospels. David Brown. 20.95 (ISBN 0-85151-016-7). Banner of Truth.

Four Gospels. 5.00 (ISBN 0-317-46838-3); 3.50 (ISBN 0-317-46839-1). Dghtrs St Paul.

Four Gospels & Acts: A Short Introduction. Harry R. Boer. 112p. 1982. pap. 3.95 (ISBN 0-8028-1901-X). Eerdmans.

Four Gospels & the Revelation. Tr. by Richard Lattimore. 288p. 1981. pap. 3.95 (ISBN 0-671-50441-X). WSP.

Four Gospels & the Revelation. Tr. by Richmond Lattimore from Greek. 320p. 1979. 14.95 (ISBN 0-374-15801-0). FS&G.

Four Gospels As One. David H. Yarn. 281p. 1982. 8.95 (ISBN 0-87747-948-8). Deseret Bk.

Four Great Heresies. John W. Wand. LC 78-63174. (Heresies of the Early Christian & Medieval Era: Second Ser.). Repr. of 1955 ed. 29.00 (ISBN 0-404-16189-8). AMS Pr.

Four Hasidic Masters & Their Struggle Against Melancholy. Elie Wiesel. LC 78-1419. (Ward-Phillips Lectures in English Language & Literature Ser: No. 9). (Illus.). 1978. 9.95 (ISBN 0-268-00944-9). U of Notre Dame Pr.

Four Hasidic Masters & Their Struggle Against Melancholy. Elie Wiesel. LC 78-1419. (Ward-Phillips Lectures in English Language & Literature: No. 9). (Illus.). 1979. pap. text ed. 4.95x (ISBN 0-268-00947-3). U of Notre Dame Pr.

Four Hundred & Fifty-Year Judgment Cycles. Gordon Lindsay. (Miracles in the Bible Ser.: Vol. 5). 0.95 (ISBN 0-89985-182-7). Christ Nations.

Four Hundred Silent Years. H. A. Ironside. pap. 3.50 (ISBN 0-87213-361-3). Loizeaux.

Four Hundred Silent Years. Gordon Lindsay. (Old Testament Ser.). 1.25 (ISBN 0-89985-158-4). Christ Nations.

Four Independents. facs. ed. Daniel Sargent. LC 68-55856. (Essay Index Reprint Ser.). 1935. 18.00 (ISBN 0-8369-0850-3). Ayer Co Pubs.

Four Leading Doctrines of the New Church. Emanuel Swedenborg. LC 71-134426. Repr. of 1882 ed. 21.00 (ISBN 0-404-08466-4). AMS Pr.

Four Letters of Pelagius: On the Grounds for Authenticity of 4 of the 20 Works Ascribed by De Plinval to Pelagius. Robert F. Evans. LC 68-11594. 1968. text ed. 12.00x (ISBN 0-685-00379-5). A R Allenson.

Four Levels of Spiritual Consciousness. Max Kappeler. LC 72-883567. 198p. 1970. 14.00 (ISBN 0-85241-091-3). Kappeler Inst Pub.

Four Loves. Dick Mills. (Orig.). 1983. pap. 0.75 minibook (HH-287). Harrison Hse.

Four Major Cults. Anthony A. Hoekema. 1963. 24.95 (ISBN 0-8028-3117-6). Eerdmans.

Four Major Mysteries of Mainland China. Paul Dong. (Illus.). 204p. 1984. 16.95 (ISBN 0-13-330572-4); pap. 8.95 (ISBN 0-13-330556-2). P-H.

Four Men of God, Neighborhood Bible Study. Marilyn Kunz & Catherine Schell. 1972. pap. 2.95 (ISBN 0-8423-0900-4). Tyndale.

Four Modern Prophets: Walter Rauschenbusch, Martin Luther King, Jr., Gustavo Gutierrez, Rosemary Radford Ruether. William M. Ramsay. LC 86-45351. 108p. (Orig.). 1986. pap. 6.95 (ISBN 0-8042-0811-5). John Knox.

Four Morality Plays. Intro. by Peter Happe. 1987. pap. 6.95 (ISBN 0-14-043119-5). Penguin.

Four Mystery Plays. Rudolf Steiner. Tr. by Adam Bittleston from Ger. 512p. (Orig.). 1982. pap. text ed. 16.00 (ISBN 0-85440-403-1). Anthroposophic.

Four Negro Spirituals. Carol Roes. 1975. pap. 3.75 (ISBN 0-930932-24-2); record incl. M Loke.

Four on an Island. Bahiyyih Nakhjavani. 144p. 10.95 (ISBN 0-85398-173-6); pap. 5.95 (ISBN 0-85398-174-4). G Ronald Pub.

Four Other Gospels: Shadows on the Contour of the Canon. John D. Crossan. 208p. (Orig.). 1985. 15.95 (ISBN 0-86683-959-3, HarpR). Har-Row.

Four Pillars of Islam. A. H. Nadvi. 14.95 (ISBN 0-686-18597-8). Kazi Pubns.

Four Portraits of Jesus. Frank Colquhoun. LC 85-4248. Orig. Title: Fourfold Portrait of Jesus. 84p. 1985. pap. 2.95 (ISBN 0-87784-450-X). Inter-Varsity.

Four Sacred Seasons. G. De Purucker. LC 79-63565. 1979. 5.00 (ISBN 0-911500-83-9); pap. 2.75 (ISBN 0-911500-84-7). Theos U Pr.

Four Sacrifices of Christ. 2nd ed. Rudolf Steiner. Ed. by Gilbert Church. Tr. by May Laird-Brown from Ger. 20p. (Orig.). 1981. pap. 1.00 (ISBN 0-88010-026-5). Anthroposophic.

Four Seasons of Shaker Life. Gerard C. Wertkin. 1986. pap. 10.95 (ISBN 0-671-61815-6, Fireside). S&S.

Four Seasons of the Spirit. Manly P. Hall. pap. 2.50 (ISBN 0-89314-315-4). Philos Res.

Four Spiritual Crises in Mid-Century American Fiction. facs. ed. Robert Detweiler. LC 78-121461. (Essay Index Reprint Ser). 1964. 12.00 (ISBN 0-8369-1799-5). Ayer Co Pubs.

Four Spiritual Crises in Mid-Century American Fiction. Robert Detweiler. LC 64-63316. (University of Florida Humanities Monographs: No. 14). 1963. pap. 3.50 (ISBN 0-8130-0058-0). U Presses Fla.

Four Steps to Pure Iman. M. R. Bawa Muhaiyaddeen. LC 81-1429. (Illus.). 70p. 1979. pap. 3.95 (ISBN 0-914390-17-1). Fellowship Pr PA.

Four Strange Books of the Bible: Jonah, Daniel, Koheleth, Esther. Elias Bickerman. (Illus.). 252p. 1984. pap. 8.95 (ISBN 0-8052-0774-0). Schocken.

Four Thousand Questions & Answers on the Old & New Testament, Vol. 1. Lincoln A. Hibler. 1986. 8.95 (ISBN 0-8062-2431-2). Carlton.

Four Trees of Christmas. Eduard M. Vajda. 1983. 16.75 (ISBN 0-89536-641-X, 0633). CSS of Ohio.

Four Trojan Horses of Humanism. Harry Conn. 141p. 1982. pap. 5.95 (ISBN 0-88062-009-9). Mott Media.

Four Views of Christ. Andrew Jukes. LC 82-7800. 128p. 1982. pap. 5.95 (ISBN 0-8254-2953-6). Kregel.

Four Weeks with God & Your Neighbor. Jay E. Adams. pap. 2.50 (ISBN 0-8010-0140-4). Baker Bk.

Four Weeks with God & Your Neighbor. Jay E. Adams. 75p. 1978. pap. 2.50 (ISBN 0-87552-020-0). Presby & Reformed.

Four Women: Four Windows on Light. Carol Murphy. Ed. by Eleanore P. Mather. LC 81-80220. 26p. 1981. pap. 2.50x (ISBN 0-87574-236-X, 236). Pendle Hill.

Foure Bookes of Offices: Enabling Privat Persons for the Service of All Good Princes & Policies. Barnabe Barnes. LC 74-28830. (English Experience Ser.: No. 712). 1975. Repr. of 1606 ed. 24.00 (ISBN 9-0221-0712-4). Walter J Johnson.

Fourfold Salvation. A. W. Pink. pap. 0.75 (ISBN 0-685-41831-6). Reiner.

Fourteen American Mothers & Fourteen American Daughters with Sri Chimnoy. 1975. 2.00 (ISBN 0-88497-212-7). Aum Pubns.

Fourteen Lessons in Yoga Philosophy. Yogi Ramacharaka. 8.00 (ISBN 0-911662-01-4). Yoga.

Fourteen Messages of Hope. Friedrich Rest. (Pulpit Library). 96p. 1985. pap. 3.95 (ISBN 0-8010-7733-8). Baker Bk.

Fourteen Witnesses. Oscar J. Rumpf & David A. Rumpf. 1985. 5.95 (ISBN 0-89536-722-X, 5805). CSS of Ohio.

Fourteen Women's Programs: Making Your House a Home. Wilma Shaffer. 96p. (Orig.). 1984. pap. 3.95 (ISBN 0-87239-743-2, 2974). Standard Pub.

Fourteenth Century English Mystics: A Comparative Analysis, 2 vols. George W. Tuma. Ed. by James Hogg. (Elizabethan & Renaissance Studies). 400p. (Orig.). 1977. pap. 30.00 (ISBN 0-317-40144-0, Pub. by Salzburg Studies). Longwood Pub Group.

Fourteenth Century English Mystics: A Comprehensive Annotated Bibliography. Ritamary Bradley & Valerie M. Lagorio. LC 79-7922. (Garland Reference Library of the Humanities). 300p. 1981. lib. bdg. 36.00 (ISBN 0-8240-9535-9). Garland Pub.

Fourteenth-Century Scholar & Primate: Richard FitzRalph in Oxford, Avignon, & Armagh. Katherine Walsh. (Illus.). 1981. 65.00x (ISBN 0-19-822637-3). Oxford U Pr.

Fourth Crusade. Donald E. Queller. LC 77-81454. (Middle Ages Ser). 1977. pap. 10.95x (ISBN 0-8122-1098-0). U of Pa Pr.

Fourth Day Guide: A Book of Prayers for Christian Pilgrims. 1969. wrps. 3.50x (ISBN 0-686-09495-6). Cellar.

Fourth Day: What the Bible & the Heavens Are Telling Us about the Creation. Howard J. Van Till. LC 85-29400. (Illus.). 286p. (Orig.). 1986. pap. 9.95 (ISBN 0-8028-0178-1). Eerdmans.

Fourth Dimension. Paul Y. Cho. LC 79-65588. 1979. pap. 5.95 (ISBN 0-88270-380-3, Pub. by Logos). Bridge Pub.

Fourth Dimension, Vol. 2. Paul Y. Cho & R. Whitney Manzano. LC 79-65588. 183p. 1983. pap. 5.95 (ISBN 0-88270-561-X). Bridge Pub.

Fourth Dimension: A Guided Tour of Higher Universes. Ruby Rucker et al. (Illus.). 228p. 1985. pap. 8.95 (ISBN 0-395-39388-4). HM.

Fourth Evangelist & His Gospel: An Examination of Contemporary Scholarship. Robert Kysar. LC 75-22711. 320p. (Orig.). 1975. pap. 11.95 (ISBN 0-8066-1504-4, 10-2365). Augsburg.

Fourth Gospel & the Jews: A Study of R. Akiba, Esther, & the Gospel of John. John Bowman. LC 75-40461. (Pittsburgh Theological Monographs: No. 8). 1975. pap. 9.00 (ISBN 0-915138-10-7). Pickwick.

Fourth Thousand Years. W. Cleon Skousen. LC 66-29887. 1966. 13.95 (ISBN 0-88494-147-7). Bookcraft Inc.

Fourth Watch of the Night. Kenneth D. Barney. 96p. 1973. 1.50 (ISBN 0-88243-724-0, 02-0724). Gospel Pub.

Fourth Way. P. D. Ouspensky. 1971. pap. 7.95 (ISBN 0-394-71672-8, Vin). Random.

Fourth Wise Man. Wadeeha Atiyeh. 1959. pap. 3.00 (ISBN 0-8315-0038-7). Speller.

Fowles, Irving, Barthes: Canonical Variations on an Apocryphal Theme. Randolph Runyon. LC 81-11125. (Illus.). 134p. 1982. 17.50x (ISBN 0-8142-0335-3). Ohio St U Pr.

Foxe's Book of Martyrs. John Foxe. Ed. by W. Grinton Berry. (Giant Summit Bks). 1978. pap. 7.95 (ISBN 0-8010-3483-3). Baker Bk.

Foxe's Book of Martyrs. John Foxe. 400p. pap. 3.95 (ISBN 0-8007-8013-2, Spire Bks). Revell.

Foxe's Book of Martyrs. John Foxe. 400p. 1981. pap. 3.95 (ISBN 0-88368-095-5). Whitaker Hse.

Foxe's Book of Martyrs. Ed. by Marie G. King. 50p. pap. 3.95 (ISBN 0-317-06922-5, 06742-3). Jove Pubns.

Foxe's Christian Martyrs of the World. John Fox. 1985. 6.95 (ISBN 0-916441-12-1). Barbour & Co.

Fox's Book of Martyrs. Ed. by W. B. Forbush. 11.95 (ISBN 0-310-24390-4, 9636); pap. 6.95 (ISBN 0-310-24391-2, 9636P). Zondervan.

Fra Filippo Lippi. Edward C. Strutt. LC 78-176460. Repr. of 1901 ed. 11.50 (ISBN 0-404-06299-7). AMS Pr.

Fra Girolamo Savonarola, Florentine Art & Renaissance Historiography. Ronald Steinberg. LC 76-8304. (Illus.). 151p. 1977. 14.00x (ISBN 0-8214-0202-1). Ohio U Pr.

Fragile Craft: The Work of Amos Niven Wilder. John D. Crossan. Ed. by Kent Richards. LC 80-19755. 1981. pap. 8.95 (ISBN 0-89130-424-X, 06 11 03). Scholars Pr GA.

Fragile Presence: Transcendence in Modern Literature. John Killinger. LC 72-91520. pap. 44.00 (2026902). Bks Demand UMI.

Fragile Universe: An Essay in the Philosophy of Religions. Patrick Burke. LC 78-17885. (Library of Philosophy & Religion). 129p. 1979. text ed. 28.50x (ISBN 0-06-490776-7, 06373). B&N Imports.

Fragmentary Illustrations of the History of the Book of Common Prayer. W. Jacobson. 122p. Repr. of 1874 ed. text ed. 33.12x (ISBN 0-576-99146-5, Pub. by Gregg Intl Pubs England). Gregg Intl.

Fragments D'une Vie de Saint Thomas de Cantorbery en Vers Accouples. Thomas a Becket. 25.00 (ISBN 0-384-60189-8); pap. 19.00 (ISBN 0-384-60179-0). Johnson Repr.

Fragments from Hellenistic Jewish Authors: Historians, Vol. I. Carl R. Holladay. LC 79-18090. (SBL Texts & Translations). 404p. 1983. pap. 16.50 (ISBN 0-89130-349-9, 06 02 20). Scholars Pr GA.

Fragments from the Cairo Genizah in the Freer Collection. Ed. by Richard J. Gottheil. Repr. of 1927 ed. 37.00 (ISBN 0-384-38813-2). Johnson Repr.

Fragments of a Faith Forgotten. 2nd ed. G. R. Mead. 633p. 1906. pap. 43.95 (ISBN 0-88697-011-3). Life Science.

Fragments of an Unknown Gospel & Other Early Christian Papyri. H. Idris Bell. 59.95 (ISBN 0-8490-0188-9). Gordon Pr.

Fragments of an Unknown Gospel & Other Early Christian Papyri. Ed. by H. Idris Bell & T. C. Skeat. (Illus.). 76p. 1935. Repr. of 1935 ed. 7.50 (ISBN 0-7141-0438-8, Pub. by British Lib). Longwood Pub Group.

Fragments of My Life. Catherine de Hueck Doherty. LC 79-56889. (Illus.). 208p. (Orig.). 1979. pap. 4.95 (ISBN 0-87793-194-1). Ave Maria.

Fraktur: The Illuminated Manuscripts of the Pennsylvania Dutch. Frances Lichten. 1958. wrappers 1.00 (ISBN 0-911132-10-4). Phila Free Lib.

Frament: The Autobiography of Mary Jane Mount Tanner. Ed. by Margery W. Ward. 231p. 1980. 15.00 (ISBN 0-941214-38-9). Signature Bks.

Framework of the New Testament Stories. Arnold A. Ehrhardt. LC 65-79. 1964. 22.50t (ISBN 0-674-31700-9). Harvard U Pr.

Frameworks: Patterns for Living & Believing Today. Douglas A. Walrath. 160p. (Orig.). 1987. pap. 8.95 (ISBN 0-8298-0743-8). Pilgrim NY.

France en Orient au XIVe Siecle, 2 vols. Joseph Delaville Le Roulx. LC 78-63335. (Crusades & Military Orders: Second Ser.). Repr. of 1886 ed. Set. 37.50 (ISBN 0-404-17020-X). AMS Pr.

France Protestante: Biographies Historiques, 12 tomes. Haag. Set. 113.75 (ISBN 0-685-36098-9). French & Eur.

Frances Hook Picture Book. Illus. by Frances Hook. Wanda Hayes. (Illus.). 1963. 7.95 (ISBN 0-87239-243-0, 2868). Standard Pub.

Francis A. Schaeffer: Portraits of the Man & His Work. LC 85-73846. 1986. pap. 7.95 (ISBN 0-89107-386-8, Crossway Bks). Good News.

Francis, a Way: The Franciscan Alternative. Constantin Pohlmann. Tr. by Davie Smith. 1988. cancelled 12.50 (ISBN 0-8199-0865-7). Franciscan Herald.

Francis & Clare: The Complete Works. Ed. by Regis J. Armstrong & Ignatius C. Brady. (Classics of Western Spirituality Ser.). 1983. pap. 8.95 (ISBN 0-8091-2446-7). Paulist Pr.

Francis & the Animals. Corinne Van Moorselaar. Ed. by Mark Hegener. Tr. by David Smith. LC 77-7391. (Dutch., Illus.). 1977. 3.50x (ISBN 0-685-81231-6). Franciscan Herald.

Francis Asbury. Charles Ludwig. 1984. pap. 6.95 (ISBN 0-88062-024-2). Mott Media.

Francis Asbury. L. C. Rudolph. 240p. (Orig.). 1983. pap. 8.95 (ISBN 0-687-13461-7). Abingdon.

Francis Asbury: God's Circuit Rider. Date not set. pap. 6.95 (ISBN 0-8010-5641-1). Baker Bk.

Francis Asbury's America: An Album of Early American Methodism. Ed. by Terry O. Bilhartz. LC 83-18275. 128p. 1984. (Pub. by F. Asbury Pr); pap. 6.95 (ISBN 0-310-44791-7, 18275). Zondervan.

Francis Bacon & His Secret Society. Constance M. Pott. LC 71-174282. Repr. of 1891 ed. 32.50 (ISBN 0-404-05096-4). AMS Pr.

Francis Book: A Celebration of the Universal Saint. Compiled By Roy M. Gasnick. (Illus.). 320p. 1980. (Collier); pap. 15.95 (ISBN 0-02-003200-5). Macmillan.

Francis: Brother of the Universe. Roy Gasnick. (Illus.). 1.00. Paulist Pr.

Francis Hopkinson, the First American Poet-Composer, & James Lyon, Patriot, Preacher, Psalmodist. 2nd ed. Oscar G. Sonneck. LC 65-23393. (Music Reprint Ser.). 213p. 1966. Repr. of 1905 ed. lib. bdg. 32.50 (ISBN 0-306-70918-X). Da Capo.

Francis Norbet Blanchet & the Founding of the Oregon Missions (1838-1848) Sr. Letitia M. Lyons. LC 73-3585. (Catholic University of America. Studies in American Church History: No. 31). Repr. of 1940 ed. 28.00 (ISBN 0-404-57781-4). AMS Pr.

Francis of Assisi. Arnaldo Fortini. Tr. by Helen Moak. 900p. 1980. 39.50x (ISBN 0-8245-0003-2). Crossroad NY.

Francis of Assisi. Ray C. Petry. LC 41-25932. Repr. of 1941 ed. 11.50 (ISBN 0-404-05017-4). AMS Pr.

Francis of Assisi: A Prophet for Our Time. N. Van Doornik. 1978. 8.95 (ISBN 0-8199-0695-6). Franciscan Herald.

Francis of Assisi: Mirror Christ. Isidore O'Brien. 1978. 6.95 (ISBN 0-8199-0691-3). Franciscan Herald.

Francis of Assisi Today, Vol. 149. Casiano Floristan & Christian Duquoc. (Concilium 1981). 128p. (Orig.). 1981. pap. 6.95 (ISBN 0-8164-2349-0, HarpR). Har-Row.

Francis of Assisi: Writer. M. A. Habig. 1981. 2.00 (ISBN 0-8199-0844-4). Franciscan Herald.

Francis Suarez: On the Essence of Finite Being as Such, on the Existence of the Essence & Their Distinction. Tr. by Norman J. Wells. (Mediaeval Philosophical Texts in Translation). 250p. 1983. pap. 24.95 (ISBN 0-87462-224-7). Marquette.

Francis: The Journey & the Dream. Murray Bodo. (Illus.). 1972. pap. 2.95 (ISBN 0-912228-07-5). St Anthony Mess Pr.

Francis: The Poor Man of Assisi. Tomie De Paola. LC 81-6984. (Illus.). 48p. 1982. reinforced 14.95 (ISBN 0-8234-0435-8). Holiday.

Francis Xavier, His Life, His Times. Georg Schurhammer. Tr. by M. Joseph Costelloe. Incl. Vol. 1. Europe, 1506-1541. (Illus.). xxxii, 791p. 1973. 35.00 (ISBN 0-8294-0354-X); Vol. 2. India, 1541-1545. (Illus.). xvi, 759p. 1977. 35.00 (ISBN 0-8294-0355-8); Vol. 3. Indonesia & India, 1545-1549. xiv, 726p. 1980. 40.00 (ISBN 0-8294-0356-6); Vol. 4. Japan, India & China, 1549-1552. xii, 713p. 1982. 45.00 (ISBN 0-8294-0357-4). LC 72-88247. (Illus.). Jesuit Hist.

Franciscan Awatovi: The Excavation & Conjectural Reconstruction of a Seventeenth Century Spanish Mission. R. G. Montgomery et al. (Harvard University Peabody Museum of Archaeology & Ethnology Papers). 1949. 24.00 (ISBN 0-527-01292-0). Kraus Repr.

Franciscan Book of Saints. Marion Habig. 988p. 1980. 30.00 (ISBN 0-8199-0751-0). Franciscan Herald.

Franciscan Calling. Lazaro De Aspurz-Iriarte. Tr. by Sr. Marie Kelly. 300p. 1975. 6.95 (ISBN 0-8199-0538-0). Franciscan Herald.

Franciscan Cartoons. Wm. Armstrong. (Armstrong Cartoon Ser.). (Illus., Orig.). 1974. pap. 1.00 (ISBN 0-913452-24-6). Jesuit Bks.

Franciscan Charism. Anselm Romb. LC 79-91837. 122p. 1969. 3.00 (ISBN 0-8199-0477-5); pap. 1.95 (ISBN 0-685-77516-X). Franciscan Herald.

Franciscan Crown Rosary. Marion A. Habig. 1977. 3.00 (ISBN 0-8199-0605-0). Franciscan Herald.

Franciscan Essay I. 128p. 1912. text ed. 33.12x (ISBN 0-576-99220-8, Pub. by Gregg Intl Pubs England). Gregg Intl.

Franciscan Essays II. 103p. 1932. text ed. 33.12x (ISBN 0-576-99222-4, Pub. by Gregg Intl Pubs England). Gregg Intl.

Franciscan Missionaries in Hispanic California 1769-1848: A Biographical Dictionary. Maynard Geiger. LC 74-79607. Repr. of 1969 ed. 60.50 (ISBN 0-8357-9191-2, 2015007). Bks Demand UMI.

Franciscan Missions in Texas (1690-1793) Thomas P. O'Rourke. LC 73-3559. (Catholic University of America. Studies in American Church History: No. 5). Repr. of 1927 ed. 19.50 (ISBN 0-404-57755-5). AMS Pr.

Franciscan Poets. facs. ed. Benjamin F. Musser. LC 67-26768. (Essay Index Reprint Ser). 1933. 17.25 (ISBN 0-8369-0732-9). Ayer Co Pubs.

Franciscan Poets of the Thirteenth Century. Frederick Ozanam. LC 68-26288. 1969. Repr. of 1914 ed. 24.50x (ISBN 0-8046-0342-1). Assoc Faculty Pr.

Franciscan Prayer Life. Ronald Mrozinski. 1983. 12.50 (ISBN 0-8199-0795-2). Franciscan Herald.

Franciscan Presence in the Americas. Ed. by Francisco Morales. (Misc. Ser.). 1984. 40.00 (ISBN 0-88382-258-X). AAFH.

Franciscan Studies. Ed. by Conrad L. Harkins. (Annual review). 16.00 (ISBN 0-686-12038-8). Franciscan Inst.

Franciscan Women. David Flood. 64p. 1976. pap. 0.95 (ISBN 0-8199-0593-3). Franciscan Herald.

Franciscans in the Indonesian Archipelago, 1300-1775. Achilles Meersman. 1967. pap. 49.50x (ISBN 0-317-27470-8). Elliots Bks.

Francisco de Osuna: The Third Spiritual Alphabet, Vol 1. Mary Giles. (Classics of Western Spirituality Ser.). 1982. 16.95 (ISBN 0-8091-0266-8); pap. 11.95 (ISBN 0-8091-2145-X). Paulist Pr.

Francisco Javier Clavigero, S. J., Figure of the Mexican Enlightment: His Life & Work. Charles E. Ronan. 1978. pap. 26.00x (ISBN 88-7041-340-3). Jesuit Hist.

Francisco of Fatima: His Life As He Might Tell It. Robert J. Fox. 14p. 1982. pap. 1.00 (ISBN 0-911988-53-X). Ami Pr.

Francois de Fenelon. Viscount St. Cyres. LC 72-113319. 1970. Repr. of 1901 ed. 25.50x (ISBN 0-8046-0998-5, Pub. by Kennikat). Assoc Faculty Pr.

Frank & Maisie: A Memoir with Parents. Wilfrid Sheed. 304p. 1986. pap. 7.95 (ISBN 0-671-62813-5, Touchstone Bks). S&S.

Frank Chamberlain Porter: Pioneer in American Biblical Interpretation. Roy A. Harrisville. LC 76-4498. (Society of Biblical Literature. Study in Biblical Scholarship). 1976. pap. 8.95 (ISBN 0-89130-104-6, 061101). Scholars Pr GA.

Frank Lloyd Wright: His Life & His Architecture. Robert C. Twombly. 1986. pap. 19.95 (ISBN 0-471-85797-1). Wiley.

Frankish Church. J. M. Wallace-Hadrill. LC 83-13051. (Oxford History of the Chri). 1983. 59.95x (ISBN 0-19-826906-4). Oxford U Pr.

Frankly Feminine: God's Idea of Womanhood. Gloria H. Hawley. LC 81-50348. 128p. (Orig.). 1981. pap. 3.50 (ISBN 0-87239-455-7, 2969). Standard Pub.

Frankly Feminine: Leader's Guide. Marie H. Frost. 48p. (Orig.). 1984. pap. 2.95 (ISBN 0-87239-746-7, 2970). Standard Pub.

Franks, Romans, Feudalism, & Doctrine: An Interplay Between Theology & Society. John S. Romanides. (Patriarch Athenagoras Memorial Lectures Ser.). 98p. (Orig.). 1982. pap. text ed. 4.95 (ISBN 0-916586-54-5). Holy Cross Orthodox.

Franz Schneider (Seventeen Thirty-Seven to Eighteen Twelve) A Thematic Catalogue of His Works. Robert N. Freeman. LC 79-15260. (Thematic Catalogues Ser.: No. 5). 1979. lib. bdg. 24.00x (ISBN 0-918728-13-4). Pendragon NY.

Franz Suarez und Die Scholastik Des Letzen Jahrhunderts, 2 Vols. rev. ed. Karl Werner. 1889. 50.50 (ISBN 0-8337-3731-7). B Franklin.

Fraternidade Shamballah. Jan Van Rijckenborgh & Catharose De Petri. (Span.). 1987. pap. 11.00. Rosycross Pr.

Fraternitas Rosae Crucis. R. Swinburne Clymer. 1929. 9.95 (ISBN 0-932785-11-5). Philos Pub.

Fraternity of the Rosy Cross. Thomas Vaughan. Ed. by A. E. Waite. 1983. pap. 5.95 (ISBN 0-916411-07-9, Pub. by Alchemical Pr). Holmes Pub.

Frau in den Religionen der Menschheit. Friedrich Heiler. Ed. by Anne M. Heiler. (Theologische Bibliothek Toepelmann: Vol. 33). 1977. 15.20x (ISBN 3-11-006583-5). De Gruyter.

Fraud Corruption & Holiness: The Controversy over the Supervision of Jewish Dietary Practice in New York City. Harold P. Gastwirt. LC 74-77649. 1974. 23.95x (ISBN 0-8046-9056-1, Pub. by Kennikat). Assoc Faculty Pr.

Fray Angelico Chavez: A Bibliography of His Published Writings (1925-1978) Phyllis S. Morales. LC 77-73462. 1980. 15.00 (ISBN 0-89016-035-X). Lightning Tree.

Fray Jose de Guadalupe Mojica: Mi Guia y Mi Estrella. Gonzalo De Jesus. (Illus.). 100p. 1976. 2.00 (ISBN 0-8199-0570-4). Franciscan Herald.

Fray Juan Crespi, Missionary Explorer on the Pacific Coast, 1769-1774. Herbert E. Bolton. LC 78-158616. Repr. of 1927 ed. 29.50 (ISBN 0-404-01838-6). AMS Pr.

Freaks of Fanaticism, & Other Strange Events. S. Baring-Gould. 59.95 (ISBN 0-8490-0193-5). Gordon Pr.

Freaks of Fanaticism & Other Strange Events. Sabine Baring-Gould. LC 68-21754. 1968. Repr. of 1891 ed. 40.00x (ISBN 0-8103-3503-4). Gale.

Freddie & the Ten Commandments. 3rd ed. Barbara M. Williams. 1978. 0.95 (ISBN 0-686-05835-6). Crusade Pubs.

Frederick Baraga: A Portrait of the First Bishop of Marquette Based on the Archives of the Congregatio De Propaganda Fide. Maksimiljan Jezernik. LC 68-16856. 155p. 1968. 8.00 (ISBN 0-686-28380-5); pap. 6.00 (ISBN 0-686-28381-3). Studia Slovenica.

Frederick Denison Maurice: Rebellious Conformist, 1805-1872. Olive J. Brose. LC 74-141380. xxiii, 308p. 1971. 16.00x (ISBN 0-8214-0092-4). Ohio U Pr.

Frederick M. Smith: Saint as Reformer. Larry E. Hunt. LC 81-7213. 1982. Vol. 1. pap. 12.00 (ISBN 0-8309-0320-8); Vol. 2. 12.00 (ISBN 0-8309-0341-0). Herald Hse.

Fredrik Franson: Model for Worldwide Evangelism. Edward P. Torjesen. LC 82-17892. 128p. (Orig.). 1983. pap. 4.95 (ISBN 0-87808-191-7). William Carey Lib.

Free & Faithful in Christ: General Moral Theology. Bernard Haring. (Free & Faithful in Christ Ser.: Vol. 1). 506p. 1987. pap. 19.50 (ISBN 0-8245-0308-2). Crossroad NY.

Free & Faithful in Christ: Light to the World, Vol. 3. Bernard Haring. 500p. 1981. 19.50 (ISBN 0-8245-0009-1). Crossroad NY.

Free & Faithful in Christ: The Truth Will Set You Free. Bernard Haring. (Free & Faithful in Christ Ser.: Vol. 2). 592p. pap. 14.95 (ISBN 0-8245-0501-8). Crossroad NY.

Free & Faithful in Christ: The Truth Will Set You Free, Vol. 2. Bernard Haring. 560p. 1979. 19.50 (ISBN 0-8245-0309-0). Crossroad NY.

Free at Last. Bob Moorehead. LC 86-71102. 88p. (Orig.). 1986. pap. 3.95 (ISBN 0-89900-212-9). College Pr Pub.

Free, but Not Cheap. Matthew Skariah. LC 85-91360. 144p. (Orig.). 1986. pap. 3.50 (ISBN 0-933495-01-3). World Prayer.

Free Church in a Free Society: The Ecclesiology of John England Bishop of Charleston, 1820-1842. Peter Clarke. 561p. 1983. (Pub. by John England Stud Inc); pap. 15.95x (ISBN 0-87921-073-7). Attic Pr.

Free Church Perspective: A Study in Ecclesiology. Stewart A. Newman. 113p. (Orig.). 1986. pap. 8.95 (ISBN 0-913029-12-2). Stevens Bk Pr.

Free Discussion of the Doctrine of Materialism and Philosophical Necessity, 1778. Richard Price. Ed. by Rene Wellek. LC 75-11247. (British Philosophers & Theologians of the 17th & 18th Centuries Ser.). 1978. lib. bdg. 51.00 (ISBN 0-8240-1798-6). Garland Pub.

Free Enquiry into the Miraculous Powers, Which Are Supposed to Have Subsisted in the Christian Church. Conyers Middleton. Ed. by Rene Wellek. LC 75-11235. (British Philosophers & Theologians of the 17th & 18th Centuries: Vol. 36). 1976. Repr. of 1749 ed. lib. bdg. 51.00 (ISBN 0-8240-1788-9). Garland Pub.

Free Enquiry into the Nature & Origin of Evil. 2nd ed. Soame Jenyns. Ed. by Rene Wellek. LC 75-11226. (British Philosophers & Theologians of the 17th & 18th Centuries: Vol. 28). 1976. Repr. of 1757 ed. lib. bdg. 51.00 (ISBN 0-8240-1780-3). Garland Pub.

Free Enterprise: A Judeo-Christian Defense. Harold Lindsell. 1982. pap. 6.95 (ISBN 0-8423-0922-5). Tyndale.

Free Enterprise & Jewish Law: Aspects of Jewish Business Ethics. Aaron Levine. 1979. 20.00 (ISBN 0-87068-702-6). Ktav.

Free from All Error: Authorship, Inerrancy, Historicity of Scripture, Church Teaching, & Modern Scripture Scholars. William G. Most. 179p. (Orig.). 1985. pap. 11.95 (ISBN 0-913382-51-5, 101-31). Prow Bks-Franciscan.

Free from Guilt & Condemnation. Don Hughes. (Orig.). 1977. pap. 0.75 minibook (ISBN 0-89274-048-5, HH-048). Harrison Hse.

Free in Christ. Warren McWilliams. LC 84-2812. 1984. pap. 3.75 (ISBN 0-8054-1609-9). Broadman.

Free Indeed! Ras Robinson. (Illus.). 1983. pap. 1.00 (ISBN 0-937778-08-7). Fulness Hse.

Free Man & the Soldier. facsimile ed. Ralph B. Perry. LC 73-24250. (Select Bibliographies Reprint Ser.). Repr. of 1916 ed. 16.00 (ISBN 0-8369-5438-6). Ayer Co Pubs.

Free Produce Movement. Ruth K. Nuermberger. LC 73-110135. (Duke University. Trinity College Historical Society. Historical Papers: No. 25). Repr. of 1942 ed. 24.50 (ISBN 0-404-51775-7). AMS Pr.

Free Pulpit in Action. facsimile ed. Ed. by Clarence R. Skinner. LC 71-156718. (Essay Index Reprint Ser.). Repr. of 1931 ed. 22.00 (ISBN 0-8369-2333-2). Ayer Co Pubs.

Free Religion: An American Faith. Stow Persons. 1947. 49.50x (ISBN 0-686-83554-9). Elliots Bks.

Free Speech in the Church. Karl Rahner. LC 79-8717. Orig. Title: Freie Wort in der Kirche. 112p. 1981. Repr. of 1959 ed. lib. bdg. 22.50x (ISBN 0-313-20849-2, RAFS). Greenwood.

Free Thoughts on Religion, the Church, & National Happiness. Bernard Mandeville. LC 77-17171. 1981. Repr. of 1720 ed. lib. bdg. 60.00x (ISBN 0-8201-1300-X). Schol Facsimiles.

Free to Be Different. American ed. Malcolm A. Jeeves et al. LC 84-10525. Repr. of 1985 ed. 40.80 (2027547). Bks Demand UMI.

Free to Be Thin. Marie Chapian. LC 79-15656. (Illus.). 192p. 1979. pap. 5.95 (ISBN 0-87123-560-9, 210560); study guide (No. 1) by Neva Coyle 64 pgs. 2.50 (ISBN 0-87123-163-8, 210163). Bethany Hse.

Free to Be Thin Study Guide Discipline, No. 2. Neva Coyle. 58p. 1982. pap. 2.25 (ISBN 0-87123-169-7, 210169). Bethany Hse.

Free to Choose. McCasland. 1983. 3.95 (ISBN 0-88207-593-4). Victor Bks.

Free to Grieve: Coping with the Trauma of Miscarriage. Maureen Rank. 176p. 1985. pap. 5.95 (ISBN 0-87123-806-3, 210806). Bethany Hse.

Free to Share. R. Edward Davenport. LC 82-62743. 183p. (Orig.). 1983. pap. text ed. 6.95 (ISBN 0-87148-337-8). Pathway Pr.

Free to Stay Home. Marilee Horton. 177p. 1984. pap. text ed. 5.95 (ISBN 0-8499-3011-1, 3011-1). Word Bks.

Free Will & Fatalism. Arthur Schopenhauer. (Illus.). 131p. 1985. 97.85 (ISBN 0-89266-508-4). Am Classical Coll Pr.

Free Will & Values. R. Kane. (Series in Philosophy). 328p. 1985. 44.50 (ISBN 0-88706-101-X); pap. 18.95 (ISBN 0-88706-102-8). State U NY Pr.

Free Will Baptist Doctrines. J. D. O'Donnell. 1974. pap. 4.95 (ISBN 0-89265-019-2). Randall Hse.

Free Will Baptist Minister's Manual. Billy A. Melvin. 1974. ringbinder 8.95 (ISBN 0-89265-024-9). Randall Hse.

Free Will Baptist Missions, Missionaries, & Their Message. Bill Jones. (Way of Life Ser.). 1972. pap. 1.50 (ISBN 0-89265-008-7, Free Will Baptist Dept); tchr's guide 3.95 (ISBN 0-89265-007-9). Randall Hse.

Free Will Baptists in America, 1727-1984. William F. Davidson. 462p. 1985. text ed. 14.95 (ISBN 0-89265-093-1). Randall Hse.

Freed to Love: A Process Interpretation of Redemption. Norman Pittenger. 1987. pap. 8.95. Morehouse.

Freeda Harris: Woman of Prayer. Ethel McIndoo. LC 84-2978. (Meet the Missionary Ser.). 1984. 5.50 (ISBN 0-8054-4286-3, 4242-86). Broadman.

Freedom. Ed. by George F. McLean. LC 77-153528. (Proceedings of the American Catholic Philosophical Association: Vol. 50). 1976. pap. 15.00 (ISBN 0-918090-10-5). Am Cath Philo.

Freedom: A Guarantee for Everybody. Kenneth D. Barney. LC 75-34644. (Radiant Life Ser.). 128p. 1976. pap. 2.50 (ISBN 0-88243-891-3, 02-0891, Radiant Bks); teacher's ed 3.95 (ISBN 0-88243-165-X, 32-0165). Gospel Pub.

Freedom & Authority in Our Time: Proceeding. Conference on Science-Philosophy & Religion in Their Relation to the Democratic Way of Live, 12th, New York. 1953. 51.00 (ISBN 0-527-00659-9). Kraus Repr.

Freedom & Civilization among the Greeks. A. J. Festugiere. Tr. & intro. by P. T. Brannan. (Princeton Theological Monograph: No. 10). Tr. of Liberte et Civilisation chez les Grecs. (Orig.). 1987. pap. price not set (ISBN 0-915138-98-0). Pickwick.

Freedom & Determinism. Ed. by Keith Lehrer. 204p. 1976. pap. text ed. 7.95x (ISBN 0-391-00537-5). Humanities.

Freedom & Equality: Civil Liberties & the Supreme Court. Gilbert L. Oddo. LC 78-25592. 1979. pap. text ed. write for info. (ISBN 0-673-16262-1). Scott F.

Freedom & Grace: The Life of Asa Mahan. Edward H. Madden & James E. Hamilton. LC 82-5724. (Studies in Evangelicalism: No. 3). 287p. 1982. 19.00 (ISBN 0-8108-1555-9). Scarecrow.

Freedom & Influence: The Role of Religion in American Society. George M. Williams. 318p. 1985. write for info.; pap. write for info. (ISBN 0-915678-15-2). World Tribune Pr.

Freedom & Reason. Richard M. Hare. (Oxford Paperbacks Ser.: No. 92). 1965. pap. text ed. 8.95x (ISBN 0-19-881092-X). Oxford U Pr.

Freedom & the Modern World. Jacques Maritain. Tr. by Richard O'Sullivan. LC 77-150414. 231p. 1971. Repr. of 1936 ed. 15.00x (ISBN 0-87752-147-6). Gordian.

Freedom & the Spirit. Nicolas Berdyaev. LC 72-2567. (Select Bibliographies Reprint Ser.). 1972. Repr. of 1935 ed. 24.50 (ISBN 0-8369-6848-4). Ayer Co Pubs.

Freedom & Transcendence. Krishna Chairanya. 1983. 28.00x (ISBN 0-8364-0953-1, Pub. by Manohar India). South Asia Bks.

Freedom & Value. Ed. by Robert O. Johann. LC 76-13969. xii, 186p. 1976. pap. 9.00 (ISBN 0-8232-1011-1). Fordham.

Freedom & Virtue: The Conservative Libertarian Debate. Ed. by George W. Carey. LC 84-19637. 164p. (Orig.). 1985. lib. bdg. 25.25 (ISBN 0-8191-4334-0, Co-Pub. by Intercollegiate Studies); pap. text ed. 9.50 (ISBN 0-8191-4335-9, Co-pub. by Intercollegiate Studies). U Pr of Amer.

Freedom, Enjoyment, & Happiness: An Essay on Moral Psychology. Richard Warner. LC 86-19696. (Illus.). 208p. 1987. text ed. 19.95x (ISBN 0-8014-1977-8). Cornell U Pr.

Freedom for Ministry: A Critical Affirmation of the Church & Its Mission. Richard J. Neuhaus. LC 78-3352. 256p. 1984. pap. 7.95 (ISBN 0-06-066095-3, RD 505, HarpR). Har-Row.

Freedom from a Self-Centered Life. William Law. Ed. by Andrew Murray. LC 77-71426. 144p. 1977. pap. 3.50 (ISBN 0-87123-104-2, 200104). Bethany Hse.

Freedom from Bad Habits. Charles Cerling. LC 84-62384. 141p. (Orig.). 1984. pap. 5.95 (ISBN 0-89840-079-1). Heres Life.

Freedom from Fear. Perry A. Gaspard. 1980. pap. 2.00 (ISBN 0-931867-06-1). Abundant Life Pubns.

Freedom from Sin: Romans Six Through Seven. John MacArthur, Jr. (John MacArthur Bible Studies Ser.). 1987. pap. 4.50 (ISBN 0-8024-5309-0). Moody.

Freedom from Sinful Thoughts: Christ Alone Breaks the Curse. Heini Arnold. LC 73-20199. 130p. 1973. 3.50 (ISBN 0-87486-115-2). Plough.

Freedom from Stress. Ernest Holmes. Ed. by Willis H. Kinnear. 96p. 1964. pap. 4.50 (ISBN 0-911336-30-3). Sci of Mind.

Freedom from the Bondage of Karma. 2nd ed. Swami Rama. 92p. pap. 5.95 (ISBN 0-89389-031-6). Himalayan Pubs.

Freedom in Christ. Robert C. Douglas. Ed. by J. D. Thomas. LC 72-140290. (Twentieth Century Sermons Ser). 1970. 11.95 (ISBN 0-89112-305-9, Bibl Res Pr). Abilene Christ U.

Freedom in God: A Guide to the Thought of Nicholas Berdyaev. E. L. Allen. LC 73-5751. lib. bdg. 12.50 (ISBN 0-8414-1740-7). Folcroft.

Freedom in Meditation. Patricia Carrington. LC 76-6240. 384p. 1977. pap. 12.00. Pace Educ Systems.

Freedom in Molina. Gerard Smith. 1966. 2.25 (ISBN 0-8294-0070-2). Loyola.

Freedom In the Spirit. Lloyd John Ogilvie. LC 83-82318. 192p. 1984. pap. 4.95 (ISBN 0-89081-444-9). Harvest Hse.

Freedom Isn't Free. Evelyn Friesen & Sam Phu. 165p. (Orig.). 1985. pap. 6.65 (ISBN 0-318-18903-8). Kindred Pr.

Freedom of Choice in Education. Virgil C. Blum. LC 77-8086. 1977. Repr. of 1958 ed. lib. bdg. 22.50x (ISBN 0-8371-9677-9, BLFC). Greenwood.

Freedom of Expression in the Jewish Tradition. Jacob J. Petuchowski. 34p. 1984. pap. 2.50 (ISBN 0-87495-062-7). Am Jewish Comm.

Freedom of Forgiveness. David Augsburger. 128p. 1973. pap. 3.50 (ISBN 0-8024-2875-4). Moody.

Freedom of Forgiveness. David Augsburger. (Moody Press Electives Ser.). 1984. pap. 3.95 (ISBN 0-8024-0695-5); leader's guide 2.50 (ISBN 0-8024-0692-0). Moody.

Freedom of God. James Daane. 5.95 (ISBN 0-8028-3421-3). Fuller Theol Soc.

Freedom of God's Sons: Studies in Galatians. Homer A. Kent, Jr. (Illus.). pap. 5.95 (ISBN 0-88469-058-X). BMH Bks.

Freedom of Morality. Christos Yannaras. Tr. by Elizabeth Briere from Gr. LC 84-9030. 272p. (Orig.). 1984. pap. text ed. 12.95 (ISBN 0-88141-028-4). St Vladimirs.

Freedom of Obedience. Martha Thatcher. (Christian Character Library). 1986. hdbk. 8.95 (ISBN 0-89109-541-1). NavPress.

Freedom of Religion. Ed. by Haig A. Bosmajian. (First Amendment in the Classroom Ser.: No. 2). 455p. 1987. text ed. 24.95 (ISBN 1-55570-002-0). Neal-Schuman.

Freedom of Religion in America: Historical Roots, Philosophical Concepts, Contemporary Problems. Henry B. Clark, II. 143p. 1982. pap. 6.95 (ISBN 0-87855-925-6). Transaction Bks.

Freedom of Religious Expression in the Public High Schools. John W. Whitehead. LC 83-72040. (Rutherford Institute Reports: No. 1). 64p. 1983. pap. 3.95 (ISBN 0-89107-295-0, Crossway Bks). Good News.

Freedom of Simplicity. Richard J. Foster. LC 80-8351. 192p. 1981. 13.45 (ISBN 0-06-062832-4, HarpR). Har-Row.

Freedom of Speech & Human Rights: An International Perspective. Daniel M. Rohrer. 1979. pap. text ed. 12.95 (ISBN 0-8403-1987-8, 40198701). Kendall-Hunt.

Freedom of the Will. Jonathan Edwards. Ed. by Arnold S. Kaufman & William K. Frankena. LC 82-18742. 300p. 1982. pap. text ed. 14.95x (ISBN 0-8290-1264-8). Irvington.

Freedom of the Will. Jonathan Edwards. Ed. by Paul Ramsey. (Works of Jonathan Edwards Ser.: Vol. 1). (Illus.). 1957. 50.00x (ISBN 0-300-00848-1). Yale U Pr.

Freedom or Order? The Eucharistic Liturgy in English Congregationalism 1645-1980. Bryan D. Spinks. (Pittsburgh Theological Monographs: New Ser. 8). (Orig.). 1984. pap. 22.50 (ISBN 0-915138-33-6). Pickwick.

Freedom Reports: The Internal Revenue Service. pap. 5.00 (ISBN 0-915598-40-X). Church of Scient Info.

Freedom, the Essence of Life. Gregory E. Penn. LC 78-75026. 1979. pap. 5.95 (ISBN 0-87516-288-6). De Vorss.

Freedom Through the Balisier. Cyril H. Boynes. LC 83-40235. 148p. (Orig.). 1984. pap. 4.75 (ISBN 0-8356-0584-1, Quest). Theos Pub Hse.

Freedom to Be Free. Arturo Paoli. Tr. by Charles U. Quinn from It. LC 72-93340. Tr. of Dialogo Della Liberazione. 320p. (Orig.). 1973. pap. 2.48 (ISBN 0-88344-143-8). Orbis Bks.

Freedom to Be Wrong. Alvin Rueter. 1985. 6.25 (ISBN 0-89536-749-1, 5855). CSS of Ohio.

Freedom to Choose. Ernest J. Gruen. 224p. 1976. pap. 2.95 (ISBN 0-88368-072-6). Whitaker Hse.

Freedom to Live. Ernest Holmes. Ed. by Willis H. Kinnear. 96p. 1969. pap. 4.50 (ISBN 0-911336-35-4). Sci of Mind.

Freedom under Siege. Madalyn M. O'Hair. 282p. cancelled (ISBN 0-911826-25-4). Am Atheist.

Freedom with Justice: Catholic Social Thought & Liberal Institutions. Michael Novak. LC 84-47731. 272p. 1984. 17.45 (ISBN 0-06-066317-0, HarpR). Har-Row.

Freedom with Order: The Doctrine of the Church in the United Church of Christ. Robert S. Paul. 160p. (Orig.). 1987. pap. 8.95 (ISBN 0-8298-0749-7). Pilgrim NY.

Freedom Years. Larry Ferguson & Dave Jackson. (Family Ministry Ser.). (Illus.). 54p. 1985. pap. text ed. 19.95 (ISBN 0-89191-966-X). Cook.

Freedom's Holy Light. Harold A. Seward. (Illus.). 88p. 1986. 10.95 (ISBN 0-8059-3021-3). Dorrance.

Freeing of the Deer & Other New Mexico Indian Myths. Carmen G. Espinosa. LC 85-16406. (Illus.). 83p. 1985. 9.95 (ISBN 0-8263-0840-6). U of NM Pr.

Freemasonry & Christianity. Alva J. McClain. 1979. pap. 1.00 (ISBN 0-88469-012-1). BMH Bks.

Freemasonry & the Anti-Christian Movement. E. Cahill. 59.95 (ISBN 0-8490-0195-1). Gordon Pr.

Freemasonry & the Vatican. Leon De Poncins. 1982. lib. bdg. 69.95 (ISBN 0-87700-351-3). Revisionist Pr.

Freemasonry & the Vatican. Leon V. DePoncins. 59.95 (ISBN 0-8490-0196-X). Gordon Pr.

Freemasonry Exposed. William Morgan. 8.50 (ISBN 0-685-19475-2). Powner.

Freemasonry Handbook. Ronayne. 9.00x (ISBN 0-685-21949-6). Wehman.

Freemasonry in American History. Allen E. Roberts. (Illus.). 504p. 1985. text ed. 20.00 (ISBN 0-88053-078-2). Macoy Pub.

Freemasonry in Federalist Connecticut, 1789-1835. Dorothy Ann Lipson. 1977. 40.00 (ISBN 0-691-04646-8). Princeton U Pr.

Freemasonry in Indonesia from Radermacher to Soekanto, 1762-1961. Paul W. Van der Veur. LC 76-620040. (Papers in International Studies: Southeast Asia Ser.: No. 40). (Illus.). 1976. pap. 4.00x (ISBN 0-89680-026-1, 82-90413, Ohio U Ctr Intl). Ohio U Pr.

Freemasonry in the Holy Land: Handmarks of Hiram's Builders. Robert Morris. Ed. by Moshe Davis. LC 77-70731. (America & the Holy Land Ser.). (Illus.). 1977. Repr. of 1872 ed. lib. bdg. 46.50x (ISBN 0-405-10270-4). Ayer Co Pubs.

Freemasonry Known by the Masonic Diploma. Apostolos Makrakis. Tr. by Denver Cummings. 135p. (Orig.). 1956. pap. 4.50 (ISBN 0-938366-42-4). Orthodox Chr.

Freemasonry of the Ancient Egyptians. Manly P. Hall. 10.50 (ISBN 0-89314-803-2). Philos Res.

Freemasonry Through Six Centuries, 2 vols. Henry W. Coil. 600p. 1976. Repr. of 1966 ed. text ed. 23.50 slipcase (ISBN 0-88053-034-0). Macoy Pub.

Freemasonry Unmasked. George E. Dillon. Pref. by Denis Fuhley. 114p. 1984. pap. 6.00 (ISBN 0-89562-095-2). Sons Lib.

Freethinker's Textbook: Christianity, Its Evidences, Its Origin, Its Morality, Its History, Pt. 2. 3rd ed. Annie Besant. LC 77-169205. (Atheist Viewpoint Ser). 288p. 1972. Repr. 21.00 (ISBN 0-405-03803-8). Ayer Co Pubs.

Freethought in the United Kingdom & the Commonwealth: A Descriptive Bibliography. Gordon Stein. LC 80-1792. xxiii, 193p. 1981. lib. bdg. 39.95 (ISBN 0-313-20869-7, SFU/). Greenwood.

Freethought Versus Religion: The Atheist Challenge. Carl Shapiro. 50p. 1977. 8.00x (ISBN 0-914937-06-5). Ind Pubns.

Freeway to Health. Paul L. Peck. (Spiritual Metaphysics: Freeways to Divine Awareness Ser.). 264p. (Orig.). 1982. pap. 7.95 (ISBN 0-941600-04-1). Harmony Pr.

Freeway to Human Love. Paul L. Peck. (Spiritual Metaphysics: Freeways to Divine Awareness Ser.). 264p. (Orig.). 1982. pap. 7.95 (ISBN 0-941600-06-8). Harmony Pr.

Freeway to Perfection: A Collection of Mormon Cartoons. Calvin Grondahl. (Illus.). 96p. (Orig.). 1980. pap. 4.50 (ISBN 0-9606760-1-5). Sunstone Found.

Freeway to Personal Growth. Paul L. Peck. (Spiritual Awareness: Freeways to Divine Awareness Ser.). 264p. (Orig.). 1982. pap. 7.95 (ISBN 0-941600-07-6). Harmony Pr.

Freeway to Work & Health. Paul L. Peck. (Spiritual Metaphysics: Freeways to Divine Awareness Ser.). 264p. (Orig.). 1982. pap. 7.95 (ISBN 0-941600-05-X). Harmony Pr.

Freewill & Responsibility: Four Lectures. Anthony Kenny. 1978. 15.00x (ISBN 0-7100-8998-8). Methuen Inc.

Freiheit Von Gedankensunden Nur Christus Bricht Den Fluch. Heini Arnold. LC 73-20198. (Ger.). 118p. 1973. text ed. 3.50. Plough.

Fremde Am Fluss. Paul Twitchell. 1979. pap. 5.95 (ISBN 0-914766-43-0). Iwp Pub.

French Catholic Missionaries in the Present United States (1604-1791) Sr. Mary D. Mulvey. LC 73-3578. (Catholic University of America. Studies in American Church History: No. 23). Repr. of 1936 ed. 23.00 (ISBN 0-404-57773-3). AMS Pr.

French Coast. Martin Collins. (Visitor's Guide Ser.). (Illus.). 144p. (Orig.). 1986. pap. 8.95. Hunter Pub NY.

French Creek Presbyterian Church. Lois M. Pinnell. (Illus.). 1971. 10.00 (ISBN 0-87012-110-3). McClain.

French Devotional Texts of the Middle Ages: A Bibliographic Manuscript Guide. Compiled by Keith V. Sinclair. LC 79-7587. 1979. lib. bdg. 49.95x (ISBN 0-313-20649-X, SFT/). Greenwood.

French Devotional Texts of the Middle Ages: A Bibliographic Manuscript Guide, First Supplement. Ed. by Keith V. Sinclair. LC 82-11773. xvi, 234p. 1982. lib. bdg. 65.00 (ISBN 0-313-23664-X, SIF/). Greenwood.

French Emigre Priests in the United States (1791-1815) Leo F. Ruskowski. LC 73-3586. (Catholic University of America. Studies in American Church History: No. 32). Repr. of 1940 ed. 21.00 (ISBN 0-404-57782-2). AMS Pr.

French Enlightenment & the Jews. Arthur Hertzberg. LC 68-18996. pap. 108.00 (ISBN 0-317-26825-2, 2023485). Bks Demand UMI.

French Existentialism, a Christian Critique. Frederick T. Kingston. LC 61-925. pap. 59.30 (ISBN 0-317-08761-4, 2014272). Bks Demand UMI.

French Foreign Policy During the Administration of Cardinal Fleury: 1726-1743; a Study in Diplomacy & Commercial Development. Arthur M. Wilson. LC 70-138193. 433p. 1972. Repr. of 1936 ed. lib. bdg. 22.50x (ISBN 0-8371-5333-6, WIFP). Greenwood.

French Freemasonry under the Third Republic. Mildred J. Headings. LC 78-64206. (Johns Hopkins University. Studies in the Social Sciences. Sixty-Sixth Ser. 1948: 1). Repr. of 1949 ed. 26.00 (ISBN 0-404-61311-X). AMS Pr.

French Huguenots. Janet G. Gray. LC 81-67172. 200p. (Orig.). 1981. pap. 8.95 (ISBN 0-8010-3758-1). Baker Bk.

French Jesuits in Lower Louisiana (1700-1763) Jean Delanglez. LC 73-3576. (Catholic University of America. Studies in American Church History: No. 21). Repr. of 1935 ed. 46.00 (ISBN 0-404-57771-7). AMS Pr.

French Laic Laws: 1879-1889. Evelyn M. Acomb. LC 67-18747. 1968. Repr. lib. bdg. 21.50 (ISBN 0-374-90038-8, Octagon). Hippocrene Bks.

French Philosophers-New England Transcendentalism. Walter L. Leighton. LC 68-19289. 1968. Repr. of 1908 ed. lib. bdg. 22.50x (ISBN 0-8371-0143-3, LEPT). Greenwood.

French Prophets: The History of a Millenarian Group in Eighteenth-Century England. Hillel Schwartz. LC 78-65459. (Illus.). 1980. 42.00x (ISBN 0-520-03815-0). U of Cal Pr.

French Protestantism, Fifteen Fifty-Nine to Fifteen Sixty-Two. Caleb G. Kelly. LC 78-63967. (Johns Hopkins University. Studies in the Social Sciences, 1918: No. 3). Repr. of 1918 ed. 24.50 (ISBN 0-404-61213-X). AMS Pr.

French Protestantism, Fifteen Fifty-Nine to Fifteen Sixty-Two. Caleb G. Kelly. LC 83-45621. Date not set. Repr. of 1918 ed. 24.50 (ISBN 0-404-19839-2). AMS Pr.

French Pulpit Oratory: Fifteen Ninety-Eight to Sixteen Fifty. P. Bayley. LC 79-50175. 1980. 57.50 (ISBN 0-521-22765-8). Cambridge U Pr.

French Reformation. Mark Greengrass. 96p. 1987. pap. text ed. 7.95 (ISBN 0-631-14516-8). Basil Blackwell.

French Revolution & the Church. John McManners. LC 82-15532. x, 161p. 1982. Repr. of 1969 ed. lib. bdg. 22.50x (ISBN 0-313-23074-9, MCFR). Greenwood.

Frenchman, a Chaplain, a Rebel: The War Letters of Pere Louis-Hippolyte Gache, S. J. Louis-Hippolyte Gache. Tr. by Cornelius M. Buckley. 282p. 1981. 8.95 (ISBN 0-8294-0376-0). Loyola.

Frente Al Cancer, Un Gigante a Mi Lado. Sara H. Martin. (Span.). 96p. 1985. pap. 4.50 (ISBN 0-311-46101-8). Casa Bautista.

Frequent Confession. Benedict Baur. 224p. 1980. 7.00 (ISBN 0-906127-20-3). Lumen Christi.

Frescoes of St. Demetrius' Cathedral. V. Plugin. 44p. 1974. 25.00x (ISBN 0-569-08164-5, Pub. by Collets UK). State Mutual Bk.

Fresh Approach to the New Testament & Early Christian Literature. Martin Dibelius. LC 78-32096. 1979. Repr. of 1936 ed. lib. bdg. 24.75x (ISBN 0-8371-4219-9, DINT). Greenwood.

Fresh Bread & Other Gifts of Spiritual Nourishment. Joyce Rupp. LC 85-70020. 160p. (Orig.). 1985. pap. 4.95 (ISBN 0-87793-283-2). Ave Maria.

Fresh Ideas for Discipleship & Nurture. Ed. by Dean Merrill. Marshall Shelley. (Fresh Ideas Ser.). 190p. 1984. pap. 6.95 (ISBN 0-917463-02-1). Chr Today.

Fresh Ideas for Preaching, Worship & Evangelism. Ed. by Dean Merrill & Marshall Shelley. (Fresh Ideas Ser.). 155p. 1984. pap. 6.95 (ISBN 0-917463-00-5). Chr Today.

Fresh Look at the Gospel. Marlene Wesner & Miles E. Wesner. LC 82-72231. (Orig.). 1983. pap. 5.95 (ISBN 0-8054-1955-1). Broadman.

Fresh New Look at God. Don Baker. LC 85-29659. 1986. 8.95 (ISBN 0-88070-104-8). Multnomah.

Fresh Suit Against Human Ceremonies in God's Worship. William Ames. 886p. Repr. of 1633 ed. text ed. 82.80x (ISBN 0-576-99734-X, Pub. by Gregg Intl Pubs England). Gregg Intl.

Fresh Wind of the Spirit. Kenneth C. Kinghorn. 128p. 1986. pap. 6.95 (ISBN 0-310-75221-3, 17033P). Zondervan.

Freske i Ikone u Makedoniji, iv-xv vek (Frescos & Icons in Macedonia, iv-xv Centory) Kosta Balabanov. 158p. 1983. 20.00 (ISBN 0-918660-26-2). Ragusan Pr.

Freud & Future Religious Experience. Anthony J. De Luca. (Quality Paperback Ser: No. 330). 263p. 1977. pap. 4.95 (ISBN 0-8226-0330-6). Littlefield.

Freud & Man's Soul. Bruno Bettelheim. LC 82-47809. 112p. 1983. 11.95 (ISBN 0-394-52481-0). Knopf.

Freud & Religious Belief. Howard L. Philp. LC 72-12635. 140p. 1974. Repr. of 1956 ed. lib. bdg. 22.50x (ISBN 0-8371-6682-9, PHFR). Greenwood.

Freud & the Problem of God. Hans Kung. Tr. by Edward Quinn. LC 78-25581. (Terry Lecture Ser.). 136p. 1980. 19.50 (ISBN 0-300-02350-2, Y-237); pap. 5.95 (ISBN 0-300-02597-1). Yale U Pr.

Freud on Ritual: Reconstruction & Critique. Volney P. Gay. LC 79-11385. (American Academy of Religion, Dissertation Ser.: No. 26). 1979. 14.00 (ISBN 0-89130-282-4, 010126); pap. 9.95 (ISBN 0-89130-301-4). Scholars Pr Ga.

Friar as Critic: Literary Attitudes in the Later Middle Ages. Judson B. Allen. LC 77-123037. 1971. 11.50x (ISBN 0-8265-1158-9). Vanderbilt U Pr.

Friar in Fiction, Sincerity in Art, & Other Essays. facs. ed. Joseph S. Kennard. LC 68-20313. (Essay Index Reprint Ser). 1923. 20.00 (ISBN 0-8369-0588-1). Ayer Co Pubs.

Friar Thomas d'Aquino: His Life, Thought, & Work. James A. Weisheipl. LC 83-14326. 487p. 1983. pap. 16.95 (ISBN 0-8132-0590-5). Cath U Pr.

Friars & the Jews: The Evolution of Medieval Anti-Judaism. Jeremy Cohen. LC 81-15210. 304p. 1984. pap. 10.95x (ISBN 0-8014-9266-1). Cornell U Pr.

Friday Afternoon: Reflections on the Seven Last Words. Neville Ward. 144p. 1984. pap. 5.95 (ISBN 0-86683-744-2, AY8397, HarpR). Har-Row.

Friedrich Schiller & Swabian Pietism. Arthur W. McCardle. (American University Studies I-Germanic Languages & Literature: Vol. 36). 236p. 1986. text ed. 40.65 (ISBN 0-8204-0196-X). P Lang Pubs.

Friedrich Schleiermacher. C. W. Christian. 157p. 1984. pap. text ed. 8.95 (ISBN 0-8499-3005-7, 3005-7). Word Bks.

Friend of Chiefs, Robert Moffat. Iris Clinton. (Stories of Faith & Fame). 1975. pap. 2.95 (ISBN 0-87508-608-X). Chr Lit.

Friend of Life: A Biography of Rufus M. Jones. 2nd ed. Elizabeth G. Vining. (Illus.). 347p. 1981. pap. 8.95 (ISBN 0-941308-00-6). Religious Soc Friends.

Friend of Little Children: Story of Our Lord's Life Told for Children. J. Sinclair Stevenson. 1978. Repr. lib. bdg. 25.00 (ISBN 0-8495-4876-4). Arden Lib.

Friend to All Men. Egide van Broeckhover. 5.95 (ISBN 0-317-06463-0). Dimension Bks.

Friend to Friend: How You Can Help a Friend Through a Problem. J. David Stone & Larry Keefauver. LC 83-80942. (Illus.). 80p. (Orig.). 1983. pap. 5.95 (ISBN 0-936664-11-8). Group Bks.

Friendless American Male: Leader's Guide. David M. Baldwin. LC 82-21518. 48p. 1984. pap. 3.95 (ISBN 0-8307-0991-6, 6101914). Regal.

Friendly Beasts: An Old English Christmas Carol. Tomie De Paola. (Illus.). 32p. 1981. 10.95 (ISBN 0-399-20739-2); pap. 4.95 (ISBN 0-399-20777-5). Putnam Pub Group.

Friendly Philosopher. Robert Crosbie. (Illus.). vii, 415p. 1934. Repr. 6.00 (ISBN 0-938998-13-7). Theosophy.

Friends. Sandy Ziegler. Ed. by Jane Buerger. 112p. 1980. 5.95 (ISBN 0-89565-174-2, 4931). Standard Pub.

Friends & Faith: How to Use Friendship Evangelism In Youth Ministry. Larry Keefauver. LC 86-7577. 156p. (Orig.). 1986. pap. 9.95 (ISBN 0-931529-10-7). Group Bks.

Friends & the Racial Crisis. Richard Taylor. LC 70-129552. (Orig.). pap. 2.50x (ISBN 0-87574-172-X). Pendle Hill.

Friends & the World of Nature. Theodor Benfey. LC 80-82941. 28p. (Orig.). 1980. pap. 2.50x (ISBN 0-87574-233-5). Pendle Hill.

Friends & Their Children: A Study in Quaker Education. Harold Loukes. LC 79-12928. 1979. Repr. of 1958 ed. lib. bdg. 22.50x (ISBN 0-313-21150-7, LOFT). Greenwood.

Friends Aren't Kept Waiting. Francis P. Lebuffe. 1975. pap. 1.75 (ISBN 0-88479-000-2). Arena Lettres.

Friends: Becoming a Friend Finder & Keeper. Ed. by Kevin Miller. (Senior High Pacesetter Ser.). 64p. 1986. pap. 7.95 (ISBN 0-89191-343-2). Cook.

Friends Face the World: Some Continuing & Current Quaker Concerns. Ed. by Leonard S. Kenworthy. 220p. 1987. pap. 6.95 (ISBN 0-913408-97-2). Friends United.

Friends: Finding & Keeping Them. Karen Dockrey. LC 85-12783. 1985. pap. 4.50 (ISBN 0-8054-5343-1). Broadman.

Friends, Followers & Factions: A Reader in Political Clientelism. Steffen W. Schmidt et al. LC 73-93060. 1977. 48.50x (ISBN 0-520-02696-9); pap. 12.95x (ISBN 0-520-03156-3, CAMPUS 167). U of Cal Pr.

Friends for Three Hundred Years. Howard H. Brinton. LC 52-5424. (Orig.). 1965. pap. 4.00 (ISBN 0-87574-903-8). Pendle Hill.

Friends Forever. William Coleman. 160p. (Orig.). 1987. pap. 5.95 (ISBN 0-87123-959-0). Bethany Hse.

Friends in East Africa. Harold Smuck. 120p. (Orig.). 1987. pap. 8.95 (ISBN 0-913408-92-1). Friends United.

Friends, Let Us Pray. Elsie H. Landstrom. LC 79-146679. (Orig.). 1970. pap. 2.50x (ISBN 0-87574-174-6, 174). Pendle Hill.

Friends of God. Shirley Beegle. (Double Trouble Puzzles Ser.). (Illus.). 48p. 1987. pap. 2.50 (ISBN 0-87403-328-4, 2768). Standard Pub.

Friends of God. Josemaria Escriva de Balaguer. Tr. of Amigos de Dios. 301p. 1981. 14.50 (ISBN 0-906138-03-5); deluxe ed. 24.00 (ISBN 0-906138-04-3); pap. 7.95 (ISBN 0-906138-02-7). Scepter Pubs.

Friends of God. Compiled by Patricia Mahany. (Story & Color Bks.). (Illus.). 64p. (Orig.). 1984. pap. 2.95 (ISBN 0-87239-795-5, 2371). Standard Pub.

Friends of God: Practical Mystics of the Fourteenth Century. Anna G. Seesholtz. 1970. Repr. of 1934 ed. 14.50 (ISBN 0-404-05697-0). AMS Pr.

Friends of Jesus. Shirley Beegle. (Double Trouble Puzzles Ser.). (Illus.). 48p. 1987. pap. 2.50 (ISBN 0-87403-327-6, 2767). Standard Pub.

Friends of the Jews. Betty J. Singer. (Illus.). 1976. pap. text ed. 2.75 (ISBN 0-917400-01-1). Options.

Friends, Partners, & Lovers. Warren L. Molton. 1979. pap. 6.95 (ISBN 0-8170-0815-2). Judson.

Friends with God. Catherine Marshall. (Illus.). 1972. pap. 1.95 (ISBN 0-380-01199-9, 52803-7). Avon.

Friendship. Martin E. Marty. LC 80-69243. 180p. 1980. pap. 4.50 (ISBN 0-89505-053-6). Argus Comm.

Friendship: A Study in Theological Ethics. Gilbert C. Meilaender. LC 81-50459. 118p. 1981. text ed. 10.95 (ISBN 0-268-00956-2). U of Notre Dame Pr.

Friendship, Altruism & Morality. Lawrence Blum. (International Library of Philosophy). 256p. 1980. 24.95x (ISBN 0-7100-0582-2); pap. 9.95x (ISBN 0-7100-9332-2). Methuen Inc.

Friendship Evangelism: The Caring Way to Share Your Faith. Arthur G. McPhee. 1979. pap. 4.95 (ISBN 0-310-37311-5, 11262P). Zondervan.

Friendship Factor: How to Get Closer to the People You Care for. Alan L. McGinniss. LC 79-50076. 1979. 12.95 (ISBN 0-8066-1710-1, 10-2410); pap. 3.95 (ISBN 0-8066-1711-X, 10-2411). Augsburg.

Friendship Factor Study Guide. Althea Daniels. 32p. (Orig.). 1984. pap. 0.95 (ISBN 0-8066-2079-X, 10-2413). Augsburg.

Friendship Gap: Reaching Out Across Cultures. Tim Stafford. LC 84-6725. 152p. (Orig.). 1984. pap. 5.95 (ISBN 0-87784-975-7). Inter-Varsity.

Friendship in the Lord. Paul Hinnebusch. LC 73-90411. 144p. 1974. pap. 2.75 (ISBN 0-87793-065-1). Ave Maria.

Friendship of Christ. Robert H. Benson & Thomas More. (Books to Live Ser.). 156p. 1984. 10.95 (ISBN 0-88347-171-X). Thomas More.

Friendship Olympics: A Young Christian Book for Boys. David A. Sorensen. LC 86-32259. 112p. 1987. pap. 4.95 (ISBN 0-8066-2248-2, 10-2430). Augsburg.

Friendship: Portraits in God's Family Album. Dee Brestin. (Fisherman Bible Studyguide Ser.). 96p. (Orig.). 1986. pap. 2.95 (ISBN 0-87788-287-8). Shaw Pubs.

Friendship: Voices from the Heart. William J. Crockett. 15p. 1985. pap. 3.00 (ISBN 0-934383-04-9). Pride Prods.

Fritz Kunkel: Selected Writings. Intro. by John A. Sanford. 400p. 1984. pap. 12.95 (ISBN 0-8091-2558-7). Paulist Pr.

Frog. 1986. 2.95 (ISBN 1-55513-175-1, Chariot Bks). Cook.

From. Beverly Beckmann. (Illus.). 1980. pap. 3.95 (ISBN 0-570-03489-2, 56-1343). Concordia.

From a Gun to a Flower. Zaher P. Kury. (Illus.). 352p. (Orig.). 1985. pap. 13.50 (ISBN 0-9615041-0-2). Unity Pr.

From a Gun to a Flower: Messages Through the Mediumship of Zaher P. Kury. Zaher P. Kury. (Illus.). 192p. 1984. 10.00 (ISBN 0-682-40160-9). Exposition Pr FL.

From a Ruined Garden: The Memorial Books of Polish Jewry. Jack Kugelmass & Jonathan Boyarin. (Illus.). 309p. 1985. pap. 8.95 (ISBN 0-8052-0789-9). Schocken.

From Acupuncture to Yoga: Alternative Methods of Healing. Brent Hafen & Katherine Frandsen. (Illus.). 136p. 1983. 12.95 (ISBN 0-13-330845-6). P-H.

From Adam to Armageddon: A Survey of the Bible. J. Benton White. LC 85-8921. 320p. 1985. pap. text ed. write for info. (ISBN 0-534-05111-1). Wadsworth Pub.

From Adam to Muhammad. A. R. Shad. 16.95 (ISBN 0-317-01593-1). Kazi Pubns.

From Adam to Noah: A Commentary on the Book of Genesis, Part 1. 3rd ed. U. Cassuto. 323p. 1978. Repr. of 1961 ed. text ed. 35.00x (Pub. by Magnes Pr Israel). Humanities.

From Age to Age a Living Witness. Leslie R. Marston. 1960. 10.95 (ISBN 0-685-14209-4). Light & Life.

From an Acorn to an Oak. Loren A. Yadon. (Illus.). 89p. 1978. pap. 4.95 (ISBN 0-912315-46-6). Word Aflame.

From Ancient Tablets to Modern Translations: A General Introduction to the Bible. David Ewert. 1986. 15.95 (ISBN 0-310-45370-4, 12384). Zondervan.

From Arapesh to Zuni: A Book of Bibleless Peoples. Karen Lewis. (Illus.). 31p. 1986. pap. text ed. 4.95 (ISBN 0-938978-07-1). Wycliffe Bible.

From Ashes to Easter. Ed. by Rita C. Dorner. 1979. pap. 9.95 (ISBN 0-918208-99-8). Liturgical Conf.

From Athens to Jerusalem: The Love of Wisdom & the Love God. Stephen R. Clark. 1984. 29.95x (ISBN 0-19-824698-6); pap. 11.95x (ISBN 0-19-824697-8). Oxford U Pr.

From Atom to Kosmos: A Theosophical Study in Evolution. L. Gordon Plummer. (Illus.). 134p. Date not set. price not set (ISBN 0-913004-49-9). Point Loma Pub.

From Babylon to Bethlehem: The People of God from the Exile to the Messiah. H. L. Ellison. LC 78-24504. 144p. 1984. pap. 5.95 (ISBN 0-8010-3412-4). Baker Bk.

From Behind Closed Doors: Acts A. (Illus.). 48p. 1981. pap. 1.95 leader's guide (ISBN 0-89367-066-9). Light & Life.

From Behind Closed Doors: Acts A. (Illus.). 68p. 1981. pap. 2.50 student's guide (ISBN 0-686-79738-8). Light & Life.

From Berlin to Berkeley: German-Jewish Identities. Reinhard Bendix. LC 85-8578. 320p. 1985. 29.95 (ISBN 0-88738-067-0). Transaction Bks.

From Bethlehem to Calvary. Alice A. Bailey. 1975. 19.00 (ISBN 0-85330-007-0); pap. 7.00 (ISBN 0-85330-107-7). Lucis.

From Bible to Mishna: The Continuity of Tradition. Jacob Weingreen. LC 75-37728. 250p. 1976. text ed. 27.00x (ISBN 0-8419-0249-6). Holmes & Meier.

From Birth to Death. David Mohr & Faye Schwartz. 1983. 2.50 (ISBN 0-89536-599-5, 0604). CSS of Ohio.

From Black Muslims to Muslims: The Transition from Separatism to Islam, 1930-1980. Clifton E. Marsh. LC 84-5611. 159p. 1984. 16.50 (ISBN 0-8108-1705-5). Scarecrow.

From Bonaventure to Bellini: An Essay in Franciscan Exegesis. John V. Fleming. LC 82-47593. (Princeton Essays on the Arts Ser.: No. 14). (Illus.). 192p. 1982. 28.00x (ISBN 0-691-07270-1); pap. 14.50 L.P.E. (ISBN 0-691-10143-4). Princeton U Pr.

From Boredom to Bliss. Gustave Ridley. Ed. by Jean Campbell. (Illus.). 160p. (Orig.). 1983. pap. 8.95 (ISBN 0-9610544-0-9). Harmonious Pr.

From Buddha to Christ. Rudolf Steiner. Ed. by Gilbert Church. Tr. of Esoterische Christentum & die geistige Fuehrung der Menschheit. 103p. 1987. pap. 5.95 (ISBN 0-88010-178-4). Anthroposophic.

From Chaos to Covenant: Prophecy in the Book of Jeremiah. Robert P. Carroll. 288p. 1981. 14.95 (ISBN 0-8245-0106-3). Crossroad NY.

From Clerk to Cleric. F. H. Cleobury. 64p. 1977. pap. 1.95 (ISBN 0-227-67825-7). Attic Pr.

From Cloister to Classroom: The Spirituality of Western Christendom III. Ed. by Rozanne Elder. (Cistercian Studies: No. 90). 1986. 26.95 (ISBN 0-87907-890-1); pap. 10.95 (ISBN 0-87907-990-8). Cistercian Pubns.

From Colonialism to World Community: The Church's Pilgrimage. John C. Smith. LC 82-12138. 334p. 1982. pap. 8.95 (ISBN 0-664-24452-1, Pub. by Geneva Press). Westminster.

From Consultation to Confrontation: A Study of the Muslim League in British Indian Politics, 1906-1912. M. Rahman. 313p. 1985. 52.00x (ISBN 0-317-39069-4, Pub. by Luzac & Co Ltd). State Mutual Bk.

From Controversy to Co-Existence: Evangelicals in the Church of England, 1914-1980. Randle Manwaring. 240p. 1985. 34.50 (ISBN 0-521-30380-X). Cambridge U Pr.

From Convincement to Conversion. Martin Cobin. LC 64-17424. (Orig.). 1964. pap. 2.50x (ISBN 0-87574-134-7). Pendle Hill.

From Copper to Gold: The Life of Dorothy Baker. Dorothy Freeman. (Illus.). 368p. 17.50 (ISBN 0-85398-177-9); pap. 10.95 (ISBN 0-85398-178-7). G Ronald Pub.

From Cover to Cover. Brian L. Harbour. LC 81-67197. 1982. pap. 7.50 (ISBN 0-8054-2241-2). Broadman.

From Creation to the Day of Eternity. Homer Hailey. (Illus.). 1982. 11.95 (ISBN 0-913814-42-3). Nevada Pubns.

From Crime to Christ. Glenn Clark. pap. 2.50 (ISBN 0-910924-61-9). Macalester.

From Darkness into Light. Sylvia Weersinghe. 1980. pap. 1.95 (ISBN 0-910924-84-8). Macalester.

From Darkness to Light: Aspects of Conversion in the New Testament. Beverly R. Gaventa. LC 85-16309. (Overtures to Biblical Theology Ser.). 176p. 1986. pap. 8.95 (ISBN 0-8006-1545-X, 1-1545). Fortress.

From Darkness to Light: The Story of Negro Progress. Mary Helm. LC 76-88433. Repr. of 1909 ed. cancelled (ISBN 0-8371-1908-1, HED&, Pub. by Negro U Pr). Greenwood.

From Darkness to the Dawn: How Belief in the Afterlife Affects Living. A. R. Van de Walle. Tr. of Tot het aanbreken van de dageraad. 272p. 1985. pap. text ed. 10.95 (ISBN 0-89622-272-1). Twenty-Third.

From Death to Rebirth. Manly P. Hall. pap. 3.50 (ISBN 0-89314-316-2). Philos Res.

From Demon Deliverance to Divine Healing. Elizabeth M. Gaitan. 1985. 5.95 (ISBN 0-8062-2394-4). Carlton.

From Dependence to Mutuality: The American Jewish Community & World Jewry. Moshe Davis. (Texts & Studies). (Hebrew.). 1970. 10.00 (ISBN 0-911934-07-3). Am Jewish Hist Soc.

From Dilemma to Delight. Gerita G. Liebelt. Ed. by Richard W. Coffen. 96p. (Orig.). 1986. pap. 6.95 (ISBN 0-8280-0298-3). Review & Herald.

From Discontent: The Biography of a Mystic. Bruce Wells. (Illus.). 224p. 1985. 13.95 (ISBN 0-85398-206-6); pap. 5.95 (ISBN 0-85398-207-4). G Ronald Pub.

From Early Judaism to Early Church. D. S. Russell. LC 85-31776. 1986. pap. 5.95 (ISBN 0-8006-1921-8). Fortress.

From Eden to Eros: Origins of the Put down of Women. Richard Roberts. (Illus.). 167p. (Orig.). 1985. pap. 8.95x (ISBN 0-942380-05-3). Vernal Equinox.

From Eden to Nazareth: Finding Our Story in the Old Testament. Leonard Foley. (Illus.). 103p. (Orig.). 1983. pap. text ed. 3.50 (ISBN 0-86716-020-9). St Anthony Mess Pr.

From Egypt to Canaan. John Ritchie. LC 82-220. 102p. 1982. pap. 4.50 (ISBN 0-8254-3614-1). Kregel.

From Egypt to Palestine: Through Sinai, the Wilderness & the South Country: History of the Israelites. Samuel C. Bartlett. Ed. by Moshe Davis. LC 77-70668. (America & the Holy Land Ser.). (Illus.). 1977. Repr. of 1879 ed. lib. bdg. 43.00x (ISBN 0-405-10227-5). Ayer Co Pubs.

From Every Nation Without Number: Racial & Ethnic Diversity in United Methodism. Roy I. Sano. LC 81-20610. (Into Our Third Century Ser.). (Orig.). 1982. pap. 3.95 (ISBN 0-687-13642-3). Abingdon.

From Evolution to Creation: A Personal Testimony. Gary E. Parker. LC 77-78020. 1978. pap. 1.00 (ISBN 0-89051-035-0). Master Bks.

From Exile to Advent. William Fairweather. Ed. by J. Moffatt. (Handbooks for Bible Classes & Private Students Ser.). 210p. 1894. 8.95 (ISBN 0-567-28128-0, Pub. by T & T Clark Ltd Uk). Fortress.

From Exodus to Advent. Morris Venden. LC 79-22389. (Orion Ser.). 1979. pap. 5.95 (ISBN 0-8127-0255-7). Review & Herald.

From Ezra to the Last of the Maccabees: Foundations of Post-Biblical Judaism. Elias Bickerman. 1962. pap. 5.95 (ISBN 0-8052-0036-3). Schocken.

From Faith to Faith. Daniel W. Bacon. 1984. pap. 5.95 (ISBN 9971-972-03-4). OMF Bks.

From Faith to Faith. Nee Watchman. Ed. by Herbert L. Fader. Tr. by Stephen Kaung. 120p. 1984. pap. 3.50 (ISBN 0-935008-62-4). Christian Fellow Pubs.

From Faith to Faith, Essays in Honor of Donald G. Miller, on His Seventieth Birthday. Ed. by Dikran Y. Hadidian. LC 79-23408. (Pittsburgh Theological Monographs: No. 31). 1979. 18.00 (ISBN 0-915138-38-7). Pickwick.

From Fear to Faith: Studies in the Book of Habakkuk. D. Martyn Lloyd-Jones. (Summit Bks.). 80p. 1982. pap. 2.95 (ISBN 0-8010-5620-9). Baker Bk.

From Fertility Cult to Worship: A Reassessment for the Modern Church. Walter J. Harrelson. LC 66-14929. (Scholars Press Reprint Ser.: No. 4). pap. 10.25x (ISBN 0-89130-379-0, 00 07 04). Scholars Pr GA.

From Fetish to God in Ancient Egypt. E. Wallis Budge. LC 72-82206. (Illus.). Repr. of 1934 ed. 33.00 (ISBN 0-405-08317-3, Blom Pubns). Ayer Co Pubs.

From Florence to Brest, Fourteen Thirty-Nine to Fifteen Ninety-Six. 2nd ed. Oscar Halecki. LC 68-26103. 456p. 1968. 35.00 (ISBN 0-208-00702-4, Archon). Shoe String.

From Font to Faith: John Wesley on Infant Baptism & the Nurture of Children. David I. Naglee. (American University Studies VII-Theology & Religion: Vol. 24). 272p. 1987. text ed. 26.00 (ISBN 0-8204-0375-X). P Lang Pubs.

From Glory to Glory: Texts from Gregory of Nyssa's Mystical Writings. Ed. by Jean Danielou. LC 79-38. 304p. 1979. pap. 9.95 (ISBN 0-913836-54-0). St Vladimirs.

From God Through Me to You. Sam Minichen. 58p. 1984. 3.95 (ISBN 0-89697-188-0). Intl Univ Pr.

From God to Us. Norman L. Geisler & William E. Nix. 302p. (Orig.). 1974. pap. 9.95 (ISBN 0-8024-2878-9). Moody.

From God with Love. Vern Worcester. pap. cancelled (ISBN 0-89900-106-8). College Pr Pub.

From Goo to You by Way of the Zoo. rev. ed. Harold Hill et al. 224p. 1984. pap. 5.95 (ISBN 0-8007-5174-4, Power Bks). Revell.

From Grace to Glory: Meditations of the Psalms. Murdoch Campbell. 1979. pap. 5.45 (ISBN 0-85151-028-0). Banner of Truth.

From Green Hills of Galilee. facsimile ed. Cathal O'Byrne. LC 71-167464. (Short Story Index Reprint Ser.). Repr. of 1935 ed. 14.00 (ISBN 0-8369-3990-5). Ayer Co Pubs.

From Guilt to Glory: The Message of Romans 9-16. Ray C. Stedman. LC 85-29659. (Authentic Christianity Bks.). 1986. pap. 7.95 (ISBN 0-88070-124-2). Multnomah.

From Guilt to Glory: The Message of Romans 1-8. Ray C. Stedman. LC 85-29657. (Authentic Christianity Bks.). 1985. pap. 8.95 (ISBN 0-88070-123-4). Multnomah.

From Harper Valley to the Mountain Top. Jeannie C. Riley & Jamie Buckingham. (Epiphany Bks.). (Illus.). 1983. pap. 2.75 (ISBN 0-345-30481-0). Ballantine.

From Haven to Conquest: Readings in Zionism & the Palestine Problem until 1948. 2nd ed. Ed. by Walid Khalidi. LC 85-237727. (Anthology Ser. (Mu'assasat Al Dirasatal-Filastiniyah): No. 2). 914p. 1987. text ed. 29.95 (ISBN 0-88728-155-9); pap. 17.50 (ISBN 0-88728-156-7). Inst Palestine.

From Heaven Come God's Weapons for the Church. Norvel Hayes. 1979. pap. 0.75 (ISBN 0-89274-366-2). Harrison Hse.

From Heaven or from Men. Hugo McCord. 1970. pap. 2.75 (ISBN 0-88027-033-0). Firm Foun Pub.

From Heaven with Love. E. G. White. 1984. 1.50 (ISBN 0-8163-0553-6). Pacific Pr Pub Assn.

From Here to Forever. Ellen G. White. 436p. 1982. pap. 1.50 (ISBN 0-317-00060-8). Pacific Pr Pub Assn.

From Here to Maturity. David Augsburger. 1982. pap. 2.50 (ISBN 0-8423-0938-1). Tyndale.

From Hiding to Healing. Laurel A. Burton. Ed. by Michael L. Sherer. (Orig.). 1987. pap. 2.75 participant bk. (ISBN 0-89536-860-9, 7819); pap. 2.25 leader's guide (ISBN 0-89536-861-7, 7820). CSS of Ohio.

From Hippie to Happy. Dan Nicholson. (Orig.). 1984. pap. write for info. (ISBN 0-88144-026-4, CPS026). Christian Pub.

From Honey to Ashes. Claude Levi-Strauss. (Science of Mythology Ser.). 1980. Repr. of 1973 ed. lib. bdg. 34.50x (ISBN 0-374-94952-2, Octagon). Hippocrene Bks.

From Honey to Ashes: Introduction to a Science of Mythology, Vol. 2. Claude Levi-Strauss. Tr. by John Weightman & Doreen Weightman. LC 82-15965. 512p. 1973. pap. 13.00x (ISBN 0-226-47489-5). U of Chicago Pr.

From Hope to Faith. Carolyn A. Jones. 134p. 1979. 9.50 (ISBN 0-87881-075-7). Mojave Bks.

From Image To Likeness: A Jungian Path in the Gospel Journey. Harold Grant et al. 224p. (Orig.). 1983. pap. 8.95 (ISBN 0-8091-2552-8). Paulist Pr.

From Intellect to Intuition. Alice A. Bailey. 1973. 18.00 (ISBN 0-85330-008-9); pap. 7.00 (ISBN 0-85330-108-5). Lucis.

From Jehovah to Jazz: Music in America from Psalmody to the Present Day. facs. ed. Helen L. Kaufmann. LC 68-54352. (Essay Index Reprint Ser). 1968. Repr. of 1937 ed. 20.00 (ISBN 0-8369-0585-7). Ayer Co Pubs.

From Jerusalem to Irian Jaya: A Biographical History of Christian Missions. Ruth Tucker. 1986. pap. 14.95 (ISBN 0-310-45931-1, 12723P). Zondervan.

From Jesus to Christ. Rudolf Steiner. 185p. 1973. 16.95 (ISBN 0-85440-277-2). Anthroposophic.

From Jesus to Paul. Joseph Klausner. Tr. by William Stinespring from Hebrew. 1978. 15.95x (ISBN 0-932232-03-5); pap. 12.95 (ISBN 0-932232-04-3). Menorah Pub.

From Jesus to Paul: Studies in Honour of Francis Wright Beare. P. Richardson & J. Hurd. 256p. 1984. pap. text ed. 16.50x (ISBN 0-88920-138-2, Pub. by Wilfrid Laurier Canada). Humanities.

From Jordan to Pentecost, Bk. III. Derek Prince. (Foundation Ser.). pap. 2.95 (ISBN 0-934920-02-8, B-12). Derek Prince.

From Joseph to Joshua: Biblical Traditions in the Light of Archaeology. H. H. Rowley. (Schweich Lectures on Biblical Archaeology). 212p. 1970. Repr. of 1948 ed. 8.25 (ISBN 0-85672-720-2, Pub. by British Acad). Longwood Pub Group.

From Jung to Jesus: Myth & Consciousness in the New Testament. Gerald H. Slusser. LC 85-45792. 180p. 1986. pap. 10.95 (ISBN 0-8042-1111-6). John Knox.

From Junk to Jesus & from Crime to Christ. George E. Woodruff. 1983. 6.50 (ISBN 0-8062-1862-2). Carlton.

From Kneepants to Romance. Benny Bristow. pap. 1.95 (ISBN 0-89137-810-3). Quality Pubns.

From Lordship to Stewardship: Religion & Social Change in Malta. Mario Vassallo. 1979. text ed. 22.00x (ISBN 90-279-7967-7). Mouton.

From Luther to Fifteen Eighty: A Pictorial Account. Ingetraut Ludolphy. (Illus.). 1977. 15.95 (ISBN 0-570-03264-4, 15-2710). Concordia.

From Luther to Popper: Studies in Critical Philosophy. Herbert Marcuse. 236p. 1984. pap. 7.95 (ISBN 0-8052-7196-1, Pub. by NLB England). Schocken.

From Luther to Tillich: The Reformers & Their Heirs. Wilhelm Pauck. Ed. by Marion Pauck. LC 84-48229. 144p. 1985. 19.45 (ISBN 0-06-066475-4, HarpR). Har-Row.

From Magic to Metaphor: A Validation of Christian Sacraments. George S. Worgul. 248p. 1986. pap. text ed. 11.75 (ISBN 0-8191-4983-7). U Pr of Amer.

From Many Centuries: A Collection of Historical Papers. facs. ed. Francis S. Betten. LC 68-16910. (Essay Index Reprint Ser). 1968. Repr. of 1938 ed. 18.00 (ISBN 0-8369-0206-8). Ayer Co Pubs.

From Mary's Side: Summons for Change. Janith Aust-Schminke. 160p. (Orig.). Date not set. price not set (ISBN 0-916865-00-2); pap. price not set (ISBN 0-916865-01-0). Sansper.

From Mishnah to Scripture: The Problem of the Unattributed Saying. Jacob Neusner. LC 84-10527. (Brown Judaic Studies). 135p. 1984. 20.95 (ISBN 0-89130-759-1, 14 00 67); pap. 13.95 (ISBN 0-89130-749-4). Scholars Pr GA.

From Morality to Religion. W. G. DeBurgh. LC 70-102568. 1970. Repr. of 1938 ed. 31.50x (ISBN 0-8046-0728-1, Pub. by Kennikat). Assoc Faculty Pr.

From Morality to Religion. W. G. De Burgh. 352p. 1985. Repr. of 1938 ed. lib. bdg. 85.00 (ISBN 0-89984-042-6). Century Bookbindery.

From Moses to Elisha: Israel to the End of the Ninth Century B. C. Leonard E. Elliott-Binns. LC 78-10639. (Illus.). 1979. Repr. of 1929 ed. lib. bdg. 27.50x (ISBN 0-313-21015-2, EBFM). Greenwood.

From Muleback to Super Jet with the Gospel. Marshall Keeble. 2.50 (ISBN 0-89225-091-7). Gospel Advocate.

From My Jewel Box. Gladys Doonan. LC 83-4439. 1983p. pap. 3.95 (ISBN 0-87227-092-0). Reg Baptist.

From My World to Yours: A Young Man's Account of the Afterlife. Jasper Swain. Ed. by Noel Langley. LC 76-52573. 103p. 1984. pap. 7.95 (ISBN 0-8027-7257-9). Walker & Co.

From Myth to Icon: Reflections of Greek Ethical Doctrine in Literature & Art. Helen North. LC 79-7619. (Cornell Studies in Classical Philology). (Illus.). 288p. 1979. 29.95x (ISBN 0-8014-1135-1). Cornell U Pr.

From New Creation to Urban Crisis: A History of Action Training Ministries, 1962-1975. George D. Younger. LC 86-70421. (Studies in Religion & Society). 260p. 1987. text ed. 25.95x (ISBN 0-913348-25-2). Ctr Sci Study.

From Noah to Abraham: A Commentary on the Book of Genesis, Pt. 2. 3rd ed. U. Cassuto. 386p. 1974. Repr. of 1964 ed. text ed. 35.00x (Pub. by Magnes Pr Israel). Humanities.

From Now till Eternity. C. C. Cribb. LC 76-21571. 12.95 (ISBN 0-932046-00-2). Manhattan Ltd NC.

From Now to Eternity: Sermons from Revelation. Nathan M. Meyer. pap. 6.00 (ISBN 0-88469-035-0). BMH Bks.

From Now to Pentecost: A Mirrored View of Development in Christianity. Elza M. Hawkins. 260p. (Orig.). 1982. pap. 11.00 (ISBN 971-10-0038-5, Pub. by New Day Philippines). Cellar.

From Office to Profession: The New England Ministry, 1750-1850. Donald M. Scott. LC 77-20304. 1978. 21.00x (ISBN 0-8122-7737-6). U of Pa Pr.

From One Language to Another: Functional Equivalence in Bible Translation. Jan de Waard & Eugene A. Nida. 224p. 1986. 15.95 (ISBN 0-8407-7555-5). Nelson.

From One to Another. Norma Jacob. LC 59-8917. (Orig.). 1959. pap. 2.50x (ISBN 0-87574-102-9). Pendle Hill.

From Order to Omega. M. D. Meilach. pap. 0.95 (ISBN 0-8199-0038-9, L38249). Franciscan Herald.

From Palm Sunday to Easter. N. Raymond Day. 45p. (Orig.). 1979. pap. 5.45 (ISBN 0-940754-01-0). Ed Ministries.

From Palmyra, New York, Eighteen Thirty to Independence, Missouri, Eighteen Ninety-Four. R. Etzenhouser. LC 73-134393. Repr. of 1894 ed. 29.50 (ISBN 0-404-08435-4). AMS Pr.

From Passion to Peace. James Allen. 64p. 1981. pap. 4.50 (ISBN 0-89540-077-4, SB-077). Sun Pub.

From Passover to Pentecost. Joseph H. King. pap. 3.95 (ISBN 0-911866-57-4). Advocate.

From Pentecost to the Present. J. B. North. LC 82-74538. 520p. (Orig.). 1983. 18.95 (ISBN 0-89900-230-7). College Pr Pub.

From Peter to John Paul II. Frank J. Korn. LC 80-65721. 300p. (Orig.). 1980. pap. 5.50 (ISBN 0-8189-1161-1, 161, Pub. by Alba Bks). Alba.

From Philo to Origen: Middle Platonism in Transition. Robert M. Berchman. (Brown Judaic Studies: No. 69). 370p. 1985. 29.95 (ISBN 0-89130-750-8, 14 00 69); pap. 25.95 (ISBN 0-89130-815-6). Scholars Pr GA.

From Pigtails to Wedding Bells. Gwen Bristow. pap. 1.95 (ISBN 0-89137-811-1). Quality Pubns.

From Place to Place: Travels with Paul Tillich, Travels Without Paul Tillich. Hannah Tillich. LC 75-34490. (Illus.). 224p. 1976. 10.00 (ISBN 0-8128-1902-0). Stein & Day.

From Plotzk to Boston. Mary Antin. Ed. by Jonathan D. Sarna. (Masterworks of Modern Jewish Writing Ser.). 140p. 1986. pap. 6.95 (ISBN 0-910129-45-2, Dist. by Schocken). Wiener Pub Inc.

From Polemics to Apologetics: Jewish-Christian Rapprochment in 17th Century Amsterdam. Ralph Melnick. 104p. 1981. pap. text ed. 8.75 (ISBN 90-232-1792-6, Pub. by Van Gorcum Holland). Longwood Pub Group.

From Politics to Piety: The Emergence of Pharisaic Judaism. Jacob Neusner. pap. 9.95 (ISBN 0-87068-677-1). Ktav.

From Praying Never to Praying Always. Mary Amlaw. 100p. (Orig.). 1985. pap. 5.95 (ISBN 0-916134-69-5). Pueblo Pub Co.

From Prejudice to Destruction: Anti-Semitism, 1700-1933. Jacob Katz. LC 80-14404. 398p. 1980. 27.50x (ISBN 0-674-32505-2). Harvard U Pr.

From Prejudice to Destruction: Anti-Semitism, 1700-1933. Jacob Katz. 400p. 1982. pap. 7.95 (ISBN 0-674-32507-9). Harvard U Pr.

From Primitives to Zen: A Thematic Sourcebook in the History of Religions. Mircea Eliade. LC 66-20775. 1978. 12.00 (ISBN 0-06-062134-6, RD 249, HarpR). Har-Row.

From Prophet to Son. Scott G. Kenney & Hyrum Smith, III. LC 81-15173. 132p. 1981. 6.95 (ISBN 0-87747-885-6). Deseret Bk.

From Radical Empiricism to Absolute Idealism. Justus Hartnack. LC 86-8603. (Studies in the History of Philosophy: Vol. 1). 222p. 1986. 49.95x (ISBN 0-88946-304-2). E Mellen.

From Rationalism to Irrationality. C. Gregg Singer. 1979. pap. 14.50 (ISBN 0-87552-428-1). Presby & Reformed.

From Reform Judaism to Ethical Culture: The Religious Evolution of Felix Adler. Benny Kraut. LC 79-14441. (Monographs: No. 5). 285p. 1979. 16.50x (ISBN 0-87820-404-0). Ktav.

From Rejection to Acceptance. Barbara Taylor. 1987. text ed. 8.95 (ISBN 0-8054-5045-9). Broadman.

From Religion to Philosophy. A Study of the Origins of Western Speculation. F. M. Cornford. 275p. 1979. text ed. o. p. (ISBN 0-391-01238-X); pap. text ed. 12.50x (ISBN 0-391-01239-8). Humanities.

From Renaissance to Renaissance: Hebrew Literature 1492-1967, Vol. I. Eisig Silberschlag. 1972. 25.00x (ISBN 0-87068-184-2). Ktav.

From Right to Left: An Autobiography. Frederick V. Field. LC 82-23407. 336p. 1983. 16.95 (ISBN 0-88208-162-4); pap. 8.95 (ISBN 0-88208-161-6). Lawrence Hill.

From Ritual to Romance. Jessie L. Weston. Tr. by Mary M. McLaughlin. 13.75 (ISBN 0-8446-3162-0). Peter Smith.

From Sabbath to Lord's Day. Ed. by D. A. Carson. 432p. (Orig.). 1982. pap. 10.95 (ISBN 0-310-44531-0, 12035P). Zondervan.

From Sacred Story to Sacred Text: Canon As Paradigm. James A. Sanders. LC 85-45483. 240p. 1987. 18.95 (ISBN 0-8006-0805-4). Fortress.

From Sacred to Profane America: The Role of Religion in American History. William A. Clebsch. LC 81-9142. (Classics & Reprints Series of the American Academy of Religion & Scholars Press). 1981. 9.95 (ISBN 0-89130-517-3, 01 05 02). Scholars Pr GA.

From Saigon to Shalom. James F. Metzler. LC 84-9313. (Mennonite Missionary Study Ser.: No. 11). 144p. (Orig.). 1985. pap. 7.95 (ISBN 0-8361-3379-X). Herald Pr.

From St. Augustine to William Temple. facsimile ed. Vivian H. Green. LC 72-148213. (Biography Index Reprint Ser.). 1948. 18.00 (ISBN 0-8369-8060-3). Ayer Co Pubs.

From Saint Francis to Dante: Translations from the Chronicle of the Franciscan Salimbene (1221-88) Salimbene Di Adam. Ed. & tr. by G. G. Coulton. LC 68-10910. 462p. 1972. pap. 10.95x (ISBN 0-8122-1053-0, Pa Paperbks). U of Pa Pr.

From Science to An Adequate Mythology. Kevin J. Sharpe. (Science, Religion & Society Ser.). 156p. (Orig.). 1984. pap. 11.95 (ISBN 0-86474-000-X, Pub. by Interface Press). ANZ Religious Pubns.

From Sea to Shining Sea. Peter Marshall & David Manuel. 448p. 1985. 14.95 (ISBN 0-8007-1451-2). Revell.

From Sea to Shining Sea. William G. Tanner. LC 86-9609. 1986. pap. 4.95 (ISBN 0-8054-5667-8). Broadman.

From Sex to Super Consciousness. Bhagwan Shree Rajneesh. Tr. by V. Vora. (Marathi.). 157p. 1975. pap. 2.95 (ISBN 0-89253-060-X). Ind-US Inc.

From Sex to Superconsciousness. Bhagwan Shree Rajneesh. Ed. by Swami Krishna Prem. LC 77-20821. (Early Discourses & Writings Ser.). (Illus.). 256p. (Orig.). 1979. 15.50 (ISBN 0-88050-064-6). Chidvilas Found.

From Shadow to Promise: Old Testament Interpretation from Augustine to the Young Luther. James S. Preus. LC 69-12732. (Illus.). xii, 301p. 1969. 20.00x (ISBN 0-674-32610-5, Belkap Pr). Harvard U Pr.

From Shadow to Substance. Roy Hession. 1976. pap. 3.95 (ISBN 0-87508-260-2). Chr Lit.

From Sheldon to Secker: Aspects of English Church History, 1660-1768. Norman Sykes. LC 59-2371. (Ford Lectures: 1958). pap. 62.50 (ISBN 0-317-20808-X, 2024534). Bks Demand UMI.

From Shtetl to Suburbia: The Family in Jewish Literary Imagination. Sol Gittleman. LC 78-53646. 1978. 12.95x (ISBN 0-8070-6364-9); pap. 5.95 o. p. (ISBN 0-8070-6365-7). Beacon Pr.

From Shylock to Svengali: Jewish Stereotypes in English Fiction. Edgar Rosenberg. (Illus.). 1960. 27.50x (ISBN 0-8047-0586-0). Stanford U Pr.

From Sin to Wholeness. Brian W. Grant. LC 81-16122. 174p. 1982. pap. 8.95 (ISBN 0-664-24399-1). Westminster.

From Slave to Priest. Caroline Hemesath. 1974. 6.95 (ISBN 0-8199-0468-6). Franciscan Herald.

From Slavery to the Bishopric in the A. M. E. Church: An Autobiography. William H. Heard. LC 69-18564. (American Negro: His History & Literature, Ser. No. 2). 1969. Repr. of 1924 ed. 10.00 (ISBN 0-405-01867-3). Ayer Co Pubs.

From Spanish Court to Italian Ghetto: Isaac Cardoso, A Study in Seventeenth-Century Marranism & Jewish Apologetics. Yosef H. Yerushalmi. LC 76-109544. (Illus.). 548p. 1981. pap. 12.50x (ISBN 0-295-95824-3). U of Wash Pr.

From Sphinx to Christ: An Occult History, Vol. 16. 2nd ed. Edouard Schure. LC 70-130818. (Spiritual Science Library). 288p. 1981. lib. bdg. 16.00 (ISBN 0-89345-011-1). Garber Comm.

From Splendor to Shadow. E. G. White. 1984. 1.50 (ISBN 0-8163-0559-5). Pacific Pr Pub Assn.

From Strength to Strength: The First Half Century of the Formative Age of the Baha'i Faith. Eunice Braun. LC 78-9424. 1978. pap. 2.95 (ISBN 0-87743-125-6, 332-030). Baha'i.

From Suburb to Shtetl: The Jews of Boro Park. Egon Mayer. (Illus.). 196p. 1979. 29.95 (ISBN 0-87722-161-8). Temple U Pr.

From Sunday School to Church School: Continuities in Protestant Church Education in the United States, 1860-1929. Jack L. Seymour. LC 82-15977. 188p. 1982. lib. bdg. 26.25 o. p. (ISBN 0-8191-2726-4); pap. text ed. 11.50 (ISBN 0-8191-2727-2). U Pr of Amer.

From Sunday to Sunday. Schmalenberger & Crotts. (Orig.). 1986. pap. 4.25 (ISBN 0-937172-63-4). JLJ Pubs.

From Temple to Meeting House: The Phenomenology & Theology of Sacred Space. Harold W. Turner. 1979. text ed. 39.20x (ISBN 90-279-7977-4). Mouton.

From Text to Sermon: Responsible Use of the New Testament in Preaching. Ernest Best. LC 77-79584. 1978. 8.95 (ISBN 0-8042-0245-1). John Knox.

From the Altar to the Upper Room. Ralph C. Horner. Ed. by Donald W. Dayton. (Higher Christian Life Ser.). 301p. 1985. 40.00 (ISBN 0-8240-6423-2). Garland Pub.

From the Apostles to Wesley. William M. Greathouse. 124p. 1979. pap. 3.50 (ISBN 0-8341-0588-8). Beacon Hill.

From the Apostolic Community to Constantine. Ed. by Hubert Jedin & John P. Dolan. (History of the Church: Vol. 1). 1980. 59.50x (ISBN 0-8245-0314-7). Crossroad NY.

From the Auroral Darkness: The Life & Poetry of Robert Hayden. John Hatcher. (Illus.). 368p. 23.50 (ISBN 0-85398-188-4); pap. 12.95 (ISBN 0-85398-189-2). G Ronald Pub.

From the Backwoods to Bethel. William R. Haney. Ed. by Amos Jones, Jr. LC 84-50332. 95p. (Orig.). 1985. pap. cancelled. Sunday School.

From the Campus to the World. Alice Poyner. LC 86-3024. 150p. (Orig.). 1986. pap. 6.95 (ISBN 0-87784-947-1). Inter-Varsity.

From the Death of Solomon to the Captivity of Judah. A. W. Heathcote. (London Divinity Ser.). 140p. 1977. pap. 3.95 (ISBN 0-227-67462-6). Attic Pr.

From the Divine to the Human: Survey of Metaphyisics & Epistemology. Frithjof Schuon. LC 82-50333. (Library of Traditional Wisdom). 156p. 1982. pap. 7.00 (ISBN 0-941532-01-1). Wrld Wisdom Bks.

From the Exile to Christ: Historical Introduction to Palestinian Judaism. Werner Foerster. Ed. by Gordon E. Harris. LC 64-18151. 264p. 1964. pap. 10.95 (ISBN 0-8006-0978-6, 1-978). Fortress.

From the Exile to Herod the Great. A. W. Heathcote. (London Divinity Ser). 140p. 1964. 3.95 (ISBN 0-227-67658-0). Attic Pr.

From the Files of the MCC. Cornelius J. Dyck. LC 80-10975. (MCC Story Ser.: Vol. 1). 168p. 1980. pap. 3.95x (ISBN 0-8361-1229-6). Herald Pr.

From the Heart of a Mother. Ruby E. Johnson. LC 82-8218. 1982. pap. 3.95 (ISBN 0-8024-5090-3). Moody.

From the Heart of a Woman. Carole Mayhall. LC 76-24066. 108p. 1976. pap. 3.95 (ISBN 0-89109-421-0). NavPress.

From the Heart of Israel. Bernard Drachman. LC 72-110183. (Short Story Index Reprint Ser.). 1905. 23.50 (ISBN 0-8369-3334-6). Ayer Co Pubs.

From the High Middle Ages to the Eve of the Reformation. Ed. by Hubert Jedin & John P. Dolan. (History of the Church: Vol. 4). 1980. 59.50x (ISBN 0-8245-0317-1). Crossroad NY.

From the Law of Moses to the Magna Carta: Essays in Ancient & Medieval History. James T. Wall. LC 79-66236. 1979. pap. text ed. 9.50 (ISBN 0-8191-0801-4). U Pr of Amer.

From the Maccabees to the Mishnah. Shaye J. Cohen. Ed. by Wayne A. Meeks. LC 86-28077. (Library of Early Christianity: Vol. 7). 252p. 1987. 20.95 (ISBN 0-664-21911-X). Westminster.

From the Memoirs of a Minister of France. Stanley J. Weyman. LC 77-113694. (Short Story Index Reprint Ser.). 1895. 24.50 (ISBN 0-8369-3423-7). Ayer Co Pubs.

From the Mountain. Alton H. McEachern. LC 82-82948. (Orig.). 1983. pap. 4.95 (ISBN 0-8054-1529-7). Broadman.

From the Mountain Top, 1 of 3 vols, Vol. I. Ed. by The Temple of the People Publications Staff. 278p. 1974. Repr. of 1914 ed. 11.25 (ISBN 0-933797-00-1). Halcyon Bk.

From the Mountain Top, Vol. 3. The Temple of the People Publications Staff. 144p. 1985. 11.25 (ISBN 0-933797-02-8). Halcyon Bk.

From the Outer Court to the Inner Sanctum. Annie Besant. Ed. by Shirley Nicholson. LC 82-42703. 130p. 1983. pap. 4.50 (ISBN 0-8356-0574-4, Quest). Theos Pub Hse.

From the Pinnacle of the Temple. Charles Farah, Jr. LC 79-89218. 1979. pap. 4.95 (ISBN 0-88270-462-1). Bridge Pub.

From the Plow to the Pulpit. Tommie F. Harper. Ed. by Elizabeth H. Neeld. LC 86-9656. (Illus.). 360p. (Orig.). 1986. pap. 9.95 (ISBN 0-937897-77-9). Centerpoint Pr.

From the Point of View of Eternity. P. Zagrebelny. 231p. 1978. pap. 4.45 (ISBN 0-8285-1076-8, Pub. by Progress Pubs USSR). Imported Pubns.

From the Prophet to the Great Sufi Mir Ghotbeddin Mohammad. Mah Talat Etemad Moghadam. Tr. by Abdosalam Peyravan & Mitra Shahrivar. 231p. (Orig.). 1982. pap. 12.50 (ISBN 0-317-01145-6). M T O Shahmag.

From the Rising of the Sun: Christians & Society in Contemporary Japan. James M. Phillips. LC 80-24609. 320p. (Orig.). 1981. pap. 14.95 (ISBN 0-88344-145-4). Orbis Bks.

From the Sociology of Symbols to the Sociology of Signs. Ino Rossi. LC 83-5261. 1983. 49.50 (ISBN 0-231-04844-0); pap. 17.50 (ISBN 0-231-04845-9). Columbia U Pr.

From the Source to the Source. Sri Chinmoy. (Orig.). 1978. pap. 8.00 (ISBN 0-88497-431-6). Aum Pubns.

From the Underside: Evangelism from a Third World Vantage Point. James A. Armstrong. LC 81-9509. 112p. (Orig.). 1981. pap. 4.95 (ISBN 0-88344-146-2). Orbis Bks.

From the Unreal to the Real. Swami Bhashyananda. Date not set. price not set. Vivekananda.

From the Vedas to the Manu-Samhita: A Cultural Study. V. B. Mishra. 160p. 1982. text ed. 19.95x (ISBN 0-391-02705-0). Humanities.

From the Wedding to the Marriage. Finbarr M. Corr. 1987. 6.95 (ISBN 0-533-07038-4). Vantage.

From the Wings: Amman Memoirs, 1947-1951. Alec Kirkbride. 194p. 1976. 28.50x (ISBN 0-7146-3061-6, F Cass Co). Biblio Dist.

From the Wisdom of Mishle. Sampson R. Hirsch. Tr. by Karin Paritzky-Joshua. 260p. 1976. pap. 7.95 (ISBN 0-87306-040-7). Feldheim.

From These Beginnings: A History of the First United Methodist Church Kirksville, Missouri. Ruth W. Towne. 100p. 1984. pap. 6.00 (ISBN 0-9613631-0-X). Journal Printing.

From These Shores. Helga Skogsbergh. (Illus.). 1975. pap. 1.50 (ISBN 0-910452-22-9). Covenant.

From this Day Forward. Jon Nilson. LC 83-73133. 88p. (Orig.). 1983. pap. 2.95 (ISBN 0-87029-192-0, 20284-6). Abbey.

From This Day Forward: Blueprint for Family Happiness. Nancy L. Van Pelt. Ed. by Richard W. Coffen. 128p. (Orig.). 1985. pap. 1.95 (ISBN 0-8280-0280-0). Review & Herald.

From This Day Forward: Thoughts about a Christian Marriage. Kenneth J. Foreman. pap. 2.95x (ISBN 0-685-02584-5). Outlook.

From Thy Bounty: Holiday Foods Around from the World. Mary V. Reilly & Margaret K. Wetterer. (Illus.). 44p. (Orig.). 1982. pap. 4.95 (ISBN 0-8192-1299-7). Morehouse.

From Tiny Beginnings. James Overholt. 64p. 1987. pap. 4.95 (ISBN 0-87178-296-0). Brethren.

From Torah to Apocalypse: An Introduction to the Bible. Francis I. Fesperman. 334p. 1983. pap. text ed. 15.25 (ISBN 0-8191-3555-0). U Pr of Amer.

From Torah to Kabbalah: A Basic Introduction to the Writings of Judaism. R. G. Musaph-Andriesse. 1982. pap. 4.95x (ISBN 0-19-520364-X). Oxford U Pr.

From Tradition to Gospel. Martin Dibelius. Tr. by Bertram L. Wooff. 328p. 1971. 27.50 (ISBN 0-227-67752-8). Attic Pr.

From Trials to Triumph. E. G. White. 1984. 1.50 (ISBN 0-8163-0565-X). Pacific Pr Pub Assn.

From Tribe to Empire: Social Organization among the Primitives & in the Ancient East. A. Moret & G. Davy. Tr. by V. Gordon Childe from Fr. LC 71-139997. (Illus.). 339p. 1971. Repr. of 1926 ed. lib. bdg. 24.50x (ISBN 0-8154-0368-2). Cooper Sq.

From Triumphalism to Maturity: An Exposition of II Corinthians 10-13. Donald A. Carson. 1984. 12.95 (ISBN 0-8010-2489-7). Baker Bk.

From Uniformity to Unity, 1662-1962. Ed. by Geoffrey F. Nuttall & O. Chadwick. LC 63-2539. 1962. 20.00x (ISBN 0-8401-1746-9). A R Allenson.

From Union Square to Rome. Dorothy Day. 17.00 (ISBN 0-405-10815-X). Ayer Co Pubs.

From UR to Nazareth: An Economic Inquiry into the Religious & Political History of Israel. Francis Neilson. 75.00 (ISBN 0-87700-010-7). Revisionist Pr.

From Utopia to Florence: The Story of a Transcendentalist Community in Northampton, Massachusetts, 1830-1852. Alice F. McBee. LC 74-31281. (American Utopian Adventure Ser). (Illus.). ix, 93p. 1975. Repr. of 1947 ed. lib. bdg. 17.50x (ISBN 0-87991-027-5). Porcupine Pr.

From Week to Week. Hillel E. Silverman. LC 74-16211. 1975. 10.95x (ISBN 0-87677-156-8). Hartmore.

From Wesley to Asbury: Studies in Early American Methodism. Frank Baker. LC 75-39454. xiv, 223p. 1976. 22.50 (ISBN 0-8223-0359-0). Duke.

From Where Shall We Begin & Machine in the Captivity of Machinism. Ali Shariati. Tr. by Fathollah Marjani from Persian. 51p. 1980. pap. 1.95x (ISBN 0-941722-10-4). Book-Dist-Ctr.

From Where They Sit. Dorothy Hutchinson. 1983. pap. 2.50x (ISBN 0-87574-084-7, 084). Pendle Hill.

From Wilderness to Wasteland: The Trial of the Puritan God in the American Imagination. Charles Berryman. (National University Publications, Literary Criticism Ser.). 1979. 21.50x (ISBN 0-8046-9235-1, Pub. by Kennikat). Assoc Faculty Pr.

From Word to Life. Perry Yoder. LC 81-20071. (Conrad Grebel Lecture Ser.). 288p. (Orig.). 1982. pap. 14.95x (ISBN 0-8361-1249-0). Herald Pr.

Frontier Camp Meeting: Religion's Harvest Time. Charles A. Johnson. LC 55-8783. (Illus.). xiv, 325p. 1985. 21.95x (ISBN 0-87074-201-9). SMU Press.

Frontier Parish: An Account of the Society for the Propagation of the Gospel & the Anglican Church in America, Drawn from the Records of the Bishop of London. Carson I. Ritchie. LC 75-3564. 210p. 1976. 18.50 (ISBN 0-8386-1735-2). Fairleigh Dickinson.

Frontier Spirit in American Christianity. P. G. Mode. 1977. lib. bdg. 59.95 (ISBN 0-8490-1870-6). Gordon Pr.

Frontiers of a Nation. H. F. Frischwasser-Ra'Anan. LC 75-6433. (Rise of Jewish Nationalism & the Middle East Ser). 168p. 1976. Repr. of 1955 ed. 18.15 (ISBN 0-88355-320-1). Hyperion Conn.

Frontiers of Hope. Horace M. Kallen. Ed. by Moshe Davis. LC 77-70711. (America & the Holy Land Ser.). 1977. Repr. of 1929 ed. lib. bdg. 37.50x (ISBN 0-405-10260-7). Ayer Co Pubs.

Frontiers of Islamic Economics. M. A. Mannan. 1985. 15.00x (ISBN 0-8364-1505-1, Pub. by Idarah). South Asia Bks.

Frontiers of Theology in Latin America. Ed. by Rosino Gibellini. Tr. by John Drury from Ital. LC 78-9147. Orig. Title: nuova frontiera della Teologia in Latina America. 333p. (Orig.). 1979. pap. 10.95 (ISBN 0-88344-144-6). Orbis Bks.

Fruehmittelaterliche Studien, Vol. 11. Ed. by Karl Hauck. (Illus.). 1977. 89.60x (ISBN 3-11-007076-6). De Gruyter.

Fruhgeschichte Des Deutschen Reims. Ulrich Pretzel. (Ger). 27.00 (ISBN 0-384-47740-2); pap. 22.00 (ISBN 0-685-02131-9). Johnson Repr.

Fruhmittelhochdeutsche Wiener Genesis. Alfred Weller. 27.00 (ISBN 0-384-66731-7); pap. 22.00 (ISBN 0-384-66730-9). Johnson Repr.

Fruit of Lips or Why Four Gospels? Eugen Rosenstock-Huessy. LC 78-8524. (Pittsburgh Theological Monographs: No. 19). 1978. pap. 6.25 (ISBN 0-915138-31-X). Pickwick.

Fruit of the Spirit. George Bethune. pap. 4.95 (ISBN 0-685-88375-2). Reiner.

Fruit of the Spirit. Leroy Brownlow. 1982. gift ed. 6.95 (ISBN 0-915720-59-0). Brownlow Pub Co.

Fruit of the Spirit. H. Ray Dunning. 38p. 1982. pap. 1.95 (ISBN 0-8341-0806-2). Beacon Hill.

Fruit of the Spirit. Donald Gee. 80p. 1975. pap. 1.95 (ISBN 0-88243-501-9, 02-0501, Radiant Bks). Gospel Pub.

Fruit of the Spirit. Hazel Offner. (LifeGuide Bible Studies). 64p. 1987. pap. 2.95. Inter-Varsity.

Fruit of the Spirit. John W. Sanderson. 192p. 1985. pap. 3.95 (ISBN 0-87552-431-1). Presby & Reformed.

Fruit of the Spirit. Betty Tapscott. 1978. pap. 4.95 (ISBN 0-917726-26-X). Hunter Bks.

Fruit of the Spirit. Stephen F. Winward. 208p. (Orig.). 1984. pap. 4.95 (ISBN 0-8028-0003-3). Eerdmans.

Fruit of the Vine. Ed. by Bryan L. McClelland. LC 85-72071. (Illus.). 392p. (Orig.). 1985. pap. 5.95 (ISBN 0-913342-50-5). Barclay Pr.

Fruitful & Responsible Love. Karol Wojtyla. (Orig.). 1979. pap. 2.95 (ISBN 0-8245-0310-4). Crossroad NY.

Fruitful or Barren? Donald Gee. 90p. 1961. pap. 1.35 (ISBN 0-88243-502-7, 02-0502). Gospel Pub.

Fruits of Anthroposophy. Rudolf Steiner. Tr. by Anna R. Meuss from Ger. Tr. of Anthroposophie, ihre Erkenntniswurzeln und Lebensfruechete. 76p. 1986. 20.00 (ISBN 0-88010-203-9); pap. 7.95 (ISBN 0-88010-202-0). Anthroposophic.

Fruits of Philosophy. Charles Knowlton. 58p. 1980. pap. 4.00 (ISBN 0-911826-16-5). Am Atheist.

Fruits of Repentance. Jerry L. Law. (Orig.). 1985. pap. 3.95 (ISBN 0-930875-00-1). Seed Life Pubns.

Fruits of Righteousness. Jerry Savelle. 32p. (Orig.). 1980. pap. 1.95 (ISBN 0-89274-069-8). Harrison Hse.

Fruits of Solitude. William Penn. pap. 5.95 (ISBN 0-913408-39-5). Friends United.

Fruits of the Spirit. Ron Hembree. (Direction Bks.). pap. 4.95 (ISBN 0-8010-4301-8). Baker Bk.

Fruits of the Spirit. Evelyn Underhill. LC 82-80477. (Treasures from the Spiritual Classics Ser.). 64p. 1982. pap. 2.95 (ISBN 0-8192-1314-4). Morehouse.

Frustration: How Christians Can Deal with It. Frances L. Carroll. 156p. 1984. pap. 6.95 (ISBN 0-13-330804-9). P-H.

Fruteful & Pleasaunt Worke of the Beste State of a Publyque Weale & the Newe Yle Called Utopia. Thomas More. Tr. by R. Robynson. LC 75-26096. (English Experience Ser.: No. 108). 1969. Repr. of 1551 ed. 21.00 (ISBN 90-221-0108-8). Walter J Johnson.

Fruto del Espiritu. Ed. by Hiram Almirudas. (Span.). 112p. 1979. pap. 3.50 (ISBN 0-87148-303-3). Pathway Pr.

FSI Hebrew Basic Course. Joseph A. Reif & Hanna Levinson. 1976. pap. text ed. 15.00X (ISBN 0-686-10730-6); 35 cassettes 210.00x (ISBN 0-686-10731-4). Intl Learn Syst.

Fuck, YES! A Guide to the Happy Acceptance of Everything. Wing F. Fing. (Illus.). 270p. (Orig.). 1987. pap. 8.50 (ISBN 0-940183-21-8). Shepherd Bks.

Fulfilled in Your Hearing (The Homily in the Sunday Assembly) 48p. 1982. pap. 2.95 (ISBN 1-55586-850-9). US Catholic.

Fulfilled Marriage. Norman Wright. LC 76-21981. (Answer Ser.). 1976. pap. 1.95 (ISBN 0-89081-060-5, 0605). Harvest Hse.

Fulfilled Promise: A Documentary Account of Religious Persecution in Albania. Gjon Sinishta. LC 76-57433. (Illus.). 253p. (Orig.). pap. 10.00 (ISBN 0-317-18715-5). Albanian Cath Info.

Fulfilled Woman. Lou Beardsley & Toni Spry. LC 74-29206. 1977. 3.25 (ISBN 0-89081-072-9). Harvest Hse.

Fulfilling the Circle: A Study of John Donne's Thought. Terry G. Sherwood. 231p. 1984. 27.50x (ISBN 0-8020-5621-0). U of Toronto Pr.

Fulfillment: Bible Studies for Women. Joyce M. Smith. 1975. pap. 2.95 (ISBN 0-8423-0980-2). Tyndale.

Fulfillment of Book of Mormon Prophecies. Ross Warner. 1975. pap. 4.95 (ISBN 0-89036-081-2). Hawkes Pub Inc.

Fulfillment of Old Age. Norbert Glas. Tr. by Stewart Easton from Fr. Tr. of Lichtvolles Alter. 141p. 1987. pap. 9.95 (ISBN 0-88010-161-X). Anthroposophic.

Fulgentius, der Mythograph und Bischof. Otto Friebel. pap. 15.00 (ISBN 0-384-16880-9). Johnson Repr.

Full Assurance. Harry A. Ironside. 1937. pap. 3.95 (ISBN 0-8024-2896-7). Moody.

Full Blessing of Pentecost. Andrew Murray. 1965. pap. 2.95 (ISBN 0-87508-376-5). Chr Lit.

Full Catechism of the Catholic Religion. Joseph Deharbe. 1979. lib. bdg. 59.95 (ISBN 0-8490-2924-4). Gordon Pr.

Full Christianity: A Catholic Response to Fundamental Questions. Richard W. Chilson. 144p. (Orig.). 1985. pap. 4.95 (ISBN 0-8091-2669-9). Paulist Pr.

Full Circle: Stories of Mennonite Women. Ed. by Mary L. Cummings. LC 78-66879. 1978. pap. 5.25 (ISBN 0-87303-014-1). Faith & Life.

Full Circle: The Moral Force of Unified Science. Ed. by Edward Haskell. LC 72-84271. (Current Topics of Contemporary Thought Ser.). (Illus.). 270p. (Orig.). 1972. 57.75 (ISBN 0-677-12480-5). Gordon & Breach.

Full History of the Wonderful Career of Moody & Sankey, in Great Britain & America. Edgar J. Goodspeed. LC 70-168154. (Illus.). Repr. of 1876 ed. 39.00 (ISBN 0-404-07227-5). AMS Pr.

Full of Grace & Truth, Vol. II. Watchman Nee. Tr. by Stephen Kaung. 1981. pap. 3.25 (ISBN 0-935008-51-9). Christian Fellow Pubs.

Full of Grace & Truth, Vol. I. Watchman Nee. Tr. by Stephen Kaung. 1980. pap. 3.25 (ISBN 0-935008-49-7). Christian Fellow Pubs.

Full of Joy. Margaret Ragland. 1980. pap. 5.25 (ISBN 0-89137-415-9). Quality Pubns.

Full Salvation. Phobe Palmer. pap. 4.95 (ISBN 0-686-27772-4). Schmul Pub Co.

Full Value: Cases in Christian Business Ethics. Oliver F. Williams & John M. Houck. LC 78-3143. 1978. pap. 8.95x S.D. (ISBN 0-06-069515-3, RD 279, HarpR). Har-Row.

Fullness in Christ (A Report on a Study of Clergy Retirement) 92p. 1979. pap. 2.95 (ISBN 1-55586-607-7). US Catholic.

Fullness of Human Experience. Dane Rudhyar. LC 85-40771. 272p. (Orig.). 1986. pap. 7.75 (ISBN 0-8356-0606-6, Quest). Theos Pub Hse.

Fullness of Humanity: Christ's Humanness & Ours. T. E. Pollard. 128p. 1982. text ed. 19.95x (ISBN 0-907459-10-2, Pub. by Almond Pr England); pap. text ed. 9.95x (ISBN 0-907459-11-0, Pub. by Almond Pr England). Eisenbrauns.

Fullness of Joy. Eric B. Hare. 1985. pap. 5.95 (ISBN 0-8163-0586-2). Pacific Pr Pub Assn.

Fullness of Life: Historical Foundations for a New Asceticism. Margaret R. Miles. LC 81-11535. 186p. 1981. pap. 11.95 (ISBN 0-664-24389-4). Westminster.

Fullness of the Spirit. V. E. Edman & R. A. Laidlaw. 36p. pap. 0.95 (ISBN 0-87509-083-4). Chr Pubns.

Fully Alive! Gloria Gaither. 208p. 1984. pap. 4.95 (ISBN 0-8407-5945-2). Nelson.

Fully Human, Fully Alive. John Powell. LC 76-41586. 1976. pap. 3.95 (ISBN 0-913592-77-3). Argus Comm.

Fully Illustrated Book in Colours of the Crucifixion. Alois Carinat. (Illus.). 101p. 1983. 275.50x (ISBN 0-86650-078-2). Gloucester Art.

Fulton's Footprints in Fiji. Eric B. Hare. 1985. pap. 5.95 (ISBN 0-8163-0583-8). Pacific Pr Pub Assn.

Fun Devotions for Kids. Louise B. Wyly. (Illus.). 64p. 1985. pap. 2.50 (ISBN 0-87239-891-9, 2821). Standard Pub.

Fun Devotions for Kids, No. 2. Marjorie H. Parker. 64p. 1985. pap. 2.50 (ISBN 0-87239-892-7, 2822). Standard Pub.

Fun Ideas for Family Devotions (with Activity Pages) Ginger Jurries & Karen Mulder. LC 81-50347. (Illus.). 176p. (Orig.). 1981. pap. 6.50 (ISBN 0-87239-415-8, 2968). Standard Pub.

Fun-in-Learning About Chanukah. James Sanders. LC 76-189390. (Illus.). 1972. 3.95 (ISBN 0-8246-0135-1). Jonathan David.

Fun-In-Learning about Passover. Alfred J. Kolatch. LC 74-175489. (Illus.). 1972. pap. 3.95 (ISBN 0-8246-0133-5). Jonathan David.

Fun 'n Festive Holiday Trimmers. Nan Aulson & Pam Aulson. (Illus.). 1983. pap. 3.00 (ISBN 0-9601896-6-1). Patch as Patch.

Fun-N-Games. Wayne Rice et al. 1977. pap. 6.95 (ISBN 0-310-35001-8, 10798P). Zondervan.

Fun to Do All Year Through. Ruth Eitzen. 32p. 1982. pap. 2.95 (ISBN 0-8170-0969-8). Judson.

Fun Ways to Holidays. Mamie G. Gamoran. 1951. pap. 2.00 (ISBN 0-8074-0136-6, 321400). UAHC.

Fun with Bible Facts. Ruby Paterson. pap. 1.75 (ISBN 0-89137-620-8). Quality Pubns.

Fun with Bible Geography. Marie Chapman. LC 80-65055. (Teaching Aid Ser.). 65p. 1980. plastic spiral 5.95 (ISBN 0-89636-044-X). Accent Bks.

Fun with Skits, Stunts, & Stories. Larry Eisenberg & Helen Eisenberg. (Game & Party Books). 64p. 1975. pap. 3.95 (ISBN 0-8010-3367-5). Baker Bk.

Function of Rebellion: Is Youth Creating New Family Values? Coles Konopka et al. LC 66-17843. 1968. pap. 2.85 (ISBN 0-686-25738-3). Jewish Bd Family.

Functional Poverty. Mildred B. Young. 1983. pap. 2.50x (ISBN 0-87574-006-5, 006). Pendle Hill.

Functioning Faith. Billy E. Simmons. 144p. 1983. pap. 4.00 (ISBN 0-914520-18-0). Insight Pr.

Functioning Leadership in the Church. Charles Moore. 1973. pap. 2.75 (ISBN 0-88027-034-9). Firm Foun Pub.

Fundamental Christian Beliefs. William Arndt. pap. text ed. 3.25 (ISBN 0-570-06324-8, 22-1144); pap. 3.75 guide (ISBN 0-570-06325-6, 22-1146); pap. tests 1.50 (ISBN 0-570-06362-0, 22-1145). Concordia.

Fundamental Christian Theology. A. M. Hills. boards 29.95 (ISBN 0-686-27770-8). Schmul Pub Co.

Fundamental Greek Grammar. James W. Voelz. 320p. 1986. 14.95 (ISBN 0-570-04226-7, 15-2185). Concordia.

Fundamental Ideas of Christianity, 2 vols. John Caird. LC 77-27231. (Gifford Lectures: 1892-93, 1895-96). Repr. of 1899 ed. Set. 49.50 (ISBN 0-404-60460-9). AMS Pr.

Fundamental Principles & Precepts of Islamic Government. Abolhassan Banisadr. Tr. by Mohammed R. Ghanoonparvar from Persian. LC 81-82634. (Iran-e NO Literary Collection Ser.). 120p. (Orig.). 1981. pap. 5.95 (ISBN 0-939214-01-6). Mazda Pubs.

Fundamental Principles of Old & New World Civilization. Zelia Nuttall. (HU PMP Ser.). 1901. 51.00 (ISBN 0-527-01190-8). Kraus Repr.

Fundamental Principles of the Metaphysic of Ethics. Immanuel Kant. Tr. by Otto Manthey-Zorn. (Century Philosophy Ser.). 1966. pap. text ed. 7.95x (ISBN 0-89197-185-8). Irvington.

Fundamental Principles of the Metaphysics of Morals. Immanuel Kant. Tr. by Thomas K. Abbott. 1949. pap. 4.24 scp (ISBN 0-672-60177-X, LLA16). Bobbs.

Fundamental Theology. Gerald O'Collins. LC 80-82809. 288p. (Orig.). 1981. pap. 8.95 (ISBN 0-8091-2347-9). Paulist Pr.

Fundamental Things Apply: Reflecting on Christian Basics. Clyde F. Crews. LC 83-71005. 104p. (Orig.). 1983. pap. 3.95 (ISBN 0-87793-272-7). Ave Maria.

Fundamentalism & American Culture: The Shaping of Twentieth-Century Evangelicalism, 1870-1925. George M. Marsden. 1980. pap. 9.95 (ISBN 0-19-503083-4). Oxford U Pr.

Fundamentalism & the Word of God. James I. Packer. 1958. pap. 6.95 (ISBN 0-8028-1147-7). Eerdmans.

Fundamentalism, Revivalists & Violence in South Asia. James Bjorkman. LC 85-61080. 210p. 1987. 19.00 (ISBN 0-913215-06-6). Riverdale Co.

Fundamentalism Today: What Makes It So Attractive? Ed. by Marla J. Selvidge. 144p. (Orig.). 1984. pap. 7.95 (ISBN 0-87178-297-9). Brethren.

Fundamentalism: What Every Catholic Needs to Know. Anthony E. Gilles. (Illus.). 72p. (Orig.). 1985. pap. text ed. 3.75 (ISBN 0-86716-043-8). St Anthony Mess Pr.

Fundamentalist Movement. Louis Gasper. (Twin Brooks Ser.). 181p. (Orig.). 1981. pap. 6.95 (ISBN 0-8010-3769-7). Baker Bk.

Fundamentalist Phenomenon: The Resurgence of Conservative Christianity. 2nd ed. Ed Dobson et al. pap. 7.95 (ISBN 0-8010-2958-9). Baker Bk.

Fundamentals of Adamic Christianity. Robert E. Birdsong. (Aquarian Academy Monograph, Series A: Lecture No. 1). 1974. pap. 1.25 (ISBN 0-917108-00-0). Sirius Bks.

Fundamentals of Catholic Dogma. Ludwig Ott. Ed. by James C. Bastible. Tr. by Patrick Lynch from Ger. Orig. Title: Grundriss der Katholischen Dogmatik. 1974. pap. 15.00 (ISBN 0-89555-009-1). TAN Bks Pubs.

Fundamentals of Catholicism: Church, Grace, Sacraments & Eschatology or the Last Things, Vol. III. Kenneth Baker. 1983. pap. 10.95 (ISBN 0-317-02736-0, Co-Pub. by Ignatius Pr-Catholic Polls). Guild Bks.

Fundamentals of Catholicism: God, Trinity, Creation, Christ, Mary, Vol. II. Kenneth Baker. LC 82-80297. 1983. pap. 10.95 (ISBN 0-89870-019-1, Co-Pub. by Ignatius Pr-Catholic Polls). Guild Bks.

Fundamentals of Catholicism: God, Trinity, Creation, Christ, Mary, Vol. 2. Kenneth S. Baker. LC 82-80297. 387p. (Orig.). 1983. pap. 11.95 (ISBN 0-89870-019-1). Ignatius Pr.

Fundamentals of Catholicism: Grace, the Church, the Sacraments, Eschatology, Vol. 3. Kenneth Baker. LC 82-80297. 388p. (Orig.). 1983. pap. 11.95 (ISBN 0-89870-027-2). Ignatius Pr.

Fundamentals of Catholocism: The Creed, the Commandments, Vol. I. Kenneth Baker. LC 82-80297. 1982. pap. 9.95 (ISBN 0-89870-017-5, Co-Pub. by Ignatius Pr-Catholic Polls). Guild Bks.

Fundamentals of Christian Education. Ellen G. White. (CHL Ser.). 1977. 8.95 (ISBN 0-8127-0307-3). Review & Herald.

Fundamentals of Human Spirituality. Peter D. Francuch. LC 81-16660. 483p. 1982. 9.95x (ISBN 0-939386-01-1). TMH Pub.

Fundamentals of Indian Philosophy. R. Puligandla. LC 85-20195. 364p. 1985. pap. text ed. 14.75 (ISBN 0-8191-4891-1). U Pr of Amer.

Fundamentals of Islam. A. A. Maududi. 12.50 (ISBN 0-686-18489-0). Kazi Pubns.

Fundamentals of Islamic Thought: God, Man & the Universe. Ayatullah M. Mutahhari. Ed. by Hamid Algar. Tr. by R. Campbell. (Comtemporary Islamic Thought Perian Ser.). Orig. Title: Per. 231p. (Orig.). 1985. 19.95 (ISBN 0-933782-14-4); pap. 8.95 (ISBN 0-933782-15-2). Mizan Pr.

Fundamentals of Judaism. Jacob Breuer. 1969. pap. 6.95 (ISBN 0-87306-208-6). Feldheim.

Fundamentals of Our Faith. Herschel H. Hobbs. LC 60-5200. (Orig.). 1960. pap. 6.95 (ISBN 0-8054-1702-8). Broadman.

Fundamentals of Preaching. John Killinger. LC 84-47926. 224p. 1985. pap. 9.95 (ISBN 0-8006-1796-7, 1-1796). Fortress.

Fundamentals of the Esoteric Philosophy. 2nd, rev. ed. G. De Purucker. Ed. by Grace F. Knoche. LC 78-74258. 1979. 14.00 (ISBN 0-911500-63-4); pap. 8.00 (ISBN 0-911500-64-2). Theos U Pr.

Fundamentals of the Faith. Robert E. Picirilli. 30p. 1973. pap. 0.95 (ISBN 0-89265-106-7). Randall Hse.

Fundamentals of the Faith. Raymond M. Pruitt. 1981. 16.95 (ISBN 0-934942-21-8). White Wing Pub.

Fundamentals of Therapy: An Extension of the Art of Healing Through Spiritual Knowledge. 4th ed. Rudolf Steiner. Tr. by Eva A. Frommer & J. M. Josephson. Tr. of Grundlegendes fur eine Erweiterung der Heilkunst nach geisteswissenschaftlichen Erkenntnissen. 128p. 1983. pap. 7.95 (ISBN 0-85440-423-6, Pub. by Steinerbooks). Anthroposophic.

Fundamentals of Thought. L. Ron Hubbard. 20.00 (ISBN 0-686-13919-4). Church Scient NY.

Fundamentals of Visistadvaita Vedanta. S. M. Chari. 1987. 36.00 (Pub. by Motilal Banarsidass). South Asia Bks.

Fundamentos de Teologia Biblica. Emery H. Bancroft. Tr. of Elemental Theology. (Span.). 496p. 1987. pap. 10.95 (ISBN 0-8254-1050-9). Kregel.

Funeral: A Service of Witness to the Resurrection. The Office of Worship for the Presbyterian Church (U. S. A.) & the Cumberland Presbyterian Church. (Supplemental Liturgical Resource Ser.: 4). 120p. (Orig.). 1986. pap. write for info. (ISBN 0-664-24034-8). Westminster.

Funeral Handbook. Friedrich Rest. 144p. 1982. 9.95 (ISBN 0-8170-0929-9). Judson.

Funeral Homilies. Ed. by Liam Swords. 2.95 (ISBN 0-8091-2784-9). Paulist Pr.

Funeral Liturgy Planning Guide. 1984. pap. 1.00 (ISBN 0-8146-1362-4). Liturgical Pr.

Funeral Orations. St. Gregory Nazianzen & St. Ambrose. LC 67-28586. (Fathers of the Church Ser: Vol. 22). 344p. 1953. 18.95x (ISBN 0-8132-0022-9). Cath U Pr.

Funeral Sermons & Outlines. F. B. Meyer et al. (Pulpit Library). 1984. pap. 3.50 (ISBN 0-8010-5873-2). Baker Bk.

Funeral Source Book. R. Earl Allen. (Preaching Helps Ser.). (Orig.). 1984. pap. 3.50 (ISBN 0-8010-0076-9). Baker Bk.

Funeral: Vestige or Value? Paul E. Irion. Ed. by Robert Kastenaum. LC 76-19578. (Death & Dying Ser.). 1977. Repr. lib. bdg. 22.00x (ISBN 0-405-09575-9). Ayer Co Pubs.

Funk & Wagnalls Standard Dictionary of Folklore, Mythology & Legend. Ed. by Leach. LC 72-78268. (Funk & W Bk.). 23.00i (ISBN 0-308-40090-9). T Y Crowell.

Funk & Wagnall's Standard Dictionary of Folklore, Mythology, & Legends. Ed. by Maria Leach & Jerome Fried. 1984. pap. 29.95 (ISBN 0-06-250511-4, HarpR). Har-Row.

Funny Thing Happened on the Way to Church. Dave Anderson & Tim Wilcox. 1981. pap. 4.50 (ISBN 0-570-03834-0, 12YY2799). Concordia.

Furnace of Affliction. 6th ed. William S. Deal. 1978. 1.50 (ISBN 0-686-05833-X). Crusade Pubs.

Furta Sacra: Thefts of Relics in the Central Middle Ages. Patrick J. Geary. LC 77-85538. 1978. 26.50 (ISBN 0-691-05261-1). Princeton U Pr.

Further Buddhist Studies: Selected Essays. Edward Conze. 238p. 1975. 40.00x (ISBN 0-317-39071-6, Pub. by Luzac & Co Ltd). State Mutual Bk.

Further Prophecies of Nostradamus Nineteen Eighty Five & Beyond. Erika Cheetham. 256p. (Orig.). 1985. pap. 6.95 (ISBN 0-399-51121-0, Perigee). Putnam Pub Group.

Further Record. P. D. Ouspensky. 352p. 1987. pap. 13.95 (ISBN 1-85063-056-9, 30569, Ark Paperbks). Methuen Inc.

Further Shore. Bhagwan Shree Rajneesh. Ed. by Ma Prem Maneesha. LC 83-181220. (Initation Talks Ser.). (Illus.). 288p. (Orig.). 1980. 22.95 (ISBN 0-88050-065-4). Chidvilas Found.

Further Studies Concerning the Origin of Paradise Lost. H. Mutschmann. LC 77-24899. lib. bdg. 10.00 (ISBN 0-8414-6211-9). Folcroft.

Fusang or the Discovery of America by Chinese Buddhist Priests. Charles G. Leland. 212p. 1981. pap. 12.00 (ISBN 0-89540-094-4, SB-094). Sun Pub.

Futile Diplomacy: Early Arab-Zionist Negotiation Attempts, 1913-1931, Vol. 1. Neil Caplan. (Illus.). 296p. 1983. text ed. 32.00x (ISBN 0-7146-3214-7, F Cass Co). Biblio Dist.

Future & a Hope. Carol Steficek. 1985. 2.95 (ISBN 0-89536-940-0, 7560). CSS of Ohio.

Future Evolution of Man. Sri Aurobindo. Ed. by P. B. Saint-Hilaire. 157p. 1982. pap. 2.95 (ISBN 0-89071-323-5, Pub. by Sri Aurobindo Ashram India). Matagiri.

Future for the Historical Jesus: The Place of Jesus in Preaching & Theology. Leander E. Keck. LC 81-43081. pap. 70.80 (2029605). Bks Demand UMI.

Future Glory. Joseph Bagiackas. LC 83-70962. 130p. (Orig.). 1983. pap. 3.95 (ISBN 0-943780-02-0, 8020). Charismatic Ren Servs.

Future Is Now. Arne Christianson. 1983. 8.95 (ISBN 0-533-05552-0). Vantage.

Future Is Now. Warren B. Davis & Richard M. Cromie. 110p. (Orig.). 1984. pap. 6.00 (ISBN 0-914733-03-6). Desert Min.

Future Life. Michel Salomon. 384p. 1983. 19.95 (ISBN 0-02-606770-6). Macmillan.

Future Life According to Orthodox Teaching. Constantine Cavarnos. Tr. by Hieromonk Auxentios & Archimandrite Chrysostomos. 100p. (Orig.). 1985. pap. 6.50 (ISBN 0-911165-06-1). Ctr Trad Orthodox.

Future of an Illusion. Sigmund Freud. Ed. by James Strachey. 1975. 10.95 (ISBN 0-393-01120-8); pap. 2.95 (ISBN 0-393-00831-2). Norton.

Future of Anglican Theology. Ed. by M. D. Bryant. LC 84-8983. (Toronto Studies in Theology: Vol. 17). 208p. 1984. 49.95x (ISBN 0-88946-763-3). E Mellen.

Future of Canon Law. Neophytos Edelby. LC 78-100004. (Concilium Ser.: No. 48). 188p. 7.95 (ISBN 0-8091-0049-5). Paulist Pr.

Future of Empirical Theology. Bernard E Meland. Ed. by J. C. Braver. LC 78-83980. (Essays in Divinty Ser: Vol. 7). 1969. 20.00x (ISBN 0-226-51955-4). U of Chicago Pr.

Future of Freedom: Notes on Christianity & Politics. facs. ed. Douglas Jerrold. LC 68-20311. (Essay Index Reprint Ser). 1938. 18.00 (ISBN 0-8369-0570-9). Ayer Co Pubs.

Future of Immortality: And Other Essays for a Nuclear Age. Robert J. Lifton. LC 86-47763. 368p. 1987. 21.95 (ISBN 0-465-02597-8). Basic.

Future of Jewish-Christian Relations. Ed. by Norma H. Thompson & Bruce Cole. LC 82-73896. 1982. 10.95 (ISBN 0-915744-27-9); pap. 8.95 (ISBN 0-915744-28-7). Character Res.

Future of Man. Pierre Teilhard De Chardin. (Orig.). 1969. pap. 7.95 (ISBN 0-06-090496-8, CN496, PL). Har-Row.

Future of Muslim Civilisation. Ziauddin Sardar. 224p. 1979. 25.00 (ISBN 0-85664-800-0, Pub. by Croom Helm Ltd). Methuen Inc.

Future of New Religious Movements. Ed. by David G. Bromley & Philip E. Hammond. 288p. 1987. 39.95 (ISBN 0-86554-237-6); pap. 19.95 (ISBN 0-86554-238-4). Mercer Univ Pr.

Future of Our Past: The Spanish Mystics Speak to Contemporary Spirituality. Segundo Galilea. LC 85-71822. 96p. (Orig.). 1985. pap. 4.95 (ISBN 0-87793-296-4). Ave Maria.

Future of Palestine. Arab Office, London Staff. LC 75-12167. (Rise of Jewish Nationalism & the Middle East Ser). 166p. 1976. Repr. of 1947 ed. 16.50 (ISBN 0-88355-229-9). Hyperion Conn.

Future of Partnership. Letty M. Russell. LC 78-20805. 198p. 1979. pap. 8.95 (ISBN 0-664-24240-5). Westminster.

Future of Religion: Secularization, Revival & Cult Formation. Rodney Stark & William S. Bainbridge. LC 83-18221. (Illus.). 600p. 1985. pap. 40.00x (ISBN 0-520-04854-7); 14.95 (ISBN 0-520-05731-7, CAMPUS 406). U of Cal Pr.

Future of Religions. Paul Tillich. Ed. by Jerald C. Brauer. LC 76-7566. 1976. Repr. of 1966 ed. lib. bdg. 22.50x (ISBN 0-8371-8861-X, TIFR). Greenwood.

Future of the American Jew. Mordecai M. Kaplan. LC 67-31309. 571p. 1981. pap. 13.95 (ISBN 0-935457-13-5). Reconstructionist Pr.

Future of the Christian Church. A. Michael Ramsey & Leon J. Suenens. (Orig.). 1970. pap. 3.95 (ISBN 0-8192-1124-9). Morehouse.

Future of the Church: The Theology of Renewal of Willem Adolf Visser't Hooft. Francois C. Gerard. LC 74-26564. (Pittsburgh Theological Monographs: No. 2). 1974. pap. 6.00 (ISBN 0-915138-01-8). Pickwick.

Future of the Methodist Theological Traditions. Ed. by M. Douglas Meeks. 224p. 1985. pap. 9.95 (ISBN 0-687-13868-X). Abingdon.

Future of Unbelief. Gerhard Szczesny. LC 60-1665. 1961. pap. 2.95 (ISBN 0-8076-0375-9). Braziller.

Future of World Evangelization: The Lausanne Movement. Ed Dayton & Samuel Wilson. 1984. 7.95 (ISBN 0-912552-42-5). Missions Adv Res Com Ctr.

Future Present: The Phenomenon of Christian Worship. Marianne H. Micks. LC 75-103844. 1970. pap. 6.95 (ISBN 0-8164-2109-9, HarpR). Har-Row.

Future Shape of Preaching. Thor Hall. LC 77-157537. pap. 40.00 (2026899). Bks Demand UMI.

Future Survival. Chuck Smith. (Illus.). 112p. (Orig.). 1980. pap. 1.50 (ISBN 0-936728-02-7). Word for Today.

Fyodor Dostoevsky. J. A. Lloyd. 1978. Repr. of 1946 ed. lib. bdg. 25.00 (ISBN 0-8495-3228-0). Arden Lib.

Fyodor Dostoevsky. J. A. Lloyd. LC 78-164532. 1971. Repr. of 1947 ed. 24.50x (ISBN 0-8154-0401-8). Cooper Sq.

Fyodor Dostyevsky. J. A. Lloyd. 1973. lib. bdg. 20.00 (ISBN 0-8414-5871-5). Folcroft.

Fyrst Boke of the Introduction of Knowledge by Andrew Borde, Vol. 2 Text. James Hogg. (Analecta Cartusiana Ser.: No. 92/2). 103p. (Orig.). 1979. pap. 25.00 (ISBN 3-7052-0161-1, Pub. by Salzburg Studies). Longwood Pub Group.

Fyrst Boke of the Introduction of Knowledge by Andrew Borde: Introduction, Vol. 1. James Hogg. (Analecta Cartusiana Ser.: No. 92/1). (Orig.). 1987. pap. 25.00 (ISBN 3-7052-0160-3, Pub. by Salzburg Studies). Longwood Pub Group.

G

G. K. Chesterton. Dudley Barker. LC 72-95988. 1975. 5.95 (ISBN 0-8128-1804-0). Stein & Day.

G. K. Chesterton. Patrick Braybrooke. LC 72-6491. (English Biography Ser., No. 31). 130p. 1972. Repr. of 1922 ed. lib. bdg. 35.95x (ISBN 0-8383-1616-6). Haskell.

G. K. Chesterton. Maurice Evans. LC 72-3187. (English Literature Ser., No. 33). 1972. Repr. of 1939 ed. lib. bdg. 39.95x (ISBN 0-8383-1504-6). Haskell.

G. K. Chesterton. W. Titterton. LC 73-14569. 1974. Repr. of 1947 ed. lib. bdg. 22.50 (ISBN 0-8414-8536-4). Folcroft.

G. K. Chesterton: A Biography. Michael Ffinch. 1987. 18.95 (ISBN 0-06-252576-X, HarpR). Har-Row.

G. K. Chesterton: A Critical Study. Julius West. LC 72-6120. 1973. Repr. of 1915 ed. lib. bdg. 30.00 (ISBN 0-8414-0112-8). Folcroft.

G. K. Chesterton: A Portrait. W. Titterton. LC 72-8980. (English Biography Ser., No. 31). 1973. Repr. of 1936 ed. lib. bdg. 49.95x (ISBN 0-8383-1679-4). Haskell.

G. K Chesterton Anthology. G. K. Chesterton. Ed. by P. J. Kavanagh. 515p. 1985. 24.95 (ISBN 0-89870-073-6); pap. 14.95 (ISBN 0-89870-096-5). Ignatius Pr.

G. K. Chesterton Calendar: A Quotation from the Works of G. K. Chesterton for Every Day in the Year. G. K. Chesterton. 75.00 (ISBN 0-87968-325-2). Gordon Pr.

Gabriel Marcel. Sam Keen. LC 67-11288. (Makers of Contemporary Theology Ser). pap. 15.00 (ISBN 0-8357-9258-7, 2015434). Bks Demand UMI.

Gabriel Marcel on Religious Knowledge. Neil Gillman. LC 80-5061. 315p. 1980. text ed. 26.75 (ISBN 0-8191-1034-5); pap. text ed. 14.25 (ISBN 0-8191-1035-3). U Pr of Amer.

Gadamer's Hermeneutics: A Reading of Truth & Method. Joel C. Weinsheimer. LC 84-27028. 288p. 1985. 20.00x (ISBN 0-300-03320-6). Yale U Pr.

Gaebelein's Concise Commentary on the Whole Bible. rev. ed. Arno C. Gaebelein. 1237p. 1985. Repr. of 1970 ed. 29.95 (ISBN 0-87213-209-9). Loizeaux.

Gaelic Pioneers of Christianity: The Work & Influence of Irish Monks & Saints in Continental Europe. Dom L. Gougaud. Tr. by Victor Collins from Fr. 166p. 1983. lib. bdg. 85.00 (ISBN 0-89984-223-2). Century Bookbindery.

Gagg for the New Gospell? No: A New Gagg for an Old Goose. Richard Montagu. LC 74-28872. (English Experience Ser.: No. 751). 1975. Repr. of 1624 ed. 26.00 (ISBN 90-221-0751-5). Walter J Johnson.

Gaina Sutras, 2 vols. H. Jacobi. lib. bdg. 200.00 (ISBN 0-87968-526-3). Krishna Pr.

Gaining Christ in Daily Life. Bill Freeman. 12p. 1983. pap. 0.25 (ISBN 0-914271-02-4). NW Christian Pubns.

Gaining Through Losing. Evelyn Christenson. LC 80-51630. 180p. 1981. 5.95 (ISBN 0-88207-795-3); pap. 5.95 (ISBN 0-88207-344-3). Victor Bks.

Gains & Losses. Robert L. Wolff. (Victorian Fiction Ser.). Orig. Title: Faith & Doubt in Victorian England. 1977. lib. bdg. 33.00 (ISBN 0-8240-1617-3). Garland Pub.

Galatas: Una Llamada a la Libertad Cristiana (Comentario Biblico Portavoz) Howard F. Vos. Orig. Title: Galatians (Everyman's Bible Commentary) (Span.). 1981. pap. 3.50 (ISBN 0-8254-1825-9). Kregel.

Galatians. Hans D. Betz. LC 77-78625. (Hermenia: A Critical & Historical Commentary on the Bible Ser.). 384p. 1979. 28.95 (ISBN 0-8006-6009-9, 20-6009). Fortress.

Galatians. rev. ed. Don E. Boatman & Kenny Boles. LC 70-1141. (Bible Study Textbook Ser.). (Illus.). 1976. 12.20 (ISBN 0-89900-039-8). College Pr Pub.

Galatians. John Brown. 1982. lib. bdg. 16.00 (ISBN 0-86524-083-3, 4802). Klock & Klock.

Galatians. G. Michael Cocoris. (Orig.). 1986. pap. text ed. write for info. (ISBN 0-935729-33-X). Church Open Door.

Galatians. (Erdman's Commentaries Ser.). 3.50 (ISBN 0-8010-3397-7). Baker Bk.

Galatians. rev. ed. Donald Guthrie. Ed. by Matthew Black. (New Century Bible Commentary Ser.). 176p. 1981. pap. 5.95 (ISBN 0-8028-1906-0). Eerdmans.

Galatians. Irving L. Jensen. (Bible Self Study Ser). 1973. pap. 3.25 (ISBN 0-8024-1048-0). Moody.

Galatians. Henry T. Mahan. 1983. pap. 1.50 (ISBN 0-686-40819-5). Pilgrim Pubns.

Galatians. Carolyn Osiek. (New Testament Message Ser.: Vol. 12). 8.95 (ISBN 0-89453-200-6); pap. 5.95 (ISBN 0-89453-135-2). M Glazier.

Galatians. Billy E. Simmons. 128p. 1983. pap. 3.00 (ISBN 0-914520-20-2). Insight Pr.

Galatians. Howard F. Vos. (Everyman's Bible Commentary Ser.). 1970. pap. 5.95 (ISBN 0-8024-2048-6). Moody.

Galatians. Geoffrey Wilson. 1979. pap. 4.95 (ISBN 0-85151-294-1). Banner of Truth.

Galatians: A Dialogical Response to Opponents. Bernard Brinsmead. LC 81-18535. (SBL Dissertation Ser.). 1982. pap. 17.25 (ISBN 0-89130-549-1, 06 01 65). Scholars Pr GA.

Galatians: A Study Guide. Roger Van Harn. (Revelation Series for Adults). 1984. pap. 2.50 (ISBN 0-933140-93-2). CRC Pubns.

Galatians & Ephesians. William Hendriksen. (New Testament Commentary Ser.). 290p. 1979. 18.95 (ISBN 0-8010-4211-9). Baker Bk.

Galatians & Ephesians. H. A. Ironside. 11.95 (ISBN 0-87213-397-4). Loizeaux.

Galatians & Ephesians. Lehman Strauss. 1957. 8.95 (ISBN 0-87213-817-8). Loizeaux.

Galatians & Romans. Frank Stagg. LC 79-92066. (Knox Preaching Guides Ser.). 128p. (Orig., John Hayes series editor). 1980. pap. 4.95 (ISBN 0-8042-3238-5); pap. 4.95. John Knox.

Galatians & Romans, No. 6. John J. Pilch & Robert J. Karris. (Collegeville Bible Commentary Ser.). 80p. 1983. pap. 2.95 (ISBN 0-8146-1306-3). Liturgical Pr.

Galatians Bible Study Commentary. Curtis Vaughan. 128p. 1972. pap. 4.95 (ISBN 0-310-33543-4, 10856P). Zondervan.

Galatians-Colossians. Archibald M. Hunter. LC 59-10454. (Layman's Bible Commentary Ser.: Vol. 22). 1959. pap. 4.95 (ISBN 0-8042-3082-X). John Knox.

Galatians-Ephesians. E. L. Lawson. (Standard Bible Studies). (Illus.). 288p. 1987. pap. price not set (ISBN 0-87403-169-9, 40109). Standard Pub.

Galatians-Ephesians. Mike McCann. (Standard Bible Study Workbooks Ser.). 80p. 1987. wkbk. 1.95 (ISBN 0-87403-189-3, 40209). Standard Pub.

Galatians, Ephesians, Philippians, & Colossians: A Daily Dialogue with God. Whitney Kuniholm. (Personal Bible Studyguide Ser.). 144p. 1983. pap. 5.95 (ISBN 0-87788-292-4). Shaw Pubs.

Galatians: Free at Last. Sandy Larsen & Dale Larsen. (Young Fisherman Bible Studyguide Ser.). (Illus.). 73p. 1982. saddle-stitched student ed. 2.95 (ISBN 0-87788-293-2); tchr's ed. 4.95 (ISBN 0-87788-294-0). Shaw Pubs.

Galatians-Philemon, Vol. IX. Beacon Bible Commentary Staff. 13.95 (ISBN 0-8010-0696-1). Baker Bk.

Galatians: The Bible Commentary for Teaching & Preaching. Charles Cousar. LC 81-82354. (Interpretation Ser.). 168p. (James Mays General Editor of the series, Paul Achtemeier New Testament editor). 1982. 13.95 (ISBN 0-8042-3138-9). John Knox.

Galatians: The Charter of Christian Liberty. rev. ed. Merrill C. Tenney. 1960. 10.95 (ISBN 0-8028-3253-9). Eerdmans.

Galatians, the Epistle of Christian Maturity. Keith L. Brooks. (Teach Yourself the Bible Ser.). 1963. pap. 2.75 (ISBN 0-8024-2925-4). Moody.

Galatians: The Gospel of Freedom. Richard A. Hufton. LC 85-80103. 130p. (Orig.). 1985. pap. 4.00 (ISBN 0-933643-00-4). Grace World Outreach.

Galatians: The Spirit-Controlled Life. Bob Yandian. 264p. (Orig.). 1985. pap. 6.95 (ISBN 0-89274-388-3). Harrison Hse.

Galatians: Why Christ Accepts Us. Jack Kuhatschek. (LifeBuilder Bible Studies). (Orig.). 1986. pap. 2.95 (ISBN 0-8308-1011-0). Inter-Varsity.

Galilean Rabbi & His Bible: Jesus' Use of the Interpreted Scripture of His Time. Bruce D. Chilton. (Good News Studies Ser.: Vol. 8). 7.95 (ISBN 0-89453-374-6). M Glazier.

Galileo: Arabic. (MacDonald Educational Ser.). (Illus.). 3.50x (ISBN 0-86685-249-2). Intl Bk Ctr.

Galileo Galilei & the Roman Curia from Authentic Sources. Karl Von Gebler. Tr. by Jane Sturge. LC 76-1124. 1977. Repr. of 1897 ed. lib. bdg. 28.50x (ISBN 0-915172-11-9). Richwood Pub.

Galileo: His Life & Work. J. J. Fahie. (Illus.). Repr. of 1903 ed. lib. bdg. 57.00x (ISBN 0-697-00003-6). Irvington.

Galileo, Science & the Church. rev. ed. Jerome J. Langford. 1971. pap. 7.95x (ISBN 0-472-06173-9, 173, AA). U of Mich Pr.

Gallia Christiana, 16 vols. Denis De Sainte Marthe. 12462p. Repr. of 1715 ed. text ed. 1863.00x (ISBN 0-576-78556-3, Pub. by Gregg Intl Pubs England). Gregg Intl.

Galut: Modern Jewish Reflections on Homelessness & Homecoming. Arnold M. Eisen. LC 85-45763. (Modern Jewish Experience Ser.). 224p. 1986. pap. 27.50x (ISBN 0-253-32550-1). Ind U Pr.

Galveston: Ellis Island of the West. Bernard Marinbach. (Modern Jewish History Ser.). 384p. 1983. 49.50x (ISBN 0-87395-700-8); pap. 17.95 (ISBN 0-87395-701-6). State U NY Pr.

Gambling: A Deadly Game. Larry Braidfoot. LC 85-19066. (Orig.). 1985. pap. 4.95 (ISBN 0-8054-5664-3). Broadman.

Game Plan II. Campus Crusade for Christ Staff. (Illus.). 100p. 1980. pap. text ed. 3.50 (ISBN 0-918956-64-1). Campus Crusade.

Game Theory, Social Choice, & Ethics. Ed. by Horace Brock. 1979. lib. bdg. 31.50 (ISBN 0-686-26826-1, Pub. by Reidel Holland). Kluwer Academic.

Gameplan: The Language & Strategy of Pro Football. Rev. ed. John Riggins & Jack Winter. Ed. by Alexandra Halsey. LC 84-40402. (Illus.). 240p. 1984. pap. 12.95x (ISBN 0-915643-08-1). Santa Barb Pr.

Games. Compiled by Mary Hohenstein. LC 80-23047. 298p. (Orig.). 1980. pap. 6.95 (ISBN 0-87123-191-3, 210191). Bethany Hse.

Games for Fun. Mildred Wade. LC 77-76616. 1977. pap. 3.95 (ISBN 0-8054-7513-3). Broadman.

Games Zen Masters Play: The Writings of R. H. Blyth. Robert Sohl & Audrey Carr. 1976. pap. 3.50 (ISBN 0-451-62416-5, Ment). NAL.

Gandhi & His Contemporaries. P. C. Roy-Chaudhury. 336p. 1972. 25.00x (ISBN 0-89684-394-7). Orient Bk Dist.

Gandhi & Khilafat. S. R. Bakshi. 1985. 18.00x (ISBN 0-8364-1491-8, Pub. by Gitanjali Prakashan). South Asia Bks.

Gandhi Remembered. Horace Alexander. LC 71-84674. (Orig.). 1969. pap. 2.50x (ISBN 0-87574-165-7). Pendle Hill.

Gandhian Approach to Communal Harmony: A Critical Study. Khan M. Afaque. 140p. 1986. 11.00 (ISBN 81-202-0163-9, Pub. by Ajanta). South Asia Bks.

Gandhian Ideas, Social Movements & Creativity. Pratibha Jain. 1986. 32.00x (ISBN 81-7033-007-6, Pub. by Rawat). South Asia Bks.

Gandhian Theology of Liberation. Ignatius Jesudasan. LC 83-19486. 192p. (Orig.). 1984. pap. 10.95 (ISBN 0-88344-154-3). Orbis Bks.

Gandhian Thought & Contemporary Society. Pyarelal et al. Ed. by J. S. Mathur. 285p. 1983. 18.00 (ISBN 0-934676-31-3). Greenlf Bks.

Gandhi's Religious Thought. Margaret Chatterjee. LC 83-5841. 224p. 1984. text ed. 19.95x (ISBN 0-268-01009-9, 85-10091). U of Notre Dame Pr.

Gandhi's Religious Thought. Margaret Chatterjee. LC 83-5841. 208p. 1986. pap. 9.95 (ISBN 0-268-01011-0). U of Notre Dame Pr.

Ganesa: Lord of Obstacles, Lord of Beginnings. Courtright. 1985. 29.95x (ISBN 0-19-503572-0). Oxford U Pr.

Gangaotri & Gaumukh: A Trek to the Holy Source. S. S. Malhotra. 1984. 12.50x (ISBN 0-8364-1175-7, Pub. by Allied India). South Asia Bks.

Ganges in Myth & History. Steven G. Darian. LC 77-21374. (Illus.). 236p. 1978. text ed. 12.00x (ISBN 0-8248-0509-7). UH Pr.

Gang's Weigh. Miriam Gang & Arthur Gang. 88p. (Orig.). 1986. pap. 9.95 (ISBN 0-941850-24-2). Sunday Pubns.

Garden & the Wilderness: Religion & Government in American Constitutional History. Mark D. Howe. (Phoenix Bks.). pap. 47.50 (ISBN 0-317-08469-0, 2020085). Bks Demand UMI.

Garden of American Methodism: The Delmarva Peninsula, 1769-1820. William H. Williams. (Illus.). xiv, 225p. 1984. 25.00 (ISBN 0-8420-2227-9). Scholarly Res Inc.

Garden of Love-Light. Sri Chinmoy. 50p. (Orig.). 1974. pap. 2.00 (ISBN 0-88497-109-0). Aum Pubns.

Garden of Love-Light, Vols 1 & 2. Sri Chinmoy. Tr. by Sri Chinmoy from Bengali. (Illus., Orig.). 1973. pap. 2.00 ea.; pap. write for info. (ISBN 0-88497-031-0); pap. write for info. (ISBN 0-88497-032-9); Vol. 1 & 2. pap. write for info. (ISBN 0-88497-030-2). Aum Pubns.

Garden of Pomegranates. Israel Regardie. LC 74-18984. (High Magick Ser.). (Illus.). 176p. 1985. pap. 6.95 (ISBN 0-87542-690-5, L-690). Llewellyn Pubns.

Garden of the Beloved. Robert Way. 80p. 1983. pap. 4.95 (ISBN 0-8091-2534-X). Paulist Pr.

Garden of the Lord. Ralph K. Beebe. LC 68-56609. (Illus.). 288p. 1968. 3.95 (ISBN 0-913342-13-0). Barclay Pr.

Gardener Looks at the Fruits of the Spirit. Phillip Keller. 1983. 6.95 (ISBN 0-8499-2958-X). Word Bks.

Gardening with Biblical Plants. Wilma James. LC 83-2290. (Illus.). 272p. 1983. 24.95x (ISBN 0-8304-1009-0). Nelson-Hall.

Gardens of Eden & Man. Laval S. Morris. 1982. 5.95 (ISBN 0-8062-1973-4). Carlton.

Gardens of Meditation. A. E. Falconar. 128p. 9.95 (ISBN 0-86140-057-7). Dufour.

Garenganze or Seven Years' Pioneer Mission Work in Central Africa. 2nd, rev. ed. Frederick S. Arnot. (Illus.). 276p. 1969. 29.50x (ISBN 0-7146-1860-8, BHA 01860, F Cass Co). Biblio Dist.

Garimus File. Gary Stanley. LC 82-72301. (Illus., Orig.). 1983. pap. 6.95 (ISBN 0-86605-107-4). Heres Life.

Garizim und Synagoge: Traditionsgeschichtliche Untersuchungen zur samaritanischen Religion der aramaeischen Periode. Hans G. Kippenberg. (Religionsgeschichtliche Versuche und Vorarbeiten, 30). (Ger). 1971. 43.20x (ISBN 3-11-001864-0). De Gruyter.

Garland for John Donne 1631-1931. Ed. by Theodore Spencer. 11.25 (ISBN 0-8446-1418-1). Peter Smith.

Garland of Letters. John Woodroffe. 18.00 (ISBN 0-89744-112-5, Pub. by Ganesh & Co. India). Auromere.

Garland of Mahamudra Practices. Khenpo K. Gyalsten. 140p. 1986. pap. 9.95 (ISBN 0-937938-35-1). Snow Lion.

Garland of Prayers. Satguru S. Keshavadas. (Illus.). 30p. (Orig.). 1975. pap. 1.99 (ISBN 0-942508-03-3). Vishwa.

Garveyism As a Religious Movement: The Institutionalization of a Black Civil Religion. Randall K. Burkett. LC 78-15728. (ATLA Monograph Ser.: No. 13). 242p. 1978. 19.00 (ISBN 0-8108-1163-4). Scarecrow.

Gate of Moon: Mythical & Magical Doorways to the Otherworld. Alan Richardson. 160p. 1984. pap. 9.95 (ISBN 0-85030-365-6). Newcastle Pub.

Gates of Eternal Life. Adrienne Von Speyr. Tr. by Corona Sharp from Ger. LC 82-84582. Tr. of Pforten des Ewigen Lebens. 140p. (Orig.). 1984. pap. 7.95 (ISBN 0-89870-025-6). Ignatius Pr.

Gates of Forgiveness: Selichot. Chaim Stern. 1980. pap. 1.00 ea. Eng. Ed (ISBN 0-916694-57-7). Hebrew Ed (ISBN 0-916694-74-7). Central Conf.

Gates of Freedom: A Passover Haggadah. Chaim Stern. LC 81-84191. (Illus.). 130p. 1986. pap. 6.95 (ISBN 0-940646-21-8). Rossel Bks.

Gates of Freedom: A Passover Haggadah. Chaim Stern. 1986. pap. 6.95 (ISBN 0-317-42655-9). Shapolsky Pubs.

Gates of Mercy. Louis E. Kaplan. LC 79-64616. (Orig.). 1979. pap. 3.75 (ISBN 0-87203-085-7). Hermon.

Gates of Mitzvah: A Guide to the Jewish Life Cycle. (Shaarei Mitzvah Ser.). (Illus.). 7.95 (ISBN 0-916694-53-4). Central Conf.

Gates of New Life. James S. Stewart. (Scholar As Preacher Ser.). 262p. 1976. pap. text ed. 11.95 (ISBN 0-567-24426-1, Pub. by T & T Clark Ltd UK). Fortress.

Gates of Prayer. pulpit ed. Ed. by Chaim Stern. 1975. English ed. 20.00 (ISBN 0-916694-46-1); Hebrew 20.00 (ISBN 0-916694-03-8). Central Conf.

Gates of Prayer. Ed. by Chaim Stern. 1978. Gift edition. 25.00 (ISBN 0-916694-69-0). Central Conf.

Gates of Prayer for Weekdays & at a House of Mourning. Ed. by Chaim Stern. 1975. pap. 2.75 (ISBN 0-916694-04-6). Central Conf.

Gates of Prayer: The New Union Prayerbook. Ed. by Chaim Stern. 1975. English ed. 15.00 (ISBN 0-916694-01-1); Hebrew ed. 16.00 (ISBN 0-916694-00-3). Central Conf.

Gates of Reincarnation. Luria. (Hebrew.). 200p. 1985. pap. 9.95 (ISBN 0-943688-49-3). Res Ctr Kabbalah.

Gates of Repentance. 1982. 10.95 (ISBN 0-87306-252-3). Feldheim.

Gates of Repentance. Ed. by Chaim Stern. 1978. 16.00 (ISBN 0-916694-38-0); pulpit ed. 20.00 (ISBN 0-916694-40-2); Hebrew ed. 15.00 (ISBN 0-916694-39-9); Hebrew pulpit ed. 20.00 (ISBN 0-686-77334-9). Central Conf.

Gates of Repentance, Shaarei Teshuvah. Rabbeinu Yonah. 1976. pap. 7.95 (ISBN 0-87306-112-8). Feldheim.

Gates of the House. Chaim Stern. 1977. cancelled (ISBN 0-916694-42-9); lib. bdg. cancelled. Central Conf.

Gates of the House (Shaarei Habayit) The New Union Home Prayerbook. 9.00 (ISBN 0-916694-35-6). Central Conf.

Gates of the Seasons: A Guide to the Jewish Year. Ed. by Peter Knobel. 200p. 1983. pap. text ed. 9.95 (ISBN 0-916694-92-5). Central Conf.

Gates of Understanding. Ed. by Lawrence Hoffman. LC 77-23488. 1977. pap. text ed. 4.95 (ISBN 0-8074-0009-2, 142689). UAHC.

Gates of Understanding, Vol. 1. Ed. by Lawrence Hoffman. 1977. 5.95 (ISBN 0-916694-43-7). Central Conf.

Gates of Understanding: for the Days of Awe, Vol. II. (Shaarei Bina Ser.). pap. 7.95 flexbook binding (ISBN 0-916694-84-4). Central Conf.

Gates to the Old City. Raphael Patai. 928p. 1980. pap. 12.95 (ISBN 0-380-76091-6, 76091-6). Avon.

Gateway to God. Simone Weil. LC 82-4688. 160p. 1982. pap. 6.95 (ISBN 0-8245-0534-4). Crossroad NY.

Gateway to Islam, 4. S. J. Doray. pap. 9.50 (ISBN 0-686-18395-9). Kazi Pubns.

Gateway to Judaism, 2 vols. Albert M. Shulman. 30.00 set (ISBN 0-8453-6896-6, Cornwall Bks). Assoc Univ Prs.

Gateway to Learning. pap. 3.95 (ISBN 0-87306-253-1). Feldheim.

Gateway to Patriarchal Son (Zen) Venerable Master Hye-Am's Dharma Talks. Master Myo-Bong & Hye-Am Choi. Tr. by Master Myo-Bong from Chinese & Korean. LC 86-50754. (Chinese Korean & Eng.). 450p. (Orig.). 1986. 18.00 (ISBN 0-938647-01-6). Western Son Acad.

Gateway to Survival Is Storage. Walter D. Batchelor. 128p. 1974. pap. 3.95 (ISBN 0-89036-127-4). Hawkes Pub Inc.

Gateway to Zen (Ch'an) Myo-Bong Master. Ed. by Hye-Am Choi. LC 86-50750. (Chinese Korean & Eng.). 355p. (Orig.). 1986. 18.00 (ISBN 0-938647-00-8). Western Son Acad.

Gateways into Light. 2nd ed. Flower A. Newhouse. LC 74-75517. 160p. 1974. pap. 8.50 (ISBN 0-910378-09-6). Christward.

Gathas of Zarathustra. Zarathustra. (Sacred Texts Ser.). viii, 104p. 1983. pap. 8.75 (ISBN 0-88695-011-2). Concord Grove.

Gathas of Zarathustra: A Reconstruction of the Text. M. C. Monna. 1978. pap. text ed. 35.00x (ISBN 90-6203-582-5). Humanities.

Gather Me Together, Lord: And Other Prayers for Mothers. Margaret B. Spiess. 96p. 1982. 4.95 (ISBN 0-8010-8229-3). Baker Bk.

Gather Round: Christian Fairy Tales for All Ages. John Aurelio. LC 81-84389. (Illus.). 128p. (Orig.). 1982. pap. 5.95 (ISBN 0-8091-2444-0). Paulist Pr.

Gather the Children: Celebrating the Word with Ideas, Activities, Prayer & Projects. Mary C. Berglund. 1987. pap. 14.95. Pastoral Pr.

Gather Together in My Name: Reflections on Christianity & Community. Arturo Paoli. Tr. by Robert R. Barr. LC 86-23806. 144p. (Orig.). 1987. pap. 9.95 (ISBN 0-88344-357-0). Orbis Bks.

Gathered Church: The Literature of the English Dissenting Interest, 1700-1930. Donald Davie. (Clark Lectures 1976). 1978. 17.50x (ISBN 0-19-519999-5). Oxford U Pr.

Gathered for Life: Official Report, VI Assembly, World Council of Vancouver of Churches, Vancouver, Canada, 24 July - 10 August 1983. World Council of Churches, Assembly (6th: 1983: Vancouver, BC) Ed. by David Gill. LC 84-141282. Repr. of 1983 ed. 91.30 (2027544). Bks Demand UMI.

Gathered Memories. Ruth Adams et al. 152p. 1985. pap. 5.00 (ISBN 0-88053-308-0, S-76). Macoy Pub.

Gathered to Pray: Understanding Liturgical Prayer. Louis Weil. LC 86-17413. (Parish Life Sourcebooks Ser.: No. 3). 148p. (Orig.). 1986. pap. 6.95 (ISBN 0-936384-35-2). Cowley Pubns.

Gathering God's People: Signs of a Successful Parish. 265p. 1982. 9.55 (ISBN 0-318-00782-7). Natl Cath Educ.

Gathering God's People: Signs of a Successful Parish. Ed. by J. Stephen O'Brien. LC 81-85241. 264p. (Orig.). 1982. pap. 7.95 (ISBN 0-87973-656-9, 656). Our Sunday Visitor.

Gathering of Hope. Helen Hayes. LC 83-1728. 112p. 1983. 9.95 (ISBN 0-8006-0705-8). Fortress.

Gathering of Hope. Helen Hayes. 222p. 1985. pap. 7.95 large print ed. (ISBN 0-8027-2467-1). Walker & Co.

Gathering of Souls. Ed. by Clare Carr. Iris Freelander. LC 81-69576. 240p. 1981. pap. 11.00 (ISBN 0-910378-17-7). Christward.

Gathering of Strangers: Understanding the Life of Your Church. rev. & updated ed. Robert C. Worley. LC 83-12343. (Illus.). 122p. 1983. pap. 8.95 (ISBN 0-664-24488-2). Westminster.

Gathering Prayers. Debra T. Hintz. 80p. (Orig.). 1986. pap. 7.95 (ISBN 0-89622-296-9). Twenty-Third.

Gathering the Fragments. Vincent M. Walsh. 64p. 1980. pap. 1.00 (ISBN 0-943374-01-4). Key of David.

Gathering the Pieces. Robert G. Davidson. 88p. (Orig.). 1985. pap. 9.95 (ISBN 0-940754-30-4). Ed Ministries.

Gatherings from Graveyards Particularly Those of London: With a Concise History of the Modes of Interment among Different Nations, from the Earliest Periods. George A. Walker. Ed. by Robert Kastenaum. LC 76-19591. (Death & Dying Ser.). 1977. Repr. of 1977 ed. lib. bdg. 25.50x (ISBN 0-405-09586-4). Ayer Co Pubs.

Gatnkamala: Or, Garland of Birth-Stories. Arya-Sura. Ed. by F. Max Muller. Tr. by J. C. Speyer from Sanskrit. LC 78-72371. Repr. of 1895 ed. 37.50 (ISBN 0-404-17218-0). AMS Pr.

Gautama: The Nyaya Philosophy. Gautama. Tr. by N. S. Junankar from Sanskrit. 1978. 25.50 (ISBN 0-89684-002-6, Pub. by Motilal Banarsidass India). Orient Bk Dist.

Gautama: The Nyaya Philosophy. N. S. Junankar. 1979. 34.00x (ISBN 0-89684-002-6). South Asia Bks.

Gay-Lesbian Liberation: A Biblical Perspective. George R. Edwards. 144p. (Orig.). 1984. pap. 9.95 (ISBN 0-8298-0725-X). Pilgrim NY.

Gay Priests: An Inner Journey. Malcolm Boyd. 208p. 1986. 14.95 (ISBN 0-312-31797-2). St Martin.

Gayatri. (Illus.). 1983. pap. 3.00 (ISBN 0-938924-14-1). Sri Shirdi Sai.

Gayatri. I. K. Taimni. 5.95 (ISBN 0-8356-7069-4). Theos Pub Hse.

Gayatri: The Highest Meditation. Satguru S. Keshavadas. LC 78-69857. (Illus.). 164p. 1978. 6.50 (ISBN 0-533-03188-5). Vishwa.

Gays & Fundamentalism. Paul R. Johnson. (Illus.). 56p. (Orig.). 1983. pap. 2.95 (ISBN 0-910097-02-X). Paul R Johnson.

Gays & the Bible. Paul R. Johnson. (Illus.). 52p. (Orig.). 1983. pap. 2.95 (ISBN 0-910097-00-3). Paul R Johnson.

Gays & the Church. Paul R. Johnson. (Illus.). 48p. (Orig.). 1983. pap. 2.95 (ISBN 0-910097-04-6). Paul R Johnson.

Gays Under Grace: A Gay Christian's Response to the Moral Majority. Maury Johnston. LC 82-51217. 250p. 1983. 15.95 (ISBN 0-938232-20-7). Winston-Derek.

Gayspeak: Gay Male & Lesbian Communication. Ed. by James W. Chesebro. LC 82-355. 384p. 1981. 17.95 (ISBN 0-8298-0472-2); pap. 9.95 (ISBN 0-8298-0456-0). Pilgrim NY.

Gazing on Truth: Meditations on Reality. Kitty Muggeridge. 96p. (Orig.). 1985. pap. 4.95 (ISBN 0-8028-0072-6). Eerdmans.

G'Dee. Helen Fine. (Illus.). 1958. text ed. 4.50 (ISBN 0-8074-0137-4, 123702). UAHC.

G'Dee's Book of Holiday Fun. Helen Fine. (Illus.). 1961. pap. 3.00 (ISBN 0-685-20737-4, 121701). UAHC.

G.E Lessing's Theology: A Reinterpretation, a Study in the Problematic Nature of the Enlightenment. Leonard P. Wessell. 1977. 20.00x (ISBN 90-279-7801-8). Mouton.

Gedenkbuch zur Erinnerung an David Kaufmann. M. Brann & F. Rosenthal. Ed. by Steven Katz. LC 79-7142. (Jewish Philosophy, Mysticism & History of Ideas Ser.). 1980. Repr. of 1900 ed. lib. bdg. 68.50x (ISBN 0-405-12292-6). Ayer Co Pubs.

Gee, You Look Good. Blaine Taylor. 137p. (Orig.). 1984. pap. 6.00 (ISBN 0-914527-32-0). C-Four Res.

Geeta. Tr. by Shri P. Swami. 96p. (Orig.). 1965. pap. 5.95 (ISBN 0-571-06157-5). Faber & Faber.

Gegen Den Strom. Emmy Arnold. (Ger.). 200p. 1983. pap. 5.50 (ISBN 3-87067-206-4, Pub. by Brendow-Verlag, West Germany). Plough.

Gegenreformation in der Furstentumern Liegnitz-Brirg-Wohlau, Ihre Vorgeschichte und Ihre Staatsrechtlichen Grundlagen. Dorothee Von Velsen. (Ger.). 34.00 (ISBN 0-384-64224-1); pap. 28.00 (ISBN 0-384-64223-3). Johnson Repr.

Geheimnis und Geheimhaltung im Rabbinischen Judentum. Gerd S. Wewers. (Religionsgeschichtliche Versuche und Vorarbeiten, Vol. 35). (Ger.). 1975. 33.60x (ISBN 3-11-005858-8). De Gruyter.

Geistige Situation der Zeit. Karl Jaspers. (Sammlung Goeschen: No. 1000). 1979. 7.80x (ISBN 3-11007-878-3). De Gruyter.

Gelatin & Jewish Law. David I. Sheinkopf. 132p. 1983. pap. 7.95x (ISBN 0-8197-0488-1). Bloch.

Gem Stones in the Breastplate. E. Raymond. (Illus.). 48p. (Orig.). 1987. pap. price not set (ISBN 0-934666-18-0). Artisan Sales.

Gemeinsamesleben-Wozu? Arnold Eberhard. (Ger.). 44p. 1978. pap. 2.50 (ISBN 3-87630-406-7, Pub. by Prasenz-Verlag, West Germany). Plough.

Gemeinschaftagedanke Bei Chesterton. Heinz Kuhn. pap. 10.00 (ISBN 0-384-30680-2). Johnson Repr.

Gemorah L'mas'chillim. Israel Rosenfeld. 4.75 (ISBN 0-914131-23-0, A40); tchr's. guide 3.00 (ISBN 0-914131-24-9, A41). Torah Umesorah.

Gems & Stones: Scientific Properties & Aspects of Twenty Two-A Comparative Study Based upon the Edgar Cayce Psychic Readings. rev. ed. Ken Carley. 1979. pap. 4.95 (ISBN 0-87604-110-1). ARE Pr.

Gems for His Crown. Holland Boring, Sr. & Bill Cox. 1977. pap. 2.25 (ISBN 0-88027-054-3). Firm Foun Pub.

Gems from Genesis. W. G. Heslop. LC 75-13661. (W. G. Heslop Bible Study Aids). 136p. 1975. pap. 4.50 (ISBN 0-8254-2825-4). Kregel.

Gems from the Sunday Gospel Lessons in the Orthodox Church, Vol. II. A. Coniaris. pap. 5.95 (ISBN 0-937032-13-1). Light&Life Pub Co MN.

Gems from the Tantras, 2nd Series. Ed. by M. P. Pandit. 1971. 3.95 (ISBN 0-89744-103-6, Pub. by Ganesh & Co. India). Auromere.

Gems from the Veda. Ed. by M. P. Pandit. Tr. by Sri Aurobindo. 102p. 1974. 3.95 (ISBN 0-89744-104-4, Pub. by Ganesh & Co. India). Auromere.

Gems from Tozer. A. W. Tozer. 96p. 1979. pap. 2.45 (ISBN 0-87509-163-6). Chr Pubns.

Gems of Islam: Lifting of the Veil, Pt. I. C. R. Jain. 196p. 1975. 6.00 (ISBN 0-88065-136-9, Pub. by Messers Today & Tomorrows Printers & Publishers India). Scholarly Pubns.

Gems of Mysticism. H. A. Curtiss & F. H. Curtiss. 83p. Date not set. pap. 5.00 (ISBN 0-89540-143-6, SB-143). Sun Pub.

Gems of Rabbi Nachman. Nachman of Breslov. Ed. by Tzvi A. Rosenfeld. Tr. by Ayreh Kaplan from Hebrew. (Illus.). 186p. (Orig.). 1980. pap. 2.00 (ISBN 0-930213-10-6). Breslov Res Inst.

Gems of Wisdom. Subramuniya. (Illus.). 234p. 1973. 7.00 (ISBN 0-87516-346-7); pap. 5.00 (ISBN 0-87516-345-9). De Vorss.

Gemstones of the Bible. 2nd ed. Percy H. Perkins, Jr. 1986. 17.95 (ISBN 0-9603090-2-0). P H Perkins Jr.

Gender & Destiny: Women Writers & the Holocaust. Marlene E. Heinemann. LC 86-367. (Contributions in Women's Studies: No. 72). 158p. 1986. 27.95 (ISBN 0-313-24665-3, HGD/). Greenwood.

Gender & God: Love & Desire in Christian Spirituality. Rachel Hosmer. LC 86-8980. 142p. (Orig.). 1986. pap. 7.95 (ISBN 0-936384-39-5). Cowley Pubns.

Gender & Religion: On the Complexity of Symbols. Ed. by Caroline W. Bynum et al. LC 86-47552. 296p. 1986. 25.00 (ISBN 0-8070-1008-1). Beacon Pr.

Genealogical Records of Utah. Laureen Jaussi & Gloria Chaston. LC 73-87713. 336p. 1974. 5.95 (ISBN 0-87747-507-5). Deseret Bk.

General Bible Knowledge Bible Drill: Flash Cards Flipbook. Ernest Clevenger, Jr. (Bible Drill Flash Cards Flipbook Ser.). 104p. 1983. pap. 4.25 (ISBN 0-88428-017-9). Parchment Pr.

General Catechetical Directory. Sacred Congregation of the Clergy, Official English Translation of the Latin Document April 11, 1971. pap. 3.75 (ISBN 1-55586-173-3, V-173). US Catholic.

General Council: Special Studies in Doctrinal & Historical Background. William J. McDonald. LC 62-20329. pap. 48.00 (ISBN 0-317-07854-2, 2005223). bks Demand UMI.

General Council: Special Studies in Doctrinal & Historical Background. Ed. by William J. McDonald. LC 78-10099. 1979. Repr. of 1962 ed. lib. bdg. cancelled (ISBN 0-313-20753-4, MCGC). Greenwood.

General Demands Concerning the Late Covenent: Together with the Answers. LC 74-80156. (English Experience Ser.: No. 635). 1974. Repr. of 1638 ed. 6.00 (ISBN 90-221-0635-7). Walter J Johnson.

General Epistle of James. Randolph V. Tasker. (Tyndale Bible Commentaries). 1957. pap. 3.95 (ISBN 0-8028-1415-8). Eerdmans.

General Epistles. (Erdmans Commentaries Ser.). 5.95 (ISBN 0-8010-3398-5). Baker Bk.

General History of Muhammadan Dynasties of Asia from 810 to 1260 AD, 2 vols. Minhaj Al-din. Tr. by H. C. Raverty from Persian. Repr. of 1881 ed. Set. text ed. 77.50x. Coronet Bks.

General History of the Baptist Denomination in America, 2 vols. David Benedict. 1985. Repr. of 1813 ed. 64.00 (ISBN 0-317-31642-7). Church History.

General History of the Baptist Denomination in America & Other Parts of the World, 2 vols. facsimile ed. David Benedict. LC 73-152974. (Select Bibliographies Reprint Ser). Repr. of 1813 ed. Set. 60.00 (ISBN 0-8369-5726-1). Ayer Co Pubs.

General History of the Christian Religion & Church, 9 vols. rev. ed. Johann A. Neander. Tr. by Joseph Torrey from Ger. Repr. of 1858 ed. Set. lib. bdg. 495.00 (ISBN 0-404-09590-9); lib. bdg. 55.00 ea. AMS Pr.

General Introduction to the Bible. rev. ed. Norman L. Geisler & William E. Nix. LC 68-18890. 1968. 29.95 (ISBN 0-8024-2916-5). Moody.

General Introduction to the New Testament. James A. Borland. (Illus.). viii, 216p. 1986. pap. 14.95x (ISBN 0-936461-00-4). Univ Book Hse.

General Introduction to the Old Testament: The Canon. William H. Green. (Twin Brooks Ser.). 1980. pap. 6.95 (ISBN 0-8010-3755-7). Baker Bk.

General Joshua. Don Thompson. (Rainy Day Survival Bk.: No. 2). 32p. pap. 0.99 (ISBN 0-87123-697-4, 220697). Bethany Hse.

General Menaion, or the Book of Services Common to the Festivals of Our Lord Jesus Christ, of the Holy Virgin, & of the Different Orders of Saints. Orthodox Eastern Church. Tr. by Nicholas Orloff from Old Slavonic. pap. 15.00 (ISBN 0-686-25551-8). Eastern Orthodox.

General Mickey. Peter Lappin. (Orig.). 1977. pap. 2.95 (ISBN 0-89944-029-0). Don Bosco Multimedia.

General Principles of Kabbalah. Moses Luzzatto. 288p. 1970. 13.75 (ISBN 0-943688-07-8); pap. 11.95 (ISBN 0-943688-31-0). Res Ctr Kabbalah.

General Psychology for Christian Counselors. Ronald L. Koteskey. 308p. (Orig.). 1983. pap. 11.95 (ISBN 0-687-14044-7). Abingdon.

General Revelation: Historical Views & Contemporary Issues. Bruce A. Demarest. 320p. 1982. 14.95 (ISBN 0-310-44550-7, 12706). Zondervan.

General Signs & Forerunners of Christ's Comming to Judgment. LC 77-7410. (English Experience Ser.: No. 875). 1977. Repr. of 1620 ed. lib. bdg. 3.50 (ISBN 90-221-0875-9). Walter J Johnson.

General Will Before Fousseau: The Transformation of the Divine into the Civic. Patrick Riley. (Studies in Moral, Political, & Legal Philosophy). 272p. 1986. text ed. 27.50 (ISBN 0-691-07720-7). Princeton U Pr.

Generalization in Ethics: An Essay in the Logic of Ethics with the Rudiments of a System of Moral Philosophy. Marcus G. Singer. LC 70-152539. (With a new introduction). 1971. Repr. of 1961 ed. 11.00x (ISBN 0-8462-1612-4). Russell.

Generation of Giants. George H. Dunne. 1962. 19.95 (ISBN 0-268-00109-X). U of Notre Dame Pr.

Generation of Wrath. Elio Romano. 228p. 1986. 14.95 (ISBN 0-7278-2039-7). Salem Hse Pubs.

Generation to Generation: Family Process in Church & Synagogue. Edwin H. Friedman. (Family Therapy Ser.). 319p. 1986. Repr. of 1985 ed. lib. bdg. 25.00 (ISBN 0-89862-059-7). Guilford Pr.

Generation to Generation: Recollections of a Chassidic Legacy. Abraham J. Twersky. 256p. 1985. 14.95 (ISBN 0-933711-17-4). Traditional Pr.

Genes, Genesis & Evolution. rev. ed. John W. Klotz. 1970. pap. 17.95 (ISBN 0-570-03212-1, 12-2637). Concordia.

Genesee Diary: Report from a Trappist Monastery. Henri J. Nouwen. LC 80-23632. 192p. 1981. pap. 4.50 (ISBN 0-385-17446-2, Im). Doubleday.

Genesee Diary: Report from a Trappist Monastery. Henri J. Nouwen. LC 85-7150. 352p. 1985. pap. 12.95 (ISBN 0-8027-2500-7). Walker & Co.

Genesee Diary: Report from a Trappist Monastery. Henri J. M. Nouwen. LC 75-38169. 192p. 1976. 9.95 (ISBN 0-385-11368-4). Doubleday.

Genesis. Albert Barnes. 13.95 (ISBN 0-8010-0835-2). Baker Bk.

Genesis, Vol. I. James M. Boice. 352p. 1982. Chapter 1-11. 16.95 (ISBN 0-310-21540-4, 10486). Zondervan.

Genesis. Walter Brueggemann. LC 81-82355. (Interpretation: the Bible Commentary for Teaching & Preaching). 432p. 1982. 23.95 (ISBN 0-8042-3101-X). John Knox.

Genesis, 2 vols. George Bush. 1981. 29.95 (ISBN 0-86524-094-9, 0103). Klock & Klock.

Genesis. John Calvin. (Geneva Commentaries Ser.). 1979. 22.95 (ISBN 0-85151-093-0). Banner of Truth.

Genesis, Vol. I. C. C. Crawford. LC 77-1140. (Bible Study Textbook Ser.). 1966. 14.30 (ISBN 0-89900-002-9). College Pr Pub.

Genesis, Vol. II. C. C. Crawford. (Bible Study Textbook Ser.). 1968. 15.90 (ISBN 0-89900-003-7). College Pr Pub.

Genesis, Vol. III. C. C. Crawford. (Bible Study Textbook Ser.). (Illus.). 1970. 14.30 (ISBN 0-89900-004-5). College Pr Pub.

Genesis. Charles R. Erdman. 128p. 1982. pap. 4.95 (ISBN 0-8010-3375-6). Baker Bk.

Genesis. Charles T. Fritsch. LC 59-10454. (Layman's Bible Commentary Ser: Vol. 2). 1959. pap. 4.95 (ISBN 0-8042-3062-5). John Knox.

Genesis. (Modern Critical Interpretations--Ancient, Medieval, & Renaissance Ser.). 1987. 19.95 (ISBN 0-87754-910-9). Chelsea Hse.

Genesis. Jeanne Guyon. 1983. pap. 5.95 (ISBN 0-940232-15-4). Christian Bks.

Genesis. Charles Hummel & Anne Hummel. (Lifebuilder Bible Studies). 96p. (Orig.). 1985. pap. text ed. 3.50 (ISBN 0-8308-1022-6). Inter-Varsity.

Genesis, 2 Bks. Ignatius Hunt. (Bible Ser.). Bk. 1. pap. 1.00 (ISBN 0-8091-5048-4); Bk. 2. pap. 1.00 (ISBN 0-8091-5049-2). Paulist Pr.

Genesis. Irving L. Jensen. (Bible Self-Study Ser.). 1967. pap. 3.25 (ISBN 0-8024-1001-4). Moody.

Genesis. F. Derek Kidner. LC 75-23851. (Tyndale Old Testament Commentary). 1968. 12.95 (ISBN 0-87784-881-5); pap. 6.95 (ISBN 0-87784-251-5). Inter-Varsity.

Genesis. Marilyn Kunz & Catherine Schell. 1981. pap. 2.95 (ISBN 0-8423-0995-0). Tyndale.

Genesis. Michael Maher. (Old Testament Message Ser.: Vol. 2). 1982. 15.95 (ISBN 0-89453-402-5); pap. 9.95 (ISBN 0-89453-237-5). M Glazier.

Genesis. Eugene F. Roop. (Believers Church Bible Comentary Ser.: No. 2). 344p. (Orig.). 1987. pap. 17.95 (ISBN 0-8361-3443-5). Herald Pr.

Genesis. Ed. by E. A. Speiser. LC 64-21724. (Anchor Bible Ser.: Vol. 1). 1964. 16.00 (ISBN 0-385-00854-6, Anchor Pr). Doubleday.

Genesis. Pauline A. Viviano. (Bible Commentary Ser.). 136p. 1985. pap. 2.95 (ISBN 0-8146-1370-5). Liturgical Pr.

Genesis. Howard F. Vos. (Everyman's Bible Commentary Ser.). 1982. pap. 5.95 (ISBN 0-8024-2001-X). Moody.

Genesis, Vol 1 chs. 1-11. John C. L. Gibson. LC 81-7477. (Daily Study Bible-Old Testament Ser.). 224p. 1981. 12.95 (ISBN 0-664-21801-6); pap. 6.95 (ISBN 0-664-24568-4). Westminster.

Genesis, Vol 2, chs. 12-50. John C. L. Gibson. LC 81-7477. (Daily Study Bible-Old Testament Ser.). 336p. 1982. 12.95 (ISBN 0-664-21804-0); pap. 7.95 (ISBN 0-664-24571-4). Westminster.

Genesis: A Bible Study Commentary. Leon J. Wood. 160p. 1975. pap. 4.95 (ISBN 0-310-34743-2, 10233P). Zondervan.

Genesis, a Commentary. rev ed. Gerhard Von Rad. LC 72-6413. (Old Testament Library). 440p. 1973. 17.95 (ISBN 0-664-20957-2). Westminster.

Genesis: A Devotional Commentary. W. H. Thomas. 507p. 1988. pap. 12.95 (ISBN 0-8254-3817-9). Kregel.

Genesis: An Expositional Commentary, Vol. 2. James M. Boice. 352p. 1985. 16.95 (ISBN 0-310-21560-9, 10487). Zondervan.

Genesis & Archaeology. rev. & enl. ed. Howard F. Vos. 1986. pap. 6.95 (ISBN 0-310-33901-4, 11154P). Zondervan.

Genesis & Common Sense. Clarence Schreur. 109p. 1983. 12.50 (ISBN 0-942078-03-9). R Tanner Assocs Inc.

Genesis & Development of a Scientific Fact. Ludwig Fleck. Ed. by Thaddeus J. Trenn & Robert K. Merton. Tr. by Fred Bradley from Ger. LC 79-12521. 224p. 1981. pap. 8.00x (ISBN 0-226-25325-2). U of Chicago Pr.

Genesis & Exodus. A. E. Cundall. (Bible Study Commentaries Ser.). 126p. 1980. pap. 4.95 (ISBN 0-87508-150-9). Chr Lit.

Genesis & Geology: A Study in the Relations of Scientific Thought, Natural Theology & Social Opinion in Great Britain, 1790-1850. Charles C. Gillispie. LC 51-10449. (Historical Monographs Ser: No. 58). 1951. 22.50x (ISBN 0-674-34480-4). Harvard U Pr.

Genesis & Judaism: The Perspective of Genesis Rabbah, an Analytical Anthology. Jacob Neusner. 1985. 28.95 (ISBN 0-89130-940-3, 14-01-08); pap. 22.95 (ISBN 0-89130-941-1). Scholars Pr GA.

Genesis & Semitic Tradition. John D. Davis. (Twin Brooks Ser.). 1980. pap. 4.95 (ISBN 0-8010-2902-3). Baker Bk.

Genesis Answer: A Scientist's Testament of Divine Creation. William L. Stokes. 1984. pap. 14.95 (ISBN 0-317-03128-7). P-H.

Genesis (CC) Stuart Briscoe. 1986. 18.95 (ISBN 0-8499-0406-4). Word Bks.

Genesis, Chapters Twelve to Fifty. Ed. by Robert Davidson. LC 78-12892. (Cambridge Bible Commentary on the New English Bible, Old Testament Ser.). (Illus.). 1979. 39.50 (ISBN 0-521-22485-3); pap. 14.95x (ISBN 0-521-29520-3). Cambridge U Pr.

Genesis, Chapters 1-11. Ed. by Robert Davidson. LC 72-93675. (Cambridge Bible Commentary on the New English Bible, Old Testament Ser.). 200p. (Orig.). 1973. pap. 8.95x (ISBN 0-521-09760-6). Cambridge U Pr.

Genesis Connection. John Wiester. LC 83-13409. (Illus.). 320p. 1983. 14.95 (ISBN 0-8407-5296-2). Nelson.

Genesis Creation Story: Its Literary Structure. Jacques B. Doukhan. (Andrews University Seminary Doctoral Dissertation Ser.: Vol. 5). xii, 303p. 1982. pap. 10.95 (ISBN 0-943872-37-5). Andrews Univ Pr.

Genesis Debate: Persistent Questions about Creation & the Flood. Ed. by Ronald Youngblood. 240p. 1986. pap. 12.95 (ISBN 0-8407-7517-2). Nelson.

Genesis-Deuteronomy, Vol. I. Beacon Bible Commentary Staff. 13.95 (ISBN 0-8010-0688-0). Baker Bk.

Genesis Effect: Personal & Organizational Transformations. Brian P. Hall. (Illus.). 376p. (Orig.). 1986. pap. 14.95 (ISBN 0-8091-2741-5). Paulist Pr.

Genesis, Exodus, Leviticus, Numbers. Foster R. McCurley. LC 78-14670. (Proclamation Commentaries: the Old Testament Witness for Preaching). 128p. 1979. pap. 4.95 (ISBN 0-8006-0593-4, 1-593). Fortress.

Genesis: Faithful to His Promises, Pt. 2. Ken Bible. Ed. by Earl Wolf. (Small Group Bible Studies). 72p. (Orig.). Date not set. pap. 2.50 (ISBN 0-8341-1108-X). Beacon Hill.

Genesis: Fifteen Lessons, Vol. 1. Bernice C. Jordan. (Footsteps of Faith Ser.). 1960. pap. text ed. 2.50 (ISBN 0-86508-027-5); figures text 11.45 (ISBN 0-86508-028-3). BCM Intl Inc.

Genesis Flood. John C. Whitcomb & Henry M. Morris. pap. 8.95 (ISBN 0-8010-9501-8). Baker Bk.

Genesis Flood. John C. Whitcomb & Henry M. Morris. pap. 8.95 (ISBN 0-88469-067-9). BMH Bks.

Genesis Flood. John C. Whitcomb, Jr. & H. M. Morris. 1960. pap. 8.95 (ISBN 0-87552-338-2). Presby & Reformed.

Genesis I Through 25: Walking with God. rev. ed. Margaret Fromer & Sharrel Keyes. (Fisherman Bible Studyguide Ser.). 80p. 1979. saddle-stitched 2.95 (ISBN 0-87788-297-5). Shaw Pubs.

Genesis I (WBC, Vol. 1. Gordon Wenham. 400p. 1987. 24.95 (ISBN 0-8499-0200-2). Word Bks.

Genesis in Space & Time. Francis A. Schaeffer. LC 72-78406. 144p. 1972. pap. 6.95 (ISBN 0-87784-636-7). Inter-Varsity.

Genesis of the New England Churches. Leonard Bacon. LC 74-38435. (Religion in America, Ser. 2). 510p. 1972. Repr. of 1874 ed. 32.00 (ISBN 0-405-04056-3). Ayer Co Pubs.

Genesis One & the Origin of the Earth. Robert C. Newman & Herman J. Eckelmann, Jr. 156p. 1981. pap. 4.95 (ISBN 0-8010-6735-9). Baker Bk.

Genesis One-Eleven. Robert A. Meyering. (Five-on-One Ser.). 96p. (Orig.). 1986. pap. text ed. 3.95 (ISBN 0-930265-16-5); tchr's. guide 7.95 (ISBN 0-930265-17-3). CRC Pubns.

Genesis One-Eleven. Claus Westermann. Tr. by John J. Scullion. LC 82-72655. 692p. cloth 34.95 (ISBN 0-8066-1962-7, 10-2543). Augsburg.

Genesis One to Twelve. D. M. Stalker. 0.50x (ISBN 0-685-33497-X). Outlook.

Genesis Principle for Parents. Pat H. Owen. 224p. 1985. pap. 6.95 (ISBN 0-8423-0996-9). Tyndale.

Genesis: Quinze Lecciones, Tomo 1. Bernice C. Jordan. (Pasos De Fe Ser.). (Span.). pap. text ed. 2.50 (ISBN 0-86508-401-7); figuras 8.95 (ISBN 0-86508-402-5). BCM Intl Inc.

Genesis Rabbah: The Judaic Commentary to the Book of Genesis, Vol. II. Jacob Neusner. 1985. 34.95 (ISBN 0-89130-933-0, 14-01-05); pap. 29.55 (ISBN 0-89130-934-9). Scholars Pr GA.

Genesis Rabbah: The Judaic Commentary to the Book of Genesis, Vol. III. Jacob Neusner. 1985. 33.95 (ISBN 0-89130-935-7, 14-01-06); pap. 28.55 (ISBN 0-89130-936-5). Scholars Pr GA.

Genesis Rabbah: The Judaic Commentary to the Book of Genesis, Vol. 1. Jacob Neusner. 1985. 35.75 (ISBN 0-89130-931-4, 14-01-04); pap. 26.75 (ISBN 0-89130-932-2). Scholars Pr GA.

Genesis Record. Henry M. Morris. 24.95 (ISBN 0-8010-6004-4). Baker Bk.

Genesis: Secrets of the Bible Story of Creation. Rudolf Steiner. Tr. by Dorothy Lenn et al from Ger. 139p. 1982. pap. 9.95 (ISBN 0-85440-391-4, Pub by Steinerbooks). Anthroposophic.

Genesis Seven. L. Farra. 1987. 8.95 (ISBN 0-533-07034-1). Vantage.

Genesis: The Book of Beginnings. David A. Leach. 96p. 1984. pap. 4.95 (ISBN 0-8170-1047-5). Judson.

Genesis: The First Book of Revelations. David Wood. 320p. 1985. 55.00x (ISBN 0-85936-180-2, Pub. by Chambers Green Ltd). State Mutual Bk.

Genesis: The Origins of Man & the Universe. John Gribbin. (Illus., Orig.). 1982. pap. 8.95 (ISBN 0-385-28321-0, Delta). Dell.

Genesis: The Student's Guide, Pt. 2. Louis Newman. pap. 4.95 (ISBN 0-8381-0404-5). United Syn Bk.

Genesis: The Teacher's Guide. Leonard Gardner. 1966. pap. 6.50 (ISBN 0-8381-0401-0). United Syn Bk.

Genesis to Deuteronomy: Notes on the Pentateuch, 6 vols. in 1. C. H. Mackintosh. LC 72-75082. 928p. 1972. 19.95 (ISBN 0-87213-617-5). Loizeaux.

Genesis: With an Introduction to Narrative. George W. Coats. (Forms of the Old Testament Literature Ser.: Vol. 1). 368p. (Orig.). 1984. pap. 21.95 (ISBN 0-8028-1954-0). Eerdmans.

Genesis 12-36: A Commentary. Claus Westermann. Tr. by John J. Scullion from Ger. LC 85-7449. Tr. of Genesis: Kapitel 12-36. 608p. 1985. text ed. 34.95 (ISBN 0-8066-2172-9, 10-2542). Augsburg.

Genesis 26 through 50: Called by God. rev. ed. Margaret Fromer & Sharrel Keyes. (Fisherman Bible Studyguide Ser.). 66p. 1979. pap. 2.95 saddle-stitched (ISBN 0-87788-298-3). Shaw Pubs.

Genesis 3. E. J. Young. 1984. pap. 4.45 (ISBN 0-85151-148-1). Banner of Truth.

Genesis 37-50: A Commentary. Claus Westermann. Tr. by John S. Scullion from Ger. LC 85-26802. 274p. 1986. 21.95 (ISBN 0-8066-2197-4, 10-2546). Augsburg.

Genetic Counseling, the Church & the Law. Gary M. Atkinson & Albert S. Moraczewski. LC 79-92084. xvii, 259p. (Orig.). 1980. pap. 9.95 (ISBN 0-935372-06-7). Pope John Ctr.

Genetic Engineering: The Ethical Issues. J. K. Anderson. 128p. (Orig.). 1982. pap. 6.95 (ISBN 0-310-45051-9, 12707). Zondervan.

Genetic History of the New England Theology. Frank H. Foster. Ed. by Bruce Kuklick. (American Religious Thought of the 18th & 19th Centuries Ser.). 56p. 1987. lib. bdg. 75.00 (ISBN 0-8240-6956-0). Garland Pub.

Genetics, Ethics & Parenthood. Karen Lebacqz. 128p. (Orig.). 1983. pap. 7.95 (ISBN 0-8298-0671-7). Pilgrim NY.

Genetics, Society, & Decisions. Richard V. Kowles. 1985. Repr. text ed. write for info. (ISBN 0-673-18678-4). Scott F.

Geneva & the Consolidation of the French Protestant Movement, 1564-1572: A Contribution to the History of Congregationalism, Presbyterianism, & Calvinist Resistance Theory. R. M. Kingdon. 244p. (Orig.). 1967. pap. text ed. 27.50x (Pub. by Droz Switzerland). Coronet Bks.

Geneva Bible: A Facsimile of the Fifteen-Sixty Edition. Intro. by Lloyd E. Barry. 1274p. 1969. 95.00x (ISBN 0-299-05251-6). U of Wis Pr.

Genius & Character of Emerson. Ed. by Franklin B. Sanborn. LC 72-122663. 1971. Repr. of 1885 ed. 27.50x (ISBN 0-8046-1312-5, Pub. by Kennikat). Assoc Faculty Pr.

Genius & Theory of Methodist Polity, or the Machinery of Methodism. Henry M. Turner. LC 75-99416. xii, 318p. 1972. Repr. of 1885 ed. lib. bdg. 16.50 (ISBN 0-8411-0089-6). Metro Bks.

Genius of Christianity. Francois R. De Chateaubriand. LC 75-25532. 1975. Repr. of 1856 ed. 40.00x (ISBN 0-86527-254-9). Fertig.

Genius of Christianity, 2 vols. Viscount De Chateaubriand. Tr. by Charles I. White. 245p. 1985. 117.35 (ISBN 0-89901-223-X). Found Class Reprints.

Genius of John: A Composition-Critical Commentary on the Fourth Gospel. Peter F. Ellis. (Orig.). 1984. pap. 10.95 (ISBN 0-8146-1328-4). Liturgical Pr.

Genius of the Few: The Story of Those who Founded the Garden of Eden. Christian O'Brien. 320p. 1985. pap. 12.95 (ISBN 0-85500-214-X). Newcastle Pub.

Genius of Willie MacMichael. George MacDonald. Ed. by Dan Hamilton. 168p. 1987. pap. 3.95 (ISBN 0-89693-750-X). Victor Bks.

Genizah Studies in Memory of Solomon Schechter, 3 vols. L. Ginzberg & I. Davidson. Incl. Vol. 1. Midrash & Haggadah. L. Ginzberg. 1969. Repr. of 1928 ed. 17.50 (ISBN 0-87203-015-6); Vol. 2. Geonic & Early Karaitic Halakah. L. Ginzberg. Repr. of 1929 ed. 17.50 (ISBN 0-87203-016-4); Vol. 3. Liturgical & Secular Poetry. I. Davidson. Repr. of 1928 ed. 17.50 (ISBN 0-87203-017-2). LC 73-76172. Hermon.

Genocide: Critical Issues of the Holocaust. Ed. by Alex Grobman et al. LC 83-3052. (Illus.). 502p. 1983. 19.95 (ISBN 0-940646-04-8, Co-pub. by Simon Wiesenthal Center); pap. 12.95 (ISBN 0-940646-38-2). Rossel Bks.

Genocide: Critical Issues of the Holocaust. Ed. by Alex Grobman et al. 1986. pap. 12.95 (ISBN 0-317-42656-7). Shapolsky Pubs.

Genocide: The Human Cancer. Israel W. Charny & Chanan Rapaport. 1983. pap. 10.95 (ISBN 0-87851-313-2). Hearst Bks.

Genozot Sefarim: Bibliographical Essays. Israel Mehlman. 10.00 (ISBN 0-405-12617-4). Ayer Co Pubs.

Genre for the Gospels: The Biographical Character of Matthew. Philip L. Shuler. LC 81-71384. 144p. 1982. 3.50 (ISBN 0-8006-0677-9). Fortress.

Genre for the Gospels: The Biographical Character of Matthew. Philip L. Shuler. LC 81-71384. pap. 35.30 (2029606). Bks Demand UMI.

Gentile Comes to Cache Valley. A. J. Simmonds. LC 72-80615. 143p. 1976. 8.95. Utah St U Pr.

Gentile Zionists: Study in Anglo-Zionist Diplomacy 1929-1939. N. A. Rose. 246p. 1973. 29.50x (ISBN 0-7146-2940-5, F Cass Co). Biblio Dist.

Gentiles & the Gentile Mission In Luke-Acts. Stephen G. Wilson. LC 72-90489. (Society for New Testament Studies, Monograpn Ser.: Vol. 23). pap. 76.80 (ISBN 0-317-26365-X, 2024566). Bks Demand UMI.

Gentle Art of Philosophical Polemics. Joseph Agassi. 304p. 1986. 28.95 (ISBN 0-912050-63-2); pap. 13.95 (ISBN 0-8126-9036-2). Open Court.

Gentle Breeze of Jesus. Mel Tari & Noni Tari. 125p. pap. 4.95 (ISBN 0-89221-122-9). New Leaf.

Gentle Brother. White Eagle. 1968. 3.95 (ISBN 0-85487-002-4). De Vorss.

Gentle Cynic. Morris Jastrow, Jr. 242p. 1980. Repr. of 1919 ed. lib. bdg. 35.00 (ISBN 0-89984-258-5). Century Bookbindery.

Gentle Cynic: Being a Translation of the Book of Koheleth Commonly Known As Ecclesiastes Stripped of Later Additions also Its Origin, Growth & Interpretation. Morris Jastrow. 255p. 1985. Repr. of 1919 ed. 50.00 (ISBN 0-8495-2810-0). Arden Lib.

Gentle Cynic: Translation of the Book of Koheleth Commonly Known As Ecclesiastes Stripped of Later Additions Also Its Origins, Growth, & Interpretation. Morris Jastrow. 1978. Repr. of 1919 ed. lib. bdg. 35.00 (ISBN 0-8495-2733-3). Arden Lib.

Gentle Death: Personal Caregiving to the Terminally Ill. Elizabeth S. Callari. 123p. 1986. 11.95 (ISBN 0-936389-00-1); pap. 7.95 (ISBN 0-936389-01-X). Tudor Pubs.

Gentle Love of the Holy Spirit. A. B. Simpson. 157p. 1983. pap. 5.95 (ISBN 0-87509-334-5). Chr Pubns.

Gentle Puritan: A Life of Ezra Stiles, 1727-1795. Edmund S. Morgan. LC 62-8257. (Institute of Early American History & Culture Ser.). 504p. 1962. 30.00x (ISBN 0-8078-1231-5). U of NC Pr.

Gentle Puritan: A Life of Ezra Stiles, 1727-1795. Edmund S. Morgan. (Illus.). 512p. 1983. pap. 9.95 (ISBN 0-393-30126-5). Norton.

Gentle Revolutionaries. Brennan Manning. 5.95 (ISBN 0-87193-012-9). Dimension Bks.

Gentle Touch. Charles J. Keating. (Illus.). 112p. (Orig.). 1985. pap. 5.95 (ISBN 0-89622-217-9). Twenty-Third.

Gentle Whisper. Duane Kelderman. 1985. 6.25 (ISBN 0-89536-752-1, 5858). CSS of Ohio.

Gentleman & the Jew. Maurice Samuel. LC 77-6666. pap. 5.95x (ISBN 0-87441-264-1). Behrman.

Gentleman from Heaven. James E. Dodds. 123p. 1962. Repr. of 1948 ed. 3.50 (ISBN 0-87516-464-1). De Vorss.

Gentlemen Theologians: American Theology in Southern Culture, 1795-1860. E. Brooks Holifield. LC 78-59580. x, 262p. 1978. 23.00 (ISBN 0-8223-0414-7). Duke.

Gentleness. Carole MacKenthun & Paulinus Dwyer. (Fruit of the Spirit Ser.). 48p. 1987. pap. 5.95 (ISBN 0-86653-395-8, SS879). Good Apple.

Geoffrey of Auxerre: On the Apocalypse, No. 42. Geoffrey of Auxerre. Tr. by Joseph Gibbons from Latin. (Cistercian Fathers Ser.). write for info (ISBN 0-87907-642-9). Cistercian Pubns.

Geoffrey of Monmouth. Ernest Jones. LC 73-20320. 1944. Repr. lib. bdg. 20.00 (ISBN 0-8414-5283-0). Folcroft.

Geoffrey of Monmouth & the Late Latin Chroniclers. Laura Keeler. LC 74-5455. 1946. Repr. lib. bdg. 27.50 (ISBN 0-8414-5493-0). Folcroft.

Geografia Biblica. J. B. Tidwell. Tr. by Carlos C. Pierson. (Span., Illus.). 144p. 1982. pap. 5.50 (ISBN 0-311-15031-4). Casa Bautista.

Geographic Influences in Old Testament Masterpieces. Laura H. Wild. 182p. 1980. Repr. of 1915 ed. lib. bdg. 30.00 (ISBN 0-8414-9701-X). Folcroft.

Geographic Influences in Old Testament Masterpieces. Laura H. Wild. 1915. 27.00 (ISBN 0-8274-2396-9). R West.

Geographical History of the Qur'an. S. M. Nadui. 1970. 10.50 (ISBN 0-87902-300-7). Orientalia.

Geographical History of the Qur'an. A. H. Nadvi. 12.50 (ISBN 0-686-18521-8). Kazi Pubns.

Geography of Early Buddhism. Ed. by Bimala C. Law. LC 78-72464. Repr. of 1932 ed. 21.00 (ISBN 0-404-17336-5). AMS Pr.

Geography of Holiness: The Photography of Thomas Merton. Ed. by Deba Patnaik. LC 80-18604. 1980. 17.50 (ISBN 0-8298-0401-3). Pilgrim NY.

Geography of Witchcraft. Montague Summers. 624p. 1973. pap. 4.95 (ISBN 0-8065-0391-2). Citadel Pr.

Geologia: Discourse Concerning the Earth Before the Deluge, Wherein the Form & Properties Ascribed to It. Erasmus Warren. LC 77-6546. (History of Geology Ser.). (Illus.). 1978. Repr. of 1690 ed. lib. bdg. 34.50x (ISBN 0-405-10470-7). Ayer Co Pubs.

Geometry of Space & Consciousness. 2nd ed. J. S. Perkins. 1973. 3.50 (ISBN 0-8356-7006-6). Theos Pub Hse.

Georg Rhaw's Publications for Vespers. Victor Mattfeld. (Wissenschaftliche Abhandlungen-Musicological Studies: Vol. 11). 361p. 1967. lib. bdg. 30.00 (ISBN 0-912024-81-X). Inst Mediaeval Mus.

Georg Sverdrup: Educator, Theologian, Churchman. James S. Hamre. 194p. 1986. 15.00 (ISBN 0-87732-071-3). Norwegian-Am Hist Assn.

George Abbot, Archbishop of Canterbury, 1562-1633: A Bibliography. Richard A. Christophers. LC 65-27845. pap. 59.00 (ISBN 0-317-10344-X, 2016440). Bks Demand UMI.

George Adams, Interpreter of Rudolf Steiner. Olive Whicher. 1978. pap. 8.95 (ISBN 0-904822-08-7). St George Bk Serv.

George Burman Foster: Religious Humanist. Alan Gragg. LC 77-92499. (Special Studies Ser.: No. 3). v, 79p. 1978. pap. 3.50 (ISBN 0-932180-02-7). NABPR.

George Carlson: The Spirit of the Tarahumara. George A. Carlson. Ed. by Gayle Maxon & Quincie Hopkins. LC 85-62063. (Illus.). 27p. (Orig.). 1985. pap. 18.00 (ISBN 0-935037-00-4). Peters Corp NM.

George Eliot & Judaism. David Kaufmann. LC 75-130251. (English Literature Ser., No. 33). 1970. Repr. of 1888 ed. lib. bdg. 27.95x (ISBN 0-8383-1141-5). Haskell.

George Eliot & Spinoza. Dorothy Atkins. Ed. by James Hogg. (Romantic Reassessment Ser.). 188p. (Orig.). 1978. pap. 15.00 (ISBN 3-7052-0535-8, Pub. by Salzburg Studies). Longwood Pub Group.

George Fox's Book of Miracles. George Fox. Ed. by Henry J. Cadbury. LC 73-735. 161p. 1973. Repr. of 1948 ed. lib. bdg. 16.50x (ISBN 0-374-92825-8, Octagon). Hippocrene Bks.

George Herbert: The Country Parson & the Temple. Ed. by John N. Wall. LC 81-80287. (Classics of Western Spirituality Ser.). 384p. 13.95 (ISBN 0-8091-0317-6); pap. 10.95 (ISBN 0-8091-2298-7). Paulist Pr.

George Lozuks: Doers of the Word. Roberta Ryan. LC 85-6615. (Meet the Missionary Ser.). 1985. 5.50 (ISBN 0-8054-4293-6, 4242-93). Broadman.

George MacDonald. Michael Phillips. 336p. 1987. 12.95 (ISBN 0-87123-944-2). Bethany Hse.

George MacDonald. Richard H. Reis. LC 71-125820. (Twayne's English Authors Ser.). 1972. lib. bdg. 17.95 (ISBN 0-8057-1356-5). Irvington.

George MacDonald: An Anthology. George MacDonald. Ed. by C. S. Lewis. 192p. 1986. pap. 6.95 (ISBN 0-02-022640-3, Collier). Macmillan.

George MacDonald & His Wife. Greville Macdonald. Repr. of 1924 ed. 50.00 (ISBN 0-384-34777-0, E240). Johnson Repr.

George Mueller. Faith C. Bailey. 160p. 1980. pap. 3.50 (ISBN 0-8024-0031-0). Moody.

George Mueller: Man of Faith. Basil Miller. 160p. 1972. pap. 3.50 (ISBN 0-87123-182-4, 200182). Bethany Hse.

George Muller: Delighted in God! rev. ed. Roger Steer. LC 81-52600. 320p. 1981. pap. 3.95 (ISBN 0-87788-304-1). Shaw Pubs.

George Muller of Bristol. Arthur T. Pierson. 336p. 1984. pap. 7.95 (ISBN 0-310-47091-9, 11669P, Clarion Class). Zondervan.

George Muller Treasury. George Muller. Ed. by Roger Steer. LC 86-72058. 192p. (Orig.). 1987. pap. 7.95 (ISBN 0-89107-416-3, Crossway Bks). Good News.

George of Lydda, the Patron Saint of England. Tr. by Ernest A. Budge. LC 77-87668. (Luzac's Semitic Texts & Translations: No. 20). (Eng. & Ethiopic., Illus.). Repr. of 1930 ed. 55.00 (ISBN 0-404-11348-6). AMS Pr.

George Rapp's Harmony Society: 1785-1847. rev. ed. Karl J. R. Arndt. LC 72-147267. (Illus.). 713p. 1972. 45.00 (ISBN 0-8386-7888-2). Fairleigh Dickinson.

George Rapp's Successors & Material Heirs: 1847-1916. Karl J. Arndt. LC 76-147268. (Illus.). 445p. 1972. 45.00 (ISBN 0-8386-7889-0). Fairleigh Dickinson.

George Ripley. Octavius B. Frothingham. LC 75-101910. Repr. of 1883 ed. 24.50 (ISBN 0-404-02625-7). AMS Pr.

George Townshend, A Life of. David Hofman. (Illus.). 448p. 23.50 (ISBN 0-85398-126-4); pap. 12.95 (ISBN 0-85398-127-2). G Ronald Pub.

George Tyrrell & the Catholic Tradition. Ellen Leonard. 208p. 1982. pap. 9.95 (ISBN 0-8091-2424-6). Paulist Pr.

George Tyrrell: In Search of Catholicism. David G. Schultenover. LC 81-38406. (Illus.). xiv, 505p. 1981. 32.50x (ISBN 0-915762-13-7). Patmos Pr.
George W. Truett Library, 4 vols. George W. Truett. 1980. Set. pap. 34.95 (ISBN 0-8054-2237-4). Broadman.
George Washington & Religion. Paul F. Boller, Jr. LC 63-9755. 1963. 12.95 (ISBN 0-87074-021-0). SMU Press.
George Whitefield's Journals. George Whitefield. 1978. 18.95 (ISBN 0-85151-147-3). Banner of Truth.
George Whitefield's Journals. George Whitefield. (Illus., Orig.). 1985. pap. 14.95 (ISBN 0-85151-482-0). Banner of Truth.
George Whitefield's Letters: Seventeen Thirty-Four to Seventeen Forty-Two. Goerge Whitefield. 1976. 16.95 (ISBN 0-85151-239-9). Banner of Truth.
Georges Rouault: Paintings & Prints. James T. Soby. LC 70-169317. (Museum of Modern Art Publications in Reprint). Repr. of 1947 ed. 24.50 (ISBN 0-405-01575-5). Ayer Co Pubs.
Gerard Manley Hopkins: A Tribute. W. A. Peters. 80p. 1984. pap. 5.95 (ISBN 0-8294-0456-2). Loyola.
Gerhard von Rad. James Crenshaw. (Makers of the Modern Theological Mind Ser.). 1978. 8.95 (ISBN 0-8499-0112-X). Word Bks.
Gerhart Hauptman: Religious Syncretism & Eastern Religions. Philip Mellen. (American University Studies I: Vol. 24). 284p. (Orig.). 1983. pap. text ed. 30.55 (ISBN 0-8204-0060-2). P Lang Pubs.
German Churches Under Hitler: Background, Struggle & Epilogue. Ernst Helmreich. LC 78-17737. 617p. 1978. 35.00x (ISBN 0-8143-1603-4). Wayne St U Pr.
German Crimes in Poland, 2 vols. in one. Central Commission for the Investigation of German Crimes in Poland Staff. 1982. Repr. of 1947 ed. 45.00x (ISBN 0-86527-336-7). Fertig.
German Hymnody of the Brethren, 1720-1903. Hedwig Durnbaugh. Ed. by William R. Eberly. (Monograph). (Illus.). 336p. 1986. 25.00x (ISBN 0-936693-21-5). Brethren Encyclopedia.
German Jew: A Synthesis of Judaism & Western Civilization, 1730-1930. H. I. Bach. (Litman Library of Jewish Civilization). 1985. 29.95x (ISBN 0-19-710033-3). Oxford U Pr.
German Jew in America: An Annotated Bibliography Including Books, Pamphlets & Articles of Special Interest. Rudolph Glanz. 1969. 39.50x (ISBN 0-87068-061-7). Ktav.
German-Jewish Refugees in England: The Ambiguities of Assimilation. Marion Berghahn. LC 83-9802. 270p. 1984. 30.00 (ISBN 0-312-32571-1). St Martin.
German Jewish Women, Vol. 2. Rudolf Glanz. 25.00x (ISBN 0-87068-462-0). Ktav.
German Pietists of Provincial Pennsylvania, 1694-1708. Julius F. Sachse. LC 70-134384. (Communal Societies Ser.). Repr. of 1895 ed. 32.50 (ISBN 0-404-07204-6). AMS Pr.
German Protestants Face the Social Question: The Conservative Phase, 1815-1871. William O. Shanahan. 1954. 22.95 (ISBN 0-268-00110-3). U of Notre Dame Pr.
German Reformation. R. Scribner. LC 85-19732. (Studies in European History). 88p. 1986. pap. text ed. 7.95x (ISBN 0-391-03362-X). Humanities.
Germania Sacra: Die Bistuemer der Kirchenprovinz Trier: Das Erzbistum Trier, 1. das Stift St. Paulin Vor Trier. Ed. by Franz J. Heyen. (Germania Sacra: Historisch-Statistische Beschreibung der Kirche Des Alten Reiches, N. F. 6). xiv, 855p. 1972. pap. 88.00 (ISBN 3-11-002273-7). De Gruyter.
Germania Sacra, New Series II: Bistuemer der Kirchenprovinz Salzburg. Edgard Krausen. 1977. 62.40x (ISBN 3-11-006826-5). De Gruyter.
Germanisches Heidentum Bei Den Angelsachsen. Ernst A. Phillippson. Repr. of 1929 ed. 20.00 (ISBN 0-384-46310-X). Johnson Repr.
Germans & Jews. George L. Mosse. LC 68-9631. 260p. 1985. 25.00x. Fertig.
Germans & Jews since the Holocaust: The Changing Situation in West Germany. Ed. by Anson Rabinbach & Jack D. Zipes. 300p. 1986. text ed. 37.50 (ISBN 0-8419-0924-5); pap. text ed. 17.95 (ISBN 0-8419-0925-3). Holmes & Meier.
Germans & Jews: The Right, the Left, & the Search for a 'Third Force' in Pre-Nazi Germany. George L. Mosse. LC 68-9631. 1970. 23.50 (ISBN 0-86527-081-3). Fertig.
Germany in the Nineteenth Century. facs. ed. A. S. Peake et al. LC 67-30189. (Manchester University Publications Historical Ser.: No. 24). 1915. 15.00 (ISBN 0-8369-0472-9). Ayer Co Pubs.
Germany-Pilgrimage of Unity & Peace. Pope John Paul II. 1981. 6.00 (ISBN 0-8198-3013-5); pap. 5.00 (ISBN 0-8198-3014-3). Dghtrs St Paul.
Germany, Turkey, & Zionism, 1897-1918. Isaiah Friedman. 1977. 59.00x (ISBN 0-19-822528-8). Oxford U Pr.
Germinal & Zola's Philosophical & Religious Thought. Philip Walker. (Purdue Univ. Monographs in Romance Languages: No. 14). 200p. (Orig.). pap. 28.00x (ISBN 90-272-1724-6). Benjamins North Am.
Gershom Scholem & the Mystical Dimension of Jewish History. Joseph Dan. 350p. 1987. 50.00x (ISBN 0-8147-1779-9). NYU Pr.
Gershom Scholem: Kabbalah & Counter-History. 2nd ed. David Biale. 240p. 1982. pap. text ed. 7.95x (ISBN 0-674-36332-9). Harvard U Pr.
Gerty's Papa's Civil War. Edward P. Smith. Ed. by William H. Armstrong. (Illus.). 128p. (Orig.). 1984. pap. 7.95 (ISBN 0-8298-0703-9). Pilgrim NY.
Gesammelte Abhandlungen Zur Romischen Religions und Stadtgeschichte. facsimile ed. Georg Wissowa. LC 75-10663. (Ancient Religion & Mythology Ser.). (Ger.). 1976. Repr. of 1904 ed. 25.50x (ISBN 0-405-07279-1). Ayer Co Pubs.
Gesammelte Schriften, 3 vols. David Kaufmann. Ed. by Steven Katz. LC 79-7143. (Jewish Philosophy, Mysticism & the History of Ideas Ser.). (Ger.). 1980. Repr. of 1915 ed. Set. lib. bdg. 120.00x (ISBN 0-405-12268-3); lib. bdg. 40.00x ea. Vol. 1 (ISBN 0-405-12269-1). Vol. 2 (ISBN 0-405-12270-5). Vol. 3 (ISBN 0-405-12271-3). Ayer Co Pubs.
Gesammelte Schriften. Moritz Steinschneider. Ed. by Steven Katz. LC 79-7152. (Jewish Philosophy, Mysticism & History of Ideas Ser.). 1980. Repr. of 1925 ed. lib. bdg. 55.50x (ISBN 0-405-12289-6). Ayer Co Pubs.
Geschichte der Alten Kirche, 4 vols. in 1. Hans Lietzmann. 1220p. 1975. Repr. 79.20x (ISBN 3-11-004625-3). De Gruyter.
Geschichte der Deutschen Reformation. Friedrich Bezold. LC 79-149654. (BCL Ser. I). (Ger.). Repr. of 1890 ed. 37.50 (ISBN 0-404-00797-X). AMS Pr.
Geschichte der Evangelischen Theologie in Deutschland seit dem Idealismus. 3rd ed. Horst Stephan & Martin Schmidt. (De Gruyter Lehrbuch). 1973. 24.80x (ISBN 3-11-003752-1). De Gruyter.
Geschichte der Israelitischen Religion. Georg Fohrer. (Ger.). xvi, 367p. 1969. 20.80x (ISBN 3-11-002652-X). De Gruyter.
Geschichte der Judischen Philosophie des Mittelalters, 3 vols. David Neumark. Ed. by Steven Katz. LC 79-7149. (Jewish Philosophy, Mysticism & History of Ideas Ser.). 1980. Repr. of 1928 ed. Set. lib. bdg. 120.00x (ISBN 0-405-12279-9); lib. bdg. 40.00x ea. Vol. 1 (ISBN 0-405-12280-2). Vol. 2, Pt. 1 (ISBN 0-405-12281-0). Vol. 2, Pt. 2 (ISBN 0-405-12282-9). Ayer Co Pubs.
Geschichte der Juedischen Religion: Von der Zeit Alexanders des Grossen bis zur Aufklaerung. Mit einem Ausblick auf das 19.-20. Jahrhundert. Johann Maier. LC 72-77437. (Ger.). xx, 641p. 1972. 29.60x (ISBN 3-11-002448-9). De Gruyter.
Geschichte der Kartause Mauerbach. Rolanda Hantschk. Ed. by James Hogg. (Analecta Cartusiana Ser.: No. 7). (Ger.). 164p. (Orig.). 1972. pap. 25.00 (ISBN 3-7052-0008-9, Pub by Salzburg Studies). Longwood Pub Group.
Geschichte der Kartause Seitz. Erwin Mayer. Ed. by James Hogg. (Analecta Cartusiana Ser.: No. 104). 116p. (Orig.). 1983. pap. 25.00 (ISBN 0-317-42574-9, Pub. by Salzburg Studies). Longwood Pub Group.
Geschichte Der Katholischen Theologie. 2nd ed. Karl Werner. 50.00 (ISBN 0-384-66815-1). Johnson Repr.
Geschichte Der Protestantischen Theologie. Isaak A. Dorner. 1867. 55.00 (ISBN 0-384-12385-6). Johnson Repr.
Geschichte Der Reformation in Polen. Theodor Wotschke. (Ger). 34.00 (ISBN 0-384-69301-6); pap. 28.00 (ISBN 0-384-69300-8). Johnson Repr.
Geschichte der urchristlichen Literatur: Einleitung in das Neue Testament, die Apokryphen und die Apostolischen Vaeter. Philipp Vielhauer. 812p. 1981. 41.00x (ISBN 3-11-007763-9). De Gruyter.
Geschichtschreiber der Husitischen Bewegung in Bohmen, Vols. 2, 6, 7. Ed. by Karl A. Hofler. (Ger). pap. 65.00 ea. vol. 2, 6; pap. 23.00 vol. 7 (ISBN 0-384-23810-6). Johnson Repr.
Geschichtsliteratur der Juden. Moritz Steinschneider. Ed. by Steven Katz. LC 79-7153. (Jewish Philosophy, Mysticism & History of Ideas Ser.). 1980. Repr. of 1905 ed. lib. bdg. 16.00x (ISBN 0-405-12290-X). Ayer Co Pubs.
Gesenius' Hebrew & Chaldee Lexicon. Tr. by Samuel P. Tregelles. (Reference Set). 919p. 1982. Repr. of 1979 ed. 24.95 (ISBN 0-915134-70-5). Mott Media.
Gesenius' Hebrew Grammar. 2nd ed. William Gesunius. Ed. by E. Kautzsch & A. E. Cowley. 1910. 29.95x (ISBN 0-19-815406-2). Oxford U Pr.
Geshikhte Fun der Yidisher Arbeterbavegung, Vol. 2. Ed. by Elias Tcherikower. LC 45-13072. (Yiddish., Illus.). 1945. 20.00 (ISBN 0-914512-18-8). Yivo Inst.
Geshikhte Fun Yidn in Varshe, 3 vols. Jacob Shatzky. LC 48-15791. (Yiddish.). 1953. Set. 10.00 (ISBN 0-914512-27-7); 10.00 ea. Vol. 1 (ISBN 0-914512-32-3). Vol. 2 (ISBN 0-914512-33-1). Vol. 3 (ISBN 0-914512-34-X). Yivo Inst.
Gestalt & the Wisdom of the Kahunas. Bethal Phaigh. LC 82-50928. 112p. 1983. pap. 5.95 (ISBN 0-87516-498-6). De Vorss.
Gestaltwander der Gotter. Leopold Ziegler. Ed. by Kees W. Bolle. LC 77-79163. (Mythology Ser.). (Ger.). 1977. Repr. of 1920 ed. lib. bdg. 35.50x (ISBN 0-405-10571-X). Ayer Co Pubs.
Gestez Urbild und Mythos. Walter F. Otto. Ed. by Kees W. Bolle. LC 77-82281. (Mytholoy Ser.). (Ger.). 1978. Repr. of 1951 ed. lib. bdg. 17.00x (ISBN 0-405-10572-X). Ayer Co Pubs.
Gesture of Balance: A Guide to Awareness, Self-Healing & Meditation. T. Tulku. 170p. 1977. 25.00x (ISBN 0-317-39074-0, Pub. by Luzac & Co Ltd). State Mutual Bk.
Gesture of Balance: A Guide to Awareness, Self-Healing & Meditation. Tarthang Tulku. LC 75-5255. (Illus.). 1976. 12.95 (ISBN 0-913546-17-8); pap. 7.95 (ISBN 0-913546-16-X). Dharma Pub.
Get Acquainted with God. Kenneth Hagin, Jr. 1983. pap. 0.50 mini bk. (ISBN 0-89276-714-6). Hagin Ministries.
Get All Excited-Jesus is Coming Soon. Charles R. Taylor. (Illus.). 108p. (Orig.). 1975. pap. 2.95 (ISBN 0-937682-00-4). Today Bible.
Get-Away Book. Doug Kamstra. (Good Things for Youth Leaders Ser.). 1984. pap. 5.95 (ISBN 0-8010-5459-1). Baker Bk.
Get Behind Me Satan. Virgil Leach. 1977. 8.75 (ISBN 0-89137-521-X); pap. 5.95 (ISBN 0-89137-520-1). Quality Pubns.
Get off My Back. Robert L. Maddox & Linda C. Maddox. (Orig.). 1987. pap. 5.95 (ISBN 0-8054-5344-X). Broadman.
Get Out of Your Own Way. Bhagwan Shree Rajneesh. Ed. by Ma Yoga Pratima. LC 83-181935. (Initation Talks Ser.). (Illus.). 374p. (Orig.). 1977. 18.95 (ISBN 0-88050-066-2). Chidvilas Found.
Get Ready for Forever. Ed. by R. A. Torrey. 176p. 1984. pap. text ed. 3.50 (ISBN 0-88368-160-9). Whitaker Hse.
Get Ready... Get Set... Grow! Gary Exman. Ed. by Michael L. Sherer. (Orig.). 1987. pap. 8.75 (ISBN 0-89536-865-X, 7824). CSS of Ohio.
Get Up & Go. Daisy Hepburn. LC 84-3362. (Life with Spice Bible Study Ser.). 64p. 1984. 2.95 (ISBN 0-8307-0946-0, 6101833). Regal.
Get Up & Grow. Daisy Hepburn. LC 84-3361. (Life with Spice Bible Study Ser.). 64p. 1984. 2.95 (ISBN 0-8307-0942-8, 6101800). Regal.
Get Well Prayer Book. John V. Bemmel. (Greeting Book Line Ser.). 48p. (Orig.). 1985. pap. 1.50 (ISBN 0-89622-231-4). Twenty Third.
Get Wise: Studies in Proverbs. Phil Ackley. (Young Fisherman Bible Studyguides). (Illus.). 80p. 1985. tchr's. ed. 4.95 (ISBN 0-87788-696-2); student ed. 2.95 (ISBN 0-87788-695-4). Shaw Pubs.
Get Your Church Involved in Missions. Michael Griffiths. 1972. pap. 1.00 (ISBN 9971-83-784-6). OMF Bks.
Getting a Grip: Bible Study for Young Teens. Ed. by Perry Gillum & Rob Allen. 41p. (Orig.). (YA) 1986. pap. 3.95 (ISBN 0-934942-55-2); tchr's. ed. 2.95 (ISBN 0-934942-56-0). White Wing Pub.
Getting a Grip on Time Management. Les Christie. 64p. 1984. pap. 5.95 (ISBN 0-88207-192-0). Victor Bks.
Getting a Job. Michael Pountney. LC 84-9039. 160p. (Orig.). 1984. pap. 4.95 (ISBN 0-87784-935-8). Inter-Varsity.
Getting Along: A Guide for Teenagers. Charles S. Mueller. LC 80-65546. 128p. (Orig.). 1980. pap. 4.95 (ISBN 0-8066-1791-8, 10-2545). Augsburg.
Getting along with People Who Don't Get Along. Dianna D. Booher. LC 83-14406. (Orig.). 1984. pap. 3.75 (ISBN 0-8054-5209-5). Broadman.
Getting Along with Your Friends. Phyllis R. Naylor. LC 79-22999. (Illus.). 1980. 8.75g (ISBN 0-687-14122-2). Abingdon.
Getting Away. Marjorie L. Sanders. LC 83-70214. 1984. pap. 5.95 (ISBN 0-8054-7523-0). Broadman.
Getting Better Acquainted with Your Bible. Berenice M. Shotwell. LC 75-173349. (Illus.). 1976. pap. 16.50 (ISBN 0-9603026-1-1). Shadwold.
Getting Better Acquainted with Your Bible. Berenice M. Shotwell. LC 75-173349. (Illus.). 1972. 24.95 (ISBN 0-9603026-0-3). Shadwold.
Getting Control of Your Inner Self. Rick Vohn. 176p. 1982. pap. 2.95 (ISBN 0-8423-0999-3). Tyndale.
Getting Even: Handling Conflict So Both Sides Win. John Vale & Robert Hughes. 128p. 1987. pap. 5.95 (ISBN 0-310-35661-X). Zondervan.
Getting Free: How Christians Can Overcome the Flesh & Conquer Persistent Personal Problems. Bert Ghezzi. (Living As a Christian Ser.). 112p. 1982. pap. 2.95 (ISBN 0-89283-117-0). Servant.
Getting in Touch with God. Jim Burns. 1986. pap. 4.95 (ISBN 0-89081-520-8). Harvest Hse.
Getting in Touch with Yourself-&-Your Parents. David Walsh. 1982. pap. 4.25 (ISBN 0-86716-009-8). St Anthony Mess Pr.
Getting into Luther's Large Catechism. F. Samuel Janzow. 1979. pap. 4.25 (ISBN 0-570-03783-2, 12-2737). Concordia.
Getting into the Formula of Concord. Eugene F. Klug. 1977. pap. 3.75 (ISBN 0-570-03742-5, 12-2646). Concordia.
Getting into the Story of Concord. David Scaer. 1978. pap. 3.95 (ISBN 0-570-03768-9, 12-2703). Concordia.
Getting into the Theology of Concord. Robert Preus. 1978. pap. 3.75 (ISBN 0-570-03767-0, 12-2702). Concordia.
Getting It All Together: The Heritage of Thomas Merton. Ed. by Timothy Mulhearn. 1984. pap. 4.95 (ISBN 0-89453-380-0). M Glazier.
Getting More from Your Bible. Hall. 1984. 5.95 (ISBN 0-88207-300-1). Victor Bks.
Getting More From Your Bible Reading. John Carlson. LC 82-14563. 137p. (Orig.). 1982. pap. 3.95 (ISBN 0-87123-256-1, 210256). Bethany Hse.
Getting More Out of Church. Wayne Kiser. 168p. 1986. pap. 5.95 (ISBN 0-89693-530-2). Victor Bks.
Getting Nowhere: Christian Hope & Utopian Dream. Peter S. Hawkins. LC 85-12758. 133p. (Orig.). 1985. pap. 8.95 (ISBN 0-936384-28-X). Cowley Pubns.
Getting Ready for Heaven. C. C. Cribb. LC 78-60614. (If God Has It I Want It!). 1979. pap. 2.95 (ISBN 0-685-96444-2). Manhattan Ltd NC.
Getting Ready for Marriage. David R. Mace. 128p. 1985. pap. 5.95 (ISBN 0-687-14136-2). Abingdon.
Getting Ready for Our New Baby. William Coleman. LC 84-432. 112p. 1984. pap. 4.95 (ISBN 0-87123-295-2, 210295). Bethany Hse.
Getting Ready for the Coming Rapture. C. C. Cribb. LC 79-88232. (If God Has It I Want It! Ser.). Date not set. pap. 2.95 (ISBN 0-932046-19-3). Manhattan Ltd NC.
Getting Rid of What You Haven't Got. Swami Muktananda. LC 74-19579. 64p. 1974. 3.25 (ISBN 0-914602-44-6). SYDA Found.
Getting Started. Gary R. Collins. 224p. (Orig.). 1984. pap. 5.95 (ISBN 0-8007-5162-0, Power Bks). Revell.
Getting Started in Adult Religious Education: A Practical Guide. James J. DeBoy, Jr. LC 79-88932. 128p. 1979. pap. 5.95 (ISBN 0-8091-2222-7). Paulist Pr.
Getting Straight about the Bible: The Creation, Interpreting Scripture, the Apocalypse, Life on Other Planets. Horace R. Weaver. LC 75-2342. 160p. (Orig.). 1975. pap. 6.95 (ISBN 0-687-14138-9). Abingdon.
Getting the Books Off the Shelves: Making the Most of Your Congregation's Library, No. 12. rev. ed. Ruth S. Smith. LC 85-11650. (CSLA Guide Ser.). (Illus.). 40p. 1985. pap. 6.95X (ISBN 0-915324-22-9). CSLA.
Getting the Buddha Mind. Chang Sheng-Yen. LC 82-73979. 147p. (Orig.). 1982. pap. text ed. 5.95 (ISBN 0-9609854-0-9). Dharma Drum Pubs.
Getting the Most Out of Being Single. rev. ed. Gien Karssen. LC 82-62240. 192p. 1983. pap. 3.95 (ISBN 0-89109-505-5). NavPress.
Getting the Most Out of Life. Spiros Zodhiates. (I Corinthians). (Illus.). 1976. pap. 4.95 (ISBN 0-89957-515-3). AMG Pubs.
Getting Them Sober, Vol. 3. Toby R. Drews. LC 85-73330. 1986. pap. 3.95 (ISBN 0-88270-610-1). Bridge Pub.
Getting Things Done: Concepts & Skills for Leaders. Lyle E. Schaller. 144p. (Orig.). 1986. pap. 10.95 (ISBN 0-687-14142-7). Abingdon.
Getting Things from God. Charles A. Blanchard. (Classic Elective Ser.: No. 1). 168p. 1985. pap. 5.95 (ISBN 0-89693-520-5); pap. 0.95. Victor Bks.
Getting Through College. Richard H. Rupp. LC 84-60726. 223p. 1984. pap. 9.95 (ISBN 0-8091-2627-3). Paulist Pr.
Getting Through to Adults. James T. Dyet. LC 79-53294. (Accent Teacher Training Ser.). (Orig.). 1980. pap. 4.95 (ISBN 0-89636-037-7). Accent Bks.
Getting to Know God. Karen Dockrey. LC 84-1702. (Orig.). 1984. pap. 4.50 (ISBN 0-8054-5341-5, 4253-41). Broadman.
Getting to Know God. Dale Larsen & Sandy Larsen. (Carpenter Studyguide). 80p. 1985. memb. ed. 1.95 (ISBN 0-87788-317-3); leader ed. 2.95 (ISBN 0-87788-318-1). Shaw Pubs.

Getting to Know God: Study Guide. Karen Dockrey. LC 86-8272. (Orig.). 1986. pap. 3.25 (ISBN 0-8054-3240-X). Broadman.

Getting to Know Jesus. Patricia Brennan-Nichols. (Illus.). 68p. (Orig.). 1984. pap. 3.95 (ISBN 0-89505-130-3). Argus Comm.

Getting to Know Jesus. George MacDonald. LC 79-93430. (Shepherd Illustrated Classics Ser.). 208p. (Orig.). 1980. pap. 5.95 (ISBN 0-87983-219-3). Keats.

Getting to Know Jesus. George MacDonald. 160p. 1987. pap. 2.95 (ISBN 0-345-34307-7, Pub. by Ballantine Epiphany). Ballantine.

Getting to Know the Bible: An Introduction to Sacred Scripture for Catholics. Melvin L. Farrell. 112p. 1986. pap. 5.95 (ISBN 0-937997-01-3). HI-Time Pub.

Getting to Know the Holy Spirit. David Mains. (Chapel Talks Ser.). 64p. 0.95 (ISBN 0-89191-262-2, 52621). Cook.

Getting to Know Your Bible. Julia R. Boone. LC 81-69259. 176p. 1984. pap. 9.95 (ISBN 0-8054-1140-2). Broadman.

Getting Together with Luke & Acts. Robert C. Cunningham. 47p. 1972. pap. 0.50 (ISBN 0-88243-930-8, 02-0930). Gospel Pub.

Getting Unstuck: Moving on after Divorce. Paul A. Lannan & LeRoy J. Spaniol. (Orig.). 1984. pap. 5.95 (ISBN 0-8091-2580-3). Paulist Pr.

Getting Your Act Together. Bob Donahue & Marilyn Donahue. (No. 4). 108p. 1983. pap. 3.95 (ISBN 0-8423-1005-3). Tyndale.

Getting Your Act Together. Theresa Hayes. LC 85-16548. 112p. 1986. pap. 4.95 (ISBN 0-87239-998-2, 3358). Standard Pub.

Getting Your House in Order. Mary Jane Preston. 130p. 1986. pap. 8.95 (ISBN 0-941478-48-3). Paraclete Pr.

Getting Your Life Out of Neutral. Gary R. Collins. 1987. 14.95. Revell.

Getting Your Share of the Spirit's Outpouring. C. C. Cribb. LC 79-88229. (If God Has It I Want It! Ser.). Date not set. pap. 2.95 (ISBN 0-932046-17-7). Manhattan Ltd NC.

Gezer One: Preliminary Report of the 1964-1966 Seasons. William G. Dever. 1971. 35.00x (ISBN 0-87820-300-1, Pub. by Hebrew Union). Ktav.

Gezer Two. William G. Dever. 1974. 35.00x (ISBN 0-685-56198-4). Ktav.

Ghandi: Portrayal of a Friend. E. Stanley Jones. 192p. 1983. pap. 3.25 (ISBN 0-687-13999-6). Abingdon.

Ghazali's Theory of Virtue. Mohamed A. Sherif. LC 71-38000. 200p. 1975. 44.50 (ISBN 0-87395-206-5). State U NY Pr.

Ghent Altarpiece & the Art of Jan Van Eyck. Lotte B. Philip. LC 73-113007. (Illus.). 380p. 1981. pap. 16.50 (ISBN 0-691-00316-5). Princeton U Pr.

Gheranda Samhita. Tr. by Srisa Chandra Vasu. LC 73-3804. (Sacred Books of the Hindus: 15, Pt. 2). Repr. of 1914 ed. 14.50 (ISBN 0-404-57836-5). AMS Pr.

Ghetto Diary. Janusz Korczak. LC 77-91911. (Illus.). 192p. 1978. 16.95 (ISBN 0-89604-004-6); pap. 10.95 (ISBN 0-317-06362-6). Holocaust Pubns.

Ghetto in Flames. Yitzhak Arad. LC 80-50198. (Illus.). 500p. 1982. pap. 14.95 (ISBN 0-89604-043-7). Holocaust Pubns.

Ghetto of Venice. Riccardo Calimani. Tr. by Katherine Wolfthal. (Illus.). 400p. 1987. 19.95 (ISBN 0-87131-484-3). M Evans.

Ghost Dance. David H. Miller. LC 85-5876. (Illus.). xviii, 318p. 1985. 23.95x (ISBN 0-8032-3099-0); pap. 8.95 (ISBN 0-8032-8130-7, BB 943, Bison). U of Nebr Pr.

Ghost Dance Messiah: The Jack Wilson Story. Paul Bailey. LC 75-135152. 12.95 (ISBN 0-87026-025-1). Westernlore.

Ghost-Dance Religion & the Sioux Outbreak of 1890. James Mooney. Ed. by Anthony F. Wallace. LC 64-24971. (Orig.). 1965. pap. 14.00 (ISBN 0-226-53517-7, P176, Phoen). U of Chicago Pr.

Ghost Dance Religion: Shakers of Puget Sound - Extracts. facsimile ed. James Mooney. (Shorey Indian Ser.). 21p. pap. 3.50 (ISBN 0-8466-0003-X, S3). Shorey.

Ghost Dance Religion: Smohalla. facs. ed. (Shorey Historical Soc). 40p. pap. 3.95 (ISBN 0-8466-0002-1, S2). Shorey.

Ghost Dancers in the West: The Sioux at Pine Ridge & Wounded Knee in 1891. 1976. pap. 1.00 (ISBN 0-916552-08-X). Acoma Bks.

Ghost of Old Capernaum. Walter A. Dawes. (Illus.). 358p. (Orig.). 1980. pap. text ed. 24.95 (ISBN 0-938792-00-8). New Capernaum.

Ghosts along the Cumberland: Deathlore in the Kentucky Foothills. William L. Montell. LC 74-32241. (Illus.). 272p. 1975. 22.50x (ISBN 0-87049-165-2). U of Tenn Pr.

Ghosts in Shakespeare. L. W. Rogers. LC 72-3658. (Studies in Shakespeare, No. 24). 1972. Repr. of 1925 ed. lib. bdg. 75.00x (ISBN 0-8383-1567-4). Haskell.

Ghosts of Fourteen Ninety-Two. Caesar C. Aronsfeld. (Conference on Jewish Social Studies). 1979. 10.00x (ISBN 0-910430-00-4, Pub by Conf Jewish Soc Studies). Columbia U Pr.

Giae Ly Can Ban. Daughters of St. Paul. Tr. by Andrew Tueng. Orig. Title: Basic Catachism. (Vietnamese.). 202p. (Orig.). 1983. pap. text ed. 2.00 (ISBN 0-8198-3035-6). Dghtrs St Paul.

Giant at the Ford & Other Legends of the Saints. Ursula Synge. LC 79-23020. (Illus.). 176p. 1980. 9.95 (ISBN 0-689-50168-4, McElderry Bk). Macmillan.

Giant Book of Superstitions. Claudia DeLys. 1979. pap. 5.95 (ISBN 0-8065-0721-7). Citadel Pr.

Giant Joshua. Maurine Whipple. Repr. 12.50 (ISBN 0-914740-17-2). Western Epics.

Giant Steps. Ed. by Warren W. Wiersbe. 496p. 1981. 15.95 (ISBN 0-8010-9648-0). Baker Bk.

Giant Steps for Little People. Kenneth N. Taylor. 64p. 1985. 6.95 (ISBN 0-8423-1023-1). Tyndale.

Giants, Lions & Fire. Joyce M. Smith. 1981. pap. 2.95 (ISBN 0-8423-1022-3). Tyndale.

Giants of Medieval Church. Frederick J. Cowie. 175p. Date not set. pap. 7.95 (ISBN 0-87973-586-4, 586). Our Sunday Visitor.

Gibbon's Antagonism to Christianity. Shelby T. McCloy. 1933. 23.50 (ISBN 0-8337-2311-1). B Franklin.

Gibeon & Israel: The Role of Gibeon & the Gibeonites in the Political and Religious History of Early Israel. J. Blenkinsopp. LC 74-171672. (Society for Old Testament Studies Monographs). 1972. 34.50 (ISBN 0-521-08368-0). Cambridge U Pr.

Gibeon, Where the Sun Stood Still: The Discovery of a Biblical City. James B. Pritchard. 1962. 31.50 (ISBN 0-691-03517-2); pap. 9.50x (ISBN 0-691-00210-X). Princeton U Pr.

Gibran of Lebanon. Suheil Bushrui. 12.00x (ISBN 0-86685-008-2). Intl Bk Ctr.

Gideon & the Early Judges. Gordon Lindsay. (Old Testament Ser.). 1.25 (ISBN 0-89985-135-5). Christ Nations.

Gideon: God's Warrior. Pat Holt. 32p. 1986. 7.95 (ISBN 0-687-14220-2). Abingdon.

Gideon, Samson & Other Judges of Israel. G. Andre. (Let's Discuss It Ser.). pap. 1.95 (ISBN 0-88172-132-8). Believers Bkshelf.

Gideonites. Devorah Omer. 256p. 1968. 3.50 (ISBN 0-88482-750-X). Hebrew Pub.

Giffard Bible. Jennifer M. Sheppard. Ed. by S. J. Freedberg. (Outstanding Dissertations in Fine Arts Ser.). (Illus.). 450p. 1985. Repr. of 1983 ed. 60.00 (ISBN 0-8240-6867-X). Garland Pub.

Gift & the Giver. Amelia Bishop. LC 84-2796. 1984. 6.25 (ISBN 0-8054-5106-4). Broadman.

Gift: Creation. Kenneth L. Schmitz. (Aquinas Lecture Ser.). 160p. 1982. 12.95 (ISBN 0-87462-149-6). Marquette.

Gift in My Arms: Thoughts for New Mothers. Lois W. Johnson. LC 77-72448. 1977. pap. 5.95 (ISBN 0-8066-1586-9, 10-2549). Augsburg.

Gift Is Already Yours. Erwin E. Prange. LC 79-55545. 1980. pap. 2.95 (ISBN 0-87123-189-1, 200189). Bethany Hse.

Gift More Precious than Gold. Ed. by Robert H. Hicks. (Illus.). 200p. 1985. Repr. 9.95 (ISBN 0-687-14691-7). Abingdon.

Gift of a Thorn. Henry G. Bosch. (Solace Ser.). 1984. pap. 1.50 (ISBN 0-8010-0866-2). Baker Bk.

Gift of Acabar. Og Mandino & Buddy Kaye. 1979. pap. 3.50 (ISBN 0-553-26084-7). Bantam.

Gift of Adminstration. Thomas C. Campbell & Gary B. Reierson. LC 80-24594. 138p. 1981. pap. 6.95 (ISBN 0-664-24357-6). Westminster.

Gift of Aid, No. 6. Robert S. Maseroni. 1983. 0.80 (ISBN 0-89536-630-4, 0738). CSS of Ohio.

Gift of Art. Gene E. Veith, Jr. LC 83-18636. 120p. 1984. pap. 6.95 (ISBN 0-87784-813-0). Inter-Varsity.

Gift of Christmas. E. L. Austin. pap. 3.95 (ISBN 0-8010-0149-8). Baker Bk.

Gift of Christmas. Jane B. Moncure. 1985. 5.95 (ISBN 0-89565-083-5, R4914). Standard Pub.

Gift of Christmas Past: A Return to Victorian Traditions. Sunny O'Neil. LC 81-14961. (Illus.). 146p. 1981. 15.95 (ISBN 0-910050-55-4). AASLH Pr.

Gift of Community: Baptism & Confirmation. Thomas A. Marsh. (Message of the Sacraments Ser.: Vol. 2). 13.95 (ISBN 0-89453-392-4); pap. 9.95 (ISBN 0-89453-228-6). M Glazier.

Gift of Courage. James Wilkes. LC 81-11507. 108p. 1981. pap. 6.95 (ISBN 0-664-24394-0). Westminster.

Gift of Encouragement, No. 4. Robert S. Maseroni. 1983. 0.80 (ISBN 0-89536-628-2, 0736). CSS of Ohio.

Gift of Faithfulness. Robert F. Hicks. Ed. by Simon Jenkins. (Gift of... Ser.). (Illus.). 24p. 1984. pap. 1.25 (ISBN 0-687-14700-X). Abingdon.

Gift of Feeling. Paul Tournier. pap. 9.95 (ISBN 0-8042-2071-9). John Knox.

Gift of Friendship. Ed. by Nick Beilenson. LC 86-63857. (Illus.). 64p. 1987. 5.95 (ISBN 0-88088-216-6). Peter Pauper.

Gift of Gentleness. Robert F. Hicks. Ed. by Simon Jenkins. (Gift of... Ser.). (Illus.). 24p. 1984. pap. 1.25 (ISBN 0-687-14703-4). Abingdon.

Gift of Giving, No. 5. Robert S. Maseroni. 1983. 0.80 (ISBN 0-89536-629-0, 0737). CSS of Ohio.

Gift of God. Gary Moore. Ed. by Mary H. Wallace. 96p. (Orig.). 1981. pap. 3.50 (ISBN 0-912315-37-7). Word Aflame.

Gift of God. Richard Seymour. pap. 1.50 (ISBN 0-686-12746-3). Grace Pub Co.

Gift of Goodness. Robert F. Hicks. Ed. by Simon Jenkins. (Gift of... Ser.). (Illus.). 24p. 1984. pap. 1.25 (ISBN 0-687-14698-4). Abingdon.

Gift of Healing. Ambrose Worrall & Olga Worrall. 240p. 1985. pap. 6.95 (ISBN 0-89804-142-2). Ariel OH.

Gift of Hope: How We Survive Our Tragedies. Robert L. Veninga. (Large Print Bks.). 404p. 1986. lib. bdg. 16.95 (ISBN 0-8161-4101-0, Large Print Bks). G K Hall.

Gift of Infallibility. 5.00 (ISBN 0-8198-3042-9); 4.00 (ISBN 0-8198-3041-0). Dghtrs St Paul.

Gift of Joy. Robert F. Hicks. Ed. by Simon Jenkins. (Gift of... Ser.). 24p. 1984. pap. 1.25 (ISBN 0-687-14704-2). Abingdon.

Gift of Life: A Message of Hope for the Seriously Ill. Randy Becton. (Illus.). 1978. pap. 4.75 (ISBN 0-89137-309-8). Quality Pubns.

Gift of Love. LC 85-19655. 181p. 1985. pap. 6.95 (ISBN 0-88141-041-1). St Vladimirs.

Gift of Love. Robert F. Hicks. Ed. by Simon Jenkins. (Gift of... Ser.). (Illus.). 24p. 1984. pap. 1.25 (ISBN 0-687-14705-0). Abingdon.

Gift of Love: Marriage As A Spiritual Journey. Ann T. Linthorst. 166p. 1985. pap. 9.95 (ISBN 0-913105-17-1). PAGL Pr.

Gift of Love: Marriage As a Spiritual Journey. Ann T. Linthorst. 9.95 (ISBN 0-8091-0299-4). Paulist Pr.

Gift of Love: Remembering the Old Anew. Patrick Mooney. (Greeting Book Line Ser.). 48p. (Orig.). 1983. pap. 1.50 (ISBN 0-89622-168-7). Twenty-Third.

Gift of Mercy, No. 7. Robert S. Maseroni. 1983. 0.80 (ISBN 0-89536-631-2, 0739). CSS of Ohio.

Gift of Ministry & Service, No. 2. Robert S. Maseroni. 1983. 0.80 (ISBN 0-89536-626-6, 0734). CSS of Ohio.

Gift of Mistletoe. (Gifts of Gold Ser.). 1972. 5.95 (ISBN 0-88088-618-8). Peter Pauper.

Gift of Music. Jane S. Smith & Betty Carlson. LC 83-70798. 255p. 1983. pap. 7.95 (ISBN 0-89107-293-4, Crossway Bks). Good News.

Gift of New Life. (Benziger Family Life Program Ser.). 5p. 1978. 2.00 (ISBN 0-02-651700-0); tchrs. ed. 4.00 (ISBN 0-02-651710-8); family handbook 1.00 (ISBN 0-02-651740-X). Benziger Pub Co.

Gift of Patience. Robert F. Hicks. Ed. by Simon Jenkins. (Gift of... Ser.). (Illus.). 24p. 1984. pap. 1.25 (ISBN 0-687-14699-2). Abingdon.

Gift of Peace. Robert F. Hicks. Ed. by Simon Jenkins. (Gift of... Ser.). (Illus.). 24p. 1984. pap. 1.25 (ISBN 0-687-14701-8). Abingdon.

Gift of Prayer. (Gifts of Gold Ser.). 1971. 4.95 (ISBN 0-88088-623-4). Peter Pauper.

Gift of Prophecy. Kenneth E. Hagin. 1969. pap. 1.00 (ISBN 0-89276-015-X). Hagin Ministries.

Gift of Prophecy, No. 8. Robert S. Maseroni. 1983. 0.80 (ISBN 0-89536-632-0, 0740). CSS of Ohio.

Gift of Prophecy in One Corinthians. Wayne A. Grudem. LC 81-40583. 358p. (Orig.). 1982. lib. bdg. 32.00 (ISBN 0-8191-2083-9); pap. text ed. 15.75 (ISBN 0-8191-2084-7). U Pr of Amer.

Gift of Self-Control. Robert F. Hicks. Ed. by Simon Jenkins. (Gift of... Ser.). (Illus.). 24p. 1984. pap. 1.25 (ISBN 0-687-14697-6). Abingdon.

Gift of Sex. Clifford Penner & Joyce Penner. 1981. pap. 11.95 (ISBN 0-8499-2893-1). Word Bks.

Gift of Simplicity. June H. McEwen. LC 84-6327. 1984. pap. 3.75 (ISBN 0-8054-5914-6). Broadman.

Gift of Suffering. F. B. Meyer. LC 79-93432. (Shepherd Illustrated Classics Ser.). (Illus.). 208p. (Orig.). 1980. pap. 5.95 (ISBN 0-87983-211-8). Keats.

Gift of Teaching, No. 3. Robert S. Maseroni. 1983. 0.80 (ISBN 0-89536-627-4, 0735). CSS of Ohio.

Gift of the Bible. R. Yehuda Ashlag. 160p. 1984. pap. 9.95 (ISBN 0-943688-22-1). Res Ctr Kabbalah.

Gift of the Magi. O. Henry. LC 82-60896. (Illus.). 32p. 1982. 14.95 (ISBN 0-907234-17-8). Picture Bk Studio USA.

Gift of the Redemption. 55p. 1984. pap. 3.95 (ISBN 1-55586-925-4). US Catholic.

Gift of the Word of Wisdom. Norvel Hayes. 1979. pap. 0.75 (ISBN 0-89274-367-0). Harrison Hse.

Gift of Time. William T. McConnell. LC 83-120. 132p. (Orig.). 1983. pap. 3.95 (ISBN 0-87784-838-6). Inter-Varsity.

Gift of Time: Family Activities for Advent, Christmas, Epiphany. Margaret Ehlen-Miller et al. (Illus.). 1977. pap. 4.95 (ISBN 0-8192-1224-5). Morehouse.

Gift of Tongues. Larry Christenson. 1963. pap. 1.25 (ISBN 0-87123-184-0, 260184). Bethany Hse.

Gift of Tongues & Interpretation. Norvel Hayes. 1980. pap. 0.75 (ISBN 0-89274-374-3). Harrison Hse.

Gift of Working of Miracles. Norvel Hayes. 1980. pap. 0.75 (ISBN 0-89274-371-9). Harrison Hse.

Gift That Grew. Yaffa Ganz. 1986. 8.95 (ISBN 0-87306-422-4). Feldheim.

Gift to Be Simple. Edward D. Andrews. (Illus.). 1940. pap. 3.95 (ISBN 0-486-20022-1). Dover.

Gift to Be Simple: Songs, Dances & Rituals of the American Shakers. Edward D. Andrews. (Illus.). 12.75 (ISBN 0-8446-1536-6). Peter Smith.

Gift Wrap, Please. Elizabeth W. Watson. (Orig.). 1966. pap. 1.95 (ISBN 0-8054-9710-2). Broadman.

Gifts: A Laity Reader, Selected Articles from the Gifts Journal 1979-1983. 124p. 1983. pap. 3.95 (ISBN 1-55586-879-7). US Catholic.

Gifts & Calling of God. Kenneth E. Hagin. 1986. pap. 0.50 (ISBN 0-89276-268-3). Hagin Ministries.

Gifts & Ministries of the Holy Spirit. Lester Sumrall. 1982. pap. 7.95 (ISBN 0-89274-189-9, HH-189). Harrison Hse.

Gifts from Korea. Larry Wilkinson & Dorcas Wilkinson. 1983. pap. 7.00 (ISBN 0-8309-0376-3). Herald Hse.

Gifts of God. Eugene V. Goetchius & Charles P. Price. LC 84-60627. 128p. (Orig.). 1984. pap. 4.95 (ISBN 0-8192-1349-7). Morehouse.

Gifts of God. Helen Schucman. LC 81-70309. 1982. 20.00 (ISBN 0-9606388-1-4). Found Inner Peace.

Gifts of Grace. Mary R. Schramm. LC 82-70946. 1982. pap. 5.95 (ISBN 0-8066-1921-X, 10-2551). Augsburg.

Gifts of Healing. H. L. Cayce. 1976. pap. 1.95 (ISBN 0-87604-070-9). ARE Pr.

Gifts of Life & Love. Ben-Zion Bokser. 193p. 1975. 7.00 (ISBN 0-88482-894-8). Hebrew Pub.

Gifts of Power: The Writings of Rebecca Jackson, Black Visionary, Shaker Eldress. Ed. by Jean M. Humez. LC 81-4684. (Illus.). 376p. 1981. lib. bdg. 22.50x (ISBN 0-87023-299-1); pap. 11.95 (ISBN 0-87023-565-6). U of Mass Pr.

Gifts of Silence. Pean Brown. 84p. 1983. pap. 6.95 (ISBN 0-942494-79-2). Coleman Pub.

Gifts of the Holy Spirit. Barbara Pursey. 40p. 1984. 1.95 (ISBN 0-934421-02-1). Presby Renewal Pubns.

Gifts of the Holy Spirit. C. R. Vaughan. 1975. 15.95 (ISBN 0-85151-222-4). Banner of Truth.

Gifts of the Lotus. Virginia Hanson. LC 74-5130. 192p. (Orig.). 1974. pap. 3.50 (ISBN 0-8356-0450-0, Quest). Theos Pub Hse.

Gifts of the Spirit. Ronald E. Baxter. LC 83-14963. 280p. (Orig.). 1983. pap. 8.95 (ISBN 0-8254-2243-4). Kregel.

Gifts of the Spirit. Duane S. Crowther. LC 65-29176. 352p. 1983. 10.95 (ISBN 0-88290-210-5). Horizon Utah.

Gifts of the Spirit. Harold Horton. 208p. 1975. pap. 2.50 (ISBN 0-88243-504-3, 02-0504, Radiant Bks). Gospel Pub.

Gifts of the Spirit. Kenneth C. Kinghorn. LC 75-22268. 128p. 1976. pap. 5.95 (ISBN 0-687-14695-X). Abingdon.

Gifts of the Spirit, 4 vols. Gordon Lindsay. 2.50 ea. Vol. 1 (ISBN 0-89985-195-9). Vol. 2 (ISBN 0-89985-196-7). Vol. 3 (ISBN 0-89985-197-5). Vol. 4 (ISBN 0-89985-199-1). Christ Nations.

Gifts of the Spirit. J. W. MacGorman. LC 75-55191. 1980. pap. 3.95 (ISBN 0-8054-1385-5). Broadman.

Gifts of the Spirit. Frank B. Stanger. 1974. pap. 0.95 (ISBN 0-87509-084-2). Chr Pubns.

Gifts of the Spirit. B. E. Underwood. 3.95 (ISBN 0-911866-64-7); pap. 2.95 (ISBN 0-911866-65-5). Advocate.

Gifts of the True Love. Elizabeth Yates. (Illus.). 1983. pap. 2.50x (ISBN 0-87574-100-2, 100). Pendle Hill.

Gifts That Differ: Lay Ministries Established & Unestablished. David N. Power. (Studies in the Reformed Rites of the Catholic Church: Vol. 8). (Orig.). 1980. pap. 9.95 (ISBN 0-916134-43-1). Pueblo Pub Co.

Gifts to Share. (Benziger Family Life Program Ser.). 1978. 2.00 (ISBN 0-02-651500-8); tchrs. ed. 4.00 (ISBN 0-02-651510-5); family handbook 1.00 (ISBN 0-02-651540-7). Benziger Pub Co.

Gigantes en Canaan: 14 Lecciones, Tomo 3. Bernice C. Jordan. (Pasos de Fe Ser.). (Span.). pap. text ed. 2.50 (ISBN 0-86508-405-X); figuras 8.95 (ISBN 0-86508-406-8). BCM Intl Inc.

Giggle Goes a Long Way. Mary A. Crum. 96p. 1986. 4.95 (ISBN 0-8010-2510-9). Baker Bk.

Gilbert Crispin, Abbot of Westminster: A Study of the Abby Under Norman Rule. Joseph A. Robinson. LC 80-2211. Repr. of 1911 ed. 37.50 (ISBN 0-404-18785-4). AMS Pr.

Gilbert Keith Chesterton. Maisie Ward. LC 83-45860. 1944. 46.50 (ISBN 0-404-20280-2, PR4453). AMS Pr.

Gilbert of Hoyland: Sermons on the Song of Songs, 1. Gilbert Of Hoyland. Tr. by Lawrence C. Braceland from Latin. LC 77-23026. (Fathers Ser.: No. 14). 1978. 15.95 (ISBN 0-87907-414-0). Cistercian Pubns.

Gilbert of Hoyland, Sermons on the Song of Songs, II. Gilbert Of Hoyland. (Fathers Ser.: No. 20). 1979. 8.95 (ISBN 0-87907-420-5). Cistercian Pubns.

Gilbert of Hoyland: Sermons on the Song of Songs, III. Gilbert Of Hoyland. Tr. by Lawrence C. Braceland. (Fathers Ser.: No. 26). 1979. 8.95 (ISBN 0-87907-426-4). Cistercian Pubns.

Gilbert of Hoyland: Treasties, Epistles, & Sermons. Gilbert. Tr. by Lawrence C. Braceland. (Fathers Ser.: No. 34). 1981. 12.95 (ISBN 0-87907-434-5). Cistercian Pubns.

Gilbert Tennent, Son of Thunder: A Case Study of Continental Pietism's Impact on the First Great Awakening in the Middle Colonies. Milton J. Coalter, Jr. LC 86-9967. (Contributions to the Study of Religion: No. 18). 247p. 1986. 35.00 (ISBN 0-313-25514-8, CGI/). Greenwood.

Gild of St. Mary & Other Documents. Ed. by F. J. Furnivall. (EETS, ES Ser.: No. 114). Repr. of 1920 ed. 10.00 (ISBN 0-527-00316-6). Kraus Repr.

Gilgal Theophany. Yoseph. 1985. 6.95 (ISBN 0-533-06448-1). Vantage.

Gilgamesh Epic & Old Testament Parallels. 2nd ed. Alexander Heidel. LC 49-5734. 1963. 8.95 (ISBN 0-226-32398-6, P136, Phoen). U of Chicago Pr.

Ginzei Droshos V'rayons, Treasures of Ideas & Thoughts: Sermons in Yiddish Language for All Holidays, Memorials, Eulogies, Installations, & for All Other Occasions. Zwi H. Kohn. 416p. 27.50 (ISBN 0-87559-149-3). Shalom.

Giotto & Assisi. Millard Meiss. (Illus.). 12.50 (ISBN 0-912158-42-5). Hennessey.

Giotto & Assisi. Millard Meiss. LC 60-9443. (Walter W. S. Cook Alumni Lecture Ser.: 1959). pap. 20.00 (ISBN 0-317-09361-4, 2050841). Bks Demand UMI.

Giotto: The Arena Chapel Frescoes. Ed. by James Stubblebine. LC 67-17689. (Critical Studies in Art History Ser). (Illus.). 1969. pap. text ed. 7.95x (ISBN 0-393-09858-3, NortonC). Norton.

Giovanni Gentile on the Existence of God. William A. Smith. Ed. & intro. by S. A. Matczak. LC 70-111087. (Philosophical Questions Ser.: No. 7). 1970. 18.00 (ISBN 0-912116-04-8). Learned Pubns.

Girl Alive. Margaret Thiele. LC 80-11623. (Orion Ser.). 1980. pap. 3.95 (ISBN 0-8127-0268-9). Review & Herald.

Girl with a Missionary Heart. John W. Duggar. (Illus.). 104p. 1975. pap. 1.95 (ISBN 0-89114-074-3). Baptist Pub Hse.

Girl with the Swansdown Seat: Aspects of Mid-Victorian Morality. Cyril Pearl. 6.95 (ISBN 0-686-85784-4, Pub. by Quartet England). Charles River Bks.

Girls in the Gang. Anne Campbell. (Illus.). 284p. 1984. 16.95 (ISBN 0-631-13374-7). Basil Blackwell.

Gita with Text, Translation & Sri Aurobindo's Comments. rev. ed. Sri Aurobindo. Ed. by Shyam S. Jhunjhunwala. 270p. 1974. 9.45 (ISBN 0-89071-207-7); pap. 4.50 (ISBN 0-89071-200-X). Matagiri.

Gittin, 2 vols. 30.00 (ISBN 0-910218-66-8). Bennet Pub.

Give It Away! Ed. by John Duckworth et al. (Pacesetter Ser.). 64p. 1987. tchr's. ed. 7.95. Cook.

Give Me a Break with Study Guide. Gary R. Collins. 192p. 1982. pap. 5.95 (Power Bks). Revell.

Give Me an Answer. Cliffe Knechtle. LC 86-10549. 132p. (Orig.). 1986. pap. 5.95 (ISBN 0-87784-569-7). Inter-Varsity.

Give Me-Make Me. Judson Cornwall. LC 79-64976. 1979. 1.25 (ISBN 0-88270-387-0). Bridge Pub.

Give Sorrow Words. Terry Creagh. 94p. (Orig.). 1982. pap. 9.95 (ISBN 0-85819-341-8, Pub. by JBCE). ANZ Religious Pubns.

Give to the Winds Thy Fears: The Women Temperance Crusade, 1873-1874. Jack S. Blocker, Jr. LC 84-15718. (Contributions in Women Studies: No. 55). (Illus.). xix, 280p. 1985. lib. bdg. 35.00 (ISBN 0-313-24556-8, BGW/). Greenwood.

Give Us Burning Hearts. Heini Arnold. 36p. 1985. pap. 1.50 (ISBN 0-87486-196-9). Plough.

Give Us This Day. (Little Remembrance Gift Edition Ser.). 4.95 (ISBN 0-87741-004-6). Makepeace Colony.

Give Us This Day. Ernest Holmes. pap. 0.75 (ISBN 0-87516-144-8). De Vorss.

Give Us This Day: A Devotional Guide for Daily Living. Leroy Brownlow. 1986. 7.95 (ISBN 0-915720-23-X). Brownlow Pub Co.

Give Us This Day Our Daily Bread: Asking for & Sharing Life's Necessities. Colleen T. Evans. 160p. 1982. pap. 3.50 (ISBN 0-687-14743-3). Abingdon.

Give What You Command. Cardinal Michael Pellegrino. flexible bdg 3.00 (ISBN 0-89942-580-1, 580/04). Catholic Bk Pub.

Given & Shed for You. Micheal Parr. Ed. by Micheal L. Sherer. (Orig.). 1987. pap. 2.50 (ISBN 0-89536-847-1, 7806). CSS of Ohio.

Givers, Takers & Other Kinds of Lovers. Josh McDowell & Paul Lewis. 1981. pap. 2.95 (ISBN 0-8423-1031-2). Tyndale.

Giving a Good Invitation. Roy J Fish. LC 74-18043. 1975. pap. 3.50 (ISBN 0-8054-2107-6). Broadman.

Giving & Becoming. Sri Chinmoy. 50p. (Orig.). 1975. pap. 2.00 (ISBN 0-88497-122-8). Aum Pubns.

Giving Away Your Faith. Barry St. Clair. (Moving Toward Maturity Ser.: No. 4). 132p. 1985. pap. 4.95 (ISBN 0-317-16074-5). Victor Bks.

Giving Birth: The Parents' Emotions in Childbirth. Sheila Kitzinger. LC 77-2518. (Orig.). 1978. pap. 4.95 (ISBN 0-8052-0573-X). Schocken.

Giving Birth to Thunder, Sleeping with His Daughter: Coyote Builds North America. Barry H. Lopez. LC 77-17395. 1978. 8.95 (ISBN 0-8362-0726-2). Andrews McMeel Parker.

Giving Book: Creative Resources for Senior High Ministry. Paul M. Thompson & Joani Lillevold. LC 84-47794. (Illus.). 144p. (Orig.). 1985. pap. 9.95 (ISBN 0-8042-1192-2). John Knox.

Giving, Christian Stewardship: Teaching Bks. Brena Price. (Illus.). 14p. 1971. pap. text ed. 2.95 (ISBN 0-86508-154-9). BCM Intl Inc.

Giving God's Way. John MacArthur. 1978. pap. 3.95 (ISBN 0-8423-1034-7). Tyndale.

Giving Good Homilies. Jay Cormier. LC 84-70383. 96p. 1984. pap. 3.95 (ISBN 0-87793-317-0). Ave Maria.

Giving Heart. Bill Swetmon. 162p. (Orig.). 1986. pap. 3.95 (ISBN 0-89225-288-X). Gospel Advocate.

Giving Yourself to God: Pursuing Excellence in Your Christian Life. Jim Burns. (Orig.). pap. 3.95; wkbk. 3.95 (ISBN 0-89081-488-0). Harvest Hse.

Glad or Sad: How Do You Feel? rev. ed. Childs World Editors. LC 79-12152. (Illus.). 1979. PLB 5.95 (ISBN 0-89565-072-X). Childs World.

Glad Reunion. John Claypool. 144p. 1985. 8.95 (ISBN 0-8499-0469-2, 0469-2). Word Bks.

Glad Tidings: Studies in Galatians. rev. ed. E. J. Waggoner. LC 72-81729. 144p. pap. 5.95 (ISBN 0-912145-06-4). MMI Pr.

Gladdys Makes Peace. Jan Hogan. (Illus.). 22p. 1985. 5.95 (ISBN 0-87178-313-4). Brethren.

Gladys Aylward. Gladys Aylward & Christine Hunter. 1970. pap. 3.50 (ISBN 0-8024-2986-6). Moody.

Glas. Jacques Derrida. Tr. by John P. Leavey, Jr. & Richard Rand. LC 85-28877. vi, 262p. 1986. 50.00x (ISBN 0-8032-1667-X). U of Nebr Pr.

Glass Christmas Ornament: Old & New. 2nd, rev. ed. Maggie Rogers & Judith Hawkins. (Illus.). 126p. (Orig.). 1983. pap. 12.95 (ISBN 0-917304-79-9). Timber.

Glass Virgin. Catherine Cookson. 352p. 1981. pap. 3.95 (ISBN 0-552-08849-8). Bantam.

Glaube und Vernunft: Eight Hundred Sixty-Three to Eighteen Hundred. Karel Macha. 350p. 1987. lib. bdg. 50.00 (ISBN 3-598-20130-3). K G Saur.

Glauben und Aberglauben. Eugenie Bormann. LC 84-70173. 120p. 23.00x (ISBN 0-938100-32-7). Camden Hse.

Glaubenszeugnisse Oberdeutscher. Ed. by Lydia Muller. (Ger). 34.00 (ISBN 0-384-40404-9); pap. 28.00 (ISBN 0-384-40403-0). Johnson Repr.

Glaubenszeugnisse Oberdeutscher Taufgesinnter, Band Zwei. Robert Friedmann. (Tauferakten Kommission Ser., Vol. 12). 318p. (Ger). 9.50x (ISBN 0-8361-1186-9). Herald Pr.

Gleanings: A Random Harvest. Douglas V. Steere. 144p. (Orig.). 1986. pap. 6.95 (ISBN 0-8358-0543-3). Upper Room.

Gleanings among the Sheaves. Charles H. Spurgeon. 1974. pap. 1.95 (ISBN 0-87509-085-0). Chr Pubns.

Gleanings: Essays in Jewish History, Letters & Art. Cecil Roth. 1967. 10.00x (ISBN 0-8197-0178-5). Bloch.

Gleanings from Elisha. Arthur W. Pink. LC 79-181591. 288p. 1972. pap. 10.95 (ISBN 0-8024-3000-7). Moody.

Gleanings from Old Shaker Journals. Clara E. Sears. LC 75-345. (Radical Tradition in America Ser). (Illus.). 311p. 1975. Repr. of 1916 ed. 30.25 (ISBN 0-88355-247-7). Hyperion Conn.

Gleanings from Paul. Arthur W. Pink. LC 67-14379. 1967. pap. 10.95 (ISBN 0-8024-3005-8). Moody.

Gleanings from the Scriptures. Arthur W. Pink. LC 73-80942. 1970. pap. 10.95 (ISBN 0-8024-3006-6). Moody.

Gleanings from the Writings of Baha'u'llah. 2nd rev. ed. Baha'u'llah. Tr. by Shoghi Effendi from Persian. LC 76-45364. (Illus.). 346p. 1976. 16.95 (ISBN 0-87743-111-6, 103-003). Baha'i.

Gleanings from the Writings of Baha'u'llah. Baha'u'llah. Tr. by Shoghi Effendi from Persian. 346p. 1983. pap. 5.95 pocket size (ISBN 0-87743-187-6). Baha'i.

GLEANINGS: Hunger Meditations for Lent. rev. ed. Ed. by Ray Buchanan. 112p. pap. 5.50 (ISBN 0-939485-02-8). St Andrew Pr.

Gleanings in Buddha-Fields. Lafcadio Hearn. LC 73-172539. Repr. of 1897 ed. 20.00 (ISBN 0-405-08609-1). Ayer Co Pubs.

Gleanings in Buddha-Fields: Studies of Hand & Soul in the Far East. Lafcadio Hearn. LC 72-146523. 1971. pap. 6.25 (ISBN 0-8048-0978-X). C E Tuttle.

Gleanings in Exodus. Arthur W. Pink. 1964. pap. 10.95 (ISBN 0-8024-3001-5). Moody.

Gleanings in Genesis. Arthur W. Pink. 1922. pap. 10.95 (ISBN 0-8024-3002-3). Moody.

Gleanings in Joshua. Arthur W. Pink. LC 64-20991. 1964. pap. 10.95 (ISBN 0-8024-3004-X). Moody.

Gleanings in the Godhead. Arthur W. Pink. LC 75-15760. 256p. pap. 10.95 (ISBN 0-8024-3003-1). Moody.

Gleanings on the Church. H. Smith. 85p. pap. 4.95 (ISBN 0-88172-150-6). Believers Bkshelf.

Glenn Clark: His Life & Writings. Miles Clark. LC 75-6877. Repr. of 1975 ed. 30.40 (ISBN 0-8357-9008-8, 2016361). Bks Demand UMI.

Glimpse into Glory. Kathryn Kuhlman. Compiled by Jamie Buckingham. LC 79-90558. 1979. pap. 3.50 pocket size (ISBN 0-88270-393-5). Bridge Pub.

Glimpse into Reality. Lynn Jay & Steve Jay. LC 81-71020. 144p. (Orig.). 1982. pap. 5.25 (ISBN 0-87516-475-7). De Vorss.

Glimpse of Glory. Gonville Ffrench-Beytagh. 128p. 1987. pap. 7.95 (ISBN 0-8091-2903-5). Paulist Pr.

Glimpse of India, Being a Collection of Extracts from the Letters of Dr. Clara A. Swain. Clara A. Swain. Ed. by Carolyn D. Gifford & Donald Dayton. (Women in American Protestant Religion 1800-1930 Ser.). 366p. 1987. lib. bdg. 50.00 (ISBN 0-8240-0677-1). Garland Pub.

Glimpse of Sion's Glory. Philip F. Gura. Incl. 1984. 30.00x (ISBN 0-8195-5095-7); Puritan Radicalism in New England,1620-1660. (Illus.). 399p. 1986. pap. 12.95 (ISBN 0-8195-6154-1). 1984. 30.00. Wesleyan U Pr.

Glimpses. Dom H. van Zeller. 260p. 1982. 5.00 (ISBN 0-8198-3027-5, SP0185); pap. 4.00 (ISBN 0-8198-3028-3). Dghtrs St Paul.

Glimpses into Revelation. Rayford Bullard. 5.95 (ISBN 0-911866-74-4). Advocate.

Glimpses into the Psychology of Yoga. I. K. Taimni. 1973. 10.95 (ISBN 0-8356-7290-5). Theos Pub Hse.

Glimpses of a Golden Childhood. Bhagwan Shree Rajneesh. Ed. by Swami Devaraj Sambuddha & Swami Devageet Mahasattva. LC 85-43069. (Biography Ser.). 788p. (Orig.). 1985. pap. 6.95 (ISBN 0-88050-715-2). Chidvilas Found.

Glimpses of a Great Soul: The Life of Swami Saradananda. Swami Aseshananda. 320p. (Orig.). 1982. pap. 7.95 (ISBN 0-87481-039-6). Vedanta Pr.

Glimpses of Abhidharma. Chogyam Trungpa. LC 86-31409. (Dragon Ser.). 100p. 1987. pap. 9.95 (ISBN 0-87773-282-5). Shambhala Pubns.

Glimpses of God's Love. James A. Tucker & Priscilla Tucker. Ed. by Raymond H. Woolsey. LC 83-61683. (Junior-Youth Devotional Ser.: 1984). 386p. 1983. 7.95 (ISBN 0-8280-0216-9). Review & Herald.

Glimpses of Hadith, 3. Azizullah. pap. 6.50 (ISBN 0-686-18380-0). Kazi Pubns.

Glimpses of Islamic History. I. Faqih. 16.50 (ISBN 0-686-63900-6). Kazi Pubns.

Glimpses of the God-Man Meher, Baba, Vol. IV. Bal Natu. LC 79-913293. (Illus.). 218p. (Orig.). 1984. pap. 7.95 (ISBN 0-913078-52-2). Sheriar Pr.

Glimpses of the God-Man, Meher Baba: Vol. III, February 1952 - February 1953. Bal Natu. LC 79-913293. (Illus.). 344p. (Orig.). 1982. pap. 7.95 (ISBN 0-913078-44-1). Sheriar Pr.

Glimpses of the God-Man, Meher Baba, Vol. 2: Jan. 1949-Jan. 1952. Bal Natu. (Illus.). 406p. 1979. pap. 7.95 (ISBN 0-913078-38-7). Sheriar Pr.

Glimpses of the Holy Quran. Azizullah. pap. 6.50 (ISBN 0-686-18517-X). Kazi Pubns.

Glimpses of the Mother's Life, Vol. 2. The Mother. Ed. by Nilima Das. 335p. 1980. 11.00 (ISBN 0-89071-291-3). Matagiri.

Glimpses of the Vedas. Siddhantalankar Satyavrata. 140p. 1980. 9.95 (ISBN 0-940500-12-4, Pub. by Milind Pubns India). Asia Bk Corp.

Glimpses of Unfamiliar Japan, 2 Vols. Lafcadio Hearn. LC 70-101093. Repr. of 1894 ed. 32.50 (ISBN 0-404-03205-2). AMS Pr.

Glimpses of Veda & Vyakarana. Ed. by G. Devasthali. 1985. 26.00x (ISBN 0-8364-1408-X, Pub. by Popular Prakashan). South Asia Bks.

Global Believer: Toward a New Imitation of Christ. Joseph G. Donders. 144p. (Orig.). 1986. pap. 5.95 (ISBN 0-89622-294-2). Twenty-Third.

Global Congress of the World's Religions. Ed. by Henry O. Thompson. LC 82-73565. (Conference Ser.: No. 15). (Orig.). 1982. pap. text ed. write for info. (ISBN 0-932894-15-1, Pub. by New Era Bks). Paragon Hse.

Global Economics & Religion. Ed. by James Finn. 277p. 1983. 26.95 (ISBN 0-87855-477-7). Transaction Bks.

Global Living Here & Now. James A. Scherer. 1974. pap. 2.25 (ISBN 0-377-00003-5). Friend Pr.

Global Mission. Winston Crawley. LC 85-3752. 1985. 11.95 (ISBN 0-8054-6340-2). Broadman.

Global, Universal, Worldwide Flood of Noah. Bert Thompson. (That You May Believe Ser.). 45p. (Orig.). 1986. pap. 1.50 (ISBN 0-932859-02-X). Apologetic Pr.

Global View of Christian Missions. J. Herbert Kane. 1971. 19.95 (ISBN 0-8010-5308-0). Baker Bk.

Globalism: America's Demise. William Bowen, Jr. LC 84-80408. 222p. (Orig.). 1984. pap. 6.95 (ISBN 0-910311-24-2). Huntington Hse Inc.

Glories & Virtues of Mary. Rev. James Alberione. 1970. 5.00 (ISBN 0-8198-3017-8); pap. 4.00 (ISBN 0-8198-3018-6). Dghtrs St Paul.

Glories of Mary. St. Alphonsus de Liguori. LC 79-112485. 1977. pap. 13.50 (ISBN 0-89555-021-0). TAN Bks Pubs.

Glories of Sri Caitanya Mahaprabhu. Ed. by Srila Hridayananda dasa Goswami. Tr. by Kusakratha dasa. LC 83-7078. 64p. (Orig.). 1984. pap. 6.00 (ISBN 0-89647-018-0). Bala Bks.

Glorification: Sermons & Papers. 2nd ed. Nathaniel D. Pendleton. 221p. 1985. Repr. of 1941 ed. 7.00 (ISBN 0-910557-10-1). Acad New Church.

Glorify God & Enjoy Him Forever. Peg Rankin. LC 81-51742. 176p. 1981. pap. 5.95 (ISBN 0-8307-0796-4, 5415209). Regal.

Glorifying God. rev. ed W. R. Smith. (Way of Life Ser.: No. 134). 1979. 3.95 (ISBN 0-89112-134-X, Bibl Res Pr). Abilene Christ U.

Glorious Caliphate. S. A. Husain. 15.50 (ISBN 0-686-18626-5). Kazi Pubns.

Glorious Church-Ephesians. 2nd ed. Wilbur Fields. LC 71-1065. (Bible Study Textbook Ser.). (Illus.). 1960. 10.60 (ISBN 0-89900-040-1). College Pr Pub.

Glorious Church of God. M. A. Tomlinson. 1968. pap. 3.50 (ISBN 0-934942-06-4). White Wing Pub.

Glorious Company. G. Avery Lee. LC 86-2601. (Orig.). 1986. pap. 3.25 (ISBN 0-8054-1536-X). Broadman.

Glorious Gospel. James A. Cross. 1956. 4.25 (ISBN 0-87148-350-5). Pathway Pr.

Glorious Is Thy Name! Robert J. Hastings. LC 85-26948. 1986. 7.95 (ISBN 0-8054-7230-4). Broadman.

Glorious Koran. bilingual ed. Ed. by Marmaduke Pickthall. 1696p. 1976. text ed. 50.00x (ISBN 0-04-297036-9). Allen Unwin.

Glorious Names of God. Mary F. Loeks. 1986. pap. 3.95 (ISBN 0-8010-5629-2). Baker Bk.

Glorious Presence. Joy Fuller. LC 81-65753. 168p. (Orig.). 1981. pap. 2.95 (ISBN 0-87516-449-8). De Vorss.

Glorious Presence. Ernest Wood. LC 74-1045. pap. 2.75 (ISBN 0-8356-0446-2, Quest). Theos Pub Hse.

Glorious Thunder. Juanita L. Gregorian. 144p. 1986. 10.95 (ISBN 0-89962-498-7). Todd & Honeywell.

Glorious Victory Thru Healing Memories. Genevieve Parkhurst. 4.95 (ISBN 0-910924-55-4). Macalester.

Glory & the Way of the Cross: The Gospel of St. Mark. Ludger Schenke. Ed. by Robert Karris. Tr. by Robin Scroggs. (Herald Biblical Bklts). 1972. pap. 1.25 (ISBN 0-8199-0517-8). Franciscan Herald.

Glory Beyond All Comparison. Betty S. Cloyd. LC 81-52216. 1981. pap. 4.50x (ISBN 0-8358-0423-2). Upper Room.

Glory Days: From the Life of Luther Allan Weigle. Richard Weigle. (Illus., Orig.). 1976. pap. 5.95 (ISBN 0-377-00058-2). Friend Pr.

Glory in the Cross-Fruit of the Spirit from the Passion of Christ. Gerhard Aho et al. 1984. pap. 7.95 (ISBN 0-570-03940-1, 12-2876). Concordia.

Glory of Bethlehem. Bargil Pixner et al. 75p. 1986. 11.95 (ISBN 0-8170-1109-9). Judson.

Glory of Hera: Greek Mythology & the Greek Family. Philip E. Slater. LC 68-24373. 540p. 1985. pap. 14.95x (ISBN 0-8070-5795-9, BPA12, Pub. by Ariadne Bks). Beacon Pr.

Glory of Israel: The Theology & Provenience of the Isaiah Targum. Bruce D. Chilton. (JSOT Supplement Ser.: No. 23). ix, 178p. 1984. text ed. 28.00x (ISBN 0-905774-46-9, Pub. by JSOT Pr England); pap. text ed. 18.50 (ISBN 0-905774-47-7, Pub. by JSOT Pr England). Eisenbrauns.

Glory of Jerusalem: An Explorer's Guide. Shlomo S. Gafni & A. Van der Heyden. LC 81-17053. 128p. 1982. o. p. 16.95 (ISBN 0-521-24613-X). Cambridge U Pr.

Glory of the Holy Land. Shlomo S. Gafni & A. Van der Heyden. LC 81-17054. (Illus.). 256p. 1982. o. p. 21.95 (ISBN 0-521-24612-1). Cambridge U Pr.

Glory of the Lord, Vol. 3. Hans U. Von Balthasar. 416p. cancelled (ISBN 0-8245-0699-5). Crossroad NY.

Glory of the Lord: A Theological Aesthetics. Hans U. Von Balthasar. Ed. by John Riches. Tr. by Andrew Louth et al from Ger. LC 82-23553. (Studies in Theological Style: Clerial Styles: Vol. 2). Orig. Title: Herrlichkeit: Eine Theologische Asthetik II Facher der Stile 1: Klerikale Style. 366p. 29.95 (ISBN 0-89870-048-5). Ignatius Pr.

Glory of the Lord; A Theological Aesthetics: Vol. I-Seeing the Form. Hans U. Von Balthasar. Ed. by Joseph Fessio & John Riches. Tr. by Erasmo Leiva-Merikakis from Ger. LC 82-23553. Tr. of Herrlickeit: Eine Theologische Asthetik, I-Schau der Gestalt. 691p. 1982. 35.00 (ISBN 0-89870-031-0). Ignatius Pr.

Glory of the New Testament. Ed. by Shlomo S. Gafni. LC 83-840322. 1984. 25.00 (ISBN 0-394-53659-2, Pub. by Villard Bks). Random.

Glory of the Old Testament. Ed. by Shlomo S. Gafni. LC 83-848323. 256p. 1984. 25.00 (ISBN 0-394-53658-4, Pub. by Villard Bks). Random.

Glory of the Only Son. Jon L. Joyce. (Orig.). 1982. pap. 4.95 (ISBN 0-937172-43-X). JLJ Pubs.

Glory of Thy People. Raphael Simon. 1986. pap. 6.95 (ISBN 0-932506-47-X). St Bedes Pubns.

Glory to God: A Candlelight Service for Christmas. Steven Bomely. 1983. pap. 2.75 (ISBN 0-89536-625-8, 0733). CSS of Ohio.

Glosario de Nombres Biblicos. Jack Enlow. 96p. 1981. pap. 2.25 (ISBN 0-311-03655-4). Casa Bautista.

Glossary: Index for "A Course in Miracles. Kenneth Wapnick. 255p. (Orig.). 1982. 16.00. Foun Miracles.

Glossary-Index for "A Course in Miracles". 2nd, enl. ed. Kenneth Wapnick. 312p. 1986. text ed. 16.00 (ISBN 0-933291-03-5). Foun Miracles.

Glossary of Buddhist Terms. A. C. March. 99p. 1986. Repr. of 1937 ed. lib. bdg. 10.50 (ISBN 81-7030-025-8, Pub. by Sri Satguru Pubns India). Orient Bk Dist.

Glossary of Liturgical & Ecclesiastical Terms. Frederick G. Lee. LC 76-174069. (Tower Bks.). (Illus.). xl, 452p. 1972. Repr. of 1877 ed. 44.00x (ISBN 0-8103-3949-8). Gale.

Glossary of Terms in Sri Aurobindo's Writings. Sri Aurobindo. 1978. 10.00 (ISBN 0-89071-271-9). Matagiri.

Glossary of the English Bible Words. J. Eastwood & W. Aldis Wright. 564p. 1981. Repr. of 1866 ed. lib. bdg. 75.00 (ISBN 0-89760-210-2). Telegraph Bks.

Glossolalia. W. J. Burgess. 64p. 1968. pap. 1.00 (ISBN 0-89114-053-0). Baptist Pub Hse.

Glossolalia: A Bibliography. Watson E. Mills. LC 85-8987. (Studies in the Bible & Early Christianity: Vol. 6). 144p. 1985. 39.95x (ISBN 0-88946-605-X). E Mellen.

Glossolalia: Behavioral Science Perspectives on Speaking in Tongues. H. Newton Malony & A. Adams Lovekin. 320p. 1985. 29.95x (ISBN 0-19-503569-0). Oxford U Pr.

Glossolalia in the New Testament. William C. MacDonald. 22p. 1964. pap. 1.50 (ISBN 0-88243-508-6, 02-0508). Gospel Pub.

Glossolalia Phenomenon. Wade H. Horton. 1966. 7.95 (ISBN 0-87148-351-3). Pathway Pr.

Glossolalia, the Gift of Tongues. Ira J. Martin. 75p. 1970. pap. 2.25 (ISBN 0-87148-352-1). Pathway Pr.

Glow in the Dark. Rick Bundschuh. LC 86-31350. (Illus.). 148p. (Orig.). pap. 4.25 (ISBN 0-8307-1091-4, S182323). Regal.

Glow Ree Bee (11 Traditional Black Spiritual Arrangements) Shirley W. McRae. Ed. by Michael D. Bennett. 28p. (Orig.). 1982. pap. text ed. 5.95 (ISBN 0-934017-02-6). Memphis Musicraft.

Glowing Moments. Intro. by Ruth Norman. 170p. (Orig.). 1982. pap. 4.95 (ISBN 0-932642-76-4). Unarius Pubns.

Gnani Yoga. Yogi Ramacharaka. 8.00 (ISBN 0-911662-04-9). Yoga.

Gnosis. Geddes MacGregor. LC 78-64908. 1979. pap. 10.75 (ISBN 0-8356-0522-1). Theos Pub Hse.

Gnosis & the Question of Thought in Vedanta. John G. Arapura. 1986. lib. bdg. 65.25 (ISBN 90-247-3061-9, Pub. by Martinus Nijhoff Netherlands). Kluwer Academic.

Gnosis: The Nature & History of Gnosticism. Kurt Rudolph. LC 81-47437. 411p. 1982. 28.45 (ISBN 0-06-067017-7, HarpR); pap. 14.95 (ISBN 0-06-067018-5, PL 4122). Har-Row.

Gnostic & Historic Christianity. Gerald Massey. 1985. pap. 5.95 (ISBN 0-916411-51-6). Sure Fire.

Gnostic Dialogue: The Early Church & Crisis of Gnosticism. Pheme Perkins. LC 80-81441. (Theological Inquiries Ser.). 256p. 1980. pap. 7.95 (ISBN 0-8091-2320-7). Paulist Pr.

Gnostic Gospels. Elaine Pagels. LC 79-4764. 1979. 14.95 (ISBN 0-394-50278-7). Random.

Gnostic Heresies of the First & Second Centuries. Henry L. Mansel. Ed. by J. B. Lightfoot. LC 78-63170. (Heresies of the Early Christian & Medieval Era: Second Ser.). Repr. of 1875 ed. 42.00 (ISBN 0-404-16185-5). AMS Pr.

Gnostic Jung & the Seven Sermons to the Dead. Stephen Hoeller. LC 82-50220. 282p. (Orig.). 1982. 13.95 (ISBN 0-8356-0573-6). Theos Pub Hse.

Gnostic Problem. Robert M. Wilson. LC 78-63175. (Heresies of the Early Christian & Medieval Era: Second Ser.). Repr. of 1958 ed. 32.00 (ISBN 0-404-16193-6). AMS Pr.

Gnostic Religion. Hans Jonas. 1958. pap. 10.95x (ISBN 0-8070-5799-1, BP259). Beacon Pr.

Gnostic Religion: The Message of the Alien God & the Beginnings of Christianity. 2nd, rev. ed. Hans Jonas. 18.00 (ISBN 0-8446-2339-3). Peter Smith.

Gnostic Scriptures: A New Translation with Annotations. Bentley Layton. LC 85-25234. (Illus.). 800p. 1987. 35.00 (ISBN 0-385-17447-0). Doubleday.

Gnosticism: A Source Book of Heretical Writings from the Early Christian Period. Ed. by Robert M. Grant. LC 77-85274. Repr. of 1961 ed. 32.50 (ISBN 0-404-16108-1). AMS Pr.

Gnosticism: Its History & Influence. Benjamin Walker. 224p. 1984. pap. 9.95 (ISBN 0-85030-324-9). Newcastle Pub.

Gnosticism: Its History & Influence. Benjamin Walker. LC 86-34294. 320p. 1986. lib. bdg. 24.95x (ISBN 0-8095-7019-X). Borgo Pr.

Gnostics & Their Remains. C. W. King. LC 73-76092. (Secret Doctrine Reference Ser.). (Illus.). 500p. 1982. Repr. of 1887 ed. 21.00 (ISBN 0-913510-34-3). Wizards.

Go Ask God. Julius Hudson. 1981. 4.75 (ISBN 0-8062-1827-4). Carlton.

Go-Between God: The Holy Spirit & the Christian Mission. John V. Taylor. 1979. pap. 7.95 (ISBN 0-19-520125-6). Oxford U Pr.

Go Book. Compiled by Dale Dieleman. (Good Things for Youth Leaders). 64p. 1982. pap. 4.50 (ISBN 0-8010-2929-5). Baker Bk.

Go Forth into the World. Edward S. Long. 1983. 3.10 (ISBN 0-89536-604-5, 0732). CSS of Ohio.

Go Free. Elliott Wright. 128p. (Orig.). 1973. pap. 1.75 (ISBN 0-377-03011-2). Friend Pr.

Go-Givers in a Go-Getter World. Paul W. Powell. 1986. pap. 5.95 (ISBN 0-8054-2546-2). Broadman.

Go-Groups: Gearing up for Reaching Out. Eleanor McMullen & Jean Sonnenfeld. (Orig.). 1977. pap. 2.50 (ISBN 0-377-00060-4). Friend Pr.

Go Home & Tell. Bertha Smith. LC 65-10342. (Orig.). 1964. pap. 5.50 (ISBN 0-8054-7202-9). Broadman.

Go in Peace. C. H. Spurgeon. 1978. pap. 0.50 (ISBN 0-685-36795-9). Reiner.

Go into the City: Sermons for a Strenuous Age. John C. Leffler. LC 85-23366. 288p. 1986. 15.95 (ISBN 0-88089-014-2). Madrona Pubs.

Go on Singing. Richard G. Champion. LC 76-20889. (Radiant Life). 128p. 1976. tchr's ed 3.95 (ISBN 0-88243-169-2, 32-0169); pap. 2.50 (ISBN 0-88243-895-6, 02-0895). Gospel Pub.

Go Preach the Kingdom Heal the Sick. Jim Wilson. 127p. 1979. pap. text ed. 2.95 (ISBN 0-227-67659-9). Attic Pr.

Go Tell Everyone: A Commentary on the Sunday Readings - Cycles A-B & C. James McKarns. LC 85-20036. 279p. 1985. 9.95 (ISBN 0-8189-0488-7). Alba.

Go, Tell It on the Mountain: Three Christmas Pageants for Church Schools. Gretchen W. Pritchard. (Illus.). 63p. (Orig.). 1985. pap. 12.50x (ISBN 0-9614022-1-0). Sunday Paper.

Go till You Guess Bible Games. Amos R. Wells. (Quiz & Puzzle Book Ser.). 128p. (Orig.). 1980. pap. 2.95 (ISBN 0-8010-9502-6). Baker Bk.

Go with Haste into the Mountains. Cornelia M. Flaherty. 230p. (Orig.). 1984. 9.95 (ISBN 0-934318-42-5); pap. write for info. Falcon Pr MT.

Go Within. Ishwar C. Puri. Ed. by Edward D. Scott. 177p. (Orig.). 1986. pap. 6.00 (ISBN 0-937067-07-5). Inst Study Hum Aware.

Go Ye Therefore & Teach: Operation Manual for Christian Day School. Paul Jehle. 300p. 1982. tchr's. ed. 10.00 (ISBN 0-942516-01-X). Plymouth Rock Found.

Go Ye to Burma. Stella Ebersole. 432p. 1986. 24.95 (ISBN 0-89962-556-8). Todd & Honeywell.

Goad & Nail: Studies in Medieval Cistercian History X. (Cistercian Studies: No. 84). pap. 14.95 (ISBN 0-87907-984-3). Cistercian Pubns.

Goal & the Way: The Vedantic Approach to Life's Problems. Swami Satprakashananda. LC 77-75279. 302p. 1977. 12.50 (ISBN 0-916356-56-6). Vedanta Soc St Louis.

Goal Setting: A Guide to Achieving the Church's Mission. Dale McConkey. (Administration for Churches Ser.). 1978. pap. 3.95 (ISBN 0-8066-1651-2, 10-2558). Augsburg.

Goals for American Education: Proceedings. Conference on Science-Philosophy & Religion in Their Relation to the Democratic Way of Life - 9th. 1950. 28.00 (ISBN 0-527-00656-4). Kraus Repr.

Goals of Economic Life. Alfred D. Ward & John M. Clark. LC 72-167432. (Essay Index Reprint Ser.). Repr. of 1953 ed. 25.00 (ISBN 0-8369-2726-5). Ayer Co Pubs.

Goat-Foot God. Dion Fortune. (Orig.). 1980. pap. 7.95 (ISBN 0-87728-500-4). Weiser.

God. Usharbudh Arya. 162p. (Orig.). pap. 7.95 (ISBN 0-89389-060-X). Himalayan Pubs.

God. Robert Hicks & Richard Bewes. (Understanding Bible Truth Ser.). (Orig.). 1981. pap. 0.95 (ISBN 0-89840-024-4). Heres Life.

God. Nicholas J. Koushiafes. LC 81-90329. (Illus.). 300p. 1982. 25.00 (ISBN 0-9607228-0-7). Gods Universe.

God. Heinrich Ott. LC 73-5350. 128p. 1974. pap. 5.95 (ISBN 0-8042-0590-6). John Knox.

God - Isn't There Any Other Way!? Walter E. Hull. 1983. 5.95 (ISBN 0-8062-2173-9). Carlton.

God: A Critical Enquiry. Antony Flew. 210p. 1984. pap. 8.95 (ISBN 0-87548-371-2). Open Court.

God a Present Help. rev. ed. Emilie H. Cady. LC 84-5002010. 1985. 5.95 (ISBN 0-87159-044-1). Unity School.

God, Action & Embodiment. Thomas F. Tracy. 208p. (Orig.). 1984. pap. 11.95 (ISBN 0-8028-1999-0). Eerdmans.

God Against Slavery. facs. ed. George B. Cheever. LC 76-78995. (Black Heritage Library Collection Ser). 1857. 13.00 (ISBN 0-8369-8537-0). Ayer Co Pubs.

God Against Slavery & the Freedom & Duty of the Pulpit to Rebuke It, As a Sin Against God. George B. Cheever. LC 79-82182. (Anti-Slavery Crusade in America Ser). 1969. Repr. of 1857 ed. 13.00 (ISBN 0-405-00621-7). Ayer Co Pubs.

God, Allah & Ju Ju: Religion in Africa Today. Jack Mendelsohn. LC 78-5872. 1978. Repr. of 1962 ed. lib. bdg. cancelled (ISBN 0-313-20483-7, MEGA). Greenwood.

God Alone: The Life & Letters of a Saint - Sri Gyanamata. Self-Realization Fellowship. LC 84-52361. (Illus.). 324p. 1984. 8.50 (ISBN 0-87612-200-4, 1805). Self Realization.

God Always Says Yes. Sue Sikking. 143p. 1984. pap. 5.95 (ISBN 0-87516-545-1). De Vorss.

God among the Zulus. Kurt E. Koch. 336p. 1981. pap. 4.95 (ISBN 0-8254-3046-1). Kregel.

God among Us. Edward Schillebeeck. 256p. 1986. pap. 9.95 (ISBN 0-8245-0732-0). Crossroad NY.

God among Us: The Gospel Proclaimed. Edward Schillebeeckx. LC 82-23575. 278p. 1983. 12.95 (ISBN 0-8245-0575-1). Crossroad NY.

God: An Enquiry & a Solution. Paul Carus. 253p. 1943. 15.95 (ISBN 0-87548-223-6); pap. 6.95 (ISBN 0-87548-224-4). Open Court.

God & Abortion. Vivian De Danois. (Science of Man Library Bk). 1979. 51.50 (ISBN 0-89266-160-7). Am Classical Coll Pr.

God & Atheism: A Philosophical Approach to the Problem of God. Bernardino M. Bonansea. LC 78-12064. 378p. 1979. 19.95x (ISBN 0-8132-0549-2). Cath U Pr.

God & Caesar: Christian Faith & Political Action. John Eidsmoe. LC 84-71423. 226p. 1984. (Crossway Bks); pap. 7.95 (ISBN 0-89107-313-2). Good News.

God & Caesar on the Potomac: A Pilgrimage of Conscience. Robert F. Drinan. 1985. 15.00 (ISBN 0-89453-458-0). M Glazier.

God & Charity: Images of Eastern Orthodox Theology, Spirituality & Practice. T. Hopko et al. Ed. by Francis D. Costa. LC 79-3027. (Pan-Am Books). 103p. (Orig.). 1979. pap. text ed. 3.95 (ISBN 0-916586-34-0). Holy Cross Orthodox.

God & Children. J. Urteaga. 241p. 1965. pap. 4.95x (ISBN 0-933932-07-3). Scepter Pubs.

God & Christ: Existence & Province. Herbert Braun et al. Ed. by Robert W. Funk & Gerhard Ebeling. lib. bdg. 17.50x (ISBN 0-88307-042-1). Gannon.

God & Creation, 2 vols. John E. Boodin. LC 75-3058. Repr. of 1934 ed. 67.50 set (ISBN 0-404-59057-8). AMS Pr.

God & Creation. Peter J. Flamming. LC 85-6647. (Layman's Liberty of Christian Doctrine Ser.). 1985. 5.95 (ISBN 0-8054-1635-8). Broadman.

God & Evil. Michael Galligan. LC 75-36172. 96p. 1976. pap. 2.95 (ISBN 0-8091-1925-0). Paulist Pr.

God & Evil: Reading on the Theological Problem of Evil. Nelson Pike. 1964. pap. 14.95 ref.ed. (ISBN 0-13-357665-5). P-H.

God & Father, Vol. 143. Edward Schillebeeckx & Johannes B. Metz. (Concilium 1981). 128p. (Orig.). 1981. pap. 6.95 (ISBN 0-8164-2310-5, HarpR). Har-Row.

God & General Longstreet: The Lost Cause & the Southern Mind. Thomas L. Connelly & Barbara Bellows. 1982. 14.95 (ISBN 0-8071-1020-5). La State U Pr.

God & Global Justice: Religion & Poverty in an Unequal World. Ed. by Frederick P. Ferre & Rita H. Mataragnon. LC 84-26538. (God Ser.). 224p. (Orig.). 1985. text ed. 21.95 (ISBN 0-913757-36-5, Pub. by New Era Bks.); pap. text ed. 12.95 (ISBN 0-913757-37-3, Pub. by New Era Bks.). Paragon Hse.

God & Government: The Separation of Church & State. Ann E. Weiss. 160p. 1982. 8.95 (ISBN 0-395-32085-2). HM.

God & His Church. Duane S. Crowther. LC 76-173392. (Scripture Guide Ser.). 244p. 1971. pap. 5.95 (ISBN 0-88290-006-4). Horizon Utah.

God & His Gifts. Ivy Compton-Burnett. 1963. 15.95 (ISBN 0-575-02578-6, Pub by Gollancz England). David & Charles.

God & His Messengers. David Hofman. (Illus.). 1986. pap. 5.95 (ISBN 0-85398-049-7). G Ronald Pub.

God & His People: Covenant & Theology in the Old Testament. Ernest W. Nicholson. 240p. 1986. 36.00x (ISBN 0-19-826684-7). Oxford U Pr.

God & History. J. Montgomery Boice. LC 80-24457. (Foundations of the Christian Faith: Vol 4). 292p. (Orig.). 1981. pap. 7.95 (ISBN 0-87784-746-0). Inter-Varsity.

God & Human Anguish. S. Paul Schilling. LC 77-5857. Repr. of 1977 ed. 76.00 (ISBN 0-8357-9009-6, 2016362). Bks Demand UMI.

God & Human Freedom: A Festschrift in Honor of Howard Thurman. Henry J. Young. 200p. 1982. text ed. 13.95 (ISBN 0-913408-81-6). Friends United.

God & Human Suffering: An Excercise in the Theology of the Cross. Douglas J. Hall. LC 86-7964. 224p. 1986. text ed. 16.95 (ISBN 0-8066-2223-7, 10-2640). Augsburg.

God & Jesus: Nothing More Than Four-Letter Words. Thomas W. Holland. 1987. 6.95 (ISBN 0-533-07206-9). Vantage.

God & Man. 2nd ed. Anthony of Sourozh. 125p. 1983. pap. text ed. 4.95 (ISBN 0-88141-024-1). St Vladimirs.

God & Man. Oscar Oppenheimer. LC 79-64099. 1979. pap. text ed. 11.25 (ISBN 0-8191-0753-0). U Pr of Amer.

God & Man in Contemporary Christian Thought. Ed. by Charles Malik. 1970. 16.95x (ISBN 0-8156-6016-2, Am U Beirut). Syracuse U Pr.

God & Man in Contemporary Islamic Thought. Ed. by Charles Malik. 1972. 16.95x (ISBN 0-8156-6035-9, Am U Beirut). Syracuse U Pr.

God & Man in Modern Spirituality. Finbarr Connolly. 276p. 1984. pap. 9.95 (ISBN 0-87061-108-9). Chr Classics.

God & Man in the Koran. Toshihiko Izutsu. LC 79-52554. (Islam Ser.). 1980. Repr. of 1964 ed. lib. bdg. 20.00x (ISBN 0-8369-9262-8). Ayer Co Pubs.

God & Man in Time. Earle E. Cairns. LC 78-73042. 1978. pap. 7.95 (ISBN 0-8010-2426-9). Baker Bk.

God & Man in Two Worlds. Joseph Rebhun. 1985. lib. bdg. 16.95 (ISBN 0-9614162-1-1). OR Pub.

God & Man: The Basic Truths. Rawley Myers. 1976. 0.50 (ISBN 0-8199-0606-9). Franciscan Herald.

God & Man: The Essential Knowledge Which Everyone, but Absolutely Everyone Ought to Possess About Human Nature & the Nature of God & How the Two Are Related. Lawrence Vinoi. (Essential Knowledge Ser. Books). (Illus.). 1978. plastic spiral bdg. 44.75 (ISBN 0-89266-118-6). Am Classical Coll Pr.

God & Man's Destiny: Inquiries into the Metaphysical Foundations of Faith. Hartley B. Alexander. LC 75-3017. 1976. Repr. of 1936 ed. 16.50 (ISBN 0-404-59010-1). AMS Pr.

God & Marriage. Geoffrey W. Bromiley. 96p. (Orig.). 1980. pap. 4.95 (ISBN 0-8028-1851-X). Eerdmans.

God & Mrs. Adam. Alma E. Blanton. (Illus.). 152p. (Orig.). 1978. lib. bdg. 4.95 (ISBN 0-938134-00-0, G-1); pap. 4.95 (ISBN 0-686-73968-X). Loving Pubs.

God & Myths of Ancient Egypt. Robert Armour. 1986. pap. 15.00 (ISBN 977-424-113-4, Pub. by Am Univ Cairo Pr). Columbia U Pr.

God & Natural Evil. Robert B. Joohariglan. 85p. (Orig.). 1985. pap. 6.95x (ISBN 0-932269-30-3). Wyndham Hall.

God & Nature: A Book of Devotions for Christians Who Love Wildlife. Norma J. Persson. 240p. 1984. pap. 6.95 (ISBN 0-13-357559-4). P-H.

God & Oneself. Lillian De Waters. pap. 3.00 (ISBN 0-686-05705-8). L De Waters.

God & Personality. C. J. Webb. (Gifford Lectures Delivered in the University of Aberdeen in 1918 & 1919 First Course). Repr. of 1918 ed. 17.00 (ISBN 0-527-94906-X). Kraus Repr.

God & Personality: Being the Gifford Lectures Delivered in the University of Aberdeen in the Years 1918 & 1919. facsimile ed. Clement C. Webb. LC 76-164632. (Select Bibliographies Reprint Ser.). Repr. of 1919 ed. 20.00 (ISBN 0-8369-5916-7). Ayer Co Pubs.

God & Philosophy. Etienne Gilson. (Powell Lectures Ser.). 1941. pap. 6.95x (ISBN 0-300-00097-9, Y8). Yale U Pr.

God & Politics. R. L. Bruckberger. LC 78-190754. (Howard Greenfield Bk.). 1971. 9.95 (ISBN 0-87955-302-2). O'Hara.

God & Reason: A Historical Approach to Philosophical Theology. Ed L. Miller. 224p. 1972. pap. text ed. write for info. (ISBN 0-02-381270-2). Macmillan.

God & Revelation, Vol. 18. Karl Rahner. (Theological Investigations Ser.). 352p. 1983. 24.50x (ISBN 0-8245-0571-9). Crossroad NY.

God & Science: The Death & Rebirth of Theism. Charles P. Henderson, Jr. LC 85-23091. 216p. 1986. pap. 10.95 (ISBN 0-8042-0668-6). John Knox.

God & Skepticism. Terence Penelhum. 1983. lib. bdg. 34.95 (ISBN 90-277-1550-5, Pub. by Reidel Holland). Kluwer Academic.

God & Temporality. Ed. by Bowman Clarke & Eugene T. Long. (God Ser.). 320p. (Orig.). 1986. pap. 12.95 (ISBN 0-913757-10-1, Pub. by New Era Bks). Paragon Hse.

God & the American Corporation. Alan S. Solowsky. (International Council for Excellence in Management Library). (Illus.). 1980. deluxe ed. 69.95 (ISBN 0-89266-266-2). Am Classical Coll Pr.

God & the Apple of His Eye. Dorothy Donnelly. LC 72-96114. 1973. pap. 2.50 (ISBN 0-913382-05-1, 101-6). Prow Bks-Franciscan.

God & the Astronomers. Robert Jastrow. (Illus.). 1978. 9.95 (ISBN 0-393-85000-5). Norton.

God & the Bible: A Review of Objections to "Literature & Dogma". Matthew Arnold. LC 75-129382. Repr. of 1875 ed. 15.00 (ISBN 0-404-00386-9). AMS Pr.

God & the Bible: A Review of Objections to Literature & Dogma. Matthew Arnold. 1973. Repr. of 1875 ed. 14.75 (ISBN 0-8274-1704-7). R West.

God & the Gods: Myths of the Bible. Walter Beltz. Tr. by Peter Heinegg. 272p. 1983. pap. 6.95 (ISBN 0-14-022192-1, Pelican). Penguin.

God & the New Haven Railway. George D. O'Brien. LC 86-47554. 144p. 1986. 14.95 (ISBN 0-8070-1010-3). Beacon Pr.

God & the New Physics. Paul Davies. 272p. 1984. pap. 7.95 (ISBN 0-671-52806-8, Touchstone Bks). S&S.

God & the "New" Psychology of Sex. Benjamin Constable. (Illus.). 265p. 1976. 53.75 (ISBN 0-89266-043-0). Am Classical Coll Pr.

God & the Poets. David Daiches. 232p. 1986. pap. 15.95x (ISBN 0-19-812862-2). Oxford U Pr.

God & the Problem of Evil. Sr. Concetta Belleggia. 1980. 3.75 (ISBN 0-8198-3007-0); pap. 2.50 (ISBN 0-8198-3008-9). Dghtrs St Paul.

God & the Procurator, Some Questions Asked. William M. Wedderspoon. 176p. 1986. 9.95 (ISBN 0-8059-3020-5). Dorrance.

God & the Rhetoric of Sexuality, No. 20. Phyllis Trible. LC 77-78647. (Overtures to Biblical Theology Ser.). 228p. 1978. pap. 8.95 (ISBN 0-8006-0464-4, 1-464). Fortress.

God & the Rich Society: A Study of Christians in a World of Abundance. Denys L. Munby. LC 85-21886. v, 218p. 1985. Repr. of 1961 ed. lib. bdg. 39.75x (ISBN 0-313-24925-3, MGRS). Greenwood.

God & the Self: Three Types of Philosophy of Religion. Wayne Proudfoot. LC 75-28983. 241p. 1976. 22.50 (ISBN 0-8387-1769-1). Bucknell U Pr.

God & the State. facsimile ed. Michael Bakunin. LC 78-148871. (Select Bibliographies Reprint Ser.). Repr. of 1916 ed. 12.00 (ISBN 0-8369-5643-5). Ayer Co Pubs.

God & the State. Michael Bakunin. LC 75-105664. 1970. pap. 3.50 (ISBN 0-486-22483-X). Dover.

God & the Story of Judaism. Dorothy K. Kripke & Meyer Levin. LC 62-17078. (Jewish Heritage Ser: Vol. 1). 1962. 5.95x (ISBN 0-87441-000-2). Behrman.

God & the Unconscious. rev. ed. Victor White. LC 82-19153. (Jungian Classics Ser.: No. 4). xxxiii, 245p. 1982. pap. 15.00 (ISBN 0-88214-503-7). Spring Pubns.

God & the World. John B. Cobb, Jr. LC 69-11374. 138p. 1969. pap. 5.95 (ISBN 0-664-24860-8). Westminster.

God & the World He Made. John Walton & Kim Walton. (Early Bible Foundations Ser.). (Illus.). 1986. pap. 2.95 (ISBN 1-55513-030-5, Chariot Bks). Cook.

God & the World of Man. 2nd ed. Theodore M. Hesburgh. 1960. 8.95x (ISBN 0-268-00112-X). U of Notre Dame Pr.

God & the Writer. 1953. pap. 10.00 (ISBN 0-527-01720-5, YFS 12). Kraus Repr.

God &... Thirty Interviews. Terrance A. Sweeney. 240p. 1985. pap. 8.95 (ISBN 0-86683-804-X, 8404, HarpR). Har-Row.

God & Us. 2.25 (ISBN 0-8198-3029-1); 1.25 (ISBN 0-8198-3030-5). Dghtrs St Paul.

God & Vitamins. Marjorie Holmes. 368p. 1982. pap. 3.50 (ISBN 0-380-56994-9, 68536-1). Avon.

God & Vitamins. Marjorie Holmes. LC 80-911. 360p. 1980. 10.95 (ISBN 0-385-15249-3, Galilee). Doubleday.

God & World in Schleiermacher's Dialektik & Glaubenslehre, Vol. 43. John E. Thiel. (Basler und Berner Studien zur Historischen und Systematischen Theologie). xiv, 239p. 1981. pap. 28.15 (ISBN 3-261-04810-7). P Lang Pubs.

God Answers Prayer. Geo. Mueller. pap. 2.95 (ISBN 0-686-27009-6). Schmul Pub Co.

God Answers Prayer. Compiled by Mary H. Wallace. LC 85-22484. (Illus.). 368p. (Orig.). 1986. pap. 6.95 (ISBN 0-912315-90-3). Word Aflame.

God Answers Prayers. Anna M. Matthews. 96p. 1981. 8.95 (ISBN 0-89962-215-1). Todd & Honeywell.

God Are You Really Real? Beverly C. Burgess. (Illus.). 30p. (Orig.). 1985. pap. 1.98 (ISBN 0-89274-309-3). Harrison Hse.

God As Form: Essays in Greek Theology with Special Reference to Christianity & the Contemporary Theological Predicament. Curtis Bennett. LC 75-43851. 1976. 39.50 (ISBN 0-87395-325-8). State U NY Pr.

God As Strategist. Samuel Brengle. (Illus.). 64p. 1978. pap. 1.50 (ISBN 0-89216-017-9). Salvation Army.

God As the Mystery of the World: On the Foundation of the Theology of the Crucified One in the Dispute Between Theism & Atheism. Eberhard Jungel. Tr. by Darrell L. Guder. (Ger.). 428p. 1983. 20.95 (ISBN 0-8028-3586-4). Eerdmans.

God at Eventide. Ed. by Arthur J. Russell. 1950. 9.95 (ISBN 0-396-03183-8). Dodd.

God at Eventide. Ed. by Arthur J. Russell. 156p. 1974. pap. 2.75 (ISBN 0-8007-8154-6, Spire Bks). Revell.

God at My Sickbed. Alfred Doerffler. 1966. 1.50 (ISBN 0-570-03062-5, 6-1114). Concordia.

God at Work in Israel. Gerhard Von Rad. Tr. by John Marks. LC 79-26281. 1980. pap. 7.75 (ISBN 0-687-14960-6). Abingdon.

God Between. Charles E. Bradford. Ed. by Richard W. Coffen. 96p. 1984. pap. 4.95 (ISBN 0-8280-0243-6). Review & Herald.

God Beyond Knowledge. H. A. Hodges. Ed. by W. D. Hudson. LC 77-22634. (Library of Philosophy & Religion Ser). 182p. 1979. text ed. 28.50x (ISBN 0-06-492922-1). B&N Imports.

God Bless. (First Prayer Ser.). 2.95 (ISBN 0-86112-195-3, Pub. by Brimax Bks). Borden.

God Builds His Church. Eve B. MacMaster. (Story Bible Ser.: No. 10). (Illus.). 184p. (Orig.). 1987. pap. 5.95 (ISBN 0-8361-3446-X). Herald Pr.

God Calling. A. J. Russell. (Christian Library). 1985. Repr. 6.95 (ISBN 0-916441-22-9). Barbour & Co.

God Calling. A. J. Russell. (Christian Library). 249p. 1986. Repr. leatherette 3.95 (ISBN 0-916441-45-8). Barbour & Co.

God Calling. Ed. by A. J. Russell. 192p. 1972. pap. 3.50 (ISBN 0-8007-8096-5, Spire Bks). Revell.

God Calling. Ed. by A. J. Russell. 208p. 1987. pap. 3.50 (ISBN 0-515-09026-3). Jove Pubns.

God Calling: A Devotional Diary. Ed. by Arthur J. Russell. 10.95 (ISBN 0-396-02621-4). Dodd.

God Can. Einar H. Mickelson. (Illus.). 301p. 1966. 2.50 (ISBN 0-87509-086-9). Chr Pubns.

God Can Be Trusted. Elizabeth Goldsmith. 1974. pap. 3.95 (ISBN 0-903843-85-4). OMF Bks.

God Can Do Anything-Bible Miracles. Compiled by Patricia Mahany. (Story & Color Bks.). (Illus.). 64p. (Orig.). 1984. pap. 2.95 (ISBN 0-87239-796-3, 2372). Standard Pub.

God, Can I Get to Know You. Keith Huttenlocker. 1979. pap. 3.95 (ISBN 0-87162-211-4, D3810). Warner Pr.

God Cares, Vol. 1. C. Mervyn Maxwell. 1981. pap. 9.95 (ISBN 0-8163-0390-8). Pacific Pr Pub Assn.

God Cares, Vol. 2. 2nd, rev. ed. 1985. pap. 14.95 (ISBN 0-8163-0611-7). Pacific Pr Pub Assn.

God Cares for Everybody, Everywhere. Alan T. Dale. (Rainbow Books (Bible Story Books for Children)). (Orig.). 1978. pap. 1.00 (ISBN 0-8192-1237-7). Morehouse.

God Cares for Me. Lynn Groth. (Cradle Roll Program Ser.). 8p. (Orig.). pap. 1.25 (ISBN 0-938272-75-6). Wels Board.

God Cares for Timothy. Margaret Anne Hooks. 1982. 6.95 (ISBN 0-686-36253-5). Rod & Staff.

God Cares for You. Richard Dayringer. LC 83-70210. (Orig.). 1984. pap. 5.95 (ISBN 0-8054-5232-X). Broadman.

God Cares When I Do Something Stupid. Elspeth Murphy. (God's Word in My Heart Ser.). (Illus.). 24p. 1984. pap. 2.95 (ISBN 0-89191-792-6). Cook.

God Cares When I Need to Talk to Somebody. Elspeth Murphy. (God's Word in My Heart Ser.). (Illus.). 24p. 1984. pap. 2.95 (ISBN 0-89191-887-6). Cook.

God Cares When I'm Disappointed. Elspeth C. Murphy. (God's Word in my Heart Ser.). (Illus.). 1983. 2.95 (ISBN 0-89191-725-X). Cook.

God Cares When I'm Sorry. Elspeth C. Murphy. (God's Word in My Heart Ser.). (Illus.). 1983. 2.95 (ISBN 0-89191-724-1). Cook.

God Cares When I'm Worried. Elspeth C. Murphy. LC 82-73572. (God's Word in My Heart Ser.). (Illus.). 1983. 2.95 (ISBN 0-89191-723-3). Cook.

God Cares When Somebody Hurts Me. Elspeth Murphy. (God's Word in My Heart Ser.). (Illus.). 24p. 1984. pap. 2.95 (ISBN 0-89191-790-X). Cook.

God Centered Evangelism. R. B. Kuiper. 1978. pap. 5.45 (ISBN 0-85151-110-4). Banner of Truth.

God-Centered Therapy. F. Bernadette Turner. 1968. pap. 4.95 (ISBN 0-8315-0182-0). Speller.

God-Christ-Church: A Practical Approach to Process Theology. Marjorie Suchocki. 224p. 1982. pap. 10.95 (ISBN 0-8245-0464-X). Crossroad NY.

God Comes to America: Father Divine & the Peace Mission Movement. Kenneth E. Burnham. 167p. 1979. 16.95x (ISBN 0-931186-01-3). Lambeth Pr.

God Comes to Nashville. Darryl E. Hicks. LC 79-89583. 1979. pap. 3.50 (ISBN 0-89221-065-6). New Leaf.

God Comforts His People. Eve B. MacHaster. LC 95-835. (Story Bible Ser: No. 7). (Illus.). 176p. (Orig.). 1985. pap. 5.95 (ISBN 0-8361-3393-5). Herald Pr.

God Comforts His People: Activity Book. Suzanne Kauffman. (Story Bible Ser.). (Illus.). 84p. (Orig.). 1986. pap. 3.00 (ISBN 0-8361-3411-7). Herald Pr.

God Created Me Too! Dot Cachiaras. (Happy Day Bks.). (Illus.). 32p. 1987. 1.59 (ISBN 0-87403-274-1, 3774). Standard Pub.

God Day by Day, Vol. 1: Lent & the Easter Season. Marcel Bastin et al. 320p. (Orig.). 1984. pap. 10.95 (ISBN 0-8091-2642-7). Paulist Pr.

God Day by Day, Vol. 2: Ordinary Time: Matthew. Marcel Bastin et al. 576p. (Orig.). 1984. pap. 14.95 (ISBN 0-8091-2643-5). Paulist Pr.

God Day by Day, Vol. 4: Advent & Christmas. Marcel Bastin et al. 184p. (Orig.). 1985. pap. 8.95 (ISBN 0-8091-2699-0). Paulist Pr.

God Demands Doctrinal Preaching. Ed. by Thomas B. Warren & Garland Elkins. 1978. pap. 9.00 (ISBN 0-934916-32-2). Natl Christian Pr.

God Did Not Create Sickness or Disease. Joe M. Parkhill. 160p. (Orig.). 1983. pap. text ed. 6.95 (ISBN 0-936744-05-7). Country Bazaar.

God Dwells with His People. Paul Zehr. LC 80-22701. 216p. 1981. pap. 7.95 (ISBN 0-8361-1939-8). Herald Pr.

God Encountered, Vol. 1. David A. Clemens. LC 79-52420. (Steps to Maturity Ser.). 1973. tchrs'. manual 17.95x (ISBN 0-86508-002-X); student's manual 15.95x (ISBN 0-86508-001-1); visuals packett 4.95x (ISBN 0-86508-007-0). BCM Intl Inc.

God Even Likes My Pantry: Devotions for Dieters. Mab G. Hoover. 128p. 1983. pap. 3.95 (ISBN 0-310-47012-9, 11269P). Zondervan.

God: Experience or Origin? Ed. by Antonio T. De Nicolas & Evanghelos Moutsopolous. (God Ser.). 256p. (Orig.). 1986. 21.95 (ISBN 0-913757-24-1, Pub. by New Era Bks); pap. 12.95 (ISBN 0-913757-25-X, Pub. by New Era Bks). Paragon Hse.

God Face to Face. Lewis Machlachlan. 160p. 1968. pap. 2.95 (ISBN 0-227-67728-5). Attic Pr.

God, Family, Country: Our Three Great Loyalties. Ezra Taft Benson. LC 74-84477. 437p. 1974. 11.95 (ISBN 0-87747-541-5). Deseret Bk.

God First: What It Means to Love God Above All Things. Ken Wilson. (Living As a Christian Ser.). 85p. 1980. pap. 2.50 (ISBN 0-89283-089-1). Servant.

God Flows Within You. Grover Thornsberry. 152p. pap. 7.95 (ISBN 0-942494-39-3). Coleman Pub.

God for a Dark Journey. George Aschenbrenner. 1984. pap. 5.95 (ISBN 0-87193-211-3). Dimension Bks.

God for Nothing. Richard MacKenna. 186p. 1986. 12.95 (ISBN 0-285-62623-X, Pub. Souvenir Pr Ltd UK). Intl Spec Bk.

God, Freedom, & Evil. Alvin Plantinga. 1978. pap. 7.95 (ISBN 0-8028-1731-9). Eerdmans.

God, Freedom & Immortality: A Critical Analysis. Antony Flew. LC 84-42543. 183p. 1984. pap. text ed. 10.95 (ISBN 0-87975-251-3). Prometheus Bks.

God Given Territory. Jackie Burgus. 96p. 1986. pap. 2.95 (ISBN 0-938612-13-1). Revival Press.

God Gives Me a Smile. Debby Anderson. LC 85-71985. (Illus.). 24p. 1985. comb bdg. 3.95 (ISBN 0-89191-669-5, 56697). Cook.

God Gives the Land. Eve Macmaster. LC 83-182. (Story Bible Ser.: Vol. 3). (Illus.). 168p. (Orig.). 1983. pap. 5.95 (ISBN 0-8361-3332-3). Herald Pr.

God Gives the Land Activity Book. Suzanne Kauffman. (Story Bible Ser.: Bk. 3). 64p. 1984. pap. 3.00 (ISBN 0-8361-3359-5). Herald Pr.

God Gives Us Seasons. Dot Cachiaras. (Happy Day Bks.). (Illus.). 24p. 1984. 1.59 (ISBN 0-87239-732-7, 3702). Standard Pub.

God Giveth Strength. Harry Hoffs. pap. 0.45 (ISBN 0-686-23472-3). Rose Pub MI.

God, Goods & the Common Good: Eleven Perspectives on Economic Justice in Dialog with the Roman Catholic Bishops' Pastoral Letter. Ed. by Charles P. Lutz. 160p. (Orig.). 1987. pap. 9.95 (ISBN 0-8066-2286-5, 10-2563). Augsburg.

God, Grant Me Serenity. Compiled by Gladys Pucillo. 1982. 4.95 (ISBN 0-8378-2030-8). Gibson.

God Guides Us. Sr. Mary Bothwell. (Christ Our Life Ser). (Illus.). 1981. pap. text ed. 4.60 (ISBN 0-8294-0365-5); tchr's ed. 12.95 (ISBN 0-8294-0366-3). Loyola.

God Guides Your Tomorrows. Rev. ed. Roger C. Palms. LC 86-27688. 96p. 1987. pap. 2.95 (ISBN 0-87784-572-7). Inter Varsity.

God, Guilt & Death: An Existential Phenomenology of Religion. Merold Westphal. LC 83-48525. (Studies in Phenomenology & Existential Philosophy). 320p. 1987. 27.50x (ISBN 0-253-32586-2); pap. 9.95 (ISBN 0-253-32586-2). Ind U Pr.

God Has a Better Idea: The Home. Roy R. Roberts. pap. 4.95 (ISBN 0-88469-023-7). BMH Bks.

God Has a Story Too: Biblical Sermons in Context. James A. Sanders. LC 77-15244. 160p. 1979. pap. 6.95 (ISBN 0-8006-1353-8, 1-1353). Fortress.

God Has Given Us Every Good Thing. 7.95 (ISBN 0-317-46978-9). CSA Pr.

God Has Many Names. John Hick. LC 82-1959. 140p. 1982. pap. 8.95 (ISBN 0-664-24419-X). Westminster.

God Has Spoken. rev. ed. J. I. Packer. LC 80-7789. (Orig.). 1980. pap. 4.95 (ISBN 0-87784-656-1). Inter-Varsity.

God Hears Me When I Pray. Elspeth C. Murphy. (Hardcover Psalm Books for Children). (Illus.). 96p. 1985. 7.95 (ISBN 0-89191-645-8, 56457). Cook.

God Helps David. Marjorie Palmer. (My Bible Story Reader Ser.: Vol. 1). (Illus.). 1983. pap. 1.95 (ISBN 0-8024-0191-0). Moody.

God Helps Me Everyday. Elspeth C. Murphy. (Hardcover Psalm Books for Children). (Illus.). 96p. 1985. 7.95 (ISBN 0-89191-642-3, 56424). Cook.

God, His Prophets & His Children. M. R. Bawa Muhaiyaddeen. LC 78-12891. (Illus.). 1978. pap. 5.95 (ISBN 0-914390-09-0). Fellowship Pr PA.

God: History & the Old Testament. Dennis Baly. LC 76-9984. 256p. 1976. pap. 10.95x (ISBN 0-06-060369-0, RD 186, HarpR). Har-Row.

God Hunt: A Discovery Book for Boys & Girls. Karen Mains & David Mains. LC 84-14204. (Illus.). 1984. Spiral 3.95 (ISBN 0-89191-886-8, 58867). Cook.

God Hunt: A Discovery Book for Men & Women. David Mains & Karen Mains. 1984. spiral wkbk. 4.95 (ISBN 0-89191-813-2, 58131). Cook.

God-Idea of the Ancients: Or Sex in Religion. Eliza B. Gamble. LC 79-66997. 339p. 1981. Repr. of 1897 ed. 30.00 (ISBN 0-8305-0110-X). Hyperion Conn.

God-Illuminated Cook: The Practice of the Presence of God. Brother Lawrence. Ed. by Robin Dawes. LC 74-84399. (Illus.). 144p. 1975. pap. 2.50 (ISBN 0-914896-00-8, Strength). East Ridge Pr.

God-Illuminated Cook: The Practice of the Presence of God. Brother Lawrence. (East Ridge Press Ser.). (Illus.). 1980. pap. 4.50 (ISBN 0-89345-217-3). Garber Comm.

God I'm Suffering, Are You Listening. Jack Van Impe. 36p. 1985. pap. 1.95 (ISBN 0-934803-00-5). J Van Impe.

God in a Nutshell. C. Alan Anderson. (Illus.). 28p. (Orig.). 1981. pap. 3.00 (ISBN 0-9607532-0-6). Squantum Pr.

God in a Rolls Royce. facsimile ed. John Hoshor. LC 70-170698. (Black Heritage Library Collection). Repr. of 1936 ed. 15.00 (ISBN 0-8369-8888-4). Ayer Co Pubs.

God in Advaita. A. G. Warrier. 1977. text ed. 15.00x (ISBN 0-8426-1047-2). Verry.

God in Africa. Malcolm McVeigh. 1982. 20.00 (ISBN 0-686-96557-4). Branden Pub Co.

God in America: Religion & Politics in the United States. Furio Colombo. Tr. by Kristin Jarrat from Ital. LC 84-4278. 208p. 1984. 20.00x (ISBN 0-231-05972-8). Columbia U Pr.

God in Christ. Horace Bushnell. LC 76-39568. Repr. of 1849 ed. 25.00 (ISBN 0-404-01245-0). AMS Pr.

God in Christ: Hartford, 1849. Horace Bushnell. Ed. by Bruce Kuklick. (American Religious Thought of the 18th & 19th Centuries Ser.). 356p. 1987. lib. bdg. 50.00 (ISBN 0-8240-6964-1). Garland Pub.

God in Contemporary Thought. Ed. by Sebastian A. Matczak. LC 75-31391. 1119p. 1977. 55.00 (ISBN 0-910621-25-X). Rose Sharon Pr.

God in Contemporary Thought: A Philosophical Perspective. Ed. by Sebastian A. Matczak. LC 75-31391. (Philosophical Questions Ser.: No. 10). 1977. 65.00x (ISBN 0-912116-12-9). Learned Pubns.

God in Creation: A New Theology of Creation & the Spirit of God. Jurgen Moltman. LC 85-42785. 384p. 1985. 25.45 (ISBN 0-06-065899-1, HarpR). Har-Row.

God in Exile: Modern Atheism. Cornelio Fabro. Tr. by Arthur Gibson. LC 68-20846. 1272p. 1968. slipcase 35.00 (ISBN 0-8091-0053-3). Paulist Pr.

God in Fragments. Jaques Pohier. 384p. 1986. 22.50 (ISBN 0-8245-0744-4). Crossroad NY.

God in Greek Philosophy to the Time of Socrates. Roy K. Hack. 1970. Repr. of 1931 ed. lib. bdg. 12.50 (ISBN 0-8337-1514-3). B Franklin.

God in Love: The Sexual Revolution of John Humphrey Noyes. Truman Nelson. write for info (ISBN 0-393-01636-6). Norton.

God in Modern Philosophy. James D. Collins. LC 77-25963. 1978. Repr. of 1959 ed. lib. bdg. 32.75x (ISBN 0-313-20079-3, COGM). Greenwood.

God in Our Hearts: Meditations from the Orthodox Church in Russia. 1987. pap. 9.95. Friend Pr.

God in Our Midst: Seeking & Receiving Ongoing Revival. James I. Packer. (Christian Essentials Ser.). 48p. (Orig.). 1987. pap. 1.95 (ISBN 0-89283-327-0). Servant.

God in Phychiatry. Thomas Hora. (Discoures in Metapsychistry Ser.). 35p. 1984. pap. 4.00 (ISBN 0-913105-06-6). PAGL Pr.

God in Search of Man: A Philosophy of Judaism. Abraham J. Heschel. 464p. 1976. pap. 10.95 (ISBN 0-374-51331-7). FS&G.

God in Search of Man: Philosophy of Judaism. Abraham J. Heschel. 437p. 1987. Repr. of 1955 ed. 30.00 (ISBN 0-87668-955-1). Aronson.

God in the American Schools: Religious Education in a Pluralistic Society. Grant E. De Forest. (Illus.). 1979. 49.50 (ISBN 0-89266-181-X). Am Classical Coll Pr.

God in the Bush is Worth Two in the Hand. George H. Harper. (Bible Adventure Ser.). 216p. (Orig.). 1985. pap. 5.95 (ISBN 0-934318-48-4). Falcon Pr MT.

God in the Dock. C. S. Lewis. Ed. by Walter Hooper. 1970. pap. 8.95 (ISBN 0-8028-1456-5). Eerdmans.

God in the Hard Times. Dale E. Rogers. LC 85-10479. 160p. 1985. pap. 8.95 (ISBN 0-8027-2516-3). Walker & Co.

God in the High Country. Otis D. Richardson. 1980. 10.00 (ISBN 0-682-49644-8). Exposition Pr FL.

God in the Midst of Every Day: Reflections on Li_'s Simple Gifts. Ruth Hackman. LC 86-7888. (Illus.). 128p. 1986. kivar paper 6.50 (ISBN 0-8066-2207-5, 10-2643). Augsburg.

God in the Present Tense. D. Shelby Corlett. 176p. 1974. 1.95 (ISBN 0-8341-0248-X). Beacon Hill.

God in the Teachings of Conservative Judaism. Seymour Siegel & Elliot Gertel. 278p. 1985. 20.00 (ISBN 0-88125-066-X). Ktav.

God in Three Persons. E. Calvin Beisner. 180p. 1984. pap. 5.95 (ISBN 0-8423-1073-8); 2.95 (ISBN 0-8423-1074-6). Tyndale.

God in Three Persons. Carl Brumback. 192p. 1959. pap. 4.95 (ISBN 0-87148-354-8). Pathway Pr.

God in You, to You, & for You. Marilyn Hickey. 199p. (Orig.). 1983. pap. text ed. 4.95 (ISBN 0-914307-13-4, Dist. by Harrison Hse). Word Faith.

God: Incidences or Divine Providence. Mary Light. 1975. pap. 1.00 (ISBN 0-910924-69-4). Macalester.

God-Inspired Orthodox Julian Calendar VS. the False Gregorian Papal Calendar. Kallistos Makris. Tr. by Jerry Vlesmas from Hellenic. 118p. (Orig.). 1971. pap. 3.25x (ISBN 0-938366-36-X). Orthodox Chr.

God Is. John Bisagno. 1981. 4.95 (ISBN 0-88207-345-1). Victor Bks.

God Is a Matchmaker. Derek Prince & Ruth Prince. 1986. pap. 5.95 (ISBN 0-8007-9058-8, B35). Revell.

God Is a Sea: The Dynamics of Christian Living. David Walker. LC 81-8072. 144p. (Orig.). 1981. pap. 5.95 (ISBN 0-8189-0420-8). Alba.

God Is All. Lillian De Waters. pap. 0.95 (ISBN 0-686-05711-2). L De Waters.

God Is Always Near. Shirley Jennings. Ed. by Michael L. Sherer. (Orig.). 1987. pap. 5.95 (ISBN 0-89536-857-9, 7816). CSS of Ohio.

God Is Calling His People to Forgiveness. Gene Lilly. 1977. pap. 3.95 (ISBN 0-917726-15-4). Hunter Bks.

God Is Enough. Hannah W. Smith. Ed. by Melvin Dieter & Hallie Dieter. 320p. 1986. 10.95 (ISBN 0-310-46260-6). Zondervan.

God Is Everywhere: Fifteen Stories to Help Children Know God. Compiled by Theresa Hayes. (Illus.). 80p. 1986. 7.95 (ISBN 0-87403-097-8, 3617). Standard Pub.

God Is Fabulous. Frances Hunter. 1978. pap. 3.25 (ISBN 0-87162-115-0). Hunter Bks.

God Is Faithful. Julius R. Scruggs. 96p. 1985. pap. 6.95 (ISBN 0-8170-1060-2). Judson.

God Is Faithful. Velma D. Stevens. LC 86-921. 1986. pap. 3.25 (ISBN 0-8054-5028-9). Broadman.

God Is for the Alcoholic. Jerry G. Dunn. Tr. of Deus e a Favor do Alcoolatra. 1986. write for info. (ISBN 0-8297-1610-6). Life Pubs Intl.

God Is for the Alcoholic. rev. ed. Jerry G. Dunn & Bernard Palmer. pap. 6.95 (ISBN 0-8024-3284-0). Moody.

God Is Gay: An Evolutionary Spiritual Work. 2nd, rev. ed. Ezekiel Wright & Daniel Inesse. 1982. pap. 4.95 (ISBN 0-934350-01-9). Tayu Pr.

God Is Good. Sr. Mary De Angelis Bothwell. LC 73-5752. (Christ Our Life Ser.). (Illus.). 138p. 1986. pap. text ed. 4.20 (ISBN 0-8294-0537-2); 12.95 (ISBN 0-8294-0570-4). Loyola.

God Is Great, God Is Good: I'd Believe Him If I Could. Michael Griffiths. LC 86-62368. Orig. Title: Down to Earth God. 170p. 1987. pap. 4.50 (ISBN 0-89109-468-7). NavPress.

God Is Greater. Rick Benjamin & Jim Richardson. 1983. pap. 1.75 (ISBN 0-911739-00-9). Abbott Loop.

God Is Here-Let's Celebrate. Leslie F. Brandt. LC 73-89877. 1969. pap. 2.95 (ISBN 0-570-03102-8, 12-2320). Concordia.

God Is in the Heart: Poetical & Symbolical Essays. M. P. Morantte. (Illus.). 78p. (Orig.). 1982. pap. 4.75 (ISBN 971-10-0040-7, Pub. by New Day Philippines). Cellar.

God Is in the Night. Connie Abrams. (Happy Day Bks.). (Illus.). 24p. 1984. 1.59 (ISBN 0-87239-733-5, 3703). Standard Pub.

God Is Light. Foster H. Shannon. LC 80-83606. (Illus.). 240p. (Orig.). 1981. pap. 6.95 (ISBN 0-938462-00-8). Green Leaf CA.

God Is Like: Three Parables for Little Children. Julie Walters & Barbara De Leu. (Illus.). 96p. 1974. pap. 1.95 (ISBN 0-87793-073-2). Ave Maria.

God Is Love: A Study in the Theology of Karl Rahner. Mark L. Taylor. (AAR-Academy Ser.). 1986. 24.95 (ISBN 0-89130-925-X, 01-01-50); pap. 18.25 (ISBN 0-89130-926-8). Scholars Pr GA.

God is Love: Communion Addresses. J. W. Alexander. 368p. 1985. pap. 5.95 (ISBN 0-85151-459-6). Banner of Truth.

God Is My Best Friend. Beverly C. Burgess. (Illus.). 32p. (Orig.). 1986. pap. 1.98 (ISBN 0-89274-293-3). Harrison Hse.

God Is My Co-Pilot. Illus. by Charles Nicholas. LC 78-50959. (Contemporary Motivators Ser.). (Illus.). 1978. pap. text ed. 1.95 (ISBN 0-88301-302-9). Pendulum Pr.

God Is My Fuehrer. Gordon C. Bennett. (Orig.). 1970. pap. 1.50 (ISBN 0-377-80611-0). Friend Pr.

God Is My Witness: The Story of the World-Famous Healer. E. G. Fricker. LC 76-50557. 1977. pap. 2.75 (ISBN 0-8128-7068-9). Stein & Day.

God Is New Each Moment: Conversations with Huub Oosterhuis & Piet Hoogeveen. Edward Schillebeeckx. LC 83-614. 160p. (Orig.). 1983. pap. 7.95 (ISBN 0-8164-2475-6, HarpR). Har-Row.

God Is Not a Gentleman & I Am That One. Da F. John. LC 83-73178. 1983. 6.95 (ISBN 0-913922-85-4). Dawn Horse Pr.

God Is Not for Sale. Bhagwan Shree Rajneesh. Ed. by Ma Yoga Pratima. LC 82-244555. (Initiation Talks Ser.). (Illus.). 450p. (Orig.). 1978. 18.95 (ISBN 0-88050-067-0). Chidvilas Found.

God Is Not Hiding. Garth Hunt. 1974. pap. 0.95 (ISBN 0-87509-087-7). Chr Pubns.

God Is Now Here. Sri Surath. 1976. 5.00 (ISBN 0-685-58439-9). Ranney Pubns.

God Is On Your Side: Fifteen Stories to Help Young Children Trust God. Compiled by Theresa Hayes. (Illus.). 80p. 1986. 7.95 (ISBN 0-87403-096-X, 3616). Standard Pub.

God Is Otherwise Engaged. Edward S. Silber. 317p. 1984. 10.95 (ISBN 0-89697-158-9). Intl Univ Pr.

God Is Our Mother: Julian of Norwich & the Medieval Image of Christian Feminine Divinity. Jennifer P. Heimmel. Ed. by James Hogg. (Elizabethan & Renaissance Studies). 111p. (Orig.). 1982. pap. 15.00 (ISBN 0-317-40145-9, Pub by Salzburg Studies). Longwood Pub Group.

God Is Red. Vine Deloria, Jr. 1983. pap. 3.95 (ISBN 0-440-33044-0, LE). Dell.

God Is Still My Co-Pilot. Robert L. Scott, Jr. 1967. 25.00 (ISBN 0-317-17716-8). Beachcomber Bks.

God Is the Answer. Dana Gattin. 1984. 5.95 (ISBN 0-317-03625-4). Unity School.

God Is the Greatest. Debby Anderson. LC 85-71986. (Illus.). 24p. 1985. comb bdg. 3.95 (ISBN 0-89191-673-3, 56739). Cook.

God Is with Me. Debby Anderson. (Happy Day Bks.). (Illus.). 24p. 1984. 1.39 (ISBN 0-87239-734-3, 3704). Standard Pub.

God Is with Me. Debby Anderson. (Sparklers Ser.). 1986. comb binding 2.95 (ISBN 0-89191-269-X, Chariot Bks). Cook.

God Is with You. Swami Muktananda. (Illus.). 40p. (Orig.). 1978. pap. 1.75 (ISBN 0-914602-57-8). SYDA Found.

God, I've Got to Talk to You Again! Carr & Paquet. LC 59-1315. (Arch Bks.). 24p. (Orig.). 1985. pap. 0.99 (ISBN 0-570-06197-0, 59-1315). Concordia.

God, Jesus & Belief: The Legacy of Theism. Stewart R. Sutherland. 160p. 1984. 29.95x (ISBN 0-631-13548-0); pap. 12.95 (ISBN 0-631-13591-X). Basil Blackwell.

God Keeps His Promise: A Bible Story Book for Young Children. Cornelia Lehn. LC 76-90377. (Illus.). 1970. 11.95x (ISBN 0-87303-291-8). Faith & Life.

God Kind of Faith for Total Prosperity. Jim Wahlie. 61p. 1986. pap. 3.95 (ISBN 0-88144-049-3). Christian Pub.

God Knows Everything. Elaine Watson. (Happy Day Bks.). (Illus.). 24p. 1986. 1.59 (ISBN 0-87403-025-0, 3485). Standard Pub.

God Knows You. Elizabeth E. Watson. LC 81-50678. (Happy Day Bks.). (Illus.). 24p. (Orig.). 1981. pap. 1.59 (ISBN 0-87239-463-8, 3596). Standard Pub.

God Laments & Our Response. Basilea Schlink. Tr. of Gott Klagt und Unsere Antwort. 64p. 1981. 0.50 (ISBN 3-87209-625-7). Evang Sisterhood Mary.

God-List in the Treaty Between Hannibal & Philip V of Macedonia: A Study in Light of the Ancient Near Eastern Treaty Tradition. Michael Barre. LC 82-13961. (Near Eastern Studies). 208p. 1983. text ed. 26.00x (ISBN 0-8018-2787-6). Johns Hopkins.

God Love You. Fulton J. Sheen. LC 80-23085. 224p. 1981. pap. 4.50 (ISBN 0-385-17486-1, Im). Doubleday.

God-Lover's Earth-Heaven Life. 1974. 2.00 (ISBN 0-88497-187-2). Aum Pubns.

God Loves Children. Barbara Hughes & Gwen Dwiggins. (God Loves...Coloring Book Ser.). (Illus.). 0.75 (ISBN 0-8091-6562-7). Paulist Pr.

God Loves Colors. Barbara Hughes & Gwen Dwiggins. (God Loves...Coloring Book Ser.). (Illus.). 0.60 (ISBN 0-8091-6566-X). Paulist Pr.

God Loves Even Me. Debby Anderson. (Happy Day Bks.). (Illus.). 24p. 1985. 1.59 (ISBN 0-87239-873-0, 3673). Standard Pub.

God Loves Fun. Barbara Hughes & Gwen Dwiggins. (God Loves...Coloring Book Ser.). (Illus.). 0.75t (ISBN 0-8091-6564-3). Paulist Pr.

God Loves His People. (Christ Our Life Ser.). 1982. text ed. 4.60 (ISBN 0-8294-0398-1); tchrs. ed 9.95 (ISBN 0-8294-0399-X). Loyola.

God Loves Laughter. William Sears. 182p. 1960. o.p. (ISBN 0-85398-018-7); pap. 6.95 (ISBN 0-85398-019-5). G Ronald Pub.

God Loves Love. Barbara Hughes & Gwen Dwiggins. (God Loves...Coloring Book Ser.). (Illus.). 0.60 (ISBN 0-8091-6565-1). Paulist Pr.

God Loves Me. Bartholomew. 1982. pap. 0.85 (ISBN 0-570-04073-6, 56-1376). Concordia.

God Loves Me. Daughters of St. Paul. 1982. pap. 1.95 (ISBN 0-8198-3032-1); tchr's. manual 3.95 (ISBN 0-8198-3031-3). Dghtrs St Paul.

God Loves Me. Florrie A. Lawton. LC 85-24342. (Bible & Me Ser.). (Illus.). 1986. 5.95 (ISBN 0-8054-4163-8). Broadman.

God Loves Me! 8 Lessons, Vol. 1. Linda M. Geiger. (Steps of Faith for Special Children Ser.). 1981. kit 19.95x (ISBN 0-86508-045-3); text ed. 4.95x (ISBN 0-86508-046-1). BCM Intl Inc.

God Loves Seasons. Barbara Hughes & Gwen Dwiggins. (God Loves...Coloring Book Ser.). (Illus.). 0.75t (ISBN 0-8091-6563-5). Paulist Pr.

God Loves the Arabs Too. Louis Hamada. Ed. by Helen Graves. LC 85-40888. 174p. 1986. 13.95 (ISBN 1-55523-044-X); pap. 10.95 (ISBN 1-55523-000-8). Winston-Derek.

God Loves Us All. Lawrence G. Lovasik. (Saint Joseph Picture Bks.). (Illus.). flexible bdg. 0.95 (ISBN 0-89942-282-9, 282). Catholic Bk Pub.

God Loves You. Catherine Marshall. 1973. pap. 0.95 (ISBN 0-380-01221-9, 14712). Avon.

God Made. (First Prayer Ser.). 2.95 (ISBN 0-86112-219-4, Pub. by Brimax Bks). Borden.

God Made Animals. (Baby's First Cloth Bks.). 6p. 1.98 (ISBN 0-8307-0814-6, 5608003). Regal.

God Made Birds. Yvonne Patterson. LC 82-62730. (Happy Day Bks.). (Illus.). 24p. 1983. 1.59 (ISBN 0-87239-634-7, 3554). Standard Pub.

God Made Chickens. Marian Bennett. (Happy Day Bks.). (Illus.). 24p. 1985. 1.59 (ISBN 0-87239-874-9, 3674). Standard Pub.

God Made Everything. Debra Stuckey. (God's Creature Ser.). (Illus.). 4.95 (ISBN 0-570-04109-0, 56-1484). Concordia.

God Made Everything. Beverly W. Wright. LC 82-80029. (Happy Day Bks.). (Illus.). 24p. (Orig.). 1982. pap. 1.59 (ISBN 0-87239-537-5, 3583). Standard Pub.

God Made Families. Debra K. Stuckey. (God's Creature Ser.). (Illus.). 24p. 1986. 4.95 (ISBN 0-570-04118-X). Concordia.

God Made Farm Animals. Sue T. Hayes. (Happy Day Bks.). (Illus.). 24p. 1984. 1.59 (ISBN 0-87239-735-1, 3705). Standard Pub.

God Made Fish. Yvonne Patterson. (Happy Day Bks.). (Illus.). 24p. 1986. 1.59 (ISBN 0-87403-026-9, 3486). Standard Pub.

God Made Food. (Baby's First Cloth Bks.). 6p. 1981. 1.98 (ISBN 0-8307-0815-4, 5608017). Regal.

God Made Kids Classroom Coloring Book. Ed. by Patricia Mahany. (Classroom Activities Bks.). (Illus.). 96p. (Orig.). 1982. pap. 2.95 (ISBN 0-87239-500-6, 2331). Standard Pub.

God Made Known. Mervyn A. Warren. Ed. by Gerald Wheeler. LC 83-17677. (Illus.). 94p. (Orig.). 1983. pap. 5.95 (ISBN 0-8280-0230-4). Review & Herald.

God Made Me. Ed. by Marian Bennett. (My Shape Book Ser.). (Illus.). 10p. 1985. 2.95 (ISBN 0-87239-908-7, 2748). Standard Pub.

God Made Me. Linda Boyer. LC 81-50677. (Happy Day Bks.). (Illus.). 24p. (Orig.). 1981. pap. 1.59 (ISBN 0-87239-464-6, 3597). Standard Pub.

God Made Me. (Baby's First Cloth Bks.). 6p. 1981. 1.98 (ISBN 0-8307-0816-2, 5608021). Regal.

God Made Me. Saundria Keck. LC 86-17572. (Bible & Me Ser.). 1987. 5.95 (ISBN 0-8054-4173-5). Broadman.

God Made Me. Debra Stuckey. (God's Creature Ser.). (Illus.). 1985. 4.95 (ISBN 0-570-04108-2, 56-1483). Concordia.

God Made Me Special. K. K. Stewart. LC 82-62731. (Happy Day Bks.). (Illus.). 24p. 1983. 1.59 (ISBN 0-87239-635-5, 3555). Standard Pub.

God Made Me Special Even Before I Was Born. Ginger A. Fulton. (Illus., Orig.). 1986. pap. 2.95 (ISBN 0-8024-3011-2). Moody.

God Made Only One Me. Gail Robinson. 32p. 1986. 4.95 (ISBN 0-570-04148-1). Concordia.

God Made Our World. (Baby's First Cloth Bks.). 6p. 1982. 1.98 (ISBN 0-8307-0817-0, 5608036). Regal.

God Made Prayer. Debra K. Stuckey. (God Made Ser.). (Illus.). 24p. 1985. 4.95 (ISBN 0-570-04117-1, 56-1528). Concordia.

God Made the One & Only Me. Barbara Linville. LC 76-8737. (Illus.). 1976. pap. text ed. 3.95 (ISBN 0-916406-28-8). Accent Bks.

God Made the Sea, the Sand & Me. Elizabeth E. Watson. (Illus.). 1979. 4.95 (ISBN 0-8054-4254-5, 4242-54). Broadman.

God Made Them Great. John Tallach. 144p. 1982. pap. 5.45 (ISBN 0-85151-190-2). Banner of Truth.

God, Make Me Brave for Life. Allen E. Zimmer. LC 81-69110. (Illus.). 128p. (Orig.). 1981. pap. 4.95 (ISBN 0-89505-057-9, 21052). Argus Comm.

God Makers. Ed Decker & Dave Hunt. LC 83-82319. 192p. 1984. pap. 6.95 (ISBN 0-89081-402-3). Harvest Hse.

God Makers. Frank Herbert. 1983. pap. 2.95 (ISBN 0-425-06388-7, Medallion). Berkley Pub.

God Makes Me His Child in Baptism. Janet Wittenback. LC 85-7689. 24p. 1985. pap. 2.95 (ISBN 0-570-04126-0, 56-1537). Concordia.

God Makes the Rivers to Flow: Passages for Meditation. Ed. by Eknath Easwaran. (Illus.). 96p. 1982. 12.00 (ISBN 0-915132-28-1); pap. 7.00 (ISBN 0-915132-29-X). Nilgiri Pr.

God, Man & Atomic War. Samuel H. Dresner. 6.95 (ISBN 0-87677-007-3). Hartmore.

God, Man & Epic Poetry: A Study in Comparative Literature, 2 Vols. Harold V. Routh. LC 69-10152. (Illus.). 1968. Repr. of 1927 ed. lib. bdg. 37.50x (ISBN 0-8371-0206-5, ROEP). Greenwood.

God, Man & Salvation. Richard Taylor & Willard Taylor. 724p. 1977. 16.95 (ISBN 0-8341-0440-7). Beacon Hill.

God, Man & State. Kathleen Freeman. LC 79-101039. 1969. Repr. of 1952 ed. 27.50x (ISBN 0-8046-0705-2, Pub. by Kennikat). Assoc Faculty Pr.

God, Man & State: Greek Concepts. Kathleen Freeman. Repr. of 1952 ed. lib. bdg. 27.50x (ISBN 0-8371-2821-8, FRGM). Greenwood.

God, Man & the Church. Vladimir Solovyev. Tr. by Donald Attwater from Rus. 192p. 1975. 10.95 (ISBN 0-227-67690-4). Attic Pr.

God, Man & the Planetary Age: Preface for a Theistic Humanism. Nicolas Yonker. LC 78-4233. 168p. 1978. 11.00x (ISBN 0-87071-322-1). Oreg St U Pr.

God-Man-Land. Paul Paetkau et al. LC 78-55244. 1978. 5.25 (ISBN 0-87303-008-7). Faith & Life.

God-Man of Galilee. Howard M. Morgan. 1983. pap. 14.95 (ISBN 0-8359-2561-7). Reston.

God-Man of Galilee: Studies in Christian Living. Howard M. Morgan & John C. Morgan. 100p. 1986. Repr. of 1983 ed. 4.95 (ISBN 0-913029-14-9). Stevens Bk Pr.

God-Man: The Life, Journeys & Work of Meher Baba with an Interpretation of His Silence & Spiritual Teaching. C. B. Purdom. LC 72-175960. (Illus.). 464p. 1971. 9.95 (ISBN 0-913078-03-4). Sheriar Pr.

God, Me, & Thee. Marvin Gilbert. (Discovery Bks.). 1980. 1.50 (ISBN 0-88243-841-7, 02-0841); tchr's ed 3.95 (ISBN 0-88243-331-8, 02-0331). Gospel Pub.

God Memorandum. new ed. Og Mandino. LC 80-81145. 112p. 1980. 6.95 (ISBN 0-8119-0337-0). Fell.

God Must Have a Sense of Humor, He Made Aadvarks & Orangutans..., & Me! David Steele. LC 82-84780. (Illus., Orig.). 1983. pap. 6.00 (ISBN 0-937088-09-9). Illum Pr.

God Never Fails. Mary L. Kupferle. 141p. 1983. pap. 4.95 (ISBN 0-87516-513-3). De Vorss.

God Never Said We'd Be Leading at the Half. Dean Spencer & Dean Nelson. 116p. (Orig.). 1980. pap. 2.95 (ISBN 0-8341-0766-X). Beacon Hill.

God of a Hundred Names: Prayers & Meditations from Many Faiths & Cultures. Ed. by Barbara Greene & Victor Gollancz. 304p. 1985. pap. 7.95 (ISBN 0-575-03645-1, Pub. by Gollancz England). David & Charles.

God of All. Claude Stark. 1982. 20.00 (ISBN 0-89007-000-8); pap. 6.00 (ISBN 0-89007-102-0). Branden Pub Co.

God of All Comfort. Hannah W. Smith. (One Evening Christian Classic Ser.). pap. 2.50 (ISBN 0-89107-008-7). Good News.

God of All Comfort. Hannah W. Smith. 1956. pap. 4.50 (ISBN 0-8024-0018-3). Moody.

God of Daniel S: In Search of the American Jew. Alan W. Miller. (Brown Classics in Judaica Ser.). 260p. 1986. pap. text ed. 13.25 (ISBN 0-8191-5047-9). U Pr of Amer.

God of Faith & Reason: Foundations of Christian Theology. Robert Sokolowski. LC 81-19813. 192p. 1982. 15.95 (ISBN 0-268-01006-4); pap. text ed. 6.95 (ISBN 0-268-01007-2). U of Notre Dame Pr.

God of Forgiveness & Healing in the Theology of Karl Rahner. J. Norman King. LC 81-40932. 100p. (Orig.). 1982. lib. bdg. 24.00 (ISBN 0-8191-2237-8); pap. text ed. 8.25 (ISBN 0-8191-2238-6). U Pr of Amer.

God of Fundamentalism & Others Studies. facs. ed. Horace J. Bridges. LC 79-86733. (Essay Index Reprint Ser.). 1925. 19.00 (ISBN 0-8369-1249-7). Ayer Co Pubs.

God of Grace, God of Glory. Fred M. Wood. LC 81-68364. 1982. pap. 4.95 (ISBN 0-8054-1221-2). Broadman.

God of Jesus Christ. rev. ed. Walter Kaspar. 450p. 1986. text ed. 14.95 (ISBN 0-8245-0777-0). Crossroad NY.

God of Jesus Christ. Walter Kasper. 1984. 24.50x (ISBN 0-8245-0629-4). Crossroad NY.

God of Jesus Christ. Joseph Cardinal Ratzinger. Tr. by Robert Cunningham from Fr. Tr. of Dieu de Jesus Christ. 1978. 6.95 (ISBN 0-8199-0697-2). Franciscan Herald.

God of Sarah, Rebekah, & Rachel. Barbara K. Shenk. LC 85-5503. 132p. 1985. 19.95 (ISBN 0-8361-3392-7). Herald Pr.

God of Seasons. Michael Moynahan. LC 79-93127. 1980. pap. text ed. 4.95 (ISBN 0-89390-019-2). Resource Pubns.

God of Shelley & Blake. John H. Clark. (English Literature Ser., No. 33). 1970. Repr. of 1930 ed. lib. bdg. 39.95x (ISBN 0-8383-0342-0). Haskell.

God of Shelley & Blake. John H. Clarke. LC 73-12459. 1973. lib. bdg. 10.00 (ISBN 0-8414-3425-5). Folcroft.

God of the Lowly: Socio-Historical Interpretation of the Bible. Ed. by Willy Schottroff & Wolfgang Stegemann. LC 84-5152. Tr. of Gott der Kleinen Leute. 192p. (Orig.). 1984. pap. 9.95 (ISBN 0-88344-153-5). Orbis Bks.

God of the Machine. Isabel B. Paterson. LC 77-172225. (Right Wing Individualist Tradition in America Ser). 1972. Repr. of 1943 ed. 25.50 (ISBN 0-405-00434-6). Ayer Co Pubs.

God of the Old Testament in Relation to War. Marion J. Rollins. LC 72-176551. (Columbia University. Teachers College. Contributions to Education Ser.: No. 263). Repr. of 1927 ed. 22.50 (ISBN 0-404-55263-3). AMS Pr.

God of the Oppressed. James Cone. 1978. pap. 6.95 (ISBN 0-8164-2607-4, HarpR). Har-Row.

God of the Philosophers. Anthony Kenny. 1979. 26.00x (ISBN 0-19-824594-7). Oxford U Pr.

God of the Poor. Victorio Araya. Tr. by Robert R. Barr from Span. 224p. (Orig.). 1987. 19.95 (ISBN 0-88344-566-2); pap. 9.95 (ISBN 0-88344-565-4). Orbis Bks.

God of the Present Age. Eric Seldon. LC 80-26149. 1981. pap. 9.00 (ISBN 0-8309-0305-4). Herald Hse.

God of the Wilderness. Hermon Pettit & Helen Wessel. LC 84-70119. (Illus.). 176p. 1984. 10.95 (ISBN 0-933082-04-5). Bookmates Intl.

God of Untold Tales. Michael E. Moynahan. LC 79-64823. 1979. pap. 4.95 (ISBN 0-89390-009-5). Resource Pubns.

God on Earth: The Lord's Prayer for Our Time. Will Campbell & Bonnie Campbell. (Illus.). 128p. 1983. pap. 12.95 (ISBN 0-8245-0586-7). Crossroad NY.

God on Our Minds. Patrick Henry & Thomas F. Stransky. LC 81-70593. 176p. 1982. pap. 6.95 (ISBN 0-8006-1600-6, 1-1600). Fortress.

God on Our Minds. Patrick Henry & Thomas F. Stransky. LC 81-70593. 176p. 1982. pap. 6.95 (ISBN 0-8146-1249-0). Liturgical Pr.

God on Our Side: The British Padre in World War I. Michael Moynihan. (Illus.). 196p. 1983. 19.95 (ISBN 0-436-29402-8, Pub. by Secker & Warburg UK). David & Charles.

God Opens the Doors. Bobbie J. Jobe. (Orig.). 1987. pap. 5.95 (ISBN 0-8054-5041-6). Broadman.

God or Beast: Evolution & Human Nature. Robert Claiborne. (Illus.). 1974. 7.95 (ISBN 0-393-06399-2). Norton.

God or Christ: The Excesses of Christocentricity. Jean Milet. LC 81-5566. 288p. 1981. 14.95 (ISBN 0-8245-0104-7). Crossroad NY.

God or Nothing? Daughters of St. Paul. 222p. 1985. 4.00 (ISBN 0-8198-3039-9); pap. 3.00 (ISBN 0-8198-3040-2). Dghtrs St Paul.

God Our Father. Florentin Boudreaux. LC 65-36485. pap. 55.00 (ISBN 0-317-10042-4, 2001664). Bks Demand UMI.

God Our Help. F. Henry Edwards. 1981. pap. 11.00 (ISBN 0-8309-0310-0). Herald Hse.

God Our Loving Enemy. W. Robertt McClelland. LC 81-12680. 160p. 1982. pap. 7.75 (ISBN 0-687-15220-8). Abingdon.

God-Players. Earl Jabay. LC 69-11637. 155p. 1970. pap. 5.95 (ISBN 0-310-26541-X, 9939P). Zondervan.

God Present. Dom G. Lefebvre. 1979. pap. 3.95 (ISBN 0-03-053436-4, HarpR). Har-Row.

God Present As Mystery: A Search for Personal Meaning in Contemporary Theology. James H. Ebner. LC 76-13750. 1976. pap. 5.95 (ISBN 0-88489-084-8). St Marys.

God Provides. Gloria L. Hayes. 64p. 1986. 6.95 (ISBN 0-89962-523-1). Todd & Honeywell.

God Pursues a Priest. George Rich. 60p. (Orig.). 1986. pap. 2.95 (ISBN 0-87227-109-9). Reg Baptist.

God-Realization Journal. Jonathan Murro. (Illus.). 337p. 1975. 10.00 (ISBN 0-917187-16-4). A R C Pub.

God Really Loves You. Norman K. Elliot. 0.50, 3 for 1.00 (ISBN 0-910924-25-2). Macalester.

God, Reason & the Evangelicals: The Case Against Evangelical Rationalism. Nicholas F. Gier. 404p. (Orig.). 1987. lib. bdg. 34.50 (ISBN 0-8191-5812-7); pap. text ed. 19.75 (ISBN 0-8191-5813-5). U Pr of Amer.

God Reigns in China. Leslie T. Lyall. 1985. pap. 4.50 (ISBN 0-340-36199-9). OMF Bks.

God Rejected: A Summary of Atheistic Thought. Maurice De Bona, Jr. LC 75-46088. 1976. 4.95 (ISBN 0-916698-00-9); pap. 2.95 (ISBN 0-916698-01-7). Desserco Pub.

God, Religion, & Family Life. Ed. by David M. Thomas. LC 79-55512. (Marriage & Family Living in Depth Book Ser.). 1979. pap. 2.45 (ISBN 0-87029-156-4, 20242-4). Abbey.

God Remembers: A Study of Zechariah. 4th ed. Charles L. Feinberg. LC 79-88530. 1979. 8.95 (ISBN 0-930014-33-2). Multnomah.

God Rescues His People Activity Book. Barbara Rogers. 72p. (Orig.). 1983. pap. 3.00 (ISBN 0-8361-3338-2). Herald Pr.

God Rescues His People: Stories of God & His People: Exodus, Leviticus, Numbers & Deuteronomy. Eve MacMaster. LC 82-2849. (Story Bible Ser.: No. 2). (Illus.). 176p. (Orig.). 1982. pap. 5.95 (ISBN 0-8361-1994-0). Herald Pr.

God Reveals Himself. John H. Scott. 1987. 7.95 (ISBN 0-533-07061-9). Vantage.

God, Revelation & Authority: God Who Speaks & Shows, Vols. 1 & 2. Carl F. Henry. Incl. Vol. 1 (ISBN 0-87680-477-6, 80477); Vol. 2 (ISBN 0-87680-485-7, 80485). LC 76-15936. 1976. 22.95 ea. Word Bks.

God, Revelation & Authority: God Who Speaks & Shows, Vols. 3, 4, 5 & 6. Carl F. Henry. 1979. Vol. 3. 24.95 (ISBN 0-8499-0091-3); Vol. 4. 24.95 (ISBN 0-8499-0126-X); Vol. 5. 24.95 (ISBN 0-8499-0320-3); Vol. 6. 24.95 (ISBN 0-8499-0333-5). Word Bks.

God Said, Part I. Patsy Eakin. 65p. (Orig.). 1981. pap. 2.95 (ISBN 0-931097-06-1). Sentinel Pub.

God Said, Part II. Patsy Eakin. 89p. 1981. pap. text ed. 2.95 (ISBN 0-931097-11-8). Sentinel Pub.

God Saves Noah. Palmer Marjorie. (My Bible Story Reader Ser.: Vol. 2). (Illus., Orig.). 1983. pap. 1.95 (ISBN 0-8024-0192-9). Moody.

God, Secularization, and History: Essays in Memory of Ronald Gregor Smith. Ed. by Eugene Thomas Long. LC 73-15712. (Illus.). xiv, 164p. 1974. 21.95x (ISBN 0-87249-293-1). U of SC Pr.

God-Seekers. Ronda Chervin & Mary Neill. 212p. (Orig.). 1986. pap. 4.95 (ISBN 0-914544-65-9). Living Flame Pr.

God Sends His Son. Eve B. MacMaster. LC 86-18342. (Story Bible Ser.: Bk. 8). (Illus.). 160p. (Orig.). 1986. pap. 5.95 (ISBN 0-8361-3420-6). Herald Pr.

God Sends His Son Activity Book. Elsie E. Lehman. (Bible Story Ser.: Bk. 8). 80p. (Orig.). 1987. pap. 3.00 (ISBN 0-8361-3429-X). Herald Pr.

God Sends the Seasons. Kathleen A. Meyer. LC 81-80712. (Illus.). 32p. 1981. 7.50 (ISBN 0-87973-668-2, 668). Our Sunday Visitor.

God, Sex, & the Social Project: The Glassboro Papers on Religion & Human Sexuality. James H. Grace. LC 78-65496. (Symposium Ser.: Vol. 2). x, 203p. 1978. 19.95x (ISBN 0-88946-900-8). E Mellen.

God, Sex & You. M. O. Vincent. 192p. 1985. pap. 3.95 (ISBN 0-916441-25-3). Barbour & Co.

God So Loved the Third World: The Bible, the Reformation & Liberation Theologies. Thomas D. Hanks. Tr. by James C. Dekker from Span. LC 83-8076. Tr. of Opresion, Podreza y Liberacion: Reflexiona Biblicas. 176p. (Orig.). 1983. pap. 8.95 (ISBN 0-88344-152-7). Orbis Bks.

God So Loved the World. William Luoma. 1986. pap. 3.95 (6806). CSS of Ohio.

God So Loved the World. Joseph F. Sica. LC 81-40441. 120p. (Orig.). 1981. lib. bdg. 21.00 o. p. (ISBN 0-8191-1677-7); pap. text ed. 9.25 (ISBN 0-8191-1678-5). U Pr of Amer.

God So Loves the World: The Immaturity of World Christianity. A. J. Van Der Bent. LC 79-4470. 160p. (Orig.). 1979. pap. 2.98 (ISBN 0-88344-159-4). Orbis Bks.

God, Soul & Universe in Science & Islam. M. Y. Khan. 1969. 3.50 (ISBN 0-87902-170-5). Orientalia.

God Spake by Moses. Oswald T. Allis. 1951. pap. 5.95 (ISBN 0-87552-103-7). Presby & Reformed.

God Spake by Moses: An Exposition of the Pentateuch. Oswald T. Allis. 1951. pap. 5.95 (ISBN 0-8010-0109-9). Baker Bk.

God Speaks from the Cross. A. M. Coniaris. 1984. pap. 4.95 (ISBN 0-937032-33-6). Light&Life Pub Co MN.

God Speaks Naturally: An Organic Perspective on the Prophets. Nathan A. Barack. LC 83-7836. 242p. 1983. 12.50 (ISBN 0-8246-0299-4). Jonathan David.

God Speaks Through His Word. Albert F. Harper. 432p. 1985. pap. 11.95 (ISBN 0-8341-1067-9). Beacon Hill.

God Speaks to Women Today. Eugenia Price. 192p. 1984. pap. 6.95 (ISBN 0-310-31301-5, 10530P). Zondervan.

God Still Loves My Kitchen. Mab G. Hoover. 208p. (Orig.). 1981. pap. 3.95 (ISBN 0-310-35622-9, 11271P). Zondervan.

God Still Loves My Kitchen Best: Devotions for the Homemaker. Mab G. Hoover. 206p. (Orig.). 1977. pap. 3.95 (ISBN 0-310-35612-1, 11270P). Zondervan.

God Stories to Scare the Hell Out of You. David J. Gerrick. 1979. pap. text ed. 4.95 (ISBN 0-916750-24-8). Dayton Labs.

God, Suffering, & Belief. Howard R. Burkle. LC 76-26496. Repr. of 1977 ed. 24.40 (ISBN 0-8357-9010-X, 2016364). Bks Demand UMI.

God-Symbol. Paul Diel. 240p. 1985. 17.95 (ISBN 0-86683-475-3, HarpR). Har-Row.

God-Talk: An Examination of the Language & Logic of Theology. John Macquarrie. 1979. pap. 7.95 (ISBN 0-8164-2205-2, HarpR). Har-Row.

God Tells the Man Who Cares. Aiden W. Tozer. Ed. by Anita Bailey. 1970. 5.95 (ISBN 0-87509-184-9); pap. 4.45 (ISBN 0-87509-185-7); mass market ed. 2.95 (ISBN 0-87509-220-9). Chr Pubns.

God Tells the World. DeWitt B. Lucas. 1964. pap. 2.50 (ISBN 0-910140-08-1). C & R Anthony.

God That Failed. Arthur Koestler. Ed. by Richard H. Crossman. LC 81-85867. 1982. pap. 7.50 (ISBN 0-89526-867-1). Regnery Bks.

God, the Bible & Common Sense. Leroy Brownlow. 1978. pap. 2.50 (ISBN 0-915720-48-5). Brownlow Pub Co.

God the Center of Value: Value Theory in the Theology of H. Richard Niebuhr. C. David Grant. LC 84-40232. 185p. 1984. 16.95x (ISBN 0-912646-92-6). Tex Christian.

God the Church & Revelation. Wade H. Phillips. 376p. (Orig.). 1986. pap. 8.95 (ISBN 0-934942-60-9, 4048). White Wing Pub.

God, the Contemporary Discussion. Ed. by Frederick Sontag & Darrol Bryant. LC 82-70771. 419p. (Orig.). 1982. pap. 13.95 (ISBN 0-318-03629-0). Rose Sharon Pr.

God: The Contemporary Discussion. Ed. by Frederick Sontag & M. Darrol Bryant. LC 82-70771. (Conference Ser.: No. 12). vi, 419p. (Orig.). 1982. pap. text ed. 12.95 (ISBN 0-932894-12-7, Pub. by New Era Bks). Paragon Hse.

God-the Cornerstone of Our Life. John C. Krol. 1978. 5.50 (ISBN 0-8198-0531-9); pap. 3.95 (ISBN 0-8198-0532-7). Dghtrs St Paul.

God the Creator: On the Transcendence & Presence of God. Robert C. Neville. LC 68-13128. (Illus.). 1968. 12.50x (ISBN 0-226-57641-8). U of Chicago Pr.

God the Evangelist: How the Holy Spirit Works to Bring Men & Women to Faith. David F. Wells. 144p. (Orig.). 1987. pap. 6.95 (ISBN 0-8028-0271-0). Eerdmans.

God the Father. Gordon T. Allred. 1979. 8.95 (ISBN 0-87747-746-9). Deseret Bk.

God the Father. Russell P. Splitter. LC 76-20888. (Radiant Life Ser.). 128p. 1976. pap. 2.50 (ISBN 0-88243-898-0, 02-0898, Radiant Bks); teacher's ed 3.95 (ISBN 0-88243-170-6, 32-0170). Gospel Pub.

God the Father Sent His Son. rev. ed. Daughters of St. Paul. (Way, Truth & Life Ser.). (Illus.). 1973. text ed. 2.00 (ISBN 0-8198-0286-7); tchrs. manual 6.25 (ISBN 0-8198-0287-5); activity bk. 1.00 (ISBN 0-8198-0288-3); parent guide 1.25 (ISBN 0-8198-0289-1). Dghtrs St Paul.

God the Father: Theology & Patriarchy in the Teaching of Jesus, No. 4. Robert Hamerton-Kelly. Ed. by Walter Brueggemann & John R. Donahue. LC 78-54551. (Overtures to Biblical Theology Ser.). 144p. 1979. pap. 8.95 (ISBN 0-8006-1528-X, 1-1528). Fortress.

God the Problem. Gordon D. Kaufman. LC 70-174543. 1972. 17.50x (ISBN 0-674-35525-3); pap. 8.95x (ISBN 0-674-35526-1). Harvard U Pr.

God: The Question & the Quest. Paul R. Sponheim. LC 85-47737. 224p. 1986. 19.95 (ISBN 0-8006-0756-2). Fortress.

God, the Rod, & Your Child's Bod. Larry Tomczak. LC 81-23507. 128p. 1982. pap. 5.95 (ISBN 0-8007-5082-9, Power Bks). Revell.

God the Son. Donald Senior. LC 81-69109. (Illus.). 95p. 1982. pap. 5.95 (ISBN 0-89505-065-X). Argus Comm.

God the Spirit. J. C. Metcalfe. 1972. pap. 1.50 (ISBN 0-87508-917-8). Chr Lit.

God the Stranger: Reflections About Resurrection. Edmund A. Steimle. LC 78-14674. 80p. 1979. pap. 4.95 (ISBN 0-8006-1354-6, 1-1354). Fortress.

God the Supreme Humorist. 1974. 2.00 (ISBN 0-88497-184-8). Aum Pubns.

God, the Universe & Self. Lonnie J. Nichols. LC 82-74521. 96p. 1983. pap. 4.50 (ISBN 0-87516-515-X). De Vorss.

God, the Unknown & the Country Music Singer. Clifford Linedecker. (Illus.). 200p. 1987. 17.95x (ISBN 0-938294-50-4); pap. 9.95x (ISBN 0-938294-51-2). Global Comm.

God They Never Knew. George Otis, Jr. 244p. 1982. pap. 5.95 (ISBN 0-915134-84-5). Mott Media.

God to Man & Man to God. Ed. by Meher Baba. 287p. 1984. 8.95 (ISBN 0-913078-27-1); pap. 6.95 (ISBN 0-913078-21-2). Sheriar Pr.

God Two Thousand: Religion Without the Bible. Paul Winchell. LC 82-71878. 329p. 1982. 20.00 (ISBN 0-9608772-0-7). April Enterp.

God under My Roof. Esther De Waal. 40p. (Orig.). 1985. pap. 1.50 (ISBN 0-941478-42-4). Paraclete Pr.

God Wants Us to Listen. Kathryn Lutz. Ed. by Patricia H. Lemon. (Christian Storybooks Ser.). 1986. pap. 5.95 (ISBN 0-939697-03-3). Graded Pr.

God Wants You Rich: And Other Enticing Doctrines. Florence Bulle. 223p. (Orig.). 1983. pap. 5.95 (ISBN 0-87123-264-2, 210264). Bethany Hse.

God Was a Stranger. Margaret Kirk. 1980. pap. 2.75 (ISBN 0-85363-130-1). OMF Bks.

God Was in Christ. Donald M. Baillie. 232p. 1977. pap. 6.50 (ISBN 0-571-05685-7). Faber & Faber.

God Was in Christ. Donald M. Baillie. 1948. pap. 8.95x (ISBN 0-684-17474-X, PG56, ScribT); lib. bdg. 20.00 lib. rep. ed. (ISBN 0-684-16470-1, PG104HRE). Scribner.

God Was in Christ. Donald M. Baillie. 230p. 1980. pap. text ed. write for info. (ISBN 0-02-305440-9, Pub. by Scribner). Macmillan.

God We Seek. Paul Weiss. LC 64-13476. 267p. 1964. 10.95x (ISBN 0-8093-0133-4). S Ill U Pr.

God We Seek. Paul Weiss. LC 72-11838. (Arcturus Books Paperbacks). 268p. 1973. pap. 7.95x (ISBN 0-8093-0628-X). S Ill U Pr.

God: What People Have Said about Him. Ed. by Lothar Kahn. 320p. 1980. 9.95 (ISBN 0-8246-0251-X). Jonathan David.

God, Where's My Daddy? Donna M. Furrey. 32p. 1985. pap. 3.50 (ISBN 0-570-04130-9, 56-1542). Concordia.

God Who Cares: A Christian Looks at Judaism. Frederick Holmgren. LC 78-52445. (Orig.). 1979. pap. 1.95 (ISBN 0-8042-0588-4). John Knox.

God Who Hears. W. Bingham Hunter. LC 86-7268. 250p. (Orig.). 1986. pap. 6.95 (ISBN 0-87784-604-9). Inter-Varsity.

God Who Is There. Francis A. Schaeffer. LC 68-29304. 1968. pap. 7.95 (ISBN 0-87784-711-8). Inter-Varsity.

God Who Responds. H. D. McDonald. 200p. (Orig.). 1986. pap. 5.95 (ISBN 0-87123-840-3, 210840). Bethany Hse.

God Who Says Yes. Walter R. L. Scragg. Ed. by Gerald Wheeler. 128p. (Orig.). 1986. pap. 6.95 (ISBN 0-8280-0376-9). Review & Herald.

God Who Sends. Francis M. DuBose. LC 83-70002. 1983. 10.95 (ISBN 0-8054-6331-3). Broadman.

God Who Shows Up. James Richardson. LC 81-47889. 55p. (Orig.). 1981. pap. 3.00 (ISBN 0-914520-16-4). Insight Pr.

God Who Understands Me: The Sermon on the Mount. Gladys Hunt. LC 75-181992. (Fisherman Bible Studyguide Ser.). 87p. 1971. saddle-stitched 2.95 (ISBN 0-87788-316-5). Shaw Pubs.

God Will See You Through. Mary Kupferle. 1983. 5.95 (ISBN 0-87159-043-3). Unity School.

God Will See You Through. Hoover Ruppert. 1976. pap. 0.75x (ISBN 0-8358-0351-1). Upper Room.

God with Us. D. A. Carson. LC 85-10849. (Bible Commentary for Laymen Ser.). 168p. (Orig.). 1985. pap. 3.95 (ISBN 0-8307-1051-5, S392106). Regal.

God with Us. S. L. Frank. 1946. 29.50x (ISBN 0-686-83560-3). Elliots Bks.

God Within. Rene Dubos. LC 76-37224. 320p. 1973. pap. 8.95 (ISBN 0-684-13506-X, SL 458, ScribT). Scribner.

God Within. Farnsworth W. Loomis. (Illus.). 1968. 5.95 (ISBN 0-8079-0122-9). October.

God Within Us: Movements, Powers, & Joys. Peter A. Fraile. 110p. 1986. 6.95 (ISBN 0-8294-0503-8). Loyola.

God Without Thunder: An Unorthodox Defense of Orthodoxy. John C. Ransom. LC 65-17410. x, 334p. 1965. Repr. of 1930 ed. 29.50 (ISBN 0-208-00085-2, Archon). Shoe String.

God, Woman & Ministry. rev. ed. Victoria B. Demarest. LC 76-42915. (Illus.). 1978. 6.95 (ISBN 0-912760-61-3). Valkyrie Pub Hse.

God Works Through Faith. Robert A. Russell. 1957. pap. 3.95 (ISBN 0-87516-325-4). De Vorss.

God Works Through You. Robert A. Russell. 1977. pap. 3.95 (ISBN 0-87516-217-7). De Vorss.

God, You Are Always With Us. Kozo Kakimoto. 28p. 9.95 (ISBN 0-687-15303-4). Abingdon.

God You Can Know. Dan DeHaan. (Moody Press Electives Ser.). 1985. pap. text ed. 3.95 (ISBN 0-8024-0697-1); leader's guide 2.50 (ISBN 0-8024-0698-X). Moody.

God You Can Know. Daniel F. DeHaan. LC 81-16948. 180p. 1982. pap. 5.95 (ISBN 0-8024-3008-2). Moody.

God You Fill Us Up with Joy. Elspeth C. Murphy. (David & I Talk to God Ser.). (Illus.). 1987. pap. 2.95 (ISBN 1-55513-037-2, Chariot Bks). Cook.

Godded with God: Hendrik Niclaes & His Family of Love. Jean D. Moss. LC 81-68192. (Transactions Ser.: Vol. 71, Pt. 8). 1981. 10.00 (ISBN 0-87169-718-1). Am Philos.

Goddess. Caitlin Matthews. (Art & Imagination Ser.). (Illus.). 1983. pap. cancelled (ISBN 0-500-81031-1). Thames-Hudson.

Goddess Cults in Ancient India. J. N. Tiwari. (Illus.). 250p. 1986. 62.50x (ISBN 0-8364-1819-0, Pub. by Chanakya India). South Asia Bks.

Goddess Durga: The Great Mother. Dulal Chaudhuri. 1985. 7.50x (ISBN 0-8364-1289-3, Pub. by Mrimol). South Asia Bks.

Goddess: Mythological Images of the Feminine. Christine Downing. 256p. 1984. pap. 9.95 (ISBN 0-8245-0624-3). Crossroad NY.

Goddess Obscured: Transformation of the Grain Protectress from Goddess to Saint. Pamela Berger. LC 85-47524. (Illus.). 250p. 1986. 19.95 (ISBN 0-8070-6722-9). Beacon Pr.

Goddesses & Gods of Old Europe, 7000 to 3500 B.C. Myths, Legends, & Cult Images. Marija Gimbutas. 1982. pap. 14.95 (ISBN 0-520-04655-2, CAL 565). U of Cal Pr.

Goddesses in Ancient India. P. K. Agrawala. 180p. 1983. text ed. 50.00x (ISBN 0-391-02960-6). Humanities.

Goddesses of Sun & Moon: Circe, Aphrodite, Medea, Niobe. Karl Kerenyi. Tr. by Murray Stein from Ger. (Dunquin Ser.: No. 11). 84p. 1979. pap. 7.50 (ISBN 0-88214-211-9). Spring Pubns.

Godding: Human Responsibility & the Bible. Virginia R. Mollencott. 144p. 1987. 12.95 (ISBN 0-8245-0824-6). Crossroad NY.

Godding: The Bible & Human Responsibility. Virginia Mollenkott. 1987. 12.95. Crossroad NY.

Godeffroy of Boloyne; or, the Siege & Conquest of Jerusalem. Guilelmus. Ed. by Mary N. Colvin. (EETS, ES Ser.: No. 64). Repr. of 1893 ed. 29.00 (ISBN 0-527-00269-0). Kraus Repr.

Godhead. Rev. ed. Kenneth V. Reeves. Ed. by Mary H. Wallace. 1984. pap. 4.50 (ISBN 0-912315-64-4). Word Aflame.

Godliness & Contentment: Studies in the Three Pastoral Epistles. Marcus L. Loane. (Canterbury Bks.). 128p. (Orig.). 1982. pap. 5.95 (ISBN 0-8010-5619-5). Baker Bk.

Godliness & Good Learning: Four Studies on a Victorian Ideal. David Newsome. (Illus.). 1961. 21.00 (ISBN 0-7195-1015-5). Transatl Arts.

Godliness Is Profitable. Kenneth E. Hagin. 1982. pap. 0.50 mini bk. (ISBN 0-89276-256-X). Hagin Ministries.

Godliness Through Discipline. Jay E. Adams. 1977. pap. 1.25 (ISBN 0-8010-0057-2). Baker Bk.

Godliness Through Discipline. Jay E. Adams. 1972. pap. 0.95 (ISBN 0-87552-021-9). Presby & Reformed.

Godly Exhortation. John Field. Incl. Sermon Preached at Pawles Crosse, 3 November 1577. Thomas White. Repr. of 1578 ed. Repr. of 1583 ed. 28.00 (ISBN 0-384-15680-0). Johnson Repr.

Godly Finances: The Bible Way to Pay off Your Home. David Crank. 50p. (Orig.). 1986. pap. 4.95 (ISBN 0-936437-00-6). D Crank Pubns.

Godly Kingdom of Tudor England: Great Books of the English Reformation. Ed. by John E. Booty. LC 81-80626. (Illus.). 288p. 1981. 15.95 (ISBN 0-8192-1287-3). Morehouse.

Godly Kings & Early Ethics. rev. ed. Tertius Chandler. (Illus.). 220p. 1981. 24.00 (ISBN 0-9603872-4-2). Gutenberg.

Godly Learning: Puritan Attitudes Towards Reason, Learning, & Education, 1560-1640. John Morgan. 378p. 1986. 49.50 (ISBN 0-521-23511-1) (ISBN 0-317-39807-5). Cambridge U Pr.

Godly Man. Gene Warr. 1978. pap. 3.95 (ISBN 2-01064-105-1, 40121). Word Bks.

Godly People: Essays on English Protestantism & Puritanism. Patrick Collinson. (No. 23). 634p. 1983. 40.00 (ISBN 0-907628-15-X). Hambledon Press.

Godly Treatise Containing & Deciding Certaine Questions. Robert Some. LC 74-80231. (English Experience Ser.: No. 696). 204p. 1974. Repr. of 1588 ed. 20.00 (ISBN 90-221-0696-9). Walter J Johnson.

Godly Woman. Irma Warr. 1978. pap. 5.95 (ISBN 2-01064-201-5, 40123). Word Bks.

Godman: Finding a Spiritual Master. 2nd ed. Kirpal Singh. LC 78-68503. (Illus.). 1979. pap. 5.95 (ISBN 0-918224-07-1). Sawan Kirpal Pubns.

Godparents, Why? Marilyn J. Bomgren. 1981. 2.50 (ISBN 0-89536-473-5, 0717). CSS of Ohio.

Gods. Alain, pseud. Tr. by Richard Pevear from Fr. LC 74-8291. 192p. 1974. 8.95 (ISBN 0-8112-0547-9); pap. 3.95 (ISBN 0-8112-0548-7, NDP382). New Directions.

Gods. (Enchanted World Ser.). 1987. 16.95 (ISBN 0-8094-5273-1). Time-Life.

God's ABC Zoo. Mary McMillan. 48p. 1987. pap. 5.95 (ISBN 0-86653-405-9, SS1802). Good Apple.

God's Abundant Supply. D. E. Thompson. (Illus., Orig.). 1984. pap. 4.95 (ISBN 0-912315-75-X). Word Aflame.

God's Activity in the World: The Contemporary Debate. Owen C. Thomas. LC 82-19148. (AAR Studies in Religion). 248p. 1983. pap. 8.50 (ISBN 0-89130-602-1, 01 00 31). Scholars Pr GA.

God's Adventurer. Hudson Taylor & Phyllis Thompson. (Illus.). 1978. pap. 2.50 (ISBN 9971-83-777-3). OMF Bks.

God's Adventurers. facs. ed. Marjorie Tiltman. LC 68-16979. (Essay Index Reprint Ser.). 1933. 18.00 (ISBN 0-8369-0945-3). Ayer Co Pubs.

God's Altar: The World & the Flesh in Puritan Poetry. Robert Daly. LC 77-76182. 1978. 23.00x (ISBN 0-520-03480-5). U of Cal Pr.

Gods & Fighting Men. Isabella A. Gregory. LC 76-115243. 1971. Repr. of 1904 ed. 23.00x (ISBN 0-403-00400-4). Scholarly.

Gods & Goddesses of Ancient Greece. Edward E. Barthell, Jr. LC 72-129664. 1981. 49.50 (ISBN 0-87024-165-6). U of Miami Pr.

Gods & Heroes. Gustav Schwab. LC 47-873. 1977. pap. 9.95 (ISBN 0-394-73402-5). Pantheon.

Gods & Heroes from Viking Mythology. Brian Branston. LC 81-14540. (World Mythologies Ser.). (Illus.). 156p. 1982. 15.95 (ISBN 0-8052-3794-1). Schocken.

Gods & Heroes in the Athenian Agora. John M. Camp. (Excavations of the Athenian Agora Picture Bks.: No. 19). (Illus.). 1980. pap. 3.00x (ISBN 0-87661-623-6). Am Sch Athens.

Gods & Heroes of the Greeks: The "Library" of Apollodorus. Tr. by Michael Simpson. LC 75-32489. (Illus.). 320p. 1976. pap. 10.95x (ISBN 0-87023-206-1). U of Mass Pr.

Gods & Men. G. S. Ghurye. 1962. 39.50x (ISBN 0-317-27474-0). Elliots Bks.

Gods & Mortals in Classic Mythology: Dictionary. Michael Grant & John Hazel. 320p. 1985. 19.95 (ISBN 0-88029-036-6, Pub. by Dorset Pr). Hippocrene Bks.

Gods & Myths of Northern Europe. H. Ellis Davidson. (Orig.). 1965. pap. 5.95 (ISBN 0-14-020670-1, Pelican). Penguin.

Gods & Myths of Northern Europe. H. R. Davidson. 250p. 1986. pap. 3.00 (ISBN 0-317-53026-7). Noontide.

Gods & Other Lectures. Robert G. Ingersoll. 69.95 (ISBN 0-87968-246-9). Gordon Pr.

Gods & Pharaohs from Egyptian Mythology. Gerladine Harris. (World Mythologies Ser.). (Illus.). 132p. 1983. 15.95 (ISBN 0-8052-3802-6). Schocken.

Gods & Rituals: Readings in Religious Beliefs & Practices. Ed. by John Middleton. LC 75-44032. (Texas Press Sourcebooks in Anthropology Ser.: No. 6). 480p. 1976. pap. 11.50x (ISBN 0-292-72708-9). U of Tex Pr.

Gods & Symbols of Ancient Egypt: An Illustrated Dictionary. Manfred Lurker. Rev. by Peter A. Clayton. (Illus.). 144p. 1980. 19.95 (ISBN 0-500-11018-2, Quest). Thames Hudson.

Gods & Symbols of Ancient Egypt: An Illustrated Dictionary. Manfred Lurker. Rev. by Peter A. Clayton. (Illus.). 142p. 1984. pap. 9.95f (ISBN 0-500-27253-0). Thames Hudson.

Gods & the One God. Robert M. Grant. LC 85-11443. (Library of Early Christianity: Vol. 1). 212p. 1986. 16.95 (ISBN 0-664-21905-5). Westminster.

Gods & Their Grand Design. Erich Von Daniken. Tr. by Michael Hemon from Ger. 1984. 18.95 (ISBN 0-399-12961-8, Putnam). Putnam Pub Group.

God's Animals. Marian Bennett. (My Shape Book Ser.). (Illus.). 10p. 1985. 2.95 (ISBN 0-87239-909-5, 2749). Standard Pub.

God's Answer for Fear. Eric Hayden. LC 85-70873. 1986. pap. 2.95 (ISBN 0-88270-581-4). Bridge Pub.

God's Answer to Overeating. Ann Thomas. (Aglow Bible Study Basic Ser.). 64p. 1975. 2.95 (ISBN 0-932305-36-9, 4220-7). Aglow Pubns.

God's Answers to Man's Problems. J. Dwight Pentecost. (Moody Press Electives Ser.). (Orig.). 1985. pap. text ed. 3.95 (ISBN 0-8024-0702-1); leader's guide 2.50 (ISBN 0-8024-0703-X). Moody.

God's Answers to Man's Questions. William MacDonald. pap. 1.95 (ISBN 0-937396-16-8). Walterick Pubs.

God's Answers to Our Anxieties. James T. Jeremiah. (Direction Bks.). 1979. pap. 1.95 (ISBN 0-8010-5083-9). Baker Bk.

God's Apology. Richard Ingrams. (Illus.). 192p. 1986. pap. 13.95 (ISBN 0-241-11746-1, Pub. by Hamish Hamilton England). David & Charles.

God's Beloved Rebel. Elizabeth S. McFadden. (Daybreak Ser.). 1982. pap. 4.95 (ISBN 0-8163-0442-4). Pacific Pr Pub Assn.

God's Beloved Son. Manolo O. Vano. 82p. (Orig.). 1984. pap. 4.00x (ISBN 971-10-0099-7, Pub. by New Day Philippines). Cellar.

God's Best for My Life. Lloyd J. Ogilvie. LC 81-82390. 390p. (Orig.). 1981. text ed. 10.95 (ISBN 0-89081-293-4, 2934). Harvest Hse.

God's Best Secrets. Andrew Murray. 1986. pap. 9.95 (ISBN 0-310-29711-7, 10391P). Zondervan.

God's Best to You. Jerry Hayner. LC 81-71257. 1982. pap. 5.95 (ISBN 0-8054-5192-7). Broadman.

God's Body. Emmett Jarrett. LC 75-8967. 32p. 1975. pap. 1.50 (ISBN 0-914610-05-8). Hanging Loose.

God's Book for God's People. John R. Stott. LC 82-21203. 96p. 1982. pap. 2.95 (ISBN 0-87784-396-1). Inter-Varsity.

God's Boot Camp. Norvel Hayes. 30p. (Orig.). 1979. pap. 1.50 (ISBN 0-89274-277-1). Harrison Hse.

God's Breath in Man. John Fandel. LC 77-76604. 1977. pap. 1.50 (ISBN 0-87957-005-9). Roth Pub.

God's Busiest Angels. Janice Ching Yee. (Illus.). 1975. pap. 3.00 (ISBN 0-931420-09-1). Pi Pr.

God's Caliph: Religious Authority in the First Centuries of Islam. Patricia Crone & Martin Hinds. (Oriental Publications Ser.: No. 37). 200p. 1986. 39.50 (ISBN 0-521-32185-9). Cambridge U Pr.

God's Call: Exodus Second Part. Albert L. Schultz. Ed. by Kenneth Bartlett. (Books of Oral Tradition: No. 4). 80p. (Orig.). 1986. pap. 9.85 (ISBN 0-936596-11-2). Quantal.

God's Call to the Single Adult. Ed. by Michael Cavanaugh. 130p. (Orig.). 1986. pap. text ed. 3.95 (ISBN 0-88368-187-0). Whitaker Hse.

God's Care. Cathy Falk. (Bible Activities for Little People Ser.: Bk. 1). 24p. (Orig.). 1983. pap. 1.50 (ISBN 0-87239-676-2, 2451). Standard Pub.

God's Care Is Everywhere. Bruce Wannamaker. LC 82-7244. (Illus.). 32p. 1982. PLB 4.95 (ISBN 0-89693-202-8). Dandelion Hse.

God's Caress: The Psychology of Puritan Religious Experience. Charles Cohen. 336p. 1986. text ed. 29.95x (ISBN 0-19-503973-4). Oxford U Pr.

God's Caring People. Eugene Sterner. 1981. pap. 3.95 (ISBN 0-87162-251-3, D3839). Warner Pr.

God's Choice: The Total World of a Fundamentalist Christian School. Alan Peshkin. LC 85-24524. x, 350p. 1986. lib. bdg. 24.95 (ISBN 0-226-66198-9). U of Chicago Pr.

God's Chosen King. Eve MacMaster. LC 83-12736. (Story Bible Ser.: Vol. 4). (Illus.). 190p. (Orig.). 1983. pap. 5.95 (ISBN 0-8361-3344-7). Herald Pr.

God's Chosen King Activity Book. Barbara Rogers. 88p. (Orig.). 1984. pap. 3.00 (ISBN 0-8361-3370-6). Herald Pr.

God's Church in the Plan of the Ages. M. A. Tomlinson. 1974. pap. 2.95 (ISBN 0-934942-07-2). White Wing Pub.

God's Church in Today's World 1. Robert Wallinga. pap. 2.25 (ISBN 0-686-14196-2). Rose Pub MI.

God's Church in Today's World 2. Robert Wallinga. pap. 2.25 (ISBN 0-686-14197-0). Rose Pub MI.

God's Co-Workers: Your Importance to God. Clyde W. Rathwick. 1985. 10.00 (ISBN 0-682-40223-0). Exposition Pr FL.

God's Commissioned People. M. Thomas Starkes. LC 84-4968. 1984. pap. 12.95 (ISBN 0-8054-6338-0). Broadman.

God's Conditions For Prosperity. rev. & enlarged ed. Charles Hunter. 1984. pap. 4.95 (ISBN 0-917726-41-3). Hunter Bks.

God's Conditions for Prosperity: How to Earn the Rewards of Christian Living in Tough Times. Charles Hunter. 110p. 1984. 12.95 (ISBN 0-13-357285-4); pap. 5.95 (ISBN 0-13-357277-3). P-H.

God's Conflict with the Dragon & the Sea in the Old Testament: Echoes of a Canaanite Myth. John Day. (University of Cambridge Oriental Publications Ser.: No. 35). 208p. 1985. 49.50 (ISBN 0-521-25600-3). Cambridge U Pr.

God's Country. Ralph Barton. 59.95 (ISBN 0-8490-0242-7). Gordon Pr.

God's Country U. S. A. Deloros S. Bailey. 1982. 17.95 (ISBN 0-913730-04-1). Robinson Pr.

God's Covenant for Your Family. Marilyn Hickey. 140p. (Orig.). 1982. pap. 4.95 (ISBN 0-89274-245-3). Harrison Hse.

God's Daughter. rev. ed. Eadie Goodboy. (Bible Study: Basic Ser.). 60p. (Orig.). 1985. pap. 2.95 (ISBN 0-932305-45-8, 521002). Aglow Pubns.

God's Daughter in Nassau. Stephen G. Burrows. 186p. 1980. 8.50 (ISBN 0-682-49497-6). Exposition Pr FL.

God's Design: A Focus on Old Testament Theology. Elmer A. Martens. pap. 10.95 (ISBN 0-8010-6209-8). Baker Bk.

God's Design for Christian Dating. 2nd ed. Greg Laurie. LC 82-83836. 96p. (YA) 1983. pap. 2.25 (ISBN 0-89081-373-6). Harvest Hse.

God's Divine Arithematic. Enoch H. Oglesby. Ed. by Amos Jones, Jr. LC 84-54498. 150p. (Orig.). 1986. pap. write for info. (ISBN 0-910683-06-9). Sunday School.

God's Eonian Purpose. Adlai Loudy. text ed. 7.00 (ISBN 0-910424-56-X). Concordant.

God's Eternal Purpose. Bill Freeman. (Illus.). 14p. 1983. pap. 0.25 (ISBN 0-914271-01-6). NW Christian Pubns.

God's Everlasting Arms of Love. Ruth M. Thorndike. 1977. 6.50 (ISBN 0-682-48736-8). Exposition Pr FL.

God's Existence & Contemporary Science. J. Qamar. pap. 1.00 (ISBN 0-686-18452-1). Kazi Pubns.

God's Exploding Love. Ed. by George Maloney. LC 86-28802. 164p. (Orig.). 1987. pap. 7.95 (ISBN 0-8189-0514-X). Alba.

God's Family. Eve MacMaster. LC 81-6551. (Story Bible Ser.: No. 1). (Illus.). 168p. 1981. pap. 5.95 (ISBN 0-8361-1964-9). Herald Pr.

God's Family Activity Book. Marjorie Waybill. 64p. (Orig.). 1983. pap. 3.00 (ISBN 0-8361-3336-6). Herald Pr.

God's Fierce Whimsy: Christian Feminism & Theological Education. The Mud Flower Collective. Ed. by Carter Heyward. (Orig.). 1985. pap. 11.95 (ISBN 0-8298-0546-X). Pilgrim NY.

God's Financial Partner: A Bible Course on God, Money & You. write for info. (ISBN 0-9607644-0-2). Financial.

God's Fire: Moses & the Management of Exodus. Alfred de Grazia. (Quantavolution Ser.). (Illus.). 340p. 1983. pap. 20.00 (ISBN 0-940268-03-5). Metron Pubns.

God's Fool: The Life of Francis of Assisi. Julien Green. LC 84-48771. 256p. 1985. 16.95 (ISBN 0-06-063462-6, HarpR). Har-Row.

God's Fools. Thomas F. Rogers. 233p. (Orig.). 1983. pap. 5.95 (ISBN 0-941214-14-1, Eden Hill Pub). Signature Bks.

God's Foreign Policy. Miriam Adeney. LC 83-25343. 152p. (Orig.). 1984. pap. 6.95 (ISBN 0-8028-1968-0). Eerdmans.

God's Foreknowledge & Man's Free Will. Richard Rice. 128p. (Orig.). 1985. pap. 4.95 (ISBN 0-87123-845-4, 210845). Bethany Hse.

God's Forgetful Pilgrims: Recalling the Church to Its Reason for Being. Michael Griffiths. LC 75-16166. Repr. of 1975 ed. 44.00 (2027545). Bks Demand UMI.

God's Friends. Cathy Falk. (Bible Activities for Little People Ser.: BK. 2). 24p. (Orig.). 1983. pap. 1.50 (ISBN 0-87239-677-0, 2452). Standard Pub.

God's Friends: Called to Believe & Belong. Wesley W. Nelson. 1985. 15.95 (ISBN 0-910452-59-8); pastor's guide 19.95. Covenant.

God's Gift. Lillian Joseph. 112p. (Orig.). 1985. pap. 5.95 (ISBN 0-916829-10-3). Apollo Bks.

God's Gift Baby. Lavonne Neff. (Arch Bks.: No. 14). 1977. pap. 0.99 (ISBN 0-570-06113-X, 59-1230). Concordia.

God's Gift of Tongues: The Nature, Purpose, & Duration of Tongues As Taught in the Bible. George W. Zeller. LC 78-100. (Orig.). 1978. pap. 2.50 (ISBN 0-87213-985-9). Loizeaux.

God's Gift of Touch. Kathryn Lutz. Ed. by Patricia H. Lemon. (Christian Storybooks Ser.). 24p. (Orig.). 1986. pap. 5.95 packaged with audio cass. (ISBN 0-939697-02-5). Graded Pr.

God's Gift-the Holy Spirit. 1978. 2.95 (ISBN 0-8198-0377-4); pap. 1.95 (ISBN 0-8198-0378-2). Dghtrs St Paul.

God's Gift: The Secrets of Financial Freedom, No. 1. John K. Graham. LC 83-83273. (God's Gift Ser.). (Illus.). 112p. 1984. 12.95 (ISBN 0-916333-00-0). King's Hse Pub.

God's Gifts. Marian Bennett. (My Shape Book Ser.). (Illus.). 10p. 1985. 2.95 (ISBN 0-87239-910-9, 2750). Standard Pub.

God's Girls: Ordination of Women in the Early Christian & Agnostic Churches. Arthur F. Ide. (Illus.). 185p. (Orig.). 1986. pap. 8.95 (ISBN 0-934667-01-2). Tangelwuld.

God's Glory, Neighbor's Good: Francke's Biography & Sermons. Gary Sattler. 272p. 1982. pap. 8.95 (ISBN 0-910452-50-4). Covenant.

Gods, Goblins & Men. V. R. Narla. 1979. 12.00x (ISBN 0-8364-0559-5, Pub. by Minerva Associates). South Asia Bks.

God's Gold Mines. C. Roy Angell. LC 62-9194. 1962. 7.95 (ISBN 0-8054-5113-7). Broadman.

God's Good Earth. Ed. by Lloyd Mattson. (Illus.). 224p. (Orig.). 1985. pap. 25.00 (ISBN 0-942684-09-5). Camp Guidepts.

God's Got a Thing about You. Bhagwan Shree Rajneesh. Ed. by Ma Prem Maneesha. LC 83-11237. (Initiation Talks Ser.). 576p. (Orig.). 1983. pap. 4.95 (ISBN 0-88050-568-0). Chidvilas Found.

God's Got Your Number. Ed. by Ken Gaub. 150p. (Orig.). 1986. pap. text ed. 3.95 (ISBN 0-88368-185-4). Whitaker Hse.

God's Grace & Human Health. J. Harold Ellens. 1982. pap. 8.75 (ISBN 0-687-15326-3). Abingdon.

God's Gracious Dealings. Fred Pruitt & Lawrence Pruitt. (Illus.). 496p. 5.00 (ISBN 0-686-29110-7). Faith Pub Hse.

God's Green Liniment. Lois J. Rew. LC 81-84183. (Illus.). 208p. (Orig.). 1981. pap. 5.95 (ISBN 0-938462-02-4). Green Leaf CA.

God's Guidance at Dawn. Mary Light. pap. 1.00 (ISBN 0-910924-68-6). Macalester.

God's Hammer: The Bible & Its Critics. 2nd rev. ed. Gordon H. Clark. 200p. 1987. pap. 6.95 (ISBN 0-940931-99-0). Trinity Found.

God's Happy Family. Edith Witmer. (Jewel Bks.). 1986. pap. 1.95. Rod & Staff.

God's Helper. Danella G. Kotrba. (Come Unto Me Ser.: Year 2, Bk. 1). 32p. 1980. pap. 1.65 (ISBN 0-8127-0211-5). Review & Herald.

Gods, Heroes & Men of Ancient Greece. W. H. Rouse. 192p. (YA) 1971. pap. 3.50 (ISBN 0-451-62366-5, Ment). NAL.

God's High Calling for Women: First Timothy Two Verses Nine through Fifteen. John MacArthur, Jr. (John MacArthur Bible Studies Ser.). 1987. pap. 3.50 (ISBN 0-8024-5308-2). Moody.

God's High Country. Mable L. Ferguson. 384p. (Orig.). pap. 14.95 (ISBN 0-930161-09-2). State of the Art Ltd.

God's Higher Ways. Clarence W. Duff. 1978. pap. 7.50 (ISBN 0-87552-257-2). Presby & Reformed.

God's Image of You. Charles Capps. 1985. 2.95 (ISBN 0-89274-376-X). Harrison Hse.

God's Images: A New Vision. James Dickey. LC 78-17465. (Illus.). 110p. (Orig.). 1978. pap. 7.95 (ISBN 0-8164-2194-3, HarpR). Har-Row.

God's in Charge Here. Harold Hill & Irene B. Harrell. 160p. (Orig.). 1982. pap. 6.95 (ISBN 0-8007-5078-0, Power Bks). Revell.

Gods in Exile. Van der Leeuw. 2.75 (ISBN 0-8356-7056-2). Theos Pub Hse.

God's in His Heaven: Prayers & Poems for Little Children. LC 84-2101. (God's in His Heaven Bks.). (Illus.). 32p. 1984. pap. 4.95 (ISBN 0-394-86760-2, BYR). Random.

God's Inerrant Word. Ed. by John W. Montgomery. pap. 8.95 (ISBN 0-87123-292-8, 210292). Bethany Hse.

God's Inspired Holy Word Says... Cathy Paul. 1981. 4.95 (ISBN 0-8062-1785-5). Carlton.

God's Joyful People: One in the Spirit. Oswald C. Hoffman. LC 72-96742. 104p. 1973. pap. 2.95 (ISBN 0-570-03152-4, 12-2537). Concordia.

God's Joyful Runner: The Story of Eric Liddell. Russell Ramsey. (Orig.). 1987. pap. 9.95 (ISBN 0-88270-624-1, P624-1). Bridge Pub.

God's Justice: Activity Book. Marjorie Waybill. (Story Bible Ser.: Vol. 6). 88p. (Orig.). 1985. pap. 3.00 (ISBN 0-8361-3397-8). Herald Pr.

God's Key to Health & Happiness. Elmer A. Josephson. 224p. 1976. pap. 6.95 (ISBN 0-8007-5018-7, Power Bks). Revell.

God's Kingdom: A Guide for Biblical Study. George V. Pixley. Tr. by Donald E. Walsh from Sp. LC 81-3946. Tr. of Reino de Dios. 128p. (Orig.). 1981. pap. 5.95 (ISBN 0-88344-156-X). Orbis Bks.

God's Last Metaphor: The Doctrine of the Trinity in New England Theology. Bruce M. Stephens. LC 80-11421. (American Academy of Religion Studies in Religion). pap. 11.95 (ISBN 0-89130-386-3, 01-00-24). Scholars Pr GA.

God's Last Word to Man: Studies in Hebrew. G. Campbell Morgan. (Morgan Library). pap. 4.95 (ISBN 0-8010-5955-0). Baker Bk.

God's Law for Modern Man: God's Law or Chaos. Vic Lockman. (Illus.). 150p. (Orig.). Date not set. pap. 9.95 (ISBN 0-936175-05-2). V Lockman.

God's Laws of Success. Robert Tilton. 224p. (Orig.). 1983. pap. text ed. 7.95 (ISBN 0-914307-04-5, Dist. by Harrison Hse). Word Faith.

God's Laws of Success. Robert Tilton. 1986. pap. 6.95 (ISBN 0-89274-405-7). Harrison Hse.

God's Life in Us. Jea Danielou. 2.95 (ISBN 0-317-06464-9). Dimension Bks.

God's Little Animals: Easy Illustrations & Bible Parallels. JoAn Summers. (Illus.). 32p. 1969. pap. 1.95 (ISBN 0-88243-718-6, 02-0718). Gospel Pub.

God's Little House. Sandol Stoddard. (Orig.). 1984. pap. 1.95 (ISBN 0-8091-6553-8). Paulist Pr.

God's Love for a Sinning World. Charles G. Finney. LC 66-19200. (Charles G. Finney Memorial Library). 122p. 1975. pap. 4.50 (ISBN 0-8254-2620-0). Kregel.

God's Love for God's Children: Story Devotion for Family Time. Eldon Weisheit. LC 86-3397. (Illus.). 256p. (Orig.). 1986. kivar paper 9.95 (ISBN 0-8066-2213-X, 10-2680). Augsburg.

God's Love for Us. Maureen Gallagher. 1983. 3.95 (ISBN 0-89837-090-6, Pub. by Pflaum Pr); 3.95 (ISBN 0-89837-091-4). Peter Li.

God's Magnified Word. Victor P. Wierwille. LC 77-87405. (Studies in Abundant Living: Vol. 4). 276p. 1977. 6.95 (ISBN 0-910068-13-5). Am Christian.

God's Man-Satan's Trap. Edward R. Skane. 180p. Repr. of 1984 ed. 12.95 (ISBN 0-917655-00-1). Dane Bks.

God's Man: The Story of Pastor Niemoeller. Clarissa S. Davidson. LC 78-21065. 1979. Repr. of 1959 ed. lib. bdg. 22.50x (ISBN 0-313-21065-9, DAGM). Greenwood.

God's Managers. Ray Bair & Lillian Bair. 48p. 1981. pap. 4.00 (ISBN 0-8361-3406-0). Herald Pr.

God's Marvelous Gifts. Faythelma Bechtel. (Christian Day School Ser.). 1982. 13.75x (ISBN 0-87813-920-6). Christian Light.

God's Marvelous Work, Bk. 1. Rosa M. Mullet. 1980. Repr. of 1975 ed. write for info. (ISBN 0-686-11149-4); tchr's. ed. avail. (ISBN 0-686-11150-8). Rod & Staff.

God's Marvelous Work, Bk. 2. Rosa M. Mullet. 1981. write for info. (ISBN 0-686-25256-X); tchr's. ed. avail. (ISBN 0-686-25257-8). Rod & Staff.

God's Master Key to Prosperity. Gordon Lindsay. 1.95 (ISBN 0-89985-001-4). Christ Nations.

Gods Master Plan. Stephen S. King. 85p. 1985. pap. 3.95 (ISBN 0-317-52285-X). Christian Pub.

God's Means of Grace. C. F. Yoder. 12.50 (ISBN 0-88469-111-X). BMH Bks.

Gods, Men & Monsters from the Greek Myths. Michael Gibson. LC 81-14542. (World Mythologies Ser.). (Illus.). 156p. 1982. 15.95 (ISBN 0-8052-3793-3). Schocken.

God's Men of Color: The Colored Catholic Priest of the U. S. 1854-1954. Albert S. Foley. LC 69-18569. (American Negro: His History & Literature, Ser. No. 2). 1969. Repr. of 1955 ed. 14.00 (ISBN 0-405-01864-9). Ayer Co Pubs.

God's Mercie Mixed with His Justice. John Cotton. LC 58-5651. 1977. Repr. of 1641 ed. 30.00x (ISBN 0-8201-1242-9). Schol Facsimiles.

God's Messengers: Religious Leadership in Colonial New England, 1700-1750. J. William T. Youngs, Jr. LC 76-8544. 192p. 1976. 19.50x (ISBN 0-8018-1799-4). Johns Hopkins.

God's Miraculous Plan of Economy. Jack R. Taylor. LC 75-27411. 168p. 1975. 8.95 (ISBN 0-8054-5565-5). Broadman.

God's Mission in the New Testament. Ernst H. Wendland. Ed. by William E. Fischer. (Bible Class Course Ser.). 40p. (Orig.). (YA) 1986. pap. 2.50 (ISBN 0-938272-55-1). WELS Board.

God's Mission in the Old Testament. Ernst H. Wendland. Ed. by William E. Fischer. (Bible Class Course Ser.). 40p. (Orig.). 1986. pap. text ed. 2.50 (ISBN 0-938272-54-3). WELS Board.

God's Mother Is My Mother. Jack Mulqueen & Ray Chatton. (Illus.). 28p. (Orig.). 1978. pap. 2.50 (ISBN 0-913382-49-3, 103-13). Prow Bks-Franciscan.

God's Mundane World in Risible Rhyme. Margaret B. Korty. LC 86-72990. (Illus.). 135p. 1986. 6.95 (ISBN 0-9603060-2-1). Church Lib.

God's New Creation. Jack R. Taylor. 1987. 8.95 (ISBN 0-8054-5046-7). Broadman.

God's New Envoys: A Bold Strategy for Penetrating "Closed Countries". Tetsunao Yamamori. (Illus.). 1987. 11.95 (ISBN 0-88070-188-9). Multnomah.

God's New Israel: Religious Interpretations of American Destiny. C. Cherry. 1971. pap. 23.95 (ISBN 0-13-357335-4). P-H.

God's Numbers in Creation, Vol. 1. Ed. by Don Kistler. 1986. pap. 4.95 (ISBN 0-940532-03-4). AOG.

Gods of China. Harvey Shell. Ed. by Roxanna Chamberlin. (Illus.). 1985. pap. 4.95 (ISBN 0-914347-02-0). Ahio Pub Co.

Gods of Flesh-Gods of Stone: The Embodiment of Divinity in India. Ed. by Joanne Punzo Waghorne et al. LC 84-18543. (Orig.). 1985. pap. 12.95 (ISBN 0-89012-037-4). Anima Pubns.

Gods of Generation. Jacques-Antoine Dulaure. LC 72-9635. Tr. of De Divinites Generatrices. Repr. of 1934 ed. 42.00 (ISBN 0-404-57433-5). AMS Pr.

Gods of India. Alain Danielou. (Illus.). 441p. (Orig.). 1985. pap. 18.95 (ISBN 0-89281-101-3). Inner Tradit.

Gods of India: A Brief Description of Their History, Character, & Worship. E. Osborn Martin. LC 77-87621. 1977. Repr. of 1914 ed. lib. bdg. 40.00 (ISBN 0-89341-302-X). Longwood Pub Group.

Gods of Japan. Harvey Shell. (Illus.). 1984. pap. 4.95 (ISBN 0-914347-01-2). Ahio Pub Co.

Gods of Mexico. L. Spence. 34.95 (ISBN 0-8490-0243-5). Gordon Pr.

Gods of Northern Buddhism. Alice Getty. LC 62-15617. (Illus.). 1962. 39.50 (ISBN 0-8048-1129-6). C E Tuttle.

Gods of Our Fathers: A Study of Saxon Mythology. Herman I. Stern. LC 77-85623. 1977. Repr. of 1898 ed. lib. bdg. 30.00 (ISBN 0-89341-303-8). Longwood Pub Group.

Gods of Roman Britain. Miranda J. Green. (Shire Archeaology Ser.: No. 34). (Illus.). 64p. (Orig.). 1983. pap. 5.95 (ISBN 0-85263-634-2, Pub. by Shire Pubns England). Seven Hills Bks.

Gods of the Ancient Northmen. Georges Dumezil. Ed. & tr. by Einar Haugen. (Center for the Study of Comparative Folklore & Mythology, UCLA Ser.: No. 3). 1974. 34.00x (ISBN 0-520-02044-8); pap. 8.95 (ISBN 0-520-03507-0, CAL 371). U of Cal Pr.

Gods of the Celts. Miranda Green. LC 86-22135. (Illus.). 224p. 1986. 27.50x (ISBN 0-389-20672-5). B&N Imports.

Gods of the Egyptians or Studies in Egyptian Mythology, 2 Vols. E. A. Budge. (Illus.). Set. 36.00 (ISBN 0-8446-0520-4). Peter Smith.

Gods of the Egyptians: Studies in Egyptian Mythology, 2 Vols. E. A. Budge. LC 67-28633. (Illus.). 1969. pap. 10.00 ea.; Vol. 1. pap. (ISBN 0-486-22055-9); Vol. 2. pap. (ISBN 0-486-22056-7). Dover.

Gods of the Greeks. C. Kerenyi. (Illus.). 1980. pap. 9.95 (ISBN 0-500-27048-1). Thames Hudson.

Gods of the New Age. Caryl Matrisciana. (Orig.). 1985. pap. 6.95 (ISBN 0-89081-445-7). Harvest Hse.

God's OK-You're OK? Perspective on Christian Worship. Richard W. Baynes. LC 79-67440. 96p. (Orig.). 1981. pap. 2.25 (ISBN 0-87239-382-8, 40088). Standard Pub.

God's Order: Is It Possible Today? L. M. Grant. pap. 0.95 (ISBN 0-88172-153-0). Believers Bkshelf.

God's Other Books. Elbert A. Dempsey. 1987. pap. 12.75 (ISBN 0-8309-0464-6). Herald Hse.

God's Other Door & the Continuity of Life. Edgar Cayce & Hugh L. Cayce. 1976. pap. 2.95 (ISBN 0-87604-007-5). ARE Pr.

God's Own Child. rev. ed. Bill Coleman & Patty Coleman. 64p. 1983. Parent's Book. pap. text ed. 3.95x (ISBN 0-89622-188-1); Leader's Guide. wkbk. 1.00 (ISBN 0-89622-187-3). Twenty-Third.

God's People. William A. Kramer. LC 75-16790. 1975. lib. bdg. 7.25 (ISBN 0-8100-0010-5, 06N552). Northwest Pub.

God's People: A Book of Children's Sermons. Gail Linam. LC 85-25736. (Orig.). 1986. pap. 4.95 (ISBN 0-8054-4928-0). Broadman.

God's People & Church Government. Robert Lemon. 64p. (Orig.). 1983. pap. 2.25 (ISBN 0-89274-282-8). Harrison Hse.

God's People in Christ: New Testament Perspectives on the Church & Judaism, No. 7. Daniel J. Harrington. Ed. by Walter Brueggemann & John R. Donahue. LC 79-7380. (Overtures to Biblical Theology Ser.). 144p. 1980. pap. 8.95 (ISBN 0-8006-1531-X, 1-1531). Fortress.

God's People: Nursery Leader's Guide. Linda Chenoweth. 64p. 1981. 2.95 (ISBN 0-686-74751-8). Westminster.

God's People on the Move. Daughters of St. Paul. LC 68-59042. (Divine Master Ser.). pap. 2.50 (ISBN 0-8198-0348-0); rev. tchr's. manual 3.95 (ISBN 0-8198-0349-9). Dghtrs St Paul.

God's People Our Story: Bible Stories from the New Testament. DeVere Ramsay. LC 83-51404. 128p. 1984. 12.95 (ISBN 0-8358-0480-1). Upper Room.

God's People Share. Linda Chenoweth. Ed. by Mary Duckert. 64p. 1981. nursery ldrs. guide 3.95 (ISBN 0-664-24337-1); pap. 1.55 students' book (ISBN 0-664-24336-3); resource Packet 8.95 (ISBN 0-664-24338-X). Westminster.

God's People: The Now & Future Church. Thomas R. Artz. 64p. 1986. pap. 1.95 (ISBN 0-89243-248-9). Liguori Pubns.

God's Pilgrims. Phillip Mauro. 192p. 1969. pap. 3.00 (ISBN 0-87509-090-7). Chr Pubns.

God's Plan & the Overcomers. Watchman Nee. Tr. by Stephen Kaung from Chinese. 1977. pap. 2.50 (ISBN 0-935008-19-5). Christian Fellow Pubs.

God's Plan for Building a Good Reputation. Gene Getz. 144p. 1987. pap. 5.95 (ISBN 0-89693-010-6). Victor Bks.

God's Plan for Christian Service. Ronald D. Tucker & Richard A. Hufton. (Illus.). 418p. 1982. 40.00 (ISBN 0-933643-17-9). Grace World Outreach.

God's Plan for Christian Service. 2nd ed. Ronald D. Tucker & Richard A. Hufton. LC 86-81343. 300p. 1987. pap. 10.00 (ISBN 0-933643-30-6). Grace World Outreach.

God's Plan for Church Leadership. Knofel Staton. LC 82-3378. 160p. (Orig.). 1982. pap. 5.95 (ISBN 0-87239-566-9, 39987). Standard Pub.

God's Plan for Church Leadership: Leader's Guide. Marshall Hayden. LC 82-3378. 64p. (Orig.). 1982. pap. 1.95 (ISBN 0-87239-567-7, 39986). Standard Pub.

God's Plan for Financial Prosperity. Elbert Willis. 1977. 3.00 (ISBN 0-89858-005-6). Fill the Gap.

God's Plan for Giving. John MacArthur, Jr. (John MacArthur's Bible Studies). 1985. pap. 3.50 (ISBN 0-8024-5107-1). Moody.

God's Plan for the Church-Growth! Michael Hamilton. LC 81-82021. (Radiant Life Ser.). 128p. (Orig.). 1981. 2.50 (ISBN 0-88243-885-9, 02-0885); teacher's ed. 3.95 (ISBN 0-88243-194-3, 32-0194). Gospel Pub.

Gods Plan for the Family. Charles Nieman. 58p. (Orig.). 1985. 4.95 (ISBN 0-914307-49-5). Word Faith.

God's Plan for the Human Race. Paul L. Giroux. 1980. 5.00 (ISBN 0-682-49270-1). Exposition Pr FL.

God's Plan for the Local Church. Donald E. Hill. 32p. 1982. pap. 2.49 (ISBN 0-88151-022-X). Lay Leadership.

God's Plan for the World, New Testament Survey. Robert Gilley. (International Correspondence Program Ser.). 169p. (Orig.). 1984. pap. 6.95 (ISBN 0-87148-362-9). Pathway Pr.

God's Plan for the World, Old Testament Survey. Laud O. Vaught. LC 82-62742. (Illus.). 183p. (Orig.). 1983. pap. text ed. 6.95 (ISBN 0-87148-360-2). Pathway Pr.

God's Plan for This Planet. Ian Macpherson. LC 76-51001. 96p. 1977. pap. 1.25 (ISBN 0-88243-517-5, 02-0517, Radiant Bks). Gospel Pub.

God's Plan for Us. Joan Mitchell. 1984. 4.95 (ISBN 0-89837-092-2, Pub. by Pflaum Press). Peter Li.

God's Plan for Us: A Practical Strategy for Communal Discernment of Spirits. Brian Hall & Benjamin Tonna. LC 80-81439. 128p. 1980. pap. 8.95 (ISBN 0-8091-2311-8). Paulist Pr.

God's Plan for Your Financial Success. Charles Nieman. 230p. (Orig.). 1985. pap. text ed. 6.95 (ISBN 0-914307-34-7). Word Faith.

God's Plan in All the Ages: The Kingdom & Redemption from Genesis to Revelation. Herbert Vander Lugt. 208p. 1980. pap. 4.95 (ISBN 0-310-42181-0, 10227P). Zondervan.

God's Plan of the Ages. Gordon Lindsay. (Prophecy Ser.). 5.00 (ISBN 0-89985-056-1). Christ Nations.

God's Plan of the Ages. Louis T. Talbot. 1936. pap. 8.95 (ISBN 0-8028-1194-9). Eerdmans.

God's Plan to Enjoy Your Children. Nita Scoggan. Ed. by Alice Tolliver. LC 84-60581. (Illus.). 52p. 1985. pap. 2.95 (ISBN 0-910487-03-0). Royalty Pub.

God's Plenty. Ruth M. Ames. 288p. 1984. 12.95 (ISBN 0-8294-0426-0). Loyola.

God's Plot: The Paradoxes of Puritan Piety, Being the Autobiography & Journal of Thomas Shepard. Ed. by Michael McGiffert. LC 71-181364. (Commonwealth Ser.: Vol. 1). (Illus.). 264p. 1972. 20.00x (ISBN 0-87023-100-6). U of Mass Pr.

God's Power Through Prayer. Ralph Wilkerson. Ed. by Marsha Countryman. 300p. 1985. leatherbound 19.95 (ISBN 0-937347-02-7). J Countryman Pubs.

God's Power Through the Laying On of Hands. Norvel Hayes. 45p. 1982. pap. 2.50 (ISBN 0-89274-280-1). Harrison Hse.

God's Power Versus Satan's Power: Christian Life Lessons. Louise Norman. (Teaching Bks.). (Illus.). 64p. (Orig.). 1985. pap. text ed. 8.95 (ISBN 0-86508-062-3). BCM Intl Inc.

God's Powerful Weapon. Denis Lane. 1977. pap. 1.25 (ISBN 9971-972-21-2). OMF Bks.

God's Presence in History. Emil L. Fackenheim. 1972. pap. 5.95x (ISBN 0-06-131690-3, TB1690, Torch). Har-Row.

God's Priests & Warriors: The Bhrgus of the Mahabharata. Robert P. Goldman. LC 76-41255. (Studies in Oriental Culture). 195p. 1977. 23.00x (ISBN 0-231-03941-7). Columbia U Pr.

God's Program of the Ages. Frederick A. Tatford. LC 67-26075. 160p. (Orig.). 1967. 4.95 (ISBN 0-8254-3800-4). Kregel.

God's Promise for Children. Eldon Weisheit. LC 80-65554. (Visual Messages on Old Testament Texts, Ser. A). 128p. 1980. pap. 6.95 (ISBN 0-8066-1799-3, 10-2692). Augsburg.

God's Promise for Children: Object Lessons on Old Testament Texts. Eldon Weisheit. LC 81-65656. (Series B). 128p. (Orig.). 1981. pap. 6.95 (ISBN 0-8066-1892-2, 10-2693). Augsburg.

God's Promise for Children: Object Lessons on Old Testament Texts. Eldon Weisheit. LC 82-70956. (Series C). 128p. (Orig.). 1982. pap. 6.95 (ISBN 0-8066-1931-7, 10-2694). Augsburg.

God's Promises & My Needs. John C. Reid. 80p. (Orig.). 1986. pap. 2.50 (ISBN 0-914733-06-0). Desert Min.

God's Promises for Living. Jack Countryman. 285p. 1984. leatherbound 19.95 (ISBN 0-937347-01-9). J Countryman Pubs.

God's Promises for Today's Believer. Ed. by Valeria Richardson. 100p. (Orig.). 1986. write for info. (ISBN 0-88368-162-5). Whitaker Hse.

God's Promises for Your Every Need. Jack Countryman. 334p. 1981. leatherbound 19.95 (ISBN 0-937347-00-0). J Countryman Pubs.

God's Promises to Preachers. Aaron Isaiah Jones. LC 81-67128. 1982. 5.50 (ISBN 0-8054-2240-4). Broadman.

God's Prophet God's Servant: A Study in Jeremiah & Isaiah 40-56. John Goldingay. 160p. 1986. pap. 11.95 (ISBN 0-85364-338-5, Pub. by Paternoster UK). Attic Pr.

God's Providence. C. H. Spurgeon. pap. 0.75 (ISBN 0-685-00749-9). Reiner.

God's Provision for Holy Living. William Culbertson. (Moody Classics Ser.). 1984. pap. 2.95 (ISBN 0-8024-3043-0). Moody.

God's Psychiatry. Charles L. Allen. 1984. pap. 2.95 (ISBN 0-515-08234-1). Jove Pubns.

God's Psychiatry. Charles L. Allen. 160p. 9.95 (ISBN 0-8007-0113-5); pap. 2.95 (ISBN 0-8007-8015-9, Spire Bks); pap. 5.95 (ISBN 0-8007-5010-1, Power Bks). Revell.

God's Purest Angels. Janice Ching Yee. (Illus.). 1976. pap. 3.00 (ISBN 0-931420-11-3). Pi Pr.

God's Purpose - Man's Plans. Edward R. Dayton. 64p. 1982. pap. 5.95 (ISBN 0-912552-11-5). Missions Adv Res Com Ctr.

God's Purpose for Man: The Spirit & the Flesh. Mollie Colbert-Thornton. 141p. 1984. 8.95 (ISBN 0-533-05913-5). Vantage.

God's Purpose-God's People: Studies in Ephesians. John A. Ishee. 36p. 1982. pap. 3.50 (ISBN 0-939298-03-1). J M Prods.

God's Rainbow of Colors. Patricia Mahany. (My Shape Bk.). (Illus.). 12p. 1984. 2.95 (ISBN 0-87239-783-1, 2723). Standard Pub.

Gods Rainbowed Week. Richard B. Jarrett. (Orig.). 1982. pap. text ed. 5.00 (ISBN 0-9606884-1-2). Jarrett.

God's Remedy for Depression. Vivian Clark. (Direction Bks.). (Orig.). 1980. pap. 3.50 (ISBN 0-8010-2444-7). Baker Bk.

God's Revolution: The Witness of Eberhard Arnold. Ebehard Arnold. Ed. by Hutterian Society of Brothers & John H. Yoder. pap. 8.95 (ISBN 0-8091-2609-5). Paulist Pr.

God's Revolution: The Witness of Eberhard Arnold. Eberhard Arnold. Ed. by Hutterian Society of Brothers & John H. Yoder. LC 83-62952. 230p. 1984. pap. 8.95 (Pub. by Paulist Pr). Plough.

God's Righteous Kingdom. Walter J. Chantry. 151p. (Orig.). 1980. pap. 4.95 (ISBN 0-85151-310-7). Banner of Truth.

God's Saving Presence. 3.27 (ISBN 0-02-649270-9); tchr's. manual 2.52 (ISBN 0-02-649280-6). Benziger Pub Co.

God's Saving World. 3.27 (ISBN 0-02-649310-1); 2.52 (ISBN 0-685-61722-X). Benziger Pub Co.

God's Secret Agent. Daughters of St. Paul. 1967. 3.00 (ISBN 0-8198-0236-0). Dghtrs St Paul.

God's Sense of Humor. Bob W. Parrott. LC 82-9142. 221p. 1984. 17.50 (ISBN 0-8022-2421-0). Philos Lib.

God's Smuggler. Brother Andrew et al. (Illus.). 224p. 1968. pap. 2.95 (ISBN 0-8007-8016-7, Spire Bks); pap. 0.79 (ISBN 0-8007-8501-0, Spire Comics). Revell.

God's Smuggler. J. Sherrill et al. 1968. pap. 2.95 (ISBN 0-451-13254-8, AE3254, Sig). NAL.

God's Son. Cathy Falk. (Bible Activities for Little People Ser.: Bk. 3). 24p. (Orig.). 1983. pap. 1.50 (ISBN 0-87239-678-9, 2453). Standard Pub.

God's Song in My Heart: Daily Devotions. Ruth Y. Nelson. LC 56-11912. 432p. 1957. 8.95 (ISBN 0-8006-0254-4, 1-254). Fortress.

God's Special Baby. Joyce Shilder. (Little Learner Ser.). 24p. 1985. 5.95 (56-1553); pap. 2.95 (ISBN 0-570-04088-4). Concordia.

God's Spotlight on Tomorrow: Seven Sevens Concerning the Return of Christ. Paul R. Alderman, Jr. 1960. pap. 1.25 (ISBN 0-87213-010-X). Loizeaux.

God's Spring Gifts. Gail Linam. (Illus., Orig.). 1980. pap. 3.25 (ISBN 0-8054-4157-3, 4142-57). Broadman.

God's Statesman: The Life & Work of John Owen. Peter Toon. 208p. 1971. 9.95 (ISBN 0-85364-133-1). Attic Pr.

God's Storehouse: Exodus 16 Lessons, Vol. 2. Bernice C. Jordan. (Footsteps of Faith Ser.). (Illus.). 1961. pap. text ed. 2.50 (ISBN 0-86508-029-1); 11.45 (ISBN 0-86508-030-5). BCM Intl Inc.

God's Story & Modern Literature: Reading Fiction in Community. Carl Ficken. LC 84-48705. 176p. 1985. pap. 9.95 (ISBN 0-8006-1823-8, 1-1823). Fortress.

God's Story-& Ours! Warren F. Groff. 148p. (Orig.). 1986. pap. 7.95 (ISBN 0-317-52618-9). Brethren.

God's Strategy in Human History. Roger T. Forster & V. Paul Marston. Tr. by Chen C. Tseng from Eng. (Chinese.). 1986. write for info. (ISBN 0-941598-92-6); pap. write for info. (ISBN 0-941598-09-8). Living Spring Pubns.

God's Strategy in Human History. Roger T. Forster & V. Paul Marston. 304p. 1984. pap. 7.95 (ISBN 0-87123-434-3, 210434). Bethany Hse.

God's Suffering Servant. Eve B. MacMaster. LC 86-19526. (Story Bible Ser.: Bk. 9). (Illus.). 120p. (Orig.). 1987. pap. 5.95 (ISBN 0-8361-3422-2). Herald Pr.

God's Surprising Goodness. Dan Ivins. 128p. 1984. pap. 4.95 (ISBN 0-8170-1044-0). Judson.

Gods, Thrones, & Peacocks: Northern Indian Painting from Two Traditions; Fifthteenth to Nineteenth Centuries. Stuart C. Welch & Milo C. Beach. LC 74-27422. (Asia Society Ser.). (Illus.). 1979. Repr. of 1965 ed. lib. bdg. 33.00x (ISBN 0-405-06570-1). Ayer Co Pubs.

God's Time for Mankind. Walter Kasper. 93p. 1983. 8.00 (ISBN 0-8199-0812-6). Franciscan Herald.

God's Time Is the Best Time. Anselm Hufstader. (Ways of Prayer Ser.: Vol. 11). 8.95 (ISBN 0-89453-386-X); pap. 4.95 (ISBN 0-89453-385-1). M Glazier.

God's Time-Records in Ancient Sediments: Evidences of Long Time Spans in Earth's History. Daniel E. Wonderly. LC 77-85681. (Illus.). 258p. (Orig.). 1977. pap. 7.00 (ISBN 0-930402-01-4). Crystal MI.

God's Tomorrow: The Life Beyond Death. Robert Shank. (Orig.). 1975. pap. 1.95 (ISBN 0-911620-03-6). Westcott.

God's Transmitters. Hannah Hurnard. 1975. pap. 2.95 (ISBN 0-8423-1085-1). Tyndale.

God's Trombones. James Weldon Johnson. (Poets Ser). 1976. pap. 4.95 (ISBN 0-14-042217-X). Penguin.

God's Twentieth Century Barnabas: The Gordon Lindsay Story. Gordon Lindsay. Ed. by Christ for the Nations. 284p. (Orig.). 1982. pap. 3.95 (ISBN 0-89985-002-2, 104). Christ Nations.

God's Ultimate Purpose. D. Martyn Lloyd-Jones. (Illus.). 12.95 (ISBN 0-8010-5591-1). Baker Bk.

God's Unfolding Plan. Sr. Mary K. Wright. 2.00 (ISBN 0-87505-307-6, Pub. by Lawrence). Borden.

God's Unfolding Purpose: A Guide to the Study of the Bible. Suzanne De Dietrich. Tr. by Robert M. Brown. LC 60-6169. 1960. Westminster.

God's Vision Promise. Sri Chinmoy. 50p. (Orig.). pap. 2.00 (ISBN 0-88497-125-2). Aum Pubns.

God's Voice. Hubberman Zavel. 8.95 (ISBN 0-8062-2496-7). Carlton.

God's Voice in the Folklore. Glenn Clark. 4.95 (ISBN 0-910924-06-6). Macalester.

God's Warriors: Dramatic Adventures of Rabbis in Uniform. Dov P. Elkins. LC 74-226. (Illus.). 92p. 1974. 7.95 (ISBN 0-8246-0168-8). Jonathan David.

God's Way of Reconciliation: Studies in Ephesians II. D. Martyn Lloyd-Jones. 1972. 12.95 (ISBN 0-8010-5519-9). Baker Bk.

God's Way Out. rev. ed. Bernard L. Ramm. Ed. by Ed Stewart. 214p. 1987. pap. 5.95 (ISBN 0-8307-1215-1, 5416514). Regal.

God's Way to Health, Wealth & Wisdom. Adrian P. Rogers. 1987. 9.95 (ISBN 0-8054-5048-3). Broadman.

God's Way to Live Successfully. Stuart D. Briscoe. 144p. 1986. pap. 2.95 (ISBN 0-8007-8582-7, Spire Bks). Revell.

God's Way to the Good Life. Robert Schuller. (Religion Ser.). 144p. 1987. pap. 2.95 (ISBN 0-553-26803-1). Bantam.

God's Way to the Good Life. Robert H. Schuller. LC 74-18978. (Pivot Family Reader Ser). 128p. 1974. pap. 1.75 (ISBN 0-87983-098-0). Keats.

God's Way to the Top. J. J. Turner. 1983. pap. 4.25 (ISBN 0-89137-539-2). Quality Pubns.

God's Way: Voices from the Heart. William J. Crockett. 15p. 1985. pap. 3.00 (ISBN 0-934383-34-0). Pride Prods.

Gods Who Walk the Rainbow. Swami Sivananda Radha. LC 81-9410. (Illus.). 240p. (Orig.). 1981. pap. 7.95 (ISBN 0-931454-07-7). Timeless Bks.

God's Will & the Christian. R. C. Sproul. 96p. 1984. 2.95 (ISBN 0-8423-1096-7). Tyndale.

God's Will Is Prosperity. Gloria Copeland. pap. 2.95 (ISBN 0-89274-090-6, HH-090). Harrison Hse.

God's Willing Knowledge: The Influence of Scotus' Analysis of Omniscience. Douglas C. Langston. LC 85-31956. 151p. 1986. 18.95x (ISBN 0-271-00429-0). PA St U Pr.

God's Winter Gifts. Gail Linam. (Illus.). 1980. pap. 3.25 (ISBN 0-8054-4158-1, 4142-58). Broadman.

God's Wisdom & Power. Eve McMaster. LC 84-8974. (Story Bible Ser.: No. 5). (Illus.). 168p. (Orig.). 1984. pap. 5.95 (ISBN 0-8361-3362-5). Herald Pr.

God's Wisdom & Power Activity Book. Elsie Lehman. (Story Bible Ser.). 80p. 1985. pap. 3.00 (ISBN 0-8361-3391-9). Herald Pr.

God's Wisdom for Daily Living. LC 84-4817. 352p. 1984. 16.95 (ISBN 0-8407-5373-X). Nelson.

God's Wisdom-God's Way: Studies in First Corinthians. John A. Ishee. 35p. (Orig.). 1983. pap. 3.50 (ISBN 0-939298-20-1). J M Prods.

God's Wonderful World & Me. Joanne L. Kepes. 1982. 9.95 (ISBN 0-89837-086-8, Pub. by Pflaum Pr). Peter Li.

God's Wonderful World: Thirteen Pupil Activities, Bk. 1. Carolyn Lehman. (God's Wonderful World Ser.). (Illus.). 32p. 1985. wkbk 1.50 (ISBN 0-87239-837-4, 3317). Standard Pub.

God's Wonderful World: Thirteen Pupil Activities, Bk. 2. Carolyn Lehman. (God's Wonderful World Ser.). (Illus.). 32p. 1985. 1.50 (ISBN 0-87239-838-2, 3318). Standard Pub.

God's Wonderful World: Twenty Six Lessons for Primary Church. Carolyn Lehman. (Children's Church Ser.). (Illus.). 144p. 1985. wkbk 8.95 (ISBN 0-87239-839-0, 3316). Standard Pub.

God's Word A. D. LeRoy Lawson. LC 83-348. 112p. (Orig.). 1984. pap. 2.95 (ISBN 0-87239-668-1, 41022). Standard Pub.

God's Word: A Living Rainbow. Maria A. Hirschmann & Betty Pershing. LC 63-1848. 167p. (Orig.). 1984. pap. 6.95 (ISBN 0-932878-07-5, HB-008). Hansi.

God's Word & Our Words: Basic Homiletics. Ronald E. Sleeth. LC 85-23777. 120p. (Orig.). 1986. pap. 7.95 (ISBN 0-8042-1577-4). John Knox.

God's Word B. C. John W. Wade. LC 83-349. (Orig.). 1983. pap. 2.95 (ISBN 0-87239-667-3, 41020). Standard Pub.

God's Word for the Church in America. Paul Trinchard. 12.95 (ISBN 0-8158-0428-8). Chris Mass.

God's Word for Today. Ed. by Wayne McCown & James Massey. (Wesleyan Theological Perspectives Ser.: Vol. II). 1982. 14.95 (ISBN 0-87162-257-2, D4851). Warner Pr.

God's Word for Today: A Daily Devotional for the Whole Year. O. Hallesby. Tr. by Clarence J. Carlsen. LC 78-67940. 1979. pap. 5.95 (ISBN 0-8066-1682-2, 10-2741). Augsburg.

God's Word for Your Healing. Robert Halverstadt. 1982. pap. 1.95 (ISBN 0-88144-003-5, CPS-003). Christian Pub.

God's Word for Your Prosperity. Robert Halverstadt. 1982. pap. 1.95 (ISBN 0-88144-002-7, CPS-002). Christian Pub.

God's Word in a Child's World: Messages & Guidelines for Sharing the Gospel with Children. Eldon Weisheit. LC 86-3442. 128p. (Orig.). 1986. pap. 6.95 (ISBN 0-8066-2214-8, 10-2745). Augsburg.

God's Word in Culture. Elena Whiteside. 233p. 1983. pap. 4.95 (ISBN 0-910068-51-8). Am Christian.

God's Word in Man's Language. Robert Branson. 83p. (Orig.). 1980. pap. 2.75 (ISBN 0-8341-0659-0). Beacon Hill.

God's Word into English. Dewey M. Beegle. LC 79-84556. 1965. pap. 8.95 (ISBN 0-933462-02-6). Pryor Pettengill.

God's Word Is Our Only Foundation. Ella S. Burton. 1983. 5.75 (ISBN 0-8062-2164-X). Carlton.

God's Word Made Plain. Kay Friederichsen. 1958. pap. 4.95 (ISBN 0-8024-3041-4). Moody.

God's Word to His Church. Carmelite Sisters of Noto, Italy Staff. Tr. by Carmelite Sisters of Cristo Rey Carmel, San Francisco Staff. LC 81-83568. Tr. of Alla Sorgente Della Parola di Dio. 144p. (Orig.). 1982. pap. text ed. 7.95 (ISBN 0-89870-016-7). Ignatius Pr.

God's Word to Israel: An Introduction to the Old Testament. Joseph Jensen. 400p. 1982. pap. 9.95 (ISBN 0-89453-289-8). M Glazier.

God's Word Written. John C. Wenger. LC 66-24292. (Conrad Grebel Lecture Ser.). (Illus., Essays on the nature of biblical revelation, inspiration, & authority). 1966. pap. 6.95 (ISBN 0-8361-1900-2). Herald Pr.

God's Words. James I. Packer. LC 81-18683. 192p. (Orig.). 1982. pap. 5.95 (ISBN 0-87784-367-8). Inter-Varsity.

God's Work. Watchman Nee. Tr. by Stephen Kaung. 1974. pap. 2.25 (ISBN 0-935008-20-9). Christian Fellow Pubs.

God's Work in a Changing World. John Farrelly. 346p. (Orig.). 1985. lib. bdg. 28.50 (ISBN 0-8191-4523-8); pap. text ed. 14.50 (ISBN 0-8191-4524-6). U Pr of Amer.

God's Work of Liberation: A Journey Through the Old Testament with the Liberation Heroes of Israel. Robert Bennett. (Illus., Orig.). 1976. pap. text ed. 5.95 (ISBN 0-8192-4067-2); tchr's guide 2.25x (ISBN 0-8192-4068-0). Morehouse.

God's Work of Salvation. Bert Dominy. LC 83-71264. (Layman's Library of Christian Doctrine Ser.). 1986. 5.95 (ISBN 0-8054-1638-2). Broadman.

God's Works Through Elvis. Marvin R. Long. 1979. 4.00 (ISBN 0-682-49294-9). Exposition Pr FL.

God's World. Barbara Ebert. 1985. pap. 0.98 (ISBN 0-317-30757-6, 2695). Standard Pub.

God's World: An Anthology of Short Stories. Nagib Mahfuz. Tr. by Akef Abadir & Roger Allen. LC 73-79201. (Studies in Middle Eastern Literatures: No. 2). 1973. pap. 12.00x student ed. (ISBN 0-88297-031-3). Bibliotheca.

God's World, God's Body. Grace Jantzen. LC 84-3697. 186p. (Orig.). 1984. pap. 10.95 (ISBN 0-664-24619-2). Westminster.

God's World-His Story. Roger L. Berry. (Christian Day School Ser.). 1976. 18.80x (ISBN 0-87813-911-7); tchr's guide 19.65x (ISBN 0-87813-914-1). Christian Light.

God's World Makes Me Feel So Little. Helen R. Caswell. (Illus.). 32p. 1985. paper over board 5.95 (ISBN 0-687-15510-X). Abingdon.

God's World, Our World. (Little Books to Treasure). (Illus.). 32p. 1985. 1.95 (ISBN 0-225-66389-9, HarpR). Har-Row.

Godswept Heart: Parables of Family Life. Marcia Hollis & Reginald Hollis. (Illus.). 96p. 1983. pap. 5.95 (ISBN 0-8164-2410-1, HarpR). Har-Row.

Godward: A Record of Religious Progress. Paul Carus. 26p. 1898. 0.95 (ISBN 0-317-40417-2). Open Court.

Godwin's Practical Encyclopedia of Cabalistic Magick. 2nd, rev. & expanded ed. David Godwin. Ed. by Carl L. Weschcke. (Sourcebook Ser.). 500p. 1987. pap. 15.00 (ISBN 0-87542-292-6, L-292). Llewellyn Pubns.

Goethe & Dostoyevsky: Two Devils, Two Geniuses, a Study of the Demonic in Their Work. Ilya Kostovski. 1974. lib. bdg. 69.95 (ISBN 0-87700-215-0). Revisionist Pr.

Goethe's Response to Protestantism. Harry Loewen. (Canadian Studies in German Language & Literature: Vol. 7). 168p. 1972. pap. 19.60. P Lang Pubs.

Goethezeit & the Metamorphosis of Catholic Theology in the Age of Idealism: Theology, Vol. 128. Donald J. Dietrich. (European University Studies: Ser. 23). 261p. 1979. pap. 26.25 (ISBN 3-261-04703-8). P Lang Pubs.

Goforth of China. Rosalind Goforth. 384p. 1969. pap. 4.95 (ISBN 0-87123-181-6, 200181). Bethany Hse.

Going Forth: Missionary Consciousness in Third World Catholic Churches. Omer Degrijse. LC 83-19337. 112p. (Orig.). 1984. pap. 6.95 (ISBN 0-88344-427-5). Orbis Bks.

Going Home. Robert Raines. LC 84-23210. 154p. 1985. pap. 6.95 (ISBN 0-8245-0692-8). Crossroad NY.

Going It - With God. 4th ed. Bishop Ian Shervill. 94p. 1985. 4.95 (ISBN 0-908175-37-X, Pub. by Boolarong Pubn Australia). Intl Spec Bk.

Going Live. Muriel Dobbin. Ed. by Joyce Engelson. 432p. 1987. 17.95 (ISBN 0-525-24473-5). Dutton.

Going Through God. Betty J. Wall. 277p. pap. 7.95 (ISBN 0-942494-36-9). Coleman Pub.

Going to America Going to School: The Jewish Immigrant Public School Encounter in Turn-of-the-Century New York City. Stephan F. Brumberg. LC 85-16791. 300p. 1986. 29.95 (ISBN 0-03-062574-2, C2030). Praeger.

Going Together: The Church of Christ. John Walsh & James DiGiacomo. (Encounter Ser.). (Illus.). 1978. pap. text ed. 4.50 (ISBN 0-03-042771-1, HarpR); resource manual 1.95 (ISBN 0-03-042776-2). Har-Row.

Going up! rev. ed. Russ Korth & Ron Wormser, Jr. 82p. 1980. pap. text ed. 5.00 (ISBN 0-934396-26-4). Churches Alive.

Going up. Charles L. Paddock. LC 53-107000078. (Dest Ser.). 1984. pap. 5.95 (ISBN 0-317-28316-2). Pacific Pr Pub Assn.

Gold Cord. Amy Carmichael. 1957. pap. 5.95 (ISBN 0-87508-068-5). Chr Lit.

Gold-Crowned Jesus & Other Writings. Chi-ha Kim. Ed. by Chong Sun Kim & Shelly Killen. LC 77-17522. pap. 44.50 (ISBN 0-317-26644-6, 2025119). Bks Demand UMI.

Gold from Golgotha. Russell B. Jones. (Orig.). 1978. pap. 1.50 (ISBN 0-89228-024-7). Impact Bks MO.

Gold from the Gospels. Edward Fudge. pap. 2.00 (ISBN 0-686-12679-3). E Fudge.

Gold in the Making. Ron L. Davis. LC 83-21931. 160p. 1984. pap. 5.95 (ISBN 0-8407-5869-3). Nelson.

Gold of Friendship: A Bouquet of Special Thoughts. Compiled by Patricia Dreier. (Illus.). 1980. 6.95 (ISBN 0-8378-1707-2). Gibson.

Gold Seals of the Vatican: Secret Archives. Ed. by Aldo Matini. (Illus.). 288p. 150.00 (ISBN 0-8478-5404-3). Rizzoli Intl.

Gold Tried in the Fire. Robert J. Wieland. (Anchor Ser.). 80p. 1983. pap. 6.95 (ISBN 0-8163-0520-X). Pacific Pr Pub Assn.

Gold Was the Mortar: The Economics of Cathedral Building. Henry Kraus. (Illus.). 1979. 37.95x (ISBN 0-7100-8728-4). Methuen Inc.

Golden Age Society & Other Studies. Mona G. Jacqueny. LC 77-87939. 183p. 1978. 12.00 (ISBN 0-8022-2219-6). Philos Lib.

Golden Alphabet (on Psalm 119) C. H. Spurgeon. 1980. pap. 4.25 (ISBN 0-686-09094-2). Pilgrim Pubns.

Golden Ark of Covenant. Dale A. Howard. (Illus.). 40p. 1987. pap. 5.00 (ISBN 0-940517-04-3). JCMC Louisiana.

Golden Ass of Apuleius. Ed. by W. E. Henley. Tr. by William Aldington from Lat. 249p. 1981. Repr. of 1893 ed. lib. bdg. 50.00 (ISBN 0-89984-233-X). Century Bookbindery.

Golden Boat, 20 vols. Sri Chinmoy. (Illus.). 50p. (Orig.). 1974. pap. 3.00 ea. Aum Pubns.

Golden Book of Eastern Saints. facsimile ed. Donald Attwater. LC 72-156607. (Essay Index Reprint Ser). Repr. of 1938 ed. 18.00 (ISBN 0-8369-2267-0). Ayer Co Pubs.

Golden Book of Management: A Historical Record of the Life & Work of Seventy Pioneers. Lyndall Urwick. Ed. by Alfred D. Chandler. LC 79-7557. (History of Management Thought & Practice Ser.). (Illus.). 1980. Repr. of 1956 ed. lib. bdg. 21.00x (ISBN 0-405-12343-4). Ayer Co Pubs.

Golden Book of Marcus Aurelius. Meric Casaubon. 1979. Repr. of 1906 ed. lib. bdg. 12.50 (ISBN 0-8482-7564-0). Norwood Edns.

Golden Booke of the Leaden Gods, Repr. Of 1577 Ed. Stephen Batman. Bd. with Third Part of the Countess of Pembroke's Yvychurch. Abraham Fraunce. Repr. of 1592 ed; Fountaine of Ancient Fiction. Richard Lynche. Repr. of 1599 ed. LC 75-27856. (Renaissance & the Gods Ser.: Vol. 13). (Illus.). 1976. lib. bdg. 88.00 (ISBN 0-8240-2062-6). Garland Pub.

Golden Booklet of the True Christian Life: Devotional Classic. John Calvin. (Summit Bks.). 1975. pap. 3.95 (ISBN 0-8010-2366-1). Baker Bk.

Golden Bough. rev., abr ed. James G. Frazer. 1985. pap. 10.95 (ISBN 0-02-095570-7, Collier). Macmillan.

Golden Caravan. Sirdar I. A. Shah. 1983. 15.95 (ISBN 0-86304-026-8, Pub. by Octagon Pr England). Ins Study Human.

Golden Chain: A Study in the Theological Anthropology of Isaac of Stella. Bernard McGinn. LC 70-152487. (Cistercian Studies: No. 15). 280p. 1972. 7.50 (ISBN 0-87907-815-4). Cistercian Pubns.

Golden Christmas Treasury. Ed. by Rick Bunsen. LC 84-72934. (Illus.). 80p. 1986. 7.95 (ISBN 0-307-15585-4, Pub. by Golden Bks). Western Pub.

Golden Dawn: Twilight of the Magicians. R. A. Gilbert. 128p. 1983. pap. 7.95 (ISBN 0-85030-278-1). Newcastle Pub.

Golden Days of the Early English Church from the Arrival of Theodore to the Death of Bede, 3 Vols. Henry H. Howorth. LC 79-153612. Repr. of 1917 ed. Set. 75.00 (ISBN 0-404-09470-8); 25.00 ea. Vol. 1 (ISBN 0-404-09471-6). Vol. 2 (ISBN 0-404-09472-4). Vol. 3 (ISBN 0-404-09473-2). AMS Pr.

Golden Door: Italian & Jewish Immigrant Mobility in New York City, 1880-1915. Thomas Kessner. 1977. text ed. 22.50x (ISBN 0-19-502116-9); pap. 8.95x (ISBN 0-19-502161-4). Oxford U Pr.

Golden Doves with Silver Dots: Semiotics & Textuality in Rabbinic Tradition. Jose Faur. LC 84-47967. (Jewish Literature & Culture Ser.). 256p. 1986. 27.50x (ISBN 0-253-32600-1). Ind U Pr.

Golden Flower. facsimile ed. Joseph A. Gobineau. Tr. by B. R. Redman. LC 68-54347. (Essay Index Reprint Ser). 1924. 15.00 (ISBN 0-8369-0477-X). Ayer Co Pubs.

Golden Fountain or the Soul's Love for God. Lilian Stavely. LC 82-70082. (Library of Traditional Wisdom). 95p. 1982. pap. 4.75 (ISBN 0-941532-02-X). Wrld Wisdom Bks.

Golden Gospel: A Pictorial History of the Restoration. Edmund C. Enriquez. (Illus.). 96p. 1981. pap. 5.95 (ISBN 0-88290-198-2). Horizon Utah.

Golden Harvest. White Eagle. 1958. 3.95 (ISBN 0-85487-017-2). De Vorss.

Golden Horns: Mythic Imagination & the Nordic Past. John L. Greenway. LC 74-30676. 232p. 1977. 20.00x (ISBN 0-8203-0384-4). U of Ga Pr.

Golden Middle Age. Roger B. Lloyd. LC 75-90654. (Essay Index Reprint Ser). 1939. 18.00 (ISBN 0-8369-1208-X). Ayer Co Pubs.

Golden Oracle: The Ancient Chinese Way to Prosperity. Ed. by Khigh Dhiegh. LC 82-18471. (Illus.). 176p. 1983. 15.95 (ISBN 0-668-05661-4); pap. 8.95 (ISBN 0-668-05913-3). Arco.

Golden Precepts of Esotericism. 3rd, rev. ed. G. De Purucker. LC 78-74257. 1979. 5.00 (ISBN 0-911500-85-5); pap. 3.00 (ISBN 0-911500-86-3). Theos U Pr.

Golden Present. Sri Swami Satchidananda. 448p. (Orig.). Date not set. pap. write for info. (ISBN 0-932040-30-6). Integral Yoga Pubns.

Golden Rosycross. Catharose De Petri. Tr. by Lectorium Rosicrucianum Staff. Orig. Title: Het Goudew Rozenkruis. Date not set. pap. 8.00. Rosycross Pr.

Golden Temple, Past & Present. Madanjit Kaur. 1985. 17.50x (ISBN 0-8364-1325-3, Pub. by Nank Dev Univ India). South Asia Bks.

Golden Thoughts for Children. Jane McDow. (Illus.). 48p. (Orig.). 1986. pap. write for info. (ISBN 0-9616464-0-3). Candy Apple Pub.

Golden Thread. Natalie N. Banks. 1979. pap. 5.00 (ISBN 0-85330-127-1). Lucis.

Golden Thread. Geoffrey S. Childs. (Illus.). 200p. 1986. write for info. (ISBN 0-910557-15-2). Acad New Church.

Golden Thread. Margaret Regehr. (Illus.). 209p. (Orig.). 1985. pap. text ed. 7.00 (ISBN 0-9614486-0-1). M Regehr.

Golden Thread. Nettie Vander Shrier. 169p. 1983. pap. 3.95 (ISBN 0-8024-0173-2). Moody.

Golden Thread: Diary of Mrs. Elsie Koll, Missionary to China. Elsie Koll. Ed. by John L. Scales. (Illus.). 180p. (Orig.). 1982. pap. 4.95 (ISBN 0-942504-00-3). Overcomer Pr.

Golden Tradition: Jewish Life & Thought in Eastern Europe. Lucy S. Dawidowicz. LC 84-5560. 512p. 1984. pap. 11.95 (ISBN 0-8052-0768-6). Schocken.

Golden Treasury of Prayers for Boys & Girls. Ed. by Esther Wilkin. (Illus.). xx, 48p. 1975. 6.95 (ISBN 0-307-13744-9, Golden Bks). Western Pub.

Golden Treasury of Psalms & Prayers. 5.95 (ISBN 0-88088-242-5). Peter Pauper.

Golden Treatise of Mental Prayer. S. Peter Alcantara. Ed. by G. S. Hollings. LC 77-18960. Repr. of 1978 ed. 35.20 (ISBN 0-8357-9135-1, 2019096). Bks Demand UMI.

Golden Words of a Sufi Sheikh. M. R. Muhaiyaddeen. LC 82-11854. 472p. 1983. 15.95 (ISBN 0-914390-24-4). Fellowship Pr PA.

Golden Years of the Hutterites. Leonard Gross. LC 80-10711. (Studies in Anabaptist & Mennonite History: Vol. 23). 1980. 17.95x (ISBN 0-8361-1227-X). Herald Pr.

Golden Years of the Hutterites, 1565-1578. Leonard Gross. LC 80-10711. 280p. 1980. 15.00 (ISBN 0-317-47160-0). Plough.

Golden Zephyr. Lama Mi-phan. Tr. by Leslie S. Kawamura from Tibetan. LC 75-5259. (Tibetan Translation Ser.: Vol.4). (Illus.). 192p. (Orig.). 1975. 12.95 (ISBN 0-913546-22-4); pap. 6.95 (ISBN 0-913546-21-6). Dharma Pub.

Golem of Prague. Gershon Winkler. (Illus.). 1980. pap. 9.95 (ISBN 0-910818-25-8). Judaica Pr.

Golem: The Story of a Legend. Ed. by Elie Wiesel. Tr. by Anne Borchardt. LC 83-9304. (Illus.). 105p. 1983. 12.95 (ISBN 0-671-45483-8); Special ed., signed, limited. 50.00 (ISBN 0-671-49624-7). Summit Bks.

Golf & the Gospel. R. Blaine Detrick. 1985. 4.95 (ISBN 0-89536-766-1, 5873). CSS of Ohio.

Golf God's Way. Gus Bernardoni. LC 77-80414. 1978. 9.95 (ISBN 0-88419-144-3). Creation Hse.

Goliath's Last Stand. Colleen Ison. LC 85-17315. 112p. 1986. pap. 4.95 (ISBN 0-87239-997-4, 3357). Standard Pub.

Golus Ugeuloh: Exile & Redemption--21 Shiurim on the Meaning of Jewish History. Joseph Grunblatt. 1987. 16.95 (ISBN 0-88125-130-5); pap. 9.95 (ISBN 0-88125-135-6). Ktav.

Gommatsara Jiva-Kanda (the Soul) Devendra Gani. Ed. & intro. by Rai B. Jaini. LC 73-3839. Repr. of 1927 ed. 48.00 (ISBN 0-404-57705-9). AMS Pr.

Gommatsara Karma-Kanda, Pts. 1 & 2. Devendra Gani. Ed. by Rai B. Jaini & Brachmachari S. Ji. LC 73-3840. Repr. of 1927 ed. Set. 72.50 (ISBN 0-404-57712-1). AMS Pr.

Gomorrah & the Rise of Homophobia. Arthur F. Ide. (Illus.). 114p. (Orig.). 1985. pap. 5.95 (ISBN 0-934659-01-X). Liberal Pr.

Gone from the Promised Land: Jonestown As American Cultural History. John R. Hall. 435p. 1987. 29.95 (ISBN 0-88738-124-3). Transaction Bks.

Gone the Golden Dream. Jan Markell. LC 79-16718. 176p. 1979. pap. 4.95 (ISBN 0-87123-049-6, 210049). Bethany Hse.

Gonzalo De Berceo. Teresa C. Goode. (Carl Ser.: No. 7). Repr. of 1933 ed. 21.00 (ISBN 0-404-50307-1). AMS Pr.

Gonzalo De Tapia, 1561-1594: Founder of the First Permanent Jesuit Mission in North America. William E. Shiels. LC 74-12835. (U. S. Catholic Historical Society Monograph: No. XIV). 1978. Repr. of 1934 ed. lib. bdg. 22.50x (ISBN 0-8371-7758-8, SHGT). Greenwood.

Good & Evil. Martin Buber. 185p. pap. text ed. 7.95 (ISBN 0-684-16990-8). Scribner.

Good & Evil. Martin Buber. 1984. 19.75 (ISBN 0-8446-6121-X). Peter Smith.

Good & Evil. Martin Buber. 143p. 1980. pap. text ed. write for info. (ISBN 0-02-316280-5, Pub. by Scribner). Macmillan.

Good & Evil: Two Interpretations. Martin Buber. 1953. pap. 3.95 (ISBN 0-684-71723-9, SL45, ScribT). Scribner.

Good-Bye Beedee. Norma J. Lutz. LC 85-12826. (Marcia Stallings Ser.). 128p. 1986. pap. 2.95 (ISBN 0-89191-738-1, 57380, Chariot Bks). Cook.

Good-Bye, I Love You. Carol L. Pearson. LC 85-23235. 240p. 1986. 15.95 (ISBN 0-394-55032-3). Random.

Good-Bye, My Son, Hello. Adolfo Quezada. LC 84-72629. 64p. (Orig.). 1985. pap. 2.95 (ISBN 0-87029-196-3). Abbey.

Good Christian Men. facsimile ed. Henry M. Davidson. LC 70-142616. (Essay Index Reprint Ser). Repr. of 1940 ed. 19.00 (ISBN 0-8369-2390-1). Ayer Co Pubs.

Good Clean Fun: Fifty Nifty Bible Games for Junior Highers. Tom Finley. 112p. 1986. pap. 8.95 (ISBN 0-310-31251-5, 18389). Zondervan.

Good Company & Violence: Sorcery & Social Action in a Lowland New Guinea Society. Bruce M. Knauft. LC 85-967. (Studies in Melanasian Anthropology). 1985. 40.00x (ISBN 0-520-05530-6). U of Cal Pr.

Good Confession. Watchman Nee. Tr. by Stephen Kaung. (Basic Lesson Ser.: Vol. 2). 1973. 4.25 (ISBN 0-935008-05-5); pap. 2.75 (ISBN 0-935008-06-3). Christian Fellow Pubs.

Good Faith & Credit. Gottlieb Hammer. LC 85-13962. (Illus.). 280p. 1986. 17.95 (ISBN 0-8453-4798-5, Cornwall Bks). Assoc Univ Prs.

Good Father in Brittany. Martin P. Harney. (Illus.). 1964. pap. 4.00 (ISBN 0-8198-0049-X). Dghtrs St Paul.

Good Friday Unchanged. Norma Leary. (Orig.). 1982. pap. 3.75 (ISBN 0-937172-34-0). JLJ Pubs.

Good Friends Again: Two - Three. Vera Groomer. (Come Unto Me Ser.: Year 2, Bk. 3). 32p. 1980. pap. 1.65 (ISBN 0-8127-0272-7). Review & Herald.

Good Genes? Emerging Values for Science, Religion & Society. David A. Ames & Colin B. Gracey. (Illus.). 136p. 1984. pap. 3.60 (ISBN 0-88028-034-4). Forward Movement.

Good God, Where in the World Are You? George Mocko. (Orig.). 1987. pap. price not set (ISBN 0-89536-878-1, 7864). CSS of Ohio.

Good Graces: Table Prayers. Julie J. McDonald. Ed. by Joan Liffring-Zug et al. (Illus.). 64p. (Orig.). 1986. pap. 7.95. Penfield.

Good Grief. Granger E. Westberg. LC 78-21233. 64p. (Orig.). 1962. pap. 1.95 (ISBN 0-8006-1114-4, 1-1114); pap. 3.95 large print ed. (ISBN 0-8006-1361-9, 1-1361). Fortress.

Good Guys Finish First: Success Strategies from the Book of Proverbs for Business Men & Women. Clinton W. McLemore. LC 83-14708. 142p. 1983. pap. 7.95 (ISBN 0-664-26004-7, A Bridgebooks Publication). Westminster.

Good Housekeeping American Family Christmas. Good Housekeeping Magazine Editors. (Brownstone Library Book). (Illus.). 168p. 1985. 19.95 (ISBN 0-916410-29-3). A D Bragdon.

Good Life: Alternatives in Ethics. Burton F. Porter. (Illus.). 1980. pap. text ed. write for info. (ISBN 0-02-396120-1). Macmillan.

Good Look at Evil. Abigail L. Rosenthal. 264p. 1987. 24.95 (ISBN 0-87722-456-0). Temple U Pr.

Good Man & the Good: An Introduction to Ethics. Mary W. Calkins. LC 75-3093. Repr. of 1918 ed. 24.50 (ISBN 0-404-59090-X). AMS Pr.

Good Minister of Jesus Christ. Joseph A. Synan. pap. 1.50 (ISBN 0-911866-81-7). Advocate.

Good Morality Is Like Good Cooking... & Other Suggestions for Right Living. Matthew F. Kohmescher. 112p. (Orig.). 1987. pap. 4.95 (ISBN 0-8091-2856-X). Paulist Pr.

Good Morning in the Dawn, Dear Son. Della A. Meadows. 200p. 1985. 11.95 (ISBN 0-8059-2952-5). Dorrance.

Good Morning, Lord: Devotions for Athletes. LeRoy Patterson. (Good Morning, Lord Ser.). 1979. 4.95 (ISBN 0-8010-7044-9). Baker Bk.

Good Morning, Lord: Devotions for Boys. William C. Hendricks. (Good Morning Lord Ser.). 1974. 4.95 (ISBN 0-8010-4100-7). Baker Bk.

Good Morning, Lord: Devotions for Campers. Floyd Todd & Pauline Todd. (Good Morning Lord Ser.). 1973. 3.95 (ISBN 0-8010-8792-9). Baker Bk.

Good Morning, Lord: Devotions for Children. Dena Korfker. (Good Morning Lord Ser.). 1973. 4.95 (ISBN 0-8010-5328-5). Baker Bk.

Good Morning, Lord: Devotions for College Students. Louis O. Caldwell. (Good Morning Lord Ser.). 1971. 4.95 (ISBN 0-8010-2324-6). Baker Bk.

Good Morning, Lord: Devotions for Hospital Patients. R. Earl Allen. 96p. 1975. 4.95 (ISBN 0-8010-0079-3). Baker Bk.

Good Morning, Lord: Devotions for New Christians. Ron Hembree. (Good Morning, Lord Ser.). 96p. 1983. 4.95 (ISBN 0-8010-4271-2). Baker Bk.

Good Morning, Lord: Devotions for Newlyweds. Ron Hembree. 128p. 1982. 4.95 (ISBN 0-8010-4262-3). Baker Bk.

Good Morning, Lord: Devotions for Teens. Paul Martin. (Good Morning Lord Ser.). 1962. 4.95 (ISBN 0-8010-5879-1). Baker Bk.

Good Morning, Lord: Devotions for Today's Homemakers. Peg Roberts. 96p. 1982. 4.95 (ISBN 0-8010-7718-4). Baker Bk.

Good Morning, Lord: Devotions for Women. Evelyn M. Anderson. (Good Morning Lord Ser.). 1971. 4.95 (ISBN 0-8010-0023-8). Baker Bk.

Good Morning, Lord: Devotions for Young Mothers. Mary F. Loeks. (Good Morning, Lord Ser.). 1977. 4.95 (ISBN 0-8010-5566-0). Baker Bk.

Good Morning, Lord: Devotions for Young People. Paul Martin. (Good Morning, Lord Ser.). 1974. 4.95 (ISBN 0-8010-5958-5). Baker Bk.

Good Morning, Lord: Devotions for Young Teens. Greta Rey. (Good Morning, Lord Ser.). 96p. 1983. 4.95 (ISBN 0-8010-7719-2). Baker Bk.

Good Morning, Lord: Devotions from Famous Hymn Stories. Lindsay Terry. (Good Morning Lord Ser.). 1974. 3.95 (ISBN 0-8010-8882-8). Baker Bk.

Good Morning, Lord: Meditations for College Students. Leland C. May. (Good Morning Lord Ser.). 64p. (Orig.). 1981. 4.95 (ISBN 0-8010-6116-4). Baker Bk.

Good Morning, Lord: Meditations for Modern Marrieds. Louis O. Caldwell. (Good Morning Lord Ser.). 1974. 3.95 (ISBN 0-8010-2351-3). Baker Bk.

Good Morning, Lord: More Devotions for Teens. Paul Martin. (Good Morning Lord Ser.). 1973. 4.95 (ISBN 0-8010-5915-1). Baker Bk.

Good Morning, Lord: More Five Minute Devotions. Ron Hembree. (Good Morning, Lord Ser.). 64p. 1977. Repr. 3.95 (ISBN 0-8010-4178-3). Baker Bk.

Good Morning, Lord: Prayers & Promises for Teens. Margaret Shiner. (Good Morning, Lord Ser.). 96p. 1976. 4.95 (ISBN 0-8010-8079-7). Baker Bk.

Good Morning to You, Valentine. Ed. by Lee B. Hopkins. LC 75-11650. (Illus.). 32p. 1976. 11.95 (ISBN 0-15-232134-9, HJ). HarBraceJ.

Good 'n' Angry. Les Carter. 128p. 1983. 8.95 (ISBN 0-8010-2488-9); pap. 5.95 (ISBN 0-8010-2481-1). Baker Bk.

Good-Natured Man: The Evolution of a Moral Ideal, 1660-1800. John K. Sheriff. LC 81-14758. 144p. 1982. text ed. 13.50 (ISBN 0-8173-0097-X). U of Ala Pr.

Good News. Compiled by Patricia Mahany. (Story & Color Bks.). (Illus.). 64p. (Orig.). 1984. pap. 2.95 (ISBN 0-87239-797-1, 2373). Standard Pub.

Good News! Beth Neuberger. (Happy Day Bks.). (Illus.). 24p. 1984. 1.59 (ISBN 0-87239-736-X, 3706). Standard Pub.

Good News about Jesus As Told by Mark. Thomas Smith. Ed. by Alphonsus Pluth. LC 77-89324. (Illus.). 1977. pap. 3.95 (ISBN 0-88489-095-3); tchrs' ed 1.00 (ISBN 0-88489-116-X). St Mary's.

Good News about Sex. David Knight. 312p. (Orig.). 1980. pap. 4.95 (ISBN 0-912228-57-1). St Anthony Mess Pr.

Good News According to Luke. Eduard Schweizer. Tr. by David E. Green. LC 83-22237. 1984. 23.95 (ISBN 0-8042-0249-4). John Knox.

Good News According to Mark. Eduard Schweizer. Tr. by Donald Madvig. LC 77-93828. 1970. 18.95 (ISBN 0-8042-0250-8). John Knox.

Good News According to Matthew. Eduard Schweizer. Tr. by David E. Green. LC 74-3717. 1975. 19.95 (ISBN 0-8042-0251-6). John Knox.

Good News & Bad News: Haru Ser. Morris Venden. 1984. pap. 4.95 (ISBN 0-8163-0484-X). Pacific Pr Pub Assn.

Good News for Children. Sheri D. Haan. 1969. pap. 5.95 (ISBN 0-8010-4073-6). Baker Bk.

Good News for Children. Michael L. Sherer. LC 80-65554. (Visual Messages on Epistle Texts, Ser. A). 128p. pap. 6.95 (ISBN 0-8066-1798-5, 10-2808). Augsburg.

Good News for Children: Object Lessons on Epistle Texts. Michael L. Sherer. LC 81-65655. (Series B). 128p. (Orig.). 1981. pap. 6.95 (ISBN 0-8066-1891-4, 10-2809). Augsburg.

Good News for Children: Object Lessons on Epistle Texts. Michael L. Sherer. LC 82-70957. (Series C). 128p. (Orig.). 1982. pap. 6.95 (ISBN 0-8066-1932-5, 10-2810). Augsburg.

Good News for Lit. Comm. Cycle A. 5.95 (ISBN 0-8198-3011-9); 4.95 (ISBN 0-8198-3012-7). Dghtrs St Paul.

Good News for the Liturgical Community: Cycle B. Valentino Del Mazza. 1980. 5.95 (ISBN 0-8198-3004-6); pap. 4.95 (ISBN 0-8198-3005-4). Dghtrs St Paul.

Good News for the Liturgical Community: Cycle C. rev. ed. Valentino Del Mazza. 1981. 5.95 (ISBN 0-8198-0573-4); pap. 4.95 (ISBN 0-8198-3003-8). Dghtrs St Paul.

Good News for Today. Barbara M. Higdon. 1981. pap. 7.00 (ISBN 0-8309-0298-8). Herald Hse.

Good News from John: Visual Messages for Children. Harold J. Uhl. LC 79-50094. 1979. pap. 6.95 (ISBN 0-8066-1712-8, 10-2811). Augsburg.

Good News from Luke: Visual Messages for Children. Lavern G. Franzen. LC 76-3869. 112p. (Orig.). 1976. pap. 6.95 (ISBN 0-8066-1528-1, 10-2813). Augsburg.

Good News from Matthew: Visual Messages for Children. Lavern G. Frazen. LC 77-72463. 1977. pap. 6.95 (ISBN 0-8066-1597-4, 10-2814). Augsburg.

Good News Is Bad News Is Good News. William K. McElvaney. LC 79-22032. 132p. (Orig.). 1980. pap. 5.95 (ISBN 0-88344-157-8). Orbis Bks.

Good News Is Better. Weiland. (Anch Ser.). 1984. pap. 6.95 (ISBN 0-8163-0592-7). Pacific Pr Pub Assn.

Good News Is for Sharing. Leighton Ford. LC 77-78496. 1977. 6.95 (ISBN 0-89191-083-2). Cook.

Good News: Mark. W. E. McCumber. 184p. 1982. pap. 4.95 (ISBN 0-8341-0699-X). Beacon Hill.

Good News of Suffering. George W. Kosicki. LC 81-13644. 87p. (Orig.). 1981. pap. 1.95 (ISBN 0-8146-1240-7). Liturgical Pr.

Good News of the Kingdom. Don W. Blomberg. 1985. 8.75 (ISBN 0-317-13203-2). Carlton.

Good News of the Kingdom Coming. J. Andrew Kirk. LC 84-19293. 164p. 1985. pap. 5.95 (ISBN 0-87784-938-2). Inter-Varsity.

Good News to the Poor: Wealth & Poverty in Luke-Acts. Walter E. Pilgrim. LC 81-65653. 208p. (Orig.). 1981. pap. 10.95 (ISBN 0-8066-1889-2, 10-2807). Augsburg.

Good News Way of Life. Jerry L. Schmalenberger. 1985. 4.75 (ISBN 0-89536-735-1, 5819). CSS of Ohio.

Good News Way of Life: Study Book. Jerry L. Schmalenberger. 1982. pap. 0.50 (ISBN 0-89536-531-6, 0729). CSS of Ohio.

Good News Way of Life: Teacher's Guide. Jerry L. Schmalenberger. 1982. pap. 3.00 (ISBN 0-89536-530-8, 0728). CSS of Ohio.

Good Night Book. William Coleman. LC 79-20002. (Illus.). 128p. 1980. pap. 4.95 (ISBN 0-87123-187-5, 210187). Bethany Hse.

Good Night, Lord. Paul Martin. 64p. 1974. 1.95 (ISBN 0-8341-0241-2). Beacon Hill.

Good Old-Fashioned Christmas. Robert Benchley. (Illus.). 96p. (Orig.). 1981. pap. 7.95 (ISBN 0-938864-02-5). Ipswich Pr.

Good Parishioner. Mark Lyons. 1983. 4.50 (ISBN 0-8199-0830-4). Franciscan Herald.

Good People Get Burned Too. Eileen Lantry. (Life Ser.). 1984. pap. 4.95 (ISBN 0-8163-0549-8). Pacific Pr Pub Assn.

Good St. Joseph. Lawrence G. Lovasik. (Saint Joseph Picture Bks.). (Illus.). flexible bdg. 0.95 (ISBN 0-89942-283-7, 283). Catholic Bk Pub.

Good Samaritan. Janice Kramer & Mathews. LC 63-23369. (Arch Bks: Set 1). (Illus.). 1964. laminated bdg 0.99 (ISBN 0-570-06000-1, 59-1102). Concordia.

Good Samaritan. Mandevile. (Ladybird Ser.). 1979. 2.50 (ISBN 0-87508-837-6). Chr Lit.

Good Samaritan. Bill Van Horn. 1983. 3.60 (ISBN 0-89536-588-X, 0730). CSS of Ohio.

Good Samaritan Faith: A Strategy for Meeting Needs in Your Community. Bernard Thompson. LC 83-24805. 210p. 1984. pap. 6.95 (ISBN 0-8307-0932-0, 5418176). Regal.

Good Samaritan: Retold by Catherine Storr. Illus. by T. Crompton. (People of the Bible Ser.). (Illus.). 32p. 1984. 10.65 (ISBN 0-8172-1988-9, Raintree Childrens Books Belitha Press Ltd. - London). Raintree Pubs.

Good Self & the Bad Self: The Moral Psychology of British Idealism & the English School of Psychoanalysis Compared. R. Wollheim. (Dawes Hicks Lectures on Philosophy). 1975. pap. 2.50 (ISBN 0-85672-278-2, Pub. by British Acad). Longwood Pub Group.

Good Shepherd: Reflections on Psalm 23. Haddon Robinson. 1987. pap. 1.95 (ISBN 0-8024-6688-5). Moody.

Good Stuff! Compiled by David Hennig. (Good Stuff, Resources for Youth Leaders Ser.: Vol. 4). 160p. 1987. tchr's wkbk. 9.95 (ISBN 0-87403-216-4, 3416). Standard Pub.

Good Stuff, Vol. 2. Ed. by David Hennig. 160p. 1986. wkbk. 9.95 (ISBN 0-87403-014-5, 3407). Standard Pub.

Good Stuff, No. 3. Richard Koffarnus et al. (Illus.). 160p. 1986. wkbk. 9.95 (ISBN 0-87403-066-8, 3411). Standard Pub.

Good That Lives after Them. Bob Wilson. Ed. by John Kings. (Illus.). 170p. 1982. 14.50 (ISBN 0-9608192-1-5); cassette 10.00. B Wilson.

Good Things Come in Small Groups. Ron Nicholas et al. LC 85-778. 200p. 1985. pap. 6.95 (ISBN 0-87784-917-X). Inter-Varsity.

Good Thoughts about Me. Jane Peifer & Marilyn Nolt. (Good Thoughts Ser.: No. 1). (Illus.). 24p. (Orig.). 1985. pap. 2.95 (ISBN 0-8361-3389-7). Herald Pr.

Good Thoughts about People. Jane Peifer & Marilyn Nolt. (Good Thoughts Ser.: No. 3). (Illus.). 24p. (Orig.). 1985. pap. 2.95 (ISBN 0-8361-3390-0). Herald Pr.

Good Thoughts at Bedtime. Jane Peifer & Marilyn Nolt. (Good Thoughts Ser.: No. 2). (Illus.). 24p. (Orig.). 1985. pap. 2.95 (ISBN 0-8361-3388-9). Herald Pr.

Good Times Bible Activities. Frances Matranga. 24p. 1983. pap. 1.50 (ISBN 0-87239-692-4, 2362). Standard Pub.

Good Times Game Book: Good Things for Youth Leaders. Compiled by Douglas Kamstra. 1981. pap. 5.95 (ISBN 0-8010-7705-2). Baker Bk.

Good to Be a Jew. Eugene Kohn. LC 59-13350. 180p. 1959. pap. 8.95 (ISBN 0-935457-23-2). Reconstructionist Pr.

Good-Wife. Pamela Urfer. 40p. (Orig.). 1983. pap. text ed. 3.95 (ISBN 0-912801-01-8). Creat Arts Dev.

Good Words for New Christians. John R. Berry. (Orig.). 1987. pap. 2.95 (ISBN 0-9616900-0-3). J R Berry.

Good Work. E. F. Schumacher & Peter N. Gillingham. LC 76-5528. 1980. pap. 6.95x (ISBN 0-06-132053-6, TB 2053, Torch). Har-Row.

Goodbye, Grandpa. Ron Koch. LC 74-14183. 96p. 1975. pap. 4.95 (ISBN 0-8066-1465-X, 10-2816). Augsburg.

Goodenough on the History of Religion & on Judaism. Ed. by Jacob Neusner & Ernest S. Frerichs. (Brown Judaic Studies). 168p. 1987. pap. 29.95 (ISBN 1-55540-062-0, 14-01-21). Scholars Pr GA.

Goodly Heritage - Pioneers for God: Devotional Readings. John Elder. Tr. by Yahya Armajani from Farsi. LC 83-62806. viii, 141p. (Orig.). 1983. pap. 3.50 (ISBN 0-9608440-1-5). Nur Pubns.

Goodly Heritage, the Episcopal Church in Florida, 1821-1892. Joseph D. Cushman, Jr. LC 65-28693. (Illus.). 1965. 7.50 (ISBN 0-8130-0054-8). U Presses Fla.

Goodness. Carole MacKenthun & Paulinus Dwyer. (Fruit of the Spirit Ser.). (Illus.). 48p. 1986. wkbk. 4.95 (ISBN 0-86653-363-X). Good Apple.

Goodness of Marriage: A Devotional Book for Newlyweds. Perry H. Biddle, Jr. LC 84-50840. 144p. 1984. 6.95 (ISBN 0-8358-0490-9). Upper Room.

Goose Is Out. Bhagwan Shree Rajneesh. Ed. by Rajneesh Foundation International. LC 82-60497. (Question & Answer Ser.). 324p. (Orig.). 1982. pap. 10.95 (ISBN 0-88050-571-0). Chidvilas Found.

Gopis' Love for Sri Krishna. Hanumanprasad Poddar. (Illus.). 51p. 1981. pap. 9.95 (ISBN 0-913922-51-X). Dawn Horse Pr.

Gordon Wetmoe's Prayers for Boys & Girls. Gordon Wetmore. (Illus.). 48p. 1986. 5.95. Ideals.

Gospel. (Ultimate Ser.). 288p. 1983. plastic comb 17.95 (ISBN 0-9607350-6-2, 00241008); pap. 14.95 (ISBN 0-9607350-7-0, 00241009). H Leonard Pub Corp.

Gospel According to Abbie Jane Wells. 143p. 1985. 9.95 (ISBN 0-88347-175-2). Thomas More.

Gospel According to Billy. Chuck Ashman. 1977. 8.95 (ISBN 0-8184-0251-2). Lyle Stuart.

Gospel According to Genesis. Charles C. Cochrane. 96p. (Orig.). 1984. pap. 4.95 (ISBN 0-8028-1971-0). Eerdmans.

Gospel According to Genesis: A Guide to Understanding Genesis 1-11. Charles C. Cochrane. LC 84-4047. Repr. of 1984 ed. 24.00 (2027539). Bks Demand UMI.

Gospel According to Grace. Chuck Smith. 176p. 1981. pap. 3.95 (ISBN 0-936728-12-4). Word for Today.

Gospel According to John. Archibald M. Hunter. (Cambridge Bible Commentary on the New English Bible, New Testament Ser.). (Orig.). 1965. pap. 11.95x (ISBN 0-521-09255-8). Cambridge U Pr.

Gospel According to John. Morgan. 1984. 13.95 (ISBN 0-8007-0119-4). Revell.

Gospel According to John. G. Campbell Morgan. Tr. by Carl Fang. (G. Campbell Morgan's Expository Ser.). 1985. write for info. (ISBN 0-941598-94-2); pap. write for info. (ISBN 0-941598-18-7). Living Spring Pubns.

Gospel According to John One - Twelve. Tr. by Raymond E. Brown. LC 66-12209. (Anchor Bible Ser.: Vol. 29). 1966. 20.00 (ISBN 0-385-01517-8, Anchor Pr). Doubleday.

Gospel According to John Thirteen - Twenty-One. Tr. by Raymond E. Brown. LC 66-12209. (Anchor Bible Ser.: Vol. 29A). 1970. 18.00 (ISBN 0-385-03761-9, Anchor Pr). Doubleday.

Gospel According to John VII the Johannine Epistles, No. 4. Neal M. Flanagan. Ed. by Robert J. Karris. LC 82-22908. (Collegeville Bible Commentary Ser.). 128p. 1983. pap. 2.95 (ISBN 0-8146-1304-7). Liturgical Pr.

Gospel According to Luke. Morgan. 1984. 13.95 (ISBN 0-8007-0120-8). Revell.

Gospel According to Luke. G. Campbell Morgan. Tr. by Lorna Chao. (G. Campbell Morgan's Expository Ser.). 1985. write for info. (ISBN 0-941598-95-0); pap. write for info. (ISBN 0-941598-17-9). Living Spring Pubns.

Gospel According to Luke. E. J. Tinsley. (Cambridge Bible Commentary on the New English Bible, New Testament Ser.). (Orig.). 1965. pap. 10.95x (ISBN 0-521-09252-3). Cambridge U Pr.

Gospel According to Luke, No. 3. Jerome Kodell. Ed. by Robert J. Karris. LC 82-20350. (Collegeville Bible Commentary Ser.). (Illus.). 128p. 1983. pap. 2.95 (ISBN 0-8146-1303-9). Liturgical Pr.

Gospel According to Luke I-IX, Vol. 28. Joseph A. Fitzmyer. LC 80-702. (Anchor Bible Ser.). 1981. 20.00 (ISBN 0-385-00515-6). Doubleday.

Gospel According to Mark. Morgan. 1984. 13.95 (ISBN 0-8007-0121-6). Revell.

Gospel According to Mark. G. Campbell Morgan. Tr. by Silas Chan from Eng. (G. Campbell Morgan's Expository Ser.). (Chinese.). 1984. write for info. (ISBN 0-941598-96-9); pap. write for info. (ISBN 0-941598-16-0). Living Spring Pubns.

Gospel According to Mark. Charles F. Moule. (Cambridge Bible Commentary on the New English Bible, New Testament Ser.). (Orig.). 1965. 15.50 (ISBN 0-521-04210-0); pap. 7.95x (ISBN 0-521-09288-4). Cambridge U Pr.

Gospel According to Mark, No. 2. Philip Van Linden. Ed. by Robert J. Karris. LC 82-20356. (Collegeville Bible Commentary Ser.). (Illus.). 96p. 1983. pap. 2.95 (ISBN 0-8146-1302-0). Liturgical Pr.

Gospel According to Matthew. Ed. by Aubrey W. Argyle. (Cambridge Bible Commentary on the New Testament Ser.). (Orig.). 1963. o. p. 19.95 (ISBN 0-521-04197-X); pap. 10.95 (ISBN 0-521-09198-5). Cambridge U Pr.

Gospel According to Matthew. Morgan. 1984. 13.95 (ISBN 0-8007-0122-4). Revell.

Gospel According to Matthew. G. Campbell Morgan. Tr. by David Chang from Eng. (G. Campbell Morgan's Expository Ser.). (Chinese.). 1984. write for info. (ISBN 0-941598-97-7); pap. write for info. (ISBN 0-941598-15-2). Living Spring Pubns.

Gospel According to Matthew, No. 1. Daniel J. Harrington. Ed. by Robert J. Karris. LC 82-20333. (Collegeville Bible Commentary Ser.). (Illus.). 128p. 1983. pap. 2.95 (ISBN 0-8146-1301-2). Liturgical Pr.

Gospel According to Matthew: A Structural Commentary on Matthew's Faith. Daniel Patte. LC 86-45218. 432p. 1986. pap. 19.95 (ISBN 0-8006-1978-1, 1-1978). Fortress.
Gospel According to Matthew in the Revised Standard Version. H. Benedict Green. (New Clarendon Bible Ser). 1975. pap. 9.95x (ISBN 0-19-836911-5). Oxford U Pr.
Gospel According to Matthew: Translation, Commentary, & Notes. F. W. Beare. LC 81-47837. 575p. 1982. 29.45 (ISBN 0-06-060731-9, HarpR). Har-Row.
Gospel According to Norton. Grady Nutt. LC 73-91610. pap. 4.50 (ISBN 0-8054-5322-9, 4253-22). Broadman.
Gospel According to Peanuts. Robert L. Short. pap. 6.95 (ISBN 0-8042-1968-0). John Knox.
Gospel According to St. John. 2nd ed. C. K. Barrett. LC 78-2587. 654p. 1978. 28.95 (ISBN 0-664-21364-2). Westminster.
Gospel According to St. John, Vol. II. Josef Blank. Ed. by John L. McKenzie. LC 81-605. (New Testament for Spiritual Reading Ser.). 282p. 1981. pap. 4.95. Crossroad NY.
Gospel According to St. John, Vol. I. John Huckle & Paul Visokay. Ed. by John L. McKenzie. LC 81-605. (New Testament for Spiritual Reading Ser.). 282p. 1981. 10.00; pap. 4.95. Crossroad NY.
Gospel According to St. John. Alfred Plummer. (Thornapple Commentaries Ser.). 380p. 1981. pap. 9.95 (ISBN 0-8010-7068-6). Baker Bk.
Gospel According to St. John, 2 vols. Rudolf Schnackenburg. 1980. 39.50x ea. Vol. 1 (ISBN 0-8245-0311-2). Vol. 2 (ISBN 0-8245-0312-0). Crossroad NY.
Gospel According to St. John. Randolph V. Tasker. (Tyndale Bible Commentaries Ser.). 1960. pap. 4.95 (ISBN 0-8028-1403-4). Eerdmans.
Gospel According to St. John, Vol. 3. Rudolf Schnackenburg. 566p. 1982. 39.50x (ISBN 0-8245-0098-9). Crossroad NY.
Gospel According to St. John: A Theological Commentary. Pheme Perkins. LC 77-12896. (Herald Scriptural Library). pap. 66.80 (ISBN 0-317-28173-9, 2022571). Bks Demand UMI.
Gospel According to Saint John: The Greek Text with Introduction & Notes, 2 vols. in 1. Brooke F. Westcott. Ed. by Arthur Westcott. 877p. 1980. pap. 16.95 (ISBN 0-8010-9644-8). Baker Bk.
Gospel According to St. John Vols. I, II & III, the New Testament for Spiritual Reading Vols. 7, 8, & 9. John Huckle. 1978. Vol. I. pap. 4.95 (ISBN 0-8245-0116-0); Vol. II. pap. 4.95 (ISBN 0-8245-0117-9); Vol. III. pap. 4.95 (ISBN 0-8245-0118-7). Crossroad NY.
Gospel According to St. Luke. Leon Morris. (Tyndale New Testament Commentaries Ser.). 1974. pap. 5.95 (ISBN 0-8028-1402-6). Eerdmans.
Gospel According to St. Luke, Vol. I. Alois Stoger. Ed. by John L. McKenzie. LC 81-605. (New Testament for Spiritual Reading Ser.). 182p. 1981. pap. 4.95 (ISBN 0-8245-0114-4). Crossroad NY.
Gospel According to St. Luke, Vol. II. Alois Stoger. Ed. by John L. McKenzie. LC 81-605. (New Testament for Spiritual Reading Ser.). 182p. 1981. pap. 4.95 (ISBN 0-8245-0115-2). Crossroad NY.
Gospel According to St. Mark. Alan Cole. (Tyndale Bible Commentaries Ser.). 1962. pap. 5.95 (ISBN 0-8028-1401-8). Eerdmans.
Gospel According to St. Mark. Alfred Plummer. (Thornapple Commentaries Ser.). 448p. 1982. pap. 12.95 (ISBN 0-8010-7072-4). Baker Bk.
Gospel According to St. Mark, Vol. II. Rudolf Schnackenburg. Ed. by John L. McKenzie. LC 81-605. (New Testament for Spiritual Reading Ser.). 182p. 1981. pap. 4.95 (ISBN 0-686-85824-7). Crossroad NY.
Gospel According to St. Mark, Vol. I. Rudolf Schnakenburg. Ed. by John L. McKenzie. LC 81-605. (New Testament for Spiritual Reading Ser.). 182p. pap. 4.95 (ISBN 0-8245-0112-8). Crossroad NY.
Gospel According to St. Matthew. A. H. McNeile. (Thornapple Commentaries Ser.). 484p. 1980. pap. 8.95 (ISBN 0-8010-6099-0). Baker Bk.
Gospel According to St. Matthew. Randolph V. Tasker. (Tyndale Bible Commentaries Ser.). 1962. pap. 5.95 (ISBN 0-8028-1400-X). Eerdmans.
Gospel According to St. Matthew, Vol. I. Wolfgang Trilling. Ed. by John L. McKenzie. LC 81-605. (New Testament for Spiritual Reading Ser.). 182p. 1981. pap. 4.95 (ISBN 0-8245-0110-1). Crossroad NY.
Gospel According to St. Matthew, Vol. II. Wolfgang Trilling. Ed. by John L. McKenzie. LC 81-605. (New Testament for Spiritual Reading Ser.). 182p. 1981. pap. 4.95 (ISBN 0-8245-0111-X). Crossroad NY.
Gospel According to St. Paul. rev. ed. Archibald M. Hunter. LC 67-10511. Orig. Title: Interpreting Paul's Gospel. 126p. 1967. pap. 7.95 (ISBN 0-664-24742-3). Westminster.
Gospel According to Thomas. Saint Thomas. (Sacred Texts Ser.). Orig. Title: Coptic. vii, 88p. 1983. pap. 8.75 (ISBN 0-88695-005-8). Concord Grove.
Gospel According to Woman. Karen Armstrong. LC 86-26610. 384p. 1987. 17.95 (ISBN 0-385-24078-3, Anchor Pr). Doubleday.
Gospel According to Zen: Beyond the Death of God. Ed. by Robert Sohl & Audrey Carr. (Orig.). 1970. pap. 2.95 (ISBN 0-451-62184-0, ME2184, Ment). NAL.
Gospel Advocate Index. 1985. 49.95 (ISBN 0-89225-280-4). Gospel Advocate.
Gospel Against Parable: Mark's Language of Mystery. James G. Williams. (Bible & Literature Ser.: No. 12). 246p. 1985. text ed. 24.95x (ISBN 0-907459-44-7, Pub. by Almond Pr England); pap. text ed. 10.95x (ISBN 0-907459-45-5). Eisenbrauns.
Gospel Among the Slaves. William P. Harrison. LC 70-168249. Repr. of 1893 ed. 27.50 (ISBN 0-404-00263-3). AMS Pr.
Gospel & Islam: A Compendium. abr. ed. Ed. by Don M. McCurry. 269p. 1979. pap. 6.95 (ISBN 0-912552-26-3). Missions Adv Res Com Ctr.
Gospel & Its Ministry. Robert Anderson. LC 78-9539. (Sir Robert Anderson Library). 224p. 1978. pap. 4.95 (ISBN 0-8254-2126-8). Kregel.
Gospel & Its Proclamation. Robert D. Sider. (Message of the Fathers of the Church Ser.: Vol. 10). 15.95 (ISBN 0-89453-350-9); pap. 9.95 (ISBN 0-89453-321-5). M Glazier.
Gospel & Kingdom: A Christian Interpretation of the Old Testament. Graeme Goldsworthy. pap. cancelled (ISBN 0-85364-218-4, Pub. by Paternoster U K). Attic Pr.
Gospel & Kingdom: A Christian's Guide to the Old Testament. Graeme Goldsworthy. 128p. 1983. pap. 6.95 (ISBN 0-86683-686-1, HarpR). Har-Row.
Gospel & Law: Contrast or Continuum? the Hermeneutics of Dispensationalism & Covenant Theology. Daniel P. Fuller. (Orig.). 1980. pap. 8.95 (ISBN 0-8028-1808-0). Eerdmans.
Gospel & Mother Goose. Donald E. Miller. 112p. (Orig.). 1987. pap. 6.95 (ISBN 0-87178-320-7). Brethren.
Gospel & Qasida. Tr. by Arthur Wormhoudt. (Arab Translation Ser.: No. 84). (Illus.). 180p. (Orig.). 1985. pap. 6.50x (ISBN 0-916358-36-4). Wormhoudt.
Gospel & the Land: Early Christianity & Jewish Territorial Doctrine. W. D. Davies. LC 72-82228. 1974. 32.50x (ISBN 0-520-02278-5). U of Cal Pr.
Gospel & the Path of Separation. R. P. Daniel. pap. 3.25 (ISBN 0-88172-016-X). Believers Bkshelf.
Gospel & the Poor. Wolfgang Stegemann. Tr. by Dietlinde Elliott from Ger. LC 83-48915. 80p. 1984. pap. 3.95 (ISBN 0-8006-1783-5, 1-1783). Fortress.
Gospel at Infant Baptism. Frederick Levinson. pap. 4.95x (ISBN 0-7152-0443-2). Outlook.
Gospel Basics Busy Book. Randall Mehew & Karen Mehew. 150p. 1980. 4.95 (ISBN 0-934126-11-9). Randall Bk Co.
Gospel Behind Bars. Lloyd N. Colbaugh. LC 79-53942. (Radiant Life Ser.). 96p. (Orig.). 1979. pap. 1.50 (ISBN 0-88243-503-5, 02-0503). Gospel Pub.
Gospel Blimp & Other Stories. Joseph Bayly. LC 83-70533. 1983. pap. 4.95 (ISBN 0-89191-731-4). Cook.
Gospel, Church, & Kingdom: Comparative Studies in World Mission Theology. James A. Scherer. 256p. (Orig.). 1987. pap. 14.95 (ISBN 0-8066-2280-6, 10-2828). Augsburg.
Gospel Church Choir Organizer. Vernetta Martin-Marrero. 150p. 1984. 3 ring hard storage binder 29.95 (ISBN 0-9613430-0-1). Martin-Marrero.
Gospel Conspiracy in the Episcopal Church. Michael E. Marshall. (Orig.). 1986. pap. 6.95 (ISBN 0-8192-1386-1). Morehouse.
Gospel Conspiracy Workbook. Charles M. Irish. 40p. 1986. wkbk. 2.95 (ISBN 0-8192-1387-X). Morehouse.
Gospel Criticism & Form Criticism. W. Emery Barnes. 84p. 1936. pap. text ed. 6.95 (ISBN 0-567-02020-7, Pub. by T & T Clark Ltd UK). Fortress.
Gospel Dialogue. Watchman Nee. Tr. by Stephen Kaung. 1975. 5.25 (ISBN 0-935008-21-7); pap. 4.00 (ISBN 0-935008-22-5). Christian Fellow Pubs.
Gospel Doctrine. Joseph F. Smith. 553p. 1975. 10.95. Deseret Bk.
Gospel Doctrine. Joseph F. Smith. 1986. text ed. 10.95 (ISBN 0-87579-063-1). Deseret Bk.
Gospel Dramas: Twelve Plays for Worship in Lent & Other Seasons. Dean Nadasdy. LC 85-22886. 96p. (Orig.). 1985. pap. 4.95 (ISBN 0-8066-2185-0, 10-2829). Augsburg.
Gospel for Children: Object Messages from the Gospel of Mark. Harold J. Uhl. LC 75-14695. 128p. 1975. pap. 6.95 (ISBN 0-8066-1493-5, 10-2830). Augsburg.
Gospel for Kids: Series A. Eldon Weishiet. 1977. 6.75 (ISBN 0-570-03265-2, 15-2711). Concordia.
Gospel for Kids: Series B. Eldon Weisheit. 1978. 6.75 (ISBN 0-570-03267-9, 15-2713). Concordia.
Gospel for Kids: Series C. Eldon Weisheit. 1979. 6.75 (ISBN 0-570-03279-2, 15-2723). Concordia.
Gospel for Little Kids. Eldon Weisheit. 1980. pap. 4.95 (ISBN 0-570-03811-1, 12-2920). Concordia.
Gospel for Sundays & Feasts: Cycle B. 1979. 7.50 (ISBN 0-8198-0573-4); pap. 6.00 (ISBN 0-8198-0574-2). Dghtrs St Paul.
Gospel for the Cities. Benjamin Tonna. Tr. by William E. Jerman from It. LC 81-18807. Orig. Title: Vangelo per le Citta. Tr. of Vangelo per le Citta. 224p. (Orig.). 1982. pap. 10.95 (ISBN 0-88344-155-1). Orbis Bks.
Gospel for the Clockaholic. Thomas L. Are. 128p. 1985. pap. 5.95 (ISBN 0-8170-1075-0). Judson.
Gospel for the Person Who Has Everything. William H. Willimon. 1978. pap. 4.95 (ISBN 0-8170-0758-X). Judson.
Gospel for Young Christians. Harold Winstone. (Illus.). 192p. 1985. 3.95 (ISBN 0-225-27392-6, HarpR). Har-Row.
Gospel from Outer Space. Robert L. Short. LC 82-48936. (Illus.). 128p. (Orig.). 1983. pap. 5.95 (ISBN 0-06-067376-1, CN4064, HarpR). Har-Row.
Gospel Guitar. Tommy Flint & Neil Griffin. 48p. 1976. wkbk 2.95 (ISBN 0-89228-018-2). Impact Bks MO.
Gospel Hymns & Social Religion: The Rhetoric of Nineteenth-Century Revivalism. Sandra S. Sizer. LC 78-10165. (American Civilization Ser.). 222p. 1979. lib. bdg. 27.95 (ISBN 0-87722-142-1). Temple U Pr.
Gospel Hyms, 6 vols, No. 1-6. facsimile ed. Ira D. Sankey et al. LC 70-171076. (Earlier American Music Ser.: No. 5). 512p. 1972. Repr. of 1895 ed. lib. bdg. 37.50 (ISBN 0-306-77305-8). Da Capo.
Gospel in Art by the Peasants of Solentiname. Commentary by Philip Scharper & Sally Sharper. Tr. by Donaldly Walsh from Span. (Illus.). 70p. 1984. 10.95 (ISBN 0-88344-382-1). Orbis Bks.
Gospel in Hymns. Albert E. Bailey. (Illus.). 1950. lib. rep. ed. 45.00x (ISBN 0-684-15554-0, PG104HHRE, ScribT). Scribner.
Gospel in Leviticus. Joseph Seiss. LC 80-8078. 408p. 1981. 12.95 (ISBN 0-8254-3743-1). Kregel.
Gospel in Madison Avenue. Peter Rudowski. 1983. 3.85 (ISBN 0-89536-644-4, 0741). CSS of Ohio.
Gospel in Solentiname, 4 vols. Ernesto Cardenal. Tr. by Donald D. Walsh from Span. LC 76-2681. Orig. Title: Evangelio en Solentiname. (Orig.). 1982. Vol. 1, 288p. pap. 8.95 (ISBN 0-88344-176-4); Vol. 2, 272p. pap. 8.95 (ISBN 0-88344-175-6); Vol. 3, 320p. pap. 8.95 (ISBN 0-88344-174-8); Vol. 4, 288p. pap. 8.95 (ISBN 0-88344-173-X). Orbis Bks.
Gospel in the Church: A Catechetical Commentary on the Lectionary Cycle C: the Creed. Quentin Quesnell. LC 82-9951. 176p. 1982. 12.95 (ISBN 0-8245-0454-2); pap. 5.95 (ISBN 0-8245-0476-3). Crossroad NY.
Gospel in the Feasts of Israel. 1954. pap. 2.95 (ISBN 0-915540-00-2). Friends Israel-Spearhead Pr.
Gospel in the Feasts of Israel. Burtis Williams. 32p. 1968. pap. 0.50 (ISBN 0-89114-011-5). Baptist Pub Hse.
Gospel in the Last Days. J. M. Little. LC 84-90258. 143p. 1985. 10.95 (ISBN 0-533-06299-3). Vantage.
Gospel in the Stars. Joseph A. Seiss. LC 72-86676. (Illus.). 1986. pap. 10.95 (ISBN 0-8254-3755-5). Kregel.
Gospel Is Not Western: Black Theologies from Aboriginal Australia & Melanesia. Ed. by G. W. Trompf. LC 86-23539. (Illus.). 224p. (Orig.). 1987. pap. 17.95 (ISBN 0-88344-269-8). Orbis Bks.
Gospel Journey. Ernest Ferlita. 120p. (Orig.). 1983. pap. 5.95 (ISBN 0-86683-685-3, HarpR). Har-Row.
Gospel Lesson Plans. Catherine Uhl. LC 79-65918. 136p. 1979. pap. 7.95 (ISBN 0-8091-2211-1). Paulist Pr.
Gospel Life of Francis of Assisi Today. Thaddee Matura. 1980. 6.95 (ISBN 0-317-46873-1). Franciscan Herald.
Gospel Light: An Indispensable Guide to the Teachings of Jesus & the Customs of His Time. George M. Lamsa. LC 86-45020. 416p. 1986. pap. 12.95 (ISBN 0-06-064928-3, HarpR). Har-Row.
Gospel Love: A Narrative Theology. John Navone. (Good News Studies Ser.: Vol. 12). 1984. pap. 8.95 (ISBN 0-89453-437-8). M Glazier.
Gospel Magic: Easy Made & Self Contained, No. 2. 1982. pap. 4.95 (ISBN 0-915398-20-6). Visual Evangels.
Gospel Magic with Homemade Stuff & Things, No. 1. Arnold C. Westphal. 1972. pap. 4.95 (ISBN 0-915398-09-5). Visual Evangels.
Gospel Manuscripts of the General Theological Seminary. C. C. Edmunds & W. H. Hatch. (Harv Theol Studies). 1918. pap. 15.00 (ISBN 0-527-01004-9). Kraus Repr.
Gospel Millennium & Obedience to the Scripture. Robert Whitelaw. pap. 0.75 (ISBN 0-685-88376-0). Reiner.
Gospel of a Poor Woman. Catherine D. Doherty. 6.95 (ISBN 0-87193-151-6). Dimension Bks.
Gospel of Barnabas. Barnabas. 1981. pap. 9.95 (ISBN 0-686-77427-2). Kazi Pubns.
Gospel of Buddha. Paul Carus. (Illus.). 1979. pap. 6.95 (ISBN 0-89744-195-8). Auromere.
Gospel of Buddha. Paul Carus. 59.95 (ISBN 0-8490-0252-4). Gordon Pr.
Gospel of Buddha. rev. & enl. ed. Paul Carus. LC 17-29837. (Illus.). 331p. 1915. deluxe ed. 24.95 (ISBN 0-87548-226-0); pap. 9.95 (ISBN 0-87548-228-7). Open Court.
Gospel of Christ. Theodore Stylianopoulos. 32p. 1981. pap. 1.95 (ISBN 0-916586-84-7). Hellenic Coll Pr.
Gospel of Emerson. Newton Dillaway. 1968. Repr. 5.95 (ISBN 0-87159-046-8). Unity School.
Gospel of Gentility: American Women Missionaries in Turn-of-the Century-China. Jane Hunter. LC 83-16668. 352p. 1984. 27.50x (ISBN 0-300-02878-4). Yale U Pr.
Gospel of Guru Granth Sahib. Greenlees. 8.95 (ISBN 0-8356-7132-1). Theos Pub Hse.
Gospel of Healing. rev. ed. A. B. Simpson. LC 86-70736. 180p. 1986. pap. 5.45 (ISBN 0-87509-376-0). Chr Pubns.
Gospel of Islam. Greenlees. 7.25 (ISBN 0-8356-7158-5). Theos Pub Hse.
Gospel of Jesus & Paul. Bill Kaiser. 152p. (Orig.). 1985. pap. text ed. 5.95 (ISBN 0-914307-37-1). Word Faith.
Gospel of Jesus Christ According to Mistress Ava. Tr. by Teta E. Moehs. (Senda de Estudios & Ensayos Ser.). (Ger. & Eng., Illus.). 176p. (Orig.). 1986. pap. 12.95 (ISBN 0-918454-53-0). Senda Nueva.
Gospel of John. James M. Boice. 1986. 34.95 (ISBN 0-310-21570-6, 10429). Zondervan.
Gospel of John. F. F. Bruce. 440p. 1984. 13.95 (ISBN 0-8028-3407-8). Eerdmans.
Gospel of John. 3rd ed. Paul Butler. LC 78-1789. (Bible Study Textbook Ser.). (Illus.). 1965. 15.90 (ISBN 0-89900-035-5). College Pr Pub.
Gospel of John. William R. Cannon. 128p. (Orig.). 1985. pap. 4.95 (ISBN 0-8358-0511-5). Upper Room.
Gospel of John. rev. ed. Arno C. Gaebelein. LC 65-26586. 1965. 9.95 (ISBN 0-87213-220-X). Loizeaux.
Gospel of John. Ernst Haenchen. Tr. by Robert W. FUnk from Ger. LC 82-48756. (Hermeneia). 1984. 34.95 (ISBN 0-8006-6013-7, 20-6013). Fortress.
Gospel of John. H. A. Ironside. 16.95 (ISBN 0-87213-373-7). Loizeaux.
Gospel of John. F. B. Meyer. 1970. pap. 6.95 (ISBN 0-87508-346-3). Chr Lit.
Gospel of John. Leon Morris. (New International Commentary of the New Testament Ser.). 1970. 24.95 (ISBN 0-8028-2296-7). Eerdmans.
Gospel of John, 2 vols. in 1. David Thomas. LC 79-15415. (Kregel Bible Study Classics Ser.). 846p. 1980. 24.95 (ISBN 0-8254-3809-8). Kregel.
Gospel of John, 2 vols. in 1. rev. ed. W. H. Van Doren. LC 80-8080. (Kregel Bible Study Classics Ser.). 1454p. 1981. text ed. 34.50 (ISBN 0-8254-3953-1). Kregel.
Gospel of John, Vol. 2. Tr. by Ernst Haenchen from Ger. Ed. by Robert W. Funk. LC 82-48756. (Hermeneia Ser.). 384p. 34.95 (ISBN 0-8006-6015-3). Fortress.
Gospel of John: A Commentary. Rudolf Bultmann. LC 70-125197. 758p. 1971. 26.50 (ISBN 0-664-20893-2). Westminster.
Gospel of John & Judaiam. Charles K. Barrett. Tr. by D. M. Smith. LC 75-15435. pap. 27.80 (2026897). Bks Demand UMI.
Gospel of John & Judaism. C. K. Barrett. Tr. by D. M. Smith. LC 75-15435. 112p. 1975. 3.95 (ISBN 0-8006-0431-8, 1-431). Fortress.
Gospel of John in Christian History. J. Louis Martyn. LC 78-70821. 160p. 1979. pap. 5.95 (ISBN 0-8091-2170-0). Paulist Pr.
Gospel of Luke. H. A. Ironside. 14.95 (ISBN 0-87213-376-1). Loizeaux.
Gospel of Luke. William Kelly. 1981. 18.50 (ISBN 0-86524-046-9, 4201). Klock & Klock.
Gospel of Luke. I. Howard Marshall. (New International Greek Testament Commentary Ser.). 1978. 35.00 (ISBN 0-8028-3512-0). Eerdmans.
Gospel of Luke, 2 vols. in 1. W. H. Van Doren. LC 80-8079. (Kregel Bible Study Classics Ser.). 1100p. 1981. 29.95 (ISBN 0-8254-3952-3). Kregel.

Gospel of Mark. Ed. by H. Anderson. (New Century Bible Ser.). 384p. 1976. 9.50 (ISBN 0-551-00579-3). Attic Pr.

Gospel of Mark. rev. ed. Hugh Anderson. (New Century Bible Commentary Ser.). 384p. 1981. pap. 8.95 (ISBN 0-8028-1887-0). Eerdmans.

Gospel of Mark. H. A. Ironside. 8.95 (ISBN 0-87213-377-X). Loizeaux.

Gospel of Mark. B. W. Johnson & Don DeWelt. LC 76-1069. (Bible Study Textbook Ser.). (Illus.). 1965. 15.90 (ISBN 0-89900-033-9). College Pr Pub.

Gospel of Mark. Philip Van Linden. 1976. 1.75 (ISBN 0-8199-0630-1). Franciscan Herald.

Gospel of Mark: A Translation for Children. Tr. by Wayne W. Martin. LC 84-50838. 112p. (Orig.). 1984. pap. 9.95 (ISBN 0-8358-0493-3). Upper Room.

Gospel of Matthew. William R. Cannon. LC 82-50948. 128p. (Orig.). 1983. pap. 4.95 (ISBN 0-8358-0450-X). Upper Room.

Gospel of Matthew, Vol. IV. Jack Cottrell. LC 85-72877. (Bible Study Textbook Ser.). 996p. text ed. 18.95 (ISBN 0-89900-032-0). College Pr Pub.

Gospel of Matthew, Vol. I. Harold Fowler. LC 78-1064. (Bible Study Textbook Ser.). (Illus.). 1975. 14.30 (ISBN 0-89900-029-0). College Pr Pub.

Gospel of Matthew, Vol. II. Harold Fowler. (Bible Study Textbook Ser.). (Illus.). 1972. 17.50 (ISBN 0-89900-030-4). College Pr Pub.

Gospel of Matthew, Vol. III. Harold Fowler. (Bible Study Textbook Ser.). (Illus.). 1978. 18.95 (ISBN 0-89900-031-2). College Pr Pub.

Gospel of Matthew. Arno C. Gaebelein. LC 61-17223. 1961. Repr. of 1910 ed. 12.95 (ISBN 0-87213-221-8). Loizeaux.

Gospel of Matthew. rev. ed. David Hill. (New Century Bible Commentary Ser.). 368p. 1981. pap. 8.95 (ISBN 0-8028-1886-2). Eerdmans.

Gospel of Matthew. H. A. Ironside. 9.95 (ISBN 0-87213-378-8). Loizeaux.

Gospel of Matthew. Donald Senior. (Read & Pray Ser.). 1974. 1.75 (ISBN 0-8199-0518-6). Franciscan Herald.

Gospel of Matthew According to a Primitive Hebrew Text. George Howard. 240p. 1987. 49.95 (ISBN 0-86554-250-3, MUP/H215). Mercer Univ Pr.

Gospel of Moses. Samuel J. Schultz. 1979. 6.95 (ISBN 0-8024-3198-4). Moody.

Gospel of Music: A Key to Understanding a Major Chord of Ministry. E. Myron Noble. LC 85-63559. 159p. (Orig.). 1986. pap. 4.95 (ISBN 0-9616056-1-8). Mid Atl Reg Pr.

Gospel of Our Salvation. Aldai Loudy. 122p. 1973. text ed. 4.00 (ISBN 0-910424-60-8). Concordant.

Gospel of Our Salvation. H. Forbes Witherby. 254p. 1986. 9.95 (ISBN 0-8254-4026-2). Kregel.

Gospel of Peace & Justice: Catholic Social Teaching Since Pope John. Ed. by Joseph Gremillion. LC 75-39892. 637p. (Orig.). 1976. pap. 14.95 (ISBN 0-88344-166-7). Orbis Bks.

Gospel of St. John. Pheme Perkins. (Read & Pray Ser.). 96p. 1975. pap. 1.75 (ISBN 0-685-55958-0). Franciscan Herald.

Gospel of St. John. Rudolf Steiner. Tr. by Maud B. Monges from Ger. LC 63-1084. (Illus.). 192p. 1984. 14.95 (ISBN 0-88010-107-5); pap. 8.95 (ISBN 0-910142-13-0). Anthroposophic.

Gospel of St. John. Rudolf Steiner. (Russian Language Ser.). 294p. 1985. pap. 12.00 (ISBN 0-89345-900-3, Steiner). Garber Comm.

Gospel of St. John. Rudolf Steiner. (Russian Language Ser.). 196p. 1985. pap. 10.00 (ISBN 0-89345-906-2, Steiner). Garber Comm.

Gospel of St. John & In Relation to the Other Gospels. rev. ed. Rudolf Steiner. Ed. by Stewart Easton. Tr. by Samuel Lockwood & Loni Lockwood. 298p. 1982. 14.00 (ISBN 0-88010-015-X); pap. 8.95 (ISBN 0-88010-014-1). Anthroposophic.

Gospel of Saint John: Commentaries. John Marsh. (Orig.). 1968. pap. 8.95 (ISBN 0-14-020491-1, Pelican). Penguin.

Gospel of St. Luke. Robert Karris. (Read & Pray Ser.). 1974. 1.75 (ISBN 0-8199-0626-3). Franciscan Herald.

Gospel of St. Luke. Rudolf Steiner. 1964. 14.95 (ISBN 0-85440-042-7). Anthroposophic.

Gospel of St. Luke. Rudolf Steiner. (Russian Language Ser.). 202p. 1985. pap. 10.00 (ISBN 0-89345-902-X, Steiner). Garber Comm.

Gospel of St. Luke: Commentaries. George B. Caird. (Orig.). 1964. pap. 7.95 (ISBN 0-14-020490-3, Pelican). Penguin.

Gospel of St. Mark: Commentaries. Dennis E. Nineham. (Orig.). 1964. pap. 7.95 (ISBN 0-14-020489-X, Pelican). Penguin.

Gospel of St. Matthew. 2nd ed. Rudolf Steiner. Tr. of Matthaeus-Evangelium. 230p. 1985. pap. 10.95 (ISBN 0-88010-134-2). Anthroposophic.

Gospel of St. Matthew: Commentaries. John Fenton. (Orig.). 1964. pap. 7.95 (ISBN 0-14-020488-1, Pelican). Penguin.

Gospel of Selfless Action or the Gita According to Gandhi. M. K. Gandhi. Ed. by Mahadev Desai. 1985. pap. 11.00x (ISBN 0-8364-1397-0, Pub. by Navajivan). South Asia Bks.

Gospel of the Comforter. Steele. pap. 5.95 (ISBN 0-686-12870-2). Schmul Pub Co.

Gospel of the Here & Now. Gordon Hyde. Ed. by Gerald Wheeler. (Illus.). 128p. (Orig.). 1984. pap. 4.95 (ISBN 0-8280-0247-9). Review & Herald.

Gospel of the Holy Mother. Tr. of Bengali. 410p. (Orig.). 1985. pap. 8.95 (ISBN 0-87481-531-2, Pub. by Ramakrishna Math Madras India). Vedanta Pr.

Gospel of the Holy Mother. Sri Sarada Devi. 409p. 1986. pap. 7.50X (ISBN 0-8364-1667-8, Pub. by Mukhopadhyaya India). South Asia Bks.

Gospel of the Holy Spirit. Alfred McBride. 1975. pap. 1.50 (ISBN 0-88479-951-4). Arena Lettres.

Gospel of the King (Matthew) Leader's Guide. (New Horizons Bible Study Ser.). 47p. (Orig.). 1986. pap. 1.95 (ISBN 0-89367-116-9). Light & Life.

Gospel of the King (Matthew) Student Guide. (New Horizons Bible Study Ser.). 64p. (Orig.). 1986. pap. 2.50 (ISBN 0-89367-115-0). Light & Life.

Gospel of the Kingdom. George E. Ladd. 1959. pap. 4.95 (ISBN 0-8028-1280-5). Eerdmans.

Gospel of the Kingdom. Philip Mauro. 6.95 (ISBN 0-685-19829-4). Reiner.

Gospel of the Kingdom (Matthew) C. H. Spurgeon. 1978. pap. 4.95 (ISBN 0-686-09110-8). Pilgrim Pubns.

Gospel of the Kingdom of Heaven. Frederick D. Maurice. 416p. 1977. Repr. of 1864 ed. 12.50 (ISBN 0-87921-037-0). Attic Pr.

Gospel of the Lord. Marcion Of Sinope. Tr. by James H. Hill. LC 78-63171. (Heresies of the Early Christian & Medieval Era: Second Ser.). Repr. of 1891 ed. 19.50 (ISBN 0-404-16186-3). AMS Pr.

Gospel of Thomas & Christian Wisdom. Stevan L. Davies. 160p. 1983. pap. 9.95 (ISBN 0-8164-2456-X, HarpR). Har-Row.

Gospel of Truth. Tr. by Kendrick Grobel. LC 78-63167. (Heresies of the Early Christian & Medieval Era: Second Ser.). Repr. of 1960 ed. 26.00. AMS Pr.

Gospel Parallels: A Synopsis of the First Three Gospels. 4th ed. Burton H. Throckmorton. 1979. 10.95 (ISBN 0-8407-5150-8). Nelson.

Gospel Perspectives: Studies of History & Tradition in the Four Gospels, Vol. II. Ed. by R. T. France & David Wenham. 375p. 1981. text ed. 14.75x (ISBN 0-905774-31-0, Pub. by JSOT Pr England). Eisenbrauns.

Gospel Perspectives: Studies of History & Tradition in the Four Gospels, Vol. 1. Ed. by R. T. France & David Wenham. 263p. 1980. text ed. 14.75x (ISBN 0-905774-21-3, Pub. by JSOT Pr England). Eisenbrauns.

Gospel Perspectives, Vol. III: Studies of History & Tradition in the Four Gospels. Ed. by R. T. France & David Wenham. 299p. 1983. text ed. 14.75x (ISBN 0-905774-56-6, Pub. by JSOT Press England). Eisenbrauns.

Gospel Poverty: Essays in Biblical Theology. Augustine George et al. Tr. by Michael D. Guinan. LC 76-44548. 167p. 1977. 6.95 (ISBN 0-8199-0610-7). Franciscan Herald.

Gospel Poverty: Witness to the Risen Christ. Michael D. Guinan. LC 81-80051. 96p. (Orig.). 1981. pap. 4.95 (ISBN 0-8091-2377-0). Paulist Pr.

Gospel Power: Toward the Revitalization of Preaching. John Burke. LC 77-14517. 1978. pap. 4.95 (ISBN 0-8189-0359-7). Alba.

Gospel Principles. 1978. Repr. 7.95 (ISBN 0-87747-716-7). Deseret Bk.

Gospel Radicalism: A Study of the Hard Sayings of Jesus. Thaddee Matura. Tr. by Maggi Despot & Paul Lachance. LC 83-6249. Orig. Title: Radicalisme Evangelique Aux Sources de la vie Chretienne. 208p. (Orig.). 1984. pap. 8.95 (ISBN 0-88344-182-9). Orbis Bks.

Gospel Shines Through. Thomas Peterson. (Orig.). 1987. pap. price not set (ISBN 0-89536-874-9, 7860). CSS of Ohio.

Gospel Showdown. Kenneth McFarland. (Outreach Ser.). 32p. 1981. pap. 1.25 (ISBN 0-8163-0435-1). Pacific Pr Pub Assn.

Gospel Sound: Good News & Bad Times. rev. updated ed. Anthony Heilbut. LC 84-26122. (Illus.). 416p. 1985. pap. 9.95 (ISBN 0-87910-034-6). Limelight Edns.

Gospel Stories. Edward W. Dolch & M. P. Dolch. (Pleasure Reading Ser.). 176p. 1951. PLB 6.57 (ISBN 0-8116-2608-3). Garrard.

Gospel Surprise Paper Tears. Arnold C. Westphal. (No. 13). 1986. pap. 4.95 (ISBN 0-915398-25-7). Visual Evangels.

Gospel, the Church & the World. Ed. by Kenneth Latourette. LC 76-134107. (Essay Index Reprint Ser). 1946. 18.00 (ISBN 0-8369-1972-6). Ayer Co Pubs.

Gospel: The Life of Jesus. Ed. by Baird W. Whitlock. LC 83-40471. 160p. 1984. 11.95 (ISBN 0-8052-3875-1). Schocken.

Gospel Themes. Donald W. Hemmingway. 90p. 1982. 3.95 (ISBN 0-934126-25-9). Randall Bk Co.

Gospel Themes: Four Portraits of Christ's Life. Jim Townsend. (Bible Mastery Ser.). 144p. 1987. pap. 5.95 (ISBN 1-55513-848-9). Cook.

Gospel Themes II. Donald W. Hemmingway. 71p. 1983. 3.95 (ISBN 0-934126-40-2). Randall Bk Co.

Gospel Time Bomb. Lowell D. Streiker. 200p. 20.95 (ISBN 0-87975-259-9). Prometheus Bks.

Gospel Trailblazer: The Exciting Story of Francis Asbury. Bettie Wilson Story. 128p. 1984. pap. 6.95 (ISBN 0-687-15652-1). Abingdon.

Gospel Truth: Classics Edition. 2nd ed. George Q. Cannon. 1987. 14.95 (ISBN 0-87579-094-1). Deseret Bk.

Gospel under Siege: A Study on Faith & Works. Zane C. Hodges. 124p. (Orig.). 1981. pap. 4.95 (ISBN 0-9607576-0-0). Redencion Viva.

Gospel Unified. Tamer Fakhry. 1984. 15.00 (ISBN 0-533-05126-6). Vantage.

Gospel Versus Gospel. Theron F. Schlabach. LC 79-15888. 352p. 1980. 17.95x (ISBN 0-8361-1220-2). Herald Pr.

Gospelof Zarathustra. Greenlees. 7.95 (ISBN 0-8356-7239-5). Theos Pub Hse.

Gospels. Albert Barnes. 19.95 (ISBN 0-8010-0843-3). Baker Bk.

Gospels. Fred B. Craddock. LC 80-26270. 160p. (Orig.). 1981. pap. 8.95 (ISBN 0-687-15655-6). Abingdon.

Gospels. (Modern Critical Interpretations--Ancient, Medieval, & Renaissance Ser.). 1987. 24.50 (ISBN 0-87754-911-7). Chelsea Hse.

Gospels. William Kelly. (Introductory Lecture Ser.). 567p. 6.95 (ISBN 0-88172-097-6). Believers Bkshelf.

Gospels. J. Ylvisaker. 1977. Repr. 24.95 (ISBN 0-8100-0052-0, 15N0363). Northwest Pub.

Gospels As a Mandala of Wisdom. Geddes MacGregor. 224p. (Orig.). 1982. pap. 6.50 (ISBN 0-8356-0554-X, Quest). Theos Pub Hse.

Gospels for Graduates. Brent D. Earles. 160p. 1987. text ed. 5.95 (ISBN 0-8010-3438-8). Baker Bk.

Gospels for Sundays & Feasts: Cycle A. Manuel Miguens. 1981. 7.50 (ISBN 0-8198-3015-1); pap. 6.00 (ISBN 0-8198-3016-X). Dghtrs St Paul.

Gospels for Sundays & Feasts: Cycle C. Manuel Miguens. 1980. 7.50 (ISBN 0-8198-3000-3); pap. 6.00 (ISBN 0-8198-3001-1). Dghtrs St Paul.

Gospels for Whole Life. William G. Thompson. 228p. (Orig.). 1983. pap. 9.95 (ISBN 0-86683-645-4, AY8336, HarpR). Har-Row.

Gospels in Current Study. rev. ed. Simon Kistemaker. 192p. 1980. pap. 7.95 (ISBN 0-8010-5316-1). Baker Bk.

Gospels: Their Origin & Their Growth. Frederick C. Grant. vii, 216p. 1983. Repr. of 1957 ed. lib. bdg. 19.00 (ISBN 0-88254-870-0, Octagon). Hippocrene Bks.

Gospels: 14 Lessons, Vol. 1. Bernice C. Jordan. (Footsteps of Faith Ser.). 1955. pap. text ed. 2.50 (ISBN 0-86508-035-6); figures text 11.45 (ISBN 0-86508-036-4). BCM Intl Inc.

Gospels: 14 Lessons, Vol. 2. Bernice C. Jordan. (Footsteps of Faith Ser.). 1956. pap. text ed. 2.50 (ISBN 0-86508-037-2); figures text 11.45 (ISBN 0-86508-038-0). BCM Intl Inc.

Gotama Buddha. Hajime Nakamura. LC 77-8589. 1977. 8.95x (ISBN 0-914910-05-1); pap. 6.95x (ISBN 0-914910-06-X). Buddhist Bks.

Gotama Buddha: A Biography. Kenneth J. Saunders. LC 78-70119. Repr. of 1922 ed. 18.00 (ISBN 0-404-17376-4). AMS Pr.

Gotama, the Man. C. Rhys Davids. LC 78-72409. Repr. of 1928 ed. 25.00 (ISBN 0-404-17273-3). AMS Pr.

Gothic Architecture & Scholasticism. Erwin Panofsky. (Illus.). pap. 7.95 (ISBN 0-452-00834-4, Mer). NAL.

Gothic Architecture in Spain, 2 Vols. George E. Street. Ed. by Georgiana G. King. LC 68-56490. (Illus.). 1968. Repr. of 1914 ed. Set. 55.00 (ISBN 0-405-09008-0); 27.50 ea. Vol. 1 (ISBN 0-405-09009-9). Vol. 2 (ISBN 0-405-09010-2). Ayer Co Pubs.

Gothic Cathedral: Origins of Gothic Architecture & the Medieval Concept of Order. Otto Von Simson. LC 72-11946. (Bollingen Ser.: No. 48). (Illus.). 300p. 1973. 31.00 (ISBN 0-691-09741-0); pap. 9.50 (ISBN 0-691-01789-1). Princeton U Pr.

Gothic Commentary on the Gospel of John. Skeireins. Tr. by W. H. Bennett. (MLA MS). 1960. 14.00 (ISBN 0-527-83350-9). Kraus Repr.

Gothic Image: Religious Art in France of the Thirteenth Century. Emile Male. Tr. by Dora Nussey from Fr. (Icon Editions). (Illus.). 440p. 1973. pap. 10.95 (ISBN 0-06-430032-3, IN-32, HarpT). Har-Row.

Gothic Stained Glass: 1200-1300. Louis Grodecki & Catherine Brisac. Tr. by Barbara D. Boehm from Fr. LC 85-71277. (Illus.). 288p. 1985. text ed. 75.00x (ISBN 0-8014-1809-7). Cornell U Pr.

Gothic Vs. Classic: Architectural Projects in Seventeenth-Century Italy. Rudolf Wittkower. LC 73-79607. (Illus.). 192p. 1974. 12.50 (ISBN 0-8076-0704-5); pap. 4.95 (ISBN 0-8076-0705-3). Braziller.

Gottesbeweise im Deutschen Idealismus: Die modaltheoretische Begruendung des Absoluten, dargestellt an Kant, Hegel und Weisse. Harald Knudsen. (Theologische Bibliothek Toepelmann 23). vi, 280p. 1972. 31.60x (ISBN 3-11-003787-4). De Gruyter.

Governance & Administration in the Catholic School. Theodore Drahmann. 45p. 1986. 6.60 (ISBN 0-318-20563-7). Natl Cath Educ.

Governance of Jesuit Colleges in the United States, 1920-1970. Paul A. FitzGerald. LC 83-25927. 328p. 1984. text ed. 20.00 (ISBN 0-268-01010-2, 85-10109). U of Notre Dame Pr.

Government & Politics in Islam. Tareq Y. Ismael & Jacqueline S. Ismael. LC 85-2265. 177p. 1985. 27.50 (ISBN 0-312-34126-1). St Martin.

Government & Religion of the Virginia Indians. Samuel R. Hendren. LC 78-63845. (Johns Hopkins University. Studies in the Social Sciences. Thirteenth Ser. 1895: 11-12). Repr. of 1895 ed. 11.50 (ISBN 0-404-61102-8). AMS Pr.

Government Intervention in Religious Affairs, No. II. Dean M. Kelley. 200p. (Orig.). 1986. pap. 11.95 (ISBN 0-8298-0564-8). Pilgrim NY.

Government Intervention in Religious Affairs, No. 1. Dean M. Kelley. LC 82-355. 224p. (Orig.). 1982. 17.95 (ISBN 0-8298-0602-4); pap. 9.95 (ISBN 0-8298-0434-X). Pilgrim NY.

Government of God: Iran's Islamic Republic. Cheryl Benard & Zalmay Khalilzad. LC 83-20880. 232p. 1984. 28.00x (ISBN 0-231-05376-2); pap. 12.50 (ISBN 0-231-05377-0). Columbia U Pr.

Governmental & Judicial Ethics in the Bible & Rabbinic Literature. Ames Priest. 1980. 20.00x (ISBN 0-87068-697-6). Ktav.

Governmental & Judicial Ethics in the Bible & Rabbinic Literature. James E. Priest. LC 79-23423. 312p. 1980. 17.95x (ISBN 0-87068-697-6). Pepperdine U Pr.

Governor Drove Us up the Wall: A Guide to Nehemiah. Paul Engle. 1985. pap. text ed. 4.95 (ISBN 0-934688-11-7); pap. text ed. 3.95 leader's guide (ISBN 0-934688-13-3). Great Comm Pubns.

Gozad del Senor. John Catoir. (Span.). 3.50 (ISBN 0-318-02209-5). Chrstphrs NY.

Gozo Al Grecer. Jessica De Summers. 48p. 1981. pap. 1.10 (ISBN 0-311-38550-8, Edit Mundo). Casa Bautista.

Graca de Dar. A. Stephen Olford. Orig. Title: Grace of Giving. (Port.). 1986. write for info. (ISBN 0-8297-1602-5). Life Pubs Intl.

Graca para Crescer. William P. Wilson. Orig. Title: Grace to Grow. (Port.). 1986. write for info. (ISBN 0-8297-0743-3). Life Pubs Intl.

Gracanica: King Milutin's Church & Its Place in Late Byzantine Architecture. Slobodan Curcic. LC 79-11984. (Illus.). 1980. 34.95x (ISBN 0-271-00218-2). Pa St U Pr.

Grace. Jane Carroll. (Illus.). 28p. 1987. 12.95 (ISBN 1-55523-041-5). Winston-Derek.

Grace. Lewis S. Chafer. pap. 11.95 (ISBN 0-310-22331-8, 6305P). Zondervan.

Grace. C. H. Spurgeon. 1976. pap. 1.50 (ISBN 0-686-16843-7). Pilgrim Pubns.

Grace Abounding to the Chief of Sinners. John Bunyan. (Summit Bks). 132p. 1986. pap. 4.95 (ISBN 0-8010-0925-1). Baker Bk.

Grace after Meals. 1982. pap. 0.35 small (ISBN 0-686-76511-7). Feldheim.

Grace All the Way Home. Mark Trotter. LC 81-52860. 1982. pap. 4.95 (ISBN 0-8358-0434-8). Upper Room.

Grace & the Gentiles. Marcus Loane. 149p. (Orig.). 1981. pap. text ed. 6.45 (ISBN 0-85151-327-1). Banner of Truth.

Grace & the Human Condition. Jean L. Segundo. Tr. by John Drury from Span. LC 72-85794. (Theology for Artisans of a New Humanity Ser.: Vol. 2). Orig. Title: Gracia y Condicion Humana. 221p. 1973. pap. 7.95 (ISBN 0-88344-488-7). Orbis Bks.

Grace at Point Zero. Loren E. Halvorson. (Orig.). 1972. pap. 1.75 (ISBN 0-377-02111-3). Friend Pr.

Grace Divine. 236p. (Orig.). 1984. pap. 3.50 (ISBN 0-87481-524-X, Pub. by Ramakrishna Math Madras India). Vedanta Pr.

Grace for Grace. Watchman Nee. Tr. by Stephen Kaung from Chinese. 1983. pap. text ed. 2.75 (ISBN 0-935008-59-4). Christian Fellow Pubs.

Grace: God's Special Gift. Donald Roberts. 1982. pap. 3.95 (ISBN 0-570-04060-4, 56-1363). Concordia.

Grace: God's Work Ethic. Paul G. Johnson. 144p. 1985. pap. 6.95 (ISBN 0-8170-1070-X). Judson.

Grace in Eclipse: A Study on Eternal Rewards. Zane C. Hodges. viii, 120p. (Orig.). 1985. pap. 4.95 (ISBN 0-9607576-3-5). Redencion Viva.

Grace in the New Testament. James Moffatt. 419p. 1981. Repr. of 1931 ed. lib. bdg. 45.00 (ISBN 0-89984-339-5). Century Bookbindery.

Grace: Living on the Friendship of God. Stephen Lee. (Orig.). 1987. pap. 3.25 (ISBN 0-8054-5437-3). Broadman.

Grace Notes & Other Fragments. Joseph A. Sittler. Ed. by Robert M. Herhold & Linda M. Delloff. LC 80-8055. 128p. (Orig.). 1981. pap. 5.95 (ISBN 0-8006-1404-6, 1-1404). Fortress.

Grace of Christ. St. Thomas Aquinas. (Summa Theologial Ser.: Vol. 49). 1974. 18.95 (ISBN 0-07-002024-8). McGraw.

Grace of Giving. Stephen Olford. 1984. pap. 4.95 (ISBN 0-8010-6703-0). Baker Bk.

Grace of Giving. Stephen Olford. 1986. write for info. (ISBN 0-8297-1263-1). Life Pubs Intl.

Grace of God. William MacDonald. pap. 1.95 (ISBN 0-937396-18-4). Walterick Pubs.

Grace of God. rev., new ed. Charles C. Ryrie. 128p. 1975. pap. 4.95 (ISBN 0-8024-3250-6). Moody.

Grace of God in the Gospel. John Cheesman et al. 1976. pap. 3.45 (ISBN 0-85151-153-8). Banner of Truth.

Grace of Law. Ernest F. Kevan. 9.95 (ISBN 0-8010-5373-0). Baker Bk.

Grace of Love. Basilea Schlink. 1974. gift edition 0.95 (ISBN 3-87209-662-1). Evang Sisterhood Mary.

Grace of Yielding. Derek Prince. 1977. pap. 2.50 (ISBN 0-934920-20-6, B-30). Derek Prince.

Grace to Be a Woman. Georgette Blaquiere. Tr. by Robert Wild from Fr. LC 83-15858. 127p. 1983. pap. 6.95 (ISBN 0-8189-0449-6). Alba.

Grace to You. Mark Mensendiek. 20p. (Orig.). 1985. pap. 0.75 (ISBN 0-933643-22-5). Grace World Outreach.

Grace Triumphant: Autobiography. Cyril Brooks. 266p. (Orig.). 1985. pap. 9.95 (ISBN 0-937396-66-4). Walterick Pubs.

Grace Unlimited. Clark H. Pinnock. LC 75-22161. 272p. 1975. pap. 8.95 (ISBN 0-87123-185-9, 210185). Bethany Hse.

Graceful Courage: A Venture in Christian Humanism. Roger Hazelton. LC 84-48706. 128p. 1985. pap. 4.95 (ISBN 0-8006-1850-5, 1-1850). Fortress.

Gracia de Dios. Charles C. Ryrie. Orig. Title: Grace of God. (Span.). 160p. 1979. pap. 3.50 (ISBN 0-8254-1630-2). Kregel.

Gracias! A Latin American Journal. Henri J. Nouwen. LC 82-48935. 224p. 1983. 13.45 (ISBN 0-06-066318-9, HarpR). Har-Row.

Gracious Woman: Developing A Servant's Heart Through Hospitality. June Curtis. 176p. (Orig.). 1985. pap. 4.95 (ISBN 0-89081-489-9). Harvest Hse.

Gradualia, Bks.1 & 2. William Byrd et al. Ed. by P. C. Buck. (Tudor Church Music: Vol. 7). 1963. Repr. of 1927 ed. 85.00x (ISBN 0-8450-1857-4). Broude.

Graduate's Guide to Success. William J. Krutza. 96p. 1976. 4.95 (ISBN 0-8010-5374-9). Baker Bk.

Graffiti: Devotions for Girls. new ed. J. David Schmidt. (Illus.). 128p. (Orig.). (YA) 1983. pap. 4.95 (ISBN 0-8007-5115-9, Power Bks). Revell.

Graffiti: Devotions for Guys. new ed. J. David Schmidt. (Illus.). 128p. (Orig.). (YA) 1983. pap. 4.95 (ISBN 0-8007-5114-0, Power Bks). Revell.

Graffiti on the Wall of Time: Thirty Poems Celebrating the Triumph of Western Heresy. John E. Whiteford-Boyle. 1983. 5.00. Wheat Forders.

Grafting Old Rootstock. Ed. by Philip A. Noss. LC 81-51153. (International Museum of Cultures Publications: No. 14). (Illus.). 246p. (Orig.). 1982. pap. 12.00x (ISBN 0-88312-165-4); microfiche (3) 6.00x (ISBN 0-88312-990-6). Summer Inst Ling.

Graham Crackers, Galoshes & God. Bernadette Snyder. LC 82-82654. 96p. 1982. pap. 2.95 (ISBN 0-89243-164-4). Liguori Pubns.

Grail Legend. Emma Jung & Marie-Louise Von Franz. 452p. (Orig.). 1986. 27.50 (ISBN 0-938434-07-1); pap. 14.95 (ISBN 0-938434-08-X). Sigo Pr.

Grail: Quest for the Eternal. John Matthews. Ed. by Jill Purce. LC 81-66807. (Illustrated Library of Sacred Imagination). (Illus.). 110p. 1981. pap. 9.95 (ISBN 0-8245-0035-0). Crossroad NY.

Grail Yoga. 2nd ed. Edward Thomas. LC 74-84399. (Grail Bk). (Illus.). 128p. 1975. pap. 2.95 (ISBN 0-914896-28-8). East Ridge Pr.

Grain of Wheat. Quentin Hakenewerth. 88p. 1966. pap. 1.75 (ISBN 0-9608124-0-7). Marianist Com Ctr.

Gramatica Elemental del Griego del Nuevo Testamento. Guillermo H. Davis. Tr. by Jorge F. McKibben. 240p. 1984. Repr. of 1980 ed. 4.75 (ISBN 0-311-42008-7). Casa Bautista.

Gramatica Griega Del Nuevo Testamento. H. E. Dana & J. R. Mantey. Tr. by Adolfo Robleto & Catalina De Clark. 1984. pap. 9.95 (ISBN 0-311-42010-9). Casa Bautista.

Grammar of Mishnaic Hebrew. M. H. Segal. 1978. pap. text ed. 15.95x (ISBN 0-19-815454-2). Oxford U Pr.

Grammar of Septuagint Greek. Frederick C. Conybeare & G. Stock. 80p. 1980. pap. 6.95 (ISBN 0-310-43001-1, 6652P). Zondervan.

Grammar of the Greek New Testament in the Light of Historical Research. Archibald T. Robertson. 1947. 45.00 (ISBN 0-8054-1308-1). Broadman.

Grammatical Aid to the Greek New Testament. Robert Hanna. 1983. 16.95 (ISBN 0-8010-4272-0). Baker Bk.

Grammatical Aids for Students of New Testament Greek. Walter Mueller. 1972. pap. 3.95 (ISBN 0-8028-1447-6). Eerdmans.

Grammatical Analysis of Greek New Testament. Max Zerwick. (Scripta Pontificii Instituti Biblici Ser.: Vol. 1). 1974. pap. 16.00 (ISBN 88-7653-553-5). Loyola.

Grammatical Insights into the New Testament. Nigel Turner. 208p. 1965. 15.95 (ISBN 0-567-01017-1, Pub. by T & T Clark Ltd UK). Fortress.

Grammatik des Samaritanischen Hebraeisch. Rudolf Macuch. (Studia Samaritana 1). (Ger). 1969. 110.00x (ISBN 3-11-000133-0). De Gruyter.

Grammatika Tserkovno-Slavjanskago Jazika. Hieromonk A. Gamanovitch. Tr. of Church Slavonic Grammer. 264p. 1984. pap. text ed. 9.00 (ISBN 0-317-30313-9). Holy Trinity.

Grand Inquisitor. Fyodor Dostoyevsky. LC 56-7503. (Milestones of Thought Ser.). pap. 2.95x (ISBN 0-8044-6125-2). Ungar.

Grand Inquisitor on the Nature of Man. Fyodor Dostoyevsky. Tr. by Constance Garnett. 1948. pap. 4.79 scp (ISBN 0-672-60237-7, LLA63). Bobbs.

Grand Miracle. C. S. Lewis. (Epiphany Ser.). 176p. 1983. pap. 2.95 (ISBN 0-345-30539-6). Ballantine.

Grand Opening. Richard W. Bimler. 1983. 3.75 (ISBN 0-89536-589-8, 0731). CSS of Ohio.

Grand Priory of the Order of the Hospital of St. John of Jerusalem in England: A Short History. Edwin J. King. LC 76-29826. Repr. of 1924 ed. 28.00 (ISBN 0-404-15420-4). AMS Pr.

Grande Chartreuse, et les Chartreuses de Portes Selignac et Pierre Chatel. James Hogg. (Analecta Cartusiana: No. 61). (Orig.). 1984. pap. 85.00 (ISBN 3-7052-0089-5, Pub. by Salzburg Studies). Longwood Pub Group.

Grande Maniere: Religious & Historical Painting in France, 1700-1800. Donald A. Rosenthal. (Illus.). 200p. 1987. pap. 24.95 (ISBN 0-295-96475-8). U of Wash Pr.

Grandees. Stephen Birmingham. 384p. 1985. pap. 4.50 (ISBN 0-425-08390-X). Berkley Pub.

Grandes Doctrinas de la Biblia. William Evans. Orig. Title: Great Doctrines of the Bible. (Span.). 1986. pap. 4.75 (ISBN 0-8254-1222-6). Kregel.

Grandes Heures of Jean, Duke of Berry. Ed. by Marcel Thomas. LC 75-167761. (Illus.). 192p. 1971. 80.00 (ISBN 0-8076-0613-8). Braziller.

Grandes Hombres de la Biblia. Leobardo Estrada. 235p. 1975. pap. 5.25 (ISBN 0-311-04656-8). Casa Bautista.

Grandeur of God. C. Samuel Storms. 80p. 1985. pap. 6.95 (ISBN 0-8010-8254-4). Baker Bk.

Grandfather Clock & Other Finger Plays, Word Rhythms, & Action Rhymes. Sharon Lee. (Illus.). 64p. 1984. pap. 5.95 (ISBN 0-86683-834-1, HarpR). Har-Row.

Grandfathers: God's Gift to Children. Mary B. Christian. 1982. pap. 2.75 (ISBN 0-570-04069-8, 56-1372). Concordia.

Grandmothers: God's Gift to Children. Mary B. Christian. 1982. pap. 2.75 (ISBN 0-570-04068-X, 56-1371). Concordia.

Grandpa Haskett Presents: Original New Christmas Stories for the Young & Young-at-Heart. William P. Haskett. Ed. by M. R. Haskett. (Illus.). 20p. (Orig.). 1982. pap. 3.00g (ISBN 0-9609724-0-4). Haskett Spec.

Grant Me a Portion. Rebecca S. Hayes. 1987. pap. 4.50 (ISBN 0-8054-6585-5). Broadman.

Grants for Religion & Religious Education. (Comsearch: Broad Topics Ser.). 1986. pap. text ed. 34.00 (ISBN 0-87954-172-5). Foundation Ctr.

Grapes of Conflict: The Faith Community & Farm Workers. Sydney D. Smith. 160p. 1987. 16.95 (ISBN 0-932727-12-3); pap. 9.95 (ISBN 0-932727-14-X); special ed. 25.00 (ISBN 0-932727-13-1). Hope Pub Hse.

Graphic History of the Jewish Heritage. Pinchas Wollman-Tsamir. (Illus.). 224p. 1982. 22.50. Shengold.

Grass Grows by Itself. Bhagwan S. Rajneesh. (Illus.). 1978. pap. 4.95 (ISBN 0-87516-251-7). De Vorss.

Grass Grows by Itself. Bhagwan Shree Rajneesh. Ed. by Ma Prema Veena. LC 77-905411. (Zen Ser.). (Illus.). 254p. (Orig.). 1978. 15.50 (ISBN 0-88050-072-7); pap. 4.95 (ISBN 0-88050-572-9). Chidvilas Found.

Grateful Heart. Margie Kirkland. LC 84-9398. 1984. pap. 3.95 (ISBN 0-8054-5012-2). Broadman.

Gratefulness, the Heart of Prayer: An Approach to Life in Fullness. David Steindl-Rast. 144p. 1984. pap. 7.95 (ISBN 0-8091-2628-1). Paulist Pr.

Gratitude. (Pocket Power Ser.). 16p. (Orig.). 1985. pap. 0.50 (ISBN 0-89486-299-5). Hazelden.

Grave Concern. Chaim Lieberman. LC 68-58650. 202p. 1968. 10.00 (ISBN 0-88400-016-8). Shengold.

Gravedigger File. Os Guiness. LC 83-10666. (Illus.). 204p. (Orig.). 1983. pap. 7.95 (ISBN 0-87784-817-3). Inter-Varsity.

Graven in the Rock or the Historical Accuracy of the Bible. Samuel Kinns. LC 77-85611. 1977. Repr. of 1891 ed. lib. bdg. 65.00 (ISBN 0-89341-319-4). Longwood Pub Group.

Gravity & Grace: Reflections & Provocations. Joseph Sittler. Ed. by Linda Marie Delloff. LC 86-3547. 128p. (Orig.). 1986. pap. 6.95 (ISBN 0-8066-2205-9, 10-2888). Augsburg.

Great Adventures from the Bible. Illus. by Andre Le Blanc. (Illus.). 200p. (Orig.). 1984. pap. 3.95 (ISBN 0-89191-848-5). Cook.

Great Adventures of the Old Testament. Paul Waterman. (Activity Book Ser.). Vol. 1. pap. 0.99 (ISBN 0-87123-751-2, 220751); Vol. 2. pap. 0.99 (ISBN 0-87123-769-5). Bethany Hse.

Great Age of Japanese Buddhist Sculpture, AD 600-1300. Kyotaro Nishikawa & Emily J. Sano. LC 82-82805. (Illus.). 152p. (Orig.). 1982. 45.00 (ISBN 0-912804-07-6, Dist by U of Wash Pr); pap. 24.95 (ISBN 0-912804-08-4). Kimbell Art.

Great Ages & Ideas of the Jewish People. Ed. by Leo W. Schwarz. LC 83-5464. 7.95 (ISBN 0-394-60413-X). Modern Lib.

Great American Foundresses. facs. ed. Joseph B. Code. LC 68-20291. (Essay Index Reprint Ser). 1929. 21.50 (ISBN 0-8369-0319-6). Ayer Co Pubs.

Great American Values Test: Influencing Behavior & Belief Through Television. Sandra Ball-Rokeach & Joel W. Grube. LC 83-48468. 208p. 1983. 25.00x (ISBN 0-02-926850-8). Free Pr.

Great & Holy Pascha. Monks of New Skete Staff. Tr. by Reverend Laurence Mancuso from Gr. & Church Slavonic. (Liturgical Music Series I: Great Feasts: Vol. 6). 60p. (Orig.). 1986. pap. text ed. 15.00 (ISBN 0-935129-07-3). Monks of New Skete.

Great Apostasy. James E. Talmage. 6.95 (ISBN 0-87747-384-6). Deseret Bk.

Great Are the Promises unto the Isle of the Sea: The Church of Jesus Christ of Latter-Day Saints in the Hawaiian Islands. Joseph H. Spurrier. (Orig.). 1978. pap. 2.95 (ISBN 0-89036-114-2). Hawkes Pub Inc.

Great Art Madonnas Classed According to Their Significance As Types of Impressive Motherhood. Vincent J. Hurlington. (Great Art Masters Library). (Illus.). 143p. 1981. 127.75 (ISBN 0-930582-97-7). Gloucester Art.

Great Asian Religions. Wing T. Chan & Ismael R. Alfaruqi. 1969. pap. write for info. (ISBN 0-02-320640-3, 32064). Macmillan.

Great Asian Religions. George C. Fry et al. 228p. 1984. pap. 9.95 (ISBN 0-8010-3511-2). Baker Bk.

Great Awakening. Jonathan Edwards. Ed. by C. C. Goen. LC 75-179472. (Works of Johathan Edwards Ser.: Vol. 4). 1972. 50.00x (ISBN 0-300-01437-6). Yale U Pr.

Great Awakening. Robert Powell. Ed. by Shirley Nicholson. LC 83-70688. Orig. Title: Zen & Reality. 179p. 1983. pap. 6.50 (ISBN 0-8356-0577-9, Quest). Theos Pub Hse.

Great Awakening: A History of the Revival of Religion in the Time of Edwards & Whitefield. Joseph Tracy. LC 72-83444. (Religion in America Ser). 1969. Repr. of 1945 ed. 21.00 (ISBN 0-405-00280-7). Ayer Co Pubs.

Great Awakening: Documents Illustrating the Crisis & Its Consequences. Ed. by Alan E. Heimert & Perry Miller. LC 66-23537. (Orig.). 1967. pap. 14.47 scp (ISBN 0-672-60044-7, AHS34). Bobbs.

Great Awakening: Documents on the Revival of Religion, 1740-1745. Ed. by Richard L. Bushman. (Institute of Early American History & Culture Ser.). xiv, 174p. 1970. 15.00x (ISBN 0-8078-1181-5). U of NC Pr.

Great Awakening: Event & Exegesis. Ed. by Darrett B. Rutman. LC 77-10540. 208p. 1977. pap. text ed. 8.00 (ISBN 0-88275-605-2). Krieger.

Great Awakening in New England. Edwin S. Gaustad. 13.75 (ISBN 0-8446-1491-2). Peter Smith.

Great Awakening in the Middle Colonies. Charles H. Maxson. 12.00 (ISBN 0-8446-1306-1). Peter Smith.

Great Awakenings & the Restoration Movement. Max W. Randall. LC 82-74537. 442p. (Orig.). 1983. pap. 9.95 (ISBN 0-89900-229-3). College Pr Pub.

Great Basin Kingdom: An Economic History of the Latter-Day Saints, 1830-1900. Leonard J. Arrington. LC 58-12961. (Illus.). xx, 550p. 1966. pap. 13.95 (ISBN 0-8032-5006-1, BB 342, Bison). U of Nebr Pr.

Great Bible Stories for Children. Ed. by Lane Easterly. (Illus.). 7.95 (ISBN 0-8407-5351-9). Nelson.

Great Bible Truths for Human Problems. Joseph Murphy. 1976. pap. text ed. 7.00 (ISBN 0-87516-214-2). De Vorss.

Great Black Robe. Jean Pitrone. (Illus.). 1965. 4.00 (ISBN 0-8198-0050-3); pap. 3.00 (ISBN 0-8198-0051-1). Dghtrs St Paul.

Great Books on Religion & Esoteric Philosophy. Manly P. Hall. pap. 5.50 (ISBN 0-89314-821-0). Philos Res.

Great Britain & the Holy See 1746-1870. Matthias Buschkuhl. (Illus.). 260p. 1982. text ed. 40.00x (ISBN 0-7165-0290-9, Pub. by Irish Academic Pr Ireland). Biblio Dist.

Great Christian Books. facsimile ed. Hugh Martin. LC 71-142666. (Essay Index Reprint Ser). Repr. of 1945 ed. 13.00 (ISBN 0-8369-2242-5). Ayer Co Pubs.

Great Christian Hymnal. Tillit S. Teddlie. 1965. 4.25 (ISBN 0-89137-600-3). Quality Pubns.

Great Christmas Craft Book. American School of Needlework Staff. (Illus.). 144p. 1983. 19.95 (ISBN 0-8069-5498-1). Sterling.

Great Church in Captivity: A Study of the Patriarchate of Constantinople from the Eve of the Turkish Conquest to the Greek War of Independence. Steven Runciman. 465p. Date not set. pap. price not set. Cambridge U Pr.

Great Church in Captivity: A Study of the Patriarchate of Constantinople from the Eve of the Turkish Conquest to the Greek War of Independence. Steven Runciman. LC 68-29330. pap. 116.30 (ISBN 0-317-26393-5, 2024531). Bks Demand UMI.

Great Churches-Today's Essentials. Don R. Pegram. 1982. pap. 1.25 (ISBN 0-89265-083-4). Randall Hse.

Great Classical Myths. Ed. & intro. by F. R. Godolphin. LC 64-10293. 7.95 (ISBN 0-394-60417-2). Modern Lib.

Great Cloud of Witnesses in Hebrews Eleven. Ethelbert W. Bullinger. LC 79-14425. 462p. 1986. pap. 12.95 (ISBN 0-8254-2247-7). Kregel.

Great Code: The Bible in Literature. Northrop Frye. LC 81-47303. 261p. 1983. pap. 5.95 (ISBN 0-15-636480-8, Harv). HarBraceJ.

Great Commitment. Jim Lewis. LC 81-71542. 120p. (Orig.). 1982. pap. 7.50 (ISBN 0-942482-03-4). Unity Church Denver.

Great Compassion Dharma Transmission Verses of the 42 Hands & Eyes. Tripitaka Master Hua. Tr. by Buddhist Text Translation Society. (Illus.). 100p. (Orig.). 1983. pap. 16.00 (ISBN 0-88139-002-X). Buddhist Text.

Great Controversy. Ellen G. White. 1950. 5.95 (ISBN 0-8163-0035-6, 07886-5); deluxe ed. 9.95 (ISBN 0-8163-0036-4, 07882-4); pap. 1.45 (ISBN 0-8163-0037-2, 07887-3). Pacific Pr Pub Assn.

Great Cosmic Mother. Monica Sjoo & Barbara Mor. 1986. pap. 14.95 (ISBN 0-317-52386-4, PL 4115, HarpR). Har-Row.

Great Day in the Morning. Robert Davis. (Jesus & His Disciples Ser.: Vol 2). (Illus.). 40p. 1986. 5.40 (ISBN 0-9615877-1-7). Davis Pub.

Great Day of the Lord. Frank Fichtl. 256p. 1986. 12.95 (ISBN 0-89962-510-X). Todd & Honeywell.

Great Day of the Lord. Gordon Lindsay. (Revelation Ser.). 1.25 (ISBN 0-89985-037-5). Christ Nations.

Great Debate on Miracles: From Joseph Glanvill to David Hume. R. M. Burns. LC 78-75197. 300p. 1981. 28.50 (ISBN 0-8387-2378-0). Bucknell U Pr.

Great Deception. Pieter Van Klaveren. 160p. 1985. 12.95 (ISBN 0-8059-2997-5). Dorrance.

Great Deliverance. J. C. Metcalfe. 1970. pap. 2.25 (ISBN 0-87508-916-X). Chr Lit.

Great Didactic of John Amos Comenius. M. W. Keatinge. (Educational Ser.). 1896. Repr. 40.00 (ISBN 0-8482-4764-7). Norwood Edns.

Great Didactic of John Maos Comenius. Ed. by M. W. Keatinge. 316p. 1981. Repr. of 1907 ed. lib. bdg. 50.00 (ISBN 0-89984-304-2). Century Bookbindery.

Great Dinosaur Mystery & the Bible. Paul Taylor. (Illus.). 63p. 1987. 9.95 (ISBN 0-89051-114-4). Master Bks.

Great Doctrines of the Bible. rev. ed. William Evans. 350p. 1974. enlarged edition 11.95 (ISBN 0-8024-3301-4). Moody.

Great Doctrines of the Bible, Vol. 1. W. A. Criswell. 144p. 1982. 9.95 (ISBN 0-310-43850-0, 9427). Zondervan.

Great Doctrines of the Bible, Vols. 1, 2, 3, & 4. W. A. Criswell. 192p. 1982. Repr. 44.75 (ISBN 0-310-43868-3, 11663). Zondervan.

Great Doctrines of the Bible, Vol. 5. W. A. Criswell. 144p. 1985. 9.95 (ISBN 0-310-43930-2). Zondervan.

Great Doctrines of the Bible, Vol. 7. W. A. Criswell. Ed. by J. Ruark. 1987. price not set (ISBN 0-310-43960-4). Zondervan.

Great Doctrines of the Bible: Christology, Vol. 2. W. A. Criswell. 192p. 1982. 9.95 (ISBN 0-310-43860-8, 11660). Zondervan.

Great Doctrines of the Bible: Ecclesiology, Vol. 3. W. A. Criswell. 128p. 1983. 8.95 (ISBN 0-310-43900-0, 11661). Zondervan.

Great Doctrines of the Bible, Vol. 4: Pneumatology. W. A. Criswell. 112p. 1984. 7.95 (ISBN 0-310-43910-8, 11662). Zondervan.

Great Doctrines of the Bible, Vol. 6: Christian Life & Stewardship. W. A. Criswell. 128p. 1986. text ed. 11.95 (ISBN 0-310-43950-7). Zondervan.

Great Doctrines Relating to Salvation. John B. Marchbanks. LC 73-123612. 1970. pap. 2.95 (ISBN 0-87213-640-X). Loizeaux.

Great Drama of Jesus: A Life of Christ for Teens Who Want to be Challenged. Victor Galeone. (Illus.). 207p. (Orig.). 1979. pap. 5.95 (ISBN 0-913382-31-0, 101-28). Prow Bks-Franciscan.

Great Dramas of the Bible. William E. Cameron. LC 81-71560. 305p. 1982. 5.95 (ISBN 0-87159-047-6). Unity School.

Great Eastern Temple: Treasures of Japanese Buddhist Art from Todai-ji. The Art Institute of Chicago. Ed. by Yutaka Mino. LC 86-45044. (Midland Bks.: No. 390). (Illus.). 180p. 1986. 45.00x (ISBN 0-253-32634-6); pap. 20.00x (ISBN 0-253-20390-2). Ind U Pr.

Great Economic Debate: An Ethical Analysis. J. Philip Wogaman. LC 77-3870. 192p. 1977. 10.95 (ISBN 0-664-20780-4); pap. 9.95 (ISBN 0-664-24141-7). Westminster.

Great Enemy. J. C. Metcalfe. 1970. pap. 2.95 (ISBN 0-87508-914-3). Chr Lit.

Great Evangelical Disaster. Francis A. Schaeffer. LC 83-73125. 192p. 1984. 14.95 (ISBN 0-89107-309-4, Crossway Bks); pap. 7.95 (ISBN 0-89107-308-6). Good News.

Great Expectations. (Pocket Power Ser.). 16p. (Orig.). 1986. pap. 0.50 (ISBN 0-89486-366-5). Hazelden.

Great Experiment. Edmond B. Szekely. (Search for the Ageless Ser.: Vol. 2). (Illus.). 328p. 1977. pap. 8.80 (ISBN 0-89564-023-6). IBS Intl.

Great Falling Away Today. Milton Green. (Orig.). 1986. pap. 6.95 (ISBN 0-910311-40-4). Huntington Hse Inc.

Great German Mystics: Eckhart, Tauler & Suso. James M. Clark. LC 73-81493. 1970. Repr. of 1949 ed. 15.00x (ISBN 0-8462-1351-6). Russell.

Great Gifts of Christmas Joy. June M. Bacher. LC 83-70005. 96p. 1983. pap. 4.95 (ISBN 0-8054-5707-0). Broadman.

Great Harmony: Teachings & Observations of the Way of the Universe. Ed. by S. Negrin. LC 77-77387. (Illus., Orig.). 1977. pap. 3.50 (ISBN 0-87810-033-4). Times Change.

Great Heresies. facs. ed. Hilaire Belloc. LC 68-16908. (Essay Index Reprint Ser). 1938. 18.00 (ISBN 0-8369-0189-4). Ayer Co Pubs.

Great Holiness Classics: The Wesley Century, Vol. 2. T. Crichton Mitchell. 504p. 1984. 21.95 (ISBN 0-8341-0910-7). Beacon Hill.

Great Holiness Classics, Vol. 3: Leading Wesleyan Thinkers. Ed. by Richard S. Taylor. 436p. 1985. 21.95 (ISBN 0-8341-1069-5). Beacon Hill.

Great Holocaust Trial. Michael A. Hoffman, II. (Illus.). 95p. (Orig.). 1985. pap. 5.95 (ISBN 0-939484-22-6). Inst Hist Rev.

Great Holocaust Trial. Michael A. Hoffman, II. (Illus.). 95p. 1986. pap. 5.95 (ISBN 0-317-53011-9). Noontide.

Great Hymns & Their Stories. W. Sheppard. lib. bdg. 69.95 (ISBN 0-87968-350-3). Gordon Pr.

Great Hymns & Their Stories. W. L. Sheppard. 1979. pap. 4.95 (ISBN 0-87508-492-3). Chr Lit.

Great I Came's of Jesus. A. M. Coniaris. 1980. pap. 7.95 (ISBN 0-686-27069-X). Light&Life Pub Co MN.

Great Ideas for Small Youth Groups. Wayne Rice. 256p. (Orig.). 1985. pap. 7.95 (ISBN 0-310-34891-9, 10823P). Zondervan.

Great Initiates: A Study of the Secret History of Religions. Edouard Schure. LC 79-3597. (Harper Library of Spiritual Wisdom). (Fr.). 528p. 1980. pap. 9.95 (ISBN 0-06-067125-4, RD 400, HarpR). Har-Row.

Great Initiates: Secret History of Religions, Vol. 3. Edward Schure. LC 61-8623. (Spiritual Science Library). 528p. 1982. Repr. of 1961 ed. lib. bdg. 23.00 (ISBN 0-89345-025-1, Spiritual Sci Lib). Garber Comm.

Great Jewish Books. Samuel Caplan & Harold Ribalow. 1983. pap. 10.95 (ISBN 0-8180-1135-1). Horizon.

Great Jewish Debates & Dilemmas: Perspectives on Moral Issues in Conflict in the 80's. Albert Vorspan. LC 80-21057. 240p. 1980. pap. text ed. 5.95 (ISBN 0-8074-0049-1). UAHC.

Great Jews in Music. Darryl Lyman. 500p. 1986. 24.95 (ISBN 0-8246-0315-X). Jonathan David.

Great Jews in Sports. Robert Slater. LC 82-19953. (Illus.). 304p. 1983. 14.95 (ISBN 0-8246-0285-4). Jonathan David.

Great Jews Since Bible Times. Elma E. Levinger. (Illus.). 2.50x (ISBN 0-87441-053-3). Behrman.

Great Judgment Throne & the Seven Seals. Gordon Lindsay. (Revelation Ser.). 1.25 (ISBN 0-89985-036-7). Christ Nations.

Great Leaps in a Single Bound. Kaaren Witte. LC 82-4163. 96p. (Orig.). 1982. pap. 3.95 (ISBN 0-87123-199-9, 210199). Bethany Hse.

Great Learning & the Doctrine of the Mean. Confucius. (Illus.). 151p. 1986. 88.85 (ISBN 0-89266-539-4). Am Classical Coll Pr.

Great Lent: Journey to Pascha. Alexander Schmemann. 1974. pap. 5.95 (ISBN 0-913836-04-4). St Vladimirs.

Great Liberation (Mahanirvana Tantra) Tr. by John Woodroffe. (Sanskrit.). 28.00 (ISBN 0-89744-237-7, Pub. by Ganesh & Co. India). Auromere.

Great Lion of Bechuanaland: The Life and Times of Roger Price, Missionary. Edwin W. Smith. LC 57-36876. 1957. text ed. 20.00x (ISBN 0-8401-2210-1). A R Allenson.

Great Living System. John R. Clark. 1984. pap. 7.95 (ISBN 0-933840-24-1). Unitarian Univ.

Great Lover's Manifesto. Dave Grant. 160p. (Orig.). 1986. 9.95 (ISBN 0-89081-481-3). Harvest Hse.

Great Magdelens. facs. ed. Hugh F. Blunt. LC 71-86731. (Essay Index Reprint Ser). 1928. 18.50 (ISBN 0-8369-1122-9). Ayer Co Pubs.

Great Men & Movements in Israel. rev. ed. Rudolf Kittel. LC 66-29121. (Library of Biblical Studies). 1968. 20.00x (ISBN 0-87068-071-4). Ktav.

Great Men As Prophets of a New Era. facs. ed. Newell D. Hillis. LC 68-16939. (Essay Index Reprint Ser). 1968. Repr. of 1922 ed. 15.00 (ISBN 0-8369-0541-5). Ayer Co Pubs.

Great Men As Prophets of a New Era. Newell D. Hillis. 1922. Repr. 20.00 (ISBN 0-8274-2445-0). R West.

Great Men of the Bible, 2 vols. F. B. Meyer. 1986. Set. pap. 20.90 (ISBN 0-310-44288-5, 12362P). Zondervan.

Great Men of the Bible, Vol. 1. F. B. Meyer & Frank Cumbers. 384p. (Orig.). 1981. pap. 10.95 (ISBN 0-310-44271-0, 12360P). Zondervan.

Great Men of the Bible, Vol. 2. F. B. Meyer & Frank Cumbers. 320p. 1982. pap. 10.95 (ISBN 0-310-44281-8, 12361P). Zondervan.

Great Men of the Christian Church. facs. ed. Williston Walker. LC 68-8502. (Essay Index Reprint Ser). 1908. 22.00 (ISBN 0-8369-0966-6). Ayer Co Pubs.

Great Miracles of Jesus. Borje Svensson. (Change-the-Picture Storybooks). (Illus.). 10p. 1985. 6.95 (ISBN 0-89191-940-6, 59402, Chariot Bks). Cook.

Great Missionaries in a Great Work. Evelyn Mangham. Ed. by E. H. Schroeder. (Illus.). 85p. 1970. pap. 1.75 (ISBN 0-87509-091-5). Chr Pubns.

Great Missionaries of the Church. facsimile ed. Charles C. Creegan & Josephine A. Goodnow. LC 73-37522. (Essay Index Reprint Ser). Repr. of 1895 ed. 24.50 (ISBN 0-8369-2541-6). Ayer Co Pubs.

Great Missionaries to China. John T. Mueller. LC 73-38329. (Biography Index Reprint Ser). Repr. of 1947 ed. 12.75 (ISBN 0-8369-8124-3). Ayer Co Pubs.

Great Missionaries to the Orient. John T. Mueller. LC 78-38330. (Biography Index Reprint Ser). Repr. of 1948 ed. 14.75 (ISBN 0-8369-8125-1). Ayer Co Pubs.

Great Moral Dilemmas. Ed. by R. M. MacIver. (Religion & Civilization Ser). 189p. 1964. Repr. of 1956 ed. 21.50x (ISBN 0-8154-0145-0). Cooper Sq.

Great Morning of the World: The Unforgettable Story of Harry Barrett. Thomas Van Braam Barrett. LC 75-16416. Repr. of 1975 ed. 47.30 (ISBN 0-8357-9011-8, 2016366). Bks Demand UMI.

Great Mother: A Gospel of the Eternally Feminine. C. H. Bjerregaard. 1977. lib. bdg. 59.95 (ISBN 0-8490-1900-1). Gordon Pr.

Great Mysteries: An Essential Catechism. Andrew M. Greeley. 192p. (Orig.). 1976. pap. 8.95x (ISBN 0-8164-0309-0, AY7823, HarpR). Har-Row.

Great Mysteries: An Essential Catechism. rev. ed. Andrew M. Greeley. 192p. 1985. pap. 6.95 (ISBN 0-86683-871-6, HarpR). Har-Row.

Great Mysteries of the Bible. John R. Bisagno. LC 81-67997. 1982. 7.95 (ISBN 0-8054-1952-7). Broadman.

Great Mystics. George Godwin. LC 74-2430. (St. Paul, Plotinus, St. Augustine, St. Francis, St. Teresa, Martin Luther, Jacob Boehme, George Fox, Emanuel Swedenborg, William Blake). 1945. lib. bdg. 27.50 (ISBN 0-8414-4499-4). Folcroft.

Great Myths & Legends. Ed. by World Book Staff. LC 65-25105. (Childcraft-The How & Why Library). 310p. 1984. PLB write for info. (ISBN 0-7166-0684-4). World Bk.

Great New England Churches: Sixty-Five Houses of Worship That Changed Our Lives. Robert Mutrux. LC 81-80425. (Illus.). 288p. (Orig.). 1981. pap. 14.95 (ISBN 0-87106-950-4). Globe Pequot.

Great Nothing. Bhagwan Shree Rajneesh. Ed. by Ma Prem Maneesha. LC 83-173216. (Initation Talks Ser.). (Illus.). 488p. (Orig.). 1978. 18.95 (ISBN 0-88050-073-5). Chidvilas Found.

Great Occasions. Carl Seaburg. 1968. pap. 9.95 (ISBN 0-933840-09-8). Unitarian Univ.

Great Omission. Robertson McQuilkin. 96p. 1984. pap. 4.95 (ISBN 0-8010-6167-9). Baker Bk.

Great Omission: Fruit That Remains. Gene Gurganus. (Illus.). 104p. 1983. pap. 3.95 (ISBN 0-89084-191-8). Bob Jones Univ Pr.

Great Passages of the Bible. Ed. by Carol Plueddemann. (Fisherman Bible Studyguide Ser.). 64p. (Orig.). 1987. pap. 2.95 (ISBN 0-87788-332-7). Shaw Pubs.

Great Penitents. facs. ed. Hugh F. Blunt. LC 67-30198. (Essay Index Reprint Ser). 1921. 17.00 (ISBN 0-8369-0220-3). Ayer Co Pubs.

Great People of the Bible. Jude Winkler. (Illus.). 160p. 1985. 11.95 (ISBN 0-89942-715-4). Catholic Bk Pub.

Great People of the Bible & How They Lived. Reader's Digest Editors. LC 73-86027. (Illus.). 1974. 21.99 (ISBN 0-89577-015-6). RD Assn.

Great Physician. G. Campbell Morgan. 416p. 1982. Repr. 16.95 (ISBN 0-8007-0485-1). Revell.

Great Physician. Lilian B. Yeomans. 80p. 1961. pap. 2.25 (ISBN 0-88243-729-1, 02-0729). Gospel Pub.

Great Power Discord in Palestine: The Anglo-American Committee of Inquiry into the Problems of European Jewry & Palestine 1945-1946. Amikam Nachmani. (Illus.). 296p. 1986. 30.00 (ISBN 0-7146-3298-8, F Cass Co). Biblio Dist.

Great Preachers of Today. Roy F. Osborne. 212p. 1966. case bound 11.95 (ISBN 0-89112-207-9, Bibl Res Pr). Abilene Christ U.

Great Promise. Karl Barth. LC 61-15239. 70p. 1963. 6.00 (ISBN 0-8022-0074-5). Philos Lib.

Great Prophecies of the Bible. Ralph Woodrow. (Illus.). 200p. 1971. 4.95 (ISBN 0-916938-02-6). R Woodrow.

Great Prophetic Themes. Keith L. Brooks. (Teach Yourself the Bible Ser.). 1962. pap. 2.75 (ISBN 0-8024-3320-0). Moody.

Great Prophets. Ruhi Afnan. 1960. 7.95 (ISBN 0-8022-0010-9). Philos Lib.

Great Pyramid: A Miracle in Stone. Joseph Seiss. LC 72-81590. (Illus.). 256p. 1973. pap. 5.00 (ISBN 0-89345-218-1, Steinerbks). Garber Comm.

Great Pyramid: A Miracle in Stone. Joseph A. Seiss. LC 80-8341. (Harper's Library of Spiritual Wisdom). 256p. 1981. pap. 5.95i (ISBN 0-06-067211-0, CN4005, HarpR). Har-Row.

Great Pyramid Decoded. rev. ed. E. Raymond Capt. LC 78-101677. (Illus.). 96p. 1978. pap. 3.00 (ISBN 0-934666-01-6). Artisan Sales.

Great Pyramid Decoded. Peter Lemesurier. (YA) 1984. pap. 4.95 (ISBN 0-380-43034-7, 43034-7). Avon.

Great Pyramid Proof of God. George R. Riffert. 1932. 8.00 (ISBN 0-685-08804-9). Destiny.

Great Pyramid: Signs in the Sun (Pyramid Design & Prophecy: Second Advent) John E. Gangstad. LC 76-24077. (Illus.). 200p. 1976. 1980-86 supplement 3.00 (ISBN 0-9603374-2-3). Di-Tri Bks.

Great Rabbis. Bernard Berniker. Ed. by Samuel Gorr. (Illus.). 1978. 10.00 (ISBN 0-87306-144-6); portfolio ed. 10.00 (ISBN 0-87306-195-0). Feldheim.

Great Rebellion: A Biblical Scrutiny of the Popular Culture of 1962-85 & Its Christian Versions. Bernard Pyron. 212p. (Orig.). 1985. pap. text ed. 7.00 (ISBN 0-9615024-0-1). Rebound Pubns.

Great Reformation. R. Tudur Jones. LC 85-23930. 272p. 1986. pap. 9.95 (ISBN 0-87784-606-5). Inter-Varsity.

Great Religions By Which Men Live. Floyd H. Ross & Tynette Hills. Orig. Title: Questions That Matter Most Asked by the World's Religions. 1977. pap. 2.50 (ISBN 0-449-30825-1, Prem). Fawcett.

Great Religions of the World. Mary L. Pastva. (Illus.). 251p. (Orig.). 1986. pap. text ed. 9.95x (ISBN 0-88489-175-5). St Mary's.

Great Reversal: Ethics & the New Testament. Allen Verhey. 288p. (Orig.). 1984. pap. 13.95 (ISBN 0-8028-0004-1). Eerdmans.

Great Revival in the West, 1797-1805. Catherine C. Cleveland. 11.25 (ISBN 0-8446-1117-4). Peter Smith.

Great Revivals. Colin Whittaker. LC 85-72333. 224p. 1986. pap. 4.50 (ISBN 0-88243-522-1, 02-0522). Gospel Pub.

Great Roman-Jewish War: A.D. 66-70. Flavius Josephus. Tr. by Whiston. 11.25 (ISBN 0-8446-0729-0). Peter Smith.

Great Sacrifice. Fred Pruitt. 31p. 1982. pap. 0.25 (ISBN 0-686-36262-4); pap. 1.00 5 copies (ISBN 0-686-37284-0). Faith Pub Hse.

Great Sacrilege. James F. Wathen. LC 76-183571. 1971. pap. 5.00 (ISBN 0-89555-014-8). TAN Bks Pubs.

Great Salvation. F. B. Hole. Ed. by R. P. Daniel. 72p. pap. 3.75 (ISBN 0-88172-142-5). Believers Bkshelf.

Great Salvation Themes. Jack Van Impe. 215p. 1984. pap. 4.95 (ISBN 0-934803-06-4). J Van Impe.

Great Satan "EBLIS". Iavad Nurbakhsh. Tr. by Terry Graham et al. 1986. pap. 6.00x (ISBN 0-933546-23-8). KhaniQahi-Nimatullahi-Sufi.

Great Schisms in Jewish History. Raphael Jospe & Stanley M. Wagner. 1980. 25.00x (ISBN 0-87068-784-0). Ktav.

Great Schoolmen of the Middle Ages. W. J. Townsend. 1977. lib. bdg. 39.95 (ISBN 0-8490-1903-6). Gordon Pr.

Great Second Advent Movement: Its Rise & Progress. J. N. Loughborough. LC 71-38453. (Religion in America, Ser. 2). 502p. 1972. Repr. of 1905 ed. 32.00 (ISBN 0-405-04073-3). Ayer Co Pubs.

Great Sermons of the Twentieth Century. Ed. by Peter F. Gunther. LC 86-70286. 224p. (Orig.). 1986. pap. 7.95 (ISBN 0-89107-397-3, Crossway Bks). Good News.

Great Shall Be Your Joy. Steven A. Cramer. 228p. 1984. 8.95 (ISBN 0-934126-48-8). Randall Bk Co.

Great Short Biographies of the World: A Collection of Short Biographies. Barrett H. Clark. 1979. Repr. of 1929 ed. lib. bdg. 40.00 (ISBN 0-8492-4037-9). R West.

Great Souls at Prayer. Mary W. Tileston. 366p. 1980. Repr. of 1898 ed. 9.50 (ISBN 0-227-67474-X). Attic Pr.

Great Souls at Prayer. Large Print ed. Ed. by Mary W. Tileston. 1983. 16.95 (ISBN 0-87983-343-2). Keats.

Great South African Christians. Horton Davies. LC 70-104242. Repr. of 1951 ed. lib. bdg. 22.50x (ISBN 0-8371-3916-3, DAGC). Greenwood.

Great Spiritual Writers of America. George H. Fitch. 1977. lib. bdg. 59.95 (ISBN 0-8490-1904-4). Gordon Pr.

Great Stories from the Bible. Borje Svensson. (Change-the-Picture Storybooks). (Illus.). 10p. 1985. 6.95 (ISBN 0-89191-939-2, 59394, Chariot Bks). Cook.

Great Tao. Stephen T. Chang. (Illus.). 464p. 1985. 26.00 (ISBN 0-942196-01-5). Tao Pub.

Great Teachings of Masonry. rev. enl. ed. Ed. by H. L. Haywood. 200p. 1971. Repr. of 1921 ed. text ed. 8.75 (ISBN 0-88053-041-3, M-90). Macoy Pub.

Great Teachings of the Buddha, 2 vols. E. Barrington. (Illus.). 211p. 1986. Set. 147.50 (ISBN 0-89901-273-6). Found Class Reprints.

Great Temple & the Aztec Gods. Doris Heyden & Luis F. Villasenor. (Illus.). 72p. 1984. pap. 4.50 (ISBN 968-7074-12-4). Ocelot Pr.

Great Temples of the East. Sacheverell Sitwell. 1962. 12.95 (ISBN 0-8392-1041-8). Astor-Honor.

Great Themes from the Old Testament. Norbert Lohfink. 1981. 10.95 (ISBN 0-8199-0801-0). Franciscan Herald.

Great Themes of the Bible. Raymond O. Corvin. (Alpha & Omega Bible Studies). 90p. (Orig.). 1986. pap. 5.95 (ISBN 0-89221-138-5). New Leaf.

Great Themes of the Christian Faith, As Presented by G. C. Morgan. facs. ed. Compiled by Charles W. Ferguson. LC 68-58788. (Essay Index Reprint Ser). 1930. 17.50 (ISBN 0-8369-1034-6). Ayer Co Pubs.

Great Themes of the New Testament. William Barclay. LC 79-18213. 122p. 1979. pap. 4.95 (ISBN 0-664-24286-3). Westminster.

Great Thoughts from the Upper Room. F. B. Meyer. 160p. 1983. pap. 5.95 (ISBN 0-310-44601-5, 12364P, Clarion Class). Zondervan.

Great Tiding: Thirtieth Part of Holy Quran. M. Ayoub. pap. 4.50 (ISBN 0-317-01597-4). Kazi Pubns.

Great Time to Be Alive: Sermons on Christianity in Wartime. Harry E. Fosdick. LC 78-167341. (Essay Index Reprint Ser.). Repr. of 1944 ed. 18.00 (ISBN 0-8369-2688-9). Ayer Co Pubs.

Great Todays - Better Tomorrows. Robert Fine. 1976. pap. 2.95 (ISBN 0-89367-001-4). Light & Life.

Great Transition: The Recovery of the Lost Centres of Modern Hebrew Literature. Ed. by Glenda Abramson & Tudor Parfitt. (Oxford Centre for Postgraduate Hebrew Studies). 184p. 1985. 35.00x (ISBN 0-8476-7437-1, Rowman & Allanheld). Rowman.

Great Trek of the Russian Mennonites to Central Asia. Fred R. Belk. LC 75-28340. (Studies in Anabaptist & Mennonite History: No. 18). pap. 63.00 (ISBN 0-317-26601-2, 2025418). Bks Demand UMI.

Great Tribulation. Gordon Lindsay. (End of the Age Ser.: Vol. 4). 1.50 (ISBN 0-89985-070-7). Christ Nations.

Great Trumpets & the Vial Judgments. Gordon Lindsay. (End of the Age Ser.: Vol. 6). 1.25 (ISBN 0-89985-072-3). Christ Nations.

Great Truths of the Bible. Raymond O. Corvin. (Alpha & Omega Bible Studies). 90p. (Orig.). 1986. pap. text ed. 5.95 (ISBN 0-89221-139-3). New Leaf.

Great Verses of the Bible. F. B. Meyer. 1984. gift ed. 6.95 (ISBN 0-915720-82-5). Brownlow Pub Co.

Great Verses Through the Bible. F. B. Meyer. 144p. 1982. pap. 13.95 (ISBN 0-310-29131-3, 10212P). Zondervan.

Great Vespers. Boris Ledkovsky. (Music Ser.). 218p. 1976. pap. 10.00 (ISBN 0-913836-26-5). St Vladimirs.

Great Warriors. H. A. Omar. 1984. pap. 15.00x (ISBN 0-7212-0631-X, Pub. by Regency Pr). State Mutual Bk.

Great Way of Wisdom: An Anthology of Written Teaching of Da Free John. Da F. John. Ed. by Georg Feuerstein. 1984. pap. 3.95 (ISBN 0-913922-88-9). Dawn Horse Pr.

Great White Throne. Gordon Lindsay. (End of the Age Ser.: Vol. 9). 1.25 (ISBN 0-89985-075-8). Christ Nations.

Great Women Initiates or the Feminine Mystic. Helene Bernard. Tr. by Michelle Ziebel from Fr. LC 84-50133. (Illus.). 151p. (Orig.). 1984. pap. 6.95 (ISBN 0-912057-36-X, G-650). AMORC.

Great Women of Faith. Hardesty. 2.95 (ISBN 0-318-18173-8). WCTU.

Great Women of Faith. Nancy A. Hardesty. (Festival Ser.). 144p. 1982. pap. 3.25 (ISBN 0-687-15728-5). Abingdon.

Great Women of the Bible. Clarence E. Macartney. (Macartney Bible Characters Library). (Orig.). 1974. pap. 5.95 (ISBN 0-8010-5961-5). Baker Bk.

Great Women of the Christian Faith. Edith Deen. (Christian Library). 410p. 1986. Repr. of 1959 ed. 6.95 (ISBN 0-916441-46-6). Barbour & Co.

Great Works of Christ in America, 2 vols. Cotton Mather. 1979. Set. 44.95 (ISBN 0-85151-280-1). Banner of Truth.

Great Writers. facs. ed. George E. Woodberry. LC 67-30236. (Essay Index Reprint Ser). 1907. 14.50 (ISBN 0-8369-1008-7). Ayer Co Pubs.

Great Writers As Interpreters of Religion. facsimile ed. Edwin Mims. LC 70-134116. (Essay Index Reprint Ser). Repr. of 1945 ed. 17.00 (ISBN 0-8369-1988-2). Ayer Co Pubs.

Great Zeus & All His Children: Greek Mythology for Adults. Donald Richardson. 312p. 1984. 16.95 (ISBN 0-13-364950-4); pap. 7.95 (ISBN 0-13-364943-1). P-H.

Greater Commission: A Theology of World Missions. Robert D. Culver. (Orig.). 1984. pap. text ed. 9.95 (ISBN 0-8024-3302-2). Moody.

Greater Health God's Way. Stormie Omartian. 208p. 1984. pap. 5.95 (ISBN 0-917143-00-0). Sparrow Pr CA.

Greater Judaism in the Making. Mordecai M. Kaplan. LC 59-15683. 565p. 1967. pap. 12.95 (ISBN 0-935457-14-3). Reconstructionist Pr.

Greater Love: A Woman's Workshop on Friendship. Jean Shaw. 96p. 1984. pap. 2.95 (ISBN 0-310-43531-5, 9596P). Zondervan.

Greater Works Shall Ye Do. Frank F. Steinke. 101p. (Orig.). 1980. pap. 2.25 (ISBN 0-686-73996-5). Impact Bks Mo.

Greatest Book in the World & Other Papers. A. Edward Newton. LC 78-86572. (Essay & General Literature Index Reprint Ser). (Illus.). 1969. Repr. 31.50x (ISBN 0-8046-0579-3, Pub. by Kennikat). Assoc Faculty Pr.

Greatest English Classic. Cleland B. McAfee. LC 77-18104. 1977. Repr. of 1912 ed. lib. bdg. 30.00 (ISBN 0-8414-6231-3). Folcroft.

Greatest Englishman: Essays on St. Boniface & the Church at Crediton. Ed. by Timothy Reuter. 140p. 1980. text ed. 15.00 (ISBN 0-85364-277-X). Attic Pr.

Greatest Fight in the World. C. H. Spurgeon. 64p. Date not set. pap. write for info. Pilgrim Pubns.

Greatest Gift in the World. Og Mandino. LC 76-43508. (Illus.). 128p. 1976. 8.95 (ISBN 0-8119-0274-9). Fell.

Greatest Gift Is Love. Baden. LC 59-1314. (Arch Bks.). 24p. 1985. pap. 0.99 (ISBN 0-570-06196-2). Concordia.

Greatest Is Love. (Illus.). 48p. 1982. Repr. 7.95 (ISBN 0-86683-688-8, AY8289, HarpR). Har-Row.

Greatest Miracle in the World. Og Mandino. 1977. pap. 3.50 (ISBN 0-553-25914-8). Bantam.

Greatest of These Is Love. Audrey McDaniel. LC 64-23538. (Illus.). 1972. 6.95 (ISBN 0-8378-1713-7). Gibson.

Greatest of These-Love. Betty R. Salls. pap. 1.75 (ISBN 0-686-12744-7). Grace Pub Co.

Greatest of These: Quotations on Fundamental Truths of Charity - The Teaching of Freemasonry. Woodrow W. Morris. (Illus.). 132p. 1985. 8.75 (ISBN 0-88053-080-4). Macoy Pub.

Greatest Salesman in the World. Og Mandino. 128p. 1974. pap. 3.50 (ISBN 0-553-26880-5). Bantam.

Greatest Secret in the World. Og Mandino. 1978. pap. 3.50 (ISBN 0-553-26545-8). Bantam.

Greatest Story Ever Told. Fulton Oursler. 1949. pap. 4.95 (ISBN 0-385-08028-X, D121, Im). Doubleday.

Greatest Story Ever Told. Fulton Oursler. 1981. pap. 2.95 (ISBN 0-671-44742-4). PB.

Greatest Thing in the World. Henry Drummond. 1959. 3.95 (ISBN 0-399-12828-X, G&D). Putnam Pub Group.

Greatest Thing in the World. Henry Drummond. 64p. 1968. pap. 2.50 (ISBN 0-8007-8018-3, Spire Bks). Revell.

Greatest Thing in the World. Henry Drummond. 64p. 1981. pap. 2.95 (ISBN 0-88368-100-5). Whitaker Hse.

Greatest Work in the World. rev. ed. Willie W. White. 1975. pap. 1.95 (ISBN 0-89900-108-4). College Pr Pub.

Greatness of the Kingdom. Alva J. McClain. 11.95 (ISBN 0-88469-011-3). BMH Bks.

Greatness of the Soul. John Bunyan. 1975. pap. 1.95 (ISBN 0-685-54807-4). Reiner.

Greece & Babylon: A Comparative Sketch of Mesopatamian, Anatolian, & Hellenic Religions. Lewis R. Farnell. 1977. lib. bdg. 59.95 (ISBN 0-8490-1906-0). Gordon Pr.

Greek & Eastern Churches. Walter F. Adeney. LC 65-22087. (Library of Religious & Philosophical Thought). 1966. Repr. of 1908 ed. lib. bdg. 45.00x (ISBN 0-678-09951-0, Reference Bk Pubs). Kelley.

Greek & Roman Myths. William A. Kottmeyer et al. 1962. pap. 7.96 (ISBN 0-07-033738-1). McGraw.

Greek & Syrian Miniatures in Jerusalem. William H. Hatch. (Illus.). 1931. 15.00x (ISBN 0-910956-04-9). Medieval Acad.

Greek Anthology, 5vols. Ed. by E. H. Warmington. Incl. Vol. 1. Book 1, Christian Epigrams. Book 2 Christoclorus of Thebes in Egypt. Book 3, Cyzicene Epigrams. Book 4, Proems of the Different Anthologies. Book 5, Amatory Epigrams. Book 6, Dedicatory Epigrams (ISBN 0-674-99074-9); Vol. 2. Book 7, Sepulchral Epigrams. Book 8, Epigrams of St. Gregory the Theologian (ISBN 0-674-99075-7); Vol. 3. Book 9, Declamatory Epigrams (ISBN 0-674-99093-5); Vol. 4. Book 10, Hortatory & Admonitory Epigrams. Book 11, Convivial & Satirical Epigrams. Book 12, Strato's Musa Puerilis (ISBN 0-674-99094-3); Vol. 5. Book 13, Epigrams in Various Metres. Book 14, Arithmetical Problems, Riddles, Oracles. Book 15, Miscellanea. Book 16, Epigrams of Planudean Anthology Not in the Palatine Manuscript (ISBN 0-674-99095-1). (Loeb Classical Library: No. 67-68, 84-86). (Gr. & Eng.). 13.95x ea. Harvard U Pr.

Greek-English Concordance. J. B. Smith. LC 55-12260. 430p. 1955. 29.95 (ISBN 0-8361-1368-3). Herald Pr.

Greek-English Lexicon of the New Testament: A Dictionary Numerically Coded to Strong's Exhaustive Concordance. Joseph H. Thayer. (Gr. & Eng.). 1977. pap. 15.95 (ISBN 0-8010-8838-0). Baker Bk.

Greek-English Lexicon of the New Testament & Other Early Christian Literature. Ed. by Walter Bauer et al. Tr. by William F. Arndt from Ger. LC 78-14293. (2nd rev. & augmented edition). 1979. lib. bdg. 47.50x (ISBN 0-226-03932-3). U of Chicago Pr.

Greek-English Lexicon of the New Testament & Other Early Christian Literature. rev 2nd. ed. Wilbur F. Gingrich et al. 1979. 45.00 (ISBN 0-310-20570-0, 6768). Zondervan.

Greek-English Lexicon of the New Testament. Joseph H. Thayer. 1956. 19.95 (ISBN 0-310-36850-2, 10906); pap. 10.95 (ISBN 0-310-36851-0, 10906P). Zondervan.

Greek-English Lexicon of the New Testament. Ed. & tr. by Joseph H. Thayer. (Gr.). 746p. 1901. 19.95 (ISBN 0-567-01015-5, Pub. by T & T Clark Ltd UK). Fortress.

Greek-English Lexicon of the New Testament. Tr. by Joseph H. Thayer. (Reference Set). Orig. Title: Grimm's Wilkes Clavis Novi Testamonti. 726p. 1982. Repr. of 1977 ed. 22.95 (ISBN 0-915134-73-X). Mott Media.

Greek Ethical Thought from Homer to the Stoics. Ed. by Hilda D. Oakeley. LC 79-173804. (Library of Greek Thought: No. 5). Repr. of 1925 ed. 10.00 (ISBN 0-404-07804-4). AMS Pr.

Greek Fathers. James Campbell. LC 63-10279. (Our Debt to Greece & Rome Ser.). 167p. 1963. Repr. of 1930 ed. 18.50x (ISBN 0-8154-0046-2). Cooper Sq.

Greek Folk Religion. Martin P. Nilsson. 1972. pap. 10.95x (ISBN 0-8122-1034-4, Pa. Paperbacks). U of Pa Pr.

Greek Gods. Bernard Evslin et al. 1972. pap. 2.25 (ISBN 0-590-06350-2, Schol Pap). Scholastic Inc.

Greek Gods. Bernard Evslin et al. (Illus.). 120p. 1984. pap. 2.25 (ISBN 0-590-33456-5, Point). Scholastic Inc.

Greek Gods & Heroes. Robert Graves. 125p. pap. 2.50 (ISBN 0-440-93221-1, LFL). Dell.

Greek Grammar of the New Testament. Curtis Vaughan & Virtus E. Gideon. LC 78-74504. 1979. 11.95 (ISBN 0-8054-1378-2). Broadman.

Greek Grammar of the New Testament & Other Early Christian Literature. F. Blass & A. Debrunner. Tr. by Robert W. Funk. 28.00 (ISBN 0-310-24780-2, 18076). Zondervan.

Greek Grammar of the New Testament & Other Early Christian Literature. Ed. by Robert W. Funk. LC 61-8077. 1961. 32.00x (ISBN 0-226-27110-2). U of Chicago Pr.

Greek-Hebrew - Aramaic Index to I Esdras. T. Muraoka. LC 83-8690. (SBL-Septuagint & Cognate Studies). 94p. 1984. pap. 8.75 (ISBN 0-89130-631-5, 06 04 16). Scholars Pr GA.

Greek Letters & the Latin Middle Ages: From Jerome to Nicholas of Cusa. Walter Berschin. Tr. by Jerold C. Frakes from Ger. Tr. of Griechisch-lateinisches mittelater von Hieronymus zu Nikolaus von Kues. 1987. price not set (ISBN 0-8132-0606-5). Cath U Pr.

Greek Mythology. Richmond Hathorn. 1977. 22.00x (ISBN 0-8156-6048-0, Am U Beirut). Syracuse U Pr.

Greek Mythology. rev. ed. John Pinsent. LC 83-71479. (Library of the World's Myths & Legends). (Illus.). 144p. 1983. 18.95 (ISBN 0-911745-08-4). P Bedrick Bks.

Greek Mythology. John Pinsent. (Library of the World's Myths & Legends). (Illus.). 144p. PLB 16.95 (ISBN 0-317-31010-0). Creative Ed.

Greek Mythology, 6 vols. Stephanides Brothers. (Series A.). (Eng.). Set. 50.00x (ISBN 0-916634-25-6). Double M Pr.

Greek Mythology: A Reader's Handbook. 2nd ed. Alexander Duthie. LC 78-12988. 1979. Repr. of 1949 ed. lib. bdg. 22.50x (ISBN 0-313-21077-2, DUGM). Greenwood.

Greek Mythology in Byzantine Art. Kurt Weitzmann. LC 84-4849. (Illus.). 380p. 1984. text ed. 95.00 (ISBN 0-691-03574-1). Princeton U Pr.

Greek Myths. Olivia Coolidge. (Illus.). 256p. 1949. 13.95 (ISBN 0-395-06721-9). HM.

Greek Myths. Robert Graves. (Illus.). 244p. 1982. 25.00 (ISBN 0-385-17790-9). Doubleday.

Greek Myths, 2 Vols. Robert Graves. (Orig.). (YA) 1955. Vol. 1. pap. 4.95 (ISBN 0-14-020508-X, Pelican); Vol. 2. pap. 4.95 (ISBN 0-14-020509-8). Penguin.

Greek Myths: A Vase Painter's Notebook. Jane Henle. LC 72-75639. (Illus.). 256p. 1973. 35.00x (ISBN 0-253-32635-4); pap. 7.95x (ISBN 0-253-32636-2). Ind U Pr.

Greek Myths & Christian Mystery. Hugo Rahner. LC 79-156736. (Illus.). 1971. Repr. of 1963 ed. 18.00 (ISBN 0-8196-0270-1). Biblo.

Greek New Testament According to the Majority Text. Ed. by Arthur L. Farstad & Zane C. Hodges. 78p. 1982. 14.95 (ISBN 0-8407-4963-5). Nelson.

Greek New Testament Analyzed. Pierre Guillemette. LC 86-81317. 480p. 1986. 29.95 (ISBN 0-8361-3418-4). Herald Pr.

Greek New Testament Insert. Benjamin Chapman. 1.95 (ISBN 0-8010-2405-6). Baker Bk.

Greek Orthodox Faith: Scriptural Presentation. Anatolius of Mohilew & Mstislaw. Tr. by Nicholas Bjerring from Rus. 1974. pap. 1.00 (ISBN 0-686-10205-3). Eastern Orthodox.

Greek Orthodox Youth Today. C. C. Moskos, Jr. & J. C. Papajohn. Intro. by N. M. Vaporis. (Saints Peter & Paul Youth Ministry Lectures Ser.). 56p. (Orig.). 1983. pap. 3.00 (ISBN 0-916586-56-1). Holy Cross Orthodox.

Greek Patristic Theolgy, Vol. 1: Eleven Studies in Eastern Orthodox Doctrine Spirituality. Constance N. Tsirpanlis. 170p. 1979. pap. 9.95 (ISBN 0-686-36327-2). EO Pr.

Greek Religion. Walter Burkert. 504p. 1987. pap. text ed. 9.95x (ISBN 0-674-36281-0). Harvard U Pr.

Greek Religion. William Burkert. Tr. by John Raffan from Ger. LC 84-25209. 493p. 1985. text ed. 30.00x (ISBN 0-674-36280-2). Harvard U Pr.

Greek Religion & Its Survivals. Walter W. Hyde. LC 63-10268. (Our Debt to Greece & Rome Ser). 1963. Repr. of 1930 ed. 18.50x (ISBN 0-8154-0117-5). Cooper Sq.

Greek Religion & Society. Ed. by P. E. Easterling & J. V. Muir. (Illus.). 264p. 1985. 39.50 (ISBN 0-521-24552-4); pap. 12.95 (ISBN 0-521-28785-5). Cambridge U Pr.

Greek Religious Thought from Homer to the Age of Alexander. Ed. by Francis M. Cornford. LC 79-98637. (Library of Greek Thought: No. 2). Repr. of 1923 ed. 21.50 (ISBN 0-404-01734-7). AMS Pr.

Greek Rhetorical Origins of Christian Faith. James L. Kinneavy. 256p. 1986. 29.95x (ISBN 0-19-503735-9). Oxford U Pr.

Greek Stories. Edward W. Dolch & M. P. Dolch. (Pleasure Reading Ser.). 176p. 1955. PLB 6.57 (ISBN 0-8116-2607-5). Garrard.

Greek Temple Builders at Epidauros. A. Burford. (Liverpool Monographs in Archaeology & Oriental Studies). 274p. 1969. text ed. 25.00x (ISBN 0-85323-080-3, Pub. by Liverpool U Pr). Humanities.

Greek Temples. Isabel H. Grinnell. LC 79-168420. (Metropolitan Museum of Art Publications in Reprint Ser.). (Illus.). 138p. 1972. Repr. of 1943 ed. 35.50 (ISBN 0-405-02258-1). Ayer Co Pubs.

Greek Testament: With English Notes, 2 vols. Samuel T. Bloomfield. 1986. Repr. of 1843 ed. Set. lib. bdg. 45.00 (ISBN 0-89941-507-5). W S Hein.

Greek Text of Ezekiel: An Examination of it's Homogeneity. Leslie J. McGregor. (SBL & SCS Ser.). 1985. 18.25 (ISBN 0-89130-902-0, 06-0418); pap. 13.95 (ISBN 0-89130-903-9). Scholars Pr GA.

Greek Text of Jeremiah: A Revised Hypothesis. Sven Soderlund. (JSOT Supplement Ser.: No. 47). 304p. 1986. text ed. 27.50x (ISBN 1-85075-028-9, Pub. by JSOT Pr England); pap. text ed. 13.50 (ISBN 0-317-46787-5). Eisenbrauns.

Greek Text of Judges: Recensional Developments. Walter R. Bodine. LC 80-12578. (Harvard Semitic Monographs: No. 23). 15.00x (ISBN 0-89130-400-2, 04-00-23). Scholars Pr GA.

Greek to Me: An Easy Way to Learn New Testament Greek Through Memory Visualization. Cullen I K Story. LC 79-1769. (Illus.). 1979. pap. text ed. 12.45 (ISBN 0-06-067705-8, RD 307, HarpR). Har-Row.

Greek Votive Offerings: An Essay in the History of Greek Religion. facsimile ed. William H. Rouse. LC 75-10654. (Ancient Religion & Mythology Ser.). (Illus.). 1976. Repr. of 1902 ed. 36.50x (ISBN 0-405-07262-7). Ayer Co Pubs.

Greek Way. Edith Hamilton. (YA) 1948. 19.95 (ISBN 0-393-04162-X). Norton.

Greek Way. Edith Hamilton. 1983. pap. 3.95 (ISBN 0-393-00230-6). Norton.

Greek Way of Death. Robert Garland. LC 85-470. (Illus.). 208p. 1985. text ed. 22.50x (ISBN 0-8014-1823-2). Cornell U Pr.

Greek Without Grief: An Outline Guide to New Testament Greek. 5th ed. Warren F. Dicharry. (Illus.). 1985. pap. 8.95 (ISBN 0-9608630-3-6). Vincentian.

Greeks & the Good Life. Ed. by David J. Depew. 280p. lib. bdg. 25.00 (ISBN 0-937622-00-1); pap. text ed. 7.95 (ISBN 0-937622-01-X). CSU Fullerton.

Greeks & Their Gods. William K. Guthrie. (Orig.). 1955. pap. 8.95x (ISBN 0-8070-5793-2, BPA16). Beacon Pr.

Green Leaf Bible Series, Year One. Foster H. Shannon. Ed. by Lois J. Rew. 1982. pap. 12.50 (ISBN 0-938462-06-7). Green Leaf CA.

Green Leaf Bible Series, Year Two. Foster H. Shannon. (Orig.). 1984. pap. 12.50 (ISBN 0-938462-11-3). Green Leaf CA.

Green Letters: Principals of Spiritual Growth. Miles J. Stanford. 128p. 1975. pap. 3.95 (ISBN 0-310-33001-7, 9473P). Zondervan.

Green Paradise Lost. Elizabeth Dodson Gray. LC 79-89193. x, 166p. 1979. pap. 8.95 (ISBN 0-934512-02-7). Roundtable Pr.

Greening of the Gospel. Roy Nichols. 1985. 6.25 (ISBN 0-89536-745-9, 5851). CSS of Ohio.

Greening: The Story of Nazarene Compassionate Ministries. R. Franklin Cook & Steve Weber. 104p. (Orig.). 1986. pap. 3.95 (ISBN 0-8341-1130-6). Beacon Hill.

Greening Wheat: Fifteen Mormon Short Stories. Ed. by Levi S. Peterson. 216p. (Orig.). 1983. pap. 5.95 (ISBN 0-941214-12-5, Orion). Signature Bks.

Gregor VII & Heinrich IV. Juergen Vogel. 1982. 59.20 (ISBN 3-11-008959-9). De Gruyter.

Gregorian Chant. Willi Apel. LC 57-10729. (Illus.). 544p. 1958. 35.00x (ISBN 0-253-32650-8). Ind U Pr.

Gregorian Chant: A History of Controversy Concerning Its Rhythm. John Rayburn. LC 80-27616. xiv, 90p. 1981. Repr. of 1964 ed. lib. bdg. 22.50x (ISBN 0-313-22811-6, RAGR). Greenwood.

Gregorian Chant, a Textbook for Seminaries, Novitiates, & Secondary Schools. Andrew F. Klarmann. (Illus.). ix, 148p. Repr. of 1945 ed. lib. bdg. 22.50x (ISBN 0-8371-9019-3, KLGC). Greenwood.

Gregory of Nyssa: The Life of Moses. Tr. by Abraham Malherbe. LC 78-56352. (Classics of Western Spirituality Ser.). (Illus.). 224p. 1978. 12.95 (ISBN 0-8091-0239-0); pap. 7.95 (ISBN 0-8091-2112-3). Paulist Pr.

Gregory of Tours-Life of the Fathers. Tr. & illus. by E. James. (Translated Texts for Historians-Latin Ser.: No. I). (Illus.). 174p. 1985. pap. text ed. 15.00x (ISBN 0-85323-115-X, Pub. by Liverpool U Pr). Humanities.

Gregory Palamas, The Triads. John Meyendorff. (Classics of Western Spirituality Ser.). 192p. 12.95 (ISBN 0-8091-0328-1); pap. 7.95 (ISBN 0-8091-2447-5). Paulist Pr.

Gretchen, I Am. Carroll E. Jay. 1979. pap. 2.25 (ISBN 0-380-42820-2, 42820-2). Avon.

Grey Friars. Harold Hoad. 1979. 6.95 (ISBN 0-8199-0779-0). Franciscan Herald.

Griechische Mythologie und Religionsgeschichte, 2 vols. facsimile ed. Otto Gruppe. LC 75-10638. (Ancient Religion & Mythology Ser.). (Ger.). 1976. Repr. of 1906 ed. 144.00x set (ISBN 0-405-07015-2). Ayer Co Pubs.

Griechische Mythology. Ludwig Preller. Ed. by Kees W. Bolle. LC 77-79153. (Mythology Ser.). (Ger.). 1978. lib. bdg. 62.00x (ISBN 0-405-10562-2). Ayer Co Pubs.

Griechischen Kultusaltertumer. facsimile ed. Paul Stengel. LC 75-10656. (Ancient Religion & Mythology Ser.). (Ger.). 1976. Repr. of 1920 ed. 22.00x (ISBN 0-405-07264-3). Ayer Co Pubs.

Grief. Haddon W. Robinson. 24p. 1976. pap. 3.50 (ISBN 0-310-32261-8, 9772P). Zondervan.

Grief & English Renaissance Elegy. C. W. Pigman, III. 192p. 1985. 29.95 (ISBN 0-521-26871-0). Cambridge U Pr.

Grief & Growth: Pastoral Resources for Emotional & Spiritual Growth. R. Scott Sullender. LC 84-61024. 240p. (Orig.). 1985. pap. 9.95 (ISBN 0-8091-2652-4). Paulist Pr.

Grief & Mourning in Cross-Cultural Perspective. Paul C. Rosenblatt et al. LC 76-29270. (Comparative Studies Ser.). 242p. 1976. pap. 7.00x (ISBN 0-87536-334-2). HRAFP.

Grief & the Meaning of the Funeral. Otto S. Margolis. 15.50 (ISBN 0-405-12501-1). Ayer Co Pubs.

Grief Is Not Forever. Jeri Krumroy. 128p. (Orig.). 1985. pap. 6.95 (ISBN 0-87178-326-6). Brethren.

Grief Observed. C. S. Lewis. 160p. 1976. pap. 3.50 (ISBN 0-553-25614-9). Bantam.

Grief Observed. C. S. Lewis. 64p. (Orig.). 1966. pap. 3.95 (ISBN 0-571-06624-0). Faber & Faber.

Grief Observed. C. S. Lewis. 1963. 6.95 (ISBN 0-8164-0137-3, HarpR). Har-Row.

Grief Observed. C. S. Lewis. 120p. 1985. pap. 5.95 large print ed. (ISBN 0-8027-2470-1). Walker & Co.

Grief: Selected Readings. Ed. by Arthur C. Carr et al. 155p. 1974. pap. 7.50 (ISBN 0-930194-76-4). Ctr Thanatology.

Grieving: A Handbook for Those Who Care. Ruth Bright. vi, 229p. 1986. pap. 19.50 (ISBN 0-918812-46-1). MMB Music.

Grieving: A Healing Process. Peter C. McDonald. 24p. (Orig.). 1985. pap. 0.95 (ISBN 0-89486-318-5). Hazelden.

Grimani Breviary. Intro. by Mario Salmi. LC 74-78138. (Illus.). 276p. 1974. 195.00 (ISBN 0-87951-022-6). Overlook Pr.

Grisez Reader for Beyond the New Morality. Germain Grisez & Russell Shaw. Ed. by Joseph H. Casey. LC 81-43481. 218p. (Orig.). 1982. lib. bdg. 29.00 (ISBN 0-8191-2243-2); pap. text ed. 11.50 (ISBN 0-8191-2244-0). U Pr of Amer.

Grist from Adams' Mill. Jay E. Adams. 96p. 1983. pap. 2.50 (ISBN 0-87552-079-0). Presby & Reformed.

Grito de Victoria! Luis Palau. Tr. by Leticia Calcada from Eng. Tr. of Moment to Shout! (Span.). 144p. 1986. pap. 5.50 (ISBN 0-311-46106-9). Casa Bautista.

Groaning Up. Ben Leach. (Uplook Ser.). 32p. 1982. pap. 0.99 (ISBN 0-8163-0513-7). Pacific Pr Pub Assn.

Groans of a Lost Soul. John Bunyan. LC 68-6571. 1967. pap. 3.25 (ISBN 0-685-19830-8). Reiner.

Grotesque in Church Art. Thomas T. Wildridge. LC 68-30633. 1969. Repr. of 1899 ed. 35.00x (ISBN 0-8103-3077-6). Gale.

Ground & Grammar of Theology. Thomas F. Torrance. LC 79-21429. 180p. 1980. 13.95x (ISBN 0-8139-0819-1). U Pr of Va.

Grounded in Love: Sacramental Theology in an Ecumenical Perspective. Frans J. Van Beeck. LC 81-40117. 162p. (Orig.). 1982. lib. bdg. 26.00 (ISBN 0-8191-2040-5); pap. text ed. 11.25 (ISBN 0-8191-2041-3). U Pr of Amer.

Grounding for the Metaphysics of Morals. Immanuel Kant. Tr. by James W. Ellington from Ger. LC 80-28839. (HPC Philosophical Classics Ser.). 80p. 1981. lib. bdg. 16.50 (ISBN 0-915145-01-4); pap. text ed. 3.45 (ISBN 0-915145-00-6). Hackett Pub.

Grounds of Hope: Essays in Faith & Freedom. Ed. by R. R. Osborn. 184p. 1968. 3.95 (ISBN 0-87921-055-9). Attic Pr.

Grounds of Secession from the M. E. Church. Orange Scott. LC 71-82219. (Anti-Slavery Crusade in America Ser). 1969. Repr. of 1848 ed. 14.00 (ISBN 0-405-00659-4). Ayer Co Pubs.

Groundwork of Biblical Studies. W. David Stacey. LC 82-70961. 448p. 1982. pap. 14.95 (ISBN 0-8066-1936-8, 10-2898). Augsburg.

Groundwork of the Metaphysics of Morals. Immanuel Kant. Tr. by H. J. Paton. Orig. Title: Moral Law. pap. 6.95x (ISBN 0-06-131159-6, TB1159, Torch). Har-Row.

Groundwork of the Philosophy of Religion. Atkinson Lee. LC 46-19011. (Studies in Theology Ser: No. 48). 1946. text ed. 6.00x (ISBN 0-8401-6048-8). A R Allenson.

Group Auditor's Handbook. L. Ron Hubbard. 50.00 (ISBN 0-686-30787-9). Church Scient NY.

Group Counseling: Dynamic Possibilities for Small Groups. Edgar N. Jackson. LC 73-91167. (Orig.). 1969. pap. 2.95 (ISBN 0-8298-0053-0). Pilgrim NY.

Group Development Through Participation Training: A Trainers Resource for Team Building. John McKinley. LC 78-71870. 162p. (Orig.). 1980. pap. text ed. 9.95 (ISBN 0-8091-2247-2); participant's bk. 2.50 (ISBN 0-8091-2299-5). Paulist Pr.

Group Magazine's Best Youth Group Programs, Vol. 1. Ed. by Cindy S. Hansen. LC 86-313. (Illus.). 224p. 1986. 17.95 (ISBN 0-931529-11-5). Group Bks.

Group Movements Throughout the Ages. Robert H. Murray. LC 72-301. (Essay Index Reprint Ser.). Repr. of 1935 ed. 22.00 (ISBN 0-8369-2810-5). Ayer Co Pubs.

Group Readings for the Church. Charlotte Arnold. (Paperback Program Ser.). (Orig.). 1975. pap. 1.95 (ISBN 0-8010-0065-3). Baker Bk.

Group Retreat Book. Arlo Reichter et al. LC 82-62532. (Illus.). 400p. (Orig.). 1983. pap. 15.95 (ISBN 0-936664-08-8). Group Bks.

Group Talk. Ed Stewart & Nina M. Fishwick. LC 85-30142. 162p. (Orig.). 1986. pap. 5.95 (ISBN 0-8307-1139-2, S411103). Regal.

Groupe Zoologique Humain, Structure et Directions Evolutives. Teilhard De Chardin. (Coll. les Savants et le Monde Ser.). pap. 6.95 (ISBN 0-685-36591-3). French & Eur.

Grow & Flourish: A Daily Guide to Personal Renewal. David Watson. Ed. by Jean Watson. (General). 392p. 1983. pap. 6.95 (ISBN 0-87788-327-0). Shaw Pubs.

Grow, Christian, Grow: Student. Knofel Staton. LC 77-82120. (New Life Ser.). (Illus.). 1978. pap. 2.25 (ISBN 0-87239-177-9, 39999). Standard Pub.

Grow in God's Love. 2nd ed. Gerard P. Weber et al. 1977. 2.64 (ISBN 0-02-658200-7); tchrs. ed. 8.00 (ISBN 0-02-658210-4); family handbook 1.00 (ISBN 0-02-658250-3). Benziger Pub Co.

Grow to Love. Jean C. Grigor. 1977. pap. 5.75x (ISBN 0-7152-0437-8). Outlook.

Grow Your Christian Life. Inter-Varsity Staff. pap. 5.95 (ISBN 0-87784-661-8). Inter-Varsity.

Growing. Evelyn Bence. 32p. 1985. 4.95 (ISBN 0-8378-2043-X). Gibson.

Growing a Healthy Family. Jim Larson. LC 85-28657. 128p. (Orig.). 1986. pap. 6.95 (ISBN 0-8066-2193-1, 10-2901). Augsburg.

Growing a Junior High Ministry. David Shaheen. LC 86-19410. 300p. (Orig.). 1986. pap. 12.95 (ISBN 0-931529-15-8). Group Bks.

Growing a Soul: The Story of A. Frank Smith. Norman W. Spellman. LC 78-20876. 1979. 17.95x (ISBN 0-87074-171-3). SMU Press.

Growing as a Disciple Conference Notebook. rev. ed. Churches Alive, Inc. Staff. 85p. 1983. pap. write for info. (ISBN 0-934396-37-X). Churches Alive.

Growing As Jesus Grew. Jane Buerger. LC 80-17187. (Illus.). 32p. 1980. PLB 5.95 (ISBN 0-89565-173-4). Childs World.

Growing as Jesus Grew. Jane Buerger. (Child's World Books of Understanding). (Illus.). 1985. PLB 5.95 (ISBN 0-89565-173-4, R4924). Standard Pub.

Growing by Discipling Pastor's Handbook. rev. ed. Churches Alive, Inc. Staff. (Illus.). 150p. 1980. pap. text ed. 9.95 (ISBN 0-934396-09-4). Churches Alive.

Growing Church School. Kenneth D. Blazier. 1978. pap. text ed. 2.50 (ISBN 0-8170-0785-7). Judson.

Growing Churches: Singapore Style. Keith Hinton. 1985. pap. 4.95 (ISBN 9971-972-24-7). OMF Bks.

Growing Closer to God. Tom Gryn. 100p. (Orig.). 1982. pap. 2.50 (ISBN 0-89283-160-X). Servant.

Growing Deep in the Christian Life: Returning to Our Roots. Charles R. Swindoll. LC 86-8661. 1986. 14.95 (ISBN 0-88070-154-4). Multnomah.

Growing Edge. Howard Thurman. LC 74-14866. 192p. 1974. pap. 6.95 (ISBN 0-913408-14-X). Friends United.

Growing Edges in the Psychology of Religion. Ed. by John R. Tisdale. LC 79-20116. 350p. 1980. text ed. 24.95x (ISBN 0-88229-338-9); pap. text ed. 12.95x (ISBN 0-88229-748-1). Nelson-Hall.

Growing Faith. Bruce P. Powers. LC 81-66990. 1982. pap. 5.50 (ISBN 0-8054-3230-2). Broadman.

Growing in Christ: Catechism. Erwin Kurth et al. (Illus.). 1953. text ed. 4.85 (ISBN 0-570-01517-0, 22-1097); wkbk. 1.95 (ISBN 0-570-01518-9, 22-1100). Concordia.

Growing in Discipleship. rev. ed. Navigators Staff. (Design for Discipleship Ser.: Bk. 6). 1980. pap. text ed. 1.95 (ISBN 0-934396-21-3). Churches Alive.

Growing in Faith. Steve B. Clark. (Living As a Christian Ser.). 1972. pap. 2.25 (ISBN 0-89283-004-2). Servant.

Growing in Faith. Joyce M. Smith. 1982. pap. 2.95 (ISBN 0-8423-1227-7). Tyndale.

Growing in Faith: Devotions for Parent-Child Interaction. Luther S. Cross. 32p. (Orig.). 1984. pap. 2.95 (ISBN 0-8066-2070-6, 23-1606). Augsburg.

Growing in Faith with Your Child. Archdiocese of Newark Staff. Ed. by Thomas P. Ivory. Tr. of Cresciendo en Fe con su Nino. 48p. (Orig.). pap. 2.95 (ISBN 0-697-01693-5). Wm C Brown.

Growing in Grace. Frank J. Gordon. (Illus.). 111p. (Orig.). 1981. pap. 6.00 (ISBN 0-686-34382-4). G Lutheran Foun.

Growing in Grace. Mike Sherer. 1986. 5.50 (ISBN 0-89536-798-X, 6816). CSS of Ohio.

Growing in His Image. Bernard Bangley. LC 82-19579. (Illus.). 155p. 1983. pap. 3.50 (ISBN 0-87788-328-9). Shaw Pubs.

Growing in Inner Freedom: A Guide for Today. Philip S. Romain. 64p. 1986. pap. 1.95 (ISBN 0-89243-259-4). Liguori Pubns.

Growing in Joy: God's Way to Increase Joy in All of Life. Ron Klug. LC 82-72637. 128p. 1983. pap. 5.95 (ISBN 0-8066-1943-0, 10-2902). Augsburg.

Growing in Perfect Union. Rev. James Alberione. 1964. 3.00 (ISBN 0-8198-3019-4); pap. 2.00 (ISBN 0-8198-3020-8). Dghtrs St Paul.

Growing in the Fruit of the Spirit. John Blattner. (Living As A Christian Ser.). 96p. 1984. pap. 3.95 (ISBN 0-89283-177-4). Servant.

Growing in the Word. Robert E. Coleman. 272p. 1982. pap. 2.95 (ISBN 0-8007-8448-0, Spire Bks). Revell.

Growing into the Blue. Ulrich Schaffer. LC 83-48463. (Illus.). 96p. (Orig.). 1984. pap. 14.95 (ISBN 0-06-067089-4, RD 509, HarpR). Har-Row.

Growing Jesus' Way. Carolyn Nystrom. (Children's Bible Basics Ser.). 1982. 4.95 (ISBN 0-8024-5999-4). Moody.

Growing Life: Devotionals for the Young in Christ. Audley B. Lyon. LC 77-82056. 1970. pap. 5.95 (ISBN 0-930014-07-3). Multnomah.

Growing Love in Christian Marriage: Couple's Manual. Joan Hunt & Richard Hunt. 1981. pap. 2.50 (ISBN 0-687-15931-8). Abingdon.

Growing Love in Christian Marriage: Pastors's Manual. Smith & Smith. 1981. pap. 4.75 (ISBN 0-687-15930-X). Abingdon.

Growing More Like Jesus. Heather Guttschuss. 128p. 1985. pap. 6.95 (ISBN 0-8163-0486-6). Pacific Pr Pub Assn.

Growing Old: A View from Within. Norma Jacob. LC 81-83072. 29p. 1981. 2.50x (ISBN 0-87574-239-4). Pendle Hill.

Growing Old & How to Cope with it. Alfons S. J. Deekken. LC 86-80786. 192p. 1986. pap. 7.95 (ISBN 0-89870-104-X). Ignatius Pr.

Growing Old-Feeling Young. John W. Drakeford. LC 84-21341. 1985. pap. 7.95 (ISBN 0-8054-5009-2). Broadman.

Growing On. Barry St. Clair. (Moving Toward Maturity Ser.: No. 5). 144p. 1986. pap. 4.95 (ISBN 0-88207-305-2). Victor Bks.

Growing Pains. Audrey M. Raphael. (Illus.). 68p. 1985. 6.95 (ISBN 0-533-06210-1). Vantage.

Growing Pains in Ministry. Sean D. Sammon. LC 83-9991. 240p. (Orig.). 1983. pap. 8.00 (ISBN 0-89571-016-1). Affirmation.

Growing Pains in Ministry. Sean D. Sammon. LC 83-9991. 240p. 1983. 12.95 (ISBN 0-89571-027-7); study guide, 77p 3.95 (ISBN 0-89571-029-3). Affirmation.

Growing Plans: Strategies to Increase Your Church's Membership. Lyle E. Schaller. 176p. 1983. pap. 7.95 (ISBN 0-687-15962-8). Abingdon.

Growing Season. Martha W. Hickman. LC 80-68983. 128p. (Orig.). 1980. pap. 4.50x (ISBN 0-8358-0411-9). Upper Room.

Growing Season. Lin Johnson. 96p. 1987. pap. 4.95 (ISBN 0-89693-009-2). Victor Bks.

Growing, Sharing, Serving. Jo Berry. LC 78-73461. 1979. pap. 3.95 (ISBN 0-89191-073-5). Cook.

Growing Spiritually. E. Stanley Jones. (Festival Books). 1978. pap. 3.25 (ISBN 0-687-15968-7). Abingdon.

Growing Strong at Broken Places. Paula Ripple. LC 86-71124. 184p. (Orig.). 1986. pap. 5.95 (ISBN 0-87793-341-3). Ave Maria.

Growing Strong in the Seasons of Life. Charles R. Swindoll. LC 83-11466. 350p. 1983. 14.95 (ISBN 0-88070-026-2). Multnomah.

Growing Strong Inside. Jane B. Moncure. LC 85-10341. (New Values Ser.). (Illus.). 32p. 1985. PLB 7.45 (ISBN 0-89565-333-8). Childs World.

Growing Stronger-Advanced. John C. Souter. 1980. study guide 2.95 (ISBN 0-8423-1234-X). Tyndale.

Growing Stronger: Two - Two. Vera Groomer. (Come Unto Me Ser.: Year 2, Bk. 2). 32p. 1980. pap. 1.65 (ISBN 0-8127-0271-9). Review & Herald.

Growing the Small Church: A Guide for Church Leaders. C. Wayne Zunkel. 109p. 1982. tchr's. ed. 12.95 (ISBN 0-89191-952-X). Cook.

Growing the Small Church: A Guide for Church Members. C. Wayne Zunkel. 120p. 1984. pap. text ed. 2.95 (ISBN 0-89191-951-1). Cook.

Growing Through Divorce: Working Guide. Jim Smoke & Lisa Guest. 96p. (Orig.). 1985. pap. 3.25 (ISBN 0-89081-477-5). Harvest Hse.

Growing Through Grief. James E. Towns. 1984. pap. 2.95 (ISBN 0-87162-395-1, D4000). Warner Pr.

Growing Through Mid-Life Crises. John Sterner. 112p. 1985. 8.95 (ISBN 0-570-04220-8, 15-2181). Concordia.

Growing through Rejection. Elizabeth Skoglund. 1983. pap. 3.95 (ISBN 0-8423-1239-0). Tyndale.

Growing to Maturity: A Messianic Jewish Guide. 2nd ed. Daniel C. Juster. (Illus.). 278p. (Orig.). 1985. pap. 7.00 (ISBN 0-9614555-0-0). Union Messianic Jew Pub.

Growing Together. Clyde T. Besson. 1987. pap. 5.95 (ISBN 0-317-54043-2). Baker Bk.

Growing Together. John Trent. 156p. 1985. pap. 5.95 (ISBN 0-89693-323-7). Victor Bks.

Growing Together: Building Your Family's Spiritual Life. 2nd ed. Mary White. 144p. 1985. pap. 4.95 (ISBN 0-89109-484-9). NavPress.

Growing Together: Prayers for Married People. Leslie Brandt & Edith Brandt. LC 75-2830. 96p. (Orig.). 1975. pap. 5.95 (ISBN 0-8066-1476-5, 10-2903). Augsburg.

Growing Together with Guys, Gals & Animal Pals. Darlene Loomis. (Illus., Orig.). 1977. pap. 2.00 (ISBN 0-686-36276-4). Drain Enterprise.

Growing Up. Josephine Colville. 1979. 6.25 (ISBN 0-8198-0575-0); pap. 5.00 (ISBN 0-8198-0576-9). Dghtrs St Paul.

Growing up Catholic: An Infinitely Funny Guide for the Faithful, the Fallen & Everyone in Between. Jeff Stone et al. LC 83-25394. 144p. 1985. pap. 5.95 (ISBN 0-385-19240-1, Dolp). Doubleday.

Growing up Christian in the Twenty-First Century. Douglas W. Johnson. 128p. 1984. pap. 4.95 (ISBN 0-8170-1048-3). Judson.

Growing up Hasidic: Education & Socialization in the Bobover Hasidic Community. Robert M. Kamen. LC 83-45358. (Immigrant Communities & Ethnic Minorities in the United States & Canada Ser.). 1985. 30.00 (ISBN 0-404-19411-7). AMS Pr.

Growing up in Christ. Eugene H. Peterson. pap. 5.50 (ISBN 0-8042-2026-3). John Knox.

Growing Up in the Church: Gospel Principles & Practices for Children. rev. ed. Jean D. Crowther. LC 67-25433. (Illus.). 84p. 1973. Repr. of 1965 ed. 6.95 (ISBN 0-88290-024-2). Horizon Utah.

Growing up Is a Family Affair. Ethel Herr. LC 78-17581. 1978. pap. 5.95 (ISBN 0-8024-3359-6). Moody.

Growing Up Isn't Easy, Lord: Story Devotions for Boys. Stephen Sorenson. LC 79-50080. 1979. pap. 3.95 (ISBN 0-8066-1713-6, 10-2904). Augsburg.

Growing up, Spiritually. Kenneth E. Hagin. 1976. pap. 3.50 (ISBN 0-89276-504-6). Hagin Ministries.

Growing up to God: A Guide for Teenagers on the Sacrement of Reconciliation. M. Loretta Pastva. LC 83-15538. 82p. (Orig.). 1983. pap. 4.95 (ISBN 0-8189-0455-0). Alba.

Growing up to Love: A Guide to Sex Education for Parents. rev. ed. H. Clair Amstutz. LC 56-11527. (Illus.). 112p. (YA) 1966. pap. 1.95 (ISBN 0-8361-1535-X). Herald Pr.

Growing up Together: A Spiritual Perspective for Parents of Adolescents. David Walsh. 124p. (Orig.). 1980. pap. 2.50 (ISBN 0-912228-73-3). St Anthony Mess Pr.

Growing When You Don't Feel Like It. Joyce M. Smith. (Good Life Bible Studies). 64p. (YA) 1985. pap. 2.95 (ISBN 0-8423-1229-3). Tyndale.

Growing with Bible Heroes: Grade 4. rev. ed. Angela R. Carl & Alice C. Holmes. Ed. by Marge Miller. (Basic Bible Readers Ser.). (Illus.). 128p. 1983. text ed. 7.95 (ISBN 0-87239-664-9, 2954). Standard Pub.

Growing with Daily Devotions. Helen Byerly. 20p. 1964. No. 4. 1.50 ea., spiral bd., wkbk. (ISBN 0-87509-337-X). No. 5 (ISBN 0-87509-338-8). No. 6 (ISBN 0-87509-339-6). No. 7 (ISBN 0-87509-340-X). No. 8 (ISBN 0-87509-341-8). No. 9 o.p (ISBN 0-87509-342-6). No. 10 (ISBN 0-87509-343-4). No. 11 (ISBN 0-87509-344-2). No.12 (ISBN 0-87509-345-0). Chr Pubns.

Growing with Doniel. Students of Bais Yaakov Academy. 1987. 9.95; pap. 7.95. Feldheim.

Growing with God. Maria De la Cruz Aymes et al. (God with Us Program). 112p. (Orig.). 1983. pap. text ed. 3.69 (ISBN 0-8215-1121-1); tchr's ed. 10.86 (ISBN 0-8215-1131-9); wkbk. 1.65 (ISBN 0-8215-1151-3); compact ed 3.18 (ISBN 0-8215-1101-7). Sadlier.

Growing with God's Forgiveness & I Celebrate Reconcilation. Maria De la Cruz Aymes et al. (Sacrament Program Ser.). 72p. 1985. pap. text ed. 3.30 (ISBN 0-8215-2371-6); tchr's. ed. 4.50 (ISBN 0-8215-2373-2); Parent Pack (10 booklets) 5.04 (ISBN 0-8215-2377-5). Sadlier.

Growing with Jesus. Maria De la Cruz Aymes et al. 144p. (Orig.). 1983. pap. text ed. 3.69 (ISBN 0-8215-1122-X); 10.86 (ISBN 0-8215-1132-7); wkbk. 1.65 (ISBN 0-8215-1152-1); compact ed. 3.18 (ISBN 0-8215-1102-5). Sadlier.

Growing with the Bible. Elaine M. Ward. 64p. (Orig.). 1986. pap. 6.95 (ISBN 0-940754-36-3). Ed Ministries.

Growing with the Bread of Life & My Mass Book. Maria De la Cruz Aymes et al. (Sacrament Program Ser.). 72p. 1985. pap. text ed. 3.30 (ISBN 0-8215-2370-8); tchr's. ed. 4.50 (ISBN 0-8215-2372-4); Parent Pack (10 booklets) 5.04 (ISBN 0-8215-2376-7). Sadlier.

Growing Within, Changing Without. Richard Reichert. (New Creation Ser.). 96p. 1985. pap. text ed. 4.05 (ISBN 0-697-01993-4); tchr's. ed. 4.50 (ISBN 0-697-01994-2). Wm C Brown.

Grown-Up's Xmas Book. Colin Walsh. 128p. 1986. pap. 7.95 (ISBN 0-907621-44-9, Pub. by Quiller Pr England). Intl Spec Bk.

Growth & Development of the Catholic School System in the United States. J. A. Burns. LC 78-89156. (American Education: Its Men, Institutions & Ideas, Ser. 1). 1969. Repr. of 1912 ed. 21.00 (ISBN 0-405-01394-9). Ayer Co Pubs.

Growth & the Essence of Buddhism. Isaac Hall. (Illus.). 148p. 1982. Repr. of 1883 ed. 89.75 (ISBN 0-89901-060-1). Found Class Reprints.

Growth Counseling for Marriage Enrichment: Pre-Marriage & the Early Years. Howard J. Clinebell. Ed. by Howard W. Stone. LC 74-26335. (Creative Pastoral Care & Counseling Ser.). 96p. 1975. pap. 4.50 (ISBN 0-8006-0551-9, 1-551). Fortress.

Growth Counseling for Mid-Years Couples. Howard J. Clinebell. Ed. by Howard W. Stone. LC 76-7863. (Creative Pastoral Care & Counseling Ser.). 1977. pap. 0.50 (ISBN 0-8006-0558-6, 1-558). Fortress.

Growth Counseling for Mid-Years Couples. Howard J. Clinebell. LC 76-7863. (Creative Pastoral Care & Counseling Ser.). pap. 24.00 (2029607). Bks Demand UMI.

Growth Group Leader's Guide. rev. ed. Churches Alive, Inc. Staff. LC 80-52536. (Illus.). 110p. 1980. pap. 7.95 (ISBN 0-934396-10-8). Churches Alive.

Growth Group Member's Notebook. Churches Alive, Inc. Staff. LC 80-52536. (Illus.). 105p. (Orig.). 1980. pap. text ed. 5.95 (ISBN 0-934396-11-6). Churches Alive.

Growth Groups: A Key to Christian Fellowship & Spiritual Maturity in the Church. Michael T. Dibbert et al. 160p. (Orig.). 1985. pap. 5.95 (ISBN 0-310-23121-3, 11673P). Zondervan.

Growth Guide for Ministers' Wives. Shirley E. Montgomery. LC 83-71066. 1984. pap. 6.95 (ISBN 0-8054-2708-2). Broadman.

Growth in Ministry. Ed. by Thomas E. Kadel. LC 79-8902. 176p. 1980. pap. 6.95 (ISBN 0-8006-1383-X, 1-1383). Fortress.

Growth in Prayer. Jim Wilson. 74p. 1969. pap. 2.95 (ISBN 0-227-67475-8). Attic Pr.

Growth of a Soul. Phylos. LC 76-15521. 10.00 (ISBN 0-912216-07-7). Angel Pr.

Growth of a Work of God. C. Stacey Woods. LC 77-6553. 1978. pap. 4.95 (ISBN 0-87784-741-X). Inter-Varsity.

Growth of Japanese Churches in Brazil. John Mizuki. LC 78-5415. (Illus.). 1978. pap. 8.95 (ISBN 0-87808-323-5). William Carey Lib.

Growth of Reform Judaism: American & European Sources Until 1948. Ed. by W. Gunther Plaut. 1965. 10.00 (ISBN 0-8074-0086-6, 382780). UAHC.

Growth of the Biblical Tradition. Klaus Koch. 1968. lib. bdg. 24.50x (ISBN 0-684-14524-3, ScribT). Scribner.

Growth of the Church in Buganda: An Attempt at Understanding. John V. Taylor. LC 78-26702. (Illus.). 1979. Repr. of 1958 ed. lib. bdg. 24.75x (ISBN 0-313-20802-6, TAGC). Greenwood.

Growth of the Gospels. Neil J. McEleney. LC 79-90141. 96p. (Orig.). 1979. pap. 4.95 (ISBN 0-8091-2243-X). Paulist Pr.

Growth of the Soul from Impiety to Ecstasy. Vicki Vann. (Illus.). 1977. pap. 3.25 (ISBN 0-87516-235-5). De Vorss.

Growth of the True Church. Van Engen. (Amsterdam Studies in Theology: Vol. III). 545p. 1981. pap. text ed. 55.00x (ISBN 90-6203-783-6, Pub. by Rodopi Holland). Humanities.

Growth Through Biblical Stewardship. J. J. Turner. 1986. pap. 4.50 (ISBN 0-89137-561-9). Quality Pubns.

Growth Through Meditation & Journal Writing: A Jungian Perspective on Christian Spirituality. Maria L. Santa-Maria. 1983. pap. 8.95 (ISBN 0-8091-2570-6). Paulist Pr.

Growth Through Virtue. Daniel L. Lowery. 64p. 1984. pap. 1.50 (ISBN 0-89243-222-5). Liguori Pubns.

Growth Unlimited. Jim Burns. 160p. (Orig.). 1987. pap. 5.95 (ISBN 0-89081-580-1). Harvest Hse.

Grumpy Prophet & 22 other Bible Stories to Read & Tell. John C. Reid. 80p. 1986. casebound 7.95 (ISBN 0-87239-917-6, 3370). Standard Pub.

Gu Mingqi Tulu. Luo Zhenyu. 1916. 300.00x (ISBN 0-317-44070-5, Pub. by Han-Shan Tang Ltd). State Mutual Bk.

Guanches of Tenerife, the Holy Image of Our Lady of Candelaria, with the Spanish Conquest & Settlement, by the Friar Alonso de Espinosa. Ed. by Clements Markham. (Hakluyt Society Ser.: No. 2, Vol. 21). (Illus.). Repr. of 1907 ed. 25.00 (ISBN 0-8115-0341-0). Kraus Repr.

Guangzhou Hanmu Excavation of the Han Tombs at Guangzhou. Guangzhou Municipal Museum. 526p. 1981. 150.00x (ISBN 0-317-44071-3, Pub. by Han-Shan Tang Ltd). State mutual Bk.

Guaranteed Steps to Managing Stress. Arnold Burron & Jerry Crews. (Orig.). 1986. pap. 6.95 (ISBN 0-8423-1249-8). Tyndale.

Guarda una Cuaresma Verdadera. Charles Fillmore. (Span.). 214p. 1983. 5.95 (ISBN 0-87159-048-4). Unity School.

Guardian I: The Answers. Fred B. Foster & Linda Foster. 224p. 1984. pap. 9.95 (ISBN 0-9613762-0-1). F B Foster Pubns.

Guardian of the Universe? Ronald Story. 1980. 8.95 (ISBN 0-312-35216-6). St Martin.

Guardian Office of the Church of Scientology. pap. 7.00 (ISBN 0-915598-25-6). Church of Scient Info.

Guardian Spirit Quest. Ella Clark. (Indian Culture Ser.). 1974. pap. 1.95 (ISBN 0-89992-045-4). Coun India Ed.

Guerre Sainte en Pays Chretien. Hippolyte Pissard. LC 78-63357. (Crusades & Military Orders: Second Ser.). Repr. of 1912 ed. 23.50 (ISBN 0-404-17027-7). AMS Pr.

Guerric of Igny Liturgical Sermons, 2 vols. Tr. by Theodore Berkeley from Latin. (Cistercian Father Ser.: No. 8 & No. 32). 378p. 1970-71. 15.00 set (ISBN 0-87907-400-0); Vol. 1. 7.95 (ISBN 0-87907-408-6); Vol. 2. o. p. 7.95 (ISBN 0-87907-432-9). Cistercian Pubns.

Guerrillas of Grace: Prayers for the Battle. 2nd ed. Ted Loder. LC 84-26096. (Illus.). 133p. (Orig.). 1984. pap. 9.95 (ISBN 0-931055-04-0). LuraMedia.

Guerrillas of Peace: Liberation Theology & the Central American Revolution. Blase Bonpane. 120p. (Orig.). 1986. 25.00 (ISBN 0-89608-311-X); pap. 8.00 (ISBN 0-89608-310-1). South End Pr.

Guess Who's Jewish in American History. Lionel Koppman & Bernard Postol. 336p. 1986. pap. 7.95 (ISBN 0-933503-55-5). Shapolsky Pubs.

Guess Who's Jewish? (You'll Never Guess) Len Chetkin. Ed. by Robert S. Friedman. LC 85-13200. (Illus.). 164p. (Orig.). 1985. pap. 4.95 (ISBN 0-89865-403-3). Donning Co.

Guessing at Truth: The Life of Julius Charles Hare 1795-1855. N. Merrill Distad. LC 78-11625. xiv, 258p. 1979. 23.50x (ISBN 0-915762-07-2). Patmos Pr.

Guest. Bhagwan Shree Rajneesh. Ed. by Ma Yoga Sudha. LC 82-203740. (Kabir Ser.). (Illus.). 604p. (Orig.). 1981. pap. 15.95 (ISBN 0-88050-574-5). Chidvilas Found.

Guest among Guests. Adriaan Van Lutsenburg Maas. 1987. 8.95 (ISBN 0-533-06965-3). Vantage.

Guest of the Soul. Samuel L. Brengle. 1978. pap. 3.95 (ISBN 0-86544-001-8). Salv Army Suppl South.

Guests in My House, Bk. 1. Samuel A. Greenburg & Helen L. Gilkey. 212p. 1984. 10.95 (ISBN 0-533-05727-2). Vantage.

Gugleilmo di Saint-Thierry: La Lettera d'Oro. James Hogg. (Analecta Cartusiana Ser.: No. 37). 144p. (Orig.). 1977. pap. 25.00 (ISBN 3-7052-0044-5, Pub by Salzburg Studies). Longwood Pub Group.

Guia De Estudios Sobre Bases Biblicas De la Etica. Julian C. Bridges & Guias de Estudio. 96p. 1982. Repr. of 1973 ed. 4.50 (ISBN 0-311-43505-X). Casa Bautista.

Guia De Estudios Sobre Doctrina Cristiana. Jorge E. Diaz. (Guias De Estudio). 88p. pap. 3.25 (ISBN 0-311-43500-9). Casa Bautista.

Guia De Estudios Sobre Estudios En el Nuevo Testamento. Carlos Allen & Guias de Estudios. (Illus.). 96p. 1981. pap. 3.25 (ISBN 0-311-43502-5). Casa Bautista.

Guia de Estudios Sobre Jesus el Maestro. J. M. Price & Guias de Estudio. 50p. 1982. pap. 3.25 (ISBN 0-311-43501-7). Casa Bautista.

Guia de Estudios Sobre Manual Para Predicadores Laicos. James Crane & Guias de Estudios. 88p. 1982. pap. 3.50 (ISBN 0-311-43502-5). Casa Bautista.

Guia de la Ensenanza Efectiva. Bernice Jordan. Tr. of Guidebook to Better Teaching. (Span.). 1976. pap. text ed. 5.95 (ISBN 0-86508-420-3). BCM Intl Inc.

Guia Para Damas Auxiliares. (Span.). 102p. pap. 2.95 (ISBN 0-87148-361-0). Pathway Pr.

Guida Spirituale. Bhagwan Shree Rajneesh. Ed. by Rajneesh Foundation International. LC 83-4435. (Western Mystics Ser.). 400p. (Orig.). 1983. pap. 4.95 (ISBN 0-88050-575-3). Chidvilas Found.

Guidance & God's Will. Tom Stark & Joan Stark. (Fisherman Bible Studyguide). 60p. 1978. saddle stitch 2.50 (ISBN 0-87788-324-6). Shaw Pubs.

Guidance from Sri Aurobindo: Letters to a Young Disciple. Sri Aurobindo. Ed. by Nagin Doshi. 285p. 1974. 6.00 (ISBN 0-89071-205-0). Matagiri.

Guidance from Sri Aurobindo: Letters to a Young Disciple, Vol. 2. Nagin Doshi. 1976. pap. 4.50 (ISBN 0-89071-265-4). Matagiri.

Guidance-Knowing the Will of God. Gwen Weising. (Workbook Ser.). 72p. 1985. pap. 4.95 (ISBN 0-930756-99-1, 581006). Aglow Pubns.

Guide for Catholic Young Women. George Deshon. 24.50 (ISBN 0-405-10816-8). Ayer Co Pubs.

Guide for New Testament Study. William W. Stevens. LC 76-62920. 1977. pap. 13.95 (ISBN 0-8054-1360-X). Broadman.

Guide for Old Testament Study. William W. Stevens. LC 73-91606. pap. 10.50 (ISBN 0-8054-1210-7). Broadman.

Guide for Preachers on Composing & Delivering Sermons. Henry Adler Sosland. (Illus.). 1987. text ed. 20.00 (ISBN 0-87334-026-4, Pub. by Jewish Theol Seminary). Ktav.

Guide for Recreation Leaders. Glenn Bannerman & Robert Fakkema. LC 74-28523. 120p. (Orig.). 1975. pap. 7.95 (ISBN 0-8042-2154-5). John Knox.

Guide for the Church Usher. Thomas L. Clark. LC 83-26211. 1984. pap. 5.50 (ISBN 0-8054-3517-4). Broadman.

Guide for the Jewish Homemaker. 2nd ed. Shonie B. Levi & Sylvia R. Kaplan. LC 59-12039. (Illus.). 1965. pap. 6.95 (ISBN 0-8052-0087-8). Schocken.

Guide for the Lay Preacher. Evan H. Boden. 1979. pap. 2.95 (ISBN 0-8170-0836-5). Judson.

Guide for the Perplexed. Moses Maimonides. Tr. by M. Friedlander. 1904. pap. 6.95 (ISBN 0-486-20351-4). Dover.

Guide for the Perplexed. 2nd ed. Moses Maimonides. 16.00 (ISBN 0-8446-2512-4). Peter Smith.

Guide for the Perplexed: Morah Nevochim. Moses Maimonides. (Heb, & Eng). 37.50 (ISBN 0-87559-079-9). Shalom.

Guide for the Still Perplexed: Heaven, Bk. I. 65p. (Orig.). 1986. pap. 4.95 (ISBN 0-940733-00-5). Dimona Pr.

Guide for Using Charisms in the Parish. John Colligan et al. LC 83-62985. 63p. (Orig.). 1983. pap. text ed. 2.95 (ISBN 0-911905-10-3). Past & Mat Rene Ctr.

Guide for Writing the History of a Church. LC 70-87728. pap. 2.95 (ISBN 0-8054-3504-2). Broadman.

Guide Lectures for Self-Transformation. Eva Pierrakos. LC 85-134343. 216p. (Orig.). 1985. 12.95 (ISBN 0-9614777-0-9); pap. 7.95 (ISBN 0-9614777-1-7). Pathwork Pr.

Guide Lectures for Self Transformation. Eva Pierrakos. LC 85-134343. 195p. 1986. pap. 9.95 (ISBN 0-913299-32-4, Dist. by NAL). Stillpoint.

Guide of the Perplexed, 2 vols. Moses Maimonides. Tr. by Shlomo Pines. LC 62-18113. 1963. 25.00x ea.; Vol. 1. (ISBN 0-226-50232-5). Vol. 2 (ISBN 0-226-50233-3). U of Chicago Pr.

Guide of the Perplexed. Moses Maimonides. Tr. by Shlomo Pines. LC 62-18113. 1974. Vol. 1. pap. 15.95 (ISBN 0-226-50230-9, P609, Phoen); Vol. 2. pap. 15.95 (ISBN 0-226-50231-7, P610). U of Chicago Pr.

Guide of the Perplexed. abr. ed. Moses Maimonodes. Ed. by Julius W. Guttman. Tr. by Chaim Rabin. 1978. pap. text ed. 5.95 (ISBN 0-85222-208-4, East & West Lib). Hebrew Pub.

Guide Through Narnia. Martha C. Sammons. LC 78-26476. (Wheaton Literary Ser.). 164p. 1979. pap. 3.95 (ISBN 0-87788-325-4). Shaw Pubs.

Guide to a Year's Reading in Luther's Works. George Kraus. (Continued Applied Christianity Ser.). 1983. pap. 2.50 (ISBN 0-570-03902-9, 12-2984). Concordia.

Guide to America-Holy Land Studies: Vol. 1, American Presence. Ed. by Nathan M. Kaganoff. LC 79-8575. (Illus.). 1980. lib. bdg. 22.00x (ISBN 0-405-12755-3). Ayer Co Pubs.

Guide to American Catholic History. 2nd, rev. ed. John T. Ellis & Robert Trisco. LC 81-17585. 265p. 1982. lib. bdg. 29.85 (ISBN 0-87436-318-7). ABC-Clio.

Guide to Baroque Rome. Anthony Blunt. LC 82-47546. (Icon Editions). (Illus.). 256p. 1982. 34.50i (ISBN 0-06-430395-0, HarpT). Har-Row.

Guide to Biblical Resources. Iris V. Cully & Kendig B. Cully. LC 81-80625. 160p. (Orig.). 1981. pap. 7.95 (ISBN 0-8192-1286-5). Morehouse.

Guide to Biography. Burton Stevenson. 1973. Repr. of 1910 ed. 25.00 (ISBN 0-8274-0867-6). R West.

Guide to Buddhist Philosophy. Kenneth K. Inada. (Reference Books - Area Studies: Area Studies). 1985. lib. bdg. 45.00 (ISBN 0-8161-7899-2). G K Hall.

Guide to Buddhist Religion. Frank E. Reynolds et al. 440p. 1981. lib. bdg. 57.50 (ISBN 0-8161-7900-X, Hall Reference). G K Hall.

Guide to Catholic Literature, 6 vols. Catholic Library Association Staff. Ed. by Walter Romig. Incl. 20.00 (ISBN 0-685-22623-9); 10.00; Vols. 3-5. 1944-1955. 15.00 ea.; Vol 6. 1956-1959. 17.50 (ISBN 0-685-22626-3); Vol. 7. 1960-1963. 25.00 (ISBN 0-685-22627-1); Vol. 8. 1964-1967. 25.00 (ISBN 0-685-22628-X). Cath Lib Assn.

Guide to Cherokee Documents in the Northeastern United States. Paul Kutsche. LC 85-11798. (Native American Bibliography Ser.: No. 7). 541p. 1986. 75.00 (ISBN 0-8108-1827-2). Scarecrow.

Guide to Chinese Religion. David C. Yu. (Reference: Asian Phil.-Rel. Ser.). 1985. lib. bdg. 45.00 (ISBN 0-8161-7902-6). G K Hall.

Guide to Christian Colleges 1984-85. rev. ed. Christian College Coalition Staff. 160p. 1984. pap. 12.95 (ISBN 0-8028-0010-6). Eerdmans.

Guide to Christian Living: A New Compendium of Moral Theology. George V. Lobo. 420p. 1984. pap. 16.95 (ISBN 0-87061-092-9). Chr Classics.

Guide to Christian Meditation. Marilyn M. Helleberg. 258p. 1985. pap. 9.95 large print ed. (ISBN 0-8027-2489-2). Walker & Co.

Guide to Church Discipline. J. Carl Laney. 160p. 1985. 8.95 (ISBN 0-87123-834-9, 230834). Bethany Hse.

Guide to Commentaries. Charles H. Spurgeon. 0.50 (ISBN 0-85151-400-6). Banner of Truth.

Guide to Confident Living. Norman V. Peale. 1977. pap. 2.25 (ISBN 0-449-24173-4, Crest). Fawcett.

Guide to Contemporary Hermeneutics: Major Trends in Biblical Interpretation. Ed. by Donald K. McKim. 312p. (Orig.). 1986. pap. 14.95 (ISBN 0-8028-0094-7). Eerdmans.

Guide to Cults & New Religions. Ronald Enroth et al. LC 83-44. 200p. (Orig.). 1983. pap. 6.95 (ISBN 0-87784-837-8). Inter-Varsity.

Guide to Daily Prayer. William Barclay. LC 62-11473. 1974. pap. 6.95 (ISBN 0-06-060401-8, RD75, HarpR). Har-Row.

Guide to Effective Scripture Study. Duane S. Crowther. LC 75-5321. (Scripture Guide Ser). 147p. 1975. pap. 4.95 (ISBN 0-88290-004-8). Horizon Utah.

Guide to Effective Sermon Delivery. Jerry Vines. 1986. text ed. 9.95 (ISBN 0-8024-4896-8). Moody.

Guide to Everything Jewish in New York. Nancy Davis & Joy Levitt. LC 86-10927. 334p. 1986. pap. 14.95 (ISBN 0-915361-47-7, Dist. by Watts). Adama Pubs Inc.

Guide to Faith. Helmut Harder. LC 79-50682. 1979. pap. 3.95 (ISBN 0-87303-022-2). Faith & Life.

Guide to Glastonbury's Temple of the Stars. K. E. Maltwood. 128p. 1983. pap. 11.95 (ISBN 0-227-67867-2, Pub. by J Clarke UK). Attic Pr.

Guide to God's Minstrel: St. Francis of Assisi. Mary S. Podles & Vicki Porter. Ed. by Carol Strohecker. (Illus.). 24p. (Orig.). 1982. pap. 1.50 (ISBN 0-911886-23-0). Walters Art.

Guide to Hebrew Lettering. Peretz Prusan. (Illus.). 64p. 1982. pap. 5.95 (ISBN 0-8074-0155-2, 282800). UAHC.

Guide to Hindu Religion. David J. Dell et al. 1981. lib. bdg. 47.00 (ISBN 0-8161-7903-4, Hall Reference). G K Hall.

Guide to Human Conduct. Shrii S. Anandamurti. LC 80-70792. 55p. 1981. pap. 3.00 (ISBN 0-88476-010-3). Ananda Marga.

Guide to I Ching. 3rd ed. Carol K. Anthony. 400p. Date not set. pap. write for info. Anthony Pub Co.

Guide to Indexed Periodicals in Religion. John J. Regazzi & Theodore C. Hines. LC 75-22277. 328p. 1975. 20.00 (ISBN 0-8108-0868-4). Scarecrow.

Guide to Islam. David Ede et al. 265p. 1983. lib. bdg. 59.50 (ISBN 0-8161-7905-0, Hall Reference). G K Hall.

Guide to Jewish Boston & New England. Ed. by Steven Feldman et al. LC 85-90430. 235p. (Orig.). pap. text ed. 10.95 (ISBN 0-9615649-0-3). Genesis Two.

Guide to Jewish History Under Nazi Impact. Jacob Robinson. 1974. 45.00x (ISBN 0-87068-231-8). Ktav.

Guide to Jewish Knowledge. rev. ed. Chaim Pearl & Reuben Brookes. LC 75-25366. 142p. 1976. 8.95 (ISBN 0-87677-138-X). Hartmore.

Guide to Jewish Religious Practice. I. Klein. (Moreshet Ser: No. 6). 20.00x (ISBN 0-87334-004-3, Pub. by Jewish Theol Seminary). Ktav.

Guide to Jewish Themes in American Fiction, 1940-1980. Murray Blackman. LC 80-24953. 271p. 1981. lib. bdg. 19.00 (ISBN 0-8108-1380-7). Scarecrow.

Guide to Liberation Theology for Middle-Class Congregations. Charles H. Bayer. Ed. by Herbert Lambert. LC 86-6111. 176p. (Orig.). 1986. pap. 10.95 (ISBN 0-8272-1233-X). CBP.

Guide to Love-Powered Living. Winifred W. Hausmann. LC 85-72282. 192p. (Orig.). 1986. pap. 7.95 (ISBN 0-87516-560-5). De Vorss.

Guide to Materials about Public Aid to Religious Schools. Jim Buchanan. (Public Administration Ser.: Bibliography P 1621). 1985. pap. 3.75 (ISBN 0-89028-291-9). Vance Biblios.

Guide to Mexican Witchcraft. William Madsen & Claudia Madsen. (Illus.). 96p. 1977. pap. 4.50 (ISBN 0-912434-10-4). Ocelot Pr.

Guide to Monastic Communities in the Northeast. Ed. by Y Wolff. 1984. pap. 2.50 (ISBN 0-317-39519-X). St Bedes Pubns.

Guide to Music for the Church Year. 4th ed. 1974. 4.95 (ISBN 0-8066-0930-3, 11-9195). Augsburg.

Guide to Myth & Religion in European Painting 1270-1700. Satia Bernen & Robert Bernen. LC 72-96070. 288p. 1973. 8.95 (ISBN 0-8076-0683-9). Braziller.

Guide to Places of Worship in & Around San Francisco. Elvira Monroe. 186p. (Orig.). 1984. pap. 6.95 (ISBN 0-933174-24-1). Wide World-Tetra.

Guide to Practical Pastoring. C. Sumner Wemp. LC 82-12562. 1982. 15.95 (ISBN 0-8407-5271-7). Nelson.

Guide to Prayer. Rueben P. Job & Norman Shawchuck. 432p. 1987. pap. 11.95 (ISBN 0-8358-0559-X). Upper Room.

Guide to Prayer for Ministers & Other Servants. Reuben Job & Norman Shawchuck. LC 83-80409. 400p. (Orig.). 1983. pap. 21.95 bible bdg. (ISBN 0-8358-0460-7). Upper Room.

Guide to Pronouncing Biblical Names. T. S. K. Scott-Craig. LC 81-84713. 112p. (Orig.). 1982. pap. 3.50 (ISBN 0-8192-1292-X). Morehouse.

Guide to Quaker Practice. Howard H. Brinton. LC 43-11899. (Orig.). 1943. pap. 2.50x (ISBN 0-87574-020-0). Pendle Hill.

Guide to Religious Education. Alex Sandri-White. 7.95x (ISBN 0-685-22753-7). Aurea.

Guide to Religious Ritual at Abydos. A. R. David. 182p. 1981. pap. text ed. 40.00x (ISBN 0-85668-060-5, Pub. by Aris & Phillips UK). Humanities.

Guide to Ritual Circumcision & Redemption of the First-Born Son. Eugene J. Cohen. 210p. 1984. 15.00x (ISBN 0-88125-017-1); pap. 9.95 (ISBN 0-88125-023-6). Ktav.

Guide to Sabbath Observance & Enjoyment. pap. 8.95 (ISBN 0-686-96036-X). United Syn Bk.

Guide to Schools & Departments of Religion & Seminaries in the U. S. & Canada. Modoc Press, Inc., Staff. 736p. 1986. reference 90.00x (ISBN 0-02-921650-8). Macmillan.

Guide to Self-Improvement in Sermon Delivery. Al Fasol. 128p. 1983. pap. 5.95 (ISBN 0-8010-3507-4). Baker Bk.

Guide to Survival. Salem Kirban. 1979. pap. 6.95 (ISBN 0-912582-24-3). Kirban.

Guide to the Archives of the Archdiocese of Boston. James O'Toole. LC 80-8989. 300p. 1981. lib. bdg. 61.00 (ISBN 0-8240-9359-3). Garland Pub.

Guide to the Archives of the South Dakota Conference of the United Church of Christ. Harry Thompson. 128p. 1986. pap. 4.00 (ISBN 0-931170-31-1). Ctr Western Studies.

Guide to the Bais Hamikosh. rev. ed. Avi Shulman. 2.75 (ISBN 0-914131-25-7, B20). Torah Umesorah.

Guide to the Bible. Monks of Maredsous. 2.25 (ISBN 0-87243-016-2). Templegate.

Guide to the Contents of the Qur'an. Ed. by Faruq Sherif. (Middle East Cultures Ser.: No. 9). 172p. 1985. 25.00 (ISBN 0-86372-030-7, Pub. by Ithaca Pr UK). Humanities.

Guide to the Gospels. W. Graham Scroggie. 664p. 1975. 23.95 (ISBN 0-8007-0127-5). Revell.

Guide to the Hymns & Tunes of American Methodism. Samuel J. Rogal. LC 85-27114. (Music Reference Collection Ser.: No. 7). 337p. 1986. lib. bdg. 45.00 (ISBN 0-313-25123-1, RGH/). Greenwood.

Guide to the Jewish Dietary Laws. 3rd ed. Y. Kemelman. 1971. pap. 2.50x (ISBN 0-685-40445-5); pap. 13.00 (ISBN 0-231-05147-6). Bloch.

Guide to the Lectionary. Ann B. Bushong. 1978. pap. 5.95 (ISBN 0-8164-2156-0, HarpR). Har-Row.

Guide to the Music of the Eastern Orthodox Church. N. Lungu et al. Tr. by Nicholas K. Apostola from Rumanian. Orig. Title: Gramatica Muzicii Psaltice. (Illus.). 180p. (Orig.). 1984. pap. 15.00 (ISBN 0-917651-00-6). Holy Cross Orthodox.

Guide to the New Testament. Alice Parmelee. (All About the Bible Ser.: Bk. 3). (Illus.). 1980. pap. 5.95 (ISBN 0-8192-1255-5). Morehouse.

Guide to the Old Testament & Apocrypha. Alice Parmelee. (All About the Bible Ser.: Bk. 2). (Illus.). 1980. pap. 5.95 (ISBN 0-8192-1254-7). Morehouse.

Guide to the Pentateuch. Charles W. Conn. 109p. 1963. 5.25 (ISBN 0-87148-004-2); pap. 4.25 (ISBN 0-87148-005-0). Pathway Pr.

Guide to the Preservation of Medieval Cathedrals & Churches. Paul E. Hardy & Bishop of Exeter. LC 82-14257. (Illus.). 160p. 1983. pap. text ed. 16.95 (ISBN 0-582-30514-4, Construction Press). Longman.

Guide to the Prophets. Stephen F. Winward. LC 68-55819. 1976. pap. 8.95 (ISBN 0-8042-0131-5). John Knox.

Guide to the Salem Witchcraft Hysteria of 1692. David C. Brown. LC 84-164658. (Illus.). 130p. (Orig.). 1984. pap. 5.95 (ISBN 0-9613415-0-5). D C Brown.

Guide to the Study of the Holiness Movement. Charles E. Jones. LC 74-659. (ATLA Bibliography Ser.: No. 1). 946p. 1974. 57.50 (ISBN 0-8108-0703-3). Scarecrow.

Guide to the Study of the Pentecostal Movement, 2 Vols, Vol. 1. Pts. 1 & 2; Vol. 2 pts 3 &4; index. Charles E. Jones. LC 82-10794. (ATLA Bibliography Ser.: No. 6). 1249p. 1983. Set. 82.50 (ISBN 0-8108-1583-4). Scarecrow.

Guide to the Thought of Saint Augustine. Eugene Portalie. Tr. by Ralph J. Bastian from Fr. LC 75-1182. 428p. 1975. Repr. of 1960 ed. lib. bdg. 25.50x (ISBN 0-8371-7992-0, POGS). Greenwood.

Guide to the Unconscious. Natalino Caputi. LC 83-24620. 172p. (Orig.). 1984. pap. 14.95 (ISBN 0-89135-042-X). Religious Educ.

Guide to the Zoroastrian Religion: A Nineteenth-Century Catechism with Modern Commentary. Firoze M. Kotwal & James W. Boyd. LC 82-3236. (Harvard University - Center for the Study of World Religions Ser.). 1982. 18.75 (ISBN 0-89130-573-4, 03-00-03); pap. 12.50 (ISBN 0-89130-574-2). Scholars Pr GA.

Guide to Thomas Aquinas. Josef Pieper. LC 86-40588. 192p. 1987. pap. text ed. 8.95x (ISBN 0-268-01013-7, Dist. by Har-Row). U of Notre Dame Pr.

Guide to Thomas Aquinas. Josef Pieper et al. Tr. by Richard Winston & Clara Winston. 182p. 1982. Repr. of 1962 ed. lib. bdg. 20.50 (ISBN 0-374-96448-3, Octagon). Hippocrene Bks.

Guide to True Peace, or the Excellency of Inward & Spiritual Prayer. Fenelon et al. LC 78-78157. 1979. pap. 6.95x (ISBN 0-87574-905-4). Pendle Hill.

Guide to Understanding Romans. Harold J. Brokke. LC 80-67446. 211p. 1980. pap. 5.95 (ISBN 0-87123-193-X, 210193). Bethany Hse.

Guide to Understanding Your Bible. Josh McDowell. LC 82-73526. 221p. 1982. pap. 6.95 (ISBN 0-86605-087-6). Here's Life.

Guide to Welsh Parish Churches. R. W. Soden. 149p. 1985. 40.50x (ISBN 0-86383-082-X, Pub. by Gomer Pr). State Mutual Bk.

Guide to Wisconsin Survivors of the Holocaust: A Documentary Project of the Wisconsin Jewish Archives. Ed. by Sara Leuchter. 192p. 1983. pap. 12.50 (ISBN 0-87020-216-2). State Hist Soc Wis.

Guidebook for Spiritual Friends. Barry A. Woodbridge. LC 84-51827. 96p. (Orig.). 1985. pap. 4.95 (ISBN 0-8358-0498-4). Upper Room.

Guidebook for Victorious Christian Living. Russel A. Jones. 192p. 1983. pap. 5.95 (ISBN 0-8170-1001-7). Judson.

Guidebook to Better Teaching. Bernice Jordan. 126p. 1980. pap. text ed. 5.95 (ISBN 0-86508-090-9). BCM Intl Inc.

Guidebook to Biblical Truth. Thomas J. Cooper. Ed. by Willia S. Cooper. (Make the Path Clear Ser.: Vol. 1). 99p. (Orig.). 1984. pap. 4.95 (ISBN 0-931429-01-3). Cooper & Cooper Pub.

Guidebook to Biblical Truth. Thomas J. Cooper. Ed. by Willia S. Cooper. (Ministry of Women in God's Plan Ser.: Vol. 6). 50p. (Orig.). 1985. pap. 4.00 (ISBN 0-931429-06-4). Cooper & Cooper Pub.

Guidebook to Biblical Truth. Thomas J. Cooper. Ed. by Willia S. Cooper. (Master of Light & Darkness Ser.: Vol. 5). 70p. (Orig.). 1985. pap. 4.75 (ISBN 0-931429-05-6). Cooper & Cooper Pub.

Guidebook to Biblical Truth. Thomas J. Cooper & Willia S. Cooper. (Stewardship Ser.: Vol. 4). 60p. (Orig.). 1985. Set. write for info. (ISBN 0-931429-00-5); Vol. 4. pap. 4.50 (ISBN 0-931429-04-8). Cooper & Cooper Pub.

Guidebook to Dating, Waiting & Choosing a Mate. Norman Wright & Marvin Inmon. LC 78-26913. 1978. pap. 4.95 (ISBN 0-89081-150-4). Harvest Hse.

Guidebook to the Aquarian Gospel of Jesus the Christ. Margaret R. Moum. 93p. 1974. pap. 3.95 (ISBN 0-917200-05-5). ESPress.

Guidebook to the True Secret of the Heart, Vol. 2. M. R. Bawa Muhaiyaddeen. LC 75-44557. (Illus.). 232p. 1976. pap. 5.95 (ISBN 0-914390-08-2). Fellowship Pr PA.

Guidelines for Diocesan Vocation Offices: May 1983. 2nd ed. 48p. 1983. pap. 5.50 (ISBN 1-55586-868-1). US Catholic.

Guidelines for Living. Harold J. Sala. (Direction Bks.). 80p. (Orig.). 1982. pap. 2.95 (ISBN 0-8010-8219-6). Baker Bk.

Guidelines for Marriage in the Orthodox Church. S. Harakas. 1980. pap. 1.45 (ISBN 0-937032-21-2). Light&Life Pub Co MN.

Guidelines for Mystical Prayer. Ruth Burrows. 5.95 (ISBN 0-87193-134-6). Dimension Bks.

Guidelines for Selected Personnel Practices in Catholic Schools II. 58p. 1977. 4.55 (ISBN 0-686-29246-4). Natl Cath Educ.

Guidelines for Singleness & Marriage. John MacArthur, Jr. (John MacArthur's Bible Studies). (Orig.). 1986. pap. 3.95 (ISBN 0-8024-5343-0). Moody.

Guidelines for Spiritual Direction. Carolyn Gratton. 8.95 (ISBN 0-87193-130-3). Dimension Bks.

Guidelines for Women's Groups in the Congregation. Oscar E. Feucht. 1981. pap. 3.95 (ISBN 0-570-03828-6, 12-2793). Concordia.

Guidelines for World Evangelism. Ed. by George P. Gurganus. 1977. 11.95 (ISBN 0-89112-040-8, Bibl Res Pr). Abilene Christ U.

Guideposts Family Topical Concordance to the Bible. Frwd. by Lloyd J. Ogilvie. LC 82-12412. 1982. 17.95 (ISBN 0-8407-4962-7). Nelson.

Guides to the Reformed Tradition: The Church. Alston M. Wallace, Jr. Ed. by John H. Leith & John W. Kuykendall. LC 83-49052. 204p. 1984. pap. 10.95 (ISBN 0-8042-3253-9). John Knox.

Guides to the Reformed Tradition: Worship. Hughes O. Old. Ed. by John H. Leith & John W. Kuykendall. LC 83-19616. 194p. 1984. pap. 11.95 (ISBN 0-8042-3252-0). John Knox.

Guiding God's Children: A Foundation for Spiritual Growth in the Home. Tolbert McCarroll. 240p. (Orig.). 1983. pap. 9.95 (ISBN 0-8091-2547-1). Paulist Pr.

Guiding Light of Lao Tzu. Henry Wei. LC 81-53011. 234p. (Orig.). 1982. 12.95 (ISBN 0-8356-0562-0, Quest); pap. 6.95 (ISBN 0-8356-0558-2, Quest). Theos Pub Hse.

Guiding Your Child: A 60-Point Checklist for Parents. Elliott D. Landau & M. Winston Egan. LC 78-70361. 48p. 1978. pap. 3.95 (ISBN 0-88290-103-6). Horizon Utah.

Guiding Your Child Toward God. C. Sybil Waldrop. LC 84-14964. 1985. pap. 4.95 (ISBN 0-8054-5660-0). Broadman.

Guiding Yourself into a Spiritual Reality: A Workbook. Peggy D. Burkan. LC 83-91310. 96p. (Orig.). 1985. pap. 7.95 (ISBN 0-935616-06-3). Reunion Pr.

Guiding Youth. Donald S. Aultman. 1977. pap. 3.95 (ISBN 0-87148-358-0). Pathway Pr.

Guidonis de Orchellis Tractatus de Sacramentis Ex Eius Summa de Sacramentis et Officiis Ecclesiae. Ed. by Damiani Van Den Eynde & Odulphi Van Den Eynde. (Text Ser). 1953. 11.00 (ISBN 0-686-11549-X). Franciscan Inst.

Guigo II: The Ladder of Monks & Twelve Meditations. Edmund Colledge & James Walsh. 14.95; pap. 6.00 (ISBN 0-87907-948-7). Cistercian Pubns.

Guigo II: The Ladder of Monks & Twelve Meditations. Guigo II. Tr. by Edmund Colledge & James Walsh. (Cistercian Studies: No. 48). (Illus.). 1981. pap. write for info. (ISBN 0-87907-748-4). Cistercian Pubns.

Guigues Du Pont: Traite Sur la Contemplation, 2 vols. Philippe DuPont. Ed. by James Hogg. (Analecta Cartusiana Ser.: No. 72). (Orig.). 1984. pap. 50.00 (ISBN 3-7052-0107-7, Pub. by Salzburg Studies). Longwood Pub Group.

Guillaume d'Auvergne: Eveque de Paris (1228-1249), Sa vie & Ses ouvrages (Medieval Studies Ser.) Noel Valois. (Medieval Studies Ser.). (Fr.). Repr. of 1880 ed. lib. bdg. 44.00x (ISBN 0-697-00019-2). Irvington.

Guillaume de Champeaux et les Ecoles de Paris. 2nd ed. E. Michaud. (Medieval Studies Reprint Ser.). (Fr.). Repr. of 1867 ed. lib. bdg. 45.00x (ISBN 0-697-00011-7). Irvington.

Guillelmi de Ockham: Opera Philosophica, Vol. 2. Ed. by Philotheus Boehner & Stephen Brown. 1978. 40.00 (ISBN 0-686-27930-1). Franciscan Inst.

Guillelmi de Ockham: Opera Philosophica, Vol. 3. Ed. by Francesco Del Punta. 1979. 29.00 (ISBN 0-686-27931-X). Franciscan Inst.

Guillelmi de Ockham: Opera Philosophica, Vol. 1, Summa Philosophica. Ed. by Philotheus Boehner et al. 1974. 52.00 (ISBN 0-686-11530-9). Franciscan Inst.

Guillelmi de Ockham: Quodlibeta Septem, Ordinatio, Opera Theologica, Vol. 9. Ed. by Joseph C. Wey. 1980. 50.00 (ISBN 0-686-28122-5). Franciscan Inst.

Guillelmi de Ockham: Scriptum in Librum Primum Sententiarum, Ordinatio, Opera Theologica, Vol. 2, Distinctiones Secunda et Tertia. Ed. by Stephen F. Brown. 1970. 37.00 (ISBN 0-686-11529-5). Franciscan Inst.

Guillelmi de Ockham: Scriptum in Librum Primum Sententiarum, Ordinatio, Opera Theologica, Vol. 3, Distinctiones 4-18. Ed. by Girard J. Etzkorn. 1977. 46.00 (ISBN 0-686-27929-8). Franciscan Inst.

Guillelmi de Ockham: Scriptum in Librum Primum Sententiarum, Ordinatio, Opera Theologica, Vol. 4, Distinctiones 19-48. Ed. by Girard J. Etzkorn & Francis E. Kelley. 1979. 48.00 (ISBN 0-686-27932-8). Franciscan Inst.

Guillelmi de Ockham: Scriptum in Librum Primum Sententiarum, Ordinatio, Opera Theologica, Vol. 1, Prologues et Distinctio Prima. Ed. by Gedeon Gal. 1967. 35.00 (ISBN 0-686-11528-7). Franciscan Inst.

Guilt & Grace. Paul Tournier. LC 82-11882. 224p. 1983. pap. 7.95 (ISBN 0-06-068331-7, RD416, HarpR). Har-Row.

Guilt & Gratitude: A Study of the Origins of Contemporary Conscience. Joseph A. Amato, II. LC 81-6991. (Contributions in Philosophy Ser.: No. 20). xxv, 218p. 1982. lib. bdg. 29.95 (ISBN 0-313-22946-5, AGG/). Greenwood.

Guilt: How to Deal with It. John Hamroque & Joseph Krastel. 48p. 1986. pap. 1.50 (ISBN 0-89243-256-X). Liguori Pubns.

Guilt: Issues of Emotional Living in an Age of Stress for Clergy & Religious. Philomena Agudo et al. Ed. by Kathleen E. Kelley. LC 80-10747. 144p. 1980. pap. 5.00 (ISBN 0-89571-008-0). Affirmation.

Guilt: Letting Go. Lucy C. Freeman & Herbert S. Strean. LC 86-15873. 288p. 1987. 14.95 (ISBN 0-471-83636-2). Wiley.

Guilt of Sin. Charles G. Finney. LC 65-25845. (Charles G. Finney Memorial Library). 124p. 1975. pap. 4.50 (ISBN 0-8254-2616-2). Kregel.

Guilt of Slavery & the Crime of Slaveholding. George B. Cheever. LC 69-16586. Repr. of 1860 ed. cancelled (ISBN 0-8371-1380-6, CHG&, Pub. by Negro U Pr). Greenwood.

Guiltfree: How to Release the Tension in Your Life. 2nd ed. Dwight L. Carlson. LC 83-80118. 1985. pap. 4.95 (ISBN 0-89081-375-2, 3752). Harvest Hse.

Gulshan-i Haqayiq. Mihdi Arjmand. (Persian.). 320p. 1982. Repr. 12.95 (ISBN 0-933770-15-4). Kalimat.

Gurdjieff: A Study of His Teaching. Kenneth Walker. (Unwin Paperbacks Ser.). 221p. (Orig.). 1980. pap. 5.95 (ISBN 0-04-294106-7). Allen Unwin.

Gurdjieff: A Very Great Enigma 1973. J. G. Bennett. LC 72-91951. 100p. (Orig.). 1984. pap. 4.50 (ISBN 0-87728-581-0). Weiser.

Gurdjieff: An Annotated Bibliography. The Gurdjieff Foundation of California & J. Walter Driscoll. LC 83-49296. (Reference Library of Social Science). 390p. 1985. lib. bdg. 50.00 (ISBN 0-8240-8972-3). Garland Pub.

Gurdjieff Group Work with Wilhem Nyland. Irmis B. Popoff. (Illus.). 80p. 1983. pap. 4.95 (ISBN 0-87728-580-2). Weiser.

Gurdjieff in Action. J. H. Reyner. 117p. 1982. 12.95 (ISBN 0-04-294117-2). Allen Unwin.

Gurdjieff: The Early Years. Kathleen R. Speeth & Ira Friedlander. LC 78-24696. (Illus.). 1979. pap. 5.95 (ISBN 0-06-090693-6, CN-693, PL). Har-Row.

Gurdjieff Today. John G. Bennett. (Transformation of Man Ser.). 1978. 4.50 (ISBN 0-900306-13-0, Pub. by Coombe Springs Pr). Claymont Comm.
Guru Amar Das. Fauja Singh. 196p. 1979. text ed. 9.95 (ISBN 0-89684-080-8, Pub. by Sterling New Delhi). Orient Bk Dist.
Guru & Disciple. Sri Swami Satchidananda. 1977. pap. 1.95 (ISBN 0-932040-18-7). Integral Yoga Pubns.
Guru & the Disciple. Daya, Sr. 1976. pap. 2.95 (ISBN 0-911564-26-8). Vedanta Ctr.
Guru Gobind Singh. Gopal Singh. (National Biography Ser.). (Orig.). 1979. pap. 2.50 (ISBN 0-89744-206-7). Auromere.
Guru Gobind Singh. Harbans Singh. 1979. text ed. 6.95 (ISBN 0-89684-073-5, Pub. by Sterling New Delhi). Orient Bk Dist.
Guru in Sikhism. W. Owen Cole. 1984. pap. 7.00x (ISBN 0-8364-1238-9, Pub. by D Longman & Todd). South Asia Bks.
Guru Nanak. P. Wylam. (Illus.). 1979. pap. 4.00 (ISBN 0-89744-154-0). Auromere.
Guru Nanak: His Life Was His Message - A Biography. Balwant S. Anand. 1985. 9.00x (ISBN 0-8364-1456-X, Pub. by Nanak Dev Univ India). South Asia Bks.
Guru Tegh Bahadur. Balwant S. Anand. 1979. text ed. 11.95 (ISBN 0-89684-076-X, Pub. by Sterling New Delhi). Orient Bk Dist.
Gurudev: The Life of Yogi Amrit Desai. Sukanya Warren & Francis Mellen. LC 82-83357. 117p. (Orig.). 1982. pap. 6.95 (ISBN 0-940258-07-2). Kripalu Pubns.
Gurus, Godman & Good People. Khushwant Singh. (Illus.). 134p. 1975. text ed. 13.95x (ISBN 0-86125-087-7, Pub. by Orient Longman India). Apt Bks.
Gustavo Gutierrez. Robert M. Brown. LC 80-82185. (Makers of Contemporary Theology Ser.). 89p. 1981. pap. 3.95 (ISBN 0-8042-0651-1). John Knox.
Gustavus Adolphus & the Struggle of Protestantism for Existence. Charles R. Fletcher. LC 73-14441. (Heroes of the Nations Ser.). Repr. of 1892 ed. 30.00 (ISBN 0-404-58260-5). AMS Pr.
Guts & Ruts: The Jewish Pioneer on the Trail in the American Southwest. Floyd S. Fierman. (Illus.). 1985. 20.00 (ISBN 0-88125-061-9). Ktav.
Guzman de Alfarache: Conversion o Proceso de Degradacion? Benito Brancaforte. vi, 230p. 1980. 11.00x (ISBN 0-942260-14-7). Hispanic Seminary.
Gypsies. Charles G. Leland. LC 75-3460. Repr. of 1882 ed. 27.00 (ISBN 0-404-16891-4). AMS Pr.
Gypsies: Their Life & Their Customs. Martin Block. Tr. by Barbara Kuczynski & Duncan Taylor. LC 75-3451. (Illus.). Repr. of 1939 ed. 31.50 (ISBN 0-404-16886-8). AMS Pr.

H

H. P. Blatavsky Returns. Robert R. Leichtman. (From Heaven to Earth Ser.). (Illus.). 95p. (Orig.). 1980. pap. 3.50 (ISBN 0-89804-059-0). Ariel OH.
H. P. Blavatsky & the Secret Doctrine Commentaries on Her Contributions to World Thought. Ed. by Virginia Hanson. LC 71-112039. (Orig.). 1971. pap. 2.25 (ISBN 0-8356-0031-9, Quest). Theos Pub Hse.
H. P. Blavatsky & the Theosophical Movement. 2nd,rev. ed. Charles J. Ryan. Ed. by Grace F. Knoche. LC 75-4433. (Illus.). 1975. 9.00 (ISBN 0-911500-79-0); pap. 6.00 (ISBN 0-911500-80-4). Theos U Pr.
H. P. Blavatsky & the Theosophical Movement: With 7 Appendixes. Charles J. Ryan. Ed. by W. Emmett Small & Helen Todd. (Illus.). 484p. 1975. pap. 7.00 (ISBN 0-913004-25-1). Point Loma Pub.
H. P. Blavatsky Collected Writings, Vol. XII. Helena P. Blavatsky. Ed. by Boris De Zirkoff. LC 80-53953. (Illus.). 849p. 1981. 16.50 (ISBN 0-8356-0228-1). Theos Pub Hse.
H. P. Blavatsky: Collected Writings, Vol. XIV. Ed. by Boris De Zirkoff. LC 84-50694. (Illus.). 750p. 1985. text ed. 16.50 (ISBN 0-8356-0234-6). Theos Pub Hse.
H. P. Blavatsky: The Key to Theosophy, an Abridgement. Ed. by Joy Mills. LC 75-18176. pap. 4.50 (ISBN 0-8356-0427-6, Quest). Theos Pub Hse.
H. P. Blavatsky: The Mystery. rev. ed. G. De Purucker & Katherine Tingley. Ed. by W. Emmett Small & Helen Todd. (Illus.). 256p. 1974. pap. 5.25 (ISBN 0-913004-14-6). Point Loma Pub.
H. P. Blavatsky: Tibet & Tulku. Geoffrey A. Barborka. (Illus.). 1974. 12.95 (ISBN 0-8356-7159-3). Theos Pub Hse.
H. P. Blavatsky to the American Conventions: 1888-1891, with a Historical Perspective. Helena P. Blavatsky. LC 78-74256. 1979. pap. 4.00 (ISBN 0-911500-88-X). Theos U Pr.
H. Richard Niebuhr. Lonnie Kliever. LC 77-92452. (Makers of the Modern Theological Mind Ser.). 1978. 8.95 (ISBN 0-8499-0078-6, 0078-6). Word Bks.
H. Richard Niebuhr: A Lifetime of Reflections on the Church & the World. Jon Diefenthaler. 144p. (Orig.). 1986. 24.95 (ISBN 0-86554-214-7, MUP-H193); pap. 9.95 (ISBN 0-86554-235-X, MUP-P33). Mercer Univ Pr.
Ha Motzi Bracha Kit. Fran Borovetz. (Illus.). 32p. (Orig.). 1985. pap. text ed. 13.95 (ISBN 0-933873-03-4). Torah Aura.
Habakkuk & Zephaniah. Cyril J. Barber. (Everyman's Bible Commentary Ser.). 1985. pap. 5.95 (ISBN 0-8024-2069-9). Moody.
Habakkuk: The Man with Honest Answers. Walter Ungerer. (Contemporary Discussion Ser.). 80p. 1976. pap. 1.45 (ISBN 0-8010-9202-7). Baker Bk.
Habit of Being. Flannery O'Connor. Ed. & intro. by Sally Fitzgerald. LC 78-11559. 639p. 1979. 15.00 (ISBN 0-374-16769-9). FS&G.
Habit of Being: Letters of Flannery O'Connor. Ed. by Sally Fitzgerald. LC 79-23319. 1980. pap. 10.95 (ISBN 0-394-74259-1, Vin). Random.
Habit of Happiness. Randal Denny. 102p. 1976. 2.50 (ISBN 0-8341-0399-0). Beacon Hill.
Habit of Happiness. Leslie Parrott. 192p. 1987. 10.95 (ISBN 0-8499-0607-5). Word Bks.
Habitation of Dragons. Keith Miller. LC 72-123009. 1983. 6.95 (ISBN 0-8499-2973-3). Word Bks.
Haboo: Native American Stories from Puget Sound. Ed. & tr. by Vi Hilbert. LC 85-40397. (Illus.). 228p. 1985. pap. 9.95 (ISBN 0-295-96270-4). U of Wash Pr.
Hacia Donde Va la Familia? Larry Christenson. 32p. 1978. 1.00 (ISBN 0-88113-110-5). Edit Betania.
Hacia la Felicidad: Como Vivir una Vida Victoriosa y Practicar la Terapia Espiritual. C. R. Solomon. 1983. Repr. of 1979 ed. 3.75 (ISBN 0-311-42060-5). Casa Bautista.
Hacia Una Teologia Evangelica Latinoamericana. Ed. by O. Costas et al. 154p. 1984. pap. 3.95 (ISBN 0-89922-238-2). Edit Caribe.
Had I Known You Better, Lord I'd a Come Runnin' with a Bucket. Billye G. Bowman. Ed. by James Goodman. 240p. (Orig.). 1986. pap. 10.00 (ISBN 0-89896-140-8, Linolean). Larksdale.
Had You Been Born a Muslim. J. B. Irving. pap. 1.50 (ISBN 0-686-18471-8). Kazi Pubns.
Hades-Abode of the Unrighteous Dead. Gordon Lindsay. (Sorcery & Spirit World Ser.). 1.25 (ISBN 0-89985-082-0). Christ Nations.
Hadewijch: The Complete Works. Tr. by Mother Columba Hart. LC 80-84500. (Classics of Western Spirituality Ser.). 440p. 1981. 13.95 (ISBN 0-8091-0311-7); pap. 10.95 (ISBN 0-8091-2297-9). Paulist Pr.
Hadha ad-Din. Sayyid Qutb. (Arabic.). 96p. (Orig.). 1978. pap. 1.75x (ISBN 0-939830-18-3, Pub. by IIFSO Kuwait). New Era Pubns MI.
Hadith: A Probe into the History of. Allama M. Al-Askari. Tr. by M. Fazal Haq. 120p. 1983. pap. 4.00 (ISBN 0-941724-16-6). Islamic Seminary.
Hadith: An Introduction. A. R. Doi. 1980. pap. 6.50 (ISBN 0-686-64661-4). Kazi Pubns.
Hadith for Children. A. Rauf. pap. 5.95 (ISBN 0-686-63901-4). Kazi Pubns.
Hadji in Syria: Three Years in Jerusalem. Sarah B. Johnson. Ed. by Moshe Davis. LC 77-70708. (America & the Holy Land Ser.). (Illus.). 1977. Repr. of 1858 ed. lib. bdg. 26.50x (ISBN 0-405-10258-5). Ayer Co Pubs.
Hafetz Hayyim on the Siddur. Tr. by C. Wengrow. 10.95 (ISBN 0-87306-996-X). Feldheim.
Hagarism: The Making of the Islamic World. Patricia Crone & M. Cook. LC 75-41714. 1980. pap. 14.95 (ISBN 0-521-29754-0). Cambridge U Pr.
Hagarism: The Making of the Islamic World. Patricia Crone & M. Cook. LC 75-41714. 268p. 1977. 37.50 (ISBN 0-521-21133-6). Cambridge U Pr.
Hagase la Luz. Elizabeth S. Turner. (Span.). 320p. 1985. 5.95 (ISBN 0-317-44746-7). Unity School.
Hageo y Malaquias: Rededicacion y Renovacion. Herbert Wolf. Orig. Title: Haggai & Malachi. (Span.). 1980. pap. 3.95 (ISBN 0-8254-1875-5). Kregel.
Haggadah. Joseph Elias. (Art Scroll Mesorah Ser.). 224p. 1977. 10.95 (ISBN 0-89906-150-8); pap. 7.95 (ISBN 0-89906-151-6). Mesorah Pubns.
Haggadah. Cecil Roth. 109p. 1975. pap. 4.95 (ISBN 0-900689-72-2). Soncino Pr.
Haggadah. Shoshana Walker. 104p. 1982. 24.95 (ISBN 965-220-017-4, Carta Maps & Guides Pub Isreal). Hippocrene Bks.
Haggadah for Children. Jacob Rudin. 1973. 2.25x (ISBN 0-8197-0032-0). Bloch.
Haggadah for the Liberated Lamb. Micah Publications Editors et al. LC 84-43165. (Illus.). 96p. (Orig.). 1985. pap. 8.95 (ISBN 0-916288-19-6). Micah Pubns.
Haggadah for the School. Hyman Chanover. (Illus.). 1964. pap. 2.25x (ISBN 0-8381-0175-5). United Syn Bk.
Haggadah-Kleinman. Tr. by Abraham Regelson. 1965. pap. 1.99 (ISBN 0-914080-33-4). Shulsinger Sales.
Haggadah of Legends & Customs. Menachem Hacohen. (Illus.). 128p. 1987. 29.95 (ISBN 0-915361-78-7, Dist. by Watts). Adama Pubs Inc.
Haggadah: The Story of Thanksgiving. Joseph H. Gelberman. 35p. (Orig.). 1983. pap. 4.00 (ISBN 0-942494-55-5). Coleman Pub.
Haggadah Treasury. Nosson Scherman. (Art Scroll Mesorah Ser.). 200p. 1978. 10.95 (ISBN 0-89906-200-8); pap. 7.95 (ISBN 0-89906-201-6). Mesorah Pubns.
Haggai & Malachi. Herbert Wolf. (Everyman's Bible Commentary Ser.). 128p. (Orig.). 1976. pap. 5.95 (ISBN 0-8024-2037-0). Moody.
Haggai & Zechariah 1-8, a Commentary. David L. Petersen. LC 84-7477. (Old Testament Library). 320p. 1984. 24.95 (ISBN 0-664-21830-X). Westminster.
Haggai, Malachi, & Zechariah. T. V. Moore. (Banner of Truth Geneva Series Commentaries). 1979. 13.95 (ISBN 0-85151-288-7). Banner of Truth.
Haggai, Zechariah & Malachi. Irving Jensen. (Bible Self Study Guide Ser.). 1976. pap. 3.25 (ISBN 0-8024-1037-5). Moody.
Haggai, Zechariah, Malachi. Joyce Baldwin. LC 72-75980. (Tyndale Old Testament Commentary Ser.). 256p. 1972. 12.95 (ISBN 0-87784-908-0); pap. 6.95 (ISBN 0-87784-276-0). Inter-Varsity.
Haggi, Zechariah, Malachi. R. J. Coggins. (Old Testament Guides Ser.). 100p. 1986. pap. text ed. 4.95x (ISBN 1-85075-025-4, Pub. by JSOT Pr England). Eisenbrauns.
Hagigah, 1 vol. 15.00 (ISBN 0-910218-61-7). Bennet Pub.
Haida Texts & Myths: Skidegate Dialect. John R. Swanton. LC 5-41613. (Landmarks in Anthropology Ser). Repr. of 1905 ed. 34.00 (ISBN 0-384-59020-9). Johnson Repr.
Hail & Farewell: Ave, Salve, Vale. George Moore. Ed. by Richard Cave. 1985. pap. 16.95 (ISBN 0-8132-0602-2). Cath U Pr.
Hail Mary. rev. ed. H. Leo Eddleman. 134p. 1983. pap. 4.00 (ISBN 0-682-40143-9). Exposition Pr FL.
Hail Mary, Are You Heeding the Blessed Virgin? In Defense of Public Schools. H. Leo Eddleman. (Orig.). 1982. pap. 4.00 (ISBN 0-682-49899-8). Exposition Pr FL.
Haiti Is Waiting. Austine Smith. 78p. 1985. pap. 3.50 (ISBN 0-88144-035-3). Christian Pub.
Hajj. Ali Shari'Ati. Tr. by Somayyah & Yaser. 1984. pap. 5.95 (ISBN 0-686-78719-6). Mizan Pr.
Hajj. 2nd ed. Ali Shariati. Tr. by A. Behzadnia from Persian. 162p. 1978. pap. 4.95 (ISBN 0-941722-09-0). Book-Dist-Ctr.
Hajj Today: A Survey of the Contemporary Pilgrimage to Makkah. David Long. (Illus.). 1979. 34.50 (ISBN 0-87395-382-7). State U NY Pr.
Hajjat-ul-Wada: Last Sermon. B. Ali. 1981. 1.25 (ISBN 0-686-97858-7). Kazi Pubns.
Hakdamot: Hebrew Text of Entrance to the Tree of Life. 1970. 10.00 (ISBN 0-943688-19-1). Res Ctr Kabbalah.
Halacha. Yechiel Galas. 192p. 1973. pap. 4.95 (ISBN 0-910818-13-4). Judaica Pr.
Halacha & Contemporary Society. Alfred S. Cohen. LC 84-741. 1985. pap. 9.95 (ISBN 0-88125-043-0). Ktav.
Halakah of Jesus of Nazareth According to the Gospel of Matthew. Phillip Sigal. 282p. (Orig.). 1986. lib. bdg. 23.75 (ISBN 0-8191-5210-2); pap. text ed. 13.25 (ISBN 0-8191-5211-0). U Pr of Amer.
Halakhah in a Theological Dimension: Essays on the Interpenetration of Law & Theology in Judaism. David Novak. Ed. by Jacob Neusner. LC 84-10661. (Brown Judaic Studies: No. 68). 1985. 19.75 (ISBN 0-89130-757-5, 14-00-68); pap. 16.25 (ISBN 0-89130-829-6). Scholars Pr GA.
Halakhic Man. Joseph B. Soloveitchik. Tr. by Lawrence Kaplan from Hebrew. 182p. 1984. 12.95 (ISBN 0-8276-0222-7, 606). Jewish Pubns.
Halakhic Mind: Rabbinic Judaism & Modern Thought. Joseph B. Soloveitchik. 128p. 1986. 16.95 (ISBN 0-02-930040-1). Free Pr.
Halakhic Process: A Systemic Analysis. Joel Roth. (Moreshet Ser.: Vol. 13). 1987. 35.00 (ISBN 0-87334-035-3). Jewish Sem.
Halel Vzimrah: Commentary in Hebrew on the Passover Haggadah. P. S. Pollak. (Heb). 12.50 (ISBN 0-87559-100-0); pap. 9.50 (ISBN 0-87559-099-3). Shalom.
Half Hours with St. John. Steele. pap. 5.95 (ISBN 0-686-12871-0). Schmul Pub Co.
Half Hours with St. Paul. Steele. pap. 5.95 (ISBN 0-686-12872-9). Schmul Pub Co.
Half Laughing, Half Crying: Songs for Myself. Malcolm Boyd. 306p. 1985. 15.95 (ISBN 0-312-35663-3). St Martin.
Half-Way Covenant: Church Membership in Puritan New England. Robert G. Pope. Repr. of 1969 ed. 63.30 (ISBN 0-8357-9500-4, 2011473). Bks Demand UMI.
Halfway Through the Door: First Steps on a Path of Enlightenment. Alan Arkin. LC 83-48415. 112p. 1984. pap. 5.95 (ISBN 0-06-060307-0, CN 4094, HarpR). Har-Row.
Halfway to Heaven. Peter Lappin. LC 80-68485. 265p. (Orig.). 1980. pap. 6.95 (ISBN 0-89944-052-5). Don Bosco Multimedia.
Hali Meidenhad, Alliterative Homily of 13th Century. Ed. by O. Cockayne. (EETS OS Ser.: No. 18). Repr. of 1922 ed. 11.00 (ISBN 0-527-00020-5). Kraus Repr.
Hall-Tonna Inventory of Values. Brian P. Hall & Benjamin Tonna. write for info. Paulist Pr.
Hallelujah! Bhagwan Shree Rajneesh. Ed. by Ma Prem Maneesha. LC 83-180760. (Initiation Talks Ser.). (Illus.). 364p. (Orig.). 1981. 25.95 (ISBN 0-88050-076-X); pap. 18.95 (ISBN 0-88050-576-1). Chidvilas Found.
Hallelujah Anyway. Richard Rogers. 57p. (Orig.). 1980. pap. text ed. 2.50 (ISBN 0-931097-03-7). Sentinel Pub.
Hallelujah Anyway, Tim. Peggy Scarborough. 1976. pap. 3.95 (ISBN 0-87148-405-6). Pathway Pr.
Hallelujah Factor. Jack R. Taylor. 180p. 1983. 8.95 (ISBN 0-8054-5531-0). Broadman.
Hallelujah: Recording Chapels & Meeting Houses. C. Stell. (Illus.). 48p. 1985. pap. text ed. 7.95 (ISBN 0-906780-49-7, Pub. by Council British Archaeology). Humanities.
Halley's Bible Handbook. Henry H. Halley. 1976. 9.95 (ISBN 0-310-25720-4, 9744); pap. 13.95 Large print (ISBN 0-310-25727-1, 12564L); large print Kivar 19.95 (ISBN 0-310-41390-7, 9840). Zondervan.
Hallucinogens & Shamanism. Ed. by Michael J. Harner. (Illus.). 1973. pap. 9.95x (ISBN 0-19-501649-1). Oxford U Pr.
Hamann on Language & Religion. Terence J. German. (Oxford Theological Monographs). 1981. text ed. 34.95x (ISBN 0-19-826717-7). Oxford U Pr.
Hamartia: The Concept of Error in the Western Tradition. Ed. by Donald V. Stump & James A. Arieti. LC 83-13087. (Texts & Studies in Religion: Vol. 16). 320p. 1984. 59.95x (ISBN 0-88946-805-2). E Mellen.
Hamlet Vocation of Coleridge & Wordsworth. Martin Greenberg. LC 85-18189. 232p. 1986. 22.50x (ISBN 0-87745-131-1). U of Iowa Pr.
Hamlet's Divinity & Other Essays. facs. ed. Christopher Devlin. (Essay Index Reprint Ser). 1963. 15.00 (ISBN 0-8369-1915-7). Ayer Co Pubs.
Hammer & the Cross. John Lawrence. LC 86-4025. 208p. 1986. text ed. 15.00x (ISBN 0-87663-470-6). Universe.
Hammer on the Rock. Bhagwan Shree Rajneesh. Ed. by Ma Prem Maneesha. LC 79-52012. (Initiation Talks Ser.). 464p. (Orig.). 1976. 22.50 (ISBN 0-88050-077-8). Chidvilas Found.
Hammer on the Rock: A Darshan Diary. Bhagwan S. Rajneesh. (Illus.). 464p. 1979. pap. 8.95 (ISBN 0-394-17090-3, E730, Ever). Grove.
Hammering Swords Into Ploughshares: Essays in Honor of Archbishop Mpilo Desmond Tutu. Ed. by Itumeleng Mosala & Buti Tlhagale. 360p. (Orig.). 1987. pap. 12.95 (ISBN 0-8028-0269-9). Eerdmans.
Hammers in the Fire. George E. Vandeman. LC 79-154293. 1971. pap. 1.25 (ISBN 0-8163-0119-0, 08010-1). Pacific Pr Pub Assn.
Han Yu & the T'ang Search for Unity. Charles Hartman. LC 85-16885. 448p. 1986. text ed. 50.00 (ISBN 0-691-06665-5). Princeton U Pr.
Hand-book of the Oneida Community, with a Sketch of Its Founder, & an Outline of Its Constitution & Doctrines, 3 vols in 1. Oneida Community. Incl. Hand-Book of the Oneida Community, Containing a Brief Sketch of Its Present Condition, Internal Economy & Leading Principles; Mutual Criticism. LC 72-2977. Repr. of 1876 ed. 23.50 (ISBN 0-404-10741-9). AMS Pr.
Hand-book on Revival. 4.95 (ISBN 0-686-27778-3). Schmul Pub Co.
Hand in Dialogue. Charles Fryer. 128p. 1983. 17.95 (ISBN 0-227-67841-9, Pub. by J Clarke UK). Attic Pr.
Hand in Hand with Jesus: A New Study Guide for Today's Youth. Robert Wallinga. pap. 2.25 (ISBN 0-686-14194-6); tchrs' ed. 0.75 (ISBN 0-686-14195-4). Rose Pub MI.
Hand List of Illuminated Oriental Christian Manuscripts. Hugo Buchtal & Otto Kurz. (Warburg Institute Studies: Vol. 12). Repr. of 1942 ed. 20.00 (ISBN 0-8115-1389-0). Kraus Repr.

Hand-List of the Ulan Bator Manuscript of the Kanjur-Rtse Them Spans-Ma. Geza Bethlenfalvy. 112p. 1982. pap. text ed. 12.50 (ISBN 963-05-3260-3, Pub. by Akademiai Kiado Hungary). Humanities.

Hand Me Another Brick: Principles of Effective Leadership: How to Motivate Yourself & Others. Charles Swindoll. LC 78-4170. 1978. pap. 6.95 (ISBN 0-8407-5650-X). Nelson.

Hand of Destiny: The Folk-Lore & Superstition of Everyday Life. C. J. Thompson. LC 70-125600. 1970. Repr. of 1932 ed. 46.00x (ISBN 0-8103-3419-4). Gale.

Hand of the Lord: A Reassessment of the "Ark Narrative" of Samuel. Patrick D. Miller & J. J. M. Roberts. LC 76-48737. (Johns Hopkins Near Eastern Studies). pap. 24.40 (ISBN 0-317-26633-0, 2010959). Bks Demand UMI.

Hand of the Lord: A Reassessment of the "Ark Narrative" of 1 Samuel. Patrick D. Miller, Jr. & J. J. Roberts. LC 76-48737. (Near Eastern Studies). 128p. 1977. 12.50x (ISBN 0-8018-1920-2). Johns Hopkins.

Hand-Size Giant Print Reference Bible. Incl. Black Genuine Leather. (semi-overlap binding, gold edges, ribbon marker). 39.95 (ISBN 0-317-18887-9, 6710S); Feora Bonded Leather. (semi-overlap binding, gold edges, ribbon marker, gift boxed). 24.95 (ISBN 0-317-18888-7); black (6708S); brown (N6708S); burgundy (R6807S); Imitation Leather. (semi-overlap binding, antique gold edges, gift boxed). 17.95 (ISBN 0-317-18889-5); black (6704S); brown (N6704S); burgundy (R6704S). 2016p. (incl. giant print concordance, harmony of the Gospels, words of Christ in red, presentation page, family record section, maps, gift boxed). thumb indexing avail. 5.00 addnl. Holman Bible Pub.

Hand That Holds Me. Michael Rogness. LC 84-14447. 112p. (Orig.). 1984. pap. 5.95 (ISBN 0-8066-2093-5, 10-2943). Augsburg.

Handbells in the Liturgical Service. John Folkening. (Illus.). 52p. (Orig.). 1984. pap. 3.00 (ISBN 0-570-01328-3, 99-1254). Concordia.

Handbook for Advanced Souls: Eternal Reminders for the Present Moment. Mark Little. (Illus.). 136p. 1984. 6.95 (ISBN 0-9613783-0-1). M A Little.

Handbook for Bible Study. Grant R. Osborne & Stephen B. Woodward. 188p. 1983. pap. 5.95 (ISBN 0-8010-6701-4). Baker Bk.

Handbook for Bible Teachers & Preachers. G. Campbell Morgan. (Paperback Reference Library). 312p. 1985. pap. 8.95 (ISBN 0-8010-6190-3). Baker Bk.

Handbook for Biblical Studies. Nicholas Turner. LC 82-7111. 156p. 1982. pap. 6.95 (ISBN 0-664-24436-X). Westminster.

Handbook for Building a Beautiful Homelife. Jan Linthorst & Joan Rubadeau. 1987. pap. 12.00 (ISBN 0-913105-20-1). PAGL Pr.

Handbook for Christian Homemakers. Edith F. Kilgo. 200p. (Orig.). 1982. pap. 5.95 (ISBN 0-8010-5439-7). Baker Bk.

Handbook for Christian Maturity. Bill Bright. 360p. (Orig.). 1981. pap. 8.95 (ISBN 0-86605-010-8). Campus Crusade.

Handbook for Church Nurseries. Debbie O'Neal. 32p. (Orig.). 1985. pap. 2.95 (ISBN 0-8066-2174-5, 10-2944). Augsburg.

Handbook for Church Officers & Boards. Conrad I. Frey. 1985. pap. 1.50 (ISBN 0-8100-0187-X, 15N0414). Northwest Pub.

Handbook for Congregational Studies. Ed. by Jackson W. Carroll et al. 192p. (Orig.). 1986. pap. 16.95 (ISBN 0-687-16562-8). Abingdon.

Handbook for Counselors: GMA. Lillian Owens. 161p. 1979. pap. 3.00 (ISBN 0-89114-023-9). Baptist Pub Hse.

Handbook for Deacons. J. D. O'Donnell. 1973. pap. 3.95 (ISBN 0-89265-011-7). Randall Hse.

Handbook for Followers of Jesus. Winkie Pratney. LC 76-44385. 336p. 1976. pap. 6.95 (ISBN 0-87123-378-9, 210378). Bethany Hse.

Handbook for Funeral & Memorial Societies. Compiled by Continental Assocation of Funeral & Memorial Societies, Inc & Memorial Society Association of Canada. Ed. by Peggy Fleming. LC 72-7963. 1976. pap. 3.50 (ISBN 0-686-18088-7). Continent Assn Funeral.

Handbook for Krishna Consciousness. Satsvarupa Dasa Goswami. 380p. 1983. 5.95 (ISBN 0-318-03098-5). Gita Nagari.

Handbook for Parish Evaluation. Ed. by Thomas P. Walters. (Orig.). 1984. pap. 10.95 (ISBN 0-8091-2587-0). Paulist Pr.

Handbook for Peer Ministry. James P. Emswiler & Joseph Moore. LC 81-84351. 128p. (Orig.). 1982. pap. 4.95 (ISBN 0-8091-2427-0). Paulist Pr.

Handbook for Preclears. L. Ron Hubbard. 20.00 (ISBN 0-686-30783-6). Church Scient NY.

Handbook for Preclears. L. Ron Hubbard. (Illus.). 192p. 1951. 38.59 (ISBN 0-88404-016-X). Bridge Pubns Inc.

Handbook for Telephone Ministry. Rev. ed. Alice E. Duncombe. 7.95 (ISBN 0-89985-110-X). Christ Nations.

Handbook for the Common Lectionary. Peter C. Bower. 300p. (Orig.). 1987. pap. 10.95 (ISBN 0-664-24048-8, A Geneva Press Publication). Westminster.

Handbook for the Humanistic Astrologer. Michael R. Meyer. LC 73-83657. 456p. 1974. pap. 8.95 (ISBN 0-385-05729-6, Anch). Doubleday.

Handbook for the Jewish Family: Understanding & Enjoying the Sabbath & Other Holidays. Alex J. Goldman. LC 58-12938. (Illus.). 1983. Repr. of 1958 ed. 14.95 (ISBN 0-8197-0085-1). Bloch.

Handbook for the Lectionary. Horace T. Allen, Jr. LC 80-19735. 254p. 1980. softcover 8.95 (ISBN 0-664-24347-9, A Geneva Press Pub.). Westminster.

Handbook for the Ultimate Church Musician. Ed. by Charles Montgomery. Jane Montgomery. 1985. pap. 3.95 (ISBN 0-916043-04-5). Light Hearted Pub Co.

Handbook for Today's Catholic: Beliefs, Practices, Prayers. A Redemptorist Pastoral Publication. 1978. pap. 1.50 (ISBN 0-89243-076-1). Liguori Pubns.

Handbook for Today's Catholic Family A Redemptorist Pastoral Publication. (Orig.). 1979. pap. 1.50 (ISBN 0-89243-112-1). Liguori Pubns.

Handbook for Today's Disciples in the Christian Church: Disciples of Christ. D. Duane Cummins. LC 81-10029. 64p. (Orig.). 1981. pap. 1.95 (ISBN 0-8272-1419-7, 10H1309). CBP.

Handbook for Writing Technical Proposals That Win Contracts. Donald V. Helgeson. LC 85-3549. 178p. 1985. pap. 24.95 (ISBN 0-13-379686-8). P-H.

Handbook for Young Christians. Tom Julien. 1976. pap. 1.00 (ISBN 0-88469-037-7). BMH Bks.

Handbook of Adult Religious Education. Ed. by Nancy T. Foltz. 272p. (Orig.). 1986. pap. 14.95 (ISBN 0-89135-052-7). Religious Educ.

Handbook of Ayurveda. Vaidya B. Dash. 221p. (Orig.). 1983. 28.00 (ISBN 0-317-17437-1, Pub. by Cultural Integration). Auromere.

Handbook of Basic Bible Texts: Every Key Passage for the Study of Doctrine & Theology. John J. Davis. 1986. pap. 6.95 (ISBN 0-310-43711-3, 12103P). Zondervan.

Handbook of Bible Lands. Guy P. Duffield. 192p. 1985. pap. 7.95 (ISBN 0-8010-2948-1). Baker Bk.

Handbook of Bible Manners & Customs. Freeman. Repr. of 1870 ed. cancelled. Guildhall Pubs.

Handbook of Biblical Criticism. rev. ed. Richard N. Soulen. LC 76-12398. 225p. 1981. pap. 11.95 (ISBN 0-8042-0045-9). John Knox.

Handbook of Biblical Hebrew, 3 vols. William S. LaSor. Set. 14.95x (ISBN 0-8028-2379-3). Eerdmans.

Handbook of Biblical Personalities. George M. Alexander. 320p. 1981. pap. 6.95 (ISBN 0-8164-2316-4, HarpR). Har-Row.

Handbook of Christian Meditation. Marjorie H. Russell. 1978. pap. 5.95 (ISBN 0-8159-5713-0). Devin.

Handbook of Christian Meditation. Marjorie H. Russell. (Illus.). pap. 5.95 (ISBN 0-8159-6110-3). Devin.

Handbook of Christian Puppetry. Grace Harp. LC 83-73204. 128p. (Orig.). 1984. pap. 5.95 plastic comb bdg. (ISBN 0-89636-125-X). Accent Bks.

Handbook of Christian Spirituality: The Major Figures & Teachings from the New Testament to the 20th Century. Michael Cox. LC 84-48236. 288p. 1985. 14.45 (ISBN 0-06-061601-6, HarpR). Har-Row.

Handbook of Christian Theologians. Ed. by Martin E. Marty & Dean G. Peerman. 736p. (Orig.). 1984. pap. 13.50 (ISBN 0-687-16563-6). Abingdon.

Handbook of Christian Theology. Marvin Halverson & Arthur Cohen. (Fount Paperback Ser.). pap. 7.95 (ISBN 0-687-16567-9). Abingdon.

Handbook of Christian Truth. Harold Lindsell & Charles J. Woodbridge. 352p. 1972. Repr. 13.95 (ISBN 0-8007-0129-1). Revell.

Handbook of Christmas Programs. William C. Hendricks & Cora Vogel. 1978. pap. 9.95 (ISBN 0-8010-4204-6). Baker Bk.

Handbook of Church Discipline. Jay E. Adams. (Jay Adams Library). 144p. 1986. pap. 6.95 (ISBN 0-310-51191-7). Zondervan.

Handbook of Classical & Modern Mandaic. Rudolf Macuch. 1965. 129.00x (ISBN 3-11-000261-2). De Gruyter.

Handbook of Concepts for Living. Bill Bright. 545p. (Orig.). 1981. pap. 8.95 (ISBN 0-86605-011-6). Campus Crusade.

Handbook of Creativity. Judy Dorsett. (Illus.). 128p. 1985. pap. 7.95 (ISBN 0-87239-729-7, 3226). Standard Pub.

Handbook of Cults, Sects, & Self-Realization Groups. Jack N. Porter. 95p. (Orig.). 1982. pap. 6.95 (ISBN 0-932270-03-4). Spencer Pr.

Handbook of Denominations in the United States. 8th ed. Frank S. Mead & Samuel S. Hill. 400p. 1985. text ed. 10.95 (ISBN 0-687-16571-7). Abingdon.

Handbook of Early Christian Fathers. Ernest Leigh-Bennett. 59.95 (ISBN 0-8490-0276-1). Gordon Pr.

Handbook of Egyptian Religions. Adolf Erman. LC 76-27517. (Illus.). 1976. Repr. of 1907 ed. lib. bdg. 30.00 (ISBN 0-89341-032-2). Longwood Pub Group.

Handbook of Freemasonry. Edmond Ronayne. 9.00 (ISBN 0-685-19476-0). Powner.

Handbook of Greek Mythology. Herbert J. Rose. 1959. pap. 7.95 (ISBN 0-525-47041-7, 0772-230). Dutton.

Handbook of Hebrew Calligraphy: The ABC's of the Alef-Bet. Cara G. Marks. (Illus.). 128p. 1983. cancelled (ISBN 0-89961-010-2); pap. cancelled (ISBN 0-89961-011-0). SBS Pub.

Handbook of Jewish Thought. Aryeh Kaplan. 307p. 13.95 (ISBN 0-940118-27-0). Maznaim.

Handbook of Legendary & Mythological Art. Clara Clement. 59.95 (ISBN 0-8490-0279-6). Gordon Pr.

Handbook of Legendary & Mythological Art. Clara E. Clement. LC 68-26616. (Illus.). 1969. Repr. of 1881 ed. 45.00x (ISBN 0-8103-3175-6). Gale.

Handbook of Legendary & Mythological Art. Clara E. Waters. LC 76-27524. (Illus.). 1976. Repr. of 1876 ed. lib. bdg. 50.00 (ISBN 0-89341-037-3). Longwood Pub Group.

Handbook of Life in Bible Times. J. A. Thompson. LC 86-3046. (Illus.). 380p. 1986. 34.95 (ISBN 0-87784-949-8). Inter-Varsity.

Handbook of Living Will Laws 1976-1980. rev. ed. Society for the Right to Die. Orig. Title: Handbook of Enacted Laws 1981 Handbook. 64p. pap. cancelled (ISBN 0-9613825-3-8). Soc Right to Die.

Handbook of Moral Development. Ed. by Gary L. Sapp. 296p. 1986. pap. 14.95 (ISBN 0-89135-054-3). Religious Educ.

Handbook of New Testament Greek: An Inductive Approach Based on the Greek Text of Acts, 2 vols. William S. LaSor. 1973. pap. text ed. 24.95 (ISBN 0-8028-2341-6). Eerdmans.

Handbook of Patrology. Patrick J. Hamell. 1968. pap. 5.95 (ISBN 0-8189-0057-1). Alba.

Handbook of Positive Prayer. Hypatia Hasbrouck. 160p. 1984. 5.95 (ISBN 0-87159-051-4). Unity School.

Handbook of Psychotherapy & Jewish Ethics. Moshe Spero. 1986. 19.95 (ISBN 0-87306-406-2). Feldheim.

Handbook of Religious Quotations. Ed. by Samuel G. Dawson & Rod MacArthur. 188p. (Orig.). 1987. pap. 5.95 (ISBN 0-938855-16-6). Gospel Themes Pr.

Handbook of Symbols in Christian Art. Gertrude G. Sill. (Illus.). 1975. pap. 10.95 (ISBN 0-02-000850-3, Collier). Macmillan.

Handbook of Synagogue Architecture. Marilyn Chiat. LC 81-9419. (Brown Judiac Studies). 1982. pap. 20.00 (ISBN 0-89130-524-6, 14-00-29). Scholars Pr GA.

Handbook of the Christian Year. Ed. by Hoyt L. Hickman et al. 304p. (Orig.). 1986. pap. 16.95 (ISBN 0-687-16575-X). Abingdon.

Handbook of the Early Church Fathers. Ernest Leigh-Bennett. 1980. lib. bdg. 75.00 (ISBN 0-8490-3107-9). Gordon Pr.

Handbook of the Mass. George Fitzgerald. 128p. 1982. pap. 4.95 (ISBN 0-8091-2401-7). Paulist Pr.

Handbook of Theological Terms. Van A. Harvey. 1964. pap. 4.95 (ISBN 0-02-085430-7, Collier). Macmillan.

Handbook of Today's Religions. Josh McDowell & Don Stewart. 512p. 1983. 18.95 (ISBN 0-86605-121-X). Campus Crusade.

Handbook of Virasaivism. S. C. Nandimath. 1979. 15.00 (ISBN 0-89684-053-0, Pub. by Motilal Banarsidass India). Orient Bk Dist.

Handbook of 1985 Living Will Laws. Society for the Right to Die. 128p. (Orig.). 1986. pap. 5.00x (ISBN 0-9613825-2-X). Soc Right to Die.

Handbook on Critical Life Issues. Donald G. McCarthy & Edward J. Bayer. 230p. (Orig.). 1982. pap. 9.95 (ISBN 0-935372-10-5). Pope John Ctr.

Handbook on Critical Sexual Issues. Ed. by Donald G. McCarthy & Edward J. Bayer. 240p. (Orig.). 1983. pap. 9.95 (ISBN 0-935372-11-3). Pope John Ctr.

Handbook on Holy Spirit Baptism. Don Basham. (Handbk. Ser: No. 1). 118p. 1969. pap. 2.95 (ISBN 0-88368-003-3). Whitaker Hse.

Handbook on the Holy Spirit. James E. Cummings. LC 77-79551. 208p. 1977. pap. 3.95 (ISBN 0-87123-541-2, 200541). Bethany Hse.

Handbook on the Pentateuch. Victor P. Hamilton. LC 82-70466. 392p. 1982. 15.95 (ISBN 0-8010-4259-3). Baker Bk.

Handbook on Tongues, Interpretation & Prophecy. Don Basham. (Handbk. Ser.: No. 2). 1971. pap. 2.95 (ISBN 0-88368-004-1). Whitaker Hse.

Handbook to Happiness. Charles Solomon. 1982. pap. 5.95 (ISBN 0-8423-1281-1); leader's guide 2.95 (ISBN 0-8423-1282-X). Tyndale.

Handbook to Higher Consciousness. 5th ed. Ken Keyes, Jr. LC 73-83071. 240p. 1975. pap. 4.95 (ISBN 0-9600688-8-0). Living Love.

Handbook to the Gospels: A Guide to the Gospel Writings & the Life & Times of Jesus. John Wijngaards. (Illus.). 300p. 1983. pap. 8.95 (ISBN 0-89283-118-9). Servant.

Handbook to the Lutheran Hymnal. 3rd rev. ed. W. G. Polack. 1975. Repr. of 1942 ed. lib. bdg. 16.95 (ISBN 0-8100-0003-2, 03-0700). Northwest Pub.

Handbook to the New Testament. Claus Westermann. Ed. & tr. by Robert H. Boyd. LC 69-14190. 1977. pap. 9.95 (ISBN 0-8066-1600-8, 10-2946). Augsburg.

Handbook to the Old Testament. Claus Westermann. Tr. by Robert H. Boyd. LC 67-25362. 1967. pap. 11.95 (ISBN 0-8066-1529-X, 10-2951). Augsburg.

Handbuch der Islam-Literatur. Gustav Pfannmueller. (Ger.). viii, 436p. 1974. Repr. of 1923 ed. 68.00x (ISBN 3-11-002488-8). De Gruyter.

Handel: A Documentary Biography. Otto Deutsch. LC 74-3118. (Music Ser.). 942p. 1974. Repr. of 1954 ed. lib. bdg. 85.00 (ISBN 0-306-70624-5). Da Capo.

Handel & The Pastoral Tradition. Ellen T. Harris. (Illus.). 1980. 47.00x (ISBN 0-19-315236-3). Oxford U Pr.

Handel, Dryden & Milton. Robert M. Myers. 1956. lib. bdg. 32.50 (ISBN 0-8414-6129-5). Folcroft.

Handel's Messiah. John Tobin. LC 69-13491. (Illus.). 1969. 35.00 (ISBN 0-312-35840-7). St Martin.

Handel's Messiah: A Devotional Commentary. Joseph E. McCabe. LC 77-25860. 120p. 1978. pap. 5.95 (ISBN 0-664-24192-1). Westminster.

Handel's Messiah: A Touchstone of Taste. Robert M. Myers. LC 72-159747. 338p. 1971. Repr. of 1948 ed. lib. bdg. 27.50x (ISBN 0-374-96035-6, Octagon). Hippocrene Bks.

Handful of Pearls: The Epistle of James. Addison J. Eastman. LC 78-5797. 106p. 1978. pap. 5.50 (ISBN 0-664-24202-2). Westminster.

Handfuls on Purpose, 5 vols. James Smith. 1943. 69.95 set (ISBN 0-8028-8139-4). Eerdmans.

Handle with Prayer. Charles Stanley. 120p. 1982. pap. 4.95 (ISBN 0-88207-309-5). Victor Bks.

Handling Church Tensions Creatively. Fred W. Prinzing. LC 86-80687. 216p. (Orig.). 1986. pap. 4.95 (ISBN 0-935797-23-8). Harvest IL.

Handling Conflicts: Taking the Tension Out of Difficult Relationships. Gerry Rauch. (Living as a Christian Ser.). 160p. (Orig.). 1985. pap. 3.95 (ISBN 0-89283-187-1). Servant.

Handling Your Hormones. Jim Burns & Carol Bostrom. (Illus.). 64p. (Orig.). 1984. involvement guide 4.95 (ISBN 0-915929-10-4); leader's guide 1.95 (ISBN 0-915929-14-7). Merit Bks.

Handmaid of the Lord. Adrienne von Speyr. LC 85-60468. Tr. of Magd des Herrn. 178p. 1985. 9.95 (ISBN 0-89870-042-6). Ignatius Pr.

Handmaid to Theology. Winfried Corduan. 176p. (Orig.). 1981. pap. 7.95 (ISBN 0-8010-2468-4). Baker Bk.

Hands & Feet of Christ. Ed. by Stanley Konieczny. 1987. pap. 1.50 (ISBN 0-8189-0515-8). Alba.

Hands that Heal. Echo B. Burns. (Orig.). 1986. pap. 7.95 (ISBN 0-917086-76-7). A C S Pubns Inc.

Hands to Work & Hearts to God. 2nd ed. Bro. Theodore E. Johnson. LC 72-78927. 64p. (Orig.). 1983. pap. 4.95 (ISBN 0-915836-08-4). Shaker Pr ME.

Handy Bible Dictionary & Concordance. Merrill C. Tenney & Alexander Cruden. 1986. pap. 6.95 (ISBN 0-310-33271-0, 11147P). Zondervan.

Handy-Book of Rules & Tables for Verifying Dates with the Christian Era. John J. Bond. LC 66-29473. 1966. Repr. of 1889 ed. 10.00x (ISBN 0-8462-1795-3). Russell.

Handy Clip Art for Church Bulletin Covers. Jack Hamm. 48p. (Orig.). 1985. pap. 9.95 (ISBN 0-933545-02-9). Knight Media.

Handy Dictionary of the Bible. Merrill C. Tenney. (Orig.). pap. 4.95 (ISBN 0-310-33151-X, 10898P). Zondervan.

Handy Dictionary of the Bible. Merrill C. Tenney. 1986. write for info. (ISBN 0-8297-0683-6). Life Pubs Intl.

Handy Helpful Household Hints. Nancy Williamson. pap. cancelled (ISBN 0-89728-066-0). Omega Pubns Or.

Hang Tough. F. Matthew Lancaster. 24p. 1985. pap. 3.95 (ISBN 0-8091-2696-6). Paulist Pr.

Hanging in There with Christ. Robert F. Waywood. 1974. 4.95 (ISBN 0-8199-0498-8). Franciscan Herald.

Hangups, Health & Heaven. large print ed. Ed. by Pearl Brians. 50p. pap. 9.95 (ISBN 0-9608650-0-4). VHI Library.
Hanna & Walter. Hanna Kohner et al. 224p. 1985. pap. 3.50 (ISBN 0-445-20109-6, Popular Lib). Warner Bks.
Hannah at the Manger. Regine Schindler. (Illus.). 31p. 1983. pap. 9.95 printed binding (ISBN 0-687-16627-6). Abingdon.
Hannah's Daughters. Bette M. Ross. Date not set. pap. 5.95 (ISBN 0-8007-5232-5, Power Bks). Revell.
Hanukah in My House. Norma Simon. (Festival Series of Picture Story Books). (Illus.). 1960. plastic cover 4.50 (ISBN 0-8381-0705-2). United Syn Bk.
Hanukkah. June Behrens. LC 82-17890. (Ethnic & Traditional Holidays Ser.). (Illus.). 32p. 1983. PLB 10.60 (ISBN 0-516-02386-1); pap. 2.95 (ISBN 0-516-42386-X). Childrens.
Hanukkah. Norma Simon. LC 66-10065. (Holiday Ser.). (Illus.). 1966. PLB 12.89 (ISBN 0-690-36953-0, Crowell Jr Bks). HarpJ.
Hanukkah Anthology. Ed. by Philip Goodman. LC 75-44637. (Illus.). xxxiv, 466p. 1976. 15.95 (ISBN 0-8276-0080-1, 392). Jewish Pubns.
Hanukkah Book. Marilyn Burns. (Illus.). 128p. 1981. 9.95 (ISBN 0-02-716140-4, Four Winds). Macmillan.
Hanukkah Book. Mae S. Rockland. (Illus.). 190p. 1985. pap. 9.95 (ISBN 0-8052-0792-9). Schocken.
Hanukkah: Eight Nights, Eight Lights. Malka Drucker. LC 80-15852. (Jewish Holidays Book). (Illus.). 96p. 1980. reinforced bdg. 12.95 (ISBN 0-8234-0377-7). Holiday.
Hanukkah Fun Book: Puzzles, Riddles, Magic & More. David A. Adler. LC 76-47459. (Illus.). 1976. pap. 3.95 (ISBN 0-88482-754-2, Bonim Bks). Hebrew Pub.
Hanukkah Game Book: Games, Riddles, Puzzles & More. David A. Adler. (Fun-to-Do Bk). (Illus.). 1978. pap. 3.95 (ISBN 0-88482-764-X, Bonim Bks). Hebrew Pub.
Hanukkah Latkes & Rothschild's Millions. David Schwartz. 1961. 14.95x (ISBN 0-8084-0036-3). New Coll U Pr.
Hanukkah Song & Story. Charles Wengrov. (Illus.). 1960. pap. 4.00 (ISBN 0-914080-29-6). Shulsinger Sales.
Hanukkah Story. Marilyn Hirsh. LC 77-22183. (Illus.). 1977. pap. 4.95 (ISBN 0-88482-761-5, Bonim Bks). Hebrew Pub.
Hanumaan Chaaleesa. Malyala Pandurangarao. (Illus.). 16p. (Orig.). 1984. pap. 2.00x (ISBN 0-317-07665-5). Sri Shirdi Sai.
Hapax Legomena in Biblical Hebrew. Frederick E. Greenspahn. LC 83-20021. (SBL Dissertation Ser.). 274p. 1984. 10.50 (ISBN 0-89130-660-9, 06 01 74); pap. 10.95 (ISBN 0-89130-785-0). Scholars Pr GA.
Happenings. Dick Hilliard & Beverly Valenti-Hilliard. (Center Celebration Ser.). (Illus.). 60p. 1981. pap. text ed. 3.95 (ISBN 0-89390-033-8). Resource Pubns.
Happiest Day. Ruth Odor. 1985. 5.95 (ISBN 0-89565-085-1, R4915). Standard Pub.
Happiest People on Earth. Demos Shakarian. 192p. 1979. 2.95 (ISBN 0-8007-8362-X, Spire Bks). Revell.
Happily Ever after Is No Accident. William Tapley. Ed. by Michael L. Sherer. (Orig.). 1987. pap. 2.75 leaders guide (ISBN 0-89536-862-5, 7821); pap. 3.45 couples bk. (ISBN 0-89536-863-3, 7822). CSS of Ohio.
Happiness & Christian Hope: A Phenomenological Analysis. William A. Marra. 1979. 8.95 (ISBN 0-8199-0770-7). Franciscan Herald.
Happiness & Harmony in Marriage. William S. Deal. pap. 2.95 (ISBN 0-686-13723-X). Crusade Pubs.
Happiness in the Home: Guidelines for Spouses & Parents. Harold Hazelip. 120p. 1985. pap. 3.95 (ISBN 0-8010-4294-1). Baker Bk.
Happiness Is a Journey. Compiled by Patricia Dreier. (Illus.). 1983. boxed 8.00 (ISBN 0-8378-1804-4). Gibson.
Happiness Is: An Introduction to Christian Life & Faith. Alfred E. Mulder. 60p. 1983. pap. 3.25 (ISBN 0-933140-88-6). CRC Pubns.
Happiness Is Being a Physically Fit Christian. Dick Couey. LC 84-12746. 1985. 9.95 (ISBN 0-8054-7525-7). Broadman.
Happiness Is... Heaven Made Marriages. LaJoyce Martin. Ed. by Mary H. Wallace. LC 85-22522. (Illus.). 313p. (Orig.). 1985. pap. 6.95 (ISBN 0-912315-86-5). Word Aflame.
Happiness: Issues of Emotional Living in an Age of Stress for Clergy & Religious. Kathleen Kelley et al. Ed. by T. A. Kane. LC 82-1733. 128p. (Orig.). 1982. pap. 5.00 (ISBN 0-89571-014-5). Affirmation.
Happiness Now. Mary K. MacDougall. 178p. 1971. 5.95 (ISBN 0-87159-053-0). Unity School.
Happiness of Heaven. J. Boudreau. LC 83-51548. 258p. 1984. pap. 6.00 (ISBN 0-89555-232-9). TAN Bks Pubs.
Happiness Rhymes for Children. Louise Eavey. 1969. pap. 1.35 (ISBN 0-915374-09-9, 09-0). Rapids Christian.
Happy Anniversary. Donald Mainprize. (Contempo Ser.). 1975. pap. 0.95 (ISBN 0-8010-5971-2). Baker Bk.
Happy Are You Poor. Thomas Dubay. 5.95 (ISBN 0-87193-141-9). Dimension Bks.
Happy Are You Who Affirm. Thomas A. Kane. LC 80-26834. (Illus.). 184p. 1980. pap. 5.00 (ISBN 0-89571-010-2). Affirmation.
Happy Birthday Planet Earth: The Instant of Co-Operation. Barbara M. Hubbard. (No. 1). (Illus.). 64p. (Orig.). 1986. pap. 6.00 perfect bdg. (ISBN 0-943734-08-8). Ocean Tree Bks.
Happy Birthday to You. Janet Herbert. 32p. 1986. 2.95 (50401, Chariot Bks). Cook.
Happy Book of Christmas Stories. William J. Lederer. (Illus.). 1984. 7.95 (ISBN 0-393-01414-2). Norton.
Happy Christmas. Ed. by William K. Seymour & John Smith. LC 68-26877. 256p. 1979. Repr. of 1968 ed. Westminster.
Happy Day for Ramona & Other Missionary Stories for Children. Illus. by Janis Timyan. (Illus., Orig.). Date not set. pap. price not set (ISBN 0-87509-392-2). Chr Pubns.
Happy Hannah. Yvonne Patterson. (Happy Day Bible Stories Bks.). (Illus.). 24p. 1984. 1.59 (ISBN 0-87239-764-5, 3724). Standard Pub.
Happy Holidays: How to Enjoy the Christmas & Chanukkah Season to the Fullest. Wayne W. Dyer. Tr. by Thomas Nast. LC 86-2448. (Illus.). 96p. 1986. 9.95 (ISBN 0-688-06466-3). Morrow.
Happy Home: Child Rearing. Jack Van Impe. 34p. 1985. pap. 1.95 (ISBN 0-934803-01-3). J Van Impe.
Happy Hour. James Bailey. 1985. 6.95 (ISBN 0-89536-750-5, 5856). CSS of Ohio.
Happy Is the Heart: A Year in the Life of a Jewish Girl. Sarah Birnhack. (Illus.). 1976. 7.95 (ISBN 0-87306-131-4); pap. 5.95. Feldheim.
Happy Journey: Thirty-Five Shaker Spirituals Compiled by Miss Clara Endicott Sears. Ed. by Roger L. Hall. LC 81-69875. (Illus.). 60p. (Orig.). 1982. 8.00 (ISBN 0-941632-00-8). Fruitlands Mus.
Happy Life & Other Works. St. Augustine. (Fathers of the Church Ser.: Vol. 5). 450p. 1948. 22.95x (ISBN 0-8132-0005-9). Cath U Pr.
Happy Life Stories. Edna K. Wenger. (Illus.). 1977. 7.50 (ISBN 0-87813-912-5). Christian Light.
Happy Purim Night. Norma Simon. (Festival Series of Picture Story Books). (Illus.). plastic cover 4.50 (ISBN 0-8381-0706-0, 10-706). United Syn Bk.
Happy Surprise Junior Objectalks. Arnold C. Westphal. 1978. 4.95 (ISBN 0-915398-11-7). Visual Evangels.
Happy Talk. Annetta Dellinger. 1982. pap. 5.95 (ISBN 0-570-03859-6, 12-2953). Concordia.
Happy Time Bible Activities. Frances Matranga. 24p. 1983. pap. 1.50 (ISBN 0-87239-691-6, 2361). Standard Pub.
Happy Times with Happy Seeds. Sally Cowell. (Happy Days Bks.). (Illus.). 24p. 1984. 1.59 (ISBN 0-87239-738-6, 3708). Standard Pub.
Happy Times with Nursery Children at Home & Church. Katherine Royer. 192p. (Orig.). 1971. pap. 7.95x (ISBN 0-8361-1275-X). Herald Pr.
Happy Times with People. Morlee Maynard. LC 85-25555. (Bible & Me Ser.). 1986. 5.95 (ISBN 0-8054-4165-4). Broadman.
Happy Together, 1977. rev. ed. Mary C. Riehle & Dolores Ready. 1977. pap. text ed. 4.95 (ISBN 0-86683-110-X, HarpR); tchr's. ed. 7.55 (ISBN 0-86683-113-4). Har-Row.
Hara-Kiri: Japanese Ritual Suicide. Jack Seward. LC 68-11973. 1968. pap. 7.95 (ISBN 0-8048-0231-9). C E Tuttle.
Hara: The Vital Centre of Man. Karlfried Von Duerckheim. Tr. by Sylvia-Monica Van Kospoth & Estelle R. Healey. (Unwin Paperbacks). 1977. pap. 6.95 (ISBN 0-04-290011-5). Allen Unwin.
Harassment & Other Collection Taboos. Lipman G. Feld. 156p. 1976. pap. 8.95 (ISBN 0-934914-08-7). NACM.
Harbinger & New England Transcendentalism: A Portrait of Associationism in America. Sterling F. Delano. 224p. 27.50 (ISBN 0-8386-3138-X). Fairleigh Dickinson.
Hard Sayings of Jesus. F. F. Bruce. LC 83-10793. (Jesus Library). 216p. 1983. pap. 7.95 (ISBN 0-87784-927-7). Inter-Varsity.
Hard Times Catalog for Youth Ministry. Marilyn Benson & Dennis Benson. LC 82-81332. (Illus.). 288p. (Orig.). 1982. pap. 14.95 (ISBN 0-936664-06-1). Group Bks.
Hardest Journey. Douglas V. Steere. 1983. pap. 2.50x (ISBN 0-87574-163-0, 163). Pendle Hill.
Hardly an Angel in Sight. Elaine Egbert. Ed. by Raymond H. Woolsey. (Banner Ser.). 128p. (Orig.). 1987. pap. 6.50 (ISBN 0-8280-0369-6). Review & Herald.
Hardships & Happy Times. Bert Russell. LC 78-75104. (Oral History Ser.: No. 1). 1982. 9.95 (ISBN 0-930344-04-9); pap. 7.95 (ISBN 0-930344-01-4). Lacon Pubs.
Hare Krishna & the Counterculture. J. Stillson Judah. LC 74-8209. (Contemporary Religious Movements Ser.). pap. 80.00 (ISBN 0-317-07867-4, 2007717). Bks Demand UMI.
Hare Krishna Character Type: A Study of the Sensate Personality. J. Frank Kenny & Tommy H. Poling. (Studies in Religion & Society: No. 15). 202p. 1986. 49.95 (ISBN 0-88946-859-1). E Mellen.
Hare Krishna Hare Krishna: Five Distinguished Scholars in Religion Discuss the Krishna Movement in the West. Ed. by Steven Gelberg. LC 82-21055. (Press Eastern Philosophy & Literature Ser.). 224p. (Orig.). 1983. pap. 7.95 (ISBN 0-394-62454-8, E845, Ever). Grove.
Hare Krishna Movement. Gelberg. 1985. lib. bdg. 23.00 (ISBN 0-8240-8751-8). Garland Pub.
Harim & the Purdah: Studies of Oriental Women. Elizabeth Cooper. LC 68-23147. 312p. 1975. Repr. of 1915 ed. 43.00x (ISBN 0-8103-3167-5). Gale.
Harley Shields: Alaskan Missionaries. Kathryn W. Kizer. LC 84-5821. (Meet the Missioanry Ser.). 1984. 5.50 (ISBN 0-8054-4285-5, 4242-85). Broadman.
Harmfully Involved: Updated for the Eighties. Ed. by William O. Manning & Jean Vinton. 168p. (Orig.). 1978. pap. 10.95 (ISBN 0-89486-056-9). Hazelden.
Harmonies De L'etre Exprimees Par les Nombres. Paul F. Lacuria. LC 75-36848. (Occult Ser.). (Fr.). 1976. Repr. of 1899 ed. 55.00x (ISBN 0-405-07964-8). Ayer Co Pubs.
Harmony & Discord: An Analysis of the Decline of Jewish Self-Government in Fifteenth Century Central Europe. Eric Zimmer. 276p. 1970. 10.00x (ISBN 0-685-26214-6, Pub. by Yeshiva U. Pr.). Bloch.
Harmony of Paul's Life & Letters. Joseph B. Harriman. 77p. (Companion vol. to A Harmony of the Four gospels). 1969. 2.50 (ISBN 0-910840-13-X). Kingdom.
Harmony of Samuel, Kings, & Chronicles. William D. Crockett. 1985. pap. 9.95 (ISBN 0-8010-2511-7). Baker Bk.
Harmony of the Four Gospels: The New International Version. Orville E. Daniel. 1987. pap. price not set (ISBN 0-8010-2974-0). Baker Bk.
Harmony of the Gospels. Loraine Boettner. 1976. pap. 3.95 (ISBN 0-87552-132-0). Presby & Reformed.
Harmony of the Gospels. Ralph D. Heim. LC 47-2807. 228p. 1974. pap. 6.95 (ISBN 0-8006-1494-1, 1-1494). Fortress.
Harmony of the Gospels. John H. Kerr. 236p. 10.95 (ISBN 0-8007-0131-3). Revell.
Harmony of the Gospels. A. T. Robertson. 1932. 12.45i (ISBN 0-06-066890-3, HarpR). Har-Row.
Harmony of the Gospels, 4 Vols. Edward Taylor. LC 82-5452. 2688p. 1983. Set. 300.00x (ISBN 0-8201-1379-4). Schol Facsimiles.
Harmony of the Gospels for Historical Study. William A. Stevens & Ernest D. Burton. 283p. 1930. text ed. write for info. (ISBN 0-02-417240-5, Pub. by Scribner). Macmillan.
Harmony of the Gospels: New American Standard Version. Robert L. Thomas & Stanley N. Gundry. 14.95x (ISBN 0-317-52392-9, HarpR). Har-Row.
Harmony of the Life of St. Paul. Frank J. Goodwin. 1951. pap. 8.95 (ISBN 0-8010-3797-2). Baker Bk.
Harmony of the Words & Works of Jesus Christ. Dwight Pentecost. 272p. 1981. 12.95 (ISBN 0-310-30950-6, 17016); pap. 8.95 (ISBN 0-310-30951-4, 17016P). Zondervan.
Harmony on Justification, Defense of the Nicene Creed, Judgement of the Catholic Church, 5 vols. George Bull. LC 71-39556. (Library of Anglo-Catholic Theology: No. 4). Repr. of 1855 ed. Set. 150.00 (ISBN 0-404-52070-7). AMS Pr.
Harmony Within: The Spiritual Vision of George MacDonald. Rolland Hein. LC 82-1488. pap. 45.80 (ISBN 0-317-30142-X, 2025325). Bks Demand UMI.
Harnessing Pegasus: Inspiration & Meditation. Elizabeth G. Vining. 1983. pap. 2.50x (ISBN 0-87574-221-1, 221). Pendle Hill.
Harold Joe Waldrum: Las Sombras de los Edificios Religiosos de Nuevo Mexico Norte. Harold J. Waldrum. Ed. by Gayle Maxon & Quincie Hopkins. (Illus., Orig.). 1985. pap. 12.50 (ISBN 0-318-18712-4). Peters Corp NM.
Harold Joe Waldrum: The Churches of Northern New Mexico. Harold J. Waldrum. Ed. by Gayle Maxon & Quincie Hopkins. (Illus.). 34p. (Orig.). 1985. pap. 12.50 (ISBN 0-935037-01-2). Peters Corp NM.
Harp of the Spirit: Eighteen Poems of Saint Ephrem. Saint Ephrem. Tr. by Sebastian Brock. LC 84-285. 89p. 1984. Repr. of 1983 ed. lib. bdg. 19.95x (ISBN 0-89370-776-7). Borgo Pr.
Harper's Bible Commentary. William Neil. LC 63-7607. 544p. 1975. pap. 7.95 (ISBN 0-06-066090-2, RD 92, HarpR). Har-Row.
Harper's Bible Dictionary. rev. ed. Madeleine S. Miller & J. Lane. 1973. 18.95i (ISBN 0-06-065673-5, HarpR). Har-Row.
Harper's Bible Dictionary. Rev. ed. Madeleine S. Miller & J. Lane. 1974. 22.07 (ISBN 0-06-065674-3, HarpR); indexed 21.95i. Har-Row.
Harper's Bible Dictionary. Ed. by Society of Biblical Literature & Paul J. Achtemeier. LC 85-42767. (Illus.). 1194p. 1985. thumb indexed 29.95 (ISBN 0-06-069863-2, HarpR); 27.50 (ISBN 0-06-069862-4). Har-Row.
Harper's Concise Book of Christian Faith. Tony Lane. LC 84-47728. (Illus.). 224p. (Orig.). 1984. pap. 9.95 (ISBN 0-06-064921-6, RD 523, HarpR). Har-Row.
Harper's Dictionary of Hinduism: Its Mythology, Folklore, Philosophy, Literature & History. Margaret Stutley & James Stutley. LC 76-9999. 400p. 1984. pap. 16.95 (ISBN 0-06-067767-8, RD 479, HarpR). Har-Row.
Harper's Encyclopedia of Bible Life. Madeleine S. Miller & J. Lane Miller. Ed. by Boyce M. Bennet, Jr. & David H. Scott. LC 78-4752. (Illus.). 416p. 1983. pap. 10.95 (ISBN 0-06-065677-8, RD-436, HarpR). Har-Row.
Harper's Introduction to the Bible. Gerald Hughes & Stephen Travis. LC 80-8607. (Illus.). 144p. (Orig.). 1981. pap. 11.95 (ISBN 0-06-064078-2, RD 350, HarpR). Har-Row.
Harper's Topical Concordance. Ed. by Charles R. Joy. LC 62-11129. 640p. 1976. pap. 10.95 (ISBN 0-06-064229-7, RD 132, HarpR). Har-Row.
Harper's World of the New Testament. Edwin Yamauchi. LC 80-8606. (Illus.). 144p. (Orig.). 1981. pap. 9.95i (ISBN 0-06-069708-3, RD349, HarpR). Har-Row.
Harpsfield's Life of More. Ed. by Elsie V. Hitchcock & R. W. Chambers. (EETS OS Ser.: Vol. 186). Repr. of 1931 ed. 40.00 (ISBN 0-8115-3377-8). Kraus Repr.
Harriet Martineau und Ihre Sittlich Religiose Weltschau. Gertrud Von Petzold. 1941. pap. 7.00 (ISBN 0-384-46100-X). Johnson Repr.
Harrowing of Hell: A Comparative Study of an Early Christian Doctrine. John A. Macculluch. LC 79-8113. 1983. Repr. of 1930 ed. 33.50 (ISBN 0-404-18426-X). AMS Pr.
Harry Emerson Fosdick: Preacher, Pastor, Prophet. Robert M. Miller. LC 84-7168. (Illus.). 608p. 1985. 34.50x (ISBN 0-19-503512-7). Oxford U Pr.
Harry, My Friend. Stephan Grosso. LC 85-82391. 80p. 1986. pap. 2.95 (ISBN 0-89243-247-0). Liguori Pubns.
Harshacarita: Text of Uchchhvasas I-VIII. Banabhatta. Ed. by P. V. Kane. 645p. 1986. Repr. 22.00 (ISBN 81-208-0032-X, Pub. by Motilal Banarsidass). South Asia Bks.
Hartford Jews: Sixteen Fifty-Nine to Nineteen Seventy. Morris Silverman. (Illus.). 449p. 1970. 10.00 (ISBN 0-940748-21-5). Conn Hist Soc.
Harvest: A Faithful Approach to Life Issues for Junior High People. Kate S. Ristow & Maureen N. Comeaux. (Illus.). 167p. 1984. pap. 24.50 (ISBN 0-940634-20-1). Puissance Pubns.
Harvest in the Desert. Maurice Samuel. LC 82-985. 316p. 1982. Repr. lib. bdg. 27.50x (ISBN 0-313-23354-3, SAHA). Greenwood.
Harvest of Hate. Leon Poliakov. LC 78-71294. 350p. 1979. pap. 12.95 (ISBN 0-89604-006-2). Holocaust Pubns.
Harvest of Hate: The Nazi Program for the Destruction of the Jews in Europe. Leon Poliakov. LC 74-110836. 1971. Repr. of 1954 ed. lib. bdg. 22.50x (ISBN 0-8371-2635-5, POHH). Greenwood.
Harvest of Hate: The Nazi Program for the Destruction of the Jews of Europe. rev ed. Leon Poliakov. LC 78-71294. 1979. pap. 5.95 (ISBN 0-8052-5006-9, Pub. by Holocaust Library). Schocken.
Harvest of Medieval Theology: Gabriel Biel & Late Medieval Nominalism. Heiko A. Oberman. xvi, 495p. 1983. pap. 17.50 (ISBN 0-939464-05-5). Labyrinth Pr.
Harvest of the Spirit. Thomas A. Langford. LC 81-50602. 64p. 1981. pap. 3.50x (ISBN 0-8358-0428-3). Upper Room.
Harvest the Day. Margot Bickel & Hermann Steigert. Ed. by Gerhard E. Frost. (Illus.). 64p. (Orig.). pap. 7.95 (ISBN 0-86683-730-2, HarpR). Har-Row.
Harvestime Guest Pulpit Library, Vol. 1. Ed. by Mary H. Wallace. 432p. (Orig.). 1982. pap. 6.95 (ISBN 0-912315-14-8). Word Aflame.
Harvestime Pulpit Library: Let Them Know, Vol. 2. Ed. by Mary H. Wallace. (Illus.). 379p. (Orig.). 1984. pap. 8.95 (ISBN 0-912315-67-9). Word Aflame.

Harvestime Pulpit Series, Vol. III. Nathaniel A. Urshan & Cleveland M. Becton. Ed. by Mary H. Wallace. (Illus.). 406p. (Orig.). 1985. pap. 14.95 (ISBN 0-912315-83-0). Word Aflame.

Has Anybody Really Seen Noah's Ark? Violet Cummings. 416p. 1982. pap. 8.95 (ISBN 0-89051-086-5). Master Bks.

Has God Given You up? Philip B. Knoche. (Uplook Ser). 1970. pap. 0.99 (ISBN 0-8163-0257-X, 08165-3). Pacific Pr Pub Assn.

Has God Rejected His People? Clark M. Williamson. LC 81-12847. 192p. (Orig.). 1982. pap. 8.75 (ISBN 0-687-16649-7). Abingdon.

Has Rome Converted. Henri Fesquet. Tr. by Harold J. Salemson. 1968. 9.50 (ISBN 0-685-11959-9). Heineman.

Has Science Discovered God: A Symposium of Modern Scientific Opinion. facs. ed. Ed. by Edward H. Cotton. LC 68-8452. (Essay Index Reprint Ser). 1931. 21.50 (ISBN 0-8369-0340-4). Ayer Co Pubs.

Has the Church a Future? Douglas J. Hall. LC 79-29647. 192p. 1980. pap. 8.95 (ISBN 0-664-24308-8). Westminster.

Has the Immigrant Kept the Faith. Gerald Shaughnessy. LC 76-83438. (Religion in America Ser). 1969. Repr. of 1925 ed. 20.00 (ISBN 0-405-00262-9). Ayer Co Pubs.

Has the Lord Indeed Spoken Only Through Moses? A Study of the Biblical Portrait of Miriam. Rita J. Burns. (Society of Biblical Literature Dissertation Ser.). 148p. 1987. 16.95 (ISBN 0-89130-964-0, 06-01-84); pap. 12.95 (ISBN 0-89130-965-9). Scholars Pr GA.

Hashmotot Zohar: Hebrew Text. Shimon Bar Yohai. 1969. 20.00 (ISBN 0-943688-20-5). Res Ctr Kabbalah.

Hasiddur Hashalem: Daily Prayer Book. Philim Birnbaum. 790p. 1977. pap. 9.95 pocket flexible ed. (ISBN 0-88482-054-8). Hebrew Pub.

Hasiddur Hashalem (Daily Prayer Book) Philip Birnbaum. 790p. 1964. 17.00 (ISBN 0-88482-045-9). Hebrew Pub.

Hasiddur Hashalem Daily Prayer Book: Sephardic. Philip Birnbaoum. 860p. 1969. 17.00 (ISBN 0-88482-053-X). Hebrew Pub.

Hasiddur: The Prayer Book. Ben Bokser. 842p. 1957. pap. 9.00 pocket flexible ed. (ISBN 0-88482-069-6). Hebrew Pub.

Hasidic Anthology. Louis I. Newman. 740p. 1987. 40.00 (ISBN 0-87668-968-3). Aronson.

Hasidic Anthology: Tales & Teachings of the Hasidim. Ed. & tr. by Louis I. Newman. LC 63-11041. 576p. 1987. pap. 12.95 (ISBN 0-8052-0836-4). Schocken.

Hasidic Legends: A Suite by H. N. Werkman. Jan Martinet. (Eng. & Dutch., Illus.). 80p. (Orig.). 1985. 175.00x (ISBN 90-6243-048-1, Pub. by Boumas Boekhuis Netherlands). Benjamins North Am.

Hasidic Prayer. Louis Jacobs. LC 72-86765. (Littman Library of Jewish Civilization). 1978. pap. 4.95 (ISBN 0-8052-0604-3). Schocken.

Hasidic Prayer. Louis Jacobs. (Littman Library of Jewish Civilization). 1972. 17.95x (ISBN 0-19-710024-4). Oxford U Pr.

Hasidic Tales of the Holocaust. Yaffa Eliach. 1982. 17.95 (ISBN 0-19-503199-7). Oxford U Pr.

Hasidic Tales of the Holocaust. Yaffa Eliach. 336p. 1983. pap. 4.95 (ISBN 0-380-64725-7, Discus). Avon.

Hasidism. Ed. by Aryeh Rubinstein. 128p. pap. 4.50 (ISBN 0-686-95129-8). ADL.

Hasidism & Modern Man. Martin Buber. LC 58-10225. 256p. 1972. pap. 5.95 (ISBN 0-8180-1326-5). Horizon.

Hasidism & the Jewish Enlightenment: Their Confrontation in Galicia & Poland in the First Half of the Nineteenth Century. Raphael Mahler. Tr. by Eugene Orenstein et al from Yiddish & Hebrew. 432p. 1985. 29.95 (ISBN 0-8276-0233-2). Jewish Pubns.

Hasidism & the State of Israel. Harry Rabinowicz. (Littman Library of Jewish Civilization). (Illus.). 1982. 24.95x (ISBN 0-19-710049-X). Oxford U Pr.

Hasidism: Continuity or Innovation? Ed. by Bezalel Safran. (Harvard Judaic Texts & Studies: No. V). 60p. 1985. text ed. 5.00x (ISBN 0-674-38120-3). Harvard U Ctr Jewish.

Haskalah: Geschichte der Aufklarungsbewegung unter den Juden in Russland. Josef Meisl. Ed. by Stephen Katz. LC 79-7147. (Jewish Philosophy, Mysticism & History of Ideas Ser.). 1980. Repr. of 1919 ed. lib. bdg. 21.00x (ISBN 0-405-12277-2). Ayer Co Pubs.

Haskalah Movement in Russia. Jacob S. Raisin. 1976. Repr. of 1913 ed. 40.00 (ISBN 0-8274-2471-X). R West.

Hasta el Armagedon. Billy Graham. Tr. by Edwin Sipowicz from Eng. Orig. Title: Till Armageddon. 272p. 1983. pap. 5.95 (ISBN 0-311-09097-4). Casa Bautista.

Hatha Yoga. rev. ed. LC 81-51182. (Illus.). 128p. 1983. pap. 6.95 (ISBN 0-914602-72-1). SYDA Found.

Hatha Yoga. Yogi Ramacharaka. 8.00 (ISBN 0-911662-06-5). Yoga.

Hatha Yoga for Kids: A Guidebook for Parents & Children. Suresh T. Bhamre. (Illus.). 1985. 8.00 (ISBN 0-682-40164-1). Exposition Pr FL.

Hatha Yoga Manual I. 2nd ed. Samskrti & Veda. (Illus.). 187p. plastic comb. 9.95 (ISBN 0-89389-053-7). Himalayan Pubs.

Hatha Yoga Manual II. Samskriti & Judith Franks. 176p. plastic comb bdg. 9.95 (ISBN 0-89389-043-X). Himalayan Pubs.

Hattie Gardner: Determined Adventurer. Judy Lathem. LC 81-70909. (Meet the Missionary Ser.). 1982. 5.50 (ISBN 0-8054-4280-4, 4242-80). Broadman.

Hatznea Lechet: Walk Humbly. Abraham Shumsky & Adaia Shumsky. Ed. by Jack D. Spiro. (Mah Tov Hebrew Teaching Ser.: Bk. 3). (Illus.). 1971. text ed. 5.00 (ISBN 0-8074-0181-1, 405307); tchrs'. guide 3.50 (ISBN 0-8074-0182-X, 205308); wkbk. 5.00 (ISBN 0-8074-0183-8, 405306). UAHC.

Hau Bong: Un Culte Vietnamien De Possession Transplante En France. Pierre J. Simon & Ida Simon-Barouh. (Cahiers De L'homme, Nouvelle Serie: No. 13). (Illus.). 1973. pap. 9.20x (ISBN 90-2797-185-4). Mouton.

Havasupai Religion & Mythology. Carma L. Smithson & Robert C. Euler. (Utah Anthropological Papers: No. 68). Repr. of 1964 ed. 14.00 (ISBN 0-404-60668-7). AMS Pr.

Havasupai Religion & Mythology. Carma L. Smithson & Robert C. Euler. viii, 112p. Repr. of 1964 ed. 19.00 (ISBN 0-384-56210-8). Johnson Repr.

Have a Great Day Every Day. Arthur G. McPhee. LC 84-565. 160p. 1984. pap. 6.50 (ISBN 0-8361-3352-8). Herald Pr.

Have a Very Merry Christmas! Skits for Elementary Schools & Families. Mabel J. Gabbott. LC 80-83034. 56p. (Orig.). 1981. pap. 4.95 (ISBN 0-88290-163-X, 2044). Horizon Utah.

Have Atheists Proved There Is No God? Thomas B. Warren. 1974. 8.00 (ISBN 0-934916-33-0). Natl Christian Pr.

Have Cart, Will Travel. Katie F Wiebe. (Trailblazer Ser.). 86p. (Orig.). 1974. pap. 1.00 (ISBN 0-919797-27-X). Kindred Pr.

Have I Committed the Unpardonable Sin? And Other Questions You Were Afraid to Ask about the Christian Faith. C. Donald Cole. LC 84-71421. 128p. 1984. pap. 5.95 (ISBN 0-89107-317-5, Crossway Bks). Good News.

Have It His Way. Opal Reddin. LC 78-73143. 128p. 1980. pap. 1.95 (ISBN 0-88243-717-8, 02-0717); tchr's ed 2.95 (ISBN 0-88243-332-6, 02-0332). Gospel Pub.

Have Miracles, Will Travel. Burt Hotchkiss. 96p. 1982. pap. 4.95 (ISBN 0-8187-0047-5). Harlo Pr.

Have the Mind of Christ. Marilyn P. Kliewer. LC 85-81041. (Faith & Life Bible Studies). 90p. 1985. pap. 4.95 (ISBN 0-87303-104-0). Faith & Life.

Have the Promises Failed: A Literary Analysis of 2 Baruch. Gwendolyn B. Sayler. LC 83-16336. (SBL Dissertation Ser.). 180p. 15.75 (ISBN 0-89130-651-X, 060172); pap. 10.50 (ISBN 0-89130-781-8). Scholars Pr GA.

Have the Time of Your Life! Maryhelen Vannier. 1986. pap. 6.50 (ISBN 0-687-16657-8). Abingdon.

Have We Lived Before? Linda Atkinson. (High Interest, Low Vocabulary Ser.). (Illus.). 112p. 1982. PLB 8.95 (ISBN 0-396-07999-7). Dodd.

Have We No Rights? Mabel Williamson. 1957. pap. 5.95 (ISBN 0-8024-3417-7). Moody.

Have You Considered Him? W. Smith. pap. 0.75 (ISBN 0-87784-108-X). Inter-Varsity.

Have You Ever Asked Yourself These Questions. Michael Hecht. LC 75-163738. 267p. 1971. 7.95 (ISBN 0-88400-034-6). Shengold.

Have You Felt Like Giving Up Lately? Wilkerson. 2.50 (ISBN 0-318-18174-6). WCTU.

Have You Felt Like Giving up Lately? David Wilkerson. 160p. 1980. pap. 6.95 (ISBN 0-8007-5042-X, Power Bks). Revell.

Have You Heard from Heaven Lately: Sermons for All Occasions. Generalee Robinson. 1984. 8.95 (ISBN 0-533-05804-X). Vantage.

Have You Lived Before This Life? L. Ron Hubbard. 20.00 (ISBN 0-686-13921-6). Church Scient NY.

Have You Lived Before This Life? A Study of Death & Evidence of Past Lives. L. Ron Hubbard. 1978. 42.87 (ISBN 0-88404-055-0). Bridge Pubns Inc.

Have You Met My Divine Uncle George? Patricia Wilson. 96p. (Orig.). pap. 5.95 (ISBN 0-8358-0529-8, Dist. by Abingdon Pr). Upper Room.

Have You Witnessed to a Mormon Lately? James R. Spencer. 1987. pap. 6.95 (Chosen Bks). Revell.

Haven & Home: A History of the Jews in America. Abraham J. Karp. LC 84-5530. 416p. 1985. 24.95 (ISBN 0-8052-3920-0). Schocken.

Haven & Home: A History of the Jews in America. Abraham. J. Karp. 416p. 1986. pap. 9.95 (ISBN 0-8052-0817-8). Schocken.

Haven in a Heartless World: The Family Besieged. Christopher Lasch. LC 77-75246. 1979. pap. 7.95x (ISBN 0-465-02884-5, TB-5047). Basic.

Haven of the Masses: A Study of the Pentecostal Movement in Chile. Christian L. D'Epinay. Tr. by Marjorie Sandle. (World Studies of Churches in Mission). 1969. pap. 4.95 (ISBN 0-377-82931-5, Pub. by Lutterworth England). Friend Pr.

Having Faith in Your Faith. Kenneth E. Hagin. 1981. pap. 0.50 mini bk. (ISBN 0-89276-252-7). Hagin Ministries.

Hawaiian Legends of Ghosts & Ghost-Gods. Ed. by William D. Westervelt. LC 63-22543. (Illus.). 1963. 7.25 (ISBN 0-8048-0238-6). C E Tuttle.

Hawaiian Mythology. Martha W. Beckwith. LC 70-97998. 1977. pap. 10.95 (ISBN 0-8248-0514-3). UH Pr.

Haworth Parsonage: Study of Wesley & the Brontes. G. E. Harrison. 1937. lib. bdg. 16.50 (ISBN 0-8414-5008-0). Folcroft.

Hawthorne, Melville, Stephen Crane: A Critical Bibliography. Theodore L. Gross & S. Wertheim. LC 75-142364. 1971. 14.95 (ISBN 0-02-913220-7). Free Pr.

Hayesod: Fundamentals of Hebrew. Uveeler & Bronznick. LC 72-86858. 16.95x (ISBN 0-87306-071-7). Feldheim.

Haysop: A Church, A Community, A People of Bibb County, Alabama. Charles E. Boyd. (Illus.). 1979. pap. 8.50. Banner Pr AL.

Hazor: The Head of All Those Kingdoms, Joshua 11: 10 with a Chapter on Israelite Megiddo. Yigael Yadin. 210p. 1979. 40.00x (ISBN 0-19-725925-1). State Mutual Bk.

Hazrat Inayat Khan: Master of Life-Modern Sufi Mystic. Wil van Beek. 1983. 12.95 (ISBN 0-533-05453-2). Vantage.

Hazy Moon of Enlightenment: On Zen Practice III. Hakuyu T. Maezumi & Bernard T. Glassman. LC 77-81974. (Zen Writings Ser.: Vol. Four). (Illus.). 1978. pap. 5.95 (ISBN 0-916820-05-X). Center Pubns.

He Arose. Jim L. Smith. 1973. pap. 1.75 (ISBN 0-88428-026-8, 317). Parchment Pr.

He Brought Me Out of a Horrible Pit. Lorraine Portilla. Ed. by Leatrice DeLellis. (Orig.). Date not set. pap. 5.00 (ISBN 0-9616892-0-X). Your New Beginning.

He Calls Me by My Name: A Pre-Membership Course for Adults. Robert Hoyer. LC 77-74385. 1977. pap. text ed. 4.75 (ISBN 0-915644-09-6). Clayton Pub Hse.

He Came Down from Heaven. Charles Williams. 160p. 1984. pap. 3.95 (ISBN 0-8028-0033-5). Eerdmans.

He Came Preaching Peace. John H. Yoder. LC 85-5474. 152p. (Orig.). 1985. pap. 8.95 (ISBN 0-8361-3395-1). Herald Pr.

He Came to Set the Captives Free. Rebecca Brown. 288p. (Orig.). 1986. pap. 7.50 (ISBN 0-937958-25-5). Chick Pubns.

He Carried Our Sorrows. (Illus.). 48p. 1983. 7.95 (ISBN 0-86683-746-9, AY8399, HarpR). Har-Row.

He Chose to Listen. Eileen E. Lantry. (Trailblazer Ser.). 85p. 1983. pap. 4.95 (ISBN 0-8163-0485-8). Pacific Pr Pub Assn.

He Freed Britains Slaves. Charles Ludwig. LC 77-9521. 208p. 1977. 7.95 (ISBN 0-8361-1822-7). Herald Pr.

He Gave Some Prophets: The Old Testament Prophets & Their Message. Sanford C. Yoder. LC 64-18733. 256p. 1964. 7.95 (ISBN 0-8361-1496-5). Herald Pr.

He His Messenger & His Message. x ed. Ayatullah B. Al-Sadr. Tr. by M. A. Ansari from Arabic. 116p. pap. 6.00 (ISBN 0-941724-12-3). Islamic Seminary.

He Is Lord. George Holmes. LC 76-20891. (Radiant Life Ser.). 128p. 1977. pap. 2.50 (ISBN 0-88243-902-2, 02-0902); teacher's ed 3.95 (ISBN 0-88243-172-2, 32-0172). Gospel Pub.

He Is Risen Indeed! Gurden Henley. 1986. 3.50 (ISBN 0-89536-795-5, 6813). CSS of Ohio.

He Is There & He Is Not Silent. Francis Schaeffer. 1972. pap. 4.95 (ISBN 0-8423-1413-X). Tyndale.

He Is Worthy. Thomas F. Zimmerman et al. LC 77-92881. 64p. 1978. pap. 0.50 (ISBN 0-88243-523-X, 02-0523, Radiant Books). Gospel Pub.

He Lifted Me. Mrs. Dennis Kellogg. 1966. pap. 3.95 (ISBN 0-88027-046-2). Firm Foun Pub.

He Lived on Our Street. Leslie R. Marston. 1979. pap. 4.95 (ISBN 0-89367-042-1). Light & Life.

He Lives Forever. Satsvarupa Dasa Goswami. Ed. by Mandalesvara Dasa. 80p. 1980. 2.00 (ISBN 0-318-03099-3). Gita Nagari.

He Loved & Served: The Story of Curtis Kelsey. Nathan Rutstein. (Illus.). 208p. 12.95 (ISBN 0-85398-120-5); pap. 7.95 (ISBN 0-85398-121-3). G Ronald Pub.

He Loves Forever. Thomas H. Olbricht. LC 80-52461. (Journey Bks). (Orig.). 1980. pap. 3.50 (ISBN 0-8344-0117-7). Sweet.

He Made Us a Kingdom: The Principles to be Applied in Establishing Christ's Kingdon Now. Richard H. Akeroyd. 1985. 5.00 (ISBN 0-916620-79-4). Portals Pr.

He Obeyed God: A Child's Life of A. B. Simpson. Pat Dys. 55p. 1986. pap. 3.95 (ISBN 0-87509-382-5). Chr Pubns.

He Pasa Ekklesia: An Original History of the Religious Denominations at Present Existing in the United States Containing Authentic Accounts of Their Rise, Progress, Statistics. Israel D. Rupp. 30.00 (ISBN 0-8369-7149-3, 7981). Ayer Co Pubs.

He Reigns from the Cross. F. Jose Gonzales. Tr. by Lemon. 1962. 3.00 (ISBN 0-8198-0054-6). Dghtrs St Paul.

He Remembered to Say "Thank You". Victor Mann. (Arch Bks: No. 13). (Illus.). 32p. 1976. pap. 0.99 (ISBN 0-570-06103-2, 59-1221). Concordia.

He Restoreth. David A. Maclennan. (Contempo Ser.). pap. 0.95 (ISBN 0-8010-6093-1). Baker Bk.

He Restoreth My Soul. Mary S. Eyer. LC 82-1363. 98p. 1982. 6.95 (ISBN 0-87747-908-9). Deseret Bk.

He Shall Be Like a Tree. Don Pate. (Horizon Ser.). 128p. 1981. pap. 5.95 (ISBN 0-8127-0315-4). Review & Herald.

He Shall Glorify Me. Oswald Chambers. 1965. 3.95 (ISBN 0-87508-111-8). Chr Lit.

He Speaks Softly. Bob Benson. 160p. 1985. 8.95 (ISBN 0-8499-0449-8, 0449-8). Word Bks.

He Speaks to You. 2.25 (ISBN 0-8198-3300-2). Dghtrs St Paul.

He Speaks to You. Camillo Zamboni. 1966. pap. 1.25 (ISBN 0-8198-0055-4). Dghtrs St Paul.

He Spoke & I Was Strengthened. Dick Mills. 1973. pap. 2.95 (ISBN 0-88368-026-2). Whitaker Hse.

He That Hath an Ear. Albert L. Burke. 101p. (Orig.). 1982. pap. 3.50 (ISBN 0-9608662-0-5). Eleventh Hour.

He That Is Spiritual. Lewis S. Chafer. 1918. 5.95 (ISBN 0-310-22341-5, 6307P, Pub. by Dunham). Zondervan.

He That Wins Souls Is Wise. David Beatty. 1982. pap. 0.75 (ISBN 0-88144-005-1, CPS-005). Christian Pub.

He Touched Me. Darlene Loomis. (Illus.). 62p. (Orig.). 1977. pap. 3.00 (ISBN 0-686-36275-6). Drain Enterprise.

He Touched Me: Conversion Stories of Norman Vincent Peale, Bruce Larson, Ernest Gordon, Bill Wilson, & Others. Irving Harris. 144p. (Orig.). pap. 8.95 (ISBN 0-687-16680-2). Abingdon.

He Touched Me: My Pilgrimage of Prayer. John Powell. 1974. pap. 2.75 (ISBN 0-913592-47-1). Argus Comm.

He Was One of Us: The Life of Jesus of Nazareth. Rien Poortvliet. LC 85-29270. 128p. 1986. 14.95 (ISBN 0-385-13576-9). Doubleday.

He Wears Orchids & Other Latin American Stories. Elizabeth M. Lee. LC 76-117327. (Biography Index Reprint Ser). 1951. 19.00 (ISBN 0-8369-8019-0). Ayer Co Pubs.

He Who Hunted Birds in His Father's Village: The Dimensions of a Haida Myth. Gary Snyder. LC 78-16935. 154p. 1979. pap. 5.95 (ISBN 0-912516-38-0). Grey Fox.

He Who Laughs...Lasts...& Lasts...& Lasts. Roy H. Hicks. (Orig.). 1976. pap. 2.95 (ISBN 0-89274-003-5). Harrison Hse.

He Who Lets Us Be. Geddes MacGregor. 194p. 1987. pap. 8.95 (ISBN 0-913729-61-2). Paragon Hse.

He Who Thinks Has to Believe. A. E. Wilder-Smith. LC 81-65988. 1981. pap. 2.95 (ISBN 0-89051-073-3). Master Bks.

He Who Thinks Has to Believe. A. E. Wilder-Smith. 91p. 1982. pap. 2.95 (ISBN 0-87123-259-6, 200259). Bethany Hse.

He Will Come. 3rd ed. Mrs. Z. W. Swafford. (Illus.). 128p. 1974. pap. 2.00 (ISBN 0-89114-009-3). Baptist Pub Hse.

Head & Face Masks in Navaho Ceremonialism. Berard Haile. LC 76-43722. Repr. of 1947 ed. 17.50 (ISBN 0-404-15565-0). AMS Pr.

Headed in the Direction of Heaven. Ed. by Lindsey D. Warren. 1980. pap. 2.00 (ISBN 0-934916-28-4). Natl Christian Pr.

Headmaster. J. A. Haig. LC 80-52617. 270p. 1982. 5.95 (ISBN 0-941478-06-8). Paraclete Pr.

Heads of Heaven, Feet of Clay: Ideas & Stories for Adult Faith Education. Charles McCollough. 192p. (Orig.). 1983. pap. 11.95 (ISBN 0-8298-0693-8). Pilgrim NY.

Heal Me or Kill Me! Cornelius Range. LC 85-71350. 1985. pap. 5.95 (ISBN 0-88270-592-X). Bridge Pub.

Heal My Heart O Lord. Joan Hutson. LC 75-30493. 112p. 1976. pap. 2.95 (ISBN 0-87793-106-2). Ave Maria.

Heal the Sick. Reginald East. LC 77-80678. 160p. (Orig.). 1977. pap. 2.95 (ISBN 0-87123-232-4, 200232). Bethany Hse.

Heal Thyself. White Eagle. 1962. 3.95 (ISBN 0-85487-015-6). De Vorss.

Heal Your Body. rev. ed. Louise L. Hay. 48p. 1984. pap. 3.00 (ISBN 0-937611-00-X). Hay House.

Healer, Ash-Shafuja, an Ismaili Treatise. Shihab Firas. Ed. by Sami N. Makarem. 1966. pap. 15.95x (ISBN 0-8156-6026-X, Am U Beirut). Syracuse U Pr.

Healers. Robert F. Baldwin. LC 85-62815. 175p. (Orig.). 1986. pap. 4.95 (ISBN 0-87973-836-7, 836). Our Sunday Visitor.

Healers & the Healing Process. Ed. by George W. Meek. LC 77-5251. (Illus., Orig.). 1977. pap. 6.75 (ISBN 0-8356-0498-5, Quest). Theos Pub Hse.

Healer's Art. Eric J. Cassell. 240p. 1985. pap. 7.95 (ISBN 0-262-53062-7). MIT Pr.

Healers, Gurus, Spiritual Guide. William Wolf. LC 76-2180. 1969. pap. 6.50 (ISBN 0-933900-07-4). Foun Human Under.

Healers in the Night. Eric De Rosny. Tr. by Robert R. Barr from Fr. LC 85-5659. Tr. of Yeaux de Ma Chevre sur les Pas des Maitres de la Nuit en Pays Douala. 304p. (Orig.). 1985. pap. 13.95 (ISBN 0-88344-199-3). Orbis Bks.

Healing. Francis MacNutt. LC 74-81446. (Illus.). 336p. 1974. pap. 4.95 (ISBN 0-87793-074-0). Ave Maria.

Healing. Francis MacNutt. 320p. 1986. pap. 4.50 (ISBN 0-553-25993-8). Bantam.

Healing. Gloria C. Stargel. (Orig.). 1982. pap. 2.50 (ISBN 0-8423-1425-3). Tyndale.

Healing. Ronald D. Tucker. 57p. (Orig.). 1985. pap. 2.50 (ISBN 0-933643-27-6). Grace World Outreach.

Healing: A Forever-Settled Subject. Kenneth Hagin, Jr. 1981. pap. 0.50 mini bk. (ISBN 0-89276-707-3). Hagin Ministries.

Healing: A Spiritual Adventure. Mary E. Peterman. LC 74-80416. 104p. 1974. pap. 3.95 (ISBN 0-8006-1086-5, 1-1086). Fortress.

Healing: A Thought Away, Vol. 2. Disciples of Donato the Christ. 438p. 1981. pap. 10.00 (ISBN 0-935146-61-X). Morningland.

Healing & Belief. Norman Cousins. LC 82-81098. 64p. 1982. 65.00 (ISBN 0-88014-041-0). Mosaic Pr OH.

Healing & Christianity. Morton Kelsey. LC 72-78065. 1976. pap. 10.95 (ISBN 0-06-064381-1, RD 161, HarpR). Har-Row.

Healing & History: Essays for George Rosen. Ed. by Charles E. Rosenberg. 1979. lib. bdg. 27.00 (ISBN 0-88202-180-X). Watson Pub Intl.

Healing & Hope. Pope John Paul II. 266p. 1982. 5.00 (ISBN 0-8198-3317-7, EP0545); pap. 3.50 (ISBN 0-8198-3318-5). Dghtrs St Paul.

Healing & Regeneration Through Color & Music. Corinne Heline. 96p. 1983. pap. 3.95 (ISBN 0-87516-512-5). DE Vorss.

Healing & the Mind World. Inayat Khan. (Sufi Message of Hazrat Inayat Khan Ser.: Vol. 4). 288p. 1979. 14.95 (ISBN 90-6077-952-5, Pub. by Servire BV Netherlands). Hunter Hse.

Healing & Wholeness. Genevieve Parkhurst. 6.95 (ISBN 0-910924-90-2). Macalester.

Healing & Wholeness. Eugene Sterner. (Doctrinal Material of the Church of God Ser.: No. 2). 1978. pap. text ed. 3.95 (ISBN 0-87162-201-7, D4285). Warner Pr.

Healing: As It Is, 2 vols. Ed. by Morningland Publications, Inc. (Illus.). 320p. (Orig.). 1981. Set. pap. 10.00 (ISBN 0-935146-59-8). Morningland.

Healing: As It Is, Vol. 4. Disciples of the Master Donato the Christ. 418p. (Orig.). pap. 10.00 (ISBN 0-935146-65-2). Morningland.

Healing As Sacrament: The Santification of the World. Martin Israel. LC 84-72482. 116p. 1985. pap. 6.00 (ISBN 0-936384-23-9). Cowley Pubns.

Healing Belongs to Us. Kenneth E. Hagin. 1969. pap. 1.00 (ISBN 0-89276-016-8). Hagin Ministries.

Healing by the Spirit. Ivan Cooke. 1955. pap. 7.95 (ISBN 0-85487-039-3). De Vorss.

Healing Choice. Ron L. Davis. 160p. 1986. 9.95 (ISBN 0-8499-0466-8, 0466-8). Word Bks.

Healing Christ. rev. ed. S. D. Gordon. 160p. (Orig.). 1985. pap. 3.95 (ISBN 0-89283-271-1, Pub. by Vine Books). Servant.

Healing Coin. Marion P. Hall. 86p. 1984. pap. 5.50 (ISBN 0-87516-542-7). De Vorss.

Healing Devotions. Anne S. White. LC 75-5218. 138p. 1975. pap. 3.95 (ISBN 0-8192-1192-3). Morehouse.

Healing: Divine Art. Manly P. Hall. 10.00 (ISBN 0-89314-510-6); pap. 6.95 (ISBN 0-89314-390-1). Philos Res.

Healing: Drawing on God's Strength. Lura J. Geiger. (Orig.). 1987. pap. 34.50; cassette incl. LuraMedia.

Healing Echoes: Values for Christian Unity. Donald C. Lacy. Ed. by Michael L. Sherer. (Orig.). 1986. pap. 6.25 (ISBN 0-89536-826-9, 6835). CSS of Ohio.

Healing Education Based on Anthroposophy's Image of Man: Living, Learning, Working with Children & Adults in Need of Special Soul Care. Ed. by Bernhard Fischer. Tr. by C. A. Mier & G. F. Mier. (Illus.). 227p. 1974. pap. 11.00 (ISBN 3-772506-39-9). Anthroposophic.

Healing Energy of Love: A Personal Journal. John Allan. LC 85-40770. (Illus.). 175p. (Orig.). 1986. pap. 7.50 (ISBN 0-8356-0603-1, Quest). Theos Pub Hse.

Healing Faith: An Annotated Bibliography of Christian Self-Help Books. Compiled by Elise Chase. LC 85-929. (Bibliographies & Indexes in Religious Studies: No. 3). xxxiv, 192p. 1985. lib. bdg. 35.00 (ISBN 0-313-24014-0, DHF/). Greenwood.

Healing: Faith or Fraud. Wayne Judd. (Uplook Ser.). 1978. pap. 0.99 (ISBN 0-8163-0199-9, 08303-0). Pacific Pr Pub Assn.

Healing Family Hurts. Ed. by Jean M. Hiesberger. LC 79-90991. (Paths of Life Ser.). 128p. (Orig.). 1979. pap. 2.95 (ISBN 0-8091-2266-9). Paulist Pr.

Healing for Damaged Emotions. David A. Seamands. 1981. pap. 5.95 (ISBN 0-88207-228-5). Victor Bks.

Healing for Everyone. 2nd, rev. ed. Evarts G. Loomis & Sig Paulson. LC 74-345. (Illus., Orig.). 1979. pap. 5.95 (ISBN 0-87516-377-7). De Vorss.

Healing for the Homosexual. Ed. by Brick Bradford. 64p. 1983. 1.95 (ISBN 0-934421-06-4). Presby Renewal Pubns.

Healing from Heaven. Lilian B. Yeomans. 145p. 1954. pap. 2.95 (ISBN 0-88243-730-5, 02-0730). Gospel Pub.

Healing Gifts of the Spirit. Agnes Sanford. 1983. pap. 2.75 (ISBN 0-515-07621-X). Jove Pubns.

Healing Gifts of the Spirit. Agness Sanford. LC 83-48998. 240p. 1984. pap. 6.95 (ISBN 0-06-067052-5, RD 519, HarpR). Har-Row.

Healing Gods of Ancient Civilizations. Walter A. Jayne. LC 75-23728. Repr. of 1925 ed. 49.00 (ISBN 0-404-13286-3). AMS Pr.

Healing: God's Work Among Us. John Bertolucci. 1987. pap. 3.95. Servant.

Healing Heart. Norman Cousins. (General Ser.). 1984. lib. bdg. 14.95 (ISBN 0-8161-3669-6, Large Print Bks). G K Hall.

Healing in Hypnosis. Milton H. Erickson et al. Ed. by Ernest L. Rossi & Florence A. Sharp. 1984. 19.95 (ISBN 0-8290-0739-3). New Horizon NJ.

Healing in the Catholic Church: Mending Wounded Hearts & Bodies. Joseph Champlin. LC 84-62226. 160p. 1985. pap. 5.50 (ISBN 0-87973-719-0, 719). Our Sunday Visitor.

Healing in the Family. Ed. by Paul F. Wilczak. LC 79-53515. (Marriage & Family Living in Depth Bk.). 1979. pap. 2.45 (ISBN 0-87029-158-0, 20244-0). Abbey.

Healing Is for Real. Malcolm Miner. pap. 4.95 (ISBN 0-8192-1132-X). Morehouse.

Healing Life's Great Hurts. Sid Cato. 64p. 5.95 (ISBN 0-914091-51-4). Chicago Review.

Healing Life's Hurts: Healing Memories Through the Five Stages of Forgiveness. Dennis Linn & Matthew Linn. LC 77-14794. 324p. 1978. pap. 5.95 (ISBN 0-8091-2059-3). Paulist Pr.

Healing Light. Agnes Sanford. pap. 4.50 (ISBN 0-910924-37-6). pocketsize o.p. 2.50 (ISBN 0-910924-52-X). Macalester.

Healing Love. Ralph A. Di Orio. LC 86-1572. 216p. 1987. 14.95 (ISBN 0-385-23694-8). Doubleday.

Healing Love: The Inner Power of All Things. Ken L. Evensen. 9.95 (ISBN 0-533-04807-9). Vantage.

Healing Love Through the Tao: Cultivating Female Sexual Energy. Mantak Chia & Maneewan Chia. LC 86-81049. (Illus.). 320p. (Orig.). 1986. 22.50 (ISBN 0-935621-04-0); pap. 12.95 (ISBN 0-935621-05-9). Heal Tao Bks.

Healing Mind. W. Glyn Evans. 160p. 1987. pap. 6.95 (ISBN 0-310-29381-2). Zondervan.

Healing Ministries: Conversations on the Spiritual Dimensions of Health Care. Joseph H. Fichter. 224p. 1986. pap. 9.95 (ISBN 0-8091-2807-1). Paulist Pr.

Healing Ministry. Emily G. Neal. 176p. 1985. pap. 7.95 (ISBN 0-8245-0688-X). Crossroad NY.

Healing Ministry of the Local Church. Robert G. Bayley. 32p. 1983. 1.95 (ISBN 0-934421-03-X). Presby Renewal Pubns.

Healing Mysteries: A Rosary for the Sick. Joanne Turpin. 25p. (Orig.). 1983. pap. text ed. 1.35 (ISBN 0-86716-018-7). St Anthony Mess Pr.

Healing of Fears. Norm Wright. LC 81-83238. 176p. (Orig.). 1982. pap. 4.95 (ISBN 0-89081-302-7). Harvest Hse.

Healing of Memories. David A. Seamands. 156p. 1985. text ed. 11.95 (ISBN 0-89693-532-9); pap. 6.95 (ISBN 0-89693-169-2). Victor Bks.

Healing of Memories: Prayers & Confession-Steps to Inner Healing. Matthew L. Linn & D. Linn. LC 74-17697. 112p. (Orig.). 1974. pap. 3.95 (ISBN 0-8091-1854-8). Paulist Pr.

Healing of Purpose: God's Call to Discipleship. John E. Biersdorf. 192p. (Orig.). 1985. pap. 11.95 (ISBN 0-687-16741-8). Abingdon.

Healing of the Mind. 4th. ed. Pat Brooks. Orig. Title: Using Your Spiritual Authority. 1983. pap. text ed. 2.50 (ISBN 0-932050-00-X). New Puritan.

Healing of the Past. Robert L. Wise. 40p. 1984. 2.00 (ISBN 0-318-04134-0). Presby Renewal Pubns.

Healing Ourselves. Naboru Muramoto. Compiled by Michael Abehsera. (Illus.). 150p. 1974. pap. 9.95 (ISBN 0-380-00900-5, 60168-0). Avon.

Healing Power of Affirmation. Ralph A. Di Orio. LC 85-4400. 216p. 1986. pap. 6.95 (ISBN 0-385-23592-5, Im). Doubleday.

Healing Power of Color: How to Use Color to Improve Your Mental, Physical & Spiritual Well-Being. Betty Wood. 112p. 1985. pap. 9.95 (ISBN 0-89281-110-2). Inner Tradit.

Healing Power of Grief. Jack S. Miller. 125p. 1985. pap. 7.95 (ISBN 0-914373-02-1). Wieser & Wieser.

Healing Power of Inversion Thinking from Soul to Body. Warner Mann. LC 85-91344. (Metaphysics for Everyone Ser.: No. 1). (Illus.). 250p. (Orig.). 1986. 14.95 (ISBN 0-9615973-0-5); pap. 9.95 (ISBN 0-9615973-1-3). Cos Sci Orange.

Healing Power of Love. Joseph Murphy. pap. 1.00 (ISBN 0-87516-334-3). De Vorss.

Healing Power of the Bible. Agnes Sanford. 224p. 1984. pap. 2.50 (ISBN 0-515-07104-8). Jove Pubns.

Healing Power of the Bible. Agnes Sanford. 1983. pap. 2.50 (ISBN 0-8007-8475-8, Spire Bks). Revell.

Healing Power of the Bible. Agnes Sanford. LC 83-48999. 1984. pap. 6.95 (ISBN 0-06-067053-3, RD 520, HarpR). Har-Row.

Healing Power of the Sacraments. Jim McManus. LC 83-83397. 112p. (Orig.). 1984. pap. 3.95 (ISBN 0-87793-313-8). Ave Maria.

Healing Power: What It Is & What to Do with It. John Gunstone. 168p. (Orig.). 1987. pap. 4.95 (ISBN 0-89283-318-1, Pub. by Vine Books). Servant.

Healing Prayer. Barbara L. Shlemon. LC 75-36056. 88p. 1975. pap. 1.95 (ISBN 0-87793-108-9). Ave Maria.

Healing Relationships: A Christian's Manual of Lay Counseling. Stephen A. Crunlan & Daniel H. Lambrides. LC 83-70103. 325p. 1984. pap. 6.45 (ISBN 0-87509-329-9); Leader's Guide. 2.95 (ISBN 0-87509-354-X). Chr Pubns.

Healing Secrets of the Ages. rev. ed. Catherine Ponder. LC 67-26503. 278p. 1985. pap. 6.95 (ISBN 0-87516-550-8). De Vorss.

Healing States. Alberto Viloldo & Stanley Krippner. (Illus.). 224p. 1987. pap. 8.95 (ISBN 0-671-63202-7, Fireside) (ISBN 0-671-60240-3). S&S.

Healing Stones. 14th ed. Doris Hodges. pap. 3.95 (ISBN 0-686-12935-0). Hiawatha Bondurant.

Healing Techniques of the Holy East. Satguru S. Keshavadas. LC 80-50447. (Illus.). 116p. (Orig.). 1980. pap. 3.95 (ISBN 0-931290-30-9). Vishwa.

Healing the Dying. Sr. Mary J. Linn et al. LC 79-53111. 128p. 1979. pap. 3.95 (ISBN 0-8091-2212-X). Paulist Pr.

Healing the Fractured Self. John F. Walters. 122p. (Orig.). 1984. pap. 10.95 (ISBN 0-86683-883-X, HarpR). Har-Row.

Healing the Greatest Hurt: Healing Grief & the Family Tree. Dennis Linn et al. LC 85-60407. 258p. (Orig.). 1985. pap. 5.95 (ISBN 0-8091-2714-8). Paulist Pr.

Healing the Heart: The Power of Biblical Heart Imagery. Joseph A. Grassi. (Orig.). 1987. 7.95 (ISBN 0-8091-2862-4). Paulist Pr.

Healing the Hidden Self. Barbara L. Shlemon. LC 81-70022. (Illus.). 128p. 1982. pap. 3.50 (ISBN 0-87793-244-1). Ave Maria.

Healing the Hurt: For Teenagers Whose Parents Are Divorced. Mildred Tickfer. 1985. pap. 4.50 (ISBN 0-8010-8876-3). Baker Bk.

Healing the Pain of Everyday Loss. Ira J. Tanner. 188p. 1980. pap. 4.95 (ISBN 0-03-057849-3, HarpR). Har-Row.

Healing the Sick. T. L. Osborn. 420p. 1981. pap. 7.95 (ISBN 0-89274-187-2, HH-187). Harrison Hse.

Healing the Wounded. John White & Ken Blue. LC 85-2358. 240p. (Orig.). 1985. 11.95 (ISBN 0-87784-939-0); pap. 6.95 (ISBN 0-87784-533-6). Inter-Varsity.

Healing the Wounded Spirit. John Sandford & Paula Sandford. LC 85-71640. 510p. 1986. pap. 8.95 (ISBN 0-932081-14-2). Victory Hse.

Healing Through Meditation & Prayer. Meredith Puryear. 1978. pap. 5.95 (ISBN 0-87604-104-7). ARE Pr.

Healing Through Spiritual Understanding. Thomas Hora. (Discourses in Metapsychiatry Ser.). 48p. (Orig.). 1983. pap. 4.00 (ISBN 0-913105-02-3). PAGL Pr.

Healing Through the Power of Christ. Jim Wilson. 64p. 1969. pap. 2.50 (ISBN 0-227-67478-2). Attic Pr.

Healing Touch. John H. Peterson. LC 81-80629. 112p. (Orig.). 1981. pap. 5.95 (ISBN 0-8192-1291-1). Morehouse.

Healing Touch of Affirmation. Thomas A. Kane. LC 76-151154. 126p. 1976. pap. 4.95 (ISBN 0-89571-001-3). Affirmation.

Healing Touch of God. Agnes Sanford. (Epiphany Ser.). 224p. 1983. pap. 2.50 (ISBN 0-345-30661-9). Ballantine.

Healings of Jesus. Michael Harper. Ed. by Michael Green. LC 86-20971. (Jesus Library). 228p. 1986. pap. 6.95 (ISBN 0-87784-987-0). Inter-Varsity.

Health: A Holistic Approach. Dennis K. Chernin & Gregory Manteuffel. LC 84-40270. (Illus.). 285p. (Orig.). 1984. pap. 7.50 (ISBN 0-8356-0590-6, Quest). Theos Pub Hse.

Health & Hatha Yoga. Swami Sivananda & Swami Venkatesananda. (Life & Works of Swami Sivananda). (Illus.). 350p. (Orig.). 1985. pap. 9.95 (ISBN 0-949027-03-0). Integral Yoga Pubns.

Health & Healing. Lilian B. Yeomans. 64p. 1973. pap. 1.95 (ISBN 0-88243-732-1, 02-0732). Gospel Pub.

Health & Healing: God's Way. Bill Owens. (Illus.). 124p. (Orig.). Date not set. pap. 5.00 (ISBN 0-936801-01-8). Christ Serv Ctrs.

Health & Healing in Yoga. The Mother. 305p. 1982. 6.00 (ISBN 0-89071-284-0, Pub. by Sri Aurobindo Ashram India); pap. 6.00 (ISBN 0-89071-283-2). Matagiri.

Health & Healing: Studies in New Testament Principles. John Wilkinson. 220p. 1980. 15.00x (ISBN 0-905312-08-2, Pub. by Scot Acad Pr). Longwood Pub Group.

Health & Healing: Understanding Conventional & Alternative Medicine. Andrew Weil. 1983. 13.95 (ISBN 0-395-34430-1). HM.

Health & Healing: Understanding Conventional & Alternative Medicine. Andrew Weil. 304p. 1985. pap. 7.95 (ISBN 0-395-37764-1). HM.

Health & Illness, Vol. 1. Rudolf Steiner. Tr. by Maria St. Goar from German. (Illus.). 155p. (Orig.). 14.00 (ISBN 0-88010-028-1); pap. 8.95 (ISBN 0-88010-000-1). Anthroposophic.

Health & Medicine & the Methodist Tradition. E. Brooks Holifield. 176p. 1986. 17.95x (ISBN 0-8245-0792-4). Crossroad NY.

Health & Medicine in Anglican Tradition. David H. Smith. 140p. 1986. 15.95x (ISBN 0-8245-0716-9). Crossroad NY.

Health & Medicine in the Islamic Tradition. Fazlur Rahman. 176p. 1987. 16.95x (ISBN 0-8245-0797-5). Crossroad NY.

Health & Medicine in the Jewish Tradition: The Pursuit of Wholeness. David M. Feldman. 176p. 1986. 15.95x (ISBN 0-8245-0707-X). Crossroad NY.

Health & Medicine in the Lutheran Tradition. Martin Marty. 192p. 1983. 16.95x (ISBN 0-8245-0613-8). Crossroad NY.

Health & Medicine in the Roman Catholic Tradition: Tradition in Transition. Richard A. McCormick. 176p. 1984. 15.95x (ISBN 0-8245-0661-8). Crossroad NY.

Health & Spiritual Healing. Richard Lynch. 140p. Date not set. pap. 8.00 (ISBN 0-89540-146-0, SB-146). Sun Pub.

Health & Wealth from Within. William E. Towne. 157p. 1981. pap. 9.00 (ISBN 0-89540-081-2, SB-081). Sun Pub.

Health & Wealth Gospel: A Fresh Look at Healing, Prosperity & Positive Confession. Bruce Barron. LC 86-27503. 206p. (Orig.). 1987. pap. 6.95 (ISBN 0-87784-327-9). Inter Varsity.

Health Care Ethics: A Theological Analysis. 2nd ed. Benedict M. Ashley & Kevin D. O'Rourke. LC 81-17973. 1982. 25.00 (ISBN 0-87125-075-6); pap. 16.00 (ISBN 0-87125-070-5). Cath Health.

Health Care Ministries. 2nd ed. Gerald Fath. LC 80-12620. 1980. pap. 8.50 (ISBN 0-87125-061-6). Cath Health.

Health, Food & Healing in Yoga. (Life Companion Library). 300p. 1983. pap. 6.95 (ISBN 0-89744-007-2). Auromere.

Health for the Glory of God. Mary M. Landis. 1976. write for info. (ISBN 0-686-15484-3); tchr's. ed. avail. (ISBN 0-686-15485-1). Rod & Staff.

Health Force. 2nd, rev. ed. Robert T. Lewanski & Robert A. Zuraw. (Illus.). 252p. 1982. 14.95 (ISBN 0-9608030-0-9). Taoist Pubs.

Health, Happiness, Humor & Holiness: As Seen Through Children's Eyes. William Armstrong. Ed. by Helen Graves. (Illus.). 150p. 1987. pap. text ed. 6.95 (ISBN 1-55523-065-2). Winston-Derek.

Health Medicine & Faith Traditions: An Inquiry into Religion & Medicine. Marty E. Martin. Ed. by Kenneth L. Vaux. LC 81-71383. pap. 90.50 (2026975). Bks Demand UMI.

Health of American Catholic Priests: A Report & a Study. 104p. 1985. pap. text ed. 3.95 (ISBN 1-55586-948-3). US Catholic.

Health Secrets from the Bible. Ronald R. Wlodyga. LC 79-64042. 1979. pap. 5.95 (ISBN 0-917182-12-X). Triumph Pub.

Health, Wealth & Happiness. Lowell Fillmore. 1964. 5.95 (ISBN 0-87159-055-7). Unity School.

Healthier & Happier Children Through Bedtime Meditations & Prayers, Bks. 1 & 2. Lee Perkins & Jim Perkins. 40p. 1982. book & tape set 14.95 (ISBN 0-87604-184-5). ARE Pr.

Healthier & Happier Children Through Bedtime Meditations & Stories. rev. ed. Lee Perkins & Jim Perkins. 1975. with tape 7.95 (ISBN 0-87604-106-3). ARE Pr.

Healthy Personality & the Christian Life. Douglas Hooker. 1977. 10.95 (ISBN 0-8158-0351-6). Chris Mass.

Hear O Israel. James Leary. 1980. pap. 3.95 (ISBN 0-88479-029-0). Arena Lettres.

Hear, O Israel: A Guide to the Old Testament. James F. Leary. 144p. 1986. pap. 4.95 (ISBN 0-88479-029-0). Chr Classics.

Hear, Oh Israel. Samuel Rosenblatt. 1958. 7.50 (ISBN 0-87306-106-3). Feldheim.

Hear the Good News. Howard Eshbaugh. 1984. 3.50 (ISBN 0-89536-656-8, 0805). CSS of Ohio.

Hear the Word, Share the Word, Guide Your People. National Catholic Educational Associations & National Conference of Directors of Religious Education. 48p. 1978. 4.80. Natl Cath Educ.

Hear with God's People. 2nd ed. Gerard P. Weber et al. (Word Is Life Ser.). 1977. 4.00 (ISBN 0-02-658600-2); tchrs. ed. 8.00 (ISBN 0-02-658610-X); family handbook 1.00 (ISBN 0-02-658650-9). Benziger Pub Co.

Hearing & Knowing: Theological Reflections on Christianity in Africa. Mercy A. Oduyoye. LC 85-29873. 176p. (Orig.). 1986. pap. 9.95 (ISBN 0-88344-258-2). Orbis Bks.

Hearing & Speaking the Word: An Anthology of the Works of James Muilenburg. Ed. by Thomas F. Best. (Scholars Press Homage Ser.: No. 7). 464p. 1985. 26.95 (ISBN 0-89130-665-X, 00 16 07). Scholars Pr GA.

Hearing Heart. Hannah Hurnard. 1975. pap. 2.95 (ISBN 0-8423-1405-9). Tyndale.

Hearing the Parables of Jesus. Pheme Perkins. LC 80-84508. 228p. (Orig.). 1981. pap. 7.95 (ISBN 0-8091-2352-5). Paulist Pr.

Hearing the Word: Scripture in Worship. Howard Eshbaugh. 1980. 4.50 (ISBN 0-89536-413-1, 0833). CSS of Ohio.

Hearken, O Ye People. Ed. by Sperry Symposium. 297p. 1984. 9.95 (ISBN 0-934126-56-9). Randall Bk Co.

Heart. rev. ed. (Agni Yoga Ser.). 1980. Repr. of 1975 ed. index 12.00 (ISBN 0-933574-08-8). Agni Yoga Soc.

Heart after God. Luis Palau. LC 78-57676. 200p. 1982. pap. 3.50 (ISBN 0-930014-83-9). Multnomah.

Heart & Church. Francis Asbury. pap. 4.95 (ISBN 0-686-23583-5). Schmul Pub Co.

Heart & Mind: Varieties of Moral Experience. Mary Midgley. 1981. 20.00x (ISBN 0-312-36588-8). St Martin.

Heart Cries: Prayers of Biblical Women. Mary Lou Carney. 128p. (Orig.). 1986. pap. 5.95 (ISBN 0-687-16762-0). Abingdon.

Heart Disease in Christ's Body. Jack Van Impe. 328p. 1984. pap. 6.95 (ISBN 0-934803-04-8). J Van Impe.

Heart for God. Sinclair Ferguson. (Christian Character Library). 150p. 1985. hdbk. 8.95 (ISBN 0-89109-507-1). NavPress.

Heart for God. Sinclair B. Ferguson. 150p. 1987. pap. 3.95 (ISBN 0-89109-176-9). NavPress.

Heart Gifts from Helen Steiner Rice. Helen S. Rice. LC 68-28438. (Illus.). 96p. 1968. 8.95 (ISBN 0-8007-0133-X). Revell.

Heart Has Its Reasons: The Sacred Heart of Jesus & the Immaculate Heart of Mary. William G. Most. 35p. (Orig.). 1985. pap. 1.50 (ISBN 0-913382-50-7, 105-40). Prow Bks-Franciscan.

Heart Has Its Seasons: A Sourcebook of Christmas Meditations. Wheaton P. Webb. LC 82-3898. 96p. (Orig.). 1982. pap. 7.75 (ISBN 0-687-16800-7). Abingdon.

Heart in Pilgrimage: Christian Guidelines for the Human Journey. Christopher Bryant. 208p. 1980. 9.95 (ISBN 0-8164-0457-7, HarpR). Har-Row.

Heart of a Distant Forest. Philip L. Williams. 1985. pap. 3.50 (ISBN 0-345-32365-3). Ballantine.

Heart of a Holy Man. 1973. 3.00 (ISBN 0-685-61431-X). Aum Pubns.

Heart of Buddhism: Being an Anthology of Buddhist Verse. Ed. by Kenneth J. Saunders. LC 78-70120. Repr. of 1915 ed. 17.00 (ISBN 0-404-17377-2). AMS Pr.

Heart of Buddhism: In Search of the Timeless Spirit of Primitive Buddhism. Takeuchi Yoshinori. LC 82-23453. 192p. (Orig.). 1983. 17.50 (ISBN 0-8245-0577-8). Crossroad NY.

Heart of Buddhist Meditation. N. Thera. 1973. pap. 7.95 (ISBN 0-87728-073-8). Weiser.

Heart of Buddhist Wisdom: A Translation of the Heart Sutra with Historical Introduction & Commentary. Douglas A. Fox. (Studies in Asian Thought & Religion: Vol. 3). 195p. 1986. lib. bdg. 39.95x (ISBN 0-88946-053-1). E Mellen.

Heart of Gold: The Light Within Life. Mary P. Fisher. LC 85-81211. (Illus.). 72p. (Orig.). 1985. pap. 6.00 (ISBN 0-9615149-5-7). Fenton Valley Pr.

Heart of Hebrew History. H. I. Hester. 1980. Repr. of 1949 ed. 12.95 (ISBN 0-8054-1217-4). Broadman.

Heart of Jesus: Symbol of Redeeming Love. Bernard Haring. 160p. 1983. pap. 4.25 (ISBN 0-89243-191-1). Liguori Pubns.

Heart of Joy: The Transforming Power of Self-Giving. Mother Teresa. 140p. (Orig.). 1987. pap. 3.95 (ISBN 0-89283-342-4). Servant.

Heart of Man: Its Genius for Good & Evil. Erich Fromm. LC 64-18053. 1980. pap. 6.95 (ISBN 0-06-090795-9, CN 795, PL). Har-Row.

Heart of Matter. Pierre Teilhard de Chardin. Tr. by Rene Hague. LC 79-24527. 276p. 1980. pap. 7.95 (ISBN 0-15-640004-9, Harv). HarBraceJ.

Heart of Qu'ran & Perfect Mizan. Shaykh F. Haeri. 140p. 1987. pap. 18.95 (ISBN 0-7103-0222-3, Kegan Paul). Methuen Inc.

Heart of the Christian Matter: An Ecumenical Approach. John Carmody. 304p. (Orig.). 1983. pap. 12.95 (ISBN 0-687-16765-5). Abingdon.

Heart of the Christian Message. school ed. Charles J. Keating. flexible bdg 1.50 (ISBN 0-89942-246-2, 246-05-SD). Catholic Bk Pub.

Heart of the Continent. Fitz H. Ludlow. LC 74-134396. (Illus.). Repr. 35.45 (ISBN 0-404-08438-9). AMS Pr.

Heart of the Gospel. 2nd rev. ed. George Townshend. 160p. (ISBN 0-85398-025-X); pap. 3.95 (ISBN 0-85398-020-9). G Ronald Pub.

Heart of the New Testament. H. I. Hester. 1980. Repr. of 1950 ed. 12.95 (ISBN 0-8054-1386-3). Broadman.

Heart of the Old Testament. Ronald Youngblood. 1971. pap. 4.50 (ISBN 0-8010-9900-5). Baker Bk.

Heart of the World. Hans Urs Von Balthasar. Tr. by Erasmo Leiva from Ger. LC 79-84879. Orig. Title: Herz der Welt. 219p. (Orig.). 1980. pap. 9.95 (ISBN 0-89870-001-9). Ignatius Pr.

Heart of the World: An Introduction to Contemplative Christianity. Thomas Keating. 96p. 1981. 8.95 (ISBN 0-8245-0014-8). Crossroad NY.

Heart of True Spirituality: John Wesley's Own Choice, Vol. 2. Ed. by Frank Baker. 1986. pap. 4.95 (ISBN 0-310-45101-9, 17079P). Zondervan.

Heart of True Spirituality: John Wesley's Own Choice, Vol. 2: Selections from Thomas a Kempis, et. al. Ed. by Frank Baker. 1985. pap. 4.95 (ISBN 0-317-46009-9). Zondervan.

Heart of True Spirituality: Selections from William Law, Vol. 1. 2nd ed. Ed. by Frank Baker. 128p. 1985. pap. 5.95 (ISBN 0-310-39621-2, 17064P). Zondervan.

Heart of Truth: Finney's Outlines of Theology. Charles G. Finney. LC 75-46128. Orig. Title: Skeletons of a Course of Theological Lectures. 256p. 1976. pap. 6.95 (ISBN 0-87123-226-X, 210226). Bethany Hse.

Heart of Wisdom, Bk. III. Bernard S. Raskas. 10.50. United Synagogue.

Heart of Wisdom-One. Bernard S. Raskas. 1962. 8.50 (ISBN 0-8381-2102-0). United Syn Bk.

Heart of Wisdom-Two. Bernard S. Raskas. 1979. 9.50 (ISBN 0-8381-2104-7). United Syn Bk.

Heart Opened Wide: Studies in II Corinthians. Homer A. Kent, Jr. (New Testament Studies). 176p. (Orig.). 1982. pap. 4.95 (ISBN 0-8010-5438-9). Baker Bk.

Heart Opened Wide: Studies in II Corinthians. Homer A. Kent, Jr. 176p. (Orig.). 1982. pap. 4.95 (ISBN 0-88469-152-7). BMH Bks.

Heart Set Free. Gloria Phillips & Irene B. Harrell. (Orig.). 1985. pap. 5.00 (ISBN 0-915541-02-5); study guide: Spiritual Warfare 5.00 (ISBN 0-915541-16-5); answer bk. avail. (ISBN 0-915541-17-3). Star Bks Inc.

Heart Song: Prophecies, Ponderings & Poetry. Helaina L. Binford. (Illus.). 50p. (Orig.). 1986. pap. 5.00 (ISBN 0-939313-11-1). Joshua-I-Minist.

Heart Sutra. Bhagwan Shree Rajneesh. Ed. by ma Yoga Sudha. LC 78-908490. (Buddha Ser.). (Illus.). 332p. (Orig.). 1978. 16.95 (ISBN 0-88050-078-6). Chidvilas Found.

Heart Sutra & Verses Without a Stand, With Prose Commentary. Tripitaka Master Hua. Tr. by Buddhist Text Translation Society. (Illus.). 160p. (Orig.). 1980. pap. 7.50 (ISBN 0-917512-27-8). Buddhist Text.

Heart Talks. C. W. Naylor. 279p. 1982. pap. 2.50 (ISBN 0-686-36257-8). Faith Pub Hse.

Heart Talks on Holiness. Samuel L. Brengle. 1978. pap. 3.95 (ISBN 0-86544-002-6). Salv Army Suppl South.

Heart Talks on the Deeper Life. William S. Deal. 1960. 1.50 (ISBN 0-686-05838-0). Crusade Pubs.

Heart-Trimmed Christmas: Christmas Inspiration for Your Heart & Home. Ruth C. Ikerman. 112p. (Orig.). 1984. pap. 7.95 (ISBN 0-687-16804-X). Abingdon.

Heart Trouble: A Woman's Workshop on Christian Character. Barbara Bush. Ed. by Janet Kobobel. (Woman's Workshop Ser.). (Orig.). 1985. pap. 2.95 (ISBN 0-310-29431-2, 12016P). Zondervan.

Heartbeat of Evangelism. Robert E. Coleman. 32p. 1985. pap. 1.95 (ISBN 0-89109-400-8). NavPress.

Heartquake. Lilya Wagner. (Daybreak Ser.). 128p. 1983. pap. 4.95 (ISBN 0-8163-0510-2). Pacific Pr Pub Assn.

Hearts Aflame. Gustaf F. Johnson. 1970. 4.50 (ISBN 0-910452-06-7). Covenant.

Hearts of Iron, Feet of Clay. Ed. by Gary Inrig. 1979. pap. 7.95 (ISBN 0-8024-3487-8). Moody.

Heartwarmers. Jim Henry. LC 77-79094. 1977. 5.95 (ISBN 0-8054-5156-0). Broadman.

Heat in the Rig Veda & Atharva Veda. Chauncey J. Blair. (American Oriental Ser.: Vol. 45). 1961. 8.00x (ISBN 0-940490-45-5). Am Orient Soc.

Heathens Primitive Man & His Religions. William Howells. 302p. pap. text ed. 9.95 (ISBN 0-88133-240-2). Sheffield Wisc.

Heather & Snow. George MacDonald. Ed. by Dan Hamilton. 288p. 1987. pap. 5.95 (ISBN 0-89693-760-7). Victor Bks.

Heaven. Joseph Bayly. LC 77-71035. (Illus.). 1977. pap. 2.95 (ISBN 0-89191-070-0). Cook.

Heaven. George Beiderwieden. 1957. 1.50 (ISBN 0-570-03680-1, 74-1008). Concordia.

Heaven. Daughters of St. Paul. 1977. 3.50 (ISBN 0-8198-0419-3); pap. 2.50 (ISBN 0-8198-0420-7). Dghtrs St Paul.

Heaven. Frank E. Stranges. 16p. (Orig.). 1985. pap. text ed. 2.00 (ISBN 0-933470-03-7). Intl Evang.

Heaven. Worcester. 1967. pap. 1.25 (ISBN 0-317-03716-1). College Pr Pub.

Heaven: A Glimpse of Your Future Home. expanded ed. Don Baker. (Orig.). 1986. pap. 3.95 (ISBN 0-88070-168-4). Multnomah.

Heaven: A Place, a City, a Home. E. M. Bounds. (Direction Bks). 152p. 1975. pap. 3.50 (ISBN 0-8010-0648-1). Baker Bk.

Heaven & Earth. Joan Hutson. (Little Learner Ser.). 24p. 1985. 5.95 (ISBN 0-570-08952-2, 56-1544). Concordia.

Heaven & Hell. large print ed. Emanuel Swedenborg. LC 81-52785. 800p. 8.25 (ISBN 0-87785-130-1). Swedenborg.

Heaven & Hell. Emanuel Swedenborg. LC 77-93044. cancelled (ISBN 0-87785-167-0); student ed. 12.00 (ISBN 0-87785-066-6); pap. 5.95 (ISBN 0-87785-153-0). Swedenborg.

Heaven & Hell: A Biblical & Theological Overview. Peter Toon. 160p. 1986. pap. 8.95 (ISBN 0-8407-5967-3). Nelson.

Heaven & Hell in Comparative Religion. Kaufmann Kohler. 1923. 25.00 (ISBN 0-8414-5601-1). Folcroft.

Heaven Born Merida & Its Destiny: The Book of Chilam Balam of Chumayel. Tr. by Munro S. Edmonson from Maya. (Texas Pan American Ser.). (Illus.). 304p. 1986. 37.50x (ISBN 0-292-73027-6). U of Tex Pr.

Heaven Bound. William A. Lauterbach. LC 74-34277. 128p. 1974. pap. 5.50 (ISBN 0-570-03028-5, 6-1156). Concordia.

Heaven for Those Who Can't Believe. Robert P. Lightner. LC 76-50303. 1977. pap. 1.95 (ISBN 0-87227-035-1). Reg Baptist.

Heaven Help the Home! Howard G. Hendricks. LC 73-78689. 143p. 1973. pap. 5.95 (ISBN 0-88207-240-4). Victor Bks.

Heaven, Here I Come. Jean Darnall. LC 77-91521. 1978. pap. 2.95 (ISBN 0-88419-148-6). Creation Hse.

Heaven: How to Get There. D. L. Moody. 112p. 1982. pap. text ed. 3.50 (ISBN 0-88368-115-3). Whitaker Hse.

Heaven in My Hand. Alice L. Humphreys. 5.95 (ISBN 0-8042-2352-1). John Knox.

Heaven in Ordinarie. Noel D. O'Donoghue. 1979. 14.95 (ISBN 0-87243-085-5). Templegate.

Heaven Is Not That Far Away. William L. Kanfield. LC 85-91401. 88p. 1986. 8.95 (ISBN 0-533-06917-3). Vantage.

Heaven is Out of This World. Don Hillis. (Illus.). 47p. 1982. pap. 2.00 (ISBN 0-89323-032-4). Bible Memory.

Heaven on Earth: A Planned Mormon Society. William J. McNiff. LC 72-8632. Repr. of 1940 ed. 14.00 (ISBN 0-404-11007-X). AMS Pr.

Heaven on Earth: A Planned Mormon Society. William J. McNiff. LC 72-187474. (American Utopian Adventure Ser.). 262p. 1973. Repr. of 1940 ed. lib. bdg. 27.50x (ISBN 0-87991-001-1). Porcupine Pr.

Heaven on Earth: Studies in Medieval Cistercian History, IX. Ed. by E. R. Elder. (Cistercian Studies: No. 68). (Orig.). 1982. pap. 7.95 (ISBN 0-87907-868-5). Cistercian Pubns.

Heaven: The Heart's Deepest Longing. Peter J. Kreeft. LC 80-7747. 160p. 1980. 10.00 (ISBN 0-06-064776-0, HarpR). Har-Row.

Heavenly City. Menaham Gerlitz. Tr. by Sheindel Weinbach from Hebrew. Tr. of Yerushalayim Shel Ma'ala. 1978. 6.95 (ISBN 0-87306-147-0). Feldheim.

Heavenly City of the Eighteenth-Century Philosophers. Carl L. Becker. (Storrs Lectures Ser.). 1932. pap. 6.95x (ISBN 0-300-00017-0, Y5). Yale U Pr.

Heavenly Comfort. Pierce Maassen. pap. 0.45 (ISBN 0-686-23473-1). Rose Pub MI.

Heavenly Contract: Ideology & Organization in Pre-Revolutionary Puritanism. David Zaret. LC 84-16473. 192p. 1985. lib. bdg. 22.50x (ISBN 0-226-97882-6). U of Chicago Pr.

Heavenly Deception. Chris Elkins. 1980. pap. 3.95 (ISBN 0-8423-1402-4). Tyndale.

Heavenly Deception. Chris Elkins. 1981. pap. 9.95 incl. cassette (ISBN 0-8423-1403-2). Tyndale.

Heavenly Footman. John Bunyan. pap. 1.25 (ISBN 0-685-19831-6). Reiner.

Heavenly Friends: A Saint for Each Day. Rosalie Levy. 7.00 (ISBN 0-8198-0638-2); pap. 6.00 (ISBN 0-8198-0639-0). Dghtrs St Paul.

Heavenly Hash: A Tasty Mix of a Mother's Meditations. Bernadette M. Snyder. LC 85-71564. 140p. (Orig.). 1985. pap. 6.95 (ISBN 0-87973-583-X, 583). Our Sunday Visitor.

Heavenly Kingdom: Aspects of Political Thought in the Talmud & Midrash. Gordon M. Freeman. 196p. (Orig.). 1986. lib. bdg. 24.75 (ISBN 0-8191-5139-4, Co-pub. by Ctr Jewish Comm Studies); pap. text ed. 11.75 (ISBN 0-8191-5140-8). U Pr of Amer.

Heavenly Ladder: A Jewish Guide to Inner Growth. Edward Hoffman. LC 85-42779. 160p. (Orig.). 1986. pap. 8.95 (ISBN 0-06-064001-4, HarpR). Har-Row.

Heavenly Life for Earthly Living. C. E. Orr. 60p. pap. 0.40 (ISBN 0-686-29111-5); pap. 1.00 3 copies (ISBN 0-686-34362-X). Faith Pub Hse.

Heavenly Muse: A Preface to Milton. A. S. Woodhouse. Ed. by Hugh R. Maccallum. LC 79-185724. 1972. 35.00x (ISBN 0-8020-5247-9). U of Toronto Pr.

Heavenly Patters for Happy Homes. Rubel Shell. 2.50 (ISBN 0-89315-109-2). Lambert Bk.

Heavenly Springs. Andrew Bonar. 211p. (Orig.). 1986. pap. 4.95 (ISBN 0-85151-479-0). Banner of Truth.

Heavenly Way. Hua-Chung Ni. LC 81-50158. (Illus.). 41p. (Orig.). 1981. pap. text ed. 2.50 (ISBN 0-937064-03-3). SEBT.

Heaven's Answer for the Home. rev. ed. Lowell Lundstrom. 142p. 1985. pap. 3.50 (ISBN 0-938220-16-0). Whitaker Hse.

Heavens Are Cleft Asunder. rev. ed. Huschmand Sabet. Tr. by Oliver Coburn from Ger. Orig. Title: Gespaltene Himmel. (Eng.). 1975. pap. 6.25 (ISBN 0-85398-055-1, 332-014). G Ronald Pub.

Heavens Are Opened. Eberhard Arnold et al. LC 73-20715. (Illus.). 190p. 1974. 8.00 (ISBN 0-87486-113-6). Plough.

Heavens Declare... William D. Banks. (Illus.). 288p. (Orig.). 1985. pap. 6.95 (ISBN 0-89228-101-4). Impact Bks MO.

Heaven's Hall of Heroes. Fred M. Barlow. LC 78-16887. (Illus.). 1978. pap. 3.95 (ISBN 0-87227-062-9). Reg Baptist.

Heavens Overflow. Ed. by Clarence M. Wagner. 73p. pap. 4.00 (ISBN 0-937498-06-8). Tru-Faith.

Heavens Resound: A History of the Latter-Day Saints in Ohio 1830-1838. Milton V. Backman, Jr. LC 83-12882. (Illus.). 480p. 1983. 14.95 (ISBN 0-87747-973-9). Deseret Bk.

Heaven's Window: Sequel to We Be Brethren. J. D. Thomas. LC 74-28950. 159p. 1975. 11.95 (ISBN 0-89112-002-5, Bibl Res Pr). Abilene Christ U.

Heavy Bread. Nancy J. Kauffman & Elizabeth J. Kauffman. LC 73-75087. (Pivot Family Reader Ser). 192p. (Orig.). 1973. pap. 1.25 (ISBN 0-87983-030-1). Keats.

Heber C. Kimball: Mormon Patriarch & Pioneer. Stanley B. Kimball. LC 80-21923. (Illus.). 345p. 1981. pap. 13.50 (ISBN 0-252-01299-2). U of Ill Pr.

Heber J. Grant: Man of Steel, Prophet of God. Francis M. Gibbons. LC 79-11649. 252p. 1979. 8.95 (ISBN 0-87747-755-8). Deseret Bk.

Hebraeische Pentateuch der Samaritaner, 5 pts. Ed. by A. Von Gall. (Ger.). xciv, 440p. 1966. Repr. of 1918 ed. Set. 45.60x (ISBN 3-11-009258-1). De Gruyter.

Hebraisms in the Authorized Version of the Bible. William Rosenau. LC 76-9047. 1976. Repr. of 1903 ed. lib. bdg. 25.00 (ISBN 0-8414-7247-5). Folcroft.

Hebreo Biblico Juego de Dos Tomos, 2 vols. Moises Chavez. (Span., Vol. I - 568 pgs., Vol. II - 240 pgs.). 1984. Set. pap. 28.95 (ISBN 0-311-42070-2, Edit Mundo). Casa Bautista.

Hebreos-Apocalipsis: Tomo IV. A. Schrolder & L. Bonnet. Tr. by A. Cotiviela from Eng. (Comentario Sobre el Nuevo Testamento). 540p. 1986. Repr. of 1983 ed. 14.95 (ISBN 0-311-03053-X). Casa Bautista.

Hebrew. Chaim Rabin. 1977. Repr. of 1949 ed. lib. bdg. 17.00 (ISBN 0-8492-2311-3). R West.

Hebrew & Aramaic Dictionary of the Old Testament. Ed. by Georg Fohrer et al. Tr. by W. A. Johnstone from Ger. LC 73-82430. (Hebrew & Aramaic.). viii, 344p. 1973. text ed. 16.75 (ISBN 3-11-004572-9). De Gruyter.

Hebrew & Chaldee Lexicon: Keyed to Strong's Exhaustive Concordance. Wilhelm Gesenius. Tr. by Samuel P. Tregelles. (Hebrew & Chaldee.). kivar 24.95 (ISBN 0-8010-3801-4); pap. 19.95 (ISBN 0-8010-3736-0). Baker Bk.

Hebrew & English Lexicon to the Old Testament. 2nd ed. William Gesenius. Ed. by Francis Brown et al. Tr. by Edward Robinson. (Hebrew & Eng.). 1959. Repr. of 1907 ed. 34.95x (ISBN 0-19-864301-2). Oxford U Pr.

Hebrew & English Lexicon to the Old Testament. William Osburn, Jr. 287p. 1981. pap. 6.95 (ISBN 0-310-20361-9, 6264P). Zondervan.

Hebrew & English: Some Likenesses, Psychic & Linguistic. J. Courtenay James. Repr. of 1920 ed. lib. bdg. 20.00 (ISBN 0-8495-2723-6). Arden Lib.

Hebrew & Heritage, 4 vols. David Bridger. LC 75-1812. (Illus.). 1976. Vol. I. pap. 3.95x (ISBN 0-87441-254-4); Vol. II. pap. 3.95x (ISBN 0-87441-252-8); Vol. III. pap. 3.95x (ISBN 0-87441-259-5); Vol. IV. pap. 3.95x (ISBN 0-87441-274-9). Behrman.

Hebrew & Heritage, Vol. II: Siddur Track. Pearl Tarnor & Norman Tarnor. 1982. 3.95x (ISBN 0-87441-375-3); tchr's. guide 12.50 (ISBN 0-87441-377-X). Behrman.

Hebrew & Lexicon to the Old Testament. Benjamin Davies & Edward Mitchell. 800p. Date not set. 22.95 (ISBN 0-8254-2453-4). Kregel.

Hebrew Anthology: A Collection of Poems & Dramas Inspired by the Old Testament & Post Biblical Tradition Gathered from Writings of English Poets, from the Elizabethan Period & Earlier to the Present Day, 2 vols. Ed. by George A. Kohut. 1399p. Repr. of 1913 ed. Set. lib. bdg. 250.00 (ISBN 0-918377-86-2). Russell Pr.

Hebrew-Arabic Dictionary of the Bible, Known As Kitab Jami al-Alfaz (Agron, 2 vols. David Ben Abraham. Ed. by Solomon L. Skoss. LC 78-63565. (Yale Oriental Ser. Researches: Nos. 20-21). (Hebrew & Arabic.). Repr. of 1945 ed. Set. 97.50 (ISBN 0-404-60290-8). AMS Pr.

Hebrew-Arabic Dictionary of the Bible Known As Kitab Jami-Al-Alfaz, 2 vols. Ed. by Solomon Skoss. (Yale Oriental Researches Ser.: No. XX, XXI). (Hebrew & Arabic.). 1945. 50.00x ea.; 95.00x set (ISBN 0-686-57837-6). Elliots Bks.

Hebrew-Aramaic-English Dictionary, a Dictionary of Talmud Babli & Talmud Yerushalmi Targum & Midrash, 2 Vols. Marcus Jastrow. (Hebrew, Aramaic & Eng.). 75.00 (ISBN 0-87559-019-5). Shalom.

Hebrew Basic Course. Foreign Service Institute. (Hebrew.). 552p. 1980. plus 24 cassettes 215.00x (ISBN 0-88432-040-5, H345). J Norton Pubs.

Hebrew Bible-A Socio-Literary Introduction. Norman K. Gottwald. LC 84-48719. (Illus.). 736p. 1985. 34.95 (ISBN 0-8006-0853-4, 1-853); pap. 19.95 (ISBN 0-8006-1853-X, 1-1853). Fortress.

Hebrew Bible & Its Modern Interpreters. Ed. by Douglas A. Knight & Gene M. Tucker. LC 83-49216. (Bible & Its Modern Interpreters Ser.). 496p. 1984. 24.95 (ISBN 0-8006-0721-X, 1-721). Fortress.

Hebrew Bible & Its Modern Interpreters. Gene M. Tucker & Douglas A. Knight. LC 83-49216. (SBL-The Bible & Its Modern Interpreters Ser.). 1985. 22.50 (ISBN 0-89130-671-4, 06 14 01); pap. 14.95 (ISBN 0-89130-784-2). Scholars Pr GA.

Hebrew Bible in Art. J. Leveen. (British Academy, London, Schweich Lectures on Biblical Archaeology Series, 1939). pap. 28.00 (ISBN 0-8115-1281-9). Kraus Repr.

Hebrew Bible in Literary Criticism. Ed. by Edward L. Greenstein & Alex Preminger. (Library of Literary Criticism). 635p. 1986. 65.00x (ISBN 0-8044-3266-X). Ungar.

Hebrew Calligraphy: A Step-by-Step Guide. Jay Seth Greenspan. LC 79-12718. (Illus.). 1980. pap. 8.95 (ISBN 0-8052-0664-7). Schocken.

Hebrew Christianity: Its Theology, History & Philosophy. Rev. ed. Arnold G. Fruchtenbaum. 142p. 1983. pap. 3.50 (ISBN 0-8010-3497-3). Ariel Pr CA.

Hebrew Conception of the World. Luis I. Stadelmann. (Analecta Biblica: Vol. 39). 1970. pap. 15.00 (ISBN 88-7653-039-8). Loyola.

Hebrew Day School Education: An Overview. 310p. 10.00 (ISBN 0-914131-32-X, E08). Torah Umesorah.

Hebrew Deluge Story in Cuneiform. Albert T. Clay. LC 78-63549. (Yale Oriental Ser. Researches: No. 5, Pt. 3). Repr. of 1922 ed. 20.00 (ISBN 0-404-60275-4). AMS Pr.

Hebrew Deluge Story in Cuneiform. Albert T. Clay. (Yale Oriental Researches Ser.: No. V, Pt. III). 1922. 19.50x (ISBN 0-685-69802-5). Elliots Bks.

Hebrew-English Dictionary: Hebrew & Chaldee Lexicon to the Old Testament. rev. ed. Gesenius Furst. Ed. by Edward C. Mitchell. (Hebrew & Eng.). 47.50 (ISBN 0-87559-021-7); thumb indexed 52.50 (ISBN 0-87559-022-5). Shalom.

Hebrew English Dictionary to the Bible. 27.50 (ISBN 0-87559-161-2). Shalom.

Hebrew-English Lexicon. (Hebrew & Eng.). 6.95 (ISBN 0-310-20360-0, Pub. by Bagster). Zondervan.

Hebrew-English Lexicon of the Bible. LC 74-26705. (Hebrew & Eng.). 296p. (Orig.). 1975. pap. 7.50 (ISBN 0-8052-0481-4). Schocken.

Hebrew for All. Harold Levy. 260p. 1976. Repr. of 1970 ed. 15.00x (ISBN 0-85303-191-6, Pub. by Vallentine Mitchell England). Biblio Dist.

Hebrew Fragments of Pseudo-Philo. Ed. & tr. by Daniel J. Harrington. LC 73-89170. (Society of Biblical Literature. Texts & Translation-Psuedepigrapha Ser.). 1974. pap. 7.50_o.s. (ISBN 0-88414-036-9, 060203). Scholars Pr GA.

Hebrew Goddess. Raphael Patai. 1984. pap. 2.95 (ISBN 0-380-39289-5, 39289, Discus). Avon.

Hebrew Greek-Key Study Bible. Ed. by Spiros Zodhiates. 59.00 (ISBN 0-89957-572-2). AMG Pubs.

Hebrew-Greek Key Study Bible. Ed. by Spiros Zodhiates. 1985. deluxe ed. 39.95 (ISBN 0-8010-9930-7). Baker Bk.

Hebrew Humanism of Martin Buber. Grete Schaeder. Tr. by Noah J. Jacobs from Ger. LC 70-39691. (Schaver Publication Fund for Jewish Studies Ser.). 504p. 1973. 29.95x (ISBN 0-8143-1483-X). Wayne St U Pr.

Hebrew Ideals in Genesis (Genesis 11-50) James Strahan. LC 82-7785. 360p. 1982. 14.95 (ISBN 0-8254-3729-6). Kregel.

Hebrew Idolatry & Superstition. Elford Higgens. 1971. Repr. of 1893 ed. 19.50x (ISBN 0-8046-1150-5, Pub. by Kennikat). Assoc Faculty Pr.

Hebrew in the Church. Pinchas Lapide. 208p. (Orig.). 1985. 24.95x (ISBN 0-8028-3615-1). Eerdmans.

Hebrew Incunables in the British Isles: A Preliminary Census. David Goldstein. (Illus.). 50p. (Orig.). 1985. pap. 14.25 (ISBN 0-7123-0047-3, Pub. by British Lib). Longwood Pub Group.

Hebrew Inscriptions & Stamps from Gibeon. James B. Pritchard. (University Museum Monographs: No. 17). (Illus.). 32p. 1959. 5.00 (ISBN 0-934718-10-5). Univ Mus of U PA.

Hebrew Kingdoms. Eric W. Heaton. (New Clarendon Bible Ser.). 1968. 10.95x (ISBN 0-19-836922-0). Oxford U Pr.

Hebrew Level Two. Bella Bergman. Ed. by Ora Band. (Illus.). 243p. 1983. pap. text ed. 7.95x (ISBN 0-87441-360-5). Behrman.

Hebrew Literature (Comprising of Talmudic Treatises, Hebrew Melodies & the Kabbalah Unveiled) Intro. by Epiphanius Wilson. 400p. 1986. Repr. of 1901 ed. PLB 60.00 (ISBN 0-89760-658-2). Telegraph Bks.

Hebrew Manuscript Painting. David Goldstein. LC 85-18995. (Illus.). 80p. (Orig.). 1985. pap. 8.95 (ISBN 0-7123-0054-6, Pub. by British Lib). Longwood Pub Group.

Hebrew Manuscript Painting. Joseph Gutmann. (Magnificent Paperback Art Ser.). 1978. 22.95 (ISBN 0-8076-0890-4); pap. 12.95 (ISBN 0-8076-0891-2). Braziller.

Hebrew Myths. Robert Graves & Raphael Patai. 1966. pap. 5.95 (ISBN 0-07-024125-2). McGraw.

Hebrew of the Dead Sea Scrolls. Elisha Qimron. (Harvard Semitic Ser.: No. 29). 1986. text ed. 13.95 (ISBN 0-89130-989-6, 04-04-29). Scholars Pr GA.

Hebrew Origins. Theophile J. Meek. 1960. 11.25 (ISBN 0-8446-2572-8). Peter Smith.

Hebrew Passover from the Earliest Times to A.D. 70. Judah B. Segal. 1963. 24.95x (ISBN 0-19-713529-3). Oxford U Pr.

Hebrew Philosophical Genius. Duncan B. Macdonald. LC 65-18819. 1965. Repr. of 1936 ed. 7.50x (ISBN 0-8462-0688-9). Russell.

Hebrew Prophets. James D. Newsome, Jr. LC 84-7601. 252p. (Orig.). 1984. pap. 12.95 (ISBN 0-8042-0113-7). John Knox.

Hebrew Saga. Gershon Rubin. LC 84-1745. 204p. 1984. 15.00 (ISBN 0-8022-2451-2). Philos Lib.

Hebrew Scriptures: An Introduction to Their Literature & Religious Ideas. Samuel Sandmel. 1978. pap. 16.95x (ISBN 0-19-502369-2). Oxford U Pr.

Hebrew Subscription Lists. Berl Kagan. 50.00x (ISBN 0-87068-282-2, Pub. by Jewish Theol. Seminary). Ktav.

Hebrew: The Eternal Language. William Chomsky. LC 57-8140. 322p. 1975. 5.95 (ISBN 0-8276-0077-1, 384). Jewish Pubns.

Hebrew Thought Compared with Greek. Thorleif Boman. Tr. by Jules L. Moreau from Ger. 1970. pap. 6.95 (ISBN 0-393-00534-8, Norton Lib). Norton.

Hebrew Union College Annual, 10 Vols. 1969. 650.00x (ISBN 0-87068-065-X). Ktav.

Hebrew Verb Tables. 1982. pap. 5.95x (ISBN 0-686-76516-8). Feldheim.

Hebrew Verbless Clause in the Pentateuch. Francis I. Andersen. (SBL Monograph). 8.95 (ISBN 0-89130-321-9, 06-00-14). Scholars Pr GA.

Hebrew Verse Structure. Michael O'Connor. 1980. 18.75x (ISBN 0-931464-02-1). Eisenbrauns.

Hebrewisms of West Africa: From Nile to Niger with the Jews. Joseph J. Williams. LC 67-19534. (Illus.). 1930. 20.00 (ISBN 0-8196-0194-2). Biblo.

Hebrews. John Brown. (Geneva Ser.). 329p. 1983. Repr. of 1862 ed. text ed. 15.95 (ISBN 0-85151-099-X). Banner of Truth.

Hebrews. Charles Capps. 39p. (Orig.). 1985. wkbk. 4.95 (ISBN 0-914307-36-3). Word Faith.

Hebrews. Juliana Casey. (New Testament Message Ser.: Vol. 18). 10.95 (ISBN 0-89453-206-5); pap. 6.95 (ISBN 0-89453-141-7). M Glazier.

Hebrews. Mr. R. De Haan. pap. 6.95 (ISBN 0-310-23371-2, 9506P). Zondervan.

Hebrews. David L. Eubanks & Robert C. Shannon. (Standard Bible Studies). 128p. 1986. pap. text ed. 5.95 (ISBN 0-87403-171-0, 40111). Standard Pub.

Hebrews. (Erdmans Commentaries Ser.). 3.95 (ISBN 0-8010-3399-3). Baker Bk.

Hebrews. Herschel H. Hobbs. LC 81-65388. 1981. pap. 4.95 (ISBN 0-8054-1323-5). Broadman.

Hebrews. Irving L. Jensen. (Bible Self-Study Ser.). 1970. pap. 3.25 (ISBN 0-8024-1058-8). Moody.

Hebrews. William G. Johnsson. LC 79-92068. (Knox Preaching Guides Ser.). 98p. (Orig., John Hayes series editor). 1980. pap. 4.95. John Knox.

Hebrews. Simon J. Kistemaker. 350p. 1984. 18.95 (ISBN 0-8010-5460-5). Baker Bk.

Hebrews. Marilyn Kunz & Catherine Schell. (Neighborhood Bible Study). 1971. pap. 2.95 (ISBN 0-8423-1410-5). Tyndale.

Hebrews. John MacArthur. (MacArthur New Testament Commentary Ser.). (Orig.). 14.95 (ISBN 0-8024-0753-6). Moody.

Hebrews. John F. MacArthur, Jr. 1983. 14.95 (ISBN 0-88469-155-1). BMH Bks.

Hebrews. Michael D. McCann. (Standard Bible Study Workbooks). 64p. 1986. pap. text ed. 1.95 (ISBN 0-87403-191-5, 40211). Standard Pub.

Hebrews. George W. MacRae. Ed. by Robert J. Karris. (Collegeville Bible Commentary Ser.: No. 10). 64p. 1983. pap. 2.95 (ISBN 0-8146-1310-1). Liturgical Pr.

Hebrews. Geoffrey Wilson. 1976. pap. 4.95 (ISBN 0-85151-278-X). Banner of Truth.

Hebrews: A Devotional Commentary. W. Griffith Thomas. 1962. pap. 4.95 (ISBN 0-8028-1552-9). Eerdmans.

Hebrews: A Good News Commentary. Donald A. Hagner. LC 82-48410. (Good News Commentary Ser.). 288p. 1983. pap. 9.95 (ISBN 0-06-063555-X, RD-425, HarpR). Har-Row.

Hebrews: A New & Better Way. Herbert W. Chilstrom. LC 83-5600. 80p. 1984. pap. 3.95 (ISBN 0-8006-1717-7, 1-1717). Fortress.

Hebrews: A Translation with Notes. Paul R. Caudill. LC 84-21415. 1985. pap. 4.95 (ISBN 0-8054-1395-2). Broadman.

Hebrews & Hermeneutics. G. Hughes. LC 77-84806. (Society for New Testament Studies Monographs: No. 36). 1980. 32.50 (ISBN 0-521-21858-6). Cambridge U Pr.

Hebrews & Perfection: An Examination of the Concept of Perfection in the Epistle to the Hebrews. David Peterson. LC 82-4188. (Society for New Testament Monograph 47). 260p. 1982. 47.50 (ISBN 0-521-24408-0). Cambridge U Pr.

Hebrews & the Pastoral Epistles. Irving L. Jensen. (Irving Jensen's Do-It-Yourself Bible Study Ser.). 139p. (Orig.). 1985. wkbk. 5.95 (ISBN 0-89840-077-5). Heres Life.

Hebrews: Bible Study Commentary. Leon Morris. 1986. pap. 5.95 (ISBN 0-310-45183-3, 12390P). Zondervan.

Hebrews: From Shadows to Reality. Gladys Hunt. (Fisherman Bible Studyguides). 79p. 1979. saddle stitch 2.95 (ISBN 0-87788-338-6). Shaw Pubs.

Hebrews in America: A Series of Historical & Biographical Sketches. facsimile ed. Isaac Markens. LC 74-29504. (Modern Jewish Experiences). 1975. Repr. of 1888 ed. 30.00x (ISBN 0-405-06731-3). Ayer Co Pubs.

Hebrews, James, I-II Peter, Vol. XI. Beacon Bible Commentary Staff. 6.95 (ISBN 0-8010-0677-5). Baker Bk.

Hebrews, James, Peter. H. A. Ironside. 9.95 (ISBN 0-87213-399-0). Loizeaux.

Hebrews, James, 1 & 2 Peter, Jude: A Daily Dialogue with God. Dale Larsen. (Personal Bible Studyguide Ser.). 144p. 1984. pap. 5.95 (ISBN 0-87788-339-4). Shaw Pubs.

Hebrews, James, 1 & 2 Peter, Jude, Revelation. Reginald H. Fuller et al. Ed. by Gerhard Krodel. LC 76-7864. (Proclamation Commentaries). 132p. 1977. pap. 4.95 (ISBN 0-8006-0584-5, 1-584). Fortress.

Hebrews-Jude. Albert Barnes. 18.95 (ISBN 0-8010-0848-4). Baker Bk.

Hebrews: Pilgrim's Progress or Regress? Jim Townsend. (Bible Mastery Ser.). 144p. 1987. pap. 5.95 (ISBN 1-55513-846-2). Cook.

Hebrews-Revelation, Vol. X. Beacon Bible Commentary Staff. 13.95 (ISBN 0-8010-0698-8). Baker Bk.

Hebrews-Second Peter. John W. Bowman. LC 59-10454. (Layman's Bible Commentary Ser: Vol. 24). 1962. pap. 4.95 (ISBN 0-8042-3084-6). John Knox.

Hebrews: The Beauty of Christ Unveiled. Keith L. Brooks. (Teach Yourself the Bible Ser.). 1961. pap. 2.75 (ISBN 0-8024-3507-6). Moody.

Hebrews, the Epistle of Warning. John Owen. LC 68-57719. 1973. pap. 9.95 (ISBN 0-8254-3407-6). Kregel.

Hebron Church Register 1750-1825, Madison, Virginia, 2 vols. George M. Smith. 1981. pap. 13.00 set (ISBN 0-917968-08-5). Shenandoah Hist.

Hechos: Colaborando en la Mision de Cristo. J. Estill Jones. Tr. by Arnoldo Canclini from Eng. (Estudios Biblicos Basicos Ser.). Orig. Title: Acts: Working Together in Christ's Mission. 157p. 1981. pap. 2.50 (ISBN 0-311-04339-9). Casa Bautista.

Hechos de los Apostoles. Ernesto Trenchard. (Span.). 686p. 1963. 13.95 (ISBN 0-8254-1742-2). Kregel.

Hechos de los Apostoles (Comentario Biblico Portavoz) Charles C. Ryrie. Orig. Title: Acts of the Apostles (Everyman's Bible Commentary) (Span.). 96p. 1981. pap. 2.95 (ISBN 0-8254-1631-0). Kregel.

Hechos de los Apostoles: Texto Programado. Weldon E. Viertel. Tr. of Early Church Growth: a Study of the Book of Acts. (Span.). 208p. 1985. pap. write for info. (ISBN 0-311-04348-8). Casa Bautista.

Hechos el Uno Para el Otro. John W. Drakeford. Tr. by Dafne C. De Plou. (Sexo en la Vida Cristiana Ser.). 1983. pap. 3.50 (ISBN 0-311-46256-1). Casa Bautista.

Hechos Epistolas-El Mar De la Vida: 14 Lecciones. Bernice C. Jordan. (Pasos De Fe Ser.). (Span.). pap. text ed. 2.50 (ISBN 0-86508-415-7); figuras 8.95 (ISBN 0-86508-416-5). BCM Intl Inc.

Hechos Epistolas-Vosotros sois Edificio de Dios: 14 Lecciones, Tomo 1. Bernice C. Jordan. (Pasos De Fe Ser.). (Span.). pap. text ed. 2.50 (ISBN 0-86508-413-0); figuras 8.95 (ISBN 0-86508-414-9). BCM Intl Inc.

Hecker Studies: Essays on the Thought of Isaac Hecker. John Farina. LC 83-60654. 196p. (Orig.). 1983. pap. 7.95 (ISBN 0-8091-2555-2). Paulist Pr.

Hectoris Boetii Murthlacensium Et Aberdonensium Episcoporum Vitae, Iterum in Lucem Editae. Hector Boece. LC 76-39462. (Bannatyne Club, Edinburgh. Publications: No. 11). Repr. of 1825 ed. 20.00 (ISBN 0-404-52711-6). AMS Pr.

Hedaya: A Commentary on the Muslim Laws. C. Hamilton. 1963. 130.00 (ISBN 0-87902-163-2). Orientalia.

Hedge of Roses: Jewish Insights into Marriage. Norman Lamm. LC 66-19539. 1977. pap. 2.95 (ISBN 0-87306-095-4). Feldheim.

Hedonism & Eudonism in Aquinas. Thomas A. Mitchell. 1983. 2.00 (ISBN 0-686-45793-5). Franciscan Herald.

Hegel, Hinrichs & Schleiermacher on Feeling & Reason in Religion: The Texts of Their 1821-22 Debate. Ed. & tr. by Eric Luft. LC 87-5550. (Studies in German Thought & History: Volume 3). 544p. 1987. lib. bdg. 79.95 (ISBN 0-88946-352-2). E Mellen.

Hegel-Kierkegaard Cosmology of the Spirit. Kurt W. Schwanktfeld. (Illus.). 103p. 1984. 87.85 (ISBN 0-89266-497-5). Am Classical Coll Pr.

Hegel, Nietzsche & the Criticism of Metaphysics. Stephen Houlgate. 304p. 1987. 39.50 (ISBN 0-521-32255-3). Cambridge U Pr.

Hegel: Phenomenology of Spirit. G. W. Hegel. Tr. by A. V. Miller & J. N. Findlay. 1977. 34.95x (ISBN 0-19-824530-0); pap. 13.95 (ISBN 0-19-824597-1). Oxford U Pr.

Hegelian Aftermath: Readings in Hegel, Kierkegaard, Freud, Proust & James. Henry Sussman. LC 82-47971. 172p. 1982. text ed. 22.50x (ISBN 0-8018-2852-X). Johns Hopkins.

Hegel's Concept of God. Quentin Lauer. 432p. 1982. 44.50 (ISBN 0-87395-597-8); pap. 16.95 (ISBN 0-87395-598-6). State U NY Pr.

Hegel's Dialectic & Its Criticism. Michael Rosen. LC 81-24211. 210p. 1982. 29.95 (ISBN 0-521-24484-6). Cambridge U Pr.

Hegel's Phenomenology, Part II: The Evolution of Ethical & Religious Consciousness to the Absolute Standpoint. Howard P. Kainz. LC 82-22444. xii, 211p. 1983. text ed. 23.95x (ISBN 0-8214-0677-9); pap. 12.95x (ISBN 0-8214-0738-4). Ohio U Pr.

Hegel's Philosophy of Spirit. Ed. by Peter G. Stillman. (SUNY Series in Hegelian Studies). 223p. 1986. 39.50x (ISBN 0-88706-476-0); pap. 12.95x (ISBN 0-88706-477-9). State U NY Pr.

Hegels System der Theologie. Erik Schmidt. LC 73-81703. (Theologische Bibliothek Toepelmann 26). 210p. 1974. 26.80x (ISBN 3-11-004463-3). De Gruyter.

Hegel's System of Ethical Life & First Philosophy of Spirit. G. W. Hegel. Ed. by H. S. Harris & T. M. Knox. Tr. by H. S. Harris & T. M. Knox. LC 79-11477. 1979. 39.50 (ISBN 0-87395-386-X). State U NY Pr.

Hegemony & Culture: Politics & Religious Change among the Yoruba. David D. Laitin. (Illus.). xiv, 252p. 1986. 30.00 (ISBN 0-226-46789-9); pap. 13.95 (ISBN 0-226-46790-2). U of Chicago Pr.

Hegesippi Qui Dicitur Historiae, Libri 5. Flavius Josephus. Ed. by V. Ussani. (Corpus Scriptorum Ecclesiasticorum Latinorum Ser: Vol. 66). 1932. 31.00 (ISBN 0-384-27880-9). Johnson Repr.

Heian Period in the Evolution of Buddhist Architecture in Japan. Alexander Coburn. (Illus.). 176p. 1985. Repr. of 1930 ed. 187.50 (ISBN 0-86650-167-3). Gloucester Art.

Heichal Hakodesh Concordance to the Old Testament, 1 vol. S. Mandelkern. 95.00 (ISBN 0-87559-163-9). Shalom.

Heidelberg Catechism. Tr. by Allen O. Miller & M. Eugene Osterhaven. LC 62-20891. 1963. pap. 2.25 (ISBN 0-8298-0060-3). Pilgrim NY.

Heidelberg Catechism with Scripture Texts. (Orig.). 1981. pap. 4.95 (ISBN 0-933140-21-5). CRC Pubns.

Heil Kahane: The Life of a Fanatic Whose Influence is Growing. Yair Kotler. Tr. by Ed Levin from Hebrew. LC 86-1035. 212p. 1986. 17.95 (ISBN 0-915361-35-3, 09712-9, Dist. by Watts). Adama Pubs Inc.

Heilige Caecilia in der Roemischen Kirche Des Altertums. Johann P. Kirsch. 1910. pap. 8.00 (ISBN 0-384-29610-6). Johnson Repr.

Heilige Mission, & Praktische Winke fur Missionaire. Franz X. Weninger. 65.00 (ISBN 0-405-10865-6, 11862). Ayer Co Pubs.

Heilige Thomas Von Aquino, 3 vols. rev. ed. Karl Werner. 1963. Set. 107.00 (ISBN 0-8337-3738-4). B Franklin.

Heine's Jewish Comedy: A Study of His Portraits of Jews & Judaism. S. S. Prawer. 846p. 1986. pap. 19.95x (ISBN 0-19-815834-3). Oxford U Pr.

Heinrich Bullinger & the Covenant: The Other Reformed Tradition. J. Wayne Baker. LC 80-14667. xxvi, 300p. 1980. 24.95x (ISBN 0-8214-0554-3). Ohio U Pr.

Heinrich Hallers Uberstzung Der'Imitatio Christi. Erika Bauer. Ed. by James Hogg. (Analecta Cartusiana Ser.: No. 88). 224p. (Orig.). 1982. pap. 25.00 (ISBN 3-7052-0145-X, Pub by. Salzburg Studies). Longwood Pub Group.

Heinrich Von Kleist: Amphithryon Materialien zur Rezeption und Interpretation. Wolfgang Wittkowski. 1978. 40.40x (ISBN 3-11-006988-1). De Gruyter.

Heirloom of Memories. Ovilene Clark. 1983. 8.50 (ISBN 0-8062-2137-2). Carlton.

Heirloom: Sermons, Lectures & Studies. Leo Jung. 1961. 7.50 (ISBN 0-87306-107-1). Feldheim.

Heirs of the Cross. James D. Wallace. 98p. (Orig.). 1984. pap. 3.25 (ISBN 0-934942-43-9, 2022). White Wing Pub.

Heirs of the Gods: A Space Age Interpretation of the Bible. Lee Gladden & Vivianne C. Gladden. LC 78-53852. (Illus.). 324p. Repr. of 1979 ed. 15.95 (ISBN 0-686-37960-8). Bel-Air.

Heirs of the Pharisees. Jacob J. Petuchowski. LC 86-1496. (Brown Classics in Judaica Ser.). 214p. 1986. pap. text ed. 12.00 (ISBN 0-8191-5256-0). U Pr of Amer.

Heirs of the Same Promise: Using Acts As a Study Guide for Evangelizing Ethnic America. Wesley Balda. 1984. 3.95 (ISBN 0-912552-44-1). Missions Adv Res Com Ctr.

Heirs Through Hope: The Episcopal Diocese of West Tennessee. Ellen Davies-Rodgers. LC 83-50733. 1983. 30.00 (ISBN 0-317-05919-X). Plantation.

Hejaz Railway & the Muslim Pilgrimage: A Case of Ottoman Political Progaganda. Jacob M. Landau. LC 78-12918. pap. 73.80 (2027676). Bks Demand UMI.

Heka-Nefer & the Dynastic Material from Toshka & Arminna. William K. Simpson. (Pubns of the Penn-Yale Expedition to Egypt: No. 1). (Illus.). xiv, 53p. 1963. 16.50x (ISBN 0-686-17767-3). Univ Mus of U PA.

Held in High Value. Robert G. Davidson. 65p. (Orig.). 1986. pap. 9.95 (ISBN 0-940754-34-7). Ed Ministries.

Held in the Heavens until... Earl Paulk. 256p. (Orig.). 1985. pap. 7.95 (ISBN 0-917595-07-6). K-Dimension.

Heliotropium: Conformity of the Human Will to the Divine. Jeremias Drexelius. LC 84-51597. 416p. 1985. pap. 8.50 (ISBN 0-89555-245-0). Tan Bks Pubs.

Hell, A Christian Doctrine. Woolsey Teller & Marshall Gauvin. (Illus.). 47p. pap. cancelled (ISBN 0-910309-01-9). Am Atheist.

Hell-Bound. Don Wilkerson & David Manuel. LC 78-60735. 199p. 1978. pap. 3.95 (ISBN 0-932260-03-9). Paraclete Pr.

Hell Is No Joke. Robert L. Sumner. 1959. pap. 3.25 (ISBN 0-914012-28-2, Pub.by Bibl Evang Pr). Sword of Lord.

Hell: Will the Wicked Burn Forever? Ralph Blodgett. (Outreach Ser.). 1981. pap. 0.99 (ISBN 0-8163-0375-4). Pacific Pr Pub Assn.

Hellenism & Christianity. facs. ed. Edwyn R. Bevan. LC 67-26714. (Essay Index Reprint Ser). 1921. 18.00 (ISBN 0-8369-0207-6). Ayer Co Pubs.

Hellenism & the Unfinished Revolution. Apostolos Makrakis. Ed. by Orthodox Christian Educational Society. Tr. by Archimandrite E. Stephanou from Hellenic. 191p. (Orig.). 1968. pap. 5.00x (ISBN 0-938366-26-2). Orthodox Chr.

Hellenistic Civilization & the Jews. Victor Tcherikover. Tr. by S. Applebaum. LC 59-8518. (Temple Bk.). 1970. pap. 9.95x (ISBN 0-689-70248-5, T22). Atheneum.

Hellenistic Magic & the Synoptic Tradition. John Hull. LC 73-77369. (Studies in Biblical Theology, 2nd Ser.: No. 28). 1974. pap. text ed. 12.00x (ISBN 0-8401-3078-3). A R Allenson.

Hellenistic Mystery-Religions. Richard Reitzenstein. Tr. by John E. Steely from Ger. LC 77-12980. (Pittsburgh Theological Monographs: No. 15). Orig. Title: Hellenistischen Mysterienreligionen Nach Ihren Arundgedanken und Wirkungen. 1978. pap. text ed. 17.75 (ISBN 0-915138-20-4). Pickwick.

Hellenistic Religions: Grant. F. C. Grant. 1953. pap. text ed. write for info. (ISBN 0-02-345640-X). Macmillan.

Hellenistic Religions: The Age of Syncretism. Ed. by Frederick C. Grant. 1953. pap. 13.24 scp (ISBN 0-672-60342-X, LLA134). Bobbs.

Hellenistic Ways of Deliverance & the Making of the Christian Synthesis. John H. Randall. LC 74-137339. 1970. 28.00x (ISBN 0-231-03327-3). Columbia U Pr.

Hello God. Alison Winn. 1985. 3.95 (ISBN 0-87162-405-2, D4310). Warner Pr.

Hello-Is God There? Richard E. Rusbuldt. 64p. 1984. pap. 5.95 (ISBN 0-8170-1043-2). Judson.

Hello, My Friend. Roger Prescott. 1981. 6.75 (ISBN 0-89536-474-3, 0800). CSS of Ohio.

Hello Neighbor. H. E. Douglass. (Outreach Ser.). 16p. 1983. pap. 0.25 (ISBN 0-8163-0523-4). Pacific Pr Pub Assn.

Hello, Tomorrow. Mary McDowell. LC 76-27935. 1977. 5.95 (ISBN 0-87212-069-4). Libra.

Hello, World, You're Mine? Winifred R. Simpson. (Illus.). 1987. pap. 3.95 (ISBN 0-570-03643-7). Concordia.

Help: Coping with Crisis. Ed. by Kevin Miller. (Senior High Pacesetter Ser.). 64p. 1986. pap. 7.95 (ISBN 0-89191-282-7). Cook.

Help for Families of the Mentally Ill. Lloyd Ahlem. LC 12-2820. (Trauma Bks.: Ser. 2). 1983. pap. 2.75 (ISBN 0-570-08257-9). Concordia.

Help for Families of the Terminally Ill. M. Tengbom. LC 12-2819. (Trauma Bks.: Ser. 2). 1983. pap. 2.75 ea. (ISBN 0-570-08256-0). Concordia.

Help for Families with a Problem Child. D. M. Nyber. LC 12-2822. (Trauma Bks.: Ser. 2). 1983. pap. 2.75 (ISBN 0-570-08259-5). Concordia.

Help for Making Difficult Decisions. Eamon Tobin. 32p. 1987. pap. 1.50 (ISBN 0-89243-267-5). Liguori Pubns.

Help for Remarried Couples & Families. Richard P. Olson & Carole D. Pia-Terry. 160p. 1984. pap. 6.95 (ISBN 0-8170-0991-4). Judson.

Help for the Evangelistic Preacher. James E. Carter. LC 83-70371. 1985. pap. 6.50 (ISBN 0-8054-6243-0). Broadman.

Help for Today. Ernest Holmes & William H. Hornaday. 256p. 1969. pap. 7.50 (ISBN 0-911336-03-6). Sci of Mind.

Help I Need a Bulletin Board. Autery & Holl. pap. 5.50 (ISBN 0-89137-621-6). Quality Pubns.

Help! I'm a Parent. S. Bruce Narramore. 1972. pap. 6.95 (ISBN 0-310-30321-4). Zondervan.

Help: I'm a Sunday School Teacher. Mary Duckert. LC 77-83133. (Illus.). 126p. 1969. pap. 3.95 (ISBN 0-664-24862-4). Westminster.

Help! I'm a Woman! Beverly Mattox. LC 77-21631. 1977. pap. 1.95 (ISBN 0-87227-053-X). Reg Baptist.

Help, I'm in College. Roy G. Gesch. LC 70-77282. 1969. pap. 3.50 (ISBN 0-570-03100-1, 12-2663). Concordia.

Help, I'm in Trouble: True-to-Life Stories for Young Teens. Louise Ulmer. LC 86-8034. (Illus.). 112p. (Orig.). 1986. pap. 3.95 (ISBN 0-8066-2215-6, 10-3008). Augsburg.

Help in Ages Past, Hope for Years to Come: Daily Devotions from the Old Testament. Robert Cate. 201p. 1983. pap. 5.95 (ISBN 0-13-387431-1). P-H.

Help Is on the Way: Overcoming Barriers to Spirit-Assisted Prayer. Robert G. Tuttle. LC 83-80412. 128p. (Orig.). 1983. pap. 4.95 (ISBN 0-8358-0461-5). Upper Room.

Help Me, God, I'm a Working Mother! Nancy B. Barcus. 64p. 1982. pap. 3.95 (ISBN 0-8170-0954-X). Judson.

Help Me God! It's Hard to Cope. Robert G. Tuttle. 1984. 4.95 (ISBN 0-89536-698-3, 4881). CSS of Ohio.

Help Me: I'm Lost. Christine Kohler. (Growing up Christian Ser.). 24p. (Orig.). 1985. pap. 3.95 (ISBN 0-570-04115-5, 56-1526). Concordia.

Help Me Understand. Amy R. Mumford. (Accent Expressions Ser.). 24p. (Orig.). 1984. pap. 4.95 (ISBN 0-89636-142-X). Accent Bks.

Help My Faith Grow, Lord! Glen Kuck. (Continued Applied Christianity Ser.). 1983. pap. 4.95 (ISBN 0-570-03894-4, 12-2976). Concordia.

Help, We're Having a Baby. H. Norman Wright & Marvin N. Inmon. LC 79-929649. 192p. 1984. pap. 5.95 (ISBN 0-8307-0997-5, 5418362). Regal.

Help Yourself to a Healthier Mind. LeRoy Dugan. 112p. (Orig.). 1980. 5.95 (ISBN 0-87123-205-7, 210205). Bethany Hse.

Help Yourself to Happiness. Maxie C. Maultsby, Jr. LC 75-15057. 1975. pap. 9.95 (ISBN 0-917476-06-9). Inst Rational-Emotive.

Helper. Catherine Marshall. 1979. pap. 3.95 (ISBN 0-380-45583-8). Avon.

Helpful Hints for Fun-filled Parenting. Carole Riddell & Kay Wallingford. LC 84-2056. 128p. 1984. pap. 6.95 spiral (ISBN 0-8407-5880-4). Nelson.

Helping Children Cope with Death. Robert V. Dodd. LC 84-6713. 56p. (Orig.). 1984. pap. 1.95 (ISBN 0-8361-3368-4). Herald Pr.

Helping Disturbed Religious. Ed. by Fintan McNamee. E. F. O'Doherty. (Synthesis Ser.). pap. 0.75 (ISBN 0-8199-0393-0, L38268). Franciscan Herald.

Helping Is. Jane Buerger & Jennie Davis. 1984. 4.95 (ISBN 0-89693-218-4). Victor Bks.

Helping Is-- Jane Buerger & Jennie Davis. LC 84-7042. (Illus.). 32p. 1984. lib. bdg. 4.95 (ISBN 0-89693-218-4). Dandelion Hse.

Helping Laity Help Others. Stanley J. Menking. LC 83-26061. (The Pastor's Handbook Ser.: Vol. 2). 114p. (Orig.). 1984. pap. 7.95 (ISBN 0-664-24615-X). Westminster.

Helping Others. Doris C. Demaree. (Bible Stories for Children Ser.). 1970. pap. 1.50 (ISBN 0-87162-237-8, D1447). Warner Pr.

Helping Ourselves: Families & the Human Network. Mary Howell. LC 75-5291. 1975. pap. 6.95x (ISBN 0-8070-2759-6, BP551). Beacon Pr.

Helping Pastors Cope: A Psycho-social Support System for Pastors. Benjamin D. Schoun. viii, 259p. 1982. pap. 9.95 (ISBN 0-943872-86-3). Andrews Univ Pr.

Helping People Care on the Job. Peter Rossman & Gaylord Noyce. 144p. 1985. pap. 5.95. Judson.

Helping People Grow. Gary Collins. LC 79-6402. (Orig.). 1980. pap. 8.95 (ISBN 0-88449-069-6, A424068). Vision Hse.

Helping the Teacher. Findley B. Edge. 1959. 10.95 (ISBN 0-8054-3403-8). Broadman.

Helping the Troubled. Richard R. De Blassie & John Anderson. 179p. 1981. pap. 3.95 (ISBN 0-8189-1163-8). Alba.

Helping Those Who Don't Want Help. Marshall Shelley. (Leadership Library). 175p. 1986. 9.95 (ISBN 0-917463-10-2). Chr Today.

Helping When It Hurts: A Practical Guide to Helping Relationships. Robert L. Hunter. LC 85-47738. 80p. 1985. pap. 3.95 (ISBN 0-8006-1879-3, 1-1879). Fortress.

Helping Women Cope with Grief. Phyllis R. Silverman. (Sage Human Services Guides Ser.: Vol. 25). 111p. 1981. pap. 9.95 (ISBN 0-8039-1735-X). Sage.

Helping Women in Crisis: A Handbook for People-Helpers. Kay M. Strom. 208p. 1986. pap. 7.95 (ISBN 0-310-33641-4, 11716P). Zondervan.

Helping Your Child Discover Faith. Delia T. Halverson. 128p. 1982. pap. 5.95 (ISBN 0-8170-0957-4). Judson.

Helping Your Child Know Right from Wrong. LC 79-91138. (Redemptorist Pastoral Publication Ser.). 1980. pap. 2.95 (ISBN 0-89243-117-2, 39900). Liguori Pubns.

Helping Your Child Stay Morally Clean. Allan K. Burgess. LC 84-71705. 100p. 1984. 6.95 (ISBN 0-87747-671-3). Deseret Bk.

Helping Your Child to Understand Death. rev. ed. Anna W. Wolf. 1973. pap. 2.30 (ISBN 0-87183-240-2). Jewish Bd Family.

Helping Your Children Love Each Other. Joyce Milburn. LC 83-15505. 160p. (Orig.). 1983. pap. 4.95 (ISBN 0-87123-307-X, 210307). Bethany Hse.

Helping Your Handicapped Child. George Paterson. LC 74-14185. 112p. (Orig.). 1975. pap. 5.95 (ISBN 0-8066-1467-6, 10-3005). Augsburg.

Helping Your Teen Develop Faith. Delia T. Halverson. 112p. 1985. pap. 5.95 (ISBN 0-8170-1046-7). Judson.

Helping Yourself with Numerology. Helen Hitchcock. LC 72-172406. (Illus.). 228p. 1972. pap. 5.95 (ISBN 0-13-386854-0, Reward). P-H.

Helping Yourself With Selected Prayers. Tr. by Original Publications. pap. 3.95 (ISBN 0-942272-01-3). Original Pubns.

Helping Yourself with White Witchcraft. A. J. Manning. 1972. 9.95 (ISBN 0-13-386565-7, Reward); pap. 4.95 (ISBN 0-13-386573-8). P-H.

Helping Youth Interpret the Bible: A Teaching Resource. A. Roger Gobbel et al. LC 84-3916. 204p. 1984. pap. 9.95 (ISBN 0-8042-1580-4). John Knox.

Helps & Hints at Bible Study. Louis M. Perschke. 176p. 1981. 8.50 (ISBN 0-682-49733-9, Testament). Exposition Pr FL.

Helps for Counselors. Jay E. Adams. (Orig.). 1980. pap. 2.95 (ISBN 0-8010-0156-0). Baker Bk.

Helps from Hebrews. Don E. Boatman. LC 75-1066. (Bible Study Textbook Ser.). (Illus.). 1960. 14.30 (ISBN 0-89900-044-4). College Pr Pub.

Helps to Holiness. Samuel L. Brengle. 1978. pap. 3.95 (ISBN 0-86544-003-4). Salv Army Suppl South.

Helps to Holy Living. C. E. Orr. 64p. pap. 0.40 (ISBN 0-686-29112-3); pap. 1.00 3 copies (ISBN 0-686-29113-1). Faith Pub Hse.

Henri Arnaud und die Waldenser. Auguste Lacoste. (Basler und Berner Studien zur historischen und systematischen: Vol. 47). 213p. 1982. 20.00 (ISBN 3-261-04890-5). P Lang Pubs.

Henri Dominique Lacordaire: Essay on the Re-establishment in France of the Order of Preachers. Henry D. Lacordaire. Ed. by Simon Tugwell. (Dominican Sources). 70p. 1983. pap. 4.00 (ISBN 0-9511202-1-2). Parable.

Henrici De Werla, O. F. M. Opera Omnia: Tractatus De Immaculata Conceptione Beatae Mariae Virginis. Ed. by Souphronius Clasen. (Text Ser). 1955. 6.00 (ISBN 0-686-11555-4). Franciscan Inst.

Henrician Reformation: The Diocese of Lincoln Under John Longland 1521-1547. Margaret Bowker. LC 80-41655. (Illus.). 256p. 1981. 49.50 (ISBN 0-521-23639-8). Cambridge U Pr.

Henry David Thoreau: A Week on the Concord & Merrimack Rivers; Walden; The Maine Woods; Cape Cod. Henry David Thoreau. 1114p. 27.50. Library of America.

Henry Ford & the Jews. Albert Lee. LC 79-3694. 252p. 1980. 12.95 (ISBN 0-8128-2701-5). Stein & Day.

Henry Grattan & His Times. facsimile ed. Stephen Gwynn. LC 78-175699. (Select Bibliographies Reprint Ser.). Repr. of 1939 ed. 26.50 (ISBN 0-8369-6614-7). Ayer Co Pubs.

Henry Hodgkin: The Road to Pendle Hill. John O. Greenwood. LC 79-91958. 1980. pap. 2.50x (ISBN 0-87574-229-7). Pendle Hill.

Henry II. W. L. Warren. (English Monarchs Ser.). 1973. pap. 14.95 (ISBN 0-520-03494-5, CAL367). U of Cal Pr.

Henry III & the Jesuit Politicians. A. L. Martin. 264p. (Orig.). 1973. pap. text ed. 48.50x (Pub. by Droz Switzerland). Coronet Bks.

Henry James & the Occult: The Great Extension. Martha Banta. LC 72-75386. Repr. of 1972 ed. 54.60 (ISBN 0-8357-9215-3, 2013010). Bks Demand UMI.

Henry James, Sr. & the Religion of the Community. Dwight W. Hoover. LC 68-57113. pap. 38.00 (ISBN 0-317-08994-3, 2012947). Bks Demand UMI.

Henry Smith: England's Silver-Tongued Preacher. R. B. Jenkins. LC 83-878. vi, 131p. 1983. 10.95 (ISBN 0-86554-077-2, H64). Mercer Univ Pr.

Henry the Eighth & the English Monasteries, 2 vols. Francis A. Gasquet. LC 74-39467. (Select Bibliography Reprint Ser.). 1972. Repr. of 1888 ed. 56.75 (ISBN 0-8369-9905-3). Ayer Co Pubs.

Henry Vaughan & the Hermetic Philosophy. Elizabeth Holmes. (English Literature Ser., No. 33). 1970. pap. 22.95x (ISBN 0-8383-0094-4). Haskell.

Henry Vaughan: The Unfolding Vision. Jonathan F. Post. LC 82-47609. 264p. 1983. 26.50 (ISBN 0-691-06527-6). Princeton U Pr.

Henry Venn: Missionary Statesman. Wilbert R. Shenk. LC 82-18779. 192p. (Orig.). 1983. pap. 2.49 (ISBN 0-88344-181-0). Orbis Bks.

Henry VIII. 2nd ed. M. D. Palmer. (Seminar Studies in History Ser.). (Illus.). 1983. pap. text ed. 6.95x (ISBN 0-582-35437-4). Longman.

Henry VIII. J. J. Scarisbrick. LC 68-10995. (English Monarchs Series). (Illus.). 1968. pap. 8.95 (ISBN 0-520-01130-9, CAL195). U of Cal Pr.

Henry VIII & the English Monasteries, 2 vols. Francis A. Gasquet. (Select Bibliographies Reprint Ser.). Repr. of 1888 ed. lib. bdg. 55.00 set (ISBN 0-8290-0849-7). Irvington.

Henry Whitney Bellows. Walter D. Kring. 1979. pap. 7.95 (ISBN 0-933840-03-9). Unitarian Univ.

Henry's Red Sea. Barbara C. Smucker. LC 55-7810. (Christian Peace Shelf Ser.). (Illus.). 108p. 1955. 3.95 (ISBN 0-8361-1372-1). Herald Pr.

Hensley Henson: A Study in the Friction Between Church & State. Owen Chadwick. 350p. 1983. text ed. 39.95x (ISBN 0-19-825445-8). Oxford U Pr.

Her-Bak Egyptian Initiate. Isha Schwaller De Lubicz. Tr. by Ronald Fraser from Fr. (Illus.). 400p. 1982. pap. 9.95 (ISBN 0-89281-002-5). Inner Tradit.

Her Door of Faith. Robert O. Donovan. LC 79-172385. (Illus.). 112p. 1971. pap. 2.95 (ISBN 0-913748-02-1). Orovan Bks.

Her Name Is Woman, 2 bks. Gien Karssen. LC 77-81187. Bk. 1, 1975. pap. 5.95 (ISBN 0-89109-420-2); Bk. 2, 1977. pap. 5.95 (ISBN 0-89109-424-5). NavPress.

Her Name Was Sojourner Truth. Hertha Pauli. (YA) 1976. pap. 1.50 (ISBN 0-380-00719-3, 29074). Avon.

Her Own Way: The Story of Lottie Moon. Helen A. Monsell. LC 82-71443. 1982. pap. 4.50 (ISBN 0-8054-4319-3, 4243-19). Broadman.

Her Story: Women in Christian Tradition. Barbara J. MacHaffie. LC 85-45494. 192p. 1986. pap. 9.95 (ISBN 0-8006-1893-9). Fortress.

Herald of Christ Louis Bourdaloue, S. J. John C. Reville. 1978. Repr. of 1922 ed. lib. bdg. 25.00 (ISBN 0-8492-2270-2). R West.

Herald of Hope (Isaiah) Leader's Guide. (New Horizons Bible Study Ser.). 48p. (Orig.). 1984. pap. 1.95 (ISBN 0-89367-101-0). Light & Life.

Herald of Hope (Isaiah) Student Guide. (New Horizons Bible Study Ser.). 68p. (Orig.). 1984. pap. 2.50 (ISBN 0-89367-100-2). Light & Life.

Heralds of the King. John G. Hogan. LC 79-107714. (Essay Index Reprint Ser.). 1934. 17.00 (ISBN 0-8369-1516-X). Ayer Co Pubs.

Heralds of Victory. Ron Holz. (Illus.). 256p. (Orig.). 1986. 8.00 (ISBN 0-89216-068-3); pap. 5.00 (ISBN 0-89216-065-9). Salvation Army.

Heralds to a New Age: Preaching for the Twenty-First Century. Don M. Aycock. 228p. 1985. 11.95 (ISBN 0-87178-352-5). Brethren.

Herbert Armstrong & His Worldwide Church of God: An Exposure & an Indictment. John Bowden. 64p. 1982. saddle stitched 3.00 (ISBN 0-911826-24-6). Am Atheist.

Herbert Butterfield on History. Herbert Butterfield. Ed. by Robin W. Winks. LC 83-49176. (History & Historiography Ser.). 204p. 1985. lib. bdg. 30.00 (ISBN 0-8240-6352-X). Garland Pub.

Herbert Fromm on Jewish Music: A Composers View. Herbert Fromm. LC 78-60716. 1979. 10.00x (ISBN 0-8197-0465-2). Bloch.

Herbert J. Taylor Story. Herbert J. Taylor. 128p. 1983. pap. 4.95 (ISBN 0-87784-836-X). Inter-Varsity.

Herbert W. Armstrong. Walter Martin. 32p. 1969. pap. 2.95 (ISBN 0-87123-213-8, 210213). Bethany Hse.

Herbs & Spices of the Bible: How to Grow & Use Them. Marian M. O'Brien. Ed. by Herbert Lambert. LC 84-256. 128p. 1984. pap. 8.95 (ISBN 0-8272-1420-0). CBP.

Herder Symbol Dictionary. Tr. by Boris Matthews from Ger. LC 85-30872. Tr. of Herder Lexikon: Symbole. (Illus.). 222p. 1986. vinyl 14.95 (ISBN 0-933029-03-9). Chiron Pubns.

Herders Theologisches Taschenlexikon. K. Rahner. (Ger.). 3180p. 1976. pap. 99.50 (ISBN 0-686-56481-2, M-7463, Pub. by Herder). French & Eur.

Here Am I! A Christian Reflection on God. Adrio Konig. LC 82-11377. pap. 62.00 (ISBN 0-317-30148-9, 2025331). Bks Demand UMI.

Here Am I; Send Aaron! Jill Bricose. 1984. pap. 2.95 (ISBN 0-89693-712-7). Victor Bks.

Here & Hereafter. William Kramer. 1978. pap. 4.95 (ISBN 0-8100-0053-9, 15-0365). Northwest Pub.

Here & Hereafter. George A. St. Paul. LC 56-9839. (Loyola Request Reprint Ser.). Repr. of 1963 ed. 59.30 (ISBN 0-8357-9427-X, 2015061). Bks Demand UMI.

Here Are Your Answers, Vol. I. 3rd ed. Flower A. Newhouse. LC 49-16192. 1948. 9.50 (ISBN 0-910378-01-0). Christward.

Here Are Your Answers, Vol. II. 2nd ed. Flower A. Newhouse. LC 76-103410. 1969. 9.50 (ISBN 0-910378-06-1). Christward.

Here Are Your Answers, Vol. III. Flower A. Newhouse. Ed. by Pamela Boult. 222p. 1983. 11.00 (ISBN 0-910378-18-5). Christward.

Here at Thy Table Lord. Alton H. McEachern. LC 77-1024. 1978. pap. 4.50 (ISBN 0-8054-2310-9). Broadman.

Here Begynneth a Lityll Treatise Spekynge of the Arte & Crafte to Knowe Well to Dye. Tr. by W. Caxton. LC 72-169. (English Experience Ser.: No. 221). 28p. Repr. of 1490 ed. 14.00 (ISBN 90-221-0221-1). Walter J Johnson.

Here Begynneth a Lytell Treatyse of the Turkes Lawe Called Alcaron. Kur'An. LC 77-7411. (English Experience Ser.: No. 876). 1977. Repr. of 1519 ed. lib. bdg. 3.50 (ISBN 90-221-0876-7). Walter J Johnson.

Here Begynneth a Treatyse to Dyspose Men to Be Vertously Occupyed in Theyr Myndes & Prayers. Martin Betson. LC 77-6854. (English Experience Ser.: No. 848). 1977. Repr. of 1500 ed. lib. bdg. 5.00 (ISBN 90-221-0848-1). Walter J Johnson.

Here Begynneth the Boke Intituled Eracles & Also Godefrey of Boloyne. Heraclius. Tr. by William Caxton. LC 73-6140. (English Experience Ser.: No. 604). 1973. Repr. of 1481 ed. 52.00 (ISBN 90-221-0604-7). Walter J Johnson.

Here Comes Adventure. Robert H. Pierson. Ed. by Gerald Wheeler. (Banner Ser.). (Illus.). 192p. (Orig.). 1984. pap. 5.95 (ISBN 0-8280-0244-4). Review & Herald.

Here Comes Jesus. Ed Stewart. LC 77-90584. 160p. 1977. pap. 3.50 (ISBN 0-8307-0553-8, S101157). Regal.

Here Endeth the Book of the Lyf of Our Lady. John Lydgate. LC 73-38207. (English Experience Ser.: No. 473). 192p. 1972. Repr. of 1484 ed. 63.00 (ISBN 90-221-0473-7). Walter J Johnson.

Here I Am Again, Lord. Betty Isler. (Continued Applied Christianity Ser.). 1983. pap. 4.95 (ISBN 0-570-03895-2, 12-2977). Concordia.

Here I Am, God, Where Are You? John Robertson. 1975. pap. 2.50 (ISBN 0-8423-1416-4). Tyndale.

Here I Stand: A Life of Martin Luther. Roland H. Bainton. (Festival Books). 1978. pap. 4.95 (ISBN 0-687-16894-5, Co-Pub. with NAL). Abingdon.

Here I Stand: A Life of Martin Luther. Roland H. Bainton. pap. 3.95 (ISBN 0-451-62404-1, ME2103, Ment). NAL.

Here I Stand: A Life of Martin Luther. Roland H. Bainton. 13.25 (ISBN 0-8446-6225-9). Peter Smith.

Here or Nowhere. Renee Hermanson. LC 83-51401. 128p. (Orig.). 1984. pap. 5.50 (ISBN 0-8358-0478-X). Upper Room.

Here We Go Again Lord. Minnie Hawthorne. 1982. 4.50 (ISBN 0-8062-1659-X). Carlton.

Hereby We Know: I, II, III John. Clinton Gill. LC 70-1464. (Bible Study Textbook Ser.). (Illus.). 1966. 10.60 (ISBN 0-89900-047-9). College Pr Pub.

Heredity: A Study in Science & the Bible. William J. Tinkle. LC 67-28034. 1967. 5.50 (ISBN 0-686-05046-0). St Thomas.

Herein Is Love. Reuel L. Howe. pap. 3.95 (ISBN 0-8170-0263-4). Judson.

Herein Lies the Treasure-Trove, Vol. 1. Triptaka Master Hua. Tr. by Buddhist Text Translation Society. (Illus.). 160p. (Orig.). 1983. pap. 6.50 (ISBN 0-88139-001-1). Buddhist Text.

Here's a Thought. J. Sig Paulson. 67p. 1982. pap. 2.00 (ISBN 0-317-20869-1). CSA Pr.

Here's How: Health Education by Extension. Ronald S. Seaton & Edith B. Seaton. LC 76-40599. 1976. pap. 3.95 (ISBN 0-87808-150-X). William Carey Lib.

Here's the Difference. William MacDonald. pap. 2.95 (ISBN 0-937396-55-9). Walterick Pubs.

Heresies et Societes Dans L'europe Pre-Industrielle 11e-18e Siecles: Communications et Debats Du Colloque De Royaumont. Jacques Le Goff. (Civilisations et Societes: No. 10). 1968. pap. 28.40x (ISBN 90-2796-079-8). Mouton.

Heresies Exposed. William C. Irvine. pap. 4.95 (ISBN 0-87213-401-6). Loizeaux.

Heresies of the Early Christian & Medieval Era, 67 titles in 92 vols. Ed. by Joseph F. O'Callaghan. (AMS Reprint Ser.). 1965. Repr. of 1816 ed. write in info. (ISBN 0-404-16090-5). AMS Pr.

Heresies: The Image of Christ in the Mirror of Heresy & Orthodoxy from the Apostles to the Present. Harold O. Brown. LC 80-2558. (Illus.). 504p. 1984. 17.95 (ISBN 0-385-15338-4). Doubleday.

Heresy & Authority in Medieval Europe. Ed. by Edward Peters. LC 79-5262. (Middle Ages Ser.). 384p. 1980. 39.00x (ISBN 0-8122-7779-1); pap. 15.95x (ISBN 0-8122-1103-0). U of Pa Pr.

Heresy & Inquisition in Narbonne. Richard W. Emery. LC 75-166031. (Columbia University Studies in the Social Sciences: No. 480). 17.50 (ISBN 0-404-51480-4). AMS Pr.

Heresy, Crusade, & Inquisition in Southern France, 1100-1250. Walter L. Wakefield. 1974. 40.00x (ISBN 0-520-02380-3). U of Cal Pr.

Heresy of Monasticism. James A. Mohler. LC 76-148683. 1971. 5.95 (ISBN 0-8189-0183-7). Alba.

Heretic. Stephen Fritchman. pap. 6.95 (ISBN 0-933840-19-5). Unitarian Univ.

Heretics. facs. ed. Gilbert K. Chesterton. LC 75-128220. (Essay Index Reprint Ser.). 1905. 19.00 (ISBN 0-8369-1869-X). Ayer Co Pubs.

Heritage & Hope: A People of Hope. Dennis E. Shoemaker. write for info. (ISBN 0-916466-04-3). Reformed Church.

Heritage & Horizons: A History of the Open Bible Standard Churches. Robert B. Mitchell. LC 81-18884. (Illus., Orig.). 1982. 6.95 (ISBN 0-9608160-0-3); pap. 4.95 (ISBN 0-9608160-1-1). Open Bible.

Heritage & Promise: Perspectives on the Church of the Brethren. rev. ed. Emmet F. Bittinger. 1983. pap. 6.95 (ISBN 0-87178-357-6). Brethren.

Heritage Book, 1985. Edna McCann. (Illus.). 192p. 1984. 5.95 (ISBN 0-02-582880-0). Macmillan.

Heritage: Civilization & the Jews. Abba Eban. (Illus.). 352p. 1984. 32.95 (ISBN 0-671-44103-5). Summit Bks.

Heritage: Civilization & the Jews. Abba Eban. 356p. 1986. pap. 16.95 (ISBN 0-671-62881-X). Summit Bks.

Heritage: Civilization & the Jews; a Study Guide. William Hallo & David Ruderman. 302p. 1984. 34.95 (ISBN 0-03-000484-5); pap. 12.95 (ISBN 0-03-000483-7). Praeger.

Heritage: Civilization & the Jews; a Source Reader. Ed. by William Hallo & David Ruderman. 332p. 1984. 34.95 (ISBN 0-03-000479-9); pap. 13.95 (ISBN 0-03-000482-9). Praeger.

Heritage in the Warmed Heart. Peter W. Gentry. 63p. 1986. pap. 2.50 (ISBN 0-8341-0955-7). Beacon Hill.

Heritage of Biblical Faith. J. P. Hyatt. LC 64-13404. 1977. pap. 9.95 (ISBN 0-8272-1416-2). CBP.

Heritage of Buddhist Poetry. W. Crown. 1986. 6.95 (ISBN 0-533-06003-6). Vantage.

Heritage of Faith. Bob Jones, Sr. et al. 183p. (Orig.). 1973. pap. 3.95 (ISBN 0-89084-009-1). Bob Jones Univ Pr.

Heritage of Faith: Two Pioneers of Judaism in America. Nancy I. Klein. 16.95 (ISBN 0-88125-119-4). Ktav.

Heritage of Holiness. Bramwell Tripp et al. 110p. 1977. pap. 3.50 (ISBN 0-89216-013-6). Salvation Army.

Heritage of the Lord. Vivia Brooks. (Illus.). 96p. 1984. 10.00 (ISBN 0-87770-314-0). Ye Galleon.

Heritage of the Sikhs. Harbans Singh. 1983. 26.00x (ISBN 0-8364-1006-8); text ed. 16.00x (ISBN 0-8364-1007-6). South Asia Bks.

Heritage of the Slavs: The Christianization of the Great Moravian Empire. Thomas J. Drobena & Wilma S. Kucharek. (Illus.). xviii, 174p. 1979. pap. 5.95 (ISBN 0-915887-01-0). Kosovo Pub Co.

Heritage Series. Power. 1976. pap. 8.00 (ISBN 0-8298-0313-0). Pilgrim NY.

Heritage Village Church Presents the Ministry of Jim & Tammy Bakker. Date not set. price not set. PTL Enterprises.

Herman Melville's "Clarel" A Spiritual Autobiography. Vincent Kenny. LC 73-3074. xvi, 272p. 1973. 26.00 (ISBN 0-208-01226-5, Archon). Shoe String.

Hermann Cohen's Judische Schriften, 3 vols. Hermann Cohen. Ed. by Steven Katz. LC 79-7128. (Jewish Philosophy, Mysticism & History of Ideas Ser.). 1980. Repr. of 1924 ed. lib. bdg. 103.50x (ISBN 0-405-12245-4). Ayer Co Pubs.

Hermanos, Ahora Cartas del Diablo. Hugo Ruiz. 64p. 1986. pap. 1.40 (ISBN 0-311-46045-3). Casa Bautista.

Hermeneutic Critique of Structuralist Exegesis: With Specific Reference to Lk. 10.29-37. Sandra W. Perpich. LC 83-21737. (Illus.). 264p. (Orig.). 1984. lib. bdg. 25.25 (ISBN 0-8191-3668-9); pap. text ed. 13.25 (ISBN 0-8191-3669-7). U Pr of Amer.

Hermeneutic of Dogma. Thomas B. Ommen. LC 75-29493. (American Academy of Religion. Dissertation Ser.). 1975. pap. 9.95 (ISBN 0-89130-039-2, 010111). Scholars Pr GA.

Hermeneutic Phenomenology: The Philosophy of Paul Ricoeur. Don Ihde. (Studies in Phenomenology & Existential Philosophy). 1971. 20.95 (ISBN 0-8101-0347-8); pap. 11.95 (ISBN 0-8101-0611-6). Northwestern U Pr.

Hermeneutical Agnosticism: A Critique of Subjectivism in Biblical Interpretation. Jody L. Apple. LC 84-62067. 195p. (Orig.). 1985. pap. 7.95 (ISBN 0-931247-00-4). New Testament Christ Pr.

Hermeneutical Essays on Vedantic Topics. J. G. Arapura. 326p. 1986. 18.00 (ISBN 81-208-0183-0, Pub. by Motilal Banarsidass). South Asia Bks.

Hermeneutical Inquiry, Vol. I: The Interpretations of Texts. Ed. by David E. Klemm. (American Academy of Religion, Studies in Religion). 299p. 1986. 22.95 (ISBN 1-55540-032-9, 01-00-43); pap. 16.95 (ISBN 1-55540-033-7). Scholars Pr GA.

Hermeneutical Inquiry, Vol. II: The Interpretation of Existence. Ed. by David E. Klemm. (American Academy of Religion, Studies in Religion). 409p. 1986. 26.95 (ISBN 1-55540-034-5, 01-00-44); pap. 19.95 (ISBN 1-55540-035-3). Scholars Pr GA.

Hermeneutical Procedure & Theological Method in Origen's Exegesis. Karen Jo Torjesen. (Patristische Texts und Studien: Vol. 28). xii, 183p. 1985. 41.00x (ISBN 3-11-010202-1). De Gruyter.

Hermeneutical Quest: Essays in Honor of James Luther Mays on His Sixty-Fifth Birthday. Ed. by Donald G. Miller. (Princeton Theological Monograph Ser.: No. 4). 1986. pap. 27.95 (ISBN 0-915138-86-7). Pickwick.

Hermeneutics. Bernard Ramm. (Practical Theology Ser.). pap. 3.95 (ISBN 0-8010-7605-6). Baker Bk.

Hermeneutics & Horizons: The Shape of the Future. Ed. by Frank Flinn. LC 82-50053. 445p. (Orig.). 1982. pap. 12.95. Rose Sharon Pr.

Hermeneutics & Horizons: The Shape of the Future. Ed. by Frank K. Flinn. LC 82-50053. (Conference Ser.: No. 11). xvii, 445p. (Orig.). 1982. pap. text ed. 11.95 (ISBN 0-932894-11-9, Pub. by New Era Bks). Paragon Hse.

Hermeneutics & Modern Philosophy. Ed. by Brice R. Wachterhauser. 536p. (Orig.). 1986. 49.50x (ISBN 0-88706-295-4); pap. 16.95x (ISBN 0-88706-296-2). State U NY Pr.

Hermeneutics & Praxis. Ed. by Robert Hollinger. LC 85-40599. (Revisions Ser.: Vol. 6). 320p. 1985. text ed. 29.95x (ISBN 0-268-01080-3, 85-10802, Dist. by Har-Row); pap. text ed. 12.95x (ISBN 0-268-01081-1, 85-10810). U of Notre Dame Pr.

Hermeneutics & the Sociology of Knowledge. Susan J. Hekman. LC 85-52311. 224p. 1986. text ed. 29.95x (ISBN 0-268-01083-8). U of Notre Dame Pr.

Hermeneutics & Unification Theology. Ed. by Darrol Bryant & Durwood Foster. LC 80-66201. (Conference Ser.: No. 5). (Illus.). 154p. (Orig.). 1980. pap. 7.95 (ISBN 0-932894-05-4, Pub. by New Era Bks). Paragon Hse.

Hermeneutics & Unification Theology. Ed. by Darrol Bryant & Durwood Foster. LC 80-66201. 154p. (Orig.). 1980. pap. 7.95. Rose Sharon Pr.

Hermeneutics, Authority & Canon. Ed. by D. A. Carson & John D. Woodbridge. 480p. 1986. pap. 14.95 (ISBN 0-310-43991-4, 12644P). Zondervan.

Hermeneutics, Inerrancy, & the Bible: Papers from ICBI Summit II. Ed. by Earl D. Radmacher & Robert D. Preus. LC 83-12314. 928p. (Orig.). 1984. pap. 16.95 (ISBN 0-310-37081-7, 12314P). Zondervan.

Hermeneutics: Interpretation Theory in Schleiermacher, Dilthey, Heidegger, & Gadamer. Richard E. Palmer. LC 68-54885. (Studies in Phenomenology & Existential Philosophy). 1969. 22.95 (ISBN 0-8101-0027-4); pap. 9.95 (ISBN 0-8101-0459-8). Northwestern U Pr.

Hermeneutics of Ultimacy: Peril or Promise? James H. Olthuis et al. (Christian Studies Today). 90p. (Orig.). 1987. lib. bdg. 19.75 (ISBN 0-8191-5800-3, Pub. by Inst Chris Stud); pap. text ed. 8.25 (ISBN 0-8191-5801-1). U Pr of Amer.

Hermeneutics: Principles & Processes of Biblical Interpretation. Henry A. Virkler. LC 80-70530. 200p. 1981. 12.95 (ISBN 0-8010-9282-5). Baker Bk.

Hermeneutics: The Handwritten Manuscripts. Friedrich Schleiermacher. Ed. by Heinz Kimmerle. Tr. by James Duke & Jack Forstman. LC 77-13969. (American Academy of Religion. Text & Translations Ser.: No. 1). 1978. pap. text ed. 10.25 (ISBN 0-89130-186-0, 010201). Scholars Pr GA.

Hermes-Guide of Souls: The Mythologem of the Masculine Source of Life. Karl Kerenyi. Tr. by Murray Stein. LC 85-18263. (Dunquin Ser.: No. 7). 104p. 1986. pap. 8.50 (ISBN 0-88214-207-0). Spring Pubns.

Hermetic Commandments in Today's World. Robert E. Birdsong. (Aquarian Academy Monograph, Ser. F: Lecture No. 7). 1977. pap. 1.25 (ISBN 0-917108-19-1). Sirius Bks.

Hermetic Wisdom. (Sacred Texts Ser.). 130p. 1986. pap. 8.75 (ISBN 0-88695-042-2). Concord Grove.

Hermetica: The Ancient Greek & Latin Writings Which Contain Religious or Philosophic Teachings Ascribed to Hermes Trismegistus, 4 vols. Ed. & tr. by Walter Scott. LC 85-8198. 1985. Vol 1; 549p. pap. 15.95 (ISBN 0-87773-338-4); Vol. 2; 482p. pap. 15.95 (ISBN 0-87773-339-2); Vol. 3; 632p. pap. 17.95 (ISBN 0-87773-340-6); Vol. 4; 576p. pap. 17.95 (ISBN 0-87773-341-4). Shambhala Pubns.

Hermit in English Literature from the Beginnings to 1660. Charles P. Weaver. LC 73-515. 1973. lib. bdg. 25.00 (ISBN 0-8414-1456-4). Folcroft.

Hermit in German Literature: From Lessing to Eichendorff. John Fitzell. LC 74-168033. (North Carolina. University. Studies in the Germanic Languages & Literatures: No. 30). Repr. of 1961 ed. 27.00 (ISBN 0-404-50930-4). AMS Pr.

Hermitage Journals. John H. Griffin. LC 82-45833. (Illus.). 240p. 1983. pap. 6.95 (ISBN 0-385-18470-0, Im). Doubleday.

Hermitage Within: Spirituality of the Desert. Tr. by Alan Neame. 160p. 1982. pap. 6.95 (ISBN 0-8091-2428-9). Paulist Pr.

Hermits & Anchorites of England. Rotha M. Clay. LC 68-21759. (Illus.). 1968. Repr. of 1914 ed. 40.00x (ISBN 0-8103-3424-0). Gale.

Hermits & the New Monasticism: A Study of Religious Communities in Western Europe, 1000-1150. Henrietta Leyser. LC 83-40611. 131p. 1984. 25.00 (ISBN 0-312-36999-9). St Martin.

Hermosa Historia de Jesus: Ordenada, Simplificada y Brevemente Explicada. Tomas De La Fuente. 1983. pap. 4.95 (ISBN 0-311-04658-4). Casa Bautista.

Hernan Cortes. (Span.). 10.95 (ISBN 84-241-5408-8). E Torres & Sons.

Hernan Cortes: Conquistador in Mexico. John Wilkes. LC 76-22436. (Cambridge Topic Bks). (Illus.). 1977. PLB 8.95 (ISBN 0-8225-1205-X). Lerner Pubns.

Hero: A Study in Tradition, Myth, & Drama. FitzRoy Raglan. LC 75-23424. 296p. 1975. Repr. of 1956 ed. lib. bdg. 45.00x (ISBN 0-8371-8138-0, RATH). Greenwood.

Hero of Auschwitz. Ed. by Franciscan Friars of Marytown. (Illus.). 47p. 1979. pap. 0.75 (ISBN 0-913382-11-6, 105-29). Prow Bks-Franciscan.

Hero of Hill House. Mabel Hale. 224p. pap. 2.00 (ISBN 0-686-29148-4). Faith Pub Hse.

Hero of Molokai. Omer Englebert. (Illus.). 1977. 4.00 (ISBN 0-8198-0057-0); pap. 3.00 (ISBN 0-8198-0058-9). Dghtrs St Paul.

Hero or Fool. G. Rostrevor Hamilton. LC 70-98995. (Studies in Milton, No. 22). 1970. pap. 19.95x (ISBN 0-8383-0038-3). Haskell.

Hero or Fool: A Study of Milton's Satan. G. Rostrevor Hamilton. LC 74-16136. 1944. lib. bdg. 17.50 (ISBN 0-8414-4860-4). Folcroft.

Hero with a Thousand Faces. rev. ed. Joseph Campbell. LC 49-8590. (Bollingen Ser.: No. 17). (Illus.). 1968. 39.50 (ISBN 0-691-09743-7); pap. 9.95 (ISBN 0-691-01784-0). Princeton U Pr.

Herod & Mariamne. Friedrich Hebbel. Tr. by Paul H. Curts. LC 51-895. (North Carolina. University. Studies in the Germanic Languages & Literatures: No. 3). Repr. of 1950 ed. 27.00 (ISBN 0-404-50903-7). AMS Pr.

Herod Antipas: A Contemporary of Jesus Christ. new ed. Harold W. Hoehner. 456p. 1980. pap. 11.95 (ISBN 0-310-42251-5, 10842P). Zondervan.

Heroes. Charles Kingsley. (Facsimilie Classics Ser.). (Illus.). 224p. 1980. 8.95 (ISBN 0-8317-4448-0, Mayflower Bks). Smith Pubs.

Heroes & Gods: Spiritual Biographies in Antiquity. facsimile ed. Moses Hadas & Morton Smith. LC 77-117800. (Essay Index Reprints - Religious Perspectives Ser.: Vol. 13). Repr. of 1965 ed. 19.00 (ISBN 0-8369-1880-0). Ayer Co Pubs.

Heroes & Heroines of Many Lands. Compiled by Harriet Ross. (Illus.). 160p. 1981. PLB 7.95 (ISBN 0-87460-214-9). Lion Bks.

Heroes & Monsters of Greek Myth. Bernard Evslin et al. (Illus.). 112p. 1984. pap. 2.25 (ISBN 0-590-33457-3, Point). Scholastic Inc.

Heroes & Zeroes. Terry Powell. 144p. 1987. pap. 3.95 (ISBN 0-89693-570-1). Victor Bks.

Heroes from Every Walk of Life. Daughters of St. Paul. 1981. 5.00 (ISBN 0-8198-3303-7); pap. 4.00 (ISBN 0-8198-3304-5). Dghtrs St Paul.

Heroes, Gods, & Emperors from Roman Mythology. Kerry Usher. LC 83-11085. (World Mythology Ser.). (Illus.). 132p. 1984. 15.95 (ISBN 0-8052-3880-8). Schocken.

Heroes, Heroines, & Holidays: Plays for Jewish Youth. Elaine Rembrandt. LC 81-67027. 148p. (Orig.). 1981. pap. 6.50 (ISBN 0-86705-002-0). AIRE.

Heroes, Monsters & Other Worlds from Russian Mythology. Elizabeth Warner. LC 85-10750. (Illus.). 132p. 1986. 15.95 (ISBN 0-8052-4007-1). Schocken.

Heroes of American Jewish History. Deborah Karp. 1972. pap. 6.95x (ISBN 0-87068-394-2). Ktav.

Heroes of American Jewish History. Deborah Karp. Ed. by Benjamin Effron. 155p. pap. 6.95 (ISBN 0-686-95130-1). ADL.

Heroes of Greek Fairy Tales for My Children. Charles Kingsley. 1889. Repr. lib. bdg. 15.00 (ISBN 0-8414-5578-3). Folcroft.

Heroes of Hanukkah. Donald Lieberman. 1980. 8.95x (ISBN 0-87068-866-9). Ktav.

Heroes of Islam. F. Karim. Incl. Bk. 1. Muhammad; Bk. 2. Abu Bakr; Bk. 3. Umar; Bk. 4. Othman; Bk. 5. Ali; Bk. 6. Khalid Bin Walid; Bk. 7. Mohammad Bin Qasim; Bk. 8. Mahmood of Ghazni; Bk. 9. Mohyuddin; Bk. 10. Sultan Tipu; Bk. 11. Aisha the Truthful; Bk. 12. Hussain the Martyr; Bk. 13. Some Companions of the Prophet-I; Bk. 14. Some Companions of the Prophet-II; Bk. 15. Some Companions of the Prophet-III. pap. 37.50 complete set (ISBN 0-686-18393-2); pap. 2.50 ea bk. Kazi Pubns.

Heroes of Jewish History: From Abraham to Moses, Vol. 1. Mordecai Lewittes. 255p. 1952. pap. 6.95x (ISBN 0-88482-626-0). Hebrew Pub.

Heroes of Jewish Thought. Deborah Karp. (Illus.). 1965. pap. 6.95x (ISBN 0-87068-538-4). Ktav.

Heroes of Modern Jewish Thought. Deborah Karp. (Illus.). 1966. pap. 6.95x (ISBN 0-87068-539-2). Ktav.

Heroes of the Dark Continent. facs. ed. J. W. Buel. LC 73-138333. (Black Heritage Library Collection). 1889. 32.75 (ISBN 0-8369-8725-X). Ayer Co Pubs.

Heroes of the New Testament Coloring Book. Illus. by LeRoy Dugan. (Illus.). 96p. (Orig.). 1981. saddle-stitched 2.95 (ISBN 0-87123-701-6). Bethany Hse.

Heroes of the Old Testament. LeRoy Dugan. 96p. (Orig.). 1981. No. 1. pap. 1.95 oversized, saddle stitched (ISBN 0-87123-704-0, 220704); No. 2. pap. 2.95 (ISBN 0-87123-705-9, 220705). Bethany Hse.

Heroes of the Old Testament, No. 3. Illus. by LeRoy Dugan. (Illus.). 96p. (Orig.). 1981. pap. 2.95 saddle stitched (ISBN 0-87123-703-2). Bethany Hse.

Heroes; or, Greek Fairy Tales. Charles Kingsley. Repr. of 1882 ed. 20.00 (ISBN 0-686-20097-7). Quality Lib.

Heroes Then, Heroes Now. Alexander Campbell. (Illus.). 89p. (Orig.). 1981. pap. 12.95 (ISBN 0-940754-08-8). Ed Ministries.

Heroic Age of Franco-German Jewry. Irving A. Agus. LC 75-94444. 1969. 20.00x (ISBN 0-8197-0053-3). Bloch.

Heroic Lives. facs. ed. Rafael Sabatini. LC 70-99648. (Essay Index Reprint Ser.). 1934. 19.50 (ISBN 0-8369-2071-6). Ayer Co Pubs.

Heroines of Jerico Ritual. 3.50 (ISBN 0-685-19478-7). Powner.

Heroines of Modern Religion. Ed. by Warren D. Foster. LC 77-107700. (Essay Index Reprint Ser.). 1913. 20.00 (ISBN 0-8369-1572-0). Ayer Co Pubs.

Herons Handbook. James Hancock & Hugh Elliott. LC 84-47576. (Illus.). 288p. 1984. 24.45i (ISBN 0-06-015331-8, HarpT). Har-Row.

Herrnhuterian Pietism in the Baltic. Valdis Mezezers. (Illus.). 160p. 1975. 8.95 (ISBN 0-8158-0322-2); pap. 6.95 (ISBN 0-8158-0413-X). Chris Mass.

Herzl. Amos Elon. (Illus.). 496p. 1986. pap. 12.95 (ISBN 0-8052-0790-2). Schocken.

Herzl Year Book: Vol. 5, Studies in the History of Zionism in America. Ed. by Raphael Patai. LC 72-117807. (Essay Index Reprint Ser). 1963. 22.00 (ISBN 0-8369-1951-3). Ayer Co Pubs.

He's Coming! Hilton Sutton. 149p. (Orig.). 1983. pap. 2.95 (ISBN 0-89274-256-9). Harrison Hse.

He's Everything to Me: Autobiography. Ralph Carmichael. 192p. 1986. 14.95 (ISBN 0-8499-0094-8). Word Bks.

Hesed in the Bible. Nelson Glueck. 1968. 12.50x (ISBN 0-87820-104-1, Pub. by Hebrew Union). Ktav.

Heshbon 1968: The First Campaign at Tell Hesban: A Preliminary Report. Roger S. Boraas & Siegfried H. Horn. (Andrews University Monographs, Studies in Religion: Vol. II). (Illus.). viii, 239p. 1969. 7.95. Andrews Univ Pr.

Heshbon 1971: The Second Campaign at Tell Hesban: A Preliminary Report. Roger S. Boraas & Siegfried H. Horn. (Andrews University Monographs, Studies in Religion: Vol. VI). (Illus.). viii, 160p. 7.95 (ISBN 0-943872-06-5). Andrews Univ Pr.

Heshbon 1973: The Third Campaign at Tell Hesban: A Preliminary Report. Roger S. Boraas & Siegfried H. Horn. (Andrews University Monographs, Studies in Religion: Vol. VIII). (Illus.). viii, 288p. 1975. 7.95 (ISBN 0-943872-08-1). Andrews Univ Pr.

Heshbon 1974: The Fourth Campaign at Tell Hesban: A Preliminary Report. Roger S. Boraas & Lawrence T. Geraty. (Andrews University Monographs, Studies in Religion: Vol. IX). (Illus.). xii, 232p. 1976. 7.95 (ISBN 0-943872-09-X). Andrews Univ Pr.

Heshbon 1976: The Fifth Campaign at Tell Hesban: A Preliminary Report. Roger S. Boraas & Lawrence T. Geraty. (Andrews University Monographs, Studies in Religion: Vol. X). (Illus.). xi, 328p. 1978. 11.95 (ISBN 0-943872-10-3). Andrews Univ Pr.

Hesiodic Catalogue of Women: Its Nature, Structure & Origins. M. L. West. (Illus.). 1985. 24.95x (ISBN 0-19-814034-7). Oxford U Pr.

Heslop Bible Study Aids, 6 vols. W. G. Heslop. 1979. Set. pap. 24.00 (ISBN 0-8254-2858-0). Kregel.

Hesoid: Theogony, Works & Days. Hesiod. Tr. by Apostolos N. Athanassakis. LC 83-6143. 184p. 1983. 20.00x (ISBN 0-8018-2998-4); pap. 6.95x (ISBN 0-8018-2999-2). Johns Hopkins.

Het Hoogste Wezen Bij De Manggaraiers. J. A. Verheijen. Repr. of 1951 ed. 46.00 (ISBN 0-384-64290-X). Johnson Repr.

Hevajra Tantra, 2 Vols. David L. Snellgrove. 1959. 59.00x (ISBN 0-19-713516-1). Oxford U Pr.

Hexameron Paradise, Cain & Abel. St. Ambrose. LC 77-81354. (Fathers of the Church Ser.: Vol. 42). 449p. 1961. 34.95x (ISBN 0-8132-0042-3). Cath U Pr.

Hexaplar Psalter, Being the Book of Psalms in Six English Versions. William A. Wright. 395p. Repr. of 1911 ed. lib. bdg. 63.00X (Pub. by G Olms BRD). Coronet Bks.

Hexaplaric Materials Preserved in the Armenian Version. Claude E. Cox. (Septuagint & Cognate Studies). 1986. text ed. 12.95 (ISBN 1-55540-028-0, 06-04-21); pap. 9.95 (ISBN 1-55540-029-9). Scholars Pr GA.

Hey God! A Large Italian Family's Amazing Experience with God. Frank Foglio. LC 72-87328. 1972. pap. 4.95 (ISBN 0-88270-007-3). Bridge Pub.

Hey, God! Hurry! Roxie C. Gibson. LC 82-60193. (Illus.). 52p. 1982. 3.95 (ISBN 0-938232-08-8, 32534). Winston-Derek.

Hey, God! Listen! Roxie C. Gibson. LC 82-60195. (Illus.). 68p. 1982. 3.95 (ISBN 0-938232-06-1, 32466). Winston-Derek.

Hey God, What about...? James T. Cumming & Hans G. Moll. (Illus.). 1977. pap. 4.50 (ISBN 0-570-03758-1, 12-2666). Concordia.

Hey, God! What Is America? Roxie C. Gibson. LC 81-71025. (Illus.). 52p. 1982. 3.95 (ISBN 0-938232-05-3, 32795). Winston-Derek.

Hey, God! What Is Christmas. Roxie C. Gibson. LC 82-60192. (Illus.). 64p. 3.95 (ISBN 0-938232-09-6, 32752). Winston-Derek.

Hey, God! Where are You? Roxie C. Gibson. LC 82-60194. (Illus.). 64p. 1982. 3.95 (ISBN 0-938232-07-X, 32485). Winston-Derek.

Hey! Is That You, God? Pasqual S. Schievella. Ed. by Richard O. Crystal. Date not set. 16.95. Sebastian Ll.

Hi, I'm Ann. Ann Kiemel. (Direction Bks). pap. 2.50 (ISBN 0-8010-5346-3). Baker Bk.

Hibernia Dominicana, Sive Historia Provinciae: Hiberniae Ordinis Praedicatorum. Thomas Burke. 966p. Repr. of 1762 ed. text ed. 124.20x (ISBN 0-576-78541-5, Pub. by Gregg Intl Pubs England). Gregg Intl.

Hidden Art of Homemaking. Edith Schaeffer. (Living Studies). 216p. 1985. pap. 6.95 (ISBN 0-8423-1398-2); Leader's Guide 2.95 (ISBN 0-8423-1399-0). Tyndale.

Hidden Battle: Strategies for Spiritual Victory. Rev. ed. David Watson. 160p. 1985. pap. 2.95 (ISBN 0-87788-343-2). Shaw Pubs.

Hidden Bible. William Leary. 1955. 19.95 (ISBN 0-910140-07-3). C & R Anthony.

Hidden Billions: The Potential of the Church in the U. S. John Ronsvalle & Sylvia Ronsvalle. 175p. (Orig.). 1984. pap. 8.00 (ISBN 0-914527-18-5). C-Four Res.

Hidden Center: Spirituality & Speculative Christology in St. Bonaventure. Zachary Hayes. LC 80-84509. 240p. (Orig.). 1981. pap. 8.95 (ISBN 0-8091-2348-7). Paulist Pr.

Hidden Childhood: A Jewish Girl's Sanctuary in a French Convent, 1942-1945. Frida S. Weinstein. Tr. by Barbara L. Kennedy. 160p. 1986. pap. 6.95 (ISBN 0-8090-1529-3). Hill & Wang.

Hidden Christian. Cliff Dudley. LC 80-80657. 160p. 1980. 7.95 (ISBN 0-89221-074-5). New Leaf.

Hidden Church of the Holy Graal. Arthur E. Waite. 710p. 1975. Repr. of 1909 ed. 12.00 (ISBN 0-911662-54-5). Yoga.

Hidden Dangers of the Rainbow: The New Age Movement & Our Coming Age of Barbarism. Constance Cumbey. LC 83-80044. 271p. (Orig.). 1983. pap. 6.95 (ISBN 0-910311-03-X). Huntington Hse Inc.

Hidden Face of Eve: Women in the Arab World. Nawal El Saadawi. Tr. by Sherif Hetata from Egyptian. LC 81-68358. 212p. 1982. pap. 9.95 (ISBN 0-8070-6701-6, BP 627). Beacon Pr.

Hidden Garden. Lucia A. Gainer. LC 84-61580. 128p. 1985. pap. 4.95 (ISBN 0-87973-598-8, 598). Our Sunday Visitor.

Hidden God. L. Boros. 132p. 1973. 5.95 (ISBN 0-8245-0313-9). Crossroad NY.

Hidden God: Studies in Hemingway, Faulkner, Yeats, Eliot & Warren. Cleanth Brooks. (Orig.). 1963. 25.00x (ISBN 0-300-00327-7). Yale U Pr.

Hidden God: The Hiding of the Face of God in the Old Testament. Samuel E. Balentine. (Oxford Theological Monographs). 1983. 34.00x (ISBN 0-19-826719-3). Oxford U Pr.

Hidden Ground of Love: Letter on Religious Experience & Social Concerns. Thomas Merton. Ed. by William H. Shannon. 1986. pap. 14.95 (ISBN 0-374-51963-3). FS&G.

Hidden Ground of Love: Letters on Religious Experience & Social Concern. Thomas Merton. Ed. by William H. Shannon. LC 84-26045. 684p. 1985. 27.95 (ISBN 0-374-16995-0). FS&G.

Hidden Half: Discovering the World of Unreached Peoples. Samuel Wilson & Gordon Aeschliman. 1984. 5.50 (ISBN 0-912552-43-3). World Vision Intl.

Hidden Harmony. Bhagwan Shree Rajneesh. Ed. by Ma Yoga Anurag. LC 83-184618. (Western Mystics Ser.). (Illus.). 364p. (Orig.). 1976. 16.95 (ISBN 0-88050-079-4). Chidvilas Found.

Hidden Histories in the United Church of Christ. Ed. by Barbara B. Zikmund. 192p. (Orig.). 1984. pap. 9.95 (ISBN 0-8298-0704-7). Pilgrim NY.

Hidden Histories in the United Church of Christ, Pt. 2. Ed. by Barbara B. Zikmund. 228p. (Orig.). 1987. pap. 10.95 (ISBN 0-8298-0753-5). Pilgrim NY.

Hidden in His Hands. Basilea Schlink. LC 79-52346. 96p. 1979. pap. 2.95 (ISBN 0-87123-208-1, 200208). Bethany Hse.

Hidden in Plain Sight: The Practice of Christian Meditation. Avery Brooke. 144p. (Orig.). 1986. pap. 7.95 (ISBN 0-8358-0547-6). Upper Room.

Hidden Life. C. E. Orr. 112p. pap. 0.75 (ISBN 0-686-29149-2). Faith Pub Hse.

Hidden Life of Prayer. David M. M'Intyre. 96p. 1962. pap. 2.50 (ISBN 0-87123-214-6, 200214). Bethany Hse.

Hidden Manna. S. Baker. pap. 5.00 (ISBN 0-686-12875-3). Schmul Pub Co.

Hidden Manna Revealed by the Comforter. Gladys Cuss. 200p. 1981. 9.00 (ISBN 0-682-49768-1). Exposition Pr FL.

Hidden Mind of Freedom. Tarthang Tulku. Ed. by Sylvia Derman. 1981. pap. 6.95 (ISBN 0-89800-120-X). Dharma Pub.

Hidden Motives of Pastoral Action: Latin American Reflections. Juan L. Segundo. Tr. by John Drury from Sp. LC 77-13420. Orig. Title: Accion Pastoral latinoamericana: Sus motivos ocultos. 141p. 1977. 12.95 (ISBN 0-88344-185-3). Orbis Bks.

Hidden Pictures in the Old Testament. Ada R. Habershon. LC 82-18676. 304p. 1983. pap. 8.95 (ISBN 0-8254-2855-6). Kregel.

Hidden Revolution: The Pharisee's Search for the Kingdom Within. Ellis Rivkin. LC 78-17180. 1978. 13.95 (ISBN 0-687-16970-4). Abingdon.

Hidden Riches. Romaine H. Stauffer. 1983. 4.70 (ISBN 0-87813-520-0). Christian Light.

Hidden Story of Scientology. Omar V. Garrison. 8.50 (ISBN 0-8065-0440-4). Church of Scient Info.

Hidden Teaching Beyond Yoga. rev. ed. Paul Brunton. LC 83-60830. 366p. (Orig.). 1984. pap. 8.95 (ISBN 0-87728-590-X). Weiser.

Hidden Treasure: Holy Mass. St. Leonard. 1971. pap. 2.50 (ISBN 0-89555-036-9). TAN Bks Pubs.

Hidden Treasure of the Gospel of Sri Ramakrishna. Ed. by Sri S. Chakravarti. 1975. Repr. of 1907 ed. 6.25 (ISBN 0-685-58386-4). Ranney Pubns.

Hidden Treasure: Parables for Kids. Margaret Freeman. LC 81-16669. (Illus.). 96p. (Orig.). 1982. pap. 3.95 (ISBN 0-87239-499-9, 2728). Standard Pub.

Hidden Treasures for Women. Ora M. Willing & C. T. Davidson. 144p. (Orig.). 1983. pap. 3.95 (ISBN 0-934942-37-4). White Wing Pub.

Hidden Treasures of the Ancient Qabalah. Elias Gewurz. 1922. 4.50 (ISBN 0-911662-31-6). Yoga.

Hidden Wisdom in the Holy Bible, Vol. 3. Geoffrey Hodson. 1971. 7.95 (ISBN 0-8356-7493-2). Theos Pub Hse.

Hidden Wisdom in the Holy Bible, Vol. 4. Geoffrey Hodson. LC 67-8724. 375p. (Orig.). 1981. pap. 5.95 (ISBN 0-8356-0548-5, Quest). Theos Pub Hse.

Hidden Words of Baha'u'llah. rev. ed. Baha'u'llah. Tr. by Shoghi Effendi. LC 54-7328. 1985. 7.95 (ISBN 0-87743-007-1, 103-005); pap. 3.50 (ISBN 0-87743-002-0, 103-006). Baha'i.

Hidden World of the Misericords. Dorothy Kraus & Henry Kraus. LC 75-10869. (Illus.). 192p. 1975. 20.00 (ISBN 0-8076-0804-1). Braziller.

Hide or Seek. expanded & updated ed. James Dobson. 192p. 1974. 11.95 (ISBN 0-8007-1070-3); pap. 6.95 (ISBN 0-8007-5146-9). Revell.

Hiding God: Jesus in the Old Testament. Raymond L. Scott. 192p. 1982. pap. 4.95 (ISBN 0-8010-8221-8). Baker Bk.

Hiding, Hurting, Healing. Mary F. Clark. 176p. (Orig.). 1985. pap. 6.95 (ISBN 0-310-30551-9, 11612). Zondervan.

Hiding the Word in Your Heart: How to Memorize Scripture. Sue K. Segerman. (Cornerstone Ser.). 40p. 1986. pap. 2.95 (ISBN 0-932305-24-5, 533012). Aglow Pubns.

Hierachy of Minds. Sri Aurobindo & Mother. Ed. by Prem Sobel & Jyoti Sobel. 174p. 1984. pap. 5.50 (ISBN 0-89071-324-3, Pub. by Sri Aurobindo Ashram India). Matagiri.

Hierarchies: The Cosmic Ladder of Life. G. Van Pelt. Ed. by W. Emmett Small & Helen Todd. (Theosophical Manual: No. 9). 1975. pap. 2.00 (ISBN 0-913004-23-5). Point Loma Pub.

Hierarchy & Democracy in Australia, 1788-1870: The Formation of Australian Catholicism. T. L. Suttor. 1965. 22.00x (ISBN 0-522-83753-0, Pub. by Melbourne U Pr). Intl Spec Bk.

Hierarchy & the Plan. Torkom Saraydarian. LC 75-39432. 1975. pap. 2.00 (ISBN 0-911794-20-4). Aqua Educ.

Hierarchy of Values. Thomas Hora. (Discourses in Metapsychiatry Ser.). 48p. (Orig.). 1983. pap. 4.00 (ISBN 0-913105-03-1). PAGL Pr.

Hieroglyphic Vocabulary to the Theban Recension of the Book of the Dead. Ernest A. Budge. LC 73-18846. Repr. of 1911 ed. 26.50 (ISBN 0-404-11335-4). AMS Pr.

Hieronimus Bosch: The Temptation of Saint Anthony. Anne F. Francis. (Illus.). 1980. 15.00 (ISBN 0-682-48910-7, University). Exposition Pr FL.

Hieronymus of Cardia. Jane Hornblower. (Classical & Philosophical Monographs). 1981. text ed. 52.00x (ISBN 0-19-814717-1). Oxford U Pr.

High above the Holy Land. Tom Dowley. Ed. by Earl O. Roe. LC 86-6422. (Illus.). 64p. 1986. 15.95 (ISBN 0-8307-1153-8, 5111590). Regal.

High Adventure: Life of Lucy Rider Meyer. Isabelle Horton. Ed. by Carolyn Gifford & Donald Dayton. (Women in American Protestant Religion 1800-1930 Ser.). 359p. 1987. lib. bdg. 50.00 (ISBN 0-8240-0665-8). Garland Pub.

High Call, High Privilege. Gail MacDonald. 1981. pap. 6.95 (ISBN 0-8423-1424-5). Tyndale.

High Cost of Indifference. Richard Cizik. LC 84-15957. 1984. pap. 6.95 (ISBN 0-8307-1000-0, 5418377). Regal.

High Cost of Indifference: Leader's Guide. John Hambrick. (Study & Grow Electives). 64p. 1985. pap. 3.95 (ISBN 0-8307-1019-1, 6102038). Regal.

High Flying Geese: Unexpected Reflections on the Church & Its Ministry. Browne Barr. (Illus.). 96p. (Orig.). 1983. pap. 6.95 (ISBN 0-86683-900-3, HarpR). Har-Row.

High Gothic. Hans Jantzen. LC 83-43099. (Illus.). 196p. 1984. 25.00x (ISBN 0-691-04026-5); pap. 7.95x (ISBN 0-691-00372-6). Princeton U Pr.

High History of the Holy Graal. Tr. by Sabastian Evans. (Illus.). 395p. 1969. 16.95 (ISBN 0-227-67727-7). Attic Pr.

High Holiday Prayer Book. Morris Silverman. 12.00 (ISBN 0-87677-051-0); simulated leather 13.50 (ISBN 0-87677-012-X). Prayer Bk.

High Holiday Prayerbook: Rosh Hashanah, Vol. 1. Ed. by Mordecai M. Kaplan et al. 360p. 1948. 9.00 (ISBN 0-935457-29-1). Reconstructionist Pr.

High Holiday Prayerbook: Yom Kippur, Vol. 2. Ed. by Mordecai M. Kaplan et al. 597p. 1948. 13.00 (ISBN 0-935457-30-5). Reconstructionist Pr.

High Holy Day Do It Yourself Dictionary. Audrey M. Friedman & Raymond Zwerin. (Illus.). 32p. 1983. pap. 5.00 (ISBN 0-8074-0162-5, 101100). UAHC.

High Lights on Hymnists & Their Hymns. Caroline L. Goodenough. LC 72-1626. Repr. of 1931 ed. 32.50 (ISBN 0-404-08310-2). AMS Pr.

High Middle Ages, One Thousand to Thirteen Hundred. Ed. by Bryce Lyon. LC 64-21207. (Orig.). 1964. pap. text ed. 13.95 (ISBN 0-02-919480-6). Free Pr.

High Mysticism. Emma C. Hopkins. 368p. 1974. pap. 8.95 (ISBN 0-87516-198-7). De Vorss.

High Sacrifice. John F. Deane. 61p. 1981. pap. text ed. 6.50x (ISBN 0-85105-382-3, Pub. by Dolmen Pr Ireland). Humanities.

High School Curriculum for Leadership. Americo D. Lapati. 1961. 14.95x (ISBN 0-8084-0375-3). New Coll U Pr.

High School Ministry. Jim Burns & Mike Yaconelli. 368p. 1986. 16.95 (ISBN 0-310-34920-6, 10826). Zondervan.

High Ways to Perfection by Abraham Maimonides, 2 vols. Rosenblatt. 35.00 (ISBN 0-87306-113-6). Feldheim.

High Ways to Perfection of Abraham Maimonides. Abraham Ben Moses Ben Maimon. Tr. by Samuel Rosenblatt. LC 74-158221. (Columbia University Oriental Studies: No. 27). 1927. 19.00 (ISBN 0-404-50517-1); Suppl., 1982. 35.00; Supp., 1983. 43.50. AMS Pr.

Higher Aspects of Greek Religion. L. R. Farnell. vii, 155p. 1977. 10.00 (ISBN 0-89005-206-9). Ares.

Higher Aspects of Greek Religion. Lewis R. Farnell. LC 77-27158. (Hibbert Lectures Ser.: 1911). Repr. of 1912 ed. 20.00 (ISBN 0-404-60413-7). AMS Pr.

Higher Call. Tom Murray. 1984. 12.95 (ISBN 0-533-06032-X). Vantage.

Higher Christian Life. W. E. Boardman. Ed. by Donald W. Dayton. (Higher Christian Life Ser.). 330p. 1985. PLB 40.00 (ISBN 0-8240-6406-2). Garland Pub.

Higher Criticism of the Pentateuch. William H. Green. (Twin Brooks Ser.). 1978. pap. 4.95 (ISBN 0-8010-3723-9). Baker Bk.

Higher Ground. Eileen Venden. (Anch Ser.). 1984. pap. 6.95 (ISBN 0-8163-0562-5). Pacific Pr Pub Assn.

Higher Ground: For the Believer Who Seeks Joy & Victory. Steve Brestin & Dee Brestin. (Fisherman Bible Studyguide Ser.). 58p. 1978. saddle-stitched 2.95 (ISBN 0-87788-345-9). Shaw Pubs.

Higher Honor. Robert Boardman. 197p. 1986. pap. 7.95 (ISBN 0-89109-552-7). NavPress.

Higher Taste: Based on Teachings of A. C. Bhaktivedanta Swami. (Contemporary Vedic Library Ser.). (Illus.). 176p. 2.95 (ISBN 0-89213-128-4). Bhaktivedanta.

Highest Yoga Tantra. Dan Cozort. 220p. (Orig.). 1986. pap. 10.95 (ISBN 0-937938-32-7). Snow Lion.

Highlands of Canaan: Agricultural Life in the Early Iron Age. David C. Hopkins. (Social World of Biblical Antiquity Ser.). 315p. 1985. text ed. 29.95x (ISBN 0-907459-38-2, Pub. by Almond Pr England); pap. text ed. 15.95 (ISBN 0-907459-39-0). Eisenbrauns.

Highlights in Church History. 9th ed. S. C. McClain. (Illus.). 66p. 1983. pap. 2.95 (ISBN 0-912315-06-7). Word Aflame.

Highlights of Hebrew History. Charles W. Conn. 1975. pap. 4.25 (ISBN 0-87148-401-3); instrs. guide 5.25 (ISBN 0-87148-404-8). Pathway Pr.

Highlights of Jewish History: From Dan to Ramban, Vol. 3. Mordecai Lewittes. 303p. 1955. pap. 6.95x (ISBN 0-88482-628-7). Hebrew Pub.

Highlights of Jewish History: From Joshua to Jeremiah, Vol. 2. Mordecai Lewittes. 288p. 1953. pap. 6.95x (ISBN 0-88482-627-9). Hebrew Pub.

Highlights of Jewish History: From Middle Ages to Modern Times, Vol. 4. Mordecai Lewittes. 319p. 1957. 6.95x (ISBN 0-88482-629-5). Hebrew Pub.

Highlights of the Bible: Genesis-Nehemiah. Ray C. Stedman. LC 79-65423. 256p. 1979. pap. 3.50 (ISBN 0-8307-0656-9, S333147). Regal.

Highlights of the Bible: New Testament. William L. Lane. LC 80-50543. 160p. 1980. pap. 3.50 (ISBN 0-8307-0676-3, S343118). Regal.

Highlights of the Bible: Poets & Prophets. Ray C. Stedman. LC 81-50589. (Bible Commentary for Laymen Ser.). 224p. 1981. pap. text ed. 3.50 (ISBN 0-8307-0774-3, S352108). Regal.

Highlights of the Story of Christianity, Bk. 5. Alice Parmelee. LC 80-81098. (All About the Bible Ser.). 136p. (Orig.). 1980. pap. 5.95 (ISBN 0-8192-1274-1). Morehouse.

Highly Informative History of the Renaissance Period of Italian Painting. Anthony C. Passavant. (Illus.). 117p. 1984. pap. 23.75 (ISBN 0-86650-128-2). Gloucester Art.

Highroad to the Stake: A Tale of Witchcraft. Michael Kunze. Tr. by William Yuill. LC 86-11230. (Illus.). 440p. 1987. 24.95 (ISBN 0-226-46221-1). U of Chicago Pr.

Highway of Our God. Catherine Booth. (Writings of Catherine Booth Ser.). 1986. Repr. of 1880 ed. deluxe ed. 4.95 (ISBN 0-86544-033-6). Salvation Army.

Higley Sunday School Commentary. Gordon Talbot et al. Ed. by Loren Triplett. (Illus.). 528p. (Orig.). 1985. text ed. 8.95 (ISBN 0-9614116-1-9); pap. text ed. 6.95 (ISBN 0-9614116-0-0). Higley.

Hijo de la Calle Tenebrosa. Victor Torres. 160p. 1975. 2.75 (ISBN 0-88113-100-8). Edit Betania.

Hilaire Belloc: A Memoir. John B. Morton. LC 74-19265. 1974. Repr. of 1955 ed. lib. bdg. 25.00 (ISBN 0-8414-6149-X). Folcroft.

Hilaire Belloc: Edwardian Radical. John P. McCarthy. LC 78-5635. (Illus.). 1979. 8.00 (ISBN 0-913966-43-6, Liberty Pr); pap. 3.00 (ISBN 0-913966-44-4). Liberty Fund.

Hilaire Belloc: No Alienated Man. Frederick Wilhelmsen. 1953. 20.00 (ISBN 0-8274-2495-7). R West.

Hilary of Poitiers: A Study in Theological Method. George M. Newlands. (European University Studies: Series 23, Vol. 108). xiii, 216p. 1978. pap. 25.25 (ISBN 3-261-03133-6). P Lang Pubs.

Hildebrand: A Life of Gregory the Seventh. Allan J. Macdonald. (Great Medieval Churchmen Ser.). 254p. 1977. Repr. of 1932 ed. lib. bdg. 17.50x (ISBN 0-915172-26-7). Richwood Pub.

Hildegard of Bingen's Book of Divine Works with Music & Letters. Hildegard of Bingen. Ed. by Matthew Fox. 408p. (Orig.). 1987. pap. 14.95 (ISBN 0-939680-32-7). Bear & Co.

Hills of Home. Amy S. Fraser. (Illus.). 250p. 1973. pap. 8.95 (ISBN 0-7102-0540-6). Methuen Inc.

Himnario Cristiano. (Span.). 6.95x (ISBN 0-8361-1198-2). Herald Pr.

Himnos de Gloria. 150p. pap. 0.75 (ISBN 0-686-29116-6). Faith Pub Hse.

Himnos de la Vida Cristiana. Tr. by Ellen Eck from Eng. 1980. 3.95 (ISBN 0-87509-277-2); pap. 2.25 (ISBN 0-87509-275-6); With music. pap. 4.50. Chr Pubns.

Hindoo Art in Its Social Setting. P. N. Dubash. (Illus.). 278p. 1986. Repr. 30.00X (ISBN 0-8364-1752-6, Pub. by Usha). South Asia Bks.

Hind's Feet on High Places. Hannah Hurnard. 1979. pap. 3.95 (ISBN 0-8423-1429-6). Tyndale.

Hindu Astronomy: Ancient Science of the Hindus. G. R. Kaye. 134p. 1981. text ed. 42.00x. Coronet Bks.

Hindu Domestic Rituals. Sindhu S. Dange. 1986. 12.00x (ISBN 81-202-0138-8, Pub. by Ajanta). South Asia Bks.

Hindu Ethics. B. Singh. 200p. 1984. text ed. 22.50 (ISBN 0-391-02933-9). Humanities.

Hindu Family in Its Urban Setting. Aileen D. Ross. LC 62-2801. pap. 84.80 (ISBN 0-317-09747-4, 2014388). Bks Demand UMI.

Hindu Gita: Ancient & Classical Interpretations of the Bhagavadgita. Arvind Sharma. LC 85-21520. 250p. 1986. 28.95 (ISBN 0-8126-9013-3). Open Court.

Hindu Goddesses: Visions of the Divine Feminine in the Hindu Religious Tradition. David Kinsley. LC 84-28000. (Hermeneutics: Studies in the History of Religions). 1985. 35.00x (ISBN 0-520-05393-1). U of Cal Pr.

Hindu Gods & Goddesses. Swami Harshananda. (Illus., Orig.). 1985. pap. 4.25 (ISBN 0-87481-522-3, Pub. by Ramakrishna Math Madras India). Vedanta Pr.

Hindu Influence on Greek Philosophy. Timothy Lomperis. 1985. 9.00x (ISBN 0-8364-1311-3). South Asia Bks.

Hindu Javanese: Tengger Tradition & Islam. Robert W. Hefner. LC 85-3426. (Illus.). 300p. 1985. text ed. 36.00x (ISBN 0-691-09413-6). Princeton U Pr.

Hindu Law. P. N. Chadha. 354p. 1982. 60.00x (Pub. by Eastern Bk India). State Mutual Bk.

Hindu Law: Edition. abr. ed. P. N. Chadha. 354p. 1982. 60.00x (Pub. by Eastern Bk India). State Mutual Bk.

Hindu Literature. 474p. 1986. Repr. 25.00X (ISBN 0-8364-1763-1, Pub. by Manohar India). South Asia Bks.

Hindu Literature: Comprising the Book of Good Counsels, Nala & Damayanti, Sakoontala, the Ramayan, & Poems of Toru Dutt. Intro. by Epiphanius Wilson. 467p. 1986. Repr. of 1900 ed. PLB 95.00 (ISBN 0-89760-654-X). Telegraph Bks.

Hindu Manners, Customs & Ceremonies. J. A. Dubois & Henry K. Beauchamp. 800p. 1986. Repr. 17.50X (ISBN 0-8364-1760-7, Pub. by Manohar India). South Asia Bks.

Hindu Metaphysics. M. N. Shastra. 247p. 1978. Repr. of 1904 ed. text ed. 15.00 (ISBN 0-89684-121-9, Pub. by Cosmo Pubns India). Orient Bk Dist.

Hindu Metaphysics. Balbir Singh. 256p. 1986. text ed. 25.00x (ISBN 0-391-03408-1). Humanities.

Hindu Music, from Various Authors. 2nd ed. Compiled by Sourindo M. Tagore. LC 74-24223. 1977. Repr. of 1882 ed. 35.00 (ISBN 0-404-12835-1). AMS Pr.

Hindu-Muslim Relations in Medieval Bengal. J. N. Sarkar. 130p. 1986. 15.00x (ISBN 0-8364-1806-9, Pub. by Chanakya India). South Asia Bks.

Hindu Mysticism. S. N. Dasgupta. 1977. 12.95 (ISBN 0-8426-0929-6). Orient Bk Dist.

Hindu Mysticism According to the Upanisads. M. Sircar. 1974. text ed. 19.00x. Coronet Bks.

Hindu Myths. Tr. by Wendy O'Flaherty. (Classics Ser.). 360p. 1975. pap. 5.95 (ISBN 0-14-044306-1). Penguin.

Hindu Pantheon. Edward Moor. 45.00 (ISBN 0-89314-409-6). Philos Res.

Hindu Pantheon. Edward Moor. Ed. by Burton Feldman & Robert D. Richardson. LC 78-60887. (Myth & Romanticism Ser.). 1984. lib. bdg. 80.00 (ISBN 0-8240-3567-4). Garland Pub.

Hindu Philosophy. Theos Bernard. LC 68-21323. 1968. Repr. of 1947 ed. lib. bdg. 22.50x (ISBN 0-8371-0311-8, BEHP). Greenwood.

Hindu Philosophy. Theos Bernard. 1981. Repr. of 1947 ed. 14.00x (ISBN 0-8364-0765-2, Pub. by Motilal Banarsidass). South Asia Bks.

Hindu Philosophy. Ram C. Bose. 420p. 1986. Repr. 28.00X (ISBN 0-8364-1757-7, Pub. by Manohar India). South Asia Bks.

Hindu Places of Pilgrimage in India: A Study in Cultural Geography. Surinder M. Bhardwaj. LC 73-174454. (Center for South & Southeast Asia Studies, U.C. Berkeley). (Illus.). 1973. 42.50x (ISBN 0-520-02135-5); pap. 8.95 (ISBN 0-520-04951-9, CAL 621). U of Cal Pr.

Hindu Primer: Yaksha Prashna. A. V. Srinivasan. (Illus.). 78p. 1984. pap. 7.70 (ISBN 0-86578-249-0, 6203). Ind-US Inc.

Hindu Quest for the Perfection of Man. Troy W. Organ. x, 439p. 1970. pap. 14.00x (ISBN 0-8214-0575-6). Ohio U Pr.

Hindu Religion & Iconology According to the Tantrasara. Pratapaditya Pal. LC 81-52893. (Tantric Tradition Ser.). Orig. Title: Tantrasara. (Illus.). 172p. 1982. pap. 10.95 (ISBN 0-941582-00-0). Vichitra Pr.

Hindu Religion, Customs & Manners. 6th ed. P. Thomas. (Illus.). 144p. 1981. text ed. 35.00x (ISBN 0-86590-036-1, Pub. by Taraporevala India). Apt Bks.

Hindu Religious Art & Architecture. S. P. Ghosh. (Illus.). 148p. 1983. text ed. 30.00x (ISBN 0-86590-124-4). Apt Bks.

Hindu Samskaras: Sacraments. Date not set. pap. price not set (ISBN 0-938924-17-6). Sri Shirdi Sai.

Hindu Sanskaras. Raj B. Pandey. 1976. Repr. 25.00 (ISBN 0-8426-0853-2). Orient Bk Dist.

Hindu Scriptures. Ed. & tr. by R. C. Zaehner. 1978. 11.95x (ISBN 0-460-10944-8, Evman); pap. 5.95x (ISBN 0-460-11944-3, Evman). Biblio Dist.

Hindu Symbology & Other Essays. Swami Swahananda. 266p. (Orig.). 1983. pap. 4.95 (ISBN 0-87481-526-6, Pub. by Ramakrishna Math Madras India). Vedanta Pr.

Hindu Temple, 2 vols. Stella Kramrisch. 1980. Repr. Set. 65.00x (ISBN 0-8364-0411-4). South Asia Bks.

Hindu Temple, 2 vols. Stella Kramrisch. 1986. Repr. 60.00 (ISBN 81-208-0222-5, Pub. by Motilal Banarsidass). South Asia Bks.

Hindu Theology, Egyptian Civilization & the Growth of European Culture. Benjamin De Maillard. (Illus.). 156p. 1986. 137.50 (ISBN 0-89266-548-3). Am Classical Coll Pr.

Hindu Tradition. Ed. by Ainslie T. Embree. 448p. 1972. pap. 5.95 (ISBN 0-394-71702-3, V696, Vin). Random.

Hindu Tribes & Castes, 3 vols. Sherring. 1219p. 1974. Repr. of 1881 ed. Set. text ed. 120.00. Vol. 1, Benares. Vol. 2, Mohamedan Tribes of the North West Frontier & Aboriginal Tribes of the Central Provinces. Vol. 3 Natural History of the Hindu Caste, Unity of the Hindu Race. Coronet Bks.

Hindu Vedic Master Operations Guide: Astrological Software for the IBM PC. Stephen C. Cratch & Anders B. Johansson. Ed. by Lilian M. Johansson. (Illus.). 200p. (Orig.). 1985. 30.00 (ISBN 0-914725-12-2); pap. 18.00 (ISBN 0-914725-10-6); spiral 24.00 (ISBN 0-914725-11-4). Astro Dynasty Pub Hse.

Hindu Vidhi (Hindu Law in Hindi) K. P. Sharma. 390p. 1980. 90.00x (Pub. by Eastern Bk India). State Mutual Bk.

Hindu View of Christ. Swami Akhilananda. pap. 12.00 (ISBN 0-8283-1355-5). Branden Pub Co.

Hindu View of Life. S. Radhakrishnan. (Unwin Paperbacks Ser.). 92p. 1980. pap. 4.95 (ISBN 0-04-294115-6). Allen Unwin.

Hindu Views & Ways & the Hindu-Muslim Interface. Agehananda Bharati. 1981. 8.00x (ISBN 0-8364-0772-5, Pub. by Munshiram). South Asia Bks.

Hindu Views & Ways & the Hindu-Muslim Interface: An Anthropological Assessment. Agehananda Bharati. 107p. 1982. Repr. of 1981 ed. 8.95 (ISBN 0-915520-54-0). Ross Erikson.

Hindu World. Patricia Bahree. LC 83-50691. (Religions of the World Ser.). 48p. 1983. lib. bdg. 14.96 (ISBN 0-382-06718-5); 9.25 (ISBN 0-382-06931-5). Silver.

Hindu World: An Encyclopedic Survey of Hinduism, 2 vols. Benjamin Walker. 1983. Set. text ed. 72.00x. Coronet Bks.

Hindu Writings in Post-Colonial India. Lothar Lutze. 1985. 27.00x (ISBN 0-8364-1422-5, Pub. by Manohar India). South Asia Bks.

Hindu-Yogi Practical Water Cure. Yogi Ramacharaka. leatherette 3.00 (ISBN 0-911662-12-X). Yoga.

Hindu Yogi Science of Breath. Yogi Ramacharaka. 88p. 1905. pap. text ed. 5.95 (ISBN 0-88697-047-4). Life Science.

Hinduism. Pat Bahree. (World Religions Ser.). (Illus.). 72p. 1984. 16.95 (ISBN 0-7134-3654-9, Pub. by Batsford England). David & Charles.

Hinduism. V. C. Channa. 1985. 17.50x (ISBN 0-8364-1451-9, Pub. by National Sahitya Akademi). South Asia Bks.

Hinduism. Yorke Crompton. 1985. 13.00 (ISBN 0-7062-3598-3, Pub. by Ward Lock Educ Co Ltd). State Mutual Bk.

Hinduism. V. P. Kanitkar. (Religions of the World Ser.). (Illus.). 48p. 1986. PLB 10.90 (ISBN 0-531-18068-9, Pub. by Bookwright). Watts.

Hinduism. Kshitimohan M. Sen. (Orig.). 1962. pap. 5.95 (ISBN 0-14-020515-2, Pelican). Penguin.

Hinduism. Robert C. Zaehner. 1962. pap. 8.95 (ISBN 0-19-888012-X). Oxford U Pr.

Hinduism: A Beautiful Mosaic. Frank R. Podgorski. LC 85-51907. i, 61p. 1984. pap. text ed. 6.95x (ISBN 0-932269-12-5). Wyndham Hall.

Hinduism: A Cultural Perspective. David Kinsley. (Illus.). 200p. 1982. 17.00 (ISBN 0-13-388975-0). P-H.

Hinduism: A Religion to Live by. Nirad C. Chaudhuri. 1979. pap. 9.95. Oxford U Pr.

Hinduism: A Select Bibliography. Ed. by Satyaprakash. 1984. 46.50x (ISBN 0-8364-1121-8, Pub. by Indian Doc Serv India). South Asia Bks.

Hinduism & Buddhism. Ananda K. Coomaraswamy. LC 78-138215. 1971. Repr. of 1943 ed. lib. bdg. 22.50x (ISBN 0-8371-5570-3, COHB). Greenwood.

Hinduism & Christianity: Jesus Christ & His Teachings in the Light of Vedanta. Swami Satprakashananda. LC 75-32598. 196p. 1975. 8.95 (ISBN 0-916356-53-1). Vedanta Soc St Louis.

Hinduism & Its Relation to Christianity. John Hobson. 1977. lib. bdg. 59.95 (ISBN 0-8490-1951-6). Gordon Pr.

Hinduism & Symbol Worship. B. C. Sinha. 1985. 17.50x (ISBN 0-8364-1297-4, Pub. by Agam Kala Prakashan). South Asia Bks.

Hinduism: Essence & Consequence. Arun Shourie. 1980. text ed. 40.00x (ISBN 0-7069-0834-1, Pub. by Vikas India). Advent NY.

Hinduism in Thai Life. Santosh N. Desai. 163p. 1980. 23.95x (ISBN 0-940500-66-3, Pub by Popular Prakashan India). Asia Bk Corp.

Hinduism: Its Meaning for the Liberation of the Spirit: a Survey of Hinduism. Swami Nikhilananda. LC 58-6155. 189p. 5.50 (ISBN 0-911206-13-2). Ramakrishna.

Hinduism: Non-Christian Religious Systems. M. Monier-Williams. lib. bdg. 79.95 (ISBN 0-87968-546-8). Krishna Pr.

Hinduism: Religion & Way of Life. Satyavrata Patel. 165p. 1980. 15.95x (ISBN 0-940500-25-6). Asia Bk Corp.

Hinduism: The Faith of the Future. R. P. Mishr. 131p. 1981. 15.95x (ISBN 0-940500-17-5, Pub. by S S Pubs India). Asia Bk Corp.

Hinduism: The Faith of the Future. R. P. Mishr. 131p. 1981. text ed. 15.00x (ISBN 0-391-02515-5). Humanities.

Hinduism: The World Ideal. H. Maitra. 34.95 (ISBN 0-8490-0302-4). Gordon Pr.

Hints on the Study of the Bhagavad Gita. Besant. 4.50 (ISBN 0-8356-7079-1). Theos Pub Hse.

Hiobkommentar Des Arianers Julian. Ed. by Dieter Hagedorn. LC 73-75486. (Patristische Texte und Studien, Vol. 14). 410p. 1973. 45.60x (ISBN 3-11-004244-4). De Gruyter.

Hippolyta's View: Some Christian Aspects of Shakespeare's Plays. J. A. Bryant, Jr. LC 61-6555. 256p. 1961. 24.00x (ISBN 0-8131-1057-2). U Pr of Ky.

Hippolytus in Drama & Myth. Euripides. Tr. by Donald Sutherland. LC 60-13112. vi, 124p. 1960. pap. 4.50x (ISBN 0-8032-5195-5, BB 103, Bison). U of Nebr Pr.

Hirsch Siddur. Samson R. Hirsch. Tr. by Samson Raphael Hirsch Publication Society Staff. Tr. of Tefilot Yisrael. 1978. 16.95 (ISBN 0-87306-141-1); compact ed 9.95 (ISBN 0-87306-142-X). Feldheim.

Hirsch Siddur. 1982. deluxe leatherbound 45.00 (ISBN 0-686-76517-6). Feldheim.

His Comfort. Norman B. Harrison. 1973. pap. 0.75 (ISBN 0-911802-32-0). Free Church Pubns.

His Cross in Your Life. Bertrand Weaver. LC 78-56766. 1978. pap. 2.25 (ISBN 0-8189-1152-2, Pub. by Alba Bks). Alba.

His Everlasting Love, Vol. 2. Norma C. Larsen. LC 81-80956. 150p. 1981. 7.95 (ISBN 0-88290-182-6, 1062). Horizon Utah.

His Everlasting Love: Stories of the Father's Help to His Children. Norma C. Larsen. LC 77-79752. 173p. 1977. 8.95 (ISBN 0-88290-083-8). Horizon Utah.

His Everlasting Words. A. Vaughn Abercrombie. 80p. 7.95 (ISBN 0-89962-326-3). Todd & Honeywell.

His Eye Is on the Sparrow. Ethel Waters & Charles Michel. 1972. pap. 2.95 (ISBN 0-515-06738-5). Jove Pubns.

His Face Shone Like the Sun: Encountering the Transfigured Christ in Scripture. Robert Wild. LC 86-8054. 126p. (Orig.). 1986. pap. 5.95 (ISBN 0-8189-0501-8). Alba.

His Glorious Name. Charles J. Rolls. (Names & Titles of Jesus Christ Ser.: No. 5). 267p. 1986. pap. 5.95 (ISBN 0-87213-735-X). Loizeaux.

His Holiness the Fourteenth Dalai Lama of Tibet Talks to Louwrier Wijers. L. Wijers. 192p. 1982. 29.00x (ISBN 0-317-39082-1, Pub. by Luzac & Co Ltd). State Mutual Bk.

His Image... My Image: Leader's Guide. Robert Massie. 86p. 1986. pap. 1.95 (ISBN 0-86605-159-7). Campus Crusade.

His Image...My Image: Biblical Principles for Improving Your Self Image. Josh McDowell. 180p. 1985. pap. 6.95 (ISBN 0-89840-103-8). Heres Life.

His in the Spirit: Confirmation Text. 1986. 3.75 (ISBN 0-8198-3319-3); tchr's manual 10.00 (ISBN 0-8198-3320-7). Dghtrs St Paul.

His Joy. Norman B. Harrison. 1973. pap. 0.75 (ISBN 0-911802-35-5). Free Church Pubns.

His Life Is Mine. Archimandrite Sophrony. Tr. by Rosemary Edmonds from Russian. LC 76-56815. 128p. 1977. pap. 5.95 (ISBN 0-913836-33-8). St Vladimirs.

His Majesties Commission & Further Declaration Concerning the Reparation of Saint Pauls Church. LC 75-171754. (English Experience Ser.: No. 379). 1971. Repr. of 1633 ed. 7.00 (ISBN 90-221-0379-X). Walter J Johnson.

His Majesties Commission to Enquire of the Decayes of the Cathedral Church of St. Paul. LC 72-185. (English Experience Ser.: No. 355). 1971. Repr. of 1631 ed. 8.00 (ISBN 90-221-0355-2). Walter J Johnson.

His Majesties Proclamation in Scotland with an Explanation of the Oath & Covenant. LC 74-80216. (English Experience Ser.: No. 692). 1974. Repr. of 1639 ed. 3.50 (ISBN 90-221-0692-6). Walter J Johnson.

His Messengers Went Forth. facs. ed. Julie Chanler. LC 77-148209. (Biography Index Reprint Ser.). (Illus.). 1948. 13.00 (ISBN 0-8369-8056-5). Ayer Co Pubs.

His Name Is Wonderful. Warren Wiersbe. (Livingg Studies). 160p. 1984. pap. 2.95 (ISBN 0-8423-1449-0); pap. 4.95 (ISBN 0-8423-1447-4). Tyndale.

His Name Shall Be Called Wonderful. Kenneth Hagin. 1983. pap. 0.50 mini bk. (ISBN 0-89276-260-8). Hagin Ministries.

His Name Was John: The Life Story of John S. Coffman, an Early Mennonite Leader. Barbara F. Coffman. LC 64-18732. (Illus.). 352p. 1964. 12.95 (ISBN 0-8361-1486-8). Herald Pr.

His Peace. Norman B. Harrison. 1972. pap. 0.75 (ISBN 0-911802-29-0). Free Church Pubns.

His People. William Tiptaft. pap. 0.75 (ISBN 0-685-88377-9). Reiner.

His Power Through You. Charles Hunter & Frances Hunter. 247p. (Orig.). 1986. pap. 4.95 (ISBN 0-917726-74-X). Hunter Bks.

His Religion & Hers: A Study of the Faith of Our Fathers & the Work of Our Mothers. Charlotte P. Gilman. LC 75-29509. (Pioneers of the Woman's Movement: An International Perspective Ser.). xi, 300p. 1976. Repr. of 1923 ed. 26.50 (ISBN 0-88355-377-5). Hyperion-Conn.

His Revelation from Apocalypses. Carlos E. Portillo. LC 85-52117. 150p. (Orig.). 1987. pap. write for info. (ISBN 0-937365-02-5). WCP Pubns.

His Saving Love. rev. ed. Daughters of St. Paul. (Way, Truth & Life Ser.). (Illus.). 1976. text ed. 2.75 (ISBN 0-8198-0340-5); tchrs. manual 6.95 (ISBN 0-8198-0341-3); activity bk. 1.60 (ISBN 0-8198-0342-1); parent guide 1.50 (ISBN 0-8198-0343-X). Dghtrs St Paul.

His Servants Speak: Statements by Latter-day Saint Leaders on Contemporary Topics. R. Clayton Brough. LC 75-17101. 298p. 1975. 10.95 (ISBN 0-88290-054-4). Horizon Utah.

His Spirit in You. Merrill Williams. 68p. 1982. 2.95 (ISBN 0-8341-0783-X). Beacon Hill.

His Story: The Life of Christ. Bill George. LC 76-53630. 1977. pap. text ed. 3.95 (ISBN 0-87148-406-4). Pathway Pr.

His Strange Ways. LaWanda Guthrie. LC 81-10854. 1986. pap. 10.95 (ISBN 0-87949-212-0). Ashley Bks.

His Stubborn Love. Joyce Landorf. pap. 2.95 (ISBN 0-310-27122-3, 9991P). Zondervan.

His Truth Is Marching On! Advanced Studies on Prophecy in the Light of History. Ralph Woodrow. (Illus.). 1977. pap. 4.95 (ISBN 0-916938-03-4). R Woodrow.

His Victory & Ours: The Temptations of Jesus. Reuben Welch. 78p. (Orig.). 1983. pap. 3.50 (ISBN 0-8341-0871-2). Beacon Hill.

His Way: An Everyday Plan for Following Jesus. David Knight. 1977. pap. 3.50 (ISBN 0-912228-39-3). St Anthony Mess Pr.

Hiscox Guide for Baptist Churches. Edward T. Hiscox. 12.95 (ISBN 0-8170-0329-0). Judson.

Hiscox Standard Baptist Manual. Edward T. Hiscox. 1965. pap. 5.95 (ISBN 0-8170-0340-1). Judson.

Hispanic Culture & Character of the Sephardic Jews. 2nd rev. ed. Mair Jose Benardete. 226p. 1981. 15.00 (ISBN 0-87203-100-4). Hermon.

Hispanic Mennonite Church in North America, 1932-1982. Rafael Falcon. LC 85-30220. (Span.). 224p. 1986. 17.95x (ISBN 0-8361-1282-2). Herald Pr.

Hispanic Presence: Challenge & Commitment. 73p. 1983. pap. 2.25 (ISBN 1-55586-891-6). US Catholic.

Hispanization of the Philippines: Spanish Aims & Filipino Responses, 1565-1700. John L. Phelan. (Illus.). 234p. 1959. 30.00x (ISBN 0-299-01810-5). U of Wis Pr.

Hispano-Jewish Culture in Transition: The Career & Controversies of Ramah. Bernard Septimus. LC 81-13275. (Harvard Judaic Monographs: No. 4). 192p. 1982. text ed. 20.00x (ISBN 0-674-39230-2). Harvard U Pr.

Histiore Des Sciences et Des Savants Depuis Deux Siecles. Alphonse De Candolle. Ed. by I. Bernard Cohen. LC 80-2116. (Development of Science Ser.). (Illus.). 1981. lib. bdg. 50.00x (ISBN 0-405-13836-9). Ayer Co Pubs.

Histoire Critique de Manichee et du Manicheisme. Isaac de Beausobre. Ed. by Burton Feldman & Robert D. Richardson. LC 78-60880. (Myth & Romanticism Ser.). 1984. lib. bdg. 160.00 (ISBN 0-8240-3552-6). Garland Pub.

Histoire de Canada, de Son Eglise et De Ses Missions. E. Ch. Brasseur De Bourbourg. (Canadiana Avant 1867: No. 4). 1968. 44.40x (ISBN 90-2796-333-9). Mouton.

Histoire de la Chartreuse Sheen Anglorum au Continent: Bruges, Louvain, Malines, Nieuport (1559-1783) Jan De Grauwe. Ed. by James Hogg. (Analecta Cartuaiana Ser.: No. 48). (Fr.). 254p. (Orig.). 1985. pap. 25.00 (ISBN 3-7052-0068-2, Pub by Salzburg Studies). Longwood Pub Group.

Histoire de la premiere croisade jusqu'a l'election de Godefroi de Bouillon. Ferdinand Chalandon. 380p. 1972. Repr. of 1925 ed. lib. bdg. 25.50 (ISBN 0-8337-0515-6). B Franklin.

Histoire de Saint Louis. Jean De Joinville. Ed. by N. De Wailly. 1868. 38.00 (ISBN 0-384-27721-7); pap. 32.00 (ISBN 0-384-27720-9). Johnson Repr.

Histoire des institutions monarchiques dans le Royaume latin de Jerusalem, 1099-1291. Gaston J. Dodu. LC 76-29820. (Fr.). Repr. of 1894 ed. 32.50 (ISBN 0-404-15415-8). AMS Pr.

Histoire des Religions, 3 vols. Henri-Charles Puech. (Historique Ser.). Vols. 1 & 2. 59.95 ea.; Vol. 2. 69.95 (ISBN 0-686-56461-8). French & Eur.

Histoire documentaire de l'Armenie, 2 Vols. Joseph Sandalgian. LC 79-175431. 1917. Repr. of 1917 ed. Set. 70.00 (ISBN 0-404-05557-5). AMS Pr.

Histoire du Canada, De Son Eglise et De Ses Missions Depuis la Decouverte De L'Amerique Jusqu'a Nos Jours, 2 vols. Charles E. Brasseur De Bourbourg. (Canadiana Before 1867 Ser). (Fr). Repr. of 1852 ed. Set. 50.00 (ISBN 0-384-05570-2). Johnson Repr.

Histoire du Catholicisme en France, 3 tomes. Incl. Tome I. Des origines a la chretiente medievale (du IIe a la fin du XIIe siecle) Palanque & Delaruelle. 7.50 (ISBN 0-685-36063-6); Tome II. Sous les Rois Tres Chretiens (Du XIIIe au XVIIIe Siecle) Delaruelle & Latreilla. 8.50 (ISBN 0-685-36064-4); Tome III. Periode Contemporaine (du XVIIIe Siecle a nos Jours) Latreille & Remona. 9.50 (ISBN 0-685-36065-2). French & Eur.

Histoire du Parlement De Paris De l'Avenememt Des Rois Valois a la Mort D'Henri Quatre, 3 Vols. Edquard Maugis. 1967. Repr. of 1913 ed. 92.50 (ISBN 0-8337-2304-9). B Franklin.

Histoire Ecclesiastique Des Francs, 4 vols. Saint Gregorius. 1967. 154.00 (ISBN 0-384-19875-9); pap. 130.00 (ISBN 0-384-19874-0). Johnson Repr.

Histoire Ecclesiastique et Civile de Bretagne, 2 vols. Dom Pierre & Hyacinthe Morice. 752p. Date not set. Repr. of 1756 ed. text ed. 310.50x (ISBN 0-576-78866-X, Pub. by Gregg Intl Pubs England). Gregg Intl.

Histoire et Absolu: Essai Sur Kierkegaard. Colette. 19.95 (ISBN 0-686-54575-3). French & Eur.

Histoire et Doctrine de la Secte des Cathares ou Albigeois, 2 vols. Charles G. Schmidt. LC 78-63191. (Heresies of the Early Christian & Medieval Era: Second Ser.). 1979. Repr. of 1849 ed. 57.50 set (ISBN 0-404-16180-4). AMS Pr.

Histoire Religieuse de la Revolution francaise, 5 Vols. Pierre F. La Gorce. LC 71-88239. (Fr). Repr. of 1923 ed. Set. 235.50 (ISBN 0-404-03810-7); 47.00 ea. Vol. 1 (ISBN 0-404-03811-5). Vol. 2 (ISBN 0-404-03812-3). Vol. 3 (ISBN 0-404-03813-1). Vol. 4 (ISBN 0-404-03814-X). Vol. 5 (ISBN 0-404-03815-8). AMS Pr.

Historia Calamitatum: Story of My Misfortunes. Peter Abelard. 59.95 (ISBN 0-8490-0305-9). Gordon Pr.

Historia Cartusiana Belgica: Esquisse Historique et Apercu des Archives, des Bibliotheques et des Oeuvres D'Art. Jan De Grauwe. Ed. by James Hogg. (Analecta Cartusiana: No. 51). (Orig.). 1985. pap. 25.00 (ISBN 3-7052-0071-2, Pub. by Salzburg Studies). Longwood Pub Group.

Historia de la Inquisicion. I. Grigulevich. (Span.). 414p. 1980. 8.95 (ISBN 0-8285-1813-0, Pub. by Progress Pubs USSR). Imported Pubns.

Historia de las Ideas sobre el Aborto en la Iglesia Catolica: Una Relacion Desconocida. Jane Hurst. Ed. by Susan J. Boyd & Jan Peterson. Tr. by Caridad Inda from Eng. (Aborto de Buena Fe Ser.). (Span., Illus.). 31p. 1985. pap. 1.00 (ISBN 0-915365-11-1). Cath Free Choice.

Historia de los Bautistas Tomo I: Sus Bases y Principios. Justo C. Anderson. 1978. pap. 5.75 (ISBN 0-311-15036-5). Casa Bautista.

Historia de Maria. M. M. Brem. (Libros Arco Ser.). Tr. of Mary's Story. (Span., Illus.). 32p. 1979. pap. 0.95 (ISBN 0-89922-145-9). Edit Caribe.

Historia de un Milagro. Justo Gonzalez, Sr. (Span.). 166p. 1984. pap. 3.95 (ISBN 0-89922-144-0). Edit Caribe.

Historia del Cristianismo, Tomo II. Kenneth S. Latourette. Tr. by Jaime C. Quarles & Lemuel C. Quarles. (Desde el Siglo XVI Hasta el Siglo XX). Orig. Title: History of the Expansion of Christianity. 968p. 1983. pap. 17.95 (ISBN 0-311-15012-8). Casa Bautista.

Historia del Cristianismo, Tomo I. Kenneth S. Latourette. Tr. by Jaime C. Quarles & Lemuel C. Quarles. (Illus.). 819p. 1984. pap. 17.95 (ISBN 0-311-15010-1). Casa Bautista.

Historia Persecutionis Africanae Provinciae. Saint Victor Of Vita. (Corpus Scriptorum Ecclesiasticorum Latinorum Ser.: Vol. 7). 1881. 30.00 (ISBN 0-384-64540-2). Johnson Repr.

Historiae Ecclesiasticae Libri Tredecim, 5 Vols. Vitalis Ordericus. Ed. by A. Le Prevost. Set. 240.00 (ISBN 0-384-43511-4); Set. pap. 210.00 (ISBN 0-384-43512-2). Johnson Repr.

Historiae Rhythmicae, 8 Vols. Ed. by Guido M. Dreves. 1889-1904. 60.00 ea. (ISBN 0-384-12880-7). Johnson Repr.

Historian & the Believer: The Morality of Historical Knowledge & Christian Belief. Van A. Harvey. LC 80-27941. 320p. 1981. Westminster.

Historians of the Church of York & Its Archbishops, 3 vols. Ed. by James Raine. (Rolls Ser.: No. 71). Repr. of 1894 ed. Set. 180.00 (ISBN 0-8115-1139-1). Kraus Repr.

Historians, Puritanism & the English Revolution: The Religious Factor in English Politics before & after the Interregnum. Michael G. Finlayson. LC 83-215172. pap. 54.50 (2026454). Bks Demand UMI.

Historias De la Biblia. Edward G. Finnegan. LC 75-18758. (Treasure House Bks). (Span., Illus.). 1978. 9.95 (ISBN 0-8326-2601-5, 5180). World Bible.

Historias de Toda la Biblia. Bethann Van Ness & Elizabeth M. De Clemente. (Illus.). 684p. 1979. pap. 19.95 (ISBN 0-311-03600-7). Casa Bautista.

Historias Extranas de Brujeria. Roger Elwood. Tr. by George Lockward from Eng. (Span.). 112p. 1974. pap. 1.95 (ISBN 0-89922-028-2). Edit Caribe.

Historias Que Jesus Conto. Margaret Ralph. (Serie Jirafa). Orig. Title: Stories Jesus Told. 28p. 1979. 3.95 (ISBN 0-311-38537-0, Edit Mundo). Casa Bautista.

Historic Albany: Its Churches & Synagogues. Ed. by Anne F. Roberts & Marcia W. Cockrell. (Illus.). 415p. (Orig.). 1986. pap. 15.00 (ISBN 0-941237-00-1). Libr Commns Servs.

Historic Background & Annals of the Swiss & German Pioneer Settlers of Southeastern Pennsylvania & of Their Remote Ancestors. H. Frank Eshleman. LC 77-86809. 386p. 1982. Repr. of 1917 ed. 20.00 (ISBN 0-8063-0105-8). Genealog Pub.

Historic Churches & Temples of Georgia. Gloria Sampson. (Illus.). 144p. 1987. 24.95 (ISBN 0-86554-242-2, MUP-H212). Mercer Univ Pr.

Historic Churches of America. Nellie U. Wallington. LC 77-85628. 1977. Repr. of 1907 ed. lib. bdg. 25.00 (ISBN 0-89341-227-9). Longwood Pub Group.

Historic Mission of Jesus: A Constructive Re-Examination of the Eschatological Teaching in the Synoptic Gospels with an Extensive Bibliography. C. John Cadoux. 1977. lib. bdg. 59.95 (ISBN 0-8490-1955-9). Gordon Pr.

Historical Account of Heathen Gods & Heroes Necessary for the Understanding of Ancient Poets. William King. LC 64-18550. (Centaur Classics Ser.). (Illus.). 290p. 1965. 15.00x (ISBN 0-8093-0150-4). S Ill U Pr.

Historical Account of the Belief in Witchcraft in Scotland. Charles K. Sharpe. LC 74-8196. 1974. Repr. of 1884 ed. 48.00x (ISBN 0-8103-3590-5). Gale.

Historical Account of the Incorporated Society for the Propagation of the Gospel in Foreign Parts - to the Year 1728. David Humphreys. LC 75-83426. (Religion in America, Ser. 1). 1969. Repr. of 1730 ed. 21.00 (ISBN 0-405-00251-3). Ayer Co Pubs.

Historical Account of the Protestant Episcopal Church, in South Carolina, from the First Settlement of the Province, to the War of the Revolution. Frederick Dalcho. LC 71-38445. (Religion in America, Ser. 2). 180p. 1972. Repr. of 1820 ed. 42.00 (ISBN 0-405-04064-4). Ayer Co Pubs.

Historical Approach to the Bible. Howard M. Teeple. LC 81-85275. (Truth in Religion Ser.: No. 2). 323p. (Orig.). 1982. pap. 7.50 (ISBN 0-914384-02-3). Religion & Ethics.

Historical Argument for the Resurrection of Jesus. William L. Craig. LC 85-21570. (Texts & Studies in Religion: Vol. 23). 688p. 1985. lib. bdg. 69.95x (ISBN 0-88946-811-7). E Mellen.

Historical Backgrounds of Early Methodist Enthusiasm. Umphrey Lee. LC 31-18047. (Columbia University. Studies in the Social Sciences: No. 339). Repr. of 1931 ed. 17.50 (ISBN 0-404-51339-5). AMS Pr.

Historical Catalogue of Printed Editions of the English Bible: 1525-1961. A. S. Herbert. 589p. 1968. 40.00 (ISBN 0-686-87735-7). A Wofsy Fine Arts.

Historical Catalogue of Printed Editions of the English Bible 1525-1961. rev. ed. Ed. by A. S. Herbert. 1968. 12.75 (ISBN 0-564-00130-9, 17066, Pub. by United Bible). Am Bible.

Historical Collections of the Life & Acts of John Aylmer, Bishop of London, in the Reign of Queen Elizabeth. John Strype. LC 74-979. 244p. 1974. Repr. of 1821 ed. lib. bdg. 22.50 (ISBN 0-8337-4427-5). B Franklin.

Historical Collections Relating to the American Colonial Church, 5 Pts. in 4 Vols. William S. Perry. LC 75-99948. Repr. of 1878 ed. Set. 245.00 (ISBN 0-404-05070-0). Vol. 1 (ISBN 0-404-05071-9). Vol. 2 (ISBN 0-404-05072-7). Vol. 3 (ISBN 0-404-05073-5). Vol. 4 (ISBN 0-404-05074-3). AMS Pr.

Historical Commentary on the Augsburg Confession. Wilhelm Maurer. Tr. by H. George Anderson from Ger. LC 86-45214. Tr. of Historischer Kommentar zur Confessio Augustana. 464p. 1986. 24.95 (ISBN 0-8006-0781-3). Fortress.

Historical Commentary on the Epistle to the Galatians. William H. Ramsay. 1978. 17.75 (ISBN 0-86524-107-4, 4801). Klock & Klock.

Historical-Critical Method. Edgar Krentz. LC 74-26345. (Guides to Biblical Scholarship: Old Testament Ser.). 96p. 1975. pap. 4.50 (ISBN 0-8006-0460-1, 1-460). Fortress.

Historical Dimensions of Irish Catholicism. Emmet Larkin. LC 76-6350. (Irish Americans Ser.). 1976. 20.00 (ISBN 0-405-09344-6). Ayer Co Pubs.

Historical Dimensions of Irish Catholicism. Emmet Larkin. LC 83-23175. 139p. 1984. pap. 9.95x (ISBN 0-8132-0594-8). Cath U Pr.

Historical Dimensions of Rational Faith: The Role of History in Kant's Religious Thought. G. E. Michalson. 1977. 12.25 (ISBN 0-8191-0308-X). U Pr of Amer.

Historical Directory of the Reformed Church in America. Peter N. Vandenberge. 1978. pap. 17.95 (ISBN 0-8028-1746-7). Eerdmans.

Historical Discourse on the Civil & Religious Affairs of the Colony of Rhode Island. facs. ed. John Callender. LC 79-150172. (Select Bibliographies Reprint Ser.). 1843. 18.00 (ISBN 0-8369-5685-0). Ayer Co Pubs.

Historical Documents Advocating Christian Union. C. A. Young. (Heritage of a Movement Book Club Ser.). 376p. Repr. of 1904 ed. text ed. 10.95 (ISBN 0-89900-276-5). College Pr Pub.

Historical Documents of Central Christian Church 1848-1979. 100p. (Orig.). 1980. pap. write for info. T H Peters.

Historical Evidence for Jesus. G. A. Wells. LC 82-60381. 350p. 1982. 20.95 (ISBN 0-87975-180-0). Prometheus Bks.

Historical Fundamentals & the Study of Religions. Rudolph Kurt. 180p. 1985. 17.95x (ISBN 0-02-927190-8). Macmillan.

Historical Geography of the Holy Land. George A. Smith. 13.25 (ISBN 0-8446-2956-1). Peter Smith.

Historical Guide to Utah Ghost Towns. Stephen L. Carr. 166p. 1972. Western Epics.

Historical Introduction to the Book of Concord. F. Bente. 1965. 12.95 (ISBN 0-570-03262-8, 15-1926). Concordia.

Historical Introduction to the Marprelate Tracts: A Chapter in the Evolution of Religious & Civil Liberty in England. William Pierce. 1908. 23.50 (ISBN 0-8337-2762-1). B Franklin.

Historical Introduction to the Rolls Series. William Stubbs. LC 77-158211. Repr. of 1902 ed. 11.50 (ISBN 0-404-06302-0). AMS Pr.

Historical Investigation & New Testament Faith. Ferdinand Hahn. Ed. by Edgar Krentz. Tr. by Robert Maddox from Ger. LC 82-48547. 112p. 1983. pap. 7.50 (ISBN 0-8006-1691-X, 1-1691). Fortress.

Historical Investigations. Ed. by Roger Aubert. LC 66-29260. (Concilium Ser.: Vol. 17). 196p. 1966. 7.95 (ISBN 0-8091-0063-0). Paulist Pr.

Historical Jesus. Michael L. Cook. (Guidelines for Contemporary Catholics). (Orig.). 1986. pap. 7.95 (ISBN 0-88347-188-4). Thomas More.

Historical Jesus & the Kingdom of God: Present & Future in the Message & Ministry of Jesus. Richard H. Hiers. LC 73-2623. (University of Florida Humanities Monographs: No. 38). 1973. pap. 3.50 (ISBN 0-8130-0386-5). U Presses Fla.

Historical Jesus of the Synoptics. Juan L. Segundo. Tr. by John Drury from Span. LC 85-7146. (Jesus of Nazareth Yesterday & Today Ser.: Vol. II). Tr. of Historia y Actualidad: Sinopticos y Pablo El Hombre de Hoy Ante Jesus de Nazareth. 240p. (Orig.). 1985. pap. 9.95 (ISBN 0-88344-220-5). Orbis Bks.

Historical Life of Christ. J. Warschauer. 1977. lib. bdg. 69.95 (ISBN 0-8490-1960-5). Gordon Pr.

Historical Meaning of Savonarola As a Religious, Moral & Political Prophet & the Progress of the Reformation in Italy. O. Gilbert & R. Whittaker. 189p. 1985. 88.45 (ISBN 0-89266-514-9). Am Classical Coll Pr.

Historical Problems of Church Renewal. Ed. by Roger Aubert. LC 65-26792. (Concilium Ser.: Vol. 7). 196p. 1965. 7.95 (ISBN 0-8091-0064-9). Paulist Pr.

Historical Records Concerning Jesus the Christ. Al Wagner. 64p. 1984. 10.50 (ISBN 0-89962-347-6). Todd & Honeywell.

Historical Reliability of the Gospels. Craig Blomberg. 288p. 1987. pap. 9.95 (ISBN 0-87784-992-7). Inter-Varsity.

Historical Review: St. Paul's Family Parish, North Canton, Ohio, Pt. II. Steven Espenschied. LC 85-29277. 240p. (Orig.). 1986. 14.95 (ISBN 0-938936-52-2). Daring Bks.

Historical Road of Eastern Orthodoxy. Alexander Schmemann. LC 77-12074. 343p. 1977. pap. 8.95 (ISBN 0-913836-47-8). St Vladimirs.

Historical Significance of Desiderius Erasmus in the Light of the Protesant Revolution & the Catholic Church As Revealed by His Most Famous Pronouncements, 2 vols. Desiderius Erasmus. (Illus.). 396p. 1985. Set. 207.50. Am Classical Coll Pr.

Historical Sites in the Holy Land. Moshe Pearlman & Yaacov Yannai. 286p. 1985. 16.95 (ISBN 0-8170-1086-6). Judson.

Historical Sketches of the Missions of the American Board. Samuel C. Bartlett. LC 78-38436. (Religion in America, Ser. 2). 210p. 1972. Repr. of 1972 ed. 21.00 (ISBN 0-405-04057-1). Ayer Co Pubs.

Historical Sketches of Western New York. Elisha W. Vanderhoof. LC 71-134434. Repr. of 1907 ed. 14.00 (ISBN 0-404-08476-1). AMS Pr.

Historical Studies of Church-Building in the Middle Ages. Charles E. Norton. LC 78-95072. (Select Bibliographies Reprint Ser.). 1902. 32.00 (ISBN 0-8369-5072-0). Ayer Co Pubs.

Historical Studies of Church Building in the Middle Ages: Venice, Sienna, Florence. Charles E. Norton. 1977. lib. bdg. 39.95 (ISBN 0-8490-1962-1). Gordon Pr.

Historical Studies of Church-Building in the Middle Ages: Venice, Siena, Florence. Charles E. Norton. LC 78-15869. 1978. Repr. of 1880 ed. lib. bdg. 35.00 (ISBN 0-89341-361-5). Longwood Pub Group.

Historical Study of Southern Baptists & Race Relations 1917-1947: Doctoral Dissertation. Ed. by Foy D. Valentine & Edwin S. Gaustad. LC 79-52579. (Baptist Tradition Ser.). 1980. lib. bdg. 23.00x (ISBN 0-405-12447-3). Ayer Co Pubs.

Historical Study of the Educational Agencies of the Southern Baptist Convention, 1845-1945. Judith Brigham. LC 77-177047. (Columbia University. Teachers College. Contributions to Education Ser.: No. 974). Repr. of 1951 ed. 17.50 (ISBN 0-404-55974-3). AMS Pr.

Historical Study of the Terms Hinayana & Mahayana & the Origin of Mahayana Buddhism. Ryukan Kimura. LC 78-72455. Repr. of 1927 ed. 26.50 (ISBN 0-404-17324-1). AMS Pr.

Historical Survey of Anti-Semitism. Richard E. Gade. pap. 5.95 (ISBN 0-8010-3747-6). Baker Bk.

Historical Survey of Old Testament. Eugene Merrill. 1966. pap. 7.95 (ISBN 0-934532-16-8). Presby & Reformed.

Historical Survey of the Old Testament. Eugene H. Merrill. pap. 7.95 (ISBN 0-8010-5884-8). Baker Bk.

Historical Theology, 2 vols. William Cunningham. 1979. Set. 38.95 (ISBN 0-85151-058-2); Vol. 1. (ISBN 0-85151-286-0); Vol. 2. (ISBN 0-85151-287-9). Banner of Truth.

Historical Theology: An Introduction. Geoffrey W. Bromiley. LC 77-17030. 1978. 14.95 (ISBN 0-8028-3509-0). Eerdmans.

Historical Tradition in the Fourth Gospel. Charles H. Dodd. 1975. pap. 17.95x (ISBN 0-521-29123-2). Cambridge U Pr.

Historical Views of Judaism: Four Selections. LC 73-2209. (Jewish People; History, Religion, Literature Ser.). 35.00 (ISBN 0-405-05273-1). Ayer Co Pubs.

Historical Works, 2 Vols. Bede. (Loeb Classical Library: No. 246, 248). 13.95x ea. Vol. 1 (ISBN 0-674-99271-7). Vol. 2 (ISBN 0-674-99273-3). Harvard U Pr.

Historicism & Faith: The Proceedings of the Fellowship of Catholic Scholars. Ed. by Paul L. Williams. LC 80-117742. 1980. pap. 5.95 (ISBN 0-937374-00-8). NE Bks.

Historicity of the Patriarchal Narratives: The Quest for the Historical Abraham. Thomas L. Thompson. LC 72-76042. (Beiheft 133 zur Zeitschrift fuer die alttestamentliche Wissenschaft). 1974. 57.00x (ISBN 3-11-004096-4). De Gruyter.

Historie of Heaven. Christopher Middleton. LC 76-57400. (English Experience Ser.: No. 816). 1977. Repr. of 1596 ed. lib. bdg. 5.00 (ISBN 90-221-0777-9). Walter J Johnson.

Historie of the Kirk of Scotland, 2 Vols. John Row & William Row. LC 70-174969. (Maitland Club. Glasgow. Publications: No. 55). Repr. of 1842 ed. Set. 57.50 (ISBN 0-404-53039-7). AMS Pr.

Histories & Prophecies of Daniel. Robert D. Culver. 192p. (Orig.). 1980. pap. 4.95 (ISBN 0-88469-131-4). BMH Bks.

Histories One. Hamish Swanston & Laurence Bright. LC 71-173033. (Scriptures Discussion Commentary Ser.: Pt. 3). 182p. 1971. pap. text ed. 4.50 (ISBN 0-87946-002-4). ACTA Found.

Histories Two. Hamish Swanston. Ed. by Laurence Bright. LC 71-173033. (Scripture Discussion Commentary Ser.: Pt. 5). 224p. 1971. pap. text ed. 4.50 (ISBN 0-87946-005-9). ACTA Found.

Historiography of the American Catholic Church, 1785-1943. John P Cadden. 14.00 (ISBN 0-405-10812-5). Ayer Co Pubs.

Historiography of the American Catholic Church: 1785-1943, No. 82. John Paul Cadden. (Studies in Sacred Theology). 134p. 1984. Repr. of 1944 ed. 35.00x (ISBN 0-939738-33-3). Zubal Inc.

Historiography of the Taiping Rebellion. Teng Ssu-Ya. LC 63-1158. (East Asian Monographs: No. 14). 1962. pap. 11.00x (ISBN 0-674-39451-8). Harvard U Pr.

History & Antiquities of the Anglo-Saxon Church, 2 vols. John Lingard. LC 77-6976. 1977. Repr. of 1845 ed. lib. bdg. 70.00 (ISBN 0-89341-212-0). Longwood Pub Group.

History & Art of the Russian Icon from the X to the XX Century. Nicolai Vorobyev. Ed. & tr. by Lucy Maxym. (Illus.). 144p. 1986. 50.00 (ISBN 0-940202-06-9). Siamese Imports.

History & Beliefs of Mormonism. Einar Anderson. LC 81-13671. Orig. Title: Inside Story of Mormonism. 176p. 1981. pap. 6.95 (ISBN 0-8254-2122-5). Kregel.

History & Character of American Revivals of Religion. Calvin Colton. LC 72-1008. Repr. of 1832 ed. 22.50 (ISBN 0-404-00018-5). AMS Pr.

History & Character of Calvinism. J. T. McNeill. 1954. pap. 12.95 (ISBN 0-19-500743-3). Oxford U Pr.

History & Christianity. John W. Montgomery. 128p. 1986. pap. 3.95 (ISBN 0-87123-890-X, 210890). Bethany Hse.

History & Chronology of the Myth-Making Age. J. F. Hewitt. LC 76-27523. (Illus.). 1976. Repr. of 1901 ed. lib. bdg. 60.00 (ISBN 0-89341-036-5). Longwood Pub Group.

History & Decoration of the Ponte S. Angelo. Mark Weil. LC 72-163216. (Illus.). 232p. 1974. 32.50x (ISBN 0-271-01101-7). Pa St U Pr.

History & Evolution of Freemasonry. D. D. Darrah. 12.00x (ISBN 0-685-21969-0). Wehman.

History & Evolution of Freemasonry. Delmore D. Darrah. (Illus.). 1951. 12.00 (ISBN 0-685-19479-5). Powner.

History & Guide to Judaic Bibliography. S. Brisman. (Bibliographica Judaica Ser.: No. 7). 35.00x (ISBN 0-87820-900-X, HUC Pr). Ktav.

History & Hate: The Dimensions of Anti-Semitism. Ed. by David Berger. 160p. 1986. 14.95 (ISBN 0-8276-0267-7). Jewish Pubns.

History & Identity. Sidney E. Mead. LC 78-26543. (American Academy of Religion. Studies in Religion: No. 19). 1979. 14.00 (ISBN 0-89130-274-3, 010019); pap. 9.95 (ISBN 0-89130-297-2). Scholars Pr GA.

History & Literature of Palestinian Jews from Cyrus to Herod 550 BC-4 BC. W. Stewart McCullough. LC 74-80889. 1975. 25.00x (ISBN 0-8020-5317-3); pap. 9.50 (ISBN 0-8020-6324-1). U of Toronto Pr.

History & Literature of the New Testament. Henry T. Fowler. LC 78-12516. 1979. Repr. of 1925 ed. lib. bdg. cancelled (ISBN 0-313-21188-4, FOHL). Greenwood.

History & Literature of the Old Testament, 2 vols. H. S. Creelman. (Illus.). 1987. Set. 189.45 (ISBN 0-89266-573-4). Am Classical Coll Pr.

History & Religion of Israel. G. W. Anderson. (New Clarendon Bible-OT Ser.). (Illus.). 1966. pap. 11.95x (ISBN 0-19-836915-8). Oxford U Pr.

History & Religion of Israel. William L. Wardle. LC 78-11741. (Clarendon Bible, Old Testament Ser.: Vol. I). (Illus.). 1979. Repr. of 1942 ed. lib. bdg. 24.75x (ISBN 0-313-21016-0, WAHR). Greenwood.

History & Teachings of the Eastern Greek Orthodox Church. G. Polyzoides. (Illus.). 96p. 4.00 (ISBN 0-686-83964-1). Divry.

History & Torah: Essays on Jewish Learning. Jacob Neusner. 128p. 1965. text ed. 8.50x (ISBN 0-686-37017-1, Pub. by Vallentine Michell England). Biblio Dist.

History & Use of Hymns & Hymn Tunes. David R. Breed. LC 76-39525. Repr. of 1903 ed. 20.00 (ISBN 0-404-09906-8). AMS Pr.

History & Use of Hymns & Hymn Tunes. David R. Breed. 59.95 (ISBN 0-8490-0313-X). Gordon Pr.

History As Apocalypse. Thomas J. Altizer. LC 84-16289. (SUNY Series in Religion). 250p. 1985. 44.50 (ISBN 0-88706-013-7); pap. 16.95 (ISBN 0-88706-014-5). State U NY Pr.

History As Experience. Aaron Steinberg. 1983. 35.00x (ISBN 0-88125-001-5). Ktav.

History from Marble, 2 Vols. Thomas Dingley. LC 70-164834. (Camden Society, London. Publications, First Ser.: Nos. 94 & 97). Repr. of 1868 ed. Set. 74.00 (ISBN 0-404-50210-5). AMS Pr.

History, Guilt, & Habit. Owen Barfield. LC 79-65333. 104p. 1981. pap. 9.95 (ISBN 0-8195-6064-2). Wesleyan U Pr.

History Historiography & Interpretation: Studies in Biblical & Cuneiform Literatures. H. Tadmor. Ed. by M. Weinfeld. 192p. 1983. pap. text ed. 22.50 (ISBN 965-223-459-1, Pub by Magnes Pr Israel). Humanities.

History in Two Dimensions: A Christian Interpretation of History as Being an Equation Between Time & Eternity. J. Spencer Trimingham. 1983. 11.95 (ISBN 0-533-05395-1). Vantage.

History, Literature & Mythology of the Hindoos, 4 vols. W. Ward. 1986. Repr. of 1817 ed. text ed. 200.00x (ISBN 81-7018-240-9, Pub. by B R Pub Corp Delhi). Vol. 1: 354. Vol. 2: 505. Vol. 3: 288. Vol. 4: 344. Apt Bks.

History, Method, & Theology: A Dialectical Comparison of Wilhelm Dilthey's Critique of Historical Reason & Bernard Lonergan's Meta-Methodology. Matthew L. Lamb. LC 78-18707. 1978. pap. 19.95_o.s. (ISBN 0-89130-238-7, 01-01-25). Scholars Pr GA.

History of Abortion in the Catholic Church. Jane Hurst. Ed. by Constance McKenna. (Illus.). 31p. 1983. pap. 1.00 (ISBN 0-915365-04-9). Cath Free Choice.

History of African Christianity: 1950-1975. A. Hastings. LC 78-16599. (Illus.). 1979. o. p. 49.50 (ISBN 0-521-22212-5); pap. 17.95 (ISBN 0-521-29397-9). Cambridge U Pr.

History of al-Tabari, Vol. 27: The Abbasid Revolution A. D. 743-750 - A. H.126-132) Ed. & tr. by John A. Williams. (Near Eastern Studies). 192p. 1985. 39.50 (ISBN 0-87395-884-5). State U NY Pr.

History of al-Tabari, Vol. 4: The Ancient Kingdoms. Al-Tabari. Ed. by Ehsan Yarshater et al. Tr. by Moshe Perlmann. (History of al-Tabari Ser.). 160p. 1986. 39.50x (ISBN 0-88706-181-8); pap. 14.95x (ISBN 0-88706-182-6). State U NY Pr.

History of al-Tabari, Vol. 7: Foundation of the Community - Muhammad at al-Madina, A. D. 622-626, Hijra-4 A.H. Al-Tabari. Ed. by V. M. McDonald & Montgomery Watt. Tr. by V. M. McDonald from Ancient Parsi. (Series in Near Eastern Studies). 154p. (Orig.). 1987. 44.50x (ISBN 0-88706-344-6); pap. 16.95x (ISBN 0-88706-345-4). State U NY Pr.

History of American Church Music. Leonard Ellinwood. LC 69-12683. (Music Reprint Ser.). 1970. Repr. of 1953 ed. lib. bdg. 32.50 (ISBN 0-306-71233-4). Da Capo.

History of American Missions to the Heathens from Their Commencement to the Present Time. Ed. by Joseph Tracy et al. LC 35-32346. (American Studies). 1970. Repr. of 1840 ed. 45.00 (ISBN 0-384-23460-7). Johnson Repr.

History of American Slavery & Methodism from 1780 to 1849. facs. ed. Lucius C. Matlack. LC 77-138342. (Black Heritage Library Collection Ser.). 1849. 19.75 (ISBN 0-8369-8734-9). Ayer Co Pubs.

History of Ancient Israel. Michael Grant. (Illus.). 360p. 1984. pap. 14.95 (ISBN 0-684-18084-7, ScribT); 19.95 (ISBN 0-684-18081-2). Scribner.

History of Ancient Israel. Michael Grant. 360p. 1984. pap. text ed. write for info. (ISBN 0-02-345620-5, Pub. by Scribner). Macmillan.

History of Ancient Israel. J. Albert Soggin. Tr. by John Bowden from Italian. LC 84-27010. (Illus.). 452p. 1985. 29.95 (ISBN 0-664-21258-1). Westminster.

History of Ancient Israel & Judah. J. Maxwell Miller & John H. Hayes. LC 85-11468. (Illus.). 524p. 1986. 27.95 (ISBN 0-664-21262-X). Westminster.

History of Anglican Liturgy. Geoffrey Cuming. (Illus.). 450p. 1980. Repr. of 1969 ed. text ed. 55.00x (ISBN 0-333-30661-9). Humanities.

History of Anti-Pedobaptism: From the Rise of Pedobaptism to A.D. 1609. Albert H. Newman. LC 71-144664. Repr. of 1897 ed. 26.45 (ISBN 0-404-04686-X). AMS Pr.

History of Anti-Semitism, Vol. 1: From the Time of Christ to the Court Jews. Leon Poliakov. LC 65-10228. 340p. 1964. 19.50 (ISBN 0-8149-0186-7). Vanguard.

History of Anti-Semitism, Vol. 2: From Mohammed to the Marranos. Leon Poliakov. Tr. by Natalie Gerardi from Fr. LC 65-10228. Tr. of Histoire De l'antisemitisme: De Mahomet Aux Marranes. 399p. 1974. 19.50 (ISBN 0-8149-0701-6). Vanguard.

History of Antichrist. P. Huchede. 1976. pap. 2.00 (ISBN 0-89555-100-4). TAN Bks Pubs.

History of Aryan Rule in India. Ernest B. Havell. LC 72-900073. (Illus.). 613p. 1972. Repr. of 1918 ed. 22.50x (ISBN 0-89684-400-5). Orient Bk Dist.

History of Auricular Confession & Indulgences in the Latin Church, 3 Vols. Henry C. Lea. LC 68-19287. 1968. Repr. of 1896 ed. lib. bdg. 67.25x (ISBN 0-8371-0140-9, LEHC). Greenwood.

History of Baptist Indian Missions. Isaac McCoy. LC 19-11605. 1970. Repr. of 1840 ed. 36.00 (ISBN 0-384-36590-6). Johnson Repr.

History of Baptists. Leon H. McBeth. LC 81-68736. 1983. cancelled 17.95 (ISBN 0-8054-6569-3). Broadman.

History of Biblical Studies in Canada: A Sense of Proportion. John S. Moir. LC 82-5979. (Society of Biblical Literature: Biblical Scholarship in North America Ser.). 132p. 1982. pap. 17.95 (ISBN 0-89130-581-5, 06 11 07). Scholars Pr GA.

History of Brethren Missionary Movements. A. T. Ronk. LC 70-184490. 1971. pap. 2.25x (ISBN 0-934970-02-5). Brethren Ohio.

History of Buddha's Religion. Bimala C. Law. (Bibliotheca Indo-Buddhica Ser.: No. 29). 174p. 1986. Repr. of 1952 ed. 24.00 (ISBN 81-7030-011-8, Pub. by SRI SATGURU Pubns India). Orient Bk Dist.

History of Buddhism in India & Tibet. E. Obermiller. 231p. 1986. Repr. of 1932 ed. 27.00 (ISBN 81-7030-026-6, Pub. by Sri Satguru Pubns India). Orient Bk Dist.

History of Buddhist Thought. Edward J. Thomas. 316p. 1981. pap. 17.00 (ISBN 0-89540-100-2, SB-100). Sun Pub.

History of Byzantine Music & Hymnography. 2nd ed. Egon Wellesz. 1961. 49.95x (ISBN 0-19-816111-5). Oxford U Pr.

History of Calvary Church of the Brethren. J. Floyd Wine. LC 72-95960. (Illus.). 1972. pap. 3.95 (ISBN 0-9604350-1-8). J F Wine.

History of Canada, or New France, 2 Vols. Francois Du Creux. Ed. by James B. Conacher. Tr. by Percy J. Robinson. LC 69-14507. 1969. Repr. of 1951 ed. Vol. 1. lib. bdg. 26.75x (ISBN 0-8371-5070-1, DUHI); Vol. 2. lib. bdg. 25.75x (ISBN 0-8371-5071-X, DUHJ). Greenwood.

History of Catholic Church Music. Karl G. Fellerer. Tr. by Francis A. Brunner. LC 78-21637. 1979. Repr. of 1951 ed. lib. bdg. 22.50x (ISBN 0-313-21147-7, FECC). Greenwood.

History of Catholic Education in Kansas: 1836-1932. Richard Joseph Bollig. 131p. 1984. 24.00x (ISBN 0-939738-22-8). Zubal Inc.

History of Catholic Life in the Diocese of Albany, 1609-1864. Martin J. Becker. LC 77-359170. (Monograph: No. 31). (Illus.). 1975. 15.00x (ISBN 0-930060-11-3). US Cath Hist.

History of Catholic Schooling in the United States. Father Harold A. Buetow. 89p. 1986. 6.60 (ISBN 0-318-20561-0). Natl Cath Educ.

History of Chinese Political Thought. Liang Chi-Chao. LC 70-100526. Repr. of 1930 ed. 17.50 (ISBN 0-404-03985-5). AMS Pr.

History of Christian Doctrine. Louis Berkhof. 1978. 14.95 (ISBN 0-85151-005-1). Banner of Truth.

History of Christian Doctrine. Ed. by Hubert Cunliffe-Jones & Benjamin Drewery. LC 79-21689. 616p. 1980. 29.95 (ISBN 0-8006-0626-4, 1-626). Fortress.

History of Christian Doctrine. George P. Fisher. LC 75-41095. Repr. of 1901 ed. 41.50 (ISBN 0-404-14663-5). AMS Pr.

History of Christian Doctrines. Louis Berkhof. (Twin Brooks Ser). 288p. 1975. pap. 8.95 (ISBN 0-8010-0636-8). Baker Bk.

History of Christian Ethics: From the New Testament to Augustine, Vol. 1. George W. Forell. LC 79-50096. 248p. 1979. 15.95 (ISBN 0-8066-1715-2, 10-3042). Augsburg.

History of Christian Missions. Stephen Neill. (History of the Church Ser.: Vol. 6). (Orig.). 1964. pap. 5.95 (ISBN 0-14-020628-0, Pelican). Penguin.

History of Christian Missions in China. Kenneth S. Latourette. LC 66-24721. 1967. Repr. of 1929 ed. 22.50x (ISBN 0-8462-0992-6). Russell.

History of Christian Spirituality, 3 vols. Jean LeClercq et al. 1982. Set. pap. 45.00 slip-cased (ISBN 0-8164-2369-5, HarpR). Har-Row.

History of Christian Spirituality: An Analytical Introduction. Urban T. Holmes, III. 176p. 1981. pap. 6.95 (ISBN 0-8164-2343-1, HarpR). Har-Row.

History of Christian Theology: An Introduction. William C. Placher. LC 83-16778. 324p. 1983. pap. 16.95 (ISBN 0-664-24496-3). Westminster.

History of Christian Theology, Vol. 1: The Science of Theology. Ed. by Paul Avis. 336p. (Orig.). 1986. pap. 14.95 (ISBN 0-8028-0195-1). Eerdmans.

History of Christian Thought, 3 vols. rev. ed. Justo L. Gonzalez. LC 74-109679. 1975. Set. 56.00 (ISBN 0-687-17181-4). Abingdon.

History of Christian Thought. rev. ed. Justo L. Gonzalez. 1987. Set. 59.95 (ISBN 0-687-17185-7). Abingdon.

History of Christian Thought. Paul Tillich. 1972. pap. 11.95 (ISBN 0-671-21426-8, Touchstone Bks). S&S.

History of Christian Thought: From Apollinaris to Erasamus, Vol. II. John R. Willis. 400p. 1984. 18.00 (ISBN 0-682-49973-0, University). Exposition Pr FL.

History of Christian Thought: From Apostolic Times to Saint Augustine. John R. Willis. LC 76-16237. 1976. 16.00 (ISBN 0-682-48583-7, University). Exposition Pr FL.

History of Christian Thought: From Luther to Marx, Vol. III. John R. Willis. LC 76-16237. 1985. 20.00 (ISBN 0-682-40256-7, University). Exposition Pr FL.

History of Christian Thought: From the Beginnings to the Council of Chalcedon in A. D. 451. rev. ed. Justo L. Gonzalez. LC 74-109679. Set. text ed. 56.00 (ISBN 0-687-17181-4); Vol. II. text ed. 18.75; Vol. I. text ed. 20.00 (ISBN 0-687-17150-4); Vol. III. text ed. 20.00. Abingdon.

History of Christianity. Edward Gibbon. LC 79-169227. (Atheist Viewpoint Ser.). (Illus.). 912p. 1972. Repr. of 1883 ed. 51.00 (ISBN 0-405-03796-1). Ayer Co Pubs.

History of Christianity. Edward Gibbon. 59.95 (ISBN 0-8490-0319-9). Gordon Pr.

History of Christianity. Perry Gillum. (Whole Man Whole World Bible Lessons Ser.). 140p. (Orig.). 1984. pap. 3.95 (ISBN 0-934942-48-X); text ed. 2.95 (ISBN 0-934942-49-8); tchr's. ed. 2.95 (ISBN 0-934942-47-1). White Wing Pub.

History of Christianity. Paul Johnson. LC 76-9002. 560p. 1976. pap. 11.95 (ISBN 0-689-70591-3, 252). Atheneum.

History of Christianity. rev. ed. Kenneth S. Latourette. Incl. Vol. 1. Beginnings to 1500. 758p. pap. 11.00 (ISBN 0-06-064952-6, RD-93); Vol. 2. Reformation to the Present. 922p. pap. 13.95 (ISBN 0-06-064953-4, RD-94). LC 74-25692. 1975. pap. (HarpR). Har-Row.

History of Christianity, 2 vols. Kenneth S. Latourette. Date not set. Vol. I. 13.95 (ISBN 0-317-52393-7, RD 93, HarpR); Vol. II. 13.95 (ISBN 0-317-52394-5, RD 94, HarpR). Har-Row.

History of Christianity from the Birth of Christ to the Abolition of Paganism in the Roman Empire, 3 Vols. new & rev. ed. Henry H. Milman. LC 78-172733. Repr. of 1863 ed. Set. 125.00 (ISBN 0-404-04350-X). AMS Pr.

History of Christianity in Belize 1776-1838. Wallace R. Johnson. (Illus.). 300p. (Orig.). 1985. lib. bdg. 26.00 (ISBN 0-8191-4552-1); pap. text ed. 13.50 (ISBN 0-8191-4553-X). U Pr of Amer.

History of Christianity in India: The Beginnings to 1707. Stephen Neill. LC 82-23475. 600p. 1984. 85.00 (ISBN 0-521-24351-3). Cambridge U Pr.

History of Christianity in India 1707-1858. Stephen Neill. (Illus.). 592p. 1985. 79.50 (ISBN 0-521-30376-1). Cambridge U Pr.

History of Christianity in Japan: Roman Catholic & Greek Orthodox Missions, 2 vols. Otis Cary. LC 75-28972. (Illus.). 1975. Repr. of 1909 ed. boxed 36.95 (ISBN 0-8048-1177-6). C E Tuttle.

History of Christianity in Japan, Roman Catholic & Greek Orthodox Missions, 2 Vols. Otis Cary. 1971. Repr. of 1909 ed. Set. 18.00 (ISBN 0-403-00252-4). Scholarly.

History of Christianity in the Middle Ages. William R. Cannon. (Twin Brooks Ser.). 1983. pap. 9.95 (ISBN 0-8010-2492-7). Baker Bk.

History of Christianity in the Philippines: The Initial Encounter, Vol. 1. T. Valentino Sitoy, Jr. (Illus.). 384p. (Orig.). 1985. pap. 18.50x (ISBN 971-10-0254-X, Pub by New Day Philippines). Cellar.

History of Christianity in the World: From Persecution to Uncertainty. 2nd ed. Clyde L. Manschreck. (Illus.). 352p. 1985. text ed. 28.67 (ISBN 0-13-389354-5). P-H.

History of Christianity, Vol. 1: From the Beginnings to the Threshold of the Reformation. Kurt Aland. Tr. by James L. Schaaf. LC 84-47913. 464p. 24.95 (ISBN 0-8006-0725-2, 1-725). Fortress.

History of Christianity, Vol. 2: From the Reformation to the Present. Kurt Aland. Tr. by James L. Schaaf from Ger. LC 85-47913. 608p. 1986. 29.95 (ISBN 0-8006-0759-7, 1-759). Fortress.

History of Christianity: Volume I, Readings in the History of the Early & Medieval Church. Ed. by Ray C. Petry. 576p. 1981. pap. 23.95 (ISBN 0-8010-7064-3). Baker Bk.

History of Christianity: Volume II, Readings in the History of the Church from the Reformation to the Present. Ed. by Clyde L. Manschreck. 576p. 1981. pap. 23.95 (ISBN 0-8010-6124-5). Baker Bk.

History of Churches of Christ in Texas, 1824-1950. Stephen D. Eckstein, Jr. 1963. 6.95 (ISBN 0-88027-098-5); 4.95. Firm Foun Pub.

History of Clementhorpe Nunnery. R. Dobson & S. Donaghey. (Archaeology of York-Historical Sources for York Archaeology after AD 1100,). 40p. 1984. pap. text ed. 10.50x (ISBN 0-906780-40-3, Pub. by Council British Archaeology England). Humanities.

History of Creation & Origin of the Species: A Scientific Theological Viewpoint (How the Universe Came into Being) 3rd ed. Reuben L. Katter. 480p. 1984. 16.95 (ISBN 0-911806-01-6, C13374); pap. 11.95 (ISBN 0-911806-00-8). Theotes.

History of Decorative Art in Mughal Architecture. R. Nath. 1986. Repr. of 1977 ed. 16.50 (ISBN 81-208-0077-X, Pub. by Motilal Banarsidass India). Orient Bk Dist.

History of Dogma, 2 vols. in 1, Vols. 2 & 3. Adolph Harnack. Tr. by Neil Buchanan from Ger. Set. 18.00 (ISBN 0-8446-2207-9). Peter Smith.

History of Dogmas, 3 vols. J. Tixeront. Ed. by Edward J. Panico. (Orig.). 1984. pap. 50.00 (ISBN 0-87061-093-7). Chr Classics.

History of Early Chinese Buddhism: From Its Introduction to the Death of Hui-Yuan, 2 vols. Zenryi Tsukamoto. Tr. by Leon Hurvitz from Japanese. (Illus.). 648p. 1985. Boxed Set. 175.00x (ISBN 0-87011-635-5). Kodansha.

History of Early Christian Doctrine Before the Council of Nicaea. Jean Danielou. Tr. by John A. Baker. Incl. Vol. 1. The Theology of Jewish Christianity. 1977; Vol. 2. Gospel Message & Hellenistic Culture. LC 72-7090. 1973; Vol. 3. The Origins of Latin Christianity. LC 76-44380. 528p. 1977. 27.50 (ISBN 0-664-21064-3). Westminster.

History of Early Christian Literature. rev. & enl. ed. Edgar J. Goodspeed. Ed. by Robert M. Grant. LC 66-13871. (Midway Reprint Ser.). 1966. pap. 13.00x (ISBN 0-226-30386-1). U of Chicago Pr.

History of Early Christian Literature in the First Three Centuries. Gustav Krueger. Tr. by Charles R. Gillet from Ger. 1969. 26.00 (ISBN 0-8337-1963-7). B Franklin.

History of Eastern Christianity. Aziz S. Atiya. LC 80-232. 1980. Repr. lib. bdg. 52.00 (ISBN 0-527-03703-6). Kraus Repr.

History of Eastern Christianity. Aziz S. Atiya. LC 67-31393. pap. 125.00 (ISBN 0-317-42117-4, 2025944). Bks Demand UMI.

History of Ecclesiastical Dress. Janet Mayo. (Illus.). 196p. 1984. text ed. 39.50x (ISBN 0-8419-0983-0). Holmes & Meier.

History of Egypt: From the Earliest Times to the End of the Eighteenth Dynasty, 2 vols. facsimile ed. James Baikie. LC 79-157323. (Select Bibliographies Reprint Ser.). Repr. of 1929 ed. Set. 66.00 (ISBN 0-8369-5782-2). Ayer Co Pubs.

History of England from the Norman Conquest to the Death of John, 1066-1216. G. B. Adams. (Political History of England Monograph). Repr. of 1905 ed. 35.00 (ISBN 0-527-00847-8). Kraus Repr.

History of Evolutionary Thought. Bert Thompson. 192p. (Orig.). 1981. pap. 3.50 (ISBN 0-932859-10-0). Apologetic Pr.

History of Fayette County Baptist Association. Herbert M. Newell & Jeanie P. Newell. 1968. 15.00 (ISBN 0-317-13829-4). Banner Pr AL.

History of First Baptist Church, Jacksonville Alabama, 1836-1986. Daniel W. Hollis, III. (Illus.). 241p. 1986. 10.00 (ISBN 0-9616158-0-X). First Bapt AL.

History of First Baptist Church Russellville. Boyce Broadus. 1967. 10.00 (ISBN 0-317-13830-8); pap. 7.00. Banner Pr AL.

History of Folkston, Ga. Methodist Church. Lois B. Mays. 37p. 1984. 3.25 (ISBN 0-9601606-1-2). Okefenokee Pr.

History of Forty Choirs. Thomas Hastings. LC 72-1620. Repr. of 1854 ed. 18.50 (ISBN 0-404-08313-7). AMS Pr.

History of Free Masonry. Joseph McCabe. 31p. pap. cancelled (ISBN 0-911826-73-4). Am Atheist.

History of Free Will Baptist State Associations. Ed. by Robert E. Picirilli. 1976. pap. 2.50 (ISBN 0-89265-061-3). Randall Hse.

History of Fundamentalism. Stewart G. Cole. LC 70-138107. 1971. Repr. of 1931 ed. lib. bdg. 22.50x (ISBN 0-8371-5683-1, COHF). Greenwood.

History of Giles, Lincoln, Franklin & Moore Counties, Tennessee. Goodspeed Publishing Company. 1979. Repr. of 1886 ed. 26.50 (ISBN 0-89308-116-7). Southern Hist Pr.

History of Hindostan. Thomas Maurice. Ed. by Burton Feldman & Robert D. Richardson. LC 78-60888. (Myth & Romanticism Ser.). 1984. lib. bdg. 240.00 (ISBN 0-8240-3566-6). Garland Pub.

History of His Own Times. Bishop Burnet. 409p. 1980. Repr. lib. bdg. 12.50 (ISBN 0-89987-056-2). Darby Bks.

History of Hymn Singing As Told Through One Hundred One Famous Hymns. LC 82-83452. (Illus.). 232p. 1982. 19.95 (ISBN 0-87319-016-5). C Hallberg.

History of Ideas about the Prolongation of Life: The Evolution of Prolongevity Hypotheses to 1800. Gerald J. Gruman. Ed. by Robert Kastenbaum. LC 76-19574. (Death & Dying Ser.). (Illus.). 1977. Repr. of 1966 ed. lib. bdg. 17.00x (ISBN 0-405-09572-4). Ayer Co Pubs.

History of India from the Sixth Century B.C. to the Mohammedan Conquest, Including the Invasion of Alexander the Great. Vincent A. Smith. LC 72-14391. (History of India Ser.: No. 2). Repr. of 1906 ed. 32.00 (ISBN 0-404-09002-8). AMS Pr.

HIstory of Interpretation of Hebrews 7, 1-10 from the Reformation to the Present. Bruce Demarest. 154p. 1976. pap. text ed. 28.50x (Pub. by J C B Mohr BRD). Coronet Bks.

History of Islam in West Africa. J. Spencer Trimingham. (Oxford Paperback Ser.). 1962. pap. 8.95x (ISBN 0-19-285038-5). Oxford U Pr.

History of Islamic Law. Noel Coulson. 264p. 1964. pap. 10.00 (ISBN 0-85224-354-5, Pub. by Edinburgh U Pr Scotland). Columbia U Pr.

History of Islamic Philosophy. 2nd ed. Majid Fakhry. LC 81-21781. 450p. 1983. 29.50x (ISBN 0-231-05532-3). Columbia U Pr.

History of Islamic Philosophy. 2nd ed. Majid Fakhry. (Studies in Oriental Culture: No. 5). 394p. 1987. pap. text ed. 16.00 (ISBN 0-231-05533-1). Columbia U Pr.

History of Israel. 3rd ed. John Bright. LC 80-22774. (Illus.). 528p. 1981. 18.95 (ISBN 0-664-21381-2). Westminster.

History of Israel. John J. Davis & John C. Whitcomb. (Old Testament Studies). 1980. 17.95 (ISBN 0-8010-2888-4). Baker Bk.

History of Israel. John J. Davis & John C. Whitcomb. 17.95 (ISBN 0-88469-061-X). BMH Bks.

History of Israel. rev. ed. H. Wheeler Robinson. Ed. by L. H. Brockington. (Studies in Theology: No. 42). 1964. pap. 8.95x (ISBN 0-8401-6042-9). A R Allenson.

History of Israel. H. Wheeler Robinson. (Studies in Theology). 206p. 1967. pap. 13.50 (ISBN 0-7156-0163-6, Pub. by Duckworth London). Longwood Pub Group.

History of Israel & Judah: From the Beginnings to the Second Century A. D. Francois Castel. 288p. (Orig.). 1985. pap. 8.95 (ISBN 0-8091-2701-6). Paulist Pr.

History of Israel: Biblical History. 2nd ed. Martin Noth. LC 58-5195. 1960. 16.95xi (ISBN 0-06-066310-3, HarpR). Har-Row.

History of Israel from Alexander the Great to Bar Kochba. Henk Jagersma. Tr. by J. H. Kok. LC 85-45497. 256p. 1986. pap. 12.95 (ISBN 0-8006-1890-4, 1-1890). Fortress.

History of Israel: From the Rise of Zionism to Our Time. Howard M. Sachar. LC 76-13710. (Illus.). 1979. 14.95 (ISBN 0-394-73679-6). Knopf.

History of Israel in Old Testament Times. 2nd, rev. & enl. ed. Siegfried Herrmann. Tr. by John Bowden from Ger. LC 81-43092. Tr. of Geschichte Israels in alttestamentlicher Zeit. 456p. 1981. pap. 16.95 (ISBN 0-8006-1499-2, 1-1499). Fortress.

History of Israel in the Old Testament Period. Henk Jagersma. Tr. by John Bowden. LC 82-48548. 320p. 1983. pap. 13.95 (ISBN 0-8006-1692-8). Fortress.

History of Japanese Religion. Masaharu Anesaki. LC 63-19395. 1963. Repr. of 1930 ed. 23.50 (ISBN 0-8048-0248-3). C E Tuttle.

History of Jewish Coinage & of Money in the Old & New Testaments. Frederic W. Madden. LC 66-26486. (Library of Biblical Studies). (Illus.). 1968. 39.50x (ISBN 0-87068-082-X). Ktav.

History of Jewish Education from 515 B. C. E. to 220 C. E. Nathan Drazin. 1979. 16.00 (ISBN 0-405-10598-3). Ayer Co Pubs.

History of Jewish Education in the Soviet Union, 1918-1948. Elias Schulman. 1971. 25.00x (ISBN 0-87068-145-1). Ktav.

History of Jewish Literature, 6 vols. Meyer Waxman. 50.00 set (ISBN 0-8453-8640-9, Cornwall Bks). Assoc Univ Prs.

History of Jewish Literature, 12 vols. Israel Zinberg. 22.50x ea. (ISBN 0-685-56219-0). Ktav.

History of Jewish Philosophy in the Middle Ages. Colette Sirat. 476p. 1985. 59.50 (ISBN 0-521-26087-6). Cambridge U Pr.

History of Johnson County Churches. Johnson County Historical Society Staff. Ed. by John Morgan. 176p. 1986. 20.00 (ISBN 0-916369-06-4). Magnolia Pr.

History of Judaism, 2 vols. Daniel J. Silver & Bernard Martin. Incl. Vol. 1. From Abraham to Maimonides; Vol. 2. Europe & the New World. pap. 10.95 o.s.i (ISBN 0-465-03005-X). LC 73-90131. 1974. Basic.

History of Judaism: The Next Ten Years. Baruch M. Bokser. Ed. by Jacob Neusner. LC 80-25501. (Brown Judaic Studies). 1980. 15.00 (ISBN 0-89130-450-9, 14-00-21); pap. 10.50 (ISBN 0-89130-451-7). Scholars Pr GA.

History of Latin Christianity, 9 Vols. Henry H. Milman. LC 71-172734. Repr. of 1887 ed. Set. lib. bdg. 145.00 (ISBN 0-404-04360-7). AMS Pr.

History of Medieval Christianity. Jeffrey Russell. LC 68-9743. 1968. pap. 8.95x (ISBN 0-88295-761-9). Harlan Davidson.

History of Medieval Islam. J. J. Saunders. (Illus.). 1978. pap. 9.95x (ISBN 0-7100-0050-2). Methuen Inc.

History of Medieval Vaishnavism in Orissa. Prabhat Mukherjee. 200p. 1986. Repr. 14.00X (ISBN 0-8364-1754-2, Pub. by Manohar India). South Asia Bks.

History of Messianic Speculation in Israel from the First Through the Seventeenth Centuries. Abba H. Silver. 11.75 (ISBN 0-8446-2937-5). Peter Smith.

History of Methodism in Alabama. Anson D. West. LC 83-19053. (Illus.). 840p. 1984. Repr. of 1893 ed. 30.00 (ISBN 0-87152-380-9). Reprint.

History of Modern Creationism. Henry M. Morris. LC 84-60865. 1984. 12.95 (ISBN 0-89051-107-1); pap. 9.95 (ISBN 0-89051-102-0). Master Bks.

History of Modern Germany, 3 vols. H. Holborn. 1982. Vol. 1, The Reformation. 47.50 (ISBN 0-691-05357-X); pap. 10.50 (ISBN 0-691-00795-0); Vol. 2, 1648-1840. 60.50 (ISBN 0-691-05358-8); pap. 11.50 (ISBN 0-691-00796-9); Vol. 3, 1840-1945. 79.00 (ISBN 0-691-05359-6); pap. 13.95 (ISBN 0-691-00797-7); Set. 155.00; Set. pap. 27.50. Princeton U Pr.

History of Modern Morals. Max Hodann. LC 72-9651. Repr. of 1937 ed. 47.50 (ISBN 0-404-57460-2). AMS Pr.

History of Monks & Monasteries. Alfred W. Wishart. 1977. lib. bdg. 59.95 (ISBN 0-8490-1980-X). Gordon Pr.

History of Music in New England, with Biographical Sketches of Reformers & Psalmists. George Hood. (American Studies). 1970. Repr. of 1846 ed. 24.00 (ISBN 0-384-24140-9). Johnson Repr.

History of Muslim Civilization in India. S. M. Ikram. 25.50 (ISBN 0-317-46089-7). Kazi Pubns.

History of Mysticism. Swami Abhayananda. 464p. (Orig.). 1987. pap. 11.95 (ISBN 0-914557-04-1). Atma Bks.

History of Neo-Arianism. Thomas A. Kopecek. LC 79-89557. (Patristic Monograph: No. 8). 1979. pap. 14.00 (ISBN 0-915646-07-2). Phila Patristic.

History of New Bethel Missionary Baptist Church. Vanderpool. 5.00x (ISBN 0-686-12400-6). Church History.

History of New England. Isaac Backus. LC 76-83410. (Religion in America, Ser. 1). 1969. Repr. of 1871 ed. 54.00 (ISBN 0-405-00231-9). Ayer Co Pubs.

History of New England Theology. George N. Boardman. Ed. by Bruce Kuklick. (American Religious Thought of the 18th & 19th Centuries Ser.). 314p. 1987. lib. bdg. 45.00 (ISBN 0-8240-6955-2). Garland Pub.

History of New-England... to the Year of Our Lord, 1700, 2 vols. Daniel Neal. LC 75-31125. Repr. of 1747 ed. Set. 64.00 (ISBN 0-404-13760-1). AMS Pr.

History of New Testament Times. Robert H. Pfeiffer. LC 77-138125. 561p. 1972. Repr. of 1949 ed. lib. bdg. 23.00x (ISBN 0-8371-3559-1, PFNT). Greenwood.

History of Northeast Arkansas. Goodspeed Publishing Company. 1978. Repr. of 1884 ed. 42.50 (ISBN 0-89308-081-0). Southern Hist Pr.

History of Oberlin College: From Its Foundation Through the Civil War, 2 vols. in 1. Robert S. Fletcher. LC 75-165716. (American Education Ser, No. 2). 1971. Repr. of 1943 ed. 60.50 (ISBN 0-405-03705-8). Ayer Co Pubs.

History of Our Lord As Exemplified in Works of Art; with That of His Type; St. John the Baptist; & Other Persons of the Old & New Testament, 2 vols. Anna B. Jameson. LC 92-167006. (Illus.). 1976. Repr. of 1890 ed. Set. 70.00x (ISBN 0-8103-4304-5). Gale.

History of Pastoral Care in America: From Salvation to Self-Realization. E. Brooks Holifield. 416p. (Orig.). 1983. pap. 16.95 (ISBN 0-687-17249-7). Abingdon.

History of Pennsylvania, 2 Vols. Robert Proud. LC 66-25101. 1967. Repr. of 1797 ed. 20.00 ea. Vol. 1 (ISBN 0-87152-031-1). Vol. 2 (ISBN 0-87152-032-X). Set. 40.00 (ISBN 0-87152-305-1). Reprint.

History of Pentateuchal Traditions. Martin Noth & Berhard W. Anderson. LC 80-24937. (Scholars Press Reproductions Ser.). 1981. 22.00_o.s. (ISBN 0-89130-446-0, 00-07-05); text ed. 17.50 (ISBN 0-89130-954-3). Scholars Pr GA.

History of Philosophy, 9 vols. Frederick Copleston. Incl. Vol. 1. Greece & Rome (ISBN 0-8091-0065-7); Vol. 2. Medieval Philosophy - Augustine to Scotus (ISBN 0-8091-0066-5); Vol. 3. Ockham to Suarez (ISBN 0-8091-0067-3); Vol. 4. Descartes to Leibniz (ISBN 0-8091-0068-1); Vol. 5. Hobbes to Hume (ISBN 0-8091-0069-X); Vol. 6. Wolff to Kant (ISBN 0-8091-0070-3); Vol. 7. Fichte to Nietzsche (ISBN 0-8091-0071-1); Vol. 8. Bentham to Russell (ISBN 0-8091-0072-X); Vol. 9. Maine de Bira to Sartre. 1976 (ISBN 0-8091-0196-3). Vols. 1-9. 19.95 ea. Paulist Pr.

History of Philosophy & Philosophical Education. Etienne Gilson. (Aquinas Lecture). 1947. 7.95 (ISBN 0-87462-112-7). Marquette.

History of Philosophy in Islam. Tjitze J. De Boer. LC 70-131638. 216p. 1903. Repr. 39.00x (ISBN 0-403-00525-6). Scholarly.

History of Pre-Buddhistic Indian Philosophy. Benimadhab Barua. 1981. Repr. of 1921 ed. 28.50x (ISBN 0-8364-0800-4, Pub. by Motilal Banarsidass). South Asia Bks.

History of Preaching, 2 Vols. Edwin C. Dargan. 1965. lib. bdg. 47.00 (ISBN 0-8337-0772-8). B Franklin.

History of Primitive Christianity. Hans Conzelmann. Tr. by John E. Steely from Ger. LC 72-8818. Orig. Title: Geschichte Des Unchristentums. 192p. 1973. pap. 8.95 (ISBN 0-687-17252-7). Abingdon.

History of Prophecy in Israel: From the Settlement in the Land to the Hellenistic Period. Joseph Blenkinsopp. LC 83-10178. 288p. (Orig.). 1983. pap. 16.95 (ISBN 0-664-24479-3). Westminster.

History of Protestant Missions in the Near East. Julius Richter. LC 79-133822. Repr. of 1910 ed. 29.50 (ISBN 0-404-05331-9). AMS Pr.

History of Protestant Theology, 2 Vols. Isaak A. Dorner. LC 72-133823. Repr. of 1871 ed. Set. 87.50 (ISBN 0-404-02147-6). AMS Pr.

History of Public Speaking in America. Robert T. Oliver. LC 78-13428. 1978. Repr. of 1965 ed. lib. bdg. 47.50 (ISBN 0-313-21152-3, OLPS). Greenwood.

History of Quakerism. Elbert Russell. LC 79-53169. 612p. 1980. pap. 14.95 (ISBN 0-913408-52-2). Friends United.

History of Religion in England, 8 vols. John Stoughton. 1977. lib. bdg. 800.00 (ISBN 0-8490-1984-2). Gordon Pr.

History of Religions, 2 vols. George F. Moore. 19.95 ea. (Pub. by T & T Clark Ltd UK). Vol. 1, 1914, 654 pgs (ISBN 0-567-07202-9). Vol. 2, 1920, 568 pgs (ISBN 0-567-07203-7). Fortress.

History of Religions: Essays in Methodology. Mircea Eliade & Joseph Kitagawa. LC 59-11621. 1959. 12.50x (ISBN 0-226-20394-8). U of Chicago Pr.

History of Religions: Essays in Methodology. Ed. by Mircea Eliade & Joseph Kitagawa. LC 59-11621. 1973. pap. 3.50 (ISBN 0-226-20395-6, P549, Phoen). U of Chicago Pr.

History of Religions: Retrospect & Prospect. Ed. by Joseph M. Kitagawa. 192p. 1985. 19.95x (ISBN 0-02-916490-7). Macmillan.

History of Religious Education: Documents & Interpretations from the Judaeo-Christian Tradition. Robert Ulich. LC 68-29433. 1968. 30.00 (ISBN 0-8147-0420-4). NYU Pr.

History of Religious Education in Connecticut to the Middle of the Nineteenth Century. George Stewart, Jr. LC 79-89238. (American Education: Its Men, Institutions & Ideas, Ser. 1). 1969. Repr. of 1924 ed. 17.00 (ISBN 0-405-01475-9). Ayer Co Pubs.

History of Religious Education in the Episcopal Church to Eighteen Thirty-Five. Clifton H. Brewer. 1924. 14.50x (ISBN 0-686-51401-7). Elliots Bks.

History of Religious Education in the Episcopal Church to 1835. Clifton H. Brewer. LC 73-89152. (American Education Its Men, Institutions & Ideas, Ser. 1). 1969. Repr. of 1924 ed. 16.00 (ISBN 0-405-01390-6). Ayer Co Pubs.

History of Religious Ideas: From the Stone Age to the Eleusinian Mysteries, Vol. 1. Mircea Eliade. Tr. by Willard R. Trask from Fr. LC 77-16784. xviii, 490p. 1979. 25.00x (ISBN 0-226-20400-6); pap. 16.95 (ISBN 0-226-20401-4). U of Chicago Pr.

History of Religious Ideas, Vol. II: From Gautama Buddha to the Triumph of Christianity. Mircea Eliade. Tr. by Willard Trask from Fr. LC 77-16784. vi, 564p. 1982. 27.50x (ISBN 0-226-20402-2). U of Chicago Pr.

History of Religious Ideas, Vol. 2: From Gautama Buddha to the Triumph of Christianity. Mircea Eliade. Tr. by Willard R. Trask. LC 77-16784. vi, 564p. 1984. pap. 15.95 (ISBN 0-226-20403-0). U of Chicago Pr.

History of Religious Ideas, Vol. 3: From Muhammad to the Age of Reforms. Mircea Eliade. Tr. by Alf Hiltebeiten & Diane Apostolos-Cappadona. LC 77-16784. xii, 352p. 1985. 27.50 (ISBN 0-226-20404-9). U of Chicago Pr.

History of Religious Sectarianism in Russia (1860s-1917) A. I. Klibanov. Ed. by Stephen P. Dunn. LC 81-12180. (Illus.). 380p. 1982. 54.00 (ISBN 0-08-026794-3). Pergamon.

History of Rome & the Popes in the Middle Ages, 3 vols. Hartmann Grisar. LC 70-154115. Tr. of Geschichte Roms und der Papste Immittelater. (Illus.). Repr. of 1912 ed. Set. 120.00 (ISBN 0-404-09370-1). AMS Pr.

History of Russian Jewish Literature: Including Russian Literature & the Jews. V. Lvov-Rogachevsky. Tr. by Arthur Levin from Rus. 1979. 15.00 (ISBN 0-88233-271-6); pap. 5.50 (ISBN 0-88233-272-4). Ardis Pubs.

History of Scepticism from Erasmus to Spinoza. Richard H. Popkin. LC 78-65469. 1979. 37.00x (ISBN 0-520-03827-4); pap. 9.50x (ISBN 0-520-03876-2, CAMPUS NO. 226). U of Cal Pr.

History of Siloam Missionary Baptist Church. J. H. Lambert. pap. 2.50x (ISBN 0-686-12399-9). Church History.

History of South Arkansas. Goodspeed Publishing Company. 1978. Repr. of 1884 ed. 47.50 (ISBN 0-89308-083-7, Goodspeed Pub Co). Southern Hist Pr.

History of Southern Baptist Landmarkism in the Light of Historical Baptist Ecclesiology: Doctoral Dissertation. James E. Tull. Ed. by Edwin S. Gaustad. LC 79-52578. (Baptist Tradition Ser.). 1980. lib. bdg. 64.00x (ISBN 0-405-12446-5). Ayer Co Pubs.

History of Spurgeons Tabernacle. Eric Hayden. 1971. 5.95 (ISBN 0-686-09091-8). Pilgrim Pubns.

History of Staffordshire Bells. T. Jennings. 1985. 22.50x (ISBN 0-317-54277-X, Pub. by J Richardson UK). State Mutual Bk.

History of Ten Baptist Churches, of Which the Author Has Been Alternately a Member. 2nd ed. John Taylor. Ed. by Edwin S. Gaustad. LC 79-5609. (Baptist Tradition Ser.). 1980. Repr. of 1827 ed. lib. bdg. 25.50x (ISBN 0-405-12474-0). Ayer Co Pubs.

History of Texas, Sixteen Seventy-Three to Seventeen Seventy-Nine, 2 pts. Fray J. Morfi. Ed. by Carlos E. Castaneda. LC 67-24718. (Quivira Society Publications Ser.: Vol. 6). 1967. Repr. of 1935 ed. 34.00 (ISBN 0-405-19053-0). Ayer Co Pubs.

History of Thanatology: Philosophical, Religious, Psychological, & Sociological Ideas Concerning Death from Primitive Times to the Present. Panos D. Bardi. LC 81-43026. 102p. (Orig.). 1981. lib. bdg. 21.00 (ISBN 0-8191-1648-3); pap. text ed. 8.25 (ISBN 0-8191-1649-1). U Pr of Amer.

History of the African Methodist Episcopal Church, 1856-1922. Charles S. Smith. 1922. 27.00 (ISBN 0-384-45261-2). Johnson Repr.

History of the African Methodist Episcopal Church. Daniel A. Payne. LC 69-18573. (American Negro: His History & Literature Ser., No. 2). 1969. Repr. of 1891 ed. 19.00 (ISBN 0-405-01885-1). Ayer Co Pubs.

History of the African Mission of the Protestant Episcopal Church in the United States. facsimile ed. Mrs. E. F. Hening. LC 77-173608. (Black Heritage Library Collection). Repr. of 1849 ed. 20.75 (ISBN 0-8369-8900-7). Ayer Co Pubs.

History of the Afro-American Group of the Episcopal Church. George F. Bragg, Jr. (Basic Afro-American Reprint Library). (Illus.). Repr. of 1922 ed. 17.00 (ISBN 0-384-05495-1). Johnson Repr.

History of the Apostolic Succession of Archbishop Emile F. Rodriguez-Fairfield from the Mexican National Catholic Church. Paul Schultz. 100p. Date not set. Repr. lib. bdg. 19.95x (ISBN 0-89370-557-8). Borgo Pr.

History of the Assassins, Derived from Oriental Sources. Joseph Von Hammer-Purgstall. Tr. by Oswald C. Wood. Repr. of 1835 ed. 22.50 (ISBN 0-8337-1562-3). B Franklin.

History of the Baptists. rev. ed. Robert G. Torbet. LC 63-8225. 592p. 1973. 21.95 (ISBN 0-8170-0074-7). Judson.

History of the Baptists. H. C. Vedder. 1977. lib. bdg. 59.95 (ISBN 0-8490-1988-5). Gordon Pr.

History of the Baptists in Missouri. R. S. Duncan. 1981. Repr. of 1882 ed. 38.00 (ISBN 0-686-77695-X). Church History.

History of the Baron DeHirsch Fund: The Americanization of the Jewish Immigrant. Samuel Joseph. LC 76-52987. (Illus.). Repr. of 1935 ed. lib. bdg. 32.50x (ISBN 0-678-01151-6). Kelley.

History of the Bible Church. Clevenger & Hill. 1973. pap. 1.50 (ISBN 0-88428-006-3, 171). Parchment Pr.

History of the Bible in English. 3rd ed. F. F. Bruce. 1978. pap. 8.95 (ISBN 0-19-520088-8). Oxford U Pr.

History of the Blessed Virgin Mary & the History of the Likeness of Christ Which the Jews of Tiberius Made to Mock At, 2 vols. Tr. by Ernest A. Budge. LC 73-18848. (Luzac's Semitic Text & Translation Ser.: Nos. 4-5). Repr. of 1899 ed. 45.00 set (ISBN 0-404-11341-9). AMS Pr.

History of the Book of Common Prayer. Leighton Pullan. LC 77-15663. 1901. 20.00 (ISBN 0-8414-6848-6). Folcroft.

History of the Book of Common Prayer. Leighton Pullan. 330p. 1981. Repr. of 1901 ed. lib. bdg. 35.00 (ISBN 0-8492-2167-6). R West.

History of the Brethren Church. A. T. Ronk. LC 68-23554. 1968. 10.95x (ISBN 0-934970-03-3). Brethren Ohio.

History of the Catechumenate. Michel Dujarier. 144p. 1982. pap. 5.95 (ISBN 0-8215-9327-7). Sadlier.

History of the Catholic Church from the Renaissaince to the French Revolution, 2 vols. facsimile ed. James MacCaffrey. LC 75-130558. (Select Bibliographies Reprint Ser.). Repr. of 1915 ed. Set. 53.00 (ISBN 0-8369-5531-5); Vol. 1. 26.50 (ISBN 0-8369-9984-3); Vol. 2. 26.50 (ISBN 0-8369-9985-1). Ayer Co Pubs.

History of the Catholic Church: From the Renaissance to the French Revolution, Vol. II. facsimile ed. James MacCaffrey. LC 75-130558. 470p. Repr. of 1915 ed. lib. bdg. 25.50 (ISBN 0-8290-0464-5). Irvington.

History of the Catholic Church: From the Renaissance to the French Revolution, Vol. I. facsimile ed. James MacCaffrey. LC 75-130558. 419p. Repr. of 1915 ed. lib. bdg. 25.50 (ISBN 0-8290-0463-7). Irvington.

History of the Catholic Church in the United States, 4 vols. John D. Shea. 216.00 (ISBN 0-405-10852-4, 11855). Ayer Co Pubs.

History of the Catholic Missions Among the Indian Tribes of the United States, 1529-1854. John D. Shea. LC 73-175853. Repr. of 1855 ed. 28.50 (ISBN 0-404-07176-7). AMS Pr.

History of the Catholic Missions Among the Indian Tribes of the United States, 1529-1854. John G. Shea. LC 70-83436. (Religion in America, Ser. 1). 1969. Repr. of 1857 ed. 26.50 (ISBN 0-405-00263-7). Ayer Co Pubs.

History of the Catholic Missions in Northeast India. C. Becker. 1980. 32.00x (ISBN 0-8364-0600-1, Pub. by Mukhopadhyay India). South Asia Bks.

History of the Catholic University of America, 3 vols. Incl. Vol.1. The Rectorship of John J. Keane, 1887-1896. Patrick H. Ahern. 220p. 1949 (ISBN 0-8132-0313-9); Vol.2. The Rectorship of Thomas J. Conaty, 1896-1903. Peter E. Hogan. 1949 (ISBN 0-8132-0314-7); Vol.3. The Rectorship of Denis J. O'Connell, 1903-1909. C. J. Barry. 212p. 1950 (ISBN 0-8132-0315-5). 5.95x ea. Cath U Pr.

History of the Celtic Religion & Learning. John Toland. LC 74-16159. 1974. Repr. lib. bdg. 40.00 (ISBN 0-8414-8553-4). Folcroft.

History of the Chaitanya Faith in Orissa. Prabhat Mukherjee. 1979. 14.00x (ISBN 0-8364-0547-1). South Asia Bks.

History of the Chartiers Hill United Presbyterian Church of Canonsburg, Pennsylvania. William W. Taylor & Thomas A. Smith, Sr. 1975. write for info. (ISBN 0-87012-210-X). McClain.

History of the Choir & Music of Trinity Church. Arthur Messiter. LC 72-137317. Repr. of 1906 ed. 21.45 (ISBN 0-404-04313-5). AMS Pr.

History of the Christian Church. George P. Fisher. LC 75-41094. 48.50 (ISBN 0-404-14662-7). AMS Pr.

History of the Christian Church, 8 vols. Philip Schaff. Incl. Vol. 1. Apostolic Christianity. 17.95 (ISBN 0-8028-8047-9); Vol. 2. Ante-Nicene. 100-325. 17.95 (ISBN 0-8028-8048-7); Vol. 3. Nicene & Post-Nicene. 311-600. 17.95 (ISBN 0-8028-8049-5); Vol. 4. Medieval Christianity. 590-1073. 17.95 (ISBN 0-8028-8050-9); Vol. 5. Middle Ages. 1049-1294. 17.95 (ISBN 0-8028-8051-7); Vol. 6. Middle Ages. 1295-1517. 17.95 (ISBN 0-8028-8052-5); Vol. 7. German Reformation. 17.95 (ISBN 0-8028-8053-3); Vol. 8. Swiss Reformation. 17.95 (ISBN 0-8028-8054-1). 1960. Repr. 17.95 ea.; 143.60 (ISBN 0-8028-8046-0). Eerdmans.

History of the Christian Church. 4th ed. Williston Walker. 1985. text ed. write for info. (ISBN 0-02-423870-8, Pub. by Scribner). Macmillan.

History of the Christian Church. 3rd, rev. ed. Williston Walker. Rev. by Robert T. Handy. 601p. 1970. text ed. write for info. (ISBN 0-02-424300-0, Pub. by Scribner). Macmillan.

History of the Christian Church, or Jones' Church History, 2 vols. William Jones. 1983. Repr. of 1826 ed. 42.50 set (ISBN 0-317-01250-9). Church History.

History of the Christian Movement: The Development of Christian Institutions. A. Daniel Frankforter. LC 77-8071. 332p. 1978. text ed. 22.95x (ISBN 0-88229-292-7); pap. 11.95x (ISBN 0-88229-568-3). Nelson-Hall.

History of the Christmas Card. George Buday. LC 74-174012. (Tower Bks.). (Illus.). xxiii, 304p. 1972. Repr. of 1954 ed. 50.00x (ISBN 0-8103-3931-5). Gale.

History of the Church, 10 Vols. 920p. 1980. complete set 595.00x (ISBN 0-8245-0318-X). Crossroad NY.

History of the Church, 7 vols. Intro. by B. H. Roberts. Incl. Vol. 1 (1820-1834) 511p. 1974 (ISBN 0-87747-074-X); Vol. 2 (1834-1837) 543p. 1974 (ISBN 0-87747-075-8); Vol. 3 (1834-1839) 478p (ISBN 0-87747-076-6); Vol. 4 (1839-1842) 620p (ISBN 0-87747-077-4); Vol. 5 (1842-1843) 563p (ISBN 0-87747-078-2); Vol. 6 (1843-1844) 641p (ISBN 0-87747-079-0); Vol. 7 (period 2, The Apostolic Interregnum) 640p (ISBN 0-87747-080-4). 15.95 ea.; index 15.95 (ISBN 0-87747-291-2). Deseret Bk.

History of the Church & State in Norway: From the 10th to the 16th Century. Thomas B. Willson. LC 72-145376. (Illus.). 1971. Repr. of 1903 ed. 49.00x (ISBN 0-403-01280-5). Scholarly.

History of the Church: From Christ to Constantine. Eusebeius. Tr. by G. A. Williamson from Latin. LC 75-22726. Orig. Title: Historia Ecclesiastica. 432p. 1975. pap. 12.95 (ISBN 0-8066-1509-5, 10-3045). Augsburg.

History of the Church from Christ to Constantine. Eusebius. Tr. by G. A. Williamson. (Classics Ser.). 1981. pap. 5.95 (ISBN 0-14-044138-7). Penguin.

History of the Church (From Christ to Constantine) Eusebius. Tr. by G. A. Williamson. 1985. Repr. of 1965 ed. 16.95 (ISBN 0-317-19661-8, Pub. by Dorset Pr). Hippocrene Bks.

History of the Church in England. 3rd rev ed. John R. Moorman. 485p. 1973. 19.95 (ISBN 0-8192-1282-2). Morehouse.

History of the Church in Latin America: Colonialism to Liberation. Enrique Dussel. Tr. by Alan Neely. 368p. 1981. 21.95 (ISBN 0-8028-3548-1). Eerdmans.

History of the Church in Venezuela. M. Walters. 1976. lib. bdg. 59.95 (ISBN 0-8490-1991-5). Gordon Pr.

History of the Church in Venezuela, 1810-1930. Mary Watters. LC 70-137303. Repr. of 1933 ed. 22.00 (ISBN 0-404-06877-4). AMS Pr.

History of the Church Known As the Moravian Church. John T. Hamilton. LC 70-134379. Repr. of 1900 ed. 37.50 (ISBN 0-404-08427-3). AMS Pr.

History of the Church of Blackburnshire. John E. Wallis. (Church Historical Society London, New Ser.: No. 7). Repr. of 1932 ed. 40.00 (ISBN 0-8115-3131-7). Kraus Repr.

History of the Church of England, 1945-80. Paul A. Welsby. 1984. 29.95x (ISBN 0-19-213231-8). Oxford U Pr.

History of the Church of Englande. Beda. (English Experience Ser.: No. 234). 382p. Repr. of 1565 ed. 55.00 (ISBN 90-221-0234-3). Walter J Johnson.

History of the Church of Russia. Andrei N. Murav'Ev. LC 76-133816. Repr. of 1842 ed. 29.45 (ISBN 0-404-04541-3). AMS Pr.

History of the Church of Scotland, 3 Vols. John Spottiswood. Ed. by Michael Russell & Mark Napier. LC 76-176004. (Bannatyne Club, Edinburgh. Publications: No. 93). Repr. of 1851 ed. Set. 145.00 (ISBN 0-404-52840-6). AMS Pr.

History of the Church of York, Ten Sixty Six-Eleven Twenty Seven. Hugh The Chantor. Ed. by Charles Johnson. (Oxford Medieval Texts Ser.). 1984. 22.00x (ISBN 0-19-822213-0). Oxford U Pr.

History of the Church of York, 1066-1127. Hugh Sottovagina. Tr. & intro. by Charles Johnson. LC 80-2227. Repr. of 1961 ed. 38.00 (ISBN 0-404-18764-1). AMS Pr.

History of the Church to A.D. 461, 3 vols. Beresford J. Kidd. LC 75-41165. Repr. of 1922 ed. Set. 135.00 (ISBN 0-404-15010-1). AMS Pr.

History of the Churches in the United States & Canada. Robert T. Handy. 1977. 29.95x (ISBN 0-19-826910-2). Oxford U Pr.

History of the Churches in the United States & Canada. Robert T. Handy. 1977. pap. 8.95 (ISBN 0-19-502531-8). Oxford U Pr.

History of the Colored Methodist Episcopal Church in America: Comprising Its Organization, Subsequent Developments & Present Status. Charles H. Phillips. LC 73-38459. (Religion in America, Ser. 2). 252p. 1972. Repr. of 1898 ed. 17.00 (ISBN 0-405-04080-6). Ayer Co Pubs.

History of the Controversy over the "Debitum Peccati". Juniper Carol. (Theology Ser.). 1978. 7.00 (ISBN 0-686-27935-2). Franciscan Inst.

History of the Councils of Baltimore, 1791-1884. Peter K. Guilday. LC 77-83421. (Religion in America, Ser. 1). 1969. Repr. of 1932 ed. 25.50 (ISBN 0-405-00246-7). Ayer Co Pubs.

History of the Councils of the Church from the Original Documents, 5 vols. Karl J. Hefele. Ed. & tr. by William R. Clark. LC 79-39294. Repr. of 1896 ed. Set. 172.50 (ISBN 0-404-03260-5); 34.50 ea.; Vol. 1. (ISBN 0-404-03261-3); Vol. 2. (ISBN 0-404-03262-1); Vol. 3. (ISBN 0-404-03263-X); Vol. 4. (ISBN 0-404-03264-8); Vol. 5. (ISBN 0-404-03265-6). AMS Pr.

History of the Criticism of the Acts of the Apostles. Ward Gasque. 334p. 1975. lib. bdg. 52.00x (Pub. by J C B Mohr BRD). Coronet Bks.

History of the Cross Creek Presbyterian Church. Alvin D. White. 1969. 6.00 (ISBN 0-87012-040-9). McClain.

History of the Crusades, 3 Vols. Joseph F. Michaud. Tr. by W. Robson. LC 72-172729. Repr. of 1852 ed. 110.00 (ISBN 0-404-04320-8). AMS Pr.

History of the Crusades, 5 vols. Ed. by Kenneth M. Setton. Incl. Vol. 1. The First Hundred Years. Ed. by Marshall W. Baldwin. (Illus.). 740p. 1969. Repr. of 1955 ed (ISBN 0-299-04831-4); Vol. 2. The Later Crusades, 1189 to 1311. 2nd ed. Ed. by Robert L. Wolff & Harry W. Hazard. (Illus.). 896p. Repr. of 1962 ed (ISBN 0-299-04841-1); Vol. 3. The Fourteenth & Fifteenth Centuries. Ed. by Harry W. Hazard & Kenneth M. Setton. (Illus.). 836p. 1975 (ISBN 0-299-06670-3); Vol. 4. The Art & Architecture of the Crusader States. Ed. by Harry W. Hazard & Kenneth M. Setton. (Illus.). 444p. 1977 (ISBN 0-299-06820-X); Vol. 5. The Impact of the Crusades on the Near East. Ed. by Kenneth M. Setton & Norman P. Zacour. (Illus.). 512p. 1985 (ISBN 0-299-09140-6). LC 68-9837. 40.00x ea. U of Wis Pr.

History of the Crusades Against the Albigenses in the Thirteenth Century. Jean C. Simonde De Sismondi. LC 72-178564. Repr. of 1826 ed. 30.00 (ISBN 0-404-56672-3). AMS Pr.

History of the Development of the Devotion to the Holy Name. Peter R. Biasiotto. 1943. 3.50 (ISBN 0-686-11579-1). Franciscan Inst.

History of the Devil & the Idea of Evil. Paul Carus. (Illus.). 496p. 1974. pap. 14.95 (ISBN 0-87548-307-0). Open Court.

History of the Dominion of the Arabs in Spain, 3 Vols. Jose A. Conde. Tr. by Mrs. Jonathan Foster. Repr. of 1855 ed. Set. 55.00 (ISBN 0-404-09270-5); 18.50 ea. Vol. 1 (ISBN 0-404-09271-3). Vol. 2 (ISBN 0-404-09272-1). Vol. 3 (ISBN 0-404-09273-X). AMS Pr.

History of the Donatists. David Benedict. 1985. Repr. of 1875 ed. 15.00 (ISBN 0-317-31641-9). Church History.

History of the Dvaita School of Vedant & Its Literature. 2nd ed. B. N. Sharma. 1981. 48.00x (ISBN 0-8364-0754-7, Pub. by Motilal Banarsidass). South Asia Bks.

History of the Early Church from A.D. 500. 4th ed. J. W. C. Wand. 300p. 1975. pap. 11.95x (ISBN 0-416-18110-4, NO. 2572). Methuen Inc.

History of the English Baptists: 1740 Ed, 4 vols. in 2 vols. Thomas Crosby. Set. 45.00 (ISBN 0-686-12405-7). Church History.

History of the English Bible. John Brown. LC 77-13187. 1977. Repr. lib. bdg. 15.00 (ISBN 0-8414-9929-2). Folcroft.

History of the English Bible. T. Harwood Pattison. 1894. 20.00 (ISBN 0-8274-2521-X). R West.

History of the English Bible. Jonathan Underwood. LC 83-577. 96p. 1983. pap. 3.50 (ISBN 0-87239-644-4, 39974). Standard Pub.

History of the English Church, 8 vols. in 9. William R. Stephens et al. Repr. of 1910 ed. Set. 265.50 (ISBN 0-404-50750-6); 29.50 ea. AMS Pr.

History of the English Church & People. Bede the Venerable. Tr. by Sherley-Price. (Classics Ser.). (Orig.). 1955. pap. 4.95 (ISBN 0-14-044042-9). Penguin.

History of the English Church & People. Bede the Venerable. Tr. by Leo Sherley-Price. 400p. 1985. 16.95 (ISBN 0-88029-042-0, Pub. by Dorset Pr). Hippocrene Bks.

History of the English Church During the Civil Wars & under the Commonwealth, 1640-1660. William A. Shaw. LC 78-184708. 1974. Repr. of 1900 ed. lib. bdg. 57.50 (ISBN 0-8337-4389-9). B Franklin.

History of the Evangelical Churches of the Valleys of Piemont. Samuel Morland. 1983. 32.00 (ISBN 0-686-42929-X). Church History.

History of the Evangelical Lutheran Church in the United States. Henry E. Jacobs. LC 83-45644. Date not set. Repr. of 1893 ed. 54.50 (ISBN 0-404-19853-8). AMS Pr.

History of the Evangelical United Brethren Church. Ed. by Kenneth W. Krueger. LC 79-14738. (Illus.). 1979. 17.95 (ISBN 0-687-17206-3). Abingdon.

History of the First Baptist Church of Boston: Sixteen Sixty-Five to Eighteen Ninty Nine. Nathan E. Wood. Ed. by Edwin S. Gaustad. LC 79-52612. (Baptist Tradition Ser.). (Illus.). 1980. Repr. of 1899 ed. lib. bdg. 34.50x (ISBN 0-405-12477-5). Ayer Co Pubs.

History of the First Dakota-District of the Evangelical-Lutheran Synod of Iowa & Other States. C. G. Eisenberg. Tr. by Anton H. Richter from Ger. LC 82-17645. 268p. (Orig.). 1983. lib. bdg. 29.25 (ISBN 0-8191-2798-1); pap. text ed. 13.75 (ISBN 0-8191-2799-X). U Pr of Amer.

History of the Foundations of Catholicism in Northern New York. Mary C. Taylor. LC 77-359034. (Monograph Ser.: No. 32). (Illus.). 13.50x (ISBN 0-930060-12-1). US Cath Hist.

History of the Franciscan Order. Lazaro Iriarte. 1983. 25.00 (ISBN 0-8199-0831-2). Franciscan Herald.

History of the Franks. Gregory - Bishop of Tours. Tr. by Ernest Brehaut. (Columbia University Records of Civilization Ser). 1969. pap. 7.95x (ISBN 0-393-09845-1, NortonC). Norton.

History of the Franks: Gregory of Tours. Gregory of Tours. Tr. by Lewis Thorpe. 720p. 1976. pap. 6.95 (ISBN 0-14-044295-2). Penguin.

History of the Free Churches. Paul Sangster. (Illus.). 224p. 1984. 29.95 (ISBN 0-434-41330-5, Pub. by W Heinemann Ltd). David & Charles.

History of the General or Six Principle in Europe & America. Richard Knight. Ed. by Edwin S. Gaustad. LC 79-52597. (Baptist Tradition Ser.). 1980. Repr. of 1827 ed. lib. bdg. 30.50x (ISBN 0-405-12464-3). Ayer Co Pubs.

History of the German Baptist Brethren in Europe & America. Martin G. Brumbaugh. LC 73-134377. (Communal Societies in America Ser.). (Illus.). Repr. of 1899 ed. 37.50 (ISBN 0-404-08425-7). AMS Pr.

History of the German People at the Close of the Middle Ages, 17 Vols. Johannes Janssen. LC 67-104463. Repr. of 1925 ed. Set. 637.50 (ISBN 0-404-03570-1); 37.50 ea. AMS Pr.

History of the German Settlements & of the Lutheran Church in North & South Carolina. Gotthardt D. Bernheim. LC 75-969. xvi, 557p. 1975. Repr. of 1872 ed. 20.00 (ISBN 0-8063-8001-2). Regional.

History of the German Settlements & of the Lutheran Church in North & South Carolina. Gotthardt D. Bernheim. LC 76-187361. 573p. 1972. Repr. of 1872 ed. 25.00 (ISBN 0-87152-089-3). Reprint.

History of the Gothic Revival. Charles Eastlake. LC 71-96937. (Library of Victorian Culture). 1975. pap. text ed. 12.00 (ISBN 0-89257-035-0). Am Life Foun.

History of the Grassy Creek Baptist Church. Robert Devin. Repr. 15.00 (ISBN 0-686-12337-9); vinyl back 8.00 (ISBN 0-686-12338-7). Church History.

History of the Holocaust. Yehuda Bauer & Nili Keren. 453p. 1982. 17.95 (ISBN 0-531-09862-1); 12.95 (ISBN 0-531-05641-4). Watts.

History of the Holy Eastern Church, 5 vols. John M. Neale. LC 74-144662. Repr. of 1850 ed. Set. 215.00 (ISBN 0-404-04670-3). AMS Pr.

History of the Holy Grail, Pts. 1-5. Henry Lovelich. Ed. by F. J. Furnivall. (EETS, ES Ser.: Nos. 20, 24, 28, 30, 95). Repr. of 1875 ed. Pts. I & II. 45.00 (ISBN 0-527-00234-8); Pts. 3-5, 1877 - 1905. 29.00 (ISBN 0-527-00235-6). Kraus Repr.

History of the Holy Rood-Tree. Ed. by Arthur S. Napier. (EETS, OS Ser.: No. 103). Repr. of 1894 ed. 12.00 (ISBN 0-527-00104-X). Kraus Repr.

History of the Hopedale Community, from Its Inception to Its Virtual Submergence in the Hopedale Parish. Adin Ballou. Ed. by William S. Heywood. LC 72-2935. (Communal Societies in America Ser.). Repr. of 1897 ed. 14.00 (ISBN 0-404-10701-X). AMS Pr.

History of the Huguenots During the Sixteenth Century, 2 vols. William S. Browning. LC 83-45604. Date not set. Repr. of 1829 ed. Set. 59.50 (ISBN 0-404-19871-6). AMS Pr.

History of the Iconoclastic Controversy. Edward J. Martin. (Church Historical Society London N. S. Ser.: No. 2). Repr. of 1930 ed. 55.00 (ISBN 0-8115-3126-0). Kraus Repr.

History of the Inquisition of Spain, 4 Vols. Henry C. Lea. LC 72-181943. Repr. of 1907 ed. Set. 145.00 (ISBN 0-404-03920-0). Vol. 1 (ISBN 0-404-03921-9). Vol. 2 (ISBN 0-404-03922-7). Vol. 3 (ISBN 0-404-03923-5). Vol. 4 (ISBN 0-404-03924-3). AMS Pr.

History of the Jainas. A. K. Roy. 1984. 22.50x (ISBN 0-8364-1136-6, Pub. by Gitanjali Prakashan). South Asia Bks.

History of the Jewish Experience: Eternal Faith, Eternal People. rev. ed. Leo Trepp. LC 73-3142. Orig. Title: Eternal Faith, Eternal People: a Journey into Judaism. 296p. 1973. pap. text ed. 9.95x (ISBN 0-87441-072-X). Behrman.

History of the Jewish People. Ed. by Haim H. Ben-Sasson. (Illus.). 1108p. 1985. pap. 18.95 (ISBN 0-674-39731-2). Harvard U Pr.

History of the Jewish People. Haim H. Ben-Sasson et al. (Illus.). 1040p. 1976. 60.00 (ISBN 0-674-39730-4). Harvard U Pr.

History of the Jewish People. Max L. Margolis & Alexander Marx. LC 70-90074. (Temple Books). 1969. pap. text ed. 10.95x (ISBN 0-689-70134-9, T8). Atheneum.

History of the Jewish People in the Age of Jesus Christ, Vol. 3, Pt. 2. Emil Schurer. Ed. by Geza Vermes et al. 250p. 1986. 29.95 (ISBN 0-567-09373-5, Pub. by T & T Clark Ltd UK). Fortress.

History of the Jewish People in the Age of Jesus Christ, Vol. 3, Pt. 1. Emil Schurer. Ed. by Geza Vermes et al. 704p. 1986. 48.50 (ISBN 0-567-02244-7, Pub. by T & T Clark Ltd UK). Fortress.

History of the Jewish People in the Time of Jesus. Emil Schurer. Ed. by Nahum N. Glatzer. LC 61-8195. 1961. pap. 7.95 (ISBN 0-8052-0008-8). Schocken.

History of the Jewish People in the Times of Jesus: From Herod the Great to Masada. Peter Connolly. LC 86-28890. 1987. 15.95. P Bedrick Bks.

History of the Jewish People in the Time of Jesus: From Herod the Great to Masada. Peter Connolly. LC 86-28890. (Illus.). 96p. 1987. 15.95 (ISBN 0-87226-007-0). P Bedrick Bks.

History of the Jewish People, Vol. 1: The Antiquity. Moses A. Shulvass. LC 81-85564. 250p. 1982. 14.95 (ISBN 0-89526-660-1). Regnery Bks.

History of the Jews. rev. ed. Solomon Grayzel. (Illus.). 908p. 1968. Repr. of 1947 ed. 12.95 (ISBN 0-8276-0142-5, 190). Jewish Pubns.

History of the Jews. Solomon Grayzel. 768p. 1968. pap. 4.95 (ISBN 0-452-00694-5, Mer). NAL.

History of the Jews. Paul Johnson. LC 85-42575. 480p. 1987. 24.50i (ISBN 0-06-015698-8, HarpT). Har-Row.

History of the Jews. rev. ed. A. L. Sachar. 1967. 20.00 (ISBN 0-394-42871-4). Knopf.

History of the Jews, Vol. 1. Simon Dubnov. 18.00 (ISBN 0-8453-6410-3, Cornwall Bks). Assoc Univ Prs.

History of the Jews, Vol. 2. Simon Dubnov. 18.00 (ISBN 0-8453-6659-9, Cornwall Bks). Assoc Univ Prs.

History of the Jews, Vol.3. Simon Dubnov. 18.00 (ISBN 0-8453-6822-2, Cornwall Bks). Assoc Univ Prs.

History of the Jews, Vol. 4. Simon Dubnov. 18.00 (ISBN 0-8453-7537-7, Cornwall Bks). Assoc Univ Prs.

History of the Jews, Vol. 5. Simon Dubnov. 18.00 (ISBN 0-8453-7691-8, Cornwall Bks). Assoc Univ Prs.

History of the Jews: From Earliest Times Through the Six Day War. rev. ed. Cecil Roth. LC 74-121042. 1970. pap. 8.95 (ISBN 0-8052-0009-6). Schocken.

History of the Jews in America. Deborah Pessin. (Illus.). 1957. pap. 4.95x (ISBN 0-8381-0189-5). United Syn Bk.

History of the Jews in Babylonia: The Parthian Period. Jacob Neusner. LC 84-5363. (Brown Judaic Studies). 292p. pap. 21.00 (ISBN 0-89130-738-9, 14 00 62). Scholars Pr GA.

History of the Jews in Baghdad. David S. Sassoon. LC 77-87645. (Illus.). 264p. Repr. of 1949 ed. 34.00 (ISBN 0-404-16427-7). AMS Pr.

History of the Jews in Canada. Benjamin G. Sack. LC 65-1899. pap. 79.00 (ISBN 0-317-28422-3, 2022315). Bks Demand UMI.

History of the Jews in Christian Spain, 2 Vols. Yitzhak Baer. LC 61-16852. 1966. pap. 6.95 ea. (ISBN 0-8276-0115-8, 425). Jewish Pubns.

History of the Jews in the Duchy of Mantua. S. Simonsohn. 35.00x (ISBN 0-87068-341-1). Ktav.

History of the Jews in Utah & Idaho, 1853-1950. Juanita Brooks. 252p. 1973. 9.95 (ISBN 0-914740-12-1). Western Epics.

History of the Jews of Philadelphia: From Colonial Times to the Age of Jackson. Edwin Wolf, 2nd & Maxwell Whiteman. LC 56-7780. (Illus.). 552p. 1975. 8.50 (ISBN 0-8276-0075-5, 372). Jewish Pubns.

History of the Jews of Spain & Portugal. Elias H. Lindo. LC 71-112055. (Research & Source Works Ser: No. 4). (Illus.). 1970. Repr. of 1848 ed. 32.50 (ISBN 0-8337-2109-7). B Franklin.

History of the Jews Since the First Century A. D. Frederick Schweltzer. 319p. pap. 1.95 (ISBN 0-686-95171-9). ADL.

History of the Kentucky Baptists from 1769 to 1885, 2 vols. J. H. Spencer. 1984. Repr. of 1886 ed. 54.00 (ISBN 0-686-12335-2). Church History.

History of the Knights Hospitallers of St. John of Jerusalem, 5 vols. Rene A. Vertot. LC 78-63372. (Crusades & Military Orders: Second Ser.). Repr. of 1757 ed. Set. 200.00 (ISBN 0-404-17040-4). AMS Pr.

History of the Legal Incorporation of Catholic Church Property in the United States (1784-1932) Patrick J. Dignan. LC 73-3569. (Catholic University of America. Studies in American Church History: No. 14). Repr. of 1933 ed. 31.00 (ISBN 0-404-57764-4). AMS Pr.

History of the Life & Sufferings of the Revered & Learned John Wiclif, D. D. John Lewis. LC 74-178543. Repr. of 1820 ed. 39.50 (ISBN 0-404-56625-1). AMS Pr.

History of the London Missionary Society. Ronald Bocking. 256p. 1986. 59.00x (ISBN 0-317-54254-0, Pub. by Elmcrest UK). State Mutual Bk.

History of the Maghrib in the Islamic Period. Jamil M. Abun-Nasr. (Illus.). 512p. Date not set. price not set (ISBN 0-521-33184-6); pap. price not set (ISBN 0-521-33767-4). Cambridge U Pr.

History of the Marranos. Cecil Roth. LC 74-10149. 448p. 1974. pap. 10.95 (ISBN 0-8052-0463-6). Schocken.

History of the Medieval Church, Five Ninety to Fifteen Hundred. 9th ed. Margaret Deanesly. 1969. pap. 12.50x (ISBN 0-416-18100-7, NO. 2163). Methuen Inc.

History of the Mennonite Brethren Church: Pilgrims & Pioneers. John A. Toews. LC 74-33718. 513p. (Orig.). 1975. pap. 13.95 (ISBN 0-318-18904-6). Kindred Pr.

History of the Mishnaic Law of Agriculture: Kilayim. Irving J. Mandelbaum. Ed. by Jacob Neusner. LC 81-1462. (Brown Judaic Studies Ser.: No. 26). 1981. pap. text ed. 18.00 (ISBN 0-89130-465-7, 14 00 26). Scholars Pr GA.

History of the Moderne Protestant Divines, Containing Their Parents, Countries, Education, with Register of Their Writings. Verheiden Jacobus. Tr. by D. Lupton from Latin. LC 79-84142. (English Experience Ser.: No. 959). 400p. 1979. Repr. of 1637 ed. lib. bdg. 28.00 (ISBN 90-221-0959-3). Walter J Johnson.

History of the Mohammedan Dynasties in Spain, 2 Vols. Ed. by Ahmed Al-Maqqari. Tr. by P. De Gayangos. 1969. Repr. of 1840 ed. Set. 175.00 (ISBN 0-384-35253-7). Johnson Repr.

History of the Monks at Tabenna. St. Pachomius. pap. 1.95 (ISBN 0-686-05644-2). Eastern Orthodox.

History of the Monks of Syria. Theodoret. Tr. by R. M. Price from Gr. (Cistercian Studies: No. 88). 1986. 26.95x (ISBN 0-87907-888-X); pap. 10.00x (ISBN 0-87907-988-6). Cistercian Pubns.

History of the Moorish Empire in Europe, 3 vols. S. P. Scott. 1977. Set. lib. bdg. 300.00 (ISBN 0-8490-2004-2). Gordon Pr.

History of the New Testament in Plain Language. Clayton Harrop. 192p. 1984. 9.95 (ISBN 0-8499-0432-3, 0432-3). Word Bks.

History of the Norwegian Baptists in America. Peder Stiansen. Ed. by Edwin S. Gaustad. LC 79-52608. (Baptist Tradition Ser.). (Illus.). 1980. Repr. of 1939 ed. lib. bdg. 32.50x (ISBN 0-405-12473-2). Ayer Co Pubs.

History of the Old Catholic Church. Karl Pruter. LC 85-13418. 76p. 1985. Repr. lib. bdg. 19.95x (ISBN 0-89370-594-2). Borgo Pr.

History of the Order of St. John of Jerusalem in Wales & on the Welsh Border: Including an Account of the Templars. William Rees. LC 76-29839. (Illus.). Repr. of 1947 ed. 26.50 (ISBN 0-404-15427-1). AMS Pr.

History of the Organization of the First Presbyterian Church of Durham, Greene County, N. Y. (Illus.). 1976. pap. 2.00 (ISBN 0-685-69663-4). Hope Farm.

History of the Origin & Establishment of the Inquisition in Portugal. Alexandre Herculano. Tr. by John C. Branner. LC 68-54274. (Stanford University. Stanford Studies in History, Economics, & Political Science: No. 1, Pt. 2). Repr. of 1926 ed. 20.00 (ISBN 0-404-50962-2). AMS Pr.

History of the Origin & Establishment of the Inquisition in Portugal. rev. ed. Alexandre Herculano. 1971. 35.00x (ISBN 0-87068-153-2). Ktav.

History of the Origin & Progress of Adult Schools: With an Account of Some Beneficial Effects. Thomas Pole. (First Ser. in the Social History of Education: No. 8). 108p. 1968. Repr. of 1814 ed. 25.00x (ISBN 0-7130-0009-0, Pub. by Woburn Pr England). Biblio Dist.

History of the Origin & Progress of the Sikhs, ISPP Vol. II, No. 4. James Brown. 74p. 1975. Repr. 2.00 (ISBN 0-88065-068-0, Pub. by Messers Today & Tommorrows Printers & Publishers India). Scholarly Pubns.

History of the Origin & Progress of Seventh-Day Adventists. Mahlon E. Olsen. LC 76-134375. Repr. of 1925 ed. 46.50 (ISBN 0-404-08423-0). AMS Pr.

History of the Orthodox Church of Cyprus from the Coming of the Apostles Paul & Barnabas to the Commencement of the British Occupation (A.D. 45-A.D. 1878) Together with Some Account of the Latin & Other Churches Existing in the Island. John Hackett. LC 79-185941. (Illus.). 760p. 1972. Repr. of 1901 ed. lib. bdg. 35.50 (ISBN 0-8337-1515-1). B Franklin.

History of the Papacy from the Great Schism to the Sack of Rome, 6 Vols. rev. ed. Mandell Creighton. LC 74-77897. Repr. of 1897 ed. Set. 165.00 (ISBN 0-404-01870-X); 27.50 ea. AMS Pr.

History of the Parish of Barwick-In-Elmet in the County of York. T. S. Colman. 1908. 34.00 (ISBN 0-384-09565-8). Johnson Repr.

History of the Parish of Tunstall. W. H. Chippindall. 1940. 16.00 (ISBN 0-384-08875-9). Johnson Repr.

History of the Parsis, 2 vols. Dosabhai F. Karaka. LC 74-21259. Repr. of 1884 ed. Set. 70.00 (ISBN 0-404-12812-2). AMS Pr.

History of the PCA: Continuing Church Movement. Frank J. Smith. 260p. 1985. 20.00 (ISBN 0-9612862-1-0). R E F Typesetting Pub.

History of the People of Israel. Carl H. Cornhill. 325p. 1943. 4.95 (ISBN 0-317-40441-5); pap. 2.95 (ISBN 0-317-40442-3). Open Court.

History of the People of Israel, Bk. 4. Alice Parmelee. LC 80-81097. (All About the Bible). 148p. (Orig.). 1980. pap. 5.95 (ISBN 0-8192-1273-3). Morehouse.

History of the Popes: Their Church & State, 3 vols. Leopold Von Ranke. 1205p. 1986. Repr. of 1901 ed. lib. bdg. 150.00 (ISBN 0-8495-4730-X). Arden Lib.

History of the Presbyterian Churches in the U. S. Robert E. Thompson. (American Church History Ser). Repr. of 1895 ed. 22.00 (ISBN 0-8337-3935-2). B Franklin.

History of the Primitive Church. Jules Lebreton & Jacques Zeiller. 80.00 (ISBN 0-8490-0361-X). Gordon Pr.

History of the Progress & Suppression of the Reformation in Spain in the Sixteenth Century. Thomas McCrie. LC 79-127433. Repr. of 1829 ed. 30.00 (ISBN 0-404-04117-5). AMS Pr.

History of the Progress & Suppression of the Reformation in Italy. Thomas McCrie. LC 72-1006. Repr. of 1856 ed. 22.45 (ISBN 0-404-04118-3). AMS Pr.

History of the Puritans, 3 vols. Daniel Neal. 1979. 54.95 (ISBN 0-86524-011-6, 9401). Klock & Klock.

History of the Ramakrishna Math & Mission. rev. ed. Swami Gambhirananda. 344p. 1983. 10.00 (ISBN 0-87481-215-1, Pub. by Advaita Ashram India). Vedanta Pr.

History of the Reformation. Merle D'Aubigne. (Religious Heritage Reprint Library). 1976. Repr. 18.95 (ISBN 0-8010-2859-0). Baker Bk.

History of the Reformation. Thomas Lindsay. (Illus.). 648p. 1908. 16.95 (ISBN 0-567-07212-6, Pub. by T & T Clark Ltd UK). Fortress.

History of the Reformation, 2 vols. facsimile ed. Thomas M. Lindsay. LC 72-37893. (Select Bibliographies Reprint Ser). Repr. of 1907 ed. Set. 54.00 (ISBN 0-8369-6730-5). Ayer Co Pubs.

History of the Reformation, 2 vols. Thomas M. Lindsay. LC 83-45664. Date not set. Repr. of 1904 ed. Set. 105.00 (ISBN 0-404-19814-7). AMS Pr.

History of the Reformation & Other Ecclesiastical Transactions in, & about, the Low Countries, from the Beginning of the Eighth Century down to the End of the Famous Synod of Dort, 4 Vols. in 2. Geeraert Brandt. LC 70-130625. Repr. of 1733 ed. Set. 285.00 (ISBN 0-404-07960-1). AMS Pr.

History of the Reformation in Europe in the Time of Calvin, 8 vols. Jean H. Merle d'Augbine. Tr. by W. L. Cates. LC 83-45624. Date not set. Repr. of 1873 ed. Set. 395.00 (ISBN 0-404-19842-2). AMS Pr.

History of the Reformation in Italy, 2 vols. Eugene V. Wallace. (Illus.). 393p. 1987. Repr. of 1843 ed. Set. 189.75 (ISBN 0-89901-317-1). Found Class Reprints.

History of the Reformation in Sweden. Lars A. Anjou. Tr. by Henry M. Mason from Swedish. LC 83-45598. Date not set. Repr. of 1859 ed. 62.50 (ISBN 0-404-19866-X). AMS Pr.

History of the Reformation of the Church of England, 7 vols. rev. ed. Gilbert Burnet. LC 83-45575. Date not set. Repr. of 1865 ed. Set. 425.00 (ISBN 0-404-19893-7). Ams Pr.

History of the Reformation of the Sixteenth-Century, 1 vol. Merle D'Aubigne. 1986. pap. 18.95 (ISBN 0-8010-2962-7). Baker Bk.

History of the Reformation of the Sixteenth Century, 5 vols. Jean H. Merle d'Aubigne. Tr. by H. White. LC 83-45666. Date not set. Repr. of 1872 ed. Set. 225.00 (ISBN 0-404-19816-3). AMS Pr.

History of the Region of Pennsylvania North of the Ohio & West of the Allegheny River. Daniel Agnew. LC 75-146371. (First American Frontier Ser). 1971. Repr. of 1887 ed. 16.00 (ISBN 0-405-02821-0). Ayer Co Pubs.

History of the Religion of Israel: From the Babylonian Captivity to the End of the Prophecy, Vol. 4. 45.00x (ISBN 0-685-56209-3). Ktav.

History of the Reorganized Church of Jesus Christ of Latter Day Saints Vol. 5: 1890-1902. F. Henry Edwards. 1969. 22.50 (ISBN 0-8309-0019-5). Herald Hse.

History of the Reorganized Church of Jesus Christ of Latter Day Saints, Vols. 6 & 7. F. Henry Edwards. Incl. Vol. 6. 1903-1914. 1970 (ISBN 0-8309-0030-6); Vol. 7. 1915-1925. 1973 (ISBN 0-8309-0075-6). 22.50 ea. Herald Hse.

History of the Reorganized Church of Jesus Christ of the Latter Day Saints, Vol. 8: 1926-1946. F. Henry Edwards. 1976. 22.50 (ISBN 0-8309-0157-4). Herald Hse.

History of the Restoration Plea. 2nd ed. Harold W. Ford. 1967. pap. 3.95 (ISBN 0-89900-110-6). College Pr Pub.

History of the Rise & Progress of the Baptists in Virginia. Robert Semple. 1976. Repr. of 1894 ed. 15.00 (ISBN 0-686-12331-X). Church History.

History of the Rise of the Huguenots of France, 2 Vols. Henry M. Baird. LC 79-130236. Repr. of 1879 ed. Set. 90.00 (ISBN 0-404-00520-9); 45.00 ea. Vol. 1 (ISBN 0-404-00521-7). Vol. 2 (ISBN 0-404-00522-5). AMS Pr.

History of the Rise of the Mahomedan Power in India till the Year A.D. 1612, 4 Vols. Muhammed Kasim Firishtah. Tr. by John Briggs. LC 79-154112. Repr. of 1910 ed. Set. 225.00 (ISBN 0-404-56300-7). AMS Pr.

History of the Rise of the Mahomedan Power in India until AD 1612, 4 vols. Muhammad Firishtah. Tr. by John Biggs. Repr. of 1910 ed. Set. text ed. 125.00x. Coronet Bks.

History of the Sabbath, 2 pts. Peter Heylyn. LC 75-26002. (English Experiene Ser.: No. 150). 272p. 1969. Repr. of 1636 ed. 49.00 (ISBN 90-221-0150-9). Walter J Johnson.

History of the Salvation Army, 6 vols. Robert Sandall & Arch Wiggins. 2093p. (Orig.). 1979. pap. 10.00 set (ISBN 0-318-04018-2). Vol. 1 (ISBN 0-89216-030-6). Vol. 2 (ISBN 0-89216-031-4). Vol. 3 (ISBN 0-89216-032-2). Vol. 4 (ISBN 0-89216-033-0). Vol. 5 (ISBN 0-89216-034-9). Vol. 6 (ISBN 0-89216-035-7). Salvation Army.

History of the Sandy Creek Baptist Association, from Its Organization in A. D. 1758 to 1858. George W. Purefoy. Ed. by Edwin S. Gaustad. LC 79-52604. (Baptist Tradition Ser.). (Illus.). 1980. Repr. of 1859 ed. lib. bdg. 26.50x (ISBN 0-405-12469-4). Ayer Co Pubs.

History of the Sikhs, 2 vols. Khushwant Singh. LC 63-7550. (Illus.). 1984. Vol. 1, 1469-1839, 430 pgs. pap. 13.50 (ISBN 0-691-00803-5); Vol. 2, 1839-1964, 408 pgs. pap. 13.50 (ISBN 0-691-00804-3); Set. pap. 25.00 (ISBN 0-691-00805-1). Princeton U Pr.

History of the Sinai. Lina Eckenstein. LC 78-63461. (Crusades & Military Orders: Second Ser.). Repr. of 1921 ed. 22.50 (ISBN 0-404-16533-8). AMS Pr.

History of the So-Called Jansenist Church of Holland. John M. Neale. LC 71-133820. Repr. of 1858 ed. 26.50 (ISBN 0-404-04656-8). AMS Pr.

History of the Society of Friends in America, 2 vols. in 1. James Bowden. LC 73-38440. (Religion in America, Ser. 2). 870p. 1972. Repr. of 1854 ed. 58.50 (ISBN 0-405-04061-X). Ayer Co Pubs.

History of the Society of Jesus. 2nd, rev. ed. William V. Bangert. Ed. by George E. Ganss. LC 85-80693. 587p. 1986. pap. 21.00 (ISBN 0-912422-73-4); smyth sewn 17.50 (ISBN 0-912422-74-2). Inst Jesuit.

History of the Synoptic Tradition. Rudolf Bultmann. LC 62-7282. 1963. pap. 9.50 (ISBN 0-06-061172-3, RD 187, HarpR). Har-Row.

History of the Tantric Religion. N. N. Bhattacharyya. 1983. 34.00x (ISBN 0-8364-0942-6, Pub. by Manohar India); pap. 17.50x (ISBN 0-8364-0943-4). South Asia Bks.

History of the Third Congregational Church of Middleborough, Known Today As North Congregational Church, United Church of Christ, North Middleboro, Massachusetts: Includes S. Hopkins Emery's Church History Reprinted from 1876 Edition. Ed. by Charles D. Townsend. (Illus.). 300p. 1982. 22.50 (ISBN 0-9607906-0-8). ACETO Bookmen.

History of the Two Tartar Conquerors of China. Pierre J. D'Orleans. LC 75-162706. 1963. Repr. of 1668 ed. 26.00 (ISBN 0-8337-3630-2). B Franklin.

History of the Universe, Vol. 2. Ruth E. Norman. (Illus.). 450p. 1982. 9.95x (ISBN 0-932642-72-1). Unarius Pubns.

History of the Vaudois Church from Its Origin & of the Vaudois of Piedmont to the Present Day. Antoine Monastier. LC 80-24096. (Heresies of the Early Christian & Medieval Era: Second Ser.). Repr. of 1849 ed. 45.00 (ISBN 0-404-16554-0). AMS Pr.

History of the Waldenses, 2 vols. 2nd enl. ed. William Jones. LC 78-63186. (Heresies of the Early Christian & Medieval Era: Second Ser.). Repr. of 1816 ed. 125.00 set (ISBN 0-404-16080-8). AMS Pr.

History of the Waldenses. J. A. Wylie. 1985. Repr. of 1870 ed. 15.00 (ISBN 0-317-38296-9). Church History.

History of the Waldenses of Italy: From Their Origin to the Reformation. Emilio Comba. LC 77-84713. Repr. of 1889 ed. 41.00 (ISBN 0-404-16119-7). AMS Pr.

History of the Warfare of Science with Theology in Christendon, 2 Vols. Andrew D. White. Set. 26.50 (ISBN 0-8446-3170-1). Peter Smith.

History of the Welsh Baptist: AD Sixty-Three to Seventeen Seventy. J. Davis. 1982. Repr. of 1835 ed. 15.00 (ISBN 0-686-91934-3). Church History.

History of the World's Great Religions. Ward McAfee. 240p. (Orig.). 1983. lib. bdg. 27.00 (ISBN 0-8191-3394-9); pap. text ed. 12.25 (ISBN 0-8191-3395-7). U Pr of Amer.

History of the Zoar Society. 3rd ed. Emilius O. Randall. LC 75-134427. 1972. Repr. of 1904 ed. 14.50 (ISBN 0-404-08467-2). AMS Pr.

History of Tithes. John Selden. LC 75-25833. (English Experience Ser.: No. 147). 1968. Repr. of 1618 ed. 49.00 (ISBN 90-221-0147-9). Walter J Johnson.

History of Union Theological Seminary in New York, 1836-1986. Robert T. Handy. (Illus.). 388p. 1987. 30.00 (ISBN 0-231-06454-3). Columbia U Pr.

History of Western Arkansas. Goodspeed Publishing Company. 1978. Repr. of 1884 ed. 37.50 (ISBN 0-89308-084-5). Southern Hist Pr.

History of Western Philosophy: Philosophy from St. Augustine to Ockham. Ralph M. McInerny. LC 63-20526. 1970. 12.00x (ISBN 0-268-00417-X). U of Notre Dame Pr.

History of Witchcraft. Montague Summers. 1970. pap. 5.95 (ISBN 0-8065-0209-6, 0209-6). Citadel Pr.

History of Witchcraft & Demonology. Montague Summers. (Illus.). 370p. 1973. pap. 8.95 (ISBN 0-7100-7613-4). Methuen Inc.

History of Witchcraft in England from 1558 to 1718. Wallace Notestein. LC 65-18824. 1965. Repr. of 1911 ed. 16.00x (ISBN 0-8462-0649-8). Russell.

History of Witchcraft: Sorcerers, Heretics & Pagans. Jeffrey B. Russell. (Illus.). 1982. pap. 10.95f (ISBN 0-500-27242-5). Thames Hudson.

History of Yaballaha III. Ed. by James A. Montgomery. 1967. lib. bdg. 14.00x (ISBN 0-374-95814-9, Octagon). Hippocrene Bks.

History of Yoga. Vivian Worthington. 176p. 1982. pap. 8.95 (ISBN 0-7100-9258-X). Methuen Inc.

History of York Minster. Ed. by G. E. Aylmer & R. C. Cant. (Illus.). 1977. 32.50x (ISBN 0-19-817199-4). Oxford U Pr.

History of Zionism. Walter Laqueur. LC 75-36491. (Illus.). 1976. pap. 12.95 (ISBN 0-8052-0523-3). Schocken.

History of Zionism, 2 Vols. in 1. rev. ed. Nahum Sokolow. LC 68-19730. (Illus.). 1969. 45.00x (ISBN 0-87068-107-9). Ktav.

History of Zoroastrianism. Maneckji N. Dhalla. LC 74-21256. Repr. of 1938 ed. 40.00 (ISBN 0-404-12806-8). AMS Pr.

History, Principles & Practice of Symbolism in Christian Art. F. E. Hulme. 35.00 (ISBN 0-8490-0364-4). Gordon Pr.

History, Principles, & Practice of Symbolism in Christian Art. F. Edward Hulme. LC 68-18027. 1969. Repr. of 1891 ed. 37.00x (ISBN 0-8103-3214-0). Gale.

History, Society & the Churches: Essays in Honour of Owen Chadwick. Ed. by D. Beales & G. Best. 335p. 1985. 49.50 (ISBN 0-521-25486-8). Cambridge U Pr.

History's Greatest Liars. Joseph McCabe. 176p. (YA) 1985. pap. 5.00. Am Atheist.

Hit the Mark. W. Q. Judge. (Sangam Texts Ser.). 126p. 1986. pap. 8.75 (ISBN 0-88695-024-4). Concord Grove.

Hitbodedouth: Ou La Porte du Ciel. Nachman of Breslov. Adapted by Its'hak Besancon. (Fr.). 110p. (Orig.). 1982. pap. 2.00 (ISBN 0-930213-27-0). Breslov Res Inst.

Hitchhiker's Guide to Missions. Ada Lum. LC 84-19149. 144p. 1984. pap. 5.95 (ISBN 0-87784-328-7). Inter-Varsity.

Hitler & the Christians. Waldemar Gurian. Tr. by E. F. Peeler. LC 78-63675. (Studies in Fascism: Ideology & Practice). 184p. Repr. of 1936 ed. 22.00 (ISBN 0-404-16937-6). AMS Pr.

Hitler & the Final Solution. Gerald Fleming. LC 83-24535. (Illus.). 219p. 1984. 25.00 (ISBN 0-520-05103-3). U of Cal Pr.

Hitler, Germans, & the "Jewish Question". Sarah Gordon. LC 83-43073. 416p. 1984. 42.00 (ISBN 0-691-05412-6); pap. 15.00 (ISBN 0-691-10162-0). Princeton U Pr.

Hitler-Himmler Order on the Jews. Austin J. App. 1984. lib. bdg. 79.95 (ISBN 0-87700-516-8). Revisionist Pr.

Hitler's Apocalypse: Jews & the Nazi Legacy. Robert Wistrich. 352p. 1986. 17.95 (ISBN 0-312-38819-5). St Martin.

Hitlers Professors. Max Weinreich. LC 47-42580. (Yiddish., Illus.). 325p. 1947. pap. 10.00x (ISBN 0-914512-26-9). Yivo Inst.

Hitler's Professors. Max Weinreich. LC 46-5155. (Yivo English Translation Ser.). (Illus.). 291p. 1946. pap. 5.00 (ISBN 0-914512-19-6). Yivo Inst.

Hitler's War Against the Jews - the Holocaust: A Young Reader's Version of the War Against the Jews: 1933-1945 by Lucy Dawidowicz. David A. Altshuler. LC 78-5418. (Illus.). 1978. 8.95x (ISBN 0-87441-293-5); pap. 6.50x (ISBN 0-87441-222-6). Behrman.

Hittites. A. E. Cowley. (British Academy, London; Schweich Lectures on Biblical Archaeology Series, 1918). pap. 19.00 (ISBN 0-8115-1260-6). Kraus Repr.

Hodge Podge. Charles B. Hodge, Jr. LC 71-92047. 1969. 6.95 (ISBN 0-89112-051-3, Bibl Res Pr). Abilene Christ U.

Hogar Cristiano. Mervin J. Baer. (Span.). pap. 1.75 (ISBN 0-686-32324-6). Rod & Staff.

Hogar Que Dios Me Dio. Josie De Smith. 80p. 1986. pap. 2.25 (ISBN 0-311-46082-8). Casa Bautista.

Hogares de la Biblia. Luis Salem. (Span.). 107p. (Orig.). pap. 2.50 (ISBN 0-89922-079-7). Edit Caribe.

Hoku & the Precious Stones. Jane E. Hartman. 1985. pap. 4.95 (ISBN 0-87613-087-2). New Age.

Hold Me Steady, Lord: And Other Prayers for Mothers. Margaret B. Spiess. 112p. 1986. text ed. 7.95 (ISBN 0-8010-8266-8). Baker Bk.

Hold Me up a Little Longer, Lord. Marjorie Holmes. LC 76-42338. (Illus.). 1977. 9.95 (ISBN 0-385-12403-1). Doubleday.

Hold Me While You Let Me Go. Rich Wilkerson. LC 82-83838. 196p. (Orig.). 1983. pap. 4.95 (ISBN 0-89081-370-1). Harvest Hse.

Holdeman People: The Church in Christ, Mennonite, 1869-1969. Clarence Hiebert. LC 72-94133. 1973. 17.95 (ISBN 0-87808-411-8). William Carey Lib.

Holderlin's "Ars Poetica" A Part-Rigorous Analysis of Information Structure in the Late Hymns. Emery George. (De Proprietatibu Litterarum Ser. Practica: No. 32). text ed. 60.80x (ISBN 90-2792-381-7). Mouton.

Holding on... While Letting Go. Joan E. Hemenway. (Looking Up Ser.). (Orig.). 1985. pap. 1.25 (ISBN 0-8298-0548-6). Pilgrim NY.

Holding the Ropes. Helen J. Parks. LC 83-70004. 156p. 1983. 6.95 (ISBN 0-8054-5194-3). Broadman.

Hole in the Sheet. Evelyn Kaye. 224p. 1987. 14.95 (ISBN 0-8184-0437-X). Lyle Stuart.

Holidays & Celebrations: Activities, Crafts & Stories for Children. Mary L. Tietjen. LC 82-62416. 1983. pap. 4.95 (ISBN 0-8091-2531-5). Paulist Pr.

Holidays & Holy Days. Dianne Ladendecker. 36p. 1986. pap. text ed. 6.95 (ISBN 0-8497-4854-2, C8630). Kjos.

Holiest of All: An Exposition of the Epistle to the Hebrews. Andrew Murray. 576p. 17.95 (ISBN 0-8007-0138-0). Revell.

Holiness. Donald Nicholl. 176p. (Orig.). 1981. pap. 8.95 (ISBN 0-8164-2336-9, HarpR). Har-Row.

Holiness. J. C. Ryle. 352p. 1977. Repr. of 1959 ed. 12.50 (ISBN 0-227-67482-0). Attic Pr.

Holiness. J. C. Ryle. (Giant Summit Bks.). pap. 11.95 (ISBN 0-8010-7686-2). Baker Bk.

Holiness. John C. Ryle. 352p. 1979. 12.95 (ISBN 0-8007-1066-5). Revell.

Holiness & Honor of Praise. Theda Holmes. LC 85-62801. 1986. pap. 3.50 (ISBN 0-88270-599-7). Bridge Pub.

Holiness & Justice: An Interpretation of Plato's "Euthyphro". Laszlo Versenyi. LC 81-43830. 164p. 1982. lib. bdg. 26.75 (ISBN 0-8191-2316-1); pap. text ed. 11.50 (ISBN 0-8191-2317-X). U Pr of Amer.

Holiness & Politics. Peter B. Hinchliff. LC 83-1749. pap. 55.80 (ISBN 0-317-30143-8, 2025326). Bks Demand UMI.

Holiness & Power for the Church & the Ministry. A. M. Hills. Ed. by Donald W. Dayton. (Higher Christian Life Ser.). 386p. 1984. 50.00 (ISBN 0-8240-6422-4). Garland Pub.

Holiness & the Human Element. H. A. Baldwin. pap. 3.95 (ISBN 0-686-12876-1). Schmul Pub Co.

Holiness & the Will of God: Perspectives on the Theology of Tertullian. Gerald L. Bray. LC 79-5211. (New Foundations Theological Library). (Peter Toon & Ralph Martin series editors). 1980. 3.25 (ISBN 0-8042-3705-0). John Knox.

Holiness: Every Christian's Calling. Roger Roberts. LC 85-11330. 1985. pap. 5.95 (ISBN 0-8054-1956-X). Broadman.

Holiness: How Obtained & Retained. Shelhamer. 2.50 (ISBN 0-686-12878-8). Schmul Pub Co.

Holiness in the Church. John A. Hardon. 1976. 3.50 (ISBN 0-8198-0417-7); pap. 2.50 (ISBN 0-8198-0418-5). Dghtrs St Paul.

Holiness in the Parables. Drysdale. pap. 2.50 (ISBN 0-686-12879-6). Schmul Pub Co.

Holiness of God. R. C. Sproul. 256p. 1985. 10.95 (ISBN 0-8423-1493-8). Tyndale.

Holiness of Pascal. H. F. Stewart. 1977. lib. bdg. 59.95 (ISBN 0-8490-2015-8). Gordon Pr.

Holiness-Pentecostal Movement. Vinson Synan. 1972. pap. 9.95 (ISBN 0-8028-1728-9). Eerdmans.

Holiness Revival of the Nineteenth Century. Melvin E. Dieter. LC 80-17259. (Studies in Evangelicalism: No. 1). 366p. 1980. 26.00 (ISBN 0-8108-1328-9). Scarecrow.

Holiness Tracts Defending the Ministry of Women. Ed. by Donald W. Dayton. (Higher Christian Life Ser.). 304p. 1985. 40.00 (ISBN 0-8240-6411-9). Garland Pub.

Holist Pilgrimage. Kelvin Van Nuys. LC 80-84738. 400p. 1981. 15.00 (ISBN 0-8022-2383-4). Philos Lib.

Holistic Economics & Social Protest. Jack Powellson. 1983. pap. 2.50x (ISBN 0-87574-250-5, 250). Pendle Hill.

Holistic Explanation: Action, Space, Interpretation. Christopher A. Peacocke. 1979. 28.50x (ISBN 0-19-824605-6). Oxford U Pr.

Holistic Healing & the Edgar Cayce Readings. Raymond Ouellette. LC 80-80446. 384p. 1980. 11.95 (ISBN 0-936450-07-X); pap. 7.75. Aero Pr.

Holistic Spirituality. John Carmody. 160p. 1984. pap. 7.95 (ISBN 0-8091-2564-1). Paulist Pr.

Holly, Reindeer, & Colored Lights: The Story of the Christmas Symbols. Edna Barth. LC 71-157731. (Illus.). 96p. 1981. pap. 4.95 (ISBN 0-89919-037-5, Clarion). HM.

Holly, Reindeer, & Colored Lights: The Story of the Christmas Symbols. Edna Barth. LC 71-157731. (Illus.). 96p. 1971. 8.95 (ISBN 0-395-28842-8, Clarion). HM.

Hollywood & the Catholic Church: The Image of Roman Catholicism in American Movies. Les Keyser & Barbara Keyser. LC 84-12556. 294p. 1984. 12.95 (ISBN 0-8294-0468-6). Loyola.

Hollywood's Image of the Jew. Lester D. Friedman. LC 81-70118. (Illus.). 408p. 1982. pap. 8.95 (ISBN 0-8044-6160-0). Ungar.

Holman Bible Atlas. Holman Bible Publishers. Ed. by Jerry L. Hooper. (Illus.). 1978. pap. 6.95 (ISBN 0-87981-099-8). Holman Bible Pub.

Holman Bible Concordance. Holman Company. Ed. by Russell Hitt. 1979. pap. 3.95 (ISBN 0-87981-093-9). Holman Bible Pub.

Holman Topical Concordance: An Index to the Bible Arranged by Subjects in Alphabetical Order. Holman Bible Publishers. LC 73-7656. 288p. 1973. 8.95 (ISBN 0-87981-019-X). Holman Bible Pub.

Holocaust. Martin Gilbert. 64p. 1979. pap. 6.95 (ISBN 0-8090-1389-4). Hill & Wang.

Holocaust. R. Conrad Stein. LC 85-31415. (World at War Ser.). (Illus.). 48p. 1986. PLB 10.60 (ISBN 0-516-04767-1); pap. 2.95 (ISBN 0-516-44767-X). Childrens.

Holocaust: A History of Courage & Resistance. Bea Stadtler. Ed. by Morrison D. Bial. LC 74-11469. Orig. Title: Test. (Illus.). 210p. 1975. pap. text ed. 5.50x (ISBN 0-87441-231-5). Behrman.

Holocaust: A History of Courage & Resistance. Bea Stadtler. 210p. Repr. 5.50 (ISBN 0-686-95067-4). ADL.

Holocaust: A History of the Jews of Europe during the Second World War. Martin Gilbert. LC 85-5523. (Illus.). 900p. 1986. 19.45 (ISBN 0-317-44733-5). H Holt & Co.

Holocaust: An Annotated Bibliography. Harry J. Cargas & John T. Corrigan. 1977. pap. text ed. 4.00 (ISBN 0-87507-005-1). Cath Lib Assn.

Holocaust & Genocide: A Search for Conscience, An Anthology for Students. Anti-Defamation League of B'nai Brith Staff. 217p. 9.95 (ISBN 0-317-03375-1). ADL.

Holocaust & Genocide: A Search for Conscience, A Curriculum Guide. Anti-Defamation League of B'nai Brith Staff. 184p. 12.00 (ISBN 0-317-03374-3). ADL.

Holocaust & Halakhah. I. Rosenbaum. (Library of Jewish Law & Ethics: No. 2). 15.00x (ISBN 0-87068-296-2); pap. 9.95. Ktav.

Holocaust & Its Perserverance: Stress, Coping, & Disorder. Ofra Ayalon et al. (Sinai-Papers, Studies in Integral Psychology). 80p. 1983. pap. text ed. 8.00 (Pub. by Van Gorcum Holland). Longwood Pub Group.

Holocaust & Its Perseverance. O. Ayalon et al. (SANAI Ser.: No. 2). 64p. 1983. pap. text ed. 9.95x (Pub. by Van Gorcum Holland). Humanities.

Holocaust & the Crisis of Human Behavior. George M. Kren & Leon H. Rappoport. LC 79-23781. 200p. 1980. text ed. 29.50x (ISBN 0-8419-0544-4). Holmes & Meier.

Holocaust & the Historians. Lucy S. Dawidowicz. LC 80-29175. (Illus.). 200p. 1983. pap. 16.50x (ISBN 0-674-40566-8); pap. text ed. 6.95 (ISBN 0-674-40567-6). Harvard U Pr.

Holocaust Debate: Revisionist Historians Versus Six Million Jews. Robert Faurisson. 1980. lib. bdg. 59.95 (ISBN 0-686-62797-0). Revisionist Pr.

Holocaust in Documents. Ed. by Yisrael Gutman. 1982. 22.50 (ISBN 0-686-85569-8). ADL.

Holocaust in Hebrew Literature: From Genocide to Rebirth. Alan J. Yuter. LC 83-9973. (Judaic Studies). 152p. 1983. 18.00x (ISBN 0-8046-5322-4, Natl U). Assoc Faculty Pr.

Holocaust in Norway: An Historical Perspective. Samuel Abrahamsen. 1987. 20.95 (ISBN 0-89604-116-6); pap. 13.95 (ISBN 0-89604-117-4). Holocaust Pubns.

Holocaust in Yiddish Literature. Elias Schulman. 96p. 1983. pap. 4.00 (ISBN 0-318-20364-2). Workmen's Circle.

Holocaust Kingdom. Alexander Donat. LC 77-89067. 361p. (Orig.). 1963. pap. 12.95 (ISBN 0-89604-001-1). Holocaust Pubns.

Holocaust Kingdom: A Memoir. Alexander Donat. 368p. pap. 5.95 (ISBN 0-686-95070-4). ADL.

Holocaust Memoirs: Jews in the Lwow Ghetto, the Janowski Concentration Camp, & as Deportees in Siberia. Joachim Schoenfeld. 1985. text ed. 17.50x (ISBN 0-88125-074-0). Ktav.

Holocaust: One Hundred Twenty Questions & Answers. Charles E. Weber. (Illus.). 60p. (Orig.). 1983. pap. 4.00 (ISBN 0-939484-07-2). Inst Hist Rev.

Holocaust Reader. Lucy Dawidowicz. LC 75-33740. pap. 9.95x (ISBN 0-87441-236-6). Behrman.

Holocaust: Sneak Attack on Christianity. Austin J. App. 1984. lib. bdg. 79.95 (ISBN 0-87700-517-6). Revisionist Pr.

Holocaust Survivors: Psychological & Social Sequelae. Ed. by Wilfred Quaytman. LC 80-80071. (Special Issue of Journal of Contemporary Psychotherapy: Vol. 11, No. 1). 88p. 1981. pap. 9.95 (ISBN 0-89885-016-9). Human Sci Pr.

Holocaust: The Destruction of European Jewry, 1933-1945. Nora Levin. LC 67-23676. (Illus.). 784p. 1973. pap. 12.95 (ISBN 0-8052-0376-1). Schocken.

Holocaust: The History of the Jews of Europe During the Second World War. Martin Gilbert. LC 85-5523. (Illus.). 488p. 1985. 24.95 (ISBN 0-03-062416-9). H Holt & Co.

Holocaust: The Nuremberg Evidence, Part I: Documents, Digest, Index & Chronological Tables. Jacob Robinson & Henry Sachs. (Yad Vashem-Yivo. Joint Documentary Projects). 1976. 30.00 (ISBN 0-914512-37-4). Yivo Inst.

Holocaust Years: Society on Trial. Roselle Chartock & Jack Spencer. 244p. Repr. 2.95 (ISBN 0-686-95069-0). ADL.

Holsom Antidotus or Counter-Poysen Agaynst the Pestylent Heresye & Secte of the Anabaptistes. Heinrich Bullinger. Tr. by J. Veron. LC 73-6106. (English Experience Ser.: No. 574). 232p. 1973. Repr. of 1548 ed. 13.00 (ISBN 90-221-0574-1). Walter J Johnson.

Holy & the Daemonic from Sir Thomas Browne to William Blake. R. D. Stock. LC 81-11974. (Illus.). 416p. 1981. 31.50 (ISBN 0-691-06495-4). Princeton U Pr.

Holy Anorexia. Rudolph M. Bell. LC 85-8460. (Illus.). xii, 248p. 1985. 22.50 (ISBN 0-226-04204-9). U of Chicago Pr.

Holy Baptism & Services for the Renewal of Baptism: The Worship of God. LC 85-3137. (Supplemental Liturgical Resource: No. 2). 114p. 1985. pap. 5.95 (ISBN 0-664-24647-8). Westminster.

Holy Baptism: Word Keys Which Unlock the Covenant. Duane E. Spencer. LC 84-81663. 170p. 1984. 9.95 (ISBN 0-939404-08-7). Geneva Ministr.

Holy Beggar Teachings: Jewish Hasidic Stories, 1975-1977. Shlomo Carlebach. Ed. by Steven L. Maimes & Elana Rappaport. 1979. pap. 4.95 (ISBN 0-917246-06-3). Maimes.

Holy Bible. Tr. by George M. Lamsa. 29.45 (ISBN 0-317-52395-3, HarpR); pap. 19.95 (ISBN 0-317-52396-1, RD 423). Har-Row.

Holy Bible at the University of Texas. rev. ed. Ed. by Edwin T. Bowden & David Farmer. Orig. Title: Holy Bible, an Exhibit. (Illus.). 1967. 8.00 (ISBN 0-87959-027-0). U of Tex H Ransom Ctr.

Holy Bible: From the Ancient Eastern Text. Tr. by George M. Lamsa. 1248p. 1986. 29.95 (ISBN 0-06-064922-4, HarpR); pap. 19.95 (ISBN 0-06-064923-2, HarpR). Har-Row.

Holy Bible in the Language of Today: An American Translation. William F. Beck. 1977. 16.95 (ISBN 0-87981-082-3). Holman Bible Pub.

Holy Book in Comparative Perspective. Frederick M. Denny & Rodney L. Taylor. LC 85-8473. (Studies in Comparative Religion). 244p. 1985. 19.95 (ISBN 0-87249-453-5). U of SC Pr.

Holy Book of Women's Mysteries, 2 vols. rev. ed. Zsuzsanna Budapest. 1986. pap. write for info. (ISBN 0-937081-03-5). SBA Coven.

Holy Book of Women's Mysteries, Pt. 1. rev. ed. Zsuzsanna Budapest. 1986. pap. text ed. write for info. (ISBN 0-937081-01-9). SBA Coven.

Holy Book of Women's Mysteries, Pt. 2. rev. ed. Zsuzsanna Budapest. 1986. pap. write for info. (ISBN 0-937081-02-7). SBA Coven.

Holy Cities of Arabia, 2 vols. Eldon Rutter. LC 78-63477. Repr. of 1928 ed. Set. 49.50 (ISBN 0-404-16543-5). AMS Pr.

Holy City with Signs & Wonders. Kristen E. Reinertson. LC 86-90554. (Illus.). 150p. (Orig.). 1987. pap. text ed. 11.95 (ISBN 0-9617564-5-4). Skoglie Storevik Pubs.

Holy Communion & Worship of the Eucharist Outside Mass. gold cloth 8.50 (ISBN 0-89942-648-4, 648/22). Catholic Bk Pub.

Holy Communion Is... R. E. Lybrand, Jr. Ed. by Michael L. Sherer. (Orig.). 1987. pap. 6.50 (ISBN 0-89536-853-6, 7812). CSS of Ohio.

Holy Company: Christian Heros & Heroines. Elliott Wright. 1980. 12.95 (ISBN 0-02-631590-4). Macmillan.

Holy Contradictions. Leslie B. Flynn. 156p. 1987. pap. 5.95 (ISBN 0-89693-239-7). Victor Bks.

Holy Cross: A Century of Anglican Monasticism. Adam D. McCoy. 1987. 29.95. Morehouse.

Holy-Days & Holidays: A Treasury of Historical Material, Sermons in Full & in Brief, Suggestive Thoughts & Poetry, Relating to Holy Days & Holidays. Ed. by Edward M. Deems. LC 68-17940. 1968. Repr. of 1902 ed. 65.00x (ISBN 0-8103-3352-X). Gale.

Holy Days & Holidays: Prayer Celebrations with Children. rev. ed. Gaynell B. Cronin. 112p. 1985. pap. 7.95 (ISBN 0-86683-226-2, HarpR). Har-Row.

Holy Days, As Outlined in Leviticus Twenty-Three. Jean Zachary. 72p. (Orig.). 1987. pap. 3.75 (ISBN 0-9617733-0-8). Pneuma Pub.

Holy Days: Holidays. Judith Ritchie & Vickie Niggemeyer. LC 78-23841. (Illus.). 1978. 7.95 (ISBN 0-915134-48-9). Mott Media.

Holy Days in the United States, Histoy, Theology, Celebration. 104p. 1984. pap. 8.95 (ISBN 0-317-46230-X). US Catholic.

Holy Days: The World of a Hasidic Family. Lis Harris. 272p. 1986. pap. 8.95 (ISBN 0-02-020970-3, Collier). Macmillan.

Holy Earth. Liberty H. Bailey. 59.95 (ISBN 0-8490-0369-5). Gordon Pr.

Holy Eucharist. Cornelius Hagerty. 77p. 1967. pap. 1.50 (ISBN 0-912414-12-X). Lumen Christi.

Holy Eucharist, Longer Form & Other Services. rev. ed. General Episcopal Synod. 44p. 1986. pap. 1.50 (ISBN 0-935461-12-4). St Alban Pr CA.

Holy Eucharist: Study Guide. Ronald H. Miller. 1977. pap. 2.95x (ISBN 0-8192-4075-3). Morehouse.

Holy Family in Egypt: In the Steps of the Tradition. Otto Meinardus. 1987. pap. 10.00 (ISBN 977-424-129-0, Pub. by Am Univ Cairo Pr). Columbia U Pr.

Holy Family of Father Moon. Joseph H. Fichter. LC 84-82549. 155p. (Orig.). 1985. pap. 7.95 (ISBN 0-934134-13-8, Leaven Pr). Sheed & Ward MO.

Holy Feast & Holy Fast: The Religious Significance of Food to Medieval Women. Caroline W. Bynum. LC 85-28896. 300p. 1986. 29.95 (ISBN 0-520-05722-8). U of Cal Pr.

Holy Fire. Robert Payne. LC 79-27594. 328p. 1980. pap. 8.95 (ISBN 0-913836-61-3). St Vladimirs.

Holy Ghost & Fire. D. N. Buntain. 100p. 1956. 1.25 (ISBN 0-88243-525-6, 02-0525). Gospel Pub.

Holy Ghost & Speaking in Tongues. R. L. Black. 180p. (Orig.). 1983. pap. 4.95 (ISBN 0-934942-35-8, 1869). White Wing Pub.

Holy God-Holy People. W. E. McCumber. 124p. 1982. pap. 3.95 (ISBN 0-8341-0779-1). Beacon Hill.

Holy Gospel. 1963. 6.00 (ISBN 0-8198-0503-3); pap. 5.00 (ISBN 0-8198-0504-1). Dghtrs St Paul.

Holy Gospel. Ed. by Nomikos M. Vaporis. 245p. 1979. 95.00 (ISBN 0-916586-25-1). Holy Cross Orthodox.

Holy Grail. Hank Harrison. (Grail Trilogy). (Illus.). 325p. (Orig.). 1987. 24.95 (ISBN 0-918501-18-0). Archives Pr.

Holy Grail: From the Works of Rudolf Steiner. 2nd ed. Ed. by Steven Roboz. 1984. pap. 4.75 (ISBN 0-919924-24-7, Steiner Bk Ctr). Anthroposophic.

Holy Grail Revealed: The Real Secret of Rennes-le-Chateau. Patricia Fanthorpe & Lionel Fanthorpe. LC 82-4303. 128p. 1982. Repr. lib. bdg. 19.95x (ISBN 0-89370-660-4). Borgo Pr.

Holy Horoscopes...for Those under the Sign of the Cross. Mary A. Magers. LC 85-50451. 112p. 1985. 6.95 (ISBN 0-938232-74-6). Winston-Derek.

Holy Hour for a New People. James Seculoff. LC 76-27491. (Orig.). 1976. pkg. of 10 17.00 (ISBN 0-87973-645-3). Our Sunday Visitor.

Holy Images: An Inquiry into Idolatry & Image-Worship in Ancient Paganism & in Christianity. Edwyn R. Bevan. LC 77-27191. (Gifford Lectures: 1933). Repr. of 1940 ed. 22.50 (ISBN 0-404-60489-7). AMS Pr.

Holy Innocents: The Story of a Historic Church & Country Parish. Ellen Davies-Rodgers. (Illus.). 12.00 (ISBN 0-685-84990-2). Plantation.

Holy Island. 2nd ed. James W. Kennedy. 144p. 1984. pap. 1.70 (ISBN 0-88028-028-X). Forward Movement.

Holy Jerusalem Voyage of Ogier VIII, Seigneure D'anglure. Ogier VIII. Tr. by Roland A. Browne. LC 75-4773. (Illus.). 163p. 1975. 10.00 (ISBN 0-8130-0513-2). U Presses Fla.

Holy Kabbalah. Arthur E. Waite. 636p. 1976. pap. 9.95 (ISBN 0-8065-0522-2). Citadel Pr.

Holy Kabbalah: A Study of the Secret Tradition in Israel. Arthur E. Waite. 1960. 20.00 (ISBN 0-8216-0025-7). Univ Bks.

Holy Koran. rev. ed. Ed. by Sayed A. Razwy. Tr. by A. Yusuf Ali. 424p. 1986. pap. 4.50 (ISBN 0-940368-77-3). Tahrike Tarsile Quran.

Holy Land. W. Joseph Clark. LC 86-61593. 204p. (Orig.). 1986. pap. 7.95 (ISBN 0-87973-546-5, 546). Our Sunday Visitor.

Holy Land. (Panorama Bks.). (Fr., Illus.). 3.95 (ISBN 0-685-11233-0). French & Eur.

Holy Land. Alice Parmelee. LC 81-80630. (All About the Bible Ser.: Bk. 6). 136p. (Orig.). 1981. pap. 5.95 (ISBN 0-8192-1290-3). Morehouse.

Holy Land: A History of the Alfred Shakers. 2nd ed. Sr. R. Mildred Barker. 53p. 1986. pap. 3.50 (ISBN 0-915836-03-3). Shaker Pr ME.

Holy Land As Jesus Knew It: Its People, Customs & Religion. David K. O'Rourke. 160p. 1983. pap. 4.95 (ISBN 0-89243-182-2). Liguori Pubns.

Holy Land in American Protestant Life, 1800 to 1948: A Documentary History. Ed. by Robert T. Handy. LC 79-1052. (Illus.). 1980. lib. bdg. 22.00x (ISBN 0-405-13466-5). Ayer Co Pubs.

Holy Land Missions & Missionaries: An Original Anthology. Ed. by Moshe Davis. LC 77-70703. (America & the Holy Land Ser.). (Illus.). 1977. lib. bdg. 20.00x (ISBN 0-405-10259-3). Ayer Co Pubs.

Holy Land Pilgrimage in the Later Roman Empire, AD 312-460. Edward D. Hunt. 1982. 47.00x (ISBN 0-19-826438-0); pap. 13.50x (ISBN 0-19-826449-6). Oxford U Pr.

Holy Land Today. rev. ed. Basilea Schlink. 1975. 4.50 (ISBN 3-87209-610-9). Evang Sisterhood Mary.

Holy Letter: A Study in Medieval Jewish Sexual Morality. Ed. by S. J. Cohen. pap. 7.95x (ISBN 0-87068-490-6). Ktav.

Holy Life & History of Saynt Werburg. Henry Bradshaw. Repr. of 1848 ed. 28.00 (ISBN 0-384-05450-1). Johnson Repr.

Holy Life: The Beauty of Christianity. John Bunyan. pap. 1.95 (ISBN 0-685-19832-4). Reiner.

Holy Living & Holy Dying. Jeremy Taylor. Ed. by Marvin D. Hinten. 80p. 1986. pap. 3.95 (ISBN 0-8423-1350-8). Tyndale.

Holy Man: Father Damien of Molokai. Gavan Daws. 328p. 1984. pap. 8.95 (ISBN 0-8248-0920-3). UH Pr.

Holy Mirth: A Theology of Laughter. Richard G. Cote. 100p. (Orig.). 1985. pap. 8.95 (ISBN 0-89571-031-5). Affirmation.

Holy Morality. Carol Murphy. LC 71-110286. (Orig.). 1970. pap. 2.50x (ISBN 0-87574-169-X). Pendle Hill.

Holy Mother: Being the Life of Sri Sarada Devi, Wife of Sri Ramakrishna & Helpmate in His Mission. Swami Nikhilananda. LC 62-13423. (Illus.). 384p. pap. 7.95 (ISBN 0-911206-20-5). Ramakrishna.

Holy Mother, Sri Sarada Devi. Swami Gambhirananda. (Illus.). 8.95 (ISBN 0-87481-434-0). Vedanta Pr.

Holy Mountain. 2nd ed. Constantine Cavarnos. LC 73-84103. (Illus.). 172p. 1977. pap. 6.50 (ISBN 0-914744-38-0). Inst Byzantine.

Holy Mountain: Approaches to the Mystery of Prayer. Noel D. O'Donoghue. 9.95 (ISBN 0-89453-430-0); pap. 6.95 (ISBN 0-89453-300-2). M Glazier.

Holy Mountain: Being the Story of a Pilgrimage to Lake Manas & of Initiation on Mount Kailas in Tibet. Bhagwan Hamsa. LC 78-72437. Repr. of 1934 ed. 27.50 (ISBN 0-404-17303-9). AMS Pr.

Holy Orthodox Church. Apostolos Makrakis. Ed. by Orthodox Christian Educational Society. Tr. by M. I. Lisney & L. Krick. 298p. (Orig.). 1980. pap. 7.95x (ISBN 0-938366-34-3). Orthodox Chr.

Holy Orthodox Church: Its Ritual, Services, & Sacraments. Sebastian Dabovich. 1898. pap. 2.95 (ISBN 0-686-00253-9). Eastern Orthodox.

Holy Path. Kirpal Singh. Ed. by Ruth Seader. (Teachings of Kirpal Singh Ser., Vol. 1). (Illus.). viii, 94p. (Orig.). 1974. pap. 3.00 (ISBN 0-89142-013-4). Sant Bani Ash.

Holy Pretence. George L. Mosse. LC 68-14552. 1968. 23.50x (ISBN 0-86527-099-6). Fertig.

Holy Quaran. Tr. by Mardaduke Peckthall. 1986. Repr. of 1983 ed. 20.00x (ISBN 0-8364-1623-6, Pub. by Rajesh). South Asia Bks.

Holy Quaran Arabic-English. A. M. Daryabadi. 24.50 (ISBN 0-686-83591-3). Kazi Pubns.

Holy Qur'an, 2 Vols. A. A. Ali. 29.50x (ISBN 0-87902-038-5). Orientalia.

Holy Qur'an. Tr. by A. Yusuf Ali from Arabic. lib. bdg. 14.00. Am Trust Pubns.

Holy Qur'an. Tr. by S. V. Ali from Arabic. 550p. 1981. text ed. 9.00 (ISBN 0-940368-08-0); pap. 4.95 (ISBN 0-940368-07-2). Tahrike Tarsile Quran.

Holy Quran. Yusef Ali. (Arabic & Eng.). 20.00x (ISBN 0-86685-167-4). Intl Bk Ctr.

Holy Quran. Yusuf Ali. LC 77-78098. 1915p. 14.00 (ISBN 0-89259-006-8). Am Trust Pubns.

Holy Quran, 2 vols. D. M. Hamidullah. (Arabic, Fr.). 1981. Set. french & arabic 69.00 (ISBN 0-686-77430-2). Kazi Pubns.

Holy Quran. (Arabic.). 19.95 (ISBN 0-686-18522-6); deluxe ed. 29.50. Kazi Pubns.

Holy Quran. 2nd ed. write for info. (ISBN 0-89259-018-1). Am Trust Pubns.

Holy Quran. (Arabic.). 14.95 (ISBN 0-686-83880-7). Kazi Pubns.

Holy Quran. Ed. by M. Pickthall. 1983. Repr. of 1977 ed. 18.50x (ISBN 0-8364-0989-2, Pub. by R Taj Co). South Asia Bks.

Holy Qur'an. Tr. by Shaikh Muhammad Sarwar from Arabic. 418p. pap. 10.00 (ISBN 0-941724-00-X). Islamic Seminary.

Holy Quran. M. H. Shakin. (Arabic & Eng.). 634p. 1982. 49.00x (ISBN 0-317-39404-5, Pub. by Luzac & Co Ltd). State Mutual Bk.

Holy Qur'an. Tr. by M. H. Shakir from Arabic. LC 82-60299. 440p. 1982. pap. 3.95 (ISBN 0-940368-18-8). Tahrike Tarsile Quran.

Holy Quran. Tr. by M. H. Shakir. (Eng. & Arabic.). 660p. 1982. 15.00 (ISBN 0-940368-17-X); pap. 9.00 (ISBN 0-940368-16-1). Tahrike Tarsile Quran.

Holy Qur'an. Mahomodali H. Shakir. 320p. 1986. text ed. 29.95 (ISBN 0-7103-0162-6); pap. text ed. 20.00 (ISBN 0-7103-0161-8). Methuen Inc.

Holy Quran: Arabic-Urdu. A. A. ThanWi. 22.50 (ISBN 0-686-83593-X). Kazi Pubns.

Holy Quran: Deluxe Arabic Only. 29.95 (ISBN 0-686-83596-4). Kazi Pubns.

Holy Quran Made Easy. M. A. Tariq. 1968. 5.35x (ISBN 0-87902-070-9). Orientalia.

Holy Quran: Text & Explanatory Translation. Pickthall. 1983. 25.50 (ISBN 0-686-18527-7). Kazi Pubns.

Holy Quran: Text, Translation & Explanatory Notes, I-VIII. A. H. Siddiqui. (Avail. in sep. parts). pap. 4.00 ea. Kazi Pubns.

Holy Quran with Arabic Text Commentary & Translation. Yousuf Ali. 25.75 (ISBN 0-686-18528-5). Kazi Pubns.

Holy Quran with English Translation. Ed. by M. M. Pickthall. 1976. Repr. 17.50x (ISBN 0-8364-0415-7). South Asia Bks.

Holy Qur'an (With Modern English Translations & Annotations) Muhammad S. Haque. 800p. 1987. text ed. 20.00 (ISBN 0-933057-05-9). Namuk Intl Inc.

Holy Roman Empire. James Bryce. 1978. Repr. of 1911 ed. lib. bdg. 65.00 (ISBN 0-8495-0333-7). Arden Lib.

Holy Roman Empire. James Bryce. 1911. 47.50 (ISBN 0-8482-7383-4). Norwood Edns.

Holy Roman Empire. new enl. rev. ed. James B. Bryce. LC 75-41045. (BCL Ser. II). Repr. of 1913 ed. 28.50 (ISBN 0-404-14516-7). AMS Pr.

Holy Roman Empire: A Dictionary Handbook. Ed. by Jonathan W. Zophy. LC 79-8282. (Illus.). xxvii, 551p. 1980. lib. bdg. 49.95 (ISBN 0-313-21457-3, ZHR/). Greenwood.

Holy Roman Republic: A Historic Profile of the Middle Ages. Giorgio Falco. Tr. by K. V. Kent from Italian. LC 80-19696. Orig. Title: Santa Romana Republica. 336p. 1980. Repr. of 1965 ed. lib. bdg. 42.50x (ISBN 0-313-22395-5, FAHR). Greenwood.

Holy Rosary. Josemaria Escriva de Balaguer. (Illus.). 49p. 1979. 5.95 (ISBN 0-933932-45-6); pap. 2.95 (ISBN 0-933932-44-8). Scepter Pubs.

Holy Rosary. Lawrence G. Lovasik. (Saint Joseph Picture Bks.). (Illus.). flexible bdg. 0.95 (ISBN 0-89942-284-5, 284). Catholic Bk Pub.

Holy Rosary. Ed. by Monks of Solesmes. 1980. 5.50 (ISBN 0-686-74345-8). Dghtrs St Paul.

Holy Science. Swami Sri Yukteswar. LC 77-88199. (Illus.). 110p. 1984. 4.50 (ISBN 0-87612-051-6); 2nd Dutch ed. 6.50x (ISBN 90-202-4529-5); German ed. 6.00x (ISBN 3-87041-176-7); Japanese ed. 7.00x (ISBN 4-627-99950-X). Self Realization.

Holy Scripture: Canon, Authority, Criticism. James Barr. LC 82-20123. 190p. 1983. 18.95 (ISBN 0-664-21395-2); pap. 9.95 (ISBN 0-664-24477-7). Westminster.

Holy Scriptures. 1917. blue cloth o.p. 11.95 (ISBN 0-685-13294-3, 101); leatherette, black or white boxed o.p. 17.95 (ISBN 0-685-13295-1, 102, 103,); small leatherette, white, boxed o.p. 17.95 (ISBN 0-8276-0035-6, 105); Heb. & Eng., two vols. 35.00 (ISBN 0-686-76879-5, 125). Jewish Pubns.

Holy Scriptures: A Survey. Robert C. Dentan. (Orig.). 1949. pap. 5.95 (ISBN 0-8164-2031-9, SP1, HarpR). Har-Row.

Holy Scriptures Holy Bible Commentary. Alexander Harkovy. 32.50 (ISBN 0-317-30500-X). Shalom.

Holy Scriptures Holy Bible Commentary. Isaac Leeser. 32.50 (ISBN 0-317-30499-2). Shalom.

Holy Shroud & Four Visions: The Holy Shroud New Evidence Compared with the Visions of St. Bridget of Sweden, Maria d'Agreda, Anne Catherine Emmerich, & Teresa Neumann. Patrick O'Connell & Charles Carty. (Illus.). 1974. pap. 1.50 (ISBN 0-89555-102-0). TAN Bks Pubs.

Holy Smoke: A Dissertation on the Utah War. Paul Bailey. (Great West & Indian Ser.: Vol. 44). (Illus.). 1977. 10.50 (ISBN 0-87026-037-5). Westernlore.

Holy Song Book: Collection Of Unification Church Songs. 2nd rev. ed. (Illus.). 60p. 1972. pap. 5.50 (ISBN 0-910621-19-5). HSA Pubns.

Holy Spirit. Edward H. Bickersteth. LC 59-13640. 192p. 1976. pap. 5.95 (ISBN 0-8254-2227-2). Kregel.

Holy Spirit. rev. ed. Garth Black. (Way of Life Ser: No. 102). 1967. pap. 3.95 (ISBN 0-89112-102-1, Bibl Res Pr). Abilene Christ U.

Holy Spirit. H. Leo Boles. 10.95 (ISBN 0-89225-102-6). Gospel Advocate.

Holy Spirit. J. Patout Burns & Gerald M. Fagin. (Message of the Fathers of the Church Ser.: Vol. 3). 16.95 (ISBN 0-89453-343-6); pap. 10.95 (ISBN 0-89453-315-0). M Glazier.

Holy Spirit. Glenn Clark. pap. 0.50 (ISBN 0-910924-07-4). Macalester.

Holy Spirit. Billy Graham. 1978. 3.95 (ISBN 0-8499-4153-9). Word Bks.

Holy Spirit. Alasdair I. Heron. LC 82-24705. 224p. (Orig.). 1983. pap. 11.95 (ISBN 0-664-24439-4). Westminster.

Holy Spirit. Robert Hicks & Richard Bewes. (Understanding Bible Truth Ser.). (Orig.). 1981. pap. 0.95 (ISBN 0-89840-021-X). Heres Life.

Holy Spirit. Arthur W. Pink. 1970. pap. 6.95 (ISBN 0-8010-7041-4). Baker Bk.

Holy Spirit. Norman Pittenger. LC 74-10839. 128p. 1974. 5.50 (ISBN 0-8298-0284-3). Pilgrim NY.

Holy Spirit. Charles C. Ryrie. LC 65-14610. (Orig.). 1965. pap. 5.95 (ISBN 0-8024-3565-3). Moody.

Holy Spirit, 2 Vols. A. B. Simpson. 7.95; Vol. 1. 7.95 ea. (ISBN 0-87509-015-X). Vol. 2 (ISBN 0-87509-016-8). pap. 5.95 ea. Vol. 1 (ISBN 0-87509-018-4). Vol. 2 (ISBN 0-87509-019-2). Chr Pubns.

Holy Spirit. C. H. Spurgeon. 1978. pap. 1.95 (ISBN 0-686-23025-6). Pilgrim Pubns.

Holy Spirit. Ronald D. Tucker. (Illus.). 34p. (Orig.). 1983. pap. 1.75 (ISBN 0-933643-15-2). Grace World Outreach.

Holy Spirit. John F. Walvoord. 1958. 15.95 (ISBN 0-310-34060-8, 6388). Zondervan.

Holy Spirit. Wayne E. Ward. (Layman's Library of Christian Doctrine). 1987. 5.95 (ISBN 0-8054-1640-4). Broadman.

Holy Spirit - the Living Love. Sri Surath. 1978. pap. 3.00 (ISBN 0-685-58453-4). Ranney Pubns.

Holy Spirit: A Pentecostal Interpretation. Thomas L. Holdcroft. LC 79-54991. (Illus.). 272p. 1979. Repr. 5.95 (ISBN 0-88243-554-X, 02-0554). Gospel Pub.

Holy Spirit & Counseling: Theology & Theory. Ed. by Marvin G. Gilbert & Raymond T. Brock. 248p. 1985. pap. 12.95 (ISBN 0-913573-41-8). Hendrickson MA.

Holy Spirit & His Gifts. Kenneth E. Hagin. 1974. pap. 5.00 (ISBN 0-89276-082-6). Hagin Ministries.

Holy Spirit & His Gifts. Gerald Rowlands. Ed. by Jo Anne Sekowsky. (Aglow Basic Bible Study Ser.). 64p. 1984. pap. 2.95 (ISBN 0-930756-83-5, 521017). Aglow Pubns.

Holy Spirit & His Gifts. J. Oswald Sanders. (Contemporary Evangelical Perspectives Ser). kivar 5.95 (ISBN 0-310-32481-5, 6520P). Zondervan.

Holy Spirit & Other Spirits. D. O. Teasley. 192p. pap. 1.75 (ISBN 0-686-29150-6). Faith Pub Hse.

Holy Spirit & Power. John Wesley. Ed. by Clare Weakley. LC 77-91883. 1977. pap. 4.95 (ISBN 0-88270-262-9). Bridge Pub.

Holy Spirit & the Christian Privilege. Thomas G. Selby. 1978. Repr. lib. bdg. 20.00 (ISBN 0-8495-4858-6). Arden Lib.

Holy Spirit & the Messianic Age. John W. Swails. 4.95 (ISBN 0-911866-73-6). Advocate.

Holy Spirit & You. Bernard Schneider. pap. 4.95 (ISBN 0-88469-119-5). BMH Bks.

Holy Spirit & You Supplement. Dennis Bennett & Rita Bennett. LC 73-75963. (To be used with The Holy Spirit & You). 1973. pap. 3.95 (ISBN 0-88270-031-6). Bridge Pub.

Holy Spirit & You: The Text Book of the Charismatic Renewal. Dennis Bennett & Rita Bennett. LC 71-140673. 224p. 1971. pap. 5.95 (ISBN 0-912106-14-X). Bridge Pub.

Holy Spirit Baptism. Joe McCormick & Tom McKenney. (Illus.). 23p. (Orig.). 1982. pap. 2.95 (ISBN 0-934527-02-4). Words Living Minis.

Holy Spirit Baptism & the Second Cleansing. R. R. Byrum. 108p. pap. 0.75 (ISBN 0-686-29114-X); pap. 2.00 3 copies (ISBN 0-686-29115-8). Faith Pub Hse.

Holy Spirit Came at 3 AM. Mariann V. Sharner. 1983. 4.95 (ISBN 0-8062-2156-9). Carlton.

Holy Spirit: Growth of Biblical Tradition. George T. Montague. LC 76-4691. 384p. 1976. pap. 10.95 (ISBN 0-8091-1950-1). Paulist Pr.

Holy Spirit, His Gifts & Power. John Owen. LC 60-16514. 1977. pap. 11.95 (ISBN 0-8254-3413-0). Kregel.

Holy Spirit: His Person & Ministry. Edwin H. Palmer. 200p. (Orig.). 1985. pap. 5.95 (ISBN 0-87552-367-6). Presby & Reformed.

Holy Spirit in Action. F. J. Sheed. 148p. 1981. pap. 3.95 (ISBN 0-89283-109-X). Servant.

Holy Spirit in Me. Carolyn Nystrom. (Children's Bible Ser.). 32p. 1980. pap. 4.95 (ISBN 0-8024-5994-3). Moody.

Holy Spirit in Missions. Adoniram J. Gordon. pap. 2.25 (ISBN 0-87509-094-X). Chr Pubns.

Holy Spirit in Salvation. Thomas Goodwin. 1979. 15.95 (ISBN 0-85151-279-8). Banner of Truth.

Holy Spirit in the New Testament. David Ewert. LC 82-95089. 336p. 1983. pap. 12.95 (ISBN 0-8361-3309-9). Herald Pr.

Holy Spirit in Your Teaching. Roy B. Zuck. 228p. 1984. pap. 7.95 (ISBN 0-88207-622-1). Victor Bks.

Holy Spirit Is a Divine Person. H. J. Heijkoop. 5.95 (ISBN 0-88172-084-4); pap. 4.95 (ISBN 0-88172-085-2). Believers Bkshelf.

Holy Spirit, Lord & Life-Giver: A Biblical Introduction to the Doctrine of the Holy Spirit. John Williams. LC 79-27891. 1980. 8.50 (ISBN 0-87213-950-6); pap. 5.95 (ISBN 0-87213-951-4); study guide 3.25 (ISBN 0-87213-952-2). Loizeaux.

Holy Spirit: Mission of, & Praying in. H. A. Ironside. pap. 2.95 (ISBN 0-87213-366-4). Loizeaux.

Holy Spirit of God. Herbert Lockyer. 240p. (Orig.). 1983. pap. 5.50 (ISBN 0-687-17323-X). Abingdon.

Holy Spirit of God. Valerie Owens. 168p. (Orig.). 1985. pap. text ed. 6.50 (ISBN 0-914307-39-8). Word Faith.

Holy Spirit of God. Richard Rogers. 85p. (Orig.). 1980. pap. text ed. 3.50 (ISBN 0-931097-04-5). Sentinel Pub.

Holy Spirit-Shy Member of the Trinity. Frederick D. Bruner & William E. Hordern. LC 83-72124. 112p. (Orig.). 1984. pap. 5.95 (ISBN 0-8066-2068-4, 10-3070). Augsburg.

Holy Spirit: The Anointing of God. Stan Abbott. (Illus.). 86p. (Orig.). 1984. pap. 2.95 (ISBN 0-915545-00-4). S R Abbott Mini.

Holy Spirit the Missing Ingredient. Frederick K. Price. 1978. pap. text ed. 1.95 (ISBN 0-89274-081-7). Harrison Hse.

Holy Spirit Today. Dick Iverson. (Illus.). 1977. pap. 5.50 (ISBN 0-914936-24-7). Bible Temple.

Holy Spirit Today. Frank Stagg. LC 73-85701. 1974. pap. 3.75 (ISBN 0-8054-1919-5). Broadman.

Holy Spirit: Who He Is & What He Does. A. Torrey. 208p. 1927. 11.95 (ISBN 0-8007-0139-9). Revell.

Holy State & the Profane State, 2 Vols. Ed. by Maximilian G. Walten & Thomas Fuller. LC 70-168072. Repr. of 1938 ed. 55.00 (ISBN 0-404-02637-0). AMS Pr.

Holy Table, Name & Thing, More Patiently, Properly, & Literally Used Under the New Treatment, Than That of an Altar. John Williams. LC 79-84146. (English Experience Ser.: No.962). 244p. 1979. Repr. of 1637 ed. lib. bdg. 22.00 (ISBN 90-221-0962-3). Walter J Johnson.

Holy Teaching of Vimalakirti: Mahayana Scripture. Tr. by Robert A. Thurman from Tibetan. LC 75-27197. (Institute for Advanced Study of World Religions Ser.). 176p. 1976. 20.00x (ISBN 0-271-01209-9); pap. 10.00 (ISBN 0-271-00601-3). Pa St U Pr.

Holy Terror: The Fundamentalist War on America's Freedoms in Religion, Politics, & Our Private Lives. Flo Conway & Jim Siegelman. 504p. 1984. pap. 10.95 (ISBN 0-385-29286-4, Delta). Dell.

Holy Terrors & Holy Parents. John G. Quesnell. 228p. 1976. 7.95 (ISBN 0-8199-0561-5). Franciscan Herald.

Holy Trinity. Cornelius J. Hagerty. 362p. 1976. 8.95 (ISBN 0-8158-0316-8). Chris Mass.

Holy Trinity. H. A. Ironside. pap. 1.50 (ISBN 0-87213-348-6). Loizeaux.

Holy Trinity Monastry: A History. (Illus.). 47p. 1983. pap. 1.00 (ISBN 0-317-30446-1). Holy Trinity.

Holy Use of Money: Personal Finance in Light of Christian Faith. John C. Haughey. LC 85-29213. 288p. 1986. 16.95 (ISBN 0-385-23448-1). Doubleday.

Holy Vessels & Furniture of the Tabernacle. Henry W. Soltau. LC 74-85428. (Illus.). 148p. 1986. pap. 12.95 (ISBN 0-8254-3751-2). Kregel.

Holy War. John Bunyan. 1975. 12.95 (ISBN 0-685-52819-7). Reiner.

Holy War. John Bunyan. 324p. 1986. pap. 6.95 (ISBN 0-8010-0924-3). Baker Bk.

Holy War & Pentecostal Peace. Paul Valliere. 176p. (Orig.). 1983. pap. 9.95 (ISBN 0-8164-2481-0, HarpR). Har-Row.

Holy Way. Yocum. pap. 8.95 (ISBN 0-686-12915-6). Schmul Pub Co.

Holy Week. Richard J. Clifford & Hays H. Rockwell. Ed. by Elizabeth Achtemeier. LC 79-7377. (Proclamation 2, Ser. C). 1980. pap. 3.75 (ISBN 0-8006-4088-8, 1-4088). Fortress.

Holy Week. David Drillock et al. (Music Ser.: Vol. I). 186p. (Orig.). 1980. 18.00 (ISBN 0-913836-67-2); pap. 14.00 (ISBN 0-913836-66-4). St Vladimirs.

Holy Week. Reginald H. Fuller. Ed. by Elizabeth Achtemeier. LC 84-6011. (Proclamation 3: Aids for Interpreting the Lessons of the Church Year Ser. B). 64p. 1984. pap. 3.75 (ISBN 0-8006-4104-3). Fortress.

Holy Week. Roy Harrisville. LC 84-18756. (Proclamation 3 C Ser.). 64p. 1985. pap. 3.75 (ISBN 0-8006-4128-0). Fortress.

Holy Week. Roy A. Harrisville & Charles D. Hackett. Ed. by Elizabeth Achtemeier et al. LC 79-7377. (Proclamation 2: Aids for Interpreting the Lessons of the Church Year, Ser. B). 64p. 1981. pap. 3.75 (ISBN 0-8006-4086-1, 1-4086). Fortress.

Holy Week. Richard L. Jeske & Browne Barr. Ed. by Elizabeth Achtemeier et al. LC 79-7377. (Proclamation 2: Aids for Interpreting the Lessons of the Church Year, Ser. A). 64p. (Orig.). 1980. pap. 3.75 (ISBN 0-8006-4094-2, 1-4094). Fortress.

Holy Week. Samuel Terrien. LC 84-18756. (Proclamation 3A Ser.). 64p. 1986. pap. 3.75 (ISBN 0-8006-4120-5). Fortress.

Holy Week Book. new ed. Eileen E. Freeman. LC 78-73510. (Illus.). 1979. pap. 19.95 (ISBN 0-89390-007-9). Resource Pubns.

Holy Week Preaching. Krister Stendahl. LC 84-48714. (Resources for Preaching Ser.). 64p. 1985. pap. 3.95 (ISBN 0-8006-1851-3, 1-1851). Fortress.

Holy Writ or Holy Church: The Crisis of the Protestant Reformation. George H. Tavard. LC 78-17085. 1978. Repr. of 1959 ed. lib. bdg. 22.75x (ISBN 0-313-20584-1, TAHO). Greenwood.

Holy Year of the Jubilee: An Account of the History & Ceremonial of the Roman Jubilee. Herbert Thurston. LC 78-63481. Repr. of 1900 ed. 38.45 (ISBN 0-404-16547-8). AMS Pr.

Homage to Guru Gobind Singh. Khushwant Singh & Suneet V. Singh. 1970. pap. 2.75 (ISBN 0-88253-088-7). Ind-US Inc.

Homage to Shravana Belgola. 1981. 35.00x (ISBN 0-8364-0761-X, Pub. by Marg India). South Asia Bks.

Hombres Claves En las Misiones. Leon McBeth. Orig. Title: Men Who Made Missions. 128p. 1980. pap. 3.75 (ISBN 0-311-01070-9). Casa Bautista.

Hombres En Su Crisis de Media Vida. Jim Conway. Orig. Title: Men in Mid-Life Crisis. (Span.). 256p. 1982. pap. 5.95 (ISBN 0-311-46088-7, Edit Mundo). Casa Bautista.

Home & Church: Ministering to Youth. Lyle Jacobson. 32p. 1977. pap. 1.50 (ISBN 0-8307-0501-5, 977208). Regal.

Home & School Connection. T. Lee Burnham. 1986. 7.95 (ISBN 0-87579-045-3, Pub. by Shadow Mountain). Deseret Bk.

Home As God Would Have It. Daisy M. Sewell. 1937. pap. 4.25 (ISBN 0-88027-047-0). Firm Foun Pub.

Home as God Would Have It & Contemporary Attacks Against It. Ed. by Thomas B. Warren & Garland Elkins. 1979. pap. 12.00 (ISBN 0-934916-34-9). Natl Christian Pr.

Home at Last. Walton J. Brown. (Discovery Ser.). 96p. pap. 5.95 (ISBN 0-317-01321-1). Review & Herald.

Home Base of American China Missions, 1880-1920. Valentin H. Rabe. (Harvard East Asian Monographs: Vol. 75). 1978. 21.00x (ISBN 0-674-40581-1). Harvard U Pr.

Home Bible Study Commentary. James M. Gray. LC 85-9750. 448p. 1985. pap. 12.95 (ISBN 0-8254-2727-4). Kregel.

Home Cell Groups & House Churches. C. KIrk Hadaway et al. 1987. 9.95 (ISBN 0-8054-6944-3). Broadman.

Home Church. Sun M. Moon. LC 82-88432. (Illus.). 474p. 1983. 14.95 (ISBN 0-318-03061-6); pap. 11.95 (ISBN 0-910621-21-7). HSA Pubns.

Home Fellowship Meetings. rev. ed. Bible Temple Staff. 1975. 6.95 (ISBN 0-914936-14-X). Bible Temple.

Home Fellowship Meetings: Creative Ideas. Don Gunstone & Gail Gunstone. 47p. 1986. pap. 3.25 (ISBN 0-914936-99-9). Bible Temple.

Home for the Homeless: A Sociological Exegesis of 1 Peter, Its Solution & Strategy. John H. Elliot. LC 80-2394. 320p. 1981. 24.95 (ISBN 0-8006-0659-0, 1-659). Fortress.

Home-Grown Kids. Raymond Moore & Dorothy Moore. 253p. 1984. pap. text ed. 7.95 (ISBN 0-8499-3007-3, 3007-3). Word Bks.

Home Invaders. Donald Wildmon. 180p. 1985. pap. 6.95 (ISBN 0-89693-521-3). Victor Bks.

Home Is a Four-Letter Word. R. E. Lybrand, Jr. 1985. 5.95 (ISBN 0-89536-719-X, 5803). CSS of Ohio.

Home Is Where the Start Is: Ideas to Help Families Grow in Love & Faith. Mary Montgomery. 132p. (Orig.). 1985. pap. 6.95 (ISBN 0-86683-868-6, HarpR). Har-Row.

Home of the Eddic Poems. Sophus Bugge. Tr. by William H. Schofield. LC 74-144524. (Grimm Library: No. 11). Repr. of 1899 ed. 21.00 (ISBN 0-404-53554-2). AMS Pr.

Home Stretch. Rogers & Thatcher. 160p. 1986. 9.95 (ISBN 0-8499-0344-0). Word Bks.

Home Study Course, 6 vols. Ed. by Chung Hwan Kwak. (Orig.). Date not set. Set. 24.95 (ISBN 0-910621-09-8). HSA Pubns.

Homemade Social Justice: Teaching Peace & Justice in the Home. 2nd ed. Michael True. 168p. 1983. pap. 5.95 (ISBN 0-89622-202-0). Twenty-Third.

Homemaking Programs, Talks & Activities. Nyla Witmore. LC 82-5626. (Illus.). 160p. (Orig.). 1982. pap. 4.95 (ISBN 0-87239-565-0, 2973). Standard Pub.

Homer & Bible: The Origin & Character of East Mediterranean Literature. Cyrus H. Gordon. 1967. pap. 4.95 (ISBN 0-911566-03-1). Ventnor.

Homer the Theologian: Neoplatonist Allegorical Rading & the Growth of the Epic Tradition. Robert Lamberton. LC 85-1184. (Transformation of the Classical Heritage Ser.: No. 9). 375p. 1986. text ed. 40.00x (ISBN 0-520-05437-7). U of Cal Pr.

Homer the Theologian: Neoplatonist Allegorical Reading & the Growth of the Epic Tradition, Vol. 10. Robert Lamberton. Date not set. price not set. Oxford U Pr.

Homeric Gods: The Spiritual Significance of Greek Religion. Walter F. Otto. Ed. by Kees W. Bolle. LC 77-79149. (Mythology Ser.). 1978. Repr. of 1954 ed. lib. bdg. 22.00x (ISBN 0-405-10558-4). Ayer Co Pubs.

Homeric Gods: The Spiritual Significance of Greek Religion. Walter F. Otto. 1978. Repr. of 1954 ed. lib. bdg. 24.00x (ISBN 0-88254-845-X, Octagon). Hippocrene Bks.

Homeric Hymns. rev. ed. Tr. by Charles Boer from Gr. (Dunquin Ser.: No. 10). vi, 182p. 1970. pap. 11.50 (ISBN 0-88214-210-0). Spring Pubns.

Homespun Schools. Raymond Moore & Dorothy Moore. 1982. 9.95 (ISBN 0-8499-0326-2). Word Bks.

Homework Manual for Biblical Counseling: Family & Marital Problems, Vol. 2. Wayne Mack. 1980. pap. 3.95 (ISBN 0-87552-357-9). Presby & Reformed.

Homework Manual for Biblical Counseling: Personal & Interpersonal Problems, Vol. 1. Wayne Mack. 1979. pap. 5.50 (ISBN 0-87552-356-0). Presby & Reformed.

Homiletic. David G. Buttrick. LC 86-45208. 544p. 1987. 24.95 (ISBN 0-8006-0777-5, 1-777). Fortress.

Homiletica Practica. Tomas Hawkins. 1986. Repr. of 1985 ed. 1.95 (ISBN 0-311-42041-9). Casa Bautista.

Homiletical Plot: The Sermon As Narrative Art Form. Eugene Lowry. LC 79-92074. 100p. (Orig.). 1980. pap. 6.95 (ISBN 0-8042-1652-5). John Knox.

Homilies, Nos. 1-59. St. Jerome. LC 64-13360. (Fathers of the Church Ser: Vol. 48). 430p. 1964. 23.95x (ISBN 0-8132-0048-2). Cath U Pr.

Homilies, Nos. 60-96. St. Jerome. LC 64-13360. (Fathers of the Church Ser: Vol. 57). 295p. 1966. 15.95x (ISBN 0-8132-0057-1). Cath U Pr.

Homilies for Sundays of the Year: Cycle A. Ganzague Motte. 1974. 7.50 (ISBN 0-8199-0535-6). Franciscan Herald.

Homilies for Sundays of the Year Cycle 'C', 1974. Gonzague Motte. Tr. by John Drury from Fr. Tr. of Homilies pour une annees. 312p. 1973. 10.00 (ISBN 0-8199-0461-9). Franciscan Herald.

Homilies for Sundays of the Year: Cycles B. G. Motte. 1976. 7.50 ea. (ISBN 0-8199-0575-5). Franciscan Herald.

Homilies for the C Cycle: Proclaiming the Good News. John J. Hughes. LC 85-60893. 160p. 1985. text ed. 14.95 (ISBN 0-87973-724-7, 724). Our Sunday Visitor.

Homilies for the Celebration of Baptism. A. M. Roguet. Tr. by Jerome Du Charme from Fr. LC 76-53546. 1977. pap. 2.75 (ISBN 0-8199-0655-7). Franciscan Herald.

Homilies for the Celebration of Marriage. A. M. Roguet. Tr. by Jerome Du Charme from Fr. LC 76-53538. 1977. pap. 3.50 (ISBN 0-8199-0656-5). Franciscan Herald.

Homilies of Photius, Patriarch of Constantinople. Tr. by Cyril Mango. (Dumbarton Oaks Studies: Vol. 3). 327p. (LC A58-6068). 1958. 20.00x (ISBN 0-88402-003-7). Dumbarton Oaks.

Homilies of St. John Chrysostom on the Letters of St. Paul to Titus & Philemon. Blake Goodall. (Univ. of California Publications in Classical Studies: Vol. 20). 1979. 19.95x (ISBN 0-520-09596-0). U of Cal Pr.

Homilies of the Anglo-Saxon Church, 2 Vols. Aelfric. Tr. by Benjamin Thorpe. Repr. of 1846 ed. 60.00 ea. (ISBN 0-384-00340-0). Johnson Repr.

Homilies on Genesis & Exodus. Origen. LC 82-4124. (Fathers of the Church Ser.: Vol. 71). 422p. 1982. 29.95x (ISBN 0-8132-0071-7). Cath U Pr.

Homilies on Genesis 1-17. St. John Chrysostom. Tr. by Robert C. Hill from Gr. (Fathers of the Church Ser.: Vol. 74). 1986. 29.95 (ISBN 0-8132-0074-1). Cath U Pr.

Homilies on St. John 1-47. St. John Chrysostom. LC 57-1545. (Fathers of the Church Ser: Vol. 33). 485p. 1957. 25.95x (ISBN 0-8132-0033-4). Cath U Pr.

Homilies, 48-88. St. John Chrysostom. LC 57-1545. (Fathers of the Church Ser.: Vol. 41). 485p. 1960. 29.95x (ISBN 0-8132-0041-5). Cath U Pr.

Homing in the Presence: Meditations for Daily Living. Gerhard Frost. 125p. 1978. pap. 5.95 (ISBN 0-86683-756-6, HarpR). Har-Row.

Homme et l'Etat. 2nd ed. Jacques Maritain. 212p. 1965. 12.95 (ISBN 0-686-56353-0). French & Eur.

Homme Revolte: Essai. Albert Camus. (Coll. Soleil). 1951. 16.50 (ISBN 0-685-11234-9); pap. 4.95 (ISBN 0-686-66425-6). French & Eur.

Homo Necans: Interpretationen altgriechischer Opferriten und Mythen. Walter Burkert. LC 72-83051. (Religionsgeschichtliche Versuche und Vorarbeiten: Vol. 32). 356p. 1972. 43.20x (ISBN 3-11-003875-7). De Gruyter.

Homo Spiritualis Nititur Fide: Martin Luther & Ignatius of Loyola, an Analytical & Comparative Study of a Hermeneutic Based on the Heuristic Structure of Discretio. Michael Proterra. LC 82-21837. 92p. (Orig.). 1983. lib. bdg. 22.00 (ISBN 0-8191-2938-0); pap. text ed. 8.50 (ISBN 0-8191-2939-9). U Pr of Amer.

Homosexuality - an Appraisal. Gerald Coleman. 1978. 0.75 (ISBN 0-685-89391-X). Franciscan Herald.

Homosexuality: A Christian Evaluation & Response. 1980. 0.75 (ISBN 0-911802-47-9). Free Church Pubns.

Homosexuality: A New Christian Ethic. Elizabeth Moberly. 64p. 1983. pap. 6.95 (ISBN 0-227-67850-8, Pub. by J Clarke UK). Attic Pr.

Homosexuality & Ethics. rev. ed. Ed. by Edward Batchelor, Jr. LC 80-10533. 1982. 15.95 (ISBN 0-8298-0392-0); pap. 8.95 (ISBN 0-8298-0615-6). Pilgrim NY.
Homosexuality & the Bible: An Interpretation. Walter Barnett. LC 79-84920. 1979. pap. 2.50x (ISBN 0-87574-226-2). Pendle Hill.
Homosexuality & the Catholic Church. Ed. by Jeannine Gramick. 176p. 1985. 8.95 (ISBN 0-88347-149-3). New Ways Min.
Homosexuality & the Christian Way of Life. Edward A. Malloy. LC 81-40385. 382p. (Orig.). 1981. lib. bdg. 32.50 (ISBN 0-8191-1794-3); pap. text ed. 14.75 (ISBN 0-8191-1795-1). U Pr of Amer.
Homosexuality & the Church. Ed. by Gordon S. Dicker. 71p. (Orig.). 1985. pap. 6.95 (ISBN 0-85819-505-4, Pub. by Uniting Church). ANZ Religious Pubns.
Homosexuality & the Judeo-Christian Tradition: An Annotated Bibliography. Tom Horner. LC 81-889. (ATLA Bibliography Ser.: No. 5). 141p. 1981. 16.50 (ISBN 0-8108-1412-9). Scarecrow.
Homosexuality & the Magisterium: Documents from the Vatican & U. S. Bishops, 1975-1985. Ed. by John Gallagher. 109p. 1986. 9.95 (ISBN 0-935877-00-2). New Ways Min.
Homosexuality & the Western Christian Tradition. D. Sherwin Bailey. LC 75-34384. xii, 181p. 1975. Repr. of 1955 ed. 22.50 (ISBN 0-208-01492-6, Archon). Shoe String.
Homosexuality in Greek Myth. Bernard Sergent. Tr. by Arthur Goldhammer from Fr. LC 85-73369. 360p. 1986. 21.95 (ISBN 0-8070-5700-2). Beacon Pr.
Homosexual's Search for Happiness. Conrad Baars. (Synthesis Ser.). 1977. pap. 1.25 (ISBN 0-8199-0709-X). Franciscan Herald.
Honest Christianity. Clinton W. McLemore. LC 84-10450. 116p. (Orig.). 1984. pap. 7.95 (ISBN 0-664-26009-8, Pub. by Bridgebooks). Westminster.
Honest Money. Gary North. (Biblical Blueprint Ser.). Date not set. pap. 6.95 (ISBN 0-8407-3094-2). Nelson.
Honest Prayer. Elsie Gibson. LC 80-39570. 120p. (Orig.). 1981. pap. 7.95 (ISBN 0-664-24348-7). Westminster.
Honest to God. John A. Robinson. LC 63-13819. 144p. 1963. pap. 7.95 (ISBN 0-664-24465-3). Westminster.
Honesty. Jane B. Moncure. LC 80-39571. (Values to Live by Ser.). (Illus.). 32p. 1981. PLB 10.35 (ISBN 0-516-06523-8). Childrens.
Honesty, Morality, & Conscience. Jerry White. LC 78-61619. 240p. 1979. pap. 5.95 (ISBN 0-89109-431-8). NavPress.
Honey & Salt. 2nd ed. Muriel Hanson. LC 78-185512. 1971. pap. text ed. 1.50 (ISBN 0-911802-26-6). Free Church Pubns.
Honey for a Child's Heart. Gladys Hunt. 1969. pap. 5.95 (ISBN 0-310-26381-6, 9891P). Zondervan.
Honey from The Rock: Ten Gates of Jewish Mysticism. Lawrence Kushner. LC 77-7832. 160p. 1983. pap. 7.95 (ISBN 0-06-064904-6, RD/442, HarpR). Har-Row.
Honi & His Magic Circle. Phillis Gershator. LC 79-84931. (Illus.). 1979. 6.95 (ISBN 0-8276-0167-0, 443). Jewish Pubns.
Honor Bound. Colleen Reece. 176p. 1983. 3.95 (ISBN 0-8024-0153-8). Moody.
Honor Thy Father. Meridel Rawlings. Ed. by Bill Keith. (Orig.). 1986. pap. 6.95 (ISBN 0-910311-39-0). Huntington Hse Inc.
Honor Thy Father & Mother. Gerald Blidstein. 15.00x (ISBN 0-87068-251-2); pap. 9.95. Ktav.
Honor Thy Womanself. Audrey Drummond. 1982. pap. 7.50 (ISBN 0-933840-12-8). Unitarian Univ.
Hooked on Horses: Bits of This & That about People & Horses after 21 Years in the Racing Game. Howard A. Jones. (Illus.). 144p. 1982. 12.50 (ISBN 0-682-49792-4, Banner). Exposition Pr FL.
Hooked on Prescription Drugs. Sue B. Jackson. Ed. by Mary H. Wallace. 112p. (Orig.). 1981. pap. 2.95 (ISBN 0-912315-33-4). Word Aflame.
Hoorays & Hosannas. Bernadette Snyder. LC 80-66937. (Illus.). 56p. (Orig.). 1980. pap. 3.95 (ISBN 0-87793-205-0). Ave Maria.
Hoosier Zion: The Presbyterians in Early Indiana. L. C. Rudolph. LC 62-8261. (Yale Publications in Religion Ser.: No. 5). (Illus.). pap. 49.00 (ISBN 0-317-09434-3, 2009008). Bks Demand UMI.
Hope: A Partner to Faith. Charles Capps. 38p. (Orig.). 1986. pap. 1.25 mini-book (ISBN 0-89274-396-4). Harrison Hse.
Hope & Fear Not. Rexella Van Impe. 32p. 1985. pap. 1.95 (ISBN 0-934803-14-5). J Van Impe.
Hope & Suffering: Sermons & Speeches. Desmond M. Tutu. 189p. (Orig.). 1984. pap. 6.95 (ISBN 0-8028-0085-8). Eerdmans.
Hope & the Purple Onion. Jackie Banas. (Illus.). 39p. (Orig.). 1984. wkbk. 5.00 (ISBN 0-9614014-1-9). Know Him Pr.
Hope for a Despairing World. Phillip E. Hughes. LC 77-89680. (Canterbury Bks.). pap. 2.95 (ISBN 0-8010-4159-7). Baker Bk.
Hope for a Troubled Nation. Kathy Graham. (Bible Puzzle Time). (Illus.). 16p. (Orig.). 1982. pap. 0.60 (ISBN 0-87403-016-1, 2176). Standard Pub.
Hope for a Troubled World. John W. Alexander. 32p. 1978. pap. 0.75 (ISBN 0-87784-165-9). Inter-Varsity.
Hope for Every Heart. Audrey McDaniel. LC 85-29110. 1986. 5.50 (ISBN 0-8054-5031-9). Broadman.
Hope for Faith: A Conversation. C. F. Naude & Dorothee Solle. 48p. (Orig.). 1986. pap. 3.95. Eerdmans.
Hope for Faith: A Conversation. C. F. Naude & Dorothee Solle. 1986. pap. 3.95 (ISBN 0-8028-0191-9). Eerdmans.
Hope for Families. Margaret M. Sarvin. 6.95 (ISBN 0-8215-9902-X). Sadlier.
Hope for the Separated. Gary D. Chapman. LC 81-18667. 160p. 1982. pap. 5.95 (ISBN 0-8024-3616-1). Moody.
Hope Is an Open Door. Mary L. Tobin. LC 80-21414. (Journeys in Faith Ser). 1981. 7.95 (ISBN 0-687-17410-4). Abingdon.
Hope of a New World. William Temple. LC 74-121507. (Essay Index Reprint Ser). 1940. 13.00 (ISBN 0-8369-1778-2). Ayer Co Pubs.
Hope of the World. C. E. McGaughey. Ed. by J. D. Thomas. LC 74-180791. (Twentieth Century Sermons Ser). 1971. 11.95 (ISBN 0-89112-306-7, Bibl Res Pr). Abilene Christ U.
Hope That Never Disappoints. Beverly M. Currin. 128p. (Orig.). 1983. pap. 8.75 (ISBN 0-687-17415-5). Abingdon.
Hope Unlimited. Ladislaus Enrody. 1962. 2.50 (ISBN 0-8198-0060-0); pap. 1.50 (ISBN 0-8198-0061-9). Dghtrs St Paul.
Hope Within History. Walter Brueggemann. LC 86-45353. 144p. (Orig.). 1986. pap. 8.95 (ISBN 0-8042-0918-9). John Knox.
Hopeful Imagination: Prophectic Voices in Exile. Walter Brueggemann. LC 86-45207. 160p. 1986. pap. 7.95 (ISBN 0-8006-1925-0). Fortress.
Hopi & Zuni Ceremonialism. Elsie C. Parsons. LC 34-5260. (American Anthro. Associatiom Memoirs). 1933. 11.00 (ISBN 0-527-00538-X). Kraus Repr.
Hopi Kachina Dolls with a Key to Their Identification. rev ed. Harold S. Colton. LC 59-5480. (Illus.). 150p. 1971. pap. 8.95 (ISBN 0-8263-0180-0). U of NM Pr.
Hopi Kachinas. 2nd ed. Edwin Earle & Edward A. Kennard. LC 71-139867. (Illus.). 1971. 12.50 (ISBN 0-934490-11-2). Mus Am Ind.
Hopi Snake Ceremonies: An Eyewitness Account. Jesse W. Fewkes. LC 86-1127. (Bureau of American Ethnology Ser.). (Illus.). 160p. 1986. Repr. of 1897 ed. 16.95 (ISBN 0-936755-00-8). Avanyu Pub.
Hoping Against All Hope. Helder Camara. Tr. by Matthew J. O'Connell from Ger. LC 83-19348. Orig. Title: Hoffer Wider Alle Hoffnung. 96p. (Orig.). 1984. pap. 4.95 (ISBN 0-88344-192-6). Orbis Bks.
Hopkins' Sanctifying Imagination. David A. Downes. LC 85-11071. 134p. (Orig.). 1985. lib. bdg. 22.00 (ISBN 0-8191-4755-9); pap. text ed. 8.75 (ISBN 0-8191-4756-7). U Pr of Amer.
Horace Bushnell: On the Vitality of Biblical Language. James O. Duke. LC 83-16312. (SBL-Biblical Schlolarship in North America). 138p. 1984. pap. 13.50 (ISBN 0-89130-650-1, 06 11 09). Scholars Pr GA.
Horace Bushnell: Selected Writings on Language, Religion & American Culture. David L. Smith. LC 83-6678. (AAR Studies in Religion). 196p. 1984. pap. 9.75 (ISBN 0-89130-636-6, 01 00 33). Scholars Pr GA.
Horace Bushnell: Sermons. Ed. by Conrad Cherry. LC 85-60410. (Sources of American Spirituality Ser.). 256p. (Orig.). 1985. 12.95 (ISBN 0-8091-0362-1). Paulist Pr.
Horace Bushnell's Theory of Language: In the Context of Other Nineteenth-Century Philosophies of Language. Donald A. Crosby. (Studies in Philosophy: No. 22). 300p. 1975. text ed. 33.60x (ISBN 90-2793-044-9). Mouton.
Horace et les Curiaces. Georges Dumezil. Ed. by Kees W. Bolle. (Mythology Ser.). (Fr.). 1978. Repr. of 1942 ed. lib. bdg. 17.00x (ISBN 0-405-10534-7). Ayer Co Pubs.
Horace Mann & Religion in the Massachusetts Public Schools. Raymond B. Culver. LC 72-89168. (American Education: Its Men, Institutions & Ideas, Ser. 1). 1969. Repr. of 1929 ed. 17.00 (ISBN 0-405-01406-6). Ayer Co Pubs.
Horace on Poetry: Epistles Book II: The Letters to Augustus & Florus, Vol. 3. Charles O. Brink. LC 63-4908. 656p. 1982. 100.00 (ISBN 0-521-20069-5). Cambridge U Pr.
Horary Art & It's Synthesis. Elsie M. Knapp. 1974. 5.00x (ISBN 0-686-17210-8). Sandollar Pr.
Horary Astrology: Course VIII, Lessons 36, 86-92. (Illus.). 1976. pap. 10.25 (ISBN 0-87887-343-0). Church of Light.
Horayoth 'Eduyyoth & Aboth, 1 vol. 15.00 (ISBN 0-910218-78-1). Bennet Pub.
Horeb, 1 vol. S. R. Hirsch. Set. 19.95x (ISBN 0-900689-40-4). Bloch.
Horizons of Criticism: An Assessment of Religious-Literary Options. Vernon Ruland. LC 75-20162. pap. 68.80 (ISBN 0-317-29363-X, 2024203). Bks Demand UMI.
Horizons of Science: Christian Scholars Speak Out. Ed. by Carl F. Henry. LC 77-7849. 1978. pap. 6.95xi (ISBN 0-06-063866-4, RD 240, HarpR). Har-Row.
Horizontal Line Synopsis of the Gospels. Reuben J. Swanson. LC 75-20997. 608p. 1984. Repr. of 1980 ed. 24.95 (ISBN 0-87808-744-3). William Carey Lib.
Horizontal Line Synopsis of the Gospels: Volume I, The Gospel of Mathew. Reuben J. Swanson. 1982. 29.95 (ISBN 0-915948-10-9). Bks Distinction.
Horkheimer's Critical Sociology of Religion: The Relative & the Transcendent. Rudolf J. Siebert. LC 78-66280. 1979. pap. text ed. 9.50 (ISBN 0-8191-0688-7). U Pr of Amer.
Horn & Crescent: Cultural Change & Traditional Islam on the East African Coast, 800-1900. Randall L. Pouwels. (African Studies Ser.: No. 53). (Illus.). 288p. Date not set. price not set (ISBN 0-521-32308-8). Cambridge U Pr.
Horn-Motif in the Hebrew Bible & Related Ancient Near Eastern Literature & Iconography. Margit L. Suring. (Andrews University Seminary Doctoral Dissertation Ser.: Vol. 4). (Illus.). xxvi, 533p. 1982. pap. 12.95 (ISBN 0-943872-36-7). Andrews Univ Pr.
Horned God. John Rowan. 160p. 1987. pap. 13.95 (ISBN 0-7102-0674-7, 06747, Ark Paperbks). Methuen Inc.
Horned Moses in Medieval Art & Thought. Ruth Mellinkoff. LC 77-85450. (California Studies in the History of Art: No. XIV). (Illus.). 1970. 40.00x (ISBN 0-520-01705-6). U of Cal Pr.
Horoscopes & the Christian. Robert A. Morey. 64p. (Orig.). 1981. pap. 2.95 (ISBN 0-87123-202-2, 210202). Bethany Hse.
Horrified & the Glorified. C. C. Cribb. LC 77-70214. pap. 2.95 (ISBN 0-932046-05-3). Manhattan Ltd NC.
Horse & the Dog in Hidatsa Culture. Gilbert L. Wilson. LC 76-43895. (AMNH Anthropological Papers: Vol. 15, Pt. 2). Repr. of 1924 ed. 23.00 (ISBN 0-404-15751-3). AMS Pr.
Horse of the Moonlight. Irene Taafaki. (Illus.). 40p. pap. 3.50 (ISBN 0-85398-111-6). G Ronald Pub,
Horseman of the King (John Wesley) Cyril Davey. 1964. pap. 2.95 (ISBN 0-87508-605-5). Chr Lit.
Hosea. Hans W. Wolff. Ed. by Paul D. Hanson. Tr. by Gary Stansell from Ger. LC 70-179634. (Hermeneia: A Critical & Historical Commentary on the Bible). Orig. Title: Dodekapropheton-Hosea. 292p. 1973. 24.95 (ISBN 0-8006-6004-8, 20-6004). Fortress.
Hosea: A Commentary. James L. Mays. LC 75-79618. (Old Testament Library). 202p. 1969. 15.95 (ISBN 0-664-20871-1). Westminster.
Hosea: An Israelite Prophet in Judean Perspective. Grace I. Emmerson. (JSOT Supplement Ser.: No. 28). 224p. 1984. text ed. 28.50x (ISBN 0-905774-68-X, Pub. by JSOT Pr England); pap. text ed. 11.95x (ISBN 0-905774-69-8, Pub. by JSOT Pr England). Eisenbrauns.
Hosea & Amos. Ed. by Gary Cohen & H. Ronald Vandermey. (Everyman's Bible Commentary). 128p. 1981. pap. 5.95 (ISBN 0-8024-2028-1). Moody.
Hosea Ballou: The Challenge to Orthodoxy. Ernest Cassara. LC 81-40859. 236p. 1982. lib. bdg. 27.75 (ISBN 0-8191-2271-8); pap. text ed. 12.50 (ISBN 0-8191-2272-6). U Pr of Amer.
Hosea: Bible Study Commentary. D. David Garland. 128p. 1975. pap. 4.95 (ISBN 0-310-24843-4, 10234P). Zondervan.
Hosea-Jonah. Jacob M. Myers. LC 59-10454. (Layman's Bible Commentary: Vol. 14). 1959. pap. 4.95 (ISBN 0-8042-3074-9). John Knox.
Hosea-Malachi, Vol. V. Beacon Bible Commentary Staff. 13.95 (ISBN 0-8010-0692-9). Baker Bk.
Hosea: The Heart & Holiness of God. G. Campbell Morgan. (Morgan Library). 1974. pap. 4.50 (ISBN 0-8010-5952-6). Baker Bk.
Hosea's Heartbreak. Jack R. Riggs. 1984. pap. 5.95 (ISBN 0-87213-724-4). Loizeaux.
Hoshanos. Avie Gold. (Art Scroll Mesorah Ser.). 160p. 1980. 11.95 (ISBN 0-89906-162-1); pap. 8.95 (ISBN 0-89906-163-X). Mesorah Pubns.
Hospice Handbook. Michael P. Hamilton & Helen F. Reid. (Orig.). 1980. pap. 7.95 (ISBN 0-8028-1820-X). Eerdmans.
Hospice Handbook: A Guide for Managers & Planners. Lenora F. Paradis. 420p. 1985. 46.50 (ISBN 0-87189-104-2). Aspen Pub.
Hospital Ministry. Lawrence Holst. Intro. by Martin E. Marty. 256p. 1985. 19.95 (ISBN 0-8245-0697-9). Crossroad NY.
Hospital Ministry. Lawrence Holst. 256p. 1987. pap. 10.95 (ISBN 0-8245-0819-X). Crossroad NY.
Hospital of Santo Spirito & Pope Sixtus IV. Eunice D. Howe. LC 77-94698. (Outstanding Dissertations in the Fine Arts Ser.). (Illus.). 444p. 1978. lib. bdg. 52.00 (ISBN 0-8240-3230-6). Garland Pub.
Hospital Strength. pap. 0.45 (ISBN 0-686-23471-5). Rose Pub MI.
Hospitality: In the Spirit of Love. Peggy Simpson. 1980. pap. 4.95 (ISBN 0-89137-416-7). Quality Pubns.
Hospitality to The Stranger: Dimension of Moral Understanding. Thomas W. Ogletree. LC 84-18763. 176p. 1985. pap. 10.95 (ISBN 0-8006-1839-4, 1-1839). Fortress.
Hospitality with Confidence. Grace Pittman. 128p. (Orig.). 1986. pap. 4.95 (ISBN 0-87123-858-6, 210858). Bethany Hse.
Hostage Game: An Exciting Simulation Game for Junior High Youth Groups. Paul Boostrom. (Best of Young Teen Action Ser.). 32p. 1985. pap. 4.95 (ISBN 0-89191-382-3). Cook.
Hostage to the Devil: The Possession of Exorcism of Five Living Americans. Malachi Martin. LC 86-46207. 488p. 1987. pap. 8.95 (ISBN 0-06-097103-7, PL 7103, PL). Har-Row.
Hot & Cold & in Between. Robert Allen. 1985. 4.25 (ISBN 0-89536-717-3, 5801). CSS of Ohio.
Hot Buttons. Compiled by Rick Bundschuh. LC 85-32323. (Light Force Ser.). (Illus.). 153p. (Orig.). 1986. pap. 4.25 (ISBN 0-8307-1092-2, S182437). Regal.
Hot Line to Heaven. Frances Hunter. 1978. pap. 3.25 (ISBN 0-87162-117-7). Hunter Bks.
Hot under the Collar: Self-Portrait of a Gay Pastor. Johannes W. DiMaria-Kuiper. LC 83-60016. 177p. (Orig.). 1983. pap. 7.95 (ISBN 0-912393-00-9). Mercury Pr.
Hound of Heaven. Francis Thompson. (Illus.). 1983. 3.95 (ISBN 0-87193-157-5). Dimension Bks.
Hour Cometh. Howard B. Rand. 1966. 5.00 (ISBN 0-685-08805-7). Destiny.
Hour of Insight. facsimile ed. Institute for Religious & Social Studies. Ed. by R. M. MacIver. LC 70-167366. (Essay Index Reprint Ser). Repr. of 1954 ed. 15.00 (ISBN 0-8369-2655-2). Ayer Co Pubs.
Hour of the Unexpected. John Shea. LC 77-73648. 1977. pap. 4.95 (ISBN 0-913592-85-4). Argus Comm.
Hour That Changes the World. Dick Eastman. (Direction Bks.). pap. 2.50 (ISBN 0-8010-3337-3). Baker Bk.
Hours of Catherine of Cleves. Intro. by John Plummer. LC 66-23096. (Illus.). 360p. 1975. 50.00 (ISBN 0-8076-0379-1). Braziller.
Hours of Etienne Chevalier. Jean Fouquet. LC 78-160131. (Illus.). 128p. 1971. slipcased 40.00 (ISBN 0-8076-0618-9). Braziller.
Hours on Sinai. Ioanna Tsatsos. Ed. by N. M. Vaporis. Tr. by Jean Demos from Gr. Orig. Title: Apo to Tetradio Mou: Hores Tou Sina. 76p. 1984. pap. text ed. 8.00 (ISBN 0-917653-00-9). Hellenic Coll Pr.
House Beautiful. Ray Patterson. (Illus.). 118p. 1987. pap. 3.95 (ISBN 0-936369-05-1). Son-Rise Pubns.
House Church Evolving. Ed. by Arthur L. Foster. LC 76-4198. (Studies in Ministry & Parish Life). 126p. 1976. 13.95x (ISBN 0-913552-04-6); pap. 6.95x (ISBN 0-913552-05-4). Exploration Pr.
House Divided. Katherine Edwards. 144p. 1984. pap. 4.95 (ISBN 0-310-43501-3, 11169P). Zondervan.
House Divided: The Origin & Development of Hindi-Hindavi. Amrit Rai. 1985. 29.95x (ISBN 0-19-561643-X). Oxford U Pr.
House Full of Prayers. Marian Bennett. (Surprise Bks.). (Illus.). 14p. (Orig.). 1982. pap. 4.95 (ISBN 0-87239-563-4, 2709). Standard Pub.
House of God. John Bunyan. pap. 0.95 (ISBN 0-685-19834-0). Reiner.
House of God: A History of Religious Architecture & Symbolism. Ernest H. Short. 75.00 (ISBN 0-8490-0374-1). Gordon Pr.
House of Holy Wisdom: A Commentary on Proverbs 9. Agioantonides Bessarion. (Illus.). 60p. (Orig.). 1986. pap. 4.95 (ISBN 0-936649-12-7). St Anthony Orthodox.
House of Neh. Thelma Park. (Illus.). 178p. (Orig.). 1986. pap. 9.95 (ISBN 1-55630-023-9). Brentwood Comm.
House of Prayer for All Nations. Leonard Spell, Sr. 174p. 1986. 12.95x (ISBN 0-9615439-1-4, 133997); pap. 9.95x (ISBN 0-9615439-2-2). Spell Assoc.

House of Si Abd Allah: The Oral History of a Moroccan Family. Henry Munson, Jr. LC 83-19837. 280p. 1984. 22.50x (ISBN 0-300-03084-3). Yale U Pr.
House of the Lord. James E. Talmage. 8.95 (ISBN 0-87747-112-6). Deseret Bk.
House of the Soul & Concerning the Inner Life. Evelyn Underhill. 150p. (Orig.). 1984. pap. 6.95 (ISBN 0-86683-882-1, 7459, HarpR). Har-Row.
House of Wisdom. John Dunne. LC 84-48767. 224p. 1985. 15.45 (ISBN 0-317-18550-0, HarpR). Har-Row.
House on the Rock. Charles Sell. 168p. 1987. pap. 5.95 (ISBN 0-89693-048-3). Victor Bks.
House Staff & Thanatology. Ed. by Robert DeBellis et al. 15.00 (ISBN 0-405-14211-0). Ayer Co Pubs.
House the Lord Built. Gordon Lindsay. 1.00 (ISBN 0-89985-015-4). Christ Nations.
Household Church. H. L. Ellison. 120p. 1979. pap. 4.95 (ISBN 0-85364-239-7). Attic Pr.
Household of Faith: Roman Catholic Devotions in Mid-Nineteenth Century America. Ann Taves. LC 85-41008. 192p. 1986. text ed. 17.95x (ISBN 0-268-01082-X). U of Notre Dame Pr.
Household of Freedom: Authority in Feminist Theology. Letty M. Russell. 132p. (Orig.). 1987. pap. 8.95 (ISBN 0-664-24017-8). Westminster.
Household of God & the Social World of the Pastoral Epistles. David C. Verner. LC 82-25015. (Society of Biblical Literature Dissertation Ser.). 218p. 1983. pap. 13.50 (ISBN 0-89130-611-0, 06 01 71). Scholars Pr GA.
Household, Village, & Village Confederation in Southeastern Europe. Paul H. Stahl. (East European Monographs: No. 200). 252p. 1986. 25.00 (ISBN 0-88033-094-5). East Eur Quarterly.
Households of God. David Parry. (Cistercian Studies: No. 39). (Orig.). 1980. pap. 7.95 (ISBN 0-87907-939-8). Cistercian Pubns.
Households of God on China's Soil. Compiled by Raymond Fung. LC 82-18974. 84p. (Orig.). 1983. pap. 5.95 (ISBN 0-88344-189-6). Orbis Bks.
Houses for the Hereafter: Funerary Temples from Guerrero, Mexico. Julie Jones. (Illus.). 32p. 1987. pap. 10.00 (ISBN 0-9617356-1-9). Metro Mus Art.
Houses of God. Jeannette Mirsky. LC 76-1536. 1976. pap. 25.00x (ISBN 0-226-53184-8, P690, Phoen). U of Chicago Pr.
How & What to Teach: A Pre-School & Kindergarten Curriculum Guide for the Day School. Sukey Gross. 8.00 (ISBN 0-914131-33-8, C04). Torah Umesorah.
How Are You Praying? Donald Demaray. 176p. (Orig.). 1985. pap. 5.95 (ISBN 0-310-23841-2, 6801P). Zondervan.
How Bad Are Your Sins? Lance Webb. 224p. (Orig.). 1983. pap. 4.95 (ISBN 0-687-17520-8, Festival). Abingdon.
How Beautiful God's Gifts. Jane B. Moncure. Ed. by Jane Buerger. LC 80-15434. (Illus.). 32p. 1980. 5.95 (ISBN 0-89565-172-6, 4923). Standard Pub.
How Big Is a Person? A Book for Loving Out Loud. George F. Simons. LC 82-61423. 72p. 1983. 3.95 (ISBN 0-8091-0336-2). Paulist Pr.
How Big Is God? Discovering Our Creator's Love & Power. Ed. by Kevin Miller. (Senior High Pacesetter Ser.). 64p. 1986. pap. 7.95 (ISBN 0-89191-328-9). Cook.
How Bishops Decide: An American Catholic Case Study. Philip F. Lawler. 45p. (Orig.). pap. 4.00 (ISBN 0-89633-101-6). Ethics & Public Policy.
How Blest You Are: A Living-Room Retreat Based on the Beatitudes. Helen C. Swift. 85p. 1984. pap. 3.50 (ISBN 0-86716-033-0). St Anthony Mess Pr.
How Came the Bible ? Edgar J. Goodspeed. (Festival Books). 1976. pap. 1.95 (ISBN 0-687-17524-0). Abingdon.
How Can I Be Blessed? Kay Arthur. 256p. (Orig.). 1984. pap. 6.95 (ISBN 0-317-06624-2, Power Bks). Revell.
How Can I Be Healed. Elbert Willis. 1978. 1.25 (ISBN 0-89858-013-7). Fill the Gap.
How Can I Be Sure: A Pre-Marriage Inventory. Bob Phillips. LC 77-94448. 160p. (Orig.). 1978. pap. 3.95 (ISBN 0-89081-073-7). Harvest Hse.
How Can I Find Healing? Jim Glennon. LC 84-73039. 1985. pap. 3.50 (ISBN 0-88270-580-6). Bridge Pub.
How Can I Live. Kay Arthur. 528p. (Orig.). 1981. pap. 7.95 (ISBN 0-8007-5077-2, Power Bks). Revell.
How Can It Be All Right When Everything Is All Wrong. Lewis B. Smedes. LC 82-47756. 128p. (Orig.). 1982. pap. 6.95 (ISBN 0-06-067409-1, RD398, HarpR). Har-Row.
How Can Mankind Find the Christ Again? 2nd ed. Rudolf Steiner. Ed. by Galdys Hahn. Tr. by Frances E. Dawson & Gladys Hahn. 1984. 15.00 (ISBN 0-88010-078-8); pap. 8.95 (ISBN 0-88010-079-6). Anthroposophic.
How Christ Said the First Mass or the Lord's Last Supper. James L. Meagher. LC 82-74246. 438p. 1985. pap. 12.00 (ISBN 0-89555-207-8). Tan Bks Pubs.
How Christians Grow. Russell T. Hitt. 1979. 12.95x (ISBN 0-19-502558-X). Oxford U Pr.
How Christmas Came to the Sunday-Schools: The Observance of Christmas in the Protestant Church Schools of the United States. Katharine L. Richards. LC 70-159860. 1971. Repr. of 1934 ed. 40.00x (ISBN 0-8103-3793-2). Gale.
How Church-Related Are Church-Related Colleges? Answers Based on a Comprehensive Survey of Supporting Constituencies of 18 LCA Colleges. Richard W. Solberg & Merton P. Strommen. LC 80-13833. 96p. (Orig.). 1980. pap. 3.95 (ISBN 0-8006-1388-0, 1-1388). Fortress.
How Churches Grow. Donald A. McGavran. (Orig.). 1965. pap. 6.95 (ISBN 0-377-40011-4). Friend Pr.
How Come Its Taking Me So Long? Lane Adams. (Living Studies). 156p. 1985. pap. 5.95 (ISBN 0-8423-1491-1); leader's guide 2.95 (ISBN 0-8423-1492-X). Tyndale.
How Could God Let This Happen. Ed. by Jim Long. (Campus Life Bks). 160p. 1986. pap. 5.95 (ISBN 0-8423-1377-X). Tyndale.
How Could I Not Be Among You? Ted Rosenthal. LC 73-80922. (Illus.). 80p. 1987. pap. 9.95 (ISBN 0-89255-117-8). Persea Bks.
How Damage is Done in The Name of Christ! Jay Dean & Claire Dean. LC 82-90134. 102p. (Orig.). 1982. pap. 3.95 (ISBN 0-943416-00-0). Plus Seven Bks.
How Do I Make Up My Mind, Lord? Robert Kelly. LC 82-70948. (Young Readers Ser.). (Orig.). 1982. pap. 3.95 (ISBN 0-8066-1923-6, 10-3168). Augsburg.
How Do Others See You? In an LDS Ward. Illus. by Rod Warren. (Illus., Orig.). 1977. pap. 2.95 (ISBN 0-89036-101-0). Hawkes Pub Inc.
How Do We Get to Heaven? Dave Eaton. (Questions, Questions Ser.). 32p. 1986. 2.95 (ISBN 0-89081-549-6). Harvest Hse.
How Do We Know There Is a God? John W. Montgomery. LC 73-16882. 96p. 1973. pap. 3.50 (ISBN 0-87123-221-9, 200221). Bethany Hse.
How Do You Decide? Ivan Friesen & Rachel Frieson. (Shalom Ser.: No. 6). (Illus.). 16p. pap. 0.50 (ISBN 0-8361-1975-4). Herald Pr.
How Do You Face Disappointments? Ruth C. Stapleton & Robert Cochran. LC 77-78468. (Lifeline Ser.). 1977. pap. 0.95 (ISBN 0-88419-136-2). Creation Hse.
How Do You Handle Life? Fritz Ridenour. LC 77-140941. 192p. 1976. pap. 3.50 (ISBN 0-8307-0430-2, S104156). Regal.
How Do You Spell Chanukah? A General-Purpose Romanization of Hebrew for Speakers of English. W. Weinberg. (Bibliographica Judaica Ser: No. 5). 10.00x (ISBN 0-87820-903-4, HUC Pr). Ktav.
How Does the Christian Confront the Old Testament. Ed. by Pierre Benoit. (Concilium Ser.: Vol. 30). 1967. 7.95 (ISBN 0-8091-0074-6). Paulist Pr.
How Faith Works. Harold T. Bryson. LC 84-17601. 1985. pap. 5.95 (ISBN 0-8054-1394-4). Broadman.
How Faith Works. Frederick K. Price. 128p. (Orig.). 1979. pap. 3.95 (ISBN 0-89274-001-9). Harrison Hse.
How Far I Can Go. Lawrence O. Richards. (Answers for Youth Ser.). 1980. pap. 4.95 (ISBN 0-310-38951-8, 18025P). Zondervan.
How God Created. John Dunne. pap. 2.00 (ISBN 0-268-00120-0). U of Notre Dame Pr.
How God Deals with Evil. W. Sibley Towner. LC 76-24916. (Biblical Perspectives on Current Issues). 186p. 1976. softcover 4.95 (ISBN 0-664-24127-1). Westminster.
How God Gives Us Popcorn. Henrietta Gambill. (Happy Days Bks.). (Illus.). 24p. 1984. 1.59 (ISBN 0-87239-739-4, 3709). Standard Pub.
How God Made the World. Mrs. Marvin Good. 1978. pap. 1.95 (ISBN 0-686-24050-2). Rod & Staff.
How God Taught Me About Prosperity. Kenneth E. Hagin. 1985. mini bk. 0.50 (ISBN 0-89276-265-9). Hagin Ministries.
How Good are your Virtues? Lance Webb. 176p. (Orig.). 1983. pap. 3.95 (ISBN 0-687-17528-3, Festival). Abingdon.
How I Can Be Real. Lawrence O. Richards. (Answers for Youth Ser.). 1980. pap. 4.95 (ISBN 0-310-38971-2, 18207P). Zondervan.
How I Can Experience God. Lawrence O. Richards. (Answers for Youth Ser.). 1980. pap. 4.95 (ISBN 0-310-38991-7, 18209P). Zondervan.
How I Can Make Decisions. Lawrence O. Richards. (Answers for Youth Ser.). 1980. pap. 4.95 (ISBN 0-310-38981-X, 18208P). Zondervan.
How I Found Out About Heaven. M. R. Keith. 1970. 4.95 (ISBN 0-910122-23-7). Amherst Pr.
How I Got Faith. Willis M. Brown. 199p. 2.00 (ISBN 0-686-29117-4). Faith Pub Hse.
How I Met God: An Unusual Conversion. Hellmut Laun. Tr. by David Smith. 163p. 1983. 10.50 (ISBN 0-8199-0871-1). Franciscan Herald.
How I Use Herbs. large print ed. Charlene Brians. 37p. 1985. pap. 5.50 (ISBN 0-914009-43-5). VHI Library.
How in the World Do I Get Along With My Parents? David Pitts. 40p. 1982. pap. 0.95 (ISBN 0-88144-046-9). Christian Pub.
How in This World Can I Be Holy? Ed. by Erwin W. Lutzer. (Moody Press Electives Ser.). 1985. pap. text ed. 3.95 (ISBN 0-8024-0730-7); leader's guide 2.50 (ISBN 0-8024-0731-5). Moody.
How Is Your Public Image? Tedra G. Smith. (Orig.). 1977. pap. 2.75 (ISBN 0-89536-096-9, 0823). CSS of Ohio.
How It All Began: (Genesis 1-11) Ronald Youngblood. LC 80-50539. (Bible Commentary for Laymen Ser.). 160p. 1980. pap. 3.50 (ISBN 0-8307-0675-5, S342103). Regal.
How It All Began: Origins of the Christian Church New Edition with Study Guide. O. C. Edwards. 1978. pap. 6.95 (ISBN 0-8164-2164-1, HarpR). Har-Row.
How Jesus Taught: The Methods & Techniques of the Master. Regina M. Alfonso. (Illus.). 129p. (Orig.). 1986. pap. 6.95 (ISBN 0-8189-0506-9). Alba.
How Jesus Won Persons. Delos Miles. LC 82-70049. 1982. pap. 5.95 (ISBN 0-8054-6236-8). Broadman.
How Karl Barth Changed My Mind. Ed. by Donald K. McKim. 216p. (Orig.). 1986. pap. 9.95 (ISBN 0-8028-0099-8). Eerdmans.
How Long? Prison Reflections from the Philippines. Karl Gaspar. Ed. by Helen Graham & Breda Noonan. LC 85-25851. 176p. (Orig.). 1986. pap. 9.95 (ISBN 0-88344-226-4). Orbis Bks.
How May I Know I Am Saved? William S. Deal. 1973. pap. 0.60, 3 for 1.50, 5 for 2.50, 10 for 5.00 (ISBN 0-686-05834-8). Crusade Pubs.
How Melanchthon Helped Luther Discover the Gospel: The Doctrine of Justification in the Reformation. Lowell C. Green. 274p. 1980. 7.95 (ISBN 0-89890-010-7). Attic Pr.
How Mennonites Came to Be. J. C. Wenger. LC 77-86332. (Mennonite Faith Ser.: No. 1). 1977. pap. 1.50 (ISBN 0-8361-1832-4). Herald Pr.
How Much of God I Express Is How Much I Profess. Herbert L. Beierle. 1982. 1.00 (ISBN 0-686-35834-1). U of Healing.
How My Mind Has Changed. Ed. by Harold E. Fey. 7.00 (ISBN 0-8446-2056-4). Peter Smith.
How New Evidence of God Can Bring You Joy. Royal Rasmussen. (Illus.). 228p. 1986. 14.95 (ISBN 0-936223-01-4). Sunshine Pr.
How Not to Eat Pork: Or Life Without the Pig. Shahrazad Ali. LC 85-70171. (Illus.). 120p. (Orig.). 1985. pap. 5.95 (ISBN 0-933405-00-6). Civilized Pubns.
How Not to Say Mass: Guidebook for All Concerned about Authentic Worship. Dennis C. Smolarski. 96p. 1986. pap. 5.95 (ISBN 0-8091-2811-X). Paulist Pr.
How One Thousand Buddhas Became Enlightened, 3 Vols. Buddhist Sutra. 1986. Set. cancelled (ISBN 0-89800-136-6). Dharma Pub.
How People Get Married. Caroline Arnold. (Ceremonies & Celebrations Ser.). (Illus.). 32p. 1987. PLB 9.90 (ISBN 0-531-10096-0). Watts.
How Praise a World That May Not Last. Mark Van Doren. 1977. pap. 6.95 handset, handbound (ISBN 0-89016-039-2). Lightning Tree.
How Rabbit Stole the Fire: A North American Indian Folk Tale. Retold by & illus. by Joanna Troughton. LC 85-15629. (Folk-Tales of the World Ser.). (Illus.). 28p. 1986. 10.95 (ISBN 0-87226-040-2, Bedrick Blackie). P Bedrick Bks.
How Sacraments Celebrate Our Story. Mary P. Ryan. LC 78-53635. (Journeys Ser). 1978. pap. text ed. 6.00x (ISBN 0-88489-104-6); tchrs. guide 6.00x (ISBN 0-88489-108-9). St Mary's.
How Shall They Hear Without a Preacher: The Life of Ernest Fremont Tittle. Robert M. Miller. LC 74-149031. xii, 524p. 1971. 35.00 (ISBN 0-8078-1173-4). U of NC Pr.
How Shall We Escape. Richard Durfield. 1983. pap. 3.95 (ISBN 0-938612-07-7). Revival Press.
How Shall We Find the Father? Meditations for Mixed Voices. Mary Neill et al. 160p. (Orig.). 1983. pap. 8.95 (ISBN 0-8164-2623-6, HarpR). Har-Row.
How Should a Christian Live? 1, 2, & 3 John. Dee Brestin. (Core Study in the Fisherman Bible Studyguides). 80p. 1985. pap. 2.95 (ISBN 0-87788-351-3). Shaw Pubs.
How Should We Then Live? Francis A. Schaeffer. LC 83-70956. 288p. 1983. pap. 9.95 (ISBN 0-89107-292-6, Crossway BKs). Good News.
How the Bible Came to Be. Willem J. Glashouwer. 1980. cancelled (ISBN 0-310-42130-6). Zondervan.
How the Great Religions Began. Joseph Gaer. LC 81-7764. 1981. pap. 6.95 (ISBN 0-396-08013-8). Dodd.
How the Hebrew Language Grew. rev. ed. Edward Horowitz. 1967. pap. 9.95x (ISBN 0-87068-066-8). Ktav.
How the Hibernators Came to Bethlehem. Norma Farber. LC 80-7685. (Illus.). 32p. 1980. PLB 7.85 (ISBN 0-8027-6353-7). Walker & Co.
How the Reformation Happened. Hilaire Belloc. 12.00 (ISBN 0-8446-0483-6). Peter Smith.
How the Spirit Filled My Life. Bertha Smith. LC 73-87068. 7.50 (ISBN 0-8054-5540-X). Broadman.
How the Thousand Buddhas Become Enlightened, 3 vols. Buddhist Sutra. 1987. 35.00 ea. (ISBN 0-89800-136-6). Dharma Pub.
How the Word Became Flesh: Story Dramas for Education & Worship. Michael E. Moynahan. LC 80-54874. 1981. pap. 10.95 (ISBN 0-89390-029-X). Resource Pubns.
How the World Began. Stephanie Caffrey & Timothy Kenslea. (Rainbow Books (Bible Story Books for Children)). 16p. 1978. pap. 1.00 (ISBN 0-8192-1233-4). Morehouse.
How the World Began. Helmut Thielicke. Tr. by J. W. Doberstein from Ger. 308p. 1978. Repr. 13.95 (ISBN 0-227-67484-7). Attic Pr.
How the World Began: Man in the First Chapters of the Bible. Helmut Thielicke. Tr. by John W. Doberstein from Ger. LC 61-6756. 324p. 1961. pap. 6.95 (ISBN 0-8006-1894-7, 1-1894). Fortress.
How They Became Friends. Howard H. Brinton. LC 61-12670. (Orig.). 1961. pap. 2.50x (ISBN 0-87574-114-2, 114). Pendle Hill.
How They Found Christ: In Their Own Words. John Bunyan et al. Ed. by Bill Freeman. LC 83-62268. 66p. (Orig.). 1983. pap. 1.40 (ISBN 0-914271-00-8). NW Christian Pubns.
How Things Began. McNeil. (Books of the World). 1975. 8.95 (ISBN 0-86020-027-2, Usborne-Hayes); PLB 12.96 (ISBN 0-88110-114-1); pap. 5.95 (ISBN 0-86020-199-6). EDC.
How to Activate Miracles in Your Life & Ministry. Burnie Davis. 125p. 1982. pap. 3.95 (ISBN 0-89274-230-5, HH-230). Harrison Hse.
How to Administer & Promote a Church Media Library. Compiled by Jacqulyn Anderson. LC 84-21452. 1985. pap. 5.95 (ISBN 0-8054-3711-8). Broadman.
How to Answer a Jehovah's Witness. Robert A. Morey. LC 79-25502. 112p. (Orig.). 1980. pap. 3.95 (ISBN 0-87123-206-5, 210206). Bethany Hse.
How to Answer a Mormon. Robert A. Morey. 119p. (Orig.). 1983. pap. 3.95 (ISBN 0-87123-260-X, 210260). Bethany Hse.
How to Avoid the Evil Eye: Five Thousand Years of Jewish Superstition. Brenda Rosenbaum. (Illus.). 96p. 1985. pap. 5.95 (ISBN 0-312-39584-1). St Martin.
How to Be a Christian in an Unchristian World. rev. ed. Fritz Ridenour. LC 72-169603. 192p. (Orig.). 1972. pap. 3.50 (ISBN 0-8307-0611-9, S123150). Regal.
How to Be a Christian Without Being Perfect. Fritz Ridenour. LC 86-6479. 250p. (Orig.). 1986. text ed. 12.95 (5111607); pap. text ed. 6.95 (ISBN 0-8307-1106-6, 5418680). Regal.
How to Be a Christian Without Being Religious. Fritz Ridenour. 1971. pap. 5.95 (ISBN 0-8423-1450-4). Tyndale.
How to Be a Christian Without Being Religious. 2nd ed. Fritz Ridenour. LC 72-169603. 176p. 1984. pap. 4.95 (ISBN 0-8307-0982-7, 5418331); Leaders Guide, Doug Van Bronkhorst 3.95 (ISBN 0-8307-0993-2, 6101930). Regal.
How to Be a Christian Without Being Religious. Fritz Ridenour. (Illus.). 166p. 1985. pap. 3.95 (ISBN 0-8307-1026-4, S182104). Regal.
How to Be a Confident Woman: A Bible Study Guide for Women. Susan J. Souter. LC 78-51904. 80p. 1978. pap. 2.95 (ISBN 0-89081-124-5). Harvest Hse.
How to Be a Growing Christian. Bennie E. Goodwin. LC 86-33737. 40p. (Orig.). 1986. pap. 1.95 (ISBN 0-87784-573-5). Inter-Varsity.
How to Be a Hero to Your Teenager. Joe White. 144p. (Orig.). 1985. pap. 4.95 (ISBN 0-8423-1495-4). Tyndale.

How to Be a Liberated Christian. Ruth Truman. LC 80-27302. 160p. 1981. 8.75 (ISBN 0-687-17710-3). Abingdon.
How to Be a Minister & a Human Being. Harold C. Warlick, Jr. 128p. 1982. pap. 7.95 (ISBN 0-8170-0961-2). Judson.
How to Be a Minister's Wife & Love It. Alice Taylor. 1968. pap. 3.95 (ISBN 0-310-33131-5, 10877P). Zondervan.
How to Be a More Effective Church Leader: A Special Edition for Pastors & Other Church Leaders. Norman Shawchuck. (Illus.). 69p. 1981. pap. 9.95 (ISBN 0-938180-07-X). Org Resources Pr.
How to be a More Effective Church Leader: A Special Edition for Pastors & Other Church Leaders. Norman Shawchuck. Orig. Title: Taking a Look at Your Leadership Styles. (Illus.). 69p. 1981. pap. 9.95 (ISBN 0-938180-07-X). Spiritual Growth.
How to Be a Motivated Christian. Stuart Briscoe. 192p. 1987. 9.95 (ISBN 0-89693-179-X). Victor Bks.
How to Be a People Helper. Gary Collins. LC 76-15112. (Orig.). 1976. pap. 5.95 (ISBN 0-88449-055-6, A424076). Vision Hse.
How to Be a Winner. Harold Hill & Irene Harrell. LC 76-31676. 1976. (Pub. by Logos); pap. 2.95 (ISBN 0-88270-456-7). Bridge Pub.
How to Be a Yogi. Swami Abhedananda. 59.95 (ISBN 0-8490-0375-X). Gordon Pr.
How to Be a Yogi. Swami Abhedananda. 5.95 (ISBN 0-87481-609-2). Vedanta Pr.
How to Be a Yogi. 6th ed. Swami Abhedananda. 64p. pap. 7.95 (ISBN 0-88697-040-7). Life Science.
How to Be Alive in the Spirit. Gerald Rowlands. (Aglow Cornerstone Ser.). 38p. 1982. pap. 2.50 (ISBN 0-930756-69-X). Aglow Pubns.
How to be an Effective Church Leader. Sam E. Stone. (Illus.). 96p. 1987. pap. price not set (ISBN 0-87403-268-7, 3182). Standard Pub.
How to Be Born Again. Billy Graham. LC 77-76057. 1977. 3.95 (ISBN 0-8499-4119-9). Word Bks.
How to Be Born Again. T. L. Osborn. 160p. pap. 2.95 (ISBN 0-89274-224-0, HH-224). Harrison Hse.
How to Be Enriched by Giving. Gordon Lindsay. 1.75 (ISBN 0-89985-012-X). Christ Nations.
How to Be Filled with the Holy Spirit. A. W. Tozer. 58p. pap. 1.75 (ISBN 0-87509-187-3). Chr Pubns.
How to Be Filled with the Spirit. Bill Bright. (Transferable Concepts Ser.). 58p. 1981. pap. 1.25 (ISBN 0-918956-90-0). Campus Crusade.
How to Be Happy. 192p. (Orig.). 1985. pap. 5.95 (ISBN 1-85063-025-9, Ark Paperbks). Methuen Inc.
How to Be Happy in an Unhappy World. Charles W. Dunn, Sr. 141p. (Orig.). 1986. pap. 6.95 (ISBN 0-89084-318-X). Bob Jones Univ Pr.
How to Be Happy in Difficult Situations: Studies in Philippians. David L. Hocking. pap. 4.95 (ISBN 0-88469-027-X). BMH Bks.
How to Be Happy No Matter What. Tom Watson, Jr. LC 77-73559. 160p. 1978. pap. 3.50 (ISBN 0-8307-0465-5, S103125). Regal.
How to Be Happy Though Married. Tim LaHaye. 1968. pap. 5.95 (ISBN 0-8423-1501-2). Tyndale.
How to Be Happy Though Married. Tim LaHaye. (Living Book Ser.). 1979. 3.50 (ISBN 0-8423-1499-7). Tyndale.
How to Be Happy Though Young. Darien Cooper. (Illus.). 224p. 1979. 5.95 (ISBN 0-8007-5048-9, Power Bks). Revell.
How to Be Parents of Happy Obedient Children. Roy Lessin. 1978. 8.95 (ISBN 0-89728-003-2, 702120); pap. 4.95 (ISBN 0-686-67298-4). Omega Pubns OR.
How to Be Perfect. Andrew Murray. 144p. 1982. pap. text ed. 3.50 (ISBN 0-88368-113-7). Whitaker Hse.
How to Be Sure of Crowns in Heaven. Salem Kirban. 1980. pap. 5.95 (ISBN 0-912582-34-0). Kirban.
How to Be Sure of Immortality. Fred T. Koepke. 1985. 6.95 (ISBN 0-533-06491-0). Vantage.
How to Be Sure You Are a Christian. Bill Bright. (Transferable Concepts Ser.). 63p. 1981. pap. 1.25 (ISBN 0-918956-88-9). Campus Crusade.
How to Be the Best Sunday School Teacher You Can Be. Terry Hall. (Orig.). 1986. pap. 6.95 (ISBN 0-8024-3631-5). Moody.
How to be the Happy Wife of an Unsaved Husband. Linda Davis. 165p. (Orig.). 1986. pap. text ed. 3.50 (ISBN 0-88368-189-7). Whitaker Hse.
How to Be the Lord's Prayer. Norman Elliott. pap. 2.95 (ISBN 0-910924-26-0). Macalester.
How to Be Your Own Good Samaritan. Howard V. Otterholt. LC 81-3465. 1982. 15.95 (ISBN 0-87949-195-7). Ashley Bks.
How to Become a Christian & Stay One. Patricia Maxwell. LC 79-4603. (Waymark Ser.). 1979. pap. 2.50 (ISBN 0-8127-0221-2). Review & Herald.
How to Become a Great Man of God. James Stone. 1981. pap. 1.95 (ISBN 0-934942-28-5). White Wing Pub.
How to Become a Masonic Lodge Officer. Ed. by H. L. Haywood. 228p. 1983. Repr. of 1958 ed. soft cover 7.50 (ISBN 0-88053-028-6, M-77). Macoy Pub.
How to Become a Skilled Intercessor. Barbara Shull. 32p. 1978. pap. 2.00 (ISBN 0-930756-35-5, 533001). Aglow Pubns.
How to Become a Star. James Stone. (How To Ser.). 72p. (Orig.). pap. 2.50 (ISBN 0-934942-38-2). White Wing Pub.
How to Become One with Your Mate. Lawrence J. Crabb, Jr. 1986. write for info. BMH Bks.
How to Become Super-Spiritual: Or Kill Yourself Trying. John Sterner. LC 82-6636. 160p. (Orig.). 1982. pap. 7.50 (ISBN 0-687-17760-X). Abingdon.
How to Become the Person You Were Meant to Be. Peter Williamson. (Living As Christian Ser.). 112p. (Orig.). 1981. pap. 2.95 (ISBN 0-89283-098-0). Servant.
How to Begin an Evangelistic Bible Study. Ada Lum. pap. 2.50 (ISBN 0-87784-317-1). Inter-Varsity.
How to Begin the Christian Life. George Sweeting. LC 75-31674. 128p. 1976. pap. 3.50 (ISBN 0-8024-3626-9). Moody.
How to Bind & Loose in Spiritual Conflict. Andrea Stoddard. 56p. (Orig.). 1986. 3.95 (ISBN 0-936371-00-5). Spirit Faith.
How to Bring Men to Christ. R. A. Torrey. LC 76-57111. 128p. 1977. pap. 2.95 (ISBN 0-87123-230-8, 200230). Bethany Hse.
How to Bring Men to Christ. R. A. Torrey. 128p. 1981. pap. 2.95 (ISBN 0-88368-098-X). Whitaker Hse.
How to Bring up a Child. Ed. by Vijay. (Illus.). 1985. pap. 3.50 (ISBN 0-89071-334-0, Pub. by Sri Aurobindo Ashram India). Matagiri.
How to Bring Up Children in the Catholic Faith. Carol Powell & David Powell. 240p. 1984. 12.95 (ISBN 0-13-402537-7). P-H.
How to Bring Your Children to Christ. Andrew Murray. 320p. 1984. pap. 3.95 (ISBN 0-88368-135-8). Whitaker Hse.
How to Build a Bus Ministry. Coggin & Spooner. 2.25 (ISBN 0-8054-9405-7). Broadman.
How to Build a Christian Lecture Series. Mike Splaine. (Illus.). 50p. 1982. wkbk. & cassette 5.00x (ISBN 0-913605-05-0). NFCLC.
How to Build a Magnetic Church. Herb Miller. 128p. 1987. pap. 7.95 (ISBN 0-687-17762-6). Abingdon.
How to Build an Evangelistic Church. John R. Bisagno. LC 78-178055. 1972. 8.50 (ISBN 0-8054-2524-1). Broadman.
How to Build Your Own Christian Character. Stanley C. Baldwin. 1982. pap. 4.95 (ISBN 0-88207-271-4). Victor Bks.
How to Celebrate Thanksgiving & Christmas. facs. ed. Ed. by Alice M. Kellogg. LC 76-139765. (Granger Index Reprint Ser). 1897. 15.00 (ISBN 0-8369-6219-2). Ayer Co Pubs.
How to Change Attitudes & Emotions. Mark Thurston. Orig. Title: A Course in Practical Spirituality. 147p. 1986. wkbk., text, 4 cassettes 29.95 (ISBN 0-87604-181-0). ARE Pr.
How to Choose the Wrong Marriage Partner & Live Unhappily Ever After. Robert L. Mason & Carrie Jacobs. LC 78-52452. 1979. pap. 2.99 (ISBN 0-8042-2093-X). John Knox.
How to Communicate in Sobriety. Luther Lord & Eileen Lord. LC 77-94793. (Illus.). 120p. (Orig.). 1978. pap. 5.95 (ISBN 0-89486-046-1). Hazelden.
How to Communicate with Single Adults. Floyd Craig. 1978. pap. 11.95 (ISBN 0-8054-3510-7). Broadman.
How to Conduct a Leadership Seminar. Allen E. Roberts. 11p. 1970. pap. 1.00 (ISBN 0-88053-013-8). Macoy Pub.
How to Conduct a Spiritual Life Retreat. Norman Shawchuck et al. (Orig.). 1986. pap. 5.95 (ISBN 0-8358-0527-1, ICN 608805, Dist. by Abingdon Pr). Upper Room.
How to Conquer Fear. Don Gossett. Orig. Title: How You Can Rise Above Fear. 160p. 1981. pap. 2.95 (ISBN 0-88368-092-0). Whitaker Hse.
How to Conquer Physical Death. Friend Stuart. 1980. vinyl 29.95 (ISBN 0-912132-02-7). Dominion Pr.
How to Converse Continually & Familiarly with God. Alphonse De Liguori. Tr. by Aubin. 2.95 (ISBN 0-8198-0062-7). Dghtrs St Paul.
How to Counsel from Scripture. Martin Bobgan & Deidre Bobgan. 1985. pap. 8.95 (ISBN 0-8024-0373-5). Moody.
How to Cure Yourself of Positive Thinking. Donald Smith. LC 77-70191. 1977. 7.95 (ISBN 0-912458-80-1). E A Seemann.
How to Deal with Depression. Timothy Foster. 132p. 1984. pap. 4.95 (ISBN 0-88207-610-8). Victor Bks.
How to Deal with Difficult People. Andrew Costello. LC 80-81751. 112p. (Orig.). 1980. pap. 3.95 (ISBN 0-89243-128-8). Liguori Pubns.
How to Deal with How You Feel. Ralph Speas. LC 80-65316. 1980. pap. 4.50 (ISBN 0-8054-5278-8). Broadman.
How to Decide What's Really Important. Fritz Ridenour. LC 78-68146. 160p. 1978. 3.50 (ISBN 0-8307-0266-0, S122154). Regal.
How to Develop a Better Self-Image. Russell M. Abata. LC 79-91440. (Orig.). 1980. pap. 2.95 (ISBN 0-89243-119-9, 41150). Liguori Pubns.
How to Develop a Team Ministry & Make It Work. Ervin F. Henkelmann & Stephen J. Carter. 1985. pap. 8.95 (ISBN 0-570-03946-0, 12-2879). Concordia.
How to Develop a Tithing Church. Charlie W. Shedd. (Orig.). 1961. pap. 5.95 (ISBN 0-687-17798-7). Abingdon.
How to Develop the Power of Transcendental Experience. Burton R. Metheny. (Illus.). 139p. 1980. 59.45 (ISBN 0-89920-014-1). Am Inst Psych.
How to Develop Your Child's Character. Nancy Van Pelt. (Better Living Ser.). 1979. pap. 0.99 (ISBN 0-8127-0232-8). Review & Herald.
How to Develop Your ESP Power. new ed. Jane Roberts. LC 66-17331. 264p. 1980. pap. 7.95 (ISBN 0-8119-0379-6). Fell.
How to Disciple Your Children. Walter A. Henrichsen. 120p. 1981. pap. 4.95 (ISBN 0-88207-260-9). Victor Bks.
How to Discipline & Build Self-Esteem in Your Child. Betty N. Chase. 46p. 1983. pap. text ed. 19.95 (ISBN 0-89191-796-9). Cook.
How to Discover God. L. L. Grubb. 1979. pap. write for info. (ISBN 0-88469-002-4). BMH Bks.
How to Distinguish the Saints in Art by Their Costumes, Symbols & Attributes. Arthur De Bles. LC 68-18018. 1975. Repr. of 1925 ed. 70.00x (ISBN 0-8103-4125-5). Gale.
How to Do All Things: Your Use of Divine Power. Mark-Age. LC 72-121118. 144p. 1970. pap. 5.00 (ISBN 0-912322-01-2). Mark-Age.
How to Effectively Study the Bible. J. J. Turner. pap. 2.50 (ISBN 0-686-73328-2). Lambert Bk.
How to Encourage Others. Bill G. Bruster & Robert D. Dale. LC 82-70868. (Orig.). 1983. pap. 6.95 (ISBN 0-8054-2247-1). Broadman.
How to Enjoy Bible Study with Others. Rice A. Pierce. LC 72-5250. 1972. 3.95 (ISBN 0-8407-5043-9). Religious Activ.
How to Enjoy Living. James A. Nelson. LC 82-70774. 160p. (Orig.). 1982. pap. 4.95 (ISBN 0-89636-087-3). Accent Bks.
How to Enjoy Plenty. T. L. Osborn. pap. 2.95 (ISBN 0-89274-222-4, HH-222). Harrison Hse.
How to Enjoy the Bible. E. W. Bullinger. LC 83-71411. 436p. 1983. 9.95 (ISBN 0-910068-48-8). Am Christian.
How to Enter the River. Jeanie Thompson. LC 84-62337. 61p. (Orig.). 1985. pap. 6.00 (ISBN 0-930100-18-2). Holy Cow.
How to Experience God's Love & Forgiveness. Bill Bright. (Transferable Concepts Ser.). 63p. 1981. pap. 1.25 (ISBN 0-918956-89-7). Campus Crusade.
How to Experience Revival. Charles G. Finney. 143p. 1984. pap. text ed. 3.50 (ISBN 0-88368-140-4). Whitaker Hse.
How to Experience Revival. Charles G. Finney. 1986. write for info. (ISBN 0-8297-0798-0). Life Pubs Intl.
How to Face Death Without Fear. St. Alphonsus Liguori. 1976. pap. 1.95 (ISBN 0-89243-029-X, 28376). Liguori Pubns.
How to Fast Successfully. Derek Prince. 1976. pap. 2.50 (ISBN 0-934920-19-2, B-28). Derek Prince.
How to Feel Great about Being a Mother. Amy Hardison. LC 86-29349. 1987. 8.95 (ISBN 0-87579-073-9). Deseret Bk.
How to Fill the Emptiness. Woodie Stevens. (Christian Living Ser.). 32p. (Orig.). 1987. pap. write for info. (ISBN 0-8341-1188-8). Beacon Hill.
How to Find & Develop Effective Illustrations. Louis P. Lehman. LC 75-12109. 102p. 1985. pap. 4.95 (ISBN 0-8254-3133-6). Kregel.
How to Find Freedom from the Power of Sin. T. A. Hegre. 96p. 1969. pap. 3.50 (ISBN 0-87123-217-0, 200217). Bethany Hse.
How to Find Fullness of Power. R. A. Torrey. Orig. Title: How to Obtain Fullness of Power. 112p. 1971. pap. 2.95 (ISBN 0-87123-219-7, 200219). Bethany Hse.
How to Find God. David Watson. LC 76-43125. 157p. 1976. pap. 1.95 (ISBN 0-87788-390-4). Shaw Pubs.
How to Find Something Big to Live for: A Spiritual Odyssey. George Bockl. 193p. (Orig.). 1984. pap. 7.95 (ISBN 0-942494-83-0). Coleman Pub.
How to Find the Perfect Will of God. Gordon Lindsay. 1.25 (ISBN 0-89985-003-0). Christ Nations.
How to Find Your Purpose in Life. Bill Greenman. 200p. (Orig.). 1987. pap. text ed. 3.95 (ISBN 0-88368-192-7). Whitaker Hse.
How to Flip Your Flab-Forever. Harold Hill. LC 79-64912. 1979. pap. 2.95 (ISBN 0-88270-377-3). Bridge Pub.
How to Follow the Shepherd When You're Being Pushed Around by the Sheep. Jill Briscoe. 192p. 1984. pap. 5.95 (ISBN 0-8007-5166-3, Power Bks). Revell.
How to Forgive Yourself & Others. Eamon Tobin. 32p. 1983. pap. 1.50 (ISBN 0-89243-197-0). Liguori Pubns.
How to Form a Christian Growth Support Group. Philip St. Romain. 48p. (Orig.). 1985. pap. 2.95 (ISBN 0-89243-242-X). Liguori Pubns.
How to Gain a Testimony of the Gospel of Jesus Christ. John J. Stewart. LC 78-52122. 74p. 1978. 5.50 (ISBN 0-88290-097-8). Horizon Utah.
How to Gain Life: Changing Insights from the Book of Books. Cyril J. Barber. 1979. pap. 1.00 (ISBN 0-88469-100-4). BMH Bks.
How to Gain the Psychological Power of Transcendental Thinking. Gaston Villamette. (Illus.). 118p. 1987. 117.55 (ISBN 0-89920-147-4). Am Classical Coll Pr.
How to Get along with Difficult People. Florence Littauer. LC 83-83371. 1984. pap. 4.95 (ISBN 0-89081-429-5). Harvest Hse.
How to Get Along with Others. Ellen G. White. (Uplook Ser.). 1964. pap. 0.99 (ISBN 0-8163-0072-0, 08835-1). Pacific Pr Pub Assn.
How to Get Married: And Stay That Way. Cliff Allbritton. LC 82-71219. (Orig.). 1983. pap. 5.95 (ISBN 0-8054-5653-8). Broadman.
How to Get More from Your Bible. Lloyd M. Perry & Robert D. Culver. (Direction Bks). 1979. pap. 3.95 (ISBN 0-8010-7048-1). Baker Bk.
How to Get More Out of the Mass. Joseph T. McGloin. LC 74-80938. 1974. pap. 3.50 (ISBN 0-89243-011-7, 41230). Liguori Pubns.
How to Get Rid of Your Wife: And No Court Will Ever Convict You. Stuart J. Faber. 200p. 1974. 7.95 (ISBN 0-685-50674-6). Good Life.
How to Get Started in Christian Music. Chris Christian. Ed. by John Styll. 167p. 1986. 12.95 (ISBN 0-9616817-0-5). Home Sweet Home.
How to Get the Most Out of Bible Study. Leo Van Dolson. (Harvest Ser.). 122p. 1980. pap. 5.95 (ISBN 0-8163-0360-6). Pacific Pr Pub Assn.
How to Get What You Pray For. Bill Austin. LC 83-50970. 160p. 1984. pap. 4.95 (ISBN 0-8423-1473-3); leader's guide 2.95 (ISBN 0-8423-1474-1). Tyndale.
How to Give a Healing Treatment. Herbert L. Beierle. 1979. 1.00 (ISBN 0-940480-07-7). U of Healing.
How to Give Away Your Faith. Paul E. Little. LC 66-20710. 1966. pap. 5.95 (ISBN 0-87784-553-0). Inter-Varsity.
How to Give Away Your Money. Simon Webley. 1979. pap. 1.95 (ISBN 0-87784-601-4). Inter-Varsity.
How to Go to Heaven. J. Glenn Harvey. 104p. (Orig.). 1982. pap. 2.95 (ISBN 0-915059-00-2). Ind Christ Pubns.
How to Grow. expanded ed. Kenneth N. Taylor. 192p. Date not set. pap. 7.95. Oliver-Nelson.
How to Grow a Church. Donald A. McGavran & Winfield C. Arn. LC 73-80207. 192p. (Orig.). 1973. pap. 6.95 (ISBN 0-8307-0238-5, 5406706). Regal.
How to Grow a Women's Minis-Tree. Daisy Hepburn & Joan B. Klope. LC 86-11812. (Illus.). 140p. (Orig.). 1986. pap. 5.95 (ISBN 0-8307-1159-7, 5418863). Regal.
How to Grow a Women's Minis-Tree. Daisy Hepburn & Joan B. Klope. (Illus., Orig.). 1986. resource manual 7.95 (ISBN 0-8307-1055-8, 5203018). Regal.
How to Grow an Adult Class. Tom Barnard. 88p. (Orig.). 1983. pap. 2.95 (ISBN 0-8341-0840-2). Beacon Hill.
How to Grow: Expanded Edition. Kenneth N. Taylor. 192p. Date not set. pap. 7.95 (ISBN 0-317-47452-9). Oliver-Nelson.
How to Grow: First Steps for New Christians. Kenneth N. Taylor. 176p. 1985. 7.95 (ISBN 0-8407-9038-4). Oliver-Nelson.
How to Grow in Christ. Jack Kinneer. 1981. pap. 2.95 (ISBN 0-87552-284-X). Presby & Reformed.
How to Grow in Grace. Garnett Reid. 1982. pap. 1.50 (ISBN 0-89265-077-X). Randall Hse.
How to Grow New Christians. John C. Souter. 1979. pap. 3.95 (ISBN 0-8423-1486-5). Tyndale.
How To Grow Up Spiritually. Steve Shamblin. (Orig.). 1986. pap. 5.95 (ISBN 0-910311-44-7). Huntington Hse Inc.
How to Handle Guilt. Marvin Moore. (Better Living Ser.). 1977. pap. 0.99 (ISBN 0-8127-0158-5). Review & Herald.

How to Have a Better Relationship with Anybody: A Biblical Approach. James Hilt. 1984. pap. 5.95 (ISBN 0-8024-1661-6). Moody.

How to Have a Creative Crisis. Norman Wright. 176p. 1986. 10.95 (ISBN 0-8499-0540-0). Word Bks.

How to Have a Daily Quiet Time. Larry Christenson. 16p. 1979. saddle stitch 0.99 (ISBN 0-87123-235-9, 200235). Bethany Hse.

How to Have a Good Marriage. Mark W. Lee. LC 78-56794. 1981. pap. 5.95 (ISBN 0-915684-89-6). Chr Pubns.

How to Have a Happier Wife. Cecil Osborne. LC 85-14255. 64p. (Orig.). 1986. pap. 2.95 (ISBN 0-310-30622-1, 10478P). Zondervan.

How to Have a Happier Year: Take a Number (Nonsense Numerology) Ransom Roberts. LC 81-90709. (Illus.). 128p. (Orig.). 1982. pap. 5.95 (ISBN 0-9607834-0-7). Uptown Bks.

How to Have a Happy Marriage. David Mace & Vera Mace. 1983. pap. 3.95 (ISBN 0-687-17831-2, Festival). Abingdon.

How to Have a Happy Marriage. Dick Mills. 91p. (Orig.). 1985. pap. 2.95 (ISBN 0-89274-381-6). Harrison Hse.

How to Have a Powerful Prayer Life. James Stone. (How To Ser.). 73p. (Orig.). 1985. pap. 2.50 (ISBN 0-934942-50-1, 2467). White Wing Pub.

How to Have a Soul Winning Church. Gene Edwards. 1963. pap. 3.95 (ISBN 0-88243-524-8, 02-0524). Gospel Pub.

How to Have Faith in Your Faith. Charles Capps. 1986. pap. 3.95 (ISBN 0-89274-415-4). Harrison Hse.

How to Have Good Health. Ted E. Chandler. LC 81-68045. 1982. 7.95 (ISBN 0-8054-5298-2). Broadman.

How to Have Powerful Daily Devotions. James Stone. (How To Ser.). 81p. (Orig.). 1983. pap. 2.50 (ISBN 0-934942-33-1). White Wing Pub.

How to Hear God. T. Howell Upchurch. (Illus.). 24p. 1985. pap. text ed. 1.00 (ISBN 0-937778-09-5). Fulness Hse.

How to Hear God Speak. Charles W. Bush. 128p. (Orig.). 1975. pap. text ed. 1.50 (ISBN 0-89228-028-X). Impact Bks MO.

How to Help a Friend. Paul Welter. 1983. pap. 8.95 (ISBN 0-8423-1505-5); 2.95 (ISBN 0-8423-1504-7). Tyndale.

How to Help a Missionary. Betsy R. Elliot. 32p. (Orig.). 1984. pap. 0.75 (ISBN 0-87784-069-5). Inter-Varsity.

How to Help Fulfill the Great Commission. Bill Bright. (Transferable Concepts Ser.). 64p. 1981. pap. 1.25 (ISBN 0-918956-94-3). Campus Crusade.

How to Help People Change. Jay E. Adams. (Jay Adams Library). 208p. 1986. pap. 7.95 (ISBN 0-310-51181-X). Zondervan.

How to Help the Hurting. Everett L. Worthington, Jr. LC 85-23070. (Illus.). 192p. 1986. pap. 5.95 (ISBN 0-87784-388-0). Inter-Varsity.

How to Improve Your Preaching. 2nd ed. Bob Jones. 151p. 1964. pap. 3.95 (ISBN 0-89084-141-1). Bob Jones Univ Pr.

How to Increase Parish Income. Henry F. DeMena. 144p. 1982. pap. 12.95 (ISBN 0-89622-160-1). Twenty-Third.

How to Increase Your Faith. Steve Ost. (Cornerstone Ser.). 32p. 1981. pap. 2.00 (ISBN 0-930756-61-4, 533003). Aglow Pubns.

How to Increase Your Sunday School Attendance. Charles L. Allen & Mildred Parker. 128p. 1980. 8.95 (ISBN 0-8007-1088-6). Revell.

How to Interpret Dreams, Omens & Fortune Telling Signs. Fred Gettings. pap. 5.00 (ISBN 0-87980-399-1). Wilshire.

How to Interpret the Bible. James M. Efird. LC 83-49051. 144p. 1984. pap. 7.95 (ISBN 0-8042-0069-6). John Knox.

How to Interpret the Bible for Yourself. Richard Mayhue. (Moody Press Electives Ser.). (Orig.). 1986. pap. text ed. 3.95 (ISBN 0-8024-0732-3); leader's guide 4.95 (ISBN 0-8024-0733-1). Moody.

How to Interpret the Bible for Yourself. Richard L. Mayhue. 1986. pap. 3.95 (ISBN 0-88469-178-0). BMH Bks.

How to Introduce Others to Christ. Bill Bright. (Transferable Concepts Ser.). 64p. 1981. pap. 1.25 (ISBN 0-918956-93-5). Campus Crusade.

How to Keep a Spiritual Journal. Ronald Klug. LC 82-14383. 144p. 1982. pap. 4.95 (ISBN 0-8407-5815-4). Nelson.

How to Keep Going When the Storms Keep Coming. Ross Campbell & Randall Gray. 288p. (Orig.). 1986. pap. 6.95 (ISBN 0-8423-1376-1). Tyndale.

How to Keep Useful Church Records. Orlando L. Tibbetts. 96p. 1983. pap. 3.95 (ISBN 0-317-00687-8). Judson.

How to Keep Your Healing. Kenneth E. Hagin. 1980. pap. 0.50 mini bk (ISBN 0-89276-059-1). Hagin Ministries.

How to Keep Your Joy. Paul Walker. 192p. 1987. 12.95 (ISBN 0-8407-9076-7). Oliver-Nelson.

How to Know God: The Yoga Aphorisms of Patanjali. Swami Prabhavananda & Christopher Isherwood. 1969. pap. 2.95 (ISBN 0-451-62330-4, ME2330, Ment). NAL.

How to Know God: The Yoga Aphorisms of Patanjali. Tr. by Swami Prabhavananda & Christopher Isherwood. 224p. 1983. pap. 6.95 (ISBN 0-87481-041-8). Vedanta Pr.

How to Know God's Will. Garnett Reid. 1982. pap. 1.50 (ISBN 0-89265-078-8). Randall Hse.

How to Know the Fullness of the Spirit. Gerald Rowlands. (Cornerstone Ser.). (Illus.). 32p. 1982. pap. 2.00 (ISBN 0-930756-68-1, 533005). Aglow Pubns.

How to Know the Will of God. Knofel Staton. LC 78-62707. 96p. (Orig.). 1979. pap. 2.95 (ISBN 0-87239-985-0, 39948). Standard Pub.

How To Know You'll Live Forever. Dick Dugan. LC 84-70727. 176p. 1984. pap. 3.95 (ISBN 0-87123-312-6, 200312). Bethany Hse.

How to Know You're Saved. Garnett Reid. 1982. pap. 1.50 (ISBN 0-89265-075-3). Randall Hse.

How to Lead a Child to Christ. Daniel H. Smith. (Orig.). 1987. pap. 2.95 (ISBN 0-8024-4622-1). Moody.

How to Lead a Small Group Bible Study. Gene Van Note. 48p. pap. 1.75 (ISBN 0-8341-0653-1). Beacon Hill.

How to Lead Small Group Bible Studies. Ed. by Navigators Staff. 72p. 1982. pap. 3.95 (ISBN 0-89109-124-6). NavPress.

How to Learn from a Course in Miracles. rev. ed. Tara Singh. LC 85-24790. (Orig.). 1985. 8.95 (ISBN 1-55531-000-1); pap. 4.50 (ISBN 1-55531-001-X). Life Action Pr.

How to Let God Help You. Myrtle Fillmore. 1956. 5.95 (ISBN 0-87159-057-3). Unity School.

How to Listen to God. Charles Stanley. 160p. 1985. 10.95 (ISBN 0-8407-9041-4). Oliver-Nelson.

How to Listen When God Speaks. Chuck Christensen & Winnie Christensen. LC 78-73294. 79p. 1979. pap. 2.95 (ISBN 0-87788-355-6). Shaw Pubs.

How to Live a Holy Life. C. E. Orr. 112p. pap. 0.75 (ISBN 0-686-29120-4). Faith Pub Hse.

How to Live (Almost) Happily with a Teenager. Lois L. Davitz & Joel R. Davitz. 230p. (Orig.). 1982. pap. 8.95 (ISBN 0-86683-624-1, AY8208, HarpR). Har-Row.

How to Live & Not Die. Norvel Hayes. (Orig.). 1986. pap. 5.95 (ISBN 0-89274-395-6). Harrison Hse.

How to Live Forever. John Phillips. (Teach Yourself the Bible Ser.). 1964. pap. 2.75 (ISBN 0-8024-3700-1). Moody.

How to Live Forever in the New Jerusalem. Lee H. Shaw, Jr. 56p. (Orig.). (YA) 1985. pap. 3.00x (ISBN 0-9614311-0-5). Elijah-John.

How to Live in High Victory. Harold Hill & Irene Harrell. LC 77-80293. 1977. pap. 2.95 (ISBN 0-88270-421-4). Bridge Pub.

How to Live in the Circle of Prayer & Make Your Dreams Come True. Stella T. Mann. (Illus.). 180p. 1975. pap. 4.95 (ISBN 0-87516-206-1). De Vorss.

How to Live Life to the Fullest: A Handbook for Seasoned Citizens. Mary L. Coakley. LC 83-63167. 168p. 1984. pap. 4.95 (ISBN 0-87973-628-3, 628). Our Sunday Visitor.

How to Live Life Victoriously. Winifred W. Hausmann. 160p. 1982. 5.95 (ISBN 0-87159-060-3). Unity School.

How to Live Like a King's Kid. Harold Hill. LC 73-93002. 1974. pap. 2.95 pocket size (ISBN 0-88270-375-7). Bridge Pub.

How to Live the Bible Like a King's Kid. Harold Hill & Irene B. Harrell. (Illus.). 128p. 1980. pap. 5.95 (ISBN 0-8007-5051-9, Power Bks). Revell.

How to Live the Christian Life. James M. Boice. LC 81-18839. 128p. 1982. pap. 5.95 (ISBN 0-8024-3666-8). Moody.

How to Live the Christian Life. Selwyn Hughes. 160p. (Orig.). 1982. pap. 6.95 (ISBN 0-8164-2395-4, HarpR). Har-Row.

How to Live the Victorious Life. Unknown Christian. Ed. by Julie Link. 112p. 1986. pap. 2.95 (ISBN 0-310-33481-0, 6660P, Clarion Classics). Zondervan.

How to Live Though an Executive: Communications Manual. L. Ron Hubbard. 132p. 1953. 32.16 (ISBN 0-88404-010-0). Bridge Pubns Inc.

How to Live Through an Executive. L. Ron Hubbard. 20.00 (ISBN 0-686-30786-0). Church Scient NY.

How to Live with Jesus - Leader's Guide. Michele Lamdon. 64p. 1981. pap. 4.95 (ISBN 0-89243-148-2). Liguori Pubns.

How to Live Your Faith. L. Perry Wilbur. 128p. 1984. 12.95 (ISBN 0-13-416850-X); pap. 5.95 (ISBN 0-13-416843-7). P-H.

How to Love. Arthur A. Rouner, Jr. (Contemporary Discussion Ser.). 1974. pap. 1.25 (ISBN 0-8010-7622-6). Baker Bk.

How to Love by Faith. Bill Bright. (Transferable Concepts Ser.). 64p. 1981. pap. 1.25 (ISBN 0-918956-95-1). Campus Crusade.

How to Love Your Neighbor. J. Sig Paulson. 184p. 1974. pap. 4.95 (ISBN 0-317-20873-X). CSA Pr.

How to Make an L.D.S. Quiet Book. Ann F. Pritt. 38p. 1976. pap. 3.95 (ISBN 0-87747-116-9). Deseret Bk.

How to Make & Use Overhead Transparancies. Anna S. Darkes. LC 77-7888. (Illus.). 1977. pap. 4.50 (ISBN 0-8024-3652-8). Moody.

How to Make Audiovisuals. rev. ed. John Hack. LC 78-72847. 1980. pap. 5.95 (ISBN 0-8054-3427-5). Broadman.

How to Make Children's Church Come Alive. Jeanne Varner. 1979. 4.95 (ISBN 0-87148-407-2). Pathway Pr.

How to Make It Through the Day. John Carmody. LC 84-51826. 112p. (Orig.). 1985. pap. 5.95 (ISBN 0-8358-0491-7). Upper Room.

How to Make People Like You When You Know They Don't. Bob Donahue & Marilyn Donahue. 1982. pap. 4.95 (ISBN 0-8423-1531-4). Tyndale.

How to Make Sunday School Fun for Everyone. Evelyn Witter. Ed. by Dolores Ronaldson. LC 82-62793. (Illus.). 80p. 1983. pap. text ed. 6.95 (ISBN 0-916260-22-4). Meriwether Pub.

How to Make the Dream God Gave You Come True. Kenneth Hagin, Jr. 1981. pap. 1.00 (ISBN 0-89276-708-1). Hagin Ministries.

How to Make the Right Decisions. John D. Arnold & Bert Tompkins. 1986. pap. 5.95 (ISBN 0-8010-0209-5). Baker Bk.

How to Make Your Church Hum. Paul W. Powell. LC 76-47791. 1977. pap. 3.95 (ISBN 0-8054-2528-4). Broadman.

How to Make Your Dreams Come True. Loyd Littlepage. (Illus.). 32p. 1981. pap. 4.50 (ISBN 0-911336-85-0). Sci of Mind.

How to Make Your Life Work. Ken Keyes, Jr. & Bruce Burkan. 1976. pap. 3.95 (ISBN 0-346-12226-0). Cornerstone.

How to Make Your Mark. Campus Crusade for Christ Staff. 540p. (Orig.). 1983. pap. 8.95 (ISBN 0-86605-142-2). Campus Crusade.

How to Manage Conflict in the Church: Conflict Interventions & Resources, Vol. II. Norman Shawchuck. (Illus.). 51p. (Orig.). 1983. pap. 9.95 (ISBN 0-938180-11-8). Org Resources Pr.

How to Manage Conflict in the Church: Understanding & Managing Conflict, Vol. I. Norman Shawchuck. (Illus.). 51p. (Orig.). 1983. pap. 9.95 (ISBN 0-938180-10-X). Org Resources Pr.

How to Manage Pressure: Before Pressure Manages You. Tim LaHaye. 240p. 1983. pap. 6.95 (ISBN 0-310-27081-2, 18336P). Zondervan.

How to Manage Your Church. Edgar Walz. 192p. 1986. pap. 8.95 (ISBN 0-570-04434-0). Concordia.

How to Manage Your Money. Larry Burkett. LC 82-7904. (Christian Financial Concepts Ser.). 1982. pap. 7.95 (ISBN 0-8024-2547-X). Moody.

How To Manual for Volunteer Youth Leaders. Joseph C. Donaldson et al. LC 86-80688. (Equipping Ser.). (Illus.). 136p. (Orig.). 1986. pap. 6.96 (ISBN 0-935797-22-X). Harvest IL.

How to Master the Miracle of Introspection for the Better Knowledge of Yourself, the Broader Dimensions of Your Intellectual Life & the Gaining of Maximal Success in Your Field of Endeavour. Irving J. Halbritter. (Illus.). 136p. 1982. 69.75 (ISBN 0-89920-044-3). Am Inst Psych.

How to Meditate: A Guide to Self-Discovery. Lawrence LeShan. 176p. 1986. pap. 3.95 (ISBN 0-553-24453-1). Bantam.

How to Meditate: A Practical Guide. Kathleen McDonald. Ed. by Robina Courtin. (Wisdom Basic Book, Orange Ser.). 200p. (Orig.). 1984. pap. 9.95 (ISBN 0-86171-009-6, Wisdom Pubns). Great Traditions.

How to Meditate God's Word. Dennis Burke. 64p. 1982. pap. 2.25 (ISBN 0-89274-241-0, HH-241). Harrison Hse.

How to Minister God's Healing Power. Gerald Rowlands. (Cornerstone Ser.). 32p. pap. 2.00 (ISBN 0-930756-73-8, 533007). Aglow Pubns.

How to Minister in Nursing Homes. Joanna M. Freeman. 40p. 1983. pap. text ed. 3.95 (ISBN 0-87148-410-2). Pathway Pr.

How to Minister to Families in Your Church. Joseph Hinkle & Melva Cook. LC 77-82925. 1978. 8.50 (ISBN 0-8054-3224-8). Broadman.

How to Minister to Senior Adults in Your Church. Horace L. Kerr. LC 77-80944. 1980. 8.50 (ISBN 0-8054-3222-1). Broadman.

How to Mobilize Church Volunteers. Marlene Wilson. LC 83-70506. 160p. (Orig.). 1983. pap. 8.95 (ISBN 0-8066-2012-9, 10-3175). Augsburg.

How to Motivate Your Child Toward Success. William S. McBirnie. 1979. pap. 3.95 (ISBN 0-8423-1528-4). Tyndale.

How to Obtain Fullness of Power. R. A. Torrey. 96p. 1982. pap. text ed. 2.95 (ISBN 0-88368-116-1). Whitaker Hse.

How to Obtain Strong Faith: Six Principles. Frederick K. Price. 184p. pap. 4.95 (ISBN 0-89274-042-6). Harrison Hse.

How to Operate a Cassette Tape Ministry. John Hack. LC 81-66822. 1981. pap. 4.25 (ISBN 0-8054-3429-1). Broadman.

How to Organize Your Church Library & Resource Center. Mary L. Hammack. 128p. 1985. pap. 5.95 (ISBN 0-8170-1066-1). Judson.

How to Overcome Evil. Jay E. Adams. (Direction Bks). 1978. pap. 1.95 (ISBN 0-8010-0126-9). Baker Bk.

How to Overcome Evil. Jay E. Adams. 116p. 1978. pap. 2.50 (ISBN 0-87552-022-7). Presby & Reformed.

How to Plan a Bible Treasure Hunt. Janice Stiefel. (Illus.). 50p. (Orig.). 1981. pap. 3.50 (ISBN 0-9605858-0-X). Second Hand.

How to Plan Children's Liturgies. Mary K. Machado. LC 86-60892. (Orig.). 1985. pap. 9.95 (ISBN 0-89390-074-5). Resource Pubns.

How to Play Twelve Christmas Carols on the Piano - This Christmas - with the Visualized Chord System. Duane Shinn. 1976. pap. 6.95 (ISBN 0-912732-19-9). Duane Shinn.

How to Pray. Bill Bright. (Transferable Concepts Ser.). 63p. 1981. pap. 1.25 (ISBN 0-918956-96-X). Campus Crusade.

How to Pray. Keith L. Brooks. (Teach Yourself the Bible Ser.). 1961. pap. 2.75 (ISBN 0-8024-3708-7). Moody.

How to Pray. Mary Francis. 84p. 1985. 1.50 (ISBN 0-8199-0931-9). Franciscan Herald.

How to Pray. Jean-Nicholas Grou. Tr. by Joseph Dalby. 154p. 1982. pap. 6.95 (ISBN 0-227-67485-5). Attic Pr.

How to Pray. rev. ed. W. Graham Scroggie. LC 80-8076. (W. Graham Scroggie Library). 112p. 1981. pap. 4.50 (ISBN 0-8254-3736-9). Kregel.

How to Pray. R. A. Torrey. 112p. 1983. pap. text ed. 3.50 (ISBN 0-88368-133-1). Whitaker Hse.

How to Pray. R. A. Torrey. Tr. by Fu H. Chen. (Chinese.). 1986. pap. write for info. (ISBN 0-941598-31-4). Living Spring Pubns.

How to Pray. Reuben A. Torrey. (Moody Classics Ser.). 1984. pap. 3.50 (ISBN 0-8024-3709-5). Moody.

How to Pray According to God's Word. Peg Neel. 72p. 1982. pap. 2.25 (ISBN 0-88144-004-3, CPS-004). Christian Pub.

How to Pray Always: Without Always Praying. Silvio Fittipaldi. LC 85-80599. (Orig.). 1985. pap. 2.95 (ISBN 0-89243-237-3). Liguori Pubns.

How to Pray: Discovering Spiritual Growth Through Prayer. Barbara Gawle. (Illus.). 204p. 1984. pap. 6.95 (ISBN 0-13-430463-2). P-H.

How to Pray Effectively. Wayne Mack. (Christian Growth Ser.). 1977. pap. 2.95 (ISBN 0-87552-331-5). Presby & Reformed.

How to Pray for Healing. Lewis Maclachlan. 112p. 1977. pap. 2.95 (ISBN 0-227-67486-3). Attic Pr.

How to Pray for Inner Healing for Yourself & Others. Rita Bennett. 126p. (Orig.). 1983. pap. 5.95 (ISBN 0-8007-5126-4, Power Bks). Revell.

How to Pray for Spiritual Growth: A Practical Handbook of Inner Healing. Theodore Dobson. LC 81-83182. 176p. (Orig.). 1982. pap. 7.95 (ISBN 0-8091-2419-X). Paulist Pr.

How to Pray for the Release of the Holy Spirit. Dennis Bennett. 1985. pap. 3.95 (ISBN 0-88270-593-8). Bridge Pub.

How to Pray for Your Children. Quin Sherrer. (Book Ser.). 112p. 1986. pap. 5.95 (ISBN 0-932305-33-4, 531022). Aglow Pubns.

How to Pray Together. John Paterson. pap. 0.75 (ISBN 0-87784-119-5). Inter-Varsity.

How to Pray with a Deck of Cards. Joseph Murphy. pap. 0.75 (ISBN 0-87516-335-1). De Vorss.

How to Preach. William Booth. 84p. (Orig.). 1979. pap. 3.95 (ISBN 0-89216-026-8). Salv Army Suppl South.

How to Preach More Powerful Sermons. Homer K. Buerlein. LC 85-26378. 140p. (Orig.). 1986. pap. 10.95 (ISBN 0-664-24683-4). Westminster.

How to Prepare Bible Messages. rev. ed. James Braga. LC 81-14132. 1982. pap. 6.95 (ISBN 0-930014-71-5). Multnomah.

How to Prepare Sermons. Jack Dunigan. 1986. pap. 3.95 (ISBN 0-932943-02-0). Life Lines.

How to Prepare Sermons. William Evans. 1964. 9.95 (ISBN 0-8024-3725-7). Moody.

How to Produce a Church Newspaper... & Other Ways Churches Communicate. Francis A. Bowen. (Illus.). 1974. 5.00 (ISBN 0-9602830-1-3). F A Bowen.

How to Profit from Bible Reading. Irving L. Jensen. (Orig.). 1985. pap. 5.95 (ISBN 0-8024-0460-X). Moody.

How to Protect Your Faith. Norvel Hayes. 70p. (Orig.). 1983. pap. 3.95 (ISBN 0-89274-279-8). Harrison Hse.

How to Protect Your Family from Terrorists. Kevin O'Neil. 106p. 1979. pap. 15.00 (ISBN 0-86627-007-8). Crises Res Pr.

How to Protect Yourself Against Black Magic & Witchcraft. Leslie Shepard. 1978. 7.95 (ISBN 0-8065-0646-6). Citadel Pr.

How to Publish a Church Newsletter. Walter W. Knight. LC 83-70372. (Orig.). 1983. pap. 6.95 (ISBN 0-8054-3108-X). Broadman.

How to Raise a Child of God. 2nd ed. Tara Singh. LC 86-82911. (Orig.). 1987. 19.95 (ISBN 1-55531-008-7); pap. 14.95 (ISBN 1-55531-009-5). Life Action Pr.

How to Raise a Child You Can Live With: And What to Do If You Haven't. Clifford Stunden. 160p. 1987. 10.95 (ISBN 0-8499-0552-4). Word Bks.

How to Raise a Young Reader. Elaine McEwan. 1987. pap. 5.95. Cook.

How to Raise Good Kids. Barbara Cook. LC 78-7844. 192p. 1978. pap. 4.95 (ISBN 0-87123-233-2, 210233). Bethany Hse.

How to Raise Money at Church Without Sales or Bingo. Daniel P. Moriarty. 1977. pap. 4.00 (ISBN 0-933968-00-0). D Moriarty.

How to Raise Self Esteem. Dair Rochau. (Life Ser.). 1983. pap. 5.95 (ISBN 0-8163-0504-8). Pacific Pr Pub Assn.

How to Raise the Level of Giving in Your Church. John McGinty. LC 78-12994. (P.A.C.E. Ser.). 1979. pap. 4.95 (ISBN 0-8272-1418-9). CBP.

How to Raise Your Children for Christ. Andrew Murray. LC 75-29344. 288p. 1975. pap. 4.95 (ISBN 0-87123-224-3, 210224). Bethany Hse.

How to Reach Out to Inactive Catholics: A Practical Parish Program. William McKee. 40p. 1982. pap. 6.95 (ISBN 0-89243-155-5). Liguori Pubns.

How to Reach the Ones You Love: Help for the Family. Nyla Witmore. LC 81-81849. 180p. (Orig.). 1981. pap. 5.95 (ISBN 0-89840-016-3). Campus Crusade.

How to Read a Spiritual Book. Kathryn Cousins et al. 1.25 (ISBN 0-8091-2415-7). Paulist Pr.

How to Read & Pray the Gospels. Marilyn Norquist. (Handbook of the Bible Ser.). 1979. pap. 1.95 (ISBN 0-89243-099-0). Liguori Pubns.

How to Read & Pray the Prophets. Marilyn Norquist. (Handbook of the Bible Ser.). (Orig.). 1980. pap. 1.50 (ISBN 0-89243-122-9, 44900). Liguori Pubns.

How to Read Creation & Evolution. C. Montenat & L. Plateaux. 144p. 1985. pap. 10.95 (ISBN 0-8245-0721-5). Crossroad NY.

How to Read Prophecy. Joel B. Green. LC 84-12838. 150p. (Orig.). 1984. pap. 6.95 (ISBN 0-87784-936-6). Inter-Varsity.

How to Read the Bible. A. J. Conyers. LC 85-23173. (How to Read Ser.). 216p. (Orig.). 1986. pap. 6.95 (ISBN 0-87784-944-7). Inter-Varsity.

How to Read the Bible. rev. ed. James A. Fischer. 1987. 14.95 (ISBN 0-396-08986-0); pap. 8.95 (ISBN 0-396-09028-1). Dodd.

How to Read the Bible: A Step by Step Manual. R. R. Evelan. 1984. 5.95 (ISBN 0-89536-700-9, 4883). CSS of Ohio.

How to Read the Bible As Literature. Leland Ryken. 200p. (Orig.). 1985. pap. text ed. 7.95 (ISBN 0-310-39021-4, 11158P). Zondervan.

How to Read the Bible for All it's Worth. Gordon Fee & Douglas Stuart. 272p. 1982. pap. 7.95 (ISBN 0-310-37361-1, 11146P). Zondervan.

How to Read the Bible: Leader's Guide. R. R. Evelan. 1984. 2.25 (ISBN 0-89536-716-5, 4891). CSS of Ohio.

How to Read the Gospels & Acts. Joel B. Green. LC 87-5572. (How to Read Ser.). 180p. (Orig.). 1987. pap. 6.95 (ISBN 0-87784-940-4). Inter-Varsity.

How to Read the Greek New Testament. Guy N. Woods. 5.00 (ISBN 0-89225-103-4). Gospel Advocate.

How to Read the Old Testament. Etienne Charpentier. LC 82-12728. 128p. 1982. pap. 10.95 (ISBN 0-8245-0540-9). Crossroad NY.

How to Really Know the Will of God. Richard Strauss. 1982. pap. 5.95 (ISBN 0-8423-1537-3); 2.95 (ISBN 0-8423-1538-1). Tyndale.

How to Really Love Your Child. D. Ross Campbell. LC 77-89470. 132p. 1977. pap. 4.95 (ISBN 0-88207-751-1). Victor Bks.

How to Really Love Your Teenager. Campbell. LC 81-51515. 1982. 4.95 (ISBN 0-88207-274-9). Victor Bks.

How to Receive God's Anointing. Ras Robinson. (Illus.). 88p. 1985. pap. text ed. 3.95 (ISBN 0-937778-10-9). Fulness Hse.

How to Receive the Holy Ghost. J. T. Pugh. 63p. (Orig.). 1969. pap. 1.95 (ISBN 0-912315-45-8). Word Aflame.

How to Recognize the Antichrist. Arthur E. Bloomfield. LC 75-29424. 160p. 1975. pap. 3.95 (ISBN 0-87123-225-1, 210225). Bethany Hse.

How to Recover from Grief. Richard L. Detrich & Nicola Steele. 128p. 1983. pap. 7.95 (ISBN 0-8170-0989-2). Judson.

How to Repair Books & Maintain Audiovisuals. Ed. by Floyd Simpson & Glynn Hill. LC 84-9618. (Orig.). 1984. pap. 2.95 (ISBN 0-8054-3708-8). Broadman.

How to Repair the Wrong You've Done. Ken Wilson. (Living As a Christian Ser.). 80p. 1982. pap. 2.25 (ISBN 0-89283-116-2). Servant.

How to Resist the Devil. F. J. Perryman. 48p. pap. 0.50 (ISBN 0-686-29122-0). Faith Pub Hse.

How to Respond to Islam. Philip H. Lochhaas. 1981. pap. 1.95 (ISBN 0-570-07687-0, 12-2788). Concordia.

How to Respond to Jehovah's Witnesses. Herbert Kern. (The Response Ser.). 1977. 1.95 (ISBN 0-570-07679-X, 12-2664). Concordia.

How to Respond to the Cults. 1977. 1.75 (ISBN 0-570-07682-X, 12-2654). Concordia.

How to Respond to the Latter Day Saints. Edgar P. Kaiser. (The Response Ser.). 1977. 1.95 (ISBN 0-570-07680-3, 12-2669). Concordia.

How to Respond to the Lodge. James Rongstad. (The Response Ser.). 1977. 1.95 (ISBN 0-570-07677-3, 12-2660). Concordia.

How to Respond to the Science Religions. Frederick R. Harm. 1981. pap. 1.75 (ISBN 0-570-07686-2, 12-2787). Concordia.

How to Respond to Transcendental Meditation. Kieth A. Gerberding. (The Response Ser.). 1977. 1.95 (ISBN 0-570-07676-5, 12-2659). Concordia.

How to Rule the World, or Seek First the Kingdom of God. 1984. write for info. Kingdom God.

How to Rule the World: Seek First the Kingdom of God. John R. Bohlen. LC 81-90513. (Illus.). 271p. 1982. pap. 3.95 (ISBN 0-9607702-0-8). Kingdom God.

How to Save the Catholic Church. Andrew Greeley. 288p. 1984. 16.95 (ISBN 0-670-38475-5, Elizabeth Sifton Bks). Viking.

How to Save Your Marriage Alone. Ed Wheat. 64p. 1983. pap. 2.50 (ISBN 0-310-42522-0, 10267P). Zondervan.

How to Say No to a Stubborn Habit. Erwin W. Lutzer. LC 79-64039. 143p. 1979. pap. 5.95 (ISBN 0-88207-787-2). Victor Bks.

How to Send Healing Energy: Diccionari Enciclopedic D'abast Universal, 8 vols. David V. Leuser. (Catalan.). 3500p. 1974. Set. 300.00 (ISBN 84-345-3560-2, S-50517). French & Eur.

How To-Sermon Outlines. Russell E. Spray. (Pulpit Library). 96p. 1984. pap. 4.50 (ISBN 0-8010-8252-8). Baker Bk.

How to Share Your Faith Without Being Offensive. Joyce Neville. 160p. (Orig.). 1983. pap. 6.95 (ISBN 0-8164-2228-1, HarpR). Har-Row.

How to Spiritualize your Marriage. 2nd, enl. ed. Swami Kriyananda. 136p. 1982. pap. 6.95 (ISBN 0-916124-21-5). Dawn Pubns CA.

How to Start a Beginning Again Ministry. Terry Hershey & Lisa McAfee. 64p. 1984. 4.95 (ISBN 0-915929-15-5). Merit Bks.

How to Start a Bible Institute. H. D. Harrison. 1978. pap. 2.95 (ISBN 0-89265-051-6). Randall Hse.

How to Start a Home Cell Ministry. 1st ed. Ed. by James D. Craig & Donald E. Hill. 32p. 1981. pap. 7.95 includes cassettes (ISBN 0-88151-019-X). Lay Leadership.

How to Start a Neighborhood Bible Study. Marilyn Kunz & Catherine Schell. (Neighborhood Bible Studies). 1970. pap. 2.00 (ISBN 0-8423-1540-3). Tyndale.

How to Start a Neighborhood Bible Study. Marilyn Kunz & Catherine Schell. incl. cassette 8.95 (ISBN 0-8423-1533-0). Tyndale.

How to Start Your Romance with God. John C. Scott. 1987. 7.95. Franciscan Herald.

How to Stay Christian. John Galloway, Jr. 144p. 1984. pap. 4.95 (ISBN 0-8170-1038-6). Judson.

How to Stick Together During Times of Tension: Directives for Christian Black Unity. Walter A. McCray. LC 83-70288. 170p. (Orig.). 1983. 11.95 (ISBN 0-933176-04-X); pap. 7.50 (ISBN 0-933176-03-1). Black Light Fellow.

How to Stop an Intermarriage. 7.95 (ISBN 0-686-76518-4). Feldheim.

How to Stop Procrastinating & Start Living. Loren Broadus. LC 82-72641. 128p. 1983. pap. 5.95 (ISBN 0-8066-1947-3, 10-3178). Augsburg.

How to Stop Worrying-Forever. Winston K. Pendleton. LC 66-19811. 80p. 1975. Repr. of 1966 ed. 4.95 (ISBN 0-88289-083-2). Pelican.

How to Study Acts. Joseph M. Gettys. 219p. 1976. pap. 4.50x (ISBN 0-87921-028-1). Attic Pr.

How to Study Ephesians. rev. ed. Joseph M. Gettys. 64p. 1976. pap. 4.00x (ISBN 0-87921-056-7). Attic Pr.

How to Study I Corinthians. Joseph M. Gettys. 128p. 1968. pap. 4.50x (ISBN 0-8042-3532-5). Attic Pr.

How to Study John. Joseph M. Gettys. 153p. 1960. pap. 4.50x (ISBN 0-8042-3568-6). Attic Pr.

How to Study Luke. rev. ed. Joseph M. Gettys. 153p. 1975. pap. 4.50x (ISBN 0-87921-027-3). Attic Pr.

How to Study Philippians, Colossians, & Philemon. Joseph M. Gettys. 87p. 1964. pap. text ed. 4.50x (ISBN 0-8042-3472-8). Attic Pr.

How to Study the Bible. James Braga. LC 82-6420. (Orig.). 1982. pap. 6.95 (ISBN 0-930014-72-3). Multnomah.

How to Study the Bible. Ralph Earle. (Christian Living Ser.). 32p. (Orig.). 1987. pap. write for info. (ISBN 0-8341-1187-X). Beacon Hill.

How to Study the Bible. Charles W. Ford. LC 77-99213. (Radiant Life Ser.). 128p. 1978. pap. text ed. 2.50 (ISBN 0-88243-912-X, 02-0912); tchr's ed. 3.95 (ISBN 0-88243-183-8, 32-0183). Gospel Pub.

How to Study the Bible. John MacArthur, Jr. (John MacArthur's Bible Studies). 1985. pap. 3.50 (ISBN 0-8024-5105-5). Moody.

How to Study the Bible. Phyllis Mitchell. (Workbook Ser.). (Illus.). 95p. 1982. pap. 4.95 (ISBN 0-930756-67-3, 581003). Aglow Pubns.

How to Study the Bible, Pt. I. Robert L. Samms. (Lay Action Ministry Program Ser.). 96p. 1987. pap. 4.95 (ISBN 0-89191-516-8). Cook.

How to Study the Bible, Pt. II. Robert L. Samms. (Lay Action Ministry Program Ser.). 96p. 1987. pap. 4.95 (ISBN 0-89191-517-6). Cook.

How to Study the Bible. K. H. Ting. Tr. by Tao Fong Shan Ecumenical Centre. Tr. of Zeyang Du Shengjing. 1981. pap. 1.95 (ISBN 0-377-00122-8). Friend Pr.

How to Study the Bible. R. A. Torrey. 155p. 1985. pap. 3.50 (ISBN 0-88368-164-1). Whitaker Hse.

How to Study the Bible for Greatest Profit. Ed. by R. A. Torrey. 1984. pap. 3.95 (ISBN 0-8010-8875-5). Baker Bk.

How to Study the Bible for Yourself. Tim LaHaye. LC 76-5568. 1976. pap. 4.95 (ISBN 0-89081-021-4, 0214). Harvest Hse.

How to Study the Revelation. rev. ed. Joseph M. Gettys. 117p. 1973. pap. 4.50x (ISBN 0-87921-029-X). Attic Pr.

How to Study Your Bible. Harold Mackay. Date not set. pap. 2.95 (ISBN 0-937396-68-0). Walterick Pubs.

How to Succeed in the Christian Life. R. A. Torrey. pap. 3.50 (ISBN 0-8024-3659-5). Moody.

How to Succeed in the Christian Life. R. A. Torrey. 128p. 1984. pap. 3.50 (ISBN 0-88368-143-9). Whitaker Hse.

How to Succeed in Winning Children to Christ. George B. Eager. 190p. 1979. pap. 3.95 (ISBN 0-9603752-0-1). Mailbox.

How to Succeed the Biblical Way. Ronald A. Jensen. 1981. pap. 4.95 (ISBN 0-8423-1541-1). Tyndale.

How to Succeed with People. Stephen R. Covey. 151p. 1971. 6.95 (ISBN 0-87747-439-7). Deseret Bk.

How to Survive & Live in Heaven on Earth. rev. ed. Martha Baker. LC 81-4234. 165p. 1981. pap. 1.95 (ISBN 0-86663-763-X). Ide Hse.

How to Survive in the Ministry. William L. Malcomson. 88p. 1982. pap. 4.95 (ISBN 0-8170-0964-7). Judson.

How to Take the Worry Out of Witnessing. George E. Worrell. LC 76-13342. 96p. 1976. pap. 4.95 (ISBN 0-8054-5568-X, 4255-68). Broadman.

How to Talk Directly with God. Azcar. 51p. 1977. pap. 1.95 (ISBN 0-931865-05-0). Psychegenics.

How to Talk to God Every Day of the Year: A Book of Devotions for Twelve Positive Months. Frances Hunter. 240p. 1984. 14.95 (ISBN 0-13-435248-3); pap. 6.95 (ISBN 0-13-435230-0). P-H.

How to Talk with Your Children about God. Frances Carroll. 1985. pap. 6.95 (ISBN 0-317-18129-7). P-H.

How to Teach, Enjoy & Survive Primary Grades. Avi Shulman. 2.50 (ISBN 0-914131-34-6, B65). Torah Umesorah.

How to Teach Origins. John N. Moore. 1987. pap. 14.95 (ISBN 0-8010-6219-5). Baker Bk.

How to Teach Peace to Children. J. Lorne Peachey. 32p. (Orig.). 1981. pap. 1.45 (ISBN 0-8361-1969-X). Herald Pr.

How to Teach the Bible. Lucien E. Coleman, Jr. LC 79-52001. 1980. 9.95 (ISBN 0-8054-3428-3). Broadman.

How to Teach Your Children about God...Without Actually Scaring them out of their Wits. Stan Berenstain & Jan Berenstain. 1984. pap. 3.95 (ISBN 0-345-29457-2). Ballantine.

How to Think About God: A Guide for the Twentieth-Century Pagan. Mortimer J. Adler. 1980. 10.95 (ISBN 0-02-500540-5). Macmillan.

How to Treat & Prevent the Crisis in the Priesthood. Conrad W. Baars. 1972. pap. 0.75 (ISBN 0-8199-0399-X). Franciscan Herald.

How to Treat Your Family As Well As You Treat Your Friends. Judson J. Swihart. LC 82-11234. 1982. pap. 5.95 (ISBN 0-8307-0855-3, 5417605). Regal.

How to Turn Minuses into Pluses. Nancy L. Van Pelt. Ed. by Richard W. Coffen. (Better Living Ser.). 32p. (Orig.). 1985. pap. 1.25 (ISBN 0-8280-0303-3). Review & Herald.

How to Turn Your Dreams into Realities. J. J. Turner. pap. 4.50 (ISBN 0-317-03774-9). Quality Pubns.

How to Turn Your Faith Loose. 2nd ed. Kenneth E. Hagin. 1983. pap. 1.00 (ISBN 0-89276-007-9). Hagin Ministries.

How to Understand & Enjoy the Scriptures. Allan K. Burgess. LC 85-29212. (Illus.). 80p. 1986. 5.95 (ISBN 0-87579-030-5). Deseret Bk.

How to Understand Church History. Jean Comby. 208p. 1985. pap. 10.95 (ISBN 0-8245-0722-3). Crossroad NY.

How to Understand Marriage. Jean-Pierre Bagot. 144p. (Orig.). 1987. pap. 9.95 (ISBN 0-8245-0810-6). Crossroad NY.

How to Understand the Bible. Ralph Herring et al. LC 74-75674. 1974. 8.95 (ISBN 0-8054-1127-5). Broadman.

How to Understand the Bible. 2nd ed. W. Robert Palmer. 118p. 1980. pap. 3.95 (ISBN 0-89900-140-8). College Pr Pub.

How to Understand the Church of God. James Stone. 1981. pap. 1.95 (ISBN 0-934942-27-7). White Wing Pub.

How to Understand the Tarot. Frank Lind. (Paths to Inner Power Ser). 1971. pap. 3.50 (ISBN 0-87728-098-3). Weiser.

How to Understand Your Bible. T. Norton Sterrett. LC 74-78674. 180p. 1974. pap. 6.95 (ISBN 0-87784-638-3). Inter-Varsity.

How to Understand Your Bible. Alan Stibbs. Rev. by David Wenham & Clare Wenham. LC 77-72351. Orig. Title: Understanding God's Word. 77p. 1978. pap. 1.95 (ISBN 0-87788-365-3). Shaw Pubs.

How to Understand Your Parents & Maybe Like the Ones You Love. Robert Baden. 1987. pap. 4.95 (ISBN 0-570-04467-7). Concordia.

How to Unlock the Secrets of Love & Sex in Marriage. Rusty Wright & Linda R. Wright. 144p. 1985. pap. 3.95 (ISBN 0-916441-08-3). Barbour & Co.

How to Use Chancel Drama Effectively. Jon L. Joyce. (Orig.). 1980. pap. 2.25 (ISBN 0-937172-00-6). JLJ Pubs.

How to Use New Testament Greek Study Aids. Walter J. Clark. 256p. 1984. pap. 6.95 (ISBN 0-87213-079-7). Loizeaux.

How to Use The Bible. James D. Robinson. 1982. pap. 3.25 (ISBN 0-570-03853-7, 12-2808). Concordia.

How to Use the Power of Mind in Everyday Life. Craig Carter. 96p. 1976. pap. 4.50 (ISBN 0-911336-65-6). Sci of Mind.

How to Use the Power of Prayer. Joseph Murphy. pap. 1.50 (ISBN 0-87516-275-4). De Vorss.

How to Use the Power of Prayer. Harold Sherman. 192p. 1985. 5.95 (ISBN 0-87159-061-1). Unity School.

How to Use the Science of Mind. Ernest Holmes. 1950. 8.95 (ISBN 0-396-03212-5). Dodd.

How to Use the Tremendous Power of Creative Prayer. Leland F. Gipson. LC 80-85276. 114p. (Orig.). 1981. pap. 2.95 (ISBN 0-9605014-0-1). Levada.

How to Use Your Bible. Wanda Milner. (Illus.). 24p. (Orig.). 1983. pap. 2.95 (ISBN 0-87239-690-8, 3200). Standard Pub.

How to Use Your Healing Power. Joseph Murphy. 158p. 1973. pap. 3.50 (ISBN 0-87516-186-3). De Vorss.

How to Use Your Twelve Gifts from God. William A. Warch. LC 76-41588. 112p. 1983. pap. 5.95 (ISBN 0-87516-530-3). De Vorss.

How to Walk in Love. Kenneth E. Hagin. 1983. pap. 0.50 mini bk. (ISBN 0-89276-262-4). Hagin Ministries.

How to Walk in the Spirit. Bill Bright. (Transferable Concepts Ser.). 64p. 1981. pap. 1.25 (ISBN 0-918956-91-9). Campus Crusade.

How to Walk in the Spirit. JoAnne Sekowsky. 32p. 1976. pap. 0.95 (ISBN 0-930756-17-7, 541004). Aglow Pubns.

How to Walk with God. Everett L. Fullam. 192p. 1987. pap. 8.95 (ISBN 0-8407-9514-9). Oliver-Nelson.

How to Walk with God. Wim Malgo. 1980. 1.95 (ISBN 0-937422-02-9). Midnight Call.

How to Win Over Depression. Tim LaHaye. 224p. 1974. pap. text ed. 6.95 (ISBN 0-310-26981-4, 18072P); pap. 3.95 (ISBN 0-310-26982-2, 18082P). Zondervan.

How to Win Over Worry. John E. Haggai. 1967. pap. 3.95 (ISBN 0-310-25712-3, 9740P). Zondervan.

How to Win Photographic Contests. 3.95 (ISBN 0-89816-087-1). Embee Pr.

How to Win Your Family to Christ. Nathanael Olson. LC 77-81561. pap. 3.95 (ISBN 0-89107-149-0). Good News.
How to Win Your Family to Christ. Stephen J. Vaudrey. 1985. 13.95 (ISBN 0-317-18081-9); pap. 6.95 (ISBN 0-317-18082-7). P-H.
How to Witness in the Spirit. Bill Bright. (Transferable Concepts Ser.). 64p. 1981. pap. 1.25 (ISBN 0-918956-92-7). Campus Crusade.
How to Witness Successfully. George Sweeting. LC 78-1959. 1978. pap. 3.95 (ISBN 0-8024-3791-5). Moody.
How to Witness to a Jehovah's Witness. William J. Schnell. Orig. Title: Christians, Awake! 160p. 1975. pap. 3.95 (ISBN 0-8010-8048-7). Baker Bk.
How to Witness to Anyone: Guidelines for Effective Evangelism. Ed. by R. A. Torrey. 1985. pap. text ed. 3.50 (ISBN 0-88368-170-6). Whitaker Hse.
How to Work for Christ. A. Torrey. 512p. 1901. 15.95 (ISBN 0-8007-0144-5). Revell.
How to Worship God. James Stone. 60p. (Orig.). 1982. pap. 1.95 (ISBN 0-934942-32-3). White Wing Pub.
How to Write for Christian Magazines. Chip Ricks & Marilyn Marsh. LC 84-23025. 1985. pap. 7.50 (ISBN 0-8054-7910-4). Broadman.
How to Write Your Own Ticket with God. Kenneth E. Hagin. 1979. mini bk. .50 (ISBN 0-89276-055-9). Hagin Ministries.
How We Got Our Bible. Ralph Earle. 119p. 1972. 2.95 (ISBN 0-8341-0226-9). Beacon Hill.
How We Got Our Bible. John P. Smyth. LC 77-24190. 1977. Repr. of 1912 ed. lib. bdg. 20.00 (ISBN 0-8414-7793-0). Folcroft.
How We Got the Bible. Neil R. Lightfoot. 1962. 7.95 (ISBN 0-8010-5502-4). Baker Bk.
How We Got the Bible. rev. ed. Neil R. Lightfoot. (Way of Life Ser.). 95p. 1986. pap. 3.95. Abilene Christ U.
How We Got the Bible. rev. ed. Neil R. Lightfoot. 1987. price not set (ISBN 0-8010-5644-6). Baker Bk.
How We Got the Bible. Lenet H. Read. LC 85-72842. 140p. 1985. 8.95 (ISBN 0-87747-799-X). Deseret Bk.
How, Why, When, Where, Bks. 1 & 2. William Coleman. 23p. 1984. Bk. 1. pap. 2.95 (ISBN 0-89191-717-9, 57174, Chariot Bks.); Bk. 2. pap. 2.95 (ISBN 0-89191-942-2, 59428, Chariot Bks.). Cook.
How Will It End? Ralph Blodgett. (Eighty-Five-Miss Ser). 1984. pap. 1.19 (ISBN 0-8163-0567-6). Pacific Pr Pub Assn.
How Would You Like to See the Slides of My Mission? A Tasteful Collection of Missionary Humor. Larry Nielson. LC 80-82708. (Illus.). 158p. (Orig.). 1980. pap. 4.95 (ISBN 0-88290-153-2, 2040). Horizon Utah.
How You Can Be a Peacemaker. Mary E. Jegen. 128p. 1985. pap. 2.95 (ISBN 0-89243-231-4). Liguori Pubns.
How You Can Be Healed. Gordon Lindsay. (Divine Healing & Health Ser.). 1.25 (ISBN 0-89985-026-X). Christ Nations.
How You Can Be Led by the Spirit of God. Kenneth E. Hagin. 1978. pap. 3.50 (ISBN 0-89276-500-3). Hagin Ministries.
How You Can Have Divine Health. Gordon Lindsay. (Divine Healing & Health Ser.). 1.25 (ISBN 0-89985-027-8). Christ Nations.
How You Can Have Joy. Vicki Jamison-Peterson. 130p. 1976. pap. 2.95 (ISBN 0-88144-054-X). Christian Pub.
How You Can Know the Will of God. 2nd ed. Kenneth E. Hagin. 1983. pap. 1.00 (ISBN 0-89276-019-2). Hagin Ministries.
How You Can Know the Will of God. Jim McKeever. 24p. 1982. 1.00 (ISBN 0-86694-095-2). Omega Pubns OR.
How You Can Pray with Power & Get Results. Lowell Lundstrom. 272p. 1984. pap. text ed. 3.50 (ISBN 0-88368-151-X). Whitaker Hse.
How You Can Talk with God. 2nd ed. Paramahansa Yogananda. (Illus.). 1985. pap. 0.95 (ISBN 0-87612-160-1); pap. 2.00 French ed. (ISBN 0-87612-163-6). Self Realization.
How You Live with Jesus: Catechism for Today's Young Catholic. Redemptorist Pastoral Publication. LC 81-80097. 96p. 1981. pap. 3.50 (ISBN 0-89243-137-7). Liguori Pubns.
Howard Florey: The Making of a Great Scientist. Gwyn MacFarlane. (Illus.). 1979. 23.95x (ISBN 0-19-858161-0). Oxford U Pr.
Howard University Bibliography of African & Afro-American Religious Studies: With Locations in American Libraries. Ethel L. Williams & Clifton F. Brown. LC 76-5604. 1977. 50.00 (ISBN 0-8420-2080-2). Scholarly Res Inc.
However Long & Hard the Road. Jeffrey R. Holland. LC 85-12945. 144p. 1985. 8.95 (ISBN 0-87747-625-X). Deseret Bk.
Hrafnkel's Saga. Tr. by Hermann Palsson. (Classics Ser). 1971. pap. 4.95 (ISBN 0-14-044238-3). Penguin.
Hsiang-Ya Journal. Ruth A. Greene. LC 76-28526. Repr. of 1977 ed. 36.70 (2011504). Bks Demand UMI.
Hsin Hsin Ming: The Book of Nothing. 2nd ed. Bhagwan Shree Rajneesh. Ed. by Ma Punito. LC 83-17783. (Zen Master Ser.). 320p. 1983. pap. 4.95 (ISBN 0-88050-597-4). Chidvilas Found.
Hsun Tzu: Basic Writings. Hsun Tzu. Tr. by Burton Watson. LC 63-20340. (Translations from Oriental Classics Ser.). (Orig.). 1963. pap. 10.00x (ISBN 0-231-08607-5). Columbia U Pr.
Hsuntze, the Moulder of Ancient Confucianism. Homer H. Dubs. 339p. Repr. of 1927 ed. text ed. 22.50x (ISBN 0-89644-006-0, Pub. by Chinese Matl Ctr). Coronet Bks.
Hua-Yen Buddhism: The Jewel Net of Indra. Francis H Cook. LC 76-43288. (Institute for Advanced Study of World Religions Ser.). 1977. 19.95x (ISBN 0-271-01245-5). Pa St U Pr.
Huai-nan-tzu, Book Eleven: Behavior, Culture, & the Cosmos. Benjamin E. Wallacker. (American Oriental Ser.: Vol. 48). 1962. pap. 5.00x (ISBN 0-940490-48-X). Am Orient Soc.
Hudson Taylor. 2nd ed. Hudson Taylor. 160p. 1987. pap. 3.50 (ISBN 0-87123-951-5). Bethany Hse.
Hudson Taylor & China's Open Century: Bk. V. Refiner's Fire, Bk. V. A. J. Broomhall. 1985. pap. 9.95 (ISBN 0-340-36866-7). OMF Bks.
Hudson Taylor: Trusting God No Matter What. Fern N. Stocker. (Guessing Bks.). (Orig.). 1986. pap. 3.95 (ISBN 0-8024-8575-8). Moody.
Hudson Taylor's Spiritual Secret. Howard Taylor & Mary G. Taylor. pap. 3.95 (ISBN 0-8024-0029-9). Moody.
Huellas del Islam en la Literatura Espanola: De Juan Ruiz a Juan Goytisola. Luce L. Baralt. 262p. 1985. 18.00 (ISBN 84-7517-152-4). U of PR Pr.
Hugh Latimer, Apostle to the English. Allan G. Chester. 1978. Repr. of 1954 ed. lib. bdg. 20.00x (ISBN 0-374-91492-3, Octagon). Hippocrene Bks.
Hugh of St. Victor: On the Sacraments of the Christian Faith. Hugh of St. Victor. Tr. by R. J. Deferrari. (Eng.). 1976. Repr. of 1951 ed. 18.00x (ISBN 0-910956-32-4). Medieval Acad.
Hugo Zuckermann: A Great Jewish Leader. Meier M. Reschke. LC 84-90055. 45p. 1985. 7.95 (ISBN 0-533-06136-9). Vantage.
Hugs for Our New Baby. Jean T. Cook. (Illus.). 1987. 3.95 (ISBN 0-570-04165-1). Concordia.
Huguenot Heritage: The History & Contribution of the Huguenots in England. Robin D. Gwynn. (Illus.). 256p. 1985. 34.95x (ISBN 0-7102-0420-5). Methuen Inc.
Huguenot Struggle for Recognition. N. M. Sutherland. LC 79-64070. 1980. text ed. 40.00x (ISBN 0-300-02328-6). Yale U Pr.
Huguenots. Arthur J. Grant. LC 69-11552. 255p. 1969. Repr. of 1934 ed. 27.50 (ISBN 0-208-00745-8, Archon). Shoe String.
Huguenots: A Biography of a Minority. George A. Rothrock. LC 78-23476. (Illus.). 228p. 1979. 21.95x (ISBN 0-88229-277-3). Nelson-Hall.
Huguenots & Henry of Navarre, 2 Vols. Henry M. Baird. LC 76-130987. Repr. of 1903 ed. Set. 74.50 (ISBN 0-404-00540-3). AMS Pr.
Huguenots & the Revocation of the Edict of Nantes, 2 vols. Henry M. Baird. LC 76-161752. Repr. of 1895 ed. Set. 74.50 (ISBN 0-404-08003-0). AMS Pr.
Huguenots & the Revocation of the Edict of Nantes, 2 vols. Henry M. Baird. 1977. lib. bdg. 250.00 (ISBN 0-8490-2025-5). Gordon Pr.
Huldrych Zwingli: His Life & Work. Ulrich Gabler. Tr. by Ruth C. Gritsch. LC 85-16199. 208p. 1986. 24.95 (ISBN 0-8006-0761-9, 1-761). Fortress.
Huldrych Zwingli: The Reformer of German Switzerland. 2nd rev. ed. Samuel M. Jackson. LC 75-170836. Repr. of 1901 ed. 24.50 (ISBN 0-404-03543-4). AMS Pr.
Huldrych Zwingli Writings in Defense of the Reformed Faith: Writings in the Defense of the Reformed Faith, Vol. 1. Tr. by E. Furcha. (Pittsburgh Theological Monographs: No. 12). 1984. pap. 19.95 (ISBN 0-915138-58-1). Pickwick.
Huldrych Zwingli-Writings in Search of True Religion: Reformation, Pastoral & Eucharistic Writings, Vol. 2. Tr. by Wayne H. Pipkin. (Pittsburgh Theological Monographs: No. 13). 1984. pap. 19.95 (ISBN 0-915138-59-X). Pickwick.
Hullin, 2 vols. 36.00 (ISBN 0-910218-81-1). Bennet Pub.
Hullo Sun. Joan Hodgson. (Illus.). 1972. 5.95 (ISBN 0-85487-019-9). De Vorss.
Human Achievement & Divine Vocation in the Message of Paul. William A. Beardslee. LC 61-4760. (Studies in Biblical Theology: No. 31). 1961. pap. 10.00x (ISBN 0-8401-3031-7). A R Allenson.
Human Action of Forgiving: A Critical Application of the Metaphysics of Alfred North Whitehead. Jean C. Lambert. (Illus.). 300p. (Orig.). 1985. lib. bdg. 26.00 (ISBN 0-8191-4596-3); pap. text ed. 14.50 (ISBN 0-8191-4597-1). U Pr of Amer.
Human Adventure. Robert Matthews. 1980. pap. 5.95 (ISBN 0-89536-426-3, 0834). CSS of Ohio.
Human Affection & Divine Love. Abhedananda. 64p. 3.95 (ISBN 0-87481-610-6, Pub. by Ramakrishna Math Madras India). Vedanta Pr.
Human & Ethical Issues in the Surgical Care of Patients with Life-Threatening Disease. Ed. by Frederic P. Herter et al. 264p. 1986. 31.50x (ISBN 0-398-05194-1). C C Thomas.
Human & the Holy: Asian Perspectives in Christian Theology. Ed. by Emerito Nacpil. Douglas J. Elwood. 1978. pap. text ed. 10.00x (ISBN 0-686-23912-1, Pub. by New Day Pub). Cellar.
Human & the Holy: Asian Perspectives in Christian Theology. Ed. by Emerito Nacpil & Douglas J. Elwood. LC 80-14134. 384p. (Orig.). 1980. pap. 3.74 (ISBN 0-88344-195-0). Orbis Bks.
Human Biological Machine As a Transformational Apparatus. E. J. Gold. Pref. by Iven Lourie. LC 85-60946. 176p. (Orig.). 1985. pap. 12.50 (ISBN 0-89556-046-1). Gateways Bks & Tapes.
Human Body. Monks of Solesmes. 1960. 6.50 (ISBN 0-8198-3309-6). Dghtrs St Paul.
Human Body - Good or Evil? Carroll M. Bates. 1986. 6.95 (ISBN 0-533-06780-4). Vantage.
Human Center: Moral Agency in the Social World. Howard L. Harrod. LC 80-2392. 160p. 1981. 3.50 (ISBN 0-8006-0657-4, 1-657). Fortress.
Human Character & Morality: Reflections from the History of Ideas. Stephen D. Hudson. 160p. 1986. 18.95 (ISBN 0-7102-0770-0, 07700). Methuen Inc.
Human Church in the Presence of Christ: The Congregation Rediscovered. Victor L. Hunter & Phillip Johnson. xii, 180p. 1985. 15.50 (ISBN 0-86554-171-X, MUP-H161). Mercer Univ Pr.
Human Condition in the Jewish & Christian Conditions. Frederick E. Greenspahn. 1985. text ed. 25.00x (ISBN 0-88125-084-8). Ktav.
Human Conduct: Problems of Ethics. 2nd ed. John Hospers. 481p. 1982. pap. text ed. 15.95 (ISBN 0-15-540094-0, HC). HarBraceJ.
Human Connection. Martin Bolt & David G. Myers. LC 83-20420. 168p. (Orig.). 1984. pap. 6.95 (ISBN 0-87784-913-7). Inter-Varsity.
Human, Criterion of Christian Existence? Ed. by Claude Geffre & Jean-Pierre Jossua. (Concilium Ser.: Vol. 155). 128p. (Orig.). 1982. pap. 6.95 (ISBN 0-8164-2386-5, HarpR). Har-Row.
Human Destiny: Some Problems for Catholic Philosophy. Joseph Owens. LC 82-21496. 126p. 1985. 16.95 (ISBN 0-8132-0604-9); pap. 7.95 (ISBN 0-8132-0605-7). Cath U Pr.
Human Development & Human Possibility: Erikson in the Light of Heidegger. Richard T. Knowles. LC 85-20498. (Illus.). 224p. (Orig.). 1986. lib. bdg. 26.00 (ISBN 0-8191-4992-6); pap. text ed. 12.25 (ISBN 0-8191-4993-4). U Pr of Amer.
Human Energy Systems. Jack Schwarz. (Illus.). 1980. pap. 7.95 (ISBN 0-525-47556-7, 0772-230). Dutton.
Human Evolution: A Philosophical Anthropology. Mary Maxwell. 288p. 1984. 38.00x (ISBN 0-231-05946-9, King's Crown Paperbacks); pap. 18.00x (ISBN 0-231-05947-7). Columbia U Pr.
Human Existence, Medicine, & Ethics. William E. May. LC 77-8149. 43p. 1977. 5.25 (ISBN 0-8199-0677-8). Franciscan Herald.
Human Experience & the Art of Counselling. Ed. by Marcus Lefebure. 160p. 1985. pap. 9.95 (ISBN 0-567-29121-9, Pub. by T&T Clark Ltd UK). Fortress.
Human Experience of God. Denis Edwards. 1984. pap. 7.95 (ISBN 0-8091-2559-5). Paulist Pr.
Human Face of God. John A. Robinson. LC 73-78. 282p. 1979. softcover 5.95 (ISBN 0-664-24241-3). Westminster.
Human Fertilization "In Vitro" A Catholic Moral Perspective. Eileen P. Flynn. LC 83-27343. 202p. (Orig.). 1984. lib. bdg. 25.00 (ISBN 0-8191-3819-3); pap. text ed. 12.25 (ISBN 0-8191-3820-7). U Pr of Amer.
Human Formation. Adrian Van Kaam. LC 84-29241. (Formative Spirituality Ser.: Vol. 2). 271p. 1985. 24.95x (ISBN 0-8245-0578-6). Crossroad NY.
Human Freedom & Social Order: An Essay in Christian Philosophy. John D. Wild. LC 59-14243. pap. 65.50 (ISBN 0-317-27300-0, 2023468). Bks Demand UMI.
Human Heritage. Alfred Taylor. LC 74-18360. 150p. (Orig.). 1975. pap. 2.50 (ISBN 0-8356-0455-1, Quest). Theos Pub Hse.
Human Immortality & Pre-Existence. John McTaggart. Repr. of 1916 ed. 23.00 (ISBN 0-527-59950-6). Kraus Repr.
Human Interest. 2nd ed. N. Sri Ram. 1968. 2.50 (ISBN 0-8356-7170-4). Theos Pub Hse.
Human Knowledge of Christ. Bertrand De Margerie. 1980. 2.95 (ISBN 0-8198-3301-0); pap. 1.50 (ISBN 0-8198-3302-9). Dghtrs St Paul.
Human Liberation in a Feminist Perspective: A Theology. Letty M. Russell. LC 74-10613. 214p. 1974. pap. 8.95 (ISBN 0-664-24991-4). Westminster.
Human Life: A Biblical Perspective for Bioethics. J. Robert Nelson. LC 83-48140. 208p. 1984. pap. 10.95 (ISBN 0-8006-1754-1, 1-1754). Fortress.
Human Life Is Sacred. Irish Bishop's Pastoral. 1977. pap. 1.50 (ISBN 0-8198-0416-9). Dghtrs St Paul.
Human Life: Problems of Birth, of Living, & of Dying. Ed. by W. C. Bier. LC 77-71939. (Pastoral Psychology Ser.: No. 9). 1977. 20.00 (ISBN 0-8232-1025-1). Fordham.
Human Love. Jean Guitton. LC 66-17110. 253p. 1966. 4.50 (ISBN 0-8199-0046-X). Franciscan Herald.
Human Love: Existential & Mystical. Ralph Harper. LC 66-24410. pap. 48.00 (2026322). Bks Demand UMI.
Human Mind & the Mind of God: Theological Promise in Brain Research. James B. Ashbrook. (Illus.). 408p. (Orig.). 1985. lib. bdg. 30.75 (ISBN 0-8191-4225-5); pap. text ed. 17.75 (ISBN 0-8191-4226-3). U Pr of Amer.
Human Mind Power: Secrets of the Vedic Gods. V. G. Rele. 136p. 1983. pap. text ed. 5.95x (ISBN 0-86590-231-3, Pub. by Taraporevala India). Apt Bks.
Human Mystery. Sir John Eccles. LC 78-12095. (Illus.). 1978. 25.00 (ISBN 0-387-09016-9). Springer-Verlag.
Human Nature & the Gospel. William L. Phelps. 1977. Repr. of 1925 ed. lib. bdg. 30.00 (ISBN 0-8414-6807-9). Folcroft.
Human Nature in the Christian Tradition. William O. Amy & James B. Recob. LC 82-45049. 118p. (Orig.). 1982. lib. bdg. 24.75 (ISBN 0-8191-2512-1); pap. text ed. 8.75 (ISBN 0-8191-2513-X). U Pr of Amer.
Human Nature of Christ: Growth & Perfection. Apostolos Makrakis. Ed. by Orthodox Christian Educational Society. Tr. by D. Cummings from Hellenic. 52p. (Orig.). 1965. pap. 1.00x (ISBN 0-938366-28-9). Orthodox Chr.
Human Organ Transplantation: Societal, Medical-Legal, Regulatory, & Reimbursement Issues. Dale H. Cowan. LC 86-29478. 1987. price not set (ISBN 0-910701-20-2). Health Admin Pr.
Human Person. Ed. by George F. McLean. LC 80-66375. (Proceedings: Vol. 53). 1979. pap. 15.00 (ISBN 0-918090-13-X). Am Cath Philo.
Human Puzzle: Psychological Research & Christian Belief. David C. Myers. LC 77-15873. 1978. pap. 8.95x (ISBN 0-06-065558-5, RD 265, HarpR). Har-Row.
Human Reality of Sacred Scripture. Ed. by Pierre Benoit et al. LC 65-28869. (Concilium Ser.: Vol. 10). 220p. 7.95 (ISBN 0-8091-0075-4). Paulist Pr.
Human Responses to the Holocaust: Perpetrators, Victims, Bystanders & Resisters-Papers of the 1979 Bernhard E. Olson Scholar's Conference on the Church Struggle & the Holocaust Sponsored by the National Conference of Christians & Jews. Ed. by Michael D. Ryan. LC 81-38331. (Texts & Studies in Religion: Vol. 9). 300p. 1981. 49.95x (ISBN 0-88946-902-4). E Mellen.
Human Revolution, Vol. 5. Daisaku Ikeda. (Illus.). 250p. 1984. 13.95 (ISBN 0-8348-0198-1). Weatherhill.
Human Rights: A Dialogue Between the First & Third Worlds. Robert A. Evans & Alice F. Evans. LC 82-18780. 236p. (Orig.). 1983. pap. 9.95 (ISBN 0-88344-194-2). Orbis Bks.
Human Rights: Amintaphil, Vol. 1. Ervin H. Pollock. LC 70-173834. xviii, 419p. 1971. lib. bdg. 37.50 (ISBN 0-930342-65-8). W S Hein.
Human Rights & American Foreign Policy. Ed. by Donald P. Kommers & Gilburt D. Loescher. LC 78-62966. 1979. pap. text ed. 9.95 (ISBN 0-268-01075-7). U of Notre Dame Pr.
Human Rights & Human Dignity: An Apologetic for the Transcendent Perspective. John W. Montgomery. 192p. 1986. pap. 10.95 (ISBN 0-310-28571-2, 18392P). Zondervan.
Human Rights & World Order. Abdul Said. LC 78-62438. 170p. 1978. pap. 5.95 (ISBN 0-87855-718-0). Transaction Bks.
Human Rights as Human & Christian Realities. Peter J. Riga. LC 81-69244. (New Studies on Law & Society). 165p. (Orig.). 1982. 26.00x (ISBN 0-86733-016-3, 5016). Assoc Faculty Pr.
Human Rights Book. Milton Meltzer. LC 79-13017. 272p. 1979. 11.95 (ISBN 0-374-33514-1). FS&G.

Human Rights in Islam. Abul A. Maududi. 39p. (Orig.). 1981. pap. 1.95 (ISBN 0-9503954-9-8, Pub. by Islamic Found UK). New Era Pubns MI.

Human Rights in Jewish Law. Haim H. Cohn. LC 83-14846. 266p. 1984. 25.00x (ISBN 0-88125-036-8). Ktav.

Human Rights in Religious Traditions. Ed. by Arlene Swidler. LC 82-15014. 128p. (Orig.). 1982. pap. 8.95 (ISBN 0-8298-0633-4). Pilgrim NY.

Human Rights Reader. Ed. by Walter Laqueur & Barry Rubin. (Orig.). 1979. pap. 9.95 (ISBN 0-452-00853-0, F661, Mer). NAL.

Human Rights Reader. Ed. by Walter Laqueur & Barry Rubin. 384p. 1979. 29.95 (ISBN 0-87722-170-7). Temple U Pr.

Human Roots: Buddhist Stories for Young Readers, Vol. 2. Dharma Realm Buddhist University Faculty. (Illus.). 140p. (Orig.). 1984. pap. 6.00 (ISBN 0-88139-017-8). Buddhist Text.

Human Roots, Fact or Fiction? Nathaniel Morrison. 1983. 4.95 (ISBN 0-8062-2218-2). Carlton.

Human Science & Human Dignity. Donald M. MacKay. LC 79-2383. 1979. pap. 3.50 (ISBN 0-87784-461-5). Inter-Varsity.

Human Sexuality. Gwenyth Dudley et al. (Illus.). 55p. (Orig.). 1984. pap. 5.95 (ISBN 0-85819-465-1, Pub. by JBCE). ANZ Religious Pubns.

Human Sexuality: A Preliminary Study - the United Church of Christ. LC 77-25398. 1977. pap. 5.95 (ISBN 0-8298-0341-6). Pilgrim NY.

Human Sexuality & Evangelical Christians. Ed. by Ernie Zimbelman. (Illus.). 394p. (Orig.). 1985. lib. bdg. 31.50 (ISBN 0-8191-4477-0); pap. text ed. 16.75 (ISBN 0-8191-4478-9). U Pr of Amer.

Human Sexuality & Personhood. LC 80-85411. ix, 254p. (Orig.). 1981. pap. 9.95 (ISBN 0-935372-09-1). Pope John Ctr.

Human Sexuality in Our Time. Ed. by George Kelly. 1979. 5.95 (ISBN 0-8198-0610-2); pap. 4.95 (ISBN 0-8198-0611-0). Dghtrs St Paul.

Human Situation. W. Macneile Dixon. 75.00 (ISBN 0-87968-062-8). Gordon Pr.

Human Society in Ethics & Politics. Bertrand Russell. 1954. text ed. 18.50x (ISBN 0-04-172004-0). Allen Unwin.

Human Soul & the Universe. Rudolf Steiner. (q). Orig. Title: Cosmic & Human Metamorphoses. 24p. 1982. pap. 2.95 (ISBN 0-919924-17-4, Pub. by Steiner Book Centre Canada). Anthroposophic.

Human Soul in Relation to World Evolution. Rudolf Steiner. Tr. by Rita Stebbing from Ger. LC 84-21703. 180p. (Orig.). 1985. 16.00 (ISBN 0-88010-114-8); pap. 9.95 (ISBN 0-88010-113-X). Anthroposophic.

Human Spirit. Ann R. Colton. 289p. 1966. 8.95 (ISBN 0-917187-05-9). A R C Pub.

Human Spirits: A Cultural Account of Trance in Mayotte. Michael Lambek. LC 81-1842. (Cambridge Studies in Cultural Systems). (Illus.). 272p. 1981. 39.50 (ISBN 0-521-23844-7); pap. 17.95 (ISBN 0-521-28255-1). Cambridge U Pr.

Human Touch. Dan Martin. Tr. by Don Rutledge. (Illus.). 1979. 6.95 (ISBN 0-937170-03-8). Home Mission.

Human Touch. Don Rutledge & Elaine S. Furlow. LC 75-2365. (Human Touch Ser.). (Illus.). 1975. 5.95 (ISBN 0-937170-13-5). Home Mission.

Human Values: An Interpretation of Ethics Based on a Study of Values. De Witt Parker. LC 75-3305. Repr. of 1931 ed. 42.50 (ISBN 0-404-59290-2). AMS Pr.

Human Values & Natural Science. Ed. by Ervin Laszlo & James B. Wilbur. (Current Topics of Contemporary Thought Ser.: Vol. 4). 310p. 1970. 63.95 (ISBN 0-677-13960-8). Gordon & Breach.

Human Values in a Changing World. Diasaku Ikeda & Bryan Wilson. 384p. (Orig.). 1987. 20.00 (ISBN 0-8184-0427-2). Lyle Stuart.

Human Way. Maurice Friedman. LC 81-8011. (Religion & Human Experience Ser.). 168p. 1982. 13.95 (ISBN 0-89012-025-0). Anima Pubns.

Human Way Out. Lewis Mumford. 1983. pap. 2.50x (ISBN 0-87574-097-9, 097). Pendle Hill.

Human Will in Judaism: The Mishnah's Philosophy of Intention. Howard Eilberg-Schwartz. (Brown Judaic Studies). 164p. 1986. 31.95 (ISBN 0-89130-938-1, 14-01-03). Scholars Pr GA.

Humanae Vitae. 2nd, rev. ed. Pope Paul VI. Tr. by Marc Caligari from Lat. 1983. pap. 1.95 (ISBN 0-89870-000-0). Ignatius Pr.

Humangrowth: An Essay on Growth, Values & the Quality of Life. Harlan Cleveland & Thomas W. Wilson, Jr. 54p. (Orig.). 1978. pap. text ed. 7.00 (ISBN 0-8191-5904-2, Pub. by Aspen Inst for Humanistic Studies). U Pr of Amer.

Humanism & Anti-Humanism. Kate Soper. 154p. 1986. 9.95 (ISBN 0-8126-9017-6). Open Court.

Humanism & Morality. Laurance Labadie. (Men & Movements in the History & Philosophy of Anarchism Ser.). 1979. lib. bdg. 59.95 (ISBN 0-685-96397-7). Revisionist Pr.

Humanism & the Church Fathers: Ambrogio Traversari (1386-1439) & the Revival of Patristic Theology in the Early Italian Renaissance. Charles L. Stinger. LC 76-21699. 1977. 49.50x (ISBN 0-87395-304-5). State U NY Pr.

Humanism & Theology. Werner Jaeger. (Aquinas Lecture). 1943. 7.95 (ISBN 0-87462-107-0). Marquette.

Humanism in Islam. Marcel Boisard. Tr. by Abdussamad Al-Jarrahi from Fr. LC 82-70456. 200p. (Orig.). Date not set. pap. 8.00 (ISBN 0-89259-035-1). Am Trust Pubns.

Humanism in the Renaissance of Islam: The Cultural Revival During the Buyid Age. Joel J. Kramer. ix, 329p. 1986. 54.50 (ISBN 90-04-07259-4, Pub. by E J Brill). Heinman.

Humanism vs Theism. Intro. by E. D. Klemke. 154p. 1982. pap. 8.50x (ISBN 0-8138-0916-9). Iowa St U Pr.

Humanisme de Bossuet. Goyet. 48.25 (ISBN 0-685-34207-7). French & Eur.

Humanist As Hero: The Life of Sir Thomas More. Theodore Maynard. 1971. Repr. of 1947 ed. 14.75x (ISBN 0-02-849040-1). Hafner.

Humanist Christology of Paul: Jesus of Nazareth Yesterday & Today, Vol. 3. Juan L. Segundo. Tr. by John Drury from Span. LC 86-8480. 256p. (Orig.). 1986. pap. 14.95 (ISBN 0-88344-221-3). Orbis Bks.

Humanist Ethics. Ed. by Morris B. Storer. LC 80-7456. 313p. 1980. 19.95 (ISBN 0-87975-117-7); pap. 13.95 (ISBN 0-87975-118-5). Prometheus Bks.

Humanist Evangel. Lucien Saumur. LC 81-85573. 128p. 1982. 16.95 (ISBN 0-87975-172-X); pap. 13.95 (ISBN 0-87975-114-2). Prometheus Bks.

Humanist Funeral Service. 3rd ed. Corliss Lamont. LC 77-76001. 48p. 1977. pap. 6.95 (ISBN 0-87975-090-1). Prometheus Bks.

Humanist Haggadah. Date not set. 5.50. Soc Humanistic.

Humanist Manifestos One & Two. Ed. by Paul Kurtz. 32p. 1973. pap. 2.95 (ISBN 0-87975-031-6). Prometheus Bks.

Humanist Scholarship & Public Order: Two Tracts Against the Pilgrimage of Grace, & a Collection of Related Contemporary Documents. Richard Morison. Ed. by David S. Berkowitz. LC 79-89983. 280p. 1983. text ed. 28.50 (ISBN 0-918016-01-0). Folger Bks.

Humanistic Ethics. Gardner Williams. 1951. 6.00 (ISBN 0-8022-1886-5). Philos Lib.

Humanistic Pragmatism: The Philosophy of F. C. S. Schiller. Ed. by Reuben E. Abel. (Orig.). 1966. pap. text ed. 6.95 (ISBN 0-02-900120-X). Free Pr.

Humanistic Psychology: A Christian Interpretation. John A. Hammes. LC 76-110448. 224p. 1971. 49.50 (ISBN 0-8089-0650-X, 791865). Grune.

Humanistic Values in the Bible. Zvi Adar. Tr. by Victor Tcherikover from Hebrew. LC 67-24730. 429p. 1967. 11.00 (ISBN 0-935457-02-X). Reconstructionist Pr.

Humanists & Holy Writ. Jerry H. Bentley. LC 83-42547. 264p. 1983. 25.50x (ISBN 0-691-05392-8). Princeton U Pr.

Humanities in Christian Higher Education in Asia: Ethical & Religious Perspectives. Ed. by Douglas J. Elwood. 1978. pap. 7.50x (ISBN 0-686-23913-X, Pub. by New Day Pub). Cellar.

Humanity & Divinity: An Essay in Comparative Metaphysics. Eliot Deutsch. LC 76-128081. 1970. 14.00x (ISBN 0-87022-190-6). UH Pr.

Humanity & Divinity of Christ. John Knox. (Orig.). pap. 9.95 (ISBN 0-521-09414-3). Cambridge U Pr.

Humanity & Self-Cultivation Essays in Confucian Thought. Tu Wei-Ming. 1980. text ed. 30.00 (ISBN 0-89581-600-8, Asian Humanities). Asian Human Pr.

Humanity Immortal: Or, Man Tried, Fallen & Redeemed. Laurens P. Hickok. LC 75-3180. Repr. of 1872 ed. 25.00 (ISBN 0-404-59183-3). AMS Pr.

Humanity in God. Elisabeth Moltmann-Wendel & Jurgen Moltmann. (Illus.). 160p. 1983. pap. 8.95 (ISBN 0-8298-0670-9). Pilgrim NY.

Humanity in the City. Edwin H. Chapin. LC 73-11901. (Metropolitan America Ser.). 254p. 1974. Repr. 19.00 (ISBN 0-405-05389-4). Ayer Co Pubs.

Humanity in the Thought of Karl Barth. Stuart McLean. 240p. 1981. 20.95 (ISBN 0-567-09304-2, Pub. by T&T Clark Ltd UK). Fortress.

Humanity of God. Karl Barth. Tr. by Thomas Weiser & John N. Thomas. LC 60-3479. 1960. pap. 5.95 (ISBN 0-8042-0612-0). John Knox.

Humanity of Jewish Law. Dayan Lew. 198p. 1986. 11.95 (ISBN 0-900689-87-0). Soncino Pr.

Humanity of the Saviour. Harry Johnson. 1962. 8.50x (ISBN 0-8401-1248-3). A R Allenson.

Humanity's Contemporary Moral Decay & the Historical Role of the Catholic Church. Karl Westheimer. LC 73-76434. (Illus.). 132p. 1973. 43.40 (ISBN 0-913314-19-6). Am Classical Coll Pr.

Humanizing America's Iconic Book. Ed. by Gene Tucker & Douglas Knight. LC 82-836. (SBL Biblical Scholarship in North America Ser.). 188p. 1982. 29.95 (ISBN 0-89130-654-4, 06-11-06); pap. 17.50 (ISBN 0-89130-570-X). Scholars Pr GA.

Humanizing Ministry. D. Timothy Estes. LC 84-15669. 160p. 1984. pap. 7.95 (ISBN 0-8361-3365-X). Herald Pr.

Humble Remonstrance to the High Court of Parliament. Joseph Hall. LC 72-203. (English Experience Ser.: No. 255). 44p. 1970. Repr. of 1640 ed. 8.00 (ISBN 90-221-0255-6). Walter J Johnson.

Humboldt Years, 1930-39. Beverly W. Brace. 1977. pap. 4.50 (ISBN 0-686-19169-2). B W Brace.

Humiliated Christ in Modern Russian Thought. N. T. Godoretzky. 59.95 (ISBN 0-8490-0376-8). Gordon Pr.

Humiliated Christ in Modern Russian Thought. Nadejda Gorodetzky. LC 79-168159. Repr. of 1938 ed. 18.75 (ISBN 0-404-02883-7). AMS Pr.

Humility, Vol. 1. Archimandrite Chrysostomos & Theodore Williams. LC 82-74509. (Themes in Orthodox Patristic Psychology Ser.). 90p. (Orig.). 1983. pap. text ed. 4.50 (ISBN 0-911165-01-0); pap. write for info. (ISBN 0-911165-02-9). Ctr Trad Orthodox.

Humility & Suffering of God. Francois Varillon. Ed. by Nelly Marans. LC 83-2724. 202p. (Orig.). 1983. pap. 8.95 (ISBN 0-8189-0448-8). Alba.

Humility of God. John Macquarrie. LC 77-18707. 96p. 1978. pap. 4.65 (ISBN 0-664-24200-6). Westminster.

Humility of Heart. Cajetan Mary da Bergamo. Tr. by Herbert C. Vaughan. 240p. 1978. pap. 4.50 (ISBN 0-89555-067-9). Tan Bks Pubs.

Humor: God's Gift. Tal. D. Bonham. 1988. text ed. 9.95 (ISBN 0-8054-5720-8). Broadman.

Humor in Pascal. Olga W. Russell. 1977. 8.95 (ISBN 0-8158-0343-5). Chris Mass.

Humor in Preaching. John W. Drakeford. 160p. 1986. pap. 6.95 (ISBN 0-310-20121-7). Zondervan.

Humor in the American Pulpit from George Whitefield Through Henry Ward Beecher. rev. ed. Doug Adams. 1981. 6.95 (ISBN 0-941500-10-1). Sharing Co.

Humor of Christ. Elton Trueblood. LC 75-12280. 128p. 1975. pap. 4.95 (ISBN 0-06-068631-6, RD 298, HarpR). Har-Row.

Humor of Jesus. Henri Cornier. Tr. by David Heiman from Fr. LC 77-9887. Orig. Title: L Humour De Jesus. 1977. pap. 5.95 (ISBN 0-8189-0356-2). Alba.

Humour & Humanism in Chemistry. John Read. LC 79-8621. Repr. of 1947 ed. 42.50 (ISBN 0-404-18487-1). AMS Pr.

Hundestammvater und Kerberos, 2 vols. Freda Kretschmar. Repr. of 1938 ed. Set. 37.00 (ISBN 0-384-30430-3). Johnson Repr.

Hundred Dharmas. Bodhisattva Vasubhandu. Commentary by Tripitaka Master Hua. Tr. by Buddhist Text Translation Society. 130p. (Orig.). 1983. pap. 6.50 (ISBN 0-88139-003-8). Buddhist Text.

Hundred Thousand Songs of Milarepa, 2 Vols. Tr. by Garma C. Chang from Tibetan. LC 76-55120. 1977. pap. 14.95 ea.; Vol. 1, 356p. (ISBN 0-87773-095-4, 73346-0); Vol. 2, 374p. (ISBN 0-87773-096-2, 72996-X). Shambhala Pubns.

Hung Society: Or the Society of Heaven & Earth, 2 Vols. J. S. Ward. 1977. 35.00 (ISBN 0-89986-003-6). Oriental Bk Store.

Hungarian Jewish Catastrophe: Selected & Annotated Bibliography. Randolph L. Braham. 501p. 1984. 45.00x (ISBN 0-88033-054-6). East Eur Quarterly.

Hungary & the Jews: Policy & Legislation 1920-1943. Nathaniel Katzburg. 299p. cancelled (ISBN 965-226-020-7). Hermon.

Hunger & Discipleship. Vicki Ross. (Orig.). 1982. pap. 8.00 (ISBN 0-8309-0346-1). Herald Hse.

Hunger for Community. J. Diedrich Snoek. LC 72-97850. (Orig.). 1973. pap. 2.50x (ISBN 0-87574-188-6). Pendle Hill.

Hunger for Meaning. 2nd ed. Calvin Miller. LC 83-26490. 180p. 1984. pap. 4.95 (ISBN 0-87784-830-0). Inter-Varsity.

Hunger of the Heart. Ron DelBene & Herb Montgomery. 96p. (Orig.). 1983. pap. 4.95 (ISBN 0-86683-801-5, HarpR). Har-Row.

Hunger, Technology & Limits to Growth: Christian Responsibility for Three Ethical Issues. Robert L. Stivers. LC 83-72120. 176p. (Orig.). 1984. pap. 9.95 (ISBN 0-8066-2064-1, 10-3184). Augsburg.

Hungry for God: Practical Help in Personal Prayer. Ralph Martin. LC 74-4830. 168p. 1974. pap. 6.50 (ISBN 0-385-09534-1). Doubleday.

Hunted Heretic: The Life & Death of Michael Servetus. R. H. Bainton. 11.25 (ISBN 0-8446-1580-3). Peter Smith.

Hunting a Hair Shirt: And Other Spiritual Adventures. Aline M. Kilmer. LC 76-39123. (Essay Index Reprint Ser.). Repr. of 1923 ed. 14.00 (ISBN 0-8369-2697-8). Ayer Co Pubs.

Hunting the Divine Fox: Images & Mystery in the Christian Faith. Robert F. Capon. 176p. 1977. pap. 6.95 (ISBN 0-8164-2137-4, AY7359, HarpR). Har-Row.

Hurban: Responses to Catastrophe in Hebrew Literature. Alan Mintz. LC 83-23979. 288p. 1984. 27.50x (ISBN 0-231-05634-6). Columbia U Pr.

Hurlbut's Story of the Bible. rev. ed. Jesse L. Hurlbut. (Illus.). 15.95 (ISBN 0-310-26520-7, 6524). Zondervan.

Hurnard Gift Set, 8 vols. Hannah Hurnard. 1975. 26.50 (ISBN 0-8423-1547-0). Tyndale.

Hurray for Birthdays. Janet Herbert. (Sparklers Ser.). 1986. comb binding 2.95 (ISBN 1-55513-040-2, Chariot Bks). Cook.

Hurry Up, Noah. Patricia S. Mahany. (Happy Day Bks.). (Illus.). 24p. 1986. 1.59 (ISBN 0-87403-028-5, 3488). Standard Pub.

Hurting. Dan Day. (Uplook Ser.). 1978. pap. 0.99 (ISBN 0-8163-0088-7, 08889-8). Pacific Pr Pub Assn.

Hurting Others. Dan Carr. (God I Need to Talk to You about...Ser.). (Illus.). 1984. pap. 0.75 (ISBN 0-570-08727-9, 56-1471). Concordia.

Hurting Parent. Margie M. Lewis & Gregg Lewis. 160p. (Orig.). 1980. pap. 5.95 (ISBN 0-310-41731-7, 11222P). Zondervan.

Husain the Savior of Islam. S. V. Ali. LC 81-51900. 252p. 1981. 5.95 (ISBN 0-940368-05-6); pap. 3.95 (ISBN 0-940368-03-X). Tahrike Tarsile Quran.

Husband & Wife in Israeli Law. Moshe Chigier. 281p. 1985. 17.50 (ISBN 0-87203-128-4, Pub. by Harry Fischel Institute for Research in Talmud Jerusalem Israel). Hermon.

Husbanding the Golden Grain: Studies in Honor of Henry W. Nordmeyer. Ed. by Luanne T. Frank & Emery E. George. 337p. 1973. 12.50x (ISBN 0-913950-01-7). M S Rosenberg.

Husbands. Patti Williams. LC 75-7477. 1976. 4.95 (ISBN 0-88270-148-7). Bridge Pub.

Husbands, Wives, Parents, Children. rev. ed. Ralph Martin. 1983. pap. 6.95 (ISBN 0-89283-149-9). Servant.

Hush, Hush. Jill Briscoe. 1978. pap. 5.95 (ISBN 0-310-21831-4, 9258P). Zondervan.

Huss et les guerres hussites. Ernest Denis. LC 77-8424. Repr. of 1930 ed. 46.50 (ISBN 0-404-16126-X). AMS Pr.

Husserl, Heidegger, Sartre, Merleau-Ponty: Phenomenology & the Problem of Intentionality. Ed. by Dorothy Leland. 640p. (Orig.). 1987. lib. bdg. 35.00 (ISBN 0-87220-005-1); pap. text ed. 19.50 (ISBN 0-87220-004-3). Hackett Pub.

Hussite Movement & the Reformation in Bohemia, Moravia & Slovakia, 1350-1650: A Bibliographic Study Guide. Jarold K. Zeman. 1977. 15.00 (ISBN 0-930042-00-X). Mich Slavic Pubns.

Hussite Movement in Bohemia. Josef Macek. Tr. by Vilem Fried & Ian Milner. LC 78-63207. (Heresies of the Early Christian & Medieval Era: Second Ser.). Repr. of 1958 ed. 39.50 (ISBN 0-404-16237-1). AMS Pr.

Hussite Revolution: Fourteen Twenty-Four to Fourteen Thirty-Seven. F. M. Bartos. 256p. 1986. 25.00 (ISBN 0-88033-097-X). East Eur Quarterly.

Hutchins' Guide to Bible Reading. John Hutchins. LC 83-102876. (Illus.). 608p. 1983. 25.00x (ISBN 0-938386-00-X). Button Gwin.

Hutterian Brethren. John Horsch. 189p. 1931. 9.95x (ISBN 0-8361-1188-5). Herald Pr.

Hutterian Brethren, 1528-1931. John Horsch. 190p. 1931. 7.00 (ISBN 0-317-47168-6). Plough.

Hutterists: Christians Who Practice a Communal Way of Life. W. S. Pickering. 1985. 20.00 (ISBN 0-7062-4163-0, Pub. by Ward Lock Educ Co Ltd). State Mutual Bk.

Hutterite Age Differences in Body Measurements. W. W. Howells. LC 78-115048. (Peabody Museum Papers: Vol. 57, No. 2). 1970. pap. 10.00x (ISBN 0-87365-168-5). Peabody Harvard.

Hutterite Life. 2nd ed. John A. Hostetler. LC 82-83962. (Illus., Orig.). 1983. pap. 4.95 (ISBN 0-8361-3329-3). Herald Pr.

Hutterite Society. John A. Hostetler. LC 74-6827. (Illus.). 420p. 1974. 30.00x (ISBN 0-8018-1584-3). Johns Hopkins.

Hutterites in North America. John A. Hostetler & Gertrude E. Huntington. LC 79-19718. 141p. 1980. pap. text ed. 9.95 (ISBN 0-03-045391-7, HoltC). HR&W.

Hyacinths to Feed the Soul. Carol Amen. LC 74-33850. (Better Living Ser.). 64p. 1975. pap. text ed. 0.99 (ISBN 0-8127-0094-5). Review & Herald.

Hye Ch'o Diary: Memoir of the Pilgrimage to the Five Regions of India. Ed. by Han-ung Yang et al. (Religions of Asia Ser.). 118p. 1984. 20.00 (ISBN 0-89581-024-7). Asian Human Pr.

Hymn & Scripture Selection Guide. Donald A. Spencer. LC 76-48529. 1977. text ed. 9.85 (ISBN 0-8170-0705-9). Judson.

Hymn As Literature. J. B. Reeves. 59.95 (ISBN 0-8490-0378-4). Gordon Pr.

Hymn Companion. Frank Colquhoun. 288p. 1985. pap. 8.95 (ISBN 0-8192-1368-3). Morehouse.

Hymn Is Born. Clint Bonner. LC 59-9694. 1959. 10.95 (ISBN 0-8054-6801-3). Broadman.

Hymn O Perle: Hymn to the Pearl. Czeslaw Milosz. (Michigan Slavic Materials Ser.: No. 21). 1982. 10.00 (ISBN 0-930042-45-X). Mich Slavic Pubns.

Hymn of Asia. L. Ron Hubbard. 40.00 (ISBN 0-686-30801-8). Church Scient NY.

Hymn of Entry. Vasileios of Stavronikita. Tr. by Elizabeth Briere from Gr. LC 84-5512. 138p. 1984. pap. text ed. 6.95 (ISBN 0-88141-026-8). St Vladimirs.

Hymn of Jesus. George R. Mead. 78p. 1973. pap. 1.00 (ISBN 0-8356-0432-2, Quest). Theos Pub Hse.

Hymn of the Day & Its Use in Lutheran Worship. Carl Schalk. 48p. (Orig.). 1983. pap. 2.50 (ISBN 0-570-01322-4, 99-1252). Concordia.

Hymn of the Universe. Pierre Teilhard De Chardin. LC 65-10375. 1969. pap. 6.95x (ISBN 0-06-131910-4, TB1910, Torch). Har-Row.

Hymn Tune Names: Their Sources & Significance. Robert G. Mc Cutchan. Repr. of 1957 ed. 39.00x (ISBN 0-403-03608-9). Scholarly.

Hymn-Tunes of Lowell Mason. H. Lowell Mason. LC 74-24144. Repr. of 1944 ed. 15.00 (ISBN 0-404-13035-6). AMS Pr.

Hymnal. 7.95 (ISBN 0-664-10033-3). Westminster.

Hymnal Companion. Ed. by Fred Bock & Bryan J. Leech. 1979. 12.95 (ISBN 0-89477-004-7). Paragon Benson.

Hymnal Companion to the Lutheran Book of Worship. Marilyn K. Stulken. LC 81-707. 672p. 1981. 34.95 (ISBN 0-8006-0300-1, 1-300). Fortress.

Hymnal for Juniors in Worship & Study. 2.25 (ISBN 0-664-10082-1). Westminster.

Hymnal Handbook for Standard Hymns & Gospel Songs. Homer A. Rodeheaver. LC 72-1686. Repr. of 1931 ed. 17.50 (ISBN 0-404-09913-0). AMS Pr.

Hymnarius Moissiancensis. Moissac France Benedictine Abbey. 1888. 60.00 (ISBN 0-384-39520-1). Johnson Repr.

Hymnary: A Table for Service Planning. Ed. by James E. Barrett. 95p. 1979. incl. binder 16.00 (ISBN 0-942466-01-2); 13.50 (ISBN 0-942466-00-4). Hymnary Pr.

Hymnary II: A Table For Service Planning. 2nd ed. James E. Barrett. Ed. by James E. Barrett. 96p. 1987. pap. text ed. 13.95 (ISBN 0-942466-11-X); 16.50 (ISBN 0-942466-12-8). Hymnary Pr.

Hymnbook for Christian Worship. Ed. by Charles H. Heaton. LC 69-14339. 1970. Red. 7.95x (ISBN 0-8272-8020-3). Blue. 7.95x (ISBN 0-8272-8021-1); Beige. 7.95x (ISBN 0-8272-8024-6); 19.50x (ISBN 0-8272-8023-8); 8.95x (ISBN 0-8272-8022-X); brown gift 8.50x (ISBN 0-8272-8027-0). CBP.

Hymnbook for Christian Worship. red 6.95 (ISBN 0-8170-9018-5). Judson.

Hymnbook: The Johannine Hymnal: Organ Edition. rev. ed. (Illus.). 1978. 24.95x (ISBN 0-915866-08-0). Am Cath Pr.

Hymne De L'univers. Pierre Teilhard De Chardin. 1966. 13.95 (ISBN 0-685-11240-3). French & Eur.

Hymnes & Songs of the Church. George Wither. (1623, 1881 Reprint 1967). 54.00 (ISBN 0-8337-3937-9). B Franklin.

Hymni Inediti, 7 Vols. Ed. by Guido M. Dreves. 1888-1903. 60.00 ea. Johnson Repr.

Hymnic Affirmation of Divine Justice. James L. Crenshaw. LC 75-22349. (Society of Biblical Literature. Dissertation Ser.: No. 24). Repr. of 1975 ed. 36.10 (ISBN 0-8357-9571-3, 2017523). Bks Demand UMI.

Hymnodia Gotica. Ed. by Clemens Blume. Repr. of 1909 ed. 60.00 ea. Vol. 1. (ISBN 0-384-04766-1); Vol. 2. (ISBN 0-384-04767-X). Johnson Repr.

Hymnodia Hiberica: Liturgische Reimofficien, Aus Spanischen Brevieren. Ed. by Guido M. Dreves. (Illus.). 1894. 60.00 (ISBN 0-384-12915-3). Johnson Repr.

Hymnodia Hiberica: Spanische Hymnen Des Mittelalters. Ed. by Guido M. Dreves. 1894. 60.00 (ISBN 0-384-12920-X). Johnson Repr.

Hymns. Fredrick W. Faber. 1977. Repr. of 1881 ed. 20.00 (ISBN 0-8274-4295-5). R West.

Hymns. Henry Newman. 1983. 9.95 (ISBN 0-87193-199-0). Dimension Bks.

Hymns: A Congregational Study. James R. Syndor. 100p. (Orig.). 1983. pap. text ed. 4.95 (ISBN 0-916642-19-4, 778); tchrs' ed 2.95 (ISBN 0-916642-20-8, 779). Agape Il.

Hymns Ancient & Modern for Use in the Services of the Church, with Accompanying Tunes. Ed. by Charles S. Hyneman. LC 74-24123. (Illus.). Repr. of 1909 ed. 150.00 (ISBN 0-404-12981-1). AMS Pr.

Hymns & Choirs. Austin Phelps et al. LC 78-144671. Repr. of 1860 ed. 29.50 (ISBN 0-404-07207-0). AMS Pr.

Hymns & Hymnwriter of Denmark. J. C. Aaberg. 170p. Repr. of 1945 ed. 29.00 (ISBN 0-932051-28-6, Pub. by Am Repr Serv). Am Biog Serv.

Hymns & Sacred Songs. Alexander Hume. Repr. of 1599 ed. 20.00 (ISBN 0-384-24880-2). Johnson Repr.

Hymns & Songs for Church Schools. Ed. by Ruth L. Olson. LC 62-13898. (Illus.). 1962. 7.95 ea. (12-1500). 25 or more 7.65 ea. Augsburg.

Hymns & Songs of the Spirit. LC 66-12542. 1966. 4.95 (ISBN 0-8272-8017-3). CBP.

Hymns & Their Uses. James R. Sydnor. LC 81-71795. 155p. (Orig.). 1982. pap. 6.95 (ISBN 0-916642-18-6). Hope Pub.

Hymns & Tunes: An Index. Katharine S. Diehl. LC 66-13743. 1242p. 1979. lib. bdg. 65.00 (ISBN 0-8108-0062-4). Scarecrow.

Hymns for Auto Harp. Meg Peterson. 56p. 1978. wkbk 4.95 (ISBN 0-89228-053-0). Impact Bks MO.

Hymns for Choirs. Ed. by David Willcocks. 1976. pap. 6.00 (ISBN 0-19-353556-4). Oxford U Pr.

Hymns for Church & School. (Orig.). 1983. 35.00x (ISBN 0-905418-05-0, Pub. by Gresham England); pap. 30.00x (ISBN 0-9502121-5-6, Pub. by Gresham England). State Mutual Bk.

Hymns for Creative Living. 3.95 (ISBN 0-8170-9009-6). Judson.

Hymns for Little Children. C. F. Armstrong. 1977. lib. bdg. 59.95 (ISBN 0-8490-2030-1). Gordon Pr.

Hymns for Praise & Worship. 1984. 7.95 (ISBN 0-916035-09-3); text ed. 15.00 organist copy (ISBN 0-916035-10-7). Evangel Indiana.

Hymns for the Drowning: Poems for Vishnu by Nammalvar. Tr. by A. K. Rananujan from Tamil. LC 81-47151. (Princeton Library of Asian Translations). 145p. 1982. 23.50 (ISBN 0-691-06492-X); pap. 8.00 (ISBN 0-691-01385-3). Princeton U Pr.

Hymns for the Family of God. Ed. by Fred Bock & Bryan J. Leech. 1976. 7.95 (ISBN 0-89477-000-4, Dist. by Alexandria House); looseleaf 6.95 (ISBN 0-89477-002-0); pap. 7.95 (ISBN 0-89477-001-2). Paragon Benson.

Hymns for Worship. 1963. 6.50 (ISBN 0-916035-02-6, BE-30); organist copy o.p. 15.00 (ISBN 0-916035-03-4). Evangel Indiana.

Hymns from the Crossroads. Ed. by Leroy J. Robertson. (Illus.). 51p. 1965. pap. 6.00 (ISBN 0-8258-0137-0, 0-4516). Fischer Inc NY.

Hymns from the Four Winds: A Collection of Asian American Hymns. 240p. (Orig.). 1983. pap. 7.50 (ISBN 0-687-18126-7). Abingdon.

Hymns from the Golden Age: Selected Hymns from the Rig Veda with Yogic Interpretation. David Frawley. 256p. 1986. 22.00 (ISBN 81-208-0072-9, Pub. by Motilal Banarsidass). South Asia Bks.

Hymns II. Ed. by Paul Beckwith et al. LC 76-47503. 1976. text ed. 12.95 (ISBN 0-87784-898-X); pap. text ed. 7.95 (ISBN 0-87784-783-5); pap. text ed. 10.95 spiral text (ISBN 0-87784-750-9). Inter-Varsity.

Hymns in Action for Everyone Nine to Ninety Dancing Today. Margaret Taylor & Doug Adams. 90p. 1985. pap. 7.95 (ISBN 0-941500-32-2). Sharing Co.

Hymns of Guru Nanak. Ed. & tr. by Khushwant Singh. Repr. of 1969 ed. cancelled (ISBN 0-8364-0302-9, Orient Longman). South Asia Bks.

Hymns of Hermes. Hermes Trismegistos. Tr. by G. R. S. Mead from Gr. 84p. (Orig.). 1985. pap. 4.00 (ISBN 0-933999-57-7). Phanes Pr.

Hymns of Luke's Infancy Narratives: Their Origin, Meaning & Significance. Stephen Farris. (JSoT Supplement Ser.: No. 44). 225p. 1985. text ed. 32.50x (ISBN 0-905774-91-4, Pub. by JSOT Pr England); pap. text ed. 13.95x (ISBN 0-905774-92-2). Eisenbrauns.

Hymns of Orpheus. Thomas Taylor. Bd. with Concerning the Beautiful, Plotinus. 15.00 (ISBN 0-89314-415-0). Philos Res.

Hymns of Our Faith. William J. Reynolds. LC 64-14049. 1964. 18.95 (ISBN 0-8054-6805-6). Broadman.

Hymns of Qumran: Translation & Commentary. Bonnie P. Kittel. Tr. by Bonnie Kittel. LC 80-11616. 1981. pap. 13.50 (ISBN 0-89130-397-9, 06 01 50). Scholars Pr GA.

Hymns of the Ages, 3 vols. F. D. Huntington. 1977. 300.00 (ISBN 0-8490-2031-X). Gordon Pr.

Hymns of the Atharva-Veda: Together with Extracts from the Ritual Books & the Commentaries. Tr. by M. Bloomfield. LC 69-14131. 716p. 1897. Repr. lib. bdg. 32.50x (ISBN 0-8371-1879-4, VEHA). Greenwood.

Hymns of the Christian Life. 698p. 1978. 7.95 (ISBN 0-87509-278-0); deluxe ed. 9.50 (ISBN 0-87509-249-7); organist-pianist version 12.95. Chr Pubns.

Hymns of the Eastern Church. John M. Neale. LC 77-131029. Repr. of 1862 ed. 17.95 (ISBN 0-404-04666-5). AMS Pr.

Hymns of the Rigveda. rev. ed. R. T. Griffith. 1976. 39.95 (ISBN 0-8426-0592-4). Orient Bk Dist.

Hymns of the Saints. World Church Congregational Music Committee. text ed. 10.50 (ISBN 0-8309-0326-7). Herald Hse.

Hymns of the Spirit. UUA. 7.50 (ISBN 0-933840-11-X). Unitarian Univ.

Hymns of Zarathustra. Avesta. Tr. by M. Henning. LC 78-20446. 1985. Repr. of 1952 ed. 21.00 (ISBN 0-88355-826-2). Hyperion Conn.

Hymns That Live. Frank Colquhoun. LC 81-1458. 320p. 1981. pap. 6.95 (ISBN 0-87784-473-9). Inter Varsity.

Hymns to the Dancing Siva. Glenn E. Yocum. 1982. 20.00x (ISBN 0-8364-0851-9). South Asia Bks.

Hymns to the Goddess - Hymn to Kali. John Woodroffe. LC 81-84749. 350p. 1982. 11.00 (ISBN 0-941524-00-0). Lotus Light.

Hymns to the Mystic Fire. Sri Aurobindo. Tr. by Sri Aurobindo. Date not set. 18.00 (ISBN 0-89744-918-5). Auromere.

Hymns to the Mystic Fire. Sri Aurobindo. 506p. 1985. pap. 14.00 (ISBN 0-89071-298-0, Pub. by Sri Aurobindo Ashram India). Matagiri.

Hypergnostic Questions & Concomitant Association for Discharging the Past. Oscar Ichazo. LC 86-70565. 90p. 1986. ring-binder 35.00 (ISBN 0-916554-13-9). Arica Inst Pr.

Hypnosis & the Christian. Martin Bobgan & Deidre Bobgan. LC 83-21401. 64p. (Orig.). 1984. pap. 2.95 (ISBN 0-87123-402-5, 210402). Bethany Hse.

Hypnotism. Albert Moll. (Hypnosis & Altered States of Consciousness Ser.). 626p. 1982. Repr. of 1902 ed. lib. bdg. 49.50 (ISBN 0-306-76079-7). Da Capo.

Hypnotism & Mysticism of India. 2nd ed. Ormond McGill. (Illus.). 208p. 1979. Repr. of 1977 ed. text ed. 12.50 (ISBN 0-930298-01-2). Westwood Pub Co.

Hypostasis of the Archons: The Coptic Text with Translation & Commentary. Ed. by Roger A. Bullard. (Patristische Texte und Studien Ser.: Vol. 10). (Coptic & Eng). 1970. 27.50x (ISBN 3-11-006356-5). De Gruyter.

I

I, a Sinner. Fray Jose G. Mojica. 1962. 5.95 (ISBN 0-685-10968-2, L38305). Franciscan Herald.

I Am a Hindu. Manju Aggarwal. LC 85-50166. (My Heritage Ser.). (Illus.). 32p. 1985. PLB 9.90 (ISBN 0-531-10018-9). Watts.

I Am a Jew. Clive Lawton. Ed. by Frank Sloan. LC 85-50167. (My Heritage Ser.). 32p. 1985. PLB 9.40 (ISBN 0-531-10019-7). Watts.

I Am a Muslim. Manju Aggarwal. (My Heritage Ser.). 32p. 1985. PLB 9.90 (ISBN 0-531-10020-0). Watts.

I Am a Possibility. Gladys Seashore. 80p. 1979. pap. 1.95 (ISBN 0-911802-44-4). Free Church Pubns.

I Am a Sikh. Manju Aggarwal. LC 85-5169. (My Heritage Ser.). (Illus.). 32p. 1985. PLB 9.90 (ISBN 0-531-10021-9). Watts.

I Am a Woman & a Jew. Leah Morton, pseud. (Masterworks of Modern Jewish Writing Ser.). (Illus.). 380p. 1986. pap. 9.95 (ISBN 0-910129-56-8, Distr. by Schocken Books). Wiener Pub Inc.

I Am a Woman by God's Design. Beverly La Haye. 160p. 1980. pap. 5.95 (ISBN 0-8007-5100-0, Power Bks); study guide o.p. 3.95 (ISBN 0-8007-1294-3). Revell.

I Am a Woman; I Am a Person. Bonnie Tinnes. 99p. (Orig.). 1986. pap. 4.95 (ISBN 0-9616611-0-0). Thoughts By Bonnie.

I Am All. James Boulden. (Illus.). 72p. 1982. pap. 2.95 (ISBN 0-87516-481-1). De Vorss.

I Am an Impure Thinker. Eugen Rosenstock-Huessy. 1970. 10.00 (ISBN 0-912148-03-9); pap. 6.95 (ISBN 0-912148-04-7). Argo Bks.

I Am Awake: A Guide to the Contemplative Life. Stephen J. Rossetti. 1987. pap. 3.95. Paulist Pr.

I Am Born Again. Compiled by Rex Kyker. (Undenominational Christianity Ser.: Vol. 2). 94p. (Orig.). 1983. pap. 2.95 (ISBN 0-88027-110-8). Firm Foun Pub.

I Am But a Child in Christ: A Basic Guide for Christian Living. Maria A. Hirschmann. LC 77-89331. (Bible Study & Sharing Ser.: No. 1). 192p. (Orig.). 1977. pap. 4.95 (ISBN 0-932878-00-8, HB-00). Hansi.

I Am Food: The Mass in Planetary Perspective. Roger Corless. LC 81-7836. 112p. 1981. 8.95 (ISBN 0-8245-0077-6). Crossroad NY.

I Am Not My Body: A Study of the International Hare Krishna Sect. Angela Burr. 352p. 1984. text ed. 35.00x (ISBN 0-7069-2296-4, Pub by Vikas India). Advent NY.

I Am One: Prayers for Singles. Carol Greene. LC 85-23015. 112p. (Orig.). 1985. pap. 5.95 (ISBN 0-8066-2186-9, 10-3191). Augsburg.

I Am Persuaded. David Read. (Scholar As Preacher Ser.). 192p. 1961. 12.95 (ISBN 0-567-04430-0, Pub. by T & T Clark Ltd UK). Fortress.

I Am That. rev. ed. Swami Muktananda. 104p. 1983. pap. 3.95 (ISBN 0-914602-27-6). SYDA Found.

I Am That. Bhagwan Shree Rajneesh. Ed. by Ma Prem Apa. LC 84-42809. (Upanishads Ser.). 416p. (Orig.). 1984. pap. 5.95 (ISBN 0-88050-580-X). Chidvilas Found.

I Am That I Am: A Metaphysical Course on Consciousness. James Thomas. (Illus.). 168p. 1984. 14.95x (ISBN 0-931290-90-2); pap. 6.95x (ISBN 0-931290-91-0). Alchemy Bks.

I Am That; Talks with Sri Nisargadatta Maharaj. Nisargadatta Maharaj. Tr. by Maurice Frydman from Marathi. Ed. by Sudhakar S. Dikshit. LC 81-66800. xx, 550p. 1986. Repr. of 1982 ed. 19.50 (ISBN 0-89386-002-6). Acorn NC.

I Am the Vine. Joel S. Goldsmith. 1972. pap. 1.00 (ISBN 0-87516-138-3). De Vorss.

I Am What I Am for God Whosoever Will. Christine Lewellen. 1987. 8.95 (ISBN 0-533-07150-X). Vantage.

I Am What I Do: Contemplation & Human Experience. Barbara Doherty. 226p. 1982. pap. 9.95 (ISBN 0-88347-129-9). Thomas More.

I Am Yahweh. Walther Zimmerli. Ed. by Walter Brueggemann. Tr. by Doug Scott from German. LC 81-85326. 160p. 1982. 15.95 (ISBN 0-8042-0519-1). John Knox.

I & II Kings: A Commentary. 2nd rev. ed. John Gray. (Old Testament Library Ser.). 27.50. Westminster.

I & II Samuel: A Commentary. Hans Hertzberg. (Old Testament Library Ser.). 22.95. Westminster.

I & the Father Are One. Frank J. Muccie, Jr. 180p. 1982. pap. 7.95 (ISBN 0-938520-01-6). Edenite.

I & Thou. Martin Buber. 13.50 (ISBN 0-8446-6219-4). Peter Smith.

I & Thou. Martin Buber et al. Tr. by Walter Kaufman & S. G. Smith. LC 72-123845. (Hudson River Edition). 1970. 20.00 (ISBN 0-684-15575-3, ScribT); pap. 6.95 (ISBN 0-684-71725-5, ScribT). Scribner.

I Asked for Wonder: A Spiritual Anthology. Abraham J. Heschel. 128p. 1983. pap. 8.95 (ISBN 0-8245-0542-5). Crossroad NY.

I Believe. Lowell L. Bennion. LC 83-70024. 87p. 1983. 5.95 (ISBN 0-87747-954-2). Deseret Bk.

I Believe... C. Donald Cole. 160p. 1983. pap. 3.95 (ISBN 0-8024-0353-0). Moody.

I Believe. Nevin C. Harner. (Orig.). 1950. 3.95 (ISBN 0-8298-0066-2); pap. 2.95 (ISBN 0-8298-0067-0). Pilgrim NY.

I Believe: A Woman's Workshop on Relational Doctrine. Robert E. Webber. (Woman's Workshop Ser.). 160p. 1986. pap. 3.95 (ISBN 0-310-36701-8). Zondervan.

I Believe Because. Batsell B. Baxter. 1971. pap. 8.95 (ISBN 0-8010-0548-5). Baker Bk.

I Believe in Evangelism. David Watson. (I Believe Ser). 1977. pap. 5.95 (ISBN 0-8028-1687-8). Eerdmans.

I Believe in God. 52p. 1975. 3.60 (ISBN 0-686-29267-7). Natl Cath Educ.

I Believe in God: The Apostles' Creed. Lawrence G. Lovasik. (Saint Joseph Picture Bks.). (Illus.). flexible bdg. 0.95 (ISBN 0-89942-276-4, 276). Catholic Bk Pub.

I Believe In Love. Jean du Couer de Jesus d' Elbee. Tr. by Marilyn Teichert & Madeline Stebbins. LC 82-24134. Tr. of Croire a l'amour. (Fr.). 1983. pap. 4.95 (ISBN 0-932506-21-6). St Bedes Pubns.

I Believe in Miracles. Kathryn Kuhlman. 1975. pap. 2.25 (ISBN 0-515-05858-0). Jove Pubns.

I Believe in Mission. Mariano DiGangi. 1979. pap. 2.95 (ISBN 0-87552-255-6). Presby & Reformed.

I Believe in Revelation. Leon Morris. (I Believe Ser.). 160p. 1976. pap. 6.95 (ISBN 0-8028-1637-1). Eerdmans.

I Believe in Satan's Downfall. Michael Green. (I Believe Ser.). 256p. (Orig.). 1981. pap. 6.95 (ISBN 0-8028-1892-7). Eerdmans.

I Believe in the Church. Watson. pap. 10.95 (ISBN 0-8028-1788-2). Eerdmans.

I Believe in the Great Commission. Max Warren. (I Believe Ser.). 1976. pap. 4.95 (ISBN 0-8028-1659-2). Eerdmans.

I Believe in the Historical Jesus. I. Howard Marshall. (I Believe Ser). 1977. pap. 4.95 (ISBN 0-8028-1691-6). Eerdmans.

I Believe in the Holy Spirit, 3 Vols. Yves Congar. Tr. by David Smith from Fr. Incl. Vol. I. The Experience of the Spirit. 173p. 24.95 (ISBN 0-8164-0518-2); Vol. 2. Lord & Giver of Life. 230p. 24.95 (ISBN 0-8164-0535-2); Vol. 3. The River of Life Flows in the East & in the West. 274p. 24.95 (ISBN 0-8164-0537-9). 300p. 1983. Set. 70.00 (ISBN 0-8164-0540-9, Winston-Seabury). Har-Row.

I Believe in the Holy Spirit. Michael Green. (I Believe Ser). 224p. 1975. pap. 8.95 (ISBN 0-8028-1609-6). Eerdmans.

I Believe in the Resurrection. George E. Ladd. (I Believe). 160p. 1975. pap. 5.95 (ISBN 0-8028-1611-8). Eerdmans.

I Believe in the Resurrection of the Body. Rubem Alves. Tr. by L. M. McCoy from Ger. & Port. LC 85-16246. 80p. 1986. pap. 4.95 (ISBN 0-8006-1885-8, 1-1885). Fortress.

I Believe in Visions. 2nd ed. Kenneth E. Hagin. 1984. pap. 3.50 (ISBN 0-89276-508-9). Hagin Ministries.

I Believe in Youth, Christ Believes in Youth. Pope John Paul II. 1981. 4.95 (ISBN 0-8198-3602-8); pap. 3.95 (ISBN 0-8198-3603-6). Dghtrs St Paul.

I Believe: The Creed. Joanne L. Kepes. 1981. 9.95 (ISBN 0-89837-067-1, Pub. by Pflaum Pr). Peter Li.

I Call It Heresy. A. W. Tozer. pap. 3.45 (ISBN 0-87509-209-8). Chr Pubns.

I Came Back Tomorrow. Edmond B. Szekely. (Illus.). 32p. 1976. pap. 3.50 (ISBN 0-89564-073-2). IBS Intl.

I Came to Love You Late. Joyce Landorf. 192p. 1981. pap. 3.50 (ISBN 0-8007-8411-1, Spire Bks). Revell.

I Can Heal Myself & I Will. new ed. Cushing Smith. LC 62-14344. 315p. 1980. pap. 7.95 (ISBN 0-8119-0384-2). Fell.

I Can Make My Own Prayers. Lucille E. Hein. LC 72-154026. (Illus.). 1971. 3.95 (ISBN 0-8170-0528-5). Judson.

I Can Pray to God. Sandra Brooks. LC 82-80031. (Happy Day Bks.). (Illus.). 24p. (Orig.). 1982. pap. 1.59 (ISBN 0-87239-540-5, 3586). Standard Pub.

I Can Read About the First Thanksgiving. J. I. Anderson. LC 76-54400. (Illus.). 1977. pap. 1.50 (ISBN 0-89375-034-4). Troll Assocs.

I Can Talk to God. Christine Tangvald. (I Am Special Bks.). (Illus.). 20p. 1985. 3.95 (ISBN 0-89191-907-4, 59071). Cook.

I Can, You Can Too! Mamie McCullough. 224p. 1986. 14.95 (ISBN 0-8407-3068-3). Nelson.

I Cannot Hear You, But I Can Hear God. Phillip Hassall. Ed. by Sylvia Mandeville. 144p. 1987. pap. 3.95 (ISBN 0-340-38268-6, Pub. by Hodder & Stoughton UK). David & Charles.

I Can't Help Singing for Jesus Gives the Song. Pearl Jacobson. 192p. (Orig.). 1983. pap. 3.95 (ISBN 0-88144-010-8, CPS-010). Christian Pub.

I Can't Turn Off My Happy. Ben Leach. (Uplook Ser.). 32p. 1982. pap. 0.79 (ISBN 0-8163-0515-3). Pacific Pr Pub Assn.

I Ching. Tr. by James Legge. 1969. pap. 4.95 (ISBN 0-553-26002-2). Bantam.

I Ching & You. Diane F. Hook. 160p. 1985. pap. 8.95 (ISBN 0-7100-8042-5). Methuen Inc.

I Ching: Book of Changes. James Legge. 449p. 1983. pap. 7.95 (ISBN 0-8065-0458-7). Citadel Pr.

I Ching of the Goddess. Barbara Walker. LC 86-45029. (Illus.). 176p. (Orig.). 1986. pap. 12.95 (ISBN 0-06-250924-1, HarpR). Har-row.

I Choose to Belong. Susan Davis. (My Church Teaches Ser.). 1979. pap. 1.65 (ISBN 0-8127-0237-9). Review & Herald.

I Come As a Brother: Bartholomew. Ed. by Mary-Margaret Moor. 192p. 1986. pap. 10.95 (ISBN 0-9614010-1-X). High Mesa Pr.

I Corinthians: Problems & Solutions in a Growing Church. Charles Hummel & Anne Hummel. (Fisherman Bible Studyguide). 93p. 1981. saddle-stitched 2.95 (ISBN 0-87788-137-5). Shaw Pubs.

I Costituti Di Don Pietro Manelfi. Ed. by Carlo Ginzburg. LC 72-3473. (Corpus Reformatorum Italicorum & Biblioteca Ser.). (Illus.). 101p. 1970. pap. 10.00 (ISBN 0-87580-510-8). N Ill U Pr.

I Dared to Live. Sandra Brand. LC 78-52142. 1978. pap. 8.95 (ISBN 0-88400-058-3). Shengold.

I Didn't Know That. Douglas Leroy. 1973. pap. 3.95 (ISBN 0-87148-425-0). Pathway Pr.

I Do Not Climb This Mountain Alone. Harold V. Smuck. (Illus.). 48p. (Orig.). 1985. pap. 3.00 (ISBN 0-913408-88-3). Friends United.

I Do Windows. Neal Stanford. 48p. 1982. 6.00 (ISBN 0-682-49865-3). Exposition Pr FL.

I Don't Want to Complain, But: Teen Conversations with God. Theodore W. Schroeder. 112p. (Orig.). 1985. pap. 4.95 (ISBN 0-570-03964-9, 12-2999). Concordia.

I Encountered God! The Spiritual Exercises with the Gospel of St. John. David M. Stanley. Ed. by George E. Ganss. LC 84-82164. (Original Studies, Composed in English: Ser. III, No. 7). 348p. 1986. 14.00 (ISBN 0-912422-72-6); pap. 11.00 Smyth sewn (ISBN 0-912422-71-8). Inst Jesuit.

I Feel My Saviour's Love: Themes from LDS Children's Songs in Counted Cross-Stitch. Sharalee S. Clawson. 9p. 1986. pap. 5.00 (ISBN 0-88290-277-6). Horizon Utah.

I Found the Key to the Heart of God. Mother Basilea Schlink. LC 75-23920. 416p. 1975. pap. 5.95 (ISBN 0-87123-239-1, 200239). Bethany Hse.

I, Francis. Carlo Carretto. Tr. by Robert R. Barr from Ital. LC 81-16913. Orig. Title: Io Francesco. 144p. (Orig.). 1982. pap. 6.95 (ISBN 0-88344-200-0). Orbis Bks.

I Gave God Time. Ann K. Anderson. 1982. 7.95 (ISBN 0-8423-1560-8); pap. 5.95 1984 (ISBN 0-8423-1559-4). Tyndale.

I Go To Church. Bartholomew. 1982. pap. 0.85 (ISBN 0-570-04072-8, 56-1375). Concordia.

I Go to Church. Marian Bennett. (My Shape Book Ser.). (Illus.). 10p. 1985. 2.95 (ISBN 0-87239-911-7, 2751). Standard Pub.

I Got the Word in Me & I Can Sing It, You Know: A Study of the Performed African American Sermon. Gerald L. Davis. LC 85-2544. (Illus.). 272p. 1986. text ed. 24.95 (ISBN 0-8122-7987-5). U of Pa Pr.

I Hate to Bother You, But: Clues for Youth on Personal Problems. rev. ed. William E. Hulme. Orig. Title: Face Your Life with Confidence. 1970. pap. 4.95 (ISBN 0-570-06617-4, 12-2327). Concordia.

I Hate Witnessing. Dick Innes. LC 84-27531. 1985. pap. 2.95 (ISBN 0-8307-1003-5, 5418403). Regal.

I Hate Witnessing: A Handbook for Effective Christian Communication. Dick Innes. LC 84-27531. 1985. pap. text ed. 2.95 (ISBN 0-8307-1003-5, 5418403). Vision Hse.

I Hate Witnessing Leader's Guide. Rob Burkhart. LC 84-18165. 64p. 1985. pap. 3.95 (ISBN 0-8307-1011-6, 6101987). Regal.

I Have a Family. Rachel Coe. LC 86-17629. (Bible-&-Me Ser.). 1987. 5.95 (ISBN 0-8054-4172-7). Broadman.

I Have Become Alive: Secrets of the Inner Journey. Swami Mukananda. Ed. by Swami Durgananda. Tr. by Swami Chidvilasananda. LC 85-50040. 240p. (Orig.). 1985. pap. 6.95 (ISBN 0-914602-89-6). SYDA Found.

I Have Been Before the Judgement Seat of Christ: A Religious Autobiography. Gladys Cuss. 189p. 1980. 7.95 (ISBN 0-682-49521-2). Exposition Pr FL.

I Have Been Here. Corbin L. Cherry. 112p. 1987. 6.95 (ISBN 1-55523-050-4). Winston-Derek.

I Have Many Feelings: With Scriptural Encouragement. (Little Shape Bks.). (Illus.). 22p. 1984. 2.50 (ISBN 0-89954-240-9). Antioch Pub Co.

I Have Seen the Lord. Junior Grant. 48p. 1982. 5.95 (ISBN 0-8059-2845-6). Dorrance.

I, He, We & They: A Literary Approach to Isaiah Fifty-Three. David J. Clines. (JSOT Supplement Ser.: No. 1). 65p. 1976. pap. text ed. 4.95x (ISBN 0-905774-00-0, Pub. by JSOT Pr England). Eisenbrauns.

I Hear the Rolling Thunder. Larry Powell. 1986. 9.25 (ISBN 0-89536-803-X, 6821). CSS of Ohio.

I Hear Two Voices, God! Donald Deffner. LC 12-2817. 1983. pap. 4.95 (ISBN 0-570-03882-0). Concordia.

I Help the Handicapped. Christine Kohler. (Growing Up Christian Ser.). 24p. (Orig.). 1985. pap. 3.95 (ISBN 0-570-04114-7, 56-1525). Concordia.

I, in Christ Arisen. Tr. by Francis Elmo from Span. LC 81-85745. Orig. Title: Yo, en Cristo Resucitado. 100p. 1982. pap. 4.00 (ISBN 0-9607590-0-X). Action Life Pubns.

I Just Saw Jesus, Still Doing Miracles, Still Touching Lives. Paul Eshleman. 224p. (Orig.). 1985. pap. 6.95 (ISBN 0-89840-100-3). Heres Life.

I Kings, with an Introduction to Historical Literature, 24 Vols, Vol. 9. Burke O. Long. Ed. by Rolf Knierim & Gene Tucker. (Forms of the Old Testament Literature Ser.). 288p. (Orig.). 1984. pap. 20.95 (ISBN 0-8028-1920-6). Eerdmans.

I Knew St. Maximilian. Juventyn Mlodozeniec. 116p. 1982. pap. 2.95 (ISBN 0-911988-48-3). AMI Pr.

I Know Christ. Gratian Of Paris. (Spirit & Life Ser). 1957. 2.00 (ISBN 0-686-11569-4). Franciscan Inst.

I Know God Loves Me. Jill Wolf. (Illus.). 24p. 1984. pap. 1.95 (ISBN 0-89954-288-3). Antioch Pub Co.

I Know His Touch. Luba Bershadsky & Ada Millington. LC 83-72042. 192p. (Orig.). 1984. pap. 6.95 (ISBN 0-89107-299-3, Crossway Bks). Good News.

I Know His Touch. Luba Bershadsky & Ada Millington. 240p. 1985. pap. 2.95 (ISBN 0-345-32164-2). Ballantine.

I Know I Can Trust You, Lord: Prayers for Girls. Lyn Klug. LC 83-70503. (Young Readers Ser.). 80p. 1983. pap. 3.95 (ISBN 0-8066-2009-9, 10-3192). Augsburg.

I Launch at Paradise: A Consideration of John Donne, Poet & Preacher. Frederick A. Rowe. LC 65-84641. 1964. 10.00x (ISBN 0-8401-2055-9). A R Allenson.

I Launch at Paradise: A Consideration of John Donne Poet & Preacher. Frederick A. Rowe. 253p. 1983. lib. bdg. 40.00 (ISBN 0-89984-841-9). Century Bookbindery.

I Learn About Jesus. Daughters of St. Paul. 1973. 5.50 (ISBN 0-8198-0246-8); pap. 4.00 (ISBN 0-8198-0247-6). Dghtrs St Paul.

I Learn About Jesus: Projects & Activities for Pre-Schoolers. Daughters of St. Paul. 1973. pap. 1.00 (ISBN 0-8198-0245-X). Dghtrs St Paul.

I Learn to Read about Jesus: Primer. rev. ed. Jane B. Moncure. (Basic Bible Readers Ser.). 128p. 1983. text ed. 7.95 (ISBN 0-87239-660-6, 2950). Standard Pub.

I Like Being a Christian. Paul W. Powell. LC 82-73370. (Orig.). 1982. pap. 5.50 (ISBN 0-8054-5212-5). Broadman.

I Like to Go to Church. Phyllis Boykin. (Bible-&-Me Ser.). 1987. 5.95 (ISBN 0-8054-4174-3). Broadman.

I Love Jesus. Patricia Mahany. (My Shape Bk.). (Illus.). 12p. 1984. 2.95 (ISBN 0-87239-785-8, 2725). Standard Pub.

I Love Me, the Only Diet There Is: A Manual. Jackie Banas. (Orig.). 1986. spiral bdg. 7.00 (ISBN 0-9614014-3-5). Know Him Pr.

I Love My Body. Louise L. Hay. 80p. 1985. pap. 5.00 (ISBN 0-937611-02-6). Hay House.

I Love the Word Impossible. Ann Kiemel. 1978. pock. pap 3.50 (ISBN 0-8423-1578-0). Tyndale.

I Love You. Muktananda. (Illus.). 40p. (Orig.). 1975. 1.75 (ISBN 0-914602-58-6). SYDA Found.

I Loved a Girl. Walter Trobisch. LC 75-12281. 128p. 1975. pap. 6.95 (ISBN 0-06-068443-7, RD 352, HarpR). Har-Row.

I, Luke. Luke the Physician. LC 81-80713. (Illus.). 120p. 1981. pap. 3.25 (ISBN 0-87973-665-8, 665). Our Sunday Visitor.

I Meet Jesus: He Tells Me "I Love You". Jean Vanier. LC 81-82109. 208p. 1982. pap. 3.95 (ISBN 0-8091-2725-3). Paulist Pr.

I Met Angels in the Tangles of Life. Irene B. Ellsworth. LC 84-52166. 118p. (Orig.). 1985. pap. 4.95 (ISBN 0-9614165-0-5). Terhell Bks.

I Need Only God. Sri Chinmoy. 50p. (Orig.). 1975. pap. 2.00 (ISBN 0-88497-133-3). Aum Pubns.

I Need Souls Like You Sharing in the Work of Charity Through Prayer & Suffering. Mother Teresa of Calcutta & Kathryn Spink. LC 83-48984. 128p. 1984. 10.45 (ISBN 0-06-068236-1, HarpR). Har-Row.

I Never Said I Didn't Love You. Robert Griffin. LC 76-24442. (Emmuas Book Ser.). 128p. 1977. pap. 2.95 (ISBN 0-8091-1989-7). Paulist Pr.

I Never Thought It Would Be This Way. James A. Jones. 5.50 (ISBN 0-89137-533-3). Quality Pubns.

I Opener. Herbert Brokering. LC 74-4912. (YA) 1974. pap. 2.50 (ISBN 0-570-06472-4, 12-2584). Concordia.

I Owe My Life to Jesus -- You Also? An Autobiography Charismatic. H. Winky-Lotz. (Illus.). 210p. 1986. 10.95 (ISBN 0-936112-00-X); pap. 6.50 (ISBN 0-936112-01-8). Willyshe Pub.

I Peter. Ernest Best. Ed. by Matthew Black. (The New Century Bible Commentary Ser.). 188p. 1982. pap. 6.95 (ISBN 0-8028-1909-5). Eerdmans.

I Pray with Jesus. Daughters of St. Paul. 1978. deluxe ed. 7.00 (ISBN 0-8198-0535-1); plastic bdg. 3.00 (ISBN 0-8198-0537-8). Dghtrs St Paul.

I Prayed, He Answered. William L. Vaswig. LC 77-72457. 1977. pap. 5.95 (ISBN 0-8066-1589-3, 10-3189). Augsburg.

I Read about God's Care: Grade 2. rev. ed. Laura Alden. (Basic Bible Readers Ser.). (Illus.). 128p. 1983. text ed. 7.95 (ISBN 0-87239-662-2, 2952). Standard Pub.

I Read about God's Love. rev. ed. Compiled by Sylvia R. Tester & Marge Miller. (Illus.). 128p. 1983. text ed. 7.95 (ISBN 0-87239-661-4, 2951). Standard Pub.

I Sat Where They Sat. William Gale. pap. 2.50 (ISBN 0-686-12884-2). Schmul Pub Co.

I Saw Heaven. Ed. by Roberts Lairdon. 31p. 1983. pap. 2.00 (ISBN 0-915693-00-3). Christian Pub.

I Saw Him. Sarah W. Miller. (Orig.). 1964. pap. 1.95 (ISBN 0-8054-9708-0). Broadman.

I Saw the Holy Shroud. Peter M. Rinaldi. LC 83-71121. (Illus.). 112p. 1983. 4.95 (ISBN 0-89944-072-X); pap. 2.85 (ISBN 0-89944-069-X). Don Bosco Multimedia.

I Say unto You, 2 vols. Bhagwan Shree Rajneesh. Ed. by Ma Prem Asha. LC 82-245650. (Jesus Ser.). (Illus., Orig.). 1980. Vol. I, 384. 19.50 (ISBN 0-88050-085-9); Vol. II. pap. 15.95 (ISBN 0-88050-586-9); pap. 4.95 wkbk. (ISBN 0-88050-585-0). Chidvilas Found.

I Scrittori De'Chierici Regolari Detti Teatini. Antonio F. Vezzosi. 1030p. Date not set. Repr. of 1780 ed. text ed. 165.60x (ISBN 0-576-72811-X, Pub. by Gregg Intl Pubs England). Gregg Intl.

I Send a Voice. Evelyn Eaton. LC 78-7273. (Illus., Orig.). 1978. 10.95 (ISBN 0-8356-0513-2). Theos Pub Hse.

I Shall Fear No Evil. Joyce Cooper. 1986. 8.95 (ISBN 0-317-43335-0). Vantage.

I Sing a Song of the Saints of God. Judith G. Brown. (Illus.). 32p. (Orig.). 1981. pap. 5.95 (ISBN 0-8164-2339-3, HarpR). Har-Row.

I Sing Your Praise All the Day Long. Fritz Pawelzik. (Illus., Orig.). 1967. pap. 1.50 (ISBN 0-377-37221-8). Friend Pr.

I Sought & I Found: My Experience of God & of the Church. Carlo Carretto. Tr. by Robert R. Barr from Ital. Tr. of Ho Cercato E. Ho Trovato. 144p. 1984. pap. 7.95 (ISBN 0-88344-202-7). Orbis Bks.

I Stay in the Church. Elizabeth Hamilton. 183p. 1973. 4.95 (ISBN 0-85478-053-X). Attic Pr.

I Support You But I Can't Sign My Name. Ed. by Constance McKenna. 20p. 1982. pap. 1.00 (ISBN 0-915365-06-5). Cath Free Choice.

I Talk Back to the Devil. A. W. Tozer. Ed. by Gerald B. Smith. Orig. Title: Tozer Pulpit, Vol. 4. Twelve Sermons on Spiritual Perfection. (Illus.). 144p. (Orig.). 1972. pap. 3.45 (ISBN 0-87509-206-3). Chr Pubns.

I Talk to God. Annetta E. Dellinger. LC 84-50287. (Little Happy Day Bks.). (Illus.). 24p. (Orig.). 1984. pap. 0.49 (ISBN 0-87239-802-1, 2162). Standard Pub.

I Tell You Truly. Hal Gulley & Nadine Gulley. LC 81-82218. 192p. 1983. pap. 4.95 (ISBN 0-89900-194-7). College Pr Pub.

I Thank God. Marie H. Frost. (First Happy Day Bks.). (Illus.). 20p. 1986. casebound 1.29 (ISBN 0-87403-134-6, 2004). Standard Pub.

I, the Prophet. Richard E. Bauerle. 1981. pap. 6.95 (ISBN 0-570-03835-9, 12YY2800). Concordia.

I: The Story of the Self. Michal J. Eastcott. LC 80-51552. (Illus.). 201p. (Orig.). 1980. pap. 5.50 (ISBN 0-8356-0541-8, Quest). Theos Pub Hse.

I Think...I Know: A Poster Book about God. Joan Hutson. (Illus.). 32p. (Orig.). 1979. pap. 1.95 (ISBN 0-87793-186-0). Ave Maria.

I Wait for You: Jesus' Lament Over Man's Indifference (Excerpts from the Way of Divine Love) Josefa Menendez. 32p. (Orig.). 1985. pap. 0.50 (ISBN 0-89555-285-X). Tan Bks Pubs.

I Walk by Faith. Ardeth G. Kapp. 1987. 9.95 (ISBN 0-87579-072-0). Deseret Bk.

I Walk with Jesus. Jean Vanier. 208p. (Orig.). 1986. pap. 7.95 (ISBN 0-8091-2786-5). Paulist Pr.

I Want My Church to Grow. C. B. Hogue. LC 77-85280. 1977. 7.95 (ISBN 0-8054-6217-1). Broadman.

I Want the Truth. Margaret J. Anderson. 96p. 1969. pap. 1.25 (ISBN 0-88243-531-0, 02-0531). Gospel Pub.

I Want to Be a Christian. J. I. Packer. 1977. pap. 8.95 (ISBN 0-8423-1842-9). Tyndale.

I Want to Be Like You, Lord: Bible Devotion for Girls. Betty S. Everett. LC 84-21563. (Young Readers Ser.). 112p. (Orig.). 1984. pap. 3.95 (ISBN 0-8066-2112-5, 10-3196). Augsburg.

I Want to Console You. Basilea Schlink. 72p. 1981. pap. 1.50 (ISBN 3-87209-626-5). Evang Sisterhood Mary.

I Want to See God - I Am a Daughter of the Church, 2 vols. in 1. P. Marie Eugene. 1216p. 1986. pap. 39.95 (ISBN 0-87061-134-8). Chr Classics.

I Was. Torkom Saraydarian. LC 77-86723. 1981. pap. 5.00 (ISBN 0-911794-43-3). Aqua Educ.

I Was a Monk. John Tettemer. LC 73-89888. pap. 1.25 (ISBN 0-8356-0300-8, Quest). Theos Pub Hse.

I Was Raised a Jehovah's Witness. Joe B. Hewitt. LC 78-73255. 1979. pap. 3.95 (ISBN 0-89636-018-0). Accent Bks.

I Was...Called To Be a Layman. Gus Gustafson. 176p. (Orig.). 1982. pap. 7.95 (ISBN 0-687-18604-8). Abingdon.

I Welcome You All with Love. Swami Muktananda. 40p. (Orig.). 1978. pap. 1.75 (ISBN 0-914602-59-4). SYDA Found.

I Went to Hell. Kenneth E. Hagin. 1982. pap. 0.50 mini bk. (ISBN 0-89276-257-8). Hagin Ministries.

I Went to School with Jesus. Frank A. Beattie, Jr. (Orig.). 1982. pap. 1.95 (ISBN 0-937172-37-5). JLJ Pubs.

I Will. 2nd ed. Emma L. Hayhurst. 1982. pap. 4.95 (ISBN 0-938736-09-4). Life Enrich.

I Will. Urban G. Steinmetz. LC 71-84816. (Illus.). 136p. 1969. pap. 1.75 (ISBN 0-87793-010-4). Ave Maria.

I Will Be a Doctor! Dorothy C. Wilson. LC 83-3862. 160p. (Orig.). 1983. pap. 7.95 (ISBN 0-687-19727-9). Abingdon.

I Will Build My Church. John W. Smith. 1985. pap. 3.95 (ISBN 0-87162-411-7, D4320). Warner Pr.

I Will Do a New Thing: The Story of the U. S. Center for World Mission. rev. ed. Frwd. by Ralph Winter. LC 78-66367. Orig. Title: Once More Around Jericho. 320p. 1987. pap. 4.95 (ISBN 0-87808-201-8). William Carey Lib.

I Will Lift up Mine Eyes. Glenn Clark. 1937. pap. 7.95 (ISBN 0-06-061393-9, RP518, HarpR). Har-Row.

I Will Lift up Mine Eyes. Glenn Clark. LC 77-7830. (Illus.). 208p. 1984. pap. 7.95 (ISBN 0-06-061394-7, RD 518, HarpR). Har-Row.

I Will Not Leave You Comfortless. Dorene Waggoner. (Illus.). 32p. 1984. 4.95 (ISBN 0-8378-2040-5). Gibson.

I Wills of Christ. P. B. Power. 382p. 1984. pap. 5.95 (ISBN 0-85151-429-4). Banner of Truth.

I Wills of the Psalms. P. B. Power. 395p. 1985. pap. 5.95 (ISBN 0-85151-445-6). Banner of Truth.

I Wish I Could Believe. Juan L. Pedraz. Tr. by Salvatore Attanasio from Span. LC 82-20606. 201p. (Orig.). 1983. pap. 7.95 (ISBN 0-8189-0445-3). Alba.

I Wish I Could Say, "I Love You". Muriel Canfield. 204p. (Orig.). 1983. pap. 5.95 (ISBN 0-87123-265-0, 210265). Bethany Hse.

I Wish I Felt Good All the Time. Mildred Tengbom. 160p. (Orig.). 1983. pap. 4.95 (ISBN 0-87123-281-2, 210281). Bethany Hse.

I Wish, I Wish. E. Elaine Watson. LC 82-62733. (Happy Day Bks.). (Illus.). 24p. 1983. 1.59 (ISBN 0-87239-637-1, 3557). Standard Pub.

I Wish Someone Understood My Divorce: A Practical Cope-Book. Harold I. Smith. LC 86-28874. 160p. (Orig.). 1987. pap. 7.95 (ISBN 0-8066-2246-6, 10-3194). Augsburg.

I Wonder from Job. Sylvia Camp. pap. 3.50 (ISBN 0-89315-127-0). Lambert Bk.

I Wouldn't Take Nothin' for My Journey: Two Centuries of an American Minister's Family. Leonidas H. Berry. 1981. 14.95 (ISBN 0-686-95206-5). Johnson Chi.

I Write for You. Eddie Hendrick. 48p. 1983. 5.95 (ISBN 0-686-82586-1). Todd & Honeywell.

Iamblichus & the Theory of the Vehicle of the Soul. John Finamore. (APA-American Classical Studies). 1985. pap. 12.95 (ISBN 0-89130-883-0, 40-04-14). Scholars Pr GA.

Ian & the Gigantic Leafy Obstacle. Sheila Miller. 1983. pap. 1.50 (ISBN 9971-83-790-0). OMF Bks.

Ibadat. A. S. Hashim. (Islamic Books for Children: Bk. 2). pap. 4.95 (ISBN 0-686-18414-9); pap. 40.00 entire ser. (ISBN 0-686-18415-7). Kazi Pubns.

Iberian Fathers Vol. 1: Marin of Braga, Paschasius, Leander. LC 70-80270. (Fathers of the Church Ser: Vol. 62). 254p. 1969. 14.95x (ISBN 0-8132-0062-8). Cath U Pr.

Iberian Fathers Vol. 2: Braulio of Saragossa, Fructuosus of Braga. LC 70-80270. (Fathers of the Church Ser: Vol. 63). 243p. 1969. 14.95x (ISBN 0-8132-0063-6). Cath U Pr.

Iberian Popular Religion, Six Hundred B. C. to Seven Hundred A. D. Celts, Romans & Visigoths. Joyce E. Salisbury. (Texts & Studies in Religion: Vol. 20). 340p. 1985. 59.95x (ISBN 0-88946-809-5). E Mellen.

IBN Abbad of Ronda, Letters on the Sufi Path. Tr. by John Renard. (Classics of Western Spirituality Ser.: No. 49). 256p. 1986. 12.95 (ISBN 0-8091-0365-6); pap. 9.95 (ISBN 0-8091-2730-X). Paulist PR.

Ibn-Al-Arabi. Husaini. pap. 1.75 (ISBN 0-686-18320-7). Kazi Pubns.

Ibn-Al-Arabi: The Bezels of Wisdom. Ed. by R. W. Austin. LC 80-83892. (Classics of Western Spirituality Ser.). 320p. 1980. 12.95 (ISBN 0-8091-0313-3); pap. 10.95 (ISBN 0-8091-2331-2). Paulist Pr.

Ibn 'Ata Illah-Kwaja Abdullah Ansari: The Book of Wisdom-Intimate Conversations. Victor Danner & Wheeler Thackston. LC 78-1022. (Classics of Western Spirituality-Sufi Ser.). 256p. 1978. 12.95 (ISBN 0-8091-0279-X); pap. 8.95 (ISBN 0-8091-2182-4). Paulist Pr.

Ibn Ezra on Leviticus: The Straightforward Meaning. pap. 9.95 (ISBN 0-88125-109-7). Ktav.

Ibn Hazm. Anver Chejne. 29.00 (ISBN 0-686-83558-1); pap. 19.95. Kazi Pubns.

Ibn Hazm al Undalasi. Anver Chejne. 320p. (Orig.). 1982. 29.00x (ISBN 0-935782-03-6); pap. 19.95x (ISBN 0-935782-04-4). Kazi Pubns.

Ibn Kammuna's Examination of the Three Faiths: A Thirteenth-Century Essay in the Comparative Study of Religion. Ed. & tr. by Moshe Perlmann. LC 73-102659. 1971. 32.00x (ISBN 0-520-01658-0). U of Cal Pr.

Ibn Khaldun's Science of Human Culture. F. Baali. 16.50 (ISBN 0-317-01604-0). Kazi Pubns.

Ibn Sina & the Muslim World. Malcolm Yapp. Ed. by Margaret Killingray & Edmund O'Connor. (World History Ser.). (Illus.). 1980. lib. bdg. 6.95 (ISBN 0-89908-037-5); pap. text ed. 2.45 (ISBN 0-89908-012-X). Greenhaven.

Ibn Taimaya's Struggle Against Popular Religion with an Annotated Translation of His Kitab Iqtida Assirat Al Mustaquin Mukhalafat Ashab Al-Jahim. Muhammed U. Memon. (Religion & Society: No. 1). 1976. text ed. 59.00x (ISBN 90-2797-591-4). Mouton.

Ibn Taymiyyah's Ethics: The Social Factor. Victor E. Makari. LC 81-1019. (American Academy of Religion Academy Ser.). pap. write for info. (ISBN 0-89130-477-0). Scholars Pr GA.

Ibn Taymiyyah's Ethics: The Social Factor. Victor E. Makari. LC 81-1019. (AAR Academy Ser.). 246p. 1983. 17.95 (ISBN 0-89130-476-2, 01 01 34). Scholars Pr GA.

Icelandic Church Saga. John C. Hood. LC 79-8720. (Illus.). xii, 241p. 1981. Repr. of 1946 ed. lib. bdg. 27.50x (ISBN 0-313-22194-4, HOIC). Greenwood.

ICH Bin Ein Jude. Herb Brin. LC 81-15256. 146p. 1983. 9.95 (ISBN 0-8246-0275-7). Jonathan David.

ICL Planbook. Incl. Adult. Ed. by Ed Stewart (ISBN 0-8307-0673-9, 99-603-09); Children. Ed. by Wesley Haystead (ISBN 0-8307-0671-2, 91-603-02); Youth. Ed. by Ed Stewart (ISBN 0-8307-0672-0, 97-603-18). 1978. pap. 1.65 ea. Regal.

ICL Planbook--Early Childhood. Ed. by Wesley Haystead. 1978. pap. 1.65 (ISBN 0-8307-0670-4, 90-603-08). Regal.

Icon. John Damascene & Oecumenical Synod Seventh. Tr. by Constantine Cavarnos from Gr. (Illus.). 11p. 1979. pap. 0.90 (ISBN 0-914744-19-4). Inst Byzantine.

Icon. Kurt Weitzmann et al. LC 82-47840. (Illus.). 419p. 1982. 60.00 (ISBN 0-394-52551-5). Knopf.

Icon & Swastika: The Russian Orthodox Church Under Nazi & Soviet Control. Harvey Fireside. LC 70-123567. (Harvard University, Russian Research Center Studies: Vol. 62). pap. 67.00 (ISBN 0-317-08921-8, 2021595). Bks Demand UMI.

Icon: Holy Images 6th to 14th Century. Kurt Weitzman. LC 78-6495. (Magnificant Paperback Art Ser.). 136p. 1978. 24.95 (ISBN 0-8076-0892-0); pap. 14.95 (ISBN 0-8076-0893-9). Braziller.

Icon Painting. John Taylor. LC 78-25925. (Mayflower Gallery Ser.). (Illus.). 1979. 12.50 (ISBN 0-8317-4813-3, Mayflower Bks); pap. 6.95 (ISBN 0-8317-4814-1). Smith Pubs.

Iconic Communication: An Annotated Bibliography. William H. Huggins & Doris R. Entwisle. LC 73-8130. (Illus.). 184p. 1974. 18.50x (ISBN 0-8018-1528-2). Johns Hopkins.

Iconmakers' Handbook of the Stroganov School of Icon Painting. 1974. 12.50 (ISBN 0-686-10192-8). Eastern Orthodox.

Iconoclasm & Poetry in the English Reformation: Down Went Dragon. Ernest B. Gilman. LC 85-28837. (Illus.). 240p. 1986. lib. bdg. 19.00x (ISBN 0-226-29382-3). U of Chicago Pr.

Iconoclastic Deity: Biblical Images of God. Clyde A. Holbrook. 240p. 1984. 29.50 (ISBN 0-8387-5069-9). Bucknell U Pr.

Iconographic Dictionary of the Indian Religions: Hinduism, Buddhism, Jainism. Gosta Liebert. (Illus.). 377p. 1986. Repr. lib. bdg. 75.00 (ISBN 81-7030-098-3, Pub. by Sri Satguru Pubns India). Orient Bk Dist.

Iconography & Ritual: A Study of Analytical Perspectives. Staale Sinding-Larsen. 260p. 1985. 30.00x (ISBN 82-00-07184-7). Oxford U Pr.

Iconography in Medieval Spanish Literature. John E. Keller & Richard P. Kinkade. LC 83-2478. (Illus.). 160p. 1984. 50.00x (ISBN 0-8131-1449-7). U Pr of Ky.

Iconography of Balarama. N. P. Joshi. 1979. 16.50x (ISBN 0-8364-0538-2). South Asia Bks.

Iconography of Chinese Buddhism in Traditional China, 2 pts. H. A. Van Oort. (Iconography of Religions Ser.: XII-5). (Illus.). 1986. Pt. 1, xii, 30p. pap. 25.50 (ISBN 90-04-07822-3, Pub. by E J Brill); Pt. 2, viii, 27p. pap. 24.75 (ISBN 90-04-07823-1). Heinman.

Iconography of New Zealand Maori Religion. D. R. Simmons. (Iconography of Religions Ser.: Pt. II/1). (Illus.). ix, 33p. 1986. pap. 27.25 (ISBN 90-04-07588-7, Pub. by E J Brill). Heinman.

Iconography of Preface & Miniature in the Byzantine Gospel Book. Robert S. Nelson. LC 80-15335. (College Art Association Monograph Ser.: Vol. 36). (Illus.). 180p. 1985. Repr. of 1980 ed. 30.00x (ISBN 0-271-00404-5). Pa St U Pr.

Iconography of Sadasiva. B. N. Sharma. LC 76-902916. 1976. 12.50 (ISBN 0-88386-823-7). South Asia Bks.

Iconography of the Conversion of Saint Paul. Thomas Martone. Ed. by S. J. Freedberg. (Outstanding Dissertations in Fine Arts Ser.). (Illus.). 325p. 1985. Repr. of 1978 ed. 45.00 (ISBN 0-8240-6882-3). Garland Pub.

Iconography of the Counter Reformation in the Netherlands: Heaven on Earth, 2 vols. John B. Knipping. LC 73-85234. (Illus.). 539p. 1974. Set. text ed. 195.00x (Pub. by B De Graaf Netherlands). Coronet Bks.

Iconography of the Facade of Saint-Gilles-Du-Gard. Carra F. O'Meara. LC 76-23668. (Outstanding Dissertations in the Fine Arts - Medieval). (Illus.). 352p. 1977. Repr. of 1975 ed. lib. bdg. 63.00 (ISBN 0-8240-2717-5). Garland Pub.

Iconography of the Hindus, Buddhists & Jains. 2nd ed. R. S. Gupte. (Illus.). xviii, 201p. 1981. text ed. 45.00x (ISBN 0-86590-028-0, Pub. by Taraporevala India). Apt Bks.

Iconography of the Teotihuacan Tlaloc. Esther Pasztory. LC 74-16543. (Studies in Pre-Columbian Art & Archaeology: No. 15). (Illus.). 22p. 1974. pap. 3.00x (ISBN 0-88402-059-2). Dumbarton Oaks.

Iconologia. Cesare Ripa. LC 75-27865. (Renaissance & the Gods Ser.: Vol. 21). (Illus.). 581p. 1976. Repr. of 1611 ed. lib. bdg. 88.00 (ISBN 0-8240-2070-7). Garland Pub.

Iconologie. J. B. Boudard. LC 75-27888. (Renaissance & the Gods Ser.: Vol. 43). (Illus.). 1976. Repr. of 1766 ed. lib. bdg. 80.00 (ISBN 0-8240-2092-8). Garland Pub.

Iconology: Image, Text, Ideology. W. J. Mitchell. LC 85-1177. x, 226p. 1986. 20.00 (ISBN 0-226-53228-3). U of Chicago Pr.

Icons in the Eastern Orthodox Church, a Brief Theological Introduction: Jeremiah, Patriarch of Constantinople & St. John of Damascus. pap. 0.50 (ISBN 0-686-01294-1). Eastern Orthodox.

Icons of America. Browne. LC 77-84917. 1978. 14.95 (ISBN 0-87972-090-5); pap. 6.95 (ISBN 0-87972-091-3). Bowling Green Univ.

Icons of Justice: Iconography & Thematic Imagery in Book Five of the Faerie Queen. Jane Aptekar. LC 79-79189. (Illus.). 218p. 1969. 32.00x (ISBN 0-231-03246-3). Columbia U Pr.

Iconum Biblicarum. Matthaeus Marien. (Illus.). 320p. 1981. Repr. of 1630 ed. 34.95 (ISBN 0-939688-06-9). Directed Media.

Idea & Essence in the Philosophies of Hobbes & Spinoza. Albert G. Balz. LC 70-161737. Repr. of 1918 ed. 17.00 (ISBN 0-404-00489-X). AMS Pr.

Idea of a Christian College. Arthur F. Holmes. 1975. pap. 5.95 (ISBN 0-8028-1592-8). Eerdmans.

Idea of A Christian College. rev. ed. Arthur F. Holmes. 104p. 1987. pap. 6.95 (ISBN 0-8028-0258-3). Eerdmans.

Idea of Apostolicity in Byzantium & the Legend of the Apostle Andrew. Francis Dvornik. (Dumbarton Oaks Studies: Vol. 4). 342p. (LC A58-8640). 1958. 25.00x (ISBN 0-88402-004-5). Dumbarton Oaks.

Idea of Biblical Poetry: Parallelism & Its History. James L. Kugel. LC 80-25227. August 1983, 351p. pap. 10.95 (ISBN 0-300-03101-7, Y-470). Yale U Pr.

Idea of Christ in the Gospels: Or, God in Man, a Critical Essay. George Santayana. LC 75-3338. Repr. of 1946 ed. 30.00 (ISBN 0-404-59341-0). AMS Pr.

Idea of Disarmament, Rethinking the Unthinkable. Alan Geyer. 256p. 1982. 17.95 (ISBN 0-87178-397-5); pap. 11.95 (ISBN 0-87178-396-7). Brethren.

Idea of Disarmament, Rethinking the Unthinkable. Alan Geyer. 256p. 1985. 11.95. Brethren.

Idea of Fertilization in the Culture of the Pueblo Indians. Herman K. Haeberlin. LC 16-25723. (American Anthro. Association Memoirs). pap. 15.00 (ISBN 0-527-00512-6). Kraus Repr.

Idea of God & Human Freedom. Wolfhart Pannenberg. LC 73-3165. 224p. 1973. 6.95 (ISBN 0-664-20971-8). Westminster.

Idea of God in Protestant Religious Education. Angus H. Maclean. LC 75-177033. (Columbia University. Teachers College. Contributions to Education: No. 410). Repr. of 1930 ed. 22.50 (ISBN 0-404-55410-5). AMS Pr.

Idea of God in the Light of Recent Philosophy: Gifford Lectures Delivered in the University of Aberdeen, 1912 & 1913. 2nd ed. rev. ed. Pattison A. Seth. Repr. of 1920 ed. 29.00 (ISBN 0-527-81500-4). Kraus Repr.

Idea of Holiness & the Humane Response: A Study of the Concept of Holiness & Its Social Consequences. John Armstrong. 177p. 1982. 16.95 (ISBN 0-04-200042-4). Allen Unwin.

Idea of Immortality. Pattison A. Seth. Repr. of 1922 ed. 18.00 (ISBN 0-527-81506-3). Kraus Repr.

Idea of Justice in Christian Perspective. K. Dengevin. 1978. pap. 2.95 (ISBN 0-88906-102-5). Radix Bks.

Idea of Personality in Sufism. R. A. Nicholson. 12.50 (ISBN 0-686-18606-0). Kazi Pubns.

Idea of Revelation in Recent Thought. John Baillie. LC 56-8158. (Bantam Lectures in America Ser.). 151p. 1956. 23.00x (ISBN 0-231-02142-9); pap. 11.00x (ISBN 0-231-08554-0). Columbia U Pr.

Idea of the Being. S. D. Philaretos. Ed. by Orthodox Christian Educational Society. Tr. by D. Cummings from Hellenic. 287p. 1963. 5.75x (ISBN 0-938366-09-2). Orthodox Chr.

Idea of the Holy. 2nd ed. Rudolf Otto. Tr. by John W. Harvey. 1950. pap. 8.95 (ISBN 0-19-500210-5). Oxford U Pr.

Idea of the Jewish State. rev. ed. Ben Halpern. LC 71-89969. (Middle Eastern Studies: No. 3). (Illus.). 1969. 30.00x (ISBN 0-674-44201-6). Harvard U Pr.

Idea of the Soul. John Laird. 1979. Repr. lib. bdg. 25.00 (ISBN 0-8495-3333-3). Arden Lib.

Idea of the Soul. John Laird. LC 76-107811. (Select Bibliographies Reprint Ser). 1924. 18.00 (ISBN 0-8369-5207-3). Ayer Co Pubs.

Idea of the Victorian Church: A Study of the Church of England 1833-1889. Desmond Bowen. 1968. 20.00x (ISBN 0-7735-0033-2). McGill-Queens U Pr.

Idea of Truth in Manzoni & Leopardi. K. Foster. (Italian Lectures). 1967. pap. 2.25 (ISBN 0-85672-283-9, Pub. by British Acad). Longwood Pub Group.

Ideal Figures in Ancient Judaism: Profiles & Paradigms. Ed. by John J. Collins & George W. Nickelsburg. LC 80-19878. 1980. 17.95 (ISBN 0-89130-434-7, 060412); pap. 11.95 (ISBN 0-89130-435-5). Scholars Pr GA.

Ideal of a Christian Church Considered in Comparison with Existing Practice. 2nd ed. William G. Ward. LC 75-30040. Repr. of 1844 ed. 49.50 (ISBN 0-404-14044-0). AMS Pr.

Ideal of the Karmayogin. Sri Aurobindo. 170p. Date not set. 7.00 (ISBN 0-317-17429-0). Auromere.

Ideal of "The New Woman" According to the Woman's Christian Temperance Union. Ed. by Carolyn G. De Swarte & Donald Dayton. (Women in American Protestant Religion 1800-1930). 394p. 1987. lib. bdg. 55.00 (ISBN 0-8240-0655-0). Garland Pub.

Ideal und Singularitat: Uber die Funktion des Gottesbegriffes in Kants theoretischer Philosophie. Svend Andersen. 278p. 1983. 28.80 (ISBN 3-11-009649-8). De Gruyter.

Ideal Womanhood. Daisy M. Sewell. 1947. pap. 1.50 (ISBN 0-88027-048-9). Firm Foun Pub.

Idealism & Naturalism in Gothic Art. Max Dyorak. Tr. by Randolph J. Klawiter. LC 67-22143. (Illus.). pap. 70.50 (ISBN 0-317-10425-X, 2022072). Bks Demand UMI.

Idealism, as a Philosophical Doctrine. R. F. Hoernle. 1979. Repr. of 1924 ed. lib. bdg. 25.00 (ISBN 0-8495-2281-1). Arden Lib.

Idealism of Giovanni Gentile. Roger W. Holmes. LC 78-63683. (Studies in Fascism: Ideology & Practice). Repr. of 1937 ed. 29.50 (ISBN 0-404-16948-1). AMS Pr.

Ideals Easter. Ideal Editors. 1985. pap. 3.50 (ISBN 0-8249-1041-9). Ideals.

Ideals of Religion. Andrew C. Bradley. LC 77-27218. (Gifford Lectures: 1907). Repr. of 1940 ed. 30.00 (ISBN 0-404-60463-3). AMS Pr.

Ideals of St. Francis of Assisi. Hilaron Felder. 1983. 12.50 (ISBN 0-8199-0845-2). Franciscan Herald.

Ideas, 39 vols. Ed. by Wayne Rice. (Ideas Library). (Illus.). 52p. (Orig.). pap. 7.95 ea.; Set. pap. 140.00 (ISBN 0-910125-00-7); index o.p. 6.95 (ISBN 0-910125-01-5). Youth Special.

Ideas & Ideals of the Hassidim. Milton Aron. 1969. 7.95 (ISBN 0-8065-0319-X). Citadel Pr.

Ideas & Ideals of the Hassidim. Milton Aron. 1980. pap. 5.95 (ISBN 0-8065-0722-5). Citadel Pr.

Ideas & Illustrations for Inspirational Talks. Jack Gulledge. LC 85-24268. (Orig.). 1985. pap. 4.95 (ISBN 0-8054-5017-3). Broadman.

Ideas & Their Consequences. Arlie J. Hoover. LC 76-3176. (Way of Life Ser: No. 129). 1976. pap. 3.95 (ISBN 0-89112-129-3, Bibl Res Pr). Abilene Christ U.

Ideas, Faiths, & Feelings: Essays on American Intellectual & Religious History, 1952-1982. Henry F. May. 1983. 25.00x (ISBN 0-19-503235-7); pap. 9.95 (ISBN 0-19-503236-5). Oxford U Pr.

Ideas for Prayer. Hubert Van Zeller. 1973. pap. 3.95 (ISBN 0-87243-046-4). Templegate.

Ideas for Use with Two's & Three's. Ed. by Grace Abbott. 176p. (Orig.). 1985. pap. 7.95 (ISBN 0-8341-1056-3). Beacon Hill.

Ideas in Fiction: The Works of Hayim Hazaz. Warren Bargad. LC 81-13621. (Brown Judiac Studies). 1982. pap. 13.50 (ISBN 0-89130-518-1, 14-00-31). Scholars Pr GA.

Ideas in Milton. William J. Grace. LC 68-12290. 1969. Repr. of 1968 ed. 6.95x (ISBN 0-268-00126-X). U of Notre Dame Pr.

Ideas of God & Conduct. Willis D. Mathias. LC 71-177059. (Columbia University. Teachers College. Contributions to Education: No. 874). Repr. of 1943 ed. 22.50 (ISBN 0-404-55874-7). AMS Pr.

Ideas of Jewish History. Ed. by Michael A. Meyer. LC 73-19960. (Library of Jewish Studies). 384p. 1974. 15.95x (ISBN 0-87441-202-1). Behrman.

Ideas of Newman: Christianity & Human Religiosity. Lee H. Yearley. LC 77-13894. 1978. 22.50x (ISBN 0-271-00526-2). Pa St U Pr.

Ideas of Order: Anglicans & the Renewal of Theological Method in the Middle Years of the 19th Century. Hamish Swanston. 256p. 1974. pap. text ed. 22.00 (ISBN 90-232-1124-3, Pub. by Van Gorcum Holland). Longwood Pub Group.

Ideas of Personality in Sufism. R. A. Nicholson. 1970. 12.50 (ISBN 0-87902-180-2). Orientalia.

Ideas of Religion: A Prolegomenon to the Philosophy of Religion. John E. Sullivan. LC 79-66230. 1979. pap. text ed. 12.25 (ISBN 0-8191-0808-1). U Pr of Amer.

Ideas of the Fall & of Original Sin: A Historical & Critical Study. Norman P. Williams. LC 79-8125. Repr. of 1927 ed. 49.00 (ISBN 0-404-18439-1). AMS Pr.

Idee du Juste Prix Chez les Theologiens et Cannonistes du Moyen Age. H. Garnier. LC 79-122228. (Fr.). 164p. 1973. Repr. of 1900 ed. lib. bdg. 20.50 (ISBN 0-8337-1286-1). B Franklin.

Idees Morales Chez les Heterodoxes Latins Au Debut Du Xiie Siecle. Paul Alphandery. LC 78-63184. (Heresies of the Early Christian & Medieval Era: Second Ser.). Repr. of 1903 ed. 27.50 (ISBN 0-404-16198-7). AMS Pr.

Identity. Ruth T. Barnhouse. LC 84-3664. (Choices: Guides for Today's Woman Ser.,: Vol. 7). 120p. (Orig.). 1984. pap. 6.95 (ISBN 0-664-24545-5). Westminster.

Identity & Community: A Social Introduction to Religion. Loyle S. Jung. LC 79-87753. pap. 51.00 (2027156). Bks Demand UMI.

Identity & Distinction in Petrus Thomae. Geoffrey G. Bridges. (Philosophy Ser). 1959. 10.00 (ISBN 0-686-11544-9). Franciscan Inst.

Identity & Faith. Maurice Martin. LC 81-82655. (Focal Pamphlet Ser.). 104p. (Orig.). 1981. pap. 3.95 (ISBN 0-8361-1979-7). Herald Pr.

Identity & Religion: International Cross-Cultural Approaches. Ed. by Hans Mol. LC 77-93700. (Sage Studies in International Sociology: Vol. 16). 246p. 1978. 28.00 (ISBN 0-8039-9890-2). Sage.

Identity Crisis of Muslims: Profiles of Lucknow Youth. Nirmala Srinivasau. 140p. 1981. text ed. 15.00x (ISBN 0-391-02279-2, Pub. by Concept Pubs India). Humanities.

Identity of Christianity. Stephen Sykes. LC 83-48907. 256p. 1984. 21.95 (ISBN 0-8006-0720-1, 1-720). Fortress.

Identity of the Individual in the Psalms. Steven J. Croft. (JSOT Supplement Ser.: No. 44). 280p. 1986. text ed. 34.00x (ISBN 1-85075-021-1, Pub. by JSOT Pr England); pap. text ed. 15.95x (ISBN 1-85075-020-3). Eisenbrauns.

Identity of the New Testament Text. rev. ed. Wilbur N. Pickering. LC 80-17369. 192p. 1980. pap. 8.95 (ISBN 0-8407-5744-1). Nelson.

Identity Search. Ed. by John Duckworth et al. (Pacesetter Ser.). 64p. 1987. tchr's. ed. 7.95. Cook.

Ideological Weapons of Death: A Theological Critique of Capitalism. Franz Hinkelammert. Tr. by Phillip Berryman from Span. LC 86-2557. Tr. of Armas Ideologicas de la Muerte. 320p. (Orig.). 1986. pap. 17.95 (ISBN 0-88344-260-4). Orbis Bks.

Ideologies of Religion. facsimile ed. George P. Conger. LC 70-93329. (Essay Index Reprint Ser). 1940. 19.00 (ISBN 0-8369-1283-7). Ayer Co Pubs.

Ideology & Consciousness, No. 5. Ed. by Diana Adlam et al. 1979. pap. text ed. 6.95x (ISBN 0-391-01189-8). Humanities.

Ideology & Experience: Anti-Semitism in France at the Time of the Dreyfus Affair. Stephen Wilson. (Littman Library of Jewish Civilization). (Illus.). 832p. 1982. 37.50x (ISBN 0-19-710052-X). Oxford U Pr.

Ideology & Experience: Antisemitism in France at the Time of the Dreyfus Affair. Stephen Wilson. LC 81-65467. (Illus.). 832p. 1982. 60.00 (ISBN 0-8386-3037-5). Fairleigh Dickinson.

Ideology on a Frontier: The Theological Foundation of Afrikaner Nationalism, 1652-1910. J. Alton Templin. LC 83-10884. (Contributions in Intercultural & Comparative Studies: No. 11). (Illus.). xiii, 360p. 1984. lib. bdg. 35.00 (ISBN 0-313-24104-X, TIF/). Greenwood.

Idiom Book of New Testament Greek. 2nd ed. Charles F. Moule. 1959. 39.50 (ISBN 0-521-05774-4); pap. text ed. 13.95 (ISBN 0-521-09237-X). Cambridge U Pr.

Idioms in the Bible Explained & a Key to the Original Gospels. George Lamsa. LC 85-42782. 128p. 1985. pap. 8.95 (ISBN 0-06-064927-5, HarpR). Har-Row.

Idol Meat in Corinth. Wendell L. Willis. (Society of Biblical Literature Dissertation Ser.: No. 68). 1985. 19.50 (ISBN 0-89130-764-8, 06 01 68); pap. 12.95 (ISBN 0-89130-606-4). Scholars Pr GA.

Idol Worshippers in Twentieth Century America. Arthur F. Ide. (Illus.). 150p. (Orig.). 1984. pap. 10.95 (ISBN 0-930383-02-8). Monument Pr.

Idolatry of Poetic Genius in German Goethe Criticism. Hans-Wilhelm Kelling. (European University Studies: Series 1, German Language & Literature: Vol. 27). 200p. 1970. pap. 9.80 (ISBN 3-261-00026-0). P Lang Pubs.

Idols Behind Altars. Anita Brenner. LC 67-19527. (Illus.). 1929. 18.00 (ISBN 0-8196-0190-X). Biblo.

Idols: Dead or Alive? Reuel J. Schulz. 7.95 (ISBN 0-686-91886-X, 12N1724). Northwest Pub.

Idols of Death & the God of Life: A Theology. Pablo Richard et al. Tr. by Barbara E. Campbell & Bonnie Shepard. LC 83-6788. Tr. of Lucha de los Dioses: la Idolos de la Opresion y la Busqueda del Dios Liberador. 240p. (Orig.). 1983. pap. 12.95 (ISBN 0-88344-048-2). Orbis Bks.

Idols of Our Time. Bob Goudzwaard. Tr. by Mark V. Vennen from Dutch. LC 84-652. Tr. of Genoodzaakt Goed te Wezen: Christelijke Hoop in Een Bezetenwereld. 120p. (Orig.). 1984. pap. 6.95 (ISBN 0-87784-970-6). Inter-Varsity.

Idylls of the Bible. Frances E. Harper. LC 75-168245. Repr. of 1901 ed. 11.50 (ISBN 0-404-00058-4). AMS Pr.

If Being a Christian Is So Great, Why Do I Have the Blahs? John A. Dobbert. LC 79-65420. 160p. 1980. pap. 4.95 (ISBN 0-8307-0729-8, 5413206). Regal.

If God Cares, Why Do I Still Have Problems? Lloyd J. Ogilvie. 208p. 1985. 12.95 (ISBN 0-8499-0454-4, 0454-4). Word Bks.

If God Is in Charge. Stephen Brown. LC 83-2240. 180p. 1983. pap. 5.95 (ISBN 0-8407-5844-8). Nelson.

If God Loves Me: Teacher's Guide. Lorraine Peterson. 128p. (Orig.). 1983. pap. 4.95 (ISBN 0-87123-586-2, 210586). Bethany Hse.

If God Loves Me, Why Can't I Get My Locker Open? Lorraine Peterson. LC 80-27014. 141p. (Orig.). 1980. pap. 4.95 (ISBN 0-87123-251-0, 210251). Bethany Hse.

If God Talked Out Loud. Clyde L. Herring. LC 76-27479. (Illus.). 1977. pap. 5.50 (ISBN 0-8054-5325-3, 4253-25). Broadman.

If God Won the War, Why Isn't It Over? Dick Winn. Ed. by Ken McFarland. (Harvest Ser.). 64p. 1982. pap. 4.95 (ISBN 0-8163-0467-X). Pacific Pr Pub Assn.

If Grandma Had Wheels: Jewish Folk Sayings. Ed. by Ruby G. Strauss. LC 85-7466. (Illus.). 64p. 1985. 8.95 (ISBN 0-689-31156-7, Childrens Bk). Macmillan.

If I Am to Lead. D. E. Hoste. 1968. pap. 0.90 (ISBN 0-85363-068-2). OMF Bks.

If I Could Change My Mom & Dad. Bill Orr & Erwin Lutzer. 128p. 1983. pap. 3.50 (ISBN 0-8024-0174-0). Moody.

If I Could Preach Just Once. facsimile ed. B. Russell et al. LC 73-167364. (Essay Index Reprint Ser). Repr. of 1929 ed. 17.00 (ISBN 0-8369-2457-6). Ayer Co Pubs.

If I Had a Bigger Drum. Marjorie L. Lloyd. (Harvest Ser.). 1981. pap. 4.50 (ISBN 0-8163-0399-1). Pacific Pr Pub Assn.

If I Only Love Jesus. Basilea Schlink. 1973. pap. 0.95 (ISBN 0-551-05288-0). Evang Sisterhood Mary.

If I Perish. Esther A. Kim. 1979. pap. 3.95 (ISBN 0-8024-4003-7). Moody.

If I Were a Clown. Floyd Shaffer. LC 84-11000. 112p. (Orig.). 1984. pap. 5.95 (ISBN 0-8066-2082-X, 10-3198). Augsburg.

If I Were a Pastor. W. McFerrin Stowe. 112p. (Orig.). 1983. pap. 6.50 (ISBN 0-687-18655-2). Abingdon.

If I Were Pope. Ed. by Candida Lund. 1987. 11.95 (ISBN 0-88347-187-6). Thomas More.

If I Were Starting My Family Again. John M. Drescher. LC 78-13278. (Festival Ser.). (Illus.). 1979. pap. 2.95 (ISBN 0-687-18674-9). Abingdon.

If I'm a Christian Why Be a Catholic? The Biblical Roots of a Catholic Faith. James E. Hanson. (Orig.). 1984. pap. 5.95 (ISBN 0-8091-2633-8). Paulist Pr.

If It Please the King. Iverna M. Tompkins. 183p. (Orig.). 1983. pap. 5.00 (ISBN 0-9611260-1-9). I Tompkins.

If Jesus Came to My House. Joan G. Thomas. (Illus.). 1951. 10.25 (ISBN 0-688-40981-4). Lothrop.

If Nobody Reaches, Nobody Gets Touched. Don Gossett. 128p. (Orig.). 1983. pap. 2.95 (ISBN 0-88368-127-7). Whitaker Hse.

If Not, Not: The Oath of the Aragonese & the Legendary Laws of the Sobrarbe. Ralph Giesey. LC 67-21023. 1968. 30.50 (ISBN 0-691-05128-3). Princeton U Pr.

If Not Now, When? Mordecai M. Kaplan & Arthur A. Cohen. LC 72-95901. 134p. 1973. 7.95 (ISBN 0-935457-15-1). Reconstructionist Pr.

If Only... Wallace Kirby. 1985. 6.25 (ISBN 0-89536-753-X, 5859). CSS of Ohio.

If Only He Knew: A Valuable Guide to Knowing, Understanding, & Loving Your Wife. Gary Smalley & Steve Scott. 144p. 1982. pap. 5.95 (ISBN 0-310-44881-6, 18247P). Zondervan.

If Only I'd Listened. (Color-a-Story Bks.). (Illus.). 1985. pap. 0.89 (ISBN 0-89191-996-1, 59964). Cook.

If Satan Can't Steal Your Joy, He Can't Have Your Goods. Jerry Savelle. 160p. 1983. pap. 3.95 (ISBN 0-89274-262-3). Harrison Hse.

If Talent Were Pizza, You'd Be a Supreme. Jack Weyland. 1986. text ed. 8.95 (ISBN 0-87579-054-2). Deseret Bk.

If That Isn't Love. Austine Smith. 132p. 1985. pap. 5.95 (ISBN 0-88144-036-1). Christian Pub.

If the World Fits, You're the Wrong Size. Bill Stearns. 1981. pap. 2.95 (ISBN 0-88207-588-8). SP Pubns.

If the World Fits, You're the Wrong Size. Bill Stearns. 1981. pap. 3.95 (ISBN 0-88207-588-8). Victor Bks.

If This Be Love: The Journey of Two People Toward Each Other in Christian Love & Marriage. Calvin Miller. LC 83-48433. 112p. 1984. 11.45 (ISBN 0-06-065755-3, HarpR). Har-Row.

If Those Who Reach Could Touch. Gail MacDonald & Gordon MacDonald. 128p. 1985. Repr. of 1984 ed. 5.95 (ISBN 0-8007-5201-5, Power Bks). Revell.

If Thou Wilt Be Perfect. Oswald Chambers. 1962. pap. 2.95 (ISBN 0-87508-113-4). Chr Lit.

If Today You Hear His Voice: Reflections on the Sunday Readings. Albert Cylwicki. LC 81-10966. 553p. (Orig.). 1981. pap. 12.95 (ISBN 0-8189-0418-6). Alba.

If We Only Have Love. Alan Cohen. (Illus.). 15p. (Orig.). 1984. pap. 1.00 (ISBN 0-910367-34-5). A Cohen.

If We Only Have Love. Alan Cohen. (Illus., Orig.). 1984. pap. 2.00 (ISBN 0-942494-86-5). Coleman Pub.

If We Were Starting Our Marriage Again. John Drescher & Betty Drescher. 96p. (Orig.). 1985. pap. 6.50 (ISBN 0-687-18672-2). Abingdon.

If Ye Continue. Guy Duty. LC 82-2314. 192p. 1966. pap. 4.95 (ISBN 0-87123-243-X, 210243). Bethany Hse.

If You Fight-Fight Fair. Day. (Out Ser.). 1984. 1.25 (ISBN 0-8163-0597-8). Pacific Pr Pub Assn.

If-You Form an Israelite Law. Harry Gilmer. LC 75-23136. (Society of Biblical Literature. Dissertation Ser.: No. 15). Repr. of 1975 ed. 36.80 (ISBN 0-8357-9572-1, 2017518). Bks Demand UMI.

If You Love Me... Kenneth D. Barney. LC 75-22611. (Radiant Life Ser.). 128p. 1977. pap. 2.50 (ISBN 0-88243-889-1, 02-0889); teacher's ed 3.95 (ISBN 0-88243-163-3, 32-0163). Gospel Pub.

If You Love Me. Patricia St. John. 1984. pap. 3.50 (ISBN 0-8024-5962-5). Moody.

If You Want to Preach. 2nd ed. Don DeWelt. LC 56-13226. 1964. pap. 3.95 (ISBN 0-89900-111-4). College Pr Pub.

If Your Doctor's Busy, Call on God: A Spiritual Journey Through Ecological Illness. Jayne Rotman. 190p. (Orig.). Date not set. pap. price not set (ISBN 0-931515-05-X). Triumph Pr.

Ifugao World. Mariano A. Dumia. Ed. by Jean Edades. (Illus.). 1979. pap. 6.00x (ISBN 0-686-24953-4, Pub. by New Day Pub). Cellar.

Igbo-Igala Borderland: Religion & Social Control in Indigenous African Colonialism. Austin J. Shelton. LC 70-141493. 1971. 44.50 (ISBN 0-87395-082-8). State U NY Pr.

Iglesia Blanceada. Ed. by Charles W. Conn. (Span.). 165p. 1979. pap. 4.95 (ISBN 0-87148-882-5). Pathway Pr.

Iglesia del Futuro. Ralph W. Neighbour, Jr. Tr. by Jose L. Martinez from Eng. Orig. Title: Future Church. 256p. 1983. pap. 7.95 (ISBN 0-311-17024-2). Casa Bautista.

Iglesia Menonita Hispana en Norte America: 1932-1982. Rafael Falcon. LC 85-61020. (Span.). 208p. 1985. 14.95x (ISBN 0-8361-1272-5). Herald Pr.

Iglesia Popular: Between Fear & Hope, Vol. 176. Ed. by Leonardo Boff & Virgil Elizondo. (Concilium Ser.). 128p. 1984. pap. 6.95 (ISBN 0-567-30056-0, Pub. by T & T Clark Ltd UK). Fortress.

Iglesia Presbiteriana: A History of Presbyterians & Mexican Americans in the Southwest. R. Douglas Brackenridge & Francisco O. Garcia-Treto. LC 74-76777. (Illus.). 262p. 1974. 8.00 (ISBN 0-911536-53-1). Trinity U Pr.

Iglesia un Companerismo Incendiario. David E. Trueblood. Tr. by Roger Velasquez from Eng. Orig. Title: Incendiary Fellowship. (Span.). 114p. 1981. pap. 4.75 (ISBN 0-311-17022-6, Edit Mundo). Casa Bautista.

Ignatius His Conclave, or His Inthronisation in a Late Election in Hell. John Conne. LC 77-6876. (English Experience Ser.: No. 868). 1977. Repr. of 1611 ed. lib. bdg. 11.50 (ISBN 90-221-0868-6). Walter J Johnson.

Ignatius Loyola. Henry D. Sedgwick. LC 83-45597. Date not set. Repr. of 1923 ed. 42.50 (ISBN 0-404-19890-2). AMS Pr.

Ignatius Loyola & the Early Jesuits. Stewart Rose. LC 83-45596. Date not set. Repr. of 1870 ed. 52.00 (ISBN 0-404-19889-9). AMS Pr.

Ignatius of Antioch: A Commentary on the Seven Letters of Ignatius. William Schoedel. LC 84-48731. (Hermeneia Ser.). 320p. 1985. 34.95 (ISBN 0-8006-6016-1, 20-6016). Fortress.

Ignatius of Loyola & the Founding of Society of Jesus. Andre Ravier. Tr. by Maura Daly et al from Fr. Tr. of Ignace de Loyola Fonde la Compagnie de Jesus. 498p. (Orig.). 1987. 29.95 (ISBN 0-89870-036-1). Ignatius Pr.

Ignatius of Loyola, Founder of the Jesuits: His Life & Work. Candido de Dalmases. Frwd. by George E. Ganss. Tr. by Jerome Aixala from Span. Index. LC 83-80349. (Series II-Scholarly Studies about the Jesuits in English Translations: No. 6). xxii, 362p. 1985. 16.00 (ISBN 0-912422-59-9); pap. 14.00 smyth sewn (ISBN 0-912422-58-0). Inst Jesuit.

Ignatius of Loyola: His Personality & Spiritual Heritage, 1556-1956, Studies on the 400th Anniversary of His Death. F. Wulf et al. LC 77-16677. (Modern Scholarly Studies About the Jesuits,in English Translations Ser.: No. 2). 318p. 1977. pap. 7.00 (ISBN 0-912422-22-X). Inst Jesuit.

Ignaz Seipel: Christian Statesman in a Time of Crisis. Klemens Von Klemperer. LC 77-166392. 420p. 1962. 49.50 (ISBN 0-691-05197-6). Princeton U Pr.

II Peter. D. Martyn Lloyd-Jones. 15.95 (ISBN 0-85151-379-4). Banner of Truth.

Iisus Khristos Pred Sudom Sovemjennogo Razuma. John of Smolensk. Tr. of Jesus Christ Before the Judgement of Contemporaty Intellect. 16p. pap. 1.00 (ISBN 0-317-28988-8). Holy Trinity.

Ijevangel'skije Poichjenija. Archimandrite Simeon. Tr. of Lessons from the Gospel. 40p. 1970. pap. 2.00 (ISBN 0-317-29123-8). Holy Trinity.

Ikkyu Sojun: A Zen Monk & His Poetry. Sonja Arntzen. LC 73-620051. (Occasional Papers: Vol. 4). (Illus.). 171p. 1973. microfiche 1.00 (ISBN 0-914584-99-5). WWUCEAS.

Iliad or the Poem of Force. Simone Weil. LC 57-6026. 1956. pap. 2.50x (ISBN 0-87574-091-X). Pendle Hill.

I'll Be Glad to Give a Devotion. Amy Bolding. (Paperback Program Ser). 1978. pap. 3.95 (ISBN 0-8010-0709-7). Baker Bk.

I'll Get to Heaven Before You Do! Meg Woodson. 96p. 1985. pap. text ed. 6.95 (ISBN 0-687-18611-0). Abingdon.

I'll Never Walk Alone: Hansi's Journal. Maria A. Hirschmann. LC 73-81015. 170p. (Orig.). 1986. pap. 6.95 (ISBN 0-932878-08-3, HB-009). Hansi.

Illegitimacy of Jesus: A Feminist Theological Interpretation. Jane Schaberg. 240p. 1985. 16.95 (ISBN 0-86683-972-0, HarpR). Har-Row.

Illimitable One. Elise N. Morgan. (Meditation Ser.). 1934. 3.50 (ISBN 0-87516-329-7). De Vorss.

Illness & Shamanistic Curing in Zinacantan: An Ethnomedical Analysis. Horacio Fabrega, Jr. & Daniel B. Silver. LC 73-80621. 304p. 1973. 22.50x (ISBN 0-8047-0844-4). Stanford U Pr.

Illuminated Haggadah. Kafra. (Illus.). 27.50 (ISBN 0-87306-078-4). Feldheim.

Illuminated Prophet Books: A Study of Byzantine Manuscripts of the Major & Minor Prophets. John Lowden. LC 86-43164. 250p. 1987. 49.75x (ISBN 0-271-00604-8). Pa St U Pr.

Illumination: Handbook of Ascended Masters. Herbert L. Beierle. 1978. 20.00 (ISBN 0-940480-02-6). U of Healing.

Illuminations from the Bhagavad-Gita. Kim Murray & Christopher Murray. LC 79-3834. (Illus.). 64p. (Orig.). pap. 8.95 (ISBN 0-06-090763-0, CN 763, PL). Har-Row.

Illuminations of the Stavelot Bible. Wayne Dynes. LC 77-94693. (Outstanding Dissertations in the Fine Arts Ser.). (Illus.). 1978. lib. bdg. 44.00 (ISBN 0-8240-3225-X). Garland Pub.

Illumined Ones. Grace Cooke. (Illus.). 1966. pap. 6.95 (ISBN 0-85487-058-X). De Vorss.

Illusion of Immortality. 4th ed. Corliss Lamont. LC 65-25140. 1965. pap. 6.95 (ISBN 0-8044-6377-8). Ungar.

Illusions of Faith: A Critique of Non-Credal Religion. Carlos G. Prado. (Orig.). 1980. pap. text ed. 9.95 (ISBN 0-8403-2176-7). Kendall-Hunt.

Illustrated Architectural History of the Greatest Cathedrals of the World, 2 vols. John Ruskin et al. (Illus.). 311p. 1986. Set. 187.75 (ISBN 0-86650-201-7). Gloucester Art.

Illustrated Articles of Faith. write for info. (ISBN 0-911712-18-6). Promised Land.

Illustrated Bible Dictionary. M. G. Easton. (Baker's Paperback Reference Library). 760p. 1983. pap. 12.95 (ISBN 0-8010-3386-1). Baker Bk.

Illustrated Bible Dictionary, 3 vols. 1980. 99.95 (ISBN 0-8423-7525-2). Tyndale.

Illustrated Bible for Children. J. F. Allen et al. (Illus.). 9.95 (ISBN 0-8407-5264-4). Nelson.

Illustrated Bible Study Outlines. F. E. Marsh. LC 79-125116. 268p. 1979. pap. 8.95 (ISBN 0-8254-3245-6). Kregel.

Illustrated Bibles from Tours. Herbert L. Kessler. LC 76-45902. (Studies in Manuscript Illumination: No. 7). (Illus.). 236p. 1977. 61.00 (ISBN 0-691-03923-2). Princeton U Pr.

Illustrated Book of Jewish Knowledge. Edith Tarcov & Oscar Tarcov. (Illus.). 1959. 6.00x (ISBN 0-87068-358-6, Pub. by Friendly Hse). Ktav.

Illustrated Book of the Great Ancient Temples. Lyman Metropulous. (Masterpieces of World Architecture Library). (Illus.). 141p. 1983. 112.50 (ISBN 0-86650-042-1). Gloucester Art.

Illustrated Catechism. Redemptorist Pastoral Publication. LC 80-84312. 112p. (Orig.). 1981. pap. 3.95 (ISBN 0-89243-135-0). Liguori Pubns.

Illustrated Catechism: Leader's Guide. Gary Johnson. (Illus.). 96p. 1981. pap. 4.95 (ISBN 0-89243-150-4). Liguori Pubns.

Illustrated Children's Bible. (Illus.). 480p. 12.95 (ISBN 0-448-14494-8). Putnam Pub Group.

Illustrated Clip Art Bible Verses. Jack Hamm. 48p. (Orig.). 1985. pap. 9.95 (ISBN 0-933545-01-0). Knight Media.

Illustrated Dictionary & Concordance of the Bible. Geoffrey Wigoder et al. (Illus.). 1000p. 1986. text ed. 100.00 (ISBN 0-02-916380-3). Macmillan.

Illustrated Dictionary of Bible Manners & Customs. A. Van Deursen. (Illus.). 1979. pap. 3.95 (ISBN 0-8065-0707-1). Citadel Pr.

Illustrated Dictionary of Bible Manners & Customs. A. Van Deursen. (Illus.). 1967. 6.95 (ISBN 0-8022-1762-1). Philos Lib.

Illustrated Dictionary of Greek & Roman Mythology. Michael Stapleton. LC 85-30692. (Library of the World's Myths & Legends). (Illus.). 224p. 1986. 17.95 (ISBN 0-87226-063-1). P Bedrick Bks.

Illustrated Dictionary of Hindu Iconography. Margaret Stutley. (Illus.). 200p. 1985. 36.95 (ISBN 0-317-17180-1). Methuen Inc.

Illustrated Dictionary of World Religions. Arthur Jones. pap. 20.00 (ISBN 0-08-024176-X). Pergamon.

Illustrated Encyclopaedia of Traditional Symbols. J. C. Cooper. LC 78-55429. (Illus.). 208p. 1987. pap. 12.95 (ISBN 0-500-27125-9). Thames Hudson.

Illustrated Gospel of St. John. (Illus.). 128p. 1986. 14.95 (ISBN 0-86350-068-4). Salem Hse Pubs.

Illustrated Guidebook to the Frescoes in the Sistine Chapel. Evelyn M. Phillips. (Illus.). 124p. 1981. Repr. of 1901 ed. 69.85 (ISBN 0-89901-029-6). Found Class Reprints.

Illustrated History of Methodism. W. H. Daniels. 1977. lib. bdg. 75.00 (ISBN 0-8490-2036-0). Gordon Pr.

Illustrated History of the Popes: St. Peter to John Paul II. Michael Walsh. (Illus.). 256p. 1980. 19.95 (ISBN 0-312-40817-X). St Martin.

Illustrated Sermon Outlines. J. B. Fowler, Jr. LC 86-2674. 1987. 4.95 (ISBN 0-8054-2261-7). Broadman.

Illustrated Sourcebook of Russian Antisemitism 1881-1977, 2 vols. Z. Szajkowski. Vol. 1, The Nineteenth Century. 50.00x (ISBN 0-87068-347-0); Vol. 2, The Twentieth Century. 45.00x (ISBN 0-87068-348-9). Ktav.

Illustrated Sourcebook on the Holocaust, Vol. III. Zosa Szajkowski. 1979. 40.00x (ISBN 0-87068-690-9). Ktav.

Illustrated Sourcebook on the Holocaust, Vols. 1 & 2. Soza Szajkowski. Incl. Vol. 1. Prelude to Holocaust: the Jew Must Disappear. o. p 50.00 (ISBN 0-87068-294-6); Vol. 2. The Ghetto & Death Camp Walls Speak (ISBN 0-87068-295-4). 45.00x ea. Ktav.

Illustrated Stories from Church History, 16 vols. Larry Porter. Ed. by Paul R. Cheesman. (Illus.). write for info (ISBN 0-911712-21-6). Promised Land.

Illustrated Stories of the Book of Mormon, 16 vols. Clinton F. Larson & Joseph N. Revill. (Illus.). write for info 0.00 (ISBN 0-911712-38-0). Promised Land.

Illustrated World of the Bible Library, 5 vols. Benjamin Mazar & Michael Avi-Yonah. Incl. Vol. 1. The Laws. 40.00 (ISBN 0-8088-1167-3); Vol. 2. The Early Prophets. 40.00 (ISBN 0-8088-1168-1); Vol. 3. The Late Prophets. 40.00 (ISBN 0-8088-1169-X); Vol. 4. The Writings. 40.00 (ISBN 0-8088-1170-3); Vol. 5. The New Testament. Michael Avi-Yonah. 40.00 (ISBN 0-8088-1171-1). 1961. Vols. 1-4. old testament ed. 160.00 (ISBN 0-8088-1080-4); Vols. 1-5. new testament ed. 200.00 (ISBN 0-8088-1081-2). Davey.

Illustrated Yorkshire Carthusian Religious Miscellany, 2 Vols. James Hogg. (Analecta Cartusiana Ser.: No. 95/1-2). (Orig.). 1985. pap. 50.00 (ISBN 3-7052-0165-4, Pub. by Salzburg Studies). Longwood Pub Group.

Illustrated Yorkshire Carthusian Religious Miscellany, Vol. 3. James Hogg. (Analecta Cartusiana Ser.: No. 95/3). 140p. (Orig.). 1981. pap. 25.00 (ISBN 3-7052-0166-2, Pub. by Salzburg Studies). Longwood Pub Group.

Illustrating Paul's Letter to the Romans. James E. Hightower, Jr. LC 84-7074. 1984. pap. 5.95 (ISBN 0-8054-2251-X). Broadman.

Illustrating the Gospel of Matthew. Church Administration Department Staff. LC 81-68044. 1982. pap. 5.25 (ISBN 0-8054-2243-9). Broadman.

Illustration of the Pauline Epistles in French & English Bibles of the Twelfth & Thirteenth Century. Luba Eleen. (Illus.). 1982. 89.00x (ISBN 0-19-817344-X). Oxford U Pr.

Illustrations from the Life of R. G. Flexon. pap. 2.95 (ISBN 0-686-12882-6). Schmul Pub Co.

Illustrations in Choir Accompaniment. Dudley Buck. LC 79-137316. Repr. of 1892 ed. 18.00 (ISBN 0-404-01145-4). AMS Pr.

Illustrations Without Sermons. Bill Lufburrow. 128p. (Orig.). 1985. pap. 7.95 (ISBN 0-687-18677-3). Abingdon.

Illustrious Relic of the Kulikovo Battle. N. Salko. 1985. 39.00x (ISBN 0-569-08567-5, Pub. by Collets (UK)). State Mutual Bk.

I'm a Good Man, But. Fritz Ridenour. LC 75-96702. 1969. pap. 3.50 (ISBN 0-8307-0429-9, S102153). Regal.

I'm All Right, Right Now. Subramuniya. pap. 1.00 (ISBN 0-87516-355-6). De Vorss.

I'm Glad You Asked. Kenneth Boa & Larry Moody. 1982. pap. 6.95 (ISBN 0-88207-354-0). Victor Bks.

I'm Glad You Asked That. rev. & updated ed. Rita Bennett. 160p. 1983. pap. 5.95 (ISBN 0-8007-5111-6, Power Bks). Revell.

I'm Glad You're Open Weekdays: Everyday Prayers to the God Who Works Between Sundays. Betty W. Skold. LC 85-3923. 112p. (Orig.). 1985. pap. 5.95 (ISBN 0-8066-2129-X, 10-3201). Augsburg.

I'm Going to Be a Missionary. Virginia B. Carter. (Orig.). 1978. pap. 2.95 (ISBN 0-89036-103-7). Hawkes Pub Inc.

I'm Going to Sing: Black American Spirituals, Vol. II. Ashley Bryan. (Illus.). 64p. 1982. 10.95 (ISBN 0-689-30915-5, Childrens Bk). Macmillan.

I'm Growing. Sylvia Stanford. (Bible & Me Ser.). (Illus.). 1986. 5.95 (ISBN 0-8054-4167-0). Broadman.

I'm Happy When I'm Good. Bessie Dean. (Children's Inspirational Coloring Bk.). (Illus.). 24p. 1979. pap. 1.25 (ISBN 0-88290-109-5). Horizon Utah.

I'm Learning, Lord, but I Still Need Help: Story Devotions for Boys. Nathan Aaseng. LC 81-65652. 112p. (Orig.). 1981. pap. 3.95 (ISBN 0-8066-1888-4, 10-3202). Augsburg.

I'm Listening, God: Psalm 19. Elspeth C. Murphy. (David & I Talk to God Ser.). (Illus.). 1983. misc. format 2.50 (ISBN 0-89191-583-4). Cook.

I'm Listening, Lord: Leader's Guide. James Aderman. Ed. by William E. Fischer. (Bible Class Course for Young Adults Ser.). 64p. 1984. pap. text ed. 2.95 (ISBN 0-938272-19-5). Wels Board.

I'm Listening, Lord: Student's Guide. James Aderman. Ed. by William E. Fischer. (Bible Class Course for Young Adults Ser.). (Illus.). 48p. 1984. pap. text ed. 2.95 (ISBN 0-938272-18-7). Wels Board.

I'm Lonely Lord-How Long? The Psalms for Today. Marva J. Dawn. LC 83-47721. 176p. 1984. 12.45 (ISBN 0-06-067201-3, HarpR). Har-Row.

I'm Looking for Mr. Right, But I'll Settle for Mr. Right Away: AIDS, True Love, the Perils of Safe Sex, & Other Spiritual Concerns of the Gay Male. Gregory Flood. 136p. (Orig.). 1987. pap. 6.95 (ISBN 0-938407-00-7). Brob Hse Bks.

I'm Not Mad at God. David Wilkerson. 96p. 1967. pap. 2.95 (ISBN 0-87123-245-6, 200245). Bethany Hse.

I'm Only One Person, What Can I Do? J. Harry Haines. (Orig.). 1985. pap. 5.95 (ISBN 0-8358-0521-2). Upper Room.

I'm Out to Change My World. Ann Kiemel. 128p. 1983. pap. 4.95 (ISBN 0-310-70141-4, 14034P). Zondervan.

I'm Scared to Witness! Roberta L. Bonnici. (Discovery Bks.). (Illus.). 48p. (Orig.). (YA) 1979. pap. 1.50 (ISBN 0-88243-931-6, 02-0931); tchr's ed 3.95 (ISBN 0-88243-330-X, 02-0330). Gospel Pub.

I'm Searching, Lord, but I Need Your Light. Nathan Aaseng. LC 82-72644. (Young Readers Ser.). 112p. 1983. pap. 3.95 (ISBN 0-8066-1950-3, 10-3203). Augsburg.

I'm Sold on Being Bold. Don Gossett. 1979. pap. 2.25 (ISBN 0-88368-085-8). Whitaker Hse.

I'm Still Here Lord! Betty Isler. 1984. pap. 4.95 (ISBN 0-570-03938-X, 12-2873). Concordia.

I'm Still Learning, Lord. 80p. 1986. pap. 5.95 (ISBN 0-8170-1112-9). Judson.

Ima on the Bima: My Mommy is a Rabbi. Rabbi Mindy Avra Portnoy. LC 86-3023. (Illus.). 32p. 1986. 10.95 (ISBN 0-930494-54-7); pap. 4.95 (ISBN 0-930494-55-5). Kar Ben.

Image & Pilgrimage in Christian Culture. Victor Turner & Edith Turner. LC 77-25442. (Lectures on the History of Religions Ser.). 1978. 25.00x (ISBN 0-231-04286-8). Columbia U Pr.

Image & Symbol in the Sacred Poetry of Richard Crashaw. 2nd edition ed. George W. Williams. LC 63-12394. x, 152p. 1967. 21.95x (ISBN 0-87249-087-4). U of SC Pr.

Image As Insight: Visual Understanding in Western Christianity & Secular Culture. Margaret R. Miles. LC 85-47528. (Illus.). 304p. 1985. 24.95 (ISBN 0-8070-1006-5). Beacon Pr.

Image As Insight: Visual Understanding in Western Christianity & Secular Culture. Margaret R. Miles. LC 85-47528. (Illus.). 200p. 1987. pap. 12.95 (ISBN 0-8070-1007-3, BP 743). Beacon Pr.

Image Before My Eyes: A Photographic History of Jewish Life in Poland, 1864-1939. L. Dobroczcki & B. Kirshenblatt-Gimblett. (Illus.). 1977. 25.00; pap. text ed. 15.00 (ISBN 0-914512-38-2). Yivo Inst.

Image Before My Eyes: A Photographic History of Jewish Life in Poland, 1864-1939. Lucjan Dobroszycki & Barbara Kirshenblatt-Gimblett. LC 75-35448. (Illus.). 1977. 29.95 (ISBN 0-8052-3607-4). Schocken.

Image Before My Eyes: A Photographic History of Jewish Life in Poland, 1864-1939. Lucjan Dobroszycki & Barbara Kirshenblatt-Gimblett. LC 75-35448. (Illus.). 1979. pap. 19.95 (ISBN 0-8052-0634-5). Schocken.

Image of Bothe Curches, After the Moste Wonderfull & Heavenly Revelation of Sainct John the Evangelist. John Bale. LC 72-5965. (English Experience Ser.: No. 498). 872p. 1973. Repr. of 1548 ed. 51.00 (ISBN 90-221-0498-2). Walter J Johnson.

Image of Guadalupe: Myth or Miracle? Jody B. Smith. LC 80-2066. (Illus.). 216p. 1984. pap. 6.95 (ISBN 0-385-19705-5, Im). Doubleday.

Image of Likeness: The Augustinian Spirituality of William of St. Thierry. David N. Bell. 19.95 (ISBN 0-87907-878-2). Cistercian Pubns.

Image of Loveliness. Joanne Wallace. (Illus.). 160p. 1978. pap. 5.95 (ISBN 0-8007-5134-5, Power Bks). Revell.

Image of Martin Luther in the Writings of Novalis & Friedrich Schlegel: The Speculative Vision of History & Religion. Sara A. Malsch. (European University Studies: Series 1, German Language & Literature: Vol. 103). 165p. 1974. pap. 18.25 (ISBN 3-261-01453-9). P Lang Pubs.

Image of Mary: According to the Evangelists. Horacio Bojorge. Tr. by Aloysius Owen from Span. LC 77-15516. (Illus.). 1978. pap. 4.00 (ISBN 0-8189-0362-7). Alba.

Image of the Jew in American Literature. Louis Harap. LC 74-12887. 608p. 1975. 10.00 (ISBN 0-8276-0054-2, 357). Jewish Pubns.

Image of the Jew in Soviet Literature. Jakub Blum & Vera Rich. LC 84-12196. 276p. 1985. 25.00 (ISBN 0-88125-062-7). Ktav.

Image of the Non-Jew in Judaism: An Historical & Constructive Study of the Noahide Laws. David Novak. LC 83-21989. (Toronto Studies in Theology: Vol. 14). 500p. 1984. 69.95x (ISBN 0-88946-759-5). E Mellen.

Image of the Word: A Study of Quranic Verses in Islamic Architecture, 2 vols. Erica C. Dodd & Shereen Khairallah. (Illus.). 434p. 1982. 95.00x (ISBN 0-8156-6061-8, Am U Beirut). Syracuse U Pr.

Image to Image, Vol. II. Rita J. Carmack. 155p. 1986. pap. 5.00 (ISBN 0-937093-00-9). Jewel Pr.

Image to Image, Vol. 1. Rita J. Carmack. 146p. 1985. pap. 5.00 (ISBN 0-88144-047-7). Jewel Pr.

Imagen de Dios. Paul Brand & Philip Yancey. Tr. by Ady Delgado. Tr. of In His Image. 272p. 1987. pap. 4.95 (ISBN 0-88113-128-8). Edit Betania.

Imagenes Del Hombre. Roger Mehl. Tr. by Felix Benlliure from Fr. Orig. Title: Images Del'homme. 64p. 1980. pap. 1.35 (ISBN 0-311-05051-4). Casa Bautista.

Imagery in Healing: Shamanism & Modern Medicine. Jeanne Achterberg. LC 84-20748. (New Science Library Ser.). 256p. (Orig.). 1985. pap. 10.95 (ISBN 0-87773-307-4, 73031-3). Shambhala Pubns.

Imagery of John Donne's Sermons. Winfried Schleiner. LC 70-91655. Repr. of 1970 ed. 66.00 (2027523). Bks Demand UMI.

Images. John W. Tranter, Jr. 180p. (Orig.). 1986. pap. text ed. 3.95 (ISBN 0-88368-183-8). Whitaker Hse.

Images & the Imageless: A Study in Religious Consciousness & Film. Thomas M. Martin. LC 79-57611. 200p. 1981. 18.50 (ISBN 0-8387-5005-2). Bucknell U Pr.

Images et Paroles. Pierre Teilhard De Chardin. 32.95 (ISBN 0-685-36592-1). French & Eur.

Images From The Bible: The Paintings of Shalom of Safed, the Words of Elie Wiesel. Shalom of Safed. LC 79-51032. (Illus.). 112p. 1980. 40.00 (ISBN 0-87951-107-9); limited, signed 400.00 (ISBN 0-87951-108-7). Overlook Pr.

Images in Covenant Beginnings. Eric G. Hawkinson. (Illus.). 1968. 3.95 (ISBN 0-910452-04-0). Covenant.

Images in Transition: The English Jew in English Literature, 1660-1830. Abba Rubin. LC 83-22730. (Contributions of the Study of World Literature Ser.: No. 4). iv, 157p. 1984. lib. bdg. 29.95 (ISBN 0-313-23779-4, RUJ/). Greenwood.

Images of Arab Women: Fact & Fiction. Mona N. Mikhail. LC 78-19969. 137p. (Orig.). 1978. 20.00 (ISBN 0-89410-023-8); pap. 10.00 (ISBN 0-89410-024-6). Three Continents.

Images of Authority: A Consideration of the Concepts of "Regnum" & "Sacerdotium". James M. Cameron. LC 66-12489. pap. 24.30 (ISBN 0-8357-9261-7, 2016769). Bks Demand UMI.

Images of Belief in Literature. Ed. by David Jasper. LC 83-40170. 195p. 1984. 22.50 (ISBN 0-312-40920-6). St Martin.

Images of Christ: An Introduction to Christology. Glenn F. Chesnut. 160p. (Orig.). 1984. pap. 8.95 (ISBN 0-86683-875-9, 7918, HarpR). Har-Row.

Images of Dharma: The Epic World of C. Rajagopalachari. Joanne P. Waghore. 1985. 25.00x (ISBN 0-8364-1426-8, Pub. by Chanakya India). South Asia Bks.

Images of Eternity. L. D. Johnson. LC 84-4987. 1984. pap. 3.75 (ISBN 0-8054-5342-3). Broadman.

Images of Eternity: Studies in the Poetry of Religious Vision, from Wordsworth to T. S. Eliot. James Benziger. LC 62-15007. (Arcturus Books Paperbacks). 333p. 1962. pap. 2.25 (ISBN 0-8093-0136-9). S Ill U Pr.

Images of God. Leo Holland. LC 84-72318. (Illus.). 112p. (Orig.). 1985. pap. 4.95 (ISBN 0-87793-276-X). Ave Maria.

Images of God: Religious Beliefs Given Life Through Counseling, Spiritual Direction, & Prayer. Brother Bernard Seif. 1987. 7.95 (ISBN 0-533-07239-5). Vantage.

Images of Kinship in "Paradise Lost" Milton's Politics & Christian Liberty. Stevie Davies. LC 82-17485. 256p. 1983. text ed. 21.00x (ISBN 0-8262-0392-2). U of Mo Pr.

Images of Leadership & Authority for the Church: Biblical Principles & Secular Models. David A. Steele. LC 86-24589. 206p. (Orig.). 1987. lib. bdg. 23.50 (ISBN 0-8191-5710-4); pap. text ed. 13.25 (ISBN 0-8191-5711-2). U Pr of Amer.

Images of Man & Death. Philippe Aries. Tr. by Janet Lloyd from Fr. LC 85-768. (Illus.). 271p. 1985. 35.00 (ISBN 0-674-44410-8). Harvard U Pr.

Images of Man & God: Old Testament Short Stories in Literary Focus. Ed. by Burke O. Long. (Bible & Literature Ser.: No. 1). 128p. 1981. text ed. 19.95x (ISBN 0-907459-00-5, Pub. by Almond Pr England); pap. text ed. 6.95x (ISBN 0-907459-01-3). Eisenbrauns.

Images of Moses. Daniel J. Silver. LC 82-70854. 1982. 16.95 (ISBN 0-465-03201-X). Basic.

Images of My Self: Meditation & Self-Exploration Through the Imagery of the Gospels. Jean Gill. 128p. 1982. pap. 3.95 (ISBN 0-8091-2463-7). Paulist Pr.
Images of Peace. Pat C. Hinton. 96p. 1983. pap. 4.95 (ISBN 0-86683-748-5, HarpR). Har-Row.
Images of Sai Baba. Alexi Allens. (Illus.). 104p. (Orig.). 1985. pap. 12.95 (ISBN 0-318-18477-X). Masterpiece Pub.
Images of the Christ: An Enquiry into Christology. George H. Tavard. LC 81-40582. 134p. (Orig.). 1982. lib. bdg. 24.25 (ISBN 0-8191-2129-0); pap. text ed. 9.50 (ISBN 0-8191-2130-4). U Pr of Amer.
Images of the Church in the New Testament. Paul S. Minear. LC 60-11331. 294p. 1970. pap. 9.95 (ISBN 0-664-24903-5). Westminster.
Images of the Future. Alan K. Waltz. LC 79-25028. (Into Our Third Century Ser.). (Orig.). 1980. pap. 3.95 (ISBN 0-687-18689-7). Abingdon.
Images of the Madonna & Child by Three Tuscan Artists of the Early Seicento: Vanni, Roncalli & Manetti. Susan E. Wegner. LC 86-70511. (Occasional Papers: No. III). (Illus.). 42p. (Orig.). 1986. pap. 9.00 (ISBN 0-916606-10-4). Bowdoin Coll.
Images of the Old Testament. Hans Holbein. (Children's Books from the Past: Vol. 1). 100p. 1973. Repr. of 1549 ed. 32.65 (ISBN 3-261-01003-7). P Lang Pubs.
Images or Shadows of Divine Things. Jonathan Edwards. Ed. by Perry Miller. LC 73-8157. 1977. Repr. of 1948 ed. lib. bdg. 29.75x (ISBN 0-8371-6952-6, EDIS). Greenwood.
Images: Women in Transition. Ed. by Janice Grana. LC 75-46441. 1977. pap. 4.95 (ISBN 0-88489-092-9). St Mary's.
Imaginal Body: Para-Jungian Reflections on Soul, Imagination & Death. Roberts Avens. LC 81-43814. 264p. (Orig.). 1982. lib. bdg. 29.00 (ISBN 0-8191-2411-7); pap. text ed. 13.25 (ISBN 0-8191-2412-5). U Pr of Amer.
Imagination & Existence: Heidegger's Retrieval of the Kantian Ethic. Frank Schalow. 192p. (Orig.). 1986. lib. bdg. 24.75 (ISBN 0-8191-5114-9); pap. text ed. 11.75 (ISBN 0-8191-5115-7). U Pr of Amer.
Imagination & Metaphysics in St. Augustine. Robert O'Connell. LC 85-82595. (Aquinas Lecture). 70p. 1986. 7.95 (ISBN 0-87462-227-1). Marquette.
Imagination & the Life of the Spirit: An Introduction to the Study of Religion & Literature. Lynn Ross-Bryant. LC 79-28464. (Scholars Press General Ser.: Vol. 2). pap. 7.95x (ISBN 0-89130-378-2, 00 03 02). Scholars Pr GA.
Imagination & the Presence of Shakespeare in Paradise Lost. Paul Stevens. LC 85-40378. 256p. 1985. text ed. 32.50x (ISBN 0-299-10420-6). U of Wis Pr.
Imagination As a Means of Grace. Ernest L. Tuveson. LC 73-21543. 218p. 1973. Repr. of 1960 ed. 20.00x (ISBN 0-87752-173-5). Gordian.
Imagination Becomes Reality Vol. 1: One Hundred Fifty Posture Solo Dance. Stuart A. Olson. Ed. by Gerald Kuehl. (T'ai Chi Ch'uan-the Teaching of Master T. T. Liang Ser.). (Illus., Orig.). 1986. pap. 19.94 (ISBN 0-938045-01-6). Bubbling Well.
Imagination: Embracing a Theology of Wonder. Cheryl Forbes. LC 86-811. (Critical Concern Bks.). 1986. 12.95 (ISBN 0-88070-136-6). Multnomah.
Imagination of the Resurrection: The Poetic Continuity of a Religious Motif in Donne, Blake, & Yeats. Kathryn R. Kremen. LC 71-168812. (Illus.). 344p. 1972. 26.50 (ISBN 0-8387-7940-9). Bucknell U Pr.
Imagination's New Beginning: Theology & Modern Literature. Frederick J. Hoffman. LC 67-12121. (Ward-Phillips Lecture Ser.: No. 1). 1967. pap. 1.95x (ISBN 0-268-00329-7). U of Notre Dame Pr.
Imagine That! Marlene Halpin. 144p. 1982. pap. 4.95 (ISBN 0-697-01812-1); videotapes avail. Wm C Brown.
Imagine That! A Child's Guide to Yoga. Kenneth K. Cohen. (Illus.). 48p. 1983. pap. 8.95 (ISBN 0-915520-55-9). Santa Barb Pr.
Imagineering for Health. Serge King. LC 80-53949. 211p. (Orig.). 1981. pap. 6.95 (ISBN 0-8356-0546-9, Quest). Theos Pub Hse.
Imaging God: Dominion As Stewardship. Douglas J. Hall. 272p. (Orig.). 1986. pap. 8.95 (ISBN 0-8028-0244-3). Eerdmans.
Imagini...Degli Dei. Vincenzo Cartari. LC 75-27855. (Renaissance & the Gods Ser.: Vol. 12). (Illus.). 602p. 1976. Repr. of 1571 ed. lib. bdg. 88.00 (ISBN 0-8240-2061-8). Garland Pub.
Imagining Religion: From Babylon to Jonestown. Jonathan Z. Smith. LC 82-2734. (Studies in the History of Judaism). 1982. 17.50x (ISBN 0-226-76358-7). U of Chicago Pr.
Imago Dei: A Study of C. G. Jung's Psychology of Religion. James W. Heisig. LC 77-74405. 256p. 1978. 26.50 (ISBN 0-8387-2076-5). Bucknell U Pr.
Imam Ali: Source of Light, Wisdom & Might. Sulayman Kattani. Tr. by I. K. Howard. 148p. Date not set. text ed. 25.00 (ISBN 0-7103-0153-7). Methuen Inc.
Iman, Basic Beliefs. A. S. Hashim. (Islamic Books for Children: Bk. 1). pap. 4.95 (ISBN 0-686-18416-5); pap. 45.00 entire ser. (ISBN 0-686-18417-3). Kazi Pubns.
Imhotep: The Egyptian God of Medicine. J. B. Hurry. (Illus.). 120p. 1978. 12.50 (ISBN 0-89005-239-5). Ares.
Imitation Christi. Ed. by J. K. Ingram. (EETS, ES Ser.: No. 63). Repr. of 1893 ed. 54.00 (ISBN 0-527-00268-2). Kraus Repr.
Imitation of Buddha: Quotations from Buddhist Literature for Each Day. E. Bowden. 59.95 (ISBN 0-8490-0386-5). Gordon Pr.
Imitation of Christ. Thomas a Kempis. 217p. 1986. 16.95 (ISBN 0-88029-078-1, Pub. by Dorset). Hippocrene Bks.
Imitation of Christ. new, rev. ed. Thomas a Kempis. Ed. by Clare L. Fitzpatrick. (Illus., Large Type). maroon, colored edges 4.95 (ISBN 0-89942-320-5, 320/00). Catholic Bk Pub.
Imitation of Christ. Thomas a Kempis. 1978. plastic bdg. 3.50 (ISBN 0-8198-0533-5). Dghtrs St Paul.
Imitation of Christ. Thomas a Kempis. LC 55-8729. 1955. pap. 4.50 (ISBN 0-385-02861-X, D17, Im). Doubleday.
Imitation of Christ. Thomas a Kempis. Tr. by E. M. Blaiklock. LC 80-54894. 228p. 1981. pap. 5.95 (ISBN 0-8407-5760-3). Nelson.
Imitation of Christ. Thomas a Kempis. 1967. 5.95 (ISBN 0-88088-320-0). Peter Pauper.
Imitation of Christ. Thomas a Kempis. 20.00 (ISBN 0-8274-2557-0). R West.
Imitation of Christ. Thomas a Kempis. Tr. by John Rooney. 214p. 1980. pap. 5.95 (ISBN 0-87243-097-9). Templegate.
Imitation of Christ. Thomas a Kempis. LC 82-80472. (Treasures from the Spiritual Classics Ser.). 64p. 1982. pap. 2.95 (ISBN 0-8192-1307-1). Morehouse.
Imitation of Christ. Thomas a Kempis. Ed. by Hal M. Helms. LC 82-61908. (Living Library Ser.). (Illus.). 280p. (Orig.). 1982. pap. 8.95 (ISBN 0-941478-07-6). Paraclete Pr.
Imitation of Christ. Thomas a Kempis. Ed. by Paul M. Bechtel. (Moody Classics Ser.). 1984. pap. 4.50 (ISBN 0-8024-4005-3). Moody.
Imitation of Christ. Thomas a Kempis. 240p. 1983. pap. 4.95 (ISBN 0-310-38441-9, 9283P, Clarion Class). Zondervan.
Imitation of Christ. Thomas a Kempis. Tr. by P. G. Zomberg. LC 84-71574. Tr. of De imitatione Christi. (Lat., Illus.). 272p. 1985. 12.00 (ISBN 0-930995-00-7, 00-7). Dunstan Pr.
Imitation of Christ: New Translation from the Original Latin Text. Joseph Tylenda. 1984. pap. 7.95 (ISBN 0-89453-432-7). M Glazier.
Imitation of the Sacred Heart of Jesus. Peter J. Arnoudt. LC 79-112463. 1974. pap. 10.00 (ISBN 0-89555-012-1). TAN Bks Pubs.
Immaculate & Powerful: The Female in Sacred Image & Social Reality. Ed. by Clarissa W. Atkinson et al. LC 85-70448. 338p. 1987. pap. 12.95 (ISBN 0-8070-1005-7, BP-732). Beacon Pr.
Immaculate Conception & the Holy Spirit: The Marian Teachings of Father Kolbe. H. M. Manteau-Bonamy. Ed. by Bernard M. Geiger. Tr. by Richard Arnandez from Fr. LC 77-93104. Tr. of Doctrine mariale du Pere Kolbe, Esprit-Saint et Conception Immaculee. (Illus.). 1977. pap. 4.00 (ISBN 0-913382-00-0, 101-20). Prow Bks-Franciscan.
Immaculate Heart of Mary: True Devotion. Robert J. Fox. 200p. (Orig.). 1986. pap. 7.50 (ISBN 0-87973-550-3, 550). Our Sunday Visitor.
Immanence of God. Borden P. Bowne. LC 75-3071. Repr. of 1905 ed. 24.50 (ISBN 0-404-59070-5). AMS Pr.
Immanuel: The Coming of Jesus in Art & the Bible. Hans-Reudi Weber. (Illus.). 128p. 1984. 12.95 (ISBN 0-8028-3603-8). Eerdmans.
Immateriality. Ed. by George F. McLean. LC 79-88689. (Proceedings: Vol. 52). 1978. pap. 15.00 (ISBN 0-918090-12-1). Am Cath Philo.
Immigrant Bishop: John England's Adaptation of Irish Catholicism to American Republicanism. Patrick Carey. LC 79-63860. (USCHS Monograph: Vol. 36). (Illus.). ix, 236p. 1982. 14.95x (ISBN 0-930060-16-4). US Cath Hist.
Immigrant Church: New York's Irish & German Catholics. Jay P. Dolan. LC 75-12552. pap. 59.30 (ISBN 0-317-08406-2, 2019817). Bks Demand UMI.
Immigrant Church: New York's Irish & German Catholics, 1815-1865. Jay P. Dolan. LC 82-23827. (Illus.). xiv, 221p. 1983. pap. text ed. 7.95x (ISBN 0-268-01151-6, 85-11511). U of Notre Dame Pr.
Immigrant Forces: Factors in the New Democracy. William P. Shriver. LC 74-145493. (American Immigration Library). 312p. 1971. Repr. of 1913 ed. lib. bdg. 20.95x (ISBN 0-89198-026-1). Ozer.
Immigrant-Survivors: Post-Holocaust Consciousness in Recent Jewish-American Literature. Dorothy S. Bilik. LC 80-15326. 217p. 1981. 17.50x. Wesleyan U Pr.
Immigrants & Religion in Urban America. Ed. by Randall M. Miller & Thomas D. Marzik. LC 76-62866. 208p. 1977. 32.95 (ISBN 0-87722-093-X); pap. 9.95 (ISBN 0-87722-146-4). Temple U Pr.
Immigrants, Baptists & the Protestant Mind in America. Lawrence B. Davis. LC 72-81264. pap. 60.00 (ISBN 0-8357-9682-5, 2019040). Bks Demand UMI.
Immigrants to Freedom: Jewish Communities in Rural New Jersey Since 1882. Joseph Brandes & Martin Douglas. LC 76-122384. 1971. 27.50x (ISBN 0-8122-7620-5). U of Pa Pr.
Immigration, the Public School, & the 20th Century American Ethos: The Jewish Immigrant As a Case Study. Alan Wieder. 124p. (Orig.). 1985. lib. bdg. 24.00 (ISBN 0-8191-4793-1); pap. text ed. 8.75 (ISBN 0-8191-4794-X). U Pr of Amer.
Immodest Acts: The Life of a Lesbian Nun in Renaissance Italy. Judith C. Brown. (Studies in the History of Sexuality). 221p. 1985. 14.95 (ISBN 0-19-503675-1). Oxford U Pr.
Immorality of the Human Soul, Demonstrated by the Light of Nature: In Two Dialogues. Walter Charleton. LC 83-46043. (Scientific AWakeningin the Restoration Ser.: No. 2). (Illus.). 224p. 1985. Repr. of 1657 ed. 87.50 (ISBN 0-404-63302-1). AMS Pr.
Immortal Dragon of Sylene & Other Faith Tales. Rafael Tilton. (Illus.). 128p. 1982. 9.95 (ISBN 0-86683-656-X, HarpR). Har-Row.
Immortal Fire. Sri Aurobindo. Ed. by Shyam S. Jhunjhuniwala. 216p. (Orig.). 1974. pap. 4.50 (ISBN 0-89071-209-3). Matagiri.
Immortal Hymns & Their Story. Louis A. Banks. LC 77-75198. 1977. Repr. of 1899 ed. lib. bdg. 30.00 (ISBN 0-89341-088-8). Longwood Pub Group.
Immortal Words of Jesus Christ. R. C. Allen. 1981. pap. 4.95 (ISBN 0-910228-11-6). Best Bks.
Immortality. J. Altasen et al. 733p. 1978. 7.45 (ISBN 0-8285-0939-5, Pub. by Progress Pubs USSR). Imported Pubns.
Immortality. Loraine Boettner. 1956. 4.50 (ISBN 0-87552-127-4). Presby & Reformed.
Immortality. William N. Clarke. 1920. 29.50x (ISBN 0-686-83578-6). Elliots Bks.
Immortality: An Essay in Discovery, Co-Ordinating Scientific, Physical, & Biblical Research. Burnett H. Streeter et al. 1977. Repr. of 1917 ed. lib. bdg. 27.50 (ISBN 0-8492-2418-7). R West.
Immortality & Human Destiny. Ed. by Geddes MacCregor. 256p. 21.95 (ISBN 0-913757-45-4); pap. 12.95 (ISBN 0-913757-46-2). Paragon Hse.
Immortality & the Present Mood. Julius S. Bixler. LC 75-3047. Repr. of 1931 ed. 16.00 (ISBN 0-404-59044-6). AMS Pr.
Immortality of the Soul & Other Works. St. Augustine. (Fathers of the Church Ser.: Vol. 4). 489p. 1947. 29.95x (ISBN 0-8132-0004-0). Cath U Pr.
Immortality of the Soul & the Perfectibility of Man. Samuel Garfield. (Illus.). 1977. 45.00 (ISBN 0-89266-026-0). Am Classical Coll Pr.
Immortality or Extinction? Paul Badham & Linda Badham. LC 81-17595. (Library of Philosophy & Religion). 156p. 1982. text ed. 28.50x (ISBN 0-389-20251-7, 07055). B&N Imports.
Immortality: The Next Giant Step for Mankind. Dr. Clem Davies Ministry Inc. et al. LC 83-90890. 138p. 1985. 10.00 (ISBN 0-533-05910-0). Vantage.
Immortality's Dance. Sri Chinmoy. 50p. (Orig.). 1974. pap. 2.00 (ISBN 0-88497-132-5). Aum Pubns.
Immortalized Words of the Past. Ed. by Ralph Lewis. LC 85-63539. 300p. (Orig.). 1986. pap. 9.95 (ISBN 0-912057-42-4, G-654). AMORC.
Immutability of God. C. H. Spurgeon. 1977. pap. 0.95 (ISBN 0-686-23221-6). Pilgrim Pubns.
Impact of a Saint. Russell Perkins. LC 80-51959. 256p. 1980. pap. 7.50 (ISBN 0-89142-037-1). Sant Bani Ash.
Impact of American Religious Liberalism. 2nd ed. Kenneth Cauthen. LC 82-23902. 308p. 1983. pap. text ed. 14.25 (ISBN 0-8191-2762-0). U Pr of Amer.
Impact of the Church Upon Its Culture: Reappraisals of the History of Christianity. Ed. by Jerald C. Brauer. Quirinus Breen & George A. Drake. LC 67-30155. (Essays in Divinity: Vol. 2). pap. 101.50 (ISBN 0-317-26159-2, 2024085). Bks Demand UMI.
Impact: The Religion of the Twenty-First Century. Walter A. Dawes. (Illus.). 79p. (Orig.). 1980. pap. text ed. 8.95 (ISBN 0-938792-05-9). New Capernaum.
Impeach the Anti-Christ. Gregory S. Gordon. 96p. (Orig.). 1986. pap. 4.95 (ISBN 0-9616971-5-6). Dynamic Reflections.
Impending Conflict. Ellen G. White. (Stories That Win Ser.). 1960. pap. 0.95 (ISBN 0-8163-0141-7, 09366-6). Pacific Pr Pub Assn.
Impending Crisis of Eighteen Sixty: The Present Connection of the Methodist Episcopal Church with Slavery. facs. ed. H. Mattison. LC 75-149870. (Black Heritage Library Collection Ser). 1858. 14.25 (ISBN 0-8369-8750-0). Ayer Co Pubs.
Imperative of Response: The Holocaust in Human Context. Robert S. Frey & Nancy Thompson-Frey. 186p. 1985. lib. bdg. 24.25 (ISBN 0-8191-4633-1); pap. text ed. 10.75 (ISBN 0-8191-4634-X). U Pr of Amer.
Imperative of Responsibility: In Search of an Ethics for the Technological Age. Hans Jonas. LC 83-18249. xii, 256p. 1985. lib. bdg. 25.00x (ISBN 0-226-40596-6); pap. 10.95 (ISBN 0-226-40597-4). U of Chicago Pr.
Imperial Abbey of Farfa. Charles B. McClendon. LC 86-3466. 336p. 1987. text ed. 35.00 (ISBN 0-300-03333-8). Yale U Pr.
Imperial Church from Constantine to the Early Middle Ages. Ed. by Hubert Jedin & John P. Dolan. (History of the Church: Vol. 2). 1980. 59.50x (ISBN 0-8245-0315-5). Crossroad NY.
Imperial Cities & the Reformation. Bernd Moeller. Ed. by H. C. Erik Midelfort & Mark U. Edwards, Jr. 128p. (Orig.). 1982. pap. text ed. 5.95x (ISBN 0-939464-04-7). Labyrinth Pr.
Imperial Cult Under the Flavians. facsimile ed. Kenneth Scott. LC 75-10655. (Ancient Religion & Mythology Ser.). 1976. Repr. of 1936 ed. 17.00x (ISBN 0-405-07263-5). Ayer Co Pubs.
Imperial Government & Catholic Missions in China During the Years 1784-1785. Bernard H. Willeke. (Missiology Ser). 1948. 3.50 (ISBN 0-686-11584-8). Franciscan Inst.
Imperial Intellect. Arthur D. Culler. LC 55-8700. Repr. of 1955 ed. lib. bdg. 22.50x (ISBN 0-8371-7683-2, CUII). Greenwood.
Imperialism & Nationalism in the Fertile Crescent: Sources & Prospects of the Arab-Israeli Conflict. Richard Allen. (Illus.). 1974. 29.95x (ISBN 0-19-501782-X). Oxford U Pr.
Imperialism & Religion: Assyria, Judah & Israel in the Eighth & Seventh Centuries B.C.E. Morton Cogan. LC 73-83723. (Society of Biblical Literature. Monograph). 1974. 13.50 (ISBN 0-89130-330-8, 060019); pap. 9.95 (ISBN 0-89130-331-6, 00-06-19). Scholars Pr GA.
Imperishable Dominion. Udo Schaefer. 320p. pap. 11.95 (ISBN 0-85398-142-6). G Ronald Pub.
Implanted Word. Bob Buess. 1978. pap. 2.50 (ISBN 0-934244-10-3). Sweeter Than Honey.
Implementation of a Diagnostic & Remedial Program at a Hebrew Day School. 1.00 (ISBN 0-686-33114-1, N02). Torah Umesorah.
Implementing Pastoral Care in Schools. Jeanette Raymond. LC 85-14978. 304p. 1985. 33.00 (ISBN 0-7099-2273-6, Pub. by Croom Helm Ltd); pap. 14.95 (ISBN 0-7099-4211-7). Methuen Inc.
Implications of Carl Michalson's Theological Method for Christian Education. Edward J. Wynne, Jr. Ed. by Henry O. Thompson. LC 82-24760. (Illus.). 400p. (Orig.). 1983. lib. bdg. 31.25 (ISBN 0-8191-3021-4); pap. text ed. 15.75 (ISBN 0-8191-3022-2). U Pr of Amer.
Implications of Death & Loss for Women. Ed. by Margot Tallmer et al. (Current Thanatology Ser.). 100p. 1986. pap. 13.95 (ISBN 0-930194-40-3). Ctr Thanatology.
Importance of Being Human. Eric L. Mascall. LC 74-12849. 118p. 1974. Repr. of 1958 ed. lib. bdg. 22.50 (ISBN 0-8371-7761-8, MABH). Greenwood.
Importance of the Ark of Covenant in Christianity. Kevin W. Sandifer. Ed. by J. Ashley Sibley, Jr. 112p. (Orig.). 1986. pap. 6.25 (ISBN 0-910653-13-5, 8101M). Archival Servs.
Importance of the Local Church. Daniel E. Wray. 15p. (Orig.). 1981. pap. 1.00 (ISBN 0-85151-330-1). Banner of Truth.
Importances of the Past: A Meditation on the Authority of Tradition. George Allan. 308p. 1985. 44.50x (ISBN 0-88706-116-8); pap. 14.95x (ISBN 0-88706-117-6). State U NY Pr.
Important Moral Issues. Ed. by A. W. Hastings & E. Hastings. 128p. 1966. pap. 6.95 (ISBN 0-567-22302-7, Pub. by T & T Clark Ltd UK). Fortress.
Important Muromachi, Momoyama & Edo Periods in the Growth of Buddhist Architecture in Japan. Charlton W. Soper. (Illus.). 101p. 1987. 127.50 (ISBN 0-86650-218-1). Gloucester Art.
Important Office of Immense Love: A Handbook for Eucharistic Ministers. Joseph M. Champlin. LC 80-80085. 152p. (Orig.). 1980. pap. 4.95 (ISBN 0-8091-2287-1). Paulist Pr.

Imposed Jewish Governing Bodies Under Nazi Rule: Yivo Colloquium Dec. 2-5, 1967. LC 73-150304. 1972. pap. 5.00 (ISBN 0-914512-03-X). Yivo Inst.

Imposibilidades Del Hombre-Posibilidades Para Dios. Kenneth Hagin, Jr. (Span.). 1983. pap. 2.50 (ISBN 0-89276-170-9). Hagin Ministries.

Impossibility of Agnosticism. L. Samuel. pap. 0.75 (ISBN 0-87784-125-X). Inter-Varsity.

Impossible Dilemma: Who Is a Jew in the State of Israel? Oscar Kraines. 1976. 8.95x (ISBN 0-8197-0392-3). Bloch.

Impossible Dream: The Spirituality of Dom Helder Camara. Mary Hall. LC 79-26888. 96p. (Orig.). 1980. pap. 2.48 (ISBN 0-88344-212-4). Orbis Bks.

Impossible Miracles. Charles Hunter & Frances Hunter. 1976. pap. 4.95 (ISBN 0-917726-05-7). Hunter Bks.

Impossible Takes a Little Longer. Harold Hill et al. 224p. 1985. pap. 6.95 (ISBN 0-8007-5192-2). Revell.

Impressions. Carol Roesel. (Illus., Orig.). 1982. pap. 3.95 (ISBN 0-89081-317-5). Harvest Hse.

Imprisoned Mind: Guru Shisya Tradition in Indian Culture. Akhileshwar Jha. 1980. 18.50x (ISBN 0-8364-0665-6, Pub. by Ambika India). South Asia Bks.

Improbable Triumvirate: John F. Kennedy, Pope John, Nikita Khrushchev. Norman Cousins. (Illus.). 176p. 1984. pap. 4.95 (ISBN 0-393-30162-1). Norton.

Improvement of College Worship. Paul N. Elbin. LC 72-176744. (Columbia University. Teachers College. Contributions to Education: No. 530). Repr. of 1932 ed. 22.50 (ISBN 0-404-55530-6). AMS Pr.

Improvement of the Moral Qualities: An Ethical Treatise of the Eleventh Century. Solomon B. Ibn-Gabirol. Ed. by Stephen S. Wise. LC 2-8360. (Columbia University. Oriental Studies: No. 1). Repr. of 1902 ed. 17.25 (ISBN 0-404-50491-4). AMS Pr.

Improving Church Education. H. W. Byrne. LC 79-10852. 352p. (Orig.). 1979. pap. 12.95 (ISBN 0-89135-017-9). Religious Educ.

Improving Parish Management: Working Smarter, Not Harder. George M. Williams. 112p. pap. 9.95 (ISBN 0-89622-176-8). Twenty-Third.

Improving Spelling Performance: Student Edition Block IV. Cedar Rapids Community School District Staff. 136p. 1981. pap. text ed. 2.55 (ISBN 0-8403-2419-7). Kendall-Hunt.

Improving Your Christian Personality. Donald Moore. 61p. 1984. pap. 2.25 (ISBN 0-88144-037-X). Christian Pub.

Improving Your Self Image. H. Norman Wright. LC 83-80119. 160p. (Orig.). 1983. pap. 4.95 (ISBN 0-89081-382-5). Harvest Hse.

Improving Your Serve. Chuck Swindoll. 1986. deluxe ed. 9.95 (ISBN 0-8499-3851-1). Word Bks.

Improving Your Serve: The Art of Unselfish Living. Charles R. Swindoll. 1981. 10.95 (ISBN 0-8499-0267-3). Word Bks.

Imprudence in Saint Thomas Aquinas. Charles J. O'Neil. (Aquinas Lecture Ser.). 1955. 7.95 (ISBN 0-87462-120-8). Marquette.

Imputation of Adam's Sin. John Murray. 1977. pap. 2.95 (ISBN 0-87552-341-2). Presby & Reformed.

In a Dark Time. Ed. by Robert J. Lifton & Nicholas Humphrey. LC 84-10816. 154p. (Orig.). 1984. 15.00 (ISBN 0-674-44538-4); pap. 5.95 (ISBN 0-674-44539-2). Harvard U Pr.

In a Day of Social Rebuilding: Lectures on the Ministry of the Church. Henry S. Coffin. 1919. 29.50x (ISBN 0-686-51402-5). Elliots Bks.

In Absolute Confidence. William G. Johnsson. LC 79-1387. (Anvil Ser.). 1979. pap. 8.95 (ISBN 0-8127-0225-5). Review & Herald.

In Accord-Let Us Worship. Justo Gonzalez & Catherine Gonzalez. (Orig.). 1981. pap. 3.95 (ISBN 0-377-00110-4). Friend Pr.

In Africa With Schweitzer. Edgar Berman. 300p. 1986. 16.95 (ISBN 0-88282-025-7). New Horizon NJ.

In After Days: Thoughts on Future Life. William D. Howells et al. Ed. by Robert Kastenaum. LC 76-19576. (Death & Dying Ser.). (Illus.). 1977. Repr. of 1910 ed. lib. bdg. 24.50x (ISBN 0-405-09574-0). Ayer Co Pubs.

In All Things I Am Not Alone. Tony Westmoreland. Ed. by Helen Graves. 230p. 1987. 8.95 (ISBN 1-55523-059-8). Winston-Derek.

In an Age of Holocaust. Ed. by Mark H. Ellis. (Chrysalis Bk). 128p. (Orig.). 1986. pap. 14.95 (ISBN 0-916349-13-6). Amity Hous Inc.

In an Eastern Rose Garden. Inayat Khan. (Sufi Message of Hazrat Inayat Khan Ser.: Vol. 7). 256p. 1979. 14.95 (ISBN 90-6325-096-7, Pub. by Servire BV Netherlands). Hunter Hse.

In & Out of Paradise: The Book of Genesis From Adam & Eve to the Tower of Babel. Conrad E. L'Heureux. LC 82-62415. 128p. 1983. pap. 3.95 (ISBN 0-8091-2530-7). Paulist Pr.

In & Out of the World: Seventh-Day Adventists in New Zealand. Ed. by Peter H. Ballis. 178p. 1986. pap. 12.95 (ISBN 0-86469-050-9, Pub. by Dunmore NZ). Intl Spec Bk.

In Behalf of Spiritual Freedom. pap. 10.00 (ISBN 0-915598-26-4). Church of Scient Info.

In Between Advents: Biblical & Spiritual Arrivals. Dennis E. Groh. LC 86-45199. (Bible for Christian Life Ser.). 64p. 1986. pap. 3.95 (ISBN 0-8006-2025-9). Fortress.

In-Between God. W. R. Scragg. Ed. by Gerald Wheeler. 128p. pap. price not set (ISBN 0-8280-0374-2). Review & Herald.

In Bloody Terms: The Betrayal of the Church in Marxist Grenada. Andrew J. Zwerneman. LC 85-82316. 113p. (Orig.). 1986. pap. text ed. 6.95 (ISBN 0-937779-00-8). Greenlawn Pr.

In But Still Out: Women in the Church. Elizabeth H. Verdesi. LC 75-34365. 218p. 1976. pap. 3.95 (ISBN 0-664-24788-1). Westminster.

In Charge. Lee E. Davis. LC 84-4969. 1984. pap. 4.95 (ISBN 0-8054-6404-2). Broadman.

In Christ. E. Stanley Jones. (Festival Bks.). 1980. pap. 2.25 (ISBN 0-687-18786-9). Abingdon.

In Christ: A New Creation. Mark Radecke. Ed. by Michael L. Sherer. (Orig.). 1986. pap. 6.25 (ISBN 0-89536-821-8, 6830). CSS of Ohio.

In Christ All Things Hold Together: An Introduction to Christian Doctrine. Jock Stein & Howard Taylor. 176p. (Orig.). 1985. pap. 5.95 (ISBN 0-8028-0083-1). Eerdmans.

In Christ Jesus. Arthur Pearson. pap. 6.95 (ISBN 0-89957-573-0). AMG Pubs.

In Christ, My Lord. Barbara O. Webb. 1982. pap. 4.95 (ISBN 0-570-03852-9, 12YY2807). Concordia.

In Crusader Greece. Eric Forbes-Boyd. (Illus.). 10.00 (ISBN 0-87556-091-1). Saifer.

In D. Pauli Epistolas ad Romanos et Galatas Commentaria. Girolamo Seripando. 568p. Repr. of 1601 ed. text ed. 99.36 (ISBN 0-576-99309-3, Pub. by Gregg Intl Pubs England). Gregg Intl.

In Darkest England & the Way Out. William Booth. 296p. 1984. Repr. of 1890 ed. 6.95 (ISBN 0-86544-024-7). Salv Army Suppl South.

In Defense of Faith: Assessing Arguments Against Latter-Day Saint Belief. Paul Hedengren. 240p. (Orig.). 1985. pap. 14.95 (ISBN 0-915073-00-5). Bradford & Wilson.

In Defense of Human Life. John F. McCarthy. 71p. 1970. pap. 1.50 (ISBN 0-912414-02-2). Lumen Christi.

In Defense of Life. John J. O'Connor. 1980. 4.00 (ISBN 0-686-74344-X); pap. 3.00 (ISBN 0-8198-3601-X). Dghtrs St Paul.

In Defense of Martin Luther. John W. Montgomery. (Illus.). 1970. 2.50 (ISBN 0-8100-0026-1, 12N0339). Northwest Pub.

In Defense of My "Life of Jesus" Against the Hegelians by David Friedrich Strauss. Ed. by Marilyn C. Massey. LC 83-10644. 112p. 1983. 17.50 (ISBN 0-208-02017-9, Archon Bks). Shoe String.

In Defense of Pretribulationism. John A. Sproule. 56p. (Orig.). 1980. pap. 2.95 (ISBN 0-88469-133-0). BMH Bks.

In Defense of Secular Humanism. Paul Kurtz. LC 83-62188. 273p. 1983. 18.95 (ISBN 0-87975-221-1); pap. 11.95 (ISBN 0-87975-228-9). Prometheus Bks.

In Defense of Theology. Gordon H. Clark. 1986. text ed. 12.95 (ISBN 0-8010-2520-6). Baker Bk.

In Dust I Sing. Francis Brabazon. 150p. 1974. 8.95 (ISBN 0-940700-08-5); pap. 4.95 (ISBN 0-940700-07-7). Meher Baba Info.

In Essentials, Unity: An Ecumenical Sampler. Edward A. Powers. (Orig.). 1982. pap. 4.95 (ISBN 0-377-00117-1). Friend Pr.

In Every Person Who Hopes... James Goff & Margaret Goff. (Orig.). 1980. pap. 3.75 (ISBN 0-377-00096-5). Friend Pr.

In Fragments: The Aphorisms of Jesus. John D. Crossan. LC 83-47719. 384p. 1983. 29.45 (ISBN 0-06-061608-3, HarpR). Har-Row.

In Galilee. Facsimile reprint ed. Thornton Chase. (Illus.). 98p. 1985. Repr. of 1921 ed. 7.95 (ISBN 0-933770-38-3). Kalimat.

In Garments All Red. Godfrey Poage. 1977. 3.00 (ISBN 0-8198-0422-3); pap. 1.50 (ISBN 0-8198-0423-1). Dghtrs St Paul.

In Ghostly Japan. Lafcadio Hearn. LC 79-138068. (Illus.). (YA) 1971. pap. 5.25 (ISBN 0-8048-0965-8). C E Tuttle.

In God They Trusted. David Manuel & Peter Marshall. 60p. (Orig.). 1983. pap. 6.95 (ISBN 0-919463-07-X). Paraclete Pr.

In God We Live. William Ostrom. (Orig.). 1986. pap. 2.50 (ISBN 0-87574-267-X). Pendle Hill.

In God We Should Trust. R. Thomas Dickman. LC 76-53146. 1977. 6.95 (ISBN 0-87212-071-6). Libra.

In Gods Gentle Arms. Richard Liddy. 1979. pap. 2.95 (ISBN 0-88479-022-3). Arena Lettres.

In God's Hand: Meditations for the Sick & Their Families. Donald D. McCall. Ed. by Herbert Lambert. LC 84-1744. 64p. 1984. pap. 4.95 (ISBN 0-8272-1606-8). CBP.

In God's Image. pap. 5.00 (ISBN 0-686-96040-8). United Syn Bk.

In God's Image. Jacob Rosin. LC 75-86507. 1969. 6.00 (ISBN 0-8022-2299-4). Philos Lib.

In God's Underground. Richard Wurmbrand. Orig. Title: Christ in the Communist Prisons. 1973. pap. text ed. 3.95 (ISBN 0-88264-003-8). Diane Bks.

In God's Waiting Room. rev. ed. Lehman Strauss. 1985. pap. text ed. 4.95 (ISBN 0-8024-3827-X). Moody.

In Gods We Trust: New Patterns of Religious Pluralism in America. Ed. by Thomas Robbins & Dick Anthony. LC 79-66441. 224p. 1980. pap. text ed. 12.95 (ISBN 0-87855-746-6). Transaction Bks.

In Good Spirits. David J. Ludwig. LC 82-70944. (Orig.). 1982. pap. 6.95 (ISBN 0-8066-1919-8, 10-3208). Augsburg.

In Heart & Home: A Woman's Workshop on Worship. Robert E. Webber. (Woman's Workshop Ser.). 112p. (Orig.). 1985. pap. 2.95 (ISBN 0-310-36681-X, 12209P). Zondervan.

In Her Own Right: The Life of Elizabeth Cady Stanton. Elisabeth Griffith. LC 83-25120. (Illus.). 1984. 19.95 (ISBN 0-19-503440-6). Oxford U Pr.

In Him. Kenneth E. Hagin. 1975. pap. 0.50 mini bk. (ISBN 0-89276-052-4). Hagin Ministries.

In Him Alone Is Our Hope: Texts on the Heart of Christ (1966-1983) Pedro Arrupe. Ed. by Jerome Aixala. Tr. by G. E. Ganss et al from Span. LC 83-80037. (Selected Letters & Addresses of: IV). xvi, 180p. 1984. pap. 7.00 Smyth sewn (ISBN 0-912422-85-8); pap. 6.00 (ISBN 0-912422-87-4). Inst Jesuit.

In His Image. Paul Brand & Philip Yancey. 224p. 1984. 12.95 (ISBN 0-310-35500-1, 10242). Zondervan.

In His Image. facsimile ed. William J. Bryan. LC 73-156618. (Essay Index Reprint Ser). Repr. of 1922 ed. 18.00 (ISBN 0-8369-2270-0). Ayer Co Pubs.

In His Image: The Jewish Philosophy of Man As Expressed in Rabbinic Tradition. Samuel Belkin. LC 78-10192. 1979. Repr. of 1960 ed. lib. bdg. 27.50x (ISBN 0-313-21234-1, BEIH). Greenwood.

In His Light. William A. Anderson. 1985. pap. 5.75 (ISBN 0-697-02111-4). Wm C Brown.

In His Likeness: A Manual of Direction for the Spiritual Life. Quentin Hakenewerth. 88p. (Orig.). 1977. pap. 1.75 (ISBN 0-9608124-1-5). Marianist Com Ctr.

In His Loving Service. Henry Hildebrand. Frwd. by Lloyd Mattson. 226p. (Orig.). 1985. pap. 6.95 (ISBN 0-942684-08-7). Camp Guidepts.

In His Name. Kirkie Morissey. 132p. 1985. pap. 4.95 (ISBN 0-89109-056-8). NavPress.

In His Presence. 2nd ed. Eva B. Werber. 1970. pap. 3.25 (ISBN 0-87516-102-2). De Vorss.

In His Presence: Appreciating Your Worship Tradition. Robert Schaper. LC 84-1305. 204p. 1984. pap. 5.95 (ISBN 0-8407-5887-1). Nelson.

In His Spirit. Richard J. Hauser. LC 81-83187. 128p. (Orig.). 1982. pap. 5.95 (ISBN 0-8091-2421-1). Paulist Pr.

In His Steps. Charles Sheldon. pap. 5.95, 250p. (ISBN 0-8007-5011-X, Power Bks); pap. 3.50, 192p. (ISBN 0-8007-8022-1, Spire Bks). Revell.

In His Steps. Charles L. Sheldon. 1980. pap. 3.95 (ISBN 0-88368-090-4). Whitaker Hse.

In His Steps. Charles M. Sheldon. (One Evening Christian Classic Ser.). 1962. pap. 2.95 (ISBN 0-89107-231-4). Good News.

In His Steps. Charles M. Sheldon. (Pivot Family Reader Ser). 256p. 1972. pap. 1.95 (ISBN 0-87983-012-3). Keats.

In His Steps. Charles M. Sheldon. 1977. large print kivar 8.95 (ISBN 0-310-32797-0, 12561L). Zondervan.

In His Steps. Charles M. Sheldon. 1982. gift ed. 7.95 (ISBN 0-915720-66-3). Brownlow Pub Co.

In His Steps. Charles M. Sheldon. 1985. pap. 4.95 (ISBN 0-916441-23-7). Barbour & Co.

In His Steps. Charles M. Sheldon. 243p. 1985. pap. 3.95 (ISBN 0-310-32751-2, Clarion Class). Zondervan.

In His Strength. Rev. ed. Gwen Wilkerson & Betty Schonauer. LC 77-92619. 144p. 1982. pap. 4.95 (ISBN 0-8307-0825-1, 5416405). Regal.

In His Time. Eileen L. Gordon-Smith. 1984. pap. 2.25 (ISBN 9971-972-04-2). OMF Bks.

In Hoc Signo? A Brief History of Catholic Parochial Education in America. Glen Gabert, Jr. LC 72-89992. 1973. 19.95x (ISBN 0-8046-9028-6, Pub. by Kennikat). Assoc Faculty Pr.

In Human Touch. Janina Babris. 17p. 1976. 5.95 (ISBN 0-912414-20-0). Lumen Christi.

In It to Win It. Roy C. Putnam. 1973. pap. 2.95 (ISBN 0-87508-440-0). Chr Lit.

In Jesus Name We Pray. 1975. 1.25 (ISBN 0-915952-01-7). Lord's Line.

In Job's Balances: On the Sources of the Eternal Truths. Lev Shestov. Tr. by Camilla Coventry & C. A. Macartney. LC 73-92902. (Eng.). l, 379p. 1975. 20.00x (ISBN 0-8214-0143-2, 82-81461). Ohio U Pr.

In Journeyings Often: Franciscan Pioneers in the Orient. Marion A. Habig. (Spirit & Life Ser). 1953. 6.50 (ISBN 0-686-11564-3). Franciscan Inst.

In Joy & in Sorrow. Large type ed. Ed. by Candida Lund. 164p. 1984. 12.95 (ISBN 0-88347-167-1). Thomas More.

In Kindling Flame: The Story of Hannah Senesh 1921-1944. Linda Atkinson. LC 83-24392. 256p. 1985. 13.50 (ISBN 0-688-02714-8). Lothrop.

In Light of Genesis. Pamela W. Hadas. LC 80-13129. (Jewish Poetry Ser.). 128p. 1980. 10.95 (ISBN 0-8276-0177-8, 462); pap. 6.95 (ISBN 0-8276-0178-6, 461). Jewish Pubns.

In Light of Wisdom. 2nd ed. Swami A. Jyoti. LC 84-50889. 74p. 1984. handbound 13.00 (ISBN 0-933572-05-0). Truth Consciousness.

In Love with Love: One Hundred of the World's Greatest Spiritual Poems. Ann Fremantle & Christopher Fremantle. LC 78-64360. (Spiritual Masters Ser.). 1978. pap. 2.95 (ISBN 0-8091-2136-0). Paulist Pr.

In Man We Trust: The Neglected Side of Biblical Faith. Walter Brueggemann. LC 72-1761. 144p. 1984. pap. 7.95 (ISBN 0-8042-0198-6). John Knox.

In Many & Various Ways. Mark W. Radecke. 1985. 5.75 (ISBN 0-89536-721-1, 5806). CSS of Ohio.

In Many Worlds. Jacob Alkow. LC 84-52110. (Illus.). 260p. 1985. pap. 13.95 (ISBN 0-88400-111-3). Shengold.

In Memoriam. Henri J. Nouwen. LC 79-56690. 64p. 1980. pap. 2.50 (ISBN 0-87793-197-6). Ave Maria.

In Memory of Her: A Feminist Theological Reconstruction of Christian Origins. Elisabeth S. Fiorenza. LC 82-19896. 275p. 1983. 22.50 (ISBN 0-8245-0493-3). Crossroad NY.

In Memory of Her: A Feminist Theological Reconstruction of Christian Origins. Ed. by Elisabeth S. Fiorenza. 384p. 1984. pap. 12.95 (ISBN 0-8245-0667-7). Crossroad NY.

In Memory of Kahil Gibran. Suheil Mutlak. (Arabic.). 1982. 14.00x (ISBN 0-86685-295-6). Intl Bk Ctr.

In My Father's House. Dorothy A. Solomon. LC 84-11964. 312p. 1984. 17.95 (ISBN 0-531-09763-3). Watts.

In My Heart Room. Mary T. Donze. 64p. 1982. pap. 1.50 (ISBN 0-89243-161-X). Liguori Pubns.

In My Own Way: An Autobiography. Alan W. Watts. 1973. pap. 5.95 (ISBN 0-394-71951-4, Vin). Random.

In My Soul I Am Free. Brad Steiger. 206p. 1968. pap. 5.95 (ISBN 0-88155-003-5). IWP Pub.

In My Upstairs Room. Mab G. Hoover. 96p. (Orig.). 1982. pap. 2.95 (ISBN 0-310-35632-6, 11272P). Zondervan.

In No Strange Land. facsimile ed. Katherine K. Burton. LC 72-99619. (Essay Index Reprint Ser). 1942. 19.50 (ISBN 0-8369-1551-8). Ayer Co Pubs.

In Our Midst. Mother Basilea Schlink. 1973. pap. 0.95 (ISBN 0-551-05289-9). Evang Sisterhood Mary.

In Parables: The Challenge of the Historical Jesus. John D. Crossan. LC 73-7067. 141p. 1985. pap. 8.95 (ISBN 0-06-061609-1, HarpR). Har-Row.

In Peter's Footsteps: Learning to Be a Disciple. M. Basil Pennington. LC 85-1541. 144p. 1985. 12.95 (ISBN 0-385-19398-X). Doubleday.

In Praise of Adam. Reuel Denney. LC 61-18887. (Phoenix Poets Ser). 1961. pap. 1.50 (ISBN 0-226-14301-5, PP3, Phoen). U of Chicago Pr.

In Praise of Constantine: A Historical Study & New Translation of Eusebius' Tricennial Orations. H. A. Drake. LC 75-62009. (UC Publications in Classical Studies: Vol. 15; California Library Reprint Ser.: No. 93). 1976. Repr. of 1975 ed. 22.50x (ISBN 0-520-03694-8). U of Cal Pr.

In Praise of God: The Rosary in Scriptural Meditation. John A. Hammes. 154p. 1983. 1.98 (ISBN 0-911988-51-3). Ami Pr.

In Praise of Homemaking: Affirming the Choice to be a Mother-at-Home. Connie F. Zimney. LC 84-71285. 144p. (Orig.). 1984. pap. 4.95 (ISBN 0-87793-322-7). Ave Maria.

In Praise of Krishna: Songs from the Bengali. Tr. by Edward C. Dimock, Jr. & Denise Levertov. (Illus.). xii, 96p. 1981. 6.95 (ISBN 0-226-15231-6, Phoen). U of Chicago Pr.

In Praise of Learning. Donald B. Rogers. LC 79-26829. (Into Our Third Century Ser.). (Orig.). 1980. pap. 3.95 (ISBN 0-687-18910-1). Abingdon.

In Praise of Leisure. Harold D. Lehman. LC 74-16399. 200p. 1974. 6.95 (ISBN 0-8361-1752-2); leader's guide o.p. 1.75 (ISBN 0-8361-1750-6). Herald Pr.

In Praise of More Folly. David I. Naglee. 208p. 1982. 10.00 (ISBN 0-682-49803-3, Banner). Exposition Pr FL.

In Prison You Came to Me. Phillip B. Singer. (Looking Up Ser.). 24p. (Orig.). 1984. pap. 1.25 (ISBN 0-8298-0473-0). Pilgrim NY.

In Pursuit of Love: Catholic Morality & Human Sexuality. Vincent Genovesi. 1987. pap. 16.95. M Glazier.

In Pursuit of Maturity. J. Oswald Sanders. 256p. 1986. pap. text ed. 7.95 (ISBN 0-310-32511-0). Zondervan.

In Pursuit of Moby Dick. Gerhard Friedrich. 1983. pap. 2.50x (ISBN 0-87574-098-7, 098). Pendle Hill.

In Pursuit of Wholeness: Healing in Today's Church. Bernard Haring. LC 85-80000. 128p. 1985. pap. 3.50 (ISBN 0-89243-236-5). Liguori Pubns.

In Quest of an Islamic Humanism: Arabic & Islamic Studies in Memory of Mohamed al-Nowaihi. Ed. by Arnold H. Green. 288p. 1986. pap. 27.50 (ISBN 977-424-027-8, Pub. by Am Univ Cairo Pr). Columbia U Pr.

In Quest of Gold: The Jim Ryun Story. Jim Ryun & Mike Philips. LC 84-47735. (Illus.). 224p. 1984. 12.45i (ISBN 0-06-067021-5, HarpR). Har-Row.

In Quest of Healing. Gordon Wright. LC 83-82030. 176p. (Orig.). 1984. pap. 4.95 (ISBN 0-88243-614-7, 02-0614). Gospel Pub.

In Quest of Jesus: A Guidebook. W. Barnes Tatum. 1983. pap. 9.95 (ISBN 0-8042-0275-3). John Knox.

In Quest of the Absolute. J. G. Weber. LC 77-3596. (Cistercian Studies: No. 51). 1977. 10.95 (ISBN 0-87907-851-0); pap. 4.95 (ISBN 0-87907-951-7). Cistercian Pub.

In Quest of the Historical Buddha & the White Cranes of Sri Ramakrishna. A. W. Sadler. LC 84-48565. (Illus.). 1984. pap. 6.50x sewn bdg. (ISBN 0-910913-02-1). Laughing B P.

In Quest of the Truth: A Survey of Medieval Jewish Thought. Israel Kane. LC 84-90191. 77p. 1985. 8.95 (ISBN 0-533-06243-8). Vantage.

In Remembrance. Ed Henry. 1978. pap. 1.50 (ISBN 0-89900-113-0). College Pr Pub.

In Remembrance of Me. Frank W. Lemons. 1975. 4.95 (ISBN 0-87148-430-7); pap. 3.95 (ISBN 0-87148-431-5). Pathway Pr.

In Search of a Faith That Works. Earl Palmer. LC 85-18421. (In Search of Ser.). 140p. 1985. write for info. (ISBN 0-8307-0889-8, 5110509). Regal.

In Search of a Father. James Robinson & Jimmie Cox. 1979. pap. 1.95 (ISBN 0-8423-1634-5). Tyndale.

In Search of a Yogi: Himalayan Pilgrimage. Dom D. Rutledge. lib. bdg. 69.95 (ISBN 0-8490-0392-X). Gordon Pr.

In Search of Ashes. Sarah B. Berkowitz. LC 83-50495. 128p. 1984. 7.95 (ISBN 0-88400-099-0). Shengold.

In Search of Bible Trivia. Bob Phillips. (Orig.). 1985. pap. 4.95 (ISBN 0-89081-458-9). Harvest Hse.

In Search of Bible Trivia II. Bob Phillips. pap. 4.95 (ISBN 0-89081-464-3). Harvest Hse.

In Search of Certainty. John Guest. LC 83-19273. (In Search of...Ser.). 1984. 9.95 (ISBN 0-8307-0919-3, 5111001). Regal.

In Search of Cumorah: New Evidences for the Book of Mormon from Ancient Mexico. David S. Palmer. LC 80-83866. (Illus.). 300p. 1981. 10.95 (ISBN 0-88290-169-9, 1063). Horizon Utah.

In Search of Deity. John Maquarrie. 288p. 14.95 (ISBN 0-8245-0682-0). Crossroad NY.

In Search of Dignity. R. C. Sproul. LC 82-18576. (In Search Of Ser.). 1983. 10.95 (ISBN 0-8307-0869-3, 5110407). Regal.

In Search of Early Christian Unity. Peter Roberts. 1985. 18.00 (ISBN 0-533-05859-7). Vantage.

In Search of Energy. Jackie Durham. Ed. by Celeste Pennington. (Home Mission Study). (Illus., Orig.). 1984. pap. 1.75 (ISBN 0-937170-27-5). Home Mission.

In Search of God. Marietta Moskin. LC 79-10493. (Illus.). 160p. 1979. 10.95 (ISBN 0-689-30719-5). Atheneum.

In Search of God & Other Poems. Swami Vivekananda. pap. 3.75 (ISBN 0-87481-121-X). Vedanta Pr.

In Search of God & Self: Renaissance & Reformation Thought. Donald J. Wilcox. (Illus.). 401p. 1987. pap. text ed. 12.95 (ISBN 0-88133-276-3). Waveland Pr.

In Search of God in the Sexual Underworld: A Mystical Journey. Edwin C. Johnson. LC 83-943. 224p. 1983. 13.95 (ISBN 0-688-01478-X). Morrow.

In Search of God-the Solar Connection. Michael Centre. LC 78-73706. (Illus.). 1978. 9.95x (ISBN 0-932876-00-5); pap. 5.95 (ISBN 0-932876-01-3). Centre Ent.

In Search of Guidance. Dallas Willard. LC 83-17743. 1983. 10.95 (ISBN 0-8307-0899-5, 5110807). Regal.

In Search of Heresy: American Literature in an Age of Conformity. John W. Aldridge. LC 74-3618. 208p. 1974. Repr. of 1956 ed. lib. bdg. 82.50x (ISBN 0-8371-7452-X, ALSH). Greenwood.

In Search of History: Historiography in the Ancient World & the Origins of Biblical History. John Van Seters. LC 82-48912. 416p. 1983. text ed. 35.00x (ISBN 0-300-02877-6); pap. 12.95 (ISBN 0-300-03633-7, Y-574). Yale U Pr.

In Search of Holiness. Loretta A. Bernard & David K. Bernard. 288p. (Orig.). 1981. pap. 6.95 (ISBN 0-912315-40-7). Word Aflame.

In Search of Humanity. rev. ed. John Macquarrie. 286p. 1985. pap. 11.95 (ISBN 0-8245-0708-8). Crossroad NY.

In Search of Humanity: A Theological & Philosophical Approach. John Macquarrie. LC 82-22077. 288p. 1983. 16.95 (ISBN 0-8245-0564-6). Crossroad NY.

In Search of Jerusalem: Religion & Ethics in the Writings of A. M. Klein. Gretl K. Fischer. LC 76-367083. pap. 66.50 (ISBN 0-317-26452-4, 2023858). Bks Demand UMI.

In Search of Peace. Helen Swift. 1983. pap. 3.75 (ISBN 0-89243-192-X). Liguori Pubns.

In Search of Self: The Soviet Jewish Intelligentsia & the Exodus. David Prital. 282p. 1983. pap. text ed. 25.00x (ISBN 965-223-420-6, Pub. by Magnes Pr Israel). Humanities.

In Search of Spiritual Excellence. Andrew Murray. Orig. Title: Full Blessing of Pentecost. 125p. 1984. pap. text ed. 3.50 (ISBN 0-88368-163-3). Whitaker Hse.

In Search of Spiritual Identity. Adrian Van Kaam. 14.95 (ISBN 0-87193-164-8). Dimension Bks.

In Search of Spiritual Leadership. Ken Hanna. 144p. 1987. pap. 5.95 (ISBN 0-89693-246-X). Victor Bks.

In Search of Talmudic Biography: The Problem of the Attributed Saying. Jacob Neusner. LC 84-10526. (Brown Judaic Studies). 148p. 1984. 19.95 (ISBN 0-89130-752-4, 14 00 70); pap. 14.95 (ISBN 0-89130-758-3). Scholars Pr GA.

In Search of the Cross. Robert J. Wieland. LC 78-184590. 120p. 1986. pap. 5.95 (ISBN 0-912145-11-0). MMI Pr.

In Search of the Divine: Some Unexpected Consequences of Interfaith Dialogue. Ed. by Shrivatsa Goswami & Larry Shinn. (God Ser.). 240p. (Orig.). 1987. text ed. 22.95 (ISBN 0-913757-28-4, Pub. by New Era Bks.); pap. text ed. 12.95 (ISBN 0-913757-29-2, Pub. by New Era Bks). Paragon Hse.

In Search of the Jewish Woman. Yisroel Miller. 149p. 1984. 8.95 (ISBN 0-87306-358-9); pap. 6.95 (ISBN 0-87306-359-7). Feldheim.

In Search of the Miraculous, Vol. 1. Bhagwan Shree Rajneesh. Ed. by Swami Anand Sambuddha. LC 84-42869. (Early Discourses & Writings Ser.). 368p. (Orig.). 1984. pap. 4.95 (ISBN 0-88050-710-1). Chidvilas Found.

In Search of the Miraculous: Fragments of an Unknown Teaching. P. D. Ouspensky. 399p. 1965. pap. 6.95 (ISBN 0-15-644508-5, Harv). HarBraceJ.

In Search of the Sacred. Rick Jarow. LC 86-40122. (Illus.). 242p. (Orig.). 1986. pap. 6.95 (ISBN 0-8356-0613-9). Theos Pub Hse.

In Search of the Shroud of Turin: New Light on Its History & Origins. Robert Drews. LC 83-24586. (Illus.). 148p. 1984. 19.95x (ISBN 0-8476-7349-9, Rowman & Allanheld). Rowman.

In Search of the Spirit. Mary M. Shideler. 272p. (Orig.). 1985. 11.95 (ISBN 0-345-32107-3, Pub. by Ballantine Epiphany). Ballantine.

In Search of the Spirit of Capitalism: An Essay on Max Weber's Protestant Ethic Thesis. Gordon Marshall. LC 81-18053. 233p. 1982. 26.50x (ISBN 0-231-05498-X); pap. 13.00x (ISBN 0-231-05499-8). Columbia U Pr.

In Search of the Yellow Submarine. Arlene Nardine. 222p. 1985. pap. write for info. (ISBN 0-88144-065-5). Christian Pub.

In Search of Tutankhamun. Piero Ventura & Gian P. Ceserani. LC 85-40416. (In Search of... Ser.). (Illus.). 48p. 1985. text ed. 12.96 (ISBN 0-382-09119-1); pap. 7.75 (ISBN 0-382-09122-1). Silver.

In Search of White Crows: Spiritualism, Parapsychology, & American Culture. R. Laurence Moore. LC 76-50720. 1977. 22.50x (ISBN 0-19-502259-9). Oxford U Pr.

In Search of Young Parents. Ruth E. Gibson. 120p. (Orig.). 1984. pap. 4.95 (ISBN 0-8341-0911-5). Beacon Hill.

In Season Out of Season. Jacques Ellul. 1983. 16.00 (ISBN 0-8446-6029-9). Peter Smith.

In Secret Tibet: In Disguise Amongst Lamas, Robbers & Wise Men. A Key to the Mysteries of Tibet. Theodore Illion. 190p. 1983. pap. 6.95 (ISBN 0-912181-01-X). East School Pr.

In-Service Education in Primary Mathematics. Mary T. Pinner & Hilary Shuard. 208p. 1985. pap. 15.00x (ISBN 0-335-15023-3, Open Univ Pr). Taylor & Francis.

In Six Days. Charles H. McGowen. 108p. 1986. pap. 3.95 (ISBN 0-936369-03-5). Son-Rise Pubns.

In Solitary Witness. rev. ed. Gordon Zahn. 1986. pap. 10.95 (ISBN 0-87243-141-X). Templegate.

In Spirit & in Truth. Ed. by Robert Fisher. (Orig.). pap. text ed. 5.95 (ISBN 0-87148-438-2). Pathway Pr.

In Spirit & in Truth: A Guide to Praying. Martha G. Rowlett. LC 82-50944. 112p. 1983. pap. 5.95 (ISBN 0-8358-0448-8). Upper Room.

In Spirit & in Truth: Charismatic Worship & the Reformed Tradition. Calvin H. Chambers. 168p. 1980. 7.95 (ISBN 0-8059-2686-0). Dorrance.

In Spirit & in Truth: Insights from Biblical Prayers. Ronald E. Clements. LC 85-228. 264p. 1985. pap. 9.95 (ISBN 0-8042-0071-8). John Knox.

In Spirit & in Truth: Ten Bible Studies on Worship. William Edgar. 72p. (Orig.). 1976. pap. 2.25 (ISBN 0-87784-458-5). Inter-Varsity.

In Step with the Spirit: A Study of the Fruit of the Spirit, Galatians 5: 22-23. Rubel Shelly. 1987. pap. price not set (ISBN 0-8010-8276-5). Baker Bk.

In Straw & Story: Christmas Resources for Home & Church. rev. ed. Joyce Erickson. (Illus.). 192p. 1983. pap. 10.95 (ISBN 0-87178-417-3). Brethren.

In Sure & Certain Hope: Funeral Messages Anthology. 1986. 6.25 (ISBN 0-89536-785-8, 6803). CSS of Ohio.

In the Arena. Isobel Kuhn. 1960. pap. 3.95 (ISBN 9971-972-19-0). OMF Bks.

In the Beginning. Behn Boruch. 1958. 4.00 (ISBN 0-88482-727-5). Hebrew Pub.

In the Beginning. Arthur Ferch. Ed. by Gerald Wheeler. LC 85-1946. 128p. (Orig.). 1985. pap. 5.95 (ISBN 0-8280-0282-7). Review & Herald.

In the Beginning. Samuel H. Hooke. LC 78-10638. (Clarendon Bible Old Testament Ser.: Vol. VI). (Illus.). 1979. Repr. of 1947 ed. lib. bdg. 22.50x (ISBN 0-313-21014-4, HOIB). Greenwood.

In the Beginning. Simeon B. Jochai. (Sacred Text Ser.). (Illus.). vii, 88p. 1983. pap. 8.75 (ISBN 0-88695-008-2). Concord Grove.

In the Beginning... Kenneth A. Skeem. Ed. by Jeanette L. Skeem. LC 81-68054. (Illus.). 256p. 1981. 12.00 (ISBN 0-9606782-0-4). Behemoth Pub.

In the Beginning. E. J. Young. 1976. pap. 3.95 (ISBN 0-85151-235-6). Banner of Truth.

In the Beginning: A Navaho Creation Myth. Stanley A. Fishler. (Utah Anthropological Papers: No. 13). Repr. of 1953 ed. 26.50 (ISBN 0-404-60613-X). AMS Pr.

In the Beginning: A New English Rendition of the Book of Genesis. Everett Fox. 288p. 1983. 14.95 (ISBN 0-8052-3870-0). Schocken.

In the Beginning: A Scientist Shows Why the Creationists Are Wrong. Chris McGowan. LC 83-62997. (Illus.). 208p. 1984. pap. 12.95 (ISBN 0-87975-240-8). Prometheus Bks.

In the Beginning: Creation Myths from Ancient Mesopotamia, Israel, & Greece. Joan O'Brien & Wilfred Major. LC 81-21311. (American Academy of Religion Academy Ser.). 1982. pap. 8.25 (ISBN 0-89130-559-9, 010311A). Scholars Pr GA.

In the Beginning God. Nina Ferguson. 1985. 6.95 (ISBN 0-8062-2430-4). Carlton.

In the Beginning God. Valarie Owen. 224p. (Orig.). 1983. pap. text ed. 6.95 (ISBN 0-914307-00-2, Dist. by Harrion Hse). Word Faith.

In the Beginning God: Jottings from Genesis. William Hartley. 96p. 1975. pap. 1.45 (ISBN 0-8010-4132-5). Baker Bk.

In the Beginning: Myths of the Western World. Lily Peter. LC 82-20274. (Illus.). 96p. 1983. 19.00x (ISBN 0-938626-15-9); pap. 7.95 (ISBN 0-938626-18-3). U of Ark Pr.

In the Beginning: Stories from the Bible. Sholem Asch. Tr. by Caroline Cunningham from Yiddish. LC 66-24907. (Illus.). 1979. pap. 3.95 (ISBN 0-8052-0626-4). Schocken.

In the Beginning: The Opening Chapters of Genesis. Henri Blocher. Tr. by David G. Preston from Fr. LC 84-12800. 180p. 1984. pap. 8.95 (ISBN 0-87784-325-2). Inter-Varsity.

In the Beginning: The Story of Creation. (Illus.). 1986. 9.95 (ISBN 0-915720-22-1). Brownlow Pub Co.

In the Beginning There Were the Parents. Dolores Curran. 1978. pap. 4.95 (ISBN 0-03-042766-5, HarpR). Har-Row.

In the Beginning Was the End. Wim Malgo. pap. 4.95 (ISBN 0-937422-33-9). Midnight Call.

In the Beginning...There Was No Sky. Walter Wangerin, Jr. 36p. 1986. 10.95 (ISBN 0-8407-6671-8). Nelson.

In the Belly of a Paradox: The Thought of Thomas Merton. Parker J. Palmer. LC 78-71769. 1979. pap. 2.50x (ISBN 0-87574-224-6). Pendle Hill.

In the Catacombs of Rome. Rodney Giffin & Sara Giffin. 1982. pap. 3.00 (ISBN 0-89536-524-3, 0902). CSS of Ohio.

In the Company of a Siddha: Interviews & Conversations with Swami Muktananda. rev. ed. Swami Muktananda. LC 78-65085. 192p. 1978. 5.95. SYDA Found.

In the Company of the Holy Mother. Orig. Title: At Holy Mother's Feet. 382p. 1980. pap. 5.95 (ISBN 0-87481-208-9). Vedanta Pr.

In the Days of Jesus: The Jewish Background & Unique Teaching of Jesus. Anthony J. Tambasco. LC 82-62919. 128p. (Orig.). 1983. pap. 3.95 (ISBN 0-8091-2536-6). Paulist Pr.

In the Days of Milton. Tudor Jenks. LC 76-170812. Repr. of 1905 ed. 19.45 (ISBN 0-404-03559-0). AMS Pr.

In the Eyes of the Ancestors: Belief & Behavior in a Mayan Community. June Nash. (Illus.). 374p. 1985. pap. text ed. 11.95x (ISBN 0-88133-142-2). Waveland Pr.

In the Flow of Life. Eric Butterworth. LC 82-50121. 181p. 1982. Repr. 5.95 (ISBN 0-87159-065-4). Unity School.

In the Footprints of the Lamb. G. Steinberger. Tr. by Bernard Christensen. LC 78-73416. 96p. 1979. pap. 2.95 (ISBN 0-87123-237-5, 200237). Bethany Hse.

In the Footsteps of the Buddha. facs. ed. Rene Grousset. Tr. by Mariette Leon from Fr. LC 77-124235. (Select Bibliographies Reprint Ser). 1932. 19.50 (ISBN 0-8369-5423-8). Ayer Co Pubs.

In the Gap: What It Means to Be a World Christian. David Bryant. LC 84-4880. 280p. 1984. pap. 7.95 (ISBN 0-8307-0952-5, 5418217). Regal.

In the Great Tradition. Ed. by Paul R. Dekar & Joseph D. Ban. 240p. 1982. 25.00 (ISBN 0-8170-0972-8). Judson.

In the Hall of the Dragon King, Bk. I. Stephen R. Lawhead. LC 82-71942. (Dragon King Trilogy Ser.). 348p. 1982. pap. 8.95 (ISBN 0-89107-257-8, Crossway Bks). Good News.

In the Hands of God. William Barclay. LC 80-25261. 154p. 1981. pap. 4.95 (ISBN 0-664-24362-2). Westminster.

In the Heart of the Seas: A Story of a Journey to the Land of Israel. S. Y. Agnon. Tr. by I. M. Lask from Hebrew. LC 66-30349. (Illus.). 128p. 1980. pap. 6.95 (ISBN 0-8052-0647-7). Schocken.

In the Hope of Nibbana: The Ethics of Theravada Buddhism. Winston L. King. LC 62-9575. 308p. 1964. 22.95 (ISBN 0-87548-230-9); pap. 9.95 (ISBN 0-87548-231-7). Open Court.

In the Hours of Meditation. Frank J. Alexander. pap. 1.75 (ISBN 0-87481-162-7). Vedanta Pr.

In the Image & Likeness of God. Vladimir Lossky. LC 76-383878. 232p. 1974. pap. 9.95 (ISBN 0-913836-13-3). St Vladimirs.

In the Image of God. Sean O'Reilly. 92p. 1982. 2.95 (ISBN 0-8198-3607-9, MS0308); pap. 1.95 (ISBN 0-8198-3608-7). Dghtrs St Paul.

In the Image of God. Robert S. Smith. 150p. (Orig.). 1987. pap. 5.95 (ISBN 0-938999-01-X). Yuganta Pr.

In the Image of God: Marriage & Chastity in Christian Life. Heini Arnold. LC 76-53542. 1977. pap. 3.50 (ISBN 0-87486-169-1). Plough.

In the Land of the Living: Health Care & the Church. Karin Granberg-Michaelson. 1984. pap. 4.95 (ISBN 0-310-27491-5, 6897P). Zondervan.

In The Lap of the Himalayas. Date not set. pap. 2.50 (ISBN 0-87481-540-1, Pub. by Ramakrishna Math Madras India). Vedanta Pr.

In the Latter Days: The Outpouring of the Holy Spirit in the Twentieth Century. Vinson Synan. 168p. (Orig.). 1984. pap. 4.95 (ISBN 0-89283-191-X). Servant.

In the Light of Healing: Sermons by Nona L. Brooks. Nona Brooks. Compiled by Patricia Zarlengo. (Illus.). 75p. (Orig.). 1986. pap. write for info. First Divine Sci Ch Denver.

In the Light of the Bible, Vols. 1 & 2. Concetta. 1976. Vol. 1. 2.00 (ISBN 0-8198-0426-6); Vol. 2. pap. 2.00 (ISBN 0-8198-0427-4). Dghtrs St Paul.

In the Likeness of God or, of Moses, of Pride & of Thorns. C. L. McDonald. 1986. 10.95 (ISBN 0-533-07031-7). Vantage.

In the Lord's Boarding House: Stories of Caring for Others. Nico Ter Linden. Tr. by Kenneth R. Mitchell from Dutch. 128p. (Orig.). 1985. pap. text ed. 7.95 (ISBN 0-687-18971-3). Abingdon.

In the Margins of the Yerushalmi: Glosses on the English Translation. Jacob Neusner. LC 83-20113. (Brown Judaic Studies). 160p. 1983. pap. 14.00 (ISBN 0-89130-663-3, 14 00 55). Scholars Pr GA.

In the Mouth of the Wolf. Rose Zar. 224p. 1983. 10.95 (ISBN 0-8276-0225-1, 611). Jewish Pubns.

In the Name of Jesus Christ. Albert A. Iacobucci. 129p. 1985. 10.95 (ISBN 0-533-06419-8). Vantage.

In the Name of Peace: Collective Statements of the United States Catholic Bishops on War & Peace, 1919-1980. Ed. by David Byers. 121p. 1983. pap. 8.95 (ISBN 1-55586-861-4). US Catholic.

In the Palm of His Hand: 1838 to 1984. Eleanor R. Lambert. LC 85-9036. (Illus.). 200p. 1985. 14.98 (ISBN 0-935304-92-4). August Hse.

In the Paradise of the Sufis. Javad Nurbakhsh. LC 79-83588. 1979. pap. 6.00x (ISBN 0-933546-01-7). KhaniQahi-Nimatullahi-Sufi.

In the Path of God: Islam & Political Power. Daniel Pipes. LC 83-70764. 373p. 1983. text ed. 22.50 (ISBN 0-465-03451-9). Basic.

In the Path of God: Islam & Political Power. Daniel Pipes. LC 83-70764. 384p. 1985. pap. 9.95 (ISBN 0-465-03452-7, PL-5138). Basic.

In the Potter's Hands Book. Sharon Tash. 32p. 1985. pap. 1.95 (ISBN 0-930756-96-7, 531020). Aglow Pubns.

In the Presence of God. Clarence Enzler. pap. 4.95 (ISBN 0-87193-055-2). Dimension Bks.

In the Presence of God. rev. ed. Otto W. Toelke. LC 61-18225. 1962. 4.95 (ISBN 0-570-03019-6, 6-1152). Concordia.

In the Presence of God: Readings for Christian Marriage. David Mace & Vera Mace. LC 84-26928. 116p. 1985. 8.95 (ISBN 0-664-21261-1). Westminster.

In the Presence of Mystery: An Introduction to the Study of Human Religiousness. Michael H. Barnes. 324p. (Orig.). 1984. pap. 9.95 (ISBN 0-89622-205-5). Twenty-Third.

In the Shade of the Qur'an, 30th Part. S. Qutb. pap. 14.95 (ISBN 0-317-46111-7). Kazi Pubns.

In the Shadow of His Cross. John F. Marshall. (Spirit & Life Ser). 1969. 2.00 (ISBN 0-686-11577-5). Franciscan Inst.

In the Shadow of Islam: The Women's Movement in Iran. Ed. by Azar Tabari & Nahid Yeganeh. 256p. 1983. 24.75x (ISBN 0-86232-022-4, Pub. by Zed Pr England); pap. 10.25 (ISBN 0-86232-039-9). Humanities.

In the Shadow of Plenty. George Grant. 1986. pap. 6.95 (ISBN 0-8407-3095-0). Nelson.

In the Shadow of the Flames: Six Lectures on the Holocaust. Kopeck. LC 82-72377. (Witness to the Holocaust Ser.: No. 4). 86p. 1982. 6.75. Witness Holocaust.

In the Shadow of the Himalayas: A Historical Narrative of the Missions of the United Presbyterian Church of North America as Conducted in the Punjab, India 1855-1940. Emma D. Anderson & Mary J. Campbell. 373p. 1983. Repr. of 1942 ed. lib. bdg. 45.00 (ISBN 0-89987-042-2). Darby Bks.

In the Shadow of the Rising Sun. Judy Hyland. LC 84-12303. 128p. (Orig.). 1984. pap. 5.95 (ISBN 0-8066-2091-9, 10-3260). Augsburg.

In the Shadow of the Temple. Meir Ben-Dov. LC 84-48639. (Illus.). 384p. 1985. 24.45i (ISBN 0-06-015362-8, HarpT). Har-Row.

In the Spirit of Hegel: A Study of G. W. F. Hegel's "Phenomenology of Spirit". Robert C. Solomon. (Illus.). 1983. 32.50x (ISBN 0-19-503169-5); pap. 14.95x (ISBN 0-19-503650-6). Oxford U Pr.

In the Steps of Jesus. Rosalyn Kendrick. 128p. 1985. pap. 8.95 (ISBN 0-7175-1309-2). Dufour.

In the Steps of John Bunyan. Vera Brittain. (Illus.). 1973. 30.00 (ISBN 0-8274-1456-0). R West.

In the Steps of St. Francis. Ernest Raymond. 380p. 1975. pap. 4.95 (ISBN 0-8199-0557-7). Franciscan Herald.

In the Steps of St. Patrick. Brian De Breffny. (Illus.). 1982. 9.98 (ISBN 0-500-24110-4). Thames Hudson.

In the Steps of St. Paul. H. V. Morton. (Illus.). 440p. 1986. Repr. of 1936 ed. lib. bdg. 45.00 (ISBN 0-89984-770-6). Century Bookbindery.

In the Steps of the Master. Douglas Baker. 1982. 40.00x (ISBN 0-9505502-4-8, Pub. by Baker Pubns England). State Mutual Bk.

In the Steps of the Master. H. V. Morton. 1935. lib. bdg. 32.59 (ISBN 0-8414-6678-5). Folcroft.

In the Steps of the Master. H. V. Morton. (Illus.). 408p. 1984. pap. 12.95 (ISBN 0-396-08415-X). Dodd.

In the Stillness Dancing: The Life of Father John Main. Neil McKinty. 192p. 1987. 14.95 (ISBN 0-8245-0799-1). Crossroad NY.

In the Tavern of Ruin: Seven Essays on Sufism. Javad Nurbakhsh. LC 78-102838. (Orig.). 1978. pap. 6.00x (ISBN 0-933546-00-9). KhaniQahi-Nimatullahi-Sufi.

In the Time of Paul. Edward G. Selden. 1900. 10.00 (ISBN 0-8414-8134-2). Folcroft.

In the Twilight of Western Thought. Herman Dooyeweerd. 1960. pap. 3.95 (ISBN 0-934532-09-5). Presby & Reformed.

In the Valley of the Mekong. Matt J. Menger. LC 79-115966. 1970. pap. 3.95 (ISBN 0-686-18632-X). Oblate.

In the Vatican. Peter Hebblethwaite. LC 86-7927. 214p. 1986. 16.95 (ISBN 0-917561-24-4). Adler & Adler.

In the Vineyard of the Lord. Helen S. Rice. (Illus.). 160p. 1979. 12.95 (ISBN 0-8007-1036-3). Revell.

In the Ways of Justice Toward Salvation. Gregory J. Polan. (American University Studies VII - Theology & Religion: Vol. 13). 360p. 1986. text ed. 46.00 (ISBN 0-8204-0280-X). P Lang Pubs.

In the Whale's Belly & Other Martyr Stories. James W. Lowry. (Illus.). (YA) 1981. 4.70 (ISBN 0-87813-513-8). Christian Light.

In the Womb of the Cave. Andre Cirino. 366p. 1981. 14.00 (ISBN 0-933402-26-0); pap. 9.00 (ISBN 0-933402-25-2). Charisma Pr.

In the World but Not of It: A Guide to More Spirituality in Your Life. Stuart Litvak & Nora Burba. 156p. 1984. pap. 5.95 (ISBN 0-13-453994-X). P-H.

In Their Footsteps. 3.75 (ISBN 0-914131-36-2, I03); tchr's guide 20.00 (ISBN 0-914131-37-0, I10). Torah Umesorah.

In This Moment. Pat A. Baker. LC 76-28802. Repr. of 1977 ed. 23.50 (ISBN 0-8357-9012-6, 2016370). Bks Demand UMI.

In Thy Presence. Lev Gillet. LC 77-1040. 144p. 1977. pap. 3.95 (ISBN 0-913836-34-6). St Vladimirs.

In Time of Need: Jesus. Johnny Hunton. 35p. (Orig.). 1983. pap. 2.25 (ISBN 0-89323-041-3). Bible Memory.

In Touch. Edythe Draper. 1983. deluxe ed. 8.95 gift ed. (ISBN 0-8423-1711-2); christmas ed. 8.95 (ISBN 0-8423-1712-0); deluxe graduation ed. 8.95 (ISBN 0-8423-1713-9); kivar 5.95 (ISBN 0-8423-1710-4). Tyndale.

In Touch with God: How God Speaks to a Prayerful Heart. Marie Shropshire. (Orig.). 1985. pap. 4.95 (ISBN 0-89081-447-3). Harvest Hse.

In Tune with the Infinite. Ralph W. Trine. LC 72-125594. 1970. pap. 4.95 (ISBN 0-672-51349-8). Bobbs.

In Tune with the Infinite. Ralph W. Trine. (Large Type Christian Classics Ser.). 1984. large print 10.95 (ISBN 0-87983-360-2). Keats.

In Verdant Pastures: From a Pastor's Diary. Peter M. Rinaldi. LC 85-72837. 228p. (Orig.). 1985. pap. 7.95 (ISBN 0-89944-202-1). Don Bosco Multimedia.

In Wisdom Thou Hast Made Them. Reverend Mother Ruth. Ed. by Patricia Galanter. (Illus.). 141p. 1986. 15.95x (ISBN 0-937431-01-X). Adams Bannister Cox.

In Word & Deed. Bruce Nicholls & Kenneth Kantzer. 224p. 1986. pap. 10.95 (ISBN 0-8028-1965-6). Eerdmans.

In Word & Deed: A Student's Beginning Guide to Understanding the Luthern Worship Service. Ronn T. Pelley. (Pass Along Ser.). (Illus.). 32p. 1986. pap. 2.95 (ISBN 0-933350-49-X). Morse Pr.

In Your Midst: Perspectives on Christian Mission. Sheila D. Collins & John A. Collins. (Orig.). 1980. pap. 3.25 (ISBN 0-377-00101-5). Friend Pr.

In Your Time of Sorrow. Albert J. Nimeth. 1976. pap. 0.50 (ISBN 0-685-77503-8). Franciscan Herald.

Inaugural Address & Defense, Eighteen Ninety-One to Eighteen Ninety-Three. Charles A. Briggs. LC 70-38442. (Religion in America, Ser. 2). 336p. 1972. Repr. of 1972 ed. 22.00 (ISBN 0-405-04062-8). Ayer Co Pubs.

Incarnate Love: Essays in Orthodox Ethics. Vigen Guroian. LC 86-40591. 208p. 1987. text ed. 22.95x (ISBN 0-268-01162-1, Dist. by Har-Row). U of Notre Dame Pr.

Incarnate Son of God. Henri DeVries. pap. 2.75 (ISBN 0-87509-095-8). Chr Pubns.

Incarnation. A. P. Shepherd. 14p. (Orig.). 1976. pap. 1.50 (ISBN 0-88010-098-2). Anthroposophic.

Incarnation & Hilton's Spirituality. David G. Kennedy. LC 85-62297. x, 312p. (Orig.). 1986. pap. 12.95x (ISBN 0-934995-00-1). OLW Editions.

Incarnation in Hinduism & Christianity: The Myth of the God-Man. Daniel E. Bassuk. (Library of Philosophy & Religion Ser.). 256p. 1987. text ed. 35.00 (ISBN 0-391-03452-9). Humanities.

Incarnation of God. Hans Kung. 660p. 1987. 34.50 (ISBN 0-8245-0793-2). Crossroad NY.

Incarnational Element in Hiltons Spirituality. David G. Kennedy. Ed. by James Hogg. (Elizabethan & Renaissance Studies). 312p. (Orig.). 1982. pap. 15.00 (ISBN 0-317-40146-7, Pub by Salzburg Studies). Longwood Pub Group.

Incense & Iconoclasm. Charles L. Moore. 343p. 1980. Repr. of 1915 ed. lib. bdg. 30.00 (ISBN 0-89987-573-4). Century Bookbindery.

Incidental Grace. Robert H. Pope. 176p. 1985. pap. 6.95 (ISBN 0-310-34651-7, 12743P). Zondervan.

Incidents in the Life of Madame Blavatsky. facsimile ed. Ed. by Alfred P. Sinnett. LC 75-36919. (Occult Ser.). Repr. of 1886 ed. 25.50x (ISBN 0-405-07974-5). Ayer Co Pubs.

Incidents in the Life of the Rev. J. Asher. facsimile ed. Jeremiah Asher. LC 74-168506. (Black Heritage Library Collection). Repr. of 1850 ed. 12.00 (ISBN 0-8369-8860-4). Ayer Co Pubs.

Inclusive Language for Psalms. National Council of Churches Staff. 1987. pap. 7.95. Pilgrim Pr.

Inclusive Language in the Church. Nancy A. Hardesty. LC 86-46036. 108p. (Orig.). 1987. pap. 7.95 (ISBN 0-8042-1686-X). John Knox.

Inclusive-Language Lectionary: Readings for Year A. rev. & enl. ed. The Inclusive-Language Lectionary Committee, Division of Education & Ministry, National Council of Churches of Christ in the U. S. A. 292p. 1986. pap. 10.95 (ISBN 0-664-24051-8). Westminster.

Inclusive-Language Lectionary: Readings for Year A. LC 83-16779. 192p. 1983. pap. 7.95 (ISBN 0-664-24506-4). Westminster.

Inclusive-Language Lectionary: Readings for Year B. LC 84-7420. 256p. 1984. pap. 9.95 (ISBN 0-664-24564-1). Westminster.

Inclusive Language Lectionary: Readings for Year B. National Council of Churches of Christ. 192p. (Orig.). 1984. pap. 8.95 (ISBN 0-8298-0719-5). Pilgrim NY.

Inclusive-Language Psalms. National Council of Churches Staff. 144p. (Orig.). 1987. pap. 7.95 (ISBN 0-8298-0747-0). Pilgrim NY.

Income Tax Law for Ministers & Religious Workers: 1986 Edition for 1985 Returns. B. J. Worth. 64p. 1984. pap. 4.95 (ISBN 0-8010-9671-5, 9671-5). Baker Bk.

Income Tax Law for Ministers & Religious Workers: 1987 Edition for Preparing 1986 Returns. B. J. Worth. 96p. 1987. pap. 4.95 (ISBN 0-8010-9676-6). Baker Bk.

Incomparable Christ. rev. ed. J. Oswald Sanders. 256p. 1982. pap. 8.95 (ISBN 0-8024-4081-9). Moody.

Incomparable Christ. Billy E. Simmons. 128p. 1983. pap. 4.00 (ISBN 0-914520-21-0). Insight Pr.

Incomparable Jewell: Shewed in a Sermon. LC 76-57393. (English Experience Ser.: No. 810). 1977. Repr. of 1632 ed. lib. bdg. 7.00 (ISBN 90-221-0810-4). Walter J Johnson.

Incomparable Story. Ralph W. Harris. LC 77-75602. (Radiant Life Ser.). 128p. 1977. pap. 2.50 (ISBN 0-88243-907-3, 02-0907); tchr's ed. 3.95 (ISBN 0-88243-177-3, 32-0177). Gospel Pub.

Incorruptibles. Joan C. Cruz. LC 77-93992. (Illus.). 1977. pap. 8.00 (ISBN 0-89555-066-0). TAN Bks Pubs.

Increase Mather Vs. Solomon Stoddard: Two Puritan Tracts. Increase Mather & Solomon Stoddard. LC 72-141117. (Research Library of Colonial Americana). 1971. Repr. of 1700 ed. 17.00 (ISBN 0-405-03328-1). Ayer Co Pubs.

Increase Your Prayer Power Tenfold. Gordon Lindsay. (School of Prayer Ser.). 1.25 (ISBN 0-89985-080-4). Christ Nations.

Increasing the Joy: Studies in I John. Harold T. Bryson. LC 81-67200. 1982. pap. 5.95 (ISBN 0-8054-1390-1). Broadman.

Incredible Christ. Jim Burns. (LifeSources for Youth Ser.: No. 3). 64p. (Orig.). 1987. wkbk. 3.95 (ISBN 0-89081-575-5). Harvest Hse.

Incredible Cover-Up. Dave Mac Pherson. 1975. 8.95 (ISBN 0-88270-143-6); pap. 3.95 (ISBN 0-88270-144-4). Omega Pubns Or.

Incredible Creed of the Jehovah Witnesses. Leslie Rumble. 1977. pap. 0.60 (ISBN 0-89555-025-3). TAN Bks Pubs.

Incredible Ideas for Youth Groups. Wayne Rice & Mike Yaconelli. 160p. (Orig.). 1982. pap. 7.95 (ISBN 0-310-45231-7, 11370P). Zondervan.

Incredible Passage: Through the Hole-in-the-Rock. Lee Reay. Ed. by Ranier Hechtle. (Illus.). 128p. (Orig.). 1981. 5.95 (ISBN 0-934826-05-6); pap. 4.50 (ISBN 0-934826-06-4). Meadow Lane.

Incredible Sai Baba: The Life & Miracles of a Modern-Day Saint. Arthur Osborne. 102p. 1985. pap. text ed. 5.00x (ISBN 0-86125-105-9, Pub. by Orient Longman Ltd India). Apt Bks.

Incubus & Ideal: Ecclesiastical Figures In Chaucer & Langland. Peter S. Taitt. Ed. by James Hogg. (Elizabethan & Renaissance Studies). 228p. (Orig.). 1975. pap. 15.00 (ISBN 3-7052-0690-7, Pub. by Salzburg Studies). Longwood Pub Group.

Incubus in English Literature: Provenance & Progeny. Nicolas Kiessling. (Illus.). 1977. pap. 12.95 (ISBN 0-87422-006-8). Wash St U Pr.

Indecision about Baptism. large print ed. Pearl Brians. 34p. 1985. pap. 5.00 (ISBN 0-914009-41-9). VHI Library.

Indentity & the Sacred. Hans J. Mol. LC 76-27153. 1977. 22.50 (ISBN 0-02-921600-1). Free Pr.

Independence of Exegesis: The Study of Christianity in the Work of Alfred Loisy, Charles Guignebert. & Maurice Goguel. Alan H. Jones. 313p. 1983. lib. bdg. 75.00x (ISBN 3-16-144451-5, Pub. by J C B Mohr BRD). Coronet Bks.

Independent Bible Study. Irving L. Jensen. LC 68-12114. 1972. pap. 6.95 (ISBN 0-8024-4050-9). Moody.

Indescribable Christ. Rev. ed. Charles J. Rolls. 1984. pap. 5.95 (ISBN 0-87213-731-7). Loizeaux.

Indestructible Jews. Max I. Dimont. 480p. 1973. pap. 4.95 (ISBN 0-451-13878-3, Sig). NAL.

Index. M. Winternitz. (Sacred Bks. of the East: Vol. 50). 15.00 (ISBN 0-89581-535-4). Asian Human Pr.

Index & Reference Volume to the Lemegeton of Solomon (1979 White Transcription of Sloane 2731) Nelson White & Anne White. LC 80-52052. 75p. (Orig.). 1980. pap. 15.00 (ISBN 0-939856-07-7). Tech Group.

Index Islamicus, Fifth Supplement 1976-1980. Compiled by J. D. Pearson & Wolfgang Behn. 944p. 1983. Set. 159.00x (ISBN 0-7201-1650-3); Pt. 1: Articles. 96.00 (ISBN 0-7201-1669-4); Pt. 2: Monographs. 64.00 (ISBN 0-7201-1668-6). Mansell.

Index Islamicus: First Supplement 1956-1960. Compiled by J. D. Pearson & Wolfgang Behn. 344p. 1978. Repr. of 1962 ed. 53.00x (ISBN 0-7201-0381-9). Mansell.

Index Islamicus, Fourth Supplement: Part 2, 1972-73. Ed. by J. D. Pearson & Ann Walsh. 108p. 1974. 64.00 (ISBN 0-7201-0286-3). Mansell.

Index Islamicus: Fourth Supplement, Part 4, 1974-1975. Ed. by J. D. Pearson & Ann Walsh. 128p. 1975. pap. 10.00x (ISBN 0-7201-0288-X). Mansell.

Index Islamicus: Primary Sequence 1906-1955. Compiled by J. D. Pearson & Wolfgang Behn. 933p. 1958. 75.00x (ISBN 0-7201-0380-0). Mansell.

Index Islamicus: Second Supplement, 1961-1965. Compiled by J. D. Pearson & Wolfgang Behn. 372p. 1967. 53.00 (ISBN 0-7201-0382-7). Mansell.

Index Islamicus: Third Supplement 1966-1970. Compiled by J. D. Pearson & Wolfgang Behn. 420p. 1972. 53.00x (ISBN 0-7201-0282-0). Mansell.

Index of Egyptian Administrative & Religious Titles of the Middle Kingdom. William Ward. 244p. 1983. text ed. 60.00x (ISBN 0-8156-6065-0, Am U Beirut). Syracuse U Pr.

Index of Icons in English Emblem Books, 1500-1700. Huston Diehl. LC 85-40950. (Illus.). 288p. 1986. 35.00x (ISBN 0-8061-1989-6). U of Okla Pr.

Index of Middle English Verse. Carleton Brown & Rossell H. Robbins. xix, 785p. 1943. 40.00x (ISBN 0-87352-017-3, Z2). Modern Lang.

Index of Quotations From the Baha'i Scared Writings. James Heggie. 824p. 39.50 (ISBN 0-85398-145-0). G Ronald Pub.

Index of Reviews of New Testament Books Between 1900-1950. repr. ed. Watson E. Mills. LC 77-72827. (Special Studies: No. 2). viii, 69p. 1984. pap. 3.50 (ISBN 0-932180-01-9). NABPR.

Index of the Spells on Egyptian Middle Kingdom Coffins & Related Documents. Leonard H. Lesko. LC 79-66500. (Orig.). 1979. pap. text ed. 6.00x (ISBN 0-930548-02-7). B C Scribe.

Index Patristicus, Sive Clavis Patrum Apostolicorum Operum. Edgar J. Goodspeed. LC 60-52358. 1960. 18.00x (ISBN 0-8401-0863-X). A R Allenson.

Index to Articles on American Jewish History. Jacob R. Marcus. 1971. 20.00x (ISBN 0-87068-139-7). Ktav.

Index to Festschriften in Jewish Studies. Charles Berlin. 1971. 50.00x (ISBN 0-87068-133-8). Ktav.

Index to Jewish Festschriften. Ed. by J. R. Marcus & A. Bilgray. Repr. of 1937 ed. 29.00 (ISBN 0-527-61300-2). Kraus Repr.

Index to Jewish Periodicals. Miriam Leikind et al. Per Volume. 80.00 (ISBN 0-686-75688-6). IJP.

Index to Leaders of Iberian Christianity. 1.00 (ISBN 0-686-23370-0). Classical Folia.

Index to Prayer Books, Pamphlets, Etc. International Partners in Prayer. 50p. 1984. pap. 2.50 (ISBN 0-917593-01-4, Pub. by Intl Partners). Prosperity & Profits.

Index to Stories of Hymns. Alice M. Richardson. LC 72-1690. Repr. of 1929 ed. 11.50 (ISBN 0-404-09911-4). AMS Pr.

Index to the American Jewish Archives, Vols. I-X. Paul F. White. 25.00x (ISBN 0-87820-004-5). Ktav.

Index to the Brown, Driver & Briggs Hebrew Lexicon. Compiled by Bruce Einspahr. LC 76-25479. (Hebrew.). 1976. 25.95 (ISBN 0-8024-4082-7). Moody.
Index to the Chant of the Mozarabic Rite. Don M. Randel. LC 72-5384. (Princeton Studies in Music Ser.: No. 6). pap. 160.00 (ISBN 0-317-09926-4, 2011400). Bks Demand UMI.
Index to the Code of Canon Law. Ed. by Canon Law Society of Great Britain & Ireland Staff. 104p. (Orig.). 1985. pap. 3.50 (ISBN 0-8028-0067-X). Eerdmans.
Index to the Evangelist & the Christian. Dennis Gulledge & David McWhirter. LC 83-70079. 160p. (Orig.). 1983. pap. 3.95 (ISBN 0-89900-231-5). College Pr Pub.
Index to the Names in the Mahabharata. S. Sorensen. 1978. Repr. 30.00 (ISBN 0-89684-011-5, Pub. by Motilal Banarsidass India). Orient Bk Dist.
Index to the Picture Collection of the American Jewish Archives. Jacob R. Marcus. 7.50 (ISBN 0-87820-005-3). Ktav.
Index to the Records of the Moravian Mission among the Indians of North America, 2 vols. Compiled by Carl J. Fliegel. 1407p. 1970. Set. 400.00 (ISBN 0-89235-018-0). Res Pubns CT.
Index to the Revised Bauer Arndt, Gingrich Greek Lexicon. 2nd ed. John R. Alsop. (Gr.). 1981. 14.95 (ISBN 0-310-44031-9, 6773P). Zondervan.
Index to the Secret Doctrine. The Theosophy Company. x, 172p. 1939. 6.00 (ISBN 0-938998-02-1). Theosophy.
Index to the Sound Recordings Collection of the American Jewish Arichives. Joel Stevens & Kerry M. Olitzky. 1980. 7.50x (ISBN 0-87820-009-6). Ktav.
Index to the Spirits Given in "Abramelin". Nelson White & Anne White. 50p. (Orig.). 1981. pap. 8.00 (ISBN 0-939856-17-4). Tech Group.
Index Verborum of the Fragments of the "Avesta". Montgomery Schuyler. LC 2-15630. (Columbia University. Indo-Iranian Ser.: No. 4). Repr. of 1901 ed. 14.50 (ISBN 0-404-50474-4). AMS Pr.
Index, with Aids to the Preacher. (Church Dogmatics Ser.: Vol. 5). 562p. 1977. 29.95 (ISBN 0-567-09046-9, Pub. by T & T Clark Ltd UK). Fortress.
India & Christendom: The Historical Connections Between Their Religions. Richard Garbe. Tr. by Lydia Robinson from Ger. 321p. 1959. 22.95 (ISBN 0-87548-232-5). Open Court.
India & the West: The Problem of Understanding-Selected Essays of J.L. Mehta. J L. Mehta. (Studies in World Religions: No. 4). 1985. 20.75 (ISBN 0-89130-826-1, 03 00 04); pap. 13.75 (ISBN 0-89130-827-X). Scholars Pr GA.
Indian & Christian Miracles of Walking on the Water. William N. Brown. LC 78-72381. Repr. of 1928 ed. 16.50 (ISBN 0-404-17243-1). AMS Pr.
Indian & Jesuit: A Seventeenth Century Encounter. James T. Moore. 1982. 12.95 (ISBN 0-8294-0395-7). Loyola.
Indian Assimilation in the Franciscan Area of Nueva Vizcaya. William B. Griffen. LC 78-14546. (Anthropological Papers: No. 33). 122p. 1979. pap. 10.95x (ISBN 0-8165-0584-5). U of Ariz Pr.
Indian Awakening in Latin America. Ed. by Yves Materne. 1980. pap. 5.95 (ISBN 0-377-00097-3). Friend Pr.
Indian Buddhism. rev. 2nd ed. A. K. Warder. 580p. 1980. text ed. 22.00 (ISBN 0-89684-094-8, Pub. by Motilal Banarsidass India). Orient Bk Dist.
Indian Buddhism: A Survey with Bibliographical Notes. Hijime Nakamura. 440p. 1986. 28.00 (Pub. by Motilal Banarsidass). South Asia Bks.
Indian Christ, the Indian King: The Historical Substrate of Maya Myth & Ritual. Victoria R. Bricker. (Illus.). 382p. 1981. text ed. 45.00x (ISBN 0-292-73824-2). U of Tex Pr.
Indian Christians of St. Thomas: An Account of the Ancient Syrian Church of Malabar. Leslie Brown. LC 81-21766. (Illus.). 330p. 1982. 39.50 (ISBN 0-521-21258-8). Cambridge U Pr.
Indian Culture. Girish C. Roy. 1977. write for info. (ISBN 0-686-22664-X). Intl Bk Dist.
Indian Dances of North America: Their Importance to Indian Life. Reginald Laubin & Gladys Laubin. LC 75-40962. (Civilization of the American Indian Ser: No.141). 1979. 32.50 (ISBN 0-8061-1319-7). U of Okla Pr.
Indian Epic Poetry: An Analysis of Ramayana. M. Monier-Williams. lib. bdg. 79.95 (ISBN 0-87968-547-6). Krishna Pr.
Indian Games & Dances with Native Songs. Alice C. Fletcher. LC 75-136369. Repr. of 1915 ed. 14.50 (ISBN 0-404-07229-1). AMS Pr.
Indian Gods & Kings: The Story of a Living Past. facs. ed. Emma Hawkridge. LC 68-24853. (Essay Index Reprint Ser). 1935. 21.50 (ISBN 0-8369-0521-0). Ayer Co Pubs.
Indian Life at the Old Missions. Edith B. Webb. LC 82-23871. (Illus.). xxx, 378p. 1983. Repr. of 1952 ed. 35.00 (ISBN 0-8032-4724-9). U of Nebr Pr.
Indian Logic & Atomism: An Exposition of the Nyaya & Vaicesika Systems. Arthur B. Keith. lib. bdg. 79.95 (ISBN 0-87968-529-8). Krishna Pr.
Indian Lore. (Illus.). 90p. 1959. pap. 1.00x (ISBN 0-8395-3358-6, 3358). BSA.
Indian Missions. Pierre-Jean DeSmet. 67p. 1985. 10.95. Ye Galleon.
Indian Mother Goddess. 2nd ed. N. N. Bhattacharyya. 1977. 16.50x (ISBN 0-88386-736-2). South Asia Bks.
Indian Muslims: A Study of Minority Problems in India. Asghar A. Engineer. 1986. 28.00x (ISBN 81-202-0139-6, Pub. by Ajanta). South Asia Bks.
Indian Muslims & World War I. Yuvaraj D. Prasad. 1985. 20.00x (ISBN 0-8364-1489-6, Pub. by Nanaki Prakashan). South Asia Bks.
Indian Myth & Legend. Donald Mackenzie. LC 77-85615. 1978. Repr. of 1913 ed. lib. bdg. 50.00 (ISBN 0-89341-316-X). Longwood Pub Group.
Indian Mythology & Iranian Mythology. A. Berriedale Keith. Bd. with Albert J. Carnoy. LC 63-19091. (Mythology of All Races Ser.: Vol. 6). (Illus.). Repr. of 1932 ed. 30.00x (ISBN 0-8154-0126-4). Cooper Sq.
Indian Myths. Ellen Emerson. 59.95 (ISBN 0-8490-0400-4). Gordon Pr.
Indian Myths from the Southeast. Beatrice Levin. (Indian Culture Ser.). 1974. 1.95 (ISBN 0-89992-071-3). Coun India Ed.
Indian Myths of the Northwest. Clarence B. Bagley. (Shorey Indian Ser.). (Illus.). 145p. pap. 8.95 (ISBN 0-8466-4041-4, I41). Shorey.
Indian Nationalism & Hindu Social Reform. Charles H. Heimsath. LC 63-20660. pap. 98.30 (ISBN 0-317-08688-X, 2000888). Bks Demand UMI.
Indian Origins & the Book of Mormon. Dan Vogel. LC 86-61016. 154p. 1986. pap. 8.95 (ISBN 0-941214-42-7). Signature Bks.
Indian Philosophy: An Analytical Study. Bijayananda Kar. 1986. 17.00x (ISBN 0-317-44233-3, Pub. by Ajanta). South Asia Bks.
Indian Philosophy: The Concept of Karma. Kewal K. Anand. 396p. 1982. 34.95 (ISBN 0-940500-91-4, Pub by Bharatiya Vidya Prakashan India). Asia Bk Corp.
Indian Priest: Philip B. Gordon, 1885-1948. Paula Delfeld. 1977. 5.95 (ISBN 0-8199-0650-6). Franciscan Herald.
Indian Religion. Ed. by Richard Burghart & Audrey Cantlie. LC 84-15115. 320p. 1985. 27.50 (ISBN 0-312-41400-5). St Martin.
Indian Religions. S. Radhakrishnan. (Orient Paperbacks Ser.). 196p. 1981. pap. 3.95 (ISBN 0-86578-084-6); 8.95 (ISBN 0-86578-117-6). Ind-US Inc.
Indian Religions. S. Radhakrishnan. 1979. 7.00x (ISBN 0-8364-0367-3). South Asia Bks.
Indian Ritual & Belief. J. Abbott. Orig. Title: Keys of Power: A Study of Indian Religion & Ritual. 1985. Repr. of 1932 ed. 40.00x (ISBN 0-8364-1294-X, Pub. by Usha). South Asia Bks.
Indian Temple Styles: The Personality of Hindu Architecture. K. V. Rajan. (Illus.). 194p. 1972. 22.50x (ISBN 0-89684-420-X). Orient Bk Dist.
Indian Testimony. Amiya Chakravarty. 1983. pap. 2.50x (ISBN 0-87574-072-3, 072). Pendle Hill.
Indian Theogony: Comparative Study of Indian Mythology from the Vedas to the Puranas. rev. ed. Sukumari Bhattacharji. 1978. Repr. of 1970 ed. 18.50x (ISBN 0-8364-0160-3). South Asia Bks.
Indian Theological Tendencies. Antony Mookenthottam. (IC-Studies in the Intercultural History of Christianity: Vol. 21). 320p. 1979. pap. 34.80 (ISBN 3-261-04613-9). P Lang Pubs.
Indian Thought & Its Development. Albert Schweitzer. 1962. 11.00 (ISBN 0-8446-2893-X). Peter Smith.
Indian Uprising in Lower California, 1734-1737. Sigismundo Taraval. LC 79-137296. Repr. of 1931 ed. 24.00 (ISBN 0-404-06337-3). AMS Pr.
Indian Wisdom. Monier Monier-Williams. 575p. 1978. Repr. of 1893 ed. 21.00x (ISBN 0-89684-105-7, Pub. by Cosmo Pubns India). Orient Bk Dist.
Indian Witchcraft. R. N. Saletore. 216p. 1981. text ed. 17.50x (ISBN 0-391-02480-9). Humanities.
India's Past: A Survey of Her Literatures, Religions, Languages & Antiquities. Arthur A. Macdonell. LC 78-20481. 1979. Repr. of 1927 ed. text ed. 29.00 (ISBN 0-88355-858-0). Hyperion Conn.
India's Religious Art: Ideas & Ideals. K. V. Rajan. (Illus.). 1982. text ed. 45.00x (ISBN 0-391-02916-9). Humanities.
Indication of the Way Into the Kingdom of Heaven. Metropolitan Innocent of Moscow. 48p. (Orig.). 1981. pap. 2.00 (ISBN 0-317-30275-2). Holy Trinity.
Indice Biblico de Bolsillo. (PocketPac Ser.). (Span.). 192p. 1984. pap. 2.95 (ISBN 0-87788-219-3). Shaw Pubs.
Indifference to Religion. Claude Geffre & Jean-Pierre Jossua. (Concilium 1983: Vol. 165). 128p. (Orig.). 1983. pap. 6.95 (ISBN 0-8164-2445-4, HarpR). Har-Row.
Indifferent Mean: Adiaphorism in the English Reformation to 1554. Bernard J. Verkamp. LC 77-13672. (Studies in the Reformation: Vol. 1). 1977. 15.00x (ISBN 0-8214-0387-7, Co-Pub by Wayne State). Ohio U Pr.
Indifferent Mean: Adiaphorism in the English Reformation to 1554. Bernard J. Verkamp. Ed. by Robert C. Walton & Philip N. Bebb. LC 77-13672. (Studies in the Reformation: Vol. I). 160p. 1978. text ed. 19.95x (ISBN 0-8143-1583-6). Wayne St U Pr.
Indigenous Church. rev. ed. Melvin L. Hodges. 160p. 1976. pap. 2.95 (ISBN 0-88243-527-2, 02-0527). Gospel Pub.
Indigenous Church & the Missionary: A Sequel to the Indigenous Church. Melvin L. Hodges. LC 77-14519. 1978. pap. 2.95 (ISBN 0-87808-151-8). William Carey Lib.
Indispensability of Scientology Press, Vol. 1, Pt. 5. Church of Scientology Information Service Staff. 1976. pap. 2.60 (ISBN 0-915598-10-8). Church of Scient Info.
Indispensable Christ: Sermons. George S. Gunn. 266p. 1962. 6.50 (ISBN 0-227-67661-0). Attic Pr.
Individual & His Religion. Gordon W. Allport. 1967. pap. 4.95 (ISBN 0-02-083130-7). Macmillan.
Individual & Society: Nature-Marx-Mao. Hugo Cartesius. 158p. 1977. 12.40 (ISBN 3-261-02063-6). P Lang Pubs.
Individualism & Holism: The Confucian & Taoist Philosophical Perspectives. Ed. by Donald J. Munro. (Michigan Monographs in Chinese Studies: No. 52). 399p. 1985. 25.00 (ISBN 0-89264-057-X); pap. 12.50 (ISBN 0-89264-058-8). U of Mich Ctr Chinese.
Individualism & Social Ethics: An Evangelical Syncretism. Dennis P. Hollinger. 284p. 1984. lib. bdg. 28.50 (ISBN 0-8191-3580-1); pap. text ed. 13.50 (ISBN 0-8191-3581-X). U Pr of Amer.
Individuals: An Essay in Descriptive Metaphysics. P. F. Strawson. 1964. pap. 12.95x (ISBN 0-416-68310-X, NO. 2535). Methuen Inc.
Indo-Tibetan Buddhism: Indian Buddhists & Their Tibetan Successors. David Snellgrove. LC 85-2453. (Illus.). 550p. 1986. Vol. I. pap. 18.95 (ISBN 0-87773-311-2); Vol. II. pap. 18.95 (ISBN 0-87773-379-1). Shambhala Pubns.
Indonesia & India, Fifteen Forty-Five to Fifteen Forty-Nine. Schurhammer. 726p. (Orig.). 1980. 40.00 (ISBN 0-8294-0356-6). Loyola.
Indonesian Religions in Transition. Ed. by Rita S. Kipp & Susan Rodgers. LC 86-30742. 304p. 1987. 29.95x (ISBN 0-8165-1020-2). U of Ariz Pr.
Indonesian Revival: Why Two Million Came to Christ. Avery T. Willis, Jr. LC 77-12811. (Illus.). 1977. pap. 6.95 (ISBN 0-87808-428-2). William Carey Lib.
Indra Web: The Renewal of Ancient Oriental Concepts in Modern Western Thought. John E. Whiteford-Boyle. 1983. 10.00. Wheat Forders.
Induction, Physics, & Ethics: Proceedings of the Colloquium in the Philosophy of Science, Salzburg, 1969. Colloquium in the Philosophy of Science Staff. Ed. by P. Weingartner & G. Zecha. LC 78-118137. (Synthese Library: No. 31). 382p. 1970. lib. bdg. 39.50 (ISBN 90-277-0158-X, Pub. by Reidel Holland). Kluwer Academic.
Inductive Approach to Biblical Study. Philip B. Harner. LC 82-40213. 132p. (Orig.). 1982. lib. bdg. 24.00 (ISBN 0-8191-2608-X); pap. text ed. 7.75 (ISBN 0-8191-2609-8). U Pr of Amer.
Inductive Preaching: Activities Guidbook. Ralph L. Lewis. 32p. 1983. pap. 3.95 (ISBN 0-9608180-2-2). Asbury Theological.
Inductive Preaching: Helping People Listen. Ralph L. Lewis & Gregg Lewis. LC 83-70321. 224p. 1983. pap. 6.95 (ISBN 0-89107-287-X, Crossway Bks). Good News.
Indwelling Presence. George A. Maloney. 112p. (Orig.). 1985. pap. 4.50 (ISBN 0-914544-62-4). Living Flame Pr.
Inequality & the American Conscience: Justice Through the Judicial System. Christopher F. Mooney. (Woodstock Studies). 144p. 1983. pap. 6.95 (ISBN 0-8091-2500-5). Paulist Pr.
Inerrancy. Norman Geisler. 1980. pap. 11.95 (ISBN 0-310-39281-0, 18157P). Zondervan.
Inerrancy & the Church. Ed. by John Hannah. (Orig.). 1984. pap. 14.95 (ISBN 0-8024-0327-1). Moody.
Inerrancy & the Scriptures. Leroy Forlines. 26p. 1978. pap. 0.95 (ISBN 0-89265-107-5). Randall Hse.
Inevitable Peace. Carl J. Friedrich. Repr. of 1948 ed. lib. bdg. 22.50x (ISBN 0-8371-2397-6, FRIN). Greenwood.
Inevitable Victory. Mehdi Bazargan. Tr. by Mohammad Yousefi from Persian. 35p. 1979. pap. 1.25x (ISBN 0-941722-03-1). Book-Dist-Ctr.
Inexhaustible God: Biblical Faith & the Challenge of Process Theism. Royce G. Gruenler. 176p. 1983. pap. 11.95 (ISBN 0-8010-3794-8). Baker Bk.
Inexhaustible Presence: The Mystery of Jesus. J. Patrick Gaffney. 210p. 1986. 11.95 (ISBN 0-87193-249-0). Dimension Bks.
Infallibility Debate. Ed. by John J. Kirvan. LC 76-168745. Repr. of 1971 ed. 40.00 (ISBN 0-8357-9485-7, 2013529). Bks Demand UMI.
Infallibility: The Crossroads of Doctrine. Peter Chirico. (Theology & Life Ser.: Vol. 1). pap. 9.95 (ISBN 0-89453-296-0). M Glazier.
Infallible? An Inquiry. Hans Kung. LC 82-45641. 288p. 1983. pap. 10.95 (ISBN 0-385-18483-2). Doubleday.
Infallible Word. Westminster Seminary Faculty Symposium. Ed. by Paul Woolley. pap. 9.95 (ISBN 0-87552-543-1). Presby & Reformed.
Infancy Narratives. Herman Hendrickx. (Commentary on Synoptic Gospels Ser.). 144p. 1984. pap. 9.95 (ISBN 0-225-66398-8, 8523, HarpR). Har-Row.
Infant & Junior Scripture Lesson. P. St. John. 274p. 1956. 4.00 (ISBN 0-227-67493-6). Attic Pr.
Infant Baptism & the Christian Community. Charles J. Keating. LC 76-25620. (Illus.). 1977. pap. 2.95 (ISBN 0-89622-022-2). Twenty-Third.
Infant Baptism: What Christian Parents Should Know. John P. Sartelle. 32p. 1985. pap. 1.95 (ISBN 0-87552-429-X); shrinkwrapped package of 12 19.50 (ISBN 0-87552-438-9). Presby & Reformed.
Infant Jesus of Prague. Ludvik Nemec. (LargeType). 2.25 (ISBN 0-89942-129-6, 129/04). Catholic Bk Pub.
Infant Joe. 128p. Date not set. pap. 4.95 (ISBN 0-937408-24-7). GMI Pubns Inc.
Infant Perdition in the Middle Ages. G. G. Coulton. 1977. lib. bdg. 59.95 (ISBN 0-8490-2058-1). Gordon Pr.
Infant Salvation. C. H. Spurgeon. 1981. pap. 0.95 (ISBN 0-686-37176-3). Pilgrim Pubns.
Infernal Poetics: Poetic Structure in Blake's Lambeth Prophecies. John Howard. LC 82-49319. (Illus.). 256p. 1984. 34.50 (ISBN 0-8386-3176-2). Fairleigh Dickinson.
Infinite God. Meldon Wass. pap. 2.25 (ISBN 0-8199-0052-4, L38345). Franciscan Herald.
Infinite Power for Richer Living. Joseph Murphy. 1969. pap. 4.95 (ISBN 0-13-464396-8, Reward). P-H.
Infinite Way. Joel S. Goldsmith. pap. 5.95 (ISBN 0-87516-309-2). De Vorss.
Infinitely Happy. G. Arthur Keough. LC 78-21952. (Horizon Ser.). 1978. pap. 5.95 (ISBN 0-8127-0213-1). Review & Herald.
Infinity I. (Agni Yoga Ser.). 1980. Repr. of 1956 ed. index 12.00 (ISBN 0-933574-05-3). Agni Yoga Soc.
Infinity II. (Agni Yoga Ser.). 1980. Repr. of 1957 ed. index 12.00 (ISBN 0-933574-06-1). Agni Yoga Soc.
Infinity of Questions. facs. ed. Cecil J. Eustace. LC 70-84356. (Essay Index Reprint Ser). 1946. 16.50 (ISBN 0-8369-1080-X). Ayer Co Pubs.
Infinity of Questions: Studies in the Art of Religion & the Religion of Art in the Lives of Helen Foley, Katherine Mansfield, et al. C. J. Eustace. 170p. 1946. 10.00 (ISBN 0-87556-595-6). Saifer.
Inflated Self: Human Illusions & the Bibical Call to Hope. David G. Myers. 176p. 1980. 12.95 (ISBN 0-8164-0459-3, HarpR); pap. 5.95 (ISBN 0-8164-2326-1). Har-Row.
Influence of Buddhism on Primitive Christianity. Arthur Lillie. LC 78-70094. 1980. Repr. of 1893 ed. 58.75 (ISBN 0-404-17343-8). AMS Pr.
Influence of Greek Ideas & Usages Upon the Christian Church. Edwin Hatch. 384p. 1972. Repr. of 1891 ed. lib. bdg. 21.50 (ISBN 0-8337-1595-X). B Franklin.
Influence of Greek Ideas on Christianity. Edwin Hatch. 11.75 (ISBN 0-8446-0683-9). Peter Smith.
Influence of Islam Upon Africa. 2nd ed. J. Spencer Trimingham. (Arab Background Ser.). (Illus.). 1980. text ed. 27.00x (ISBN 0-582-78499-9). Longman.
Influence of Islam Upon Africa. Spencer Trimingham. 25.00x (ISBN 0-685-85423-X). Intl Bk Ctr.
Influence of Islam Upon Medieval Europe. W. M. Watt. 125p. 1973. pap. 10.00x (ISBN 0-85224-439-8, Pub. by Edinburgh U Pr Scotland). Columbia U Pr.

Influence of Puritanism. John S. Flynn. LC 72-102569. 1970. Repr. of 1920 ed. 23.00x (ISBN 0-8046-0729-X, Pub. by Kennikat). Assoc Faculty Pr.

Influence of Quaker Women on American Society: Biographical Studies. Ed. by John Stoneburner & Carol Stoneburner. (Studies in Women & Religion: Vol. 21). 496p. 1986. text ed. 69.95x (ISBN 0-88946-528-2). E Mellen.

Influence of the English Bible Upon the English Language & Upon English & American Literature. O. L. Joseph. 59.95 (ISBN 0-8490-0409-8). Gordon Pr.

Influence of the Enlightenment on the Catholic Theory of Religious Education in France, 1750-1850. Clarence E. Elwell. LC 66-27064. 1967. Repr. of 1944 ed. 10.00x (ISBN 0-8462-0980-2). Russell.

Influence of the Holy Spirit: The Popular View of the Apostolic Age & the Teaching of the Apostle Paul. Hermann Gunkel. Tr. by Roy A. Harrisville & Philip A. Quanbeck, II. LC 78-20022. 144p. 1979. 3.00 (ISBN 0-8006-0544-6, 1-544). Fortress.

Influence of the Spanish Mystics on the Works of Saint Francis De Sales. Mother Mary M. Rivet. LC 79-115355. (Catholic University of America. Studies in Romance Languages & Literatures: No. 22). Repr. of 1941 ed. 20.00 (ISBN 0-404-50322-5). AMS Pr.

Influences of Lucifer & Ahriman: Man's Responsibility for the Earth. Rudolf Steiner. Tr. by D. S. Osmond from Ger. 84p. 1976. pap. 6.95 (ISBN 0-919924-00-X). Anthroposophic.

Influential Theologians on Wo-Man. William E. Phipps. LC 79-5431. 1980. lib. bdg. 23.00 (ISBN 0-8191-1383-2); pap. text ed. 9.50 (ISBN 0-8191-0880-4). U Pr of Amer.

Informal Groups in the Church: Papers of the Second Cerdic Colloquium, Strasbourg, May 13-15, 1971. Ed. by Rene Metz & Jean Schlick. Tr. by Matthew J. O'Connell. LC 75-25591. (Pittsburgh Theological Monographs: No. 7). 1975. pap. 5.25 (ISBN 0-915138-08-5). Pickwick.

Information for Pilgrims Unto the Holy Land. Ed. by E. Gordon Duff. LC 78-63464. Repr. of 1893 ed. 16.50 (ISBN 0-404-16536-2). AMS Pr.

Ingathering Experience, Vol. 1. large print ed. Pearl Brians. 33p. 1985. pap. 5.00 (ISBN 0-914009-32-X). VHI Library.

Ingeld & Christ: Heroic Conceptions & Values in Old English Christian Poetry. Michael D. Cherniss. (Studies in English Literature: No. 74). 267p. 1972. text ed. 29.60x (ISBN 90-2792-335-3). Mouton.

Ingulph's Chronicle of the Abbey of Croyland. Abbot Ingulf. Tr. by H. T. Riley. LC 68-55553. (Bohn's Antiquarian Library Ser). Repr. of 1854 ed. 34.50 (ISBN 0-404-50018-8). AMS Pr.

Inherit the Kingdom. F. B. Meyer. 168p. 1985. pap. 5.95 (ISBN 0-89693-396-2). Victor Bks.

Inherit the Kingdom. rev. ed. Paul L. Peck. (Spiritual Metaphysics: Freeways to Divine Awareness Ser.). (Orig.). 1982. pap. 7.95 (ISBN 0-941600-02-5). Harmony Pr.

Inherited Wealth: Studies in Ephesians. Tom Julien. pap. 4.95 (ISBN 0-88469-034-2). BMH Bks.

Inheriting the Master's Cloak: Creative Biblical Spirituality. John Wijngaards. LC 85-71535. 192p. (Orig.). 1985. pap. 4.95 (ISBN 0-87793-288-3). Ave Maria.

Initiates & the People, 1928-1932, 5 vols. R. Swinburne Clymer. 1933. Repr. Set. 37.95 (ISBN 0-686-15595-5). Vol. I, 204 pp (ISBN 0-932785-18-2). Vol. II, 208 pp (ISBN 0-932785-19-0). Vol. III, 200 pp (ISBN 0-932785-20-4). Vol. IV, 192 pp (ISBN 0-932785-21-2). Vol. V, 207 pp (ISBN 0-932785-22-0). Philos Pub.

Initiation & Conversion. Regis Duffy et al. Ed. by Lawrence Johnson. 96p. 1985. pap. 4.95 (ISBN 0-8146-1431-0). Liturgical Pr.

Initiation & Its Results. Rudolf Steiner. 134p. 1984. pap. 8.00 (ISBN 0-89540-148-7, SB-148). Sun Pub.

Initiation into Hermetics. 4th ed. Franz Bardon. Tr. by A. Radspieler from Ger. (Illus.). 294p. 1981. 17.00 (ISBN 0-914732-10-2). Bro Life Inc.

Initiation into Yoga. Krishna Prem. LC 76-10790. (Orig.). 1976. pap. 3.25 (ISBN 0-8356-0484-5, Quest). Theos Pub Hse.

Initiation to Adulthood: An Ancient Rite of Passage in Contemporary Form. William O. Roberts. LC 82-18544. 208p. (Orig.). 1983. pap. 7.95 (ISBN 0-8298-0629-6). Pilgrim NY.

Ink on His Fingers. Louise A. Vernon. LC 73-171105. (Illus.). 128p. 1972. 4.95 (ISBN 0-8361-1660-7); pap. 4.50 (ISBN 0-8361-1673-9). Herald Pr.

Inklings of Grace. Terry A. Moe. 64p. 1981. pap. 3.95 (ISBN 0-8170-0941-8). Judson.

Inmenso Amor De Dios. Jose Borras. (Span.). 96p. 1981. pap. 3.95 (ISBN 0-311-43038-4). Casa Bautista.

Inn of the Samaritan. Donald X. Burt. 96p. (Orig.). 1983. pap. 5.95 (ISBN 0-8146-1315-2). Liturgical Pr.

Innenland: Ein Wegweiser In Die Seele Der Bibel und In Den Kampf Um Die Wirklichkeit. Eberhard Arnold. (Ger.). 492p. 1936. 9.00 (ISBN 0-87486-150-0). Plough.

Inner & Outer Peace. Sri Chinmoy. 113p. (Orig.). 1984. pap. 5.95 (ISBN 0-88497-769-2). Aum Pubns.

Inner Calm: A Christian Answer to Modern Stress. Paul DeBlassie, III. LC 84-52377. 128p. 1985. pap. 3.95 (ISBN 0-89243-229-2). Liguori Pubns.

Inner Chamber. Andrew Murray & Leona Choy. (Orig.). 1980. pap. 2.50 (ISBN 0-87508-405-2). Chr Lit.

Inner Dimensions of Islamic Worship. Al-Ghazali. Tr. by Muhtar Holland from Arabic. 142p. (Orig.). 1983. pap. 6.95 (ISBN 0-86037-125-5, Pub. by Islamic Found UK). New Era Pubns MI.

Inner Eye of Love: Mysticism & Religion. William Johnston. LC 78-4428. 1978. pap. 6.95 (ISBN 0-06-064195-9, RD-349, HarpR). Har-Row.

Inner Fire. rev. ed. Allen W. Brown. 1984. pap. 1.95 (ISBN 0-88028-033-6). Forward Movement.

Inner Freedom Through Qabala. Bob Lancer. (Illus.). 134p. (Orig.). 1986. pap. 6.95 (ISBN 0-917913-02-7). Limitless Light.

Inner Growth-Outer Change: An Educational Guide to Church Renewal. John H. Westerhoff, III. (Orig.). pap. 4.95 (ISBN 0-8164-2213-3, HarpR). Har-Row.

Inner Guide Meditation. 4th ed. Edwin C. Steinbrecher. LC 78-60489. (Illus.). 1978. 12.95 (ISBN 0-685-65266-1); pap. 6.75 (ISBN 0-685-65267-X). Blue Feather.

Inner Guide Meditation: A Spiritual Technology for the 21st Century. Edwin Steinbrecher. 240p. (Orig.). 1987. pap. 7.95 (ISBN 0-87728-657-4). Weiser.

Inner Healing. Theodoree Dobson. 384p. 1985. 12.95 (ISBN 0-8027-2488-4). Walker & Co.

Inner Healing. Michael Scanlan. LC 74-81901. 96p. (Orig.). 1974. pap. 3.95 (ISBN 0-8091-1846-7). Paulist Pr.

Inner Healing: Deliverance or Deception? Don Matzat. 224p. (Orig.). 1987. pap. 6.95 (ISBN 0-89081-584-4). Harvest Hse.

Inner Healing: Deliverance or Deception. Don Matzat. 1987. pap. 5.95. Har-Row.

Inner Healing: God's Great Assurance. Theodore Dobson. LC 78-65129. 216p. 1978. pap. 7.95 (ISBN 0-8091-2161-1). Paulist Pr.

Inner Healing Through Healing of Memories. Betty Tapscott. 1975. pap. 4.95 (ISBN 0-917726-29-4). Hunter Bks.

Inner Heart of Ministry. Doran C. McCarthy. LC 85-15152. (Orig.). 1985. pap. 3.25 (ISBN 0-8054-6942-7). Broadman.

Inner History of the Great Schism of the West, 1378-1417; a Problem in Church Unity. George J. Jordan. LC 72-80392. 216p. 1972. Repr. of 1930 ed. lib. bdg. 19.50 (ISBN 0-8337-4193-4). B Franklin.

Inner Impulses of Human Evolution: The Mexican Mysteries & the Knights Templar. Rudolf Steiner. Ed. by Gilbert Church et al. 180p. (Orig.). 1984. 16.00 (ISBN 0-88010-119-9); pap. 9.95 (ISBN 0-88010-118-0). Anthroposophic.

Inner Islands. Winifred Rawlins. 1983. pap. 2.50x (ISBN 0-87574-073-1, 073). Pendle Hill.

Inner Land: A Guide into the Heart & Soul of the Bible. Eberhard Arnold. LC 74-30356. 608p. 1976. 12.00 (ISBN 0-87486-152-7). Plough.

Inner Land, Vol. 1: The Inner Life. Eberhard Arnold. LC 74-18434. 1975. postpaid 3.50 (ISBN 0-87486-153-5). Plough.

Inner Land, Vol. 2: The Struggle of the Conscience. Eberhard Arnold. LC 75-1335. 1975. 3.50 (ISBN 0-87486-154-3). Plough.

Inner Land, Vol. 3: The Experience of God. Eberhard Arnold. LC 75-9720. 1975. 3.50 (ISBN 0-87486-155-1). Plough.

Inner Land, Vol. 4: Light & Fire & the Holy Spirit. Eberhard Arnold. LC 75-16303. 1975. 3.50 (ISBN 0-87486-156-X). Plough.

Inner Land, Vol. 5: The Living Word. Eberhard Arnold. LC 75-33241. 1975. 3.50 (ISBN 0-87486-157-8). Plough.

Inner Liberty. Peter Viereck. 1983. pap. 2.50x (ISBN 0-87574-095-2, 095). Pendle Hill.

Inner Life. C. H. Bjerregaard. Incl. Tao-Teh-King. 1977. lib. bdg. 49.00 (ISBN 0-8490-2061-1). Gordon Pr.

Inner Life. Inayat Khan. (Sufi Message of Hazrat Inayat Khan Ser.: Vol. 1). 256p. 1979. 14.95 (ISBN 90-6325-094-0, Pub. by Servire BV Netherlands). Hunter Hse.

Inner Life. Andrew Murray. 1980. pap. 2.95 (ISBN 0-310-29752-4). Zondervan.

Inner Life. Andrew Murray. 144p. 1984. pap. 5.95 (ISBN 0-310-29751-6, 10364P, Clarion Class). Zondervan.

Inner Life. Andrew Murray. 160p. 1984. pap. text ed. 3.50 (ISBN 0-88368-138-2). Whitaker Hse.

Inner Life: An Introduction to Sufism. Hazrat I. Khan. (Orient Paperbacks Ser.). 1980. pap. 3.25 (ISBN 0-86578-082-X). Ind-US Inc.

Inner Life of Christ. W. G. Blaikie & R. Law. 459p. 1982. lib. bdg. 17.25 Smythe Sewn (ISBN 0-86524-156-2, 9515). Klock & Klock.

Inner Loneliness. Sebastian Moore. LC 82-14862. 125p. 1982. 9.95 (ISBN 0-8245-0515-8). Crossroad NY.

Inner Loneliness. Sebastian Moore. 1984. pap. 6.95 (ISBN 0-8245-0619-7). Crossroad NY.

Inner Path from Where You Are to Where You Want to Be: A Spiritual Odyssey. Terry Cole-Whittaker. LC 84-42930. 239p. 1986. 14.95 (ISBN 0-89256-283-8). Rawson Assocs.

Inner Paths. Himalayan International Institute. 110p. pap. 3.95 (ISBN 0-89389-049-9). Himalayan Pubs.

Inner Peace: Finding Serenity Within. Lura J. Geiger. 1987. pap. 34.50; cassette incl. LuraMedia.

Inner Quest. Hoyt Stone. 1980. pap. 6.25 (ISBN 0-87148-435-8). Pathway Pr.

Inner Radiance. H. H. Curtiss & F. H. Curtiss. 369p. Date not set. pap. 20.00 (ISBN 0-89540-149-5, SB-149). Sun Pub.

Inner Rainbow: The Imagination in Christian Life. Kathleen R. Fischer. 160p. 1983. pap. 6.95 (ISBN 0-8091-2498-X). Paulist Pr.

Inner Reaches of Outer Space: Metaphor As Myth & As Religion. Joseph Campbell. LC 84-40776. (Illus.). 160p. 1986. 16.95 (ISBN 0-912383-09-7). Van der Marck.

Inner Sanctuary. Charles Ross. 1967. pap. 2.95 (ISBN 0-85151-042-6). Banner of Truth.

Inner Stage: An Essay on the Conflict of Vocations in the Early Works of Paul Claudel. Richard Berchan. 1966. 3.50 (ISBN 0-87013-097-8). Mich St U Pr.

Inner Story: Myth & Symbol in the Bible & Literature. Helen Luke. 112p. 1982. 8.95 (ISBN 0-8245-0443-7). Crossroad NY.

Inner Teachings of Taoism. Chang Po-tuan & Liu I-ming. Tr. & intro. by Thomas Cleary. LC 86-11841. 100p. (Orig.). 1986. pap. 9.95 (ISBN 0-87773-363-5). Shambhala Pubns.

Inner Voice Speaks. Betty W. Sprague. 59p. pap. 7.95 (ISBN 0-942494-30-X). Coleman Pub.

Inner Words for Every Day of the Year. Ed. by Emmy Arnold. LC 77-164915. 1963. 3.50 (ISBN 0-87486-101-2). Plough.

Inner World. Gopi Krishna. 12p. 1978. pap. 3.95 (ISBN 0-88697-001-6). Life Science.

Inner World: A Psycho-Analytic Study of Childhood & Society in India. 2nd ed. Sudhir Kakar. (Illus.). 1981. pap. text ed. 8.95x (ISBN 0-19-561508-5). Oxford U Pr.

Inner World of Qoehelet. Frank Zimmerman. 1972. 15.00x (ISBN 0-87068-181-8). Ktav.

Inner Worlds of Meditation. John-roger. LC 76-56625. pap. 5.00 (ISBN 0-914829-11-4). Baraka Bk.

Inneres Wort Fur Jeden Tag Des Jahres. Emmy Arnold. LC 76-10987. 192p. 1976. 4.50 (ISBN 0-87486-166-7). Plough.

Innkeeper's Wife. Becky Kaaikaula. (Illus.). 12p. (Orig.). 1983. write for info. (ISBN 0-914599-00-3). Kaaikaula.

Innocence of G. K. Chesterton. Gerald Bullett. 1973. Repr. of 1923 ed. 17.50 (ISBN 0-8274-1799-3). R West.

Innocence: The Story of Steve Linscott, the Emmaus Bible School Student Convicted of Murder. Gordon Haresign. 224p. 1986. 7.95 (ISBN 0-310-43801-2, 12056P). Zondervan.

Innocent Ecstasy: How Christianity Gave America an Ethic of Sexual Pleasure. Peter Gardella. LC 84-27253. (Illus.). 1985. 17.95 (ISBN 0-19-503612-3). Oxford U Pr.

Innocent III. L. Elliott-Binns. LC 68-15343. xi, 212p. 1968. Repr. of 1931 ed. 19.50 (ISBN 0-208-00393-2, Archon). Shoe String.

Innocent Three, Church Defender. Charles E. Smith. LC 79-88939. 1971. Repr. of 1951 ed. lib. bdg. 55.00x (ISBN 0-8371-3145-6, SMIN). Greenwood.

Innocent XI, Pope of Christian Unity. Raymond J. Maras. (Church & the World Ser.). xiv, 356p. 1984. 42.85x (ISBN 0-317-52635-9); lib. bdg. 42.85x. Cross Cultural Pubns.

Innokenty of Alaska. Lazar Puhalo. 86p. (Orig.). 1986. pap. 5.00 (ISBN 0-913026-86-7). Synaxis Pr.

Innovations in Counseling (RCC) Gary Collins. 224p. 1986. 12.95 (ISBN 0-8499-0510-9). Word Bks.

Innovations of the Roman Church. Apostolos Makrakis. 82p. (Orig.). 1966. pap. 3.75x (ISBN 0-938366-39-4). Orthodox Chr.

Inquest on the Shroud of Turin. Joe Nickell. LC 82-62457. (Illus.). 178p. 1982. 18.95 (ISBN 0-87975-194-0). Prometheus Bks.

Inquiry Concerning the Principles of Morals: With a Supplement, a Dialogue. David Hume. Ed. by Charles W. Hendel. 1957. pap. 7.20 scp (ISBN 0-672-60236-9, LLA62). Bobbs.

Inquiry Concerning Virtue, or Merit. A. A. Cooper. Ed. by D. E. Walford. 152p. 1977. 23.00 (ISBN 0-7190-0657-0, Pub. by Manchester Univ Pr). Longwood Pub Group.

Inquiry into Scriptural Views of Slavery. Albert Barnes. LC 75-92415. 1855. 23.00x (ISBN 0-403-00151-X). Scholarly.

Inquiry into the Accordancy of War with the Principles of Christianity. Jonathan Dymond. LC 79-147432. (Library of War & Peace; Proposals for Peace: a History). 1973. lib. bdg. 46.00 (ISBN 0-8240-0222-9). Garland Pub.

Inquiry into the Animism & Folklore of the Guiana Indians. Walter E. Roth. LC 16-9897. (Landmarks in Anthropology Ser). Repr. of 1915 ed. 23.00 (ISBN 0-384-52130-4). Johnson Repr.

Inquiry into the Authenticity of Moses Maimonides' Treatise on Resurrection. Lea N. Goldfield. 1985. text ed. 19.95x (ISBN 0-88125-088-0). Ktav.

Inquiry into the Heresies of the Apostolic Age. Edward Burton. LC 78-63166. (Heresies of the Early Christian & Medieval Era: Second Ser.). Repr. of 1829 ed. 62.50 (ISBN 0-404-16179-0). AMS Pr.

Inquiry into the Local Variations in Vulgar Latin As Reflected in the Vocalism of Christian Inscriptions. Paul A. Gaeng. (Studies in the Romance Languages & Literatures: No. 77). 300p. 1968. pap. 16.50x (ISBN 0-8078-9077-4). U of NC Pr.

Inquiry into the Original of Our Ideas of Beauty & Virtue. 4th ed. Francis Hutcheson. 1986. lib. bdg. 20.00X (ISBN 0-935005-22-6); pap. text ed. 12.50X (ISBN 0-935005-33-1). Ibis Pub VA.

Inquiry into the Philosophy & Religion of Shakespeare. W. J. Birch. LC 72-3660. (Studies in Shakespeare, No. 24). 1972. Repr. of 1848 ed. lib. bdg. 59.95x (ISBN 0-8383-1569-0). Haskell.

Inquiry into the Philosophy & Religion of Shakespeare. William Birch. LC 76-39446. Repr. of 1848 ed. 15.00 (ISBN 0-404-00868-2). AMS Pr.

Inquisition. George G. Coulton. LC 74-18020. 1974. Repr. of 1929 ed. lib. bdg. 16.50 (ISBN 0-8414-3647-9). Folcroft.

Inquisition: A Critical & Historical Study of the Coercive Power of the Church. Elphege Vacandard. Tr. by Bertrand L. Conway from Fr. LC 76-1127. 195p. 1977. Repr. of 1926 ed. lib. bdg. 20.00 (ISBN 0-915172-09-7). Richwood Pub.

Inquisition & Society in Early Modern Europe. Ed. by Stephen Haliczer. LC 86-26493. 208p. 1987. 28.50x (ISBN 0-389-20700-4). B&N Imports.

Inquisition & Society in Spain in the Sixteenth & Seventeenth Centuries. Henry Kamen. LC 85-10804. (Illus.). 320p. 1985. 27.50x (ISBN 0-253-33015-7); pap. 10.95x (ISBN 0-253-22775-5). Ind U Pr.

Inquisition Dans le Midi De la France Au Treizieme et Au Quatorzieme Seicle: Etude Sur les Sources De Son Histoire. Charles Molinier. 1965. Repr. of 1880 ed. 32.00 (ISBN 0-8337-2421-5). B Franklin.

Inquisition in Early Modern Europe: Studies on Sources & Methods. Ed. by Gustav Henningsen & John Tedeschi. 254p. 1986. 27.50 (ISBN 0-87580-102-1). N Ill U Pr.

Inquisitors. Jerzy Andrzejewski. Tr. by Konrad Syrop from Polish. LC 76-6896. 1976. Repr. of 1960 ed. lib. bdg. 22.50x (ISBN 0-8371-8868-7, ANIN). Greenwood.

Inquisitors & the Jews in the New World: Summaries of Procesos 1500-1810, & Bibliographical Guide. Seymour B. Liebman. LC 72-85110. 160p. 1973. 12.95x (ISBN 0-87024-245-8). U of Miami Pr.

Inquistio De Fide: A Colloquy by Desiderius Erasmus Roterodamus, 1524. 2nd ed. Erasmus. Ed. by Craig Thompson. LC 74-31476. xiii, 137p. 1975. Repr. of 1950 ed. 20.00 (ISBN 0-685-51693-8, Archon). Shoe String.

Inscape: God at the Heart of the Matter. George Maloney. 1978. pap. 4.95 (ISBN 0-87193-095-1). Dimension Bks.

Inscape: The Christology & Poetry of Gerald Manley Hopkins. James F. Cotter. LC 73-189857. pap. 92.30 (ISBN 0-317-26639-X, 2025436). Bks Demand UMI.

Inscriptiones Graecae Aegypti, No. 5: Christian Inscriptions. Ed. by G. Lefebvre. xlii, 173p. 1978. 30.00 (ISBN 0-89005-248-4). Ares.

Insecurity of Freedom: Essays on Human Existence. Abraham J. Heschel. LC 66-16293. 320p. 1985. pap. 7.95 (ISBN 0-8052-0361-3). Schocken.

Inside a Mormon Mission. Jack S. Bailey. 190p. pap. 3.95 (ISBN 0-89036-076-6). Hawkes Pub Inc.

Inside & Occupied. Nancy S. Williamson. LC 82-3139. 192p. (Orig.). 1982. pap. 9.95 (ISBN 0-8361-3304-8). Herald Pr.

Inside My Head. Cee Cee, pseud. 1985. 6.50 (ISBN 0-8062-2521-1). Carlton.

Inside the Church: Finding Your Place Within God's Family. Ed. by Kevin Miller. (Senior High Pacesetter Ser.). 64p. 1986. pap. 7.95 (ISBN 0-89191-325-4). Cook.

Inside the Jewish Schools: A Study of the Cultural Setting for Jewish Education. Samuel Heilman. 50p. 1984. pap. 2.50 (ISBN 0-87495-057-0). Am Jewish Comm.

Inside the Synagogue. rev. ed. Grace Freeman & Joan Sugarman. (Illus.). 64p. 1984. pap. 6.00 (ISBN 0-8074-0268-0, 301785). UAHC.

Inside the Tuplic Contoversy: Calvinism Rebuked & Revisited. Kent Kelly. LC 86-70927. (Illus.). 264p. 1986. 9.95 (ISBN 0-9604138-4-7). Calvary Pr.

Inside the Vatican. George Bull. 294p. 1983. 13.95 (ISBN 0-312-41884-1). St Martin.

Insight & Creativity in Christian Counseling: An Antidote to Rigid & Mechanical Approaches. Jay E. Adams. (Jay Adams Library). 144p. 1986. pap. 6.95 (ISBN 0-310-51131-3, 12125P). Zondervan.

Insights: Building a Successful Youth Ministry, Vol. I. Campus Crusade Staff. (Insight Ser.). (Orig.). 1981. pap. text ed. 5.95 (ISBN 0-86605-017-5). Campus Crusade.

Insights for Daily Living: A Guide to Scriptural Prayer. rev. ed. Andrew Murray. 208p. Date not set. pap. 3.95 (ISBN 0-89283-329-7, Pub. by Vine Books). Servant.

Insights for the Age of Aquarius. Gina Cerminara. LC 76-6173. 314p. 1976. pap. 6.95 (ISBN 0-8356-0483-7, Quest). Theos Pub Hse.

Insights for Today: The Wisdom of the Proverbs. F. LaGard Smith. LC 85-80483. 1985. leather 19.95 (ISBN 0-89081-499-6). Harvest Hse.

Insights for Young Mothers. Carol Rischer. pap. 5.95 (ISBN 0-89081-485-6). Harvest Hse.

Insights from the Psalms, Vol. 1. John Thomas Willis. LC 73-93946. (Way of Life Ser: No. 131). 1974. pap. text ed. 3.95 (ISBN 0-89112-131-5, Bibl Res Pr). Abilene Christ U.

Insights from the Psalms, Vol. 2. John T. Willis. LC 73-93946. (Way of Life Ser.: No. 132). 111p. 1974. pap. 3.95 (ISBN 0-89112-132-3, Bibl Res Pr). Abilene Christ U.

Insights from the Psalms, Vol. 3. John T. Willis. LC 73-93946. (Way of Life Ser: No. 133). 114p. 1974. pap. 3.95 (ISBN 0-89112-133-1, Bibl Res Pr). Abilene Christ U.

Insights into Buddhism. Ed. by Sunil K. Gupta. 212p. 1986. 15.00 (ISBN 81-7030-022-3, Pub. by Sri Satguru Pubns India). Orient Bk Dist.

Insights into Reality. 2nd ed. Flower A. Newhouse et al. LC 75-36869. 1975. pap. 8.50 (ISBN 0-910378-10-X). Christward.

Insights into Religious Life. James Alberione. 1977. 3.00 (ISBN 0-8198-0424-X); pap. 2.00 (ISBN 0-8198-0425-8). Dghtrs St Paul.

Insights into the Beyond. Paul B. Zacharias. LC 76-6756. pap. 1.00 (ISBN 0-87785-156-5). Swedenborg.

Insights to Scripture. Eli L. Cooper. 196p. (Orig.). 1986. lib. bdg. 24.00 (ISBN 0-8191-5121-1); pap. text ed. 10.25 (ISBN 0-8191-5122-X). U Pr of Amer.

Inspiration. A. A. Hodge & B. B. Warfield. 1979. pap. 2.95 (ISBN 0-8010-4222-4). Baker Bk.

Inspiration & Authority of Bible. B. B. Warfield. 12.95 (ISBN 0-8010-9586-7). Baker Bk.

Inspiration & Authority of Scripture. Rene Pache. 1970. pap. 10.95 (ISBN 0-8024-4091-6). Moody.

Inspiration & Authority of the Bible. 2nd ed. Benjamin B. Warfield. 1948. 12.95 (ISBN 0-87552-527-X). Presby & Reformed.

Inspiration & Canonicity of the Bible. R. Laird Harris. (Contemporary Evangelical Perspectives Ser.). kivar 8.95 (ISBN 0-310-25891-X, 9766P). Zondervan.

Inspiration & Motivation. LC 81-23459. 1982. 9.95 (ISBN 0-9603174-6-5). Bks of Value.

Inspiration & Revelation in the Old Testament. Henry W. Robinson. LC 78-9891. 1979. Repr. of 1946 ed. lib. bdg. 24.75x (ISBN 0-313-21068-3, ROIR). Greenwood.

Inspiration-Garden & Aspiration-Leaves. Sri Chinmoy. 58p. (Orig.). 1977. pap. 2.00 (ISBN 0-88497-379-4). Aum Pubns.

Inspiration of Responsibility, & Other Papers. facs. ed. Charles H. Brent. LC 67-22081. (Essay Index Reprint Ser). 1915. 13.00 (ISBN 0-8369-0251-3). Ayer Co Pubs.

Inspiration of Scripture: Problems & Proposals. Paul J. Achtemeier. LC 80-10286. (Biblical Perspectives on Current Issues). 188p. 1980. pap. 8.95 (ISBN 0-664-24313-4). Westminster.

Inspiration of the Bible. Alva J. McClain. 1980. pap. 1.00 (ISBN 0-88469-115-2). BMH Bks.

Inspiration Three, Vol. 3: Three Famous Classics in One Book - Wisdom of Luther, Calvin & Wesley. Compiled by David Poling. LC 73-80032. (Pivot Family Reader Ser). 1973. pap. 1.25 (ISBN 0-87983-043-3). Keats.

Inspiration Three, Vol. 5: Three Famous Classics in One Book. O. Henry et al. LC 73-80032. (Pivot Family Reader Ser.). 1973. pap. 1.25 (ISBN 0-87983-045-X). Keats.

Inspirational Lines. Chiaki Sato. 1986. 5.95 (ISBN 0-533-06789-8). Vantage.

Inspirational Meditations for Sunday Church School Teachers. Richard Andersen. 1980. pap. 2.25 (ISBN 0-570-03810-3, 12-2919). Concordia.

Inspirational Resources for Women's Groups. Helen L. Marshall. 64p. 1985. pap. 3.95 (ISBN 0-8010-6196-2). Baker Bk.

Inspirational Series, 12 bks. Susan Powers. (Illus.). 1980. 2.95 ea. (Mayflower Bks). Smith Pubs.

Inspirationally Yours. Ellwood Foster. LC 80-53330. 1984. 5.95 (ISBN 0-533-04843-5). Vantage.

Inspirations from Isaiah. Nelle Vander Ark. (Good Morning Lord Ser.). 96p. 1980. 3.95 (ISBN 0-8010-9281-7). Baker Bk.

Inspirations of God & the Emotions of Life. Jim Belcher, Jr. 64p. 1987. 6.95 (ISBN 0-89962-588-6). Todd & Honeywell.

Inspirations Unbidden: The "Terrible Sonnets" of Gerard Manley Hopkins. Daniel A. Harris. LC 81-11497. 200p. 1982. 26.50x (ISBN 0-520-04539-4). U of Cal Pr.

Inspirations Unlimited. Claire Schneider. 48p. (Orig.). 1985. pap. 4.95 (ISBN 0-9601982-2-9). Greenwood Hse.

Inspired Principles of Prophetic Interpretation. John Wilmot. pap. 10.95 (ISBN 0-686-48168-2). Reiner.

Inspired Scriptures. Charles W. Ford. LC 78-60267. (Radiant Life Ser.). 128p. 1978. pap. 2.50 (ISBN 0-88243-914-6, 02-0914); tchr's ed. 3.95 (ISBN 0-88243-185-4, 32-0185). Gospel Pub.

Inspired Talks. Swami Vivekananda. pap. 5.50 (ISBN 0-87481-455-3). Vedanta Pr.

Inspired Thoughts of Swami Rama. Swami Rama. 260p. (Orig.). pap. 8.95 (ISBN 0-89389-086-3). Himalayan Pubs.

Inspiring Devotional Programs for Women's Groups. Leila T. Ammerman. (Paperback Program Ser). 1971. pap. 3.50 (ISBN 0-8010-0015-7). Baker Bk.

Inspiring Devotions for Church Groups. Amy Bolding. 144p. 1985. pap. 4.95 (ISBN 0-8010-0889-1). Baker Bk.

Inspiring Messages for Daily Living. Norman V. Peale. 1981. pap. 2.50 (ISBN 0-449-92383-5, Crest). Fawcett.

Inspiring Poems. Carl Frasier. 6.00 (ISBN 0-8062-2493-2). Carlton.

Inspiring Thoughts for Your Marriage. Charles L. Allen. 1985. 7.95 (ISBN 0-8007-1401-6). Revell.

Installation Services for All Groups. Amy Bolding. 1984. pap. 4.95 (ISBN 0-8010-0863-8). Baker Bk.

Installation Services That Inspire. Leila T. Ammerman. LC 81-67371. 1982. pap. 5.50 (ISBN 0-8054-3616-2). Broadman.

Installations with Corresponding Devotionals. Gladyce E. White. Ed. by Andrea Crankshaw. 70p. (Orig.). Date not set. pap. 6.50 (ISBN 0-9615371-0-8). Adlen Bks.

Instant Cartoons for Church Newsletters, No. 1. Compiled by George W. Knight. 4.95 (ISBN 0-8010-5451-6). Baker Bk.

Instant Cartoons for Church Newsletters, No. 2. Compiled by George W. Knight. (Illus.). 112p. 1984. pap. 4.95 (ISBN 0-8010-5457-5). Baker Bk.

Instant Cartoons for Church Newsletters, No. 3. Compiled by George W. Knight. 1986. pap. 4.95 (ISBN 0-8010-5473-7). Baker Bk.

Instant Piano Fun for Christmas. Nancy Poffenberger. 24p. 1986. pap. text ed. 4.95 (ISBN 0-938293-28-1). Fun Pub OH.

Instant Sermons for Busy Pastors. Russell E. Spray. (Sermon Outline Ser.). (Orig.). 1981. pap. 1.95 (ISBN 0-8010-8192-0). Baker Bk.

Instead of Death: New & Expanded Edition. rev. ed. William Stringfellow. 1976. pap. 3.95 (ISBN 0-8164-2120-X, HarpR). Har-Row.

Instead of God? A Pragmatic Reconsideration of Beliefs & Values. James Hemming. 244p. 1986. 19.95 (ISBN 0-7145-2835-8, Dist. by Kampmann). M Boyars Pubs.

Institute of Chartered Accountants in England & Wales Library Catalogue, 1913, 2 vols. Ed. by Richard P. Brief. LC 80-1501. (Dimensions of Accounting Theory & Practice Ser.). 1981. Repr. of 1913 ed. Set. lib. bdg. 92.00x (ISBN 0-405-13526-2). Ayer Co Pubs.

Institutes of Biblical Law. Rousas J. Rushdoony. 1973. 24.00 (ISBN 0-87552-410-9). Presby & Reformed.

Institutes of Moral Philosophy. 2nd rev. ed. Adam Ferguson. LC 75-11219. (British Philosophers & Theologians of the 17th & 18th Centuries Ser.: Vol. 22). 1978. Repr. of 1773 ed. lib. bdg. 51.00 (ISBN 0-8240-1773-0). Garland Pub.

Institutes of the Christian Religion, 1536 Edition. John Calvin. Tr. by Ford L. Battles from Lat. 464p. 1986. 25.00 (ISBN 0-8028-2319-X). Eerdmans.

Institutes of the Christian Religion: Beveridge Translation, 2 Vols. John Calvin. 1953. Set. pap. 16.95 (ISBN 0-8028-8026-6). Eerdmans.

Institutes of Vishnu. J. Jolly. lib. bdg. 79.95 (ISBN 0-87968-528-X). Krishna Pr.

Institutes of Vishnu. Ed. by Julius Jolly. (Sacred Bks. of the East: Vol. 7). 15.00 (ISBN 0-89581-517-6). Asian Human Pr.

Institution, Laws & Ceremonies of the Most Noble Order of the Garter. Elias Ashmole. LC 78-147882. (Illus.). 720p. 1971. Repr. of 1672 ed. 50.00 (ISBN 0-8063-0467-7). Genealog Pub.

Institution of a Christen Man. LC 76-57371. (English Experience Ser.: No. 789). 1977. Repr. of 1537 ed. lib. bdg. 20.00 (ISBN 90-221-0789-2). Walter J Johnson.

Institutionalized Language Planning: Documents & Analysis of the Revival of Hebrew. Scott B. Saulson. (Contributions to the Sociology of Language Ser.: No. 23). 1979. text ed. 24.80x (ISBN 90-279-7567-1). Mouton.

Instrucciones En la Meditacion. Eknath Easwaran. 1980. pap. 2.00 (ISBN 0-915132-23-0). Nilgiri Pr.

Instrucciones Practicas para Nuevos Creyentes. Rodolfo A. Cruz. LC 77-71308. (Span.). 78p. (Orig.). 1970. pap. text ed. 1.95 (ISBN 0-89922-002-9). Edit Caribe.

Instructed Conscience: The Shaping of the American National Ethic. Donald H. Meyer. LC 76-175512. (Illus.). 1972. 18.95x (ISBN 0-8122-7651-5); pap. 9.95x (ISBN 0-8122-1066-2). U of Pa Pr.

Instruction & Instructional Facilities in the Colleges of the United Lutheran Church in America. Donald P Cottrell. LC 79-176672. (Columbia University. Teachers College. Contributions to Education: No. 376). Repr. of 1929 ed. 22.50 (ISBN 0-404-55376-1). AMS Pr.

Instruction in Christian Love. Martin Bucer. John Knox.

Instruction in God's Law. Peter Smirnoff. 1974. pap. 5.00 (ISBN 0-686-10199-5). Eastern Orthodox.

Instruction on Christian Freedom & Liberation. 60p. (Orig.). 1986. pap. 1.95 (ISBN 1-55586-995-5). US Catholic.

Instructions for Practical Living & Other Neo-Confucian Writings. Wang Yang Ming. Tr. by Wing tsit Chan from Chinese. 358p. 1985. pap. 14.00x (ISBN 0-231-06039-4). Columbia U Pr.

Instructions in the Life of Prayer. 2nd ed. Charles Whiston. 96p. 1985. pap. 1.50 (ISBN 0-88028-046-8). Forward Movement.

Instructions of St. Pachomius. Saint Pachomius. Tr. by E. Wallis Budge. pap. text ed. 1.95 (ISBN 0-686-25553-4). Eastern Orthodox.

Instructions to Beginners in the Christian Life. Ed. by John L. Horst. 121p. 1934. pap. 1.95 (ISBN 0-8361-1378-0). Herald Pr.

Instructions to Christian Converts. Clark. pap. 1.95 (ISBN 0-686-12883-4). Schmul Pub Co.

Instrument of Thy Peace. Alan Paton. 124p. 1985. pap. text ed. 8.95 large print ed. (ISBN 0-8027-2494-9). Walker & Co.

Instrumental Music in Worship. M. C. Kurfees. 10.95 (ISBN 0-89225-106-9). Gospel Advocate.

Instruye al Nino. Kathleen Demaray. Orig. Title: Train up a Child. (Span., Illus.). 24p. 1982. Spiral Wire Bound 5.95 (ISBN 0-89367-085-5). Light & Life.

Insular & Anglo-Saxon Illuminated Manuscripts: An Iconographic Catalogue c. A.D. 625 to 1100. Compiled by Thomas H. Ohlgren. LC 85-20446. (Illus.). 480p. 75.00 (ISBN 0-8240-8651-1). Garland Pub.

Insured by Hope. Mildred B. Young. LC 56-8831. (Orig.). pap. 2.50x (ISBN 0-87574-090-1). Pendle Hill.

Insurrection - Resurrection. N. J. (Illus.). 1976. pap. 1.25 (ISBN 0-686-16521-7). Working Peoples Art.

Insurrection of the Old-Ritualist Monks at the Solovetsk Monastery in the Seventeenth Century. V. L. Syrtsov. 316p. Repr. of 1888 ed. text ed. 33.12 (ISBN 0-576-99180-5, Pub. by Gregg Intl Pubs England). Gregg Intl.

Integral Yoga. Haridas Chaudhuri. LC 73-17170. 1981. pap. 4.95 (ISBN 0-8356-0444-6, Quest). Theos Pub Hse.

Integral Yoga Hatha Booklet & Tape. Integral Yoga Institutes. 1979. 6.95 (ISBN 0-932040-23-3). Integral Yoga Pubns.

Integral Yoga of Sri Aurobindo. 2nd ed. Richabhchand. 1979. 20.00 (ISBN 0-89744-939-8); pap. 16.00 (ISBN 0-89744-940-1). Auromere.

Integral Yoga of Sri Aurobindo. Rishabhchand. 473p. 1974. pap. 5.30 (ISBN 0-89071-281-6). Matagiri.

Integral Yoga: The Yoga Sutras of Patanjali. Pocket ed. Sri Swami Satchidananda. LC 85-125. 124p. (Orig.). 1985. pap. 3.95 (ISBN 0-932040-28-4). Integral Yoga Pubns.

Integral Yoga Today. Maya N. Swami Jyotir. 96p. (Orig.). 1983. pap. 2.50 (ISBN 0-934664-43-9). Yoga Res Foun.

Integrating Psychology & Theology: Elbows Together but Hearts Apart. Kirk E. Farnsworth. LC 81-40100. 94p. 1982. lib. bdg. 23.50 (ISBN 0-8191-1851-6); pap. text ed. 8.25 (ISBN 0-8191-1852-4). U Pr of Amer.

Integration Musings: Thoughts on Being A Christian Professional. H. Newton Malony. LC 86-81512. (Orig.). 1986. pap. 12.95 (ISBN 0-9609928-3-9). Integ Pr.

Integration of Human Values. Cornelius J. Van Der Poel. 5.95 (ISBN 0-87193-004-8). Dimension Bks.

Integration of Psychology & Theology: An Introduction. Bruce S. Narramore & John Carter. (Rosemead Ser.). (Orig.). 1979. pap. 8.95 (ISBN 0-310-30341-9, 11190P). Zondervan.

Integrative Preaching: The Pulpit at the Center. William H. Willimon. LC 80-39628. (Abingdon Preacher's Library). 112p. (Orig.). 1981. pap. 6.95 (ISBN 0-687-19129-7). Abingdon.

Integrative Theology: Knowing Ultimate Reality; The Living God, Vol. 1. Gordon R. Lewis & Bruce A. Demarest. 352p. 1986. 16.95 (ISBN 0-310-39230-6). Zondervan.

Integrity & Compromise: Problems of Public & Private Conscience. facsimile ed. Institute for Religious & Social Studies. Ed. by R. M. MacIver. LC 76-167367. (Essay Index Reprints - Religion & Civilization Ser). Repr. of 1957 ed. 15.00 (ISBN 0-8369-2656-0). Ayer Co Pubs.

Integrity of Leviticus Rabbah: The Problem of the Autonomy of a Rabbinic Document. Jacob Neusner. (Brown Judaic Studies). 1985. 25.95 (ISBN 0-89130-852-0, 14-00-93); pap. 21.50 (ISBN 0-89130-853-9). Scholars Pr Ga.

Integrity of Life: Allegorical Imagery in the Plays of John Webster. Eloise K. Goreau. Ed. by James Hogg. (Jacobean Drama Studies). 194p. (Orig.). 1974. pap. 15.00 (ISBN 0-317-40056-8, Pub. by Salzburg Studies). Longwood Pub Group.

Integrity of Mission: The Inner Life & Outreach of the Church. Orlando E. Costas. LC 79-1759. 1979. pap. 5.95 (ISBN 0-06-061586-9, RD 235, HarpR). Har-Row.

Integrity of the Church. E. Glenn Hinson. LC 77-82400. 1978. 8.95 (ISBN 0-8054-1616-1). Broadman.

Intellect & Beyond: Developing a Christian Mind. Oliver R. Barclay. 144p. (Orig.). 1985. pap. 6.95 (ISBN 0-310-33291-5, 12280P). Zondervan.

Intellectual Conquest of Peru: The Jesuit College of San Pablo, 1568-1767. Luis Martin. LC 67-26159. (Orig.). 1968. 25.00 (ISBN 0-8232-0785-4). Fordham.

Intellectual Crisis in English Catholicism: Liberal Catholics, Modernists, & the Vatican in the Late Nineteenth & Early Twentieth Centuries. William J. Schoenl. Ed. by Peter Stanmsky & Leslie Hume. LC 81-48368. 360p. 1982. lib. bdg. 52.00 (ISBN 0-8240-5164-5). Garland Pub.

Intellectual Freedom & Its Limitations in the University of Paris in the Thirteenth & Fourteenth Centuries. Mary M. McLaughlin. Ed. by Walter P. Metzger. LC 76-55187. (Academic Profession Ser.). 1977. Repr. lib. bdg. 34.50x (ISBN 0-405-10018-3). Ayer Co Pubs.

Intellectual Heritage of the Early Middle Ages. Max L. Laistner. 1966. lib. bdg. 24.00x (ISBN 0-88254-852-2, Octagon). Hippocrene Bks.

Intellectual History of Islamic India. Aziz Ahmad. 1970. 13.00x (ISBN 0-85224-057-0, Pub. by Edinburgh U Pr Scotland). Columbia U Pr.

Intellectual Legacy of Paul Tillich. Ed. by James R. Lyons. LC 68-63714. (Slaughter Foundation Lectures: 1966). pap. 29.80 (2027636). Bks Demand UMI.

Intellectual Life of Colonial New England. Samuel E. Morison. LC 79-20246. 1980. Repr. of 1956 ed. lib. bdg. 24.75x (ISBN 0-313-22032-8, MOIL). Greenwood.

Intellectual Modernism of Shibli Nu'mani: An Exposition of His Religious & Political Ideas. M. A. Murd. pap. 19.95 (ISBN 0-317-46099-4). Kazi Pubns.

Intellectual Mysticism. Ben Sheiner. LC 78-50531. (Illus.). 120p. 1978. 8.95 (ISBN 0-8022-2228-5). Philos Lib.

Intellectual Origins of the European Reformation. Alister E. McGrath. 272p. 1987. text ed. 39.95 (ISBN 0-631-15144-3). Basil Blackwell.

Intellectual Schizophrenia. Rousas J. Rushdoony. 1961. pap. 5.50 (ISBN 0-87552-411-7). Presby & Reformed.

Intellectual Struggle of the English Catholics in the Seventeenth Century: The Catholic Dilemma. Kenneth L. Campbell. LC 86-23893. (Texts & Studies in Religion Ser.: Vol. 30). 256p. 1986. text ed. 49.95 (ISBN 0-88946-818-4). E Mellen.

Intellectual Tradition in the Old Testament. R. N. Whybray. LC 73-78236. (Beiheft zur Zeitschrift fuer die Alttestamentliche Wissenschaft). 1974. 44.25x (ISBN 3-11-004424-2). De Gruyter.

Intellectual Virtues According to the Philosophy of St. Thomas. Sr. M. Rose Brennan. (Orig.). 1957. pap. text ed. 4.95x (ISBN 0-87015-075-8). Pacific Bks.

Intellectuals Speak Out About God. Ed. by Roy A. Varghese. 1984. pap. 7.95 (ISBN 0-89526-827-2). Regnery Bks.

Intellektualmythologie: Betrachtungen Uber das Wesen das Mythus und Die Mythologische Methode. Fritz Langer. Ed. by Kees W. Bolle. LC 77-79136. (Mythology Ser.). (Ger.). 1978. Repr. of 1916 ed. lib. bdg. 21.00x (ISBN 0-405-10546-0). Ayer Co Pubs.

Intelligent Prayer. Lewis Maclachlan. 104p. 1965. pap. 3.50 (ISBN 0-227-67496-0). Attic Pr.

Intelligent Theology, Vol. 1: The Trinity Lives in Us As We Celebrate Life. P. Fransen. LC 77-85505. 148p. pap. 2.50 (ISBN 0-8199-0400-7). Franciscan Herald.

Intelligent Theology, Vol. 2: Confirmation & Priesthood. P. Fransen. 157p. pap. 2.50 (ISBN 0-8199-0401-5). Franciscan Herald.

Intelligent Theology, Vol. 3: A Universal Theology. P. Fransen. 183p. pap. 2.50 (ISBN 0-8199-0402-3). Franciscan Herald.

Intelligent Understanding of Sculptures & Mosaics in the Early Church. Christopher L. Gunter. (Illus.). 138p. 1982. 75.45 (ISBN 0-86650-037-5). Gloucester Art.

Intelligible Universe: A Cosmological Argument. Hugo A. Meynell. LC 81-19065. 164p. 1982. 28.50x (ISBN 0-389-20253-3, 07057). B&N Imports.

Intelligible World: Metaphysics & Value. Wilbur M. Urban. LC 76-51208. 1977. Repr. of 1929 ed. lib. bdg. 26.75x (ISBN 0-8371-9437-7, URIW). Greenwood.

Intended for Pleasure. rev. ed. Ed Wheat & Gaye Wheat. (Illus.). 256p. 1981. 12.95 (ISBN 0-8007-1253-6). Revell.

Intensive Spiritual Hypnotherapy. Peter D. Francuch & Arthur E. Jones. LC 82-62015. 543p. 1983. 9.95 (ISBN 0-939386-04-6). TMH Pub.

Intention der Verkuendigung Jesajas. Hans W. Hoffmann. LC 74-80632. (Beiheft 136 zur Zeitschrift fuer die alttestamentliche Wissenschaft). 125p. 1974. 30.00 (ISBN 3-11-004672-5). De Gruyter.

Inter-Faith Organizations 1893-1979: An Historical Directory. Marcus Braybrooke. LC 79-91620. (Texts & Studies in Religion: Vol. 6). xiv, 228p. 1980. 49.95x (ISBN 0-88946-971-7). E Mellen.

Interaction of Italians & Jews in America. Ed. by Jean Scarpaci. 1974. 9.95 (ISBN 0-934675-07-4). Am Italian.

Interceding Christian. 2nd ed. Kenneth E. Hagin. 1983. pap. 1.00 (ISBN 0-89276-018-4). Hagin Ministries.

Interceding Faith. Elbert Willis. 1978. 1.25 (ISBN 0-89858-018-8). Fill the Gap.

Intercession of Christ. John Bunyan. pap. 1.95 (ISBN 0-685-19835-9). Reiner.

Interesting Men of the Bible. E. T. Burgess. 1970. pap. 0.50 (ISBN 0-89114-007-7). Baptist Pub Hse.

Interfaith Marriages: Who & Why. Paul H. Besanceney. 1970. 12.95x (ISBN 0-8084-0164-5); pap. 8.95x (ISBN 0-8084-0165-3). New Coll U Pr.

Interim Report on the Books Jesus & Christ. Edward Schillebeeckx. 160p. 1980. 9.95 (ISBN 0-8245-0029-6). Crossroad NY.

Interior Acts: Teleology, Justice, & Friendship in the Religious Ethics of Thomas Aquinas. Steven A. Edwards. LC 85-29530. 184p. (Orig.). 1986. lib. bdg. 24.75 (ISBN 0-8191-5212-9); pap. text ed. 11.75 (ISBN 0-8191-5213-7). U Pr of Amer.

Interior & Exterior in Zen Buddhism. Toshihiko Izutsu. LC 84-5580. (Eranos Lectures Ser.: No. 1). 36p. (Orig.). 1984. pap. 7.00 (ISBN 0-88214-401-4). Spring Pubns.

Interior Castle. St. Teresa of Avila. 1972. pap. 4.50 (ISBN 0-385-03643-4, Im). Doubleday.

Interior Castle or the Mansions, 2 vols. Teresa. (Illus.). 325p. 1984. Set. 197.85 (ISBN 0-89266-488-6). Am Classical Coll Pr.

Interior Decorating: A Reflection of the Creator's Design. Georg Andersen & Edith Dean. 192p. 1983. 16.95 (ISBN 0-87123-288-X, 230288). Bethany Hse.

Interior Realization. Hubert Benoit. Tr. by John F. Mahoney from Fr. (Illus.). 128p. (Orig.). 1987. pap. 6.95 (ISBN 0-87728-624-8). Weiser.

Interlinear Bible, 4 vols. Jay P. Green, Sr. 2952p. 1986. 89.95 (ISBN 0-913573-31-0). Hendrickson MA.

Interlinear Bible. Jay P. Green, Sr. 736p. 1986. 21.95 (ISBN 0-913573-29-9). Hendrickson MA.

Interlinear Bible. Jay P. Green, Sr. 960p. 1986. 44.95 (ISBN 0-913573-25-6). Hendrickson MA.

Interlinear Greek-English New Testament: Coded to Strong's. 1984. deluxe ed. 24.95 (ISBN 0-8010-5036-7). Baker Bk.

Interlinear Greek-English New Testament. George R. Berry. LC 78-54242. 1978. pap. 15.95 (ISBN 0-8054-1372-3). Broadman.

Interlinear Greek-English New Testament. George R. Berry. 24.95 (ISBN 0-310-21170-0, 9216). Zondervan.

Interlinear Greek-English New Testament. George R. Berry & James Strong. (Reference Set). 1187p. 24.95 (ISBN 0-915134-74-8). Mott Media.

Interlinear Greek-English New Testament. Alfred Marshall. 27.95 (ISBN 0-310-20380-5, 6254, Pub. by Bagster). Zondervan.

Interlinear Greek-English New Testament: With Greek-English Lexicon & New Testament Synonyms. 1977. pap. 14.95 (ISBN 0-8010-0700-3). Baker Bk.

Interlude of Widowhood. Patricia DeStefano. (Greeting Book Line Ser.). 48p. (Orig.). 1983. pap. 1.50 (ISBN 0-89622-200-4). Twenty-Third.

Intermarriage & Conversion: A Halakhic Solution. Jack S. Cohen. 1987. 14.95 (ISBN 0-88125-124-0); pap. 9.95 (ISBN 0-88125-125-9). Ktav.

Intermarriage & the Jewish Future. Egon Mayer & Carl Sheingold. LC 79-63378. 46p. 1980. pap. 2.00 (ISBN 0-87495-031-7). Am Jewish Comm.

Intermediary World & Patterns of Perfection in Philo & Hebrews. Lala K. Dey. LC 75-22457. (Society of Biblical Literature Dissertation Ser.: No.25). pap. 62.80 (ISBN 0-317-12981-3, 2017524). Bks Demand UMI.

Intermediate Christian Training. Jean Gibson. 1981. pap. 7.50 (ISBN 0-937396-60-5). Walterick Pubs.

Intermediate Hebrew Grammar. Bruce K. Waltke. 1987. text ed. write for info. (ISBN 0-931464-31-5). Eisenbrauns.

Intermediate Spiritual Metaphysics. Paul L. Peck. LC 78-61985. (Spiritual Metaphysics Ser.: Vol. 2). 1979. 15.95 (ISBN 0-87881-081-1); pap. 13.50 (ISBN 0-87881-082-X). Mojave Bks.

International Aspect of the Missionary Movement in China. Chao-Kwang Wu. LC 75-41300. (Johns Hopkins University. Studies in Historical & Political Science: Extra Volumes; New Ser.: No. 11). Repr. of 1930 ed. 18.50 (ISBN 0-404-14708-9). AMS Pr.

International Bible Commentary. rev. ed. Ed. by F. F. Bruce. 1664p. 1986. text ed. 24.95 (ISBN 0-310-22020-3, 6404). Zondervan.

International Bible Dictionary. 1977. (Pub. by Logos); pap. 6.95 (ISBN 0-88270-235-1). Bridge Pub.

International Bibliography of Explanatory Essays on Individual Proverbs & Proverbial Expressions: German Language & Literature. Wolfgang Mieder. (European University Studies Ser.: No.1, Vol. 191). 146p. 1977. pap. 18.25 (ISBN 3-261-02932-3). P Lang Pubs.

International Bibliography of Jewish Affairs 1966-1967: A Select List of Books & Articles Published in the Diaspora. Ed. by Elizabeth E. Eppler. LC 74-84654. 365p. 1976. 35.00x (ISBN 0-8419-0177-5). Holmes & Meier.

International Bibliography of Jewish History & Thought. Ed. by Jonathan Kaplan. 483p. 1984. lib. bdg. 41.00 (ISBN 3-598-07503-0). K G Saur.

International Book of Christmas Carols. Walter Ehret & George K. Evans. LC 80-13105. (Illus.). 352p. 1980. pap. 14.95 (ISBN 0-8289-0378-6). Greene.

International Buddhist Directory 1985. Compiled by Tushita Meditation Centre. (Wisdom Reference Bk.). 150p. (Orig.). 1985. pap. write for info. (ISBN 0-86171-025-8, Wisdom Bks). Great Traditions.

International Calvinism. Ed. by Menna Prestwich. (Illus.). 414p. 1985. 49.95x (ISBN 0-19-821933-4). Oxford U Pr.

International Catechetical Congress: Selected Documentation: Rome, 1971. Ed. by William Tobin. cancelled (ISBN 0-686-18988-4, V-199). US Catholic.

International Children's Bible Handbook. Larry Richards. LC 86-5995. (Illus.). 1986. 13.95 (ISBN 0-8344-0133-9, BB600C). Sweet.

International Conference for World Peace & Social Reform & Human Rights Prayer Day--1976: Proceedings. (Illus.). 1976. pap. 11.50 (ISBN 0-915598-14-0). Church of Scient Info.

International Conflict in the Twentieth Century. Herbert Butterfield. LC 74-6777. 123p. 1974. Repr. of 1960 ed. lib. bdg. 65.00 (ISBN 0-8371-7569-0, BUIC). Greenwood.

International Congress of Psychology, 10th: Copenhagen, 1932 (Papers Read) Repr. 53.00 (ISBN 0-8115-3551-7). Kraus Repr.

International Dictionary of Religion. Richard Kennedy. LC 83-27209. (Illus.). 1984. 24.50x (ISBN 0-8245-0632-4). Crossroad NY.

International Dictionary of Religion. Richard Kennedy. 256p. 1986. pap. 12.95 (ISBN 0-8245-0733-9). Crossroad NY.

International Ethics: A Philosophy & Public Affairs Reader. Ed. by Charles R. Beitz et al. LC 84-42938. 352p. 1985. text ed. 24.50 (ISBN 0-691-07683-9); pap. 8.95 (ISBN 0-691-02234-8). Princeton U Pr.

International Implications of the Papal Assassination Attempt: A Case of State-Sponsored Terrorism. Zbigniew Brzezinski & Robert H. Kupperman. (Significant Issues Ser.: Vol. VI, No. 20). 23p. 1984. 12.95 (ISBN 0-89206-073-5). CSI Studies.

International Implications of the Papal Assassination Attempt: A Case of State-Sponsored Terrorism. Linnea P. Raine. (Significant Issues Ser.: Vol. VI, No. 20). 32p. (Orig.). 1985. pap. text ed. 6.95 (ISBN 0-8191-5935-2, Pub. by CSIS). U Pr of Amer.

International Jew. Henry Ford. 59.95 (ISBN 0-8490-0418-7). Gordon Pr.

International Jew. Henry Ford. 1978. pap. 5.00x (ISBN 0-911038-45-0). Noontide.

International Jew, 4 vols. Henry Ford. 1984. lib. bdg. 500.95 (ISBN 0-87700-586-9). Revisionist Pr.

International Lesson Annual, 1986-1987. Ed. by Horace R. Weaver. 448p. (Orig.). 1986. pap. 7.95 (ISBN 0-687-19150-5). Abingdon.

International Lesson Annual, 1987-1988. Horace R. Weaver. 448p. 1987. pap. 7.95 (ISBN 0-687-19151-3). Abingdon.

International Organization for Masoretic Studies, 1972 & 1973 Proceedings & Papers. Harry M. Orlinsky. LC 74-16568. (Society of Biblical Literature, Masoretic Studies). Repr. of 1974 ed. 33.30 (ISBN 0-8357-9573-X, 2017535). Bks Demand UMI.

International Partners in Prayer Triumpeting News: Packet of Past Issues. International Partners in Prayers. 6p. 1984. pap. 0.50 (ISBN 0-917593-04-9, Pub. by Intl Partners). Prosperity & Profits.

International Standard Bible Encyclopedia, Vol. III, K-P. rev. ed. Ed. by Geoffrey W. Bromiley. (International Standard Bible Encyclopedia Ser.). (Illus.). 1080p. 1986. 37.50 (ISBN 0-8028-8163-7). Eerdmans.

International Standard Bible Encyclopedia, 4 vols. Ed. by James Orr. 1930. 89.95 (ISBN 0-8028-8045-2). Eerdmans.

International Standard Bible Encyclopedia, Vol. 1, A-D. rev. ed. Ed. by Geoffrey W. Bromiley. LC 79-12280. (Illus.). 1979. 37.50 (ISBN 0-8028-8161-0). Eerdmans.

International Standard Bible Encyclopedia, Vol. 2: E-J. rev. ed. Ed. by Geoffrey W. Bromiley. 1132p. 1981. 37.50 (ISBN 0-8028-8162-9). Eerdmans.

International Theological Commentary, 6 vols. Ed. by Frederick Holmgren & George A. Knight. Incl. Vol. 1. Joshua. E. J. Hamlin. 8.95. 1983. pap. write for info. Eerdmans.

International Theological Commentary on Daniel. R. A. Anderson. Ed. by George A. Knight. (International Theological Commentary Ser.). 192p. (Orig.). 1984. pap. 7.95 (ISBN 0-8028-1038-1). Eerdmans.

International Theological Commentary on Joshua. E. J. Hamlin. Ed. by Frederick Holmgren & George A. Knight. (International Theological Commentary Ser.). 200p. (Orig.). 1983. pap. 8.95 (ISBN 0-8028-1041-1). Eerdmans.

International Theological Commentary on Amos & Lamentations. R. Martin-Achard & P. Re'emi. (International Theological Commentary Ser.). 160p. (Orig.). 1983. pap. 8.95 (ISBN 0-8028-1040-3). Eerdmans.

International Theological Commentary on Isaiah 40-55. George A. Knight. Ed. by Frederick Holmgren. (International Theological Commentary Ser.). 208p. (Orig.). 1983. pap. 9.95 (ISBN 0-8028-1039-X). Eerdmans.

International Yoga Bibliography, 1950 to 1980. Howard R. Jarrell. LC 81-13518. 231p. 1981. 17.50 (ISBN 0-8108-1472-2). Scarecrow.

Internationales Abkuerzungsverzeichnis fuer Theologie und Grenzgebiete. Siegfried Schwertner. LC 72-77418. 1974. pap. 35.20x (ISBN 3-11-004027-1). De Gruyter.

Internationales Jahrbuch fuer interdisziplinaere Forschung, Vol. 1: 1974. Wissenschaft als interdisziplinaeres Problem. Ed. by Richard Schwarz. 1974. 44.00x (ISBN 3-11-004633-4). De Gruyter.

Interplay: A Theory of Religion & Education. Gabriel Moran. LC 80-53203. 125p. (Orig.). 1981. pap. 8.95 (ISBN 0-88489-125-9). St Mary's.

Interplay of Realistic & Flamboyant Art Elements in the French Mysteres. Sr. M. Faith McKean. LC 74-94196. (Catholic University of America Studies in Romance Languages & Literatures Ser: No. 60). Repr. of 1959 ed. 23.00 (ISBN 0-404-50360-8). AMS Pr.

Interpretation & Dionysos: Method in the Study of a God. Park McGinty. (Religon & Reason Ser.: No. 16). 1978. 37.50x (ISBN 90-279-7844-1). Mouton.

Interpretation of Acts. Richard C. Lenski. 1934. 22.95 (ISBN 0-8066-9009-7, 10-3365). Augsburg.

Interpretation of Ancient, Strange Mythological Symbols. Richard P. Knight. (Illus.). 137p. 1983. 147.75 (ISBN 0-89901-125-X). Found Class Reprints.

Interpretation of Belief: Coleridge, Schleiermacher & Romanticism. Ed. by David Jasper. LC 85-26204. 192p. 1986. 25.00x (ISBN 0-312-42401-9). St Martin.

Interpretation of Christian Ethics. Reinhold Niebuhr. 1979. pap. 8.95 (ISBN 0-8164-2206-0, HarpR). Har-Row.

Interpretation of Colossians, Thessalonians First & Second, Timothy First & Second, Titus, & Philemon. Richard C. Lenski. 1937. 21.95 (ISBN 0-8066-9006-2, 10-3369). Augsburg.

Interpretation of Existence. Joseph Owens. LC 84-23805. 162p. 1985. pap. text ed. 7.95 (ISBN 0-268-01157-5, 85-11578, Dist. by Harper & Row). U of Notre Dame Pr.

Interpretation of First & Second Corinthians. Richard C. Lenski. 1935. 22.95 (ISBN 0-8066-9008-9, 10-3367). Augsburg.

Interpretation of First & Second Peter, First, Second & Third John, Jude. Richard C. Lenski. 1938. 21.95 (ISBN 0-8066-9011-9, 10-3371). Augsburg.

Interpretation of Galatians, Ephesians, & Philippians. Richard C. Lenski. 1937. 21.95 (ISBN 0-8066-9007-0, 10-3368). Augsburg.

Interpretation of Hebrews & James. Richard C. Lenski. 1938. 21.95 (ISBN 0-8066-9010-0, 10-3370). Augsburg.

Interpretation of John. Ed. by John Ashton. LC 85-45536. (Issues in Religion & Theology Ser.). 176p. 1986. pap. 7.95 (ISBN 0-8006-1774-6, 1-1774). Fortress.

Interpretation of Mark. Ed. by William R. Telford. LC 84-18708. (Issues in Religion & Theology Ser.). 176p. 1985. pap. 7.95 (ISBN 0-8006-1772-X, 1-1772). Fortress.

Interpretation of Material Shapes in Puritanism: A Study of Rhetoric, Prejudice & Violence. Ann Kibbey. (Cambridge Studies in American Literature & Culture). (Illus.). 256p. 1986. 27.95 (ISBN 0-521-26509-6). Cambridge U Pr.

Interpretation of Matthew. Ed. by Graham Stanton. LC 83-5508. (Issues in Religion & Theology Ser.). 176p. 1983. pap. 7.95 (ISBN 0-8006-1766-5, 1-1766). Fortress.

Interpretation of Otherness: Literature Religion & the American Imagination. Giles Gunn. 1979. 24.95x (ISBN 0-19-502453-2). Oxford U Pr.

Interpretation of Plainchant: A Preliminary Study. Alec Robertson. Repr. of 1937 ed. lib. bdg. 22.50x (ISBN 0-8371-4322-5, ROPL). Greenwood.

Interpretation of Prophecy. 4th ed. Paul L. Tan. LC 73-85613. 1979. Repr. 8.95 (ISBN 0-932940-01-3). Assurance Pubs.

Interpretation of Prophecy. Paul L. Tan. 1975. 8.95 (ISBN 0-88469-000-8). BMH Bks.

Interpretation of Religious Experience, 2 vols. John Watson. LC 77-27216. (Gifford Lectures: 1910-12). Repr. of 1912 ed. Set. 67.50 (ISBN 0-404-60510-9). AMS Pr.

Interpretation of Romans. Richard C. Lenski. 1936. 21.95 (ISBN 0-8066-9005-4, 10-3366). Augsburg.

Interpretation of St. John. R. Swinburne Clymer. 266p. 1953. 9.95 (ISBN 0-932785-23-9). Philos Pub.

Interpretation of St. John's Gospel. R. C. Lenski. 1936. 22.95 (ISBN 0-8066-9000-3, 10-3364). Augsburg.

Interpretation of St. John's Revelation. R. C. Lenski. 1935. 21.95 (ISBN 0-8066-9001-1, 10-3372). Augsburg.

Interpretation of St. Luke's Gospel. R. C. Lenski. 1934. 22.95 (ISBN 0-8066-9002-X, 10-3363). Augsburg.

Interpretation of St. Mark's Gospel. R. C. Lenski. 1946. 21.95 (ISBN 0-8066-9003-8, 0-3362). Augsburg.

Interpretation of St. Matthew, 2 Vols. 1945. Set. 16.95 (ISBN 0-686-00813-8). Vol. I, 285 pp (ISBN 0-932785-24-7). Vol. II, 284 pp (ISBN 0-932785-25-5). Philos Pub.

Interpretation of St. Matthew's Gospel. R. C. Lenski. 1933. 22.95 (ISBN 0-8066-9004-6, 10-3361). Augsburg.

Interpretation of the Book of Revelation. Apostolos Makrakis. Ed. by Orthodox Christian Educational Society. Tr. by A. G. Alexander from Hellenic. 564p. 1972. 11.00x (ISBN 0-938366-12-2). Orthodox Chr.

Interpretation of the Entire New Testament (Revelation Not Incl), 2 vols. Apostolos Makrakis. Ed. by Orthodox Christian Educational Society. Tr. by Albert G. Alexander from Hellenic. 2052p. (Vol. 1, 1127 pp.;vol. 2, 925 pp.). 1949. Set. 28.00x (ISBN 0-938366-08-4). Orthodox Chr.

Interpretation of the Fourth Gospel. Charles H. Dodd. 67.50 (ISBN 0-521-04848-6); pap. text ed. 18.95 (ISBN 0-521-09517-4). Cambridge U Pr.

Interpretation of the Gospel Law. Apostolos Makrakis. Ed. by Orthodox Christian Educational Society. Tr. by Denver Cummings from Hellenic. 453p. 1955. 9.00x (ISBN 0-938366-10-6). Orthodox Chr.

Interpretation of the New Testament, 12 Vols. Richard C. Lenski. 1933-46. Set. 235.00 (ISBN 0-8066-9012-7, 10-3360). Augsburg.

Interpretation of the New Testament, 1861-1961. Stephen Neill. 1964. pap. 10.95x (ISBN 0-19-283005-8). Oxford U Pr.

Interpretation of Whitehead's Metaphysics. William A. Christian. LC 77-5619. 1977. Repr. of 1959 ed. lib. bdg. 35.00x (ISBN 0-8371-9638-8, CHIW). Greenwood.

Interpretations of Difficult Passages in Rashi, Vol. I. Pinchas Doron. (Hebrew.). 1985. text ed. 20.00x (ISBN 0-88125-080-5). Ktav.

Interpretations of Greek Mythology. Ed. by Jan Bremmer & Fritz Graf. LC 86-20638. (Illus.). 304p. 1987. 28.50x (ISBN 0-389-20679-2). B&N Imports.

Interpretations of Islam: Past & Present. Emmanuel Sivan. LC 84-70415. 256p. 1985. 19.95 (ISBN 0-87850-049-9). Darwin Pr.

Interpretations of Poetry & Religion. George Santayana. 11.25 (ISBN 0-8446-0893-9). Peter Smith.

Interpretaton of William Blake's Job. Emily S. Hamblen. LC 70-100759. 1970. pap. 39.95x (ISBN 0-8383-0037-5). Haskell.

Interpreter, Wherein Three Principal Terms of State Are Clearly Unfolded. Thomas Scott. LC 74-80194. (English Experience Ser.: No. 673). 1974. Repr. of 1624 ed. 3.50 (ISBN 90-221-0281-5). Walter J Johnson.

Interpreter's Bible, 12 vols. George A. Buttrick. Incl. Vol. 1. General Articles, Genesis, Exodus. 1952 (ISBN 0-687-19207-2); Vol. 2. Leviticus - Samuel. 1953 (ISBN 0-687-19208-0); Vol. 3. Kings - Job. 1954 (ISBN 0-687-19209-9); Vol. 4. Psalms, Proverbs. 1955 (ISBN 0-687-19210-2); Vol. 5. Ecclesiates - Jeremiah. 1956 (ISBN 0-687-19211-0); Vol. 6. Lamentations - Malachi. 1956 (ISBN 0-687-19212-9); Vol. 7. General Articles, Matthew, Mark. 1951 (ISBN 0-687-19213-7); Vol. 8. Luke, John. 1952 (ISBN 0-687-19214-5); Vol. 9. The Acts, Romans. 1954 (ISBN 0-687-19215-3); Vol. 10. Corinthians, Ephesians. 1953 (ISBN 0-687-19216-1); Vol. 11. Philippians - Hebrews. 1955 (ISBN 0-687-19217-X); Vol. 12. James - Revelation. 1957 (ISBN 0-687-19218-8). LC 51-12276. 1957. 22.95 (ISBN 0-686-76914-7); 260.00 (ISBN 0-687-19206-4). Abingdon.

Interpreter's Concise Commentary, 8 vols. Set. slipcased 34.95 (ISBN 0-687-19231-5). Abingdon.

Interpreter's Concise Commentary, Vol. II: Old Testament History. 4.95 (ISBN 0-687-19233-1). Abingdon.

Interpreter's Concise Commentary, Vol. IV: The Major Prophets. 4.95 (ISBN 0-687-19235-8). Abingdon.

Interpreter's Concise Commentary, Vol. I: The Pentateuch, 8 vols. 368p. (Orig.). 1983. pap. 4.95 (ISBN 0-687-19232-3). Abingdon.

Interpreter's Concise Commentary, Vol. III: Wisdom Literature & Poetry. 4.95 (ISBN 0-687-19234-X). Abingdon.

Interpreter's Concise Commentary, Vol. VII: Acts & Paul's Letters. 4.95 (ISBN 0-687-19238-2). Abingdon.

Interpreter's Concise Commentary, Vol. VIII: Revelation & the General Epistles. 4.95 (ISBN 0-687-19239-0). Abingdon.

Interpreter's Concise Commentary, Vol. VI: The Gospels, 8 vols. 368p. (Orig.). 1983. pap. 4.95 (ISBN 0-687-19237-4). Abingdon.

Interpreter's Concise Commentary, Vol. V: The Minor Prophets & the Apocrypha. 4.95 (ISBN 0-687-19236-6). Abingdon.

Interpreter's Dictionary of the Bible, 5 vols. Ed. by George A. Buttrick & Keith R. Crim. LC 62-9387. 1976. Set. 112.00 (ISBN 0-687-19268-4). Abingdon.

Interpreter's Dictionary of the Bible, Supplementary Volume. Ed. by Keith R. Crim et al. LC 62-9387. (Illus.). 1976. 22.95 (ISBN 0-687-19269-2). Abingdon.

Interpreters of Reality: Lao-Tse, Heraclitus & the Christian Faith. Gwilym O. Griffith. 1977. lib. bdg. 59.95 (ISBN 0-8490-2065-4). Gordon Pr.

Interpreter's One-Volume Commentary on the Bible. Ed. by Charles M. Laymon. (Illus.). 1971. 24.95 (ISBN 0-687-19299-4); thumb indexed 28.95 (ISBN 0-687-19300-1). Abingdon.

Interpreting Acts. Everett F. Harrison. (Interpreting Ser.: No. 2). 352p. 1986. pap. 14.95 (ISBN 0-310-31850-5). Zondervan.

Interpreting Christian Holiness. W. T. Purkiser. 70p. (Orig.). 1971. pap. 1.95 (ISBN 0-8341-0221-8). Beacon Hill.

Interpreting Disciples: Practical Theology in the Disciples of Christ. Ed. by L. Dale Richesin & Larry D. Bouchard. LC 86-30072. 295p. (Orig.). 1987. pap. text ed. 14.95x (ISBN 0-87565-072-4). Tex Christian.

Interpreting Isaiah: The Suffering & Glory of the Messiah. Herbert M. Wolf. 272p. (Orig.). 1985. pap. 9.95 (ISBN 0-310-39061-3, 12713P). Zondervan.

Interpreting Jesus. Gerald O'Collins. 1983. pap. 9.95 (ISBN 0-8091-2572-2). Paulist Pr.

Interpreting Kant. Ed. by Moltke S. Gram. LC 82-13627. 1982. text ed. 18.00 (ISBN 0-87745-118-4). U of Iowa Pr.

Interpreting Orthodoxy. N. Nissiotis. 1980. pap. 2.95 (ISBN 0-937032-23-9). Light&Life Pub Co MN.

Interpreting Revelation. Merrill C. Tenney. 1957. 15.95 (ISBN 0-8028-3254-7). Eerdmans.

Interpreting Scripture: A Catholic Response to Fundamentalism. Edwin Daschbach. 144p. 1985. pap. 6.95 (ISBN 0-697-02110-6). Wm C Brown.

Interpreting the Atonement. Robert H. Culpepper. 170p. 1986. pap. 6.95 (ISBN 0-913029-13-0). Stevens Bk Pr.

Interpreting the Bible. A. Berkeley Mickelsen. 1963. 20.95 (ISBN 0-8028-3192-3). Eerdmans.

Interpreting the Bible: A Popular Introduction to Biblical Hermeneutics. Terence J. Keegan. 224p. (Orig.). 1986. pap. 8.95 (ISBN 0-8091-2747-4). Paulist Pr.

Interpreting the Bible in Theology & the Church. Henry V. Vander Goot. LC 84-9027. (Symposium Ser.: Vol. II). 128p. 1984. pap. 19.95 (ISBN 0-88946-701-3). E Mellen.

Interpreting the Gospels. Ed. by James L. Mays. LC 80-8057. pap. 79.30 (2027872). Bks Demand UMI.

Interpreting the Gospels for Preaching. Dwight M. Smith. LC 79-8900. pap. 32.00 (2029609). Bks Demand UMI.

Interpreting the Hebrew Bible. Ed. by J. A. Emerton & Stefan C. Reif. LC 81-21668. (University of Cambridge Oriental Publication Ser.: No. 32). 1982. 52.50 (ISBN 0-521-24424-2). Cambridge U Pr.

Interpreting the New Testament: A Practical Guide. Daniel J. Harrington. (New Testament Message Ser.: Vol. 1). 1979. 10.95 (ISBN 0-89453-189-1); pap. 6.95 (ISBN 0-89453-124-7). M Glazier.

Interpreting the New Testament Today. rev. ed. R. C. Briggs. LC 73-8024. 288p. (Orig.). 1973. pap. 9.95 (ISBN 0-687-19327-3). Abingdon.

Interpreting the Old Testament: A Practical Guide. Daniel J. Harrington. (Old Testament Message Ser.: Vol. 1). 1981. 10.95 (ISBN 0-89453-401-7); pap. 6.95 (ISBN 0-89453-236-7). M Glazier.

Interpreting the Parables. Archibald M. Hunter. LC 61-5122. 126p. 1976. pap. 5.95 (ISBN 0-664-24746-6). Westminster.

Interpreting the Prophets. Ed. by James L. Mays & Paul J. Achtemeier. LC 86-45223. 336p. 1987. pap. 16.95 (ISBN 0-8006-1932-3). Fortress.

Interpreting the Psalms. Patrick D. Miller, Jr. LC 85-16258. 176p. 1986. pap. 10.95 (ISBN 0-8006-1896-3). Fortress.

Interpreting the Religious Experience: A Worldview. John T. Carmody & Denise L. Carmody. 240p. Date not set. text ed. price not set (ISBN 0-13-475609-6). P-H.

Interpreting the Revelation with Edgar Cayce. J. Everett Irion. 440p. 1982. 19.95 (ISBN 0-87604-137-3). ARE Pr.

Interpreting the Scriptures. Kevin J. Conner & Ken P. Malmin. 1976. pap. 9.95 (ISBN 0-914936-20-4). Bible Temple.

Interpreting Tradition: The Art of Theological Reflection. Ed. by Jane Kopas. (College Theology Society - Annual Publications Ser.). 1984. pap. 11.95 (ISBN 0-89130-621-8, 34 10 83). Scholars Pr GA.

Interpreting Worship. Alan Dunstan. 102p. 1985. pap. 5.95 (ISBN 0-8192-1357-8). Morehouse.

Interpretive Outline of Romans. David H. Steele & Curtis C. Thomas. (Illus.). 1963. pap. 5.95 (ISBN 0-87552-443-5). Presby & Reformed.

Interpretive Theories of Religion. Donald A. Crosby. (Religion & Reason Ser.: No.20). 336p. 1981. 34.25x (ISBN 90-279-3039-2). Mouton.

Interpretive Views: Opinions on Evaluating Interpretation. Ed. by Gary E. Machlis. LC 86-61991. (Illus., Orig.). 1986. pap. 9.95 (ISBN 0-940091-15-1). Natl Parks & Cons.

Interrelationship Between Atom-Body-Universe (Anda-Pinda-Brah Manda) Panduranga R. Malyala. Date not set. 1.99 (ISBN 0-938924-08-7). Sri Shirdi Sai.

Interreligious Dialogue: Facing the Next Frontier. Ed. by Richard W. Rousseau. LC 81-52035. (Modern Theological Themes Ser.: Selection from the Literature: Vol. I). 234p. (Orig.). 1981. pap. 13.50 (ISBN 0-940866-00-5). Ridge Row.

Interreligious Haggadah. write for info. ADL.

Interrupted Life: The Diaries of Etty Hillesum 1941-1943. Etty Hillesum. Tr. by Arno Pomerans. LC 83-47750. 226p. 1984. 13.45 (ISBN 0-394-53217-1). Pantheon.

Interruption of Eternity: Modern Gnosticism & the Origins of the New Religious Consciousness. Carl A. Raschke. LC 79-16460. 280p. 1980. 21.95x (ISBN 0-88229-374-5). Nelson-Hall.

Intersection & Beyond, Vol. II. Elizabeth Boyden Howes. LC 86-3067. 200p. (Orig.). 1986. pap. 8.50 (ISBN 0-917479-07-6). Guild Psy.

Intertestamental Literature. Martin McNamara. (Old Testament Message Ser.: Vol. 23). 16.95 (ISBN 0-89453-423-8); pap. 12.95 (ISBN 0-89453-256-1). M Glazier.

Interview with Chiara Lubich. William Proctor. 72p. (Orig.). 1983. pap. 4.95 (ISBN 0-911782-44-3). New City.

Interview with Santa Claus. Margaret Mead & Rhoda Metraux. (Illus.). 1978. 4.95 (ISBN 0-8027-0620-7). Walker & Co.

Interview with the Dalai Lama. John F. Avedon. LC 80-83015. (Illus.). 83p. (Orig.). 1980. pap. 6.95 (ISBN 0-937896-00-4). Littlebird.

Interviewing & Supporting the Catholic Educator. Alfred McBride. 1983. 3.35 (ISBN 0-318-00784-3). Natl Cath Educ.

Intimacy: Issues of Emotional Living in an Age of Stress for Clergy & Religious. Ed. by Anna Polcino. LC 78-104617. 1978. pap. 5.00 (ISBN 0-89571-003-X). Affirmation.

Intimacy: Where Do I Go To Find Love? Terry Hershey. 144p. 1984. text ed. 9.95 (ISBN 0-915929-06-6). Merit Bks.

Intimacy with God. Richard Booker. LC 84-70055. 196p. 1983. pap. 5.95 (ISBN 0-88270-552-0). Bridge Pub.

Intimacy with Jesus: An Introduction. Richard J. Huelsman. LC 82-60587. 1983. pap. 5.95 (ISBN 0-8091-2492-0). Paulist Pr.

Intimate Analysis of a Lost Life, 2 vols. George Santayana. (Illus.). 285p. 1986. 147.55 (ISBN 0-86650-196-7). Gloucester Art.

Intimate Gospel: Studies in John. Earl F. Palmer. 1978. pap. 5.95 (ISBN 0-8499-2941-5). Word Bks.

Intimate Husband. Richard Furman. 1986. pap. 8.95 (ISBN 0-89081-557-7). Harvest Hse.

Intimate Marriage. R. C. Sproul. 160p. (Orig.). 1986. pap. 5.95 (ISBN 0-8423-1595-0). Tyndale.

Intimate Moments: Teaching Your Child to Walk with God. Eva Gibson. 1987. pap. 5.95. Heres Life.

Intimate Notebook of a Recent Convert to Catholicism: The Confessions of an Anguished Soul. Walter Powell. (Illus.). 1977. 41.45 (ISBN 0-89266-079-1). Am Classical Coll Pr.

Intimations of Reality: Critical Realism in Science & Religion. Arthur Peacocke. LC 84-40357. (Mendenhall Lectures). 96p. 1984. text ed. 10.95 (ISBN 0-268-01155-9, 85-11552); pap. text ed. 4.95 (ISBN 0-268-01156-7, 85-11560). U of Notre Dame Pr.

Into Battle. Arthur Wallis. 1973. pap. 2.95 (ISBN 0-87508-560-1). Chr Lit.

Into Denominationalism. William Swatos. LC 79-53776. (Monograph: No. 2). 1979. pap. 5.50 (ISBN 0-932566-01-4). Soc Sci Stud Rel.

Into His Presence: Perspectives on Reformed Worship. James De Jong. 1985. pap. 7.95 (ISBN 0-933140-99-1); pap. text ed. 3.95 leader's guide (ISBN 0-930265-08-4). CRC Pubns.

Into Meditation Now: A Course on Direct Enlightenment. Christopher Hills. LC 79-5124. (Illus.). 128p. 1979. pap. 5.95 (ISBN 0-916438-30-9). Univ of Trees.

Into One Body... by the Cross, Vol. 1. Karl A. Olsson. 1985. pap. 8.95 (ISBN 0-910452-62-8). Covenant.

Into the Christian Community: Religious Education with Disabled Persons. 115p. 1982. 6.35 (ISBN 0-686-40033-X). Natl Cath Educ.

Into the Copper River Valley. Faye E. Crandall. 1983. 9.95 (ISBN 0-8062-2025-2). Carlton.

Into the Fourth Dimension. Hanlon. 3.95 (ISBN 0-8356-7529-7). Theos Pub Hse.

Into the Highways & Hedges. Raymond T. Brock. LC 61-18608. 1961. 1.25 (ISBN 0-88243-533-7, 02-0533). Gospel Pub.

Into the Midst of Suffering: A Woman's Workshop on Job. Diane B. Bloem. (Woman's Workshop Ser.). (Orig.). 1985. Leader's ed., 64pp. pap. 3.95 (ISBN 0-310-42771-1, 11213P); Student's ed., 112pp. pap. 2.95 (ISBN 0-310-42781-9, 11213P). Zondervan.

Into the Needle's Eye. William Reiser. LC 83-72741. 144p. (Orig.). 1984. pap. 4.50 (ISBN 0-87793-306-5). Ave Maria.

Into the Whirlwind: The Future of the Church. John S. Spong. 224p. 1983. 9.95 (ISBN 0-86683-899-6, HarpR). Har-Row.

Into This Land: Centennial History of the Cleveland Poor Clare Monastery of the Blessed Sacrament. Camilla Koester. LC 80-83390. (Illus.). 274p. 1981. 8.95 (ISBN 0-934906-28-9). R J Liederbach.

Into Your Hands, Lord. Dom H. Camara. 80p. 1987. text ed. 9.95 (ISBN 0-940989-06-9). Meyer Stone Bks.

Intolerance in the Reign of Elizabeth, Queen of England. Arthur J. Klein. LC 67-27614. 1968. Repr. of 1917 ed. 26.50x (ISBN 0-8046-0249-2, Pub. by Kennikat). Assoc Faculty Pr.

Intra Muros: My Dream of Heaven. Rebecca R. Springer. LC 78-67820. 1985. pap. 1.75 (ISBN 0-932484-01-8). Book Searchers.

Intrareligious Dialogue. Raimundo Panikkar. LC 78-58962. 136p. 1978. 6.95 (ISBN 0-8091-2728-8). Paulist Pr.

Intriguing Bible Quizzes. Erma Reynolds. (Quiz & Puzzle Books). 112p. 1976. pap. 2.95 (ISBN 0-8010-7640-4). Baker Bk.

Introduccion a la Teologia Sistematica. G. H. Lacy. (Span.). 417p. 1983. pap. 6.95 (ISBN 0-311-09032-X). Casa Bautista.

Introduccion a los Cuatro Evangelios. Ernesto Trenchard. (Span.). 686p. 1961. 9.95 (ISBN 0-8254-1744-9); pap. 8.75 (ISBN 0-8254-1743-0). Kregel.

Introduccion a los Libros de Sabiduria y Job. Ernesto Trenchard. (Span.). 152p. 1972. 4.50 (ISBN 0-8254-1746-5); pap. 3.50 (ISBN 0-8254-1745-7). Kregel.

Introduccion a los Libros Profeticos e Isaias. Ernesto Trenchard. (Span.). 192p. 1974. 4.95 (ISBN 0-8254-1748-1); pap. 3.95 (ISBN 0-8254-1747-3). Kregel.

Introduccion Al Antiguo Testamento. C. T. Francisco. Tr. by Juan J. Lacue from Eng. Tr. of Introducing the Old Testament. (Span.). 350p. 1983. pap. 5.25 (ISBN 0-311-04010-1). Casa Bautista.

Introduccion Al Estudio Del Nuevo Testamento. H. I. Hester. Tr. by Felix Benlliure from Eng. Tr. of Heart of the New Testament. (Span.). 366p. 1980. pap. 7.95 (ISBN 0-311-04330-5). Casa Bautista.

Introducing Biblical Literature: A More Fantastic Country. Leonard L. Thompson. LC 78-6632. (Illus.). ref. ed. 28.95 (ISBN 0-13-498824-8). P-H.

Introducing Buddhism. Kodo Matsunami. LC 75-28970. (Illus.). 304p. 1976. pap. 7.50 (ISBN 0-8048-1192-X). C E Tuttle.

Introducing Christian Ethics. Henlee H. Barnette. LC 61-5629. 1961. 9.95 (ISBN 0-8054-6102-7). Broadman.

Introducing Church Growth. Tetsunao Yamamori & E. Leroy Lawson. LC 74-24577. (New Life Books). (Illus.). 256p. 1974. 7.95 (ISBN 0-87239-000-4, 40002). Standard Pub.

Introducing Dance in Christian Worship. Ronald Gagne et al. (Illus.). 184p. 1984. pap. 7.95 (ISBN 0-912405-04-X). Pastoral Pr.

Introducing Liberation Theology. Leonardo Boff & Clodovis Boff. Tr. by Paul Burns from Port. LC 87-5672. Tr. of Como Fazer Teologia da Libertacao. 112p. (Orig.). 1987. 16.95 (ISBN 0-88344-575-1); pap. 7.95 (ISBN 0-88344-550-6). Orbis Bks.

Introducing Old Testament Books: With an Emphasis on Their Chronological Relationship. S. S. Urberg. 1979. pap. 5.95 (ISBN 0-8010-9203-5). Baker Bk.

Introducing Religion: From Inside & Outside. Robert S. Ellwood, Jr. (Illus.). 240p. 1983. pap. text ed. write for info. (ISBN 0-13-477497-3). P-H.

Introducing Southern Baptists. C. B. Hastings. LC 81-80052. 168p. (Orig.). 1981. pap. 7.95 (ISBN 0-8091-2364-9). Paulist Pr.

Introducing the Bible. Neil Fugita. LC 81-80874. 224p. (Orig.). 1981. pap. 5.95 (ISBN 0-8091-2392-4). Paulist Pr.

Introducing the Bible. Alice Parmalee. (Epiphany Ser.). 128p. 1983. pap. 2.25 (ISBN 0-345-30575-2). Ballantine.

Introducing the Bible. Alice Parmelee. (All About the Bible Ser.: Bk. 1). (Illus.). 1979. pap. 5.95 (ISBN 0-8192-1253-9). Morehouse.

Introducing the Books of the Bible: A Devotional Summary. Rudolph Norden. 64p. 1987. pap. 3.95 (ISBN 0-570-04452-9, 12-3061). Concordia.

Introducing the Holy Land. J. Maxwell Miller. LC 82-14424. x, 189p. 1982. 13.95 (ISBN 0-86554-034-9, MUP-H38). Mercer Univ Pr.

Introducing the Lessons of the Church Year: A Guide for Lay Readers & Congregations. Frederick H. Borsch. 240p. (Orig.). 1984. pap. 8.95 (ISBN 0-8164-2496-9, 6102, HarpR). Har-Row.

Introducing the New Testament. 3rd. rev. ed. Archibald M. Hunter. LC 72-7110. 224p. 1973. pap. 7.95 (ISBN 0-664-24965-5). Westminster.

Introducing the Old Testament. rev. ed. Clyde T. Francisco. LC 76-24060. 1977. bds. 13.95 (ISBN 0-8054-1213-1, 4212-13). Broadman.

Introducing the Orthodox Church. A. M. Coniaris. 1982. pap. 7.95. Light&Life Pub Co MN.

Introducing the Prophets. M. S. Raza. 1970. 5.00x (ISBN 0-87902-184-5). Orientalia.

Introducing the Sermon: The Art of Compelling Beginnings. Michael J. Hostetler. 96p. 1986. pap. 5.95 (ISBN 0-310-30741-4, 10570P). Zondervan.

Introducing the Shakers: An Explanation & Directory. Diana Van Kolken. (Illus.). 64p. (Orig.). 1985. pap. 3.95 (ISBN 0-911861-04-1). Gabriel's Horn.

Introduction. William Hordern. (New Directions in Theology Today: Vol. 1). 168p. 1966. pap. 4.95 (ISBN 0-664-24706-7). Westminster.

Introduction of the Observant Friars into England. A. G. Little. 1925. pap. 2.25 (ISBN 0-85672-686-9, Pub. by British Acad). Longwood Pub Group.

Introduction to a Faith. Joseph R. Narot. pap. 1.00 (ISBN 0-686-15807-5). Rostrum Bks.

Introduction to a Philosophy of Religion. Alice J. Von Hildebrand. LC 79-139972. 1971. 6.95 (ISBN 0-8199-0426-0). Franciscan Herald.

Introduction to a Scientific System of Mythology. Karl O. Muller. Ed. by Kees W. Bolle. LC 77-79144. (Mythology Ser.). 1978. Repr. of 1844 ed. lib. bdg. 30.00x (ISBN 0-405-10553-3). Ayer Co Pubs.

Introduction to African Religion. John S. Mbiti. (Orig.). 1975. pap. text ed. 10.00x (ISBN 0-435-94001-5). Heinemann Ed.

Introduction to Ancient Iranian Religion: Readings from the "Avesta" & "Achaemenid" Inscriptions. William W. Malandra. (Minnesota Publications in the Humanities Ser.: No. 2). 201p. 1983. 29.50 (ISBN 0-8166-1114-9); pap. 14.95x (ISBN 0-8166-1115-7). U of Minn Pr.

Introduction to Ancient Philosophy. 3rd ed. A. H. Armstrong. LC 81-3731. (Quality Paperback Ser.: No. 418). 260p. 1981. pap. 7.45 (ISBN 0-8226-0418-3). Littlefield.

Introduction to Anselm's Argument. Gregory Schufreider. 131p. 1978. 29.95 (ISBN 0-87722-133-2); pap. 14.95 (ISBN 0-87722-129-4). Temple U Pr.

Introduction to Asian Religions. Geoffrey Parrinder. 1976. pap. 7.95 (ISBN 0-19-519858-1). Oxford U Pr.

Introduction to Augustine. Robert Meagher. LC 77-99085. 1978. 30.00x (ISBN 0-8147-5423-6). NYU Pr.

Introduction to Basic Theology. James Stone. 123p. (Orig.). 1983. pap. text ed. 5.95 (ISBN 0-934942-39-0). White Wing Pub.

Introduction to Bible Archaeology. Rev. ed. Howard F. Vos. 1983. pap. 5.95 (ISBN 0-8024-0325-5). Moody.

Introduction to Bible Geography. Rev. ed. Howard F. Vos. 1983. pap. 6.95 (ISBN 0-8024-0326-3). Moody.

Introduction to Biblical Christian Education. Ed. by Werner Graendorf. LC 81-1608. 1981. 16.95 (ISBN 0-8024-4128-9). Moody.

Introduction to Biblical Hebrew. Thomas O. Lambin. 345p. 1971. text ed. write for info. (ISBN 0-02-367250-1, Pub. by Scribner). Macmillan.

Introduction to Biblical Literature. O. B. Davis. 1976. pap. text ed. 9.25x (ISBN 0-8104-5834-9). Boynton Cook Pubs.

Introduction to Bioethics. 2nd. ed. Thomas A. Shannon. 160p. 1987. pap. 6.95. Paulist Pr.

Introduction to Books of the Bible. 7.00 (ISBN 0-8198-3605-2); 6.00 (ISBN 0-8198-3606-0). Dghtrs St Paul.

Introduction to Buddhist Esoterism. Benoytosh Bhattacharyya. 1980. Repr. of 1931 ed. 19.00x (ISBN 0-686-69019-2, Pub. by Motilal Banarsidas). South Asia Bks.

Introduction to Buddhist Psychology. Padmasiri De Silva. (Library of Philosophy & Religion Ser.). 134p. 1979. text ed. 28.50x (ISBN 0-06-491666-9). B&N Imports.

Introduction to Buddhist Thought: A Philosophic History of Indian Buddhism. A. L. Herman. (Illus.). 480p. (Orig.). 1984. lib. bdg. 35.75 (ISBN 0-8191-3594-1); pap. text ed. 13.50 (ISBN 0-8191-3595-X). U Pr of Amer.

Introduction to C. H. Spurgeon. Bob L. Ross. 1985. pap. 0.95 (ISBN 0-686-18093-3). Pilgrim Pubns.

Introduction to Catholic Sacramental Theology. Alexandre Ganoczy. 1984. pap. 8.95 (ISBN 0-8091-2568-4). Paulist Pr.

Introduction to Christian Camping. Rev. ed. Lloyd Mattson & Werner Graendorf. (Illus.). pap. 7.95 (ISBN 0-942684-07-9). Camp Guidepts.

Introduction to Christian Counseling. Malcom F. George. (Parchment Psychology Ser.). 64p. 1975. pap. 2.25 (ISBN 0-88428-038-1). Parchment Pr.

Introduction to Christian Doctrine. Herman A. Di Brandi. 128p. (Orig.). 1976. pap. 4.95 (ISBN 0-8192-1194-X). Morehouse.

Introduction to Christian Doctrine. John Lawson. Ed. by Harold Burgess. 1980. pap. 9.95 (ISBN 0-310-75021-0). Zondervan.

Introduction to Christian Doctrine. John Lawson. 1986. 14.95 (ISBN 0-310-75020-2). Zondervan.

Introduction to Christian Education. 2nd, rev. ed. Daniel et al. 352p. 1987. pap. text ed. price not set (ISBN 0-87403-211-3, 88591). Standard Pub.

Introduction to Christian Education. Eleanor Daniel et al. LC 79-92587. (Bible College Textbooks Ser.). 352p. (Orig.). 1980. pap. text ed. 6.95 (ISBN 0-87239-394-1, 88581). Standard Pub.

Introduction to Christian Education. Marvin J. Taylor. LC 66-11452. 412p. 1975. pap. 8.95 (ISBN 0-687-19498-9). Abingdon.

Introduction to Christian Faith. Walter Kasper. Tr. by David Smith from Ger. LC 80-82808. 224p. 1981. pap. 4.95 (ISBN 0-8091-2324-X). Paulist Pr.

Introduction to Christian Worship. James F. White. LC 79-21073. (Orig.). 1980. pap. 9.50 (ISBN 0-687-19509-8). Abingdon.

Introduction to Christian Writing. Ethel Herr. 315p. 1983. pap. 8.95 (ISBN 0-8423-1590-X). Tyndale.

Introduction to Christianity. Joseph Ratzinger. 1970. 8.95 (ISBN 0-8245-0319-8). Crossroad NY.

Introduction to Christianity: A Case Method Approach. Alice F. Evans & Robert A. Evans. pap. 3.99 (ISBN 0-8042-1314-3). John Knox.

Introduction to Church History. Howard F. Vos. (Orig.). 1984. pap. 7.95 (ISBN 0-8024-0315-8). Moody.

Introduction to Contemporary Preaching. J. Daniel Baumann. 1972. 14.95 (ISBN 0-8010-0572-8). Baker Bk.

Introduction to Doctrina Christiana. 1.00 (ISBN 0-317-46857-X). Dghtrs St Paul.

Introduction to Early American Jewish History. Jacob R. Marcus. (Texts & Studies). (Hebrew.). 1971. 10.00 (ISBN 0-911934-09-X). Am Jewish Hist Soc.

Introduction to English Church Architecture: From the 11th to the 16th Century. Francis Bond. LC 77-94546. 1979. Repr. of 1908 ed. lib. bdg. 25.00 (ISBN 0-89341-225-2). Longwood Pub Group.

Introduction to Ethics. Robert E. Dewey & Robert H. Hurlbutt. 1977. write for info. (ISBN 0-02-329480-9, 32948). Macmillan.

Introduction to Ethics: A Philosophical Orientation. Ed. by Thomas R. Koenig. 187p. 1974. pap. text ed. 8.95x (ISBN 0-8422-0444-X). Irvington.

Introduction to Evangelism. Delos Miles. LC 82-73078. 1983. 19.95 (ISBN 0-8054-6239-2). Broadman.

Introduction to Existentialism. Marjorie Grene. LC 84-2725. (Midway Ser.). x, 150p. 1984. pap. text ed. 7.00x (ISBN 0-226-30823-5). U of Chicago Pr.

Introduction to Green's Moral Philosophy. William D. Lamont. LC 78-20478. 1980. Repr. of 1934 ed. 21.45 (ISBN 0-88355-855-6). Hyperion Conn.

Introduction to Hebrew. Moshe Greenberg. 1964. text ed. write for info. (ISBN 0-13-484469-6). P-H.

Introduction to Hegel's Philosophy of Religion. Raymond K. Williamson. (Hegelian Studies). 376p. 1984. 49.50 (ISBN 0-87395-827-6); pap. 17.95 (ISBN 0-87395-826-8). State U NY Pr.

Introduction to Hindu & Mohammedan Law. William Markby. LC 78-58189. 1978. Repr. of 1906 ed. lib. bdg. 25.00 (ISBN 0-89341-509-X). Longwood Pub Group.

Introduction to Homiletics. Donald E. Demaray. 140p. 1978. pap. 5.95 (ISBN 0-8010-2892-2). Baker Bk.

Introduction to Islam. Bruce Barnes. (Illus.). 192p. (Orig.). 1984. pap. text ed. 7.00 (ISBN 0-913811-01-7). Northeast A S.

Introduction to Islam. Frederick M. Denny. 368p. 1985. text ed. write for info. (ISBN 0-02-328520-6). Macmillan.

Introduction to Islam. M. Hameedullah. pap. 14.95 (ISBN 0-686-18488-2). Kazi Pubns.

Introduction to Islam. Muhammad Hameedullah. 276p. (Orig.). 1977. pap. 6.50 (ISBN 0-939830-13-2, Pub. by IIFSO Kuwait). New Era Pubns MI.

Introduction to Islam: The First & Final Religion. abr. ed. Imam. 18p. (Orig.). 1983. pap. 1.50 (ISBN 0-916157-01-6). African Islam Miss Pubns.

Introduction to Islamic History. Gerhard Endress. 220p. 1986. cancelled (ISBN 0-85224-496-7, Pub. by Edinburgh U Pr Scotland). Columbia U Pr.

Introduction to Islamic Law. Joseph Schacht. 1964. pap. 18.95x (ISBN 0-19-825473-3). Oxford U Pr.

Introduction to Islamic Political System. Muhammad B. Sadr. Tr. by M. A. Ansari. 112p. 1985. pap. 6.00 (ISBN 0-941724-34-4). Islamic Seminary.

Introduction to Islamic Theology & Law. Ignaz Goldziher. Ed. by Bernard Lewis. Tr. by Andras Hamori & Ruth Hamori. LC 80-7523. (Modern Classics in Near Eastern Studies). 325p. 1981. 32.00 (ISBN 0-691-07257-4); pap. 14.50 LPE (ISBN 0-691-10099-3). Princeton U Pr.

Introduction to Jesuit Life: The Constitutions & History Through 435 Years. Thomas H. Clancy. Ed. by George E. Ganss. LC 75-46080. (Study Aids on Jesuit Topics Ser.: No. 3). 422p. 1976. 12.00 (ISBN 0-912422-15-7). Inst Jesuit.

Introduction to Jesus of Nazareth. Eric W. Johnson. (Illus.). 512p. (Orig.). 1981. pap. 11.95x (ISBN 0-88334-146-8). Ind Sch Pr.

Introduction to Jewish History. Seymour Rossel. Ed. by Neil Kozodoy. (Illus.). 128p. 1981. pap. text ed. 5.95x (ISBN 0-87441-335-4). Behrman.

Introduction to John & the Acts of the Apostles. William Barclay. LC 75-38902. 352p. 1976. softcover 5.95 (ISBN 0-664-24771-7). Westminster.

Introduction to Judaism. Joseph Kalir. LC 79-6758. 170p. 1980. text ed. 25.00 (ISBN 0-8191-0948-7); pap. text ed. 10.75 (ISBN 0-8191-0949-5). U Pr of Amer.

Introduction to Kings, Later Prophets & Writings, Vol. 3. Shirley Newman. Ed. by Seymour Rossel. (Child's Introduction to Bible Ser.). (Illus.). 160p. (Orig.). 1981. pap. text ed. 6.95x (ISBN 0-87441-336-2); wkbk. by Morris Sugarman 3.50x; tchr's ed. 12.50x. Behrman.

Introduction to Liturgical Theology. Alexander Schmemann. LC 66-69197. 170p. 1966. pap. 9.95 (ISBN 0-913836-18-4). St Vladimirs.

Introduction to Mahayana Buddhism. William M. McGovern. LC 70-149665. Repr. of 1922 ed. 17.00 (ISBN 0-404-04129-9). AMS Pr.

Introduction to Medieval Islamic Philosophy. Oliver Leaman. 224p. 1985. 34.50 (ISBN 0-521-24707-1); pap. 12.95 (ISBN 0-521-28911-4). Cambridge U Pr.

Introduction to Mennonite History. rev. ed. C. J. Dyck. LC 81-1958. 400p. 1981. 12.95 (ISBN 0-8361-1955-X). Herald Pr.

Introduction to Missiology. Alan R. Tippett. LC 86-9605. 300p. (Orig.). 1987. pap. text ed. 15.95x (ISBN 0-87808-206-9, WCL206-9). William Carey Lib.

Introduction to Myth. Peter R. Stillman. 1977. pap. text ed. 9.25x (ISBN 0-8104-5890-X). Boynton Cook Pubs.

Introduction to Natural Theology. Maurice R. Holloway. LC 59-6522. 1959. text ed. 19.95x (ISBN 0-89197-244-7). Irvington.

Introduction to Navaho Chant Practice. Clyde Kluckhohn & L. C. Wyman. LC 42-2722. (HU PMP Ser.). 1940. 21.00 (ISBN 0-527-00552-5). Kraus Repr.

Introduction to New Testament Greek. 2nd ed. Huber L. Drumwright. LC 78-59982. 1980. 11.95 (ISBN 0-8054-1368-5). Broadman.

Introduction to New Testament Greek. Raymond Martin. 1980. text ed. 7.50x (ISBN 0-915948-07-9). Bks Distinction.

Introduction to New Testament Literature. Donald Juel et al. LC 77-18036. (Illus.). 1978. 16.50 (ISBN 0-687-01360-7); pap. 10.95 (ISBN 0-687-01361-5). Abingdon.

Introduction to New Testament Textual Criticism. J. Harold Greenlee. 1964. pap. 7.95 (ISBN 0-8028-1724-6). Eerdmans.

Introduction to Nichiren Shoshu Buddhism. Kevin O'Neil. 111p. 1980. pap. 5.00 (ISBN 0-86627-002-7). Crises Res Pr.

Introduction to Old Testament Poetic Books. C. Hassell Bullock. 1979. 11.95 (ISBN 0-8024-4143-2). Moody.

Introduction to Old Testament Study. John H. Hayes. LC 78-20993. 1979. pap. text ed. 14.50 (ISBN 0-687-01363-1). Abingdon.

Introduction to Paradise Lost. John Broadbent. (Milton for Schools & Colleges Ser.). (Illus.). 1971. 34.50 (ISBN 0-521-08068-1); pap. 11.95 (ISBN 0-521-09639-1). Cambridge U Pr.

Introduction to Pastoral Care. William V. Arnold. LC 81-16092. 222p. 1982. pap. 10.95 (ISBN 0-664-24400-9). Westminster.

Introduction to Pastoral Counseling. Wayne E. Oates. 1959. 14.95 (ISBN 0-8054-2404-0). Broadman.

Introduction to Philo Judaeus. 2nd ed. Erwin R. Gookenough. (Brown Classics in Judaica Ser.). 194p. 1986. pap. text ed. 12.75 (ISBN 0-8191-5335-4). U Pr of Amer.

Introduction to Physics in the Waldorf Schools: The Balance Between Art & Science. 2nd ed. Hermann Von Baravalle. 1967. pap. 2.95 (ISBN 0-916786-10-2, Pub by Waldorf School Monographs). St George Bk Serv.

Introduction to Plato's Metaphysics. Robert J. O'Connell. LC 84-73309. xii, 235p. 1985. pap. 6.25 (ISBN 0-8232-1132-0). Fordham.

Introduction to Praise. Ruth Collingridge & JoAnne Sekowsky. (Workbook Ser.). (Orig.). 1981. pap. 4.95 (ISBN 0-930756-60-6, 581001). Aglow Pubns.

Introduction to Protestant Theology. Helmut Gollwitzer. Tr. by David Cairns. LC 82-4798. 236p. 1982. pap. 12.95 (ISBN 0-664-24415-7). Westminster.

Introduction to Psychology & Counseling: Christian Perspectives & Applications. Paul D. Meier et al. LC 82-70462. 432p. 1982. 21.95 (ISBN 0-8010-6128-8). Baker Bk.

Introduction to Religious Archival Science. Kevin W. Sandifer. Ed. by Rowland P. Gill. 16p. (Orig.). 1985. students guide 3.50 (ISBN 0-910653-05-4, 8101-F). Archival Servs.

Introduction to Saint Thomas Aquinas. St. Thomas Aquinas. Ed. by Anton C. Pegis. (Modern Library College Editions Ser.). 1965. pap. 3.75x (ISBN 0-394-30974-X, T74, RanC). Random.

Introduction to Science of Missions. John H. Bavinck. 1960. pap. 5.95 (ISBN 0-87552-124-X). Presby & Reformed.

Introduction to Scientology Ethics. L. Ron Hubbard. 20.00 (ISBN 0-686-13916-X). Church Scient NY.

Introduction to Scientology Ethics. L. Ron Hubbard. 74p. 1968. 32.16 (ISBN 0-88404-015-1). Bridge Pubns Inc.

Introduction to Sharing the Light of Faith. 48p. 1979. pap. 2.75 (ISBN 1-55586-685-9). US Catholic.

Introduction to Shi'i Islam. Moojan Momen. LC 85-40438. 480p. 1987. pap. 15.95x (ISBN 0-300-03531-4). Yale U Pr.

Introduction to Shi'i Islam: The History & Doctrines of Twelver Shi'ism. Moojan Momen. LC 85-40438. (Illus.). 397p. 1985. 25.00x (ISBN 0-300-03499-7). Yale U Pr.

Introduction to Shii Law: A Bibliographical Study. Hossein M. Tabatabai. 258p. 1985. text ed. 22.00 (ISBN 0-86372-015-3, Pub. by Ithaca England). Evergreen Dist.

Introduction to Soul Winning. Ed. by Clayton Pepper. pap. 2.25 (ISBN 0-89137-204-0). Quality Pubns.

Introduction to Spiritual Brotherhood: Science, Mysticism & the New Age. Samuel L. Lewis. Ed. by Saadi Klotz. (Bismillah Bks.: No. 3). (Illus.). 112p. (Orig.). 1981. pap. 4.50 (ISBN 0-915424-07-X). Sufi Islamia-Prophecy.

Introduction to Sufi Doctrine. D. M. Matheson & T. Burckhardt. 1971. pap. 4.75x (ISBN 0-87902-175-6). Orientalia.

Introduction to Swedenborg's Religious Thought. J. Howard Spalding. LC 77-78682. 1973. pap. 2.95 (ISBN 0-87785-121-2). Swedenborg.

Introduction to Systematic Theology. Louis Berkhof. (Twin Brooks Ser.). 1979. pap. 7.95 (ISBN 0-8010-0768-2). Baker Bk.

Introduction to Systematic Theology. Cornelius Van Til. 1974. pap. 8.95 syllabus (ISBN 0-87552-488-5). Presby & Reformed.

Introduction to Talmud Study. Ed. by B. Haskelevich. (Rus.). 400p. 1982. pap. 6.00x (ISBN 0-938666-01-0). CHAMAH Pubs.

Introduction to Tantra. Lama T. Yeshe. Ed. by Jonathan Landaw. (Wisdom Basic Bk. Orange). 150p. (Orig.). 1984. pap. 8.95 (ISBN 0-86171-021-5, Wisdom Pubns). Great Traditions.

Introduction to Tantra Shastra. John Woodroffe. 9.00 (ISBN 0-89744-114-1, Pub. by Ganesh & Co. India). Auromere.

Introduction to the Arguments for God. Charles J. Caes. LC 82-82548. 1983. 8.95 (ISBN 0-87212-162-3). Libra.

Introduction to the Bible. Dianne Bergant. (Bible Commentary Ser.). 72p. 1985. pap. 2.95 (ISBN 0-8146-1369-1). Liturgical Pr.

Introduction to the Bible. Stanley A. Cook. LC 78-12762. 1979. Repr. of 1945 ed. lib. bdg. 22.50x (ISBN 0-313-21028-4, COIB). Greenwood.

Introduction to the Bible. Henry J. Flanders, Jr. et al. 588p. 1973. text ed. 25.75 (ISBN 0-394-34416-2, RandC). Random.

Introduction to the Bible. Kenneth J. Foreman et al. Ed. by Balmer H. Kelly et al. LC 59-10454. (Layman's Bible Commentary, Vol. 1). 1959. pap. 4.95 (ISBN 0-8042-3061-7). John Knox.

Introduction to the Bible. John H. Hayes. LC 76-105395. (Illus.). 556p. 1971. pap. 13.95 (ISBN 0-664-24883-7). Westminster.

Introduction to the Bible, 2 Vols. D. J. Selby & J. K. West. 1971. Set. text ed. write for info. (ISBN 0-02-408850-1). Macmillan.

Introduction to the Bible: A Journey into Three Worlds. Christian E. Hauer & William A. Young. (Illus.). 400p. 1985. text ed. 29.67 (ISBN 0-13-478488-X). P-H.

Introduction to the Bible As Literature. Robert Burns Wallace. 1929. 20.00 (ISBN 0-8274-2583-X). R West.

Introduction to the Books of the Bible. C. F. Drewes. 1929. 4.95 (ISBN 0-570-03185-0, 12-2110). Concordia.
Introduction to the Buddhist Tantric System. F. D. Lessing & Alex Wayman. 1978. 21.00 (ISBN 0-89684-037-9, Pub. by Motilal Banarsidass India). Orient Bk Dist.
Introduction to the Buddhist Tantric System. Alex Wayman & F. D. Lessing. 382p. 1980. pap. 7.95 (ISBN 0-87728-450-4). Weiser.
Introduction to the Chakras. Peter Rendel. (Paths to Inner Power Ser). (Illus.). 1981. pap. 3.50 (ISBN 0-85030-161-0). Weiser.
Introduction to the Code of Maimonides (Mishneh Torah) Moses Maimonides & Isadore Twersky. LC 79-10347. (Yale Judaica Ser.: No. XXII). 1980. 50.00x (ISBN 0-300-02319-7); pap. 11.95x (ISBN 0-300-02846-6). Yale U Pr.
Introduction to the Critical Study of the Text of the Hebrew Bible. Jacob Weingreen. 1982. 8.95x (ISBN 0-19-815453-4). Oxford U Pr.
Introduction to the Devout Life. rev. ed. St. Francis De Sales. Ed. by John K. Ryan. 1972. pap. 5.50 (ISBN 0-385-03009-6, IM). Doubleday.
Introduction to the Episcopal Church. rev ed. Joseph B. Bernardin. (Orig.). 1978. pap. 4.95 (ISBN 0-8192-1231-8). Morehouse.
Introduction to the Fante & Accra (GA) Languages & J. E. J. C. Proten. (Capiteins Fante Catechism Ser.). 69p. 1971. 19.00x (ISBN 0-317-39089-9, Pub. by Luzac & Co Ltd). State Mutual Bk.
Introduction to the Fifth Book of Hooker's Treatise of the Laws of Ecclesiastical Polity. Francis Paget. 265p. 1981. Repr. of 1899 ed. lib. bdg. 85.00 (ISBN 0-8495-4402-5). Arden Lib.
Introduction to the First Three Gospels: A Revised Edition of the First Three Gospels. William Barclay. LC 75-37545. 314p. 1976. pap. 9.95 (ISBN 0-664-24798-9). Westminster.
Introduction to the Franciscan Literature of the Middle Ages. John V. Fleming. 274p. 1977. 10.95 (ISBN 0-8199-0651-4). Franciscan Herald.
Introduction to the History of Early New England Methodism. George C. Baker, Jr. LC 70-95393. 1969. Repr. of 1941 ed. 16.00 (ISBN 0-404-00466-0). AMS Pr.
Introduction to the History of Mysticism. Margaret Smith. 69.95 (ISBN 0-87968-437-2). Gordon Pr.
Introduction to the History of Religions. Crawford H. Toy. LC 76-126655. Repr. of 1913 ed. 27.50 (ISBN 0-404-06498-1). AMS Pr.
Introduction to the History of the Church of England, from the Earliest Times to the Present Day. 7th ed. Henry O. Wakeman. LC 77-137302. Repr. of 1908 ed. 32.50 (ISBN 0-404-06802-2). AMS Pr.
Introduction to the Jesuit Theater: A Posthumous Work. William H. McCabe. Intro. by Louis J. Oldani. LC 83-81114. (Series III-Original Studies, Composed in English: No. 6). xxiv, 338p. 1983. pap. 19.00 smyth sewn (ISBN 0-912422-62-9). Inst Jesuit.
Introduction to the Literature of the New Testament. James Moffatt. 704p. 1981. 19.95 (ISBN 0-567-07213-4, Pub. by T & T Clark Ltd UK). Fortress.
Introduction to the Literature of the New Testament. James Moffatt. 630p. 1983. Repr. of 1911 ed. lib. bdg. 75.00 (ISBN 0-89984-820-6). Century Bookbindery.
Introduction to the Literature of the Old Testament. S. R. Driver. 640p. 1913. 19.95 (ISBN 0-567-07205-3, Pub. by T & T Clark Ltd UK). Fortress.
Introduction to the Literature of the Old Testament. S. R. Driver. 16.50 (ISBN 0-8446-1998-1). Peter Smith.
Introduction to the Massoretico Critical Edition of the Hebrew Bible. rev. ed. Christian D. Ginsburg. 1966. 79.50x (ISBN 0-87068-060-9). Ktav.
Introduction to the Medieval Mystics of Europe. Ed. by Paul E. Szarmach. 368p. 1984. 44.50 (ISBN 0-87395-834-9); pap. 14.95x (ISBN 0-87395-835-7). State U NY Pr.
Introduction to the Metaphysics of St. Thomas Aquinas. James F. Anderson. LC 53-6515. 1969. pap. 6.50 (ISBN 0-89526-970-8). Regnery Bks.
Introduction to the Mimamsa Sutras of Jaimini. Mohan L. Sandal. LC 73-3821. (Sacred Books of the Hindus: No. 28). Repr. of 1925 ed. 24.50 (ISBN 0-404-57828-4). AMS Pr.
Introduction to the Mystical Life. Abbe P. Lejeune. 1977. lib. bdg. 59.95 (ISBN 0-8490-2070-0). Gordon Pr.
Introduction to the Mystical Qabalah. Alan Richardson. (Paths to Inner Power Ser). 1974. pap. 3.50 (ISBN 0-85030-264-1). Weiser.
Introduction to the New Testament. Edward W. Bauman. LC 61-10616. 190p. 1979. pap. 5.95 (ISBN 0-664-24279-0). Westminster.
Introduction to the New Testament. Raymond F. Collins. LC 82-45070. (Illus.). 480p. 1983. 24.95 (ISBN 0-385-18126-4). Doubleday.
Introduction to the New Testament. Raymond F. Collins. 480p. 1987. pap. 10.95 (ISBN 0-385-23534-8, Im). Doubleday.
Introduction to the New Testament. Robert W. Crapps et al. 566p. 1969. text ed. 25.00 (ISBN 0-394-34415-4, RandC). Random.
Introduction to the New Testament. Everett F. Harrison. 1964. 22.95 (ISBN 0-8028-3106-0). Eerdmans.
Introduction to the New Testament. Helmut Koester. 1982. Vol. 1: History, Culture, & Religion of the Hellenistic Age. 24.95 (ISBN 0-89925-198-6); Vol. 2: History & Literature of Early Christianity. 22.95 (ISBN 0-89925-199-4). De Gruyter.
Introduction to the New Testament. rev. ed. Werner G. Kuemmel. Tr. by Howard C. Kee from Ger. LC 74-26804. 624p. 1975. 16.95 (ISBN 0-687-19575-6). Abingdon.
Introduction to the New Testament. rev. ed. Adam W. Miller. 1984. pap. 1.50 (ISBN 0-87162-141-X, D2403). Warner Pr.
Introduction to the New Testament. Henry C. Thiessen. 1943. 14.95 (ISBN 0-8028-3259-8). Eerdmans.
Introduction to the New Testament, 3 vols. Theodor Zahn. 1977. 48.00 (ISBN 0-86524-119-8, 8003). Klock & Klock.
Introduction to the New Testament: An Approach to Its Problems. Willi Marxsen. Tr. by G. Buswell from Ger. LC 68-15419. 304p. 1968. pap. 8.50 (ISBN 0-8006-1181-0, 1-1181). Fortress.
Introduction to the New Testament: The Word Became Flesh. D. J. Selby. 1971. text ed. write for info. (ISBN 0-02-408870-6). Macmillan.
Introduction to the Old Testament. Adam W. Miller. 1981. pap. 1.75 (ISBN 0-87162-193-2, D2401). Warner Pr.
Introduction to the Old Testament. Rev. ed. J. Alberto Soggin. Tr. by John Bowden. LC 81-3422. (Old Testament Library). 544p. 1982. 27.50 (ISBN 0-664-21385-5). Westminster.
Introduction to the Old Testament. 2nd ed. James West. 1981. text ed. write for info. (ISBN 0-02-425920-9). Macmillan.
Introduction to the Old Testament. rev ed. Edward J. Young. 1958. 14.95 (ISBN 0-8028-3310-1). Eerdmans.
Introduction to the Old Testament & Its Study. Robert L. Cate. (Orig.). 1987. 19.95 (ISBN 0-8054-1233-6). Broadman.
Introduction to the Old Testament As Scripture. Brevard S. Childs. LC 78-14665. 688p. 1979. 29.95 (ISBN 0-8006-0532-2, 1-532). Fortress.
Introduction to the Old Testament Prophetic Books. C. Hassell Bullock. 1986. text ed. 19.95 (ISBN 0-8024-4142-4). Moody.
Introduction to the Parables of Jesus. Robert H. Stein. LC 81-11564. 180p. 1981. pap. 8.95 (ISBN 0-664-24390-8). Westminster.
Introduction to the Philosophy of Religion. John Caird. LC 75-113569. (BCL Ser. I). Repr. of 1901 ed. 12.50 (ISBN 0-404-01363-5). AMS Pr.
Introduction to the Philosophy of Religion. Kai Nielsen. LC 82-16843. 200p. 1983. 22.50x (ISBN 0-312-43310-7). St Martin.
Introduction to the Principles of Morals & Legislation. Jeremy Bentham & H. L. Hart. 385p. 1982. 14.95x (ISBN 0-416-31910-6, NO. 3710). Methuen Inc.
Introduction to the Psychology of Religion. Robert W. Crapps. 384p. 1986. text ed. 49.95 (ISBN 0-86554-194-9); pap. text ed. 24.95 (ISBN 0-86554-195-7). Mercer Univ Pr.
Introduction to the Psychology of Religion. 3rd ed. R. H. Thouless. LC 76-184142. 160p. 1972. pap. 10.95 (ISBN 0-521-09665-0). Cambridge U Pr.
Introduction to the Psychology of Religion. Robert H. Thouless. 286p. 1980. Repr. of 1925 ed. lib. bdg. 25.00 (ISBN 0-89987-802-4). Darby Bks.
Introduction to the Rabbinic Bible of 1525. rev. ed. Ben Chayyim Jacob. (Library of Biblical Studies Ser). 1969. 39.50x (ISBN 0-87068-067-6). Ktav.
Introduction to the Reformed Tradition: A Way of Being the Christian Community. rev. ed. John H. Leith. LC 81-5968. (Illus.). 253p. 1981. pap. 10.95 (ISBN 0-8042-0479-9). John Knox.
Introduction to the Restoration Ideal. Marshall Leggett. 240p. 1986. pap. text ed. 7.95 (ISBN 0-87403-067-6, 3175). Standard Pub.
Introduction to the Sacraments. John P. Schanz. 180p. (Orig.). 1983. pap. 9.95 (ISBN 0-916134-57-1). Pueblo Pub Co.
Introduction to the Sacred Language of the Sikhs. C. Shackle. 1983. pap. 25.00x (ISBN 0-8364-1009-2, Pub. by London U Pr). South Asia Bks.
Introduction to the Saints Church. Peter Judd & Bruce Lindgren. LC 75-35763. 1976. 14.00 (ISBN 0-8309-0154-X). Herald Hse.
Introduction to the Science of Christian Science. Max Kappeler. LC 79-313991. 169p. 1978. 12.00 (ISBN 0-85241-099-9). Kappeler Inst Pub.
Introduction to the Science of Comparative Mythology & Folklore. G. W. Cox. 69.95 (ISBN 0-8490-0420-9). Gordon Pr.
Introduction to the Science of Comparative Mythology & Folklore. George W. Cox. 1976. lib. bdg. 59.95 (ISBN 0-8490-2071-9). Gordon Pr.
Introduction to the Science of Missions. J. H. Bavinck. 1977. pap. 5.95 (ISBN 0-8010-0600-7). Baker Bk.
Introduction to the Science of Prayer. 2nd ed. Ernest Wood. 1980. pap. text ed. 1.95 (ISBN 0-918980-08-9). St Alban Pr.
Introduction to the Science of Religion. Friedrich M. Muller. Ed. by Kees W. Bolle. LC 77-79145. (Mythology Ser.). 1978. lib. bdg. 32.00x (ISBN 0-405-10554-1). Ayer Co Pubs.
Introduction to the Seven Rays. Kurt Abraham. LC 86-80170. 108p. (Orig.). 1986. pap. 6.95 (ISBN 0-9609002-2-5). Lampus Pr.
Introduction to the Sociology of the New Testament. Derek Tidball. 1982. pap. text ed. 9.95 cancelled (ISBN 0-85364-301-6). Attic Pr.
Introduction to the Study of Dogmatics. Hendrikus Berkhof. Tr. by John Vriend from Dutch. 120p. (Orig.). 1985. pap. 7.95 (ISBN 0-8028-0045-9). Eerdmans.
Introduction to the Study of Religion. Ed. by T. William Hall. LC 78-4427. (Orig.). 1978. pap. text ed. 10.95xi (ISBN 0-06-063572-X, RD 281, HarpR). Har-Row.
Introduction to the Study of the Holy Qur'an. M. M. Ali. 5.25x (ISBN 0-87902-040-7). Orientalia.
Introduction to the Study of the Middle Ages: 375-814. Ephraim Emerton. 1979. Repr. of 1895 ed. lib. bdg. 30.00 (ISBN 0-8495-1325-1). Arden Lib.
Introduction to the Study of the Middle Ages (375-814) Ephraim Emerton. 1978. Repr. of 1900 ed. lib. bdg. 35.00 (ISBN 0-8482-0713-0). Norwood Edns.
Introduction to the Study of Theravada Buddhism in Burma: A Study of Indo-Burmese Historical & Cultural Relations from the Earliest Times to the British Conquest. Nihar-Ranjan Ray. LC 77-87021. Repr. of 1946 ed. 25.00 (ISBN 0-404-16853-1). AMS Pr.
Introduction to the Talmud. 4th ed. Moses Mielziner. LC 68-29908. 1969. 17.95 (ISBN 0-8197-0156-4); pap. 12.95 (ISBN 0-8197-0015-0). Bloch.
Introduction to the Talmud & Midrash. Hermann L. Strack. LC 59-7191. (Temple Books). 1969. pap. text ed. 8.95x (ISBN 0-689-70189-6, T10). Atheneum.
Introduction to the Tantraloka. Navjivan Rastogi. 400p. 1986. 22.00 (ISBN 81-208-0180-6, Pub. by Motilal Banarsidass). South Asia Bks.
Introduction to the Theology of Karl Barth. Geoffrey W. Bromiley. LC 79-15397. (Orig.). pap. 8.95 (ISBN 0-8028-1804-8). Eerdmans.
Introduction to the Tiberian Masorah. Israel Yeivin. LC 79-24755. (Society of Biblical Literature Masoretic Studies: No. 5). pap. 14.50x (ISBN 0-89130-374-X, 06 05 05A). Scholars Pr Ga.
Introduction to the Works of St. Bonaventure. Guy J. Bougerol. 1964. 7.50 (ISBN 0-8199-0525-9). Franciscan Herald.
Introduction to the Yoga Philosophy. Srisa Chandra Vasu. LC 73-3806. (Scared Books of the Hindus: No. 15, Pt. 4). Repr. of 1915 ed. 14.50 (ISBN 0-404-57838-1). AMS Pr.
Introduction to Theological German. J. D. Manton. 1973. pap. 4.95 (ISBN 0-8028-1514-6). Eerdmans.
Introduction to Theological Research. Cyril J. Barber. 1982. pap. 9.95 (ISBN 0-8024-4134-3). Moody.
Introduction to Theology. Young O. Kim. LC 82-84722. 190p. 1983. pap. 8.95 (ISBN 0-318-11687-1). Rose Sharon Pr.
Introduction to Theology. Young Oon Kim. LC 82-94722. 190p. (Orig.). 1983. pap. 7.50 (ISBN 0-910621-25-X). HSA Pubns.
Introduction to Theology. rev. ed. Marianne H. Micks. 160p. 1983. pap. 9.95 (ISBN 0-8164-2465-9, HarpR). Har-Row.
Introduction to Theology. 2nd ed. Owen C. Thomas. LC 82-61890. 304p. 1983. pap. 13.95 (ISBN 0-8192-1319-5). Morehouse.
Introduction to Theology. J. C. Wenger. LC 53-9049. 418p. 1954. pap. 12.95 (ISBN 0-8361-1791-3). Herald Pr.
Introduction to Theology: An Invitation to Reflection upon the Christian Mythos. Theodore W. Jennings. LC 76-7867. pap. 48.00 (2027873). Bks Demand UMI.
Introduction to Utopia. Henry W. Donner. LC 78-94268. (Select Bibliographies Reprint Ser). 1946. 18.00 (ISBN 0-8369-5042-9). Ayer Co Pubs.
Introduction to Wesleyan Theology. William Greathouse & H. Ray Dunning. 128p. 1982. 4.95 (ISBN 0-8341-0762-7). Beacon Hill.
Introduction to Wisdom Literature, Proverbs. Lawrence E. Boadt. (Collegeville Bible Commentary: Old Testament Ser.: Vol. 18). 104p. 1986. pap. 2.95 (ISBN 0-8146-1475-2). Liturgical Pr.
Introduction to Yoga. Annie Besant. 1972. 3.50 (ISBN 0-8356-7120-8). Theos Pub Hse.
Introduction to Yoga. Sachindra Kumar Majundar. 1977. pap. 4.95 (ISBN 0-8065-0542-7). Citadel Pr.
Introduction to Zen Buddhism. D. T. Suzuki. 1964. pap. 3.95 (ISBN 0-394-17474-7, B341, BC). Grove.
Introductions to the Books of the New Testament. Daughters of St. Paul. 1977. pap. 1.00 (ISBN 0-8198-0421-5). Dghtrs St Paul.
Introductory Ethics. Fred Feldman. 1978. text ed. write for info. (ISBN 0-13-501783-1). P-H.
Introductory Hebrew: Method & Manual. rev. ed. William R. Harper. Ed. by James M. Smith. LC 59-7624. (Midway Reprint Ser.). 1974. pap. 15.00x (ISBN 0-226-31683-1). U of Chicago Pr.
Introductory New Testament Greek Course. Francis T. Gignac. 4.20 (ISBN 0-8294-0223-3). Loyola.
Introductory Readings in Ethics. William K. Frankena & John T. Granrose. 496p. 1974. text ed. write for info. (ISBN 0-13-502112-X). P-H.
Introductory Theology. Zoltan Alszeghy & Maurizio Flick. 1983. 8.95 (ISBN 0-87193-198-2). Dimension Bks.
Introits & Responses for Contemporary Worship. Ed. by Paul Hamill. (Orig.). 1983. pap. 2.95 (ISBN 0-8298-0649-0). Pilgrim NY.
Introvert's Guide to Spontaneous Witnessing. Selwyn Hughes. LC 83-22390. 192p. 1984. pap. 5.95 (ISBN 0-87123-428-9, 210428). Bethany Hse.
Inuective Agenste Treason. Richard Morison. LC 72-38212. (English Experience Ser.: No. 477). 104p. 1972. Repr. of 1539 ed. 9.50 (ISBN 90-221-0477-X). Walter J Johnson.
Invaded by God: Mysticism & the Indwelling Trinity. George Maloney. 1979. 5.95 (ISBN 0-87193-107-9). Dimension Bks.
Inventory of the Roman Catholic Church Records of New Hampshire. Historical Records Survey, WPA Staff. 19p. 1985. pap. 3.50 (ISBN 0-935207-18-X). DanBury Hse Bks.
Inventory of Unpublished Material for American Religion History in Protestant Church Archives & Other Repositories. W. H. Allison. (CI.G Ser.). 1910. 21.00 (ISBN 0-527-00683-1). Kraus Repr.
Investigating God's Orderly World, Bk. 1. Lester Showalter. (YA) 1970. write for info. (ISBN 0-686-05588-8); tchr's. ed. avail. (ISBN 0-686-05589-6). Rod & Staff.
Investigating God's Orderly World, Bk 2. Lester Showalter. (YA) 1975. write for info. (ISBN 0-686-11144-3); tchr's. ed. avail. (ISBN 0-686-11145-1). Rod & Staff.
Investiture Controversy: Issues, Ideals & Results. Ed. by Karl E. Morrison. LC 77-15654. (European Problem Studies). 144p. 1976. pap. text ed. 5.95 (ISBN 0-88275-634-6). Krieger.
Invincible Power of Praise. James R. Swanson & Don Tanner. LC 86-19151. (Illus.). 64p. 1986. pap. 2.95 (ISBN 0-88005-004-7). Uplift Bks.
Invisible & Invincible. Clarence M. Wagner. 78p. 1982. pap. 4.00 (ISBN 0-937498-05-X). Tru-Faith.
Invisible Helpers. Leadbeater. 6.95 (ISBN 0-8356-7160-7). Theos Pub Hse.
Invisible Ministry Annual Reports. Ed. by A. S. Otto. 60p. 1985. vinyl 19.95 (ISBN 0-912132-12-4). Dominion Pr.
Invisible Parade: The Fiction of Flannery O'Connor. Miles Orvell. LC 72-91132. 246p. 1975. 27.95 (ISBN 0-87722-023-9). Temple U Pr.
Invisible Partners. John A. Sanford. LC 79-56604. 139p. (Orig.). 1980. pap. 6.95 (ISBN 0-8091-2277-4). Paulist Pr.
Invisible Strands in African Methodism: A History of the African Union Methodist Protestant & Union American Methodist Episcopal Churches, 1805-1980. Lewis V. Baldwin. LC 83-15039. (ATLA Monographs: No. 19). (Illus.). 306p. 1983. 27.50 (ISBN 0-8108-1647-4). Scarecrow.
Invisible Way: A Sufi Love Story. Reshad Feild. LC 78-19501. 176p. 1983. pap. 7.95 (ISBN 0-06-062588-0, RD/457, HarpR). Har-Row.
Invisible Woman: Target of the Religious New Right. Shirley R. Radl. LC 83-5345. 264p. 1983. 17.95 (ISBN 0-385-29232-5, Sey Lawr). Delacorte.
Invisible Woman: Target of the Religious New Right. Shirley R. Radl. LC 83-5345. 264p. 1983. pap. 9.95 (ISBN 0-385-29210-4, Delta). Dell.

Invisible World: A Study of Pneumatology in Elizabethan Drama. Robert H. West. LC 74-31118. 1939. lib. bdg. 30.00 (ISBN 0-8414-9582-3). Folcroft.

Invitation to a Great Experiment. 3rd ed. Thomas E. Powers. LC 74-16887. Orig. Title: First Questions on the Life of the Spirit. (Illus.). 238p. 1986. pap. 8.95 (ISBN 0-914896-33-4). East Ridge Pr.

Invitation to Action: The Lutheran-Reformed Dialogue, Ser. III, 1981-1983; A Study of Ministry, Sacraments & Recognition. James E. Andrews & Joseph A. Burgess. LC 84-47885. 144p. 1984. pap. 2.00 (ISBN 0-8006-1818-1, 1-1818). Fortress.

Invitation to American Catholic History. Martin Marty. (Basics of Christian Thought Ser.). 1986. 14.95 (ISBN 0-88347-189-2). Thomas More.

Invitation to Faith. John A. Hostetler. 40p. (Orig.). 1957. pap. 1.00 (ISBN 0-8361-1381-0). Herald Pr.

Invitation to Faith: Christian Belief Today. Paul T. Jersild. LC 77-84097. 1978. pap. 9.95 (ISBN 0-8066-1623-7, 10-3395). Augsburg.

Invitation to Holiness. James C. Fenhagen. LC 85-42774. 128p. 1985. 12.45 (ISBN 0-06-062351-9, HarpR). Har-Row.

Invitation to Holy Company. Swami Jnanatmananda. Tr. by J. N. Dey from Bengali. (Illus.). 1979. pap. 2.95 (ISBN 0-87481-491-X). Vedanta Pr.

Invitation to John: A Commentary on the Gospel of John with Complete Text from the Jerusalem Bible. George W. Macrae. LC 77-91559. 1978. pap. 3.95 (ISBN 0-385-12212-8, Im). Doubleday.

Invitation to Philosophy: Issues & Options. 4th ed. Stanley M. Honer & Thomas C. Hunt. 272p. 1981. pap. text ed. write for info. (ISBN 0-534-00997-2). Wadsworth Pub.

Invitation to Religious Education. Harold W. Burgess. LC 75-14980. 173p. 1975. lib. bdg. 12.95 (ISBN 0-89135-004-7); pap. 10.95 (ISBN 0-89135-019-5). Religious Educ.

Invitation to Shabbat. Rosalyn Moss & David Moss. (Illus.). 160p. 1981. cancelled (ISBN 0-89961-013-7); pap. cancelled (ISBN 0-89961-014-5). SBS Pub.

Invitation to the Feast. Danny E. Bush. LC 85-13314. 1985. pap. 3.75 (ISBN 0-8054-5019-X). Broadman.

Invitation to the Psychology of Religion. Raymond F. Paloutzian. 1983. pap. text ed. 13.50x (ISBN 0-673-15343-6). Scott F.

Invitation to the Talmud. Rev. ed. Jacob Neusner. LC 83-48422. 320p. 1984. 19.45 (ISBN 0-06-066099-6, HarpR). Har-Row.

Invitations to Communion. Alec J. Langford. Ed. by Herbert Lambert. LC 86-6116. 112p. (Orig.). 1986. pap. 7.95 (ISBN 0-8272-1607-6). CBP.

Inviting the Mystic, Supporting the Prophet: An Introduction to Spiritual Direction. L. Patrick Carroll & Katharine M. Dyckman. LC 81-80053. 112p. (Orig.). 1981. pap. 5.95 (ISBN 0-8091-2378-9). Paulist Pr.

Involved. Wilfred M. Hillock. LC 77-78102. (Anvil Ser.). 1977. pap. 8.95 (ISBN 0-8127-0140-2). Review & Herald.

Involvement, Vol. I: Being a Responsible Christian in a Non-Christian Society. John Stott. (Crucial Questions Ser.). 224p. 1985. 13.95 (ISBN 0-8007-1418-0). Revell.

Involving the People in Dancing Worship: Historic & Contemporary Patterns. Doug Adams. 1975. 2.00 (ISBN 0-941500-11-X). Sharing Co.

Involving Youth in Youth Ministry. Thom Schultz & Joani Schultz. 200p. (Orig.). 1987. pap. 9.95 (ISBN 0-931529-20-4). Group Bks.

Inward Arc: Healing & Wholeness in Psychotherapy & Spirituality. Frances Vaughan. LC 85-2504. (Illus.). 238p. (Orig.). 1986. pap. 10.95 (ISBN 0-87773-324-4, 74201-X, Pub. by New Sci Lib-Shambhala). Shambhala Pubns.

Inward Journey. Gene Edwards. 250p. 1982. pap. 5.95 (ISBN 0-940232-06-5). Christian Bks.

Inward Journey. Howard Thurman. LC 77-70182. 1973. pap. 7.95 (ISBN 0-913408-03-4). Friends United.

Inward Journey of Isaac Penington. Isaac Penington. Ed. by Robert J. Leach. LC 44-280. (Orig.). 1944. pap. 2.50x (ISBN 0-87574-029-4). Pendle Hill.

Inward Legacy. Forbes Robinson & Gilbert Kilpack. 1983. pap. 5.00x (ISBN 0-87574-092-8, 092). Pendle Hill.

Inward Light. Harold Fielding-Hall. LC 78-72431. Repr. of 1908 ed. 27.00 (ISBN 0-404-17294-6). AMS Pr.

Inward Stillness. George Maloney. 6.95 (ISBN 0-87193-062-5). Dimension Bks.

Iohannis Philoponi: De Vocabulis Quae Diversum Significatum Exhibent Secundum Differentiam Accentus. Lloyd W. Daly. LC 81-72156. (Memoirs Ser.: Vol. 151). 1983. 20.00 (ISBN 0-87169-151-5). Am Philos.

Iona, Tara, & Soissons: The Origin of the Royal Anointing Ritual in Francia. Michael J. Enright. (Arbeiten zur Fruehmittelalterforschung: Vol. 17). x, 198p. 1985. 67.25x (ISBN 3-11-010628-0). De Gruyter.

Iqbal & the Concept of Islamic Socialism. A. K. Brohi. pap. 1.00 (ISBN 0-686-18447-5). Kazi Pubns.

Iqbal's Concept of God. M. S. Rashid. 120p. 1986. pap. text ed. 12.95 (ISBN 0-7103-0004-2). Methuen Inc.

Iran & Islam. Ed. by C. E. Bosworth. 574p. 1972. 35.00x (ISBN 0-85224-200-X, Pub. by Edinburgh U Pr Scotland). Columbia U Pr.

Iranian Jewry's Hour of Peril & Heroism. Vera B. Moreen. (Study of the American Academy for Jewish Research). 247p. 1987. text ed. 25.00 (ISBN 0-231-06578-7). Columbia U Pr.

Iran's Islamic Revolution: Popular Liberation or Religious Dictatorship? Suroosh Irfani. (Illus.). 278p. 1983. 29.50x (ISBN 0-86232-157-3, Pub. by Zed Pr England); pap. 10.75 (ISBN 0-86232-158-1). Humanities.

Ireland: In the Footsteps of St. Patrick. Pope John Paul II. 1979. 3.95 (ISBN 0-8198-0624-2); pap. 2.95 (ISBN 0-8198-0625-0). Dghtrs St Paul.

Irina's Story. Hermann Hartfeld. 318p. 1983. pap. 5.95 (ISBN 0-87123-261-8, 210261). Bethany Hse.

Irish American Voluntary Organizations. Ed. by Michael F. Funchion. LC 83-6712. (Ethnic American Voluntary Organizations Ser.). xviii, 323p. 1983. lib. bdg. 45.00 (ISBN 0-313-22948-1, FIA/). Greenwood.

Irish Catholic Experience. Patrick Corish. 1985. 25.00 (ISBN 0-317-42754-7). M Glazier.

Irish Christmas Book. Ed. by John Killen. (Illus.). 132p. (Orig.). 1986. pap. 8.95 (ISBN 0-85640-345-8, Pub. by Blackstaff Pr). Longwood Pub Group.

Irish Churches & Monastic Buildings, 3 Vols. Harold G. Leask. Vol. I: First Phases & Romanesque, 173p. 16.95 (ISBN 0-85221-016-7); Vol. II: Gothic to A.D. 1400, 162p. 16.95 (ISBN 0-85221-011-6). Dufour.

Irish Dance & Spirituality: Relating Folkdance & Faith. Cynthia D. Sautter. Ed. by Doug Adams. (Orig.). 1985. pap. text ed. 3.00 (ISBN 0-941500-39-X). Sharing Co.

Irish Druids & Old Irish Religions. James Bonwick. LC 75-36830. (Occult Ser.). 1976. Repr. of 1894 ed. 25.50x (ISBN 0-405-07942-7). Ayer Co Pubs.

Irish Medieval Figure Sculpture 1200-1600: A Study of Irish Tombs with Notes on Costume & Armour, 2 vols. John Hunt. (Illus.). 550p. 1974. 75.00 (ISBN 0-85667-012-X). Sotheby Pubns.

Irish Monasticism: Origins & Early Development. John Ryan. 520p. 1986. 60.00x (ISBN 0-7165-2374-4, Pub. by Irish Academic Pr Ireland). Biblio Dist.

Irish Mythology. H. James Cousins. 59.95 (ISBN 0-8490-0425-X). Gordon Pr.

Irish Mythology: A Dictionary. Peter Kavanagh. (Illus.). 150p. (Hand Set & Printed). 100.00 (ISBN 0-914612-00-X). Kavanagh.

Irish Pilgrimage. Daphne Pochin-Mould. 1957. 12.95 (ISBN 0-8159-5816-1). Devin.

Irish Saints for Boys & Girls. Alice Cartayne. (Illus.). 96p. 1978. pap. 3.95 (ISBN 0-86167-018-3, Pub. by Educ Co of Ireland). Longwood Pub Group.

Iron Collar. Fedor Sommer. Tr. by Andrew S. Berky. 261p. 1982. pap. 4.00 (ISBN 0-935980-01-6). Schwenkfelder Lib.

Iron Cow of Zen. Albert Low. LC 85-40413. 226p. (Orig.). 1985. pap. 6.50 (ISBN 0-8356-0598-1, Quest). Theos Pub Hse.

Iron Wall: Zionist Revisionism from Jabotinsky to Shamir. Lenni Brenner. 230p. 1984. 26.25x (ISBN 0-86232-216-2, Pub. by Zed Pr England); pap. text ed. 9.25 (ISBN 0-86232-217-0, Pub. by Zed Pr England). Humanities.

Irony & Consciousness: American Historiography & Reinhold Niebuhr's Vision. Richard Reinitz. LC 77-92574. 232p. 23.50 (ISBN 0-8387-2062-5). Bucknell U Pr.

Irony in the Fourth Gospel. Paul D. Duke. LC 85-42822. 228p. 1985. pap. 11.95 (ISBN 0-8042-0242-7). John Knox.

Irony in the Old Testament. Edwin M. Good. (Bible & Literature Ser.: No. 3). (Orig.). 1981. pap. text ed. 9.95x (ISBN 0-907459-05-6, Pub. by Almond Pr England). Eisenbrauns.

Irony of American Morality. Henry Clark. 1972. 13.95x (ISBN 0-8084-0036-3); pap. 9.95x (ISBN 0-8084-0037-1). New Coll U Pr.

Iroquoian Cosmology, 2 pts. in 1. John N. Hewitt. LC 73-8095. Repr. of 1928 ed. 60.00 (ISBN 0-404-11202-1). AMS Pr.

Iroquois Book of Rites. Ed. by Horatio E. Hale. LC 74-83458. (Library of Aboriginal American Literature: No. 2). Repr. of 1883 ed. 30.00 (ISBN 0-404-52182-7). AMS Pr.

Iroquois Music & Dance: Ceremonial Arts of Two Seneca Longhouses. Gertrude P. Kurath. Repr. of 1964 ed. 39.00x (ISBN 0-403-03618-6). Scholarly.

Irrational Season. Madeleine L'Engle. (Crosswicks Journal Trilogy). 224p. 1977. 12.95 (ISBN 0-8164-0324-4, HarpR); pap. 7.95 (ISBN 0-8164-2261-3); Three Volume Set 19.95 (ISBN 0-8164-2617-1). Har-Row.

Irrational Season. Madeleine L'Engle. 430p. 1985. pap. 13.95 large print ed. (ISBN 0-8027-2476-0). Walker & Co.

Irregular People. Joyce Landorf. 1982. 9.95 (ISBN 0-8499-0291-6). Word Bks.

Irreverent Pilgrims: Melville, Browne & Mark Twain in the Holy Land. Franklin Walker. LC 74-10644. (Illus.). 246p. 1974. 16.50x (ISBN 0-295-95344-6). U of Wash Pr.

Irruption of the Third World: Challenge to Theology. Ed. by Virginia Fabella & Sergio Torres. LC 82-18851. 304p. (Orig.). 1983. pap. 10.95 (ISBN 0-88344-216-7). Orbis Bks.

Irving Jensen's Do-It-Yourself Bible Study: Mark. Irving Jensen. (Irving Jensen's Do-It-Yourself Bible Study Ser.). 118p. (Orig.). 1983. wkbk 5.95 (ISBN 0-89840-035-X). Heres Life.

Is Adam a "Teaching Model" in the New Testament? J. P. Versteeg. pap. 1.75 (ISBN 0-8010-9276-0). Baker Bk.

Is Adam a Teaching Model in the New Testament? J. P. Versteeg. 1978. pap. 1.75 (ISBN 0-87552-500-8). Presby & Reformed.

Is Anybody Listening When I Pray? Phoebe Cranor. LC 79-27475. 112p. (Orig.). 1980. pap. 3.95 (ISBN 0-87123-200-6, 210200). Bethany Hse.

Is Anybody Up There. Donald Barnhouse. LC 76-51734. 1977. 6.95 (ISBN 0-9606562-0-0, BT1102-B26). L Victor Pr.

Is Anyone Out There Building Mother's Self Esteem? Marilyne Linford. 1986. text ed. 8.95 (ISBN 0-87579-048-8). Deseret Bk.

Is Bible God's Word? A. Deedat. 1981. 2.75 (ISBN 0-686-97857-9). Kazi Pubns.

Is Bible Reliable, Bk. 2. Richard L. Saucy. Tr. by Ernest Wong. (Basic Doctrine Ser.). (Chinese.). 1985. pap. write for info. (ISBN 0-941598-28-4). Living Spring Pubns.

Is Bible Reliable? Leader's Guide. Nelda Cockman. Tr. by Loran Y. Chao. (Basic Doctrine Ser.). (Chinese.). 1986. pap. write for info. (ISBN 0-941598-34-9). Living Spring Pubns.

Is Capitalism Christian? Ed. by Franky Schaeffer. LC 85-70471. 400p. (Orig.). 1985. pap. 9.95 (ISBN 0-89107-362-0, Crossway Bks). Good News.

Is Christ Infallible & the Bible True? Hugh McIntosh. 1981. lib. bdg. 27.00 (ISBN 0-86524-076-0, 8603). Klock & Klock.

Is Christ the End of the Law? Gerard S. Sloyan. LC 77-27454. (Biblical Perspectives on Current Issues). 210p. 1978. softcover 4.95 (ISBN 0-664-24190-5). Westminster.

Is Christ the Only Way. S. Mark Heim. 160p. 1984. pap. 7.95 (ISBN 0-317-18066-5). Judson.

Is Christian Life Possible Today? Karl Rahner. 1984. pap. 6.95 (ISBN 0-87193-210-5). Dimension Bks.

Is Christianity Credible. Kenneth Taylor. pap. 0.75 (ISBN 0-87784-110-1). Inter-Varsity.

Is Christianity the Only Way? Paul L. Walker. 1975. pap. 3.95 (ISBN 0-87148-429-3). Pathway Pr.

Is Christianity True? Michael Arnheim. LC 84-42861. (Skeptic's Bookshelf Ser.). 198p. 1984. 20.95 (ISBN 0-87975-262-9). Prometheus Bks.

Is Death for Real? Jack Provonsha. (Outreach Ser.). 1981. pap. 3.95 (ISBN 0-8163-0406-8). Pacific Pr Pub Assn.

Is Death Necessary? Harvey Jackins. 1970. pap. 0.50 (ISBN 0-911214-22-4). Rational Isl.

Is Each Individual Born with a Purpose? Manly P. Hall. pap. 2.50 (ISBN 0-89314-325-1). Philos Res.

Is Easter Just for Bunnies? Beverly C. Burgess. (Illus.). 30p. (Orig.). 1985. pap. 1.98 (ISBN 0-89274-310-7). Harrison Hse.

Is Evolutionism the Answer. Ed. by Commission For Christian Literature. (Truth Unchanging Series). (Illus.). 1968. pap. 2.50 (ISBN 0-8100-0023-7, 12-0331). Northwest Pub.

Is Faith Obsolete? Robert M. Brown. LC 74-13420. 160p. 1979. pap. 3.95 (ISBN 0-664-24230-8). Westminster.

Is God a Creationist? Religious Arguments Against Creation-Science. Ed. by Roland M. Frye. 256p. 1983. 15.95 (ISBN 0-684-17993-8, ScribT). Scribner.

Is God a Creationist? The Religious Case Against Creation Science. Roland M. Frye. 256p. 1983. pap. text ed. write for info. (ISBN 0-02-339560-5, Pub. by Scribner). Macmillan.

Is God a Separate Being? Parker L. Johnstone. LC 76-706635. 1977. cloth 7.95 (ISBN 0-917802-01-2). Theoscience Found.

Is God Dead? Ed. by Johannes B. Metz. LC 66-25679. (Concilium Ser.: Vol. 16). 189p. 7.95 (ISBN 0-8091-0078-9). Paulist Pr.

Is God Dead Within You? Shirley O. Crawford. 112p. 1981. 6.50 (ISBN 0-682-49789-4). Exposition Pr FL.

Is God Endangered by Believers? A Critical Study of the Gap Between Religion & Real Faith. Jean-Francois Six. 1983. 11.95 (ISBN 0-87193-207-5). Dimension Bks.

Is God God? Ed. by Alexel D. Steuer & James W. McClendon, Jr. LC 81-1927. 288p. (Orig.). 1981. pap. 10.95 (ISBN 0-687-19703-1). Abingdon.

Is God Really Fair? Dick Dowsett. 1985. pap. 3.95 (ISBN 0-8024-3277-8). Moody.

Is God Really Good? Conversations with a Theodicist. George B. Wall. LC 82-24854. 130p. (Orig.). 1983. pap. text ed. 9.50 (ISBN 0-8191-3032-X). U Pr of Amer.

Is God Still Here: Q-Book No. 15. C. Alton Robertson. (Orig.). 1968. pap. 0.75 (ISBN 0-377-86371-8). Friend Pr.

Is God the Only Reliable Father. Diane Tennis. LC 84-20899. 118p. (Orig.). 1985. pap. 7.95 (ISBN 0-664-24594-3). Westminster.

Is He the One? James Aderman. Ed. by William E. Fischer. (Bible Class Course for Young Adults Ser.). (Illus.). 64p. 1985. pap. 2.95 leaders guide (ISBN 0-938272-21-7); pap. 2.95 students guide (ISBN 0-938272-20-9). WELS Board.

Is Healing for All? Frederick K. Price. 127p. (Orig.). 1979. pap. 3.95 (ISBN 0-89274-005-1). Harrison Hse.

Is Human Forgiveness Possible? A Pastoral Care Perspective. John Patton. 192p. (Orig.). 1985. pap. 10.95 (ISBN 0-687-19704-X). Abingdon.

Is Irish Catholicism Dying? Peadar Kirby. 93p. 1984. pap. 5.95 (ISBN 0-87061-112-7). Chr Classics.

Is It a Saint's Name? William P. Dunne. 1977. pap. 1.25 (ISBN 0-89555-024-5). TAN Bks Pubs.

Is It Any of God's Business? A Provocative Look at Faith in the Workplace. Walter Henrichsen. LC 86-63651. 204p. (Orig.). 1987. pap. price not set (ISBN 0-89109-138-6). NavPress.

Is It God? Donald Gee. (Charismatic Bks.). 30p. 1972. pap. 0.69 (ISBN 0-88243-916-2, 02-0916). Gospel Pub.

Is It the Watchtower? E. B. Price. LC 67-30889. 1967. pap. 1.25 (ISBN 0-8163-0106-9, 09665-1). Pacific Pr Pub Assn.

Is Jesus Coming in a Flying Saucer? Margaret MacKeeby. 1984. 8.95 (ISBN 0-533-05998-4). Vantage.

Is Life Worth Living? A. B. Simpson. 30p. pap. 0.95 (ISBN 0-87509-045-1). Chr Pubns.

Is Love in & Sin Out? Russell M. Abata. LC 85-81325. 80p. 1985. pap. 2.95 (ISBN 0-89243-246-2). Liguori Pubns.

Is Man a Free Agent. The Mystic Jhamom Editors. (Conversations with a Mystic: No. 1). (Illus.). 128p. 1985. pap. 9.95 (ISBN 0-933961-01-4). Mystic Jhamom.

Is Man a Fress Agent Illustrations Booklet: Supplement. Ed. by Mystic Jhamom Publishers Staff. (Conversations with a Mystic Ser.: No. 1). 12p. 1985. pap. 1.75 (ISBN 0-933961-02-2). Mystic Jhamom.

Is Mark a Roman Gospel? Benjamin W. Bacon. (Harvard Theological Studies: Vol. 7). 1919. 11.00 (ISBN 0-527-01007-3). Kraus Repr.

Is Mormonism Christian? Gordon H. Fraser. 1977. pap. 3.95 (ISBN 0-8024-4169-6). Moody.

Is-Ought Question. Ed. by W. D. Hudson. LC 79-106390. (Controversies in Philosophy Ser). 1970. 12.95 (ISBN 0-312-43715-3). St Martin.

Is the Baptist Church Relevant to the Black Community. B. A. Meshack. LC 75-38304. 1976. perfect bdg. softcover 9.95 (ISBN 0-88247-385-9). R & E Pubs.

Is the Homosexual My Neighbor? Another Christian View. Letha Scanzoni & Virginia R. Mollenkott. LC 77-20445. 176p. 1980. pap. 8.95 (ISBN 0-06-067076-2, RD 337, HarpR). Har-Row.

Is the Order of St. John Masonic? James F. Wathen. 84p. 1973. pap. 3.50 (ISBN 0-89555-250-7). TAN Bks Pubs.

Is the Position of Atheism Growing Stronger. Joseph McCabe. 30p. pap. cancelled (ISBN 0-911826-85-8). Am Atheist.

Is the United States in Prophecy? Herman A. Hoyt. 1979. pap. 1.00 (ISBN 0-88469-040-7). BMH Bks.

Is the Virgin Mary Appearing at Medjugorje? Rene Laurentin & Ljudevit Rupcic. Tr. by Francis Martin from Fr. (Illus.). 170p. 1984. 12.95 (ISBN 0-932085-02-4); pap. 6.95 (ISBN 0-932085-00-8). Word Among Us.

Is There a Difference Between a Khazar Jew & a Palestinian Jew? L. Keech. 1982. lib. bdg. 59.95 (ISBN 0-87700-335-1). Revisionist Pr.

Is There a Shrink in the Lord's House? How Psychologists Can Help the Church. Ed. by H. Newton Malony. LC 86-81513. (Orig.). 1986. pap. 12.00 (ISBN 0-9609928-4-7). Integ Pr.

Is There Hope for the City? Karl A. Ostrom & Donald W. Shriver, Jr. LC 77-22187. (Biblical Perspectives on Current Issues). 204p. 1977. softcover 4.95 (ISBN 0-664-24147-6). Westminster.

Is There Life after Divorce in the Church? Richard L. Morgan. LC 85-42825. 200p. 1985. pap. 12.95 (ISBN 0-8042-1123-X). John Knox.

Is There Life after High School. P. David Klinsing et al. LC 79-53677. 116p. 1979. pap. 2.50 (ISBN 0-87509-264-0). Chr Pubns.

Is There Salvation Outside the Catholic Church? S. J. Bainvel. LC 79-55461. 1979. pap. 1.50 (ISBN 0-89555-132-2). TAN Bks Pubs.

Is This My Neighbor? The Union Gospel Mission. J. R. Braun. (Illus.). 60p. (Orig.). 1980. pap. text ed. 8.95 (ISBN 0-933656-08-4). Trinity Pub Hse.

Is Your Miracle Passing You By? Kenneth Hagin, Jr. 1985. mini bk. 0.50 (ISBN 0-89276-718-9). Hagin Ministries.

Isaac. W. Kelly. 135p. pap. 4.95 (ISBN 0-88172-144-1). Believers Bkshelf.

Isaac & Rebekah. Gordon Lindsay. (Old Testament Ser.). 1.25 (ISBN 0-89985-127-4). Christ Nations.

Isaac Backus - Puritan & Baptist. Stanley Grenz. (Dissertation Ser.: No. 4). vii, 346p. 1983. pap. 21.95 (ISBN 0-86554-067-5). NABPR.

Isaac Backus: Puritan & Baptist; His Place in History, His Thought, & the Implications for Modern Baptist Theology. Stanley Grenz. LC 83-12140. vii, 346p. pap. 21.95 (ISBN 0-86554-067-5, P12). Mercer Univ Pr.

Isaac ben Abraham ibn Ezra Poems (in Hebrew) Menahem Schmelzer. 15.00x (ISBN 0-87334-011-6). Ktav.

Isaac Hecker & His Friends. Joseph McSorley. 314p. 1972. pap. 1.45 (ISBN 0-8091-1605-7). Paulist Pr.

Isaac Hecker & the First Vatican Council, Including Hecker's Notes in Italy: 1869-1870. William L. Portier. LC 85-3034. (Studies in American Religion: Vol. 15). 360p. 1984. 59.95x (ISBN 0-88946-653-X). E Mellen.

Isaac of Stella: Sermons on the Christian Year, Vol. 1. Isaac Of Stella. Tr. by Hugh McCaffrey. LC 78-868. (Cistercian Fathers Ser.: No. 11). 1979. 15.95 (ISBN 0-87907-611-9). Cistercian Pubns.

Isaac: The Link in the Chain. Chaim Stern. 1977. text ed. 9.95 (ISBN 0-8315-0077-8). Speller.

Isaac Watts's Hymns & Spiritual Songs (1707) A Publishing History & a Bibliography. Selma L. Bishop. LC 73-78316. 1974. 29.50 (ISBN 0-87650-033-5). Pierian.

Isaac's Chosen Wife. Lucille B. Golphenee. (Arch Book Ser.: No. 21). 1984. pap. 0.99 (59-1282). Concordia.

Isabel la Catolica. (Span.). 9.50 (ISBN 84-241-5417-7). E Torres & Sons.

Isaiah, 2 Vols. Joseph A. Alexander. 1981. Set. lib. bdg. 29.95 (ISBN 0-86524-072-8, 2302). Klock & Klock.

Isaiah. Albert Barnes. 23.95 (ISBN 0-8010-0840-9). Baker Bk.

Isaiah, Vol. III. Paul Butler. (Bible Study Textbook). (Illus.). 1978. 14.30 (ISBN 0-89900-022-3). College Pr Pub.

Isaiah, Vol. I. Paul Butler. LC 75-328170. (Bible Study Textbook Ser.). (Illus.). 1980. cancelled (ISBN 0-89900-020-7). College Pr Pub.

Isaiah, Vol. II. Paul Butler. (Bible Study Textbook Ser.). (Illus.). 1976. cancelled (ISBN 0-89900-021-5). College Pr Pub.

Isaiah, Vol. I, II. Paul Butler. (Bible Study Textbook). 694p. 1980. 15.90 (ISBN 0-89900-061-4). College Pr Pub.

Isaiah. John J. Collins. (Collegeville Bible Commentary Ser.). 144p. 1986. pap. 2.95 (ISBN 0-8146-1420-5). Liturgical Pr.

Isaiah. Charles R. Erdman. 160p. 1982. pap. 4.50 (ISBN 0-8010-3380-2). Baker Bk.

Isaiah, 2 pts. John S. Huesman. (Bible Ser.). Pt. 1. pap. 1.00 (ISBN 0-8091-5069-7); Pt. 2. pap. 1.00 (ISBN 0-8091-5070-0). Paulist Pr.

Isaiah. H. A. Ironside. 9.95 (ISBN 0-87213-369-9). Loizeaux.

Isaiah. rev. ed. F. C. Jennings. LC 55-41748. 1935. 14.95 (ISBN 0-87213-420-2). Loizeaux.

Isaiah, 2 vols. James Montgomery. 2.50 ea. (ISBN 0-686-73329-0); Vol. 1. (ISBN 0-89315-125-4); Vol. 2. (ISBN 0-89315-126-2). Lambert Bk.

Isaiah. G. Campbell Morgan. Tr. by Lorna Chao. (G. Campbell Morgan's Expository Ser.). 1985. write for info (ISBN 0-941598-93-4); pap. write for info. (ISBN 0-941598-20-9). Living Spring Pubns.

Isaiah. Carroll Stuhlmueller. 1976. 1.75 (ISBN 0-8199-0628-X). Franciscan Herald.

Isaiah. G. Ernest Wright. LC 59-10454. (Layman's Bible Commentary, Vol. 11). 1964. pap. 4.95 (ISBN 0-8042-3071-4). John Knox.

Isaiah, Vol. I, Chs. 1-32. John F. Sawyer. LC 84-22098. (Daily Study Bible Ser. Old Testament). 280p. 1984. 14.95 (ISBN 0-664-21812-1); pap. 7.95 (ISBN 0-664-24579-X). Westminster.

Isaiah: A Commentary. Solomon B. Freehof. 1972. 15.00 (ISBN 0-8074-0042-4, 383015). UAHC.

Isaiah: A New Translation. LC 78-188581. (Illus.). 192p. 1973. 12.50 (ISBN 0-686-73768-7, 150); pap. 4.00 (ISBN 0-8276-0005-4, 151). Jewish Pubns.

Isaiah: An Ensign to the Nations. Loren D. Martin. LC 81-92840. (Isaiah Ser.: Vol. 1). (Illus.). 180p. 1982. 9.95 (ISBN 0-9608244-0-5); Set of Multivolumes. write for info. (ISBN 0-9608244-2-1). Valiant Pubns.

Isaiah & Jeremiah. rev. ed. Irving L. Jensen. (Bible Self-Study Ser.). (Illus., Orig.). 1968. pap. 3.25 (ISBN 0-8024-1023-5). Moody.

Isaiah & Jeremiah. Gordon Lindsay. (Old Testament Ser.). 1.25 (ISBN 0-89985-155-X). Christ Nations.

Isaiah & the Deliverance of Jerusalem. R. E. Clements. (Journal for the Study of the Old Testament, Supplement Ser.: No. 13). 1980. text ed. 18.95x (ISBN 0-905774-23-X, Pub. by JSOT Pr England); pap. text ed. 10.95 (ISBN 0-905774-62-0). Eisenbrauns.

Isaiah: Bible Study Commentary. D. David Garland. (Orig.). 1968. pap. 4.95 (ISBN 0-310-24853-1, 9672P). Zondervan.

Isaiah Chapters XL-LV: Literary Criticism & History. Sidney Smith. (British Academy, London, Schweich Lectures on Biblical Archaeology Series, 1940). pap. 28.00 (ISBN 0-8115-1282-7). Kraus Repr.

Isaiah-Daniel, Vol. IV. Beacon Bible Commentary Staff. 13.95 (ISBN 0-8010-0691-0). Baker Bk.

Isaiah Fifty-Six to Sixty-Six. George A. Knight. Ed. by Frederick Holmgern. (International Theological Commentary Ser.). 148p. (Orig.). 1985. pap. 5.95 (ISBN 0-8028-0021-1). Eerdmans.

Isaiah Forty-Jeremiah. Alan Cole. 1983. pap. 4.95 (ISBN 0-87508-161-4). Chr Lit.

Isaiah Forty to Sixty-Six. John Scullion. (Old Testament Message Ser.: Vol. 12). 1982. 12.95 (ISBN 0-89453-412-2); pap. 9.95 (ISBN 0-89453-246-4). M Glazier.

Isaiah Forty to Sixty-Six. R. N. Whybray. Ed. by Ronald E. Clements. (New Century Bible Commentary). 320p. (Orig.). 1981. pap. 8.95 (ISBN 0-8028-1884-6). Eerdmans.

Isaiah Forty to Sixty-Six. Ed. by R. N. Whybray. (New Century Bible Ser.). 304p. 1975. 9.95 (ISBN 0-551-00573-4). Attic Pr.

Isaiah Forty to Sixty-Six: A Commentary. Claus Westermann. Tr. by David M. Stalker. LC 69-18647. (Old Testament Library). 446p. 1969. 19.95 (ISBN 0-664-20851-7). Westminster.

Isaiah: Messenger for God. Fred Heifner. (BibLearn Ser.). (Illus.). 1978. 5.95 (ISBN 0-8054-4243-X, 4242-43). Broadman.

Isaiah One & Two. A. Cohen. 330p. 1949. 10.95 (ISBN 0-900689-28-5). Soncino Pr.

Isaiah One to Thirty-Nine. Joseph Jensen. (Old Testament Message Ser.: Vol. 8). 1984. 15.95 (ISBN 0-89453-408-4); pap. 10.95 (ISBN 0-89453-243-X). M Glazier.

Isaiah, One to Twelve, A Commentary. 2nd ed. Otto Kaiser. LC 82-23785. (The Old Testament Library Ser.). 288p. 1983. 19.95 (ISBN 0-664-21827-X). Westminster.

Isaiah: Prophecies, Promises, Warnings. W. E. Vine. pap. 7.95 (ISBN 0-310-33771-2, 6621P). Zondervan.

Isaiah: Prophet, Poet, & Seer. Victor L. Ludlow. LC 82-1444. (Illus.). 578p. 1982. 13.95 (ISBN 0-87747-884-8). Deseret Bk.

Isaiah: Scroll of a Prophetic Heritage. William L. Holladay. 270p. 1987. pap. 9.95 (ISBN 0-8298-0658-X). Pilgrim NY.

Isaiah Speaks to Modern Times. Cleon W. Skousen. 800p. 1984. 15.95 (ISBN 0-910558-25-6). Ensign Pub.

Isaiah: The Glory of the Messiah. Alfred Martin & John A. Martin. (Orig.). 1983. pap. 9.95 (ISBN 0-8024-0168-6). Moody.

Isaiah: The Salvation of Jehovah. Alfred Martin. (Everyman's Bible Commentary Ser.). 1967. pap. 5.95 (ISBN 0-8024-2023-0). Moody.

Isaiah Thirteen to Thirty-Nine, A Commentary. Otto Kaiser. LC 73-21949. (Old Testament Library). 432p. 1974. 19.95 (ISBN 0-664-20984-X). Westminster.

Isaiah Twenty-Four to Twenty-Seven & the Origin of Apocalyptic. William R. Millar. LC 76-3561. (Harvard Semetic Museum Ser.). 1976. pap. 11.95 (ISBN 0-89130-102-X, 04-00-11). Scholars Pr GA.

Isaiah Two. Ed. by John L. McKenzie. LC 68-10565. (Anchor Bible Ser.: Vol. 20). 1968. 14.00 (ISBN 0-385-05390-8, Anchor Pr). Doubleday.

Isaiah Two (WBC, Vol. 25. John Watts. 400p. 1987. 24.95 (ISBN 0-8499-0224-X). Word Bks.

Isaiah XXI: A Palimpsest. A. A. Macintosh. LC 79-41375. 160p. 1980. 34.50 (ISBN 0-521-22943-X). Cambridge U Pr.

Isaias: La Salvacion del Senor (Comentario Biblico Portavoz) Alfred Martin. Orig. Title: Isaiah: The Salvation of Jehovah (Everyman's Bible Commentary) (Span.). 112p. 1979. pap. 3.50 (ISBN 0-8254-1455-5). Kregel.

Isavasyopanisad. Tr. by Swami Sarvananda. (Sanskrit & English). pap. 1.00 (ISBN 0-87481-456-1). Vedanta Pr.

Isha Upanishad. Sri Aurobindo. Tr. by Sri Aurobindo. 1979. pap. 6.00 (ISBN 0-89744-922-3). Auromere.

Isidore of Seville on the Pagan Gods, Vol. 70, Pt. 3. Katherine N. MacFarlane. 1980. 6.00 (ISBN 0-87169-703-3). Am Philos.

Isidors Geschichte der Gothen, Vandalen, Sueven, Nebst Auszugen Aus der Kirchengeschichte Des Beda Venerablis. Isidorus. pap. 8.00 (ISBN 0-384-25980-4). Johnson Repr.

Isis und Sarapis bei den Griechen und Roemern: Epigraphische Studien zur Verbreitung und zu den Traegern des aegyptischen Kultes. Ladislav Vidman. (Religionsgeschichtliche Versuche und Vorarbeiten, No. 29). (Ger). 1970. 26.00x (ISBN 3-11-006392-1). De Gruyter.

Isis Unveiled, 2 Vols. Helena P. Blavatsky. Ed. by Boris De Zirkoff. 1971. Set. 30.00 (ISBN 0-8356-0193-5). Theos Pub Hse.

Isis Unveiled, 2 vols. Helena P. Blavatsky. LC 72-186521. 1976. Set. 20.00 (ISBN 0-911500-02-2); Set. pap. 14.00 (ISBN 0-911500-03-0). Theos U Pr.

Isis Unveiled: A Master-Key to the Mysteries of Ancient & Modern Science & Theology, 2 vols. in 1. Helena P. Blavatsky. (Illus.). xlix, 1260p. 1931. Repr. of 1877 ed. 17.00 (ISBN 0-938998-01-3). Theosophy.

Islam. Christopher Barlow. (Today's World Ser.). (Illus.). 72p. 1983. 16.95 (ISBN 0-7134-3659-X, Pub. by Batsford England). David & Charles.

Islam. Riadh El Droubie. 1985. 13.00 (ISBN 0-7062-3595-9, Pub. by Ward Lock Educ Co Ltd). State Mutual Bk.

Islam. Alfred Guillaume. 1954. pap. 6.95 (ISBN 0-14-020311-7, Pelican). Penguin.

Islam. Solomon Nigosian. (Crucible Ser.). 208p. 1987. pap. 9.95 (ISBN 0-85030-490-3). Thorsons Pubs.

Islam. 2nd ed. Fazlur Rahman. LC 78-68547. 1979. pap. 9.95 (ISBN 0-226-70281-2, P806, Phoen). U of Chicago Pr.

Islam: A Christian Perspective. M. Nazir-Ali. 160p. (Orig.). 1982. pap. text ed. 9.95 cancelled (ISBN 0-85364-333-4). Attic Pr.

Islam: A Christian Perspective. Michael Nazir-Ali. LC 84-3615. 186p. 1984. pap. 11.95 (ISBN 0-664-24527-7). Westminster.

Islam: A Code of Social Life. 4.00. Islamic Seminary.

Islam: A Concise Introduction. Dennis Roberts. LC 81-47845. 224p. 1982. pap. 7.95 (ISBN 0-06-066880-6, CN 4026, HarpR). Har-Row.

Islam: A Cultural Orientation. Ali B. Sheik. 10.00x (ISBN 0-8364-0802-0, Pub. by Macmillan India). South Asia Bks.

Islam: A Cultural Perspective. Richard C. Martin. (Illus.). 192p. 1982. pap. text ed. 17.00 (ISBN 0-13-506345-0). P-H.

Islam, a General Picture. M. Hameedullah. pap. 4.50 (ISBN 0-686-63903-0). Kazi Pubns.

Islam: A Historical Introduction. Gerhard Endress. Tr. by Carole Hillenbrand from Ger. 205p. 1987. text ed. 25.00 (ISBN 0-231-06580-9); pap. text ed. 12.00 (ISBN 0-231-06579-5). Columbia U Pr.

Islam: A Primer. J. Sabini. 127p. 1984. 30.00x (ISBN 0-317-39197-6, Pub. by Luzac & Co Ltd). State Mutual Bk.

Islam: A Primer. John Sabini. LC 83-61987. (Illus.). 127p. 1983. pap. 7.50x (ISBN 0-918992-05-2). Middle East Edit.

Islam: A Way of Life. Philip K. Hitti. 1971. pap. 7.50 (ISBN 0-89526-992-9). Regnery Bks.

Islam, A Way of Life & a Movement. Ed. by M. Tariq Quraishi. LC 83-71408. 221p. (Orig.). 1986. pap. 9.50 (ISBN 0-89259-055-6). Am Trust Pubns.

Islam Against the West: Shakib Arslan & the Campaign for Islamic Nationalism. William L. Cleveland. (Modern Middle East Ser.: No. 10). (Illus.). 247p. 1985. 19.95 (ISBN 0-292-77594-6). U of Tex Pr.

Islam & Alcoholism. M. C. Badri. LC 76-42173. 1976. pap. 2.75 (ISBN 0-89259-005-X). Am Trust Pubns.

Islam & Christian Theology: A Study of the Interpretations of Theological Ideas in the Two Religions, 3 vols. James W. Sweetman. 1980. Set. lib. bdg. 229.95 (ISBN 0-8490-3136-2). Gordon Pr.

Islam & Christian Witness. Martin Goldsmith. LC 83-6112. 160p. 1983. pap. 4.95 (ISBN 0-87784-809-2). Inter-Varsity.

Islam & Christianity. U. Aziz-us-Samad. 150p. 1985. write for info. (Pub. by IIFSO Kuwait). New Era Pubns MI.

Islam & Christianity. Donald S. Tingle. 32p. (Orig.). 1985. pap. 0.75 (ISBN 0-87784-073-3). Inter-Varsity.

Islam & Christianity in the Modern World. F. R. Ansari. pap. 14.95 (ISBN 0-686-18577-3). Kazi Pubns.

Islam & Christianity Today. W. Montgomery Watt. LC 83-10949. 157p. 1984. 19.95x (ISBN 0-7100-9766-2, Kegan Paul). Methuen Inc.

Islam & Colonialism. Rudilph Peters. (Religion & Society Ser.). 1984. text ed. 37.75x (ISBN 90-279-3347-2); pap. 14.95 (ISBN 3-11-010022-3). Mouton.

Islam & Communism. K. A. Hakim. pap. 15.95 (ISBN 0-686-18576-5). Kazi Pubns.

Islam & Contemporary Society. Salem Azzam. LC 82-253. 256p. 1982. 16.95x (ISBN 0-582-78323-2); pap. 7.95x (ISBN 0-582-78322-4). Longman.

Islam & Development: Religion & Sociopolitical Change. Ed. by John L. Esposito. LC 80-25119. (Contemporary Issues in the Middle East Ser.). 292p. 1980. pap. text ed. 9.95x (ISBN 0-8156-2230-9). Syracuse U Pr.

Islam & Imperialism in Senegal: Sine-Saloum, 1847-1914. Martin A. Klein. 1968. 25.00x (ISBN 0-8047-0621-2). Stanford U Pr.

Islam & International Relations. Ed. by Jesse H. Proctor. LC 80-1914. 1981. Repr. of 1965 ed. 27.50 (ISBN 0-404-18969-5). AMS Pr.

Islam & Modernism. M. Jameelah. pap. 10.50 (ISBN 0-686-18574-9). Kazi Pubns.

Islam & Modernity: Transformation of an Intellectual Tradition. Fazlur Rahman. LC 82-2720. (Publications of the Center for Middle Eastern Studies: No. 15). 184p. 1984. pap. 6.95x (ISBN 0-226-70284-7). U of Chicago Pr.

Islam & Muslims in Red Regimes. A. S. Kyani. pap. 4.50 (ISBN 0-686-18575-7). Kazi Pubns.

Islam & Muslims: Some Basic Information. Michael J. Diamond & Peter G. Gowing. 100p. 1981. pap. 3.75x (ISBN 0-686-30367-9, Pub. by New Day Publishers Philippines). Cellar.

Islam & Nationalism. S. Ramadhan. pap. 1.00 (ISBN 0-686-18586-2). Kazi Pubns.

Islam & Orientalism. M. Jameelah. pap. 6.50 (ISBN 0-686-18573-0). Kazi Pubns.

Islam & Pan-Africanism. Agadem L. Diara. LC 72-91318. (Illus.). 120p. 1973. pap. 3.75 (ISBN 0-913358-04-5). El-Shabazz Pr.

Islam & Politics in the Modern Middle East. Ed. by Metin Heper & Raphael Israeli. LC 84-40042. 131p. 1984. 25.00 (ISBN 0-312-43742-0). St Martin.

Islam & Power in the Contemporary Muslim World. Ed. by Alex Cudsi & Ali E. Hillal Dessouki. LC 81-47608. 208p. 1981. text ed. 25.00x (ISBN 0-8018-2697-7). Johns Hopkins.

Islam & Remaking of Humanity. A. H. Siddiqui. 14.95 (ISBN 0-686-83885-8); pap. 9.95 (ISBN 0-686-83886-6). Kazi Pubns.

Islam & Resistance in Afghanistan. Olivier Roy. (Cambridge Middle East Library). (Illus.). 256p. 1986. 24.95 (ISBN 0-521-32833-0). Cambridge U Pr.

Islam and Revolution: Basic Issues Facing the Muslim World. Kaukab Siddique. LC 82-154032. 112p. 1981. pap. 10.00 (ISBN 0-942978-00-5). Am Soc Ed & Rel.

Islam & Revolution: Writings & Declarations. Imam Khomeini. Tr. by Hamid Algar. 460p. 1986. pap. 19.95 (ISBN 0-7103-0098-0, Kegan Paul). Methuen Inc.

Islam & Revolution: Writings & Declarations of Imam Khomeini. Ruh A. Khumayni. Tr. by Hamid Algar. LC 80-24032. 480p. 1981. 24.95 (ISBN 0-933782-04-7); pap. 11.95 (ISBN 0-933782-03-9). Mizan Pr.

Islam & Schools of Economics. Muhammad B. Al Sadr. Tr. by M. A. Ansari. 160p. 1983. pap. text ed. 6.00 (ISBN 0-686-90405-2). Islamic Seminary.

Islam & the Destiny of Man. Charles Le Gai Eaton. (Islam Ser.). 256p. 1985. 44.50x (ISBN 0-88706-161-3); pap. 14.95 (ISBN 0-88706-163-X). State U NY Pr.

Islam & the Divine Comedy. Miguel A. Palacios. 295p. 1968. Repr. of 1926 ed. 30.00x (ISBN 0-7146-1995-7, F Cass Co). Biblio Dist.

Islam & the Medieval West. Ed. by Stanley Ferber. (Illus.). 1979. pap. 29.50x (ISBN 0-87395-802-0). State U NY Pr.

Islam & the Medieval West: Aspects of Intercultural Relations. LC 79-18678. 1979. 44.50x (ISBN 0-87395-409-2); pap. 16.95x (ISBN 0-87395-455-6). State U NY Pr.

Islam & the Modern Age. Ilse Lichtenstadter. 228p. 1958. text ed. 29.00x (ISBN 0-8290-0179-4). Irvington.

Islam & the Plight of Modern Man. Seyyed H. Nasr. LC 75-29014. (World of Islam Ser.). 1976. text ed. 26.00x (ISBN 0-582-78053-5). Longman.

Islam & the Politics of Meaning in Palestinian Nationalism. Nels Johnson. 111p. 1983. 21.95x (ISBN 0-7103-0021-2). Methuen Inc.

Islam & the Psychology of the Musulman. Andre Servier. 1977. lib. bdg. 59.95 (ISBN 0-8490-2079-4). Gordon Pr.

Islam & the Race Question. A. Abd-Al-Qadir Kamil. 65p. (Orig.). 1970. pap. 5.00 (ISBN 92-3-100833-1, U342, UNESCO). Bernan-Unipub.

Islam & the Remaking of Humanity. A. H. Siddiqui. pap. 9.95 (ISBN 0-686-63904-9). Kazi Pubns.

Islam & the Search for Social Order in Modern Egypt: A Biography of Muhammad Husayn Haykal. Charles D. Smith. (Middle East Studies). 256p. 1983. 49.50 (ISBN 0-87395-710-5); pap. 18.95 (ISBN 0-87395-711-3). State U NY Pr.

Islam & the West. K. Ahmad. pap. 2.00 (ISBN 0-686-18572-2). Kazi Pubns.

Islam & the West. Norman A. Daniel. 26.00x (ISBN 0-85224-109-7, Pub. by Edinburgh U Pr Scotland). Columbia U Pr.

Islam & the West: A Historical Cultural Survey. Philip K. Hitti. LC 78-10793. (Anvil Ser.). 192p. 1979. pap. 7.50 (ISBN 0-88275-787-3). Krieger.

Islam & the West: The Moriscos. Anwar G. Chejne. LC 82-703. 368p. 1983. 49.50 (ISBN 0-87395-603-6); pap. 19.95 (ISBN 0-87395-606-0). State U NY Pr.

Islam & the Western Civilization. F. R. Ansari. pap. 1.50 (ISBN 0-686-18533-1). Kazi Pubns.

Islam & the World. Abul H. Nadawi. Tr. by Mohammad A. Kidwai from Arabic. Tr. of Madha Khasira al-Alam bi-Inhtat al-Muslimin. 218p. (Orig.). 1977. pap. 5.95x (ISBN 0-939830-04-3, Pub. by IIFSO Kuwait). New Era Pubns MI.

Islam & the World. A. H. Nadvi. 14.50 (ISBN 0-686-18625-7). Kazi Pubns.

Islam & Universal Peace. Sayyed Qutb. LC 77-89635. 1977. pap. 2.85 (ISBN 0-89259-007-6). Am Trust Pubns.

Islam & Urban Labor in Northern Nigeria: The Making of a Muslim Working Class. Paul M. Lubeck. (African Studies Ser.: No. 52). (Illus.). 368p. Date not set. 49.50 (ISBN 0-521-30942-5). Cambridge U Pr.

Islam & World Peace. M. R. Muhaiyaddeen. LC 87-11921. 150p. 1987. 6.95 (ISBN 0-914390-25-2). Fellowship Pr PA.

Islam Assembled: The Advent of the Muslim Congresses. Martin Kramer. LC 84-21407. 280p. 1985. 30.00x (ISBN 0-231-05994-9). Columbia U Pr.

Islam at a Glance. Ed. by Hakeem A. Hameed. 125p. 1981. (Pub. by Vikas India); pap. 4.95x (ISBN 0-7069-1413-9). Advent NY.

Islam at the Cross Roads: A Brief Survey of the Present Position & Problems of the World of Islam. De Lacy E. O'Leary. LC 80-1916. 1981. Repr. of 1923 ed. 26.50 (ISBN 0-404-18983-0). AMS Pr.

Islam at the Crossroads. Muhammad Asad. 104p. (Orig.). 1982. 8.95 (ISBN 0-317-52459-3, Pub. by Dar Al Andalus). New Era Pubns MI.

Islam: Belief & Practices. Arthur S. Tritton. LC 79-2883. 200p. 1986. Repr. of 1950 ed. 20.00 (ISBN 0-8305-0051-0). Hyperion Conn.

Islam: Beliefs & Institutions. Henri Lammens. 1976. lib. bdg. 59.95 (ISBN 0-8490-2080-8). Gordon Pr.

Islam: Beliefs & Institutions. Henri Lammens. Tr. by E. Denison Ross from Fr. 265p. Repr. of 1929 ed. text ed. 23.50x. Coronet Bks.

Islam: Beliefs & Observances. rev. ed. Caesar E. Farah. LC 72-135505. (Orig.). (YA) 1970. pap. 6.50 (ISBN 0-8120-0277-6). Barron.

Islam Between East & West. Alija A. Izetbegovic. LC 84-45552. 248p. (Orig.). 1984. pap. 12.00 (ISBN 0-89259-057-2). Am Trust Pubns.

Islam Between Ignorant Followers & Incapable Scholars. A. Q. Audah. pap. 4.50 (ISBN 0-686-18505-6). Kazi Pubns.

Islam Between Ignorant Followers & Incapable Scholars. Adbul Q. Audah. Tr. of Al-Islam bain Jahl 'Abna'ihi wa Ajz Ulama'ihi. 115p. (Orig.). pap. 3.50 (ISBN 0-939830-01-9, Pub. by IIFSO Kuwait). New Era Pubns MI.

Islam: Continuity & Change in the Modern World. John O. Voll. LC 82-2829. 398p. 1982. 32.00x (ISBN 0-89158-931-7); pap. text ed. 14.50x (ISBN 0-89158-983-X). Westview.

Islam Debate. Josh McDowell & John Gilchrist. (Orig.). 1983. pap. 6.95 (ISBN 0-86605-104-X). Campus Crusade.

Islam: Faith & Practice. Manazir Ahsan. (Illus.). 48p. (Orig.). 1980. pap. 3.00 (ISBN 0-86037-001-1, Pub. by Islamic Found UK). New Era Pubns MI.

Islam in a World of Nation-States. Royal Institute of International Affairs & James P. Piscatori. LC 86-8275. 1986. 34.50 (ISBN 0-521-32985-X); pap. 12.95 (ISBN 0-521-33867-0). Cambridge U Pr.

Islam in Africa. Anson P. Atterbury. LC 73-91254. Repr. of 1899 ed. 22.50x (ISBN 0-8371-2064-0, ATI&, Pub. by Negro U Pr). Greenwood.

Islam in Africa South of the Sahara: A Select Bibliographic Guide. Patrick E. Ofori. 223p. 1977. lib. bdg. 42.00 (ISBN 3-262-00003-5). Kraus Intl.

Islam in China: A Neglected Problem. Marshall Broomhall. 1980. lib. bdg. 75.00 (ISBN 0-8490-3137-0). Gordon Pr.

Islam in East Africa. John S. Trimingham. LC 79-52567. (Islam Ser.). 1980. Repr. of 1964 ed. lib. bdg. 18.00x (ISBN 0-8369-9270-9). Ayer Co Pubs.

Islam in Egypt Today: Social & Political Aspects of Popular Religion. Morroe Berger. LC 70-113597. 1970. 34.50 (ISBN 0-521-07834-2). Cambridge U Pr.

Islam in Ethiopia. J. Spencer Trimingham. (Illus.). 299p. 1965. Repr. of 1952 ed. 29.50x (ISBN 0-7146-1731-8, F Cass Co). Biblio Dist.

Islam in Focus. 2nd ed. Hammudah Abdalati. LC 75-4382. (Illus.). 211p. 1975. pap. 5.00 (ISBN 0-89259-000-9). Am Trust Pubns.

Islam in Focus. H. A. Ati. pap. 9.50 (ISBN 0-686-18504-8). Kazi Pubns.

Islam in Foreign Policy. Ed. by Adeed Dawisha. LC 83-7458. 250p. 1984. 29.95 (ISBN 0-521-25815-4). Cambridge U Pr.

Islam in Foreign Policy. Ed. by Adeed Dawisha. 202p. 1985. pap. 11.95 (ISBN 0-521-27740-X). Cambridge U Pr.

Islam in India-Studies & Commentaries: Vol. 1, The Akbar Mission & Miscellaneous Studies. Ed. by Christian W. Troll. 240p. 1982. text ed. 32.50x (ISBN 0-7069-1889-4, Pub. by Vikas India). Advent NY.

Islam in Indian Politics. Moin Shakir. 1983. 11.00x (ISBN 0-8364-1032-7, Pub. by Ajanta). South Asia Bks.

Islam in India's Transition to Modernity. Maheshwar A. Karandikar. 1972. lib. bdg. 35.00 (ISBN 0-8371-2337-2, KAI/). Greenwood.

Islam in Iran. I. P. Petrushevsky. Tr. by Hubert Evans. (Series in Near Eastern Studies). 400p. 1985. 49.50x (ISBN 0-88706-070-6). State U NY Pr.

Islam in Modern History. Wilfred C. Smith. 1957. 37.00 (ISBN 0-691-03030-8); pap. 10.50x (ISBN 0-691-01991-6). Princeton U Pr.

Islam in Practical Life. A. M. Muhajir. 1968. 7.25x (ISBN 0-87902-067-9). Orientalia.

Islam in Practical Life. M. R. Muhajir. 12.50 (ISBN 0-686-18502-1). Kazi Pubns.

Islam in Revolution: Fundamentalism in the Arab World. R. Hrair Dekmejian. (Contemporary Issues in the Middle East Ser.). 224p. 1985. text ed. 28.00x (ISBN 0-8156-2329-1); pap. text ed. 13.95x (ISBN 0-8156-2330-5). Syracuse U Pr.

Islam in Secular India. Mushir-Ul-Hag. (Indian Institute of Advanced Study Monographs Ser). 110p. 1972. 8.00x (ISBN 0-89684-426-9). Orient Bk Dist.

Islam in South East Asia. Ed. by M. B. Hooker. 272p. 1983. text ed. 39.95x (ISBN 0-686-46644-6, Pub. by EJ Brill Holland). Humanities.

Islam in the Modern World. Ed. by Denis MacEoin & Ahmed Al-Shahi. LC 83-8992. 148p. 1983. 22.50 (ISBN 0-317-13515-5). St Martin.

Islam in the Political Process. Ed. by James P. Piscatori. LC 82-9745. 272p. 1983. 42.50 (ISBN 0-521-24941-4); pap. 16.95 (ISBN 0-521-27434-6). Cambridge U Pr.

Islam in the World. Zaki Ali. LC 74-180314. (Mid-East Studies). Repr. of 1947 ed. 31.00 (ISBN 0-404-56209-4). AMS Pr.

Islam in Theory & Practice. M. Jameelah. pap. 14.50 (ISBN 0-686-18501-3). Kazi Pubns.

Islam in Transition: Muslim Perspectives. Ed. by John J. Donohue & John L. Esposito. 1982. 28.00x (ISBN 0-19-503022-2); pap. 12.95x (ISBN 0-19-503023-0). Oxford U Pr.

Islam in Tribal Societies: From the Atlas to the Indus. Ed. by Akbar S. Ahemd & David M. Hart. 320p. (Orig.). 1984. pap. 21.95x (ISBN 0-7100-9320-9). Methuen Inc.

Islam in Tropical Africa. 2nd ed. Ed. by I. M. Lewis. LC 79-3292. 324p. 1980. 25.00x (ISBN 0-253-14956-8); pap. 10.95x (ISBN 0-253-28514-3). Ind U Pr.

Islam in Uganda. Arye Oded. 382p. 1974. casebound 19.95x (ISBN 0-87855-171-9). Transaction Bks.

Islam in West Africa. John S. Trimingham. 1959. 29.95x (ISBN 0-19-826511-5). Oxford U Pr.

Islam: Its Belief & Practices. S. A. Subhan. 1938. 5.25x (ISBN 0-87902-190-X). Orientalia.

Islam: Its Meaning & Message. Ed. by Khurshid Ahmad. 279p. (Orig.). 1976. pap. 8.95 (ISBN 0-86037-000-3, Pub. by Islamic Found UK). New Era Pubns MI.

Islam Observed: Religious Development in Morocco & Indonesia. Clifford Geertz. 1971. pap. 6.00x (ISBN 0-226-28511-1, P439, Phoen). U of Chicago Pr.

Islam: Outline of a Classification Scheme. Ziauddin Sardar. 81p. 1979. 17.50 (ISBN 0-85157-285-5, Pub. by Bingley England). Shoe String.

Islam: Politics & Religion in the Muslim World. Thomas W. Lippman. (Headline Series 258). (Illus.). 64p. 1982. pap. 4.00 (ISBN 0-87124-075-0). Foreign Policy.

Islam, Politics & the State - The Pakistan Experience. Ed. by Mohammad Asghar Khan. 320p. 1985. 32.95x (ISBN 0-86232-471-8, Pub. by Zed Pr England); pap. 12.95 (ISBN 0-86232-472-6, Pub. by Zed Pr England). Humanities.

Islam: Religions of the World Ser. Abdul Latif Al Hood. (Illus.). 48p. 1987. lib. bdg. 11.40 (ISBN 0-531-18063-8, Pub. by Bookwright Pr). Watts.

Islam, Secularism & the Philosophy of the Future. Syed Muhammad Al-Naquib Al-Attas. LC 84-26108. 239p. 1985. 31.00x (ISBN 0-7201-1740-2). Mansell.

Islam: Study Notes. Steven Roboz & Rudolf Steiner. Ed. by Steven Roboz. 33p. 1980. pap. 2.95 (ISBN 0-88010-050-8, Pub. by Steiner Book Centre Canada). Anthroposophic.

Islam (Textual Sources for the Study of Islam) Ed. by A. Rippin & J. Knappert. LC 86-22190. (Textual Sources for the Study of Religion). 256p. 1986. 23.50x (ISBN 0-389-20677-6); pap. 11.75 (ISBN 0-389-20678-4). B&N Imports.

Islam: The Misunderstood Religion. M. Qutb. pap. 8.50 (ISBN 0-686-18500-5). Kazi Pubns.

Islam: The Misunderstood Religion. Muhammad Qutb. Tr. of Shubuhat haul al-Islam. 199p. (Orig.). 1977. pap. 5.95 (ISBN 0-939830-05-1, Pub. by IIFSO Kuwait). New Era Pubns MI.

Islam: The Only Way. A. Nadvi. pap. 1.00 (ISBN 0-686-18499-8). Kazi Pubns.

Islam: The Perfect Religion & a Way of Life. A. H. Nadui. pap. 1.00 (ISBN 0-686-18498-X). Kazi Pubns.

Islam: The Religious & Political Life of a World Community. Ed. by Marjorie Kelly. LC 84-13307. 336p. 1984. 42.95 (ISBN 0-275-91204-3); pap. 16.95 (ISBN 0-03-001087-X); study guide 9.95 (ISBN 0-03-001084-5). Praeger.

Islam: The Religious & Political Life of a World Community. Ed. by Marjorie Kelly. LC 84-13307. 325p. 1984. 39.95; pap. 16.95. Foreign Policy.

Islam the Straight Path: Islam Interpreted by Muslims. Ed. by Kenneth W. Morgan. LC 58-9807. pap. 115.80 (ISBN 0-317-08489-5, 2012383). Bks Demand UMI.

Islam-the Wave of the Future. Kaukab Siddique. LC 82-83624. 75p. (Orig.). 1983. pap. 2.00 (ISBN 0-942978-04-8). Am Soc Ed & Rel.

Islam: The Way of Submission. Solomon Nigosian. 1987. pap. 9.95. Inner Tradit.

Islam Under the Double Eagle: The Muslims of Bosnia & Hercegovina, 1878-1914. Robert J. Donia. (East European Monographs: No. 78). 237p. 1981. 22.00x (ISBN 0-914710-72-9). East Eur Quarterly.

Islam vs, Ahl-al-Kitab, Past & Present. M. Jameelah. pap. 15.95 (ISBN 0-686-18570-6). Kazi Pubns.

Islam vs. Socialism. M. N. Hussain. pap. 6.50 (ISBN 0-686-18569-2). Kazi Pubns.

Islam vs the West. M. Jameelah. pap. 1.75 (ISBN 0-686-18568-4). Kazi Pubns.

Islamic & Christian Spain in the Early Middle Ages: Comparative Perspectives on Social & Cultural Formation. Thomas F. Glick. LC 78-70296. 1978. 41.50 (ISBN 0-691-05274-3). Princeton U Pr.

Islamic Architecture. John D. Hoag. LC 76-41805. (Masters of Art Ser.). (Illus.). 1977. 50.00 (ISBN 0-8109-1010-1). Abrams.

Islamic Architecture & Culture in India. R. Nath. (Illus.). 228p. 1983. text ed. 40.00x (ISBN 0-86590-135-X). Apt Bks.

Islamic Architecture: Style, Function, & Form. Robert Hillenbrand. (Illus.). 200p. 1986. 22.50x (ISBN 0-85224-391-X, Pub. by Edinburgh U Pr Scotland). Columbia U Pr.

Islamic Arms. Anthony North. (Victoria & Albert Introductions to Decorative Arts Ser.). (Illus.). 48p. 1986. 9.95 (ISBN 0-88045-078-9). Stemmer Hse.

Islamic Art & Architecture. LC 76-14076. (Garland Library of the History of Art: XIII). 1977. lib. bdg. 61.00 (ISBN 0-8240-2423-0). Garland Pub.

Islamic Calligraphy. Annemarie Schimmel. (Illus.). 1970. 103.25x (ISBN 0-685-00757-X). Adlers Foreign Bks.

Islamic Civilization, Nine Fifty - Eleven Fifty. D. S. Richards. 284p. 1983. 50.00x (ISBN 0-317-39090-2, Pub. by Luzac & Co Ltd). State Mutual Bk.

Islamic Concept of God. Mohammad Z. Ullah. 100p. (Orig.). 1984. 26.95x (ISBN 0-7103-0076-X, Kegan Paul). Methuen Inc.

Islamic Concept of God. Mohammad Z. Ullah. 116p. 1985. pap. 9.95 (ISBN 0-7103-0127-8, Kegan Paul). Methuen Inc.

Islamic Concept of Religion & Its Revival. A. H. Siddigui. 1981. 19.00 (ISBN 0-686-77428-0). Kazi Pubns.

Islamic Cultures in North America. E. Allen Richardson. LC 81-2876. 84p. (Orig.). 1981. pap. 3.95 (ISBN 0-8298-0449-8). Pilgrim NY.

Islamic Dynasties. C. E. Bosworth. 243p. 1980. pap. 10.00 (ISBN 0-85224-402-9, Pub. by Edinburgh U Pr Scotland). Columbia U Pr.

Islamic Education in Indonesia: A Bibliography. Muljanto Sumarti. 133p. (Orig.). 1984. pap. text ed. 21.00x (ISBN 9971-902-57-5, Pub. by Inst Southeast Asian Stud). Gower Pub Co.

Islamic Education: Its Traditions & Modernization into the Arab National Systems. A. L. Tibawl. 256p. 1979. Repr. 60.00x (ISBN 0-317-39091-0, Pub. by Luzac & Co Ltd). State Mutual Bk.

Islamic Ethics. A. S. Hashim. (Islamic Books for Children: Bk. 7). pap. 4.95 (ISBN 0-686-18404-1); pap. 45.00 entire set (ISBN 0-686-18405-X). Kazi Pubns.

Islamic Geomancy & a Thirteenth-Century Divinatory Device. E. Smith-Savage & M. B. Smith. LC 79-65001. (Studies in Near Eastern Culture & Society: Vol. 2). 91p. 1981. pap. 15.25x (ISBN 0-89003-038-3). Undena Pubns.

Islamic History: A.D. 750 to 1055, (A.H. 132 to 448) New Interpretation II. M. A. Shaban. LC 75-39390. (Illus.). 190p. 1976. 49.50 (ISBN 0-521-21198-0); pap. 16.95 (ISBN 0-521-29453-3). Cambridge U Pr.

Islamic Ideology. K. A. Hakim. 16.50 (ISBN 0-686-18571-4). Kazi Pubns.

Islamic Impact. Ed. by Yvonne Y. Haddad et al. (Contemporary Issues in the Middle East Ser.). (Illus.). 264p. 1983. text ed. 30.00x o. p. (ISBN 0-8156-2304-6); pap. text ed. 13.95x (ISBN 0-8156-2299-6). Syracuse U Pr.

Islamic Iran: Revolution & Counter-Revolution. Asaf Hussain. LC 85-40078. 250p. 1985. 27.50 (ISBN 0-312-43745-5). St Martin.

Islamic Jesus: An Annotated Bibliography of Sources in English & French. Don Wismer. LC 76-24737. (Reference Library of the Humanities Ser.: Vol. 58). 1977. lib. bdg. 40.00 (ISBN 0-8240-9940-0). Garland Pub.

Islamic Jurisprudence in the Modern World. A. A. Qadri. 45.00 (ISBN 0-317-46102-8). Kazi Pubns.

Islamic Jurisprudence in the Modern World. A. A. Quadri. 35.00 (ISBN 0-317-01602-4). Kazi Pubns.

Islamic Law & Constitution. A. Maududi. 1969. pap. 14.95 (ISBN 0-87902-176-4). Orientalia.

Islamic Law & Society in the Sudan. Carolyn Fluehr-Lobban. 275p. 1986. 32.50x (ISBN 0-7146-3280-5, F Cass Co). Biblio Dist.

Islamic Law in the Modern World. James N. Anderson. LC 75-31816. 106p. 1976. Repr. of 1959 ed. lib. bdg. 22.50x (ISBN 0-8371-8451-7, ANIL). Greenwood.

Islamic Law of Nations: Shaybani's Siyar. Intro. by & tr. by Majid Khadduri. 366p. 1966. 34.50x (ISBN 0-8018-0334-9). Johns Hopkins.

Islamic Law of Personal Status. Jamal J. Nasir. Date not set. 79.00 (ISBN 0-317-53173-5); deluxe ed. 132.00 (ISBN 0-86010-503-2). Graham & Trotman.

Islamic Law: Social & Historical Contents. Ed. by Aziz Al-Azmeh. 1986. 39.00 (ISBN 0-7099-0588-2, Pub. by Croom Helm Ltd). Longwood Pub Group.

Islamic Life & Thought. S. H. Nasn. 232p. 1981. 35.00x (ISBN 0-317-39093-7, Pub. by Luzac & Co Ltd). State Mutual Bk.

Islamic Life & Thought. Seyyed H. Nasr. LC 81-4723. 232p. 1981. 44.50 (ISBN 0-87395-490-4); pap. 14.95x (ISBN 0-87395-491-2). State U NY Pr.

Islamic Medicine. Muhammad S. Khan. (Illus.). 102p. Date not set. lib. bdg. 24.95 (ISBN 0-7102-0329-2). Methuen Inc.

Islamic Messianism: The Idea of Mahdi in Twelver Shi'ism. Abdulaziz A. Sachedina. LC 80-16767. 1980. 49.50x (ISBN 0-87395-442-4); pap. 19.95x (ISBN 0-87395-458-0). State U NY Pr.

Islamic Middle East 700-1900: Studies in Economic & Social History. Ed. by A. L. Udovitch. LC 79-52703. (Illus.). 838p. 1981. 29.95x (ISBN 0-87850-030-8). Darwin Pr.

Islamic Monuments of Cairo: A Practical Guide. 3rd ed. Richard B. Parker & Robin Sabin. Ed. by Caroline Williams. 1986. pap. 12.50x (ISBN 977-424-036-7, Pub. by Am Univ Cairo Pr). Columbia U Pr.

Islamic Movement & the Threat to Western Civilization. Richard N. Sanderson. (Illus.). 141p. 1980. deluxe ed. 67.45x (ISBN 0-930008-59-6). Inst Econ Pol.

Islamic Movement & the Threat to Western Civilization, 2 vols. Richard N. Sanderson. (Illus.). 309p. 1985. Set. 227.50 (ISBN 0-86722-113-5). Inst Econ Finan.

Islamic Movement: Problems & Perspective. Fathi Yakan. Tr. by Maneh Al-Johani from Arabic. pap. 5.00 (ISBN 0-89259-051-3). Am Trust Pubns.

Islamic Movements in Egypt, Pakistan & Iran: An Annotated Bibliography. Asaf Hussain. 182p. 1983. 36.00x (ISBN 0-7201-1648-1). Mansell.

Islamic Perspective to the Divine Principle. LC 80-84970. 198p. (Orig.). 1980. pap. 7.00 (ISBN 0-910621-18-7). HSA Pubns.

Islamic Philosophical Theology. Ed. by Parviz Morewedge. LC 79-14405. 1979. 55.50x (ISBN 0-87395-242-1). State U NY Pr.

Islamic Philosophy. M. Saeed Sheikh. 1982. 16.95 (ISBN 0-900860-50-2, Pub. by Octagon Pr England). Ins Study Human.

Islamic Philosophy & Mysticism. Ed. by Parviz Morewedge. LC 80-14364. (Studies in Islamic Philosophy & Science). 1981. 45.00x (ISBN 0-88206-302-2). Caravan Bks.

Islamic Philosophy & the Classical Tradition. Stern et al. 549p. 1972. 100.00x (ISBN 0-317-39094-5, Pub. by Luzac & Co Ltd). State Mutual Bk.

Islamic Pious Foundations in Jerusalem. A. L. Tibawl. 163p. 1978. 20.00x (ISBN 0-317-39095-3, Pub. by Luzac & Co Ltd). State Mutual Bk.

Islamic Practical Law, Pts. I & II. Ayatullah Al-Khu'i. Tr. by Shaikh Muhammad Sarwar from Arabic. 1981. 15.00 (ISBN 0-941724-08-5); pap. 10.00 (ISBN 0-941724-01-8). Islamic Seminary.

Islamic Reassertion in Pakistan: Islamic Laws in a Modern State. Ed. by Anita M. Weiss. (Contemporary Issues in the Middle East Ser.). 176p. 1986. text ed. 19.95x (ISBN 0-8156-2375-5). Syracuse U Pr.

Islamic Religious Knowledge, 3 vols. M. A. Rauf. 9.50 (ISBN 0-686-18392-4). Kazi Pubns.

Islamic Response to Imperialism: Political & Religious Writings of Sayyid Jamal ad-Din "al-Afghani". Hikke R. Keddie. LC 68-13224. (California Library Reprint Ser. Near Eastern Center, UCLA: No. 119). 224p. 1983. 35.00x (ISBN 0-520-04766-4); pap. 7.95 (ISBN 0-520-04774-5, CAL 586). U of Cal Pr.

Islamic Resurgence in the Arab World. Ali E. Hillal Dessouki. LC 81-12135. 286p. 1982. 40.95 (ISBN 0-03-059673-4). Praeger.

Islamic Revival in British India: Deoband, 1860-1900. Barbara D. Metcalf. LC 81-47934. (Illus.). 400p. 1982. 31.50 (ISBN 0-691-05343-X). Princeton U Pr.

Islamic Revivalism in a Changing Peasant Economy: Central Sumatra, 1784-1847. Christine Dobbin. 328p. 1981. 40.00x (ISBN 0-7007-0155-9, Pub. by Curzon England). State Mutual Bk.

Islamic Sharia & the Muslims. M. S. Siddiqui. pap. 2.50 (ISBN 0-686-63905-7). Kazi Pubns.

Islamic Social Framework. M. Sharif. 14.50 (ISBN 0-686-18446-7). Kazi Pubns.

Islamic Society & Culture: Essays in Honour of Professor Aziz Ahmad. Ed. by Milton Israel & N. K. Wagle. 1983. 32.50x (ISBN 0-8364-1047-5, Pub. by Manohar India). South Asia Bks.

Islamic Society on the South Asian Frontier: The Mappilas of Malabar, 1498 - 1922. Stephen F. Dale. (Illus.). 1980. 55.00x (ISBN 0-19-821571-1). Oxford U Pr.

Islamic Spirituality. Ed. by Seyyed H. Nasr. (World Spirituality Ser.). (Illus.). 496p. 1987. 49.50x (ISBN 0-8245-0767-3). Crossroad NY.

Islamic State: A Study Based on the Qur'an & Sunnah. Abdulrahman A. Kurdi. 147p. 1984. 33.00x (ISBN 0-7201-1725-9). Mansell.

Islamic Struggle in Syria. Umar F. Abdallah. 24.95 (ISBN 0-933782-10-1). Mizan Pr.

Islamic Studies. S. K. Bukhsh. 16.50 (ISBN 0-686-18357-6). Kazi Pubns.

Islamic Syncretistic Tradition in Bengal. Asim Roy. LC 83-42574. 312p. 1984. 31.50x (ISBN 0-691-05387-1). Princeton U Pr.

Islamic Teaching, V. Tr. by M. Fazal Haq. 102p. 1985. pap. 6.00 (ISBN 0-317-19682-0). Islamic Seminary.

Islamic Teachings, VI. Tr. by M. Fazal Haq. 140p. 1985. pap. 6.00 (ISBN 0-317-19685-5). Islamic Seminary.

Islamic Teachings, VII. Tr. by M. Fazal Haq. 192p. 1985. pap. 9.00 (ISBN 0-941724-33-6). Islamic Seminary.

Islamic Technology: An Illustrated History. Ahmed Al-Hassan & Donald Hill. (Illus.). 300p. 1987. 39.50 (ISBN 0-521-26333-6). Cambridge U Pr.

Islamic Theology & Philosophy: Studies in Honor of George F. Hourani. Ed. by Michael E. Marmura. 344p. 1983. 49.50 (ISBN 0-87395-746-6); pap. 18.95 (ISBN 0-87395-747-4). State U NY Pr.

Islamic Tradition. John B. Christopher. (Major Traditions in World Civilization Ser.). 1972. pap. text ed. 11.95 scp (ISBN 0-06-041283-6, HarpC). Har-Row.

Islamic Tradition & Its Problems. Ed. by Malcolm H. Kerr. LC 80-53523. (Giorgio Levi Della Vida Conference: Vol. 7). 140p. (Orig.). 1983. pap. 18.50x (ISBN 0-89003-069-3). Undena Pubns.

Islamic Understanding of Death & Resurrection. Jane I. Smith & Yvonne Y. Haddad. LC 80-21303. 270p. 1981. 49.50x (ISBN 0-87395-506-4); pap. 19.95 (ISBN 0-87395-507-2). State U NY Pr.

Islamic Unity & Happiness. Ed. by Muhammad K. Ali. Tr. by Alaedin Pazargali from Persian. 1985. pap. 3.95 (ISBN 0-940368-47-1). Tahrike Tarsile Quran.

Islamic View of Women & the Family. Muhammad Abdul-Rauf. 1977. text ed. 11.95 (ISBN 0-8315-0156-1). Speller.

Islamic Way of Life. A. A. Maududi. pap. 3.50 (ISBN 0-686-18496-3). Kazi Pubns.

Islamic World. Ed. by William H. McNeill & Marilyn Robinson Waldman. LC 83-18246. xviii, 468p. 1984. pap. 15.00x (ISBN 0-226-56155-0). U of Chicago Pr.

Islamic World since the Peace Settlement. Arnold J. Toynbee. Repr. of 1927 ed. 50.00 (ISBN 0-384-61120-6). Johnson Repr.

Islamische Funde in Balaguer und die Aljaferia in Zaragoza. Christian Ewert. (Madrider Forschungen, Vol. 7). (Illus.). 281p. 1971. 96.00 (ISBN 3-11-003613-4). De Gruyter.

Islamization among the Upper Pokomo. 2nd ed. Robert L. Bunger. LC 80-242. (Foreign & Comparative Studies-African Ser.: No. 33). 128p. (Orig.). 1979. pap. 7.00x (ISBN 0-915984-55-5). Syracuse U Foreign Comp.

Islamization of Pakistan. Afzal Iqbal. 1985. 15.00x (ISBN 0-8364-1493-4, Pub. by Idarah). South Asia Bks.

Islam's Understanding of Itself. Ed. by Richard G. Hovannisian & Speros Vryonis, Jr. LC 82-50987. (Giorgio Levi Della Vida Biennial Conference Ser.: Vol. 8). viii, 151p. 1983. pap. 18.50x (ISBN 0-89003-135-5). Undena Pubns.

Island Churches of the South Pacific: Emergence in the Twentieth Century. Charles W. Forman. LC 81-18666. 304p. (Orig.). 1982. pap. 17.50 (ISBN 0-88344-218-3). Orbis Bks.

Island of the Blest: Islam in a Libyan Oasis Community. John P. Mason. LC 77-620016. (Papers in International Studies: Africa Ser.: No. 31). (Illus.). 1977. pap. 10.00x (ISBN 0-89680-063-6, Ohio U Ctr Intl). Ohio U Pr.

Islands of Light. Ann R. Colton. 203p. 1953. 6.95 (ISBN 0-917187-14-8). A R C Pub.

Isles & Continents. Maurice L. Draper. (Orig.). 1982. pap. 14.00 (ISBN 0-8309-0343-7). Herald Hse.

Isness of Your Life. Anna Cook. (Illus.). 56p. 1986. pap. 3.95 (ISBN 0-936029-03-X). Western Bk Journ.

Isn't It Amazin'? A Book about the Love of God. Tommy Lewis & Irene B. Harrell. 184p. (Orig.). 1983. pap. 6.00 (ISBN 0-915541-00-9). Star Bks Inc.

Isotoriia Dogmaticheskikh Divhenii v Epokhu Vselenskikh Soborov. A. Spasskii. 656p. Repr. of 1914 ed. text ed. 74.52x (ISBN 0-576-99173-2, Pub. by Gregg Intl Pubs England). Gregg Intl.

Israel. Lily Edelman. 1958. 20.00 (ISBN 0-686-17232-9). Scholars Ref Lib.

Israel. (Library of Nations). (YA) 1986. lib. bdg. 18.60 (ISBN 0-8094-5313-4, Pub. by Time-LIfe). Silver.

Israel. Ludwig Lewisohn. LC 76-138122. 1971. Repr. of 1925 ed. lib. bdg. 22.50x (ISBN 0-8371-5698-X, LEIS). Greenwood.

Israel. F. B. Meyer. 1972. pap. 4.50 (ISBN 0-87508-347-1). Chr Lit.

Israel. Danah Zohar. LC 77-88352. (Countries Ser.). (Illus.). 1978. PLB 14.96 (ISBN 0-382-06146-2). Silver.

Israel: A History of the Jewish People. Israel Goldberg. LC 72-162629. 715p. 1949. Repr. lib. bdg. 29.50x (ISBN 0-8371-6196-7, GOIS). Greenwood.

Israel after the Exile: Sixth & Fifth Centuries B. C. William F. Lofthouse. LC 78-10629. (Illus.). 1979. Repr. of 1928 ed. lib. bdg. 24.75x (ISBN 0-313-21008-X, LOIS). Greenwood.

Israel Alive Again: Ezra & Mehemiah. Fredrick C. Holmgren. Ed. by G. A. Knight. (International Theological Commentary Ser.). 200p. (Orig.). 1987. pap. 9.95 (ISBN 0-8028-0259-1). Eerdmans.

Israel among the Nations: A Study of the Jews & Antisemitism. facsimile ed. Anatole Leroy-Beaulieu. Tr. by Frances Hellman from Fr. LC 74-27996. (Modern Jewish Experience Ser.). (Eng.). 1975. Repr. of 1904 ed. 32.00x (ISBN 0-405-06723-2). Ayer Co Pubs.

Israel & Iran in Talmudic Times: A Political History. Jacob Neusner. (Illus.). 266p. (Orig.). 1987. lib. bdg. 27.50 (ISBN 0-8191-5729-5, Pub. by Studies in Judaism); pap. text ed. 14.75 (ISBN 0-8191-5730-9). U Pr of Amer.

Israel & Me. Morris Alexander. (Illus.). 278p. 1977. 14.50x (ISBN 0-87073-204-8). Schenkman Bks Inc.

Israel & the Arabs: Cambridge Introduction to the History of Mankind. Geoffrey B. Regan. (Illus.). 48p. 1984. pap. 4.95 (ISBN 0-521-27580-6). Cambridge U Pr.

Israel & the Arabs: Prelude to the Jewish State. Ed. by Anne Sinai & Robert I. Sinai. LC 78-161364. (Facts on File Publication). pap. 64.00 (2025158). Bks Demand UMI.

Israel & the Aramaeans of Damascus. Merrill F. Unger. (BSBA Ser.). 1980. pap. 5.95 (ISBN 0-8010-9204-3). Baker Bk.

Israel & the Dead Sea Scrolls. Edmund Wilson. 416p. 1978. pap. 9.25 (ISBN 0-374-51341-4). FS&G.

Israel & the Mind of America. Peter Grose. 1983. 17.95 (ISBN 0-394-51658-3). Random.

Israel & the Nations. Ed. by Frederick F. Bruce. LC 63-22838. 1963. pap. 7.95 (ISBN 0-8028-1450-6). Eerdmans.

Israel & the New Covenant. Roderick Campbell. LC 82-142978. 364p. 1982. Repr. of 1954 ed. 12.95 (ISBN 0-939404-01-X). Geneva Ministr.

Israel & the New Covenant. Roderick Campbell. 1982. 12.95 (ISBN 0-87552-161-4). Presby & Reformed.

Israel & the Prophecies. Benjamin M. Sanchez. pap. 3.10 (ISBN 0-913558-06-0). Educator Pubns.

Israel & the World: Essays in a Time of Crisis. Martin Buber. LC 48-9322. 1963. pap. 6.50 (ISBN 0-8052-0066-5). Schocken.

Israel Becomes a Nation. C. M. Amos. (Discovering the Bible Ser.). pap. 8.95 (ISBN 0-7175-1160-X). Dufour.

Israel: Covenant People, Covenant Land. Seymour Rossel. (Illus.). 256p. 1985. pap. 8.95 (ISBN 0-941232-06-9, 147500). UAHC.

Israel Exploration Journal Reader, 2 vols. H. M. Orlinsky. (Library of Biblical Studies). 1982. Set. 99.50x (ISBN 0-87068-267-9). Ktav.

Israel for Christians. A. James Rudin. LC 82-7241. 160p. (Orig.). 1983. pap. 8.95 (ISBN 0-8006-1643-X, 1-1643). Fortress.

Israel, from Its Beginning to the Middle of the Eighth Century. Adolphe Lods. Tr. by S. H. Hooke. LC 75-41180. 1948. 34.75 (ISBN 0-404-14569-8). AMS PR.

Israel Haggadah. rev. ed. Meyer Levin. LC 70-99933. (Illus.). 1977. pap. 5.95 (ISBN 0-8109-2040-9). Abrams.

Israel: Idea & Reality. Emil Lehman. (Illus.). 3.95x (ISBN 0-8381-0205-0, 10-205). United Syn Bk.

Israel in Egypt. Siegfried Herrmann. LC 73-77371. (Studies in Biblical Theology, Second Ser.: No. 27). (Orig.). 1973. pap. text ed. 10.00x (ISBN 0-8401-3077-5). A R Allenson.

Israel in Exile: A Theological Interpretation. Ralph W. Klein. Tr. by Walter Brueggemann & John R. Donahue. LC 79-7382. (Overtures to Biblical Theology Ser.). 180p. (Orig.). 1979. pap. 8.95 (ISBN 0-8006-1532-8, 1-1532). Fortress.

Israel in Prophecy. John F. Walvoord. 1978. pap. 4.95 (ISBN 0-310-34081-0, 10970P). Zondervan.

Israel in Space & Time: Basic Themes in Jewish Spirituality. Alexander Safran. 1987. 25.00. Feldheim.

Israel in the Book of Chronicles. H. G. Williamson. LC 76-11096. 1977. 42.50 (ISBN 0-521-21305-3). Cambridge U Pr.

Israel in the Period of the Judges. Andrew D. Mayes. (Studies in Biblical Theology, Second Ser.: No. 29). 1974. pap. text ed. 10.00x (ISBN 0-8401-3079-1). A R Allenson.

Israel in the Plan of God. David Baron. LC 82-18678. 320p. 1983. 14.95 (ISBN 0-8254-2241-8). Kregel.

Israel into Palestine. Ed. by Gwyn Rowley. LC 83-22167. 198p. 1983. 31.00x (ISBN 0-7201-1674-0). Mansell.

Israel: Its Role in Civilization. Ed. by Moshe Davis. LC 77-70673. (America & the Holy Land Ser.). 1977. Repr. of 1956 ed. lib. bdg. 31.00 (ISBN 0-405-10241-0). Ayer Co Pubs.

Israel Jacobson: The Founder of the Reform Movement in Judaism. Jacob R. Marcus. 12.50x (ISBN 0-87820-000-2, Pub. by Hebrew Union). Ktav.

Israel, Land of Promise, Land of Peace. Gary Cohen & Salem Kirban. LC 74-77252. (Illus.). 1974. pap. 5.95 (ISBN 0-912582-16-2). Kirban.

Israel: Land of Tradition & Conflict. Bernard Reich. (Profiles-Nations of the Contemporary Middle East Ser.). 240p. 1985. 28.00x (ISBN 0-8133-0211-0); pap. text ed. 13.95x (ISBN 0-8133-0215-3). Westview.

Israel Now: Portrait of a Troubled Land. Lawrence Meyer. 1982. 16.95 (ISBN 0-385-28475-6). Delacorte.

Israel of God in Prophecy: Principles of Prophetic Interpretation. Hans K. LaRondelle. LC 82-74358. (Andrews University Monographs, Studies in Religion: Vol.13). viv, 226p. 1983. 14.95 (ISBN 0-943872-13-8); pap. 8.50 (ISBN 0-943872-14-6). Andrews Univ Pr.

Israel of the Alps: A Complete History of the Waldenses & Their Colonies, 2 vols. Alexis Muston. Tr. by John Montgomery. LC 77-84718. Repr. of 1875 ed. 84.50 set (ISBN 0-404-16140-5). AMS Pr.

Israel Passover Haggadah. Menachem M. Kasher. LC 64-17316. (Illus.). 1983. Repr. of 1964 ed. 15.00 (ISBN 0-88400-018-4). Shengold.

Israel: Promised Land to Modern State. Rinna Samuel. (Illus.). 175p. 1971. Repr. of 1969 ed. 18.50x (ISBN 0-85303-135-5, Pub. by Vallentine Mitchell England). Biblio Dist.

Israel: Prophetic Signs. Gordon Lindsay & Jarry Autry. 72p. (Orig.). 1982. Repr. of 1968 ed. 2.95 (ISBN 0-89985-189-4). Christ Nations.

Israel Salanter: Text, Structure, Idea. Hillel Goldberg. 1982. 25.00x (ISBN 0-87068-709-3). Ktav.

Israel Shall Do Valiantly. Wim Malgo. 3.95 (ISBN 0-937422-05-3). Midnight Call.

Israel: The Eternal Idea. Irving Miller. 1955. 19.50x (ISBN 0-686-50046-6). Elliots Bks.

Israel, the False Prophet & the Two Witnesses, Vol. 5. Gordon Lindsay. (End of the Age Ser.). 1.25 (ISBN 0-89985-071-5). Christ Nations.

Israel: The Sword & the Harp. Ferdynand Zweig. LC 74-86291. 326p. 1970. 24.50 (ISBN 0-8386-7534-4). Fairleigh Dickinson.

Israel Today. rev. ed. Harry Essrig & Abraham Segal. LC 77-7536. (Illus.). (YA) 1977. text ed. 8.50 (ISBN 0-8074-0007-6, 142601); tchr's guide o.p. 5.00 (ISBN 0-686-83000-8, 202601). UAHC.

Israel under Babylon & Persia. Peter R. Ackroyd. (New Clarendon Bible Ser.). 1970. 15.95x (ISBN 0-19-836917-4). Oxford U Pr.

Israel y las Naciones. F. F. Bruce. Orig. Title: Israel & the Nations. (Span.). 298p. 1979. 8.95 (ISBN 0-8254-1076-2). Kregel.

Israeli Childhood Stories of the Sixties. Gideon Telpaz. LC 83-14202. (Brown Judaic Studies). 222p. 1983. pap. 18.00 (ISBN 0-89130-610-2, 14 00 40). Scholars Pr GA.

Israeli Humor: The Content & Structure of the Chizbat of the Palmah. Elliott Oring. LC 80-25483. (Modern Jewish Literature & Culture Ser.). 210p. 1981. 44.50 (ISBN 0-87395-512-9); pap. 14.95x (ISBN 0-87395-513-7). State U NY Pr.

Israeli Love Story. Zola Levitt. LC 77-27611. 1977. pap. 3.95 (ISBN 0-8024-4181-5). Moody.

Israelian Heritage of Judaism. Louis H. Ginsberg. 15.00x (ISBN 0-87334-013-2). Ktav.

Israelis Speak: About Themselves & the Palestinians. Ed. by Larry L. Fabian & Ze'ev Schiff. LC 75-51150. 1977. text ed. 10.00 (ISBN 0-87003-007-8); pap. text ed. 5.00 (ISBN 0-87003-008-6). Carnegie Endow.

Israelite Religion. Helmer Ringgren. Tr. by David E. Green from Ger. LC 66-10757. 408p. 1975. pap. 7.95 (ISBN 0-8006-1121-7, 1-1121). Fortress.

Israelite Wisdom: Theological & Literary Essays in Honor of Samuel Terrien. Ed. by John G. Gammie. LC 77-17862. 1978. pap. 18.00 (ISBN 0-89130-208-5, 00-16-03). Scholars Pr GA.

Israelite Woman: Social Role & Literary Type in Biblical Narrative. Athalya Brenner. (Biblical Seminar Ser.: No. 2). 144p. 1985. pap. text ed. 7.95x (ISBN 0-905774-83-3, Pub. by JSOT Pr England). Eisenbrauns.

Israelitische Lehrerbildungsanstalt Wurzburg. Ed. by Max Ottensoser & Alex Roberg. LC 81-81930. (Illus.). 256p. 1982. 12.95 (ISBN 0-8187-0046-7). Harlo Pr.

Israelitische Pfingstfest und der Plejadenkult. Hubert Grimme. 1907. pap. 12.00 (ISBN 0-384-20060-5). Johnson Repr.

Israel's Apostasy & Restoration in Prophetic Thought: Essays in Honor of Roland Kenneth Harrison. Ed. by Avraham Gileadi. 336p. 1986. 26.95 (ISBN 0-8407-7532-6). Nelson.

Israel's Final Holocaust. Jack Van Impe. 172p. 1979. pap. 4.95 (ISBN 0-934803-08-0). J Van Impe.

Israel's Forty-Eight Signs of Christ Return. Gordon Lindsay. 2.25 (ISBN 0-89985-186-X). Christ Nations.

Israel's God Does Not Lie. Wim Malgo. 4.95 (ISBN 0-937422-06-1). Midnight Call.

Israel's Holy Days: In Type & in Prophecy. Daniel Fuchs. LC 85-13172. 96p. 1985. pap. 3.95 (ISBN 0-87213-198-X). Loizeaux.

Israel's Hope Encouraged. John Bunyan. pap. 1.95 (ISBN 0-685-19836-7). Reiner.

Israel's Impact, Nineteen Hundred Fifty to Fifty-One: A Personal Record. Allen Lesser. LC 84-12013. (Orig.). 1984. lib. bdg. 28.00 (ISBN 0-8191-4125-9); pap. text ed. 15.50 (ISBN 0-8191-4126-7). U Pr of Amer.

Israel's Politics in Sasanian Iran: Jewish Self-Government in Talmudic Times. Jacob Neusner. (Studies in Judaism). (Illus.). 202p. (Orig.). 1987. lib. bdg. 24.75 (ISBN 0-8191-5725-2, Pub. by Studies in Judaism); pap. text ed. 12.25 (ISBN 0-8191-5726-0). U Pr of Amer.

Israel's Prophetic Tradition. Ed. by R. J. Coggins & Anthony C. Phillips. LC 81-17065. (Illus.). 290p. 1982. 44.50 (ISBN 0-521-24223-1). Cambridge U Pr.

Israel's Prophetic Tradition: Essays in Honour of Peter Ackroyd. Ed. by Richard Coggins et al. 294p. 1985. 18.95 (ISBN 0-521-31886-6). Cambridge U Pr.

Israel's Prophets: Envoys of the King. Walter Wifall. (Biblical Booklets). 1975. pap. 1.25 (ISBN 0-8199-0521-6). Franciscan Herald.

Israel's Sacred Songs: A Study of Dominant Themes. Harvey H. Guthrie, Jr. 256p. 1984. pap. text ed. 11.50 (ISBN 0-8191-4027-9, Co-Pub. by Episcopal Div Sch). U Pr of Amer.

Israel's Settlement in Canaan: The Biblical Tradition & Its Historical Background. 3rd ed. C. F. Burney. (British Academy, London, Schweich Lectures on Biblical Archaeology Series, 1917). pap. 19.00 (ISBN 0-8115-1259-2). Kraus Repr.

Israel's United Monarchy. Leon J. Wood. 1980. 12.95 (ISBN 0-8010-9622-7). Baker Bk.

Israel's Wisdom in Modern Life: Essays & Interpretations of Religious & Cultural Problems Based on the Talmudic & Midrashic Literature. Mordecai Mayer. 32.50 (ISBN 0-87559-147-7). Shalom.

Issues: A Biblical Perspective on Current Social Themes. Ed. by Perry Gillum & Rob Allen. 128p. (Orig.). 1986. pap. 3.95 (ISBN 0-934942-57-9); discussion kit 2.95 (ISBN 0-934942-83-8). White Wing Pub.

Issues in American Protestantism: A Documentary History from the Puritans to the Present. Ed. by Robert L. Ferm. 15.25 (ISBN 0-8446-2052-1). Peter Smith.

Issues in Christian Ethics. Ed. by Paul D. Simmons. LC 79-52983. 1980. pap. 8.95 (ISBN 0-8054-6122-1). Broadman.

Issues in Missiology. Edward C. Pentecost. LC 82-70467. 192p. 1982. 11.95 (ISBN 0-8010-7071-6). Baker Bk.

Issues in Science & Religion. Ian G. Barbour. 1971. pap. 8.95x (ISBN 0-06-131566-4, TB1566, Torch). Har-Row.

Issues in the Jewish Christian Dialogue. Ed. by Helga Croner. LC 79-88933. 200p. 1979. pap. 7.95 (ISBN 0-8091-2238-3). Paulist Pr.

Issues in the Jewish-Christian Dialogue: Jewish Perspectives on Covenant Mission & Witness. Ed. by Helga Croner & Leon Klenicki. 190p. 7.95 (ISBN 0-686-95172-7). ADL.

Issues in the Sociology of Religion: A Bibliography. Anthony J. Blasi & Michael W. Cuneo. Ed. by Dan A. Chekki. (Bibliographies in Sociology-Reference Library of Social Science). 392p. 1986. 53.00 (ISBN 0-8240-8585-X). Garland Pub.

Issues in the Wake of Vatican II: Proceedings of the Eighth Convention of the Fellowship of Catholic Scholars. Ed. by Paul L. Williams. 128p. (Orig.). 1985. pap. 6.95 (ISBN 0-937374-02-4). NE Bks.

Issues of Theological Conflict: Evangelicals & Liberals. Rev. ed. Richard J. Coleman. LC 79-19494. pap. 74.00 (ISBN 0-317-19816-5, 2023209). Bks Demand UMI.

Istoria Degli Scrittori Fiorentini. Giulio Negri. 570p. Date not set. Repr. of 1722 ed. text ed. 144.90x (ISBN 0-576-72205-7, Pub. by Gregg Intl Pubs England). Gregg Intl.

Istoriia Russkago Raskola Starobriadstva. P. S. Smirnov. 314p. Repr. of 1895 ed. text ed. 62.10x (ISBN 0-576-99245-3, Pub. by Gregg Intl Pubs England). Gregg Intl.

Istorija Kristijanskoj Tserkvi. N. D. Talberg. Tr. of History of the Christian Church. 494p. 1964. pap. text ed. 20.00 (ISBN 0-317-30289-2); pap. 15.00 (ISBN 0-317-30290-6). Holy Trinity.

Istorija Russkoi Tserkvi. N. D. Talberg. Tr. of History of the Russuan Church. 927p. 1959. pap. text ed. 25.00 (ISBN 0-317-30295-7). Holy Trinity.

It Began in an Upper Room. Kenneth D. Barney. LC 78-67445. 128p. 1978. pap. 1.50 (ISBN 0-88243-528-0, 02-0528, Radiant Bks). Gospel Pub.

It Begins with Friendship: A Fresh Approach to Prayer. Greg Friedman. 73p. (Orig.). 1984. pap. text ed. 3.95 (ISBN 0-86716-038-1). St Anthony Mess Pr.

It Came upon the Midnight Clear: Christmas Photo Sermon. Merle G. Franke. 1977. pap. 9.50 (ISBN 0-89536-291-0, 0916). CSS of Ohio.

It Can Happen to You. Ernest Holmes & Willis H. Kinnear. 96p. 1959. pap. 4.50 (ISBN 0-911336-25-7). Sci of Mind.

It Can Happen Today. G. Edwin Bontrager & Nathan Showalter. LC 86-15036. 96p. (Orig.). 1986. pap. 5.95 (ISBN 0-8361-3419-2); pap. 14.95x tchrs. manual (ISBN 0-8361-1286-5). Herald Pr.

It Happened This Way. Edward B. Vargesko. (Orig.). 1982. pap. 2.25 (ISBN 0-937172-35-9). JLJ Pubs.

It Hurts So Bad, Lord! Andrew D. Lester. LC 75-42860. 1976. 5.95 (ISBN 0-8054-5238-9). Broadman.

It Hurts to Lose a Special Person. Amy Ross Mumford. (Accent Expressions Ser.). (Illus.). 24p. (Orig.). 1982. gift book 4.95 (ISBN 0-89636-093-8). Accent Bks.

It Is No Dream. LC 78-51766. 1978. pap. 4.95 (ISBN 0-915540-21-5). Friends Israel-Spearhead Pr.

It Is Not Lawful for Me to Fight. Jean-Michel Hornus. LC 79-26846. (Christian Peace Shelf Ser.). 376p. 1980. pap. 15.95 (ISBN 0-8361-1911-8). Herald Pr.

It Is Written. Cecil J. Blay. 120p. 1973. text ed. 4.00 (ISBN 0-910424-62-4). Concordant.

It Only Hurts Between Paydays. Amy R. Mumford. LC 80-70679. 160p. 1986. pap. 5.95 (ISBN 0-89636-067-9). Accent Bks.

It Removes the Misconceptions about Caliphs' Caliphate. M. A. Sattar. 416p. 1985. pap. 19.00 (ISBN 0-941724-36-0). Islamic Seminary.

It Seems to Me. Philip E. Collier. 1982. 4.95 (ISBN 0-86544-019-0). Salv Army Suppl South.

It Shouldn't Hurt to Be a Child. Dianne Vasi. Ed. by Richard W. Coffen. (Better Living Ser.). 32p. (Orig.). 1985. pap. 0.99 (ISBN 0-8280-0310-6). Review & Herald.

It Takes so Little to Be above Average. Florence Litthauer. 192p. 1983. pap. 4.95 (ISBN 0-89081-376-0). Harvest Hse.

It Was Always Africa. Pam Brown. LC 86-2240. (YA) 1986. pap. 4.95 (ISBN 0-8054-4335-5). Broadman.

It Works. 31st ed. R. H. Jarrett. 1976. pap. 1.00 (ISBN 0-87516-323-8). De Vorss.

Itala: Das Neue Testament in Altlateinischer Ueberlieferung, Vols. 1-2 & 4. Ed. by A. Juelicher et al. Incl. Vol. 1. Matthaeus-Evangelium. rev. 2nd ed. viii, 160p. 1972. 84.00 (ISBN 3-11-002256-7); Vol. 2. Marcus-Evangelium. x, 230p. 1970. 76.00 (ISBN 3-11-001244-8); Vol. 4. Johannes-Evangelium. x, 230p. 1963. 96.00x (ISBN 3-11-001243-X). (Ger.). De Gruyter.

Itala: Das Neue Testament in Altlateinischer Ueberlieferung, Vol. 3. 2nd ed. Ed. by A. Juelicher et al. viii, 282p. 1976. 162.25x (ISBN 3-11-002255-9). De Gruyter.

Italian-American History: The Italian Contribution to the Catholic Church in America. Giovanni E. Schiavo. LC 74-17948. (Italian American Experience Ser: Vol. No. 2). (Illus.). 1975. Repr. 70.50x (ISBN 0-405-06429-2). Ayer Co Pubs.

Italian Benedictine Scholars & the Reformation: The Congregation of Santa Giustina of Padua. Barry Collett. (Historical Monographs). 300p. 1985. 48.00x (ISBN 0-19-822934-8). Oxford U Pr.

Italian Cardinals, Reform, & the Church As Property, 1492-1563. Barbara M. Hallman. LC 84-8501. (Center for Medieval & Renaissance Studies, UCLA Publications: No. 22). 1985. 35.00x (ISBN 0-520-04937-3). U of Cal Pr.

Italian Crusade: The Papal-Angevin Alliance & the Crusades Against Christian Lay Powers, 1254-1343. Norman Housley. (Illus.). 1982. 47.50x (ISBN 0-19-821925-3). Oxford U Pr.

Italian Renaissance Illuminations. Ed. by J. J. Alexander. LC 77-2841. (Magnificent Paperback Ser.). (Illus.). 1977. 19.95 (ISBN 0-8076-0863-7); pap. 11.95 (ISBN 0-8076-0864-5). Braziller.

Italian Ritual. (Rubrics in Italian & English). Blue Cloth 4.95 (ISBN 0-89942-111-3, 111/22). Catholic Bk Pub.

Italians & the Holocaust: Persecution, Rescue & Survival. Susan Zuccotti. LC 86-47738. (Illus.). 344p. 1987. 19.95 (ISBN 0-465-03622-8). Basic.

Italy & the Vatican at War: A Study of Their Relations from the Outbreak of the Franco-Prussian War to the Death of Pius 9th. Samuel W. Halperin. LC 68-57606. (Illus.). 1968. Repr. of 1939 ed. lib. bdg. 22.50x (ISBN 0-8371-0461-0, HAIV). Greenwood.

Italy, Mount Athos & Muscovy: The Three Worlds of Maximos the Greek. D. Obolensky. (Raleigh Lectures on History). 1981. pap. 3.00 (ISBN 0-85672-323-1, Pub. by British Acad). Longwood Pub Group.

Itching Ears. Kenneth Hagin, Jr. 1982. pap. 0.50 mini bk. (ISBN 0-89276-711-1). Hagin Ministries.

Itinera Hierosolymitana, Saeculi 3-8. Ed. by Paul Geyer. (Corpus Scriptorum Ecclesiasticorum Latinorum Ser: Vol. 39). Repr. of 1898 ed. 40.00 (ISBN 0-384-18270-4). Johnson Repr.

Itineraire De Paris a Jerusalem. Rene de Chateaubriand & Jean Mourot. 448p. 1968. 3.50 (ISBN 0-686-54365-3). French & Eur.

Itinerario De la Pasion: Meditaciones De la Semana Santa. Cecilio Arrastia. 1985. pap. 2.95 (ISBN 0-311-43036-8). Casa Bautista.

Itinerarium Mentis in Deum. Philotheus Boehner. (Works of Saint Bonaventure Ser). 1956. 3.50 (ISBN 0-686-11591-0). Franciscan Inst.

Itinerary of Benjamin of Tudela. Adler. Tr. by Marcus N. Adler. LC 68-9344. 1964. 25.00 (ISBN 0-87306-033-4). Feldheim.

It's a Different World! The Challenge for Today's Pastor. Lyle E. Schaller. 240p. 1987. pap. 10.95 (ISBN 0-687-19729-5). Abingdon.

It's a Mystery to Me, Lord: Bible Devotions for Boys. David A. Sorensen. LC 85-22993. (Young Readers Ser.). 112p. (Orig.). 1985. pap. 3.95 (ISBN 0-8066-2183-4, 10-3445). Augsburg.

It's a Young World after All. Paul D. Ackerman. 128p. 1986. pap. 6.95 (ISBN 0-8010-0204-4). Baker Bk.

It's All about Jesus. Allan H. Jahsmann. LC 74-21233. (Illus.). 160p. 1975. pap. 5.95 (ISBN 0-570-03031-5, 6-1157). Concordia.

It's All There If You Want It: And Here Is the Map. Jack E. Blalock, Jr. LC 80-69519. 200p. (Orig.). 1981. 12.95 (ISBN 0-9605156-0-7); pap. 10.95 (ISBN 0-9605156-1-5). J Blalock.

It's Beautiful & Other Salvationist Verse. Ed. by The Salvation Army Literary Staff. (Illus.). 105p. (Orig.). 1984. pap. 3.50 (ISBN 0-89216-052-7). Salvation Army.

It's Been One of Those Days, Lord. Bob W. Brown. 144p. (Orig.). 1985. pap. 2.95 (ISBN 0-310-28912-2, 12773P). Zondervan.

It's Chanukah. Ellie Gellman. LC 85-80782. (Illus.). 12p. 1985. bds. 4.95 (ISBN 0-930494-51-2). Kar Ben.

It's Christmas! Poems & Stories for the Holiday Season. Laurene J. Tibbetts. 97p. 1981. write for info. Rector Pub.

It's Easy to Play Hymns. Cyril Watters. 1981. pap. 5.95. Music Sales.

It's Getting Gooder & Gooder. Hymie Rubenstein. (Orig.). 1976. pap. 4.95 (ISBN 0-89350-006-2). Fountain Pr.

It's Getting Late. Stanley M. Horton. LC 74-33869. 1975. pap. 1.25 (ISBN 0-88243-570-1, 02-0570). Gospel Pub.

It's Incredible. Ann Kiemel. 1977. pap. 2.50 (ISBN 0-8423-1818-6). Tyndale.

It's Midnight, Lord. Helder Camara. Tr. by Joseph Gallagher et al. (Illus., Orig.). 1984. pap. 7.95 (ISBN 0-912405-02-3). Pastoral Pr.

It's My Birthday, God: Psalm 90. Elspeth C. Murphy. (David & I Talk to God Ser.). (Illus.). 1982. misc. format 2.50 (ISBN 0-89191-580-X). Cook.

It's My Life: True-to-Life Stories for Young Teens. Michael L. Sherer. (Illus.). 112p. (Orig.). 1986. pap. 3.95 (ISBN 0-8066-2216-4, 10-3454). Augsburg.

It's My Move: Older Adults Choose How to Live. Dorthy Gager. 80p. (Orig.). 1987. pap. 7.95 (ISBN 0-88177-045-0, DR045B). Discipleship Res.

It's Not the Jewish Christmas. Norman Geller. (Illus.). 20p. 1985. pap. 4.95 (ISBN 0-915753-09-X). N Geller Pub.

It's Not the Same Old Me. Nils Donnell. 1975. pap. 2.00 (ISBN 0-88027-007-1). Firm Foun Pub.

It's OK to Be an MK. William C. Viser. (Orig.). 1986. pap. 7.95 (ISBN 0-8054-6337-2). Broadman.

It's Real. Mary H. Wallace. (Illus.). 224p. (Orig.). 1981. pap. 5.95 (ISBN 0-912315-17-2). Word Aflame.

It's Rosh-Hashanah. Ellie Gellman. LC 85-80783. (Illus.). 12p. 1985. bds. 4.95 (ISBN 0-930494-50-4). Kar Ben.

It's Sabbath. Leila M. Ashton. (My Church Teaches Ser.). (Illus.). 1978. pap. 1.95 (ISBN 0-8127-0177-1). Review & Herald.

It's So Simple. Frances Hunter. 1978. pap. 3.25 (ISBN 0-87162-130-4). Hunter Bks.

It's Sooner Than You Think. Gordon Lindsay. (Prophecy Ser.). 1.25 (ISBN 0-89985-057-X). Christ Nations.

It's Sunday Night Again? Donna Gladman. Ed. by Arthur L. Zapel. LC 79-84726. (Illus.). 1979. pap. text ed. 4.95 (ISBN 0-916260-04-6). Meriwether Pub.

It's the Truth, Christopher. Patricia C. McKissack. LC 84-71376. (Christopher Bks.). (Illus.). 32p. (Orig.). 1984. pap. 3.95 (ISBN 0-8066-2111-7, 10-3457). Augsburg.

It's Tough Being a Mother. Mari Rippey. 32p. 1983. pap. 2.95 (ISBN 0-8170-0995-7). Judson.

It's Tuesday Night Again: Planning This Week's Program for Youth Group & Clubs. Mary R. Marshall. (Australian Youth Leadership Ser.). (Illus.). 56p. (Orig.). 1983. pap. 6.95 (ISBN 0-85819-416-3, Pub. by JBCE). ANZ Religious Pubns.

It's Your Choice. Edwin L. Groenhoff. 1975. pap. 1.75 (ISBN 0-911802-38-X). Free Church Pubns.

It's Your Death, Make the Most of It. Harold Billnitzer. LC 79-88402. 1979. pap. 7.95 (ISBN 0-933350-27-9). wkbk. 0.90 (ISBN 0-933350-28-7). Morse Pr.

It's Your Souls We Want. Stewart W. Herman. LC 72-180406. Repr. of 1943 ed. 29.50 (ISBN 0-404-56130-6). AMS Pr.

Iustitia Dei: A History of the Doctrine of Justification. Alister E. McGrath. 250p. 1986. 39.50 (ISBN 0-521-30887-9). Cambridge U Pr.

Iustitia Dei: A History of the Doctrine of Justification, Vol. II--From the Reformation to the Present Day. Alister E. McGrath. 272p. 1986. 39.50 (ISBN 0-521-32274-X). Cambridge U Pr.

I've Found the Sheep. Alan T. Dale. (Rainbow Books, Bible Story Books for Children). 1976. pap. 1.00 (ISBN 0-8192-1206-7). Morehouse.

I've Got Mixed-Up Feelings, God. John Brown. 64p. 1984. pap. 3.95 (ISBN 0-8170-1035-1). Judson.

I've Got to Talk to Somebody. Marjorie Holmes. 144p. 1984. pap. 2.95 (ISBN 0-8007-8080-9, Spire Bks). Revell.

I've Got to Talk to Somebody, God. Marjorie Holmes. 160p. 1985. pap. 3.50 (ISBN 0-553-26428-1). Bantam.

I've Got to Talk to Somebody, God. Marjorie Holmes. LC 69-10938. 1969. 8.95 (ISBN 0-385-05209-X). Doubleday.

I've Got to Talk to Somebody, God. 15th, anniversary ed. Marjorie Holmes. LC 84-28724. 144p. 1985. pap. 5.95 (ISBN 0-385-19751-9, Galilee). Doubleday.

I've Taken a Page in the Bible. Alfred Marks. 208p. 1987. 14.95 (ISBN 0-86051-348-3). Parkwest Pubns.

Iz Missionersko-pastirskoj dejatel'nosti na Nivje Khristovoj v Emigratsii. Archpriest Mitrophan Znosko-Borovsky. Tr. of From My Missionary-Pastoral Activities in Christ's Field in the Immigration. 320p. 1985. pap. 12.00 (ISBN 0-317-29117-3). Holy Trinity.

J

J. B. Phillips: The Wounded Healer. Vera Phillips & Edwin Robertson. 120p. (Orig.). 1985. pap. 5.95 (ISBN 0-8028-0073-4). Eerdmans.

J. C. Ryle: A Self-Portrait. Peter Toon. 1975. 4.95 (ISBN 0-685-52822-7). Reiner.

J. J. Griesbach. Ed. by D. B. Orchard & R. W. Longstaff. LC 77-27405. (Society for New Testament Studies Monographs: No. 34). 1979. 32.50 (ISBN 0-521-21706-7). Cambridge U Pr.

J. M. Grant's Rigdon. J. M. Grant. 16p. (Orig.). 1984. pap. 1.95 (ISBN 0-942284-06-2). Restoration Re.

J. N. Andrews: The Man & the Mission. Ed. by Harry Leonard. xii, 355p. (Orig.). 1985. pap. 11.95 (ISBN 0-943872-91-X). Andrews Univ Pr.

J. Reuben Clark: The Public Years. Frank W. Fox. LC 80-17903. (J. Reuben Clark Three Vol. Ser.). (Illus.). 706p. 1980. 10.95 (ISBN 0-8425-1832-0). Brigham.

J. Ross Browne: A Biography. Francis J. Rock. 90p. 1984. Repr. of 1929 ed. 22.00x (ISBN 0-939738-21-X). Zubal Inc.

J. S. Bach & Liturgical Life in Liepzig. Gunther Stiller. Ed. by Robin A. Leaver. Tr. by Herbert J. Boutman et al from Ger. Tr. of Johann Sebastian Bach und das Leipziger Gottesdienstliche Leben Seiner Zeit. (Illus.). 312p. (Orig.). 1984. pap. 24.95 (ISBN 0-570-01320-8, 99-1247). Concordia.

Jacinta, Flower of Fatima. Joseph De Oliveira. 192p. 1972. pap. 3.95 (ISBN 0-911988-45-9). AMI Pr.

Jacinta of Fatima: Her Life as She Might Tell It. Robert J. Fox. 22p. 1982. pap. 1.00 (ISBN 0-911988-52-1). Ami Pr.

Jack: C. S. Lewis & His Times. George Sayer. LC 84-48778. (Illus.). 416p. 1985. 25.95 (ISBN 0-06-067072-X, HarpR). Har-Row.

Jacksonian Jew: The Two Worlds of Mordecai Noah. Jonathan D. Sarna. LC 79-24379. 245p. 1981. text ed. 35.00x (ISBN 0-8419-0567-3). Holmes & Meier.

Jacob. 1979. 0.75 (ISBN 0-8198-0581-5). Dghtrs St Paul.

Jacob & Esau. Adapted by Diana Craig. LC 84-51684. (Bible Stories Ser.). (Illus.). 24p. 1984. 5.45 (ISBN 0-382-06944-7); PLB 5.96 (ISBN 0-382-06795-9). Silver.

Jacob & Esau. LC 78-133688. (Tudor Facsimile Texts. Old English Plays: No. 40). Repr. of 1908 ed. 49.50 (ISBN 0-404-53340-X). AMS Pr.

Jacob & His Son, Joseph. Gordon Lindsay. (Old Testament Ser.). 1.25 (ISBN 0-89985-129-0). Christ Nations.

Jacob & the Angel: An Essay in Sociologies of Religion. Henri Desroche. Ed. & tr. by John K. Savacool. LC 72-77575. 196p. 1973. 15.00x (ISBN 0-87023-109-X). U of Mass Pr.

Jacob & the Star. Mary Matthews. 1986. pap. 7.95 (ISBN 0-8192-1384-5). Morehouse.

Jacob Boehme: Insights into the Challenge of Evil. Ann Liem. LC 77-79823. 32p. (Orig.). 1977. pap. 2.50x (ISBN 0-87574-214-9). Pendle Hill.

Jacob Boehme, "The Way to Christ". Peter C. Erb. LC 77-95117. (Classics of Western Spirituality). 336p. 1978. 13.95 (ISBN 0-8091-0237-4); pap. 7.95 o. p. (ISBN 0-8091-2102-6). Paulist Pr.

Jacob Boehme's "The Way to Christ". Jacob Boehme. Tr. by John J. Stoudt. LC 78-13976. 1979. Repr. of 1947 ed. lib. bdg. 22.50x (ISBN 0-313-21075-6, BOTW). Greenwood.

Jacob Fontaine: From Slavery to the Greatness of the Pulpit, Press, & Public Service. Jacob Fontaine, III & Gene Burd. 96p. 1984. pap. 6.95 (ISBN 0-89015-438-4). Eakin Pr.

Jacob: God's Plain Man. Lillian Cantleberry. 1984. pap. 7.95 (ISBN 0-570-03928-2, 12-2863). Concordia.

Jacob Hamblin: Mormon Apostle to the Indians. Juanita Brooks. LC 80-80395. (Illus.). 160p. 1980. pap. 6.95 (ISBN 0-935704-03-5). Howe Brothers.

Jacob, The Supplanter Who Became a Prince with God. Gordon Lindsay. (Old Testament Ser.). 1.25 (ISBN 0-89985-128-2). Christ Nations.

Jacob's Ladder: A Choral Reading. Wally M. Shearburn. 1980. 4.00 (ISBN 0-89536-441-7, 1014). CSS of Ohio.

Jacob's Ladder & the Tree of Life: Concepts of Hierarchy & the Great Chain of Being. Paul G. Kuntz & Marion L. Kuntz. (American University Studies V-Philosophy: Vol. 14). 444p. 1987. text ed. 40.00 (ISBN 0-8204-0233-8). P Lang Pubs.

Jacob's Ladder: Bible Picture Book from Anglo-Saxon & 12th Century English MSS. Ed. by Nicolette Gray. 1978. Repr. of 1949 ed. lib. bdg. 25.00 (ISBN 0-8495-1948-9). Arden Lib.

Jacob's Ladder: Theology & Spirituality in the Thought of Austin Farrer. Charles C. Hefling, Jr. LC 80-117760. xiii, 132p. (Orig.). 1979. pap. 5.00 (ISBN 0-936384-01-8). Cowley Pubns.

Jacob's Pillar. E. Raymond Capt. LC 79-116385. (Illus.). 96p. 1977. pap. 3.00 (ISBN 0-934666-03-2). Artisan Sales.

Jacob's Well, an English Treatise on the Cleansing of Man's Conscience, Pt. 1. Ed. by Arthur Brandeis. (EETS, OS Ser.: No. 115). Repr. of 1900 ed. 54.00 (ISBN 0-527-00114-7). Kraus Repr.

Jacopo Sannazaro & the Uses of Pastoral. William J. Kennedy. LC 83-40011. 248p. 1983. pap. 22.50x (ISBN 0-87451-268-9). U Pr of New Eng.

Jacques Maritain & the French Catholic Intellectuals. Bernard Doering. LC 82-40377. 288p. 1983. text ed. 22.95. U of Notre Dame Pr.

Jacques Maritain, Antimodern or Ultramodern? B. W. Smith. 1976. 27.95 (ISBN 0-444-99013-5, SIM/, Pub. by Elsevier). Greenwood.

Jacques Maritain: Homage in Words & Pictures. John H. Griffin & Yves R. Simon. LC 73-85056. (Illus.). 1974. 12.95x (ISBN 0-87343-046-8). Magi Bks.

Jade: A Study in Chinese Archaeology & Religion. Berthold Laufer. LC 74-81085. (Illus.). 480p. 1975. pap. 6.95 (ISBN 0-486-23123-2). Dover.

Jade: A Study in Chinese Archaeology & Religion. Berthold Laufer. (Field Museum of Natural History). (Illus.). 1912. 41.00 (ISBN 0-527-01870-8). Kraus Repr.

Jade: A Study in Chinese Archaeology & Religion. Berthold Laufer. (Illus.). 15.25 (ISBN 0-8446-5214-8). Peter Smith.

Jahwe, Juda und die anderen Voelker beim Proheton Jesaja. Friedrich Huber. (Beiheft 137 Zur Zeitschrift Fuer die Alttestamentliche Wissenschaft). (Ger.). 1976. 46.40 (ISBN 3-11-005729-8). De Gruyter.

Jain Cosmology. Collette Caillat. (Illus.). 192p. 1982. 55.00 (ISBN 0-517-54662-0, Harmony). Crown.

Jaina Art & Architecture, 3 vols. A. Ghosh. (Illus.). 1974. Set. text ed. 110.00x. Coronet Bks.

Jaina Community. 2nd ed. Vilas Sanghavi. 455p. 1980. 29.95 (ISBN 0-317-12346-7, Pub. by Popular Pubns India). Asia Bk Corp.

Jaina Path of Purification. Padmanabh S. Jaini. LC 77-73496. 1979. 35.95x (ISBN 0-520-03459-7). U of Cal Pr.

Jaina Philosophy of Non-Absolutism. Satkari Mookerjee. 1978. 15.00 (ISBN 0-89684-021-2, Pub. by Motilal Banarsidass India). Orient Bk Dist.

Jaina Philosophy of Non-Absolutism. 2nd ed. Satkari Mookerjee. 24.00x (ISBN 0-89684-021-2). South Asia Bks.

Jaina Stories. Tr. by K. C. Lalwani. 1985. 15.00x (ISBN 0-317-31633-8, Pub. by Arthat Prakashon). South Asia Bks.

Jaina, Sutras. T. W. Davids. (Sacred Bks. of the East Ser.: Vol. 22, 45). both vols. 36.00 (ISBN 0-89581-525-7); 15.00 ea. Asian Human Pr.

Jaina Theories of Reality & Knowledge. Umrao S. Bist. 1985. 6.50x (ISBN 0-8364-1362-8, Pub. by Eastern). South Asia Bks.

Jaina Theory of Perception. Pushpa Bothra. 1976. 11.95 (ISBN 0-89684-229-0). Orient Bk Dist.

Jainism: A Select Bibliography. Satyaprakash. 1984. 12.50x (ISBN 0-8364-1224-9, Pub. by Indian Doc Serv India). South Asia Bks.

Jainism in Early Medieval Karnataka. R. B. Singh. 1976. 9.95 (ISBN 0-8426-0981-4). Orient Bk Dist.

Jajal Al-Din Al-Suywti, 2 vols. E. M. Sartain. Incl. Vol. 1. Biography & Background. 230p. 44.50 (ISBN 0-521-20547-6); Vol. 2. Al-Tahadduth bini'mat allah. 370p. 52.50 (ISBN 0-521-20546-8). LC 74-82226. (Oriental Publications Ser.: Nos. 23 & 24). 1975. Set. 86.00 (ISBN 0-521-20633-2). Cambridge U Pr.

Jamaa & the Church: A Bantu Catholic Movement in Zaire. Willy De Craemer. (Oxford Studies in African Affairs). 1977. 58.00x (ISBN 0-19-822708-6). Oxford U Pr.

Jamaica: Its Past & Present State. James M. Phillippo. LC 70-109998. (Illus.). Repr. of 1843 ed. 23.75x (ISBN 0-8371-4132-X, PIA&, Pub. by Negro U Pr). Greenwood.

Jambalaya: The Natural Woman's Book of Personal Charms & Practical Rituals. Luisah Teish. LC 85-42793. (Illus.). 240p. 1985. 15.95 (ISBN 0-06-250860-1, HarpR). Har-Row.

James. Martin Dibelius. Ed. by Helmut Koester. Tr. by Michael A. Willims. LC 74-80428. (Hermeneia: a Critical & Historical Commentary on the Bible). 308p. 1975. 24.95 (ISBN 0-8006-6006-4, 20-6006). Fortress.

James. Vernon Doerkson. (Everyman's Bible Commentaries Ser.). (Orig.). 1983. pap. 5.95 (ISBN 0-8024-0242-9). Moody.

James. Irving L. Jensen. (Bible Self-Study Ser). (Illus.). 1972. pap. 3.25 (ISBN 0-8024-1059-6). Moody.

James. Robert Johnstone. (Geneva Commentaries Ser.). 1977. 15.95 (ISBN 0-85151-257-7). Banner of Truth.

James. Thomas Manton. 1983. 15.95 (ISBN 0-85151-074-4). Banner of Truth.

James. Douglas Moo. Ed. by R. V. Tasker. (Tyndale New Testament Commentary Ser.). 176p. (Orig.). 1987. pap. 4.95 (ISBN 0-8028-0079-3). Eerdmans.

James. Lehman Strauss. 1956. 8.95 (ISBN 0-87213-818-6). Loizeaux.

James, Pt. 1. rev. ed. G. Michael Cocoris. 51p. 1984. pap. text ed. 1.00 (ISBN 0-935729-12-7). Church Open Door.

James, Pt. 2. rev. ed. G. Michael Cocoris. 43p. 1984. pap. text ed. 1.00 (ISBN 0-935729-13-5). Church Open Door.

James: A Good News Commentary. Peter H. Davids. LC 83-47720. (Good News Commentary Ser.). 176p. (Orig.). 1983. pap. 7.95 (ISBN 0-06-061697-0, RD-499, HarpR). Har-Row.

James Alberione: A Marvel for Our Times. Stephen Lamera. (Illus.). 1977. 4.00 (ISBN 0-8198-0428-2); pap. 3.00 (ISBN 0-8198-0429-0). Dghtrs St Paul.

James & Jude. Richard Kugelman. (New Testament Message Ser.: Vol. 19). 10.95 (ISBN 0-89453-207-3); pap. 5.95 (ISBN 0-89453-142-5). M Glazier.

James: Apostle of Practical Christianity. Robert P. Lightner. LC 81-70775. (Chosen Messengers Ser.). 128p. (Orig.). 1982. pap. text ed. 3.50 (ISBN 0-89636-079-2). Accent Bks.

James Barr & the Bible: Critique of a New Liberalism. Paul R. Wells. 1980. pap. 12.00 (ISBN 0-87552-546-6). Presby & Reformed.

James: Belief in Action. Keith L. Brooks. (Teach Yourself the Bible Ser.). 1961. pap. 2.75 (ISBN 0-8024-4227-7). Moody.

James: Bible Study Commentary. Curtis Vaughan. pap. 4.95 (ISBN 0-310-33553-1, 10955P). Zondervan.

James Burnett Monboddo (1714-1799) Antient Metaphysics, 6 Vol., 1779-99. Ed. by Rene Wellek. LC 75-11236. (British Philosophers & Theologians of the 17th & 18th Centuries Ser.). 1977. lib. bdg. 46.00 (ISBN 0-8240-1789-7). Garland Pub.

James City County, Virginia 1634-1659, Vol. 4. Lindsay O. Duvall. (Virginia Colonial Abstracts, Series II). 1979. Repr. of 1957 ed. 20.00 (ISBN 0-89308-065-9). Southern Hist Pr.

James Duhig. T. P. Boland. LC 86-15654. (Illus.). 435p. 1987. text ed. 37.50x (ISBN 0-7022-2011-6). U of Queensland Pr.

James: Faith in Action. Chuck Christensen & Winnie Christensen. LC 75-33442. (Fisherman Bible Studyguide Ser.). 55p. 1975. saddle-stitched 2.95 (ISBN 0-87788-421-8). Shaw Pubs.

James: Faith in Action. Richard A. Hufton. 146p. (Orig.). 1984. pap. 4.00 (ISBN 0-933643-03-9). Grace World Outreach.

James: Faith That Works. Andrew T. LePeau & Phyllis J. LePeau. (LifeGuide Bible Studies). 64p. (Orig.). 1987. pap. 2.95. Inter-Varsity.

James Grenehalgh As Textual Critic. Michael G. Sargent. Ed. by James Hogg. (Analecta Cartusiana Ser.: No. 85/1&2). 589p. (Orig.). 1984. pap. 50.00 (ISBN 3-7052-0142-5, Pub. by Salzburg Studies). Longwood Pub Group.

James: Hear It! Live It! Bob Couchman & Win Couchman. (Carpenter Studyguide Ser.). 1982. saddle-stitched leader's handbook, 61p 2.95 (ISBN 0-87788-423-4); member's handbook, 64p 1.95 (ISBN 0-87788-422-6). Shaw Pubs.

James: Hebrews, Peter. H. A. Ironside. 9.95 (ISBN 0-87213-399-0). Loizeaux.

James Joyce's Pauline Vision: A Catholic Exposition. Robert Boyle. LC 78-18901. 133p. 1978. 10.95x (ISBN 0-8093-0861-4). S Ill U Pr.

James, Jude & II Peter. E. M. Sidebottom. (New Century Bible Ser). 142p. 1967. 7.50 (ISBN 0-551-00590-4). Attic Pr.

James, Jude, II Peter. E. M. Sidebottom. Ed. by Matthew Black. (The New Century Bible Commentary Ser.). 130p. 1982. pap. 5.95 (ISBN 0-8028-1936-2). Eerdmans.

James Madison on Religious Liberty. Ed. by Robert Alley. LC 85-42957. 343p. 1985. 19.95 (ISBN 0-87975-298-X). Prometheus Bks.

James Nayler: The Quaker Indicted by Parliament. Willliam G. Bittle. 248p. (Orig.). 1987. pap. 14.95x (ISBN 1-85072-015-0). Friends United.

James: Roadmap for Down-to-Earth Christians. Margaret Fromer & Carolyn Nystrom. (Young Fisherman Bible Studyguide Ser.). (Illus.). 89p. 1982. saddle-stiched tchr's. ed. 4.95 (ISBN 0-87788-420-X); student ed. 2.95 (ISBN 0-87788-419-6). Shaw Pubs.

James Shore's Daughter. Stephen V. Benet. 277p. 1985. Repr. of 1934 ed. lib. bdg. 30.00 (ISBN 0-918377-67-6). Russell Pr.

James Stewart, Earl of Moray: A Political Study of the Reformation in Scotland. Maurice Lee. LC 73-104251. 1971. Repr. of 1953 ed. lib. bdg. 22.50x (ISBN 0-8371-3975-9, LEJS). Greenwood.

James the Just in the Habakkuk Pesher. Robert H. Eisenman. (Studia Post-Biblica Ser.: Vol. 35). x, 110p. 1986. pap. 17.25 (ISBN 90-04-07587-9, Pub. by E J Brill). Heinman.

James: The Man & His Message. James B. Adamson. 432p. (Orig.). 1987. pap. 16.95 (ISBN 0-8028-0167-6). Eerdmans.

James: The Most American Book in the Bible. Henry R. Rust. 70p. (Orig.). 1985. pap. 6.95 (ISBN 0-940754-31-2). Ed Ministries.

James Ussher, Archbishop of Armagh: 1581-1656. Robert B. Knox. 205p. 1968. text ed. 17.50x (ISBN 0-7083-0061-8, Pub. by U of Wales). Humanities.

James Warrington: Short Titles of Books, Relating to or Illustrating the History & Practice of Psalmody in the United States,1620-1820. Ed. by Theodore M. Finney. LC 70-18250. (Bibliographia Tripotamopolitana: No.1). 1970. 6.00x (ISBN 0-931222-00-1). Pitts Theolog.

James White. Virgil Robinson. LC 75-16921. (Illus.). 1976. 9.95 (ISBN 0-8280-0049-2). Review & Herald.

Jami: Yusuf & Zulaika. David Pendlebury. 1980. 16.95 (ISBN 0-900860-77-4). Ins Study Human.

Jamieson, Fausset & Brown's Commentary on the Whole Bible. 1957. 24.95 (ISBN 0-310-26570-3, 9930). Zondervan.

Jamil: The Child Christ. Gene Savoy. LC 73-92360. (Sacred Teachings of Light Ser.: Codex I). 118p. 1976. text ed. 25.00 (ISBN 0-936202-00-9). Intl Comm Christ.

Janissa. Robert T. Newcomb. 1943. 8.00 (ISBN 0-685-08807-3). Destiny.

Jansenism in Seventeenth-Century France: Voices from the Wilderness. Alexander Sedgwick. LC 77-2812. 243p. 1977. 20.00x (ISBN 0-8139-0702-0). U Pr of Va.

Jansenists & the Expulsion of the Jesuits from France, 1757-1765. Dale Van Kley. LC 74-26390. (Yale Historical Publication. Miscellany Ser.: No. 107). pap. 70.50 (ISBN 0-317-09445-9, 2022046). Bks Demand UMI.

Jap Ji: Message of Guru Nanak. 5th ed. Ed. & tr. by Kirpal Singh. 182p. 1976. pap. 3.50 (ISBN 0-89142-029-0). Sant Bani Ash.

Japa. Sri M. Pandit. 41p. 1979. Repr. of 1959 ed. 1.95 (ISBN 0-941524-09-4). Lotus Light.

Japa Reform Notebook. Satsvarupa das Goswami. Ed. by Bimala Dasi & Mandalesvara Dasa. 144p. (Orig.). 1982. pap. text ed. 3.95 (ISBN 0-911233-07-5). Gita Nagari.

Japan Journey: The Columban Fathers in Nippon. Edward Fischer. LC 84-14228. 208p. 1984. pap. 9.95 (ISBN 0-8245-0656-1). Crossroad NY.

Japanese Bon Dance in Hawaii. Judy Van Zile. (Illus.). 96p. 1982. pap. 5.95 (ISBN 0-916630-27-7). Pr Pacifica.

Japanese Buddhism: Its Tradition, New Religions & Interaction with Christianity. Ed. by Minoru Kiyota et al. 1987. 24.50 (ISBN 0-914910-76-0). Buddhist Bks.

Japanese Lacquer: Selected Pieces. Pierre-F. Schneeberger. Tr. by K. Watson. (Baur Collection Ser.). (Illus.). 193p. 1985. 195.00 (ISBN 0-7102-0320-9). Methuen Inc.

Japanese Mythology. rev. ed. Juliet Piggott. LC 83-71480. (Library of the World's Myths & Legends). (Illus.). 144p. 1983. 18.95 (ISBN 0-911745-09-2). P Bedrick Bks.

Japanese Mythology. Juliet Piggott. (Library of the World's Myths & Legends). (Illus.). 144p. PLB 16.95 (ISBN 0-317-31009-7). Creative Ed.

Japanese New Religion: Rissho Kosei-Kai in a Mountain Hamlet. Stewart E. Guthrie. LC 86-33446. (Michigan Papers in Japanese Studies: No. 16). 1987. text ed. 20.00 (ISBN 0-939512-33-5); pap. 10.00 (ISBN 0-939512-34-3). U Mi Japan.

Japanese Pilgrimage. Oliver Statler. (Illus.). 352p. 1985. pap. 9.95 (ISBN 0-688-04834-X, Quill). Morrow.

Japanese Religion: A Cultural Perspective. Robert S. Ellwood & Richard Pilgrim. (Illus.). 192p. 1985. pap. text ed. 16.00 (ISBN 0-13-509282-5). P-H.

Japanese Religion: A Survey by the Agency for Cultural Affairs. LC 80-85584. (Illus.). 272p. 1981. pap. 6.25 (ISBN 0-87011-467-0). Kodansha.

Japanese Religion in the Modern Century. Shigeyoshi Murakami. Tr. by H. Byron Earhart. 186p. 1979. 18.50x (ISBN 0-86008-260-1, Pub. by U of Tokyo Japan). Columbia U Pr.

Japanese Religion: Unity & Diversity. 3rd ed. H. Byron Earhart. 288p. 1982. pap. text ed. write for info. (ISBN 0-534-01028-8). Wadsworth Pub.

Japanese Spirit. Y. Okakura. lib. bdg. 79.95 (ISBN 0-87968-549-2). Krishna Pr.

Japanese Traditions of Christianity: Being Some Old Translations from the Japanese, with British Consular Reports of the Persecutions of 1868-1872. Ed. by Montague Paske-Smith. (Studies in Japanese History & Civilization). 1979. Repr. of 1930 ed. 17.50 (ISBN 0-89093-257-3). U Pubns Amer.

Japan's New Buddhism: An Objective Account of Soka Gakkai. Kiyoaki Murata. LC 74-83640. (Illus.). 216p. 1969. 8.50 (ISBN 0-8348-0040-3). Weatherhill.

Japan's Religious Ferment: Christian Presence Amid Faiths Old & New. Raymond Hammer. LC 85-14867. (Christian Presence Ser.). 207p. 1985. Repr. of 1962 ed. lib. bdg. 39.75x (ISBN 0-313-24921-0, HAJR). Greenwood.

Japji. Guru Nanak. Tr. by Sangat Singh from Punjabi. 128p. (Orig.). 1974. pap. 2.25 (ISBN 0-88253-317-7). Ind-US Inc.

Japuji: The Immortal Prayer-Chant. Gurbachan Singh Talib. 1977. 7.00x (ISBN 0-88386-967-5). South Asia Bks.

Jason & the Golden Fleece. Adapted by C. J. Naden. LC 80-50068. (Illus.). 32p. 1980. PLB 9.79 (ISBN 0-89375-360-2); pap. 2.50 (ISBN 0-89375-364-5). Troll Assocs.

Jason Lee: Prophet of the New Oregon. Cornelius J. Brosnan. LC 84-71620. (Illus.). 376p. 1985. pap. text ed. 12.00 (ISBN 0-914960-52-0). Academy Bks.

Java Saga. David Bentley-Taylor. Orig. Title: Weathercocks Reward. 1975. pap. 2.25 (ISBN 0-85363-100-X). OMF Bks.

Jazz Chants for Children. Carolyn Graham. (Illus.). 1979. pap. text ed. 7.50x (ISBN 0-19-502496-6); tchrs ed. 10.95x (ISBN 0-19-502497-4); cassette 12.00x (ISBN 0-19-502575-X); tchrs' ed & cassette 16.00x (ISBN 0-19-502576-8). Oxford U Pr.

Je Crois en Dieu. Paul Claudel. 432p. 1961. 8.95 (ISBN 0-686-54394-7). French & Eur.

Je m'explique. Pierre Teilhard De Chardin. 13.50 (ISBN 0-685-36593-X). French & Eur.

Jean-Paul Sartre: The Existentialist Ethic. Norman N. Greene. LC 80-12203. vii, 213p. 1980. Repr. of 1960 ed. lib. bdg. 22.50x (ISBN 0-313-22422-6, GRJP). Greenwood.

Jean Rhys: Woman in Passage. Helen Nebeker. 250p. (Orig.). 1981. pap. 8.95 (ISBN 0-920792-04-9). Eden Pr.

Jeanne d'Arc. Margaret O. Oliphant. LC 73-14460. (Heroes of the Nations Series). Repr. of 1896 ed. 30.00 (ISBN 0-404-58278-8). AMS Pr.

Jeddah Old & New. rev. ed. Ed. by James Buchan et al. (Illus.). 144p. 1986. Repr. of 1980 ed. 32.50 (ISBN 0-905743-22-9, Pub. by Stacey Intl UK). Humanities.

Jeddah Old & New. Stacey. (Illus.). 1980. 45.00x (ISBN 0-686-47159-8). Intl Bk Ctr.

Jedidiah Morse: A Champion of New England Orthodoxy. James K. Morse. LC 39-11247. Repr. of 1939 ed. 10.00 (ISBN 0-404-04504-9). AMS Pr.

Jedidiah Morse & New England Congregationalism. Joseph W. Phillips. 305p. 1983. 30.00x (ISBN 0-8135-0982-3). Rutgers U Pr.

Jefferson on Religion in Public Education. Robert M. Healey. LC 73-114422. xi, 294p. 1970. Repr. of 1962 ed. 27.50 (ISBN 0-208-00841-1, Archon). Shoe String.

Jefferson's Extracts from the Gospels: "The Philosophy of Jesus" & "The Life & Morals of Jesus". Ed. by Dickinson W. Adams. LC 82-61371. (Papers of Thomas Jefferson, Second Ser.). 456p. 1986. text ed. 31.50 (ISBN 0-691-04699-9); pap. text ed. 14.50 (ISBN 0-691-10210-4). Princeton U Pr.

Jeff's Happy Day. Beverly Fiday. (Happy Day Bks.). (Illus.). 24p. 1984. 1.59 (ISBN 0-87239-740-8, 3710). Standard Pub.

Jehad in Islam. A. H. Siddiqui. pap. 2.75 (ISBN 0-686-63906-5). Kazi Pubns.

Jehovah of the Watchtower. Walter Martin & Norman H. Klann. 192p. 1981. pap. 5.95 (ISBN 0-87123-267-7, 210267). Bethany Hse.

Jehovah's Witness & Kindred Groups: An Historical Compendium & Bibliography. Jerry Bergman. LC 83-47603. (Social Science Ser.). 414p. 1985. lib. bdg. 58.00 (ISBN 0-8240-9109-4). Garland Pub.

Jehovah's Witness Finds the Truth. Ed. by Richard Hickman. 115p. (Orig.). 1983. pap. 4.95 (ISBN 0-914605-00-3). Love Agape Min.

Jehovah's Witness: Not Just Another Denomination. Gordon E. Duggar. (Illus.). 144p. 1982. 8.00 (ISBN 0-682-49874-2). Exposition Pr FL.

Jehovah's Witnesses. Anthony A. Hoekema. 1974. pap. 4.95 (ISBN 0-8028-1489-1). Eerdmans.

Jehovah's Witnesses. Salem Kirban. (Illus.). 1972. pap. 4.95 (ISBN 0-912582-03-0). Kirban.

Jehovah's Witnesses. Walter Martin. 64p. 1969. pap. 2.95 (ISBN 0-87123-270-7, 210270). Bethany Hse.

Jehovah's Witnesses & Prophetic Speculation. Edmond C. Gruss. pap. 5.95 (ISBN 0-8010-3710-7). Baker Bk.

Jehovah's Witnesses & Prophetic Speculation. Edmond C. Gruss. 1972. pap. 5.95 (ISBN 0-87552-306-4). Presby & Reformed.

Jehovah's Witnesses Answered Verse By Verse. David A. Reed. 1987. pap. 5.95 (ISBN 0-8010-7739-7). Baker Bk.

Jehovah's Witnesses Errors Exposed. William J. Schnell. pap. 6.95 (ISBN 0-8010-8074-6). Baker Bk.

Jehovah's Witnesses' New Testament: A Critical Analysis. Robert H. Countess. 1982. pap. 5.95 (ISBN 0-87552-210-6). Presby & Reformed.

Jehovah's Witnesses: Watchout for the Watchtower! Gordon E. Duggar. 144p. 1985. pap. 5.95 (ISBN 0-8010-2955-4). Baker Bk.

Jekyll & Hyde Syndrome. Stephen H. Shoemaker. (Orig.). 1987. text ed. 9.95 (ISBN 0-8054-1538-6). Broadman.

Jellyfish Bones the Humor of Zen. Donald Gilbert. Ed. by Richard Angilly. (Illus.). 168p. (Orig.). 1980. pap. 7.95x (ISBN 0-931290-25-2). Blue Dragon.

Jenny Wren. Dawn L. Watkins. (English Skills for Christian Schools Ser.). (Illus., Orig.). 1986. pap. 4.95 (ISBN 0-89084-324-4). Bob Jones Univ Pr.

Jensen's Survey of the New Testament. Irving L. Jensen. 608p. 1981. text ed. 19.95 (ISBN 0-8024-4308-7). Moody.

Jensen's Survey of the Old Testament. Irving L. Jensen. 1978. text ed. 19.95 (ISBN 0-8024-4307-9). Moody.

Jephthah & His Vow. David Marcus. 80p. 1986. 25.00 (ISBN 0-89672-136-1); pap. 15.00 (ISBN 0-89672-135-3). Tex Tech Univ Pr.

Jephthah & Samson. Gordon Lindsay. (Old Testament Ser.). 1.25 (ISBN 0-89985-136-3). Christ Nations.

Jeremiah. Elizabeth Achtemeier. Ed. by John H. Hayes. LC 86-45402. (Preaching Guides). 120p. (Orig.). 1987. pap. 7.95 (ISBN 0-8042-3222-9). John Knox.

Jeremiah. Tr. by John Bright. LC 65-13603. (Anchor Bible Ser.: Vol. 21). 1965. 20.00 (ISBN 0-385-00823-6, Anchor Pr). Doubleday.

Jeremiah. A. Cohen. 369p. 1949. 10.95 (ISBN 0-900689-29-3). Soncino Pr.

Jeremiah, 2 pts. Neal Flanagan. (Bible Ser.). Pt. 1. pap. 1.00 (ISBN 0-8091-5071-9); Pt. 2. pap. 1.00 (ISBN 0-8091-5072-7). Paulist Pr.

Jeremiah. Theodore Laetsch. pap. 13.95 (ISBN 0-570-03218-0, 15-2003). Concordia.

Jeremiah. Elmer A. Martens. LC 86-9958. (Believers Church Bible Commentary Ser.). 328p. (Orig.). 1986. pap. 17.95 (ISBN 0-8361-3405-2). Herald Pr.

Jeremiah. F. B. Meyer. 1972. pap. 4.50 (ISBN 0-87508-355-2). Chr Lit.

Jeremiah, a Commentary. Robert P. Carroll. LC 85-13655. (Old Testament Library). 880p. 1986. 38.95 (ISBN 0-664-21835-0). Westminster.

Jeremiah: A New Translation. Illus. by Nikos Stavroulakis. (Illus.). 92p. 1973. 12.50 (ISBN 0-8276-0027-5). Jewish Pubns.

Jeremiah: A Study in Ancient Hebrew Rhetoric. Jack R. Lundbom. LC 75-15732. (Society of Biblical Literature. Dissertation Ser.: No. 18). Repr. of 1975 ed. 39.80 (ISBN 0-8357-9574-8, 2017520). Bks Demand UMI.

Jeremiah & Lamentations. R. K. Harrison. LC 72-97951. 240p. 1973. 12.95 (ISBN 0-87784-864-5); pap. 6.95 (ISBN 0-87784-271-X). Inter-Varsity.

Jeremiah & Lamentations. Irving L. Jensen. (Everyman' Bible Commentary Ser.). (Orig.). 1966. pap. 5.95 (ISBN 0-8024-2024-9). Moody.

Jeremiah & Lamentations. James E. Smith. LC 72-77951. (Bible Study Textbook Ser.). (Illus.). 1972. 18.95 (ISBN 0-89900-023-1). College Pr Pub.

Jeremiah & the Fall of Jerusalem. Constance Head. (Arch Bks.). (Illus.). 24p. 1986. pap. 0.99 saddlestitched (ISBN 0-570-06201-2, 59-1424). Concordia.

Jeremiah, Baruch. Peter F. Ellis. (Collegeville Bible Commentary Ser.). 136p. 1986. pap. 2.95 (ISBN 0-8146-1421-3). Liturgical Pr.

Jeremiah: Bible Study Commentary. F. B. Huey, Jr. (Bible Study Commentary Ser.). 144p. (Orig.). 1981. pap. 4.95 (ISBN 0-310-36063-3, 11063P). Zondervan.

Jeremiah: Chapters 1-25, Vol. 1. William McKane. Ed. by Charles E. Cranfield & John A. Emerton. (International Critical Commentary Ser.). 784p. 1986. 39.95 (ISBN 0-567-05042-4, Pub. by T & T Clark Ltd UK). Fortress.

Jeremiah, Lamentations. Howard T. Kuist. LC 59-10454. (Layman's Bible Commentary Ser: Vol. 12). 1960. pap. 4.95 (ISBN 0-8042-3072-2). John Knox.

Jeremiah, Lamentations: God's Unfailing Love. Winn O. Allison. Ed. by Earl C. Wolf. (Small-Group Bible Studies). 96p. (Orig.). 1986. pap. text ed. 2.50 (ISBN 0-8341-1106-3). Beacon Hill.

Jeremiah, Man & Prophet. Sheldon Blank. 1961. 12.50x (ISBN 0-87820-100-9, Pub. by Hebrew Union). Ktav.

Jeremiah One. William L. Holladay. LC 85-45498. (Hermeneia Ser.). 752p. 1986. 44.95 (ISBN 0-8006-6017-X, 20-6017). Fortress.

Jeremiah One to Twenty-Five. Lawrence Boadt. (Old Testament Message Ser.: Vol. 9). 1982. 15.95 (ISBN 0-89453-409-2); pap. 9.95 (ISBN 0-89453-262-6). M Glazier.

Jeremiah: Prophecy & Lamentations. H. A. Ironside. 10.95 (ISBN 0-87213-371-0). Loizeaux.

Jeremiah: Spokesman Out of Time. William L. Holladay. LC 74-7052. 160p. 1974. pap. 5.95 (ISBN 0-8298-0283-5). Pilgrim NY.

Jeremiah: The Iron Prophet. George T. Dickinson. (Horizon Ser.). 1978. pap. 5.95 (ISBN 0-8127-0183-6). Review & Herald.

Jeremiah, the Prophet. G. Andre. (Let's Discuss It Ser.). pap. 1.95 (ISBN 0-88172-135-2). Believers Bkshelf.

Jeremiah: The Prophet Who Wouldn't Quit. William J. Petersen. 168p. 1984. pap. 5.95 (ISBN 0-88207-243-9). Victor Bks.

Jeremiah Twenty-Six to Fifty-Two, Habakkuk, Zephaniah, Nahum. Lawrence Boadt. (Old Testament Message Ser.: Vol. 10). 1982. 15.95 (ISBN 0-89453-410-6); pap. 9.95 (ISBN 0-89453-244-8). M Glazier.

Jeremiah, Vol. 1: Chapters 1 to 20. Robert Davidson. LC 83-14598. (Daily Study Bible - Old Testament Ser.). 176p. 1983. 12.95 (ISBN 0-664-21394-4); pap. 6.95 (ISBN 0-664-24476-9). Westminster.

Jeremias y Lamentaciones (Commentario Biblico Portavoz) Irving L. Jensen. Orig. Title: Jeremiah & Lamentations (Everyman's Bible Commentary) (Span.). 142p. 1979. pap. 3.95 (ISBN 0-8254-1352-4). Kregel.

Jeremy Belknap: A Biography. George B. Kirsch. 25.00 (ISBN 0-405-14112-2). Ayer Co Pubs.

Jeremy Taylor. Edmund Gosse. 1904. Repr. 9.50 (ISBN 0-8274-2609-7). R West.

Jeremy Taylor. Edmund W. Gosse. LC 4-1683. 1969. Repr. of 1904 ed. 11.00x (ISBN 0-403-00088-2). Scholarly.

Jeremy Taylor. Hugh Ross Williamson. LC 73-15705. 1902. lib. bdg. 20.00 (ISBN 0-8414-9472-X). Folcroft.

Jeremy Taylor: A Selection from His Works. Martin Armstrong. 1973. lib. bdg. 15.00 (ISBN 0-8414-1165-4). Folcroft.

Jericho. John A. Bartlett. Ed. by Graham I. Davies. (Cities of the Biblical World Ser.). 128p. (Orig.). 1983. pap. 6.95 (ISBN 0-8028-1033-0). Eerdmans.

Jericho Walls. Sisters of the Community of Jesus. (Illus.). 72p. (Orig.). 1984. pap. 7.95 incl. cassette (ISBN 0-941478-18-1). Paraclete Pr.

Jerome. 15th ed. James W. Brewer, Jr. (Illus.). 1976. pap. 0.50 (ISBN 0-911408-16-9). SW Pks Mnmts.

Jerome Biblical Commentary. Ed. by Raymond E. Brown et al. 1969. 59.95 (ISBN 0-13-509612-X). P-H.

Jerome, Chrysostom, & Friends: Essays & Translations. Elizabeth A. Clark. LC 79-66374. (Studies in Women & Religion: Vol. 2). xi, 270p. 1979. soft cover 34.95x (ISBN 0-88946-548-7). E Mellen.

Jerome, Chrysostom, & Friends: Essays & Translations. Elizabeth A. Clark. LC 82-20829. (Studies in Women & Religion: Vol. 2). xi, 270p. 1983. Repr. of 1979 ed. 49.95x (ISBN 0-88946-541-X). E Mellen.

Jerome's Commentary on Daniel: A Study of Comparative Jewish & Christian Interpretations of the Hebrew Bible. Jay Braverman. LC 78-55726. (Catholic Biblical Quarterly Monographs: No. 7). xvi, 162p. 1978. 4.00 (ISBN 0-915170-06-X). Catholic Biblical.

Jerry Falwell & the Jews. Merill Simon. LC 83-22266. 172p. 1983. 12.50 (ISBN 0-8246-0300-1). Jonathan David.

Jerry McAuley, an Apostle to the Lost. facsimile ed. Ed. by R. M. Offord. LC 75-124248. (Select Bibliographies Reprint Ser). (Illus.). Repr. of 1907 ed. 19.00 (ISBN 0-8369-5436-X). Ayer Co Pubs.

Jerusalem. Pierre Loti. 15.00 (ISBN 0-8482-4859-7). Norwood Edns.

Jerusalem, 2 vols. in 4. Hughes Vincent. LC 78-63368. (Crusades & Military Orders: Second Ser.). Repr. of 1926 ed. Set. 495.00 (ISBN 0-404-17060-9). AMS Pr.

Jerusalem: A Geopolitical Perspective. Saul B. Cohen. 1977. 10.00 (ISBN 0-930832-54-X). Herzl Pr.

Jerusalem: A Universal Cultural & Historical Resource. Colin Williams. 18p. (Orig.). 1975. pap. text ed. 5.00 (ISBN 0-8191-5907-7, Pub. by Aspen Inst for Humanistic Studies). U Pr of Amer.

Jerusalem & Its Vicinity: Familiar Lectures on the Sacred Localities Connected with the Week Before the Resurrection. William H. Odenheimer. Ed. by Moshe Davis. (America & the Holy Land Ser.). (Illus.). 1977. Repr. of 1855 ed. lib. bdg. 20.00x (ISBN 0-405-10272-0). Ayer Co Pubs.

Jerusalem & Mecca: The Typology of the Holy City in the Near East. F. E. Peters. 272p. 1987. 45.00 (ISBN 0-8147-6598-X). NYU Pr.

Jerusalem Cathedra: Studies in the History, Archaeology, Geography, & Ethnography of the Land of Israel, Vol. 1. Ed. by Lee I. Levine. (Illus.). 362p. 1982. 35.00x (ISBN 0-8143-1691-3). Wayne St U Pr.

Jerusalem Cathedra: Studies in the History, Archaeology, Geography & Ehthnography of the Land of Israel, Vol. 2. Ed. by Lee I. Levine. 355p. 1983. 35.00x (ISBN 0-8143-1715-4). Wayne St U Pr.

Jerusalem: City of Jesus: An Exploration of the Traditions, Writings, & Remains of the Holy City from the Time of Christ. Richard M. Mackowski. LC 79-28093. pap. 57.80 (ISBN 0-317-30152-7, 2025334). Bks Demand UMI.

Jerusalem Community: Rule of Life. Frwd. by Carlo Coretto. 144p. (Orig.). 1985. pap. 5.95 (ISBN 0-8091-2712-1). Paulist Pr.

Jerusalem: Focal Point of the World. Wim Malgo. 3.95 (ISBN 0-937422-08-8). Midnight Call.

Jerusalem in the Time of Jesus: An Investigation into Economic & Social Conditions During the New Testament Period. Joachim Jeremias. Tr. by F. H. Cave & C. H. Cave. LC 77-81530. 434p. 1975. pap. 7.95 (ISBN 0-8006-1136-5, 1-1136). Fortress.

Jerusalem, Key to Peace. Evan M. Wilson. LC 70-119026. (James Terry Duce Ser.: Vol. 2). 1970. 5.95 (ISBN 0-916808-08-4). Mid East Inst.

Jerusalem Mission: Under the Direction of the American Christian Missionary Society. Compiled by David S. Burnet & Moshe Davis. (America & the Holy Land Ser.). 1977. Repr. of 1853 ed. lib. bdg. 26.50x (ISBN 0-405-10233-X). Ayer Co Pubs.

Jerusalem: Or on Religious Power & Judaism. Moses Mendelssohn. Intro. by Alexander Altmann. Tr. by Allan Arkush. LC 83-40015. 262p. 1983. 20.00x (ISBN 0-87451-263-8); pap. 10.00x (ISBN 0-87451-264-6). U Pr of New Eng.

Jerusalem: Problems & Prospects. Ed. by Joel L. Kraemer. LC 80-19418. 256p. 1980. 38.95 (ISBN 0-03-057733-0); pap. 17.95 (ISBN 0-03-057734-9). Praeger.

Jerusalem Question: 1917-1968. H. Eugene Bovis. LC 73-149796. (Studies Ser.: No. 29). (Illus.). 175p. 1971. 9.95x (ISBN 0-8179-3291-7). Hoover Inst Pr.

Jerusalem Sinner Saved. John Bunyan. pap. 3.25 (ISBN 0-685-88378-7). Reiner.

Jerusalem: The Holy City in the Eyes of Chroniclers, Visitors, Pilgrims, & Prophets from the Days of Abraham to the Beginnings of Modern Times. F. E. Peters. LC 85-42699. (Illus.). 712p. 1985. 37.00 (ISBN 0-691-07300-7). Princeton U Pr.

Jerusalem the Holy: History of Ancient Jerusalem with an Account of the Modern City & Its Conditions Political, Religious & Social. Edwin S. Wallace. Ed. by Moshe Davis. LC 77-70753. (America & the Holy Land Ser.). (Illus.). 1977. Repr. of 1898 ed. lib. bdg. 30.00x (ISBN 0-405-10298-4). Ayer Co Pubs.

Jerusalem: The Tragedy & the Triumph. Charles Gulston. 1977. 12.95 (ISBN 0-310-35510-9). Zondervan.

Jerusalem to Rome: Studies in Acts. Homer A. Kent, Jr. (Illus.). pap. 5.95 (ISBN 0-88469-056-3). BMH Bks.

Jerusalem to Rome: Studies in the Book of Acts. Homer A. Kent, Jr. (New Testament Studies Ser.). pap. 5.95 (ISBN 0-8010-5313-7). Baker Bk.

Jerusalem Trilogy. Samuel L. Lewis. Intro. by Wali A. Meyer et al. (Illus.). 336p. (Orig.). 1975. pap. 5.95 (ISBN 0-915424-03-7, Prophecy Pressworks). Sufi Islamia-Prophecy.

Jerusalem Undivided. Saul B. Cohen. 1980. pap. 3.00 (ISBN 0-930832-58-2). Herzl Pr.

Jerusalem Windows of Marc Chagall. Intro. by Jean Leymarie. LC 62-18146. (Illus.). 120p. 1975. 15.00 (ISBN 0-8076-0423-2); pap. 9.95 (ISBN 0-8076-0807-6). Braziller.

Jesse Tree: A Cutout Book. Marlene Konrady. (Learning Connections Ser.). 48p. (Orig.). 1984. pap. 8.95 (ISBN 0-86683-830-9, 8439, HarpR). Har-Row.

Jesse Tree Devotions: A Family Activity for Lent. Marilyn S. Breckenridge. 40p. (Orig.). 1985. pap. 4.95 (ISBN 0-8066-2154-0, 10-3475). Augsburg.

Jesucristo Sana (Jesus Christ Heals) Charles Fillmore. (Span.). 200p. 1984. 5.95 (ISBN 0-87159-071-9). Unity School.

Jesuit Education. Robert Schwickerat. 59.95 (ISBN 0-8490-0442-X). Gordon Pr.

Jesuit Educational Tradition & Saint Louis University: Some Bearings for the University's Sesquicentennial, 1818-1968. George E. Ganss. LC 75-87922. (Illus.). 70p. 1969. 3.25 (ISBN 0-912422-02-5). Inst Jesuit.

Jesuit Heritage in New England. Vincent A. Lapomarda. LC 76-42896. (Illus., Orig.). 1977. 8.00x (ISBN 0-9606294-0-8). Jesuits Holy Cross.

Jesuit Mission of St. Mary's County. 2nd ed. LC 77-75320. 422p. 1976. 20.00 (ISBN 0-686-24147-9). E W Beitzell.

Jesuit Ranches & the Agrarian Development of Colonial Argentina, 1650-1767. Nicholas P. Cushner. 350p. 1982. 49.50x (ISBN 0-87395-707-5); pap. 19.95 (ISBN 0-87395-706-7). State U NY Pr.

Jesuit Relations, Baja California, 1716-1762. Ed. by Ernest J. Burrus. (Baja California Travels Ser.: Vol. 47). (Illus.). 280p. 1984. 60.00 (ISBN 0-87093-243-8). Dawsons.

Jesuit Relations of Canada, 1632-1673: A Bibliography. James C. McCoy. LC 76-153038. (Illus.). xv, 346p. 1972. Repr. of 1937 ed. lib. bdg. 23.50 (ISBN 0-8337-2314-6). B Franklin.

Jesuit Religious Life Today: The Principal Features of its Spirit, in Excerpts... from Official Documents. Ed. by George E. Ganss. LC 77-78816. (Jesuit Primary Sources in English Translation Ser.: No. 3). 190p. 1977. pap. 3.00 (ISBN 0-912422-27-0). Inst Jesuit.

Jesuit Rings from Fort Michilimackinac & Other European Contact Sites. Judith A. Hauser. LC 83-100548. (Archaeological Completion Report Ser.: No. 5). (Illus.). 69p. (Orig.). 1983. pap. 5.00 (ISBN 0-911872-45-0). Mackinac Island.

Jesuit Saints & Martyrs. Joseph N. Tylenda. 503p. 1984. 15.95 (ISBN 0-8294-0447-3). Loyola.

Jesuit School Drama: Critical Literature. Nigel Griffin. (Research Bibliographies & Checklists Ser.: 12). 54p. 1976. pap. 6.50 (ISBN 0-7293-0003-X, Pub. by Grant & Cutler). Longwood Pub Group.

Jesuit Thinkers of the Renaissance. Ed. by Gerard Smith. 1939. 8.95 (ISBN 0-87462-431-2). Marquette.

Jesuits. J. C. Aveling. LC 81-40482. 396p. 1982. 19.95 (ISBN 0-8128-2838-0). Stein & Day.

Jesuits. H. Boehmer. 69.95 (ISBN 0-87968-199-3). Gordon Pr.

Jesuits: A Complete History of Their Open & Secret Proceedings, 2 vols. Theodor Griesinger. 1977. Set. lib. bdg. 200.00 (ISBN 0-8490-2092-1). Gordon Pr.

Jesuits: A Study in Counter-Reformation. Francis A. Ridley. LC 83-45595. Date not set. Repr. of 1938 ed. 35.00 (ISBN 0-404-19888-0). AMS Pr.

Jesuits & Jacobins: Enlightenment & Enlightened Despotism in Austria. Paul P. Bernard. LC 78-151997. 207p. 1971. 19.95 (ISBN 0-252-00180-X). U of Ill Pr.

Jesuits & Music. Thomas D. Culley. 401p. 1970. 29.00 (ISBN 88-7041-582-1). Jesuit Hist.

Jesuits & the Great Mogul. E. MacLagan. LC 71-159212. 1971. Repr. of 1932 ed. lib. bdg. 26.00x (ISBN 0-374-95248-5, Octagon). Hippocrene Bks.

Jesuits & the Indian Wars of the Northwest. Robert Burns. LC 65-22314. 550p. (Orig.). 1985. pap. 12.95 (ISBN 0-89301-110-X). U of Idaho Pr.

Jesuits at the Court of Peking. (Studies in Chinese History & Civilization). Repr. of 1935 ed. 23.00 (ISBN 0-89093-077-5). U Pubns Amer.

Jesuits' Estates Question, 1760-1888: A Study of the Background for the Agitation of 1889. Roy C. Dalton. LC 74-393033. (Canada Studies in History & Government: No. 11). pap. 53.30 (ISBN 0-317-26918-6, 2023608). Bks Demand UMI.

Jesuits, Fifteen Thirty-Four to Nineteen Twenty-One, 2 vols. Thomas J. Campbell. 1977. lib. bdg. 250.00 (ISBN 0-8490-2093-X). Gordon Pr.

Jesuits: Fifteen Thirty-Four to Nineteen Twenty-One. Thomas J. Campbell. LC 77-82144. (Reprints Ser). 1970. Repr. of 1921 ed. lib. bdg. 45.00 (ISBN 0-87821-018-0). Milford Hse.

Jesuits: History & Legend of the Society of Jesus. Manfred Barthel. Tr. by Mark Howson. 324p. 1987. pap. 8.95 (ISBN 0-688-06970-3, Quill). Morrow.

Jesuits in England from 1850 to the Present Day. Francis Edwards. LC 85-12048. 333p. text ed. cancelled (ISBN 0-268-01204-0, Pub. by Burns & Oates London). U of Notre Dame Pr.

Jesuits in North America. Francis Parkman. 586p. 1970. Repr. of 1895 ed. 22.50 (ISBN 0-87928-016-6). Corner Hse.

Jesuits in Poland. Alfred F. Pollard. LC 76-116799. (Studies in Philosophy, No. 40). 1970. Repr. of 1902 ed. lib. bdg. 39.95x (ISBN 0-8383-1041-9). Haskell.

Jesuits: Legend & Truth of the Society of Jesus - Yesterday, Today, Tomorrow. Manfred Barthel. Tr. by Mark Howson. LC 84-60446. (Illus.). 384p. 1984. 17.95 (ISBN 0-688-02861-6). Morrow.

Jesuits, Lutherans, & the Printing Press in South India. Katharine S. Diehl. (Printers & Printing in the East Indies to 1850 Ser.: Vol. III). write for info. Caratzas.

Jesuits of the Middle United States, 3 vols. Gilbert J. Garraghan. 162.00 (ISBN 0-405-10831-1, 11838). Ayer Co Pubs.

Jesuits: Revolt of Angels. Malachi Martin. 704p. 1987. 19.95 (ISBN 0-671-54505-1, Linden Pr). S&S.

Jesuits: Their Spiritual Doctrine & Practice. Joseph De Guibert. Tr. by W. J. Young. LC 64-21430. 717p. 1964. pap. 15.00 (ISBN 0-912422-09-2). Inst Jesuit.

Jesus. Humphrey Carpenter. (Past Masters Ser.). 1980. pap. 4.95 (ISBN 0-19-283016-3). Oxford U Pr.

Jesus. Hans Conzelmann. Ed. by John Reumann. Tr. by J. Raymond Lord from Gr. LC 73-79011. 128p. 1973. pap. 4.25 (ISBN 0-8006-1000-8, 1-1000). Fortress.

Jesus. Grace Dickerson. 1985. 5.50 (ISBN 0-533-03936-3). Vantage.

Jesus. 1979. 0.75 (ISBN 0-8198-0582-3). Dghtrs St Paul.

Jesus. 23p. 1982. pap. 7.55 (ISBN 0-88479-034-7). Arena Lettres.

Jesus. rev. ed. (Time of Life Learning Ser.). (Illus.). 32p. pap. 2.95 (ISBN 0-89622-244-6). Twenty-Third.

Jesus. Malcolm Muggeridge. LC 74-28794. 176p. 1976. pap. 9.95 (ISBN 0-06-066042-2, RD149, HarpR). Har-Row.

Jesus. Eduard Schweizer. LC 76-107322. 1979. pap. 7.95 (ISBN 0-8042-0331-8). John Knox.

Jesus: A Biblical Defense of His Deity. Josh McDowell & Bart Larson. 144p. (Orig.). 1983. pap. 5.95. Campus Crusade.

Jesus: A Biography. Ed B. Lorenz. (Illus.). 1977. 4.95 (ISBN 0-89328-011-9). Lorenz Pr.

Jesus: A Disciple's Search. Murray Bodo. 1987. pap. 5.95. St Anthony Mess Pr.

Jesus: A Gospel Portrait. Donald Senior. 192p. (Orig.). 1975. pap. 2.95 (ISBN 0-8278-9003-6, Pub. by Pflaum Pr). Peter Li.

Jesus, a New Biography. Shirley J. Case. LC 70-95149. (BCL Ser. II). Repr. of 1927 ed. 17.50 (ISBN 0-404-01406-2). AMS Pr.

Jesus: A New Biography. Shirley J. Case. LC 68-57594. 1968. Repr. of 1927 ed. lib. bdg. 22.50x (ISBN 0-8371-0342-8, CAJE). Greenwood.

Jesus, a New Biography. Shirley J. Case. 1928. 30.00 (ISBN 0-932062-36-9). Sharon Hill.

Jesus: A Poet, Prophet, Mystic & Man of Freedom. Carl H. Bjerregard. 1976. lib. bdg. 59.95 (ISBN 0-8490-2094-8). Gordon Pr.

Jesus: A Portrait of Love. Martyria Madauss 1972. 6.50 (ISBN 3-87209-603-6). Evang Sisterhood Mary.

Jesus: A Savior or the Savior? Religious Pluralism in Christian Perspective. Russell Aldwinckle. LC 81-19033. viii, 232p. 1982. 15.95 (ISBN 0-86554-023-3, MUP-H24). Mercer Univ Pr.

Jesus: A Story Color Book. Laura M. Stoner. (Illus.). 80p. (Orig.). 1985. pap. 3.95 wkbk. (ISBN 0-934426-07-4). Napsac Reprods.

Jesus: A Whole in One Down. George Harper. (H. B. & His-Her Adventures Ser.). 224p. (Orig.). 1986. pap. 5.95 (ISBN 0-937959-12-X). Falcon Pr Mt.

Jesus According to a Woman. Rachel C. Wahlberg. LC 74-27461. 112p. 1975. pap. 4.95 (ISBN 0-8091-1861-0). Paulist Pr.

Jesus According to Luke. William Sydnor. 144p. (Orig.). 1982. pap. 7.95 (ISBN 0-8164-2393-8, HarpR). Har-Row.

Jesus Against the Rapture: Seven Unexpected Prophecies. Robert Jewett. LC 78-31759. 148p. 1979. pap. 5.95 (ISBN 0-664-24253-7). Westminster.

Jesus Alias Christ. S. Levin. LC 71-81814. 1969. 6.95 (ISBN 0-8022-2293-5). Philos Lib.

Jesus Alimenta. Gordon Stowell. Tr. by Violeta S. De Martinez from Span. (Libros Pescaditos Sobre Jesus). Tr. of Jesus Feeds the People. (Illus.). 24p. pap. 0.60 (ISBN 0-311-38614-8). Casa Bautista.

Jesus Alive in Our Lives. Philip St. Romain. LC 85-71676. 104p. (Orig.). 1985. pap. 4.95 (ISBN 0-87793-293-X). Ave Maria.

Jesus Alive! The Mighty Message of Mark. Thomas J. Smith. LC 73-81824. 1973. pap. 6.00x (ISBN 0-88489-015-5); teaching guide 3.00x (ISBN 0-88489-117-8). St Marys.

Jesus Ama. Gordon Stowell. Tr. by Violeta S. De Martinez from Span. (Libros Pescaditos Sobre Jesus). Tr. of Jesus Loves. (Illus.). 24p. 1984. pap. 0.60 (ISBN 0-311-38611-3). Casa Bautista.

Jesus: An Experiment in Christology. Edward Schillebeeckx. 1979. pap. 12.95 (ISBN 0-8245-0405-4). Crossroad NY.

Jesus: An Historian's Review of the Gospels. Michael Grant. LC 77-70218. 1978. text ed. 12.50 (ISBN 0-684-14889-7, ScribT); pap. text ed. 9.95 (ISBN 0-684-17439-1). Scribner.

Jesus: An Historian's View of the Gospels. Michael Grant. 261p. 1978. pap. text ed. write for info. (ISBN 0-02-345630-2, Pub. by Scribner). Macmillan.

Jesus & Christ. Rudolf Steiner. 1976. pap. 2.00 (ISBN 0-910142-74-2). Anthroposophic.

Jesus & Christian Origins Outside the New Testament. F. F. Bruce. 1974. pap. 5.95 (ISBN 0-8028-1575-8). Eerdmans.

Jesus & Community: The Social Dimension of Christian Faith. Gerhard Lohfink. Tr. by John P. Galvin. LC 84-47928. 224p. 1984. pap. 9.95 (ISBN 0-8006-1802-5). Fortress.

Jesus & Community: The Social Dimension of Christian Faith. Gerhard Lohfink. 224p. 1985. pap. 9.95 (ISBN 0-8091-2661-3). Paulist Pr.

Jesus & Divorce: The Problem with the Evangelical Consensus. William A. Heth & Gordon J. Wenham. 288p. 1985. pap. 7.95 (ISBN 0-8407-5962-2). Nelson.

Jesus & Freedom. Sebastian Kappen. LC 76-25927. 186p. (Orig.). 1977. 4.48 (ISBN 0-88344-232-9). Orbis Bks.

Jesus & His Coming. 2nd ed. John A. Robinson. LC 79-14078. 192p. 1979. pap. 6.95 (ISBN 0-664-24278-2). Westminster.

Jesus & His Friends. Ruth Odor. (Flip-a-Bible-Story Bks.). (Illus.). 16p. (Orig.). 1982. pap. 3.95 (ISBN 0-87239-560-X, 2734). Standard Pub.

Jesus & His Mother. Andre Feuillet. Tr. by Leonard Maluf from Fr. LC 84-6790. (Studies in Scripture Ser.: Vol. I). Tr. of Jesus et sa Mere. 266p. (Orig.). 1984. pap. 19.95 (ISBN 0-932506-27-5). St Bedes Pubns.

Jesus & His Parables. Joanne L. Kepes. 1982. 9.95 (ISBN 0-89837-087-6, Pub. by Pflaum Pr). Peter Li.

Jesus & Human Conflict. H. A. Fast. LC 58-10315. 215p. 1959. 7.95 (ISBN 0-8361-1382-9). Herald Pr.

Jesus & I. Aloysius J. Heeg. pap. text ed. 1.00 (ISBN 0-8294-0214-4). Loyola.

Jesus & Jim Jones. Stephen Rose. LC 79-17285. (Orig.). 1979. 8.95 (ISBN 0-8298-0379-3); pap. 6.95 (ISBN 0-8298-0373-4). Pilgrim NY.

Jesus & John the Baptist. Laurent Lalo. LC 83-25075. (Illus.). 24p. 1985. 4.95 (ISBN 0-88070-045-9). Multnomah.

Jesus & John the Baptist. As told by Catherine Storr. (People of the Bible Ser.). (Illus.). 32p. 1985. PLB 10.65 (ISBN 0-8172-2037-2). Raintree Pubs.

Jesus & Judaism. E. P. Sanders. LC 84-48806. 448p. 1985. 19.95 (ISBN 0-8006-0743-0, 1-743). Fortress.

Jesus & Man's Hope: Pittsburgh Festival on the Gospels, April 6-10, 1970, 2 vols. Vols. 1 & 2. 12.00 ea.; Vol. 1. pap. 8.00 (ISBN 0-686-36876-2). Pitts Theolog.

Jesus & Mary. William Bramley. 450p. 1987. 21.95 (ISBN 0-940291-02-9). Dahlin Family Pr.

Jesus & Me. Gladys Seashore. 1975. pap. 2.25 (ISBN 0-911802-37-1). Free Church Pubns.

Jesus & Me Teacher: Primary Study in the Life of Christ. Compiled by Tessa Colina & Jacqueline Westers. 1978. pap. 7.95 (ISBN 0-87239-165-5, 3243). Standard Pub.

Jesus & Passover. Anthony J. Saldarini. (Orig.). 1984. pap. 4.95 (ISBN 0-8091-2595-1). Paulist Pr.

Jesus & Paul: Places They Knew. F. F. Bruce. 128p. 1983. Repr. of 1981 ed. 12.95 (ISBN 0-8407-5281-4). Nelson.

Jesus & Socrates. W. F. Bostick. 59.95 (ISBN 0-89190-443-8). Gordon Pr.

Jesus & the Big Storm. Elspeth Murphy. (Tubable Hugable Ser.). (Illus.). 1984. pap. 2.95 (ISBN 0-89191-816-7). Cook.

Jesus & the Children: Biblical Resources for Study & Preaching. Hans-Ruedi Weber. LC 79-87754. 1980. pap. 5.95 (ISBN 0-8042-1316-X). John Knox.

Jesus & the Christian. William Manson. 236p. 1967. 14.00 (ISBN 0-227-67723-4). Attic Pr.

Jesus & the Christian in a Pop Culture. Tony Jasper. 224p. 1984. 29.00x (ISBN 0-947728-02-3, Pub. by R Royce Ltd Publ England). State Mutual Bk.

Jesus & the Demon World. Spiros Zodhiates. LC 82-71842. 1982. pap. 5.95 (ISBN 0-89957-556-0). AMG Pubs.

Jesus & the Disinherited. Howard Thurman. LC 81-70333. 112p. 1981. pap. 5.95 (ISBN 0-913408-77-8). Friends United.

Jesus & the End-Time. Everett L. Wilson. 1977. pap. 3.95 (ISBN 0-910452-32-6). Covenant.

Jesus & the Eucharist. Tad W. Guzie. LC 73-90069. 168p. 1974. pap. 5.95 (ISBN 0-8091-1858-0). Paulist Pr.

Jesus & the Fisherman. Gordon Stowell. (Little Fish Bks.: Bk. II). (Illus.). 14p. 1982. pap. 0.59 (ISBN 0-8307-0831-6, 5608150). Regal.

Jesus & the Freed Woman. Rachel C. Wahlberg. LC 78-61718. 176p. (Orig.). 1978. pap. 3.95 (ISBN 0-8091-2139-5). Paulist Pr.

Jesus & the Gospel. James Denny. 1977. lib. bdg. 59.95 (ISBN 0-8490-2095-6). Gordon Pr.

Jesus & the Gospel. William R. Farmer. LC 81-43078. 320p. 1982. 22.95 (ISBN 0-8006-0666-3). Fortress.

Jesus & the Gospels. D. R. De Lacey. (Discovering the Bible Ser.). pap. 8.95 (ISBN 0-7175-1162-6). Dufour.

Jesus & the Gospels. John Drane. LC 77-20448. 1979. pap. 9.95 (ISBN 0-06-062066-8, RD264, HarpR). Har-Row.

Jesus & the Greeks. William Fairweather. 1977. lib. bdg. 59.95 (ISBN 0-8490-2096-4). Gordon Pr.

Jesus & the Hope of the Poor. Luise Schottroff & Wolfgang Stegemann. Tr. by Matthew O'Connell from Ger. LC 86-5435. (Jesus von Nazareth-Hoffnung der Armen Ser.). 144p. (Orig.). 1986. pap. 9.95 (ISBN 0-88344-255-8, CIP). Orbis Bks.

Jesus & the Hunger for Things Unknown. Pierre Talec. Tr. by Joachim Neugroschel from Fr. Orig. Title: Choses de la Foi. 250p. 1982. 12.95 (ISBN 0-8164-0510-7, HarpR). Har-Row.

Jesus & the Kingdom of God. George R. Beasley-Murray. 512p. 1986. 29.95 (ISBN 0-8028-3609-7). Eerdmans.

Jesus & the Language of the Kingdom: Symbol & Metaphor in New Testament Interpretation. Norman Perrin. LC 80-20822. 240p. 1980. pap. 11.95 (ISBN 0-8006-1432-1, 1-1432). Fortress.

Jesus & the Laws of Purity: Tradition History & Legal History in Mark 7. Roger P. Booth. (JSoT Supplement Ser.: No. 13). 300p. 1986. text ed. 27.50x (ISBN 1-85075-023-8, Pub. by JSOT Pr England); pap. text ed. 13.50x (ISBN 1-85075-022-X). Eisenbrauns.

Jesus & the Moralists. Edward W. Hirst. 1977. lib. bdg. 59.95 (ISBN 0-8490-2097-2). Gordon Pr.

Jesus & the New Age According to St. Luke. Frederick W. Danker. 1983. pap. text ed. 12.00 (ISBN 0-915644-25-8). Clayton Pub Hse.

Jesus & the Nonviolent Revolution. Andre Trocme. Tr. by Michel Shenk from Fr. LC 73-9934. (Christian Peace Shelf Ser.). 216p. 1974. pap. 12.95 (ISBN 0-8361-3320-X). Herald Pr.

Jesus & the Pharisees. John Bowker. 240p. 1973. 42.50 (ISBN 0-521-20055-5). Cambridge U Pr.

Jesus & the Politics of His Day. Ed. by E. Bammel & C. F. Moule. 320p. 1985. pap. 17.95 (ISBN 0-521-31344-9). Cambridge U Pr.

Jesus & the Spirit: A Study of the Religious & Charismatic Experience of Jesus & the First Christians as Reflected in the New Testament. James D. Dunn. LC 75-9802. 528p. 1979. pap. 15.95 (ISBN 0-664-24290-1). Westminster.

Jesus & the Synoptic Gospels: A Bibliographic Study Guide. David E. Aune. Ed. by Mark L. Branson. (TSF - IBR Bibliographic Study Guides Ser.). 99p. (Orig.). 1981. pap. 2.95 (ISBN 0-8308-5498-3). Inter-Varsity.

Jesus & the Transformation of Judaism. John Riches. 264p. (Orig.). 1982. pap. 10.95 (ISBN 0-8164-2361-X, HarpR). Har-Row.

Jesus & the Witchdoctor: An Approach to Healing & Wholeness. Aylward Shorter. 268p. (Orig.). 1985. pap. 10.95 (ISBN 0-88344-225-6). Orbis Bks.

Jesus & the Word. Rudolf Bultmann. (Hudson River Edition). 20.00 (ISBN 0-684-17596-7, ScribT). Scribner.

Jesus & the World of Judaism. Geza Vermes. LC 83-16535. 224p. 1984. pap. 10.95 (ISBN 0-8006-1784-3, 1-1784). Fortress.

Jesus & Woman: An Exciting Discovery of What He Offered Her. Lisa Sergio. LC 75-4365. 139p. 1980. pap. 4.95 (ISBN 0-914440-44-6). EPM Pubns.

Jesus & You. Josephine F. Nellen. 1987. 8.95 (ISBN 0-533-07355-3). Vantage.

Jesus & You: Student Text. rev. ed. Michael Pennock. LC 84-70384. (High School Religion Text Ser.). (Illus.). 224p. 1984. pap. 5.95 (ISBN 0-87793-315-4). Ave Maria.

Jesus & You: Teacher Manual. Rev. ed. Michael Pennock. (High School Religion Text Ser.). 144p. 1984. pap. 7.95 (ISBN 0-87793-316-2). Ave Maria.

Jesus Appeals to the World. Lorenzo Sales. 1955. 5.95 (ISBN 0-8189-0069-5). Alba.

Jesus As an Anarchist. Laurance Labadie. (Men & Movements in the History & Philosophy of Anarchism Ser.). 1979. lib. bdg. 59.95 (ISBN 0-685-96404-3). Revisionist Pr.

Jesus As Counselor. Robert C. Leslie. (Festival Ser.). 144p. 1982. pap. 4.50 (ISBN 0-687-19930-1). Abingdon.

Jesus As Friend. Salvatore Canals. 117p. (Orig.). 1979. pap. 6.95 (ISBN 0-906127-11-4, Pub. by Four Courts Pr Ireland). Scepter Pubs.

Jesus As Mother: Studies in the Spirituality of the High Middle Ages. Caroline W. Bynum. LC 81-13137. (Center for Medieval & Renaissance Studies. UCLA Publications: No. 16). 280p. 1982. pap. text ed. 7.95 (ISBN 0-520-05222-6, CAL 697). U of Cal Pr.

Jesus as Others Saw Him: A Retrospect A.D. 54. Joseph Jacobs. LC 73-2211. (Jewish People; History, Religion, Literature Ser.). Repr. of 1925 ed. 21.00 (ISBN 0-405-05275-8). Ayer Co Pubs.

Jesus As They Saw Him. William Barclay. LC 78-18224. 1978. pap. 7.95 (ISBN 0-8028-1775-0). Eerdmans.

Jesus As We Knew Him. Weston A. Stevens. LC 85-73771. (Illus.). 137p. 1986. pap. 5.95 (ISBN 0-9605818-2-0). John Alden Bks.

Jesus at the Temple. Retold by Pamela Broughton. LC 85-81162. (Golden Bible Stories). (Illus.). 32p. 1986. 3.95 (ISBN 0-307-11624-7, Pub. by Golden Bks). Western Pub.

Jesus: Author & Finisher. Compiled by Morris H. Chapman. 1987. pap. 6.95 (ISBN 0-8054-5047-5). Broadman.

Jesus Before Christianity. Albert Nolan. LC 78-6708. 156p. (Orig.). 1978. pap. 8.95 (ISBN 0-88344-230-2). Orbis Bks.

Jesus Begins His Work. Ella K. Lindvall. (People of the Bible Ser.). (Illus.). 1983. 4.95 (ISBN 0-8024-0394-8). Moody.

Jesus Begins His Work. Catherine Storr. LC 82-9037. (People of the Bible). (Illus.). 32p. 1982. PLB 10.65 (ISBN 0-8172-1978-1). Raintree Pubs.

Jesus Book. Kate C. Dooley. LC 82-61422. 48p. (Orig.). 1983. pap. 2.95 (ISBN 0-8091-2514-5). Paulist Pr.

Jesus Book: Extended Study. Ronald J. Wilkins. (To Live Is Christ Ser.). 168p. 1984. pap. 5.75 (ISBN 0-697-01917-9); tchrs. manual 5.00 (ISBN 0-697-01927-6); spirit master 10.95 (ISBN 0-697-01692-7). Wm C Brown.

Jesus Book: Short Ed. Ronald J. Wilkins. (To Live Is Christ Ser.). 112p. 1979. pap. 4.20 (ISBN 0-697-01695-1); tchr's manual 4.00 (ISBN 0-697-01714-1). Wm C Brown.

Jesus by the Sea of Galilee. Lucy Diamond. (Ladybird Ser). (Illus.). 1958. bds. 2.50 (ISBN 0-87508-840-6). Chr Lit.

Jesus Calls His Disciples. Lucy Diamond. (Ladybird Ser). (Illus.). 1959. bds. 2.50 (ISBN 0-87508-842-2). Chr Lit.

Jesus Came to Me. 2nd rev. ed. Barin. LC 86-60047. (Illus.). 150p. (Orig.). 1986. Repr. of 1973 ed. 17.95 (ISBN 0-935075-06-2). Sri Aurobindo.

Jesus Cares for Me. Nancee Berry. (Come Unto Me Ser.). 16p. 1979. pap. 1.65 (ISBN 0-8127-0252-2). Review & Herald.

Jesus Changes People. Janet Helm. Ed. by Mary Duckert. (New Vacation Venture Ser.). leader's guide 3.95; 1.95 (ISBN 0-664-24172-7); resource packet 11.95 (ISBN 0-664-24174-3); New Life Songbook. 0.95 (ISBN 0-664-24171-9). Westminster.

Jesus Chist's One Hundred Rule Communication Program: An Axumatyation of the New Testament. (Analysis Ser.: No. 12). 1983. pap. 10.00 (ISBN 0-686-42848-X). Inst Analysis.

Jesus Christ. Robert Hicks & Richard Bewes. (Understanding Bible Truth Ser.). (Orig.). 1981. pap. 0.95 (ISBN 0-89840-026-0). Heres Life.

Jesus Christ & Mythology. Rudolf Bultmann. 1958. pap. text ed. 5.95 (ISBN 0-684-17228-3, ScribT). Scribner.

Jesus Christ & Mythology. Rudolf Bultmann. 94p. 1981. pap. text ed. write for info. (ISBN 0-02-305570-7, Pub. by Scribner). Macmillan.

Jesus Christ & the Faith: A Collection of Studies by Philippe H. Menoud. LC 78-15551. (Pittsburgh Theological Monographs: No. 18). Orig. Title: Jesus-Christ et la Foi. 1978. 16.75 (ISBN 0-915138-22-0). Pickwick.

Jesus Christ & the Temple. Georges A. Barrois. LC 80-19700. 163p. (Orig.). 1980. pap. 5.95 (ISBN 0-913836-73-7, BS680 T4837). St Martin.

Jesus Christ & the Temple. Georges A. Barrois. LC 80-19700. 163p. 1980. pap. 6.95 (ISBN 0-913836-73-7). St Vladimirs.

Jesus Christ, Disciplemaker. Bill Hull. LC 84-70471. 216p. 1984. 5.95 (ISBN 0-89109-516-0). NavPress.

Jesus Christ for Today. George W. Stroup. LC 82-13494. (Library of Living Faith: Vol. 7). 116p. 1982. pap. 5.95 (ISBN 0-664-24450-5). Westminster.

Jesus Christ for Today's Filipino. Nicomedes T. Yatco. 124p. (Orig.). 1984. pap. 6.50x (ISBN 971-10-0053-9, Pub. by New Day Philipines). Cellar.

Jesus Christ Heals. Charles Fillmore. 1939. 5.95 (ISBN 0-87159-070-0). Unity School.

Jesus Christ, His Life & Teaching. Dennis E. Clark. 324p. pap. 4.95 (ISBN 0-89191-117-0, 23341). Cook.

Jesus Christ: His Times, Life & Work. E. De Pressense. 1978. Repr. of 1898 ed. lib. bdg. 50.00 (ISBN 0-8495-1032-5). Arden Lib.

Jesus Christ Hope of the Homes. Robert R. Taylor, Jr. 2.50 (ISBN 0-89315-131-9). Lambert Bk.

Jesus Christ in Matthew, Mark, & Luke. Jack D. Kingsbury. Ed. by Gerhard Krodel. LC 80-69755. (Proclamation Commentaries Ser.: The New Testament Witnesses for Preaching). 144p. (Orig.). 1981. pap. 4.95 (ISBN 0-8006-0596-9, 1-596). Fortress.

Jesus Christ in the Talmud, Midrash, Zohar, & the Liturgy of the Synagogue. Gustaf Dalman. LC 73-2190. (Jewish People; History, Religion, Literature Ser.). Repr. of 1893 ed. 11.00 (ISBN 0-405-05256-1). Ayer Co Pubs.

Jesus Christ Is God! 329p. 1985. pap. 9.95 (ISBN 0-914012-23-1, Pub. by Bibl Evang Pr). Sword of Lord.

Jesus Christ Is Lord: Adoration Viewed Through the New Testament. Ernest Lussier. LC 79-15581. 1980. 7.95 (ISBN 0-8189-0382-1). Alba.

Jesus Christ Is Not God. Victor P. Wierwille. LC 81-66710. 180p. 1981. 6.95 (ISBN 0-910068-33-X). Am Christian.

Jesus Christ Liberator: A Critical Christology for Our Time. Leonardo Boff. Tr. by Patrick Hughes from Portuguese. LC 78-969. Tr. of Jesus Cristo Libertador Ensaio de Crista logia Critica para o nosso Tempo. 335p. (Orig.). 1978. pap. 9.95 (ISBN 0-88344-236-1). Orbis Bks.

Jesus Christ Our Lord. J. C. Metcalfe. 1970. pap. 2.25 (ISBN 0-87508-919-4). Chr Lit.

Jesus Christ Our Lord. John F. Walvoord. LC 70-80941. 318p. 1974. pap. 8.95 (ISBN 0-8024-4326-5). Moody.

Jesus Christ Our Passover. Victor P. Wierwille. LC 80-68401. 527p. 1980. 10.95 (ISBN 0-910068-30-5). Am Christian.

Jesus Christ Our Promised Seed. Victor P. Wierwille. LC 82-72672. 306p. 1982. 10.95 (ISBN 0-910068-42-9). Am Christian.

Jesus Christ: Prophet-Priest. Andrew Murray. 64p. 1967. pap. 2.95 (ISBN 0-87123-271-5, 200271). Bethany Hse.

Jesus Christ Returns by 1988? Gordon McDowell. LC 83-90836. 66p. 1984. 5.95 (ISBN 0-533-05838-4). Vantage.

Jesus Christ-Sam. Samuel W. Slomowitz. 1987. 7.95 (ISBN 0-533-07158-5). Vantage.

Jesus Christ: The Divine Executive; Architect of the Universe (Why the Universe Was Created) Reuben L. Katter. 400p. 1986. 18.95. Theotes.

Jesus Christ: The Man from Nazareth & the Exalted Lord. Eduard Schweizer. Ed. by Hulitt Gloer. 128p. (Orig.). 1986. 14.95 (ISBN 0-86554-225-2, MUP-H201); pap. 9.95 (ISBN 0-86554-226-0, MUP-P30). Mercer Univ Pr.

Jesus Christ the Only Way: Christian Responsibility in the Multicultural Society. Patrick Sookhdeo. 159p. 1978. pap. 5.95 (ISBN 0-85364-236-2). Attic Pr.

Jesus Christ: The Witness of History. Norman Anderson. LC 84-15703. 210p. 1985. pap. 6.95 (ISBN 0-87784-336-8). Inter-Varsity.

Jesus Christ Through History. Dennis C. Duling. 324p. 1979. pap. text ed. 13.95 (ISBN 0-15-547370-0, HC). HarBraceJ.

Jesus Christ Today. Neil R. Lightfoot. LC 76-42590. 360p. 1976. pap. 8.95 (ISBN 0-8010-5604-7). Baker Bk.

Jesus Christ's World Utopia. rev. ed. Dale L. Harris. (Illus.). 1984. pap. text ed. 4.95 (ISBN 0-318-00118-7). Christian Freedom.

Jesus' Church. John A. Chalk. Ed. by J. D. Thomas. (Twentieth Century Sermons Ser). 1969. 11.95 (ISBN 0-89112-303-2, Bibl Res Pr). Abilene Christ U.

Jesus' Claims-Our Promise: A Study of the "I Am" Sayings of Jesus. Maxie Dunnam. LC 84-51831. 128p. (Orig.). 1984. pap. 5.95 (ISBN 0-8358-0502-6). Upper Room.

Jesus Comes: the Story of Jesus' Birth for Children. Ron Klug & Lyn Klug. LC 86-81808. (Illus.). 32p. (Orig.). 1986. pap. 4.95 saddlestitch (ISBN 0-8066-2234-2, 10-3497). Augsburg.

Jesus Connection: To Triumph over Anti-Semitism. Leonard C. Yaseen. (Illus.). 192p. 1985. pap. 9.95 (ISBN 0-8245-0718-5). Crossroad NY.

Jesus Cuenta. Gordon Stowell. Tr. by Violeta S. De Martinez from Span. (Libros Pescaditos Sobre Jesus). Tr. of Jesus Tells Stories. (Illus.). 24p. 1984. pap. 0.60 (ISBN 0-311-38613-X). Casa Bautista.

Jesus Debate: A Survey & Synthesis. William M. Thompson. 512p. (Orig.). 1985. pap. 12.95 (ISBN 0-8091-2666-4). Paulist Pr.

Jesus Difference: And Other Youth Ministry Activities. Kieran Sawyer. LC 86-72571. 168p. (Orig.). 1987. spiral binding 8.95 (ISBN 0-87793-353-7). Ave Maria.

Jesus: El Amigo De los Ninos. Richard Hook & Frances Hook. Tr. of Jesus, the Friend of Children. (Illus.). 112p. 1981. 19.50 (ISBN 0-311-38552-4, Edit Mundo); pap. 14.95 (ISBN 0-311-38553-2). Casa Bautista.

Jesus en Nuestras Vidas - Hoy. Juan Carlos Ortiz. Tr. by Juan S. Araujo from Eng. Tr. of Living with Jesus Today. (Span.). 160p. 1987. pap. 4.25 (ISBN 0-88113-157-1). Edit Betania.

Jesus Ensena. Gordon Stowell. Tr. by Violeta S. De Martinez from Span. (Libros Pescaditos Sobre Jesus). Tr. of Jesus Teaches. (Illus.). 24p. 1984. pap. 0.60 (ISBN 0-311-38609-1). Casa Bautista.

Jesus: Essential Readings. Anthony Duncan. (Crucible Ser.). 176p. 1987. pap. 9.95 (ISBN 0-85030-395-8). Thorsons Pubs.

Jesus Event & Our Response. Martin R. Tripole. LC 79-27896. 248p. (Orig.). 1980. pap. 7.95 (ISBN 0-8189-0399-6). Alba.

Jesus Exultant. Steele. pap. 2.95 (ISBN 0-686-12885-0). Schmul Pub Co.

Jesus: Fact, Fable or Myth. A. F. Kralik. 1985. 6.50 (ISBN 0-8062-2480-0). Carlton.

Jesus Feeds the People. Gordon Stowell. (Little Fish Bks.: Bk. II). (Illus.). 14p. 1982. pap. 0.59 (ISBN 0-8307-0832-4, 5608167). Regal.

Jesus for Children. Henry W. Griffin. (Illus.). 132p. 1985. 12.95 (HarpR); pap. 4.95 (ISBN 0-86683-866-X). Har-Row.

Jesus Forgives Peter. McElroy. (Arch Bks.). 24p. (Orig.). 1985. pap. 0.99 (ISBN 0-570-06192-X, 59-1293). Concordia.

Jesus: Friend, Teacher, Leader. Ed. by Aline Baumgartner & Carl Fisher. (Illus.). 1986. dupl. masterbook 9.95 (ISBN 0-89837-104-X, Pub. by Pflaum Pr). Peter Li.

Jesus, God & Man. Raymond E. Brown. LC 67-29587. (Impact Books). 1967. pap. 4.95 (ISBN 0-02-084000-4, Collier). Macmillan.

Jesus: God & Man. 2nd ed. Wolfhart Pannenberg. Tr. by Lewis L. Wilkins & Duane A. Priebe. LC 76-26478. 428p. 1982. pap. 13.95 (ISBN 0-664-24468-8). Westminster.

Jesus God's Gift of Peace to You. Hazel S. Craft. 100p. (Orig.). 1983. pap. 5.95 (ISBN 0-88144-013-2, CPS-013). Christian Pub.

Jesus, God's Son. Marian Bennett. (Surprise Bks.). (Illus.). 14p. (Orig.). 1982. pap. 4.95 (ISBN 0-87239-564-2, 2705). Standard Pub.

Jesus: God's Son, Saviour, Lord. Eugene Chamberlain. (BibLearn Ser.). (Illus.). pap. 5.95 (ISBN 0-8054-4226-X, 4242-26). Broadman.

Jesus God's Way of Healing & Power to Promote Health. Wilford H. Reidt & John G. Lake. 171p. 1981. pap. 5.95 (ISBN 0-89274-197-X). Harrison Hse.

Jesus Heals. Gordon Stowell. (Little Fish Bks.: Bk. II). (Illus.). 14p. 1982. pap. 0.59 (ISBN 0-8307-0828-6, 5608122). Regal.

Jesus' Helpers Classroom Dot-to-Dot Book. Ed. by Patricia Mahany. (Classroom Activity Bks.). (Illus.). 96p. pap. 2.95 (ISBN 0-87239-503-0, 2334). Standard Pub.

Jesus Himself. Andrew Murray. 27p. 1966. pap. 0.95 (ISBN 0-87509-096-6). Chr Pubns.

Jesus: His Story for Children. Alice Brown & Pat Kirk. (Illus.). 1986. 10.95 (ISBN 0-915720-21-3). Brownlow Pub Co.

Jesus, His Story: The Four Gospels As One Narrative in Language for Today. Tr. by Robert Shank. LC 62-17864. (Illus.). 256p. 1962. 7.95 (ISBN 0-911620-00-1). Westcott.

Jesus: Historias de su Vida. Margaret Ralph. Tr. by Teresa LaValle. (Serie Jirafa). Orig. Title: Life of Jesus. (Illus.). 28p. 1979. 3.95 (ISBN 0-311-38536-2, Edit Mundo). Casa Bautista.

Jesus, Hope Drawing Near: Reflections on the Gospels for the C-Cycle. Joseph G. Donders. LC 85-5125. 272p. (Orig.). 1985. pap. 10.95 (ISBN 0-88344-244-2). Orbis Bks.

Jesus I Knew. Hugh L. Cayce. 81p. (Orig.). 1984. pap. 4.95 (ISBN 0-87604-156-X). ARE Pr.

Jesus I: The Man. Patricia. Ed. by Morningland Publications, Inc. (Ser. of Three Books Called Jesus). (Illus.). 439p. 1980. pap. 10.00 (ISBN 0-935146-15-6). Morningland.

Jesus, I Want to Talk with You: Contemporary Prayers. Edward Carter. LC 73-75617. (Illus.). 1977. pap. 1.95 (ISBN 0-8189-1142-5, Pub. by Alba Bks). Alba.

Jesus II: The Mission. Patricia. Ed. by Morningland Publications, Inc. (Ser. of Three Books Called Jesus). (Illus.). 461p. 1980. pap. 10.00 (ISBN 0-935146-17-2). Morningland.

Jesus III: The Return. Patricia. Ed. by Morningland Publications, Inc. (Ser. of Three Books Called Jesus). (Illus.). 470p. (Orig.). 1980. pap. 10.00 (ISBN 0-935146-18-0). Morningland.

Jesus in Bad Company. Adolf Holl. 1978. pap. 1.65 (ISBN 0-380-00022-9, 19281, Discus). Avon.

Jesus in European Protestant Thought, 1778-1860. Colin Brown. (Studies in Historical Theology: Vol. 1). 380p. 1985. lib. bdg. 35.00x (ISBN 0-939464-18-7). Labyrinth Pr.

Jesus in Focus: A Life in Its Setting. Gerard S. Sloyan. 207p. (Orig.). 1983. pap. 7.95 (ISBN 0-89622-191-1). Twenty-Third.

Jesus in History: An Approach to the Study of the Gospels. 2nd ed. Howard C. Kee. LC 77-75349. 312p. 1977. pap. text ed. 13.95 (ISBN 0-15-547382-4, HC). HarBraceJ.

Jesus in History & Myth. R. Joseph Hoffmann & Gerald Larue. 300p. 1986. 21.95 (ISBN 0-87975-332-3). Prometheus Bks.

Jesus in Latin America. Jon Sobrino. LC 86-23485. Tr. of Jesus en America Latina: Su significada para la fe y la cristologia. 192p. (Orig.). 1987. pap. 11.95 (ISBN 0-88344-412-7). Orbis Bks.

Jesus in Nazareth. Erich Graesser et al. (Beiheft 40 zur Zeitschrift fuer die alttes tamentliche Wissenschaft). 153p. 1972. 41.50x (ISBN 3-11-004004-2). De Gruyter.

Jesus in Our Affluent Society. Joseph B. Carl. 208p. 1981. 9.95 (ISBN 0-938234-01-3); pap. 5.95 (ISBN 0-938234-00-5). Ministry Pubns.

Jesus in the Church's Gospels: Modern Scholarship & the Earliest Sources. John Reumann. LC 68-10983. 564p. 1973. pap. 9.95 (ISBN 0-8006-1091-1, 1-1091). Fortress.

Jesus in the Experience of Men. T. R. Glover. LC 78-23617. 1921. 30.00 (ISBN 0-8414-4616-4). Folcroft.

Jesus in the Eyes of the Sufis. Nurbakhsh Javad. Tr. by Terry Graham et al. 1983. pap. 6.00 (ISBN 0-317-07015-0). KhaniQahi-Nimatullahi-Sufi.

Jesus in the Gospel. (Illus.). 1980. 12.00 (ISBN 0-8198-0618-8). Dghtrs St Paul.

Jesus in the Gospel of John. Jacob Jervell. Tr. by Harry T. Cleven. LC 84-14547. 96p. (Orig.). 1984. pap. 5.95 (ISBN 0-8066-2089-7, 10-3516). Augsburg.

Jesus In the Gospels: Old Stories Told Anew. Richard Mazziotta. LC 86-70132. 200p. (Orig.). 1986. pap. 5.95 (ISBN 0-87793-336-7). Ave Maria.

Jesus in the Midst: Spiritual Writings. Chiara Lubich. LC 76-18455. 80p. 1976. pap. 2.95 (ISBN 0-911782-26-5). New City.

Jesus in Two Perspectives. Pinchas Lapide & Ulrich Luz. LC 85-15760. Tr. of Jude Jesus. 176p. 1985. pap. 8.95 (ISBN 0-8066-2171-0, 10-3517). Augsburg.

Jesus: Introducing His Life & Teaching. Leonard F. Badia. 208p. (Orig.). 1985. pap. 7.95 (ISBN 0-8091-2689-3). Paulist Pr.

Jesus Is a Special Person. Willa R. Garlow. LC 85-24361. (Bible & Me Ser.). (Illus.). 1986. 5.95 (ISBN 0-8054-4166-2). Broadman.

Jesus Is Alive! & Five Other Stories. Peter Enns & Glen Forsberg. (Stories that Live Ser.: Bk. 6). 24p. 1985. book & cassette 4.95 (ISBN 0-936215-06-2). STL Intl.

Jesus Is Born. Marie H. Frost. (First Happy Day Bks.). (Illus.). 20p. 1986. casebound 1.29 (ISBN 0-87403-131-1, 2001). Standard Pub.

Jesus is Born. Ed. by Patricia Mahany. (Classroom Activity Bks.). (Illus.). 48p. (Orig.). 1984. pap. 2.95 (ISBN 0-87239-719-X, 2449). Standard Pub.

Jesus Is Born. Gordon Stowell. (Little Fish Bks.: Bk. II). (Illus.). 14p. 1982. pap. 0.59 (ISBN 0-8307-0827-8, 5608119). Regal.

Jesus Is Coming. Paul L. Tan. 1982. pap. 2.95 (ISBN 0-88469-095-4). BMH Bks.

Jesus Is Coming Again. H. M. Riggle. 111p. pap. 1.00 (ISBN 0-686-29123-9). Faith Pub Hse.

Jesus Is Coming-Get Ready Christian. C. S. Lovett. 1969. pap. 4.25 (ISBN 0-938148-04-4). Personal Christianity.

Jesus Is Different. Wolfgang Heiner. 112p. 1983. pap. 4.50 (ISBN 0-85364-344-X, Pub. by Paternoster UK). Attic Pr.

Jesus Is for Now! Paul W. Powell. LC 85-4115. 1985. pap. 3.75 (ISBN 0-8054-5006-8). Broadman.

Jesus Is Here: Devotions to the Sacred Heart & Precious Blood. Rawley Myers. LC 85-63066. 144p. (Orig.). 1986. pap. 5.95 (ISBN 0-87973-520-1, XXX 520). Our Sunday Visitor.

Jesus Is Lord! Thomas Zanzig. LC 82-62337. (Illus.). 208p. pap. 7.95 (ISBN 0-88489-149-6). St Marys.

Jesus Is My Special Friend. Susan S. Balika. LC 81-86702. (Happy Day Bks.). (Illus.). 24p. (Orig.). 1982. pap. 1.59 (ISBN 0-87239-541-3, 3587). Standard Pub.

Jesus Is My Very Best Friend. Barbara Young. 1984. 4.95 (ISBN 0-570-04097-3, 56-1465). Concordia.

Jesus Is No Secret. Carolyn Nystrom. (Children's Bible Basics Ser.). (Illus.). 1983. 4.95 (ISBN 0-8024-0193-7). Moody.

Jesus Is Really Alive Again! Alan T. Dale. (Rainbow Books, Bible Story Books for Children). 1976. pap. 1.00 (ISBN 0-8192-1209-1). Morehouse.

Jesus Is Victor. Corrie ten Boom. 288p. 1984. pap. 6.95 (ISBN 0-8007-5176-0, Power Bks). Revell.

Jesus Is Victor! Karl Barth's Doctrine of Salvation. Donald G. Bloesch. LC 76-14360. Repr. of 1976 ed. 33.50 (ISBN 0-8357-9013-4, 2016373). Bks Demand UMI.

Jesus, Jefferson & the Task of Friends. Newton Garver. 1983. pap. 2.50x (ISBN 0-87574-251-3, 251). Pendle Hill.

Jesus Jewels. Marie M. Hald. 118p. 1983. pap. 5.00 (ISBN 0-682-49963-3). Exposition Pr FL.

Jesus' Journey, Our Journey: A Way of the Cross for the Sick & Shut-in. Joanne Turpin. 1987. pap. 2.25. St Anthony Mess Pr.

Jesus, Joy of the Suffering. Lawrence Lovasik. 3.00 (ISBN 0-8198-0641-2); pap. 2.00 (ISBN 0-8198-0642-0). Dghtrs St Paul.

Jesus King of Love. Mateo Crawley-Boevey. 1978. 5.50 (ISBN 0-8198-0521-1); pap. 3.95 (ISBN 0-8198-0522-X). Dghtrs St Paul.

Jesus, Liberation & the Biblical Jubilee: Images for Ethics & Christology. Sharon H. Ringe. LC 85-4609. (Overtures to Biblical Theology Ser.). 144p. 1985. pap. 8.95 (ISBN 0-8006-1544-1). Fortress.

Jesus Life: A Guide for Young Christians. Alvin N. Rogness. LC 72-90260. 112p. (Orig.). (YA) 1973. pap. 5.95 (ISBN 0-8066-1307-6, 10-3521). Augsburg.

Jesus Life Songbook. Richard H. Crockett & James E. Horsch. 134p. 1975. pap. 3.95 (ISBN 0-317-37867-8). Herald Pr.

Jesus Life Songbook. Ed. by Richard H. Crockett & James E. Horsch. 134p. 1975. pap. 3.95 (ISBN 0-8361-2785-4). Herald Pr.

Jesus Lives. Ron Klug & Lyn Klug. LC 82-72848. 32p. (Orig.). 1983. pap. 3.95 (ISBN 0-8066-1952-X, 10-3527). Augsburg.

Jesus Lives. Gordon Stowell. (Little Fish Bks.: Bk. II). (Illus.). 14p. 1982. pap. 0.59 (ISBN 0-8307-0834-0, 5608181). Regal.

Jesus Living the Father's Values. Megan McKenna & Darryl Ducote. LC 78-71530. (Followers of the Way Ser.: Vol. 3). 1979. 22.50 (ISBN 0-8091-9544-5); cassette 7.50 (ISBN 0-8091-7668-8). Paulist Pr.

Jesus Llama. Gordon Stowell. Tr. by Violeta S. De Martinez from Span. (Libros Pescaditos Sobre Jesus). Tr. of Jesus & the Fisherman. (Illus.). 24p. 1984. pap. 0.60 (ISBN 0-311-38612-1). Casa Bautista.

Jesus Lord. Charles Dollen. (Orig.). 1964. 3.00 (ISBN 0-8198-0066-X); pap. 2.00 (ISBN 0-8198-0067-8). Dghtrs St Paul.

Jesus: Lord & Savior. F. F. Bruce. Ed. by Michael Green. LC 86-7157. (Jesus Library). 228p. 1986. pap. 7.95 (ISBN 0-87784-932-3). Inter-Varsity.

Jesus' Lost Gospels: The Discovery at Nag Hammadi. Ed. by J. Frank O'Quinn. (Illus.). 48p. 1981. pap. text ed. 6.95 (ISBN 0-9609802-0-2). Life Science.

Jesus Loved Them. Omar V. Garrison. (Illus.). 133p. 1983. 19.95 (ISBN 0-931116-06-6). Ralston-Pilot.

Jesus Loves. Gordon Stowell. (Little Fish Bks.: Bk. II). 14p. 1982. pap. 0.59 (ISBN 0-8307-0830-8, 5608145). Regal.

Jesus Loves Children. Ed. by C. Brusselmans. 5.95 (ISBN 0-8215-9889-9). Sadlier.

Jesus Loves Children. Lynn Groth. (Cradle Roll Program Ser.). 16p. (Orig.). 1985. pap. 1.25 (ISBN 0-938272-78-0). Wels Board.
Jesus Loves Me All the Time. E. Elaine Watson. (Happy Day Bks.). (Illus.). 24p. 1984. 1.59 (ISBN 0-87239-741-6, 3711). Standard Pub.
Jesus Loves Me, Too. Ed. by Clara S. Schuster. 160p. (Orig.). 1985. pap. 6.95 (ISBN 0-8341-1074-1). Beacon Hill.
Jesus Loves: Stories about Jesus for Children. Ron Klug et al. LC 86-81807. (Illus.). 32p. (Orig.). 1986. pap. 4.95 saddlestitch (ISBN 0-8066-2235-0, 10-3526). Augsburg.
Jesus Loves You. Redemptorist Pastoral Publication. 80p. 1983. 4.95 (ISBN 0-89243-175-X). Liguori Pubns.
Jesus Loves You: A Catholic Catechism for the Primary Grades. Redemptorist Pastoral Publication Staff. LC 82-8000658. 96p. 1982. pap. 4.95 (ISBN 0-89243-157-1). Liguori Pubns.
Jesus Makes Me Happy. Wanda Hayes. (Happy Day Book). (Illus.). 24p. 1979. 1.59 (3620). Standard Pub.
Jesus Makes Me Well. Christine Kohler. (Growing up Christian Ser.). (Illus.). 24p. (Orig.). 1985. pap. 3.95 (ISBN 0-570-04113-9, 56-1524). Concordia.
Jesus Makes the Difference! The Gospel in Human Experience. James A. Harnish. 144p. (Orig.). 1987. pap. 6.95 (ISBN 0-8358-0554-9). Upper Room.
Jesus Means Freedom. Ernst Kasemann. Tr. by Frank Clarke from Ger. LC 75-94357. 168p. (Orig.). 1972. pap. 6.50 (ISBN 0-8006-1235-3, 1-1235). Fortress.
Jesus Meets Nick. Robert W. Davis. (Jesus & His Disciples Ser.: Vol. I). (Illus.). 24p. 1985. 4.95 (ISBN 0-9615877-0-9). Davis Pub.
Jesus Messages. Alan Ross. Ed. by Gregory Boster. (Illus.). 24p. (Orig.). pap. 3.49 (ISBN 0-9617038-0-6). Divine Love Pub.
Jesus' Mission to Jerusalem: Theology, Vol. 80. Helmuth L. Egelkraut. (European University Studies: Ser. 23). x, 258p. 1977. pap. 28.70 (ISBN 3-261-02133-0). P Lang Pubs.
Jesus, My Forever Friend. William Coleman. (Wonderful World of the Bible Ser.). (Illus.). 1981. 9.95 (ISBN 0-89191-370-X, 53702). Cook.
Jesus, My Friend. Ed. by Tessa Colina. (Jesus & Me Pupil Activities Books: No. 3). (Illus.). 1978. pap. 1.50 (ISBN 0-87239-270-8, 2442). Standard Pub.
Jesus, My Lord. Ed. by Tessa Colina. (Jesus & Me Pupil Activities Books: No. 4). (Illus.). 1978. pap. 1.50 (ISBN 0-87239-271-6, 2443). Standard Pub.
Jesus, My Lord So Hated Today. Basilea Schlink. 1978. pap. 0.50 (ISBN 3-87209-653-2). Evang Sisterhood Mary.
Jesus, My Saviour. Ed. by Tessa Colina. (Jesus & Me Pupil Activities Books: No. 1). (Illus.). 1978. pap. 1.50 (ISBN 0-87239-268-6, 2440). Standard Pub.
Jesus, My Teacher: (Pupil Activities Book Two) Ed. by Tessa Colina. (Jesus & Me Ser.). (Illus.). 16p. 1978. pap. 1.50 (ISBN 0-87239-269-4, 2441). Standard Pub.
Jesus Mystery: Of Lost Years & Unknown Travels. Janet L. Bock. LC 80-67420. (Illus.). 231p. (Orig.). 1980. pap. 6.95 (ISBN 0-937736-00-7). Aura Bks.
Jesus Nace. Gordon Stowell. Tr. by Violeta S. De Martinez from Span. (Libros Pescaditos Sobre Jesus). Tr. of Jesus Is Born. (Illus.). 24p. 1984. pap. 0.60 (ISBN 0-311-38608-3). Casa Bautista.
Jesus Never Said Everyone Was Lovable. Clay F. Lee. 112p. 1987. pap. 6.95 (ISBN 0-687-19980-8). Abingdon.
Jesus Nos Habla Por Medio De Sus Parabolas. Tomas R. De La Fuente. 160p. 1978. 2.95 (ISBN 0-311-04344-5). Casa Bautista.
Jesus Now. Leslie Brandt. 1978. 8.50 (ISBN 0-570-03268-7, 15-2714). Concordia.
Jesus of Faith: A Study in Christology. Michael L. Cook. LC 80-84510. 192p. (Orig.). pap. 6.95 (ISBN 0-8091-2349-5). Paulist Pr.
Jesus of History. T. R. Glover. LC 78-25986. 30.00 (ISBN 0-8414-4488-9). Folcroft.
Jesus of History, Christ of Faith. Thomas Zanzig. LC 81-86361. (Illus.). 192p. (Orig.). 1981. pap. text ed. 7.20x (ISBN 0-88489-145-3); tchr's. manual 9.00 (ISBN 0-88489-146-1); spiritmasters 9.95. St Mary's.
Jesus of Nazareth. William Barclay. 1977. pap. 1.95 (ISBN 0-345-27253-6). Ballantine.
Jesus of Nazareth. William Barclay. 288p. 1985. pap. 12.95 (ISBN 0-8407-5759-X). Nelson.
Jesus of Nazareth. Gunther Bornkamm. LC 61-5256. 240p. 1975. pap. 6.00 (ISBN 0-06-060932-X, RD113, HarpR). Har-Row.
Jesus of Nazareth. David M. Harralson. (Literacy Volunteers of America Readers Ser.). 48p. (Orig.). 1983. pap. 1.95 (ISBN 0-8428-9608-2). Cambridge Bk.
Jesus of Nazareth: A Life Worth Living. Ronald Modras. (Nazareth Bks). 128p. 1983. pap. 4.95 (ISBN 0-86683-713-2, HarpR). Har-Row.
Jesus of Nazareth: His Life, Times & Teaching. Joseph Klausner. Tr. by Herbert Danby from Hebrew. 1978. 15.95x (ISBN 0-932232-01-9); pap. 12.95 (ISBN 0-932232-02-7). Menorah Pub.
Jesus of Nazareth in New Testament Preaching. G. N. Stanton. LC 73-92782. (Society of New Testament Studies: No. 27). 228p. 1975. 44.50 (ISBN 0-521-20465-8). Cambridge U Pr.
Jesus of Nazareth: Meditations on His Humanity. Jose Comblin. Tr. by Carl Kabat from Port. LC 75-29580. Orig. Title: Jesus De Nazare. 176p. (Orig.). 1976. pap. 3.48 (ISBN 0-88344-239-6). Orbis Bks.
Jesus of Nazareth: The Man, the Myth, the Enigma. George Christopher, Jr. 50p. 1984. 4.95 (ISBN 0-89697-176-7). Intl Univ Pr.
Jesus of Nazareth, Who Is He. Arthur Wallis. 1959. pap. 1.50 (ISBN 0-87508-558-X). Chr Lit.
Jesus of Nazareth Yesterday & Today. Juan L. Segundo. Tr. by John Drury from Span. LC 83-19386. (Faith & Ideologies Ser.: Vol. 1). Tr. of Hombre de Hoy Ante Jesus de Nazaret: Fe e Ideologia Ser. 368p. (Orig.). 1984. pap. 14.95 (ISBN 0-88344-127-6). Orbis Bks.
Jesus of Poets & Prophets. Richard Roberts. LC 74-118546. 1971. Repr. of 1919 ed. 22.50x (ISBN 0-8046-1171-8, Pub. by Kennikat). Assoc Faculty Pr.
Jesus of Poets & Prophets. Richard Roberts. 1977. Repr. of 1920 ed. lib. bdg. 25.00 (ISBN 0-8492-2312-1). R West.
Jesus of the Bible. Ed. by Clevenger & Hill. 1973. pap. 1.50 (ISBN 0-88428-007-1, 101). Parchment Pr.
Jesus of the Gospels: A Worktext Approach to Understanding Scripture. Mark Quinn. (YA) 1987. pap. text ed. write for info. (ISBN 0-697-02233-1); write for info. tchr's. ed. (ISBN 0-697-02234-X). Wm C Brown.
Jesus of the Parables. Charles W. Smith. LC 74-26816. 255p. 1975. 8.95 (ISBN 0-8298-0267-3). Pilgrim NY.
Jesus on Our Hands. Jon L. Joyce. (Orig.). 1983. pap. 4.95 (ISBN 0-937172-57-X). JLJ Pubs.
Jesus on the Cross. Frank Beattie. (Orig.). 1981. pap. 2.95 (ISBN 0-937172-17-0). JLJ Pubs.
Jesus on the Mountain: A Study in Matthean Theology. Terence L. Donaldson. (JSNT Supplement Ser.: No. 8). 326p. 1985. text ed. 28.50x (ISBN 0-905774-74-4, Pub. by JSOT Pr England); pap. text ed. 13.50x (ISBN 0-905774-75-2, Pub. by JSOT Pr England). Eisenbrauns.
Jesus on Trial. Penny Frank. Ed. by P. Alexander. (Lion Story Bible Ser.). 24p. 1987. 2.95. Lion USA.
Jesus on Trial: The Development of the Passion Narratives & Their Historical & Ecumenical Implications. Gerard S. Sloyan. (Illus.). 156p. pap. 3.75 (ISBN 0-686-95173-5). ADL.
Jesus: One of Us. Ed. by Chris Davies et al. 148p. 1981. pap. 3.95 (ISBN 0-87784-618-9). Inter Varsity.
Jesus Our Life: Activity Book. Mary E. Podhaizer. Ed. by Patricia I. Puccetti. (Faith & Life Ser.: bk. 2). 76p. (Orig.). 1984. pap. 2.50 (ISBN 0-89870-063-9). Ignatius Pr.
Jesus, Our Man in Glory. Compiled by Gerald B. Smith. Date not set. pap. price not set (ISBN 0-87509-390-6). Chr Pubns.
Jesus, Our Savior. Donna Holly. (Illus.). 16p. (Orig.). 1984. pap. 0.60 (ISBN 0-87239-701-7, 2307). Standard Pub.
Jesus Outside the Gospels. R. Joseph Hoffmann. LC 84-42862. (Skeptic's Bookshelf Ser.). 132p. 1984. 17.95 (ISBN 0-87975-263-7). Prometheus Bks.
Jesus' Parables & the War of Myths: Essays on Imagination in the Scriptures. Amos N. Wilder. LC 81-43083. 176p. 1982. 3.50 (ISBN 0-8006-0668-X, 1-668). Fortress.
Jesus' Pattern for a Happy Life: The Beatitudes. Marilyn Norquist. 112p. 1986. pap. 3.50 (ISBN 0-89243-136-9). Liguori Pubns.
Jesus' Pattern of Prayer. John MacArthur, Jr. LC 81-3947. 200p. 1981. 5.95 (ISBN 0-8024-4962-X). Moody.
Jesus People. John J. Ryan. 1970. text ed. 2.95 (ISBN 0-914070-03-7). ACTA Found.
Jesus Person Pocket Promise Book. David Wilkerson. LC 72-86208. 96p. 1979. pap. 2.50 (ISBN 0-8307-0191-5, 5007801). Regal.
Jesus, Politics, & Society: A Study of Luke's Gospel. Richard J. Cassidy. LC 78-735. 238p. (Orig.). 1978. 15.95 (ISBN 0-88344-238-8); pap. 7.95 (ISBN 0-88344-237-X). Orbis Bks.
Jesus Prayed. Arthur Wallis. 1966. pap. 1.50 (ISBN 0-87508-559-8). Chr Lit.
Jesus Prayer. Per-Olof Sjogren. Tr. by Sydney Linton from Swedish. LC 75-18789. 96p. 1975. pap. 3.95 (ISBN 0-8006-1216-7, 1-1216). Fortress.
Jesus Prayer for Today. Arthur A. Vogel. LC 81-84349. 128p. (Orig.). 1982. pap. 5.95 (ISBN 0-8091-2413-0). Paulist Pr.
Jesus' Predictions of Vindication & Resurrection: The Provenance, Meaning, & Correlation of the Synoptic Predictions. Hans F. Bayer. 290p. 1986. pap. 50.00x (ISBN 3-16-145014-0, Pub. by J C B Mohr BRD). Coronet Bks.
Jesus Present & Coming: Daily Meditations on the Advent & Christmas Masses. Emeric Lawrence. LC 82-20380. 128p. 1982. pap. 7.95 (ISBN 0-8146-1284-9). Liturgical Pr.
Jesus' Proclamation of the Kingdom of God. Johannes Weiss. Ed. by Richard H. Hiers & Larrimore D. Holland. (Reprints & Translations). 1985. pap. 9.75 (ISBN 0-89130-859-8, 00-07-08). Scholars Pr GA.
Jesus Psychi Super Star. Alan Crossley. 64p. 1984. 29.00x (ISBN 0-7212-0683-2, Pub. by Regency Pr). State Mutual Bk.
Jesus Purusha. Ian Davie. LC 85-23113. 176p. (Orig.). 1985. pap. 8.95 (ISBN 0-89281-069-6, Lindisfarne Pr). Inner Tradit.
Jesus Put on a Happy Face: The Healing Power of Joy & Humor. Cal Samra. LC 85-60257. (Illus.). 234p. (Orig.). 1985. pap. 7.95 (ISBN 0-933453-00-0). Rosejoy Pubns.
Jesus Quizzes. Shirley Beegle. 1985. pap. 0.69 (ISBN 0-87239-824-2, 2814). Standard Pub.
Jesus Rediscovered. Malcolm Muggeridge. 1979. pap. 7.95 (ISBN 0-385-14654-X, Galilee). Doubleday.
Jesus Reveals His Heart: Letters of St. Margaret Mary. Tr. by Clarence Hebert. 1980. 4.75 (ISBN 0-8198-3905-1); pap. 3.50 (ISBN 0-8198-3906-X). Dghtrs St Paul.
Jesus' Revelation of What Is True. Emil R. Lindemann. Ed. by Wilfried W. Wegener. 154p. (Orig.). 1983. pap. text ed. 4.00 (ISBN 0-9612192-0-3). E R Lindemann.
Jesus Rey De Amor. Mateo Crawley-Boevey. (Span.). 1980. pap. 3.95 (ISBN 0-8198-3909-4). Dghtrs St Paul.
Jesus Rides into Jerusalem. Joyce Coe. (Illus.). 24p. 1987. pap. 00.99 (ISBN 0-570-09007-5, 59-1435). Concordia.
Jesus Risen: An Historical, Fundamental & Systematic Examination of Christ's Resurrection. Gerald O'Collins. 240p. 1987. 13.95 (ISBN 0-8091-2849-7); pap. 16.95 (ISBN 0-8091-0393-1). Paulist Pr.
Jesus Said "Leave Her Alone". Shirley M. Dail. (Illus.). 1979. pap. 2.95x (ISBN 0-9602440-0-X). Jesus-First.
Jesus Sana. Gordon Stowell. Tr. by Violeta S. De Martinez from Eng. (Libros Pescaditos Sobre Jesus). Tr. of Jesus Heals. (Illus.). 24p. 1984. pap. 0.60 (ISBN 0-311-38610-5). Casa Bautista.
Jesus' Saving Questions. Gloria Hutchinson. 118p. (Orig.). 1984. pap. text ed. 4.95 (ISBN 0-86716-028-4). St Anthony Mess Pr.
Jesus' Second Family. M. Marquart. (Arch Book Series Fourteen). 1977. pap. 0.99 (ISBN 0-570-06111-3, 59-1229). Concordia.
Jesus, Set Me Free! Inner Freedom Through Contemplation. George Maloney. 4.95 (ISBN 0-87193-096-X). Dimension Bks.
Jesus, Shelley, & Malthus. Charles Bradlaugh. 1978. Repr. of 1877 ed. lib. bdg. 10.00 (ISBN 0-8495-0441-4). Arden Lib.
Jesus Silences His Critics: Mattew Twenty-Two Verses Fifteen Through Forty-Six. John MacArthur, Jr. (John MacArthur Bible Studies Ser.). 1987. pap. 3.50 (ISBN 0-8024-5313-9). Moody.
Jesus, Son of God? Ed. by Edward Schillebeeckx & Johannes-Baptist Metz. (Concilium Ser.: Vol. 153). 128p. 1982. pap. 6.95 (ISBN 0-8164-2384-9, HarpR). Har-Row.
Jesus, Son of Man. Barnabas Lindars. 256p. (Orig.). 1984. pap. 9.95 (ISBN 0-8028-0022-X). Eerdmans.
Jesus, Son of Mary: A Book for Children. Fulton J. Sheen. (Illus.). 32p. 1980. 8.95 (ISBN 0-8164-0470-4, HarpR). Har-Row.
Jesus Speaks Today. John E. Hunter. LC 81-68042. 1982. pap. 4.25 (ISBN 0-8054-5184-6). Broadman.
Jesus Still Has Something to Say. Robert C. Campbell. 192p. 1987. pap. 9.95 (ISBN 0-8170-1114-5). Judson.
Jesus Story. Ann R. Colton. 396p. 1969. 10.00 (ISBN 0-917187-04-0). A R C Pub.
Jesus Story. Mary Montgomery & Herb Montgomery. 1974. pupil pack 5.55 (ISBN 0-03-012951-6, 125, HarpR); tchr's. manual 8.95 (ISBN 0-03-012956-7, 126). Har-Row.
Jesus Story & Color Book. Rilda Humphrey. (Illus.). 64p. (Orig.). 1982. pap. 2.95 (ISBN 0-87239-583-9, 2398). Standard Pub.
Jesus: Stranger from Heaven & Son of God. Marinus De Jonge. Ed. by John E. Steely. LC 77-9984. (Society of Biblical Literature. Sources for Biblical Studies: No. 11). Repr. of 1977 ed. 61.50 (ISBN 0-8357-9575-6, 2017532). Bks Demand UMI.
Jesus Style. Gayle D. Erwin. 211p. 1985. 9.95 (ISBN 0-8499-0509-5, 0509-5). Word Bks.
Jesus, Symbol-Maker for the Kingdom. Bernard B. Scott. LC 80-2388. pap. 47.50 (2029610). Bks Demand UMI.
Jesus Taught Me to Cast Out Devils. Norvel Hayes. 90p. (Orig.). 1982. pap. 2.75 (ISBN 0-89274-272-0). Harrison Hse.
Jesus Teaches. Gordon Stowell. (Little Fish Bks.: Bk. II). (Illus.). 14p. 1982. pap. 0.59 (ISBN 0-8307-0829-4, 5608138). Regal.
Jesus Teaches Me. Bartholomew. 1982. pap. 0.85 (ISBN 0-570-04071-X, 56-1374). Concordia.
Jesus Teaches Me. Linda Corbin & Pat Dys. (Discipleship Workbook for Parent & Child Ser.: Bk. 4). (Illus.). 35p. Date not set. wkbk. 3.95 (ISBN 0-87509-389-2). Chr Pubns.
Jesus Tells Some Stories. Gordon Stowell. (Little Fish Bks.: Bk. II). (Illus.). 14p. 1982. pap. 0.59 (ISBN 0-8307-0833-2, 5608176). Regal.
Jesus, the Children's Friend. Miriam J. Hall. 64p. (Orig.). 1983. pap. 1.95 (ISBN 0-8341-0815-1). Beacon Hill.
Jesus the Christ. Walter Kasper. LC 76-20021. 294p. 1977. pap. 9.95 (ISBN 0-8091-2081-X). Paulist Pr.
Jesus the Christ. James E. Talmage. (Classics in Mormon Literature Ser.). 804p. 1982. 10.95 (ISBN 0-87747-903-8). Deseret Bk.
Jesus, the Compassion of God: New Perspectives on the Tradition of Christianity. Monika K. Hellwig. 1983. 12.95 (ISBN 0-89453-365-7); pap. 7.95 (ISBN 0-89453-375-4). M Glazier.
Jesus: The Death & Resurrection of God. Donald G. Dawe. LC 85-5192. 252p. 1985. pap. 15.95 (ISBN 0-8042-0527-2). John Knox.
Jesus: The Evidence. Ian Wilson. LC 84-48234. (Illus.). 208p. 1985. 17.45 (ISBN 0-06-069433-5, HarpR). Har-Row.
Jesus: The First Human Behaviorist. Warren D. Burtis. 128p. 1981. pap. text ed. 5.95 (ISBN 0-939530-00-7). Burtis Ent.
Jesus, the Friend of Children. D. C. Cook Editors. LC 77-72722. (Illus.). 1977. 9.95 (ISBN 0-89191-077-8). Cook.
Jesus the Healer. As told by Catherine Storr. (People of the Bible Ser.). (Illus.). 32p. 1985. PLB 10.65 (ISBN 0-8172-2041-0). Raintree Pubs.
Jesus the Jew: A Historian's Reading of the Gospels. Geza Vermes. LC 80-2381. 288p. 1981. pap. 9.95 (ISBN 0-8006-1443-7, 1-1443). Fortress.
Jesus: The King & His Kingdom. George Wesley Buchanan. LC 83-24939. xx, 348p. 1984. 21.95 (ISBN 0-86554-072-1, H66). Mercer Univ Pr.
Jesus the Life Changer. Ada Lum. 40p. 1978. pap. 2.25 (ISBN 0-87784-316-3). Inter-Varsity.
Jesus the Magician. Morton Smith. LC 76-9986. 224p. 1982. pap. 12.95 (ISBN 0-06-067413-X, RD 372, HarpR). Har-Row.
Jesus: The Man. Edward W. H. Vick. LC 78-10253. (Anvil Ser.). 1979. pap. 6.95 (ISBN 0-8127-0220-4). Review & Herald.
Jesus, the Man & the Myth. James P. Mackey. LC 78-61627. 320p. 1979. pap. 10.95 (ISBN 0-8091-2169-7). Paulist Pr.
Jesus: The Man, the Mission, & the Message. 2nd ed. C. Milo Connick. (Illus.). 512p. 1974. 29.95 (ISBN 0-13-509521-2). P-H.
Jesus, the Man Who Changes Lives. Denise R. Adler. 1982. pap. 2.50 (ISBN 0-8423-1872-0). Tyndale.
Jesus the Master Respondent. James Bales. 2.50 (ISBN 0-89315-130-0). Lambert Bk.
Jesus the Messiah. Alfred Edersheim. 1959. pap. 10.95 (ISBN 0-8028-8131-9). Eerdmans.
Jesus the Messiah. Donald Guthrie. 400p. 1981. pap. 12.95 (ISBN 0-310-25431-0, 12223P). Zondervan.
Jesus the Pagan. Ed. by Pearl Ross. 84p. 1972. 7.00 (ISBN 0-8022-2097-5). Philos Lib.
Jesus the Pattern: Library. Compiled by Association for Research & Enlightenment, Readings Research Dept. (Vol. 10). 336p. 1980. 10.95 (ISBN 0-87604-123-3). ARE Pr.
Jesus the Pharisee: New Look at the Jewishness of Jesus. Harvey Falk. (Orig.). 1985. pap. 8.95 (ISBN 0-8091-2677-X). Paulist Pr.
Jesus: The Servant. Karen Melang. (Concept Ser.). (Illus.). 24p. (Orig.). 1986. pap. 3.95 saddlestitched (ISBN 0-570-08532-2, 56-1559). Concordia.
Jesus the Servant: From the Gospel of Mark. William R. Cannon. LC 78-62578. 1978. pap. text ed. 2.95x (ISBN 0-8358-0376-7). Upper Room.
Jesus, the Son of Man. Illus. by Carl Bloch. (Illus.). 80p. 1983. pap. 12.95 (ISBN 0-87973-652-6, 652). Our Sunday Visitor.
Jesus the Son of Man. Kahlil Gibran. (Illus.). 1928. 14.95 (ISBN 0-394-43124-3). Knopf.
Jesus: the Story of His Life: A Modern Retelling Based on the Gospels. Walter Barnett. LC 75-28260. 1976. 19.95x (ISBN 0-88229-308-7). Nelson Hall.
Jesus, the Stranger. Joseph G. Donders. LC 77-21783. 298p. (Orig.). 1978. pap. 8.95x (ISBN 0-88344-235-3). Orbis Bks.
Jesus the Teacher. Penny Frank. Ed. by P. Alexander. (Lion Story Bible Ser.). 24p. 1987. 2.95 (ISBN 0-85648-760-0). Lion USA.

Jesus the Teacher: A Socio-Rhetorical Interpretation of Mark. Vernon K. Robbins. LC 83-16504. 256p. 1984. 23.95 (ISBN 0-8006-0719-8, 1-719). Fortress.

Jesus the Teacher Word Search. John H. Tiner. 48p. 1986. pap. 2.50 (ISBN 0-87403-049-8, 2693). Standard Pub.

Jesus: The Ultimate E.T. Bill Clancy. Ed. by Dick Howard. 40p. (Orig.). 1983. pap. 1.75 (ISBN 0-912573-00-7). Believers Faith.

Jesus: The Way to Freedom. Donald P. Gray. LC 79-66823. (Illus.). 1979. pap. text ed. 4.95 (ISBN 0-88489-112-7). St Mary's.

Jesus, the Word to Be Spoken. Mother Teresa. 176p. (Orig.). 1986. pocket-size 3.95 (ISBN 0-89283-304-1). Servant.

Jesus, the Word to Be Spoken: A Daily Devotional. Mother Teresa. 1987. 9.95 (ISBN 0-8027-2574-0). Walker & Co.

Jesus Then & Now. David Watson & Simon Jenkins. Ed. by R. Keely. 192p. 1987. pap. 9.95 (ISBN 0-7459-1318-0). Lion USA.

Jesus Through Many Eyes: Introduction to the Theology of the New Testament. Stephen Neill. LC 75-36455. 228p. 1976. pap. 7.95 (ISBN 0-8006-1220-5, 1-1220). Fortress.

Jesus Through the Centuries: His Place in the History of Culture. Jaroslav Pelikan. LC 85-2428. (Illus.). 272p. 1985. 22.50 (ISBN 0-300-03496-2). Yale U Pr.

Jesus Through the Centuries: His Place in the History of Culture. Jaroslav Pelikan. LC 86-45679. (Illus.). 288p. 1987. pap. 8.95 (ISBN 0-06-097080-4, PL 7080, PL). Har-Row.

Jesus Tradition: Images of Jesus in the West. Gerard S. Sloyan. 128p. (Orig.). 1986. pap. 5.95 (ISBN 0-89622-285-3). Twenty-Third.

Jesus Tradition Outside the Gospels. David Wenham. (Gospel Perspectives Ser.: No. 5). 419p. 1985. text ed. 24.50x (ISBN 1-85075-006-8, Pub by JSOT Pr England); pap. text ed. 13.50x (ISBN 1-85075-007-6). Eisenbrauns.

Jesus' Twelve Disciples: Arch Bks. Louise Ulmer. 1982. pap. 0.99 (ISBN 0-570-06160-1, 59-1307). Concordia.

Jesus Two: The Life & Wisdom of Jesus. Ed. by Chet Olson. 216p. 1982. 8.95 (ISBN 0-940298-04-X); pap. 5.95 (ISBN 0-940298-03-1). Spiritwarrior Pub.

Jesus' Vigil of the Hour "Watch with Me". 1965. 1.95 (ISBN 0-685-79133-5). Summit Univ.

Jesus Vive. Gordon Stowell. Tr. by Violeta S. De Martinez from Span. (Libros Pescaditos Sobre Jesus). Tr. of Jesus Lives. (Illus.). 24p. 1984. pap. 0.60 (ISBN 0-311-38615-6). Casa Bautista.

Jesus Wants You Well. C. S. Lovett. 1973. pap. 6.45 (ISBN 0-938148-29-X). Personal Christianity.

Jesus Was a Helper. Kay V. Henry. LC 86-17540. (Bible-&-Me Ser.). 1987. pap. 5.95 (ISBN 0-8054-4176-X). Broadman.

Jesus Was a Jew. Rev. ed. Arnold G. Fruchtenbaum. LC 74-75670. 156p. 1981. pap. 2.95 (ISBN 0-8054-6209-0). Ariel Pr CA.

Jesus Was a Vegetarian. Frank J. Muccie, Jr. 62p. pap. 1.95 (ISBN 0-938520-03-2). Edenite.

Jesus Was an Anarchist. Elbert Hubbard. 1974. lib. bdg. 59.95 (ISBN 0-87700-304-1). Revisionist Pr.

Jesus, Way, Truth, Life. 7.00 (ISBN 0-8198-3913-2); 6.00 (ISBN 0-8198-3914-0). Dghtrs St Paul.

Jesus Went about Doing Good. Jean H. Richards. LC 80-70475. 1983. 5.95 (ISBN 0-8054-4289-8, 4242-89). Broadman.

Jesus, What Are You Doing Tonight? Cathy Carlin. (Outreach Ser.). 32p. 1982. pap. 0.99 (ISBN 0-8163-0492-0). Pacific Pr Pub Assn.

Jesus Who? The Greatest Mystery Never Told. Francis B. Drohan. LC 84-16654. 270p. 1985. 15.00 (ISBN 0-8022-2475-X). Philos Lib.

Jesus Years: A Chronological Study of the Life of Christ. Thomas D. Thurman. LC 77-80314. (Illus.). 1977. pap. 5.95 (ISBN 0-87239-136-1, 40061). Standard Pub.

Jew According to the Talmud. A. Rohling. 1982. lib. bdg. 69.95 (ISBN 0-87700-361-0). Revisionist Pr.

Jew & Greek: Tutors Unto Christ. G. H. MacGregor & A. C. Purdy. 59.95 (ISBN 0-8490-0444-6). Gordon Pr.

Jew & His Duties. Hyman E. Goldin. 246p. 1953. pap. 6.95 (ISBN 0-88482-429-2). Hebrew Pub.

Jew & His Family. Benjamin Kaplan. LC 67-21376. 1967. 25.00x (ISBN 0-8071-0545-7). La State U Pr.

Jew & His History. Lionel Kochan. (Scholars Press Reprints & Translations: No. 1). 1985. pap. 8.25 (ISBN 0-89130-821-0, 00 07 06). Scholars Pr GA.

Jew & His Home. 14th ed. A. E. Kitov. Tr. by Nathan Bulman. LC 63-17660. 233p. 1976. 12.50 (ISBN 0-88400-004-4). Shengold.

Jew & Palestine in Prophecy. M. R. DeHaan. 1978. pap. 5.95 (ISBN 0-310-23381-X, 9497P). Zondervan.

Jew & the Christian Missionary: A Jewish Response to Missionary Christianity. Gerald Sigal. 1981. 20.00x (ISBN 0-87068-886-3). Ktav.

Jew & the Cross. Dagobert D. Runes. 1966. pap. 0.95 (ISBN 0-8065-0111-1, 216). Citadel Pr.

Jew & the Universe. Solomon Goldman. LC 73-2200. (Jewish People; History, Religion, Literature Ser.). Repr. of 1936 ed. 23.50 (ISBN 0-405-05265-0). Ayer Co Pubs.

Jew As Ally of the Muslim: Medieval Roots of Anti-Semitism. Allan H. Cutler & Helen E. Cutler. LC 84-40295. 594p. 1986. text ed. 50.00 (ISBN 0-268-01190-7, 85-11909). U of Notre Dame Pr.

Jew at Home: Impressions of Jewish Life in Russia & Austria. Joseph Pennell. 1976. lib. bdg. 134.95 (ISBN 0-8490-2098-0). Gordon Pr.

Jew Examines Christianity. Rachel Zurer. LC 83-82999. 181p. (Orig.). 1985. 12.50 (ISBN 0-941752-03-8); pap. 8.50 (ISBN 0-941752-01-1). Jenna Pr.

Jew in America: A History. rev. ed. Rufus Learsi. 1972. 11.95x (ISBN 0-87068-177-X). Ktav.

Jew in Drama. Myer J. Landa. LC 68-26290. 1968. Repr. of 1926 ed. 23.00x (ISBN 0-8046-0257-3, Pub. by Kennikat). Assoc Faculty Pr.

Jew in English Drama: An Annotated Bibliography. rev. ed. Edward D. Coleman. LC 67-11901. 1969. 25.00x (ISBN 0-87068-011-0). Ktav.

Jew in English Drama: An Annotated Bibliography. Edward D. Coleman. LC 67-11901. 1968. Repr. of 1943 ed. with The Jew in Western Drama by Edgar Rosenberg 8.95 (ISBN 0-87104-101-4, Co-Pub by Ktav). NY Pub Lib.

Jew in English Fiction. David Philipson. LC 76-42290. 1889. lib. bdg. 25.00 (ISBN 0-8414-6796-X). Folcroft.

Jew in English Fiction. David Philipson. LC 76-30568. (English Literature Ser, No. 33). 1977. lib. bdg. 47.95x (ISBN 0-8383-2150-X). Haskell.

Jew in the Medieval Community. James W. Parkes. 456p. 1976. pap. 12.95 (ISBN 0-87203-060-1). Hermon.

Jew in the Medieval World: A Source Book: 315-1791. Jacob R. Marcus. LC 60-8666. (Temple Books). 1969. pap. text ed. 10.95x (ISBN 0-689-70133-0, T7). Atheneum.

Jew in the Medieval World: A Source Book, 315-1791. Jacob R. Marcus. LC 71-97295. 504p. 1975. Repr. of 1938 ed. lib. bdg. 22.50x (ISBN 0-8371-2619-3, MAJM). Greenwood.

Jew in the Victorian Novel: Some Relationships Between Prejudice & Art. Anne A. Naman. LC 79-8634. (AMS Studies in the 19th Century: No. 1). 1980. 29.50 (ISBN 0-404-18023-X). AMS Pr.

Jew of Juif? Jews in Canada, 1759-1914. Michael Brown. (Illus.). 336p. 1987. 16.95 (ISBN 0-8276-0271-5). Jewish Pubns.

Jew, the Gypsy & el Islam. Richard F. Burton. 1974. Repr. of 1898 ed. 6.00 (ISBN 0-913022-11-X). Angriff Pr.

Jew Today. Elie Wiesel. Tr. by Marion Weisel from Fr. LC 79-11251. 1979. pap. 4.95 (ISBN 0-394-74057-2, Vin). Random.

Jewel in the Lotus. Grace Cooke. 1973. pap. 5.95 (ISBN 0-85487-032-6). De Vorss.

Jewel in the Lotus. Ed. by Raghavan Iyer. 606p. (Orig.). 1983. pap. 19.75 (ISBN 0-88695-000-7). Concord Grove.

Jewel in the Lotus: Outline of Present Day Buddhism in China. John E Blofeld. LC 74-10096. (China Studies: from Confucius to Mao Ser). 193p. 1986. Repr. of 1948 ed. 20.50 (ISBN 0-88355-161-6). Hyperion Conn.

Jewel of Happiness: The Sukhmani of Guru Arjan. Ajaib Singh. Ed. by Russell Perkins & Judith Perkins. Tr. by Raaj K. Bagga. LC 84-50910. (Illus.). 384p. (Orig.). 1984. pap. 15.00 (ISBN 0-89142-042-8). Sant Bani Ash.

Jewel of Humility. Sri Chinmoy. (Illus.). 56p. (Orig.). 1980. pap. 2.00 (ISBN 0-88497-493-6). Aum Pubns.

Jewel Ornament of Liberation. SGam po pa. Tr. by Herbert V. Guenther. LC 86-11839. 353p. (off). 1986. pap. 14.95 (ISBN 0-87773-378-3). Shambhala Pubns.

Jeweled Sword. Ruth L. Hill. 1987. pap. 5.95 (ISBN 0-89081-565-8). Harvest Hse.

Jewels from the Bible. (The Inspirational Library). 24p. 3.95 (ISBN 0-8326-2008-4, 3255). World Bible.

Jewels of the Qur'an: Al-Ghazali's Theory. Muhammad A. Quasem. 1977. 12.00 (ISBN 0-686-23467-7). Quasem.

Jewels of the Qur'an: Al-Ghazali's Theory. Muhammad A. Quasem. 240p. (Orig.). 1984. pap. 12.95 (ISBN 0-7103-0034-4, Kegan Paul). Methuen Inc.

Jewish Activism in Imperial Germany: The Struggle for Civil Equality. Marjorie Lamberti. LC 77-17325. (Yale Historical Publications: No. 119). 1978. 27.50x (ISBN 0-300-02163-1). Yale U Pr.

Jewish Agency for Palestine: The Jewish Plan for Palestine. Repr. of 1947 ed. 77.00 (ISBN 3-601-00327-9). Kraus Repr.

Jewish Alternatives in Love, Dating & Marriage. Pinchas Stopler. 100p. (Orig.). 1985. lib. bdg. 10.50 (ISBN 0-8191-4475-4); pap. text ed. 5.95 (ISBN 0-8191-4476-2). U Pr of Amer.

Jewish America. Seymour Kurtz. LC 84-10065. (Illus.). 250p. 1985. 29.95 (ISBN 0-07-035655-6). McGraw.

Jewish-American Literature: An Anthology. Ed. by Abraham Chapman. 727p. pap. 2.25 (ISBN 0-686-95132-8). ADL.

Jewish-American Stories. Ed. by Irving Howe. 1977. pap. 4.95 (ISBN 0-451-62515-3, ME2302, Ment). NAL.

Jewish Americana. Jacob R. Marcus. 1954. 7.50x (ISBN 0-87068-799-9, Pub. by Hebrew Union). Ktav.

Jewish Americans: Three Generations in a Jewish Community. Sidney Goldstein & Calvin Goldscheider. (Brown Classics in Judaica Ser.). (Illus.). 294p. 1985. pap. text ed. 13.50 (ISBN 0-8191-4721-4). U Pr of Amer.

Jewish & Christian Apocalypses. F. C. Burkitt. (British Academy, London, Schweich Lectures on Biblical Archaeology Series, 1914). pap. 19.00 (ISBN 0-8115-1255-X). Kraus Repr.

Jewish & Christian Self-Definition, Vol. 1: The Shaping of Christianity in the Second & Third Centuries. Ed. by E. P. Sanders. LC 79-7390. 336p. 1980. 5.00 (ISBN 0-8006-0578-0, 1-578). Fortress.

Jewish & Christian Self-Definition, Vol. 2: Aspects of Judaism in the Greco-Roman Period. Ed. by E. P. Sanders et al. LC 79-7390. 450p. 1981. 5.00 (ISBN 0-8006-0660-4, 1-660). Fortress.

Jewish & Christian Self-Definition, Vol. 3: Self-Definition in the Greco-Roman World. Ed. by Ben F. Meyer & E. P. Sanders. LC 79-7390. 320p. 1983. 24.95 (ISBN 0-8006-0690-6, 1-690). Fortress.

Jewish & Gnostic Man. Gilles Quispel & Gershom Scholem. LC 85-26137. (Eranos Lectures Ser.: No. 3). 46p. (Orig.). 1986. pap. 7.50 (ISBN 0-88214-403-0). Spring Pubns.

Jewish & Hebrew Onomastics: A Bibliography. Robert Singerman. (Reference Library of the Humanities: Vol. 92). (LC 76-052684). 1977. lib. bdg. 23.00 (ISBN 0-8240-9881-1). Garland Pub.

Jewish & Pauline Studies. W. D. Davies. LC 82-48620. 432p. 1983. text ed. 29.95 (ISBN 0-8006-0694-9). Fortress.

Jewish & Roman Law, 2 Vols. Boaz Cohen. 1966. Set. 15.00x (ISBN 0-8381-4100-5). United Syn Bk.

Jewish Anthology. Edmond Fleg. Tr. by Maurice Samuel. LC 72-142934. 399p. 1975. Repr. of 1925 ed. lib. bdg. 22.50x (ISBN 0-8371-5824-9, FLJA). Greenwood.

Jewish Apostasy in the Modern World. Ed. by Todd M. Endelman. 300p. 1987. 34.50 (ISBN 0-8419-1029-4). Holmes & Meier.

Jewish Apostle to the Gentiles: Paul As He Saw Himself. Philip A. Cunningham. 112p. (Orig.). 1986. pap. 5.95 (ISBN 0-89622-302-7). Twenty-Third.

Jewish Awareness Worksheets, 2 vols. Sharon Eichenbaum & Alice Goldin. pap. 2.95x ea. Vol. 1 (ISBN 0-87441-266-8). Vol. 2 (ISBN 0-87441-270-6). Behrman.

Jewish Background of Christianity: 586 B.C. to A.D. 1. N. Levison. 1977. lib. bdg. 59.95 (ISBN 0-8490-2100-6). Gordon Pr.

Jewish Background of the Christian Liturgy. William O. Oesterley. 1925. 11.75 (ISBN 0-8446-1329-0). Peter Smith.

Jewish Background to the Lord's Prayer. Brad Young. 54p. (Orig.). 1984. pap. 3.95 (ISBN 0-918873-02-9). Ctr Judaic-Christ Studies.

Jewish Barbers & the Holy See: From the Thirteenth to the Seventeenth-Century. Leon Poliakov. Tr. by Miriam Kochan from Fr. (Littman Library of Jewish Civilization). 288p. 1977. 29.00x (ISBN 0-19-710028-7). Oxford U Pr.

Jewish Baseball Stars. Harld V. Ribalow & Meir Ribalow. (Illus.). 1984. 12.95 (ISBN 0-88254-898-0). Hippocrene Bks.

Jewish Bioethics. Fred Rosner et al. 1979. (Sanhedrin Pr); pap. 11.95 (ISBN 0-88482-935-9, Sanhedrin Pr). Hebrew Pub.

Jewish Book Annual, Vol. 35. Jacob Kabakoff. 1977. 10.00 (ISBN 0-914820-05-2). JWB.

Jewish Book Annual, Vol. 36. Ed. by Jacob Kabakoff. 1978. 10.00 (ISBN 0-914820-06-0). JWB.

Jewish Book Annual, Vol. 37. Jacob Kabakoff. 1979. 12.00 (ISBN 0-914820-07-9). JWB.

Jewish Book Annual, Vol. 38. Ed. by Jacob Kabakoff. 1980. 15.00 (ISBN 0-914820-33-8). JWB.

Jewish Book Annual, Vol. 39. Ed. by Jacob Kabakoff. 1981. 15.00 (ISBN 0-914820-34-6). JWB.

Jewish Book Annual, Vol. 40. Ed. by Jacob Kabakoff. 1982. 17.50 (ISBN 0-914820-10-9). JWB.

Jewish Book Annual, Vol. 41. Jacob Kabakoff. 1983. 17.50 (ISBN 0-914820-12-5). JWB.

Jewish Book Annual, Vol. 42. Jacob Kabakoff. 18.00 (ISBN 0-914820-13-3). JWB.

Jewish Book Annual, Vol. 43. Jacob Kabakoff. 1985. 18.00 (ISBN 0-914820-14-1). JWB.

Jewish Book of Days. (Illus.). 128p. 1987. 9.95 (ISBN 0-88363-388-4). H L Levin.

Jewish Book of Why. Alfred J. Kolatch. 1981. 12.95 (ISBN 0-8246-0256-0). Jonathan David.

Jewish Book of Why's. A. J. Kolatch. 1985. gift set 28.95 (ISBN 0-8246-0314-1). Jonathan David.

Jewish Buildings & Cemeteries Guide to Visual Resources: International Holdings in Israel, Vol. I. Ethel S. Hirsh. 75p. 1982. pap. 10.00 (ISBN 0-943376-17-3). Magnes Mus.

Jewish Bund in Russia from Its Origins to 1905. Henry J. Tobias. LC 75-153820. 1972. 30.00x (ISBN 0-8047-0764-2). Stanford U Pr.

Jewish Campus Life: A Survey of Student Attitudes Toward Marriage & Family. Rela G. Monson. LC 84-70026. 52p. 1984. pap. 3.00 (ISBN 0-87495-060-0). Am Jewish Comm.

Jewish Catalog: A Do-It Yourself Kit. Compiled by Michael Strassfeld et al. LC 73-11759. (Illus.). 1973. pap. 8.95 (ISBN 0-8276-0042-9, 338). Jewish Pubns.

Jewish Celebrities Hall of Fame. Tim Boxer. 1986. pap. 7.95 (ISBN 0-318-21398-2). Shapolsky Pubs.

Jewish Ceremonial: A Guide to Jewish Prayer & Ritual. Eli Kellerman. 69p. 1983. pap. 9.95 (ISBN 965-220-038-7, Carta Pub Isreal). Hippocrene Bks.

Jewish Ceremonial Designs. Rimma Reider. (International Design Library). (Illus.). 48p. 1987. pap. 3.95 (ISBN 0-88045-087-8). Stemmer Hse.

Jewish Ceremonial Institutions & Customs. rev. ed. 3rd. ed. William Rosenau. LC 70-78222. (Illus.). 1971. Repr. of 1925 ed. 35.00x (ISBN 0-8103-3402-X). Gale.

Jewish Characters in Eighteenth Century Fiction & Drama. H. R. Van Der Veen. 1970. 25.00x (ISBN 0-87068-076-5). Ktav.

Jewish Child: Halakhic Perspectives. Shoshana Matzner-Bekerman. LC 83-19950. 314p. 1984. 20.00x (ISBN 0-88125-017-1); pap. 11.95 (ISBN 0-88125-024-4). Ktav.

Jewish-Christian Relations in Today's World. Ed. by James E. Wood, Jr. 164p. pap. 1.95 (ISBN 0-686-95175-1). ADL.

Jewish-Christian Relations in Today's World. Ed. by James E. Wood, Jr. LC 74-185826. 164p. 1971. 8.95 (ISBN 0-918954-09-6); pap. 4.50 (ISBN 0-918954-10-X). Baylor Univ Pr.

Jewish Christians in the U. S. A Bibliography. Karl Pruter. LC 84-48881. 250p. 1985. lib. bdg. 30.00 (ISBN 0-8240-8741-0). Garland Pub.

Jewish Christians in the United States: A Bibliography Sects & Cults in America. Karl Pruter. LC 86-48881. (Garland Reference Library of Social Sciences Ser.). 1987. lib. bdg. 38.00. Garland Pub.

Jewish Chrononomy. Levi. 12.95 (ISBN 0-87306-213-2). Feldheim.

Jewish Communities of Nazi-Occupied Europe. American Jewish Committee. 400p. 1982. Repr. of 1944 ed. 42.50x (ISBN 0-86527-337-5). Fertig.

Jewish Community, 3 vols. Salo W. Baron. LC 74-97269. 1972. Repr. of 1942 ed. Set. lib. bdg. 53.50x (ISBN 0-8371-3274-6, BAJC). Greenwood.

Jewish Community & Children of Divorce: A Pilot Study of Perceptions & Responses. Natalie Friedman & Theresa F. Rogers. 32p. 1983. pap. 2.00 (ISBN 0-87495-051-1). Am Jewish Comm.

Jewish Community in America: An Annotated & Classified Bibliographical Guide. Ed. & compiled by William E. Brickman. (Ethnic Bibliographical Ser: No. 2). 1977. PLB 19.95 (ISBN 0-89102-057-8). B Franklin.

Jewish Community of Indianapolis, 1849 to the Present. Judith E. Endelman. LC 83-49513. (Modern Jewish Experience Ser.). (Illus.). 316p. 1985. 17.50x (ISBN 0-253-33150-1). Ind U Pr.

Jewish Concepts & Reflections. Samuel Umen. LC 62-9774. 190p. 1962. 10.00 (ISBN 0-8022-1748-6). Philos Lib.

Jewish Connection: To Triumph over Anti-Semitism. Leonard C. Yaseen. (Illus.). 1985. pap. 9.95 (ISBN 0-317-39020-1). Crossroad NY.

Jewish Consciousness Raising: A Handbook of 50 Experiential Exercises for Jewish Groups. Dov P. Elkins. LC 77-83775. 1977. softbound 10.00 (ISBN 0-918834-03-1). Growth Assoc.

Jewish Continuity & Change: Emerging Patterns in America. Calvin Goldscheider. LC 84-48746. (Jewish Political & Social Studies). (Illus.). 214p. 1986. 24.95x (ISBN 0-253-33157-9). Ind U Pr.

Jewish Contribution to Civilizaton. Cecil Roth. 1978. pap. 5.95 (ISBN 0-85222-217-3, East & West Lib). Hebrew Pub.

Jewish Cookery. Leah W. Leonard. (International Cook Book Ser.). 512p. 1949. 10.95 (ISBN 0-517-09758-3). Crown.
Jewish Days & Holidays. Greer F. Cashman. LC 79-66167. (Illus.). 64p. 1979. Repr. of 1976 ed. 10.95 (ISBN 0-89961-000-5). SBS Pub.
Jewish Days & Holidays. Greer F. Cashman & Alona Frankel. LC 86-70789. (Illus.). 61p. 1986. 9.95 (ISBN 0-915361-58-2, Dist. by Watts). Adama Pubs Inc.
Jewish Design for Living. S. M. Lehrman. LC 76-24242. 1976. 11.95 (ISBN 0-88400-003-6). Shengold.
Jewish Dietary Laws. rev. ed. Samuel Dresner & Seymour Siegel. LC 83-235401. 110p. pap. 2.95x (ISBN 0-8381-2105-5). United Syn Bk.
Jewish Dietary Laws, 2 vols. Grunfeld. 1973. Set. 32.95x (ISBN 0-900689-09-9). Bloch.
Jewish Dietary Laws, 2 vols. Dayan I. Grunfeld. 246p. 1972. Vol. 1, 246 pgs. pap. 29.95 (ISBN 0-900689-10-2); Vol. 2, 285 pgs. pap. 32.95 slipcased (ISBN 0-900689-11-0). Soncino Pr.
Jewish Education: Selected Writings. Alexander M. Dushkin. 180p. 1980. text ed. 10.00x (ISBN 965-223-353-6, Pub. by Magnes Pr Israel). Humanities.
Jewish Emancipation & Self-Emancipation. Jacob Katz. 179p. 1986. 14.95 (ISBN 0-8276-0261-8). Jewish Pubns.
Jewish Emergence from Powerlessness. Yehuda Bauer. LC 78-25830. pap. 25.80 (ISBN 0-317-26941-0, 2023592). Bks Demand UMI.
Jewish Emigration from 1933 to the Evian Conference of 1938. John Mendelsohn & Donald S. Detwiler. LC 81-80313. (Holocaust Ser.). 260p. 1982. lib. bdg. 61.00 (ISBN 0-8240-4879-2). Garland Pub.
Jewish Emigration: The SS St. Louis Affair & Other Cases. John Mendelsohn. LC 81-80315. (Holocaust Ser.: Vol. 7). 274p. 1982. lib. bdg. 61.00 (ISBN 0-8240-4881-4). Garland Pub.
Jewish Emigration 1938-1940: Rublee & Intergovernmental Committee. John Mendelsohn. LC 81-80314. (Holocaust Ser.). 250p. 1982. lib. bdg. 61.00 (ISBN 0-8240-4880-6). Garland Pub.
Jewish Encyclopedia, 12 vols. Ed. by I. Singer. 1976. Set. lib. bdg. 998.95 (ISBN 0-8490-2101-4). Gordon Pr.
Jewish Ethics & Halakhah for Our Time. Basil F. Herring. 1984. 15.00 (ISBN 0-88125-044-9); pap. 9.95 (ISBN 0-88125-045-7). Ktav.
Jewish Ethics, Philosophy & Mysticism. Louis Jacobs. LC 71-80005. (Chain of Tradition Ser). 1969. pap. 5.95x (ISBN 0-87441-012-6). Behrman.
Jewish Experience, Bk. 2. Frieda C. Hyman. (Illus.). 1978. text ed. 6.95x (ISBN 0-8381-0192-5). United Syn Bk.
Jewish Experience: A Guide to Manuscript Sources in the Library of Congress. Gary J. Kohn. (Monographs of the American Jewish Archives). 250p. 1986. text ed. write for info. (ISBN 0-87820-014-2, Pub. by Am Jewish Archives). Ktav.
Jewish Experience: Book I. Frieda C. Hyman. 1975. 5.25x (ISBN 0-8381-0191-7). United Syn Bk.
Jewish Experience in America: A Historical Bibliography. LC 82-22823. (ABC-Clio Research Guides Ser.: No. 1). 190p. 1982. lib. bdg. 25.00 (ISBN 0-87436-034-X). ABC-Clio.
Jewish Experience in Latin America, 2 Vols. Martin Cohen. 1971. Set. 50.00x (ISBN 0-87068-136-2, Pub by Am Jewish Hist Soc). Ktav.
Jewish Experience in the Art of the Twentieth-Century. Avram Kampf. (Illus.). 240p. 1984. 49.50 (ISBN 0-89789-039-6). Bergin & Garvey.
Jewish Experience in Western Pensylvania, 1755-1945. Jacob Feldman. (Illus.). 1986. 9.95 (ISBN 0-936340-03-7). Hist Soc West Pa.
Jewish Experiential Book: The Quest for Jewish Identity. Bernard Reisman. 1979. 35.00x (ISBN 0-87068-688-7). Ktav.
Jewish Expression. Ed. & Judah Goldin. LC 75-27866. 512p. 1976. pap. 10.95 (ISBN 0-300-01975-0). Yale U Pr.
Jewish Expressions on Jesus. Ed. by T. Weiss-Rosmarin. 14.95x (ISBN 0-87068-470-1). Ktav.
Jewish Face. (Illus.). 1.50 (ISBN 0-914131-38-9, D44). Torah Umesorah.
Jewish Fairy Tales & Legends. Aunt Naomi, pseud. 16.95 (ISBN 0-89190-314-3, Pub. by Am Repr). Amereon ltd.
Jewish Fairy Tales & Stories. Gerald Friedlander. LC 78-67711. (Folktale). (Illus.). Repr. of 1919 ed. 20.00 (ISBN 0-404-16088-3). AMS Pr.
Jewish Family. Ed. by Steven M. Cohen & Paula E. Hyman. 256p. 1986. text ed. 42.50x (ISBN 0-8419-0860-5). Holmes & Meier.
Jewish Family: A Survey & Annotated Bibliography. Benjamin Schlesinger. Ed. by Florence Strakhovsky. LC 79-151389. pap. 46.80 (ISBN 0-317-09749-0, 2014401). Bks Demand UMI.
Jewish Family: Authority & Tradition in Modern Perspectives. Norman Linzer. 217p. 1984. 34.95 (ISBN 0-89885-149-1); pap. 14.95 (ISBN 0-89885-191-2). Human Sci Pr.
Jewish Family Celebrations. Arlene Cardozo. (Illus.). 288p. 1985. pap. 6.95 (ISBN 0-312-44232-7). St Martin.
Jewish Family Celebrations: Shabbat, Festivals & Traditional Ceremonies. Arlene R. Cardozo. LC 82-5566. (Illus.). 288p. 1982. 17.50 (ISBN 0-312-44231-9). St Martin.
Jewish Female in America: Two Female Generations, 1820-1929, Vol. 1. Rudolf Glanz. The Eastern European Jewish Woman 25.00x (ISBN 0-87068-461-2). Ktav.
Jewish Feminist Movement in Germany: The Campaigns of the Judischer Frauenbund, 1904-1938. Marion Kaplan. LC 78-67567. (Contributions in Women's Studies: No. 8). (Illus.). lib. bdg. 29.95 (ISBN 0-313-20736-4, KGJ/). Greenwood.
Jewish Festivals: From Their Beginnings to Our Own Day. rev. ed. Hayyim Schauss. (Illus.). (YA) 1969. 8.00 (ISBN 0-8074-0095-5, 383202); course syll. 1.25 (ISBN 0-686-66555-4, 247330). UAHC.
Jewish Festivals: History & Observance. Hayyim Schauss. LC 62-13140. 1973. pap. 7.50 (ISBN 0-8052-0413-X). Schocken.
Jewish Folk Art: From Biblical Days to Modern Times. Joy Ungerleider-Mayerson. 272p. 1986. 50.00 (ISBN 0-671-63007-5). Summit Bks.
Jewish Folklore: An Annotated Bibliography. Eli Yassif. LC 83-48282. 500p. 1985. lib. bdg. 65.00 (ISBN 0-8240-9039-X). Garland Pub.
Jewish Foundation of Islam. rev. ed. Charles C. Torrey. LC 67-18817. 1968. 20.00x (ISBN 0-87068-117-6). Ktav.
Jewish-Gentile Courtships: An Exploratory Study of a Social Process. John E. Mayer. LC 80-16130. x, 240p. 1980. Repr. of 1961 ed. lib. bdg. 24.75x (ISBN 0-313-22465-X, MAJG). Greenwood.
Jewish Gnosticism, Merkabah Mysticism & Talmudic Tradition. Gersham G. Scholem. 1960. 10.00x (ISBN 0-685-31427-8, Pub. by Jewish Theol Seminary). Ktav.
Jewish Grandparents' Book of Memories. Ron Isaacs & Leora Isaacs. 100p. 1987. 20.00 (ISBN 0-87668-976-4). Aronson.
Jewish Heart: Essays on Jewish Sensitivities. Jack S. Cohen. LC 84-27837. 217p. 1985. 15.00 (ISBN 0-88125-065-1). Ktav.
Jewish Historical Treasures. Azriel Eisenberg. LC 68-57432. (Illus.). 300p. 1969. 12.50 (ISBN 0-8197-0076-2). Bloch.
Jewish History - Moments & Methods: An Activity Source Book for Teachers. Sorel G. Loeb & Barbara B. Kadden. LC 82-71283. (Illus.). 150p. (Orig.). 1982. pap. text ed. 10.00 (ISBN 0-86705-008-X). AIRE.
Jewish History: An Essay in the Philosophy of History. Semen M. Dubnow. LC 72-5481. (Select Bibliographies Reprint Ser.). 1972. Repr. of 1903 ed. 16.00 (ISBN 0-8369-6903-0). Ayer Co Pubs.
Jewish Holiday Do-Book. new ed. Lois Englander et al. 1977. 9.95x (ISBN 0-685-76976-3). Bloch.
Jewish Holiday Fun. Judith H. Corwin. 1987. 4.95. Wanderer Bks.
Jewish Holidays. pap. 1.19 (9059). Garrard.
Jewish Holidays. Michael Strassfeld. LC 84-48196. (Illus.). 1985. 24.45i (ISBN 0-06-015406-3, HarpT); pap. 15.95 (ISBN 0-06-091225-1). Har-Row.
Jewish Holidays & Festivals. Isidor Margolis & Sidney L. Markowitz. (Orig.). 1962. pap. 3.95 (ISBN 0-8065-0285-1). Citadel Pr.
Jewish Holy Days: Their Prophetic & Christian Significance. Coulson Shepherd. LC 61-16660. 1961. pap. 3.25 (ISBN 0-87213-780-5). Loizeaux.
Jewish Horizons. Berl Frymer. LC 81-65057. 256p. 1982. 12.95 (ISBN 0-8453-4705-5, Cornwall Bks). Assoc Univ Prs.
Jewish Idea of Community. 1982. 9.95 (ISBN 0-686-76521-4). Feldheim.
Jewish Ideals & Other Essays. Joseph Jacobs. LC 72-311. (Essay Index Reprint Ser.). Repr. of 1896 ed. 18.00 (ISBN 0-8369-2795-8). Ayer Co Pubs.
Jewish Identities in France: An Analysis of Contemporary French Jewry. Dominique Schnapper. Tr. by Arthur Goldhammer. LC 82-17495. (Illus.). 224p. 1983. lib. bdg. 25.00x (ISBN 0-226-73910-4). U of Chicago Pr.
Jewish Identity. Litvin & Hoenig. 13.95 (ISBN 0-87306-096-2). Feldheim.
Jewish Identity & Self-Esteem: Healing Wounds Through Ethnotherapy. Judith W. Klein. 64p. 1980. 2.75. Am Jewish Comm.
Jewish Identity in an Age of Ideologies. Jacob B. Agus. LC 76-14230. 1978. 25.00 (ISBN 0-8044-5018-8). Ungar.
Jewish Illustrated Book. Jane Levy & Florence B. Helzel. LC 86-80427. (Illus.). 150p. (Orig.). 1986. pap. 16.00 (ISBN 0-943376-33-5). Magnes Mus.
Jewish Immigrants of the Nazi Period in the U. S. A, 6 Vols. Ed. by Herbert Strauss. Set. lib. bdg. 130.00 (ISBN 0-317-11838-2); Vol. 1. 35.00 (ISBN 3-598-08006-9). Vol. 2 (ISBN 3-598-08007-7). Vol. 3, Pt. 1 (ISBN 3-598-08008-5). Vol. 3, Pt. 2 (ISBN 3-598-08013-1). K G Saur.
Jewish Immigrants of the Nazi Period in the U. S. A. Essays on the History, Persecution, & Emigration of the German Jews. Ed. by Herbert A. Strauss. (Jewish Immigrants of the Nazi Period in the U. S. A. Ser.: Vol. 6). 430p. 1987. lib. bdg. 74.00 (ISBN 3-598-08011-5). K G Saur.
Jewish Immigrants of the Nazi Period in the U. S. A. The Expulsion & Migration of German Jews 1933-45 - Annotated Sources. Ed. by Herbert A. Strauss & Norbert Kampe. (Jewish Immigrants of the Nazi Period in the U. S. A. Ser.: Vol. 4). 225p. 1988. lib. bdg. 50.00 (ISBN 3-598-08009-3). K G Saur.
Jewish Immigrants of the Nazi Period in the U. S. A. An Oral History Record. Ed. by Herbert A. Strauss & Dennis Rogrbaugh. (Jewish Immigrants of the Nazi Period in the U. S. A. Ser.: Vol. 5). 308p. 1986. lib. bdg. 60.00 (ISBN 3-598-08010-7). K G Saur.
Jewish Immigration to the United States from 1881 to 1910. Samuel Joseph. LC 14-15042. (Columbia University. Studies in the Social Sciences: No. 145). Repr. of 1914 ed. 7.50 (ISBN 0-404-51145-7). AMS Pr.
Jewish Immigration to the United States from 1881 to 1910. Samuel Joseph. LC 69-18781. (American Immigration Collection Ser., No. 1). (Illus.). 1969. Repr. of 1914 ed. 10.00 (ISBN 0-405-00529-6). Ayer Co Pubs.
Jewish Influence on Christian Reform Movements. Louis I. Newman. LC 26-883. (Columbia University. Oriental Studies: No. 23). Repr. of 1925 ed. 45.00 (ISBN 0-404-50513-9). AMS Pr.
Jewish Influences on European Thought. Charles C. Lehrmann. Tr. by George Klin & Victor Carpenter. LC 72-3264. 323p. 1976. 27.50 (ISBN 0-8386-7908-0). Fairleigh Dickinson.
Jewish Jurisprudence: Its Sources & Modern Applications. Emanuel B. Quint & Neil S. Hecht. (Jewish Jurisprudence Ser.: Vol. 2). 193p. 1986. text ed. 65.00 (ISBN 3-7186-0064-1); pap. text ed. 18.00 (ISBN 3-7186-0293-8). Harwood Academic.
Jewish Jurisprudence: Its Sources & Modern Applications Ser, Vol. 1. Emanuel Quint & Neil S. Hecht. (Jurisprudence-Its Sources & Modern Applications Ser.). 268p. 1980. 46.25 (ISBN 3-7186-0054-4); pap. 13.95 (ISBN 3-7186-0055-2). Harwood Academic.
Jewish Kids Catalog. Chaya M. Burstein. (Illus.). 224p. 1983. pap. 10.95 (ISBN 0-8276-0215-4, 603). Jewish Pubns.
Jewish Labor in the U. S. A., 1882-1952. rev. ed. Melech Epstein. 1969. 45.00x (ISBN 0-87068-042-0). Ktav.
Jewish Laffs. Henry D. Spalding. LC 82-9990. (Illus.). 96p. 1982. pap. 3.95 (ISBN 0-8246-0290-0). Jonathan David.
Jewish Landmarks of New York: A Travel Guide & History. Bernard Postal & Lionel Koppman. LC 76-27400. (Orig.). 1978. 15.95 (ISBN 0-8303-0153-4). Fleet.
Jewish Law. Louis Jacobs. LC 68-27329. (Chain of Tradition Ser). 1968. pap. text ed. 5.95x (ISBN 0-87441-010-X). Behrman.
Jewish Law & Decision-Making: A Study Through Time. Aaron Schreiber. 456p. 1980. lib. bdg. 39.95 (ISBN 0-87722-120-0). Temple U Pr.
Jewish Law & Jewish Life, 8 bks. in 4 vols. Jacob Bazak. Ed. by Stephen M. Passamaneck. Incl. Bk. 1. Selected Rabbinical Response (ISBN 0-8074-0034-3, 180210); Bks. 2-4. Contracts, Real Estate, Sales & Usury (180211); Bks. 5-6. Credit, Law Enforcement & Taxation (180212); Bks. 7-8. Criminal & Domestic Relations (ISBN 0-8074-0037-8, 180213). 1978. pap. 12.50 complete vol. (ISBN 0-8074-0038-6, 180218); pap. 5.00 ea. UAHC.
Jewish Law & Modern Ideology. Elliot Dorff. 1970. pap. 6.50x (ISBN 0-8381-0209-3). United Syn Bk.
Jewish Law Association Studies II: The Jerusalem Conference Volume. Ed. by Bernard S. Jackson. (Occasional Papers & Proceedings). 208p. 26.95 (ISBN 0-89130-950-0, 15-00-02); pap. 19.95 (ISBN 0-89130-951-9). Scholars Pr GA.
Jewish Law in American Trials & Tribunals. Bernard Meislin. 25.00x (ISBN 0-87068-288-1). Ktav.
Jewish Law in Our Time. Ruth Link-Salinger. 183p. 22.50x (ISBN 0-8197-0486-5); pap. 12.95x (ISBN 0-8197-0487-3). Bloch.
Jewish Legends of the Middle Ages. Claud H. Field. LC 76-48141. 1976. Repr. of 1930 ed. lib. bdg. 25.00 (ISBN 0-8414-6771-4). Folcroft.
Jewish Legends of the Second Commonwealth. Judah Nadich. 508p. 1983. 25.00 (ISBN 0-8276-0212-X, 490). Jewish Pubns.
Jewish Library. Leo Jung. Incl. Vol. 1. Faith. 9.50x (ISBN 0-685-23058-9); Vol. 2. Folk. 9.50x (ISBN 0-685-23059-7); Vol. 3. Women. 9.50x (ISBN 0-685-23060-0); Vol. 4. Judaism in a Changing World. 9.50x (ISBN 0-685-23061-9); Vol. 5. Panorama of Judaism: Part 1. 9.50x (ISBN 0-685-23062-7); Vol. 6. Panorama of Judaism: Part 2. 9.50x (ISBN 0-685-23063-5). Bloch.
Jewish Life in America: Historical Perspectives. Gladys Rosen. 12.50x (ISBN 0-87068-346-2); pap. 9.95 (ISBN 0-686-52683-X). Ktav.
Jewish Life in America: Historical Perspectives. Ed. by Gladys L. Rosen. LC 78-16560. 198p. 1978. pap. 6.95 (ISBN 0-686-74514-0). Am Jewish Comm.
Jewish Life in Los Angeles: A Window to Tomorrow. Neil C. Sandberg. LC 86-11025. (Illus.). 224p. 1986. lib. bdg. 17.50 (ISBN 0-8191-5439-3). U Pr of Amer.
Jewish Life in Philadelphia, 1830-1940. Ed. by Murray Friedman. LC 83-10763. (Illus.). 360p. 1983. 19.95 (ISBN 0-89727-050-9). ISHI PA.
Jewish Life in the Middle Ages. Israel Abrahams. LC 58-11933. (Temple Books). 1969. pap. text ed. 7.95x (ISBN 0-689-70001-6, T1). Atheneum.
Jewish Life in Twentieth Century America: Challenge & Accommodation. Milton Plesur. LC 81-11196. (Illus.). 264p. 1982. text ed. 21.95x (ISBN 0-88229-639-6). Nelson-Hall.
Jewish Life in Village Communities of Southern Germany. Hugo Mandelbaum. (Illus.). 96p. 1986. 6.95 (ISBN 0-87306-382-1). Feldheim.
Jewish Life of Christ: Being Sepher Toldoth Jeshu. Ed. by G. W. Foote & J. M. Wheeler. (Illus.). 49p. 1982. pap. 3.00 (ISBN 0-910309-02-7). Am Atheist.
Jewish Life on Campus: A Directory of B'nai B'rith Hillel Foundations & Other Campus Agencies. Ed. by Ruth G. Fredman. 1986. pap. 8.95 (ISBN 0-9603058-5-8). B'nai B'rith Hillel.
Jewish Life under Islam: Jerusalem in the Sixteenth Century. Amnon Cohen. (Illus.). 288p. 1984. text ed. 30.00x (ISBN 0-674-47436-8). Harvard U Pr.
Jewish Life under the Tsars: The Autobiography of Chaim Aronson, 1825-1888, Vol. 3. Ed. by Norman Marsden. LC 81-10963. (Publications of the Oxford Centre for Postgraduate Hebrew Study). 368p. 1983. 23.95 (ISBN 0-86598-066-7). Allanheld.
Jewish Lights: Substitute Teachers Kit. Rabin. 1984. 3.00x (ISBN 0-940646-28-5). Rossel Bks.
Jewish Literary Marketplace: A Directory of the Press, Periodicals, Publishers, & Booksellers. Ed. by Howard M. Berliant & Bruce Arbit. LC 79-18114. 1979. pap. 9.95 (ISBN 0-930038-16-9). Arbit.
Jewish Literature & Other Essays. facsimile ed. Gustav Karpeles. LC 78-37159. (Essay Index Reprint Ser). Repr. of 1895 ed. 22.00 (ISBN 0-8369-2512-2). Ayer Co Pubs.
Jewish Literature Between the Bible & the Mishnah: A Historical & Literary Introduction. George W. Nickelsburg. LC 80-16176. 352p. 1981. 19.95 (ISBN 0-8006-0649-3, 1-649). Fortress.
Jewish Literature for Children: A Teaching Guide. Cheryl S. Grossman & Suzy Engman. 230p. (Orig.). 1985. text ed. 19.00 (ISBN 0-86705-018-7); pap. text ed. 15.00. AIRE.
Jewish Literature: The Bible Through 1789. Ed. & intro. by Harold Bloom. (Critical Cosmos--Other European & Latin American Literature Ser.). 1987. 49.95 (ISBN 1-55546-101-8). Chelsea Hse.
Jewish Liturgy: Prayer & Synagogue Service Through the Ages. Ed. by Raphael Posner et al. (Illus.). 1976. 25.00 (ISBN 0-8148-0596-5). L Amiel Pub.
Jewish Magic & Superstition. Joshua Trachtenberg. LC 39-14212. (Temple Bks). 1970. pap. text ed. 6.95x (ISBN 0-689-70234-5, T15). Atheneum.
Jewish Marriage. Joseph Breur. 3.95 (ISBN 0-87306-097-0). Feldheim.
Jewish Marriage Anthology. Ed. by Philip Goodman. Hanna Goodman. LC 65-17045. (Illus.). 1965. 13.95 (ISBN 0-8276-0145-X, 236). Jewish Pubns.
Jewish Marriage Contract: A Study in the Status of the Woman in Jewish Law. Louis M. Epstein. LC 73-2195. (Jewish People; History, Religion, Literature Ser.). Repr. of 1927 ed. 33.00 (ISBN 0-405-05261-8). Ayer Co Pubs.
Jewish Martyrs of Pawiak. Julien Hirshaut. LC 81-85301. 256p. 1982. 16.95 (ISBN 0-8052-5039-5); pap. 10.95 (ISBN 0-8052-5040-9). Holocaust Pubns.
Jewish Meditation: A Practical Guide. Aryeh Kaplan. LC 84-23589. 174p. 1985. 17.95 (ISBN 0-8052-4006-3); pap. 9.95 (ISBN 0-8052-0781-3). Schocken.
Jewish Mind. Raphael Patai. LC 76-58040. 1977. 14.95 (ISBN 0-684-14878-1, ScribT). Scribner.

Jewish Mind. Raphael Patai. 384p. 1985. pap. 14.95 (ISBN 0-684-16321-7, ScribT). Scribner.
Jewish Mothers' Hall of Fame. Fred Bernstein. LC 85-24541. (Illus.). 192p. 1986. pap. 6.95 (ISBN 0-385-23377-9, Dolp). Doubleday.
Jewish Music in Its Historical Development. Abraham Z. Idelsohn. LC 80-24235. (Illus.). xi, 535p. 1981. Repr. of 1948 ed. lib. bdg. 35.00 (ISBN 0-313-22749-7, IDJM). Greenwood.
Jewish Music: In Its Historical Development. Abraham Z. Idelsohn. LC 67-25236. 1967. pap. 12.50 (ISBN 0-8052-0165-3). Schocken.
Jewish Mystical Testimonies. Louis Jacobs. LC 76-46644. 1977. pap. 8.95 (ISBN 0-8052-0585-3). Schocken.
Jewish Mysticism: An Annotated Bibliography on the Kabbalah in English. Sheila A. Spector. LC 83-48224. (Reference Library of Social Science Ser.). 1984. lib. bdg. 45.00 (ISBN 0-8240-9042-X). Garland Pub.
Jewish Mysticism: An Introduction to Kabbalah. Joshua Abelson. LC 80-54593. (Judaic Studies Library: SHP 7). 192p. 1981. pap. 6.95 (ISBN 0-87203-096-2). Hermon.
Jewish Mysticism & Jewish Ethics. Joseph Dan. LC 85-40358. 158p. 1986. 20.00x (ISBN 0-295-96265-8). U of Wash Pr.
Jewish Mystique. Ernest Van Den Haag. LC 76-56974. 1977. pap. 6.95 (ISBN 0-8128-2189-0). Stein & Day.
Jewish Neo-Platonism: Selected Essays. An Original Anthology. Ed. by Steven Katz. LC 79-7178. (Jewish Philosophy, Mysticism & History of Ideas Ser.). 1980. lib. bdg. 48.50x (ISBN 0-405-12236-5). Ayer Co Pubs.
Jewish Origins of the Psychoanalytic Movement: With a New Preface. Dennis B. Klein. 224p. 1985. pap. 8.95 (ISBN 0-226-43960-7). U of Chicago Pr.
Jewish Partisans: A Documentary of Jewish Resistance in the Soviet Union During World War II, Vol. II. Ed. by Jack N. Porter. LC 81-40258. 314p. (Orig.). 1982. lib. bdg. 29.00 (ISBN 0-8191-2537-7); pap. text ed. 14.25 (ISBN 0-8191-2538-5). U Pr of Amer.
Jewish Partisans of Eastern Europe. Moshe Kaganovich. 340p. 1985. 15.95 (ISBN 0-8052-5053-0); pap. 11.95 (ISBN 0-8052-5054-9). Schocken.
Jewish Partisans of Eastern Europe. Moshe Kaganovoch. 1984. 17.95 (ISBN 0-89604-048-8); pap. 13.95 (ISBN 0-89604-049-6). Holocaust Pubns.
Jewish Party Book: A Contemporary Guide to Customs, Crafts & Foods. Mae S. Rockland. LC 78-54387. (Illus.). 284p. 1987. pap. 10.95 (ISBN 0-8052-0829-1). Schocken.
Jewish People, 3 Vols. Deborah Pessin. (Illus.). 1951-53. pap. 4.25x ea. Vol. I (ISBN 0-8381-0182-8). Vol. II (ISBN 0-8381-0185-2). Vol. III (ISBN 0-8381-0187-9). pap. 2.50x ea. pupils' activity bks. Vol. I Activity Bk (ISBN 0-8381-0183-6). Vol. II Activity Bk (ISBN 0-8381-0186-0). Vol. III Activity Bk (ISBN 0-8381-0188-7). United Syn Bk.
Jewish People: A Biological History. Harry L. Shapiro. 1978. lib. bdg. 59.95 (ISBN 0-685-62297-5). Revisionist Pr.
Jewish People & Jesus Christ. Jakob Jocz. 1979. pap. 7.95 (ISBN 0-8010-5085-5). Baker Bk.
Jewish People & Jesus Christ After Auschwitz. Jakob Jocz. 172p. (Orig.). 1981. pap. 9.95 (ISBN 0-8010-5123-1). Baker Bk.
Jewish People: Four Thousand Years of Survival. rev. ed. Max Wurmbrand & Cecil Roth. (Illus.). 480p. 1987. 39.95 (ISBN 0-915361-64-7, Dist. by Watts). Adama Pubs Inc.
Jewish People: History, Religion, Literature, 41 bks. Ed. by Jacob B. Agus et al. 1973. Set. 1106.50 (ISBN 0-405-05250-2). Ayer Co Pubs.
Jewish People, Jewish Thought. Robert M. Seltzer. (Illus.). 1980. text ed. write for info. (ISBN 0-02-408950-8). Macmillan.
Jewish Philosophers. Steven T. Katz. LC 75-7590. (Illus.). 300p. 1975. 10.95x (ISBN 0-8197-0387-7); pap. 8.95x (ISBN 0-8197-0010-X). Bloch.
Jewish Philosophical Polemics Against Christianity in the Middle Ages. D. J. Lasker. 25.00x (ISBN 0-87068-498-1). Ktav.
Jewish Philosophical Polemics Against Christianity in the Middle Ages. Daniel J. Lasker. 320p. 15.00 (ISBN 0-686-95177-8). ADL.
Jewish Philosophy. 1982. 15.95 (ISBN 0-686-76523-0). Feldheim.
Jewish Philosophy: A Study in Personalism. Leon D. Stitskin. 1976. 15.00x (ISBN 0-685-84458-7). Bloch.
Jewish Philosophy & Pattern of Life. Simon Greenberg. LC 81-2153. (Moreshet Series, Studies in Jewish History, Literature & Thought: Vol. 9). 550p. 1982. 25.00x (ISBN 0-87334-012-4, Pub. by Jewish Theol Seminary). Ktav.
Jewish Philosophy, Mysticism & History of Ideas Series, 50 bks. Ed. by Steven T. Katz. (Illus.). 1980. Set. lib. bdg. 2389.00x (ISBN 0-405-12229-2). Ayer Co Pubs.
Jewish Physicians: A Biographical Index. Ed. by Nathan Koren. 275p. 1973. 25.00 (ISBN 0-87855-184-0). Transaction Bks.
Jewish Physicians in the Netherlands 1600-1940. Hindle S. Hes. 248p. 1980. pap. text ed. 14.50 (ISBN 0-317-51979-4, Pub. by Van Gorcum Holland). Longwood Pub Group.
Jewish Pleasure Principle. Reuven P. Bulka. LC 86-20839. 168p. 1987. text ed. 24.95 (ISBN 0-89885-328-1). Human Sci Pr.
Jewish Policies & Right-Wing Politics in Imperial Russia. Hans Rogger. LC 85-1006. 1985. 30.00x (ISBN 0-520-04596-3). U of Cal Pr.
Jewish Political Traditions. Ed. by International Center for University Teaching of Jewish Civilization Staff et al. LC 85-40516. (Selected Course Outlines & Curriculum Resources from Leading Universities Ser.). 250p. 1985. pap. text ed. 14.50 (ISBN 0-910129-29-0). Wiener Pub Inc.
Jewish Polity: Jewish Political Organization from Biblical Times to the Present. Daniel J. Elazar & Stuart A. Cohen. LC 83-48648. (Jewish Political & Social Studies). (Illus.). 384p. 1984. 27.50x (ISBN 0-253-33156-0). Ind U Pr.
Jewish Power: Myth or Reality. Max M. Kampelman. 21p. 1.50 (ISBN 0-686-74974-X). ADL.
Jewish Prayer: Concepts & Customs. Earl Klein. LC 85-23944. (Hebraica-Judaica Bookshelf Ser.). (Orig.). 1986. 17.95 (ISBN 0-933771-01-0). Alpha Pub Co.
Jewish Preschool Teachers Handbook. Sandy S. Furfine & Nancy C. Nowak. LC 81-67023. (Illus.). 132p. (Orig.). 1981. pap. 13.50 (ISBN 0-86705-004-7). AIRE.
Jewish Presence: Essays on Identity & History. Lucy Dawidowicz. LC 78-6236. 308p. 1978. pap. 3.95 (ISBN 0-15-646221-4, Harv). HarBraceJ.
Jewish Presence: Essays on Identity & History. Lucy Dawidowicz. 13.75 (ISBN 0-8446-6217-8). Peter Smith.
Jewish Presence in Eliot & Kafka. Melvin Wilk. (Brown Judaic Studies). 228p. 1986. 31.95 (ISBN 0-89130-915-2, 14-00-82). Scholars Pr GA.
Jewish Presence in Latin America. Ed. by Judith L. Elkin & Gilbert Merkx. (Thematic Studies in Latin America). 256p. 1987. text ed. 34.95x (ISBN 0-04-497012-9); pap. text ed. 13.95x (ISBN 0-04-497013-7). Allen Unwin.
Jewish Principals Handbook. Ed. by Audrey F. Marcus & Raymond A. Zwerin. LC 83-70198. 525p. 1983. text ed. 45.00 (ISBN 0-86705-035-7); pap. text ed. 39.95 (ISBN 0-86705-010-1). AIRE.
Jewish Problem. Alva J. McClain. 1979. pap. 1.00 (ISBN 0-88469-014-8). BMH Bks.
Jewish Problem as Dealt with by the Popes. 1982. lib. bdg. 59.95 (ISBN 0-87700-344-0). Revisionist Pr.
Jewish Problem in South Africa. Eric Louw. 1982. lib. bdg. 59.95 (ISBN 0-87700-342-4). Revisionist Pr.
Jewish Problem in the Soviet Union: Analysis & Solution. Ben Z. Goldberg. LC 82-15842. (Illus.). x, 374p. 1982. Repr. of 1961 ed. lib. bdg. 45.00x (ISBN 0-313-23692-5, GOJE). Greenwood.
Jewish Quest: Essays on Basic Concepts of Jewish Theology. Jacob B. Agus. LC 83-258. 264p. 1983. 25.00x (ISBN 0-88125-012-0). Ktav.
Jewish Question: A Marxist Interpretation. Abram Leon. LC 76-108721. 1971. 23.00 (ISBN 0-87348-133-X); pap. 7.95 (ISBN 0-87348-134-8). Path Pr NY.
Jewish Radicals & Radical Jews. Ed. by P. S. Cohen. LC 80-41227. 1981. 53.00 (ISBN 0-12-178780-X). Acad Pr.
Jewish Reference Sources: A Select, Annotated Bibliographic Guide. Charles Cutter & Micha F. Oppenheim. LC 82-15434. (Reference Library of Social Science: Vol. 126). 180p. 1982. lib. bdg. 24.00 (ISBN 0-8240-9347-X). Garland Pub.
Jewish Reflections on Death. Ed. by Jack Riemer. LC 74-18242. 192p. 1976. pap. 5.95 (ISBN 0-8052-0516-0). Schocken.
Jewish Religion: Describing & Explaining the Philosophy & Rituals of the Jewish Faith. M. Friedlander. 35.00 (ISBN 0-87559-117-5). Shalom.
Jewish Religion in the Soviet Union. Joshua Rothenberg. 1971. 20.00x (ISBN 0-87068-156-7). Ktav.
Jewish Religion: Its Influence Today. Elizabeth Dilling. (Illus.). 300p. 1983. pap. 8.00 (ISBN 0-939482-07-X). Noontide.
Jewish Religious Polemic. rev. ed. Oliver S. Rankin. 1969. 20.00x (ISBN 0-87068-007-2). Ktav.
Jewish Resistance During the Holocaust. Herbert Druks. LC 83-14. 132p. 1983. text ed. 14.95x (ISBN 0-8290-1295-8). Irvington.
Jewish Resistance In France. Anny Latour. LC 80-84246. (Illus.). 287p. 1981. 16.95 (ISBN 0-89604-025-9); pap. 10.95 (ISBN 0-89604-026-7). Holocaust Pubns.
Jewish Resistance in France, Nineteen Forty to Nineteen Forty-Four. Anny Latour. (Illus.). 1981. 14.95 (ISBN 0-8052-5025-5, Pub. by Holocaust Library); pap. 8.95 (ISBN 0-8052-5024-7). Schocken.
Jewish Response to German Culture: From the Enlightenment to the Second World War. Ed. by Jehuda Reinharz & Walter Schatzberg. LC 85-14185. 368p. 1985. 32.50x (ISBN 0-87451-345-6). U Pr of New Eng.
Jewish Responses to Nazi Persecution. Isaiah Trunk. (Illus.). 371p. Repr. 13.00 (ISBN 0-686-95071-2). ADL.
Jewish Return into History: Reflections in the Age of Auschwitz & a New Jerusalem. Emil L. Fackenheim. LC 77-87861. 1978. 14.95 (ISBN 0-8052-3677-5). Schocken.
Jewish Sanctuary. Joseph Gutmann. (Inconography of Religions, Section Ser.: Vol. 23). (Illus.). 33p. 1983. pap. text ed. 32.50x (ISBN 90-04-06893-7, Pub. by EJ Brill Holland). Humanities.
Jewish Sects & Parties in the Time of Jesus. John W. Lightley. 1980. lib. bdg. 75.00 (ISBN 0-8490-3150-8). Gordon Pr.
Jewish Self-Government in Medieval Egypt: The Origins of the Office of the Head of the Jews. Mark R. Cohen. LC 80-7514. (Princeton Studies on the Near East). 425p. 1981. 41.00 (ISBN 0-691-05307-3). Princeton U Pr.
Jewish Self-Hatred: Anti-Semitism & the Hidden Language of the Jews. Sander L. Gilman. LC 85-45050. 480p. 1986. text ed. 28.50x (ISBN 0-8018-3276-4). Johns Hopkins.
Jewish Serials of the World: A Research Bibliography of Secondary Sources. Robert Singerman. LC 86-344. 399p. 1986. lib. bdg. 55.00 (ISBN 0-313-24493-6, SJE/). Greenwood.
Jewish Services in Synagogue & Home. facs. ed. Lewis N. Dembitz. LC 74-27977. (Modern Jewish Experience Ser.). 1975. Repr. of 1898 ed. 40.00x (ISBN 0-405-06706-2). Ayer Co Pubs.
Jewish Socialist Movements, Eighteen Seventy-One to Nineteen Seventeen: While Messiah Tarried. Nora Levin. (Littman Library of Jewish Civilization). (Illus.). 566p. 1978. 32.00x (ISBN 0-19-710029-5). Oxford U Pr.
Jewish Societies in the Middle East: Community, Culture & Authority. Shlomo Deshen & Walter P. Zenner. LC 80-6285. (Illus.). 328p. (Orig.). 1982. lib. bdg. 30.50 (ISBN 0-8191-2578-4); pap. text ed. 14.25 (ISBN 0-8191-2579-2). U Pr of Amer.
Jewish Sources of the Sermon on the Mount. Gerald Friedlander. 1976. lib. bdg. 59.95 (ISBN 0-8490-2102-2). Gordon Pr.
Jewish Sources of the Sermon on the Mount. rev. ed. Gerald Friedlander. (Library of Biblical Studies). 1969. 14.95x (ISBN 0-87068-054-4). Ktav.
Jewish Spirituality: Vol 1. Arthur Green. Ed. by Ewert Cousins. (World Spirituality Ser.). 496p. 1985. 49.50x (ISBN 0-8245-0762-2). Crossroad NY.
Jewish Stories & Hebrew Melodies. Heinrich Heine. Ed. by Jonathan D. Sarna. Tr. by Charles G. Leyland from Ger. LC 86-40567. (Masterworks of Modern Jewish Writing Ser.). (Illus.). 200p. 1987. text ed. 18.95 (ISBN 0-910129-68-1); pap. 8.95 (ISBN 0-910129-62-2). Wiener Pub Inc.
Jewish Stories One Generation Tells Another. Peninnah Schram. 350p. 1987. 30.00 (ISBN 0-87668-967-5). Aronson.
Jewish Studies in Memory of Israel Abrahams. Alexander Kohut Memorial Foundation Staff. Ed. by Steven Katz. LC 79-7164. (Jewish Philosophy, Mysticism & History of Ideas Ser.). (Illus.). 1980. Repr. of 1927 ed. lib. bdg. 45.00x (ISBN 0-405-12274-8). Ayer Co Pubs.
Jewish Survival. T. Weiss-Rosmarin. 6.95x (ISBN 0-87068-426-4). Ktav.
Jewish Symbols. Charles Wengrov. (Illus.). 1960. pap. 0.99 (ISBN 0-914080-24-5). Shulsinger Sales.
Jewish Symbols in the Greco-Roman Period, 13 vols. E. R. Goodenough. Incl. Vols. 1-3. Archeological Evidence from Palestine & the Diaspora. 1953; Vol. 4. Problem of Method; Symbols from Jewish Cult. 1954; Vols. 5 & 6. Fish, Bread, & Wine, 2 vols. 1956; Vols. 7 & 8. Pagan Symbols in Judaism. 1958. o.p. (ISBN 0-691-09755-0); Vols. 9-11. Symbolism in the Dura Synagogue. 1964; Vol. 12. Summary & Conclusions. 1965. 34.00x (ISBN 0-691-09757-7); Vol. 13. General Index & Maps. 1969. (Bollingen Ser.). Princeton U Pr.
Jewish Tales. L. Sacher-Masoch. 59.95 (ISBN 0-8490-0445-4). Gordon Pr.
Jewish Tales & Legends. Menachem Glenn. 441p. 1929. 6.95 (ISBN 0-88482-857-3). Hebrew Pub.
Jewish Theology. Louis Jacobs. LC 73-17442. 384p. 1973. pap. 9.95x (ISBN 0-87441-248-X). Behrman.
Jewish Thought & the Scientific Revolution of the Sixteenth Century: David Gans (1541-1613) & His Times. Andre Neher. Tr. by David Maisel. (Littman Library of Jewish Civilization). (Illus.). 240p. 1986. 29.95x (ISBN 0-19-710057-0). Oxford U Pr.
Jewish Thought in the Seventeenth Century. Ed. by Isadore Twersky & Bernard Septimus. (Harvard Judaic Texts & Studies: VI). 425p. 1986. text ed. 25.00x (ISBN 0-674-47465-1); pap. text ed. 12.50x (ISBN 0-674-47466-X). Harvard U Pr.
Jewish Thought of Emil Fackenheim: A Reader. Ed. by Michael L. Morgan & Emil Fackenheim. LC 87-2116. 400p. 1987. 39.95X (ISBN 0-8143-1820-7); pap. 15.95X (ISBN 0-8143-1821-5). Wayne St U Pr.
Jewish Thought Today. Louis Jacobs. LC 73-116679. (Chain of Tradition Ser). (Illus.). 1970. pap. 5.95x (ISBN 0-87441-014-2). Behrman.
Jewish Tradition & Corporate Morality. Lester Eckman. LC 85-63013. 96p. 1986. 10.95. Shengold.
Jewish Tradition in the Diaspora: Studies in Memory of Professor Walter J. Fischel. Ed. by M. M. Caspi. 314p. 1981. 19.95 (ISBN 0-943376-16-5). Magnes Mus.
Jewish Tradition of Peace. Ed. by Jewish Peace Fellowship. 1984. lib. bdg. 79.95 (ISBN 0-87700-626-1). Revisionist Pr.
Jewish Travel Guide, 1986. Ed. by Sidney Lightman. (Illus.). 296p. (Orig.). 1986. pap. 9.25 (ISBN 0-317-39976-4, Pub. by Jewish Chronicle Pubns England). Hermon.
Jewish Traveler. Hadassah Magazine Staff. Ed. by Alan M. Tigay. LC 86-8917. (Illus.). 416p. 1987. 19.95 (ISBN 0-385-23811-8); pap. 12.95 (ISBN 0-385-23451-1). Doubleday.
Jewish Travellers in the Middle Ages: Nineteen Firsthand Accounts. Ed. by Elkan N. Adler. 416p. 1987. pap. 8.95 (ISBN 0-486-25397-X). Dover.
Jewish Trivia. Dode B. Levenson et al. LC 84-63112. (Illus.). 195p. (Orig.). 1985. pap. 7.95 (ISBN 0-9611268-7-6). Quinlan Pr.
Jewish Trivia & Information Book. Ian Shapolsky. 400p. 1985. pap. 5.95 (ISBN 0-317-39894-6). Shapolsky Pubs.
Jewish Understanding of the New Testament. Samuel Sandmel. 1974. 11.95x (ISBN 0-87068-102-8); pap. 9.95x (ISBN 0-87068-262-8). Ktav.
Jewish Understanding of the New Testament. Samuel Sandmel. 356p. pap. 9.95 (ISBN 0-686-95179-4). ADL.
Jewish Values. Louis Jacobs. LC 75-103241. 10.95x (ISBN 0-87677-001-4). Hartmore.
Jewish Values in Bioethics. Ed. by Levi Meier. 195p. 1986. text ed. 26.95 (ISBN 0-89885-299-4). Human Sci Pr.
Jewish Views of Jesus: An Introduction & an Appreciation. Thomas T. Walker. LC 73-2229. (Jewish People; History, Religion, Literature Ser.). Repr. of 1931 ed. 16.00 (ISBN 0-405-05290-1). Ayer Co Pubs.
Jewish War. Flavius Josephus. Ed. by E. Mary Smallwood. Tr. by G. A. Wiliiamson. (Classics Ser.). 512p. (Orig.). 1984. pap. 6.95 (ISBN 0-14-044420-3). Penguin.
Jewish War Against the Jews: Reflections on Golah, Shoah, & Torah. Jacob Neusner. LC 84-9657. 157p. 1984. 12.95 (ISBN 0-88125-050-3). Ktav.
Jewish War of Survival. A. Leese. 1982. lib. bdg. 59.95 (ISBN 0-87700-347-5). Revisionist Pr.
Jewish Way. David H. Weisenberg. (Illus.). 1969. 8.95 (ISBN 0-8158-0026-6). Chris Mass.
Jewish Way in Death & Mourning. rev. ed. Maurice Lamm. LC 69-11684. 1972. pap. 7.95 (ISBN 0-8246-0126-2). Jonathan David.
Jewish Way of Life. David Aronson. 1957. 5.00x (ISBN 0-8381-1107-6). United Syn Bk.
Jewish Way of Life & Thought. Abraham J. Karp. 1981. pap. 9.95x (ISBN 0-87068-717-4). Ktav.
Jewish Wedding. Neil A. Lash & Jamie S. Lash. (Jewish Jewels Ser.: Vol. 2). (Illus.). 24p. 1985. pap. 1.50 (ISBN 0-915775-03-4). Love Song Mess Assn.
Jewish Wedding Book: A Practical Guide to the Traditions & Social Customs of the Jewish Wedding. Lilly S. Routtenberg & Ruth R. Seldin. LC 67-13723. (Illus.). 1969. pap. 6.95 (ISBN 0-8052-0186-6). Schocken.
Jewish Woman in America. Charlotte Brown & Paula Hyman. 1977. pap. 7.95 (ISBN 0-452-25786-7, Z5282, Plume). NAL.
Jewish Woman in Jewish Law. M. Meiselman. (Library of Jewish Law & Ethics: Vol. 6). 9.95x (ISBN 0-87068-329-2). Ktav.
Jewish Woman in Judaism: The Significance of Women's Status in Religious Culture. Solomon Appleman. 1979. 10.00 (ISBN 0-682-49431-3). Exposition Pr FL.

Jewish Woman in Rabbinic Literature: A Psychohistorical Perspective. Menachem M. Brayer. 400p. 1986. text ed. 20.00x (ISBN 0-88125-073-2); pap. text ed. 11.95x (ISBN 0-88125-072-4). Ktav.

Jewish Woman in Rabbinic Literature: A Psychosocial Perspective. Menachem M. Brayer. 300p. 1986. text ed. 20.00x (ISBN 0-88125-071-6); pap. text ed. 11.95x (ISBN 0-88125-070-8). Ktav.

Jewish Woman: New Perspectives. Ed. by Elizabeth Koltun. LC 75-35445. 320p. 1976. pap. 7.95 (ISBN 0-8052-0532-2). Schocken.

Jewish Woman: 1900-1985 Bibliography. 2nd ed. Ed. by Aviva Cantor & Ora Hamelsdorf. 200p. 1987. pap. 8.95 (ISBN 0-930395-04-2). Biblio NY.

Jewish Women & Jewish Law: Bibliography. Compiled by Ora Hamelsdorf et al. 60p. 1981. pap. 3.00 (ISBN 0-9602036-2-1). Biblio NY.

Jewish Women's Studies Guide. 2nd ed. Compiled by Sue L. Elwell. 1987. pap. 19.75 (Co-Pub by U Press of America); pap. 9.75 (Co-Pub. by U Press of America). Biblio NY.

Jewish Working Parent: Determining Priorities. Jane G. Epstein. 4.95. United Synagogue.

Jewish World. Douglas Charing. LC 83-50693. (Religions of the World Ser.). 48p. 1983. PLB 14.96 (ISBN 0-382-06720-7); 9.25 (ISBN 0-382-06930-7). Silver.

Jewish Worship. Abraham E. Millgram. LC 77-151316. (Illus.). 1971. 15.95 (ISBN 0-8276-0003-8, 179). Jewish Pubns.

Jewish Writing & Identity in the Twentieth Century. Leon I. Yudkin. LC 82-827. 180p. 1982. 22.50x (ISBN 0-312-44234-3). St Martin.

Jewish Writings of the Second Temple Period: Apocrypha, Pseudipigrapha, Qumran, Sectarian Writings, Philo, Josephus. Ed. by Michael E. Stone. LC 83-48926. (Compendia Rerum Iudaicarum ad Novum Testamentum Ser.). 656p. 1984. 35.95 (ISBN 0-8006-0603-5, 1-603). Fortress.

Jewish Wry: Essays on Jewish Humor. Ed. by Sarah B. Cohen. (Jewish Literature & Culture Ser.). 1987. 27.50 (ISBN 0-253-33185-4). Ind U Pr.

Jewish You Wouldn't Believe It Book. M. Hirsch Goldberg. (Illus.). 252p. 1986. pap. 7.95 (ISBN 0-933503-51-2). Shapolsky Pubs.

Jewish Youth Comes Home. Norman D. Bentwich. LC 75-6422. (Rise of Jewish Nationalism & the Middle East Ser). 159p. 1976. Repr. of 1944 ed. 19.25 (ISBN 0-88355-309-0). Hyperion Conn.

Jewishness & Jesus. Daniel Juster. 1977. pap. 0.75 (ISBN 0-87784-163-2). Inter-Varsity.

Jews. Hilaire Belloc. 1981. lib. bdg. 75.00 (ISBN 0-8490-3220-2). Gordon Pr.

Jews. Hilaire Belloc. 1986. pap. 6.50 (ISBN 0-317-53001-1). Noontide.

Jews. Ed. by Fred L. Israel. (Let's Meet the Peoples of North America Ser.). (Illus.). 112p. 1987. lib. bdg. 15.95 (ISBN 0-87754-887-0). Chelsea Hse.

Jews. Alan Unterman. (Library of Religious Beliefs & Practices). 212p. 1986. pap. text ed. 14.95 (ISBN 0-7100-0842-2). Methuen Inc.

Jews Among the Greeks & Romans. Max Radin. LC 73-2224. (Jewish People; History, Religion, Literature Ser.). Repr. of 1915 ed. 33.00 (ISBN 0-405-05286-3). Ayer Co Pubs.

Jews Among the Nations. Bernard L. Cohen. LC 77-79171. 338p. 1978. 10.95 (ISBN 0-8022-2209-9). Philos Lib.

Jews & Arabs. Albert Memmi. Tr. by Eleanor Levieux from Fr. LC 75-10697. (Eng.). 224p. 1975. 9.95 (ISBN 0-87955-327-8); pap. 7.95 (ISBN 0-87955-328-6). O'Hara.

Jews & Arabs in Palestine: Studies in a National & Colonial Problem. Ed. by Ezo H. Sereni & R. E. Ashery. LC 75-6455. (Rise of Jewish Nationalism & the Middle East Ser). 416p. 1975. Repr. of 1936 ed. 31.35 (ISBN 0-88355-341-4). Hyperion Conn.

Jews & Arabs: Their Contacts Through the Ages. 3rd ed. S. D. Goitein. LC 74-9141. 271p. 1974. pap. 6.95 (ISBN 0-8052-0464-4). Schocken.

Jews & Christians after the Holocaust. Ed. by Abraham J. Peck. LC 81-70665. pap. 31.80 (2029611). Bks Demand UMI.

Jews & Christians, Getting Our Stories Straight: The Exodus & the Passion...Resurrection. Michael Goldberg. 240p. (Orig.). 1985. pap. 12.95 (ISBN 0-687-20330-9). Abingdon.

Jews & Christians: Graeco-Roman Views. Molly Whittaker. (Commentaries on Writings of the Jewish & Christian World 200 B.C. to A.D. 200: Vol. 6). 304p. 1985. 47.50 (ISBN 0-521-24251-7); pap. 18.95 (ISBN 0-521-28556-9). Cambridge U Pr.

Jews & Christians in Antioch in the First Four Centuries of the Common Era. Wayne A. Meeks & Robert L. Wilken. LC 78-3760. 1978. pap. 9.95 (ISBN 0-89130-229-8, 06-03-13). Scholars Pr GA.

Jews & Christians in Dialogue: New Testament Foundations. John Koenig. LC 79-17583. 188p. 1979. pap. 8.95 (ISBN 0-664-24280-4). Westminster.

Jews & Christians: The Contemporary Meeting. A. Roy Eckardt. LC 85-45327. 192p. 1986. 19.95x (ISBN 0-253-33162-5). Ind U Pr.

Jews & Divorce. Jacob L. Fried. 1968. 12.50x (ISBN 0-87068-049-8). Ktav.

Jews & Freemasons in Europe, 1723-1939. Jacob Katz. Tr. by Leonard Oschry from Heb. LC 71-115475. 1970. 22.50x (ISBN 0-674-47480-5). Harvard U Pr.

Jews & Hispanics in America: The Meeting of Two Historic Cultures. Ed. by Lori Santo. 31p. 1982. pap. 2.50 (ISBN 0-87495-061-9). Am Jewish Comm.

Jews & Jewish Christianity. David Berger & Michael Wyschogrod. 3.95x (ISBN 0-87068-675-5). Ktav.

Jews & Judaism During the Greek Period: The Background of Christianity. William O. Oesterley. LC 74-102580. 1970. Repr. of 1941 ed. 23.00x (ISBN 0-8046-0740-0, Pub. by Kennikat). Assoc Faculty Pr.

Jews & Judaism in a Midwestern Community: Columbus, Ohio, 1840-1975. Marc L. Raphael. (Illus.). 296p. 1979. 10.00 (ISBN 0-318-00876-9). Ohio Hist Soc.

Jews & Judaism in the United States: A Documentary History. Ed. by Marc L. Raphael. 352p. 1983. pap. text ed. 9.95x (ISBN 0-87441-347-8). Behrman.

Jews & Medicine & Jewish Luminaries in Medical History, 3 Vols. rev. ed. Harry Friedenwald. 1967. 50.00x (ISBN 0-87068-053-6). Ktav.

Jews & Minority Rights, 1898-1919. Oscar I. Janowsky. LC 33-31678. (Columbia University. Studies in the Social Sciences: No. 384). Repr. of 1933 ed. 24.50 (ISBN 0-404-51384-0). AMS Pr.

Jews & Modern Capitalism. Werner Sombart. LC 81-16152. (Social Science Classics Ser.). 475p. 1982. pap. 19.95 (ISBN 0-87855-837-3). Transaction Bks.

Jews & Non-Jews Falling in Love. Sandford Seltzer. 1976. 4.00 (ISBN 0-8074-0098-X, 164050). UAHC.

Jews & Non-Jews: Getting Married. Sanford Seltzer. 1984. pap. 4.00 (ISBN 0-8074-0300-8, 164055). UAHC.

Jews & Non-Jews in Eastern Europe, 1918-1945. Ed. by Bela Vago & George L. Mosse. pap. 88.00 (ISBN 0-317-27256-X, 2024158). Bks Demand UMI.

Jews & the American Revolution: A Bicentennial Documentary. Ed. by J. R. Marcus. 7.50x (ISBN 0-87068-875-8). Ktav.

Jews & the Crusaders: The Hebrew Chronicles of the First & Second Crusades. Ed. by Shlomo Eidelberg. (Illus.). 200p. 1977. 24.95x (ISBN 0-299-07060-3). U of Wis Pr.

Jews & the Cults: Bibliography-Guide. Compiled by Jack N. Porter. LC 81-67448. 50p. 1981. pap. 3.50 (ISBN 0-9602036-4-8). Biblio NY.

Jews & the Founding of the Republic. Jonathan D. Sarna et al. LC 85-40513. (American History in Documents Ser.). (Illus.). 240p. (Orig.). 1985. pap. text ed. 14.50x (ISBN 0-910129-44-4). Wiener Pub Inc.

Jews & the French Revolution of 1789, 1830 & 1848. Soza Szajkowski. 1969. 59.50x (ISBN 0-87068-112-5). Ktav.

Jews Are Like That. facs. ed. James W. Wise. LC 70-84348. (Essay Index Reprint Ser). 1928. 16.75 (ISBN 0-8369-1114-8). Ayer Co Pubs.

Jews, Are They Human? Wyndham Lewis. LC 72-82188. 1972. Repr. of 1939 ed. lib. bdg. 75.00 (ISBN 0-87968-008-3). Gordon Pr.

Jews at the Crossroads. Yitshak Korn. LC 81-86479. 208p. 1983. 12.95 (ISBN 0-8453-4754-3, Cornwall Bks). Assoc Univ Prs.

Jews, Christians & the Theory of the Soul: New Discoveries in Classical Theology. Massimiliano Tebaldus. (Illus.). 138p. 1984. 88.95 (ISBN 0-89266-480-0). Am Classical Coll Pr.

Jews for Nothing: On Cults, Assimilation & Intermarriage. Dov A. Fisch. 368p. 1984. 13.95 (ISBN 0-87306-347-3). Feldheim.

Jews from Alexander to Herod. D. S. Russell. 1967. pap. 13.95x (ISBN 0-19-836913-1). Oxford U Pr.

Jews, God & History. Max I. Dimont. 1972. pap. 4.95 (ISBN 0-451-14694-8, AE2181, Sig). NAL.

Jews: God's People. Hilla Jacoby & Max Jacoby. (Illus.). 224p. 1984. 49.95 (ISBN 0-310-42430-5, 18369). Zondervan.

Jews in a Free Society: Challenges & Opportunities. Ed. by Edward A. Goldman. 12.50x (ISBN 0-87820-112-2). Ktav.

Jews in a Gentile World: The Problem of Anti-Semitism. Isacque Graeber & Steuart H. Britt. LC 78-26329. (Illus.). 1979. Repr. of 1942 ed. lib. bdg. 32.50x (ISBN 0-313-20878-6, GRJE). Greenwood.

Jews in America. Max Dimont. 1980. 6.95 (ISBN 0-671-25412-X, Touchstone). S&S.

Jews in America. Burton J. Hendrick. Ed. by Gerald Grob. LC 76-46081. (Anti-Movements in America). 1977. Repr. of 1923 ed. lib. bdg. 17.00x (ISBN 0-405-09954-1). Ayer Co Pubs.

Jews in America: A Picture Album. Milton Meltzer. LC 84-14344. (Illus.). 1985. 12.95 (ISBN 0-8276-0246-4). Jewish Pubns.

Jews in America: Heritage & History. Jacob I. Hartstein & Benjamin Miller. (Illus.). 1978. 6.50 (ISBN 0-686-26239-5). Board Jewish Educ.

Jews in America 1621-1977: A Chronology & Fact Book. 2nd ed. Irving J. Sloan. LC 77-26768. (No. 3). 1978. lib. bdg. 8.50 (ISBN 0-379-00530-1). Oceana.

Jews in an Arab Land: Libya, 1835-1970. Renzo De Felice. Tr. by Judith Roumani. 436p. 1985. 27.50x (ISBN 0-292-74016-6). U of Tex Pr.

Jews in Barbarian Europe. Bernard S. Bachrach. 1977. 7.50x (ISBN 0-87291-088-1). Coronado Pr.

Jews in Early Mississippi. Leo Turitz & Evelyn Turitz. LC 82-25093. (Illus.). 144p. (Orig.). 1983. pap. 20.00 (ISBN 0-87805-178-3). U Pr of Miss.

Jews in Hellenistic & Roman Egypt: The Struggle for Equal Rights. Aryek Kasher. 442p. 1985. lib. bdg. 90.00x (ISBN 3-16-144829-4, Pub. by J C B Mohr BRD). Coronet Bks.

Jews in India & the Far East. James H. Lord. LC 70-97292. 1976. Repr. of 1907 ed. lib. bdg. 22.50x (ISBN 0-8371-2615-0, LOJI). Greenwood.

Jews in Luke-Acts. Jack T. Sanders. LC 86-45926. 432p. 1987. pap. 19.95 (ISBN 0-8006-0837-2, 1-1969). Fortress.

Jews in Music: From the Age of Enlightenment to the Mid-Twentieth Century. rev. ed. Ed. by Artur Holde & Irene Heskes. LC 74-83942. 364p. 1974. 10.00 (ISBN 0-8197-0372-9). Bloch.

Jews in Nazi Germany. American Jewish Committee. x, 177p. 1982. Repr. of 1935 ed. 22.50x (ISBN 0-86527-110-0). Fertig.

Jews in New Spain: Faith, Flame & the Inquisition. Seymour B. Liebman. LC 70-91213. (Illus.). 1970. 19.95x (ISBN 0-87024-129-X). U of Miami Pr.

Jews in Oklahoma. Henry J. Tobias. LC 79-6723. (Newcomers to a New Land Ser.: Vol. 10). (Illus.). 96p. (Orig.). 1980. pap. 3.95 (ISBN 0-8061-1676-5). U of Okla Pr.

Jews in Old China: Studies by Chinese Historians. Ed. by Sidney Shapiro. (Illus.). 224p. 1984. 15.95 (ISBN 0-88254-996-0). Hippocrene Bks.

Jews in Poland. Antony Polonsky et al. 288p. 1986. 24.95 (ISBN 0-631-14857-4). Basil Blackwell.

Jews in Poland & Russia: Bibliographical Essays. Gershon D. Hundert & Gershon C. Bacon. LC 83-49285. (Modern Jewish Experience Ser.). 288p. 1985. 25.00x (ISBN 0-253-33158-7). Ind U Pr.

Jews in Review: The World's Greatest Minds on Zionism. Zudhi Al-Fatih. 1984. lib. bdg. 79.95 (ISBN 0-87700-581-8). Revisionist Pr.

Jews in Rhode Island: A Brief History. Geraldine S. Foster. Ed. by Patrick T. Conley. (Rhode Island Ethnic Heritage Pamphlet Ser.). (Illus.). 48p. (Orig.). 1985. pap. 2.75 (ISBN 0-917012-80-1). RI Pubns Soc.

Jews in Russia. Nikolai Leskov. Ed. & tr. by Harold K. Schefski. 143p. 1986. 21.00 (ISBN 0-940670-29-1). Kingston Pr.

Jews in Russia: The Last Four Centuries. Jonathan D. Porath. 1973. pap. 3.75x (ISBN 0-8381-0220-4). United Syn Bk.

Jews in Russia: The Struggle for Emancipation, 2 Vols. in 1. Louis Greenberg. LC 79-161769. Repr. of 1965 ed. 27.50 (ISBN 0-404-09023-0). AMS Pr.

Jews in Russia: The Struggle for Emancipation, 1772-1917, 2 vols. in 1. Louis Greenberg. Ed. by Mark Wishnitzer. LC 75-36489. 234p. 1976. pap. 11.95 (ISBN 0-8052-0525-X). Schocken.

Jews in Soviet Culture. Ed. by Jack Miller. 325p. 1983. 24.95 (ISBN 0-87855-495-5). Transaction Bks.

Jews in Soviet Russia Since 1917. 3rd ed. Ed. by Lionel Kochan. (Illus.). 1978. pap. 9.95 (ISBN 0-19-281199-1). Oxford U Pr.

Jews in Spain & Portugal: A Bibliography. Robert Singerman. LC 75-1166. (Reference Library of Social Science: No. 11). 376p. 1975. lib. bdg. 52.00 (ISBN 0-8240-1089-2). Garland Pub.

Jews in Spain: Their Social, Political & Cultural Life During the Middle Ages, 2 vols. Abraham A. Neuman. LC 70-105964. 1970. Repr. of 1942 ed. lib. bdg. 54.50x (ISBN 0-374-96061-5, Octagon). Hippocrene Bks.

Jews in Suburbia. Albert I. Gordon. LC 73-11749. 264p. 1973. Repr. of 1959 ed. lib. bdg. 15.00x (ISBN 0-8371-7088-5, COJS). Greenwood.

Jews in the East, 2 vols. Ludwig A. Frankl. Tr. by P. Beaton. LC 78-97278. 1975. Repr. of 1859 ed. Set. lib. bdg. 28.50x (ISBN 0-8371-2596-0, FRJE). Greenwood.

Jews in the Economic & Political Life of Medieval Islam. rev. ed. Walter Fischel. LC 68-25719. 1969. Repr. of 1937 ed. 15.00x (ISBN 0-87068-047-1). Ktav.

Jews in the Eyes of the Germans: From the Enlightenment to Imperial Germany. Alfred D. Low. LC 79-334. (Illus.). 528p. 1979. 19.95 (ISBN 0-915980-86-X). ISHI PA.

Jews in the French Foreign Legion. Soza Szajkowski. 25.00x (ISBN 0-87068-285-7). Ktav.

Jews in the Hellenistic World: Josephus, Aristeas, the Sibylline Oracles, Eupolemus. (Cambridge Commentaries on the Writings of the Jewish & Christian World 200 B. C. to 200 A. D.). (Illus.). 224p. 1985. 42.50 (ISBN 0-521-24246-0); pap. 12.95 (ISBN 0-521-28551-8). Cambridge U Pr.

Jews in the Renaissance. Cecil Roth. LC 59-8516. (Illus.). 378p. 1978. pap. 8.95 (ISBN 0-8276-0103-4, 321). Jewish Pubns.

Jews in the Roman World. Michael Grant. LC 72-11118. 1973. lib. rep. ed. 20.00x (ISBN 0-684-15494-3, ScribT). Scribner.

Jews in the South. Ed. by Leonard Dinnerstein & Mary D. Palsson. LC 72-89114. viii, 392p. 1973. 32.50x (ISBN 0-8071-0226-1). La State U Pr.

Jews in the Soviet Satellites. Peter Meyer. LC 79-97297. 1971. Repr. of 1953 ed. lib. bdg. 45.00x (ISBN 0-8371-2621-5, MEJS). Greenwood.

Jews in the Soviet Union. Solomon M. Schwarz. LC 72-4298. (World Affairs Ser.: National & International Viewpoints). 398p. 1972. Repr. of 1951 ed. 22.00 (ISBN 0-405-04589-1). Ayer Co Pubs.

Jews in the Soviet Union: A History from 1917 to the Present, 2 vols. Nora Levin. (Illus.). 864p. 1987. Set. text ed. 75.00 (ISBN 0-8147-5018-4); Vol. 1 (432p.) text ed. 45.00 (ISBN 0-8147-5034-6); Vol. 2 (432p.) text ed. 45.00 (ISBN 0-8147-5035-4). NYU Pr.

Jews in the U. S. S. R. Figures, Facts, Comment. Avtandil Rukhadze. 112p. 1984. pap. 5.00x (ISBN 0-317-53875-6, Pub. by Collets (UK)). State Mutual Bk.

Jews in the Visigothic & Frankish Kingdoms of Spain & Gaul. S. Katz. (Mediaeval Academy of America Publications). 1937. 21.00 (ISBN 0-527-01697-7). Kraus Repr.

Jews in Their Land in the Talmudic Age, Vol. 1. Gedaliah Alon. Tr. by Levi Gershon from Hebrew. 324p. 1980. text ed. 32.50x (ISBN 965-223-352-8, Pub. by Magnes Pr Israel). Humanities.

Jews in Weimar Germany. Donald L. Niewyk. LC 79-26234. 262p. 1980. 27.50x (ISBN 0-8071-0661-5). La State U Pr.

Jews, Judaism & the Classical World. Gedalyahu Alon. Tr. by Israel Abrahams from Hebrew. 499p. 1977. text ed. 38.50x (Pub. by Magnes Pr Israel). Humanities.

Jews Must Live. Samuel Roth. 1980. lib. bdg. 69.95 (ISBN 0-8490-3204-0). Gordon Pr.

Jews of Africa, Especially in the 16th & 17th Centuries. Sidney Mendelssohn. 59.95 (ISBN 0-8490-0446-2). Gordon Pr.

Jews of America: History & Sources. Frances Butwin. Ed. by Arthur C. Blecher. LC 73-2253. (Illus.). 160p. 1973. pap. text ed. 3.95x (ISBN 0-87441-062-2). Behrman.

Jews of Arab & Islamic Countries: History, Problems & Solutions. Heskel M. Haddad. LC 83-5065. 168p. 1984. 12.95 (ISBN 0-88400-100-8). Shengold.

Jews of Arab Lands: A History & Source Book. Norman A. Stillman. LC 78-70078. (Illus.). 416p. 1979. 10.95 (ISBN 0-8276-0116-6, 426). Jewish Pubns.

Jews of Asia: Especially in the Sixteenth & Seventeenth Centuries. Sidney Mendelssohn. LC 77-87612. (Illus.). 256p. Repr. of 1920 ed. 29.50 (ISBN 0-404-16436-6). AMS Pr.

Jews of Barnow. facsimile ed. Karl E. Franzos. Tr. by M. W. Macdowall from Ger. LC 74-27985. (Modern Jewish Experience Ser.). (Eng.). 1975. Repr. of 1883 ed. 30.00x (ISBN 0-405-06712-7). Ayer Co Pubs.

Jews of Byzantium: Twelve Four to Fourteen Fifty-Three. Steven B. Bowman. LC 83-17230. (Judaic Studies Ser.). (Illus.). 400p. 1985. 42.50 (ISBN 0-8173-0198-4). U of Ala Pr.

Jews of Czechoslovakia, Vol. III. Ed. by Avigdor Dagan et al. (Illus.). 700p. 1984. 29.95 (ISBN 0-8276-0230-8). Jewish Pubns.

Jews of Detroit: From the Beginning, 1762-1914. Robert Rockaway. LC 86-15866. (Illus.). 175p. 1986. 15.95X (ISBN 0-8143-1808-8). Wayne St U Pr.

Jews of East Central Europe between the World Wars. Ezra Mendelsohn. LC 81-48676. (Illus.). 320p. 1983. 27.50x (ISBN 0-253-33160-9). Ind U Pr.

Jews of Europe & The Inquisition of Venice, 1550-1670. Brian Pullan. LC 83-7147. 364p. 1983. 32.50x (ISBN 0-389-20414-5). B&N Imports.

Jews of Hope. Martin Gilbert. (Nonfiction Ser.). 272p. 1985. pap. 7.95 (ISBN 0-14-008510-6). Penguin.

Jews of Hope: The Plight of Soviet Jewry Today. Martin Gilbert. LC 84-40461. (Illus.). 237p. 1985. 15.95 (ISBN 0-670-80377-4, E. Sifton Bks). Viking.

Jews of Iraq. Nissim Rejwan. 288p. 1986. 30.00 (ISBN 0-8133-0348-6). Westview.

Jews of Islam. Bernard Lewis. LC 84-42575. (Illus.). 259p. 1984. 42.50x (ISBN 0-691-05419-3). Princeton U Pr.

Jews of Islam. Bernard Lewis. 280p. 1987. pap. 8.95 (ISBN 0-691-00807-8). Princeton U Pr.

Jews of Israel: History & Sources. Nora B. Kubie. Ed. by Mark Silberman. LC 75-18510. (Illus.). 128p. (Orig.). 1975. pap. text ed. 3.95x (ISBN 0-87441-246-3). Behrman.

Jews of Jannina. Rachel Dalven. 1986. write for info. (ISBN 0-930685-02-4). Cadmus Press.

Jews of Los Angeles, No. 3. Compiled by Sara Cogan. (Western Jewish Americana Ser. Publications). 237p. 1980. 24.95 (ISBN 0-943376-12-2); pap. 14.95 (ISBN 0-943376-11-4). Magnes Mus.

Jews of Majorca. A. Lionel Isaacs. 1976. lib. bdg. 59.95 (ISBN 0-8490-2105-7). Gordon Pr.

Jews of Medieval Poland. A. Vetulani. 1978. lib. bdg. 59.95 (ISBN 0-685-62298-3). Revisionist Pr.

Jews of Moslem Spain, Vol. III. Eliyahu Ashtor. Tr. by Aaron Klein & Jenny M. Klein. 380p. 1985. 19.95 (ISBN 0-8276-0237-5). Jewish Pubns.

Jews of Moslem Spain, Vol. 1. Eliyahu Ashtor. Tr. by Aaron Machlowitz Klein from Heb. LC 73-14081. (Illus.). 469p. 1974. 12.00 (ISBN 0-8276-0017-8, 352). Jewish Pubns.

Jews of Moslem Spain, Vol. 2. Eliyahu Ashtor. 381p. 1978. 12.00 (ISBN 0-8276-0100-X, 411). Jewish Pubns.

Jews of Odessa: A Cultural History, 1794-1881. Steven J. Zipperstein. LC 84-50152. 232p. 1986. 32.50x (ISBN 0-8047-1251-4). Stanford U Pr.

Jews of Poland: Recollections & Recipes. Edouard De Pomiane. Tr. by Josephine Bacon from Fr. (Jewish Cookery Classics Ser.). Tr. of Cuisine Juive: Ghettos Modernes. (Illus.). 256p. 1985. 9.95 (ISBN 0-910231-02-8); pap. 9.95. Pholiota.

Jews of San Francisco & the Greater Bay Area: 1849 to 1919. Compiled by Sara Cogan. (Western Jewish Americana Ser.: No. 2). 1972. 22.00 (ISBN 0-943376-03-3). Magnes Mus.

Jews of Silence: A Personal Report on Soviet Jewry. Elie Wiesel. LC 63-11041. 160p. 1987. pap. 8.95 (ISBN 0-8052-0826-7). Schocken.

Jews of South Carolina, from the Earliest Times to the Present Day. Barnett A. Elzas. LC 77-187364. (Illus.). 352p. 1972. Repr. of 1905 ed. 23.50 (ISBN 0-87152-092-3). Reprint.

Jews of the Ottoman Empire in the Late Fifteenth & the Sixteenth Centuries. A. Shmuelevitz. 201p. 1984. pap. text ed. 35.00x (ISBN 90-04-07071-0, Pub. by EJ Brill Holland). Humanities.

Jews of the South: Selected Essays. Ed. by Samuel Proctor et al. LC 83-25060. viii, 131p. 1984. 12.95 (ISBN 0-86554-102-7, H94). Mercer Univ Pr.

Jews of the United States, 1790-1840: A Documentary History, 3 Vols. Ed. by Joseph L. Blau et al. LC 64-10108. 1034p. 1964. Set. 140.00x (ISBN 0-231-02651-X). Columbia U Pr.

Jews of the West: The Metropolitan Years. Ed. by Moses Rischin. (Illus.). 1979. 5.95 (ISBN 0-911934-11-1). Am Jewish Hist Soc.

Jews of the West: The Metropolitan Years. Ed. by Moses Rischin. (Illus.). 156p. 1975. pap. 5.95 (ISBN 0-943376-10-6). Magnes Mus.

Jews of Vienna, 1867-1914: Assimilation & Identity. Marsha L. Rozenblit. (Modern Jewish History Ser.). 368p. 1984. 44.50 (ISBN 0-87395-844-6); pap. 16.95 (ISBN 0-87395-845-4). State U NY Pr.

Jews of Warsaw, 1939-1943: Ghetto, Underground, Revolt. Yisrael Gutman. Tr. by Ina Friedman. LC 81-47570. (Illus.). 512p. 1982. 24.95x (ISBN 0-253-33174-9). Ind U Pr.

Jews: Story of a People. Howard Fast. 384p. 1978. pap. 3.95 (ISBN 0-440-34444-1). Dell.

Jews' Struggle for Religious & Civil Liberty in Maryland. E. Milton Altfeld. LC 78-99859. (Civil Liberties in American History Ser). 1970. Repr. of 1924 ed. lib. bdg. 29.50 (ISBN 0-306-71859-6). Da Capo.

Jews, Turks, & Infidels. Morton Borden. LC 83-19863. xii, 163p. 1984. 17.95x (ISBN 0-8078-1592-6). U of NC Pr.

Jews under Roman & Byzantine Rule: A Political History of Palestine from the Bar-Kokhba War to the Arab Conquest. Michael Avi-Yonah. LC 84-5612. Orig. Title: Jews of Palestine. (Illus.). 304p. 1984. Repr. 23.00x (ISBN 0-8052-3580-9). Schocken.

Jews under the Italian Occupation. Leon Poliakov & Jacques Sabille. LC 81-22202. 208p. 1983. Repr. of 1955 ed. 23.50x (ISBN 0-86527-344-8). Fertig.

Jews, War & Communism. Soza Szjakowski. Incl. Vol. 1. Attitude of American Jews to World War I, the Russian Revolution of 1917, and Communism, 1917 to 1945. 1972. 35.00x (ISBN 0-87068-182-6); Vol. 2. 1974. 35.00x (ISBN 0-87068-239-3). Ktav.

Jews Were Expendable: Free World Diplomacy & the Holocaust. Monty N. Penkower. LC 82-17490. 446p. 1983. 27.50 (ISBN 0-252-00747-6). U of Ill Pr.

Jews without Mercy: A Lament. Earl Shorris. 1982. 14.95 (ISBN 0-385-17853-0). Brown Bk.

Jews, Zionism & the Bible. S. Hadawi. 1984. lib. bdg. 79.95 (ISBN 0-87700-572-9). Revisionist Pr.

Jhamom's Story of Creation. Ed. by Mystic Jhamom Staff. (Conversations Mystic Ser.: No. 3). (Illus.). 136p. 1986. pap. 9.95 (ISBN 0-933961-07-3). Mystic Jhamom.

Jim Burn's Youth Series 1--Leaders' Guide. Jim Burns. (Orig.). 1985. pap. 7.95 (ISBN 0-89081-495-3). Harvest Hse.

Jim Crow Comes to Church: The Establishment of Segregated Catholic Parishes in South Louisiana. Dolores E. Labbe. 14.00 (ISBN 0-405-10838-9, 11845). Ayer Co Pubs.

Jim Hart Story. Thomas Barnidge & Douglas Grow. LC 77-12538. (Illus.). 1977. 6.95 (ISBN 0-8272-1705-6); pap. 4.95 (ISBN 0-8272-1704-8). CBP.

Jimmy Carter-Jimmy Carter. Gary Allen. 96p. pap. 1.00 (ISBN 0-686-31145-0). Concord Pr.

Jimshoes in Vietman. James R. Klassen. LC 86-9801. (Illus.). 400p. (Orig.). 1986. pap. 14.95 (ISBN 0-8361-3412-5). Herald Pr.

Jnana-Yoga. Swami Vivekananda. pap. 4.95 (ISBN 0-87481-158-9). Vedanta Pr.

Jnana Yoga (Yoga Secrets of Wisdom) Swami Jyotir Maya Nanda. (Illus.). 1974. pap. 1.99 (ISBN 0-934664-05-6). Yoga Res Foun.

Jnanagarbha's Commentary on the Distinction Between the Two Truths. Malcolm D. Eckel. (Buddhist Studies). 196p. (Orig.). 1986. 39.50x (ISBN 0-88706-301-2); pap. 12.95x (ISBN 0-88706-302-0). State U NY Pr.

Jnaneshwari. Jnanadev. Tr. by Ramachandra K. Bhagwat. (Illus.). 1979. 36.00 (ISBN 0-89744-188-5). Auromere.

Joan Antida Thouret: When God Was the Voice of the Poor. Gino Lubich & Piero Lazzarin. Tr. by Joel Brody from Ital. LC 84-62540. 1985. pap. 5.95 (ISBN 0-911782-47-8). New City.

Joan of Arc. Jules Michelet. Tr. by Albert Guerard. 1957. pap. 6.95 (ISBN 0-472-06122-4, 122, AA). U of Mich Pr.

Joan of Arc. Catherine Storr. LC 84-18346. (Raintree Stories Ser.). (Illus.). 32p. 1985. PLB 14.65 (ISBN 0-8172-2111-5); pap. 9.27 (ISBN 0-8172-2254-5). Raintree Pubs.

Joan of Arc: By Herself & Her Witnesses. Regine Pernoud. LC 66-24807. 1969. pap. 10.95 (ISBN 0-8128-1260-3). Stein & Day.

Joan of Arc: Heretic, Mystic, Shaman. Anne L. Barstow. LC 86-12756. (Studies in Women & Religion: No. 17). (Illus.). 156p. 1986. lib. bdg. 49.95 (ISBN 0-88946-532-0). E Mellen.

Joan of Arc: The Image of Female Heroism. Marina Warner. LC 80-2720. (Illus.). 1981. 19.95 (ISBN 0-394-41145-5). Knopf.

Joan of Arc: The Image of Female Heroism. Marina Warner. LC 81-69565. (Illus.). 400p. 1982. pap. 9.95 (ISBN 0-394-75333-X, Vin). Random.

Joan, the Brave Soldier: Joan of Arc. Dolores Ready. LC 77-86597. (Stories About Christian Heroes). (Illus.). 1977. pap. 1.95 (ISBN 0-86683-764-7, HarpR). Har-Row.

Job. Francis I. Andersen. Ed. by D. J. Wiseman. LC 76-12298. (Tyndale Old Testament Commentary Ser.). 1976. 12.95 (ISBN 0-87784-869-6); pap. 6.95 (ISBN 0-87784-263-9). Inter-Varsity.

Job. Albert Barnes. 18.95 (ISBN 0-8010-0837-9). Baker Bk.

Job. Myles M. Bourke. (Bible Ser.). Pt. 1. pap. 1.00 (ISBN 0-8091-5073-5); Pt. 2. pap. 1.00 (ISBN 0-8091-5074-3). Paulist Pr.

Job. A. Cohen. 233p. 1946. 10.95 (ISBN 0-900689-34-X). Soncino Pr.

Job. J. H. Eaton. (Old Testament Guides Ser.). 69p. 1985. pap. text ed. 3.95x (ISBN 0-905774-97-3, Pub by. JSOT Pr England). Eisenbrauns.

Job. Harold M. Freligh. pap. 1.95 (ISBN 0-87509-097-4). Chr Pubns.

Job. John C. Gibson. LC 85-13652. (Daily Study Bible - Old Testament). 294p. 1985. 16.95 (ISBN 0-664-21815-6); pap. 8.95 (ISBN 0-664-24584-6). Westminster.

Job. Michael D. Guinan. (Collegeville Bible Commentary: Old Testament Ser.: Vol. 19). 88p. 1986. pap. 2.95 (ISBN 0-8146-1476-0). Liturgical Pr.

Job. Norman C. Habel. LC 80-82193. (Knox Preaching Guides). 100p. (Orig., John Hayes series editor). 1981. pap. 4.95 (ISBN 0-8042-3216-4). John Knox.

Job. Irving L. Jensen. (Bible Self Study Guide Ser.). 1975. pap. 3.25 (ISBN 0-8024-1018-9). Moody.

Job. rev. ed. Ed. by Marvin H. Pope. (Anchor Bible Ser.: Vol. 15). 1973. 18.00 (ISBN 0-385-00894-5, Anchor Pr). Doubleday.

Job. Samuel Ridout. 1919. pap. 3.95 (ISBN 0-87213-719-8). Loizeaux.

Job. rev. ed. H. H. Rowley. (New Century Bible Ser.). 302p. 1976. 9.95 (ISBN 0-551-00596-3). Attic Pr.

Job. Roy Zuck. (Everyman's Bible Commentary Ser.). 1978. pap. 5.95 (ISBN 0-8024-2017-6). Moody.

Job: A Bible Commentary for Teaching & Preaching. Ed. by J. Gerald Jansen et al. LC 84-48512. (Interpretation Ser.). 288p. 1985. 18.95 (ISBN 0-8042-3114-1). John Knox.

Job: A Practical Commentary. A. Van Selms. Ed. by A. S. Van Der Woude. (Text & Interpretation Ser.). (Dutch.). 192p. (Orig.). 1985. pap. 8.95 (ISBN 0-8028-0101-3). Eerdmans.

Job & Jonah: Questioning the Hidden God. Bruce Vawter. LC 82-62413. 1983. pap. 4.95 (ISBN 0-8091-2524-2). Paulist Pr.

Job & the Silence of God. Christian Duquoc & Casiano Floristan. (Concilium Ser. 1983: Vol. 169). 128p. (Orig.). 1983. pap. 6.95 (ISBN 0-8164-2449-7, 9671P). Har-Row.

Job: Bible Study Commentary. D. David Garland. 160p. 1971. pap. 4.95 (ISBN 0-310-24863-9, 9671P). Zondervan.

Job (CC) David McKenna. 320p. 1986. 18.95 (ISBN 0-317-43277-X). Word Bks.

Job (CC, Vol. 12. David McKenna. 320p. 1986. 18.95 (ISBN 0-8499-0418-8). Word Bks.

Job, Ecclesiastes. Dianne Bergant. (Old Testament Message Ser.: Vol. 18). 1982. 12.95 (ISBN 0-89453-418-1); pap. 9.95 (ISBN 0-89453-252-9). M Glazier.

Job: God's Answer to Suffering. Ron Klug. (Fisherman Bible Studyguide Ser.). 61p. 1982. saddle-stitched 2.95 (ISBN 0-87788-430-7). Shaw Pubs.

Job: Living Patiently. J. Allen Blair. LC 66-25720. 1966. pap. 5.95 (ISBN 0-87213-051-7). Loizeaux.

Job on Trial: A Book for Our Time. Isreal J. Gerber. 217p. 1982. 14.95 (ISBN 0-318-01102-6). E P Press.

Job Shattering of Silence. James D. Strauss. LC 77-155412. (Bible Study Textbook Ser.). (Illus.). 1976. 15.90 (ISBN 0-89900-015-0). College Pr Pub.

Job-Song of Solomon, Vol. III. Beacon Bible Commentary Staff. 13.95 (ISBN 0-8010-0690-2). Baker Bk.

Job: The Story of a Simple Man. Joseph Roth. Tr. by Dorothy Thompson from Ger. LC 81-18901. (Tusk Bk.). 252p. 1985. 22.50 (ISBN 0-87951-149-4); pap. 8.95 (ISBN 0-87951-202-4). Overlook Pr.

Job: The Trial & Triumph of Faith. David G. Grosse. (Small Group Bible Studies). 88p. (Orig.). 1986. pap. 2.50 (ISBN 0-8341-1138-1). Beacon Hill.

Jodie: One Little Ewe Lamb. Elizabeth P. Dean. 96p. 1984. pap. 4.95 (ISBN 0-8010-2938-4). Baker Bk.

Jodoshinshu Book. Monto Hikkei Kai. (Illus.). 92p. 1973. pap. 2.50 (ISBN 0-685-65547-4). Nembutsu Pr.

Joel & Amos. Hans W. Wolff, Jr. Ed. by Dean McBride. Tr. by Waldemar Janzen from Ger. LC 75-76932. (Hermeneia: a Critical & Historical Commentary on the Bible). 416p. 1977. 29.95 (ISBN 0-8006-6007-2, 20-6007). Fortress.

Joel Goldsmith's Gift of Love. Joel S. Goldsmith. LC 82-11891. 96p. 1983. 8.95 (ISBN 0-686-92026-0, HarpR). Har-Row.

Joel Litu: African Quaker. Rose Adede. LC 82-81325. 32p. 1982. pap. 2.50x (ISBN 0-87574-243-2). Pendle Hill.

Joel, Obadiah, Haggai, Zechariah, Malachi. Mary M. Pazdan. (Collegevile Bible Commentary Ser.). 128p. 1986. pap. 2.95 (ISBN 0-8146-1424-8). Liturgical Pr.

Joel, Obadiah, Jonah, Micah. Leslie Allen. (New International Commentary on Old Testament Ser.). 16.95 (ISBN 0-8028-2373-4). Eerdmans.

Joel: The Outpouring of God's Glory. Bob Yandian. (Commentaries for Laymen Ser.). 160p. (Orig.). 1986. pap. 5.95 (ISBN 0-89274-402-2). Harrison Hse.

Joey. Daughters of St. Paul. 1980. 3.00 (ISBN 0-8198-3907-8); pap. 2.00 (ISBN 0-8198-3908-6). Dghtrs St Paul.

Joey Meets His People. Herbert L. Kruckman. 44p. 1940. 2.95 (ISBN 0-88482-732-1). Hebrew Pub.

Jog for Your Life. new ed. Haydn Gilmore. (Illus.). 1979. pap. 1.95 (ISBN 0-310-25022-6). Zondervan.

Jogging with God. LeRoy L. Hamilton. 56p. 1985. 5.95 (ISBN 0-8059-2983-5). Dorrance.

Jogging with Jesus. C. S. Lovett. (Illus.). 1978. pap. 3.95 (ISBN 0-938148-34-6). Personal Christianity.

Johan the Evangelist. LC 71-133689. (Tudor Facsimile Texts. Old English Plays: No. 24). Repr. of 1907 ed. 49.50 (ISBN 0-404-53324-8). AMS Pr.

Johann Arndt: True Christianity. Peter Erb. LC 78-72046. (Classics of Western Spirituality). 320p. 1979. 12.95 (ISBN 0-8091-0281-1); pap. 9.95 (ISBN 0-8091-2192-1). Paulist Pr.

Johann Christian Edelmann: From Orthodoxy to Enlightenment. Walter Grossman. (Religion & Society Ser: No. 3). 209p. 1976. text ed. 22.25x (ISBN 90-2797-691-0). Mouton.

Johann Conrad Beissel: Mystic & Martinet 1690-1768. Walter C. Klein. LC 74-187453. (American Utopian Adventure Ser.). 218p. 1973. Repr. of 1942 ed. lib. bdg. 22.50x (ISBN 0-87991-012-7). Porcupine Pr.

Johann Sleidan's Commentaries: Vantage Point of a Second Generation Lutheran. Ingeborg B. Vogelstein. 176p. 1987. lib. bdg. 21.75 (ISBN 0-8191-5641-8); pap. text ed. 11.50 (ISBN 0-8191-5642-6). U Pr of Amer.

Johannes Amos Comenius. Jan Jakubec. LC 70-135811. (Eastern Europe Collection Ser). 1970. Repr. of 1928 ed. 12.00 (ISBN 0-405-02753-2). Ayer Co Pubs.

Johannes, Jesus und die Juden. Volker Schoenle. (Beitroge zur Biblischen Exegese und Theologie: Vol. 17). (Ger.). 288p. 1982. 40.00 (ISBN 3-8204-5877-8). P Lang Pubs.

Johannes von Apamea. Werner Strothmann. (Patristische Texte und Studien 11). 1972. 48.40x (ISBN 3-11-002457-8). De Gruyter.

Johannine Christianity: Essays on Its Setting, Sources, & Theology. Moody D. Smith. 233p. 1985. 19.95x (ISBN 0-87249-449-7). U of SC Pr.

Johannine Christianity in Conflict: Authority, Rank & Succession in the First Farwell Discourse. D. Bruce Woll. LC 81-1795. (SBL Dissertation Ser.). 1981. pap. 12.00 (ISBN 0-89130-471-1, 060160). Scholars Pr GA.

Johannine Epistles. Rudolf Bultmann. Ed. by Robert W. Funk. Tr. by R. Philip O'Hara et al from Gr. LC 75-171510. (Hermeneia: a Critical & Historical Commentary on the Bible). 158p. 1973. 19.95 (ISBN 0-8006-6003-X, 20-6003). Fortress.

Johannine Epistles. Kenneth Grayston. Ed. by Ronald Clements & Matthew Black. (New Century Bible Commentary Ser.). 180p. (Orig.). 1984. pap. 5.95 (ISBN 0-8028-1981-8). Eerdmans.

Johannine Epistles. J. L. Houlden. LC 74-4634. (New Testament Commentary Ser.). 176p. 1974. 10.95 (ISBN 0-06-064020-0, HarpR). Har-Row.

Johannine Epistles. Pheme Perkins. (New Testament Ser.: Vol. 21). 120p. 1980. 10.95 (ISBN 0-89453-209-X); pap. 6.95 (ISBN 0-89453-144-1). M Glazier.

Johannine Hymnal. Joseph Cirou et al. LC 75-14542. (Melody ed). 1970. 3.95 (ISBN 0-915866-00-5). Am Cath Pr.

Johannine Polemic: The Role of Tradition & Theology. Rodney A. Whitacre. LC 82-5457. (SBL Dissertation Ser.). 292p. 1982. pap. 13.00 (ISBN 0-89130-579-3, 06-01-67). Scholars Pr GA.

Johannine School: An Evaluation of the Johannine-School Hypothesis Based on an Investigation of the Nature of Ancient Schools. R. Alan Culpepper. LC 75-34235. (Society of Biblical Literature. Dissertation Ser.: No. 26). Repr. of 1975 ed. 62.40 (ISBN 0-8357-9576-4, 2017525). Bks Demand UMI.

Johannine Writings & Other Epistles. E. Ridley Lewis. (London Divinity Ser). 144p. 1961. 3.95 (ISBN 0-227-67663-7). Attic Pr.

John, Vol. IV. Beacon Bible Commentary Staff. 6.95 (ISBN 0-8010-0777-1). Baker Bk.

John. rev. ed. G. Michael Cocoris. 181p. 1985. pap. text ed. 3.00 (ISBN 0-935729-07-0). Church Open Door.

John. Fred B. Craddock. Ed. by John H. Hayes. LC 82-48095. (Knox Preaching Guides Ser.). 149p. 1982. pap. 6.95. John Knox.

John. Floyd V. Filson. LC 59-10454. (Layman's Bible Commentary Ser: Vol. 19). 1963. pap. 4.95 (ISBN 0-8042-3079-X). John Knox.

John. Lewis Foster. (Standard Bible Studies). (Illus.). 272p. 1987. pap. price not set (ISBN 0-87403-164-8, 40104). Standard Pub.

John. William Hendriksen. (New Testament Commentary Ser.). 1961. 24.95 (ISBN 0-8010-4051-5). Baker Bk.

John. Giles Hibbert et al. LC 71-173033. (Scripture Discussion Commentary Ser.: Pt. 9). 256p. 1972. pap. text ed. 4.50 (ISBN 0-87946-008-3). ACTA Found.

John. J. R. Hill. (Bible Study Commentaries Ser.). 112p. 1980. pap. 4.95 (ISBN 0-87508-169-X). Chr Lit.
John. George Hutcheson. (Geneva Commentary Ser.). 448p. 1985. Repr. of 1657 ed. 17.95 (ISBN 0-85151-155-4). Banner of Truth.
John. Irving L. Jensen. (Bible Self-Study Guide). 1970. pap. 3.25 (ISBN 0-8024-1043-X). Moody.
John. Irving L. Jensen. (Irving Jensen's Do-It-Yourself Bible Study Ser.). 160p. (Orig.). 1983. wkbk. 5.95 (ISBN 0-89840-051-1). Heres Life.
John. (Erdmans Commentaries Ser.). 4.50 (ISBN 0-8010-3400-0). Baker Bk.
John. James McPolin. (New Testament Message Ser.: Vol. 6). 244p. 1979. 14.95 (ISBN 0-89453-194-8); pap. 9.95 (ISBN 0-89453-129-8). M Glazier.
John. Mark Plunkett. (Standard Bible Study Workbooks Ser.). 80p. 1987. wkbk. 1.95 (ISBN 0-87403-184-2, 40204). Standard Pub.
John. 2nd, rev., & enl. ed. D. Moody Smith. Ed. by Gerhard Krodel. LC 75-13046. (Proclamation Commentaries: The New Testament Witnesses for Preaching Ser.). 144p. 1986. pap. 7.95 (ISBN 0-8006-1917-X, 1-1917). Fortress.
John. Guy N. Woods. 1981. 10.95 (ISBN 0-89225-261-8). Gospel Advocate.
John: A Daily Dialogue with God. Whitney Kuniholm. (Personal Bible Studyguide Ser.). 155p. 1982. pap. 4.95 (ISBN 0-87788-431-5). Shaw Pubs.
John: A Good News Commentary. J. Ramsey Michaels. LC 83-47729. (Good News Commentary Ser.). 288p. (Orig.). 1983. pap. 9.95 (ISBN 0-06-065575-5, RD-462, HarpR). Har-Row.
John: A Study Guide. David E. Holwerda. (Revelation Series for Adults). 1977. pap. text ed. 2.50 (ISBN 0-933140-06-1). CRC Pubns.
John: A Study Guide Commentary. Herschel H. Hobbs. 96p. 1973. pap. 4.95 (ISBN 0-310-26113-9). Zondervan.
John: Acts, Vol. VII. Beacon Bible Commentary Staff. 13.95 (ISBN 0-8010-0694-5). Baker Bk.
John Alexander Dowie: A Life of Tragedies & Triumphs. Gordon Lindsay. 1980. 4.95 (ISBN 0-89985-985-2). Christ Nations.
John Allen Moores: Good News in War & Peace. Mary Butler & Trent Butler. LC 85-6656. (Meet the Missionary Ser.). 1985. 5.50 (ISBN 0-8054-4295-2, 4242-95). Broadman.
John Amos Comenius, Bishop of the Moravians, His Life & Educational Works. Simon S. Laurie. LC 72-10020. (Illus.). 272p. 1973. Repr. of 1893 ed. 21.00 (ISBN 0-8337-2028-7). B Franklin.
John: An Access Guide for Scripture Study. Peter F. Ellis & Judith M. Ellis. 174p. 1983. pap. 3.95 (ISBN 0-8215-5936-2); leader's guide 3.25 (ISBN 0-8215-5918-4). Sadlier.
John & Charles Wesley. Samuel J. Rogal. (English Authors Ser.: No. 368). 197p. 1983. lib. bdg. 16.95 (ISBN 0-8057-6854-8, Twayne). G K Hall.
John & Charles Wesley: Selected Writings & Hymns. Ed. by Frank Whaling. LC 81-82207. 432p. 1981. 13.95 (ISBN 0-8091-0318-4); pap. 10.95. Paulist Pr.
John & Jude, Epistles. H. A. Ironside. 9.95 (ISBN 0-87213-372-9). Loizeaux.
John & One John. Chip Ricks. 1982. pap. 2.50 (ISBN 0-8423-1890-9). Tyndale.
John-Apostle of Love. Earl McQuay. LC 81-70774. (Chosen Messenger Ser.). 128p. (Orig.). 1982. pap. text ed. 3.50 (ISBN 0-89636-080-6). Accent Bks.
John Bale. facs. ed. Jesse W. Harris. LC 72-119958. (Select Bibliographies Reprint Ser). 1940. 17.00 (ISBN 0-8369-5401-7). Ayer Co Pubs.
John Bale. Jesse W. Harris. LC 73-12898. 1940. Repr. lib. bdg. 20.00 (ISBN 0-8414-4742-X). Folcroft.
John Bale: Dramatist & Antiquary. facsimile ed. Honor C. McCusker. LC 79-148890. (Select Bibliographies Reprint Ser). Repr. of 1942 ed. 17.00 (ISBN 0-8369-5678-8). Ayer Co Pubs.
John Bale: Mythmaker for the English Reformation. Leslie P. Fairfield. LC 75-19953. 250p. 1976. 9.75 (ISBN 0-911198-42-3). Purdue U Pr.
John Baptist Scalabrini: Apostle to Emigrants. Marco Caliaro & Mario Francesconi. Tr. by Alba I. Zizzamia from It. LC 76-44922. (Illus.). 580p. 1977. lib. bdg. 15.00x (ISBN 0-913256-24-2). Ctr Migration.
John: Beloved Apostle. Dorothy Laux. (BibLearn Ser.). (Illus.). 1977. bds. 5.95 (ISBN 0-8054-4234-0, 4242-34). Broadman.
John, Book One. Marilyn Kunz & Catherine Schell. 1978. pap. 2.95 (ISBN 0-8423-1895-X). Tyndale.
John, Book Two. Marilyn Kunz & Catherine Schell. 1979. pap. 2.95 (ISBN 0-8423-1896-8). Tyndale.
John Brown of Haddington. Robert Mackenzie. 1964. pap. 2.95 (ISBN 0-85151-113-9). Banner of Truth.
John Bunyan. Robert B. Coats. LC 77-9277. 1977. lib. bdg. 15.00 (ISBN 0-8414-1804-7). Folcroft.
John Bunyan. Charles H. Firth. LC 74-11062. 1911. lib. bdg. 10.00 (ISBN 0-8414-4212-6). Folcroft.
John Bunyan. Gwilym O. Griffith. 1973. Repr. of 1927 ed. lib. bdg. 20.00 (ISBN 0-8414-4623-7). Folcroft.
John Bunyan. W. H. Hutton. LC 77-24947. Repr. of 1927 ed. lib. bdg. 15.00 (ISBN 0-8414-4861-2). Folcroft.
John Bunyan. Roger Sharrock. LC 84-6728. 163p. 1984. Repr. lib. bdg. 25.00x (ISBN 0-313-24528-2, SHJO). Greenwood.
John Bunyan: Allegory & Imagination. E. Beatrice Batson. LC 83-21341. 168p. 1984. 27.50x (ISBN 0-389-20442-0, 08004). B&N Imports.
John Bunyan: His Life & Times. Richard W. Harding. LC 76-27749. 1976. Repr. of 1928 ed. lib. bdg. 20.00 (ISBN 0-8414-4933-3). Folcroft.
John Bunyan in Relation to His Times. Edmund A. Knox. 1928. lib. bdg. 12.50 (ISBN 0-8414-5598-8). Folcroft.
John Bunyan: Maker of Myths. Jack Lindsay. LC 77-85138. 1969. Repr. of 1937 ed. 25.00x (ISBN 0-678-00523-0). Kelley.
John Bunyan: Maker of Myths. Jack Lindsay. LC 73-86039. 1969. Repr. of 1937 ed. 23.00x (ISBN 0-8046-0623-4, Pub. by Kennikat). Assoc Faculty Pr.
John Bunyan, Pilgrim & Dreamer. William H. Harding. LC 77-9369. 1977. 25.00 (ISBN 0-8414-4782-9). Folcroft.
John Bunyan: Pilgrim's Prayer Book. rev. ed. John Bunyan & Louis G. Parkhurst, Jr. 136p. 1986. pap. 5.95 (ISBN 0-8423-4933-2). Tyndale.
John Bunyan: The Man & His Work. Augustus R. Buckland. LC 76-16025. 1976. Repr. of 1928 ed. lib. bdg. 20.00 (ISBN 0-8414-3319-4). Folcroft.
John Bunyan: The Man & His Works. Henri A. Talon. 1978. lib. bdg. 35.00 (ISBN 0-8495-5114-5). Arden Lib.
John Bunyan: The Man & His Works. Henri A. Talon. 340p. 1980. Repr. of 1951 ed. lib. bdg. 35.00 (ISBN 0-89987-810-5). Darby Bks.
John Bunyan: The Man & His Works. Henri A. Talon. LC 76-8161. 1976. lib. bdg. 47.50 (ISBN 0-8414-8611-5). Folcroft.
John Bunyan, (1628-1688) His Life, Times & Work. John Brown. Ed. by Frank M. Harrison. (Illus.). xxiv, 515p. 1969. Repr. of 1928 ed. 37.50 (ISBN 0-208-00726-1, Archon). Shoe String.
John Calvin. Patricia Fillingham. (Illus.). 42p. 1983. pap. 5.00 (ISBN 0-942292-04-9). Warthog Pr.
John Calvin. T. H. Parker. Ed. by Simon Jenkins. 240p. 1987. pap. 7.95 (ISBN 0-7459-1219-2). Lion USA.
John Calvin. Ed. by G. R. Potter & M. Greengrass. LC 82-23088. (Documents of Modern History Ser.). 180p. 1983. 20.00x (ISBN 0-312-44277-7). St Martin.
John Calvin: A Biography. T. H. Parker. LC 75-33302. (Illus.). 208p. 1976. 10.95 (ISBN 0-664-20810-X). Westminster.
John Calvin: His Life, Letters & Work. Hugh Y. Reyburn. LC 83-45630. Date not set. Repr. of 1914 ed. 45.00 (ISBN 0-404-19847-3). AMS Pr.
John Calvin: Many Sided Genius. Alfred T. Davies. LC 83-45609. Date not set. Repr. of 1947 ed. 18.50 (ISBN 0-404-19827-9). AMS Pr.
John Calvin: Selections from His Writings. Ed. by John Dillenberger. LC 75-26875. (American Academy of Religion. Aids for the Study of Religion). 590p. 1975. pap. 10.95 (ISBN 0-89130-025-2, 010302). Scholars Pr GA.
John Calvin, the Church, & the Eucharist. Kilian McDonnell. LC 65-17149. pap. 105.00 (ISBN 0-317-08461-5, 2010572). Bks Demand UMI.
John Calvin: The Man & His Ethics. Georgia E. Harkness. 1977. lib. bdg. 59.95 (ISBN 0-8490-2106-5). Gordon Pr.
John Calvin: The Man & His Ethics. Georgia E. Harkness. LC 83-45612. Date not set. Repr. of 1931 ed. 32.50 (ISBN 0-404-19830-9). AMS Pr.
John Calvin: The Organiser of Reformed Protestantism, 1509-1564. Williston Walker. Repr. of 1906 ed. 27.50 (ISBN 0-404-06807-3). AMS Pr.
John Calvin Vs. the Westminster Confession. Holmes Rolston, III. LC 75-37422. (Orig.). 1972. pap. 4.95 (ISBN 0-8042-0488-8). John Knox.
John Calvin's Sermons on the Ten Commandments. John Calvin. Ed. by Benjamin W. Farley. 544p. 1980. 12.95 (ISBN 0-8010-2443-9). Baker Bk.
John Calvin's Treatises Against the Anabaptists & Against the Libertines. John Calvin. Tr. by Benjamin W. Farley. 360p. (Orig.). 1982. pap. 16.95 (ISBN 0-8010-2476-5). Baker Bk.
John Cassian. 2nd ed. Owen Chadwick. 1968. 32.50 (ISBN 0-521-04607-6). Cambridge U Pr.
John Cassian: Conferences. John Cassian. Tr. by Colm Luibheid. (Classics of Western Spirituality Ser.). 201p. 1985. 12.95 (ISBN 0-8091-0361-3); pap. 9.95 (ISBN 0-8091-2694-X). Paulist Pr.
John Charles Ryle, Evangelical Bishop. Peter Toon. 5.95 (ISBN 0-685-88379-5). Reiner.
John Checkley, or, Evolution of Religious Tolerance in Massachusetts, 2 vols. Ed. by Edmund F. Slafter & Edmund F. Slafter. (Prince Soc. Pubns: Nos. 22 & 23). 1966. 39.00 (ISBN 0-8337-0553-9). B Franklin.
John Chrysostom: On Virginity; Against Remarriage. Tr. by Sally R. Shore. Elizabeth A. Clark. LC 83-8193. (Studies in Women & Religion: Vol. 9). 200p. 1984. 49.95x (ISBN 0-88946-543-6). E Mellen.
John Clifford: A Fighting Free Churchman. G. W. Byrt. 192p. 1947. Repr. 2.95 (ISBN 0-87921-011-7). Attic Pr.
John Climacus, The Ladder of Divine Ascent. Colm Lubheid. (Classics of Western Spirituality). 224p. pap. 12.95 (ISBN 0-8091-0312-5); pap. 9.95 (ISBN 0-8091-2330-4). Paulist Pr.
John Colet & Marsilio Ficino. Sears R. Jayne. LC 80-17262. (Illus.). 172p. 1980. Repr. of 1963 ed. lib. bdg. 24.75x (ISBN 0-313-22606-7, JACF). Greenwood.
John Colet & the Platonic Tradition. Leland Miles. LC 60-16716. 258p. 1961. 11.95 (ISBN 0-87548-005-5); pap. 6.95 (ISBN 0-87548-006-3). Open Court.
John Colet's Commentary on First Corinthians. John Colet. Ed. & tr. by Bernard O'Kelly. LC 82-12403. (Medieval & Renaissance Texts & Studies: Vol. 21). (Illus.). 352p. 1985. 20.00 (ISBN 0-86698-056-3). Medieval & Renaissance NY.
John Cotton. Everett H. Emerson. (Twayne's United States Authors Ser). 1965. pap. 8.95x (ISBN 0-8084-0180-7, T80, Twayne). New Coll U Pr.
John de la Rochelle: Eleven Marian Sermons. Ed. by Kilian F. Lynch. (Text Ser). 1961. 7.00 (ISBN 0-686-11557-0). Franciscan Inst.
John Donne in Meditation: The Anniversaries. Louis L. Martz. LC 70-99172. (English Literature Ser., No. 33). 1970. Repr. of 1947 ed. lib. bdg. 39.95x (ISBN 0-8383-0335-8). Haskell.
John Donne: Life, Mind & Art. John Carey. 1981. 25.00x (ISBN 0-19-520242-2). Oxford U Pr.
John Donne: Preacher. William R. Mueller. 1977. Repr. of 1962 ed. lib. bdg. 19.50x (ISBN 0-374-95988-9, Octagon). Hippocrene Bks.
John Donne Since 1900: A Bibliography of Periodical Articles. William White. LC 77-25861. 1942. lib. bdg. 17.50 (ISBN 0-8414-9557-2). Folcroft.
John Donne: Sometime Dean of St. Paul's AD 1621-1631. Augustus Jessopp. LC 71-39284. (English Biography Ser. 31). 238p. 1972. Repr. of 1897 ed. lib. bdg. 49.95x (ISBN 0-8383-1395-7). Haskell.
John Donne's Biathanatos: A Modern-Spelling Critical Edition. Ed. by Margaret Battin & Michael Rudick. (Garland English Texts Ser.). 1982. lib. bdg. 55.00 (ISBN 0-8240-9481-6). Garland Pub.
John Donne's Christian Vocation. Robert Jackson. 1970. 19.95 (ISBN 0-8101-0289-7). Northwestern U Pr.
John Donne's Sermons on the Psalms & Gospels: With a Selection of Prayers & Meditations. John Donne. Ed. & intro. by Evelyn M. Simpson. LC 63-16249. 1963. pap. 7.95 (ISBN 0-520-00340-3, CAL84). U of Cal Pr.
John Doyle Lee: Zealot, Pioneer Builder, Scapegoat. Juanita Brooks. LC 84-12849. 406p. 1984. pap. 12.50 (ISBN 0-935704-21-3). Howe Brothers.
John Duns Scotus: God & Creatures; the Quodlibetal Questions. Tr. by Felix Alluntis & Allan B. Wolter. LC 80-28098. Orig. Title: Quaestiones Quodlibetales. (Illus.). 548p. pap. 16.95x (ISBN 0-8132-0557-3). Cath U Pr.
John Duns Scotus: Reason & Revelation. (Franciscan Educational Conferences Ser). 1976. pap. 0.75 (ISBN 0-685-77549-6). Franciscan Herald.
John Duns Scotus, Twelve Sixty Five-Nineteen Sixty Five. John K. Ryan. Ed. by Bernardine M. Bonansea. LC 61-66336. (Studies in Philosophy & the History of Philosophy Ser.: Vol. 3). pap. 98.00 (ISBN 0-317-08040-7, 2022584). Bks Demand UMI.
John Elias: Life & Letters. Edward Morgan. 1973. 13.95 (ISBN 0-85151-174-0). Banner of Truth.
John: Evangelist & Interpreter. Stephen S. Smalley. 285p. 1983. cancelled; pap. 10.95 (ISBN 0-85364-345-8). Attic Pr.
John: Eyewitness. Gladys Hunt. LC 70-158130. (Fisherman Bible Studyguide Ser.). 87p. 1971. pap. 2.95 saddle stitch (ISBN 0-87788-245-2). Shaw Pubs.
John Foxe & His Book. James F. Mozley. LC 76-120651. 1970. Repr. of 1940 ed. lib. bdg. 18.50x (ISBN 0-374-95977-3, Octagon). Hippocrene Bks.
John Foxe & the Elizabethan Church. V. Norskov Olsen. 1973. 38.50x (ISBN 0-520-02075-8). U of Cal Pr.
John Fred Craddock. Ed. by John Hayes. (Knox Preaching Guide Ser.). 1983. pap. 6.95 (ISBN 0-8042-3236-9). John Knox.
John G. Lake: Apostle to Africa. Gordon Lindsay. 1.75 (ISBN 0-89985-011-1). Christ Nations.
John G. Lake: Sermons on Dominion over Demons, Disease, & Death. Gordon Lindsay. (Divine Healing & Health Ser.). 3.50 (ISBN 0-89985-028-6). Christ Nations.
John Gerson: Reformer & Mystic. J. L. Connolly. (Medieval Studies Ser.). (Illus.). Repr. of 1928 ed. lib. bdg. 44.00x (ISBN 0-697-00031-1). Irvington.
John: Gospel of Light & Life. rev. & expanded ed. Don W. Hillis. (Teach Yourself the Bible Ser.). Date not set. pap. 2.75 (ISBN 0-8024-4375-3). Moody.
John Greenleaf Whittier: His Life, Genius & Writings. Kennedy W. Sloane. 373p. 1982. Repr. of 1903 ed. lib. bdg. 25.00 (ISBN 0-89760-432-6). Telegraph Bks.
John Henry Newman. 2nd ed. Charles S. Dessain. 1971. 17.50x (ISBN 0-8047-0778-2). Stanford U Pr.
John Henry Newman. John Moody. 1946. Repr. 20.00 (ISBN 0-8482-5070-2). Norwood Edns.
John Henry Newman: A Bibliograhical Catalogue of His Writings. Vincent F. Blehl. LC 77-12141. 148p. 1978. 20.00x (ISBN 0-8139-0738-1). U Pr of Va.
John Henry Newman: An Annotated Bibliography of His Tract & Pamphlet Collection. James D. Earnest & Gerard Tracey. LC 84-48069. (Reference Library of Social Science). 600p. 1984. lib. bdg. 78.00 (ISBN 0-8240-8958-8). Garland pub.
John Henry Newman: His Inner Life. Zeno Capuchin. LC 86-81424. 340p. (Orig.). 1987. 29.95 (ISBN 0-89870-149-X); pap. 12.95 (ISBN 0-89870-112-0). Ignatius Pr.
John Henry Newman: His Life & Work. Brian W. Martin. (Illus.). 1982. 22.50x (ISBN 0-19-520387-9). Oxford U Pr.
John Henry Newman, 1801-1890: A Preliminary Register of Editions from 1818 to 1890. Compiled by Robert D. Allenson. 1976. pap. text ed. 5.00x (ISBN 0-8401-0050-7, Aleph Pr). A R Allenson.
John Heyl Vincent: A Biographical Sketch. facs. ed. Leon H. Vincent. LC 71-124263. (Select Bibliographies Reprint Ser). 1925. 18.00 (ISBN 0-8369-5451-3). Ayer Co Pubs.
John Humphrey Noyes: The Putney Community. Ed. by George W. Noyes. (Illus.). 1931. 30.00x (ISBN 0-8156-8059-7). Syracuse U Pr.
John Hus: A Biography. Matthew Spinka. LC 78-14366. (Illus.). 1978. Repr. of 1968 ed. lib. bdg. 37.50 (ISBN 0-313-21050-0, SPJH). Greenwood.
John Huss. D. S. Schaff. 59.95 (ISBN 0-8490-0451-9). Gordon Pr.
John Hyde. Francis McGaw. 64p. 1986. pap. 3.50. Bethany Hse.
John I, II, III: Twenty-Six Daily Bible Studies. David Jeremiah. (Steps to Higher Ground Ser.). 1983. pap. 1.95 (ISBN 0-86508-206-5). BCM Intl Inc.
John J. Zubly: Colonial Georgia Minister. Roger A. Martin. 25.00 (ISBN 0-405-14095-9). Ayer Co Pubs.
John Jasper: Negro Philosopher & Preacher. W. Hatcher. 59.95 (ISBN 0-8490-0452-7). Gordon Pr.
John Jasper, the Unmatched Negro Philosopher & Preacher. William E. Hatcher. LC 71-88413. Repr. of 1908 ed. 22.50x (ISBN 0-8371-1842-5, HAJ&, Pub. by Negro U Pr). Greenwood.
John Jewel & the Problem of Doctrinal Authority. Wyndham M. Southgate. LC 62-9430. (Historical Monographs: No. 49). (Illus.). 1962. 16.50x (ISBN 0-674-47750-2). Harvard U Pr.
John Keble. Walter Lock. 1977. Repr. of 1895 ed. lib. bdg. 20.00 (ISBN 0-8495-3221-3). Arden Lib.
John Keble. Walter Lock. 1895. Repr. 20.00 (ISBN 0-8274-2626-7). R West.
John Keble: An Essay on the Author of the 'Christian Year' J. C. Shairp. 1866. Repr. 15.00 (ISBN 0-8274-3919-9). R West.
John Keble: Leaders of the Church 1800-1900. Edward L. Wood. Ed. by George W. Russell. 1909. Repr. 25.00 (ISBN 0-8274-2627-5). R West.

John Keble: Priest, Professor & Poet. Brian W. Martin. 191p. 1976. 25.00 (ISBN 0-85664-381-5, Pub. by Croom Helm Ltd). Methuen Inc.
John Keble, Saint of Anglicanism. John R. Griffin. 128p. 1987. 24.95 (ISBN 0-86554-249-X). Mercer Univ Pr.
John Knox. Marion Harland. 1900. 25.00 (ISBN 0-686-19912-X). Quaker City.
John Knox. A. Taylor Innes. 1978. Repr. of 1896 ed. lib. bdg. 17.50 (ISBN 0-8414-5057-9). Folcroft.
John Knox. G. R. Pearce. 1936. Repr. 25.00 (ISBN 0-8274-3855-9). R West.
John Knox: Apostle of the Scottish Reformation. G. Barnett Smith & Dorothy Martin. LC 82-12608. (Golden Oldies Ser.). 128p. 1982. pap. 3.95 (ISBN 0-8024-4354-0). Moody.
John Knox: Historia of the Reformation in Scotland. Ralph S. Walker. 72p. 1985. 22.00x (ISBN 0-85411-021-6, Pub. by Saltire Soc.). State Mutual Bk.
John Knox: Portrait of a Calvinist. facsimile ed. Edwin Muir. LC 76-148892. (Select Bibliographies Reprint Ser). Repr. of 1929 ed. 21.00 (ISBN 0-8369-5656-7). Ayer Co Pubs.
John Knox: Portrait of a Calvinist. Edwin Muir. 1978. Repr. of 1930 ed. lib. bdg. 30.00 (ISBN 0-8414-6246-1). Folcroft.
John Knox: Portrait of a Calvinist. Edwin Muir. LC 78-159096. 1971. Repr. of 1929 ed. 28.00x (ISBN 0-8046-1639-6, Pub. by Kennikat). Assoc Faculty Pr.
John Knox: The Hero of the Scottish Reformation. Henry Cowan. LC 70-133817. (Illus.). Repr. of 1905 ed. 27.50 (ISBN 0-404-01788-6). AMS Pr.
John: Living Eternally. J. Allen Blair. LC 77-28529. 1978. pap. 4.95 (ISBN 0-87213-046-0). Loizeaux.
John Locke's Moral Philosophy. John Colman. 280p. 1982. 27.50x (ISBN 0-85224-445-2, Pub. by Edinburgh U Pr Scotland). Columbia U Pr.
John McCullough: Pioneer Presbyterian Missionary in Texas. William W. McCullough, Jr. (Illus.). 9.50 (ISBN 0-8363-0055-6). Jenkins.
John Masefields Stellung Zum Religiosen. Adelheid Gfollner. Ed. by James Hogg. (Poetic Drama & Poetic Theory). 129p. (Orig.). 1979. pap. 15.00 (ISBN 3-7052-0880-2, Pub. by Salzburg). Longwood Pub Group.
John Milton. W. Grinton Berry. LC 73-10007. 1909. lib. bdg. 17.50 (ISBN 0-8414-3150-7). Folcroft.
John Milton. Ed. by Alan Rudrum. LC 71-127553. (Modern Judgement Ser). 1978. pap. text ed. 2.50 (ISBN 0-87695-100-0). Aurora Pubs.
John Milton. Rex Warner. LC 72-12371. Repr. of 1949 ed. lib. bdg. 12.50 (ISBN 0-8414-9389-8). Folcroft.
John Milton: A Biography. Cyrus R. Edmonds. LC 72-194753. 1851. lib. bdg. 20.00 (ISBN 0-8414-3886-2). Folcroft.
John Milton: A Short Study of His Life & Works. William P. Trent. LC 71-177572. Repr. of 1899 ed. 12.00 (ISBN 0-404-06523-6). AMS Pr.
John Milton: A Short Study of His Life & Work. William P. Trent. LC 72-187004. 1899. lib. bdg. 30.00 (ISBN 0-8414-8430-9). Folcroft.
John Milton & the Transformation of Ancient Epic. Charles Martindale. LC 86-3408. 254p. 1986. 28.50x (ISBN 0-389-20624-5). B&N Imports.
John Milton: His Life & Times, Religious & Political Opinions. Joseph Ivimey. LC 72-190658. 1833. lib. bdg. 37.50 (ISBN 0-8414-5069-2). Folcroft.
John Milton: Poet, Priest & Prophet: A Study of Divine Vocation in Milton's Poetry & Prose. John S. Hill. 233p. 1979. 24.50x (ISBN 0-8476-6124-5). Rowman.
John Milton: Puritan, Patriot, Poet. W. Melville Harris. LC 77-3593. lib. bdg. 5.00 (ISBN 0-8414-4919-8). Folcroft.
John Milton: The Supreme Englishman. H. L. Senior. lib. bdg. 15.50 (ISBN 0-8414-8126-1). Folcroft.
John Milton: 1608-1674. John Cooke. LC 74-5138. 1973. Repr. of 1908 ed. lib. bdg. 10.00 (ISBN 0-8414-3549-9). Folcroft.
John Milton's Epitaphium Damonis. Walter W. Skeat. LC 75-44069. 1933. lib. bdg. 15.00 (ISBN 0-8414-7644-6). Folcroft.
John of Ford: Sermons on the Final Verses of the Song of Songs, IV. Tr. by Wendy M. Beckett from Latin. (Cistercian Fathers Ser.: No. 44). 1983. 24.95 (ISBN 0-87907-644-5). Cistercian Pubns.
John of Ford: Sermons on the Final Verses of the Song of Songs, V (Sermons 62-82) Tr. by Wendy M. Beckett from Latin. (Cistercian Fathers Ser.: No. 45). 1983. 24.95 (ISBN 0-87907-645-3). Cistercian Pubns.
John of Ford: Sermons on the Final Verses of the Song of Songs, Vol. 6. John of Ford. Tr. by Wendy M. Beckett from Latin. (Cistercian Fathers Ser.: No. 46). 26.95 (ISBN 0-87907-646-1). Cistercian Pubns.
John of Ford: Sermons on the Final Verses of the Song of Songs, Vol. 7. John of Ford. Tr. by Wendy M. Beckett from Latin. (Cistercian Fathers Ser.: No. 47). 1985. 26.95 (ISBN 0-87907-647-X). Cistercian Pubns.
John of Ford: Sermons on the Song of Songs I. Tr. by Wendy M. Bechett. LC 77-3697. (Cistercian Fathers Ser.: No. 29). 1977. 14.95 (ISBN 0-87907-629-1). Cistercian Pubns.
John of God: His Place in the History of Psychiatry & Medicine. Ruben D. Rumbaut. LC 77-91668. 1978. pap. 8.00 (ISBN 0-89729-198-0). Ediciones.
John of Paris on Royal & Papal Power: A Translation with Introduction of the de Postestate Regia et Papali of John of Paris. Arthur P. Monahan. LC 73-16302. (Records of Civilation Ser). 197p. 1974. 27.50x (ISBN 0-231-03690-6). Columbia U Pr.
John of Saint Thomas: Outlines of Formal Logic. 2nd ed. Francis C. Wade. (Medieval Philosophical Texts in Translation: No. 8). 1962. pap. 7.95 (ISBN 0-87462-208-5). Marquette.
John of the Cross: Selected Writings. Ed. & intro. by Kiernan Kavanaugh. (Classics of Western Spirituality Ser.: No. 53). 1987. 16.95 (ISBN 0-8091-0384-2); pap. 12.95 (ISBN 0-8091-2839-X). Paulist Pr.
John, One, & James: Neighborhood Bible Study. Marilyn Kunz & Catherine Schell. 1978. pap. 2.95 (ISBN 0-8423-1930-1). Tyndale.
John P. Williamson: A Brother to the Sioux. Winifred W. Barton. LC 80-53176. (Illus.). 308p. 1980. Repr. of 1919 ed. 16.00 (ISBN 0-9610012-0-8). Sunnycrest Pub.
John Paul II: The Pilgrim Pope. Robert W. Douglas. LC 79-24930. (Picture-Story Biographies Ser.). (Illus.). 32p. 1980. PLB 10.60 (ISBN 0-516-03563-0). Childrens.
John Pecham: Tractatus De Perspectiva. Ed. by David C. Lindberg. (Text Ser). 1972. 13.00 (ISBN 0-686-11561-9). Franciscan Inst.
John Ploughman's Pictures. C. H. Spurgeon. 1974. pap. 2.50 (ISBN 0-686-10526-5). Pilgrim Pubns.
John Ploughman's Talk. C. H. Spurgeon. 1975. pap. 2.50 (ISBN 0-686-16833-X). Pilgrim Pubns.
John R. Mott, Eighteen Sixty-Five to Nineteen Fifty-Five: A Biography. C. Howard Hopkins. LC 79-15069. 22.50 (ISBN 0-8028-3525-2). Eerdmans.
John Redford: Organist & Almoner of St. Paul's Cathedral in the Reign of Henry VIII. Carl F. Pfatteicher. LC 74-24184. Repr. of 1934 ed. 24.00 (ISBN 0-404-13088-7). AMS Pr.
John Robinson & the English Separatist Tradition. Timothy F. George. LC 82-14201. (National Association of Baptist Professors of Religion Dissertation Ser.: No. 1). ix, 263p. 1982. text ed. 18.50 (ISBN 0-86554-043-8, MUP-P006). Mercer Univ Pr.
John Robinson & the English Separatist Tradition. Timothy F. George. (Dissertation Ser.: No. 1). ix, 263p. 1982. pap. 18.50 (ISBN 0-86554-043-8). NABPR.
John Ruskin: The Portrait of a Prophet. Peter Quennell. 1973. Repr. of 1949 ed. 35.00 (ISBN 0-8274-0472-7). R West.
John Sergeant: A Forgotten Critic of Descartes & Locke. Norman C. Bradish. 65p. 1929. 6.95 (ISBN 0-87548-363-1). Open Court.
John, Son of Thunder. Ellen G. Traylor. 1980. pap. 4.95 (ISBN 0-8423-1903-4). Tyndale.
John Strachan, Seventeen Hundred Seventy-Eight to Eighteen Hundred Sixty-Seven. John L. Henderson. LC 70-408188. (Canadian Biographical Studies: No. 1). pap. 30.50 (ISBN 0-317-09154-9, 2019176). Bks Demand UMI.
John Sullivan Dwight: A Biography. George W. Cooke. LC 79-90210. (Music Reprint Ser). 1969. Repr. of 1898 ed. 39.50 (ISBN 0-306-71818-9). Da Capo.
John Taverner: Part 1. Ed. by P. C. Buck. (Tudor Church Music Ser.: Vol. 1). 1963. Repr. of 1923 ed. write for info. (ISBN 0-8450-1851-5). Broude.
John Taverner: Part 2. Ed. by P. C. Buck. (Tudor Church Music Ser.: Vol. 3). 1963. Repr. of 1924 ed. 85.00x (ISBN 0-8450-1853-1). Broude.
John Taylor: Mormon Philosopher, Prophet of God. Francis M. Gibbons. LC 84-73532. 312p. 1985. 10.95 (ISBN 0-87747-714-0). Deseret Bk.
John the Baptist. Ronald Klus. (Arch Book Ser.: No. 21). 1984. pap. 0.99 (ISBN 0-570-06189-X, 59-1290). Concordia.
John the Baptist. F. B. Meyer. 1975. pap. 4.50 (ISBN 0-87508-345-5). Chr Lit.
John the Baptist: Forerunner of Jesus. Johnnie Human. (BibLearn Ser.). (Illus.). 1978. 5.95 (ISBN 0-8054-4240-5, 4242-40). Broadman.
John: The Different Gospel... A Reflective Commentary. Michael J. Taylor. LC 83-15485. 269p. 1983. pap. 9.95 (ISBN 0-8189-0456-9). Alba.
John: The Gospel of Belief. Merrill C. Tenney. 1948. 14.95 (ISBN 0-8028-3252-0). Eerdmans.
John: The Gospel of Faith. Everett F. Harrison. (Everyman's Bible Commentary Ser.). 1967. pap. 5.95 (ISBN 0-8024-2043-5). Moody.
John: The Gospel of Life. Oliver Trimiew, Jr. (Orig.). 1987. pap. text ed. 4.95 (ISBN 0-940955-00-8); tchr's. ed. 3.95 (ISBN 0-940955-01-6). Urban Ministries.
John: The Gospel of Life. D. George Vanderlip. 1979. pap. 5.95 (ISBN 0-8170-0826-8). Judson.
John: The Martyr's Gospel. Paul S. Minear. 192p. (Orig.). 1985. pap. 8.95 (ISBN 0-8298-0718-7). Pilgrim NY.
John, the Maverick Gospel. Robert Kysar. LC 76-12393. (Biblical Foundations Ser.). 1976. pap. 7.95 (ISBN 0-8042-0302-4). John Knox.
John Toland & the Deist Controversy: A Study in Adaptations. Robert E. Sullivan. LC 81-7137. (Harvard Historical Studies: 101). (Illus.). 384p. 1982. text ed. 27.50x (ISBN 0-674-48050-3). Harvard U Pr.
John Tucker Daland House. Bryant F. Tolles, Jr. LC 76-27382. (Historic House Booklet Ser.). 1978. 2.00 (ISBN 0-88389-065-8). Essex Inst.
John Twenty Third: Simpleton or Saint. Giacomo Lecaro. 1968. 3.50 (ISBN 0-8199-0055-9, L38351). Franciscan Herald.
John Updike & the Three Great Secret Things: Sex, Religion & Art. George W. Hunt. LC 80-23796. pap. 60.50 (ISBN 0-317-20577-3, 2023218). Bks Demand UMI.
John Webster: Politics & Tragedy. Robert P. Griffin. Ed. by James Hogg. (Jacobean Drama Studies). 179p. (Orig.). 1972. pap. 15.00 (ISBN 3-7052-0311-8, Pub. by Salzburg Studies). Longwood Pub Group.
John Wesley. Stanley Ayling. 1983. 16.95 (ISBN 0-687-20376-7). Abingdon.
John Wesley. Bonamy Dobree. LC 74-7428. 1973. lib. bdg. 17.50 (ISBN 0-8414-3739-4). Folcroft.
John Wesley. May McNeer & Lynd Ward. 1957. pap. 3.95 (ISBN 0-687-20430-5). Abingdon.
John Wesley. Basil Miller. 144p. 1969. pap. 3.50 (ISBN 0-87123-272-3, 200272). Bethany Hse.
John Wesley. Ed. by Albert Outler. 1964. pap. 13.95 (ISBN 0-19-502810-4). Oxford U Pr.
John Wesley. John Vickers. (Ladybird Ser.). 1977. 2.50 (ISBN 0-87508-841-4). Chr Lit.
John Wesley. C. E. Vulliamy. (Heroes of the Faith Ser.). 359p. 1985. Repr. 6.95 (ISBN 0-916441-14-8). Barbour & Co.
John Wesley: A Blueprint for Church Renewal. Blaine Taylor. 221p. (Orig.). 1984. pap. 10.00 (ISBN 0-914527-19-3). C-Four Res.
John Wesley: A Portrait. Abram Lipsky. LC 76-155619. Repr. of 1928 ed. 20.50 (ISBN 0-404-03994-4). AMS Pr.
John Wesley & Authority: A Psychological Perspective. Robert L. Moore. LC 79-13709. (American Academy of Religion. Dissertation Ser.: No. 29). 1979. 14.00 (ISBN 0-89130-290-5, 010129); pap. 9.95 (ISBN 0-89130-291-3). Scholars Pr GA.
John Wesley & the Methodists. Cyril Davey. 49p. (Orig.). 1986. 6.95 (ISBN 0-687-20434-8). Abingdon.
John Wesley As a Social Reformer. facsimile ed. D. D. Thompson. LC 70-164396. (Black Heritage Library Collection). Repr. of 1898 ed. 12.25 (ISBN 0-8369-8855-8). Ayer Co Pubs.
John Wesley: His Life & Theology. Robert G. Tuttle, Jr. 368p. 1982. pap. 9.95 (ISBN 0-310-36661-5, 11260P). Zondervan.
John Wesley, His Way of Knowing God. Robert O. Reddish, Jr. 1972. soft cover 4.00 (ISBN 0-686-08730-5). Rorge Pub Co.
John Wesley North & the Reform Frontier. Merlin Stonehouse. LC 65-15075. pap. 73.00 (ISBN 0-317-29473-3, 2055921). Bks Demand UMI.
John Wesley on the Sacraments. Ole E. Borgen. 312p. 1986. pap. 12.95 (ISBN 0-310-75191-8, 17085P). Zondervan.
John Wesley the Soul Winner. pap. 4.95 (ISBN 0-686-27010-X). Schmul Pub Co.
John Wesley's England: A Nineteenth Century Pictorial History Based on an 18th Century Journal. Ed. by Richard Bewes. (Illus.). 128p. (Orig.). 1981. pap. 9.95 (ISBN 0-8164-2319-9, HarpR). Har-Row.
John Wesley's Fifty-Three Sermons. 800p. 1983. stamped, flexible bdg. 17.95 (ISBN 0-687-20493-3). Abingdon.
John Wesley's Message for Today. Steve Harper. Ed. by Ben Chapman. 1983. pap. 4.95 (ISBN 0-310-45711-4, 12382P). Zondervan.
John Wesley's Theology: A Collection from His Works. Ed. by Robert W. Burtner & Robert E. Chiles. 304p. 1982. pap. 7.95 (ISBN 0-687-20529-8). Abingdon.
John Wesley's Theology Today. Colin W. Williams. LC 60-5238. 256p. 1983. pap. 9.95 (ISBN 0-687-20531-X). Abingdon.
John Wheatley, Catholic Socialism, & Irish Labour in the West of Scotland, 1906-1924. Gerry C. Gunnin. Ed. by William H. McNeil & Peter Stansky. (Modern European History Ser.). 375p. 1987. lib. bdg. 55.00 (ISBN 0-8240-7811-X). Garland Pub.
John Wheelwright: His Writings, Including His Fast-Day Sermon, 1637. John Wheelwright. 1966. 24.00 (ISBN 0-8337-3763-5). B Franklin.
John Wheelwright's Writings, Including His Fast-Day Sermon, 1637, & His Mercurius Americanus, 1645. facs. ed. John Wheelwright. LC 70-128897. (Select Bibliographies Reprint Ser). 1876. 18.00 (ISBN 0-8369-5517-X). Ayer Co Pubs.
John Wilkins, Sixteen Fourteen to Sixteen Seventy-Two: An Intellectual Biography. Barbara J. Shapiro. LC 73-84042. 1969. 40.00x (ISBN 0-520-01396-4). U of Cal Pr.
John Woolman. Paul Rosenblatt. (Great American Thinkers Ser.). 1969. lib. bdg. 17.95 (ISBN 0-89197-813-5). Irvington.
John Woolman & the Twentieth Century. Reginald Reynolds. 1983. pap. 2.50x (ISBN 0-87574-096-0, 096). Pendle Hill.
John Wycliffe. Lewis Sergeant. LC 73-14468. (Heroes of the Nations Ser.). Repr. of 1893 ed. 30.00 (ISBN 0-404-58286-9). AMS Pr.
John Wycliffe & His English Precursors. Gotthard V. Lechler. LC 78-63197. (Heresies of the Early Christian & Medieval Era: Second Ser.). Repr. of 1884 ed. 49.50 (ISBN 0-404-16235-5). AMS Pr.
John Wycliffe & Reform. John Stacey. LC 78-63199. (Heresies of the Early Christian & Medieval Era: Second Ser.). 1979. Repr. of 1964 ed. 24.50 (ISBN 0-404-16239-8). AMS Pr.
John Wycliffe: Last of the Schoolmen & First of the Reformers. Sergeant Lewis. 1978. Repr. of 1892 ed. lib. bdg. 25.00 (ISBN 0-8492-8060-5). R West.
John Wycliffe: Last of the Schoolmen & First of the English Reformers. Lewis Seargent. 1908. 30.00 (ISBN 0-8274-2629-1). R West.
John Wycliffe: Patriot & Reformer. Life & Writings. Rudolf Buddensieg. 1979. Repr. of 1884 ed. lib. bdg. 40.00 (ISBN 0-8495-0535-6). Arden Lib.
John XXII & Papal Taching Authority. James Heft. (Texts & Studies in Religion: Vol. 27). 282p. 1986. lib. bdg. 49.95x (ISBN 0-88946-815-X). E Mellen.
John Zizka & the Hussite Revolution. Frederick G. Heymann. LC 71-77671. (Illus.). 1969. Repr. of 1955 ed. 17.50x (ISBN 0-8462-1344-3). Russell.
John's Magic: John Bosco. Dolores Ready. LC 77-86595. (Stories About Christian Heroes). (Illus.). 1977. pap. 1.95 (ISBN 0-86683-765-5, HarpR). Har-Row.
John's Story of Jesus. Robert Kysar. LC 83-16537. 96p. 1984. pap. 4.50 (ISBN 0-8006-1775-4, 1-1775). Fortress.
John's Wonderful Gospel. Ivor Powell. LC 83-16192. 448p. 1983. 16.95 (ISBN 0-8254-3514-5). Kregel.
Johnson: Selected Writings. Samuel Johnson. Ed. by Patrick Cruttwell. 1982. pap. 6.95 (ISBN 0-14-043033-4). Penguin.
Joining the Army That Sheds No Blood. Susan C. Steiner. LC 82-81510. (Christian Peace Shelf Ser.). 176p. (Orig.). 1982. pap. 6.95 (ISBN 0-8361-3305-6). Herald Pr.
Joining the Club: A History of Jews & Yale. Dan A. Oren. LC 85-14252. (Yale Scene, University Ser.: No. 4). 448p. 1986. 29.95x (ISBN 0-300-03330-3). Yale U Pr.
Joining the Conversation: Jesus, Matthew, Luke & Us. Barbara Hall. LC 84-72480. (Parish Life Sourcebooks: Vol. 1). 103p. (Orig.). 1985. pap. 6.95 (ISBN 0-936384-25-5). Cowley Pubns.
Joint & Visible Fellowship. Beatrice S. Snell. LC 65-19207. (Orig.). 1965. pap. 2.50x (ISBN 0-87574-140-1). Pendle Hill.
Joint Heirs in Christ. Darlene Loomis. (Illus., Orig.). 1977. pap. 2.00 (ISBN 0-686-36277-2). Drain Enterprise.
Joke of Christianizing China. B. W. Williams. 40p. 1983. pap. 3.00 (ISBN 0-910309-13-2). Am Atheist.
Jon & the Little Lost Lamb. Jane Latourette & Betty Wind. LC 65-15145. (Arch Bks: Set 2). 1965. pap. 0.99 (ISBN 0-570-06008-7, 59-1106). Concordia.
Jonah. Allen Artos. 52p. (Orig.). 1984. cancelled 10.00 (ISBN 0-934852-00-6); pap. 3.50 (ISBN 0-934852-24-3). Lorien Hse.
Jonah. Samuel C. Burn. 1981. lib. bdg. 11.25 (ISBN 0-86524-071-X, 3201). Klock & Klock.
Jonah. G. Michael Cocoris. 74p. 1986. pap. text ed. 2.00 (ISBN 0-935729-32-1). Church Open Door.
Jonah. Rebecca Daniel. (Our Greatest Heritage Ser.). (Illus.). 32p. 1983. wkbk. 3.95 (ISBN 0-86653-141-6, SS 810). Good Apple.

Jonah. (Burl Ives Bible-Time Stories). incl. tape 4.95 (ISBN 0-89191-799-3, 97998). Cook.

Jonah. LC 76-11275. (Sunshine Bks). (Illus.). 20p. 1976. pap. 1.50 (ISBN 0-8006-1577-8, 1-1577). Fortress.

Jonah. Hugh Martin. (Geneva Series Commentaries). 1978. 12.95 (ISBN 0-85151-115-5). Banner of Truth.

Jonah: A Bible Study Commentary. John H. Walton. 80p. (Orig.). 1982. pap. 3.95 (ISBN 0-310-36303-9, 11616P). Zondervan.

Jonah & the Big Fish. Sekiya Miyoshi. LC 81-3635. 1982. 8.95g (ISBN 0-687-20541-7). Abingdon.

Jonah & the Big Fish. John Walton & Kim Walton. (Early Bible Foundations Ser.). (Illus.). 1986. pap. 2.95 (ISBN 1-55513-035-6, Chariot Bks). Cook.

Jonah & the Great Fish. Belinda Hollyer. LC 84-50451. (Bible Stories Ser.). (Illus.). 24p. 1984. 5.45 (ISBN 0-382-06792-4); pap. 5.96 (ISBN 0-382-06941-2). Silver.

Jonah & the Great Fish. Warwick Hutton. LC 83-15477. (Illus.). 32p. 1984. 12.95 (ISBN 0-689-50283-4, McElderly Bk). Macmillan.

Jonah & the Great Fish. 2nd ed. Ella K. Lindvall. (People of the Bible Ser.). (Illus.). 1984. 4.95 (ISBN 0-8024-0398-0). Moody.

Jonah & the Whale. Retold by Catherine Storr. LC 82-23023. (People of the Bible). (Illus.). 32p. 1983. PLB 10.65 (ISBN 0-8172-1984-6). Raintree Pubs.

Jonah & the Worm. Jill Briscoe. LC 83-6323. (Illus.). 120p. 1983. 5.95 (ISBN 0-8407-5289-X). Nelson.

Jonah Complex. Andre Lacocque & Pierre Lacocque. LC 80-84649. 1981. pap. 8.95 (ISBN 0-8042-0092-0). John Knox.

Jonah, Habakkuk, Malachi: Living Responsibly. Margaret Fromer & Sharrel Keyes. (Fisherman Bible Studyguide Ser.). 68p. 1982. saddle-stitch 2.95 (ISBN 0-87788-432-3). Shaw Pubs.

Jonah: His Life & Mission. Thomas Kirk. 344p. 1983. lib. bdg. 12.95 (ISBN 0-86524-166-X, 3202). Klock & Klock.

Jonah Legend: A Suggestion of Interpretation. William Simpson. LC 72-177422. (Illus.). vi, 182p. 1971. Repr. of 1899 ed. 35.00x (ISBN 0-8103-3820-3). Gale.

Jonah: Living Obediently. J. Allen Blair. LC 63-18265. 1963. pap. 3.95 (ISBN 0-87213-050-9). Loizeaux.

Jonah-Nahum. John R. Kohlenberger, III. (Everyman's Bible Commentary Ser.). (Orig.). 1984. pap. 5.95 (ISBN 0-8024-0352-2). Moody.

Jonah, Speak for God. Charlotte Graeber. (Speak for Me Ser.). (Illus.). 24p. 1986. 3.95 (ISBN 0-8407-6702-1). Nelson.

Jonah: The Spirituality of a Reluctant Prophet. Roman Ginn. (Orig.). pap. 2.95 (ISBN 0-914544-21-7). Living Flame Pr.

Jonah, Tobit, Judith. Irene Nowell. (Collegeville Bible Commentary: Old Testament Ser.: Vol. 25). 112p. 1986. pap. 2.95 (ISBN 0-8146-1481-7). Liturgical Pr.

Jonathan Edwards. Clarence H. Faust & Thomas H. Johnson. 1981. Repr. of 1935 ed. lib. bdg. 40.00 (ISBN 0-89760-234-X). Telegraph Bks.

Jonathan Edwards. Edward M. Griffin. (Pamphlets on American Writers Ser: No. 97). (Orig.). 1971. pap. 1.25x (ISBN 0-8166-0601-3, MPAW97). U of Minn Pr.

Jonathan Edwards. Arhtur C. McGiffert. LC 75-3134. (Philosophy of American Ser.). Repr. of 1932 ed. 28.00 (ISBN 0-404-59143-4). AMS Pr.

Jonathan Edwards. Perry Miller. LC 72-7877. (American Men of Letters Ser.). (Illus.). 348p. 1973. Repr. of 1949 ed. lib. bdg. 25.00x (ISBN 0-8371-6551-2, MIJE). Greenwood.

Jonathan Edwards. Perry Miller. LC 81-4496. (New England Writers Ser.). 384p. 1981. pap. text ed. 11.95x (ISBN 0-87023-328-9). U of Mass Pr.

Jonathan Edwards: His Life & Influence. Conrad Cherry et al. Ed. by Charles Angoff. LC 74-4516. (Leverton Lecture Series II). 65p. 1975. 9.50 (ISBN 0-8386-1571-6). Fairleigh Dickinson.

Jonathan Edwards Jr. Works, 2 vols. Bruce Kuklick. (American Religious Thought of the 18th & 19th Centuries Ser.). 1114p. 1987. Set. lib. bdg. 145.00 (ISBN 0-8240-6953-6). Garland Pub.

Jonathan Edward's Moral Thought & Its British Context. Norman Fiering. LC 80-26755. (Institute of Early American History & Culture Ser.). xi, 391p. 1981. 32.50x (ISBN 0-8078-1473-3). U of NC Pr.

Jonathan Edwards on Evangelism. Ed. by Carl J. Wolf. LC 81-2266. xii, 137p. 1981. Repr. of 1958 ed. lib. bdg. 22.50x (ISBN 0-8371-6588-1, EDOE). Greenwood.

Jonathan Edwards on Nature & Destiny: A Systematic Analysis. Paula M. Cooey. LC 85-21499. (Studies in American Religion: Vol. 16). 296p. 1985. lib. bdg. 49.95x (ISBN 0-88946-660-2). E Mellen.

Jonathan Edwards: On Revival. 1984. pap. 5.45 (ISBN 0-85151-431-6). Banner of Truth.

Jonathan Edwards, Pastor: Religion & Society in Eighteenth-Century Northampton. Patricia Tracy. (American Century Ser.). 288p. 1980. 14.95 (ISBN 0-8090-6195-3); pap. 5.95 (ISBN 0-8090-0149-7). Hill & Wang.

Jonathan Edwards, Seventeen Fifty-Six to Nineteen Seventy-Eight: Bibliographical Synopses. Nancy Manspeaker. LC 81-9491. (Studies in American Religion: Vol. 3). (Illus.). xviii, 278p. 1981. 49.95x (ISBN 0-88946-907-5). E Mellen.

Jonathan Edwards: Seventeen Three to Seventeen Fifty-Eight. Alexander Allen. lib. bdg. 23.50 (ISBN 0-8337-3926-3). B Franklin.

Jonathan Edwards, the Fiery Puritan. Henry B. Parkes. LC 75-3135. Repr. of 1930 ed. 30.00 (ISBN 0-404-59144-2). AMS Pr.

Jonathan Edwards: The Narrative of a Puritan Mind. Edward H. Davidson. LC 68-7254. pap. 43.80 (ISBN 0-317-07848-8, 2005489). Bks Demand UMI.

Jonathan Edwards to Aaron Burr, Jr. From Great Awakening to Democratic Politics. Suzanne B. Geissler. LC 81-38353. (Studies in American Religion: Vol. 1). xii, 298p. 1981. 49.95x (ISBN 0-88946-906-7). E Mellen.

Jonathan Goforth. Rosalind Goforth. (Men of Faith Ser.). 3.95 (ISBN 0-87123-842-X, 200842). Bethany Hse.

Jonathan Loved David: Homosexuality in Biblical Times. Tom Horner. LC 77-15628. 164p. 1978. pap. 8.95 (ISBN 0-664-24185-9). Westminster.

Jones' Dictionary of Old Testament Proper Names: Keyed to Strong's Numbering System. rev. ed. Alfred Jones. Ed. & frwd. by Gleason L. Archer, Jr. LC 86-3001. 400p. 1988. Repr. of 1856 ed. 24.95 (ISBN 0-8254-2961-7). Kregel.

Jonestown Letters Correspondence of the Moore Family. Rebecca Moore. LC 86-18192. (Studies in American Religion Ser.: Vol. 23). (Illus.). 398p. 1986. lib. bdg. 59.95 (ISBN 0-88946-667-X). E Mellen.

Joni. Joni Eareckson & Joe Musser. 1984. pap. 2.95 (ISBN 0-553-22886-2). Bantam.

Joni. Joni Eareckson & Joe Musser. (Illus.). 256p. 1980. pap. 3.95 (ISBN 0-310-23982-6, 12009P). Zondervan.

Joni. Joni Eareckson & Joe Musser. 1976 (12563L). kivar, large print o.p. 7.95 (ISBN 0-310-23967-2); pap. 6.95 (ISBN 0-310-23961-3, 12005P). Zondervan.

Jordan of Saxony: On the Beginnings of the Order of Preachers. Jordan of Saxony. Ed. & tr. by Simon Tugwell. (Dominican Sources: New Editions in English). 35p. 1982. pap. 4.00 (ISBN 0-9511202-0-4). Parable.

Jordanville: A Portrait of Holy Trinity Monastery. 1985. pap. 5.00 (ISBN 0-317-30449-6). Holy Trinity.

Jornada. Myrna Grant. 208p. 1980. 1.00 (ISBN 0-88113-200-4). Edit Betania.

Joscelyn I, Prince of Edessa. Robert L. Nicholson. LC 78-63352. (Crusades & Military Orders: Second Ser.). 120p. Repr. of 1954 ed. 21.50 (ISBN 0-404-17025-0). AMS Pr.

Joseph. Ethel Barrett. LC 79-65232. (Bible Biography Bible Ser.). 128p. 1979. pap. 1.95 (ISBN 0-8307-0715-8, 5607701). Regal.

Joseph. Rebecca Daniel. (Our Greatest Heritage Ser.). (Illus.). 32p. 1983. wkbk. 3.95 (ISBN 0-86653-134-3, SS 803). Good Apple.

Joseph. 1979. 0.75 (ISBN 0-8198-0583-1). Dghtrs St Paul.

Joseph. Joyce Landorf. 1985. pap. 7.95 (ISBN 0-8007-5197-3, Power Bks.). Revell.

Joseph. Joe Maniscalco. LC 74-28725. (Bible Hero Stories). (Illus.). 48p. (Orig.). 1975. pap. 2.00 (ISBN 0-87239-332-1, 2737). Standard Pub.

Joseph. F. B. Meyer. 1975. pap. 4.50 (ISBN 0-87508-356-0). Chr Lit.

Joseph & His Brethren. Gordon Lindsay. (Old Testament Ser.). 1.25 (ISBN 0-89985-130-4). Christ Nations.

Joseph & His Brothers. Ella K. Lindvall. (People of the Bible Ser.). (Illus.). 1983. 4.95 (ISBN 0-8024-0395-6). Moody.

Joseph & His Brothers. Thomas Mann. (YA) 1948. 35.00 (ISBN 0-394-43132-4). Knopf.

Joseph & His Brothers. Adapted by Philip Steele. LC 85-40308. (Bible Stories Ser.). (Illus.). 24p. 1985. 5.45 (ISBN 0-382-09092-6); PLB 6.96 (ISBN 0-382-09089-6). Silver.

Joseph & His Brothers. Retold by Catherine Storr. LC 82-9087. (People of the Bible). (Illus.). 32p. 1982. PLB 10.65 (ISBN 0-8172-1976-5). Raintree Pubs.

Joseph & Me. Judy Hoffman. 1979. pap. 5.95x (ISBN 0-87068-655-0). Ktav.

Joseph & the Coat of Many Colors. Retold by Pamela Broughton. LC 85-81156. (Golden Bible Stories). (Illus.). 32p. 1986. 3.95 (ISBN 0-307-11627-1, Pub. by Golden Bks). Western Pub.

Joseph & the Coat of Many Colors. Philip Steele. LC 85-40309. (Bible Stories Ser.). (Illus.). 24p. 1985. 5.45 (ISBN 0-382-09091-8); PLB 6.96 (ISBN 0-382-09088-8). Silver.

Joseph & the Famine. As told by Catherine Storr. (People of the Bible Ser.). (Illus.). 32p. 1985. PLB 10.65 (ISBN 0-8172-2038-0). Raintree Pubs.

Joseph & the King. 2nd ed. Ella K. Lindvall. (People of the Bible Ser.). (Illus.). 1984. 4.95 (ISBN 0-8024-0400-6). Moody.

Joseph Campbell on Myth: An Introduction. Robert A. Segal. LC 84-45374. (Reference Library on the Humanities). 125p. 1987. lib. bdg. 18.00 (ISBN 0-8240-8827-1). Garland Pub.

Joseph Conrad's Bible. Dwight H. Purdy. LC 83-40331. 160p. 1984. 16.95x (ISBN 0-8061-1876-8). U of Okla Pr.

Joseph F. Smith. Francis Gibbons. LC 84-70071. (Illus.). 1984. 10.95 (ISBN 0-87747-988-7). Deseret Bk.

Joseph: From Prison to Palace. Gene A. Getz. LC 82-18571. 1983. pap. 5.95 (ISBN 0-8307-0870-7, 5417907). Regal.

Joseph Hall: A Study in Satire & Meditation. Richard A. McCabe. (Illus.). 1982. 72.00x (ISBN 0-19-812807-X). Oxford U Pr.

Joseph Hatch, the Ulcombe Bellfounder. J. Hilton. 1985. 11.25x (ISBN 0-317-54278-8, Pub. by J Richardson UK). State Mutual Bk.

Joseph Ibn Kaspi's Gevia' Kesef: A Study in Medieval Jewish Philosophical Bible Commentary. Basil Herring. 1982. 35.00x (ISBN 0-87068-716-6). Ktav.

Joseph: Non Stop Faith. Sandy Larsen. (Young Fisherman Bible Studyguides). 64p. (Orig.). 1987. pap. 4.95 tchr's. ed. (ISBN 0-87788-438-2); pap. 2.95 student ed. (ISBN 0-87788-437-4). Shaw Pubs.

Joseph of Arimathea: An Easter Play. Thomas J. Hatton. 1980. 4.25 (ISBN 0-89536-417-4, 1013). CSS of Ohio.

Joseph of Nazareth. Federico Suarez. Tr. by Ives Mascarenhas & Patrick Kearns. Tr. of Jose, Esposo de Maria. 222p. (Orig.). 1984. pap. 7.95 (ISBN 0-906138-08-6). Scepter Pubs.

Joseph Smith. Karen D. Merrell. 24p. 4.95 (ISBN 0-87747-561-X). Deseret Bk.

Joseph Smith & the Beginnings of Mormonism. Richard L. Bushman. LC 84-2451. 270p. 1984. 17.95 (ISBN 0-252-01143-0). U of Ill Pr.

Joseph Smith & the Law of Consecration. Lyndon W. Cook. 100p. 1985. 8.95 (ISBN 0-910523-24-X). E B Grandin.

Joseph Smith & the Origins of "The Book of Mormon". David Persuitte. LC 84-42734. (Illus.). 303p. 1985. lib. bdg. 19.95x (ISBN 0-89950-134-6). McFarland & Co.

Joseph Smith & the Restoration: A History of the LDS Church to 1846. rev. ed. Ivan J. Barrett. LC 70-167990. (Illus.). 1973. pap. 9.95 (ISBN 0-8425-0672-1). Brigham.

Joseph Smith & World Government. Hyrum L. Andrus. 144p. 1972. pap. 3.95 (ISBN 0-89036-032-4). Hawkes Pub Inc.

Joseph Smith: The First Mormon. Donna Hill. 552p. 1983. pap. 5.95 (ISBN 0-941214-16-8). Signature Bks.

Joseph Smith's New Translation of the Bible. Ed. by Paul A. Wellington. LC 74-127097. 1970. 16.00 (ISBN 0-8309-0032-2). Herald Hse.

Joseph the Dream Teller: Retold by Catererine Storr. Illus. by Chris Molan. (People of the Bible Ser.). (Illus.). 32p. 1984. 10.65 (ISBN 0-8172-1989-7, Raintree Children's Books Belitha Press Ltd. - London). Raintree Pubs.

Joseph the Dreamer & Five Other Stories. Peter Enns & Glen Forsberg. (Stories that Live Ser.: Bk. 2). (Illus.). 24p. 1985. book & cassette 4.95 (ISBN 0-936215-02-X). STL Intl.

Joseph: the Forgiver. Jester Summers. (BibLearn Ser.). (Illus.). 1976. bds. 5.95 (ISBN 0-8054-4224-3, 4242-24). Broadman.

Joseph, the Just Man. Rosalie M. Levy. 4.00 (ISBN 0-8198-3901-9); pap. 3.00 (ISBN 0-8198-3902-7). Dghtrs St Paul.

Joseph's Wardrobe. Paul J. Citrin. (Illus.). 1987. pap. 6.95 (ISBN 0-8074-0319-9). UAHC.

Josephus: A Historical Romance. Lion Feuchtwanger. LC 32-28823. (Temple Bks). 1972. pap. 12.95 (ISBN 0-689-70345-7, T25). Atheneum.

Josephus & Modern Scholarship: 1937-1980. Louis H. Feldman. LC 84-1879. xvi, 1055p. 1984. 248.00x (ISBN 3-11-008138-5). De Gruyter.

Josephus, Judaism & Christianity. Ed. by Louis Feldman. Tr. by Gohei Hata from Japanese. 336p. 1987. 39.95X (ISBN 0-8143-1831-2); pap. 13.95X (ISBN 0-8143-1832-0). Wayne St U Pr.

Josephus: The Historian & His Society. Tessa Rajak. LC 83-16538. 256p. 1984. 24.95 (ISBN 0-8006-0717-1, 1-717). Fortress.

Josephus: The Jewish War. Ed. by Cornfeld & Gaalyah. 560p. 1982. 44.95 (ISBN 0-310-39210-1, 10265). Zondervan.

Joshua. Ethel Barrett. LC 79-65233. (Bible Biography Ser.). 128p. 1979. pap. 2.50 (ISBN 0-8307-0707-7, 5607000). Regal.

Joshua. rev. ed. G. Michael Cocoris. 125p. 1986. pap. text ed. 3.00 (ISBN 0-935729-34-8). Church Open Door.

Joshua. Rebecca Daniel. (Our Greatest Heritage Ser.). (Illus.). 32p. 1983. wkbk. 3.95 (ISBN 0-86653-136-X, SS 805). Good Apple.

Joshua. Joseph F. Girzone. 320p. 1983. 12.00 (ISBN 0-911519-03-3). Richelieu Court.

Joshua. rev. ed. Irving L. Jensen. (Bible Self-Study Ser). (Illus.). 80p. 1967. pap. 3.25 (ISBN 0-8024-1006-5). Moody.

Joshua. (Burl Ives Bible-Time Stories). incl. tape 4.95 (ISBN 0-89191-610-5, 26104). Cook.

Joshua. F. B. Meyer. 1977. pap. 4.50 (ISBN 0-87508-357-9). Chr Lit.

Joshua, Pt. 1. G. Michael Cocoris. 44p. (Orig.). 1984. pap. text ed. 1.00 (ISBN 0-935729-18-6). Church Open Door.

Joshua, Pt. 2. G. Michael Cocoris. 42p. (Orig.). 1984. pap. text ed. 1.00 (ISBN 0-935729-19-4). Church Open Door.

Joshua, Pt. 3. G. Michael Cocoris. 44p. (Orig.). 1984. pap. text ed. 1.00 (ISBN 0-935729-20-8). Church Open Door.

Joshua, Vol. 6. Robert G. Boling & Ernest Wright. LC 79-6583. (Anchor Bible Ser.). (Illus.). 432p. 1982. 18.00 (ISBN 0-385-00034-0). Doubleday.

Joshua: A Commentary. J. Alberto Soggin. Tr. by R. A. Wilson. LC 72-76954. (Old Testament Library). 264p. 1972. 14.95 (ISBN 0-664-20938-6). Westminster.

Joshua & Judges. George Bush. 1981. 17.95 (ISBN 0-86524-100-7, 0602). Klock & Klock.

Joshua & Judges. Ed. by A. Cohen. 332p. 1950. 10.95 (ISBN 0-900689-20-X). Soncino Pr.

Joshua & Samuel. Peter Broughton. (Bible Study Commentaries Ser.). 126p. 1984. pap. 4.95 (ISBN 0-317-43371-7). Chr Lit.

Joshua & the Battle of Jericho. Illus. by Hanna-Barbera. (Greatest Adventure: Stories from the Bible). (Illus., Orig.). Date not set. 5.95 (ISBN 0-687-15743-9). Abingdon.

Joshua & the Flow of Biblical History. Francis A. Schaeffer. LC 74-31847. 216p. 1975. pap. text ed. 7.95 (ISBN 0-87784-773-8). Inter-Varsity.

Joshua: Bible Study Commentary. Paul P. Enns. (Bible Study Commentary). 160p. (Orig.). 1981. pap. 4.95 (ISBN 0-310-44041-6, 11830P). Zondervan.

Joshua (CC, Vol. 6. John Huffman. 320p. 1986. 18.95 (ISBN 0-8499-0411-0). Word Bks.

Joshua, Conqueror of Canaan. Gordon Lindsay. (Old Testament Ser.). 1.25 (ISBN 0-89985-134-7). Christ Nations.

Joshua: Defeat to Victory. Gene Getz. LC 78-53358. 176p. 1979. pap. 5.95 (ISBN 0-8307-0643-7, 5410509). Regal.

Joshua-Esther, Vol. II. Beacon Bible Commentary Staff. 13.95 (ISBN 0-8010-0689-9). Baker Bk.

Joshua, Ezra, Nehemiah, Esther. H. A. Ironside. 11.95 (ISBN 0-87213-396-6). Loizeaux.

Joshua in the Light of the New Testament. W. Graham Scroggie. LC 80-8074. (W. Graham Scroggie Library). 88p. 1981. pap. 4.50 (ISBN 0-8254-3734-2). Kregel.

Joshua-Judges. John Garstang. LC 78-9518. (Kregel Limited Edition Library). 464p. 1978. 19.95 (ISBN 0-8254-2719-3). Kregel.

Joshua, Judges. John Grindel. (Bible Commentary Ser.). 120p. 1985. pap. 2.95 (ISBN 0-8146-1414-0). Liturgical Pr.

Joshua, Judges. Max Kappeler. Tr. by Rory Larson from Ger. LC 82-80904. (Bible in the Light of Christian Science Ser.: Vol. 3). Orig. Title: Wissenschaft der Bibel, Das Buch Josua und Das Buch der Richter. 210p. (Orig.). 1983. pap. 12.00 (ISBN 0-942958-07-1). Kappeler Inst Pub.

Joshua, Judges, & Ruth. A. Graeme Auld. LC 84-22076. (Daily Study Bible-Old Testament). 290p. 1985. 15.95 (ISBN 0-664-21809-1); pap. 8.95 (ISBN 0-664-24576-5). Westminster.

Joshua, Judges & Ruth. rev. ed. John Gray. (New Century Bible Ser). 337p. 1977. 14.50 (ISBN 0-551-00784-2). Attic Pr.

Joshua, Judges, Ruth. rev. ed. John Gray. (New Century Bible Commentary Ser.). 432p. 1986. pap. 12.95 (ISBN 0-8028-0018-1). Eerdmans.

Joshua, Judges, Samuel, Kings. Walter E. Rast. Ed. by Foster R. McCurley. LC 78-54559. (Proclamation Commentaries: the Old Testament Witnesses for Preaching). 132p. 1978. pap. 4.95 (ISBN 0-8006-0594-2, 1-594). Fortress.

Joshua Judges: The Foundations of Bible History. John Garstang. 1977. lib. bdg. 59.95 (ISBN 0-8490-2109-X). Gordon Pr.

Joshua, Judges, with Excursus on Charismatic Leadership in Israel. Leslie Hoppe. (Old Testament Message Ser.: Vol. 5). 1982. text ed. 12.95 (ISBN 0-89453-405-X); pap. 8.95 (ISBN 0-89453-240-5). M Glazier.

Joshua: Leader under Fire. Donald K. Campbell. 144p. pap. 5.95 (ISBN 0-89693-502-7). Victor Bks.

Joshua, Moses & the Land. A. Graeme Auld. 158p. 1981. 19.95 (ISBN 0-567-09306-9, Pub. by T & T Clark Ltd UK). Fortress.

Joshua: Promises to Keep. Roberta Green. (Young Fisherman Bible Studyguide Ser.). (Illus.). 70p. 1982. tchr's ed. 4.95 (ISBN 0-87788-434-X); student ed. 2.95 (ISBN 0-87788-433-1). Shaw Pubs.

Joshua: Rest-Land Won. Irving L. Jensen. (Everyman's Bible Commentary Ser.). (Orig.). 1966. pap. 5.95 (ISBN 0-8024-2006-0). Moody.

Joshua's Long Day. C. A. Totten. 1968. 5.00 (ISBN 0-685-08808-1). Destiny.

Josquin Des Prez's "Missa Pange Lingua" An Edition, with Notes for Performance & Commentary. Thomas Warburton. LC 76-22703. (Early Musical Masterworks--Critical Editions & Commentaries). ix, 63p. 1977. 21.00x (ISBN 0-8078-1296-X). U of NC Pr.

Josue. Joseph J. Devault. (Bible Ser.). pap. 1.00 (ISBN 0-8091-5075-1). Paulist Pr.

Josue: La Tierra de Reposo, Conquistada (Comentario Biblico Portavoz) Irving L. Jensen. Orig. Title: Joshua: Rest-Land Won (Everyman's Bible Commentary) (Span.). 118p. 1980. pap. 3.50 (ISBN 0-8254-1353-2). Kregel.

Journal & Major Essays of John Woolman. Ed. by Phillips P. Moulton. (Library of Protestant Thought). (Illus.). 336p. 1971. pap. text ed. 7.95 (ISBN 0-19-501419-7). Religious Soc Friends.

Journal & the Journey. Mary Morrison. LC 81-85559. (Pendle Hill Pamphlets Ser.). 32p. (Orig.). 1982. pap. 2.50x (ISBN 0-87574-242-4). Pendle Hill.

Journal des Jesuites. Ed. by Laverdiere & Casgrain. (French-Canadian Civilization Ser.). (Fr.). Repr. of 1871 ed. lib. bdg. 46.00x (ISBN 0-697-00050-8). Irvington.

Journal for Life: Discovering Faith & Values Through Journal Keeping-Theology from Experience, Pt. 2, Pt. 2. George F Simons. LC 75-17161. (Illus.). 1977. pap. 1.95 (ISBN 0-914070-10-X). ACTA Found.

Journal from an Obscure Place. Judith Miles. LC 78-60279. 144p. 1978. pap. 3.95 (ISBN 0-87123-273-1, 200273). Bethany Hse.

Journal of a College Student. Joseph Havens. LC 65-19208. (Orig.). pap. 2.50x (ISBN 0-87574-141-X). Pendle Hill.

Journal of a Parish Priest. Rawley Myers. LC 81-82022. 144p. (Orig.). 1982. pap. 3.75 (ISBN 0-87973-675-5, 675). Our Sunday Visitor.

Journal of a Two-Months Tour, with a View to Promoting Religion. Charles Beatty. LC 72-108459. 1768. 25.00x (ISBN 0-403-00456-X). Scholarly.

Journal of George Fox. Rufus M. Jones. 576p. 1976. pap. 8.50 (ISBN 0-913408-24-7). Friends United.

Journal of Holistic Health: Vol. VI. Anastas Harris. (Illus.). 144p. 1981. pap. 12.00 (ISBN 0-939410-07-9). Mandala Holistic.

Journal of Jewish Bibliography, 4 vols. Ed. by Bloch. Set. 35.00 (ISBN 0-685-48593-5). Feldheim.

Journal of John Woolman. John Woolman. 256p. 1972. pap. 5.95 (ISBN 0-8065-0294-0). Citadel Pr.

Journal of John Woolman & a Plea for the Poor. John Woolman. 17.00 (ISBN 0-8446-0297-3). Peter Smith.

Journal of Pastoral Practice, Vol. IV, No. II. Jay E. Adams. pap. 5.00 (ISBN 0-8010-0169-2). Baker Bk.

Journal of Pastoral Practice, Vol. 1, No. 1 - Winter, 1977. Jay E. Adams. 1977. pap. 3.50 (ISBN 0-8010-0116-1). Baker Bk.

Journal of Pastoral Practice, Vol. V, No. 1. Jay E. Adams. 1981. pap. 5.00 (ISBN 0-87552-035-9). Presby & Reformed.

Journal of Pastoral Practice, Vol. IV, No. 1. Jay E. Adams. 1979. 5.00 (ISBN 0-87552-031-6). Presby & Reformed.

Journal of Pastoral Practice, Vol. V, No.1. Jay E. Adams. 1981. pap. 5.00 (ISBN 0-8010-0178-1). Baker Bk.

Journal of Pastoral Practice, Vol. I, No. 2. J. Adams. 1978. 3.50 (ISBN 0-87552-024-3). Presby & Reformed.

Journal of Pastoral Practice, Vol. I, No. 2. Jay E. Adams. 1977. pap. 3.50 (ISBN 0-8010-0125-0). Baker Bk.

Journal of Pastoral Practice, Vol. V, No. 2. Jay E. Adams. 1981. pap. 5.00 (ISBN 0-87552-036-7). Presby & Reformed.

Journal of Pastoral Practice, Vol. V, No. 2. Jay E. Adams. 1981. pap. 5.00 (ISBN 0-8010-0183-8). Baker Bk.

Journal of Pastoral Practice, Vol. IV, No. 3. Jay E. Adams. pap. 5.00 (ISBN 0-8010-0170-6). Baker Bk.

Journal of Pastoral Practice, Vol. IV, No. 3. Jay E. Adams. 1981. pap. 5.00 (ISBN 0-87552-033-2). Presby & Reformed.

Journal of Pastoral Practice, Vol. V, No 3. Jay E. Adams. 1982. pap. 5.00 (ISBN 0-8010-0186-2). Baker Bk.

Journal of Pastoral Practice, Vol. IV, No. 4. Jay E. Adams. pap. 5.00 (ISBN 0-8010-0177-3). Baker Bk.

Journal of Pastoral Practice, Vol. IV, No. 4. Jay E. Adams. 1981. pap. 5.00 (ISBN 0-87552-034-0). Presby & Reformed.

Journal of Practical Practice, Vol. IV, No. 2. Ed. by Jay E. Adams. 1980. pap. 5.00 (ISBN 0-87552-032-4). Presby & Reformed.

Journal of Tears. Elizabeth Lapp. 1984. 2.95 (ISBN 0-87813-522-7). Christian Light.

Journal of the Rev. Godfrey Drehr, Eighteen Nineteen to Eighteen Fifty-One. Ed. by Brent H. Holcomb. 104p. 1978. 15.00 (ISBN 0-89308-060-8). Southern Hist Pr.

Journal of the Spirit. Yogi A Desai. (Illus.). 160p. 1985. pap. 4.95 (ISBN 0-940258-18-8). Kripalu Pubns.

Journal of Thomas Chalkley. Thomas Chalkley. LC 75-31088. (Incl. a collection of author's works). Repr. of 1808 ed. 45.00 (ISBN 0-404-13506-4). AMS Pr.

Journals of George Whitefield, 1737-1741. George Whitefield. LC 73-81363. (Illus.). 1969. Repr. of 1905 ed. 75.00x (ISBN 0-8201-1069-8). Schol Facsimiles.

Journals of Jim Elliot. Jim Elliot. Ed. by Elisabeth Elliot. 416p. 1978. 7.95 (Power Bks). Revell.

Journals of Jim Elliot. Jim Elliot. Ed. by Elisabeth Elliot. 416p. 1983. pap. 7.95 (ISBN 0-8007-5147-7, Power Bks). Revell.

Journals of the Rev. James Frederick Schon & Mr. Samuel Crowther Who with the Sanction of Her Majesty's Government; Accompanied the Expedition Up the Niger in 1841 on Behalf of the Church Missionary Society. 2nd ed. James F. Schon & Samuel Crowther. 394p. 1970. 37.50x (ISBN 0-7146-1877-2, F Cass Co). Biblio Dist.

Journey: A Home & Group Bible Study Program. Ed. by Marcel Gervais. (Illus.). Set. 60.00; Old Testament, Set 20 Bklts. 30.00 (ISBN 0-8091-9279-9); New Testament Set, 20 Bklts. 30.00 (ISBN 0-8091-9280-2); bklt. 1.50 ea. Paulist Pr.

Journey Homeward. Susan Muto. 6.95 (ISBN 0-87193-001-3). Dimension Bks.

Journey in Becoming. Compiled by Stanley A. Nelson. (Orig.). 1983. pap. 4.95 (ISBN 0-8054-6320-8). Broadman.

Journey in East Africa: Towards the Mountains of the Moon. new ed. M. A. Pringle. LC 72-3957. (Black Heritage Library Collection Ser.). Repr. of 1886 ed. 27.50 (ISBN 0-8369-9105-2). Ayer Co Pubs.

Journey in Faith. Raymond Kemp. pap. 5.95 (ISBN 0-8215-9329-3). Sadlier.

Journey in Faith. Warren T. Smith. 1984. 5.50 (ISBN 0-89536-679-7, 4855). CSS of Ohio.

Journey in Faith: A History of the Christian Church. Lester G. McAllister & William E. Tucker. LC 75-11738. 512p. 1975. 14.95 (ISBN 0-8272-1703-X). CBP.

Journey in Faith: An Inquirer's Program. rev. ed. Barbara Wolf. 144p. 1982. pap. 5.95 (ISBN 0-8164-2402-0, HarpR). Har-Row.

Journey in Faith: Leader's Manual. Frederick B. Wolf. 80p. (Orig.). 1982. pap. 4.95 (ISBN 0-8164-2400-4, HarpR). Har-Row.

Journey in Faith: Things to Know. Frederick B. Wolf. 48p. (Orig.). 1982. pap. 3.50 (ISBN 0-8164-2401-2, HarpR). Har-Row.

Journey into Christ. Alan W. Jones. 1977. pap. 6.95 (ISBN 0-8164-0338-4, HarpR). Har-Row.

Journey into Contemplation. George A. Maloney. 144p. (Orig.). 1983. pap. 3.95 (ISBN 0-914544-51-9). Living Flame Pr.

Journey into Fullness. James Mahoney. LC 73-91615. pap. 5.95 (ISBN 0-8054-5221-4). Broadman.

Journey into His Presence. Ferne H. Murray. LC 78-73439. (Illus.). 1979. pap. 3.95 (ISBN 0-932994-00-8). Day Star.

Journey into Life. Ernest Holmes. Ed. by Willis H. Kinnear. 88p. 1967. pap. 5.50 (ISBN 0-911336-05-2). Sci of Mind.

Journey into Light & Joy. Howard R. Carey. LC 79-53905. (Illus.). 180p. 1979. pap. 4.50 (ISBN 0-87516-380-7). De Vorss.

Journey into Wholeness. Stephen L. Manley. 96p. (Orig.). 1983. pap. 2.95 (ISBN 0-8341-0832-1). Beacon Hill.

Journey Inward: Interior Conversations 1960 to the Present. Catherine D. Doherty. LC 84-443. 116p. (Orig.). 1984. pap. 6.95 (ISBN 0-8189-0468-2). Alba.

Journey Inward, Journey Outward. Elizabeth O'Connor. LC 75-9313. 192p. 1975. pap. 5.95 (ISBN 0-06-066332-4, RD100, HarpR). Har-Row.

Journey Is Home: The Distinguished Feminist Theologian Traces the Development of Her Personal & Theoretical Vision. Nelle Morton. LC 85-42342. 285p. 1986. pap. 8.95 (ISBN 0-8070-1133-9, BP 718). Beacon Pr.

Journey of Awakening: A Mediator's Guidebook. Ram Dass. 1978. pap. 4.95 (ISBN 0-553-25845-1). Bantam.

Journey of Conscience: Young People Respond to the Holocaust. Leatrice Rabinsky & Gertrude Mann. 112p. Repr. 1.50 (ISBN 0-686-95073-9). ADL.

Journey of Forgiveness. Barbara Howard. 1986. pap. 7.50 (ISBN 0-8309-0463-8). Herald Hse.

Journey of God's People. Robert Mathias. 1982. pap. 4.95 (ISBN 0-89536-528-6, 1016). CSS of Ohio.

Journey of No Return. Bette M. Ross. Date not set. pap. 5.95 (ISBN 0-8007-5231-7, Power Bks). Revell.

Journey of the Heart. Thomas S. Kane. LC 81-5278. 1981. pap. 4.95 (ISBN 0-932506-13-5). St Bedes Pubns.

Journey of the Soul. John-Roger. LC 77-81387. 1977. pap. 5.00 (ISBN 0-914829-12-2). Baraka Bk.

Journey of the Soul: The Story of Hai bin Yaqzan. Tr. by R. Kocache. 1982. 11.95 (ISBN 0-900860-90-1, Pub. by Octagon Pr England). Ins Study Human.

Journey of the Three Jewels: Japanese Buddhist Paintings from Western Collections. John M. Rosenfield & Elizabeth Ten Grotenhuis. LC 79-15072. (Illus.). 1979. 19.95 (ISBN 0-87848-054-4). Asia Soc.

Journey of the Universe As Expounded in the Qur'an. Shaykh F. Haeri. 120p. 1985. 29.95x (ISBN 0-7103-0149-9, Kegan Paul). Methuen Inc.

Journey of Western Spirituality. A. W. Sadler. 234p. 1986. lib. bdg. 23.00 (ISBN 0-8191-5722-8, Pub. by College Tehology Society); pap. text ed. 13.00 (ISBN 0-8191-5618-3). U Pr of Amer.

Journey of Western Spirituality: CTS Annual Publication, 1980. Ed. by A. W. Sadler. LC 81-5831. 1981. text ed. 18.00 (ISBN 0-89130-505-X, 34 10 80). Scholars Pr GA.

Journey Out of Chaos. Sr. Clare. LC 81-22885. 248p. (Orig.). 1981. pap. 8.00 (ISBN 0-89571-012-9). Affirmation.

Journey: Spiritual Insights. Chiara Lubich. Tr. by Hugh Moran & William Hartnett. 158p. 1984. pap. 4.95 (ISBN 0-911782-51-6). New City.

Journey Through Jewish History, Vol. II. Seymour Rossel. (Illus.). 128p. 1983. pap. text ed. 5.95x (ISBN 0-87441-366-4). Behrman.

Journey Through the Bible. Ralph J. Brewer. 167p. (Orig.). 1983. pap. text ed. 5.95 (ISBN 0-87148-450-1); instrs. guide 2.50 (ISBN 0-87148-451-X). Pathway Pr.

Journey to Ararat. Friedrich Parrot. LC 73-115576. (Russia Observed, Series I). 1970. Repr. of 1846 ed. 20.00 (ISBN 0-405-03057-6). Ayer Co Pubs.

Journey to Bethlehem. Akiko Kageyama. 26p. 1983. 7.95 (ISBN 0-8170-1012-2). Judson.

Journey to Great Salt-Lake City, 2 vols. Jules Remy & Julius Brenchley. LC 75-134399. (Illus.). Repr. of 1861 ed. Set. 49.50 (ISBN 0-404-08441-9). Vol. 1 (ISBN 0-404-08442-7). Vol. 2 (ISBN 0-404-08443-5). AMS Pr.

Journey to Healing. Kenneth C. Farnsworth. Ed. by Herbert Lambert. LC 85-3838. (Orig.). 1985. pap. 8.95 (ISBN 0-8272-1706-4). CBP.

Journey to Inner Peace. Paul A. Feider. LC 84-71863. 112p. (Orig.). 1984. pap. 3.95 (ISBN 0-87793-275-1). Ave Maria.

Journey to Ixtlan. Carlos Castaneda. 1983. pap. 4.95 (ISBN 0-671-60658-1). WSP.

Journey to Jerusalem. Marian Hostetler. LC 77-19347. (Illus.). 128p. 1978. pap. 3.95 (ISBN 0-8361-1848-0). Herald Pr.

Journey to Jerusalem. Frank Rothfuss. 1982. pap. 9.25 (ISBN 0-89536-522-7, 1015). CSS of Ohio.

Journey to Resurrection. Richard S. Hanson. 81p. (Orig.). 1986. pap. 4.95 (ISBN 0-8091-2737-7). Paulist Pr.

Journey to the Father. Bob Grgic. (YA) 1987. pap. text ed. write for info. (ISBN 0-697-02225-0); write for info. tchr's. ed. (ISBN 0-697-02226-9). Wm C Brown.

Journey to the Lonely Christ: The Little Mandate of Catherine de Hueck Doherty. Ed. by Robert Wild. LC 86-17388. 164p. 1987. pap. 7.95 (ISBN 0-8189-0509-3). Alba.

Journey to the Lord of Power: A Sufi Manual on Retreat. Ibn Arabi. Tr. by Rabia Harris from Arab. (Illus.). 144p. 1981. pap. 8.95 (ISBN 0-89281-018-1). Inner Tradit.

Journey to the Magical City: A Quadriplegic Person's Reflections on Suffering & Love. Robert T. Standhardt. LC 83-80413. 96p. (Orig.). 1983. pap. 4.50 (ISBN 0-8358-0458-5). Upper Room.

Journey to the Unknown: Catholic Doctrine on Ethnicity & Migration. Andrew N. Woznicki. LC 82-83230. 105p. (Orig.). 1982. pap. text ed. 3.95 (ISBN 0-910727-01-5). Golden Phoenix.

Journey to Totality. Ishwar C. Puri. Ed. by Edward D. Scott. 121p. (Orig.). 1985. pap. 6.00 (ISBN 0-937067-05-9). Inst Study Hum Aware.

Journey to Tradition: The Odyssey of a Born-Again Jew. Michael G. Levin. 129p. 1986. 14.95 (ISBN 0-88125-093-7). Ktav.

Journey Toward Freedom. Paul G. King & David O. Woodyard. (Illus.). 248p. 1982. 28.50 (ISBN 0-8386-3115-0). Fairleigh Dickinson.

Journey Toward Jesus. Bruce Edwards & Edward Fudge. 1.50 (ISBN 0-686-12687-4). E Fudge.

Journey Toward Wholeness: A Jungian Model of Adult Spiritual Growth. Helen Thompson. LC 81-83184. 96p. (Orig.). 1982. pap. 5.95 (ISBN 0-8091-2422-X). Paulist Pr.

Journey Towards Easter. Joseph Ratzinger. 160p. 1987. 12.95 (ISBN 0-8245-0803-3). Crossroad NY.

Journey Towards Holiness. Alan Kreider. LC 86-22838. 304p. (Orig.). 1987. pap. 9.95 (ISBN 0-8361-3423-0). Herald Pr.

Journey with Jesus. Carol A. Lund. (Illus.). 214p. (Orig.). 1982. pap. 4.95x (ISBN 0-9608418-0-6). MasterSon Pub.

Journey with Jonah. rev. ed. Thomas J. Carlisle. 96p. 1984. pap. 1.95 (ISBN 0-88028-035-2). Forward Movement.

Journey with Matthew. Pat Backman. (Orig.). 1984. tchr's. ed. 4.95 (ISBN 0-931055-03-2). LuraMedia.

Journey with the Master. Eva B. Werber. 1950. pap. 3.25 (ISBN 0-87516-103-0). De Vorss.

Journey with the Saints. facs. ed. Thomas S. Kepler. LC 70-148223. (Biography Index Reprint Ser.). 1951. 17.00 (ISBN 0-8369-8070-0). Ayer Co Pubs.

Journey Without Goal: The Tantric Wisdom of the Buddha. Chogyam Trungpa. LC 85-8175. 150p. 1985. pap. 8.95 (ISBN 0-87773-334-1, 74194-3). Shambhala Pubns.

Journeying in His Light. William Anderson. 160p. 1982. wire coil 4.95 (ISBN 0-697-01858-X). Wm C Brown.

Journeying Self: The Gospel of Mark through a Jungian Perspective. Dairmuid McGann. 144p. (Orig.). 1985. pap. 7.95 (ISBN 0-8091-2662-1). Paulist Pr.

Journeying Through a Jungle. Sandy F. Ray. LC 79-84787. 1979. 5.50 (ISBN 0-8054-5169-2). Broadman.

Journeying Through the Days, 1986. 1985. spiral bdg. 10.95 (ISBN 0-8358-0523-9, Dist. by Abingdon Press). Upper Room.

Journeying Through the Days 1987. 272p. (Orig.). 1986. pap. 10.95 (ISBN 0-8358-0541-7). Upper Room.

Journeying Together: A Study on the Psalms. Nancy V. Phillips & Mary T. Van Andel. write for info. (ISBN 0-916466-03-5). Reformed Church.

Journeying Together: Proceedings of Three Regional Convocations on Shared Responsibility in America. Ed. by Dolores R. Leckey. 48p. 1986. pap. 4.95 (ISBN 1-55586-975-0). US Catholic.

Journeying Toward Marriage. William Anderson. (Journeying with Christ Ser.). 176p. 1985. pap. 6.75 (ISBN 0-697-02059-2). Wm C Brown.

Journeys: An Introductory Guide to Jewish Mysticism. William E. Kaufman. LC 80-69017. 1980. 12.50 (ISBN 0-8197-0482-2); pap. 7.95 (ISBN 0-686-77548-1). Bloch.

Journeys into the Fifth Dimension. Helena E. Ruhnau. LC 75-149286. (Illus.). 1975. 12.95 (ISBN 0-941036-02-2). Colleasius Pr.

Journeys Not Regreeted. Edward Fischer. 1986. pap. 10.95 (ISBN 0-317-42448-3). Crossroad NY.

Journeys on Your Spiritual Path. L. Richard Batzler. 1982. 7.95 (ISBN 0-935710-04-3). Hid Valley MD.

Journeys: The Impact of Personal Experience on Religious Thought. Gregory Baum. LC 75-31401. pap. 52.90 (ISBN 0-8357-9486-5, 2013525). Bks Demand UMI.

Journeys to Orthodoxy. T. Doulis. 1986. pap. 6.95 (ISBN 0-937032-42-5). Light&Life Pub Co MN.

Journeys with Mary. Zerlina De Santis. (Encounter Ser.). 155p. 1982. 3.00 (ISBN 0-8198-3900-0, EN0165); pap. 2.00 (ISBN 0-8198-3910-8). Dghtrs St Paul.

Joven y Su Dios. Winkey Pratney. (Joven y Sus Inquietudes Ser.). 1982. 2.95 (ISBN 0-88113-163-6). Edit Betania.

Joven y Su Mundo. Winkey Pratney. (Joven y Sus Inquietudes). 1982. 2.50 (ISBN 0-88113-164-4). Edit Betania.

Joven y Sus Amigos. Winkey Pratney. (Joven y Sus Inquietudes Ser). 1982. 2.25 (ISBN 0-88113-162-8). Edit Betania.

Joven y Sus Dilemas. Winkey Pratney. (Joven y Sus Inquietudes). 1982. 2.50 (ISBN 0-88113-165-2). Edit Betania.

Jovita Galan: Unselfish Teacher. Lou Sherrill. LC 86-6110. (Meet the Missionary Ser.). 1986. 5.50 (ISBN 0-8054-4326-6). Broadman.

Joy. Carole MacKenthun & Paulinus Dwyer. (Fruit of the Spirit Ser.). (Illus.). 48p. 1986. wkbk. 4.95 (ISBN 0-86653-360-5). Good Apple.

Joy. Jane B. Moncure. LC 82-1145. (What Does the Bible Say? Ser.). (Illus.). 32p. 1982. PLB 5.95 (ISBN 0-89565-222-6, 4940, Pub. by Childs World). Standard Pub.

Joy. Jane B. Moncure. (Values to Live by Ser.). 1982. 10.35 (ISBN 0-516-06527-0). Childrens.

Joy. Charles R. Rogers. 1979. pap. 1.00 (ISBN 0-89841-001-0). Zoe Pubns.

Joy & Adventure of Growing Younger. M. Kimbrough. LC 12-2969. 1983. pap. 4.95 (ISBN 0-570-03876-6). Concordia.

Joy & Remembrance. Max Arzt. 1979. 12.50 (ISBN 0-87677-147-9). Hartmore.

Joy & Responsibility: Israel, Modernity & the Renewal of Judaism. David Hartman. 286p. 12.50 (ISBN 0-686-95138-7). ADL.

Joy Before Us. Janice M. Townsend. LC 81-7198. 1982. pap. 8.00 (ISBN 0-8309-0327-5). Herald Hse.

Joy Beyond. Gwynn M. Day. 1979. 3.95 (ISBN 0-8010-2893-0). Baker Bk.

Joy Every Morning. Muriel Larson. (Quiet Time Books). 1979. pap. 3.50 (ISBN 0-8024-4396-6). Moody.

Joy Explosion. Barry St. Clair. 128p. 1986. pap. 9.95 (ISBN 0-88207-306-0). Victor Bks.

Joy Five. rev. ed. Winston Staff. (Joy Religion Ser.). (Illus.). 1978. pap. text ed. 5.87 (ISBN 0-86683-035-9, HarpR); tchr's. manual 8.95 (ISBN 0-03-041871-2). Har-Row.

Joy Four. rev. ed. Winston Staff. (Joy Religion Ser.). (Illus.). 1978. pap. text ed. 5.87 (ISBN 0-86683-034-0, HarpR); tchr's. manual 8.95 (ISBN 0-86683-044-8). Har-Row.

Joy in a Roman Jail. John Moran. 208p. (Orig.). 1984. pap. 6.25 (ISBN 0-934998-17-5). Bethel Pub.

Joy in Christ: Studies in Philippians. Steve Lemke. 36p. 1981. pap. 3.50 (ISBN 0-939298-10-4). J M Prods.

Joy in His Presence: Christian Reflections on Everyday Life. Lily M. Gyldenvand. LC 81-67806. 112p. (Orig.). 1981. pap. 4.95 (ISBN 0-8066-1896-5, 10-3596). Augsburg.

Joy in the Classroom. Stephanie Herzog. Ed. by Ann Ray. LC 82-4724. (Illus.). 224p. 1982. text ed. 7.95 (ISBN 0-916438-46-5). Univ of Trees.

Joy in the New Testament. William G. Morrice. 144p. (Orig.). 1982. pap. 11.95 (ISBN 0-85364-340-7). Attic Pr.

Joy Is the Promise. Holly Coors. 1978. pap. 1.50 (ISBN 0-88419-182-6). Creation Hse.

Joy Joy, the Mass: Our Family Celebration. J. Leichner. (Illus.). 1978. pap. 2.75 (ISBN 0-87973-350-0). Our Sunday Visitor.

Joy of All Creation: An Anglican Meditation on the Place of Mary. A. M. Allchin. LC 84-72479. 162p. 1985. pap. 7.50 (ISBN 0-936384-24-7). Cowley Pubns.

Joy of Being Human: Reflections for Every Day of the Year. Eugene C. Kennedy. 360p. 1976. pap. 5.95 (ISBN 0-385-00943-7, Im). Doubleday.

Joy of Belonging. Richard L. Dresselhaus. LC 78-66868. (Radiant Life Ser.). 128p. 1978. pap. 2.50 (ISBN 0-88243-526-4, 02-0526); tchr's ed. 3.95 (ISBN 0-88243-186-2, 32-0186). Gospel Pub.

Joy of Bible Study. Joe Pendleton. (Illus.). 64p. (Orig.). 1981. pap. 1.95 (ISBN 0-89114-106-5); P. 32. tchr's ed. 1.50 (ISBN 0-89114-107-3). Baptist Pub Hse.

Joy of Christmas. Cleo Kapilla et al. 96p. 1983. pap. 7.95 (ISBN 0-9611466-0-5). Wimmer Bks.

Joy of Christmas: A Manual for Holiday Survival. Cleo Kapilla & Eleanor Simons. LC 83-90104. 96p. (Orig.). 1983. pap. 7.95 (ISBN 0-686-88978-9). K & S.

Joy of Committed Love: A Valuable Guide to Knowing, Understanding & Loving Each Other. Gary Smalley & Steve Scott. LC 83-18248. 336p. 1984. 12.95 (ISBN 0-310-44900-6, 18248). Zondervan.

Joy of Discipleship. Robert W. Bailey. LC 81-69402. 1982. pap. 5.95 (ISBN 0-8054-5188-9). Broadman.

Joy of Discovery in Bible Study. rev. ed. Oletta Wald. LC 75-22710. 96p. 1975. pap. 4.95 (ISBN 0-8066-1513-3, 10-3600). Augsburg.

Joy of Feeling Body-Mind: Acupressure--Jin Shin Do. Iona M. Teeguarden. LC 85-80534. (Illus.). 176p. (Orig.). 1986. pap. 13.95 (ISBN 0-87040-634-5). Japan Pubns USA.

Joy of Feeling Good: Eight Keys to a Happy & Abundant Life. William A. Miller. LC 86-20574. 192p. (Orig.). (YA) 1986. pap. 4.50 (ISBN 0-8066-2236-9, 10-3601). Augsburg.

Joy of Fellowship: A Study of First John. J. Dwight Pentecost. 1977. pap. 5.95 (ISBN 0-310-30921-2, 17013P). Zondervan.

Joy of Full Surrender. Jean-Pierre De Caussade. (Living Library Ser.). 160p. 1986. pap. 5.95 (ISBN 0-941478-49-1). Paraclete Pr.

Joy of Knowing God. Richard L. Strauss. 305p. 1984. pap. 8.95 (ISBN 0-87213-834-8). Loizeaux.

Joy of Listening to God. Joyce Huggett. LC 86-27689. 240p. (Orig.). 1987. pap. 6.95 (ISBN 0-87784-729-0). Inter-Varsity.

Joy of Living. Willard Scott. (Epiphany Bks.). 192p. (Orig.). 1983. pap. 2.50 (ISBN 0-345-31073-X). Ballantine.

Joy of Living: A Study of Philippians. J. Dwight Pentecost. 160p. 1973. pap. text ed. 6.95 (ISBN 0-310-30871-2, 17012P). Zondervan.

Joy of Marriage. Clayton C. Barbeau. Orig. Title: Creative Marriage: the Middle Years. 132p. 1980. pap. 5.95 (ISBN 0-86683-759-0, HarpR). Har-Row.

Joy of Meditation. Jack Addington & Cornelia Addington. LC 78-75078. 1979. pap. 4.95 (ISBN 0-87516-292-4). De Vorss.

Joy of Ministry: My Role in Christian Education. (Christian Education Ministries Ser.). 1978. pap. 3.50 (ISBN 0-89367-026-X). Light & Life.

Joy of My Heart. Basilea Schlink. 1978. pap. 0.95 (ISBN 3-87209-623-0). Evang Sisterhood Mary.

Joy of Personal Worship. Lynne Hybels. 156p. 1984. pap. 5.95 (ISBN 0-89693-373-3). Victor Bks.

Joy of Remembering Our Guests. Ruth Cording. 1982. gift padded cover 7.95 (ISBN 0-87162-258-0, J1016). Warner Pr.

Joy of Sacrifice: Secrets of the Sufi Way. E. J. Gold. LC 78-54140. (Illus.). 1978. pap. 5.95 (ISBN 0-89556-003-8, Pub. by IDHHB & HOHM Press). Gateways Bks & Tapes.

Joy of Teaching Discovery Bible Study. Oletta Wald. LC 76-3857. (Orig.). 1976. pap. 4.95 (ISBN 0-8066-1530-3, 10-3603). Augsburg.

Joy of the Lord. Mary Light. pap. 0.50 (ISBN 0-910924-67-8). Macalester.

Joy of the Psalms. Herb Montgomery & Mary Montgomery. (Illus.). 64p. (Orig.). 1982. pap. 7.95 (ISBN 0-86683-631-4, HarpR). Har-Row.

Joy of Understanding Your Faith. Cecil G. Osborne. 192p. (Orig.). 1983. pap. 7.75 (ISBN 0-687-20594-8). Abingdon.

Joy of Worship. Marianne H. Micks. LC 81-19667. (Library of Living Faith: Vol, 1). 120p. 1982. pap. 5.95 (ISBN 0-664-24402-5). Westminster.

Joy Six. rev. ed. Winston Press Editorial Staff. (Joy Religious Ser.). 1979. pap. 5.87 (ISBN 0-86683-036-7, 665, HarpR); tchr's. ed. 8.95 (ISBN 0-86683-046-4). Har-Row.

Joy That Lasts: How to Have an Overflowing Life. Gary Smalley. 144p. 1986. pap. 11.95 (ISBN 0-310-46290-8, 18254). Zondervan.

Joy to the World: An Introduction to Kingdom Evangelism. Robert T. Henderson. LC 80-14597. 207p. (Orig.). 1980. pap. 6.50 (ISBN 0-8042-2096-4). John Knox.

Joy to You & Me. Gurden Henley. Ed. by Michael L. Sherer. (Orig.). 1986. pap. 4.75 (ISBN 0-89536-832-3, 6846). CSS of Ohio.

Joy Unspeakable: Power & Renewal in the Holy Spirit. Ed. by Martyn Lloyd-Jones. 284p. 1985. pap. 7.95 (ISBN 0-87788-441-2). Shaw Pubs.

Joy Without a Cause: Selected Essays of Christopher Derrick. Christopher Derrick. 254p. 1979. pap. 5.95 (ISBN 0-89385-004-7). Sugden.

Joyce among the Jesuits. Kevin Sullivan. LC 84-25241. x, 259p. 1985. Repr. of 1957 ed. lib. bdg. 39.75x (ISBN 0-313-24745-5, SUJJ). Greenwood.

Joyful Christ: The Healing Power of Humor. Cal Samra. 1986. pap. 7.95 (ISBN 0-06-067032-0). Har-Row.

Joyful Christian: One Hundred Readings from the Works of C. S. Lewis. C. S. Lewis. LC 77-21685. 1977. 11.95 (ISBN 0-02-570900-3). Macmillan.

Joyful Christian: 127 Readings. C. S. Lewis. 256p. 1984. 5.95 (ISBN 0-02-086930-4, Collier). Macmillan.

Joyful Community: An Account of the Bruderhof, a Communal Movement Now in Its Third Generation. Benjamin Zablocki. 1980. pap. 5.95 (ISBN 0-226-97749-8, P885, Phoen). U of Chicago Pr.

Joyful Heart. Watchman Nee. 1977. pap. 3.95 (ISBN 0-87508-417-6). Chr Lit.

Joyful Heart. Watchman Nee. 1977. pap. 4.50 (ISBN 0-8423-1975-1). Tyndale.

Joyful Heart. Watchman Nee. Tr. by Ruth T. Chen. (Chinese.). 1985. write for info. (ISBN 0-941598-91-8); pap. write for info. (ISBN 0-941598-24-1). Living Spring Pubns.

Joyful Heart: Meditations for Lent. Martin Thornton. LC 86-32841. 76p. 1987. pap. 6.95 (ISBN 0-936384-45-X). Cowley Pubns.

Joyful Hospitality. Mona Mobley. pap. 4.95 (ISBN 0-89137-431-0). Quality Pubns.

Joyful Sound: Christian Hymnody. 2nd ed. William J. Reynolds & Milburn Price. LC 77-12048. 1978. 26.95 (ISBN 0-03-040831-8, HoltC). HR&W.

Joyful Teaching - Joyful Learning. Judy G. Smith. LC 86-71007. 104p. (Orig.). 1986. pap. 6.95 (ISBN 0-88177-031-0, DR031B). Discipleship Res.

Joyous Days: A Collection of Advent & Christmas Activities. Sharon Lee. (Learning Connections Ser.). 96p. (Orig.). 1984. pap. 7.95 (ISBN 0-86683-833-3, 8443, HarpR). Har-Row.

Joys of Jewish Folklore. Ed. by David M. Eichhorn. LC 80-13936. 534p. 1981. 16.95 (ISBN 0-8246-0254-4). Jonathan David.

Joys of Jewish Humor. Ed. by H. D. Spalding. LC 84-23822. (Illus.). 360p. 1985. pap. 8.95 (ISBN 0-8246-0257-9). Jonathan David.

Joys of Yiddish. Leo Rosten. 1968. 19.95 (ISBN 0-07-053975-8). McGraw.

Joys of Yiddish. Leo Rosten. 534p. 1970. pap. 4.95 (ISBN 0-671-47349-2). WSP.

Juan Colon, Alias Cristobal Colon, Alias Christopher Columbus, Was a Spanish Jew. Nectario M. Ed. by E. Josephson. 1985. lib. bdg. 79.95 (ISBN 0-87700-867-1). Revisionist Pr.

Juan de Cartagena, O.F.M. (1563-1618) The Mariology of His Homiliae Catholicae & Its Baroque Scripturism. Sabino A. Vengco. (Theology Ser.). 1978. 13.00 (ISBN 0-686-27934-4). Franciscan Inst.

Juan: El Evangelio de la Fe (Comentario Biblico Portavoz) Everett F. Harrison. Orig. Title: John: The Gospel of Faith (Everyman's Bible Commentary) (Span.). 128p. 1981. pap. 3.50 (ISBN 0-8254-1304-4). Kregel.

Juan Testifica de Jesus. James L. Sullivan. Tr. by J. C. Quarles from Eng. Orig. Title: John's Witness to Jesus. 128p. 1986. pap. 3.25 (ISBN 0-311-04324-0). Casa Bautista.

Juan y Hechos: Tomo II. L. Bonnet A. Schroeder. Tr. by A. Cativiela. 1986. Repr. of 1983 ed. 14.95 (ISBN 0-311-03051-3). Casa Bautista.

Jubilate Deo Omnis Terra: Psalm 99, Score & Brass Parts Accompaniment 1954. Flor Peeters. pap. 20.00 (ISBN 0-317-09824-1, 2003407). Bks Demand UMI.

Jubilate!(Church Music in the Evangelical Tradition) Donald P. Hustad. LC 80-85185. 368p. 1981. 17.95 (ISBN 0-916642-17-8). Hope Pub.

Jubilee: A Monk's Journal. M. Basil Pennington. LC 81-82336. 208p. (Orig.). 1981. 6.95 (ISBN 0-8091-2402-5). Paulist Pr.

Jubilee of the World: The Sabbath As a Day of Gladness. Charles W. Scriven. (Flame Ser.). 1978. pap. 0.99 (ISBN 0-8127-0188-7). Review & Herald.

Jubilee Singers, & Their Campaign for Twenty Thousand Dollars. Gustavus D. Pike. LC 72-1692. Repr. of 1873 ed. 18.50 (ISBN 0-404-08329-3). AMS Pr.

Jubilee Time: Celebrating Gods Grace & Justice. Carol M. Cox. 112p. (Orig.). 1984. pap. 8.25 (ISBN 0-687-20609-X). Abingdon.

Judaeo Christian Tradition. Jack H. Hexter. (Orig.). 1966. pap. text ed. 10.95 scp (ISBN 0-06-042815-5, HarpC). Har-Row.

Judah's Sceptre & Joseph's Birthright. John H. Allen. 1946. 8.00 (ISBN 0-685-08809-X). Destiny.

Judaic Ethics for a Lawless World. Robert Gordis. 185p. 1986. 20.00. Ktav.

Judaic Lore in Heine. Israel Tabak. LC 78-19266. 25.50 (ISBN 0-405-10632-7). Ayer Co Pubs.

Judaic or Semitic Legends & Customs Amongst South African Natives. S. Mendelssohn. 1976. lib. bdg. 59.95 (ISBN 0-8490-2111-1). Gordon Pr.

Judaic Perspectives on Ancient Israel. Ed. by Jacob Neusner et al. LC 86-45908. 356p. 1987. 34.95 (ISBN 0-8006-0832-1, 1-832). Fortress.

Judaic Tradition. Nahum Glatzer. 352p. 1982. pap. text ed. 9.95x (ISBN 0-87441-344-3). Behrman.

Judaica. Ernst Bammel. 330p. 1986. lib. bdg. 82.50x (ISBN 3-16-144971-1, Pub. by J C B Mohr BRD). Coronet Bks.

Judaica Festschrift zu Hermann Cohens Siebzigstem Geburtstage. Ed. by Steven Katz et al. LC 79-7156. (Jewish Philosophy, Mysticism & History of Ideas Ser.). 1980. Repr. of 1912 ed. lib. bdg. 60.00x (ISBN 0-405-12246-2). Ayer Co Pubs.

Judaism. Ed. & tr. by Philip Alexander. (Textual Sources for the Study of Religion). 240p. 1987. pap. 11.75 (ISBN 0-389-20719-5). B&N Imports.

Judaism. Ed. by Philip S. Alexander. LC 84-6199. (Textual Sources for the Study of Religion Ser.). 208p. 1984. 23.50x (ISBN 0-389-20477-3, BNB 08039); pap. 11.75x (ISBN 0-389-20719-5). B&N Imports.

Judaism. Nicholas De Lange. 224p. 1986. 14.95 (ISBN 0-19-219198-5). Oxford U Pr.

Judaism. Myer Domnitz. 1985. 13.00 (ISBN 0-7062-3596-7, Pub. by Ward Lock Educ Co Ltd). State Mutual Bk.

Judaism. Myer Domnitz. (Religions of the World Ser.). (Illus.). 48p. 1986. PLB 10.90 (ISBN 0-531-18066-2, Pub. by Bookwright). Watts.

Judaism. Isidore Epstein. (Orig.). 1959. pap. 6.95 (ISBN 0-14-020440-7, Pelican). Penguin.

Judaism. Harry Essrig. 1984. Barron.

Judaism. Michael Fishbane. LC 85-42775. (Religious Traditions of the World Ser.). 128p. (Orig.). 1985. 6.95 (ISBN 0-06-062655-0, HarpR). Har-Row.

Judaism. Lady Queenborough. 1982. lib. bdg. 55.95 (ISBN 0-87700-410-2). Revisionist Pr.

Judaism. Solomon Nigosian. (Crucible Ser.). 208p. 1987. pap. 9.95 (ISBN 0-85030-429-6). Thorsons Pubs.

Judaism. Stuart E. Rosenberg. 159p. pap. 2.45 (ISBN 0-686-95139-5). ADL.

Judaism. Jay G. Williams. LC 80-51551. 204p. 1981. pap. 5.50 (ISBN 0-8356-0540-X, Quest). Theos Pub Hse.

Judaism. Angela Wood. (World Religions Ser.). (Illus.). 72p. 1984. 16.95 (ISBN 0-7134-3656-5, Pub. by Batsford England). David & Charles.

Judaism, a Portrait. Leon Roth. LC 61-5918. 240p. 1972. pap. 4.95 (ISBN 0-8052-0344-3). Schocken.

Judaism: A Sociology. Stephen Sharot. LC 75-37727. 240p. 1976. text ed. 29.50x (ISBN 0-8419-0250-X). Holmes & Meier.

Judaism: An Eternal Covenant. Howard R. Greenstein. LC 82-17601. 176p. 1983. pap. 10.95 (ISBN 0-8006-1690-1, 1-1690). Fortress.

Judaism & Christianity: Selected Accounts, 1892-1962. Arno Press Staff. LC 73-2212. (Jewish People; History, Religion, Literature Ser.). 22.00 (ISBN 0-405-05276-6). Ayer Co Pubs.

Judaism & Christian Beginnings. Samuel Sandmel. pap. 11.95x (ISBN 0-19-502282-3). Oxford U Pr.

Judaism & Christianity. William B. Silverman. LC 68-27330. pap. 5.95x (ISBN 0-87441-016-9). Behrman.

Judaism & Christianity: A Guide to the Reference Literature. Edward D. Starkey. (Reference Sources in the Humanities Ser.). 250p. 1987. lib. bdg. 27.50 (ISBN 0-87287-533-4). Libs Unl.

Judaism & Christianity: Origins, Developments & Recent Trends. Robert H. Ayers. LC 83-3548. (Illus.). 478p. (Orig.). 1983. lib. bdg. 35.75 (ISBN 0-8191-3156-3); pap. text ed. 16.50 (ISBN 0-8191-3157-1). U Pr of Amer.

Judaism & Christianity: Perspectives & Traditions. Luther H. Harshbarger & John A. Mourant. 490p. Date not set. text ed. price not set (ISBN 0-8290-0294-4); pap. text ed. price not set (ISBN 0-8290-0295-2). Irvington.

Judaism & Christianity: The Differences. Trude Weiss-Rosmarin. 1965. pap. 4.95 (ISBN 0-8246-0044-4). Jonathan David.

Judaism & Ethics. Daniel J. Silver. 1970. 20.00x (ISBN 0-87068-010-2). Ktav.

Judaism & Healing: Halakhic Perspectives. David J. Bleich. 1981. pap. 9.95 (ISBN 0-87068-890-1). Ktav.

Judaism & Hellenism: Studies in Their Encounter in Palestine During the Early Hellenistic Period, 2 Vols. Martin Hengel. pap. 160.00 (2027202). Bks Demand UMI.

Judaism & It's History: In Two Parts. Abraham Geiger. Tr. by Charles Newburgh from Ger. LC 85-9043. (Brown Classics in Judaica Ser.). 414p. 1985. pap. text ed. 17.50 (ISBN 0-8191-4491-6). U Pr of Amer.

Judaism & Modern Man. Ben Zion Bokser. 153p. 1958. 5.95 (ISBN 0-8022-0148-2). Philos Lib.

Judaism & Modern Man. Will Herberg. LC 59-12913. (Temple Bks). 1970. pap. text ed. 8.95x (ISBN 0-689-70232-9, T13). Atheneum.

Judaism & Mysticism According to Gershom Scholem: A Critical Analysis & Programmatic Discussion. ELiezer Schweid. Tr. by David A. Weiner. (Reprints & Translations). 1985. 22.95 (ISBN 0-89130-982-9, 00-07-09); pap. 16.95 (ISBN 0-89130-887-3). Scholars Pr Ga.

Judaism & Peacemaking. Ed. by Jewish Peace Fellowship. 1984. lib. bdg. 79.95 (ISBN 0-87700-627-X). Revisionist Pr.

Judaism & Psychology. Amsel. pap. 5.95 (ISBN 0-87306-064-4). Feldheim.

Judaism & Psychology: Halakhic Perspectives. Moshe H. Spero. 25.00x (ISBN 0-87068-693-3). Ktav.

Judaism & St. Paul. Claude G. Montefiore. LC 73-2222. (Jewish People; History, Religion, Literature Ser.). Repr. of 1914 ed. 23.50 (ISBN 0-405-05284-7). Ayer Co Pubs.

Judaism & Scripture: The Evidence of Leviticus Rabbah. Jacob Neusner. LC 85-20497. (CSHJ Ser.). 664p. 1986. 50.00x (ISBN 0-226-57614-0). U. of Chicago Pr.

Judaism & the American Idea. Milton R. Konvitz. LC 78-58028. 265p. 1978. 19.50x (ISBN 0-8014-1181-5). Cornell U Pr.

Judaism & the American Mind: In Theory & Practice. Philip D. Bookstaber. LC 78-26404. 1979. Repr. of 1939 ed. lib. bdg. cancelled (ISBN 0-313-20875-1, BOJU). Greenwood.

Judaism & the Christian Seminary Curriculum. Ed. by J. B. Long. 166p. pap. 2.95 (ISBN 0-686-95180-8). ADL.

Judaism & the New Woman. Sally Priesand. LC 75-21951. (Jewish Concepts & Issues Ser.). 162p. (Orig.). 1975. pap. 2.50x (ISBN 0-87441-230-7). Behrman.

Judaism & the Vatican. Leon De Poncins. 1982. lib. bdg. 65.00 (ISBN 0-87700-381-5). Revisionist Pr.

Judaism & the Vatican. Leon V. DePoncins. 59.95 (ISBN 0-8490-0466-7). Gordon Pr.

Judaism & Zionism: Principles & Definitions. Neturei Karta. 1980. lib. bdg. 59.95 (ISBN 0-87700-305-X). Revisionist Pr.

Judaism As a Civilization: Toward a Reconstruction of American-Jewish Life. Mordecai M. Kaplan. LC 81-6057. 601p. 1981. 25.00 (ISBN 0-8276-0193-X, 474); pap. 12.95 (ISBN 0-8276-0194-8, 480). Jewish Pubns.

Judaism at Bay: Essays Toward the Adjustment of Judaism to Modernity. Horace M. Kallen. LC 74-38451. (Religion in America, Ser. 2). 268p. 1972. Repr. of 1932 ed. 20.00 (ISBN 0-405-04071-7). Ayer Co Pubs.

Judaism Beyond God. Sherwin T. Wine. LC 85-61942. 286p. (Orig.). 1985. pap. 13.95 (ISBN 0-912645-08-3). Soc Humanistic.

Judaism Beyond God: A Radical New to Be Jewish. Sherwin T. Wine. 286p. 1986. pap. 13.95 (ISBN 0-87975-363-3). Prometheus Bks.

Judaism, Christianity & Germany. Faulhaber. Tr. by George D. Smith from Ger. 116p. 1981. Repr. of 1934 ed. lib. bdg. 30.00 (ISBN 0-89987-263-8). Darby Bks.

Judaism, Christianity & Zoroastrianism in Talmudic Babylonia. Jacob Neusner. (Studies in Judaism). 240p. (Orig.). 1987. lib. bdg. 26.50 (ISBN 0-8191-5727-9, Pub. by Studies in Judaism); pap. text ed. 13.50 (ISBN 0-8191-5728-7). U Pr of Amer.

Judaism: Development & Life. 3rd ed. Leo Trepp. 384p. 1981. pap. text ed. write for info. (ISBN 0-534-00999-9). Wadsworth Pub.

Judaism Eternal, 2 Vols. S. R. Hirsch. 1956. Set. 29.95 (ISBN 0-900689-70-6). Soncino Pr.

Judaism for Beginners. Charles Szlakmann. (Documentary Comic Bks.). (Illus.). 189p. Date not set. pap. 6.95 (ISBN 0-86316-101-4). Writers & Readers.

Judaism in a Changing Civilization. Samuel Dinin. LC 70-176722. (Columbia University. Teachers College. Contributions to Education: No. 563). Repr. of 1933 ed. 22.50 (ISBN 0-404-55563-2). AMS Pr.

Judaism in a Changing World. Leo Jung. 273p. 1971. 9.50 (ISBN 0-900689-08-0). Soncino Pr.

Judaism in America: From Curiosity to Third Faith. Joseph L. Blau. LC 75-5069. (Chicago History of American Religion Ser.). 176p. 1976. 6.00x (ISBN 0-226-05727-5). U of Chicago Pr.

Judaism in German Christian Theology since 1945: Christianity & Israel Considered in Terms of Mission. Eva Fleischner. LC 75-22374. (ATLA Monograph: No. 8). 205p. 1975. 17.50 (ISBN 0-8108-0835-8). Scarecrow.

Judaism in Islam: Biblical & Talmudic Background of the Koran & Its Commentaries. 3rd ed. Abraham I. Katsh. LC 80-50001. 1980. pap. 9.75 (ISBN 0-87203-086-5). Hermon.

Judaism in Music. Richard Wagner. 1982. lib. bdg. 79.95 (ISBN 0-87700-354-8). Revisionist Pr.

Judaism in Society: The Evidence of the Yerushalmi, Toward the Natural History of a Religion. Jacob Neusner. LC 83-4916. (Chicago Studies in the History of Judaism). 272p. 1984. lib. bdg. 25.00x (ISBN 0-226-57616-7). U of Chicago Pr.

Judaism in the American Humanities. Jacob Neusner. LC 81-1798. (Brown Judaic Studies). 1981. pap. text ed. 20.00 (ISBN 0-89130-480-0, 14-00-28). Scholars Pr GA.

Judaism in the American Humanities: Second Series. Jacob Neusner. (Brown Judaic Ser.). 136p. 1983. pap. 13.50 (ISBN 0-89130-618-8, 14 00 42). Scholars Pr GA.

Judaism in the Beginning of Christianity. Jacob Neusner. LC 83-48000. 112p. 1984. pap. 5.95 (ISBN 0-8006-1750-9, 1-1750). Fortress.

Judaism in the Matrix of Christianity. Jacob Neusner. LC 85-45492. 160p. 1986. pap. 12.95 (ISBN 0-8006-1897-1, 1-1897). Fortress.

Judaism-Law & Ethics. Isaac Herzog. 227p. 1974. 9.95 (ISBN 0-900689-73-0). Soncino Pr.

Judaism Looks at Christianity: 7 BC-1985 C. E. Stanley J. Marks & Ethel M. Marks. 1985. pap. 19.95; 24.95. Bur Intl Aff.

Judaism of the Next Generation. Morris Janowitz. pap. 2.00 (ISBN 0-686-15805-9). Rostrum Bks.

Judaism on Trial: Jewish-Christian Disputations in the Middle Ages. Hyman Maccoby. (Littman Library of Jewish Civilization). 246p. 1982. 34.00x (ISBN 0-19-710046-5). Oxford U Pr.

Judaism or Zionism? What Difference for the Middle East? Eaford & Ajaz. 320p. 1986. 32.50 (ISBN 0-86232-475-0, Pub. by Zed Pr England); pap. 12.50 (ISBN 0-86232-476-9, Pub. by Zed Pr England). Humanities.

Judaism: The Classical Statement, the Evidence of the Bavli. Jacob Neusner. LC 85-28875. (CSHJ Ser.). 288p. 1986. 37.00 (ISBN 0-226-57620-5). U of Chicago Pr.

Judaism: The Evidence of the Mishnah. Jacob Neusner. LC 80-26080. xx, 420p. 1981. 25.00x (ISBN 0-226-57617-5); pap. 15.95 (ISBN 0-226-57619-1). U of Chicago Pr.

Judaism: The Way of Holiness. Solomon Nigosian. 1987. pap. 9.95. Inner Tradit.

Judaism: The Way of Sanctification. Samuel Dresner & Byron Sherwin. 1978. text ed. 6.50 (ISBN 0-8381-0222-0). United Syn Bk.

Judaism, Thought & Legend. Meir Meiseles. Tr. by Rebecca Schonfeld-Brand & Aryeh Newman. 1978. pap. 9.95 (ISBN 0-87306-140-3). Feldheim.

Judaism under Freedom. Ira Eisenstein. LC 56-12814. 262p. 1956. pap. 6.95 (ISBN 0-935457-05-4). Reconstructionist Pr.

Judaism Viewed from Within & from Without: Anthropological Studies. Ed. by Harvey E. Goldberg. (Anthropolgy & Judaic Studies). 348p. 1986. 44.50X (ISBN 0-88706-354-3); pap. 16.95X (ISBN 0-88706-356-X). STate U NY Pr.

Judaism Without Guilt. Joseph R. Narot. pap. 0.75 (ISBN 0-686-15811-3). Rostrum Bks.

Judaism Without Supernaturalism. Mordecai M. Kaplan. LC 58-10056. 254p. 1958. pap. 6.50 (ISBN 0-935457-18-6). Reconstructionist Pr.

Judaism, Zionism, & Anti-Semitism. Rabbi E. Berger et al. 72p. (Orig.). 1985. pap. 2.50 (ISBN 0-935177-01-9). Palestine Focus.

Judaism's Truth versus the Missionaries. Beth Moshe. 354p. 1987. 14.95 (ISBN 0-8197-0515-2). Bloch.

Judas: Los Hechos de los Apostatas (Comentario Biblico Portavoz) Maxwell S. Coder. Orig. Title: Jude: the Acts of the Apostates (Everyman's Bible Commentary. (Span.). 134p. 1980. pap. 3.95 (ISBN 0-8254-1125-4). Kregel.

Judas Maccabeus. Ed. by William P. Hansen & John Haney. (World Leaders--Past & Present Ser.). (Illus.). 112p. 1987. lib. bdg. 16.95 (ISBN 0-87754-539-1). Chelsea Hse.

Judas: The Unforgiven Man. Ethel L. Schaumberg. 1981. 4.75 (1002). CSS of Ohio.

Judas Within. Kenneth Zanca. (Illus.). 96p. (Orig.). 1978. pap. 2.95 (ISBN 0-914544-25-X). Living Flame Pr.

Jude: John. H. A. Ironside. 9.95 (ISBN 0-87213-372-9). Loizeaux.

Jude: The Acts of the Apostates. S. Maxwell Coder. (Everyman's Bible Commentary Ser). 1967. pap. 5.95 (ISBN 0-8024-2065-6). Moody.

Judenrat. Isaiah Trunk. LC 70-173692. 1977. pap. 8.95 (ISBN 0-8128-2170-X). Stein & Day.

Judeo-Christian Vision & the Modern Business Corporation. Ed. by Oliver Williams & John Houck. LC 81-40448. 336p. 1982. pap. text ed. 10.95 (ISBN 0-268-01201-6). U of Notre Dame Pr.

Judge: An Untrue Tale. Harve Zemach. LC 79-87209. (Illus.). 48p. 1969. 14.95 (ISBN 0-374-33960-0). FS&G.

Judge for Yourself. Steve Lawhead & Alice Lawhead. 160p. 1985. pap. 3.95 (ISBN 0-88207-597-7). Victor Bks.

Judgement of the Synode at Dort Touching Conradus Vortius. (English Experience Ser.: No. 678). 1974. Repr. of 1619 ed. 10.50 (ISBN 90-221-0678-0). Walter J Johnson.

Judgement Seat of Christ: Your Day in Court. Leonard Ravenhill. 200p. (Orig.). 1986. pap. 6.95 (ISBN 0-910311-34-X). Huntington Hse Inc.

Judgement unto Victory. Robert S. Yoder. 1983. 6.75 (ISBN 0-8062-1964-5). Carlton.

Judges. Philip J. King. (Bible Ser.). pap. 1.00 (ISBN 0-8091-5077-8). Paulist Pr.

Judges. A. D. Mayes. (Old Testament Guides Ser.). 98p. 1985. pap. text ed. 3.95x (ISBN 0-905774-58-2, Pub. by JSOT Pr England). Eisenbrauns.

Judges, Vol. 6A. Tr. & intro. by Robert G. Boling. LC 72-96229. (Anchor Bible Ser). (Illus.). 360p. 1975. 18.00 (ISBN 0-385-01029-X). Doubleday.

Judges: A Bible Study Commentary. Paul P. Enns. (Bible Study Commentary Ser.). 160p. (Orig.). 1982. pap. 5.95 (ISBN 0-310-44051-3, 11831P). Zondervan.

Judges: A Commentary. J. Alberto Soggin. Tr. by John Bowden from Ital. LC 81-7600. (Old Testament Library). 324p. 1981. text ed. 21.95 (ISBN 0-664-21368-5). Westminster.

Judges & Kings: God's Chosen Leaders. William E. McElrath. (Illus.). 1979. 5.95 (ISBN 0-8054-4249-9, 4242-49). Broadman.

Judges & Ruth. Arthur E. Cundall & Leon Morris. LC 68-31426. (Tyndale Old Testament Commentary Ser). (Illus.). 1968. 12.95 (ISBN 0-87784-896-3); pap. 6.95 (ISBN 0-87784-257-4). Inter-Varsity.

Judges & Ruth. F. C. Jennings. 9.95 (ISBN 0-88172-152-2). Believers Bkshelf.

Judges & Ruth. rev. ed. Irving L. Jensen. (Bible Self-Study Ser). (Illus.). 96p. 1967. pap. 3.25 (ISBN 0-8024-1007-3). Moody.

Judges & Ruth. Arthur Lewis. (Everyman's Bible Commentary Ser.). 1979. pap. 5.95 (ISBN 0-8024-2007-9). Moody.

Judges & Ruth. rev. ed. Samuel Ridout. 415p. 1981. pap. 7.25 (ISBN 0-87213-720-1). Loizeaux.

Judges: God's War Against Humanism. James B. Jordan. (Trinity Biblical Commentary Ser.). xxi, 333p. 1985. 14.95 (ISBN 0-939404-10-9). Geneva Ministr.

Judges, Ruth, First & Second Samuel. Eric C. Rust. LC 59-10454. (Layman's Bible Commentary Ser: Vol. 6). 1961. pap. 4.95 (ISBN 0-8042-3066-8). John Knox.

Judgment in the Gate. Ed. by Richie Martin. LC 86-70285. (Orig.). 1986. pap. 6.95 (ISBN 0-89107-396-5, Crossway Bks). Good News.

Judgment of a Catholicke English-Man Living in Banishment for His Religion. Robert Parsons. LC 57-9033. 1978. Repr. of 1608 ed. 30.00x (ISBN 0-8201-1240-2). Schol Facsimiles.

Judgment Seat of Christ, Vol. 7. Gordon Lindsay. (End of the Age Ser.). 1.25 (ISBN 0-89985-073-1). Christ Nations.

Judicial Doctrines of Religious Rights in America. William G. Torpey. LC 78-132289. (Civil Liberties in American History Ser). 1970. Repr. of 1948 ed. lib. bdg. 42.50 (ISBN 0-306-70067-0). Da Capo.

Judicial System & the Jews in Nazi Germany. J. Mendelsohn. LC 81-80321. (Holocaust Ser.). 245p. 1982. lib. bdg. 61.00 (ISBN 0-8240-4887-3). Garland Pub.

Judische Apologetik. Moritz Gudemann. Ed. by Steven Katz. LC 79-7133. (Jewish Philosophy, Mysticism & History of Ideas Ser.). 1980. Repr. of 1906 ed. lib. bdg. 23.00x (ISBN 0-405-12258-6). Ayer Co Pubs.

Judische Schriften. Moses Hess. Ed. by Steven Katz. LC 79-7135. (Jewish Philosophy, Mysticism & History of Ideas Ser.). 1980. Repr. of 1905 ed. lib. bdg. 14.00x (ISBN 0-405-12261-6). Ayer Co Pubs.

Judischen Frauen in der Geschichte, Literatur und Kunst. Meyer Kayserling. Ed. by Steven Katz. (Jewish Philosophy, Mysticism & the History of Ideas Ser.). 1980. Repr. of 1879 ed. lib. bdg. 21.50x (ISBN 0-405-12273-X). Ayer Co Pubs.

Judith. Carey A. Moore. LC 83-11694. (Anchor Bible Ser.: Vol. 40). (Illus.). 312p. 1985. 14.00 (ISBN 0-385-14424-5). Doubleday.

Judith. N. I. Saloff-Astakhoff. 160p. 1980. 1.00 (ISBN 0-88113-290-X). Edit Betania.

Jueces y Rut (Comentario Biblico Portavoz) Arthur H. Lewis. Orig. Title: Judges & Ruth (Everyman's Bible Commentary) (Span.). 128p. 1982. pap. 3.50 (ISBN 0-8254-1434-2). Kregel.

Juengste Gericht Philologische Studien zu den Eschatologie Vorstellungen in den Alt-und Fruehmittel-Hochdeutschen Denkmaelern. Wilfried Kettler. (Quellen und Forschungen Zur Sprach-und Kulturgeschichte der Germanischen Voelker: Vol.70). 1977. 38.80x (ISBN 3-11-007345-5). De Gruyter.

Juergen Moltmanns Theologie in Auseinandersetzung mit Ernst Bloch. Marko Matic. (European University Studies Ser.: No. 23, Vol. 209). (Ger.). 428p. 1983. 41.05 (ISBN 3-8204-7741-1). P Lang Pubs.

Juguemos. Viola D. Campbell. (Illus.). 199p. 1983. pap. 3.50 (ISBN 0-311-11006-1). Casa Bautista.

Juifs de Paris Pendant la Revolution. Leon Kahn. (Research & Source Works Ser.: No. 198). 1968. Repr. of 1899 ed. 30.50 (ISBN 0-8337-1892-4). B Franklin.

Julian: A Play Based on the Life of Julian of Norwich. J. Janda. 112p. (Orig.). 1984. pap. 6.95 (ISBN 0-8164-2632-5, 6464, HarpR). Har-Row.

Julian of Norwich. Paolo Molinari. LC 74-13160. 1974. Repr. of 1958 ed. lib. bdg. 32.50 (ISBN 0-8414-6168-6). Folcroft.

Julian of Norwich, "Showings". Ed. by Edmund Colledge et al. LC 77-90953. (Classics of Western Spirituality). 384p. 1978. 13.95 (ISBN 0-8091-0234-X); pap. 9.95 (ISBN 0-8091-2091-7). Paulist Pr.

Julian: Scenes in Judea, 2 vols. in one. William Ware. Ed. by Moshe Davis. LC 77-70754. (America & the Holy Land Ser.). 1977. Repr. of 1841 ed. lib. bdg. 40.00x (ISBN 0-405-10299-2). Ayer Co Pubs.

Julian: Woman of Our Day. Ed. by Robert Llewelyn. 1987. pap. 6.95 (ISBN 0-89622-334-5). Twenty-Third.

Julianus Pomerius, the Contemplative Life. Ed. by W. J. Burghardt et al. LC 78-62457. (ACW Ser.: No. 4). 220p. 1947. 9.95 (ISBN 0-8091-0245-5). Paulist Pr.

Julius Africanus & the Early Christian View of Magic. Francis C. Thee. 549p. 1984. lib. bdg. 73.50x (ISBN 3-16-144552-X, Pub. by J C B Mohr BRD). Coronet Bks.

July Fourth Is Every Day! To Serve, Is to Be Served! Richard B. Jarrett. (Orig.). 1981. pap. text ed. write for info. Jarrett.

July Secret: The Prohetic Meaning of Fatima about Russia & the Future of the Church. Sergius Wroblewski. (Illus.). 90p. (Orig.). 1985. pap. 4.50 (ISBN 0-913382-15-9, 105-39). Prow Bks-Franciscan.

Jung & Christianity: The Challenge of Reconciliation. Wallace B. Clift. 169p. 1982. 12.95 (ISBN 0-8245-0409-7). Crossroad NY.

Jung & Christianity: The Challenge of Reconciliation. Wallace B. Clift. LC 81-17395. 192p. 1983. pap. 8.95 (ISBN 0-8245-0552-2). Crossroad NY.

Jung & Eastern Thought. Harold C. Coward. (Series in Transpersonal & Humanistic Philosophy). 229p. 1985. 39.50 (ISBN 0-88706-052-8); pap. 12.95 (ISBN 0-88706-051-X). State U NY Pr.

Jung & the Bible. Wayne G. Rollins. LC 82-48091. 156p. 1983. pap. 10.95 (ISBN 0-8042-1117-5). John Knox.

Jung & the Christian Way. Christopher Bryant. 144p. (Orig.). 1984. pap. 7.95 (ISBN 0-86683-872-4, 7917, HarpR). Har-Row.

Jung, Gods, & Modern Man. Antonio Moreno. LC 73-122047. pap. 72.00 (ISBN 0-317-29683-3, 2022073). Bks Demand UMI.

Jungian Symbolism in Astrology. Alice O. Howell. LC 86-40406. 238p. (Orig.). 1987. pap. 6.95 (ISBN 0-8356-0618-X). Theos Pub Hse.

Jung's Challenge to Contemporary Religion. Ed. by Murray Stein & Robert Moore. 175p. 1987. pap. 14.95 (ISBN 0-933029-09-8). Chiron Pubns.

Jung's Treatment of Christianity: The Psychotherapy of a Religious Tradition. 2nd ed. Murray Stein. LC 85-4739. 194p. 1985. 24.95 (ISBN 0-933029-14-4). Chiron Pubns.

Junior Contemporary Prayer Book for the High Holidays. Sidney Greenberg & Allan S. Sugarman. pap. 4.95 (ISBN 0-87677-054-5). Prayer Bk.

Junior Encyclopedia of Sikhism. H. S. Singha. 181p. 1985. text ed. 12.50x (ISBN 0-7069-2844-X, Pub. by Vikas India). Advent NY.

Junior High Ministry. Wayne Rice. 220p. 1987. text ed. 12.95 (ISBN 0-310-34970-2). Zondervan.

Junior High Ministry: A Guidebook for the Leading & Teaching of Early Adolescents. Wayne Rice. 1978. pap. 6.95 (ISBN 0-310-34971-0, 10825P). Zondervan.

Junior Jewish Encyclopedia. 10th, rev. ed. Ed. by Naomi Ben-Asher & Hayim Leaf. LC 84-51583. (Illus.). 1984. 19.95 (ISBN 0-88400-110-5). Shengold.

Junior Judaica, 6 vols. (Encyclopedia Judaica for Youth Ser.). 69.00 (ISBN 0-942500-00-8, Keter Pub). Maccabee Pub.

Junior Saints: The Rich Rare Humor of Kids in Church. Oren Arnold. LC 75-12108. (Illus.). 128p. 1976. pap. 4.95 (ISBN 0-8254-2117-9). Kregel.

Junior Surprise Sermons with Handmade Objects, 2 bks. Arnold C. Westphal. Set. pap. 9.90 (ISBN 0-686-70924-1); No. 1. pap. 4.50 (ISBN 0-915398-18-4); No. 2. pap. 4.95 (ISBN 0-915398-19-2). Visual Evangels.

Junior Worker's Handbook. Mavis Weidman. pap. 1.95 (ISBN 0-87509-098-2). Chr Pubns.

Junior's Praise. Kenneth W. Osbeck. LC 57-1012. 184p. 1981. 5.95x (ISBN 0-8254-3400-9). Kregel.

Juniper: Friend of Francis, Fool of God. Murray Bodo. 90p. pap. text ed. cancelled (ISBN 0-86716-021-7). St Anthony Mess Pr.

Junipero Serra: Pioneer of the Cross. Bernice Scott. (Illus.). 248p. 1985. pap. 9.95 (ISBN 0-317-44750-5). Panorama West.

Junipero Serra: The Illustrated Story of the Franciscan Founder of California's Missions. Don DeNevi & Noel Moholy. LC 84-47718. (Illus.). 256p. 1985. 14.45 (ISBN 0-06-061876-0, HarpR). Har-Row.

Juntarum Typographiae Annales. Angelo M. Bandini. 474p. Date not set. Repr. of 1791 ed. text ed. 82.80x (ISBN 0-576-72349-5, Pub. by Gregg Intl Pubs England). Gregg Intl.

Jupiter-Saturn Conference Lectures: New Insights in Modern Astrology. Stephen Arroyo & Liz Greene. LC 82-45632. (Lectures on Modern Astrology). 1983. pap. 8.95 (ISBN 0-916360-16-4). CRCS Pubns NV.

Jurisdiction Regall, Episcopall, Papall. George Carleton. LC 68-54625. (English Experience Ser.: No. 34). 302p. 1969. Repr. of 1610 ed. 30.00 (ISBN 90-221-0034-0). Walter J Johnson.

Jurisprudence of Freemasonry. Albert G. Mackey. 12.00 (ISBN 0-685-19480-9). Powner.

Just a Minute, Lord: Prayers for Girls. Lois Johnson. LC 73-78265. (Illus.). 96p. (Orig.). 1973. pap. 3.95 (ISBN 0-8066-1329-7, 10-3605). Augsburg.

Just a Taste of Honey. K. Norline Rendall. (Quiet Time Bks.). 1975. pap. 3.50 (ISBN 0-8024-4494-6). Moody.

Just a Touch of Nearness. Fred Bauer. 48p. 1985. 6.95 (ISBN 0-8378-5082-7). Gibson.

Just Add Water: How to Use Dehydrated Foods & TVP. Barbara G. Salsbury. 92p. 1972. 5.50 (ISBN 0-88290-011-0). Horizon Utah.

Just Around the Corner. Bhagwan S. Rajneesh. Ed. by Swami Krishna Mahasattva. LC 84-42870. (Initiation Talks Ser.). 224p. (Orig.). 1984. pap. 3.95 (ISBN 0-88050-588-5). Chidvilas Found.

Just As I Am. Harvey Cox. LC 82-11631. 160p. 1983. 10.95 (ISBN 0-687-20687-1). Abingdon.

Just Balance. Al-Ghazzali. 6.50 (ISBN 0-317-01603-2). Kazi Pubns.

Just Because They're Jewish. M. Hirsh Goldberg. 1978. 9.95 (ISBN 0-8128-2518-7). Stein & Day.

Just Between God & Me. Sandra Drescher. 1977. girls o.p. 9.95 (ISBN 0-310-23940-0); boys gift ed. o.p. 9.95 (ISBN 0-310-23950-8, 18111B); pap. 4.95 (ISBN 0-310-23941-9, 18111P). Zondervan.

Just Complaint Against an Unjust Doer, Mr. J. Paget. John Davenport. LC 76-57376. (English Experience Ser.: No. 793). 1977. Repr. of 1634 ed. lib. bdg. 5.00 (ISBN 90-221-0793-0). Walter J Johnson.

Just Follow the Signs. Daniel Mueller. 1984. 5.00 (ISBN 0-89536-676-2, 4851). CSS of Ohio.

Just for Today: Selections from St. Therese of Lisieux & the Imitation of Christ. Thomas a Kempis & St. Therese of Lisieux. 250p. 1983. pap. 7.95 (ISBN 0-87243-121-5). Templegate.

Just Friends? Andre Bustanoby. 160p. (Orig.). 1985. pap. 6.95 (ISBN 0-310-45431-X, 9254P). Zondervan.

Just in Time: A Novel about Medieval Jewish Community. Marcus Lehmann. 1982. pap. 6.95 (ISBN 0-87306-257-4). Feldheim.

Just King: Monarchical Judicial Authority in Ancient Israel. Keith W. Whitelam. (Journal for the Study of the Old Testament Supplement Ser.: No. 12). 1979. text ed. 19.95x (ISBN 0-905774-18-3, Pub. by JSOT Pr England). Eisenbrauns.

Just Like Jesus. Bob Wolf. (Illus.). 24p. (Orig.). 1982. pap. 0.75 (ISBN 0-89323-034-0). Bible Memory.

Just Like That. Bhagwan Shree Rajneesh. Ed. by Swami Anand Somendra. (Sufi Ser.). (Illus.). 488p. (Orig.). 1975. 19.50 (ISBN 0-88050-089-1). Chidvilas Found.

Just Like Us: Twenty-One Character Studies from the Bible. J. Oswald Sanders. 1985. pap. 6.95 (ISBN 0-8024-6516-1). Moody.

Just Mary. Effie M. Williams. 96p. pap. 0.75 (ISBN 0-686-29124-7). Faith Pub Hse.

Just Me & the Kids. Patricia Brandt & Dave Jackson. (Family Ministry Ser.). (Illus.). 54p. 1985. pap. text ed. 19.95 (ISBN 0-89191-750-0). Cook.

Just One Victory. Becky Tirabassi & Gregg Lewis. (Campus Life Bks.). (Orig.). 1987. pap. 5.95 (ISBN 0-8423-1998-0). Tyndale.

Just Passing Through. G. E. Hutches. LC 78-71390. (Stories That Win Ser.). 1979. pap. 1.25 (ISBN 0-8163-0320-7, 10617-9). Pacific Pr Pub Assn.

Just Passing Through. Steven LaVelle. (Illus.). 32p. (Orig.). 1980. pap. 1.50 (ISBN 0-87516-402-1). De Vorss.

Just This Much: Healing Into Life & Death. Stephen Levine. 288p. 1987. 16.95 (ISBN 0-385-23371-X, Anch); pap. 8.95 (ISBN 0-385-23372-8, Anch). Doubleday.

Just to Love Him: Talks & Essays about Meher Baba. Adi K. Irani. Ed. by Steve Berry & Peter Booth. LC 85-10709. 160p. (Orig.). 1985. pap. 8.95 (ISBN 0-913078-56-5). Sheriar Pr.

Just War Theory in the Nuclear Age. John D. Jones & Marc F. Griesbach. LC 85-6092. 236p. (Orig.). 1985. lib. bdg. 25.50 (ISBN 0-8191-4659-5); pap. text ed. 10.75 (ISBN 0-8191-4660-9). U Pr of Amer.

Just When You Need Him. R. Earl Allen. (Contempo Ser). pap. 0.95 (ISBN 0-8010-0074-2). Baker Bk.

Justice & Health Care: Christian Perspectives. Ed. by Margaret Kelly. LC 84-9459. 1985. pap. 16.50 (ISBN 0-87125-097-7). Cath Health.

Justice & History in the Old Testament: The Evolution of Divine Retribution in the Historiographies of the Wilderness Generation. Richard Adamiak. 1982. 14.95x (ISBN 0-939738-08-2). Zubal Inc.

Justice & Peace Education: Models for College & University Faculty. Ed. by David M. Johnson. LC 85-25808. 256p. (Orig.). 1986. pap. 16.95 (ISBN 0-88344-247-7). Orbis Bks.

Justice Church: The New Function of the Church in North American Christianity. Frederick Herzog. LC 80-15091. 176p. (Orig.). 1980. pap. 6.95 (ISBN 0-88344-249-3). Orbis Bks.

Justice Department & Abuse of the Judicial System. pap. 3.00 (ISBN 0-915598-22-1). Church of Scient Info.

Justice for the Unborn: Why We Have Legal Abortion & How We Can Stop It. Randall Hekman. 200p. (Orig.). 1984. pap. 5.95 (ISBN 0-89283-194-4). Servant.

Justice, Human Nature, & Political Obligation. Morton A. Kaplan. LC 76-8145. 1976. 18.95 (ISBN 0-02-916890-2). Free Pr.

Justice in the Marketplace: Collected Statements of the Vatican & the United States Catholic Bishops on Economic Policy, 1891-1984. Ed. by David Byers. 554p. 1985. pap. 14.95 (ISBN 1-55586-933-5). US Catholic.

Justice, Justice, Shalt Thou Pursue. Ronald Sobel & Sidney Wallach. 10.00x (ISBN 0-87068-458-2). Ktav.

Justice-Light & Satisfaction-Delight. Sri Chinmoy. (Soulful Questions & Fruitful Answers on Law & Justice). 41p. (Orig.). 1977. pap. 2.00 (ISBN 0-88497-338-7). Aum Pubns.

Justice of Zeus. 2nd ed. Hugh Lloyd-Jones. (Sather Classical Lectures: No. 41). 290p. 1983. pap. 8.95 (ISBN 0-520-04688-9). U of Cal Pr.

Justice Seekers Peace Makers: 32 Portraits in Courage. Michael True. (Illus.). 160p. 1985. pap. 5.95 (ISBN 0-89622-212-8). Twenty Third.

Justice with Faith Today: Selected Letters & Addresses--II. Pedro Arrupe. Ed. by Jerome Aixala. LC 80-81055. 336p. 1980. 8.00 (ISBN 0-912422-51-3); pap. 7.00 smyth sewn (ISBN 0-912422-50-5). Inst Jesuit.

Justification. pap. 1.25 (ISBN 0-686-12888-5). Schmul Pub Co.

Justification: An Ecumenical Study. George H. Tavard. 144p. (Orig.). 1983. pap. 7.95 (ISBN 0-8091-2549-8). Paulist Pr.

Justification & Sanctification. Peter Toon. LC 83-70317. (Foundations for Faith Ser.). 160p. 1983. pap. 8.95 (ISBN 0-89107-288-8, Crossway Bks). Good News.

Justification by an Imputed Righteousness. John Bunyan. pap. 2.95 (ISBN 0-685-88380-9). Reiner.

Justification by Faith. John MacArthur, Jr. (John MacArthur's Bible Studies). 1985. pap. 4.95 (ISBN 0-8024-5120-9). Moody.

Justification by Faith: A Matter of Death & Life. Gerhard O. Forde. LC 81-70663. 112p. 1982. pap. 5.95 (ISBN 0-8006-1634-0, 1-1634). Fortress.

Justification by Faith in Modern Theology. Henry P. Hamann. 114p. 1957. write for info. Concordia Schl Grad Studies.

Justification by Faith: Lutherans & Catholics in Dialogue VII. Ed. by H. George Snderson et al. LC 84-28412. 320p. (Orig.). 1984. pap. 6.95 (ISBN 0-8066-2103-6, 10-3626). Augsburg.

Justification of God: An Exegetical & Theological Study of Romans 9: 1-23. John Piper. 312p. (Orig.). 1983. pap. 8.95 (ISBN 0-8010-7079-1). Baker Bk.

Justification of Knowledge. Robert Reymond. 1976. pap. 6.95 (ISBN 0-87552-406-0). Presby & Reformed.

Justification of Man by Faith Only. Philipp Melanchthon. Tr. by Nicholas Lesse. LC 79-84123. (English Experience Ser.: No. 942). 204p. 1979. Repr. of 1548 ed. lib. bdg. 15.00 (ISBN 90-221-0942-9). Walter J Johnson.

Justification of Religious Belief. Basil Mitchell. (Orig.). 1981. pap. 7.95x (ISBN 0-19-520124-8). Oxford U Pr.

Justification of Separation from the Church of England. John Robinson. LC 77-7427. (English Experience Ser.: No. 888). 1977. Repr. of 1610 ed. lib. bdg. 46.00 (ISBN 90-221-0888-0). Walter J Johnson.

Justification: The Chief Article of Christian Doctrine. Martin Chemnitz. Tr. by J. A. Preus. 200p. 1986. 16.95 (ISBN 0-570-04227-5, 15-2186). Concordia.

Justification: The Doctrine of Karl Barth & a Catholic Reflection. Hans Kung. LC 80-26001. 378p. 1981. pap. 14.95 (ISBN 0-664-24364-9). Westminster.

Justifying Faith. Thomas Goodwin. 593p. 1985. 15.95 (ISBN 0-85151-447-2). Banner of Truth.

Justin: Heaven's Baby. Sharon Marshall. 128p. (Orig.). 1983. pap. 3.95 (ISBN 0-8341-0833-X). Beacon Hill.

Justinian the Great: The Emperor & Saint. Asterios Gerostergios. LC 82-82095. (Illus.). 312p. 1982. 15.95 (ISBN 0-914744-58-5); pap. 11.95 (ISBN 0-914744-59-3). Inst Byzantine.

K

K. A. C. Cresswell Library of Islamic Art & Architecture. 1986. 39.50 (ISBN 977-424-101-0, Pub. by Am Univ Cairo Pr). Columbia U Pr.

K. H. Letters to C. W. Leadbeater. Jinarajadasa. 5.95 (ISBN 0-8356-7552-1). Theos Pub Hse.

K Sorokaljetiju pagubnago evlogijanskago raskola. N. D. Talberg. Tr. of Fortieth Anniversary of the Ruinous Evlogian Schism. 128p. 1966. pap. 4.00 (ISBN 0-317-30373-2). Holy Trinity.

K Tchemu Privodit Bezbozhije. N. Ivanoff. Tr. of What are the Consequeces of Godlessness. 24p. 1983. pap. 1.50 (ISBN 0-317-29144-0). Holy Trinity.

Kabala of Numbers. Sepharial. LC 80-53342. 423p. 1980. Repr. of 1974 ed. lib. bdg. 16.95x (ISBN 0-89370-627-2). Borgo Pr.

Kabala of Numbers. Sepharial. LC 74-6128. 425p. 1974. pap. 6.95 (ISBN 0-87877-027-5, P-27). Newcastle Pub.

Kaballah & Jewish Mysticism. Israel Gutwirth. 1987. 15.00. Philos Lib.

Kabbala: An Introduction to Jewish Mysticism & Secret Doctrine. Erich Bischoff. LC 84-52262. 96p. 1985. pap. 5.95 (ISBN 0-87728-564-0). Weiser.

Kabbala Unveiled: Books of the Zohar. Tr. by S. L. Mathers. lib. bdg. 100.00 (ISBN 0-87968-124-1). Krishna Pr.

Kabbalah. Adolphe Franck. 1979. pap. 5.95 (ISBN 0-8065-0708-X). Citadel Pr.

Kabbalah. Charles Ponce. LC 78-7385. (Illus.). 1978. pap. 6.50 (ISBN 0-8356-0510-8, Quest). Theos Pub Hse.

Kabbalah. Gershom Scholem. 1978. pap. 10.95 (ISBN 0-452-00791-7, Mer). NAL.

Kabbalah & Criticism. Harold Bloom. LC 75-12820. 100p. 1975. 8.95 (ISBN 0-8264-0124-4). Continuum.

Kabbalah & Criticism. Harold Bloom. LC 82-4674. 126p. 1983. pap. 7.95 (ISBN 0-8245-0487-9). Crossroad NY.

Kabbalah & Jewish Mysticism. Israel Gutwirth. LC 86-18693. 288p. 1986. 15.00 (ISBN 0-8022-2516-0). Philos Lib.

Kabbalah & Psychology. Z'ev Ben Shimon Halevi. (Illus.). 260p. (Orig.). 1986. pap. 12.50 (ISBN 0-87728-671-X). Weiser.

Kabbalah & the Philosophy of Plato. Adolf Franck. (Illus.). 81p. 1986. 98.85 (ISBN 0-89901-288-4). Found Class Reprints.

Kabbalah Connection. Philip S. Berg. 224p. 1983. 12.95 (ISBN 0-943688-02-7); pap. 9.95 (ISBN 0-943688-03-5). Res Ctr Kabbalah.

Kabbalah Decoded. Ed. by Rodney Dale. Tr. by George Sassoon. 240p. 1978. 55.00 (ISBN 0-7156-1289-1, Pub. by Duckworth London); pap. 17.00 (ISBN 0-7156-1374-X). Longwood Pub Group.

Kabbalah Decoded. George Sassoon. Ed. by Rodney Dale. 240p. 1978. pap. 9.95 (ISBN 0-7156-1289-1). US Games Syst.

Kabbalah for the Layman. Philip S. Berg. (Span.). 224p. 1986. 12.95 (ISBN 0-943688-43-4); pap. 9.95 (ISBN 0-943688-44-2). Res Ctr Kabbalah.

Kabbalah for the Layman II. Philip S. Berg. 224p. 1987. 14.95 (ISBN 0-943688-24-8); pap. 9.95 (ISBN 0-943688-26-4). Res Ctr Kabbalah.

Kabbalah for the Layman III. Philip S. Berg. 1987. 14.95 (ISBN 0-943688-69-8); pap. 9.95 (ISBN 0-943688-70-1). Res Ctr Kabbalah.

Kabbalah for the Modern World. 2nd, rev. & expanded ed. Migene Gonzalez-Wippler. LC 83-80133. (New Age Ser.). 250p. 1987. pap. 9.95 (ISBN 0-87542-294-2). Llewellyn Pubns.

Kabbalah or the Religious Philosophy of the Hebrews. Adolph Franck. LC 73-2199. (Jewish People; History, Religion, Literature Ser.). Repr. of 1926 ed. 30.00 (ISBN 0-405-05264-2). Ayer Co Pubs.

Kabbalah: The Light of Redemption. Levi Krakovsky. 1970. 14.95 (ISBN 0-943688-06-X); pap. 11.95 (ISBN 0-943688-32-9). Res Ctr Kabbalah.

Kabbalah: Tradition of Hidden Knowledge. Z'Ev ben Shimon Halevi. (Art & Imagination Ser.). (Illus.). 1980. pap. 10.95 (ISBN 0-500-81023-0). Thames Hudson.

Kabbalah Unveiled. S. L. Mathers. LC 71-16504. 373p. (Orig.). 1983. pap. 12.50 (ISBN 0-87728-557-8). Weiser.

Kabbalistic Discoveries into Hebrew & Aegyptian Mysteries, 2 Vols. Spencer Cleghorn. (Illus.). 121p. 1983. 177.75 (ISBN 0-89920-057-5). Am Inst Psych.

Kabir: The Weaver of God's Name. V. K. Sethi. 762p. 1986. 23.00X (ISBN 0-8364-1673-2, Pub. by Manohar India). South Asia Bks.

Kabirenheiligtum Bei Theben: Die Bauten Im Kabirenheiligtum Bei Theben, Vol. 2. Wolfgang Heyder & Alfred Mallwitz. (Illus.). 1978. 52.00 (ISBN 3-11-005754-9). De Gruyter.

Kaddish. Nosson Scherman. (Art Scroll Mesorah Ser.). 64p. 1980. 6.95 (ISBN 0-89906-160-5). Mesorah Pubns.

Kadima Hagim Series, 8 vols. Incl. No. 1-Pesach, Pesach, Pesach Time Is Here; No. 2-Tikun Lel Chatzot Shavuot; No. 3-Rosh Chodesh Programming; No. 4-Purim Programming; No. 5-Shlosha Yamim: Three New Holidays; No. 6-A Kadima Chanukah Party; No. 7-Yom Yerushalayim; No. 8-Dreidel Factory. Set. pap. 6.50 (ISBN 0-686-95960-4); pap. 1.00 ea. vol. United Syn Bk.

Kadima Kesher Series, 16 vols. Incl. No. 1. Bar-Bat Mitzvah Simulation Game; No. 2. Build Your Own Sukkah; No. 3. Russian Jewry Situation Game; No. 4. Izzy Queer; No. 5. Kasher In; No. 6. Teaching Shira is More Than Clapping Hands; No. 7. T-O-R-A-H; No. 8. Values Auction; No. 9. Kadima Family Programming Seudah Shleesheet; No. 10. How to Create a Creative Service; No. 11. Kadima Sports Manual; No. 12. Grandparents Shabbat; No. 13. Shabbat Cantata; No. 14. Prejudice; No. 15. Yad B'Yad Bowl-A-Thon; No. 16. Different Choices-A Game of Jewish Survival. Set. 11.00 (ISBN 0-686-95953-1); vol. 1.00 ea. United Syn Bk.

Kadimah. Intercollegiate Zionist Association of America. Ed. by Moshe Davis. LC 77-70704. (America & the Holy Land Ser.). (Illus.). 1977. Repr. of 1918 ed. lib. bdg. 20.00x (ISBN 0-405-10255-0). Ayer Co Pubs.

Kadmos the Phoenician: A Study in Greek Legends & the Mycenaean Age. R. B. Edwards. xiv, 258p. 1979. pap. text ed. 67.50x (Pub. by A. M. Hakkert). Coronet Bks.

Kafra Haggadah. 1982. 27.50 (ISBN 0-686-76527-3). Feldheim.

Kahlil Gibran: Collection of His Famous Works. (Arabic.). 25.00x (ISBN 0-86685-149-6). Intl Bk Ctr.

Kahlil Gibran: Wings of Thought. Joseph P. Ghougassian. LC 73-77402. (Illus.). 255p. 1973. 7.50 (ISBN 0-8022-2115-7). Philos Lib.

Kahtahah. Frances L. Paul. LC 76-17804. (Illus., Orig.). 1976. pap. 7.95 (ISBN 0-88240-058-4). Alaska Northwest.

Kahuna: Authentic Chants, Prayers & Rituals of the Legendary Hawaiians. Timothy G. Beckley & Maria Carta. (Illus.). 200p. Date not set. 17.95x (ISBN 0-938294-52-0); pap. 9.95x (ISBN 0-938294-53-9). Global Comm.

Kahuna Sorcerers of Hawaii, Past & Present: With a Glossary of Ancient Religious Terms & the Books of the Hawaiian Royal Dead. Julius S. Rodman. (Illus.). 1979. 20.00 (ISBN 0-682-49196-9, Banner). Exposition Pr FL.

Kahuna: Versatile Mystics of Old Hawaii. L. R. McBride. pap. 4.25 (ISBN 0-912180-18-8). Petroglyph.

Kailash Journal: Pilgrimage into the Himalayas. Sri Swami Satchidananda. LC 84-25296. 1984. pap. 6.95 (ISBN 0-932040-25-X). Integral Yoga Pubns.

Kairos & Logos: Studies in the Roots & Implications of Tillich Society. John J. Carey. LC 84-6738. xxii, 284p. 1984. Repr. of 1978 ed. 15.95 (ISBN 0-86554-106-X, MUP/H100). Mercer Univ Pr.

Kairos: Confessions of a Gay Priest. Zalmon Sherwood. 150p. (Orig.). 1987. pap. 7.95 (ISBN 1-55583-102-8). Alyson Pubns.

Kairos Document: Challenge to the Churches. 80p. (Orig.). 1986. pap. 4.95 (ISBN 0-8028-0189-7). Eerdmans.

Kalam Cosmological Argument. William L. Craig. LC 77-17232. (Library of Philosophy & Religion Ser.). 216p. 1979. text ed. 28.50x (ISBN 0-06-491308-2). B&N Imports.

Kalendarium Manuale Utriusque Ecclesiae Orientalis & Occidentalis. Nicolaus Nilles. (Fr.). 1509p. Date not set. Repr. of 1897 ed. text ed. 310.50x (ISBN 0-576-99195-3, Pub by Gregg Intl Pubs England). Gregg Intl.

Kali the Mother. Margaret Noble. 110p. 1985. pap. 2.00 (ISBN 0-87481-104-X, Pub. by Advaita Ashrama India). Vedanta Pr.

Kalila & Dimna. Ramsey Wood. 1980. 10.95 (Pub. by Octagon Pr England). Ins Study Human.

Kaliya: King of Serpents. LC 79-4669. (Childhood Pastimes of Krishna). (Illus.). pap. 4.00 (ISBN 0-89647-009-1). Bala Bks.

Kalumburu: The Benedictine Mission & the Aborigines 1908-1975. Eugene Perez. (Illus.). 1978. pap. 15.00x (ISBN 0-9596887-0-6, Pub. by U of W Austral Pr). Intl Spec Bk.

Kama Kalpa or the Hindu Ritual of Love. 14th ed. P. Thomas. (Illus.). ix, 151p. 1981. text ed. 35.00x (ISBN 0-86590-031-0, Pub. by Taraporevala India). Apt Bks.

Kama Sutra of Vatsyayana. Ed. by Mulk R. Anand. 276p. 1981. text ed. 125.00x (ISBN 0-391-02224-5). Humanities.

Kama Sutra of Vatsyayana. Tr. by Richard Burton. (Hindustani.). 340p. 1986. 16.95 (ISBN 0-88029-089-7, Pub. by Dorset). Hippocrene Bks.
Kama Sutra of Vatsyayana. Tr. by S. C. Upadhyaya from Sanskrit. (Illus.). xvi, 270p. 1981. Repr. of 1961 ed. text ed. 45.00x (ISBN 0-86590-027-2, Pub. by Taraporevala India). Apt Bks.
Kamakura Period in the Evolution of Buddhist Architecture in Japan. Charlton W. Soper. (Illus.). 143p. 1987. 147.75 (ISBN 0-86650-217-3). Gloucester Art.
Kambuja-Desa; or, an Ancient Hindu Colony in Cambodia. R. C. Majumdar. LC 80-18307. 178p. 1980. Repr. of 1944 ed. text ed. 19.95 (ISBN 0-915980-28-2). ISHI PA.
Kamo Grjadeshi: Quo Vadis. Heinrich Sindevitch. 523p. 23.00 (ISBN 0-317-30246-9); pap. 18.00 (ISBN 0-317-30247-7). Holy Trinity.
Kant. Ralph C. Walker. 1982. pap. 10.95 (ISBN 0-7100-0009-X). Methuen Inc.
Kant & His Philosophical Revolution. R. M. Wenley. 302p. 1982. Repr. of 1910 ed. lib. bdg. 40.00 (ISBN 0-89987-894-6). Darby Bks.
Kant: Einzig Mogliche Beweisgrund. Gordon Treash. LC 77-86227. Tr. of One Possible Basis for a Demonstration of the Existence of God. 1978. 20.00 (ISBN 0-913870-37-4). Abaris Bks.
Kant on Pure Reason. Ed. by Ralph C. Walker. (Illus.). 1982. pap. text ed. 7.95x (ISBN 0-19-875056-0). Oxford U Pr.
Kant's Cosmogony. Immanuel Kant. Ed. by W. Hastie. 1971. Repr. 25.00 (ISBN 0-384-28575-9). Johnson Repr.
Kant's Ethical Theory: A Commentary on the Grundlegung zur Metaphysik der Sitten. Sir William D. Ross. LC 78-6730. 1978. Repr. of 1954 ed. lib. bdg. 22.50x (ISBN 0-8371-9059-2, ROKE). Greenwood.
Kant's Moral Teleology. Thomas Auxter. LC 82-7838. xvi, 194p. 1982. 16.95 (ISBN 0-86554-022-5, MUP-H23). Mercer Univ Pr.
Kant's Moral Theology. W. H. Walsh. (Dawes Hicks Lectures on Philosophy). 1963. pap. 2.25 (ISBN 0-85672-270-7, Pub. by British Acad). Longwood Pub Group.
Kant's Philosophy of Religion. C. J. Webb. Repr. of 1926 ed. 18.00 (ISBN 0-527-94912-4). Kraus Repr.
Kant's Political Philosophy. Patrick Riley. LC 82-573. (Philosophy & Society Ser.). 224p. 1983. text ed. 31.50x (ISBN 0-8476-6763-4). Rowman.
Kant's Rational Theology. Allen W. Wood. LC 78-58059. 144p. 1978. 22.50x (ISBN 0-8014-1200-5). Cornell U Pr.
Kant's Theory of Morals. Bruce Aune. LC 79-17938. 1980. 26.50 (ISBN 0-691-07238-8). Princeton U Pr.
Kant's Transcendental Idealism. Henry E. Allison. LC 85-5756. 400p. 1986. 12.95x (ISBN 0-300-03629-9, Y-567). Yale U Pr.
Karaite Anthology: Excerpts from the Early Literature. Tr. by Leon Nemoy. (Judaica Ser.: No. 7). 1952. 45.00x (ISBN 0-300-00792-2). Yale U Pr.
Karaites in Byzantium: The Formative Years, 970-1100. Zvi Ankori. LC 71-158258. (Columbia University Studies in the Social Sciences: No. 597). Repr. of 1959 ed. 28.50 (ISBN 0-404-51597-5). AMS Pr.
Kareem & Fatimah. Zeba Siddiqui. Ed. by Hamid Quinlan. LC 82-70452. (Illus.). 50p. 1982. pap. 3.50 (ISBN 0-89259-032-7). Am Trust Pubns.
Karen! Karen! Karen Mains. 1980. 6.95 (ISBN 0-8423-2026-1). Tyndale.
Kari. John Benton. 192p. 1984. pap. 2.95 (ISBN 0-8007-8491-X, New Hope). Revell.
Karl Barth. David Mueller. Ed. by Bob E. Patterson. LC 70-188066. (Makers of the Modern Theological Mind Ser). 1972. 8.95 (ISBN 0-87680-254-4, 80254). Word Bks.
Karl Barth. David L. Mueller. 172p. 1984. pap. text ed. 8.95 (ISBN 0-8499-3002-2, 3002-2). Word Bks.
Karl Barth, a Theological Legacy. Eberhard Jungel. Tr. by Garrett E. Paul. LC 86-7793. 96p. (Orig.). 1986. pap. 13.95 (ISBN 0-664-24031-3). Westminster.
Karl Barth & Evangelicalism. Gregory G. Bolich. (Orig.). 1979. pap. 6.95 (ISBN 0-87784-615-4). Inter-Varsity.
Karl Barth & Radical Politics. Ed. by George Hunsinger. LC 76-976. 236p. 1976. softcover 6.45 (ISBN 0-664-24797-0). Westminster.
Karl Barth: Church Dogmatics - A Selection with Introduction. Helmut Gollwitzer. Ed. & tr. by G. W. Bromiley. 272p. Date not set. pap. 8.50 (ISBN 0-567-29051-4, Pub. by T & T Clark Ltd UK). Fortress.
Karl Barth in Review: Posthumous Works Introduced & Assessed. H. Martin Rumscheidt. (Pittsburgh Theological Monograph: No. 30). xxviii, 118p. (Orig.). 1981. pap. 11.75 (ISBN 0-915138-33-6). Pickwick.
Karl Barth: Letters 1961-1968. Ed. & tr. by G. W. Bromiley. 288p. Date not set. 21.75 (ISBN 0-567-09321-2, Pub. by T & T Clark Ltd UK). Fortress.
Karl Barth on God: Our Knowledge of the Divine Existence. Sebastian A. Matczak. LC 62-15994. 358p. 1962. 7.25 (ISBN 0-912116-06-4). Learned Pubns.
Karl Barth: Preaching Through the Christian Year. Karl Barth. Ed. by John B. McTavish & Harold G. Wells. 288p. 1978. 11.95 (ISBN 0-567-29052-2, Pub. by T&T Clark Ltd UK). Fortress.
Karl Barth: Studies of His Theological Method. S. W. Sykes. 1979. text ed. 34.95x (ISBN 0-19-826649-9). Oxford U Pr.
Karl Barth's Christology: Its Basic Alexandrian Character. Charles T. Waldrop. LC 84-20701. (Religion & Reason: Vol. 21). xvi, 265p. 1984. 52.50 (ISBN 90-279-3109-7). Mouton.
Karl Barth's Doctrine of Election. William J. Hausmann. LC 74-81812. 1969. 5.95 (ISBN 0-8022-2281-1). Philos Lib.
Karl Barth's Theology of Mission. Waldron Scott. Ed. by Klaus Bockmuehl. (World Evangelical Fellowship: Outreach & Identity Theological Monograph). 40p. 1978. pap. 1.95 (ISBN 0-87784-541-7). Inter-Varsity.
Karl Jaspers: An Introduction to His Philosophy. Charles F. Wallraff. 1970. 27.50 (ISBN 0-691-07164-0); pap. 10.50 (ISBN 0-691-01971-1). Princeton U Pr.
Karl Jaspers: Philosophy As Faith. Leonard H. Ehrlich. LC 73-79505. 292p. 1975. 20.00x (ISBN 0-87023-153-7). U of Mass Pr.
Karl Marx: A Christian Assessment of His Life & Thought. David Lyon. LC 81-8268. 192p. (Orig.). 1981. pap. 5.95 (ISBN 0-87784-879-3). Inter-Varsity.
Karl Marx & Religion: In Europe & India. Trevor Ling. LC 79-55947. 168p. 1980. text ed. 28.50x (ISBN 0-06-494294-5). B&N Imports.
Karl Marx & the Radical Critique of Judaism. Julius Carlebach. (Littman Library of Jewish Civilization). 478p. 1978. 45.00x (ISBN 0-19-710031-7). Oxford U Pr.
Karl Rahner: An Introduction to His Theology. Karl-Heinz Weger. 1980. 10.95 (ISBN 0-8245-0324-4). Crossroad NY.
Karl Rahner in Dialogue. Karl Rahner. 352p. 1986. 18.95 (ISBN 0-8245-0749-5). Crossroad NY.
Karl Rahner, S. J., Theology & Discovery: Essays in Honor of Karl Rahner, S. J. William J. Kelly. 320p. 24.95 (ISBN 0-87462-521-1). Marquette.
Karl Rahner's Spirituality of the Pierced Heart: A Reinterpretation of Devotion to the Sacred Heart. Annice Callahan. LC 84-29170. 198p. (Orig.). 1985. lib. bdg. 25.25 (ISBN 0-8191-4568-8); pap. text ed. 11.75 (ISBN 0-8191-4569-6). U Pr of Amer.
Karlstadt As the Father of the Baptist Movements. Calvin A. Pater. 350p. 1984. 37.50x (ISBN 0-8020-5555-9). U of Toronto Pr.
Karma. 10th ed. Annie Besant. 1975. 3.50 (ISBN 0-8356-7035-X). Theos Pub Hse.
Karma. 2nd rev. ed. Ed. by Virginia Hanson. Rosemarie Stewart. LC 80-53951. 200p. 1980. pap. 4.95 (ISBN 0-8356-0543-4, Quest). Theos Pub Hse.
Karma: An Anthropological Inquiry. Charles F. Keyes & E. Valentine Daniel. LC 81-19719. 328p. 1983. text ed. 33.00x (ISBN 0-520-04429-0). U of Cal Pr.
Karma & Creativity. Christopher Chapple. (Religion Ser.). 128p. (Orig.). 1986. 29.50x (ISBN 0-88706-250-4); pap. 9.95x (ISBN 0-88706-251-2). State U NY Pr.
Karma & Destiny in the I Ching. Guy Damian-Knight. 256p. 1987. pap. 12.95 (ISBN 1-85063-038-0, 30380, Ark Paperbks). Methuen Inc.
Karma & Rebirth. Christmas Humphreys. 110p. 1983. pap. 5.75 (ISBN 0-8356-0306-7, Quest). Theos Pub Hse.
Karma & Rebirth in Classical Indian Traditions. Wendy D. O'Flaherty. LC 79-64475. 400p. 1980. 41.00x (ISBN 0-520-03923-8). U of Cal Pr.
Karma Lore: One. Helena P. Blavatsky et al. 71p. (Orig.). 1983. pap. 3.95 (ISBN 0-912181-02-8). East School Pr.
Karma-Mimamsa. Arthur B. Keith. LC 78-72451. Repr. of 1921 ed. 27.00 (ISBN 0-404-17318-7). AMS Pr.
Karma Nirvana: Two Buddhist Tales. Paul Carus. LC 73-82781. (Illus.). 160p. 1973. 15.95 (ISBN 0-87548-249-X); pap. 6.95 (ISBN 0-87548-359-3). Open Court.
Karma of Materialism. Rudolf Steiner. Tr. of Menschliche und menschheitliche Entwicklungswahrheiten. 173p. (Orig.). 1986. 20.00 (ISBN 0-88010-130-X); pap. 9.95 (ISBN 0-88010-129-6). Anthroposophic.
Karma of Vocation. 2nd ed. Rudolf Steiner. Ed. by Peter Mollenhauer & Gilbert Church. Tr. by Olin Wannamaker et al from Ger. 270p. 1984. 17.00 (ISBN 0-88010-085-0); pap. 10.95 (ISBN 0-88010-086-9). Anthroposophic.
Karma of Words: Buddhism & the Literary Arts in Medieval Japan. William R. LaFleur. LC 82-45909. 232p. 1983. text ed. 30.00x (ISBN 0-520-04600-5); pap. 9.95 (ISBN 0-520-05622-1, CAL764). U of Cal Pr.
Karma Yoga. Yogi Bhikshu. 1928. 6.00 (ISBN 0-911662-20-0). Yoga.
Karma Yoga. Swami Sivananda. Ed. by Swami Venkatesananda. (Life & Works of Swami Sivananda). 192p. (Orig.). 1985. pap. 6.95 (ISBN 0-949027-05-7). Integral Yoga Pubns.
Karma-Yoga. Swami Vivekananda. pap. 1.50 (ISBN 0-87481-159-7). Vedanta Pr.
Karma-Yoga & Bhakti-Yoga. Swami Vivekananda. LC 55-8657. 336p. pocket ed. 6.95 (ISBN 0-911206-07-8); pap. 6.95 large size (ISBN 0-911206-22-1). Ramakrishna.
Karmapa the Black Hat Lama of Tibet. N. Douglas & M. White. 248p. 1976. 40.00x (ISBN 0-317-39097-X, Pub. by Luzac & Co Ltd). State Mutual Bk.
Karmasiddhi Prakarana of Vasubandhu. Tr. by Leo Pruden. 1987. 20.00 (ISBN 0-89581-907-4). Asian Human Pr.
Karmic Astrology: Retrogrades & Reincarnation. Martin Schulman. LC 83-104490. (Vol. 2). 1977. pap. 5.95 (ISBN 0-87728-345-1). Weiser.
Karmic Relationships. Martin Schulman. LC 84-51376. 1984. pap. 7.95 (ISBN 0-87728-508-X). Weiser.
Karmic Relationships, 8 vols. Rudolf Steiner. Incl. Vol. 1. 205p. 14.50 (ISBN 0-85440-260-8); Vol. 2. 1974. 14.50 (ISBN 0-85440-281-0); Vol. 3. 12.95 (ISBN 0-85440-313-2); Vol. 4. 157p. 1983. 14.00 (ISBN 0-85440-412-0); Vol. 5. 10.95 (ISBN 0-685-36131-4); Vol. 6. 14.50 (ISBN 0-85440-242-X); Vol. 7. 140p. 1973. 9.95 (ISBN 0-85440-276-4); Vol. 8. 102p. 1975. 9.95 (ISBN 0-85440-018-4). Anthroposophic.
Karmic Relationships: Esoteric Studies, Vol. I. Rudolf Steiner. Tr. by George Adams from Ger. 205p. 1981. 14.50 (ISBN 0-85440-260-8, Pub. by Steinerbooks). Anthroposophic.
Karmic Relationships: Esoteric Studies, Vol. 2. Rudolf Steiner. Tr. by George Adams & M. Cotterell. C. Davy & D. S. Osmond. 1974. 14.50 (ISBN 0-85440-281-0, Pub. by Steinerbooks). Anthroposophic.
Karmic Relationships: Esoteric Studies, Vol. 4. 2nd ed. Rudolf Steiner. Tr. by George Adams et al. 157p. 1983. 14.00 (ISBN 0-85440-412-0, Pub by Steinerbooks). Anthroposophic.
Karmic Relationships: Esoteric Studies, Vol. 7. Rudolf Steiner. Tr. by D. S. Osmond from Ger. 140p. 1973. 9.95 (ISBN 0-85440-276-4, Pub. by Steinerbooks). Anthroposophic.
Karmic Relationships: Esoteric Studies, Vol. 8. Rudolf Steiner. Tr. by D. S. Osmond from Ger. Orig. Title: Cosmic Christianity & the Impulse of Michael. 102p. 1975. 9.95 (ISBN 0-85440-018-4, Pub. by Steinerbooks). Anthroposophic.
Karmic Relationships: Esoteric Studies (The Karmic Relationships of the Anthroposophics Movement, Vol. 3. 3rd ed. Rudolf Steiner. Tr. by George Adams. 179p. 1977. 12.95 (ISBN 0-85440-313-2, Pub. by Steinerbooks). Anthroposophic.
Karmic Theater: Self, Society & Astrology in Jaffna. R. S. Perinbanayagam. LC 82-6997. 224p. 1982. lib. bdg. 22.50x (ISBN 0-87023-374-2). U of Mass Pr.
Karok Myths. Alfred L. Kroeber & E. W. Gifford. Ed. by Grace Buzaljko. LC 78-66022. 450p. 1980. 31.00 (ISBN 0-520-03870-3). U of Cal Pr.
Karol from Poland. Daughters of St. Paul. write for info. Dghtrs St Paul.
Kartause Buxheim, 2 Vols. Friedrich Stohlker. Ed. by James Hogg. (Analecta Cartusiana Ser.: No. 96). (Orig.). 1985. pap. 50.00 (ISBN 3-7052-0167-0, Pub. by Salzburg Studies). Longwood Pub Group.
Kartause Gaming. Heienrich Jelinek. Ed. by James Hogg. (Analecta Cartusiana Ser.: No. 58-2). (Ger., Illus.). 175p. 1981. pap. 25.00 (ISBN 3-7052-0085-2, Pub. by Salzburg Studies). Longwood Pub Group.
Kartauser In Osterreich, Vol. 1. James Hogg et al. Ed. by James Hogg. (Analecta Cartusiana Ser.: No. 83-1). (Ger.). 236p. (Orig.). 1980. pap. 25.00 (ISBN 3-7052-0128-X, Pub. by Salzburg Studies). Longwood Pub Group.
Kartauser In Osterreich, Vol. 2. Ed. by James Hogg. Tr. by Janet Wharton. (Analecta Cartusiana Ser.: No. 83-2). (Ger. Ital. & Eng., Illus.). 308p. (Orig.). 1981. pap. 25.00 (ISBN 3-7052-0129-8, Pub. by Salzburg Studies). Longwood Pub Group.
Kartauser und die Reformation: Internationaler Kongress Vom 24 bis 27 1983, 2 vols. James Hogg. (Analecta Cartusiana Ser.: No. 108). 320p. (Orig.). 1984. pap. 50.00 (ISBN 0-317-42576-5, Pub. by Salzburg Studies). Longwood Pub Group.
Kartauserliturgie. Ed. by James Hogg. (Analecta Cartusiana Ser.: No. 116). (Orig.). 1987. pap. 25.00 (ISBN 3-7052-0196-4, Pub. by Salzburg Studies). Longwood Pub Group.
Kartausermystik und Mystiker, Vol. 1. Ed. by James Hogg. (Analecta Cartusiana Ser.: No. 55-1). 238p. (Orig.). 1981. pap. 25.00 (ISBN 0-317-40525-X, Pub. by Salzburg Studies). Longwood Pub Group.
Kartausermystik und Mystiker, Vol. 2. Ed. by James Hogg. (Analecta Cartusiana Ser.: No. 55-2). 226p. (Orig.). 1981. pap. 25.00 (ISBN 3-7052-0077-1, Pub. by Salzburg Studies). Longwood Pub Group.
Kartausermystik und Mystiker, Vol. 3. Ed. by James Hogg. (Analecta Cartusiana Ser.: No. 55-3). 198p. 1982. pap. 25.00 (ISBN 3-7052-0078-X, Pub. by Salzburg Studies). Longwood Pub Group.
Kartausermystik und Mystiker, Vol. 4. Ed. by James Hogg. (Analecta Cartusiana Ser.: No. 55-4). 172p. (Orig.). 1982. pap. 25.00 (ISBN 3-7052-0079-8, Pub. by Salzburg Studies). Longwood Pub Group.
Kartausermystik und Mystiker, Vol. 5. Ed. by James Hogg. (Analecta Cartusiana Ser.: No. 55-5). 103p. (Orig.). 1982. pap. 25.00 (ISBN 3-7052-0080-1, Pub. by Salzburg Studies). Longwood Pub Group.
Kartauserregel und Kartauserleben: Internationaler Kongress Vom XX, 30 Mai bis 3 Juni 1984, Sift Heilgenkrezv, 3 vols. Ed. by James Hogg. (Analecta Cartusiana Ser.: No. 113/1-3). 744p. (Orig.). 1984. pap. 85.00 (ISBN 0-317-42577-3, Pub. by Salzburg Studies). Longwood Pub Group.
Kartauserschriftsteller. Ed. by James Hogg. (Analecta Cartusiana Ser.: No. 117). (Orig.). 1988. pap. 25.00 (ISBN 0-317-42580-3, Pub. by Salzburg Studies). Longwood Pub Group.
Karthaus Und Sein Kloster "Marienparadies", Ein "Bildband" Zum Heimatbuch Des Kreises Karthaus. Wilhelm Brauer. Ed. by James Hogg. (Analecta Cartusiana Ser.: No. 93). 178p. (Orig.). 1980. pap. 25.00 (ISBN 3-7052-0162-X, Pub. by Salzburg Studies). Longwood Pub Group.
Kashef-Al-Mahjub. Ali Bin Uthman. 19.95 (ISBN 0-317-01606-7). Kazi Pubns.
Kashf al-Mahjub: The Oldest Persian Treatise on Sufism by Ali B. Uthman al-Hullabi al-Hujwiri. R. A. Nicholson. 441p. 1976. Repr. 30.00x (ISBN 0-317-39100-3, Pub. by Luzac & Co Ltd). State Mutual Bk.
Kashmir Shaivaism. J. C. Chatterji. (Cultural Perspectives Ser.). 176p. (Orig.). 1986. 29.50x (ISBN 0-88706-179-6); pap. 9.95x (ISBN 0-88706-180-X). State U NY Pr.
Kasturba, Wife of Gandhi. Sushila Nayyar. 1983. pap. 2.50x (ISBN 0-87574-000-6, 000). Pendle Hill.
Kasyapa's Book of Wisdom: A Ritual Handbook of the Vaikhanasas. Tr. by T. Goudriaan. (Disputationes Rheno-Trajectinae Ser.: No. 10). 1965. pap. text ed. 37.60 (ISBN 90-2790-036-1). Mouton.
Kate Magevney & the Christmas Miracle: A Child's Christmas in Memphis (1850) Sue Olsen. Ed. by Roger R. Easson. LC 84-11612. (Child's Christmas in Memphis Ser.: Vol. 2). (Illus.). 48p. 1984. 9.95 (ISBN 0-918518-34-2). St Luke TN.
Katechesis. Daniel Sahas. 70p. 1981. pap. 3.00 (ISBN 0-916586-45-6). Holy Cross Orthodox.
Katha Upanishad. Tr. by Swami Gambhirananda from Sanskrit. (Upanishads with Shankara's Commentary Ser.). 136p. pap. 2.95 (ISBN 0-87481-201-1). Vedanta Pr.
Katharine Luther, Liberated Nun. Alice E. Walter. LC 81-65305. (Illus., Orig.). 1981. pap. text ed. 3.95 (ISBN 0-915644-22-3). Clayton Pub Hse.
Kathavatthu, 2 vols. in one. Ed. by Arnold C. Taylor. LC 78-72450. Repr. of 1894 ed. 56.00 (ISBN 0-404-17317-9). AMS Pr.
Katherine: Life of Luther. Clara S. Schreiber. 1981. 6.95 (ISBN 0-8100-0144-6, 15N0385). Northwest Pub.
Kathopanisad. Tr. by Swami Sarvananda. (Sanskrit & English). pap. 1.00 (ISBN 0-87481-458-8). Vedanta Pr.
Kathy. Barbara Miller & Charles P. Conn. (Illus.). 160p. 1981. pap. 2.75 (ISBN 0-8007-8415-4, Spire Bks). Revell.
Katie & Luther Speak. Jewell Makolin. 1985. 4.95 (ISBN 0-89536-943-5, 7558). CSS of Ohio.
Kausitaki Upanisat. Tr. by Srisa Chandra Vidyarnava & Mohan L. Sandal. LC 73-3825. (Sacred Books of the Hindus: No. 31, Pt. 1). Repr. of 1925 ed. 14.50 (ISBN 0-404-57831-4). AMS Pr.

Kautiliya Arthasastra, 3 pts. R. P. Kangle. 1986. Repr. of 1965 ed. Set. 75.00 (Pub. by Motilal Banarsidass). Pt. 1 (ISBN 81-208-0039-7). Pt. 2. 36.00 (ISBN 81-208-0040-0); Pt. 3. 46.00 (ISBN 81-208-0024-9). South Asia Bks.

Keep a True Lent. Charles Fillmore. 1982. 5.95 (ISBN 0-87159-076-X). Unity School.

Keep in the Step with the Spirit. J. T. Packer. Date not set. pap. 7.95 (ISBN 0-8007-5235-X, Power Bks). Revell.

Keep on Keeping on. Harold L. Fickett, Jr. LC 75-23517. 160p. (Orig.). 1977. pap. 3.50 (ISBN 0-8307-0371-3, S311100). Regal.

Keep the Fire Glowing: How a Loving Marriage Builds a Loving Family. Pat Williams & Jill Williams. 160p. 1986. 9.95 (ISBN 0-317-46133-8). Revell.

Keep the Fruit on the Table. Frances Ward. 48p. 1982. pap. 1.75 (ISBN 0-88144-006-X, CPS-006). Christian Pub.

Keep the River Flowing. Sylvia A. Culver. 92p. 1979. pap. 2.50 (ISBN 0-8341-0592-6). Beacon Hill.

Keep the Wonder. Paul M. Bassett. 61p. 1979. pap. 1.95 (ISBN 0-8341-0608-6). Beacon Hill.

Keepers of the Vineyard: The Puritan Ministry & Collective Culture in Colonial New England. George Selement. 128p. (Orig.). 1984. lib. bdg. 22.00 (ISBN 0-8191-3876-2); pap. text ed. 9.50 (ISBN 0-8191-3877-0). U Pr of Amer.

Keeping a Good Thing Going. Stephen J. Carter & Charles McKinney. 1979. pap. 3.25 (ISBN 0-570-03787-5, 12-2745). Concordia.

Keeping Body & Soul Together. Denis Lane. 1982. pap. 2.25 (ISBN 0-85363-144-1). OMF Bks.

Keeping Christmas: An Edwardian-Age Memoir. William F. Stricker. LC 81-9406. (Illus.). 128p. 1981. 15.00 (ISBN 0-916144-60-7). Stemmer Hse.

Keeping Converts & Restoring the Erring. Ed. by Clayton Pepper. pap. 2.25 (ISBN 0-89137-205-9). Quality Pubns.

Keeping Festival. Suzanne Toolan. 1979. pap. 4.95 (ISBN 0-89390-011-7). Resource Pubns.

Keeping Free. Frank Pollard. LC 82-73932. 1983. 4.95 (ISBN 0-8054-5216-8). Broadman.

Keeping off the Casualty List. Leroy Eims. 132p. 1986. pap. 4.95 (ISBN 0-89693-152-8). Victor Bks.

Keeping Promises: The Challenge of the Sober Parent. Kay M. Porterfield. 172p. (Orig.). 1984. pap. 4.95 (ISBN 0-89486-245-6). Hazelden.

Keeping the Church Year. H. Boone Porter. 1978. pap. 5.95 (ISBN 0-8164-2161-7, HarpR). Har-Row.

Keeping the Faith: A Guide to the Christian Message. David G. Truemper & Frederick A. Niedner, Jr. LC 81-43072. 144p. 1981. pap. 6.95 (ISBN 0-8006-1608-1, 1-1608). Fortress.

Keeping the Faith: American Catholicism Past & Present. Philip Gleason. LC 86-40579. 320p. 1987. text ed. 24.95x (ISBN 0-268-01227-X, Dist. by Har-Row). U of Notre Dame Pr.

Keeping the Lock in Wedlock. Thomas B. Warren. 1980. pap. 11.00 (ISBN 0-934916-26-8). Natl Christian Pr.

Keeping the Sunday School Alive. Cecil B. Knight. 1959. 5.25 (ISBN 0-87148-475-7). Pathway Pr.

Keeping up with Kundalini Yoga. LC 85-13215. 1985. Repr. of 1980 ed. lib. bdg. 19.95x (ISBN 0-89370-884-4). Borgo Pr.

Keeping Your Balance. Byrd & Horton. 1986. 6.95 (ISBN 0-8499-3056-1). Word Bks.

Keeping Your Eye on Television. Les Brown. LC 79-15828. (Orig.). 1979. pap. 4.95 (ISBN 0-8298-0376-9). Pilgrim NY.

Keepsake Book of Christmas Carols: Complete Lyrics to the Most Beloved Yuletide Songs. (Illus.). 48p. 1984. pap. 4.95 (ISBN 0-89471-281-0); lib. bdg. 12.90 (ISBN 0-89471-282-9). Running Pr.

Ken Pike: Scholar & Christian. Eunice V. Pike. LC 81-51058. (Illus.). 270p. (Orig.). 1981. pap. 5.00 (ISBN 0-88312-920-5); microfiche (3) 6.00 (ISBN 0-88312-986-8). Summer Inst Ling.

Ken Prickett: Man of Joy. Belew M. Wendell. LC 85-6208. (Meet the Missionary Ser.). 1985. 5.50 (ISBN 0-8054-4296-0, 4242-96). Broadman.

Kena Upanishad. Sri Aurobindo. Tr. by Sri Aurobindo. (Life Companion Library). 1979. pap. 5.95 (ISBN 0-89744-923-1). Auromere.

Kendra. Gretchen Booz & Reed M. Holmes. LC 79-12285. 1979. 2.00 (ISBN 0-8309-0234-1). Herald Hse.

Kenneth E. Hagin's Fifty Years in the Ministry, 1934-1984. Kenneth E. Hagin. 1984. pap. write for info. (ISBN 0-89276-093-1). Hagin Ministries.

Kenopanisad. Tr. by Swami Sarvananda. (Sanskrit & Eng.). pap. 1.00 (ISBN 0-87481-457-X). Vedanta Pr.

Kenotic Christology: In the Humanity of Jesus the Christ, the Compassion of Our God. Lucien J. Richard. LC 80-40915. 342p. (Orig.). 1982. lib. bdg. 32.00 (ISBN 0-8191-2199-1); pap. text ed. 14.50 (ISBN 0-8191-2200-9). U Pr of Amer.

Kentucky Harmony: A Collection of Psalms, Tunes, Hymns & Anthems. Ed. by A. Davisson. 1976. 16.00 (ISBN 0-8066-1546-X, 11-9249). Augsburg.

Kentucky Presbyterians. Louis Weeks. LC 83-8372. 228p. 1983. 8.95 (ISBN 0-8042-0920-0); after Sept. 1, 1983 9.95 (ISBN 0-686-46122-3). John Knox.

Kentucky Shakers. Julia Neal. LC 82-1871. (Illus.). 120p. 1982. 10.00 (ISBN 0-8131-1458-6). U Pr of Ky.

Kepelino's Traditions of Hawaii. Kepelino. Ed. by Martha W. Beckwith. (BMB). Repr. of 1932 ed. 25.00 (ISBN 0-527-02201-2). Kraus Repr.

Kept by Grace: A Centennial History of First Congregational Church of Pasadena. Ed. by Randi J. Walker. 128p. (Orig.). 1986. text ed. 8.95 (ISBN 0-932727-10-7). Hope Pub Hse.

Kept by the Power of God. I. Howard Marshall. LC 74-23996. 288p. 1975. pap. 8.95 (ISBN 0-87123-304-5, 210304). Bethany Hse.

Kept for the Master's Use. Frances R. Havergal. (Large Print Christian Classic Ser.). 1982. 11.95 (ISBN 0-87983-290-8). Keats.

Kept for the Master's Use. Frances Havergel. 120p. 1986. pap. 4.95 (ISBN 0-89693-279-6). Victor Bks.

Kept Moments. Gerhard E. Frost. 96p. (Orig.). 1982. pap. 5.95 (ISBN 0-86683-668-3, HarpR). Har-Row.

Kerithoth, 1 vol. 15.00 (ISBN 0-910218-85-4). Bennet Pub.

Kerygma & Didache: The Articulation & Structure of the Earliest Christian Message. J. H. McDonald. LC 77-95446. (Society for New Testament Studies Monograph: No. 37). 1980. 29.95 (ISBN 0-521-22055-6). Cambridge U Pr.

Keshub Chunder Sen. rev. ed. F. Max Mueller. Ed. by Nanda Mookerjee. 1976. 6.00x (ISBN 0-88386-862-8). South Asia Bks.

Keshub Chunder Sen: A Search for Cultural Synthesis in India. Meredith Borthwick. 1978. 13.50x (ISBN 0-88386-904-7). South Asia Bks.

Keswick: A Bibliographic Introduction to the Higher Life Movements. David D. Bundy. LC 76-369083. (Occasional Bibliographic Papers of the B. L. Fisher Library: No. 3). 89p. 1975. 3.00 (ISBN 0-914368-03-6). Asbury Theological.

Keswick from Within. John B. Figgis. Ed. by Donald W. Dayton. (Higher Christian Ser.). 192p. 1985. 25.00 (ISBN 0-8240-6417-8). Garland Pub.

Kethuboth, 3 vols. 45.00 (ISBN 0-910218-65-X). Bennet Pub.

Ketuba: Jewish Marriage Contracts Through the Ages. 2nd ed. David Davidovitch. (Illus.). 1974. 29.50 (ISBN 0-87203-054-7). Hermon.

Ketuba: Jewish Marriage Contracts Through the Ages. David Davidovitch. LC 82-1247. (Illus.). 120p. 1985. 29.95 (ISBN 0-915361-21-3, 09745-5, Dist. by Watts). Adama Pubs Inc.

Kevod Elohim. Abraham I. Migas. 27.50 (ISBN 0-405-12616-6). Ayer Co Pubs.

Key Concepts in Sufi Understanding. Ed. by Hafiz Jamal. (Sufi Research Ser.). 47p. 1980. pap. 4.95 (ISBN 0-86304-006-3, Pub. by Octagon Pr England). Ins Study Human.

Key Concepts of the Old Testament. Albert Gelin. Tr. by George Lamb. 96p. pap. 2.95 (ISBN 0-8091-1610-3, Deus). Paulist Pr.

Key Ideas of Paul Tillich's Systematic Theology. Walter Eisenbeis. LC 82-21834. (Ger. & Eng.). 268p. (Orig.). 1983. lib. bdg. 27.50 (ISBN 0-8191-2948-8); pap. text ed. 13.25 (ISBN 0-8191-2949-6). U Pr of Amer.

Key of David: David the True Messiah. Warder Cresson. Ed. by Moshe Davis. LC 77-70671. (America & the Holy Land Ser.). (Illus.). 1977. Repr. of 1852 ed. lib. bdg. 26.50x (ISBN 0-405-10239-9). Ayer Co Pubs.

Key of Knowledge: The Key to Unlock the Mysteries of Important Religions of the World. C. R. Jain. 1012p. 1975. 35.00 (ISBN 0-88065-137-7, Pub. by Messers Today & Tomorrows Printers & Publishers India). Scholarly Pubns.

Key of Truth. Fred C. Conybeare. cancelled 93.00 (ISBN 0-686-12403-0). Church History.

Key Plans Showing Locations of Theban Temple Decorations. Harold H. Nelson. LC 42-21551. (Oriental Institute Pubns. Ser: No. 56). (Illus.). 1941. 30.00x (ISBN 0-226-62154-5, OIP56). U of Chicago Pr.

Key Thoughts for Talks. Reed L. Hart. (Orig.). 1978. pap. 3.50 (ISBN 0-89036-105-3). Hawkes Pub Inc.

Key to a Successful Church Library. rev. ed. Erwin E. John. LC 58-13940. (Orig.). 1967. pap. 5.95 (ISBN 0-8066-0711-4, 10-3684). Augsburg.

Key to Abundant Living. Helen Julian. 1977. tchr's manual 2.00 (ISBN 0-87509-099-0); student manual 1.25 (ISBN 0-87509-100-8). Chr Pubns.

Key to Biblical Hebrew Step by Step, No. 1. Menahem Mansoor. pap. 7.95 (ISBN 0-8010-6100-8). Baker Bk.

Key to Charismatic Renewal in the Catholic Church. Vincent M. Walsh. LC 74-82238. 286p. 1974. pap. 6.00 (ISBN 0-686-32791-8). Key of David.

Key to Dooyeweerd. S. Wolfe. 1978. pap. 2.95 (ISBN 0-87552-542-3). Presby & Reformed.

Key to Health, Wealth, & Love. Julia Seton-Sears. 32p. 1976. pap. 4.95 (ISBN 0-88697-025-3). Life Science.

Key to Inerrancy. Rudy Ydur. 1980. pap. 3.00 (ISBN 0-930592-05-0). Lumeli Pr.

Key to Inner Peace. John H. Hampsch & Clint Kelly. LC 85-61758. (Keyhole Ser.: No. 2). 112p. (Orig.). 1985. pap. 6.95 (ISBN 0-9613575-2-5). Perf Pr.

Key to Israel's Future-The Forgotten Covenant. Gordon Lindsay. 1.95 (ISBN 0-89985-191-6). Christ Nations.

Key to Lasting Joy. T. W. Wilson. 192p. 1987. 12.95 (ISBN 0-8499-0534-6). Word Bks.

Key to Scriptural Healing. 2nd ed. Kenneth E. Hagin. 1983. pap. 1.00 (ISBN 0-89276-008-7). Hagin Ministries.

Key to Spiritual Growth. James C. Lewis. 128p. 1985. 5.95 (ISBN 0-87159-004-2). Unity School.

Key to the Ancient Parish Registers of England & Wales. Arthur M. Burke. LC 62-6577. (Illus.). 163p. 1981. Repr. of 1908 ed. 15.00 (ISBN 0-8063-0445-6). Genealog Pub.

Key to the Biblical Hebrew, No. 2. Menham Mansoor. 7.95 (ISBN 0-8010-6182-2). Baker Bk.

Key to the Catholic Pentecostal Renewal, Vol. 2. Vincent M. Walsh. 232p. 1985. pap. 8.00 (ISBN 0-943374-12-X). Key of David.

Key to the Colloquies of Erasmus. P. Smith. (Harvard Theological Studies). 1927. pap. 15.00 (ISBN 0-527-01013-8). Kraus Repr.

Key to the Kingdom. Bill Van Horn. 1982. 4.25 (ISBN 0-89536-555-3, 1101). CSS of Ohio.

Key to the Missionary Problem. Andrew Murray & Leona Choy. (Orig.). 1980. pap. 3.95 (ISBN 0-87508-401-X). Chr Lit.

Key to the Prison. Louise A. Vernon. LC 86-11054. (Illus.). 144p. 1968. 4.50 (ISBN 0-8361-1813-8). Herald Pr.

Key to the Problems of Existence. rev. ed. Omraam M. Aivanhov. (Complete Works: Vol. 11). (Illus.). 263p. (Orig.). 1985. pap. 9.95 (ISBN 2-85566-111-0). Prosveta USA.

Key to the Universe. H. A. Curtiss & F. H. Curtiss. 391p. 1981. pap. 21.00 (ISBN 0-89540-069-3, SB-069). Sun Pub.

Key to the Universe. Darwin Gross. 75p. (Orig.). 1986. pap. 3.00 (ISBN 0-931689-08-2). SOS Pub OR.

Key to Theosophy. H. P. Blavatsky. 7.50 (ISBN 0-8356-5131-2). Theos Pub Hse.

Key to Theosophy. Helena P. Blavatsky. xii, 310p. 1930. Repr. of 1889 ed. 6.00 (ISBN 0-938998-03-X). Theosophy.

Key to Theosophy Simplified. Ed. by Clara Codd & Blavatsky. 5.25 (ISBN 0-8356-7060-0). Theos Pub Hse.

Key to Theosophy: Verbatim with 1889 Edition. Helena P. Blavatsky. LC 72-95701. 1972. 9.00 (ISBN 0-911500-06-5); pap. 6.00 (ISBN 0-911500-07-3). Theos U Pr.

Key to Triumphant Living. Jack Taylor. LC 76-166582. 1971. 8.95 (ISBN 0-8054-5514-0). Broadman.

Key to Triumphant Living. Jack R. Taylor. 208p. 1986. pap. 3.50 (ISBN 0-553-26031-6). Bantam.

Key to Whitehead's "Process & Reality". Ed. by Donald W. Sherburne. LC 81-11661. 264p. 1981. pap. 10.00x (ISBN 0-226-75293-3). U of Chicago Pr.

Key to Your Child's Heart. Gary Smalley. 160p. 1984. 10.95 (ISBN 0-8499-0433-1, 0433-1). Word Bks.

Key to Yourself. Venice Bloodworth. 1986. pap. 4.95 (ISBN 0-87516-296-7). De Vorss.

Keyen of Fu Tze: The Wise Sayings of Confucious. Charles L. Fontenay. 1977. 5.95 (ISBN 0-900306-50-5, Pub. by Coombe Springs Pr). Claymont Comm.

Keynes Schumpeter & the Effort to Save Capitalism from Total Collapse. Samuel Slater. (Illus.). 137p. 1984. 93.00x (ISBN 0-86654-134-9). Inst Econ Finan.

Keys of the Kingdom: A Tool's Witness to Truth. Stanley L. Jaki. (Illus.). 1986. 9.95 (ISBN 0-8199-0898-3). Franciscan Herald.

Keys to Contentment. Sharon A. Steele. (Aglow Bible Study Basic Ser.). 80p. 1981. pap. 2.95 (ISBN 0-930756-65-7, 521013). Aglow Pubns.

Keys to Effective Motivation. Reginald McDonough. LC 77-26532. 1979. pap. 4.25 (ISBN 0-8054-3226-4). Broadman.

Keys to Prosperity. Elbert Willis. 1978. 1.25 (ISBN 0-89858-016-1). Fill the Gap.

Keys to Spiritual Growth. John F. MacArthur, Jr. 132p. 1976. pap. 5.95 (ISBN 0-8007-5013-6, Power Bks). Revell.

Keys to Successful Bible Study. John R. Martin. LC 81-6459. 184p. 1981. pap. 6.95 (ISBN 0-8361-1963-0). Herald Pr.

Keys to the Bhagavad Gita. Swami Kriyananda. 48p. 1979. pap. 3.00 (ISBN 0-916124-15-0). Dawn Pubns CA.

Keys to the Deeper Life. A. W. Tozer. 56p. 1973. pap. 1.95 (ISBN 0-310-33362-8). Zondervan.

Keys to the Kingdom. F. A. Walton. (Illus.). 80p. 1985. 8.00 (ISBN 0-682-40247-8). Exposition Pr FL.

Keys to the Universe & the Mind. Ruth E. Norman. (Tesla Speaks Ser.: Vol. 11). (Illus.). 1977. 12.50 (ISBN 0-932642-34-9). Unarius Pubns.

Keys to Unlock Yourself. Frank Morgan, Jr. LC 84-21418. 1985. pap. 6.95 (ISBN 0-8054-5003-3). Broadman.

Keys to Wisdom. Ernest Holmes. Ed. by Willis H. Kinnear. 96p. 1965. pap. 5.50 (ISBN 0-911336-06-0). Sci of Mind.

Khadijih Bagum: The Wife of the Bab. H. M. Balyuzi. (Illus.). 52p. 7.95 (ISBN 0-85398-100-0); pap. 3.75 (ISBN 0-85398-101-9). G Ronald Pub.

Khajuraho. Eliky Zannas. (Illus.). 1960. 132.00x (ISBN 0-686-21868-X). Mouton.

Khanum: The Greatest Holy Leaf. Marzieh Gail. (Illus.). 48p. 6.95 (ISBN 0-85398-112-4); pap. 3.50 (ISBN 0-85398-113-2). G Ronald Pub.

Kharma, Rebirth, God, & Computers. Lionel J. Seneviratne. 1987. 6.95 (ISBN 0-533-07145-3). Vantage.

Khatirat-i Nuh Salih. Yunis Khan Afrukhtih. (Persian., Illus.). 1983. 15.95 (ISBN 0-933770-20-0, P-31). Kalimat.

Khazarian Hebrew Documents of the Tenth Century. Norman Golb & Omeljan Pritsak. 152p. 1982. 45.00x (ISBN 0-8014-1221-8). Cornell U Pr.

Khotanese Buddhist Texts. rev. ed. Harold W. Bailey. LC 80-41425. (University of Cambridge Oriental Publications Ser.: No. 31). 168p. 1981. 57.50 (ISBN 0-521-23717-3). Cambridge U Pr.

Khoumani, Islamic Fundamentalists & the Contributions of Islamic Sciences to Modern Civilization. Antoine J. Abraham. 60p. (Orig.). 1985. pap. 5.95x (ISBN 0-932269-51-6). Wyndham Hall.

Khram Bozhij i Tserkovnija Sluzhbi. N. R. Antonov. Tr. of Temple of God & Church Services. 300p. 1983. pap. text ed. 10.00 (ISBN 0-317-30284-1). Holy Trinity.

Khristianskaya Zhizn' po Dobrotolijubiju. Ed. by Arcimndrite Juvenaly. Tr. of Christian Life According to the Philokalia. 216p. 13.00 (ISBN 0-317-28893-8); pap. 8.00 (ISBN 0-317-28894-6). Holy Trinity.

Khristianskoje Uchenijr o Zlikh Dukhakh. Tr. of Christian Teaching on Evil Spirits. 30p. pap. 2.00 (ISBN 0-317-29008-8). Holy Trinity.

Khristianstvo ili Tserkov. Saint Hilacion Troitsky. Tr. of Christianity or the Church. 64p. pap. 2.00 (ISBN 0-317-28982-9). Holy Trinity.

Khristijanskaja Zhizn' po Dobrotoljubiju: Izbrannija Mjesta iz Tborenji Svjatikh Otsoff i Utchitjeljej Tserkvi. Ed. by Archimandrite Juvenaly. Tr. of Christian Life by the Philokalia; Selected Passages from the Writings of the Holy Fathers. (Rus.). 216p. (Orig.). 1972. 13.00x (ISBN 0-88465-031-6); pap. 8.00x (ISBN 0-88465-032-4). Holy Trinity.

Khudaka Patha. Ed. by Maung Tin. LC 78-70126. Repr. of 1913 ed. 18.00 (ISBN 0-404-17385-3). AMS Pr.

Khuddaka-Nikaya: The Minor Anthologies of the Pali Canon, 4 vols. Ed. by C. Rhys Davids. Repr. of 1931 ed. 105.00 set (ISBN 0-404-17640-2). AMS Pr.

Khuddaka-Patha. Ed. by Helmer Smith. LC 78-72454. Repr. of 1915 ed. 28.50 (ISBN 0-404-17323-3). AMS Pr.

Kibbutz Judaism: A New Tradition in the Making. Shalom Lilker. LC 80-70886. (Norwood Editions, Kibbutz, Cooperative Societies, & Alternative Social Policy Bk.: Vol. 7). 240p. 1982. 14.95 (ISBN 0-8453-4740-3, Cornwall Bks). Assoc Univ Prs.

Kibbutz Judaism: A New Tradition in the Making. Shalom Lilker. (Kibbutz, Cooperative Society, & Alternative Social Policy Ser.: Vol. 7). 264p. 1982. lib. bdg. 19.50 (ISBN 0-8482-4876-7). Norwood Edns.

Kick-Starting the Bible. Simon Jenkins. (Illus.). 160p. 1987. pap. 5.95 (ISBN 0-7459-1004-1). Lion USA.

Kicked Out of the Kingdom. Charles Trombley. 1974. pap. 2.95 (ISBN 0-88368-044-0). Whitaker Hse.

Kicking over Sacred Cows. Charles Capps. 132p. (Orig.). 1984. pap. 4.95 (ISBN 0-914307-18-5, Dist. by Harrison Hse). Word Faith.

Kicking Those Habits. Stephen S. Wilburn. 48p. 1985. 4.95 (ISBN 0-8378-5403-2). Gibson.

Kiddushin, 2 vols. 30.00 (ISBN 0-910218-67-6). Bennet Pub.

Kids Are Gone, Lord, but I'm Still Here: Prayers for Mothers. Betty W. Skold. LC 80-67801. 96p. (Orig.). 1981. pap. 5.95 (ISBN 0-8066-1863-9, 10-3703). Augsburg.

Kids Grieve Too! Victor S. Lombardo & Edith F. Lombardo. (Illus.). 88p. 1986. 17.75x (ISBN 0-398-05275-1). C C Thomas.

Kids in Cults: Why They Join, Why They Stay, Why They Leave. Rev. ed. Jack N. Porter & Irvin Doress. 22p. (Orig.). 1982. pap. 2.95 (ISBN 0-932270-02-6). Spencer Pr.

Kidstories: Seasonal & Topical Sermons for Children. Betsy Larson. (Paperback Program Ser.). 128p. 1980. pap. 2.95 (ISBN 0-8010-5598-9). Baker Bk.

Kierkegaard, 2 vols. Walter Lowrie. Set. 28.50 (ISBN 0-8446-0778-9). Peter Smith.

Kierkegaard Handbook. Frederick Sontag. LC 79-87741. 1980. pap. 7.25 (ISBN 0-8042-0654-6). John Knox.

Kierkegaard's Dialectic of Existence. Hermann Diem. Tr. by Harold Knight from German. LC 77-18886. 1978. Repr. of 1959 ed. lib. bdg. 22.50x (ISBN 0-313-20220-6, DIKD). Greenwood.

Kierkegaard's Existential Ethics. George J. Stack. LC 75-16344. (Studies in Humanities: No. 16). 240p. 1977. 15.00 (ISBN 0-8173-6624-5); pap. 5.50 (ISBN 0-8173-6626-1). U of Ala Pr.

Kierkegaard's Philosophy of Religion. Reidar Thomte. Repr. of 1948 ed. lib. bdg. 27.50x (ISBN 0-8371-0979-5, THKI). Greenwood.

Kierkegaard's Thought. Gregor Malantschuk. Tr. by Howard V. Hong & Edna H. Hong. LC 77-155000. (Eng.). 400p. 1972. 38.50 (ISBN 0-691-07166-7, 317); pap. 10.00 (ISBN 0-691-01982-7). Princeton U Pr.

Kievo-Petchersky Paterik. Tr. of Kiev Caves Patericon. 252p. pap. 10.00 (ISBN 0-317-29241-2). Holy Trinity.

Killing. Richard Holloway. 77p. 1985. pap. 5.95 (ISBN 0-8192-1367-5). Morehouse.

Killing Effects of Calvinism. Bob L. Ross. 1980. pap. 1.25 (ISBN 0-686-29039-9). Pilgrim Pubns.

Killing Giants, Pulling Thorns. Charles R. Swindoll. LC 78-57675. (Illus.). 1978. pap. 9.95 (ISBN 0-930014-25-1). Multnomah.

Killing in Defense of Private Property: The Development of a Roman Catholic Moral Teaching, Thirteenth to Eighteenth Centuries. Shaun J. Sullivan. LC 75-38843. (American Academy of Religion. Dissertation Ser.). (Illus.). 1976. pap. 9.95 (ISBN 0-89130-067-8, 010115). Scholars Pr GA.

Kilvert's Diary 1870-1879. Francis Kilvert. LC 86-80573. 288p. 1986. 24.95 (ISBN 0-87923-637-X). Godine.

Kimbangu: An African Prophet & His Church. Marie-Louise Martin. Tr. by D. M. Moore. LC 75-45371. pap. 55.50 (ISBN 0-317-08451-8, 2012735). Bks Demand UMI.

Kinaalada: A Navajo Puberty Ceremony. rev. ed. Shirley M. Begay & Verna Clinton-Tullie. LC 83-61661. (Illus.). 171p. 1983. 15.00x (ISBN 0-936008-11-3); pap. 11.00x. Navajo Curr.

Kind Kristy. Vera Groomer. (Come Unto Me Library). 1979. pap. 1.65 (ISBN 0-8127-0209-3). Review & Herald.

Kind Stranger. Meryl Doney. (Illus.). 16p. 1982. pap. 0.99 (ISBN 0-86683-666-7, AY8244, HarpR). Har-Row.

Kind Words for Our Kind of Faith. Robert G. Kemper. 144p. (Orig.). 1986. pap. 8.95 (ISBN 0-8298-0738-1). Pilgrim NY.

Kindergarten Curriculum for the Day School. Esther Galupkin. 1.50 (ISBN 0-914131-39-7, C05). Torah Umesorah.

Kindness. Carole MacKenthun & Paulinus Dwyer. (Fruit of the Spirit Ser.). (Illus.). 48p. 1987. pap. 5.95 (ISBN 0-86653-379-6, SS880). Good Apple.

Kindness. Jane B. Moncure. LC 80-15286. (What Does the Bible Say? Ser.). (Illus.). 32p. 1980. PLB 5.95 (ISBN 0-89565-167-X). Childs World.

Kindness, Clarity & Insight. The Fourteenth Dalai Lama His Holiness Tenzin Gyatso. Ed. by Jeffrey Hopkins & Elizabeth Napper. LC 84-51198. (Illus.). 250p. (Orig.). 1984. pap. 10.95 (ISBN 0-937938-18-1). Snow Lion.

Kindred Spirits. Kathy Narramore & Alice Hill. 144p. (Orig.). 1985. pap. 5.95 (ISBN 0-310-30531-4, 11245P). Zondervan.

Kinerhythm Meditation: A Multfaceted Concentration. Oscar Ichazo. (Illus.). 54p. 1978. pap. 12.95 (ISBN 0-916554-07-4). Arica Inst Pr.

King. Ann R. Colton. 72p. 1968. 5.00 (ISBN 0-917187-08-3). A R C Pub.

King Alfred's Version of St. Augustine's Soliloquies. Ed. by Thomas A. Carnicelli. LC 69-12719. 1969. 7.50x (ISBN 0-674-50360-0). Harvard U Pr.

King Alfred's West-Saxon Version of Gregory's Pastoral Care, 2 pts. Ed. by Henry Sweet. (EETS, OS Ser.: No. 50). Repr. of 1872 ed. Pt. I. 18.00 (ISBN 0-527-00041-8); Pt. II. 13.00 (ISBN 0-527-00042-6). Kraus Repr.

King Alfred's West-Saxon Version of Gregory's Pastoral Care. Henry Sweet. 1979. Repr. of 1871 ed. lib. bdg. 200.00 (ISBN 0-8492-8102-4). R West.

King & His Kingdom. Reuel Lemmons. Ed. by J. D. Thomas. LC 68-59307. (Twentieth Century Sermons Ser). 1968. 11.95 (ISBN 0-89112-301-6, Bibl Res Pr). Abilene Christ U.

King & Kin: Political Allegory in the Hebrew Bible. Joel Rosenberg. LC 85-45160. (Indiana Studies in Biblical Literature: Midland Bks: No. 396). 256p. 1986. 29.50x (ISBN 0-253-14624-0); pap. 10.95x (ISBN 0-253-20396-1). Ind U Pr.

King & the Corpse: Tales of the Soul's Conquest of Evil. Heinrich Zimmer. Ed. by Joseph Campbell. (Bollingen Ser.: Vol. 11). 1971. pap. 9.50 (ISBN 0-691-01776-X). Princeton U Pr.

King & the Kingdom of Heaven. Watchman Nee. Tr. by Stephen Kaung from Chinese. 1978. pap. 5.00 (ISBN 0-935008-24-1). Christian Fellow Pubs.

King Arthur & the Grail: The Arthurian Legends & Their Meaning. Richard Cavendish. LC 79-14034. 238p. 1985. pap. 6.95 (ISBN 0-8008-4466-1). Taplinger.

King David. Penny Frank. Ed. by P. Alexander. (Lion Story Bible Ser.). 24p. 1987. 2.95 (ISBN 0-85648-744-9). Lion USA.

King David. Mary McMillan. (Color, Cut & Paste Ser.). (Illus.). 48p. 1987. pap. 5.95 (ISBN 0-86653-392-3). Good Apple.

King David. Purves. (Ladybird Ser.). 1980. 2.50 (ISBN 0-87508-843-0). Chr Lit.

King David. As told by Catherine Storr. (People of the Bible Ser.). (Illus.). 32p. 1985. PLB 10.65 (ISBN 0-8172-2042-9). Raintree Pubs.

King in the Garden. Leon Garfield. LC 84-10064. (Illus.). 32p. 1985. 11.75 (ISBN 0-688-04106-X). Lothrop.

King Is Coming. David McCord. 112p. (Orig.). 1984. pap. 2.95 (ISBN 0-87239-670-3, 41026). Standard Pub.

King James Bible Translators. Olga S. Opfell. LC 81-20885. (Illus.). 179p. 1982. lib. bdg. 18.95x (ISBN 0-89950-041-2). McFarland & Co.

King James-Simple English Parallel: New Testament. 19.00 (ISBN 0-89957-571-4). AMG Pubs.

King James Version Debate. D. A. Carson. LC 79-50443. 1978. pap. 4.95 (ISBN 0-8010-2427-7). Baker Bk.

King James Version Defended. 4th ed. Edward F. Hills. (Illus.). 280p. 1984. pap. 8.95x (ISBN 0-915923-00-9). Christian Res Pr.

King James Version of the English Bible. David Daiches. LC 68-16338. vii, 228p. 1968. Repr. of 1941 ed. 21.50 (ISBN 0-208-00493-9, Archon). Shoe String.

King Jesus. Robert Graves. 356p. 1983. Repr. of 1946 ed. lib. bdg. 25.00 (ISBN 0-8495-2139-4). Arden Lib.

King of Creation. Henry M. Morris. LC 80-80558. 1980. pap. 6.95 (ISBN 0-89051-059-8). Master Bks.

King of Kings. Jack T. Chick. (Sword Ser.: Vol. 1). (Illus.). 64p. (Orig.). 1980. pap. 1.65 (ISBN 0-937958-07-7). Chick Pubns.

King of the Earth. Erich Sauer. 256p. 1979. pap. 10.95 (ISBN 0-85364-009-2). Attic Pr.

King of the Jews. Leslie Epstein. 352p. 1986. pap. 7.95 (ISBN 0-452-25823-5, Plume). NAL.

King Saul, Man after the Flesh. S. Ridout. 8.50 (ISBN 0-88172-118-2). Believers Bkshelf.

King Saul, the Tragic Hero: A Study in Individuation. John A. Sanford. LC 84-61023. 160p. (Orig.). 1985. pap. 7.95 (ISBN 0-8091-2658-3). Paulist Pr.

King Solomon. Frederic Thieberger. (Illus.). 313p. 1978. pap. 6.95 (ISBN 0-85222-200-9). Hebrew Pub.

King Solomon & His Followers, No. 13, Minnesota. 200p. (Printed cipher code). fabricord 13.50 (ISBN 0-88053-255-6). Macoy Pub.

King Solomon & His Followers: No. 5, Ohio. 200p. (Printed cipher code). fabricord bdg. 13.50 (ISBN 0-88053-250-5). Macoy Pub.

King Solomon's Temple. E. Raymond Capt. LC 79-54774. (Illus.). 96p. 1979. pap. 3.00 (ISBN 0-934666-05-9). Artisan Sales.

King Udrayana & the Wheel of Life: The History & Meaning of the Buddhist Teaching of Dependent Origination. Sermey G. Tharchin et al. LC 84-61266. (Illus.). 248p. (Orig.). 1984. 14.50 (ISBN 0-918753-06-6); pap. 9.50 (ISBN 0-918753-05-8). Mahayana.

King Who Lives Forever. Alice Schrage. LC 81-50590. (Bible Biography Ser.). 128p. 1981. pap. text ed. 1.95 (ISBN 0-8307-0766-2, 5810604). Regal.

Kingdom. Larry Christenson. (Trinity Bible Ser.). 160p. 1972. pap. 5.95x (ISBN 0-87123-548-X, 240548). Bethany Hse.

Kingdom & Community: The Social World of Early Christianity. John G. Gager. 160p. 1975. pap. text ed. write for info. (ISBN 0-13-516203-3). P-H.

Kingdom & the Glory. Alfred McBride. 1977. pap. 1.75 (ISBN 0-88479-003-7). Arena Lettres.

Kingdom & the Power. Gay Talese. 672p. 1981. pap. 5.95 (ISBN 0-440-14397-7). Dell.

Kingdom at Hand. Vincent M. Walsh. 340p. 1982. pap. 6.00 (ISBN 0-943374-00-6). Key of David.

Kingdom Citizens. John Driver. LC 80-16171. 160p. (Orig.). 1980. pap. 6.95 (ISBN 0-8361-1935-5). Herald Pr.

Kingdom Come. Lawrence Kearney. 64p. 1980. 15.00x (ISBN 0-8195-2098-5); pap. 7.95 (ISBN 0-8195-1098-X). Wesleyan U Pr.

Kingdom Conflict. Joseph M. Stowell. 156p. 1984. pap. 5.95 (ISBN 0-89693-376-8). Victor Bks.

Kingdom, Cross, & Community. Ed. by J. R. Burkholder & Calvin Redekop. LC 76-29663. 312p. 1976. 14.95 (ISBN 0-317-37847-3). Herald Pr.

Kingdom Life in a Fallen World: Living out the Sermon on the Mount. Sinclair B. Ferguson. (Christian Character Library). 224p. 1986. 8.95 (ISBN 0-89109-492-X). NavPress.

Kingdom Living. Sharon Tash. (Bible Study Basic Ser.). 64p. 1984. 2.95 (521018). Aglow Pubns.

Kingdom Living for the Family. Frank Hammond & Ida Mae Hammond. 175p. (Orig.). 1985. pap. 4.95 (ISBN 0-89228-100-6). Impact Bks MO.

Kingdom Living Here & Now. John MacArthur, Jr. LC 79-25326. 1980. pap. 5.95 (ISBN 0-8024-4562-4). Moody.

Kingdom Lost & Found: A Fable for Everyone. Sr. M. Terese Donze. LC 82-71983. (Illus.). 64p. (Orig.). 1982. pap. 3.95 (ISBN 0-87793-253-0). Ave Maria.

Kingdom Manifesto. Howard A. Snyder. LC 85-10725. 108p. (Orig.). 1985. pap. 5.95 (ISBN 0-87784-408-9). Inter-Varsity.

Kingdom of Christ. James DeVries. LC 84-90313. 155p. (Orig.). 1984. pap. 3.50 (ISBN 0-9613181-0-4). Kingdom Bks.

Kingdom of God. John Allan. pap. 2.50 (ISBN 0-87516-286-X). De Vorss.

Kingdom of God. rev. ed. John Bright. (Series A). 1957. pap. 7.50 (ISBN 0-687-20908-0, Apex). Abingdon.

Kingdom of God & the Church. Geerhardus Vos. 1972. pap. 3.50 (ISBN 0-87552-502-4). Presby & Reformed.

Kingdom of God & the Church of God. Robert J. Pruitt. 1977. pap. 1.95 (ISBN 0-934942-09-9). White Wing Pub.

Kingdom of God & the One Thousand Years Reign. H. M. Riggle. 160p. pap. 1.50 (ISBN 0-686-29153-0). Faith Pub Hse.

Kingdom of God in the Synoptic Tradition. Richard H. Hiers. LC 70-630982. (U of Fla. Humanities Monograph Ser.: No. 33). Repr. of 1970 ed. 29.00 (ISBN 0-8357-9821-6, 2015531). Bks Demand UMI.

Kingdom of God in the Teaching of Jesus. Ed. by Bruce Chilton. LC 83-20569. (Issues in Religion & Theology Ser.). 192p. 1984. pap. 7.95 (ISBN 0-8006-1769-X, 1-769). Fortress.

Kingdom of God Is Within You. Leo Tolstoy. Tr. by Constance Garnett from Rus. LC 84-10471. xxii, 368p. 1984. 26.95x (ISBN 0-8032-4411-8); pap. 8.50 (ISBN 0-8032-9404-2, BB 897, Bison). U of Nebr Pr.

Kingdom of God's Justice: As Foretold by Isaiah. Marlys Swinger. 60p. (Choral edition). 1972. pap. 2.50 (ISBN 0-87486-012-1); L.P. Record-Mono 4.95. Plough.

Kingdom of Heaven. Hilton Hotema. 45p. 1960. pap. 8.95 (ISBN 0-88697-030-X). Life Science.

Kingdom of Heaven As Seen by Swedenborg. John H. Spalding. LC 72-8245. Repr. of 1916 ed. 18.00 (ISBN 0-404-11006-1). AMS Pr.

Kingdom of Heaven Taken by Prayer. Wm Huntington. pap. 2.50 (ISBN 0-686-48162-3). Reiner.

Kingdom of Light. Joe White. 83p. 1984. pap. 2.50 (ISBN 0-88144-033-7). Christian Pub.

Kingdom of Love & Knowledge: The Encounter Between Orthodoxy & the West. A. M. Allchin. 224p. (Orig.). 1982. 14.95 (ISBN 0-8164-0532-8, HarpR). Har-Row.

Kingdom of Priests. Bob E. Lyons. LC 77-92990. 160p. 1984. pap. text ed. 5.95 (ISBN 0-87148-478-1). Pathway Pr.

Kingdom of Self. Earl Jabay. LC 73-89494. 1974. pap. 3.95 (ISBN 0-88270-062-6). Bridge Pub.

Kingdom of Servants. Dwight L. Dye. 1979. 3.95 (ISBN 0-87162-218-1, D5050). Warner Pr.

Kingdom of Surprises. Cecil E. Sherman. LC 85-4699. (Orig.). 1985. pap. 3.75 (ISBN 0-8054-1533-5). Broadman.

Kingdom of the Crusaders. Dana C. Munro. LC 65-20472. 1966. Repr. of 1935 ed. 22.50x (ISBN 0-8046-0326-X, Pub. by Kennikat). Assoc Faculty Pr.

Kingdom of the Cults. rev. ed. Walter Martin. 450p. 1985. 14.95 (ISBN 0-87123-796-2, 230796). Bethany Hse.

Kingdom of the Gods. 7th ed. Geoffrey Hodson. (Illus.). 1972. 15.95 (ISBN 0-8356-7081-3). Theos Pub Hse.

Kingdom of Wundle. Robert Siegel. 48p. 1982. 8.95 (ISBN 0-89107-261-6, Crossway Bks). Good News.

Kingdom Revisited: An Essay on Christian Social Ethics. Charles L. Kammer, 3rd. LC 81-40045. 188p. (Orig.). 1981. lib. bdg. 26.00 (ISBN 0-8191-1737-4); pap. text ed. 12.50 (ISBN 0-8191-1738-2). U Pr of Amer.

Kingdom: Teacher's Guide. Sandra Hall. 96p. (Orig.). 1985. pap. 6.95. Bethany Hse.

Kingdom Transformed: Themes in the Development of Mormonism. Gordon Shepherd & Gary Shepherd. 320p. 1984. 19.95 (ISBN 0-87480-233-4). U of Utah Pr.

Kingdom Within: A Study of the Inner Meaning of Jesus' Sayings. John A. Sanford. LC 77-105548. 1970. Har-Row.

Kingdom Within: Discourses to Mixed Congregations. John H. Newman. 1984. pap. 14.95 (ISBN 0-87193-216-4). Dimension Bks.

Kingdom Without God. Paul Eldridge. 15p. 1951. pap. cancelled (ISBN 0-911826-50-5). Am Atheist.

Kingdoms of the Lord: A History of the Hebrew Kingdoms from Saul to the Fall of Jerusalem. David F. Payne. LC 81-3197. (Illus.). pap. 85.00 (ISBN 0-317-11122-1, 2020852). Bks Demand UMI.

Kingly Priesthood of the Saints. C. H. Spurgeon. 1978. pap. 0.95 (ISBN 0-686-26195-X). Pilgrim Pubns.

Kings Bishop. Barbara Denny. 376p. 1986. 49.00 (ISBN 0-946619-16-6, Pub. by Alderman Pr). State Mutual Bk.

King's Book. Louise A. Vernon. LC 80-18998. (Illus.). 128p. 1980. pap. 4.50 (ISBN 0-8361-1933-9). Herald Pr.

King's Book, or a Necessary Doctrine & Erudition for Any Christian Man, 1543. Ed. by Thomas A. Lacey. (Church Historical Society, London, N.S. Ser.: No. 10). Repr. of 1932 ed. 40.00 (ISBN 0-8115-3134-1). Kraus Repr.

King's Daughters. Judy Overrein. 116p. (Orig.). 1982. pap. text ed. 3.00 (ISBN 0-941630-00-5). Freedom Pr.

King's Diamond. Harvey. 3.95 (ISBN 0-686-27782-1). Schmul Pub Co.

Kings I. Walter Brueggemann. (Knox Preaching Guide Ser.). 132p. 1983. pap. 4.95 (ISBN 0-8042-3212-1). John Knox.

Kings II. Walter Brueggemann. Ed. by John Hayes. LC 82-48094. (Knox Preaching Guide Ser.). 120p. 1983. pap. 4.95 (ISBN 0-8042-3214-8). John Knox.

Kings of Judah & Israel. Rev. ed. Christopher Knapp. 1982. pap. 5.95 (ISBN 0-87213-461-X). Loizeaux.

Kings of the Hittites. D. G. Hogarth. (British Academy, London, Schweich Lectures on Biblical Archaeology Ser.). pap. 19.00 (ISBN 0-8115-1266-5). Kraus Repr.

Kings on the Hill. George Harper. (H. B. Bible Adventures Ser.). 224p. (Orig.). 1985. pap. 5.95 (ISBN 0-934318-70-0). Falcon Pr MT.

Kings One & Two. A. Cohen. 337p. 1950. 10.95 (ISBN 0-900689-27-7). Soncino Pr.

Kings School Canterbury Hymn Book. 578p. (Orig.). 1983. 38.00x (ISBN 0-905418-93-X, Pub. by Gresham England). State Mutual Bk.

King's Son: Readings in the Contemporary Psychologies & Contemporary Thoughts on Man. Ed. by Robert Cecil & Richard Rieu. 181p. 1981. 14.95 (ISBN 0-900860-88-X, Pub. by Octagon Pr England). Ins Study Human.

Kingship According to Deuteronomistic History. Gerald E. Gerbrandt. (Society of Biblical Literature Dissertation Ser.). 1986. 17.95 (ISBN 0-89130-968-3, 06 01 87); pap. 12.95 (ISBN 0-89130-969-1). Scholars Pr GA.

Kingship & Community in Early India. Charles Drekmeier. LC 62-9565. 1962. 27.50x (ISBN 0-8047-0114-8). Stanford U Pr.

Kingship & Sacrifice: Ritual & Society in Ancient Hawaii. Valerio Valeri. Tr. by Paula Wissing from Hawaiian. LC 84-23991. (Fr. & Eng., Illus.). 392p. 1985. lib. bdg. 55.00x (ISBN 0-226-84559-1); pap. text ed. 22.50x (ISBN 0-226-84560-5). U of Chicago Pr.

Kingship & the Gods: A Study of Ancient Near Eastern Religion As the Integration of Society & Nature. Henri Frankfort. LC 48-5158. 1978. pap. 12.95 (ISBN 0-226-26011-9, P766, Phoen). U of Chicago Pr.

Kingship & the Psalms. John Eaton. (Biblical Seminar Ser.: No. 3). 240p. 1986. pap. text ed. 9.95x (ISBN 0-905774-89-2, Pub. by JSOT Pr England). Eisenbrauns.

Kingship of Christ: The Story of the World Council of Churches. George K. Bell. LC 78-10482. 1979. Repr. of 1954 ed. lib. bdg. 22.50x (ISBN 0-313-21121-3, BEKC). Greenwood.

Kingship of Jesus: Composition & Theology in Mark Fifteen. Frank Matera. LC 82-708. (SBL Dissertation Ser.). 1982. pap. 12.75 (ISBN 0-89130-564-5, 060166). Scholars Pr GA.
Kink & I: A Psychiatrist's Guide to Untwisted Living. James D. Mallory & Stanley C. Baldwin. LC 73-78688. 224p. 1973. pap. 5.95 (ISBN 0-88207-237-4). Victor Bks.
Kino Guide II. Charles Polzer. LC 82-50218. (Illus.). 76p. 1982. pap. 5.00 (ISBN 0-915076-07-1). SW Mission.
Kinot for the Ninth of Av. Abraham Rosenfield. 482p. 1956. 12.95 (ISBN 0-910818-16-9). Judaica Pr.
Kinship & Consent: The Jewish Political Tradition & Its Contemporary Uses. Daniel J. Elazar. LC 82-21851. 412p. 1983. lib. bdg. 29.50 (ISBN 0-8191-2800-7, Co-pub. by Ctr Jewish Comm Studies); pap. text ed. 14.50 (ISBN 0-8191-2801-5). U Pr of Amer.
Kinship & Marriage among the Nuer. Edward E. Evans-Pritchard. (Illus.). 1951. 32.50x (ISBN 0-19-823104-0). Oxford U Pr.
Kinship & Pilgrimage: Rituals of Reunion in American Protestant Culture. Gwen K. Neville. 1987. 18.95. Oxford U Pr.
Kirby Page & the Social Gospel: Pacifist & Socialist Aspects. Charles Chatfield. LC 70-147695. (Library of War & Peace: Documentary Anthologies). 1976. lib. bdg. 46.00 (ISBN 0-8240-0451-5). Garland Pub.
Kirche Aethiopiens: Eine Bestandsaufnahme. Friedrich Heyer. (Theologische Bibliothek Toepelmann 22). 360p. 1971. 32.25 (ISBN 3-11-001850-0). De Gruyter.
Kirchenrecht der Morgenlandischen Kirche. 2nd ed. Nikodim Milash. LC 80-2360. Repr. of 1905 ed. 83.00 (ISBN 0-404-18910-5). AMS Pr.
Kiri & the First Easter. Carol Greene. (Arch Bks: Set 9). (Illus.). 32p. 1972. pap. 0.99 (ISBN 0-570-06064-8, 59-1182). Concordia.
Kirigami. Frederick Kemper. 1979. pap. 4.95 (ISBN 0-570-03782-4, 12-2736). Concordia.
Kirpal Singh: The Story of a Saint. 2nd ed. Juliet Scotti & Ricki Linksman. LC 77-79840. (Children's Ser.: No. 1). (Illus.). 96p. 1982. pap. 4.95 (ISBN 0-918224-05-5). Sawan Kirpal Pubns.
Kirtland Economy Revisited: A Market Critique of Sectarian Economics. Marvin S. Hill & C. Keith Rooker. LC 78-3848. (Studies in Mormon History: No. 3). (Illus.). 1977. pap. 4.95 (ISBN 0-8425-1230-6). Brigham.
Kirtland Temple: A Historical Narrative. Roger D. Launius. 1986. pap. 12.50 (ISBN 0-8309-0449-2). Herald Hse.
Kisare, A Mennonite of Kiseru: An Autobiography As Told to Joseph C. Shenk. Kisare. As told to Joseph C. Shenk. (Illus.). 194p. 1984. 5.00 (ISBN 0-9613368-1-1). E Mennonite Bd.
Kiss of God. Shiva Das Floating Eagle Feather. (Illus.). 100p. 1979. pap. 3.50 (ISBN 0-686-95426-2). Ananda Marga.
Kissing, Hugging, &... Wayne Judd. LC 79-20362. (Nugget Ser.). 1979. pap. 0.79 (ISBN 0-8127-0249-2). Review & Herald.
Kitab Al-Anwar Wal-Maraoib: Code of Karaite Law, 3 vols. Ya'Qub Al-Qirqisani. Incl. Vol. 1. First Discourse - Historical Introduction; Second Discourse - Philosophical & Theological Principles of JurisPrudence; Vol. 2. Third Discourse - Criticism of Sectarian Doctrines; Fourth Discourse - Methods of Construction & Interpretation of Law; Vol. 3. Fifth Discourse - Circumcion - Sabbath; Sixth Discourse - Civil & Criminal Law Liturgy. pap. 49.50 ea. in arabic; Set. pap. 125.00x (ISBN 0-686-52167-6). Elliots Bks.
Kitab Al-Irshad: The Book of Guidance into the Lives of the Twelve Imams. Shaykh Al-Mufid. Tr. by I. K. Howard. 616p. 1986. lib. bdg. 55.00 (ISBN 0-7103-0151-0). Methuen Inc.
Kitab Al Tawhid. Muhammad I. Al-Wahhab. (Arabic.). 120p. (Orig.). 1978. pap. 4.95 (ISBN 0-939830-20-5, Pub. by IIFSO Kuwait). New Era Pubns MI.
Kitab Jawi: Islamic Thought of the Malay Muslim Scholars. Nor bin Ngah. 64p. (Orig.). 1982. pap. text ed. 7.50x (ISBN 9971-902-48-6, Pub. by Inst Southeast Asian Stud). Gower Pub Co.
Kitab Mu'id an-Ni'am Wa-Mubid an-Niqam: The Restorer of Favours & the Restrainer of Chastisements. Taj Adb al-Wahhab ibn Ali. LC 78-53829. (Luzac's Semitic Text & Translation Ser.: Vol. 18). 1978. Repr. of 1908 ed. 32.50 (ISBN 0-404-11291-9). AMS Pr.
Kitchen Connection. Omaha Section National Council of Jewish Women. Ed. by Sandy Kutler & Sheila Polikov. (Illus., Orig.). 1983. pap. 11.95 (ISBN 0-9612406-0-1). Omaha Sec Nat.
Kitchen Sink Prayer Book. Bernadette M. Snyder. 96p. 1984. pap. 3.25 (ISBN 0-89243-217-9). Liguori Pubns.
Kitto's Daily Bible Illustrations, 2 vols. John Kitto. LC 80-8069. 1934p. 1982. 64.95 (ISBN 0-8254-3025-9). Kregel.
Kitve Ari: Hebrew Text, 17 vols. Luria. 1985. 340.00 set (ISBN 0-943688-16-7); 25.00 ea. Res Ctr Kabbalah.
KJV Vest Pocket Companion. Reuben A. Torrey. pap. 1.95 (ISBN 0-310-33321-0, 12151P). Zondervan.
Kleines Stuttgarter-Bibellexikon. 3rd ed. H. Obermayer. (Ger.). 344p. 1976. 9.95 (ISBN 3-460-30053-1, M-7507, Pub. by Vlg. Katholisches Bibelwerk). French & Eur.
Kleines Theologisches Woerterbuch. Rahner & Vorgrimmler. (Ger.). 460p. 1976. 11.95 (ISBN 0-686-56624-6, M-7508, Pub. by Herder). French & Eur.
Kleines Woerterbuch Des Christlichen Orients. 1st ed. Julius Assfalg & P. Krueger. (Ger.). 1975. 52.00 (ISBN 3-447-01707-4, M-7514, Pub. by Harrassowitz). French & Eur.
Knaves, Fools, Madmen & That Subtile Effluvium: A Study of the Opposition to the French Prophets in England, 1706-1710. Hillel Schwartz. LC 78-1692. (University of Florida Social Sciences Monographs: No. 62). 1978. pap. 5.50 (ISBN 0-8130-0505-1). U Presses Fla.
Kneeling Christian. Ed. by Julie Link. 112p. 1986. pap. 5.95 (ISBN 0-310-33491-8, 6659P, Clarion Class). Zondervan.
Kneeling Christian. Unknown Christian. 1979. pap. 2.95 (ISBN 0-310-33492-6, 6657P); large print kivar o.p. 6.95 (ISBN 0-310-33497-7). Zondervan.
Kneeling in Bethlehem. Ann Weems. (Illus.). 96p. (Orig.). 1987. pap. price not set (ISBN 0-664-21323-5). Westminster.
Knight-Errant of Assisi. Ed. by Thomas Sheehan. Tr. by B. Little. Repr. 7.00. Franciscan Inst.
Knight in History. Frances Gies. LC 84-47571. (Illus.). 192p. 1984. 16.45 (ISBN 0-06-015339-3, HarpT). Har-Row.
Knight of Onions & Knight of Garlic. Hayyim N. Bialik. 55p. 1934. 4.95 (ISBN 0-88482-734-8). Hebrew Pub.
Knight Templarism. rev. ed. J. Blanchard. 9.50x (ISBN 0-685-22013-3). Wehman.
Knight Templarism. E. H. Cook. 9.50 (ISBN 0-685-19481-7). Powner.
Knights Hospitallers in England. Philippus De Thame. Repr. of 1857 ed. 37.00 (ISBN 0-384-46330-4). Johnson Repr.
Knights Hospitallers in England: Being the Report of Prior Phillip De Thame to the Grand Master Elyan De Villanova for A. D. 1338. Philippus De Thame. Ed. by Lambert B. Larking. (Camden Society, London Publications, First Ser.: No. 65). Repr. of 1857 ed. 37.00 (ISBN 0-404-50165-6). AMS Pr.
Knights Hospitallers of the Venerable Tongue of England in Malta. Alfred Mifsud. LC 78-63348. (Crusades & Military Orders: Second Ser.). (Illus.). Repr. of 1914 ed. 34.50 (ISBN 0-404-17009-9). AMS Pr.
Knight's Master Book of New Illustrations. Walter B. Knight. 1956. pap. 13.95 (ISBN 0-8028-1699-1). Eerdmans.
Knights of St. Crispin, Eighteen Sixty-Seven to Eighteen Seventy-Four. Don D. Lescohier. LC 77-89748. (American Labor from Conspiracy to Collective Bargaining, Ser. 2). 101p. 1969. Repr. of 1910 ed. 14.00 (ISBN 0-405-02136-4). Ayer Co Pubs.
Knights of the Golden Rule: The Intellectual As Christian Social Reformer in the 1890s. Peter J. Frederick. LC 76-9497. 344p. 1976. 28.00x (ISBN 0-8131-1345-8). U Pr of Ky.
Knights Templar History. rev. ed. Charles G. Addison. LC 76-29832. Repr. of 1912 ed. 59.50 (ISBN 0-404-15407-7). AMS Pr.
Knights Templars in England. Thomas W. Parker. LC 63-11983. pap. 48.80 (ISBN 0-317-08903-X, 2055370). Bks Demand UMI.
Knights Templars, Their Rise & Fall. George A. Campbell. LC 78-63330. (Crusades & Military Orders: Second Ser.). Repr. of 1937 ed. 35.00 (ISBN 0-404-17005-6). AMS Pr.
Knoche Writes Again. Keith Knoche. (Friendship Ser.). 64p. 1983. pap. 4.95 (ISBN 0-8163-0508-0). Pacific Pr Pub Assn.
Knock & Enter. Chad Walsh. (Orig.). 1953. pap. 4.95 (ISBN 0-8192-1076-5). Morehouse.
Knock on a Door. Mary T. Blanton. 32p. 1984. 4.95. Victor Bks.
Knock Wood! Superstition Through the Ages. Daniel Deerforth. LC 79-164220. 200p. 1974. Repr. of 1928 ed. 43.00x (ISBN 0-8103-3964-1). Gale.
Knom: Father Jim Poole Story. Louis L. Renner. LC 85-71950. (Illus.). 184p. (Orig.). 1985. pap. 8.95 (ISBN 0-8323-0444-1). Binford-Metropolitan.
Knots Untied: Being Plain Statements on Some of the Weightier Matters of Christianity. John Charles Ryle. 342p. 1977. Repr. of 1964 ed. 12.95 (ISBN 0-227-67511-8). Attic Pr.
Know & Grow, Vol. 1. Cheryl Fawcett. LC 82-21567. 1983. pap. 4.95 (ISBN 0-87227-086-6). Reg Baptist.
Know & Grow, Vol. 2. Cheryl Fawcett. LC 82-21567. 1983. pap. 4.95 (ISBN 0-87227-090-4). Reg Baptist.
Know Jewish Living & Enjoy It. Morris Golomb. LC 78-54569. (Illus.). 1981. 11.95 (ISBN 0-88400-054-0). Shengold.
Know, Love & Serve: General Principles & the Christo-Centric Method. Michael A. McGuire & Rose M. Mangieri. (Know, Love & Serve Cathechism Ser.). 30p. (Orig.). 1973. pap. 2.50 (ISBN 0-913382-44-2). Prow Bks-Franciscan.
Know the Marks of Cults. Dave Breese. LC 74-21907. 128p. 1975. pap. 4.95 (ISBN 0-88207-704-X). Victor Bks.
Know the Truth. Bruce Milne. LC 82-4711. 288p. 1982. pap. 9.95 (ISBN 0-87784-392-9). Inter-Varsity.
Know the Way, Keep the Truth, Win the Life. Donald Macleod. (Orig.). 1987. pap. price not set (ISBN 0-89536-872-2, 7858). CSS of Ohio.
Know Thyself. Richard Lynch. 1967. 5.95 (ISBN 0-87159-077-8). Unity School.
Know Thyself. Ishwar C. Puri. Ed. by Leonard Ingram. 66p. 1983. pap. 3.00 (ISBN 0-937067-01-6). Inst Study Hum Aware.
Know Thyself: Collected Readings on Identity. Ed. by David Cernic & Linda Longmire. 1987. pap. 12.95 (ISBN 0-8091-2872-1). Paulist Pr.
Know Thyself: Jnani Yoga. Omraam M. Aivanhov. (Complete Works: Vol. 17). (Illus.). 271p. 1981. pap. 9.95 (ISBN 2-85566-162-5). Prosveta USA.
Know What You Believe. Paul Little. 192p. 1985. pap. 2.95 (ISBN 0-89693-526-4). Victor Bks.
Know Why You Believe. rev. ed. Paul E. Little. LC 68-8267. 1968. pap. 5.95 (ISBN 0-87784-529-8). Inter-Varsity.
Know Why You Believe. Paul E. Little. 160p. 1984. pap. 2.95 (ISBN 0-89693-717-8). Victor Bks.
Know Your Bible. W. Graham Scroggie. 608p. 1965. 23.95 (ISBN 0-8007-0169-0). Revell.
Know Your Child. Joe Temple. 1974. pap. 5.95 (ISBN 0-8010-8820-8). Baker Bk.
Know Your Islam. Yousuf N. Lalljee. LC 81-51707. 256p. 1981. pap. 7.00 (ISBN 0-940368-02-1). Tahrike Tarsile Quran.
Know Your Neighbor's Faith. Bernard E. Deitrick. LC 83-7259. (Orig.). 1983. pap. 3.95x (ISBN 0-915324-19-9); pap. 3.00 members. CSLA.
Know Your Self. David Freeman. 1976. pap. 3.95 (ISBN 0-934532-11-7). Presby & Reformed.
Know Yourself! Ernest Holmes. Ed. by Willis H. Kinnear. 96p. (Orig.). 1970. pap. 4.50 (ISBN 0-911336-36-2). Sci of Mind.
Knowing & Doing God's Will. Jerry Glisson. LC 86-2617. (Orig.). 1986. pap. 5.95 (ISBN 0-8054-5027-0). Broadman.
Knowing & Helping Youth. Ed. by G. Temp Sparkman. LC 77-75621. 1978. 8.50 (ISBN 0-8054-3219-1, 4232-19). Broadman.
Knowing Christ Through Mark's Gospel. Philip Van Linden. 1977. pap. 1.25 (ISBN 0-8199-0727-8). Franciscan Herald.
Knowing God. J. I. Packer. LC 73-81573. 1973. pap. 7.95 (ISBN 0-87784-770-3). Inter-Varsity.
Knowing God. rev. ed. Mrs. A. W. Swafford. (God & Us Ser.). Tr. of God & Us. 32p. 1980. tchrs' ed. 2.00 (ISBN 0-89114-090-5). Baptist Pub Hse.
Knowing God Intimately. Dennis Burke. 1985. pap. 2.95 (ISBN 0-89274-349-2). Harrison Hse.
Knowing God: Religious Knowledge in the Theology of John Baillie. William P. Tuck. LC 78-52865. 1978. pap. text ed. 9.50 (ISBN 0-8191-0484-1). U Pr of Amer.
Knowing God: Study Guide. Pref. by James I. Packer. 1975. pap. 2.95 (ISBN 0-87784-413-5). Inter-Varsity.
Knowing God's Will. Steve B. Clark. (Living As a Christian Ser.). 1974. pap. 2.50 (ISBN 0-89283-005-0). Servant.
Knowing God's Will. M. Blaine Smith. LC 78-24756. 1979. pap. 4.95 (ISBN 0-87784-610-3). Inter-Varsity.
Knowing God's Will & Doing It! J. Grant Howard, Jr. 116p. 1983. pap. 4.95 (ISBN 0-310-26281-X, 9986P). Zondervan.
Knowing Jesus. Peter Rodgers. LC 82-14832. 64p. (Orig.). pap. 1.95 (ISBN 0-87784-383-X). Inter-Varsity.
Knowing Man. J. I. Packer. LC 79-52495. 1979. pap. 3.95 (ISBN 0-89107-175-X, Crossway Bks). Good News.
Knowing Religiously. Leroy S. Rouner. LC 85-8689. (Boston University Studies in Philosophy & Religion: Vol. 7). 240p. 1985. text ed. 22.95x (ISBN 0-268-01224-5, 85-12246, Dist. by Har-Row). U of Notre Dame Pr.
Knowing Scripture. R. C. Sproul. LC 77-11364. 1977. pap. text ed. 5.95 (ISBN 0-87784-733-9). Inter-Varsity.
Knowing the Doctrines of the Bible. Myer Pearlman. 400p. 1937. 7.95 (ISBN 0-88243-534-5, 02-0534). Gospel Pub.
Knowing the Face of God. Tim Stafford. 256p. Date not set. pap. 8.95 (ISBN 0-310-32851-9). Zondervan.
Knowing the Face of God: The Search for a Personal Relationship with God. Tim Stafford. 256p. 1986. text ed. 12.95 (ISBN 0-310-32850-0, 10836). Zondervan.
Knowing the Future. Paul L. Walker. LC 76-710. 1976. pap. 1.99 (ISBN 0-87148-477-3). Pathway Pr.
Knowing the Old Testament. James P. Berkeley. (Illus.). (YA) 1954. pap. text ed. 5.95 (ISBN 0-8170-0088-7). Judson.
Knowing the Unknowable God: Ibn-Sina, Maimonides, Aquinas. David B. Burrell. LC 85-40600. 160p. 1986. text ed. 15.95x (ISBN 0-268-01225-3, 85-12253). U of Notre Dame Pr.
Knowing the Unknowable God: Ibn-Sina, Maimonides, Aquinas. David B. Burrell. 130p. 1986. pap. text ed. 8.95x (ISBN 0-268-01226-1, Dist. by Har-Row). U of Notre Dame Pr.
Knowing the Whole Truth: Basic Christianity & What It Means in Your Life. D. James Kennedy. 192p. 1985. 11.95 (ISBN 0-8007-1407-5). Revell.
Knowing Your Tefilen & Mezuzos: A Layman's Guide to Understanding & Appreciating Tefilin & Mezuzos. Zeev Rothschild. 80p. (Orig.). 1982. pap. 2.50 (ISBN 0-686-76528-1). Feldheim.
Knowing Yourself. (Benziger Family Life Program Ser.). 4p. 1978. 2.00 (ISBN 0-02-651650-0); tchrs. ed. 4.00 (ISBN 0-02-651660-8); 1.00 (ISBN 0-02-651690-X). Benziger Pub Co.
Knowledge & Belief. Ed. by A. Philips Griffiths. 1967. pap. 9.95x (ISBN 0-19-875003-X). Oxford U Pr.
Knowledge & Cosmos: Development & Decline of the Medieval Perspective. Robert K. DeKosky. LC 79-66226. 1979. text ed. 26.00 (ISBN 0-8191-0814-6); pap. text ed. 15.25 (ISBN 0-8191-0815-4). U Pr of Amer.
Knowledge & Deceit in the Intellectual Life of Man. Matthew of Aquasparta. (Illus.). 87p. 1984. pap. 23.75 (ISBN 0-89266-491-6). Am Classical Coll Pr.
Knowledge & Initiation: Cognition of the Christ through Anthroposophy. Rudolf Steiner. Tr. by George Adams from Ger. 31p. 1983. pap. 3.25 (ISBN 0-919924-21-2). Anthroposophic.
Knowledge & Liberation. Anne Klein. LC 86-1784. 283p. (Orig.). 1986. 27.50 (ISBN 0-937938-24-6); pap. 15.95 (ISBN 0-937938-23-8). Snow Lion.
Knowledge & Power in Morocco: The Education of a Twentieth-Century Notable. Dale F. Eickelman. LC 85-3444. (Princeton Studies on the Near East). (Illus.). 325p. 1985. text ed. 32.50x (ISBN 0-691-09415-2). Princeton U Pr.
Knowledge & the Sacred. Ed. by Seyyed H. Nasr. 228p. 1982. 17.50 (ISBN 0-8245-0095-4). Crossroad NY.
Knowledge, Belief & Opinion. John Laird. LC 72-6560. 515p. 1972. Repr. of 1930 ed. 37.50 (ISBN 0-208-01215-X, Archon). Shoe String.
Knowledge, Belief, & Trancendence: Philosophical Problems in Religion. James Hall. LC 82-21757. 254p. 1983. pap. text ed. 12.25 (ISBN 0-8191-2912-7). U Pr of Amer.
Knowledge, Belief & Witchcraft. Barry Hallen & J. O. Sodipo. 144p. 1986. text ed. 24.95x (ISBN 0-936508-19-1, Ethnographica). Barber Pr.
Knowledge, Life & Reality: An Essay in Systemic Philosophy. George T. Ladd. LC 75-3221. Repr. of 1909 ed. 37.50 (ISBN 0-404-59217-1). AMS Pr.
Knowledge of God. Stephen Charnock. 598p. 1985. 15.95 (ISBN 0-85151-448-0). Banner of Truth.
Knowledge of God & Its Historical Development, 2 vols. Henry M. Gwatkin. LC 77-27219. (Gifford Lectures: 1904-05). 1978. Repr. of 1906 ed. Set. 49.50 (ISBN 0-404-60490-0). AMS Pr.
Knowledge of God & the Service of God According to the Teaching of the Reformation: Recalling the Scottish Confession of 1560. Karl Barth. LC 77-27187. (Gifford Lectures: 1937-38). Repr. of 1939 ed. 30.00 (ISBN 0-404-60495-1). AMS Pr.
Knowledge of God the Creator. John Calvin. 2.50 (ISBN 0-686-23485-5). Rose Pub MI.
Knowledge of Good & Evil. Jim McKeever. 1981. 1.00 (ISBN 0-86694-084-7). Omega Pubns OR.
Knowledge of the Higher Worlds & Its Attainment. 3rd ed. Rudolf Steiner. Tr. by Henry B. Monges. 1969. pap. 6.95 (ISBN 0-910142-20-3). Anthroposophic.
Knowledge of the Higher Worlds & Its Attainment. Rudolf Steiner. Tr. by George Metaxa & Henry B. Monges. LC 79-101595. 224p. 1983. 14.00 (ISBN 0-88010-045-1); pap. 6.95 (ISBN 0-88010-046-X). Anthroposophic.
Knowledge of the Holy. A. W. Tozer. LC 75-12279. 128p. 1978. pap. 6.95 (ISBN 0-06-068412-7, RD 291, HarpR). Har-Row.

Knowledge of the Holy. A. W. Tozer. LC 85-42794. 208p. 1985. pap. 12.95 large print (ISBN 0-06-068413-5, HarpR). Har-Row.

Knowledge of the Truth - Two Doctrines: The Book of Thomas the Contender(CGII, 7) & the False Teachers in the Pastoral Epistles. Jesse Sell. (European University Studies Ser.: No. 23, Vol. 194). 114p. 1982. pap. 14.20 (ISBN 3-8204-7224-X). P Lang Pubs.

Knowledge Without Goodness Is Dangerous: Moral Education in Boarding Schools. 2nd ed. Ed. by Charles L. Terry. LC 81-81105. 144p. (Orig.). 1981. pap. 6.95 (ISBN 0-939618-00-1). Phillips Exeter.

Knowth: And the Passage Tombs of Ireland. George Eogan. LC 86-50218. (New Aspects of Antiquity Ser.). (Illus.). 248p. 1987. 29.95 (ISBN 0-500-39023-1). Thames Hudson.

Koenig Herodes: Der Mann und sein Werk. Abraham Schalit. Tr. by Jehoshua Amir. (Studia Judaica, No. 4). (Ger). 1969. 80.00x (ISBN 3-11-001346-0). De Gruyter.

Koheles-Ecclesiastes. Meir Zlotowitz. (Art Scroll Ser.). 224p. 1976. 11.95 (ISBN 0-89906-006-4); pap. 8.95 (ISBN 0-686-63976-6). Mesorah Pubns.

Koheleth. Harold I. Leiman. 1978. 8.95 (ISBN 0-87306-143-8); pap. 2.95. Feldheim.

Koheleth: His Language & Thought. C. F. Whitley. (Beihefte zur Zeitschrift fuer die Alttestamentliche Wissenschaft: 148). 1979. 50.50x (ISBN 3-11-007602-0). De Gruyter.

Koheleth: The Man & His World: A Study of Ecclesiastes. rev. ed. Robert Gordis. LC 67-26988. 1968. pap. 10.95 (ISBN 0-8052-0166-1). Schocken.

Kokoro: Hints & Echoes of Japanese Inner Life. Lafcadio Hearn. LC 79-184814. 1972. pap. 6.50 (ISBN 0-8048-1035-4). C E Tuttle.

Kokoro: Hints & Echoes of Japanese Inner Life. Lafcadio Hearn. Repr. of 1896 ed. lib. bdg. 22.50x (ISBN 0-8371-1633-3, HEKO). Greenwood.

Kol Rom, Vol. I. 3rd ed. Avraham Fishelis. (Hebrew.). 208p. 5.50 (ISBN 0-9605560-0-1). A Fishelis.

Kol Rom, Vol. II. Avraham Fishelis. (Hebrew.). 292p. 6.50 (ISBN 0-9605560-2-8). A Fishelis.

Kol Rom, Vol. III. Avraham Fishelis. (Hebrew.). 431p. 12.00 (ISBN 0-9605560-3-6). A Fishelis.

Kolbe Novena in Honor of the Immaculate Conception & Novena in Honor of St. Maximilin Kolbe. Ed. by Franciscan Friars of Marytown Staff. (Illus.). 31p. 1983. pap. 0.50 (ISBN 0-913382-14-0, 105-38). Prow Bks-Franciscan.

Kolbe Reader. Anselm Romb. (Orig.). Date not set. pap. price not set (ISBN 0-913382-35-3, 101-35). Prow Bks-Franciscan.

Kolel in America. Herbert W. Bomzer. LC 85-63012. 184p. 1986. 15.95 (ISBN 0-88400-118-0). Shengold.

Kommmentar Zu Boethius De Consolatione Philosophiae. Joachim Gruber. (Texte und Kommentare: Vol. 9). 1978. 62.00x (ISBN 3-11-007223-8). De Gruyter.

Konfessionskunde. Friedrich Heyer. 1977. 39.20 (ISBN 3-11-006651-3). De Gruyter.

Konigsweg Zu Wiedergeburt und Vergottung Bei Philon Von Alexandreia. Josef Pascher. Repr. of 1931 ed. 22.00 (ISBN 0-384-45050-4). Johnson Repr.

Konziliarismus als Problem der Neueren Katholischen Theologie. Hans Schneider. (Arbeiten Zur Kirchengeschichte Ser.). 1976. 50.80x (ISBN 3-11-005744-1). De Gruyter.

Koptischen Quellen Zum Konzil Von Nicaa. Felix A. Haase. 12.00 (ISBN 0-384-20630-1). Johnson Repr.

Koran. Mufassir M. Ahmad. LC 81-52147. (Illus.). 600p. 1981. pap. 30.00 (ISBN 0-940368-04-8). Tahrike Tarsile Quran.

Koran. Tr. by Mir Ahmad Ali. LC 83-80220. 440p. Date not set. pap. 4.95 (ISBN 0-940368-36-6). Tahrike Tarsile Quran.

Koran. Ed. & tr. by J. M. Rodwell. 1978. pap. 3.50x (ISBN 0-460-01380-7, Evman). Biblio Dist.

Koran. Tr. by H. M. Shakir. LC 85-51993. (Arabic & Eng.). 672p. 1985. pap. text ed. 6.00 (ISBN 0-940368-56-0). Tahrike Tarsile Quran.

Koran. Tr. by M. H. Shakir from Arabic. 440p. 1985. 15.00 (ISBN 0-933543-05-0); pap. 9.00 (ISBN 0-933543-04-2). Aza Khana.

Koran & the Kafir: Islam & the Infidel. A. Ghosh. (Illus.). 190p. 1983. pap. 5.95 (ISBN 0-9611614-0-X). Ghosh A.

Koran & the Kafir: Islam & the Infidel. rev., 2nd ed. A. Ghosh. (Illus.). 200p. (Orig.). 1983. pap. 7.35 (ISBN 0-9611614-1-8). Ghosh A.

Koran, Hadith, & Islam. R. A. Khalifa. 90p. (Orig.). 1983. 6.00 (ISBN 0-934894-35-3). Islamic Prods.

Koran in the Light of Christ. Giulio Basetti-Sami. 1977. 8.50 (ISBN 0-8199-0713-8). Franciscan Herald.

Koran: The Final Scripture. Rashad Khalifa. 600p. (Orig.). 1981. 13.30 (ISBN 0-934894-19-1). Islamic Prods.

Korean Approach to Zen: The Collected Works of Chinul. Chinul. Tr. by Robert E. Buswell, Jr. LC 82-23873. 484p. 1983. text ed. 29.95x (ISBN 0-8248-0785-5). UH Pr.

Korean Buddhism: History-Condition-Art: Three Lectures. Frederick Starr. LC 78-70123. Repr. of 1918 ed. 25.00 (ISBN 0-404-17379-9). AMS Pr.

Korean Buddhist Canon: A Descriptive Catalogue. Ed. by Lewis R. Lancaster. LC 75-40662. (Center for Korean Studies, UC Berkeley). 1980. 60.00x (ISBN 0-520-03159-8). U of Cal Pr.

Korean Immigrant Churches Today in Southern California. Steve S. Shim. LC 76-24724. 1977. soft bdg. 11.00 (ISBN 0-88247-426-X). R & E Pubs.

Korean Minjung Theology: An Old Testament Perspective. Cyris H. Moon. 96p. (Orig.). 1986. pap. 7.95 (ISBN 0-88344-250-7). Orbis Bks.

Korean Shamanistic Rituals. Jung Y. Lee. (Religion & Society Ser.: No. 12). 250p. 1980. 39.50 (ISBN 90-279-3378-2). Mouton.

Koren Tanach. 1982. small 7.95 (ISBN 0-686-76529-X); medium 14.95 (ISBN 0-686-76530-3); large 75.00 (ISBN 0-686-76531-1). Feldheim.

Korinthisch-dorische Tempel am Forum von Paestum. Friedrich Krauss & Reinhard Herbig. (Denkmaeler antiker Architektur, Vol. 7). (Ger., Illus.). xii, 82p. 1978. Repr. of 1939 ed. 79.20x (ISBN 3-11-004991-0). De Gruyter.

Korrespondenz und die Liber Exhortacionis des Heinrich Von Kalkar: Eine Kritische Ausgabe. A. P. Orban. Ed. by James Hogg. (Analecta Cartusiana Ser.: No. 111). 303p. (Orig.). 1984. pap. 25.00 (ISBN 0-317-42581-1, Pub. by Salzburg Studies). Longwood Pub Group.

Korwars & Korwar Style: Art & Ancestor Worship in North-West New Guinea. T. P. Van Baaren. (Art in Its Context, Studies in Ethno-Aesthetics, Museum Ser.: No. 2). (Illus.). 1968. 26.75x (ISBN 0-686-21795-0). Mouton.

Kosher Calories. Tziporah Spear. 1985. 12.95 (ISBN 0-317-38550-X); pap. 9.95 (ISBN 0-317-38551-8). Mesorah Pubns.

Kosher Code of the Orthodox Jew. S. I. Levin & Edward A. Boyden. LC 76-76170. (Illus.). 264p. 1983. pap. 9.75 (ISBN 0-87203-011-3). Hermon.

Kosher for Pessach Cookbook. Yeshivat Aish HaTorah Woman's Organization. 1982. spiral bd. 5.95 (ISBN 0-87306-223-X). Feldheim.

Kosher Konnection: The Los Angeles Dining Guide to the Best of Kosher, Delis & Natural Foods. Bennet Simon. LC 79-67671. (Orig.). 1980. pap. 4.95 (ISBN 0-935618-00-7). Rossi Pubns.

Kosher Yoga: Cabalistic Roots of Western Mysticism. Albert Schutz & Hilda W. Schaps. LC 83-60144. 128p. (Orig.). 1983. 12.95 (ISBN 0-936596-09-0); pap. 8.95 (ISBN 0-936596-08-2). Quantal.

Koyasan: Sanctuary of Buddhism. Manly P. Hall. pap. 2.50 (ISBN 0-89314-326-X). Philos Res.

Krater & the Grail: Hermetic Sources of the Parzival. Henry Kahane & Renee Kahane. LC 84-16179. 216p. 1965. 31.00 (ISBN 0-252-01196-1). U of Ill Pr.

Kratkaja Grammatika Tserkovno-Slavjanskago Jazika. S. Mitropolsky. Tr. of Concise Grammer of the Church-Slavonic Language. 92p. 1980. pap. 5.00 (ISBN 0-317-30307-4). Holy Trinity.

Krauter: Die Magischen Heiler. Paul Twitchell. 1978. pap. 3.95 (ISBN 0-914766-39-2). IWP Pub.

Krinkle Nose: A Prayer of Thanks. Dean Turner. LC 77-78424. 1978. 6.95 (ISBN 0-8159-6002-6). Devin.

Kripalu Yoga: Meditation-in-Motion, - Focusing Inward, Bk. II. Amrit Desai. Ed. by Laura Tennen. (Illus.). 120p. 1987. wkbk. 9.95 (ISBN 0-940258-16-1). Kripalu Pubns.

Krishna: A Hindu Vision of God. Jeremiah P. Losty. (Illus.). 52p. (Orig.). 1980. pap. 3.75 (ISBN 0-904654-51-6, Pub. by British Lib). Longwood Pub Group.

Krishna & Orpheus. Edward Schure. 69.95 (ISBN 0-8490-0475-6). Gordon Pr.

Krishna & the Demons. Illus. by Marie T. Guelinboin. (Illus.). 16p. 1978. pap. 2.50 (ISBN 0-89647-005-9). Bala Bks.

Krishna: Devotional Songs of Mirabai. Mirabai & Pritish Nandy. 68p. (Orig.). 1982. pap. text ed. O.P. (ISBN 0-7069-1495-3, Pub. by Vikas India); text ed. 5.25x (ISBN 0-7069-1494-5). Advent NY.

Krishna, Master of All Mystics. Retold by Joshua Greene. (Illus.). 16p. 1981. pap. 4.00 (ISBN 0-89647-010-5). Bala Bks.

Krishna: Myths, Rites, & Attitudes. Ed. by Milton Singer. LC 65-20585. 1969. pap. 12.00x (ISBN 0-226-76101-0, P329, Phoen). U of Chicago Pr.

Krishna: Myths, Rites, & Attitudes. Ed. by Milton B. Singer. LC 80-29194. xvii, 277p. 1981. Repr. of 1966 ed. lib. bdg. 27.50x (ISBN 0-313-22822-1, SIKR). Greenwood.

Krishna: Pastoral & Kingmaker. Swami Ramakrishnananda. pap. 2.25 (ISBN 0-87481-447-2). Vedanta Pr.

Krishna Reddy: A Retrospective. Una Johnson et al. (Illus.). 78p. (Orig.). 1981. pap. 10.00 (ISBN 0-89062-138-1, Pub by Bronx Museum Arts). Pub Ctr Cult Res.

Krishna Smiled: Assignment in Southeast Asia. Judith L. Elkin. LC 72-737. pap. 63.30 (2027638). Bks Demand UMI.

Krishna: The Cowherd King. P. Pal. LC 70-185825. 1972. pap. 4.95x (ISBN 0-87587-048-1). LA Co Art Mus.

Krishna: The Divine Lover. Ed. by Enrico Isacco & Anna L. Dallapiccola. LC 82-83044. (Illus.). 224p. 1983. 75.00 (ISBN 0-87923-457-1). Godine.

Krishna: The Man & His Philosophy. Bhagwan Shree Rajneesh. Ed. by Swami Anand Sambuddha. LC 85-43055. (Early Writings & Discourses Ser.). 880p. 1985. pap. 5.95 (ISBN 0-88050-713-6). Chidvilas Found.

Krishnamurti: A Biography. Pupul Jayakar. LC 85-45739. (Illus.). 525p. 1986. 22.95 (ISBN 0-06-250401-0, HarpR). Har-Row.

Krishnamurti: A Biography. A. J. Methorst-Kuiper. 1974. lib. bdg. 79.95 (ISBN 0-87968-545-X). Krishna Pr.

Krishnamurti & the Unity of Man. Carlo Suares. 1974. lib. bdg. 69.95 (ISBN 0-8490-0476-4). Gordon Pr.

Krishnamurti: The Man & His Teaching. Rene Fouere. 1974. lib. bdg. 69.95 (ISBN 0-8490-0477-2). Gordon Pr.

Krishnamurti: The Years of Fulfillment. Mary Lutyens. 248p. 1983. 15.50 (ISBN 0-374-18224-8). FS&G.

Krishnamurti's Journal. Krishnamurti. Ed. by Mary Lutyens. LC 81-48210. 1982. pap. 5.95 (ISBN 0-06-064841-4, RD-396, HarpR). Har-Row.

Kritische Gesamtausgabe: Erste Abteilung (Schriften und Entwuerfe), Band 7, Teil 3 - Der Christliche Glaube, 1821-1822. Friedrich D. Schleiermacher. (Ger.). 1984. 128.00 (ISBN 3-11-008593-3). De Gruyter.

Kritische Gesamtausgabe: Fuenfte Abteilung (Briefwechsel & Biographische Dokumente) Briefwechsel, 1774-1796, Band 1. Friedrich D. Schleiermacher. Ed. by Andreas Arndt & Wolfgang Virmond. (Illus.). lxxii, 489p. 1986. 120.00x (ISBN 3-11-008595-X). De Gruyter.

Kritischer Rationalismus In Theologischer Pruefung. Peter Suchla. (European University Studies Series No. 23: Vol. 187). (Ger.). 443p. 1982. 41.60 (ISBN 3-8204-5828-X). P Lang Pubs.

Krsna Consciousness: The Matchless Gift. Swami A. C. Bhaktivedanta. LC 73-76634. (Illus.). 1974. pap. 1.95 (ISBN 0-912776-61-7). Bhaktivedanta.

Krsna: The Supreme Personality of Godhead, 3 vols. Swami A. C. Bhaktivedanta. LC 74-118081. (Illus.). 1970. Vol. 1. pap. 12.95 (ISBN 0-89213-136-5). Bhaktivedanta.

Kukai: Major Works, Translated with an Account of His Life & a Study of His Thought. Tr. by Yoshita S. Hakeda from Japanese. LC 72-3124. (Records of Civilization, Sources, Studies & Translations of the Oriental Classics Ser.). 303p. 1972. 30.00x (ISBN 0-231-03627-2); pap. 14.00x (ISBN 0-231-05933-7). Columbia U Pr.

Kularnava Tantra. T. Vidyaratna & A. Avalon. (Sanskrit.). 1975. Repr. 25.00 (ISBN 0-8426-0966-0). Orient Bk Dist.

Kum Nye Relaxation, Vols. 1 & 2. Tarthang Tulku. (Nyingma Psychology Ser.). 1978. 14.95 ea. Vol. 1 (ISBN 0-913546-10-0). Vol. 2 (ISBN 0-913546-74-7). pap. 7.95 ea. Vol. 1 (ISBN 0-913546-25-9). Vol. 2 (ISBN 0-913546-75-5). Dharma Pub.

Kumarasambhava. Kalidasa. Ed. by M. R. Kale. 1986. Repr. 17.50 (ISBN 81-208-0160-1, Pub. by Motilal Banarsidass). South Asia Bks.

Kumuhonua Legends: A Study of Late 19th Century Hawaiian Stories of Creation & Origins. Dorothy B. Barrere. (Pacific Anthropological Records: No. 3). 47p. 1969. pap. 5.00 (ISBN 0-910240-59-0). Bishop Mus.

Kumulipo: The Hawaiian Hymn of Creation. Rubellite K. Johnson. Ed. by John D. Holt. (Illus.). 1981. text ed. 19.95 (ISBN 0-914916-53-X); leather 100.00 (ISBN 0-914916-59-9). Topgallant.

Kundalini. George S. Arundale. 1972. 4.95 (ISBN 0-8356-7102-X). Theos Pub Hse.

Kundalini & the Third Eye. Earlyne Chaney & William L. Messick. Ed. by Sita Chaney. LC 80-67635. (Illus.). 127p. 1982. pap. 12.95 (ISBN 0-918936-08-X). Astara.

Kundalini Experience: Psychosis or Transcendence. rev. ed. Lee Sannella. (Illus.). 160p. 1987. pap. 9.95 (ISBN 0-941255-29-8). Integral Pub.

Kundalini for the New Age. Gene Kieffer. 288p. (Orig.). 1987. pap. 7.95 (ISBN 0-553-34433-1). Bantam.

Kundalini in the Physical World. Mary Scott. (Illus.). 240p. (Orig.). 1983. pap. 11.95 (ISBN 0-7100-9417-5). Methuen Inc.

Kundalini Meditation: Manual for Intermediate Students. LC 85-11044. 70p. 1985. Repr. of 1984 ed. lib. bdg. 19.95x (ISBN 0-89370-885-2). Borgo Pr.

Kundalini: Secret of the Ancient Yogis. Anna Billion. 1982. pap. 4.95 (ISBN 0-686-97516-2, Reward). P-H.

Kundalini Stavaha. Swami Muktananda. 45p. 1980. pap. 2.50 (ISBN 0-914602-55-1). SYDA Found.

Kundalini: The Evolutionary Energy in Man. Gopi Krishna. LC 73-75656. 252p. 1971. pap. 8.95 (ISBN 0-87773-043-1). Shambhala Pubns.

Kundalini: The Mother - Power. 2nd rev. ed. Sri Chinmoy. 1974. pap. 3.95 (ISBN 0-88497-104-X). Aum Pubns.

Kundalini: The Secret of Life. Swami Muktananda. (Illus.). 64p. (Orig.). 1983. pap. 3.95 (ISBN 0-914602-47-0). SYDA Found.

Kundalini West. Ann R. Colton. (Illus.). 403p. 1978. 12.95 (ISBN 0-917187-01-6). A R C Pub.

Kundalini Yoga. M. P. Pandit. LC 79-88734. 1979. 4.95 (ISBN 0-89744-004-8); pap. 3.00 (ISBN 0-89744-005-6). Auromere.

Kundalini Yoga. M. P. Pandit. pap. 3.00 (ISBN 0-89744-106-0). Auromere.

Kundalini Yoga for the West. Sivananda Radha. LC 81-40488. (Illus.). 379p. 1981. pap. 14.95 (ISBN 0-87773-211-6). Shambhala Pubns.

Kundalini Yoga for the West. Swami Sivananda Radha. LC 78-1857. (Illus.). 1978. 24.95 (ISBN 0-931454-01-8). Timeless Bks.

Kundalini Yoga-Sadhana Guidelines. LC 85-9918. 107p. 1985. Repr. of 1978 ed. lib. bdg. 19.95x (ISBN 0-89370-886-0). Borgo Pr.

Kung Fu Meditations & Chinese Proverbial Wisdom. Adapted by Ellen K. Hua. LC 73-7731. (Illus.). 1973. o. p. 3.95 (ISBN 0-87407-511-4); pap. 3.00 (ISBN 0-87407-200-X, FPI). Thor.

K'ung-Tzu or Confuscius? The Jesuit Interpretation of Confucianism. Paul A. Rule. 292p. (Orig.). 1987. pap. text ed. 18.95x (ISBN 0-86861-913-2). Allen Unwin.

Kurozumikyo & the New Religions of Japan. Helen Hardacre. LC 85-43287. (Illus.). 232p. 1986. text ed. 28.00 (ISBN 0-691-06675-2). Princeton U Pr.

Kut: Korean Shamanist Rituals. Halla Pai Huhm. 102p. 1980. 14.50x (ISBN 0-930878-18-3). Hollym Intl.

Kuzari: An Argument for the Faith of Israel. Judah Halevi. LC 64-15222. 1966. pap. 6.95 (ISBN 0-8052-0075-4). Schocken.

Kwakiutl Culture As Reflected in Mythology. Franz Boas. LC 36-6760. (American Folklore Society Memoirs). Repr. of 1935 ed. 19.00 (ISBN 0-527-01080-4). Kraus Repr.

Kyriakodromion (Sunday Sermonary) Apostolos Makrakis. Ed. by Orthodox Christian Educational Society. Tr. by D. Cummings from Hellenic. 637p. 1951. 12.00x (ISBN 0-938366-20-3). Orthodox Chr.

KZ: A Pictoral Report from Five Concentration Camps. (Witness to the Holocaust Ser.: No. 5). (Illus.). 54p. 1983. 3.00 (ISBN 0-317-46949-5). Witness Holocaust.

L

L. D. S. Children's Comments, Vol. 1. Compiled by Arthur Wallace. 60p. 1978. pap. 1.95x (ISBN 0-937892-03-3). LL Co.

Labor of Love. Spiros Zodhiates. (Trilogy Ser.: Vol. 3). (Illus.). pap. 8.95 (ISBN 0-89957-541-2). AMG Pubs.

Labor Peacemaker: The Life & Works of Father Leo. C. Brown, S. J. Gladys W. Gruenberg. Ed. by George E. Ganss. LC 80-83552. (Original Studies Composed in English Ser.: No. 4). (Illus.). 176p. 1981. 8.50 (ISBN 0-912422-54-8); pap. 7.00 smythsewn paperbound (ISBN 0-912422-53-X); pap. 6.00 (ISBN 0-912422-52-1). Inst Jesuit.

Labor-Religion Prophet: The Times & Life of Harry F. Ward. Eugene P. Link. (Academy of Independent Scholars Retrospections Ser.). 270p. 1984. 22.00x (ISBN 0-86531-621-X). Westview.

Laborers for the Vineyard: Proceedings of a Conference on Church Vocations. 180p. 1984. pap. 7.50 (ISBN 1-55586-908-4). US Catholic.

Laboring in the Harvest. LeRoy Eims. 108p. 1985. pap. 4.95 (ISBN 0-89109-530-6). NavPress.

Labyrinth of the World & the Paradise of the Heart. John A. Komensky. LC 73-135812. (Eastern Europe Collection Ser). 1970. Repr. of 1901 ed. 22.00 (ISBN 0-405-02754-0). Ayer Co Pubs.

Lach a Bisl: Laugh a Little. Isador Kleinman. 1985. pap. 5.95 (ISBN 0-910818-61-4). Judaica Pr.
Lactantius & Milton. Kathleen Hartwell. LC 74-17014. (Studies in Milton, No. 22). 1974. lib. bdg. 46.95x (ISBN 0-8383-1743-X). Haskell.
Ladies, God Bless 'Em. Georgianna Summers. 1983. 3.75 (ISBN 0-89536-581-2, 1264). CSS of Ohio.
Lady, A Healer. Russell Ramsey. Ed. by Helen Graves. LC 85-40891. 213p. (Orig.). 1986. pap. 3.95 (ISBN 1-55523-006-7). Winston-Derek.
Lady & the Virgin: Image, Attitude & Experience in Twelfth-Century France. Penny S. Gold. LC 84-23701. (Women in Culture & Society Ser.). (Illus.). 228p. 1985. lib. bdg. 20.00x (ISBN 0-226-30087-0). U of Chicago Pr.
Lady Hester Stanhope. Martin Armstrong. (Women Ser.). 1928. 17.50 (ISBN 0-8482-7275-7). Norwood Edns.
Lady of Faith. Lois M. Nester. (Illus.). 112p. 1987. 7.95 (ISBN 0-8059-3040-X). Dorrance.
Lady of the Dance: A Movement Approach to the Biblical Figures of Wisdom in Worship & Education. Hal Taussig. (Orig.). 1981. pap. 2.50 (ISBN 0-941500-24-1). Sharing Co.
Lady of the Holy Alliance: The Life of Julie De Krudener. Ernest J. Knapton. LC 39-14081. Repr. of 1939 ed. 22.45 (ISBN 0-404-03732-1). AMS Pr.
Lady Preacher: Or, the Life & Labors of Mrs. Hannah Reeves, the Late Wife of the Rev. William Reeves of the Methodist Church. George Brown. Ed. by Carolyn G. De Swarte & Donald Dayton. (Women in American Protestant Religion Series 1800-1930). 341p. 1987. lib. bdg. 50.00 (ISBN 0-8240-0660-7). Garland Pub.
Ladybug & Country Preacher. Nan Olmstead. LC 84-29264. 1985. pap. 3.95 (ISBN 0-8054-4297-9). Broadman.
Laghu-Vakya-Vritti. Shankara. (Sanskrit & English). pap. 1.50 (ISBN 0-87481-067-1). Vedanta Pr.
Laghu-Yoga-Vasistha. Tr. by K. Narayanaswami Aiyer. 1971. 19.95 (ISBN 0-8356-7497-5). Theos Pub Hse.
Laity: A Bibliography. Leonard Doohan. LC 87-45006. (Theological & Biblical Resources). 160p. (Orig.). 1987. pap. 8.95 (ISBN 0-89453-617-6). M Glazier.
Laity in Ministry. Ed. by George Peck & John S. Hoffman. 176p. 1984. pap. 7.95 (ISBN 0-8170-1041-6). Judson.
Laity Stirring the Church: Prophetic Questions. Dolores R. Leckey. LC 86-45213. (Laity Exchange Ser.). 128p. pap. 6.95 (ISBN 0-8006-1659-6, 1-1659). Fortress.
Laity Today & Tomorrow. Edmund Flood. 120p. (Orig.). 1987. pap. 4.95 (ISBN 0-8091-2848-9). Paulist Pr.
Laity's Mission in the Local Church. Leonard Doohan. 204p. (Orig.). 1986. pap. 8.95 (ISBN 0-86683-490-7, HarpR). Har-Row.
Lake Kinneret: Lake of Tiberias, Sea of Galilee. Colette Serruya. (Monographiae Biologicae: No.32). 1978. lib. bdg. 68.50 (ISBN 90-619-3085-5, Pub. by Junk Pubs Netherlands). Kluwer Academic.
Lakeside Story. Anderson. LC 86-70041. (Illus.). 242p. 1986. 12.50 (ISBN 0-87483-010-9). August Hse.
Lakota Belief & Ritual. James R. Walker. Ed. by Raymond J. DeMallie & Elaine A. Jahner. LC 79-19816. (Illus.). xxx, 369p. 1980. 21.50 (ISBN 0-8032-2551-2). U of Nebr Pr.
Lakota Myth. James R. Walker. Ed. by Elaine A. Jahner. LC 83-3454. xiv, 428p. 1983. 29.95x (ISBN 0-8032-4726-5); pap. 14.95 (ISBN 0-8032-9706-8, BB 848, Bison). U of Nebr Pr.
Lalleshwari. Swami Muktananda. LC 81-50160. 92p. 1981. pap. 3.95. SYDA Found.
Lalmai, a Cultural Center of Early Bengal: An Archaeological Report & Historical Analysis. Barrie M. Morrison. LC 74-9892. (Publications on Asia of the School of International Studies: No. 24). (Illus.). 160p. 1974. 18.50x (ISBN 0-295-95342-X). U of Wash Pr.
Lama Knows: A Tibetan Legend Is Born. Robert B. Ekvall. LC 81-4160. (Illus.). 144p. 1981. pap. 5.95 (ISBN 0-88316-541-4). Chandler & Sharp.
Lamb. Frederick W. Kemper. LC 12-2983. (Christian Education & the Church Ser.). 1983. pap. 5.95 (ISBN 0-570-03901-0). Concordia.
Lamb & the Elephant: Ideal Imitation & the Context of Renaissance Allegory. John M. Steadman. LC 73-93874. 254p. 1974. 29.95 (ISBN 0-87328-062-8). Huntington Lib.
Lamb of God; the Theme Eternal. Willard S. Hall. 35p. 1974. 4.95 (ISBN 0-87881-033-1). Mojave Bks.
Lambeth Conferences: The Solution for Pan-Anglican Organization. William R. Curtis. LC 68-58565. (Columbia University Studies in the Social Sciences: No. 488). Repr. of 1942 ed. 24.50 (ISBN 0-404-51488-X). AMS Pr.
Lame Deer Seeker of Visions: The Life of a Sioux Medicine Man. John Lame Deer & Richard Erdoes. 288p. 1976. pap. 3.95 (ISBN 0-671-45586-9, 80391). WSP.
Lame Man Who Walked Again. Mary P. Warren & Betty Wind. (Arch Bks: Set 3). 1966. laminated bdg. 0.99 (ISBN 0-570-06020-6, 59-1129). Concordia.
Lamentations. Tr. by Delbert R. Hillers. LC 70-176347. (Anchor Bible Ser: Vol. 7A). (Illus.). 168p. 1972. 14.00 (ISBN 0-385-00738-8, Anchor Pr). Doubleday.
Lamentations. Dan G. Kent. (Bible Study Commentary Ser.). 80p. 1983. pap. 3.95 (ISBN 0-310-44011-4, 12482P). Zondervan.
Lamentations, Baruch, Sophonia, Nahum, Habacuc. Edward J. Crowley. (Bible Ser.). pap. 1.00 (ISBN 0-8091-5078-6). Paulist Pr.
Lamentations-Daniel. Joyce Baldwin. (Bible Study Commentaries Ser.). 128p. 1984. pap. 4.95 (ISBN 0-317-43378-4). Chr Lit.
Lamentations: From the Matins of Holy & Great Saturday. Tr. by Holy Transfiguration Monastery. 65p. (Orig.). 1981. pap. 4.95x (ISBN 0-913026-51-4). St Nectarios.
Lamentations, Haggai, Zechariah, Second Zechariah, Malachi, Obadiah, Joel, Baruch. Jerome Kodell. (Old Testament Ser.: Vol. 14). 1982. 12.95 (ISBN 0-89453-414-9); pap. 8.95 (ISBN 0-89453-248-0). M Glazier.
Lamp for My Feet: The Bible's Light for Daily Living. Elisabeth Elliot. 210p. (Orig.). 1985. pap. 9.95 (ISBN 0-89283-234-7, Pub. by Vine Books). Servant.
Lamp for Orchid. Mary Mellows. 126p. 1986. pap. 22.00X (ISBN 0-7223-1987-8, Pub. by A H Stockwell England). State Mutual Bk.
Lamp unto My Feet. Doris Wallace. LC 83-91018. 49p. 1985. 5.95 (ISBN 0-533-06008-7). Vantage.
Lamp Unto Our Faith. Clarice Albritton & Grace Newby. LC 76-24514. 1976. pap. 3.95 (ISBN 0-87516-218-5). De Vorss.
Lamplighter & Son. Craig Skinner. LC 82-82947. 1984. 13.95 (ISBN 0-8054-5705-4). Broadman.
Lamps of Fire. Robert A. Herrera. 168p. (Orig.). 1986. pap. 7.95 (ISBN 0-932506-40-2). St Bedes Pubns.
Lancashire Elizabethan Recusants. J. Stanley Leatherbarrow. Repr. of 1947 ed. 24.00 (ISBN 0-384-31910-6). Johnson Repr.
Lancaster County Churches in the Revolutionary War Era. Martin E. Ressler et al. Ed. by Matthew W. Harrison, Jr. LC 76-21210. (Illus.). 96p. 1976. pap. 3.50 (ISBN 0-915010-11-9, Co-Pub by Lancaster County Bicentennial Committee). Sutter House.
Lancaster County, Virginia Records, Vol. 2. Lindsay O. Duvall. (Virginia Colonial Abstracts, Series II). 1979. Repr. 20.00 (ISBN 0-89308-063-2). Southern Hist Pr.
Land & People Jesus Knew. J. Robert Teringo. 250p. 1985. 24.95 (ISBN 0-87123-797-0, 230797). Bethany Hse.
Land & People of Israel. rev. ed. Gail Hoffman. LC 77-37286. (Portraits of the Nations Ser.). (Illus.). 1972. PLB 11.89i (ISBN 0-397-31258-X, Lipp Jr Bks). HarpJ.
Land Flowing with Milk & Honey: Perspectives on Feminist Theology. Elisabeth Moltmann-Wendel. 224p. 1986. 14.95 (ISBN 0-8245-0791-6). Crossroad NY.
Land for the Chosen People Racket. C. H. Douglas. 1982. lib. bdg. 55.00 (ISBN 0-87700-415-3). Revisionist Pr.
Land of Israel. Photos by Hilla Jacoby & Max Jacoby. (Illus.). 1978. 25.00f. Thames Hudson.
Land of Israel: Jewish Perspectives. Lawrence A. Hoffman. LC 86-40241. (Studies in Judaism & Christianity in Antiquity: Vol. 6). 352p. 1986. text ed. 29.95x (ISBN 0-268-02180-5). U of Notre Dame Pr.
Land of Miracles. Nathan M. Meyer. (Illus.). pap. 2.00 (ISBN 0-88469-021-0). BMH Bks.
Land of Promise. Robert Thompson. pap. 5.95 (ISBN 0-89728-042-3, 670209). Omega Pubns OR.
Land of Promise: A Critique of Political Zionism. Abdelwahab M. Elmessiri. LC 77-83664. 1977. text ed. 11.95x (ISBN 0-930244-02-8); pap. text ed. 7.95x (ISBN 0-930244-01-X). North American Inc.
Land of the Bible: A Historical Geography. rev. & enlarged ed. Yohanan Aharoni. Tr. by Anson F. Rainey. LC 80-14168. 496p. 1980. pap. 19.95 (ISBN 0-664-24266-9). Westminster.
Land of Upside Down. Ludwig Tieck. Tr. by Oscar Mandel. LC 76-50288. 123p. 1978. 17.50 (ISBN 0-8386-2061-2). Fairleigh Dickinson.
Land or Religion? The Sardar & Kherwar Movements in Bihar, 1858-1895. John MacDougall. 1986. 27.00x (ISBN 0-8364-1591-4, Pub. by Manohar India). South Asia Bks.
Land, Piety & Peoplehood. Richard K. MacMaster. LC 84-15790. (Mennonite Experience in America Ser.: Vol. 1). 344p. (Orig.). 1984. pap. 12.00x (ISBN 0-8361-1261-X). Herald Pr.
Land: Place As Gift, Promise & Challenge in Biblical Faith. Walter Brueggemann. Ed. by John R. Donahue. LC 76-15883. (Overtures to Biblical Theology Ser.: No. 1). 228p. 1977. pap. 8.95 (ISBN 0-8006-1526-3, 1-1526). Fortress.
Land Rush: The Secret World of Real Estate's Super Brokers & Developers. Mark Stevens. 1985. pap. 6.95 (ISBN 0-07-061274-9). McGraw.
Landmarks in the Struggle Between Science & Religion. James Y. Simpson. LC 75-118549. 1971. Repr. of 1925 ed. 26.50x (ISBN 0-8046-1174-2, Pub. by Kennikat). Assoc Faculty Pr.
Landmarks of Church History to the Reformation. new rev. & enl. ed. Henry Cowan. LC 70-144590. Repr. of 1896 ed. 17.00 (ISBN 0-404-01787-8). AMS Pr.
Landmarks of Freemasonry. Elbert Bede. 56p. 1980. pap. text ed. 3.00 (ISBN 0-88053-020-0). Macoy Pub.
Landmarks of the Spirit: One Man's Journey. David H. Sandstrom. 192p. (Orig.). 1984. pap. 11.95 (ISBN 0-8298-0726-8). Pilgrim NY.
Landmauer von Konstantinopel, Part 2: Aufnahme, Beschreibung und Geschichte. Meyer-Plath & A. M. Schneider. (Denkmaeler antiker Architektur, Vol. 8). (Ger., Illus.). x, 170p. 1978. Repr. of 1943 ed. 120.00 (ISBN 3-11-004992-9). De Gruyter.
Landybird Bible Storybook. Jenny Robertson. (Illus.). 384p. 1983. 14.95 (ISBN 0-310-44440-3, 11361). Zondervan.
Lane Rebels: Evangelicalism & Antislavery in Antebellum America. Lawrence T. Lesick. LC 80-24123. (Studies in Evangelicalism: No. 2). 287p. 1980. 21.00 (ISBN 0-8108-1372-6). Scarecrow.
Lanfranc of Bec. Margaret Gibson. 1978. 47.00x (ISBN 0-19-822462-1). Oxford U Pr.
Langenscheidt Greek (Classical) Pocket Dictionary. 428p. plastic 7.95 (ISBN 0-88729-081-7). Langenscheidt.
Language & Gnosis: Form & Meaning in the Acts of Thomas Chapters 1-10. J. Michael LaFargue. LC 84-45191. (Harvard Dissertations in Religion Ser.). 288p. 1984. pap. 14.95 (ISBN 0-8006-7016-7, 1-7016). Fortress.
Language & Imagery of the Bible. G. B. Caird. LC 79-27586. 288p. 1980. 20.00 (ISBN 0-664-21378-2). Westminster.
Language & Logic of the Bible: The Road to Reformation. G. R. Evans. 200p. 1985. 32.50 (ISBN 0-521-30548-9). Cambridge U Pr.
Language & Myth. Ernst Cassirer. Tr. by Susanne K. Langer. 1946. pap. 2.95 (ISBN 0-486-20051-5). Dover.
Language & Myth. Ernst Cassirer. 13.50 (ISBN 0-8446-1820-9). Peter Smith.
Language & Natural Theology. Bowman L. Clarke. (Janua Linguarum, Ser. Minor: No. 47). (Orig.). 1966. pap. text ed. 18.00 (ISBN 90-2790-580-0). Mouton.
Language & Reality: An Introduction to Indian Philosophical Studies. Bimal K. Matilal. 450p. 1986. 31.00X (ISBN 0-317-53529-3, Pub. by Motilal Banarsidass). South Asia Bks.
Language & Theology. Gordon H. Clark. 1979. pap. 4.95 (ISBN 0-87552-141-X). Presby & Reformed.
Language for Madness: The Abuse & the Use of Christian Creeds. Hamish F. Swanston. 154p. 1976. pap. text ed. 12.50 (ISBN 90-232-1426-9, Pub. by Van Gorcum Holland). Longwood Pub Group.
Language in Indian Philosophy & Religion. Ed. by Harold G. Coward. 98p. 1978. pap. text ed. 9.95x (ISBN 0-919812-07-4, Pub. by Wilfrid Laurier Canada). Humanities.
Language, Logic, & God. Frederick Ferre. LC 81-27305. viii, 184p. 1987. pap. text ed. 10.00 (ISBN 0-226-24457-1, Midway Reprint). U of Chicago Pr.
Language of Canaan & the Grammar of Feminism: An Exercise in Wittgensteinian Analysis. Vernard Eller. 64p. 1982. pap. 2.95 (ISBN 0-8028-1902-8). Eerdmans.
Language of Canaan: Metaphor & Symbol in New England from the Puritans to the Transcendentalists. Mason I Lowance, Jr. LC 79-21179. 1980. 22.50x (ISBN 0-674-50949-8). Harvard U Pr.
Language of Counseling. Jay E. Adams. 90p. 1981. pap. 2.45 (ISBN 0-87552-009-X). Presby & Reformed.
Language of Counseling & the Christian Counselor's WordBook. Jay E. Adams. (Jay Adams Library). 160p. 1986. pap. 7.95 (ISBN 0-310-51061-9, 12118P). Zondervan.
Language of Exixtence & Faith. J. Donald Butler. LC 86-30549. 1987. 19.95 (ISBN 0-8022-2532-2). Philos Lib.
Language of Faith. Aaron Bin-Nun. LC 78-65723. 1979. 8.95 (ISBN 0-88400-061-3). Shengold.
Language of Jewish Education. Barry Chazan. LC 77-21638. 1978. 10.00 (ISBN 0-87677-146-0). Hartmore.
Language of Judaism. rev. ed. Simon Glustrom. 1973. pap. 9.95x (ISBN 0-87068-224-5). Ktav.
Language of Mining & Metallurgy in English. Eugene J. Hall. (English for Careers Ser.). 1978. pap. text ed. 4.25 (ISBN 0-88345-307-X, 18521). Regents Pub.
Language of Parable. William F. Worcester. LC 76-6008. 1976. pap. 4.00 (ISBN 0-87785-155-7). Swedenborg.
Language of Puritan Feeling: An Exploration in Literature, Psychology, & Social History. David Leverenz. 1980. 32.00x (ISBN 0-8135-0882-7). Rutgers U Pr.
Language of the Consciousness Soul. Carl Unger. 1983. 25.00 (ISBN 0-916786-56-0). St George Bk Serv.
Language of the Cross. Ed. by Aelred Lacomara. 1977. 5.95 (ISBN 0-8199-0617-4). Franciscan Herald.
Language of the New Testament. Eugene Van Ness Goetchius. 349p. 1966. text ed. write for info. (ISBN 0-02-344530-0, Pub. by Scribner). Macmillan.
Language of the Rite. Roger Grainger. 192p. 1984. pap. 8.95 (ISBN 0-232-51246-9). Chr Classics.
Language of the Soul. Robert Crosbie. (Sangam Texts). 130p. 1986. pap. 8.75 (ISBN 0-88695-026-0). Concord grove.
Language Silenced: Hebrew Culture in the Soviet Union. Yehoshuna A. Gilboa. LC 80-70920. 320p. 1982. 25.00 (ISBN 0-8386-3072-3). Fairleigh Dickerson.
Lankavatara Sutra: A Mahayana Text. Tr. by Daisetz T. Suzuki. (Illus.). 1972. Repr. of 1932 ed. 27.00 (ISBN 0-7100-2165-8). Methuen Inc.
Lantern in the Dawn: Selections from Writings of John E. Zercher. E. Morris Sider & Paul Hostetler. 1980. 6.95 (ISBN 0-916035-08-5). Evangel Indiana.
Lantern in the Moonlight. Doras R. Benbow. (Illus.). 1974. lib. bdg. 3.00 (ISBN 0-931611-06-7); pap. 1.50. D R Benbow.
Lao-Tzu & Taoism. Max Kaltenmark. Tr. by Roger Greaves. LC 69-13179. 1969. 15.00x (ISBN 0-8047-0688-3); pap. 5.95 (ISBN 0-8047-0689-1, SP96). Stanford U Pr.
Lao-Tzu: My Words Are Very Easy to Understand. 2nd ed. Cheng Men-Ching. Tr. by Tam Gibbs & Juh-Hua Huang. (Eng. & Chinese.). 256p. 1981. pap. 8.95 (ISBN 0-913028-91-6). North Atlantic.
Laodecian Church. 28p. (Orig.). 1982. pap. 0.95 (ISBN 0-937408-17-4). GMI Pubns Inc.
Lapsed & the Unity of the Church. St. Cyprian. pap. 2.95 (ISBN 0-686-05646-9). Eastern Orthodox.
Large Catechism of Martin Luther. Martin Luther. Tr. by Robert H. Fischer from Ger. LC 61-3802. 112p. 1959. 4.95 (ISBN 0-8006-0885-2, 1-885). Fortress.
Large Church. John N. Vaughan. 1985. pap. 7.95 (ISBN 0-8010-9298-1). Baker Bk.
Large Sutra on Perfect Wisdom: With the Divisions of the Abhisamayalankara. Edward Conze. LC 71-189224. (Center for South & Southeastern Asia Studies, UC Berkeley). 697p. 1985. pap. 12.95 (ISBN 0-520-05321-4, CAL 668). U of Cal Pr.
Large Type Treasury of Inspiration. 1986. 8.98 (625334). Outlet Bk Co.
Larger Christian Life. Albert B. Simpson. 3.95 (ISBN 0-87509-025-7); pap. 3.45 mass market (ISBN 0-87509-026-5). Chr Pubns.
Larger Hope, Vol. 1. Russell Miller. 25.00 (ISBN 0-933840-00-4). Unitarian Univ.
Larger Hope, Vol. 2. Russell Miller. 1986. 25.00 (ISBN 0-933840-25-X). Unitarian Univ.
Larger Life. Ernest Holmes. Ed. by Willis H. Kinnear. 84p. 1969. pap. 5.50 (ISBN 0-911336-07-9). Sci of Mind.
Larger Meaning of Religion. James I. Wedgwood. 80p. 1981. pap. text ed. 3.00 (ISBN 0-918980-10-0). St Alban Pr.
Lark. Jean Anouilh. Tr. by Christopher Fry. 1956. 10.95x (ISBN 0-19-500393-4). Oxford U Pr.
Larousse Des Prenoms et Des Saints. Pierre Pierradrd. (Fr.). 256p. 1976. 42.50 (ISBN 0-686-57079-0, M-6454). French & Eur.
Larousse Dictionnaire des Proverbs, Sentences et Maximes. Larousse. 37.50 (ISBN 0-317-45655-5). French & Eur.
Larry the Lamb. Jane Hammond. (God's Animals Story Bks.). 1983. pap. 1.50 (ISBN 0-87162-286-6, D5600). Warner Pr.
Larson's Book of Cults. Bob Larson. 1982. 9.95 (ISBN 0-8423-2104-7). Tyndale.
Last American Puritan: The Life of Increase Mather. Michael Hall. 1987. 35.00 (ISBN 0-8195-5128-7). Wesleyan U Pr.
Last Arab Jews: The Communities of Jerba. Lucette Valensi & Abraham L. Udovitch. (Social Orders: A Series of Monographs & Tracts). 180p. 1984. 36.00 (ISBN 3-7186-0135-4). Harwood Academic.

Last Barrier. Reshad Feild. LC 75-9345. 1977. pap. 8.95 (ISBN 0-06-062586-4, RD 202, HarpR). Har-Row.

Last Barrier to Freedom: Internment of Jewish Holocaust Survivors on Cyprus 1946-1949. Morris Laub. LC 84-82475. (Illus., Orig.). 1985. pap. 8.95 (ISBN 0-943376-25-4). Magnes Mus.

Last Call. Jack T. Chick. (Illus.). 64p. (Orig.). 1963. pap. 1.95 (ISBN 0-937958-06-9). Chick Pubns.

Last Call to the Godly Remnant. Philip Mauro. pap. 1.75 (ISBN 0-685-88381-7). Reiner.

Last Christian: Release of the Siberian Seven. Timothy Chmykhaler & Danny Smith. 208p. 1985. pap. 7.95 (ISBN 0-310-34021-7, 12411P). Zondervan.

Last Crusade: The Church of England in the First World War. Albert Marrin. LC 72-97471. xv, 303p. 1973. 19.75 (ISBN 0-8223-0298-5). Duke.

Last Dalai Lama. Michael H. Goodman. LC 85-27906. 400p. 1987. pap. 14.95 (ISBN 0-87773-400-3). Shambhala Pubns.

Last Day of Jesus. Gerhard Lohfink. Tr. by Salvator Attanasio from Ger. LC 83-73026. Tr. of De Letzte Tag Jesu. 80p. 1984. pap. 2.95 (ISBN 0-87793-312-X). Ave Maria.

Last Days. William F. Dankenbring. LC 77-79265. 1977. 11.95 (ISBN 0-917182-05-7). Triumph Pub.

Last Days Collection: A Treasury of Articles from Last Days Ministries. Catherine Booth et al. (Illus.). 224p. (Orig.). 1986. pap. text ed. 10.95. Pretty Good TX.

Last Days of David & His Contemporaries. Gordon Lindsay. (Old Testament Ser.). 1.25 (ISBN 0-89985-144-4). Christ Nations.

Last Days of Greco-Roman Paganism. J. Geffcken. (Europe in the Middle Ages Selected Studies: Vol. 8). 344p. 1978. 74.50 (ISBN 0-444-85005-8, North-Holland). Elsevier.

Last Days of Jesus. T. V. Moore. 212p. (Orig.). 1981. pap. 4.95 (ISBN 0-85151-321-2). Banner of Truth.

Last Days of the Lancashire Monasteries & the Pilgrimage of Grace. C. Haigh. 182p. 1969. 30.00 (ISBN 0-7190-1150-7, Pub. by Manchester Univ Pr). Longwood Pub Group.

Last Eight Days. Ester M. Smith & Maurice L. Sutton. LC 85-40202. 125p. (Orig.). 1985. pap. 6.95 (ISBN 0-938232-82-7). Winston-Derek.

Last Enemy. Robert L. Richter. 1983. 3.75 (ISBN 0-89536-960-5, 7511). CSS of Ohio.

Last Eve. Gail White. LC 85-91011. 160p. 1985. 10.00 (ISBN 0-682-40244-3). Exposition Pr FL.

Last Great Conflict. A. J. Tomlinson. 241p. 1984. Repr. of 1913 ed. 8.95 (ISBN 0-317-14173-2, 1925). White Wing Pub.

Last Great Conflict. A. J. Tomlinson. (Higher Christian Life Ser.). 219p. 1985. lib. bdg. 30.00 (ISBN 0-8240-6446-1); pap. 8.95 (ISBN 0-317-14532-0, 1925). Garland Pub.

Last Hours of Jesus. Ralph Gorman. 1960. 4.50 (ISBN 0-8362-0221-X, Pub. by Sheed). Guild Bks.

Last Jews of Eastern Europe. Yale Strom & Brian Blue. LC 86-25354. (Illus.). 250p. 1986. 29.95 (ISBN 0-8022-2520-9). Philos Lib.

Last Jews of Radauti. Ayse Gursan-Salzmann & Laurence Salzmann. LC 82-22176. (Illus.). 192p. 1983. 29.95 (ISBN 0-385-27808-X, Dial). Doubleday.

Last, Least & Lowest. Julia Taylor. LC 78-70663. 1979. pap. 2.95 (ISBN 0-89221-058-3). New Leaf.

Last Lectures. facs. ed. Wilfrid P. Ward. LC 67-26793. (Essay Index Reprint Ser). 1918. 22.50 (ISBN 0-8369-0976-3). Ayer Co Pubs.

Last of the Crusaders. Roderick Cavaliero. LC 78-63337. (Crusades & Military Orders: Second Ser.). Repr. of 1960 ed. 34.25 (ISBN 0-404-17006-4). AMS Pr.

Last of the Fathers. Basil Pennington. LC 82-24098. 1983. pap. 14.95 (ISBN 0-932506-24-0). St Bedes Pubns.

Last of the Fathers: Saint Bernard of Clairvaux & the Encyclical Letter, Doctor Mellifluus. Thomas Merton. Repr. of 1954 ed. lib. bdg. 22.50x (ISBN 0-8371-4434-5, MELF). Greenwood.

Last of the Fathers: Saint Bernard of Clairvaux & the Encyclical Letter, Doctor Mellifluus. Thomas Merton. LC 81-4105. 128p. 1981. pap. 4.95 (ISBN 0-15-649438-8, Harv). HarBraceJ.

Last One Chosen. Dorothy Hamilton. LC 82-3150. (Illus.). 112p. (Orig.). 1982. pap. 3.95 (ISBN 0-8361-3306-4). Herald Pr.

Last Outpost of Texas: A History of First Baptist Church, El Paso, Texas--The First Fifty Years. William I. Latham. 1987. 20.00 (ISBN 0-930208-21-8). Mangan Bks.

Last Page in the Diary. Colleen L. Reece. Ed. by Gerald Wheeler. (Banner Ser.). 128p. (Orig.). 1986. pap. 6.50 (ISBN 0-8280-0304-1). Review & Herald.

Last Reformation. F. G. Smith. 256p. 5.00 (ISBN 0-686-29154-9); pap. 3.50 (ISBN 0-686-29155-7). Faith Pub Hse.

Last Sayings of the Savior from the Cross. G. Michael Cocoris. 25p. (Orig.). 1985. pap. 1.00 (ISBN 0-935729-01-1). Church Open Door.

Last Supper & Lord's Supper. I. Howard Marshall. (Orig.). 1981. pap. 6.95 (ISBN 0-8028-1854-4). Eerdmans.

Last Temptation of Christ. Nikos Kazantzakis. 1966. Translation 1971. pap. 9.95 (ISBN 0-671-21170-6, Touchstone Bks). S&S.

Last Testament. William J. Duda. 1987. 7.95 (ISBN 0-533-07114-3). Vantage.

Last Testament, Vol. I. Bhagwan Shree Rajneesh. Ed. by Swami Svadesh et al. LC 85-63289. (Interview Ser.). (Illus.). 832p. (Orig.). 1986. pap. 7.95x (ISBN 0-88050-250-9, 250-9). Chidvilas Found.

Last Things. James Alberione. (Orig.). 1965. 4.50 (ISBN 0-8198-0072-4). Dghtrs St Paul.

Last Things. Robert Hicks & Richard Bewes. (Understanding Bible Truth Ser.). (Orig.). 1981. pap. 1.50 (ISBN 0-89840-020-1). Heres Life.

Last Things. George E. Ladd. 1978. pap. 3.95 (ISBN 0-8028-1727-0). Eerdmans.

Last Things First. Gayraud S. Wilmore. LC 81-23136. (Library of Living Faith.: Vol. 3). 118p. (Orig.). 1982. pap. 5.95 (ISBN 0-664-24412-2). Westminster.

Last Things in Shakespeare. Harry Morris. LC 85-1453. (Illus.). 360p. 1986. 30.00 (ISBN 0-8130-0794-1). U Presses Fla.

Last Trial: On the Legend & Lore of the Command to Abraham to Offer Isaac As a Sacrifice - the Akedah. Shalom Spiegel. LC 79-12664. (Jewish Legacy Ser.). 1979. pap. 7.95x (ISBN 0-87441-290-0). Behrman.

Last Trump. Ingemar Linden. (IC-Studies in the Intercultural History of Christianity: Vol. 17). 372p. 1978. pap. 34.10 (ISBN 3-261-02370-8). P Lang Pubs.

Last Warning. Kenneth L. Smith. LC 79-53625. 1979. pap. 4.95 (ISBN 0-89412-030-1). Aegean Park Pr.

Last Week. Richard Rouse & Susan Rouse. 1985. 1.00 (ISBN 0-89536-726-2, 5810). CSS of Ohio.

Last Will Be First. John MacArthur, Jr. (John MacArthur's Bible Studies). (Orig.). 1987. pap. 3.95 (ISBN 0-8024-5347-3). Moody.

Last Word. Jamie Buckingham. LC 78-56932. 1978. pap. 4.95 (ISBN 0-88270-303-X). Bridge Pub.

Last Words. H. Smith. pap. 4.75 (ISBN 0-88172-124-7). Believers Bkshelf.

Last World War & the End of Time. Emmett J. Culligan. (Illus.). 210p. 1981. pap. 6.00 (ISBN 0-89555-034-2). TAN Bks Pubs.

Last Writings. Lionel Swain et al. LC 71-173033. (Scripture Discussion Commentary Ser.: Pt. 12). 192p. 1972. pap. text ed. 4.50 (ISBN 0-87946-011-3). ACTA Found.

Last Writings: Nothingness & the Religious Worldview. Nishida Kitaro. Tr. by David A. Dilworth. 176p. 1987. text ed. 18.00x (ISBN 0-8248-1040-6). UH Pr.

Lasting Peace. Carol L. Pearson. 110p. 1983. 7.95 (ISBN 0-934126-38-0). Randall Bk Co.

Lasting Spring: Jessie Catherine Kinsley, Daughter of the Oneida Community. Ed. by Jane K. Rich & Nelson M. Blake. LC 82-19200. (York State Bks.). (Illus.). 300p. (Orig.). 1983. 32.00x (ISBN 0-8156-0183-2); pap. 14.95 (ISBN 0-8156-0176-X). Syracuse U Pr.

Lasting Words of Jesus. Howard W. Roberts. LC 85-12288. 1986. pap. 4.95 (ISBN 0-8054-2257-9). Broadman.

Late Antique, Early Christian & Mediaeval Art: Selected Papers, Vol. III. Meyer Schapiro. (Illus.). 422p. 1979. 25.00 (ISBN 0-8076-0927-7). Braziller.

Late Antique-Early Christian Painting. Kurt Weitzmann. LC 76-16444. (Magnificent Paperback Art Ser.). 128p. 1977. 19.95 (ISBN 0-8076-0830-0); pap. 11.95 (ISBN 0-8076-0831-9). Braziller.

Late Baroque Churches of Venice. Douglas Lewis. LC 78-94704. (Outstanding Dissertations in the Fine Arts Ser.). 1979. lib. bdg. 63.00 (ISBN 0-8240-3236-5). Garland Pub.

Late Bronze Palestinian Pendants: Innovation in a Cosmopolitian Age. Patrick E. McGovern. (JSOT-ASOR Monographs: No. 1). (Illus.). xx, 184p. 1985. text ed. 35.00x (ISBN 0-905774-90-6, Pub. by JSOT Pr England). Eisenbrauns.

Late Byzantine & Slavonic Communion Cycle: Liturgy & Music. Dimitri E. Conomos. LC 84-12176. (Dumbarton Oaks Studies: Vol. 21). (Illus.). 222p. 1985. 25.00x (ISBN 0-88402-134-3). Dumbarton Oaks.

Late Fifteenth Century Carthusian Rubrics for the Deacon & The Sacristan: (From the Ms. Valsainte 42-T.I.8) Ed. & intro. by James Hogg. (Analecta Cartusiana Ser.: No. 4). (Lat. & Eng.). 169p. (Orig.). 1971. pap. 25.00 (ISBN 3-7052-0004-6, Pub by Salzburg Studies). Longwood Pub Group.

Late Friendship: The Letters of Carl Zuckmayer & Karl Barth. Karl Barth & Carl Zuckmayer. Tr. by Geoffrey W. Bromiley. 80p. 1983. 8.95 (ISBN 0-8028-3574-0). Eerdmans.

Late Great Book: The Bible. Nicholas Carter. Ed. by David McCalden. 230p. (Orig.). 1985. pap. 10.00 (ISBN 0-910607-01-X). Truth Missions.

Late Great Planet Earth. Hal Lindsey & C. C. Carlson. 192p. 1980. pap. 3.50 (ISBN 0-553-23958-9). Bantam.

Late Great Planet Earth. Hal Lindsey & C. C. Carlson. 1976. pap. 3.95 mass market (ISBN 0-310-27772-8, 18093P); pap. 5.95 (ISBN 0-310-27771-X, 18089P); study guide o.p. 0.75 (ISBN 0-310-27773-6). Zondervan.

Late Medieval Mysticism. Ed. by Ray C. Petry. LC 57-5092. (Library of Christian Classics). 420p. 1980. pap. 12.95 (ISBN 0-664-24163-8). Westminster.

Late Medieval Religious Plays of Bodleian Manuscripts Digby 133 & E Museo 160. Ed. by Donald C. Baker & J. L. Murphy. (Early English Text Society Ser.). (Illus.). 1982. 37.50x (ISBN 0-19-722285-4). Oxford U Pr.

Lateinische Ubersetzung der Didache. Teaching of the Twelve Apostles. 142p. Repr. of 1913 ed. 12.00 (ISBN 0-384-59780-7). Johnson Repr.

Lateinische Vorlage der Westsaechsischen Evangelienversion. Hans Glunz. pap. 8.00 (ISBN 0-384-18955-5). Johnson Repr.

Latent Power of the Soul. Watchman Nee. Tr. by Stephen Kaung. 1972. pap. 2.50 (ISBN 0-935008-25-X). Christian Fellow Pubs.

Later Christian Fathers: A Selection from the Writings of the Fathers from St. Cyril of Jerusalem to St. Leo the Great. Ed. & tr. by Henry Bettenson. 1972. pap. 8.95x (ISBN 0-19-283012-0). Oxford U Pr.

Later Greek Religion. Ed. by Edwyn R. Bevan. LC 76-179282. (Library of Greek Thought: No. 9). Repr. of 1927 ed. 12.50 (ISBN 0-404-07807-9). AMS Pr.

Later Heidegger & Theology. Ed. by James M. Robinson & John B. Cobb, Jr. LC 78-23619. 1979. Repr. of 1963 ed. lib. bdg. 22.50x (ISBN 0-313-20783-6, ROLH). Greenwood.

Later Latin Fathers. William G. Rusch. (Studies in Theology). 214p. 1977. pap. 13.50 (ISBN 0-7156-1674-9, Pub. by Duckworth London). Longwood Pub Group.

Later Middle Ages: From the Norman Conquest to the Eve of the Reformation. J. C. Dickinson. (Ecclesiastical History of England Ser.). 487p. 1979. text ed. 30.00x (ISBN 0-06-491678-2). B&N Imports.

Later Periods of Quakerism, 2 vols. Rufus M. Jones. LC 74-109758. 1921. Repr. Set. lib. bdg. 95.00x (ISBN 0-8371-4248-2, JOQU). Greenwood.

Later Writings of Bishop Hooper. John Hooper. 1852. 55.00 (ISBN 0-384-24211-1). Johnson Repr.

Latest Word on the Last Days. C. S. Lovett. (Illus., Orig.). 1980. pap. 6.95 (ISBN 0-938148-00-1). Personal Christianity.

Latimer: Apostle to the English. Clara Stuart. 320p. 1986. 15.95 (ISBN 0-310-41370-2). Zondervan.

Latin American Christian Democratic Parties. Edward J. Williams. LC 67-13159. Repr. of 1967 ed. 79.00 (2027567). Bks Demand UMI.

Latin American Jewry: A Research Guide. Martin H. Sable. LC 77-18527. (Bibliographica Judaica: No. 6). Repr. of 1978 ed. 160.00 (ISBN 0-317-42036-4, 2025695). Bks Demand UMI.

Latin American Mythology. Hartley B. Alexander. LC 63-19096. (Mythology of All Races Ser.: Vol. 11). (Illus.). 1964. Repr. of 1932 ed. 30.00x (ISBN 0-8154-0006-3). Cooper Sq.

Latin & Teutonic Christendom: An Historical Sketch. George W. Cox. LC 77-94557. 1979. Repr. of 1870 ed. lib. bdg. 30.00 (ISBN 0-89341-259-7). Longwood Pub Group.

Latin Church Music in England, Fourteen Sixty to Fifteen Seventy-Five. Hugh Benham. (Music Reprint Ser.: 1980). (Illus.). 1980. Repr. of 1977 ed. lib. bdg. 35.00 (ISBN 0-306-76025-8). Da Capo.

Latin Compositions in the Sixth Fasciale of the Notre-Dame Manuscript Wolfenbuttel 1099. Gordon A. Anderson. (Wissenschaftliche Abhandlungen-Musicological Studies Ser.: Vol. 24). Pt. 1. lib. bdg. 50.00 (ISBN 0-931902-02-9); Pt. 2. lib. bdg. 50.00 (ISBN 0-931902-03-7). Inst Mediaeval Mus.

Latin Hymn-Writers & Their Hymns. Samuel W. Duffield. 1980. Repr. of 1889 ed. lib. bdg. 50.00 (ISBN 0-89341-440-9). Longwood Pub Group.

Latin Kingdom of Jerusalem, 2 Pts. J. Richard. (Europe in the Middle Ages Selected Studies: Vol. 11). 514p. 1978. Set. 91.50 (ISBN 0-444-85092-9, North-Holland). Elsevier.

Latin Lives of the Saints. Edmund Hogan. LC 78-72684. (Royal Irish Academy. Todd Lecture Ser.: Vol. 5). Repr. of 1894 ed. 21.50 (ISBN 0-404-60565-6). AMS Pr.

Latin Monasticism in Norman Sicily. L. T. White, Jr. 1967. Repr. of 1938 ed. 9.00x (ISBN 0-910956-12-X). Medieval Acad.

Latin Version of The Cloud of Unknowing. James Hogg. (Analecta Cartusiana Ser.: No. 120). (Orig.). 1988. pap. 25.00 (ISBN 0-317-42582-X, Pub. by Salzburg Studies). Longwood Pub Group.

Latin Writings of the Italian Humanists. Ed. by Florence A. Gragg. (College Classical Ser.). xxxvi, 434p. 1981. lib. bdg. 30.00 (ISBN 0-89241-356-5); pap. text ed. 17.50 (ISBN 0-89241-110-4). Caratzas.

Latins in the Levant: A History of Frankish Greece. William Miller. LC 75-41193. Repr. of 1908 ed. 57.50 (ISBN 0-404-14689-9). AMS Pr.

Latter-Day Saints' Emigrants' Guide. William Clayton. Ed. by Stanley B. Kimball & James B. Allen. LC 83-2473. (Illus.). vi, 111p. 1983. 12.95 (ISBN 0-935284-27-3). Patrice Pr.

Latter Day Shepherds & Sheepfolds. Kenneth F. Haney. Ed. by Mary Wallace. (Illus.). 78p. 1984. pap. 4.50 (ISBN 0-912315-72-5). Word Aflame.

Latter Rain. large print ed. Michele Moss & Charlene Brians. 24p. 1984. pap. 5.00 (ISBN 0-914009-03-6). VHI Library.

Lausiac History: Palladius. Tr. by E. A. Budge. 1977. pap. 5.95 (ISBN 0-686-19350-4). Eastern Orthodox.

Laudate Pueri. Giacomo Antonio Perti. Ed. by Jean Berger. LC 65-26097. (Penn State Music Series, No. 10). 35p. 1965. pap. 4.00x (ISBN 0-271-73075-7). Pa St U Pr.

Laugh with Your Teenager. Byron W. Arledge. 128p. 1985. pap. 4.95 (ISBN 0-8423-2102-0). Tyndale.

Laughing Out Loud & Other Religious Experiences. Tom Mullen. 1983. 8.95 (ISBN 0-8499-0329-7). Word Bks.

Laughing Together: The Value of Humor in Family Life. Dotsey Welliver. Ed. by David Eller. 128p. (Orig.). 1986. pap. 6.95 (ISBN 0-87178-226-X). Brethren.

Laughter Is the Best Meditation: The Best of the Inner Jester. Laren Bright. LC 78-4491. 1979. pap. 5.00 (ISBN 0-686-10176-6). Baraka Bk.

Laughter, Joy, & Healing. Donald E. Demaray. 160p. 1987. pap. 7.95 (ISBN 0-8010-2969-4). Baker Bk.

Laughter Lives Here. Evelyn Kliewer. LC 81-70476. 1982. pap. 4.95 (ISBN 0-8054-5203-6). Broadman.

Launch Out! Frances J. Roberts. 1964. 2.95 (ISBN 0-932814-21-2). Kings Farspan.

Laurie Miracle by Miracle. Barbara J. Spaeth. 48p. 1986. 6.95 (ISBN 0-317-43316-4). Todd & Honeywell.

Law Above the Law. John W. Montgomery. LC 75-31395. 168p. 1975. pap. 3.95 (ISBN 0-87123-329-0, 200329). Bethany Hse.

Law & Bioethics: Selected Cases. Thomas Shannon & Jo Ann Manfra. LC 81-80876. 448p. (Orig.). 1981. pap. 14.95 (ISBN 0-8091-2353-3). Paulist Pr.

Law & Gospel: Selected Writings of C.F.W. Walther. Tr. by Herbert J. Bouman. 1981. 12.95 (ISBN 0-570-08275-7, 15-2733). Concordia.

Law & Grace. Alva J. McClain. pap. 1.75 (ISBN 0-88469-001-6). BMH Bks.

Law & Liberation. Robert E. Rodes. LC 85-41011. 240p. 1986. text ed. 24.95 (ISBN 0-268-01279-2). U of Notre Dame Pr.

Law & Morality. D. Don Welch. LC 86-45195. 192p. 1987. pap. text ed. 14.95 (ISBN 0-8006-1974-9, 1-1974). Fortress.

Law & Morality in Modern Society. Aaron Soloveitchik. (Annual Fryer Memorial Lecture Ser.). 0.75 (ISBN 0-914131-40-0, I33). Torah Umesorah.

Law & Narrative in the Bible: The Evidence of the Deuteronomic Laws & the Decalogue. Calum M. Carmichael. LC 85-4214. 352p. 1985. text ed. 35.00x (ISBN 0-8014-1792-9). Cornell U Pr.

Law & Religion. Timothy L. Fort. LC 86-43082. 153p. 1987. pap. 13.95 (ISBN 0-89950-265-2). McFarland & Co.

Law & Religion. Wake Forest University Law School. 1985. 10.00 (ISBN 0-318-18444-3). Wake Forest Law.

Law & Society in Puritan Massachusetts: Essex County, 1629-1692. David T. Konig. xxi, 215p. 1981. pap. 9.95x (ISBN 0-8078-4081-5). U of NC Pr.

Law & the Promise. Neville. 156p. 1984. pap. 5.50 (ISBN 0-87516-532-X). De Vorss.

Law & Theology in Deuteronomy. J. G. McConville. (JSOT Supplement Ser.: No. 33). 200p. 1985. text ed. 28.50x (ISBN 0-905774-78-7, Pub. by JSOT Pr England); pap. text ed. 13.50x (ISBN 0-905774-79-5, Pub. by JSOT Pr England). Eisenbrauns.

Law & Tradition in Judaism. Boaz Cohen. 1959. 12.50x (ISBN 0-87068-023-4). Ktav.

Law As Gospel: Revival & Reform in the Theology of Charles G. Finney. David L. Weddle. LC 85-8303. (Studies in Evangelicalism: No. 6). 293p. 1985. 23.50 (ISBN 0-8108-1819-1). Scarecrow.

Law, Church, & Society: Essays in Honor of Stephan Kuttner. Ed. by Robert Somerville & Kenneth Pennington. LC 76-53199. 1977. 27.95x (ISBN 0-8122-7726-0). U of Pa Pr.

Law Given Through Moses. Neil J. McEleney. (Bible Ser.). pap. 0.50 (ISBN 0-8091-5079-4). Paulist Pr.

Law in Paul's Thought. Hans Hubner. Ed. by John Riches. Tr. by James Greig. 186p. 26.95 (ISBN 0-567-09313-1, Pub. by T & T Clark Ltd UK). Fortress.

Law in the Apocrypha. Ralph Marcus. LC 29-9822. (Columbia University. Oriental Studies: No. 26). Repr. of 1927 ed. 15.00 (ISBN 0-404-50516-3). AMS Pr.

Law, Liberty & Love. Columbia Cary-Elwes. 1950. 5.00 (ISBN 0-8159-6104-9). Devin.

Law of Christ, 3 vols. Bernard Haring. 646p. Vol. 1. 17.95 (ISBN 0-8091-0084-3). Paulist Pr.

Law of Church-State Relations in a Nutshell. Leonard F. Manning. LC 80-22991. (Nutshell Ser.). 305p. 1981. pap. text ed. 10.95 (ISBN 0-8299-2113-3). West Pub.

Law of Crime & Punishment in Ancient Hindu Society. Damayanti Doongaji. 310p. 1986. 48.50X (ISBN 81-202-0168-X, Pub. by Ajanta). South Asia Bks.

Law of Faith. Norman P. Grubb. 1969. pap. 3.95 (ISBN 0-87508-223-8). Chr Lit.

Law of Love & Love As a Law: Or, Christian Ethics. 3rd ed. Mark Hopkins. LC 75-3196. Repr. of 1871 ed. 42.50 (ISBN 0-404-59197-3). AMS Pr.

Law of Nations & the Book of Nature. George H. Williams. Ed. by R. W. Franklin. LC 84-72274. (New Essays in Christian Humanism: Vol. 1). (Illus.). 60p. (Orig.). 1985. pap. 4.95x (ISBN 0-9613867-0-3). St Johns Univ Christ Hum.

Law of Sacrifice. B. P. Wadia. (Sangam Texts). 135p. 1986. pap. 8.75 (ISBN 0-88695-023-6). Concord Grove.

Law of Success. Paramahansa Yogananda. 1980. pap. 0.95 (ISBN 0-87612-150-4); pap. 1.00x Span. ed. (ISBN 0-87612-151-2); pap. 2.00 French ed. (ISBN 0-87612-152-0). Self Realization.

Law of the Harvest. Sterling W. Sill. 392p. 1980. 10.95 (ISBN 0-88290-142-7). Horizon Utah.

Law of the Offerings. Andrew Jukes. LC 68-19198. 220p. 1976. pap. 6.95 (ISBN 0-8254-2957-9). Kregel.

Law of the Rhythmic Breath. Ella A. Fletcher. LC 80-19750. 372p. 1980. Repr. of 1979 ed. lib. bdg. 19.95x (ISBN 0-89370-644-2). Borgo Pr.

Law of War & Peace in Islam: A Study of Moslem International Law. Majid Khadduri. LC 76-147599. (Library of War & Peace; International Law). lib. bdg. 42.00 (ISBN 0-8240-0360-8). Garland Pub.

Law, Resistance & the State: The Opposition to Roman Law in Reformation Germany. Gerald Strauss. LC 85-43315. 312p. 1986. text ed. 34.50 (ISBN 0-691-05469-X). Princeton U Pr.

Law, the Student, & the Catholic School. Steve Permuth et al. 96p. 1981. 6.00 (ISBN 0-686-39898-X). Natl Cath Educ.

Lawful & the Prohibited in Islam. Yusuf Al-Qaradawi. Tr. by Mohammed M. Siddiqui et al from Arabic. LC 80-81562. Orig. Title: Al-Halal Wal-Haram Fil Islam. (Eng.). 355p. (Orig.). 1981. pap. 10.00 (ISBN 0-89259-016-5). Am Trust Pubns.

Lawrie Tatum: Indian Agent. Robert Hixon. LC 81-81684. 28p. 1981. pap. 2.50x (ISBN 0-87574-238-6, 238). Pendle Hill.

Laws in the Pentateuch. Martin Noth. 304p. pap. 13.95 (ISBN 0-317-31484-X, 30-870-259). Fortress.

Laws of Chanukah. Aryeh Kaplan. 124p. pap. 5.45 (ISBN 0-940118-28-9). Maznaim.

Laws of Christian Living: The Commandments. Perry McDonald & William Odell. 170p. (Orig.). 1986. pap. 6.95 (ISBN 0-87973-593-7, 593). Our Sunday Visitor.

Laws of Love. Margaret Pounders. LC 79-64898. 1979. 5.95 (ISBN 0-87159-083-2). Unity School.

Laws of Manu. G. Buhler. lib. bdg. 79.95 (ISBN 0-87968-492-5). Krishna Pr.

Laws of Success for Christians: There's Only One-Way to Success Both for Today & Forever. Richard H. LeTourneau. LC 85-91034. (LeTourneau One-Way Ser.: Vol. 7). 130p. (Orig.). 1985. pap. 5.95 (ISBN 0-935899-03-0). LeTourneau Pr.

Laws of the Fraternity of the Rosie Crosse (Themis Aurea) Michael Maier. 12.50 (ISBN 0-89314-402-9). Philos Res.

Laws of the Pilgrims. John D. Cushing. 1978. facsimile ed. 8.50 (ISBN 0-940628-00-7). Pilgrim Soc.

Laws of the Spirit. Bob Buess. 1968. pap. 2.50 (ISBN 0-934244-01-4). Sweeter Than Honey.

Laws That Liberate. Bill Hybels. 132p. 1985. pap. 4.95 (ISBN 0-89693-394-6). Victor Bks.

Lawyer Looks at Judgement. Ken Hopp. (Anchor Ser.). 1984. 5.95 (ISBN 0-8163-0557-9). Pacific Pr Pub Assn.

Lay Action: The Church's Third Force. Cameron P. Hall. (Orig.). 1974. pap. 3.50 (ISBN 0-377-00018-3). Friend Pr.

Lay & Religious States of Life. James O'Reilly. LC 76-43048. 1977. pap. text ed. 0.75 (ISBN 0-685-81233-2). Franciscan Herald.

Lay Authority & Reformation in the English Church. Robert Rodes. LC 82-7038. 319p. 1982. 25.00 (ISBN 0-268-01265-2). U of Notre Dame Pr.

Lay Buddhism in Contemporary Japan. Helen Hardacre. LC 83-43075. (Illus.). 328p. 1984. 35.00x (ISBN 0-691-07284-1). Princeton U Pr.

Lay Caregiving. Diane Detwiler-Zapp & William C. Dixon. LC 81-66519. (Creative Pastoral Care & Counseling Ser.). 1982. pap. 4.50 (ISBN 0-8006-0567-5, 1-567). Fortress.

Lay-Centered Church: Theology & Spirituality. Leonard Doohan. 204p. 1984. pap. 8.95 (ISBN 0-86683-808-2; AY8403, HarpR). Har-Row.

Lay Evangelism Calling: Participants Manual. Walter Schmidt. 1986. 4.50 (ISBN 0-89536-805-6, 6825); training manual 2.95 (ISBN 0-89536-800-5, 6818). CSS of Ohio.

Lay Folks Mass Book: Four Texts. Ed. by T. F. Simmons. (EET OS Ser.: Vol. 71). Repr. of 1879 ed. 63.00 (ISBN 0-8115-3359-X). Kraus Repr.

Lay Guide to Romans. J. C. Wenger. LC 82-15789. 160p. (Orig.). 1983. pap. 8.95 (ISBN 0-8361-3316-1). Herald Pr.

Lay Mission Handbook. Ed. by Jeff Bolle. 100p. binder 20.00 (ISBN 0-318-21725-2). Intl Liaison.

Lay People in the Church. Yves Congar. 518p. 1985. pap. 14.95 (ISBN 0-87061-114-3). Chr Classics.

Lay Psalter: Selections from the Psalms with Meditations. John V. Sheridan. LC 84-62159. 216p. (Orig.). 1985. pap. 7.50 (ISBN 0-87973-716-6, 716). Our Sunday Visitor.

Lay Reader's Guide to the Book of Common Prayer. Clifford W. Atkinson. 1981. pap. 3.95 (ISBN 0-8192-1222-9). Morehouse.

Lay Shepherding. Rudolph E. Grantham. 1980. pap. 5.95 (ISBN 0-8170-0863-2). Judson.

Lay Theology in the Reformation: Popular Pamphleteers in Southwest Germany, 1521-1525. Paul A. Russell. (Illus.). 303p. 1986. 39.50 (ISBN 0-521-30727-9). Cambridge U Pr.

Laying on of Hands. Kenneth E. Hagin. 1980. pap. 0.50 mini bk. (ISBN 0-89276-250-0). Hagin Ministries.

Laying on of Hands. Derek Prince. (Foundation Ser.: Bk. V). 1965-66. pap. 1.95 (ISBN 0-934920-04-4, B-14). Derek Prince.

Laying the Foundation. James L. Beall. LC 76-42084. 389p. 1976. pap. 5.95 (ISBN 0-88270-198-3). Bridge Pub.

Layla & Majnun. Nizami. Ed. & tr. by R. Gelpke. LC 78-58219. 206p. 1978. pap. 8.95 (ISBN 0-87773-133-0). Shambhala Pubns.

L'ayla L'ayla. pap. 6.95 (ISBN 0-686-96043-2); tchr's guide 4.00 (ISBN 0-686-99686-0). United Syn Bk.

Layman & the Book. A. E. Robinson. pap. 1.95 (ISBN 0-911866-58-2). Advocate.

Layman Looks at the Lamb of God. W. Phillip Keller. LC 82-4568. 122p. (Orig.). 1982. 7.95 (ISBN 0-87123-313-4, 230314); pap. 3.95 (ISBN 0-87123-314-2, 210314). Bethany Hse.

Layman Looks at the Lord's Prayer. W. Phillip Keller. 160p. 1976. pap. 5.95 (ISBN 0-8024-4644-2). Moody.

Layman Looks at the Lord's Prayer. W. Phillip Keller. (Moody Press Electives Ser.). 1985. pap. text ed. 3.95 (ISBN 0-8024-0699-8); leader's guide 2.50 (ISBN 0-8024-0701-3). Moody.

Layman Looks at the Love of God. Phillip Keller. 122p. 1984. pap. 7.95 (ISBN 0-87123-618-4). Bethany Hse.

Layman Looks at the Love of God. Phillip Keller. (Orig.). 1982. pap. 4.95 (210314). Bethany Hse.

Layman Looks at the Names of Jesus. John Timmerman. 1985. pap. 4.95 (ISBN 0-8423-2110-1). Tyndale.

Layman's Bible Book Commentary: Acts, Vol. 19. Robert L. Maddox, Jr. LC 78-67926. 1979. 5.95 (ISBN 0-8054-1189-5). Broadman.

Layman's Bible Book Commentary: Exodus, Vol. 2. Robert L. Cate. LC 78-59976. 1979. 5.95 (ISBN 0-8054-1172-0). Broadman.

Layman's Bible Book Commentary: Ezekiel, Daniel, Vol. 12. F. B. Huey, Jr. LC 81-66848. 1984. 5.95 (ISBN 0-8054-1182-8). Broadman.

Layman's Bible Book Commentary: Ezra, Nehemiah, Esther, Job, Vol. 7. Mary F. Owens. 1984. 5.95 (ISBN 0-8054-1177-1). Broadman.

Layman's Bible Book Commentary: First & Second Samuel & First Chronicles, Vol. 5. Joe O. Lewis. LC 79-54796. 1981. 5.95 (ISBN 0-8054-1175-5). Broadman.

Layman's Bible Book Commentary: First, Second, Third John, Jude & Revelation, Vol. 24. Fred D. Howard. LC 80-66807. 1982. 5.95 (ISBN 0-8054-1194-1). Broadman.

Layman's Bible Book Commentary: Genesis, Vol.1. Sherrill Stevens. LC 78-50377. 1978. 5.95 (ISBN 0-8054-1171-2). Broadman.

Layman's Bible Book Commentary: Isaiah, Vol. 10. Trent C. Butler. LC 80-68890. 1983. 5.95 (ISBN 0-8054-1180-1). Broadman.

Layman's Bible Book Commentary: Jeremiah, Lamentations, Vol. 11. Edward H. Dalglish. LC 81-65801. 1984. 5.95 (ISBN 0-8054-1181-X). Broadman.

Layman's Bible Book Commentary: John, Vol. 18. James E. Carter. LC 81-65391. 1984. 5.95 (ISBN 0-8054-1188-7). Broadman.

Layman's Bible Book Commentary: Joshua, Judges, Ruth, Vol. 4. Dan G. Kent. LC 79-51136. 1980. 5.95 (ISBN 0-8054-1174-7). Broadman.

Layman's Bible Book Commentary: Leviticus, Numbers, Deuteronomy, Vol. 3. Roy L. Honeycutt, Jr. LC 78-73278. 1979. 5.95 (ISBN 0-8054-1173-9). Broadman.

Layman's Bible Book Commentary: Luke, Vol. 17. Robert J. Dean. 1983. 5.95 (ISBN 0-8054-1187-9). Broadman.

Layman's Bible Book Commentary: Mark, Vol. 16. Johnnie C. Godwin. LC 78-54774. 1979. 5.95 (ISBN 0-8054-1186-0). Broadman.

Layman's Bible Book Commentary: Matthew, Vol. 15. Clair M. Crissey. LC 79-56691. 1981. 5.95 (ISBN 0-8054-1185-2). Broadman.

Layman's Bible Book Commentary: Micah, Nahum, Habbakuk, Zephaniah, Haggai, Zechariah, Malachi, Vol. 14. Page H. Kelley. LC 83-26288. 1984. 5.95 (ISBN 0-8054-1184-4). Broadman.

Layman's Bible Book Commentary: One & Two Kings, Two Chronicles, Vol. 6. John H. Traylor, Jr. LC 80-67148. 1982. 5.95 (ISBN 0-8054-1176-3). Broadman.

Layman's Bible Book Commentary: Phillppians - Philemon, Vol. 22. Malcolm O. Tolbert. LC 79-51998. 1980. 5.95 (ISBN 0-8054-1192-5). Broadman.

Layman's Bible Book Commentary: Proverbs, Ecclesiastes, Song of Solomon, Vol. 9. L. D. Johnson. LC 80-66543. 1982. 5.95 (ISBN 0-8054-1179-8). Broadman.

Layman's Bible Book Commentary: Psalms Vol. 8. Alton H. McEachern. LC 79-56593. 1981. 5.95 (ISBN 0-8054-1178-X). Broadman.

Layman's Bible Book Commentary: Second Corinthians, Galatians, Ephesians, Vol. 21. David C. George. LC 78-74202. 1980. 5.95 (ISBN 0-8054-1191-7). Broadman.

Layman's Bible Book Commentary: Vol. 13 Hosea, Joel, Amos, Abadiah, Jonah. Billy K. Smith. LC 80-68536. 1982. 5.95 (ISBN 0-8054-1183-6). Broadman.

Layman's Bible Commentary, 25 vols. Incl. Vol. 1. Introduction to the Bible; Vol. 2. Genesis; Vol. 3. Exodus; Vol. 4. Leviticus, Numbers; Vol. 5. Deuteronomy, Joshua; Vol. 6. Judges - 2 Samuel; Vol. 7. 1 Kings - 2 Chronicles; Vol. 8. Ezra - Job; Vol. 9. Psalms; Vol. 10. Proverbs - Song of Solomon; Vol. 11. Isaiah; Vol. 12. Jeremiah, Lamentations; Vol. 13. Ezekiel, Daniel; Vo. 14. Hosea - Jonah; Vol. 15. Micah - Malachi; Vol. 16. Matthew; Vol. 17. Mark; Vol. 18. Luke; Vol. 19. John; Vol. 20. Acts of the Apostles; Vol. 21. Romans - Second Corinthians; Vol. 22. Galatians - Colossians; Vol. 23. First Thessalonians - Philemon; Vol. 24. Hebrews - Second Peter; Vol. 25. First John - Revelation. LC 59-10454. 1959-64. 4.95 ea.; Set. 115.00 (ISBN 0-8042-3086-2). John Knox.

Layman's Bible Commentary: Romans, I Corinthians, Vol. 20. J. W. MacGorman. LC 79-51501. 1980. 5.95 (ISBN 0-8054-1190-9). Broadman.

Layman's Bible Study Notebook. parallel new testament ed. Irving Jensen. LC 77-93518. (King James & New International Version Ser.). (Orig.). 1978. pap. 26.95 (ISBN 0-89081-116-4). Harvest Hse.

Layman's Guide to Applying the Bible. Walter A. Henrichsen & Gayle Jackson. 224p. (Orig.). 1985. pap. 7.95 (ISBN 0-310-37691-2, 11233P, Pub. by Lamplight); Set pack. pap. 19.95 (ISBN 0-310-37698-X, 11238P, Pub. by Lamplight). Zondervan.

Layman's Guide to Interpreting the Bible. Walter A. Henrichsen. 112p. (Orig.). 1985. pap. 5.95 (ISBN 0-310-37681-5). Zondervan.

Layman's Guide to Protestant Theology. rev. ed. William E. Hordern. 1968. pap. 5.95 (ISBN 0-02-085470-6, Collier). Macmillan.

Layman's Guide to Studying the Bible. Walter A. Henrichsen. 144p. (Orig.). 1985. pap. 6.95 (ISBN 0-310-37631-9, 11236P). Zondervan.

Layman's Guide to the New Testament. William M. Ramsay. LC 79-87742. (Layman's Bible Commentary Ser.). 273p. (Orig.). 1980. pap. 11.95 (ISBN 0-8042-0322-9). John Knox.

Layman's Handbook of Christian Doctrine. Herschel H. Hobbs. LC 74-78615. 1975. 5.75 (ISBN 0-8054-1927-6). Broadman.

Layman's Harmony of the Gospel. John F. Carter. 1961. 12.95 (ISBN 0-8054-1326-X). Broadman.

Layman's Introduction to the New Testament. Carl H. Morgan. LC 68-22756. (Illus.). 1968. pap. text ed. 4.95 (ISBN 0-8170-0399-1). Judson.

Layman's Introduction to the Old Testament. Robert B. Laurin. 1970. pap. 4.95 (ISBN 0-8170-0451-3). Judson.

Layman's Look at Starting a Religious Archives. Kevin W. Sandifer. Ed. by Renee Hall et al. 48p. (Orig.). 1982. pap. text ed. 4.50 (ISBN 0-910653-00-3, 8101-A). Archival Servs.

Layman's Overview of the Bible. Ed. by George Knight & James R. Edwards. 224p. 1987. pap. text ed. 8.95 (ISBN 0-8407-3109-4). Nelson.

Layman's Overview of the Bible. Ed. by George W. Knight & James R. Edwards. 1987. 14.95 (ISBN 0-8407-7560-1). Nelson.

Lazarus & His Beloved. Kahlil Gibran. 64p. 1973. 5.95 (ISBN 0-8464-1165-2). Beekman Pubs.

Lazarus Interlude: A Story of God's Healing Love in a Moment of Ministry. Dennis O'Neill. LC 83-60438. 80p. (Orig.). 1983. pap. 2.95 (ISBN 0-87793-271-9). Ave Maria.

Lazarus Spengler: A Lay Leader of the Reformation. Harold J. Grimm. LC 78-13508. (Illus.). 249p. 1979. 22.50x (ISBN 0-8142-0290-X). Ohio St U Pr.

Lazarus Spengler und Die Reformation in Nurnberg. Hans Von Schubert. 29.00 (ISBN 0-685-92689-3); pap. 28.00 (ISBN 0-384-54287-5). Johnson Repr.

LDS Roots in Egypt. Arthur Wallace. 63p. 1981. pap. 3.50x (ISBN 0-937892-08-4). LL Co.

LDSF: Latter-Day Science Fiction, Vol. 2. Ed. by Benjamin Urrutia. 192p. (Orig.). 1985. pap. text ed. 4.95 (ISBN 0-9614960-0-2). Parables.

Le Mans Forgeries: A Chapter from the History of Church Property in the Ninth Century. Walter A. Goffart. LC 66-18246. (Historical Studies: No. 76). 1966. 25.00x (ISBN 0-674-51875-6). Harvard U Pr.

Lead, Follow or Get Out of the Way! Daisy Hepburn. LC 81-84568. (Orig.). 1982. pap. 4.95 (ISBN 0-8307-0822-7, 5416209); Resource Manual o.p. 5.95 (ISBN 0-8307-0872-3, 5202802). Regal.

Lead, Kindly Light. Desmond L. Morse-Boycott. LC 70-107728. (Essay Index Reprint Ser). 1933. 16.00 (ISBN 0-8369-1529-1). Ayer Co Pubs.

Lead My People. Vincent M. Walsh. 104p. 1980. pap. 4.00 (ISBN 0-943374-02-2). Key of David.

Lead Us Not into Penn Station. Anne N. Gaylor. 1983. 5.00 (ISBN 0-318-00995-1). Freedom Rel Found.

Lead Us Not into Temptation. Don Basham. (Quality Paper Ser.). 1986. pap. 6.95 (ISBN 0-8007-9082-0, Chosen Bks). Revell.

Lead Us on the Way. Heini Arnold. 36p. 1985. pap. 1.50 (ISBN 0-87486-194-2). Plough.

Leader Led. Guy H. King. 1971. pap. 3.95 (ISBN 0-87508-283-1). Chr Lit.

Leader's Guide for Jay E. Adams's Christian Living in the Home: A Teaching Manual for Use in Adult Study Groups. Dorothy P. Anderson. (Orig.). 1977. pap. 2.95 (ISBN 0-934688-05-2). Great Comm Pubns.

Leader's Guide for John W. Sanderson's "The Fruit of the Spirit" A Teaching Manual for Use in Adult Study Groups. Allen D. Curry. (Orig.). 1978. pap. 2.95 (ISBN 0-934688-07-9). Great Comm Pubns.

Leader's Guide for T. Norton Sterrett's "How to Understand Your Bible" A Teaching Manual for Use in Adult Study Groups. Joseph A. Pipa. (Orig.). 1977. pap. 2.95 (ISBN 0-934688-06-0). Great Comm Pubns.

Leader's Guide for Use with Persons Can Change, by Francis Gerald Ensley. Francis G. Ensley. LC 69-101739. pap. 20.00 (ISBN 0-317-10063-7, 2001430). Bks Demand UMI.

Leader's Guide: Meeting Jesus in Holy Communion. Lynn Queck. 96p. 1985. pap. 3.95 (ISBN 0-89243-224-1). Liguori Pubns.

Leader's Guide: Meeting the Forgiving Jesus. Mary E. Loren. 48p. 1985. pap. 2.95 (ISBN 0-89243-225-X). Liguori Pubns.

Leader's Guide to Facing the Issues, No. 3 & 4. William J. Krutza. (Contemporary Discussion Ser.). pap. 1.95 (ISBN 0-8010-5387-0). Baker Bk.

Leader's Manual: A Woman's Workshop on Bible Women. Diane B. Bloem. 128p. 1983. pap. 3.95 student Manual (ISBN 0-310-23151-5); tchr's. manual avail. (ISBN 0-310-23141-8, 10747). Zondervan.

Leaders of Iberian Christianity. Ed. by J. M. Marique. 5.00 (ISBN 0-686-23369-7). Classical Folia.

Leaders of the Reformation. Ed. by Richard L. DeMolen. LC 83-51423. 360p. 1984. 39.50 (ISBN 0-941664-05-8, Pub. Susquehanna U Pr). Assoc Univ Prs.

Leaders of the Reformation: Luther, Calvin et al. John Tulloch. 34.95 (ISBN 0-8490-0492-6). Gordon Pr.

Leaders of Thought in the Modern Church. Reuen Thomas. LC 72-8559. (Essay Index Reprint Ser.). 1972. Repr. of 1892 ed. 18.00 (ISBN 0-8369-7333-X). Ayer Co Pubs.

Leadership. Barry St. Clair. 1984. pap. 9.95 (ISBN 0-88207-193-9). Victor Bks.

Leadership & Church Growth. J. J. Turner. pap. 2.75 (ISBN 0-89315-137-8). Lambert Bk.

Leadership & Conflict. Speed B. Leas. (Creative Leadership Ser.). 128p. (Orig.). 1982. pap. 7.50 (ISBN 0-687-21264-2). Abingdon.

Leadership Book. rev. ed. Charles J. Keating. LC 77-99300. 144p. 1982. pap. 4.95 (ISBN 0-8091-2504-8). Paulist Pr.

Leadership Communication. Richard L. Stoppe. 254p. (Orig.). 1982. pap. text ed. 5.95 (ISBN 0-87148-519-2). Pathway Pr.

Leadership for Youth Ministry. Zeni Fox et al. (Illus.). 200p. (Orig.). 1984. pap. 8.95 (ISBN 0-88489-157-7). St Mary's.

Leadership, Greatness, & Servanthood. Philip Greenslade. 208p. (Orig.). 1986. pap. 5.95 (ISBN 0-87123-871-3, 210871). Bethany Hse.

Leadership in a Successful Parish. Thomas P. Sweetser & Carol W. Holden. LC 86-45386. 160p. 1986. pap. 8.95 (ISBN 0-86683-517-2, RD 569, HarpR). Har-Row.

Leadership in Crisis. Donald Gerig. LC 81-51741. 128p. 1981. pap. 3.95 (ISBN 0-8307-0797-2, 5415304). Regal.

Leadership in Paul. Helen Doohan. (Good News Studies Ser.: Vol. 11). 1984. pap. 7.95 (ISBN 0-89453-435-1). M Glazier.

Leadership in Voluntary Organizations: The Controversy Over Social Action in Protestant Churches. James R. Wood. 155p. 1981. 17.00x (ISBN 0-8135-0920-3). Rutgers U Pr.

Leadership Lifestyles: A Study of 1 Timothy. Ajith Fernando. (Living Studies). 224p. 1985. pap. 6.95 (ISBN 0-8423-2130-6); leader's guide 2.95 (ISBN 0-8423-2131-4). Tyndale.

Leadership Multiplication Books: Book A, World Vision. Hal Perkins. 30p. 1983. pap. 2.50 (ISBN 0-8341-0858-5); Set of 8 bks. pap. 19.95 (YD-1495). Beacon Hill.

Leadership Multiplication Books: Book B, Knowing the Father. Hal Perkins. 30p. (Orig.). 1983. pap. 2.50 (ISBN 0-8341-0859-3); Set of 8 bks. pap. 19.95 (YD-1495). Beacon Hill.

Leadership Multiplication Books: Book C, Coming to Jesus. Hal Perkins. (Bk. C). (Orig.). 1983. pap. 2.50 (ISBN 0-8341-0852-6). Beacon Hill.

Leadership Multiplication Books: Book D, Following Jesus. Hal Perkins. 30p. (Orig.). (YA) 1983. pap. 2.50 (ISBN 0-8341-0860-7); Set of 8 bks. pap. 19.95 (YD-1495). Beacon Hill.

Leadership Multiplication Books: Book E, Becoming Like Jesus. Hal Perkins. 30p. (Orig.). 1983. pap. 2.50 (ISBN 0-8341-0861-5); Set of 8 bks. pap. 19.95 (YD-1495). Beacon Hill.

Leadership Multiplication Books: Book F, Making Leaders in Families. Hal Perkins. 30p. (Orig.). (YA) 1983. pap. 2.50 (ISBN 0-8341-0862-3); Set of 8 bks. pap. 19.95 (YD-1495). Beacon Hill.

Leadership Multiplication Books: Book G, Making Leaders in the Church. Hal Perkins. 30p. (Orig.). (YA) 1983. pap. 2.50 (ISBN 0-8341-0866-6); Set of 8 bks. pap. 19.95 (YD-1495). Beacon Hill.

Leadership Multiplication Books: Book H, Making Leaders in the World. Hal Perkins. 30p. (Orig.). (YA) 1983. pap. 2.50 (ISBN 0-8341-0867-4); Set of 8 bks. pap. 19.95 (YD-1495). Beacon Hill.

Leadership of the American Zionist Organization, 1897-1930. Yonathan Shapiro. LC 71-126521. pap. 77.50 (ISBN 0-317-11047-0, 2022265). Bks Demand UMI.

Leadership of Worship. H. Grady Hardin. LC 79-26863. 1980. 6.95 (ISBN 0-687-21160-3). Abingdon.

Leadership Questions Confronting the Church. Jack Lewis. 1985. pap. 5.95 (ISBN 0-89225-275-8). Gospel Advocate.

Leadership Strategies for Ministers. Charles Somervill. Ed. by H. Wayland Cummings. LC 86-26788. 132p. (Orig.). 1987. pap. 8.95 (ISBN 0-664-24062-3). Westminster.

Leadership Style of Jesus. Michael Youssef. 168p. 1986. pap. 5.95 (ISBN 0-89693-168-4). Victor Bks.

Leadership Through Values: A Study in Personal & Organizational Development. Brian P. Hall. LC 80-81438. (Illus.). 112p. (Orig.). 1980. pap. 8.95 (ISBN 0-8091-2313-4). Paulist Pr.

Leading & Being Led. Paul A. Lacey. LC 85-63379. (Orig.). 1985. pap. 2.50 (ISBN 0-87574-264-5). Pendle Hill.

Leading Bible Discussions. rev. ed. James F. Nyquist & Jack Kuhatschek. 60p. 1985. pap. 2.95 (ISBN 0-8308-1000-5). Inter-Varsity.

Leading Cases in the Bible. David W. Amram. ix, 220p. 1985. Repr. of 1905 ed. lib. bdg. 22.50x (ISBN 0-8377-0218-6). Rothman.

Leading Children in Worship, Vol. 1, 2, 3. Ed. by Donna Fillmore. 216p. 1982. Vol. 2. pap. 7.95 each (ISBN 0-8341-0767-8). Vol. 1 (ISBN 0-8341-0677-9). Vol. 3 (ISBN 0-8341-0676-0). Beacon Hill.

Leading Churches Through Change. Douglas A. Walrath. LC 79-4456. (Creative Leadership Ser.). 1979. pap. 6.95 (ISBN 0-687-21270-7). Abingdon.

Leading Dynamic Bible Study. Rice A. Pierce. LC 74-78835. 1979. 3.95 (ISBN 0-8054-3420-8). Religious Activ.

Leading Edge of Now: The Living Love of God. Susan S. Hykes. 24p. (Orig.). 1982. pap. 3.00 (ISBN 0-9608894-0-X). S S Hykes.

Leading Little Ones to God: A Child's Book of Bible Teaching. rev., 2nd ed. Marian M. Schoolland. (Illus.). 96p. 1981. 14.95 (ISBN 0-8028-4035-3). Eerdmans.

Leading Our Children to God. William Brinkmann & William Ditewig. LC 83-72992. (Illus.). 96p. (Orig.). 1984. pap. 4.95 (ISBN 0-87793-310-3). Ave Maria.

Leading the Family of God. Paul M. Miller. LC 81-2267. 215p. 1981. pap. 8.95 (ISBN 0-8361-1950-9). Herald Pr.

Leading the First Century Church in the Space Age. F. Dale Simpson. 1972. 8.75 (ISBN 0-89137-003-X); pap. 5.95. Quality Pubns.

Leading the Little Ones to Mary. Mary Lelia. pap. 1.00 (ISBN 0-910984-13-1). Montfort Pubns.

Leading the Lord's Singing. Jack Boyd. 1981. pap. 5.95 (ISBN 0-89137-603-8). Quality Pubns.

Leading Your Church in Evangelism. Lewis Drummond. LC 75-30135. 168p. 1976. pap. 5.50 (ISBN 0-8054-6210-4). Broadman.

Leading Your Church to Growth. C. Peter Wagner. LC 83-19272. 224p. 1984. pap. 6.95 (ISBN 0-8307-0922-3, 5418091). Regal.

Leap of Faith. Paul Y. Cho. 120p. 1984. pap. 2.95 (ISBN 0-88270-574-1). Bridge Pub.

Leaps of Faith: Improvisational Dance in Worship & Education. Cynthia Winton-Henry. Ed. by Doug Adams. 1985. pap. 3.00 (ISBN 0-941500-33-0). Sharing Co.

Learn Mishnah. Jacob Neusner. LC 78-5482. (Illus.). 1978. pap. 4.95x (ISBN 0-87441-310-9). Behrman.

Learn Mishnah Notebook. Priscilla Fishman. 128p. 1983. pap. 3.50x (ISBN 0-87441-369-9). Behrman.

Learn of Me: A Study of the Teachings of Christ. Maria A. Hirschmann & Betty Pershing. LC 79-90958. (Bible Study & Sharing Ser.: No. 3). 144p. (Orig.). 1980. pap. 4.95 (ISBN 0-932878-02-4, HB-02). Hansi.

Learn or Review New Testament Greek: The Answer Book. Ed. by Spiros Zodhiates. 1977. pap. 2.95 (ISBN 0-89957-519-6); wkbk. 9.95 (ISBN 0-89957-566-8); answer bk. avail. (ISBN 0-89957-567-6). AMG Pubs.

Learn Talmud. Jacob Neusner. (Illus.). 1979. pap. 4.95x (ISBN 0-87441-292-7). Behrman.

Learn to Grow Old. Paul Tournier. LC 72-78078. 256p. 1983. pap. 7.95 (ISBN 0-06-068361-9, RD-475, HarpR). Har-Row.

Learn to Live. Ervin Seale. 256p. 1966. pap. 6.95 (ISBN 0-911336-08-7). Sci of Mind.

Learn to Read the Greek New Testament. B. Ward Powers. 300p. 1982. 21.00 (ISBN 0-85364-291-5); pap. text ed. 13.95 cancelled (ISBN 0-85364-292-3). Attic Pr.

Learn to Read the Greek New Testament. Ward Powers. 336p. 1982. 19.95 (ISBN 0-8028-3578-3). Eerdmans.

Learn to Reign. Frances J. Roberts. 1963. 2.95 (ISBN 0-932814-22-0). Kings Farspan.

Learn While You Play. Compiled by Chava Shairo. 20p. 1.50 (B68). Torah Umesorah.

Learned Doctor William Ames: Dutch Backgrounds of English & American Puritanism. Keith L. Sprunger. LC 77-175172. pap. 76.30 (ISBN 0-317-08400-3, 2020215). Bks Demand UMI.

Learning about God & Jesus: An Overview of the Gospel in Simple English. Beverly J. Doswald. LC 86-81297. 50p. (Orig.). 1986. pap. 3.25 (ISBN 0-938783-00-9). Helpful Beginnings.

Learning about God's Love: Word-Picture Activities for Children in Grades 1 & 2. Lois M. Borchardt. 48p. 1986. pap. 2.95 (ISBN 0-570-04354-9). Concordia.

Learning about Jesus. rev. ed. Francis Schraff et al. 80p. 1980. pap. 1.95 (ISBN 0-89243-129-6). Liguori Pubns.

Learning Center Book of Bible People. Karen L. Goodis. LC 81-67026. (Learning Center Book Ser.). (Illus.). 123p. (Orig.). 1981. pap. 14.50 (ISBN 0-86705-005-5). AIRE.

Learning Christian Leadership. Donald S. Aultman. 1960. 4.95 (ISBN 0-87148-501-X). Pathway Pr.

Learning Clubs for the Poor. Lea A. Hunter & Magdalen Sienkiewicz. LC 83-82024. (Orig.). 1984. pap. 4.95 (ISBN 0-8091-2602-8). Paulist Pr.

Learning Disabled Child in Your Church School. J. Cherne. LC 12-2818. (09). 1983. pap. 3.25 (ISBN 0-570-03883-9). Concordia.

Learning from God's Animals. Ruth J. Jay. (Illus.). 36p. (Orig.). 1981. pap. 3.25 (ISBN 0-934998-04-3). Bethel Pub.

Learning from God's Birds. Ruth J. Jay. (Illus.). 34p. (Orig.). 1981. pap. 3.25 (ISBN 0-934998-05-1). Bethel Pub.

Learning from God's Wonderful Wildwood. Ruth J. Jay. (Learning From...Ser.). (Illus.). 36p. 1982. pap. 3.25 (ISBN 0-934998-13-2). Bethel Pub.

Learning from Hebrews. Charles W. Ford. LC 80-67467. (Radiant Life Ser.). 127p. (Orig.). 1980. 2.50 (ISBN 0-88243-915-4, 02-0915); teacher's ed 3.95 (ISBN 0-88243-188-9, 32-0188). Gospel Pub.

Learning from Jesus. Seth Wilson. Ed. by Lynn Gardner. LC 77-155407. (Bible Study Textbook Ser.). (Illus.). 1977. 15.90 (ISBN 0-89900-056-8). College Pr Pub.

Learning from Little Ones: Insights from the Gospel. Mary M. Fenocketti. 48p. 1984. pap. 1.95 (ISBN 0-89243-203-9). Liguori Pubns.

Learning from the Apostles. Amos D. Millard. 128p. 1971. pap. 1.25 (ISBN 0-88243-537-X, 02-0537). Gospel Pub.

Learning God's Word, 3 bks. Carroll. 1971. Bk. 1. pap. 1.75 (ISBN 0-87148-502-8); Bk. 2. pap. 1.35 (ISBN 0-87148-503-6); Bk. 3. pap. 1.35 (ISBN 0-87148-504-4). Pathway Pr.

Learning How to Learn. Idries Shah. 302p. 1978. 14.95 (ISBN 0-900860-59-6, Pub. by Octagon Pr England). Ins Study Human.

Learning How to Learn: Psychology & Spirituality in the Sufi Way. Idries Shah. LC 80-8892. 304p. 1981. pap. 9.95 (ISBN 0-06-067255-2, CN4015, HarpR). Har-Row.

Learning Is Change. Martha M. Leypoldt. LC 70-144082. 1971. pap. 4.95 (ISBN 0-8170-0526-9). Judson.

Learning Jesus Christ Through the Heidelberg Catechism. Karl Barth. 144p. (Orig.). 1982. pap. 4.95 (ISBN 0-8028-1893-5). Eerdmans.

Learning of God. Amy Carmichael. 1986. pap. 4.95 (ISBN 0-87508-086-3). Chr Lit.

Learning Process for Religious Education. Richard J. Reichert. LC 74-14308. (Orig.). 1974. pap. 3.95 (ISBN 0-8278-0001-0, Pub. by Pflaum Pr). Peter Li.

Learning the Pacific Way: A Guide for All Ages. Janet M. DeVries. (Orig.). 1982. pap. 3.95 (ISBN 0-377-00119-8). Friend Pr.

Learning the Skills of Peacemaking. Naomi Drew. Ed. by Janet Lovelady. 200p. (Orig.). 1987. pap. 17.95x (ISBN 0-915190-46-X). Jalmar Pr.

Learning Through Liturgy. Gwen K. Neville & John H. Westerhoff, III. 189p. 1983. pap. 6.95 (ISBN 0-8164-2423-3, HarpR). Har-Row.

Learning to Be a Family: Leader's Guide. Ken Smith & Floy Smith. (Orig.). 1985. pap. 3.95 (ISBN 0-934688-17-6). Great Comm Pubns.

Learning to Be a Woman. Kenneth G. Smith & Floy Smith. LC 76-127932. (Orig.). 1970. pap. 3.95 (ISBN 0-87784-693-6). Inter-Varsity.

Learning to Be Thankful. 2.98 (ISBN 0-8010-5111-8). Baker Bk.

Learning to Celebrate: The Mass & Its Music. Joseph Gelineau. 1985. pap. 6.95 (ISBN 0-317-38557-7). Pastoral Pr.

Learning to Die. Samuel Gerber. Tr. by Peter Dyck from Ger. LC 84-10809. 104p. (Orig.). 1984. pap. 5.95 (ISBN 0-8361-3369-2). Herald Pr.

Learning to Forget. Kenneth E. Hagin. 1985. mini bk. 0.50 (ISBN 0-89276-266-7). Hagin Ministries.

Learning to Forgive. Doris Donnelly. (Festival Ser.). 144p. 1982. pap. 4.95 (ISBN 0-687-21324-X). Abingdon.

Learning to Know God As Provider. Russell Bixler. 96p. 1982. pap. 3.50 (ISBN 0-88368-120-X). Whitaker Hse.

Learning to Lead. Fred Smith. (Leadership Library). 182p. 1986. write for info. (ISBN 0-917463-08-0). Chr Today.

Learning to Let Go. Carol Kuykendall. 160p. (Orig.). 1985. pap. 6.95 (ISBN 0-310-33621-X, 12763P). Zondervan.

Learning to Live. Keith M. Bailey. 64p. (Orig.). 1978. pap. 0.95 (ISBN 0-87509-158-X). Chr Pubns.

Learning to Live from Within: A Glimpse of Jesus As Healer. George F. Freemesser. 1985. 8.95 (ISBN 0-87193-242-3). Dimension Bks.

Learning to Live, Learning to Love: A Book about You, A Book about Everyone. Joanne Haynes-Klassen. (Illus.). 150p. 1984. pap. 7.95 (ISBN 0-915190-38-9). Jalmar Pr.

Learning to Live with the People You Love. D. James Kennedy. 200p. (Orig.). 1987. pap. text ed. 3.95 (ISBN 0-88368-190-0). Whitaker Hse.

Learning to Love. 1982. 3.00 (ISBN 0-89858-040-4). Fill the Gap.

Learning to Love. J. R. Miller. Ed. by Joan Zodhiates. Orig. Title: Lesson of Love. 1977. pap. 3.95 (ISBN 0-89957-521-8). AMG Pubs.

Learning to Love like Jesus. Large Type ed. Wanda Winburn. (Twenty-Six Children's Church Programs Ser.). (Illus.). 112p. 1984. 7.95 (ISBN 0-87239-708-4, 3319). Standard Pub.

Learning to Love, Vol. II: God's People Make the Best Lovers. Patsy R. Dawson. LC 86-22746. (Marriage: A Taste of Heaven Ser.). (Illus.). 544p. (Orig.). 1987. pap. 12.95 (ISBN 0-938855-41-7); Set. 25.90 (ISBN 0-938855-44-1). Gospel Themes Pr.

Learning to Manage Our Fears. James W. Angell. LC 81-1878. 128p. 1981. 7.75 (ISBN 0-687-21329-0). Abingdon.

Learning to Pray. Arnold Prater. 144p. (Orig.). 1986. pap. 6.50 (ISBN 0-687-21330-4). Abingdon.

Learning to Pray. Howard W. Roberts. LC 82-74296. 1984. pap. 4.95 (ISBN 0-8054-5195-1). Broadman.

Learning to Talk with God. Joyce M. Smith. 1976. pap. 2.95 (ISBN 0-8423-2140-3). Tyndale.

Learning to Worship As a Way of Life. Graham Kendrick. 214p. 1985. pap. 4.95 (ISBN 0-87123-863-2, 210863). Bethany Hse.

Learning Together. Ronald G. Held. LC 76-9515. 128p. 1976. pap. 1.25 (ISBN 0-88243-571-X, 02-0571). Gospel Pub.

Least of These. Edith B. Dumas. 128p. 1982. 7.95 (ISBN 0-89962-261-5). Todd & Honeywell.

Least of These: What Everyone Should Know About Abortion. Curt Young. 1984. 7.95 (ISBN 0-8024-0355-7). Moody.

Leave It to God. Christian D. Larson. pap. 1.00 (ISBN 0-87516-191-X). De Vorss.

Leave Your Life Alone. Hubert Van Zeller. 6.95 (ISBN 0-87243-043-X). Templegate.

Leave Yourself Alone. Eugenia Price. 128p. 1982. pap. 5.95 (ISBN 0-310-31431-3, 16244P). Zondervan.

Leaven for Doughfaces: Parables Touching Slavery. facs. ed. Darius Lyman, Jr. LC 78-146266. (Black Heritage Library Collection Ser). 1856. 18.00 (ISBN 0-8369-8741-1). Ayer Co Pubs.

Leaves from the Notebook of a Tamed Cynic. Reinhold Niebuhr. LC 79-2992. (Harper's Ministers Paperback Library). 224p. 1980. pap. 5.95i (ISBN 0-06-066231-X, RD 311, HarpR). Har-Row.

Leaves of Morya's Garden, Vol. I: The Call. 3rd ed. Incl. Leaves of Morya's Garden, Vol. II: Illumination. (Agni Yoga Ser.). 1979. pap. 12.00, Repr. of 1952 ed. (ISBN 0-933574-01-0). (Agni Yoga Ser.). 1978. Repr. of 1953 ed. softbound 12.00 (ISBN 0-933574-00-2). Agni Yoga Soc.

Leaving Matters to God. Louise B. Cantoni. (Illus.). 164p. 1984. 3.00 (ISBN 0-8198-4424-1); pap. 2.00 (ISBN 0-8198-4425-X). Dghtrs St Paul.

Lebanese Prophets of New York. Nadeem Naimy. 112p. 1985. text ed. 18.00x (ISBN 0-8156-6073-1, Am U Beirut). Syracuse U Pr.

Leben Des Abtes Eigil Von Fulda und der Aebtissin Hathumoda Von Gandersheim Nebst der Uebertragung Des Hl. Liborius und Des Hl. Vitus. Ed. & tr. by Georg Grandaur. (Ger). pap. 10.00 (ISBN 0-384-19640-3). Johnson Repr.

Leben Des Bischofs Adalbert Von Prag. Johannes Canaparius. Tr. by Hermann Hueffer. xiv, 54p. (Ger.). pap. 8.00 (ISBN 0-384-31946-7). Johnson Repr.

Leben des Bischofs Benno der Zweiter von Osnabruck. Norbert. Bd. with Ausfuehrliches Namenregister und Sachregister Mit Genauem Inhalsverzeichnis der Seither Erschienene Baende 1-90. (Geschichtschreiber der Deutschen Vorzeit Ser: Vol. 91). (Ger.). 12.00 (ISBN 0-384-41895-3). Johnson Repr.

Leben Des Bischofs Otto Von Bamberg. Wolfger Von Prufening. xxix, 78p. (Ger.). Repr. of 1928 ed. 12.00 (ISBN 0-384-69065-3). Johnson Repr.

Leben Des Heiligen Gallus & Des Abtes Otmar Von Sanktgallen. Walahfrid Strabo. Tr. by A. Potthast. x, 86p. (Ger.). pap. 10.00 (ISBN 0-384-31951-3). Johnson Repr.

Leben Des Heiligen Severin. 3rd ed. Eugippius. Tr. by C. Rodenbery. (Ger.). Repr. of 1912 ed. 12.00 (ISBN 0-384-14820-4). Johnson Repr.

Leben Schleiermachers, 2 vols. Wilhelm Dilthey. Incl. Vol. 1, Pt. 1. 1768-1802. 3rd ed. Ed. by Martin Redeker. xlvi, 567p. 1970. 48.00x (ISBN 3-11-006348-4); Vol. 1, Pt. 2. 1803-1807. Ed. by H. Mulert. xxiv, 251p. 1970. 24.00x (ISBN 3-11-006437-5); Vol. 2. Schleiermachers System als Philosophie und Theologie, 2 vols. in 1. Ed. by Martin Redeker. lxxx, 811p. 1966. 72.00x (ISBN 3-11-001266-9). (Ger.). De Gruyter.

Lecciones Para Nuevos Creyentes Student. James D. Crane & Jorge E. Diaz. 64p. 1984. pap. 1.65 (ISBN 0-311-13835-7); teacher ed. 2.95 (ISBN 0-311-13838-1). Casa Bautista.

Lecciones...la Vida Victoriosa. Chris Schlabach. Orig. Title: Lessons in Victorious Living. (Span.). 1986. write for info. (ISBN 0-8297-0730-1). Life Pubs Intl.

Lectionary, 3 vols. Geoffrey Chapman. 3500p. 1985. Vol. 1: The Proper of the Seasons, Sundays in Ordinary Time. 60.00 (ISBN 0-225-66350-3, HarpR). Vol. 2: Weekdays in Ordinary Time, Proper of Saints, Commons. Vol. 3: Rituals Celebrations, Masses for Various Needs & Occasions, Votive Masses, Masses for the Dead. Har-Row.

Lectionary for Mass: Cycle A, Sundays & Solemnities. Catholic Church, Sacred Congregation for Divine Worship. Ed. by Steven J. Hartdegen. Tr. by International Committee on English in the Liturgy Confraternity of Christian Doctrine for the New American Bible. (Lectionary for Mass Ser.). 1974. 14.50 (ISBN 0-916134-01-6). Pueblo Pub Co.

Lectionary for Mass: Cycle B, Sundays & Solemnities. Catholic Church, Sacred Congregation for Divine Worship. Ed. by Steven J. Hartdegen. (Lectionary for Mass Ser.). 1972. 27.50 (ISBN 0-916134-02-4). Pueblo Pub Co.

Lectionary for Mass: Cycle C, Sundays & Solemnities. Catholic Church, Sacred Congregation of Divine Worship Staff. Ed. by Steven J. Hartdegen. Tr. by International Committee on English in the Liturgy Confraternity of Christian Doctrine for the New American Bible. (Lectionary for Mass). 1973. 27.50 (ISBN 0-916134-03-2). Pueblo Pub Co.

Lectionary: New American Bible Version. small size ed. 23.00 (ISBN 0-89942-025-7, 25/22). Catholic Bk Pub.

Lectionary: New American Bible Version. large size ed. (Large Red & Black type, Ribbon Markers). red simulated leather 42.00 (ISBN 0-89942-035-4, 35/02); protective jacket o.s.i. 1.50; genuine leather, gold edges 75.00 (ISBN 0-89942-036-2, 35/13). Catholic Bk Pub.

Lectionary Preaching Resources. Francis Rossow & Gerhard Aho. (Illus.). 224p. 1987. pap. 14.95 (ISBN 0-570-04468-5). Concordia.

Lectionary Preaching Workbook B: Series II. Perry Biddle, Jr. (Orig.). 1987. pap. price not set (ISBN 0-89536-879-X, 7865). CSS of Ohio.

Lectionary Preaching Workbook on the Psalms. Hagen Staack. (Ser. C). 1982. 14.25 (ISBN 0-89536-573-1, 1263). CSS of Ohio.

Lectionary Reader C (Common, RSV) 1985. 14.25 (ISBN 0-89536-772-6, 5877). CSS of Ohio.

Lectionary Reader C (Common, TEV) 1985. 14.25 (ISBN 0-89536-776-9, 5879). CSS of Ohio.

Lectionary Series from the Common (Consensus) Lectionary: Series B (TEV) 1984. 14.25 (ISBN 0-89536-693-2, 4870). CSS of Ohio.

Lectionary Series from the Common Lectionary: Series A (RSV) rev. ed. Ed. by Michael L. Sherer. 1986. 14.25 (ISBN 0-89536-810-2, 6839). CSS of Ohio.

Lectionary Series from the Common Lectionary: Series A (TEV) rev. ed. Ed. by Michael L. Sherer. 1986. 14.25 (ISBN 0-89536-811-0, 6840). CSS of Ohio.

Lectionary Series from the Common Lectionary: Series B (RSV) Ed. by Michael L. Sherer. (Orig.). 1987. pap. price not set (ISBN 0-89536-884-6, 7870). CSS of Ohio.

Lectionary Texts, Year C: From the Common Lectionary RSV. 312p. 1985. UM 49.95 (ISBN 0-687-21337-1). Plain (ISBN 0-687-21334-7). Abingdon.

Lectionary Worship Aids A: Common Lectionary. rev. ed. Heth H. Corl. Ed. by Michael L. Sherer. 1986. pap. 9.95 (ISBN 0-89536-814-5, 6843). CSS of Ohio.

Lectionary Worship Aids B: Series II. Paul A. Laughlin. (Orig.). 1987. pap. price not set (ISBN 0-89536-886-2, 7872). CSS of Ohio.

Lectionary Worship Aids C (Common) Heth Corl. 1985. 9.95 (ISBN 0-89536-760-2, 5867). CSS of Ohio.

Lector's Guide to Biblical Pronunciations. Joseph M. Staudacher. LC 75-14609. 72p. (Orig.). 1975. pap. 2.95 (ISBN 0-87973-773-5). Our Sunday Visitor.

Lecture on the Doctrine of Baptism for the Dead. new ed. George J. Adams. (Orig.). 1983. pap. 1.00 (ISBN 0-942284-04-6). Restoration Re.

Lectures & Articles on Christian Science. Edward A. Kimball. (Illus.). 1976. 12.50 (ISBN 0-911588-01-9); pap. 8.00; leatherette 18.00. N S Wait.

Lectures & Miscellanies. Henry James, Sr. LC 72-923. (Selected Works of Henry James, Sr.: Vol. 3). 456p. 1983. Repr. of 1852 ed. 42.50 (ISBN 0-404-10083-X). AMS Pr.

Lectures from Colombo to Almora. Swami Vivekananda. pap. 8.95 (ISBN 0-87481-171-6). Vedanta Pr.

Lectures in Godmanhood. Vladimir Solovyev. 214p. 1981. 37.00x (ISBN 0-234-77047-3, Pub. by Dobson Bks England). State Mutual Bk.

Lectures in Systematic Theology. R. L. Dabney. 1985. pap. 24.95 (ISBN 0-8010-2956-2). Baker Bk.

Lectures in Systematic Theology. rev. ed. Henry C. Thiessen. Rev. by Vernon C. Doerksen. 1981. 16.95 (ISBN 0-8028-3529-5). Eerdmans.

Lectures on Calvinism. Abraham Kuyper. pap. 3.95 (ISBN 0-8028-1607-X). Eerdmans.

Lectures on Church Co-Operation & Orphan Homes. Thomas B. Warren. 1958. pap. 7.00 (ISBN 0-934916-48-9). Natl Christian Pr.

Lectures on Counseling. Jay E. Adams. 281p. 1977. kivar 4.50 (ISBN 0-87552-041-3). Presby & Reformed.

Lectures on Counseling. Jay E. Adams. (Jay Adams Library). 288p. 1986. pap. 9.95 (ISBN 0-310-51121-6, 12124P). Zondervan.

Lectures on Ethics. Immanuel Kant. Tr. by Louis Infield from Ger. LC 80-22092. 272p. 1980. pap. text ed. 6.95 (ISBN 0-915144-26-3). Hackett Pub.

Lectures on Ethics. Immanuel Kant. 11.25 (ISBN 0-8446-2348-2). Peter Smith.

Lectures on Faith. Joseph Smith. LC 84-73495. 96p. 1985. 6.95 (ISBN 0-87747-897-X). Deseret Bk.

Lectures on Kant's Political Philosophy. Hannah Arendt. Ed. by Ronald Beiner. LC 82-4817. 192p. 1982. 17.50 (ISBN 0-226-02594-2). U of Chicago Pr.

Lectures on Moral Philosophy. John Witherspoon. Ed. by Varnum L. Collins. LC 75-3424. Repr. of 1912 ed. 12.00 (ISBN 0-404-59420-4). AMS Pr.

Lectures on Moral Science. Mark Hopkins. LC 75-3197. Repr. of 1862 ed. 37.50 (ISBN 0-404-59198-1). AMS Pr.

Lectures on Mysticism & Nature Worship. C. H. Bjerregaard. 1977. lib. bdg. 59.95 (ISBN 0-8490-2138-3). Gordon Pr.

Lectures on Philosophical Theology. Immanuel Kant. Tr. by Allen W. Wood & Gertrude M. Clark. LC 78-58034. 192p. 1986. pap. text ed. 7.95x (ISBN 0-8014-9379-X). Cornell U Pr.

Lectures on the Bases of Religious Belief. 2nd ed. Charles B. Upton. LC 77-27161. (Hibbert Lectures: 1893). Repr. of 1897 ed. 39.50 (ISBN 0-404-60411-0). AMS Pr.

Lectures on the Book of Job Delivered in Westminster Abbey. Ed. by George G. Bradley. 334p. 1981. Repr. of 1888 ed. lib. bdg. 50.00 (ISBN 0-89984-069-8). Century Bookbindery.

Lectures on the Church of God. W. Kelly. 7.50 (ISBN 0-88172-092-5). Believers Bkshelf.

Lectures on the Council of Trent, Delivered at Oxford 1892-3. James A. Froude. LC 68-8244. 1969. Repr. of 1901 ed. 27.00x (ISBN 0-8046-0159-3, Pub. by Kennikat). Assoc Faculty Pr.

Lectures on the Doctrine of the Holy Spirit. W. Kelly. 7.95 (ISBN 0-88172-095-X). Believers Bkshelf.

Lectures on the Epistle of James. Robert Johnstone. 1977. 16.50 (ISBN 0-86524-111-2, 5901). Klock & Klock.

Lectures on the Epistle of Jude. W. Kelly. 6.95 (ISBN 0-88172-101-8). Believers Bkshelf.

Lectures on the First & Second Epistles of Peter. John Lillie. 1978. 19.75 (ISBN 0-86524-116-3, 7102). Klock & Klock.

Lectures on the Gospel of Matthew. W. Kelly. 6.95 (ISBN 0-88172-104-2). Believers Bkshelf.

Lectures on the Influence of the Apostle Paul on the Development of Christianity. Otto Pfleiderer. Tr. by J. Frederick Smith. LC 77-27166. (Hibbert Lectures: 1885). Repr. of 1885 ed. 29.00 (ISBN 0-404-60406-4). AMS Pr.

Lectures on the Influence of the Institutions, Thought & Culture of Rome, on Christianity & the Development of the Catholic Church. Ernest Renan. Tr. by Charles Beard. LC 77-27170. (Hibbert Lectures: 1880). Repr. of 1898 ed. 24.50 (ISBN 0-404-60402-1). AMS Pr.

Lectures on the Moral Government of God: New York, 1859, 2 vols. Nathaniel W. Taylor. Ed. by Bruce Kuklick. (American Religious Thought of the 18th & 19th Centuries Ser.). 840p. 1987. lib. bdg. 110.00 (ISBN 0-8240-6961-7). Garland Pub.

Lectures on the Origin & Growth of Religion as Illustrated by the Religion of the Ancient Hebrews. 3rd ed. Claude J. Montefiore. LC 77-27162. (Hibbert Lectures: 1892). Repr. of 1892 ed. 46.50 (ISBN 0-404-60410-2). AMS Pr.

Lectures on the Origin & Growth of Religion, as Illustrated by the Religions of India. Friedrich M. Mueller. LC 73-18816. Repr. of 1882 ed. 34.50 (ISBN 0-404-11440-7). AMS Pr.

Lectures on the Origin & Growth of Religion as Illustrated by the Religion of Ancient Egypt. 2nd ed. Peter L. Renouf. LC 77-27171. (Hibbert Lectures: 1879). Repr. of 1884 ed. 30.00 (ISBN 0-404-60401-3). AMS Pr.

Lectures on the Origin & Growth of Religion as Illustrated by the Native Religions of Mexico & Peru. Albert D. Reville. 1977. lib. bdg. 59.95 (ISBN 0-8490-2140-5). Gordon Pr.

Lectures on the Origin & Growth of Religion as Illustrated by Celtic Heathendom. John Rhys. LC 77-27165. (Hibbert Lectures: 1886). Repr. of 1898 ed. 53.00 (ISBN 0-404-60407-2). AMS Pr.

Lectures on the Origin & Growth of the Conception of God as Illustrated by Anthropology & History. Eugene F. Goblet D'Alviella. Tr. by P. H. Wicksteed. LC 77-27163. (Hibbert Lectures: 1887). Repr. of 1892 ed. 34.00 (ISBN 0-404-60409-9). AMS Pr.

Lectures on the Philosophy of Religion. G. W. Hegel. Ed. by Peter Hodgson. Incl. Vol. 1. Introduction & the Concept of Religion. 1984. lib. bdg. 50.00x (ISBN 0-520-04676-5); Vol. 3. Consumate Religion. 1985. lib. bdg. 45.00x (ISBN 0-520-05514-4); Vol. II. Determinate Religion. G. W. Hegel. Ed. & tr. by Peter C. Hodgson. 816p. 1987. text ed. 50.50 (ISBN 0-520-05513-6). LC 83-9132. 450p. U of Cal Pr.

Lectures on the Philosophy of Religion, 3 vols. Georg W. Hegel. Tr. by E. B. Speirs & J. B. Sanderson. 1968. Repr. of 1895 ed. Set. text ed. 70.00x (ISBN 0-7100-6080-7). Humanities.

Lectures on the Philosophy of Swedenborg's Principia. George De Charms. 68p. 1970. pap. 3.00 (ISBN 0-915221-39-X). Swedenborg Sci Assn.

Lectures on the Reunion of the Churches. Johann J. Von Dollinger. LC 74-131579. (Sources in the History of Interpretation: No. 2). 1973. 15.00x (ISBN 0-8401-0567-3). A R Allenson.

Lectures on the Revival of Religion by Ministers of the Church of Scotland. Ed. by William M. Hetherington. (Revival Library). xxvi, 444p. 1980. Repr. of 1840 ed. lib. bdg. 15.95 (ISBN 0-940033-15-1). R O Roberts.

Lectures on the Science of Religion: With a Paper on Buddhist Nihilism, & a Translation of the Dhammapada or Path of Virtue. Friedrich M. Mueller. LC 73-18818. Repr. of 1872 ed. 15.00 (ISBN 0-404-11444-X). AMS Pr.

Lectures on the Tabernacle. Samuel Ridout. (Illus.). 1973. Repr. of 1914 ed. 13.95 (ISBN 0-87213-715-5); chart only 0.15 (ISBN 0-87213-716-3). Loizeaux.

Lectures on Yoga. Swami Rama. LC 79-114571. (Illus.). 208p. pap. 7.95 (ISBN 0-89389-050-2); 6.95 (ISBN 0-89389-051-0). Himalayan Pubs.

Lectures to My Students. Charles H. Spurgeon. 1977. pap. 12.95 (ISBN 0-8010-8097-5). Baker Bk.

Lectures to My Students. 2nd ed. Charles H. Spurgeon. 443p. 1980. pap. 9.95 (ISBN 0-310-32911-6, 10845P). Zondervan.

Lectures to Professing Christians. Charles G. Finney. (Higher Christian Life Ser.). 348p. 1985. lib. bdg. 45.00 (ISBN 0-8240-6418-6). Garland Pub.

Lee's Modified Tai Chi for Health. Lee Ying-Arng. 10.95x (ISBN 0-685-70688-5). Wehman.

Lefevre: Pioneer of Ecclesiastical Renewal in France. Philip E. Hughes. 224p. (Orig.). 1984. pap. 15.95x (ISBN 0-8028-0015-7). Eerdmans.

Left Alive: After a Suicide Death in the Family. Linda Rosenfeld & Marilynne Prupas. 120p. 1984. 20.75 (ISBN 0-398-04953-X). C C Thomas.

Legacy for My Loved Ones. Cassandre Maxwell. 1984. 12.95 (ISBN 0-317-13919-3). Revell.

Legacy of Egypt. Stephen R. Glanville. LC 76-44448. (Illus.). 1976. Repr. of 1942 ed. lib. bdg. 34.00x (ISBN 0-8371-9092-4, GLLE). Greenwood.

Legacy of Egypt. 2nd ed. Ed. by J. R. Harris. (Legacy Ser.). (Illus.). 1971. 35.00x (ISBN 0-19-821912-1). Oxford U Pr.

Legacy of Hatred: Why Christians Must Not Forget the Holocaust. David A. Rausch. 1984. 9.95 (ISBN 0-8024-0341-7). Moody.

Legacy of Herman Dooyeweerd: Reflections on Critical Philosophy in the Christian Tradition. Ed. by C. T. McIntire. (Illus.). 198p. (Orig.). 1986. lib. bdg. 25.25 (ISBN 0-8191-5033-9, Pub. by Inst Christ Stud); pap. text ed. 12.00 (ISBN 0-8191-5034-7). U Pr of Amer.

Legacy of Islam. T. W. Arnold & A. Guillaume. 1976. lib. bdg. 75.00 (ISBN 0-8490-2141-3). Gordon Pr.

Legacy of Islam. 2nd ed. Ed. by Joseph Schacht & C. E. Bosworth. (Legacy Ser). (Illus.). 1974. text ed. 29.95x (ISBN 0-19-821913-X). Oxford U Pr.

Legacy of Islam. 2nd ed. Ed. by Joseph Schacht & C. E. Bosworth. (Illus.). 1974. pap. 8.95 (ISBN 0-19-285081-4). Oxford U Pr.

Legacy of Jesus. John MacArthur, Jr. pap. 5.95 (ISBN 0-8024-8524-3). Moody.

Legacy of Jewish Migration: Eighteen Eighty-One & Its Impact. David Berger. (Social Science Monographs, Brooklyn College Studies on Society in Change). 189p. 1983. 26.00x (ISBN 0-88033-026-0). East Eur Quarterly.

Legacy of Luther: Martin Luther & the Reformation in the Estimation of the German Lutherans from Luther's Death to the Beginning of the Age of Goethe. Ernest W. Zeeden. Tr. by Ruth M. Bethell from Ger. LC 83-45685. Date not set. Repr. of 1954 ed. 30.00 (ISBN 0-404-19865-1). AMS Pr.

Legacy of Michael Sattler. Ed. by John H. Yoder. LC 72-6333. (Classics of the Radical Reformation Ser., No. 1). 208p. 1973. 12.95 (ISBN 0-8361-1187-7). Herald Pr.

Legacy of Night: The Literary Universe of Elie Wiesel. Ellen S. Fine. LC 81-14601. (Modern Jewish Literature & Culture Ser.). 276p. 1982. 44.50 (ISBN 0-87395-589-7); pap. 14.95 (ISBN 0-87395-590-0). State U NY Pr.

Legacy of Reinhold Niebuhr. Ed. by Nathan A. Scott, Jr. LC 74-30714. xxiv, 124p. 1975. 10.00X (ISBN 0-226-74297-0). U of Chicago Pr.

Legacy of St. Patrick. Martin Harney. 1972. 3.50 (ISBN 0-8198-4407-1); pap. 2.25 (ISBN 0-8198-4408-X). Dghtrs St Paul.

Legacy of the Middle Ages. Ed. by C. G. Crump & E. F. Jacob. (Legacy Ser.). (Illus.). 1926. 32.50x (ISBN 0-19-821907-5). Oxford U Pr.

Legacy of Thomas Merton. Ed. by Patrick Hart. (Cistercian Studies: No. 92). 1985. 25.95 (ISBN 0-87907-892-8); pap. 7.95 (ISBN 0-87907-992-4). Cistercian Pubns.

Legacy of Wisdom: The Egyptian Contribution to the Wisdom of Israel. Glendon E. Bryce. LC 74-4984. 336p. 1979. 24.50 (ISBN 0-8387-1576-1). Bucknell U Pr.

Legacy Remembered: The Relief Society Magazine. Ed. by Carol Clark. (Illus.). 1982. 7.95 (ISBN 0-87747-926-7). Deseret Bk.

Legal Education & Religious Perspective. Raymond C. O'Brien. LC 85-220822. (Illus.). 95p. Date not set. price not set. Cambridge U Pr.

Legal Problems of Religious & Private Schools. R. Mawdsley & S. Permuth. 1983. 9.95 (ISBN 0-318-02068-8). NOLPE.

Legal Status of Church-State Relationships in the United States with Special Reference to the Public Schools. Alvin W. Johnson. ix, 332p. 1982. Repr. of 1934 ed. lib. bdg. 30.00x (ISBN 0-8377-0739-0). Rothman.

Legal Status of Soviet Jewry: De Jure Equality & De Facto Discrimination. Menachem Z. Rosensaft. 30p. 1.00 (ISBN 0-686-74962-6). ADL.

Legatio & De Resurrectione. Athenagoras. Ed. by William R. Schoedel. (Oxford Early Christian Texts Ser). 1972. 34.95x (ISBN 0-19-826808-4). Oxford U Pr.

Legend & the Apostle: The Battle for Paul in Story & Canon. Dennis R. MacDonald. LC 82-21953. 144p. (Orig.). 1983. pap. 9.95 (ISBN 0-664-24464-5). Westminster.

Legend of Etana. J. Kinnier Wilson. (Assyriology Ser.). (Illus.). 150p. 1985. pap. 36.00 (ISBN 0-86516-116-X). Bolchazy-Carducci.

Legend of Etana. J. V. Wilson. 140p. 1985. pap. text ed. 44.00 (ISBN 0-85668-258-6, Pub. by Aris & Phillips UK). Humanities.

Legend of Job in the Middle Ages. Lawrence L. Besserman. LC 78-14936. (Illus.). 1979. 15.00x (ISBN 0-674-52385-7, Belknap Pr). Harvard U Pr.

Legend of King Asoka: A Study & Translation of the Asokavadana. John S. Strong. LC 83-42579. (Princeton Library of Asian Translations). 336p. 1984. 30.00x (ISBN 0-691-06575-6). Princeton U Pr.

Legend of Noah: Renaissance Rationalism in Art, Science, & Letters. Don C. Allen. LC 49-49065. (Reprint of Studies in Language & Literature Ser.: Vol. 33, No. 3-4, 1949). (Illus.). 1963. pap. 8.95 (ISBN 0-252-72516-6). U of Ill Pr.

Legend of St. Dismas & Other Poems. Ed. by Peter Gallwey. LC 83-82115. 126p. (Orig.). 1984. pap. 6.95 (ISBN 0-89870-034-5). Ignatius Pr.

Legend of Saint Nicholas. Bernice Krasovec. (Illus.). 48p. 1985. 5.95 (ISBN 0-89962-467-7). Todd & Honeywell.

Legend of Shamballa. Torkom Saraydarian. LC 76-12895. 1976. 12.00 (ISBN 0-911794-40-9); pap. 10.00 (ISBN 0-911794-41-7). Aqua Educ.

Legend of the Baal-Shem. Martin Buber. LC 76-86849. 1969. pap. 7.95 (ISBN 0-8052-0233-1). Schocken.

Legend of the Christmas Donkey. William C. Zimmann, Sr. 1984. 1.95 (ISBN 0-89536-989-3, 7540). CSS of Ohio.

Legend of the Great Stupa. Guru Padmasambhava. LC 73-79059. (Tibetan Translation Ser., Vol. 2). (Illus.). 144p. 1973. pap. 6.95 (ISBN 0-913546-03-8). Dharma Pub.

Legend of the Holy Child of Atocha. J. Janda. (Illus.). 48p. (Orig.). 1986. pap. 2.95 (ISBN 0-8091-6559-7). Paulist Pr.
Legend of the Holy Grail. G. M. Harper. 59.95 (ISBN 0-8490-0502-7). Gordon Pr.
Legend of the Sons of God: A Fantasy. T. C. Lethbridge. (Illus.). 126p. 1983. pap. 5.95 (ISBN 0-7100-9500-7). Methuen Inc.
Legend of the Truant Tree. Jovan DeRocco. (Illus.). 112p. 1982. 6.50 (ISBN 0-682-49804-1). Exposition Pr FL.
Legend of the Wandering Jew. George K. Anderson. LC 65-14290. (Brown University Bicentennial Publication Ser.). pap. 125.80 (ISBN 0-317-52056-3, 2027498). Bks Demand UMI.
Legendary Lore of the Holy Wells of England. Robert C. Hope. LC 68-21775. (Illus.). 1968. Repr. of 1893 ed. 35.00x (ISBN 0-8103-3445-3). Gale.
Legende Doree Ou Legenda Aurea: The First Ten Chapters. Gwendolyn C. Stanford. LC 85-90222. 125p. 1986. 8.95 (ISBN 0-533-06725-1). Vantage.
Legendes de Constantin et de methode vues de Byzance. Francis Dvornik. (Russian Ser: No. 12). 1969. Repr. of 1933 ed. 35.00 (ISBN 0-87569-009-2). Academic Intl.
Legends & Traditions of Christmas. Trudie W. Revoir. (Illus.). 112p. 1985. pap. 5.95 (ISBN 0-8170-1082-3). Judson.
Legends from the Future. Ewald Bash. (Illus., Orig.). 1972. pap. 1.75 (ISBN 0-377-02101-6). Friend Pr.
Legends of Abraham the Patriarch. S. Shimoni. (Biblical Ser.). (Illus.). 1975. 3.00 (ISBN 0-914080-07-5). Shulsinger Sales.
Legends of Babylon & Egypt in Relation to Hebrew Tradition. L. W. King. 59.95 (ISBN 0-8490-0504-3). Gordon Pr.
Legends of Babylonia & Egypt in Relation to the Hebrew Tradition. Leonard W. King. LC 77-94593. 1979. Repr. of 1918 ed. lib. bdg. 20.00 (ISBN 0-89341-310-0). Longwood Pub Group.
Legends of Daniel. S. Shimoni. (Biblical Ser.). (Illus.). 1975. 3.00 (ISBN 0-914080-14-8). Shulsinger Sales.
Legends of Earth, Air, Fire & Water. Eric Hadley & Tessa Hadley. (Illus.). 32p. 1985. 10.95 (ISBN 0-521-26311-5). Cambridge U Pr.
Legends of Elijah. S. Shimoni. (Biblical Ser.). (Illus.). 1975. 3.00 (ISBN 0-914080-13-X). Shulsinger Sales.
Legends of Galilee, Jordan & Sinai. Zev Vilnay. LC 73-168156. (Sacred Land Ser.: Vol. 3). (Illus.). 378p. 1978. 10.95 (ISBN 0-8276-0106-9, 419). Jewish Pubns.
Legends of Genesis: The Biblical Saga & History. Hermann Gunkel. LC 64-22609. 1984. pap. 5.50 (ISBN 0-8052-0086-X). Schocken.
Legends of Gods & Ghosts from Hawaiian Mythology. W. D. Westervelt. 1977. lib. bdg. 59.95 (ISBN 0-8490-2147-2). Gordon Pr.
Legends of Greece & Rome. Grace H. Kupfer. 1911. 20.00 (ISBN 0-686-20105-1). Quality Lib.
Legends of Israel. Joel Snowman. Tr. by J. B. Levner from Hebrew. (Illus.). 233p. 1983. Repr. of 1946 ed. lib. bdg. 85.00 (ISBN 0-8495-5060-2). Arden Lib.
Legends of Jerusalem. Zev Vilnay. LC 72-12180. (Sacred Land Ser.: Vol. 1). (Illus.). 338p. 1973. 8.95 (ISBN 0-8276-0004-6, 323). Jewish Pubns.
Legends of Joseph & His Brothers. S. Shimoni. (Biblical Ser.). (Illus.). 1975. 3.00 (ISBN 0-914080-11-3). Shulsinger Sales.
Legends of Joshua. S. Shimoni. (Biblical Ser.). (Illus.). 1975. 3.00 (ISBN 0-914080-12-1). Shulsinger Sales.
Legends of Our Time. Elie Wiesel. 1980. pap. 2.50 (ISBN 0-380-00931-5, 49429, Bard). Avon.
Legends of the Bible. Louis Ginzberg. LC 56-9915. 620p. 1956. 14.95 (ISBN 0-8276-0036-4, 168). Jewish Pubns.
Legends of the Hasidim: An Introduction to Hasidic Culture & Oral Tradition in the New World. Jerome R. Mintz. LC 68-16707. 504p. 1974. pap. 14.95 (ISBN 0-226-53103-1, P612, Phoen). U of Chicago Pr.
Legends of the Holy Grail. Alfred T. Nutt. LC 78-139176. (Popular Studies in Mythology, Romance & Folklore: No. 14). Repr. of 1902 ed. 5.50 (ISBN 0-404-53514-3). AMS Pr.
Legends of the Jews, 7 Vols. Louis Ginzberg. LC 76-58650. 1956. Set. 80.00 (ISBN 0-8276-0148-4); 11.95 ea. Vol. 1 (172). Vol. 2 (173). Vol. 3 (174). Vol. 4 (175). Vol. 5 (176). Vol. 6 (177). Vol. 7 (178). Jewish Pubns.
Legends of the Madonna, As Represented in the Fine Arts. Anna B. Jameson. LC 70-89273. (Tower Bks.). (Illus.). lxxvi, 344p. 1972. Repr. of 1890 ed. 42.00x (ISBN 0-8103-3114-4). Gale.
Legends of the Monastic Orders As Represented in the Fine Arts. Anna B. Jameson. LC 75-41154. 1976. Repr. of 1866 ed. 29.50 (ISBN 0-404-14767-4). AMS Pr.
Legends of the Patriarchs & Prophets & Other Old Testament Characters. S. Baring-Gould. LC 74-9741. 1872. lib. bdg. 42.00 (ISBN 0-8414-3205-8). Folcroft.
Legends of the Saints. Hippolyte Delehaye. LC 77-26797. 1907. 30.00 (ISBN 0-8414-3657-6). Folcroft.
Legends of the Saints, in the Scottish Dialect of the Fourteenth Century, 3 Vols. Ed. by W. M. Metcalfe. 1896. Set. 140.00 (ISBN 0-384-32090-2). Johnson Repr.
Legends of the Sufis. Ed. by Shemsu-D-Din Ahmed. 1977. pap. 7.95 (ISBN 0-7229-5050-0). Theos Pub Hse.
Legends of the Wagner Drama. Jessie L. Weston. LC 74-24255. Repr. of 1896 ed. 24.00 (ISBN 0-404-13132-8). AMS Pr.
Legends of the Wagner Drama: Studies in Mythology & Romance. Jessie L. Weston. LC 76-22354. 1976. Repr. of 1903 ed. lib. bdg. 35.00 (ISBN 0-89341-003-9). Longwood Pub Group.
Legends of Zion. S. Z. Kahana. 256p. 1986. pap. 9.95 (ISBN 0-943688-63-9). Res Ctr Kabbalah.
Legislating Morality: Private Choices on the Public Agenda. Ed. by Kim E. Shienbaum. 256p. 1987. 28.95 (ISBN 0-87073-689-2); pap. 18.95 (ISBN 0-87073-690-6). Schenkman Bks Inc.
Lehavin Ulehaskil. 1982. 8.95 (ISBN 0-686-76535-4); pap. 6.95. Feldheim.
Lehmann's Little Dictionary of Liturgical Terms. Arnold O. Lehmann. 1980. 3.75 (ISBN 0-8100-0127-6, 15N0371). Northwest Pub.
Lehntafel der Prinzessin Antonia, 2 Vol. Ed. by Friederich Haeusermann & Reinhard Breymayer. (Texte Zur Geschichte Des Pietismus: Sec. 7, Vol. 1). 1977. 112.00x (ISBN 3-11-004130-8). De Gruyter.
Lehre der Alten: II Das Testament als Literaturgattung im Alten Testament und im Alten Vorderen Orient. Eckhard Von Nordheim. (Arbeiten zur Literatur und Geschichte des hellenistischen Judentums Ser.: No. 18). (Ger.). xii, 184p. 1986. 25.50 (ISBN 90-04-07313-2, Pub. by E J Brill). Heinman.
Leib und das Heil. Meinulf Blechschmidt. (European University Studies: No. 23, Vol. 207). (Ger.). 435p. 1983. 22.10 (ISBN 3-261-03264-2). P Lang Pubs.
Leibniz Philosophical Writings. Gottfried W. Leibniz & G. H. Parkinson. Tr. by Mary Morris from Ger. (Rowman & Littlefield University Library). 270p. 1973. 13.50x (ISBN 0-87471-659-4). Rowman.
Leisure Crisis. John Oswalt. 168p. 1987. pap. 5.95 (ISBN 0-89693-241-9). Victor Bks.
Lemba, Sixteen Fifty to Nineteen Thirty: A Drum of Affliction in Africa & the New World. John M. Janzen. 1982. lib. bdg. 91.00 (ISBN 0-8240-9306-2). Garland Pub.
Lemegeton, Clavicula Salomonis: Or the Complete Lesser Key of Solomon the King. rev ed. Ed. by Nelson White & Anne White. LC 79-91961. (Illus.). 130p. (Orig.). 1979. pap. 30.00 (ISBN 0-939856-06-9). Tech Group.
Lemniscatory Ruled Surface in Space & Counterspace. George Adams. Tr. by Stephen Eberhart from Ger. & Eng. (Illus.). 83p. 1979. pap. 9.95x (ISBN 0-686-43395-5, Pub. by Steinerbooks). Anthroposophic.
Lemuria, el Continente Perdido del Pacifico. Wishar S. Cerve. Tr. by AMORC Staff. (Span., Illus.). 191p. (Orig.). 1980. pap. 7.00 (ISBN 0-912057-68-8, GS-512). AMORC.
Lena. Margaret Jensen. LC 84-62381. 150p. (Orig.). 1985. pap. text ed. 9.95 (ISBN 0-89840-074-0). Heres Life.
Lenape & Their Legends. Ed. by Daniel G. Brinton. LC 77-102641. (Library of Aboriginal American Literature Ser.: No. 5). Repr. of 1884 ed. 30.00 (ISBN 0-404-52185-1). AMS Pr.
Lenape & Their Legends. Walam Olum. Tr. by Daniel G. Brinton. LC 74-108462. 262p. 1973. Repr. of 1884 ed. 29.00 (ISBN 0-403-00449-7). Scholarly.
Lenin on the Jewish Question. V. I. Lenin. Ed. by Hyman Lumer. LC 74-6278. (Eng.). 156p. 1974. 7.50 (ISBN 0-7178-0398-8); pap. 2.75 (ISBN 0-7178-0399-6). Intl Pubs Co.
Lent. Elisabeth S. Fiorenza & Urban T. Holmes. Ed. by Elizabeth Achtemeier & Gerhard Krodel. LC 79-7377. (Proclamation 2: Aids for Interpreting the Lessons of the Church Year, Ser. B). 64p. 1981. pap. 3.75 (ISBN 0-8006-4070-5, 1-4070). Fortress.
Lent. Victor Furnish. LC 84-18756. (Proclamation 3A Ser.). 64p. 1986. pap. 3.75 (ISBN 0-8006-4119-1, 1-4119). Fortress.
Lent. Peter Gomes. LC 84-18756. (Proclamation 3 C Ser.). 64p. 1985. pap. 3.75 (ISBN 0-8006-4127-2). Fortress.
Lent. Jack D. Kingsbury & Chester Pennington. Ed. by Elizabeth Achtemeier et al. LC 79-7377. (Proclamation 2: Aids for Interpreting the Lessons of the Church Year, Ser. A). 64p. (Orig.). 1980. pap. 3.75 (ISBN 0-8006-4093-4, 1-4093). Fortress.
Lent. Marianne H. Micks & Thomas E. Ridenhour. Ed. by Elizabeth Achtemeier et al. LC 79-7377. (Proclamation 2: Aids for Interpreting the Lessons of the Church Year Ser. C). 64p. 1979. pap. 3.75 (ISBN 0-8006-4082-9, 1-4082). Fortress.
Lent, a Guide to the Eucharist & Hours. Kevin Irwin. (Liturgical Seasons Ser.). 300p. (Orig.). 1985. pap. 12.95 (ISBN 0-916134-68-7). Pueblo Pub Co.
Lent: A Journey to Resurrection Prayers & Reflections for the Penitential Season. Rawley Myers. LC 83-63084. 192p. 1984. pap. 5.95 (ISBN 0-87973-605-4). Our Sunday Visitor.
Lent: A Time of Tears. John R. Brokhoff. 1984. 4.25 (ISBN 0-89536-649-5, 1267). CSS of Ohio.
Lent Begins at Home. Pat Ryan & Rosemary Ryan. 1979. pap. 1.50 (ISBN 0-89243-101-6). Liguori Pubns.
Lent, Good Friday & Easter. Ralph Becker. pap. 0.50 (ISBN 0-685-41825-1). Reiner.
Lent Is for Remembering. Donna R. Rathert. LC 56-1613. 24p. (Orig.). 1987. pap. 2.95 (ISBN 0-570-04147-3). Concordia.
Lent: Series B. Pheme Perkins. Ed. by Elizabeth Achtemeier. LC 84-6010. (Proclamation 3: Aids for Interpreting the Lessons of the Church Year Ser.). 64p. 1984. pap. 3.75 (ISBN 0-8006-4103-5). Fortress.
Lenten Journey with Jesus. Joan Cole. 48p. 1982. pap. 1.50 (ISBN 0-89243-172-5). Liguori Pubns.
Lenten Pilgrimage-Dying & Rising in the Lord: A Manual for Ministry in the Lenten Catechumenate. Richard W. Chilson. (Orig.). 1984. pap. 8.95 (ISBN 0-8091-2589-7); handbook 4.95 (ISBN 0-8091-2569-2). Paulist Pr.
Lenten Pilgrimage: Scriptural Meditations in the Holy Land. David E. Rosage. (Orig.). 1980. pap. 3.50 (ISBN 0-89283-081-6). Servant.
Lenten Spring. Thomas Hopko. LC 83-4278. 229p. 1983. pap. text ed. 5.95 (ISBN 0-88141-014-4). St Vladimirs.
Lenten Triodion. Tr. by Mother Mary & Archimandrite Kallistos Ware. LC 83-20750. 699p. (Orig.). 1984. pap. 17.95 (ISBN 0-571-13243-X). Faber & Faber.
Leo Baeck Institute Yearbook, Vol. 17. 1972. 28.00 (ISBN 0-436-24425-X, Pub. by Secker & Warburg UK). David & Charles.
Leo Baeck Institute Yearbook, Vol. 18. 400p. 1973. 28.00 (ISBN 0-436-24426-8, Pub. by Secker & Warburg UK). David & Charles.
Leo Baeck Institute Yearbook, Vol. 19. 380p. 1974. 28.00 (ISBN 0-436-24427-6, Pub. by Secker & Warburg UK). David & Charles.
Leo Baeck Institute Yearbook, Vol 20. 420p. 1975. 28.00 (ISBN 0-436-24428-4, Pub. by Secker & Warburg UK). David & Charles.
Leo Baeck Institute Yearbook, Vol. 22. (Illus.). 388p. 1977. 28.00 (ISBN 0-436-24430-6, Pub. by Secker & Warbug UK). David & Charles.
Leo Baeck Institute Yearbook, Vol. 23. 486p. 1978. 28.00 (ISBN 0-436-24431-4, Pub. by Secker & Warburg UK). David & Charles.
Leo Baeck Institute Yearbook, Vol. 25. 504p. 1980. 28.00 (ISBN 0-436-24433-0, Pub. by Secker & Warburg UK). David & Charles.
Leo Baeck Institute Yearbook, Vol. 26. 504p. 1981. 28.00 (ISBN 0-436-24434-9, Pub. by Secker & Warburg UK). David & Charles.
Leo Baeck Institute Yearbook: The Jewish Questions & Antisemitism II, Vol. 21. (Leo Baeck Institute Yearbooks Ser.). (Illus.). 388p. 1976. 28.00 (ISBN 0-317-24492-2, Pub. by Secker & Warburg UK). David & Charles.
Leo Baeck Institute Yearbook, Vol. 29: Enlightenment & Acculturation Persecution under the Nazi Regime. (Illus.). 560p. 1984. 28.00 (ISBN 0-436-25543-X, Pub. by Secker & Warburg UK). David & Charles.
Leo Baeck Institute Yearbook XXXI. Leo Baeck Institute Staff. 1987. 35.00 (ISBN 0-436-25545-6, Pub. by Secker & Warburg UK). David & Charles.
Leo Baeck Institute Yearbooks Index: Volumes I-XX, 1956-1975. 224p. 1982. 32.00 (ISBN 0-436-25541-3, Pub. by Secker & Warburg UK). David & Charles.
Leo Baek Institute Yearbook: Jewry in the German Reich II, No. 28. 464p. 1983. 28.00 (ISBN 0-436-25542-1, Pub. by Secker & Warburg UK). David & Charles.
Leo Jung Jubilee Volume. cancelled (ISBN 0-686-76536-2). Feldheim.
Leon Bloy: A Study in Impatience. Albert Beguin. Tr. by Edith M. Riley from Fr. 247p. 1982. Repr. of 1947 ed. lib. bdg. 45.00 (ISBN 0-89984-081-7). Century Bookbindery.
Leon Trotsky on the Jewish Question. Leon Trotsky. pap. 0.95 (ISBN 0-87348-157-7). Path Pr NY.
Leonardo, 3 vols. Carlo Pedretti & David A. Brown. (Illus.). 1985. Set. pap. 29.95 (ISBN 0-295-96323-9, Pub. by Natl Gallery of Art). U of Wash Pr.
Leoni Meadows Experiences. large print ed. Bert Brians. 62p. 1984. pap. 9.00 (ISBN 0-914009-07-9). VHI Library.
Leopold Brenner, Historia Cartusia Mauerancensis. James Hogg. (Analecta Cartusiana Ser.: No. 32). (Orig.). 1987. pap. 25.00 (ISBN 3-7052-0033-X, Pub by Salzburg Studies). Longwood Pub Group.
Lesbian Nuns: Breaking Silence. Rosemary Curb & Nancy Manahan. 400p. 1986. pap. 3.95 (ISBN 0-446-32659-3). Warner Bks.
Lesbian Nuns: Breaking Silence. Ed. by Rosemary Curb & Nancy Manahan. LC 84-29594. 432p. 1985. 16.95 (ISBN 0-930044-63-0); pap. 9.95 (ISBN 0-930044-62-2). Naiad Pr.
Leslie D. Weatherhead Library, 8 vols. Leslie D. Weatherhead. Set in Slipcase. 17.50 (ISBN 0-687-21373-8). Abingdon.
Leslie Stephen & Matthew Arnold As Critics of Wordsworth. John D. Wilson. LC 72-2060. (English Biography Ser., No. 31). 1972. Repr. of 1939 ed. lib. bdg. 40.95x (ISBN 0-8383-1455-4). Haskell.
Less Than Conquerors. Douglas W. Frank. 336p. (Orig.). 1986. pap. 14.95 (ISBN 0-8028-0228-1). Eerdmans.
Less Than Slaves: Jewish Forced Labor & the Quest for Compensation. Benjamin B. Ferencz. LC 79-10690. 1979. 17.50x (ISBN 0-674-52525-6). Harvard U Pr.
Lesser Eastern Churches. Adrian Fortescue. LC 79-168124. Repr. of 1913 ed. 31.50 (ISBN 0-404-02517-X). AMS Pr.
Lesser Festivals 1: Saints' Days & Special Occasions. Richard L. Thulin. Ed. by Elizabeth Achtemeier et al. LC 79-7377. (Proclamation 2: Aids for Interpreting the Lessons of the Church Year). 64p. (Orig.). 1980. pap. 3.75 (ISBN 0-8006-1393-7, 1-1393). Fortress.
Lesser Festivals 2: Saints' Days & Special Occasions. John B. Trotti. Ed. by Elizabeth Achtemeier et al. LC 79-7377. (Proclamation 2: Aids for Interpreting Thee Lessons of the Church Year). 64p. (Orig.). 1980. pap. 3.75 (ISBN 0-8006-1394-5, 1-1394). Fortress.
Lesser Festivals 3: Saints' Days & Special Occasions. Richard Reid & Milton Crum, Jr. Ed. by Elizabeth Achtemeier et al. LC 79-7377. (Proclamation 2: Aids for Interpreting the Lessons of the Church Year). 64p. (Orig.). 1981. pap. 3.75 (ISBN 0-8006-1395-3, 1-1395). Fortress.
Lesser Festivals 4: Saints' Days & Special Occasions. Lorenz Nieting. Ed. by Elizabeth Achtemeier et al. LC 79-7377. (Proclamation Two Ser.: Aids for Interpreting the Lessons of the Church Year). 64p. (Orig.). 1981. pap. 3.75 (ISBN 0-8006-1396-1, 1-1396). Fortress.
Lesser Parables of Our Lord. William Arnot. LC 80-8066. 464p. 1981. 12.95 (ISBN 0-8254-2121-7). Kregel.
Lessing & the Drama. F. J. Lamport. 1981. text ed. 39.00x (ISBN 0-19-815767-3). Oxford U Pr.
Lessing's Theological Writings: Selections in Translation. Gotthold Lessing. Tr. by Henry Chadwick. 1957. pap. 3.25x (ISBN 0-8047-0335-3). Stanford U Pr.
Lessing's "Ugly Ditch" A Study of Theology & History. Gordon E. Michalson, Jr. LC 84-42991. 224p. 1985. 22.50x (ISBN 0-271-00385-5). Pa St U Pr.
Lesson of Life. The Mother. 180p. 1985. pap. 5.25 (ISBN 0-89071-322-7, Pub. by Sri Aurobindo Ashram India). Matagiri.
Lesson of the Christmas Donkey. Pope John Paul I. Tr. by David Smith & Robert Cunningham. LC 79-21337. 104p. 1982. 6.95 (ISBN 0-8199-0774-X). Franciscan Herald.
Lessons for Living: Reflections on the Weekly Bible Readings & on the Festivals. Sidney Greenberg. 236p. 1985. 15.95x (ISBN 0-87677-157-6). Hartmore.
Lessons for the Children of Godly Ancestors. Ed. by Ronald A. Bosco. LC 82-5844. (Sermon in America Ser.). 1982. 60.00x (ISBN 0-8201-1381-6). Schol Facsimiles.
Lessons from a Sheepdog. W. Phillip Keller. 1983. 8.95 (ISBN 0-8499-0335-1). Word Bks.
Lessons from Exodus. F. W. Grant. 6.25 (ISBN 0-88172-074-7). Believers Bkshelf.
Lessons from Our Living Past. Jules Harlow. LC 72-2055. (Illus.). 128p. 1972. text ed. 6.95x (ISBN 0-87441-085-1). Behrman.
Lessons from the Stories of the Quran. Muhajir. pap. 14.95 (ISBN 0-686-18515-3). Kazi Pubns.
Lessons from the Stories of the Quran. A. M. Muhajir. 1969. 14.95x (ISBN 0-87902-066-0). Orientalia.
Lessons in Islam, 5. Ashraf. 8.50 (ISBN 0-686-18391-6). Kazi Pubns.
Lessons in Leadership from the Bible. Kenneth O. Gangel. 1980. pap. 5.95 (ISBN 0-88469-109-8). BMH Bks.
Lessons in Talmud. 1982. 3.00 (ISBN 0-686-76537-0). Feldheim.
Lessons in Victorious Living. Chris Schlabach. 160p. (Orig.). 1984. pap. 3.95 (ISBN 0-88368-141-2). Whitaker Hse.

Lessons in Yoga: Fourteen Steps to Higher Awareness. 2nd, rev. ed. Swami Kriyanada. 1979. pap. write for info. (ISBN 0-916124-16-9). Dawn Pubns CA.

Lessons Jesus Taught. Bessie Dean. (Children's Inspirational Coloring Books). (Illus.). 72p. (Orig.). 1980. pap. 2.50 (ISBN 0-88290-146-X). Horizon Utah.

Lessons on Assurance. The Navigators Staff. (Growing in Christ Ser.). 32p. 1982. pap. text ed. 2.45 (ISBN 0-934396-28-0). Churches Alive.

Lessons on Christian Living. The Navigators. (Growing in Christ Ser.). 46p. 1982. pap. text ed. 2.45 (ISBN 0-934396-29-9). Churches Alive.

Lessons on Doctrine: For Youth (Teacher) Ronald Christman & Linda Schibilla. 48p. (Orig.). 1982. pap. 1.95 (ISBN 0-87239-604-5, 3376). Standard Pub.

Lessons on Doctrine: For Youth (Workbook) Ronald Christman & Linda Schibilla. (Illus.). 64p. (Orig.). 1982. pap. 3.50 (ISBN 0-87239-603-7, 3377). Standard Pub.

Lessons on Love from Critter County. Paula Bussard & Christine Wyrtzen. 144p. 1986. wkbk. 9.95 (ISBN 0-87403-000-5, 3340). Standard Pub.

Lessons on New Testament Evidences. Wallace Wartick. 250p. 1980. pap. 4.95 (ISBN 0-89900-141-6). College Pr Pub.

Lessons on Praise from Critter County: Helping Children Praise God. Paula J. Bussard & Patti Jefferson. (Critter County Ser.). 144p. 1987. pap. 9.95 (ISBN 0-87403-217-2, 3337). Standard Pub.

Lessons on the Holy Spirit. George D. King. (Orig.). 1987. pap. 6.95 (ISBN 0-8054-1153-4). Broadman.

Lest We Forget. Margaret Eck. 72p. pap. 0.75 (ISBN 0-686-29125-5); pap. 2.00 3 copies (ISBN 0-686-29126-3). Faith Pub Hse.

Lest We Forget. William G. Storey. 176p. (Orig.). 1985. pap. 4.95 (ISBN 0-8091-2718-0). Paulist Pr.

Lestvitsa. Saint John Climacus. Tr. of Ladder. 363p. 18.00 (ISBN 0-317-28895-4); pap. 13.00 (ISBN 0-317-28896-2). Holy Trinity.

Let Earth Receive Its King: Christmas Service for Children. Kathy Sader. (Orig.). 1986. pap. 0.90 (ISBN 0-8066-9202-2, 23-1682). Augsburg.

Let Go! Fenelon. 1973. pap. 3.50 (ISBN 0-88368-010-6). Whitaker Hse.

Let Go! Bhagwan Shree Rajneesh. Ed. by Ma Prem Maneesha. LC 83-181279. (Initiation Talks Ser.). (Illus.). 654p. (Orig.). 1980. 22.95 (ISBN 0-88050-091-3). Chidvilas Found.

Let Go & Let God. A. E. Cliffe. 1951. pap. 5.95 (ISBN 0-13-531509-3). P-H.

Let Go, Let God. John E. Keller. LC 85-11048. 128p. 1985. pap. 6.95 (ISBN 0-8066-2162-1, 10-3815). Augsburg.

Let Go of the Ring. Ralph Moore & Dan Beach. (Religion Ser.). (Illus.). 150p. (Orig.). 1983. pap. 4.95 (ISBN 0-941018-10-5). Martin Pr CA.

Let God Be God: An Interpretation of the Theology of Martin Luther. Philip S. Watson. LC 83-45675. Date not set. Repr. of 1947 ed. 30.00 (ISBN 0-404-19864-3). AMS Pr.

Let God Love You. Lloyd Ogilvie. 1978. pap. 7.95 (ISBN 0-8499-2831-1, 2831-1). Word Bks.

Let It Begin in Me. R. Earl Allen. LC 84-19934. 1985. pap. 3.75 (ISBN 0-8054-5005-X). Broadman.

Let It Grow: Your Church Can Chart a New Course. Marvin G. Rickard. LC 84-22733. 1985. pap. 5.95 (ISBN 0-88070-074-2). Multnomah.

Let Judah Go up First: A Study in Praise, Prayer, & Worship. Roy B. Blizzard, Jr. 46p. (Orig.). 1984. pap. 3.50 (ISBN 0-918873-01-0). Ctr Judaic-Christ Studies.

Let Justice Roll Down. John M. Perkins. LC 74-30172. 224p. 1976. pap. 5.95 (ISBN 0-8307-0345-4, 5404002). Regal.

Let Me Be a Woman. Elisabeth Elliott. 1977. pap. 5.95 (ISBN 0-8423-2161-6); pap. 3.95 (ISBN 0-8423-2162-4). Tyndale.

Let Me Hear Your Voice: Portraits of Aging Immigrant Jews. Mimi Handlin & Marilyn S. Layton. LC 83-47974. (Illus.). 112p. 1984. 19.95 (ISBN 0-295-96039-6). U of Wash Pr.

Let Me Illustrate: Stories & Quotations for Christian Communicators. Albert P. Stauderman. LC 83-70511. 192p. (Orig.). 1983. pap. 9.95 (ISBN 0-8066-2017-X, 10-3817). Augsburg.

Let Me Introduce You to the Bible. William MacDonald. 1980. pap. 2.50 (ISBN 0-937396-22-2). Walterick Pubs.

Let Me Keep Laughter. Audre Pitts. 106p. 1986. pap. 3.95 (ISBN 0-8341-1090-3). Beacon Hill.

Let Me Out: I'm a Prisoner in a Stained Glass Jail. Wally Armbruster. LC 85-11561. 1985. pap. 6.95 (ISBN 0-88070-111-0). Multnomah.

Let Me Stand at Your Side. Basilea Schlink. 1975. 2.95 (ISBN 3-87209-614-1). Evang Sisterhood Mary.

Let Mercy Abound: Social Concern in the Greek Orthodox Church. Stanley S. Harakas. 188p. 1983. text ed. 18.95 (ISBN 0-686-90967-4); pap. text ed. 12.95 (ISBN 0-686-90968-2). Holy Cross Orthodox.

Let My People Go. Valarie Owen. 395p. (Orig.). 1983. pap. text ed. 9.95 (ISBN 0-914307-10-X, Dist. by Harrison Hse). Word Faith.

Let My People Go. Aiden W. Tozer. pap. 4.45 (ISBN 0-87509-189-X). Chr Pubns.

Let My People Go: Empowering Laity for Ministry. Alvin J. Lindgren & Norman Shawchuck. LC 80-16035. 144p. (Orig.). 1982. pap. 7.95 (ISBN 0-687-21377-0). Abingdon.

Let My People Live. Dagobert D. Runes. LC 74-75083. 84p. 1975. 6.00 (ISBN 0-8022-2141-6). Philos Lib.

Let No Man Put Asunder: The Control of Marriage in the German Southwest, 1550-1600. Thomas M. Safley. (Studies and Essays: Vol. II). 210p. 1984. 25.00x (ISBN 0-940474-02-6). Sixteenth Cent.

Let Not Your Heart Be Troubled. E. J. Saleska. 1945. 0.95 (ISBN 0-570-03676-3, 74-1001). Concordia.

Let Our Children Go! Ted Patrick & Tom Dulack. 1977. pap. 2.25 (ISBN 0-345-28343-0). Ballantine.

Let Peace & Justice Prevail. Mary-Angela Harper. 10p. 1977. 1.55 (ISBN 0-686-39920-X). Natl Cath Educ.

Let Peace Begin With Me: Peace Book. Mary Lou Kownacki & Carol Clark. 1983. pap. 1.00 (ISBN 0-89622-186-5). Twenty-Third.

Let Peace Begin With Me: Teacher Manual. Mary L. Kownacki & Carol Clark. 1983. pap. 2.95 (ISBN 0-89622-185-7). Twenty-Third.

Let Rome Speak for Herself. John E. Millheim. LC 82-16616. 1982. pap. 3.95. Reg Baptist.

Let the Bible Speak...About Tongues. Richard C. Schwab. LC 85-8098. (Illus.). 144p. (Orig.). 1985. pap. 6.95 (ISBN 0-8254-3753-9). Kregel.

Let the Children Come. Elizabeth B. Jones. 112p. 1980. pap. 2.95 (ISBN 0-8010-5102-9). Baker Bk.

Let the Children Come. Stewart R. McChesney. LC 81-67995. 1982. pap. 4.25 (ISBN 0-8054-4925-6). Broadman.

Let the Church Counsel Together. M. A. Tomlinson. 1978. pap. 3.25 (ISBN 0-934942-10-2). White Wing Pub.

Let the Earth Bless the Lord: A Christian Perspective on Land Use. Ed. by C. A. Cesaretti & Stephen Commins. 160p. (Orig.). 1981. pap. 6.95 (ISBN 0-8164-2296-6, HarpR). Har-Row.

Let the Earth Rejoice! William A. Dyrness. 192p. (Orig.). 1983. pap. 6.95 (ISBN 0-89107-282-9, Crossway Bks). Good News.

Let the Fire Fall. Michael Scanlan. 180p. 1986. pap. 6.95 (ISBN 0-89283-296-7). Servant.

Let the Hallelujahs Roll. Naomi Shaw. LC 76-52280. (YA) 1977. pap. 1.95 (ISBN 0-89221-028-1). New Leaf.

Let the Hammer Down. Jerry Clower. 1979. pap. 1.95 (ISBN 0-671-82626-3). PB.

Let the People Sing. Harold E. Hannum. Ed. by Tom Davis. 112p. 1981. pap. 7.95 (ISBN 0-8280-0029-8). Review & Herald.

Let Them Go Free: A Family Prayer Service & Guidelines for the Withdrawal of Life Support Systems. Thomas A. Shannon & Charles N. Faso. 1987. pap. 2.95. Paulist Pr.

Let There Be Light... Bernice Dittmer. Date not set. 40.00 (ISBN 0-930208-23-4). Mangan Bks.

Let There Be Light. Elizabeth S. Turner. 1954. 5.95 (ISBN 0-87159-085-9). Unity School.

Let There Be Light - Words of the Christ. Helena E. Ruhnau. (Illus.). 220p. (Orig.). 1987. pap. text ed. 9.95 (ISBN 0-941036-60-X). Colleasius Pr.

Let There Be Light: The Seven Keys. Rocco A. Errico. 180p. (Orig.). 1985. pap. 9.95 (ISBN 0-87516-555-9). De Vorss.

Let There Be Peace on Earth. (Chrysalis Bk). 128p. (Orig.). 1986. pap. 7.95 (ISBN 0-916349-00-4). Amity Hous Inc.

Let There Be Praise. Jerome Boone. (International Correspondence Program Ser.). 226p. (Orig.). pap. 6.95 (ISBN 0-87148-524-9). Pathway Pr.

Let This Cup Pass. Jane McWhorter. (Illus.). 1979. pap. 4.95 (ISBN 0-89137-414-0). Quality Pubns.

Let Us Abide. Judson Cornwall. LC 77-23143. 155p. 1984. pap. 4.95 (ISBN 0-8007-5065-9). Bridge Pub.

Let Us Be Holy. Judson Cornwall. LC 87-70993. 1978. pap. 4.95 (ISBN 0-88270-278-5). Bridge Pub.

Let Us Be What We Are. Clarence J. Enzler. 5.95 (ISBN 0-87193-136-2). Dimension Bks.

Let Us Draw Near. Judson Cornwall. LC 77-24832. 1977. pap. 4.95 (ISBN 0-88270-226-2, Pub. by Logos). Bridge Pub.

Let Us Draw Nigh. Andrew Murray. 1962. pap. 2.95 (ISBN 0-87508-379-X). Chr Lit.

Let Us Enjoy Forgiveness. Judson Cornwall. LC 78-8306. 159p. 1978. pap. 4.95 (ISBN 0-8007-5090-X). Bridge Pub.

Let Us Give. David McCord. 64p. 1986. pap. 2.95 (ISBN 0-87403-098-6, 3024). Standard Pub.

Let Us Give Thanks: Meal Prayers for All Occasions. Gary Boelhower et al. 42p. (Orig.). 1986. pap. 3.00 (ISBN 0-937997-04-8). Hi-Time Pub.

Let Us Love. Dale E. Rogers. 1982. 8.95 (ISBN 0-8499-0298-3). Word Bks.

Let Us Make Man: Self Esteem Through Jewishness. 208p. 1987. 14.95 (ISBN 0-933711-01-8). Traditional Pr.

Let Us Praise: A Prominent Charismatic Leader Tells How & Why to Praise God. Judson Cornwall. LC 73-75957. 1973. pap. 4.95 (ISBN 0-88270-039-1). Bridge Pub.

Let Us Pray. David McCord. 64p. 1986. pap. 2.95 (ISBN 0-87403-099-4, 3025). Standard Pub.

Let Us Pray. Watchman Nee. Tr. by Stephen Kaung from Chinese. 1977. pap. 2.50 (ISBN 0-935008-26-8). Christian Fellow Pubs.

Let Us Remember. David McCord. 64p. 1986. pap. 2.95 (ISBN 0-87403-071-4, 3023). Standard Pub.

Let Us See Jesus. Judson Cornwall. LC 80-20645. 160p. 1981. pap. 4.95 (ISBN 0-8007-5052-7). Bridge Pub.

Let Us Worship. Judson Cornwall. LC 82-74089. 1983. pap. 4.95 (ISBN 0-88270-542-3). Bridge Pub.

Let Wives Be Submissive: The Domestic Code in 1 Peter. David Balch. LC 80-21203. (Society of Biblical Literature Monograph). 196p. 1981. pap. 21.00 (ISBN 0-89130-429-0). Scholars Pr GA.

Let Yesterday Go. Mickey Jordan & Irene B. Harrell. LC 84-51995. 285p. 1984. pap. 6.00 (ISBN 0-915541-01-7). Star Bks Inc.

Let Your Light Shine. 64p. 1983. 3.75 (ISBN 0-317-36762-5). Forum Script.

Let Your Light So Shine. Ernest A. Miller. 218p. (Orig.). 1981. pap. 7.50 (ISBN 0-89216-046-2). Salvation Army.

Let Your Lives Speak. Elfrida V. Foulds. 1983. pap. 2.50x (ISBN 0-87574-071-5, 071). Pendle Hill.

Let Your Words Be Few: Symbolism of Speaking & Silence Among Seventeenth Century Quakers. Richard Bauman. LC 83-1982. (Cambridge Studies in Oral & Literate Culture Ser.: No. 8). 208p. 1984. 34.50 (ISBN 0-521-25506-6); pap. 10.95 (ISBN 0-521-27514-8). Cambridge U Pr.

Lethal Speech: Daribi Myth As Symbolic Obviation. Roy Wagner. LC 78-58049. (Symbol, Myth, & Ritual Ser). (Illus.). 272p. 1979. 27.50x (ISBN 0-8014-1193-9). Cornell U Pr.

Let's All Pray Together. Willlam J. Krutza. 128p. 1984. pap. 3.95 (ISBN 0-8170-1024-6). Judson.

Let's Be Friends. Gwendolyn Miller. 64p. 1971. pap. 1.50 (ISBN 0-87178-933-7). Brethren.

Let's Be Realistic about Your Church Budget. Douglas W. Johnson. 112p. 1984. pap. 3.95 (ISBN 0-8170-1025-4). Judson.

Let's Celebrate: Fifty-Seven Jewish Holiday Crafts for Young Children. Ruth E. Brinn. (Illus.). 72p. 1977. pap. 4.95 (ISBN 0-930494-02-4). Kar Ben.

Let's Choose Our Worship: Prayers for Women's Meetings. Church of Scotland, the Woman's Guild Staff. 1980. pap. 1.65 (ISBN 0-7152-0461-0). Outlook.

Let's Communicate. Roger Campbell. (Orig.). 1979. pap. 3.50 (ISBN 0-87508-060-X). Chr Lit.

Let's Count. Marilyn McAuley. (Peek & Find Bks.). (Illus.). 28p. 1984. board book 3.95 (ISBN 0-89191-879-5, 58792). Cook.

Let's Get Moving. D. Stuart Briscoe. LC 77-91773. 160p. 1978. pap. 3.50 (ISBN 0-8307-0538-4, S322102). Regal.

Let's Go to Church. Bessie Dean. LC 76-3995. (Books for Lds Children Ser.). (Illus.). 63p. 1976. pap. 3.95 (ISBN 0-88290-062-5). Horizon Utah.

Let's Go to Meherabad. Bhau Kalchuri. 120p. 1981. 10.95 (ISBN 0-940700-12-3); pap. 5.95 (ISBN 0-940700-11-5). Meher Baba Info.

Let's Go to Synagogue. Ceil Olivestone & David Olivestone. LC 81-516. (Illus.). 24p. 1981. 4.95 (ISBN 0-89961-018-8). SBS Pub.

Let's Go Witnessing. Frances Hunter. 1978. pap. 3.25 (ISBN 0-685-90803-8). Hunter Bks.

Let's Grow & Make Disciples! Charles L. Sattenfield. 92p. (Orig.). 1980. 2.75 (ISBN 0-88027-080-2). Firm Foun Pub.

Let's Have a Banquet: Or will One Dollar & thirtysix cents be Enough. Joyce Landorf. 1968. pap. 4.95 (ISBN 0-310-27131-2, 9994P). Zondervan.

Lets Have Church, Children, No. 1. Ernest Quinley & Rachel Quinley. 1981. pap. 7.95 (ISBN 0-87148-512-5). Pathway Pr.

Let's Have Church, Children, No. 2. Ernest Quinley & Rachel Quinley. 1981. pap. 7.95 (ISBN 0-87148-513-3). Pathway Pr.

Let's Learn About Jewish Symbols. Heidi Steinberger. LC 68-9347. (Illus.). 1969. pap. text ed. 6.00 (ISBN 0-8074-0144-7, 101035). UAHC.

Let's Learn God's Plan. Bessie Dean. LC 78-52114. (Illus.). 1978. pap. 3.95 (ISBN 0-88290-092-7). Horizon Utah.

Let's Learn of God's Love. Bessie Dean. LC 79-89367. (Books for LDS Children). (Illus.). 64p. 1979. pap. 3.95 (ISBN 0-88290-124-9). Horizon Utah.

Let's Learn the First Principles. Bessie Dean. LC 78-70366. (Books for LDS Children). (Illus.). 64p. 1978. pap. 3.95 (ISBN 0-88290-104-4). Horizon Utah.

Let's Listen to Jesus: Reflections on the Farewell Discourse. Reuben R. Welch. Ed. by Joseph D. Allison. 144p. (Orig.). 1985. pap. 5.95 (ISBN 0-310-75101-2, 17044P). Zondervan.

Let's Look at This the Right Way: A Guide for Christian Parents in Conflict with Their Teens. Theodore W. Schroeder. 112p. (Orig.). 1986. pap. 4.95 (ISBN 0-570-03987-8, 12-3015). Concordia.

Let's Love One Another. Bessie Dean. LC 77-74492. (Books for Lds Children Ser.). (Illus.). 64p. 1978. pap. 3.95 (ISBN 0-88290-077-3). Horizon Utah.

Let's Make a Memory. Shirley Dobson & Gloria Gaither. 1986. pap. write for info. Word Bks.

Let's Meet the Holy Spirit. Myer Pearlman. (Radiant Bks.). 64p. 1975. pap. 0.95 (ISBN 0-88243-565-5, 02-0565). Gospel Pub.

Let's Plan: A Guide to the Planning Process for Voluntary Organizations. John C. DeBoer. LC 72-124329. (Illus., Orig.). 1970. pap. 3.95 (ISBN 0-8298-0177-4). Pilgrim NY.

Let's Play Bible Detective. R. P. Daniel. 36p. pap. 2.95 (ISBN 0-88172-017-8). Believers Bkshelf.

Let's Pray: Fifty Services for Praying Communities. Charles Reutemann. LC 75-197. 1975. pap. 5.95 (ISBN 0-9600824-1-7). St Marys.

Let's Pray Together: Studies in Prayer. Margaret Fromer & Sharrel Keyes. LC 74-76160. (Fisherman Bible Studyguide Ser.). 63p. 1974. saddle-stitched 2.95 (ISBN 0-87788-801-9). Shaw Pubs.

Let's Pray Two. Charles Reutemann. LC 82-60612. (Illus.). 224p. (Orig.). 1982. pap. 6.95 (ISBN 0-88489-148-8). St Mary's.

Let's Read the Old Testament. Raymond Brown. 1972. pap. 2.95 (ISBN 0-87508-034-0). Chr Lit.

Let's Share Jesus-Together. Wesley T. Runk. 1982. 4.50 (ISBN 0-89536-554-5, 1243). CSS of Ohio.

Let's Sing Together. Ed. by Walford Davies. 25.00x (ISBN 0-946095-14-0, Pub. by Gresham England); pap. 20.00x (ISBN 0-946095-13-2, Pub. by Gresham England). State Mutual Bk.

Let's Sing Together: Favorite Primary Songs of Members of the Church of Jesus Christ of Latter-day Saints. Ed. by Frances B. Perry. (Illus.). 96p. 1981. 10.98 (ISBN 0-941518-00-0). Perry Enterprises.

Let's Study Greek. rev. ed. Clarence B. Hale. LC 82-3619. 1982. 14.95 (ISBN 0-8024-4666-3). Moody.

Let's Talk about Church Staff Relationships. Ronald W. Wiebe & Bruce A. Rowlison. 64p. 1983. pap. 3.95 (ISBN 0-938462-12-1). Green Leaf CA.

Let's Talk About Jesus. Gladys Seashore. (Illus.). 1978. pap. 1.75 (ISBN 0-911802-40-1). Free Church Pubns.

Let's Talk about Sex: The Truth & God's Power to Live It. rev. ed. Larry Tomczak. 123p. 1987. pap. 4.95 (ISBN 0-89283-353-X, Pub. by Vine Books). Servant.

Lets Talk about the Jewish Holidays. Dorothy K. Kripke. 1982. pap. 5.95 (ISBN 0-8246-0267-6). Jonathan David.

Let's Talk it Over God! Hattie Smith. LC 84-50077. 105p. 1984. 5.95 (ISBN 0-938232-46-0). Winston-Derek.

Let's Try This Way. Clifford Fuller. pap. 1.00 (ISBN 0-87516-196-0). De Vorss.

Letter. Donald M. Smith. Ed. by Diane Parker et al. LC 83-91201. (Illus.). 217p. 20.00 (ISBN 0-914731-00-9). DMS Publishing Co.

Letter-Book of Samuel Sewall, 1685-1729, 2 vols. Samuel Sewall. LC 75-31101. Repr. of 1838 ed. 67.50 set (ISBN 0-404-13580-3). AMS Pr.

Letter Excerpts, Statements on Christian Science. Herbert W. Eustace. 36p. 1976. pap. 3.00 (ISBN 0-9611156-1-0). Eustace CSB.

Letter of Consolation. Henri J. Nouwen. LC 81-48212. 96p. 1982. 10.45 (ISBN 0-686-81488-6, HarpR). Har-Row.

Letter of Jesus Christ. John Of Landsburg. Ed. by John Griffiths. LC 81-126. (Spiritual Classics Ser.). 176p. 1981. 9.95 (ISBN 0-8245-0080-6). Crossroad NY.

Letter of John to James. John Kater. (Illus.). 64p. (Orig.). 1981. pap. 3.95 (ISBN 0-8164-2344-X, HarpR). Har-Row.

Letter of Meric Casaubon to Peter du Moulin Concerning Natural Experimental Philosophie. Meric Casaubon. LC 76-47045. 1976. Repr. of 1669 ed. 90.00x (ISBN 0-8201-1284-4). Schol Facsimiles.

Letter of Paul to the Galatians. William Neil. (Cambridge Commmentary on the New English Bible, New Testament Ser.). (Orig.). 1967. pap. 6.95x (ISBN 0-521-09402-X). Cambridge U Pr.

Letter of Paul to the Romans: Cambridge Bible Commentary on the New English Bible. Ed. by Ernest Best. (New Testament Ser.). (Orig.). 1967. 21.95 (ISBN 0-521-04213-5); pap. 8.95x (ISBN 0-521-09401-1, 401). Cambridge U Pr.

Letter of Peter to Philip. Marvin W. Meyer. Ed. by Howard C. Kee. LC 80-28612. (Society of Biblical Literature Dissertation Ser.). 1981. pap. text ed. 13.50 (ISBN 0-89130-463-0, 06-01-53). Scholars Pr GA.

Letter of Private Direction. Ed. by John Griffiths. LC 81-126. (Spiritual Classics Ser.). 176p. 1981. 9.95 (ISBN 0-8245-0081-4). Crossroad NY.

Letter of Private Direction. Tr. by James Walsh. 1979. pap. 5.95 (ISBN 0-87243-083-9). Templegate.

Letter of Unity: A Woman's Workshop on Ephesians. Martha Hook. (Woman's Workshop Ser.). 1987. Leader's Guide, 80p. pap. 4.95 (ISBN 0-310-26181-3); Student's Guide, 64p. pap. 3.95 (ISBN 0-310-26191-0). Zondervan.

Letter: The Crucifixion by an Eye Witness. 7th ed. Ed. by James M. Harvey. LC 70-186124. (Supplemental Harmonic Ser.: Vol. 4). 107p. 1972. pap. 3.95 (ISBN 0-686-01242-9). Harvey J M.

Letter to Pilgrims. Robert Jewett. LC 80-28102. 244p. (Orig.). 1981. pap. 7.95 (ISBN 0-8298-0425-0). Pilgrim NY.

Letter to the Colossians: A Commentary. Edward Schweizer. Tr. by Andrew Chester. LC 81-65657. 352p. (Orig.). 1982. pap. 14.95 (ISBN 0-8066-1893-0, 10-3823). Augsburg.

Letter to the Hebrews. Ed. by J. H. Davies. (Cambridge Bible Commentary on the New English Bible, New Testament Ser.). 1967. 16.95 (ISBN 0-521-04222-4); pap. 9.95x (ISBN 0-521-09408-9). Cambridge U Pr.

Letter to the Pope on His Visit to Auschwitz. Leon Degrelle. 1982. lib. bdg. 59.95 (ISBN 0-87700-346-7). Revisionist Pr.

Letter to Titus. William MacDonald. pap. 2.50 (ISBN 0-937396-46-X). Walterick Pubs.

Letter Writing in Greco-Roman Antiquity. Stanley K. Stowers. LC 86-9082. (Library of Early Christianity: Vol. 5). 192p. 1986. 18.95 (ISBN 0-664-21909-8). Westminster.

Letters. Saint Bernard de Clairvaux. Tr. by Bruno S. James. LC 78-63344. (Crusades & Military Orders: Second Ser.). Repr. of 1953 ed. 47.50 (ISBN 0-404-17004-8). AMS Pr.

Letters. Joel S. Goldsmith. 299p. 1980. pap. 5.95 (ISBN 0-87516-386-6). De Vorss.

Letters, Nos. 1-82. St. Augustine. LC 64-19948. (Fathers of the Church Ser.: Vol. 12). 420p. 1951. 22.95x (ISBN 0-8132-0012-1). Cath U Pr.

Letters, Nos. 1-185. St. Basil. (Fathers of the Church Ser.: Vol. 13). 345p. 1951. 18.95x (ISBN 0-8132-0013-X). Cath U Pr.

Letters, Nos. 131-164. St. Augustine. (Fathers of the Church Ser.: Vol. 20). 398p. 1953. 34.95x (ISBN 0-8132-0020-2). Cath U Pr.

Letters, Nos. 83-130. St. Augustine. LC 64-19948. (Fathers of the Church Ser.: Vol. 18). 401p. 1953. 34.95x (ISBN 0-8132-0018-0). Cath U Pr.

Letters, Nos. 186-368. St. Basil. LC 65-18318. (Fathers of the Church Ser.: Vol. 28). 369p. 1955. 19.95x (ISBN 0-8132-0028-8). Cath U Pr.

Letters Addressed to the Daughter of a Nobleman on the Formation of the Religious & the Moral Principle, 2 vols. Elizabeth Hamilton. Ed. by Gina Luria. (Feminist Controversy in England, 1788-1810 Ser.). 1974. Set. lib. bdg. 121.00 (ISBN 0-8240-0865-0). Garland Pub.

Letters & Charters of Gilbert Foliot. G. Foliot. Ed. by A. Morey & C. N. Brooke. 1967. Cambridge U Pr.

Letters & Diaries of John Henry Cardinal Newman: Consulting the Laity, January 1859-June 1861, Vol. 19. John H. Newman. 38.50x (ISBN 0-19-920051-3). Oxford U Pr.

Letters & Diaries of John Henry Cardinal Newman: Ealing, Trinity, Oriel, February 1801 to December 1826, Vol. I. John H. Newman. Ed. by Ian Ker & Thomas Gornall. 1978. 52.00x (ISBN 0-19-920102-1). Oxford U Pr.

Letters & Diaries of John Henry Cardinal Newman: The Oxford Movement, July 1833 to December 1834, Vol. IV. John H. Newman. Ed. by Ian Ker & Thomas Gornall. 1980. 55.00x (ISBN 0-19-920112-9). Oxford U Pr.

Letters & Diaries of John Henry Newman: A Cardinal's Apostolate, October 1881-December 1884, Vol. 30. John H. Newman. Ed. by Charles S. Dessain. 1976. 47.00x (ISBN 0-19-920060-2). Oxford U Pr.

Letters & Diaries of John Henry Newman: New Bearings, January 1832 to June 1833, Vol. 3. John H. Newman. Ed. by Ian Ker & Thomas Gornall. 1979. 52.00x (ISBN 0-19-920109-9). Oxford U Pr.

Letters & Diaries of John Henry Newman: Standing Firm Amid Trials, July 1861-December 1863, Vol. 20. John H. Newman. 38.50x (ISBN 0-19-920052-1). Oxford U Pr.

Letters & Diaries of John Henry Newman: The Cardinalate, January 1878-September 1881, Vol. 29. John H. Newman. Ed. by Charles S. Dessain & Thomas Gornall. 1976. 47.00x (ISBN 0-19-920059-9). Oxford U Pr.

Letters & Diaries of John Henry Newman: The Last Years, January 1885 to August 1890, Vol.31. John H. Newman. Ed. by Charles S. Dessain & Thomas Gornall. 1977. 52.00x (ISBN 0-19-920083-1). Oxford U Pr.

Letters & Diaries of John Henry Newman: Tutor of Oriel, January 1827 to December 1831, Vol. II. John H. Newman. Ed. by Ian Ker & Thomas Gornall. 1979. 55.00x (ISBN 0-19-920108-0). Oxford U Pr.

Letters & Diaries of John Henry Newman. John H. Newman. Ed. by Charles S. Dessain & Thomas Gornall. Incl. Vol. 23. Defeat at Oxford-Defence at Rome, January to December 1867. 38.50x (ISBN 0-19-920040-8); Vol. 24. A Grammar of Ascent, January 1868 to December 1869. 38.50x (ISBN 0-19-920043-2); Vol. 25. The Vatican Council, January 1870 to December 1871. 42.00x (ISBN 0-19-920055-6); Vol. 26. Aftermaths, January 1872 to December 1873. 42.00x (ISBN 0-19-920056-4). 1973. Oxford U Pr.

Letters & Diaries of John Henry Newman, Vols. 27 & 28. John H. Newman. Ed. by Stephen Dessain & Thomas Gornall. Incl. Vol. 27. Controversy with Gladstone, January 1874-December 1875 (ISBN 0-19-920057-2); Vol. 28. Fellow of Trinity, January 1876-December 1878 (ISBN 0-19-920058-0). 1975. 38.50x ea. Oxford U Pr.

Letters & Lectures of Idries Shah. Ed. by Adam Musa. 40p. 1981. pap. 4.95 (ISBN 0-86304-010-1, Pub. by Octagon Pr England). Ins Study Human.

Letters & Memorials of Emanuel Swedenborg, Vols. I & II. Ed. & tr. by Alfred Acton. 1948. Set. 17.00 (ISBN 0-915221-04-7); Vol. I, 1709-1748, 508p. 9.00 (ISBN 0-915221-29-2); Vol. II, 1748-1772, 803p. 8.00 (ISBN 0-915221-30-6). Swedenborg Sci Assn.

Letters & Papers from Prison. enl. ed. Dietrich Bonhoeffer. 1972. pap. 7.95 (ISBN 0-02-083920-0, Collier). Macmillan.

Letters & Religion. John J. Chapman. 1977. Repr. 29.00x (ISBN 0-403-07361-8). Scholarly.

Letters, Compiled from the Original Manuscripts & Edited with Historical Notes, 4 vols. Jean Calvin. Ed. by Jules Bonnet. Tr. by M. R. Gilchrist & David Constable. LC 70-185936. 1973. Repr. of 1858 ed. Set. 110.00 (ISBN 0-8337-4021-0). B Franklin.

Letters Concerning Mythology. Thomas Blackwell. LC 75-27887. (Renaissance & the Gods Ser.: Vol. 42). (Illus.). 1976. Repr. of 1748 ed. lib. bdg. 88.00 (ISBN 0-8240-2091-X). Garland Pub.

Letters Concerning the English Nation. Voltaire. LC 74-728. 224p. 1974. Repr. of 1926 ed. lib. bdg. 19.00 (ISBN 0-8337-4467-4). B Franklin.

Letters Concerning the Spread of the Gospel. Samuel S. Haury. 50p. 1982. pap. 3.95 (ISBN 0-8361-1252-0). Herald Pr.

Letters for God's Name. Gail Ramshaw-Schmidt. (Illus.). 1984. pap. 4.95 (ISBN 0-86683-880-5, 7458, HarpR). Har-Row.

Letters from a Hermit. William Paulsell & Matthew Kelty. 1978. 7.95 (ISBN 0-87243-086-3). Templegate.

Letters from a Roman Catholic. Carolynne Simms. 27p. 1987. pap. 3.00 (ISBN 0-911826-11-4). Am Atheist.

Letters from an Understanding Friend: Jesus on the Way to Jerusalem. Isaias Powers. 112p. (Orig.). 1985. pap. 4.95 (ISBN 0-89622-215-2). Twenty-Third.

Letters from Egypt & Palestine. Maltbie D. Babcock. Ed. by Moshe Davis. LC 77-70662. (America & the Holy Land Ser.). (Illus.). 1977. Repr. of 1902 ed. lib. bdg. 19.00x (ISBN 0-405-10223-2). Ayer Co Pubs.

Letters from Ireland, 1228-1229. Tr. by Barry W. O'Dwyer from Lat. (Cistercian Fathers Ser.: No. 28). Orig. Title: Registrum epistolarum Stephani de Lexinton abbatis de Stannlegia et de Saviagnaco. 1982. 24.95 (ISBN 0-87907-428-0). Cistercian Pubns.

Letters from Peter. Bruce Oberst. LC 74-1071. (Bible Study Textbook Ser.). (Illus.). 1962. 10.60 (ISBN 0-89900-046-0). College Pr Pub.

Letters from Srila Prabhupada, Vol. 1. Satsvarupa Das Goswami. Ed. by Mandalesvara dasa & Gaura Purnima dasa. 274p. (Orig.). 1982. pap. text ed. 3.95 (ISBN 0-911233-03-2). Gita Nagari.

Letters from the Desert. Carlo Carretto. 1976. pap. write for info (ISBN 0-515-09573-7). Jove Pubns.

Letters from the Heart: Christian Monasticism & the Renewal of Community. John Main. 1982. pap. 6.95 (ISBN 0-8245-0444-5). Crossroad NY.

Letters from the Mandali of Avatar Meher Baba, Vol 1. Compiled by Jim Mistry. LC 83-142831. 152p. (Orig.). 1981. pap. 6.75 (ISBN 0-913078-42-5). Sheriar Pr.

Letters from the Mandali of Avatar Meher Baba, Vol. 2. Jim Mistry. LC 83-142831. 176p. (Orig.). 1983. pap. 7.95 (ISBN 0-913078-46-8). Sheriar Pr.

Letters From the Masters of the Wisdom. Jinarajadasa. (Series 1). 3.50 (ISBN 0-8356-7135-6). Theos Pub Hse.

Letters From the Masters of Wisdom. Jinarajadasa. (Series 2). 3.50 (ISBN 0-8356-7311-1). Theos Pub Hse.

Letters from the Mughal Court: The First Jesuit Mission to Akbar (1580-1583) Ed. & tr. by John Correia-Afonso. LC 81-81766. (Jesuit Primary Sources in English Translation Ser.: No. 4). (Illus.). 150p. 1982. 9.00 (ISBN 0-912422-57-2). Inst Jesuit.

Letters from the Ursuline 1852-1853. Ed. by Catherine McDowell. LC 77-85460. 1978. boxed 20.00 (ISBN 0-911536-69-8); 18.00. Trinity U Pr.

Letters from Westerbork. Etty Hillesum. Tr. by Arnold Pomerans. LC 86-42625. (Dutch.). 160p. 1986. 14.95 (ISBN 0-394-55350-0). Pantheon.

Letters I Never Wrote, Conversations I Never Had: Dealing with Unresolved Grief & Anger. Charles B. Bissell, III. 58p. (Orig.). 1983. pap. 4.95 (ISBN 0-9612604-0-8). C Bissell.

Letters in Primitive Christianity. William G. Doty. Ed. by Dan O. Via, Jr. LC 72-87058. (Guides to Biblical Scholarship: New Testament Ser.). 96p. 1973. pap. 4.50 (ISBN 0-8006-0170-X, 1-170). Fortress.

Letters, Nineteen Sixty-One to Nineteen Sixty-Eight. Karl Barth. Ed. by Jurgen Fangmeier & Hinrich Stoevesand. LC 80-29140. pap. 99.50 (ISBN 0-317-41616-2, 2023208). Bks Demand UMI.

Letters of A. W. Pink. A. W. Pink. 1978. pap. 2.95 (ISBN 0-85151-262-3). Banner of Truth.

Letters of Adam of Perseigne. Tr. by Grace Perigo. LC 76-15486. (Cistercian Father Ser.: No. 21). 1976. 11.95 (ISBN 0-87907-621-6). Cistercian Pubns.

Letters of Armand Jean de Rance Abbot & Reformer of La Trappe, 2 vols. Ed. by A. J. Krailsheimer. Vol. I. 25.00; Vol. II. 25.00. Cistercian Pubns.

Letters of C. S. Lewis. Ed. by W. H. Lewis. LC 74-13416. (Illus.). 308p. 1975. pap. 5.95 (ISBN 0-15-650870-2, Harv). HarBraceJ.

Letters of Francis A. Schaeffer: Spiritual Reality in the Personal Christian Life. Ed. by Lane T. Dennis. LC 85-70473. 264p. (Orig.). 1986. 15.95 (ISBN 0-89107-361-2, Crossway Bks); pap. 7.95 (ISBN 0-89107-409-0, Crossway Bks). Good News.

Letters of H. P. Blavatsky to A. P. Sinnett. facsimile of 1925 ed. Compiled by A. Trevor Barker. LC 73-84138. 1973. 12.00 (ISBN 0-911500-23-5). Theos U Pr.

Letters of Helena Roerich, Vol. I. 1979. Repr. of 1954 ed. flexible cover 16.00 (ISBN 0-933574-14-2). Agni Yoga Soc.

Letters of Helena Roerich, Vol. II. 1982. Repr. of 1967 ed. index 16.00 (ISBN 0-933574-15-0). Agni Yoga Soc.

Letters of J. N. Darby, 3 vols. J. N. Darby. Set. 18.95 (ISBN 0-88172-061-5); 6.95 ea. Believers Bkshelf.

Letters of Jews Through the Ages, Vol. 1. Ed. by Franz Kobler. 1978. pap. 7.95 (ISBN 0-85222-212-2, East & West Lib). Hebrew Pub.

Letters of Jews Through the Ages, Vol. 2. Franz Kobler. 1978. pap. 7.95 (ISBN 0-85222-213-0, East & West Lib). Hebrew Pub.

Letters of John & James. Ed. by Ronald R. Williams. (Cambridge Bible Commentary on the New English Bible, New Testament Ser.). (Orig.). 1965. 17.95 (ISBN 0-521-04206-2); pap. 8.95 (ISBN 0-521-09250-7, 250). Cambridge U Pr.

Letters of John & Jude. W. Donald Reeder. (Teach Yourself the Bible Ser.). 1965. pap. 2.75 (ISBN 0-8024-4674-4). Moody.

Letters of John Davenport, Puritan Divine. John Davenport. Ed. by Isabel M. Calder. 1937. 65.00x (ISBN 0-685-69794-0). Elliots Bks.

Letters of John Newton. John Newton. 1976. pap. 3.95 (ISBN 0-85151-120-1). Banner of Truth.

Letters of John the Apostle. Donald W. Burdick. (Orig.). 1985. pap. 13.95 (ISBN 0-8024-2356-6). Moody.

Letters of Ludwig Tieck, Hitherto Unpublished, 1792-1853. Johann L. Tieck. Ed. by Edwin H. Zeydel et al. LC 73-9682. (MLA Gen. Ser.: No. 7). 636p. 1973. Repr. of 1937 ed. 41.00 (ISBN 0-527-90100-8). Kraus Repr.

Letters of Maimonides. 1982. pap. 7.95 (ISBN 0-686-76539-7). Feldheim.

Letters of Narcissa Whitman. Narcissa P. Whitman. 245p. 1986. 14.95 (ISBN 0-87770-386-8). Ye Galleon.

Letters of Paul: Complete Outlines & Notes on the Epistles of Paul. P. C. Nelson. 144p. 1976. pap. 2.00 (ISBN 0-88243-546-9, 02-0546). Gospel Pub.

Letters of Paul: Conversations in Context. 2nd ed. Calvin J. Roetzel. LC 81-85334. (Biblical Foundations Ser.). 144p. 1982. pap. 9.95 (ISBN 0-8042-0209-5). John Knox.

Letters of Paul, Hebrews & Psalms. Arthur S. Way. LC 81-1092. 504p. 1981. text ed. 14.95 (ISBN 0-8254-4016-5). Kregel.

Letters of Paul to the Ephesians, Colossians & Philemon. G. H. Thompson. (Cambridge Bible Commentary on the New English Bible, New Testament Ser.). 18.95 (ISBN 0-521-04227-5); pap. 9.95x (ISBN 0-521-09410-0, 410). Cambridge U Pr.

Letters of Peter & Jude. Alfred R. Leaney. (Cambridge Bible Commentary on the New English Bible, New Testament Ser.). (Orig.). 16.95 (ISBN 0-521-04216-X); pap. 8.95x (ISBN 0-521-09403-8). Cambridge U Pr.

Letters of Peter the Venerable, 2 Vols. Peter The Venerable. Ed. by Giles Constable. LC 67-10086. (Historical Studies: No. 78). 1967. Set. 55.00x (ISBN 0-674-52775-5). Harvard U Pr.

Letters of Rebecca Gratz. facsimile ed. Rebecca Gratz. LC 74-27987. (Modern Jewish Experience Ser.). 1975. Repr. of 1929 ed. 38.50x (ISBN 0-405-06714-3). Ayer Co Pubs.

Letters of Saint Boniface. Saint Boniface. Ed. by Ephraim Emerton. 1967. lib. bdg. 21.50x (ISBN 0-374-92584-4, Octagon). Hippocrene Bks.

Letters of St. Cyprian, Vol. 1. Tr. by Graehme W. Clarke. (Ancient Christian Writers Ser.: No. 43). 416p. 1983. 24.95 (ISBN 0-8091-0341-9). Paulist Pr.

Letters of St. Cyprian, Vol. 2. Tr. by Graeme W. Clarke. (Ancient Christian Writers Ser.: No. 44). 352p. 1983. 22.95 (ISBN 0-8091-0342-7). Paulist Pr.

Letters of St. Cyprian: Vol. 3, Letters 55-66. Ed. by Graeme W. Clarke. (ACW Ser.: No. 46). 352p. 1986. 24.95 (ISBN 0-8091-0369-9). Paulist Pr.

Letters of Saint Ignatius of Loyola. Saint Ignatius of Loyola. Ed. by William J. Young. LC 59-13459. 1959. 8.95 (ISBN 0-8294-0085-0). Loyola.

Letters of Saint Jerome, Vol. 1. Saint Jerome. Ed. by Quasten & Burqhardt. (Ancient Christian Writers Ser: Vol. 33). 1963. 11.95 (ISBN 0-8091-0087-8). Paulist Pr.

Letters of Saint Paulinus of Nola. Saint Paulinus of Nola. Ed. by Quasten & Burqhardt. (Ancient Christian Writers Ser.: Nos. 35-36). Vol. 1. 11.95 (ISBN 0-8091-0088-6); Vol. 2. 13.95 (ISBN 0-8091-0089-4). Paulist Pr.

Letters of St. Teresa, 4 vols. Saint Teresa. Ed. by Cardinal Gasquet. 1977. Set. lib. bdg. 400.00 (ISBN 0-8490-2154-5). Gordon Pr.

Letters of Samuel Rutherford. Samuel Rutherford. 1985. Repr. 17.95 (ISBN 0-85151-388-3). Banner of Truth.

Letters of Sir Thomas Copley to Queen Elizabeth & Her Ministers. Thomas Copley. Ed. by Richard C. Christie. LC 74-80263. (Research & Source Works Ser.: No. 631). 1971. Repr. lib. bdg. 32.00 (ISBN 0-8337-0655-1). B Franklin.

Letters of Still. William Still. (Religious Ser.). 192p. (Orig.). 1984. pap. 5.95x (ISBN 0-85151-378-6). Banner of Truth.

Letters on Demonology & Witchcraft. Walter Scott. 1887. Repr. 25.00 (ISBN 0-8274-2850-2). R West.

Letters on the Healing Ministry. Albert E. Day & James K. Wagner. 144p. 1986. pap. 6.95 incl. study guide (ISBN 0-317-30215-9, ICN 606462, Dist. by Abingdon Pr). Upper Room.

Letters on the Spanish Inquisition. Tr. by Joseph M. De Maistre. LC 77-24949. 1977. Repr. of 1843 ed. 35.00x (ISBN 0-8201-1293-3). Schol Facsimiles.

Letters on Yoga, Vol. I. Sri Aurobindo. 502p. 1979. 16.00 (ISBN 0-89744-984-3, Pub. by Sri Aurogindo Ashram Trust); pap. 12.00 (ISBN 0-89744-985-1). Auromere.

Letters on Yoga, Vol. III. Sri Aurobindo. 720p. 1979. 22.00 (ISBN 0-89744-988-6, Pub. by Sri Aurobindo Ashram Trust); pap. 19.00 (ISBN 0-89744-989-4). Auromere.

Letters on Yoga, Vol. II. Sri Aurobindo. 587p. 1979. 19.00 (ISBN 0-89744-986-X, Pub. by Sri Arobindo Ashram Trust); pap. 16.00 (ISBN 0-89744-987-8). Auromere.

Letters on Yoga, 2 vols. Sri Aurobindo. (Life Companion Library Bible Paper Ser.). 1984p. 40.00 (ISBN 0-89744-014-5). Auromere.

Letters on Yoga, 3 vols. Sri Aurobindo. 1979. Vol. 1. 11.25 (ISBN 0-89071-236-0); Vol. 2. 12.50 (ISBN 0-89071-238-7); Vol. 3. 14.50 (ISBN 0-89071-240-9); Vol. 1. pap. 10.00 (ISBN 0-89071-237-9); Vol. 2. pap. 11.25 (ISBN 0-89071-239-5); Vol. 3. pap. 12.50 (ISBN 0-89071-241-7). Matagiri.

Letters, Principal Doctrines, & Vatican Sayings: Epicurus. Russell Geer. 1964. pap. text ed. write for info. (ISBN 0-02-341200-3). Macmillan.

Letters That Have Helped Me. William Q. Judge. Ed. & intro. by Jasper Niemand. (Illus.). x, 300p. 1946. 6.00 (ISBN 0-938998-08-0). Theosophy.

Letters to a Devastated Christian. Gene Edwards. 68p. 1983. pap. 3.95 (ISBN 0-940232-13-8). Christian Bks.

Letters to a New Elder: The Melchizedek Priesthood, Its Duty & Fulfillment. Robb Russon. pap. 2.95 (ISBN 0-89036-144-4). Hawkes Pub Inc.

Letters to a Retired Couple. David Mace & Vera Mace. 160p. 1984. pap. 6.95 (ISBN 0-8170-1005-X). Judson.

Letters to a Roman Catholic Priest. H. A. Ironside. pap. 1.25 (ISBN 0-87213-349-4). Loizeaux.

Letters to a Soul. Hubert Van Zeller. 1976. 7.95 (ISBN 0-87243-067-7). Templegate.

Letters to a Young Bride. Ruth H. Calkin. 112p. 1985. 10.95 (ISBN 0-8423-2134-9). Tyndale.

Letters to an American Jewish Friend: A Zionist's Polemic. Hillel Halkin. LC 76-58650. 246p. 1977. pap. 6.95 (ISBN 0-8276-0207-3, 402). Jewish Pubns.

Letters to an Ex-Priest. Emmett McLoughlin. 1965. 4.95 (ISBN 0-8184-0050-1). Lyle Stuart.

Letters to Eva in Heaven. Russell Shull. 3.95 (ISBN 0-910924-51-1). Macalester.

Letters to Malcolm: Chiefly on Prayer. C. S. Lewis. LC 64-11536. 124p. 1973. pap. 3.95 (ISBN 0-15-650880-X, Harv). HarBraceJ.

Letters to Margaret Bridges. John Masefield. Ed. by Donald Stanford. 123p. 1984. 18.50 (ISBN 0-85635-477-5). Carcanet.

Letters to My Little Sisters. Jami L. Buchanan. LC 84-27612. (Orig.). 1985. pap. 3.95 (ISBN 0-8307-0999-1, S185100). Regal.

Letters to Philip. Charlie W. Shedd. (Orig.). 1985. pap. 2.95 (ISBN 0-515-08465-4). Jove Pubns.

Letters to Philip. Charlie W. Shedd. 128p. 1969. pap. 2.95 (ISBN 0-8007-8025-6, Spire Bks). Revell.

Letters to Scattered Pilgrims. Elizabeth O'Connor. LC 78-3361. 176p. 1982. (HarpR); pap. 8.95 (ISBN 0-06-066334-0, RD-374). Har-Row.

Letters to Serena. John Toland. Ed. by Rene Wellek. LC 75-11259. (British Philosophers & Theologians of the 17th & 18th Centuries: Vol. 58). 295p. 1976. Repr. of 1704 ed. lib. bdg. 51.00 (ISBN 0-8240-1809-5). Garland Pub.

Letters to the Martyrs. facs. ed. Helen Homan. LC 79-148220. (Biography Index Reprint Ser.). 1951. 20.00 (ISBN 0-8369-8067-0). Ayer Co Pubs.

Letters to the Modern Church. Wayne Hoffman. LC 79-88401. 1979. pap. 3.75 (ISBN 0-933350-23-6). Morse Pr.

Letters to the Now Generation. Joseph R. Narot. pap. 1.95 (ISBN 0-686-15801-6). Rostrum Bks.

Letters to the People on Health & Happiness. Catherine E. Beecher. (Works of Catherine E. Beecher Ser.). vi, 222p. Repr. of 1855 ed. lib. bdg. 29.00 (ISBN 0-932051-03-0, Pub by Am Repr Serv). Am Biog Serv.

Letters to the Right Rev. John Hughes, Roman Catholic Bishop of New York. Nicholas Murray. Ed. by Gerald Grob. LC 76-46091. (Anti-Movements in America). 1977. Repr. of 1855 ed. 29.00 (ISBN 0-405-09964-9). Ayer Co Pubs.

Letters to the Seven Churches. William Barclay. LC 82-2760. 128p. 1982. pap. 6.95 (ISBN 0-664-24433-5). Westminster.

Letters to the Seven Churches. William M. Ramsay. (William M. Ramsay Library). 476p. 1985. pap. 12.95 (ISBN 0-8010-7681-1). Baker Bk.

Letters to the Seven Churches of Asia in Their Local Setting. C. J. Hemer. (JSoT Supplement Ser.: No. 11). 375p. 1986. text ed. 32.50x (ISBN 0-905774-95-7, Pub. by JSOT Pr England); pap. text ed. 14.95x (ISBN 0-905774-96-5). Eisenbrauns.

Letters to the Thessalonians. Margaret Fromer & Sharrel Keyes. LC 75-33441. (Fisherman Bible Studyguide Ser.). 47p. 1975. saddle-stitched 2.95 (ISBN 0-87788-489-7). Shaw Pubs.

Letters to the Thessalonians. rev. ed. William McDonald. 1982. pap. 3.50 (ISBN 0-937396-43-5). Walterick Pubs.

Letters to Timothy. Gary Leggett. LC 80-82830. (Radiant Life Ser.). 128p. (Orig.). 1981. 2.50 (ISBN 0-88243-877-8, 02-0877); teacher's ed. 3.95 (ISBN 0-88243-189-7, 32-0189). Gospel Pub.

Letters to Timothy: Discipleship in Action. Margaret Fromer & Sharrel Keyes. LC 74-19763. (Fisherman Bible Study Guide Ser.). 80p. 1974. saddle-stitched 2.95 (ISBN 0-87788-490-0). Shaw Pubs.

Letters to Young People: A World Spiritual Legacy for Our Future Earth. Ed. by Richard Payne. (Patterns of World Spirituality Ser.). 240p. pap. 9.95 (ISBN 0-913757-72-1). Paragon Hse.

Letters, 1-50. St. Cyril of Alexandria. (Fathers of the Church: Vol. 76). 350p. 1987. 29.95x (ISBN 0-8132-0076-8). Cath U Pr.

Letters: 165-203. St. Augustine. (Fathers of the Church Ser.: Vol. 30). 421p. 1955. 21.95x (ISBN 0-8132-0030-X). Cath U Pr.

Letters: 204-270. St. Augustine. (Fathers of the Church Ser.: Vol. 32). 317p. 1956. 17.95x (ISBN 0-8132-0032-6). Cath U Pr.

Letting Go: A Holistic & Meditative Approach to Living & Dying. Richard W. Boerstler. LC 81-71653. (Illus.). 112p. (Orig.). 1982. pap. 3.95 (ISBN 0-9607928-0-5). Assocs Thanatology.

Letting Go with Love: The Grieving Process. Nancy O'Connor. LC 84-61538. 186p. 1985. 18.95x (ISBN 0-9613714-1-2); pap. 9.95x (ISBN 0-9613714-0-4). La Mariposa.

Letting the Lion Loose. Eric W. Hayden. 1984. pap. 3.95 (ISBN 0-907927-05-X). Pilgrim Pubns.

Lettre a M. d'Alembert sur les Spectacles. Jean-Jacques Rousseau. 208p. 1948. 7.95 (ISBN 0-686-55352-7). French & Eur.

Lettres Escrites a un Provincial. Blaise Pascal & Antoine Adam. 320p. 1967. 4.50 (ISBN 0-686-54847-7). French & Eur.

Lettres Philosophiques. Voltaire. Ed. by Rene Pomeau. 192p. 1964. 18.95 (ISBN 0-686-55754-9). French & Eur.

Leveller Movement. T. C. Pease. 11.75 (ISBN 0-8446-1345-2). Peter Smith.

Leveller Tracts: 1647-1653. Ed. by William Haller & Godfrey Davies. 1964. 11.75 (ISBN 0-8446-1218-9). Peter Smith.

Leviticus. Lloyd R. Bailey. Ed. by John H. Hayes. LC 86-46035. (Knox Preaching Guide Series). 108p. (Orig.). 1987. pap. 5.95 (ISBN 0-8042-3203-2). John Knox.

Leviticus. Andrew Bonar. (Banner of Truth Geneva Series Commentaries). 1978. 15.95 (ISBN 0-85151-086-8). Banner of Truth.

Leviticus. George Bush. 1981. 10.50 (ISBN 0-86524-098-1, 0302). Klock & Klock.

Leviticus. Don DeWelt. LC 75-328945. (Bible Study Textbook Ser.). (Illus.). 1975. 14.95 (ISBN 0-89900-007-X). College Pr Pub.

Leviticus. Irving L. Jensen. (Bible Self Study Ser.). 1970. pap. 3.25 (ISBN 0-8024-1003-0). Moody.

Leviticus. George A. Knight. LC 81-3007. (Daily Study Bible-Old Testament Ser.). 182p. 1981. 12.95 (ISBN 0-664-21802-4); pap. 6.95 (ISBN 0-664-24569-2). Westminster.

Leviticus. J. R. Porter. LC 75-20831. (Cambridge Bible Commentary on the New English Bible, Old Testament Ser.). (Illus.). 250p. 1976. 29.95 (ISBN 0-521-08638-8); pap. 11.95x (ISBN 0-521-09773-8). Cambridge U Pr.

Leviticus. Samuel J. Schultz. (Everyman's Bible Commentary Ser.). (Orig.). 1983. pap. 5.95 (ISBN 0-8024-0247-X). Moody.

Leviticus. Carroll Stuhlmueller. (Bible Ser.). pap. 1.00 (ISBN 0-8091-5082-4). Paulist Pr.

Leviticus. Wayne A. Turner. (Bible Commentary Ser.). 112p. 1985. pap. 2.95 (ISBN 0-8146-1372-1). Liturgical Pr.

Leviticus: An Introduction & Commentary. R. K. Harrison & D. J. Wiseman. LC 80-7985. (Tyndale Old Testament Commentaries Ser.). 180p. 1980. 12.95 (ISBN 0-87784-890-4); pap. 6.95 (ISBN 0-87784-253-1). Inter-Varsity.

Leviticus: Bible Study Commentary. Louis Goldberg. (Study Guide Commentary Ser.). 128p. (Orig.). 1980. pap. 4.95 (ISBN 0-310-41813-5, 18198P). Zondervan.

Leviticus-Deuteronomy. M. Goldsmith. (Bible Study Commentary Ser.). 126p. 1980. pap. 4.95 (ISBN 0-87508-151-7). Chr Lit.

Leviticus, Numbers. James L. Mays. LC 59-10454. (Layman's Bible Commentary Ser: Vol. 4). 1963. pap. 4.95 (ISBN 0-8042-3064-1). John Knox.

Lexical Aids for Students of New Testament Greek. 3rd ed. Bruce M. Metzger. LC 70-73197. 1969. pap. 4.95x (ISBN 0-8401-1618-7). A R Allenson.

Lexical Study of the Septuagint Version of the Pentateuch. J. A. Lee. LC 82-5460. (Septuagint & Cognate Studies). 186p. 1983. pap. 12.50 (ISBN 0-89130-576-9, 06 04 14). Scholars Pr GA.

Lexico-Concordancia del Nuevo Testamento en Griego y Espanol. George Parker. (Span.). 1000p. 1982. pap. 19.95 (ISBN 0-311-42066-4). Casa Bautista.

Lexicon in Veteris Testamenti Libros: Hebrew-Aramaic Lexicon, Incl. Supplement. Ludwig Koehler & Walter Baumgartner. (Hebrew & Aramaic.). 1951-53. 49.50x (ISBN 0-8028-2176-6). Eerdmans.

Lexicon of Accadian Prayers in the Rituals of Expiation. Cecil J. Weir. LC 78-72774. (Ancient Mesopotamian Texts & Studies). Repr. of 1934 ed. 35.00 (ISBN 0-404-18236-4). AMS Pr.

Lexicon to the English Poetical Works of John Milton. Laura E. Lockwood. LC 68-56596. (Bibliography & Reference Ser: No. 323). 1968. Repr. of 1907 ed. 32.00 (ISBN 0-8337-2132-1). B Franklin.

Lexicon to the Syriac New Testament. LC 79-91407. 243p. 1979. 4.95 (ISBN 0-910068-18-6). Am Christian.

Lexikon der Griechischen und Roemischen Mythologie. H. Hunger. (Ger.). 452p. 1974. pap. 7.95 (ISBN 3-499-16178-8, M-7252). French & Eur.

Lexikon der Mythologie der Eurpaeischen Voelker. Herbert Gottschalk. (Ger.). 42.00 (ISBN 3-7934-1184-2, M-7246). French & Eur.

Lexikon Zur Bibel. 3rd ed. Fritz Rienecker. (Ger.). 1974. 40.00 (ISBN 3-417-00403-9, M-7192). French & Eur.

Lexikon Zur Weltmission. S. E. Neill. (Ger.). 48.00 (ISBN 3-7974-0054-3, M-7190). French & Eur.

Ley Divina: La Senda Hacia la Maestria. R. Swinburne Clymer. (Span., Orig.). 1972. pap. 6.95 (ISBN 0-932785-55-7). Philos Pub.

Ley e Historia del Antiguo Testamento. Samuel Schultz. Tr. by Fernando P. Villalobos from Eng. (Curso Para Maestros Cristianos Ser.: No. 1). (Span., Illus.). 122p. 1972. pap. 3.50 (ISBN 0-89922-008-8); instructor's manual 1.50 (ISBN 0-89922-009-6). Edit Caribe.

Ley Lines in Question. Tom Williamson & Lin Bellamy. (Illus.). 272p. 1984. 22.50 (ISBN 0-437-19205-9, Pub. by Worlds Work). David & Charles.

Lhasa the Holy City. facsimile ed. F. Spencer Chapman. LC 75-37875. (Select Bibliographies Reprint Ser). Repr. of 1940 ed. 32.00 (ISBN 0-8369-6712-7). Ayer Co Pubs.

Li Chi: Book of Rites, 2 Vols. Ed. by Ch'U Chai & Winberg Chai. 1966. 25.00 (ISBN 0-8216-0107-5). Univ Bks.

Libellus De Diversis Ordinibus et Professionibus Qui Sunt in Aecclesia: Orders & Callings of the Church. Ed. by G. Constable & B. Smith. (Oxford Medieval Texts Ser). 1972. 45.00x (ISBN 0-19-822218-1). Oxford u Pr.

Liber Null & Psychonaut. Peter Carroll. (Illus.). 128p. (Orig.). 1987. pap. 12.50 (ISBN 0-87728-639-6). Weiser.

Liber Pontificalis Graecae. Isaac Habert. 790p. Repr. of 1643 ed. text ed. 124.20x (ISBN 0-576-99140-6, Pub. by Gregg Intl Pubs England). Gregg Intl.

Liber Qvi Appellatvr Specvlvm et Liber De Divinis Scriptvris. Saint Aurelius Augustinus. (Corpus Scriptorum Ecclesiasticorum Latinorum Ser: Vol. 12). 50.00 (ISBN 0-384-02505-6). Johnson Repr.

Liber S. Marie De Calchou, Registrum Abbacie Tironensis De Kelso, 1113-1567, 2 Vols. Kelso Abbey. Ed. by Cosmo Innes. LC 71-171552. Repr. of 1846 ed. 75.00 (ISBN 0-404-52805-8). AMS Pr.

Liberacion del Espiritu. Watchman Nee. 112p. 1968. 2.95 (ISBN 0-88113-255-1). Edit Betania.

Liberacion del Planeta Tierra. Hal Lindsey. Tr. of Liberation of Planet Earth. (Span.). 192p. 1982. pap. 3.95 (ISBN 0-311-13023-2). Casa Bautista.

Liberacion: El Evangelo de Dios. James E. Adams. 1980. pap. 2.95 (ISBN 0-85151-417-0). Banner of Truth.

Liberal Arts & the Jesuit College System. Aldo Scaglione. LC 86-17507. (Paperback Ser.: No. 6). (Illus.). v, 229p. 1986. 44.00x (ISBN 0-915027-76-3); pap. 20.00x (ISBN 0-915027-77-1). Benjamins North Am.

Liberal Christian Orthodoxy. F. H. Cleobury. 164p. 1963. 9.50 (ISBN 0-227-67668-8). Attic Pr.

Liberal Judaism. Eugene Borowitz. LC 83-17997. 468p. (Orig.). 1984. pap. 8.95 (ISBN 0-8074-0264-8, 306050). UAHC.

Liberal Judaism at Home: The Practices of Modern Reform Judaism. rev. ed. Morrison D. Bial. 1971. pap. 5.00 (ISBN 0-8074-0075-0, 383110); tchrs'. guide 1.50 (ISBN 0-8074-0225-7, 203110). UAHC.

Liberal Learning & Religion. Ed. by Amos N. Wilder. LC 77-86072. (Essay & General Literature Index Reprint Ser). 1969. Repr. of 1951 ed. 24.50x (ISBN 0-8046-0595-5, Pub. by Kennikat). Assoc Faculty Pr.

Liberal Protestantism. Robert S. Michaelsen & Wade C. Roof. 200p. (Orig.). 1986. pap. 11.95 (ISBN 0-8298-0584-2). Pilgrim NY.

Liberal Protestantism. Ed. by Bernard M. Reardon. 1968. 18.50x (ISBN 0-8047-0647-6). Stanford U Pr.

Liberal Religion: Principles & Practices. Frank Opton. LC 81-81129. (Library of Liberal Religion). 295p. 1981. 20.95 (ISBN 0-87975-155-X). Prometheus Bks.

Liberal Tradition. William A. Orton. 1945. 12.50x (ISBN 0-686-83606-5). Elliots Bks.

Liberalism: A Rope of Sand. Don Boys. 1979. 4.95 (ISBN 0-686-25591-7). Freedom Univ-FSP.

Liberalism & Liberal Politics in Edwardian England. George L. Bernstein. 256p. 1986. text ed. 34.95x (ISBN 0-04-942198-0); pap. text ed. 14.95x (ISBN 0-04-942199-9). Allen Unwin.

Liberalism & Sociology: L. T. Hobhouse & Political Argument in English, 1880-1914. Stefan Collini. LC 78-23779. 1979. 37.50 (ISBN 0-521-22304-0). Cambridge U Pr.

Liberalism & Tradition. B. Reardon. LC 75-7214. 320p. 1975. Cambridge U Pr.

Liberalization of American Protestantism: A Case Study in Complex Organizations. Henry J. Pratt. LC 74-38837. 345p. 1972. 24.95 (ISBN 0-8143-1475-9). Wayne St U Pr.

Liberals Among the Orthodox: Unitarian Beginnings in New York City, 1819-1839. Walter D. Kring. LC 73-21275. (Illus.). 1974. 14.95x (ISBN 0-8070-1662-4). Beacon Pr.

Liberated for Life a Christian Declaration of Indepence. Nina M. Fishwick. (Study & Grow Electives Ser.). 64p. 1985. pap. 3.95 (ISBN 0-8307-1039-6, 6102095). Regal.

Liberated for Life a Christian Declaration of Indepence. John F. MacArthur, Jr. LC 75-23511. 1984. pap. 4.95 (ISBN 0-8307-0931-2, 5418165). Regal.

Liberated Traditionalism: Men & Women in Balance. Ronald Allen & Beverly Allen. LC 85-8969. (Critical Concern Bks.). 1985. 11.95 (ISBN 0-88070-112-9). Multnomah.

Liberating Bond: Covenants Biblical & Contemporary. Wolfgang Roth & Rosemary R. Ruether. (Orig.). 1978. pap. 2.95 (ISBN 0-377-00076-0). Friend Pr.

Liberating Creation: Foundations of Religious Social Ethics. Gibson Winter. LC 81-5364. 1981. 12.95 (ISBN 0-8245-0032-6). Crossroad NY.

Liberating Faith: Bonhoeffer's Message for Today. Geffrey B. Kelly. LC 84-15863. 208p. (Orig.). 1984. pap. 11.95 (ISBN 0-8066-2092-7, 10-3832). Augsburg.

Liberating Grace. Leonardo Boff. Tr. by John Drury from Port. LC 79-4206. Tr. of graca libertadoro no mundo. 256p. (Orig.). 1979. pap. 9.95 (ISBN 0-88344-282-5). Orbis Bks.

Liberating Leadership: Practical Styles of Pastoral Ministry. Bernard F. Swain. 96p. (Orig.). 1986. pap. 6.95 (ISBN 0-86683-483-4, HarpR). Har-Row.

Liberating the Church: The Ecology of Church & Kingdom. Howard A. Snyder. 280p. (Orig.). 1982. pap. 8.95 (ISBN 0-87784-385-6); cloth 12.95 (ISBN 0-87784-894-7). Inter-Varsity.

Liberating the Laity. R. Paul Stevens. LC 85-10856. 192p. (Orig.). 1985. pap. 5.95 (ISBN 0-87784-613-8). Inter-Varsity.

Liberating the Leader's Prayer Life. Terry Muck. 160p. 1985. 9.95 (ISBN 0-8499-0549-4, 0549-4). Word Bks.

Liberating the Leader's Prayer Life. Terry C. Muck. (Leadership Library). 176p. 1985. 9.95 (ISBN 0-917463-05-6). Chr Today.

Liberating the Pulpit: Selected Sermons. Oscar S. Suarez. 164p. (Orig.). 1984. pap. 8.25 (ISBN 0-318-20555-6, Pub. by New Day Philippines). Cellar.

Liberating Word: A Guide to Non-Sexist Interpretation of the Bible. Ed. by Letty M. Russell. LC 76-18689. 120p. 1976. pap. 7.95 (ISBN 0-664-24751-2). Westminster.

Liberation. Wesley W. Nelson. 1974. pap. 2.95 (ISBN 0-910452-19-9). Covenant.

Liberation & Ethics: Essays in Religious Social Ethics in Honor of Gibson Winter. Ed. by Charles Amjad-Ali & W. Alvin Pitcher. LC 83-73425. (Studies in Religion & Society). 233p. 1985. text ed. 24.95x (ISBN 0-913348-22-8). Ctr Sci Study.

Liberation & Human Wholeness: The Conversion Experiences of Black People in Slavery & Freedom. Edward P. Wimberly & Anne Streaty. 144p. (Orig.). 1986. pap. 10.95 (ISBN 0-687-21698-2). Abingdon.

Liberation from Karma & Rebirth. Satguru S. Keshavadas. (Illus.). 164p. (Orig.). 1970. pap. 3.50 (ISBN 0-942508-02-5). Vishwa.

Liberation of Life: From the Cell to the Community. L. C. Birch & J. B. Cobb. LC 80-42156. 300p. 1982. 42.50 (ISBN 0-521-23787-4). Cambridge U Pr.

Liberation of Planet Earth. Hal Lindsey. 256p. 1976. pap. 3.95 (ISBN 0-553-25307-7). Bantam.

Liberation of the Laity. Anne W. Rowthorn. 232p. (Orig.). 1986. pap. 9.95 (ISBN 0-8192-1395-0). Morehouse.

Liberation of Theology. Juan L. Segundo. Tr. by John Drury from Spanish. LC 76-7049. Orig. Title: Liberation de la Tealogia. 248p. (Orig.). 1976. pap. 10.95 (ISBN 0-88344-286-8). Orbis Bks.

Liberation Preaching: The Pulpit & the Oppressed. Justo L. Gonzalez & Catherine G. Gonzalez. LC 79-27858. (Abingdon Preacher's Library). 1980. pap. 6.95 (ISBN 0-687-21700-8). Abingdon.

Liberation, Revolution & Freedom-Theological Perspectives: Proceedings of the College Theology Society. Ed. by Thomas M. McFadden. 222p. 1984. pap. text ed. 13.00 (ISBN 0-8191-4021-X). U Pr of Amer.

Liberation, the Jesus Mode: Reflections on the Gospels for the B-Cycle. Joseph G. Donders. LC 87-5700. 228p. (Orig.). 1987. pap. 10.95 (ISBN 0-88344-553-0). Orbis Bks.

Liberation Theology. Ed. by Ron Nash. 1984. 15.95 (ISBN 0-88062-121-4). Mott Media.

Liberation Theology. Ed. by Ronald H. Nash. 1986. text ed. 15.95 (ISBN 0-8010-6745-6). Baker Bk.

Liberation Theology. Emilio Nunez. 1985. text ed. 15.95 (ISBN 0-8024-4893-3). Moody.

Liberation Theology: An Evangelical View from the Third World. J. Andrew Kirk. LC 79-5212. (New Foundations Theological Library). 246p. (Peter Toon & Ralph Martin series editor). 1980. 12.95 (ISBN 0-8042-3704-2). John Knox.

Liberation Theology & the Message of Salvation: Proceedings of the Cerdic Colloquium, 4th, Strasbourg, May 10-12, 1973. Cerdic Colloquium Staff. Ed. by Rene Metz & Jean Schlick. Tr. by David G. Gelzer. LC 78-7540. (Pittsburgh Theological Monographs: No. 20). 1978. pap. 8.75 (ISBN 0-915138-26-3). Pickwick.

Liberation Theology: Essential Facts about the Revolutionary Movement in Latin America & Beyond. Phillip Berryman. LC 86-42638. 224p. 1986. 16.95 (ISBN 0-394-55241-5); pap. 6.95 (ISBN 0-394-74652-X). Pantheon.

Liberation Theology from Below: The Life & Thought of Manuel Quintin Lame. Gonzalo Castillo-Cardenas. LC 86-21812. 224p. (Orig.). 1987. pap. 16.95 (ISBN 0-88344-408-9). Orbis Bks.

Liberation Theology: From Dialogue to Confrontation. Leonardo Boff & Clodovis Boff. 120p. (Orig.). 1986. pap. 8.95 (ISBN 0-86683-528-8, HarpR). Har-Row.

Liberation Theology: Human Hope Confronts Christian History & American Power. Rosemary Ruether. LC 72-92263. Repr. of 1972 ed. 50.50 (ISBN 0-8357-9487-3, 2015212). Bks Demand UMI.

Liberation Theology in Latin America. James V. Schall. LC 80-82266. 412p. (Orig.). 1982. pap. 13.95 (ISBN 0-89870-006-X). Ignatius Pr.

Liberation Theology: The Church's Future Shock. Gerard Berghoef & Lester DeKoster. 197p. 1984. 14.95 (ISBN 0-934874-07-7). Chr Lib Pr.

Liberator, Eleutherios. Da Free John. (Illus.). 114p. 1982. 12.95 (ISBN 0-913922-66-8); pap. 6.95 (ISBN 0-913922-67-6). Dawn Horse Pr.

Libertins en France au Dix-Septieme Siecle. Francois T. Perrens. LC 72-168701. (Fr.). 428p. 1973. Repr. of 1896 ed. lib. bdg. 29.00 (ISBN 0-8337-2728-1). B Franklin.

Liberty. Everett D. Martin. 307p. 1981. Repr. of 1930 ed. lib. bdg. 20.00 (ISBN 0-8495-3828-9). Arden Lib.

Liberty & Reformation in the Puritan Revolution. William Haller. LC 54-6482. 410p. 1955. pap. 14.00x (ISBN 0-231-08547-8). Columbia U Pr.

Liberty Bible Commentary. Ed. by Jerry Falwell & Edward E. Hindson. LC 83-7280. (Illus.). 2736p. 1983. 29.95 (ISBN 0-8407-5295-4). Nelson.

Liberty, Equality, Sisterhood: On the Emancipation of Women in Church & Society. Elizabeth Moltmann-Wendel. Tr. by Ruth Gritsch. LC 77-15240. pap. 23.80 (2026919). Bks Demand UMI.

Liberty in Christ. John J. MacArthur. (John MacArthur's Bible Studies). (Orig.). 1986. pap. 3.50 (ISBN 0-8024-5094-6). Moody.

Liberty, Justice, & Morals: Contemporary Value Conflicts. 2nd ed. Burton M. Leiser. (Illus.). 1979. text ed. write for info. (ISBN 0-02-369510-2). Macmillan.

Liberty of Conscience & the Growth of Religious Diversity in Early America, 1636-1786. Carla G. Pestana. (Illus.). 104p. 1986. pap. 30.00 (ISBN 0-916617-02-5); bibliographical suppl. 10.00 (ISBN 0-916617-03-3). J C Brown.

Liberty of Prophesying: With Its Just Limits & Temper Considered with Reference to the Circumstances of the Modern Church. H. H. Henson. 1910. 39.50x (ISBN 0-686-51411-4). Elliots Bks.

Liberty of the Press, Speech & Public Worship: Being Commentaries on the Liberty of the Subject & the Laws of England. James Paterson. xxxi, 568p. 1985. Repr. of 1880 ed. lib. bdg. 42.50x (ISBN 0-8377-1019-7). Rothman.

Library, 2 Vols. Apollodorus. (Loeb Classical Library: No. 121, 122). 13.95x ea. Vol. 1, Bks. 1-3 (ISBN 0-674-99135-4). Vol. 2 (ISBN 0-674-99136-2). Harvard U Pr.

Library Manual for Missionaries. Ed. by Clara R. Stone. LC 79-116205. (Illus., Orig.). 1979. pap. 4.95 (ISBN 0-686-31591-X). Assn Chr Libs.

Library of Anglo-Catholic Theology, 18 titles in 81 vols. Ed. by W. J. Copeland et al. Repr. of 1841 ed. Set. 2627.50 (ISBN 0-404-52010-3); write for info. AMS Pr.

Library of Christian Hymns, 3 vols. in 2. Ed. by John Dahle. LC 72-1649. Repr. of 1928 ed. 74.50 set (ISBN 0-404-13202-2). AMS Pr.

Library of Congress Headings for Judaica. Daniel D. Stuhlman. LC 82-73398. (Orig.). 1983. pap. 5.00 (ISBN 0-934402-13-2); pap. 1.50 (ISBN 0-934402-15-9). BYLS Pr.

Library of Early Christianity. Ed. by Wayne A. Meeks. 200p. 1987. 18.95. Westminster.

Library of Jesus College, Oxford: With an Appendix on the Books Bequeathed Thereto by Lord Herbert of Cherbury. rev. ed. C. J. Fordyce & T. M. Knox. (Oxford Bible Society Ser.: Vol. 5, Pt. 2). Repr. of 1937 ed. 13.00 (ISBN 0-8115-1238-X). Kraus Repr.

Library of Religious Poetry. Arthur Gilman. 59.95 (ISBN 0-8490-0521-3). Gordon Pr.

Library Research Guide to Religion & Theology: Illustrated Search Strategy & Sources. 2nd Rev. ed. James Kennedy, Jr. LC 73-90317. (Library Research Guides Ser.: No. 1). 1984. 19.50 (ISBN 0-87650-185-4); pap. 12.50 (ISBN 0-87650-184-6). Pierian.

Libre Dentro de la Carcel. Roger Arienda & Marichelle Roque. (Span.). 176p. 1986. pap. 2.95 (ISBN 0-311-46102-6). Casa Bautista.

Libre Para Vivir. T. A. Hegre. 96p. 1964. 2.25 (ISBN 0-88113-020-6). Edit Betania.

Libri Tres, Id Est: De Sacramentis in Genere, De Sacramento Eucharistiae, De Sacrificio Eucharistiae. William Allen. 699p. Repr. of 1576 ed. text ed. 124.20x (ISBN 0-576-99475-8, Pub. by Gregg Intl Pubs England). Gregg Intl.

Libro De Formacion De Catequistas: Creciendo y Compartiendo. Maruja Sedano et al. 1982. pap. 7.95 (ISBN 0-8091-2439-4). Paulist Pr.

Libro Llamado la Biblia. J. C. Wenger. Tr. by Milka Rindzinski from Eng. LC 84-80158. (Mennonite Faith Ser.: No. 8). 72p. (Orig.). 1984. pap. 1.50 (ISBN 0-8361-1268-7). Herald Pr.

Libros Cristianos En Existencia. Association of Christian Publishers & Booksellers. (Span.). 384p. (Orig.). 1984. write for info. (ISBN 0-943258-01-4). Assn Christian Pub.

Lider No Nace, Se Hace. Ted W. Engstrom. 256p. 1980. 4.25 (ISBN 0-88113-330-2). Edit Betania.

Lie: Evolution. Ken Ham. 188p. 1987. 10.95 (ISBN 0-89051-117-9). Master Bks.

Liedersammlung, 2 vols. Incl. Vol. B. Collection of 148 German Hymns Without Notes. 1917. 5.95x (ISBN 0-8361-1144-3); Vol. G. Collection of 317 German Hymns Without Notes. 6.95x (ISBN 0-8361-1163-X). Repr. of 1928 ed. Herald Pr.

Life. Omraam M. Aivanhov. (Complete Works: Vol. 5). (Illus.). 266p. 1978. pap. 9.95 (ISBN 2-85566-108-0). Prosveta USA.

Life: A Gift of God. 7.00 (ISBN 0-8198-4441-1). Dghtrs St Paul.

Life after Birth: Spirituality for College Students. William Toohey. 112p. 1980. pap. 4.95 (ISBN 0-8164-2290-7, HarpR). Har-Row.

Life after Death. Leadbeater. 4.50 (ISBN 0-8356-7148-8). Theos Pub Hse.

Life after Death. Gordon Lindsay. (Sorcery & Spirit World Ser.). 3.00 (ISBN 0-89985-083-9). Christ Nations.

Life after Death. Albert J. Nevins. LC 83-61888. 136p. (Orig.). 1983. pap. 5.95 (ISBN 0-87973-612-7, 612). Our Sunday Visitor.

Life after Death!? Spiros Zodhiates. Tr. by Spiros Zodhiates from Greek. Orig. Title: What Happens After Death? (Illus.). 1977. pap. 3.95 (ISBN 0-89957-525-0). AMG Pubs.

Life after Divorce. Dorothy Payne. (Looking Up Ser.). 24p. (Orig.). 1982. pap. 1.25 booklet (ISBN 0-8298-0610-5). Pilgrim NY.

Life after Life: The Theory of Reincarnation. Eustace Miles. 180p. 1985. pap. 10.00 (ISBN 0-89540-126-6, SB-126). Sun Pub.

Life after Youth. Ed. by Luella Slover. 1981. pap. 4.50 (ISBN 0-8309-0303-8). Herald Hse.

Life & Adventures of a Quaker among the Indians. Thomas C. Battey. 339p. 1972. Repr. of 1875 ed. 20.00 (ISBN 0-87928-025-5). Corner Hse.

Life & Character of Erasmus. Arthur R. Pennington. 1977. lib. bdg. 59.95 (ISBN 0-8490-2159-6). Gordon Pr.

Life & Character of the Late Reverend, Learned, & Pious Mr. Jonathan Edwards, President of the College in New Jersey. Jonathan Edwards. LC 75-31090. Repr. of 1804 ed. 28.50 (ISBN 0-404-13508-0). AMS Pr.

Life & Character of the Reverend Benjamin Colman, D. D. Ebenezer Turell. LC 72-4539. 256p. 1972. Repr. of 1749 ed. 40.00x (ISBN 0-8201-1104-X). Schol Facsimiles.

Life & Correspondence of Theodore Parker. John Weiss. LC 70-83446. (Religion in America, Ser. 1). 1969. Repr. of 1864 ed. 52.00 (ISBN 0-405-00279-3). Ayer Co Pubs.

Life & Correspondence of Theodore Parker, 2 Vols. facs. ed. John Weiss. LC 69-16854. (Select Bibliographies Reprint Ser). 1863. 52.00 (ISBN 0-8369-5018-6). Ayer Co Pubs.

Life & Correspondence of Theodore Parker, 2 Vols. John Weiss. LC 76-106987. (American Public Figures Ser). 1864. Set. lib. bdg. 95.00 (ISBN 0-306-71874-X). Da Capo.

Life & Correspondence of Theodore Parker, Minister of the Twenty-Eighth Congregational Society, Boston. John Weiss. LC 74-97443. Repr. of 1864 ed. 42.00x (ISBN 0-8371-2723-8, WEQ&, Pub. by Negro U Pr). Greenwood.

Life & Correspondence of Thomas Arnold D. D, 2 vols. Arthur P. Stanley. LC 75-29624. Repr. of 1845 ed. Set. 72.50 (ISBN 0-404-13980-9). AMS Pr.

Life & Death. Catherine Booth. (Writings of Catherine Booth Ser.). 1986. Repr. of 1883 ed. deluxe ed. 4.95 (ISBN 0-86544-034-4). Salvation Army.

Life & Death in the New Testament. Xavier Leon-Dufour. 1986. 18.45 (ISBN 0-317-52379-1, HarpR). Har-Row.

Life & Death of Mary Magdalene. T. Robinson. Ed. by H. O. Sommer. (EETS ES Ser.: Vol. 78). pap. 15.00 (ISBN 0-8115-3401-4). Kraus Repr.

Life & Death of Saint Malachy the Irishman. Bernard of Clairvaux. (Cistercian Fathers Ser.: No. 10). 170p. 7.95. Cistercian Pubns.

Life & Epistles of St. Paul. W. J. Conybeare & J. S. Howson. 1949. 16.95 (ISBN 0-8028-8086-X). Eerdmans.

Life & Epistles of St. Paul. W. J. Conybeare & J. S. Howson. 1977. lib. bdg. 59.95 (ISBN 0-8490-2160-X). Gordon Pr.

Life & Faith of Martin Luther. Adolph Fehlauer. 1981. pap. 5.95 (ISBN 0-8100-0125-X, 15N0376). Northwest Pub.

Life & Faith of the Baptists. H. Wheeler Robinson. 158p. 1985. pap. 6.95 (ISBN 0-913029-09-2). Stevens Bk Pr.

Life & Faith: Psychoanalytic Perspectives on Religious Experience. W. W. Meissner. 302p. 1987. 19.95 (ISBN 0-87840-429-5); pap. 11.95. Georgetown U Pr.

Life & Genius of Rembrandt. Joseph Cundall. LC 77-94567. 1979. Repr. of 1867 ed. lib. bdg. 30.00 (ISBN 0-89341-235-X). Longwood Pub Group.

Life & Glories of St. Joseph. Edward H. Thompson. LC 80-53744. 1980. pap. 7.50 (ISBN 0-89555-161-6). Tan Bks Pubs.

Life & Holiness. Thomas Merton. 1964. pap. 2.95 (ISBN 0-385-06277-X, D183, Im). Doubleday.

Life & Illustrious Martyrdom of Sir Thomas More. Stapleton. LC 66-23617. 206p. 1984. 7.50 (ISBN 0-8232-0731-5). Fordham.

Life & Labors of Mrs. Maggie Newton Van Cott, the First Lady Licensed to Preach in the Methodist Episcopal Church in the United States. John O. Foster. Ed. by Carolyn Gifford & Donald Dayton. (Women in American Protestant Religion 1800-1930 Ser.). 339p. 1987. lib. bdg. 50.00 (ISBN 0-8240-0663-1). Garland Pub.

Life & Labors of Rev. Jordan W. Early: One of the Pioneers of African Methodism in the West & South. facsimile ed. Sarah J. Early. LC 72-164386. (Black Heritage Library Collection). Repr. of 1894 ed. 16.00 (ISBN 0-8369-8845-0). Ayer Co Pubs.

Life & Labours of Asahel Nettleton. Bennet Tyler & Andrew Bonar. 1975. 10.95 (ISBN 0-85151-208-9). Banner of Truth.

Life & Letters in the Fourth Century. Terrot R. Glover. LC 68-10923. 1968. Repr. of 1901 ed. 11.00x (ISBN 0-8462-1065-7). Russell.

Life & Letters of Charles Inglis: His Ministry in America & Consecration As First Colonial Bishop from 1759 to 1787. John W. Lydekker. (Church Historical Society London N. S. Ser.: No. 20). Repr. of 1936 ed. 50.00 (ISBN 0-8115-3144-9). Kraus Repr.

Life & Letters of Dean Church. Ed. by Mary C. Church. 428p. 1981. Repr. of 1897 ed. lib. bdg. 45.00 (ISBN 0-8495-0859-2). Arden Lib.

Life & Letters of Elizabeth Prentiss. George L. Prentiss. Ed. by Carolyn D. Gifford & Donald Dayton. (Women in American Protestant Religion 1800-1930 Ser.). 573p. 1987. lib. bdg. 80.00 (ISBN 0-8240-0672-0). Garland Pub.

Life & Letters of Erasmus. James A. Froude. LC 70-155628. Repr. of 1895 ed. 24.50 (ISBN 0-404-02627-3). AMS Pr.

Life & Letters of Erasmus & the Unknown Historical Significance of the Protestant Reformation, 2 vols. J. A. Froude. (Illus.). 157p. 1984. 147.55x set (ISBN 0-89266-469-X). Am Classical Coll Pr.

Life & Letters of Father Andrew. Father Andrew. LC 82-80473. (Treasures from the Spiritual Classics Ser.). 64p. 1982. pap. 2.95 (ISBN 0-8192-1310-1). Morehouse.

Life & Letters of Henry Martyn. John Sargent. 496p. 1985. pap. 6.95 (ISBN 0-85151-468-5). Banner of Truth.

Life & Letters of Laura Askew Haygood. Oswald E. Brown & Anna M. Brown. Ed. by Carolyn G. De Swarte. (Women in American Protestant Religion Series 1800-1930). 522p. 1987. lib. bdg. 75.00 (ISBN 0-8240-0661-5). Garland Pub.

Life & Letters of Mrs. Phoebe Palmer. Phoebe Palmer & Richard Wheatley. Ed. by Donald W. Dayton. (Higher Christian Life Ser.). 636p. 1985. 80.00 (ISBN 0-8240-6432-1). Garland Pub.

Life & Letters of Saint Paul. Ed. by David Smith. 1977. lib. bdg. 69.95 (ISBN 0-8490-2161-8). Gordon Pr.

Life & Letters of the Rev. John Philip Boehm: Founder of the Reformed Church in Pennsylvania, 1683-1749. Ed. by William J. Hinke. LC 71-38784. (Religion in America, Ser. 2). 572p. 1972. Repr. of 1916 ed. 35.00 (ISBN 0-405-04069-5). Ayer Co Pubs.

Life & Liberation of Padmasambhava, 2 vols. Yeshe Tsogyal. Tr. by G. C. Toussaint & Kenneth Douglas. (Tibetan Translation Ser.). (Illus.). 1978. 60.00 set (ISBN 0-685-80849-1). Vol. I (ISBN 0-913546-18-6). Vol. II (ISBN 0-913546-20-8). Dharma Pub.

Life & Ministry of Charles Finney. Lewis Drummond. 272p. 1985. pap. 5.95 (ISBN 0-87123-818-7, 210818). Bethany Hse.

Life & Ministry of Jesus. F. H. Edwards. 1982. pap. 14.00 (ISBN 0-686-95353-3). Herald Hse.

Life & Miracles of Pope Kirillos VI. Ernest Abdel-Massih. 139p. (Orig.). 1982. pap. text ed. 3.00 (ISBN 0-932098-20-7). St Mark Coptic Orthodox.

Life & Miracles of Saint Benedict: Book Two of Dialogues. Gregorius I. Tr. by Odo J. Zimmermann & Benedict R. Avery. LC 80-19624. xv, 87p. 1980. Repr. of 1949 ed. lib. bdg. 22.50x (ISBN 0-313-22766-7, GRLI). Greenwood.

Life & Morals: An Introduction to Ethics. A. K. Bierman. 596p. 1980. pap. text ed. 14.95 (ISBN 0-15-550725-7, HC). HarBraceJ.

Life & Morals of Jesus of Nazareth. Thomas Jefferson. LC 76-17582. 1976. Repr. of 1904 ed. lib. bdg. 30.00 (ISBN 0-8414-5323-3). Folcroft.

Life & Morals of Jesus of Nazareth. Thomas Jefferson. 82p. 1983. Repr. of 1904 ed. lib. bdg. 25.00 (ISBN 0-8492-5611-9). R West.

Life & Opinions of John de Wycliffe, D. D, 2 vols. 2nd ed. Robert Vaughan. LC 71-178561. Repr. of 1831 ed. Set. 75.00 (ISBN 0-404-56678-2). Vol. 1 o.p (ISBN 0-404-56679-0). Vol. 2 o.p (ISBN 0-404-56680-4). AMS Pr.

Life & Philosophy of Shree Swaminarayan. new ed. H. T. Dave. Ed. by Leslie Shepard. (Illus.). 274p. 1974. 8.95 (ISBN 0-04-294082-6). Weiser.

Life & Pontificate of Pope Leo the Tenth, 2 vols. rev. ed. 6th ed. William Roscoe. Ed. by Thomas Roscoe. LC 75-174965. Repr. of 1853 ed. 92.50 (ISBN 0-404-05430-7). AMS Pr.

Life & Prayer. Valentine Breton. 189p. 1960. 5.95 (ISBN 0-933932-21-9). Scepter Pubs.

Life & Religion. Friedrich M. Mueller. LC 73-18821. Repr. of 1905 ed. 19.75 (ISBN 0-404-11448-2). AMS Pr.

Life & Religion of Muhammad. Muhammad B. Al-Majlisi. Tr. by James Merrick. 463p. 1987. pap. 19.95 (ISBN 0-7103-0216-9, 02169, Kegan Paul). Methuen Inc.

Life & Religion of Muhammad, 3 vols, Vol. 2. Allama Muhammad Al-Majlisi Balquir. Tr. by J. L. Merrick from Persian. Tr. of Hiyat al-Qulub. 483p. 1982. 35.00x (ISBN 0-317-39115-1, Pub. by Luzac & Co Ltd). State Mutual Bk.

Life & Revelations of St. Gertrude. St. Gertrude. 570p. 1983. pap. 15.00 (ISBN 0-87061-079-1). Chr Classics.

Life & Ritual in Old Siam: Three Studies of Thai Life & Customs. Rajadhon Phraya Anuman. Ed. by William J. Gedney. LC 78-23833. (Illus.). 1979. Repr. of 1961 ed. lib. bdg. 24.75x (ISBN 0-313-21193-0, ARLF). Greenwood.

Life & Sacrament: Reflections on the Catholic Vision. Donal Murray. (Theology & Life Ser.: Vol. 4). 1983. pap. 6.95 (ISBN 0-89453-299-5). M Glazier.

Life & Sufferings of Saint Catherine the Great Martyr. Tr. by Leonidas J. Papadopulos & Georgia Lizardos. (Illus.). 1986. pap. 3.00 (ISBN 0-913026-63-8). St Nectarios.

Life & Teaching of Jesus. Edward W. Bauman. LC 60-7038. 240p. 1978. pap. 6.95 (ISBN 0-664-24221-9). Westminster.

Life & Teaching of Jesus Christ. James S. Stewart. 1982. pap. 3.95 (ISBN 0-687-21744-X, Festival). Abingdon.

Life & Teaching of Jesus Christ: According to the Synoptic Gospels. E. R. Lewis. (London Divinity Ser.). 170p. 1977. pap. 3.95 (ISBN 0-227-67519-3). Attic Pr.

Life & Teaching of Ludwig Hesser: Leader & Martyr of the Anabaptists, 1500-1529. Frederick L. Weis. LC 83-45633. Date not set. Repr. of 1930 ed. 31.50 (ISBN 0-404-19875-9). AMS Pr.

Life & Teaching of Satguru Sant Keshavadas. Satguru S. Keshavadas. LC 77-81277. (Illus.). 150p. (Orig.). 1977. pap. 3.50 (ISBN 0-942508-12-2). Vishwa.

Life & Teaching of the Masters of the Far East, 5 vols. Baird T. Spalding. pap. 4.00 ea. Vol. 1 (ISBN 0-87516-363-7). Vol. 2 (ISBN 0-87516-364-5). Vol.3 (ISBN 0-87516-365-3). Vol. 4 (ISBN 0-87516-366-1). Vol. 5 (ISBN 0-87516-367-X). 20.00 set (ISBN 0-87516-538-9). De Vorss.

Life & Teachings of Buddha. Sandor K. Csoma. LC 78-72399. Repr. of 1957 ed. 21.50 (ISBN 0-404-17258-X). AMS Pr.

Life & Teachings of Christ, Vol. 1. Gordon Lindsay. (Life of Christ & Parable Ser.). 238p. (Orig.). 1980. pap. 5.00 (ISBN 0-89985-967-4, 4101). Christ Nations.

Life & Teachings of Christ, Vol. 2. Gordon Lindsay. (Life of Christ & Parable Ser.). 244p. (Orig.). 1980. pap. 5.00 (ISBN 0-89985-968-2). Christ Nations.

Life & Teachings of Christ, Vol. 3. Gordon Lindsay. (Life of Christ & Parable Ser.). 288p. 1980. pap. 5.75 (ISBN 0-89985-969-0). Christ Nations.

Life & Teachings of Jesus. rev. ed. T. Franklin Miller. 1971. pap. 1.95 (ISBN 0-87162-114-2, D5200). Warner Pr.

Life & the Teaching of Carrie Judd Montgomery. Carrie J. Montgomery. Ed. by Donald W. Dayton. (Higher Christian Life Ser.). 420p. 1985. 50.00 (ISBN 0-8240-6430-5). Garland Pub.

Life & Thought in the Early Middle Ages. Ed. by Robert S. Hoyt. LC 67-15065. (Illus.). 1968. pap. 1.95 (ISBN 0-8166-0464-9, MP11). U of Minn Pr.

Life & Thought of Michael Sattler. C. Arnold Snyder. LC 83-22835. (Studies in Anabaptist & Mennonite History: No. 27). 264p. 1984. 19.95x (ISBN 0-8361-1264-4). Herald Pr.

Life & Times of an MK. C. John Buffam. LC 84-27482. (Mission Candidate Aids Ser.). 224p. (Orig.). 1985. pap. 9.95 (ISBN 0-87808-198-4). William Carey Lib.

Life & Times of Cotton Mather. Abijah P. Marvin. LC 72-1979. (American Biography Ser., No. 32). 1972. Repr. of 1892 ed. lib. bdg. 59.95x (ISBN 0-8383-1454-6). Haskell.

Life & Times of Girolamo Savonarola. P. Villari. LC 68-25276. (World History Ser., No. 48). 1969. Repr. of 1888 ed. lib. bdg. 79.95x (ISBN 0-8383-0174-6). Haskell.

Life & Times of Girolamo Savonarola. Pagquale Villart. Tr. by Linda Villari from Ital. (Illus.). 792p. 1985. Repr. of 1888 ed. lib. bdg. 85.00 (ISBN 0-89987-906-3). Darby Bks.

Life & Times of Jesus the Messiah. Alfred Edersheim. 1972. 25.95 (ISBN 0-8028-8027-4). Eerdmans.

Life & Times of Jesus the Messiah. Alfred Edersheim. 1568p. Date not set. 24.95 (ISBN 0-917006-12-7). Hendrickson MA.

Life & Times of John Calvin, 2 vols. Paul E. Henry. Tr. by Henry Stebbing from Ger. LC 83-45613. Date not set. Repr. of 1851 ed. Set. 95.00 (ISBN 0-404-19831-7). AMS Pr.

Life & Times of John Calvin: With an Earnest Appeal for the Adoption of Open-Air Preaching. Charles W. Banks. LC 83-45599. Date not set. Repr. of 1891 ed. 21.50 (ISBN 0-404-19867-8). Ams Pr.

Life & Times of John England. Peter K. Guilday. LC 70-83422. (Religion in America, Ser. 1). 1969. Repr. of 1927 ed. 54.00 (ISBN 0-405-00247-5). Ayer Co Pubs.

Life & Times of John Huss: The Bohemian Reformation of the Fifteenth Century, 2 vols. Ezra H. Gillett. LC 77-85271. Repr. of 1863 ed. Set. 94.50 (ISBN 0-404-16150-2). AMS Pr.

Life & Times of John Milton. Carlos Martyn. LC 76-39970. 1976. Repr. of 1866 ed. lib. bdg. 37.50 (ISBN 0-8414-6009-4). Folcroft.

Life & Times of Master John Hus. Franz Lutzow. LC 77-84728. (Illus.). Repr. of 1909 ed. 40.00 (ISBN 0-404-16128-6). AMS Pr.

Life & Times of St. Bernard of Clairvaux. James C. Morison. 1977. lib. bdg. 59.95 (ISBN 0-8490-2162-6). Gordon Pr.

Life & Times of Sydney Smith. Stuart J. Reid. Repr. of 1901 ed. lib. bdg. 30.00 (ISBN 0-8495-4533-1). Arden Lib.

Life & Times of the Rev. John Wesley, 3 vols. Luke Tyerman. LC 72-82522. 1973. Repr. of 1872 ed. Set. lib. bdg. 89.00 (ISBN 0-8337-4710-X). B Franklin.

Life & Words of Jesus. Ed. by Patricia Alexander. LC 83-47715. (Illus.). 96p. 1983. 10.95 (ISBN 0-06-065255-1, HarpR). Har-Row.

Life & Work of Gerardus Joannes Vossius 1577-1649. C. S. Rademaker. (Respublica Literaria Neerlandica: No. 5). 472p. 1981. text ed. 39.50 (ISBN 90-232-1785-3, Pub. by Van Gorcum Holland). Longwood Pub Group.

Life & Work of Morgan Edwards: First Baptist Historian in the United States. Thomas R. McKibbens, Jr. & Kenneth Smith. Ed. by Edwin S. Gaustad. LC 79-5269. (Baptist Tradition Ser.). 1980. lib. bdg. 23.00x (ISBN 0-405-12438-4). Ayer Co Pubs.

Life & Work of Muhammed Jalal-ud-Din Rumi. Afzal Iqbal. 1983. 29.95 (ISBN 0-86304-033-0, Pub. by Octagon England). Ins Study Human.

Life & Work of St. Paul. F. W. Farrar. 1980. 2 vol. set 43.95 (ISBN 0-86524-055-8, 8402). Klock & Klock.

Life & Work of the Minister. Daniel D. Preston. 1968. 5.95 (ISBN 0-934942-11-0). White Wing Pub.

Life & Work on the Mission Field. J. Herbert Kane. LC 80-65010. 1980. 16.95 (ISBN 0-8010-5406-0). Baker Bk.

Life & Works of Charles Harmon. Jack Brown & David Armbrister. 136p. 1986. 16.95; pap. 12.95. Commonwealth Pr.

Life & Works of Michelangelo Buonarroti. Charles H. Wilson. Repr. of 1876 ed. 65.00 (ISBN 0-686-19837-9). Ridgeway Bks.

Life & Works of St. Cyprian of Carthage, 4 vols. St. Cyprian. Vols. 1, 2, & 4. pap. 1.50 ea.; Vol. 3. pap. 2.95 (ISBN 0-686-05649-3); pap. 6.95 set (ISBN 0-686-05650-7). Eastern Orthodox.

Life & Writings of Jeremy Taylor. C. J. Stranks. LC 73-11259. 1973. lib. bdg. 35.00 (ISBN 0-8414-7595-4). Folcroft.

Life & Writings of John Bunyan. Harold E. Speight. 1928. 40.00 (ISBN 0-8274-2916-9). R West.

Life & Writings of John Bunyan. Harold E. Speight. 224p. 1983. lib. bdg. 50.00 (ISBN 0-8495-5063-7). Arden Lib.

Life & Writings of St. John of the Cross. James M. MacDonald. 1977. lib. bdg. 59.95 (ISBN 0-8490-2164-2). Gordon Pr.

Life & Writings of the Historical St. Patrick. R. P. Hanson. 144p. 1983. 11.95 (ISBN 0-8164-0523-9, HarpR). Har-Row.

Life & Writings of Theodore Parker. Albert Reville. 59.95 (ISBN 0-8490-0525-6). Gordon Pr.

Life as Laughter: Following Bhagwan Shree Rajneesh. Bob Mullan. (Illus.). 204p. 1984. 26.95x (ISBN 0-7102-0141-9); pap. 12.95 (ISBN 0-7102-0043-9). Methuen Inc.

Life As Parable: Reinterpreting the Religious Life. John M. Lozano. 208p. (Orig.). 1986. pap. 8.95 (ISBN 0-8091-2825-X). Paulist Pr.

Life As Revealed Through Early American Court Records, Including the Story of Col. John Custis of Arlington, Queen's Creek & Williamsburg. Elmer T. Crowson. (Illus.). 1981. 20.00 (ISBN 0-89308-146-9). Southern Hist Pr.

Life As Worship: Prayer & Praise in Jesus' Name. Theodore W. Jennings. LC 82-7283. pap. 37.80 (ISBN 0-317-30146-2, 2025329). Bks Demand UMI.

Life As Yoga: Discourses at Chorwad, 2 bks. Vimala Thakar. Tr. by Devendra Singh. 286p. 1977. 14.00 (ISBN 0-89684-242-8, Pub. by Motilal Banarsidass India); pap. 10.95 (ISBN 0-89684-241-X). Orient Bk Dist.

Life Before Birth. Gary Parker. (Orig.). 1987. 9.95 (ISBN 0-89051-115-2); read-along cassette 5.95. Master Bks.

Life Begins at Death. Leslie D. Weatherhead. (Festival Ser.). 112p. 1981. pap. 2.25 (ISBN 0-687-21806-3). Abingdon.

Life Between Death & New Birth. Rudolf Steiner. (Russian Language Ser.). 90p. 1985. pap. 6.00 (ISBN 0-89345-904-6, Steiner). Garber Comm.

Life Between Death & Rebirth. Rudolf Steiner. Tr. by R. M. Querido from Ger. LC 68-57429. 308p. (Orig.). 1975. pap. 9.95 (ISBN 0-910142-62-9). Anthroposophic.

Life Between Life: Scientific Explorations into the Void Separating One Incarnation from the Next. Joel Whitton. LC 86-4573. 192p. 1986. 14.95 (ISBN 0-385-23274-8, Dolp). Doubleday.

Life Between the Questions. Carolyn Huffman & Lu Ann Barrow. 80p. 1985. 8.95 (ISBN 0-8499-0446-3, 0446-3). Word Bks.

Life Beyond. Ray Summers. LC 83-20874. 1973. pap. 8.95 (ISBN 0-8054-1608-0). Broadman.

Life Beyond Death. John C. Tormey. 64p. 1981. pap. 1.50 (ISBN 0-89243-151-2). Liguori Pubns.

Life Beyond Death: A Critical Study of Spiritualism. Swami Abhedananda. 6.95 (ISBN 0-87481-616-5). Vedanta Pr.

Life Beyond the Final Curtain. Samuel Porrath. 250p. text ed. 17.95 (ISBN 0-88125-083-X). Ktav.

Life Can Begin Again: Sermons on the Sermon on the Mount. Helmut Thielicke. Tr. by John W. Doberstein from Ger. LC 63-12535. 240p. 1963. pap. 5.95 (ISBN 0-8006-1934-X, 1-1934). Fortress.

Life Can Begin Again: Sermons on the Sermon on the Mount. Helmut Thielicke. Tr. by J. W. Doberstein from Ger. 224p. pap. 10.95 (ISBN 0-227-67854-0, Pub. by J Clarke UK). Attic Pr.

Life-Changing Answers to Depression. Harold I. Smith. 192p. (Orig.). 1986. 9.95 (ISBN 0-89081-529-1). Harvest Hse.

Life-Changing Learning for Adults. Jeff Hoyer. (C. E. Ministries Ser.). 96p. (Orig.). 1984. pap. 3.50 (ISBN 0-89367-097-9). Light & Life.

Life Changing Learning for Children: Resources That Work. Betty Hockett & Grace Abbott. (C. E. Ministries Ser.). 1977. pap. 3.50 (ISBN 0-89367-020-0). Light & Life.

Life, Character & Influence of Desiderius Erasmus of Rotterdam, 2 Vols. John J. Mangan. LC 73-147113. Repr. of 1927 ed. 78.50 (ISBN 0-404-04178-7). AMS Pr.

Life Choices: Confronting the Life & Death Decisions Created by Modern Medicine. Howard Levine. 304p. 1986. 16.95 (ISBN 0-671-55385-2). S&S.

Life Choices: Tackling the Biggest Decisions You'll Ever Make. Ed. by Kevin Miller. (Senior High Pacesetter Ser.). 64p. 1986. pap. 7.95 (ISBN 0-89191-327-0). Cook.

Life Companion Paperback Supplement Series. Aurobindo. (Life Companion Ser.). 1339p. (Orig.). 1984. pap. 39.25 (ISBN 0-89744-013-7, Pub. by Madanlal Himatsinghlea). Auromere.

Life, Conversion, Preaching, Travels & Suffering of Elias Smith. Elias Smith. Ed. by Edwin S. Gaustad. LC 79-52606. (Baptist Tradition Ser.). 1980. Repr. of 1816 ed. lib. bdg. 34.50x (ISBN 0-405-12471-6). Ayer Co Pubs.

Life Cycle Chapter Study Kit. pap. 3.00 (ISBN 0-686-96087-4). United Syn Bk.

Life Cycle Theory & Pastoral Care. Donald Capps. LC 83-5585. (Theology & Pastoral Care Ser.). 128p. 1983. pap. 7.95 (ISBN 0-8006-1726-6, 1-1726). Fortress.

Life, Death & Hereafter. Parker L. Johnstone. LC 76-21518. 1976. cloth 7.95 (ISBN 0-917802-00-4). Theoscience Found.

Life, Death & Miracles of Saint Francois De Paule. Antoine Donde. (Printed Sources of Western Art Ser.). (Fr., Illus.). 258p. 1981. pap. 40.00 slipcase (ISBN 0-915346-64-8). A Wofsy Fine Arts.

Life, Death & the Law: A Study of the Relationship Between Law & Christian Morals in the English & American Legal Systems. Norman St. John-Stevas. 375p. 1981. Repr. of 1961 ed. lib. bdg. 32.50x (ISBN 0-8377-1119-3). Rothman.

Life, Death, Eternity & the Secret of the Universe. Brian C. Lawson. (Illus.). 1979. 47.45 (ISBN 0-89266-207-7). Am Classical Coll Pr.

Life Divine. Sri Aurobindo. (Life Companion Library Bible Paper Ser.). 1112p. 1983. Repr. of 1949 ed. deluxe ed. 24.95 (ISBN 0-89744-008-0); write for info. Auromere.

Life Divine. Sri Aurobindo. 1112p. 1982. 19.50 (ISBN 0-89071-301-4, Pub. by Sri Aurobindo Ashram India); pap. 15.00 (ISBN 0-89071-300-6, Pub. by Sri Aurobindo Ashram India). Matagiri.

Life Divine: A Commentary on Isha Upanished. Sri Aurobindo. 108p. (Orig.). 1981. pap. 7.50 (ISBN 0-89744-230-X, Pub. by Sri Aurobindo Ashram Trust India). Auromere.

Life Essential: The Hope of the Gospel. 2nd ed. George MacDonald. Ed. by Rolland Hein. LC 74-16732. (Wheaton Literary Ser.). 102p. 1978. pap. 4.95 (ISBN 0-87788-499-4). Shaw Pubs.

Life Everlasting. Murdo MacDonald-Bayne. 165p. 1981. pap. 9.50 (ISBN 0-85243-365-4). Ariel OH.

Life Experience & Gospel Labors of the Rt. Rev. Richard Allen. Richard Allen. 96p. (Orig.). 1983. pap. 3.95 (ISBN 0-687-21844-6). Abingdon.

Life Forces from Anthroposophy. Carl Unger. 1982. pap. 1.95 (ISBN 0-916786-63-3). St George Bk Serv.

Life in a Fifteenth Century Monastery. Anne Boyd. LC 76-22452. (Cambridge Topic Bks). (Illus.). 1978. PLB 8.95 (ISBN 0-8225-1208-4). Lerner Pubns.

Life in a Medieval Monastery. Ed. by Trevor Cairns. (Cambridge Introduction to World History Ser.). (Illus.). 48p. Date not set. pap. 4.95 (ISBN 0-521-33724-0). Cambridge U Pr.

Life in a New Dimension. Don Double. 1979. pap. 2.95 (ISBN 0-88368-083-1). Whitaker Hse.

Life in Abundance: A Contemporary Spirituality. Francis Baur. 240p. 1983. pap. 7.95 (ISBN 0-8091-2507-2). Paulist Pr.

Life in Ancient Egypt. Adolf Erman. Tr. by H. M. Tirard. (Illus.). pap. 8.50 (ISBN 0-486-22632-8). Dover.

Life in Ancient Egypt. Adolph Erman. LC 68-56523. (Illus.). Repr. of 1894 ed. 25.00 (ISBN 0-405-08488-9, Blom Pubns). Ayer Co Pubs.

Life in Ancient Egypt. Adolph Erman. 16.75 (ISBN 0-8446-0090-3). Peter Smith.

Life in Ancient India as Depicted in Jaina Canon & Commentaries. 2nd ed. J. Jain. 1984. text ed. 34.00x. Coronet Bks.

Life in Bible Times. Christ Tarrant. 48p. (Orig.). 1986. pap. 5.95 (ISBN 0-687-21850-0). Abingdon.

Life in Bible Times & Places. Joanne L. Kepes. 1982. 9.95 (Pub. by Pflaum Pr). Peter Li.

Life in California Before the Conquest. Alfred Robinson. LC 68-30553. (American Scene Ser). (Illus.). 1969. Repr. of 1846 ed. lib. bdg. 39.50 (ISBN 0-306-71142-7). Da Capo.

Life in Christ. Nicholas Cabasilas. Tr. by Carmino J. Decatanzaro. 229p. 1974. pap. 8.95 (ISBN 0-913836-12-5). St Vladimirs.

Life in Christ. rev. ed. James Killgallon et al. LC 76-26451. 1976. pap. 2.25 (ISBN 0-914070-08-8). ACTA Found.

Life in Christ. Theo Preiss. LC 55-1608. (Studies in Biblical Theology: No. 13). 1954. pap. 10.00x (ISBN 0-8401-3013-9). A R Allenson.

Life in Christ. Tony Salerno. 288p. (Orig.). 1985. pap. 9.95 (ISBN 0-87123-887-X, 210887). Bethany Hse.

Life in Faith & Freedom: An Essay Presenting Gaston Fessard's Analysis of the Dialectic of the Spiritual Exercises of St. Ignatius. Edouard Pousset. Frwd. by G. E. Ganss. LC 79-84200. (Modern Scholarly Studies About Jesuits, in English Translation Ser.: No. 4). 286p. 1980. 9.00 (ISBN 0-912422-41-6); pap. 8.00 smythsewn (ISBN 0-912422-40-8); pap. 7.00 (ISBN 0-912422-39-4). Inst Jesuit.

Life in Her Hands. Shirlee Evans. 192p. (Orig.). 1987. pap. 5.95 (ISBN 0-8361-3441-9). Herald Pr.

Life in His Body: Discovering Purpose, Form & Freedom in His Church. Gary Inrig. 182p. 1975. pap. 5.95 (ISBN 0-87788-500-1). Shaw Pubs.

Life in Large Families: Views of Mormon Women. Howard M. Bahr et al. LC 82-45005. 264p. (Orig.). 1982. lib. bdg. 29.25 (ISBN 0-8191-2551-2); pap. text ed. 13.25 o. p. (ISBN 0-8191-2552-0). U Pr of Amer.

Life in the Afterlife. Tim LaHaye. Tyndale.

Life in the Balance: Exploring the Abortion Controversy. Robert Wennberg. 192p. (Orig.). 1985. pap. 7.95 (ISBN 0-8028-0061-0). Eerdmans.

Life in the Fifth Dimension. Bonnie B. O'Brien & Dorothy E. Sample. 1984. pap. 6.50 (ISBN 0-8054-5214-1). Broadman.

Life in the Holy Spirit. Alan Walker. LC 86-71315. 72p. 1986. pap. 3.95 (ISBN 0-88177-036-1, DR036B). Discipleship Res.

Life in the Middle Ages. George G. Coulton. Cambridge U Pr.

Life in the Pressure Cooker: Studies in James. Roy R. Roberts. pap. 4.95 (ISBN 0-88469-033-4). BMH Bks.

Life in the Roman World of Nero & St. Paul. T. G. Tucker. 1924. 45.00 (ISBN 0-8274-3984-9). R West.

Life in the Son: A Study of the Doctrine of Perseverance. Robert Shank. LC 59-15488. 380p. 1960. 8.95 (ISBN 0-911620-01-X). Westcott.

Life in the Spirit. Jessie Penn-Lewis. 1962. pap. 3.95 (ISBN 0-87508-948-8). Chr Lit.

Life in the Spirit. Bramwell H. Tillsley. 109p. (Orig.). 1986. pap. 4.95 (ISBN 0-86544-037-9). Salv Army Suppl South.

Life in the Spirit: In Marriage, Home & Work. D. Martyn Lloyd-Jones. 372p. 1975. Repr. 12.95 (ISBN 0-8010-5550-4). Baker Bk.

Life in the Spirit: Reflections, Meditations, & Prayers. Mother Teresa of Calcutta. LC 82-48938. 128p. 1983. 10.45i (ISBN 0-06-066021-X, HarpR). Har-Row.

Life in the Spirit Seminars Team Manual: Catholic Edition. 1979. pap. 4.95 (ISBN 0-89283-065-4). Servant.

Life in the Spirit Seminars Team Manual. rev. ed. 1979. pap. 4.95 (ISBN 0-89283-064-6). Servant.

Life in the Upanishads. Shubhra Sharma. 1985. 15.00x (ISBN 81-7017-202-0, Pub. by Abhinav India). South Asia Bks.

Life in the Word. Philip Mauro. pap. 1.25 (ISBN 0-87509-101-6). Chr Pubns.

Life into Autobiography: A Study of Goethe's "Dichtung und Wahrheit". Derek Bowman. (Germanic Studies in America: Vol. 5). 162p. 1972. 19.60 (ISBN 3-261-00311-1). P Lang Pubs.

Life Is a Trust. Frederick A. Meyer. (Religious Ser.). 95p. 1986. 8.95 (ISBN 0-935087-09-5). Wright Pub Co.

Life Is for Growth. Samuel S. Stoesz. 1977. pap. 2.25 (ISBN 0-87509-102-4); leaders guide 1.25 (ISBN 0-87509-169-5). Chr Pubns.

Life Is for Loving. Eric Butterworth. LC 73-6326. 128p. 1974. 10.53 (ISBN 0-06-061268-1, HarpR). Har-Row.

Life Is Forever. Helen S. Rice. (Illus.). 32p. 1974. 8.95 (ISBN 0-8007-0681-1). Revell.

Life Is Real Only Then, When "I Am". G. I. Gurdjieff. 177p. 1981. 17.50 (ISBN 0-525-14547-8, 01699-510). Dutton.

Life Is Too Short. Margaret Foth. 144p. (Orig.). 1985. pap. 5.95 (ISBN 0-310-42681-2, 12779P). Zondervan.

Life Is Worth Living. Fulton J. Sheen. 1978. pap. 4.50 (ISBN 0-385-14510-1, Im). Doubleday.

Life, Journals & Correspondence of Rev. Manasseh Cutler, L.L.D, 2 vols. William P. Cutler & Julia P. Cutler. (Illus.). 1032p. 1987. Set. text ed. 40.00x (ISBN 0-8214-0859-3). Ohio U Pr.

Life Journey & the Old Testament: An Experiential Approach to the Bible & Personal Transformations. Conrad E. L'Heureux. 184p. 1986. pap. 8.95 (ISBN 0-8091-2828-4). Paulist Pr.

Life Journey of a Quaker Artist. Dorothea Blom. LC 80-80916. 32p. (Orig.). 1980. 2.50x (ISBN 0-87574-232-7). Pendle Hill.

Life, Letters & Travels of Father Pierre Jean de Smet, 4 vols. Pierre J. De Smet. LC 75-83418. (Religion in America Ser. I). 1969. Repr. of 1905 ed. 88.00 set (ISBN 0-405-00237-8); Vols. 1-2. 22.00 ea. Vol. 1 (ISBN 0-405-00238-6). Vol. 2 (ISBN 0-405-00239-4). Vols. 3-4. 22.00 ea. Vol. 3 (ISBN 0-405-00240-8). Vol. 4 (ISBN 0-405-00241-6). Ayer Co Pubs.

Life Lines: Quotations of Victor Paul Wierwille. Victor P. Wierwille. LC 85-52028. 136p. 1985. 5.95 (ISBN 0-910068-64-X). Am Christian.

Life, Man & Time. 2nd ed. Frank L. Marsh. LC 66-21121. (Illus.). (YA) 1967. 8.95 (ISBN 0-911080-15-5). Outdoor Pict.

Life More Abundant. Charles L. Allen. pap. 2.25 (ISBN 0-515-06412-2). Jove Pubns.

Life, Nature & Cultivation of Anthroposophy. Rudolf Steiner. Tr. by George Adams from Ger. 68p. 1976. pap. 5.95 (ISBN 0-85440-061-3, Pub. by Steinerbooks). Anthroposophic.

Life Never Ends. Kay Leedy. 141p. pap. 7.95 (ISBN 0-942494-41-5). Coleman Pub.

Life of a Rich Man. Mrs. W. N. Paschal. (Illus.). 180p. 1976. pap. 2.50 (ISBN 0-89114-075-1). Baptist Pub Hse.

Life of A. W. Pink. Iain H. Murray. (Illus.). 272p. (Orig.). 1981. pap. 5.95 (ISBN 0-85151-332-8). Banner of Truth.

Life of Adam. Giovanni Loredano. LC 67-26617. 1967. Repr. of 1659 ed. 25.00x (ISBN 0-8201-1031-0). Schol Facsimiles.

Life of All Living. Fulton J. Sheen. 1979. pap. 3.50 (ISBN 0-385-15458-5, Im). Doubleday.

Life of Anne Catherine Emmerich, 2 vols. Carl E. Schmoger. 1976. Set. pap. 33.00 (ISBN 0-89555-061-X); Vol. 1. pap. 12.00 (ISBN 0-89555-059-8); Vol. 2. pap. 24.00 (ISBN 0-89555-060-1). TAN Bks Pubs.

Life of Baptists in the Life of the World. Ed. by Walter B. Shurden. LC 85-1401. 1985. pap. 7.95 (ISBN 0-8054-6582-0). Broadman.

Life of Bishop Wilfrid. Eddius Stephanus. Ed. by Bertram Colgrave. 207p. 1985. 37.50 (ISBN 0-521-30927-1); pap. 12.95 (ISBN 0-521-31387-2). Cambridge U Pr.

Life of Blessed Margaret of Castello. William R. Bonniwell. LC 83-70524. 113p. 1983. pap. 4.00 (ISBN 0-89555-213-2). TAN Bks Pubs.

Life of Buddha. B. Asvaghosha. lib. bdg. 79.95 (ISBN 0-87968-473-9). Krishna Pr.

Life of Buddha: According to the Legend of Ancient India. A. Ferdinand Herold. LC 55-12748. 1954. pap. 6.95 (ISBN 0-8048-0382-X). C E Tuttle.

Life of Buddha & the Early History of His Order. Ed. by William W. Rockhill. 285p. Repr. of 1884 ed. text ed. 19.50x (ISBN 0-89563-149-0, Pub. by Chinese Matl Ctr). Coronet Bks.

Life of Buddha on the Stupa of Barabudur, According to the Lalitavistara-Text. Ed. by N. J. Krom. LC 78-72460. Repr. of 1926 ed. 30.00 (ISBN 0-404-17328-4). AMS Pr.

Life of Cardinal Manning, Archbishop of Westminster, 2 vols. Edmund S. Purcell. LC 70-126605. (Europe 1815-1945 Ser.). 1534p. 1973. Repr. of 1896 ed. Set. lib. bdg. 115.00 (ISBN 0-306-70050-6). Da Capo.

Life of Cardinal Manning, Archbishop of Westminster, 2 vols. Edmund S. Purcell. 1973. Repr. of 1896 ed. 50.00 set (ISBN 0-8274-1075-1). R West.

Life of Cardinal Wolsey. George Cavendish. 1887. Repr. 15.00 (ISBN 0-8274-2879-0). R West.

Life of Charles F. Parham, Founder of the Apostolic Faith Movement. Charles F. Parham & Sarah E. Parham. (Higher Christian Life Ser.). 468p. 1985. lib. bdg. 60.00 (ISBN 0-8240-6436-4). Garland Pub.

Life of Charles Hodge, Professor in the Theological Seminary, Princeton, New Jersey. Archibald A. Hodge. LC 71-83425. (Religion in America, Ser. 1). 1969. Repr. of 1881 ed. 32.00 (ISBN 0-405-00250-5). Ayer Co Pubs.

Life of Christ. Hall Caine. 1310p. 1985. Repr. of 1938 ed. lib. bdg. 45.00 (ISBN 0-89987-194-1). Darby Bks.

Life of Christ. Robert D. Culver. LC 76-17967. 272p. 1976. pap. 9.95 (ISBN 0-8010-2498-6). Baker Bk.

Life of Christ. Frederic W. Farrar. 1980. 15.00 (ISBN 0-911376-01-1). Fountain Publications Oregon.

Life o. Christ. Frederic W. Farrar. 1982. lib. bdg. 24.95 (ISBN 0-86524-089-2, 9508). Klock & Klock.

Life of Christ. Irving R. Jensen. (Bible Self Study Ser.). pap. 3.25 (ISBN 0-8024-1067-7). Moody.

Life of Christ. Armin J. Panning. 1971. pap. 2.50 (ISBN 0-8100-0018-0, 09-0932). Northwest Pub.

Life of Christ. Fulton J. Sheen. LC 77-81295. 1977. pap. 8.95 (ISBN 0-385-13220-4, Im). Doubleday.

Life of Christ. Clifford Stevens. LC 83-60102. 196p. (Orig.). 1983. pap. 5.95 (ISBN 0-87973-617-8, 617). Our Sunday Visitor.

Life of Christ, Vols. 1 & 2. 6.49 ea. (0140594). CEF Press.

Life of Christ: A Stanzaic Life of Christ Compiled from Higden's Polychronicon & the Legenda Aurea. (EETS, OS Ser.: No. 166). Repr. of 1926 ed. 70.00 (ISBN 0-527-00163-5). Kraus Repr.

Life of Christ in Stereo. Johnston M. Cheney. Ed. by Stanley A. Ellisen. LC 84-8280. 275p. 1984. pap. 6.95 (ISBN 0-88070-068-8). Multnomah.

Life of Christ in the Conception & Expression of Chinese & Oriental Artists. Ed. by James C. Emerson. (Great Art Masters of the World Ser.). (Illus.). 117p. 1983. 97.50 (ISBN 0-86650-054-5). Gloucester Art.

Life of Christ in the Paintings by Tissot. Virgil Beauchamp. 1979. deluxe ed. 49.75 (ISBN 0-930582-29-2). Gloucester Art.

Life of Christ Story-N-Puzzle Book. Ruby Maschke. 48p. (Orig.). 1981. pap. 2.50 (ISBN 0-87239-449-2, 2839). Standard Pub.

Life of D. L. Moody. A. P. Fitt. pap. 3.50 (ISBN 0-8024-4727-9). Moody.

Life of David, 2 vols. in one. Arthur W. Pink. (Giant Summit Ser.). 768p. 1981. pap. 14.95 (ISBN 0-8010-7061-9). Baker Bk.

Life of David. Arthur W. Pink. 14.95 (ISBN 0-685-19837-5). Reiner.

Life of David Brainerd: The Works of Jonathan Edwards, Vol. 7. Jonathan Edwards. Ed. by Norman Pettit. LC 83-23445. (Illus.). 640p. 1984. text ed. 50.00x (ISBN 0-300-03004-5). Yale U Pr.

Life of Doctor C. F. W. Walther. Lewis W. Spitz, Sr. (Illus.). 1961. 3.95 (ISBN 0-570-03247-4, 15-1246). Concordia.

Life of Dwight L. Moody. W. R. Moody. (Heroes of the Faith Ser.). 508p. 1985. Repr. of 1900 ed. 6.95 (ISBN 0-916441-15-6). Barbour & Co.

Life of Eknath. Justin E. Abbott. cancelled (ISBN 0-8364-0746-6, Pub. by Motilal Banarsidass). South Asia Bks.

Life of Elijah. A. W. Pink. 1976. pap. 5.95 (ISBN 0-85151-041-8). Banner of Truth.

Life of Emerson. Van Wyck Brooks. LC 80-2528. Repr. of 1932 ed. 37.00 (ISBN 0-404-19252-1). AMS Pr.

Life of Emerson. Richard Garnett. LC 73-21630. (American Biography Ser., No. 32). 1974. lib. bdg. 49.95x (ISBN 0-8383-1775-8). Haskell.

Life of Emerson. Denton J. Snider. 1973. Repr. of 1921 ed. 30.00 (ISBN 0-8274-0462-X). R West.

Life of Ernest Renan. Darmesteter. 1898. Repr. 25.00 (ISBN 0-8274-2884-7). R West.

Life of Ernest Renan. Francis Espinasse. 1895. Repr. 20.00 (ISBN 0-8274-2925-8). R West.

Life of Excellence. Charles Nieman. 32p. (Orig.). 1985. wkbk. 4.95 (ISBN 0-914307-37-1). Word Faith.

Life of Faith. C. Nuzum. 96p. 1956. pap. 1.95 (ISBN 0-88243-539-6, 02-0539). Gospel Pub.

Life of Faith. Thomas C. Upham. (Higher Christian Life Ser.). 480p. 1985. lib. bdg. 60.00 (ISBN 0-8240-6447-X). Garland Pub.

Life of Father De Smet, S. J. Eighteen Hundred One to Eighteen Seventy-Three. E. Laveille. Tr. by Marian Lindsay. (Loyola Request Reprint Ser.). 398p. 1981. Repr. of 1915 ed. 8.95 (ISBN 0-8294-0372-8). Loyola.

Life of Father Hecker. Walter Elliott. LC 75-38446. (Religion in America, Ser. 2). 456p. 1972. Repr. of 1891 ed. 28.00 (ISBN 0-405-04065-2). Ayer Co Pubs.

Life of Francis Place. Graham Wallas. 1898. 21.00 (ISBN 0-8337-3674-4). B Franklin.

Life of Fray Antonio Margil De Jesus. Tr. by Benedict Leutenegger. (Illus.). 1967. 10.00 (ISBN 0-88382-254-7). AAFH.

Life of Frederick Denison Maurice, Chiefly Told in His Own Letters. J. F. D. Maurice. 1294p. Repr. of 1884 ed. text ed. 99.36x (ISBN 0-576-02191-1). Gregg Intl.

Life of George Muller. William H. Harding. (Heroes of the Faith Ser.). 384p. 1985. Repr. of 1914 ed. 6.95 (ISBN 0-916441-13-X). Barbour & Co.

Life of Girolamo Savonarola. Roberto Ridolfi. LC 76-8001. (Illus.). 1976. Repr. of 1959 ed. lib. bdg. 65.00x (ISBN 0-8371-8873-3, RIGS). Greenwood.

Life of Gotama Buddha (Compiled Exclusively from the Pali Canon) Compiled by Earl H. Brewster. LC 78-72380. Repr. of 1926 ed. 27.50 (ISBN 0-404-17229-6). AMS Pr.

Life of Grace. David R. Previtali. (Faith & Life). (Illus.). 176p. (Orig.). 1985. pap. 7.50 (ISBN 0-89870-083-3); pap. 2.50 activity bk. (ISBN 0-89870-084-1). Ignatius Pr.

Life of Handel: The Kelkel Edition. James C. Hadden. LC 74-24096. Repr. of 1904 ed. 15.00 (ISBN 0-404-12941-2). AMS Pr.

Life of Hilaire Belloc. facs. ed. Robert Speaight. LC 78-136655. (Biography Index Reprint Ser.). 1957. 29.00 (ISBN 0-8369-8050-6). Ayer Co Pubs.

Life of Hilaire Belloc. Robert Speaight. 552p. 1981. Repr. of 1957 ed. lib. bdg. 35.00 (ISBN 0-89987-773-7). Darby Bks.

Life of Jacob Boehme. Franz Hartmann. 1985. pap. 4.95 (ISBN 0-916411-97-4, Pub by Sure Fire). Holmes Pub.

Life of Jehudi Ashmun. facs. ed. Ralph R. Gurley. LC 73-149867. (Black Heritage Library Collection Ser). 1835. 22.50 (ISBN 0-8369-8749-7). Ayer Co Pubs.

Life of Jesus. Shirley Beegle. (Double Trouble Puzzles Ser.). (Illus.). 48p. 1987. pap. 2.50 (ISBN 0-87403-326-8, 2766). Standard Pub.

Life of Jesus. Retold by Pamela Broughton. LC 85-51852. (Golden Bible Stories). (Illus.). 32p. 1986. 3.95 (ISBN 0-307-11626-3, Pub. by Golden Bks). Western Pub.

Life of Jesus. Shusaku Endo. Tr. by Richard Schuchert from Japanese. LC 78-61721. 192p. 1979. pap. 3.95 (ISBN 0-8091-2319-3). Paulist Pr.

Life of Jesus. Maurice Goguel. Tr. by Olive Wyon. LC 75-41114. Repr. of 1933 ed. 32.50 (ISBN 0-404-14546-9). AMS Pr.

Life of Jesus. Edgar J. Goodspeed. LC 78-21540. 1979. Repr. of 1950 ed. lib. bdg. 24.75x (ISBN 0-313-20728-3, GOLJ). Greenwood.

Life of Jesus. Greg L. LeFevre. (Bible Quiz 'N Tattletotals Ser.). 16p. (Orig.). 1982. pap. 0.98 (ISBN 0-87239-579-0, 2806). Standard Pub.

Life of Jesus. Basil Mathews. (Illus.). 1979. Repr. of 1931 ed. lib. bdg. 25.00 (ISBN 0-8495-3817-3). Arden Lib.

Life of Jesus. J. Middleton Murry. 1982. Repr. of 1927 ed. lib. bdg. 35.00 (ISBN 0-8495-3939-0). Arden Lib.

Life of Jesus. Charles Nieman. 55p. (Orig.). 1984. wkbk. 2.75 (ISBN 0-914307-25-8). Word Faith.

Life of Jesus. Ruth Odor. (Flip-a-Bible-Story Bks.). (Illus.). 16p. (Orig.). 1982. pap. 3.95 (ISBN 0-87239-559-6, 2733). Standard Pub.

Life of Jesus. Humberto Rasi. 9.95 ea. (ISBN 0-8163-0573-0). No.1, 1984. No.2, 1985 (ISBN 0-8163-0602-8). No. 3, 1985 (ISBN 0-8163-0607-9). Pacific Pr Pub Assn.

Life of Jesus. Connie Sherlock. (Think 'N Check Quizzes Ser.). (Illus.). 16p. (Orig.). 1983. pap. 1.95 (ISBN 0-87239-689-4, 2793). Standard Pub.

Life of Jesus. Isobel Tallach. (Orig.). 1984. pap. 1.75 (ISBN 0-85151-345-X). Banner of Truth.

Life of Jesus Christ. Albert J. Nevins. 248p. (Orig.). 1987. pap. 12.95 (ISBN 0-87973-500-7, 500). Our Sunday Visitor.

Life of Jesus Christ. James Stalker. Ed. by A. Whyte & J. Moffatt. (Handbooks for Bible Classes & Private Students Ser.). 160p. 1922. pap. 7.95 (ISBN 0-567-28130-2, Pub. by T & T Clark Ltd UK). Fortress.

Life of Jesus Christ. James A. Stalker. (Stalker Trilogy Ser.). 160p. 1984. pap. 5.95 (ISBN 0-310-44191-9, 12618P). Zondervan.

Life of Jesus Christ. James M. Stalker. 160p. 10.95 (ISBN 0-8007-0177-1). Revell.

Life of Jesus Christ & Biblical Revelations, 4 vols. Anne C. Emmerich. Ed. by C. E. Schmoeger. LC 79-90066. 1979. Set. pap. 30.00 (ISBN 0-89555-127-6); Vol. 1. (ISBN 0-89555-123-3); Vol. 2. pap. (ISBN 0-89555-124-1); Vol. 3. (ISBN 0-89555-125-X); Vol. 4. (ISBN 0-89555-126-8). TAN Bks Pubs.

Life of Jesus Christ & Biblical Revelations. Anne C. Emmerich. Ed. by Carl E. Schmoger. LC 86-50154. 1986. Repr. of 1914 ed. Set. 67.00 (ISBN 0-89555-293-0); Vol. 1, 486 p. 16.75 ea (ISBN 0-89555-289-2). Vol. 2, 481 p (ISBN 0-89555-290-6). Vol. 3, 594 p (ISBN 0-89555-291-4). Vol. 4, 476 p (ISBN 0-89555-292-2). TAN Bks Pubs.

Life of Jesus Critically Examined, 2 Vols. David F. Strauss. Tr. by Marian Evans. LC 74-107193. 1970. Repr. of 1860 ed. Set. 59.00x (ISBN 0-403-00238-9). Scholarly.

Life of Jesus for Everyman. William Barclay. LC 75-12282. 96p. 1975. pap. 5.72 (ISBN 0-06-060404-2, RD 319, HarpR). Har-Row.

Life of John Bunyan. Edmund Venables. LC 77-20805. 1977. Repr. of 1888 ed. lib. bdg. 35.00 (ISBN 0-8414-9157-7). Folcroft.

Life of John Colet. Joseph H. Lupton. 1887. 20.50 (ISBN 0-8337-4243-4). B Franklin.

Life of John Dryden. Sir Walter Scott. Ed. by Bernard Kreissman. LC 63-8121. xx, 471p. 1963. pap. 5.95x (ISBN 0-8032-5177-7, BB 157, Bison). U of Nebr Pr.

Life of John Eliot: The Apostle to the Indians. Convers Francis. 1972. Repr. of 1854 ed. lib. bdg. 29.00 (ISBN 0-8422-8049-9). Irvington.

Life of John Henry Newman Based on His Private Journals & Correspondence, 2 vols. Wilfred Ward. 1912. Repr. 50.00 (ISBN 0-8274-2889-8). R West.

Life of John Kline. Benjamin Fink. 7.95 (ISBN 0-87178-516-1). Brethren.

Life of John Knox. Thomas McCrie. LC 83-45584. (Illus.). Date not set. Repr. of 1898 ed. 57.50 (ISBN 0-404-19902-X). AMS Pr.

Life of John Knox. George R. Preedy. 1940. Repr. 35.00 (ISBN 0-8274-2933-9). R West.

Life of John Milton. Richard Garnett. LC 77-112638. Repr. of 1890 ed. 10.00 (ISBN 0-404-02686-9). AMS Pr.

Life of John Milton. Richard Garnett. 1890. lib. bdg. 9.75 (ISBN 0-8414-4638-5). Folcroft.

Life of John Milton. 3rd ed. Charles Symmons. LC 71-128979. 1970. Repr. of 1822 ed. 25.50 (ISBN 0-404-06325-X). AMS Pr.

Life of John Milton. John Toland. LC 76-40068. 1761. lib. bdg. 30.00 (ISBN 0-8414-8619-0). Folcroft.

Life of John Milton, Englishman. John A. Hamilton. LC 74-16133. 1974. Repr. lib. bdg. 9.50 (ISBN 0-8414-4874-4). Folcroft.

Life of John Milton: Narrated in Connection with the Political, Literary & Ecclesiastical History of His Time, 7 vols. David Masson. Set. 117.25 (ISBN 0-8446-1303-7); 16.75 ea. Peter Smith.

Life of John Murray. Iain Murray. 1984. pap. 6.95 (ISBN 0-85151-426-X). Banner of Truth.

Life of Joseph. Thomas Kirk. 319p. 1985. smythe sewn 12.75 (ISBN 0-86524-193-7, 8408). Klock & Klock.

Life of Joseph Smith the Prophet. George Q. Cannon. (Classics in Mormon Literature Ser.). 572p. 1986. Repr. of 1964 ed. 14.95 (ISBN 0-87747-148-7). Deseret Bk.

Life of las Casas: The Apostle of the Indies. Arthur Helps. 1976. lib. bdg. 75.00 (ISBN 0-8490-2165-0). Gordon Pr.

Life of Luther. Julius Kostlin. 1883. Repr. 50.00 (ISBN 0-8274-2894-4). R West.

Life of Mahavira. Manak C. Jaini. 1986. 8.00X (ISBN 0-8364-1559-0, Pub. by Academic India). South Asia Bks.

Life of Mahomet. H. De Boulainvilliers. Ed. by Luzac & Co. Ltd. Staff. 400p. 1985. 60.00 (ISBN 0-317-39040-6, Pub. by Luzac & Co Ltd). State Mutual Bk.

Life of Marpa the Translator. Tsang N. Heruka. Tr. by The Nalanda Translation Committee & Chogyam Trungpa. LC 86-11837. 320p. 1986. pap. 12.95 (ISBN 0-87773-377-5). Shambhala Pubns.

Life of Mary Magdalene in the Paintings of the Great Masters, 2 vols. Ralph De Jong. (Illus.). 1979. deluxe ed. 117.45 (ISBN 0-930582-30-6). Gloucester Art.

Life of Melania the Younger: Introduction, Translation & Commentary. Elizabeth A. Clark. LC 84-20635. (Studies in Women & Religion: Vol. 14). 305p. 1985. 49.95x (ISBN 0-88946-535-5). E Mellen.

Life of Michael Angelo, 2 Vols. Herman F. Grimm. Tr. by Fanny E. Bunnett. Repr. of 1900 ed. Set. lib. bdg. 48.00x (ISBN 0-8371-2750-5, GRMA). Greenwood.

Life of Michael Angelo, 2 Vols. Herman F. Grimm. 45.00x (ISBN 0-403-00399-7). Scholarly.

Life of Michaelangelo, 2 vols. H. Grimm. 200.00 (ISBN 0-8490-0533-7). Gordon Pr.

Life of Milton. William Hayley. LC 76-26849. Repr. of 1796 ed. lib. bdg. 45.00 (ISBN 0-8414-4739-X). Folcroft.

Life of Milton. William Hayley. LC 78-122485. 1970. Repr. of 1796 ed. 50.00x (ISBN 0-8201-1081-7). Schol Facsimiles.

Life of Milton. Louis Racine. LC 74-16189. 1930. lib. bdg. 17.00 (ISBN 0-8414-7258-0). Folcroft.

Life of Mind. Paul S. Delp. LC 82-61238. (Illus.). 125p. (Orig., PB). 1983. pap. 10.00 (ISBN 0-935356-05-3). Mills Pub Co.

Life of Mohammad from Original Sources. new rev. ed. William Muir. Ed. by Thomas H. Weir. LC 78-180366. Repr. of 1923 ed. 57.50 (ISBN 0-404-56306-6). AMS Pr.

Life of Muhammad. M. H. Haykal. Tr. by R. I. Faruqi. LC 76-3060. 1976. 15.95 (ISBN 0-89259-002-5); pap. 12.95. Am Trust Pubns.

Life of Muhammad. A. H. Siddiqui. 15.50 (ISBN 0-686-18307-X). Kazi Pubns.

Life of Muhammad: A Translation of Ishaq's Sirat Rasul Allah. I. Ishaq. Intro. by A. Guillaume. 1979. pap. text ed. 24.95x (ISBN 0-19-636034-X). Oxford U Pr.

Life of My Years. A. Taylor, Jr. 160p. (Orig.). 1983. pap. 9.95 (ISBN 0-687-21854-3). Abingdon.

Life of Newman. Robert Sencourt. 1973. Repr. of 1948 ed. 30.00 (ISBN 0-8274-1085-9). R West.

Life of Obedience. Kenneth Hagin, Jr. 1986. pap. 1.00 (ISBN 0-89276-720-0). Hagin Ministries.

Life of Ogyu Sorai: A Tokugawa Philosopher. Olof Lidin. (Scandinavian Institute of Asian Studies Monograph Ser.: No. 19). 250p. 1982. pap. text ed. 18.95x (ISBN 0-7007-0068-4, Pub. by Curzon Pr England). Apt Bks.

Life of Our Lord. Charles Dickens. LC 80-22131. (Illus.). 128p. 1981. Repr. of 1934 ed. 10.95 (ISBN 0-664-21382-0). Westminster.

Life of Our Lord. Marigold Hunt. 191p. 1959. 5.00 (ISBN 0-912414-25-1). Lumen Christi.

Life of Our Lord in Art. E. M. Hurll. 59.95 (ISBN 0-8490-0534-5). Gordon Pr.

Life of Our Lord in Art: With Some Account of the Artistic Treatment of the Life of St. John the Baptist. Estelle M. Hurll. LC 76-89272. 1969. Repr. of 1898 ed. 31.00 (ISBN 0-8103-3137-3). Gale.

Life of Pachomius. Apostolos N. Athanassakis. LC 84-4046. (Society of Biblical Literature. Texts & Translation-Early Christian Literature Ser.). 216p. 1975. pap. 14.25 (ISBN 0-89130-065-1, 06 02 07). Scholars Pr GA.

Life of Paul. Benjamin W. Robinson. 1918. 20.00 (ISBN 0-8414-7468-0). Folcroft.

Life of Paul. 2nd ed. Benjamin W. Robinson. LC 18-19810. (Midway Reprint Ser). 1973. pap. 16.00x (ISBN 0-226-72261-9). U of Chicago Pr.

Life of Prayer. St. Teresa of Avila. Ed. by James M. Houston. LC 83-12185. (Classics of Faith & Devotion). 1983. 11.95 (ISBN 0-88070-022-X). Multnomah.

Life of Prayer. A. B. Simpson. 122p. 1975. pap. 2.50 (ISBN 0-87509-164-4). Chr Pubns.

Life of Prayer & the Way to God. Mary C. Vincent. LC 81-21257. (Illus.). 96p. (Orig.). 1982. pap. 3.50 (ISBN 0-932506-11-9). St Bedes Pubns.

Life of Promise: Poverty, Chastity & Obedience. Francis J. Moloney. (Consecrated Life Studies Ser.: Vol. 1). 1983. 8.95 (ISBN 0-89453-370-3). M Glazier.

Life of Prophet Muhammad-I. A. S. Hashim. (Islamic Books for Children: Bk. 4). pap. 4.95 (ISBN 0-686-18410-6); pap. 45.00 entire ser. (ISBN 0-686-18411-4). Kazi Pubns.

Life of Prophet Muhammad-II. A. S. Hashim. (Islamic Books for Children: Bk 5). pap. 4.95 (ISBN 0-686-18408-4); pap. 45.00 entire ser. (ISBN 0-686-18409-2). Kazi Pubns.

Life of R. M. M'Cheyne. Andrew Bonar. 1978. pap. 3.45 (ISBN 0-85151-085-X). Banner of Truth.

Life of Ralph Waldo Emerson. Richard Garnett. LC 73-12352. 1972. Repr. of 1888 ed. lib. bdg. 12.50 (ISBN 0-8414-4404-8). Folcroft.

Life of Ramakrishna. Romain Rolland. 5.95 (ISBN 0-87481-080-9). Vedanta Pr.

Life of Reason: Reason in Religion, Vol. 3. George Santayana. 288p. 1982. pap. 5.95 (ISBN 0-486-24253-6). Dover.

Life of Religion: A Marquette University Symposium on the Nature of Religious Belief. Ed. by Stanley M. Harrison & Richard C. Taylor. 124p. (Orig.). 1986. lib. bdg. 22.50 (ISBN 0-8191-5558-6); pap. text ed. 8.75 (ISBN 0-8191-5559-4). U Pr of Amer.

Life of Robert Lewis Dabney. Thomas C. Johnson. 1977. 16.95 (ISBN 0-85151-253-4). Banner of Truth.

Life of Rt. Rev. Joseph Rosati, D. M., First Bishop of St. Louis, 1789-1843. Frederick J. Easterly. LC 73-3587. (Catholic University of America. Studies in American Church History: No. 33). Repr. of 1942 ed. 27.00 (ISBN 0-404-57783-0). AMS Pr.

Life of Rudolf Steiner. Sonia T. Clark. (Rudolf Steiner Publications Ser.). 40p. 1985. pap. 4.00 (ISBN 0-89345-905-4, Steiner). Garber Comm.

Life of St. Alexis, the Man of God. 1985. pap. 1.50 (ISBN 0-317-30438-0). Holy Trinity.

Life of St. Aloysius Gonzaga: Patron of Christian Youth. Maurice Meschler. LC 85-52294. 344p. 1985. pap. 7.00 (ISBN 0-89555-275-2). Tan Bks Pubs.

Life of St. Anselm, Archbishop of Canterbury. Eadmer. Ed. & tr. by R. W. Southern. (Oxford Medieval Texts Ser.). 1972. 49.00x (ISBN 0-19-822225-4). Oxford U Pr.

Life of St. Anthony Mary Claret. Fanchon Royer. LC 85-52248. 302p. (Orig.). 1985. pap. 8.00 (ISBN 0-89555-288-4). Tan Bks Pubs.

Life of St. Anthony the Great. Saint Athanasius. pap. 2.95 (ISBN 0-686-16367-2). Eastern Orthodox.

Life of Saint Benedict: Book II of the Dialogues of Gregory the Great. Gregory The Great. Tr. by Myra L. Uhlfelder. LC 66-30611. (Orig.). 1967. pap. 3.56 scp (ISBN 0-672-60468-X, LLA216). Bobbs.

Life of St. Benedict: St. Gregory's Dialogues, Book 2. Myra L. Uhlfelder. 1967. pap. text ed. write for info. (ISBN 0-02-422100-7). Macmillan.

Life of Saint Cuthbert. Tr. by W. Forbes-Leith from Latin. pap. 6.95 (ISBN 0-317-52092-X). Eastern Orthodox.

Life of St. Cyprian. St. Pontus. pap. 1.50 (ISBN 0-686-05651-5). Eastern Orthodox.

Life of St. Dominie in Old French Verse. Saint Domingo De Guzman. Ed. by Warren F. Manning. (Harv Studies in Romance Languages). 1944. 32.00 (ISBN 0-527-01118-5). Kraus Repr.

Life of Saint Francis. Pedro E. Subercaseaux. 1977. buckram 25.00 (ISBN 0-8199-0615-8). Franciscan Herald.

Life of St. Francis & the Soul of Modern Man. Maurice F. Egan. (Illus.). 131p. 1983. 88.85 (ISBN 0-89266-427-4). Am Classical Coll Pr.

Life of Saint Francis of Assisi. E. E. Reynolds. 128p. 1983. pap. 5.95 (ISBN 0-87061-081-3). Chr Classics.

Life of St. Francis of Assisi. Paul Sabatier. 1977. lib. bdg. 59.95 (ISBN 0-8490-2167-7). Gordon Pr.

Life of Saint Hilarion. Jerome. 1976. 1.95 (ISBN 0-686-15462-2). Eastern Orthodox.

Life of St. John the Almsgiver. pap. 1.25 (ISBN 0-317-11384-4). Eastern Orthodox.

Life of St. Katharine of Alexandria. John Capgrave. Ed. by Carl Horstmann. (EETS, OS Ser.: No. 100). Repr. of 1893 ed. 70.00 (ISBN 0-527-00102-3). Kraus Repr.

Life of St. Macrina. St. Gregory. 1974. pap. 2.95 (ISBN 0-686-10202-9). Eastern Orthodox.

Life of Saint Martin of Tours. Sulpicius Severus. pap. 1.95 (ISBN 0-686-05653-1). Eastern Orthodox.

Life of St. Maximus the Confessor. Ed. by Holy Transfiguration Monastery. Tr. by Christopher Birchall from Greek, & Russian. (Illus.). 73p. (Orig.). 1982. pap. 5.00 (ISBN 0-913026-52-2). St Nectarios.

Life of St. Patrick: His Place in History. facsimile ed. John B. Bury. LC 79-175691. (Select Bibliographies Reprint Ser). Repr. of 1905 ed. 24.50 (ISBN 0-8369-6606-6). Ayer Co Pubs.

Life of St. Paul. James A. Stalker. (Stalker Trilogy Ser.). 176p. 1984. pap. 5.95 (ISBN 0-310-44181-1, 12617P). Zondervan.

Life of Saint Severin & Other Minor Works. Eugippius. LC 65-12908. (Fathers of the Church Ser: Vol. 55). 132p. 1965. 14.95x (ISBN 0-8132-0055-5). Cath U Pr.

Life of St. Stanislaus Kosta, of the Society of Jesus, Patron of Novices. 1978. Repr. of 1850 ed. lib. bdg. 20.00 (ISBN 0-8495-0127-X). Arden Lib.

Life of Saint Teresa of Avila. Elizabeth Hamilton. 190p. 1982. pap. 6.95 (ISBN 0-87061-089-9, Pub. by A Clarke Bks UK). Chr Classics.

Life of St. Vincent Pallotti. John S. Gaynor. 1980. 4.00 (ISBN 0-8198-4401-2); pap. 3.00 (ISBN 0-8198-4402-0). Dghtrs St Paul.

Life of Salvation. Gilbert W. Stafford. 1979. pap. 3.95 (ISBN 0-87162-216-5, D5210). Warner Pr.

Life of Samuel of Kalamon. T. Alcock. 144p. 1983. pap. text ed. 35.00x (ISBN 0-85668-219-5, Pub. by Aris & Phillips UK). Humanities.

Life of Sir Thomas More. William Roper. pap. 6.95 (ISBN 0-87243-118-5). Templegate.

Life of Spirit, Vol. I. Robert R. Leichtman & Carl Japikse. (Illus.). 216p. (Orig.). 1986. pap. 7.95 (ISBN 0-89804-132-5). Ariel OH.

Life of Spirit Series. Robert R. Leichtman & Carl Japikse. (Orig.). 1982. pap. 2.25 ea. Ariel OH.

Life of Sri Aurobindo. A. B. Purani. (Illus.). 1978. 13.50 (ISBN 0-89071-230-1); pap. 11.25 (ISBN 0-89071-229-8). Matagiri.

Life of Sri Ramakrishna. Compiled by Advaita Ashrama Staff. 12.00 (ISBN 0-87481-077-9). Vedanta Pr.

Life of Sri Ranauja. Swami Ramakrisnananda. 1979. pap. 8.95 (ISBN 0-87481-446-4). Vedanta Pr.

Life of Swami Vivekananda, 2 Vols. rev. ed. Eastern & Western Disciples of Vivekananda. Vol. 1, 1980, 629p. 12.95x (ISBN 0-87481-196-1); Vol. 2. 16.00x (ISBN 0-87481-197-X). Vedanta Pr.

Life of Tecumseh & of His Brother the Prophet: With a Historical Sketch of the Shawanoe Indians. Benjamin Drake. LC 78-90173. (Mass Violence in America Ser). Repr. of 1841 ed. 14.00 (ISBN 0-405-01307-8). Ayer Co Pubs.

Life of Teresa of Jesus. E. Alison Peers. 1960. pap. 5.50 (ISBN 0-385-01109-1, Im). Doubleday.

Life of the Blessed Virgin Mary. Anne C. Emmerich. Tr. by Michael Palairet from Ger. 1970. pap. 10.00 (ISBN 0-89555-048-2). TAN Bks Pubs.

Life of the Blessed Virgin Mary. A. C. Emmerick. (Roman Catholic Ser.). 1979. lib. bdg. 69.95 (ISBN 0-8490-2959-7). Gordon Pr.

Life of the Buddha. Alfred C. Foucher. Tr. by Simone B. Boas. LC 72-6195. 272p. 1972. Repr. of 1963 ed. lib. bdg. 22.50x (ISBN 0-8371-6476-1, FOLB). Greenwood.

Life of the Church. Lavonn D. Brown. 1987. 5.95 (ISBN 0-8054-1643-9). Broadman.

Life of the Rev. George Whitefield, 2 vols. Luke Tyerman. LC 75-31102. Repr. of 1877 ed. 97.50 (ISBN 0-404-13540-4). AMS Pr.

Life of the Rev. John S. Inskip. William McDonald & John E. Searless. Ed. by Donald W. Dayton. (Higher Christian Life Ser.). 374p. 1985. 45.00 (ISBN 0-8240-6424-0). Garland Pub.

Life of the Rev. Rowland Hill, A. M. Edwin Sidney. 1978. Repr. of 1834 ed. lib. bdg. 25.00 (ISBN 0-8495-4870-5). Arden Lib.

Life of the Reverend Mr. George Trosse. George Trosse. Ed. by A. W. Brink. LC 73-79097. pap. 37.50 (ISBN 0-317-26445-1, 2023853). Bks Demand UMI.

Life of the Servant. Henry Suso. 144p. 1983. pap. 11.95 (ISBN 0-227-67862-1, Pub. by J Clarke UK). Attic Pr.

Life of the Spirit in Women: A Jungian Approach. Helen M. Luke. 1983. pap. 2.50x (ISBN 0-87574-230-0, 230). Pendle Hill.

Life of the Spirit: The Immortality of the Soul & the Perfectibility of Man. Samuel Garfield. (Illus.). 1978. deluxe bdg. 41.45 (ISBN 0-930582-04-7). Gloucester Art.

Life of Vivekananda. Romain Rolland. 1987. 7.95 (ISBN 0-87481-090-6, Pub. by Advaita Ashrama). Vedanta Pr.

Life of William Blake: With Selections from His Poems & Other Writings, 2 vols. enl. ed. Alexander Gilchrist. (Illus.). 993p. 1969. Set. 75.00x (ISBN 0-87753-017-3). Phaeton.

Life of William Penn. Mason L. Weems. LC 75-31139. Repr. of 1822 ed. 17.50 (ISBN 0-404-13613-3). AMS Pr.

Life of William Penn: With Selections from His Correspondence & Autobiography. facsimile ed. Samuel M. Janney. LC 74-130555. (Select Bibliographies Reprint Ser.). Repr. of 1851 ed. 24.00 (ISBN 0-8369-5528-5). Ayer Co Pubs.

Life of William Wilberforce: By His Sons, 5 vols. Robert I. Wilberforce & Samuel Wilberforce. LC 72-5506. (Black Heritage Library Collections Ser). 1972. Repr. of 1838 ed. Set. 121.00 (ISBN 0-8369-9151-6). Ayer Co Pubs.

Life of Zoroaster: In the Words of His Own Hymns the "Gathas". Tr. by Kenneth S. Guthrie. LC 73-131036. Repr. of 1914 ed. 14.50 (ISBN 0-404-02964-7). AMS Pr.

Life on the Highest Plane: A Study of the Spiritual Nature & Needs of Man. Ruth Paxson. pap. 12.95 (ISBN 0-8010-7091-0). Baker Bk.

Life, or Legend of Gaudama: The Buddha of the Burmese, 2 vols. 4th ed. Paul A. Bigandet. LC 77-8749. Repr. of 1912 ed. Set. 52.50 (ISBN 0-404-16800-0). AMS Pr.

Life out of Death: Meditations on the Easter Mystery. Hans U. Von Balthasar. LC 84-48704. 64p. 1985. pap. 3.50 (ISBN 0-8006-1821-1, 1-1821). Fortress.

Life Planning. Kirk E. Farnsworth & Wendell H. Lawhead. 96p. (Orig.). 1981. pap. 7.95 (ISBN 0-87784-840-8). Inter-Varsity.

Life Planning Guide for Women. Mary Vander Goot. 128p. 1982. pap. 9.95x (ISBN 0-88946-512-6). E Mellen.

Life Problems. G. Campbell Morgan. (Morgan Library). 1978. pap. 3.95 (ISBN 0-8010-6056-7). Baker Bk.

Life Records of John Milton, 1608-1674, 5 Vols. Ed. by J. Milton French. LC 66-20024. 2368p. 1966. Repr. of 1958 ed. Set. 150.00x (ISBN 0-87752-039-9). Gordian.

Life Sentence. Charles W. Colson. (Illus.). 320p. 1981. pap. 7.95 (ISBN 0-8007-5059-4, Power Bks). Revell.

Life-Size Living. Leonard Mann. Ed. by Michael L. Sherer. (Orig.). 1986. pap. 6.25 (ISBN 0-89536-820-X, 6829). CSS of Ohio.

Life Songs Number Two. Ed. by S. F. Coffman. 288p. (With Responsive Readings). 1938. 6.95x (ISBN 0-8361-1116-8). Herald Pr.

Life Story of Brigham Young. facsimile ed. Susa Y. Gates & Leah D. Widtsoe. LC 74-164602. (Select Bibliographies Reprint Ser). Repr. of 1930 ed. 24.00 (ISBN 0-8369-5886-1). Ayer Co Pubs.

Life Story of His Divine Grace A. C. Bhaktivedanta Swami Prabhupada. Satsvarupa dasa Goswami. 32p. 1984. saddlestitch 3.50 (ISBN 0-89647-019-9). Bala Bks.

Life-style Evangelism: Crossing Traditional Boundaries to Reach the Unbelieving World. Joseph C. Aldrich. LC 80-27615. (Critical Concern Bks.). 1981. 10.95 (ISBN 0-930014-46-4). Multnomah.

Life-Style Evangelism: Crossing Traditional Boundaries to Reach the Unbelieving World. Joseph C. Aldrich. LC 80-27615. (Critical Concern Ser.). 246p. 1983. pap. 6.95 (ISBN 0-88070-023-8). Multnomah.

Life-Style Evangelism: Study Guide. Joseph C. Aldrich. 1983. pap. 2.95 (ISBN 0-88070-020-3). Multnomah.

Life Styled by God: A Woman's Workshop on Spiritual Discipline for Weight Control. Pam Snyder. (Woman's Workshop Ser.). 112p. (Orig.). 1985. pap. 2.95 (ISBN 0-310-42791-6, 11378P). Zondervan.

Life that Wins. Watchman Nee. Ed. by Herbert L. Fader. Tr. & intro. by Stephen Kaung. 157p. (Orig.). 1986. 9.00 (ISBN 0-935008-65-9); pap. 4.00 (ISBN 0-935008-66-7). Christian Fellow Pubs.

Life-There's More to It Than Meets the Eye. Charles Moore. 1983. 5.95 (ISBN 0-8062-2110-0). Carlton.

Life, Time. 1st ed. Jane F. Rittmayer. pap. 31.80 (ISBN 0-317-26230-0, 2055572). Bks Demand UMI.

Life to Live - a Way to Pray. John Coburn. 160p. (Orig.). 1973. pap. 5.95 (ISBN 0-8164-2079-3, SP80, HarpR). Har-Row.

Life Together. Dietrich Bonhoeffer. LC 54-6901. 128p. 1976. pap. 6.95 (ISBN 0-06-060851-X, RD292, HarpR). Har-Row.

Life Triumphant. James Allen. 112p. 1983. pap. 6.50 (ISBN 0-89540-125-8, SB-125). Sun Pub.

Life: Voices from the Heart. William J. Crockett. 15p. 1985. pap. 3.00 (ISBN 0-934383-05-7). Pride Prods.

Life, Walk & Triumph of Faith: With an Account of His Life and Work by Peter Toon. William Romaine. 439p. 1970. 14.00 (ISBN 0-227-67744-7). Attic Pr.

Life We Never Dared Hope For. Roger Schutz. 80p. (Orig.). 1981. pap. 3.95 (ISBN 0-8164-2322-9, HarpR). Har-Row.

Life When Jesus Was a Boy. Cassandre. 48p. 1981. pap. 6.95 (ISBN 0-8170-0913-2). Judson.

Life with Elvis. David Stanley. (Illus.). 1986. 12.95 (ISBN 0-8007-1490-3). Revell.

Life with God. Herman C. Theiss. pap. 5.95 (ISBN 0-933350-05-8); tchrs. manual 3.00 (ISBN 0-933350-44-9). Morse Pr.

Life with Promise: Marriage as a Covenant Venture. Larry Martens. LC 82-81266. 76p. (Orig.). 1982. pap. 4.95 (ISBN 0-937364-03-7). Kindred Pr.

Life with Spice Resource Manual. Daisy Hepburn. 1984. 5.95 (ISBN 0-8307-0936-3, 5203006). Regal.

Life with the Perfect Master. Satsvarupa Das Goswami. Ed. by Mathuresa Dasa. 110p. 1983. pap. text ed. 3.50 (ISBN 0-911233-17-2). Gita Nagari.

Life with Your Parents. Herman C. Ahrens, Jr. (Looking Up Ser.). 24p. 1983. pap. 1.25 booklet (ISBN 0-8298-0667-9). Pilgrim NY.

Life Without Compromise. John R. Bisagno. LC 81-71253. 1983. 3.95 (ISBN 0-8054-1503-3). Broadman.

Life Without End. Bob Hendren. LC 80-54164. (Journey Adult Ser.). 144p. 1981. pap. 3.50 (ISBN 0-8344-0118-5). Sweet.

Lifelines: God's Frame Work For Christian Living. Edith Schaeffer. LC 83-71240. 224p. (Orig.). 1982. (Crossway Bks); pap. 6.95 (ISBN 0-89107-294-2). Good News.

Lifelong Fitness & Fulfillment. Richard Couey. LC 80-65844. 1980. 7.95 (ISBN 0-8054-5426-8). Broadman.

Lifemating: New Hope for Those Who've Loved & Lost. Mark Dana. 1985. 7.75 (ISBN 0-8062-2447-9). Carlton.

Lifer. Ted Winters & Al Janssen. (Living Books). 320p. 1985. pap. 3.95 (ISBN 0-8423-2142-X). Tyndale.

Life's Candle Light. Yvonne Schneider. 82p. pap. 5.95 (ISBN 0-942494-29-6). Coleman Pub.

Life's Choices: Discovering the Consequences of Sowing & Reaping. John Lawrence. LC 82-3438. 120p. 1982. pap. 5.95 (ISBN 0-930014-85-5). Multnomah.

Life's Deeper Aspects. N. Sri Ram. 1968. 3.50 (ISBN 0-8356-7172-0). Theos Pub Hse.

Life's Golden Gleanings. Ruby E. Stover. 94p. pap. 1.00 (ISBN 0-686-29127-1). Faith Pub Hse.

Life's Priorities. Keith Johnson. LC 79-63739. 1979. pap. 3.95 (ISBN 0-89841-000-2). Zoe Pubns.

Life's Riddle. Nils Amneus. 1975. pap. 5.25 (ISBN 0-913004-26-X). Point Loma Pub.

Life's Story & Healings. Nellie Poulos. 160p. pap. 1.50 (ISBN 0-686-29128-X). Faith Pub Hse.

Lifesigns: Intimacy, Fecundity, Ecstasy in Christian Perspective. Henri J. Nouwen. LC 86-4572. (Illus.). 128p. 1986. pap. 11.95 (ISBN 0-385-23627-1). Doubleday.

Lifestyle: Conversations with Members of the Unification Church. Ed. by Richard Quebedeaux. LC 82-50799. (Conference Ser.: No. 13). (Orig.). 1982. 12.95 (ISBN 0-932894-18-6, Pub. by New Era Bks); pap. 9.95 (ISBN 0-932894-13-5, Pub. by New Era Bks). Paragon Hse.

Lifestyle in the Eighties: An Evangelical Commitment to Simple Lifestyle. Ed. by Ronald J. Sider. LC 82-7067. (Contemporary Issues in Social Ethics Ser.). 258p. 1982. pap. 10.95 (ISBN 0-664-24437-8). Westminster.

Lifestyles. Ed. by Richard Quebedeaux. LC 82-50799. 214p. (Orig.). 1982. 14.95; pap. 10.95. Rose Sharon Pr.

Lifetime. Anthony J. Marquis. 48p. 1986. 5.95 (ISBN 0-89962-521-5). Todd & Honeywell.

Lifetime Beginner: An Autobiography. Nikkyo Niwano. Tr. by Richard L. Gage from Japanese. Orig. Title: Shoshin Issho & Niwano Nikkyo Jiden. (Illus.). 344p. 1978. 14.95 (Pub. by Kosei Publishing Co). C E Tuttle.

Lifetime in Preparation: Srila Prabhupada-lilamrta, Vol. 1. Satsvarupa dasa Goswami. (Illus.). 357p. 1980. 12.95 (ISBN 0-686-71685-X). Bhaktivedanta.

Lifetime of a Jew: Throughout the Ages of Jewish History. rev. ed. Hayyim Schauss. (Illus.). (YA) 1976. pap. 7.95 (ISBN 0-8074-0096-3, 383473). UAHC.

Lifetime of Love. S. L. Hart. LC 67-29163. 1969. 6.50 (ISBN 0-8198-0076-7); pap. 5.50 (ISBN 0-8198-4426-8). Dghtrs St Paul.

Lifetimes: True Accounts of Reincarnation. Frederick Lenz. 224p. 1986. pap. 2.95 (ISBN 0-449-20908-3, Crest). Fawcett.

Lift My Spirits, Lord: Prayers of a Struggling Christian. Bryan J. Leech. LC 84-9351. 128p. (Orig.). 1984. pap. 5.95 (ISBN 0-8066-2090-0, 10-3850). Augsburg.

Lift of Love. Bo Baker. 1986. 7.95 (ISBN 0-8054-5039-4). Broadman.

Lift up Your Heart. Fulton J. Sheen. 280p. 1975. pap. 4.50 (ISBN 0-385-09001-3, Im). Doubleday.

Lift up Your Hearts. Caryll Houselander. 1979. pap. 2.25 (ISBN 0-88479-020-7). Arena Lettres.

Lift Your Eyes to the Mountain. David Knight. 8.95 (ISBN 0-87193-137-0); pap. 6.95 (ISBN 0-87193-190-7). Dimension Bks.

Lifting the Veil (Kundalini Yoga) A Compendium of Rajneesh's Essential Teachings. R. C. Prasad. 1975. pap. 6.50 (ISBN 0-89684-244-4). Orient Bk Dist.

Lifting up for the Downcast. William Bridge. 1979. pap. 5.45 (ISBN 0-85151-298-4). Banner of Truth.

Light. Ernest Holmes et al. Ed. by Willis H. Kinnear. 96p. 1971. pap. 5.50 (ISBN 0-911336-09-5). Sci of Mind.

Light a Small Candle. Bernard Palmer & Marjorie Palmer. LC 82-84439. 1982. 10.95 (ISBN 0-911802-54-1). Free Church Pubns.

Light after Ellen White. large print ed. Charline Brians. 32p. 1985. pap. 5.00 (ISBN 0-914009-06-0). VHI Library.

Light & Life in the Fourth Gospel. Howard Brinton. LC 76-128679. (Orig.). 1971. pap. 2.50x (ISBN 0-87574-179-7). Pendle Hill.

Light & Peace. R. P. Quadrupani. LC 79-67860. 193p. 1980. pap. 3.50 (ISBN 0-89555-133-0). TAN Bks Pubs.

Light & the Glory. Peter Marshall & David Manuel. 352p. 1977. 14.95 (ISBN 0-8007-0886-5); pap. 7.95 (ISBN 0-8007-5054-3, Power Bks). Revell.

Light & the Glory Study Guide. Peter Marshall & David Manuel. 1981. pap. 5.95 (ISBN 0-8007-1279-X); photo enrichment pack o.p. 12.50. Revell.

Light Another Candle: The Story & Meaning of Hanukkah. Miriam Chaikin. LC 80-28137. (Illus.). 80p. 1981. 10.50 (ISBN 0-395-31026-1, Clarion); pap. 3.95 (ISBN 0-89919-057-X). HM.

Light at the Center: Context & Pretext of Modern Mysticism. Agehananda Bharati. 1976. lib. bdg. 11.95 (ISBN 0-915520-03-6); pap. 6.95 (ISBN 0-915520-04-4). Ross-Erikson.

Light Beyond: Adventure in Hassidic Thought. Aryeh Kaplan. 384p. 1981. 15.95 (ISBN 0-940118-33-5). Maznaim.

Light-Delight-Journeys. Sri Chinmoy. 67p. (Orig.). 1975. pap. 2.00 (ISBN 0-88497-102-3). Aum Pubns.

Light for All People. Bill Van Horn. 1981. 3.50 (ISBN 0-89536-469-7, 1215). CSS of Ohio.

Light for My Life. Desmond B. Hills. Ed. by Bobbie J. Van Dolson. 384p. 1981. 7.95 (ISBN 0-8280-0041-7). Review & Herald.

Light for Students: Compiled from the Writings of Sri Aurobindo & the Mother. Sri Aurobindo. 1984. pap. 3.50 (ISBN 0-89071-272-7). Matagiri.

Light for the Journey: Living the Ten Commandments. Ernest Lewis. 1985. 10.95. Word Bks.

Light for the Way: Old Testament, 2 bks. Frank Starr. (Illus.). 96p. 1987. pap. 2.95 ea. Bk. 3 (ISBN 0-570-04450-2, 12-3057). Bk. 4 (ISBN 0-570-04451-0, 12-3058). Concordia.

Light for Them That Sit in Darkness. John Bunyan. pap. 3.50 (ISBN 0-685-19838-3). Reiner.

Light from Above. Alfred W Koehler. 1960. 3.95 (ISBN 0-570-03506-6, 14-1260). Concordia.

Light from Heaven. Christmas Carol Kauffman. 1965. pap. 5.95 (ISBN 0-8024-3814-8). Moody.

Light from Jewish Lamps: A Modern Treasury of Jewish Thoughts. Ed. by Sidney Greenberg. LC 86-71270. 465p. 1986. 30.00 (ISBN 0-87668-918-7). Aronson.

Light from Light. Jack Perry. 208p. 1987. 11.95 (ISBN 0-310-23850-1). Zondervan.

Light from Light: What Catholics Believe about Jesus. Ronald Lawler. 240p. (Orig.). 1987. pap. 7.50 (ISBN 0-87973-547-3, 547). Our Sunday Visitor.

Light from Many Lamps. Lillian E. Watson. 1951. 15.95 (ISBN 0-671-42300-2). S&S.

Light from the Ancient Past, 2 vols. 2nd ed. Jack Finegan. (Illus.). 1959. Vol. 1 2nd Ed. 52.50 (ISBN 0-691-03550-4); Vol. 1 2nd Edition. pap. 16.50 (ISBN 0-691-00207-X); Vol. 2. 50.00 (ISBN 0-691-03551-2); Vol. 2. pap. 15.50x (ISBN 0-691-00208-8); Set. 90.00 (ISBN 0-686-76901-5). Princeton U Pr.

Light from the East: Studies in Japanese Confucianism. Robert C. Armstrong. lib. bdg. 79.95 (ISBN 0-87968-134-9). Krishna Pr.

Light from the West. Selig Schachnowitz. Tr. by Joseph Leftwich. 7.95 (ISBN 0-87306-124-1). Feldheim.

Light in Babylon. Carole Carlson. 256p. 1985. 12.95 (ISBN 0-8499-0452-8, 0452-8). Word Bks.

Light in Britain. Grace Cooke & Ivan Cooke. (Illus.). 1971. pap. 5.95 (ISBN 0-85487-056-3). De Vorss.

Light in the Darkness. Benjamin Gorodetsky. Tr. by Mordecai Schreiber. LC 85-63010. (Illus.). 224p. 1986. 14.95 (ISBN 0-88400-120-2). Shengold.

Light in the Darkness. Homer A. Kent, Jr. (New Testament Studies Ser.). 1974. pap. 5.95 (ISBN 0-8010-5343-9). Baker Bk.

Light in the Darkness: Studies in the Gospel of John. Homer A. Kent, Jr. (Illus.). pap. 5.95 (ISBN 0-88469-055-5). BMH Bks.

Light in the Grotto. Daughters of St. Paul. 1972. 3.00 (ISBN 0-8198-4409-8); pap. 2.00 (ISBN 0-8198-4410-1). Dghtrs St Paul.

Light in the Valley: The McCurdy Mission School Story. Robert H. Terry. LC 84-50388. (Illus.). 148p. (Orig.). 1984. pap. 9.95 (ISBN 0-86534-051-X). Sunstone Pr.

Light is Life: Eastern Rite Religious Emblem Record. 1980. pap. 1.60 (ISBN 0-8395-3011-0, 3011). BSA.

Light of All Nations: Essays on the Church in New Testament Research. Daniel Harrington. (Good News Studies Ser.: Vol. 3). 1982. pap. 7.95 (ISBN 0-89453-291-X). M Glazier.

Light of Asia. Edwin Arnold. LC 79-4436. 1969. pap. 4.50 (ISBN 0-8356-0405-5, Quest). Theos Pub Hse.

Light of Asia: Buddha Sakyamuni in Asian Art. Pratapaditya Pal. LC 84-788. (Illus.). 344p. 1984. 35.00 (ISBN 0-295-96123-6, Pub. by LA County Museum of Art). U of Wash Pr.

Light of Asia: Buddha Sakyamuni in Asian Art. Pratapaditya Pal et al. (Illus.). 332p. 1984. 35.00 (ISBN 0-87587-116-X, Dist. by U of Wash Pr); pap. 16.95 (ISBN 0-87587-116-X). LA Co Art Mus.

Light of Asia or, the Great Renunciation (Mahabhinishkramana) Being the Life & Teaching of Gautama, Prince of India, Founder of Buddhism. Edwin Arnold. x, 176p. 1972. pap. 5.00 (ISBN 0-7100-7006-3). Methuen Inc.

Light of Asia: The Life & Teaching of Gautama Buddha. Edwin Arnold. xi, 238p. 1977. 5.00 (ISBN 0-938998-17-X). Theosophy.

Light of Christ. Pope John Paul II. 256p. 1987. pap. 9.95 (ISBN 0-8245-0820-3). Crossroad NY.

Light of Consciousness: Explorations in Transpersonal Psychology. Richard D. Mann. 208p. 1984. 39.50 (ISBN 0-87395-905-1); pap. 10.95 trade disc. (ISBN 0-87395-906-X). State U NY Pr.

Light of Exploration. R. P. Kaushik. LC 76-39622. 1977. pap. 5.95 (ISBN 0-918038-00-6). Journey Pubns.

Light of Kirpal. Kirpal Singh. LC 80-52537. xv, 446p. 1984. pap. 12.00 (ISBN 0-89142-033-9). Sant Bani Ash.

Light of Life: A Compendium of the Writings of Rabbi Chaim Ben Attar. Chaim B. Attar. 236p. 1986. pap. 9.95 (ISBN 0-87877-090-9). Newcastle Pub.

Light of Life: A Compendium of the Writings of Rabbi Chaim ben Moshe Attar. Chaim ben Moshe Attar. 160p. 1986. Repr. lib. bdg. 19.95x (ISBN 0-89370-690-6). Borgo Pr.

Light of Nature Pursued, 7 vols. Abraham Tucker. Ed. by Rene Wellek. LC 75-11262. (British Philosophers & Theologians of the 17th & 18th Centuries: Vol. 60). 4075p. 1984. Repr. of 1805 ed. Set. lib. bdg. 355.00 (ISBN 0-8240-1811-7). Garland Pub.

Light of the Bhagavat. Bhaktivedanta Swami. 1985. 12.95 (ISBN 0-89213-135-7). Bhaktivedanta.

Light of the Mind: St. Augustine's Theory of Knowledge. Ronald H. Nash. LC 69-19765. Repr. of 1969 ed. 39.80 (ISBN 0-8357-9790-2, 2016099). Bks Demand UMI.

Light of the Soul. Alice A. Bailey. 1972. 20.00 (ISBN 0-85330-012-7); pap. 9.00 (ISBN 0-85330-112-3). Lucis.

Light of the Vedas. Manly P. Hall. (Adepts Ser.). pap. 3.95 (ISBN 0-89314-530-0). Philos Res.

Light of the World. Serge S. Verhovskoy. LC 82-16963. 163p. 1982. pap. 6.95 (ISBN 0-88141-004-7). St Vladimirs.

Light on a Dark Trail. Helen Parker. LC 82-71560. 1982. pap. 4.95 (ISBN 0-8054-5430-6). Broadman.

Light on a Mountain. Helena E. Ruhnau. (Illus.). 1976. 12.95 (ISBN 0-941036-00-6); pap. 6.50 (ISBN 0-941036-01-4). Colleasius Pr.

Light on Ananda Yoga. Shiv Brat Lal. Tr. by Steve Morrow. LC 82-61990. 134p. 1982. pap. 10.00 (ISBN 0-89142-041-X). Sant Bani Ash.

Light on Synanon. David Mitchell & Cathy Mitchell. 1982. pap. 7.50 (ISBN 0-87223-761-3, Wideview Bks). Putnam Pub Group.

Light on the Path. Collins. 1.50 (ISBN 0-8356-7192-5). Theos Pub Hse.

Light on the Path. Mabel Collins. 1970. pap. 1.75 (ISBN 0-8356-0299-0, Quest). Theos Pub Hse.

Light on the Path. Mabel C. Collins. leatherette 3.00 (ISBN 0-911662-13-8). Yoga.

Light on the Path. Swami Muktananda. LC 81-51377. 112p. 1972. 4.95 (ISBN 0-914602-54-3). SYDA Found.

Light on the Path: Daily Scripture Readings in Hebrew & Greek. Ed. by Heinrich Bitzer. 400p. (Orig.). 1982. pap. 9.95 (ISBN 0-8010-0822-0). Baker Bk.

Light on the Spiritual Path. Roy E. Davis. 138p. 1984. pap. 3.95 (ISBN 0-317-20861-6). CSA Pr.

Light Over Tibet. Jan Van Rijckenborgh. 40p. (Orig.). 1987. pap. 1.75. Rosycross Pr.

Light Shines in the Darkness. Georgianna Summers. (Orig.). 1987. pap. price not set (ISBN 0-89536-888-9, 7874). CSS of Ohio.

Light Shineth in Darkness: Five Studies in Revelation after Christ. Udo Schaefer. Tr. by Helene M. Neri & Oliver Coburn. 208p. 1977. 15.95 (ISBN 0-85398-091-8); pap. 9.95 (ISBN 0-85398-072-1). G Ronald Pub.

Light Through an Eastern Window. K. C. Pillai. pap. 4.95 (ISBN 0-8315-0057-3). Speller.

Light Through an Eastern Window. K. C. Pillai. LC 85-51634. 144p. 1986. 4.95 (ISBN 0-910068-63-1). Am Christian.

Light to Light. Betty Streib. 1981. 10.00 (ISBN 0-89536-486-7, 1238). CSS of Ohio.

Light to Live By (Wedding Edition) Ed. by Herbert Lockyer. 384p. 1981. graduation ed. 9.95 (ISBN 0-310-28230-6, 10145); pap. 9.95 all-occasion ed. (ISBN 0-310-28211-X, 10124P). Zondervan.

Light to the Nations. 201p. 1983. pap. 3.95 (ISBN 0-88479-036-3). Arena Lettres.

Light to the Nations: A Guide to the New Testament. James F. Leary. 144p. 1986. pap. 4.95 (ISBN 0-88479-036-3). Chr Classics.

Light Triumphant. Esther Lense. 1978. pap. 3.25 (ISBN 0-89536-301-1, 1253). CSS of Ohio.

Light Unto My Path. Mary L. Merrill et al. (Illus.). 185p. 1981. Repr. of 1982 ed. 10.00 (ISBN 0-686-33180-X). Pathway Pubns.

Light unto My Path: Old Testament Studies in Honor of Jacob M. Myers. Ed. by Howard N. Bream et al. LC 73-85042. (Gettysburg Theological Studies, No. 4). 576p. 1974. 27.95 (ISBN 0-87722-026-3). Temple U Pr.

Light upon the Land. Elaine Furlow et al. (Home Mission Study). 110p. (Orig.). 1984. pap. 2.85 (ISBN 0-937170-28-3). Home Mission.

Light Will Dawn. Mary L. Kupferle. LC 77-91310. 1978. 5.95 (ISBN 0-87159-087-5). Unity School.

Light Within. Zev K. Nelson. LC 78-56774. 1979. 8.95 (ISBN 0-88400-060-5). Shengold.

Light Within: The Inner Path of Meditation. Laurence Freeman. 112p. 1987. pap. 7.95 (ISBN 0-8245-0785-1). Crossroad NY.

Light Within Us. Albert Schweitzer. (Philosophical Paperback Ser.). 58p. 1985. pap. 3.95 (ISBN 0-8022-2484-9). Philos Lib.

Light Within You: Looking at Life Through New Eyes. John Claypool. 1983. 9.95 (ISBN 0-8499-0273-8). Word Bks.

Light Your Own Lamp. Harriet Richards. LC 66-26971. 1967. 5.95 (ISBN 0-8022-1333-2). Philos Lib.

Lighten Our Darkness: Toward an Indigenous Theology of the Cross. Douglas J. Hall. LC 75-38963. 252p. 1980. pap. 9.95 (ISBN 0-664-24359-2). Westminster.

Lightgarment of the New Man. Jan Van Rijckenborgh & Catharose De Petri. Tr. of Het Lichtkleed van de Niewe Mens. 100p. (Orig.). Date not set. pap. 11.00. Rosycross Pr.

Lighthouse of Langdon: Presenting 20th Century Jehovah to Doomsday Man. Rohen Langdon. 207p. 1980. 9.00 (ISBN 0-682-49637-5). Exposition Pr FL.

Lightning East to West: Jesus, Gandhi & the Nuclear Age. James W. Douglass. 112p. 1983. pap. 6.95 (ISBN 0-8245-0587-5). Crossroad NY.

Lights: A Fable of Hanukahkah. Yehuda Wurtzel & Sara Wurtzel. LC 84-18297. (Illus.). 64p. 1985. pap. 7.95 (ISBN 0-940646-56-0). Rossel Bks.

Lights on the Tantra. M. P. Pandit. 3.95 (ISBN 0-89744-107-9, Pub. by Ganesh & Co. India). Auromere.

Lights on Yoga. Sri Aurobindo. 1979. pap. 3.00 (ISBN 0-89744-916-9). Auromere.

Lights Out, Christopher. Patricia A. McKissack. LC 84-71375. (Christopher Bks.). (Illus.). 32p. (Orig.). 1984. pap. 3.95 (ISBN 0-8066-2110-9, 10-3870). Augsburg.

Like a Meteor Across the Horizon: The Jesse B. Ferguson Story & History of the Church of Christ in Nashville. Johnny Tucker et al. (Illus., Orig.). 1978. pap. 2.95 (ISBN 0-686-26617-X). Tucker Pubns.

Like a Mighty Army. rev. ed. Charles W. Conn. LC 77-82067. 1977. 12.95 (ISBN 0-87148-510-9). Pathway Pr.

Like a Mighty Army. Charles W. Conn. 1955. 7.95 (ISBN 0-87148-505-2). Pathway Pr.

Like a Mighty River. David Manuel. LC 77-90948. (Illus.). 220p. 1977. 5.95 (ISBN 0-932260-02-0). Rock Harbor.

Like a Mighty River. Lois Wilson. (Illus.). 125p. (Orig.). 1981. pap. 6.95 (ISBN 0-919599-01-X). Wood Lake Pr.

Like a Mighty Wind. Mel Tari & Cliff Dudley. 171p. 1978. pap. 4.95 (ISBN 0-89221-123-7). New Leaf.

Like a Miracle. Ernest C. Wilson. 202p. 1971. 5.95 (ISBN 0-87159-088-3). Unity School.

Like a Promise. Phyllis C. Gobbell. LC 83-71490. 1983. 8.95 (ISBN 0-8054-7319-X). Broadman.

Like a River. Carl Brumback. LC 76-58782. (Illus.). 176p. 1977. pap. 2.95 (ISBN 0-88243-564-7, 02-0564). Gospel Pub.

Like Angels from a Cloud: The English Metaphysical Preachers 1588-1645. Horton Davies. 500p. 1986. 30.00 (ISBN 0-87328-088-1). Huntington Lib.

Like Christ. Andrew Murray. 240p. 1981. pap. 2.95 (ISBN 0-88368-099-8). Whitaker Hse.

Like Falling in Love. David W. Augsburger. (New Life Ser.). pap. 3.00 (ISBN 0-8361-1686-0). Herald Pr.

Likeness of Thomas More: An Iconographical Survey of Three Centuries. Stanley Morison. Ed. by Nicolas Barker. (Illus.). 1964. 50.00 (ISBN 0-8232-0575-4). Fordham.

Likrat Shabbat. Sidney Greenberg & Jonathan Levine. LC 78-669313. 10.00 (ISBN 0-87677-076-6); large type ed. 14.95; 10.95. Prayer Bk.

Likutey Moharan, Vol. 1. Rabbi Nachman of Breslov. Tr. by Simcha Bergman & Moshe Mykoff. 213p. 1986. pap. text ed. 10.00 (ISBN 0-930213-76-9). Breslov Res Inst.

Lilamrta, Vol. 5. Satsvarupa Das Goswami. (Illus.). 297p. 12.95 (ISBN 0-89213-119-5). Bhaktivedanta.

Lilies, Rabbits, & Painted Eggs: The Story of the Easter Symbols. Edna Barth. LC 74-79033. (Illus.). 1970. 8.95 (ISBN 0-395-28844-4, Clarion). HM.

Lilith's Daughters: Women & Religion in Contemporary Fiction. Barbara H. Rigney. LC 81-70012. 136p. 1982. 17.50x (ISBN 0-299-08960-6). U of Wis Pr.

Lillooet Indians. James A. Teit. LC 73-3520. (Jesup North Pacific Expedition. Publications: No. 2, Pt. 5). Repr. of 1906 ed. 20.00 (ISBN 0-404-58121-8). AMS Pr.

Lilmarta, Vol. 6. Satsvarupa Das Goswami. (Illus.). 12.95 (ISBN 0-89213-120-9). Bhaktivedanta.

Lilmod u-Lelamed: Studies in Jewish Education & Judaica in Honor of Louis Newman. Ed. by Alexander M. Shapiro. 1984. 20.00x (ISBN 0-88125-038-4). Ktav.

Lilmod Ulelamade: From the Teachings of Our Sages on Judges. Mordechai Katz. (Rothman Foundation Ser.). 1986. 8.95 (ISBN 0-87306-207-8); pap. 6.95 (ISBN 0-87306-928-5). Feldheim.

Lilmod Ulelamade on Joshua. Mordechai Katz. (Rothman Foundation Ser.). 1984. 8.95 (ISBN 0-87306-925-0); pap. 6.95 (ISBN 0-87306-926-9). Feldheim.

Lily Among the Thorns. Howard G. Hageman. 1978. write for info. (ISBN 0-916466-00-0). Reformed Church.

Lily Montagu & the Advancement of Liberal Judaism: From Vision to Vocation. Ellen M. Umansky. LC 83-22005. (Studies in Women & Religion: Vol. 12). 305p. 1984. 49.95x (ISBN 0-88946-537-1). E Mellen.

Lily Montagu: Sermons, Addresses, Letters & Prayers. Ellen J. Umansky. LC 85-3053. (Studies in Women & Religion: Vol. 15). (Illus.). 415p. 1985. 69.95x (ISBN 0-88946-534-7). E Mellen.

Limited to Everyone: An Invitation to Christian Faith. Robert Jones. 144p. (Orig.). 1982. pap. 7.95 (ISBN 0-8164-2381-4, HarpR). Har-Row.

Limits of Literary Criticism. Helen Gardner. LC 74-16242. 1956. lib. bdg. 8.00 (ISBN 0-8414-4558-3). Folcroft.

Limits of Religious Thought. 5th ed. H. L. Mansel. 1986. Repr. of 1870 ed. lib. bdg. 25.00X (ISBN 0-935005-46-3). Ibis Pub VA.

Limits of Religious Thought Examined. Henry L. Mansel. LC 72-172840. Repr. of 1859 ed. 25.00 (ISBN 0-404-04182-5). AMS Pr.

Limping along: Confessions of a Pilgrim Theologian. Bela Vassady. 248p. (Orig.). 1985. pap. 13.95 (ISBN 0-8028-0095-5). Eerdmans.

Lincoln & the Preachers. Edgar D. Jones. (Biography Index Reprint Ser). 1948. 21.00 (ISBN 0-8369-8018-2). Ayer Co Pubs.

Lincoln, English: Lincoln Diocese Documents. (EETS, OS Ser.: No. 149). Repr. of 1914 ed. 28.00 (ISBN 0-527-00145-7). Kraus Repr.

Lincoln's Religion. William J. Wolf. LC 70-123035. Orig. Title: Almost Chosen People. 1970. pap. 2.25 (ISBN 0-8298-0181-2). Pilgrim NY.

Lincoln's Use of the Bible. Samuel T. Jackson. LC 74-26790. 1974. Repr. of 1909 ed. lib. bdg. 17.00 (ISBN 0-8414-5329-2). Folcroft.

Linda's Song. Genny Waddell & Agnes Smith. 136p. (Orig.). 1985. pap. 5.95 (ISBN 0-89265-095-8). Randall Hse.

Lindisfarne Gospels. Janet Backhouse. LC 81-65990. (Cornell Phaidon Bks.). (Illus.). 96p. 1981. 29.95 (ISBN 0-8014-1354-0). Cornell U Pr.

Lines to Live By. Ed. by Clinton T. Howell. 200p. 1984. Repr. 12.95 (ISBN 0-8407-5389-6). Nelson.

Lines to the Mountain Gods: Nazca & the Mysteries of Peru. Evan Hadingham. LC 86-10137. (Illus.). 256p. 1986. 22.50 (ISBN 0-394-54235-5). Random.

Linger with Me: Moments Aside with Jesus. David E. Rosage. 212p. (Orig.). 1979. pap. 3.95 (ISBN 0-914544-29-2). Living Flame Pr.

Lingering at Calvary. S. Franklin Logsdon. 157p. (Orig.). 1981. pap. 3.95 (ISBN 0-89323-025-1). Bible Memory.

Lingering with my Lord: Post-Communion Experiences of St. Teresa of Avila. Tr. by Michael D. Griffin from Span. LC 84-18590. Orig. Title: Obras Completas de Teresa de Jesus Doctora de la Iglesia. 79p. 1985. pap. 3.95 (ISBN 0-317-19366-X). Alba.

Linguistic Concordance of Ruth & Jonah: Hebrew Vocabulary & Idiom. Francis I. Andersen & A. Dean Forbes. (Computer Bible Ser.: Vol. IX). 1976. pap. 15.00 (ISBN 0-935106-12-X). Biblical Res Assocs.

Linguistic Density Plots in Ezekiel: The Computer Bible, Vol. XXVII A & B. Van Dyke H. Parunak. Ed. by Arthur J. Baird & David Freedman. 528p. 1984. pap. 70.00x (ISBN 0-935106-22-7). Biblical Res Assocs.

Linguistics & Theology: The Significance of Noam Chomsky for Theological Construction. Irene Lawrence. LC 80-24210. (ATLA Monograph: No. 16). 214p. 1980. 17.50 (ISBN 0-8108-1347-5). Scarecrow.

Linquistic Key to the Greek New Testament. Fritz Rienecker & Cleon Rogers. 912p. 1982. 29.95 (ISBN 0-310-32050-X, 6277). Zondervan.

L'Integration des Juifs Nord-Africains en France. Doris Bensimon-Donath. (Publications de l'Institut d'Etudes et de Recherches Interethniques et Interculturelles: No. 1). 1971. pap. 14.00x (ISBN 90-2796-930-2). Mouton.

Lion & the Lamb. John P. Newport. LC 85-29887. 1986. 11.95 (ISBN 0-8054-1324-3). Broadman.

Lion Becomes Man: The Gnostic Leontomorphic Creator & the Creator & the Platonic Tradition. Howard Jackson. (SBL Dissertation Ser.). 1985. 17.95 (ISBN 0-89130-872-5, 06-01-81); pap. 11.95 (ISBN 0-89130-873-3). Scholars Pr GA.

Lion Encyclopedia of the Bible. Ed. by Pat Alexander. 352p. 1986. 24.95 (ISBN 0-7459-1113-7). Lion USA.

Lion Roars. Arthur H. Kolsti. 1985. 4.95 (ISBN 0-89536-720-3, 5804). CSS of Ohio.

Lion Story. Incl. The Battle of Jericho (ISBN 0-85648-736-8); ComeDown, Zacchaeus; David & Goliath (ISBN 0-85648-743-0); Enemies All Around (ISBN 0-85648-749-X); The First Christmas (ISBN 0-85648-757-0); Journey to the Promised Land (ISBN 0-85648-736-8); Little Lion & Friends (ISBN 0-7459-1029-7); Little Lion & the Butterfly (ISBN 0-7459-1030-0); Little Lion & the Thunderstorm (ISBN 0-7459-1031-9); Little Lion at Home (ISBN 0-7459-1028-9); Paul at Damascus (ISBN 0-85648-775-9); When Jesus Was Young (ISBN 0-85648-758-9). (Illus.). 24p. 1986. pap. 2.95 ea. Lion USA.

Lion's Roar of Queen Srimala. Tr. by Alex Wayman & Hideko Wayman. 160p. 1974. 24.00x (ISBN 0-231-03726-0). Columbia U Pr.

Lisbon Massacre of 1506 & the Royal Image in the Shebet Yehuda. Y. H. Yerushalmi. (Hebrew Union College Annual Supplements: Vol. 1). 12.50x (ISBN 0-87820-600-0, HUC Pr). Ktav.

Lishmor Velaasos: Guide to Basic Principles of Jewish Law & Their Applications in Theory & Practice. Mordechai Katz. (Rothman Foundation Ser.). 159p. 1981. 8.95 (ISBN 0-87306-974-9); pap. 6.95 (ISBN 0-317-42416-5). Feldheim.

L'Islam Contemporain. Roger Le Tourneau. LC 80-1922. Repr. of 1950 ed. 24.50 (ISBN 0-404-18975-X). AMS Pr.

L'islam Dans le Miroir De L'Occident: Comment Quelques Orientalistes Occidentaux Se Sont Penches Sur L'islam et Se Sont Forme une Image De Cette Religion. 3 ed. Jean-Jacques Waardenburg. (Recherches Mediterraneennes: Etudes 3). 1970. 26.80x (ISBN 90-2796-304-5). Mouton.

List of Editions of the Bay Psalm Book or New England Version of the Psalms, 2 vols. in 1. Ed. by Wilberforce Eames. Incl. Bible. O. T. Psalms. English. Paraphrases. 1912 Bay Psalm Book. facsimile ed. New England Society. 1912. Repr. LC 1-538. 1885. Repr. 23.50 (ISBN 0-8337-0987-9). B Franklin.

List of Editions of the Holy Scriptures & Parts Thereof Printed in American Previous to 1860. Edmund B. O'Callaghan. LC 66-25690. 1966. Repr. of 1861 ed. 43.00x (ISBN 0-8103-3313-9). Gale.

List of New Testament Words Sharing Common Elements. Xavier Jacques. (Scripta Pontificci Instituti Biblici: Vol. 119). 1969. pap. 13.00 (ISBN 88-7653-497-0). Loyola.

Listen & Help Tell the Story. Bernice W. Carlson. (Illus.). 1965. 9.95 (ISBN 0-687-22096-3). Abingdon.

Listen, Beloved. Martha Smock. LC 80-50624. 177p. 1980. 5.95 (ISBN 0-87159-101-4). Unity School.

Listen! Jesus Is Praying. Warren W. Wiersbe. 1982. pap. 4.95 (ISBN 0-8423-2167-5); leader's guide 2.95 (ISBN 0-8423-2168-3). Tyndale.

Listen Listen Listen. Louis Gittner. Ed. by Starr Farish. 320p. (Orig.). 1980. pap. 8.95 (ISBN 0-9605492-0-X). Touch Heart.

Listen, My Son. Rev. ed. William MacDonald. pap. 3.00 (ISBN 0-937396-23-0). Walterick Pubs.

Listen! Our Dying Savior Speaks. Lehman Strauss. Orig. Title: Day God Died. 113p. 1987. pap. 5.95 (ISBN 0-87213-828-3). Loizeaux.

Listen, Prophets! George Maloney. 5.95 (ISBN 0-87193-059-5). Dimension Bks.

Listen...The Speaking Heart. Doris. LC 79-50254. 1979. pap. 3.75 (ISBN 0-87516-361-0). De Vorss.

Listen to Him. David E. Rosage. 112p. (Orig.). 1981. pap. 3.50 (ISBN 0-89283-108-1). Servant.

Listen to the Animals. William L. Coleman. LC 79-11312. 128p. 1979. pap. 4.95 (ISBN 0-87123-341-X, 210341). Bethany Hse.

Listen to the King: Meditations Just from the Scriptures. Compiled By Walter E McAlister. (Direction Bks.). 96p. (Orig.). 1980. pap. 2.95 (ISBN 0-8010-6104-0). Baker Bk.

Listen to the Light. John S. Niendorff. 96p. 1983. pap. 4.50 (ISBN 0-911336-84-2). Sci of Mind.

Listen to the Silence. Mildred Long. (Orig.). 1970. pap. 2.50 (ISBN 0-87516-049-2). De Vorss.

Listen to the Silence. Frances J. Roberts. 1964. 2.95 (ISBN 0-932814-23-9). Kings Farspan.

Listen to Your Children. Marie H. Frost. LC 80-50320. 144p. (Orig.). 1980. pap. 2.95 (ISBN 0-87239-396-8, 3000). Standard Pub.

Listen to Your Children: Leader's Guide. Marie H. Frost. 48p. (Orig.). 1984. pap. 2.95 (ISBN 0-87239-747-5, 2999). Standard Pub.

Listen to Yourself: Think Everything Over, Vol. II. Tripitaka Master Hua. Tr. by Buddhist Text Translation Society. 172p. 1983. pap. 7.00 (ISBN 0-88139-010-0). Buddhist Text.

Listen to Yourself; Think Everything Over, Vol 1. Tripitaka Master Hua. Tr. by Buddhist Text Translation Society Staff. (Illus.). 153p. (Orig.). 1978. pap. 7.00 (ISBN 0-917512-24-3). Buddhist Text.

Listening at Prayer. Benedict J. Groeschel. 80p. (Orig.). 1984. 4.95 (ISBN 0-8091-2582-X). Paulist Pr.

Listening Ear: Reflections on Christian Caring. Paul Tournier. Tr. by Paul Hudson from Fr. Tr. of Vivre a l'ecoute. 144p. 1987. pap. 7.95 (ISBN 0-8066-2266-0, 10-3900). Augsburg.

Listening Heart. Joyce M. Smith. 1981. pap. 2.95 (ISBN 0-8423-2375-9). Tyndale.

Listening on Sunday for Sharing on Monday. William D. Thompson. 64p. 1983. pap. 3.95 (ISBN 0-317-00858-7). Judson.

Listening to God: Lessons from Everyday Places. Janice Kempe. (Orig.). 1985. pap. 2.95 (ISBN 0-310-34822-6, 12748P). Zondervan.

Listening to Life. Ray Owen. Ed. by Mary Penoi & Kay Condit. 124p. (Orig.). 1987. pap. 5.95 (ISBN 0-942316-14-2). Pueblo Pub Pr.

Listening to People of Hope. Brother Leonard of Taize. 180p. 1985. pap. 6.95 (ISBN 0-8298-0544-3). Pilgrim NY.

Listening to the Giants. Warren W. Wiersbe. 1979. 14.95 (ISBN 0-8010-9618-9). Baker Bk.

Listening to the Inner Self. Ed. by Lucy Freeman. LC 83-9988. 206p. 1984. 20.00 (ISBN 0-87668-640-4). Aronson.

Listenings. Judy Ball. (Orig.). 1987. pap. 7.00 (ISBN 0-915541-12-2). Star Bks Inc.

Lists of Personal Naames from the Temple School of Nippur: A Syllabary of Personal Names. E. Chiera. (Publications of the Babylonian Section: Vol. 11-1). (Illus.). 88p. 1916. soft bound 10.50x (ISBN 0-686-11923-1). Univ Mus of U PA.

Lists of Personal Names from the Temple School of Nippur: Lists of Akkadian Personal Names. E. Chiera. (Publications of the Babylonian Section: Vol. 11-2). (Illus.). 85p. 1916. soft bound 10.50x (ISBN 0-686-11924-X). Univ Mus of U PA.

Lists of Personal Names from the Temple School of Nippur: Lists of Sumerian Personal Names. Edward Chiera. LC 17-5006. (University of Pennsylvania, University Museum, Publications of the Babylonian Section: Vol. 11, No. 3). pap. 34.00 (ISBN 0-317-28537-8, 2052027). Bks Demand UMI.

LITE Manual. James L. Garlow. 177p. 1982. pap. 6.95 spiral binding (ISBN 0-8341-0883-6, S-2000); Leader's Guide 14.95. Beacon Hill.

Literacy, Bible Reading & Church Growth Through the Ages. Morris Watkins. LC 78-15315. (Illus.). 1978. pap. 5.95 (ISBN 0-87808-325-1). William Carey Lib.

Literal Interpretation of the Bible. Paul L. Tan. LC 78-73220. 1978. pap. text ed. 2.95 (ISBN 0-932940-04-8). Assurance Pubs.

Literal Interpretation of the Bible. Paul L. Tan. 114p. 1979. pap. 3.95 (ISBN 0-88469-098-9). BMH Bks.

Literarischen Widersacher der Paepste Zur Zeit Ludwig Des Baiers. Sigmund Riezler. 336p. 1874. Repr. 25.50 (ISBN 0-8337-2994-2). B Franklin.

Literary & Biographical History; or Bibliographical Dictionary of English Catholics from the Breach with Rome, in 1534, to the Present Time, 5 Vols. Joseph Gillow. 1962. Repr. of 1892 ed. 205.00 (ISBN 0-8337-1356-6). B Franklin.

Literary Approach to the New Testament. John P. Pritchard. (Illus.). 350p. 1972. 17.95x (ISBN 0-8061-1011-2); pap. 11.95x (ISBN 0-8061-1710-9). U of Okla Pr.

Literary Aspects of North American Mythology. Paul Radin. 1979. Repr. of 1915 ed. lib. bdg. 15.50 (ISBN 0-8414-7304-8). Folcroft.

Literary Aspects of North American Mythology. Paul Radin. (Folklore Ser). 20.00 (ISBN 0-8482-5887-8). Norwood Edns.

Literary Characteristics & Achievements of the Bible. W. Trail. 335p. 1983. Repr. of 1863 ed. lib. bdg. 85.00 (ISBN 0-89984-471-5). Century Bookbindery.

Literary Concordances: A Complete Handbook for the Preparation of Manual & Computer Concordances. T. H. Howard-Hill. 1979. text ed. 18.00 (ISBN 0-08-023021-0). Pergamon.

Literary Criticism & Biblical Hermeneutics. Lynn M. Poland. (American Academy of Religion Academy Ser.: No. 48). 1985. 15.25 (ISBN 0-89130-825-3, 01 01 48); pap. 10.25 (ISBN 0-89130-836-9). Scholars Pr GA.

Literary Criticism & Myth. Ed. by Joseph P. Strelka. LC 79-15111. (Yearbook of Comparative Criticism Ser.: Vol. 9). 1980. text ed. 25.00x (ISBN 0-271-00225-5). Pa St U Pr.

Literary Criticism for New Testament Critics. Norman R. Petersen. Ed. by Dan O. Via, Jr. LC 77-15241. (Guides to Biblical Scholarship: New Testament Ser.). 96p. (Orig.). 1978. pap. 4.50 (ISBN 0-8006-0465-2, 1-465). Fortress.

Literary Criticism of the New Testament. William A. Beardslee. Ed. by Dan O. Via, Jr. LC 77-94817. (Guides to Biblical Scholarship: New Testament Ser.). 96p. (Orig.). 1970. pap. 4.50 (ISBN 0-8006-0185-8, 1-185). Fortress.

Literary Criticism of the Old Testament. Norman C. Habel. Ed. by Coert Rylaarsdam. LC 78-157548. (Guides to Biblical Scholarship: Old Testament Ser.). 96p. 1971. pap. 4.50 (ISBN 0-8006-0176-9, 1-176). Fortress.

Literary Function of Possession in Luke-Acts. Luke T. Johnson. LC 77-21055. (Society of Biblical Literature. Dissertation Ser.: No. 39). 1985. pap. 11.25 (ISBN 0-89130-200-X, 060139). Scholars Pr GA.

Literary Genius of the New Testament. P. C. Sands. 1932. 20.00 (ISBN 0-8274-2953-3). R West.

Literary Genius of the New Testament. Percy C. Sands. Repr. of 1932 ed. lib. bdg. 22.50x (ISBN 0-8371-4328-4, SANT). Greenwood.

Literary Genius of the Old Testament. Percy C. Sands. LC 75-35756. 1975. Repr. of 1924 ed. lib. bdg. 27.50 (ISBN 0-8414-7646-2). Folcroft.

Literary Guide to the Bible. Laura H. Wild. LC 74-9861. 1976. lib. bdg. 35.00 (ISBN 0-8414-9533-5). Folcroft.

Literary History of Early Christianity, 2 Vols. Charles T. Cruttwell. LC 76-129369. Repr. of 1893 ed. 65.00 (ISBN 0-404-01877-7). AMS Pr.

Literary History of Sanskrit Buddhism. Gushtaspshah K. Nariman. LC 78-70106. Repr. of 1920 ed. 37.50 (ISBN 0-404-17356-X). AMS Pr.

Literary History of Sanskrit Buddhism. 2nd ed. J. K. Nariman. 1972. 13.95 (ISBN 0-8426-0453-7). Orient Bk Dist.

Literary Impact of the Authorized Version. C. S. Lewis. Ed. by John Reumann. LC 63-17883. (Facet Bks). 48p. (Orig.). 1963. pap. 2.50 (ISBN 0-8006-3003-3, 1-3003). Fortress.

Literary Interpretations of Biblical Narratives 11. Kenneth R. Louis. LC 74-12400. 320p. (Orig.). 1982. pap. 10.95 (ISBN 0-687-22132-3). Abingdon.

Literary Life of the Early Friends, 1650-1725. Luella M. Wright. LC 32-25426. Repr. of 1932 ed. 19.50 (ISBN 0-404-07046-9). AMS Pr.

Literary Man's Bible: A Selection of Passages from the Old Testament, Historic, Poetic & Philosophic, Illustrating Hebrew Literature. 414p. 1982. Repr. of 1908 ed. lib. bdg. 40.00 (ISBN 0-89987-133-X). Darby Bks.

Literary Origin of the Gospel of John. Howard M. Teeple. LC 73-87487. x, 297p. (Orig.). 1974. pap. 6.00 (ISBN 0-914384-00-7). Religion & Ethics.

Literary Outlook. Samuel L. Bethell. LC 73-9787. 1943. lib. bdg. 15.00 (ISBN 0-8414-3145-0). Folcroft.

Literary Patterns, Theological Themes & the Genre of Luke-Acts. Charles H. Talbert. LC 74-78620. (Society of Biblical Literature. Monograph: No. 20). Repr. of 1974 ed. 42.00 (ISBN 0-8357-9577-2, 2017509). Bks Demand UMI.

Literary Study of the Bible. R. G. Moulton. 34.95 (ISBN 0-8490-0544-2). Gordon Pr.

Literary Study of the Bible. Richard G. Moulton. LC 70-4534. 1898. 59.00x (ISBN 0-403-00113-7). Scholarly.

Literary Temper of the English Puritans. Lawrence A. Sasek. Repr. of 1961 ed. lib. bdg. 22.50x (ISBN 0-8371-2333-X, SAEP). Greenwood.

Literary Transcendentalism: Style & Vision in the American Rennaisance. Lawrence Buell. LC 73-8409. 336p. (Orig.). 1975. pap. 9.95x (ISBN 0-8014-9152-5). Cornell U Pr.

Literary Uses of Typology from the Late Middle Ages to the Present. Ed. by Earl Miner. LC 76-45904. 1977. 47.50 (ISBN 0-691-06327-3). Princeton U Pr.

Literature & Dogma. Matthew Arnold. Repr. of 1873 ed. lib. bdg. 20.00 (ISBN 0-8414-3076-4). Folcroft.

Literature & Dogma. Matthew Arnold. Ed. by James C. Livingston. LC 79-107032. (Milestones of Thought Ser). 1970. pap. 3.95x (ISBN 0-8044-6011-6). Ungar.

Literature & Dogma: An Essay Towards a Better Apprehension of the Bible. Matthew Arnold. LC 78-126650. 1970. Repr. of 1883 ed. 15.00 (ISBN 0-404-00387-7). AMS Pr.

Literature & Meaning of Scripture. Ed. by Morris A. Inch & C. Hassell Bullock. 360p. 1981. 14.95 (ISBN 0-8010-5032-4). Baker Bk.

Literature & Occult Traditions. Denis Saurat. LC 68-759. (Studies in Comparative Literature, No. 35). 1969. Repr. of 1930 ed. lib. bdg. 49.95x (ISBN 0-8383-0617-9). Haskell.

Literature & Religion: A Study in Conflict. Charles I. Glicksberg. LC 77-23753. 1977. Repr. of 1960 ed. lib. bdg. 22.50x (ISBN 0-8371-9753-8, GLLR). Greenwood.

Literature & the Occult Tradition. Denis Saurat. Tr. by D. Bolton. LC 65-27133. 1930. Repr. 23.00x (ISBN 0-8046-0405-3, Pub. by Kennikat). Assoc Faculty Pr.

Literature & the Pastoral. Andrew V. Ettin. LC 83-26052. 212p. 1984. 22.50x (ISBN 0-300-03160-2). Yale U Pr.

Literature & Theology in Colonial New England. Kenneth B. Murdock. LC 78-104247. xi, 235p. Repr. of 1949 ed. lib. bdg. 22.50x (ISBN 0-8371-3990-2, MUCN). Greenwood.

Literature, Arts & Religion. Harry Garvin. LC 80-70270. (Bucknell Review Ser.: Vol. 26, No. 2). (Illus.). 192p. 1982. 16.50 (ISBN 0-8387-5021-4). Bucknell U Pr.

Literature De L'angleterre Puritaine 1603-1660. Floris Delattre. 1978. Repr. lib. bdg. 25.00 (ISBN 0-8492-0692-8). R West.

Literature in Protestant England: 1560-1660. Alan Sinfield. LC 82-18408. 168p. 1983. text ed. 26.50x (ISBN 0-389-20341-6, 07185). B&N Imports.

Literature of American Jews. Theodore L. Gross. LC 72-93311. 1973. 14.95 (ISBN 0-02-913190-1). Free Pr.

Literature of Modern Israel. Reuben Wallenrod. LC 80-12709. 256p. 1980. Repr. of 1956 ed. lib. bdg. 20.00x (ISBN 0-374-98198-1, Octagon). Hippocrene Bks.

Literature of Mysticism in Western Tradition. Patrick Grant. LC 83-5789. 200p. 1983. 22.50x (ISBN 0-312-48808-4). St Martin.

Literature of the New Testament. Ernest F. Scott. Ed. by Austin P. Evans. LC 84-25243. (Records of Civilization Sources & Studies: No. xv). xv, 312p. 1985. Repr. of 1936 ed. lib. bdg. 45.00x (ISBN 0-313-24743-9, SCNT). Greenwood.

Literature of the Old Testament. 3rd ed. Julius A. Bewer & Emil G. Kraeling. LC 62-17061. (Records of Civilization: Sources & Studies: No. 5). pap. 128.00 (ISBN 0-317-26423-0, 2024975). Bks Demand UMI.

Literature of the Old Testament. Herbert R. Purinton. 1926. 20.00 (ISBN 0-8274-2966-5). R West.

Literature of Theology. John F. Hurst. LC 77-85625. 1977. Repr. of 1896 ed. lib. bdg. 50.00 (ISBN 0-89341-196-5). Longwood Pub Group.

Literature of Theology: A Guide for Students & Pastors. John A. Bollier. LC 78-10962. 208p. 1979. pap. 5.95 (ISBN 0-664-24225-1). Westminster.

Literature, Religion & Society in Wales: 1660-1730. G. H. Jenkins. (Studies in Welsh History: Vol. 2). 357p. 1980. text ed. 32.50x (ISBN 0-7083-0669-1, Pub. by U of Wales). Humanities.

Lithuania Calling Collect: An Exploration of the Roads to Love. Elbert Rynberg. 160p. 1983. 8.50 (ISBN 0-682-49970-6). Exposition Pr FL.

Little Benjamin & the First Christmas. Betty Forell & Betty Wind. (Arch Bks: Set 1). (Illus.). 1964. laminated bdg. 0.99 (ISBN 0-570-06005-2, 59-1113). Concordia.

Little Bishop. Paschal Turbet. 1977. 3.50 (ISBN 0-8198-0430-4); pap. 2.50 (ISBN 0-8198-0431-2). Dghtrs St Paul.

Little Bit of Everything Good. Null & Watts. pap. 5.50 (ISBN 0-89137-619-4). Quality Pubns.

Little Blank Book. Betty Sprague. (Illus.). 64p. 1982. pap. 5.95 (ISBN 0-942494-24-5). Coleman Pub.

Little Boat That Almost Sank. Mary P. Warren & Rada. LC 64-23371. (Arch Bks: Set 2). 1965. pap. 0.99 (ISBN 0-570-06010-9, 59-1111). Concordia.

Little Book about God. Lauren Ford. LC 81-43749. (Illus.). 48p. 1985. 9.95 (ISBN 0-385-17691-0). Doubleday.

Little Book for Christmas. facsimile ed. Cyrus T. Brady. LC 73-167443. (Short Story Index Reprint Ser). (Illus.). Repr. of 1917 ed. 17.00 (ISBN 0-8369-3969-7). Ayer Co Pubs.

Little Book of Good: Spiritual Values for Parents & Children. Joan Rubadeau. 58p. 1986. pap. 7.00 (ISBN 0-913105-19-8). PAGL Pr.

Little Book of Inspiration: Seven Famous Classics, 1 vol. 290p. Date not set. pap. 9.95 (ISBN 0-87983-424-2). Keats.

Little Book of Life After Death. Gustav T. Fechner. Ed. by Robert Kastenbaum. LC 76-19570. (Death & Dying Ser.). 1977. Repr. of 1904 ed. lib. bdg. 15.00x (ISBN 0-405-09565-1). Ayer Co Pubs.

Little Book of the Work of Infinite Love. Louise M. De La Touche. LC 79-90490. 1979. pap. 1.50 (ISBN 0-89555-130-6). TAN Bks Pubs.

Little Book on Religion: For People Who Are Not Religious. Samuel Sandmel. LC 75-1831. 1975. pap. 3.95 cancelled (ISBN 0-89012-002-1). Anima Pubns.

Little Book: Why I Am a Mormon. Leon N. Christensen. 1976. 12.00 (ISBN 0-8283-1606-6). Branden Pub Co.

Little Children Sing to God! Arthur W. Gross & Allan H. Jahsmann. 1960. 8.95 (ISBN 0-570-03471-X, 56-1036). Concordia.

Little Christian's Songbook. Compiled by Daniel R. Burow & Carol Greene. 64p. 1975. pap. 5.50 (56-1266). Concordia.

Little Commonwealth: Family Life in Plymouth Colony. John Demos. (Illus.). 1970. pap. 6.95x (ISBN 0-19-501355-7). Oxford U Pr.

Little Exercise for Young Theologians. Helmut Thielicke. (Orig.). 1962. pap. 2.95 (ISBN 0-8028-1198-1). Eerdmans.

Little Faith Builders. Judy Shaw. 30p. (Orig.). 1983. pap. 0.75 (ISBN 0-89274-290-9). Harrison Hse.

Little Flower of St. Francis. Tr. by Raphael Brown. 1971. pap. 5.50 (ISBN 0-385-07544-8, Im). Doubleday.

Little Flowers of St. Francis. Tr. by E. M. Blaiklock & A. C. Keys. 176p. 1985. pap. 3.95 (ISBN 0-89283-300-9). Servant.

Little Flowers of St. Francis. 1976. pap. 1.95 (ISBN 0-8198-0434-7). Dghtrs St Paul.

Little Folded Hands. rev. ed. LC 59-12074. 1959. 3.50 (ISBN 0-570-03417-5, 56-1038); pap. 1.85 laminated (ISBN 0-570-03416-7, 56-1037). Concordia.

Little Grey Donkey. Marjorie Procter. (Very First Bible Stories Ser.). 1984. 1.59 (ISBN 0-87162-272-6, D8501). Warner Pr.

Little Heroes. Arthur Dobrin. (Ethical Humanist Society Monograph: No. 1). (Illus.). 1977. pap. 2.50x (ISBN 0-89304-200-5, CCC111). Cross Cult.

Little Journey. June Strong. Ed. by Gerald Wheeler. 126p. (Orig.). 1984. pap. 5.95 (ISBN 0-8280-0236-3). Review & Herald.

Little Journeys Through the Old Testament. Jeanette Groth. 128p. (Orig.). 1986. pap. 5.95 (ISBN 0-570-03985-1, 12-3012). Concordia.

Little Journeys with Jesus. Jeanette L. Groth. pap. 5.95 (ISBN 0-570-03924-X, 12-2858). Concordia.

Little Lamb & the Good Shepherd. Virginia Lane. (Illus.). 48p. 1983. 6.95 (ISBN 0-89274-254-2). Harrison Hse.

Little Library of Inspiration for Sunday School Teachers. Richard Andersen. 1982. pap. 2.25 (ISBN 0-570-03846-4, 12-2949). Concordia.

Little Lips Shall Praise Thee. Emily Hunter. (Illus.). 96p. 1986. 11.95 (ISBN 0-89081-543-7). Harvest Hse.

Little Lives of the Great Saints. John O. Murray. LC 82-50593. 495p. 1985. pap. 12.00 (ISBN 0-89555-190-X). Tan Bks Pubs.

Little Lost Lamb. 1.75 (ISBN 0-8198-4415-2). Dghtrs St Paul.

Little Lost Lamb. Marjorie Procter. (Very First Bible Stories Ser.). 1984. 1.59 (ISBN 0-87162-276-9, D8505). Warner Pr.

Little Martins Learn to Love. Ada Nighswander. 6.50 (ISBN 0-686-30775-5). Rod & Staff.

Little Masonic Library, 5 vols. Silas H. Shepherd et al. 1977. Repr. cloth 35.00 set (ISBN 0-88053-005-7, M-5). Macoy Pub.

Little Missionaries. Mary R. Zook. 184p. (YA) 1979. 6.75 (ISBN 0-686-30764-X). Rod & Staff.

Little Office of the Blessed Virgin. cloth o.p. 3.00 (ISBN 0-8199-0063-X, L38395); pap. 2.25 (ISBN 0-8199-0062-1, 38396). Franciscan Herald.

Little Ones Praise. Martha Mellinger. 1981. 4.35 (ISBN 0-87813-518-9). Christian Light.

Little Prayers. Esther Wilkin. (Golden Look-Look Ser.). (Illus.). 24p. 1980. pap. 1.50 (ISBN 0-307-11858-4, Golden Bks.). Western Pub.

Little Sermons on Sin: The Archpriest of Talavera. Alfonso Martinez De Toledo. Tr. by Leslie Byrd. 1977. pap. 2.85 (ISBN 0-520-03281-0, CAL 346). U of Cal Pr.

Little Sleeping Beauty. Brenda Prior. (Arch Bks: Set 6). 1969. laminated bdg. 0.99 (ISBN 0-570-06041-9, 59-1156). Concordia.

Little Stories About God. Mary R. McDonald. (Illus.). 1964. 5.50 (ISBN 0-8198-0080-5). pap. 4.50 (ISBN 0-8198-0081-3). Dghtrs St Paul.

Little Talks about God & You. V. Gilbert Beers. 224p. (Orig.). 1986. pap. 7.95 (ISBN 0-89081-519-4). Harvest Hse.

Little Talks About Life. Patrick Fontaine. 1956. 4.50 (ISBN 0-8198-0082-1). Dghtrs St Paul.

Little Talks with Jesus. Nancy B. Irland. Ed. by Gerald Wheeler. 1985. 9.95 (ISBN 0-8280-0251-7). Review & Herald.

Little Things Mean a Lot: Minute Meditations. Marie McIntyre. (Greeting Book Line Ser.). (Illus.). 48p. 1982. pap. 1.50 (ISBN 0-89622-155-5). Twenty-Third.

Little Visits with God. Allan H. Jahsmann & Martin P. Simon. 1957. 9.50 (ISBN 0-570-03016-1, 6-1055); pap. 6.95 (ISBN 0-570-03032-3, 6-1158). Concordia.

Little World of Don Camillo. Giovanni Guareschi. LC 86-8845. (Illus.). 144p. 1986. pap. 5.95 (ISBN 0-385-23242-X, Im). Doubleday.

Liturgiae Britannicae. William Keeling. 498p. Repr. of 1851 ed. text ed. 74.52x (ISBN 0-576-99718-8, Pub. by Gregg Intl Pubs England). Gregg Intl.

Liturgical & Mystical Theology of Nicolas Cabasilas. 2nd ed. Constance N. Tsirpanlis. 103p. 1979. pap. 6.99 (ISBN 0-686-36328-0). EO Pr.

Liturgical Calendar & Ordo, 1987, United States of America. 128p. 1986. pap. 6.95 (ISBN 1-55586-986-6). US Catholic.

Liturgical Coordinator. James E. Hamilton. 64p. (Orig.). 1984. pap. text ed. 10.00 (ISBN 0-942466-06-3); Looseleaf 9.50 (ISBN 0-942466-05-5). Hymnary Pr.

Liturgical Formation in Seminaries: A Commentary. 120p. 1984. pap. 4.95 (ISBN 1-55586-917-3). US Catholic.

Liturgical Foundations of Social Policy in the Catholic & Jewish Traditions. Ed. by Eugene J. Fisher & Daniel F. Polish. LC 82-40378. 180p. 1983. text ed. 16.95 (ISBN 0-268-01267-9); pap. text ed. 9.95 (ISBN 0-268-01268-7). U of Notre Dame Pr.

Liturgical Guitarist. Bill Bay. 360p. 1980. spiral bdg. 9.95 (ISBN 0-89228-055-7). Impact Bks MO.

Liturgical Law Today: New Style, New Spirit. Thomas Richstatter. LC 77-3008. pap. 67.80 (ISBN 0-317-28483-5, 2019104). Bks Demand UMI.

Liturgical Ministry of the Deacon. Michael Kwatera. (Ministry Ser.). 96p. 1985. pap. 1.95 (ISBN 0-8146-1386-1). Liturgical Pr.

Liturgical Music: Dogmatica & Other Selections, Vol. II. Laurence Mancuso. (New Skete). 107p. (Orig.). 1978. pap. 15.00 (ISBN 0-9607924-2-2). Monks of New Skete.

Liturgical Music: Selection for Vespers, Matins, & Liturgy, Vol. I. Laurence Mancuso. (New Skete). 172p. (Orig.). 1975. 18.00x (ISBN 0-9607924-0-6); pap. 15.00x (ISBN 0-9607924-1-4). Monks of New Skete.

Liturgical Narrative on the Service for the Day. Dennis C. Johnson. 1984. 3.50 (ISBN 0-89536-657-6, 1268). CSS of Ohio.

Liturgical Objects in the Walters Art Gallery: A Picture Book. LC 67-9432. (Illus.). 1967. pap. 3.50 (ISBN 0-911886-11-7). Walters Art.

Liturgical Piety. Louis Bouyer. (Liturgical Studies Ser). 1965. 10.95x (ISBN 0-268-00158-8). U of Notre Dame Pr.

Liturgical Terms for Music Students: A Dictionary. Compiled by Dom A. Hughes. LC 70-166236. 1972. Repr. of 1940 ed. 29.00x (ISBN 0-403-01363-1). Scholarly.

Liturgical Year in Puzzles. Arlene W. Murphy. 1982. 9.95 (Pub. by Pflaum Pr). Peter Li.

Liturgical Year: Its History & Its Meaning after the Reform of the Liturgy. Adolf Adam. Tr. by Matthew J. O'Connell from Ger. 1981. pap. 16.60 (ISBN 0-916134-47-4). Pueblo Pub Co.

Liturgies & Lessons: Childrens Homilies. Patricia Brennan-Nichols. 1984. pap. 9.95 (ISBN 0-941850-13-7). Sunday Pubns.

Liturgies & Occasional Forms of Prayer Set Forth in the Reign of Queen Elizabeth. 1847. 55.00 (ISBN 0-384-32940-3). Johnson Repr.

Liturgies & Trials: The Secularization of Religious Language. Richard K. Fenn. LC 81-19250. 256p. 1982. 15.95 (ISBN 0-8298-0495-1). Pilgrim NY.

Liturgies for Little Ones: Thirty-Eight Complete Celebrations for Grades One Through Three. Carol Rezy. LC 78-59926. (Illus.). 160p. 1978. pap. 4.95 (ISBN 0-87793-160-7). Ave Maria.

Liturgies of Saints Mark, James, Clement, Chrysostom, & the Church of Malabar. Orthodox Eastern Church. LC 76-83374. Repr. of 1859 ed. 18.50 (ISBN 0-404-04658-4). AMS Pr.

Liturgies of Saints Mark, James, Clement, Chrysostom, Basil. Orthodox Eastern Church. LC 79-80721. (Gr). 1969. Repr. of 1859 ed. 18.50 (ISBN 0-404-04657-6). AMS Pr.

Liturgies of the Western Church. Ed. by Bard Thompson. LC 80-8044. 448p. 1980. pap. 9.95 (ISBN 0-8006-1428-3, 1-1428). Fortress.

Liturgies on the Holocaust: An Interfaith Anthology. Ed. by Marcia S. Littell. LC 86-23507. 208p. 1986. lib. bdg. 39.95x (ISBN 0-88946-030-2). E Mellen.

Liturgisches Woerterbuch. Wolfgang Jung. (Ger.). 1964. leatherette 13.50 (ISBN 3-87537-023-6, M-7544, Pub. by Merseburger Berlin). French & Eur.

Liturgy According to the Use of the Liberal Catholic Church, Prepared for the Use of English-Speaking Congregations. 3rd ed. General Episcopal Synod. 421p. 1987. Repr. of 1942 ed. price not set (ISBN 0-935461-11-6). St Alban Pr CA.

Liturgy: Advent, Christmas, Epiphany, Vol. 4, No. 3. Rachel Reeder. (The Quarterly Journal of the Lit. Conference Ser.). (Illus.). 88p. (Orig.). 1984. pap. 7.95 (ISBN 0-918208-36-X). Liturgical Conf.

Liturgy Against Itself. Ralph A. Keifer. 128p. (Orig.). 1986. pap. 7.95 (ISBN 0-06-254480-2, HarpR). Har-Row.

Liturgy & Architecture. Louis Bouyer. 1967. 6.95x (ISBN 0-268-00159-6). U of Notre Dame Pr.

Liturgy & Learning Through the Life Cycle. John H. Westerhoff, III & William H. Willimon. 192p. (Orig.). 1985. pap. 9.95 (ISBN 0-86683-980-1, HarpR). Har-Row.

Liturgy & Personality. Dietrich Von Hildebrand. LC 85-18388. 182p. 1986. 11.95 (ISBN 0-918477-03-4); pap. 7.95 (ISBN 0-918477-04-2). Sophia Inst Pr.

Liturgy & Ritual of the Ante-Nicene Church. 2nd rev. ed. Frederick E. Warren. LC 78-177851. Repr. of 1912 ed. 25.00 (ISBN 0-404-06847-2). AMS Pr.

Liturgy & Ritual of the Celtic Church. Frederick E. Warren. 1987. 39.50 (ISBN 0-85115-473-5); pap. 12.50. Eastern Orthodox.

Liturgy & Ritual: The Liturgy of the Holy Apostles Adai & Mari. Nestorian Church. LC 79-131032. Repr. of 1893 ed. 14.50 (ISBN 0-404-03997-9). AMS Pr.

Liturgy & Social Justice. Ed. by Mark Searle. LC 80-27011. 102p. 1980. pap. 5.50 (ISBN 0-8146-1209-1). Liturgical Pr.

Liturgy As Dance & the Liturgical Dancer. Carolyn Deitering. (Illus.). 144p. 1984. pap. 8.95 (ISBN 0-8245-0654-5). Crossroad NY.

Liturgy: Celebrating Marriage, Vol. 4, No. 2. Ed. by Rachel Reeder. (Illus.). 80p. 1984. pap. text ed. 7.95 (ISBN 0-918208-34-3). Liturgical Conf.

Liturgy Committee Basics: A No-nonsense Guide. Thomas Baker & Frank Ferrone. (Orig.). 1985. pap. 6.95 (ISBN 0-912405-11-2). Pastoral Pr.

Liturgy Constitution. Ed. by Paulist Editorial Committee. 192p. 1964. pap. 1.95 (ISBN 0-8091-1620-0, 192, Deus). Paulist Pr.

Liturgy: Diakonia. Ed. by Rachel Reeder. (Journal of The Liturgical Conference: Vol. 2, No. 4). (Illus.). 84p. (Orig.). 1982. pap. 7.95 (ISBN 0-918208-28-9). Liturgical Conf.

Liturgy: Dressing the Church. Ed. by Rachel Reeder. (Quarterly Journal of the Liturgical Conference Ser.: Vol.5, No. 4). (Illus.). 103p. (Orig.). Date not set. pap. 7.95 (ISBN 0-918208-40-8). Liturgical Conf.

Liturgy: Easter's Fifty Days. Ed. by Rachel Reeder. (Journal of The Liturgical Conference: Vol. 3, No. 1). (Illus.). 72p. 1982. pap. text ed. 7.95 (ISBN 0-918208-29-7). Liturgical Conf.

Liturgy Explained. Thomas Howard. (Illus.). 48p. (Orig.). 1981. pap. 2.95 (ISBN 0-8192-1285-7). Morehouse.

Liturgy: Feasts & Fasting. Ed. by Rachel Reeder. (Quarterly Journal of the Liturgical Conference: Vol. 2, No. 1 of Liturgy). (Illus.). 80p. (Orig.). 1981. pap. text ed. 7.95 (ISBN 0-918208-25-4). Liturgical Conf.

Liturgy for Living. Charles P. Price & Louis Weil. (Church's Teaching Ser.: Vol. 5). 1979. 5.95 (ISBN 0-8164-0422-4, HarpR); pap. 4.95 (ISBN 0-8164-2218-4); user guide 1.50 (ISBN 0-8164-2225-7). Har-Row.

Liturgy for the Free Church. John R. Johnson. LC 86-18782. 176p. 1986. lib. bdg. 19.95x (ISBN 0-89370-527-6). Borgo Pr.

Liturgy: Holy Places. Rachel Reeder. (Quarterly Journal of the Liturgical Conference: Vol. 3, No. 4). (Illus.). 96p. (Orig.). 1983. pap. text ed. 7.95 (ISBN 0-918208-32-7). Liturgical Conf.

Liturgy: In Spirit & Truth. Ed. by Rachel Reeder. (Quarterly Journal of the Liturgical Conference: Vol. 5, No. 3). (Illus.). 96p. (Orig.). pap. text ed. 7.95 (ISBN 0-918208-39-4). Liturgical Conf.

Liturgy: Language & Metaphor, Vol. 4, No.4. Ed. by Rachel Reeder. (The Quarterly Journal of the Lit. Conference Ser.). (Illus.). 95p. (Orig.). 1985. pap. 7.95 (ISBN 0-918208-35-1). Liturgical Conf.

Liturgy Made Simple. Mark Searle. LC 81-4807. 96p. (Orig.). 1981. pap. 2.95 (ISBN 0-8146-1221-0). Liturgical Pr.

Liturgy: Ministries to the Sick. Ed. by Rachel Reeder. (Quarterly Journal of the Liturgical Conference Ser.: Vol. 2, No. 2 of Liturgy). (Illus.). 80p. 1982. 7.95 (ISBN 0-918208-26-2). Liturgical Conf.

Liturgy of Funerary Offerings: The Egyptian Texts with English Translations. E. Wallis Budge. LC 72-83744. (Illus.). Repr. of 1909 ed. 22.00 (ISBN 0-405-08322-X, Blom Pubns). Ayer Co Pubs.

Liturgy of St. John Chrysostom. (Eng. & Arabic.). 104p. 1978. pap. 3.00 (ISBN 0-911726-39-X). Alleluia Pr.

Liturgy of the Eucharist. 79p. (Orig.). 1984. pap. 3.95 (ISBN 0-908682-01-8, Pub. by Genesis). ANZ Religious Pubns.

Liturgy of the Hours, 4 vols. Incl. Vol. 1. Advent & Christmas. 24.50 (ISBN 0-89942-401-5, 401/10); Vol. 2. Lent & Easter. 26.00 (ISBN 0-89942-402-3, 402/10); Vol. 3. Ordinary Time-Weeks 1 to 17. 24.50 (ISBN 0-89942-403-1, 403/10); Vol. 4. Ordinary Time-Weeks 18 to 34. 24.50 (ISBN 0-89942-404-X, 404/10). Boxed. gift set 96.00 (ISBN 0-89942-409-0, 409-05); St. Joseph guide for 1986 o.s.i. 1.25 (ISBN 0-89942-400-7, 400-G); Boxed. deluxe gift set 136.00, leather, gold edges (ISBN 0-89942-411-2, 409/13). Blue (401C). Red (402C). Brown (403C). Green (404C). Catholic Bk Pub.

Liturgy of the Hours. Dominic Scotto. 1986. pap. 9.95 (ISBN 0-932506-48-8). St Bedes Pubns.

Liturgy of the Hours in East & West. Robert Taft. 440p. 1986. pap. 14.95 (ISBN 0-8146-1405-1). Liturgical Pr.

Liturgy of the Word for Children. Sr. Jan Ihli. LC 79-90003. 176p. 1979. pap. 9.95 (ISBN 0-8091-2176-X). Paulist Pr.

Liturgy: One Church, Many Churches. Ed. by Rachel Reeder. (Quarterly Journal of The Liturgical Conference: Vol. 3, No. 2). (Illus.). 96p. (Orig.). 1983. pap. text ed. 7.95 (ISBN 0-918208-30-0). Liturgical Conf.

Liturgy: One Hundred Sixty-Nine Pronouncements from Benedict Fourteenth to John Twenty-Third. Ed. by Monks Of Solesmes. 5.00 (ISBN 0-8198-0083-X). Dghtrs St Paul.

Liturgy: Our School of Faith. Anthony Buono. 177p. (Orig.). 1982. pap. 6.95 (ISBN 0-8189-0435-6). Alba.

Liturgy, Prayer & Spirituality. Kevin W. Irwin. 1984. pap. 9.95 (ISBN 0-8091-2560-9). Paulist Pr.

Liturgy: Putting on Christ, Vol. 4, No. 1. Ed. by Rachel Reeder. (Illus.). 80p. 1983. pap. text ed. 7.95 (ISBN 0-918208-33-5). Liturgical Conf.

Liturgy: Scripture & the Assembly. Ed. by Rachel Reeder. (Quarterly Journal of the Liturgical Conference Ser.: Vol. 2, No. 3 of Liturgy). (Illus.). 80p. 1982. 7.95 (ISBN 0-918208-27-0). Liturgical Conf.

Liturgy: Teaching Prayer. Ed. by Rachel Reeder. (Quarterly Journal of the Liturgical Conference Ser.: Vol. 5, No. 1). (Illus.). 96p. (Orig.). pap. text ed. 7.95 (ISBN 0-918208-37-8). Liturgical Conf.

Liturgy: The Church & Culture. Ed. by Rachel Reeder. (Quarterly Journal of the Liturgical Conference Ser.: Vol. 6, No. 1). (Illus.). 96p. (Orig.). Date not set. pap. 7.95 (ISBN 0-918208-41-6). Liturgical Conf.

Liturgy: With All the Saints. Ed. by Rachel Reeder. (Quarterly Journal of the Liturgy Conference Ser.: Vol. 5, No. 2). (Illus.). 112p. (Orig.). pap. text ed. 7.95 (ISBN 0-918208-38-6). Liturgical Conf.

Liturgy: With Lyre & Harp. Ed. by Rachel Reeder. (Quarterly Journal of The Liturgical Conference: Vol. 3, No. 3). (Illus.). 88p. (Orig.). 1983. pap. text ed. 7.95 (ISBN 0-918208-31-9). Liturgical Conf.

Liturgy: Work of the People. William J. Freburger. 112p. (Orig.). 1984. pap. 4.95 (ISBN 0-89622-214-4). Twenty-Third.

Liutprand of Cremona, Mission to Constantinople 968 A.D. Lynn H. Nelson & Melanie Shirk. 62p. 1972. pap. 1.00x (ISBN 0-87291-039-3). Coronado Pr.

Live & Be Well: A Celebration of Yiddish Culture in America from the First Immigrants to the Second World War. Richard F. Shepard et al. (Illus.). 192p. 1982. 19.50 (ISBN 0-345-30752-6); pap. 9.95 (ISBN 0-345-29435-1). Ballantine.

Live & Learn with Your Teenager. Virginia E. Pipe. LC 85-18451. (Family Life Ser.). 160p. 1985. pap. 6.95 (ISBN 0-8170-1069-6). Judson.

Live Free. Tom C. McKenney. LC 84-91415. (Illus.). 317p. 1985. 9.95 (ISBN 0-934527-04-0). Words Living Minis.

Live, Grow & Be Free: A Guide to Self-Parenting. Dennis L. Gibson. LC 82-82412. 136p. 1982. pap. 5.95 (ISBN 0-89840-030-9). Here's Life.

Live in God's World. 2nd ed. Gerard P. Weber et al. (Word Is Life Ser.). 1977. 2.64 (ISBN 0-02-658100-0); tchrs. ed. 8.00 (ISBN 0-02-658110-8); family handbook 1.00 (ISBN 0-02-658150-7). Benziger Pub Co.

Live Like a King. rev. ed. Warren Wiersbe. (Moody Press Elective Ser.). 1983. pap. 3.95 (ISBN 0-8024-0256-9); pap. 2.50 leaders guide (ISBN 0-8024-0306-9). Moody.

Live the Mass. rev. ed. Daughters of St. Paul. (Way, Truth & Life Ser.). (Illus.). text ed. 1.75 (ISBN 0-8198-0272-7); tchr's. manual 6.25 (ISBN 0-8198-0273-5); activity bk. 0.85 (ISBN 0-8198-0274-3); parent guide 0.69 (ISBN 0-8198-0275-1). Dghtrs St Paul.

Live the Truth-Give the Truth. rev. ed. Daughters of St. Paul. (Way, Truth & Life Ser.). (Illus.). 1976. text ed. 2.75 (ISBN 0-8198-0304-9); tchr's. manual 8.00 (ISBN 0-8198-0305-7); activity bk. 1.60 (ISBN 0-8198-0306-5); parent guide 1.50 (ISBN 0-8198-0307-3). Dghtrs St Paul.

Live This Gift: A Program for Confirmation Preparation. Mary Montgomery & Herb Montgomery. 1975. student guide 3.25 (ISBN 0-03-014266-0, 127, HarpR); parent guide 1.95 (ISBN 0-03-014271-7, 128); tchr's. guide 4.35 (ISBN 0-03-014276-8, 129). Har-Row.

Live until You Die. Randolph C. Miller. LC 73-8657. 144p. 1973. 5.95 (ISBN 0-8298-0253-3). Pilgrim NY.

Live up to Your Faith: Studies in Titus. James T. Draper, Jr. 1983. pap. 3.95 (ISBN 0-8423-3687-7); leader's guide 2.95 (ISBN 0-8423-3688-5). Tyndale.

Live with Jesus. Alexander Campbell & Gerry Haff. 90p. (Orig.). 1984. pap. 12.95 (ISBN 0-940754-20-7). Ed Ministries.

Live with Meaning. Bernard Mandlebaum. 1980. pap. 7.95 (ISBN 0-87677-182-7). Hartmore.

Live with Moses. Alexander Campbell & Gerry Haff. 90p. (Orig.). 1982. pap. 12.95 (ISBN 0-940754-13-4). Ed Ministries.

Live, with Peace, Power & Purpose. Joe R. Barnett. Ed. by J. D. Thomas. (Twentieth Century Sermons Ser.). 1978. 11.95 (ISBN 0-89112-311-3, Bibl Res Pr). Abilene Christ U.

Live Your Faith! Russell McIntire. LC 78-25579. 167p. 1979. 6.95 (ISBN 0-88289-217-7). Pelican.

Live Youthfully Now. Russell A. Kemp. LC 69-93890. 1969. 5.95 (ISBN 0-87159-232-0). Unity School.

Lively Experiment Continued: Essays in Honor of Sidney E. Mead. Ed. by Jerald C. Brauer. 288p. 1987. 39.95 (ISBN 0-86554-264-3, H225). Mercer Univ Pr.

Lively Experiment: The Shaping of Christianity in America. Sidney E. Mead. 1963. pap. 6.95xi (ISBN 0-06-065545-3, RD-194, HarpR). Har-Row.

Lively Image: Four Myths in Literature. Richard E. Hughes. 1975. pap. text ed. 12.00 (ISBN 0-316-38034-2). Little.

Lively Jewish Classroom: Games & Activities for Learning. Rita Kopin. (Illus.). 132p. 1980. pap. text ed. 8.75 (ISBN 0-86705-014-4). AIRE.

Lively Legacy: Essays in Honor of Robert Preus. Ed. by Kurt E. Marquart et al. 224p. (Orig.). 1985. 13.95 (ISBN 0-9615927-0-2); pap. 11.95 (ISBN 0-9615927-1-0). Concordia Theo Sem.

Lively Oracles. Ann R. Colton. 151p. 1962. 5.95 (ISBN 0-917187-13-X). A R C Pub.

Lives: An Anthropological Approach to Biography. L. L. Langness & Gelya F. Frank. Ed. by R. B. Edgerton. LC 81-15460. (Chandler & Sharp Publications in Anthropology Ser.). 232p. (Orig.). 1981. pap. 9.95x (ISBN 0-88316-542-2). Chandler & Sharp.

Lives & Legends of the Georgian Saints. Ed. by David M. Lang. 179p. 1976. pap. 4.95 (ISBN 0-913836-29-X). St Vladimirs.

Lives of Eminent Korean Monks: The Haedong Kosung Chon. Kakhun. Tr. by Peter H. Lee. LC 69-18037. (Harvard-Yenching Institute Studies: No. 25). 1969. pap. text ed. 7.00x (ISBN 0-674-53662-2). Harvard U Pr.

Lives of Great Men & Women: Charles Kingsley, John Ruskin, William Morris. Catherine Webb. 1911. Repr. 25.00 (ISBN 0-8274-2976-2). R West.

Lives of Jesus: A History & Bibliography. Warren S. Kissinger. LC 83-48284. 200p. 1985. lib. bdg. 39.00 (ISBN 0-8240-9035-7). Garland Pub.

Lives of St. Augustine & St. Gilbert of Sempringham. J. Capgrave. (EETS, OS Ser.: No. 140). Repr. of 1910 ed. 40.00 (ISBN 0-527-00137-6). Kraus Repr.

Lives of St. Eugenia & St. Antipas. 1981. pap. 1.00 (ISBN 0-317-30436-4). Holy Trinity.

Lives of Saints for Young People, Vol. 1. Lev Puhalo. 1975. pap. 2.50x (ISBN 0-913026-11-5). St Nectarios.

Lives of the Buddha in the Art & Literature of Asia. Mary Cummings. LC 80-67341. (Michigan Papers on South & Southeast Asia: No. 20). (Illus.). xiii, 225p. 1982. 19.95 (ISBN 0-89148-022-6); pap. 10.95 (ISBN 0-89148-023-4). Ctr S&SE Asian.

Lives of the Desert Fathers. Tr. by Norman Russell. 192p. 1981. 40.00x (ISBN 0-264-66581-3, Pub. by Mowbrays Pub Div). State Mutual Bk.

Lives of the Desert Fathers: The Historia Monachorum in Aegypto. Tr. by Benedicta Ward & Norman Russell. (Cistercian Studies: No. 34). 1981. 17.95 (ISBN 0-87907-834-0); pap. 8.95 (ISBN 0-87907-934-7). Cistercian Pubns.

Lives of the Saints, 4 vols. Alban Butler. Ed. by Thurston Attwater. 1956. Set. 140.00 (ISBN 0-87061-045-7); Set. pap. 95.00 (ISBN 0-87061-137-2). Chr Classics.

Lives of the Saints. H. Hoever. (Illus.). maroon cloth, colored edges 4.75 (ISBN 0-89942-870-3, 870/22). Catholic Bk Pub.

Lives of the Saints. Augustine Kalberer. (Illus.). 380p. 1976. 18.50 (ISBN 0-8199-0539-9). Franciscan Herald.

Lives of the Saints, Vols. 2. L. Puhalo. 1977. pap. 2.50x ea.; Vol. 2. (ISBN 0-913026-75-1); St Nectarios.

Lives of the Serbian Saints. Voyeslav Yanich. (Illus.). 1973. 3.95 (ISBN 0-686-05412-1). Eastern Orthodox.

Lives of the Welsh Saints. G. H. Doble. Ed. by D. Simon Evans. 258p. 1984. text ed. 15.00x (ISBN 0-7083-0870-8, Pub. by U of Wales). Humanities.

Lives of Three English Saints. Aelfric. Ed. by G. I. Needham. (Old English Ser.). 1966. pap. text ed. 9.95x (ISBN 0-89197-564-0). Irvington.

Lives of Three English Saints. rev. ed. Ed. by G. I. Needham. 119p. 1979. pap. text ed. 7.95x (ISBN 0-85989-076-7, Pub. by U Exeter UK). Humanities.

Lives on Borrowed Time. Rudolph G. Roden & Eva Roden. 1984. 6.95 (ISBN 0-8062-2316-2). Carlton.

Living. J. C. Van Rijn. 49p. (Orig.). 1986. pap. 7.00 (ISBN 0-9617483-0-3). What Is Pr.

Living. 2nd ed. J. C. Van Rijn. 130p. Date not set. pap. 8.95 (ISBN 0-9617483-1-1). What Is Pr.

Living a Biblical Faith. Donald H. Juel. LC 82-8652. (Library of Living Faith: Vol. 6). 118p. 1982. pap. 5.95 (ISBN 0-664-24429-7). Westminster.

Living a Thousand Lives. Halford E. Luccock & Walter Rauschenbusch. LC 82-9091. 80p. (Orig.). 1982. pap. 5.95 (ISBN 0-8298-0622-9). Pilgrim NY.

Living above the Level of Mediocrity: A Commitment to Excellence. Charles Swindoll. 256p. 1987. 14.95 (ISBN 0-8499-0564-8). Word Bks.

Living Alone. Martin Israel. Intro. by Morton T. Kelsey. LC 82-72725. 144p. (Orig.). 1983. pap. 8.95 (ISBN 0-8245-0503-4). Crossroad NY.

Living & Active Word: A Way to Preach from the Bible Today. O. C. Edwards. 166p. 1975. 1.50 (ISBN 0-8164-0265-5, HarpR). Har-Row.

Living & Active Word of God: Studies in Honor of Samuel J. Schultz. Ed. by Ronald Youngblood & Morris Inch. 1983. 20.00 (ISBN 0-931464-11-0). Eisenbrauns.

Living & Celebrating Advent Season. 3.50 (ISBN 0-8198-4418-7); 2.50 (ISBN 0-8198-4419-5). Dghtrs St Paul.

Living & Dying: An Inquiry into the Enigma of Death & After-Life. Vidya Dehejia. 1979. 8.95x (ISBN 0-7069-0815-5, Pub. by Vikas India). Advent NY.

Living & Growing Through the Eucharist. Daughters of St. Paul. 1976. 7.00 (ISBN 0-8198-0432-0); pap. 6.00 (ISBN 0-8198-0433-9). Dghtrs St Paul.

Living & Learning with Nursery Children. Joy Latham. (Teaching Helps Ser.). 128p. 1976. pap. 2.95 (ISBN 0-8010-5562-8). Baker Bk.

Living Animals of the Bible. Walter W. Ferguson. (Encore Edition). 1974. 3.95 (ISBN 0-684-15245-2, ScribT). Scribner.

Living As a Winner. Richard H. Stadler. Ed. by William E. Fischer. (Bible Class Course for Young Adults Ser.). (Illus.). 64p. 1985. pap. 2.95 leaders guide (ISBN 0-938272-23-3); pap. 2.95 students guide (ISBN 0-938272-22-5). WELS Board.

Living As God's People. Helmut Harder. LC 86-80675. (Faith & Life Bible Studies). 64p. (Orig.). 1986. pap. 4.95 (ISBN 0-87303-108-3). Faith & Life.

Living As if: How Positive Faith Can Change Your Life. William R. Miller. LC 84-13001. 132p. (Orig.). 1985. pap. 7.95 (ISBN 0-664-24635-4). Westminster.

Living at the Edge of Faith. Lawrence D. Reimer. 96p. 1984. pap. 6.95 (ISBN 0-8170-1023-8). Judson.

Living Between Two Worlds. Joel S. Goldsmith. LC 73-18679. 1974. 8.95 (ISBN 0-06-063191-0, HarpR). Har-Row.

Living Beyond Crisis: Essays on Discovery & Being in the World. Ed. by Stephen Rowe. LC 80-18135. 261p. 1980. pap. 8.95 (ISBN 0-8298-0402-1). Pilgrim NY.

Living Beyond Depression. Matilda Nordtvedt. LC 78-58082. 128p. 1978. pap. 3.50 (ISBN 0-87123-339-8, 200339). Bethany Hse.

Living Beyond Divorce: Working Guide. Jim Smoke & Lisa McAfee. LC 83-82321. (Orig.). 1985. pap. 5.95 (ISBN 0-89081-407-4); working guide 3.95 (ISBN 0-89081-467-8). Harvest Hse.

Living Beyond Worry & Anger. LC 79-83659. 1979. 7.95 (ISBN 0-89081-194-6). Harvest Hse.

Living Bible: A Topical Approach to the Jewish Scriptures. Sylvan D. Schwartzman & Jack D. Spiro. (Illus.). 1962. text ed. 5.00 (ISBN 0-8074-0097-1, 161751). UAHC.

Living Bible Story Book. Kenneth N. Taylor. 7.95 (ISBN 0-8423-2307-4). Tyndale.

Living Bread. Thomas Merton. 157p. 1956. 12.95 (ISBN 0-374-14613-6); pap. 7.95 (ISBN 0-374-51520-4). FS&G.

Living Bread. Christine Stugard. (Illus.). 80p. (Orig.). 1983. pap. 4.95 (ISBN 0-88028-023-9). Forward Movement.

Living Bread, Saving Cup: Readings on the Eucharist. Ed. by R. Seasoltz. LC 81-20813. 350p. 1982. pap. 12.95 (ISBN 0-8146-1257-1). Liturgical Pr.

Living Buddha. R. Horniman. LC 78-72441. Repr. of 1903 ed. 33.00 (ISBN 0-404-17307-1). AMS Pr.

Living Buddha. Edmond B. Szekely. (Illus.). 70p. 1977. pap. 4.50 (ISBN 0-89564-059-7). IBS Intl.

Living Buddha: An Interpretive Biography. Daisaku Ikeda. LC 75-40446. (Illus.). 164p. 1975. 7.95 (ISBN 0-8348-0117-5). Weatherhill.

Living by Faith. Stuart Y. Blanch. LC 84-10182. Repr. of 1984 ed. 39.00. Bks Demand UMI.

Living by Faith: A Study of Romans. Muriel Larson. 60p. 1984. pap. 2.95 (ISBN 0-930756-80-0, 521016). Aglow Pubns.

Living by Faith: How an Active Faith Can Change Your Life. Don Mallough. LC 77-91484. 128p. 1978. pap. 1.50 (ISBN 0-88243-552-3, 02-0552). Gospel Pub.

Living by Grace. William Hordern. LC 75-6548. 208p. 1975. pap. 7.95 (ISBN 0-664-24763-6). Westminster.

Living by the Power of Faith. Gene R. Cook. 120p. 1985. 8.95 (ISBN 0-87747-745-0). Deseret Bk.

Living by the Word. O. W. Polen. LC 77-79942. 1977. pap. 1.95 (ISBN 0-87148-509-5). Pathway Pr.

Living by Zen. D. T. Suzuki. pap. 5.95 (ISBN 0-87728-194-7). Weiser.

Living Cameos. Helen K. Hosier. 192p. (Orig.). 1984. pap. 8.95 (ISBN 0-8007-1398-2). Revell.

Living Cells: Developing Small Christian Community. James O'Halloran. LC 83-22076. 132p. (Orig.). 1984. pap. 4.95 (ISBN 0-88344-288-4). Orbis Bks.

Living Christ: Church of Illumination. R. Swimburne Clymer. 58p. 1979. pap. 2.95 (ISBN 0-932785-27-1). Philos Pub.

Living Church: A Guide for Revitalization. Donald J. MacNair. (Illus.). 167p. (Orig.). 1980. pap. 4.95 (ISBN 0-934688-00-1). Great Comm Pubns.

Living Churches: A Reconsideration of Their Basis of Life & Leadership. John Williams. 144p. 1975. pap. 4.95 (ISBN 0-85364-122-6). Attic Pr.

Living Churches: The Essence of Their Life - Love to Christ & Love to the Brothers, Vol. 1. Eberhard Arnold. LC 73-21273. 1974. pap. 2.50 (ISBN 0-87486-116-0). Plough.

Living Churches: The Essence of Their Life - the Meaning & Power of Prayer Life, Vol. 2. Eberhard Arnold. LC 75-42829. 1976. pap. 2.50 (ISBN 0-87486-159-4). Plough.

Living Confidently in God's Love. Hannah W. Smith. Orig. Title: Living in the Sunshine the God of All Comfort. 192p. 1984. pap. text ed. 3.50 (ISBN 0-88368-150-1). Whitaker Hse.

Living Covenant: The Innovative Spirit in Traditional Judaism. David Hartman. 384p. 1985. 21.60x (ISBN 0-02-914140-0). Free Pr.

Living Divine Love: Transformation, the Goal of Christian Life. Dominic M. Hoffman. LC 82-11552. 200p. (Orig.). 1982. pap. 7.95 (ISBN 0-8189-0443-7). Alba.

Living Each Day by the Power of Faith. Barbara Shlemon. 140p. (Orig.). 1986. pap. 4.95 (ISBN 0-89283-289-4). Servant.

Living Faith & Ultimate Goals: Salvation & World Religions. Ed. by S. J. Samartha. LC 75-7610. 119p. (Orig.). 1975. pap. 1.98 (ISBN 0-88344-297-3). Orbis Bks.

Living Fellowship. Richard C. Halverson. 195p. 1985. pap. 5.95 (ISBN 0-310-25781-6, Pub. by Pyranee). Zondervan.

Living for Christ. rev. ed. William A. Kramer. LC 72-96585. 1973. 3.25 (ISBN 0-570-03157-5, 12-2542). Concordia.

Living for God. Z. W. Swafford. (God & Us Ser.). 32p. 1981. pap. 2.00 (ISBN 0-89114-099-9); coloring book 0.69 (ISBN 0-89114-102-2). Baptist Pub Hse.

Living for Jesus. Doris C. Demaree. (Bible Stories for Children Ser.). 1974. pap. 1.50 (ISBN 0-87162-238-6, D1448). Warner Pr.

Living for Others When You'd Rather Live for Yourself. Gene A. Getz. LC 85-24283. (Biblical Renewal Ser.). 126p. 1985. pap. write for info. (ISBN 0-8307-1125-2, 5418606). Regal.

Living Fully: Producing Spiritual Fruit. George O. Wood. 1985. pap. 3.95 (ISBN 0-932305-23-7, 531021). Aglow Pubns.

Living Gita. Sri Swami Satchidananda. LC 84-27861. (Orig.). Date not set. pap. price not set (ISBN 0-932040-27-6). Integral Yoga Pubns.

Living God. Thomas C. Oden. 1986. 29.45 (ISBN 0-317-52383-X, HarpR). Har-Row.

Living God. Rene Voillaume. 1971. 5.95 (ISBN 0-87193-169-9). Dimension Bks.

Living God: Basal Forms of Personal Religion. Nathan Soderblom. LC 77-27196. (Gifford Lectures: 1931). Repr. of 1933 ed. 40.00 (ISBN 0-404-60485-4). AMS Pr.

Living God's Love. Douglas Cooper. LC 74-27171. (Redwood Ser.). 1975. pap. 4.95 (ISBN 0-8163-0176-X, 12523-7). Pacific Pr Pub Assn.

Living God's Way. F. E. Marsh. LC 80-8073. 230p. (Reprint of The Spiritual Life). 1981. pap. 7.95 (ISBN 0-8254-3233-2). Kregel.

Living God's Word. E. A. Jiede. 1947. pap. 2.25 (ISBN 0-570-03505-8, 14-1262). Concordia.

Living Gospels. J. B Phillips. 288p. 1981. 24.95 (ISBN 0-8317-3948-7, Rutledge Pr). Smith Pubs.

Living Happily Ever after: Toward a Theology of Christian Marriage. Thomas Hart. LC 79-89475. 96p. 1979. pap. 3.95 (ISBN 0-8091-2213-8). Paulist Pr.

Living Hebrew. Samuel Steinberg. (YA) 1958. 17.95 (ISBN 0-517-00133-0); records, manual & dictionary incl. Crown.

Living Here & Hereafter. David E. Rosage. (Christian Dying, Death & Resurection Ser.). 128p. (Orig.). 1982. pap. 2.95 (ISBN 0-914544-44-6). Living Flame Pr.

Living Heritage of Hanukkah. David Greenberg & Solomon S. Bernards. 47p. 1.50 (ISBN 0-686-74963-4). ADL.

Living Heritage of the High Holy Days. Ed. by Solomon S. Bernards. 31p. 0.50 (ISBN 0-686-74964-2). ADL.

Living Holiness. Helen Roseveare. 192p. (Orig.). 1987. pap. 5.95 (ISBN 0-87123-952-3). Bethany Hse.

Living Hope: A Commentary on I & II Peter. Robert Mounce. 1982. pap. 4.95 (ISBN 0-8028-1915-X). Eerdmans.

Living Hope: Studies in I Peter. Steve Lemke. 35p. (Orig.). 1982. pap. 3.50 (ISBN 0-939298-12-0, 120). J M Prods.

Living Human Document: Re-Visioning Pastoral Counseling in a Hermeneutical Mode. Charles V. Gerkin. 224p. 1984. pap. 10.95 (ISBN 0-687-22372-5). Abingdon.

Living Hymn Stories. Wilbur Konkel. 128p. 1982. pap. 3.95 (ISBN 0-87123-317-7, 210317). Bethany Hse.

Living Illustrations. J. B. Fowler, Jr. LC 85-4175. 1985. pap. 5.95 (ISBN 0-8054-2260-9). Broadman.

Living in a Larger World: The Life of Murray S. Kenworthy. Leonard Kenworthy. (Illus.). 120p. (Orig.). 1987. pap. 8.95 (ISBN 0-913408-93-X). Friends United.

Living in Christ. Ralph M. Riggs. LC 67-25874. 1967. pap. 1.50 (ISBN 0-88243-538-8, 02-0538). Gospel Pub.

Living in Christian Community. Arthur G. Gish. LC 79-11848. 384p. 1979. pap. 9.95 (ISBN 0-8361-1887-1). Herald Pr.

Living in Christ's Church. Edmund P. Clowney. 1986. pap. text ed. 4.95 (ISBN 0-934688-22-2); leader's guide 3.95 (ISBN 0-934688-24-9). Great Comm Pubns.

Living in Divine Prosperity. Jerry Savelle. 256p. 1983. pap. 4.95 (ISBN 0-89274-247-X). Harrison Hse.

Living in God's Love. Allan B. Wolter. 172p. 1958. pap. 1.75 (ISBN 0-8199-0059-1, L38375). Franciscan Herald.

Living in God's Power. George W. Swank. 112p. 1983. pap. 5.95 (ISBN 0-8170-0968-X). Judson.

Living in Harmony: Through Kahuna Wisdom. Allan P. Lewis. LC 84-25244. (Illus.). 192p. (Orig.). 1985. pap. 10.95 (ISBN 0-915563-01-0). Homana Pubns.

Living in His Love: Essays on Prayer & Christian Living. Bernard J. Bush. LC 78-11809. 115p. 1978. pap. 3.95 (ISBN 0-89571-005-6). Affirmation.

Living in Light of Eternity. Christian Character Library Staff & Stacy Rinehart. 176p. 1986. 8.95 (ISBN 0-89109-551-9). NavPress.

Living in Our Finest Hour. Douglas Cooper. Ed. by Max Phillips. (RWD Ser.). 112p. 1982. pap. 4.95 (ISBN 0-8163-0465-3). Pacific Pr Pub Assn.

Living in the Power of Pentecost. Joseph C. McKinney. 112p. (Orig.). 1987. pap. 4.95 (ISBN 0-89283-311-4). Servant.

Living in the Presence of God. Eugene B. Hines. LC 84-24305. 1985. pap. 4.95 (ISBN 0-8054-5229-X). Broadman.

Living in the Shadow of the Second Coming: American Premillennialism, 1875-1982. rev. & enl. ed. Timothy P. Weber. xiv, 306p. 1987. pap. 12.95 (ISBN 0-226-87732-9). U of Chicago Pr.

Living in the Spirit. R. Hollis Gause. 136p. 1980. pap. 5.25 (ISBN 0-87148-515-X). Pathway Pr.

Living in the Spirit. Rachel Hosmer & Alan Jones. (Church's Teaching Ser.: Vol. 7). 272p. 1979. 5.95 (ISBN 0-8164-0424-0, HarpR); pap. 4.95 (ISBN 0-8164-2220-6); pap. text ed. 1.50 (ISBN 0-8164-2227-3). Har-Row.

Living in the Spirit: Ephesians Five Eighteen Through Twenty. John MacArthur, Jr. (John MacArthur Bible Studies Ser.). 1987. pap. 3.95 (ISBN 0-8024-5315-5). Moody.

Living in the Tower. Nathanael Pugh. LC 86-18888. 96p. (Orig.). 1986. pap. 4.95 (ISBN 0-932581-01-3). Word Aflame.

Living in Two Worlds: Communication Between a White Healer & Her Black Counterparts. M. Vera Buhrmann. 108p. 1986. pap. 9.95 (ISBN 0-933029-10-1). Chiron Pubns.

Living Is Now. Ed. by D. A. Blaiklock. 1972. pap. 1.50 (ISBN 0-8010-0579-5). Baker Bk.

Living Issues in Ethics. Richard T. Nolan & Frank G. Kirkpatrick. 400p. 1982. pap. text ed. write for info. (ISBN 0-534-01140-3). Wadsworth Pub.

Living Issues in Religious Thought, from George Fox to Bertrand Russell. facs. ed. Herbert G. Wood. LC 67-22128. (Essay Index Reprint Ser). 1924. 14.25 (ISBN 0-8369-1007-9). Ayer Co Pubs.

Living Issues in Religious Thought: From George Fox to Betrand Russell. facsimile ed. Herbert G. Wood. LC 67-22128. (Essay Index Reprint Ser.). 187p. 1967. Repr. of 1924 ed. lib. bdg. 13.50 (ISBN 0-8290-0489-0). Irvington.

Living Jesus. Harold Cooper. (Illus.). 1977. PBK:106. pap. text ed. 1.50 (ISBN 0-89114-077-8); PBK:48. tchrs. ed. 1.00 (ISBN 0-89114-078-6). Baptist Pub Hse.

Living Jewish: The Lore & the Law of the Practicing Jew. Michael Asheri. 446p. 1983. pap. 9.95 (ISBN 0-396-08263-7). Dodd.

Living Letter for the Children's Hour. Kenneth N. Taylor. LC 68-26407. (Illus.). 192p. 1968. pap. 3.95 (ISBN 0-8024-0062-0). Moody.

Living Life By God's Law. Gordon K. Reed. 124p. (Orig.). 1984. pap. 6.00 (ISBN 0-317-03221-6). Word Ministries.

Living Life to the Fullest. Maxine Kipp. LC 79-52997. (Radiant Life Ser.). 160p. 1980. pap. 2.95 (ISBN 0-88243-896-4, 02-0896); teacher's ed 3.95 (ISBN 0-88243-187-0, 32-0187). Gospel Pub.

Living Light. Edythe Draper. Incl. Large Print Edition. 1976. kivar 8.95 (ISBN 0-8423-2652-9). 1972. leatherette o.p. 8.95 (ISBN 0-8423-2651-0). Tyndale.

Living Like a King. Edward O'Rourke. 1979. 3.95 (ISBN 0-87243-087-1). Templegate.

Living Love. J. A. Ferrara. (Illus.). 142p. 1961. 9.45 (ISBN 0-933961-04-9). Mystic Jhamom.

Living Love: Meditations on Texts from the New Testament. Ruth Burrows. 1985. 5.95 (ISBN 0-87193-243-1). Dimension Bks.

Living Marriage. H. Norman Wright. (Illus.). 128p. 1975. 12.95 (ISBN 0-8007-0722-2). Revell.

Living Messages of the Books of the New Testament. Ed. by Thomas B. Warren & Garland Elkins. 1976. 13.00 (ISBN 0-934916-35-7). Natl Christian Pr.

Living Messages of the Books of the Old Testament. Ed. by Thomas B. Warren & Garland Elkins. 1977. 14.00 (ISBN 0-934916-36-5). Natl Christian Pr.

Living More Simply. Ed. by Ronald J. Sider. LC 79-3634. (Orig.). 1980. pap. 4.95 (ISBN 0-87784-808-4). Inter-Varsity.

Living Non-Christian Religions. 160p. 1984. pap. write for info. (ISBN 0-311-72940-1). Casa Bautista.

Living Now. Joel S. Goldsmith. Ed. by Lorraine Sinkler. 192p. 1984. pap. 5.95 (ISBN 0-8065-0911-2). Citadel Pr.

Living on Less & Liking It More. Maxine Hancock. 160p. 1982. pap. 4.95 (ISBN 0-89081-414-7). Harvest Hse.

Living on the Cutting Edge: Joshua & the Challenge of Spiritual Leadership. R. Kent Hughes. LC 86-72055. 176p. (Orig.). 1987. pap. 6.95 (ISBN 0-89107-414-7, Crossway Bks). Good News.

Living on the Mountain. Roger C. Palms. 288p. 1985. 11.95 (ISBN 0-8007-1449-0). Revell.

Living on the Ragged Edge: Ecclesiastes. Charles Swindoll. 224p. 1985. 12.95 (ISBN 0-8499-0463-3, 0463-3). Word Bks.

Living Options in Protestant Theology: A Survey of Methods. John B. Cobb, Jr. 336p. 1986. pap. text ed. 14.75 (ISBN 0-8191-5488-1). U Pr of Amer.

Living Options in World Philosophy. John A. Hutchison. LC 76-46489. 323p. 1977. 16.00x (ISBN 0-8248-0455-4). UH Pr.

Living Our Commitment. James Alberione. 1968. 4.00 (ISBN 0-8198-4411-X); pap. 3.00 (ISBN 0-8198-4412-8). Dghtrs St Paul.

Living Our Future: St. Francis of Assisi & the Church Tomorrow. new ed. Mario Von Galli. (Illus.). 239p. 1976. pap. 4.95 (ISBN 0-8199-0439-2). Franciscan Herald.

Living Our Visions of Peace. Connie Johnson. (Illus.). 35p. (Orig.). 1984. pap. 4.95 (ISBN 0-377-00141-4). Friend Pr.

Living Peacefully: First Peter. J. Allen Blair. 1959. pap. 3.50 (ISBN 0-87213-052-5). Loizeaux.

Living Portraits from the Old Testament. Paul Culbertson. 192p. 1978. pap. 2.95 (ISBN 0-8341-0507-1). Beacon Hill.

Living Powerfully One Day at a Time. Robert H. Schuller. 400p. 1983. pap. 7.95 (ISBN 0-8007-5113-2, Power Bks). Revell.

Living Prayer. Metropolitan A. Bloom. 1975. pap. 6.95 (ISBN 0-87243-054-5). Templegate.

Living Prayer. Glenn Clark. 1980. pap. 0.50 (ISBN 0-910924-88-0). Macalester.

Living Prayer. Mother Angelica. 126p. (Orig.). 1985. pap. 4.95 (ISBN 0-89283-280-0). Servant.

Living Presence of the Past: The Dynamic of Christian Tradition. A. M. Allchin. 192p. (Orig.). 1981. pap. 7.95 (ISBN 0-8164-2334-2, HarpR). Har-Row.

Living Prophet. Dean Zimmerman. 1974. pap. 2.95 (ISBN 0-89036-041-3). Hawkes Pub Inc.

Living Reliantly: Twenty-Third Psalm. J. Allen Blair. 1958. pap. 2.75 (ISBN 0-87213-054-1). Loizeaux.

Living Religions & a World Faith. William E. Hocking. LC 75-3187. (Hibbert Lectures Ser. 1938). Repr. of 1940 ed. 28.50 (ISBN 0-404-59189-2). AMS Pr.

Living Religions of the World: Our Search for Meaning. Carl H. Voss. (Library of Liberal Religion). 192p. 1977. pap. 6.95 (ISBN 0-87975-215-7). Prometheus Bks.

Living Reminder: Service & Prayer in Memory of Jesus Christ. Henri J. Nouwen. 80p. 1981. pap. 4.95 (ISBN 0-86683-915-1, HarpR). Har-Row.

Living-Room Retreat: Meditations for Home Use with a 12-Week Plan for Group Sharing. Helen C. Swift. 100p. 1981. pap. text ed. 3.25 (ISBN 0-912228-95-4). St Anthony Mess Pr.

Living Sacrifice. Watchman Nee. Tr. by Stephen Kaung. (Basic Lesson Ser.: Vol. 1). 1972. 4.25 (ISBN 0-935008-07-1); pap. 2.75 (ISBN 0-935008-08-X). Christian Fellow Pubs.

Living Saints Witness at Work. T. Edward Barlow. 1976. 6.00 (ISBN 0-8309-0153-1). Herald Hse.

Living Securely in an Unstable World: God's Solution to Man's Dilemma. Rick Yohn. LC 85-4895. (Living Theology Ser.). 1985. pap. 8.95 (ISBN 0-88070-082-3). Multnomah.

Living Securely with Insecurity. Rev. William F. Maestri. LC 86-60328. 185p. (Orig.). 1986. pap. 6.95 (ISBN 0-87973-543-0, 543). Our Sunday Visitor.

Living Simply. Daisy Hepburn. LC 84-3360. (Life with Spice Bible Study Ser.). 1984. 2.95 (ISBN 0-8307-0947-9, 6101848). Regal.

Living Simply: An Examination of Christian Lifestyles. Ed. by David Crean & Eric Ebbeson. 128p. (Orig.). 1981. pap. 5.95 (ISBN 0-8164-2340-7, HarpR). Har-Row.

Living Simply Through the Day. Tilden Edwards. 444p. 1985. pap. 9.95 large print ed. (ISBN 0-8027-2492-2). Walker & Co.

Living Spirit-Filled Life. Douglas Cooper. (Red Ser.). 1985. pap. 4.95 (ISBN 0-8163-0595-1). Pacific Pr Pub Assn.

Living Stories of Famous Hymns. Ernest K. Emurian. (Interlude Bks). 1971. pap. 4.95 (ISBN 0-8010-3260-1). Baker Bk.

Living Talmud. Judah Goldin. 1957. pap. 3.95 (ISBN 0-451-62344-4, Ment). NAL.

Living Testament: The Essential Writings of Christianity since the Bible. M. Basil Pennington et al. LC 85-42790. 400p. 1985. 22.45 (ISBN 0-06-066499-1, HarpR); pap. 14.95 (ISBN 0-06-066498-3). Har-Row.

Living Text: Essays in Honor of Ernest W. Saunders. Ed. by Dennis E. Groh & Robert Jewett. (Illus.). 272p. (Orig.). 1985. lib. bdg. 27.50 (ISBN 0-8191-4584-X); pap. text ed. 14.25 (ISBN 0-8191-4585-8). U Pr of Amer.

Living the Catholic Faith Today. John F. Whealon. LC 75-6801. 1975. 2.50 (ISBN 0-8198-0491-6); pap. 1.50 (ISBN 0-8198-0492-4). Dghtrs St Paul.

Living the Christ Life. James Stalker. LC 81-81097. (Shepherd Illustrated Classics Ser.). (Illus.). 1981. pap. 5.95 (ISBN 0-87983-259-2). Keats.

Living the Christian Life. A. N. Martin. 32p. 1986. pap. 1.00 (ISBN 0-85151-493-6). Banner of Truth.

Living the Faith Community: The Church That Makes a Difference. John H. Westerhoff, III. 1985. pap. cancelled (ISBN 0-317-18159-9). Whitaker Hse.

Living the Faith Community: The Church That Makes a Difference. John H. Westerhoff, III. 120p. (Orig.). 1985. pap. 6.95 (ISBN 0-86683-870-8, HarpR). Har-Row.

Living the Good Life: How to Live Sanely & Simply in a Troubled World. Helen Nearing & Scott Nearing. LC 73-127820. (Illus.). 1971. pap. 5.25 (ISBN 0-8052-0300-1). Schocken.

Living the Good News: An Introduction to Moral Theology. Nicholas Lohkamp. 170p. (Orig.). 1982. pap. text ed. 4.50 (ISBN 0-86716-016-0). St Anthony Mess Pr.

Living the Heidelberg, the Heidelberg Catechism & the Moral Life. Allen Verhey. LC 85-31386. 120p. (Orig.). 1986. pap. text ed. 7.95 (ISBN 0-930265-21-1). CRC Pubns.

Living the Infinite Way. rev. ed. Joel S. Goldsmith. LC 61-9646. 1961. 11.45 (ISBN 0-06-063190-2, HarpR). Har-Row.

Living the Liturgy. S. Harakas. 1974. pap. 4.95 (ISBN 0-937032-17-4). Light&Life Pub Co MN.

Living the Lord's Prayer. Everett L. Fullman. (Epiphany Ser.). 128p. 1983. pap. 2.50 (ISBN 0-345-30432-2). Ballantine.

Living the New Life. Andrew Murray. 256p. 1982. pap. text ed. 3.50 (ISBN 0-88368-108-0). Whitaker Hse.

Living the Richness of the Cross. John Dalrymple. LC 83-70945. 128p. (Orig.). 1983. pap. 3.95 (ISBN 0-87793-274-3). Ave Maria.

Living the Sacraments: A Call to Conversion. David M. Knight. LC 85-60888. 140p. (Orig.). 1985. pap. 6.50 (ISBN 0-87973-815-4, 815). Our Sunday Visitor.

Living the Truth in a World of Illusions. William S. Coffin. LC 84-48766. 160p. 1985. 12.45 (ISBN 0-06-061512-5, HarpR). Har-Row.

Living the Vows. Robert J. McAllister. Date not set. 19.45 (ISBN 0-317-52397-X, HarpR). Har-Row.

Living Theology in Asia. Ed. by John C. England. LC 82-2288. 256p. (Orig.). 1982. pap. 9.95 (ISBN 0-88344-298-1). Orbis Bks.

Living Thoughts. Ernest Miner. (Book of Inspirational Thoughts Ser.). 84p. 1985. 7.95 (ISBN 0-935087-00-1). Wright Pub Co.

Living Thoughts. Ed. by Bernard S. Raskas. LC 76-22418. 1976. 12.50 (ISBN 0-87677-145-2). Hartmore.

Living Thoughts for the Children's Hour. Kenneth N. Taylor. LC 72-77943. (Illus.). 128p. 1972. pap. 3.95 (ISBN 0-8024-0121-X). Moody.

Living Thoughts of Cardinal Newman. Henry Tristram. 167p. 1983. Repr. of 1948 ed. lib. bdg. 25.00 (ISBN 0-8495-5218-4). Arden Lib.

Living Thoughts of Confucius. Alfred Doerblin. 182p. 1983. Repr. of 1940 ed. lib. bdg. 25.00 (ISBN 0-89987-173-9). Darby Bks.

Living Thoughts of Gotama, the Buddha. Ananda K. Coomaraswamy & I. B. Horner. LC 78-72397. Repr. of 1948 ed. 34.50 (ISBN 0-404-17256-3). AMS Pr.

Living Thoughts of St. Paul. 2nd ed. 4.76 (ISBN 0-02-659680-6, 65968). Benziger Pub Co.

Living Thoughts of Saint Paul. Jacques Maritain. 135p. 1983. Repr. of 1942 ed. lib. bdg. 20.00 (ISBN 0-8495-3946-3). Arden Lib.

Living Thoughts of Swedenborg. Eric A. Sutton. 122p. 1981. Repr. of 1944 ed. lib. bdg. 20.00 (ISBN 0-8495-5041-6). Arden Lib.

Living Through Loss: God's Help in Bereavement. David Winter. 96p. (Orig.). 1986. pap. 3.50 (ISBN 0-87788-507-9). Shaw Pubs.

Living Through Your Separation or Divorce. P. Mark Watts. Ed. by Michael L. Sherer. (Orig.). 1987. pap. 2.25 (ISBN 0-89536-864-1, 7823). CSS of Ohio.

Living to Please God. Andrew Murray. 100p. 1985. pap. text ed. 3.50 (ISBN 0-88368-166-8). Whitaker Hse.

Living Today for God. Roger Schutz. 80p. (Orig.). 1981. pap. 3.95 (ISBN 0-8164-2323-7, HarpR). Har-Row.

Living Together in a Jesuit Community. Carlos G. Valles. LC 84-81259. (Study Aids on Jesuit Topics: Ser. IV, No. 10). 128p. 1985. pap. 4.00 Smyth Sewn (ISBN 0-912422-66-1). Inst Jesuit.

Living Together on God's Earth. John D. Martin. (Christian Day School Ser.). 1974. 12.95x (ISBN 0-87813-915-X); tchr's. guide 19.65x (ISBN 0-87813-910-9). Christian Light.

Living Toward a Vision: Biblical Reflections on Shalom. rev. ed. Walter Brueggemann. LC 76-22172. (Shalom Resource Ser.). 1982. pap. 6.95 (ISBN 0-8298-0613-X). Pilgrim NY.

Living Tradition. John Meyendorff. LC 78-2031. 202p. 1978. pap. 7.95 (ISBN 0-913836-48-6). St Vladimirs.

Living Tree: Materials on the Jewish Legal Tradition with Comparative Notes. Elliot N. Dorff & Arthur Rosett. 680p. 1987. 49.50x (ISBN 0-88706-459-0); pap. 19.95x (ISBN 0-88706-460-4). State U NY Pr.

Living True. Coleen Evans. 132p. 1985. pap. 4.95 (ISBN 0-89693-321-0). Victor Bks.

Living Victoriously: Philippians. J. Allen Blair. LC 62-290. 1962. pap. 2.75 (ISBN 0-87213-056-8). Loizeaux.

Living Voice of the Gospel: The Gospels Today. Francis J. Moloney. 1987. pap. 10.95. Paulist Pr.

Living Water. Frances J. Roberts. 1965. 2.95 (ISBN 0-932814-20-4). Kings Farspan.

Living Water: Prayers of Our Heritage. Janaan Manternach & Carl J. Pfeifer. LC 78-58965. (Illus.). 128p. 1978. pap. 3.95 (ISBN 0-8091-2128-X). Paulist Pr.

Living Waters: Psalms for Your Quiet Time with God. Commentary by E. M. Blaiklock. (Illus.). 256p. 1985. Repr. 10.95 (ISBN 0-687-22378-4). Abingdon.

Living We've Just Begun. Douglas Cooper. (Redwood Ser.). 96p. 1983. pap. 4.95 (ISBN 0-8163-0505-6). Pacific Pr Pub Assn.

Living When a Loved One Has Died. Earl A. Grollman. LC 76-48508. (Illus.). 1977. pap. 6.95 (ISBN 0-8070-2741-3, BP560). Beacon Pr.

Living with a Clear Conscience: A Christian Strategy for Overcoming Guilt & Self-Condemnation. Mark Kinzer. (Living As a Christian Ser.). 160p. 1982. pap. 3.50 (ISBN 0-89283-115-4). Servant.

Living with a Purpose. S. Radhakrishnan. 136p. 1982. 9.00 (ISBN 0-86578-204-0); pap. 4.25 (ISBN 0-86578-137-0). Ind-US Inc.

Living with Angels. 5th ed. Dorie D'Angelo. 1980. pap. 10.00 (ISBN 0-912216-22-0). Angel Pr.

Living with Antisemitism: Modern Jewish Responses. Ed. by Jehuda Reinharz. (Tauber Institute Ser.: No. 6). 1987. 45.00 (ISBN 0-87451-388-X). U Pr of New Eng.

Living with Anxiety. Randolph C. Miller. LC 75-168525. 190p. 1971. 5.95 (ISBN 0-8298-0206-1). Pilgrim NY.

Living with Dying. Glen W. Davidson. LC 74-14186. 112p. (Orig.). 1975. pap. 5.95 (ISBN 0-8066-1468-4, 10-3980); study guide 00.30 (10-3981). Augsburg.

Living with Fire. Sydney Martin. 120p. (Orig.). 1983. pap. 3.95 (ISBN 0-8341-0845-3). Beacon Hill.

Living with God in My Heart. A. A. Noser. 1980. 2.50 (ISBN 0-8198-4406-3); pap. 1.50 (ISBN 0-8198-4404-7). Dghtrs St Paul.

Living with God's Kids. Kay Kuzma. LC 83-61552. 1983. pap. 5.95 (ISBN 0-910529-03-5). Parent Scene.

Living with Jesus Today. Juan C. Ortiz. 1982. 4.95 (ISBN 0-88419-187-7). Creation Hse.

Living with Joy. Donald McKinney. LC 76-8203. Repr. of 1976 ed. 24.00 (ISBN 0-8357-9014-2, 2016375). Bks Demand UMI.

Living with Joy: Keys to Personal Power & Spiritual Transformation. Sanaya Roman. Ed. by Elaine Ratner. (Earth Life Ser.). 216p. (Orig.). 1986. pap. 9.95 (ISBN 0-915811-03-0). H J Kramer Inc.

Living with Luther. J. M. Weidenschilling. 1945. pap. text ed. 1.10 (ISBN 0-570-03523-6, 14-1155). Concordia.

Living with Money. Everald Compton. 47p. (Orig.). 1983. pap. 5.95 (ISBN 0-340-34299-4, Pub. by Genesis). ANZ Religious Pubns.

Living with Others. Leslie H. Stobbe. 1986. pap. 4.95 (ISBN 0-8010-8275-7). Baker Bk.

Living with Purpose. J. Sig Paulson. 142p. 1968. pap. 3.95 (ISBN 0-317-20871-3). CSA Pr.

Living with Suffering. Paul Heubach. Ed. by Richard W. Coffen. (Better Living Ser.). 32p. (Orig.). 1986. pap. 1.25 (ISBN 0-8280-0322-X). Review & Herald.

Living with the Church. Joseph Ratzinger & Karl Lehmann. Tr. by Zachary Hayes from Ger. LC 78-15509. Orig. Title: Mit der Kirche Leben. 53p. 1978. pap. 1.50 (ISBN 0-8199-0742-1). Franciscan Herald.

Living with the Himalayan Masters: Spiritual Experiences of Swami Rama. Ed. by Swami Ajaya. LC 80-82974. 490p. 1980. pap. 12.95 (ISBN 0-89389-070-7). Himalayan Pubs.

Living with the Lama. T. Lobsang Rampa. pap. 2.95 (ISBN 0-552-08408-5). Weiser.

Living with the Parables: Jesus & the Reign of God. J. Edward Carothers. 141p. (Orig.). 1984. pap. 9.95 (ISBN 0-377-00146-5). Friend Pr.

Living with the Psalms. Leroy Brownlow. 386p. 1976. 7.95 (ISBN 0-915720-17-5). Brownlow Pub Co.

Living with the Scriptures, Vol. 1. Satsvarupa Dasa Goswaini. Ed. by Dattatreya dasa. 120p. 1984. text ed. 5.00 (ISBN 0-911233-26-1). Gita Nagari.

Living with the Scriptures, Vol. 2. Satsvarupa Das Goswami. Ed. by Dattatreya dasa. 120p. 1985. text ed. 5.00 (ISBN 0-911233-27-X). Gita Nagari.

Living with the Unexpected. Barry Bailey. 128p. 1984. 8.95 (ISBN 0-687-22366-0). Abingdon.

Living with Your Body. Walther Buhler. Tr. by L. Maloney from Ger. Tr. of Leib als Instrument der Seele. 117p. (Orig.). 1979. pap. 9.95 (ISBN 0-85440-345-0, Pub. by Steinerbooks). Anthroposophic.

Living with Your Emotions: Self-Image & Depression. Norman Wright. LC 79-83661. 1979. 7.95 (ISBN 0-89081-193-8); avail. tchr's guide. Harvest Hse.

Living with Your Passion. Lutzer. 1983. 5.95 (ISBN 0-686-46315-3). Victor Bks.

Living Without Fear. Ernest Holmes. Ed. by Willis H. Kinnear. 96p. 1962. pap. 4.50 (ISBN 0-911336-28-1). Sci of Mind.

Living Without Fear. James M. Tolle. 1977. 4.95 (ISBN 0-915378-13-2). Tolle Pubns.

Living Without Losing. Don Polston. LC 75-27142. 1976. pap. 5.95 (ISBN 0-89081-015-X). Harvest Hse.

Living Without Strain. Joseph Murphy. 157p. 1973. pap. 3.95 (ISBN 0-87516-187-1). De Vorss.

Living Witness: Art in the Concentration Camps & Ghettos. Mary S. Costanza. 1982. 19.95 (ISBN 0-02-906660-3). Free Pr.

Living Witness of John Woolman. Phillips P. Moulton. LC 72-94969. 36p. (Orig.). 1973. 2.50x (ISBN 0-87574-187-8, 187). Pendle Hill.

Living Word (God's Self-Disclosure) Marlene Wesner & Miles E. Wesner. LC 86-70752. 164p. (Orig.). pap. cancelled (ISBN 0-936715-27-8). Diversity Okla.

Living Word of St. John. new ed. White Eagle. 208p. 1979. pap. 13.95 (ISBN 0-85487-044-X). De Vorss.

Living Word of the Bible. Bernhard W. Anderson. LC 78-27108. 118p. 1979. pap. 4.95 (ISBN 0-664-24247-2). Westminster.

Living Word: Scripture & Myth, Vol. 1. William J. O'Malley. LC 80-80534. 180p. (Orig.). 1980. pap. text ed. 4.95 (ISBN 0-8091-9558-5). Paulist Pr.

Living Words. Michel Quoist. 5.95 (ISBN 0-87193-196-6). Dimension Bks.

Living Yoga. Ed. by S. Satchidananda. (Psychic Studies). 336p. 1977. 30.95 (ISBN 0-677-05230-8). Gordon & Breach.

Living Your Life... As God Intended. Jim Burns. (Illus., Orig.). 1985. pap. 3.95 (ISBN 0-89081-450-3). Harvest Hse.

Living Your Religion in the Real World. Madeline M. Daniels. LC 84-18209. 192p. 14.95 (ISBN 0-13-539016-8); pap. 6.95 (ISBN 0-13-539008-7). P-H.

Living Zen. Robert Linssen. Tr. by Diana Abrahams-Curiel. 1960. pap. 3.95 (ISBN 0-394-17391-0, E578, Ever). Grove.

Livingstone. Reginald J. Campbell. LC 77-138212. (Illus.). 295p. 1972. Repr. of 1930 ed. lib. bdg. 22.50x (ISBN 0-8371-5567-3, CALI). Greenwood.

Livre de Seyntz Medicines. Henry Duke Of Lancaster. Ed. by E. J. Arnould. 1967. Repr. of 1940 ed. 19.00 (ISBN 0-384-22400-8). Johnson Repr.

Livres des Miracles & Autres Opuscules, 4 Vols. Saint Gregorius. 1863. Set. 149.00 (ISBN 0-384-19888-0); 38.00 ea.; pap. 32.00 ea.; Set. pap. 125.00 (ISBN 0-384-19889-9). Johnson Repr.

Liz: A Life of Courage. Liz Herron. LC 85-60126. 176p. (Orig.). 1986. pap. 4.95 (ISBN 0-89081-472-4, 4724). Harvest Hse.

Ljestvitsa. St. John Climacus. Tr. of Ladder. (Rus.). 266p. (Orig.). 1963. 18.00x (ISBN 0-88465-033-2); pap. 13.00x (ISBN 0-317-38080-X). Holy Trinity.

Llamados a Ensenar. Lois Lebar & Miguel Berg. Tr. by Jose M. Blanch from Eng. LC 77-5183. (Span., Illus.). 160p. 1970. pap. 3.95 (ISBN 0-89922-006-1). Edit Caribe.

Llamas No Me Destruyeron. Mary E. Ton. Tr. by Edna L. De Gutierrez. (Span.). 160p. 1985. pap. 4.95 (ISBN 0-311-46103-4). Casa Bautista.

Llave para una Vida de Triunfo. Jack R. Taylor. Tr. by Juan P. Guzman from Eng. Orig. Title: Key to Triumphant Living. 240p. 1982. pap. 6.25 (ISBN 0-311-46095-X, Edit Mundo). Casa Bautista.

Lloyd John Ogilvie Anthology. Lloyd J. Olgilvie. 1987. 10.95 (ISBN 0-8307-1189-9, 5419003). Regal.

Lloyd-Jones Expositions of Ephesians, 8 Vols. D. Martyn Lloyd-Jones. 1983. 95.00 (ISBN 0-8010-5623-3). Baker Bk.

Lloyd's Church Musicians Directory. Ed. by Frederick E. Lloyd. LC 72-1733. Repr. of 1910 ed. 14.75 (ISBN 0-404-08319-6). AMS Pr.

Lo Que Dios Espera de Mi. William T. George. LC 82-60829. (Illus.). 157p. (Orig.). 1983. pap. text ed. 6.95 (ISBN 0-87148-517-6). Pathway Pr.

Lo Que los Jovenes Deben Saber Acerca de las Drogas. Guillermo H. Perez. 80p. 1983. pap. 1.10 (ISBN 0-311-46070-4). Casa Bautista.

Lo Que los Padres y Maestros Deben Saber Acerca de las Drogas. Guillermo H. Vasquez. 128p. 1984. pap. 1.20 (ISBN 0-311-46080-1). Casa Bautista.

Lo! the Bridegroom. Peter C. Krey. LC 66-20393. 1966. 3.95 (ISBN 0-686-05043-6). St Thomas.

Loaves & Fishes: Foods from Bible Times. Malvina Kinard & Janet Crisler. LC 75-19544. (Illus.). 224p. 1975. pap. 4.95 (ISBN 0-87983-173-1). Keats.

Loaves & Fishes: The Function of the Feeding Stories in the Gospel of Mark. Robert M. Fowler. Ed. by William Baird. LC 81-2749. (Society of Biblical Literature Dissertation Ser.). 1981. pap. 15.00 (ISBN 0-89130-486-X, 06-01-54). Scholars Pr GA.

Loaves & Fishes: The Story of the Catholic Worker Movement. Dorothy Day. LC 82-48433. (Illus.). 240p. 1983. pap. 4.95 (ISBN 0-06-061771-3, RD/434, HarpR). Har-Row.

Local Church Administration. Larry Wade. (Illus.). 122p. 1978. pap. 8.95 (ISBN 0-914936-32-8). Bible Temple.

Local Church in Ministry. Pinson. LC 73-75629. 7.50 (ISBN 0-8054-6304-6). Broadman.

Local Church Planning Manual. Richard E. Rusbuldt et al. 1977. pap. 14.95 (ISBN 0-8170-0753-9). Judson.

Local Religion in 16th Century Spain. William A. Christian, Jr. LC 80-7513. 296p. 1981. 28.00 (ISBN 0-691-05306-5). Princeton U Pr.

Local Styles of the English Parish Church. William Addison. (Illus.). 192p. 1982. text ed. 35.00x (ISBN 0-8419-6401-7). Holmes & Meier.

Locating & Preserving Your Church's Records. Pat Brown. Ed. by Charles W. Deweese. (Resource Kit for Your Church's History Ser.). 8p. 1984. 0.50 (ISBN 0-939804-15-8). Hist Comm S Baptist.

Loci Communes of Philip Melanchthon. Philip Melanchthon. Tr. by Charles L. Hill. LC 83-45649. Date not set. Repr. of 1944 ed. 32.50 (ISBN 0-404-19858-9). AMS Pr.

Locke on War & Peace. Richard H. Cox. LC 82-42514. 240p. 1983. pap. text ed. 12.50 (ISBN 0-8191-2662-4). U Pr of Amer.

Locke, Wesley & the Method of English Romanticism. Richard E. Brantley. LC 83-26026. 311p. 1984. 30.00 (ISBN 0-8130-0783-6). U Presses Fla.

Lodge & the Craft. Rollin C. Blackmer. 295p. 1976. text ed. 7.95 s.p. (ISBN 0-88053-043-X). Macoy Pub.

Lodge of Sorrows. pap. 1.75 (ISBN 0-685-19483-3). Powner.

Loftier Way. Blaine M. Yorgason & Brenton G. Yorgason. LC 85-70919. 143p. 1985. 8.95 (ISBN 0-87747-785-X). Deseret Bk.

Logic. Gordon H. Clark. (Trinity Papers: No. 9). 123p. (Orig.). 1985. pap. 8.95 (ISBN 0-940931-09-5). Trinity Found.

Logic & Debate Tradition of India, Tibet & Mongolia: History, Reader & Sources. Compiled by Debate Study Group & Sermey G. Tharchin. 281p. (Orig.). 1979. pap. 9.50 (ISBN 0-918753-00-7, Pub by Rashi Gempil Ling). Mahayana.

Logic & the Basis of Ethics. Arthur N. Prior. 1949. 17.95x (ISBN 0-19-824157-7). Oxford U Pr.

Logic & the Bible. Thomas B. Warren. 1983. 11.00 (ISBN 0-934916-01-2). Natl Christian Pr.

Logic & Virtue of Atheism. Joseph McCabe. 58p. 1980. saddle stitched 3.00 (ISBN 0-911826-13-0). Am Atheist.

Logic, Language & Reality: An Introduction to Indian Philosophical Studies. Bimal K. Matilal. 447p. 1985. 29.50 (ISBN 81-208-0008-7, Pub. by Motilal Banarsidass India). Orient Bk Dist.

Logic of Abelard. M. T. Beonio-Brocchieri Fumagalli. Tr. by Simon Pleasance from It. (Synthese Library: No. 1). 101p. 1969. lib. bdg. 18.50 (ISBN 90-277-0068-0, Pub. by Reidel Holland). Kluwer Academic.

Logic of Faith. Phillip Schmahl. LC 65-20327. 250p. 1965. 5.95 (ISBN 0-8022-1503-3). Philos Lib.

Logic of God Incarnate. Thomas V. Morris. LC 85-21252. (Illus.). 224p. 1986. text ed. 19.95x (ISBN 0-8014-1846-1). Cornell U Pr.

Logic of Gotama. Kisor K. Chakrabarti. LC 77-13853. (Society for Asian & Comparative Philosophy Monograph: No. 5). 168p. 1978. pap. text ed. 7.00x (ISBN 0-8248-0601-8). UH Pr.

Logic of Love. Swami Chetanananda. 288p. 1987. pap. 10.95 (ISBN 0-915801-05-1). Rudra Pr.

Logic of Perfection & Other Essays in Neoclassical Metaphysics. Charles Hartshorne. LC 61-11286. 351p. 1973. pap. 8.95 (ISBN 0-87548-037-3). Open Court.

Logic of Promise in Moltmann's Theology. Christopher Morse. LC 78-54556. 192p. 1979. 12.95 (ISBN 0-8006-0523-3, 1-523). Fortress.

Logic of Subjectivity: Kierkegaard's Philosophy of Religion. Louis P. Pojman. LC 83-1053. 174p. 1984. 17.50x (ISBN 0-8173-0166-6). U of Ala Pr.

Logic of Theology. Dietrich Ritschl. Tr. by John Bowden. LC 86-45920. 336p. 1987. pap. 24.95 (ISBN 0-8006-1975-7). Fortress.

Logic of Unity: The Discovery of Zero & Emptiness in Prajanaparamita Thought. Hosaku Matsuo. Tr. by Kenneth K. Inada. (Buddhist studies). 144p. 1987. 29.50 (ISBN 0-88706-391-8); pap. 9.95 (ISBN 0-88706-392-6). State U NY Pr.

Logic: Or, the Right Use of Reason in the Enquiry after Truth, with a Variety of Rules to Guard Against Error, in the Affairs of Religion & Human Life as Well as the Sciences. Issac Watts. LC 83-48579. (Philosophy of John Locke Ser.). 365p. 1984. lib. bdg. 44.00 (ISBN 0-8240-5615-9). Garland Pub.

Logica Magna of Paul of Venice, Part 1, Fascicule 1. Paul Of Venice. Ed. by Norman Kretzmann. (British Academy Ser.). 1979. text ed. 98.00x (ISBN 0-19-725980-4). Oxford U Pr.

Logical Criticisms of Textual Criticism. Gordon H. Clark. (Trinity Papers: No. 16). 49p. (Orig.). 1986. pap. 2.95 (ISBN 0-940931-16-8). Trinity Found.

Logical Status of God. Michael Durrant. LC 72-93886. (New Studies in the Philosophy of Religion). 132p. 1973. 18.95 (ISBN 0-312-49455-6). St Martin.

Logique & Religion: L'Atomisme Logique de L. Wittgenstein & la Possibilite des Propositions Religieuses. Jacques Poulain. (Religion & Reason: No. 7). 1974. 18.40x (ISBN 90-2797-284-2). Mouton.

Logos: Mathematics & Christian Theology. Granville C. Henry, Jr. LC 74-25529. 361p. 1976. 25.00 (ISBN 0-8387-1653-9). Bucknell U Pr.

Logos of the Soul. Evangelos Christou. Ed. by James Hillman. (Dunquin Ser.: No. 2). 1963. pap. 6.50 (ISBN 0-88214-202-X). Spring Pubns.

Logotherapy in Action. Ed. by Joseph B. Fabry et al. LC 79-51917. 379p. 1979. 19.95 (ISBN 0-317-06212-3). Inst Logo.

Lollard Bible & Other Medieval Biblical Versions. Margaret Deanesly. LC 77-84722. Repr. of 1920 ed. 49.50 (ISBN 0-404-16125-1). AMS Pr.

Lollard Themes in Reformation Theology of William Tyndale. Donald Smeeton. (Sixteenth Century Essays & Studies: Vol. VI). (Illus.). 240p. 1986. smyth sewn 30.00x (ISBN 0-940474-06-9). Sixteenth Cent.

Lollards & Protestants in the Diocese of York. A. G. Dickens. (No. 10). 280p. 1983. 27.00 (ISBN 0-907628-05-2); pap. 12.00 (ISBN 0-907628-06-0). Hambledon Press.

Lollards & Reformers: Images & Literacy in Late Medieval Religion. Margaret Aston. 405p. 1984. 35.00 (ISBN 0-907628-03-6). Hambledon Press.

Lollards of the Chiltern Hills. William H. Summers. LC 80-12770. (Heresies of the Early Christian & Medieval Era: Second Ser.). Repr. of 1906 ed. 31.51 (ISBN 0-404-16245-2). AMS Pr.

Lollardy & the Reformation in England: An Historical Survey, 4 Vols. James Gairdner. 1965. Repr. of 1913 ed. 141.00 (ISBN 0-8337-1268-3). B Franklin.

London Churches at the Reformation: With an Account of Their Contents. Henry B. Walters. (Church Historical Society London N. S. Ser.: No. 37). Repr. of 1939 ed. 95.00 (ISBN 0-8115-3160-0). Kraus Repr.

London Mission: The First Critical Years. Jack L. Cross. x, 180p. 1969. 6.00 (ISBN 0-87013-128-1). Mich St U Pr.

London Missionary Society's Report of the Proceedings Against the Late Rev. J. Smith of Demerara, Who Was Tried Under Martial Law & Condemned to Death, on a Charge of Aiding & Assisting in a Rebellion of Negro Slaves. London Missionary Society. LC 78-79809. Repr. of 1824 ed. 22.50x (ISBN 0-8371-1506-X, LMS&, Pub. by Negro U Pr). Greenwood.

London Theatres & Music Halls, 1850-1950. Diana Howard. 291p. 1986. text ed. 40.00x (ISBN 0-85365-471-9, L471-9). ALA.

London's Churches: A Visitor's Companion. Elizabeth Young & Wayland Young. (Illus.). 252p. (Orig.). 1986. pap. 14.95 (ISBN 0-88162-212-5). Salem Hse Pubs.

Lone-Star Vanguard: The Catholic Re-Occupation of Texas (1838-1848) Ralph Bayard. LC 45-10779. 453p. 1982. lib. bdg. 59.95x (ISBN 0-89370-723-6). Borgo Pr.

Lone Traveler. Manly P. Hall. pap. 2.50 (ISBN 0-89314-329-4). Philos Res.

Loneliness. Ed. by Paul A. Wellington. 1980. pap. 4.50 (ISBN 0-8309-0287-2). Herald Hse.

Loneliness & Everyday Problems. Eugene Kennedy. LC 82-45971. 160p. 1983. pap. 3.95 (ISBN 0-385-18797-1, Im). Doubleday.

Loneliness Factor: Its Religious & Spiritual Meaning. Ronald Rolheiser. 8.95 (ISBN 0-87193-168-0). Dimension Bks.

Loneliness Is for Loving. Robert E. Lauder. LC 77-94033. (Illus.). 144p. 1978. pap. 2.95 (ISBN 0-87793-147-X). Ave Maria.

Loneliness Is Not a Disease. Tim Timmons. (Epiphany Bks.). 1983. pap. 2.25 (ISBN 0-345-30509-4). Ballantine.

Loneliness, Solitude, & Companionship. Robert E. Neale. LC 83-26065. 132p. (Orig.). 1984. pap. 9.95 (ISBN 0-664-24621-4). Westminster.

Lonely House: Strength for Times of Loss. Lowell O. Erdahl. LC 77-1907. Repr. of 1977 ed. 21.30 (ISBN 0-8357-9015-0, 2016377). Bks Demand UMI.

Lonergan, Spirituality, & the Meeting of Religions. Vernon Gregson. LC 85-3312. (College Theology Society-Studies in Religion: No. 2). 170p. (Orig.). 1985. lib. bdg. 24.50 (ISBN 0-8191-4619-6, Co-Pub by College Theo Soc); pap. text ed. 10.75 (ISBN 0-8191-4620-X). U Pr of Amer.

Long & the Short & the All. Bhagwan Shree Rajneesh. Ed. by Swami Krishna Prabhu. LC 84-42806. (Early Writings & Discourses Ser.). 320p. 1984. pap. 4.95 (ISBN 0-88050-708-X). Chidvilas Found.

Long Darkness: Psychological & Moral Perspectives on Nuclear Winter. Ed. & intro. by Lester Grinspoon. LC 85-40986. 224p. 1986. text ed. 25.00 (ISBN 0-300-03663-9); pap. 7.95 (ISBN 0-300-03664-7, YF-31). Yale U Pr.

Long Journey to the Country of the Hurons. Gabriel Sagard-Theodat. Ed. by George M. Wrong. Tr. by H. H. Langton. LC 68-28613. 1968. Repr. of 1939 ed. lib. bdg. 29.25x (ISBN 0-8371-3861-2, SAJC). Greenwood.

Long Loneliness: An Autobiography. Dorothy Day. LC 81-4727. (Illus.). 1981. pap. 7.95 (ISBN 0-06-061751-9, RD363, HarpR). Har-Row.

Long Night's Journey into Day - Life & Faith After the Holocaust. A. Roy Eckardt & Alice L. Eckardt. LC 81-14788. 206p. 1982. 19.50x (ISBN 0-8143-1692-1). Wayne St U Pr.

Long Obedience in the Same Direction. Eugene H. Peterson. LC 79-2715. 1980. pap. 6.95 (ISBN 0-87784-727-4). Inter-Varsity.

Long Pilgrimage: The Life & Teaching of Shivapuri Baba. John G. Bennett. LC 81-66139. 191p. pap. 7.95 (ISBN 0-913922-54-4). Dawn Horse Pr.

Long Term Marriage. Floyd Thatcher & Harriett Thatcher. 1981. 5.95 (ISBN 0-8499-2963-6). Word Bks.

Long Way Home, the Short Way of Love. John F. Marshall. (Spirit & Life Ser). 1968. 3.50 (ISBN 0-686-11575-9). Franciscan Inst.

Longest Step: Searching for God. James Digiacomo et al. (Encounter Ser.). (Illus.). 1977. pap. text ed. 4.50 (ISBN 0-86683-180-0, 315, HarpR); resource manual 1.95 (ISBN 0-86683-181-9, 316). Har-Row.

Longest War. Kenneth D. Barney. LC 82-83915. 128p. (Orig.). 1984. pap. 2.50 (ISBN 0-88243-536-1, 02-0536). Gospel Pub.

Longing for Love. Walter Trobisch. LC 86-72059. Orig. Title: Living with Unfulfilled Desires. 128p. 1987. pap. 5.95 (ISBN 0-89107-417-1, Crossway Bks). Good News.

Longinus: On the Sublime. Tr. by James A. Arieti & John M. Crossett. LC 84-25435. (Studies in Art & Religious Interpretation: Vol.21). 275p. 1985. 59.95x (ISBN 0-88946-554-1). E Mellen.

Look at Fourth Way Work: A System of Esoteric Exercises Based on the Work of Gurdjieff. Nicholas Tereshchenko. 1987. pap. 10.00. Phanes Pr.

Look at Mormonism. Gary J. Coleman. pap. 3.95 (ISBN 0-89036-142-8). Hawkes Pub Inc.

Look at the Modern Healing Movement. Charles W. Mayes. 1979. pap. write for info. (ISBN 0-88469-113-6). BMH Bks.

Look Down, Harmonious Saint. George F. Handel. Ed. by Denis Stevens. LC 63-21369. (Penn State Music Series, No. 1). 22p. 1963. pap. 3.00x (ISBN 0-271-73079-X). Pa St U Pr.

Look for Me in Heaven: The Life of John Lewis Dyer. Mark Fiester. LC 80-14913. (Illus.). 400p. 1980. 19.95 (ISBN 0-87108-564-X). Pruett.

Look of Distance: Reflections on Suffering & Sympathy in Modern Literature - Auden to Agee, Whitman to Woolf. Walter J. Slatoff. LC 85-10447. 309p. 1985. 25.00x (ISBN 0-8142-0385-X). Ohio St U Pr.

Look on the Fields. Serena M. Hodges. 202p. 1956. pap. 2.00 (ISBN 0-88243-540-X, 02-0540). Gospel Pub.

Look-the Madonna Is Weeping. H. Jongen. pap. 3.00 (ISBN 0-910984-12-3). Montfort Pubns.

Look to the East. Lester. 8.95x (ISBN 0-685-22017-6). Wehman.

Look to the East. Ralph P. Lester. 8.50 (ISBN 0-685-19484-1). Powner.

Look unto the Rock: A History of the Presbyterian Church, in West Virginia from 1719 to 1974. Dorsey D. Ellis. LC 82-60889. (Illus.). 372p. (Orig.). 1982. pap. 14.95 (ISBN 0-9609076-0-2). McClain.

Look up & Live: Dance in Prayer & Meditation. Margaret F. Taylor. Ed. by Doug Adams. 96p. 1980. 4.95 (ISBN 0-941500-12-8). Sharing Co.

Look What They've Done to My Church. Leonard Urban. 1985. pap. 5.95 (ISBN 0-8294-0499-6). Loyola.

Look What You've Done Now Moses! Fredrick McKissack & Patricia McKissack. (Early Readers Ser.). (Illus.). 1984. 4.95 (ISBN 0-89191-839-6); pap. 2.95 (ISBN 0-89191-812-4). Cook.

Look Who's Coming. Richard E. Orchard. LC 74-33870. (Radiant Bks.). 128p. 1975. pap. 1.25 (ISBN 0-88243-541-8, 02-0541). Gospel Pub.

Look Who's Talking: A Guide for Lay Speakers in the Church. Ronald E. Sleeth. LC 77-1171. 1982. pap. 5.50 (ISBN 0-687-22630-9). Abingdon.

Look, You're a Leader. Daisy Hepburn. LC 85-19637. 284p. 1985. pap. write for info. (ISBN 0-8307-1098-1, 5418647); resource manual avail. (ISBN 0-8307-1074-4, 5203023). Regal.

Looking Ahead: Planning the Year's Program for Youth Groups & Clubs. Mary R. Marshall. (Australian Youth Leadership Ser.). 32p. (Orig.). 1983. pap. 4.95 (ISBN 0-85819-417-1, Pub. by JBCE). ANZ Religious Pubns.

Looking Ahead to Marriage. Daughters of St. Paul Editorial Staff. (Divine Master Ser.). (Illus.). 1969. 5.25 (ISBN 0-8198-0259-X); pap. 4.25 (ISBN 0-8198-0260-3); discussion & projects manual 2.75 (ISBN 0-8198-0261-1). Dghtrs St Paul.

Looking at Jesus with Luke. Marjorie Stewart. 24p. 1978. pap. 0.75 (ISBN 0-88243-756-9, 02-0756). Gospel Pub.

Looking at the Episcopal Church. William Sydnor. LC 80-81103. 142p. (Orig.). 1981. pap. 5.95 (ISBN 0-8192-1279-2). Morehouse.

Looking Beyond. Frank W. Lemons. 78p. 1969. 3.95 (ISBN 0-87148-506-0); pap. 2.95 (ISBN 0-87148-507-9). Pathway Pr.

Looking Beyond. Jeffrey A. Watson. 132p. 1986. pap. 4.95 (ISBN 0-89693-155-2). Victor Bks.

Looking Both Ways: A Theology for Midlife. David J. Maitland. 240p. 1985. pap. 10.95 (ISBN 0-8042-1127-2). John Knox.

Looking Deeper. Klong-chen rab-byams pa. Tr. by Herbert V. Guenther from Tibetan. (Illus.). 64p. (Orig.). 1984. pap. 3.50 (ISBN 0-931454-09-3). Timeless Bks.

Looking for Jesus. Adrian Van Kaam. pap. 4.95 (ISBN 0-87193-146-X); 7.95. Dimension Bks.

Looking for Leaven. Neil A. Lash & Jamie S. Lash. (Jewish Jewels: Vol. 1). (Illus.). 21p. (Orig.). 1985. pap. 1.50 (ISBN 0-915775-02-6). Love Song Mess Assn.

Looking Forward to a New Day. LaNell Compton. 1984. 7.95 (ISBN 0-8158-0418-0). Chris Mass.

Looking in the Mirror: Self-Appraisal in the Local Church. Lyle E. Schaller. 208p. 1984. pap. 9.50 (ISBN 0-687-22635-X). Abingdon.

Looking into Being a Muslim. Michael Keene. (Looking into World Religions Ser.). (Illus.). 64p. 1987. 16.95 (ISBN 0-7134-4667-6, Pub. by Batsford England). David & Charles.

Looking into Being Jewish. Michael Keene & Angela Wood. (Looking into World Religions Ser.). (Illus.). 64p. 1987. 16.95 (ISBN 0-7134-4668-4, Pub. by Batsford England). David & Charles.

Looking Unto Jesus. C. H. Spurgeon. 1976. pap. 0.10 (ISBN 0-686-16841-0). Pilgrim Pubns.

Looking unto Jesus. George B. Wall. 160p. 1986. pap. 7.95 (ISBN 0-8170-1098-X). Judson.

Looking up When You Feel Down Based on Ephesians 1-3. Gene A. Getz. LC 85-2041. 158p. 1985. pap. 5.95 (ISBN 0-8307-1028-0, 5418463). Regal.

Looking Up...While Lying Down. Biegert. (Looking Up Ser.). 1979. pap. 1.25 booklet (ISBN 0-8298-0364-5). Pilgrim NY.

Lord. Romano Guardini. 1978. pap. 9.95 (ISBN 0-89526-909-0). Regnery Bks.

Lord & Giver of Life. Pope John Paul II. 144p. (Orig.). 1986. pap. 3.95 (ISBN 1-55586-103-2). US Catholic.

Lord Be with You. George W. Hoyer. LC 77-85172. (Child of God Ser.: Vol. 1). 1977. pap. text ed. 4.95 (ISBN 0-915644-11-8). Clayton Pub Hse.

Lord Bishop: The Life of Samuel Wilberforce, 1805-1873. Standish Meacham. LC 70-102669. 1970. 20.00x (ISBN 0-674-53913-3). Harvard U Pr.

Lord Blesses Me. Dick Hilliard. LC 78-61308. (Illus.). 1978. pap. 11.95 (ISBN 0-89390-005-2). Resource Pubns.

Lord, Break Me. William MacDonald. pap. 1.75 (ISBN 0-937396-24-9). Walterick Pubs.

Lord Buddha & His Doctrine. Vasu Kunjavihari. LC 78-72458. Repr. of 1927 ed. 39.50 (ISBN 0-404-17326-8). AMS Pr.

Lord, Change Me. Evelyn Christenson. LC 77-81219. 192p. 1977. pap. 5.95 (ISBN 0-88207-756-2). Victor Bks.

Lord, Could You Hurry a Little. Ruth H. Calkin. 1983. pap. 2.95 (ISBN 0-8423-3816-0). Tyndale.

Lord, Don't Let Me Be Bored. G. Lloyd Rediger. LC 85-26379. 132p. 1986. pap. 9.95 (ISBN 0-664-24700-8). Westminster.

Lord, Empower Us! George P. Mocko. Ed. by Michael L. Sherer. (Orig.). 1987. pap. 2.75 (ISBN 0-89536-851-X, 7810). CSS of Ohio.

Lord from Heaven. Robert Anderson. LC 78-9533. (Sir Robert Anderson Library). 120p. 1978. pap. 3.50 (ISBN 0-8254-2127-6). Kregel.

Lord Gauranga: Love Incarnate. 2.00 (ISBN 0-685-61441-7). Aum Pubns.

Lord Giveth & Taketh. Manly P. Hall. pap. 2.50 (ISBN 0-89314-330-8). Philos Res.

Lord God of Truth Within. M. 1976. Repr. of 1940 ed. 12.00 (ISBN 0-911662-56-1). Yoga.

Lord Have I Got Problems. (Out Ser.). 1984. 1.25 (ISBN 0-8163-0599-4). Pacific Pr Pub Assn.

Lord Hear Our Prayer. Ed. by Thomas McNally & William G. Storey. LC 78-67423. (Illus.). 1978. 5.95 (ISBN 0-87793-163-1). Ave Maria.

Lord, Help Me Love My Sister. Clair G. Cosby. LC 86-4831. 80p. (Orig.). 1986. pap. 4.95 (ISBN 0-8361-3413-3). Herald Pr.

Lord, Help Me! The Desperate Dieter. Beth Hammond. (Continued Applied Christianity Ser.). 1983. pap. 4.50 (ISBN 0-570-03896-0, 12-2978). Concordia.

Lord, Help Me When I'm Hurting. Harold Hazelip. pap. 3.95 (ISBN 0-8010-4285-2). Baker Bk.

Lord, I Am One of Your Little Ones. Enric Puig. 93p. 1987. 5.95 (ISBN 0-8294-0545-3). Loyola.

Lord, I Ask You for One Favour. Sri Chinmoy. 50p. (Orig.). 1975. pap. 2.00 (ISBN 0-685-61224-4). Aum Pubns.

Lord, I Can Resist Anything but Temptation. Harold Bussell. (Orig.). 1985. pap. 5.95 (ISBN 0-310-37271-2, 12389P). Zondervan.

Lord, I Keep Running Back to You. Ruth Calkin. 1983. pap. 3.50 (ISBN 0-8423-3819-5). Tyndale.

Lord, I Need an Answer: Story Devotions for Girls. Betty W. Skold. LC 81-52279. 112p. (Orig.). 1982. pap. 3.95 (ISBN 0-8066-1911-2, 10-4099). Augsburg.

Lord, I Need You. Sri Chinmoy. 50p. 1975. pap. 2.00 (ISBN 0-88497-211-9). Aum Pubns.

Lord, I Want to Celebrate. Rich Bimler & Herb Brokering. 1980. pap. 2.95 (ISBN 0-570-03069-2, 06-1185). Concordia.

Lord, I Want to Have a Quiet Time: Learning to Study the Bible for Yourself. Carolyn Nystrom. 156p. 1984. pap. 6.95 (ISBN 0-87788-516-8). Shaw Pubs.

Lord, I Want to Know You. Kay Arthur. 192p. (Orig.). 1984. pap. 6.95 (ISBN 0-8007-5159-0, Power Bks). Revell.

Lord, I Want to Know You Better: Story Devotions for Boys. Stephen W. Sorenson. LC 81-52280. 112p. (Orig.). 1982. pap. 3.95 (ISBN 0-8066-1912-0, 10-4103). Augsburg.

Lord, I Want to Tell You Something: Prayers for Boys. Chris Jones. LC 73-78266. (Illus.). 96p. (Orig.). 1973. pap. 3.95 (ISBN 0-8066-1330-0, 10-4100). Augsburg.

Lord, If. Herbert Brokering. 1977. pap. 2.95 (ISBN 0-570-03046-3, 6-1171). Concordia.

Lord, If I Ever Needed You, It's Now! Creath Davis. 138p. Date not set. pap. 5.95 (ISBN 0-8010-2968-6). Baker Bk.

Lord, I'm Afraid. Roger Campbell. (Orig.). 1980. pap. 2.50 (ISBN 0-87508-056-1). Chr Lit.

Lord, I'm Back Again: Story Devotions for Girls. Mary P. Warren. LC 81-65651. 112p. (Orig.). 1981. pap. 3.95 (ISBN 0-8066-1887-6, 10-4098). Augsburg.

Lord Is My Counsel: A Businessman's Personal Experiences with the Bible. Marion E. Wade & Glenn D. Kittler. 192p. 1984. pap. 4.95 (ISBN 0-13-540658-7). P-H.

Lord Is My Shepherd. (Illus.). 48p. 1982. Repr. 7.95 (ISBN 0-86683-687-X, AY8288, HarpR). Har-Row.

Lord Is My Shepherd. 2.98 (ISBN 0-8010-5113-4). Baker Bk.

Lord Is My Shepherd: Expositions of Selected Psalms. William Barclay. LC 79-27096. 154p. 1980. pap. 5.95 (ISBN 0-664-24317-7). Westminster.

Lord Is My Shepherd: Praying the Psalms. David E. Rosage. 196p. (Orig.). 1984. pap. 3.50 (ISBN 0-89283-196-0). Servant.

Lord is My Shepherd: Selections from the Psalms. Ed. by Pritish Nandy. (Vikas Library of Modern Morian Writing: No. 12). (Orig.). 1982. text ed. 5.95x (ISBN 0-7069-1492-9, Pub. by Vikas India). Advent NY.

Lord Is My Strength. Joan Rosenthal. 1976. pap. 1.25 (ISBN 0-89129-086-9). Jove Pubns.

Lord Is Present. David Champlin. 7.95 (ISBN 0-87193-175-3). Dimension Bks.

Lord, It Keeps Happening...& Happening. Ruth H. Calkin. LC 83-91404. 112p. 1984. pap. 2.95 (ISBN 0-8423-3823-3). Tyndale.

Lord I've Been Thinking: Prayer Thoughts for High School Boys. Ron Klug. LC 78-52183. 1978. pap. 3.95 (ISBN 0-8066-1657-1, 10-4105). Augsburg.

Lord Jesus. Lawrence G. Lovasik. (Illus.). hard bd 3.95 (ISBN 0-89942-419-8, 419/22). Catholic Bk Pub.

Lord, Let Me Love. Marjorie Holmes. 288p. 1981. pap. 3.95 (ISBN 0-553-25859-1). Bantam.

Lord, Let Me Love: A Marjorie Holmes Treasury. Marjorie Holmes. LC 77-26516. 1978. 12.95 (ISBN 0-385-14093-2, Galilee). Doubleday.

Lord Loves His People. 1980. plastic bdg. 5.00 (ISBN 0-8198-4400-4). Dghtrs St Paul.

Lord, Make My Days Count. Ely Moskowitz. LC 83-2430. 231p. 1983. 14.95 (ISBN 0-8022-2423-7). Philos Lib.

Lord, Make My Life a Miracle! Raymond C. Ortlund. LC 73-89714. (Orig.). 1974. pap. 3.50 (ISBN 0-8307-0284-9, 5011701); study guide 1.59 (ISBN 0-8307-0626-7, 6101305). Regal.

Lord, Make My Life Count. Raymond C. Ortlund. LC 75-6188. 144p. 1975. pap. 3.50 (ISBN 0-8307-0348-9, S112175). Regal.

Lord, Make Us One. John W. Sloat. 144p. 1986. pap. 7.95 (ISBN 0-8170-1101-3). Judson.

Lord of Confusion. Ladislas Orsy. 5.00 (ISBN 0-87193-064-1). Dimension Bks.

Lord of History. Eugene Kevane. 1980. 4.00 (ISBN 0-8198-0636-6); pap. 3.00 (ISBN 0-8198-0637-4). Dghtrs St Paul.

Lord of Parables: Instructor Edition. LeRoy Lawson. LC 83-12640. 128p. (Orig.). 1984. pap. 2.95 (ISBN 0-87239-706-8, 39980); pap. 2.50 student edition (ISBN 0-87239-707-6, 39981). Standard Pub.

Lord of Promises. LeRoy Lawson. LC 82-17034. 112p. 1983. pap. 2.50 (ISBN 0-87239-611-8, 39988). Standard Pub.

Lord of Song: The Messiah Revealed in the Psalms. Ronald B. Allen. LC 85-21693. (Living Theology Bks.). 1985. pap. 7.95 (ISBN 0-88070-129-3). Multnomah.

Lord of the Dance: The Beauty of the Disciplined Life. Deidre Bobgan. 160p. (Orig.). 1987. pap. 5.95 (ISBN 0-89081-583-6). Harvest Hse.

Lord of the Four Seasons. Malcolm Nygren. 144p. (Orig.). 1986. pap. 7.95 (ISBN 0-9617890-1-8). Doxology Lane.

Lord of the Horizon. Joan Cerart. 300p. 1987. pap. 7.95 (ISBN 0-89804-147-3). Ariel OH.

Lord of the Impossible. Lloyd J. Ogilvie. 224p. (Orig.). 1984. pap. 9.95 (ISBN 0-687-22710-0). Abingdon.

Lord of the Marketplace. Myron Rush. 192p. 1986. pap. 7.95 (ISBN 0-89693-278-8). Victor Bks.

Lord of the Temple: A Study of the Relation Between Cult & Gospel. Ernst Lohmeyer. LC 62-18409. 1961. text ed. 8.50x (ISBN 0-8401-1423-0). A R Allenson.

Lord of What's Left. rev. ed. Vance Havner. 124p. 1985. pap. 4.95 (ISBN 0-8010-4286-0). Baker Bk.

Lord, Please Zip Up My Armor. Mab G. Hoover. 112p. 1986. pap. 3.95 (ISBN 0-310-35642-3). Zondervan.

Lord, Receive This Little Undying Cry. Sri Chinmoy. 50p. (Orig.). 1975. pap. 2.00. Aum Pubns.

Lord Sri Venkateswara. Date not set. 5.00 (ISBN 0-938924-33-8). Sri Shirdi Sai.

Lord, Teach Me Wisdom. Carole Mayhall. LC 78-78013. 180p. 1979. pap. 5.95 (ISBN 0-89109-432-6). NavPress.

Lord, Teach Me Your Ways: Children's Stories with Biblical Parallels. Stephen Sorenson. LC 81-2067. 96p. 1982. 6.95 (ISBN 0-687-22660-0). Abingdon.

Lord, Teach Us to Live. Norman P. Madsen. LC 84-62161. 112p. 1985. pap. 4.95 (ISBN 0-87973-718-2, 718). Our Sunday Visitor.

Lord, Teach Us to Pray. James Alberione. Tr. by Daughters of St. Paul. 295p. 1982. 4.00 (ISBN 0-8198-4422-5, SP0408); pap. 3.00 (ISBN 0-8198-4423-3). Dghtrs St Paul.

Lord, Teach Us to Pray. Norman P. Madsen. LC 83-61890. 96p. (Orig.). 1983. pap. 3.95 (ISBN 0-87973-611-9, 611). Our Sunday Visitor.

Lord Teach Us to Pray. Leonard Mullens. 1963. pap. 1.00 (ISBN 0-686-75248-1). Firm Foun Pub.

Lord, the Lion & Mutn. Sue Delaney. pap. 0.95 (ISBN 0-89985-995-X). Christ Nations.

Lord Went with Them. Stanley Sayers. pap. 2.50 (ISBN 0-89315-143-2). Lambert Bk.

Lord, When? Arthur Katterjohn & Mark Fackler. LC 76-16284. 1976. pap. 1.50 (ISBN 0-88419-003-X). Creation Hse.

Lord, Where Are You? I'm Hip-Deep in Alligators. Merle G. Franke. 1985. 4.95 (ISBN 0-89536-740-8, 5824). CSS of Ohio.

Lord, You Love to Say Yes. Ruth H. Calkin. (Living Books). 160p. (Orig.). 1985. pap. 2.95 (ISBN 0-8423-3824-1). Tyndale.

Lord's Balance. Steve Ost. 32p. 1979. pap. 0.95 (ISBN 0-930756-43-6, 541007). Aglow Pubns.

Lord's Day. James P. Wesberry. pap. 8.95 (ISBN 0-8054-2264-1). Broadman.

Lord's Hidden Message in Money. Jovah. 1986. 5.75 (ISBN 0-8062-2404-5). Carlton.

Lords of the Ghostland: A History of the Ideal. Edgar Saltus. LC 71-116003. Repr. of 1907 ed. 17.50 (ISBN 0-404-05539-7). AMS Pr.

Lord's Portion: A Scriptural Study of Tithing. Roy L. Moss. (Illus.). 80p. (Orig.). 1980. pap. 2.95 (ISBN 0-912315-48-2). Word Aflame.

Lord's Prayer. Henry Bast. 2.50 (ISBN 0-686-23480-4). Rose Pub MI.

Lord's Prayer. Glenn Clark. pap. 0.50 (ISBN 0-910924-08-2). Macalester.

Lord's Prayer. Ronald E. Cottle. 48p. 1980. 0.95 (ISBN 0-88243-566-3, 02-0566). Gospel Pub.

Lords Prayer. Anna M. Hernandez. (Illus.). 32p. 1987. 6.95 (ISBN 0-89962-601-7). Todd & Honeywell.

Lord's Prayer. Joan Hutson. LC 82-62736. (Happy Day Bks.). (Illus.). 24p. 1983. 1.59 (ISBN 0-87239-640-1, 3560). Standard Pub.

Lord's Prayer. Joachim Jeremias. Ed. & tr. by John Reumann. LC 64-11859. (Facet Bks.). 56p. 1964. pap. 2.50 (ISBN 0-8006-3008-4, 1-3008). Fortress.

Lord's Prayer. St. Cyprian of Carthage. Ed. by Edmond Bonin. 112p. (Orig.). 1983. pap. 6.95 (ISBN 0-87061-076-7). Chr Classics.

Lord's Prayer. Ingrid Shelton. (Arch Bks.). 1982. pap. 0.99 (ISBN 0-570-06161-X, 59-1308). Concordia.

Lord's Prayer. Alice Very. 1975. 10.00 (ISBN 0-8283-1629-5). Branden Pub Co.

Lord's Prayer. Thomas Watson. 1978. 9.95 (ISBN 0-85151-145-7). Banner of Truth.

Lord's Prayer. Spiros Zodhiates. 352p. pap. 8.95 (ISBN 0-89957-049-6). AMG Pubs.

Lord's Prayer: A Way of Life. Donald W. Shriver, Jr. LC 83-9843. 108p. (Orig.). 1983. pap. 4.95 (ISBN 0-8042-2409-9). John Knox.

Lord's Prayer: An Esoteric Study. Rudolf Steiner. Tr. by Floyd McKnight from Ger. 26p. 1977. pap. 2.95 (ISBN 0-88010-029-X). Anthroposophic.

Lord's Prayer for Children. Reda Lucy, pseud. (Illus.). 24p. (Orig.). 1981. pap. 2.25 (ISBN 0-87516-437-4). De Vorss.

Lord's Prayer: St. Cyprian. pap. 1.95 (ISBN 0-686-01296-8). Eastern Orthodox.

Lord's Prayer: The Prayer Jesus Taught. Barbara O. Webb. (Concept Ser.). (Illus.). 24p. (Orig.). 1986. pap. 3.95 saddlestitched (ISBN 0-570-08529-2, 56-1556). Concordia.

Lord's Prayer: The Prayer of Integral Liberation. Leonardo Boff. Tr. by Theodore Morrow from Portuguese. LC 82-18811. Tr. of O Pai-nosso: A Oracao da Libertacao. 144p. (Orig.). 1983. pap. 6.95 (ISBN 0-88344-299-X). Orbis Bks.

Lord's Presence. Alton H. McEachern. LC 85-29055. 1986. pap. 4.95 (ISBN 0-8054-2314-1). Broadman.

Lord's Sermons. Jakob Lorber. Tr. by Violet Ozols & Hildegard Von Koerber. LC 80-50280. (Jakob Lorber Ser.). 278p. 1981. 15.95 (ISBN 0-934616-06-X). Valkyrie Pub Hse.

Lord's Supper. William Barclay. LC 82-2774. 128p. 1982. pap. 7.95 (ISBN 0-664-24432-7). Westminster.

Lord's Supper. 1979. 15.95 (ISBN 0-570-03275-X, 15-2720). Concordia.

Lord's Supper. Martin E. Marty. LC 79-6550. 80p. (Orig.). 1980. pap. 3.50 (ISBN 0-8006-1386-4, 1-1386). Fortress.

Lord's Supper from Wycliffe to Crammer. David B. Knox. 75p. 1986. pap. 6.25 (ISBN 0-85364-379-2, Pub. by Paternoster UK). Attic Pr.

Lord's Supper: Mattew Twenty-six Vs Seventeen to Thirty, Corinthians Eleven Seventeen Through Thirty-four. John MacArthur, Jr. (John MacArthur Bible Studies). 1987. pap. 3.50 (ISBN 0-8024-5310-4). Moody.

Lord's Supper: More Than a Ritual. Bob Lamb. 1983. pap. 2.95 (ISBN 0-910709-08-4). PTL Repro.

Lord's Supper: The Church's Love Feast. Donald L. Norbie. 1986. pap. 2.25 (ISBN 0-937396-67-2). Walterick Pubs.

Lord's Table. Andrew Murray & Leona Choy. (Orig.). 1980. pap. 2.95 (ISBN 0-87508-380-3). Chr Lit.

Lord's Table: Eucharist & Passover in Early Christianity. Gillian Feeley-Harnik. 1981. text ed. 23.50x (ISBN 0-8122-7786-4). U of Pa Pr.

Lords Temporal & Lords Spiritual. Boden Clarke. LC 80-10979. (Stokvis Studies in Historical Chronology & Thought: No. 1). 160p. 1985. lib. bdg. 19.95x (ISBN 0-89370-800-3); pap. 9.95x (ISBN 0-89370-900-X). Borgo Pr.

Lord's Unconquerable Church. D. O. Silvey. 256p. 1972. 4.95 (ISBN 0-89114-052-2); pap. 2.95 (ISBN 0-89114-051-4). Baptist Pub Hse.

Lordship of Jesus. W. T. Purkiser. 70p. (Orig.). 1986. pap. 2.95 (ISBN 0-8341-1135-7). Beacon Hill.

Lordship Salvation-Is It Biblical? G. Michael Cocoris. 24p. (Orig.). 1983. pap. 1.25 (ISBN 0-9607576-2-7). Redencion Viva.

Lore & Legend of the English Church. George S. Tyack. 1979. Repr. of 1899 ed. lib. bdg. 50.00 (ISBN 0-8495-5135-8). Arden Lib.

Lore & Science in Ancient Pythagoreanism. Walter Burkert. Tr. by Edwin L. Minar, Jr. from Ger. LC 70-162856. (Illus.). 512p. 1972. 35.00x (ISBN 0-674-53918-4). Harvard U Pr.

Lore Power is "Man" Power. Thomas Adams. 64p. 1981. pap. write for info. (ISBN 0-969242-0-5). T Adams.

Los Alamos Experience. Phyllis K. Fisher. (Illus.). 240p. 1985. 12.95 (ISBN 0-87040-623-X, Dist. by Harper & Row). Japan Pubns USA.

Los Angeles Times Book of Christmas Entertaining. Dawn Navarro. Compiled by Betsy Balsley. (Illus.). 176p. 1985. 24.95 (ISBN 0-8109-1290-2). Abrams.

Loser, a Winner, & a Wise-Guy: Saul, David & Solomon. David McCord. LC 79-67438. 96p. 1980. pap. 2.25 (ISBN 0-87239-380-1, 40084). Standard Pub.

Losing a Loved One. Jeannette Partridge. 3.50 (ISBN 0-913420-86-7). Olympus Pub Co.

Losing Control of Your Teenager: Ten Rules for Raising an Adult While Keeping a Friend. Roger McIntire. 290p. 1985. pap. 15.00x (ISBN 0-87425-017-X). Human Res Dev Pr.

Loss & Anticipatory Grief. Ed. by Therese A. Rando. LC 85-45082. 256p. 1986. 27.00 (ISBN 0-669-11144-9). Lexington Bks.

Loss & How to Cope with It. Joanne Bernstein. LC 76-50027. 8.95 (ISBN 0-395-28891-6, Clarion). HM.

Loss & How to Cope with It. Joanne Bernstein. 160p. 1981. pap. 4.95 (ISBN 0-395-30012-6, Clarion). HM.

Lost & Found Cat. (Color-a-Story Bks.). (Illus.). 1985. pap. 0.89 (ISBN 0-89191-994-5, 59949). Cook.

Lost Art of Disciple Making. Leroy Eims. pap. 6.95 (ISBN 0-310-37281-X, 9233P). Zondervan.

Lost Books of the Bible & the Forgotten Books of Eden. 562p. 9.95 (ISBN 0-529-03385-2); pap. 7.95 (ISBN 0-529-02061-0). World Bible.

Lost, but not Forever. Mary J. Warkentin. 1986. pap. cancelled (ISBN 0-88270-605-5). Bridge Pub.

Lost Chapter of Acts of the Apostles. E. Raymond Capt. 32p. 1982. pap. 2.00 (ISBN 0-934666-09-1). Artisan Sales.

Lost Christianity: A Journey of Rediscovery. Jacob Needleman. LC 84-48227. 224p. 1985. pap. 6.95 (ISBN 0-06-066102-X, HarpR). Har-Row.

Lost Cities of Paraguay: The Art & Architecture of the Jesuit Reductions. C. J. McNaspy. 1982. 24.95 (ISBN 0-8294-0396-5). Loyola.

Lost Fatherland: The Story of the Mennonite Emigration from Soviet Russia, 1921-1927. John B. Toews. LC 67-23294. (Studies in Anabaptist & Mennonite History: No. 12). pap. 65.50 (ISBN 0-317-26609-8, 2025421). Bks Demand UMI.

Lost Generation: Children in the Holocaust. Ed. by Azriel Eisenberg. 384p. 1982. 17.95 (ISBN 0-8298-0498-6). Pilgrim NY.

Lost Goddesses of Early Greece: A Collection of Pre-Hellenic Myths. Charlene Spretnak. LC 84-45068. 132p. 1984. pap. 6.95 (ISBN 0-8070-1345-5, BP682). Beacon Pr.

Lost Gospel of Jesus of Nazareth. LC 85-72544. write for info. (ISBN 0-936435-00-3). Church Man Pub.

Lost Gospel of Jesus: The Hidden Teachings of Christ. authorized millennium ed. Gene Savoy. LC 78-71277. (The Sacred Teachings of Light, Codex VIII Ser.). (Illus.). xv, 91p. 1984. text ed. 39.50 (ISBN 0-936202-08-4). Intl Comm Christ.

Lost Gospel of the Ages: Key to Immortality & Companion to the Holy Bible. Ed. by John C. Androgeus. (Illus.). 979p. 1978. pap. text ed. 95.00 (ISBN 0-9609802-3-7). Life Science.

Lost Honesty. Joseph R. Narot. pap. 1.25 (ISBN 0-686-15804-0). Rostrum Bks.

Lost in Wonder: Charles Wesley - The Meaning of His Hymns Today. S. Kimbrough, Jr. 176p. (Orig.). 1987. pap. 6.95 (ISBN 0-8358-0558-1). Upper Room.

Lost Key to Prediction: The Arabic Parts in Astrology. Robert Zoller. 350p. 1980. pap. 8.95 (ISBN 0-89281-013-0). Inner Tradit.

Lost Keys of Freemasonry. Manly P. Hall. 8.95 (ISBN 0-89314-500-9). Philos Res.

Lost Keys of Freemasonry: Or, the Secret of Hiram Abiff. rev. and enl. ed. Manly P. Hall. 190p. 1981. Repr. text ed. 8.95 (ISBN 0-88053-044-8). Macoy Pub.

Lost Paradise: Early Reminiscences. facsimile ed. Samuel Chotzinoff. LC 74-27970. (Modern Jewish Experience Ser.). 1975. Repr. of 1955 ed. 31.00x (ISBN 0-405-06700-3). Ayer Co Pubs.

Lost Sheep. Meryl Doney. (Illus.). 16p. 1982. pap. 0.99 (ISBN 0-86683-663-2, AY8243, HarpR). Har-Row.

Lost Sheep. Mandeville. (Ladybird Ser.). 1979. pap. 2.50 (ISBN 0-87508-849-X). Chr Lit.

Lost Sheep. Heidi Petach. (Happy Day Bible Stories Bks.). (Illus.). 24p. 1984. 1.59 (ISBN 0-87239-765-3, 3725). Standard Pub.

Lost Sheep. Regine Schindler. LC 80-68546. Orig. Title: Das Verlorene Shaf. (Illus.). 32p. 1982. Repr. 7.95g (ISBN 0-687-22780-1). Abingdon.

Lost Ship of Noah: In Search of the Ark at Ararat. Charles Berlitz. (Illus.). 224p. 1986. 17.95 (ISBN 0-399-13182-5, Perigee). Putnam Pub Group.

Lost Son & Other Stories. Ella K. Lindvall. (People of the Bible Ser.). (Illus.). 1984. 4.95 (ISBN 0-8024-0399-9). Moody.

Lost Spirituals. facsimile ed. Lily Y. Cohen. LC 74-39081. (Black Heritage Library Collection). (Illus.). Repr. of 1928 ed. 17.25 (ISBN 0-8369-9019-6). Ayer Co Pubs.

Lost Teachings of Jesus, Vol. I. Mark L. Prophet & Elizabeth C. Prophet. LC 81-52784. (Illus.). 425p. (Orig.). 1986. 19.95 (ISBN 0-916766-45-4). Summit Univ.

Lost Teachings of Jesus, Vol. 1. Mark L. Prophet & Elizabeth C. Prophet. LC 81-52784. (Illus.). 425p. (Orig.). pap. 14.95 (ISBN 0-916766-71-3). Summit Univ.

Lost Teachings of Jesus, Vol. 2. Mark L. Prophet & Elizabeth C. Prophet. LC 81-52784. (Illus.). 598p. (Orig.). 1986. pap. 21.95 (ISBN 0-916766-72-1). Summit Univ.

Lost Tradition: Women Writers of the Early Church. Patricia Wilson-Kastner et al. LC 80-6290. 210p. (Orig.). 1981. lib. bdg. 25.00 (ISBN 0-8191-1642-4); pap. text ed. 11.50 (ISBN 0-8191-1643-2). U Pr of Amer.

Lost Tribes: History Doctrine, Prophecies & Theories About Israel's Lost Ten Tribes. R. Clayton Brough. LC 79-89351. 1979. 7.95 (ISBN 0-88290-123-0). Horizon Utah.

Lost Tribes of Israel: Or, the First of the Red Men. Charles Even. 26.50 (ISBN 0-405-10243-7, 14436). Ayer Co Pubs.

Lost Years of Jesus. Elizabeth C. Prophet. (Illus.). 401p. 1984. pap. 14.95 (ISBN 0-916766-61-6). Summit Univ.

Lost Years of Jesus Revealed. C. F. Potter. 1982. pap. 2.25 (ISBN 0-449-12468-1, GM). Fawcett.

Lot & Lots Wife. Gordon Lindsay. (Old Testament Ser.: Vol. 4). pap. 1.25 (ISBN 0-89985-958-5). Christ Nations.

Lotus of the Heart. Subramuniya. (On the Path Ser.). (Illus.). 72p. 1972. pap. 2.00 (ISBN 0-87516-352-1). De Vorss.

Lotus of the Wonderful Law, or the Lotus Gospel. W. E. Soothill. (Illus.). 288p. 1987. pap. 9.95 (ISBN 0-391-03465-0, Pub. by Curzon Pr England). Humanities.

Lotus Petals: The Life & Work of Rudolf Steiner. C. J. Furness. 59.95 (ISBN 0-8490-0557-4). Gordon Pr.

Lotus Prayer Book. Ed. by Swami Karunananda Ma. LC 86-10384. 224p. (Orig.). 1986. pap. 9.95 (ISBN 0-932040-33-0). Integral Yoga Pubns.

Lotus Textbook. Kanjitsu Ijima. 62p. (Orig.). 1984. pap. 10.00 (ISBN 0-86627-010-8). Crises Res Pr.

Louis Martin: Father of a Saint. Joyce R. Emert. LC 83-2728. 208p. (Orig.). 1983. pap. 9.95 (ISBN 0-8189-0446-1). Alba.

Louis Massignon: Christian Ecumenist. Biuolio Basetti-Sani. 1974. 6.95 (ISBN 0-8199-0496-1). Franciscan Herald.

Louis the IX: The Challenge of the Crusade. William C. Jordan. LC 79-83996. (Illus.). 1979. 37.00 (ISBN 0-691-05285-9). Princeton U Pr.

Louisiana Church Architecture. R. Warren Robison. LC 84-70619. (USL Architecture Ser.: No. 2). 90p. 1984. 19.95 (ISBN 0-940984-20-2). U of SW LA Ctr LA Studies.

Lourdes: A History of Its Apparitions & Cures. G. Bertrin. 59.95 (ISBN 0-8490-0560-4). Gordon Pr.

Lourdes: A Modern Pilgrimage. Patrick Marnham. LC 82-45299. 272p. 1982. pap. 4.95 (ISBN 0-385-18252-X, Im). Doubleday.

Love. Ernesto Cardenal. 160p. 1981. pap. 4.95 (ISBN 0-8245-0043-1). Crossroad NY.

Love. (The Inspirational Library Ser.). 24p. 3.95 (ISBN 0-8326-2006-8, 3253). World Bible.

Love. 1986. 8.95 (ISBN 0-87579-059-3). Deseret Bk.

Love. Carole MacKenthun & Paulinus Dwyer. (Fruit of the Spirit Ser.). (Illus.). 48p. Date not set. wkbk. 4.95 (ISBN 0-86653-359-1). Good Apple.

Love. rev. ed. Jane B. Moncure. LC 80-27479. (What Is It? Ser.). (Illus.). 32p. 1981. PLB 7.45 (ISBN 0-89565-205-6). Childs World.

Love. Helen S. Rice. (Illus.). 128p. 1980. 12.95 (ISBN 0-8007-1072-X). Revell.

Love. John Souter. (Campus Magazine Ser.). 96p. (Orig.). 1985. pap. 4.95 (ISBN 0-8423-3851-9). Tyndale.

Love a Feast. Frederick Buechner. LC 84-47714. (Books of Bebb). 380p. 1984. pap. 3.95 (ISBN 0-06-061167-7, P-5009, HarpR). Har-Row.

Love: A Guide for Prayer. Jacqueline Bergan & S. Marie Schwan. (Take & Receive Ser.). 96p. (Orig.). 1984. pap. 5.95 (ISBN 0-88489-168-2). St Mary's.

Love, Acceptance & Forgiveness: Leader's Guide. Margaret Parker. LC 79-63763. 128p. 1984. pap. 3.95 (ISBN 0-8307-0989-4, 6101895). Regal.

Love Adds the Chocolate. Linda Andersen. 1984. 4.95 (ISBN 0-8010-0198-6). Baker Bk.

Love Affairs of the Vatican. Angelo S. Rappoport. 35.00 (ISBN 0-8490-0561-2). Gordon Pr.

Love & a Wooden Spoon. Charmaine Solomon & Dee Huxley. LC 83-25446. 168p. 1985. pap. 10.00 (ISBN 0-385-19387-4). Doubleday.

Love & Be Loved. Marie Chapian. 192p. 1983. pap. 6.95 (ISBN 0-8007-5092-6, Power Bks). Revell.

Love & Be Loved: A How-To Book. John Tamiazzo. 176p. 1986. pap. 7.95 (ISBN 0-87877-087-9, Greenbriar Books). Newcastle Pub.

Love & Being: An Investigation into the Metaphysics of St. Thomas Aquinas. Bernard J. Diggs. 180p. 1947. 6.75 (ISBN 0-913298-45-X). S F Vanni.

Love & Conflict: A Covenantal Model of Christian Ethics. Joseph L. Allen. 336p. 1984. pap. 12.95 (ISBN 0-687-22806-9). Abingdon.

Love & Control in Sexuality. W. Norman Pittinger. LC 73-19833. 128p. 1974. 4.25 (ISBN 0-8298-0268-1). Pilgrim NY.

Love & Creation. Richard McBride et al. pap. text ed. 2.16 (ISBN 0-317-39314-6); 3.99 (ISBN 0-8215-5842-0); Parent Guidebook 1.98 (ISBN 0-317-39315-4). Sadlier.

Love & Estrangement in the Baha'i Community. Arnie Nerenberg. (Orig.). 1986. 9.95 (ISBN 0-933770-47-2). Kalimat.

Love & Exile: A Memoir. Isaac B. Singer. LC 79-7211. (Illus.). 384p. 1984. 17.95 (ISBN 0-385-14060-6). Doubleday.

Love & Gratitude. Joel S. Goldsmith. 1972. pap. 1.75 (ISBN 0-87516-139-1). De Vorss.

Love & Justice: Selections from the Shorter Writings of Reinhold Niebuhr. Reinhold Niebuhr. Ed. by D. B. Robertson. 12.50 (ISBN 0-8446-2659-7). Peter Smith.

Love & Learning. Sidney E. Mead. Ed. by Mary L. Doyle. 1978. lib. bdg. 12.95x (ISBN 0-914914-13-8); pap. 5.00 (ISBN 0-914914-12-X). New Horizons.

Love & Life. Leo Jung. LC 79-87873. 84p. 1979. 7.50 (ISBN 0-8022-2355-9). Philos Lib.

Love & Life: A Christian Sexual Morality Guide for Teens. Coleen K. Mast et al. 118p. 1986. pap. 7.95 (ISBN 0-89870-106-6). Ignatius Pr.

Love & Life: A Christian Sexual Morality Guide for Teens Parents' Guide. Coleen K. Mast et al. LC 86-80604. 48p. 1986. pap. 5.95 (ISBN 0-89870-107-4). Ignatius Pr.

Love & Life: A Christian Sexual Morality Guide for Teens Teacher's Guide. Coleen K. Mast. 150p. 1986. pap. 10.95 (ISBN 0-89870-108-2). Ignatius Pr.

Love & Lifestyles. Mary T. Judd. LC 80-54285. (Illus.). 200p. (Orig.). 1981. pap. text ed. 6.80x (ISBN 0-88489-132-1); teacher's guide 9.00x (ISBN 0-88489-134-8). St Mary's.

Love & Marriage in the Spirit. Eberhard Arnold. LC 64-24321. 1965. 7.00 (ISBN 0-87486-103-9). Plough.

Love & Responsibility. Pope John Paul II. Tr. by H. T. Willetts. 320p. 1981. 15.00 (ISBN 0-374-19247-2); pap. 7.95 (ISBN 0-374-51685-5). FS&G.

Love & Selfishness. Alice Von Hildebrand. 54p. 1970. pap. 0.75 (ISBN 0-8199-0376-0). Franciscan Herald.

Love & Sex: A Modern Jewish Perspective. Robert Gordis. 290p. 1978. 8.95 (ISBN 0-374-19252-9). FS&G.

Love & Sexuality, Pt. I. Omraam M. Aivanhov. (Complete Works: Vol. 14). (Illus.). 250p. 1976. pap. 9.95 (ISBN 2-85566-114-5). Prosveta USA.

Love & Sympathy in Theravada Buddhism. Harvey B. Aronson. cancelled (ISBN 0-8364-0627-3, Pub. by Motilal Banarsidass). South Asia Bks.

Love & Thunder: A Spirituality of the Old Testament. John F. Craghan. 248p. 1983. pap. text ed. 11.00 (ISBN 0-8146-1279-2). Liturgical Pr.

Love & Tradition: Marriage Between Jews & Christians. Egon Mayer. 312p. 1985. (full discount avail.) 17.95 (ISBN 0-306-42043-0, Plenum Pr). Plenum Pub.

Love & Tradition: Marriage Between Jews & Christians. Egon Mayer. LC 86-24823. 312p. 1987. pap. 8.95 (ISBN 0-8052-0828-3). Schocken.

Love Bade Me Welcome. Robert Llewelyn. 96p. (Orig.). 1985. pap. 5.95 (ISBN 0-8091-2715-6). Paulist Pr.

Love, Beauty, & Harmony in Sufism. Nasrollah S. Fatemi & Faramarz S. Fatemi. 12.95 (ISBN 0-8453-2248-6, Cornwall Bks). Assoc Univ Prs.

Love Book. Karen Casey. (Hazelden Meditation Ser.). (Illus.). 110p. 1986. pap. 7.00 (ISBN 0-86683-505-9, HarpJ). Har-Row.

Love Book. Karen Casey. (Hazelden Bks.). scp 7.50t (ISBN 0-317-46481-7). Har-Row.

Love Book. Karen Casey. (Meditation Ser.). 110p. 1985. 7.95 (ISBN 0-89486-339-8). Hazelden.

Love Carved in Stone. Daniel R. Seagren. LC 82-23195. 1983. pap. text ed. 3.50 (ISBN 0-8307-0840-5, S371101). Regal.
Love: Christian Romance, Marriage, Friendship. Diogenes Allen. 149p. (Orig.). 1987. pap. 8.95 (ISBN 0-936384-47-6). Cowley Pubns.
Love Commandment: How to Find Its Meaning for Today. Mary Patrick. Ed. by Herbert Lambert. LC 84-7083. 112p. 1984. pap. 6.95 (ISBN 0-8272-2118-5). CBP.
Love Commands in the New Testament. Pheme Perkins. 144p. (Orig.). 1982. pap. 5.95 (ISBN 0-8091-2450-5). Paulist Pr.
Love Covenant. 3.25 (ISBN 0-8198-4432-2); 2.25 (ISBN 0-8198-4433-0). Dghtrs St Paul.
Love Covers. Paul Billheimer. 1981. pap. 4.95 (ISBN 0-87508-006-5). Chr Lit.
Love Covers. Paul E. Billheimer. LC 83-15823. 174p. (Orig.). 1983. pap. 4.95 (ISBN 0-87123-400-9, 210400). Bethany Hse.
Love, Dating & Marriage. George B. Eager. LC 86-90552. (Illus.). 136p. (Orig.). 1987. pap. 5.95 (ISBN 0-9603752-5-2). Mailbox.
Love Enthroned. Steele. kivar 4.95 (ISBN 0-686-12891-5). Schmul Pub Co.
Love Explosion: Human Experience & the Christian Mystery. Robert E. Lauder. 128p. (Orig.). 1979. pap. 2.95 (ISBN 0-914544-22-5). Living Flame Pr.
Love-Feasts: A History of the Christian Agape. Richard L. Cole. 59.95 (ISBN 0-8490-0563-9). Gordon Pr.
Love for a Lifetime: Wise Words from Those Who've Gone Before. James C. Dobson. Date not set. price not set (ISBN 0-88070-174-9). Multnomah.
Love for All Your Worth! A Quest for Personal Value & Lovability. Joseph C. Aldrich. LC 85-11420. 1985. pap. 6.95 (ISBN 0-88070-119-6). Multnomah.
Love from the Living Bible. Perry Tanksley. 1976. 4.95 (ISBN 0-686-17793-2). Allgood Bks.
Love-God's Greatest Gift. Douglas R. Benn. (Illus.). 1981. pap. 4.00 (ISBN 0-682-49736-3). Exposition Pr FL.
Love Goes 'Round the Circle. Carol V. Amen. (Better Living Ser.). pap. 0.99 (ISBN 0-8280-1268-7). Review & Herald.
Love Has a Price Tag. Elisabeth Elliot. 152p. 1982. pap. 5.95 (ISBN 0-89283-153-7, Pub. by Vine Books). Servant.
Love Holds No Grievances: The Ending of Attack. 2nd ed. Tara Singh. LC 86-14834. 1986. 8.95 (ISBN 1-55531-120-2); pap. 4.95 (ISBN 1-55531-007-9). Life Action Pr.
Love-Hungry Priest. Sidney Custodio & Cliff Dudley. LC 82-61308. 192p. (Orig.). 1983. pap. 2.95 (ISBN 0-89221-099-0). New Leaf.
Love in Action. Beth Holzbauer. 1987. Instrs's., 128 pgs. pap. price not set (ISBN 0-87403-043-9, 39968); Student's, 112 pgs. pap. price not set (ISBN 0-87403-044-7, 39967). Standard Pub.
Love in Action: Reflections on Christian Service. Bernard Hayes. 120p. (Orig.). pap. 5.95 (ISBN 0-914544-57-8). Living Flame Pr.
Love in Fearful Land: A Guatemalan Story. Henri J. Nouwen. LC 85-71913. (Illus.). 120p. (Orig.). 1985. pap. 5.95 (ISBN 0-87793-294-8). Ave Maria.
Love Is. Ronald D. Tucker. (Illus.). 76p. (Orig.). 1983. pap. 2.50 (ISBN 0-933643-10-1). Grace World Outreach.
Love Is a Challenge. Matilda A. Gocek. LC 78-12327. (Keepers of the Light Ser.). (Illus.). 72p. 1978. pap. 3.95 (ISBN 0-912526-22-X). Lib Res.
Love Is Always. Michael Miles. LC 86-2378. 320p. 1986. 17.95 (ISBN 0-688-06218-0). Morrow.
Love Is an Awakening. Yogi A. Desai. Ed. by Lisa Sarasohn. (Illus.). 40p. (Orig.). 1985. pap. 2.00 (ISBN 0-940258-14-5). Kripalu Pubns.
Love Is an Everyday Thing. rev. ed. Colleen T. Evans. 128p. 1984. pap. 4.95 (ISBN 0-8007-5157-4, Power Bks). Revell.
Love Is Better Than Wine. Herbert Lockyer. LC 80-84903. 1981. pap. 3.95 (ISBN 0-89221-083-4). New Leaf.
Love Is for Living. Carlo Carretto. Tr. by Jeremy Moiser from Ital. LC 76-49878. Orig. Title: Cio Che Conta E Amare. 158p. 1977. pap. 7.95 (ISBN 0-88344-293-0). Orbis Bks.
Love Is for Tomorrow. Hope Traver. 271p. 1978. pap. 3.95 (ISBN 0-930756-37-1, 531006). Aglow Pubns.
Love Is Forever. May Mapou. 1984. 4.95 (ISBN 0-8062-2196-8). Carlton.
Love Is Freedom. Joseph Murphy. pap. 1.25 (ISBN 0-87516-337-8). De Vorss.
Love Is God. Marie H. Frost. (First Happy Day Bks.). (Illus.). 20p. 1986. casebound 1.29 (ISBN 0-87403-133-8, 2003). Standard Pub.
Love Is Kind. Janet Herbert. (Sparkler Bks.). (Illus.). 32p. 1986. plastic comb bndg. 2.95 (ISBN 0-89191-928-7, 59287, Chariot Bks). Cook.
Love Is Like the Sunlight. Mary A. Vandermey. 1985. pap. 5.95 (ISBN 0-8010-9294-9). Baker Bk.
Love Is Not a Special Way of Feeling. Charles G. Finney. Orig. Title: Attributes of Love. 144p. 1963. pap. 3.50 (ISBN 0-87123-005-4, 200005). Bethany Hse.
Love Is Now. new ed. Peter E. Gillquist. 1970. 4.95 (ISBN 0-310-36941-X, 18054P). Zondervan.
Love Is Prayer - Prayer Is Love. St. Alphonsus Liguori. LC 72-97592. 1973. pap. 2.95 (ISBN 0-89243-047-8, 41500). Liguori Pubns.
Love Is So Much More, Lord. Ruth H. Calkin. LC 79-51739. 1979. pap. 2.50 (ISBN 0-89191-187-1). Cook.
Love Is Something You Do. John R. Bisagno. LC 75-9314. 1979. pap. 6.95 (ISBN 0-06-060793-9, RD-238, HarpR). Har-Row.
Love Is Stronger Than Death. Peter J. Kreeft. LC 78-15839. 1979. 8.95 (ISBN 0-06-064774-4, HarpR). Har-Row.
Love Is the Answer. Robert V. Ozment. 160p. 1986. pap. 5.95 (ISBN 0-8007-5227-9). Revell.
Love Is the Greatest. Audrey Williamson. (Direction Bks). 64p. 1976. pap. 1.25 (ISBN 0-8010-9579-4). Baker Bk.
Love It, Don't Label It: A Practical Guide for Using Spiritual Principles in Everyday Life. Carlin J. Diamond. Ed. by Kim Peterson. (Illus.). 200p. (Orig.). 1986. pap. 10.00 (ISBN 0-911761-03-9). Fifth Wave Pr.
Love Leaves Home. Erich H. Heintzen & Frank Starr. LC 72-94586. 1973. 3.50 (ISBN 0-570-03513-9, 14-2017). Concordia.
Love Letters. Madeleine L'Engle. (Epiphany Ser.). 384p. 1983. pap. 2.95 (ISBN 0-345-30617-1). Ballantine.
Love Life for Every Married Couple. Ed Wheat. 288p. 1980. pap. 5.95 (ISBN 0-310-42511-5, 10266P). Zondervan.
Love Life: I Cor. 13. W. Graham Scroggie. LC 79-2551. (W. Graham Scroggie Library). 96p. 1980. pap. 4.50 (ISBN 0-8254-3733-4). Kregel.
Love Lives Here. Mary A. Forehand. (Orig.). 1975. pap. 1.95 (ISBN 0-377-00028-0). Friend Pr.
Love Lyrics from the Bible: A Translation & Literary Study of the Song of Songs. Marcia Falk. (Bible & Literature Ser.: No. 4). 1981. text ed. 19.95x (ISBN 0-907459-06-4, Pub. by Almond Pr England); pap. text ed. 9.95x (ISBN 0-907459-07-2, Pub. by Almond Pr England). Eisenbrauns.
Love-Magic & Butterfly People: The Slim Curly Version of the Ajilee & Mothway Myths. Berard Haile. LC 78-59705. (American Tribal Religions Ser.: Vol. 2). (Illus.). xii, 172p. 1978. pap. 13.95x (ISBN 0-89734-026-4, Pub by Mus Nothern Ariz). U of Nebr Pr.
Love Must Be Tough. James Dobson. 1986. write for info. Word Bks.
Love Never Ends. Joyce G. Rice. pap. 3.95 (ISBN 0-89036-147-9). Hawkes Pub Inc.
Love Never Ever Ends. Joan Hutson. LC 82-6737. (Happy Day Bks.). (Illus.). 24p. 1983. 1.59 (ISBN 0-87239-641-X, 3561). Standard Pub.
Love Never Faileth: The Inspiration of St. Francis, St. Augustine, St. Paul & Mother Teresa. Eknath Easwaran. (Illus.). 208p. (Orig.). 1985. 15.00 (ISBN 0-915132-31-1); pap. 8.00 (ISBN 0-915132-32-X). Nilgiri Pr.
Love Never Fails. Kenneth E. Hagin. 1984. pap. 0.50 mini bk. (ISBN 0-89276-264-0). Hagin Ministries.
Love Not the World. John MacArthur, Jr. (John MacArthur's Bible Studies). (Orig.). 1986. pap. 3.50 (ISBN 0-8024-5098-9). Moody.
Love Not the World. Watchmans Nee. 1977. pap. 3.50 (ISBN 0-8423-3850-0). Tyndale.
Love of Christ. Richard Rogers. 26p. 1981. pap. text ed. 1.50 (ISBN 0-931097-12-6). Sentinel Pub.
Love of Christ: Spiritual Counsels. Mother Teresa of Calcutta. LC 81-48216. 128p. 1982. 8.45 (ISBN 0-06-068229-9, HarpR). Har-Row.
Love of Enemies: The Way to Peace. William Klassen. LC 84-47927. (Overtures to Biblical Theology Ser.). 176p. 1984. pap. 8.95 (ISBN 0-8006-1539-5). Fortress.
Love of Eternal Wisdom. St. Louis De Montfort. 4.95 (ISBN 0-910984-51-4); pap. 2.95 (ISBN 0-910984-05-0). Montfort Pubns.
Love of God. Bernard of Clairvaux & William of St. Thierry. Ed. by James M. Houston. LC 83-10533. (Classics of Faith & Devotion). Orig. Title: Life & Works of St. Bernard. 1983. 11.95 (ISBN 0-88070-017-3). Multnomah.
Love of God. Mir Valiuddin. LC 85-27481. 216p. 1985. Repr. lib. bdg. 19.95x (ISBN 0-89370-577-2). Borgo Pr.
Love of God. Bernard N. Schneider. 1985. pap. 5.95 (ISBN 0-88469-167-5). BMH Bks.
Love of God. Mir Valiuddin. (Orig.). 1979. pap. 9.95 (ISBN 0-900217-02-2, Pub. by Sufi Pub Co England). Hunter Hse.
Love of God & Social Duty in the Ramcaritmanas. Edmour J. Babineau. 1979. 13.95 (ISBN 0-89684-050-6, Pub. by Motilal Banarsidass India). Orient Bk Dist.
Love of Jesus & the Love of Neighbor. Karl Rahner. LC 82-23523. 96p. 1983. pap. 5.95 (ISBN 0-8245-0570-0). Crossroad NY.
Love of Knowledge. Tarthang Tulku. (Psychology Ser.). 300p. (Orig.). 1987. pap. 12.95 (ISBN 0-89800-138-2). Dharma Pub.
Love of Krishna: The Krsnakarnamrta of Lilasuka Bilvamangala. Ed. & tr. by Frances Wilson. LC 74-153426. (Haney Foundation Ser.). 448p. 1975. 24.00x (ISBN 0-8122-7655-8). U of Pa Pr.
Love of Learning & Desire for God: A Study of Monastic Culture. 3rd ed. Jean Leclercq. LC 60-53004. x, 282p. 1985. pap. 10.00 (ISBN 0-8232-0407-3). Fordham.
Love of Mary. D. Roberto. LC 83-51545. 240p. 1985. pap. 5.00 (ISBN 0-89555-235-3). Tan Bks Pubs.
Love One Another. Watchman Nee. Tr. by Stephen Kaung. (Basic Lesson Ser.: Vol. 6). 1975. 5.50 (ISBN 0-935008-09-8); pap. 4.25 (ISBN 0-935008-10-1). Christian Fellow Pubs.
Love One Another Bible Study Series, 7 vols. LC 79-52132. 1979. pap. 16.80 (ISBN 0-934396-00-0). Churches Alive.
Love One Another Leader's Guide. Churches Alive, Inc. Staff. LC 79-52128. (Love One Another Ser.). (Illus.). 85p. (Orig.). 1981. pap. text ed. 4.95 (ISBN 0-934396-13-2). Churches Alive.
Love, Peace & Joy: Devotion to the Sacred Heart of Jesus According to St. Gertrude. Andre Prevot. LC 84-51822. 224p. 1985. pap. 4.00 (ISBN 0-89555-255-8). Tan Bks Pubs.
Love, Power & Justice. Paul Tillich. 1954. pap. 7.95 (ISBN 0-19-500222-9). Oxford U Pr.
Love Power: New Dimensions for Building Strong Families. Alan Stine. LC 78-70360. 1978. 8.95 (ISBN 0-88290-105-2). Horizon Utah.
Love Prescription. E. Delafield. (Stories That Win Ser.). 64p. 1980. pap. 0.95 (ISBN 0-8163-0410-6). Pacific Pr Pub Assn.
Love, Sex & Marriage: A Jewish View. Roland B. Gittelsohn. (Illus.). 1980. pap. 7.95x (ISBN 0-8074-0046-7, 142683). UAHC.
Love Slaves. Samuel L. Brengle. 1960. Repr. of 1923 ed. 3.95 (ISBN 0-86544-004-2). Salv Army Suppl South.
Love So Amazing... Memories of Meher Baba. Bili Eaton. LC 84-23597. 144p. 1984. pap. 8.95 (ISBN 0-913078-55-7). Sheriar Pr.
Love Song in Harvest. Geoffrey Bull. 1977. pap. 3.95 (ISBN 0-87508-042-1). Chr Lit.
Love Songs: Daily Meditations for Married Couples. Al Bryant. 8.95 (ISBN 0-8499-3036-7). Word Bks.
Love Songs: Musical Activities for Christian Celebration. Herb Brokering & Lois Brokering. 36p. (Orig.). 1981. pap. 3.95 (ISBN 0-942562-01-1). Brokering Pr.
Love Story. Gabriel Delgado. 64p. (Orig.). pap. 1.25 (ISBN 0-89228-046-8). Impact Bks MO.
Love That Heals. Ed. by Edward E. Thornton. LC 83-21083. 1984. pap. 3.75 (ISBN 0-8054-5105-6). Broadman.
Love the Greatest Enchantment: The Sorceries of Sin, the Devotion of the Cross. Denis Florence Mac Carthy. 1861. 50.00 (ISBN 0-8274-3002-7). R West.
Love Them In: The Proclamation Theology of D. L. Moody. Stanley N. Gundry. 252p. 1982. pap. 8.95 (ISBN 0-8010-3783-2). Baker Bk.
Love Theory in Later Hanbalite Islam. Joseph N. Bell. LC 78-5904. 1979. PLB 49.50x (ISBN 0-87395-244-8). State U NY Pr.
Love Treasures: "The Mother", Book One. Sri Aurobindo. (Illus.). 98p. 1985. 36.00x (ISBN 0-89071-333-2, Pub. by Sri Aurobindo Ashram India). Matagiri.
Love Until It Hurts: The Work of Mother Teresa & Her Missionaries of Charity. Daphne Rae. LC 81-47424. (Illus., Orig.). 1981. pap. 9.95 (ISBN 0-06-066729-X, RD 368, HarpR). Har-Row.
Love Was Born at Christmas. Susan E. Luttrell. (Orig.). 1981. pap. 3.25 (ISBN 0-89536-483-2, 1234). CSS of Ohio.
Love with No Strings: The Human Touch in Christian Social Ministries. Elaine Furlow. Ed. by Everett Hullum. (Human Touch Photo-Text Ser.: Volume IV). (Illus.). 1977. 6.95 (ISBN 0-937170-15-1). Home Mission.
Love with Your Eyes Open. Clement Renirkens. Tr. by Marc Lucas & Claudia Lucas. LC 85-28669. 145p. (Orig.). 1986. pap. 7.95 (ISBN 0-8189-0491-7). Alba.
Love Within Limits: A Realist's View of I Corinthians 13. Lewis B. Smedes. 1978. pap. 4.95 (ISBN 0-8028-1753-X). Eerdmans.
Love Your Enemies. John Piper. LC 77-95449. (Society for New Testament Studies: No. 38). 1980. 34.50 (ISBN 0-521-22056-4). Cambridge U Pr.
Love Your Neighbor: A Woman's Workshop on Fellowship. Larry Richards. Ed. by Janet Kobobel. 144p. 1986. pap. 3.95 (18139). Zondervan.
Love Your Neighbour: A Woman's Workshop on Fellowship. Lawrence O. Richards. (Woman's Workshop Ser.). 160p. (Orig.). 1981. pap. 3.95 (ISBN 0-310-43451-3, 18139P). Zondervan.
Love Yourself. J. B. Livingston. 2.70 (ISBN 0-89137-421-3). Quality Pubns.
Love Yourself. Edward Richardson. 1970. pap. 1.50 (ISBN 0-89243-028-1, 28849). Liguori Pubns.
Lovebook. Karen Casey. 110p. 1985. pap. 5.95 (ISBN 0-89486-376-2). Hazelden.
Loved & Forgiven. Lloyd J. Ogilvie. LC 76-29889. 160p. 1977. pap. 3.50 (ISBN 0-8307-0442-6, S313103). Regal.
Lovers: Whatever Happened to Eden? Donald Joy. 220p. 1987. 12.95 (ISBN 0-8499-0541-9). Word Bks.
Love's Abiding Joy. Janette Oke. LC 83-15503. 224p. (Orig.). 1983. pap. 4.95 (ISBN 0-87123-401-7, 210401). Bethany Hse.
Love's Abiding Joy. Janette Oke. 217p. 1985. Large Print. pap. 6.95 (ISBN 0-317-20707-5). Bethany Hse.
Love's Humility. John MacArthur, Jr. (John MacArthur's Bible Studies). (Orig.). 1986. pap. 3.95 (ISBN 0-8024-5097-0). Moody.
Love's Long Journey. Janette Oke. 207p. 1985. Large Print. pap. 6.95 (ISBN 0-317-20714-8). Bethany Hse.
Love's Old Song. Dorothy Augur. 1984. pap. 6.95 (ISBN 0-89221-129-6, Pub. by Sonlife Intl). New Leaf.
Love's Unending Legacy. Janette Oke. 224p. (Orig.). 1984. pap. 4.95 (ISBN 0-87123-616-8, 210616). Bethany Hse.
Love's Unending Legacy. Janette Oke. 224p. 1985. Large Print. pap. 6.95 (ISBN 0-87123-855-1). Bethany Hse.
Lovest Thou Me? Frances J. Roberts. 1967. 2.95 (ISBN 0-932814-19-0). Kings Farspan.
Lovett's Lights on Acts. C. S. Lovett. 1972. pap. 6.95 (ISBN 0-938148-28-1). Personal Christianity.
Lovett's Lights on Galatians, Ephesians, Philippians, Colossians, 1 & 2 Thessalonians. C. S. Lovett. 1970. pap. 5.95 (ISBN 0-938148-25-7). Personal Christianity.
Lovett's Lights on John. C. S. Lovett. 1970. pap. 6.45 (ISBN 0-938148-24-9). Personal Christianity.
Lovett's Lights on Romans. C. S. Lovett. 1975. pap. 6.95 (ISBN 0-938148-30-3). Personal Christianity.
Lovett's Lights on the Sermon on the Mount. C. S. Lovett. 176p. (Orig.). 1985. pap. 5.45 (ISBN 0-938148-40-0). Personal Christianity.
Loving Each Other. Yogi A. Desai. Ed. by Lisa Sarasohn. (Illus.). 40p. 1985. pap. 2.00 (ISBN 0-940258-19-6). Kripalu Pubns.
Loving Father. Meryl Doney. (Illus.). 16p. 1982. pap. 0.99 (ISBN 0-86683-665-9, AY8245, HarpR). Har-Row.
Loving God. Charles W. Colson. 288p. 1983. 12.95 (ISBN 0-310-47030-7, 11306); study guide 3.95 (ISBN 0-310-47038-2, 11307). Zondervan.
Loving God & a Suffering World. Jon T. Murphree. LC 81-11759. 144p. (Orig.). 1981. pap. 4.50 (ISBN 0-87784-877-7). Inter-Varsity.
Loving Hands for Jesus. Edith P. Galambos. (Little Learner Ser.). 24p. 1985. 5.95 (ISBN 0-570-08951-4, 56-1543). Concordia.
Loving Kindness of the Sovereign God. Norman Douty. pap. 0.50 (ISBN 0-685-88383-3). Reiner.
Loving One Another. Gene Getz. LC 79-63450. 143p. 1979. pap. 5.95 (ISBN 0-88207-786-4). Victor Bks.
Loving Promises. Helen S. Rice. (Illus.). 128p. 1975. 12.95 (ISBN 0-8007-0736-2); large-print ed., 176p. 12.95 (ISBN 0-8007-1333-8). Revell.
Loving Relationships. Robert R. Shelton. 272p. (Orig.). 1987. pap. 11.95 (ISBN 0-87178-542-0). Brethren.
Loving Says It All. Norman Pittenger. 128p. 1978. 6.95 (ISBN 0-8298-0352-1). Pilgrim NY.
Loving Search for the Lost Servant. Swami B. Sridhara. Ed. by B. S. Goswami & B. V. Mahayogi. (Illus.). 120p. 1987. pap. text ed. 9.95 (ISBN 0-940431-05-X). Guardian Devot Pr.
Loving Truth about Jesus. Harold Cooper. 136p. 1976. pap. 1.50 (ISBN 0-89114-100-6); tchr's ed 1.00 (ISBN 0-89114-101-4). Baptist Pub Hse.
Lowell's Religious Outlook. Leo Martin Shea. 124p. 1983. Repr. of 1926 ed. 16.00x (ISBN 0-939738-13-9). Zubal Inc.
Lower East Side: A Guide to Its Jewish Past with Ninety-Nine New Photographs. Ronald Sanders & Edmund V. Gillon. (Illus.). 1980. pap. 5.95 (ISBN 0-486-23871-7). Dover.
Loyalty by Oath. Hallock Hoffman. 1983. pap. 2.50x (ISBN 0-87574-094-4, 094). Pendle Hill.

Loyd Corder: Traveler for God. Eugene Chamberlain. LC 82-73663. (Meet the Missionary Ser.). 1983. 5.50 (ISBN 0-8054-4284-7, 4242-84). Broadman.
Loyola & the Educational System of the Jesuits. Thomas A. Hughes. 34.95 (ISBN 0-8490-0565-5). Gordon Pr.
Loyola & the Educational System of the Jesuits. Thomas A. Hughes. LC 83-45594. Date not set. Repr. of 1892 ed. 35.00 (ISBN 0-404-19887-2). AMS Pr.
Loyola & the Educational Systems of the Jesuits. Thomas A. Hughes. 1892. 39.00 (ISBN 0-403-00121-8). Scholarly.
Lu Hsiang-Shan: A 12th Century Chinese Idealist Philosopher. Hsiu-Chi Huang. LC 75-39028. (China Studies: from Confucius to Mao Ser.). (Illus.). 116p. 1976. Repr. of 1944 ed. 18.15 (ISBN 0-88355-384-8). Hyperion-Conn.
Luca & Andrea Della Robbia. Maud Crutwell. LC 79-155625. (Illus.). Repr. of 1902 ed. 29.50 (ISBN 0-404-01869-6). AMS Pr.
Luca della Robbia. John Pope-Hennessy. LC 79-13566. (Illus.). 282p. 1980. 125.00x (ISBN 0-8014-1256-0). Cornell U Pr.
Luces Bajo el Almud. Justo L. Gonzalez. LC 77-11753. (Span.). 76p. (Orig.). 1977. pap. 2.50 (ISBN 0-89922-102-5). Edit Caribe.
Luces Encendidas Para Cada Dia. Miguel Limardo. 376p. 1983. Repr. of 1981 ed. 5.50 (ISBN 0-311-40038-8). Casa Bautista.
Lucian. W. Lucas Collins. 1877. Repr. 25.00 (ISBN 0-8274-3005-1). R West.
Lucifer & Prometheus: A Study of Milton's Satan. Raphael J. Werblowsky. LC 79-153359. Repr. of 1952 ed. 7.50 (ISBN 0-404-06906-1). AMS Pr.
Lucifer Connection. Joseph Carr. 1986. pap. 6.96 (ISBN 0-910311-42-0). Huntington Hse Inc.
Lucifer: The Devil in the Middle Ages. Jeffrey B. Russell. LC 84-45153. (Illus.). 384p. 1984. 24.95x (ISBN 0-8014-1503-9). Cornell U Pr.
Lucifer: The Devil in the Middle Ages. Jeffrey B. Russell. LC 84-45153. (Illus.). 360p. 1986. pap. text ed. 12.95x (ISBN 0-8014-9429-X). Cornell U Pr.
Lucifer's Handbook. Lee Carter. LC 76-55893. 1977. pap. text ed. 5.95 (ISBN 0-918260-01-9). Acad Assoc.
Lucky Hans. Jacob Grimm & Wilhelm K. Grimm. LC 86-2520. (Illus.). 32p. 1986. 12.45 (ISBN 0-8050-0009-7, North South Bks). H Holt & Co.
Lucretia Mott Speaking: Excerpts from the Sermons & Speeches of a Famous 19th Century Quaker Minister & Reformers. Margaret Hope Bacon. LC 80-84890. 31p. (Orig.). 1980. pap. 2.50x (ISBN 0-87574-234-3). Pendle Hill.
Ludus Coventriae, Or, the Place Called Corpus Christi. Ed. by K. S. Block. (Early English Text Society Ser.). 1922. 26.00x (ISBN 0-19-722560-8). Oxford U Pr.
Ludwig-Missionsverein & the Church in the United States (1838-1918) Theodore Roemer. LC 73-3571. (Catholic University of America. Studies in American Church History: No. 16). Repr. of 1933 ed. 22.00 (ISBN 0-404-57766-0). AMS Pr.
Ludwig Schaffrath, Stained Glass & Mosaic. Konrad Stephany. LC 77-79948. 1977. write for info. (ISBN 0-686-05497-0). C & R Loo.
Ludwig Tieck & America. Percy Matenko. LC 54-62860. (North Carolina University. Studies in the Germanic Languages & Literatures: No. 12). Repr. of 1954 ed. 27.00 (ISBN 0-404-50912-6). AMS Pr.
Ludwig Tieck & the Medieval Church. Sr. Mary M. Scheiber. LC 74-140028. (Catholic University Studies in German: No. 12). Repr. of 1939 ed. 22.00 (ISBN 0-404-50232-6). AMS Pr.
Ludwig Tieck's Early Concept of Catholic Clergy & Church. Edgar A. Lang. LC 74-140044. (Catholic University Studies in German Ser.: No. 8). Repr. of 1936 ed. 28.00 (ISBN 0-404-50228-8). AMS Pr.
Ludwig's Handbook of New Testament Cities & Rulers. Charles Ludwig. LC 83-71619. 244p. (Orig.). 1983. pap. 6.95 (ISBN 0-89636-111-X). Accent Bks.
Ludwig's Handbook of Old Testament Rulers & Cities. Charles Ludwig. LC 84-70426. 244p. (Orig.). 1984. pap. 6.95 (ISBN 0-89636-130-6). Accent Bks.
Lug Dukhovnij. Tr. of Spiritual Meadow. 400p. 20.00 (ISBN 0-317-28903-9); pap. 15.00 (ISBN 0-317-28904-7). Holy Trinity.
Lugbara Religion: Ritual & Authority among an East African People. John Middleton. LC 60-51074. pap. 71.00 (ISBN 0-317-28622-6, 2055387). Bks Demand UMI.
Lugbara Religion: Ritual & Authority among East African People. John Middleton. LC 86-21889. (Illus.). 294p. 1987. pap. 14.95x (ISBN 0-87474-667-1). Smithsonian.
Luis de Leon: Names of Christ. Tr. by Manuel Duran & William Kluback. (Classics of Western Spirituality Ser.). 1984. 14.95 (ISBN 0-8091-0346-X); pap. 11.95 (ISBN 0-8091-2561-7). Paulist Pr.
Luis Palau: Calling the Nations to Christ. As told to Jerry B. Jenkins. (Illus.). 1983. pap. 4.95 (ISBN 0-8024-0461-8). Moody.
Lukac's Road to God: The Early Criticism Against Its Pre-Marxist Background. Michael Holzman. (Current Continental Research Ser.: No. 208). 196p. (Orig.). 1985. lib. bdg. 25.00 (ISBN 0-8191-4719-2); pap. text ed. 11.25 (ISBN 0-8191-4720-6). U Pr of Amer.
Lukan Voice: Confusion & Irony in the Gospel of Luke. James M. Dawsey. 208p. 1986. 19.50 (ISBN 0-86554-193-0, MUP-H178). Mercer Univ Pr.
Luke, Vol. III. Beacon Bible Commentary Staff. 6.95 (ISBN 0-8010-0678-3). Baker Bk.
Luke. Paul Butler. LC 81-68817. (Bible Study Textbook Ser.). 627p. 1981. 17.50 (ISBN 0-89900-062-2). College Pr Pub.
Luke. Frederick W. Danker. Ed. by Gerhard Krodel. LC 76-5954. (Proclamation Commentaries: the New Testament Witnesses for Preaching Ser.). 128p. 1976. pap. 4.95 (ISBN 0-8006-0583-7, 1-583). Fortress.
Luke. 2nd, rev. ed. Frederick W. Danker. LC 86-45905. (Proclamation Commentary, New Testament Ser.). 144p. 1987. pap. 7.95 (ISBN 0-8006-0598-5, 1-598). Fortress.
Luke. Lewis A. Foster. (Standard Bible Studies). 336p. 1986. pap. text ed. 9.95 (ISBN 0-87403-163-X, 40103). Standard Pub.
Luke. William Hendriksen. (New Testament Commentary Ser.). 1978. 24.95 (ISBN 0-8010-4191-0). Baker Bk.
Luke. Irving L. Jensen. (Bible Self Study Ser.). 1970. pap. 3.25 (ISBN 0-8024-1042-1). Moody.
Luke. Marilyn Kunz & Catherine Schell. (Neighborhood Bible Studies). 1973. pap. 2.95 (ISBN 0-8423-3880-2). Tyndale.
Luke. Eugene LaVerdiere. (New Testament Message Ser.: Vol. 5). 15.95 (ISBN 0-89453-193-X); pap. 10.95 (ISBN 0-89453-128-X). M Glazier.
Luke. (Erdmans Commentaries Ser.). 4.95 (ISBN 0-8010-3401-9). Baker Bk.
Luke. Duncan Macpherson et al. LC 71-173033. (Scripture Discussion Commentary Ser.: Pt. 8). 192p. 1971. pap. text ed. 4.50 (ISBN 0-87946-007-5). ACTA Found.
Luke. Donald G. Miller. LC 59-10454. (Layman's Bible Commentary Ser.: Vol. 18). 1959. pap. 4.95 (ISBN 0-8042-3078-1). John Knox.
Luke. J. C. Ryle. (Expository Thoughts on the Gospel Ser.: Vol. 2). 530p. 1986. pap. 6.95 (ISBN 0-85151-498-7). Banner of Truth.
Luke. J. C. Ryle. (Expository Thoughts on the Gospel Ser.: Vol. 1). 390p. 1986. pap. 5.95 (ISBN 0-85151-497-9). Banner of Truth.
Luke. David A. Underwood. (Standard Bible Study Workbooks Ser.). 64p. 1986. pap. text ed. 1.95 (ISBN 0-87403-183-4, 40203). Standard Pub.
Luke: A Challenge to Present Theology. Eduard Schwizer. LC 81-85332. 144p. 1982. pap. 10.50 (ISBN 0-8042-0686-4). John Knox.
Luke: A Daily Dialogue with God. Gladys Hunt. (Personal Bible Studyguide Ser.). 192p. (Orig.). 1986. pap. 5.95 (ISBN 0-87788-510-9). Shaw Pubs.
Luke, a Plagiarist. George Rice. (Anchor Ser.). 1984. pap. 6.95 (ISBN 0-8163-0542-0). Pacific Pr Pub Assn.
Luke Acts: A Story of Prophet & People. Luke T. Johnson. LC 81-4520. 65p. 1.75 (ISBN 0-8199-0524-0). Franciscan Herald.
Luke-Acts: The Promise of History. Donald Juel. LC 82-25845. 136p. 1983. pap. 8.95 (ISBN 0-8042-0321-0). John Knox.
Luke: An Access Guide for Scripture Study. Daniel J. Harrington & Edmund F. Gordon. (Access Guides for Scripture Study). 1983. pap. 3.20 (ISBN 0-8215-5929-X); leader's ed. 3.45 (ISBN 0-8215-5934-6). Sadlier.
Luke & the Last Things. A. J. Mattill, Jr. 1979. pap. 8.95 (ISBN 0-915948-03-6). Bks Distinction.
Luke & the Law. S. G. Wilson. LC 83-7263. (Society for New Testament Studies Monograph: No. 50). 200p. 1984. 29.95 (ISBN 0-521-25284-9). Cambridge U Pr.
Luke & the People of God: A New Look at Luke-Acts. Jacob Jervell. LC 72-78565. 208p. 1979. pap. 10.95 (ISBN 0-8066-1730-6, 10-4136). Augsburg.
Luke, Artist & Theologian. Robert J. Karris. LC 84-61030. 144p. (Orig.). 1985. pap. 7.95 (ISBN 0-8091-2651-6). Paulist Pr.
Luke: Doctor-Writer. Robert Brown. (BibLearn Ser.). (Illus.). 1977. bds. 5.95 (ISBN 0-8054-4233-2, 4242-33). Broadman.
Luke: Following Jesus. Sharrel Keyes. (Fisherman Bible Studyguide Ser.). 96p. 1983. pap. 2.95 saddlestitched (ISBN 0-87788-511-7). Shaw Pubs.
Luke: Gospel of the Son of Man. Paul Benware. (Everyman's Bible Commentary Ser.). 1985. pap. 5.95 (ISBN 0-8024-2074-5). Moody.
Luke: Historian & Theologian. I. Howard Marshall. (Contemporary Evangelical Perspective Ser). 1971. kivar 7.95 (ISBN 0-310-28761-8, 10105P). Zondervan.
Luke-John. William G. Scroggie. 1981. pap. 4.95 (ISBN 0-87508-485-0). Chr Lit.
Luke: Study Guide Commentary. Virtus E. Gideon. (Orig.). 1967. pap. 4.95 (ISBN 0-310-24973-2, 9084P). Zondervan.
Luke, the Gospel of God's Man. Keith L. Brooks. (Teach Yourself the Bible Ser.). 1964. pap. 2.75 (ISBN 0-8024-5047-4). Moody.
Luke: The Perennial Spirituality. Leonard Doohan. LC 85-71858. 214p. (Orig.). 1985. pap. 9.95 (ISBN 0-939680-24-6). Bear & Co.
Luke the Theologian: Thirty-Five Years of Research (1950-1985) Francois Bovon. Tr. by Ken McKinney from Fr. (Princeton Theological Monograph Ser.: No. 12). Tr. of Luc la theologien: Vingt-cinq ans de recherches (1950-1975) (Orig.). 1987. pap. price not set (ISBN 0-915138-93-X). Pickwick.
Luke's Story of Jesus. O. C. Edwards, Jr. LC 81-43076. 96p. 1981. pap. 4.50 (ISBN 0-8006-1611-1, 1-1611). Fortress.
Luke's Thrilling Gospel. Ivor Powell. LC 84-9637. 508p. 1984. 18.95 (ISBN 0-8254-3513-7). Kregel.
Luminous Vision: Six Medieval Mystics & Their Teachings. Anne Bancroft. 194p. 1983. text ed. 18.50x (ISBN 0-04-189001-9). Allen Unwin.
Lunation Process. Leyla Rael Rudhyar. pap. 3.95 (ISBN 0-943358-15-9). Aurora Press.
Lure of Divine Love. Norman Pittenger. LC 79-15611. (Orig.). 1979. pap. 6.95 (ISBN 0-8298-0370-X). Pilgrim NY.
Lure of God: A Biblical Background for Process Theism. Lewis S. Ford. 158p. 1985. Repr. of 1978 ed. lib. bdg. 8.75 (ISBN 0-8191-4902-0). U Pr of Amer.
Lure of the Cults. rev. ed. Ronald Enroth. 130p. 1987. pap. 5.95 (ISBN 0-87784-994-3). Inter-Varsity.
Lure of Zion--the Case of the Iraqi Jews. Abbas Shiblak. 178p. 1986. 29.95 (ISBN 0-86356-121-7, Pub. by Al Saqi Bks UK); pap. 9.95 (ISBN 0-86356-033-4, Pub. by Al Saqi Bks UK). Humanities.
Luther. Ed. by William P. Hansen & John Haney. (World Leaders--Past & Present Ser.). (Illus.). 112p. 1986. lib. bdg. 16.95 (ISBN 0-87754-538-3). Chelsea Hse.
Luther. John Osborne. pap. 3.95 (ISBN 0-451-14474-0, Sig). NAL.
Luther: A Life. John Todd. 416p. 1982. 17.50x (ISBN 0-8245-0479-8). Crossroad NY.
Luther: A Reformer for the Churches. Mark Edwards & George Tavard. 1983. pap. 4.95 (ISBN 0-8091-2575-7). Paulist Pr.
Luther: A Reformer for the Churches; An Ecumenical Study Guide. Mark Edwards & George H. Tavard. LC 83-48005. 96p. 1983. pap. 5.50 (ISBN 0-8006-1718-5, 1-1718). Fortress.
Luther: An Experiment in Biography. H. G. Haile. LC 82-48569. 460p. 1983. 31.50x (ISBN 0-691-05374-X); pap. 10.50x (ISBN 0-691-00798-5). Princeton U Pr.
Luther: An Introduction to His Thought. Gerhard Ebeling. Tr. by R. A. Wilson from Ger. LC 77-99612. 288p. 1970. pap. 6.95 (ISBN 0-8006-1162-4, 1-1162). Fortress.
Luther & Erasmus: Free Will & Salvation. Ed. by E. Gordon Rupp & Philip S. Watson. LC 76-79870. (Library of Christian Classics). 356p. 1978. softcover 10.95 (ISBN 0-664-24158-1). Westminster.
Luther & His Spiritual Legacy. Jared Wicks. (Theology & Life Ser.: Vol. 7). pap. 7.95 (ISBN 0-89453-338-X). M Glazier.
Luther & His Times: The Reformation from a New Perspective. Ernest G. Schwiebert. (Illus.). 1950. 24.95 (ISBN 0-570-03246-6, 15-1164). Concordia.
Luther & Late Medieval Thomism: A Study in Theological Anthropology. Denis Janz. 191p. 1984. text ed. 25.00x (ISBN 0-88920-132-3). Humanities.
Luther & Learning: The Wittenberg University Luther Symposium. Marilyn J. Harran. LC 84-40810. (Illus.). 144p. 1985. 19.50 (ISBN 0-941664-13-9, Pub. by Susquehanna U Pr). Assoc Univ Prs.
Luther & Staupitz: An Essay in the Intellectual Origins of the Protestant Reformation. David C. Steinmetz. LC 80-23007. (Duke Monographs in Medieval & Renaissance Studies: No. 4). xi, 149p. 1980. 18.50 (ISBN 0-8223-0447-3). Duke.
Luther & the English Bible. Albert H. Gerberich. LC 83-45643. Date not set. Repr. of 1933 ed. 17.50 (ISBN 0-404-19852-X). AMS Pr.
Luther & the False Brethren. Mark U. Edwards, Jr. LC 75-181. 1975. 20.00x (ISBN 0-8047-0883-5). Stanford U Pr.
Luther & the Germany Reformation. facsimile ed. Thomas M. Lindsay. LC 71-133524. (Select Bibliographies Reprint Ser.). Repr. of 1900 ed. 18.00 (ISBN 0-8369-5556-0). Ayer Co Pubs.
Luther & the Modern State in Germany. James D. Tracy. (Sixteenth Century Essays & Studies: Vol. VII). 110p. 1986. smyth sewn 25.00 (ISBN 0-940474-07-7). Sixteenth Cent.
Luther & the Papacy: Stages in a Reformation Conflict. Scott H. Hendrix. LC 80-2393. pap. 56.30 (2027874). Bks Demand UMI.
Luther & the Peasants' War. Hubert Kirchner. LC 73-171507. (Facet Books-Historical Ser.: No. 22). pap. 20.00 (2027181). Bks Demand UMI.
Luther & the Reformation. Heather Cubitt. Ed. by Marjorie Reeves. (Then & There Ser.). (Illus.). 96p. 1976. pap. text ed. 4.75 (ISBN 0-582-20542-5). Longman.
Luther & the Reformation, 4 vols. James Mackinnon. LC 83-45648. Date not set. Repr. of 1925 ed. Set. 157.50 (ISBN 0-404-19857-0). AMS Pr.
Luther & the Reformation in the Light of Modern Research. Heinrich Boehmer. LC 83-45639. Date not set. Repr. of 1930 ed. 44.50 (ISBN 0-404-19823-6). AMS Pr.
Luther As an Educator. Gustav M. Bruce. LC 77-114482. (Illus.). 318p. Repr. of 1928 ed. lib. bdg. 35.00x (ISBN 0-8371-4771-9, BRLD). Greenwood.
Luther As Interpreter of Scripture. G. S. Robbert. LC 12-2960. 1982. pap. 9.95 (ISBN 0-570-03867-7). Concordia.
Luther: By Those Who Knew Him. Elizabeth R. Charles. 1983. pap. 5.95 (ISBN 0-8024-0314-X). Moody.
Luther: Early Theological Works. Ed. by James Atkinson. LC 62-12358. (Library of Christian Classics). 376p. 1980. pap. 9.95 (ISBN 0-664-24166-2). Westminster.
Luther, Erasmus & Loyola. Peter Amey et al. Ed. by Malcolm Yapp et al. (World History Ser.). (Illus.). 1980. lib. bdg. 6.95 (ISBN 0-89908-043-X); pap. text ed. 2.45 (ISBN 0-89908-018-9). Greenhaven.
Luther, Erasmus & the Reformation: A Catholic-Protestant Reappraisal. Ed. by John C. Olin & James D. Smart. LC 82-15500. x, 150p. 1982. Repr. of 1969 ed. lib. bdg. 22.50x (ISBN 0-313-23652-6, OLLE). Greenwood.
Luther Had a Wife. Jon L. Joyce. (Orig.). 1985. pap. 2.95 (ISBN 0-937172-60-X). JLJ Pubs.
Luther: His Life & Work. Gerhard Ritter. Tr. by John Riches from Ger. LC 78-2717. 1978. Repr. of 1963 ed. lib. bdg. 24.25x (ISBN 0-313-20347-4, RILU). Greenwood.
Luther in Context. David Steinmetz. LC 85-45313. (Midland Bks: No. 405). 160p. 1986. 25.00x (ISBN 0-253-33647-3); pap. 7.95x (ISBN 0-253-20405-4). Ind U Pr.
Luther in Mid-Career, 1521-1530. Heinrich Bornkamm. Tr. by E. Theodore Bachmann from German. LC 82-48591. 736p. 1983. 36.95 (ISBN 0-8006-0692-2, 1-692). Fortress.
Luther in the Light of Recent Research. Heinrich Boehmer. 1977. lib. bdg. 59.95 (ISBN 0-8490-2189-8). Gordon Pr.
Luther Journey. Herb Brokering. (Illus.). 96p. (Orig.). 1983. pap. 6.95 (ISBN 0-942562-02-X). Brokering Pr.
Luther: Lectures on Romans. Ed. by Wilhelm Pauck. LC 61-13626. (Library of Christian Classics). 502p. 1977. pap. 11.95 (ISBN 0-664-24151-4). Westminster.
Luther Legacy: An Introduction to Luther's Life & Thought for Today. George W. Forell. LC 83-72106. 80p. 1983. pap. 5.95 (ISBN 0-8066-2050-1, 10-4142). Augsburg.
Luther on Conversion: The Early Years. Marilyn J. Harran. LC 83-7194. 224p. 1983. 29.95x (ISBN 0-8014-1566-7). Cornell U Pr.
Luther on Justification. Robin A. Leaver. LC 74-11781. 1975. pap. 4.75 (ISBN 0-570-03188-5, 12-2590). Concordia.
Luther on Ministerial Office & Congregational Function. Gert Haendler. Ed. by Eric W. Gritsch. Tr. by Ruth C. Gritsch from Ger. LC 81-43075. Tr. of Amt und Gemeinde bei Luther im Kontext der Kirchengeschichte. 112p. 1981. 9.95 (ISBN 0-8006-0665-5, 1-665). Fortress.
Luther the Expositor. Ed. by Jaroslav Pelikan. 1959. 13.95 (ISBN 0-570-06431-7, 15-1741). Concordia.
Luther the Preacher. Fred W. Meuser. LC 83-72107. 80p. 1983. pap. 5.95 (ISBN 0-8066-2051-X, 10-4147). Augsburg.
Luther the Reformer: The Story of the Man & His Career. James M. Kittelson. LC 86-17266. (Illus.). 320p. 1986. text ed. 24.95 (ISBN 0-8066-2240-7, 10-4148). Augsburg.
Luther: Theologian for the Catholics & Protestants. Ed. by George Yule. 208p. 1985. pap. 12.95 (ISBN 0-567-29119-7, Pub. by T&T Clark Ltd UK). Fortress.
Luther Translator of Paul: Studies in Romans & Galatians. Heinz Bluhm. 580p. 1984. text ed. 49.80 bndg. text (ISBN 0-8204-0186-2). P Lang Pubs.

Luther und der Deutsche Volksaberglaube. Erich Klingner. 18.00 (ISBN 0-384-29830-3); pap. 13.00 (ISBN 0-685-02277-3). Johnson Repr.

Luther: Witness to Jesus Christ: Stages & Themes of the Reformer's Christology. Marc Lienhard. Tr. by Edwin H. Robertson. LC 81-52285. 432p. 1982. text ed. 24.95 (ISBN 0-8066-1917-1, 10-4149). Augsburg.

Lutheran Book of Prayer. rev. ed. LC 76-119916. 1970. 4.50 (ISBN 0-570-03005-6, 6-1141). Concordia.

Lutheran Book of Worship. Inter-Lutheran Commission on Worship. 10.50 (ISBN 0-8006-3330-X). Bd of Pubn LCA.

Lutheran Book of Worship, 7 vols. Incl. Pew Edition. 11.50 (ISBN 0-685-92595-1, 12-2000); Ministers Edition. 65.00 (ISBN 0-685-92596-X, 12-2001); Accompaniment Edition, Liturgy. 22.00 (ISBN 0-685-92597-8, 12-2002); Organist Edition, Hymns. 17.00 (ISBN 0-685-92598-6, 12-2003); Ministers Desk Edition. 18.00 (ISBN 0-685-92599-4, 12-2004); Gift Edition. 15.00 (ISBN 0-686-52336-9, 12-2005); Pocket Edition. 21.00 (ISBN 0-686-52337-7, 12-2006). LC 77-92169. 1978. Augsburg.

Lutheran Book of Worship, 13 Vols. Incl. Pew Edition. 10.50 (ISBN 0-317-12649-0); Ministers Altar Book. 50.00 (ISBN 0-317-12650-4); Minister Desk Edition. 16.50 (ISBN 0-317-12651-2); Accompaniment Edition. 20.00 (ISBN 0-317-12652-0); Organist Edition. 15.00 (ISBN 0-317-12653-9); Gift Edition. 21.50 (ISBN 0-317-12654-7); Pocket Edition. 19.00 (ISBN 0-317-12655-5); Braille Edition. 55.00 (ISBN 0-317-12656-3); Hymns Large. 5.25 (ISBN 0-317-12657-1); Holy Communion. 2.25 (ISBN 0-317-12658-X); Hymnal Companion. 32.50 (ISBN 0-317-12659-8); LBW Occasional Service. 23.50 (ISBN 0-317-12660-1); LBW Large Print. 40.00 (ISBN 0-317-12661-X). LC 77-92160. 1978-84. Fortress.

Lutheran Church in North American Life: 1776-1976, 1580-1980. Ed. by John E. Groh & Robert H. Smith. LC 78-71233. 1979. 5.95 (ISBN 0-915644-17-7, Clayton). Luth Acad.

Lutheran Ethic: The Impact of Religion on Laymen & Clergy. Lawrence K. Kersten. LC 71-102200. 310p. 1970. 25.00x (ISBN 0-8143-1416-3). Wayne St U Pr.

Lutheran Higher Education in North America. Richard W. Solberg. LC 85-28757. 400p. (Orig.). 1985. pap. 9.95 (ISBN 0-8066-2187-7, 10-4168). Augsburg.

Lutheran Historical Conference: Essays & Reports. Concordia Historical Institute Staff & Lutheran Historical Conference Staff. Ed. by August R. Suelflow. 7.50 (ISBN 0-318-04799-3). Concordia Hist.

Lutheran Zion-Pine Church Record, 1786-1827-Stony Creek, Virginia, Vol. I & II. Ed. by Klaus Wust. Tr. by Ilse Martin & George M. Smith. (Shenandoah Genealogical Source Bks.: Nos. 8 & 9). (Illus.). 1985. pap. 15.00 set (ISBN 0-917968-13-1). Vol. I, 49p. Vol. II, 44p. Shenandoah Hist.

Lutheranism in Colonial New York. Harry J. Kreider. LC 78-38452. (Religion in America, Ser. 2). 184p. 1972. Repr. of 1942 ed. 13.00 (ISBN 0-405-04072-5). Ayer Co Pubs.

Lutheranism: The Theological Movement & Its Confessional Writings. Eric W. Gritsch & Robert W. Jenson. LC 76-7869. 228p. 1976. pap. 8.95 (ISBN 0-8006-1246-9, 1-1246). Fortress.

Lutherans & Catholics in Dialogue I-III. Ed. by Paul C. Empie et al. LC 74-83330. 1974. pap. 8.95 (ISBN 0-8066-1451-X, 10-4190). Augsburg.

Lutherans & Catholics in Dialogue: Personal Notes for a Study. Paul C. Empie. Ed. by Raymond Tiemeyer. LC 80-69754. pap. 40.00 (2029612). Bks Demand UMI.

Lutherans & Roman Catholicism: The Changing Conflict, 1917-1963. Myron A. Marty. 1968. 14.95 (ISBN 0-268-00162-6). U of Notre Dame Pr.

Lutherans in North America. rev. ed. Ed. by E. Clifford Nelson. LC 74-26337. (Illus.). 576p. 1980. 22.50x (ISBN 0-8006-0409-1); pap. 16.95 (ISBN 0-8006-1409-7, 1-1409). Fortress.

Lutherpredigten Des Johannes Mathesius. Hans Volz. (Ger). 34.00 (ISBN 0-384-64913-0); pap. 28.00 (ISBN 0-384-64912-2). Johnson Repr.

Luther's Catechism. David P. Kuske. (Illus.). 383p. 1982. text ed. 7.50 (ISBN 0-938272-11-X); pap. 2.50 catechism aid bklet. (ISBN 0-938272-13-6). WELS Board.

Luther's Ecumenical Significance: An Interconfessional Consultation. Ed. by Peter Manns & Harding Meyer. LC 83-48001. 336p. 1983. pap. 24.95 (ISBN 0-8006-1747-9, 1-1747). Fortress.

Luther's English Connection. J. E. McGoldrick. 1979. pap. 7.50 (ISBN 0-8100-0070-9, 15-0368). Northwest Pub.

Luther's Faith: The Cause of the Gospel in the Church. D. Olivier. LC 12-2961. 1982. pap. 13.95 (ISBN 0-570-03868-5). Concordia.

Luther's German Bible. Johann M. Reu. LC 83-45651. Date not set. Repr. of 1934 ed. 75.00 (ISBN 0-404-19860-0). AMS Pr.

Luther's House of Learning: Indoctrination of the Young in the German Reformation. Gerald Strauss. LC 77-18705. pap. 101.30 (ISBN 0-317-20464-5, 2023003). Bks Demand UMI.

Luther's Hymns. James F. Lambert. LC 83-45646. Date not set. Repr. of 1917 ed. 34.50 (ISBN 0-404-19855-4). AMS Pr.

Luther's Large Catechism. Martin Luther. Tr. by J. M. Lenker. 1967. flexible bdg. 6.95 (ISBN 0-8066-0720-3, 10-4211). Augsburg.

Luther's Last Battles: Politics & Polemics, 1531-1546. Mark U. Edwards, Jr. LC 82-72363. (Illus.). 272p. 1986. pap. text ed. 9.95x (ISBN 0-8014-9393-5). Cornell U Pr.

Luther's Last Battles: Politics & Polemics, 1531-46. Mark U. Edwards, Jr. 272p. 1983. 24.95x (ISBN 0-8014-1564-0). Cornell U Pr.

Luther's Ninety-Five Theses. Martin Luther. Tr. by C. M. Jacobs. 1957. pap. 0.95 (ISBN 0-8006-1265-5, 1-1265). Fortress.

Luther's Ninety-Five Theses. E. G. Schwiebert. pap. 0.75 (ISBN 0-570-03519-8, 14-1253). Concordia.

Luther's Pastors: The Reformation in the Ernestine Countryside. Susan C. Karant-Nunn. LC 79-51539. (Transactions Ser.: Vol. 69, Pt. 8). 1979. 8.00 (ISBN 0-87169-698-3). Am Philos.

Luthers Prayers. Ed. by Herbert F. Brokering. Tr. by Charles E. Kistler. LC 67-25366. 1967. lea. bdg. 7.95 (ISBN 0-8066-0721-1, 10-4231). Augsburg.

Luther's Table Talk. Preserved Smith. LC 78-127457. (Columbia University Studies in the Social Sciences: No. 69). 1970. Repr. of 1907 ed. 14.50 (ISBN 0-404-51069-8). AMS Pr.

Luther's Theological Development from Erfurt to Augsburg. Albert Hyma. LC 76-137247. Repr. of 1928 ed. 12.50 (ISBN 0-404-03479-9). AMS Pr.

Luther's Theology of the Cross. Regin Prenter. Ed. by Charles S. Anderson. LC 71-152368. (Facet Bks.). 32p. 1971. pap. 2.50 (ISBN 0-8006-3062-9, 1-3062). Fortress.

Luther's Theology of the Cross. Walter Von Loewenich. Tr. by Herbert J. Bouman. LC 75-2845. 224p. (Orig.). 1982. pap. 10.95 (ISBN 0-8066-1490-0, 10-4233). Augsburg.

Luther's Theology of the Cross: Martin Luther on Justification 1509-1519. Alister E. McGrath. 224p. 1985. 34.95x (ISBN 0-631-13855-2). Basil Blackwell.

Luther's Variations in Sentence Arrangement From the Modern Literary Usage With Primary Reference to the Position of the Verb. Paul Curts. 1910. 39.50x (ISBN 0-686-83611-1). Elliots Bks.

Luther's View of Church History. John M. Headley. 1963. 49.50x (ISBN 0-686-51413-0). Elliots Bks.

Luthers Werke, 4 vols. Martin Luther. (Ger.). 1920p. 1982. Set. pap. 67.50 (ISBN 3-11-008942-4). De Gruyter.

Luthers Werke in Auswahl, 8 vols. Martin Luther. Ed. by Otto Clemen. Incl. Vol. 1. Schriften von 1517 bis 1520. 6th rev. ed. (Illus.). xxxii, 512p. 1966. 20.00x (ISBN 3-11-003152-3); Vol. 2. Schriften von 1520 bis 1524. 6th rev. ed. vi, 464p. 1967. 20.00x (ISBN 3-11-003153-1); Vol. 3. Schriften von 1524 bis 1528. 6th rev. ed. vi, 516p. 1966. 20.00x (ISBN 3-11-003154-X); Vol. 4. Schriften von 1529 bis 1545. 6th rev. ed. vi, 428p. 1967. 20.00x (ISBN 3-11-003151-5); Vol. 5. Junge Luther. 3rd rev. ed. Ed. by Erich Vogelsang. xi, 434p. 1963. 22.10 (ISBN 3-11-005609-7); Vol. 6. Luthers Briefe. 3rd rev. ed. Ed. by Hanns Rueckert. xv, 451p. 1966. 22.10x (ISBN 3-11-005610-0); Vol. 7. Predigten. 3rd ed. Ed. by Emanuel Hirsch. xii, 420p. 1962. 22.10x (ISBN 3-11-005611-9); Vol. 8. Tischreden. 3rd ed. Ed. by Otto Clemen. x, 387p. 1962. 22.10 (ISBN 3-11-005612-7). De Gruyter.

Luther's Works, Vol. 6. Tr. by Paul D. Pahl. LC 55-9893. 1969. 16.95 (ISBN 0-570-06406-6, 15-1748). Concordia.

Luther's Works, Vol 7. Tr. by Paul D. Pahl. LC 55-9893. 1964. 15.95 (ISBN 0-570-06407-4, 15-1749). Concordia.

Luther's Works, Vol. 9. Ed. by Jaroslav Pelikan. LC 55-9893. 1960. 14.95 (ISBN 0-570-06409-0, 15-1751). Concordia.

Luther's Works, Vol. 11. Ed. by Hilton Oswald. Tr. by Herbert J. Bowman from Lat. LC 55-9893. 560p. 1976. 17.95 (ISBN 0-570-06411-2, 15-1753). Concordia.

Luther's Works, Vol. 12 Psalms. Martin Luther. LC 55-9893. 1955. 15.95 (ISBN 0-570-06412-0, 15-1754). Concordia.

Luther's Works, Vol. 14 Selected Psalms 3. Martin Luther. LC 55-9893. 1958. 14.95 (ISBN 0-570-06414-7, 15-1756). Concordia.

Luther's Works, Vol. 15, Letters On Ecclesiastes, Song Of Solomon, & The Last Words Of David. Tr. by Jaroslav Pelikan et al from Lat. LC 55-9893. 1971. 15.95 (ISBN 0-570-06415-5, 15-1757). Concordia.

Luther's Works, Vol. 16. Tr. by Herbert J. Bouman. 1968. 14.95 (ISBN 0-570-06416-3, 15-1758). Concordia.

Luther's Works, Vol. 17. Martin Luther. Tr. by Herbert J. Bouman. LC 55-9893. 1972. 16.95 (ISBN 0-570-06417-1, 15-1759). Concordia.

Luther's Works, Vol. 20. Tr. by W. M. Miller & R. J. Dinda. LC 55-9893. 300p. 1973. 14.95 (ISBN 0-570-06420-1, 15-1762). Concordia.

Luther's Works, Vol. 21. Ed. by Jaroslav Pelikan. LC 55-9893. 16.95 (ISBN 0-570-06421-X, 15-1763). Concordia.

Luther's Works, Vol. 22. Ed. by Jaroslav Pelikan. Tr. by Martin Bertram. LC 55-9893. 1957. 17.95 (ISBN 0-570-06422-8, 15-1764). Concordia.

Luther's Works, Vol. 23. Tr. by Martin H. Bertram. LC 55-9893. 1958. 16.95 (ISBN 0-570-06423-6, 15-1765). Concordia.

Luther's Works, Vol. 24. Ed. by Jaroslav Pelikan. Tr. by Martin H. Bertram. LC 55-9893. 1961. 16.95 (ISBN 0-570-06424-4, 15-1766). Concordia.

Luther's Works, Vol. 28. Martin Luther. LC 55-9893. 1973. 15.95 (ISBN 0-570-06428-7, 15-1770). Concordia.

Luther's Works, Vol. 29. 1968. 13.95 (ISBN 0-570-06429-5, 15-1771). Concordia.

Luther's Works: Career of the Reformer I, Vol. 31. Ed. by Harold J. Grimm & Helmut T. Lehmann. LC 55-9893. 1957. 19.95 (ISBN 0-8006-0331-1, 1-331). Fortress.

Luther's Works: Career of the Reformer II, Vol. 32. Ed. by George W. Forell & Helmut T. Lehmann. LC 55-9893. 1958. 19.95 (ISBN 0-8006-0332-X, 1-332). Fortress.

Luther's Works: Career of the Reformer III, Vol. 33. new ed. Ed. by Philip S. Watson & Helmut T. Lehmann. LC 55-9893. 1972. 19.95 (ISBN 0-8006-0333-8, 1-333). Fortress.

Luther's Works: Career of the Reformer IV, Vol. 34. Ed. by Lewis W. Spitz & Helmut T. Lehmann. LC 55-9893. 1960. 19.95 (ISBN 0-8006-0334-6, 1-334). Fortress.

Luther's Works: Catholic Epistles, Vol. 30. Martin Luther. Ed. by Jaroslav Pelikan. LC 55-9893. 1967. 14.95 (ISBN 0-570-06430-9, 15-1772). Concordia.

Luther's Works: Church & Ministry I, Vol. 39. Ed. by Eric W. Gritsch & Helmut T. Lehmann. LC 55-9893. 1970. 19.95 (ISBN 0-8006-0339-7, 1-339). Fortress.

Luther's Works: Church & Ministry II, Vol. 40. Ed. by Conrad Bergendoff & Helmut H. Lehman. LC 55-9893. 1958. 19.95 (ISBN 0-8006-0340-0, 1-340). Fortress.

Luther's Works: Church & Ministry III, Vol. 41. Ed. by Helmut T. Lehmann & Eric W. Gritsch. LC 55-9893. 1966. 19.95 (ISBN 0-8006-0341-9, 1-341). Fortress.

Luther's Works: Devotional Writings I, Vol. 42. Ed. by Martin O. Dietrich & Helmut T. Lehmann. LC 55-9893. (Prog. Bk.). 1969. 19.95 (ISBN 0-8006-0342-7, 1-342). Fortress.

Luther's Works: Devotional Writings II, Vol. 43. Ed. by Gustav K. Wiencke & Helmut T. Lehman. LC 55-9893. 1968. 19.95 (ISBN 0-8006-0343-5, 1-343). Fortress.

Luther's Works: Genesis Chapters 1-5, Vol. 1. Ed. by Jaroslav Pelikan. Tr. by George V. Schick. LC 55-9893. 1958. 15.95 (ISBN 0-570-06401-5, 15-1743). Concordia.

Luther's Works: Genesis Chapters 15-20, Vol. 3. Ed. by Jaroslav Pelikan. Tr. by George V. Schick. LC 55-9893. 1961. 15.95 (ISBN 0-570-06403-1, 15-1745). Concordia.

Luther's Works: Genesis Chapters 21-25, Vol. 4. Tr. by G. V. Schick. LC 55-9893. 1964. 16.95 (ISBN 0-570-06404-X, 15-1746). Concordia.

Luther's Works: Genesis Chapters 26-30, Vol. 5. LC 55-9893. 1967. 15.95 (ISBN 0-570-06405-8, 15-1747). Concordia.

Luther's Works: Genesis Chapters 45-50, Vol. 8. Tr. by Paul D. Pahl. LC 55-9893. 1965. 14.95 (ISBN 0-570-06408-2, 15-1750). Concordia.

Luther's Works: Genesis Chapters 6-11, Vol. 2. Ed. by Jaroslav Pelikan. Tr. by George V. Schick. LC 55-9893. 1960. 16.95 (ISBN 0-570-06402-3, 15-1744). Concordia.

Luther's Works-Index. Ed. by Joel W. Lundeen. LC 86-45197. 512p. 1986. 24.95 (ISBN 0-8006-0355-9). Fortress.

Luther's Works: Index. Ed. by Joel W. Lundeen. through 12/31/86 19.95 (ISBN 0-317-52515-8, 1-355). Fortress.

Luther's Works: Lectures on Galatians, Vols. 26 & 27. Martin Luther. Incl. Vol. 26. Ed. by Jaroslav Pelikan. 1962; Vol. 27. Ed. by Jaroslav Pelikan. Tr. by Richard Jungkuntz. 1963. 16.95 (ISBN 0-570-06427-9, 15-1769). LC 55-9893. 16.95 (ISBN 0-570-06426-0, 15-1768). Concordia.

Luther's Works: Lectures on Romans Glosses & Scholia, Vol. 25. Martin Luther. LC 55-9893. (Luther's Works). 1972. 17.95 (ISBN 0-570-06425-2, 15-1767). Concordia.

Luther's Works: Lectures on the Minor Prophets, 2: Jonah & Habakkuk, Vol. 19. Ed. by H. Oswald. LC 55-9893. 1974. 13.95 (ISBN 0-570-06419-8, 15-1761). Concordia.

Luther's Works: Letters I, Vol. 48. Ed. by Gottfried G. Krodel & Helmut T. Lehman. LC 55-9893. 1963. 19.95 (ISBN 0-8006-0348-6). Fortress.

Luther's Works: Letters II, Vol. 49. Ed. & tr. by Krodel. LC 55-9893. 480p. 1972. 19.95 (ISBN 0-8006-0349-4, 1-349). Fortress.

Luther's Works: Letters III, Vol. 50. Ed. by Gottfried G. Krodel & Helmut T. Lehmann. LC 74-76934. 416p. 1975. 19.95 (ISBN 0-8006-0350-8, 1-350). Fortress.

Luther's Works: Liturgy & Hymns, Vol. 53. Ed. by Ulrich S. Leupold & Helmut T. Lehmann. LC 55-9893. 1965. 19.95 (ISBN 0-8006-0353-2, 1-353). Fortress.

Luther's Works: Selected Psalms 2, Vol. 13. Martin Luther. Ed. by Jaroslav Pelikan. LC 55-9893. 1956. 16.95 (ISBN 0-570-06413-9, 15-1755). Concordia.

Luther's Works: Sermons I, Vol. 51. Ed. by Helmut T. Lehmann & John W. Doberstein. Tr. by John W. Doberstein. LC 55-9893. 1959. 19.95 (ISBN 0-8006-0351-6, 1-353). Fortress.

Luther's Works: Sermons II, Vol. 52. Ed. by Hans J. Hillerbrand & Helmut T. Lehmann. LC 55-9893. 416p. 1974. 19.95 (ISBN 0-8006-0352-4, 1-352). Fortress.

Luther's Works: Table Talk, Vol. 54. Ed. by Theodore G. Tappert & Helmut T. Lehmann. Tr. by Theodore G. Tappert. LC 55-9893. 1967. 19.95 (ISBN 0-8006-0354-0, 1-354). Fortress.

Luther's Works: The Christian in Society I, Vol. 44. Ed. by Helmut T. Lehmann & James Atkinson. LC 55-9893. 1966. 19.95 (ISBN 0-8006-0344-3, 1-344). Fortress.

Luther's Works: The Christian in Society II, Vol. 45. Ed. by Walter I. Brandt & Helmut T. Lehmann. LC 55-9893. 1962. 19.95 (ISBN 0-8006-0345-1, 1-345). Fortress.

Luther's Works: The Christian in Society III, Vol. 46. Ed. by Robert C. Schultz & Helmut T. Lehmann. LC 55-9893. 1967. 19.95 (ISBN 0-8006-0346-X, 1-346). Fortress.

Luther's Works: The Christian in Society IV, Vol. 47. Ed. by Franklin Sherman & Helmut T. Lehman. LC 55-9893. 1971. 19.95 (ISBN 0-8006-0347-8, 1-347). Fortress.

Luther's Works, Vol. 10. Tr. by H. J. Bouman. 1981. 16.95 (ISBN 0-570-06410-4, 15-1752). Concordia.

Luther's Works, Vol. 18. Tr. by R. J. Dinda. 1980. 16.95 (ISBN 0-570-06418-X, 15-1760). Concordia.

Luther's Works: Word & Sacrament I, Vol. 35. Ed. by Theodore Bachmann & Helmut T. Lehmann. LC 55-9893. 426p. 1960. 19.95 (ISBN 0-8006-0335-4, 1-335). Fortress.

Luther's Works: Word & Sacrament II, Vol. 36. Ed. by Abdel R. Wentz & Lehmann. LC 55-9893. 400p. 1959. 19.95 (ISBN 0-8006-0336-2, 1-336). Fortress.

Luther's Works: Word & Sacrament III, Vol. 37. Ed. by Robert H. Fischer & Helmut T. Lehmann. LC 55-9893. 1961. 19.95 (ISBN 0-8006-0337-0, 1-337). Fortress.

Luther's Works: Word & Sacrament IV, Vol. 38. Ed. by Martin E. Lehman & Helmut T. Lehman. LC 55-9893. 1971. 19.95 (ISBN 0-8006-0338-9, 1-338). Fortress.

Luz Diaria Para el Camino Diario. 284p. 1984. pap. 5.50 (ISBN 0-311-40045-0). Casa Bautista.

Luz Que No Se Apaga. Mirtha F. Siccardi. Tr. of Bright Light. (Span.). 256p. 1983. pap. 4.75 (ISBN 0-8254-1665-5). Kregel.

Lycidas: A Monograph. W. Tuckwell. LC 77-22476. 1911. lib. bdg. 10.00 (ISBN 0-8414-8588-7). Folcroft.

Lying. Dan Carr. (God I Need to Talk to You About...Ser.). (Illus.). 1984. pap. 0.75 (ISBN 0-570-08732-5, 56-1476). Concordia.

Lying...Not a Very Fun Thing. Gloria G. Morrell. 1986. pap. 3.95 (ISBN 0-8054-4338-X). Broadman.

Lyman Beecher & the Reform of Society: Four Sermons, 1804-1828. Lyman Beecher. LC 71-38437. (Religion in America Series Two). 214p. 1972. Repr. of 1972 ed. 19.00 (ISBN 0-405-04058-X). Ayer Co Pubs.

Lyric Psalms: Half a Psalter. Francis P. Sullivan. (Illus.). 192p. (Orig.). 1983. pap. 5.95 (ISBN 0-9602378-8-7). Pastoral Pr.

Lyric Religion: The Romance of Immortal Hymns. H. Augustine Smith. 517p. Repr. of 1931 ed. lib. bdg. 75.00 (ISBN 0-918377-84-6). Russell Pr.

Lytle Treatise of the Maner & Forme of Confession. Desiderius Erasmus. LC 79-39487. (English Experience Ser.: No. 553). (Illus.). 232p. 1973. Repr. of 1535 ed. 16.00 (ISBN 90-221-0553-9). Walter J Johnson.

Lzhe-Pravoslavije na podjomje. Tr. of False-Orthodoxy on the Rise. 212p. 1954. pap. 7.00 (ISBN 0-317-30370-8). Holy Trinity.

M

M. Derings Workes: More at Large Than Ever Hath Heer-to-Fore Been Printed, 3 pts. Edward Dering. LC 74-38171. (English Experience Ser.: No. 448). 692p. 1972. Repr. of 1597 ed. 95.00 (ISBN 90-221-0448-6). Walter J Johnson.

Ma alim fi at-Tariq. Sayyid Qutb. (Arabic.). 186p. (Orig.). 1978. pap. 3.75x (ISBN 0-939830-17-5, Pub. by IIFSO Kuwait). New Era Pubns MI.

Ma-Ha-Bone: Ritual. E. Ronayne. 11.00x (ISBN 0-685-22019-2). Wehman.

Maasaw: Profile of a Hopi God. Ekkehart Malotki & Michael Lomatuway'ma. LC 87-163. (American Tribal Religions Ser.: Vol. 11). (Illus.). vi, 432p. 1987. 24.95x (ISBN 0-8032-3118-0); pap. 14.95x (ISBN 0-8032-8148-X, Bison). U of Nebr Pr.

Ma'aseh Book: Book of Jewish Tales & Legends. Tr. by Moses Gaster from Judeo-German. LC 81-80356. 694p. 1981. pap. 10.95 (ISBN 0-8276-0189-1, 471). Jewish Pubns.

Maaser Kesafim. 1982. 9.95 (ISBN 0-87306-238-8). Feldheim.

Mabinogion. Charlotte Guest. (Illus.). 504p. 1978. pap. 9.95 (ISBN 0-89733-000-5). Academy Chi Pubs.

Mabon & the Mysteries of Britain. Caitlin Matthews. 256p. 1987. pap. 11.95 (ISBN 1-85063-052-6, 30526, Ark Paperbks). Methuen Inc.

M'aleph V'ad Tav: Spirit Duplicating Primer. Avivia Langsam. text ed. 15.00 (ISBN 0-915152-02-9, A04). Torah Umesorah.

Maccabees One. Tr. & intro. by Jonathan A. Goldstein. LC 75-32719. (Anchor Bible Ser.: Vol. 41). (Illus.). 18.00 (ISBN 0-385-08533-8, Anchor Pr). Doubleday.

McCarthyism: The Seed Is in Us. James E. Bristol. 1983. pap. 2.50x (ISBN 0-87574-076-6, 076). Pendle Hill.

MacDonald Presentation Volume: A Tribute to Duncan Black Macdonald, Consisting of Articles by Former Students, Presented to Him on His Seventieth Birthday, April 9, 1933. facs. ed. LC 68-22109. (Essay Index Reprint Ser.). 1933. 24.25 (ISBN 0-8369-0645-4). Ayer Co Pubs.

Machiavelli's Thoughts on the Management of Men. Niccolo Machiavelli. (Illus.). 119p. 1982. 107.50 (ISBN 0-89266-364-2). Am Classical Coll Pr.

Machzorim-Rosh Hashana & Yom Kippur. 1982. 9.00 (ISBN 0-686-76540-0). Feldheim.

Mackey's Jurisprudence of Freemasonry. Albert G. Mackey. 1985. Repr. 12.75 (ISBN 0-88053-026-X). Macoy Pub.

Mackintosh Treasury: Miscellaneous Writings of C. H. Mackintosh. rev. ed. C. H. Mackintosh. LC 75-44323. 1976. 6 vols. in 1 19.95 (ISBN 0-87213-609-4). Loizeaux.

Macknight on the Epistles. James Macknight. 784p. 1984. Repr. of 1966 ed. 24.95 (ISBN 0-8010-6031-1). Baker Bk.

Macmillan Atlas History of Christianity. Franklin H. Littell. LC 75-22113. (Illus.). 176p. 1976. 24.95 (ISBN 0-02-573140-8, 57314). Macmillan.

Macmillan Atlas of the Holocaust. Martin Gilbert. (Quality Paperbacks Ser.). (Illus.). 256p. 1984. pap. 13.95 (ISBN 0-306-80218-X). Da Capo.

Macmillan Bible Atlas. rev. ed. Yohanon Aharoni & Michael Avi-Yonah. LC 77-4313. (Illus.). 183p. 1977. 25.95 (ISBN 0-02-500590-1). Macmillan.

Macmillan Book of Greek Gods & Heroes. Alice Low. LC 85-7170. (Illus.). 192p. 1985. 15.95 (ISBN 0-02-761390-9). Macmillan.

Macoy's Short Addresses & Ceremonies for Matron's Use. Vee Hansen et al. 24p. 1983. pap. 1.50 (ISBN 0-88053-330-7). Macoy Pub.

Macoy's Short Addresses for Matron: Forty-Five Sentiments. Vee Hansen & Opal Shaw. 28p. 1975. pap. 1.50 (ISBN 0-88053-329-3, S-83). Macoy Pub.

Macro Plays. Ed. by David M. Bevington. LC 72-3905. 1972. 50.00 (ISBN 0-384-34920-X). Johnson Repr.

Macro Plays: The Castle of Perseverance, Wisdom, Mankind. Ed. by Mark Eccles. (Early English Text Society Ser.). 1969. 17.95x (ISBN 0-19-722265-X). Oxford U Pr.

Macrocosm & Microcosm. Rudolf Steiner. Tr. of Makrokosmos und Mikosmos. Seelenfragen, Lebensfragen, Geistesfragen. 205p. 1986. 20.00 (ISBN 0-88010-201-2); pap. 10.95 (ISBN 0-88010-200-4). Anthroposophic.

Mac's Giant Book of Quips & Quotes. E. C. McKenzie. 1983. pap. 12.95 (ISBN 0-8010-6164-4). Baker Bk.

Madagascar & the Protestant Impact. Bonar A. Gow. LC 78-11216. (Dalhousie African Studies). 256p. 1980. text ed. 49.50x (ISBN 0-8419-0463-4, Africana). Holmes & Meier.

Madagascar & the Protestant Impact: The Work of the British Missions, 1818-95. Bonar A. Gow. (Dalhousie African Studies Ser.). pap. 71.00 (ISBN 0-317-27749-9, 2025229). Bks Demand UMI.

Madame Jeanne Guyon: Child of Another World. Dorothy Coslet. 219p. (Orig.). 1984. pap. 3.95 (ISBN 0-87508-144-4). Chr Lit.

Made According to Pattern. Charles W. Slemming. 1964. pap. 2.95 (ISBN 0-87508-506-7). Chr Lit.

Made for Each Other: Devotions for Newly Married Couples. Roy Gesch. 112p. 1987. pap. 4.95 (ISBN 0-570-04453-7, 12-3059). Concordia.

Made in God's Image. Del Olsen. 128p. (Orig.). 1986. pap. 5.95 (ISBN 0-310-46381-5, 18382P). Zondervan.

Made in Heaven. Carlo Carretto. 4.95 (ISBN 0-87193-135-4). Dimension Bks.

Made, Not Born: New Perspectives on Christian Initiation & the Catechumenate. Murphy Center for Liturgical Research. 192p. 1976. pap. 6.95 (ISBN 0-268-01337-3). U of Notre Dame Pr.

Made to Be Mastered: Managing Your Emotions Successfully--God's Way. Jon T. Murphree. 126p. (YA) 1984. pap. 5.95 (ISBN 0-8010-6169-5). Baker Bk.

Made to Grow. Annelle Harty & Robert Harty. (Sexuality in Christian Living Ser.). 32p. 1973. 6.95 (ISBN 0-8054-4222-7). Broadman.

Madera: The Rich, Colorful & Exciting Historical Heritage of That Area Now Known As Madera County, California. Charles W. Clough. (Illus.). 108p. 1983. casebound 14.95 (ISBN 0-317-44752-1); pap. 9.95 (ISBN 0-317-44753-X). Panorama West.

Madha Khasira al-Alam bi-Inhtat al-Muslimin. 4th ed. Abul H. Nadawi. (Arabic.). 432p. (Orig.). 1978. pap. 8.50x (ISBN 0-939830-14-0, Pub. by IIFSO Kuwait). New Era Pubns MI.

Madhusudan Saraswati on the Bhagavaddita. S. K. Gupta. 1977. 28.00 (ISBN 0-89684-246-0, Pub. by Motilal Banarsidass India). Orient Bk Dist.

Madhyantavibhagatika: An Analysis of the Middle Path & the Extremes. Sthiramati Maitreya. Tr. by David L. Friedman from Sanskrit. 154p. 1984. Repr. of 1937 ed. lib. bdg. 19.50x (ISBN 0-88181-004-5). Canon Pubns.

Madman of Ch'u: The Chinese Myth of Loyalty & Dissent. Laurence A. Schneider. LC 78-54800. (Center for Chinese Studies). 1980. 35.95x (ISBN 0-520-03685-9). U of Cal Pr.

Madman's Guide to Enlightenment. Bhagwan Shree Rajneesh. Ed. by Ma Prem Maneesha. (Initiation Talks Ser.). (Illus.). 388p. (Orig.). 1980. pap. 18.95 (ISBN 0-88050-593-1). Chidvilas Found.

Madonna. (Illus.). 64p. (Orig.). 1984. 19.95 (ISBN 0-86683-827-9, 8467, HarpR); pap. 9.95 (ISBN 0-86683-812-0, 8291). Har-Row.

Madonna in the Paintings of the Great Masters. Marcel Belvianes. (Illus.). 1980. Repr. 107.50 (ISBN 0-89901-010-5). Found Class Reprints.

Madonna: Mary in the Catholic Tradition. Rev. Frederick K. Jelly. LC 86-61598. 210p. (Orig.). 1986. pap. 7.50 (ISBN 0-87973-536-8, 536). Our Sunday Visitor.

Madonna of One Hundred Fifteenth Street: Faith & Community in Italian Harlem, 1880 to 1950. Robert A. Orsi. LC 85-10799. (Illus.). 366p. 1985. 29.95x (ISBN 0-300-03262-5). Yale U Pr.

Madonna or Courtesan: The Jewish Woman in Christian Literature. Livia Bitton-Jackson. 160p. 1983. pap. 7.95 (ISBN 0-8164-2440-3, HarpR). Har-Row.

Maestro de Dolores. Robert Lazear. (Span., Illus.). 342p. (Orig.). 1979. pap. 4.50 (ISBN 0-89922-138-6). Edit Caribe.

Maftechoth Hamidrash Rabba: Keys to the Midrash Rabba. 35.00 (ISBN 0-87559-159-0). Shalom.

Mag. Johannis Hus Tractatus Responsiyus. Jan Hus. LC 78-63201. (Heresies of the Early Christian & Medieval Era: Second Ser.). Repr. of 1927 ed. 34.50 (ISBN 0-404-16229-0). AMS Pr.

Maggid of Dubno & His Parables. rev ed. Benno Heineman. 1978. 11.95 (ISBN 0-87306-156-X). Feldheim.

Maggidim & Hasidim: Their Wisdom. Ed. by Louis I. Newman. 1962. 14.95x (ISBN 0-8197-0161-0). Bloch.

Maggie Kuhn on Aging. Margaret E. Kuhn. Ed. by Dieter Hessel. LC 77-24294. 140p. 1977. pap. 3.95 (ISBN 0-664-24146-8). Westminster.

Maggiorino. Stephen Lamera. 1976. pap. 1.75 (ISBN 0-8198-0437-1). Dghtrs St Paul.

Magian Gospel of Brother Yeshua. Charles C. Wise, Jr. LC 79-84277. (Illus.). 306p. 1979. 11.95 (ISBN 0-917023-05-6); pap. 5.95 (ISBN 0-917023-06-4). Magian Pr.

Magic & Meaning of Voodoo. Barbara Christesen. LC 77-12781. (Myth, Magic & Superstition Ser.). (Illus.). 1977. PLB 14.65 (ISBN 0-8172-1030-X). Raintree Pubs.

Magic & Music: The Language of the Gods Revealed. Juanita Wescott. LC 85-71700. (Illus.). 145p. (Orig.). 1983. pap. 7.95 (ISBN 0-913407-00-3). Abbetira Pubns.

Magic & Religion. Andrew Lang. 59.95 (ISBN 0-8490-0576-0). Gordon Pr.

Magic & Religion. Andrew Lang. Repr. of 1901 ed. lib. bdg. 22.50x (ISBN 0-8371-0933-7, LAMR). Greenwood.

Magic & the Qabbalah. W. E. Butler. 1972. pap. 8.95 (ISBN 0-85030-155-6). Weiser.

Magic Background of Modern Anti-Semitism. Adolf Leschnitzer. LC 55-6501. x, 236p. (Orig.). pap. text ed. 12.95 (ISBN 0-8236-8134-3). Intl Univs Pr.

Magic Carpet: Aleppo in Flatbush: The Story of a Unique Ethnic Jewish Community. 3rd ed. Joseph A. D. Sutton. LC 79-65516. (Illus.). 336p. 1986. text ed. 19.95x (ISBN 0-686-27080-0). Thayer-Jacoby.

Magic Cauldron: Witchcraft for Good & Evil. Margaret O'Connell. LC 75-26757. (Illus.). 256p. 1975. 15.95 (ISBN 0-87599-187-4). S G Phillips.

Magic Dance: The Display of the Self-Nature of the Five Wisdom Dakinis. rev. ed. Thinley Norbu. LC 85-59. 166p. (Orig.). 1981. pap. 10.00 (ISBN 0-9607000-0-5). Jewel Pub Hse.

Magic in Your Mind. Uell S. Andersen. pap. 7.00 (ISBN 0-87980-089-5). Wilshire.

Magic Monastery. Idries Shah. 208p. 1972. 16.95 (ISBN 0-900860-89-8, Pub. by Octagon Pr England). Ins Study Human.

Magic, Myth & Medicine. John Camp. LC 73-18793. 200p. 1974. 8.50 (ISBN 0-8008-5046-7). Taplinger.

Magic of Faith. Joseph Murphy. pap. 1.50 (ISBN 0-87516-291-6). De Vorss.

Magic People. Arland Ussher. 12.95 (ISBN 0-8159-6200-2). Devin.

Magic Power of Witchcraft. Frost & Frost. 1977. 14.95 (ISBN 0-13-545376-3, Reward); pap. 5.95 (ISBN 0-13-545368-2). P-H.

Magic Power of Your Mind. Walter M. Germain. pap. 7.00 (ISBN 0-87980-093-3). Wilshire.

Magic, Witchcraft, & Religion. Arthur C. Lehmann & James E. Myers. (Illus.). 416p. 1985. pap. text ed. 22.95 (ISBN 0-87484-685-4). Mayfield Pub.

Magical Jewels of the Middle Ages & the Renaissance Particularly in England. Joan Evans. LC 75-26288. (Illus.). 288p. 1976. pap. 5.95 (ISBN 0-486-23367-7). Dover.

Magical Rites from the Crystal Well. Ed Fitch & Janine Renee. Ed. by Carl L. Weschcke. LC 83-80134. (Practical Magick Ser.). (Illus.). 166p. 1984. pap. 9.95 (ISBN 0-87542-230-6, L-230). Llewellyn Pubns.

Magician, the Witch & the Law. Edward Peters. LC 78-51341. (Middle Ages Ser.). 1982. 23.50x (ISBN 0-8122-7746-5); pap. 9.95x (ISBN 0-8122-1101-4). U of Pa Pr.

Magick & the Law: Or, How to Set-Up & Operate Your Own Occult Shop. Nelson H. White. LC 80-50273. (Magick & the Law Ser.: Vol. 5). (Illus.). 85p. (Orig.). 1982. pap. 15.00 (ISBN 0-939856-31-X). Tech Group.

Magickal Qaballah. Frater Zarathustra. LC 86-50965. (Illus.). 75p. (Orig.). 1986. pap. 15.00 (ISBN 0-939856-63-8). Tech Group.

Magie dans L'Inde Antique: Paris, 1904. Victor Henry. LC 78-74261. (Oriental Religions Ser.: Vol. 5). 325p. 1980. lib. bdg. 40.00 (ISBN 0-8240-3903-3). Garland Pub.

Magisterium: Teaching Authority in the Catholic Church. Francis A. Sullivan. 1984. pap. 9.95 (ISBN 0-8091-2577-3). Paulist Pr.

Magna Carta Latina: The Privilege of Singing, Articulating & Reading a Language & Keeping It Alive. 2nd ed. Eugen Rosenstock-Huessy & Ford L. Battles. LC 75-23378. (Pittsburgh Reprint Ser.: No. 1). 1975. pap. text ed. 9.95 (ISBN 0-915138-07-7). Pickwick.

Magna Charta of the Christian Church. Karl F. Althoff. Tr. by Werner Grimm from Ger. 19p. 1982. pap. 3.00 (ISBN 0-919924-15-8, Pub. by Steiner Book Centre Canada). Anthroposophic.

Magna Charta of Woman. Jessie Penn-Lewis. LC 75-28655. 112p. 1975. pap. 3.50 (ISBN 0-87123-377-0, 200377). Bethany Hse.

Magna Vita Sancti Hugonis: The Life of St. Hugh of Lincoln. Ed. by Decima L. Douie & David H. Farmer. (Medieval Texts Ser.). (Illus.). 1985. Vol. I. 45.00x (ISBN 0-19-822207-6); Vol. II. 45.00x (ISBN 0-19-822208-4). Oxford U Pr.

Magnalia Christi Americana, Bks. I & II In 1 vol. Cotton Mather. Ed. by Kenneth B. Murdock. (John Harvard Library). 512p. 1976. text ed. 35.00x (ISBN 0-674-54155-3, Belknap Pr). Harvard U Pr.

Magnalia Christi Americana, or the Ecclesiastical History of New-England from the Year 1620, Unto the Year 1698, 7 Bks. Cotton Mather. LC 74-141092. (Research Library of Colonial Americana). (Illus.). 1971. Repr. of 1702 ed. Set. 58.00 (ISBN 0-405-03297-8). Ayer Co Pubs.

Magnalia Christi Americana: Or the Ecclesiastical History of New England. Cotton Mather. Ed. by Raymond J. Cunningham. LC 75-12340. (Milestones of Thought Ser). 1971. pap. 5.95x (ISBN 0-8044-6478-2). Ungar.

Magnificat: Homilies in Praise of the Blessed Virgin Mary. Bernard Of Clairvaux & Amadeus Of Lausanne. LC 78-6249. (Cistercian Fathers Ser.: No. 18). 1979. 15.95 (ISBN 0-87907-118-4). Cistercian Pubns.

Magnificat Quinti Toni. Pierre De La Rue. Ed. by Nigel Davison. LC 65-26095. (Penn State Music Series, No. 8). 19p. 1965. pap. 3.00x (ISBN 0-271-73081-1). Pa St U Pr.

Magnificent Marriage. Gordon MacDonald. 1976. pap. 3.50 1980 (ISBN 0-8423-3891-8). Tyndale.

Magnificent Mind. Gary R. Collins. 224p. 1985. 9.95 (ISBN 0-8499-0385-8, 0385-8). Word Bks.

Magnificent Muslims. Marguerite Brown. LC 81-80056. 98p. 1981. 8.00 (ISBN 0-911026-10-X). New World Press NY.

Magnificent Prayers of Saint Bridget of Sweden. Bridget. (Illus.). 19p. 1983. pap. 1.00 (ISBN 0-89555-220-5). TAN Bks Pubs.

Magnificent Promise: The Unifying Power of Prayer. Helen S. Shoemaker. 128p. (Orig.). 1985. pap. 6.95 (ISBN 0-687-22904-9). Abingdon.

Magnificent Strangers. Ann Wedgeworth. LC 78-67446. 128p. 1979. pap. 1.95 (ISBN 0-88243-568-X, 02-0568, Radiant Bks). Gospel Pub.

Magus: A Complete System of Occult Philosophy. Francis Barrett. 200p. 1975. pap. 12.00 (ISBN 0-8065-0462-5). Citadel Pr.

Mah Hah Bone. Edmond Ronayne. 11.00 (ISBN 0-685-19485-X). Powner.

Mahabarata. Besant. 5.25 (ISBN 0-8356-7539-4). Theos Pub Hse.

Mahabharata. William Buck. 272p. 1979. pap. 3.95 (ISBN 0-451-62347-9, ME1783, Ment). NAL.

Mahabharata. William Buck. (Illus.). 1973. pap. 8.95 (ISBN 0-520-04393-6, CAL 491). U of Cal Pr.

Mahabharata. P. Lal. 352p. 1980. (Pub. by Vikas India); pap. 14.50 (ISBN 0-686-77530-9). Advent NY.

Mahabharata. John Murdoch. 160p. 1986. Repr. 14.00X (ISBN 0-8364-1762-3, Pub. by Manohar Inida). South Asia Bks.

Mahabharata. Tr. by Chakravarthi V. Narasimhan. LC 64-10347. 254p. (English Version Based on Selected Verses). 1973. pap. 12.00x (ISBN 0-231-08321-1). Columbia U Pr.

Mahabharata. 2nd ed. Tr. by S. Rameshwar Rao. Orig. Title: Children's Mahabharata. 219p. 1976. pap. text ed. cancelled (ISBN 0-89253-041-3). Ind-US Inc.

Mahabharata. Ed. & tr. by J. A. Van Buitenen. Incl. Vol. 1. Book 1: The Book of the Beginning. 1974. 32.00x (ISBN 0-226-84648-2); Vol. II. Book 2: The Book of the Assembly Hall. 1976; Book 3: The Book of the Forest. 1976. LC 72-97802. lib. bdg. 42.00x set (ISBN 0-226-84649-0). U of Chicago Pr.

Mahabharata. 6th ed. Vyasa. Ed. by Chakravarti Rajagopalachari. Tr. by Chakravarti Rajagopalachari & N. R. Rao. 332p. 1980. pap. 5.50 (ISBN 0-934676-16-X). Greenlf Bks.

Mahabharata, Vol. 2, Bks. 2 & 3. Ed. & tr. by J. A. Van Buitenen. LC 75-5067. 880p. 1981. Book 2 The Book Of The Assembly Hall. 15.00x (ISBN 0-226-84664-4, Phoen). Book 3 The Book Of The Forest. U of Chicago Pr.

Mahabharata: Bhagvat-Geeta. LC 59-6527. (Eng.). 174p. 1972. Repr. of 1785 ed. 25.00x (ISBN 0-8201-1109-0). Schol Facsimiles.

Mahabharata: The Book of the Beginning, Vol. 1. J. A. Van Buitenen. LC 72-97802. (Illus.). lii, 492p. 1980. pap. 18.00x (ISBN 0-226-84663-6, P879). U of Chicago Pr.

Mahalia Jackson: Queen of Gospel Song. Jean G. Cornell. LC 73-14713. (Americans All Ser.). (Illus.). 96p. 1974. PLB 7.12 (ISBN 0-8116-4581-9). Garrard.

Mahamudra: The Quintessance of Mind & Meditation. Takpo Tashi Namgyal. Tr. by Lobsang P. Lhalungpa from Tibetan. LC 85-27963. (Orig.). 1986. pap. 25.00 (ISBN 0-87773-360-0). Shambhala Pubns.

Mahanarayanopanisad. Tr. by Swami Vimalananda from Sanskrit. 1979. pap. 6.50 (ISBN 0-87481-492-8). Vedanta Pr.

Mahanirvana Tantra. Arthur Avalon, pseud. (Sanskrit.). 473p. 1982. text ed. 28.00 (ISBN 0-89744-237-7). Auromere.

Maharaja Ranjit Singh. Gobind Sigh Mansukhana. (Illus.). 1982. 6.25 (ISBN 0-89744-247-4). Auromere.

Maharishi Effect: A Revolution Through Meditation. Elaine Aron & Arthur Aron. 235p. (Orig.). 1986. pap. 9.95 (ISBN 0-913299-26-X, Dist. by NAL). Stillpoint.

Maharishi Mahesh Yogi on the Bhagavad-Gita. Tr. by Mahesh Yogi Maharishi. (Orig.). 1969. pap. 8.95 (ISBN 0-14-002913-3). Penguin.

Mahatma Gandhi & Comparative Religion. K. L. Rao. 1979. 15.00x (ISBN 0-89684-034-4). South Asia Bks.

Mahatma Letters to A. P. Sinnett. 3rd ed. Ed. by A. Trevor Barker. 1972. 11.50 (ISBN 0-8356-7013-9). Theos Pub Hse.

Mahatma Letters to A. P. Sinnett. facsimile of 1926, 2nd ed. Compiled by A. Trevor Barker. LC 75-10574. 1975. 12.00 (ISBN 0-911500-20-0); pap. 7.00 (ISBN 0-911500-21-9). Theos U Pr.

Mahavansi. the Raja-Ratnacari. & the Raja-Vali, Forming the Sacred & Historical Books of Ceylon, 3 vols. Edward Upham. LC 78-70132. Repr. of 1833 ed. 115.00 set (ISBN 0-404-17670-4). AMS Pr.

Mahayana Buddhism. rev. ed. Nalinaksha Dutt. 1978. 12.95 (ISBN 0-89684-032-8, Pub. by Motilal Banarsidass India). Orient Bk Dist.

Mahayana Buddhism. Nalinaksha Dutt. 1976. Repr. of 1973 ed. 11.00x (ISBN 0-8364-0430-0). South Asia Bks.

Mahayana Buddhist Meditation: Theory & Practice. Minoru Kiyota. 327p. 1978. text ed. 17.50x (ISBN 0-8248-0556-9). UH Pr.

Mahayana Buddhist Sculpture of Ceylon. Diran D. Dohanian. LC 76-23613. (Outstanding Dissertations in the Fine Arts). (Illus.). 1977. Repr. of 1964 ed. lib. bdg. 58.00 (ISBN 0-8240-2685-3). Garland Pub.

Mahayana Way to Buddhahood. Susumu Yamaguchi. Tr. by Buddhist Books International. LC 82-4416. 1982. 10.95x (ISBN 0-914910-11-6). Buddhist Bks.

Mahayogi: Life, Sadhana & Teachings of Sri Aurobindo. R. R. Diwakar. 292p. 1976. pap. 6.00 (ISBN 0-89744-240-7, Pub. by Bharatiya Vidya Bhavan India). Auromere.

Mahdi of Allah: The Story of the Dervish, Mohammed Ahmed. Richard A. Bermann. Tr. by Robin John. LC 80-1935. Repr. of 1932 ed. 36.00 (ISBN 0-404-18955-5). AMS Pr.

Mahdiism & Egyptian Sudan. 2nd ed. F. R. Wingate. (Illus.). 618p. 1968. 45.00x (ISBN 0-7146-1738-5, F Cass Co). Biblio Dist.

Mahomet & His Successors, 2 Vols. Washington Irving. 1983. Repr. of 1868 ed. lib. bdg. 200.00 set (ISBN 0-89987-405-3). Darby Bks.

Mahomet & the Political Theory of the Arab Empire, 2 vols. Edward Gibbon. (Illus.). 328p. 1984. Repr. of 1901 ed. 217.85 set (ISBN 0-89901-181-0). Found Class Reprints.

Mahommed "the Great Arabian". Meredith Townsend. 86p. 1981. Repr. of 1912 ed. lib. bdg. 20.00 (ISBN 0-89984-454-5). Century Bookbindery.

Mahommedan History, 3 vols. David Price. Orig. Title: Chronological Retrospect or the Principal Events of Mahommedan History. (Illus.). 2291p. 1984. Repr. of 1811 ed. Set. text ed. 400.00x (ISBN 0-86590-393-X, Inter India Pubns Delhi). Apt Bks.

Mahzor Hadash. rev. ed. Sidney Greenberg & Jonathan D. Levine. 12.50 (ISBN 0-87677-075-8); simulated leather 14.95. Prayer Bk.

Mahzor Hashalem: High Holiday Prayer Book, Vol. 1, Rosh Hashahah. Philip Birnbaum. 646p. 1960. 14.00 (ISBN 0-88482-246-X). Hebrew Pub.

Mahzor Hashalem: High Holyday Prayer Book, 5 Vols. Philip Birnbaum. 1971. Set. 58.00 (ISBN 0-88482-169-2). Hebrew Pub.

Mahzor Hashalem: High Holyday Prayer Book, 2 Vols. Philip Birnbaum. 1960. Set. 26.50 (ISBN 0-88482-170-6). Hebrew Pub.

Mahzor Hashalem: High Holyday Prayer Book, 1 Vol. Philip Birnbaum. 1042p. 1951. 17.00 (ISBN 0-88482-240-0). Hebrew Pub.

Mahzor Hashalem: Prayer Book for Pesah, Vol. 4. Philip Birnbaum. 459p. 1971. 11.50 (ISBN 0-88482-172-2). Hebrew Pub.

Mahzor Hashalem: Prayer Book for Shavuot, Vol. 5. Philip Birnbaum. 358p. 1971. 11.50 (ISBN 0-88482-173-0). Hebrew Pub.

Mahzor Hashalem: Prayer Book for Sukkot, Vol. 3. Philip Birnbaum. 478p. 1971. 11.50 (ISBN 0-88482-174-9). Hebrew Pub.

Mahzor Leshalosh Regalim: Prayer Book for Three Festivals. Philip Birnbaum. 641p. 1971. 15.00 (ISBN 0-88482-149-8). Hebrew Pub.

Maiden of Orleans. 2nd rev. ed. Friedrich Von Schiller. Tr. by John T. Krumpelmann. LC 63-62703. (North Carolina. University. Studies in the Germanic Languages & Literatures: No. 37). Repr. of 1962 ed. 18.50 (ISBN 0-404-50937-1). AMS Pr.

Maimonides. Abraham J. Heschel. Tr. by Joachim Neugroschel from Ger. 273p. 1982. 15.00 (ISBN 0-374-19874-8); pap. 7.25 (ISBN 0-374-51759-2). FS&G.

Maimonides & Abravanel on Prophecy. Alvin J. Reines. 1971. 15.00x (ISBN 0-87820-200-5, Pub. by Hebrew Union). KTAV.

Maimonides & Aquinas: A Contemporary Appraisal. Jacob Haberman. 25.00x (ISBN 0-87068-685-2). Ktav.

Maimonides & St. Thomas Aquinas. Jacob I. Dienstag. 1974. 39.50x (ISBN 0-87068-249-0). Ktav.

Maimonides Codex: The Laws of Moses Ben Maimon (1135-1204) (Jewish Legal System in Hebrew Ser.). 1982. 390.00x (ISBN 0-686-44755-7, Pub. by Collets (UK)). State Mutual Bk.

Maimonides' Commentary on Avoth. Paul Forchheimer. pap. 5.95 (ISBN 0-87306-332-5). Feldheim.

Maimonides' Commentary on Mishnah Sanhedrin. Fred Rosner. LC 81-51800. 224p. 1981. 14.95 (ISBN 0-87203-099-7). Hermon.

Maimonides' Commentary on the Mishnah. Rosner. cancelled (ISBN 0-87306-083-0). Feldheim.

Maimonides: Essays & Texts, 850th Anniversary. Norman D. Roth. 1986. 10.00x (ISBN 0-942260-59-7). Hispanic Seminary.

Maimonides: His Life & Works. David Yellin & Israel Abrahams. (Judaic Studies Library: No. SHP 10). (Illus.). 240p. 1987. 12.95 (ISBN 0-87203-120-9); pap. 9.75 (ISBN 0-87203-121-7). Hermon.

Maimonides Octocentennial Series, No. I-IV. Asher Ginzberg et al. (Jewish People; History, Religion, Literature Ser.). Repr. of 1935 ed. 15.00 (ISBN 0-405-05278-2). Ayer Co Pubs.

Maimonides Reader. Isadore Twersky. LC 76-160818. pap. 9.95x (ISBN 0-87441-206-4). Behrman.

Maimonides: Selected Essays, Original Anthology. Ed. by Steven Katz. LC 79-7176. (Jewish Philosophy, Mysticism & the History of Ideas Ser.). 1980. lib. bdg. 51.50x (ISBN 0-405-12234-9). Ayer Co Pubs.

Maimonides-Torah & Philosophic Quest. David Hartman. LC 76-6305. 288p. 1977. pap. 7.95 (ISBN 0-8276-0089-5, 392). Jewish Pubns.

Main Institutions of Jewish Law, 2 Vols. Isaac Herzog. Set. pap. 15.95x (ISBN 0-900689-14-5). Bloch.

Main Institutions of Jewish Law, 2 vols. Isaac Herzog. 1939. Set. pap. 15.95 (ISBN 0-900689-14-5). Soncino Pr.

Main Issues in Bioethics. Andrew C. Varga. LC 80-82084. 240p. (Orig.). 1984. pap. 10.95 (ISBN 0-8091-2327-4). Paulist Pr.

Main Route to Bethlehem. Mary E. Shoemaker. (Orig.). 1981. pap. 4.50 (ISBN 0-937172-26-X). JLJ Pubs.

Main Street Gospel. Robert A. Noblett. 1983. 4.75 (ISBN 0-89536-608-8, 1341). CSS of Ohio.

Mainline Churches & the Evangelicals. Richard G. Hutcheson, Jr. LC 80-84648. 192p. (Orig.). 1981. pap. 9.95 (ISBN 0-8042-1502-2). John Knox.

Mainstreaming: Feminist Research for Teaching Religious Studies. Ed. by Arlene Swidler & Walter E. Conn. 96p. (Orig.). 1985. lib. bdg. 20.25 (ISBN 0-8191-4724-9, Co-Pub by College Theo Soc); pap. text ed. 7.75 (ISBN 0-8191-4725-7). U Pr of Amer.

Maintaining a Spirit Filled Life. Buddy Harrison. 1985. 0.75 (ISBN 0-89274-383-2). Harrison Hse.

Maintaining the Foundations. French Arrington. 1983. pap. 4.95 (ISBN 0-8010-0192-7). Baker Bk.

Maintaining the Right Fellowship. John L. Ruth. LC 83-18579. (Anabaptist & Mennonite History Ser.: No. 26). 608p. 1984. 24.95x (ISBN 0-8361-1259-8). Herald Pr.

Maintaining Unity. Churches Alive, Inc. Staff. LC 79-52134. (Love One Another Bible Study Ser.). (Illus.). 1979. wkbk. 3.00 (ISBN 0-934396-07-8). Churches Alive.

Maitrayaniya Upanisad: A Critical Essay with Text, Translation & Commentary. J. A. Van Buitenen. (Disputationes Rheno-Trajectinae: No. 6). 1962. pap. 17.60x (ISBN 90-2790-032-9). Mouton.

Maitri Upanisat. Tr. by Srisa Chandra Vidyarnava & Mohan L. Sandal. LC 73-3827. (Sacred Books of the Hindus: No. 31, Pt. 2). Repr. of 1926 ed. 14.50 (ISBN 0-404-57832-2). AMS Pr.

Majestic Hymnal, No. 2. Ed. by Reuel Lemmons. 1959. 2.75x (ISBN 0-88027-056-X). Firm Foun Pub.

Majestic Tapestry: How the Power of Early Christian Tradition Can Enrich Contemporary Faith. Robert Webber. 160p. 1986. 12.95 (ISBN 0-8407-5536-8). Nelson.

Majesty of Books. Sterling W. Sill. LC 74-81407. 336p. 1974. 9.95 (ISBN 0-87747-532-6). Deseret Bk.

Majesty of Man: The Dignity of Being Human. Ronald B. Allen. LC 84-984. (Critical Concern Ser.). 1984. 11.95 (ISBN 0-88070-065-3). Multnomah.

Majesty of Snowy Whiteness. Frank W. Sandford. 1963. pap. 1.50 (ISBN 0-910840-10-5). Kingdom.

Majesty! The God You Should Know. J. Sidlow Baxter. LC 84-47805. 228p. 1984. 12.95 (ISBN 0-89840-070-8). Heres Life.

Majjhima-Nikaya, 4 vols. Ed. by V. Trenckner. LC 78-70099. Repr. of 1888 ed. 137.50 set (ISBN 0-404-17660-7); Vol. 1. (ISBN 0-404-17661-5); Vol. 2. (ISBN 0-404-17662-3); Vol. 3. (ISBN 0-404-17663-1); Vol. 4. (ISBN 0-404-17664-X). AMS Pr.

Major Bible Themes. rev. ed. Lewis S. Chafer & John F. Walvoord. 11.95 (ISBN 0-310-22390-3, 6203P). Zondervan.

Major Cities of the Biblical World. Ed. by R. K. Harrison. 320p. 1985. 15.95 (ISBN 0-8407-7520-2). Nelson.

Major Ideas of the New Revelation. Peter D. Francuch. LC 84-51914. 266p. 1985. pap. 8.95 (ISBN 0-939386-08-9). TMH Pub.

Major Prophets of To-Day. facs. ed. Edwin E. Slosson. LC 68-8493. (Essay Index Reprint Ser.). 1914. 20.00 (ISBN 0-8369-0882-1). Ayer Co Pubs.

Major Religions of the World. Marcus Bach. 128p. 1984. pap. 4.95 (ISBN 0-87516-543-5). De Vorss.

Major Themes from the Minor Prophets. Gerald H. Twombly. (Adult Study Guide Ser.). 144p. (Orig.). 1981. pap. 4.95 (ISBN 0-88469-132-2). BMH Bks.

Major Themes in Modern Philosophies of Judaism. Eliezer Berkovits. 1974. 25.00x (ISBN 0-87068-264-4); pap. 11.95. Ktav.

Major Themes of the Qur'an. Fazlur Rahman. LC 79-54189. 1980. 30.00x (ISBN 0-88297-026-7); pap. 16.00x (ISBN 0-88297-027-5). Bibliotheca.

Major Trends in Formative Judaism: First Series. Jacob Neusner. LC 83-20176. (Brown Judaic Studies). 126p. 1983. pap. 14.25 (ISBN 0-89130-668-4, 14 00 60). Scholars Pr GA.

Major Trends in Formative Judaism: Second Series: Texts, Contents, & Contexts. Jacob Neusner. LC 83-20176. (Brown Judaic Studies). 160p. 1984. pap. text ed. 15.00 (ISBN 0-89130-727-3, 14 00 61). Scholars Pr GA.

Major Trends in Formative Judaism: Third Series: The Three Stages in the Formation of Judaism. Jacob Neusner. (Brown Judaic St00553869x). 1985. 22.95 (ISBN 0-89130-898-9, 14-00-99); pap. 18.25 (ISBN 0-89130-899-7). Scholars Pr GA.

Major Trends in Jewish Mysticism. 3rd ed. Gershom Scholem. LC 61-8991. 1961. pap. 8.95 (ISBN 0-8052-0005-3). Schocken.

Major United Methodist Beliefs. rev. & enl. ed. Mack B. Stokes. LC 77-173955. 128p. (Orig.). 1971. pap. 2.00 (ISBN 0-687-22923-5). Abingdon.

Make a Joyful Noise! James Haas & Lynne Haas. (Illus.). 40p. (Orig.). 1973. pap. 1.95 (ISBN 0-8192-1146-X). Morehouse.

Make a Joyful Noise! Bible Verses for Children. Carolyn Haywood. LC 84-2401. (Illus.). 96p. 1984. 11.95 (ISBN 0-664-32711-7). Westminster.

Make a Joyful Noise Unto the Lord: Hymns As a Reflection of Victorian Social Attitudes. Susan S. Tamke. LC 76-51693. 209p. 1978. 12.00x (ISBN 0-8214-0371-0); pap. text ed. 5.00x (ISBN 0-8214-0382-6). Ohio U Pr.

Make a Joyful Noise unto the Lord: The Life of Mahalia Jackson, Queen of Gospel Singers. Jesse Jackson. LC 72-7549. (Women of America Ser.). 1974. 12.70 (ISBN 0-690-43344-1, Crowell Jr Bks). HarpJ.

Make All Things New. Caryl Porter. (Orig.). 1987. 9.95 (ISBN 0-8054-7324-6). Broadman.

Make Disciples. Joel D. Heck. 1984. pap. 6.50 (ISBN 0-570-03934-7, 12-2869). Concordia.

Make Friends with Your Shadow: How to Accept & Use Positively the Negative Side of Your Personality. William A. Miller. LC 80-67793. 144p. (Orig.). 1981. pap. 6.95 (ISBN 0-8066-1855-8, 10-4238). Augsburg.

Make It an Adventure. Marcus Bach. LC 75-32232. 206p. 1975. pap. 6.95 (ISBN 0-918936-01-2). Astara.

Make Love Your Aim. Eugenia Price. 192p. 1983. pap. 5.95 (ISBN 0-310-31311-2, 16243P). Zondervan.

Make Me A Sabbath of Your Heart. David M. Knight. 6.95 (ISBN 0-87193-191-5). Dimension Bks.

Make Noise, Make Merry: The Story & Meaning of Purim. Miriam Chaikin. LC 82-12926. (Illus.). 96p. 1983. 11.95 (ISBN 0-89919-424-9, Pub. by Clarion); pap. 4.95. Ticknor & Fields.

Make or Break: A Guide to Marriage Counselling. Jack Dominian. (Pastoral Help Bks.: Vol. 1). 1985. pap. 8.95 (ISBN 0-89453-473-4). M Glazier.

Make Ready the Way: An Advent-Christmas Journal Book. Jean Evans. LC 81-52596. 64p. (Orig.). 1981. pap. text ed. 4.95 (ISBN 0-89390-030-3). Resource Pubns.

Make Space, Make Symbols. Keith Clark. LC 78-73826. (Illus.). 112p. 1979. pap. 2.95 (ISBN 0-87793-173-9). Ave Maria.

Make the Bible Live. Glenn O'Neal. pap. 3.50 (ISBN 0-88469-020-2). BMH Bks.

Make Us Ready. Heini Arnold. 36p. 1985. pap. 1.50 (ISBN 0-87486-198-5). Plough.

Make Way for Jesus Christ. Ed. by Marcel Gendrot. pap. 4.95 (ISBN 0-910984-52-2). Montfort Pubns.

Make Way for the King: Psalm 145 & 24. Elspeth C. Murphy. (David & I Talk to God Ser.). (Illus.). 1983. 2.95 (ISBN 0-89191-581-8). Cook.

Make Your Illness Count: A Hospital Chaplain Shows How God's Healing Power Can Be Released in Your Life. Vernon J. Bittner. LC 76-3862. 128p. (Orig.). 1976. pap. 6.95 (ISBN 0-8066-1532-X, 10-4260). Augsburg.

Make Your Life Worthwhile. Emmet Fox. LC 83-48456. 256p. 1984. pap. 7.95 (ISBN 0-06-062913-4, RD 508, HarpR). Har-Row.

Make Your Own Nativity Scene. pap. 2.95 (ISBN 0-89191-810-8, 28100). Cook.

Make Your Teaching Count! Wesley Willis. 144p. 1985. pap. 5.95 (ISBN 0-89693-324-5). Victor Bks.

Make Your Tomorrow Better: A Psychological Resource for Singles, Parents & the Entire Family. Michael E. Cavanagh. LC 80-80638. 360p. (Orig.). 1980. pap. 9.95 (ISBN 0-8091-2293-6). Paulist Pr.

Make Yours a Happy Marriage. O. A. Geiseman. 1981. pap. 3.95 (ISBN 0-570-03133-8, 12-2383). Concordia.

Make Yourself an Ark. Barbara Doherty. 1984. 10.95 (ISBN 0-88347-162-0). Thomas More.

Maker of Heaven & Earth: The Christian Doctrine of Creation in the Light of Modern Knowledge. Langdon Gilkey. 392p. 1986. pap. text ed. 14.75 (ISBN 0-8191-4976-4). U Pr of Amer.

Makers of Hebrew Books in Italy. David Amram. 350p. 1983. 55.00 (ISBN 0-87556-013-X). Saifer.

Makers of Puritan History. Marcus L. Loane. (Canterbury Bks). Orig. Title: Pioneers of Religious Freedom. 240p. 1980. pap. 6.95 (ISBN 0-8010-5593-8). Baker Bk.

Making a Life: Career, Commitment & the Life Process. Gene Ruyle. 144p. (Orig.). 1983. pap. 7.95 (ISBN 0-8164-2408-X, HarpR). Har-Row.

Making All Things New: An Invitation to Life in the Spirit. Henri J. Nouwen. LC 80-8897. 96p. 1981. 10.45 (ISBN 0-06-066326-X, HarpR). Har-Row.

Making an Apostolic Community of Love: The Role of the Superior According to St. Ignatius of Loyola. John C. Futrell. LC 73-139365. (Original Studies Composed in English Ser.). 239p. 1970. smyth sewn 5.00 (ISBN 0-912422-19-X); pap. 4.00 (ISBN 0-912422-08-4). Inst Jesuit.

Making Christian Sense. Paul L. Holmer. LC 83-27373. (Spirituality & the Christian Life Ser.: Vol. 3). 118p. (Orig.). 1984. pap. 7.95 (ISBN 0-664-24614-1). Westminster.

Making Church More Enjoyable. David Mains. (Chapel Talks Ser.). 64p. 0.95 (ISBN 0-89191-256-8, 52563). Cook.

Making Eucharistic Vestments on a Limited Budget. 2nd ed. Linda B. Hall. Ed. by James E. Barrett. (Illus.). 48p. 1985. pap. text ed. 8.50 (ISBN 0-942466-07-1). Hymnary Pr.

Making Evangelism Personal, Pt. 1. G. Michael Cocoris. 56p. (Orig.). 1984. pap. text ed. 1.00 (ISBN 0-935729-16-X). Church Open Door.

Making Evangelsim Personal, Pt. 2. G. Michael Cocoris. 41p. (Orig.). 1984. pap. text ed. 1.00 (ISBN 0-935729-17-8). Church Open Door.

Making Friends & Making Them Count. Em Griffin. LC 87-2619. (Illus.). 220p. (Orig.). 1987. pap. 7.95 (ISBN 0-87784-996-X). Inter-Varsity.

Making Friends for Christ. Wayne McDill. LC 79-55290. 1980. pap. 4.95 (ISBN 0-8054-6224-4). Broadman.

Making God Real in the Orthodox Christian Home. A. M. Coniaris. 1977. pap. 5.95 (ISBN 0-937032-07-7). Light&Life Pub Co MN.

Making God's Good News Known. T. M. Moore. (Orig.). 1985. pap. text ed. 4.95 (ISBN 0-934688-18-4); pap. text ed. 3.95 leader's guide (ISBN 0-934688-19-2). Great Comm Pubns.

Making Good Marriages Better. Robert D. Dale & Carrie Kondy Dale. LC 78-60052. 1978. 6.95 (ISBN 0-8054-5631-7). Broadman.

Making Happiness a Habit. Paul N. Elbin. (Festival Ser.). 192p. 1981. pap. 2.75 (ISBN 0-687-23030-6). Abingdon.

Making Happiness Happen. Leith Anderson. 132p. 1987. pap. 5.95 (ISBN 0-89693-776-3). Victor Bks.

Making Higher Education Christian: The History & Mission of Evangelical Colleges in America. Ed. by Joel A. Carpenter & Kenneth W. Shipps. 304p. (Orig.). 1987. pap. 16.95 (ISBN 0-8028-0253-2). Eerdmans.

Making Holy the Day: A Commentary in the Liturgy of the Hours. Charles E. Miller. red flexible bdg. 0.95 (ISBN 0-89942-410-4, 410/04). Catholic Bk Pub.

Making It. Joann Mills. 1986. pap. 4.95 (ISBN 0-89137-439-6). Quality Pubns.

Making Jesus Lord. Barry St. Clair. 1983. pap. 4.95 (ISBN 0-88207-303-6). Victor Bks.

Making Love Grow: Love That Can Make Incompatibility a Myth. Lance Webb. LC 83-80410. 176p. (Orig.). 1983. pap. 6.50 (ISBN 0-8358-0462-3). Upper Room.

Making Mission Happen. Arthur O. Bauer. 1974. pap. 4.50 (ISBN 0-377-00019-1). Friend Pr.

Making Moral Choices. Joan Mitchell & Irene O'Neill. Ed. by Carl Fisher. (Illus.). 1985. Dupl. Masterbook 9.95 (ISBN 0-89837-103-1, Pub. by Pflaum Pr). Peter Li.

Making Moral Decisions. rev. ed. Richard Reichert. LC 83-60316. (Illus.). 1983. pap. text ed. 7.20x (ISBN 0-88489-150-X); tchrs. guide 9.00x (ISBN 0-88489-151-8). St Marys.

Making Moral Decisions. rev. ed. Edward Stevens. LC 81-80877. 96p. 1981. pap. 4.95 (ISBN 0-8091-2397-5). Paulist Pr.

Making More of Holy Week. Edmund Flood. 1984. pap. 3.95 pamphlet (ISBN 0-8091-5184-7). Paulist Pr.

Making of a Christian Leader. Ted W. Engstrom. 1976. pap. 6.95 (ISBN 0-310-24221-5, 9573P). Zondervan.

Making of a Christian Mind. Arthur F. Holmes et al. LC 84-22476. 160p. (Orig.). 1984. pap. 6.95 (ISBN 0-87784-525-5). Inter-Varsity.

Making of a Disciple. Keith Phillips. LC 80-24908. 160p. 1983. 2.50 (ISBN 0-8007-8485-5, Spire Bks). Revell.

Making of a Leader. Robert L. Russell. 256p. 1987. pap. price not set (ISBN 0-87403-267-9, 3181). Standard Pub.

Making of a Man of God: Studies in I & II Timothy. Dean Fetterhoff. pap. 4.95 (ISBN 0-88469-030-X). BMH Bks.

Making of a Man of God: Studies in the Life of David. Alan Redpath. 256p. 1962. 12.95 (ISBN 0-8007-0189-5). Revell.

Making of a Missionary. J. Herbert Kane. 160p. 1975. pap. 5.95 (ISBN 0-8010-5481-8). Baker Bk.

Making of a Missionary. Martha Odom. Ed. by Raymond H. Woolsey. 128p. (Orig.). 1985. pap. 5.95 (ISBN 0-8280-0289-4). Review & Herald.

Making of a Moonie: Choice or Brainwashing? Eileen Barker. (Illus.). 299p. 1984. 19.95 (ISBN 0-631-13246-5). Basil Blackwell.

Making of a Pastoral Person. Gerald R. Niklas. 159p. (Orig.). 1981. pap. 6.95 (ISBN 0-8189-0409-7). Alba.

Making of a Spiritual Movement: The Untold Story of Paul Twitchell & Eckankar. David C. Lane. (Understanding Cults & Spiritual Movements Ser.: No. 1). (Illus.). 154p. (Orig.). 1983. pap. 9.95 (ISBN 0-9611124-0-9). Del Mar Pr.

Making of a Sunday School. Harris Jansen. 128p. 1972. pap. 1.95 (ISBN 0-88243-737-2, 02-0737). Gospel Pub.

Making of a Theologian. Martin H. Scharlemann. 182p. 1984. pap. 6.50 (ISBN 0-911770-54-2). Concordia Schl Grad Studies.

Making of Christian Doctrine. Maurice F. Wiles. 1967. 32.50 (ISBN 0-521-06803-7). Cambridge U Pr.

Making of Israel. James Cameron. LC 77-76041. (Illus.). 1977. 7.95 (ISBN 0-8008-5084-X). Taplinger.

Making of Man. Kenneth Walker. 1963. 14.95 (ISBN 0-7100-2248-4). Methuen Inc.

Making of Modern English Religion. Bernard L. Manning. LC 70-161528. 1929. text ed. 6.00x (ISBN 0-8401-1558-X). A R Allenson.

Making of Modern German Christology: From the Enlightenment to Pannenberg. Alister E. McGrath. 240p. 1986. text ed. 34.95x (ISBN 0-631-14512-5). Basil Blackwell.

Making of Modern Zionism: Intellectual Origins of the Jewish State. Shlomo Avineri. LC 81-66102. 272p. 1981. 15.50 (ISBN 0-465-04328-3). Basic.

Making of Modern Zionism: The Intellectual Origins of the Jewish State. Shlomo Avineri. LC 81-66102. 244p. 1984. pap. 7.95 (ISBN 0-465-04330-5, CN 5113). Basic.

Making of Moral Theology: A Study of the Roman Catholic Tradition. John Mahoney. 1987. 55.00. Oxford U Pr.

Making of the English Bible. Gerald Hammond. LC 83-13264. 249p. 1983. 19.95 (ISBN 0-8022-2419-9). Philos Lib.

Making of the English Bible. S. McComb. 59.95 (ISBN 0-8490-0578-7). Gordon Pr.

Making of the First American Book of Common Prayer. Marion J. Hatchett. 224p. 1982. 19.95 (ISBN 0-8164-0512-3, HarpR). Har-Row.

Making of the Middle Ages. Richard W. Southern. (Illus.). 1953. pap. 8.95x 1961 (ISBN 0-300-00230-0, Y46). Yale U Pr.

Making of the Modern Christmas. J. M. Golby & A. W. Purdue. LC 86-7083. (Illus.). 144p. 1986. 19.95 (ISBN 0-8203-0879-X). U of GA Pr.

Making of the Modern Family. Edward Shorter. LC 75-7266. (Illus.). 1975. pap. 13.50x (ISBN 0-465-09722-7, TB-5042). Basic.

Making of the Modern Jew. Milton Steinberg. (Brown Classics in Judaica Ser.). 318p. 1987. pap. text ed. 14.50 (ISBN 0-8191-4492-4). U Pr of Amer.

Making of the Old Testament. Ed. by E. B. Mellor. (Cambridge Bible Commentary on the New English Bible, Old Testament Ser.). (Illus.). 226p. 1972. 22.95 (ISBN 0-521-08184-X); pap. 10.95 (ISBN 0-521-09673-1). Cambridge U Pr.

Making of the Roman Catholic Church in Ireland, 1850-1860. Emmet Larkin. LC 79-19560. xxiv, 520p. 1980. 32.50x (ISBN 0-8078-1419-9). U of NC Pr.

Making of the Vedanta. T. G. Mainkar. 1980. 14.00x (ISBN 0-8364-0623-0, Pub. by Ajanta). South Asia Bks.

Making of William Penn. facs. ed. Mabel R. Brailsford. LC 77-124227. (Select Bibliographies Reprint Ser.). 1930. 22.00 (ISBN 0-8369-5416-5). Ayer Co Pubs.

Making Peace in the Global Village. Robert M. Brown. LC 80-27213. 118p. 1981. pap. 5.95 (ISBN 0-664-24343-6). Westminster.

Making Peace with Your Past. H. Norman Wright. 1984. 10.95 (ISBN 0-8007-1228-5). Revell.

Making Scripture Yours. David Mains. (Chapel Talks Ser.). 64p. 0.95 (ISBN 0-89191-272-X, 52720). Cook.

Making Sense of the Jonestown Suicides: A Sociological History of Peoples Temple. Judith M. Weightman. LC 83-21999. (Studies in Religion & Society: Vol. 7). 240p. 1984. 49.95x (ISBN 0-88946-871-0). E Mellen.

Making Sense of the Ministry. David Wiersbe & Warren Wiersbe. 128p. (Orig.). 1983. pap. 5.95 (ISBN 0-8024-0164-3). Moody.

Making Sense Out of Suffering. Peter Kreeft. 160p. (Orig.). 1986. pap. 6.95 (ISBN 0-89283-219-3). Servant.

Making Sexuality Human. Norman Pittenger. LC 79-126862. 1979. pap. 4.95 (ISBN 0-8298-0368-8). Pilgrim NY.

Making Sunday Special. Karen Mains. 192p. 1987. 12.95 (ISBN 0-8499-0612-1). Word Bks.

Making the Bible Our Own. George Drew. 65p. 1985. pap. 6.95 (ISBN 0-940754-29-0). Ed Ministries.

Making the Bible Yours. 13th ed. Earl C. Wolf. 102p. 1984. pap. 3.95 (ISBN 0-8341-0892-5). Beacon Hill.

Making the Connections: Essays in Feminist Social Ethics. Beverly W. Harrison. Intro. by Carol S. Robb. LC 84-45718. (Illus.). 352p. 1985. 22.95 (ISBN 0-8070-1524-5). Beacon Pr.

Making the Contact. Robert A. Russell. 90p. 1980. Repr. of 1956 ed. lexitone cover 3.95 (ISBN 0-87516-391-2). De Vorss.

Making the Good News Relevant: Keeping the Gospel Distinctive in Any Culture. Morris A. Inch. 128p. 1986. pap. 8.95 (ISBN 0-8407-7540-7). Nelson.

Making the Grade: A Guide to Excellence in College. 2nd ed. Jerry White. 108p. 1985. pap. 4.95 (ISBN 0-89109-447-4). NavPress.

Making the Jesuits More Modern. Thomas P. Faase. LC 81-40388. (Illus.). 478p. (Orig.). 1981. lib. bdg. 31.50 o. p. (ISBN 0-8191-1761-7); pap. text ed. 18.75 (ISBN 0-8191-1762-5). U Pr of Amer.

Making the Most of Life. Charles C. Ryrie. 1983. pap. 3.95 (ISBN 0-88207-587-X). SP Pubns.

Making the Most of Single Life. Bobbie Reed. 1980. pap. 3.95 (ISBN 0-570-03809-X, 12-2918). Concordia.

Making the Most of Your Mind. Stephen B. Douglass & Lee Roddy. 250p. (Orig.). 1982. pap. 6.95 (ISBN 0-86605-109-0). Heres Life.

Making the Second Half the Best Half. Edmund W. Janss. LC 83-15779. 192p. (Orig.). 1984. pap. 4.95 (ISBN 0-87123-404-1, 210404). Bethany Hse.

Making the Shift to Peace. Ed. by Don Carlson & Craig K. Comstock. (Ark Reflections: No. 2). 368p. 1986. 14.95 (ISBN 0-934325-02-2). Ark Comm Inst.

Making the Small Church Effective. Carl S. Dudley. LC 78-2221. 1983. pap. 7.95 (ISBN 0-687-23044-6). Abingdon.

Making the Small Church Grow. Robert E. Maner. 101p. 1982. pap. 2.95 (ISBN 0-8341-0741-4). Beacon Hill.

Making the World Safe for Pornography. E. J. Mishan. LC 73-83001. 262p. 1973. 1.95 (ISBN 0-912050-41-1, Library Pr). Open Court.

Making Things Right: The Sacrament of Reconciliation. Jeannine T. Leichner. (Illus.). 62p. (Orig.). 1980. pap. 3.50 (ISBN 0-87973-351-9, 351). Our Sunday Visitor.

Making Things Right, When Things Go Wrong. Paul Faulkner. LC 86-61405. 1986. 11.95 (ISBN 0-8344-0137-1, BA130H). Sweet.

Making TV Work for Your Family. William L. Coleman. LC 83-11881. 112p. (Orig.). 1983. pap. 4.95 (ISBN 0-87123-322-3, 210322). Bethany Hse.

Making Your Home a Missionary Training Center. Joe J. Christensen & Barbara K. Christensen. 140p. 1985. 7.95 (ISBN 0-87747-589-X). Deseret Bk.

Making Your Life Count. Jim Burns. (Illus.). 64p. Wkbk 3.95 (ISBN 0-89081-392-2). Harvest Hse.

Making Your Marriage Work. Mary Jensen & Andrew Jensen. LC 85-7528. 144p. 1985. pap. 6.95 (ISBN 0-8066-2124-9, 10-4265). Augsburg.

Makings for Meditation. Elsa Gidlow. (Illus.). 1973. 2.00 (ISBN 0-9606568-0-4). Druid Heights.

Makkoth, 1 vol. 15.00 (ISBN 0-910218-76-5). Bennet Pub.

Malachi & the Great & Dreadful Day. Mark E. Petersen. 76p. 1983. 5.95 (ISBN 0-87747-962-3). Deseret Bk.

Malachi: Bible Study Commentary. Charles D. Isbell. (Bible Study Commentary Ser.). 128p. (Orig.). 1980. pap. 4.95 (ISBN 0-310-41673-6, 9350P). Zondervan.

Malachi: God's Unchanging Love. Walter Kaiser. 1984. pap. 6.95 (ISBN 0-8010-5464-8). Baker Bk.

Malachi: Lessons for Today. W. A. Lickley. pap. 3.95 (ISBN 0-88172-114-X). Believers Bkshelf.

Malachi: Messenger of Divine Love. Thomas J. Delaughter. LC 75-40410. 160p. (Orig.). 1976. 6.00 (ISBN 0-914520-08-3); pap. text ed. 5.00 (ISBN 0-914520-07-5). Insight Pr.

Malachi: Twenty-Six Daily Bible Studies. David Jeremiah. (Steps to Higher Ground Ser.). 1983. pap. 1.95 (ISBN 0-86508-207-3). BCM Intl Inc.

Malachi's Message for Today. G. Campbell Morgan. (Morgan Library). 131p. 1972. pap. 3.95 (ISBN 0-8010-5912-7). Baker Bk.

Malay Magic: Being an Introduction to the Folklore & Popular Religion of the Malay Peninsula. Walter W. Skeat. LC 70-174437. (Illus.). 1973. Repr. of 1900 ed. lib. bdg. 28.00 (ISBN 0-405-08980-5). Ayer Co Pubs.

Male Sexual Fantasies: The Destruction of the Feminine Personality; The Christian Mandate Against Pornography. J. R. Braun. 48p. (Orig.). 1980. pap. 1.95 (ISBN 0-933656-05-X). Trinity Pub Hse.

Maledicta 1980. Ed. by Reinhold Aman. LC 77-649633. (Maledicta: International Journal of Verbal Aggression Ser.: Vol. 4, No. 1 & 2). (Illus.). 320p. 1980. pap. 20.00 (ISBN 0-916500-55-1). Maledicta.

Malleus Maleficarum. Montague Summers. 288p. 1971. pap. 7.50 (ISBN 0-486-22802-9). Dover.

Malleus Maleficarum. Ed. & tr. by Montague Summers. LC 68-57193. 1969. Repr. of 1928 ed. 27.50 (ISBN 0-405-09016-1, Pub. by Blom). Ayer Co Pubs.

Malleus Maleficarum: The Witches Hammer of Heinrich Kramer & James Sprenger. Heinrich Kramer & James Sprenger. Tr. by Montague Summers. 15.50 (ISBN 0-8446-0169-1). Peter Smith.

Malta of the Knights. Elizabeth W. Schermerhorn. LC 76-29838. Repr. of 1929 ed. 40.00 (ISBN 0-404-15429-8). AMS Pr.

Mama's Life on a Missouri Farm. large print ed. Pearl Brians. 86p. pap. 8.00 (ISBN 0-914009-26-5). VHI Library.

Mamre, Essays in Religion. Martin Buber. Tr. by Greta Hort. LC 72-97271. Repr. of 1946 ed. lib. bdg. 15.00x (ISBN 0-8371-2591-X, BUMA). Greenwood.

Man. Robert Hicks & Richard Bewes. (Understanding Bible Truth Ser.). (Orig.). 1981. pap. 0.95 (ISBN 0-89840-025-2). Heres Life.

Man & Faith. Morteza Mutahhari. Tr. by Amir F. Abri & Mohammad Talebinejad. LC 82-60360. 64p. 1985. pap. 3.95 (ISBN 0-940368-48-X). Tahrike Tarsile Quran.

Man & God. Lois Degler. LC 74-28943. (Illus.). 1975. pap. 3.00 (ISBN 0-930422-04-X). Dennis-Landman.

Man & God. (Miniature Ser.). 0.50 (ISBN 0-685-61383-6). Aum Pubns.

Man & His Approach to God in John Duns Scotus. B. M. Bonansea. 258p. (Orig.). 1983. lib. bdg. 29.75 (ISBN 0-8191-3299-3); pap. text ed. 13.50 o. p. (ISBN 0-8191-3300-0). U Pr of Amer.

Man & His Bodies. 12th ed. Annie Besant. 1967. 4.50 (ISBN 0-8356-7083-X). Theos Pub Hse.

Man & His Destiny. Tr. by M. A. Ansari from Persian. Tr. of Insan wa Sarnawisht. 124p. 1985. pap. 5.00 (ISBN 0-941724-39-5). Islamic Seminary.

Man & His Problems. Rene Latourelle. Tr. by Matthew O'Connell. LC 82-24334. (Fr.). 395p. (Orig.). 1983. pap. 9.95 (ISBN 0-8189-0450-X). Alba.

Man & Islam. Ali Shariati. Tr. by Fathollah Marjani from Persian. 150p. (Orig.). 1981. 9.95 (ISBN 0-941722-02-3); pap. 4.95 (ISBN 0-941722-00-7). Book Dist Ctr.

Man & Mind. Jeanne L. De Groot. ix, 441p. 1985. text ed. 45.00x (ISBN 0-8236-3087-0). Intl Univs Pr.

Man & Salvation in Literature. Charles Moeller. Tr. by Charles U. Quinn. LC 77-122048. Orig. Title: Homme Moderne Devant le Salut. 208p. 1973. 11.95 (ISBN 0-268-00351-3); pap. 6.95x (ISBN 0-268-00489-7). U of Notre Dame Pr.

Man & Sin: A Theological View. Piet Schoonenberg. 1965. 7.95 (ISBN 0-268-00167-7). U of Notre Dame Pr.

Man & the Incarnation: The Study of Philippians 2 & Psalm 110. Samuel J. Andrews & E. H. Gifford. 1981. lib. bdg. 15.00 (ISBN 0-86524-078-7, 9510). Klock & Klock.

Man & the Sacred. Roger Caillois. Tr. by Meyer Barash from Fr. LC 79-8709. 190p. 1980. Repr. of 1959 ed. lib. bdg. 22.50x (ISBN 0-313-22196-0, CAMS). Greenwood.

Man & the State. Jacques Maritain. LC 51-555. 1956. pap. 4.45x (ISBN 0-226-50552-9, P5, Phoen). U of Chicago Pr.

Man & Woman. Dietrich von Hildebrand. LC 65-25840. pap. 25.80 (ISBN 0-317-28166-6, 2022575). Bks Demand UMI.

Man & Woman, & Child. Harold W. Percival. LC 52-6126. 1979. pap. 6.95 (ISBN 0-911650-08-3). Word Foun.

Man & Woman He Made Them. Jean Vanier. 192p. 1985. pap. 6.95 (ISBN 0-8091-2751-2). Paulist Pr.

Man & Woman in Biblical Perspective. James B. Hurley. 288p. (Orig.). 1981. pap. 9.95 (ISBN 0-310-42731-2, 10460P). Zondervan.

Man & Woman in Christ: An Examination of the Roles of Men & Women in Light of Scripture & the Social Sciences. Stephen B. Clark. 754p. (Orig.). 1980. 24.95 (ISBN 0-89283-084-0). Servant.

Man & World in the Light of Anthroposophy. Rev. ed. Stewart C. Easton. 536p. 1982. pap. 11.95 (ISBN 0-88010-006-0). Anthroposophic.

Man & World in the Light of Anthroposophy. 2nd ed. Stewart C. Easton. 543p. 1982. pap. 21.00 (ISBN 0-88010-077-X). Anthroposophic.

Man as a Being of Sense & Perception. Rudolf Steiner. Tr. by Dorothy Lenn from Ger. 53p. 1981. pap. 6.00 (ISBN 0-919924-11-5, Pub. by Steiner Book Centre Canada). Anthroposophic.

Man as a Picture of the Living Spirit. Rudolf Steiner. Tr. by George Adams from Ger. 31p. (Orig.). 1972. pap. 1.95 (ISBN 0-85440-253-5, Pub. by Steinerbooks). Anthroposophic.

Man As Infinite Spirit. James H. Robb. (Aquinas Lecture). 1974. 7.95 (ISBN 0-87462-139-9). Marquette.

Man As Man & Believer. Ed. by Edward Schillebeeckx & Boniface Willems. LC 67-17789. (Concilium Ser.: Vol. 21). 188p. 7.95 (ISBN 0-8091-0093-2). Paulist Pr.

Man As Sinner. John H. McClanahan. LC 84-20036. (Layman's Library of Christian Doctrine Ser.). 1987. 5.95 (ISBN 0-8054-1637-4). Broadman.

Man: Believer & Unbeliever. Francis M. Tyrrell. LC 73-20055. 475p. (Orig.). 1974. pap. 7.95 (ISBN 0-8189-0283-3). Alba.

Man Beneath the Gift: The Story of My Life. Ralph A. DiOrio & Donald Gropman. LC 80-17619. (Illus.). 239p. 1981. 9.95 (ISBN 0-688-03740-2); pap. 7.95 (ISBN 0-688-00795-3). Morrow.

Man Born to Be King. Dorothy L. Sayers. 343p. 1983. 13.95 (ISBN 0-575-00366-9, Pub. by Gollancz England). David & Charles.

Man Called Martin Luther. Kathleen Benson. 1980. 7.50 (ISBN 0-570-03625-9, 39-1067). Concordia.

Man Called Mr. Pentecost. David DuPlessis. LC 76-53322. 1977. pap. 5.95 (ISBN 0-88270-184-3). Bridge Pub.

Man Called Peter. Catherine Marshall. 1971. pap. 4.50 (ISBN 0-380-00894-7). Avon.

Man Christian Anthropology in the Conflicts of the Present. Jurgen Moltmann. LC 73-88350. pap. 34.00 (2026872). Bks Demand UMI.

Man Cures, God Heals: Religion & Medical Practice Among the Akans of Ghana. Kofi Appiah-Kubi. LC 81-65019. (Illus.). 188p. 1981. text ed. 18.95x (ISBN 0-86598-011-X). Allanheld.

Man Cures, God Heals: Religion & Medical Practice Among the Akans of Ghana. Kofi Appiah-Kubi. (Orig.). 1981. pap. 10.95 (ISBN 0-377-00114-7). Friend Pr.

Man Discovers God. facs. ed. George S. Eddy. LC 68-24849. (Essay Index Reprint Ser). 1968. Repr. of 1942 ed. 18.00 (ISBN 0-8369-0401-X). Ayer Co Pubs.

Man Does Survive Death. D. Scott Rogo. 1977. pap. 3.95 (ISBN 0-8065-0582-6). Citadel Pr.

Man for All Seasons. Robert Bolt. 1962. 10.95 (ISBN 0-394-40623-0). Random.

Man for All Seasons. Robert Bolt. 1966. pap. 2.95 (ISBN 0-394-70321-9, V321, Vin). Random.
Man for All Time. C. Stephen Mann. LC 75-161567. 1971. pap. 2.50 (ISBN 0-8192-1127-3). Morehouse.
Man for Others: Maximilian Kolbe, Saint of Auschwitz. Patricia Treece. 208p. 1986. pap. 5.95 (ISBN 0-87973-519-8, 519). Our Sunday Visitor.
Man from Galilee. Charles P. Conn. LC 74-83547. 1974. pap. 1.99 (ISBN 0-87148-565-6). Pathway Pr.
Man from Nazareth: As His Contemporaries Saw Him. Harry E. Fosdick. LC 78-16469. 1978. Repr. of 1949 ed. lib. bdg. 24.25x (ISBN 0-313-20603-1, FOMN). Greenwood.
Man from the Past. 2nd ed. Roy C. Higby. (Illus.). pap. 4.25 (ISBN 0-914692-02-X). Big Moose.
Man, God & the Universe. I. K. Taimni. LC 74-4167. (Illus.). 447p. 1974. pap. 3.45 (ISBN 0-8356-0447-0, Quest). Theos Pub Hse.
Man Heal Thyself. Narvella Matthews. Ed. by Helen Graves. LC 85-51970. 65p. 1986. 6.95 (ISBN 1-55523-004-0). Winston-Derek.
Man in Chains, St. Paul. Rosalie M. Levy. 1951. 4.00 (ISBN 0-8198-4704-6); pap. 3.00 (ISBN 0-8198-4705-4). Dghtrs St Paul.
Man in Christ. James S. Stewart. (James S. Stewart Library). 1975. pap. 7.95 (ISBN 0-8010-8045-2). Baker Bk.
Man in Demand. Rev. ed. Emily Hunter & Wayne Hunter. (Illus.). 1986. Repr. of 1975 ed. tchr's ed., 224 pp. 7.95 (ISBN 0-89081-511-9, 5119); student's wkbk. 80 pp 4.95 (ISBN 0-89081-510-0, 5100). Harvest Hse.
Man in Evolution. 2nd rev. ed. G. De Purucker. Ed. by Grace F. Knoche. LC 76-45503. 1977. pap. 6.00 (ISBN 0-911500-55-3). Theos U Pr.
Man in God's World. Helmut Thielicke. Tr. by J. W. Doberstein from Ger. 224p. 1978. Repr. 13.95 (ISBN 0-227-67709-9). Attic Pr.
Man in His Right Mind. Harold W. Darling. 158p. 1977. pap. 5.95 (ISBN 0-85364-097-1). Attic Pr.
Man in Qur'an & the Meaning of Furqan. Shaykh F. Haeri. 210p. 1987. pap. 18.95 (ISBN 0-7103-0223-1, Pub. by Routledge UK). Methuen Inc.
Man in Revolt: A Christian Anthropology. Emil Brunner. Tr. by Olive Wyon. LC 47-2442. 564p. 1979. softcover 9.95 (ISBN 0-664-24245-6). Westminster.
Man in Search of Immortality. Swami Nikhilananda. LC 68-101793. 112p. 4.95 (ISBN 0-911206-12-4). Ramakrishna.
Man in the Cosmic Ocean. Edmond B. Szekely. (Illus.). 56p. 1970. pap. 3.50 (ISBN 0-89564-054-6). IBS Intl.
Man in the Manse, Eighteen Hundred to Nineteen Hundred. Ronald S. Blakey. 160p. 1979. 10.00x (ISBN 0-905312-05-8, Pub. by Scot Acad Pr). Longwood Pub Group.
Man in the Modern Age. Karl Jaspers. LC 75-41155. Repr. of 1933 ed. 28.50 (ISBN 0-404-14558-2). AMS Pr.
Man in the Past, the Present, & the Future: The Sun-Initiation of the Druid Priest & His Moon-Science. Rudolf Steiner. Tr. by E. Goddard from Ger. 82p. 1982. pap. 5.00 (ISBN 0-85440-403-1, Pub by Steinerbooks). Anthroposophic.
Man in the Universe: Some Cultural Continuities in Indian Thought. W. Norman Brown. LC 66-12648. (Rabindranath Tagore Memorial Lectures). 1966. 24.00x (ISBN 0-520-00185-0). U of Cal Pr.
Man in the World: The Political Theology of Johannes Baptist Metz. Roger D. Johns. LC 76-26491. (American Academy of Religion. Dissertation Ser.). 1976. pap. 9.95 (ISBN 0-89130-079-1, 010116). Scholars Pr GA.
Man into Wolf: An Anthropological Interpretation of Sadism, Masochism, & Lycanyhropy. Robert Eisler. LC 77-2497. 264p. 1978. lib. bdg. 11.95 (ISBN 0-915520-16-8); pap. text ed. 5.95 (ISBN 0-915520-06-0). Ross-Erikson.
Man Is Not Alone: A Philosophy of Religion. Abraham J. Heschel. 320p. 1976. pap. 8.95 (ISBN 0-374-51328-7). FS&G.
Man Is Not Alone: A Philosophy of Religion. Abraham J. Heschel. LC 74-169258. 306p. 1972. Repr. of 1951 ed. lib. bdg. 25.50x (ISBN 0-374-93879-2, Octagon). Hippocrene Bks.
Man Jesus Christ. W. J. Dawson. 1977. lib. bdg. 59.95 (ISBN 0-8490-2199-5). Gordon Pr.
Man Kann Wieder Christ Sein: Eine Abrechnung mit der Theologie und der "kritischen" Bibelwissenschaft. Frans Simons. 231p. 1978. 27.80 (ISBN 3-261-03011-9). P Lang Pubs.
Man Master of His Destiny. Omraam M. Aivanhov. (Izvor Collection Ser.: Vol. 202). 194p. 1982. pap. 4.95 (ISBN 0-911857-01-X). Prosveta USA.
Man Nobody Knows. Bruce Barton. 1925. pap. 6.95 (ISBN 0-672-50743-9). Bobbs.
Man Nobody Knows. Bruce Barton. 128p. 1987. pap. 5.95 (ISBN 0-02-083620-1, Collier). Macmillan.
"Man of Books & a Man of the People" E. Y. Mullins & the Crisis Moderate Southern Baptist Leadership. William E. Ellis. xi, 228p. 1985. text ed. 18.95 (ISBN 0-86554-175-2, MUP-H165). Mercer Univ Pr.
Man of Faith: Learning from the Life of Abraham. Ray C. Stedman. LC 85-21772. (Authentic Christianity Bks.). 1985. pap. 7.95 (ISBN 0-88070-125-0). Multnomah.
Man of Galilee. Clifford Stevens. LC 79-88086. 1979. pap. 2.50 (ISBN 0-87973-302-0). Our Sunday Visitor.
Man of His Counsel. Effie Williams. 112p. pap. 1.00 (ISBN 0-686-29156-5). Faith Pub Hse.
Man of Peace: Casimir Michael Cypher, OFM Conv: His Meaning in Life Was Found in Death. Anselm Romb. (Illus.). 67p. (Orig.). 1985. pap. 3.75 (ISBN 0-913382-17-5, 105-42). Prow Bks-Franciscan.
Man of Zen: The Recorded Sayings of Layman P'ang. Tr. by Ruth F. Sasaki et al. LC 77-157273. (Illus.). 124p. 1976. 6.95 (ISBN 0-8348-0057-8); pap. 4.95 (ISBN 0-8348-0121-3). Weatherhill.
Man on Three Dimensions. Kenneth E. Hagin. 1973. pap. 1.00 (ISBN 0-89276-020-6). Hagin Ministries.
Man Overboard. Sinclair Ferguson. 1982. pap. 3.95 (ISBN 0-8423-4015-7); leader's guide 2.95 (ISBN 0-8423-4016-5). Tyndale.
Man Sent by God: The Life of Patriarch Athenagoras of Constantinople. Demetrios Tsakonas. Tr. by George Angeloglou from Greek. LC 77-77699. (Illus.). 99p. 1977. pap. 3.95 (ISBN 0-916586-07-3). Holy Cross Orthodox.
Man, Son of Man. Sri Madhava Ashish. LC 79-98267. 1970. 8.50 (ISBN 0-8356-0011-4). Theos Pub Hse.
Man Spoke, a World Listened. Paul L. Maier. 1980. pap. 8.95 (ISBN 0-570-03822-7, 12-2762). Concordia.
Man: The Broken Image. Carol R. Murphy. LC 68-30960. (Orig.). pap. 2.50x (ISBN 0-87574-158-4). Pendle Hill.
Man, the Dwelling Place of God. Aiden W. Tozer. 5.95 (ISBN 0-87509-188-1); pap. 4.45 (ISBN 0-87509-165-2); mass market 2.95 (ISBN 0-87509-166-0). Chr Pubns.
Man, the Image of God & Modern Psychology. Heini Arnold. 14p. 1973. pap. 1.25 (ISBN 0-87486-176-4). Plough.
Man: The Measure of All Things. Sri K. Prem & Sri Madhava Ashish. LC 74-87256. 1969. 8.50 (ISBN 0-8356-0006-8). Theos Pub Hse.
Man, the Message, & the Mission. George M. Bass. 1982. 6.95 (ISBN 0-89536-565-0, 1336). CSS of Ohio.
Man the Saint. J. Urteaga. 218p. 1963. pap. 4.95 (ISBN 0-933932-06-5). Scepter Pubs.
Man to Match His Mountains: Badshah Khan, Nonviolent Soldier of Islam. Eknath Easwaran. (Illus.). 1985. 15.95 (ISBN 0-915132-33-8); pap. 7.95 (ISBN 0-915132-34-6). Nilgiri Pr.
Man Triumphant. Annalee Skarin. 1966p. pap. 5.95 (ISBN 0-87516-091-3). De Vorss.
Man, Visible & Invisible. Charles W. Leadbeater. 9.95 (ISBN 0-8356-7388-X). Theos Pub Hse.
Man Was Not Born to Cry. Joel S. Goldsmith. 1984. pap. 5.95 (ISBN 0-8065-0915-5). Citadel Pr.
Man Who Carried the Cross for Jesus. Constance Head. (Arch Bk.: No. 16). (Illus.). 1979. 0.99 (ISBN 0-570-06124-5, 59-1242). Concordia.
Man Who Could Do No Wrong. Charles Blair & John Sherrill. 1982. pap. 3.50 (ISBN 0-8423-4002-5). Tyndale.
Man Who Cried Justice. Aeschliman Perkins. 1987. pap. 5.95 (ISBN 0-8307-1075-2, 5418545). Regal.
Man Who Freed Slaves: Wilberforce. Elsie Johnson. (Stories of Faith, Fame Ser.). (YA) 1975. pap. 2.95 (ISBN 0-87508-615-2). Chr Lit.
Man Who Lost His Shadow. John A. Sanford. LC 82-62414. 1983. 6.95 (ISBN 0-8091-0337-0). Paulist Pr.
Man Who Met Jesus at Bethesda. Neal A. Boehlke. (Arch Bk.). 1981. pap. 0.99 (ISBN 0-570-06143-1, 59-1260). Concordia.
Man Who Moved a Mountain. Richard C. Davids. LC 75-99609. (Illus.). 270p. 1972. pap. 5.95 (ISBN 0-8006-1237-X, 1-1237). Fortress.
Man Who Rode the Tiger: The Life of Judge Samuel Seabury. Herbert Mitgang. (Illus.). 1979. pap. 5.95 (ISBN 0-393-00922-X). Norton.
Man Who Slept Through a Sermon. Evelyn Marxhausen. (Arch Bk.: No. 16). (Illus.). 1979. 0.99 (ISBN 0-570-06128-8, 59-1246). Concordia.
Man Who Talked With Angels. Sharon White. 226p. (Orig.). 1982. pap. 5.95 (ISBN 0-89221-088-5, Pub. by SonLife). New Leaf.
Man Who Was Different. Gien Karssen. 1987. price not set (ISBN 0-89109-136-X). NavPress.
Man Who Wouldn't Listen. Connie W. Nowlan. (Trailblazer Ser.). 1982. pap. 5.95 (ISBN 0-8163-0441-6). Pacific Pr Pub Assn.
Man Who Wrestled with God: Light from the Old Testament on the Psychology of Individuation. John A. Sanford. LC 80-84829. 128p. 1981. pap. 7.95 (ISBN 0-8091-2367-3). Paulist Pr.
Man with a Dream. Peter M. Rinaldi. (Illus.). 1978. pap. 2.95 (ISBN 0-89944-035-5). Don Bosco Multimedia.
Man with a Song. Francis R. Line & Helen E. Line. 1978. 8.95 (ISBN 0-8199-0756-1). Franciscan Herald.
Man-Woman. 1982. pap. 1.95 (ISBN 0-686-76542-7). Feldheim.
Management: A Biblical Approach. Myron D. Rush. 1983. pap. 7.95 (ISBN 0-88207-607-8). Victor Bks.
Management Ethics: An Intercultural Perspective. William A. Evans. (Dimensions in International Business Ser.). 256p. 1981. lib. bdg. 15.00 (ISBN 0-89838-055-3). Kluwer-Nijhoff.
Management for the Christian Leader. Olan Hendrix. 1986. text ed. 8.95 (ISBN 0-8010-4313-1). Baker Bk.
Management for Your Church: How to Realize Your Church's Potential Through a Systems Approach. Norman Shawchuck & Alvin J. Lindgren. (Illus.). 160p. 1985. pap. 8.95 (ISBN 0-938180-14-2). Org Resources Pr.
Management of Ministry. James D. Anderson & Ezra E. Jones. LC 76-62942. 1978. 13.45 (ISBN 0-06-060235-X, HarpR). Har-Row.
Management Series. L. Ron Hubbard. (Vol. I). 100.00 (ISBN 0-686-30799-2). Church Scient NY.
Management Series Volume 1: Data, Public Relations, Personnel, Organizing, Finance, Executive, Establishment Officer. 578p. 1974. 120.04 (ISBN 87-7336-107-0). Bridge Pubns Inc.
Managing God's Organization: The Catholic Church in Society. Scott R. Safranski. Ed. by Richard Farmer. LC 85-16540. (Research for Business Decisions: No. 79). 200p. 1985. 44.95 (ISBN 0-8357-1669-4). UMI Res Pr.
Managing Stress in Ministry. William Hulme. LC 84-48221. 160p. 1985. 13.45 (ISBN 0-06-064077-4, HarpR). Har-Row.
Managing Your Emotions. Erwin Lutzer. 180p. 1983. pap. 5.95 (ISBN 0-88207-386-9). Victor Bks.
Managing Your Life & Time. Jo Berry. 192p. 1986. pap. 6.95 (ISBN 0-310-34181-7). Zondervan.
Managing Your Stress. Wayne E. Oates. LC 85-47715. 64p. 1985. pap. 3.95 (ISBN 0-8006-1880-7, 1-1880). Fortress.
Manantiales en el Desierto. Charles E. Cowman & Antonio Serrano. Orig. Title: Stream in the Desert. 1986. pap. 4.95 (ISBN 0-311-40028-0, Edit Mundo). Casa Bautista.
Mandala. Jose Arguelles & Miriam Arguelles. LC 70-189856. (Illus.). 144p. 1972. pap. 14.95 (ISBN 0-87773-033-4, 73000-3). Shambhala Pubns.
Mandalas: The Dynamics of Vedic Symbolism. James N. Powell. Ed. by S. K. Ghai. 127p. 1980. 9.95 (ISBN 0-914794-36-1). Wisdom Garden.
Mandan-Hidatsa Myths & Ceremonies. Martha W. Beckwith. LC 38-19412. (American Folklore Society Memoirs). Repr. of 1938 ed. 29.00 (ISBN 0-527-01084-7). Kraus Repr.
Mandarins, Jews & Missionaries: The Jewish Experience in the Chinese Empire. Michael Pollak. LC 79-84732. (Illus.). 439p. 1983. pap. 10.95 (ISBN 0-8276-0229-4). Jewish Pubns.
Mandatory Motherhood: The True Meaning of "Right to Live". Garrett Hardin. LC 74-4880. 136p. 1974. 6.95 (ISBN 0-8070-2176-8). Beacon Pr.
Mandie & the Abandoned Mine. Lois G. Leppard. (Mandie Ser.). 144p. (Orig.). 1987. pap. 2.95 (ISBN 0-87123-932-9). Bethany Hse.
Mandukya Upanishad. Tr. by Swami Gambhirananda from Sanskrit. (Upanishads with Shankara's Commentary Ser.). 240p. 1980. pap. 3.50 (ISBN 0-87481-202-X). Vedanta Pr.
Manet & the Nude, a Study in Iconography in the Second Empire. Beatrice Farwell. LC 79-57509. (Outstanding Dissertations in the Fine Arts Ser.: No. 5). 290p. 1981. lib. bdg. 61.00 (ISBN 0-8240-3929-7). Garland Pub.
Mani Rimdu-Nepal: The Buddhist Dance Drama of Tengpoche (1976) Mario Fantin. (Illus.). 1978. 40.00. Heinman.
Manichaean Literature: Representative Texts, Chiefly from Middle Persian & Parthian Writings. Compiled by Jes P. Asmussen. LC 74-22063. (Unesco Collection of Representative Works, Oriental Ser.). 160p. 1975. lib. bdg. 30.00x (ISBN 0-8201-1141-4). Schol Facsimiles.
Manichaeism in the Later Roman Empire & Medieval China. Samuel N. Lieu. LC 84-26093. 240p. 1985. 54.00 (ISBN 0-7190-1088-8, Pub. by Manchester Univ Pr). Longwood Pub Group.
Manifest Destiny: A Study of Nationalist Expansionism in American History. Albert K. Weinberg. LC 75-41293. Repr. of 1935 ed. 41.50 (ISBN 0-404-14706-2). AMS Pr.
Manifest Destiny & Mission in American History: A Reinterpretation. Federick Merk & Lois B. Merk. LC 82-25146. ix, 265p. 1983. Repr. lib. bdg. 35.00x (ISBN 0-313-23844-8, MERM). Greenwood.
Manifestations of Karma. 3rd ed. Rudolf Steiner. 262p. 1984. pap. 10.95 (ISBN 0-317-18543-8, Pub. by Steinerbooks). Anthroposophic.
Manifesto for a Global Civilization. Matt Fox & Brian Swimme. LC 82-71450. 54p. (Orig.). 1982. pap. 3.95 (ISBN 0-939680-05-X). Bear & Co.
Manifesto, or a Declaration of the Doctrines & Practice of the Church of Christ. John Dunlavy. LC 74-134416. Repr. of 1818 ed. 34.50 (ISBN 0-404-08460-5). AMS Pr.
Manifold & the One. Agnes Arber. 1967. pap. 1.45 (ISBN 0-8356-0018-1, Quest). Theos Pub Hse.
Manipulated Man: The Power of Man Over Man, Its Risks & Its Limits. European Studies. Strasbourg, September 24-29, 1973. Ed. by Charles Robert. Tr. by C. P. Frank. LC 77-24330. (Pittsburgh Theological Monographs: No. 16). 1977. pap. 8.00 (ISBN 0-915138-21-2). Pickwick.
Manipulating the Machine: Changing the Pattern of Ministerial Departments, 1960-83. Christopher Pollitt. 296p. 1984. text ed. 29.95x (ISBN 0-04-351064-7). Allen Unwin.
Mankind's Greatest Invention. John M. Fontana. LC 64-5232. 112p. 1964. 4.95 (ISBN 0-9600034-1-X). J M Fontana.
Mankind's Greatest Life. Zygmunt V. Szarnicki. 188p. (Orig.). 1985. pap. 9.95 (ISBN 0-939332-12-4). J Pohl Assocs.
Manna: A Book of Table Devotions. Ed. by Floyd D. Carey & James F. Byrd. 1973. pap. 3.95 (ISBN 0-87148-564-8). Pathway Pr.
Manna in the Desert. George A. Maloney. 120p. (Orig.). 1984. pap. 5.95 (ISBN 0-914544-54-3). Living Flame Pr.
Manna in the Morning. Ruth B. Vernon. 5.75 (ISBN 0-8062-2491-6). Carlton.
Manner & Method: A Translation of the French Reformed Church's Liturgy. Blair Reynolds. 85p. (Orig.). 1985. pap. 6.95x (ISBN 0-932269-40-0). Wyndham Hall.
Manners & Customs of Bible Lands. Fred H. Wight. 1953. 10.95 (ISBN 0-8024-5175-6). Moody.
Manners & Customs of Bible Lands. Fred Wright. (Affordables Ser.). 336p. pap. 5.50 (ISBN 0-8024-0416-2). Moody.
Manners & Customs of the Bible. James M. Freeman. (Illus.). 515p. 1972. (Pub. by Logos); pap. 8.95 (ISBN 0-88270-022-7). Bridge Pub.
Manners & Morals of the Nineteen Twenties: A Survey of the Religious Press. Mary P. Thaman. LC 77-8129. 1977. Repr. of 1954 ed. lib. bdg. 22.50x (ISBN 0-8371-9679-5, THMM). Greenwood.
Manners in God's House. Ethel Uhrich. (Illus.). 1972. pap. 3.95 (ISBN 0-87239-272-4, 2586). Standard Pub.
Manning: Anglican & Catholic. Ed. by John Fitzsimmons. LC 78-11571. 1979. Repr. of 1951 ed. lib. bdg. cancelled (ISBN 0-313-21005-5, FIMA). Greenwood.
Man's Being, His Destiny & World Evolution. 3rd ed. Rudolf Steiner. Tr. by Erna McArthur & William Riggins. 123p. (Orig.). 1984. pap. 7.95 (ISBN 0-88010-090-7). Anthroposophic.
Man's Crown of Glory. Jerry Savelle. 96p. (Orig.). 1983. pap. 2.75 (ISBN 0-89274-169-4, HH-169). Harrison Hse.
Man's Destiny in Eternity. Arthur H. Compton. LC 75-117821. (Essay Index Reprint Ser). 1949. 19.00 (ISBN 0-8369-1762-6). Ayer Co Pubs.
Man's Divine Parentage & Destiny: The Great Rounds & Races. G. Van Pelt. Ed. by W. Emmett Small & Helen Todd. (Theosophical Manual: No. 7). 64p. 1975. pap. 2.00 (ISBN 0-913004-24-3, 913004-24). Point Loma Pub.
Man's Earth-Lease Is About to Expire. C. C. Cribb. LC 77-70210. pap. 2.95 (ISBN 0-932046-01-0). Manhattan Ltd NC.
Man's Eternal Quest. Paramahansa Yogananda. LC 75-17183. (Illus.). 503p. 1982. 9.95 (ISBN 0-87612-233-0); Italian ed. 10.00x (ISBN 0-87612-237-3). Self Realization.
Man's Eternal Quest. Paramahansa Yogananda. LC 75-17183. (Illus.). 503p. 1982. pap. 5.50 (ISBN 0-87612-232-2). Self Realization.
Man's Freedom. Paul Weiss. LC 67-23318. (Arcturus Books Paperbacks). 335p. 1967. pap. 8.95x (ISBN 0-8093-0277-2). S Ill U Pr.
Man's Impossibility, God's Possibility. Kenneth Hagin, Jr. 1978. pap. 2.50 (ISBN 0-89276-700-6). Hagin Ministries.

Man's Judgement Call-the Irrevocable Master Contract. Kenna. Date not set. price not set. Port Love Intl.

Man's Natural Powers: Essays for & About C. S. Lewis. Ed. by R. P. Tripp, Jr. (Orig.). 1975. pap. 5.00 (ISBN 0-905019-01-6). Soc New Lang Study.

Man's Need & God's Gift: Readings in Christian Theology. Ed. by Millard J. Erickson. LC 76-17965. 512p. 1976. pap. 12.95 (ISBN 0-8010-3324-1). Baker Bk.

Man's Origin, Man's Destiny. 1987. 9.95 (210356). Bethany Hse.

Man's Origin, Man's Destiny. A. W. Wilder-Smith. LC 74-28508. 320p. 1975. pap. 7.95 (ISBN 0-87123-356-8, 210356). Bethany Hse.

Man's Quest for God: Studies in Prayer & Symbolism. Abraham J. Heschel. LC 54-10371. (Hudson River Edition Ser.). 1981. 22.50x (ISBN 0-684-16829-4, ScribT). Scribner.

Man's Quest for God: Studies in Prayer & Symbolism. Abraham J. Heschel. LC 54-10371. 1954. 5.95 (ISBN 0-684-13582-5, ScribT). Scribner.

Man's Religion. 7th ed. John B. Noss & Davis S. Noss. (Illus.). 608p. 1984. text ed. write for info. (ISBN 0-02-388470-3). Macmillan.

Man's Subtle Bodies & Centers: The Aura, The Solar Plexus, The Chakras, Vol. 219. Omraam M. Aivanhov. (IZVOR Collection). 154p. (Orig.). 1986. pap. 4.95 (ISBN 2-85566-383-0, 219). Prosveta USA.

Man's Touch. Charles F. Stanley. LC 77-80948. 120p. 1977. pap. 3.95 (ISBN 0-88207-753-8). Victor Bks.

Mansion of the Gods. Rene De Goscinny. (Asterix Ser.). (Illus.). 1976. 7.95x (ISBN 0-340-17719-5); pap. 4.95x (ISBN 2-2050-6916-0). Intl Learn Syst.

Mansiones del Alma. 16th ed. H. Spencer Lewis. Tr. by AMORC Staff. (Span., Illus.). 235p. 1981. pap. 7.00 (ISBN 0-912057-67-X, GS-511). AMORC.

Mansions of the Soul. 19th ed. H. Spencer Lewis. LC 30-34218. 1981. 11.95 (ISBN 0-912057-07-6, G-511). AMORC.

Mansions of the Soul. Spencer H. Lewis. LC 30-34218. 338p. 1986. pap. 9.95 (ISBN 0-912057-43-2, G-655). AMORC.

Mantel's Folks Redner: Mantel's Sermons & Address in Yiddish Language for All Jewish Holidays & Many Other Occasions. Herman Mantel & Hugo Mantel. 320p. 27.50 (ISBN 0-87559-148-5). Shalom.

Mantique Apollinienne a Delphes: Essai Sur le Fonctionnement De L'Oracle. facsimile ed. Pierre Amandry. LC 75-10627. (Ancient Religion & Mythology Ser.). (Fr., Illus.). 1976. Repr. of 1950 ed. 23.50x (ISBN 0-405-07003-9). Ayer Co Pubs.

Mantle of Christ: A History of the Sydney Central Methodist Mission. Don Wright. (Illus.). 179p. 1985. text ed. 25.00x. U of Queensland Pr.

Mantle of the Prophet: Religion & Politics in Iran. Roy Mottahedeh. LC 86-42737. 416p. 1986. pap. 9.95 (ISBN 0-394-74865-4). Pantheon.

Mantra & Meditation. Usharbudh Arya & D. Litt. LC 81-84076. 237p. (Orig.). 1981. pap. 8.95 (ISBN 0-89389-074-X). Himalayan Pubs.

Mantra, Kirtana, Yantra & Tantra. Swami Jyotir Maya Nanda. (Illus.). 1974. pap. 3.99 (ISBN 0-934664-06-4). Yoga Res Foun.

Mantra Meditation. rev. ed. Lalita Sanadi. Ed. by Laura D'Auri. (Illus.). 160p. pap. cancelled (ISBN 0-87407-204-2, FP-4). Thor.

Mantramanjari: An Anthology of the Veclas for Modern Man & Contemporary Celebration. Raimundo Panikkar. 1977. 55.00x (ISBN 0-520-02854-6). U of Cal Pr.

Mantras for the Evening. Robert F. Morneau. LC 82-83587. (Illus.). 116p. (Orig.). 1982. pap. text ed. 4.95 (ISBN 0-8146-1269-5). Liturgical Pr.

Mantras for the Morning: An Introduction to Holistic Prayer. Robert F. Morneau. LC 81-1085. (Illus.). 120p. 1981. pap. 4.95 (ISBN 0-8146-1210-5). Liturgical Pr.

Mantras: Words of Power. Swami Sivananda Radha. LC 80-10293. (Illus.). 150p. 1980. pap. 7.95 (ISBN 0-931454-05-0). Timeless Bks.

Manual Biblico de Abingdon. Edward P. Blair. LC 81-12774. Tr. of Abingdon Bible Handbook. (Span.). 400p. (Orig.). 1982. pap. 12.95 (ISBN 0-687-23170-1). Abingdon.

Manual Biblico de Unger. Merrill F. Unger. Orig. Title: Unger's Bible Handbook. (Span.). 954p. 1976. pap. 12.95 (ISBN 0-8254-1778-3). Kregel.

Manual Comprensivo de Sicologia Pastoral. Ed. by Esdras Betancourt. (Span.). 168p. 1980. pap. 4.95 (ISBN 0-87148-580-X). Pathway Pr.

Manual de Ceremonias Matrimoniales. Ed. by Mario Ruiz. (Span.). 184p. 1982. 6.95 (ISBN 0-87148-581-8). Pathway Pr.

Manual de Eclesiologia. H. E. Dana. Tr. by Adolfo Robleto. Orig. Title: Manual of Ecclesiology. write for info. (ISBN 0-311-17018-8). Casa Bautista.

Manual de Finanzas Para Iglesias. F. W. Patterson. (Illus.). 118p. 1986. pap. 2.50 (ISBN 0-311-17005-6). Casa Bautista.

Manual for Acolytes: The Duties of the Server at Liturgigal Celebrations. Dennis G. Michno. LC 80-81096. (Illus., Orig.). 1981. pap. 4.95 (ISBN 0-8192-1272-5). Morehouse.

Manual for Altar Guilds. Victor Gebauer. 72p. (Orig.). 1986. pap. 9.50 (ISBN 0-8066-2203-2, 10-4267). Augsburg.

Manual for Biblical Preaching. Lloyd M. Perry. pap. 12.95 (ISBN 0-8010-7047-3). Baker Bk.

Manual for Design for Church Growth. Charles L. Chaney & Ron S. Lewis. 1978. pap. text ed. 2.50 (ISBN 0-8054-6219-8). Broadman.

Manual for Editors & Writers. Church of God Editorial Department. 1976. pap. 4.95 (ISBN 0-87148-568-0). Pathway Pr.

Manual for Lectors. Judith Tate. (Orig.). 1975. 2.95 (ISBN 0-8278-0030-4, Pub. by Pflaum Pr). Peter Li.

Manual for Missionaries on Furlough. Marjorie A. Collins. LC 72-92747. 1978. pap. 4.45 (ISBN 0-87808-119-4). William Carey Lib.

Manual for Today's Missionary: From Recruitment to Retirement. rev. ed. Marjorie A. Collins. LC 85-27603. (Mission Candidate Aids Ser.). 400p. 1986. pap. 9.95x (ISBN 0-87808-204-2, WCL204-2). William Carey Lib.

Manual Grammar of the Greek New Testament: With Index. H. E. Dana & R. Mantey. 1957. text ed. write for info. (ISBN 0-02-327070-5, 32707). Macmillan.

Manual Greek Lexicon of the New Testament. 3rd ed. G. Abbott-Smith. 528p. 1937. 21.95 (ISBN 0-567-01001-5, Pub. by T & T Clark Ltd UK). Fortress.

Manual of Bible History: Reading Lessons, Explanations, Questions & Geographical Notes, 2 vols. Charles Baker. 1980. lib. bdg. 195.95 (ISBN 0-8490-3117-6). Gordon Pr.

Manual of Buddhism for Advanced Students. Carolina A. Davids. LC 78-72410. Repr. of 1932 ed. 32.50 (ISBN 0-404-17274-1). AMS Pr.

Manual of Buddhism in Its Modern Development. Robert S. Hardy. LC 78-72439. Repr. of 1853 ed. 46.50 (ISBN 0-404-17305-5). AMS Pr.

Manual of Buddhist Philosophy. William M. McGovern. LC 78-70097. Repr. of 1923 ed. 27.50 (ISBN 0-404-17346-2). AMS Pr.

Manual of Christian Doctrine. Louis Berkhof. 1933. pap. 7.95 (ISBN 0-8028-1647-9). Eerdmans.

Manual of Christian Reformed Church Government, 1980. rev. ed. William P. Brink & Richard R. DeRidder. LC 80-24129. 1980. pap. text ed. 7.95 (ISBN 0-933140-19-3). CRC Pubns.

Manual of Church History, 2 vols. Albert H. Newman. 1977. Set. lib. bdg. 250.00 (ISBN 0-8490-2205-3). Gordon Pr.

Manual of Church History, 2 Vols. Franz X. Von Funk. Tr. by Luigi Cappadelta. LC 78-168077. 1910. Set. 67.50 (ISBN 0-404-02646-X). AMS Pr.

Manual of Eastern Orthodox Prayer. 2nd ed. pap. text ed. 3.95 (ISBN 0-88141-012-8). St Vladimirs.

Manual of Ecclesiastical Architecture. W. W. Martin. 1977. lib. bdg. 75.00 (ISBN 0-8490-2206-1). Gordon Pr.

Manual of Exorcism: Useful for Priests & Ministers of the Church. LC 74-84092. 141p. 1975. pap. 2.95 (ISBN 0-913456-73-X, Pub. by Hispanic Soc). Interbk Inc.

Manual of Field Excavation. William G. Dever & Lance H. Darrel. 1979. 15.00x (ISBN 0-87820-303-6). Ktav.

Manual of Greek Forms. James L. Boyer. pap. 4.95 (ISBN 0-88469-007-5). BMH Bks.

Manual of Indian Buddhism. H. Kern. 1974. Repr. 6.95 (ISBN 0-8426-0674-2). Orient Bk Dist.

Manual of Life: The New Testament for Daily Living. M. B. Pennington. 128p. (Orig.). 1985. pap. 4.95 (ISBN 0-8091-2710-5). Paulist Pr.

Manual of Mythology. George W. Cox. LC 77-94556. 1979. Repr. of 1867 ed. lib. bdg. 30.00 (ISBN 0-89341-307-0). Longwood Pub Group.

Manual of Pastoral Problems & Procedures. Lloyd M. Perry & Edward J. Lias. 8.95 (ISBN 0-8010-7063-5). Baker Bk.

Manual of Scandinavian Mythology: Containing a Popular Account of the Two Eddas & of the Religion of Odin. Grenville Pigott. Ed. by Kees W. Bolle. LC 77-79152. (Mythology Ser.). 1978. Repr. of 1839 ed. lib. bdg. 27.50x (ISBN 0-405-10561-4). Ayer Co Pubs.

Manual of Textual Analysis. Vinton A. Dearing. LC 82-20947. ix, 108p. 1983. Repr. of 1959 ed. lib. bdg. 32.50x (ISBN 0-313-23734-4, DEMA). Greenwood.

Manual of the Mother Church, 11 vols. Mary B. Eddy. Incl. Vol. 1. Danish. 12.50 (ISBN 0-87952-104-X); Vol. 2. Dutch. 12.50 (ISBN 0-87952-110-4); Vol. 3. French. 12.50 (ISBN 0-87952-118-X); Vol. 4. German. 12.50 (ISBN 0-87952-153-8); Vol. 5. Italian. 12.50 (ISBN 0-87952-181-3); Vol. 6. Norwegian. 12.50 (ISBN 0-87952-196-1); Vol. 7. Portuguese. 12.50 (ISBN 0-87952-206-2); Vol. 8. Spanish. 12.50 (ISBN 0-87952-228-3); Vol. 9. Swedish. 12.50 (ISBN 0-87952-251-8); Vol. 10. Greek. 12.50 (ISBN 0-87952-171-6); Vol. 11. Japanese. 12.50 (ISBN 0-87952-191-0). First Church.

Manual of the Mother Church, The First Church of Christ, Scientist, in Boston, Massachusetts. Mary B. Eddy. standard ed. 9.50 (ISBN 0-87952-061-2); century ed. 11.00 (ISBN 0-87952-063-9); leather 35.00 (ISBN 0-87952-064-7). First Church.

Manual of the Orthodox Church's Divine Services. D. Archpriest Sokoloff. 172p. (Orig.). 1975. pap. 6.00 (ISBN 0-317-30302-3). Holy Trinity.

Manual of Theology... Christian Doctrine... Church Order, 2 vols. in one. John L. Dagg. Ed. by Edwins. Gausted. LC 79-52592. (Baptist Tradition Ser.). 1980. Repr. of 1858 ed. lib. bdg. 57.50x (ISBN 0-405-12459-7). Ayer Co Pubs.

Manual of Zen Buddhism. D. T. Suzuki. (Orig.). 1960. pap. 5.95 (ISBN 0-394-17224-8, E231, Ever). Grove.

Manual on the Liturgy: Lutheran Book of Worship. Philip H. Pfatteicher & Carlos R. Messerli. LC 78-68179. 1979. 18.00 (ISBN 0-8066-1676-8, 12-2015). Augsburg.

Manual para el Catolico de Hoy. Redemptorist Pastoral Publication. 1978. pap. 1.95 (ISBN 0-89243-091-5). Liguori Pubns.

Manual para la Familia Catolica Hispana de Hoy. Ed. by John McPhee. Tr. by Olimpia Diaz. (Span.). 1980. pap. 1.50 (ISBN 0-89243-123-7, 51900). Liguori Pubns.

Manual para los Discipulos de Hoy. D. Duane Cummins. Tr. by Conchita Delgado & Zayda N. Sanchez. LC 83-15489. Tr. of Handbook for Today's Disciples. (Span., Illus.). 64p. (Orig.). 1983. pap. 2.25 (ISBN 0-8272-2316-1). CBP.

Manual para Predicadores Laicos. J. D. Crane. 122p. 1983. pap. 2.10 (ISBN 0-311-42039-7). Casa Bautista.

Manual Rosacruz. 8th ed. H. Spencer Lewis. Tr. by AMORC Staff. (Span., Illus.). 268p. (Orig.). 1981. pap. 8.00 (ISBN 0-912057-60-2, GS-508). AMORC.

Manual: School Library-Media Skills Test. Anne M. Hyland. 50p. 1986. pap. text ed. 5.00 (ISBN 0-87287-524-5). Libs Unl.

Manuductio Administerium, Directions for a Candidate of the Ministry. Cotton Mather. LC 75-41190. Repr. of 1938 ed. 17.25 (ISBN 0-404-14685-6). AMS Pr.

Manuel de l'Inquisiteur, 2 vols. in 1. Bernardus Guidonis. Ed. by G. Mollat. LC 78-63183. (Heresies of the Early Christian & Medieval Era: Second Ser.). Repr. of 1927 ed. 57.50 set (ISBN 0-404-16199-5). AMS Pr.

Manuel des cures pour le bon Gouvernement Temporel Des Paroisses et des Fabriques dans le Bas-Canada. Joseph Desautels. 1864. 24.00 (ISBN 0-384-11480-6). Johnson Repr.

Manuel d'iconographie Chretienne, Grecque et Latine. Dionysius Of Fourna. Tr. by Paul Durand. 1963. Repr. of 1845 ed. 32.00 (ISBN 0-8337-0868-6). B Franklin.

Manuel du Traducteur pour l'Evangile de Marc. Robert G. Bratcher & Eugene A. Nida. Tr. by C. Weber. (Auxiliaires Du Traducteur Ser.). 542p. 1963. pap. 7.05x (ISBN 0-8267-0250-3, 51972, Pub. by United Bible). Am Bible.

Manufacturer's Handbook. Ed. by Irene B. Harrell & Alie H. Benson. (Orig.). 1987. pap. 7.00 (ISBN 0-915541-04-1). Star Bks Inc.

Manuscript Catalog of the American Jewish Archives, 4 vols. Ed. by American Jewish Archives, Cincinnati Staff. 1971. Set. lib. bdg. 400.00 (ISBN 0-8161-0899-4, Hall Library). G K Hall.

Manuscript Catalog of the American Jewish Archives, Cincinnati: First Supplement. Ed. by American Jewish Archives, Cincinnati Staff. 1978. lib. bdg. 105.00 (ISBN 0-8161-0934-6, Hall Library). G K Hall.

Manuscript History of the Psalms of Solomon. Robert R. Hann. LC 81-21212. (SBL Septuagint & Cognate Studies). 1982. pap. 15.00 (ISBN 0-89130-557-2, 06-04-13). Scholars Pr GA.

Manuscripts of the Bible. T. S. Pattie. (Illus.). 32p. (Orig.). 1979. pap. 2.95 (ISBN 0-904654-13-3, Pub. by British Lib). Longwood Pub Group.

Manuscripts of the Greek Bible: An Introduction to Paleography. Bruce M. Metzger. (Illus.). 1981. 19.95x (ISBN 0-19-502924-0). Oxford U Pr.

Many Are Called but Few Are Chosen. Verlan Andersen. 96p. 1967. pap. 2.95 (ISBN 0-89036-002-2). Hawkes Pub Inc.

Many Faces of Anti-Semitism. George Salomon & Rose Feitelson. 44p. 1978. 1.50 (ISBN 0-87495-045-7). Am Jewish Comm.

Many Faces of Judaism. Gilbert S. Rosenthal. Ed. by Seymour Rossel. LC 78-25898. 1979. pap. 4.95x (ISBN 0-87441-311-7). Behrman.

Many Faces of Religion & Society. Ed. by M. Darrol Bryant & Rita H. Mataragnon. LC 84-26539. (God Ser.). 208p. (Orig.). 1985. 21.95 (ISBN 0-913757-20-9, Pub. by New Era Bks.); pap. 12.95 (ISBN 0-913757-21-7, Pub. by New Era Bks). Paragon Hse.

Many Infallible Proofs. Henry M. Morris. LC 74-81484. 384p. 1974. pap. 8.95 (ISBN 0-89051-005-9). Master Bks.

Many Meanings of Myth. Martin S. Day. 574p. 1984. lib. bdg. 28.75 (ISBN 0-8191-3821-5); pap. text ed. 20.75 (ISBN 0-8191-3822-3). U Pr of Amer.

Many Peoples, Many Faiths. 2nd ed. Robert S. Ellwood, Jr. (Illus.). 416p. 1982. 27.95 (ISBN 0-13-556001-2). P-H.

Many Religions: One God. Carol R. Murphy. LC 66-30689. (Orig.). 1966. pap. 2.50x (ISBN 0-87574-150-9). Pendle Hill.

Maori Religion & Mythology. Elsdon Best. LC 75-35236. Repr. of 1924 ed. 45.00 (ISBN 0-404-14412-8). AMS Pr.

Maori Religion & Mythology. Edward Shortland. LC 75-35268. Repr. of 1882 ed. 22.50 (ISBN 0-404-14437-3). AMS Pr.

Maori Tohunga & His Spirit World. Johannes C. Andersen. LC 75-35224. Repr. of 1948 ed. 20.00 (ISBN 0-404-14403-9). AMS Pr.

Map of Life. F. J. Sheed. 1979. pap. 2.95 (ISBN 0-88479-017-7). Arena Lettres.

Map of the New Country: Women & Christianity. Sara Maitland. LC 82-13142. 218p. 1983. pap. 8.95 (ISBN 0-7100-9301-2). Methuen Inc.

Mapilla Muslims of Kerala: A Study of Islamic Trends. Roland Miller. LC 76-901758. 1976. 14.00x (ISBN 0-88386-080-5). South Asia Bks.

Maps of the Holy Land: Cartobibliography of Printed Maps, 1475-1900. Eran Laor. LC 86-15298. 224p. 1986. 77.50 (ISBN 0-8451-1705-X). A R Liss.

Maps of the Holy Land: Images of Terra Sancta Through Two Millennia. Kenneth Nebenzahl. LC 86-675055. (Illus.). 164p. 1986. 55.00 (ISBN 0-89659-658-3). Abbeville Pr.

Marantha: The Mouse in the Tomb. Wanda L. Spangler. 1986. 6.95 (ISBN 0-8062-2500-9). Carlton.

Maravillas De la Creacion. Orig. Title: Wonders of Creation. 124p. 1979. 18.95 (ISBN 0-311-09092-3, Edit Mundo). Casa Bautista.

Marbin Besimho. P. S. Pollak. (Heb). 9.50 (ISBN 0-87559-083-7); pap. 5.00 saddle stitched (ISBN 0-87559-084-5). Shalom.

Marc Chagall: A Biography. Sidney Alexander. (Illus.). 525p. 1979. 26.95x (ISBN 0-8464-1196-2). Beekman Pubs.

March of Faith: Samuel Morris. Lindley Baldwin. 96p. 1969. pap. 2.95 (ISBN 0-87123-360-6, 200360). Bethany Hse.

March of Faith: The Story of Religion in America Since 1865. Winfred E. Garrison. LC 79-138112. 1971. Repr. of 1933 ed. lib. bdg. 22.50x (ISBN 0-8371-5688-2, GAMF). Greenwood.

March of Holiness Through the Centuries. William S. Deal. 1978. pap. 2.50 (ISBN 0-686-05528-4). Crusade Pubs.

March of Methodism. Cyril J. Davey. 1952. 5.95 (ISBN 0-8022-0345-0). Philos Lib.

March of the Institutions: A Commentary on the Interdependence of Rulers & Learned. Eunice Braun. 112p. 9.95 (ISBN 0-85398-182-5); pap. 5.95 (ISBN 0-85398-183-3). G Ronald Pub.

March to Zion: United States Policy & the Founding of Israel. Kenneth R. Bain. LC 79-7413. 256p. 1980. 18.50 (ISBN 0-89096-076-3). Tex A&M Univ Pr.

Marchin' the Pilgrims Home: Leadership & Decision-Making in an Afro-Caribbean Faith. Stephen D. Glazier. LC 82-24179. (Contributions to the Study of Religion Ser.: No. 10). (Illus.). xx, 165p. 1983. lib. bdg. 29.95 (ISBN 0-313-23464-7, GPI/). Greenwood.

Marching Orders for the End Battle. Corrie ten Boom. 1970. pap. 1.95 (ISBN 0-87508-024-3). Chr Lit.

Marching to Glory. Edward H. McKinley. 290p. pap. 4.95 (ISBN 0-86544-039-5). Salv Army Suppl South.

Marcion. Robert S. Wilson. LC 78-63176. (Heresies of the Early Christian & Medieval Era: Second Ser.). Repr. of 1933 ed. 32.00 (ISBN 0-404-16194-4). AMS Pr.

Marcion & the New Testament. John Knox. LC 78-63168. (Heresies of the Early Christian & Medieval Era: Second Ser.). Repr. of 1942 ed. 31.00 (ISBN 0-404-16183-9). AMS Pr.

Marcion: On the Restitution of Christianity. R. Joseph Hoffmann. LC 83-9008. (AAR Academy Ser.). 356p. 1984. 16.50 (ISBN 0-89130-638-2, 01 01 46). Scholars Pr GA.

Marcion: The Gospel of the Alien God. Adolf Von Harnack. Tr. by John E. Steely & Lyle D. Bierma. Orig. Title: Marcion, das Evangelium vom Fremden Gott. 265p. 1987. lib. bdg. 24.95 (ISBN 0-939464-16-0). Labyrinth Pr.

Marcos: Estudios Para un Joven En Busca De Identidad. Jack Greever. Orig. Title: Mark: an Inductive Bible Study. (Span.). 64p. 1982. pap. 2.50 (ISBN 0-311-12325-2, Edit Mundo). Casa Bautista.

Marcos Presenta Al Salvador. Raymond B. Brown. Tr. by Olivia Y Alfredo Lerin. Orig. Title: Mark - the Saviour for Sinners. 160p. 1982. pap. 4.25 (ISBN 0-311-04346-1). Casa Bautista.

Marcus & Narcissa Whitman & the Opening of Old Oregon. Clifford M. Drury. (Illus.). 911p. 1986. pap. 21.84 (ISBN 0-914019-08-2). Pacif NW Natl Pks.

Mardi Gras Syndrome: Rethinking Christian Sexuality. Joan Timmerman. 144p. 1984. pap. 8.95 (ISBN 0-8245-0641-3). Crossroad NY.

Margaret & Her Friends; or, Ten Conversations with Margaret Fuller Upon the Mythology of the Greeks & Its Expression in Art. Caroline H. Dall. LC 72-4961. (Romantic Tradition in American Literature Ser.). 166p. 1972. Repr. of 1895 ed. 18.00 (ISBN 0-405-04633-2). Ayer Co Pubs.

Margaret Fell Speaking. Hugh Barbour. LC 76-4224. (Orig.). 1976. pap. 2.50x (ISBN 0-87574-206-8). Pendle Hill.

Margery Kempe, Genius & Mystic. Katharine Cholmeley. LC 78-7811. 1978. Repr. of 1947 ed. lib. bdg. 17.50 (ISBN 0-8414-0296-5). Folcroft.

Marginal Notes for the New Testament. Ed. by R. G. Bratcher. 125p. 1980. softcover 2.50x (ISBN 0-8267-0026-8, 08558, Pub. by United Bible). Am Bible.

Marginal Notes for the Old Testament. Ed. by R. G. Bratcher. 186p. 1980. softcover 5.00x (ISBN 0-8267-0025-X, 08557, Pub. by United Bible). Am Bible.

Maria Reina de Los Apostolos. (Span.). 1.25 (ISBN 0-8198-4713-5). Dghtrs St Paul.

Maria Woodworth Etter: Her Life & Ministry. Gordon Lindsay. 2.50 (ISBN 0-89985-022-7). Christ Nations.

Mariage En Droit Canonique, 2 Vols. Adhemar Esmein. (Fr). 1969. Repr. of 1891 ed. Set. 47.00 (ISBN 0-8337-1072-9). B Franklin.

Marian Era, Vol. 11. Ed. by Marion A. Habig. (Illus.). 132p. 1973. 6.95 (ISBN 0-8199-0215-2). Franciscan Herald.

Marian Paintings of Jan Van Eyck. Carol J. Purtle. LC 81-47943. (Illus.). 288p. 1982. 52.50x (ISBN 0-691-03989-5). Princeton U Pr.

Marian Studies: Proceedings, Vol. 35. Mariological Society of America. Washington, D.C. Convention, 1984. 190p. 10.00 (ISBN 0-318-17634-3). Mariological Soc.

Marian Studies: Proceedings, Vol. 37. Mariological Society of America. Tampa, Fla. Convention, 1986. 1987. 10.00. Mariological Soc.

Marian's Big Book of Bible Stories. Marian M. Schoolland. 1947. 12.95 (ISBN 0-8028-5003-0). Eerdmans.

Marian's Favorite Bible Stories. Marian M. Schoolland. 1948. 5.95 (ISBN 0-8028-5002-2); pap. 3.95 (ISBN 0-8028-5007-3). Eerdmans.

Marie Magdalens Funeral Teares. Robert Southwell. LC 74-22099. 180p. 1975. 30.00x (ISBN 0-8201-1144-9). Schol Facsimiles.

Marind-Anim Von Hollandischsud-Neu-Guinea, 2 vols. in 1. Paul Wirz. Ed. by Kees W. Bolle. (Mythology Ser.). (Ger.). 1978. Repr. of 1922 ed. lib. bdg. 54.00x (ISBN 0-405-10569-X). Ayer Co Pubs.

Marists & Melanesians: A History of Catholic Missions in the Solomon Islands. Hugh Laracy. 222p. 1976. text ed. 15.00x (ISBN 0-8248-0361-2). UH Pr.

Maritain Volume of "The Thomist", Dedicated to Jacques Maritain on the Occasion of His 60th Anniversary. Ed. by Dominican Fathers of the Province of St. Joseph. LC 77-92509. (Essay Index in Reprint Ser.). 1978. Repr. 24.50x (ISBN 0-8486-3003-3). Roth Pub Inc.

Marital Breakdown. J. Dominian. 1969. 5.95 (ISBN 0-8199-0151-2, L38436). Franciscan Herald.

Marital Counseling: A Biblical Behavioral Cognitive Approach. H. Norman Wright. 370p. 1981. 16.95 (ISBN 0-938786-00-8). Chr Marriage.

Marital Intimacy: A Catholic Perspective. Joan Anzia & Mary Durkin. 81p. pap. 6.95. Loyola.

Marital Love. Emanuel Swedenborg. LC 38-13542. 760p. 1974. student ed. 12.00 (ISBN 0-87785-150-6). Swedenborg.

Marital Relations, Birth Control, & Abortion in Jewish Law. David M. Feldman. LC 68-15338. 336p. 1974. pap. 8.95 (ISBN 0-8052-0438-5). Schocken.

Mark. rev., enl., 2nd ed. Paul J. Achtemeier. Ed. by Gerhard Krodel. LC 85-46020. (Proclamation Commentaries: The New Testament Witnesses for Preaching Ser.). 144p. 1986. pap. 4.50 (ISBN 0-8006-1916-1, 1-1916). Fortress.

Mark. J. A. Alexander. (Geneva Series Commentaries). 1984. 15.95 (ISBN 0-85151-422-7). Banner of Truth.

Mark. Joseph A. Alexander. (Thornapple Commentaries Ser.). 1980. pap. 8.95 (ISBN 0-8010-0150-1). Baker Bk.

Mark, Vol. II. Beacon Bible Commentary Staff. 6.95 (ISBN 0-8010-0755-0). Baker Bk.

Mark. Wilfrid Harrington. (New Testament Message Ser.: Vol. 4). 270p. 1979. 14.95 (ISBN 0-89453-192-1); pap. 9.95 (ISBN 0-89453-127-1). M Glazier.

Mark. William Hendriksen. (New Testament Commentary Ser). 708p. 1975. 21.95 (ISBN 0-8010-4114-7). Baker Bk.

Mark. James Hoover. (Lifebuilder Bible Studies). 96p. (Orig.). 1985. pap. text ed. 2.95 (ISBN 0-8308-1004-8). Inter-Varsity.

Mark. Irving L. Jensen. (Bible Self-Study Ser.). (Illus.). 1972. pap. 3.25 (ISBN 0-8024-1041-3). Moody.

Mark. Matthew Lipman. LC 80-80849. (Philosophy for Children Ser.). 86p. 1980. pap. 8.00 (ISBN 0-916834-13-1, TX 752-903). First Mntn Foun.

Mark. (Erdmans Commentaries Ser.). 4.50 (ISBN 0-8010-3410-8). Baker Bk.

Mark. Ralph Martin. Ed. by John Hayes. LC 81-82350. (Knox Preaching Guides). 96p. 1981. pap. 4.95 (ISBN 0-8042-3234-2). John Knox.

Mark. Paul S. Minear. LC 59-10454. (Layman's Bible Commentary, Vol. 17). 1962. pap. 4.95 (ISBN 0-8042-3077-3). John Knox.

Mark. James Morison. 1981. lib. bdg. 21.00 (ISBN 0-86524-069-8, 4102). Klock & Klock.

Mark. Maurice Nicoll. LC 84-22116. 216p. 1985. pap. 9.95 (ISBN 0-87773-315-5, 72998-6). Shambhala Pubns.

Mark. J. C. Ryle. 370p. 1984. pap. 5.95 (ISBN 0-85151-441-3). Banner of Truth.

Mark. Michael Wilcock. 1983. pap. 4.50 (ISBN 0-87508-167-3). Chr Lit.

Mark: A Bible Commentary for Teaching & Preaching. Lamar Williamson, Jr. Ed. by James L. Mays & Paul J. Achtemeier. LC 82-17161. (Interpretation Ser.). 289p. 1983. 17.95 (ISBN 0-8042-3121-4). John Knox.

Mark: A Bible Study Commentary. Howard F. Vos. pap. 4.95 (ISBN 0-310-33873-5, 11044P). Zondervan.

Mark: A Daily Dialogue with God. Ron Klug. (Personal Bible Studyguide Ser.). 156p. 1984. pap. 5.95 (ISBN 0-87788-539-7). Shaw Pubs.

Mark: A Good News Commentary. Larry Hurtado. LC 82-48930. 288p. (Orig.). 1983. pap. 9.95 (ISBN 0-06-064085-5, RD/447, HarpR). Har-Row.

Mark: A New Translation with Introduction & Commentary, Vol. 27. C. S. Mann. LC 85-4433. (Illus.). 744p. 1986. 20.00 (ISBN 0-385-03253-6, Anchor). Doubleday.

Mark: A Study Guide. John Timmer. (Revelation Series for Adults). (Orig.). 1980. pap. 2.50 (ISBN 0-933140-13-4). CRC Pubns.

Mark: An Access for Scripture Study. Daniel J. Harrington & Edmund F. Gordon. (Access Guide for Scripture Study). 128p. 1983. pap. 3.45 (ISBN 0-8215-5928-1); leader's ed. 4.20 (ISBN 0-8215-5933-8). Sadlier.

Mark & Matthew. Sean Freyne & Henry Wansbrough. Ed. by Laurence Bright. LC 71-173033. (Scripture Discussion Commentary Ser.: Pt. 7). 256p. 1971. pap. text ed. 4.50 (ISBN 0-87946-006-7). ACTA Found.

Mark As Story: An Introduction to the Narrative of a Gospel. Donald Michie & David Rhoads. LC 81-43084. 176p. 1982. pap. 8.95 (ISBN 0-8006-1614-6). Fortress.

Mark Buntain Story. Ron Hembree. LC 83-73187. 256p. 1984. pap. 3.95 (ISBN 0-87123-593-5, 200593). Bethany Hse.

Mark: Evangelist & Theologian. Ralph P. Martin. (Contemporary Evangelical Perspective Ser.). 249p. 1973. kivar 7.95 (ISBN 0-310-28801-0). Zondervan.

Mark: God in Action. Chuck Christensen & Winnie Christensen. LC 72-88935. (Fisherman Bible Studyguide Ser.). 94p. 1972. saddle-stitched 2.95 (ISBN 0-87788-309-2). Shaw Pubs.

Mark: God on the Move. Carolyn Nystrom. (Young Fisherman Bible Studyguide Ser.). 96p. 1978. pap. 4.95 tchr's ed. (ISBN 0-87788-312-2); student ed. 2.95 (ISBN 0-87788-311-4). Shaw Pubs.

Mark: Good News for Hard Times. George T. Montague. 200p. (Orig.). 1981. pap. 6.95 (ISBN 0-89283-096-4). Servant.

Mark: Good News for Today. Dale & Sandy Larsen. (Carpenter Studyguide). 80p. 1984. member's handbook 1.95 (ISBN 0-87788-540-0); saddle-stitched leader's handbook 2.95 (ISBN 0-87788-541-9). Shaw Pubs.

Mark: Gospel of Action. Ralph Earle. LC 73-15084. (Everyman's Bible Commentary Ser.). 1970. pap. 5.95 (ISBN 0-8024-2041-9). Moody.

Mark: Gospel of God's Servant. rev. ed. Keith Brooks. (Teach Yourself the Bible Ser.). 1987. pap. 2.75 (ISBN 0-8024-5200-0). Moody.

Mark: Gospel of God's Servant. Keith L. Brooks. (Teach Yourself the Bible Ser.). 64p. 1961. pap. 2.75 (ISBN 0-8024-5183-7). Moody.

Mark Gruner's Numbers of Life: An Introduction to Numerology. Mark Gruner & Christopher K. Brown. LC 78-57560. 1979. 9.95 (ISBN 0-8008-5639-2); pap. 3.95 (ISBN 0-08-805640-6). Taplinger.

Mark: Meditations. August Van Ryn. 1957. pap. 2.25 (ISBN 0-87213-892-5). Loizeaux.

Mark, Neighborhood Bible Study. Marilyn Kunz & Catherine Schell. 1970. pap. 2.95 (ISBN 0-8423-4101-3). Tyndale.

Mark of a Man. Elisabeth Elliot. LC 80-25108. 176p. 1981. pap. 5.95 (ISBN 0-8007-5121-3, Power Bks). Revell.

Mark of the Beast. Sydney Watson. 256p. 1974. 5.95 (ISBN 0-8007-5199-X, Power Bks); (Spire Bks). Revell.

Mark of the Christian. Francis A. Schaeffer. pap. 2.50 (ISBN 0-87784-434-8). Inter-Varsity.

Mark: The Gospel as Story. Ernest Best. Ed. by John Riches. 154p. 1983. 21.95 (ISBN 0-567-09342-5, Pub. by T&T Clark Ltd UK). Fortress.

Mark: The Way for All Nations. rev. ed. Willard M. Swartley. LC 78-27917. 224p. 1981. pap. 9.95 (ISBN 0-8361-1977-0). Herald Pr.

Mark: Visionary of Early Christianity. Leonard Doohan. LC 86-72485. 192p. (Orig.). 1986. pap. 9.95 (ISBN 0-939680-33-5). Bear & Co.

Markan Public Debate: Literary Technique, Concentric Structure & Theology in Mark 2: 1-3: 6. Joanna Dewey. LC 79-17443. (Society of Biblical Literature Ser.: No. 48). 14.95 (ISBN 0-89130-337-5, 06-01-48); pap. 9.95 (ISBN 0-89130-338-3). Scholars Pr GA.

Markers III: The Journal of the Association for Gravestone Studies. Ed. by David Watters. LC 81-642903. (Illus.). 162p. (Orig.). 1985. lib. bdg. 25.25 (ISBN 0-8191-4537-8); pap. text ed. 11.50 (ISBN 0-8191-4538-6). U Pr of Amer.

Market Day of the Soul: The Puritan Doctrine of the Sabbath in England, 1532-1700. James T. Dennison, Jr. LC 83-6990. (Illus.). 188p. (Orig.). 1983. lib. bdg. 25.00 (ISBN 0-8191-3204-7); pap. text ed. 11.25 (ISBN 0-8191-3205-5). U Pr of Amer.

Marketing. David L. Appel. (How to Ser.). 43p. 1986. 5.65 (ISBN 0-318-20575-0). Natl Cath Educ.

Marketing Religious Health Care. Robin S. MacStravic. 140p. (Orig.). 1987. pap. 24.00 (ISBN 0-87125-121-3). Cath Health.

Marking the Scriptures. Daniel H. Ludlow. 105p. (Orig.). 1980. pap. 4.95 (ISBN 0-87747-815-5). Deseret Bk.

Markings. Dag Hammarskjold. (Epiphany Bks.). 1985. pap. 3.50 (ISBN 0-345-32741-1). Ballantine.

Mark's Gospel: A History of Its Interpretation. Sean Kealy. LC 81-84384. 144p. (Orig.). 1982. pap. 8.95 (ISBN 0-8091-2417-3). Paulist Pr.

Marks of a True Believer: First John Two Vs Eighteen Through Four Twenty-One. John MacArthur, Jr. (John MacArthur Bible Studies Ser.). 1987. pap. 3.95 (ISBN 0-8024-5312-0). Moody.

Mark's Sketch Book of Christ. Helen Tenney. 1975. spiral bound 6.45 (ISBN 0-85151-075-2). Banner of Truth.

Mark's Story of Jesus. Werner H. Kelber. LC 78-14668. 96p. 1979. pap. 4.50 (ISBN 0-8006-1355-4, 1-1355). Fortress.

Mark's Superb Gospel. Ivor C. Powell. LC 85-25615. 432p. 1986. 16.95 (ISBN 0-8254-3523-4). Kregel.

Markus-Stoff Bei Lukas. Tim Schramm. LC 79-96099. (New Testament Studies Monographs: No. 14). (Ger). 1971. 34.50 (ISBN 0-521-07743-5). Cambridge U Pr.

Marla. Ethel Van Pelt. 154p. (Orig.). 1982. pap. 2.95 (ISBN 0-89084-155-1). Bob Jones Univ Pr.

Marmaduke Pickthall: British Muslim. Peter Clark. (Illus.). 156p. 1987. 19.95 (ISBN 0-7043-2514-4, Pub. by Quartet Bks). Salem Hse Pubs.

Maronites in History. Matti Moosa. 350p. 1986. text ed. 35.00x (ISBN 0-8156-2365-8). Syracuse U Pr.

Marrano Poets of the Seventeenth Century: An Anthology of the Poetry of Joao Pinto Delgado, Antonio Enriquez Gomez & Miguel de Barrios. Ed. & tr. by Timothy Oelman. (Littman Library of Jewish Civilization). (Illus.). 1985. 24.95x (ISBN 0-19-710047-3). Oxford U Pr.

Marriage. Spencer W. Kimball. LC 78-4132. (Illus.). 1978. 5.95 (ISBN 0-87747-675-6). Deseret Bk.

Marriage. Karl Rahner. 1.50 (ISBN 0-87193-118-4). Dimension Bks.

Marriage According to God's Word: How to Succeed at Marriage. Woody McGraw. LC 83-9121. 86p. (Orig.). 1983. pap. 2.95 (ISBN 0-913309-00-1). Trinity House.

Marriage: According to the New Code of Canon Law. Bernad A. Siegle. LC 86-10806. 297p. (Orig.). 1986. pap. 14.95 (ISBN 0-8189-0497-6). Alba.

Marriage: According to the New Code of Canon Law. new ed. Bernard Siegle. LC 72-4055. 297p. (Orig.). Date not set. pap. 14.95 (ISBN 0-8189-0497-6). Alba.

Marriage Affair. Compiled by J. Allan Petersen. 1971. pap. 9.95 (ISBN 0-8423-4171-4). Tyndale.

Marriage Among Christians: A Curious Tradition. James T. Burtchaell et al. LC 77-81396. (Illus.). 192p. 1977. pap. 3.50 (ISBN 0-87793-139-9). Ave Maria.

Marriage: An Orthodox Perspective. John Meyendorff. LC 75-14241. 144p. 1975. pap. 5.95 (ISBN 0-913836-05-2). St Vladimirs.

Marriage & Death Notices from Southern Christian Advocate, 1837-1860, Vol. 1. Brent Holcomb. 1979. 40.00 (ISBN 0-89308-111-6). Southern Hist Pr.

Marriage & Divorce: What the Bible Says. James M. Efird. (Contemporary Christian Concerns Ser.). 96p. (Orig.). 1985. pap. 4.95 (ISBN 0-687-23619-3). Abingdon.

Marriage & Family Enrichment: New Perspectives & Programs. Ed. by Herbert A. Otto. LC 75-30743. 1976. pap. 9.95 (ISBN 0-687-23620-7). Abingdon.

Marriage & Family Life: A Jewish View. Ed. by Abraham B. Shoulson. 19.95x (ISBN 0-8084-0378-8). New Coll U Pr.

Marriage & Family Life Code of the Jewish Faith. Bernard Abramowitz. (Hebrew., Heb, & Eng). 12.50 (ISBN 0-87559-098-5). Shalom.

Marriage & Priesthood: Six Sermons on Commitment. (Sermon Ser.: No. 3). 33p. (Orig.). 1984. pap. 5.00 (ISBN 0-936384-16-6). Cowley Pubns.

Marriage & Sexuality in Islam: A Translation of al-Ghazali's Book on the Etiquette of Marriage from the Ihya' Madelain Farah. 192p. 1984. 20.00 (ISBN 0-87480-231-8). U of Utah Pr.

Marriage & the Family: A Christian Perspective. Stephen A. Grunlan. 384p. 1984. pap. 10.95 (ISBN 0-310-36341-1, 11282P). Zondervan.

Marriage & the Family Medicine, Psychology & Religion: New Directions, New Integrations. Ed. by John T. Chirban. (Series on Medicine, Psychology & Religion). (Illus.). 94p. (Orig.). 1983. pap. text ed. 4.95 (ISBN 0-916586-63-4). Holy Cross Orthodox.

Marriage & the Family: The Domestic Church. Luis Alessio & Hector Munoz. Tr. by Aloysius Owen from Span. LC 82-6853. 121p. 1982. pap. 3.95 (ISBN 0-8189-0433-X). Alba.

Marriage As Equal Partnership. Dwight H. Small. 1980. pap. 3.95 (ISBN 0-8010-8177-7). Baker Bk.

Marriage at Its Best. John A. Lavender. LC 82-71375. 160p. (Orig.). 1982. pap. 4.95 (ISBN 0-89636-091-1). Accent Bks.

Marriage Builder: A Blueprint for Couples & Counselors. Lawrence J. Crabb, Jr. 176p. 1982. 9.95 (ISBN 0-310-22580-9, 10181). Zondervan.

Marriage Can Be Meaningful. Jerry Hayner & Karen Hayner. (Orig.). 1983. pap. 3.95 (ISBN 0-8054-2303-6). Broadman.

Marriage, Divorce, And... Robert C. Kistler. Ed. by Raymond H. Woolsey. 160p. (Orig.). 1987. 10.95 (ISBN 0-8280-0367-X). Review & Herald.

Marriage, Divorce & Purity. Joe D. Schubert. (Way of Life Ser: No. 101). 1966. pap. 3.95 (ISBN 0-89112-101-3, Bibl Res Pr). Abilene Christ U.

Marriage, Divorce, & Remarriage in the Bible. Jay E. Adams. (Jay Adams Library). 128p. 1986. pap. 6.95 (ISBN 0-310-51111-9, 12123P). Zondervan.

Marriage, Divorce, & the Believer. Appolles T. Sweatte. LC 85-91361. 53p. 1986. 6.95. Vantage.

Marriage Enrichment in the Church. David Mace & Vera Mace. LC 76-49710. 1977. pap. 4.50 o. p. (ISBN 0-8054-5621-X). Broadman.

Marriage, Faith & Love. Jack Dominian. 288p. 1982. 14.95 (ISBN 0-8245-0425-9). Crossroad NY.

Marriage: God's Design for Intimacy. James Reapsome & Martha Reapsome. (LifeBuilder Bible Studies). 64p. (Orig.). 1986. pap. 2.95 (ISBN 0-8308-1056-0). Inter-Varsity.

Marriage Hats. Mary Sue Hubbard. 1970. pap. 12.87 (ISBN 0-88404-068-2). Bridge Pubns Inc.

Marriage Homilies. Ed. by Liam Swords. 2.95. Paulist Pr.

Marriage: Ideals & Realizations. William F. Wunsch. 155p. 1973. 1.75 (ISBN 0-87785-122-0). Swedenborg.

Marriage in Islam: A Manual. Muhammed Abdul-Rauf. LC 75-186483. 1972. 8.50 (ISBN 0-682-47431-2, Banner). Exposition Pr FL.
Marriage in Today's World. H. Clair Amstutz. LC 78-955. 160p. 1978. pap. 6.95 (ISBN 0-8361-1849-9). Herald Pr.
Marriage Is a Loving Business. Paul A. Hauck. LC 77-2202. 116p. 1977. pap. 6.95 (ISBN 0-664-24137-9). Westminster.
Marriage Is for Love. Richard L. Strauss. 1982. pap. 4.95 (ISBN 0-8423-4178-1); leader's guide 2.95 (ISBN 0-8423-4179-X). Tyndale.
Marriage is for Those Who Love God & One Another. Thomas B. Warren. 1976. 8.00 (ISBN 0-934916-37-3). Natl Christian Pr.
Marriage is for Two: How to Build a Marriage That Lasts & Works. Omar Stuenkel. LC 81-65640. 96p. (Orig.). 1981. pap. 4.95 (ISBN 0-8066-1876-0, 10-4290). Augsburg.
Marriage Laws in the Bible & the Talmud. Louis M. Epstein. 1942. 25.00 (ISBN 0-384-14535-3). Johnson Repr.
Marriage Made in Heaven: The Story of Billy & Ruth Graham. Jhan Robbins. 192p. 1983. 13.95 (ISBN 0-399-12849-2, Putnam). Putnam Pub Group.
Marriage of Equals. Dennis L. Lythgoe. 160p. 1985. 8.95 (ISBN 0-87747-700-0). Deseret Bk.
Marriage Personalities. David Field. 192p. (Orig.). 1986. pap. 5.95 (ISBN 0-89081-476-7). Harvest Hse.
Marriage Puzzle. Shirley Cook. 128p. (Orig.). 1985. pap. 5.95 (ISBN 0-310-33611-2, 11742P). Zondervan.
Marriage Readiness. Bobbye Wood & Britton Wood. 1984. pap. 4.95 (ISBN 0-8054-5657-0). Broadman.
Marriage Rituals & Songs of Bengal. Buddhaved Roy. 1985. 6.50x (ISBN 0-8364-1290-7, Pub. by Mukhopadhyaya India). South Asia Bks.
Marriage: Sacrament of Hope & Challenge. William P. Roberts. 136p. 1983. pap. text ed. 4.75 (ISBN 0-86716-019-5). St Anthony Mess Pr.
Marriage Service. boxed 4.50 (ISBN 0-664-21050-3); moire boxed 5.95 (ISBN 0-664-21075-9); pap. 15.50 pkg. of 10 (ISBN 0-664-29035-3). Westminster.
Marriage, Sexuality & Celibacy: A Greek Orthodox Perspective. D. J. Constantelos. 1975. pap. 4.95 (ISBN 0-937032-15-8). Light&Life Pub Co MN.
Marriage Should Be Honored by All. Herbert A. Birner. 5.95 (ISBN 0-686-76769-1, 12N1719). Northwest Pub.
Marriage Studies: Reflections in Canon Law & Theology, Vol. 1. Ed. by Thomas P. Doyle. 155p. (Orig.). 1980. pap. 4.00 (ISBN 0-943616-03-4). Canon Law Soc.
Marriage Studies: Reflections in Canon Law & Theology, Vol. 2. Ed. by Thomas P. Doyle. 202p. (Orig.). 1982. pap. 4.50 (ISBN 0-943616-04-2). Canon Law Soc.
Marriage Studies, Vol. 3: Reflections in Canon Law & Theology. Ed. by Thomas P. Doyle. 207p. (Orig.). 1985. pap. 6.00 (ISBN 0-943616-25-5). Canon Law Soc.
Marriage Takes More Than Love. Jack Mayhall & Carole Mayhall. LC 77-85736. 240p. 1978. pap. 5.95 (ISBN 0-89109-426-1). NavPress.
Marriages That Work. Ed. by Don A. Augsburger. LC 84-15637. 112p. (Orig.). 1984. pap. 6.95 (ISBN 0-8361-3374-9). Herald Pr.
Married for Good. R. Paul Stevens. LC 86-2881. 220p. (Orig.). 1986. pap. 5.95 (ISBN 0-87784-603-0). Inter-Varsity.
Married Priests & the Reforming Papacy: The 11th Century Debates. Anne L. Barstow. LC 82-7914. (Texts & Studies in Religion: Vol. 12). 288p. 1982. 49.95x (ISBN 0-88946-987-3). E Mellen.
Married Saints. facs. ed. Selden P. Delany. LC 69-17573. (Essay Index Reprint Ser). 1935. 18.00 (ISBN 0-8369-0071-5). Ayer Co Pubs.
Marrow of Theology. William Ames. Ed. & tr. by John D. Eusden. Orig. Title: Medulla Theologiae. xiv, 354p. 1983. pap. 14.95 (ISBN 0-939464-14-4). Labyrinth Pr.
Marry Me, Marybeth. Jeanne Jordan. Ed. by Raymond Woolsey. 96p. 1987. pap. price not set (ISBN 0-8280-0379-3). Review & Herald.
Marrying Again: A Guide for Christians. David Hocking. 160p. 1983. 5.95 (ISBN 0-8007-5188-4, Power Bks). Revell.
Marrying for Life. Raymond E. Vath & Daniel W. O'Neill. (Illus., Orig.). 1981. pap. 8.00 (ISBN 0-939336-00-6). Messenger Comm.
Marrying for Life: A Handbook of Marriage Skills. Raymond E. Vath & Daniel O'Neill. (Illus.). 144p. (Orig.). 1982. pap. 6.95 (ISBN 0-86683-674-8, HarpR). Har-Row.
Marrying Well: Stages on the Journey of Christian Marriage. Evelyn Whitehead & James Whitehead. LC 81-43046. 504p. 1983. pap. 9.95 (ISBN 0-385-18829-3, Im). Doubleday.
Mars Underground Cities Discovered. Ruth E. Norman. (Tesla Speaks Ser.: Vol. 12). (Illus.). 1977. 7.95 (ISBN 0-932642-35-7); pap. 6.95 (ISBN 0-932642-46-2). Unarius Pubns.
Martha & Mary: A Woman's Relationship to Her Home. Josephine M. Benton. 1983. pap. 2.50x (ISBN 0-87574-036-7, 036). Pendle Hill.
Martha Berry, the Sunday Lady of Possum Trot. Tracy Byers. LC 72-159905. 1971. Repr. of 1932 ed. 40.00x (ISBN 0-8103-3783-5). Gale.
Martha Root: Lioness at the Threshold. M. R. Garis. LC 83-3913. (Illus.). 500p. 1983. 22.95 (ISBN 0-87743-184-1); pap. 15.95 (ISBN 0-87743-185-X). Baha'i.
Marthe Robin: The Cross & the Joy. Raymond Peyret. Tr. by Clare W. Faulhaber from Fr. LC 83-15591. (Illus.). 135p. 1983. pap. 6.95 (ISBN 0-8189-0464-X). Alba.
Martin - God's Court Jester: Luther in Retrospect. Eric W. Gritsch. LC 83-48004. 304p. 1983. pap. 15.95 (ISBN 0-8006-1753-3, 1-1753). Fortress.
Martin Buber. Stephen M. Panko. Ed. by Bob E. Patterson. LC 76-2869. (Markers of the Modern Theological Mind Ser.). 1976. 8.95 (ISBN 0-87680-470-9, 80470). Word Bks.
Martin Buber: A Centenary Volume. Haim Gordon. 1983. 49.50x (ISBN 0-88125-026-0). Ktav.
Martin Buber & the Covenant of Peace. Ed. by Jewish Peace Fellowship. 1984. lib. bdg. 79.95 (ISBN 0-87700-629-6). Revisionist Pr.
Martin Buber: Jewish Existentialist. Malcolm L. Diamond. 1968. lib. bdg. 17.50x (ISBN 0-88307-077-4). Gannon.
Martin Buber: The Life of Dialogue. 3rd, rev. ed. Maurice Friedman. 1976. pap. 13.00x (ISBN 0-226-26356-8). U of Chicago Pr.
Martin Buber's Ontology: An Analysis of I & Thou. Robert E. Wood. LC 73-82510. (Studies in Phenomenology & Existential Philosophy). 160p. 1969. 19.95 (ISBN 0-8101-0256-0); pap. 10.95 (ISBN 0-8101-0650-7). Northwestern U Pr.
Martin Buber's Philosophy of Interhuman Relation. Alexander Kohanski. LC 80-70626. 300p. 1981. 28.50 (ISBN 0-8386-3085-5). Fairleigh Dickinson.
Martin Heidegger. John Macquarrie. LC 68-11970. (Makers of Contemporary Theology Ser). 1968. pap. 3.95 (ISBN 0-8042-0659-7). John Knox.
Martin Heidegger's Philosophy of Religion. John R. Williams. 190p. 1977. pap. text ed. 9.95x (ISBN 0-919812-03-1, Pub. by Wilfrid Laurier Canada). Humanities.
Martin John Spalding: American Churchman. Thomas W. Spalding. LC 74-171040. pap. 96.80 (2029524). Bks Demand UMI.
Martin Luther. Gustav Freytag. LC 78-144612. Repr. of 1897 ed. 27.50 (ISBN 0-404-02577-3). AMS Pr.
Martin Luther. Judith O'Neill. LC 74-12959. (Cambridge Introduction to the History of Mankind). (Illus.). 48p. 1975. pap. text ed. 4.95 (ISBN 0-521-20403-8). Cambridge U Pr.
Martin Luther. Judith O'Neill. LC 78-56804. (Cambridge Topic Bks). (Illus.). 1978. PLB 8.95 (ISBN 0-8225-1215-7). Lerner Pubns.
Martin Luther. Estelle Ross. LC 83-45673. (Illus.). Date not set. Repr. of 1927 ed. 28.00 (ISBN 0-404-19862-7). AMS Pr.
Martin Luther. Ed. by E. G. Rupp & Benjamin Drewery. (Documents of Modern History Ser.). 1970. pap. text ed. 11.95 (ISBN 0-312-51660-6). St Martin.
Martin Luther - Reformer or Revolutionary? 3rd ed. Ed. by Brian Tierney et al. (Historical Pamphlets Ser.). 1977. pap. text ed. 1.95x (ISBN 0-394-32055-7). Random.
Martin Luther: A Destiny. Lucien P. Febvre. Tr. by Roberts Tapley. LC 83-45640. Date not set. Repr. of 1929 ed. 37.50 (ISBN 0-404-19850-3). AMS Pr.
Martin Luther: An Illustrated Biography. Peter Manns. LC 83-1083. (Illus.). 128p. 1983. 14.95 (ISBN 0-8245-0563-8). Crossroad NY.
Martin Luther: An Introduction to His Life & Work. Bernhard Lohse. Tr. by Robert C. Schultz from Ger. LC 85-45496. 304p. 1986. 26.95 (ISBN 0-8006-0764-3, 1-764); pap. 16.95 (ISBN 0-8006-1964-1, 1-1964). Fortress.
Martin Luther & Charismatic Ecumenism. Theodore P. Letis. (Orig.). 1979. pap. 1.95 (ISBN 0-936592-00-1). Reformation Res.
Martin Luther & the Birth of Protestantism. James Atkinson. LC 81-82356. 348p. 1981. pap. 5.25 (ISBN 0-8042-0941-3). John Knox.
Martin Luther & the Modern Mind: Freedom, Conscience, Toleration, Rights. Manfred Hoffman. LC 85-3054. (Toronto Studies in Theology: Vol. 22). 281p. 1985. 49.95x (ISBN 0-88946-766-8). E Mellen.
Martin Luther & the Reformation: An Annotated Bibliography. Leona R. Phillips. 1985. lib. bdg. 79.95 (ISBN 0-8490-3242-3). Gordon Pr.
Martin Luther & the Reformation in Germany until the Close of the Diet of Worms. Charles Beard. LC 83-45638. Date not set. Repr. of 1889 ed. 49.50 (ISBN 0-404-19822-8). AMS Pr.
Martin Luther Christmas Book with Celebrated Woodcuts by His Contemporaries. Tr. by Roland H. Bainton. LC 59-2930. 80p. 1948. pap. 3.95 (ISBN 0-8006-1843-2, 1-1843). Fortress.
Martin Luther: Companion of the Contemporary Christian. R. Kolb & D. Lumpp. LC 12-2959. 1982. pap. 9.95 (ISBN 0-570-03866-9). Concordia.
Martin Luther Easter Book. Roland Bainton. LC 82-15996. 88p. 1983. pap. 3.95 (ISBN 0-8006-1685-5). Fortress.
Martin Luther Had a Wife. William J. Petersen. 1983. pap. 3.95 (ISBN 0-8423-4104-8). Tyndale.
Martin Luther: Hero of Faith. Frederick Nohl. LC 62-14146. (Illus.). 1962. pap. 5.25 (ISBN 0-570-03727-1, 12-2629). Concordia.
Martin Luther: His Life & Teachings. James A. Nestingen. LC 82-71829. 80p. 1982. pap. 4.50 (ISBN 0-8006-1642-1, 1-1642). Fortress.
Martin Luther: His Life & Work. Hartmann Grisar. Ed. by Arthur Preuss. LC 71-137235. Repr. of 1930 ed. 29.50 (ISBN 0-404-02935-3). AMS Pr.
Martin Luther: His Road to Reformation, 1483-1521. Martin Brecht. Tr. by James L. Schaaf. LC 84-47911. 592p. 1985. 36.95 (ISBN 0-8006-0738-4, 1-738). Fortress.
Martin Luther: Hitler's Spiritual Ancestor. Peter F. Wiener. (Illus.). 92p. 1985. saddle stiched 4.00 (ISBN 0-910309-21-3). Am Atheist.
Martin Luther King. Nancy F. Shuker. (World Leaders: Past & Present Ser.). (Illus.). 112p. 1985. lib. bdg. 16.95x (ISBN 0-87754-567-7). Chelsea Hse.
Martin Luther King, Jr. His Religion, His Philosophy. Philip A. Rahming. LC 86-911950. 96p. (Orig.). 1986. pap. text ed. 10.00 (ISBN 0-682-40301-6). Exposition Pr FL.
Martin Luther: Knowledge and Mediation in the Renaissance. Jan Lindhardt. (Texts and Studies in Religion: Vol. 29). 270p. lib. bdg. 49.95 (ISBN 0-88946-817-6). E Mellen.
Martin Luther: Man for Whom God Had Great Plans. Ruth Hatznung. 1974. pap. 1.95 (ISBN 0-8100-0060-1, 16-0757). Northwest Pub.
Martin Luther: Portfolio Of Letters & Translations from Aesop. 126p. 150.00 (ISBN 0-8115-0906-0). Kraus Repr.
Martin Luther: Prophet to the Church Catholic. James Atkinson. LC 83-16462. Repr. of 1983 ed. 58.00 (2027535). Bks Demand UMI.
Martin Luther Quincentennial. Ed. by Gerhard Dunnhaupt. LC 84-15239. 329p. 1984. 29.95x (ISBN 0-8143-1774-X). Wayne St U Pr.
Martin Luther: Selections from His Writings. Martin Luther. Ed. by John Dillenberger. LC 61-9503. pap. 7.95 (ISBN 0-385-09876-6, Anch). Doubleday.
Martin Luther, the Hero of the Reformation. Henry E. Jacobs. LC 72-170838. Repr. of 1898 ed. 27.50 (ISBN 0-404-03544-2). AMS Pr.
Martin Luther: The Man & His Work. Walther von Loewenich. Tr. by Lawrence W. Denef from Ger. LC 83-70513. Tr. of Martin Luther: Der Mann und das Werk. 448p. 1986. text ed. 19.95 (ISBN 0-8066-2019-6, 10-4296). Augsburg.
Martin Luther, the Man & His Work. Arthur C. McGiffert. LC 83-45647. Date not set. Repr. of 1911 ed. 42.50 (ISBN 0-404-19856-2). AMS Pr.
Martin Luther: The Man & the Image. Herbert D. Rix. 335p. 1983. text ed. 37.50x (ISBN 0-8290-0554-4). Irvington.
Martin Luther's Last Will & Testament: A Facsimile of the Original Document, with an Account of Its Origins, Composition & Subsequent History. T. Fabiny. 51p. 1984. text ed. 25.00x (ISBN 0-904720-15-2, Pub. by Ussher Pr Ireland). Humanities.
Martin of Tours: Parish Priest, Mystic & Exorcist. Christopher Donaldson. (Illus.). 171p. 1985. pap. 8.95 (ISBN 0-7102-0682-8). Methuen Inc.
Martyn Lloyd-Jones: Chosen by God. Ed. by Christopher Catherwood. LC 86-70463. 288p. (Orig.). 1986. pap. 7.95 (ISBN 0-89107-404-X, Crossway Bks). Good News.
Martyr. Murtaza Mutahhery. Tr. by M. A. Ansari. 62p. 1983. pap. 4.00 (ISBN 0-941724-13-1). Islamic Seminary.
Martyr Bishop Confessors under Communism. Elena Lopeshinskaya. (Rus.). pap. 5.00 (ISBN 0-686-05413-X). Eastern Orthodox.
Martyr Bishop: The Life of St. Oliver Plunkett. John McKee. 181p. 1975. 7.95 (ISBN 0-912414-21-9). Lumen Christi.
Martyrdom of Lovejoy: An Account of the Life, Trials, & Perils of Rev. Elijah P. Lovejoy. Henry Tanner. LC 68-18603. (Illus.). 1971. Repr. of 1881 ed. lib. bdg. 25.00x (ISBN 0-678-00744-6). Kelley.
Martyrdom of St. Polycarp: The Encyclical Epistle of the Church at Smyrna Concerning the Martyrdom of the Holy Polycarp. Tr. by James Donaldson & Alexander Roberts. pap. 1.50 (ISBN 0-317-11392-5). Eastern Orthodox.
Martyrdom of Women in the Early Christian Church. Arthur F. Ide. LC 85-14741. (Illus.). 100p. 1985. pap. 6.95 (ISBN 0-934667-00-4). Tangelwuld.
Martyrdom Today. Edward Schillebeeckx & Johannes Baptist-Metz. (Concilium 1983: Vol. 163). 128p. 1983. pap. 6.95 (ISBN 0-8164-2443-8, HarpR). Har-Row.
Martyrology of St. Aengus. Saint Aengus. pap. 12.50 (ISBN 0-686-25554-2). Eastern Orthodox.
Martyrology of Ukrainian Churches: Vol. 1, Ukrainian Catholic Church. Osyp Zinkewych & Taras Lonchyna. (Ukrainian Ser.). 839p. 1985. 29.75 (ISBN 0-914834-36-3). Smoloskyp.
Martyrology Pronouncing Dictionary. Anthony I. Russo-Alesi. LC 79-167151. 1973. Repr. of 1939 ed. 35.00x (ISBN 0-8103-3272-8). Gale.
Martyrs' Mirror. Thieleman J. Van Braght. (Illus.). 1157p. 1938. 29.95 (ISBN 0-8361-1390-X). Herald Pr.
Martyrs of Our Time. William Purcell. Ed. by Herbert Lambert. LC 85-4104. 1985. pap. 9.95 (ISBN 0-8272-2317-X). CBP.
Martyrs of the Oblong & Little Nine. Defost Smith. 1948. 6.00 (ISBN 0-910294-11-9). Brown Bk.
Marvelous Companion: Life Stories of the Buddha. Aryasura. (Illus.). 250p. 1983. 25.00 (ISBN 0-913546-88-7). Dharma Pub.
Marvelous Ministry. Charles Ray. 100p. 1985. pap. 2.95. Pilgrim Pubns.
Marvelous Work & a Wonder. Le Grand Richards. 424p. 14.00 (ISBN 0-87747-686-1); pap. 2.95 (ISBN 0-87747-614-4). Deseret Bk.
Marvelous Work & a Wonder. LeGrand Richards. 5.95 (ISBN 0-87747-161-4); pocket black leather o.p. 8.50 (ISBN 0-87747-163-0); pocket brown leather o.p. 11.95 (ISBN 0-87747-383-8). Deseret Bk.
Marvels & Mysteries. Marie S. Bordner. 96p. (Orig.). 1986. pap. 4.95 (ISBN 0-912661-09-7). Woodsong Graph.
Marvels of Prophecy. Howard B. Rand. 1959. 5.00 (ISBN 0-685-08810-3). Destiny.
Marx Against the Marxists: The Christian Humanism of Karl Marx. Jose P. Miranda. Tr. by John Drury from Span. LC 80-14415. Orig. Title: Christianism de Marx. 336p. (Orig.). 1980. pap. 12.95 (ISBN 0-88344-322-8). Orbis Bks.
Marx & Marxism. Ed. by Peter Worsley. LC 81-6848. (Key Sociologists Ser.). 126p. 1982. pap. 4.95x (ISBN 0-85312-375-6, NO. 3675 TAVISTOCK). Methuen Inc.
Marx & Satan. Richard Wurmbrand. 143p. 1986. pap. 5.95 (ISBN 0-89107-379-5, Crossway Bks). Good News.
Marx & Teilhard: Two Ways to the New Humanity. Richard Lischer. LC 79-4438. 192p. (Orig.). 1979. pap. 3.48 (ISBN 0-88344-303-1). Orbis Bks.
Marx & the Bible: A Critique of the Philosophy of Oppression. Jose P. Miranda. Tr. by John Eagleson from Span. LC 73-89053. Orig. Title: Marx y la Biblia: Critica a la filosofia de la oppresion. Tr. of Marx y la Biblia. 360p. (Orig.). 1974. pap. 8.95x (ISBN 0-88344-307-4). Orbis Bks.
Marx-Engels-Marxism. V. I. Lenin. 176p. 1977. pap. 1.40 (ISBN 0-8285-2194-8, Pub. by Progress Pubs USSR). Imported Pubns.
Marx Versus Tolstoy: A Debate. Clarence S. Darrow & Arthur M. Lewis. LC 73-137537. (Peace Movement in America Ser). 124p. 1972. Repr. of 1911 ed. lib. bdg. 12.95x (ISBN 0-89198-066-0). Ozer.
Marxism: An American Christian Perspective. Arthur McGovern. LC 79-27257. 352p. (Orig.). 1980. pap. 12.95 (ISBN 0-88344-301-5). Orbis Bks.
Marxism & Christianity. Alasdair MacIntyre. LC 83-40600. 143p. 1984. pap. text ed. 6.95 (ISBN 0-268-01358-6, 85-13590). U of Notre Dame Pr.
Marxism & Christianity. Denys Turner. LC 82-22713. 268p. 1983. text ed. 27.50x (ISBN 0-389-20351-3). B&N Imports.
Marxism & Christianity: The Quarrel & the Dialogue in Poland. Josef Tischner. (Orig.). 1987. 9.95 (ISBN 0-87840-419-8). Georgetown U Pr.
Marxism & Judaism. A. Salluste. 1982. lib. bdg. 69.95 (ISBN 0-87700-329-7). Revisionist Pr.
Marxism & Religion in Eastern Europe. Ed. by R. T. De George & J. P. Scanlan. LC 75-33051. (Sovietica Ser: No. 36). 180p. 1976. lib. bdg. 39.50 (ISBN 90-277-0636-0, Pub. by Reidel Holland). Kluwer Academic.

Marxist Analysis & Christian Faith. Rene Coste. Tr. by Roger A. Couture et al from Fr. LC 85-3119. Tr. of Analyse Marxiste et foi Chretienne. 256p. (Orig.). 1985. pap. 11.95 (ISBN 0-88344-342-2). Orbis Bks.

Marxist-Leninist 'Scientific Atheism' & the Study of Religion & Atheism in the U. S. S. R. James Thrower. (Ger.). 500p. 1983. 78.00 (ISBN 90-279-3060-0). Mouton.

Marx's Kapital for Beginners. David Smith. (Illus.). 1982. pap. 3.95 (ISBN 0-394-71265-X). Pantheon.

Mary. Marlee Alex. (Women of the Bible Ser.). 32p. 1987. 8.95 (ISBN 0-8028-5018-9). Eerdmans.

Mary According to Women. Carol F. Jegen. LC 84-82550. 163p. (Orig.). 1985. pap. 7.95 (ISBN 0-934134-31-6, Leaven Pr). Sheed & Ward MO.

Mary & Scripture. Candido Pozo. Date not set. price not set (ISBN 0-8199-0906-8). Franciscan Herald.

Mary & Your Everyday Life. Bernard Haring. LC 77-92897. 1978. pap. 4.95 (ISBN 0-89243-075-3). Liguori Pubns.

Mary Andrews: Companion of Sorrow. Carolyn Byers. Ed. by Gerald Wheeler. LC 83-21121. (Banner Bk.). (Illus.). 91p. (Orig.). 1984. pap. 5.95 (ISBN 0-8280-0212-6). Review & Herald.

Mary at My Side. Bob Guste. 64p. (Orig.). 1985. pap. 3.95 (ISBN 0-89622-247-0). Twenty-Third.

Mary Baker Eddy: Her Spiritual Footsteps. Gilbert C. Carpenter, Sr. & Gilbert C. Carpenter, Jr. 290p. 1985. pap. 20.00 (ISBN 0-930227-02-6). Pasadena Pr.

Mary Bethune & Her Somedays. Jan Johnson. (Stories About Christian Heroes Ser.). (Illus.). 1979. pap. 1.95 (ISBN 0-03-049421-4, HarpR). Har-Row.

Mary Bunyan: Blind Daughter of John Bunyan. Sallie R. Ford. 9.95 (ISBN 0-685-00748-0). Reiner.

Mary God's Mother & Ours. Pope Paul VI. 1979. 4.75 (ISBN 0-8198-0571-8); pap. 3.50 (ISBN 0-8198-0572-6). Dghtrs St Paul.

Mary, in Bethlehem. Edith Cutting. (Paper People Ser.). 48p. 1986. wkbk. 4.95 (ISBN 0-86653-370-2). Good Apple.

Mary in Modern Spirituality. Quentin Hakenewerth. 52p. (Orig.). 1966. pap. 1.25 (ISBN 0-9608124-2-3). Marianist Com Ctr.

Mary in the Churches. Ed. by Hans Kung & Jurgen Moltmann. (Concilium 1983: Vol. 168). 128p. (Orig.). 1983. pap. 6.95 (ISBN 0-8164-2448-9, HarpR). Har-Row.

Mary in the Franciscan Order: Proceedings Third National Meeting of Franciscan Teaching Sisterhoods, Vol. 3. 1955. 4.00 (ISBN 0-686-11578-3). Franciscan Inst.

Mary in the New Testament. Ed. by Raymond E. Brown et al. LC 78-8797. 336p. 1978. pap. 6.95 (ISBN 0-8091-2168-9). Paulist Pr.

Mary in the New Testament: A Collaborative Assessment by Protestant & Roman Catholic Scholars. Ed. by Raymond E. Brown et al. LC 78-8797. 336p. 1978. pap. 6.95 (ISBN 0-8006-1345-7, 1-1345). Fortress.

Mary McLeod Bethune. Eloise Greenfield. LC 76-11522. (Biography Ser.). (Illus.). 1977. PLB 12.89 (ISBN 0-690-01129-6, Crowell Jr Bks). HarpJ.

Mary McLeod Bethune: Her Own Words of Inspiration. Florence J. Hicks. LC 75-18004. 96p. 1975. 4.95 (ISBN 0-912444-00-2). Gaus.

Mary Magdalen. Edgar Saltus. LC 78-116002. Repr. of 1891 ed. 17.50 (ISBN 0-404-05517-6). AMS Pr.

Mary Magdalene & the Theory of Sin, 2 vols. Felix De Simoni. LC 72-84832. (Illus.). 35p. 1972. 179.50 (ISBN 0-913314-04-8). Am Classical Coll Pr.

Mary, Michael, & Lucifer: Folk Catholicism in Central Mexico. John M. Ingham. (Latin American Monographs: No. 69). (Illus.). 228p. 1986. text ed. 25.00x (ISBN 0-292-75089-7). U of Tex Pr.

Mary: Model of Justice: Reflections on the Magnificat. Ed. by William Maestri. LC 86-22304. 87p. (Orig.). 1987. pap. 4.95 (ISBN 0-8189-0511-5). Alba.

Mary Mother of Christ & of Christians. Joseph-Marie Perrin. Tr. by Jean D. Finley from Fr. LC 77-26608. (Illus.). 1978. pap. 3.50 (ISBN 0-8189-0367-8). Alba.

Mary: Mother of Jesus. Barbara Hintze. (BibLearn Ser.). (Illus.). 1977. bds. 5.95 (ISBN 0-8054-4232-4, 4242-32). Broadman.

Mary, Mother of the Church: What Recent Popes Have Said about the Blessed Mother's Role in the Church. Francis J. Ripley. 1973. pap. 2.00 (ISBN 0-89555-094-6). TAN Bks Pubs.

Mary My Hope. rev. ed. Lawrence Lavasik. (Illus., LargeType). blue bdg., colored edges 4.95 (ISBN 0-89942-365-5, 365/00). Catholic Bk Pub.

Mary My Mother. rev. ed. Lawrence G. Lovasik. (Saint Joseph Picture Bks). (Illus., LargeType). flexible bdg. 0.95 (ISBN 0-89942-280-2, 280). Catholic Bk Pub.

Mary Myth: On the Femininity of God. Andrew M. Greeley. 240p. 1977. 9.95 (ISBN 0-8164-0333-3, HarpR). Har-Row.

Mary of Nazareth. Igino Giordani. (Orig.). 1965. 6.00 (ISBN 0-8198-0092-9); pap. 5.00 (ISBN 0-8198-0093-7). Dghtrs St Paul.

Mary of Nazareth. F. Suarez. 259p. 1979. pap. 4.95x (ISBN 0-933932-42-1). Scepter Pubs.

Mary of the Koran: A Meeting Point Between Islam & Christianism. Nilo Geagea. Tr. by Lawrence T. Fares. LC 82-3804. 324p. 1984. 17.50 (ISBN 0-8022-2395-8). Philos Lib.

Mary Our Hope. John Wright. Pref. by Stephen Almagno. LC 84-80015. 227p. (Orig.). 1984. pap. 8.95 (ISBN 0-89870-046-9). Ignatius Pr.

Mary: Pathway to Fruitfulness. John Randall et al. (Orig.). 1978. pap. 2.95 (ISBN 0-914544-28-4). Living Flame Pr.

Mary Queen & Mother. John Carberry. 1979. 5.50 (ISBN 0-8198-0584-X); pap. 3.95 (ISBN 0-8198-0585-8). Dghtrs St Paul.

Mary, Queen of Apostles. rev. ed. James Alberione. 1976. 4.00 (ISBN 0-8198-0438-X); pap. 3.00 (ISBN 0-8198-0439-8). Dghtrs St Paul.

Mary, Queen of Peace: Is the Mother of God Appearing in Medjugorje? Lucy Rooney & Robert Faricy. 98p. (Orig.). 1985. pap. 4.95 (ISBN 0-317-19369-4). Alba.

Mary, Servant of the Lord. M. Miguens. 1978. 3.75 (ISBN 0-8198-0538-6); pap. 2.25 (ISBN 0-8198-0539-4). Dghtrs St Paul.

Mary Slessor. Basil Miller. 144p. 1985. pap. 3.50 (ISBN 0-87123-849-7, 200849). Bethany Hse.

Mary Slessor of Calabar. W. P. Livingstone. LC 83-9286. 352p. 1984. 7.95 (ISBN 0-310-27451-6, 9286P, Clarion class). Zondervan.

Mary Slessor of Calabar. W. P. Livingstone. (Heroes of the Faith Ser.). 1986. Repr. 6.95 (ISBN 0-916441-49-0). Barbour & Co.

Mary, the Faithful Disciple. Bertrand Budy. 160p. (Orig.). 1985. pap. 6.95 (ISBN 0-8091-2703-2). Paulist Pr.

Mary-the Feminine Face of the Church. Rosemary R. Ruether. LC 77-7652. 106p. 1977. pap. 6.95 (ISBN 0-664-24759-8). Westminster.

Mary, the Perfect Prayer Partner. Kenneth J. Roberts. Ed. by Anna Marie Waters. LC 83-61151. (Illus.). 128p. (Orig.). 1983. pap. 3.95 (ISBN 0-9610984-1-4). Pax Tapes.

Mary the Second Eve. John H. Newman. 40p. 1982. pap. 1.50 (ISBN 0-89555-181-0). TAN Bks Pubs.

Mary, the Womb of God. George Maloney. 6.95 (ISBN 0-87193-057-9). Dimension Bks.

Mary Today: The Challenging Woman. M. Basil Pennington. LC 86-29183. (Illus.). 168p. 1987. 13.95 (ISBN 0-385-23609-3). Doubleday.

Mary-Verse in "Meistergesang". M. J. Schroeder. (Catholic University Studies in German: No. 16). 1970. Repr. of 1942 ed. 30.00 (ISBN 0-404-50236-9). AMS Pr.

Mary-Verse of the Teutonic Knights. M. E. Goenner. LC 72-140022. (Catholic University of America Studies in German: No. 19). Repr. of 1943 ed. 20.00 (ISBN 0-404-50239-3). AMS Pr.

Mary, Woman of Faith. Mary A. Watson. 32p. 1986. pap. 1.50 (ISBN 0-89243-260-8). Liguori Pubns.

Maryland German Church Records, Vol. 1: Christ Reformed Church, Middletown. Ed. by Frederick S. Weiser. LC 86-61245. (Maryland German Church Records Ser.). 108p. (Orig.). 1986. pap. 15.00x (ISBN 0-913281-03-4). Noodle Doosey.

Maryland German Church Records, Vol. 2: Zion Lutheran Church, Middletown. Ed. by Frederick S. Weiser. Tr. by Charles T. Zahn. LC 86-62419. (Orig.). 1986. pap. 15.00x (ISBN 0-913281-04-2). Noodle-Doosey.

Maryland German Church Records, Vol. 3: Monocacy Lutheran Congregation & Evangelical Lutheran Church - Baptisms 1742-1779. Ed. & tr. by Frederick S. Weiser. LC 86-63901. (Orig.). 1987. pap. 20.00x (ISBN 0-913281-05-0). Noodle-Doosey.

Maryland German Church Records, Vol. 4: Evangelical Lutheran Church Baptisms, 1780-1811, Frederick, Maryland. Ed. & tr. by Frederick S. Weiser. 150p. (Orig.). 1987. pap. 20.00x (ISBN 0-913281-06-9). Noodle Doosey.

Maryland German Church Records, Vol. 5: Evangelical Reformed Church 1746-1789, Frederick. Ed. by Frederick S. Weiser. Tr. by William J. Hinke. (Maryland German Church Records Ser.). (Orig.). 1987. pap. 20.00x (ISBN 0-913281-07-7). Noodle Doosey.

Maryland German Church Records, Vol. 6: Evangelical Reformed Church 1790-1835, Frederick. Ed. by Frederick S. Weiser. Tr. by William J. Hinke. (Maryland German Church Records Ser.). (Orig.). 1987. pap. 20.00x (ISBN 0-913281-08-5). Noodle Doosey.

Maryland German Church Records, Vol. 7: St. Mary's Lutheran Church 1783-1863, St. Mary's Reformed Church 1812-1866, & Jerusalem Lutheran Church 1799-1859. Ed. by Frederick S. Weiser. (Maryland German Church Records Ser.). (Orig.). 1987. pap. 15.00x (ISBN 0-913281-09-3). Noodle Doosey.

Maryland in Africa: The Maryland State Colonization Society, 1831-1857. Penelope Campbell. LC 75-131058. pap. 68.00 (ISBN 0-317-41903-X, 2025915). Bks Demand UMI.

Mary's Immaculate Heart: A Way of God. Gabriel Allegra. 156p. 1985. 9.50 (ISBN 0-8199-0875-4). Franciscan Herald.

Mary's Journey. Louis Cameli. 5.95 (ISBN 0-8215-9911-9). Sadlier.

Mary's Pilgrim. Pat Balskus. LC 68-58160. (Encounter Ser.). 3.00 (ISBN 0-8198-0279-4). Dghtrs St Paul.

Mary's Place in Christian Dialogue. Ed. by Alberic Stacpoole. LC 83-61204. 282p. (Orig.). 1983. pap. 10.95 (ISBN 0-8192-1333-0). Morehouse.

Mary's Spiritual Maternity. Patrick Gaffney. 4.95 (ISBN 0-910984-18-2); pap. 2.95 (ISBN 0-910984-19-0). Montfort Pubns.

Mary's Story. M. M. Brem. (Arch Bks.: Set 4). 1967. laminated bdg. 0.99 (ISBN 0-570-06029-X, 59-1140). Concordia.

Masaryk on Thought & Life. Thomas G. Masaryk. LC 78-135840. (Eastern Europe Collection Ser.). 1970. Repr. of 1938 ed. 16.00 (ISBN 0-405-02782-6). Ayer Co Pubs.

Masculine Cross & Ancient Sex Worship. Sha Rocco. (Illus.). 65p. 1873. pap. 7.95 (ISBN 0-88697-014-8). Life Science.

Masinaigans: The Little Book. Bernard Coleman & Verona LaBud. (Illus.). 368p. 1972. 10.00 (ISBN 0-686-05025-8). North Central.

Mask for Privilege: Anti-Semitism in America. Carey McWilliams. LC 78-26197. 1979. Repr. of 1948 ed. lib. bdg. 24.75x (ISBN 0-313-20880-8, MCMP). Greenwood.

Mask of Evil. Anthony Tatlow. (European University Studies: Series 18, Comparative Literature, Vol. 12). 1977. 52.20 (ISBN 3-261-02905-6). P Lang Pubs.

Mask of Religion. G. Peter Fleck. LC 79-9644. (Library of Liberal Religion). 204p. 1980. 12.95 (ISBN 0-87975-125-8). Prometheus Bks.

Masks of God: Creative Mythology. Joseph Campbell. (Illus.). 730p. 1970. pap. 7.95 (ISBN 0-14-004307-1). Penguin.

Masks of God: Occidental Mythology. Joseph Campbell. (Illus.). 564p. 1976. pap. 7.95 (ISBN 0-14-004306-3). Penguin.

Masks of God: Oriental Mythology. Joseph Campbell. (Illus.). 576p. 1970. pap. 7.95 (ISBN 0-14-004305-5). Penguin.

Masks of God: Primitive Mythology. Joseph Campbell. (Illus.). 528p. 1976. pap. 7.95 (ISBN 0-14-004304-7). Penguin.

Masks of God 4: Creative Mythology. Joseph Campbell. 1968. 19.95 (ISBN 0-670-46111-3). Viking.

Masks of Odin: Wisdom of the Ancient Norse. Elsa-Brita Titchenell. LC 85-40652. (Illus.). 316p. 1985. 15.00 (ISBN 0-911500-72-3); pap. 8.00 (ISBN 0-911500-73-1). Theos U Pr.

Masks of Satan: The Demonic in History. Christopher Nugent. 216p. 1984. 22.50 (ISBN 0-89860-128-2, Sheed & Ward). Eastview.

Masnavi, Vol. 1. Mowlana Jalal ud-Din Mohammad Rumi. Ed. by Mohammad Estelami. (Mazda Special Persian Language Publications). (Persian.). 580p. 1987. lib. bdg. 25.00 (ISBN 0-939214-40-7). Mazda Pubs.

Masochism: A Jungian View. Lyn Cowan. LC 82-16957. 137p. (Orig.). 1982. pap. 12.00 (ISBN 0-88214-320-4). Spring Pubns.

Mason City District - A History: The United Methodist Church. Lyle Johnston. (Illus.). 109p. (Orig.). 1984. pap. 6.50 (ISBN 0-9616365-2-1). Grt Plains Emporium.

Mason Locke Weems, His Works & Ways, 3 vols. Mason L. Weems. Ed. by Emily E. Skeel. LC 75-31140. Repr. of 1929 ed. 120.00 set (ISBN 0-404-13670-2). AMS Pr.

Masonic Burial Service. 3.00 (ISBN 0-685-19486-8). Powner.

Masonic Lodge Methods. Louis B. Blakemore. 320p. 1981. Repr. of 1953 ed. text ed. 11.50 (ISBN 0-88053-027-8, M-76). Macoy Pub.

Masonic Orders of Fraternity. Manly P. Hall. 5.95 (ISBN 0-89314-536-X). Philos Res.

Masonic Quiz. William Petersen. 12.00x (ISBN 0-685-22032-X). Wehman.

Masonic Quiz: Ask Me Another, Brother. 12.00 (ISBN 0-685-19487-6). Powner.

Masonic Ritual. rev. ed. M. C. Duncan. 12.50x (ISBN 0-685-22033-8). Wehman.

Masonic Ritual & Monitor, 2 Pts. Malcolm Duncan. 1946. 8.50 ea.; 1 vol. ed. 12.50 (ISBN 0-685-19489-2). Powner.

Masonry & Its Symbols, in Light of "Thinking & Destiny". Harold W. Percival. LC 52-2237. 1979. pap. 3.95 (ISBN 0-911650-07-5). Word Foun.

Masonry & Medieval Mysticism. Cooper & Oakley. pap. 9.25 (ISBN 0-8356-5301-3). Theos Pub Hse.

Masonry & Medieval Mysticism. Cooper & Oakley. 12.95 (ISBN 0-8356-5309-9). Theos Pub Hse.

Masoretic Studies. Ed. by Harry M. Orlinsky. 10.00x (ISBN 0-685-56221-2). Ktav.

Masques of God: Form & Theme in the Poetry of Henry Vaughan. James D. Simmonds. LC 78-170144. 1972. 24.95x (ISBN 0-8229-3236-9). U of Pittsburgh Pr.

Mass: Ancient Liturgies & Patristic Texts. Adelbert Hamman. Ed. by Thomas Halton. LC 67-15202. 1967. 5.95 (ISBN 0-8189-0086-5). Alba.

Mass: Finding Its Meaning for You & Getting More Out of It. Gerard Weber. (Illus., Orig.). 1985. pap. 4.95 (ISBN 0-86716-049-7). St Anthony Mess Pr.

Mass for Young Catholics. Ed Curley. 1978. 9.95 (ISBN 0-686-89575-4, Pub. by Pflaum Pr). Peter Li.

Mass: Great Common Prayer. Gaynell Cronin & Jim Cronin. 1977. pap. 7.55 (ISBN 0-88479-006-1). Arena Lettres.

Mass Murderers in White Coats: Psychiatric Genocide in Nazi Germany & the United States. Lenny Lapon. (Orig.). 1986. pap. 9.00 (ISBN 0-9614961-9-3). Psych Genocide Res.

Mass of the Roman Rite: Its Origins and Development, 2 vols. Joseph A. Jungmann. Tr. by Francis A. Brunner from German. 1050p. 1986. pap. 39.95 (ISBN 0-87061-129-1). Chr Classics.

Massachusetts Bay Company & Its Predecessors. Frances Rose-Troup. LC 68-56574. 1973. Repr. of 1930 ed. 22.50x (ISBN 0-678-00871-X). Kelley.

Massada English-Hebrew Student Dictionary. Reuben Alcalay. (Eng. & Hebrew.). 734p. 1980. Repr. 18.95 (ISBN 0-89961-006-4). SBS Pub.

Masses Are Asses. Albert Dugan. 256p. (Orig.). 1987. pap. 9.95 (ISBN 0-89896-047-9). Larksdale.

Masses, Cantiones, Motets. William Byrd et al. Ed. by P. C. Buck. (Tudor Church Music Ser.: Vol. 9). 1963. Repr. of 1928 ed. write for info. (ISBN 0-8450-1859-0). Broude.

Masses of Francesco Soriano: A Style-Critical Study. S. Philip Kniseley. LC 67-22198. (University of Florida Humanities Monographs: No. 26). (Illus.). 1967. pap. 3.50 (ISBN 0-8130-0131-5). U Presses Fla.

Massora Magna. rev. ed. Salomon Frensdorff. LC 67-11896. (Library of Biblical Studies). (Heb). 1968. 35.00x (ISBN 0-87068-052-8). Ktav.

Massoreth Ha Massoreth. rev. ed. Elijah Levita. LC 67-11894. (Library of Biblical Studies). 1969. 39.50x (ISBN 0-87068-081-1). Ktav.

Master. Diane M. Cary. 1981. 9.95 (ISBN 0-8062-1763-4). Carlton.

Master: A Life of Jesus. John Pollack. 240p. 1985. 12.95 (ISBN 0-89693-315-6). Victor Bks.

Master Alcuin, Liturgist. Gerald Ellard. LC 56-8943. (Jesuit Studies). 1956. 2.95 (ISBN 0-8294-0027-3). Loyola.

Master & Mastership. Murtaza Mutahhery. Tr. by M. A. Ansari. 124p. 1983. pap. 5.00 (ISBN 0-941724-15-8). Islamic Seminary.

Master & the Disciple. Sri Chinmoy. LC 85-72172. 115p. (Orig.). 1985. pap. 3.95 (ISBN 0-317-46896-0). Aum Pubns.

Master & the Disciple. D. S. Sarma. pap. 1.00 (ISBN 0-87481-466-9). Vedanta Pr.

Master As I Saw Him. Sr. Nivedita. 6.95 (ISBN 0-87481-088-4). Vedanta Pr.

Master Catechist Guide for the Catechist Formation Book. Don Boyd & Maruja Sedano. LC 82-60853. 1982. pap. 3.95 (ISBN 0-8091-2471-8). Paulist Pr.

Master Christian. Marie Corelli. 604p. 1983. Repr. of 1900 ed. lib. bdg. 45.00 (ISBN 0-8495-0961-0). Arden Lib.

Master in Akka: Including Recollections of the Greatest Holy Leaf. Myron H. Phelps. Orig. Title: Abbas Effendi: His Life & Teachings. (Illus.). 1985. Repr. of 1912 ed. 12.95 (ISBN 0-933770-49-9). Kalimat.

Master John Milton of the Citie of London. McEwan Lawson. LC 72-10632. 1973. Repr. lib. bdg. 12.50 (ISBN 0-8414-0725-8). Folcroft.

Master of Men. fascimile ed. Ed. by Thomas C. Clark. LC 72-116396. (Granger Index Reprint Ser.). 1930. 15.00 (ISBN 0-8369-6137-4). Ayer Co Pubs.

Master of Wisdom: Writings of the Buddhist Master Nagarjuna. Tr. by Christian Lindtner from Sanskrit, Chinese, Tibetan. (Tibetan Translation Ser.). 420p. 1987. 28.00 (ISBN 0-89800-139-0). Dharma Pub.

Master Plan of Discipleship. Robert E. Coleman. 9.95; pap. 5.95. Revell.

Master Plan of Evangelism. Robert E. Coleman. 128p. 1978. pap. 5.95 (ISBN 0-8007-5007-1, Power Bks); pap. 2.50 (ISBN 0-8007-8303-4, Spire Bks). Revell.

Master Plan Revealed. Daughters of St. Paul. (Divine Master Ser.). pap. 3.00 (ISBN 0-8198-0346-4); rev. project & discussion manual o.s.i. 3.95 (ISBN 0-8198-0347-2). Dghtrs St Paul.

Master Principles of Evangelism. Delos Miles. LC 81-66291. 1982. pap. 3.95 (ISBN 0-8054-6232-5). Broadman.

Master Sculptor. Pershing Tousley. LC 81-7189. 1981. pap. 10.00 (ISBN 0-8309-0316-X). Herald Hse.

Master Speaks. Joel Goldsmith. 192p. 1984. pap. 5.95 (ISBN 0-8065-0912-0). Citadel Pr.

Master Teacher: Nadia Boulanger. Don G. Campbell. (Illus.). 151p. 1984. text ed. 19.95 (ISBN 0-912405-03-1). Pastoral Pr.

Master Theme of the Bible, Pt. I: The Doctrine of the Lamb. J. Sidlow Baxter. (Living Studies). 160p. 1985. pap. 5.95 (ISBN 0-8423-4187-0); study guide 2.95 (ISBN 0-8423-4191-9). Tyndale.

Master Thoughts, 3 vols. Friend Stuart. 600p. 1985. Set. vinyl 50.00 (ISBN 0-912132-05-1). Dominion Pr.

Mastering New Testament Facts, 4 bks. Madeline H. Beck & Lamar Williamson, Jr. Incl. Bk. 1. Introduction & Synoptic Gospels (ISBN 0-8042-0326-1); Bk. 2. The Fourth Gospel & Acts (ISBN 0-8042-0327-X); Bk. 3. Pauline Letters (ISBN 0-8042-0328-8); Bk. 4. The General Letters & Revelation (ISBN 0-8042-0329-6). (Illus., Orig.). 1973. pap. 4.95 ea.; pap. 14.95 set. John Knox.

Mastering New Testament Greek. W. Harold Mare. 1979. 14.95 (ISBN 0-8010-6064-8). Baker Bk.

Mastering Old Testament Facts, 4 bks. Madeline H. Beck & Lamar Williamson, Jr. Incl. Bk. 1. Introduction on-Deut. 1979 (ISBN 0-8042-0134-X); Bk. 2. Joshua-Esther. 1979 (ISBN 0-8042-0135-8). (Illus., Orig.). pap. text ed. 4.95 ea.; pap. text ed. 14.95 set. John Knox.

Mastering Old Testament Facts, Bk. 4: Isaiah-Malachi. Madeline H. Beck & Lamar Williamson, Jr. (Mastering Old Testament Facts Ser.). (Illus.). 112p. (Orig.). 1981. pap. 4.95 (ISBN 0-8042-0137-4). John Knox.

Mastering the Meaning of the Bible. John L. McKenzie. 140p. 1986. 4.95 (ISBN 0-87193-252-0). Dimension Bks.

Mastering the Problems of Living. new ed. Haridas Chaudhuri. LC 75-4172. 222p. 1975. pap. 2.75 (ISBN 0-8356-0463-2, Quest). Theos Pub Hse.

Masterpiece in Progress. Jeff Steinberg & James C. Hefley. 288p. 1986. 11.95 (ISBN 0-8423-4194-3). Tyndale.

Masterpieces of Catholic Literature, 2 vols. 1139p. 1965. Set. 60.00x (ISBN 0-89356-154-1). Salem Pr.

Masterpieces of Christian Literature, 2 vols. 1203p. 1963. Set. 60.00x (ISBN 0-89356-150-9). Salem Pr.

Masterpieces of Hebrew Literature: A Treasury of Two Thousand Years of Jewish Creativity. Curt Leviant. 1969. pap. 14.95x (ISBN 0-87068-079-X). Ktav.

Masterpieces of Indian Temples. Rustam J. Mehta. LC 75-901641. (Illus.). 110p. 1974. 22.00x (ISBN 0-89684-433-1). Orient Bk Dist.

Masterpieces of the Vatican. Mario Fellucci. (Science of Man Library Bk). (Illus.). 40p. 1975. 97.45 (ISBN 0-913314-54-4). Am Classical Coll Pr.

Masters & Astara. 2nd ed. Earlyne Chaney. (Illus.). 100p. 1982. pap. 8.95 (ISBN 0-918936-13-6). Astara.

Master's Blesseds: The Sermon on the Mount. J. R. Miller. pap. 1.50 (ISBN 0-685-88384-1). Reiner.

Master's Book of Short Speeches. rev. ed. Walter E. Willets. 65p. 1984. Repr. s.p. soft cover 2.95 (ISBN 0-88053-050-2). Macoy Pub.

Master's Carpet. Edmond Ronayne. 9.00 (ISBN 0-685-19490-6). Powner.

Master's Hands: Understanding the Parable of the Potter & the Clay. Phillip Keller. (Christian Essentials Ser.). 48p. (Orig.). Date not set. pap. 1.95 (ISBN 0-89283-330-0, Pub. by Vine Books). Servant.

Master's Indwelling. Andrew Murray. LC 76-23363. 192p. 1977. pap. 2.95 (ISBN 0-87123-355-X, 200355). Bethany Hse.

Master's Men. William Barclay. (Festival Books). 1976. pap. 3.25 (ISBN 0-687-23732-7). Abingdon.

Master's Men. William Barclay. LC 85-6395. 224p. 1985. pap. 8.95 (ISBN 0-8027-2496-5). Walker & Co.

Master's Men. John MacArthur, Jr. (John MacArthur's Bible Studies). 1985. pap. text ed. 3.50 (ISBN 0-8024-5106-3). Moody.

Masters of Deception. Fred W. Thomas. pap. 4.95 (ISBN 0-8010-8779-1). Baker Bk.

Masters of Mahamudra: Songs & Histories of Eighty-Four Siddhas. Keith Dowman. (Buddhist Studies). 320p. 1986. 44.50x (ISBN 0-88706-158-3); pap. 10.95x (ISBN 0-88706-160-5). State U NY Pr.

Masters of the Path: A History of the Masters of the Nimatullahi Sufi Order. Javad Nurbakhsh. LC 80-80902. (Illus.). 144p. 1980. pap. 6.00x (ISBN 0-933546-03-3). KhaniQahi-Nimatullahi-Sufi.

Masters of the Reformation: Rival Roads to a New Ideology. H. A. Oberman. Tr. by D. Martin from German. 432p. 1981. 57.50 (ISBN 0-521-23098-5). Cambridge U Pr.

Masters Speak, 2 vols. Ruth E. Norman et al. (Tesla Speaks Ser.: No. 8). (Illus.). 1975. 8.95 ea.; Vol. 1. (ISBN 0-932642-30-6); Vol. 2. (ISBN 0-932642-29-2). Unarius Pubns.

Master's Touch: Disciples' Stories. Compiled by Sita Bordow. LC 84-28857. 1984. pap. 4.95 (ISBN 0-932040-26-8). Integral Yoga Pubns.

Mastery Through Accomplishment: Developing Inner Strength for Life's Challenges. rev. ed. Hazrat I. Khan. LC 79-101639. (Collected Works of Hazrat Inayat Khan Ser.). 336p. 1985. pap. 11.95 (ISBN 0-930872-07-X). Omega Pr NM.

Mater Larum: Zum Wesen der Larenreligion. facsimile ed. Ernst Tabeling. LC 75-10657. (Ancient Religion & Mythology Ser.). (Ger.). 1976. Repr. of 1932 ed. 12.00x (ISBN 0-405-07265-1). Ayer Co Pubs.

Material for Thought, No.7. Far West Editions. LC 77-89507. 76p. 1977. pap. 2.50 (ISBN 0-914480-03-0). Far West Edns.

Material for Thought, No. 8. Far West Editions. LC 79-56899. 88p. 1979. pap. 2.95 (ISBN 0-914480-05-7). Far West Edns.

Material for Thought, No. 9. Far West Editions. LC 81-68048. 94p. 1981. pap. 3.95 (ISBN 0-914480-07-3). Far West Edns.

Material for Thought, Vol.74 & 76, Nos. 7 & 8. Far West Editions. Bound Vol. pap. 7.95 (ISBN 0-686-47075-3). Far West Edns.

Material For Thought: Spring 1976. Far West Editions. LC 73-94407. 1976. pap. 2.95 (ISBN 0-914480-02-2). Far West Edns.

Material for Thought: 1970. Far West Editions. 31p. 1970. pap. 0.50 (ISBN 0-686-47079-6). Far West Edns.

Material for Thought: 1971. Far West Editions. 47p. 1971. pap. 0.50 (ISBN 0-686-47081-8). Far West Edns.

Material for Thought: 1972. Far West Editions. 63p. 1972. pap. 0.50 (ISBN 0-686-47082-6). Far West Edns.

Material for Thought: 1974. Far West Editions. LC 73-94407. 114p. 1974. pap. 2.00 (ISBN 0-914480-01-4). Far West Edns.

Materialist Approaches to the Bible. Michel Clevenot. Tr. by William Nottingham. LC 84-14711. 160p. (Orig.). 1985. pap. 8.95 (ISBN 0-88344-343-0). Orbis Bks.

Materialist Reading of the Gospel of Mark. Fernando Belo. Tr. by Matthew O'Connell from Fr. LC 80-24756. Tr. of Lectero Materialiste de L'evangele de Marc. 384p. (Orig.). 1981. pap. 12.95 (ISBN 0-88344-323-6). Orbis Bks.

Materials for the History of the Text of the Qur'an. Ed. by Arthur Jeffery. LC 79-180350. Repr. of 1937 ed. 57.50 (ISBN 0-404-56282-5). AMS Pr.

Materials for the History of Thomas Becket, 7 vols. Ed. by James C. Robertson & J. B. Sheppard. (Rolls Ser.: No. 67). Repr. of 1885 ed. Set. 308.00 (ISBN 0-8115-1135-9). Kraus Repr.

Materials for the Physical Anthropology of the Eastern European Jews. Maurice Fishberg. LC 6-2111. (American Anthro. Association Memoirs). 1905. 14.00 (ISBN 0-527-00500-2). Kraus Repr.

Materials Toward a History of the Baptists, 2 vols. Morgan Edwards. 1984. 36.00 (ISBN 0-317-38301-9). Church History.

Mathematical Metrological & Chronological Tablets from the Temple Library of Nippur. Hermann V. Hilprecht. LC 8-33648. (University of Pennsylvania, Babylonian Expedition, Series A: Cuneiform Texts: Vol. 20, Pt. 1). pap. 33.80 (ISBN 0-317-28568-8, 2052019). Bks Demand UMI.

Mathematics of the Cosmic Mind. rev. ed. L. Gordon Plummer. LC 77-114206. (Illus.). 1970. 18.95 (ISBN 0-8356-0030-0). Theos Pub Hse.

Mathers: Three Generations of Puritan Intellectuals, 1596-1728. Robert Middlekauff. LC 79-140912. 1971. pap. 7.95 (ISBN 0-19-502115-0). Oxford U Pr.

Mathew: A Gospel for the Church. Donald Senior. 1976. pap. 1.25 (ISBN 0-685-77500-3). Franciscan Herald.

Mathnawi of Jalalu'ddin Rumi, 3 vols. Jalalu'ddin Rumi. Tr. by R. A. Nicholson from Persian. 1444p. 1985. 175.00x (ISBN 0-317-39128-3, Pub. by Luzac & Co Ltd). State Mutual Bk.

Matrimonial Jurisprudence United States, 1975-1976: Summaries of Selected Cases. Reporting Tribunal Jurisprudence Committee. 158p. (Orig.). 1977. pap. 3.50 (ISBN 0-943616-11-5). Canon Law Soc.

Matrimonial Trials of Henry VIII. Henry A. Kelly. LC 75-7483. xiv, 334p. 1976. 27.50x (ISBN 0-8047-0895-9). Stanford U Pr.

Matrimonio Sorprendente. Pancho Pico. 96p. 1981. pap. 1.90 (ISBN 0-311-37022-5). Casa Bautista.

Matrimonio y la Familia en la Vida Cristiana. Guillermo Goff. (Span.). 240p. 1985. pap. 7.00 (ISBN 0-311-46097-6). Casa Bautista.

Matrimono y Familia Cristiana. P. Pedro Rodriguez. LC 84-7000069. 116p. 1984. pap. 2.95 (ISBN 0-915388-20-0). Buckley Pubns.

Matrimony: One Hundred & Thirty-Eight Pronouncements from Benedict Fourteenth to John Twenty-Third. Ed. by Monks Of Solesmes. 5.50 (ISBN 0-8198-0098-8); pap. 4.50 (ISBN 0-8198-0099-6). Dghtrs St Paul.

Matrix of Mystery: Scientific & Humanistic Aspects of rDzogs-chen Thought. Herbert V. Guenther. LC 83-2306. (Illus.). 317p. 1984. 22.50 (ISBN 0-87773-291-4, 54073-5). Shambhala Pubns.

Matsyendranath & Gorakshanath: Two Spiritual Lions. Sri Chinmoy. 64p. (Orig.). 1974. pap. 2.00 (ISBN 0-88497-093-0). Aum Pubns.

Matt Talbot: His Life & Times. Mary Purcell. 250p. 1977. 7.00 (ISBN 0-8199-0657-3). Franciscan Herald.

Matter & Spirit. William R. Clayton. LC 80-81694. 136p. 1981. 9.95 (ISBN 0-8022-2368-0). Philos Lib.

Matter of Choice. Angela R. Carl. LC 84-7040. (Illus.). 32p. 1984. lib. bdg. 4.95 (ISBN 0-89693-223-0). Dandelion Hse.

Matter of Faith. Charles P. Price. LC 83-50559. 80p. 1983. pap. 5.95 (ISBN 0-8192-1335-7). Morehouse.

Matter of Hope: A Theologian's Reflections on the Thought of Karl Marx. Nicholas Lash. LC 82-1980. 312p. 1982. text ed. 19.95 (ISBN 0-268-01352-7). U of Notre Dame Pr.

Matter of Hope: A Theologian's Reflections on the Thought of Karl Marx. Nicholas Lash. LC 82-1980. 312p. 1984. pap. text ed. 9.95 (ISBN 0-268-01360-8, 85-13608). U of Notre Dame Pr.

Matter of Life & Death. Robert P. Sikking. 1978. pap. 4.95 (ISBN 0-87516-256-8). De Vorss.

Matter of Personal Survival. Michael Marsh. LC 84-40514. (Illus.). 209p. (Orig.). 1985. pap. 7.50 (ISBN 0-8356-0596-5). Theos Pub Hse.

Matter of Return. 1982. pap. 4.95 (ISBN 0-686-76543-5). Feldheim.

Matters of Faith & Matter of Principle: Religious Truth Claims & Their Logic. John H. Whittaker. LC 80-51940. (Trinity University Monograph Series in Religion: Vol. 6). 173p. 1981. 12.00 (ISBN 0-911536-87-6). Trinity U Pr.

Matters of Life & Death: New Introductory Essays in Moral Philosophy. Ed. by Tom Regan. 368p. 1980. 32.95 (ISBN 0-87722-181-2). Temple U Pr.

Matthew. Ed. by William F. Albright & C. S. Mann. LC 77-150875. (Anchor Bible Ser.: Vol. 26). 1971. 18.00 (ISBN 0-385-08658-X, Anchor Pr). Doubleday.

Matthew, Vol. I. Beacon Bible Commentary Staff. 6.95 (ISBN 0-8010-0676-7). Baker Bk.

Matthew. George Beasley-Murray. (Bible Study Commentaries Ser.). 122p. 1984. pap. 4.95 (ISBN 0-317-43380-6). Chr Lit.

Matthew. David Dickson. (Geneva Ser. Commentaries). Orig. Title: Brief Exposition of the Evangel of Jesus Christ According to Matthew. 416p. 1981. 15.95 (ISBN 0-85151-319-0). Banner of Truth.

Matthew. Suzanne Dietrich. LC 59-10454. (Layman's Bible Commentary Ser.: Vol. 16). 1961. pap. 4.95 (ISBN 0-8042-3076-5). John Knox.

Matthew. William Hendriksen. (New Testament Commentary Ser.). 1973. 24.95 (ISBN 0-8010-4066-3). Baker Bk.

Matthew. Irving L. Jensen. (Bible Self Study Ser.). 1974. pap. 3.25 (ISBN 0-8024-1040-5). Moody.

Matthew. 2nd, enl. & rev. ed. Jack D. Kingsbury. LC 84-45212. (Proclamation Commentaries Ser.). 144p. 1986. pap. 6.95 (ISBN 0-8006-0597-7). Fortress.

Matthew. E. Leroy Lawson. (Standard Bible Studies). 352p. 1986. pap. 9.95 (ISBN 0-87403-161-3, 40101). Standard Pub.

Matthew. (Erdmans Commentaries Ser.). 4.95 (ISBN 0-8010-3402-7). Baker Bk.

Matthew. John P. Meier. (New Testament Message Ser.: Vol. 3). 15.95 (ISBN 0-89453-191-3); pap. 12.95 (ISBN 0-89453-126-3). M Glazier.

Matthew. James Morison. 1981. lib. bdg. 24.95 (ISBN 0-86524-068-X, 4001). Klock & Klock.

Matthew. Arthur Robertson. (Everyman's Bible Commentary Ser.). (Orig.). 1983. pap. 5.95 (ISBN 0-8024-0233-X). Moody.

Matthew. J. C. Ryle. (Expository Thoughts on the Gospel Ser.). 368p. 1986. pap. 5.95 (ISBN 0-85151-483-9). Banner of Truth.

Matthew. Jonathan Underwood. (Standard Bible Study Workbooks Ser.). 64p. 1986. pap. text ed. 1.95 (ISBN 0-87403-181-8, 40201). Standard Pub.

Matthew: A Bible Study Commentary. Howard F. Vos. (Study Guide Commentary Ser.). 1979. pap. 6.95 (ISBN 0-310-33883-2, 11152P). Zondervan.

Matthew: A Commentary on His Literary & Theological Art. Robert Gundry. 600p. 1982. 24.95 (ISBN 0-8028-3549-X). Eerdmans.

Matthew: A Good News Commentary. Robert H. Mounce. LC 84-48775. (Good News Commentary Ser.). 288p. (Orig.). 1985. pap. 9.95 (ISBN 0-06-066032-5, HarpR). Har-Row.

Matthew: An Access Guide for Scripture Study. John P. Meier & Edmund F. Gordon. 174p. 1983. pap. 4.20 (ISBN 0-8215-5932-X); manual 3.45 (ISBN 0-8215-5935-4). Sadlier.

Matthew & Paul: A Comparison of Ethical Perspectives. Roger Mohrlang. LC 83-10147. (Society for New Testament Studies Monograph: No. 48). 220p. 1984. 37.50 (ISBN 0-521-25093-5). Cambridge U Pr.

Matthew Arnold. John D. Jump. LC 76-7983. 1955. lib. bdg. 20.00 (ISBN 0-8414-5348-9). Folcroft.

Matthew Arnold. Alexander Kelso. 1978. lib. bdg. 10.00 (ISBN 0-8492-1444-0). R West.

Matthew Arnold. Hugh Kingsmill. 1973. Repr. of 1928 ed. 40.00 (ISBN 0-8274-0720-3). R West.

Matthew Arnold. Carlton W. Stanley. 1978. Repr. of 1938 ed. 20.00 (ISBN 0-8492-2595-7). R West.

Matthew Arnold: A Critic of the Victorian Period. Charles H. Harvey. LC 69-18273. 256p. 1969. Repr. of 1931 ed. 27.50 (ISBN 0-208-00732-6, Archon). Shoe String.

Matthew Arnold: A Life. Park Honan. LC 80-26131. (Illus.). 544p. 1981. 19.95 (ISBN 0-07-029697-9). McGraw.

Matthew Arnold & Carlyle. Kathleen Tillotson. LC 73-16394. 1956. lib. bdg. 12.50 (ISBN 0-8414-8560-7). Folcroft.

Matthew Arnold & Christianity: His Religious Prose Writings. James C. Livingston. 250p. 1986. text ed. 17.95x (ISBN 0-87249-462-4). U of SC Pr.

Matthew Arnold & His Critics: A Study of Arnold's Controversies. Sidney Coulling. LC 74-82498. xiv, 351p. 1974. 20.00x (ISBN 0-8214-0161-0). Ohio U Pr.

Matthew Arnold & the Philosophy of Vico. Paul W. Day. 1964. 10.00 (ISBN 0-8274-2691-7). R West.

Matthew Arnold: How to Know Him. Stuart P. Sherman. 1973. lib. bdg. 20.00 (ISBN 0-8414-8083-4). Folcroft.

Matthew Arnold, How to Know Him. Stuart P. Sherman. 326p. 1968. Repr. of 1917 ed. 29.50 (ISBN 0-208-00453-X, Archon). Shoe String.

Matthew Arnold: Prose Writings. Ed. by Carl Dawson & John Pfordresher. (Critical Heritage Ser.). 1979. 34.00x (ISBN 0-7100-0244-0). Methuen Inc.

Matthew Arnold, the Critic & France. Frank J. Harding. LC 76-50106. 1977. Repr. of 1964 ed. lib. bdg. 25.00 (ISBN 0-8414-4721-7). Folcroft.

Matthew Arnold: The Message & Meaning of a Life. T. W. Lund. LC 76-28474. 1888. lib. bdg. 8.50 (ISBN 0-8414-5807-3). Folcroft.

Matthew As Story. Jack D. Kingsbury. LC 85-16204. 160p. 1986. pap. 9.95 (ISBN 0-8006-1891-2). Fortress.

Matthew: Being Discipled by Jesus. Stephen Eyre & Jackie Eyre. (LifeBuilder Bible Studies). 64p. (Orig.). 1987. pap. 2.95 (ISBN 0-8308-1003-X). Inter-Varsity.

Matthew Book One. Marilyn Kunz & Catherine Schell. 1980. pap. 2.50 (ISBN 0-8423-4188-9). Tyndale.

Matthew Book Two. Marilyn Kunz & Catherine Schell. 1980. pap. 2.95 (ISBN 0-8423-4189-7). Tyndale.

Matthew Eight-Fifteen. John MacArthur, Jr. (MacArthur New Testament Commentary Ser.). 1986. text ed. 14.95 (ISBN 0-8024-0763-3). Moody.

Matthew Henry Concise Commentary on the Whole Bible. Mathew Henry & Thomas Scott. (Affordable Ser.). 1024p. 13.95 (ISBN 0-8024-0417-0). Moody.

Matthew Henry Concise Commentary on the Whole Bible. Matthew Henry & Thomas Scott. 25.95 (ISBN 0-8024-5190-X). Moody.

Matthew Henry's Commentary in One Volume. Matthew Henry. Ed. by Leslie F. Church. 1966. 29.95 (ISBN 0-310-26010-8, 9802). Zondervan.

Matthew Henry's Commentary on the New Testament, 10 vols. Ed. by Matthew Henry. 1983. 59.95 (ISBN 0-8010-4277-1). Baker Bk.

Matthew Henry's Commentary on the Whole Bible, 6 vols. Matthew Henry. 7152p. Date not set. Set. 79.95 (ISBN 0-917006-21-6). Hendrickson MA.

Matthew Henry's Sermon Outlines. Ed. by Sheldon B. Quincer. 1955. pap. 5.95 (ISBN 0-8028-1155-8). Eerdmans.

Matthew-Luke, Vol. VI. Beacon Bible Commentary Staff. 13.95 (ISBN 0-8010-0693-7). Baker Bk.

Matthew-Luke Commentary of Philoxenus. Douglas J. Fox. LC 78-12852. 1979. 14.50 (ISBN 0-89130-350-2); pap. 9.95 (ISBN 0-89130-266-2, 060143). Scholars Pr GA.

Matthew-Mark. William G. Scrogie. 1981. pap. 4.95 (ISBN 0-87508-484-2). Chr Lit.

Matthew One-Seven. John F. MacArthur, Jr. 1985. 14.95 (ISBN 0-88469-168-3). BMH Bks.

Matthew, Part 2: Come & Learn from Me. Frank Carver. Ed. by Earl Wolf. (Small-Group Bible Studies). 84p. 1986. pap. 2.50 (ISBN 0-8341-1076-8). Beacon Hill.

Matthew: Spirituality for the 80's & 90's. Leonard Doohan. LC 85-70838. 199p. (Orig.). 1985. pap. 9.95 (ISBN 0-939680-19-X). Bear & Co.

Matthew, the Gospel of God's King. Keith L. Brooks. (Teach Yourself the Bible Ser.). 1963. pap. 2.75 (ISBN 0-8024-5212-4). Moody.

Matthew: The Teacher's Gospel. Paul S. Minear. LC 82-10178. 160p. (Orig.). 1982. pap. 7.95 (ISBN 0-8298-0617-2). Pilgrim NY.

Matthew 1-7. John MacArthur, Jr. (MacArthur New Testament Commentary Ser.). 1985. text ed. 14.95 (ISBN 0-8024-0755-2). Moody.

Matthew 8-15. John MacArthur, Jr. 1986. 14.95 (ISBN 0-88469-172-1). BMH Bks.

Matthew's Gospel. John Gilchrist & Judy Andrews. 1.77 (ISBN 0-8091-9335-3). Paulist Pr.

Matthew's Majestic Gospel. Ivor Powell. LC 86-10401. 528p. 1986. 18.95 (ISBN 0-8254-3525-0). Kregel.

Matthew's Story of Jesus. Richard A. Edwards. LC 84-48711. 96p. 1985. pap. 4.50 (ISBN 0-8006-1619-7, 1-1619). Fortress.

Matthieu de Vendome, ars Versificatoria. Roger P. Parr. Ed. by James Robb. LC 80-84768. 1981. pap. 9.95 (ISBN 0-87462-222-0). Marquette.

Mattie Loves All. Mildred H. Grimley. (Illus.). 22p. 1985. 5.95 (ISBN 0-87178-552-8). Brethren.

Mature Christianity: The Recognition & Repudiation of the Anti-Jewish Polemic of the New Testament. Norman A. Beck. LC 83-51047. (Illus.). 328p. 1985. 19.50 (ISBN 0-941664-03-1). Assoc Univ Prs.

Mature Faith: A Spiritual Pilgrimage. Glenn H. Asquith. LC 84-12890. 120p. (Orig.). 1984. pap. 6.95 (ISBN 0-8361-3366-8). Herald Pr.

Maturing a Christian Conscience. John Carmody. 160p. (Orig.). 1985. pap. 6.95 (ISBN 0-8358-0510-7). Upper Room.

Maturing Christian. Douglas J. Simpson. 1977. pap. 1.50 (ISBN 0-89265-047-8). Randall Hse.

Maturing in the Christian Life: A Pastor's Guide. Neill Q. Hamilton. LC 83-20661. 192p. (Orig.). 1984. pap. 10.95 (ISBN 0-664-24515-3). Westminster.

Maturing Ministry. Elwood Matthews. 1981. pap. 3.50 (ISBN 0-934942-22-6). White Wing Pub.

Maturing Salesian. David DeBurgh. 1977. pap. 3.95 (ISBN 0-89944-028-2). Don Bosco Multimedia.

Maturing the Spirit. new ed. Dominic M. Hoffman. 1973. 5.00 (ISBN 0-8198-0257-3); pap. 4.00 (ISBN 0-8198-0258-1). Dghtrs St Paul.

Maturity in an Immature World. Levi A. Olan. 1984. 15.00 (ISBN 0-88125-049-X). Ktav.

Maududi, Thought & Movements. A. Gilani. 25.00 (ISBN 0-317-46091-9). Kazi Pubns.

Mauerbach und die Kartauser: Symposium Uber die Kartausegeschichte und - Spiritualitat 27, 28 May 1983. Ed. by James Hogg. (Analecta Cartusiana Ser.: No. 110). 98p. (Orig.). 1984. pap. 25.00 (ISBN 0-317-42585-4, Pub. by Salzburg Studies). Longwood Pub Group.

Maui Now. Jack H. Stephens et al. (Illus., Orig.). 1969. pap. 1.70 (ISBN 0-941200-02-7). Aquarius.

Maury, Hijo Del Dolor. Maury Blair & Doug Brendel. Tr. by Juan S. Araujo from Eng. Tr. of Maury, Wednesday's Child. (Span.). 144p. 1986. pap. 3.75 (ISBN 0-88113-204-7). Edit Betania.

Max Scheler: The Man & His Works. John H. Nota. 1983. 12.00 (ISBN 0-8199-0852-5). Franciscan Herald.

Maximes et Pensees. Blaise Pascal. 4.95 (ISBN 0-686-54848-5). French & Eur.

Maximized Manhood. Edwin L. Cole. 176p. (Orig.). 1982. pap. text ed. 3.95 (ISBN 0-88368-107-2). Whitaker Hse.

Maximum Marriage. rev. & updated ed. Tim Timmons. 160p. pap. 5.95 (ISBN 0-8007-5106-X, Power Bks). Revell.

Maximum Marriage. Tim Timmons & Lisa McAfee. 64p. (Orig.). 1984. pap. 4.95 (ISBN 0-915929-08-2); leader's guide 1.95 (ISBN 0-915929-17-1). Merit Bks.

Maximus the Confessor. Ed. by George C. Berthold. (Classics of Western Spirituality Ser.: Vol. 45). 1985. 12.95 (ISBN 0-8091-0353-2); pap. 9.95 (ISBN 0-8091-2659-1). Paulist Pr.

May I Divorce & Remarry. Spiros Zodhiates. write for info. (ISBN 0-89957-600-1). AMG Pubs.

May I Hate God? Pierre Wolff. LC 78-70815. 80p. 1979. pap. 2.95 (ISBN 0-8091-2180-8). Paulist Pr.

May the Light Shine. Heini Arnold. 36p. 1985. pap. 1.50 (ISBN 0-87486-197-7). Plough.

May They All Be One. Chiara Lubich. Tr. of Tutti Siano Uno. 96p. (Orig.). 1983. pap. 3.95 (ISBN 0-911782-46-X). New City.

May They All Be One: Origins & Life of the Focolare Movement. Chiara Lubich. LC 71-77438. 1977. pap. 2.50 cancelled (ISBN 0-911782-28-1). New City.

May Thy Light Shine: Prayers. Heini Arnold. Ed. by Hutterian Brethren. LC 86-9387. (Illus.). 240p. 1986. 6.00 (ISBN 0-87486-199-3, BV245.A748 1986 242.80973). Plough.

Maya Astronomy. Ed. by John Teeple. (Classics of Anthropology Ser.). 20.00 (ISBN 0-8240-9624-X). Garland Pub.

Maya Book of the Dead: The Ceramic Codex. Francis Robicsek & Donald Hale. LC 81-86395. (Illus.). 288p. 48.50 (ISBN 0-8061-9911-3). U of Okla Pr.

Maya Divine & Human. Teun Goudriaan. 1978. 19.95 (ISBN 0-89684-040-9, Pub. by Motilal Banarsidass India). Orient Bk Dist.

Maya, Divine & Human. Teun Goudriaan. 1979. 26.00x (ISBN 0-685-95754-3). South Asia Bks.

Maya History & Religion. J. Eric Thompson. LC 72-88144. (Civilization of the American Indian Ser.: Vol. 99). 1976. Repr. of 1970 ed. 24.95 (ISBN 0-8061-0884-3). U of Okla Pr.

Maya Veeram or the Forces of Illusion. Bawa Muhaiyaddeen. Ed. by Sharon Marcus. Tr. by K. Ganesan & R. Ganesan. (Illus.). 232p. 1982. pap. 10.95 (ISBN 0-87728-550-0). Weiser.

Mayan Factor: Path Beyond Technology. Jose Arguelles. (Illus.). 160p. (Orig.). 1987. pap. 10.95 (ISBN 0-939680-38-6). Bear & Co.

Maya's Own Words: An Anthology Comprising Abridgements of the Popol-Vuh, Warrior of Rabinal, & Selections from the Memorial of Solola, the Book of Chilam Balam of Chumayel, & the Title of the Lords Of Totonicapan. Ed. by Thomas B. Irving. LC 84-81822. (Illus.). 102p. (Orig.). 1985. pap. 12.00X (ISBN 0-911437-14-2). Labyrinthos.

Mayer Boulding Dialogue on Peace Research. Kenneth E. Boulding & Milton Mayer. Ed. by Carol Murphy. LC 67-23313. (Orig.). 1967. pap. 2.50x (ISBN 0-87574-153-3). Pendle Hill.

Mayflower Essays: On the Story of the Pilgrim Fathers, As Told in Governor Bradford's Ms. History of the Plimoth Plantation. G. Cuthbert Blaxland. LC 78-39713. (Essay Index Reprint Ser.). Repr. of 1896 ed. 13.00 (ISBN 0-8369-2748-6). Ayer Co Pubs.

Mayflower II: On Buddhist Voyage to Liberation. C. T. Shen. LC 83-81198. (Basic Buddhism Ser.). (Illus.). 1983. pap. 4.95 (ISBN 0-915078-03-1, P-02). Inst Adv Stud Wld.

Mayim. Nachman & Nathan. Ed. by Moshe Mykoff. 64p. (Orig.). 1987. pap. 1.50 (ISBN 0-930213-28-9). Breslov Res Inst.

Mayo Indians of Sonora: A People Who Refuse to Die. N. Ross Crumrine. LC 76-8563. 167p. 1977. 12.50x (ISBN 0-8165-0605-1); pap. text ed. 5.95x (ISBN 0-8165-0473-3). U of Ariz Pr.

Mazarin. facs. ed. Arthur Hassall. LC 73-137379. (Select Bibliographies Reprint Ser.). 1903. 17.00 (ISBN 0-8369-5580-3). Ayer Co Pubs.

Mazdak: Geschichte einer sozialen Bewegung im sassanidischen Persien. Otakar Klima. Ed. by Moses Finley. LC 79-4986. (Ancient Economic History Ser.). (Ger.). 1980. Repr. of 1957 ed. lib. bdg. 27.50x (ISBN 0-405-12371-X). Ayer Co Pubs.

Maze of Mormonism. Walter Martin. LC 78-66067. (Orig.). 1979. pap. 6.95 (ISBN 0-88449-017-3, A424365). Vision Hse.

Mazhor Hashalem High Holiday Prayer Book, Vol. 2: Yom Kippur. Philip Birnbaum. 770p. 1960. 14.00 (ISBN 0-88482-247-8). Hebrew Pub.

Me & My Mustang. Anne Brady. (Illus.). 50p. (Orig.). 1986. pap. 4.95 (ISBN 0-937689-02-5). Chisum Pub.

Me, Believing. Joan Mitchell. (Infinity Ser.: No. 8). 1972. text ed. 2.50 (ISBN 0-03-004061-2, 241, HarpR). Har-Row.

Me, Myself & I. Christine Tangvald. (I Am Special Bks.). (Illus.). 20p. 1985. 3.95 (ISBN 0-89191-925-2, 59253). Cook.

Me, Myself & You. rev. ed. Vincent P. Collins. LC 74-17734. 1974. pap. 2.95 (ISBN 0-87029-001-0, 20033-7). Abbey.

Meah Shaerim Centennial: A Study of the Neturei Karta. 1980. lib. bdg. 59.95 (ISBN 0-686-68746-9). Revisionist Pr.

Mealtime Prayers. Mildred Tengbom. LC 85-9041. 128p. (Orig.). 1985. pap. 4.95 (ISBN 0-8066-2127-3, 10-4306). Augsburg.

MeAm Lo'ez Haggadah. Tr. & intro. by Aryeh Kaplan. 216p. pap. 6.45 (ISBN 0-940118-24-6). Maznaim.

Meanest Man in Texas. Don Umphrey. LC 84-3383. 288p. 1984. pap. 6.95 (ISBN 0-8407-5870-7). Nelson.

Meaning Across Cultures: A Study on Bible Translating. Eugene A. Nida & William D. Reyburn. LC 81-38374. 96p. (Orig.). 1981. pap. 2.98 (ISBN 0-88344-326-0). Orbis Bks.

Meaning & End of Religion. Wilfred C. Smith. LC 77-20440. 1978. pap. 9.95 (ISBN 0-06-067465-2, RD 252, HarpR). Har-Row.

Meaning & End of Suffering for Freud & the Buddhist Tradition. Gordon E. Pruett. LC 86-26735. 524p. 1987. lib. bdg. 34.50 (ISBN 0-8191-5758-9). U Pr of Amer.

Meaning & Measurement of Moral Development. Ed. by L. Hohlberg. (Heinz Werner Lecture: No. 13). 1979. pap. 6.00 (ISBN 0-914206-18-4). Clark U Pr.

Meaning & Mode of Baptism. Jay E. Adams. 63p. 1975. pap. 3.75 (ISBN 0-87552-043-X). Presby & Reformed.

Meaning & Place: An Introduction to the Social Scientific Study of Religion. Hans Mol. (Orig.). 1983. pap. 6.95 (ISBN 0-8298-0638-5). Pilgrim NY.

Meaning & Reason in Ethics. rev. ed. W. L. LaCroix. LC 79-52963. 1979. pap. text ed. 8.75 (ISBN 0-8191-0786-7). U Pr of Amer.

Meaning & Value of Mysticism. 3rd facsimile ed. E. Herman. LC 72-164607. (Select Bibliographies Reprint Ser.). Repr. of 1922 ed. 22.00 (ISBN 0-8369-5891-8). Ayer Co Pubs.

Meaning & Value of Mysticism. E. Herman. 1977. lib. bdg. 59.95 (ISBN 0-8490-2216-9). Gordon Pr.

Meaning & Value of the Sacraments. Flower A. Newhouse. LC 77-186123. 123p. 1971. 7.50 (ISBN 0-910378-07-X). Christward.

Meaning in History: The Theological Implications of the Philosophy of History. Karl Lowith. LC 57-7900. 1957. pap. 7.50x (ISBN 0-226-49555-8, P16, Phoen). U of Chicago Pr.

Meaning in Suffering: Comfort in Crisis Through Logotherapy. Elisabeth Lukas. Tr. by Joseph Fabry from Ger. Tr. of Auch Dein Leiden hat Sinn. 160p. (Orig.). 1986. pap. 7.95 (ISBN 0-917867-05-X). Inst Logo.

Meaning of Agapao & Phileo in the Greek New Testament. Roy F. Butler. 1977. 6.50x (ISBN 0-87291-089-X). Coronado Pr.

Meaning of Authority. John E. Skinner. LC 82-25098. 88p. (Orig.). 1983. lib. bdg. 22.00 (ISBN 0-8191-3044-3, Co-pub. by Episcopal Div Sch); pap. text ed. 8.50 (ISBN 0-8191-3045-1). U Pr of Amer.

Meaning of Bama in the Old Testament. P. H. Vaughan. LC 73-89004. (Society for Old Testament Study Monographs: No. 3). (Illus.). 96p. 1974. 29.95 (ISBN 0-521-20425-9). Cambridge U Pr.

Meaning of Christ. Robert C. Johnson. LC 58-6120. (Layman's Theological Library). 96p. 1958. pap. 3.45 (ISBN 0-664-24009-7). Westminster.

Meaning of Christianity. Garry De Young. 96p. 1982. pap. 7.95x (ISBN 0-936128-02-X). tchrs' ed. o. p. 7.95. De Young Pr.

Meaning of Christianity. Peter Nemeshegyi. 128p. 1982. pap. 3.95 (ISBN 0-8091-2464-5). Paulist Pr.

Meaning of Christmas. Phyllis Hobe. LC 75-12627. 1982. Repr. of 1975 ed. 7.95 (ISBN 0-8054-5118-8). Broadman.

Meaning of Church Membership. Wayne C. Clark. pap. 4.50 (ISBN 0-8170-0103-4). Judson.

Meaning of Creations. Conrad Hyers. LC 84-47795. 212p. pap. 11.95 (ISBN 0-8042-0125-0). John Knox.

Meaning of Faith. Harry E. Fosdick. (Festival Bks). 352p. 1982. pap. 3.95 (ISBN 0-687-23959-1). Abingdon.

Meaning of Gifts. Paul Tournier. LC 63-19122. 1976. 5.95 (ISBN 0-8042-2124-3); pap. 1.25 (ISBN 0-8042-3604-6). John Knox.

Meaning of God in Modern Jewish Religion. Mordecai M. Kaplan. 1975. pap. 10.95 (ISBN 0-935457-19-4). Reconstructionist Pr.

Meaning of Happiness: The Quest for Freedom of the Spirit in Modern Psychology & the Wisdom of the East. Alan W. Watts. 1979. pap. 6.95 (ISBN 0-06-090676-6, CN 676, PL). Har-Row.

Meaning of Health: Relation of Religion & Health. 2nd ed. Paul Tillich. 64p. 1981. 20.00 (ISBN 0-913028-87-8); pap. 7.95 (ISBN 0-913028-81-9). North Atlantic.

Meaning of Human Existence. Leslie A. Paul. LC 73-148642. 1971. Repr. of 1949 ed. lib. bdg. 22.50x (ISBN 0-8371-6008-1, PAHE). Greenwood.

Meaning of Human Suffering. Ed. by Flavian Dougherty. LC 81-6267. 349p. 1982. 39.95 (ISBN 0-89885-011-8). Human Sci Pr.

Meaning of Icons. Vladimir Lossky & Leonid Ouspensky. 1981. pap. 52.50x (ISBN 0-913836-77-X, Pub. by Mowbrays Pub Div). State Mutual Bk.

Meaning of Immortality in Human Experience, Including Thoughts on Death & Life. rev. ed. William E. Hocking. 263p. 1973. Repr. of 1957 ed. lib. bdg. 27.50x (ISBN 0-8371-6621-7, HOMI). Greenwood.

Meaning of Job & Other Biblical Studies: Essays on the Literature & Religion of the Hebrew Bible. Matitiahu Tsevat. 1981. 25.00x (ISBN 0-87068-714-X). Ktav.

Meaning of Kahlil Gibran. M. S. Daoudi. 160p. 1982. 9.95 (ISBN 0-8065-0804-3). Citadel Pr.

Meaning of Kahlil Gibran. M. S. Daoudi. 140p. 1984. pap. 5.95 (ISBN 0-8065-0929-5). Citadel Pr.

Meaning of Life. Gene Liberty. (Orig.). 1975. pap. text ed. 8.67 (ISBN 0-87720-010-6). AMSCO Sch.

Meaning of Love. Phyllis Hobe. LC 76-23415. 1982. Repr. of 1976 ed. 7.95 (ISBN 0-8054-5119-6). Broadman.

Meaning of Love. rev. ed. Vladimir Solovyov. 144p. 1985. pap. 7.95 (ISBN 0-89281-068-8, Lindisfarne Pr). Inner Tradit.

Meaning of Mysticism. Isaac H. Riley. LC 75-26512. 1975. lib. bdg. 20.00 (ISBN 0-8414-7227-0). Folcroft.

Meaning of Other Faiths. Willard G. Oxtoby. LC 83-1090. (Library of Living Faith: Vol. 10). 120p. (Orig.). 1983. pap. 5.95 (ISBN 0-664-24443-2). Westminster.

Meaning of Persons. Paul Tournier. LC 57-9885. 244p. 1982. pap. 7.95 (ISBN 0-686-97228-7, RD 411, HarpR). Har-Row.

Meaning of Prayer. Harry E. Fosdick. 1982. pap. 2.95 (ISBN 0-687-23960-5, Festival). Abingdon.

Meaning of Prayer. Harry E. Fosdick. LC 76-50560. 1976. Repr. of 1946 ed. lib. bdg. 18.50 (ISBN 0-8414-4159-6). Folcroft.

Meaning of Religious Conversion in Africa: The Case of the Igbo of Nigeria. Cyril Okoroche. 354p. 1987. text ed. 55.00x (ISBN 0-566-05030-7, Pub. by Gower Pub England). Gower Pub Co.

Meaning of Revelation. H. Richard Niebuhr. 1967. pap. 5.95 (ISBN 0-02-087750-1, Collier). Macmillan.

Meaning of Revelation. H. Richard Niebuhr. 1983. 14.00 (ISBN 0-8446-6033-7). Peter Smith.

Meaning of Righteousness in Paul: A Linguistic & Theological Enquiry. J. A. Ziesler. LC 75-164455. (Society for New Testament Studies, Monograph Ser.: Vol. 20). pap. 66.80 (ISBN 0-317-26359-5, 2024567). Bks Demand UMI.

Meaning of Sacrifice. Roger E. Money-Kyrle. Repr. of 1930 ed. 17.00 (ISBN 0-384-39690-9). Johnson Repr.

Meaning of Sanctorum Communio. Stephen Benko. LC 64-55292. (Studies in Historical Theology: No. 3). 1964. pap. 10.00x (ISBN 0-8401-0178-3). A R Allenson.

Meaning of Service. Harry E. Fosdick. 224p. 1983. pap. 4.35 (ISBN 0-687-23961-3). Abingdon.

Meaning of Sexual Pleasure: A Christian Understanding of Sexuality. J. R. Braun. 203p. (Orig.). 1976. pap. 4.95 (ISBN 0-933656-02-5). Trinity Pub Hse.

Meaning of the Cross. Leslie D. Weatherhead. (Festival Ser.). 192p. 1982. pap. 2.75 (ISBN 0-687-23970-2). Abingdon.

Meaning of the Dead Sea Scrolls. A. Davies. pap. 2.95 (ISBN 0-451-62447-5, ME2097, Ment). NAL.

Meaning of the Glorious Koran. Tr. by Mohammed M. Pickthall. pap. 4.50 (ISBN 0-451-62305-3, ME2305, Ment). NAL.

Meaning of the Glorious Qur'an, 2 Vols. Abdullah Y. Ali & Abdullah Y. Ali. Set. 24.00 (ISBN 0-686-37146-1). New World Press NY.

Meaning of the Glorious Quran. Pickthall. pap. 4.95 (ISBN 0-686-18531-5). Kazi Pubns.

Meaning of the Illustrious Qur'an: Arabic & English. Tr. by M. M. Pickthall. 1970. 45.00x (ISBN 0-87902-182-9). Orientalia.

Meaning of the Millennium. Robert G. Clouse. 212p. 1978. pap. 5.95 (ISBN 0-88469-099-7). BMH Bks.

Meaning of the Millennium: Four Views. Ed. by Robert G. Clouse. 1977. pap. 7.95 (ISBN 0-87784-794-0). Inter-Varsity.

Meaning of the Quran, 12 vols. A. A. Maududi. 10.50 ea. Kazi Pubns.

Meaning of the Sacraments. Monika Hellwig. 1.95 (ISBN 0-686-13702-7, Pub. by Pflaum Pr). Peter Li.

Meaning of Things in Life. Harbhajan S. Bajaj. 1986. 6.95 (ISBN 0-533-06697-2). Vantage.

Meaning of Transcendence. Robert P. Orr. Ed. by Wendell Dietrich. LC 80-12872. (American Academy of Religion Dissertation Ser.). 172p. 1981. pap. 9.95 (ISBN 0-89130-408-8, 01 01 35). Scholars Pr GA.

Meaningful Learning in the Church. Donald M. Joy. 1969. 3.25 (ISBN 0-89367-019-7). Light & Life.

Meanings: The Bible As Document & Guide. Krister Stendahl. LC 83-5601. 240p. 1984. pap. 14.95 (ISBN 0-8006-1752-5, 1-1752). Fortress.

Means of Grace. Edward M. Matthews. 58p. 1946. pap. 1.50 (ISBN 0-935461-08-6). St Alban Pr CA.

Meant to Last. Steele & Ryrie. 1983. 5.95 (ISBN 0-686-46323-4). Victor Bks.

Meanwhile, Back at the Flock: A Christmas Puppet Play. Mary E. Shoemaker. (Orig.). 1980. pap. 1.85 (ISBN 0-937172-09-X). JLJ Pubs.

Measure of a Church. Gene A. Getz. LC 75-17160. (Orig.). 1975. pap. 3.50 (ISBN 0-8307-0398-5, 5014700). Regal.

Measure of a Man. Gene A. Getz. LC 74-175983. 224p. (Orig.). 1974. pap. 4.95 (ISBN 0-8307-0291-1, 5012104). Regal.

Measure of a Man. John Richardson. (Study & Grow Electives). 64p. 1985. pap. 3.95 (ISBN 0-8307-1018-3, 6102023). Regal.

Measure of a Marriage. Gene A. Getz. LC 78-53356. 144p. 1980. pap. 3.50 (ISBN 0-8307-0638-0, 5017203). Regal.

Measure of a Woman. Sarah Fryman. LC 77-74533. (Measure of... Ser.). 64p. 1985. pap. 3.95 (ISBN 0-8307-0988-6, 6101888). Regal.

Measure of My Days. Florida Scott-Maxwell. 1979. pap. 5.95 (ISBN 0-14-005164-3). Penguin.

Measured Pace. William Coleman. 144p. (Orig.). 1986. pap. 4.95 (ISBN 0-87123-671-0, 210671). Bethany Hse.

Measurement of Moral Judgement, 2 vols, Vols. 1-2. Anne Colby & Lawrence Kohlberg. Date not set. Vol. 1: Theoretical Foundations & Research, 425 pgs. price not set (ISBN 0-521-24447-1); Vol. 2: Standard Issue Scoring Manual, 1200 pgs. price not set (ISBN 0-521-32501-3); price not set (ISBN 0-521-32565-X). Cambridge U Pr.

Measurement of Values. Rollo Handy. LC 79-110107. 232p. 1970. 12.50 (ISBN 0-87527-040-9). Fireside Bks.

Measurement of Values. Louis L. Thurstone. LC 58-11960. (Midway Reprint Ser.). pap. 82.50 (2026748). Bks Demand UMI.

Measures of Wisdom: The Cosmic Dance in Classical & Christian Antiquity. James Miller. 672p. 1986. 60.00 (ISBN 0-8020-2553-6). U of Toronto Pr.

Measuring Old English Rhythm: An Application of the Principles of Gregorian Chant Rhythm to the Meter of Beowolf. Jane-Marie Luecke. LC 66-25869. (Literary Monographs: Vol. 9). 168p. 1978. 25.00x (ISBN 0-299-07510-9). U of Wis Pr.

Measuring Religious Dimensions: Studies of Congregational Involvement. Morton B. King & Richard A. Hunt. (Studies in Social Science: No. 1). 1972. pap. 5.95x (ISBN 0-87074-174-8). SMU Press.

Meat for Men. Leonard Ravenhill. 144p. 1979. pap. 4.95 (ISBN 0-87123-362-2, A-510418). Bethany Hse.

Meatless Recipes. Mattie L. Gebhardt. LC 75-4315. (Illus.). 130p. (Orig.). 1975. pap. 2.50 (ISBN 0-8356-0304-0, Quest). Theos Pub Hse.

Mecca, the Pilgrimage City: A Study of Pilgrim Accomodation. Ghazy A. Makky. (Illus.). 95p. 1978. 28.00 (ISBN 0-85664-591-5, Pub. by Croom Helm Ltd). Methuen Inc.

Mecca Today. Jean Hureau. (J. A. Editions: Today Ser.). (Illus.). 240p. 1980. 14.95 (ISBN 2-85258-214-7, Pub. by J. A. Editions France). Hippocrene Bks.

Meccan Trade & the Rise of Islam. Patricia Crone. 320p. 1986. text ed. 30.00 (ISBN 0-691-05480-0). Princeton U Pr.

Medallion. Dawn L. Watkins. (English Skills for Christian Schools Ser.). (Illus.). 223p. (Orig.). 1985. pap. 5.95 (ISBN 0-89084-282-5). Bob Jones Univ Pr.

Media & Catechetics Today: Towards the Year 2000. Pref. by Francis D. Kelley. 24p. 1980. 3.60 (ISBN 0-686-29243-X). Natl Cath Educ.

Media Impact & You. Daughters of St. Paul. 1981. 2.95 (ISBN 0-8198-4702-X); pap. 1.95 (ISBN 0-686-73820-9). Dghtrs St Paul.

Media Mirror: A Study Guide on Christian Values & Television. 3.60 (ISBN 0-318-03691-6); tchrs. guide 4.00 (ISBN 0-318-03692-4). Natl Cath Educ.

Media-Wasteland Or Wonderland: Opportunities & Dangers for Christians in the Electronic Age. John W. Bachman. LC 84-24319. 176p. (Orig.). 1984. pap. 7.95 (ISBN 0-8066-2116-8, 10-4307). Augsburg.

Mediaeval Art: From the Peace of the Church to the Eve of the Renaissance, 312-1350. facsimile ed. William R. Lethaby. LC 70-157345. (Select Bibliographies Reprint Ser). Repr. of 1904 ed. 33.00 (ISBN 0-8369-5806-3). Ayer Co Pubs.

Mediaeval Church. Marshall W. Baldwin. (Development of Western Civilization Ser). 124p. (Orig.). 1953. pap. 4.95x (ISBN 0-8014-9842-2). Cornell U Pr.

Mediaeval Church. Marshall W. Baldwin. LC 82-2992. (Development of Western Civilization Ser.). xii, 124p. 1982. Repr. of 1953 ed. lib. bdg. 22.50x (ISBN 0-313-23554-6, BAME). Greenwood.

Mediaeval Church Architecture of England. facsimile ed. Charles H. Moore. LC 74-37900. (Select Bibliographies Reprint Ser). Repr. of 1912 ed. 29.00 (ISBN 0-8369-6738-0). Ayer Co Pubs.

Mediaeval Church Vaulting. Clarence Ward. LC 72-177847. Repr. of 1915 ed. 19.50 (ISBN 0-404-06836-7). AMS Pr.

Mediaeval Legends of Christ. Angelo S. Rappoport. LC 76-15555. 1976. Repr. of 1934 ed. lib. bdg. 32.50 (ISBN 0-8414-7346-3). Folcroft.

Mediaeval Musical Relics of Denmark. Angul Hammerich. LC 74-24104. Repr. of 1912 ed. 24.50 (ISBN 0-404-12952-8). AMS Pr.

Mediaeval Russian Churches. Samuel H. Cross. 1949. 10.00x (ISBN 0-910956-27-8). Medieval Acad.

Mediaeval Society. Sidney Painter. (Development of Western Civilization Ser). (Illus.). 109p. 1951. pap. 5.95x (ISBN 0-8014-9850-3). Cornell U Pr.

Mediation of Christ. Thomas F. Torrance. LC 83-25330. Repr. of 1984 ed. 27.00 (2027551). Bks Demand UMI.

Mediation Process: Practical Strategies for Resolving Conflicts. Christopher W. Moore. LC 85-23675. (Social & Behavioral Science Ser.). 1986. text ed. 24.95x (ISBN 0-87589-673-1). Jossey Bass.

Mediations for Those Who Live with Alcoholism. Ed. by Judy Osgood. 72p. 1987. pap. 5.95 (ISBN 0-916895-04-1). Gilgal Pubns.

Mediations on the Supper of Our Lord. Ed. by J. M. Cowper & Robert Manning. (EETS, OS Ser.: No. 60). Repr. of 1875 ed. 15.00 (ISBN 0-527-00054-X). Kraus Repr.

Mediations with Nicolas of Cusa. James F. Yockey. (Illus.). 144p. (Orig.). 1987. pap. 6.95 (ISBN 0-939680-40-8). Bear & Co.

Medical Care of the Dying Patient. Ed. by Robert DeBellis et al. 30.00 (ISBN 0-405-13947-0). Ayer Co Pubs.

Medical Experiments on Jewish Inmates of Concentration Camps. John Mendelsohn. LC 81-80317. (Holocaust Ser.). 282p. 1982. lib. bdg. 61.00 (ISBN 0-8240-4883-0). Garland Pub.

Medical Hulacha for Everyone. 1982. 10.95 (ISBN 0-87306-218-3). Feldheim.

Medical Ministry. Ellen G. White. 1963. deluxe ed. 8.95 (ISBN 0-8163-0158-1, 13370-2). Pacific Pr Pub Assn.

Medicina De Dios. Kenneth E. Hagin. (Span.). 1982. pap. 0.50 mini bk. (ISBN 0-89276-153-9). Hagin Ministries.

Medicinal Plants of the Bible. James A. Duke. (Traditional Healing Ser.: No. 10). (Illus.). 300p. 1983. lib. bdg. 49.95 (ISBN 0-932426-23-9). Trado-Medic.

Medicine Among the American Indians. Eric P. Stone. LC 75-23657. (Clio Medica: 7). (Illus.). Repr. of 1932 ed. 20.00 (ISBN 0-404-58907-3). AMS Pr.

Medicine & Christian Morality. Thomas J. O'Donnell. LC 75-41471. 1976. 9.95 (ISBN 0-8189-0323-6). Alba.

Medicine & Religion: Strategies of Care. Ed. by Donald W. Shriver, Jr. LC 79-23420. (Contemporary Community Health Ser.). 1980. 14.95x (ISBN 0-8229-3412-4). U of Pittsburgh Pr.

Medicine & the Mormons: An Introduction to the History of Latter-day Saint Health Care. Robert T. Divett. LC 81-84588. 230p. 1981. pap. 9.95 (ISBN 0-88290-194-X, 2050). Horizon Utah.

Medicine in the Bible & the Talmud: Selections from Classical Jewish Sources. F. Rosner. (Library of Jewish Law & Ethics: Vol. 5). 9.95x (ISBN 0-87068-326-8). Ktav.

Medicine in the Mishneh Torah of Maimonides. Fred Rosner. 1983. 20.00x (ISBN 0-88125-020-1); pap. 11.95 (ISBN 0-88125-021-X). Ktav.

Medicine Man: A Sociological Study of the Character & Evolution of Shamanism. J. L. Maddox. 1977. lib. bdg. 59.95 (ISBN 0-8490-2219-3). Gordon Pr.

Medicine Man: A Sociological Study of the Character & Evolution of Shamanism. John L. Maddox. LC 75-23737. Repr. of 1923 ed. 45.00 (ISBN 0-404-13294-4). AMS Pr.

Medicine-Man of the American Indian & His Cultural Background. William T. Corlett. LC 75-23699. Repr. of 1935 ed. 47.50 (ISBN 0-404-13249-9). AMS Pr.

Medicine Men of the Apache. John G. Bourke. LC 71-175003. (Illus.). 150p. 13.50 (ISBN 0-87026-049-9). Westernlore.

Medicine, Miracle & Magic in New Testament Times. Howard C. Kee. (Society for New Testament Studies Monographs: No. 55). 200p. 1986. 29.95 (ISBN 0-521-32309-6). Cambridge U Pr.

Medicine Woman. Lynn V. Andrews. LC 81-47546. 224p. 1983. pap. 7.95 (ISBN 0-06-250026-0, CN 4062, HarpR). Har-Row.

Medidas Principales en la Planificacion de la Iglesia Local: Key Steps in Local Church Planning. Richard E. Rusbuldt et al. Tr. by Oscar E. Rodriguez from Eng. (Span.). 134p. 1981. pap. 5.95 (ISBN 0-8170-0933-7). Judson.

Medieval Agriculture, the Southern French Countryside & the Early Cistercians: A Study of Forty-Three Monasteries. Constance H. Berman. LC 84-71079. (Transaction Ser.: Vol. 76, Pt. 5). 179p. 1986. 18.00 (ISBN 0-87169-765-3). Am Philos.

Medieval & Renaissance Miniatures from the National Gallery of Art. Ed. by Carl Nordenfalk. LC 74-28397. (Illus.). pap. 8.95 (ISBN 0-89468-017-X). Natl Gallery Art.

Medieval Buda. Martyn C. Rady. 1985. 32.00 (ISBN 0-88033-074-0). East Eur Quarterly.

Medieval Carthisian Costomaries, Pt. 2. James Hogg. (Analecta Carusiana Ser.: No. 2). (Orig.). 1986. pap. 25.00 (ISBN 3-7052-0002-X, Pub by Salzburg Studies). Longwood Pub Group.

Medieval Church. Roland H. Bainton. LC 78-11433. (Anvil Ser.). 192p. 1979. pap. 7.50 (ISBN 0-88275-786-5). Krieger.

Medieval Church. John M. O'Brien. (Quality Paperback: No. 227). 120p. (Orig.). 1968. pap. 2.95 (ISBN 0-8226-0227-X). Littlefield.

Medieval Church Music-Dramas: A Repertory of Complete Plays. Ed. by Fletcher Collins, Jr. LC 75-33896. Repr. of 1976 ed. 128.50 (ISBN 0-8357-9809-7, 2013180). Bks Demand UMI.

Medieval Colonialism: Post-Crusade Exploitation of Islamic Valencia. Robert I. Burns. (Illus.). 432p. 1975. 44.50 (ISBN 0-691-05227-1). Princeton U Pr.

Medieval Contribution to Political Thought: Thomas Aquinas, Marsilius of Padua, Richard Hooker. Alexander P. D'Entreves. 1959. Repr. of 1939 ed. text ed. 12.50x (ISBN 0-391-00513-8). Humanities.

Medieval Contributions to Modern Civilization. Ed. by Fossey J. Hearnshaw. LC 66-25917. 1966. Repr. of 1921 ed. 18.00x (ISBN 0-8046-0198-4, Pub. by Kennikat). Assoc Faculty Pr.

Medieval Cosmology: Theories of Infinity, Place, Time, Void, & the Plurality of Worlds. Pierre Duhem. Ed. by Roger Ariew. LC 85-8115. 642p. 1986. lib. bdg. 35.00x (ISBN 0-226-16922-7). U of Chicago Pr.

Medieval Drama. David Bevington. 1975. text ed. 34.95 (ISBN 0-395-13915-5). HM.

Medieval Drama. Ed. by Sandro Sticca. LC 78-152517. (Illus.). 154p. 1972. 39.50 (ISBN 0-87395-085-2). State U NY Pr.

Medieval England. new ed. Ed. by H. W. Davis. Orig. Title: Bernard's Companion to English History. 1977. Repr. of 1924 ed. lib. bdg. 45.00 (ISBN 0-8495-1006-6). Arden Lib.

Medieval England: A Social History & Archaeology from the Conquest to 1600 A. D. Colin Platt. (Illus.). 1978. encore ed. 9.95 (ISBN 0-684-17247-X, ScribT). Scribner.

Medieval English Episcopal Registers. Louis A. Haselmayer. (Church Historical Society, London, New Ser.: No. 33). pap. 16.00 (ISBN 0-8115-3157-0). Kraus Repr.

Medieval English Religious & Ethical Literature. Ed. by Gregory Kratzmann & James Simpson. 224p. 1986. 37.50 (ISBN 0-85991-220-5, Pub. by Boydell & Brewer). Longwood Pub Group.

Medieval English Stage: Corpus Christi Pageants & Plays. Alan H. Nelson. LC 73-85247. (Patterns of Literary Criticism Ser). 288p. 1974. 21.00x (ISBN 0-226-57173-4). U of Chicago Pr.

Medieval Essays. facs. ed. Christopher H. Dawson. LC 68-58785. (Essay Index Reprint Ser). 1954. 18.00 (ISBN 0-8369-0070-7). Ayer Co Pubs.

Medieval Europe. Ed. by William H. McNeill & Schuyler O. Houser. (Oxford Readings in World History Ser: Vol. 8). 1971. pap. 7.95x (ISBN 0-19-501312-3). Oxford U Pr.

Medieval Exegesis of Wisdom Literature: Essays by Beryl Smalley. Ed. & intro. by Roland E. Murphy. (Scholars Press Reprints & Translations Ser.). 1986. 13.95 (ISBN 1-55540-026-4, 00 07 16). Scholars Pr GA.

Medieval Faith & Fable. J. Arnott MacCulloch. 1978. Repr. of 1932 ed. lib. bdg. 47.50 (ISBN 0-8492-1662-1). R West.

Medieval Foundations of Western Civilization. G. C. Sellery & A. C. Krey. LC 68-24116. (World History Ser., No. 48). (Illus.). 1968. Repr. 74.95x (ISBN 0-8383-0926-7). Haskell.

Medieval Franciscan Houses. John R. Moorman. Ed. by George Marcel. (History Ser.: No. 4). 1983. 40.00 (ISBN 0-318-00515-8). Franciscan Inst.

Medieval French Drama. Grace Frank. 1954. 34.95x (ISBN 0-19-815317-1). Oxford U Pr.

Medieval Hagiography & Romance. Ed. by Paul M. Clogan. LC 75-16872. (Medievalia et Humanistica Ser.: No. 6). pap. 59.30 (2029216). Bks Demand UMI.

Medieval Handbooks of Penance. John T. McNeill & Helena M. Gamer. 1965. lib. bdg. 40.00x (ISBN 0-374-95548-4, Octagon). Hippocrene Bks.

Medieval Heresy: Popular Movements from Bogomil to Hus. Malcolm Lambert. LC 76-49949. 446p. 1977. 54.50x (ISBN 0-8419-0298-4). Holmes & Meier.

Medieval History & Civilization. Daniel D. McGarry. (Illus.). 896p. 1976. text ed. write for info. (ISBN 0-02-379100-4). Macmillan.

Medieval Humanism: And Other Stories. R. W. Southern. (Illus.). 288p. 1984. pap. 12.95x (ISBN 0-631-13649-5). Basil Blackwell.

Medieval Humanist: Michael Akominatos. Ida T. Hill. LC 73-3164. 48p. 1974. Repr. of 1923 ed. lib. bdg. 14.00 (ISBN 0-8337-3497-0). B Franklin.

Medieval India under Mohammedan Rule: A. D. 712-1764, 2 Vols. in 1. S. Lane-Poole. LC 52-33515. Repr. of 1951 ed. 29.00 (ISBN 0-527-54300-4). Kraus Repr.

Medieval Inquisition. Jean Guiraud. Tr. by E. C. Messenger. LC 78-63181. (Heresies of the Early Christian & Medieval Era: Second Ser.). Repr. of 1929 ed. 31.00 (ISBN 0-404-16222-3). AMS Pr.

Medieval Inquisition. Bernard Hamilton. 112p. 1981. 25.00x (ISBN 0-7131-6251-1, Pub. by E Arnold England). State Mutual Bk.

Medieval Inquisition. Albert C. Shannon. 168p. 1983. 15.00 (ISBN 0-9612336-0-5, 83-72869); pap. 10.00 (ISBN 0-9612336-1-3). Augustinian Coll Pr.

Medieval Inquisition: Foundations of Medieval History. Bernard Hamilton. LC 80-27997. 110p. (Orig.). 1981. 24.50x (ISBN 0-8419-0718-8); pap. text ed. 14.95x (ISBN 0-8419-0695-5). Holmes & Meier.

Medieval Jewish Mind. Chaim Pearl. LC 76-184221. 208p. 1973. 8.95 (ISBN 0-87677-043-X). Hartmore.

Medieval Jewish Philosophy: Original Anthology. Ed. by Steven Katz. LC 79-7177. (Jewish Philosophy, Mysticism & the History of Ideas Ser.). (Ger., Eng., Ital, Fr. Span.). 1980. lib. bdg. 44.00x (ISBN 0-405-12235-7). Ayer Co Pubs.

Medieval Jewry in Northern France: A Poltical & Social History. Robert Chazan. LC 73-8129. (Johns Hopkins University Studies in Historical & Political Science: 91st; 2). pap. 63.00 (ISBN 0-317-20643-5, 2024132). Bks Demand UMI.

Medieval Latin Liturgy: A Select Bibliography. Richard W. Pfaff. (Toronto Medieval Bibliographies Ser.). 128p. 1982. pap. 12.50 (ISBN 0-8020-6488-4). U of Toronto Pr.

Medieval Manichee: A Study of the Christian Dualist Heresy. Steven Runciman. LC 82-4123. 224p. 1982. 39.50 (ISBN 0-521-06166-0); pap. 13.95 (ISBN 0-521-28926-2). Cambridge U Pr.

Medieval Manuscript Library of the Charterhouse of St. Barbara in Cologne, Vols. 1 & 2. Richard B. Marks. Ed. by James Hogg. (Analecta Cartusiana Ser.: Nos. 21 & 22). (Illus.). 473p. (Orig.). 1974. Set. pap. 50.00 (ISBN 3-7052-0022-4, Pub by Salzburg Studies). Longwood Pub Group.

Medieval Manuscripts for Mass & Office: A Guide to Their Organization & Terminology. Andrew Hughes. 496p. 1981. 65.00x (ISBN 0-8020-5467-6). U of Toronto Pr.

Medieval Miscellany. C. B. Caples et al. (Rice University Studies: Vol. 62, No. 2). (Illus.). 120p. (Orig.). 1976. pap. 10.00x (ISBN 0-89263-228-3). Rice Univ.

Medieval Monastery: Then & There Ser. Marjorie Reeves. (Illus.). 90p. (Orig.). 1980. pap. text ed. 4.75 (ISBN 0-582-20372-4). Longman.

Medieval Monasticism: A Select Bibliography. Giles Constable. LC 75-42284. 1976. 20.00x (ISBN 0-8020-2200-6). U of Toronto Pr.

Medieval Monasticism: Forms of Religious Life, Western Europe in the Middle Ages. C. H. Lawrence. 288p. 1984. pap. text ed. 12.95 (ISBN 0-582-49186-X). Longman.

Medieval Monk. Giovanni Caselli. LC 86-70451. (Everyday Life of Ser.). (Illus.). 30p. 1986. 9.95 (ISBN 0-87226-105-0). P Bedrick Bks.

Medieval Mysteries, Moralities & Interludes. Ed. by Vincent F. Hopper & Gerald B. Lahey. LC 61-18362. 1962. pap. text ed. 5.95 (ISBN 0-8120-0135-4). Barron.

Medieval Myths. rev. ed. Norma L. Goodrich. 224p. (YA) 1977. pap. 3.95 (ISBN 0-451-62359-2, Ment). NAL.

Medieval Papacy. Geoffrey Barraclough. (Library of World Civilization). (Illus.). 1979. pap. text ed. 7.95x (ISBN 0-393-95100-6). Norton.

Medieval Papalism: The Political Theories of the Medieval Canonists. Walter Ullman. LC 79-1644. 1981. Repr. of 1949 ed. 21.50 (ISBN 0-88355-946-3). Hyperion Conn.

Medieval Philosophers from St. Augustine to St. Anselm. Richard M. Macauley. (Illus.). 196p. 1984. 88.85 (ISBN 0-89266-483-5). Am Classical Coll Pr.

Medieval Philosophy: From St. Augustine to Nicholas of Cusa. Ed. by John F. Wippel & Allen B. Wolter. LC 69-10043. 1969. pap. text ed. 14.95 (ISBN 0-02-935650-4). Free Pr.

Medieval Plays in Scotland. Anna J. Mill. LC 68-56497. 1969. Repr. of 1927 ed. 24.50 (ISBN 0-405-08789-6, Pub. by Blom). Ayer Co Pubs.

Medieval Reformation. Brenda Bolton. (Foundations of Medieval History). (Illus.). 112p. 1983. text ed. 22.50x (ISBN 0-8419-0879-6); pap. text ed. 14.75x (ISBN 0-8419-0835-4). Holmes & Meier.

Medieval Religion & Technology: Collected Essays. Lynn White, Jr. LC 77-83113. (Center for Medieval & Renaissance Studies, UCLA: Publication: No. 13). 1978. pap. 11.95x (ISBN 0-520-05896-8, CAMPUS 371). U of Cal Pr.

Medieval Religious Houses, England & Wales. David Knowles & R. Neville Hadcock. LC 72-181783. pap. 147.00 (ISBN 0-317-08419-4, 2016312). Bks Demand UMI.

Medieval Religious Lyric: An Ars Poetria. Patrick S. Diehl. LC 83-6557. 475p. 1984. text ed. 40.00x (ISBN 0-520-04673-0). U of Cal Pr.

Medieval Religious Stage: Shapes & Phantoms. A. M. Nagler. LC 75-43328. (Illus.). 1976. 22.00x (ISBN 0-300-01986-6). Yale U Pr.

Medieval Religious Women I: Distant Echoes. Ed. by John A. Nichols & M. Thomas Shank. (Cistercian Studies: No. 71). 1984. 29.95 (ISBN 0-87907-871-5); pap. 11.95 (ISBN 0-87907-971-1). Cistercian Pubns.

Medieval Slavic Lives of Saints & Princes. Ed. by Marvin Kantor. (Michigan Slavic Translations: No. 5). 1983. 15.00 (ISBN 0-930042-44-1). Mich Slavic Pubns.

Medieval Studies: A Bibliographical Guide. Everett U. Crosby et al. LC 83-48259. (Reference Library of the Humanities: Vol. 427). 1156p. 1985. 109.00 (ISBN 0-8240-9107-8). Garland Pub.

Medieval Texts & Studies. C. R. Cheney. 1973. 55.00x (ISBN 0-19-822399-4). Oxford U Pr.

Medieval Ties Between Italy & Ireland. Martin P. Harney. 1963. 1.50 (ISBN 0-8198-0101-1). Dghtrs St Paul.

Medieval Tradition of Natural Law. Harold J. Johnson. LC 86-31126. (Studies in Medieval Culture: No. 22). Date not set. price not set (ISBN 0-918720-81-8). Medieval Inst.

Medieval Women. Ed. by Derek Baker. (Studies in Church History: Subsidia 1). (Illus.). 412p. 1979. 45.00x (ISBN 0-631-19260-3). Basil Blackwell.

Medieval Women. Ed. by Derek Baker. (Studies in Church History: Subsidia 1). 412p. 1981. pap. 9.95x (ISBN 0-631-12539-6). Basil Blackwell.

Medieval World: Europe Eleven Hundred to Thirteen Fifty. Friedrick Heer. 1964. pap. 5.95 (ISBN 0-451-62542-0, ME2165, Ment). NAL.

Medina vor dem Islam, Muhammeds Gemeindeordnung Von Medina: Seine Schriften und Die Gesandtschaften an Ihn. Julius Wellhausen. (Skizzen und Vorarbeiten: 4 Heft). (Ger. & Arabic.). 272p. 1985. 63.00x (ISBN 3-11-009764-8). De Gruyter.

Medinet Habu - Epigraphic Survey: The Temple Proper, Part Three, the Third Hypostyle Hall, All Rooms Accessible from It, with Friezes of Scenes from the Roof Terraces & Exterior Walls of the Temple. George R. Hughes. LC 30-22847. (Oriental Institute Pubns. Ser). 1964. 65.00x (ISBN 0-226-62196-0, OIP93). U of Chicago Pr.

Medinet Habu - Epigraphic Survey: The Temple Proper, Part Two, the Re Chapel, the Mortuary Complex, & Adjacent Rooms with Miscellaneous Material from Pylons, the Forecourts & the First Hypostyle Hall, Vol. 6. George R. Hughes. LC 30-22847. (Oriental Institute Pubns. Ser). 1963. 65.00x (ISBN 0-226-62185-5, OIP84). U of Chicago Pr.

Medinet Habu, Nineteen Twenty Four-Twenty Eight. Harold H. Nelson & Uvo Holscher. LC 29-13423. (Illus.). 1929. pap. 5.00x (ISBN 0-226-62320-3, OIC5). U of Chicago Pr.

Meditacion Segun la Mas Antigua Tradicion Budista. Luis Mojica Sandoz. (Coleccion Uprex; Serie Manuales: No. 54). (Span., Illus.). 1979. pap. text ed. 1.85 (ISBN 0-8477-0054-2). U of PR Pr.

Meditaciones. Mateo Crawley-Boevey. (Span.). 1978. plastic bdg. 2.00 (ISBN 0-8198-4706-2). Dghtrs St Paul.

Meditaciones para la Nueva Madre. H. G. Brenneman. 80p. 1982. Repr. of 1978 ed. 2.85 (ISBN 0-311-40032-9). Casa Bautista.

Meditaciones para la Nueva Madre. Helen G. Brenneman. Tr. by Maria T. La Valle. Tr. of Meditations for the New Mother. (Span., Illus.). 80p. 1978. pap. 2.85 (ISBN 0-8361-1212-1). Herald Pr.

Meditaciones para Ninos. Kenneth N. Taylor. Orig. Title: Devotions for the Children's Hour. (Span.). 252p. 1983. pap. 4.75 (ISBN 0-8254-1707-4). Kregel.

Meditaciones Sobre el Padrenuestro. Rogelio Archilla. (Span.). 96p. 1984. pap. 3.95 (ISBN 0-311-40046-9, Edit Mundo). Casa Bautista.

Meditacoes De Um Leigo. Tr. by Phillip Keller. (Portugese Bks.). Tr. of Layman Looks at the Lord's Prayer. (Port.). 1979. 1.60 (ISBN 0-8297-0788-3). Life Pubs Intl.

Meditate. Muktananda. LC 80-20477. 84p. 1980. 9.95x (ISBN 0-87395-471-8); pap. 4.95x (ISBN 0-87395-472-6). State U NY Pr.

Meditate Upon These Things. 2nd ed. Compiled by Linda Lee. (Illus.). 160p. 1981. pap. 5.00 (ISBN 0-87516-463-3). De Vorss.

Meditating for Success. Paul Meier. Ed. by Jane Mack. 25p. (Orig.). 1985. pap. 2.95 (ISBN 0-8010-6207-1). Baker Bk.

Meditating on the Word. Dietrich Bonhoeffer. Ed. & tr. by David Gracie. LC 86-16839. 152p. (Orig.). 1986. 11.95 (ISBN 0-936384-43-3); pap. 6.95 (ISBN 0-936384-41-7). Cowley Pubns.

Meditating the Sunday Gospels. P. McHuch. 1976. 5.95 (ISBN 0-8198-0443-6); pap. 4.95 (ISBN 0-8198-0444-4). Dghtrs St Paul.

Meditating with Children: New Age Meditations for Children. Deborah A. Rozman. LC 76-10480. (Illus.). 160p. (Orig.). 1975. pap. 7.95 (ISBN 0-916438-23-6). Univ of Trees.

Meditation. Juan Benet. Tr. by Gregory Rabassa from Span. Tr. of Una Meditacion. 366p. 1983. 15.95; pap. 8.95 (ISBN 0-89255-065-1). Persea Bks.

Meditation. Grace Cooke. 1955. pap. 4.95 (ISBN 0-85487-059-8). De Vorss.

Meditation. Monks of the Ramakrishna Order. Ed. by Swami Bhavyananda. 1977. pap. 8.50 (ISBN 0-7025-0019-4). Vedanta Pr.

Meditation. Sadhu. pap. 7.00 (ISBN 0-87980-096-8). Wilshire.

Meditation: A Practical Guide to a Spiritual Discipline. Thomas McCormick & Sharon Fish. 132p. (Orig.). 1983. pap. 3.95 (ISBN 0-87784-844-0). Inter-Varsity.

Meditation According to Yoga-Vedanta. Swami Siddheswarananda. pap. 4.95 (ISBN 0-87481-467-7). Vedanta Pr.

Meditation: An Eight-Point Program. Eknath Easwaran. LC 78-10935. 240p. 1978. 15.00 (ISBN 0-915132-15-X); pap. 8.00. Nilgiri Pr.

Meditation & Its Methods According to Swami Vivekananda. Swami Vivekananda. Compiled by Swami Chetanananda. LC 75-36392. (Orig.). 1976. pap. 4.95 (ISBN 0-87481-030-2). Vedanta Pr.

Meditation & Kabbalah. Aryeh Kaplan. LC 81-70150. 368p. (Orig.). 1985. pap. 12.50 (ISBN 0-87728-616-7). Weiser.

Meditation & Other Spiritual Disciplines. Swami Swahananda. 171p. 6.50 (ISBN 0-87481-214-3, Pub. by Advaita Ashrama India). Vedanta Pr.

Meditation & Prayer. F. Henry Edwards. LC 79-23708. 1980. pap. 12.00 (ISBN 0-8309-0271-6). Herald Hse.

Meditation & Reality: A Critical View. Douglas Fox. LC 85-45459. 192p. 1986. pap. 12.95 (ISBN 0-8042-0662-7). John Knox.

Meditation & Spiritual Life. Swami Yatiswarananda. 700p. 1980. 15.00x (ISBN 0-87481-403-0). Vedanta Pr.

Meditation & the Art of Dying. Usharbudh Arya. 196p. pap. 7.95 (ISBN 0-89389-056-1). Himalayan Pubs.

Meditation & the Bible. reprinting ed. Aryeh Kaplan. 1978. pap. 9.95 (ISBN 0-87728-617-5). Weiser.

Meditation & the Fullness of Life. Jim Wilson. 76p. 1974. pap. text ed. 2.95 (ISBN 0-227-67810-9). Attic Pr.

Meditation & the Mind of Man. rev. ed. Herbert B. Puryear & Mark Thurston. 1975. pap. 6.95 (ISBN 0-87604-105-5). ARE Pr.

Meditation & Yoga Retreats: An International Directory. Compiled by Frieda Carrol. 200p. 1983. text ed. 4.75 (ISBN 0-913597-06-6, Pub. by Alpha Pyramis). Prosperity & Profits.

Meditation as an Intervention in Stress Reactivity. (Stress in Modern Society Ser.: No. 10). 1986. write for info. (ISBN 0-404-63260-2). AMS Pr.

Meditation: Classic & Contemporary Perspectives. Ed. by Deane H. Shapiro, Jr. & Roger N. Walsh. LC 84-300. 722p. 1984. lib. bdg. 64.95x (ISBN 0-202-25136-5). De Gruyter Aldine.

Meditation: Cybernetics of Consciousness. Benito F. Reyes. Ed. by Fred J. Volz. 152p. 1978. pap. 7.50 (ISBN 0-939375-04-4). World Univ Amer.

Meditation Disciplines. Manly P. Hall. pap. 3.50 (ISBN 0-89314-800-8). Philos Res.

Meditation for Beginners. Wedgewood. 2.50 (ISBN 0-8356-5050-2). Theos Pub Hse.

Meditation for Healing: Particular Meditations for Particular Results. rev. ed. Justin F. Stone. LC 86-61661. (Illus.). 192p. 1986. pap. 11.95 (ISBN 0-937277-01-0). Satori Resources.

Meditation for Little People. Anne Langford. LC 75-46191. (Illus.). 40p. 1976. pap. 3.00 (ISBN 0-87516-211-8). De Vorss.

Meditation: Gateway to Light. rev. ed. Elsie Sechrist. 53p. 1972. pap. 3.95 (ISBN 0-87604-062-8). ARE Pr.

Meditation in Action. Chogyam Trungpa. 74p. (Orig.). 1969. pap. 4.95 (ISBN 0-87773-000-8). Shambhala Pubns.

Meditation in Christianity. rev. ed. Himalayan Institute. 130p. pap. 5.95 (ISBN 0-89389-085-5). Himalayan Pubs.

Meditation in Motion. Susan A. Muto. LC 86-4690. 144p. 1986. 5.95 (ISBN 0-385-23533-X, Im). Doubleday.

Meditation, Its Practice & Results. 4th ed. Clara M. Codd. 1968. 2.25 (ISBN 0-8356-7212-3). Theos Pub Hse.

Meditation: Its Process, Practice, & Culmination. Swami Satprakashananda. LC 76-15722. 264p. 1976. 10.00 (ISBN 0-916356-55-8). Vedanta Soc St Louis.

Meditation Made Easy. W. P. Petersen & Terry Fehr. (Concise Guides Ser.). (Illus.). 1979. s&l 9.90 (ISBN 0-531-02894-1). Watts.

Meditation: Man-Perfection in God-Satisfaction. Sri Chinmoy. (Illus.). 1979. pap. 6.95 (ISBN 0-88497-444-8). Aum Pubns.

Meditation Moments for Women. Millie Stamm. 1967. pap. 7.95 (ISBN 0-310-32981-7). Zondervan.

Meditation of the Sad Soul. B. Hayya Abraham. Tr. by Geoffrey Wigoder. (Littman Library of Jewish Civilization Ser.). 1969. 14.50x (ISBN 0-19-710018-X). Oxford U Pr.

Meditation on Emptiness. Jeffrey Hopkins. Ed. by Elizabeth Napper. (Wisdom Advanced Book: Blue Ser.). (Illus.). 700p. 1983. 35.00 (ISBN 0-86171-014-2, Pub. by Wisdom Pubns). Great Traditions.

Meditation on the Sand. Alessandro Pronzato. LC 82-24513. (Ital.). 104p. (Orig.). 1983. pap. 5.95 (ISBN 0-8189-0457-7). Alba.

Meditation Prayer on Mary Immaculate. Padre Pio. (Illus.). 28p. 1974. pap. 0.75 (ISBN 0-89555-099-7). Tan Bks Pubs.

Meditation: Self-Regulation Strategy & Altered States of Consciousness. Deane H. Shapiro, Jr. LC 80-66454. 318p. 1980. 28.95x (ISBN 0-202-25132-2). De Gruyter Aldine.

Meditation Techniques of the Kabalists, Vedantins & Taoists. R. A. Straughn. (Illus.). 1976. pap. 6.95 (ISBN 0-917650-02-6). Maat Pub.

Meditation: The Art of Ecstasy. Bhagwan S. Rajneesh. Ed. by Ma S. Bharti. 1978. pap. 3.50 (ISBN 0-06-080394-0, P394, PL). Har-Row.

Meditation, The Highway to Happiness. 3rd ed. Richard J. Green. 40p. 1980. pap. 3.00 (ISBN 0-87516-407-2). De Vorss.

Meditation, 1: Healing, Prayer, & the Revelation. Compiled by Association for Research & Enlightenment, Readings Research Dept. (Library: Vol. 2). 306p. 1974. 10.95 (ISBN 0-87604-072-5). ARE Pr.

Meditation, 2: Meditation, Endocrine Glands, Prayer, & Affirmations. Ed. by Association for Research & Enlightenment, Readings Research Dept. (Library: Vol. 3). 274p. 1975. 10.95 (ISBN 0-87604-082-2). ARE Pr.

Meditational Therapy. Ed. by Swami Ajaya. 100p. (Orig.). pap. 3.95 (ISBN 0-89389-032-4). Himalayan Pubs.

Meditations. Marcus Aurelius. Ed. & tr. by G. M. A. Grube. LC 83-22722. (HPC Philosophical Classics Ser.). 170p. 1984. lib. bdg. 16.50 (ISBN 0-915145-78-2); pap. text ed. 4.95 (ISBN 0-915145-79-0). Hackett Pub.

Meditations. Anthony Bloom. 3.95 (ISBN 0-87193-010-2). Dimension Bks.

Meditations. Toyohiko Kagawa. LC 78-12761. 1979. Repr. of 1950 ed. lib. bdg. 22.50x (ISBN 0-313-21180-9, KAMD). Greenwood.

Meditations. Chiara Lubich. LC 74-79452. 148p. 1974. pap. 4.95 (ISBN 0-911782-20-6). New City.

Meditations & Inspirations. Virginia Satir. LC 85-13302. 96p. (Orig.). 1985. pap. 5.95 (ISBN 0-89087-421-2). Celestial Arts.

Meditations Based on the Lord's Prayer. Evelyn Underhill. 59.95 (ISBN 0-8490-0601-5). Gordon Pr.

Meditations-Dorothy Day. Stanley Vishnewski. LC 73-133570. 104p. 1970. pap. 4.95 (ISBN 0-8091-1636-7). Paulist Pr.

Meditations du Bienheureux de Guigues de Saint Romain: Cinquieme Prieur de Chartreuse (1109-1136) Gaston Hocquard. Ed. by James Hogg. (Analecta Cartusiana Ser.: No. 112). 311p. (Orig.). 1984. pap. 25.00 (ISBN 0-317-42589-7, Pub. by Salzburg Studies). Longwood Pub Group.

Meditations for Bereaved Parents. Ed. by Judy Osgood. LC 86-15003. (Gilgal Meditations Ser.). 70p. (Orig.). 1984. pap. 5.95 (ISBN 0-916895-00-9). Gilgal Pubns.

Meditations for Lent. Paul J. Hayes. 1985. pap. 1.95 (ISBN 0-8198-4719-4). Dghtrs St Paul.

Meditations for Mature Christians. B. C. Schreiber. LC 85-90050. 1985. 13.95 (ISBN 0-533-06578-X). Vantage.

Meditations for Priests. David M. Knight. 1978. write for info. (ISBN 0-915488-05-1). Clarity Pub.

Meditations for Religious. Richard J. Cushing. 1959. 3.00 (ISBN 0-8198-0102-X). Dghtrs St Paul.

Meditations for Spiritual Misfits. Robert Badra. (Illus.). 93p. (Orig.). 1982. pap. 7.95 (ISBN 0-9610274-0-1). JCL Hse.

Meditations for the Divorced. Ed. by Judy Osgood. (Gilgal Meditations Ser.). 167p. (Orig.). 1987. pap. text ed. 5.95 (ISBN 0-916895-02-5). Gilgal Pubns.

Meditations for the Expectant Mother. Helen G. Brenneman. LC 68-12025. (Illus.). 80p. (Orig.). 1968. 8.95 (ISBN 0-8361-1639-9); pap. 4.50 (ISBN 0-8361-1567-8). Herald Pr.

Meditations for the New Mother. Helen G. Brenneman. LC 53-7585. (Illus.). 78p. (Orig.). 1953. 8.95 (ISBN 0-8361-3400-1); pap. 4.50 (ISBN 0-8361-3399-4). Herald Pr.

Meditations for the Newly Married. John M. Drescher. LC 69-10835. 142p. 1969. gift-boxed 9.95 (ISBN 0-8361-1571-6). Herald Pr.

Meditations for the Suddenly Single. Ragan Courtney. pap. 5.95 (ISBN 0-310-70301-8). Zondervan.

Meditations for the Widowed. Ed. by Judy Osgood. LC 86-15002. (Gilgal Meditations Ser.). 70p. (Orig.). 1985. pap. 5.95 (ISBN 0-916895-01-7). Gilgal Pubns.

Meditations in the Mountains. Marion R. Vuilleumier. 128p. (Orig.). 1983. pap. 7.75 (ISBN 0-687-24260-6). Abingdon.

Meditations of a Maverick Rabbi. Albert S. Axelrad. Ed. by Stephen Whitfield. 256p. (Orig.). 1985. pap. 8.95 (ISBN 0-940646-12-9). Rossel Bks.

Meditations of the Heart. Howard Thurman. LC 76-18287. 216p. 1976. pap. 6.95 (ISBN 0-913408-25-5). Friends United.

Meditations of the Masters. Ellen K. Hua. LC 76-47649. (Illus., Orig.). 1977. pap. 3.00 (ISBN 0-87407-203-4, FP-3). Thor.

Meditations on a Loving God. L. Brandt. LC 12-2812. 1983. 10.95 (ISBN 0-570-03858-8). Concordia.

Meditations on Ecclesiastes. F. C. Jennings. 143p. 5.95 (ISBN 0-88172-090-9). Believers Bkshelf.

Meditations on Freedom & the Spirit. Karl Rahner. 1978. pap. 3.95 (ISBN 0-8245-0325-2). Crossroad NY.

Meditations on Hope & Love. Karl Rahner. LC 77-76614. 1977. pap. 3.95 (ISBN 0-8245-0326-0). Crossroad NY.

Meditations on Joshua. H. Rossier. 7.25 (ISBN 0-88172-119-0). Believers Bkshelf.

Meditations on St. John. Burns K. Seeley. Ed. by Jerome F. Coniker & Dale Francis. LC 81-65808. (Living Meditation & Prayerbook Ser.). (Illus.). 245p. (Orig.). 1981. pap. text ed. 5.00 (ISBN 0-932406-03-3). AFC.

Meditations on St. Paul. Burns K. Seeley. Ed. by Jerome F. Coniker. LC 82-72201. (Living Meditation & Prayerbook Ser.). (Illus.). 270p. (Orig.). 1982. pap. text ed. 5.00 (ISBN 0-932406-06-8). AFC.

Meditations on the Book of Job. Christine L. Benagh. LC 64-25262. 1964. 3.95 (ISBN 0-686-05041-X). St Thomas.

Meditations on the Divine Liturgy. Nikolai Gogol. 58p. (Orig.). 1985. pap. 3.00 (ISBN 0-317-30300-7). Holy Trinity.

Meditations on the Life & Passion of Christ. (EETS, OS Ser.: No. 158). Repr. of 1921 ed. 34.00 (ISBN 0-527-00155-4). Kraus Repr.

Meditations on the Life of Christ: An Illustrated Manuscript of the Fourteenth Century. Ed. by Isa Ragusa & Rosalie B. Green. (Monographs in Art & Archeology: No. 35). (Illus.). 501p. 1975. 52.50x (ISBN 0-691-03829-5). Princeton U Pr.

Meditations on the Lord's Prayer. 2nd ed. Martin Cecil. 1982. 10.95 (ISBN 0-686-27652-3). Cole-Outreach.

Meditations on the Mass. Marie McIntyre. (Greeting Book Line Ser.). 48p. 1983. pap. 1.50 (ISBN 0-89622-201-2). Twenty-Third.

Meditations on the Mystery of Christmas. Charles A. Ramm. Ed. by Sr. Catherine M. Lilly. LC 59-15709. (Illus.). 1959. 6.95 (ISBN 0-87015-092-8). Pacific Bks.

Meditations on the Passion. Johannes B. Metz & Jurgen Moltmann. LC 78-70823. 48p. 1979. pap. 2.50 (ISBN 0-8091-2184-0). Paulist Pr.

Meditations on the Rosary. Lawrence Lovasik. LC 82-72204. (Living Meditation & Prayerbook Ser.). (Illus.). 270p. (Orig.). 1985. pap. text ed. 5.00 (ISBN 0-932406-09-2). AFC.

Meditations on the Siddur. 1982. 9.95 (ISBN 0-686-76545-1). Feldheim.

Meditations on the Way of the Cross. Mother Teresa of Calcutta & Roger of Taize. (Illus.). 64p. (Orig.). 1987. pap. 5.95 (ISBN 0-8298-0585-0). Pilgrim NY.

Meditations Through the Quran: Tonal Images in an Oral Culture. Ernest G. McClain. LC 81-82124. (Illus.). 166p. 1981. 12.95 (ISBN 0-89254-009-5). Nicolas-Hays.

Meditations Through the Rg Veda: Four-Dimensional Man. Antonio T. De Nicolas. LC 76-39692. 1976. 12.95 (ISBN 0-89254-004-4). Nicolas-Hays.

Meditations With Animals: A Native American Bestiary. Gerald Hausman. LC 86-70259. (Meditations With Ser.). (Illus.). 141p. (Orig.). 1986. pap. 6.95 (ISBN 0-939680-26-2). Bear & Co.

Meditations with Native Americans: Lakota Spirituality. Paul Steinmetz. LC 83-71961. (Meditations with Ser.). (Illus.). 144p. (Orig.). 1984. pap. 6.95 (ISBN 0-939680-13-0). Bear & Co.

Meditations with Nicholas of Cusa. James F. Yockey. 1987. pap. 6.95. Bear & Co.

Meditations With Teresa of Avila. Camille Campbell. LC 85-71856. (Meditations With Ser.). 142p. (Orig.). 1985. pap. 6.95 (ISBN 0-939680-23-8). Bear & Co.

Meditations With the Hopi. Robert Boissiere. LC 86-70257. (Meditations With Ser.). (Illus.). 144p. (Orig.). 1986. pap. 6.95 (ISBN 0-939680-27-0). Bear & Co.

Meditations with TM Hildegard of Bingen. Gabriele Uhlein. LC 82-74151. (Meditations with TM). 129p. (Orig.). 1982. pap. 6.95 (ISBN 0-939680-12-2). Bear & Co.

Meditations with TM Julian of Norwich. Brendan Doyle. LC 82-73955. (Meditations with TM). (Illus.). 135p. (Orig.). 1983. pap. 6.95 (ISBN 0-939680-11-4). Bear & Co.

Meditations with TM Mechtild of Magdeburg. Sue Woodruff. LC 82-73366. (Meditations with TM Ser.). (Illus.). 132p. (Orig.). 1982. pap. 6.95 (ISBN 0-939680-06-8). Bear & Co.

Meditations with TM Meister Eckhart. Matthew Fox. LC 82-71451. (Meditations with TM Ser.). (Illus.). 131p. (Orig.). 1982. pap. 6.95 (ISBN 0-939680-04-1). Bear & Co.

Meditative Relaxation. The G-Jo Institute. 1980. pap. 4.50 (ISBN 0-916878-13-9). Falkynor Bks.

Meditative Status in Tibetan Buddhism. Lati Rinbochay et al. Ed. by Leah Zahler. Tr. by Jeffrey Hopkins from Tibetan. (Wisdom Advanced Book: Blue Ser.). (Illus.). 288p. (Orig.). 1983. pap. 10.95 (ISBN 0-86171-011-8, Pub. by Wisdom Pubns). Great Traditions.

Meditator. Subramuniya. (On the Path Ser.). (Illus.). 72p. 1973. pap. 2.00 (ISBN 0-87516-351-3). De Vorss.

Mediterranean Society: The Jewish Communities of the Arab World As Portrayed in the Documents of the Cairo Geniza. S. D. Goitein. Bd. with Vol. I. Economic Foundations. 1968; Vol. 2. The Community. 1971; Vol. 3. The Family. 1978. 48.50x (ISBN 0-520-03265-9); Vol. 4. Daily Life. 1983. 42.00x (ISBN 0-520-04869-5). LC 67-22430. (Near Eastern Center, UCLA). U of Cal Pr.

Mediums, & Spirit Rappers, & Roaring Radicals: Spiritualism in American Literature, 1850-1900. Howard Kerr. LC 78-170964. pap. 67.80 (ISBN 0-317-41918-8, 2025919). Bks Demand UMI.

Medusa's Hair: An Essay on Personal Symbols & Religious Experiences. Gananath Obeyesekere. LC 80-27372. (Illus.). 252p. 1981. lib. bdg. 22.50x (ISBN 0-226-61600-2). U of Chicago Pr.

Meek & the Militant: Religion & Power Across the World. Paul N. Siegel. 260p. 1986. 35.00 (ISBN 0-86232-349-5, Pub. by Zed Pr UK); pap. 12.50 (ISBN 0-86232-350-9, Pub. by Zed Pr UK). Humanities.

Meekins' Ceremonies. Inez P. Meekins. 48p. 1981. soft cover 3.00 (ISBN 0-88053-326-9). Macoy Pub.

Meet It with Faith. Martha Smock. 1966. 5.95 (ISBN 0-87159-097-2). Unity School.

Meet Jesus in Luke. Desmond O'Donnell. LC 80-67126. (Praying the Scriptures Ser.). 56p. (Orig.). 1980. pap. 1.75 (ISBN 0-87793-206-9). Ave Maria.

Meet Jesus in the Sunday Gospels, Vol. 1. 1986. pap. 8.95 (ISBN 0-937032-41-7). Light&Life Pub Co MN.

Meet Mary & Martha. Irene Brand. 144p. 1985. pap. 4.95 (ISBN 0-87239-899-4, 2978). Standard Pub.

Meet Moses: Fifty-Four Drawings in Color. Mortimer Borne. LC 77-74180. (Illus.). 1981. 18.50 (ISBN 0-913870-39-0). Abaris Bks.

Meet My Friend David. Jane McWhorter. 4.95 (ISBN 0-89137-420-5). Quality Pubns.

Meet Southern Baptists. Compiled by Albert McClellan. LC 78-52960. (Illus.). 1978. pap. 7.95 (ISBN 0-8054-6534-0). Broadman.

Meet the Brethren. Ed. by Donald F. Durnbaugh. (Illus.). 120p. 1984. pap. 2.95 (ISBN 0-936693-11-8). Brethren Encyclopedia.

Meet the Brethren. (Illus.). 120p. pap. 2.95x (ISBN 0-87178-559-5). Brethren.

Meet the Holy Family. Gladys E. Deck. 139p. 1978. 7.50 (ISBN 0-913382-24-8, 101-24). Prow Bks-Franciscan.

Meet the Lord & His Church. Richard H. Stadler. Ed. by William E. Fischer. (Bible Class Course for Young Adults Ser.). (Illus.). 64p. (Orig.). 1987. pap. text ed. 2.95 (ISBN 0-938272-26-8); tchr's ed. 2.95 (ISBN 0-938272-27-6). Wels Board.

Meet the Lord: Encounters with Jesus. James DiGiacomo et al. (Encounter Ser.). 1977. pap. 3.98 (ISBN 0-03-021281-2, 317, HarpR); resource manual 1.95 (ISBN 0-03-021866-7, 318). Har-Row.

Meet the Mennonites. (Pennsylvania Dutch Books Ser.). (Illus.). 1961. 3.00 (ISBN 0-911410-05-8). Applied Arts.

Meet the Methodists: An Introduction to the United Methodist Church. Charles L. Allen. 96p. 1986. pap. 3.50 (ISBN 0-687-24650-4). Abingdon.

Meet the Overcomers: The Story of a Special Family. Bonnie G. Wheeler. (Orig.). 1984. pap. 5.95 (ISBN 0-8024-0440-5). Moody.

Meet the Pilgrim Fathers. Elizabeth Payne. (Step-up Books Ser). (Illus.). 1966. PLB 5.99 (ISBN 0-394-90063-4, BYR). Random.

Meet the Witnesses. John M. Haffert. (Illus.). 160p. 1981. pap. 3.25 (ISBN 0-911988-39-4). AMI Pr.

Meet Yourself in the Psalms. Warren W. Wiersbe. 192p. 1983. pap. 5.95 (ISBN 0-88207-740-6). Victor Bks.

Meeting Challenges: Scripture References. Greetings Etc. by Alfreda. 1984. pap. text ed. 2.95 (ISBN 0-318-04372-6, Pub. by Greetings). Prosperity & Profits.

Meeting Christ in Handel's Messiah: Lent & Easter Messages Based on Handel's Texts & Music. Roger T. Quillin. 96p. 1984. pap. 4.95 (ISBN 0-8066-2118-4, 10-4318). Augsburg.

Meeting Christ in the Sacraments. Colman E. O'Neill. LC 64-20111. 1964. pap. 3.95 (ISBN 0-8189-0090-3). Alba.

Meeting Famous Christians. Brian G. Cooper. (Illus.). 111p. 1977. pap. text ed. 3.50 (ISBN 0-85597-205-X). Attic Pr.

Meeting God. J. I. Packer. (LifeBuilder Bible Studies). 64p. (Orig.). 1986. pap. 2.95. Inter-Varsity.

Meeting God. Michel Quoist. 1985. 4.95 (ISBN 0-87193-222-9). Dimension Bks.

Meeting God at Every Turn. Catherine Marshall. 224p. 1985. pap. 3.50 (ISBN 0-553-23977-5). Bantam.

Meeting House & Counting House. Frederick B. Tolles. (Illus.). 1963. pap. 8.95 (ISBN 0-393-00211-X, Norton Lib). Norton.

Meeting House & Farm House. Howard H. Brinton. LC 72-80096. (Orig.). 1972. pap. 2.50x (ISBN 0-87574-185-1). Pendle Hill.

Meeting House to Camp Meeting: Toward a History of American Free Church Worship from 1620-1835. Doug Adams. 160p. (Orig.). 1981. pap. text ed. 6.95 (ISBN 0-941500-26-8). Sharing Co.

Meeting Jesus in Holy Communion. Roger Marchand. 32p. 1984. pap. 1.75 (ISBN 0-89243-202-0). Liguori Pubns.

Meeting Life's Challenges with Pastoral Counseling. Ed. by Joseph Rothstein. 1986. 14.95 (ISBN 0-533-06612-3). Vantage.

Meeting the Challenge. Herbert C. Gabhart. 1984. 6.95 (ISBN 0-8054-5340-7, 4253-40). Broadman.

Meeting the Challenge of Change: A Sixty-Year History of the St. Stephens Baptist Church, Kansas City, Mo. 15.00 (ISBN 0-685-02662-0). Univ Place.

Meeting the Forgiving Jesus: A Child's First Penance Book. Joann Angers. 32p. 1984. pap. 1.75 (ISBN 0-89243-201-2). Liguori Pubns.

Meeting the Living God. 2nd, rev. ed. William J. O'Malley. 1983. pap. 5.95 (ISBN 0-8091-9565-8). Paulist Pr.

Meeting the Messiah. Donald J. Shelby. LC 79-57363. 96p. (Orig.). 1980. pap. 3.50x (ISBN 0-8358-0398-8). Upper Room.

Meetinghouse Hill, Sixteen Thirty to Seventy Eighty-Three. Ola E. Winslow. 1972. pap. 2.95x (ISBN 0-393-00632-8, Norton Lib). Norton.

Meetingplace: A History of the Mennonite Church of Normal 1912-1987. Rachel W. Goossen. Ed. by Terry Stutzman. LC 86-63769. (Illus.). 192p. 1987. text ed. 25.00 (ISBN 0-9617978-0-0); pap. text ed. 18.00 (ISBN 0-9617978-1-9). Mennonite Church.

Meetings. Martin Buber. Ed. & tr. by Maurice Friedman. LC 73-82780. 123p. 1973. 9.95 (ISBN 0-87548-085-3). Open Court.

Meetings at the Edge: Conversations with the Grieving & the Dying, the Healing & the Healed. Stephen Levine. LC 82-45931. 264p. 1984. pap. 7.95 (ISBN 0-385-18786-6, Anchor Pr). Doubleday.

Meetings with the Master. William G. Jozwiak. LC 84-91374. 118p. 1985. 10.00 (ISBN 0-533-06459-7). Vantage.

Meg. Meg Ashley. LC 83-1332. 128p. 1983. pap. text ed. 2.95 (ISBN 0-88449-101-3, A324581). Vision Hse.

Megasthenes & Indian Religion. Allan Dahlquist. 1977. 11.50 (ISBN 0-89684-277-0, Pub. by Motilal Banarsidass India). Orient Bk Dist.

Megatruth: The Church in the Age of Information. David McKenna. 1987. 12.95. Heres Life.

Megillah & Shekalim, 1 vol. 15.00 (ISBN 0-910218-59-5). Bennet Pub.

Megillah: Book of Esther. Arthur Szyk. 1974. 25.00x (ISBN 0-685-84454-4). Bloch.

Megillah-the Book of Esther. Meir Zlotowitz. (Art Scroll Tanach Ser.). 160p. 1976. 11.95 (ISBN 0-89906-000-5); pap. 8.95 (ISBN 0-89906-001-3). Mesorah Pubns.

Megillat Esther: The Mascretic Hebrew Text with Introduction, New Translation & Commentary. Robert Gordis. 1977. 3.95x (ISBN 0-87068-763-8). Ktav.

Megillat Esther: The Story of Esther. Ed. & tr. by Meir H. Letteris. 1979. pap. 0.95 (ISBN 0-88482-583-3). Hebrew Pub.

Megillath Esther. A. J. Rosenberg. 86p. 1985. pap. 6.95 (ISBN 0-900689-97-8). Soncino Pr.

Megilloth. Ed. by T. H. Robinson et al. (Biblia Hebraica Stuttgartensia Ser.). 62p. 1975. pap. 2.50x (ISBN 3-438-05213-X, 61304, Pub. by United Bible). Am Bible.

Meher Baba Is Love. 2nd ed. Adah Shifrin. (Illus.). 56p. pap. 6.95. Sheriar Pr.

Meher Baba Journal, Vol. 1, No. 11. Meher Baba et al. Ed. by Elizabeth Patterson. (No. 11). (Illus.). 66p. 1974. pap. 2.50x (ISBN 0-913078-18-2). Sheriar Pr.

Meher Baba Journal, Vol. 1, No. 6. Meher Baba et al. Ed. by Elizabeth C. Patterson. (Illus.). 68p. 1972. pap. 2.50x (ISBN 0-913078-10-7). Sheriar Pr.

Meher Baba Journal, Vol. 1, No. 7. Meher Baba et al. Ed. by Elizabeth C. Patterson. (Illus.). 68p. 1972. pap. 2.50x (ISBN 0-913078-11-5). Sheriar Pr.

Meher Baba Journal, Vol. 1, No. 9. Meher Baba et al. Ed. by Elizabeth C. Patterson. (Illus.). 1973. pap. 2.50x (ISBN 0-913078-13-1). Sheriar Pr.

Meher Baba Journal, Vol. 1, No. 10. Meher Baba et al. Ed. by Elizabeth C. Patterson. (Illus.). 1973. pap. 2.50x (ISBN 0-913078-14-X). Sheriar Pr.

Meher Roshani. Bhau Kalchuri. 144p. (Orig.). Date not set. pap. 10.00 (ISBN 0-932947-06-9). Manifestation.

Me'ilah, Kimmin, Tamid & Middoth, 1 vol. 15.00 (ISBN 0-910218-86-2). Bennet Pub.

Meir Kahane, Ideologue, Hero, & Thinker. S. Daniel Breslauer. LC 86-21703. (Jewish Studies: Vol. 1). 168p. 1986. text ed. 39.95x (ISBN 0-88946-252-6). E Mellen.

Meister Eckhart, 2 vols. Franz Pfeiffer. 1977. lib. bdg. 250.00 (ISBN 0-8490-2222-3). Gordon Pr.

Meister Eckhart: A Modern Translation. Meister Eckhart. pap. 8.95x (ISBN 0-06-130008-X, TB8, Torch). Har-Row.

Meister Eckhart: Mystic & Philosopher. Meister Eckhart. Tr. by Reiner Schurmann. LC 76-26416. (Studies in Phenomenology & Existential Philosophy Ser.). 320p. 1978. 22.50x (ISBN 0-253-35183-9). Ind U Pr.

Meister Eckhart: Teacher & Preacher. Bernard McGinn et al. (Classics of Western Spirituality Ser.: Vol. 52). 448p. 1986. 15.95 (ISBN 0-8091-0377-X); pap. 12.95 (ISBN 0-8091-2827-6). Paulist Pr.

Meister Eckhart und seine Juenger: Ungedruckte Texte zur Geschichte der deutschen Mystik. Ed. by Franz Jostes. (Deutsche Neudrucke Texte des Mittelalters Ser.). (Ger.). 216p. 1972. 17.40 (ISBN 3-11-004356-4). De Gruyter.

Mejda: The Family & the Early Life of Paramahansa Yogananda. Sananda L. Ghosh. LC 80-54206. (Illus.). 330p. 1980. 8.50 (ISBN 0-87612-265-9). Self Realization.

Mekilta De-Rabbi Ishmael, 3 vols. Intro. by & tr. by Jacob Z. Lauterbach. LC 75-40823. (JPS Library of Jewish Classics). 808p. 1976. pap. 19.95 (ISBN 0-8276-0078-X, 382). Jewish Pubns.

Mel Bay's Deluxe Guitar Praise Book. Bill Bay. 64p. (Orig.). 1973. pap. 2.95 (ISBN 0-89228-007-7). Impact Bks MO.

Mel Bay's Guitar Hymnal. Bill Bay. 80p. (Orig.). 1972. pap. 2.95 (ISBN 0-89228-009-3). Impact Bks MO.

Melanchthon: Alien or Ally. Franz Hildebrandt. LC 46-3804. 1968. Repr. of 1946 ed. 16.00 (ISBN 0-527-40600-7). Kraus Repr.

Melanchthon & Bucer. Ed. by Wilhelm Pauck. LC 69-12309. (Library of Christian Classics). 422p. 1980. pap. 9.95 (ISBN 0-664-24164-6). Westminster.

Melanchthon on Christian Doctrine: Loci Communes 1555. Philip Melanchthon. Ed. & tr. by Clyde L. Manschreck. (Twin Brooks Ser.). 414p. 1982. pap. 11.95 (ISBN 0-8010-6143-1). Baker Bk.

Melanchthon: The Quiet Reformer. Clyde L. Manschreck. LC 73-21263. (Illus.). 350p. 1975. Repr. of 1958 ed. lib. bdg. 27.25x (ISBN 0-8371-6131-2, MAMQ). Greenwood.

Melanes: French-Arabic Text, Vol. 14. Institut Dominicain d'Etudes Orientales du Caire. 1980. 30.00x (ISBN 0-86685-284-0). Intl Bk Ctr.

Melanges Philosophie Juive et Arabe. Salomon Munk. Ed. by Steven Katz. LC 79-7148. (Jewish Philosophy, Mysticism & History of Ideas Ser.). 1980. Repr. of 1927 ed. lib. bdg. 51.50x (ISBN 0-405-12278-0). Ayer Co Pubs.

Melanges: Tables Generales Tomes 1-13 (1954-1977) Institut Dominicain D'Etudes Orientales du Caire. (Fr. & Arabic.). 1980. 10.00x (ISBN 0-86685-283-2). Intl Bk Ctr.

Melchior Hoffman: Social Unrest & Apocalyptic Visions in the Age of Reformation. Klaus Deppermann. Tr. by Malcolm Wren. 450p. 1986. 38.95 (ISBN 0-567-09338-7, Pub. by T & T Clark Ltd UK). Fortress.

Melchizedek Tradition. F. L. Horton. LC 75-32479. (Society for New Testament Studies Monographs: No. 30). 220p. 1976. 42.50 (ISBN 0-521-21014-3). Cambridge U Pr.

Melchizedek Truth Principles. Frater Achad. pap. 6.95 (ISBN 0-87516-166-9). De Vorss.

Melhor Relacionamento com. James Hilt. Orig. Title: How to Have a Better Relationship with Anybody. (Port.). 1986. write for info. (ISBN 0-8297-0542-2). Life Pubs Intl.

Melissa. Eva Gibson. 137p. (Orig.). 1982. pap. 2.95 (ISBN 0-87123-575-7, 200575). Bethany Hse.

Melody of Israel. Neil J. McEleney. (Bible Ser.). pap. 1.00 (ISBN 0-8091-5089-1). Paulist Pr.

Melody of Prayer: How to Personally Experience the Divine Liturgy. Stanley Harakas. pap. 1.95 (ISBN 0-686-27068-1). Light&Life Pub Co MN.

Melody of the Twenty-Third Psalm. Anna Warner. pap. 1.95 (ISBN 0-685-88385-X). Reiner.

Melville & the Gods. William Hamilton. (Scholars Press Studies in the Humanities: No. 7). 1985. pap. 13.25 (ISBN 0-89130-741-9, 00 01 07). Scholars Pr GA.

Member Missionary? Hey...I Can Do That! Gary Coleman. LC 83-80527. 79p. 1983. pap. 4.95 (ISBN 0-88290-220-2). Horizon-Utah.

Membership. Ed. by Bob Korth. (Discipleship Booklets Ser.). (Illus.). 1984. 0.95 (ISBN 0-87239-788-2, 1152). Standard Pub.

Membership in the Reformed Church. Herman Ridder. pap. 1.65 (ISBN 0-686-23484-7). Rose Pub MI.

Membership: Interpol Dossier, Pt. Two. pap. 5.75 (ISBN 0-905931-00-9). Church of Scient Info.

Memo to a Weary Sunday School Teacher. David S. McCarthy. LC 77-92877. 1978. pap. 3.95 (ISBN 0-8170-0807-1). Judson.

Memoir & Remains of R. M. M'cheyne. Andrew A. Bonar. 1978. 16.95 (ISBN 0-85151-084-1). Banner of Truth.

Memoir of Jemima Wilkinson, a Preacheress of the 18th Century. David Hudson. LC 78-134417. Repr. of 1844 ed. 23.00 (ISBN 0-404-08475-3). AMS Pr.

Memoir of Mrs. Harriet L. Winslow, Thirteen Years a Member of the American Mission in Ceylon. Miron Winslow. Ed. by Carolyn D. Gifford & Donald Dayton. (Women in American Protestant Religion 1800-1930 Ser.). 480p. 1987. lib. bdg. 70.00 (ISBN 0-8240-0684-4). Garland Pub.

Memoir of Rev. Levi Parsons: Late Missionary to Palestine. Daniel O. Morton. Ed. by Moshe Davis. (America & the Holy Land Ser.). 1977. Repr. of 1824 ed. lib. bdg. 33.00x (ISBN 0-405-10271-2). Ayer Co Pubs.

Memoir of the Late Martha Hazeltine Smith. Sarah Sleeper. Ed. by Carolyn D. Gifford & Donald Dayton. (Women in American Protestant Religion 1800-1930 Ser.). 294p. 1987. lib. bdg. 40.00 (ISBN 0-8240-0686-0). Garland Pub.

Memoir of the Life & Character of the Rev. Samuel Bacon. facs. ed. Samuel Bacon. Ed. by Jehudi Ashmun. (Black Heritage Library Collection). 1822. 20.25 (ISBN 0-8369-8781-0). Ayer Co Pubs.

Memoir of the Life & Labors of Francis Wayland, D. D., L. L. D. Francis Wayland & H. L. Wayland. LC 76-38465. (Religion in America, Ser. 2). 818p. 1972. Repr. of 1867 ed. 52.00 (ISBN 0-405-04092-X). Ayer Co Pubs.

Memoir of the Life & Times of the Reverend Isaac Backus. Alvah Hovey. LC 73-148598. (Era of the American Revolution Ser.). 367p. 1972. Repr. of 1858 ed. lib. bdg. 47.50 (ISBN 0-306-70415-3). Da Capo.

Memoir of the Life of Laurence Oliphant & of Alice Oliphant, His Wife. Margaret Oliphant. LC 75-36915. (Occult Ser.). 1976. Repr. of 1892 ed. 32.00x (ISBN 0-405-07970-2). Ayer Co Pubs.

Memoir of the Nature of the Church of Christ. Apostolos Makrakis. Ed. by Orthodox Christian Educational Society. Tr. by Denver Cummings from Hellenic. 175p. 1947. 4.75x (ISBN 0-938366-21-1). Orthodox Chr.

Memoir of the Rev. Elijah P. Lovejoy. facsimile ed. Joseph C. Lovejoy & Owen Lovejoy. LC 72-117882. (Select Bibliographies Reprint Ser). Repr. of 1838 ed. 21.00 (ISBN 0-8369-5335-5). Ayer Co Pubs.

Memoir of the Rev. Francis Hodgson, B.D., Scholar, Poet, & Divine, 2 vols. James T. Hodgson. LC 75-26864. 1975. Repr. of 1878 ed. lib. bdg. 75.00 (ISBN 0-8414-4804-3). Folcroft.

Memoir of the Rev. John Keble, 2 vols. in 1. 2nd rev. ed. John T. Coleridge. LC 75-30019. Repr. of 1869 ed. 38.50 (ISBN 0-404-14024-6). AMS Pr.

Memoir of the Reverend Jesse Lee, with Extracts from His Journals. Jesse Lee & Minton Thrift. LC 72-83428. (Religion in America, Ser. 1). 1969. Repr. of 1823 ed. 19.00 (ISBN 0-405-00253-X). Ayer Co Pubs.

Memoir of the Reverend Sydney Smith by His Daughter, Lady Holland, 2 vols. Ed. by Mrs. Austin. 1973. Repr. of 1855 ed. 45.00 set (ISBN 0-8274-1210-X). R West.

Memoire of Mrs. Ann R. Page. C. W. Andrews. Ed. by Carolyn G. De Swarte & Donald Dayton. (Women in American Protestant Religion Series 1800-1930). 95p. 1987. lib. bdg. 25.00 (ISBN 0-8240-0657-7). Garland Pub.

Memoires, 2 vols. Charlotte A. De Mornay. 1869. Set. 67.00 (ISBN 0-384-40148-1); Set. pap. 55.00 (ISBN 0-384-40149-X). Johnson Repr.

Memoirs & Memories. Gary MacEoin. 308p. (Orig.). 1986. pap. 9.95 (ISBN 0-89622-317-5). Twenty-Third.

Memoirs, Incidents, Reminiscences of the Early History of the New Church in Michigan, Indiana, Illinois, & Adjacent States, & Canada. G. Field. LC 70-134423. 1972. Repr. of 1879 ed. 27.00 (ISBN 0-404-08463-X). AMS Pr.

Memoirs of a Fortunate Jew: An Italian Story. Dan V. Segre. LC 86-17495. 274p. 1987. 16.95 (ISBN 0-917561-32-5). Adler & Adler.

Memoirs of a Protestant Condemned to the Galleys of France for His Religion, 2 Vols. Jean Marteilhe. Tr. by Oliver Goldsmith. 290p. 1983. Repr. of 1895 ed. Set. lib. bdg. 75.00 (ISBN 0-8495-2138-6). Arden Lib.

Memoirs of a Special Case. rev. ed. Chaim Raphael. LC 62-9548. 208p. 1985. 12.95 (ISBN 0-940646-16-1); pap. 7.95 (ISBN 0-940646-17-X). Rossel Bks.

Memoirs of an Anti-Zionist Jew. Elmer Berger. 159p. 1978. 4.00 (ISBN 0-88728-127-3). Inst Palestine.

Memoirs of Ber of Bolechow (1723-1805) Ber Of Bolechow. LC 73-2186. (Jewish People; History, Religion, Literature Ser.). Repr. of 1922 ed. 19.00 (ISBN 0-405-05252-9). Ayer Co Pubs.

Memoirs of George E. Harmon. (Illus.). 56p. 0.60 (ISBN 0-686-29129-8); 2 copies 1.00 (ISBN 0-686-29130-1). Faith Pub Hse.

Memoirs of Gluckel of Hameln. Gluckel. Tr. by Marvin Lowenthal from Ger. LC 77-75290. 1977. pap. 7.95 (ISBN 0-8052-0572-1). Schocken.

Memoirs of Mary Baker Eddy. Adam H. Dickey. 51p. 1985. pap. 6.00 (ISBN 0-930227-04-2). Pasadena Pr.

Memoirs of Peter. Arthur Pitcher. 1981. 3.95 (ISBN 0-86544-015-8). Salv Army Suppl South.

Memoirs of the Crusades. Geoffroi De Villehardouin & Joinville. LC 83-1515. (Everyman's Library: History: No. 333). xli, 340p. 1983. Repr. of 1908 ed. lib. bdg. 45.00x (ISBN 0-313-23856-1, VIME). Greenwood.

Memoirs of the Rev. Eleazar Wheelock, D. D. David M'Clure & Elijah Parish. LC 75-38454. (Religion in America, Ser. 2). 338p. 1972. Repr. of 1811 ed. 22.00 (ISBN 0-405-04074-1). Ayer Co Pubs.

Memoirs of the Rev. Francis Hodgson, 2 Vols. James T. Hodgson. LC 76-169470. Repr. of 1878 ed. Set. 65.00 (ISBN 0-404-07374-3). Vol. 1 (ISBN 0-404-07375-1). Vol. 2 (ISBN 0-404-07376-X). AMS Pr.

Memoirs of the Reverend David Brainerd: Missionary to the Indians on the Border of New York, New Jersey & Pennsylvania. Ed. by David Brainerd. LC 70-108477. (American Indian History Sers). 1970. Repr. of 1822 ed. 49.00x (ISBN 0-403-00233-8). Scholarly.

Memoirs of the Reverend Noah Worcester, D. D. Henry Ware. LC 78-137557. (Peace Movement in America Ser). xii, 155p. 1972. Repr. of 1844 ed. lib. bdg. 14.95x (ISBN 0-89198-088-1). Ozer.

Memoirs of William Miller. Sylvester Bliss. LC 72-134374. Repr. of 1853 ed. 30.00 (ISBN 0-404-08422-2). AMS Pr.

Memoirs to Serve for the Future Ecclesiastical History of the Diocese of Boston. Benedict J. Fenwick. Ed. by Joseph M. McCarthy. LC 78-64366. (Monograph: No. 35). (Illus.). 270p. 1979. 10.95x (ISBN 0-686-65388-2). US Cath Hist.

Memorable Ceremonies & Poems: Including Material from "Along the Story Trail". J. L. Alexander. 192p. 1986. Repr. of 1928 ed. 5.50 (ISBN 0-88053-302-1, S-109). Macoy Pub.

Memorbook: Pictorial History of Dutch Jewry from the Renaissance to 1940. Mozes Heiman Gans. (Illus.). 852p. 1983. 125.00x (ISBN 0-8143-1749-9). Wayne St U Pr.

Memorial & Genealogical Record of Southwest Texas. Goodspeed Publishing Company. 661p. 1978. Repr. of 1894 ed. 40.00 (ISBN 0-89308-122-1). Southern Hist Pr.

Memorial Service at the Cemetery. Morris Silverman. pap. 0.95 (ISBN 0-685-64878-8). Prayer Bk.

Memorials of Bishop Waynflete, Founder of St. Mary Magdalen College, Oxford. Peter Heylyn. Ed. by John R. Bloxam. 1851. 24.00 (ISBN 0-8337-0311-0). B Franklin.

Memorials of Saint Anselm, Vol. I. Ed. by R. W. Southern & F. S. Schmitt. (Auctores Britannici Medii Aevi). 370p. 1969. 22.50 (ISBN 0-85672-693-1, Pub. by British Acad). Longwood Pub Group.

Memorials of South Africa. Barnabas Shaw. LC 71-109358. Repr. of 1840 ed. cancelled (ISBN 0-8371-3737-3, SMS&, Pub. by Negro U Pr). Greenwood.

Memorials of the Faithful. Abdu'l-Baha. Tr. by Marzieh Gail. LC 77-157797. 1971. 10.95 (ISBN 0-87743-041-1, 106-012). Baha'i.

Memorie Degli Scrittori Filippini o Siano Della Congregazione Dell' Oratorio de S. Filippo Neri, 2 vols. Carlantonio De Rosa Villarosa. 1380p. Date not set. Repr. of 1842 ed. text ed. 74.52x (ISBN 0-576-72217-0, Pub. by Gregg Intl Pubs England). Gregg Intl.

Memories & Meditations of a Workcamper. David S. Richie. LC 73-84213. 36p. (Orig.). 1973. pap. 2.50x (ISBN 0-87574-190-8, 189). Pendle Hill.

Memories & Visions of Paradise. Richard Heinberg. (Illus.). 61p. (Orig.). 1985. pap. 4.95 (ISBN 0-932869-00-9). Emissaries Divine.

Memories of a Catholic Girlhood. Mary McCarthy. LC 57-8842. 245p. 1972. pap. 5.95 (ISBN 0-15-658650-9, Harv). HarBraceJ.

Memories of a Loving Soul. Tr. by Swami Prabhavananda. (Orig.). 1968. pap. 4.95 (ISBN 0-87481-015-9). Vedanta Pr.

Memories of Abdu'l-Baha: Recollections of the Early Days of the Baha'i Faith in California. Ramona A. Brown. LC 79-16412. (Illus.). 1980. 10.95 (ISBN 0-87743-128-0, 332-010); pap. 6.95 (ISBN 0-87743-139-6, 332-011). Baha'i.

Memories of an American Jew. facsimile ed. Philip Cowen. LC 74-27974. (Modern Jewish Experience Ser.). (Illus.). 1975. Repr. of 1932 ed. 37.50x (ISBN 0-405-06703-8). Ayer Co Pubs.

Memories of Gurdjieff. A. L. Staveley. LC 78-56109. 1978. 8.95 (ISBN 0-89756-000-0). Two Rivers.

Memories of Stambourne. C. H. Spurgeon. 1975. pap. 1.95 (ISBN 0-686-16838-0). Pilgrim Pubns.

Memories of the Future. Paul Horgan. 216p. 1966. 4.95 (ISBN 0-374-20756-9). FS&G.

Memories of the Life of the Priest Don Antonio Jose Martinez. Pedro Sanchez. Tr. by Ray J. De Aragon. LC 78-51462. (Span. & Eng.). 1978. 12.00 (ISBN 0-89016-044-9); pap. 6.95 (ISBN 0-89016-045-7). Lightning Tree.

Memorized Torah: The Mnemonic System of the Mishnah. Jacob Neusner. (Brown Judaic Studies). 1985. 22.95 (ISBN 0-89130-866-0, 14-00-96); pap. 17.95 (ISBN 0-89130-867-9). Scholars Pr GA.

Memorizing Bible Verses with Games & Crafts. Beth Short. LC 12-2872. 1984. pap. 4.95 teacher's material (ISBN 0-570-03937-1). Concordia.

Memory Palace of Matteo Ricci. Jonathan D. Spence. (Nonfiction Ser.). 368p. 1985. pap. 7.95 (ISBN 0-14-008098-8). Penguin.

Men & Ideas in the Sixteenth Century. Hans J. Hillerbrand. 130p. 1984. pap. text ed. 7.95x (ISBN 0-88133-080-9). Waveland Pr.

Men & Women of the Renaissance & Reformation 1300-1600. Thomas R. Rumsey. 487p. (Orig.). 1981. pap. text ed. 10.95 (ISBN 0-686-81286-7). Ind Sch Pr.

Men & Women: Partners in Service. Lillian V. Grissen & Gordon J. Spykman. 100p. (Orig.). 1981. pap. text ed. 4.50 (ISBN 0-933140-36-3). CRC Pubns.

Men in the Sunlight of the Word. Cummings. pap. 5.95 (ISBN 0-686-27771-6). Schmul Pub Co.

Men in White Apparel. Ann R. Colton. (Illus.). 202p. 1961. 6.95 (ISBN 0-917187-10-5). A R C Pub.

Men Made New: An Exposition of Romans 5-8. John R. Stott. 108p. 1984. pap. 4.95 (ISBN 0-8010-8244-7). Baker Bk.

Men of Conviction. facs. ed. Henry B. Washburn. LC 74-134152. (Essay Index Reprint Ser). 1931. 18.00 (ISBN 0-8369-2081-3). Ayer Co Pubs.

Men of Maryknoll. James G. Keller & Meyer Berger. LC 78-142650. (Essay Index Reprint Ser.). Repr. of 1943 ed. 18.00 (ISBN 0-8369-2775-3). Ayer Co Pubs.

Men of Power: Benjamin Franklin, Ralph Waldo Emerson, George Fox, Charles Darwin, Vol. 3. facs. ed. Fred Eastman. LC 74-128236. (Essay Index Reprint Ser). 1939. 18.00 (ISBN 0-8369-1993-9). Ayer Co Pubs.

Men of Power: Francis of Assisi, Leonardo Da Vinci, Oliver Cromwell, John Milton, Vol. 2. facs. ed. Fred Eastman. LC 74-128236. (Essay Index Reprint Ser). 1938. 18.00 (ISBN 0-8369-1992-0). Ayer Co Pubs.

Men of Power: Nicolai Lenin, Mahatma Gandhi, Edward Livingston Trudeau, Robest Louis Stevenson, Vol. 5. facs. ed. Fred Eastman. LC 74-128236. (Essay Index Reprint Ser). 1940. 18.00 (ISBN 0-8369-1995-5). Ayer Co Pubs.

Men of Science, Men of God. Henry M. Morris. (Illus.). 1982. pap. 2.95 (ISBN 0-89051-080-6). Master Bks.

Men of the Cloth & the Social-Cultural Fabric of the Norwegian Ethnic Community in North Dakota. Duane R. Lindberg. Ed. by Francesco Cordasco. LC 80-877. (American Ethnic Groups Ser.). 1981. lib. bdg. 38.00x (ISBN 0-405-13438-X). Ayer Co Pubs.

Men of the Outposts: The Romance of the Modern Christian Movement. facs. ed. Herbert Welch. LC 69-17594. (Essay Index Reprint Ser). 1937. 16.50 (ISBN 0-8369-1162-8). Ayer Co Pubs.

Men of the Spirit. Jung. cancelled (ISBN 0-685-48594-3). Feldheim.

Men, the Meaning, the Message of the New Testament Books. William Barclay. LC 77-22184. 156p. 1978. pap. 4.95 (ISBN 0-664-24188-3). Westminster.

Men Who Change the World, 7 vols. Gordon Lindsay. 0.95 ea. Christ Nations.

Men Who Left the Movement. facs. ed. Gertrude Donald. LC 67-23207. (Essay Index Reprint Ser). 1933. 20.00 (ISBN 0-8369-0385-4). Ayer Co Pubs.

Men Who Shape Belief. David W. Soper. LC 76-86061. (Essay & General Literature Index Reprint Ser). 1969. Repr. of 1955 ed. 24.00x (ISBN 0-8046-0588-2, Pub. by Kennikat). Assoc Faculty Pr.

Menace of the Religious Movie. A. H. Tozer. 1974. pap. 1.00 (ISBN 0-915374-51-X, 51-X). Rapids Christian.

Menahoth, 2 vols. 30.00 (ISBN 0-910218-80-3). Bennet Pub.

Menasseh ben Israel: The Hope of Israel. Ed. by Henry Mechoulan & Gerard Nahon. (Litman Library of Jewish Civilzation). (Illus.). 224p. 37.00 (ISBN 0-19-710054-6). Oxford U Pr.

Mended Speech: The Crisis of Religious Study & Theology. P. Joseph Cahill. 272p. 1982. 14.95 (ISBN 0-8245-0421-6). Crossroad NY.

Mendele Mocher Seforim. Theodore L. Steinberg. (World Authors Ser.). 1977. lib. bdg. 16.95 (ISBN 0-8057-6308-2, Twayne). G K Hall.

Mender of Broken Hearts: How Christ Gives Us Courage to Live. Conrad M. Thompson. LC 81-52270. 128p. (Orig.). 1982. pap. 5.95 (ISBN 0-8066-1902-3, 10-4343). Augsburg.

Mending. Dorothy Hsu. 1982. pap. 2.95 (ISBN 0-87508-263-7). Chr Lit.

Mending of Life: Being an Anonymous Version of about A. D. 1400 from the De Emendatione Vitae of Richard Rolle of Hampole. Richard Rolle. 95p. 1981. Repr. of 1913 ed. lib. bdg. 30.00 (ISBN 0-89987-374-X). Darby Bks.

Mending Our Nets. Rosemary Torrence. 176p. 1980. 10.95 (ISBN 0-697-01757-5). Wm C Brown.

Mending the Nets: Taiwan Church Growth & Loss in the 1980's. Allen J. Swanson. LC 86-47704. 320p. 1986. pap. 7.95 (ISBN 0-87808-207-7, WCL 207-7). William Carey Lib.

Mending the World: Quaker Insights on the Social Order. Kenneth E. Boulding. LC 86-60283. 1986. pap. 2.50 (ISBN 0-87574-266-1). Pendle Hill.

Menno Simons su Vida y Escritos. Harold S. Bender & John Horsch. Tr. by Carmen Palomeque. 160p. 1979. 4.95x (ISBN 0-8361-1218-0). Herald Pr.

Mennonite Bibliography, 2 vols. Ed. by Nelson Springer & A. J. Klassen. LC 77-9105. 1977. 78.00x ea. Vol. 1 (ISBN 0-8361-1206-7). Vol. 2 (ISBN 0-8361-1207-5). Set. 147.50. Herald Pr.

Mennonite Brethren Church: A Bibliographic Guide. Herbert Giesbrecht. 99p. (Orig.). 1983. pap. 7.95 (ISBN 0-919797-28-8). Kindred Pr.

Mennonite Brethren Church Gesangbuch. 590p. 1955. 9.95x (ISBN 0-919797-17-2). Kindred Pr.

Mennonite Brethren Mission in Latin America. J. J. Toews. 255p. (Orig.). 1975. pap. 3.00 (ISBN 0-318-18905-4). Kindred Pr.

Mennonite Brotherhood in Russia (1789-1910) rev. ed. P. M. Friesen. LC 78-52664. 1065p. 1980. 24.95 (ISBN 0-919797-19-9). Kindred Pr.

Mennonite Church in America. John C. Wenger. LC 66-23903. (Mennonite History Vol. 2). 384p. 1967. 14.95x (ISBN 0-8361-1179-6). Herald Pr.

Mennonite Church in India: Eighteen Ninety-Seven to Nineteen Sixty-Two. John A. Lapp. LC 75-186445. 248p. 1972. 12.95 (ISBN 0-8361-1122-2). Herald Pr.

Mennonite Church in Zaire. J. B. Toews. 255p. (Orig.). 1978. pap. 3.00 (ISBN 0-919797-23-7). Kindred Pr.

Mennonite Confession of Faith. Mennonite Church. LC 63-22593. 32p. (Orig.). 1963. pap. 0.95 (ISBN 0-8361-1314-4). Herald Pr.

Mennonite Encyclopedia, 4vols. Ed. by Harold S. Bender & C. Henry Smith. 1956-1969. Set. 160.00x (ISBN 0-8361-1018-8); 45.00x ea. Vol. 1 (ISBN 0-8361-1118-4). Vol. 2 (ISBN 0-8361-1119-2). Vol. 3 (ISBN 0-8361-1120-6). Vol. 4 (ISBN 0-8361-1121-4). Herald Pr.

Mennonite Encyclopedia, 4 vols. 3800p. Set. 160.00x (ISBN 0-8361-1018-8); 45.00ea (ISBN 0-317-37852-X). Herald Pr.

Mennonite Hymnal. Ed. by Lester Hostetler & Walter E. Yoder. LC 69-18131. 1969. 7.50x (ISBN 0-87303-515-1). Faith & Life.

Mennonite Hymnal. 640p. 1960. round notes 7.95 (ISBN 0-317-37871-6); shape notes 7.95 (ISBN 0-317-37872-4); large print 11.95 (ISBN 0-317-37873-2). Herald Pr.

Mennonite Hymnal Loose-Leaf Edition. 640p. 1969. round notes 14.95 (ISBN 0-317-37874-0); shape notes 14.95 (ISBN 0-317-37875-9). Herald Pr.

Mennonite Identity & Literary Art. John L. Ruth. 72p. 1978. pap. 1.95 (ISBN 0-8361-1861-8). Herald Pr.

Mennonite Life. 2nd ed. John A. Hostetler. LC 82-83963. (Illus.). 48p. 1983. pap. 4.95 (ISBN 0-8361-1995-9). Herald Pr.

Mennonite Quarterly Review: Goshen, Ind., 1927-1976, Vols. 1-50. Set. lib. bdg. 2375.00 (ISBN 0-686-77268-7); lib. bdg. 47.50 ea. AMS Pr.

Mennonite Statements on Peace. Richard C. Detweiler. 80p. (Orig.). 1968. pap. 2.95 (ISBN 0-8361-1581-3). Herald Pr.

Mennonite Tourguide to Western Europe. Jan Gleysteen. LC 84-683. 340p. (Orig.). 1984. pap. 17.95 (ISBN 0-8361-3360-9). Herald Pr.

Mennonite Women: A Story of God's Faithfulness. Elaine S. Rich. LC 82-15452. 256p. 1983. pap. 9.95 (ISBN 0-8361-3311-0). Herald Pr.

Mennonites in Canada, Nineteen Twenty to Nineteen Forty, Vol. II. Frank H. Epp. LC 82-81339. 640p. 1982. text ed. 21.95x (ISBN 0-8361-1255-5). Herald Pr.

Mennonites in Europe. John Horsch. (Illus.). 414p. 1950. 12.95 (ISBN 0-8361-1395-0). Herald Pr.

Mennonites in Illinois, No. 24. Willard H. Smith. LC 83-152. (Studies in Anabaptist & Mennonite History Ser.). 616p. 1983. 24.95x (ISBN 0-8361-1253-9). Herald Pr.

Mennonites in the Confederacy. Samuel L. Horst. LC 67-15991. 148p. 1967. 6.95 (ISBN 0-317-37856-2). Herald Pr.

Mennonites in the World War: Or, Nonresistance under Test. Jonas S. Hartzler. LC 76-137543. (Peace Movement in America Ser). 246p. 1972. Repr. of 1922 ed. lib. bdg. 18.95x (ISBN 0-89198-071-7). Ozer.

Mennonites: Who & Why. Leroy Kennel. LC 63-17081. 32p. 1966. pap. 1.00 (ISBN 0-8361-1396-9). Herald Pr.

Mennonities in the Confederacy: A Study in Civil War Pacifism. Samuel L. Horst. LC 67-15991. (Illus.). 148p. 1967. 8.95x (ISBN 0-8361-1180-X). Herald Pr.

Menominee Music. Frances Densmore. LC 72-1882. (Music Ser.). (Illus.). 286p. 1972. Repr. of 1932 ed. lib. bdg. 29.50 (ISBN 0-306-70510-9). Da Capo.

Men's House: Masonic Papers & Addresses. Joseph F. Newton. 253p. 1969. text ed. 5.00 (ISBN 0-88053-037-5, M-86). Macoy Pub.

Mensaje a la Conciencia. Dardo Bruchez. (Span.). 128p. (Orig.). 1979. pap. 3.50 (ISBN 0-89922-143-2). Edit Caribe.

Mensaje de los Salmos, Tomo III. Rolando C. Gutierrez. 160p. 1983. pap. 5.95 (ISBN 0-311-04028-4). Casa Bautista.

Mensaje de los Salmos en Nuestro Contexto, Tomo II. Rolando C. Gutierrez. 160p. 1980. pap. 4.95 (ISBN 0-311-04025-X). Casa Bautista.

Mensaje de los Salmos en Nuestro Contexto Tomo I. Rolando C. Gutierrez. 160p. 1984. Repr. of 1979 ed. 5.95 (ISBN 0-311-04023-3). Casa Bautista.

Mental Alchemy. 3rd ed. Ralph Lewis. LC 79-66799. 270p. 1984. 11.95 (ISBN 0-912057-38-6, G-639). AMORC.

Mental Body. A. E. Powell. 1975. 11.95 (ISBN 0-8356-5504-0). Theos Pub Hse.

Mental Health Skills for Clergy. Dana Charry. 160p. 1981. 10.95 (ISBN 0-8170-0886-1). Judson.

Mental Philosophy of John Henry Newman. Jay Newman. 224p. 1986. pap. 22.95x (ISBN 0-88920-186-2, Pub. by Wilfrid Laurier Canada). Humanities.

Mental, Physical, Spiritual Health. Faye W. Parker. LC 79-56170. 80p. 1980. pap. 2.95 (ISBN 0-87516-397-1). De Vorss.

Mental Poisons & Their Antidotes. Joseph Murphy. pap. 1.50 (ISBN 0-87516-339-4). De Vorss.

Mentchkins Make Shabbos. Chaya L. Rothstein. (Sifrei Rimon Ser.). 1986. pap. 2.50 (ISBN 0-317-42728-8). Feldheim.

Mente Renovada. Larry Christenson. 128p. 1975. 2.50 (ISBN 0-88113-199-7). Edit Betania.

Menucha Vesimcha. Mordechai Katz. (Rothman Foundation Ser.). 1982. 7.95 (ISBN 0-87306-977-3); pap. 5.95 (ISBN 0-317-42411-4). Feldheim.

Mephistopheles: The Devil in the Modern World. Jeffrey B. Russell. LC 86-47648. (Illus.). 352p. 1986. text ed. 24.95x (ISBN 0-8014-1808-9). Cornell U Pr.

Mercies of a Covenant God. John Warburton. pap. 6.95 (ISBN 0-686-66520-1). Reiner.

Mercy for the Mankind, Vol. II. A. Ghazi. 1981. 4.00 (ISBN 0-686-97848-X). Kazi Pubns.

Mercy Lord, My Husband's in the Kitchen & Other Equal Opportunity Conversations with God. Toby D. Schwartz. 96p. 1982. pap. 2.95 (ISBN 0-380-57943-X, 57943-X). Avon.

Mercy Oceans: Teachings of Maulana Abdullah al-Faiza ad-Daghestani. Shaykh N. Al-Qibrisi. 190p. (Orig.). 1980. pap. 4.75x (ISBN 0-939830-11-6, Pub. by Leon). New Era Pubns MI.

Mercy of Qur'an & the Advent of Zaman. Shykh F. Haeri. 164p. 1987. pap. 18.95 (ISBN 0-7103-0224-X, 02231, Kegan Paul). Methuen Inc.

Mercy: The Gift Before & Beyond Faith. Doyle Harrison & Michael Landsman. 64p. (Orig.). 1984. pap. 2.25 (ISBN 0-89274-305-0). Harrison Hse.

Mere Christian. Kathryn Lindskoog. 264p. Date not set. pap. 9.95 (ISBN 0-87788-543-5). Shaw Pubs.

Mere Christianity. C. S. Lewis. 1964. 10.95 (ISBN 0-02-570610-1); pap. 3.95 (ISBN 0-02-086830-8). Macmillan.

Mere Christianity. C. S. Lewis. (Illus.). 211p. 1981. 12.95 (ISBN 0-02-570590-3). Macmillan.

Mere Christianity. C. S. Lewis. 1978. pap. 3.95 (Collier). Macmillan.

Mere Christianity. C. S. Lewis. (Christian Library). 1985. Repr. 6.95 (ISBN 0-916441-18-0). Barbour & Co.

Mere Christianity. C. S. Lewis. 180p. 1986. pap. 4.95 (ISBN 0-02-086940-1, Collier). Macmillan.

Mere Morality: What God Expects from Ordinary People. Lewis B. Smedes. 292p. 1987. pap. 9.95 (ISBN 0-8028-0257-5). Eerdmans.

Meredith's Book of Bible Lists. Joel L. Meredith. LC 80-14486. 288p. (Orig.). 1980. text ed. 10.95 (ISBN 0-87123-022-4, 230022); pap. 6.95 (ISBN 0-87123-023-2, 210023). Bethany Hse.

Meredith's Second Book of Bible Lists. J. M. Meredith. LC 83-3807. 192p. (Orig.). 1983. pap. 5.95 (ISBN 0-87123-319-3, 210319). Bethany Hse.

Merging Mission & Unity. Donald Black. LC 86-14847. 180p. (Orig.). 1986. pap. 9.95 (ISBN 0-664-24047-X, A Geneva Press Publication). Westminster.

Meridian Handbook of Classical Mythology. Edward Tripp. pap. 10.95 (ISBN 0-452-00785-2, Mer). NAL.

Merkabah in Rabbinic Literature. David Halperin. (American Oriental Ser.: Vol. 62). 1980. 14.00x (ISBN 0-940490-62-5). Am Orient Soc.

Mermaid & the Minotaur: Sexual Arrangements & Human Malaise. Dorothy Dinnerstein. LC 72-23879. 1977. pap. 7.95 (ISBN 0-06-090587-5, CN 587, PL). Har-Row.

Merrie Christmas Cookbook. 64p. 1955. 5.95 (ISBN 0-88088-429-0). Peter Pauper.

Merry Christmas: Things to Make & Do. Robyn Supraner. LC 80-23884. (Illus.). 48p. 1981. PLB 9.49 (ISBN 0-89375-422-6); pap. 1.95 (ISBN 0-89375-423-4). Troll Assocs.

Merry Christmas, Thomas! A. Vesey. (Illus.). 32p. 9.95 (ISBN 0-87113-096-3). Atlantic Monthly.

Merry Missionary: A Story About Philip Neri. Kenneth Christopher. (Stories About Christian Heroes Ser.). (Illus.). 32p. pap. 1.95 (ISBN 0-03-056876-5, HarpR). Har-Row.

Merry-Mouse Book of Prayers & Graces. Illus. by Priscilla Hillman. LC 82-45497. (Balloon Bks.). (Illus.). 32p. 1983. 4.95 (ISBN 0-385-18337-2). Doubleday.

Merton: A Biography. Monica Furlong. LC 84-48218. (Illus.). 368p. 1985. pap. 8.95 (ISBN 0-06-063078-7, RD 529, HarpR). Har-Row.

Merton: By Those Who Knew Him Best. Ed. by Paul Wilkes. LC 84-47824. (Illus.). 160p. 1984. 13.95 (ISBN 0-06-069416-5, HarpR). Har-Row.

Merton's Palace of Nowhere. James Finley. LC 78-58738. 160p. 1978. pap. 3.95 (ISBN 0-87793-159-3). Ave Maria.

Mesrob Mashtotz: A Fifth Century Life. Elise A. Bayizian. (Armenian Church Classics Ser.). (Illus.). 39p. (Orig.). 1984. pap. 4.00 (ISBN 0-934728-14-3). D O A C.

Message. Jafar Subhani. Tr. by M. Fazal Haq from Persian. 784p. 1985. pap. 25.00 (ISBN 0-941724-38-7). Islamic Seminary.

Message & Existence: An Introduction to Christian Theology. Langdon Gilkey. 272p. 1980. 12.95 (ISBN 0-8164-0450-X, HarpR); pap. 7.95 (ISBN 0-8164-2023-8). Har-Row.

Message Delivered. C. Stephen Mann. 128p. (Orig.). 1973. pap. 2.50 (ISBN 0-8192-1143-5). Morehouse.

Message Delivered: Leader's Guide. Helen S. Thomsen. (Orig.). 1973. pap. 2.50x (ISBN 0-8192-4048-6). Morehouse.

Message for the Human Race. Paul G. Lemons. 1984. 15.95 (ISBN 0-533-06058-3). Vantage.

Message from Calvary. Ellen G. White. (Outreach Ser.). 64p. 1981. pap. 1.25 (ISBN 0-8163-0394-0). Pacific Pr Pub Assn.

Message from Heaven & Things to Think about. LC 76-18436. 1976. 2.95 (ISBN 0-686-16284-6). W R Inman.

Message from Infinity: A Space-Age Correlation of Science & Religion. Gordon N. Patterson. (Illus.). 96p. 1984. 6.50 (ISBN 0-682-40149-8). Exposition Pr FL.

Message in Our Time: The Life & Teachings of the Sufi Master, Hazrat Inayat Khan. Pir V. Khan. LC 78-4751. (Illus.). 1979. 15.45 (ISBN 0-06-064237-8, HarpR). Har-Row.

Message of an Indian Relic: Seattle's Own Totem Pole. facs. ed. J. P. Lloyd. (Shorey Indian Ser.). (Illus.). 29p. pap. 1.95 (ISBN 0-8466-4006-6, I6). Shorey.

Message of Aquaria. H. A. Curtiss & F. H. Curtiss. 487p. 1981. pap. 25.00 (ISBN 0-89540-065-0, SB-065). Sun Pub.

Message of Christ & the Counselor. John Q. Quesnell. (Synthesis Ser). 1975. 2.00 (ISBN 0-8199-0534-8). Franciscan Herald.

Message of Colossians & Philemon. R. J. Lucas. Ed. by J. A. Motyer & J. R. Stott. LC 79-3635. (Bible Speaks Today Ser.). 1980. pap. 6.95 (ISBN 0-87784-284-1). Inter-Varsity.

Message of Daniel. Arthur Petrie. pap. 2.95 (ISBN 0-87509-103-2). Chr Pubns.

Message of Daniel. Ronald S. Wallace. LC 79-1996. (Bible Speaks Today Ser.). 1979. pap. 6.95 (ISBN 0-87784-285-X). Inter-Varsity.

Message of Ecclesiastes. Derek Kidner. LC 76-21460. (Bible Speaks Today Ser.). 1976. pap. 5.95 (ISBN 0-87784-286-8). Inter-Varsity.

Message of Ephesians. John R. Stott. Ed. by J. A. Motyer. (Bible Speaks Today Ser.). 1980. pap. text ed. 7.95 (ISBN 0-87784-287-6). Inter-Varsity.

Message of Exodus. Lester Meyer. LC 83-70519. 176p. (Orig.). 1983. pap. 8.95 (ISBN 0-8066-2025-0, 10-4347). Augsburg.

Message of Galatians. John R. Stott. pap. 6.95 (ISBN 0-87784-288-4). Inter-Varsity.

Message of Genesis 12-50: From Abraham to Joseph. Joyce G. Baldwin. Ed. by J. A. Motyer & John R. Stott. LC 86-10615. (Bible Speaks Today). 224p. (Orig.). 1986. pap. 7.95 (ISBN 0-87784-298-1). Inter Varsity.

Message of Hebrews. Raymond Brown. Ed. by J. A. Motyer & John R. Stott. LC 82-15321. (Bible Speaks Today Ser.). 272p. (Orig.). 1982. pap. 7.95 (ISBN 0-87784-289-2). Inter-Varsity.

Message of Hosea. Derek Kidner. Ed. by J. A. Motyer & John R. Stott. (Bible Speaks Today Ser.). 132p. (Orig.). 1982. text ed. 5.95 (ISBN 0-87784-290-6). Inter-Varsity.

Message of I Corinthians. David Prior. Ed. by John R. Stott & J. A. Motyer. LC 85-239. (Bible Speaks Today Ser.). 270p. 1985. pap. 7.95 (ISBN 0-87784-297-3). Inter-Varsity.

Message of James. Alec Motyer. Ed. by John R. Stott. LC 85-4316. (Bible Speaks Today Ser.). 156p. 1985. pap. 6.95 (ISBN 0-87784-292-2). Inter-Varsity.

Message of Jesus Christ. Mohandas K. Gandhi. Ed. by A. T. Hingorani. 64p. (Orig.). 1980. pap. 1.25 (ISBN 0-934676-20-8). Greenlf Bks.

Message of Job: A Theological Commentary. Daniel J. Simundson. LC 84-24214. (Augsburg Old Testament Studies). 192p. (Orig.). 1986. pap. 9.95 (ISBN 0-8066-2218-0, 10-4349). Augsburg.

Message of Jonah: A Theological Commentary. Terence E. Fretheim. LC 77-72461. pap. 8.95 (ISBN 0-8066-1591-5, 10-4350). Augsburg.

Message of Life: Studies in the Epistle of St. John (Missionary Message of the New Testament) J. Ireland Hasler. 96p. 1949. 3.95 (ISBN 0-87921-013-3). Attic Pr.

Message of Luke. Michael Wilcock. Ed. by J. A. Motyer & John R. Stott. LC 79-2720. (Bible Speaks Today Ser.). (Orig.). 1979. pap. 6.95 (ISBN 0-87784-291-4). Inter-Varsity.

Message of Marienfried: According to Our Lady's Apparitions in 1946. Ami Press Staff. 20p. 1983. 1.00 (ISBN 0-911988-50-5). AMI Pr.

Message of Medjugorje: The Marian Message to the Modern World. Mark I. Miravalle. LC 86-1588. 168p. 1986. lib. bdg. 23.75 (ISBN 0-8191-5288-9); pap. 9.75 (ISBN 0-8191-5289-7). U Pr of Amer.

Message of One & Two Chronicles. Michael Wilcock. Ed. by John R. Stott & J. A. Motyer. LC 86-27700. (Bible Speaks Today Ser.). 240p. (Orig.). 1987. pap. 8.95 (ISBN 0-87784-299-X). Inter-Varsity.

Message of Our Master. Ramakrishna's Disciples. pap. 1.95 (ISBN 0-87481-102-3). Vedanta Pr.

Message of Philippians. Alec Motyer. Ed. by John R. Stott. LC 83-22684. (Bible Speaks Today Ser.). 252p. 1983. pap. 7.95 (ISBN 0-87784-310-4). Inter-Varsity.

Message of Revelation. M. Wilcock. LC 74-31845. (Bible Speaks Today Ser.). 1975. pap. 6.95 (ISBN 0-87784-293-0). Inter-Varsity.

Message of Ruth. David Atkinson. LC 84-27785. (Bible Speaks Today Ser.). 128p. 1983. pap. 5.95 (ISBN 0-87784-294-9). Inter-Varsity.

Message of St. John: The Spiritual Teachings of the Beloved Disciple. Thomas E. Crane. LC 80-11779. 184p. (Orig.). 1980. pap. 5.95 (ISBN 0-8189-0402-X). Alba.

Message of Second Timothy. John R. Stott. LC 73-75890. (Bible Speaks Today Ser.). 144p. 1973. text ed. 5.95 (ISBN 0-87784-295-7). Inter-Varsity.

Message of the Bible: An Orthodox Christian Perspective. George Cronk. LC 82-7355. 293p. (Orig.). 1982. pap. 8.95 (ISBN 0-913836-94-X). St Vladimirs.

Message of the Buddha. K. N. Jayatilleke. Ed. by Ninian Smart. LC 75-15431. 1975. 12.95 (ISBN 0-02-916350-1). Free Pr.

Message of the Gita: With Text, Translation & Notes. Sri Aurobindo. Ed. by Anilbaran Roy. (Sanskrit & Eng.). 1979. (Pub. by Sri Aurobindo Ashram Trust India); pap. 9.00 (ISBN 0-89744-977-0, Pub. by Sri Aurobindo Ashramtrust India). Auromere.

Message of the Gita: With Text, Translation & Notes As Interpreted by Sri Aurobindo. Sri Aurobindo. Ed. by Anilbaran Roy. 1984. pap. 7.95 (ISBN 0-89071-225-5). Matagiri.

Message of the Lord's Prayer. Igor I. Sikorsky. 1963. 10.95 (ISBN 0-8392-1068-X). Astor-Honor.

Message of the New Testament. Frederick F. Bruce. 120p. 1973. pap. 4.95 (ISBN 0-8028-1525-1). Eerdmans.

Message of the New Testament-Ephesians & Colossians. Thomas H. Olbricht. LC 82-74323. (Way of Life Ser.: No. 170). 91p. 1983. pap. 3.95 (ISBN 0-89112-170-6, Biblo Res Pr). Abilene Christ U.

Message of the New Testament-First Corinthians. J. D. Thomas. (Way of Life Ser.: No. 167). 1984. pap. 3.95 (ISBN 0-89112-167-6, Bibl Res Pr). Abilene Christ U.

Message of the New Testament: Revelation I & II, 2 vols. Frank Pack. (Way of Life Ser.: No. 176 & 177). 1984. pap. 3.95 ea. (Bibl Res Pr). Vol. I (ISBN 0-89112-176-5). Vol. II (ISBN 0-89112-177-3). Abilene Christ U.

Message of the New Testament-Romans. J. D. Thomas. LC 82-70933. (Way of Life Ser.: 166). (Illus.). 108p. 1982. pap. 3.95 (ISBN 0-89112-166-8, Bibl Res Pr). Abilene Christ U.

Message of the New Testament: The Letters of John. Everett Ferguson. (Way of Life Ser.: No. 175). 1984. pap. 3.95 (ISBN 0-89112-175-7, Bibl Res Pr). Abilene Christ U.

Message of the Old Testament. John T. Willis. Incl. Vol. I, No. 141. Adam to Moses (ISBN 0-89112-141-2); Vol. II, No. 142. Joshua to Ruth (ISBN 0-89112-142-0); Vol. III, No. 143. Samuel to Solomon (ISBN 0-89112-143-9); Vol. IV, No. 144. Rehoboam to Nehemiah (ISBN 0-89112-144-7). (Way of Life Ser.). 1977. pap. 3.95 ea. (Bibl Res Pr). Abilene Christ U.

Message of the Prophets. Gerhard Von Rad. Tr. by D. M. Stalker from Ger. LC 72-183633. 288p. 1972. pap. 10.95xi (ISBN 0-06-068929-3, RD45, HarpR). Har-Row.

Message of the Psalms: A Theological Commentary. Walter Brueggemann. LC 84-21734. (Augsburg Old Testament Studies). 224p. (Orig.). 1984. pap. 11.95 (ISBN 0-8066-2120-6, 10-4370). Augsburg.

Message of the Quran. Muhammad Asad. 998p. (Orig.). 1980. 49.95 (ISBN 0-317-52456-9, Pub. by Dar Al Andalus). New Era Pubns MI.

Message of the Qur'an: Presented in Perspective. Hashim Amir-Ali. LC 73-84906. 1974. 25.00 (ISBN 0-8048-0976-3). C E Tuttle.

Message of the Scrolls. Yigael Yadin. 1957. (Touchstone Bks); pap. 3.95 (ISBN 0-686-66285-7). S&S.

Message of the Semon on the Mount. John R. Stott. LC 84-27763. (Bible Speaks Today Ser.). 1978. pap. 6.95 (ISBN 0-87784-296-5). Inter-Varsity.

Message of the Sunday Gospel Readings, Vol. 1. A. M. Coniaris. 1982. pap. 7.95 (ISBN 0-937032-26-3). Light&Life Pub Co MN.

Message of the Sunday Gospels, Vol. 2. A. M. Coniaris. 1983. pap. 7.95 (ISBN 0-937032-29-8). Light&Life Pub Co MN.

Message of the Wesleys: A Reader of Instruction & Devotion. Ed. by Philip S. Watson. 270p. 1983. pap. 9.95 (ISBN 0-310-75031-8, 17027P). Zondervan.

Message of Thomas Merton. Ed. by Patrick Hart. (Cistercian Studies: No. 42). (Illus.). 1981. 15.95 (ISBN 0-87907-842-1); pap. 5.50 (ISBN 0-87907-942-8). Cistercian Pub.

Messages from Maitreya the Christ, Vol. 1. Benjamin Creme. LC 80-52483. 209p. 1980. pap. 5.00 (ISBN 0-936604-01-8). Tara Ctr.

Messages from the Depths: (Selections from the Writings of Reinhold Schneider) Reinhold Schneider. Ed. by Curt Winterhalter. Tr. by Robert Cunningham from Ger. 1977. pap. 2.50 (ISBN 0-8199-0683-2). Franciscan Herald.

Messages from the Universal House of Justice: 1968-1973. The Universal House of Justice. LC 75-11795. 1976. 9.95 (ISBN 0-87743-076-4, 225-005); pap. 4.95 (ISBN 0-87743-096-9, 225-006). Baha'i.

Messages from Within. Peter D. Francuch. LC 82-60513. 220p. 1982. pap. 7.95 (ISBN 0-939386-03-8). TMH Pub.

Messages of Israel's Lawgivers. Charles F. Kent. Ed. by Frank K. Sanders. 386p. 1981. Repr. of 1916 ed. lib. bdg. 25.00 (ISBN 0-89760-430-X). Telegraph Bks.

Messages on Revival. Vance Havner. (Pulpit Library). 128p. 1983. pap. 4.50 (ISBN 0-8010-4275-5). Baker Bk.

Messages to a Nation in Crisis: An Introduction to the Prophecy of Jeremiah. Steven M. Fettke. LC 82-19997. (Illus.). 72p. (Orig.). 1983. pap. text ed. 7.75 (ISBN 0-8191-2839-2). U Pr of Amer.

Messe: Etudes Archeologiques sur ses Monuments, 8 vols. C. Rohault Fleury. (Fr., Illus.). 1722p. Repr. of 1889 ed. lib. bdg. 600.00x (ISBN 0-89241-153-8). Caratzas.

Messe sur le Monde. Pierre Teilhard De Chardin. pap. 6.25 (ISBN 0-685-36598-0). French & Eur.

Messenger. Virginia Howard. 1971. pap. 3.95 (ISBN 0-910122-31-8). Amherst Pr.

Messenger of Allah, Vol. II. A. Ghazi. 1981. 4.50 (ISBN 0-686-97851-X). Kazi Pubns.

Messenger of Grace: A Biography of C. N. Hostetter Jr. E. Morris Sider. LC 82-71583. 1982. cloth 7.95 (ISBN 0-916035-06-9); pap. 5.95 (ISBN 0-916035-07-7). Evangel Indiana.

Messenger of the Cross. Watchman Nee. Tr. by Stephen Kaung. (Orig.). 1980. pap. text ed. 3.25 (ISBN 0-935008-50-0). Christian Fellow Pubs.

Messenger: The Life of Mohammed. Ronald V. Bodley. LC 70-92296. Repr. of 1946 ed. lib. bdg. 35.00x (ISBN 0-8371-2423-9, BOTM). Greenwood.

Messengers of God: Biblical Portraits & Legends. Elie Wiesel. 224p. 1985. 16.95 (ISBN 0-671-52333-3); pap. 7.95 (ISBN 0-671-54134-X). Summit Bks.

Messengers of God's Word: A Handbook for Lectors. Joseph M. Champlin. 1983. pap. 4.95 (ISBN 0-8091-2484-X). Paulist Pr.

Messengers of Grace: Evangelical Missionaries in the South Seas 1797-1860. Niel Gunson. (Illus.). 1978. 49.95x (ISBN 0-19-550517-4). Oxford U Pr.

Messengers of Hope. Carol W. Parrish-Harra. 1983. pap. 7.95 (ISBN 0-87613-079-1). New Age.

Messiah, a Study in Interpretation. Percy M. Young. (Student's Music Library Ser.). 1961. 13.95 (ISBN 0-234-77215-8). Dufour.

Messiah: An Aramaic Interpretation. Samson H. Levey. 1974. 20.00x (ISBN 0-87820-402-4, Pub. by Anti-Defamation League). Ktav.

Messiah & Temple: The Trial of Jesus in the Gospel of Mark. Donald Juel. LC 76-46397. (Society of Biblical Literature. Dissertation Ser.: No. 31). Repr. of 1977 ed. 43.60 (ISBN 0-8357-9578-0, 2017527). Bks Demand UMI.

Messiah Book: The Life & Times of G. F. Handel's Greatest Hit. Peter Jacobi. (Illus.). 169p. 1982. 10.95 (ISBN 0-312-53072-2). St Martin.

Messiah Idea in Jewish History. Julius H. Greenstone. LC 70-97284. 347p. 1972. Repr. of 1906 ed. lib. bdg. 22.50x (ISBN 0-8371-2606-1, GRMI). Greenwood.

Messiah in Context: Israel's History & Destiny in Formative Judaism. Jacob Neusner. LC 83-20542. (Foundations of Judaism Ser.). 304p. 1984. 26.95 (ISBN 0-8006-0716-3, 1-716). Fortress.

Messiah of Midtown Park. Rolf Gompertz. LC 83-50871. 136p. 1983. velo binding 10.00 (ISBN 0-918248-05-1). Word Doctor.

Messiah Texts. Raphael Patai. 1979. pap. 7.95 (ISBN 0-380-46482-9, 46482-9). Avon.

Messiah Texts: Jewish Legends of Three Thousand Years. Raphael Patai. LC 79-5387. 426p. 1979. 25.95x (ISBN 0-8143-1652-2). Wayne St U Pr.

Messiah Witness-Israel's Destiny & Coming Deliverer. Gordon Lindsay. 0.95 (ISBN 0-89985-187-8). Christ Nations.

Messiahship of Christ. P. J. Gloag & F. Delitzsch. 628p. 1983. lib. bdg. 23.50 Smythe Sewn (ISBN 0-86524-146-5, 9514). Klock & Klock.

Messiahship of Shakespeare. Charles Downing. LC 76-57998. (Studies in Shakespeare, No. 24). 1977. lib. bdg. 39.95x (ISBN 0-8383-2172-0). Haskell.

Messianic Expectation in the Old Testament. Joachim Becker. Tr. by David E. Green. LC 79-8891. pap. 24.00 (2027875). Bks Demand UMI.

Messianic Hope. Arthur W. Kac. pap. 4.95 (ISBN 0-8010-5362-5). Baker Bk.

Messianic Idea in Judaism: And Other Essays on Jewish Spirituality. Gershom Scholem. LC 70-130212. 384p. 1972. pap. 8.95 (ISBN 0-8052-0362-1). Schocken.

Messianic Idea in Judaism & Other Essays on Jewish Spirituality. Gershom Scholem. 376p. pap. 7.95 (ISBN 0-686-95141-7). ADL.

Messianic Judaism: Its History, Theology & Polity. David A. Rausch. LC 82-20382. (Texts & Studies in Religion: Vol. 14). 304p. 1983. 49.95x (ISBN 0-88946-802-8). E Mellen.

Messianic Movements: A Comparative Analysis of the Sabbatians, the People's Temple & the Unification Church. Sture Ahlberg. 128p. (Orig.). pap. text ed. 19.00x (ISBN 91-22-00787-3, Pub. by Almqvist & Wiksell). Coronet Bks.

Messianic Psalms. Ernest T. Wilson. pap. 3.95 (ISBN 0-87213-963-8). Loizeaux.

Messianic Secret. Ed. by Christopher Tuckett. LC 83-5499. (Issues in Religion & Theology Ser.). 176p. 1983. pap. 7.95 (ISBN 0-8006-1767-3). Fortress.

Messianism in the Talmudic Era. Ed. by L. Landman. 59.50x (ISBN 0-87068-445-0). Ktav.

Messianism, Mysticism, & Magic: A Sociological Analysis of Jewish Religious Movements. Stephen Sharot. LC 81-11688. (Studies in Religion). ix, 306p. 1987. pap. 12.95x (ISBN 0-8078-4170-6). U of NC Pr.

Metalogicon of John of Salisbury: A Twelfth-Century Defense of Verbal & Logical Arts of the Trivium. John of Salisbury. Tr. by Daniel D. McGarry from Latin. LC 82-2989. xxvii, 305p. 1982. Repr. of 1955 ed. lib. bdg. 39.75x (ISBN 0-313-23539-2, JOME). Greenwood.

Metamorphose des Dieux: L'Intemporel. Andre Malraux. (Illus.). 424p. 1976. 125.00 (ISBN 0-686-56329-8). French & Eur.

Metamorphoseon. Ovid. Ed. by Jacobus Pontanus. LC 75-27868. (Renaissance & the Gods Ser.: Vol. 24). (Illus.). 1977. Repr. of 1618 ed. lib. bdg. 88.00 (ISBN 0-8240-2073-1). Garland Pub.

Metamorphoseon...Ovidianarum. Antonio Tempesta. LC 75-27861. (Renaissance & the Gods Ser.: Vol. 19). (Illus.). 1976. Repr. of 1606 ed. lib. bdg. 88.00 (ISBN 0-8240-2067-7). Garland Pub.

Metamorphoses. Ovid. Tr. by Garth et al. LC 75-27884. (Renaissance & the Gods Ser.: Vol. 39). (Illus.). 1976. Repr. of 1732 ed. lib. bdg. 88.00 (ISBN 0-8240-2088-X). Garland Pub.

Metamorphoses of the Soul: Path of Experience, 2 vols. 2nd ed. Rudolf Steiner. Tr. by Charles Davy & Christian Von Arnim. 1983. Set. pap. 12.00 ea. (ISBN 0-317-13485-X). Vol. 1: 171 pgs (ISBN 0-85440-414-7, Pub. by Steinerbooks). Vol. 2: 150 pgs (ISBN 0-85440-415-5, Pub. by Steinerbooks). Anthroposophic.

Metamorphosis of a Death Symbol: The Transi Tomb in the Late Middle Ages & the Renaissance. Kathleen R. Cohen. LC 78-138511. (California Studies in the History of Art: Vol. 15). 1974. 77.00x (ISBN 0-520-01844-3). U of Cal Pr.

Metaphor & Myth in Science & Religion. Earl R. MacCormac. LC 75-23941. pap. 46.80 (2052207). Bks Demand UMI.

Metaphoric Process: The Creation of Scientific & Religious Understanding. Mary Gerhart & Allan M. Russell. LC 83-15614. 217p. 1984. 16.95x (ISBN 0-912646-82-9); pap. 10.95x (ISBN 0-912646-86-1). Tex Christian.

Metaphorical Theology: Models of God in Religious Language. Sallie McFague. LC 82-7246. 240p. 1982. pap. 11.95 (ISBN 0-8006-1687-1, 1-1687). Fortress.

Metaphors for the Contemporary Church. Susan B. Thistlethwaite. 192p. (Orig.). 1983. pap. 8.95 (ISBN 0-8298-0692-X). Pilgrim NY.

Metaphors of Christ. Donald Fraser. 384p. 1985. smythe sewn 15.25 (ISBN 0-86524-188-0, 9523); lib. bdg. 15.25 smythe sewn (ISBN 0-317-40599-3). Klock & Klock.

Metaphors of Interpretation: Essays in Honour of W. E. H. Stanner. D. Barwick et al. LC 84-71361. (Illus.). 318p. 1987. pap. 28.00 (ISBN 0-08-029875-3). Pergamon.

Metaphors of Social Control in a Pentecostal Sect. Tom C. Darrand & Anson D. Shupe. LC 83-9006. (Studies in Religion & Society: Vol. 6). 232p. 1984. 49.95x (ISBN 0-88946-870-2). E Mellen.

Metaphysic of Experience, 4 vols. Shadworth H. Hodgson & Maurice Nathanson. LC 78-66730. (Phenomenology Ser.). 858p. 1980. lib. bdg. 233.00 (ISBN 0-8240-9564-2). Garland Pub.

Metaphysical Analysis. John W. Yolton. LC 68-88650. pap. 58.30 (ISBN 0-317-08857-2, 2014464). Bks Demand UMI.

Metaphysical Bible Dictionary. Unity School Of Christianity. 1931. 10.00 (ISBN 0-87159-098-0). Unity School.

Metaphysical Disputation, XXXI, De Ento Finito, on Finite Being. Norman Wells. cancelled. Marquette.

Metaphysical Elements of Justice: Part I of the Metaphysics of Morals. Immanuel Kant. Tr. by John Ladd. (Orig.). 1965. pap. 7.20 scp (ISBN 0-672-60250-4, LLA72). Bobbs.

Metaphysical Imperative: A Critique of the Modern Approach to Science. Ronald E. Pubek. LC 82-40244. 166p. (Orig.). 1983. lib. bdg. 26.00 (ISBN 0-8191-2663-2); pap. text ed. 11.25 (ISBN 0-8191-2664-0). U Pr of Amer.

Metaphysical Knowledge & Transcendental Problems. Immanuel Kant. (Illus.). 167p. 1985. Repr. 89.55 (ISBN 0-89901-200-0). Found Class Reprints.

Metaphysical Mediations. pap. 8.95 (ISBN 0-937134-17-1). Amrita Found.

Metaphysical Meditations. 11th ed. Paramahansa Yogananda. LC 40-16548. 124p. 1964. pap. 1.95 (ISBN 0-87612-041-9). pap. 5.00x German ed. (ISBN 3-87041-111-2); pap. 1.25x Span. ed. (ISBN 0-87612-043-5); pap. 3.00x Italian ed. (ISBN 0-87612-046-X). Self Realization.

Metaphysical Poets: A Study in Religious Experience. Helen C. White. LC 83-45866. 1936. 39.50 (ISBN 0-404-20285-3, PR549). AMS Pr.

Metaphysical Themes in Thomas Aquinas. John F. Wippel. LC 82-7296. (Studies in Philosophy & the History of Philosophy: Vol. 10). 294p. 1984. 31.95x (ISBN 0-8132-0578-6). Cath U Pr.

Metaphysical Thought of Godfrey of Fontaines: A Study in Late Thirteenth-Century Philosophy. John F. Wippel. LC 80-16900. 413p. 1981. 31.95x (ISBN 0-8132-0556-5). Cath U Pr.

Metaphysics, a Bridge to ECKANKAR. Thomas Flamma. LC 81-80177. 232p. 1981. pap. 3.95 (ISBN 0-914766-65-1, 0193). IWP Pub.

Metaphysics & Science in Christian Science. Max Kappeler. (Orig.). 1985. pap. 3.50 (ISBN 0-942958-11-X). Kappeler Inst Pub.

Metaphysics in Islamic Philosophy. Fadlou Shehadi. LC 81-18069. 1983. 35.00x (ISBN 0-88206-049-X). Caravan Bks.

Metaphysics in Midwestern America. Melinda B. Wagner. LC 83-2158. 241p. 1983. 20.00x (ISBN 0-8142-0346-9). Ohio St U Pr.

Metaphysics of Experience: A Companion to Whitehead's "Process & Reality". Elizabeth M. Kraus. LC 78-70564. xiv, 190p. 1979. 22.50 (ISBN 0-8232-1038-3); pap. 9.00 (ISBN 0-8232-1039-1). Fordham.

Metaphysics of Haji Mulla Hadi Sabzavari. Hadi Ibn Mahdi Sabzavari. Tr. by Toshihiku Izutsu & Mehdi Mohaghegh. LC 76-18174. 248p. 1977. lib. bdg. 35.00x (ISBN 0-88206-011-2). Caravan Bks.

Metaphysics of Ibn Rushd: Averroes. C. F. Genequand. LC 83-15428. (Studies in Islamic Philosophy & Science). write for info. cancelled (ISBN 0-88206-059-7). Caravan Bks.

Metaphysics of Modern Existence. Vine Deloria, Jr. LC 76-8708. (Native American Publishing Program Ser.). 1978. 8.45 (ISBN 0-06-450250-3, HarpR). Har-Row.

Metaphysics of Rumi. K. A. Hakim. 1959. 3.95x (ISBN 0-87902-061-X). Orientalia.

Metaphysics of Rumi. Khalifa A. Hakim. 157p. 1981. pap. 3.95 (ISBN 0-88004-004-1). Sunwise Turn.

Metaphysics of Sex. Julius Evola. Tr. by J. A. Ormrod from Ital. LC 82-11909. (Illus.). 384p. 1983. pap. 9.95 (ISBN 0-89281-025-4). Inner Tradit.

Metaphysics of the Jewish, the Aegyptian & the Assyrian Spirit. Georg W. Hegel. (Illus.). 177p. 1981. 67.85 (ISBN 0-89266-280-8). Am Classical Coll Pr.

Metaphysics: The Elements. Bruce Aune. LC 85-2540. xiv, 235p. 1985. 25.00 (ISBN 0-8166-1412-1); pap. 12.95 (ISBN 0-8166-1414-8). U of Minn Pr.

Method & Meaning in Ancient Judaism. Jacob Neusner. LC 79-9881. (Brown Judaic Ser.: No. 10). 1979. 18.00 (ISBN 0-89130-281-6, 140010); pap. 13.50 (ISBN 0-89130-300-6). Scholars Pr GA.

Method & Meaning in Ancient Judaism II. Jacob Neusner. LC 80-21781. (Brown Judaic Studies). 1981. pap. 27.50 (ISBN 0-89130-416-9, 140015). Scholars Pr GA.

Method & Meaning in Ancient Judiasm III. Jacob Neusner. LC 80-19449. (Brown Judaic Studies). 1981. pap. 27.50 (ISBN 0-89130-418-5, 14-00-16). Scholars Pr GA.

Method & Message of Jesus' Teachings. Robert H. Stein. LC 78-16427. 202p. 1978. pap. 8.95 (ISBN 0-664-24216-2). Westminster.

Method & Message of Jewish Apocalyptic. D. S. Russell. LC 64-18683. (Old Testament Library). 464p. 1964. 19.95 (ISBN 0-664-20543-7). Westminster.

Method & Speculation in Hegel's Phenomenology. Ed. by Merold Westphal. 137p. 1982. text ed. 15.00x (ISBN 0-391-02336-5, Pub. by Harvester Pr UK). Humanities.

Method in Ministry: Theological Reflection & Christian Ministry. James D. Whitehead & Evelyn E. Whitehead. 224p. 1980. (HarpR); pap. 9.95 (ISBN 0-86683-459-1). Har-Row.

Method in Theology. Bernard Lonergan. LC 78-181008. 1979. pap. 11.50 (ISBN 0-8164-2204-4, HarpR). Har-Row.

Method in Theology: An Organon for Our Time. Frederick E. Crowe. LC 80-81015. (Pere Marquette Ser.). 68p. 1980. 7.95 (ISBN 0-87462-519-X). Marquette.

Method of the Siddhas. rev. ed. Da Free John. LC 78-53869. (Illus.). 364p. 1978. pap. 9.95 (ISBN 0-913922-44-7). Dawn Horse Pr.

Method of Zen. Eugene Herrigel. Ed. by R. F. Hull & Alan Watts. LC 74-5120. 1974. pap. 2.95 (ISBN 0-394-71244-7, Vin). Random.

Methodical Bible Study. Robert A. Traina. 1985. 12.95 (ISBN 0-317-38919-X, 17031). Zondervan.

Methodical Bible Study. Robert A. Traina. 1985. 14.95 (ISBN 0-310-31230-2). Zondervan.

Methodism & Politics in British Society, 1750-1850. David Hempton. LC 84-51419. 276p. 1984. 27.50x (ISBN 0-8047-1269-7). Stanford U Pr.

Methodism & the Frontier: Indiana Proving Ground. Elizabeth K. Nottingham. LC 41-19465. Repr. of 1941 ed. 7.00 (ISBN 0-404-04798-X). AMS Pr.

Methodism & the Literature of the 18th Century. T. B. Shepherd. LC 68-4718. (Studies in Comparative Literature, No. 35). 1969. Repr. of 1940 ed. lib. bdg. 75.00x (ISBN 0-8383-0680-2). Haskell.

Methodism & the Working-Class Movements of England 1800-1850. Robert F. Wearmouth. LC 73-139523. 1972. Repr. of 1937 ed. 29.50x (ISBN 0-678-00829-9). Kelley.

Methodism in Mississippi, 2 Vols. in 1. John G. Jones. 25.00 (ISBN 0-87511-592-6). Claitors.

Methodist Conference Minutes & Traveling Preachers: 1773-1794. Ed. by Richard Heitzenrater. LC 79-51893. Date not set. pap. 9.25 (ISBN 0-914960-18-0). Academy Bks.

Methodist Episcopal Church & Education up to 1869. Sylvanus M. Duvall. LC 79-176735. (Columbia University. Teachers College. Contributions to Education: No. 284). Repr. of 1928 ed. 22.50 (ISBN 0-404-55284-6). AMS Pr.

Methodist Episcopal Church in Georgia. Edmund J. Hammond. 1935. 10.00 (ISBN 0-88289-286-X). Pelican.

Methodist Hymnal Concordance. Robert F. Klepper. LC 86-29811. 800p. 1987. 62.50 (ISBN 0-8108-1968-6). Scarecrow.

Methodist Mass. Donald C. Lacy. 1984. 2.95 (ISBN 0-89536-977-X, 7533). CSS of Ohio.

Methodist Publishing House: A History, Vol. 1. James P. Pilkington. LC 68-21894. (Illus.). 1968. 8.25 (ISBN 0-687-26700-5). Abingdon.

Methodist Riots: The Testing of Charles Wesley. Franklin Wilder. (Illus.). 160p. 1982. 8.95 (ISBN 0-89962-236-4). Todd & Honeywell.

Methodist Secessions. D. A. Gowland. 192p. 1979. 40.00 (ISBN 0-7190-1335-6, Pub. by Manchester Univ Pr). Longwood Pub Group.

Methodist Trail Blazer: Philip Gatch. rev. ed. Elizabeth Connor. LC 76-101704. (Illus.). 260p. pap. 12.00 smythsewn (ISBN 0-914960-51-2). Academy Bks.

Methodist Union Catalog: Pre-1976 Imprints, Vol. V:G-Haz. Kenneth E. Rowe. LC 75-33190. 371p. 1981. 29.00 (ISBN 0-8108-1454-4). Scarecrow.

Methodist Union Catalog: Pre-1976 Imprints, 20 vols, Vol. I, A-bj. Ed. by Kenneth E. Rowe. LC 75-33190. 438p. 1975. 29.00 (ISBN 0-8108-0880-3). Scarecrow.

Methodist Union Catalog: Pre-1976 Imprints, Vol. VI: He-I. Ed. by Kenneth E. Rowe. LC 75-33190. 360p. 1985. 29.00 (ISBN 0-8108-1725-X). Scarecrow.

Methodist Union Catalog: Pre-1976 Imprints, Vol. 3, Che-Dix. Ed. by Kenneth E. Rowe. LC 75-33190. 431p. 1978. 29.00 (ISBN 0-8108-1067-0). Scarecrow.

Methodist Worship: In Relation to Free Church Worship. rev. ed. John Bishop. LC 75-20379. xvii, 173p. 1976. lib. bdg. 6.95 (ISBN 0-89177-001-1). Scholars Studies.

Methodists & the Making of America. Charles W. Ferguson. 480p. 1983. 17.95 (ISBN 0-89015-424-4); pap. 12.95 (ISBN 0-89015-405-8). Eakin Pr.

Methodological Issues in Religious Studies. Ed. by Robert D. Baird. LC 75-44170. (Orig.). 1976. lib. bdg. 14.95x (ISBN 0-914914-08-1); pap. text ed. 5.95x (ISBN 0-914914-07-3). New Horizons.

Methodology in the Academic Teaching of Judaism. Ed. by Zev Garber. (Studies in Judaism). 308p. (Orig.). 1987. lib. bdg. 28.00 (ISBN 0-8191-5723-6, Pub. by Studies in Judaism); pap. text ed. 15.75 (ISBN 0-8191-5724-4). U Pr of Amer.

Methods & Techniques of Holistic Education. Ed. by Isadore L. Sonnier. (Illus.). 184p. 1985. 21.50 (ISBN 0-398-05054-6). C C Thomas.

Methods for Youth Ministry. Ed. by Jon Underwood & David Roadcup. 272p. 1986. pap. 7.95 (ISBN 0-87239-991-5, 88589). Standard Pub.

Methods of Achieving the Paths: Stages of Philosophical & Ethical Development According to the Madhyamika Svatantrika School of Buddhism. Sermey G. Tharchin. Ed. by Barbara D. Taylor. Tr. of Lam-thob-tsul. 59p. (Orig.). 1981. pap. 5.00 (ISBN 0-918753-02-3). Mahayana.

Methods of Bible Study. Robert Conn & Steve Clapp. (C-Four Youth Bible Materials Ser.). (Illus.). 91p. (Orig.). 1982. pap. 8.00 (ISBN 0-914527-14-2). C-Four Res.

Methods of Ethics. Henry Sidgwick. LC 81-85772. (Philosophical Classics Ser.). 568p. 1981. 30.00 (ISBN 0-915145-29-4); pap. 12.50 (ISBN 0-915145-28-6). Hackett Pub.

Methods of Knowledge According to Advaita Vedanta. Swami Satprakashananda. 366p. 1975. Repr. of 1965 ed. 10.00 (ISBN 0-87481-154-6). Vedanta Pr.

Methods of Teaching in the Catholic School. Mary L. Welch. 1986. 6.60 (ISBN 0-318-20570-X). Natl Cath Educ.

Metodologia Pedagogica. Findley B. Edge. Tr. by Celia Mendoza & Sara P. Molina. Orig. Title: Helping the Teacher. 155p. 1982. pap. 3.75 (ISBN 0-311-11026-6). Casa Bautista.

Metropolitan Innocent of Moscow, the Apostle of Alaska. Charles R. Hale. pap. 1.25 (ISBN 0-686-05655-8). Eastern Orthodox.

Metropolitan Tabernacle Pulpit. Charles H. Spurgeon. 1971. Vol. 31. 14.95. Banner of Truth.

Metropolitan Tabernacle Pulpit, 1861-1917, Vols. 7-63. C. H. Spurgeon. (C. H. Spurgeon's Sermon Ser.). Repr. black or gold bdgs. (vols. 7-61) 12.95 ea.; (vols. 62-63 combined) 15.95 (ISBN 0-686-31695-9). Pilgrim Pubns.

Meu Livro de Historias Biblicas. Hayes & Hook. (Portugese Bks.). Tr. of My Book of Bible Stories. (Port.). 1979. 3.00 (ISBN 0-8297-0758-1). Life Pubs Intl.

Mexican & Central American Mythology. Irene Nicholson. LC 84-45598. (Library of the World's Myths & Legends). (Illus.). 144p. 1985. 18.95 (ISBN 0-87226-003-8). P Bedrick Bks.

Mexican & Native American Dances in Christian Worship & Education. Martha A. Kirk. Ed. by Doug Adams. (Orig.). 1981. pap. 3.00 (ISBN 0-941500-22-5). Sharing Co.

Mexican Revolution & the Catholic Church, 1910-1929. Robert E. Quirk. LC 85-30209. 276p. 1986. Repr. of 1973 ed. lib. bdg. 45.00x (ISBN 0-313-25121-5, QUMC). Greenwood.

Mexico Mystique: The Coming Sixth World of Consciousness. Frank Waters. LC 74-18579. (Illus.). 326p. 1975. 13.95 (ISBN 0-8040-0663-6, SB). Ohio U Pr.

Mexico's Bishops: From Fifteen Twenty-eight to Nineteen Seventy-six from Abad to Zumarraga. Clarence A. Liederbach. LC 76-29279. 80p. 1977. pap. 2.95 (ISBN 0-913228-18-4). R J Liederbach.

Meyersville, Md., Lutheran Baptisms. Margaret E. Myers. Ed. by Donna V. Russell. (Illus.). 70p. 1986. pap. 10.00 (ISBN 0-914385-04-6). Catoctin Pr.

Mi Camino de Damasco. Francisco Lacueva. Orig. Title: My Way from Damascus. (Span.). 112p. 1982. pap. 2.75 (ISBN 0-8254-1426-1). Kregel.

Mi Desarrollo Sexual. Paul D. Simmons & Kenneth Crawford. Tr. by Dafne Sabanes De Plou from Eng. (El Sexo En la Vida Cristiana). (Span.). 96p. 1985. pap. 2.50 (ISBN 0-311-46257-X, Edit Mundo). Casa Bautista.

Mi Diario Personal de Oracion. Catherine Marshall & Leonard LeSourd. 416p. 1981. 4.95 (ISBN 0-88113-306-X). Edit Betania.

Mi la Ras Pa'i Rnam Thar: Texte Tibetian De la Vie De Milarepa. Ed. by J. W. De Jong. (Indo-Iranian Monographs: No. 4). 1959. 22.00x (ISBN 90-2790-052-3). Mouton.

Mi Maquina Maravillosa. William L. Coleman. 144p. 1982. 3.25 (ISBN 0-88113-309-4). Edit Betania.

Mi Primer Diccionario Biblico. William N. McElrath. Tr. by Ruth G. McElrath from Eng. (Span., Illus.). 128p. 1985. pap. 2.95 (ISBN 0-311-03656-2). Casa Bautista.

Mi Primer Diccionario Biblico. William N. McElrath. (Span.). 122p. 1978. pap. 4.95 (S-37577). French & Eur.

Micacles, My Father's Delight. Joseph E. Chambers. 136p. (Orig.). text ed. 8.95 (ISBN 0-87148-585-0); pap. 6.95 (ISBN 0-87148-586-9). Pathway Pr.

Micah. Delbert R. Hillers. LC 83-48002. (Hermenaia Ser.). 192p. 1983. 17.95 (ISBN 0-8006-6012-9, 20-6012). Fortress.

Micah: A Commentary. James L. Mays. LC 76-2599. (Old Testament Library). 180p. 1976. 15.95 (ISBN 0-664-20817-7). Westminster.

Micah-Malachi. James H. Gailey, Jr. LC 59-10454. (Layman's Bible Commentary Ser: Vol. 15). 1962. pap. 4.95 (ISBN 0-8042-3075-7). John Knox.

Micah the Prophet. Hans W. Wolff. Tr. by Ralph D. Gehrke from Ger. LC 80-2380. Tr. of Mit Micha reden: Prophetie einst und jetzt. 240p. 1981. 19.95 (ISBN 0-8006-0652-3, 1-652). Fortress.

Michael Augustine Corrigan & the Shaping of Conservative Catholism in America, 1878-1902. Robert E. Curran. 46.50 (ISBN 0-405-10814-1). Ayer Co Pubs.

Michael Jackson, Superstar. Patricia McKissack. LC 84-12170. (Today's Superstars Ser.). 96p. 1984. lib. bdg. 13.25 (ISBN 0-516-04380-3); pap. 4.50 (ISBN 0-516-44380-1). Childrens.

Michael Mystery: Letters to the Members of the Anthroposophical Society with Their Accompanying Guidelines. Rudolf Steiner. Tr. by Marjorie Spock. 1985. 15.95 (ISBN 0-916786-77-3); pap. 9.95 (ISBN 0-317-30085-7). St George Bk Serv.

Michael Servetus: A Case Study in Total Heresy. J. Friedman. 154p. (Orig.). 1978. pap. text ed. 34.00x (Pub. by Droz Switzerland). Coronet Bks.

Michael Servetus, His Life & Teachings. Carl T. Odhner. LC 83-45626. Date not set. Repr. of 1910 ed. 18.50 (ISBN 0-404-19844-9). AMS Pr.

Michael Servetus, Humanist & Martyr. John F. Fulton & Madeline E. Stanton. (Illus.). 99p. 40.00 (ISBN 0-8139-1089-7). H Reichner.

Michalina, Daughter of Israel: True Story of A Jewish Girl Abducted by the Catholic Church. Rachel S. Araten. 1986. 12.95 (ISBN 0-87306-412-7). Feldheim.

Michel Foucault: An Introduction to the Study of His Thought. Barry Cooper. LC 82-8260. (Studies in Religion & Society: Vol. 2). 176p. 1982. 39.95x (ISBN 0-88946-867-2). E Mellen.

Michelangelo, 6 vols. Charles Q. De Tolnay. Incl. Vol. 1. The Youth of Michelangelo. 1969. 90.00x (ISBN 0-691-03858-9); Vol. 2. The Sistine Ceiling. 1969. 90.00x (ISBN 0-691-03856-2); Vol. 3. The Medeci Chapel. 1970. 90.00 (ISBN 0-691-03854-6); Vol. 4. The Tomb of Julius Two. 1970. 91.50x (ISBN 0-691-03857-0); Vol. 5. The Final Period. 1970. 90.00x (ISBN 0-691-03855-4); Vol. 6. Michelangelo, Architect. 68.00x (ISBN 0-691-03853-8); Michelangelo: Sculpter-Painter-Architect. (One vol. condensation). 52.50 (ISBN 0-691-03876-7); pap. 20.50 (ISBN 0-691-00337-8). Princeton U Pr.

Michelangelo. 2nd ed. Herbert Von Einem. 1973. 43.00x (ISBN 0-416-15140-X, NO. 2183). Methuen Inc.

Michelangelo. Ed. by Frederick Hartt. (Library of Great Painters). 1965. 45.00 (ISBN 0-8109-0299-0). Abrams.

Michelangelo. Lutz Heuzinger. (Illus.). 96p. (Orig.). 1982. pap. 13.95 (ISBN 0-935748-43-1). Scala Books.

Michelangelo. Howard Hibbard. LC 74-6576. (Icon Editions). (Illus.). 348p. 1975. 20.00i (ISBN 0-06-433323-X, HarpT); (HarpT). Har-Row.

Michelangelo: A Record of His Life As Told in His Own Letters & Papers. Michelangelo Buonarroti. Tr. by Robert W. Carden. 1976. lib. bdg. 59.95 (ISBN 0-8490-2256-8). Gordon Pr.

Michelangelo: Pieta. Robert Hupka. (Illus.). 96p. 1975. pap. 6.95 (ISBN 0-517-52414-7). Crown.

Michelangelo: Six Lectures by Johannes Wilde. Johannes Wilde. Ed. by John Shearman & Michael Hirst. (Oxford Studies in the History of Art & Architecture). (Illus.). 1979. pap. 13.95x (ISBN 0-19-817346-6). Oxford U Pr.

Michelangelo: The Bruges Madonna & the Piccolomini Altar. Harold R. Mancusi-Ungaro, Jr. LC 70-151582. (College Ser.: No. 11). (Illus.). Repr. of 1971 ed. 45.60 (ISBN 0-8357-9387-7, 2013192). Bks Demand UMI.

Michelangelo: The Sistine Chapel Ceiling. Ed. & intro. by Charles Seymour, Jr. (Critical Studies in Art History). (Illus.). 243p. 1972. pap. 7.95x (ISBN 0-393-09889-3). Norton.

Michelle. Carolyn Phillips. 1982. 3.95 (ISBN 0-88113-205-5). Edit Betania.

Michigan Manuscript 18 of the Gospels. William M. Read. LC 44-13750. (Publications in Language & Literature Ser.: No. 11). (Illus.). 75p. 1942. pap. 5.00x (ISBN 0-295-95219-9). U of Wash Pr.

Microcosm & Mediator: The Theological Anthropology of Maximus the Confessor. Lars Thunberg. Rev. by A. L. Allchin. LC 80-2368. 1981. Repr. of 1965 ed. 58.00 (ISBN 0-404-18917-2). AMS Pr.

Mid-Life Crises. William E. Hulme. LC 80-11539. (Christian Care Bks.: Vol, 7). 118p. 1980. pap. 7.95 (ISBN 0-664-24324-X). Westminster.

Mid-Life Directions, Praying & Playing Sources of New Dynamism. Anne Brennan & Brewi Janice. LC 84-62157. 192p. (Orig.). 1985. pap. 7.95 (ISBN 0-8091-2681-8). Paulist Pr.

Mid Life: Psyhological & Spiritual Perspectives. Ed. by Janice Brewi & Anne Brennan. 224p. 1982. 12.95 (ISBN 0-8245-0417-8); pap. 8.95. Crossroad NY.

Middle Ages. abr. ed. Morris Bishop. LC 70-95728. 1970. pap. 7.95 (ISBN 0-07-005466-5). McGraw.

Middle Ages. Trevor Cairns. (Cambridge Introduction to the History of Mankind Ser.: Bk. 4). (Illus.). 1971. 8.95 (ISBN 0-521-07726-5). Cambridge U Pr.

Middle Ages. Alan Clifford. Ed. by Malcolm Yapp et al. (World History Ser.). (Illus.). 1980. lib. bdg. 6.95 (ISBN 0-89908-028-6); pap. text ed. 2.45 (ISBN 0-89908-003-0). Greenhaven.

Middle Ages, 900-1300. Enzo Bellini. Ed. & tr. by John Drury. (Illustrated History of the Church). 126p. 12.95 (ISBN 0-03-056828-5, HarpR). Har-Row.

Middle East, Its Religion & Culture. Edward J. Jurji. LC 72-9809. 159p. 1973. Repr. of 1956 ed. lib. bdg. 22.50x (ISBN 0-8371-6597-0, JUME). Greenwood.

Middle Eastern Muslim Women Speak. Ed. by Elizabeth W. Fernea & Basima Q. Bezirgan. (Illus.). 452p. 1977. 23.50x (ISBN 0-292-75033-1); pap. 12.50x (ISBN 0-292-75041-2). U of Tex Pr.

Middle Eastern Mythology. Samuel H. Hooke. (Orig.). 1963. pap. 5.95 (ISBN 0-14-020546-2, Pelican). Penguin.

Middle English Bible: Prefatory Epistles of St. Jerome. Conrad Lindberg. 172p. 1978. text ed. 19.50x. Oxford U Pr.

Middle English Bible: The Book of Baruch. Conrad Lindberg. 174p. 1986. 45.00 (ISBN 82-00-06057-8); pap. 23.00x. Oxford U Pr.

Middle English Metrical Paraphrase on the Old Testament. Ingrid Melander. 116p. (Orig.). 1971. pap. text ed. 30.00x. Coronet Bks.

Middle English Penitential Lyric. Frank A. Patterson. LC 11-26002. Repr. of 1911 ed. 17.50 (ISBN 0-404-04908-7). AMS Pr.

Middle High German Translation of the "Summa Theologica". St. Thomas Aquinas. Ed. by Bayard Q. Morgan & Friedrich W. Strothmann. LC 50-8471. (Stanford University. Stanford Studies in Language & Literature: No. 8). (Lat. & Ger., Glossary). Repr. of 1950 ed. 42.50 (ISBN 0-404-51816-8). AMS Pr.

Middle High German Translations of the Regula Sancti Benedicti. Saint Benedictus. Ed. & intro. by Carl Selmer. (Mediaeval Academy of America Publications). 1933. 28.00 (ISBN 0-527-01689-6). Kraus Repr.

Middle-Sized Church: Problems & Prescriptions. Lyle E. Schaller. 160p. (Orig.). 1985. pap. 6.95 (ISBN 0-687-26948-2). Abingdon.

Middle Sphere. Mara. LC 81-67349. (Earth Song Ser.). (Illus.). 57p. (Orig.). 1981. pap. 4.95 (ISBN 0-9605170-1-4). Earth-Song.

Middletown. Robert S. Lynd & Helen M. Lynd. 550p. 1959. pap. 8.95 (ISBN 0-15-659550-8, Harv). HarBraceJ.

Middletown in Transition: A Study in Cultural Conflicts. Robert S. Lynd & Helen M. Lynd. LC 37-27243. 604p. 1982. pap. 9.95 (ISBN 0-15-659551-6, Harv). HarBraceJ.

Midlife: Triumph-Not Crisis. Elizabeth Burg. 96p. (Orig.). 1986. pap. 4.50 (ISBN 0-914544-63-2). Living Flame Pr.

Midlife Wanderer: The Woman Religious in Midlife Transition. Sheila M. Murphy. LC 83-25806. 176p. (Orig.). 1983. pap. 8.00 (ISBN 0-89571-018-8). Affirmation.

Midnight Cry: A Defense of William Miller & the Millerites. Francis D. Nichol. LC 72-8249. Repr. of 1944 ed. 36.00 (ISBN 0-404-11003-7). AMS Pr.

Midrash & Literature. Geoffrey Hartman. LC 85-17898. 424p. 1986. 28.50 (ISBN 0-300-03453-9). Yale U Pr.

Midrash Bamidbar Rabba: Numbers Rabba, Hebrew & English, 4 vols. 80.00 (ISBN 0-87559-153-1). Shalom.

Midrash Bet HaShem: The Alphabet. 3rd, rev. ed. Shmuel Ben Aharon. (Illus.). 22p. 1986. pap. text ed. write for info. (ISBN 0-9616488-1-3). Alef Bet Comns.

Midrash Devorim Rabba: Deuteronomy, Hebrew & English. 20.00 (ISBN 0-87559-154-X). Shalom.

Midrash Eicha Rabba: Lamentation Rabba, Hebrew & English. 20.00 (ISBN 0-87559-157-4). Shalom.

Midrash Esther Rabba & Midrash Ruth Rabba: Hebrew & English. 20.00 (ISBN 0-87559-155-8). Shalom.

Midrash in Context. Jacob Neusner. LC 83-5705. 240p. 1983. 23.95 (ISBN 0-8006-0708-2, 1-708). Fortress.

Midrash Koheleth Rabba: Ecclesiastes Rabba, Hebrew & English. 20.00 (ISBN 0-87559-158-2). Shalom.

Midrash, Mishnah & Gemara: The Jewish Predilection for Justified Law. David W. Halivni. 176p. 1986. text ed. 22.50x (ISBN 0-674-57370-6). Harvard U Pr.

Midrash Pesher of Habakkuk. William H. Brownlee. LC 76-30560. (Society of Biblical Literature Monograph). 220p. 1979. pap. 9.95 (ISBN 0-89130-147-X, 06 00 24). Scholars Pr GA.

Midrash Rabbah: Midrashim on the Pentateuch & the Five Scrolls with the Matnoth Kehunah Commentary, 5 Vols. (Hebrew & Yiddish.). Set. leatherette 95.00 (ISBN 0-87559-096-9). Shalom.

Midrash Shemoth Rabba: Exodus Rabba, Hebrew & English, 2 vols. 40.00 (ISBN 0-87559-151-5). Shalom.

Midrash Shirashirim Rabba: Songs of Rabba, Hebrew & English. 20.00 (ISBN 0-87559-156-6). Shalom.

Midrash Tanhuma, 2 vols. John T. Townsend. 800p. 1987. price not set (ISBN 0-88125-087-2). Ktav.

Midrash: The Search for a Contemporary Past. pap. 3.00 (ISBN 0-686-96071-8); discussion leader's guide 2.00 (ISBN 0-686-99696-8). United Syn Bk.

Midrash Vayikra Rabba: Leviticus Rabba, Hebrew & English, 2 vols. 40.00 (ISBN 0-87559-152-3). Shalom.

Midrashic Interpretations of the Song of Moses. Herbert W. Basser. LC 83-49003. (American University Studies VII: Vol. 2). 312p. 1983. pap. text ed. 28.85 (ISBN 0-8204-0065-3). P Lang Pubs.

Midwives of the Future: American Sisters Tell Their Story. Joan Chittister et al. Ed. by Ann P. Ware. LC 84-82554. 237p. (Orig.). 1984. pap. 8.95 (ISBN 0-934134-11-1, Leaven Pr). Sheed & Ward MO.

Miftah-ul-Quran: Glossary of Quran, 2 vols. A. Shah. 22.50 (ISBN 0-686-18525-0). Kazi Pubns.

Mighty Act of God. Clifford A. Cole. 192p. 1984. pap. text ed. 12.00 (ISBN 0-8309-0393-3). Herald Hse.

Mighty Acts of God. Arnold B. Rhodes. (Orig.). 1964. pap. 7.95 (ISBN 0-8042-9010-5); tchrs' ed. 6.95 (ISBN 0-8042-9012-1). John Knox.

Mighty from Their Thrones: Power in the Biblical Tradition. J. P. Walsh. LC 86-45198. (Overtures to Biblical Theology Ser.). 224p. 1987. pap. 12.95 (ISBN 0-8006-1546-8). Fortress.

Mighty Man of Valor. W. Phillip Keller. 128p. 1979. pap. 4.95 (ISBN 0-8007-5072-1, Power Bks). Revell.

Migration of Symbols & Their Relations to Beliefs & Customs. Donald A. Mackenzie. LC 68-18029. 1968. Repr. of 1926 ed. 34.00x (ISBN 0-8103-3074-1). Gale.

Miguel De Unamuno: The Agony of Belief. Ed. by M. Nozick. 1982. 23.50 (ISBN 0-691-06498-9); pap. 10.50x (ISBN 0-691-01366-7). Princeton U Pr.

Mike: A Mother's Prayers. Bette Lawrence. LC 84-21247. 64p. 1985. pap. 2.95 (ISBN 0-8006-1857-2, 1-1857). Fortress.

Mike King Story. Mike King. LC 85-81940. (Illus.). 176p. (Orig.). 1985. 15.95 (ISBN 0-934672-33-4). Good Bks PA.

Mike King Story. Mike King. LC 85-81940. (Illus.). pap. 5.95 (ISBN 0-934672-42-3). Good Bks PA.

Mikhail Bulgakov: Life & Work. Ellendea Proffer. LC 83-16199. 1984. 45.00 (ISBN 0-88233-198-1). Ardis Pubs.

Mikron Euchologion: An Orthodox Prayer Book. Ed. by Nomikos M. Vaporis. Tr. & pref. by Michael Gelsinger. LC 77-77642. 288p. 1977. 18.95 (ISBN 0-916586-09-X). Holy Cross Orthodox.

Milagro de Kathy. Barbara Miller & Charles P. Conn. 144p. 1982. 2.75 (ISBN 0-88113-170-9). Edit Betania.

Milagros Tambien Son Parabolas. Plutarco Bonilla. LC 78-59240. (Span.). 166p. (Orig.). 1978. pap. 3.95 (ISBN 0-89922-114-9). Edit Caribe.

Miles Beyond in Brazil. Vera F. Barnes. 3.50 (ISBN 0-87509-104-0); pap. 2.00 (ISBN 0-87509-105-9). Chr Pubns.

Milestone. S. Qutb. 1981. pap. 7.50 (ISBN 0-686-77426-4). Kazi Pubns.

Milestones. Sayyid Qutb. Tr. of Ma alim fi at-Tariq. 303p. (Orig.). 1978. pap. 5.95 (ISBN 0-939830-07-8, Pub. by IIFSO Kuwait). New Era Pubns MI.

Milestones in the Life of a Jew. Donald G. Frieman. LC 65-15710. 1980. pap. 3.95 (ISBN 0-8197-0002-9). Bloch.

Milestones of the Way. rev. ed. Paul L. Peck. (Spiritual Metaphysics: Freeways to Divine Awareness Ser.). 250p. (Orig.). 1982. pap. 7.95 (ISBN 0-941600-03-3). Harmony Pr.

Milieu Divin. Pierre Teilhard De Chardin. (Coll. Livre de vie). 1958. pap. 3.95 (ISBN 0-685-11395-7). French & Eur.

Milieu Divin. Pierre Teilhard De Chardin. 8.95 (ISBN 0-685-36583-2). French & Eur.

Militant Gospel: A Critical Introduction to Political Theologies. Alfredo Fierro. Tr. by John Drury from Span. LC 77-1652. Orig. Title: Evangelio Beligerente. 459p. (Orig.). 1977. pap. 3.48 (ISBN 0-88344-311-2). Orbis Bks.

Militant Ministry: People & Pastors of the Early Church. Hans R. Weber. LC 64-12990. (Knubel-Miller Lectures for 1963). pap. 30.00 (2027186). Bks Demand UMI.

Militarism for America. Grover L. Hartman. 1983. pap. 2.50x (ISBN 0-87574-025-1, 025). Pendle Hill.

Militia Christi: The Christian Religion & the Military in the First Three Centuries. Adolf Harnack. Tr. by David M. Gracie from Ger. LC 81-43089. Tr. of Militia Christi: Die christliche Religion und der Soldatenstand in den ersten drei Jahrhunderten. 112p. 1981. 3.00 (ISBN 0-8006-0673-6, 1-673). Fortress.

Milk & Honey. E. E. Cleveland. Ed. by Gerald Wheeler. 1985. write for info. (ISBN 0-8280-0301-7). Review & Herald.

Milk of the World. Peter Barnes. 80p. (Orig.). 1985. pap. 2.95 (ISBN 0-85151-434-0). Banner of Truth.

Millenarian Piety of Roger Williams. W. Clark Gilpin. LC 78-20786. 1979. lib. bdg. 19.00x (ISBN 0-226-29397-1). U of Chicago Pr.

Millenial Harbinger - Index. David McWhirter. LC 81-65031. (Millenial Harbinger Ser.). 776p. 1981. 19.95 (ISBN 0-89900-228-5). College Pr Pub.

Millennial Kingdom of the Franciscans in the New World. 2nd rev ed. John L. Phelan. 1970. 35.95x (ISBN 0-520-01404-9). U of Cal Pr.

Millennial Messiah. Bruce R. McConkie. LC 81-19599. 726p. 1982. 17.95 (ISBN 0-87747-896-1). Deseret Bk.

Millennial Mistake. Roger Dickson. 2.50 (ISBN 0-89315-160-2). Lambert Bk.

Millennialism: The Two Major Views. Charles Feinberg. 1985. 12.95 (ISBN 0-88469-166-7). BMH Bks.

Millennium. Ralph Blodgett. (Outreach Ser.). 1981. pap. 1.25 (ISBN 0-8163-0398-3). Pacific Pr Pub Assn.

Millennium. Gordon Lindsay. (Revelation Ser.). 1.25 (ISBN 0-89985-048-0). Christ Nations.

Millennium Edition of the Decoded New Testament: Origins & History of the Paradosis or Secret Tradition of the Oral Law Called the Gospel, with Commentary on the Canonical New Testament, Apocrypha, Pseudepigrapha, Old Testament, Dead Sea Scrolls, Ancient Fragments, & Other Religious Texts. Revised ed. Gene Savoy. LC 83-80523. (The Sacred Teachings of Light, Codex II Ser.). Orig. Title: Decoded New Testament. (Illus.). 207p. 1983. text ed. 39.50 (ISBN 0-936202-06-8). Intl Comm Christ.

Millennium Edition of the Essaei Document: Secrets of an Eternal Race. Revised ed. Gene Savoy. LC 83-83221. Orig. Title: Essaei Document. (Illus.). xii, 140p. 1983. text ed. 39.50 (ISBN 0-936202-07-6). Intl Comm Christ.

Millennium in America: From the Puritan Migration to the Civil War, 41 vols. Incl. Vol. 1. Puritan Interpretation of Scripture. LC 78-67510 (ISBN 0-404-60901-5); Vol. 2. Puritan Doctrine of the Last Judgment. LC 78-67512 (ISBN 0-404-60902-3); Vol. 3. Puritan Vision of New Jerusalem. LC 78-67513 (ISBN 0-404-60903-1); Vol. 4. Increase Mather: Selected Works. LC 78-67514 (ISBN 0-404-60904-X); Vol. 5. Samuel Willard: Selected Works. LC 78-67515 (ISBN 0-404-60905-8); Vol. 6. Cotton Mather: Selected Works. LC 78-67516 (ISBN 0-404-60906-6); Vol. 7. Representative Writings of the Eighteenth Century: Scriptural Interpretations. LC 78-67517 (ISBN 0-404-60907-4); Representative Writings of the Eighteenth Century: Applications of Prophecy. LC 78-67518 (ISBN 0-404-60908-2); Vol. 9. Earthquakes of the Apocalypse. LC 78-67519 (ISBN 0-404-60909-0); Vol. 10. Edwardsian Revivalism from the Great Awakening to the Revolution. LC 78-67520 (ISBN 0-404-60910-4); Vol. 11. Charles Chauncy. LC 78-67586 (ISBN 0-404-60911-2); Vol. 12. French & Indian Wars. LC 78-67587 **(ISBN 0-404-60912-0); Vol. 13. Sermons of the American Revolution. LC 78-67588 (ISBN 0-404-60913-9); Vol. 14. Celebration of Nationhood. LC 78-67590 (ISBN 0-404-60914-7); Vol. 15. Loyalist Millenarians. LC 78-67591 (ISBN 0-404-60915-5); Vol. 16. Poems on the Rising Glory of America. LC 78-67592 (ISBN 0-404-60916-3); Vol. 17. Interpretations of the French Revolution. LC 78-67599 (ISBN 0-404-60917-1); Vols. 18 & 19, Pts. 1 & 2. Signs of the Times: The Late Eighteenth Century. LC 78-67595. Set. 115.00 (ISBN 0-404-60942-2). Vol. 18 (ISBN 0-404-60918-X). Vol. 19 (ISBN 0-404-60919-8); Vols. 20 & 21. Elhanan Winchester. LC 78-67596. Set. 115.00 (ISBN 0-404-60943-0). Vol. 20 (ISBN 0-404-60920-1). Vol. 21 (ISBN 0-404-60921-X); Vol. 22. Timothy Dwight: Selected Writings. LC 78-67598 (ISBN 0-404-60922-8). Vols. 1-17, & 22-41. write for info. ea.; Set. write for info. (ISBN 0-404-60900-7). AMS Pr.**

Millennium in America: From the Puritan Migration to the Civil War, 41 vols. Incl. Vol. 23. Representative Writings of the Early Nineteenth Century (1800-1839) LC 78-67600 (ISBN 0-404-60923-6); Vol. 24. Garden of the West. LC 78-67601 (ISBN 0-404-60924-4); Vol. 25. Three Women Prophets: Harriet Livermore. LC 78-67603 (ISBN 0-404-60925-2); Vol. 26. Three Women Prophets: Phoebe Palmer. LC 78-67604 (ISBN 0-404-60926-0); Vol. 27. Three Women Prophets: Ellen Gould White. LC 78-67605 (ISBN 0-404-60927-9); Vol. 28. Allegorical Narratives. LC 78-67606 (ISBN 0-404-60928-7); Vol. 29, Pt. 1. Slavery & Abolition. LC 78-67607 (ISBN 0-404-60929-5); Vol. 30, Pt. 2. Slavery & Abolition. LC 78-67608 (ISBN 0-404-60930-9); Vol. 31. Millennial Optimism & Despair. LC 78-67610 (ISBN 0-404-60931-7); Vol. 32. Hymns to the Millennium. LC 78-67611 (ISBN 0-404-60932-5); Vol. 33. Millenarian Anthologies. LC 78-67612 (ISBN 0-404-60933-3); Vol. 34. Elias Smith: Selected Writings. LC 78-67613 (ISBN 0-404-60934-1); Vol. 35. Elias Boudinot. LC 78-67614 (ISBN 0-404-60935-**X); Vol. 36. Ethan Smith: Selected Writings. LC 78-67615 (ISBN 0-404-60936-8); Vol. 37. Lyman Beecher: Selected Works. LC 78-67616 (ISBN 0-404-60937-6); Vol. 38. Millennial Debate: Owen vs. Campbell. LC 78-67618 (ISBN 0-404-60938-4); Vol. 39. George Duffield: Selected Works. LC 78-67619 (ISBN 0-404-60939-2); Vol. 40. William Miller: Selected Works. LC 78-67620 (ISBN 0-404-60940-6); Vol. 41. Representative Writings, 1840-1860. LC 78-67621 (ISBN 0-404-60941-4). Vols. 1-17 & 22-41. write for info.; Set. write for info. (ISBN 0-404-60900-7). AMS Pr.**

Miller Heresy, Millenialism, & Amercian Culture. Ruth A. Doan. 270p. 1987. price not set (ISBN 0-87722-481-1). Temple U Pr.

Millhands & Preachers: A Study of Gastonia. Liston Pope. (Studies in Religious Education: No. 15). (Illus.). 1965. pap. 11.95x (ISBN 0-300-00182-7). Yale U Pr.

Millionaire for God (C. T. Studd) John T. Erskine. 1968. pap. 2.95 (ISBN 0-87508-611-X). Chr Lit.

Millionaire from Nazareth. Catherine Ponder. (Millionaires of the Bible Ser.). 1979. pap. 6.95 (ISBN 0-87516-370-X). De Vorss.

Millionaire Joshua. Catherine Ponder. LC 77-86719. (Millionaires of the Bible Ser.). 1978. pap. 5.95 (ISBN 0-87516-253-3). De Vorss.

Millionaire Moses. Catherine Ponder. LC 77-71459. (Millionaires of the Bible Ser.). 1977. pap. 5.95 (ISBN 0-87516-232-0). De Vorss.

Millionaires of Genesis. Catherine Ponder. (Millionaires of the Bible Ser.). 1976. pap. 4.95 (ISBN 0-87516-215-0). De Vorss.

Milly: A Tribute to Amelia E. Collins. A. Q. Faizi. 52p. pap. 2.95 (ISBN 0-85398-074-8). G Ronald Pub.

Milstater Genesis und Exodus: Eine Grammatisch-Stillistische Ist Untersuchung. Fritz Bulthaupt. (Ger). 21.00 (ISBN 0-384-06341-1); pap. 16.00 (ISBN 0-685-02228-5). Johnson Repr.

Milton. John C. Bailey. LC 73-12210. 1973. lib. bdg. 17.50 (ISBN 0-8414-3218-X). Folcroft.

Milton. Hilaire Belloc. LC 78-100142. Repr. of 1935 ed. lib. bdg. 24.75x (ISBN 0-8371-3248-7, BEMI). Greenwood.

Milton. William Blake. Ed. by A. Russell & E. Maclagan. LC 73-16264. 1907. lib. bdg. 15.00 (ISBN 0-8414-3345-3). Folcroft.

Milton. David Daiches. (Orig.). 1966. pap. 4.95x (ISBN 0-393-00347-7, Norton Lib). Norton.

Milton. Rose Macaulay. LC 74-7050. (Studies in Milton, No. 22). 1974. lib. bdg. 75.00x (ISBN 0-8383-1911-4). Haskell.

Milton. Mark Pattison. Ed. by John Morley. LC 68-58393. (English Men of Letters). Repr. of 1887 ed. lib. bdg. 12.50 (ISBN 0-404-51725-0). AMS Pr.

Milton. Mark Pattison. 1896. Repr. 12.00 (ISBN 0-8274-2735-2). R West.

Milton. Walter A. Raleigh. LC 67-13336. 1967. Repr. of 1900 ed. 17.00 (ISBN 0-405-08873-6). Ayer Co Pubs.

Milton. Walter A. Raleigh. 1973. 10.00 (ISBN 0-8274-1323-8). R West.

Milton. George C. Williamson. LC 75-19089. 1975. Repr. of 1905 ed. lib. bdg. 15.00 (ISBN 0-88305-757-3). Norwood Edns.

Milton: A Poem. William Blake. LC 78-58177. (Illus.). 178p. 1978. pap. 17.95 (ISBN 0-87773-129-2). Shambhala Pubns.

Milton, A Sheaf of Gleanings. Joseph Hunter. LC 76-26898. 1850. lib. bdg. 12.50 (ISBN 0-8414-4737-3). Folcroft.

Milton Agonistes. E. H. Visiak. (Studies in Milton, No. 22). 1970. pap. 39.95x (ISBN 0-8383-0102-9). Haskell.

Milton & Forbidden Knowledge. H. Schultz. (MLA RFS). 1955. 22.00 (ISBN 0-527-80600-5). Kraus Repr.

Milton & His Sonnets. William C. Hall. LC 73-4268. 1973. lib. bdg. 12.50 (ISBN 0-8414-2071-8). Folcroft.

Milton & Jakob Boehme. Margaret L. Bailey. LC 65-15885. (Studies in Comparative Literature, No. 35). 1969. Repr. of 1914 ed. lib. bdg. 39.95x (ISBN 0-8383-0505-9). Haskell.

Milton & Scriptural Tradition: The Bible into Poetry. Ed. by James H. Sims & Leland Ryken. LC 83-16781. 192p. 1984. text ed. 19.50x (ISBN 0-8262-0427-9). U of MO Pr.

Milton & the Art of Sacred Song. J. Max Patrick & Roger H. Sundell. LC 78-65014. 248p. 1979. 32.50x (ISBN 0-299-07830-2). U of Wis Pr.

Milton & the Book of Revelation: The Heavenly Cycle. Austin C. Dobbins. LC 73-22715. (Studies in the Humanities: No. 7). 176p. 1975. o. p. 12.50 (ISBN 0-8173-7320-9); pap. 4.95 (ISBN 0-8173-7321-7). U of Ala Pr.

Milton & the Christian Tradition. C. A. Patrides. LC 79-10846. xvi, 302p. 1979. Repr. 28.00 (ISBN 0-208-01821-2, Archon). Shoe String.

Milton & the Drama of the Soul: A Study of the Theme of the Restoration of Man in Milton's Later Poetry. George M. Muldrow. LC 76-89796. (Studies in English Literature: Vol. 51). 1970. text ed. 23.20x (ISBN 90-2790-530-4). Mouton.

Milton & the English Mind. F. Hutchinson. LC 74-7187. (Studies in Milton, No. 22). 1974. lib. bdg. 49.95x (ISBN 0-8383-1906-8). Haskell.

Milton & the English Mind. F. E. Hutchinson. LC 74-28171. 1946. Repr. lib. bdg. 17.50 (ISBN 0-8414-4897-3). Folcroft.

Milton & the Middle Ages. Ed. by John Mulryan. LC 81-694400. 192p. 1982. 22.50 (ISBN 0-8387-5036-2). Bucknell U Pr.

Milton & the Miltonic Dryden. Anne D. Ferry. LC 68-25608. 1968. 16.50x (ISBN 0-674-57576-8). Harvard U Pr.

Milton & the Pauline Tradition: A Study of Theme & Symbolism. Timothy J. O'Keeffe. LC 80-5842. 356p. (Orig.). 1982. PLB 32.25 (ISBN 0-8191-2453-2); pap. text ed. 15.75 (ISBN 0-8191-2454-0). U Pr of Amer.

Milton & the Puritan Dilemma, 1641-1660. Arthur E. Barker. LC 58-3195. 1942. 30.00x (ISBN 0-8020-5025-5); pap. 8.50 o. p. (ISBN 0-8020-6306-3). U of Toronto Pr.

Milton & the Renaissance Ovid. David P. Harding. LC 76-47466. 1977. Repr. of 1946 ed. lib. bdg. 17.50 (ISBN 0-8414-4941-4). Folcroft.

Milton in Early America. George Sensabaugh. LC 79-14332. 322p. 1979. 32.50x (ISBN 0-87752-180-8). Gordian.

Milton in Holland. H. Scherpbier. LC 76-41928. 1933. lib. bdg. 30.00 (ISBN 0-8414-7580-6). Folcroft.

Milton in the Puritan Revolution. Don M. Wolfe. 1963. text ed. 22.50x (ISBN 0-391-00477-8). Humanities.

Milton, Man & Thinker. D. Saurat. LC 76-121151. (Studies in Milton, No. 22). 1970. Repr. of 1925 ed. lib. bdg. 49.95x (ISBN 0-8383-1093-1). Haskell.

Milton: Man & Thinker. Denis Saurat. LC 73-153352. Tr. of Pensee De Milton. Repr. of 1925 ed. 24.50 (ISBN 0-404-05565-6). AMS Pr.

Milton Memorial Lectures. Percy W. Ames. 1974. Repr. 32.50 (ISBN 0-8274-2738-7). R West.

Milton Memorial Lectures 1909. Percy Ames. LC 65-15895. (Studies in Milton, No. 22). 1969. Repr. of 1909 ed. lib. bdg. 49.95x (ISBN 0-8383-0501-6). Haskell.

Milton on Plagiary; Or a Detection of the Forgeries. John Douglas. LC 72-187954. Repr. of 1756 ed. lib. bdg. 10.00 (ISBN 0-8414-0508-5). Folcroft.

Milton on the Nature of Man. William Hunter. LC 76-48905. 1946. lib. bdg. 12.50 (ISBN 0-8414-4908-2). Folcroft.

Milton on the Nature of Man. Wm. Bridges Hunter. 1978. Repr. of 1946 ed. lib. bdg. 15.00 (ISBN 0-8492-1186-7). R West.

Milton on the Son of God & the Holy Spirit (From the Treatise on Christian Doctrine) Ed. by Alexander Gordon. LC 73-4827. 1973. lib. bdg. 15.00 (ISBN 0-8414-2028-9). Folcroft.

Milton Papers. David H. Stevens. LC 75-176438. Repr. of 1927 ed. 5.00 (ISBN 0-404-06262-8). AMS Pr.

Milton Papers. David H. Stevens. LC 76-27340. 1927. lib. bdg. 12.00 (ISBN 0-8414-7615-2). Folcroft.

Milton Poete De la Bible Dans le Paradis Perdu. Jacques Blondel. LC 73-13668. 1959. lib. bdg. 12.50 (ISBN 0-8414-3252-X). Folcroft.

Milton Studies, Vol. III. Ed. by James D. Simmonds. LC 69-12335. (Milton Studies). 1971. 32.95x (ISBN 0-8229-3218-0). U of Pittsburgh Pr.

Milton Studies, Vol. II. Ed. by James D. Simmonds. LC 69-12335. (Milton Studies). 1970. 32.95x (ISBN 0-8229-3194-X). U of Pittsburgh Pr.

Milton Studies, Vol. V. Ed. by James D. Simmonds. LC 69-12335. (Milton Studies). 1973. 32.95x (ISBN 0-8229-3272-5). U of Pittsburgh Pr.

Milton Studies, Vol. VI. Ed. by James D. Simmonds. LC 69-12335. (Milton Studies). 1974. 32.95x (ISBN 0-8229-3288-1). U of Pittsburgh Pr.

Milton Studies, Vol. VIII. Ed. by James D. Simmonds. LC 69-12335. (Milton Studies). 1975. 39.95x (ISBN 0-8229-3310-1). U of Pittsburgh Pr.

Milton Studies, Vol. IX. Ed. by James D. Simmonds. LC 69-12335. (Milton Studies). 1976. 32.95x (ISBN 0-8229-3329-2). U of Pittsburgh Pr.

Milton Studies in Honor of Harris Francis Fletcher. Harris F. Fletcher. LC 74-16488. 1974. Repr. of 1961 ed. lib. bdg. 30.00 (ISBN 0-8414-4247-9). Folcroft.

Milton Tercentenary: The Portraits, Prints & Writings of John Milton. George C. Williamson. LC 72-194902. 1973. lib. bdg. 18.50 (ISBN 0-8414-9743-5). Folcroft.

Milton: The Individualist in Metre. Hugh C. Candy. 1930. lib. bdg. 7.50 (ISBN 0-8414-3630-4). Folcroft.

Milton the Poet. A. S. Woodhouse. LC 73-785. 1955. lib. bdg. 10.00 (ISBN 0-8414-1606-0). Folcroft.

Milton the Puritan: Portrait of a Mind. A. L. Rowse. 298p. 1985. pap. text ed. 12.50 (ISBN 0-8191-4778-8). U Pr of Amer.

Milton: Tractate of Education. Edward E. Morris. LC 73-13795. 1895. Repr. lib. bdg. 12.50 (ISBN 0-8414-6000-0). Folcroft.

Milton's Agonistes: A Metaphysical Criticism. E. H. Visiak. LC 77-9361. 1922. lib. bdg. 12.50 (ISBN 0-8414-9187-9). Folcroft.

Milton's Conception of Sin As Developed in Paradise Lost. John M. Patrick. 1930. Repr. 25.00 (ISBN 0-8274-2740-9). R West.

Milton's Fame on the Continent. John G. Robertson. Repr. of 1908 ed. lib. bdg. 8.50 (ISBN 0-8414-7462-1). Folcroft.

Milton's God. William Empson. LC 80-40109. 320p. 1981. pap. 18.95 (ISBN 0-521-29910-1). Cambridge U Pr.

Milton's God. William Empson. LC 78-14409. 1978. Repr. of 1961 ed. lib. bdg. 27.50x (ISBN 0-313-21021-7, EMMG). Greenwood.

Milton's Good God: A Study in Literary Theodicy. Dennis Danielson. LC 81-15535. 272p. 1982. 39.50 (ISBN 0-521-23744-0). Cambridge U Pr.

Milton's Imagery & the Visual Arts: Iconographic Tradition in the Epic Poems. Roland M. Frye. LC 77-24541. 1978. 83.00x (ISBN 0-691-06349-4). Princeton U Pr.

Milton's Inward Jerusalem: "Paradise Lost" & the Ways of Knowing. Frederick Plotkin. LC 76-159468. (Studies in English Literature: No. 72). 155p. 1971. text ed. 17.60x (ISBN 0-686-22493-0). Mouton.

Milton's Ode on the Morning of Christ's Nativity, L'allegro, Il Penseroso, & Lycidas. A. W. Verity. LC 73-12943. 1974. Repr. of 1931 ed. lib. bdg. 22.50 (ISBN 0-8414-9150-X). Folcroft.

Milton's Ontology, Cosmogony & Physics. Walter C. Curry. LC 57-5833. (Illus.). 226p. 1957. pap. 6.00x (ISBN 0-8131-0102-6). U Pr of Ky.

Milton's Paradise Lost. Helen Darbishire. LC 74-3031. 1951. lib. bdg. 15.00 (ISBN 0-8414-3750-5). Folcroft.

Milton's "Paradise Lost.". new ed. John Milton. Ed. by Richard Bentley. LC 74-5237. Repr. of 1732 ed. 67.50 (ISBN 0-404-11537-3). AMS Pr.

Milton's Paradise Lost, 3 Vols. John Milton. Ed. by A. W. Verity. LC 72-4906. 1921. lib. bdg. 120.00 (ISBN 0-8414-0012-1). Folcroft.

Milton's Paradise Lost. Ed. by A. W. Verity. 1974. Repr. of 1921 ed. lib. bdg. 47.50 (ISBN 0-685-45197-6). Folcroft.

Milton's Paradise Lost. M. Wilding. (Sydney Studies in Literature Ser.). 1969. 15.00x (ISBN 0-424-05850-2, Pub. by Sydney U Pr). Intl Spec Bk.

Milton's Paradise Regained: Two Eighteenth-Century Critiques, 2 vols. in 1. Richard Meadowcourt. Ed. by Joseph A. Wittreich, Jr. LC 76-161937. 1971. Repr. of 1732 ed. 50.00x (ISBN 0-8201-1087-6). Schol Facsimiles.

Milton's Pastoral Vision: An Approach to "Paradise Lost". John R. Knott, Jr. LC 79-145576. 1971. text ed. 15.00x (ISBN 0-226-44846-0). U of Chicago Pr.

Milton's Poetic Art: A Mask, Lycidas, & Paradise Lost. John Reesing. LC 68-17632. Repr. of 1968 ed. 55.50 (ISBN 0-8357-9166-1, 2017011). Bks Demand UMI.

Milton's Rabbinical Readings. Harris F. Fletcher. LC 67-30701. 344p. 1967. Repr. of 1930 ed. 29.50x (ISBN 0-87752-034-8). Gordian.

Milton's Rabbinical Readings. Harris F. Fletcher. LC 67-22303. 344p. 1967. Repr. of 1930 ed. 29.50 (ISBN 0-208-00335-5, Archon). Shoe String.

Milton's Samson Agonistes. Christian E. Kreipe. LC 76-10958. (Ger.). 1926. lib. bdg. 20.00 (ISBN 0-8414-5458-2). Folcroft.

Milton's Samson Agonistes. Christian E. Kreipe. 59.95 (ISBN 0-8490-0638-4). Gordon Pr.

Milton's Semitic Studies. Harris F. Fletcher. LC 74-18236. 1973. lib. bdg. 27.50 (ISBN 0-8414-4249-5). Folcroft.

Milton's Semitic Studies & Some Manifestations of Them in His Poetry. Harris F. Fletcher. LC 66-29575. 155p. 1966. Repr. of 1926 ed. 14.50x (ISBN 0-87752-035-6). Gordian.

Milton's Tercentenary. Henry A. Beers. LC 73-39421. Repr. of 1910 ed. 7.50 (ISBN 0-404-00725-2). AMS Pr.

Milton's Tercentenary. Henry A. Beers. LC 73-9747. 1910. lib. bdg. 8.50 (ISBN 0-8414-3168-X). Folcroft.

Milton's Theories Concerning Epic Poetry. Ralph W. Condee. LC 77-861. 1977. lib. bdg. 8.50 (ISBN 0-8414-3421-2). Folcroft.

Mimamsa Sutras of Jaimini. Jaimini. Tr. by Mohan L. Sandal. LC 73-3820. (Sacred Books of the Hindus: No. 27). (Eng. & Sanskrit.). Repr. of 1925 ed. 79.50 (ISBN 0-404-57827-6). AMS Pr.

Mimekor Yisrael: Classical Jewish Folktales, 3 vols. Ed. by Micha J. bin Gorion & Emanuel bin Gorion. Tr. by I. M. Lask from Heb. LC 74-15713. 1666p. 1976. 100.00 (ISBN 0-253-15330-1). Ind U Pr.

Mimesis: From Mirror to Method, Augustine to Descartes. Ed. by John D. Lyons & Stephen G. Nichols, Jr. LC 82-40340. (Illus.). 287p. 1982. 25.00x (ISBN 0-87451-244-1). U Pr of New Eng.

Mimosa. Amy Carmichael. 1958. pap. 2.95 (ISBN 0-87508-074-X). Chr Lit.

Minature Book of Hours. 480p. 250.00 (ISBN 0-8115-0905-2). Kraus Repr.

Minchah-Maariv: Pocket Size Siddur. 0.60 (ISBN 0-914131-45-1, B75). Torah Umesorah.

Mind Al-Quran Builds. S. A. Latif. 200p. 1983. 9.95 (ISBN 0-935782-16-8). Kazi Pubns.

Mind: An Essay on Human Feeling. Susanne K. Langer. Incl. Vol. I. Mind. (Illus.). 512p. 1967. 34.50x (ISBN 0-8018-0360-8); pap. 11.95 (ISBN 0-8018-1150-3); Vol. II. 412p. 1973. 28.50x (ISBN 0-8018-1428-6); pap. 9.95 (ISBN 0-8018-1607-6); Vol. III. 264p. Set of 3 vols. 26.50 (ISBN 0-8018-2756-6); pap. 8.95 (ISBN 0-8018-2511-3); pap. 28.85x (ISBN 0-8018-2555-5). LC 66-26686. Johns Hopkins.

Mind & Deity. John Laird. LC 70-114424. 322p. 1970. Repr. of 1941 ed. 32.50 (ISBN 0-208-00937-X, Archon). Shoe String.

Mind & Its Control. Swami Budhananda. 119p. (Orig.). 1972. pap. 1.75 (ISBN 0-87481-128-7). Vedanta Pr.

Mind & Memory Training. Wood. 10.50 (ISBN 0-8356-5115-0). Theos Pub Hse.

Mind & Memory Training. Wood. pap. 7.95 (ISBN 0-8356-5126-6). Theos Pub Hse.

Mind & Spirit. Christopher A. Anderson. LC 86-72816. (Illus.). 90p. 1987. pap. 7.50 (ISBN 0-931353-09-2). Andersons Pubns.

Mind & Spirit of India. N. K. Devaraja. 1967. 5.95 (ISBN 0-89684-281-9). Orient Bk Dist.

Mind at Ease. rev. ed. Alfred Doerffler. LC 75-43869. (Large Print Ser.). 104p. 1976. pap. 5.50 (ISBN 0-570-03040-4, 6-1163). Concordia.

Mind Awake: An Anthology of C. S. Lewis. Ed. by Clyde S. Kilby. LC 80-14133. 256p. 1980. pap. 3.95 (ISBN 0-15-659772-1, Harv). HarBraceJ.

Mind Beyond Mind: Perceptive Meditation, Form & Function. Yuvacharya Shri Mahaprajna. 186p. 1980. 9.00 (ISBN 0-88065-214-4, Pub. by Messers Today & Tomorrows Printers & Publishers India). Scholarly Pubns.

Mind Changers. Em Griffin. 1976. pap. 7.95 (ISBN 0-8423-4290-7). Tyndale.

Mind, Character, & Personality: Guidelines to Mental & Spiritual Health, 2 vols. Ellen G. White. (Christian Home Library). 1978. 8.95 ea. Vol. 1 (ISBN 0-8127-0148-8). Vol. 2 (ISBN 0-8127-0149-6). Review & Herald.

Mind Control Papers, Vol. I. pap. 6.00 (ISBN 0-915598-35-3). Church of Scient Info.

Mind Cure in New England: From the Civil War to World War I. Gail T. Parker. LC 72-92704. 209p. 1973. 18.00x (ISBN 0-87451-073-2). U Pr of New Eng.

Mind Forg'd Manacles: Evil in the Poetry of Blake & Shelley. Melanie Bandy. LC 80-18779. (Illus.). 210p. 1981. text ed. 19.95 (ISBN 0-8173-0046-5). U of Ala Pr.

Mind in Buddhist Psychology: The Necklace of Clear Understanding, an Elucidation of the Workings of Mind & Mental Events. Ye-Shes Rgyal-Mtshan. Tr. by Herbert V. Guenther & Leslie S. Kawamura. LC 74-24373. (Tibetan Translation Ser.: Vol. 3). (Illus.). 168p. 1975. 12.95 (ISBN 0-913546-07-0); pap. 7.95 (ISBN 0-913546-06-2). Dharma Pub.

Mind in Ferment: Mikhail Bulgakov's Prose. K. Sahni. 251p. 1984. text ed. 12.50x (ISBN 0-391-03201-1, Pub. by Arnold Heinemann). Humanities.

Mind in Tibetan Buddhism. Lati Rinbochay. Ed. by Elizabeth Napper. LC 86-3799. 172p. (Orig.). 1980. lib. bdg. 12.95 cancelled (ISBN 0-937938-03-3); pap. 10.95 (ISBN 0-937938-02-5). Snow Lion.

Mind Invaders. Linda Stafford. (YA) 1982. pap. 1.95. Victor Bks.

Mind Is It: Meditation, Prayer, Healing, & the Psychic. Charles C. Wise, Jr. LC 77-82923. 191p. (Orig.). 1978. pap. 3.75 (ISBN 0-917023-02-1). Magian Pr.

Mind of Chesterton. Christopher Hollis. LC 76-130447. 1970. 14.95x (ISBN 0-87024-184-2). U of Miami Pr.

Mind of China. Edwin D. Harvey. LC 73-874. (China Studies: from Confucius to Mao Ser). x, 321p. 1973. Repr. of 1933 ed. 25.50 (ISBN 0-88355-069-5). Hyperion Conn.

Mind of Clover: Essays in Zen Buddhist Ethics. Robert Aitken. 224p. (Orig.). 1984. pap. 11.50 (ISBN 0-86547-158-4). N Point Pr.

Mind of Jesus. William Barclay. LC 61-7332. 352p. 1976. pap. 8.95 (ISBN 0-06-060451-4, RD143, HarpR). Har-Row.

Mind of John Paul II: Origins of His Thought & Action. George H. Williams. LC 80-19947. 415p. 1981. 26.95 (ISBN 0-8164-0473-9, HarpR). Har-Row.

Mind of St. Bernard of Clairvaux. G. Rosemary Evans. 1983. text ed. 37.00x (ISBN 0-19-826667-7). Oxford U Pr.

Mind of St. Paul. William Barclay. LC 75-9310. 256p. 1975. pap. 8.95 (ISBN 0-06-060471-9, RD110, HarpR). Har-Row.

Mind of the Bible-Believer. Edmund D. Cohen. 425p. 1986. 19.95 (ISBN 0-87975-341-2). Prometheus Bks.

Mind of the Maker. Dorothy L. Sayers. Repr. of 1941 ed. lib. bdg. 22.50x (ISBN 0-8371-3372-6, SAMM). Greenwood.

Mind of the Oxford Movement. Ed. by Owen Chadwick. 1961. 18.50x (ISBN 0-8047-0342-6). Stanford U Pr.

Mind of Whittier: A Study of Whittier's Fundamental Religious Ideas. C. Hawkins. LC 73-6984. (American Literature Ser., No. 49). 1973. Repr. of 1904 ed. lib. bdg. 39.95x (ISBN 0-8383-1700-6). Haskell.

Mind of William Paley: A Philosopher & His Age. D. L. LeMahieu. LC 75-22547. xiv, 215p. 1976. 18.50x (ISBN 0-8032-0865-0). U of Nebr Pr.

Mind Polluters. Jerry Kirk. 224p. 1985. pap. 6.95 (ISBN 0-8407-5965-7). Nelson.

Mind Power: The Secret of Mental Magic. limited ed. William W. Atkinson. limited ed. 9.00 (ISBN 0-911662-27-8). Yoga.

Mind: The Master Power. Charles Roth. 1984. 5.95 (ISBN 0-87159-099-9). Unity School.

Minding God's Business. Ray S. Anderson. 176p. (Orig.). 1986. pap. 9.95 (ISBN 0-8028-0168-4). Eerdmans.

Mind's Journey to God (Itinerarium Mentis Ad Deum) St. Bonaventure. Tr. by Lawrence S. Cunningham. 1979. 6.95 (ISBN 0-8199-0765-0). Franciscan Herald.

Mind's Road to God: Bonaventura. George Boas. 1953. pap. text ed. write for info. (ISBN 0-02-311250-6). Macmillan.

Mindszenty the Man. Joseph Vecsey & Phyllis Schlafly. LC 72-93906. 1972. 2.00 (ISBN 0-934640-04-1). Pere Marquette.

Mine to Choose. Sue Schaeffer. LC 78-73144. 128p. 1979. 2.50 (ISBN 0-88243-553-1, 02-0553, Radiant Bks.); tchr's manual 2.50 (ISBN 0-88243-337-7, 02-0337). Gospel Pub.

Miners, Merchants & Missionaries: The Roles of Missionaries & Pioneer Churches in the Colorado Gold Rush & Its Aftermath, 1858-1870. Alice C. Cochran. LC 80-16895. (ATLA Monographs: No. 15). x, 287p. 1980. 21.00 (ISBN 0-8108-1325-4). Scarecrow.

Minerva Britanna, or a Garden of Heroical Devises. Henry Peacham. LC 73-171783. (English Experience Ser.: No. 407). 232p. 1971. Repr. of 1612 ed. 33.50 (ISBN 90-221-0407-9). Walter J Johnson.

Minhagim: The Customs & Ceremonies of Judaism, Their Origins & Rationale. 2nd corrected ed. Abraham Chill. LC 78-62153. (Illus.). 339p. 1980. 14.95 (ISBN 0-87203-076-8); pap. 10.95 (ISBN 0-87203-077-6). Hermon.

Minhah & Maariv Service. Tr. by Ben Z. Bokser. 45p. 1958. pap. 1.50 (ISBN 0-88482-125-0). Hebrew Pub.

Minhas Marheshes: Commentary on Genesis. P. S. Pollak. (Heb). 9.50 (ISBN 0-87559-101-9). Shalom.

Mini-Guide to the Contents of the Books of the Bible. pap. 0.50 (ISBN 0-686-70364-2). Reiner.

Mini Messages on Stewardship. Raymond Bayne. 130p. 1984. pap. 3.95 (ISBN 0-8010-0858-1). Baker Bk.

Mini Miracles & Words with a Little Wisdom. Albert C. Scott. 1984. 6.95 (ISBN 0-8062-2320-0). Carlton.

Miniature Cathedral & Other Poems. Walter Wangerin, Jr. 1987. 16.95; pap. 10.95. Har-Row.

Miniatures & Silhouettes of Early American Jews. Hannah R. London. LC 78-87797. (Illus.). 1969. Repr. 16.50 (ISBN 0-8048-0657-8). C E Tuttle.

Miniatures & Silhouttes of Early American Jews. Hannah London. (Illus.). 199p. 25.00 (ISBN 0-686-47008-7). Apollo.

Miniatures in the Gospels of St. Augustine: Corpus Christi College Ms. 286. Francis Wormald. LC 54-4312. (Sandars Lectures in Bibliography Ser.: 1948). (Illus.). pap. 20.00 (ISBN 0-317-09509-9, 2051474). Bks Demand UMI.

Miniatures of the Paris Psalter: A Study in Middle Byzantine Painting. Hugo Buchtal. (Warburg Institute Studies: Vol. 2). Repr. of 1938 ed. 88.00 (ISBN 0-8115-1379-3). Kraus Repr.

Minister as Crisis Counselor. rev. ed. David L. Switzer. 304p. 1986. pap. 13.95 (ISBN 0-687-26954-7). Abingdon.

Minister As Diagnostician: Personal Problems in Pastoral Perspective. Paul W. Pruyser. LC 76-8922. 144p. 1976. pap. 7.95 (ISBN 0-664-24123-9). Westminster.

Minister As Shepherd. Jefferson. (Orig.). 1970. pap. 3.25 (ISBN 0-87508-290-4). Chr Lit.

Minister Heal Thyself. William H. Armstrog. 64p. (Orig.). 1985. pap. 4.95 (ISBN 0-8298-0551-6). Pilgrim NY.

Minister-Mayor. William H. Hudnut, III & Judy Keene. LC 86-32512. 192p. 1987. 12.95 (ISBN 0-664-21321-9). Westminster.

Minister of God: Effective & Fulfilled. Helen Doohan. LC 86-14099. 127p. (Orig.). 1986. pap. 6.95 (ISBN 0-8189-0507-7). Alba.

Minister on the Spot. James E. Dittes. LC 79-114051. 1970. pap. 3.95 (ISBN 0-8298-0155-3). Pilgrim NY.

Ministerial Competency Report. Steve Clapp. (Practice of Ministry Ser.). 123p. (Orig.). 1982. pap. 8.00 (ISBN 0-914527-10-X). C-Four Res.

Ministerial Education in the American Methodist Movement. Gerald O. McCulloh. LC 80-69028. (Informed Ministry Ser.: 200 Years of American Methodist Thought). 342p. (Orig.). 1980. pap. 3.95 (ISBN 0-938162-00-4). United Meth Educ.

Ministerial Training in Eighteenth-Century New England. Mary L. Gambrell. (Columbia University. Studies in the Social Sciences: No. 428). Repr. of 1937 ed. 16.50 (ISBN 0-404-51428-6). AMS Pr.

Ministering Church. Gaines S. Dobbins. LC 60-9530. 1960. 9.95 (ISBN 0-8054-2505-5). Broadman.

Ministering in the Pauline Churches: Partners for Christ. Pheme Perkins. LC 82-60849. 1982. pap. 4.95 (ISBN 0-8091-2473-4). Paulist Pr.

Ministering Parish: Methods & Procedures for the Pastoral Organization. Robert R. Newsome. LC 81-85381. 128p. (Orig.). 1982. pap. 8.95 (ISBN 0-8091-2435-1). Paulist Pr.

Ministering Teacher. Frank E. Dunn. 112p. 1982. pap. 4.95 (ISBN 0-8170-0958-2). Judson.

Ministering to Abortion's Aftermath. Bill Banks & Sue Banks. 144p. (Orig.). 1982. pap. 3.95 (ISBN 0-89228-057-3). Impact Bks MO.

Ministering to Alcoholics. rev. ed. John E. Keller. LC 66-22560. 1966. pap. 8.95 (ISBN 0-8066-0922-2, 10-4439). Augsburg.

Ministering to Families. Royce Money. 300p. 1987. pap. 10.95 (ISBN 0-915547-92-9). Abilene Christ U.

Ministering to Single Adults. Gene Van Note. 109p. 1978. pap. 2.95 (ISBN 0-8341-0556-X). Beacon Hill.

Ministering to the Aging. Bartholomew J. Laurello. LC 79-90992. (Paths of Life Ser.). 96p. (Orig.). 1979. pap. 2.95 (ISBN 0-8091-2268-5). Paulist Pr.

Ministering to the Lord. Roxanne Brant. 80p. (Orig.). 1973. pap. 3.95 (ISBN 0-89228-031-X). Impact Bks MO.

Ministering to the Oppressed. 2nd ed. Kenneth E. Hagin. 1983. pap. 1.00 (ISBN 0-89276-027-3). Hagin Ministries.

Ministering to the Sick. Tay Wallace. 60p. (Orig.). 1981. pap. 3.00 (ISBN 0-933643-06-3). Grace World Outreach.

Ministering to Young Adults. Carol Gura. (Illus.). 200p. 1987. spiralbound 28.95 (ISBN 0-88489-179-8). St Mary's.

Ministering to Your Family. Kenneth E. Hagin & Kenneth Hagin, Jr. 1986. pap. 1.50 (ISBN 0-89276-407-4). Hagin Ministries.

Ministering to Youth. Cecil R. Guiles. 1973. 5.25 (ISBN 0-87148-551-6); pap. 4.25 (ISBN 0-87148-552-4); instrs. guide 4.95 (ISBN 0-87148-834-5). Pathway Pr.

Ministering to Youth. David Roadcup. LC 79-92586. (Bible College Textbooks Ser.). 256p. (Orig.). 1980. pap. text ed. 6.95 (ISBN 0-87239-395-X, 88582). Standard Pub.

Ministering to Youth: A Guide for Parents, Teachers & Youth Workers. Michael G. Wensing. 120p. (Orig.). 1982. pap. 4.95 (ISBN 0-8189-0444-5). Alba.

Ministerio de Todo Creyente. David Haney. Ed. by Jose Luis Martinez. Tr. by Guillermo Kratzig. 200p. 1984. pap. 4.75 (ISBN 0-311-09099-0). Casa Bautista.

Ministerio Ideal, 2 vols, Vols. 1 & 2. C. H. Spurgeon. Vol. 1. 3.95 (ISBN 0-85151-410-3); Vol. 2. 3.95 (ISBN 0-85151-411-1). Banner of Truth.

Minister's Annual: Preaching in 1987. Jim Morentz & Doris Morentz. 432p. 1986. 9.95 (ISBN 0-687-26990-3). Abingdon.

Minister's Annual: Preaching in 1988. Jim Morentz & Doris Morentz. 496p. 1987. 12.95 (ISBN 0-687-26991-1). Abingdon.

Ministers As Leaders. Robert D. Dale. LC 84-9501. (Broadman Leadership Ser.). 1984. pap. 4.95 (ISBN 0-8054-3110-1). Broadman.

Ministers for the Nineteen Eighties. Ed. by Jock Stein. 120p. 1980. pap. 6.00x (ISBN 0-905312-09-0, Pub. by Scot Acad Pr). Longwood Pub Group.

Minister's Guide for Special Occasions. Ed. by Zeno C. Tharp. Repr. 7.95 (ISBN 0-87148-553-2). Pathway Pr.

Minister's Handbook. Orlando L. Tibbetts. 224p. 1986. 9.95 (ISBN 0-8170-1088-2). Judson.

Minister's Library, Vol. I. Cyril J. Barber. 1985. 19.95 (ISBN 0-8024-5296-5). Moody.

Minister's Library, Vol. 2. Cyril J. Barber. 1987. text ed. 23.95 (ISBN 0-8024-5299-X). Moody.

Ministers Manual. Ed. by Herbert L. Beierle. 1978. 10.00 (ISBN 0-940480-03-4). U of Healing.

Minister's Manual. 2nd ed. Ed. by Herbert L. Beierle. 1985. 10.00 (ISBN 0-940480-20-4). U of Healing.

Minister's Manual. rev. ed. 1970. Repr. of 1960 ed. 5.95 (ISBN 0-916035-04-2). Evangel Indiana.

Ministers Manual for Nineteen Eighty-Six. Ed. by James W. Cox. LC 25-21658. 352p. 1985. 14.45 (ISBN 0-06-061595-8, HarpR). Har-Row.

Ministers Manual for 1987. Ed. by James W. Cox. 1986. 14.45 (ISBN 0-317-52366-X, HarpR). Har-Row.

Ministers Manual Ser, 3 vols. Compiled by William E. Pickthorn. Incl. Vol. 1, Services for Special Occasions (ISBN 0-88243-547-7, 02-0547); Vol. 2, Services for Weddings & Funerals (ISBN 0-88243-548-5, 02-0548); Vol. 3, Services for Ministers & Workers (ISBN 0-88243-549-3, 02-0549). LC 65-13222. 1965. Set. 13.95 (ISBN 0-88243-544-2, 02-0544); 4.95 ea. Gospel Pub.

Minister's Marriage Handbook. rev. ed. James L. Christensen. 160p. 1974. Repr. 10.95 (ISBN 0-8007-1424-5). Revell.

Minister's Marriage Manual. Samuel W. Hutton. 1968. 6.95 (ISBN 0-8010-4031-0). Baker Bk.

Ministers of Christ. John P. Meyer. 1963. 6.95 (ISBN 0-8100-0042-3, 15N0328). Northwest Pub.

Ministers of God, Ministers of the People: Testimonies of Faith from Nicaragua. Teofilo Cabestrero. Tr. by Robert R. Barr from Span. LC 83-6306. Orig. Title: Ministros De Dios, Ministros Del Pueblo. (Illus.). 160p. (Orig.). 1983. pap. 6.95 (ISBN 0-88344-335-X). Orbis Bks.

Minister's Prayer Book: An Order of Prayers & Readings. Ed. by John W. Doberstein. LC 85-16212. 512p. 1986. 12.95 (ISBN 0-8006-0760-0, 1-760). Fortress.

Minister's Saturday Night. Robert L. Eddy. LC 79-23819. (Orig.). 1980. pap. 6.95 (ISBN 0-8298-0382-3). Pilgrim NY.

Minister's Service Book. Jesse Jai McNeil. 212p. 1982. 7.95 (ISBN 0-8028-3580-5). Eerdmans.

Minister's Service Book. Myer Pearlman. 4.95 (ISBN 0-88243-551-5, 02-0551). Gospel Pub.

Minister's Service Manual. Clyne Buxton. text ed. 8.95 (ISBN 0-87148-584-2). Pathway Pr.

Ministers Service Manual. Free Church. 1981. 5.95 (ISBN 0-911802-48-7). Free Church Pubns.

Minister's Service Manual. Samuel W. Hutton. 1964. 8.95 (ISBN 0-8010-4035-3). Baker Bk.

Minister's Spiritual Life. E. W. McMillan. 1959. 4.50 (ISBN 0-88027-009-8). Firm Foun Pub.

Minister's Wife: Her Role in Nineteenth Century American Evangelicalism. Leonard Sweet. 323p. 1983. text ed. 29.95 (ISBN 0-87722-283-5). Temple U Pr.

Ministries for the Lord: A Resource Guide & Directory of Catholic Church Vocations for Men, 1985. The National Conference of Religious Vocation Directors. 128p. (Orig.). 1985. pap. 4.95 (ISBN 0-8091-2724-5). Paulist Pr.

Ministries: Sharing God's Gifts. James B. Dunning. LC 80-52058. (Illus.). 136p. (Orig.). 1980. pap. 5.95 (ISBN 0-88489-123-2). St Marys.

Ministries Through Non-Parish Institutions. William E. Ramsden. LC 80-22294. (Into Our Third Century Ser.). 96p. (Orig.). 1981. pap. 4.95 (ISBN 0-687-27037-5). Abingdon.

Ministry. Joseph T. Lienhard. (Message of the Fathers of the Church Ser.: Vol. 8). 15.00 (ISBN 0-89453-348-7); pap. 7.95 (ISBN 0-89453-320-7). M Glazier.

Ministry. Edward Schillebeeckx. 160p. 1981. 12.95 (ISBN 0-8245-0030-X). Crossroad NY.

Ministry. Edward Schillebeeckx. Tr. by John Bowden. 176p. 1984. pap. 9.95 (ISBN 0-8245-0638-3). Crossroad NY.

Ministry after Freud. Allison Stokes. (Illus.). 256p. 1985. pap. 10.95 (ISBN 0-8298-0569-9). Pilgrim NY.

Ministry & Education in Conversation. Ed. by Mary C. Boys. LC 80-53204. 160p. (Orig.). 1981. pap. 6.95 (ISBN 0-88489-126-7). St Mary's.

Ministry & Imagination. Urban T. Holmes, III. 288p. 1981. pap. 5.50 (ISBN 0-8164-2351-2, HarpR). Har-Row.

Ministry & Medicine in Human Relations. facs. ed. New York Academy Of Medicine. Ed. by Iago Galdston. LC 77-142682. (Essay Index Reprint Ser). 1955. 17.00 (ISBN 0-8369-2120-8). Ayer Co Pubs.

Ministry & Message of Paul. Richard N. Longenecker. (Contemporary Evangelical Perspective Ser). 1971. kivar 6.95 (ISBN 0-310-28341-8, 12234P). Zondervan.

Ministry & Mission: Theological Reflections for the Life of the Church. James F. Hopewell et al. Ed. by Barbara B. Taylor. 192p. (Orig.). 1985. pap. 9.95x (ISBN 0-935311-00-9). Post Horn Pr.

Ministry & Music. Robert H. Mitchell. LC 77-20815. 164p. 1978. pap. 8.95 (ISBN 0-664-24186-7). Westminster.

Ministry & Solitude: The Ministry of Laity & Clergy in Church & Society. James C. Fenhagen. 128p. 1981. 9.95 (ISBN 0-8164-0498-4, HarpR). Har-Row.

Ministry Burnout. John A. Sanford. 144p. 1982. 5.95 (ISBN 0-8091-2465-3). Paulist Pr.

Ministry by Objectives. Daniel L. Mead & Darrel J. Allen. LC 78-59182. (Evangelical Leadership Preparation Ser.). 80p. 1978. pap. 3.95 (ISBN 0-910566-84-4). Evang Tchr.

Ministry by the People: Theological Education by Extension. Ed. by F. Ross Kinsler. 348p. (Orig.). 1983. pap. 12.95 (ISBN 0-88344-334-1). Orbis Bks.

Ministry Explosion. Robert J. Hater. 96p. (Orig.). 1979. pap. 3.25 (ISBN 0-697-01709-5). Wm C Brown.

Ministry Gifts Study Guide. Kenneth E. Hagin. 1981. pap. 10.00 spiral bdg. (ISBN 0-89276-092-3). Hagin Ministries.

Ministry Ideabank. John H. Krahn & Betty J. Foster. 136p. (Orig.). 1981. pap. text ed. 6.75 (ISBN 0-89536-488-3, 1314). CSS of Ohio.

Ministry Ideabank III. John Krahn & Betty J. Foster. (Orig.). 1987. pap. price not set (ISBN 0-89536-895-1, 7881). CSS of Ohio.

Ministry Ideabank No. 2. John Krahn & Betty J. Foster. 1986. 7.50 (ISBN 0-89536-801-3, 6819). CSS of Ohio.

Ministry in Historical Perspectives. rev. ed. Ed. by H. Richard Niebuhr & Daniel D. Williams. LC 80-8899. (Ministers Paperback Library). 384p. 1983. pap. 8.95 (ISBN 0-06-066232-8, RD 354, HarpR). Har-Row.

Ministry in Transition: A Case Study of Theological Education. Yoshio Fukuyama. LC 72-1395. 200p. 1973. 22.50x (ISBN 0-271-01129-7). Pa St U Pr.

Ministry of a Prophet. Kenneth E. Hagin. 1968. pap. 1.00 (ISBN 0-89276-009-5). Hagin Ministries.

Ministry of All Christians. Norman Pittenger. 96p. 1983. pap. 5.95 (ISBN 0-8192-1323-3). Morehouse.

Ministry of Angels. Gordon Lindsay. 1.25 (ISBN 0-89985-018-9). Christ Nations.

Ministry of Angels. Joy Shell. 1977. pap. 3.95 (ISBN 0-8065-0586-9). Citadel Pr.

Ministry of Believers. Emeric A. Lawrence. 24p. (Orig.). 1982. pap. text ed. 1.25 (ISBN 0-8146-1276-8). Liturgical Pr.

Ministry of Casting Out Demons, Vol. 7. Gordon Lindsay. (Sorcery & Spirit World Ser.). 1.25 (ISBN 0-89985-090-1). Christ Nations.

Ministry of Christian Teaching. Donald S. Aultman. 111p. 1966. 4.95 (ISBN 0-87148-554-0); pap. 3.95 (ISBN 0-87148-555-9). Pathway Pr.

Ministry of Clowning. Compiled by Everett Robertson. LC 82-71444. 1983. pap. 5.95 (ISBN 0-8054-7522-2). Broadman.

Ministry of Communion. Michael Kwatera. (Illus.). 48p. 1983. pap. text ed. 1.25 (ISBN 0-8146-1292-X). Liturgical Pr.

Ministry of Counseling. Carol Murphy. 1983. pap. 2.50x (ISBN 0-87574-067-7, 067). Pendle Hill.

Ministry of Development in Evangelical Perspective: A Symposium on the Social & Spiritual Mandate. Ed. by Carl F. Henry & Robert L. Hancock. LC 78-27821. 1979. pap. 4.95 (ISBN 0-87808-164-X). William Carey Lib.

Ministry of God's Word. Watchman Nee. Tr. by Stephen Kaung. 1971. 5.50 (ISBN 0-935008-27-6); pap. 4.25 (ISBN 0-935008-28-4). Christian Fellow Pubs.

Ministry of Healing: Readings in the Catholic Health Care Ministry. Catholic Health Association Staff. LC 81-12201. 120p. 1981. pap. 7.50 (ISBN 0-686-85771-2). Cath Health.

Ministry of Health & Healing. Ed. by Otto Elser. 1986. pap. 7.50 (ISBN 0-8309-0451-4). Herald Hse.

Ministry of Helps Study Course. Buddy Bell. 40p. (Orig.). 1983. pap. 1.95 (ISBN 0-89274-292-5). Harrison Hse.

Ministry of Intercession. F. J. Huegel. LC 76-15861. (Orig.). 1971. pap. 2.95 (ISBN 0-87123-365-7, 200365). Bethany Hse.

Ministry of Intercession. Andrew Murray. 208p. 1982. pap. text ed. 3.50 (ISBN 0-88368-114-5). Whitaker Hse.

Ministry of Intercessory Prayer. rev. ed. Andrew Murray. LC 81-18011. 1981. pap. 3.95 (ISBN 0-87123-353-3, 210353). Bethany Hse.

Ministry of Lectors. James Wallace. 48p. 1981. softcover 1.25 (ISBN 0-8146-1229-6). Liturgical Pr.

Ministry of Liturgical Environment. Thomas G. Simon & James M. Fitzpatrick. 48p. (Orig.). 1984. pap. 1.25 (ISBN 0-8146-1354-3). Liturgical Pr.

Ministry of Love: A Handbook for Visiting the Aged. Stephen V. Doughty. LC 84-71674. 96p. (Orig.). 1984. pap. 3.95 (ISBN 0-87793-324-3). Ave Maria.

Ministry of Music. Kenneth W. Osbeck. LC 61-14865. 192p. 1975. pap. 5.95x (ISBN 0-8254-3410-6). Kregel.

Ministry of Music in the Black Church. J. Wendell Mapson, Jr. 1984. pap. 5.95 (ISBN 0-8170-1057-2). Judson.

Ministry of Musicians. Edward J. McKenna. 40p. (Orig.). 1983. pap. 1.25 (ISBN 0-8146-1295-4). Liturgical Pr.

Ministry of Pastoral Counseling. James D. Hamilton. (Source Books for Ministers Ser). 1972. pap. 5.95 (ISBN 0-8010-4069-8). Baker Bk.

Ministry of Peter, John & Paul. A. E. Booth. 1982. pap. 1.25 (ISBN 0-88172-004-6). Believers Bkshelf.

Ministry of Prayer. 3rd ed. Donald W. Bartow. 165p. 1983. pap. 7.95 (ISBN 0-938736-22-1). LIFE ENRICH.

Ministry of Prayer. Womens Anglow Staff. (Cornerstone Ser.). 32p. 1983. pap. 2.00 (ISBN 0-930756-77-0, 533008). Aglow Pubns.

Ministry of Reconciliation: Modern Lessons from Scripture & Sacrament. David W. Barry. LC 75-4630. 129p. (Orig.). 1975. pap. 2.95 (ISBN 0-8189-0317-1). Alba.

Ministry of Servers. Michael Kwatera. (Illus.). 48p. (Orig.). 1982. pap. 1.25 (ISBN 0-8146-1300-4). Liturgical Pr.

Ministry of Service. Cardinal Joseph Bernardin. 40p. 1986. pap. 1.25 (ISBN 0-8146-1485-X). Liturgical Pr.

Ministry of Teaching. David C. Plake & Roberta S. Plake. LC 82-81509. (Workers Training Ser.). 128p. (Orig.). 1982. pap. 2.50 (ISBN 0-88243-567-1, 02-0567). Gospel Pub.

Ministry of Teaching Toddlers. Lynda T. Boardman. 92p. (Orig.). 1983. pap. 3.95 (ISBN 0-8341-0820-8). Beacon Hill.

Ministry of the Cantor. James Hansen. (Ministry Ser.). 40p. 1985. pap. 1.25 (ISBN 0-8146-1387-X). Liturgical Pr.

Ministry of the Christian School Guidance Counselor. James W. Deuink. (Illus.). 175p. (Orig.). 1984. pap. 6.60 (ISBN 0-89084-273-6). Bob Jones Univ Pr.

Ministry of the Church & Pastor. Paul L. Walker. 107p. 1965. 5.25 (ISBN 0-87148-556-7); pap. 4.25 (ISBN 0-87148-557-5). Pathway Pr.

Ministry of the Cradle Roll. Betty Bowes. (Orig.). 1970. pap. 1.95 (ISBN 0-8341-0190-4). Beacon Hill.

Ministry of the Laity. James D. Anderson & Ezra E. Jones. LC 84-48211. 224p. 1985. 14.45 (ISBN 0-06-060194-9, HarpR). Har-Row.

Ministry of the Small Group Leader. Eugene A. Skelton. 48p. 1986. pap. 1.25 (ISBN 0-8146-1487-6). Liturgical Pr.

Ministry of the Spirit. A. J. Gordon. 160p. 1986. pap. 3.95 (ISBN 0-87123-843-8, 210843). Bethany Hse.

Ministry of the Volunteer Teacher. Charles R. Foster. 96p. 1986. pap. 6.95 (ISBN 0-687-27040-5). Abingdon.

Ministry of Ushering: Leader's Guide. Malcolm C. Fry & Milton Crowson. 1980. pap. 2.50 (ISBN 0-89265-066-4). Randall Hse.

Ministry of Ushers. Gregory F. Smith. 32p. (Orig.). 1980. pap. 1.25 (ISBN 0-8146-1207-5). Liturgical Pr.

Ministry of Visitation. John T. Sisemore. LC 54-2969. 1954. 1.25 (ISBN 0-88243-550-7, 02-0550). Gospel Pub.

Ministry of Welcome: A Guide for Ushers & Greeters. Paul Blom. 32p. (Orig.). 1980. pap. 2.95 (ISBN 0-8066-1806-X, 10-4442). Augsburg.

Ministry of Worship. Paul L. Walker. LC 81-84605. 199p. (Orig.). 1981. pap. text ed. 5.95 (ISBN 0-87148-576-1). Pathway Pr.

Ministry to Inactives: A Manual for Establishing a Listening Witness to Inactive Members. Gerhard Knutson. 40p. (Orig.). 1983. pap. 3.95 (ISBN 0-8066-1729-2, 10-4443). Augsburg.

Ministry to Persons: Organization & Administration. Robert Crandall. (Illus.). 96p. (Orig.). 1981. pap. 3.50 (ISBN 0-89367-070-7). Light & Life.

Ministry to Single Adults. Ed Toews. pap. 1.95 (ISBN 0-919797-48-2). Herald Pr.

Ministry to the Bereaved. L. Wayne Updike. 1986. pap. 6.00 (ISBN 0-8309-0450-6). Herald Hse.

Ministry to the Divorced: Guidance, Structure & Organization That Promote Healing in the Church. Sue Richards & Stanley Hagemeyer. 112p. 1986. text ed. 6.95 (ISBN 0-310-20051-2, 9604P). Zondervan.

Ministry to the Sick. Gerals R. Niklas & Charlotte Stefanics. LC 82-4083. 143p. (Orig.). 1982. pap. 7.95 (ISBN 0-8189-0429-1). Alba.

Ministry to the Sick & Dying. Jude J. McGeehan. (Synthesis Ser.). 1981. 1.75 (ISBN 0-8199-0836-3). Franciscan Herald.

Ministry to Word & Sacraments: History & Theology. Bernard Cooke. LC 75-36459. 688p. 1980. pap. 16.95 (ISBN 0-8006-1440-2, 1-1440). Fortress.

Ministry: Traditions, Tensions, Transitions. William J. Bausch. LC 81-86345. 192p. 1982. pap. 7.95 (ISBN 0-89622-153-9). Twenty-Third.

Ministry with Older Persons: A Guide for Clergy & Congregations. Arthur H. Becker. LC 86-1101. 228p. (Orig.). 1986. pap. 12.95 (ISBN 0-8066-2196-6, 10-4444). Augsburg.

Ministry with Remarried Persons. Richard P. Olson & Carole D. Pia-Terry. 160p. 1984. pap. 6.95 (ISBN 0-8170-0990-6). Judson.

Ministry with the Aging: Designs-Challenges-Foundations. Ed. by William M. Clements. LC 80-7739. 1983. pap. 9.95 (ISBN 0-06-061497-8, RD/452, HarpR). Har-Row.

Ministry with the Community College: A Lutheran Perspective. Ed. by Phil Schroeder. (Illus.). 75p. 1982. pap. text ed. 2.75 (ISBN 0-9609438-0-3). Luth Coun IL.

Ministry with the Confined. Ed. by Luella H. Slover. (Orig.). 1981. pap. 4.50 (ISBN 0-8309-0318-6). Herald Hse.

Ministry with the Divorced. Peter R. Monkers. 128p. 1985. pap. text ed. 7.95 (ISBN 0-8298-0566-4). Pilgrim NY.

Ministry with Young Adults. Luella H. Slover. 1980. pap. 4.00 (ISBN 0-8309-0283-X). Herald Hse.

Ministry with Young Couples: A Pastor's Planbook. Douglas W. Johnson. 128p. (Orig.). 1985. pap. 6.95 (ISBN 0-687-27043-X). Abingdon.

Ministry, Word, & Sacraments: An Enchiridion. Martin Chemitz. Tr. by Luther Poellot. 1981. pap. 17.50 (ISBN 0-570-03295-4, 15-2730). Concordia.

Minjung Theology: People As the Subjects of History. Ed. by Theological Concerns of the Christian Conference of Asia Commission. LC 83-7279. 224p. (Orig.). 1983. pap. 9.95 (ISBN 0-88344-336-8). Orbis Bks.

Minnesota Christmas Book. Patricia C. Johnston. LC 85-90344. (Illus.). 96p. 1985. text ed. 27.50 (ISBN 0-942934-08-3). Johnston Pub.

Minoan-Mycenaean Religion. Martin P. Nilsson. LC 70-162300. 1950. 15.00 (ISBN 0-8196-0273-6). Biblo.

Minor Buddhist Texts, 2 parts in 1. Giuseppe Tucci. 1986. Repr. 28.00 (ISBN 81-208-0190-3, Pub. by Motilal Banarsidass). South Asia Bks.

Minor Ecclesiastical, Domestic & Garden Architecture of Southern Spain. A. Whittlesey. 1976. lib. bdg. 75.00 (ISBN 0-8490-2259-2). Gordon Pr.

Minor Prophets. Albert Barnes. 23.95 (ISBN 0-8010-0842-5). Baker Bk.

Minor Prophets. G. Campbell-Morgan. 160p. 1960. 10.95 (ISBN 0-8007-0208-5). Revell.

Minor Prophets. rev ed. Charles L. Feinberg. LC 76-44088. 384p. 1976. 17.95 (ISBN 0-8024-5306-6). Moody.

Minor Prophets. H. A. Ironside. 11.95 (ISBN 0-87213-379-6). Loizeaux.

Minor Prophets. Theodore Laetsch. 1956. 16.95 (ISBN 0-570-03249-0, 15-1719). Concordia.

Minor Prophets. Jack P. Lewis. 1966. pap. 3.95 (ISBN 0-8010-5509-1). Baker Bk.

Minor Prophets. Rubel Shelly. pap. 2.50 (ISBN 0-89315-161-0). Lambert Bk.

Minor Prophets, 3 vols. Frederick A. Tatford. 1214p. 1982. Set. lib. bdg. 44.95 Smythe Sewn (ISBN 0-86524-135-X, 7000). Klock & Klock.

Minor Prophets: A Study of Micah Through Malachi. Clinton R. Gill. (Bible Study Textbook Ser.). (Illus.). 1971. 15.90 (ISBN 0-89900-027-4). College Pr Pub.

Minor Prophets: An Expositional Commentary (Hosea-Jonah, Vol. 1. James M. Boice. 272p. 1983. 12.95 (ISBN 0-310-21550-1, 10423). Zondervan.

Minor Prophets: An Expositional Commenatry (Micah-Malachi, Vol. 2. James M. Boice. 1986. 14.95 (ISBN 0-310-21580-3, 10424). Zondervan.

Minor Prophets: Hosea, Joel, Amos, Obadiah, Jonah, Micah. Gordon Lindsay. (Old Testament Ser.). 1.25 (ISBN 0-89985-156-8). Christ Nations.

Minor Prophets in the Light of Christian Science. Max Kappeler. LC 64-36062. 214p. 1962. 14.00 (ISBN 0-85241-041-7). Kappeler Inst Pub.

Minor Prophets: Nahum, Habakkuk, Zephaniah, Haggai. Zechariah, Malachi. Gordon Lindsay. (Old Testament Ser.). 1.25 (ISBN 0-89985-157-6). Christ Nations.

Minor Prophets of Israel. Irving L. Jensen. (Bible Self-Study Guides Ser.). 112p. (Orig.). 1975. pap. 3.25 (ISBN 0-8024-1028-6). Moody.

Minor Prophets of Judah. Irving L. Jensen. (Bible Self-Study Guide Ser.). 112p. 1976. pap. 3.25 (ISBN 0-8024-1029-4). Moody.

Minor Prophets: The Prophets of the Decline: Hosea-Jonan. P. T. Butler. LC 79-1493. (Bible Study Textbook). 1968. 15.90 (ISBN 0-317-03548-7). College Pr Pub.

Minor Prophets: With a Commentary Explanatory & Practical & Introductions to the Several Books, 2 vols. Edward B. Pusey. 1986. Repr. of 1885 ed. Set. lib. bdg. 45.00 (ISBN 0-89941-505-9). W S Hein.

Minor Tractates. I. Epstein. 480p. 1965. write for info. (ISBN 0-900689-86-2). Soncino Pr.

Minor Traditions of British Mythology. Lewis Spence. LC 72-84001. Repr. of 1948 ed. 31.00 (ISBN 0-405-08989-9). Ayer Co Pubs.

Minor Upanishads. Tr. by Swami Madhavananda. pap. 2.00 (ISBN 0-87481-061-2). Vedanta Pr.

Minor Works. Lactantius. (Fathers of the Church Ser: Vol. 54). 1965. 15.95x (ISBN 0-8132-0054-7). Cath U Pr.

Minority Religions in America. rev. ed. William J. Whalen. LC 81-3664. 222p. (Orig.). 1981. pap. 7.95 (ISBN 0-8189-0413-5). Alba.

Minority Religions in America. William J. Whalen. LC 79-38979. 312p. (Orig.). 1972. pap. 7.95 (ISBN 0-8189-0239-6). Alba.

Minsk Ghetto. Hersh Smolar. Tr. by Max Rosenfeld from Yiddish. 1987. 18.95 (ISBN 0-89604-068-2); pap. 13.95 (ISBN 0-89604-069-0). Holocaust Pubns.

Minute in the Morning: One Hundred & Fifty Devotionals for Women. Pat A. Baker. 1984. pap. 4.95 (ISBN 0-8010-0864-6). Baker Bk.

Minutes of the General Assembly of the Church of God 1980. 107p. 1981. pap. 1.50 (ISBN 0-87148-575-3). Pathway Pr.

Minutes of the General Assembly of the Church of God, 1978. 114p. 1979. 4.75 (ISBN 0-87148-572-9); pap. 1.00 (ISBN 0-87148-573-7). Pathway Pr.

Minutes of the General Assembly of the Church of God: 1982. 1983. text ed. 6.95 (ISBN 0-87148-577-X); pap. 5.95 (ISBN 0-87148-578-8). Pathway Pr.

Minutes of the Presbyterian Church in America: 1706-1788. Date not set. text ed. price not set (ISBN 0-685-84634-2). Presby Hist.

Mir Trogn Agezang Yiddish Songbook. Eleanor G. Mlotek. 239p. 1977. pap. 8.50. Workmen's Circle.

Miracle & Power of Blessing. Maurice Berquist. 1984. pap. 2.95 (ISBN 0-87162-408-7, D8556). Warner Pr.

Miracle at the Manger. Sisters of the Community of Jesus. LC 84-62045. (Illus., Orig.). 1984. pap. 9.95 (ISBN 0-941478-32-7). Paraclete Pr.

Miracle for Sarah. Regine Schindler. Tr. of Und Sara Lacht. (Illus.). 28p. 1985. 7.95 (ISBN 0-687-27044-8). Abingdon.

Miracle in Darien. Bob Slosser. LC 79-83791. 1979. 5.95 (ISBN 0-88270-355-2). Bridge Pub.

Miracle in the Early Christian World: A Study in Sociohistorical Method. Howard C. Kee. LC 83-40004. 304p. 1983. 30.00x (ISBN 0-300-03008-8); pap. 9.95 (ISBN 0-300-03632-9, Y-570). Yale U Pr.

Miracle in the Mirror. Mark Buntain et al. LC 81-70999. (Illus.). 155p. 1982. pap. 3.50 (ISBN 0-87123-352-5, 210352). Bethany Hse.

Miracle Man of Japan: The Life & Work of Masaharu Taniguchi, One of the Most Influential Spiritual Leaders of Our Time. Roy E. Davis. (Illus.). 160p. (Orig.). pap. 3.00 (ISBN 0-87707-048-2). CSA Pr.

Miracle of Abduction. William J. Williams. LC 84-82540. 160p. (Orig.). 1985. 12.95 (ISBN 0-930371-02-X); pap. 8.95 (ISBN 0-930371-03-8). Epistemics.

Miracle of Agape Love. Joseph F. Manning. 160p. 1977. pap. 2.95 (ISBN 0-88368-079-3). Whitaker Hse.

Miracle of Anne. Bruce Shelly. 90p. 1974. pap. 4.50 (ISBN 0-911336-55-9). Sci of Mind.

Miracle of Christmas. Kay M. Glaesner. (Orig.). 1982. pap. 2.95 (ISBN 0-937172-39-1). JLJ Pubs.

Miracle of Dialogue. Reuel L. Howe. 1963. pap. 6.95 (ISBN 0-86683-886-4, SP9, HarpR). Har-Row.

Miracle of Existence. Henry Margenau. 143p. 1987. pap. 9.95 (ISBN 0-87773-407-0). Shambhala Pubns.

Miracle of Israel. Gordon Lindsay. 1.95 (ISBN 0-89985-188-6). Christ Nations.

Miracle of Jesus: Then & Now. Alfons Weiser. Ed. by Robert Karris. Tr. by David L. Tiede. (Herald Biblical Bklts.). 1972. pap. 1.25 (ISBN 0-8199-0519-4). Franciscan Herald.

Miracle of Love: Mother Teresa of Calcutta, Her Missionaries of Charity, & Her Co-Workers. Kathryn Spink. LC 81-47717. (Illus.). 256p. 1982. 15.00 (ISBN 0-06-067497-0, HarpR). Har-Row.

Miracle of Love: Stories About Neem Karoli Baba. Ram Dass. (Illus.). 1979. pap. 12.95 (ISBN 0-525-47611-3, 01257-380). Dutton.

Miracle of Mindfulness! A Manual on Meditation. Thich N. Hanh. LC 76-7747. (Illus.). 1976. pap. 7.95 (ISBN 0-8070-1119-3, BP546). Beacon Pr.

Miracle of Prayer: Operation Esther. Harvey Ward. Ed. by Diane Floyd & Judith Kinnaird. LC 87-70021. 128p. 1987. pap. 5.95 (ISBN 0-89221-146-6). New Leaf.

Miracle of Salvation. Carroll J. Thompson. (Illus.). 178p. (Orig.). 1986. pap. 9.95 (ISBN 1-55630-010-7). Brentwood Comm.

Miracle of the Loaves & Fishes. Illus. by Pamela F. Johnson. (Golden Bible Stories Ser.). (Illus.). 32p. 1986. 3.95 (ISBN 0-307-11622-0, Pub. by Golden Bks). Western Pub.

Miracle of the Scarlet Thread. Richard Booker. LC 80-84802. (Orig.). 1981. pap. 4.95 (ISBN 0-88270-499-0). Bridge Pub.

Miracle of the Second Advent: The Emerging New Christianity. Gene Savoy. LC 84-81232. (Illus.). 68p. 1984. text ed. 14.50 (ISBN 0-936202-04-1). Intl Comm Christ.

Miracle of Theism. J. L. Mackie. 1982. text ed. 32.50x (ISBN 0-19-824665-X); pap. text ed. 10.95x (ISBN 0-19-824682-X). Oxford U Pr.

Miracle of Touching. John Hornbrook & Dorothy F. Bakker. Ed. by Bill Keith. 160p. (Orig.). 1985. pap. 5.95 (ISBN 0-910311-28-5). Huntington Hse Inc.

Miracle on the Sepik. 2nd ed. Clarence Hall. (Illus.). 100p. 1980. pap. 3.95. Full Gospel.

Miracle on the Sepik. 2nd ed. Clarence Hall. (Illus.). 100p. 1981. pap. 3.95. Gift Pubns.

Miracle Play in England. Sidney M. Clarke. LC 65-15874. 1970. Repr. of 1897 ed. text ed. 75.00x (ISBN 0-8383-0529-6). Haskell.

Miracle Plays of Mathura. Norvin Hein. LC 75-99826. pap. 81.30 (ISBN 0-317-09863-2, 2022003). Bks Demand UMI.

Miracle Power of Believing. Theoder Laurence. 1976. (Parker). P-H.

Miracle Stories in Christian Antiquity. Susan M. Praeder. LC 86-45909. 288p. 1987. pap. 22.95 (ISBN 0-8006-2115-8, 1-2115). Fortress.

Miracle Stories of the Early Christian Tradition. Gerd Theissen. Ed. by John Riches. Tr. by Francis McDonagh. LC 82-48546. 416p. 1983. 29.95 (ISBN 0-8006-0700-7). Fortress.

Miracle to Proclaim: First-Hand Experience of Healing. Ralph A. Diorio. LC 83-18218. 224p. 1984. pap. 4.50 (ISBN 0-385-19241-X, Im). Doubleday.

Miracles. C. S. Lewis. 1978. pap. 3.95 (ISBN 0-02-086760-3, Collier). Macmillan.

Miracles. Toni Pickett. 1983. 5.95 (ISBN 0-8062-2201-8). Carlton.

Miracles: A Catholic View. Ralph McInerny. LC 86-61141. 153p. (Orig.). 1986. pap. 6.95 (ISBN 0-87973-540-6). Our Sunday Visitor.

Miracles Among You. R. Gaveston Knight. 100p. 1985. 13.50x (ISBN 0-85088-379-2, Pub. by Gomer Pr). State Mutual Bk.

Miracles & Modern Thought. Norman L. Geisler. 208p. (Orig.). 1982. pap. 7.95 (ISBN 0-310-44681-3, 12560P). Zondervan.

Miracles & Prophecies in Nineteenth-Century France. Thomas A. Kselman. (Illus.). 312p. 1983. 30.00 (ISBN 0-8135-0963-7). Rutgers U Pr.

Miracles & the Critical Mind. Colin Brown. LC 83-16600. 432p. 1984. 19.95 (ISBN 0-8028-3590-2). Eerdmans.

Miracles & the Medieval Mind: Theory, Record, & Event, 1000 to 1215. Benedicta Ward. LC 81-23106. (Middle Ages Ser.). (Illus.). 300p. 1982. 29.95x (ISBN 0-8122-7836-4). U of Pa Pr.

Miracles & the Sumrall Family. Leona S. Murphy. 205p. (Orig.). 1984. pap. 6.95 (ISBN 0-89274-325-5). Harrison Hse.

Miracles by the Sea. Ella Lindvall. (People of the Bible Ser.). (Illus.). 1984. 4.95 (ISBN 0-8024-0397-2). Moody.

Miracles by the Sea. Retold by Catherine Storr. LC 82-23022. (People of the Bible). (Illus.). 32p. 1983. PLB 10.65 (ISBN 0-8172-1983-8). Raintree Pubs.

Miracles De Nostre Dame Par Personnages, 8 Vols. 1876-1893. Set. 265.00 (ISBN 0-384-39105-2); pap. 28.00 ea.; Set. pap. 220.00 (ISBN 0-685-13516-0). Johnson Repr.

Miracles Do Happen. Briege McKenna & Henry Libersat. 170p. (Orig.). 1987. pap. 4.95 (ISBN 0-89283-316-5). Servant.

Miracles: From God or Men. Jimmy Jividen. 288p. 1987. 9.95 (ISBN 0-915547-93-7). Abilene Christ U.

Miracles In Dispute: A Continuing Debate. Ernst Keller & Marie-Luise Keller. 256p. pap. 8.95 (ISBN 0-317-31482-3, 30-1012-259). Fortress.

Miracles in El Paso. Rene Laurentin. (Illus.). 135p. 1982. pap. 6.95 (ISBN 0-89283-150-2). Servant.

Miracles in the Slums. Seth C. Rees. (Higher Christian Life Ser.). 301p. 1985. lib. bdg. 40.00 (ISBN 0-8240-6440-2). Garland Pub.

Miracles of Christ. A. B. Bruce. 1980. 20.00 (ISBN 0-86524-060-4, 9504). Klock & Klock.

Miracles of Christ. Tomie DePaola. LC 86-18297. (Illus.). 1987. price not set reinforced bdg. (ISBN 0-8234-0635-0). Holiday.

Miracles of Christ, 2 parts, Vols. 2 & 3. Gordon Lindsay. (Miracles in the Bible Ser.). 0.95 ea. Vol. 2 (ISBN 0-89985-960-7). Vol. 3 (ISBN 0-89985-960-7). Christ Nations.

Miracles of Divine Discipline, Vol. 7. Gordon Lindsay. (Miracles in the Bible Ser.). 0.95 (ISBN 0-89985-184-3). Christ Nations.

Miracles of Jesus. Lawrence G. Lovasik. (Saint Joseph Picture Bks.). flexible dg. 0.95 (ISBN 0-89942-279-9, 279). Catholic Bk Pub.

Miracles of Jesus. Rawson & Lloyd. (Children's Picture Bible Ser.). 1982. 7.95 (ISBN 0-86020-518-5, Usborne-Hayes); PLB 12.96 (ISBN 0-88110-099-4); pap. 4.95 (ISBN 0-86020-523-1). EDC.

Miracles of Jesus. David Wenham & Craig Blomberg. (Gospel Perspectives Ser.: No. 6). 1986. text ed. 30.00x (ISBN 1-85075-008-4, Pub. by JSOT Pr England); pap. text ed. 14.95x (ISBN 1-85075-009-2, Pub. by JSOT Pr England). Eisenbrauns.

Miracles of Jesus for the Intellectual. Ed. by William Tregay. LC 85-63853. 128p. (Orig.). 1986. pap. text ed. write for info. (ISBN 0-936435-03-8). Church Man pub.

Miracles of Jesus: What Really Happened? Hubert J. Richards. (What Really Happened? Ser.). 128p. 1986. pap. 5.95 (ISBN 0-89622-287-X). Twenty-Third.

Miracles of Our Lord. George MacDonald. Ed. by Rolland Hein. LC 79-22261. (Wheaton Literary Ser.). 166p. 1980. pap. 6.95 (ISBN 0-87788-547-8). Shaw Pubs.

Miracles of Prophet Muhammad. M. A. Qazi. pap. 3.50 (ISBN 0-686-18629-X). Kazi Pubns.

Miracles of the Apostles, Vol. 4. Gordon Lindsay. (Miracles in the Bible Ser.). 0.95 (ISBN 0-89985-181-9). Christ Nations.

Miracles on Tap. Frank Duff. 5.00 (ISBN 0-910984-14-X); pap. 3.50 (ISBN 0-910984-15-8). Montfort Pubns.

Miracles or Magic? rev. ed. Andre Kole & Al Janssen. 1987. pap. 5.95 (ISBN 0-89081-579-8). Harvest Hse.

Miracles or Mirages? James D. Bales. 1956. 3.00 (ISBN 0-88027-010-1). Firm Foun Pub.

Miracles: Proof of God's Power. T. L. Osborn. 96p. (Orig.). 1981. pap. 1.50 (ISBN 0-89274-185-6, HH-185). Harrison Hse.

Miracles Today. Rodney A. Kvamme. 96p. (Orig.). 1986. pap. 4.95 (ISBN 0-570-04439-1). Concordia.

Miraculous Gifts: Are They for Today? Thomas R. Edgar. 384p. 1983. 11.95 (ISBN 0-87213-133-5). Loizeaux.

Miraculous Journey of Mahomet. Marie-Rose Seguy. LC 77-5140. (Library of Illuminated Manuscripts). (Illus.). 1977. 40.00 (ISBN 0-8076-0868-8). Braziller.

Miraculous Laws of Universal Dynamics. Al G. Manning. 1964. pap. 5.95 (ISBN 0-317-46046-3). Pan Ishtar.

Mirage of the Ages: A Critique of Christianity. Andrew Tomas. 152p. 1983. 9.00 (ISBN 0-682-49999-4). Exposition Pr FL.

Mirages in the Sea of Time: The Taoist Poetry of Ts'ao T'ang. Edward H. Schafer. 1985. 18.00x (ISBN 0-520-05429-6). U of Cal Pr.

Mirando Hacia Arriba en Medio de la Enfermedad: (Looking Up...While Lying Down) John E. Biegert. (Looking Up Ser.). (Span.). 24p. (Orig.). 1983. pap. 1.25 booklet (ISBN 0-8298-0663-6). Pilgrim NY.

Miriam & the Princess of Egypt. Illus. by Graham Round. (Illus.). 16p. 1982. pap. 0.99 (ISBN 0-86683-659-4, AY8240, HarpR). Har-Row.

Miriam's Well: Rituals for Jewish Women Around the Year. Penina V. Adelman. LC 84-71828. (Illus.). 143p. (Orig.). 1986. pap. 9.95 (ISBN 0-930395-00-X); music cassette 6.00. Biblio NY.

Mirk's Festial: A Collection of Homilies. T. Erbe. (EETS ES Ser.: No. 96). Repr. of 1905 ed. 28.00 (ISBN 0-527-00296-8). Kraus Repr.

Mirour of Mans Saluacioune: A Middle English Translation of Speculum Humanae Salvationis. Avril Henry. LC 86-19364. (Middle Ages Ser.). (Illus.). 347p. 1987. text ed. 49.95x (ISBN 0-8122-8054-7). U of Pa Pr.

Mirror & the Skylight. Colin Evans. 1986. 40.00x (ISBN 0-317-54255-9, Pub. by Elmcrest Uk). State Mutual Bk.

Mirror Mind: Spirituality & Transformation. William Johnston. LC 80-8350. 192p. 1981. 10.45 (ISBN 0-06-064197-5, HarpR). Har-Row.

Mirror Mind: Spirituality & Transformation. William Johnston. LC 80-8350. 192p. 1984. pap. 6.95 (ISBN 0-06-064206-8, RD 516, HarpR). Har-Row.

Mirror, Mirror. Alice Gray & Marilyn McAuley. 144p. (Orig.). 1985. pap. 5.95 (ISBN 0-310-42951-X, 11344). Zondervan.

Mirror, Mirror... Please Lie. Pat Wellman. 86p. (Orig.). 1984. pap. 3.50 (ISBN 0-8341-0931-X). Beacon Hill.

Mirror of Charity. Aelred of Rievaulx. Tr. by Elizabeth Connor from Latin. (Cistercian Fathers Ser.: No. 17). Orig. Title: Speculum Caritatis. Date not set. pns (ISBN 0-87907-217-2); pap. pns (ISBN 0-87907-717-4). Cistercian Pubns.

Mirror of Faith. William of St. Thierry. Ed. by E. Rozanne Elder. Tr. by Thomas X. Davis from Lat. LC 78-12897. (Cistercian Fathers Ser.). (Illus.). 1979. 12.95 (ISBN 0-87907-315-2). Cistercian Pubns.

Mirror of God's Love. JoAnn H. Hunter & John Freund. 64p. 1984. pap. 2.50 (ISBN 0-916134-60-1). Pueblo Pub Co.

Mirror of Life & Death. Laurence J. Bendit. 1965. pap. 1.35 (ISBN 0-8356-0411-X, Quest). Theos Pub Hse.

Mirror of Life & Death. Laurence J. Bendit. 7.25 (ISBN 0-8356-7394-4). Theos Pub Hse.

Mirror of Light. Rodney Collin. LC 84-22141. 89p. 1985. pap. 6.95 (ISBN 0-87773-314-7, 72996-X). Shambhala Pubns.

Mirror of Medusa. Tobin Siebers. LC 82-20071. (Illus.). 180p. 1983. text ed. 26.95x (ISBN 0-520-04856-3). U of Cal Pr.

Mirror of Simple Souls. Ed. by John Griffiths. LC 81-126. (Spiritual Classics Ser.). 176p. 1981. 9.95 (ISBN 0-8245-0083-0). Crossroad NY.

Mirror of the Ministry in Modern Novels. facsimile ed. Horton Davies. LC 70-111824. (Essay Index Reprint Ser.). 1959. 19.00 (ISBN 0-8369-1601-8). Ayer Co Pubs.

Mirroring Christ's Splendour. Rev. ed. Arthur H. Ryan. 216p. 1984. pap. 7.00 (ISBN 0-912414-40-5). Lumen Christi.

Mirrors of God. Joseph Goetz. 1984. pap. 4.95 (ISBN 0-86716-031-4). St Anthony Mess Pr.

Mirrors of the Hidden Wisdom: Threads of Theosophy in Literature - I. Henry T. Edge et al. (Study Ser.: No. 7). 122p. 1981. pap. 5.95 (ISBN 0-913004-42-1). Point Loma Pub.

Miryam of Nazareth: Woman of Strength & Wisdom. Ann Johnson. LC 84-71347. 128p. (Orig.). 1984. pap. 4.95 (ISBN 0-87793-321-9). Ave Maria.

Miscarriage of Marriage. Dr. Andrew Telford. pap. 1.45 (ISBN 0-686-12750-1). Grace Pub Co.

Miscellanea Cartusiensia, Vol. 3. Raymond Boyer & Marie Brisson. Ed. by James Hogg. (Analecta Cartusiana Ser.: No. 42). (Fr. & Lat.). 101p. (Orig.). 1978. pap. 25.00 (ISBN 3-7052-0058-5, Pub by Salzburg Studies). Longwood Pub Group.

Miscellaneous Church Music. Ed. by Ernest Warburton. (John Christian Bach, 1735-1782 The Collected Works Ser.). 75.00 (ISBN 0-8240-6073-3). Garland Pub.

Miscellaneous Coptic Texts in the Dialect of Upper Egypt, 2 vols. Ed. by Ernest A. Budge. LC 77-3587. (Coptic Texts: Vol. 5). (Illus.). Repr. of 1915 ed. 135.00 (ISBN 0-404-11555-1). AMS Pr.

Miscellaneous Theological Works. Emanuel Swedenborg. LC 76-46143. 1970. cancelled (ISBN 0-87785-071-2); student ed. 12.00 (ISBN 0-87785-070-4). Swedenborg.

Miscellaneous Works of John Bunyan, Vols. 8 & 9. John Bunyan. Ed. by Richard L. Greaves. (Oxford English Texts). 1979. 79.00x (ISBN 0-19-812736-7); Vol. 9, 1981 95.00x, (ISBN 0-19-812737-5). Oxford U Pr.

Miscellaneous Writings, Eighteen Eighty-Three to Eighteen Ninety-Six. Mary B. Eddy. 1982. pap. 5.50 (ISBN 0-87952-229-1). First Church.

Mischief, Messes & God's Grace. Mimi Varberg. LC 53-1019. (Book Ser.). 56p. 1985. pap. 3.50 (ISBN 0-932305-34-2). Aglow Pubns.

Mischling, Second Degree: My Childhood in Nazi Germany. Ilse Koehn. LC 77-6189. 240p. 1977. 13.00 (ISBN 0-688-80110-2); PLB 12.88 (ISBN 0-688-84110-4). Greenwillow.

Mishkat Al-Anwar: A Niche for Lights. Al-Ghazzali. 1952. 4.25x (ISBN 0-87902-051-2). Orientalia.

Mishkat Al-Masabih, 2 vols. Tr. by J. Robson. Set. 65.00x (ISBN 0-87902-068-7); Vol. 1. 35.00 (ISBN 0-87902-297-3); Vol. 2. 35.00 (ISBN 0-87902-298-1). Orientalia.

Mishna Berurah, Vol. 3A. 1980. regular ed. 12.95 (ISBN 0-87306-233-7); large ed. 15.95 (ISBN 0-87306-198-5). Feldheim.

Mishna Berurah: Laws of Shabbath, Section, 325-344, Sec. 325-344, Vol. 3-D. 1986. 17.95 (ISBN 0-87306-408-9); pap. 13.95 (ISBN 0-87306-409-7). Feldheim.

Mishna of Idolatry Aboda Zara. Ed. by W. A. Elmslie. (Texts & Studies Ser.: No. 1, Vol. 8, Pt. 2). pap. 19.00 (ISBN 0-8115-1709-8). Kraus Repr.

Mishnah, 7 vols. with index vol. Tr. by Philip Blackman. (Eng. & Hebrew.). 4050p. 1962. 75.00 (ISBN 0-910818-00-2). Judaica Pr.

Mishnah. Yaacov D. Herzog. 15.00x (ISBN 0-686-84235-9). Bloch.

Mishnah Bervrah, Vol. 3C. Yisroel Meir Ha-Cohen. Tr. by Aviel Orenstein from Herbrew. 1984. 13.95 (ISBN 0-87306-351-1); large type ed. 17.95 (ISBN 0-87306-350-3). Feldheim.

Mishnah Bervrah, Vol. 3B. Yisroel Meir Ha-Cohen. Tr. by Aharon Feldman & Aviel Orenstein. 402p. 1981. 12.95 (ISBN 0-87306-276-0); large type ed. 15.95 (ISBN 0-87306-275-2). Feldheim.

Mishnah-Moed, Vol. 2. Hersh Goldworm. (Artscroll Mishnah Ser.). 416p. 1981. 16.95 (ISBN 0-89906-254-7); pap. 13.95 (ISBN 0-89906-255-5). Mesorah Pubns.

Mishnah-Moed, Vol. 3. Hersh Goldwurm et al. (Art Scroll Mishnah Ser.). 1980. 16.95 (ISBN 0-89906-256-3); pap. 13.95 (ISBN 0-89906-257-1). Mesorah Pubns.

Mishnah: Pirkay Avot-Ethics of the Fathers. (Home Study Program Ser.: No. 401). 7.00 (ISBN 0-686-96126-9). United Syn Bk.

Mishnah-Seder Moed, Vol. 4. Avrohom Y. Rosenberg. (Art Scroll Mishnah Ser.). 352p. 1979. 14.95 (ISBN 0-89906-258-X); pap. 11.95 (ISBN 0-89906-259-8). Mesorah Pubns.

Mishnah, the Oral Law. Harry Gersh & Robert S. Platzner. 64p. 1984. pap. 2.95 (ISBN 0-87441-390-7); tchr's 6.95 (ISBN 0-317-15397-8). Behrman.

Mishnah's Division of Agriculture: A History & Theology of Seder Zeriam. Alan J. Avery-Peck. (Brown Judaic Studies). 1985. 39.25 (ISBN 0-89130-888-1, 14-00-79); pap. 32.25 (ISBN 0-89130-889-X). Scholars Pr GA.

Mishnah's Theology of Tithing: A Study of Tractate Maaserot. Martin Jaffee. Ed. by Jacob Neusner. LC 80-29333. (Brown Judaic Studies). 1981. pap. text ed. 15.00 (ISBN 0-89130-459-2, 14-00-19). Scholars Pr GA.

Mishnayoth Tohoroth, 2 vols. 36.00 (ISBN 0-910218-88-9). Bennet Pub.

Mishnayoth Zera im, 2 vols. 30.00 (ISBN 0-910218-52-8). Bennet Pub.

Mishneh Torah. Abr. ed. Moses Maimonides. Tr. by Philip Birnbaum. (Eng. & Hebrew.). 755p. 1944. 19.50 (ISBN 0-88482-437-3). Hebrew Pub.

Mishneh Torah. Abr. ed. Moses Maimonides. Tr. by Philip Birnbaum. 344p. 1944. pap. 9.95 (ISBN 0-317-26820-1). Hebrew Pub.

Mishpokhe: A Study of New York City Jewish Family Clubs. William E. Mitchell. (New Babylon Studies in the Social Sciences Ser.: No. 30). (Illus.). 1978. 20.50x (ISBN 90-279-7695-3). Mouton.

Mision Cosmica Cumplida. 4th ed. Ralph M. Lewis. Tr. by AMORC Staff. (Span., Illus.). 403p. (Orig.). 1981. pap. 7.00 (ISBN 0-912057-73-4, GS-631). AMORC.

Misli na Kazhdij Den' Goda. Theophan the Recluse. Tr. of Thoughts on Every Day of the Year. 186p. 1982. pap. 7.00 (ISBN 0-317-28912-8). Holy Trinity.

Misli o Bogosluzhenii Pravoslavnoi Tserkvi. Saint John Kronstadt. Tr. of Thoughts on the Divine Services of the Orthdox Church. 141p. 1954. 5.00 (ISBN 0-317-28907-1). Holy Trinity.

Missing: A Family's Triumph in the Tragedy No Parent Ever Wants to Face. Fay Overly. LC 84-72590. 210p. (Orig.). 1985. pap. 6.95 (ISBN 0-89636-151-9). Accent Bks.

Missing Link: Building Quality Time with Teens. Mark J. Singer & Stephen A. Shechtman. 176p. 1985. pap. 7.95 (ISBN 0-687-27078-2). Abingdon.

Missing Message of Revelation: Natural Catastrophes Ordained by God. Judy Becker. Ed. by Evelyn Campbell. (Illus.). 374p. (Orig.). 1986. pap. 9.95 (ISBN 0-9617493-0-X). Landmark Pr GA.

Missiological Abstracts. Ed. by Doris M. Wagner. LC 84-82346. 180p. (Orig.). 1984. pap. text ed. write for info. (ISBN 0-9602638-3-7). Fuller Theol Soc.

Mission: A Film Journal. Daniel Berrigan. LC 86-45012. 160p. 1986. 14.95 (ISBN 0-06-250056-2, HarpR). Har-Row.

Mission Accomplished: What Today's Christian Must Know About God & Salvation. Michael S. Horton. 192p. 1985. pap. 6.95 (ISBN 0-8407-5947-9). Nelson.

Mission & Ministry: A Vision for the Church. John Colligan et al. LC 83-62365. 84p. (Orig.). 1983. pap. text ed. 3.95 (ISBN 0-911905-07-3). Past & Mat Rene Ctr.

Mission & Ministry: History & Theology in the Sacrament of Order. Nathan Mitchell. (Message of the Sacraments Ser.: Vol. 6). 1982. text ed. 16.95 (ISBN 0-89453-396-7); pap. 12.95 (ISBN 0-89453-292-8). M Glazier.

Mission & the Peace Witness. Robert L. Ramseyer. LC 79-16738. (Christian Peace Shelf Ser.: No. 7). 144p. 1979. pap. 6.95 (ISBN 0-8361-1896-0). Herald Pr.

Mission-Book of the Congregation of the Most Holy Redeemer. Alfonso M. Liguori & Redemptorists. 38.50 (ISBN 0-405-10843-5, 11848). Ayer Co Pubs.

Mission, Church, & Sect in Oceania. Ed. by James A. Boutilier et al. (Asao Monograph: No. 6). (Illus.). 514p. 1984. lib. bdg. 38.25 (ISBN 0-8191-3837-1, Assoc Soc Anthro Oceania); pap. text ed. 20.75 (ISBN 0-8191-3838-X, Assoc Soc Anthro Oceania). U Pr of Amer.

Mission, Church & State in a Colonial Setting: Uganda 1890-1925. H. B. Hansen. LC 84-16052. 608p. 1985. 39.95 (ISBN 0-312-53474-4). St Martin.

Mission Focus: Current Issues. Ed. by Wilbert R. Shenk. LC 80-15686. pap. 122.00 (ISBN 0-317-26607-1, 2025420). Bks Demand UMI.

Mission for Caribbean Change. Kortright Davis. (IC-Studies in the Intercultural History of Christianity: Vol. 28). 300p. 1982. pap. 32.10 (ISBN 3-8204-5732-1). P Lang Pubs.

Mission Handbook. 13th ed. North American Protestant Ministries Overseas. 1986. write for info. World Vision Intl.

Mission Handbook. 13th ed. Samuel Wilson & John Siewert. write for info. (ISBN 0-912552-55-7). Missions Adv Res Com Ctr.

Mission Impossible-Unless... Cyril Powles & Rob Nelson. (Orig.). 1973. pap. 2.95 (ISBN 0-377-03009-0). Friend Pr.

Mission in Dialogue: The Sedos Research Seminar on the Future of Mission. Ed. by Mary Motte & Joseph R. Lang. LC 82-2258. 704p. (Orig.). 1982. 35.00 (ISBN 0-88344-332-5). Orbis Bks.

Mission into Time. L. Ron Hubbard. 20.00 (ISBN 0-686-13923-2). Church Scient NY.

Mission Mania: A Cartoonist's View of the Best Two Years of Life. Val C. Bagley. (Illus.). 98p. (Orig.). 1980. pap. 3.95 (ISBN 0-88290-140-0). Horizon Utah.

Mission Music of California. Tr. by Owen F. Silva. Ed. by Arthur Bienbar. LC 77-16531. (Music Reprint Ser.). (Illus.). 1978. Repr. of 1941 ed. lib. bdg. 39.50 (ISBN 0-306-77524-7). Da Capo.

Mission of a Covenant. Paul E. Larsen. 1985. pap. 6.95 (ISBN 0-910452-61-X). Covenant.

Mission of Baha'u'llah & Other Literary Pieces. George Townshend. 160p. 1952. 10.95 (ISBN 0-85398-021-7). G Ronald Pub.

Mission of Israel. Jacob Baal-Teshuva. 1963. 10.95 (ISBN 0-8315-0046-8). Speller.

Mission of Jesus. Howard Belben. 96p. 1985. pap. 4.95 (ISBN 0-89109-529-2). NavPress.

Mission of Sorrows: Jesuit Guevari & the Pimas, 1691-1767. John L. Kessell. LC 79-101098. pap. 60.00 (ISBN 0-317-28586-6, 2055248). Bks Demand UMI.

Mission of The Messiah (Three) Ed. by Chung Hwan Kwak. (Home Study Course Ser.). 40p. (Orig.). 1980. pap. 4.00 (ISBN 0-910621-12-8). HSA Pubns.

Mission on a Mountain: The Story of Abraham & Isaac. Cecil P. Golann. LC 73-7498. (Foreign Lands Ser.). (Illus.). 32p. 1975. PLB 5.95 (ISBN 0-8225-0363-8). Lerner Pubns.

Mission Possible. Robert Schindler & Marian Schindler. 168p. 1984. pap. 5.95 (ISBN 0-88207-618-3). Victor Bks.

Mission San Xavier del Bac: A Photographic Essay on the Desert People & Their Church. Helga Teiwes. (Illus.). 32p. 1973. pap. 3.50 (ISBN 0-8165-0423-7). U of Ariz Pr.

Mission Santa Ines. Zephyrin Engelhardt. LC 85-23977. (Missions & Missionaries of California Ser.). (Illus.). 202p. (Orig.). 1986. 16.50 (ISBN 0-87461-063-X); pap. 7.50 (ISBN 0-87461-062-1). McNally & Loftin.

Mission Tales: Stories of the Historic California Missions: Missions San Diego, San Luis Rey, San Juan Capistrano, Vol. 1. Helen M. Roberts. LC 62-11254. (Illus.). 91p. 1962. 5.95x (ISBN 0-87015-244-0). Pacific Bks.

Mission Tales: Stories of the Historic California Missions: Missions San Gabriel, San Fernando Rey, San Buenaventura, Vol. 2. Helen M. Roberts. LC 62-11254. (Illus.). 92p. 1962. 5.95x (ISBN 0-87015-245-9). Pacific Bks.

Mission Tales: Stories of the Historic California Missions: Missions Santa Barbara, Santa Ines, Purisima, Vol. 3. Helen M. Roberts. LC 62-11254. (Illus.). 95p. 1962. 5.95x (ISBN 0-87015-246-7). Pacific Bks.

Mission Tales: Stories of the Historic California Missions: Missions San Luis Obispo, San Miguel, San Antonio, Vol. 4. Helen M. Roberts. LC 62-11254. (Illus.). 92p. 1962. 5.95x (ISBN 0-87015-247-5). Pacific Bks.

Mission Tales: Stories of the Historic California Missions: Missions Soledad, San Carlos, San Juan Bautista, Vol. 5. Helen M. Roberts. LC 62-11254. (Illus.). 88p. 1962. 5.95x (ISBN 0-87015-248-3). Pacific Bks.

Mission Theology, Nineteen Forty Eight to Nineteen Seventy-Five: Years of Worldwide Creative Tension--Ecumenical, Evangelical & Roman Catholic. Rodger C. Bassham. LC 79-17116. 1980. 10.95 (ISBN 0-87808-330-8). William Carey Lib.

Mission to Asia. Christopher Dawson. (Medieval Academy Reprints for Teaching Ser.). 228p. 1981. pap. 6.95 (ISBN 0-8020-6436-1). U of Toronto Pr.

Mission to Latin America: The Successes & Failures of a Twentieth-Century Crusade. Gerald M. Costello. LC 78-12974. 319p. (Orig.). 1979. pap. 2.49 (ISBN 0-88344-312-0). Orbis Bks.

Mission to the Poorest. M. R. Loew. 184p. 1984. pap. 7.95 (ISBN 0-7220-5524-2). Chr Classics.

Mission Trends: Crucial Issues in Mission Today, No. 1. Ed. by Gerald H. Anderson & Thomas F. Stransky. LC 74-81222. (Mission Trend Ser.). (Orig.). 1974. pap. 4.95 (ISBN 0-8091-1843-2). Paulist Pr.

Mission Trends: "Evangelization", No. 2. Gerald H. Anderson & Thomas F. Stranskey. LC 75-29836. (Mission Trend Ser.). 288p. 1976. pap. 4.95 (ISBN 0-8091-1900-5). Paulist Pr.

Mission Trends: Faith Meets Faith, No. 5. Ed. by Gerald Anderson & Thomas Stransky. LC 81-80983. 320p. (Orig.). 1981. pap. 4.95 (ISBN 0-8091-2356-8). Paulist Pr.

Mission Trends: Faith Meets Faith, No. 5. Ed. by Gerald H. Anderson & Thomas F. Stransky. (Mission Trends Ser.). 320p. (Orig.). 1981. pap. 3.95 (ISBN 0-8028-1821-8). Eerdmans.

Mission Trends: Liberation Theologies, No. 4. Ed. by Thomas Stransky & Gerald H. Anderson. LC 78-70827. (Mission Trend Ser.). 304p. 1979. pap. 4.95 (ISBN 0-8091-2185-9). Paulist Pr.

Mission Trends: Liberation Theologies in North America & Europe, No. 4. Ed. by Gerald Anderson & Thomas Stransky. LC 78-70827. 1978. pap. 3.95 (ISBN 0-8028-1709-2). Eerdmans.

Mission Trends: Third World Theologies, No. 3. Ed. by Gerald H. Anderson & Thomas F. Stansky. LC 76-24451. (Mission Trend Ser.). 264p. 1976. pap. 4.95 (ISBN 0-8091-1984-6). Paulist Pr.

Missionaries, Chinese & Diplomats. Paul A. Varg. LC 76-30301. 1977. Repr. lib. bdg. 23.00x (ISBN 0-374-98071-3, Octagon). Hippocrene Bks.

Missionary Administration in the Local Church. Reginald L. Matthews. 1972. 3.95 (ISBN 0-87227-002-5); pap. 2.95 (ISBN 0-87227-011-4). Reg Baptist.

Missionary Adventures in the South Pacific. David Crawford & Leona Crawford. LC 67-15137. 1967. 5.50 (ISBN 0-8048-0403-6). C E Tuttle.

Missionary Censuses of Hawaii. Robert C. Schmitt. (Pacific Anthropological Records: No. 20). 50p. pap. 5.00 (ISBN 0-910240-66-3). Bishop Mus.

Missionary Conversations with Protestant Sectarians. Kyrill Archpriest Zaits. 49p. (Orig.). 1985. pap. 2.00 (ISBN 0-317-30291-4). Holy Trinity.

Missionary Discipleship: The Story of R. E. & Ella Thompson. R. E. Thompson & Ella Thompson. (Illus.). 42p. (Orig.). 1982. pap. 3.95 (ISBN 0-942726-00-6). Missionary Intern.

Missionary Enterprise in China & America. Ed. by John K. Fairbank. LC 74-82191. (Studies in American-East Asian Relations: No. 6). 442p. 1974. text ed. 25.00x (ISBN 0-674-57655-1). Harvard U Pr.

Missionary Family. Betty Jo Kenney. LC 83-6572. (Mission Candidate Aids Ser.). 120p. 1983. pap. 5.95 (ISBN 0-87808-193-3). William Carey Lib.

Missionary Handbook. Lazar Puhalo. 49p. (Orig.). 1985. pap. text ed. 3.00 (ISBN 0-911523-00-6). Synaxis Pr.

Missionary Heroes, 2 vols. pap. 3.95 ea. Schmul Pub Co.

Missionary Heroes of Africa. James H. Morrison. LC 79-89010. Repr. of 1922 ed. 22.50x (ISBN 0-8371-1738-0, MOM&, Pub. by Negro U Pr). Greenwood.

Missionary Impact on Modern Nigeria, 1842-1914. Emmanuel A. Ayandele. (Ibadan History Ser.). 1967. pap. text ed. 17.50x (ISBN 0-582-64512-3). Humanities.

Missionary Journalist in China: Young J. Allen & His Magazines, 1860-1883. Adrian A. Bennett. LC 81-19761. (Illus.). 336p. 1983. 28.00x (ISBN 0-8203-0615-0). U of Ga Pr.

Missionary Kid, MK. rev. ed. Edward E. Danielson. LC 84-12655. (Mission Candidate Aids Ser.). (Illus.). 104p. 1985. pap. 5.95 (ISBN 0-87808-745-1). William Carey Lib.

Missionary Labours & Scenes in Southern Africa. Robert Moffat. (Landmarks in Anthropology Ser). (Illus.). 1969. Repr. of 1842 ed. 32.00 (ISBN 0-384-39470-1). Johnson Repr.

Missionary Landscapes in the Dark Continent. James Johnston. LC 72-3911. (Black Heritage Library Collection Ser.). Repr. of 1892 ed. 16.00 (ISBN 0-8369-9100-1). Ayer Co Pubs.

Missionary Methods: St. Paul's or Our's? Roland Allen. 1962. pap. 5.95x (ISBN 0-8028-1001-2). Eerdmans.

Missionary Moments. Phyllis Cammack. LC 66-30364. (Illus.). 134p. 1966. 3.50 (ISBN 0-913342-09-2). Barclay Pr.

Missionary of Moderation: Henry Melchior Muhlenberg & the Lutheran Church in English America. Leonard R. Riforgiato. LC 78-75203. 256p. 23.50 (ISBN 0-8387-2379-9). Bucknell U Pr.

Missionary Society of Connecticut Papers, 1759-1948: A Guide to the Microform Edition. Ed. by Jack T. Ericson. 49p. 1976. pap. 15.00 (ISBN 0-667-00289-8). Microfilming Corp.

Missionary Spirit in the Augustana Church. George F. Hall. LC 84-72945. (Publications Ser.: No. 32). 166p. 1985. 7.50 (ISBN 0-910184-32-1). Augustana.

Missionary Story Sketches: Folk-Lore from Africa. facsimile ed. Alexander P. Camphor. LC 79-173603. (Black Heritage Library Collection). Repr. of 1909 ed. 20.00 (ISBN 0-8369-8915-5). Ayer Co Pubs.

Missionary to Tanganyika: 1877-1888. Edward C. Hore. Ed. by James B. Wolf. 200p. 1971. 28.50x (ISBN 0-7146-2605-8, F Cass Co). Biblio Dist.

Missionary to the Mountain West: The Reminiscences of Episcopal Bishop Daniel S. Tuttle, 1866-1886. Daniel S. Tuttle. 509p. 1987. Repr. of 1906 ed. 20.00 (ISBN 0-87480-305-5). U of Utah Pr.

Missionary Travels & Researches in South Africa. David Livingston. LC 5-15250. 1971. Repr. of 1857 ed. 62.00 (ISBN 0-384-32983-7). Johnson Repr.

Missionary Travels & Researches in South Africa. David Livingstone. LC 72-5439. (Select Bibliographies Reprint Ser.). 1972. Repr. of 1857 ed. 52.00 (ISBN 0-8369-6918-9). Ayer Co Pubs.

Missions: A Family Affair. Jack B. Scott. 1985. pap. 4.95 (ISBN 0-934688-15-X). Great Comm Pubns.

Missions: A Family Affair, Leader's Guide. (Orig.). 1985. pap. text ed. 3.95 (ISBN 0-934688-20-6). Great Comm Pubns.

Missions & Missionaries in the Pacific. Ed. by Char Miller. LC 85-5074. (Symposium Ser.: Vol. 14). 136p. 1985. 19.95x (ISBN 0-88946-705-6). E Mellen.

Missions & Missionaries of California, 4 Vols. Zephyrin Engelhardt. (Illus.). lib. bdg. 185.00 (ISBN 0-87821-019-9). Milford Hse.

Missions & Theological Education in World Perspective. Ed. by Harvie M. Conn & Samuel F. Rowen. LC 84-72527. 484p. (Orig.). 1984. pap. text ed. 11.95 (ISBN 0-930957-00-8). Assocs Urbanus.

Missions, Basic: Questions & Answers. (Teaching Bks.). (Illus.). 10p. (Orig.). 1970. pap. text ed. 2.95 (ISBN 0-86508-156-5). BCM Intl Inc.

Missions, Evangelism, & Church Growth. Norman C. Kraus. LC 80-10922. (Mennonite Central Committee Story Ser.). 176p. 1980. pap. 6.95 (ISBN 0-8361-1925-8). Herald Pr.

Missions for Marrieds. Barbara Jacobs & Briant Jacobs. LC 83-70189. 136p. 1983. 6.95 (ISBN 0-87747-953-4). Deseret Bk.

Missions Growth: A Case Study on Finnish Free Foreign Missions. Lauri Ahonen. LC 84-12636. 96p. (Orig.). 1984. pap. 5.95 (ISBN 0-87808-335-9). William Carey Lib.

Missions Have Come Home to America. Jerry Appleby. 120p. 1986. pap. 3.95 (ISBN 0-8341-1132-2). Beacon Hill.

Missions in Africa: Relevant or Relic? A Conference. Curtis A. Keim & Howard Brown. (African Humanities Ser.). 89p. (Orig.). 1980. pap. text ed. 5.00 (ISBN 0-941934-30-6). Indiana Africa.

Missions in the Mountains. Mrs. H. W. Darst. (Illus.). 116p. 1979. pap. 2.50 (ISBN 0-89114-085-9). Baptist Pub Hse.

Missions of New Mexico Since 1776. John L. Kessell. LC 79-4934. (Illus.). 320p. 1980. 45.00x (ISBN 0-8263-0514-8). U of NM Pr.

Missions of San Antonio. Emilie Toepperwein & Fritz Toepperwein. pap. text ed. 1.50 (ISBN 0-910722-12-9). Highland Pr.

Missions on Trial. Walbert Buhlmann. Tr. by A. P. Dolan from Fr. & Ger. LC 78-23922. Orig. Title: Missions prozess in Addis Abeba. 160p. (Orig.). 1979. pap. 2.98 (ISBN 0-88344-316-3). Orbis Bks.

Missions Strategy of the Local Church. 10p. 1976. pap. 2.95 (ISBN 0-912552-14-X). Missions Adv Res Com Ctr.

Missions Studies: Australia. Amelia Hughes. (Illus.). 32p. (Orig.). 1984. pap. 1.00 (ISBN 0-89114-117-0). Baptist Pub Hse.

Missions Studies: Bolivia. Amelia Hughes. 32p. (Orig.). 1982. pap. text ed. 1.00 (ISBN 0-89114-109-X). Baptist Pub Hse.

Missions Studies: Brazil. Mrs. Jim Beasley. (Illus.). 32p. (Orig.). 1985. pap. 1.00 (ISBN 0-89114-155-3). Baptist Pub Hse.

Missions Studies: Japan. Amelia Hughes. pap. 1.00 (ISBN 0-89114-113-8). Baptist Pub Hse.

Missions Studies: Mexico. Sandra Gambill & Clara Ashley. pap. 1.00 (ISBN 0-89114-095-6). Baptist Pub Hse.

Missions Studies: Taiwan. Sandra Gambill & Clara Ashley. pap. 1.00 (ISBN 0-89114-123-5). Baptist Pub Hse.

Missions Studies: The Philippines. Sandra Gambill & Clara Ashley. (Vacation Bible School Ser.). (Illus.). 32p. (Orig.). 1981. pap. 1.00 (ISBN 0-89114-105-7). Baptist Pub Hse.

Missions Trends, No. 2. Gerald H. Anderson & Thomas Stansky. LC 75-29836. 1975. pap. 3.95 (ISBN 0-8028-1624-X). Eerdmans.

Missions U. S. A. Earl Parvin. (Orig.). 1985. pap. text ed. 14.95 (ISBN 0-8024-5975-7). Moody.

Mississippi Methodists, Seventeen Ninety-Nine to Nineteen Eighty-Three: A Moral People "Born of Conviction". Ray Holder. Date not set. 11.95 (ISBN 0-9612932-0-9); pap. 8.95 (ISBN 0-9612932-1-7). Maverick Prints.

Missy Doe & Other Benjy Stories. Helen C. Noordewier. (Voyager Ser.). 96p. (Orig.). 1981. pap. 2.50 (ISBN 0-8010-6732-4). Baker Bk.

Mister Blue. Myles Connolly. pap. 3.50 (ISBN 0-385-02866-0, Im). Doubleday.

Mr. Pickwick's Pilgrimages. W. Dexter. 59.95 (ISBN 0-8490-0645-7). Gordon Pr.

Mistere Du Viel Testament, 6 Vols. (Illus.). 200.00 (ISBN 0-384-39180-X); pap. 165.00 (ISBN 0-384-39179-6). Johnson Repr.

Misticos en Oracion. Many Cihlar. Tr. by AMORC Staff. (Span.). 59p. (Orig.). 1982. pap. 7.00 (ISBN 0-912057-82-3, GS-509). AMORC.

Mists of Danger. B. J. Hoff. LC 86-70567. 196p. 1986. pap. 6.95 (ISBN 0-89636-206-X). Accent Bks.

Mithras. Esme Wynne-Tyson. 1985. 50.00x (ISBN 0-900000-79-1, Pub. by Centaur Bks). State Mutual Bk.

Mithras-Orion: Greek Hero & Roman Army God. Michael P. Speidel. (Illus.). 56p. 1980. pap. text ed. 19.95 (ISBN 90-04-06055-3). Humanities.

Miti E. Leggende: Myths & Legends, 4 vols. in 1. Ed. by Raffaele Pettazzoni & Kees W. Bolle. LC 77-79151. (Mythology Ser.). (Ital.). 1978. Repr. of 1959 ed. lib. bdg. 186.00x (ISBN 0-405-10560-6). Ayer Co Pubs.

Mitra & Aryaman. Paul Thieme. (Connecticut Academy of Arts & Sciences Transaction: Vol. 41). 1967. 18.00 (ISBN 0-208-01104-8). Shoe String.

Mittelalterliche Caerimonialia der Kartauser, Pr. 1. Ed. by James Hogg. (Analecta Cartusiana Ser.: No. 2). (Ger. & Lat.). 354p. 1971. pap. 25.00 (ISBN 3-7052-0001-1, Pub by Salzburg Studies). Longwood Pub Group.

Mitzvah: Basic Jewish Ideas. Jacob Neusner. (Ser.). (Orig.). 1981. pap. 4.95 (ISBN 0-940646-25-0). Rossel Bks.

Mitzvot. Amye Rosenberg. (Illus.). 30p. pap. text ed. 2.95x (ISBN 0-87441-387-7). Behrman.

Mitzvoth. cancelled (ISBN 0-686-76550-8). Feldheim.

Mixed Blessings: Jews & Gentiles Confront Intermarriage. Paul Cowan & Rachael Cowan. LC 87-480. 288p. 1987. 17.95 (ISBN 0-385-19502-8). Doubleday.

Mixed Pasture. facs. ed. Evelyn Underhill. LC 68-8501. (Essay Index Reprint Ser). 1933. 17.00 (ISBN 0-8369-0958-5). Ayer Co Pubs.

Mixing: Catholic-Protestant Marriages in the 1980's. Barbara D. Schiappa. LC 81-84387. 144p. (Orig.). 1982. pap. 5.95 (ISBN 0-8091-2443-2). Paulist Pr.

Mobiles, Banners & Chariots. Artie Kamiya & Elizabeth Kamiya. (Helping Hand Ser.). (Illus.). 48p. (YA) 1984. wkbk 4.95 (ISBN 0-86653-184-X). Good Apple.

Mobilizing Social Movement Organization: The Formation, Institionalization & Effectiveness of Economical Urban Ministries. James Davidson. (Monograph: No. 6). 1985. pap. 8.00 (ISBN 0-932566-05-7). Soc Sci Stud Rel.

Moby Dick & Calvinism: A World Dismantled. T. Walter Herbert, Jr. 1977. 27.00x (ISBN 0-8135-0829-0). Rutgers U Pr.

Modeh Ani Means Thank You. Ruth Lipson. (Illus.). 1986. 5.95 (ISBN 0-317-42732-6). Feldheim.

Model Building of Solar Systems. Pandurangarao Malyaya. (Worship Technology Around the World Ser.: No. 1). Orig. Title: Sri Satyanarayana Katha. (Illus.). 100p. (Orig.). 1981. 9.99 (ISBN 0-938924-00-1). Sri Shirdi Sai.

Model for Christian Wholeness. Dan Ivins. LC 84-9436. 1985. pap. 4.25 (ISBN 0-8054-2252-8). Broadman.

Model Four Semester Syllabus for Transcultural Theology Overseas. Ed. by Michael C. Kirwen. LC 86-8618. 224p. 1986. 49.95 (ISBN 0-88946-047-7). E Mellen.

Modelos Para el Proceso de Ensenanza-Aprendizaje. LeRoy Ford. Tr. by Nelda B. de Gaydou & Jorge E. Diaz. Tr. of Design for Teaching & Training. (Span., Illus.). 320p. (Orig.). 1986. pap. 5.95 (ISBN 0-311-11042-8). Casa Bautista.

Models for Ministry: Creative Administration in the Local Church. Raymond B. Knudsen. (Orig.). 1978. pap. 5.95 (ISBN 0-377-00082-5). Friend Pr.

Models of Jesus. John F. O'Grady. LC 82-45076. (Illus.). 224p. 1982. pap. 4.95 (ISBN 0-385-17321-0, Im). Doubleday.

Models of Revelation. Avery Dulles. LC 82-45243. 360p. 1983. 16.95 (ISBN 0-385-17975-8). Doubleday.

Models of Revelation. Avery Dulles. LC 82-45243. 360p. 1985. pap. 8.95 (ISBN 0-385-23235-7, Im). Doubleday.

Models of the Church. Avery Dulles. LC 77-11246. 1987. pap. 4.95 (ISBN 0-385-13368-5, Im). Doubleday.

Models of Theological Reflections. Raymond F. Collins. LC 83-21733. (Illus.). 240p. (Orig.). 1984. lib. bdg. 25.75 (ISBN 0-8191-3661-1); pap. text ed. 12.25 (ISBN 0-8191-3662-X). U Pr of Amer.

Moderate Puritans & the Elizabethan Church. Peter Lake. LC 81-17052. 345p. 1982. 57.50 (ISBN 0-521-24010-7). Cambridge U Pr.
Moderates & Conservatives in Western Europe. Roger Morgan & Stefano Silvestri. LC 83-5662. 288p. 1983. 27.50 (ISBN 0-8386-3201-7). Fairleigh Dickinson.
Modern American Religion, Vol. 1: The Irony of It All, 1893-1919. Martin E. Marty. LC 86-16524. (Illus.). 398p. 1986. 24.95 (ISBN 0-226-50893-5). U of Chicago Pr.
Modern Arab Woman: A Bibliography. Michelle Raccagni. LC 78-15528. 272p. 1978. lib. bdg. 19.00 (ISBN 0-8108-1165-0). Scarecrow.
Modern Catholic Dictionary. John A. Hardon. LC 77-82945. 624p. 1980. 22.95 (ISBN 0-385-12162-8). Doubleday.
Modern Catholic Thinkers. facs. ed. Ed. by Aloysius R. Caponigri. LC 78-117775. (Essay Index Reprint Ser). 1960. 38.50 (ISBN 0-8369-1787-1). Ayer Co Pubs.
Modern Catholic Thinkers: An Anthology. Aloysius R. Caponigri. (Essay Index Reprint Ser.). 650p. Repr. of 1960 ed. lib. bdg. 37.50 (ISBN 0-8290-0784-9). Irvington.
Modern Christian Revolutionaries. facsimile ed. Ed. by Donald Attwater. LC 76-156608. (Essay Index Reprint Ser). Repr. of 1947 ed. 23.00 (ISBN 0-8369-2304-9). Ayer Co Pubs.
Modern Christian Thought: From the Enlightenment to Vatican Two. James C. Livingston. 1971. text ed. write for info. (ISBN 0-02-371420-4). Macmillan.
Modern Cities & Their Religious Problems. Samuel L. Loomis. LC 73-112558. (Rise of Urban America). 1970. Repr. of 1887 ed. 23.50 (ISBN 0-405-02464-9). Ayer Co Pubs.
Modern Commentators of Veda. A. K. Pateria. 120p. 1986. text ed. 22.50x (ISBN 81-7018-252-2, Pub. by B R Pub Corp Delhi). Apt Bks.
Modern Concordance to the New Testament. Ed. by Michael Darton. LC 75-34831. 1977. 12.95 (ISBN 0-385-07901-X). Doubleday.
Modern Cosmology: A Survey in Four Lectures. P. J. Willcox. LC 82-90241. (Illus.). 96p. 1982. pap. 4.50 (ISBN 0-9608436-0-4). P J Willcox.
Modern Drama & the Death of God. George E. Wellwarth. LC 86-40064. 192p. 1986. text ed. 25.75x (ISBN 0-299-10850-3). U of Wis Pr.
Modern Greek Philosophers on the Human Soul. Constantine Cavarnos. LC 86-83011. (Illus.). 144p. 1987. pap. 6.95. Inst Byzantine.
Modern Growth of the Totem Pole on the Northwest Coast. facs. ed. Marius Barbeau. (Shorey Indian Ser.). 16p. pap. 0.95 (ISBN 0-8466-0098-6, S98). Shorey.
Modern Hebrew: An Introductory Course. D. J. Kamhi. (OUP for the School of Oriental & African Studies Ser.). 1982. 15.95x (ISBN 0-19-713594-3). Oxford U Pr.
Modern Hebrew for Biblical Scholars: An Annotated Chrestomathy with an Outline Grammar & Glossary. T. Muraoka. (Journal for the Study of the Old Testament Ser.: Manuals 2). 220p. 1982. text ed. 25.00 (ISBN 0-905774-36-1, Pub. by JSOT Pr England); pap. text ed. 14.50 (ISBN 0-905774-37-X, Pub. by JSOT Pr England). Eisenbrauns.
Modern Hebrew: Ivrit Hayah, Vol. 1. 3rd ed. Harry Blumberg & Mordecai Lewittes. 449p. pap. 8.95x (ISBN 0-88482-718-6). Hebrew Pub.
Modern Hebrew Literature. Ed. by Robert Alter. LC 75-9928. (Library of Jewish Studies). 384p. 1975. pap. text ed. 9.95x (ISBN 0-87441-235-8); cloth 15.95x. Behrman.
Modern Hebrew Literature Reader for Advanced Students, 2 vols. Menahem Mansoor. 1971. Vol. 1. 14.95x; Vol. 2. 16.95x (ISBN 0-685-27921-9). Ktav.
Modern Hindu Law. R. C. Nagpal. (Hindi.). 815p. 1984. 225.00x (Pub. by Eastern Bk India). State Mutual Bk.
Modern Hindu Law. R. C. Nagpal. 992p. 1983. 360.00x (Pub. by Eastern Bk India). State Mutual Bk.
Modern Impulse of Traditional Judaism. Zvi Kurzweil. LC 84-28892. 156p. 1985. 12.95 (ISBN 0-88125-068-6). Ktav.
Modern Indian Interpreters of the Bhagavadgita. Ed. by Robert N. Minor. (Religious Studies Ser.). 288p. (Orig.). 1986. 44.50x (ISBN 0-88706-297-0); pap. 14.95x (ISBN 0-88706-298-9). State U NY Pr.
Modern Indian Mysticism. K. P. Choudhary. 1981. 17.00x (ISBN 0-8364-0744-X, Pub. by Motilal Banarsidass). South Asia Bks.
Modern Industry & the African. 2nd ed. International Missionary Council - Department of Social & Economic Research & Council. Ed. by J. Mearle Davis. LC 67-24749. 1961. Repr. of 1932 ed. 37.50x (ISBN 0-678-05042-2). Kelley.
Modern Introduction to Astrology. Henry Weingarten. LC 74-15939. 1974. pap. 1.95 (ISBN 0-88231-014-3). ASI Pubs Inc.
Modern Introduction to Biblical Hebrew. John F. Sawyer. (Orig.). 1976. pap. 14.95x (ISBN 0-85362-159-4, Oriel). Methuen Inc.
Modern Islam in India. W. C. Smith. 1985. Repr. of 1946 ed. 18.50x (ISBN 0-8364-1338-5, Pub. by Usha). South Asia Bks.
Modern Islam in India: A Social Analysis. Wilfred C. Smith. LC 70-179243. Repr. of 1946 ed. 17.00 (ISBN 0-404-54869-5). AMS Pr.
Modern Islam: The Search for Cultural Identity. Gustave E. Von Grunebaum. LC 83-11508. viii, 303p. 1983. Repr. of 1962 ed. lib. bdg. 39.75x (ISBN 0-313-24087-6, VGMI). Greenwood.
Modern Jew Faces Eternal Problems. Barth. 7.50 (ISBN 0-685-48595-1). Feldheim.
Modern Jew in Search of a Soul. Ed. by J. Marvin Spiegelman & Abraham Jacobson. 320p. 1986. pap. 12.95 (ISBN 0-941404-33-1). Falcon Pr AZ.
Modern Jewish Ethics: Theory & Practice. Ed. by Marvin Fox. LC 74-28395. 274p. 1975. 14.50 (ISBN 0-8142-0192-X). Ohio St U Pr.
Modern Jewish Experience, 59 vols. Ed. by Moses Rischin. 1975. Set. 1630.50x (ISBN 0-405-06690-2). Ayer Co Pubs.
Modern Jewish Life in Literature, 2 Vols. Azriel Eisenberg. 1952-1968. Vol. 1. 4.50x (ISBN 0-8381-0201-8); Vol. 2. 4.50x (ISBN 0-8381-0207-7). United Syn Bk.
Modern Jewish Literature. Ed. & intro. by Harold Bloom. (Critical Cosmos--Other European & Latin American Literature Ser.). 1987. 49.95 (ISBN 1-55546-102-6). Chelsea Hse.
Modern Jewish Morality: A Bibliographical Survey. Compiled by S. Daniel Breslauer. LC 86-12145. 249p. 1986. 39.95 (ISBN 0-313-24700-5, BJM/). Greenwood.
Modern Jewish Religious Movements. 3rd rev. ed. David Rudavsky. LC 79-11266. 1979. pap. text ed. 9.95x (ISBN 0-87441-286-2). Behrman.
Modern Jewish Thought: A Source Reader. Ed. by Nahum N. Glatzer. LC 76-9139. 1976. pap. 7.50 (ISBN 0-8052-0542-X). Schocken.
Modern Jewish Thought: Selected Issues, 1889-1966. LC 73-2221. (Jewish People; History, Religion, Literature Ser.). 22.00 (ISBN 0-405-05283-9). Ayer Co Pubs.
Modern Job: An Essay on the Problem of Evil. Etienne Giran. 92p. 1916. 1.95 (ISBN 0-317-40399-0). Open Court.
Modern Kongo Prophets: Religion in a Plural Society. Wyatt MacGaffey. LC 82-48554. (African Systems of Thought: Midland Bks: No. 307). (Illus.). 304p. 1983. 22.50x (ISBN 0-253-33865-4); pap. 15.00X (ISBN 0-253-20307-4, MB 307). Ind U Pr.
Modern Liturgy Index. 2nd ed. Ed. by Helen M. Gilsdorf. 1984. pap. 6.95 (ISBN 0-89390-040-0). Resource Pubns.
Modern Liturgy Planning Guide. Robert Zappula et al. 350p. 1987. 19.95 (ISBN 0-89390-088-5). Resource Pubns.
Modern Man & An Old-Fashioned God. David Kinigsberg. 1985. 7.95 (ISBN 0-533-06659-X). Vantage.
Modern Man & Religion. facsimile ed. Thomas G. Masaryk. LC 74-107816. (Select Bibliographies Reprint Ser). 1938. 24.50 (ISBN 0-8369-5216-2). Ayer Co Pubs.
Modern Man & Religion. Tomas G. Masaryk. Tr. by H. E. Kennedy et al. LC 78-109783. viii, 320p. Repr. of 1938 ed. lib. bdg. 22.50x (ISBN 0-8371-4273-3, MAMR). Greenwood.
Modern Management Technology Defined. L. Ron Hubbard. 94.00 (ISBN 0-686-30806-9). Church Scient NY.
Modern Management Technology Defined. L. Ron Hubbard. 1977. text ed. 107.18 (ISBN 0-88404-040-2). Bridge Pubns Inc.
Modern Marriage & the Clergy. Ed. by David R. Mace. LC 74-19593. (Special Issues of Pastoral Psychology). 84p. 1978. 9.95 (ISBN 0-87705-368-5). Human Sci Pr.
Modern Masters of Religious Education. Ed. by Marlene Mayr. LC 82-25009. 323p. (Orig.). 1983. pap. 14.95 (ISBN 0-89135-033-0). Religious Educ.
Modern Medicine & Jewish Ethics. Fred Rosner. LC 86-2910. 1986. text ed. 22.50 (ISBN 0-88125-091-0); pap. text ed. 14.95 (ISBN 0-88125-102-X). Ktav.
Modern Medicine & Jewish Law: Studies in Torah Judaism. Fred Rosner. 1972. 9.95x (ISBN 0-8197-0389-3). Bloch.
Modern Midrash: The Retelling of Traditional Jewish Narratives by Twentieth-Century Hebrew Writers. David C. Jacobson. (SUNY Series in Modern Jewish Literature & Culture). 208p. 1986. 34.50x (ISBN 0-88706-323-3); pap. 10.95x (ISBN 0-88706-325-X). State U NY Pr.
Modern Movement in American Theology. facs. ed. Frank H. Foster. LC 76-86751. (Essay Index Reprint Ser). 1939. 14.50 (ISBN 0-8369-1131-8). Ayer Co Pubs.
Modern Movements among Moslems. S. G. Wilson. 1977. lib. bdg. 59.95 (ISBN 0-8490-2270-3). Gordon Pr.
Modern Movements among Moslems. S. G. Wilson. LC 74-83190. (Islam & Mideast Ser.). 1976. Repr. of 1916 ed. 33.00 (ISBN 0-8420-1753-4). Scholarly Res Inc.
Modern Mysticism. Francis Grierson. 1977. lib. bdg. 59.95 (ISBN 0-8490-2271-1). Gordon Pr.
Modern Mysticism. Francis Grierson. LC 77-102570. 1970. Repr. of 1899 ed. 22.50x (ISBN 0-8046-0730-3, Pub. by Kennikat). Assoc Faculty Pr.
Modern Mystics. Francis Younghusband. 322p. 1970. 7.95 (ISBN 0-8216-0118-0). Univ Bks.
Modern Mystics. facs. ed. Francis E. Younghusband. LC 67-28774. (Essay Index Reprint Ser). 1935. 17.75 (ISBN 0-8369-1015-X). Ayer Co Pubs.
Modern Mythology. Andrew Lang. LC 68-54279. Repr. of 1897 ed. 16.75 (ISBN 0-404-03852-2). AMS Pr.
Modern Nationalism & Religion. facs. ed. Salo W. Baron. LC 79-134050. (Essay Index Reprint Ser). 1947. 19.50 (ISBN 0-8369-2142-9). Ayer Co Pubs.
Modern Numerology. Morris C. Goodman. pap. 5.00 (ISBN 0-87980-102-6). Wilshire.
Modern Orthodox Saints: St. Methodia of Kimolos, Vol. 9. Constantine Cavarnos. (Illus.). 123p. 1987. 8.95 (ISBN 0-914744-75-5); pap. 5.95 (ISBN 0-914744-76-3). Inst Byzantine.
Modern Orthodox Saints: St. Nikephoros of Chios, Vol. 4. 2nd, rev. ed. Constantine Cavarnos. LC 86-82207. (Illus.). 124p. 1986. pap. 4.95 (ISBN 0-914744-74-7). Inst Byzantine.
Modern Orthodox Saints, Vol. 1: St. Cosmas Aitolos. 3rd. rev. & enl. ed. Ed. by Constantine Cavarnos. LC 85-80440. (Illus.). 118p. 1985. 8.95 (ISBN 0-914744-64-X); pap. 5.95 (ISBN 0-914744-65-8). Inst Byzantine.
Modern Orthodox Saints: Vol. 2-St. Macarios of Corinth. 2nd ed. Constantine Cavarnos. LC 72-85116. (Illus.). 1977. pap. 4.50 (ISBN 0-914744-35-6). Inst Byzantine.
Modern Orthodox Saints: Vol. 3-St. Nicodemos the Hagiorite. 2nd ed. Constantine Cavarnos. LC 78-71478. (Illus.). 167p. 1979. 8.00 (ISBN 0-914744-41-0); pap. 4.50. Inst Byzantine.
Modern Orthodox Saints: Vol. 5-St. Seraphim of Sarov. Constatine Cavarnos & Mary B Zeldin. LC 80-80124. (Illus.). 167p. 1980. 9.00 (ISBN 0-914744-47-X); pap. 6.00 (ISBN 0-914744-48-8). Inst Byzantine.
Modern Orthodox Saints: Vol. 6-St. Arsenios of Paros. Constantine Cavarnos. LC 78-54384. (Illus.). 123p. 1978. 8.00 (ISBN 0-914744-39-9); pap. 4.50 (ISBN 0-914744-40-2). Inst Byzantine.
Modern Orthodox Saints: Vol. 7-St. Nectarios of Aegina. Constantine Cavarnos. LC 81-82963. (Illus.). 222p. 1981. 10.00 (ISBN 0-914744-53-4); pap. 7.00 (ISBN 0-914744-54-2). Inst Byzantine.
Modern Orthodox Saints: Vol. 8, St. Savvas the New. Constantine Cavarnos. LC 85-60117. (Illus.). 144p. 1985. 8.95 (ISBN 0-914744-62-3); pap. 5.95 (ISBN 0-914744-63-1). Inst Byzantine.
Modern Panarion. H. P. Blavatsky. 504p. 1981. Repr. of 1895 ed. 15.00 (ISBN 0-938998-22-6). Theosophy.
Modern Pathfinders of Christianity: The Lives & Deeds of Seven Centuries of Christian Leaders. facs. ed. Henry K. Rowe. LC 68-16973. (Essay Index Reprint Ser). 1928. 15.00 (ISBN 0-8369-0839-2). Ayer Co Pubs.
Modern Poets & Christian Teaching: Richard Watson Gilder, Edwin Markham, Edward Rowland Sill. David G. Downey. 1973. Repr. of 1906 ed. 25.00 (ISBN 0-8274-1700-4). R West.
Modern Poets & Christian Teaching: Richard Watson Gilder, Edwin Markham, Edward Rowland Sill. David G. Downey. 183p. 1982. Repr. lib. bdg. 40.00 (ISBN 0-89984-013-2). Century Bookbindery.
Modern Priestess of Isis. Vsevolod S. Solovyoff. Tr. by Walter Leaf. LC 75-36921. (Occult Ser.). 1976. Repr. of 1895 ed. 26.50x (ISBN 0-405-07976-1). Ayer Co Pubs.
Modern Problems & Religion. Swami Akhilananda. pap. 9.00 (ISBN 0-8283-1146-3). Branden Pub Co.
Modern Promethean: A Dialogue with Today's Youth. Maurice Friedman. LC 73-104050. (Orig.). 1969. pap. 2.50x (ISBN 0-87574-168-1). Pendle Hill.
Modern Reader in the Philosophy of Religion. Ed. by Willard E. Arnett. LC 66-20470. (Century Philosophy Ser.). 1966. 39.50x (ISBN 0-89197-482-2); pap. text ed. 24.50x (ISBN 0-89197-483-0). Irvington.
Modern Reader's Book of Psalms. Ed. by Harry Mayer. (Black & Gold Lib). 1968. 6.95 (ISBN 0-87140-879-1, Co-Pub with Tudor). Liveright.
Modern Reform Response. Solomon B. Freehof. 1971. 15.00x (ISBN 0-87820-101-7, Pub. by Hebrew Union). Ktav.
Modern Religious Cults & Movements. Gaius Atkins. LC 74-126684. Repr. of 1923 ed. 26.50 (ISBN 0-404-00415-6). AMS Pr.
Modern Religious Cults & Society. Louis R. Binder. LC 77-113556. Repr. of 1933 ed. 10.00 (ISBN 0-404-00867-4). AMS Pr.
Modern Religious Verse. Ed. by Timothy Beaumont. (Pocket Poet Ser.). 1966. pap. 2.95 (ISBN 0-8023-9039-0). Dufour.
Modern Religious Verse & Prose: An Anthology. Ed. by Fred Merrifield. LC 79-51964. (Granger Poetry Library). 1980. Repr. of 1925 ed. 32.50x (ISBN 0-89609-186-4). Roth Pub Inc.
Modern Research As Illustrating the Bible. S. R. Driver. (British Academy, London, Schweich Lectures on Biblical Archaeology, 1908). pap. 19.00 (ISBN 0-8115-1250-9). Kraus Repr.
Modern Rival of Christian Faith: An Analysis of Secularism. Georgia E. Harkness. LC 77-27000. 1978. Repr. of 1952 ed. lib. bdg. 20.50x (ISBN 0-313-20174-9, HAMR). Greenwood.
Modern Sacred Art & the Church of Assy. William S. Rubin. LC 61-15469. (Illus.). pap. 61.30 (ISBN 0-317-10614-7, 2051858). Bks Demand UMI.
Modern Saints: Their Lives & Faces. Ann Ball. LC 82-50357. (Illus.). 457p. 1983. pap. 10.00 (ISBN 0-89555-222-1). TAN Bks Pubs.
Modern Science & Moral Values: Proceedings. International Conference on the Unity of the Sciences, 2nd, Tokyo, Nov. 18-21, 1973. LC 75-306280. 608p. 1974. casebound smythesewn 20.00x (ISBN 0-89226-000-9, Pub. by ICF Pr). Paragon Hse.
Modern Scriptural Approach to the Spiritual Exercises. David M. Stanley. Frwd. by George E. Ganss. LC 67-25219. (Series III: No. 1). xviii, 358p. 1986. pap. 6.95 (ISBN 0-912422-07-6). Inst Jesuit.
Modern Sons of the Pharaohs. S. H. Leeder. LC 73-6288. (Middle East Ser.). Repr. of 1918 ed. 29.00 (ISBN 0-405-05346-0). Ayer Co Pubs.
Modern Spiritual Exercises: A Contemporary Reading of the Spiritual Exercises of St. Ignatius. David L. Fleming. LC 82-46055. 152p. 1983. pap. 3.95 (ISBN 0-385-18853-6, Im). Doubleday.
Modern Spirituality: An Anthology. Ed. by John Garvey. 156p. 1985. 12.95 (ISBN 0-87243-132-0). Templegate.
Modern Study in the Book of Proverbs: Charles Bridges Classic Revised for Today's Reader. George F. Santa. LC 78-7667. (Illus.). 1978. kiver bdg. 17.95 (ISBN 0-915134-27-6); incl. study guide (ISBN 0-915134-49-7). Mott Media.
Modern Theologians, Christians & Jews. 2nd ed. Ed. by Thomas E. Bird. 1967. 15.95 (ISBN 0-268-00183-9). U of Notre Dame Pr.
Modern Theories of Religion. Eric S. Waterhouse. 1977. lib. bdg. 59.95 (ISBN 0-8490-2272-X). Gordon Pr.
Modern Tongues Movement. Robert G. Gromacki. pap. 4.95 (ISBN 0-8010-3708-5). Baker Bk.
Modern Tongues Movement. Robert G. Gromacki. 1967. pap. 4.95 (ISBN 0-87552-304-8). Presby & Reformed.
Modern Trends in Hinduism. Philip H. Ashby. LC 73-20262. (Lectures in the History of Religions Ser.: No. 10). 143p. 1974. 22.50x (ISBN 0-231-03768-6). Columbia U Pr.
Modern Trends in World-Religions. facs. ed. Ed. by Albert E. Haydon. LC 68-29214. (Essay Index Reprint Ser). 1934. 18.00 (ISBN 0-8369-0522-9). Ayer Co Pubs.
Modern Use of the Bible. Harry E. Fosdick. 1925. 35.00 (ISBN 0-8274-2758-1). R West.
Modern Varieties of Judaism. Joseph L. Blau. LC 66-10732. (Lectures on the History of Religion Ser.). 217p. 1966. 24.50x (ISBN 0-231-02867-9); pap. 11.00x (ISBN 0-231-08668-7). Columbia U Pr.
Modern Witch's Spellbook. Sarah L. Morrison. LC 71-135588. 256p. 1973. pap. 5.95 (ISBN 0-8065-0372-6). Citadel Pr.
Modern Witch's Spellbook, Vol. 2. Sarah L. Morrison. 224p. 1986. pap. 6.95 (ISBN 0-8065-1015-3). Citadel Pr.
Modern Work & Human Meaning. John C. Raines & Donna C. Day-Lower. LC 85-26370. (Illus.). 152p. (Orig.). 1986. pap. 12.95 (ISBN 0-664-24703-2). Westminster.
Moderne Gemeinschaftsbewegung in Deutschland. Paul Fleisch. Ed. by Donald W. Dayton. (Higher Christian Life Ser.). 605p. 1985. 75.00 (ISBN 0-8240-6419-4). Garland Pub.
Modernism: A Record & Review. Alfred L. Lilley. LC 75-102575. 1970. Repr. of 1908 ed. 25.00x (ISBN 0-8046-0735-4, Pub. by Kennikat). Assoc Faculty Pr.
Modernist Impulse in American Protestantism. William R. Hutchison. (Illus.). 384p. 1976. 22.50x (ISBN 0-674-58058-3). Harvard U Pr.
Modernist Impulse in American Protestantism. William R. Hutchison. (Illus.). 1982. pap. 9.95x (ISBN 0-19-503084-2). Oxford U Pr.

Modernist Movement in the Roman Church. Alexander R. Vidler. 69.95 (ISBN 0-8490-0889-1). Gordon Pr.

Modernity of Milton. Martin A. Larson. LC 76-23120. 1927. lib. bdg. 7.95 (ISBN 0-8414-5800-6). Folcroft.

Modernity of Milton: A Theological & Philosophical Interpretation. Martin A. Larson. LC 76-124764. Repr. of 1927 ed. 18.75 (ISBN 0-404-03880-8). AMS Pr.

Modernization & Social Change among Muslims in India. Ed. by Imtiaz Ahmad. 1983. 28.00x (ISBN 0-88386-892-X). South Asia Bks.

Modernization of French Jewry: Consistory & Community in the Nineteenth Century. Phyllis C. Albert. LC 76-50680. (Illus.). 472p. 1977. 40.00x (ISBN 0-87451-139-9). U Pr of New Eng.

Modes of Scepticism: Ancient Texts & Modern Interpretations. Julia Annas & Jonathan Barnes. 216p. 1985. 29.50 (ISBN 0-521-25682-8); pap. 9.95 (ISBN 0-521-27644-6). Cambridge U Pr.

Modestianischen und Die Konstantinischen Bauten Am Heiligen Grabe Zu Jerusalem. Anton Baumstark. Repr. of 1915 ed. 15.00 (ISBN 0-384-03585-X). Johnson Repr.

Mo'ed Katan, 1 vol. 15.00 (ISBN 0-910218-63-3). Bennet Pub.

Moehler & Baur in Controversy Eighteen Thirty-Two to Thirty-Eight: Romantic-idealist Assesment of the Reformation & Counter-Reformation. Joseph Fitzer. LC 74-77619. (American Academy of Religion. Studies in Religion). 1974. 9.95 (ISBN 0-88420-111-2, 010007). Scholars Pr GA.

Mohammed. E. Bey. 336p. 1985. 50.00x (ISBN 0-317-39181-X, Pub. by Luzac & Co Ltd). State Mutual Bk.

Mohammed. David S. Margoliuth. LC 79-2875. 151p. 1981. Repr. of 1939 ed. 23.00 (ISBN 0-8305-0044-8). Hyperion Conn.

Mohammed & Charlemagne. Henri Pirenne. (B & N Paperback Ser.). 239p. (Orig.). 1983. pap. 9.95x (ISBN 0-389-20134-0, 06641, 444). B&N Imports.

Mohammed & the Rise of Islam. David S. Margoliouth. LC 73-14455. Repr. of 1905 ed. 30.00 (ISBN 0-404-58273-7). AMS Pr.

Mohammed & the Rise of Islam. David S. Margoliouth. LC 73-38361. (Select Bibliographies Reprint Ser.). Repr. of 1905 ed. 34.00 (ISBN 0-8369-6778-X). Ayer Co Pubs.

Mohammed: The Man & His Faith. facsimile ed. Tor Andrae. Tr. by Theophil Menzel. LC 79-160954. (Select Bibliographies Reprint Ser). Repr. of 1936 ed. 19.00 (ISBN 0-8369-5821-7). Ayer Co Pubs.

Mohammedanism: An Historical Survey. 2nd ed. Hamilton A. Gibb. 1953. pap. 5.95x (ISBN 0-19-500245-8, 90). Oxford U Pr.

Mohammedanism: Lectures in Its Origin, Its Religious & Political Growth, & Its Present State. Christian S. Hurgronje. LC 79-2865. 184p. 1980. Repr. of 1916 ed. 18.00 (ISBN 0-8305-0038-3). Hyperion Conn.

Moja pervaja Svjashchennaja Istorija, dlja detjej. P. Vozdvizhensky. Tr. of My First Sacred History, for Children. (Illus.). 101p. 1968. pap. 4.00 (ISBN 0-317-30407-0). Holy Trinity.

Moksha: Writings on Psychedelics & the Visionary Experience (1931-1963) Aldous Huxley. Ed. by Michael Horowitz & Cynthia Palmer. LC 81-21239. 300p. 1982. pap. 7.95 (ISBN 0-87477-208-7). J P Tarcher.

Molchanie: The Silence of God. Catherine D. Doherty. 112p. 1982. 8.95 (ISBN 0-8245-0407-0). Crossroad NY.

Molchanie: The Silence of God. Catherine de Hucck Doherty. 128p. 1984. pap. 7.95 (ISBN 0-8245-0672-3). Crossroad NY.

Mom, Can We Still Keep Roger? Freda I. Briggs. 96p. 1985. pap. 4.95 (ISBN 0-8010-0888-3). Baker Bk.

Mom LeTourneau. Norman B. Rohrer. Ed. by Isabel A. Throop. 144p. 1985. 6.95 (ISBN 0-8423-4502-7). Tyndale.

Mom, Take Time. Pat A. Baker. 128p. 1976. pap. 3.95 (ISBN 0-8010-0857-3). Baker Bk.

Moment of Christ: The Path of Meditation. John Main. 144p. 1984. 10.95 (ISBN 0-8245-0679-0); pap. 7.95 (ISBN 0-8245-0660-X). Crossroad NY.

Moment of Truth for Protestant America: Interchurch Campaigns Following World War I. Eldon Ernst. LC 74-16567. (American Academy of Religion. Dissertation Ser.). 1974. pap. 9.95 (010103). Scholars Pr GA.

Moment of Truth: The Confession of the Dutch Reformed Mission Church, 1982. Ed. by G. D. Cloete. 176p. (Orig.). 1984. pap. 10.95x (ISBN 0-8028-0011-4). Eerdmans.

Moment to Decide. Jan S. Doward. Ed. by Raymond H. Woolsey. (Daily Devotional Ser.). 384p. 1984. 7.95 (ISBN 0-8280-0234-7). Review & Herald.

Moment to Shout. Luis Palau. LC 77-4593. 250p. 1982. pap. 3.50 (ISBN 0-930014-84-7). Multnomah.

Momentos Felices Con Dios. Margaret Anderson. 192p. 1977. 3.95 (ISBN 0-88113-312-4). Edit Betania.

Momentous Century: Personal & Eyewitness Accounts of the Rise of the Jewish Homeland & State, 1875-1978. Ed. by Levi Shoshuk & Azriel Eisenberg. LC 81-86164. (Illus.). 472p. 1984. 25.00 (ISBN 0-8453-4748-9, Cornwall Bks). Assoc Univ Prs.

Momentous Decisions in Missions Today. Donald A. McGavran. 1984. pap. 11.95 (ISBN 0-8010-6176-8). Baker Bk.

Momentous Event. W. J. Grier. 1976. pap. 2.95 (ISBN 0-85151-020-5). Banner of Truth.

Moments Bright & Shining: Three Hundred & Sixty-Five Thoughts to Enjoy Day by Day. Compiled by Peter Seymour. (Illus.). 1979. 6.95 (ISBN 0-8378-1706-4). Gibson.

Moments for Prayer. Daughters of St. Paul. plastic bdg. 1.00 (ISBN 0-8198-0277-8); pap. 0.40 (ISBN 0-8198-0278-6). Dghtrs St Paul.

Moments of Decision. Daughters of St Paul. 1976. 5.00 (ISBN 0-8198-0445-2); pap. 4.00 (ISBN 0-8198-0446-0). Dghtrs St Paul.

Moments of Decision. Vance Havner. 128p. 1980. 8.95 (ISBN 0-8007-1091-6). Revell.

Moments of Decision: Guidelines for the Most Important Choices of Your Life. Vance Havner. 128p. 1985. pap. 4.95 (ISBN 0-8010-4287-9). Baker Bk.

Moments of Grace: Lessons from Grief. Roberta Carlson. 128p. (Orig.). 1987. pap. 4.95 (ISBN 0-8423-4602-3). Tyndale.

Moments to Hold Close. Mouzon Biggs, Jr. 144p. 1983. 9.95 (ISBN 0-687-27147-9). Abingdon.

Moments to Live By - Years to Enjoy. Kermit R. Carr. 1986. 8.95 (ISBN 0-533-06945-9). Vantage.

Moments with Martha. Martha Ferrin. LC 83-60477. 1983. pap. text ed. 2.50 (ISBN 0-932050-18-2). New Puritan.

Moments with the Master. T. R. Applebury. 1974. pap. 1.50 (ISBN 0-89900-115-7). College Pr Pub.

Moments Without Self. 4th ed. Benito F. Reyes. LC 61-21760. 198p. Date not set. Repr. of 1970 ed. 10.00 (ISBN 0-939375-36-2). World Univ Amer.

Momentum. Wallace Alcorn. (Living Studies Ser.). 128p. (Orig.). 1986. pap. 5.95 (ISBN 0-8423-4538-8); guide 2.95study (ISBN 0-8423-4539-6). Tyndale.

Mommy Book: Advice to New Mothers from Those Who've Been There. Karen Hull. 240p. 1986. pap. 8.95 (ISBN 0-310-32241-3). Zondervan.

Mommy's Lesson. Pat Holt. 32p. 1985. pap. 3.95 (ISBN 0-570-04131-7, 56-1545). Concordia.

Mom's Quiet Corner. Mary F. Locks. (Comtempo Ser.). 1977. pap. 1.25 (ISBN 0-8010-5576-8). Baker Bk.

Mon Univers. Pierre Teilhard De Chardin. pap. 6.95 (ISBN 0-685-36599-9). French & Eur.

Mona Antiqua Restaurata. Henry Rowlands. Ed. by Burton Feldman & Robert D. Richardson. LC 78-60894. (Myth & Romanticism Ser.: Vol. 21). 399p. 1979. lib. bdg. 80.00 (ISBN 0-8240-3570-4). Garland Pub.

Monad. Leadbeater. 3.00 (ISBN 0-8356-7646-3). Theos Pub Hse.

Monarch Notes in Kant's Philosophy. pap. 2.95 (ISBN 0-671-00530-8). Monarch Pr.

Monarch Notes on Milton's Paradise Lost. Mariam Seldin. (Orig.). pap. 3.50 (ISBN 0-671-00513-8). Monarch Pr.

Monarch Notes on Mythology. (Orig.). pap. 3.50 (ISBN 0-671-00523-5). Monarch Pr.

Monarch Notes on Shaw's Saint Joan. Grace H. Schwartz. (Orig.). pap. 2.95 (ISBN 0-671-00725-4). Monarch Pr.

Monarch Notes on the New Testament. Unicio J. Violi. (Orig.). pap. 4.50 (ISBN 0-671-00625-8). Monarch Pr.

Monarch Notes on the Old Testament As Living Literature. 1976. pap. 3.95 (ISBN 0-671-00964-8). Monarch Pr.

Monarchia. Dante Alighieri. LC 74-147412. (Library of War & Peace; Proposals for Peace: a History). lib. bdg. 46.00 (ISBN 0-8240-0210-5). Garland Pub.

Monasteries. R. J. Unstead. (Junior Reference Ser.). (Illus.). 1961. 10.95 (ISBN 0-7136-1043-3). Dufour.

Monasteries of the Wadi 'n Natrun: Metropolitan Museum of Art Egyptian Expedition Publications, 3 vols. Hugh G. White & Walter Hauser. Incl. Vol. 1. New Coptic Texts from the Monastery of Saint Macarius. (Illus.). 308p. Repr. of 1926 ed. 42.00 (ISBN 0-405-02243-3); Vol. 2. the History of the Monasteries of Nitria & of Scetis. Walter Hauser. (Illus.). Repr. of 1932 ed. 57.50 (ISBN 0-405-02244-1); Vol. 3. Walter Hauser. (Illus.). 480p. Repr. of 1933 ed. 57.50 (ISBN 0-405-02245-X). LC 77-168409. (Metropolitan Museum of Art Publications in Reprint). (Illus.). 1340p. 172.00 set (ISBN 0-405-02242-5). Ayer Co Pubs.

Monasteries of Western Europe: The Architecture of the Orders. Wolfgang Braunfels. LC 73-2472. (Illus.). 263p. 1973. 55.50 (ISBN 0-691-03896-1); pap. 19.95 (ISBN 0-691-00313-0). Princeton U Pr.

Monastery. David Birt. (Resource Units: Middle Ages, 1066-1485 Ser.). (Illus.). 1974. pap. text ed. 12.95x 10 copies & tchr's guide (ISBN 0-582-39380-9). Longman.

Monastery. Charles E. Ziavras. LC 85-81279. (Illus.). 1985. 12.95 (ISBN 0-915940-05-1); pap. 4.95 (ISBN 0-915940-06-X). Ithaca Pr MA.

Monastery & Cathedral in France: Medieval Architecture, Sculpture, Stained Glass, Manuscripts, the Art of the Church Treasuries. Whitney S. Stoddard. LC 66-23923. 412p. 1966. 35.00x (ISBN 0-8195-3071-9). Wesleyan U Pr.

Monastery of Epiphanius at Thebes, 2 bks in one, Pt. 1. Incl. The Archaeological Material. H. E. Winlock; The Literary Material. W. E. Crum. (Metropolitan Museum of Art Egyptian Expedition Publications Ser., Vol. 3). 1972. Repr. of 1926 ed. 40.00 (ISBN 0-405-02250-6). Ayer Co Pubs.

Monastery of Epiphanius at Thebes, 2 bks in one, Pt. 2. Incl. Coptic Ostraca & Papyri. W. E. Crum; Greek Ostraca & Papyri. H. G. White. (Metropolitan Museum of Art Egyptian Expedition Publication Ser., Vol. 4). 1972. Repr. of 1926 ed. 45.00 (ISBN 0-405-02251-4). Ayer Co Pubs.

Monastery of Epiphanius at Thebes: Metropolitan Museum of Art Egyptain Expedition Publications, Vols. 3 & 4, 2 vols. Herbert E. Winlock et al. LC 72-168413. (The Metropolitan Museum of Art Publication in Reprint Ser.). 1926. 88.00 set (ISBN 0-405-02249-2). Ayer Co Pubs.

Monastery of Saint Catherine at Mount Sinai: The Church & Fortress of Justinian: Plates. George H. Forsyth & Kurt Weitzmann. LC 68-29257. (Illus.). 236p. 1973. 65.00 (ISBN 0-472-33000-4). U of Mich Pr.

Monastery of Saint Catherine at Mount Sinai, The Icons I: From the Sixth to the Tenth Century. Kurt Weitzmann. LC 75-3482. 276p. 1976. 205.00x (ISBN 0-691-03543-1). Princeton U Pr.

Monastic Archaeology in Egypt. C. C. Walters. 354p. 1974. text ed. 38.50x (ISBN 0-85668-008-7, Pub. by Aris & Phillips UK). Humanities.

Monastic Breviary. 1976. 14.95x (ISBN 0-8192-1220-2). Morehouse.

Monastic Chronicler & the Early School of St. Albans: A Lecture. Claude Jenkins. LC 74-19113. 1974. Repr. of 1922 ed. lib. bdg. 20.00 (ISBN 0-8414-5320-9). Folcroft.

Monastic Iconography in France from the Renaissance to the Revolution. Joan Evans. LC 67-12317. (Illus.). 1969. 80.00 (ISBN 0-521-06960-2). Cambridge U Pr.

Monastic Impulse. Walter Capps. LC 82-14866. 224p. 1982. 10.95 (ISBN 0-8245-0490-9). Crossroad NY.

Monastic Journey. Thomas Merton. Ed. by Patrick Hart. LC 77-27714. 1978. pap. 4.50 (ISBN 0-385-14094-0, Im). Doubleday.

Monastic Journey to India. M. Basil Pennington. 144p. (Orig.). 1982. pap. 9.95 (ISBN 0-8164-2398-9, HarpR). Har-Row.

Monastic Life in Medieval England. John C. Dickinson. LC 78-25804. (Illus.). 1979. Repr. of 1961 ed. lib. bdg. 24.75x (ISBN 0-313-20774-7, DIML). Greenwood.

Monastic Life in the Middle Ages. Cardinal Gasquet. 59.95 (ISBN 0-8490-0657-0). Gordon Pr.

Monastic Life in the Middle Ages, 1792-1806. facs. ed. Francis A. Gasquet. LC 76-137377. (Select Bibliographies Reprint Ser). 1922. 16.00 (ISBN 0-8369-5578-1). Ayer Co Pubs.

Monastic Order in England. 2nd ed. David Knowles. 1963. 89.50 (ISBN 0-521-05479-6). Cambridge U Pr.

Monastic Order in South Wales: 1066-1349. F. G. Cowley. (Studies in Welsh History: No. 1). 325p. 1977. text ed. 32.50x (ISBN 0-7083-0648-9, Pub. by U of Wales Pr). Humanities.

Monastic Practices. Charles Cummings. pap. 7.95 (ISBN 0-87907-975-4). Cistercian Pubns.

Monastic Realm. Reginald Gregoire et al. LC 85-43046. (Illus.). 288p. 1985. 75.00 (ISBN 0-8478-0664-2). Rizzoli Intl.

Monastic Rule of Losif Volotsky. Ed. by David Goldfrank. 1983. pap. 14.95 (ISBN 0-87907-936-3). Cistercian Pubns.

Monastic Rule of St. Carthach: St. Mochuda the Younger. St. Carthach. pap. 1.50 (ISBN 0-686-05656-6). Eastern Orthodox.

Monastic Rules of Ireland. pap. 1.50 (ISBN 0-686-05654-X). Eastern Orthodox.

Monastic Typicon. The Monks of New Skete. 49p. (Orig.). 1980. pap. 10.00 (ISBN 0-9607924-6-5). Monks of New Skete.

Monasticism: A Historical Overview. (Word & Spirit Ser.: Vol. VI). 1984. pap. 7.00 (ISBN 0-932506-33-X). St Bedes Pubns.

Monasticism & the Arts. Ed. by Timothy G. Verdon & John Dally. (Illus.). 368p. 1984. text ed. 34.95x (ISBN 0-8156-2291-0); pap. text ed. 16.95x (ISBN 0-8156-2292-9). Syracuse U Pr.

Monasticism in the Orthodox Church. N. F. Robinson. LC 72-131506. Repr. of 1916 ed. 18.50 (ISBN 0-404-05375-0). AMS Pr.

Monasticon Praemonstratense, Vol. 1. 274p. 1983. 99.20 (ISBN 3-11-008917-3). De Gruyter.

Moncado. Dominga D. Ramos. 1985. 9.75 (ISBN 0-8062-2452-5). Carlton.

Monday Morning Jesus. Joseph Moore. 96p. (Orig.). 1984. pap. 3.95 (ISBN 0-8091-2591-9). Paulist Pr.

Money & Power. Jacques Ellul. Tr. by LaVonne Neff from Fr. LC 83-22647. Orig. Title: Homme et l'Argent. 216p. 1984. pap. 7.95 (ISBN 0-87784-916-1). Inter-Varsity.

Money & Your Church. Manfred Holck, Jr. LC 74-75979. (Illus.). 189p. 1974. 7.95 (ISBN 0-87983-080-8). Keats.

Money: Christ's Perspective on the Use & Abuse of Money. Andrew Murray. 80p. 1978. pap. 2.95 (ISBN 0-87123-382-7, 200382). Bethany Hse.

Money God. Dolly Hildreth et al. (Indian Culture Ser.). 1972. 1.95 (ISBN 0-89992-031-4). Coun India Ed.

Money in the Church. Joe E. Walker. LC 81-20583. (Into Our Third Century Ser.). (Orig.). 1982. pap. 3.95 (ISBN 0-687-27160-6). Abingdon.

Money Management: Dollars & Sense for Christian Homemakers. Edith F. Kilgo. 200p. 1980. pap. 5.95 (ISBN 0-8010-5422-2). Baker Bk.

Money Matters. R. C. Sproul, Jr. 192p. (Orig.). 1985. pap. 5.95 (ISBN 0-8423-4540-X). Tyndale.

Money, Sex & Power: Study Guide. Richard J. Foster. LC 84-48785. 96p. (Orig.). 1985. pap. 4.95 (ISBN 0-06-062827-8, HarpR). Har-Row.

Money, Sex & Power: The Challenge of the Disciplined Life. Richard J. Foster. LC 84-48769. 192p. 1985. 13.45 (ISBN 0-06-062826-X, HarpR). Har-Row.

Moneys of the Bible. R. S. Yeoman. (Illus.). 1982. Repr. of 1961 ed. softcover 7.00 (ISBN 0-915262-77-0). S J Durst.

Mongol Mission. Ed. by Christopher H. Dawson. LC 78-63334. (Crusades & Military Orders: Second Ser.). Repr. of 1955 ed. 33.00 (ISBN 0-404-17008-0). AMS Pr.

Monicas Hannukah House. Janie D'Addio & Othello Bach. (Illus.). 64p. 1983. 14.95 (ISBN 0-914759-01-9). Preferred Pr.

Monk. facsimile ed. Julian Corbett. LC 72-154148. (Select Bibliographies Reprint Ser). Repr. of 1889 ed. 18.00 (ISBN 0-8369-5764-4). Ayer Co Pubs.

Monk of Mount Athos: Staretz Silouan 1866-1938. Archimandrite Sophrony. LC 61-4333. 124p. 1975. pap. 4.95 (ISBN 0-913836-15-X). St Vladimirs.

Monk Who Shook the World (Martin Luther) Cyril Davey. 1960. pap. 2.95 (ISBN 0-87508-614-4). Chr Lit.

Monks, Bishops, & Pagans: Christian Culture in Gaul & Italy. Ed. by Edward Peters. Incl. Selections from the Minor Writings. Gregory Of Tours. Ed. by William C. McDermott. LC 74-33702. (Middle Ages Ser.). 252p. 1975. (Pa Paperbks); pap. text ed. 10.95x (ISBN 0-8122-1069-7). U of Pa Pr.

Monks, Hermits & the Ascetic Tradition. Ed. by W. J. Sheils. (Studies in Church History: Vol. 22). 500p. 1985. 45.00x (ISBN 0-631-14351-3). Basil Blackwell.

Monks of Durham. Anne Boyd. LC 74-14438. (Introduction to the History of Mankind Ser). (Illus.). 48p. 1975. text ed. 4.95 (ISBN 0-521-20647-2). Cambridge U Pr.

Monks of Kublai Khan, Emperor of China. Ernest A. Budge. LC 71-38051. Repr. of 1928 ed. 32.50 (ISBN 0-404-56905-6). AMS Pr.

Monks of the West from St. Benedict to St. Bernard, 6 vols. Charles Montalembert, pseud. LC 3-11386. Repr. of 1896 ed. Set. 195.00 (ISBN 0-404-04410-7). Vol. 1 (ISBN 0-404-04411-5). Vol. 2 (ISBN 0-404-04412-3). Vol. 3 (ISBN 0-404-04413-1). Vol. 4 (ISBN 0-404-04414-X). Vol. 5 (ISBN 0-404-04415-8). Vol. 6 (ISBN 0-404-04416-6). AMS Pr.

Monks on Marriage: A Twelfth-Century View. Jean LeClercq. 144p. 1982. 10.95 (ISBN 0-8164-0507-7, HarpR). Har-Row.

Monographie & Iconographie der Oedogoniaceen. K. E. Hirn. (Illus.). 1960. pap. 95.00x (ISBN 3-7682-7056-4). Lubrecht & Cramer.

Monographs on Church Architecture, 2 vols. Mary Vance. (Architecture Ser.: Bibliography A1209). 249p. 1984. Set. pap. 20.00 (ISBN 0-89028-019-3). Vance Biblios.

Monolithic Jinas. Jose Pereira. 1977. 11.50 (ISBN 0-8426-1027-8, Pub. by Motilal Banarsidass India). Orient Bk Dist.

Monotheism, Vol. 177. Ed. by Claude Geffre & Jean-Pierre Jossua. (Concilium Ser.). 128p. pap. 6.95 (ISBN 0-567-30057-9, Pub. by T & T Clark Ltd UK). Fortress.

Monotheism: A Philosophic Inquiry into the Foundations of Theology & Ethics. Lenn E. Goodman. LC 79-24818. (Publications of the Oxford Centre for Postgraduate Hebrew Study). 228p. 1981. 22.50x (ISBN 0-86598-068-3). Allanheld.

Monotheism & the Prophetic Minority: An Essay in Biblical History & Sociology. Bernhard Lang. (Social World of Biblical Antiquity: No. 1). 191p. 1983. text ed. 22.95x (ISBN 0-907459-30-7, Pub. by Almond Pr England); pap. text ed. 10.95x (ISBN 0-907459-31-5). Eisenbrauns.

Monotheistic Point of View. Murtaza Mutahhery. 70p. 1984. pap. 3.95 (ISBN 0-940368-39-0). Tahrike Tarsile Quran.

Mons Perfectionis. John Alcock. LC 74-28823. (English Experience Ser.: No. 706). 1974. Repr. of 1497 ed. 6.00 (ISBN 90-221-0706-X). Walter J Johnson.

Monsters: A Guide to Information on Unaccounted for Creatures, Including Bigfoot, Many Water Monsters, & Other Irregular Animals. George M. Eberhart. LC 82-49029. (Supernatural Studies). 358p. 1983. lib. bdg. 28.00 (ISBN 0-8240-9213-9). Garland Pub.

Mont-Saint-Michel. Germain Bazin. LC 75-24825. (Fr.). 1978. Repr. of 1933 ed. lib. bdg. 100.00 (ISBN 0-87817-190-8). Hacker.

Mont Saint-Michel. Rene-Jacques. (Panorama Bks.). (Fr.). 62p. 3.95 (ISBN 0-685-23348-0). French & Eur.

Mont Saint Michel & Chartres. Henry Adams. LC 36-27246. 397p. 1978. 18.95 (ISBN 0-910220-94-8). Berg.

Mont-Saint-Michel & Chartres. Henry B. Adams. LC 82-14018. 408p. 1982. 25.00 (ISBN 0-89783-019-9). Larlin Corp.

Mont-Saint-Michel & Chartres: A Study of 13th Century Unity. H. Adams. LC 81-47279. (Illus.). 448p. 1981. 40.00x (ISBN 0-691-03971-2); pap. 9.95x (ISBN 0-691-00335-1). Princeton U Pr.

Montecassino Passion & the Poetics of Medieval Drama. Robert Edwards. LC 75-22655. 1977. 36.50x (ISBN 0-520-03102-4). U of Cal Pr.

Montesquieu et l'Esclavage: Etude Sur les Origines De l'Opinion Antiesclavage En France Au Dix-Huitieme Siecle. Russell P. Jameson. LC 72-171409. (Research & Source Works Ser.: No. 859). (Fr.). 371p. (Philosophy & Religious History Monographs, No. 81). 1972. Repr. of 1911 ed. lib. bdg. 23.50 (ISBN 0-8337-4185-3). B Franklin.

Monteverdi Church Music. Denis Arnold. LC 81-71298. (BBC Music Guides Ser.). 64p. (Orig.). 1983. pap. 4.95 (ISBN 0-295-95923-1). U of Wash Pr.

Month of Mondays: Poems & Prayers for the Monday Morning Homemaker Blues. Mary Lou Carney. 112p. (Orig.). 1984. pap. 5.95 (ISBN 0-687-27164-9). Abingdon.

Month with Jesus. Gerald O'Collins. pap. 2.95 (ISBN 0-87193-097-8). Dimension Bks.

Month with Saint Paul. James Alberione. 1952. pap. 2.25 (ISBN 0-8198-0104-6). Dghtrs St Paul.

Monumenta Ritualia Ecclestiae Anglicanae, 3 vols. William Maskell. 1710p. 1882. text ed. 186.30x (ISBN 0-576-99784-6, Pub. by Gregg Intl Pub England). Gregg Intl.

Monumental Christianity: The Art & Symbolism of the Primitive Church. John P. Lundy. 1977. lib. bdg. 59.95 (ISBN 0-8490-2278-9). Gordon Pr.

Monuments des Croises dans le Royaume de Jerusalem, 4 vols. Camille Enlart. LC 78-63336. (Crusades & Military Orders: Second Ser.). Repr. of 1927 ed. Set. 495.00 (ISBN 0-404-17050-1). AMS Pr.

Monuments of Romanesque Art: The Art of Church Treasures in North-Western Europe. 2nd ed. Hanns Swarzenski. LC 55-937. (Illus.). 1967. 40.00x (ISBN 0-226-78605-6). U of Chicago Pr.

Mood of Christmas. Howard Thurman. LC 85-16018. 127p. 1985. pap. 9.95 (ISBN 0-913408-90-5). Friends United.

Moods. John Souter. 96p. (Orig.). 1986. 4.95 (ISBN 0-8423-4498-5). Tyndale.

Moody Atlas of Bible Lands. Barry J. Beitzel. 1985. text ed. 31.95 (ISBN 0-8024-0438-3). Moody.

Moody Bible Atlas. 1985. 29.95 (ISBN 0-88469-169-1). BMH Bks.

Moody Guide to Bible Lands. Tim Dowley. 1987. text ed. 7.95 (ISBN 0-8024-5563-8). Moody.

Moody Guide to the Bible. Tim Dowley. 1986. Repr. text ed. 7.95 (ISBN 0-8024-5562-X). Moody.

Moon for the Misbegotten. Eugene O'Neill. LC 74-5218. 1974. pap. 2.95 (ISBN 0-394-71236-6, Vin). Random.

Moon: Its Creation, Form & Significance. John C. Whitcomb & Donald B. DeYoung. 7.95 (ISBN 0-88469-102-0). BMH Bks.

Moon Lore. Timothy Harley. 1976. Repr. 13.00x (ISBN 0-85409-828-3). Charles River Bks.

Moon Lore & Moon Magic. Al G. Manning. 1980. 14.95 (ISBN 0-13-600668-X). Pan Ishtar.

Moon, Moon. Anne K. Rush. 1976. pap. 7.95 (ISBN 0-394-73230-8). Random.

Moonies: A Critical Look at a Controversial Group. R. J. Owen. 1985. 20.00x (ISBN 0-7062-4149-5, Pub. by Ward Lock Educ Co Ltd). State Mutual Bk.

Moonies in America: Cult, Church, & Crusade. David G. Bromley & Anson D. Shupe, Jr. LC 79-16456. (Sage Library of Social Research: Vol. 92). 269p. 1979. 29.00 (ISBN 0-8039-1060-6). Sage.

Moonshine Special. Julia C. Cardwell. (Illus.). 1983. 5.75 (ISBN 0-8062-1908-4). Carlton.

Moral & Philosophical Essays. Caleb S. Henry. LC 75-3178. Repr. of 1839 ed. 10.50 (ISBN 0-404-59181-7). AMS Pr.

Moral & Political Philosophy. David Hume. Ed. by Henry D. Aiken. (Library of Classics Ser.: No. 3). 1975. pap. text ed. 8.95x (ISBN 0-02-846170-3). Hafner.

Moral & Political Philosophy of the Abbe de Saint-Pierre. M. L. Perkins. 160p. (Orig.). 1959. pap. text ed. 20.00x (Pub. by Droz Switzerland). Coronet Bks.

Moral & Political Thought of Mahatma Gandi. Raghavan Iyer. (Illus.). xviii, 478p. pap. 17.50 (ISBN 0-88695-002-3). Concord Grove.

Moral & Religious Education in County Primary Schools. H. Blackham. 6.00x (ISBN 0-85633-115-5, Pub. by NFER Nelson UK). Taylor & Francis.

Moral Basis of Faith. Tom Wells. 28p. (Orig.). 1986. pap. 1.45 (ISBN 0-85151-469-3). Banner of Truth.

Moral Behavior in Chinese Society. Ed. by Richard W. Wilson et al. LC 81-4581. 232p. 1981. 35.95 (ISBN 0-03-056922-2). Praeger.

Moral Choice. Daniel C. Maguire. 1979. pap. 12.95 (ISBN 0-86683-771-X, AY8112, HarpR). Har-Row.

Moral Choices: A Religious Perspective. Joseph Asher. 50p. (Orig.). 1984. pap. write for info. (ISBN 0-936434-14-7, Pub. by Zellerbach Fam Fund). SF Study Ctr.

Moral Conduct & Authority: The Place of Adab in Sout h Asian Islam. Ed. by Barbara D. Metcalf. LC 83-1361. 350p. 1984. text ed. 40.00x (ISBN 0-520-04660-9). U of Cal Pr.

Moral Context of Pastoral Care. Don S. Browning. LC 76-5858. 144p. 1983. pap. 8.95 (ISBN 0-664-24483-1). Westminster.

Moral Cosmos of Paradise Lost. Lawrence Babb. 1970. 7.50 (ISBN 0-87013-154-0). Mich St U Pr.

Moral Development. Bonnidell Clouse. 368p. 1985. pap. 13.95 (ISBN 0-8010-2507-9). Baker Bk.

Moral Development: A Guide to Piaget & Kohlberg. Ronald Duska & Mariellen Whelan. LC 75-20863. 136p. 1975. pap. 5.95 (ISBN 0-8091-1892-0). Paulist Pr.

Moral Development: A Practical Guide for Jewish Teachers. Earl Schwartz. LC 83-70196. 188p. 1983. pap. text ed. 10.00 (ISBN 0-86705-037-3). AIRE.

Moral Development: Advances in Research & Theory. James R. Rest. LC 86-21708. 241p. 1986. lib. bdg. 36.95 (ISBN 0-275-92254-5, C2254). Praeger.

Moral Development: Current Theory & Research. David J. DePalma & Jeanne M. Foley. LC 75-14211. 206p. 1975. text ed. 24.95x (ISBN 0-89859-116-3). L Erlbaum Assocs.

Moral Development Foundations: Judeo-Christian Alternatives to Piaget-Kohlberg. Ed. by Donald M. Joy. 240p. (Orig.). 1983. pap. 13.95 (ISBN 0-687-27177-0). Abingdon.

Moral Dimensions of International Conduct. Shirley Williams & Jose Zalaquett. Ed. by James Devereux. (Jesuit Community Lectures Ser.: 1982). 128p. (Orig.). pap. 5.95 (ISBN 0-87840-406-6). Georgetown U Pr.

Moral Education: A First Generation of Research & Development. Ed. by Ralph Mosher. LC 80-18607. 426p. 1980. 42.95 (ISBN 0-03-053961-7). Praeger.

Moral Education: International Perspectives. Ed. by Marvin W. Berkowitz & Fritz Oser. 472p. 1985. text ed. 45.00 (ISBN 0-89859-557-6). L Erlbaum Assocs.

Moral en la Educacion. Ramon M. Parsons. LC 83-10594. (Span.). 90p. 1984. write for info. (ISBN 0-8477-2746-7). U of PR Pr.

Moral Evaluation of Contraception & Sterilization: A Dialogical Study. Gary M. Atkinson & Albert S. Moraczewski. LC 79-90971. viii, 115p. (Orig.). 1979. pap. 4.95 (ISBN 0-935372-05-9). Pope John Ctr.

Moral Exhortation, a Greco-Roman Sourcebook. Abraham J. Malherbe. LC 86-5499. (Library of Early Christianity: Vol. 4). 180p. 1986. 18.95 (ISBN 0-664-21908-X). Westminster.

Moral Fiber: Character & Belief in Recent American Fiction. Wesley A. Kort. LC 81-71389. 160p. 1982. pap. 1.00 (ISBN 0-8006-1624-3, 1-1624). Fortress.

Moral Foundations of Life. Oswald Chambers. 1961. pap. 2.95 (ISBN 0-87508-117-7). Chr Lit.

Moral Foundations of Professional Ethics. Alan H. Goldman. LC 80-11696. (Philosophy & Society Ser.). 305p. 1980. 28.95x (ISBN 0-8476-6274-8); pap. 11.95x (ISBN 0-8476-6285-3). Rowman.

Moral Foundations of the American Republic. 2nd ed. Robert H. Horwitz. LC 79-20387. 275p. 1982. 15.00x (ISBN 0-8139-0853-1). U Pr of Va.

Moral Foundations of the American Republic. 3rd ed. Ed. by Robert H. Horwitz. LC 85-17772. (Kenyon Public Affairs Conference Center Ser.). xii, 347p. 1986. 25.00x (ISBN 0-8139-1081-1); pap. 5.95x (ISBN 0-8139-1082-X). U Pr of Va.

Moral Idea of the Main Dogmas of the Faith. Antony Khrapovitsky. Tr. by Varlaam Novakshonoff & Lazar Puhalo. 170p. (Orig.). 1984. pap. text ed. 8.00 (ISBN 0-911523-01-4). Synaxis Pr.

Moral Idea of the Main Dogmas of the Faith. Antony Khrapovitsky. Tr. by V. Novakshonoff & L. Puhalo. 96p. (Orig.). 1986. pap. 7.50. Synaxis Pr.

Moral Ideals of Our Civilization. R. A. Tsanoff. 1977. lib. bdg. write for info. (ISBN 0-8490-2279-7). Gordon Pr.

Moral Ideals of Our Civilization. facsimile ed. Radoslav A. Tsanoff. LC 70-38738. (Essay Index Reprint Ser). Repr. of 1942 ed. 36.50 (ISBN 0-8369-2675-7). Ayer Co Pubs.

Moral Imperatives of Human Rights: A World Survey. Ed. by Kenneth W. Thompson. LC 79-3736. 1980. text ed. 25.00 (ISBN 0-8191-0920-7); pap. text ed. 9.75 (ISBN 0-8191-0921-5). U Pr of Amer.

Moral Issues & Christian Responses. 3rd ed. Paul T. Jersild & Dale A. Johnson. 1983. pap. text ed. 25.95 (ISBN 0-03-062464-9). HR&W.

Moral Issues: If Christ Is Lord. Lyman Coleman. (Serendipity Ser.). (Orig.). 1981. pap. 4.95 leader's guide 64 pgs. (ISBN 0-687-37330-1); pap. 1.25 student's bk 32 pgs (ISBN 0-687-37331-X). Abingdon.

Moral Issues in the Control of Birth. new ed. Duane Friesen. LC 74-76587. (Illus.). 64p. 1974. pap. 1.95 (ISBN 0-87303-561-5). Faith & Life.

Moral Judgment. David D. Raphael. LC 77-28440. 1978. Repr. of 1955 ed. lib. bdg. 22.25x (ISBN 0-313-20246-X, RAMJ). Greenwood.

Moral Justification of Suicide. Jerry Jacobs. (Illus.). 148p. 1982. pap. 16.25x spiral bdg. (ISBN 0-398-04725-1). C C Thomas.

Moral Language. Mary G. Forrester. 240p. 1982. 27.50x (ISBN 0-299-08630-5). U of Wis Pr.

Moral Law in Christian Social Ethics. Walter G. Muelder. LC 66-15972. 198p. lib. bdg. 19.95x (ISBN 0-88946-011-6). E Mellen.

Moral Letters, 3 vols. Seneca. (Loeb Classical Library: No. 75-77). 12.50x (ISBN 0-686-76874-4). Vol. 1 (ISBN 0-674-99084-6). Vol. 2 (ISBN 0-674-99085-4). Vol. 3 (ISBN 0-674-99086-2). Harvard U Pr.

Moral Life. Hugo L. Odhner. 142p. 1985. Repr. of 1957 ed. write for info. (ISBN 0-910557-08-X). Acad New Church.

Moral Majority: Right or Wrong. Robert E. Webber. 190p. 1981. 9.95. Cornerstone.

Moral Man & Immoral Society. Reinhold Niebuhr. 16.75 (ISBN 0-8446-6221-6). Peter Smith.

Moral Man & Immoral Society: A Study in Ethics & Politics. Reinhold Niebuhr. 1932. pap. 9.95 (ISBN 0-684-71857-X, ScribT). Scribner.

Moral Mystic. James Horne. 144p. 1983. pap. text ed. 9.25x (ISBN 0-88920-149-8, Pub. by Wilfrid Lauries Canada). Humanities.

Moral Norms: A Tentative Systemization. M. Ossowska. 264p. 1980. 47.00 (ISBN 0-444-85454-1, North-Holland). Elsevier.

Moral Obligation & Duty & Interest: Essays & Lectures. Harold A. Prichard. (Oxford Paperbacks Ser). (Orig.). 1968. pap. 4.95x (ISBN 0-19-881151-9). Oxford U Pr.

Moral Order of the World in Ancient & Modern Thought. Alexander B. Bruce. LC 77-527224. (Gifford Lectures: 1898). Repr. of 1899 ed. 40.00 (ISBN 0-404-60456-0). AMS Pr.

Moral Paradox of Paradise Lost. John E. Seaman. LC 74-135665. (Studies in English Literature: Vol. 61). 1971. text ed. 17.00x (ISBN 90-2791-715-9). Mouton.

Moral Perspective in Webster's Major Tragedies. Joseph H. Stodder. Ed. by James Hogg. (Jacobean Drama Studies). 164p. (Orig.). 1974. pap. 15.00 (ISBN 3-7052-0343-6, Salzburg Studies). Longwood Pub Group.

Moral Philosopher in a Dialogue Between Philalethes, a Christian Deist, & Theophanes, a Christian Jew. Thomas Morgan. LC 75-11239. (British Philosophers & Theologians of the 17th & 18th Centuries Ser.: Vol. 39). 463p. 1977. Repr. of 1737 ed. lib. bdg. 51.00 (ISBN 0-8240-1791-9). Garland Pub.

Moral Philosophers: An Introduction to Ethics. Richard Norman. 1983. 29.95x (ISBN 0-19-875060-9); pap. 10.95x (ISBN 0-19-875059-5). Oxford U Pr.

Moral Philosophies in Shakespeare's Plays. Ben Kimpel. (Studies in Art & Religious Interpretation). 262p. 1987. text ed. 49.95 (ISBN 0-88946-558-4). E Mellen.

Moral Philosophy. D. D. Raphael. (Oxford Paperbacks University Ser.). (Orig.). 1981. pap. text ed. 8.95x (ISBN 0-19-289136-7). Oxford U Pr.

Moral Philosophy, Vol. 9. Richardson, J. & Co. Staff. 1982. 62.50x (ISBN 0-317-54279-6, Pub. by J Richardson UK); pap. 47.50x (ISBN 0-317-54280-X, Pub. by J Richardson UK). State Mutual Bk.

Moral Philosophy at Seventeenth-Century Harvard: A Discipline in Transition. Norman Fiering. LC 80-18282. (Institute of Early American History & Culture Ser.). xiii, 323p. 1981. 27.50x (ISBN 0-8078-1459-8). U of NC Pr.

Moral Philosophy for Education. Robin Barrow. (Unwin Education Books). 1975. pap. text ed. 9.95x (ISBN 0-04-370060-8). Allen Unwin.

Moral Problems & Christian Personalism. Ed. by Franz Bockle. LC 65-24045. (Concilium Ser.: Vol. 5). 191p. 7.95 (ISBN 0-8091-0099-1). Paulist Pr.

Moral Problems & Mental Health. Richard Egenter & Paul Matussek. 1967. 4.95 (ISBN 0-8189-0095-4). Alba.

Moral Problems in Contemporary Society: Essays in Humanistic Ethics. 2nd ed. Ed. by Paul Kurtz. 301p. 1973. pap. 10.95 (ISBN 0-87975-022-7). Prometheus Bks.

Moral Problems of Contraception. James O'Reilly. (Synthesis Ser). 62p. 1975. pap. 0.75 (ISBN 0-8199-0363-9). Franciscan Herald.

Moral Problems: Student Text. Michael Pennock. LC 79-51015. (Illus.). 240p. 1979. pap. text ed. 5.50 (ISBN 0-87793-177-1); tchr's manual 2.95 (ISBN 0-87793-178-X). Ave Maria.

Moral Psychology of the Virtues. N. J. Dent. LC 83-26208. (Cambridge Studies in Philosophy). 240p. 1984. 37.50 (ISBN 0-521-25726-3). Cambridge U Pr.

Moral Reasoning: A Psychological-Philosophical Integration. William D. Boyce & Larry C. Jensen. LC 78-5935. xii, 291p. 1978. 22.50x (ISBN 0-8032-0982-7). U of Nebr Pr.

Moral Reasoning & Truth: An Essay in Philosophy & Jurisprudence. Thomas D. Perry. 1976. 38.00x (ISBN 0-19-824532-7). Oxford U Pr.

Moral Reasoning: Ethical Theory & Some Contemporary Moral Problems. Victor Grassian. 400p. 1981. pap. text ed. write for info. (ISBN 0-13-600759-7). P-H.

Moral Response to Industrialism: The Lectures of Reverend Cook in Lynn, Massachusetts. John T. Cumbler. LC 81-9338. (American Social History Ser.). 180p. 1982. 39.50 (ISBN 0-87395-558-7); pap. 10.95 (ISBN 0-87395-559-5). State U NY Pr.

Moral Responsibility in Conflicts: Essays on Nonviolence, War, & Conscience. James F. Childress. LC 82-15197. 224p. 1982. text ed. 25.00x (ISBN 0-8071-1019-1). La State U Pr.

Moral Responsibility: Situation Ethics at Work. Joseph Fletcher. LC 67-14515. 256p. (Orig.). 1967. pap. 4.95 (ISBN 0-664-24770-9). Westminster.

Moral Revolution. Daniel C. Maguire. 224p. (Orig.). 1986. pap. 12.95 (ISBN 0-06-254539-6, HarpR). Har-Row.

Moral Revolution: A Christian Humanist Vision. Daniel C. Maguire. LC 85-51826. 224p. pap. 12.95 (ISBN 0-86683-520-2, RD 572, HarpR). Har-Row.

Moral Situations. N. Fotion. LC 68-31034. 135p. 1968. 8.00x (ISBN 0-87338-076-2); pap. 4.95x (ISBN 0-87338-077-0). Kent St U Pr.

Moral Teaching of the New Testament. Rudolf Schnackenburg. pap. 7.95 (ISBN 0-8245-0329-5). Crossroad NY.

Moral Theology Today: Certitudes & Doubts. LC 84-11714. 372p. (Orig.). 1984. pap. 17.95 (ISBN 0-935372-14-8). Pope John Ctr.

Moral Thinking: Its Levels, Methods, & Point. R. M. Hare. 1981. 27.00x (ISBN 0-19-824659-5); pap. 9.95x (ISBN 0-19-824660-9). Oxford U Pr.

Moral Tradition in English Fiction, 1785-1850. Samuel Pickering, Jr. LC 74-12540. 194p. 1976. text ed. 16.00x (ISBN 0-87451-109-7). U Pr of New Eng.

Moral Training in the Public Schools. Charles E. Rugh. 203p. 1980. Repr. lib. bdg. 25.00 (ISBN 0-8492-7749-3). R West.

Moral Universe: A Preface to Christian Living. facs. ed. Fulton J. Sheen. LC 67-28766. (Essay Index Reprint Ser). 1936. 15.00 (ISBN 0-8369-0873-2). Ayer Co Pubs.

Moral Values & the Idea of God. William R. Sorley. LC 77-27215. (Gifford Lectures: 1914-15). 1978. Repr. of 1918 ed. 37.50 (ISBN 0-404-60465-X). AMS Pr.

Moral Wisdom of St. Thomas: An Introduction. Peter A. Redpath. LC 83-3590. 216p. (Orig.). 1983. lib. bdg. 26.00 (ISBN 0-8191-3144-X); pap. text ed. 11.00 (ISBN 0-8191-3145-8). U Pr of Amer.

Moral World of the First Christians. Wayne A. Meeks. LC 86-5504. (Library of Early Christianity: Vol. 6). 180p. 1986. 18.95 (ISBN 0-664-21910-1). Westminster.

Morale Proberbes of Christyne. Christine Du Castel. LC 73-25783. (English Experience Ser.: No. 241). 8p. 1970. Repr. of 1478 ed. 14.00 (ISBN 90-221-0241-6). Walter J Johnson.

Moralism & Christianity: Or Man's Experience & Destiny in Three Lectures. Henry James, Sr. LC 72-917. (Selected Works of Henry James, Sr.: Vol. 4). 192p. 1983. Repr. of 1850 ed. 28.50 (ISBN 0-404-10084-8). AMS Pr.

Moralist Tradition in France. Theodore P. Fraser & Richard L. Kopp. LC 81-69245. 286p. (Orig.). 1982. text ed. 22.50x (ISBN 0-86733-017-1). Assoc Faculty Pr.

Moralities of Everyday Life. Jon Sabini & Maury Silver. 1982. 22.50x (ISBN 0-19-503016-8); pap. 8.95 (ISBN 0-19-503017-6). Oxford U Pr.

Morality: An Introduction to Ethics. Bernard Williams. LC 70-172503. 1972. pap. 5.95x (ISBN 0-06-131632-6, TB1632, Torch). Har-Row.

Morality & Conflict. Stuart Hampshire. 176p. 1987. pap. text ed. 9.50x (ISBN 0-674-58732-4). Harvard U Pr.

Morality & Ethics in Early Christianity. Jan L. Womer. LC 86-45903. (Sources in Early Christian Thought Ser.). 144p. 1987. pap. 7.95 (ISBN 0-8006-1417-8). Fortress.

Morality & Its Beyond. Dick Westley. 324p. (Orig.). 1984. pap. 8.95 (ISBN 0-89622-207-1). Twenty-Third.

Morality & Population Policy. Michael D. Bayles. LC 79-23965. 208p. 1980. 15.75 (ISBN 0-8173-0032-5); pap. text ed. 7.50 (ISBN 0-8173-0033-3). U of Ala Pr.

Morality & the Bomb: An Ethical & Assessment of Nuclear Deterrence. David Fisher. LC 85-2210. 136p. 1985. 25.00 (ISBN 0-312-54784-6). St Martin.

Morality & the Human Future in the Thought of Teilhard De Chardin: A Critical Study. Joseph A. Grau. LC 74-4976. 389p. 1976. 28.50 (ISBN 0-8386-1579-1). Fairleigh Dickinson.

Morality & the Immorality of the Human Race. Giuseppe Mazzini. (Illus.). 144p. Repr. of 1862 ed. 127.45 (ISBN 0-89901-115-2). Found Class Reprints.

Morality & the Perfect Life. Henry James, Sr. LC 72-918. (Selected Works of Henry James, Sr.: Vol. 5). 88p. 1983. Repr. of 1906 ed. 18.00 (ISBN 0-404-10085-6). AMS Pr.

Morality, Halakha & the Jewish Tradition. Shubert Spero. 1983. 20.00x (ISBN 0-87068-727-1). Ktav.

Morality: How to Live It Today. Leonard F. Badia & Ronald Sarno. LC 79-20498. 1980. pap. 9.95 (ISBN 0-8189-0391-0). Alba.

Morality in the Making: Thought, Action & the Social Context. Helen Weinreich-Haste & Don Locke. (Developmental Psychology & Its Application Ser.). 300p. 1983. 73.95 (ISBN 0-471-10423-X, Pub. by Wiley Interscience). Wiley.

Morality Maze. Ward Patterson. LC 81-14539. 128p. (Orig.). 1982. pap. 2.25 (ISBN 0-87239-478-6, 41010). Standard Pub.

Morality: Memory & Desire. Luigi Guissani. Tr. by Kenneth D. Whitehead. LC 86-80476. Tr. of Italian. 174p. 1986. pap. 8.95 (ISBN 0-89870-090-6). Ignatius Pr.

Morality of Abortion: Legal & Historical Perspectives. Intro. by John T. Noonan, Jr. LC 70-129118. 276p. 1970. pap. text ed. 6.95x (ISBN 0-674-58727-8). Harvard U Pr.

Morality: Religious & Secular. Basil Mitchell. 176p. 1986. pap. 10.95x (ISBN 0-19-824928-4). Oxford U Pr.

Morality-Religious & Secular: The Dilemma of the Traditional Conscience. Basil Mitchell. 1980. 29.95x (ISBN 0-19-824537-8). Oxford U Pr.

Morality, Sex & the Constitution: A Christian Perspective on the Power of Government to Regulate Private Sexual Conduct Between Consenting Adults. G. Sidney Buchanan. LC 85-3249. 242p. (Orig.). 1985. lib. bdg. 26.25 (ISBN 0-8191-4602-1); pap. text ed. 11.75 (ISBN 0-8191-4603-X). U Pr of Amer.

Morality Today: The Bible in My Life. Daughters of St Paul. 1979. 3.25 (ISBN 0-8198-0620-X); pap. 2.25 (ISBN 0-8198-0621-8). Dghtrs St Paul.

Morals for Mankind. Herbert W. Schneider. LC 60-14882. 96p. 1960. 5.00x (ISBN 0-8262-0006-0). U of Mo Pr.

Morals Game. Edward Stevens. LC 74-18855. 216p. 1975. pap. 5.95 (ISBN 0-8091-1852-1). Paulist Pr.

Morals in Review. Arthur K. Rogers. LC 72-126697. Repr. of 1927 ed. 31.50 (ISBN 0-404-05379-3). AMS Pr.

Morals in World History. Archibald Robertson. LC 74-6354. (World History Ser., No. 48). 1974. lib. bdg. 49.95x (ISBN 0-8383-1918-1). Haskell.

Morals, Law & Life. Cahal Daly. 228p. 1966. 5.95 (ISBN 0-933932-08-1). Scepter Pubs.

Morals, Value, & Motivation: Ethics for Today. Ed Curley. 1978. 9.95 (ISBN 0-89837-039-6, Pub. by Pflaum Pr). Peter Li.

Morals Without Religion. Margaret Knight. 124p. 1981. 25.00x (ISBN 0-686-97044-6, Pub. by Dobson Bks England). State Mutual Bk.

Moravian & Methodist. Clifford W. Towlson. LC 57-3559. 1957. 20.00x (ISBN 0-8401-2387-6, 8401-2387-6). A R Allenson.

Moravians in Jamaica. facsimile ed. J. H. Buchner. LC 77-178470. (Black Heritage Library Collection Ser.). Repr. of 1854 ed. 17.50 (ISBN 0-8369-8918-X). Ayer Co Pubs.

Moravians in Two Worlds: A Study of Changing Communities. Gillian L. Gollin. LC 67-19653. 302p. 1967. 31.00x (ISBN 0-231-03033-9). Columbia U Pr.

Mordecai M. Kaplan: An Evaluation. Ed. by Ira Eisenstein & Eugene Kohn. 324p. 1952. 12.00 (ISBN 0-935457-11-9). Reconstructionist Pr.

Mordecai M. Kaplan Jubilee Volume, 2 Vols. Moshe Davis. 1953. Set. 50.00x (ISBN 0-685-13740-6, Pub. by Jewish Theol Seminary). Ktav.

Mordecai's Ride. Gladys S. Stump. (Books I Can Read). (Illus.). 1978. pap. 1.95 (ISBN 0-8127-0161-5). Review & Herald.

More about Fatima. J. Dacruz. Tr. by V. Montes De Oca from Port. Tr. of Prodige Prow de Fatima. 1979. pap. 1.00 (ISBN 0-913382-16-7, 102-95). Prow Bks-Franciscan.

More about My Magnificent Machine. William L. Coleman. LC 79-21140. (Illus.). 128p. (Orig.). 1980. pap. 4.95 (ISBN 0-87123-386-X, 210386). Bethany Hse.

More Bible Study Puzzles. Thomas J. Marks. (Orig.). 1983. pap. 2.95 (ISBN 0-8054-9108-2). Broadman.

More Brief Prayers for Bread & Cup. Russell F. Harrison. Ed. by Herbert Lambert. LC 86-6076. 80p. (Orig.). 1986. pap. 4.95 (ISBN 0-8272-2319-6). CBP.

More Bulletin Boards-ers. Helen Eisenberg & Larry Eisenberg. 1984. 5.25 (ISBN 0-89536-704-1, 4887). CSS of Ohio.

More Celebrating the Seasons with Children. Philip E. Johnson. 112p. 1985. pap. 7.95 (ISBN 0-8298-0731-4). Pilgrim NY.

More Children's Church Time. Mary Rose Pearson. LC 82-70390. 220p. (Orig.). 1982. 14.95 (ISBN 0-89636-082-2). Accent Bks.

More Children's Liturgies. Ed. by Maria Bruck. LC 81-80877. 256p. (Orig.). 1981. pap. 9.95 (ISBN 0-8091-2362-2). Paulist Pr.

More Class Notes. Arthur Corey. pap. 2.50 (ISBN 0-87516-016-6). De Vorss.

More Difficult Sayings of Jesus. William Neil & Stephen Travis. 128p. (Orig.). 1982. pap. 5.95 (ISBN 0-8028-1937-0). Eerdmans.

More Drawings of Rembrandt. Stephen Longstreet. (Master Draughtsman Ser). 48p. treasure trove bdg. 10.95x (ISBN 0-87505-054-9); pap. 4.95 (ISBN 0-87505-207-X). Borden.

More Effective Choir Ministry: A Manual for Church Musicians. Dean C. Schield. LC 86-42932. 32p. (Orig.). 1986. pap. 4.00 (ISBN 0-937021-02-4). Sagamore Bks MI.

More Essays on Religion. facsimile ed. Arthur Clutton-Brock. LC 76-156632. (Essay Index Reprint Ser). Repr. of 1928 ed. 18.00 (ISBN 0-8369-2349-9). Ayer Co Pubs.

More Evidence That Demands a Verdict. rev. ed. Josh McDowell. 425p. 1981. pap. 7.95 (ISBN 0-918956-73-0). Campus Crusade.

More Fun with Bible Facts. Ruby Paterson. pap. 1.75 (ISBN 0-89137-617-8). Quality Pubns.

More Funny Things on the Way to Church. Dave Anderson. Ed. by Tim Wilcox. (Continued Applied Christianity Ser.). 1983. pap. 4.50 (ISBN 0-570-03893-6, 12-2975). Concordia.

More Gospel According to Mother Goose. Edmund Wells. 159p. (Orig.). 1981. pap. 2.95 (ISBN 0-8341-0727-9). Beacon Hill.

More Graffiti: Devotions for Girls. J. David Schmidt. (Illus.). 128p. (Orig.). 1984. pap. 4.95 (ISBN 0-8007-5143-4, Power Bks). Revell.

More Graffiti: Devotions for Guys. J. David Schmidt. (Illus.). 128p. 1984. pap. 4.95 (ISBN 0-8007-5142-6, Power Bks). Revell.

More Graham Crackers, Galoshes, & God. Bernadette M. Snyder. LC 85-80929. 96p. (Orig.). 1985. pap. 2.95 (ISBN 0-89243-243-8). Liguori Pubns.

More Hours in My Day. Emilie Barnes. (Orig.). 1982. pap. 5.95 (ISBN 0-89081-355-8). Harvest Hse.

More Light. 8.50 (ISBN 0-685-19492-2). Powner.

More Lights on Yoga. Sri Aurobindo. 1979. pap. 3.50 (ISBN 0-89744-950-9). Auromere.

More Little Visits with God. Allan H. Jahsmann & Martin P. Simon. 1961. 9.50 (ISBN 0-570-03017-X, 6-1080); pap. 6.95 (ISBN 0-570-03033-1, 6-1159). Concordia.

More Notices from Methodist Papers 1830-1857. Donald A. McKenzie. 424p. 1986. lib. bdg. 22.00 (ISBN 0-912606-29-0). Hunterdon Hse.

More of a Good Thing. Stephen Carter & Charles McKinney. 1982. pap. 3.50 (ISBN 0-570-03840-5, 12-2943). Concordia.

More of Jesus, Less of Me. Joan Cavanaugh & Pat Forseth. 1976. pap. 3.95 (ISBN 0-88270-174-6). Bridge Pub.

More of My Changeless Friend. Francis P. Lebuffe. 1977. pap. 1.95 (ISBN 0-88479-007-X). Arena Lettres.

More Old Testament Stories. Elaine M. Ward. 65p. 1984. pap. 6.95 (ISBN 0-940754-23-1). Ed Ministries.

More on Tantras. M. P. Pandit. 152p. 1986. text ed. 22.50x (ISBN 81-207-0122-4, Pub. by Sterling Pubs India). Apt Bks.

More Parables For Now. Edmund Flood. 4.95 (ISBN 0-87193-192-3). Dimension Bks.

More Power to You! Charles Roth. LC 82-50122. 158p. 1982. 5.95 (ISBN 0-87159-093-X). Unity School.

More Prayers. Tasha Tudor. LC 67-19929. (Illus.). 1967. 4.95 (ISBN 0-8098-1954-6). McKay.

More Precious Than Gold. Basilea Schlink. 1978. pap. 4.95 (ISBN 0-88419-178-8). Creation Hse.

More Precious Than Gold: Psalm 19. 48p. (Orig.). 7.95 (ISBN 0-86683-845-7, HarpR). Har-Row.

More Rock, Country & Backward Masking. Jacob Aranza. 1985. pap. 5.95 (ISBN 0-910311-30-7). Huntington Hse Inc.

More Roman Than Rome: English Catholicism in the Nineteenth Century. J. Derek Holmes. LC 77-92886. (Illus.). 278p. 1978. 21.95x (ISBN 0-915762-05-6). Patmos Pr.

More Salt in My Kitchen. Jeanette Lockerbie. LC 80-12357. (Quiet Time Bks.). 1980. pap. 3.50 (ISBN 0-8024-5668-5). Moody.

More Seasonings for Sermons. Phil Barnhart. 1985. 6.25 (ISBN 0-89536-723-8, 5807). CSS of Ohio.

More Simulation Games. Pat Baker & Mary R. Marshall. (Youth Work Guide Ser.). (Illus.). 88p. (Orig.). 1977. pap. 7.95 (ISBN 0-85819-194-6, Pub. by JBCE). ANZ Religious Pubns.

More Skits That Win. Ruth Vaughn. 1977. pap. 2.95 (ISBN 0-310-33671-6, 10942X). Zondervan.

More Songs of Gladness (Suppl.) Llewellyn McKernan. (Arch Bks.). (Illus.). 24p. 1987. pap. 0.99 (ISBN 0-570-09004-0, 59-1432). Concordia.

More Special Times with God. David Shibley & Naomi Shibley. LC 84-3485. 168p. 1984. 5.95 (ISBN 0-8407-5363-2). Nelson.

More Steeple Stories. Ed. by Oren Arnold. LC 77-76437. (Church Humor Series). 1969. pap. 1.95 (ISBN 0-8254-2105-5). Kregel.

More Stepping Stones to Jewish Christian Relations. Helga Croner. (Stimulus Bk.). 240p. (Orig.). 1985. pap. 7.95 (ISBN 0-8091-2708-3). Paulist Pr.

More Stories to See & Share. Maline Crockett. (Illus.). 64p. 1981. pap. 3.95 (ISBN 0-87747-886-4). Deseret Bk.

More Sunshine on the Soapsuds. Beneth P. Jones. 110p. (Orig.). 1983. pap. 2.95 (ISBN 0-89084-192-6). Bob Jones Univ Pr.

More Than a Carpenter. Josh McDowell. 1980. pap. 2.95 (ISBN 0-8423-4552-3). Tyndale.

More Than a Dream. Loren A. Yadon. Ed. by Mary Wallace. 128p. (Orig.). 1984. pap. 4.95 (ISBN 0-912315-66-0). Word Aflame.

More Than a Job. YMCA of the USA. 139p. 1984. 3-ring notebook 25.00x (ISBN 0-931250-76-5). Human Kinetics.

More Than a Knight. Daughters of St. Paul. (Encounter Ser.). (Illus.). 100p. 1982. 3.00 (ISBN 0-8198-4714-3, EN0204); pap. 2.00 (ISBN 0-8198-4715-1). Dghtrs St Paul.

More Than a Prophet: On John the Baptist. Philip Mauro. pap. 1.50 (ISBN 0-685-36794-0). Reiner.

More Than an Ark on Ararat. James B. Irwin & Monte Unger. LC 85-4157. 1985. 6.95 (ISBN 0-8054-5018-1). Broadman.

More Than Burnt Offerings. Wayne Ham. LC 78-17646. 1978. pap. 7.00 (ISBN 0-8309-0217-1). Herald Hse.

More Than Candlelighting: A Guide for Training Acolytes. Philip C. Peace. LC 82-18973. (Illus.). 64p. (Orig.). 1983. pap. 4.95 (ISBN 0-8298-0642-3). Pilgrim NY.

More Than Conquerors. William Hendriksen. Commeritive ed. 11.95 (ISBN 0-8010-4026-4). Baker Bk.

More Than Conquerors. rev ed. Terry Mize. 224p. 1981. pap. text ed. 3.95 (ISBN 0-89274-200-3, HH-200). Harrison Hse.

More Than Earthlings. James B. Irwin. LC 83-70369. 1983. 6.95 (ISBN 0-8054-5255-9). Broadman.

More Than Enough. C. C. Gibb. 83p. pap. 4.95 (ISBN 0-88172-071-2). Believers Bkshelf.

More Than Harps of Gold. Penny E. Wheeler. (Outreach Ser.). 1981. pap. 1.25 (ISBN 0-8163-0424-6). Pacific Pr Pub Assn.

More Than "I Do" An Engaged Couple's Premarital Handbook. Harold I. Smith. (Orig.). 1983. pap. 2.95 (ISBN 0-8341-0864-X). Beacon Hill.

More Than "I Do" Devotions for the Engaged Couple. Harold I. Smith. 1983p. (Orig.). 1983. pap. 2.95 (ISBN 0-8341-0805-4). Beacon Hill.

More Than "I Do" Pastor's Resource Book for Premarital Counseling. (Orig.). 1983. pap. 4.95 (ISBN 0-8341-0865-8). Beacon Hill.

More Than Just Talk. Tim Nicholas & Ken Touchton. Ed. by Elaine S. Furlow. (Human Touch Photo-Text Ser.). (Illus.). 1977. 6.95g (ISBN 0-937170-16-X). Home Mission.

More Than Meets the Eye: Ritual & Parish Liturgy. Patrick W. Collins. LC 82-62920. 160p. (Orig.). 1983. pap. 6.95 (ISBN 0-8091-2539-0). Paulist Pr.

More Than Redemption. Jay E. Adams. 350p. 1979. pap. 10.95 (ISBN 0-87552-039-1). Presby & Reformed.

More Than Survivors: God's Way of Restoration for Women. Ruth Sanford. 200p. (Orig.). 1981. pap. 4.95 (ISBN 0-89283-102-2). Servant.

More Than Symbol. Eli Landrum, Jr. LC 81-86669. (Orig.). 1983. pap. 3.95 (ISBN 0-8054-2304-4). Broadman.

More Than Wanderers: Spiritual Disciplines for Christian Ministry. James C. Fenhagen. 1985. pap. 7.95 (ISBN 0-86683-978-X, HarpR). Har-Row.

More Than You Know. Richard E. Wentz. 60p. (Orig.). 1983. pap. 1.25 (ISBN 0-88028-027-1). Forward Movement.

More Training When Meeting. Evangelical Teacher Training Association. 32p. 1982. pap. 2.95 (ISBN 0-317-02858-8); leader's planbook 3.95 (ISBN 0-910566-36-4). Evang Tchr.

More Unholy Writ: Jewish Verses & Vices. Mollee Kruger. 100p. 1973. pap. 2.25 (ISBN 0-913184-02-0). Maryben Bks.

More Wise Men of Helm. Solomon Simon. LC 65-14594. (Illus., Orig.). 1979. pap. 4.95 (ISBN 0-87441-126-2). Behrman.

More-with-Less Cookbook. Doris Longacre. LC 75-23563. 320p. 1976. pap. 9.95 (ISBN 0-8361-1786-7). Herald Pr.

More Word Search Puzzles. Edward M. Seagrist. (Quiz & Puzzle Bks.). 80p. 1986. pap. 3.95 (ISBN 0-8010-8263-3). Baker Bk.

Morei Ha'umah, Bk. 2. Israel Shurin. (Illus.). 4.00 (ISBN 0-914131-46-X, D45). Torah Umesorah.

Morenita: Evangelizadora de las Americas. Virgilio P. Elizondo. (Span.). 96p. 1981. pap. 2.50 (ISBN 0-89243-145-8). Liguori Pubns.

More's Utopia: The Biography of an Idea. Jack H. Hexter. LC 76-15177. (History of Ideas Ser.: No. 5). 1976. Repr. of 1952 ed. lib. bdg. 22.50x (ISBN 0-8371-8947-0, HEMU). Greenwood.

More...Try This One. Ed. by Thom Schultz. LC 80-80947. (Illus.). 80p. (Orig.). 1980. pap. 5.95 (ISBN 0-936664-00-2). Group Bks.

Morgantown Disciples. Earl L. Core. (Illus.). 1960. 8.00 (ISBN 0-87012-024-7). McClain.

Moriscos of Spain. Henry C. Lea. LC 68-56783. 1968. Repr. of 1901 ed. 20.50 (ISBN 0-8337-4218-3). B Franklin.

Moriscos of Spain, Their Conversion & Expulsion. Henry Lea. LC 68-26358. (Studies in Spanish Literature, No. 36). 1969. Repr. of 1901 ed. lib. bdg. 51.95x (ISBN 0-8383-0266-1). Haskell.

Moriscos of Spain: Their Conversion & Expulsion. Henry C. Lea. 1968. Repr. of 1901 ed. lib. bdg. 23.50x (ISBN 0-8371-0141-7, LEMS). Greenwood.

Mormans, Jehovah's Witnesses & Christian Scientists. Lucinda Beier. 1985. 13.00x (ISBN 0-7062-3880-X, Pub. by Ward Lock Educ Co Ltd). State Mutual Bk.

Mormon Answer to Skepticism: Why Joseph Smith Wrote the Book of Mormon. Ed. by Robert N. Hullinger. LC 79-54055. 201p. (Orig.). 1980. pap. 14.95x (ISBN 0-915644-18-5). Clayton Pub Hse.

Mormon Bibliography, 1830-1930: Books, Pamphlets, Periodicals, & Broadsides Relating to the First Century of Mormonism. Ed. by Chad J. Flake. LC 74-22639. (Illus.). 1978. 80.00x (ISBN 0-87480-016-1). U of Utah Pr.

Mormon Chronicle: The Diaries of John D. Lee, 1848-1876, 2 vols. Ed. by Robert G. Cleland & Juanita Brooks. (Illus.). xxxii, 824p. 1955. Set. 39.95 (ISBN 0-87480-230-X). U of Utah Pr.

Mormon Conflict, 1850-1859. Norman F. Furniss. LC 77-5424. (Illus.). 1977. Repr. of 1960 ed. lib. bdg. 23.75x (ISBN 0-8371-9636-1, FUMC). Greenwood.

Mormon Corporate Empire: The Eye-Opening Report on the Church & Its Political & Financial Agenda. John Heinerman & Anson Shupe. LC 85-47527. 352p. 1986. 19.95 (ISBN 0-8070-0406-5). Beacon Pr.

Mormon Country. John T. Codman. LC 70-134392. Repr. of 1874 ed. 18.25 (ISBN 0-404-08481-8). AMS Pr.

Mormon Country. Wallace Stegner. LC 81-3410. x, 362p. 1981. 25.50x (ISBN 0-8032-4129-1); pap. 8.50 (ISBN 0-8032-9125-6, BB 778, Bison). U of Nebr Pr.

Mormon Doctrine of Deity: The Roberts-Van der Donckt Discussion. Brigham H. Roberts. 296p. 1975. 9.95 (ISBN 0-88290-058-7). Horizon Utah.

Mormon Enigma: Emma Hale Smith, Prophet's Wife, Elect Lady, Polygamy's Foe. Linda K. Newell & Valeen T. Avery. LC 80-2400. (Illus.). 394p. 1984. 19.95 (ISBN 0-385-17166-8). Doubleday.

Mormon Experience: A History of the Latter-Day Saints. Leonard J. Arrington & Davis Bitton. LC 78-20561. (Illus.). 1979. 17.50 (ISBN 0-394-46566-0). Knopf.

Mormon Experience: A History of the Latter-Day Saints. Leonard J. Arrington & Davis Bitton. LC 80-11843. (Illus.). 404p. 1980. pap. 5.95 (ISBN 0-394-74102-1, Vin). Random.

Mormon Experience: A Young Couple's Fascinating Journey to Truth. Jolene Coe & Greg Coe. 176p. (Orig.). 1985. pap. 5.95 (ISBN 0-89081-486-4). Harvest Hse.

Mormon Family Cookbook. Helen Thackeray & Beth Brown. LC 82-73085. (Illus.). 180p. 1982. 12.95 (ISBN 0-87747-930-5). Deseret Bk.

Mormon Gold: The Story of the Mormon Argonauts. J. K. Davies. 440p. (Orig.). 1984. pap. 12.95 (ISBN 0-913420-20-4). Olympus Pub Co.

Mormon Illusion. rev. ed. Floyd McElveen. LC 76-57036. 1980. pap. text ed. 3.95 (ISBN 0-8307-0735-2, 5017807). Regal.

Mormon Landscape: Existence, Creation & Perception of a Unique Image in the American West. Richard V. Francaviglia. LC 77-83791. (Studies in Social History: No. 2). (Illus.). 39.50 (ISBN 0-404-16020-4). AMS Pr.

Mormon Mind Puzzlers. Fern Oviatt & Joan Oviatt. 60p. 1983. 1.99 (ISBN 0-934126-30-5). Randall Bk Co.

Mormon Mirage. Latayne C. Scott. 276p. 1982. pap. 7.95 (ISBN 0-310-38911-9, 10450P). Zondervan.

Mormon Neo-orthodoxy: A Crisis Theology. O. Kendall White, Jr. 250p. 1987. pap. 8.95 (ISBN 0-941214-52-4). Signature Bks.

Mormon Papers. rev. ed. Harry L. Ropp. LC 77-2681. (Illus., Orig.). 1987. pap. 5.95 (ISBN 0-87784-469-0). Inter-Varsity.

Mormon Polygamy: A History. Richard S. Van Wagoner. 275p. 1985. 19.95 (ISBN 0-941214-35-4). Signature Bks.

Mormon Question in Its Economic Aspects. Dyer D. Lum. 1973. lib. bdg. 59.95 (ISBN 0-8490-0672-4). Gordon Pr.

Mormon Role in the Settlement of the West. Ed. by Richard H. Jackson. LC 78-24728. (Charles Redd Monographs in Western History Ser.: No. 9). (Illus.). 1978. pap. 6.95 (ISBN 0-8425-1321-3, Dist. by Signature Bks). C Redd Ctr.

Mormon Settlement in Arizona. James McClintock. LC 78-134397. Repr. of 1921 ed. 27.00 (ISBN 0-404-08439-7). AMS Pr.

Mormon Settlement in Arizona. James H. McClintock. LC 85-8458. (Illus.). 384p. 1985. pap. 9.95 (ISBN 0-8165-0953-0). U of Ariz Pr.

Mormon Sisters: Women in Early Utah. Claudia L. Bushman et al. LC 76-53854. (Illus.). 320p. 1980. pap. 9.95 (ISBN 0-913420-95-6). Olympus Pub Co.

Mormon Songs from the Rocky Mountains: A Compilation of Mormon Folksong. Ed. by Thomas E. Cheney. 224p. 1968. pap. 9.95 (ISBN 0-87480-196-6). U of Utah Pr.

Mormon Towns in the Region of the Colorado. Leland H. Creer. Incl. Activities of Jacob Hamblin in the Region of the Colorado. (Glen Canyon Ser.: Nos. 3-4). Repr. of 1958 ed. 20.00 (ISBN 0-404-60633-4). AMS Pr.

Mormon Village: A Study in Social Origins. Lowry Nelson. 59.95 (ISBN 0-8490-0673-2). Gordon Pr.

Mormon Women Speak. Ed. by Mary L. Bradford. LC 82-62366. 1982. 9.95 (ISBN 0-913420-94-8). Olympus Pub Co.

Mormoneniand Als Beispiel Eines Sozialgeographischen Raumes. Hermann Lautensach. Repr. of 1953 ed. 20.00 (ISBN 0-384-31640-9). Johnson Repr.

Mormones: Sus Doctrinas Refutadas a la Luz De la Biblia. Marvin W. Cowan. Tr. by Tomas De La Fuente from Eng. 160p. 1985. pap. 3.50 (ISBN 0-311-05763-2). Casa Bautista.

Mormonism. Anthony A. Hoekema. 1974. pap. 2.95 (ISBN 0-8028-1491-3). Eerdmans.

Mormonism. Salem Kirban. (Illus.). 1971. pap. 4.95 (ISBN 0-912582-13-8). Kirban.

Mormonism. Walter Martin. 32p. 1968. pap. 2.95 (ISBN 0-87123-367-3, 210367). Bethany Hse.

Mormonism. rev. ed. Donald S. Tingle. (Viewpoints Ser.). 32p. 1987. pap. 1.95 (ISBN 0-8308-1103-6). Inter-Varsity.

Mormonism & Me: A True Story. Thelma Geer. 1986. pap. 6.95 (ISBN 0-8024-5633-2). Moody.

Mormonism & the American Experience. Klaus J. Hansen. LC 80-19312. (History of American Religion Ser.). 224p. 1981. 15.00x (ISBN 0-226-31552-5). U of Chicago Pr.

Mormonism & the American Experience. Klaus J. Hansen. LC 80-19312. (Chicago History of American Religions Ser.). xx, 258p. 1983. pap. 8.50 (ISBN 0-226-31553-3). U of Chicago Pr.

Mormonism & the Mormons. Danuiel P. Kidder. 59.95 (ISBN 0-8490-0674-0). Gordon Pr.

Mormonism & the Negro. John J. Stewart. LC 78-52123. 92p. 1978. 5.50 (ISBN 0-88290-098-6). Horizon Utah.

Mormonism: Challenge & Defense. Rodger S. Gunn. 1979. pap. 8.95 (ISBN 0-89036-126-6). Hawkes Pub Inc.

Mormonism in Conflict: The Nauvoo Years. Annette P. Hampshire. LC 84-27263. (Studies in Religion & Society: Vol. II). 350p. 1985. 59.95x (ISBN 0-88946-874-5). E Mellen.

Mormonism in Mexico. F. LaMond Tullis. (Illus.). 275p. 1987. 22.50 (ISBN 0-87421-130-1). Utah St U Pr.

Mormonism in Transition: The Latter-day Saints & Their Church, 1890-1930. Thomas G. Alexander. LC 84-22164. (Illus.). 396p. 1986. 19.95 (ISBN 0-252-01185-6). U of Ill Pr.

Mormonism: Its Rise, Progress & Present Condition. N. W. Green. LC 79-134401. Repr. of 1870 ed. 32.50 (ISBN 0-404-08445-1). AMS Pr.

Mormonism, Mama & Me. 3rd, rev. ed. Thelma Geer. LC 81-146846. (Illus.). 228p. 1983. pap. 3.95 (ISBN 0-912375-00-0). Calvary Miss Pr.

Mormonism, Mama, & Me. Thelma Geer. 1983. pap. 4.95 (ISBN 0-87508-192-4). Chr Lit.

Mormonism, Mama & Me. 4th ed. Ed. by Thelma Geer. (Illus.). 252p. 1984. pap. 4.95 (ISBN 0-912375-01-9). Calvary Miss Pr.

Mormonism, Now & Then. G. T. Harrison. 357p. cancelled (ISBN 0-686-96149-8). Am Atheist.

Mormonism: The Story of a New Religious Tradition. Jan Shipps. LC 84-2672. (Illus.). 232p. 1985. 14.50 (ISBN 0-252-01159-7). U of Ill Pr.

Mormonism Unvailed; or, a Faithful Account of That Singular Imposition & Delusion, from Its Rise to the Present Time. Eber D. Howe. LC 72-2967. Repr. of 1834 ed. 32.50 (ISBN 0-404-10730-3). AMS Pr.

Mormonismo. Walter Martin. 48p. 1982. 1.95 (ISBN 0-88113-208-X). Edit Betania.

Mormonismo Refutado. Jay Jacobson. (Modern Doctrines Collection). 32p. 1984. Repr. of 1981 ed. 0.75 (ISBN 0-311-05030-1). Casa Bautista.

Mormonismo Revelacion Divina o Invencion Humana. Domingo Fernandez. 32p. 1984. pap. 1.00 (ISBN 0-311-05762-4). Casa Bautista.

Mormons. Thomas F. O'Dea. LC 57-6984. 1964. pap. 10.00x (ISBN 0-226-61744-0, P162, Phoen). U of Chicago Pr.

Mormons & Mormonism, 15 vols. W. A. Linn et al. 1973. lib. bdg. 50.00 (ISBN 0-8490-0675-9). Gordon Pr.

Mormons at Home. B. G. Ferris. LC 70-134395. Repr. of 1856 ed. 24.00 (ISBN 0-404-08437-0). AMS Pr.

Mormons in American History. William Mulder. (University of Utah Frederick William Reynolds Lecture Ser.: No. 21). 1981. pap. 4.95 (ISBN 0-87480-184-2). U of Utah Pr.

Mormons, Indians & the Ghost Dance Religion of 1890. Garold D. Barney. LC 85-29509. (Illus.). 258p. (Orig.). 1986. lib. bdg. 28.00 (ISBN 0-8191-5227-7); pap. text ed. 13.50 (ISBN 0-8191-5228-5). U Pr of Amer.

Mormons: Or, Latter Day Saints. Henry Mayhew. LC 71-134398. Repr. of 1852 ed. 24.75 (ISBN 0-404-08440-0). AMS Pr.

Mormons: Or, Latter-Day Saints, in the Valley of the Great Salt Lake; a History of Their Rise & Progress, Peculiar Doctrines, Present Condition & Prospects, Derived from Personal Observation During a Residence Among Them. John W. Gunnison. LC 70-38355. (Select Bibliographies Reprint Ser.). Repr. of 1852 ed. 16.00 (ISBN 0-8369-6772-0). Ayer Co Pubs.

Morning after Death. L. D. Johnson. LC 77-99255. 1978. 7.50 (ISBN 0-8054-2412-1). Broadman.

Morning & Evening. Charles H. Spurgeon. 736p. 1980. Repr. 13.95 (ISBN 0-310-32940-X, 10873); large print kivar 11.95 (ISBN 0-310-32927-2). Zondervan.

Morning & Evening. Charles H. Spurgeon. 774p. Date not set. 13.95 (ISBN 0-917006-26-7). Hendrickson MA.

Morning Answer. John Fandel. 1984. pap. 3.35 (ISBN 0-88028-041-7). Forward Movement.

Morning Bells. F. R. Havergal. pap. 2.25 (ISBN 0-685-88387-6). Reiner.

Morning by Morning. C. H. Spurgeon. 368p. 1984. pap. text ed. 3.95 (ISBN 0-88368-156-0). Whitaker Hse.

Morning, Evening Thoughts. 1967. 5.95 (ISBN 0-88088-444-4). Peter Pauper.

Morning Joy. Helen G. Brenneman. LC 80-26449. 80p. 1981. pap. 3.95 (ISBN 0-8361-1942-8). Herald Pr.

Morning Light. Lenora Boneck. (Illus.). 270p. (Orig.). 1986. pap. 12.95 (ISBN 0-940415-00-3). B & K Pub Hse.

Morning Light. White Eagle. 1957. 3.95 (ISBN 0-85487-018-0). De Vorss.

Morning Meditations. Austin B. Tucker. 99p. 1980. pap. 2.00 (ISBN 0-89323-011-1, 450). Bible Memory.

Morning Prayer & the Psalter: Large Type Edition. 1981. pap. 12.95 (ISBN 0-8192-1284-9). Morehouse.

Morning Stars Sang: The Bible in Popular & Folk Art. Anita Schorsch & Martin Greif. LC 78-52197. (Illus.). 128p. 1980. 12.95x (ISBN 0-87663-316-5); pap. 8.95 (ISBN 0-87663-985-6). Universe.

Morningland Color Book. Gopi Gyan. 1979. pap. 7.95 (ISBN 0-935146-09-1). Morningland.

Moro: Ellis Heywood's Dialogue in Memory of Thomas More. Ellis Heywood. Tr. by Roger L. Deakins. LC 75-184107. 176p. 1972. 12.50x (ISBN 0-674-58735-9). Harvard U Pr.

Moroccan Islam: Tradition & Society in a Pilgrimage Center. Dale F. Eickelman. (Modern Middle East Ser.: No. 1). 323p. 1976. pap. text ed. 12.95x (ISBN 0-292-75062-5). U of Tex Pr.

Morphophonemics of Modern Hebrew. Noam Chomsky. Ed. by Jorge Hankamer. LC 78-66579. (Outstanding Dissertations in Linguistics Ser.). 1979. 15.00 (ISBN 0-8240-9688-6). Garland Pub.

Morrison on Acts. rev. ed. George H. Morrison. Ed. by Joan Zodhiates. LC 80-69541. (Glasgow Pulpit Ser.). 1981. pap. 4.95 (ISBN 0-89957-050-X). AMG Pubs.

Morrison on Galatians through Hebrews. G. H. Morrison. LC 82-71841. (Glasgow Pulpit Ser.). 1982. pap. 4.95 (ISBN 0-89957-557-9). AMG Pubs.

Morrison on Genesis. Ed. by G. H. Morrison. (Glasgow Pulpit Ser.). 72p. 1976. pap. 4.95 (ISBN 0-89957-520-X). AMG Pubs.

Morrison on James to Revelation. Morrison. pap. 4.95 (ISBN 0-89957-563-3). AMG Pubs.

Morrison on John, Vol. I. new ed. G. H. Morrison. (Glasgow Pulpit Ser.). 1979. pap. 4.95 (ISBN 0-89957-534-X). AMG Pubs.

Morrison on John, Vol. II. new ed. G. H. Morrison. (Glasgow Pulpit Ser.). 1979. pap. 4.95 (ISBN 0-89957-535-8). AMG Pubs.

Morrison on Luke, Vol. I. new ed. G. H. Morrison. (Glasgow Pulpit Ser.). 1979. pap. 4.95 (ISBN 0-89957-532-3). AMG Pubs.

Morrison on Luke, Vol. II. new ed. G. H. Morrison. (Glasgow Pulpit Ser.). 1979. pap. 4.95 (ISBN 0-89957-533-1). AMG Pubs.

Morrison on Mark. new ed. G. H. Morrison. (Glasgow Pulpit Ser.). 1979. pap. 4.95 (ISBN 0-89957-531-5). AMG Pubs.

Morrison on Matthew, Vol. I. new ed. G. H. Morrison. (Glasgow Pulpit Ser.). 1979. pap. 4.95 (ISBN 0-89957-528-5). AMG Pubs.

Morrison on Matthew, Vol. II. new ed. G. H. Morrison. (Glasgow Pulpit Ser.). 1979. pap. 4.95 (ISBN 0-89957-529-3). AMG Pubs.

Morrison on Matthew, Vol. III. new ed. G. H. Morrison. (Glasgow Pulpit Ser.). 1979. pap. 4.95 (ISBN 0-89957-530-7). AMG Pubs.

Morrison on Romans & Corinthians. G. H. Morrison. (Glasgow Pulpit Ser.). 96p. 1982. pap. 4.95 (ISBN 0-89957-547-1). AMG Pubs.

Morrow & Miracles. Faye V. Alberding. (Illus.). 1983. 5.95 (ISBN 0-8062-2203-4). Carlton.

Mortal Messiah: From Bethlehem to Calvary, 4 vols, Bk. 1. Bruce R. McConkie. LC 79-19606. 536p. 1979. 16.95 (ISBN 0-87747-784-1). Deseret Bk.

Mortal Messiah: From Bethlehem to Calvary, Bk. 2. Bruce R. McConkie. LC 79-19606. 424p. 1980. 16.95 (ISBN 0-87747-803-1). Deseret Bk.

Mortal Messiah, from Bethlehem to Calvary, Bk. 3. Bruce R. McConkie. LC 79-19606. 486p. 1980. 14.95 (ISBN 0-87747-825-2). Deseret Bk.

Mortal Messiah: From Bethlehem to Calvary, Bk. 4. Bruce R. McConkie. LC 79-19606. (Mortal Messiah Ser.). 447p. 1981. 14.95 (ISBN 0-87747-856-2). Deseret Bk.

Mortal Questions. T. Nagel. LC 78-58797. 1979. 32.50 (ISBN 0-521-22360-1); pap. 10.95 (ISBN 0-521-29460-6). Cambridge U Pr.

Mortality & Immortality: The Anthropology & Archaeology of Death. Ed. by S. C. Humphreys & H. King. LC 81-67910. (Research Seminars in Archaeology Ser.). 1982. 54.50 (ISBN 0-12-361550-X). Acad Pr.

Mortals in the Immortal Profession: An Oral History of Teaching. Alice D. Rinehart. LC 82-17200. 410p. 1983. pap. text ed. 19.95x (ISBN 0-8290-1049-1). Irvington.

Mortmain Legislation & the English Church, 1279-1500. S. Raban. LC 81-21685. (Cambridge Studies in Medieval Life & Thought: No. 17). (Illus.). 244p. 1982. 47.50 (ISBN 0-521-24233-9). Cambridge U Pr.

Morya. El Morya. Ed. by Elizabeth C. Prophet. LC 81-85570. 412p. 1982. pap. 9.95 (ISBN 0-916766-52-7). Summit Univ.

Mosaics. Beatrice E. Harmon. LC 74-144725. (Yale Ser. of Younger Poets: No. 18). Repr. of 1923 ed. 18.00 (ISBN 0-404-53818-5). AMS Pr.

Mosaics & Frescoes of St. Mary Pammakaristos (Fethiye Camii) at Istanbul. Hans Belting et al. LC 77-99268. (Dumbarton Oaks Studies: Vol. 15). (Illus.). 118p. 1978. 30.00x (ISBN 0-88402-075-4). Dumbarton Oaks.

Mosaics of Saint Peter's: Decorating the New Basilica. Frank DiFederico. LC 82-42777. (Illus.). 176p. 1983. 42.50x (ISBN 0-271-00344-8). Pa St U Pr.

Mosaics of the National Shrine of the Immaculate Conception. Frank DiFederico. (Illus.). 96p. 1981. 16.95 (ISBN 0-916276-09-0). Decatur Hse.

Mosaiques De la Grande Mosquee De Cordoue. Henri Stern. (Madrider Forschungen, Ser., Vol. 11). (Illus.). 55p. 1976. 64.00x (ISBN 3-11-002126-9). De Gruyter.

Moscow & East Rome: A Political Study of the Relation of Church & State in Muscovite Russia. William K. Medlin. LC 79-2913. 252p. 1980. Repr. of 1952 ed. 23.00 (ISBN 0-8305-0082-0). Hyperion Conn.

Moscow & the Vatican. Alexis Floridi. 365p. 1986. 23.50 (ISBN 0-88233-647-9). Ardis Pubs.

Moscow, the Third Rome. 2nd ed. Nicholas Zernov. LC 76-149664. Repr. of 1938 ed. 12.50 (ISBN 0-404-07075-2). AMS Pr.

Moscow Was My Parish. Georges Bissonnette. LC 78-16489. 1978. Repr. of 1956 ed. lib. bdg. 22.50x (ISBN 0-313-20594-9, BIMM). Greenwood.

Moscow's Muslim Challenge: Soviet Central Asia. Michael Rywkin. LC 81-14414. (Illus.). 232p. 1982. pap. 13.95 (ISBN 0-87332-262-2). M E Sharpe.

Moses. Elias Auerbach. Tr. by Israel O. Lehman & R. A. Barclay. LC 72-6589. 255p. 1975. text ed. 25.00x (ISBN 0-8143-1491-0). Wayne St U Pr.

Moses. Ethel Barrett. LC 82-16521. (Bible Biographies Ser.). 1982. pap. text ed. 2.50 (ISBN 0-8307-0772-7, 5811201). Regal.

Moses. Rebecca Daniel. (Our Greatest Heritage Ser.). (Illus.). 32p. 1983. wkbk. 3.95 (ISBN 0-86653-135-1, SS 804). Good Apple.

Moses. F. B. Meyer. 1972. pap. 4.50 (ISBN 0-87508-354-4). Chr Lit.

Moses. 1979. 0.75 (ISBN 0-8198-0586-6). Dghtrs St Paul.

Moses: A Psychodynamic Study. Ed. by Dorothy F. Zeligs. 384p. 1986. 39.95 (ISBN 0-89885-236-6). Human Sci Pr.

Moses & Egypt: The Documentation to the Motion Picture "the Ten Commandments". Henry S. Noerdlinger. LC 56-12886. 202p. 1956. pap. 1.95 (ISBN 0-88474-007-2). U of S Cal Pr.

Moses & Gods of Egypt. John J. Davis. (Old Testament Studies). pap. 11.95 (ISBN 0-8010-2957-0). Baker Bk.

Moses & His Contemporaries. Gordon Lindsay. (Old Testament Ser.). 1.25 (ISBN 0-89985-133-9). Christ Nations.

Moses & Monotheism. Sigmund Freud. Ed. by Katherine Jones. 1955. pap. 4.95 (ISBN 0-394-70014-7, V14, Vin). Random.

Moses & Pharaoh: Dominion Religion vs. Power Religion. Gary North. 430p. 1985. pap. text ed. 12.50 (ISBN 0-930464-05-2). Inst Christian.

Moses & the Awful Plagues. John Walton & Kim Walton. (Early Bible Foundations Ser.). (Illus.). 1986. pap. 2.95 (ISBN 1-55513-041-0, Chariot Bks). Cook.

Moses & the Church in the Wilderness. Gordon Lindsay. (Old Testament Ser.). 1.25 (ISBN 0-89985-132-0). Christ Nations.

Moses & the Deuteronomist: A Literary Study of the Deuteronomic History. Robert M. Polzin. 224p. 1981. 17.95 (ISBN 0-8164-0456-9, HarpR); pap. 8.95 (ISBN 0-8164-2284-2). Har-Row.

Moses & the Flight from Egypt. Diana Craig. LC 84-50448. (Bible Stories Ser.). (Illus.). 24p. 1984. 5.45 (ISBN 0-382-06945-5); PLB 6.96 (ISBN 0-382-06797-5). Silver.

Moses & the Gods of Egypt: Studies in Exodus. Rev. ed. John J. Davis. (Illus.). 1985. pap. 11.95 (ISBN 0-88469-177-2). BMH Bks.

Moses & the Golden Age. Tertius Chandler. (Illus.). 88p. 1986. 9.95 (ISBN 0-8059-3024-8). Dorrance.

Moses & the Plagues. Catherine Storr. LC 84-18077. (People of the Bible Ser.). (Illus.). 32p. 1985. PLB 10.65 (ISBN 0-8172-1999-4). Raintree Pubs.

Moses & the Ten Plagues. Hodges. (Arch Bks.). 24p. (Orig.). 1985. pap. 0.99 (ISBN 0-570-06190-3, 59-1291). Concordia.

Moses: Founder of Preventive Medicine. P. Wood. 1976. lib. bdg. 59.95 (ISBN 0-8490-2285-1). Gordon Pr.

Moses: From the Egyptian Mysteries to the Judges of Israel. Emil Bock. 208p. (Orig.). 1986. pap. 12.95 (ISBN 0-89281-117-X). Inner Tradit.

Moses: God's Helper. William E. Young. (BibLearn Ser.). (Illus.). 5.95 (ISBN 0-8054-4225-1, 4242-25). Broadman.

Moses in Graeco-Roman Paganism. John G. Gager. (SBL Monograph). 8.95 (ISBN 0-89130-323-5, 06-00-16). Scholars Pr GA.

Moses in the Bulrushes. Warwick Hutton. LC 85-72261. (Illus.). 32p. 1986. 12.95 (ISBN 0-689-50393-8, McElderry Bk). Macmillan.

Moses in the Bulrushes. Retold by Elaine Ife & Rosalind Sutton. (Now You Can Read Stories from the Bible Ser.). (Illus.). 24p. 1985. 2.50 (ISBN 0-8407-5481-7). Nelson.

Moses in the Fourth Gospel. T. Francis Glasson. LC 63-5666. (Studies in Biblical Theology: No. 40). 1963. pap. 10.00x (ISBN 0-8401-3040-6). A R Allenson.

Moses in the Letter to the Hebrews. Mary R. D'Angelo. LC 78-12917. (Society of Biblical Literature, Dissertation Ser.: No. 42). 1979. pap. 9.95 (ISBN 0-89130-333-2). Scholars Pr GA.

Moses in the Wilderness. Ed. by Catherine Storr. (People of the Bible Ser.). (Illus.). 32p. 1985. PLB 10.65 (ISBN 0-8172-2039-9). Raintree Pubs.

Moses Let My People Go. Illus. by Hanna-Barbera. (Greatest Adventure: Stories from the Bible). (Illus.). 48p. (Orig.). Date not set. 5.95 (ISBN 0-687-15740-4). Abingdon.

Moses Maimonides' Treatise on Resurrection. Tr. by Fred Rosner. 12.50x (ISBN 0-87068-764-6); pap. 7.95. Ktav.

Moses: Moments of Glory...Feet of Clay. Gene A. Getz. LC 75-23519. 160p. (Orig.). 1976. pap. 4.95 (ISBN 0-8307-0400-0, 5403200). Regal.

Moses of Rovno: The Stirring Story of Fritz Graeve, a German Christian Who Risked His Life to Lead Hundreds of Jews to Safety During the Holocaust. Douglas K. Huneke. (Holocaust Studies). (Illus.). 236p. 1985. 17.95 (ISBN 0-396-08714-0). Dodd.

Moses of the Bullrushes: Retold by Catherine Storr. Illus. by Jim Russell. (People of the Bible Ser.). (Illus.). 32p. 1984. 10.65 (ISBN 0-8172-1990-0, Raintree Children's Books Belitha Press Ltd. - London). Raintree Pubs.

Moses, Prince & Shepherd. Lucy Diamond. (Ladybird Ser). (Illus.). 1954. bds. 2.50 (ISBN 0-87508-850-3). Chr Lit.

Moses: Prince, Servant, Prophet. Lillian Cantleberry. 208p. (Orig.). 1985. pap. 7.95 (ISBN 0-570-03970-3, 12-3005). Concordia.

Moses Principle: Leadership & the Venture of Faith. Michael Baughen. LC 78-27498. 118p. 1978. pap. 2.95 (ISBN 0-87788-558-3). Shaw Pubs.

Moses, Speak for God! Charlotte Graeber. (Speak for Me Ser.). (Illus.). 24p. 1986. 3.95 (ISBN 0-8407-6704-8). Nelson.

Moses, The Deliverer. Gordon Lindsay. (Old Testament Ser.). 1.25 (ISBN 0-89985-131-2). Christ Nations.

Moses the Lawgiver. Gordon Lindsay. (Old Testament Ser.: Vol. 10). pap. 1.25 (ISBN 0-89985-959-3). Christ Nations.

Moses the Leader. Retold by Rosalind Sutton & Elaine Ife. (Now You Can Read Stories from the Bible Ser.). (Illus.). 24p. 1985. 2.50 (ISBN 0-8407-5391-8). Nelson.

Moses, the Man of God. G. Andre. 47p. pap. 1.95 (ISBN 0-88172-131-X). Believers Bkshelf.

Moses, the Man of God. James Hamilton. 388p. 1985. Repr. lib. bdg. 14.75 (ISBN 0-86524-187-2, 8407). Klock & Klock.

Moses, the Servant of Yahweh. Dewey M. Beegle. LC 79-84558. 368p. 1972. pap. text ed. 8.95 (ISBN 0-933462-03-4). Pryor Pettengill.

Moslem Brethren: The Greatest of the Modern Islamic Movements. Ishak M. Al-Husaini. LC 79-2866. 186p. 1987. Repr. of 1956 ed. 21.00 (ISBN 0-8305-0039-1). Hyperion Conn.

Moslem Egypt & Christian Abyssinia. William M. Dye. LC 78-97365. Repr. of 1880 ed. 23.00x (ISBN 0-8371-2432-8, DYM&, Pub. by Negro U Pr). Greenwood.

Moslem Rebellion in Northwest China, 1862-1878. Wen-Djang Chu. (Central Asiatic Studies: No. 5). 1966. pap. text ed. 31.20x (ISBN 90-2790-017-5). Mouton.

Moslem Schisms & Sects: Being the History of the Various Philosophic Systems Developed in Islam. Abu M. Abd-Al-Kahir Ibn-Tahir Ibn Muhammad. Tr. by Kate C. Seelye. LC 75-158216. (Columbia University Oriental Studies: No. 15). 1920. 20.00 (ISBN 0-404-50505-8). AMS Pr.

Moslem Sects & Divisions: The Section on Muslim Sects in Kitab Al-Milal Wa L-Nihal. Muhammad B. Shahrastani. Tr. by A. K. Kazi & J. G. Flynn. 180p. 1984. 29.95x (ISBN 0-7103-0063-8, Kegan Paul). Methuen Inc.

Moslem Women Enter a New World. Ruth F. Woodsmall. LC 75-180309. Repr. of 1936 ed. 31.50 (ISBN 0-404-56334-1). AMS Pr.

Moslem World of Today. John R. Mott. xv, 420p. 1986. text ed. 50.00x (ISBN 81-210-0016-5, Pub. by Inter India Pubns N Delhi). Apt Bks.

Mosque in Early Ottoman Architecture. Aptullah Kuran. LC 68-16701. (Publications of the Center for Middle Eastern Studies Ser). (Illus.). 1968. 25.00x (ISBN 0-226-46293-5). U of Chicago Pr.

Mosquitoes in Paradise. John Aurelio. 144p. 1985. pap. 7.95 (ISBN 0-8245-0698-7). Crossroad NY.

Mosses. Sylvia A. Johnson. LC 83-17488. (Lerner Natural Science Bks.). (Illus.). 48p. 1983. PLB 12.95 (ISBN 0-8225-1482-6). Lerner Pubns.

Most Ancient Testimony: Sixteenth-Century Christian-Hebraica in the Age of Renaissance Nostalgia. Jerome Friedman. LC 82-18830. x, 279p. 1983. text ed. 26.95x (ISBN 0-8214-0700-7). Ohio U Pr.

Most Compelling Sayings by Confucius. Confucius. Tr. by Leonard D. Lynall. (Most Meaningful Classics in World Culture Ser.). (Illus.). 166p. 1983. 83.45 (ISBN 0-89266-387-1). Am Classical Coll Pr.

Most Excellent Treatise of the Thre Kynges of Coleyne. LC 74-80169. (English Experience Ser: No. 648). (Illus.). 91p. 1974. Repr. of 1499 ed. 9.50 (ISBN 9-0221-0648-9). Walter J Johnson.

Most High God. LC 82-90990. 1982. pap. 5.95 (ISBN 0-915540-30-4). Frnds Israel.

Most Important Thing in Our Lives Is... Elvie L. Foster. LC 86-90082. 47p. 1986. 5.95 (ISBN 0-533-07047-3). Vantage.

Most Meaningful Writings by Epictetus. Epictetus. Tr. by Steve C. Roswell. (Most Meaningful Classics in World Culture Ser.). (Illus.). 1979. 49.75 (ISBN 0-89266-183-6). Am Classical Coll Pr.

Most Memorable Passages of the New Testament Fully & Dramatically Illustrated. Harvey P. Brymer. (Promotion of the Arts Library). (Illus.). 141p. 1982. 69.85 (ISBN 0-86650-039-1). Gloucester Art.

Most Memorable Utterances of Our Lord & Master Jesus Christ. Ed. by V. V. Grace. (Illus.). 98p. 1987. 97.85 (ISBN 0-89266-580-7). Am Classical Coll Pr.

Most of All They Taught Me Happiness. Robert Muller. LC 78-52110. 1985. pap. 7.95 (ISBN 0-385-19914-7, Im). Doubleday.

Most Quoted Scriptures. Kay Briggs. 417p. 1981. Repr. of 1980 ed. 11.95 (ISBN 0-934126-13-5). Randall Bk Co.

Most Revealing Book of the Bible: Making Sense Out of Revelation. Vernard Eller. 1974. pap. 4.95 (ISBN 0-8028-1572-3). Eerdmans.

Most Wonderful King. Dave Hill. (Arch Bks.: Set 5). (Illus.). 1968. laminated bdg. 0.99 (ISBN 0-570-06032-X, 59-1145). Concordia.

Mother. Sri Aurobindo. 62p. 1980. 19.00 (ISBN 0-89744-914-2, Pub. by Sri Aurobindo Ashram Trust India); pap. 2.00 (ISBN 0-89744-915-0, Pub. by Sru Aurobindo Ashram Trust India); pap. 1.00 miniature size 1980 (ISBN 0-89744-148-6). Auromere.

Mother as I Saw Her. Saradeshananda. Tr. by J. N. Dey from Bengali. 247p. 1985. pap. 4.95 (ISBN 0-87481-530-4, Pub. by Ramakrishna Math Madras India). Vedanta Pr.

Mother Cabrini. Daughters of St. Paul. 1977. 3.50 (ISBN 0-8198-0440-1); pap. 2.50 (ISBN 0-8198-0441-X). Dghtrs St Paul.

Mother Cabrini: Italian Immigrant of the Century. Mary L. Sullivan. 250p. 1987. 19.50 (ISBN 0-934733-06-6). Ctr Migration.

Mother-Daughter-Father-Son Banquets & Programs, No. 7. Ed. by Laurie Hoard. 64p. (Orig.). 1984. pap. 2.95 (ISBN 0-87239-769-6, 8737). Standard Pub.

Mother Goddess in Indian Art, Archaeology & Literature. Srivastava. 1980. 32.00x (ISBN 0-686-65576-1, Pub. by Agam India). South Asia Bks.

Mother India's Lighthouse: India's Spiritual Leaders. Sri Chinmoy. LC 74-189998. 288p. 1973. pap. cancelled (ISBN 0-89345-219-X, Steinerbks). Garber Comm.

Mother India's Lighthouse: India's Spiritual Leaders & Flame-Heights of the West. LC 74-189998. 1973. 1.95 (ISBN 0-685-61448-4). Aum Pubns.

Mother Is the Baby's First Guru: Pregnancy, Infant Care & Yoga. Sri Swami Satchidananda. 1976. pap. 3.95 (ISBN 0-932040-15-2). Integral Yoga Pubns.

Mother Knot. Jane Lazarre. LC 85-47944. 210p. 1986. pap. 8.95 (ISBN 0-8070-6725-3, BP710). Beacon Pr.

Mother Nature & Beauty, Vol. 1. Ed. by Thomas L. Hakes. 16p. 1984. pap. 3.25x (ISBN 0-915020-17-3). Bardic.

Mother of Agni Yoga. 1977. pap. 3.00 (ISBN 0-933574-18-5). Agni Yoga Soc.

Mother of God. Valentine Long. 1977. 7.95 (ISBN 0-8199-0619-0). Franciscan Herald.

Mother of Jesus: Present with Us. Paul Hinnebusch. LC 79-93231. 1980. pap. 5.95 (ISBN 0-913382-32-9, 101-27). Prow Bks-Franciscan.

Mother of Knowledge: The Enlightenment of Yeshes Mtsho-Rgyal. Namkhay Nyingpo. Tr. by Tarthang Tulka. (Translation Ser.). Orig. Title: Tibetan. (Illus.). 250p. 1983. 21.95 (ISBN 0-913546-90-9); pap. 12.95 (ISBN 0-913546-91-7). Dharma Pub.

Mother of Royalty. Yehoshua Bachrach. Tr. by Leonard Oschry. 1973. pap. 6.95 (ISBN 0-87306-018-0). Feldheim.

Mother of the World. 1977. pap. 3.00 (ISBN 0-933574-17-7). Agni Yoga Soc.

Mother or the New Species. Satprem. LC 83-4370. Orig. Title: Mere Ou L'espece Nouvelle. 530p. 1983. pap. 8.95 (ISBN 0-938710-03-6). Inst Evolutionary.

Mother Person. Virginia Barber & Merrill M. Skaggs. LC 76-48850. 1977. pap. 7.95 (ISBN 0-8052-0565-9). Schocken.

Mother Seton. Daughters of St. Paul. 1975. 3.95 (ISBN 0-8198-0487-8). Dghtrs St Paul.

Mother Seton: Saint Elizabeth of New York. Leonard Feeney. LC 75-23224. 212p. 1975. 6.95 (ISBN 0-911218-05-X); pap. 3.95 (ISBN 0-911218-06-8). Ravengate Pr.

Mother Shares: Meditations on Parenting. Susan Nethery. 128p. 1981. 5.95 (ISBN 0-8010-6736-7). Baker Bk.

Mother Shipton Investigated. William H. Harrison. LC 77-3412. 1977. Repr. of 1881 ed. lib. bdg. 17.00 (ISBN 0-8414-4911-2). Folcroft.

Mother Teresa. Mary Craig. (Profiles Ser.). (Illus.). 64p. 1983. 8.95 (ISBN 0-241-10933-7, Pub. by Hamish Hamilton England). David & Charles.

Mother Teresa. Vanora Leigh. LC 85-72245. (Great Lives Ser.). 32p. 1986. lib. bdg. 10.40 (ISBN 0-531-18033-6, Pub. by Bookwright Pr). Watts.

Mother Teresa: A Biography. Edward Le Joly. LC 84-48238. (Illus.). 352p. 1985. 16.30 (ISBN 0-06-065217-9, HarpR). Har-Row.

Mother Teresa: A Sister to the Poor. Patricia R. Giff. LC 85-40885. (Illus.). 64p. 1986. 9.95 (ISBN 0-670-81096-7, Viking Kestrel). Viking.

Mother Teresa & India. B. Srinivasa Murthy. LC 82-80522. (Illus.). 144p. (Orig.). 1983. pap. 6.95x (ISBN 0-941910-00-8). Long Beach Pubns.

Mother Teresa: Caring for All God's Children. Betsy Lee. LC 80-20286. (Taking Part Ser.). (Illus.). 48p. 1981. PLB 8.95 (ISBN 0-87518-205-4). Dillon.

Mother Teresa: Contemplative in the Heart of the World. Mother Teresa. 154p. 1985. pap. 8.95 (ISBN 0-89283-279-7). Servant.

Mother Teresa: Friend of the Friendless. Carol Greene. LC 83-7386. (Picture-Story Biographies Ser.). (Illus.). 32p. 1983. PLB 10.60 (ISBN 0-516-03559-2). Childrens.

Mother Teresa: Her Work & Her People. Desmond Doig. LC 75-39857. (Illus.). 176p. 1980. pap. 11.95 (ISBN 0-06-061941-4, RD336, HarpR). Har-Row.

Mother Teresa of Calcutta. Roy Gasnick. 1.25. Paulist Pr.

Mother Teresa Story. Maria Shrady. 1987. pap. 2.50. Paulist Pr.

Mother Teresa: The Early Years. David Porter. 120p. (Orig.). 1986. pap. 5.95 (ISBN 0-8028-0185-4). Eerdmans.

Mother Teresa Treasury: Mother Teresa of Calcutta, 3 vols. Mother Teresa of Calcutta. Incl. Vol. 1. Gift for God. 96p; Vol. 2. Love of Christ. 128p; Vol. 3. Life in the Spirit. 96p. LC 85-42786. 1985. 19.95 (ISBN 0-06-068228-0, HarpR). Har-Row.

Mother, with Letters on the Mother & Translations of Prayers & Meditations. Sri Aurobindo. 500p. 1982. 11.95 (ISBN 0-89071-311-1, Pub. by Sri Aurobindo Ashram India); pap. 8.95 (ISBN 0-89071-310-3, Pub. by Sri Aurobindo Ashram India). Matagiri.

Mother Worship: Theme & Variations. Ed. by James J. Preston. LC 81-3336. (Studies in Religion). xxiv, 360p. 1982. text ed. 29.00x (ISBN 0-8078-1471-7). U of NC Pr.

Mother Worship: Theme & Variations. Ed. by James J. Preston. (Studies in Religion). xxiv, 360p. 1983. pap. text ed. 9.95x (ISBN 0-8078-4114-5). U of NC Pr.

Motherhood. Pierce Maassen. pap. 0.45 (ISBN 0-686-23476-6). Rose Pub MI.

Motherhood & God. Margaret Hebbelthwaite. 144p. 1984. pap. 5.95 (ISBN 0-225-66384-8, HarpR). Har-Row.

Motherhood of the Church. Henri De Lubac. Tr. by Sr. Sergia Englund from Fr. LC 81-83857. Tr. of Eglises particulieres & La maternite de l'eglise. 363p. (Orig.). 1983. pap. 12.95 (ISBN 0-89870-014-0). Ignatius Pr.

Motherpeace: A Way to the Goddess Through Myth, Art & Tarot. Vicki Noble. LC 82-47752. (Illus.). 240p. (Orig.). 1982. pap. 12.95 (ISBN 0-06-066300-6, CN4039, HarpR). Har-Row.

Mothers are a Gift of Love. Helen S. Rice. (Illus.). 128p. 1980. 12.95 (ISBN 0-8007-1135-1). Revell.

Mothers Are People Too: A Contemporary Analysis of Motherhood. Anita Spencer. 1984. pap. 5.95 (ISBN 0-8091-2616-8). Paulist Pr.

Mothers Are Special. John W. Drakeford & Robina Drakeford. LC 78-73137. 1979. 8.95 (ISBN 0-8054-5636-8). Broadman.

Mothers: At the Heart of Life. Sheree Phillips. 140p. (Orig.). 1985. pap. 4.95 (ISBN 0-89283-274-6, Pub. by Vine Books). Servant.

Mother's Day Is over. Shirley Radl. 288p. 1987. 17.95 (ISBN 0-87795-864-5). Arbor Hse.

Mother's Day: Voices from the Heart. William J. Crockett. 15p. 1985. pap. 3.00 (ISBN 0-934383-33-2). Pride Prods.

Mothers, Fathers, & Children: Practical Advice to Parents. A. Furutan. 280p. pap. 8.95 (ISBN 0-85398-095-0). G Ronald Pub.

Mother's Gifts: A Book of Praise & Inspiration. E. Jane Mall. LC 75-33082. pap. 15.00 (ISBN 0-8357-9017-7, 2016382). Bks Demand UMI.

Mother's Joy. June M. Bacher. 1984. pap. 6.95 (ISBN 0-8010-0852-2). Baker Bk.

Mother's Joy. June Masters Bacher. 128p. 1984. pap. 6.95 6x (ISBN 0-89081-415-5). Harvest Hse.

Mother's Love. Leon R. Hartshorn. LC 80-81506. 76p. 1980. 5.95 (ISBN 0-88290-143-5). Horizon Utah.

Mothers of Feminism: The Story of Quaker Women in America. Margaret H. Bacon. 1986. 16.95 (ISBN 0-06-250043-0, HarpR). Har-Row.

Mother's Prayer. Jean D. Crowther. 14p. 1978. pap. 1.00 (ISBN 0-88290-099-4). Horizon Utah.

Mother's Soliloquy. Gladys E. Deck. 115p. 1986. 7.50 (ISBN 0-913382-38-8, 101-38). Prow Bks-Franciscan.

Mother's Songs: Images of God the Mother. Meinrad Craighead. LC 85-50408. 96p. (Orig.). 1985. pap. 9.95 (ISBN 0-8091-2716-4). Paulist Pr.

Mother's Touch. Elise Arndt. 156p. 1983. pap. 5.95 (ISBN 0-88207-101-7). Victor Bks.

Mother's World. Gayle G. Roper. (Ultra Bks Ser). 96p. 1975. 3.50 (ISBN 0-8010-7631-5). Baker Bk.

Motif Symbolism in the Disciples of Mallarme. John A. Frey. LC 73-94193. (Catholic University of America Studies in Romance Languages & Literatures Ser: No. 55). Repr. of 1957 ed. 23.00 (ISBN 0-404-50355-1). AMS Pr.

Motifs of Spirituality. James M. Houston. Date not set. pap. cancelled (ISBN 0-88070-106-4). Multnomah.

Motion & Motion's God: Thematic Variations in Aristotle, Cicero, Newton, & Hegel. Michael J. Buckley. LC 73-132234. 1971. 30.50 (ISBN 0-691-07124-1). Princeton U Pr.

Motivate with Bulletin Boards, No. 2. Eva Lee. (Illus.). 48p. 1985. pap. 2.95 (ISBN 0-87239-919-2, 3289). Standard Pub.

Motivation to Last a Lifetime. Ted W. Engstrom. 96p. 1983. gift ed. 8.95 (ISBN 0-310-24250-9, 9570L); pap. 4.95 (ISBN 0-310-24251-7, 9570P). Zondervan.

Motivational Ideas for Changing Lives. Neil E. Jackson, Jr. LC 81-68366. 1982. pap. 4.95 (ISBN 0-8054-5647-3). Broadman.

Motive Clauses in Hebrew Law: Biblical Forms & Near Eastern Parallels. Rifat Sonsino. LC 79-15024. (Society of Biblical Literature Dissertation Ser.: No. 45). 15.95 (ISBN 0-89130-317-0, 060145); pap. 10.95 (ISBN 0-89130-318-9). Scholars Pr GA.

Motivi Moijej Zhizni. Archbishop Vitaly Maximenko. Tr. of Motives of My Life. 205p. 1955. pap. 7.00 (ISBN 0-317-29054-1). Holy Trinity.

Motse, the Neglected Rival of Confucius. Mei Yi-Pac. LC 73-892. (China Studies). (Illus.). xi, 222p. 1973. Repr. of 1934 ed. 20.75 (ISBN 0-88355-084-9). Hyperion Conn.

Moulds of Understanding: A Pattern of Natural Philosophy. Joseph Needham. LC 75-37252. 320p. 1976. 27.50 (ISBN 0-312-54950-4). St Martin.

Moulids of Egypt: Egyptian Saints-Days. Joseph W. McPherson. LC 77-87654. Repr. of 1941 ed. 28.50 (ISBN 0-404-16408-0). AMS Pr.

Mount Athos: An Illustrated Guide to the Monasteries & their Histories. (Illus.). 200p. pap. 20.00 (ISBN 0-89241-369-7). Caratzas.

Mount Fuji & Mount Sinai: A Critique of Idols. Kosuke Koyama. LC 84-16556. Orig. Title: Mount Fui & Mount Sinai - A Pilgramage in Theology. 288p. (Orig.). 1985. pap. 12.95 (ISBN 0-88344-353-8). Orbis Bks.

Mount Grace Charterhouse & Late English Medieval Spirituality: John Norton, Vol. 3. James Hogg. (Analecta Cartusiana Ser.: No. 64-3). (Orig.). 1987. pap. 25.00 (ISBN 3-7052-0094-1, Pub. by Salzburg Studies). Longwood Pub Group.

Mount Grace Charterhouse & Late Medieval English Spirituality, Vol. 2. James Hogg. (Analecta Cartusiana Ser.: No. 64-2). 144p. (Orig.). 1978. pap. 25.00 (ISBN 3-7052-0093-3, Pub. by Salzburg Studies). Longwood Pub Group.

Mount Grace Charterhouse & Late Medieval English Spirituality: Richard Methley, Vol. 1. James Hogg. (Analecta Cartusiana Ser.: No. 64-1). (Orig.). 1987. pap. 25.00 (ISBN 3-7052-0092-5, Pub. by Salzburg Studies). Longwood Pub Group.

Mount-Orgueil. William Prynne. LC 83-20361. 1984. Repr. of 1641 ed. 40.00x (ISBN 0-8201-1392-1). Schol Facsimiles.

Mount to the Sky Like Eagles, Vol. 9. Bernard Perner & Majorie Perner. (Heritage Ser.). 1986. 10.95 (ISBN 0-911802-64-9). Free Church Pubns.

Mountain Dialogues. Frank Waters. LC 81-732. x, 237p. 1981. 16.95 (ISBN 0-8040-0361-0, SB). Ohio U Pr.

Mountain Meadows Massacre. Juanita Brooks. (Illus.). 342p. 1985. Repr. of 1963 ed. 18.95 (ISBN 0-8061-0549-6). U of Okla Pr.

Mountain Preacher, Vol. III. R. Paul Caudill. LC 84-71992. (Illus.). 165p. (Orig.). 1986. pap. 3.00 (ISBN 0-938980-05-X). Blue Ridge.

Mountain Preacher, Vol. 3. R. Paul Caudill. LC 84-71992. 1986. pap. 3.00 (ISBN 0-938980-05-X). Blue Ridge.

Mountain Rain. Eileen Crossman. 1982. pap. 3.95 (ISBN 9971-972-05-0). OMF Bks.

Mountain Trailways for Youth: Devotions for Young People. Mrs. Charles E. Cowman. 1979. pap. 6.95 (ISBN 0-310-37641-6, 6880P). Zondervan.

Mountains into Goldmines: Robert Schuller & the Gospel of Success. Dennis Voskuil. LC 83-1729. pap. 47.00 (ISBN 0-317-30165-9, 2025347). Bks Demand UMI.

Mountains of Spices. Hannah Hurnard. 1975. pap. 3.50 (ISBN 0-8423-4611-2). Tyndale.

Mountainway of the Navajo. Leland C. Wyman. LC 74-83333. 271p. 1975. 14.50x (ISBN 0-8165-0412-1). U of Ariz Pr.

Mourning & Liberation. George Pollock. 1987. lib. bdg. price not set (ISBN 0-8236-3485-X). Intl Univs Pr.

Mourning Cry & Woe Oracle. Waldemar Janzen. (Beiheft 125 zur Zeitschrift fuer die alttestamentliche Wissenschaft). 120p. 1972. 27.50x (ISBN 3-11-003848-X). De Gruyter.

Mourning Song. Joyce Landorf. 192p. 1974. 10.95 (ISBN 0-8007-0680-3). Revell.

Mouth of Witnesses: Biblical Exegesis & the Dead Sea Scrolls. Kate M. McClelland. LC 76-48407. 1978. 10.00 (ISBN 0-916620-09-3). Portals Pr.

Mouvement religieux a Paris pendant la Revolution: 1789-1801, 2 vols. Jean F. Robinet. LC 70-174331. (Collection de documents relatifs a l'histoire de Paris pendant la Revolution francaise). Repr. of 1898 ed. Set. 169.00 (ISBN 0-404-52567-9); 84.50 ea. Vol. 1 (ISBN 0-404-52568-7). Vol. 2 (ISBN 0-404-52569-5). AMS Pr.

Move Ahead with Possibility Thinking. Robert H. Schuller. 224p. 1973. pap. 2.95 (ISBN 0-8007-8105-8, Spire Bks). Revell.

Move in Our Midst: Looking at Worship in the Life of the Church. Kenneth I. Morse. 1977. pap. 2.95 (ISBN 0-87178-583-8). Brethren.

Move of God: Azusa Street to Now. Clara Davis. 80p. (Orig.). 1983. pap. 2.95 (ISBN 0-88144-016-7, CPS-016). Christian Pub.

Move over, Elijah. Arthur O. Roberts. LC 67-24903. 161p. 1967. 3.50 (ISBN 0-913342-11-4). Barclay Pr.

Movement & Emptiness. L. C. Beckett. 1969. pap. 1.45 (ISBN 0-8356-0414-4, Quest). Theos Pub Hse.

Movement in Prayer in a Hasidic Mode. Clifford Trolin. 1979. 2.50 (ISBN 0-941500-13-6). Sharing Co.

Movement of Theology since the Council. Ed. by Edward Schillebeeckx. (Concilium 1983: Vol. 170). 128p. (Orig.). 1983. pap. 6.95 (ISBN 0-8164-2450-0, HarpR). Har-Row.

Movements & Issues in American Judaism: An Analysis & Sourcebook of Developments Since 1945. Ed. by Bernard Martin. LC 77-87971. 1978. lib. bdg. 35.00 (ISBN 0-313-20044-0, MCJ/). Greenwood.

Movements & Issues in World Religions: A Sourcebook & Analysis of Developments since 1945; Religion, Ideology, & Politics. Ed. by Charles W. Fu & Gerhard E. Spiegler. LC 86-4634. 576p. 1987. lib. bdg. 75.00 (ISBN 0-313-23238-5, FUR). Greenwood.

Movers of Mountains. Elaine M. Ward. 88p. (Orig.). (YA) 1984. pap. 12.95 (ISBN 0-940754-24-X). Ed Ministries.

Moving Frontiers. Ed. by Carl S. Meyer. 524p. 1986. pap. 12.95 (ISBN 0-570-04461-8). Concordia.

Moving Meditation: Enlightenment of the Mind & Total Fitness. Van H. Ho. LC 79-88748. (Illus.). 214p. 1979. pap. 15.00 (ISBN 0-9602904-1-9). V H Ho.

Moving Out: The Story of Student Initiative in World Missions. David M. Howard. 80p. 1984. pap. 2.95 (ISBN 0-87784-565-4). Inter-Varsity.

Moving Right Along in the Spirit. Dennis Bennett. 160p. 1982. 5.95 (ISBN 0-8007-5184-1, Power Bks). Revell.

Moving the Hand That Moves the World. C. C. Cribb. LC 79-88930. (If God Has It I Want It! Ser.). Date not set. pap. 2.95 (ISBN 0-932046-18-5). Manhattan Ltd NC.

Mozart & Masonry. Paul Nettl. LC 78-114564. (Music Ser.). 1970. Repr. of 1957 ed. lib. bdg. 25.00 (ISBN 0-306-71922-3). Da Capo.

Mrs. C. H. Spurgeon. Charles Ray. 1979. pap. 2.50 (ISBN 0-686-09102-7). Pilgrim Pubns.

Mrs. Eddy: The Biography of a Virginal Mind. Edwin F. Dakin. 13.25 (ISBN 0-8446-0570-0). Peter Smith.

Mrs. Grundy: A History of Four Centuries of Morals Intended to Illuminate Present Problems in Great Britain & the United States. Leo Markun. 1930. 69.00 (ISBN 0-403-00130-7). Scholarly.

Mrs. Preacher. Karen Norheim. 160p. (Orig.). 1985. pap. 3.95 (ISBN 0-89900-204-8). College Pr Pub.

Msgr. Josemaria Escriva de Balaguer: A Profile of the Founder of Opus Dei. 360p. 1977. 14.95 (ISBN 0-933932-31-6); pap. 6.95 large ed. (ISBN 0-933932-30-8); small ed. 4.95 (ISBN 0-933932-34-0). Scepter Pubs.

Mt. Angel Abbey: A Centennial History of the Benedictine Community & Its Library, 1882-1982. Compiled by Lawrence J. McCrank. LC 83-10536. 176p. 1983. pap. 15.00 (ISBN 0-8420-2212-0). Scholarly Res Inc.

Much Beloved Daughter: The Story of Florence Li. Ted Harrison. 110p. 1986. pap. 6.95 (ISBN 0-8192-1378-0). Morehouse.

Much More! Jack Taylor. LC 72-79179. 160p. 1972. 8.95 (ISBN 0-8054-5523-X). Broadman.

Much More Than Giving. Roy Bleick. 112p. (Orig.). 1985. pap. 6.95 (ISBN 0-570-03951-7, 12-2886). Concordia.

Much Silence: The Life & Work of Meher Baba. 3rd ed. Tom Hopkinson & Dorothy Hopkinson. LC 74-26821. 232p. 1982. pap. 4.95 (ISBN 0-913078-53-0, Pub. by Meher Foun Australia). Sheriar Pr.

Mucho Mas Que Numeros. Paul Y. Cho & R. Whitney Manzano. Ed. by Luis L. Bernal. Tr. by M. Francisco Lievano. Tr. of More Than Numbers. (Span.). 208p. 1985. pap. text ed. 2.95 (ISBN 0-8297-0531-7). Life Pubs Intl.

Mudra: A Study of Symbolic Gestures in Japanese Buddhist Sculpture. E. Dale Saunders. (Bollingen Ser.: Vol. 58). (Illus.). 1960. 37.00x (ISBN 0-691-09796-8). Princeton U Pr.

Mudras: The Ritual Hand-Poses of the Buddha Priests & the Shiva Priests of Bali. Tyra De Kleen. 1970. 5.00 (ISBN 0-8216-0119-9). Univ Bks.

Muhammad. Michael Cook. (Past Masters Ser.). (Illus.). 1983. 13.95x (ISBN 0-19-287606-6); pap. 4.95 (ISBN 0-19-287605-8). Oxford U Pr.

Muhammad. Martin Lings. LC 83-49. 349p. 1983. 24.95 (ISBN 0-89281-046-7). Inner Tradit.

Muhammad. Maxime Rodinson. Tr. by Anne Carter. LC 69-20189. 1980. pap. 9.95 (ISBN 0-394-73822-5). Pantheon.

Muhammad & the Arab Empire. John Duckworth et al. Ed. by Malcolm Yapp & Margaret Killingray. (World History Ser.). (Illus.). 1980. lib. bdg. 6.95 (ISBN 0-89908-036-7); pap. text ed. 2.45 (ISBN 0-89908-011-1). Greenhaven.

Muhammad & the Christian: A Question of Response. Kenneth Cragg. 192p. (Orig.). 1984. pap. 8.95 (ISBN 0-88344-349-X). Orbis Bks.

Muhammad & the Islamic Tradition. Emile Dermenghem. Tr. by Jean M. Watt from Fr. LC 81-47412. (Spiritual Masters Ser.). (Illus.). 192p. 1981. 18.95 (ISBN 0-87951-130-3). Overlook Pr.

Muhammad & the Islamic Tradition. Emile Dermenghem. Tr. by Jean M. Watt. LC 81-47412. 192p. pap. 9.95 (ISBN 0-87951-170-2). Overlook Pr.

Muhammad & the World of Islam. H. O. McWilliam. Ed. by Marjorie Reeves. (Then & There Ser.). (Illus.). 96p. (Orig.). 1977. pap. text ed. 4.75 (ISBN 0-582-20537-9). Longman.

Muhammad as a Military Leader. A. Rahman. pap. 12.50 (ISBN 0-317-46107-9). Kazi Pubns.

Muhammad at Medina. W. Montgomery Watt. 1981. Repr. of 1956 ed. 39.95x (ISBN 0-19-577307-1). Oxford U Pr.

Muhammad in the Holy Quran. A. Musa Raza. 15.95 (ISBN 0-317-14646-7). Kazi Pubns.

Muhammad in the Mirror of Islam. Muhammad Tabatabai. Tr. by William Chittick from Persian. 21p. 1979. pap. 1.00 (ISBN 0-941722-18-X). Book-Dist-Ctr.

Muhammad: Man of Allah. S. H. Nasr. 61p. 1982. 20.00x (ISBN 0-317-39130-5, Pub. by Luzac & Co Ltd). State Mutual Bk.

Muhammad: Prophet & Statesman. W. Montgomery Watt. 1961. pap. 7.95 (ISBN 0-19-881078-4). Oxford U Pr.

Muhammad: Seal of the Prophets. Muhammad Z. Khan. 400p. 1980. pap. 10.50 (ISBN 0-7100-0610-1). Methuen Inc.

Muhammad the Benefactor of Humanity. N. Siddiqui. pap. 9.50 (ISBN 0-686-18434-3). Kazi Pubns.

Muhammad the Educator. A. Rehman. pap. 15.00 (ISBN 0-686-18433-5). Kazi Pubns.

Muhammad the Holy Prophet. G. Sawar. pap. 14.50 (ISBN 0-686-18432-7). Kazi Pubns.

Muhammad: The Last Prophet. V. Ismail. 8.50 (ISBN 0-686-83579-4). Kazi Pubns.

Muhammad, the Prophet of Islam. Chattapadhyaya. 1981. 1.25 (ISBN 0-686-97878-1). Kazi Pubns.

Muhammadam Festivals: Typical Elements of Islamic Rituals, Prayers & Pilgrimage. G. E. Von Grunebaum. 144p. 1981. 20.00x (ISBN 0-7007-0087-0, Pub. by Curzon England). State Mutual Bk.

Muhammadan Architecture in Egypt & Palestine. Martin S. Briggs. LC 74-1287. (Architecture & Decorative Arts Ser.). (Illus.). 255p. 1974. Repr. of 1924 ed. lib. bdg. 39.50 (ISBN 0-306-70590-7). Da Capo.

Muhammadan Mysticism in Sumatra. Raymond L. Archer. LC 77-87487. (Royal Asiatic Society, Malayan Branch. Journal: Vol. 15). Repr. of 1937 ed. 16.50 (ISBN 0-404-16695-4). AMS Pr.

Muhammaden Festivals: Typical Elements of Islamic Ritual, Prayer & Pilgrimage. new ed. G. E. Von Grunebaum. (Illus.). 1976. text ed. 9.95x (ISBN 0-7007-0087-0). Humanities.

Muhammed: Man of Allah. Seyyed H. Nasr. 61p. (Orig.). 1986. pap. text ed. 9.95 (ISBN 0-7103-0154-5). Methuen Inc.

Muhammedan Law of Marriage & Divorce. Ahmed Shukri. (Columbia University. Contributions to Oriental History & Philology: No. 7). Repr. of 1917 ed. 15.25 (ISBN 0-404-50537-6). AMS Pr.

Mujer en su Crisis de Media Vida. Jim Conway & Sally Conway. Tr. by Alicia De Zorzoli from Span. Tr. of Women in Mid-Life Crisis. 352p. 1985. pap. 6.50 (ISBN 0-311-46105-0). Casa Bautista.

Mujer: Su Mision, Posicion y Ministerio. Perry B. Fitzwater. Orig. Title: Woman: Mission, Position, Ministry. (Span.). 76p. 1972. pap. 2.25 (ISBN 0-8254-1233-1). Kregel.

Mujer Sujeta al Espiritu. Beverly LaHaye. 208p. 1978. 3.25 (ISBN 0-88113-210-1). Edit Betania.

Muktananda: Selected Essays. Paul Zweig. LC 76-9994. 1977. pap. 7.95i (ISBN 0-06-069860-8, RD185, HarpR). Har-Row.

Mukteshwari, Vol. II. Swami Muktananda. LC 79-101943. 188p. 1973. 6.00 (ISBN 0-914602-62-4). SYDA Found.

Mule Musings. Basil Overton. 6.95 (ISBN 0-89137-105-2); pap. 4.25. Quality Pubns.

Multi-Media Methods for Christian Ministries. Clark Greer. LC 82-16132. 1982. pap. 2.95 (ISBN 0-87227-085-8). Reg Baptist.

Multiformity of Man. Eugen Rosenstock-Huessy. 1973. pap. 3.50 (ISBN 0-912148-06-3). Argo Bks.

Multiple Church-Staff Handbook. Harold J. Westing. LC 85-9811. (Illus.). 208p. (Orig.). 1985. pap. 10.95 (ISBN 0-8254-4031-9). Kregel.

Multiple Faith Relationships. Deborah Premoe & David Premoe. (Pastoral Care Office Pamphlet Ser.). 84p. 1984. pap. text ed. 5.00 (ISBN 0-8309-0390-9). Herald Hse.

Multiple Marriage: A Study of Polygamy in Light of the Bible. Robert J. Hitchens. LC 86-72269. 160p. (Orig.). 1987. pap. 6.95 (ISBN 0-9617379-1-3). Doulos Pubs.

Multiple Staff & the Larger Church. Lyle E. Schaller. LC 79-20796. 1980. pap. 6.95 (ISBN 0-687-27297-1). Abingdon.

Multipurpose Tools for Bible Study. rev. ed. Frederick W. Danker. 1970. pap. 12.50 (ISBN 0-570-03734-4, 12-2638). Concordia.

Mummy. 2nd ed. E. A. Budge. LC 64-13391. (Illus.). 1894. 25.00 (ISBN 0-8196-0139-X). Biblo.

Munajat: The Intimate Prayers. Khwajih Abd Allah Ansarti. Tr. by Lawrence Morris & Rustam Sarfeh. LC 75-30173. (Eng. & Persian.). 1975. 7.50 (ISBN 0-917220-00-5). Khaneghah & Maktab.

Mundaka Upanishad with Commentary of Shankara. Tr. by Swami Gambhirananda from Sanskrit. 100p. pap. 1.25 (ISBN 0-87481-203-8). Vedanta Pr.

Mundakopanisad. Tr. by Swami Sarvananda. (Sanskrit & English). pap. 1.00 (ISBN 0-87481-460-X). Vedanta Pr.

Mundo Del Nuevo Testamento. H. E. Dana. Tr. by Ildefonso Villarello. 288p. 1982. pap. 4.95 (ISBN 0-311-04342-9). Casa Bautista.

Mundo en Llamas. Billy Graham. Orig. Title: World Aflame. (Span.). 272p. 1983. pap. 5.25 (ISBN 0-311-46091-7). Casa Bautista.

Munirih Khanum: Memoirs & Letters. Munirih Khanum. Tr. by Sammireh A. Smith. (Persian., Illus.). 1987. 7.95 (ISBN 0-933770-51-0). Kalimat.

Muqarnas: An Annual on Islamic Art & Architecture: The Art of the Mamluks, Vol. II. Ed. by Oleg Grabar. LC 83-643765. (Illus.). 240p. 1984. 35.00x (ISBN 0-300-03137-8). Yale U Pr.

Murbacher Hymnen, nach den Handschriften Herausgegeben. Eduard Sievers. Repr. of 1874 ed. 27.00 (ISBN 0-384-55359-1). Johnson Repr.

Murder & Difference: Gender, Genre & Scholarship Sisera's Death. Mieke Bal. (Indiana Studies in Biblical Literature). (Illus.). Date not set. price not set. Ind U Pr.

Murder of Archbishop Thomas. Tom Corfe. LC 76-22419. (Cambridge Topic Bks). (Illus.). 1977. PLB 8.95 (ISBN 0-8225-1202-5). Lerner Pubns.

Murder of Becket. David Birt. (Resource Units: Middle Ages, 1066-1485 Ser.). (Illus.). 24p. 1974. pap. text ed. 12.95 10 copies & tchr's guide (ISBN 0-582-39376-0). Longman.

Murder of Jacob De Haan by the Zionists: A Martyr's Message. Emil Marmorstein. 1980. lib. bdg. 59.95 (ISBN 0-686-68747-7). Revisionist Pr.

Murdered Heiress, Living Witness. Petti Wagner. LC 84-80413. 211p. (Orig.). 1984. pap. 6.95 (ISBN 0-910311-09-9). Huntington Hse Inc.

Music & Dance: In the Worship Program of the Church. Constance L. Fisher. (Orig.). 1981. pap. 2.50 (ISBN 0-941500-20-9). Sharing Co.

Music & Language: The Rise of Western Music Exemplified in Settings of the Mass. Thrysbulos Georgiades. Tr. by Marie-Louise Gollner. LC 82-4246. (Illus.). 150p. 1983. 29.95 (ISBN 0-521-23309-7); pap. 9.95 (ISBN 0-521-29902-0). Cambridge U Pr.

Music & Ministry: A Biblical Counterpoint. Calvin M. Johansson. 152p. 1984. pap. 6.95 (ISBN 0-913573-07-8). Hendrickson MA.

Music & Religion. Ed. by Stanley A. Hunter. LC 72-1615. Repr. of 1930 ed. 19.00 (ISBN 0-404-08316-1). AMS Pr.

Music & Ritual at Papal Avignon, 1309-1403. Andrew Tomasello. Ed. by George Buelow. LC 83-18296. (Studies in Musicology: No. 75). 314p. 1983. 49.95 (ISBN 0-8357-1493-4). UMI Res Pr.

Music & Worship. Edward W. Nelson. 176p. 1985. spiral bdg. 13.50 (ISBN 0-311-72642-9). Casa Bautista.

Music & Worship in the Church. rev. ed. Austin C. Lovelace & William C. Rice. LC 76-13524. pap. 64.00 (ISBN 0-317-09866-7, 2020266). Bks Demand UMI.

Music, Dance & Religion: The Performing Arts in Worship. Norman Mealy & Judith Rock. (Illus.). 192p. 1985. 15.95 (ISBN 0-13-607219-4); pap. 8.95 (ISBN 0-13-607201-1). P-H.

Music: Does It Really Matter? 2nd ed. Nathanael Pugh. Ed. by Mary H. Wallace. (Illus.). 79p. 1984. pap. 2.50 (ISBN 0-912315-73-3). Word Aflame.

Music for a King: George Herbert's Style & the Metrical Psalms. Coburn Freer. LC 76-179136. pap. 67.50 (ISBN 0-317-42332-0, 2025815). Bks Demand UMI.

Music for Vespers II. Johann C. Bach. (Johann Christian Bach: The Collected Works). 400p. 1985. lib. bdg. 85.00 (ISBN 0-8240-6072-5). Garland Pub.

Music in Early Christian Literature. James W. McKinnon. (Cambridge Readings in the Literature of Music Ser.). 300p. Date not set. price not set (ISBN 0-521-30497-0). Cambridge U Pr.

Music in Lutheran Worship. Carl Schalk. 16p. (Orig.). 1983. pap. 1.25 (ISBN 0-570-01323-2, 99-1253). Concordia.

Music in Missions: Discipling Through Music. T. W. Hunt. LC 86-28333. (Orig.). 1987. pap. 9.95 (ISBN 0-8054-6343-7). Broadman.

Music in Terezin Nineteen Forty-One to Nineteen Forty Five. Joza Karas. LC 84-24411. (Illus.). 212p. 1985. 16.95x (ISBN 0-918728-34-7). Pendragon NY.

Music in the Christian Community. Dale Topp. LC 76-20471. Repr. of 1976 ed. 51.30 (ISBN 0-8357-9130-0, 2019340). Bks Demand UMI.

Music in the Church. Peter C. Lutkin. LC 72-135722. Repr. of 1910 ed. 21.45 (ISBN 0-404-04069-1). AMS Pr.

Music in the History of the Western Church. E. Dickinson. LC 68-25286. (Studies in Music, No. 42). 1969. Repr. of 1902 ed. lib. bdg. 49.95x (ISBN 0-8383-0301-3). Haskell.

Music in the History of the Western Church. Edward Dickinson. LC 77-127454. Repr. of 1902 ed. 14.50 (ISBN 0-404-02127-1). AMS Pr.

Music in the History of the Western Church, with an Introduction in Religious Music Among the Primitive & Ancient Peoples. Edward Dickinson. LC 69-13884. Repr. of 1902 ed. lib. bdg. 22.50x (ISBN 0-8371-1062-9, DIMW). Greenwood.

Music in the History of the Western Church, with an Introduction in Religious Music Among the Primitive & Ancient Peoples. Edward Dickinson. 1977. Repr. 19.00 (ISBN 0-403-08194-7). Scholarly.

Music in the Pentecostal Church. Delton L. Alford. 113p. 1969. 5.25 (ISBN 0-87148-561-3); pap. 4.25 (ISBN 0-87148-562-1). Pathway Pr.

Music in the Service of the Church: The Funeral Sermon for Heinrich Schuetz. Robin A. Leaver. 68p. (Orig.). 1985. pap. 6.75 (ISBN 0-570-01331-3, 99-1261). Concordia.

Music in the Southwest, 1825-1950. Howard Swan. LC 77-5421. (Music Reprint Ser.). 1977. Repr. of 1952 ed. lib. bdg. 39.50 (ISBN 0-306-77418-6). Da Capo.

Music Leadership in the Church. Erik Routley & Carlton R. Young. 136p. 1985. pap. text ed. 6.95 (ISBN 0-916642-24-0). Agape IL.

Music Locator. Orig. Title: MusiCatalog. 584p. 1987. pap. 89.95 (ISBN 0-89390-098-2). Resource Pubns.

Music, Mysticism & Magic: A Source Book. Joscelyn Godwin. 384p. 1986. text ed. 50.00 (ISBN 0-7102-0904-5, 0905W, Pub. by Routledge UK). Methuen Inc.

Music of the Angels. Sir Michael Tippett. (Eulenburg Music Ser.). 1982. pap. text ed. 19.50 (ISBN 0-903873-60-5). Da Capo.

Music of the Bay Psalm Book: Ninth Edition (1698) Richard G. Appel. LC 75-34880. (I.S.A.M. Monographs: No. 5). 44p. (Orig.). 1975. pap. 4.00 (ISBN 0-914678-04-3). Inst Am Music.

Music of the Bible. John Stainer. LC 74-100657. (Music Ser). (Illus.). 1970. Repr. of 1914 ed. lib. bdg. 32.50 (ISBN 0-306-71862-6). Da Capo.

Music of the English Parish Church, 2 vols. Nicholas Temperley. LC 77-84811. (Cambridge Studies in Music). (Illus.). 1980. Vol. 1. 100.00 (ISBN 0-521-22045-9); Vol. 2. 52.50 (ISBN 0-521-22046-7). Cambridge U Pr.

Music of the English Parish Church, Vol. 1. Nicholas Temperley. LC 77-84811. (Cambridge Studies in Music). 1983. pap. 23.95 (ISBN 0-521-27457-5). Cambridge U Pr.

Music of the Ephrata Cloister. Julius F. Sachse. LC 77-134386. (Communal Societies Ser.). Repr. of 1903 ed. 15.00 (ISBN 0-404-05500-1). AMS Pr.

Music of the French Psalter of 1562. Waldo S. Pratt. LC 40-4909. Repr. of 1939 ed. 15.00 (ISBN 0-404-05119-7). AMS Pr.

Music of the Ghetto & the Bible. Lazare Saminsky. LC 74-24220. Repr. of 1934 ed. 16.00 (ISBN 0-404-12833-5). AMS Pr.

Music of the Moravians in America from the Archives of the Moravian Church at Bethlehem Pa, 2 vols. Hans T. David. Incl. Vol. 1. Ten Sacred Songs. J. Dencke et al; Vol. 2. Six Quintets. John F. Peter. write to C. F. Peters Corp., NY for prices (ISBN 0-685-22862-2). NY Pub Lib.

Music of the Pilgrims: A Description of the Psalm-Book Brought to Plymouth in Sixteen Twenty. Waldo S. Pratt. 1980. lib. bdg. 59.00 (ISBN 0-8490-3180-X). Gordon Pr.

Music of the Spheres: The Material Universe from Atom to Quasar, Simply Explained, 2 vols. Guy Murchie. (Illus.). 28.00 set (ISBN 0-8446-0815-7). Peter Smith.

Music That is Soundless: An Introduction to God for the Graduate. Philip McShane. 1977. pap. text ed. 9.25 (ISBN 0-8191-0236-9). U Pr of Amer.

Musica Divina Selectus Novus Missarum, 10 vols in 8. Ed. by Karl Proske. 1973. Repr. of 1855 ed. 545.00 (ISBN 0-384-48055-1). Johnson Repr.

Musical Calender of Festivals: Folk Songs of Feast-Days & Holidays from Around the World. Barbara Cass-Beggs. (Ward Lock Educational Ser.). 1985. 25.00x (ISBN 0-7062-4226-2, Pub. by Ward Lock Educ Co Ltd). State Mutual Bk.

Musical Letters from Abroad. 2nd ed. Lowell Mason. LC 67-13035. (Music Ser). 1967. Repr. of 1854 ed. lib. bdg. 37.50 (ISBN 0-306-70940-6). Da Capo.

Musical Ministries in the Church. Waldo S. Pratt. LC 74-24193. Repr. of 1923 ed. 18.75 (ISBN 0-404-13095-X). AMS Pr.

Musical Scales of the Hindus. Sourindo M. Tagore. LC 74-24225. Repr. of 1884 ed. 21.50 (ISBN 0-404-12837-8). AMS Pr.

Musical Setting for the Liturgy of St. John Chrysostom. Joseph Raya & Jose D. Vinck. (Illus.). 44p. 1971. pap. 2.00 (ISBN 0-911726-05-5). Alleluia Pr.

Musical Variations on Jewish Thought. Olivier R. D'Allonnes. Tr. by Judith Greenberg. LC 83-15640. 169p. 1984. 12.95 (ISBN 0-8076-1091-7). Braziller.

Musical Wesleys. Erik Routley. LC 75-36511. (Illus.). 1976. Repr. of 1968 ed. text ed. 22.50x (ISBN 0-8371-8644-7, ROMW). Greenwood.

MusiCatalog. Resource Publications, Inc. Staff. Ed. by W. P. Cunningham. 1978. pap. 54.90x (ISBN 0-89390-013-3). Resource Pubns.

Musician's Guide to Church Music. Joy Lawrence & John Ferguson. LC 80-27567. 280p. 1981. 16.95 (ISBN 0-8298-0424-2). Pilgrim NY.

Musician's Quest. George MacDonald. Ed. by Michael Phillips. 272p. 1984. pap. 5.95 (ISBN 0-87123-444-0, 210444). Bethany Hse.

Musing, Meditations, & Meanderings. Doris Gvillo. 1984. 5.95 (ISBN 0-89536-982-6, 7531). CSS of Ohio.

Musings for Meditation. Arleen Lorrance. LC 76-14783. (Illus.). 180p. (Orig.). 1976. pap. 4.50 (ISBN 0-916192-03-2). L P Pubns.

Musings of a Chinese Mystic: Selections from the Philosophy of Chuang Tzu. Ed. & tr. by Herbert A. Giles. 112p. Repr. of 1926 ed. text ed. 17.50x (ISBN 0-89644-497-X, Pub. by Chinese Matl Ctr). Coronet Bks.

Musique et Liturgie: Le Graduel et l'Antiphonaire Romains; Histoire et Description. Amedee Gastoue. LC 70-178577. (Fr.). Repr. of 1913 ed. 32.50 (ISBN 0-404-56608-1). AMS Pr.

Muslim Architecture of Egypt, 2 vols. K. A. Creswell. LC 75-11056. (Illus.). 1978. Repr. of 1952 ed. lib. bdg. 350.00 (ISBN 0-87817-175-4). Hacker.

Muslim Attitudes Toward British Rule & Western Culture in India. Mujeeb Ashraf. 1983. 19.00x (ISBN 0-8364-1076-9, Pub. by Idarah). South Asia Bks.

Muslim Brotherhoods & Politics in Senegal. Lucy Behrman. LC 70-95918. 1970. 15.00x (ISBN 0-674-59490-8). Harvard U Pr.

Muslim Brotherhoods in 19th Century Africa. B. G. Martin. LC 75-35451. (African Studies Ser.: No. 18). 1977. 44.50 (ISBN 0-521-21062-3). Cambridge U Pr.

Muslim-Christian Relations & Inter-Christian Rivalries in the Middle East: The Case of the Jacobites in an Age of Transition. John Joseph. LC 82-870. 320p. 1983. 49.50x (ISBN 0-87395-600-1); pap. 19.95 (ISBN 0-87395-601-X). State U NY Pr.

Muslim Civilization & the Crisis in Iran. Ravi Batra. 218p. 1980. pap. 2.00 (ISBN 0-686-95468-8). Ananda Marga.

Muslim Community in North America. Ed. by E. H. Waugh et al. xii, 316p. 1983. pap. 15.00x (ISBN 0-88864-034-X, Pub. by Univ of Alta Pr Canada). U of Nebr Pr.

Muslim Contribution to Civilization. Haidar Bammate. Date not set. 2.50 (ISBN 0-89259-029-7). Am Trust Pubns.

Muslim Contributions to Geography. Nafis Ahmad. (Illus.). 178p. (Orig.). 1981. pap. 10.25 (ISBN 0-88004-014-9). Sunwise Turn.

Muslim Creed: Its Genesis & Historical Development. Arent J. Wensinck. 311p. 1932. Repr. text ed. 22.00x. Coronet Bks.

Muslim Dilemma in India. M. R. Baig. 1974. 7.50 (ISBN 0-7069-0311-0). Intl Bk Dist.

Muslim Discovery of Europe. Bernard Lewis. (Illus.). 352p. 1982. 19.95 (ISBN 0-393-01529-7). Norton.

Muslim Economic Thinking: A Survey of Contemporary Literature. Muhammad N. Siddiqi. 130p. (Orig.). 1981. 10.50x (ISBN 0-86037-082-8, Pub. by Islamic Found UK); pap. 5.25x (ISBN 0-86037-081-X). New Era Pubns MI.

Muslim Ethics & Modernity. S. McDonough. (Comparative Ethics Ser.: No. 1). 126p. 1984. pap. 11.95x (ISBN 0-88920-162-5, Pub. by Wilfrid Laurier Canada). Humanities.

Muslim Etiquettes. A. R. Shad. 1981. 16.50 (ISBN 0-686-77429-9). Kazi Pubns.

Muslim Family Law: A Sourcebook. Keith Hodkinson. 401p. (Orig.). 1984. pap. 25.00 (ISBN 0-7099-1256-0, Pub. by Croom Helm Ltd). Methuen Inc.

Muslim Filipinos: Heritage & Horizon. Peter G. Gowing. (Illus.). 1979. pap. 11.00x (ISBN 0-686-25217-9, Pub. by New Day Pub). Cellar.

Muslim Inscriptions in the Punjab, Haryana & Himachal Pradesh. Subhash Parihar. (Illus.). 79p. 1986. text ed. 40.00x (ISBN 81-210-0017-3, Pub. by Inter India Pubns N Delhi). Apt Bks.

Muslim Institutions. Maurice Gaudefroy-Demombynes. LC 84-12953. 216p. 1984. Repr. of 1950 ed. lib. bdg. 35.00x (ISBN 0-313-24287-9, GAMU). Greenwood.

Muslim Law. Khalid Rashid. 376p. 1985. 60.00x (Pub. by Eastern Bk India). State Mutual Bk.

Muslim Law. 4th ed. K. P. Saxena. 1306p. 1963. 105.00x (Pub. by Eastern Bk India). State Mutual Bk.

Muslim Mind. 2nd ed. Charis Waddy. LC 82-7778. (Illus.). 232p. 1983. 25.00x (ISBN 0-582-78346-1); pap. 8.95x (ISBN 0-582-78345-3). Longman.

Muslim Minorities in the World Today. M. Ali Kettani. 267p. 1986. 56.00x (ISBN 0-7201-1802-6). Mansell.

Muslim Minorities in the World Today. M. Ali Kettani. 267p. 1986. 56.00 (ISBN 0-7201-1802-6). Wilson.

Muslim Politics in India. S. K. Ghosh. 1986. 18.50 (ISBN 81-7024-070-0, Pub. by Ashish India). South Asia Bks.

Muslim Population of the World. M. S. A. pap. 1.00 (ISBN 0-686-18438-6). Kazi Pubns.

Muslim Puritans: Reformist Psychology in Southeast Asian Islam. James L. Peacock. LC 76-55571. 1978. 36.00x (ISBN 0-520-03403-1). U of Cal Pr.

Muslim Society. Ernest Geller. LC 80-41103. (Cambridge Studies in Social Anthropology: No. 32). 267p. 1983. pap. 12.95 (ISBN 0-521-27407-9). Cambridge U Pr.

Muslim Spain: Its History & Culture. Anwar G. Chejne. LC 73-87254. (Illus.). 616p. 1974. 32.50 (ISBN 0-8166-0688-9). U of Minn Pr.

Muslim Studies. Ignac Goldziher. Ed. & tr. by S. M. Stern. Incl. Vol. 1. Muhammedanische Studien. LC 67-20745. 1967. 44.50 (ISBN 0-87395-234-0); Vol. 2. Hadith: The 'Traditions', Ascribed to Muhammed. LC 72-11731. 1972. State U NY Pr.

Muslim Theologian's Response to Christianity: A Translation of Ibn Taymiyya's Jawab al-Sahih li-man Baddala din al-Masih. Ibn Taymiyah. Tr. by Thomas F. Michel. LC 83-15430. (Studies in Islamic Philosophy & Science). 60.00x (ISBN 0-88206-058-9). Caravan Bks.

Muslim Theology. Arthur S. Tritton. LC 79-2885. 218p. 1980. Repr. of 1947 ed. 22.00 (ISBN 0-8305-0052-9). Hyperion Conn.

Muslim Thought, Its Origin & Achievements. A. A. Shariff. pap. 10.50 (ISBN 0-317-46100-1). Kazi Pubns.

Muslim Tradition: Studies in Chronology, Provenance & Authorship of Early Hadith. G. H. Juynboll. LC 82-19778. (Cambridge Studies in Islamic Civilization). 264p. 1983. 62.50 (ISBN 0-521-25382-9). Cambridge U Pr.

Muslim Women: The Ideal & Contextual Realities. Ed. by Freeda Hussain. LC 83-11189. 240p. 1984. 22.50 (ISBN 0-312-55586-5). St Martin.

Muslim World. Richard Tames. LC 83-50694. (Religions of the World Ser.). 48p. 1983. 14.96 (ISBN 0-382-06719-3); pap. 9.25 (ISBN 0-382-06932-3). Silver.

Muslim World: A Historical Survey of Modern Times, Pt. IV, Fascicule 1. Ed. by Bertold Spuler. x, 370p. 1981. text ed. 49.95x (ISBN 90-04-06196-7, Pub. by E J Brill Holland). Humanities.

Muslim World: A Selected Bibliography on Its Socio-Economic Development. Akhtar H. Siddiq. (Public Administration Ser.: P 1372). 74p. 1984. pap. 11.25 (ISBN 0-88066-832-6). Vance Biblios.

Muslims & India's Freedom Movement. Ed. by B. K. Ahluwalia. 1985. 26.50x (ISBN 0-8364-1349-0, Pub. by Heritage India). South Asia Bks.

Muslims & Modernization. Sushila Jain. 1986. 27.50x (ISBN 81-7033-009-2, Pub. by Rawat). South Asia Bks.

Muslims, Christians & Jews in the Crusader Kingdom of Valencia: Societies in Symbiosis. Robert I. Burns. LC 83-2007. (Cambridge Iberian & Latin American Studies). 300p. 1984. 65.00 (ISBN 0-521-24374-2). Cambridge U Pr.

Muslims in China: A Study in Cultural Confrontation. Raphael Israeli. (Scandinavian Institute of Asian Studies: No. 29). 272p. 1981. pap. text ed. 17.50x (ISBN 0-391-00718-1, Pub. by Curzon Pr UK). Humanities.

Muslims in India: A Bibliography of Their Religious, Socio-Economic & Political Literature. Satyaprakash. 1986. 34.00x (ISBN 0-8364-1558-2, Pub. by Indian Doc Serv India). South Asia Bks.

Muslims in India: A Biographical Dictionary, Vol. II. Ed. by Naresh K. Jain. 1984. 40.00x (ISBN 0-8364-1150-1, Pub. by Manohar India). South Asia Bks.

Muslims in the West: The Message & the Mission. Abul H. Nadwi. Ed. by Khurram Murad. 191p. (Orig.). 1983. pap. 6.95x (ISBN 0-86037-130-1, Pub by Islamic Found UK). New Era Pubns MI.

Muslims of British India. P. Hardy. LC 77-184772. (South Asian Studies: No. 13). (Illus.). 300p. 1973. pap. 15.95 o. p. (ISBN 0-521-09783-5). Cambridge U Pr.

Muslims of British India. Peter Hardy. LC 77-184772. (Cambridge South Asian Studies: No. 13). pap. 79.30 (ISBN 0-317-27996-3, 2025585). Bks Demand UMI.

Muslim's Reflections on Democratic Capitalism. Muhammad Abdul-Rauf. 1984. pap. 4.95 (ISBN 0-8447-3537-X). Am Enterprise.

Must Christians Suffer? Kenneth E. Hagin. 1982. pap. 1.50 (ISBN 0-89276-404-X). Hagin Ministries.

Must Walls Divide? The Creative Witness of the Churches in Europe. James E. Will. (Orig.). 1981. pap. 3.75 (ISBN 0-377-00106-6). Friend Pr.

Must We Choose Sides? Ed. by Harry Strharsky. (Christian Committment for the '80s: Vol. 1). (Illus.). 128p. (Orig.). 1980. pap. 5.95 (ISBN 0-936476-01-X). Inter-Religious Task.

Mustard Seed. rev. ed. Bhagwan Shree Rajneesh. Ed. by Swami Krishna Prabhu. LC 84-43009. (Jesus Ser.). 560p. 1984. pap. 5.95 (ISBN 0-88050-595-8). Chidvilas Found.

Mustard Seed Conspiracy. Tom Sine. 1981. 7.95 (ISBN 0-8499-2939-3). Word Bks.

Mutu Finds the Way to Heaven. Sue Delaney. pap. 0.95 (ISBN 0-89985-996-8). Christ Nations.

Mutual Effects of the Islamic & Judeo-Christian Worlds: The East European Pattern. Ed. by A. Ascher et al. LC 77-90629. (Studies on Society in Change: No. 3). 1979. write for info (ISBN 0-930888-00-6). Brooklyn Coll Pr.

Mutual Irradiation: A Quaker View of Ecumenism. Douglas V. Steere. LC 73-146680. (Orig.). 1971. pap. 2.50x (ISBN 0-87574-175-4). Pendle Hill.

Mutual Ministry: New Vitality for the Local Church. James C. Fenhagen. 1986. 7.95 (ISBN 0-8164-0332-5, HarpR). Har-Row.

Muwata. Imam Malik & M. R. Din. 25.50 (ISBN 0-686-83588-3). Kazi Pubns.

Muybridge's Complete Human & Animal Locomotion: All 781 Plates from the 1887 Animal Locomotion, 3 vols. Eadweard Muybridge. Incl. Vol. 1. 33.34 (ISBN 0-486-23792-3); Vol. 2. 33.33 (ISBN 0-486-23793-1); Vol. 3. 33.33 (ISBN 0-486-23794-X). (Illus.). 1979. Repr. of 1887 ed. Set. 100.00. Dover.

My All for Him. Basilea Schlink. 160p. 1971. pap. 3.95 (ISBN 0-87123-370-3, 200370). Bethany Hse.

My Angel Will Go Before You. Georges Huber. Tr. by Michael Adams from Fr. Tr. of Mon Ange Marchera Devant Toi. 135p. 1983. pap. 9.95. Chr Classics.

My Answer to the Moscow's Bible. Richard Wurmbrand. pap. 4.95 (ISBN 0-88264-001-1). Diane Bks.

My Appetite Control. large print ed. Pearl Brians. 1985. pap. 6.00 (ISBN 0-914009-40-0). VHI Library.

My Baba & I. John S. Hislop. LC 85-61733. 1985. pap. 6.30 (ISBN 0-9600958-8-8). Birth Day.

My Baby Jesus Book. Patricia Mahany. (My Surprise Book Ser.). (Illus.). 12p. 1984. 4.95 (ISBN 0-87239-800-5, 2732). Standard Pub.

My Bad Temper. Dan Carr. (God I Need to Talk to You About...Ser.). (Illus.). 1984. pap. 0.75 (ISBN 0-570-08730-9, 56-1474). Concordia.

My Bar Mitzvah. Richard Rosenblum. LC 84-16685. (Illus.). 32p. 1985. 10.25 (ISBN 0-688-04143-4, Morrow Junior Books); PLB 10.88 (ISBN 0-688-04144-2, Morrow Junior Books). Morrow.

My Beginning Mass Book. JoAnn M. Angers. (Illus.). 32p. (Orig.). 1978. pap. 1.95 (ISBN 0-89622-082-6). Twenty-Third.

My Beloved Sisters. Spencer W. Kimball. LC 79-3620. 1979. 5.95 (ISBN 0-87747-798-1). Deseret Bk.

My Bible Alphabet. Maida Silverman. (Golden Storytime Book). (Illus.). 24p. 1987. pap. 2.95 (ISBN 0-307-11968-8, Golden Bks). Western Pub.

My Bible Book. Marian Bennett. (Wipe-Clean Bks.). (Illus.). 12p. 1985. pap. 1.39 (ISBN 0-87239-956-7, 3516). Standard Pub.

My Bible Number Book. Joyce Rottschafer. LC 81-50675. (Happy Day Book). (Illus.). 24p. (Orig.). 1981. pap. 1.59 (ISBN 0-87239-465-4, 3598). Standard Pub.

My Bible Says. Marilyn McAuley. (Peek & Find Bks.). (Illus.). 28p. 1984. board book 3.95 (ISBN 0-89191-877-9, 58776). Cook.

My Bible Story Picture Book. Brenda Mills. (Illus.). 128p. 1982. text ed. 12.95 (ISBN 0-89081-319-1). Harvest Hse.

My Bible Story Reader, 5 vols. Faris. pap. 2.95 ea. Schmul Pub Co.

My Book about Jesus. (Little Books to Treasure). (Illus.). 32p. 1985. 1.95 (ISBN 0-225-66388-0, HarpR). Har-Row.

My Book of Bible Rhymes. John Knapp, II. (Illus.). 1987. 11.95. Cook.

My Book of Bible Stories. Wanda Hayes. (Illus.). 1964. board cover 5.95 (ISBN 0-87239-240-6, 3047). Standard Pub.

My Book of Christmas Carols. Compiled by B. Rosenkrans. (All Aboard Bks.). (Illus.). 32p. 1986. pap. 1.95 (ISBN 0-448-19079-6, G&D). Putnam Pub Group.

My Book of Feelings. 1977. 6.95 (ISBN 0-8065-0585-0). Citadel Pr.

My Book of Gold & Other Writings. Loraine C. Frank. 1987. 6.95 (ISBN 0-533-07072-4). Vantage.

My Book of Gospel Treasures. Rhonda Schomas. (Illus.). 63p. (Orig.). 1980. pap. 3.95 (ISBN 0-87747-839-2). Deseret Bk.

My Book of Prayers. Helen Gompertz. (Illus.). 32p. 1986. pap. 3.95 (ISBN 0-8170-1104-8). Judson.

My Book of Prayers. Frances Matranga. (Happy Day Bks.). (Illus.). 24p. 1985. 1.59 (ISBN 0-87239-877-3, 3677). Standard Pub.

My Brothers Keeper? Pat Boone. 1975. pap. 1.75 (ISBN 0-89129-028-1). Jove Pubns.

My Calling: Here I Am Lord. Lyman Coleman. (Serendipity Ser.). (Orig.). 1981. pap. 4.95 leader's guide 64 pgs (ISBN 0-687-37336-0); pap. 1.25 student's bk 32 pgs (ISBN 0-687-37337-9). Abingdon.

My Calvary Road. Roy Hession. 1978. pap. 4.95 (ISBN 0-87508-262-9). Chr Lit.

My Child & God: Religious Education in the Family. Annamaria Zanzucchi. Ed. by Thomas Hartman. Tr. by Lenny Sczesniak. LC 78-52599. 100p. 1978. pap. 2.95 (ISBN 0-911782-31-1). New City.

My Child Within. Ruth Heil. LC 82-83901. 128p. 1983. pap. 5.95 (ISBN 0-89107-268-3). Good News.

My Church. J. B. Moody. 325p. 1974. Repr. of 1890 ed. 8.50 (ISBN 0-87921-030-3). Attic Pr.

My Comforters. Helen G. Brenneman. LC 66-13156. 80p. (Orig.). 1966. deluxe ed. 3.95 o. p. (ISBN 0-8361-1751-4); pap. 2.50 (ISBN 0-8361-1529-5). Herald Pr.

My Companion to Know, Love, & Serve. Rose M. Mangieri. LC 73-158919. (Know, Love, & Serve Catechisms Ser.). (Illus.). 85p. (Orig.). 1977. pap. 5.50 (ISBN 0-913382-45-0, 103-7). Prow Bks-Franciscan.

My Confirmation Book. Randolph E. Haugan. (Illus.). 1942. pap. 2.50 ea. (ISBN 0-8066-0078-0, 10-4631). Augsburg.

My Confirmation Journal. Bill Coleman & Patty Coleman. 95p. 1979. pap. 3.95 (ISBN 0-89622-114-8). Twenty-Third.

My Conscience Speaks. Ed. by Constance McKenna et al. (Illus.). 48p. 1981. pap. 1.00 (ISBN 0-915365-05-7). Cath Free Choice.

My Conversion to Christ. Paul Photiou. Ed. by Orthodox Christian Educational Society. (Gr., Orig.). 1970. Repr. of 1952 ed. 0.50x (ISBN 0-938366-41-6). Orthodox Chr.

My Country Right or Wrong? Selective Conscientious Objection in the Nuclear Age. Eileen P. Flynn. 1985. pap. 3.95 (ISBN 0-317-18110-6). Loyola.

My Creator, My Friend. Bruce Larson. 192p. 1986. 10.95 (ISBN 0-8499-0458-7). Word Bks.

My Credo. Cornelius Van Til. 1971. pap. 3.50 (ISBN 0-87552-490-7). Presby & Reformed.

My Dateless Diary. R. K. Narayan. 1960. pap. 3.25 (ISBN 0-86578-118-4). Ind-US Inc.

My Diary Secrets by Mrs. Lindsay. Lindsay. 3.95 (ISBN 0-89985-021-9). Christ Nations.

My Doctrine Book. George Douma. pap. 2.25 (ISBN 0-686-23469-3). Rose Pub MI.

My Duel with the Vatican: The Autobiography of a Catholic Modernist. Alfred F. Loisy. Tr. by Richard W. Boynton. 1968. Repr. of 1924 ed. lib. bdg. 22.50 (ISBN 0-8371-0148-4, LODV). Greenwood.

My Ego, Higher Self & I. Jerry Hirschfield. 281p. (Orig.). 1986. pap. 11.95 (ISBN 0-87418-014-7, 151). Coleman Pub.

My Enemy Is My Guest. J. Massyngbaerd Ford. LC 84-5812. 192p. 1984. pap. 9.95 (ISBN 0-88344-348-1). Orbis Bks.

My Experience with Clinical Depression. rev. ed. Gerald F. Mundfrom. (Illus.). 184p. 1986. pap. 5.50x (ISBN 0-9615494-1-6). Mercy & Truth.

My Family. Hazel Morris. LC 85-24334. (Bible & Me Ser.). (Illus.). 1986. 5.95 (ISBN 0-8054-4164-6). Broadman.

My Family Seder. Norma Simon. (Festival Series of Picture Story Books). (Illus.). 1961. plastic cover 4.50 (ISBN 0-8381-0710-9, 10-710). United Syn Bk.

My Father. Maria Rasputin. 1970. 5.00 (ISBN 0-8216-0120-2). Univ Bks.

My Father, Edward Bransten: His Life & Letters. Frances Rothman. (Illus.). 109p. 1983. pap. 5.00 (ISBN 0-943376-18-1). Magnes Mus.

My Father I Trust You. Basilea Schlink. 1976. pap. 1.00 (ISBN 3-87209-617-6). Evang Sisterhood Mary.

My Father-in-Law: Memories of Karl Barth. Max Zellweger-Barth. Tr. by Martin Rumscheidt from Ger. (Princeton Theological Monograph Ser.: No. 5). Tr. of Mein Schwiegervater. (Orig.). 1986. pap. 6.00 (ISBN 0-915138-84-0). Pickwick.

My Father My Teacher: A Spiritual Journey. Nichiko Niwano. Tr. by Richard L. Gage from Jap. 143p. (Orig.). 1982. pap. 3.50 (ISBN 4-333-01095-0, Pub. by Kosei Pub Co Japan). C E Tuttle.

My Father Took Me to the Circus: Religious Life from Within. Prue Wilson. 144p. 1985. pap. 5.95 (ISBN 0-87193-218-0). Dimension Bks.

My Father's Business: Creating a New Future for the People of God. Louis De Thomasis. 168p. (Orig.). 1984. pap. 6.95 (ISBN 0-87061-107-0). Chr Classics.

My Father's Testament. David Nyvall. 1974. pap. 5.95 (ISBN 0-910452-20-2). Covenant.

My Favorite Bible Stories. Allan H. Jahsmann. LC 67-15957. 1967. 5.95 (ISBN 0-570-03415-9, 56-1064). Concordia.

My Favorite Prayers & Reflections. Daughters of St. Paul. 1973. plastic bdg. 5.00 (ISBN 0-8198-0276-X). Dghtrs St Paul.

My Favorite Reflections. Charles W. Turner. pap. 1.75 (ISBN 0-88469-029-6). BMH Bks.

My Favorite Verse. Cynthia Clawson. LC 86-73189. (My Favorite Verse Ser.). 24p. 1987. pap. 4.95 (ISBN 0-89636-222-1). Accent Bks.

My Favorite Verse. Jerry Falwell. LC 86-72750. (My Favorite Verse Ser.). 24p. 1987. pap. 4.95 (ISBN 0-89636-235-3). Accent Bks.

My Favorite Verse. Harold Sala. LC 86-72986. (My Favorite Verse Ser.). 24p. 1987. pap. 4.95 (ISBN 0-89636-228-0). Accent Bks.

My Favorite Verse. Luci Swindoll. LC 85-73591. (My Favorite Verse Ser.). 24p. 1986. pap. 4.95 (ISBN 0-89636-204-3). Accent Bks.

My Favorite Verse: Favorite Ser. Ann K. Anderson. LC 85-70000. 24p. 1986. pap. 4.95 (ISBN 0-89636-209-4). Accent Bks.

My "Feel Good" Secrets. Leila M. Ashton. (My Church Teaches Ser.). (Illus.). 1978. pap. 1.50 (ISBN 0-8127-0178-X). Review & Herald.

My First Bible Board Books. Incl. Noah & the Ark (ISBN 0-528-82490-2); Baby Jesus (ISBN 0-528-82491-0); Daniel in the Lion's Den (ISBN 0-528-82492-9); Joseph & His Brothers (ISBN 0-528-82493-7); Jesus Our Friend (ISBN 0-528-82494-5); Jonah & the Great Fish (ISBN 0-528-82495-3). 14p. 1984. pap. 2.95 ea. Macmillan.

My First Bible Wordbook. Russell. 1984. 8.95 (ISBN 0-528-82421-X). Macmillan.

My First Book about Baptism. H. Roger Bothwell. (My Church Teaches Ser.). (Illus.). 1978. pap. 1.95 (ISBN 0-8127-0179-8). Review & Herald.

My First Book About Communion. H. Roger Bothwell. (My Church Teaches Ser.). (Illus.). 1978. pap. 1.95 (ISBN 0-8127-0180-1). Review & Herald.

My First Book about Jesus. Walter Wangerin, Jr. 1984. 8.95 (ISBN 0-528-82403-1). Macmillan.

My First Book of Mitzvos. Isaiah Karlinsky & Ruth Karlinsky. (Illus.). 1986. 7.95 (ISBN 0-87306-388-0). Feldheim.

My First Communion. Dorothy Haas. Ed. by Kathleen Tucker. (Illus.). 48p. 1987. PLB 9.25 (ISBN 0-8075-5331-X). A Whitman.

My First Haggadah. new ed. Lois E. Rakov. (Illus.). 1978. 3.95 (ISBN 0-87243-075-8). Templegate.

My First Prayer Book. (Little Books To Treasure). (Illus.). 32p. 1985. 1.95 (ISBN 0-225-66387-2, HarpR). Har-Row.

My First SDA Camp Meeting. large print ed. Pearl Brians. 44p. 1985. pap. 6.00 (ISBN 0-914009-27-3). VHI Library.

My First Two Thousand Years. George S. Viereck & Paul Eldridge. 1984. Repr. 25.00 (ISBN 0-911378-16-2). Sheridan.

My Flute. Sri Chinmoy. (Orig.). 1972. pap. 3.00 (ISBN 0-88497-227-5). Aum Pubns.

My Friend Consider. Dru A. Kenner. LC 84-51459. 100p. (Orig.). 1985. pap. 4.95 (ISBN 0-930551-00-1). Vistara Pubns.

My Friend God: This Amazing Universe! Who Made It? Theron A. Newell. LC 82-73698. (Illus.). 92p. 1983. 9.95 (ISBN 0-9610080-0-8). Dentan Pr.

My Friend Jesus. Margaret Wyatt. LC 86-90051. (Illus.). 20p. (Orig.). 1986. pap. 2.25 (ISBN 0-9616117-0-7). M Wyatt.

My Friend, My Father. Stanley Burnshaw. (Galaxy Books). 160p. 1986. pap. 7.95 (ISBN 0-19-503723-5). Oxford U Pr.

My Friend Paul. Alfred Yale. 1986. pap. 8.25 (ISBN 0-8309-0433-6). Herald Hse.

My Friend Will. Charles F. Lummis. 1972. 3.50 (ISBN 0-87516-161-8). De Vorss.

My Friends. Bob Jones, Sr. (Illus.). 131p. 1983. pap. 3.95 (ISBN 0-89084-230-2). Bob Jones Univ Pr.

My Friends the Adventists. large print ed. Charline Brians. (Illus.). 57p. 1982. pap. 9.50 (ISBN 0-9608650-6-3). VHI Library.

My Generations: A Course in Jewish Family History. Arthur Kurzweil & Ruby Strauss. (Illus.). 128p. 1984. pap. 6.50x (ISBN 0-87441-383-4). Behrman.

My Glimpse of Eternity. B. Maltz. 128p. 3.50 (ISBN 0-8007-8363-8, Spire Bks). Revell.

My God & My All. Marion A. Habig. 1977. 4.50 (ISBN 0-685-77278-0). Franciscan Herald.

My God Is Real. Dory Peters. 1984. pap. 3.95 (ISBN 0-938612-08-5). Revival Press.

My God Is Real. David Watson. LC 81-71343. 95p. 1982. pap. 4.95 (ISBN 0-89107-248-9). Good News.

My God, My Life. 71p. pap. 5.95 (ISBN 0-9616007-0-5). M F Turner Pub.

My God, Why? A Mastectomy from a Husbands Point of View. Jim Pollnow. LC 79-55888. 127p. 1980. pap. 2.95x (ISBN 0-9603708-0-3). J L Pollnow.

My Good Shepherd Bible Story Book. A. C. Mueller. LC 70-89876. 1969. bds. 12.50 (ISBN 0-570-03400-0, 56-1126). Concordia.

My Grace Is Sufficient: Devotional Thoughts for Hospital Patients. Cornelius Oldenburg. (Solace Ser.). 1983. pap. 1.25 (ISBN 0-8010-6705-7). Baker Bk.

My Guru & His Disciple. Christopher Isherwood. 352p. 1981. pap. 4.95 (ISBN 0-14-005837-0). Penguin.

My Hand in His. rev. ed. Herman W. Gockel. LC 60-15577. 1975. pap. 6.50 (12-2613). Concordia.

My Hand in His. J. G. Malphurs. 1961. 5.00 (ISBN 0-88027-012-8). Firm Foun Pub.

My Head Is Bloody But Unbowed. Matsu Crawford. 111p. (Orig.). 1983. pap. 5.00 (ISBN 0-9612862-0-2). R E F Typesetting Pub.

My Healing Secrets. Boris R. Chaitow. 128p. 1980. 14.95 (ISBN 0-8464-1066-4). Beekman Pubs.

My Heart a Hiding Place. Paul Lee. 1986. pap. 7.95 (ISBN 0-87508-316-1). Chr Lit.

My Heart-Christ's Home. rev. ed. Robert B. Munger. 32p. 1986. pap. 0.75 (ISBN 0-87784-075-X). Inter-Varsity.

My Heart Is Happy. Dick Hilliard. LC 79-64822. 1979. pap. 4.95 (ISBN 0-89390-008-7). Resource Pubns.

My Heart Speaks to Thee, Vol. 1. Ed. by Carolyn E. Cardwell. (Illus.). 250p. 1985. pap. 8.45 (ISBN 0-916395-02-2, MH-1). Hieroglyphics.

My Heart Speaks to Thee, Vol. 2. Ed. by Carolyn E. Cardwell. (Illus.). 250p. (Orig.). 1985. pap. 8.45 (ISBN 0-916395-05-7, MH-2). Hieroglyphics.

My Holiday Story Book. rev. ed. Morris Epstein. 1958. pap. 4.50x (ISBN 0-87068-368-3). Ktav.

My Hopes Were Shattered at Age Six: Read How God Blessed Me. Ida B. Scott. 1981. 4.95 (ISBN 0-8062-1837-1). Carlton.

My Imprisonment. John Bunyan. pap. 1.75 (ISBN 0-686-64391-7). Reiner.

My Jesus Book. Wanda Hayes. (Illus.). 32p. 1963. pap. 5.95 (ISBN 0-87239-239-2, 3046). Standard Pub.

My Jesus Pocketbook of a Very Special Birth Day. Stirrup Associates Inc. Ed. by Bonnie C. Harvey & Cheryl M. Phillips. LC 84-50919. (My Jesus Pocketbook Ser.). (Illus.). 32p. 1984. pap. 0.49 (ISBN 0-937420-15-8). Stirrup Assoc.

My Jesus Pocketbook of ABC's. Cynthia H. Fletcher. LC 81-80218. (Illus.). 32p. (Orig.). 1981. pap. 0.49 (ISBN 0-937420-01-8). Stirrup Assoc.

My Jesus Pocketbook of Daniel in the Lion's Den. Stirrup Associates Inc. Ed. by Bonnie C. Harvey & Cheryl M. Phillips. LC 84-50916. (My Jesus Pocketbook Ser.). (Illus.). 32p. (Orig.). 1984. pap. text ed. 0.49 (ISBN 0-937420-12-3). Stirrup Assoc.

My Jesus Pocketbook of God's Fruit. Ed. by Cheryl Phillips & Bonnie C. Harvey. LC 83-50194. (My Jesus Pocketbook Ser.). (Illus.). 32p. 1983. pap. 0.49 (ISBN 0-937420-08-5). Stirrup Assoc.

My Jesus Pocketbook of Jonah & the Big Fish. Stirrup Associates, Inc. Ed. by Bonnie C. Harvey & Cheryl M. Phillips. LC 83-51679. (My Jesus Pocketbook Ser.). (Illus.). 32p. 1984. pap. 0.49 (ISBN 0-937420-09-3). Stirrup Assoc.

My Jesus Pocketbook of Li'l Critters. Stirrup Associates, Inc. Staff. Ed. by Cheryl M. Phillips. LC 82-63139. (Illus.). 32p. (Orig.). 1983. pap. text ed. 0.49 (ISBN 0-937420-05-0). Stirrup Assoc.

My Jesus Pocketbook of Manners. Stirrup Associates, Inc. Staff. Ed. by Cheryl M. Phillips. LC 82-63141. (Illus.). 32p. 1983. pap. 0.49 (ISBN 0-937420-06-9). Stirrup Assoc.

My Jesus Pocketbook of Noah & the Floating Zoo. Stirrup Associates, Inc. Ed. by Bonnie C. Harvey & Cheryl M. Phillips. LC 83-51680. (My Jesus Pocketbook Ser.). (Illus.). 32p. 1984. pap. 0.49 (ISBN 0-937420-10-7). Stirrup Assoc.

My Jesus Pocketbook of Scripture Pictures. Stirrup Associates, Inc. LC 82-80351. (Illus.). 32p. (Orig.). 1982. pap. 0.49 (ISBN 0-937420-02-6). Stirrup Assoc.

My Jesus Pocketbook of the Beginning. Stirrup Associates Inc. Ed. by Bonnie C. Harvey & Cheryl M. Phillips. LC 84-50918. (Jesus Pocketbook Ser.). (Illus.). 32p. (Orig.). 1984. pap. 0.49 (ISBN 0-937420-14-X). Stirrup Assoc.

My Jesus Pocketbook of the Big Little Person: The Story of Zacchaeus. Stirrup Associates Inc. Ed. by Cheryl M. Phillips & Bonnie C. Harvey. LC 84-50917. (My Jesus Pocketbook Ser.). (Illus.). 32p. 1984. pap. 0.49 (ISBN 0-937420-13-1). Stirrup Assoc.

My Jesus Pocketbook of the Lord's Prayer. Ed. by Cheryl M. Phillips & Bonnie C. Harvey. LC 83-50193. (My Jesus Pocketbook Ser.). (Illus.). 32p. 1983. pap. 0.49 (ISBN 0-937420-07-7). Stirrup Assoc.

My Jesus Pocketbook of the 23rd Psalm. Stirrup Associates, Inc. Staff. Ed. by Cheryl M. Phillips. LC 82-63140. (Illus.). 32p. (Orig.). 1983. pap. text ed. 0.49 (ISBN 0-937420-04-2). Stirrup Assoc.

My Jewish Brother Jesus. Rolf Gompertz. LC 76-55591. 200p. 1977. 15.00 (ISBN 0-918248-03-5); pap. 10.00 (ISBN 0-918248-02-7). Word Doctor.

My Jewish Holidays. Azriel Eisenberg & Jessie B. Robinson. 208p. 3.95x (ISBN 0-8381-0176-3, 10-176). United Syn Bk.

My Jewish Home: Sinchah Ba'ambatyah - Fun in the Bathtub. Martin Lemelman. (Illus.). 10p. 1987. polyvinyl 3.95 (ISBN 0-8074-0327-X). UAHC.

My Journal. 2nd ed. Narcissa Whitman. 74p. 1985. 7.50 (ISBN 0-87770-348-5); pap. 4.95; pap. 9.95. Ye Galleon.

My Journey Homeward. Walter Trobisch. 140p. (Orig.). 1986. pap. 4.95 (ISBN 0-89283-299-1, Pub. by Vine Books). Servant.

My Journey into God's Realm of Light. Agnes M. Fenwick. 1974. 3.50 (ISBN 0-682-47865-2). Exposition Pr FL.

My Journey into Self Phase One. Diane K. Pike. LC 79-12179. 161p. 1979. pap. 4.95 (ISBN 0-916192-13-X). L P Pubns.

My Journey to Lhasa. Alexandra David-Neel. LC 85-47947. (Illus.). 320p. 1986. lib. bdg. 22.00x (ISBN 0-8070-5900-5); pap. 10.95 (ISBN 0-8070-5901-3, BP713). Beacon Pr.

My King. F. R. Havergal. pap. 2.25 (ISBN 0-685-88388-4). Reiner.

My Land & My People. 3rd ed. Tenzin Gyatso. (Illus.). 271p. 1983. Repr. of 1962 ed. 6.95. Potala.

My Life & the Story of the Gospel Hymns & of Sacred Songs & Solos. Ira D. Sankey. LC 72-1682. Repr. of 1907 ed. 32.50 (ISBN 0-404-08332-3). AMS Pr.

My Life as a Maine-iac. Muriel Young. Ed. by Constance Hunting. (Illus.). 150p. 1984. pap. 6.95 (ISBN 0-913006-30-0). Puckerbrush.

My Life for the Poor: Mother Teresa of Calcutta. Ed. by Jose L. Gonzalez & Jane Playfoot. 1987. pap. 2.95 (ISBN 0-345-33780-8, Pub. by Ballantine Epiphany). Ballantine.

My Life for the Poor: The Story of Mother Teresa in Her Own Words. Ed. by Jose L. Gonzalez-Balado & Janet Playfoot. LC 85-42787. 128p. 1985. 10.95 (ISBN 0-06-068237-X, HarpR). Har-Row.

My Life in Christ. Saint John of Kronstadt. Tr. by E. E. Goulaeff from Rus. LC 84-81775. 558p. 1984. 25.00 (ISBN 0-88465-018-9); pap. 20.00 (ISBN 0-88465-017-0). Holy Trinity.

My Life in Christ: A Momento of My Confirmation. S. H. Fenske. LC 76-5729. 1976. pap. 2.50 (ISBN 0-8100-0056-3, 16N0514). Northwest Pub.

My Life, My Destiny. Norman Gilmovsky. LC 82-46083. (Illus.). 320p. 1984. 22.50 (ISBN 0-317-02674-7, Cornwall Bks). Assoc Univ Prs.

My Life-Tree. Sri Chinmoy. 50p. (Orig.). 1975. pap. 2.00 (ISBN 0-88497-221-6). Aum Pubns.

My Life with Christ. Anthony J. Paone. LC 62-17359. 1962. pap. 4.95 (ISBN 0-385-03361-3, D185, Im). Doubleday.

My Life Without God. William J. Murray. LC 83-14269. 252p. 1984. pap. 5.95 (ISBN 0-8407-5884-7). Nelson.

My Listening Ears. Joanne E. De Jonge. LC 85-7372. (My Father's World Ser.). (Illus.). 144p. 1985. pap. 3.95 (ISBN 0-930265-09-2). CRC Pubns.

My Little Book of Prayer. Muriel Strode. 73p. 1942. pap. 1.95 (ISBN 0-87548-237-6). Open Court.

My Living Counselor: Daily Readings form the Living Bible. LC 76-43126. (Illus.). 736p. 1976. kivar bdg. 4.95 (ISBN 0-87788-573-7). Shaw Pubs.

My Lord & My God. Charles Allen. 48p. 1985. 6.95 (ISBN 0-8378-5083-5). Gibson.

My Lord Knows the Way. Austin B. Tucker. (Illus.). 80p. (Orig.). 1982. pap. 1.50 (ISBN 0-89323-036-7). Bible Memory.

My Lord of Belmont: A Biography of Leo Haid. Paschal M. Baumstein. (Illus.). xxii, 396p. 1985. 20.00 (ISBN 0-9614976-0-2). Archives Belmont.

My Lord, What a Morning: An Autobiography. Marian Anderson. 312p. Repr. of 1956 ed. lib. bdg. 39.00 (Pub. by Am Repr Serv). Am Biog Serv.

My Lord's Secrets Revealed. Sri Chinmoy. 102p. text ed. 10.00 (ISBN 0-88497-793-5); pap. 5.00 (ISBN 0-317-46895-2). Aum Pubns.

My Love Remembers. Betty R. Salls. pap. 1.75 (ISBN 0-686-12740-4). Grace Pub Co.

My Marks & Scars I Carry: The Story of Ernst Kisch. Thoburn T. Brumbaugh. (Bold Believers Ser.). 1969. pap. 0.95 (ISBN 0-377-84151-X). Friend Pr.

My Massbook. Daughters of St Paul. 1978. plastic bdg. 2.00 (ISBN 0-8198-0361-8); pap. 1.25 (ISBN 0-8198-0362-6). Dghtrs St Paul.

My Memories of Baha'u'llah: Ustad Muhammad-'Aliy-Salmani, the Barber. Ustad Muhammad-'Aliy-Salmani. Tr. by Marzieh Gail from Persian. (Illus.). xii, 148p. 1982. 11.95 (ISBN 0-933770-21-9). Kalimat.

My Million Faces. Wayne Ham & Marlene Ham. (World Religion Ser.). 74p. 1985. Set. pap. 3.00 (ISBN 0-8309-0415-8); Faces from India. pap. 3.00 (ISBN 0-8309-0416-6); Faces from the Orient. pap. 3.00 (ISBN 0-8309-0417-4); Faces fron the Eternal. pap. 3.00 (ISBN 0-8309-0418-2). Herald Hse.

My Music Workbook. Kenneth W. Osbeck. 144p. 1982. pap. 5.95x (ISBN 0-8254-3415-7). Kregel.

My Name Is Christian Woman. Mary H. Wallace. LC 85-31575. (Illus., Orig.). 1982. pap. 6.95 (ISBN 0-912315-20-2). Word Aflame.

My Name Is Nabil. Wendy Heller. (Illus.). 48p. 1981. 5.95 (ISBN 0-933770-17-0). Kalimat.

My Neighbors, the Billy Grahams. Betty Frist. LC 83-70368. 1983. 8.95 (ISBN 0-8054-7229-0). Broadman.

My New Life with Christ: Baptismal Certificate. Dana Eynon. (Certificate Booklets Ser.). (Illus.). 16p. 1982. pap. 0.95 self-cover (ISBN 0-87239-529-4, 1177). Standard Pub.

My New Sister, the Bully. Deane Durrett. 128p. 1985. 7.95 (ISBN 0-687-27551-2). Abingdon.

My Oneness with God. Josephine C. Natividad. 1984. 8.95 (ISBN 0-533-05995-X). Vantage.

My Other Self. Clarence Enzler. pap. 5.95 (ISBN 0-87193-056-0). Dimension Bks.

My Own Hanukah Story. Daniel D. Stuhlman. (Illus., Orig.). 1980. pap. 3.95 personalized version (ISBN 0-934402-07-8); decorations 1.00 (ISBN 0-934402-08-6); trade version 2.50 (ISBN 0-934402-12-4). BYLS Pr.

My Own Pesah Story. Daniel D. Stuhlman. (My Own Holiday Stories: No. 2). (Illus., Orig.). 1981. Personalized Version. pap. 3.95x (ISBN 0-934402-09-4); Trade Version. pap. 3.00 (ISBN 0-934402-10-8); Seder cards 1.50 (ISBN 0-934402-11-6). BYLS Pr.

My Own Special Body. Christine Tangvald. (I Am Special Bks.). (Illus.). 20p. 1985. pap. 3.95 (ISBN 0-89191-903-1, 59030). Cook.

My People: Abba Eban's History of the Jews, Vol. II. David Bamberger. (Illus.). 1979. pap. 6.95x (ISBN 0-87441-280-3); tchr's guide by Geoffrey Horn 12.50 (ISBN 0-87441-341-9). Behrman.

My People: Abba Eban's History of the Jews, Vol. I. David Bamberger. LC 77-10667. (Illus.). 1978. pap. text ed. 6.95x (ISBN 0-87441-263-3). Behrman.

My People: The Story of the Jews. Abba Eban. LC 68-27328. (Illus.). 1968. 25.00 (ISBN 0-87441-294-3). Behrman.

My Personal Experiences with the Poor Souls. Maria Simma. Tr. by M. Helena from Ger. 1978. 6.95 (ISBN 0-8199-0744-8). Franciscan Herald.

My Personal Fulfillment Plan Workbook. Roy E. Davis. 32p. 1984. pap. 3.95 (ISBN 0-317-20868-3). CSA Pr.

My Personal Pentecost. Martha Koch & Roy Koch. LC 77-79229. 296p. 1977. pap. 4.95 (ISBN 0-8361-1816-2). Herald Pr.

My Personal Pentecost. Rodney Lensch. 60p. (Orig.). 1972. pap. 1.25 (ISBN 0-89228-025-5). Impact Bks MO.

My Personal Prayer Diary. Catherine Marshall & Leonard Le Sourd. (Epiphany Bks.). 1983. pap. 3.95 (ISBN 0-345-30612-0). Ballantine.

My Picture Bible to See & to Share. V. Gilbert Beers. 1982. text ed. 11.95 (ISBN 0-88207-818-6, Sonflower Bks). SP Pubns.

My Picture Bible to See & to Share. V. Gilbert Beers. 1982. text ed. 12.95 (ISBN 0-88207-818-6). Victor Bks.

My Picture Missal. Lawrence G. Lovasik. (Saint Joseph Picture Bks.). (Illus.). flexible bdg. 0.95 (ISBN 0-89942-275-6, 275). Catholic Bk Pub.

My Pilgrimage for Peace. George Lansbury. Bd. with Peace Through Economic Cooperation. George Lansbury. LC 70-147723. (Library of War & Peace; Peace Leaders: Biographies & Memoirs). 1972. lib. bdg. 46.00 (ISBN 0-8240-0251-2). Garland Pub.

My Prayer Book. Daughters of St Paul. 1978. plastic bdg. 2.00 (ISBN 0-8198-0359-6); pap. 1.25 (ISBN 0-8198-0360-X). Dghtrs St Paul.

My Prayer Book. 235p. 1983. 4.50 (ISBN 0-570-03059-5, 06-1184). Concordia.

My Prayer Journal. Ronald Klug. LC 12-2964. 1982. pap. 3.95 (ISBN 0-570-03871-5). Concordia.

My Promise to God. Sri Chinmoy. 50p. (Orig.). 1975. pap. 2.00 (ISBN 0-88497-222-4). Aum Pubns.

My Quest: Voices from the Heart. William J. Crockett. 15p. 1985. pap. 3.00 (ISBN 0-934383-32-4). Pride Prods.

My Redeemer Lives. Emmeline S. Miller. 1982. 4.35 (ISBN 0-89536-529-4, 1315). CSS of Ohio.

My Religion. M. K. Gandhi. Ed. by B. Kumarappa. 178p. (Orig.). 1983. pap. 5.00 (ISBN 0-934676-54-2). Greenlf Bks.

My Religion. Emil G. Hirsch. Ed. by Gerson B. Levi. Incl. Crucifixion Viewed from a Jewish Standpoint (1908. LC 73-2207. (Jewish People; History, Religion, Literature Ser.). Repr. of 1925 ed. 33.00 (ISBN 0-405-05271-5). Ayer Co Pubs.

My Religion. Helen Keller. LC 74-11654. 1972. pap. 2.95 (ISBN 0-87785-103-4); Span. ed. leatherette o.s.i. 5.00 (ISBN 0-87785-114-X). Swedenborg.

My Religion: Large Print Edition. Helen Keller. LC 74-11645. 1979. 4.75 (ISBN 0-87785-158-1). Swedenborg.

My Response. Luis Palau. 1985. pap. 3.95 (ISBN 0-8024-8782-3). Moody.

My Room at Church. Anita Hale. LC 85-24344. (Bible & Me Ser.). (Illus.). 1986. 5.95 (ISBN 0-8054-4168-9). Broadman.

My Sabbath Fun Book. Cecilia Watson. 1983. Bk. 1. pap. 4.95 ea. Bk. 2 (ISBN 0-8163-0463-7). Pacific Pr Pub Assn.

My Search for Absolutes: A Credo Perspective. Paul Tillich. Ed. by Ruth N. Anshen. (Illus.). 1984. pap. 6.95 (ISBN 0-671-50585-8, Touchstone Bks). S&S.

My Sermon Notes, 4 vols. Charles H. Spurgeon. (Spurgeon Library). 1981. Set. pap. 21.95 (ISBN 0-8010-8201-3); pap. 5.95 ea. Baker Bk.

My Servants the Prophets. Edward J. Young. 1952. pap. 8.95 (ISBN 0-8028-1697-5). Eerdmans.

My Servants the Prophets, Vol. 1. John T. Willis. LC 76-180789. (Way of Life Ser.: No. 116). 1971. pap. 3.95 (ISBN 0-89112-116-1, Bibl Res Pr). Abilene Christ U.

My Servants the Prophets, Vol. 3. John T. Willis. LC 76-180789. (Way of Life Ser.: No. 118). (Orig.). 1972. pap. 3.95 (ISBN 0-89112-118-8, Bibl Res Pr). Abilene Christ U.

My Servants the Prophets, Vol. 4. John T. Willis. (Way of Life Ser.: No. 119). 1982. pap. 3.95 (ISBN 0-89112-119-6, Bibl Res Pr). Abilene Christ U.

My Sister Alma & I. Alonzo Baker. (Daybreak Ser.). 1981. pap. 4.50 (ISBN 0-8163-0373-8). Pacific Pr Pub Assn.

My Son, My Mother: Indestructible Chain of Love. Adalu Justus & Ira J. Marlin. LC 86-3884. 200p. (Orig.). 1986. pap. 7.95 (ISBN 0-937109-00-2). Silo Pubs.

My Son, My Son. Bernard Palmer. (Living Bks.). 288p. (Orig.). 1987. pap. 3.95 (ISBN 0-8423-4639-2). Tyndale.

My Soul Doth Magnify the Lord! rev. ed. Mark Prophet & Elizabeth Prophet. (Illus.). 350p. 1980. pap. 7.95 (ISBN 0-916766-35-7). Summit Univ.

My Soul Looks Back. James H. Cone. 144p. 1986. pap. 8.95 (ISBN 0-88344-355-4). Orbis Bks.

My Soul Thirsts Still. Zalman A. Hilsenrad. 1985. 13.95 (ISBN 0-87306-923-4). Feldheim.

My Special Book of Jewish Celebrations. Grace C. Mack. (Illus.). 36p. (Orig.). 1984. pap. 8.95 (ISBN 0-9602338-4-9). Rockdale Ridge.

My Special Place. Mrs. Bill Martin. 136p. 1980. pap. 5.95 (ISBN 0-89114-111-1). Baptist Pub Hse.

My Summer in a Mormon Village. F. Bailey. 59.95 (ISBN 0-8490-0692-9). Gordon Pr.

My Sweet Lord: The Hare Krishna Movement. Kim Knott. 112p. 1986. pap. 11.95. Newcastle Pub.

My Sweet Lord: The Hare Krishna Movement. Kim Knott. LC 86-18810. 176p. 1986. lib. bdg. 19.95x (ISBN 0-8095-7023-8). Borgo Pr.

My Synagogue. M. Weisser. (Illus.). 25p. 1984. pap. text ed. 2.95x (ISBN 0-87441-386-9). Behrman.

My Testimony. Ella M. Wilson. 70p. 1986. pap. 6.95 (ISBN 1-55523-060-1). Winston-Derek.

My Thank You Book. Wanda Hayes. (Illus.). 32p. 1964. 5.95 (ISBN 0-87239-241-4, 3048). Standard Pub.

My Triumphant Life. Harvey Childress. 1978. pap. 2.25 (ISBN 0-88027-087-X). Firm Foun Pub.

My Unusual Adventures on the Five Continents in Search for the Ageless. Edmond B. Szekely. (Search for the Ageless Ser.: Vol. 1). (Illus.). 212p. 1977. pap. 7.80 (ISBN 0-89564-022-8). IBS Intl.

My Very First Prayer-Time Book. Mary Fletcher. (Very First Bible Stories Ser.). 1984. 1.59 (ISBN 0-87162-274-2, D8503). Warner Pr.

My Very Own Chanukah Book. Judyth R. Saypol & Madeline Wikler. LC 77-23682. (Illus.). 32p. 1977. pap. 2.95 (ISBN 0-930494-03-2). Kar-Ben.

My Very Own Haggadah. Rev. ed. Judyth Saypol & Madeline Wikler. LC 83-6. (Illus.). 32p. pap. text ed. 2.95 (ISBN 0-930494-23-7). Kar Ben.

My Very Own Jewish Community. Judyth S. Groner & Madeline Wikler. LC 83-22215. (Illus.). 40p. 1984. pap. 4.95 (ISBN 0-930494-32-6). Kar Ben.

My Very Own Megillah. Judyth R. Saypol & Madeline Wikler. (Illus.). 32p. 1977. pap. 2.95 (ISBN 0-930494-01-6). Kar Ben.

My Very Own Simchat Torah. Illus. by Judyth Saypol & Madeline Wikler. (Illus.). 24p. 1981. pap. 2.95 (ISBN 0-930494-11-3). Kar Ben.

My Very Own Sukkot Book. Judyth R. Saypol & Madeline Wikler. LC 83-26738. (Illus.). 40p. 1980. pap. 2.95 (ISBN 0-930494-09-1). Kar Ben.

My Very Own Yom Kippur Book. Judyth R. Saypol & Madeline Wikler. (Illus.). 32p. 1978. pap. 2.95 (ISBN 0-930494-05-9). Kar Ben.

My Vocation, by Eminent Americans; or, What Eminent Americans Think of Their Callings. Compiled by Earl G. Lockhart. LC 72-5602. (Essay Index Reprint Ser.). 1972. Repr. of 1938 ed. 32.00 (ISBN 0-8369-2997-7). Ayer Co Pubs.

My Way: The Way of the White Clouds. rev. ed. Bhagwan Shree Rajneesh. Ed. by Swami Ananda Teertha. LC 79-2303. (Questions & Answers Ser.). (Illus.). 640p. 1975. 29.95 (ISBN 0-88050-096-4). Chidvilas Found.

My Wife the Prophetess. large print ed. Bert Brians. (Illus.). 55p. 1982. pap. 9.50 (ISBN 0-9608650-7-1). VHI Library.

My Wife the Prophetess. rev. ed. Ed. by Bert Brians. (Illus.). 24p. 1985. pap. 4.50 (ISBN 0-914009-73-7). VHI Library.

My Will Be Done. Clayton A. Parker. 201p. 1982. pap. 3.00 (ISBN 0-686-86578-2, 0-9606438). C A Parker Pubns.

My Wonderful Salvation. Harvey Childress. 1978. pap. 1.75 (ISBN 0-88027-088-8). Firm Foun Pub.

My World as a Jew, Vol. 1. Israel Goldstein. LC 82-42721. (Illus.). 352p. 1984. 27.50 (ISBN 0-8453-4765-9, Cornwall Bks). Assoc Univ Prs.

My World as a Jew, Vol. 2. Israel Goldstein. LC 82-42621. (Illus.). 416p. 1984. 27.50 (ISBN 0-8453-4780-2, Cornwall Bks). Assoc Univ Prs.

Mycenaean Origins of Greek Mythology. Martin P. Nilsson. 16.50 (ISBN 0-8446-6208-9). Peter Smith.

Mycenaean Origins of Greek Mythology. Martin P. Nilsson. (Sather Classical Lectures: Vol.80). 278p. 1983. pap. 7.95 (ISBN 0-520-05073-8, CAL 655). U of Cal Pr.

Myriam & the Mystic Brotherhood. Maude L. Howard. 370p. 1981. pap. 20.00 (ISBN 0-89540-105-3, SB-105). Sun Pub.

Myron Here. Myron C. Cole. LC 82-61064. (Illus.). 260p. (Orig.). 1983. pap. 5.00 (ISBN 0-935356-04-5). Mills Pub Co.

Myroure of Oure Lady. Ed. by J. H. Blunt. (EETS, ES Ser.: No. 19). Repr. of 1873 ed. 40.00 (ISBN 0-527-00232-1). Kraus Repr.

Mystere d'Israel. Jacques Maritain. 260p. 1965. 9.95 (ISBN 0-686-56358-1). French & Eur.

Mysteres d'Eleusis. facsimile ed. Paul F. Foucart. LC 75-10636. (Ancient Religion & Mythology Ser.). (Fr.). 1976. Repr. of 1914 ed. 37.50x (ISBN 0-405-07013-6). Ayer Co Pubs.

Mysteres Provencaux Du XVe Siecle. Repr. of 1893 ed. 35.00 (ISBN 0-384-40753-6). Johnson Repr.

Mysteries. John Allan. (Book of Beliefs). 1981. 9.95 (ISBN 0-89191-477-3, 54775). Cook.

Mysteries: Encounters with the Unexplained. John Blashford-Snell. 256p. 1984. 16.95 (ISBN 0-370-30479-9, Pub. by Bodley Head). Salem Hse Pubs.

Mysteries' End: An Investigation of the Last Days of the Medieval Religious Stage. Harold C. Gardiner. LC 67-26652. (Yale Studies in English Ser.: No. 103). xiv, 139p. 1967. Repr. of 1946 ed. 21.50 (ISBN 0-208-00385-1, Archon). Shoe String.

Mysteries of All Nations. James Grant. LC 79-150243. 1971. Repr. of 1880 ed. 70.00x (ISBN 0-8103-3391-0). Gale.

Mysteries of Almsgiving. Al-Ghazzali. Tr. by Nabik A. Faris. 1966. 12.95x (ISBN 0-8156-6002-2, Am U Beirut). Syracuse U Pr.

Mysteries of Almsgiving. N. A. Faris. pap. 4.50 (ISBN 0-686-18616-8). Kazi Pubns.

Mysteries of Chartres Cathedral. Louis Charpentier. 1980. pap. 1.75 (ISBN 0-380-00386-4, 24596). Avon.

Mysteries of Fasting. Al-Ghazzali. 1970. 3.50x (ISBN 0-87902-052-0). Orientalia.

Mysteries of Fasting. N. A. Faris. pap. 3.75 (ISBN 0-686-18615-X). Kazi Pubns.

Mysteries of Genesis. Charles Fillmore. 1936. 5.95 (ISBN 0-87159-104-9). Unity School.

Mysteries of God in the Universe: Including the Reincarnation & Karma in the Gathas, the Bible, & Koran, 2 vols. H. S. Spencer. Repr. of 1967 ed. Set. text ed. 35.00x. Coronet Bks.

Mysteries of John. Charles Fillmore. 1946. 5.95 (ISBN 0-87159-105-7). Unity School.

Mysteries of Life & Death. Acharya Rajneesh. Tr. by Malini Bisen from Hindi. 1978. pap. 3.50 (ISBN 0-89684-045-X, Pub. by Motilal Banarsidass India). Orient Bk Dist.

Mysteries of Mind. Yuvacharya Mahaprajna. 225p. 1982. 11.00 (ISBN 0-88065-223-3, Pub. by Messers Today & Tomorrow Printers & Publishers). Scholarly Pubns.

Mysteries of Mithra. 2nd ed. Franz Cumont. Tr. by Thomas J. McCormack. (Illus., Fr). 1911. pap. 5.95 (ISBN 0-486-20323-9). Dover.

Mysteries of Mithra. Franz Cumont. (Illus.). 14.00 (ISBN 0-8446-1926-4). Peter Smith.

Mysteries of Osiris: Egyptian Initiation. R. Swinburne Clymer. 287p. 1951. 8.95 (ISBN 0-932785-31-X). Philos Pub.

Mysteries of Purity. Al-Ghazzali. 1966. 4.50x (ISBN 0-87902-053-9). Orientalia.

Mysteries of Purity. N. A. Faris. pap. 4.75 (ISBN 0-686-18614-1). Kazi Pubns.

Mysteries of Religion: An Introduction to Philosophy through Religion. Stephen R. Clark. 288p. text ed. 45.00 (ISBN 0-631-13419-0); pap. text ed. 12.95 (ISBN 0-631-14295-9). Basil Blackwell.

Mysteries of the Creation. Dovid Brown. (Illus.). 400p. 1987. 19.99 (ISBN 0-939833-24-7). Mosdos Pubs.

Mysteries of the Holy Grail. Corinne Heline. pap. 3.95 (ISBN 0-87613-015-5). New Age.

Mysteries of the Holy Grail: Archangel Gabriel. Ed. by Elizabeth C. Prophet. LC 83-51154. (Illus.). 430p. 1984. pap. 12.95 (ISBN 0-916766-64-0). Summit Univ.

Mysteries of the Qabalah. Elias Gewurz. 1922. 4.50 (ISBN 0-911662-32-4). Yoga.

Mysteries of the Qabalah, or the Occult Agreement of the Two Testaments. Eliphas Levi. (Studies in Hermetic Tradition Ser.: Vol. 2). (Illus.). 1974. pap. 12.95 (ISBN 0-85030-274-9). Weiser.

Mysteries of the Rosary. Edith Myers. (Illus.). 41p. 1977. Repr. of 1968 ed. 2.50 (ISBN 0-912414-13-8). Stella Maris Bks.

Mysteries of the Unexplained. Reader's Digest Editors. LC 82-60791. (Illus.). 320p. 1983. 21.95 (ISBN 0-89577-146-2, Pub. by RD Assn). Random.

Mysteries of Worship in Islam. E. E. Calverley. 1981. 6.50 (ISBN 0-686-97865-X). Kazi Pubns.

Mysteries of Worship in Islam: The Book of the Ihya' on Worship Translated with Commentary & Introduction. Al Ghazzali. Tr. by E. E. Calverley. pap. 11.00 (ISBN 0-87902-200-0). Orientalia.

Mysteries of Yesod. Omraam M. Aivanhov. (Complete Works: Vol. 7). (Illus.). 217p. (Orig.). 1982. pap. 9.95 (ISBN 2-85566-109-9). Prosveta USA.

Mysterio de la Vide e de la Muerta. Jan Van Rijckenborgh. (Span.). 1987. pap. 2.00. Rosycross Pr.

Mysterious Alabaster Bottle. Elizabeth R. Handford & Joy R. Martin. 28p. (Orig.). 1987. pap. 1.50 (ISBN 0-912623-04-7). Joyful Woman.

Mysterious Encounters at Mamre & Jabbok. William T. Miller. (Brown Judaic Studies: No. 50). 252p. 1985. 24.95 (ISBN 0-89130-816-4, 14 00 50); pap. 18.25 (ISBN 0-89130-817-2). Scholars Pr GA.

Mysterious Fundamental Option. Theodore Hall. (Synthesis Ser.). 1979. 0.75 (ISBN 0-8199-0746-4). Franciscan Herald.

Mysterious Marvelous Snowflake. Harvey D. Moore & Patsie S. Moore. LC 80-20996. 128p. (Orig.). 1981. pap. 5.50 (ISBN 0-687-27640-3). Abingdon.

Mysterious Numbers of the Hebrew Kings. New rev. ed. Edwin R. Thiele. 256p. 1984. pap. 11.95 (ISBN 0-310-36011-0, 10116P). Zondervan.

Mystery & Lore of Apparitions, with Some Account of Ghosts, Spectres, Phantoms & Boggarts in Early Times. C. J. Thompson. LC 70-167225. (Illus.). 331p. 1975. Repr. of 1930 ed. 40.00x (ISBN 0-8103-3981-1). Gale.

Mystery & Miracle. Robert S. Bachelder. 1983. 3.00 (ISBN 0-89536-606-1, 1340). CSS of Ohio.

Mystery & Morality. Neil King. (Drama Ser.). pap. 8.95 (ISBN 0-7175-1231-2). Dufour.

Mystery & Mysticism. A. Pie et al. 1956. 5.95 (ISBN 0-8022-1988-8). Philos Lib.

Mystery & Philosophy. Michael B. Foster. LC 79-8721. (Library of Philosophy & Theology). 96p. 1980. Repr. of 1957 ed. lib. bdg. 24.75x (ISBN 0-313-20792-5, FOMP). Greenwood.

Mystery & Truth. John MacQuarrie. (Pere Marquette Theology Lectures). 1970. 6.95 (ISBN 0-87462-518-1). Marquette.

Mystery Doctrines of the New Testament: God's Sacred Secrets. T. Ernest Wilson. LC 74-78881. 128p. 1975. pap. text ed. 2.50 (ISBN 0-87213-962-X). Loizeaux.

Mystery Hid from All Ages & Generations. Charles Chauncy. LC 70-83414. (Religion in American, Ser. 1). 1969. Repr. of 1784 ed. 23.50 (ISBN 0-405-00235-1). Ayer Co Pubs.

Mystery Man of Darkness No. 666. Frank E. Stranges. 16p. 1985. pap. text ed. 2.00 (ISBN 0-933470-05-3). Intl Evang.

Mystery of... America's Future... Destruction... Revealed! Gilbert W. Rucker. 1985. 6.95 (ISBN 0-8062-2440-1). Carlton.

Mystery of Being, Vol. I: Reflection & Mystery. Gabriel Marcel. 238p. 1984. pap. text ed. 8.50 (ISBN 0-8191-3310-8). U Pr of Amer.

Mystery of Being, Vol. II: Faith & Reality. Gabriel Marcel. 198p. 1984. pap. text ed. 7.75 (ISBN 0-8191-3311-6). U Pr of Amer.

Mystery of Christian Hope. Jean Galot. LC 77-1222. 1977. 4.95 (ISBN 0-8189-0346-5). Alba.

Mystery of Creation. Watchman Nee. Tr. by Stephen Kaung. 1981. pap. 3.10 (ISBN 0-935008-52-7). Christian Fellow Pubs.

Mystery of Death. Ladislaus Boros. 216p. 1973. pap. 3.95 (ISBN 0-8245-0330-9). Crossroad NY.

Mystery of Faith: The Ministers of Music. Lawrence J. Johnson. 128p. (Orig.). 1983. pap. 5.95 (ISBN 0-9602378-9-5). Pastoral Pr.

Mystery of God: St. Augustine on the Trinity. Edmund Hill. (Catholic Theology Ser.). 200p. pap. 14.95 (ISBN 0-225-66470-4, HarpR). Har-Row.

Mystery of God's Providence. Paul Billheimer. 1983. pap. 3.95 (ISBN 0-8423-4664-3). Tyndale.

Mystery of Healing. Theosophical Research Centre, London. 1968. pap. 3.50 (ISBN 0-8356-0114-5, Quest). Theos Pub Hse.

Mystery of Holy Spirit. Manly P. Hall. pap. 2.50 (ISBN 0-89314-333-2). Philos Res.

Mystery of Humanity: Tranquilty & Survival. Molana-al-Moazam Hazrat Shah & Maghsoud Sadegh-ibn-Mohammad Angha. 74p. (Orig.). 1986. lib. bdg. 19.75 (ISBN 0-8191-5329-X); pap. text ed. 8.75 (ISBN 0-8191-5330-3). U Pr of Amer.

Mystery of Israel: An Exposition of Romans 9-11. 3rd ed. H. L. Ellison. 117p. 1976. pap. 4.95 (ISBN 0-85364-169-2). Attic Pr.

Mystery of Jeane Dixon. Gordon Lindsay. (Sorcery & Spirit World Ser.). 0.95 (ISBN 0-89985-084-7). Christ Nations.

Mystery of Jesus & of the Jewish People, 2 vols. Blaise Pascal. (Illus.). 245p. 1985. 207.50 (ISBN 0-89901-228-0). Found Class Reprints.

Mystery of Life & Death. Jan Van Rijckenborgh. Tr. by Lectorium Rosicrucianum. 50p. 1987. pap. 6.00. Rosycross Pr.

Mystery of Marriage: As Iron Sharpens Iron. Mike Mason. LC 85-3048. 190p. 1985. 10.95 (ISBN 0-88070-097-1). Multnomah.

Mystery of Peace. Arthur C. Cochrane. 224p. 1985. pap. 11.95 (ISBN 0-87178-695-8). Brethren.

Mystery of Providence. John Flavel. 1976. pap. 3.95 (ISBN 0-85151-104-X). Banner of Truth.

Mystery of Redemption. James B. Coffman. 1976. 5.95 (ISBN 0-88027-089-6). Firm Foun Pub.

Mystery of Salvation. Paul De Surgy. Tr. by Rosemary Sheed. 1966. pap. 6.95 (ISBN 0-268-00185-5). U of Notre Dame Pr.

Mystery of Stonehenge. Franklyn M. Branley. LC 69-11823. (Illus.). 1969. PLB 12.89 (ISBN 0-690-57046-5, Crowell Jr Bks). HarpJ.

Mystery of Stonehenge. Nancy Lyon. LC 77-10044. (Great Unsolved Mysteries). (Illus.). 1977. PLB 14.65 (ISBN 0-8172-1049-0). Raintree Pubs.

Mystery of Stonehenge. Nancy Lyon. LC 77-10044. (Great Unsolved Mysteries Ser.). (Illus.). 48p. 1983. pap. 9.27 (ISBN 0-8172-2164-6). Raintree Pubs.

Mystery of Suffering & Death. Ed. by Michael J. Taylor. LC 72-13294. 203p. 1973. pap. 5.95 (ISBN 0-8189-0263-9). Alba.

Mystery of the Beatitudes. Jan Van Rijckenborgh. 104p. (Orig.). 1987. pap. 10.50. Rosycross Pr.

Mystery of the Eucharist. Max Thurian. 88p. (Orig.). 1984. pap. 4.95 (ISBN 0-8028-0028-9). Eerdmans.

Mystery of the Gospel. A. E. Knoch. 297p. 1976. pap. text ed. 4.00 (ISBN 0-910424-55-1). Concordant.

Mystery of the Incarnation. Norman Anderson. LC 79-13879. 1979. pap. 3.95 (ISBN 0-87784-530-1). Inter-Varsity.

Mystery of the Kingdom of God. Joel Marcus. (Dissertation Ser.). 270p. 1986. 17.95 (ISBN 0-89130-983-7, 06-01-90); pap. 12.95 (ISBN 0-89130-984-5). Scholars Pr GA.

Mystery of the Kingdom of God: The Secret of Jesus' Messiahship & Passion. Albert Schweitzer. LC 85-60625. 174p. 1985. pap. 11.95 (ISBN 0-87975-294-7). Prometheus Bks.

Mystery of the Mind. Swami Muktananda. LC 81-50159. (Illus.). 64p. (Orig.). 1983. pap. 3.95 (ISBN 0-914602-70-5). SYDA Found.

Mystery of the Oracles: World Famous Archaeologists Reveal the Best Kept Secrets of Antiquity. Philipp Vandenberg. Tr. by George Unwin. (Illus.). 288p. 1982. 14.95 (ISBN 0-02-621590-X). Macmillan.

Mystery of the Ordinary: Discovering the Richness of Everyday Experiences. Charles Cummings. LC 81-47846. 144p. 1982. 9.57 (ISBN 0-06-061652-0, HarpR). Har-Row.

Mystery of the Soul: Katha Upanishad. Swami Jyotir Maya Nanda. (Illus.). 1976. pap. 1.99 (ISBN 0-934664-07-2). Yoga Res Foun.

Mystery of Transforming Love. Adrian Van Kaam. 6.95 (ISBN 0-87193-182-6). Dimension Bks.

Mystery of Womanhood. Debra Evans. LC 86-72262. 256p. (Orig.). 1987. pap. 8.95 (ISBN 0-89107-426-0, Crossway Bks). Good News.

Mystery Religions. Samuel Angus. LC 74-12637. 360p. 1975. pap. 6.95 (ISBN 0-486-23124-0). Dover.

Mystery Religions & Christianity. Samuel Angus. 1977. lib. bdg. 59.95 (ISBN 0-8490-2314-9). Gordon Pr.

Mystery Religions: In the Ancient World. Joscelyn Godwin. LC 81-47423. (Illus.). 180p. (Orig.). 1981. pap. 9.95 (ISBN 0-06-063140-6, CN4020, HarpR). Har-Row.

Mystery Teachings in World Religions. Florice Tanner. LC 73-8887. (Quest Book Original Ser). 160p. (Orig.). 1973. pap. 2.45 (ISBN 0-8356-0439-X, Quest). Theos Pub Hse.

Mystic Americanism or the Spiritual Heritage of America Revealed. R. Swineburn Clymer & Grace K. Morey. 328p. 1975. 7.95 (ISBN 0-932785-33-6). Philos Pub.

Mystic & Pilgrim: The "Book" & the World of Margery Kempe. Clarissa W. Atkinson. LC 82-22219. 248p. (Orig.). 1983. 27.50x (ISBN 0-8014-1521-7); pap. text ed. 8.95x (ISBN 0-8014-9895-3). Cornell U Pr.

Mystic Approach to the Veda & the Upanishad. M. P. Pandit. 4.25 (ISBN 0-89744-108-7, Pub. by Ganesh & Co. India). Auromere.

Mystic As a Force for Change. rev. ed. Sisirkumar Ghose. LC 80-53954. 144p. 1980. pap. 4.75 (ISBN 0-8356-0547-7, Quest). Theos Pub Hse.

Mystic Christianity. Yogi Ramacharaka. 8.00 (ISBN 0-911662-08-1). Yoga.

Mystic Experience. Bhagwan S. Rajneesh. Ed. by Ma A. Prem. Tr. by Dolly Diddee. 543p. 1977. text ed. 25.00 (ISBN 0-89684-292-4, Pub. by Motilal Banarsidass India). Orient Bk Dist.

Mystic Gnosis. J. M. Fisher. 1977. lib. bdg. 59.95 (ISBN 0-8490-2316-5). Gordon Pr.

Mystic Healers. Paris Flammonde. LC 73-91856. (Illus.). 256p. 1974. 8.95 (ISBN 0-8128-1680-3). Stein & Day.

Mystic Masonry & the Bible. Corinne Heline. pap. 1.00 (ISBN 0-87613-017-1). New Age.

Mystic of Liberation: A Portrait of Bishop Pedro Casaldaliga of Brazil. Teofilo Cabestrero. Tr. by Donald D. Walsh from Span. & Fr. LC 80-25402. Orig. Title: Dialogos en Mato Grosso con Pedro Casadaliga. (Illus.). 176p. (Orig.). 1981. pap. 7.95 (ISBN 0-88344-324-4). Orbis Bks.

Mystic, Rebel, Saint: A Study on St. Joan of the Cross. J. C. Nieto. (Illus.). 148p. (Orig.). 1979. pap. text ed. 38.00x (Pub. by Droz Switzerland). Coronet Bks.

Mystic Shrine Illustrated. 3.50 (ISBN 0-317-13711-5). Powner.

Mystic Spiral: Journey of the Soul. Jill Purce. (Art & Imagination Ser.). (Illus.). 128p. 1980. pap. 10.95 (ISBN 0-500-81005-2). Thames Hudson.

Mystic Spiral: Journey of the Soul. Jill Purce. 1983. 17.00 (ISBN 0-8446-5993-2). Peter Smith.

Mystic Test Book. Olney H. Richmond. (Orig.). 1983. pap. 9.95 (ISBN 0-87877-064-X). Newcastle Pub.

Mystic Vision in the Grail Legend & in the Divine Comedy. Lizette A. Fisher. LC 79-168029. Repr. of 1917 ed. 16.50 (ISBN 0-404-02389-4). AMS Pr.

Mystic Will. Charles G. Leland. 1976. Repr. of 1907 ed. 6.00 (ISBN 0-911662-58-8). Yoga.

Mystical & Ethical Experience. Gerry C. Heard. LC 84-29569. viii, 82p. 1985. 8.50 (ISBN 0-86554-149-3, MUP/H140). Mercer Univ Pr.

Mystical & Mythological Explanatory Works of Assyrian & Babylonian Scholars. Alasdair Livingstone. 280p. 1986. 55.00x (ISBN 0-19-815462-3). Oxford U Pr.

Mystical & Visionary Treatises of Shihabuddin Yahya Suhrawardi. Shihabuddin Yahya Suhrawardi. Tr. by W. H. Thackston, Jr. 1982. 16.95 (ISBN 0-900860-92-8, Pub. by Octagon Pr England). Ins Study Human.

Mystical Babylon. 31p. (Orig.). pap. 0.95 (ISBN 0-937408-21-2). GMI Pubns Inc.

Mystical Body of Christ. John H. Collins. 1977. 2.00 (ISBN 0-8198-0435-5); pap. 0.95 (ISBN 0-8198-0436-3). Dghtrs St Paul.

Mystical Christ. Manly P. Hall. 10.95 (ISBN 0-89314-514-9). Philos Res.

Mystical City of God: A Popular Abridgement. abr. ed. Mary Agreda. Tr. by Fiscar Marison & George J. Blatter. LC 78-62255. 1978. pap. 15.00 (ISBN 0-89555-070-9). TAN Bks Pubs.

Mystical Consciousness: Exploring an Extraordinary State of Awareness. Martin V. Riccardo. 1977. pap. 5.00 (ISBN 0-686-19170-6). MVR Bks.

Mystical Design of "Paradise Lost". Galbraith M. Crump. 194p. 1975. 18.00 (ISBN 0-8387-1519-2). Bucknell U Pr.

Mystical Dimensions of Islam. Annemarie Schimmel. LC 73-16112. (Illus.). xxi, 506p. 1975. 30.00x (ISBN 0-8078-1223-4); pap. 8.95x (ISBN 0-8078-1271-4). U of NC Pr.

Mystical Element in Heidegger's Thought. John D Caputo. LC 77-92251. xvi, 292p. 1978. 28.95x (ISBN 0-8214-0372-9). Ohio U Pr.

Mystical Element in Heidegger's Thought. rev. ed. John D. Caputo. xxviii, 292p. 1986. pap. 12.50 (ISBN 0-8232-1153-3). Fordham.

Mystical Element in the Metaphysical Poets of the Seventeenth Century. Itrat-Husain. LC 66-23522. 1948. 15.00 (ISBN 0-8196-0177-2). Biblo.

Mystical Element of Religion As Studied in Saint Catherine of Genoa & Her Friends, 2 vols. F. Von Huegel. 1977. lib. bdg. 200.00 (ISBN 0-8490-2317-3). Gordon Pr.

Mystical Elements in Mohammed. John C. Archer. LC 80-26396. (Yale Oriental Ser. Researches: No. 11 Pt. 1; All Published). Repr. of 1924 ed. 22.50 (ISBN 0-404-60281-9). AMS Pr.

Mystical Evolution, 2 vols. John G. Arintero. Tr. by Jordan Aumann from Sp. LC 78-62254. Orig. Title: Evolucion Mistica. 1979. Set. pap. 24.00 (ISBN 0-89555-071-7); Vol. I. pap. (ISBN 0-89555-072-5); Vol. II. pap. (ISBN 0-89555-073-3). TAN Bks Pubs.

Mystical Experience & Religious Doctrine: An Investigation of the Study of Mysticism in World Religions. Philip C. Almond. (Religion & Reason: No. 26). 197p. 1982. text ed. 40.00 (ISBN 90-279-3160-7). Mouton.

Mystical Experience in Abraham Abulafia. Moshe Idel. (SUNY Series in Judaica: Hermeneutics, Mysticism & Religion). 240p. 1987. text ed. 39.50x (ISBN 0-88706-552-X); pap. 12.95x (ISBN 0-88706-553-8). State U NY Pr.

Mystical Ferryboat. Stuart Perrin. (Metaphysics Ser.). 121p. (Orig.). 1987. 12.95 (ISBN 0-943920-67-1); pap. price not set (ISBN 0-943920-64-7). Metamorphous Pr.

Mystical I. Joel S. Goldsmith. Ed. by Lorraine Sinkler. LC 73-149745. 1971. 10.45 (ISBN 0-06-063195-3, HarpR). Har-Row.

Mystical Life of Jesus. 25th ed. H. Spencer Lewis. LC 54-20988. 1982. 11.95 (ISBN 0-912057-06-8, G-503). AMORC.

Mystical Life of Jesus. H. Spencer Lewis. LC 54-20988. (Illus.). 320p. 1986. pap. 9.95 (ISBN 0-912057-46-7, G-658). AMORC.

Mystical Marriage of Science & Spirit. Frances Paelian. LC 81-70272. (Illus.). 200p. 1981. pap. 11.95 (ISBN 0-918936-11-X). Astara.

Mystical Meaning of Jesus the Christ: Significant Episodes in the Life of the Master. 2nd ed. Helen Brungardt. (Illus.). 64p. 1983. pap. 5.00 (ISBN 0-941992-03-9). Los Arboles Pub.

Mystical Philosophy of Muhyid Din Ibn-Ul-Arabi. A. E. Affifi. 1964. 12.00x (ISBN 0-87902-035-0). Orientalia.

Mystical Philosophy of Muhyid Din-Ibnul 'Arabi. Abul E. Affifi. LC 77-180312. (Mid-East Studies). Repr. of 1939 ed. 12.00 (ISBN 0-404-56205-1). AMS Pr.

Mystical Poets of the English Church. Percy H. Osmond. LC 72-5166. 1919. lib. bdg. 48.50 (ISBN 0-8414-6542-8). Folcroft.

Mystical Qabalah. Dion Fortune. 311p. 1984. 8.95 (ISBN 0-87728-596-9). Weiser.

Mystical Symbolism of Universal Love. Benjamin Constable. (Illus.). 1978. 47.50 (ISBN 0-89266-113-5). Am Classical Coll Pr.

Mystical Teachings of Christianity. Jim Lewis. 150p. 1980. pap. 7.95 (ISBN 0-942482-01-8). Unity Church Denver.

Mystical Theology & Social Dissent: The Life & Works of Judah Loew of Prague. Byron L. Sherwin. (Littman Library of Jewish Civilization). 256p. 1982. 24.95x (ISBN 0-19-710051-1). Oxford U Pr.

Mystical Theology of the Eastern Church. Vladimir Lossky. 252p. 1973. Repr. of 1957 ed. 17.95 (ISBN 0-227-67536-3). Attic Pr.

Mystical Theology of the Eastern Church. Vladimir Lossky. LC 76-25448. Orig. Title: Essai sur la theologie mystique de L'eglise d'orient. 252p. 1976. pap. 8.95 (ISBN 0-913836-31-1). St Vladimirs.

Mystical Transformations: The Imagery of Liquids in the Work of Mechthild Von Magdeburg. James C. Franklin. LC 75-5248. 192p. 1976. 18.50 (ISBN 0-8386-1738-7). Fairleigh Dickinson.

Mystical Vision of Existence in Classical Islam. Gerhard Boewering. (Studien zur Sprache, Geschichte und Kultur des islamischen Orients, Beihefte zur "der Islam"). 296p. 1979. text ed. 70.50x (ISBN 3-11-007546-6). De Gruyter.

Mystical Vocabulary of Venerable Mere Marie De L'Incarnation & Its Problems. Mother Aloysius G. L'Heureux. LC 72-94190. (Catholic University of America Studies in Romance Languages & Literatures Ser: No. 53). (Fr.). Repr. of 1956 ed. 24.00 (ISBN 0-404-50353-5). AMS Pr.

Mystical Way in the Fourth Gospel: Crossing over into God. L. William Countryman. LC 86-45913. 160p. 1987. pap. text ed. 9.95 (ISBN 0-8006-1949-8, 1-1949). Fortress.

Mystical Way of Life. Mary Valla. LC 74-14058. 176p. 1975. pap. 4.95 (ISBN 0-685-52237-7). De Vorss.

Mystical Writings of St. Isaac the Syrian. Isaac The Syrian. Tr. by A. J. Wensinck from Syriac. 1977. pap. 6.95 (ISBN 0-686-19231-1). Eastern Orthodox.

Mysticism. Frank C. Happold. (Orig.). 1963. pap. 6.95 (ISBN 0-14-020568-3, Pelican). Penguin.

Mysticism. Sven S. Hartman & C. M. Edsman. (Illus.). 258p. (Orig.). 1970. pap. text ed. 16.95x (Pub. by Almqvist & Wiksell). Coronet Bks.

Mysticism. Evelyn Underhill. 1955. pap. 12.95 (ISBN 0-452-00840-9, Mer). NAL.

Mysticism. William J. Wainwright. LC 81-50821. 264p. 1982. 40.00x (ISBN 0-299-08910-X). U of Wis Pr.

Mysticism - the Ultimate Experience. Cecil A. Poole. LC 81-86628. 166p. 1982. 8.95 (ISBN 0-912057-33-5, G-647). AMORC.

Mysticism - Window on a World View: Introduction to Mysticism As a Pattern of Thought & Practice. Margaret L. Furse. LC 76-56816. Repr. of 1977 ed. 55.00 (ISBN 0-8357-9018-5, 2016384). Bks Demand UMI.

Mysticism & Aldous Huxley. D. S. Savage. LC 77-23247. 1947. lib. bdg. 12.50 (ISBN 0-8414-7805-8). Folcroft.

Mysticism & Catholicism. Hugh E. Stutfield. 1977. lib. bdg. 59.95 (ISBN 0-8490-2318-1). Gordon Pr.

Mysticism & Dissent: Religious Ideology & Social Protest in the Sixteenth Century. Steven E. Ozment. LC 72-91316. 272p. 1973. 33.00x (ISBN 0-300-01576-3). Yale U Pr.

Mysticism & Dissent: Socioreligious Thought in Qajar Iran. Mangol Bayat. LC 82-5498. 320p. 1982. 25.00x (ISBN 0-8156-2260-0). Syracuse U Pr.

Mysticism & Logic & Other Essays. 2nd ed. Bertrand Russell. LC 81-119829. 168p. 1981. pap. 8.95x (ISBN 0-389-20135-9, 06657). B&N Imports.

Mysticism & Magic in Turkey: An Account of the Religious Doctrines, Monastic Organisation & Ecstatic Powers of the Dervish Orders. Lucy M. Garnett. LC 77-87628. (Illus.). Repr. of 1912 ed. 22.00 (ISBN 0-404-16453-6). AMS Pr.

Mysticism & Mental Healing. Manly P. Hall. pap. 2.50 (ISBN 0-89314-336-7). Philos Res.

Mysticism & Philosophical Analysis. Steven T. Katz. 1978. 19.95x (ISBN 0-19-520010-1); pap. 8.95x (ISBN 0-19-520011-X). Oxford U Pr.

Mysticism & Philosophy. W. T. Stace. 1960. text ed. 17.50x (ISBN 0-333-08274-5). Humanities.

Mysticism & Philosophy. W. T. Stace. 384p. 1987. pap. 10.95 (ISBN 0-87477-416-0). J P Tarcher.

Mysticism & Religious Traditions. Steven T. Katz. 1983. 19.95x (ISBN 0-19-503313-2, 739); pap. 9.95 (ISBN 0-19-503314-0, GB). Oxford U Pr.

Mysticism & the Early South German-Austrian Anabaptist 1525-1531. Werner O. Packull. LC 76-46557. (Studies in the Anabaptist & Mennonite History: No. 19). 296p. 1977. 19.95x (ISBN 0-8361-1130-3). Herald Pr.

Mysticism & the Eastern Church. Nicholas Arseniev. 173p. 1979. pap. 7.95 (ISBN 0-913836-55-9). St Vladimirs.

Mysticism & the Eastern Church. Nicholas Arseniew. 1977. lib. bdg. 59.95. Gordon Pr.

Mysticism & the Experience of Love. Howard Thurman. LC 61-13708. (Orig.). 1961. pap. 2.50x (ISBN 0-87574-115-0). Pendle Hill.

Mysticism at the Dawn of the Modern Age. Rudolf Steiner. (Russian Language Ser.). 102p. 1985. pap. 7.00 (ISBN 0-89345-901-1, Steiner). Garber Comm.

Mysticism at the Dawn of the Modern Age, Vol. 6. 2nd ed. Rudolf Steiner. Ed. by Paul M. Allen. Tr. by Karl E. Zimmer from Ger. LC 60-15703. (Major Writings of Rudolf Steiner in English Translation Ser.: The Centennial Edition). 256p. 1981. lib. bdg. 16.00 (ISBN 0-89345-026-X, Spiritual Sci Lib); pap. 9.50 (ISBN 0-89345-206-8, Steinerbks). Garber Comm.

Mysticism: Christian & Buddhist. D. T. Suzuki. 160p. 1982. pap. 5.95 (ISBN 0-04-149053-3). Allen Unwin.

Mysticism: Christian & Buddhist. Daisetz T. Suzuki. LC 75-31442. 214p. 1976. Repr. of 1957 ed. lib. bdg. 25.00x (ISBN 0-8371-8516-5, SUMY). Greenwood.

Mysticism Debate. Paul Murray. 1978. 6.26 (ISBN 0-8199-0722-7). Franciscan Herald.

Mysticism East & West. Rudolf Otto. Tr. by Bertha L. Bracey & Richenda C. Payne. 289p. 1987. pap. 8.75 (ISBN 0-8356-0619-8). Theos Pub Hse.

Mysticism, Freudianism & Scientific Psychology. facsimile ed. Knight Dunlap. (Select Bibliographies Reprint Ser). Repr. of 1920 ed. 17.00 (ISBN 0-8369-5838-1). Ayer Co Pubs.

Mysticism in Blake & Wordsworth. Jacomina Kortelling. LC 68-2111. (Studies in Poetry, No. 38). 1969. Repr. of 1928 ed. lib. bdg. 39.95x (ISBN 0-8383-0577-6). Haskell.

Mysticism in India: The Poet Saints of Maharashtra. R. D. Ranade. LC 82-10458. (Illus.). 534p. 1982. 44.50x (ISBN 0-87395-669-9); pap. 12.95 (ISBN 0-87395-670-2). State U NY Pr.

Mysticism in Religion. William R. Inge. LC 76-15407. 1976. Repr. of 1948 ed. lib. bdg. 22.50x (ISBN 0-8371-8953-5, INMR). Greenwood.

Mysticism in Robert Browning. Rufus M. Jones. 1924. Repr. 15.00 (ISBN 0-8274-2784-0). R West.

Mysticism in Seventeenth Century English Literature. Elbert N. Thompson. LC 78-100788. 1970. pap. text ed. 39.95x (ISBN 0-8383-0076-6). Haskell.

Mysticism in the Bhagavad-Gita. M. N. Sircar. 1977. 12.00x (ISBN 0-686-22667-4). Intl Bk Dist.

Mysticism in the Neo-Romanticists. B. C. Broers. LC 68-767. (Studies in Comparative Literature: No. 35). 1969. Repr. of 1923 ed. text ed. 75.00x (ISBN 0-8383-0514-8). Haskell.

Mysticism in the World's Religions. Geoffrey Parrinder. 1976. pap. text ed. 6.95 (ISBN 0-19-502185-1). Oxford U Pr.

Mysticism in World Religion. Sidney Spencer. 11.75 (ISBN 0-8446-0927-7). Peter Smith.

Mysticism of Hindu Gods & Goddesses. Swami Jyotir Maya Nanda. (Illus.). 1974. pap. 3.99 (ISBN 0-934664-08-0). Yoga Res Foun.

Mysticism of Innerworldly Fulfillment: A Study of Jacob Boehme. David Walsh. LC 83-6554. (University of Florida Humanities Monographs: No. 53). x, 142p. (Orig.). 1983. pap. 12.50 (ISBN 0-8130-0751-8). U Presses Fla.

Mysticism of Masonry. R. Swinburne Clymer. 1924. 4.95 (ISBN 0-686-00820-0). Philos Pub.

Mysticism of St. Francis of Assissi. D. H. Nicholson. 1977. lib. bdg. 59.95 (ISBN 0-8490-2319-X). Gordon Pr.

Mysticism of Sound. Inayat Khan. (Sufi Message of Hazrat Inayat Khan Ser.: Vol. 2). 262p. 1979. 14.95 (ISBN 90-6077-569-4, Pub. by Servire BV Netherlands). Hunter Hse.

Mysticism of the Cloud of Unknowing: A Modern Interpretation. William Johnston. LC 74-30738. (Religious Experience Ser.: Vol. 8). pap. 74.30 (2052172). Bks Demand UMI.

Mysticism: Old & New. Arthur W. Hopkinson. LC 77-118528. 1971. Repr. of 1946 ed. 21.50x (ISBN 0-8046-1151-3, Pub. by Kennikat). Assoc Faculty Pr.

Mysticism, Psychology & Oedipus. Israel Regardie et al. LC 85-81908. 96p. (Orig.). 1986. pap. 6.95 (ISBN 0-941404-38-2). Falcon Pr AZ.

Mysticism: Sacred & Profane. Robert C. Zaehner. 1957. pap. 7.95x (ISBN 0-19-500229-6). Oxford U Pr.

Mysticism: Spiritual Quest or Psychic Disorder, Vol. 9. GAP Committee on Psychiatry & Religion. LC 76-45931. (Report: No. 97). 1976. pap. 5.00 (ISBN 0-87318-134-4, Pub. by GAP). Brunner-Mazel.

Mysticism: The Direct Experience of God. Michael Cox. 256p. 1984. pap. 9.95 (ISBN 0-85030-280-3). Newcastle Pub.

Mysticism: The Journey Within. Robert Chaney. LC 79-52959. 1979. softcover 12.50 (ISBN 0-918936-06-3). Astara.

Mysticism: The Search for Ultimate Meaning. John Chrisci. 78p. 1986. text ed. 17.50 (ISBN 0-8191-5609-4); pap. text ed. 7.75 (ISBN 0-8191-5610-8). U Pr of Amer.

Mysticism Through the Ages. E. Gall. 59.95 (ISBN 0-8490-0697-X). Gordon Pr.

Mystics & Heretics in Italy at the End of the Middle Ages. E. Gebhart. 1977. lib. bdg. 59.95 (ISBN 0-8490-2321-1). Gordon Pr.

Mystics & Medics: A Comparison of Mystical & Psychotherapeutic Encounters. Ed. by Reuven P. Bulka. LC 79-87593. 120p. 1979. pap. 12.95 (ISBN 0-87705-377-4). Human Sci Pr.

Mystics & Men of Miracles in India. Mayah Balse. (Illus.). 1976. 5.95 (ISBN 0-913244-10-4). Hapi Pr.

Mystics & Poets. William T. Davison. LC 77-924. 1977. lib. bdg. 25.00 (ISBN 0-8414-3680-0). Folcroft.

Mystics & Poets. William T. Davison. 167p. 1980. Repr. of 1936 ed. lib. bdg. 32.50 (ISBN 0-8482-0639-8). Norwood Edns.

Mystics & Zen Masters. Thomas Merton. 303p. 1986. pap. 8.95 (ISBN 0-374-52001-1). FS&G.

Mystics, Ascetics & Saints of India. John C. Oman. lib. bdg. 75.00 (ISBN 0-8490-0698-8). Gordon Pr.

Mystics, Ascetics & Saints of India: A Study of Sadhmaism with an Account of the Yogis, Sanyasis, Bairagis, & other Strange Hindu Sectarians. J. C. Oman. 308p. 1984. text ed. 38.50x (ISBN 0-89563-650-6). Coronet Bks.

Mystics at Prayer. 19th ed. Compiled by Many Cihlar. LC 36-17108. 57p. 1982. 7.95 (ISBN 0-912057-08-4, G-509). AMORC.

Mystics of Islam. Manly P. Hall. pap. 3.95 (ISBN 0-89314-532-7). Philos Res.

Mystics of Islam: An Introduction to Sufism. Reynold A. Nicholson. LC 75-10713. 192p. 1975. pap. 5.95 (ISBN 0-8052-0492-X). Schocken.

Mystics of Spain. E. Allison Peers. 1977. lib. bdg. 59.95 (ISBN 0-8490-2322-X). Gordon Pr.

Mystics of the Church. Evelyn Underhill. 260p. 1975. 13.95 (ISBN 0-227-67820-6). Attic Pr.

Mystics, Philosophers, & Politicians: Essays in Jewish Intellectual History in Honor of Alexander Altman. Ed. by Jehuda Reinharz et al. LC 81-5540. (Duke Monographs in Medieval & Renaissance Studies: No. 5). xv, 372p. 1982. 36.75 (ISBN 0-8223-0446-5). Duke.

Mystique of Enlightenment. Alvin Bobroff & U. G. Krishnamurti. 190p. 1985. pap. 9.95 (ISBN 0-87418-020-1, 156). Coleman Pub.

Myth. M. I. Steblin-Kamenskij. 165p. 1981. 15.50 (ISBN 0-89720-053-5); pap. 8.50 (ISBN 0-89720-054-3). Karoma.

Myth: A Symposium. Ed. by Thomas A. Sebeok. LC 65-29803. (Midland Bks.: No. 83). 192p. 1955. pap. 4.95 (ISBN 0-253-20083-0). Ind U Pr.

Myth, Allegory, & Gospel. Ed. by John W. Montgomery. LC 74-1358. Orig. Title: Names & Titles of Christ. 160p. 1974. pap. 5.95 (ISBN 0-87123-358-4, 210358). Bethany Hse.

Myth & Cosmos: Readings in Mythology & Symbolism. Ed. by John Middleton. LC 75-43817. (Texas Press Sourcebooks in Anthropology: No. 5). 382p. 1976. pap. 9.95x (ISBN 0-292-75030-7). U of Tex Pr.

Myth & Cult Among Primitive Peoples. Adolf E. Jensen. LC 63-20909. 1963. 10.00x (ISBN 0-226-39823-4). U of Chicago Pr.

Myth & Legend of Ancient Israel, 3 Vols. rev. ed. Angelo S. Rappoport. 1966. Set. 39.50x (ISBN 0-87068-099-4). Ktav.

Myth & Literature in the American Renaissance. Robert D. Richardson, Jr. LC 77-22638. 320p. 1978. 22.50x (ISBN 0-253-33965-0). Ind U Pr.

Myth & Meaning. Claude Levi-Strauss. LC 78-25833. 1979. pap. 3.95 (ISBN 0-8052-0622-1). Schocken.

Myth & Meaning in Early Taoism: The Themes of Chaos (hun-tun) N. J. Girardot. LC 81-21964. (Hermeneutics Studies in the History of Religions). (Illus.). 430p. 1983. 39.50x (ISBN 0-520-04330-8). U of Cal Pr.

Myth & Miracle: An Essay on the Mystic Symbolism of Shakespeare. G. Wilson Knight. 59.95 (ISBN 0-8490-0699-6). Gordon Pr.

Myth & Miracle: Essay on the Mystic Symbolism of Shakespeare. G. Wilson Knight. 1978. Repr. of 1929 ed. lib. bdg. 17.50 (ISBN 0-8495-3014-8). Arden Lib.

Myth & Philosophy. Ed. by George F. McLean. LC 72-184483. (Proceedings of the American Catholic Philosophical Association: Vol. 45). 1971. pap. 15.00 (ISBN 0-918090-05-9). Am Cath Philo.

Myth & Prayers of the Great Star Chant & the Myth of the Coyote Chant. Mary C. Wheelwright. (Illus.). 191p. 1987. 14.00 (ISBN 0-912586-58-3); pap. 10.00 (ISBN 0-912586-61-3). Navajo Coll Pr.

Myth & Reality. Mircea Eliade. pap. 5.95x (ISBN 0-06-131369-6, TB1369, Torch). Har-Row.

Myth & Reason: A Symposium. Ed. by Walter D. Wetzels. LC 72-3096. (Germanic Languages Symposium Ser). 206p. 1973. 9.95x (ISBN 0-292-75003-X). U of Tex Pr.

Myth & Religion of the North. E. O. Turville-Petre. LC 75-5003. (Illus.). 340p. 1975. Repr. of 1964 ed. lib. bdg. 49.75x (ISBN 0-8371-7420-1, TUMR). Greenwood.

Myth & Ritual in Christianity. Alan W. Watts. (Illus.). 1968. pap. 9.95x (ISBN 0-8070-1375-7, BP301). Beacon Pr.

Myth & Science. Tito Vignoli. 1976. lib. bdg. 59.95 (ISBN 0-8490-2323-8). Gordon Pr.

Myth & Thought Among the Greeks. Jean P. Vernant. 400p. 1983. 29.95x (ISBN 0-7100-9544-9). Methuen Inc.

Myth, Faith & Hermeneutics. Mary E. Hansburg. 85p. (Orig.). 1985. pap. 6.95x (ISBN 0-932269-23-0). Wyndham Hall.

Myth, Faith & Hermeneutics: Toward Cross-Cultural Religious Understanding. Raimundo Panikkar. LC 77-99306. 528p. 1980. 22.95 (ISBN 0-8091-0232-3). Paulist Pr.

Myth, History & Faith: The Re-Mythologizing of Christianity. Morton Kelsey. LC 73-94216. 192p. 1974. pap. 5.95 (ISBN 0-8091-1827-0). Paulist Pr.

Myth in Old Testament Interpretation. J. W. Rogerson. LC 73-78234. (Beiheft zur Zeitschrift fuer die Alttestamentliche Wissenschaft). 1974. 50.00x (ISBN 3-11-004220-7). De Gruyter.

Myth in Primitive Psychology. Bronislaw Malinowski. LC 79-152394. 94p. 1972. Repr. of 1926 ed. text ed. 22.50x (ISBN 0-8371-5954-7, MMP&, Pub. by Negro U Pr). Greenwood.

Myth: Its Meaning & Functions in Ancient & Other Cultures. G. S. Kirk. LC 72-628267. (Sather Classical Lectures: No. 40). 1970. pap. 8.95x (ISBN 0-520-02389-7, CAMPUS 94). U of Cal Pr.

Myth, Legend & Custom in the Old Testament: A Comparative Study with Chapters from Sir James G. Frazer's Folklore in the Old Testament, 2 vols. Theodore H. Gaster. Set. 36.00 (ISBN 0-8446-5189-3). Peter Smith.

Myth, Mensch & Umwelt. Ed. by Adolf E. Jensen & Kees W. Bolle. LC 77-79134. (Mythology Ser.). (Ger., Illus.). 1978. Repr. of 1950 ed. lib. bdg. 36.50x (ISBN 0-405-10544-4). Ayer Co Pubs.

Myth of Apollo & Daphne from Ovid to Quevedo. Mary E. Barnard. (Duke Monographs in Medieval & Renaissance Studies: No. 8). (Illus.). 190p. 1986. lib. bdg. 25.00 (ISBN 0-8223-0701-4). Duke.

Myth of Certainty. Dan Taylor. 128p. 1986. 10.95 (ISBN 0-8499-0547-8). Word Bks.

Myth of Christian Beginnings. Robert L. Wilken. LC 80-11884. 218p. 1980. 17.95 (ISBN 0-268-01347-0); pap. text ed. 6.95 (ISBN 0-268-01348-9). U of Notre Dame Pr.

Myth of Evolution. Donald A. McWilliams. LC 73-88018. 1973. 3.95x (ISBN 0-916434-08-7). Plycon Pr.

Myth of Freedom & the Way of Meditation. Chogyam Trungpa. LC 75-40264. (Illus.). 176p. (Orig.). 1976. pap. 7.95 (ISBN 0-87773-084-9). Shambhala Pubns.

Myth of God Incarnate. Ed. by John Hick. LC 77-9965. 224p. 1978. pap. 7.95 (ISBN 0-664-24178-6). Westminster.

Myth of Hiawatha, & Other Oral Legends, Mythologic & Allegoric, of the North American Indians. H. R. Schoolcraft. Repr. of 1856 ed. 28.00 (ISBN 0-527-80350-2). Kraus Repr.

Myth of Innocence: Mark & Christian Origins. Burton L. Mack. LC 86-45906. (Foundations and Facets Ser.). 448p. 1987. text ed. 9.95 (ISBN 0-8006-2113-1). Fortress.

Myth of Mormon Inspiration. Brodie Crouch. 7.50 (ISBN 0-89315-158-0). Lambert Bk.

Myth of Over-Population. Colin Clark. 133p. 1975. pap. 3.50 (ISBN 0-912414-26-X). Lumen Christi.

Myth of the Cross. A. D. Ajijola. pap. 9.50 (ISBN 0-686-63907-3). Kazi Pubns.

Myth of the Eternal Return. Mircea Eliade. Tr. by Willard R. Trask. (Bollingen Ser.: Vol. 46). 1954. 24.00 (ISBN 0-691-09798-4); pap. 8.50 (ISBN 0-691-01777-8). Princeton U Pr.

Myth of the Great Secret: A Search for Spiritual Meaning in the Face of Emptiness. Edwin C. Johnson. 1982. 10.50 (ISBN 0-688-00781-3). Morrow.

Myth of the Greener Grass. J. Allan Petersen. 1983. 8.95 (ISBN 0-8423-4656-2); pap. 6.95 (ISBN 0-8423-4651-1). Tyndale.

Myth of the Magus. E. M. Butler. 283p. 1982. Repr. of 1948 ed. lib. bdg. 65.00 (ISBN 0-89984-084-1). Century Bookbindery.

Myth of the State. Ernst Cassirer. 1961. pap. 8.95x (ISBN 0-300-00036-7, y33). Yale U Pr.

Myth, Religion & Society: Structuralist Essays by M. Detienne, L. Gernet, J. P. Vernant & P. Vidal-Naquet. Ed. by R. L. Gordon. (Illus.). 250p. 1982. text ed. 44.50 (ISBN 0-521-22780-1); pap. text ed. 15.95 (ISBN 0-521-29640-4). Cambridge U Pr.

Myth, Ritual & Religion, 2 Vols in 1. Andrew Lang. LC 68-54280. Repr. of 1906 ed. 35.00 (ISBN 0-404-03868-9). AMS Pr.

Myth, Symbol & Reality. Ed. by Alan M. Olson. LC 80-11617. 189p. 1982. pap. text ed. 7.95 (ISBN 0-268-01349-7). U of Notre Dame Pr.

Mythenbildung und Erkenntnis: Eine Abhandlung Uber Die Grundlagen der Philosophie. Gottlob F. Lipps. Ed. by Kees W. Bolle. LC 77-79141. (Mythology Ser.). 1978. lib. bdg. 27.50x (ISBN 0-405-10550-9). Ayer Co Pubs.

Mythengeschichte der Asiatischen Welt: Mit einen Anhang: Beitrage aus den Heidelberger Jahrbuchern. Joseph Gorres. Ed. by Kees W. Bolle. (Mythology Ser.). (Ger.). 1978. Repr. of 1935 ed. lib. bdg. 54.00x (ISBN 0-405-10538-X). Ayer Co Pubs.

Mythic Image. Joseph Campbell & M. J. Abadie. LC 79-166363. (Bollingen Series C). (Illus.). 560p. 1981. pap. 19.95 (ISBN 0-691-01839-1). Princeton U Pr.

Mythic Masks in Self-Reflexive Poetry: A Study of Pan & Orpheus. Dorothy Z. Baker. LC 85-16468. (Studies in Comparative Literature Ser.: No. 62). x, 186p. 1986. 20.00x (ISBN 0-8078-7062-5). U of NC Pr.

Mythical Intentions in Modern Literature. Eric Gould. LC 81-47132. 304p. 1981. 30.50 (ISBN 0-691-06482-2). Princeton U Pr.

Mythmaker: Paul & the Invention of Christianity. Hyam Maccoby. LC 85-45680. 256p. 1986. 17.45 (ISBN 0-06-015582-5, HARPT). Har-Row.

Mythmakers. Mary Barnard. LC 66-20061. 213p. 1979. 16.95 (ISBN 0-8214-0024-X); pap. 6.50 (ISBN 0-8214-0562-4). Ohio U Pr.

Mythmakers. Mary Barnard. LC 66-20061. 213p. 1986. 12.95 (ISBN 0-932576-36-2); pap. 6.95 (ISBN 0-932576-37-0). Breitenbush Bks.

Mythography: The Study of Myths & Rituals. William G. Doty. LC 85-991. 384p. 1986. 28.50 (ISBN 0-8173-0269-7). U of Ala Pr.

Mythologiae. Natalis Comes. LC 75-27853. (Renaissance & the Gods Ser.: Vol. 11). (Illus.). 1976. Repr. of 1567 ed. lib. bdg. 88.00 (ISBN 0-8240-2060-X). Garland Pub.

Mythological Bonds Between East & West. Dorothea Chaplin. 1976. lib. bdg. 59.95 (ISBN 0-8490-2325-4). Gordon Pr.

Mythological Painting. Michael Jacobs. LC 78-25563. (Mayflower Gallery Ser.). (Illus.). 1979. 12.50 (ISBN 0-8317-6282-9, Mayflower Bks); pap. 6.95 (ISBN 0-8317-6283-7). Smith Pubs.

Mythologie universelle: Universal Mythology. Alexandre H. Krappe. Ed. by Kees W. Bolle. LC 77-79135. (Mythology Ser.). 1978. Repr. of 1930 ed. lib. bdg. 36.50x (ISBN 0-405-10545-2). Ayer Co Pubs.

Mythologies & Philosophies of Salvation in the Theistic Traditions of India. K. Klostermaier. (Editions SR Ser.: No. 5). 549p. 1984. pap. text ed. 23.95x (ISBN 0-88920-158-7, Pub. by Wilfrid Laurier Canada). Humanities.

Mythologies of Ancient Mexico & Peru. Lewis Spence. 80p. 1983. Repr. of 1907 ed. lib. bdg. 30.00 (ISBN 0-89987-949-7). Darby Bks.

Mythologies of Ancient Mexico & Peru. Lewis Spence. 80p. 1921. 0.95 (ISBN 0-317-40437-7). Open Court.

Mythologies of the Ancient World. Ed. by Samuel Noah Kramer. LC 60-13538. 1961. pap. 6.95 (ISBN 0-385-09567-8, A229, Anch). Doubleday.

Mythologies of the World: A Concise Encyclopedia. Rhoda A. Hendricks. Ed. by Max S. Shapiro. (McGraw-Hill Paperbacks Ser.). 240p. 1981. pap. 5.95 (ISBN 0-07-056421-3). McGraw.

Mythologische Forschungen Aus Dem Nachlasse, 2 vols. in 1. Wilhelm Mannhardt. Ed. by Kees W. Bolle. LC 77-79142. (Mythology Ser.). (Ger.). 1978. Repr. of 1868 ed. lib. bdg. 38.50x (ISBN 0-405-10551-7). Ayer Co Pubs.

Mythology. Edith Hamilton. (Illus.). 1942. 15.45 (ISBN 0-316-34114-2). Little.

Mythology. Edith Hamilton. 336p. (YA) 1971. pap. 3.50 (ISBN 0-451-62523-4, Ment). NAL.

Mythology. James Weigel, Jr. 210p. 1973. pap. 3.95 (ISBN 0-8220-0865-3). Cliffs.

Mythology & Cosmology in the Narratives of Bernard Dadie & Birago Diop: A Structural Approach. Marie S. Tollerson. LC 81-51668. 152p. 1985. 20.00 (ISBN 0-89410-156-0); pap. 10.00 (ISBN 0-89410-157-9). Three Continents.

Mythology & Folktales: Their Relation & Interpretation. Edwin S. Hartland. LC 75-144519. (Popular Studies in Mythology, Romance & Folklore: No. 7). Repr. of 1900 ed. 5.50 (ISBN 0-404-53507-0). AMS Pr.

Mythology & the Bible. Corinne Heline. 1972. pap. 4.50 (ISBN 0-87613-018-X). New Age.

Mythology & the Bible. Corinne Heline. 75p. pap. text ed. 4.50 (ISBN 0-933963-13-0). New Age Bible.

Mythology & Values: An Analysis of Navaho Chantway Myths. Katherine Spencer. (American Folklore Society Memoir Ser: No. 48). 248p. 1957. pap. 6.95x (ISBN 0-292-73528-6). U of Tex Pr.

Mythology, Archeology, Architecture. Diane Sylvester & Mary Wiemann. (Gifted & Talented Ser.). 112p. 1982. 8.95 (ISBN 0-88160-081-4, LW 901). Learning Wks.

Mythology: Greek & Roman. Thomas H. Carpenter & Robert J. Gula. (Illus.). 1977. pap. text ed. 6.95x (ISBN 0-88334-089-5). Ind Sch Pr.

Mythology in American Education. Harold H. Punke. 480p. 1981. pap. 14.75x (ISBN 0-8134-2136-5). Inter Print Pubs.

Mythology of Ancient Britain & Ireland. Charles Squire. LC 73-13769. 1974. Repr. of 1909 ed. lib. bdg. 17.50 (ISBN 0-8414-7650-0). Folcroft.

Mythology of Brahma. G. M. Bailey. 1983. 27.00x (ISBN 0-19-561411-9). Oxford U Pr.

Mythology of Modern Geology: A Refutation of Evolution's Most Influential Argument. Wayne Jackson. 45p. (Orig.). 1980. pap. 1.95 (ISBN 0-932859-13-5). Apologetic Pr.

Mythology of North America: Intro to Classic American Gods, Heroes & Tricksters. John Bierhorst. LC 86-12207. (Illus.). 256p. 1986. pap. 6.95 (ISBN 0-688-06666-6, Quill). Morrow.

Mythology of Plato & Dante & the Future Life. W. T. Harris. (Essential Library of the Great Philosophers). (Illus.). 107p. 1983. Repr. of 1896 ed. 71.85 (ISBN 0-89901-091-1). Found Class Reprints.

Mythology of the Bella Coola Indians. Franz Boas. LC 73-3510. (Jesup North Pacific Expedition. Publications: Vol. 1, Pt. 2). Repr. of 1898 ed. 20.00 (ISBN 0-404-58113-7). AMS Pr.

Mythology of the Blackfoot Indians. Clark Wissler & D. C. Duvall. LC 74-9019. (Anthropological Papers of the American Museum of Natural History: Vol. 2, Pt. 1). (Illus.). Repr. of 1909 ed. 17.00 (ISBN 0-404-11916-6). AMS Pr.

Mythology of the British Islands. Charles Squire. LC 77-94622. 1979. Repr. of 1905 ed. lib. bdg. 45.00 (ISBN 0-89341-306-2). Longwood Pub Group.

Mythology of the Thompson Indians. James A. Teit. LC 73-3529. (Jesup North Pacific Expeditions. Publications: No. 8, Pt. 2). Repr. of 1912 ed. 27.50 (ISBN 0-404-58125-0). AMS Pr.

Mythology Series, 39 vols. Ed. by Kees W. Bolle. (Illus.). 1978. Set. lib. bdg. 1807.50x (ISBN 0-405-10529-0); Set. lib. bdg. 669.00 (ISBN 0-405-18984-2). Ayer Co Pubs.

Mythology: The Voyage of the Hero. 2nd ed. David A. Leeming. (Illus.). 370p. 1980. pap. text ed. 14.50 scp (ISBN 0-06-043942-4, HarpC); instr's manual avail. (ISBN 0-06-363950-5). Har-Row.

Mythopoesis: Mythic Patterns in the Literary Classics. Harry Slochower. LC 96-11337. (Waynebooks Ser: No. 35). 363p. 1970. 29.95x (ISBN 0-8143-1395-7); pap. text ed. 9.95x (ISBN 0-8143-1511-9). Wayne St U Pr.

Myths & Folk-Lore of Ireland. Jeremiah Curtin. 1976. Repr. 18.00x (ISBN 0-7158-1090-1). Charles River Bks.

Myths & Folk Tales of Ireland. Jeremiah Curtin. LC 69-18206. 256p. 1975. pap. 4.50 (ISBN 0-486-22430-9). Dover.

Myths & Hunting Stories of the Mandan & Hidatsa Sioux. Martha W. Beckwith. LC 76-43665. (Vassar College Folklore Foundation: Publication No. 10). 1977. Repr. of 1930 ed. 16.00 (ISBN 0-404-15498-0). AMS Pr.

Myths & Legends of All Nations. Herbert S. Robinson & Knox Wilson. (Quality Paperback Ser.: No. 319). 244p. 1978. pap. 5.95 (ISBN 0-8226-0319-5). Littlefield.

Myths & Legends of Ancient Greece & Rome. E. M. Berens. LC 77-91528. 1977. Repr. of 1880 ed. lib. bdg. 30.00 (ISBN 0-89341-029-2). Longwood Pub Group.

Myths & Legends of Australia. A. W. Reed. LC 72-779. (Illus.). 1973. 7.50 (ISBN 0-8008-5463-2). Taplinger.

Myths & Legends of Babylonia & Assyria. Lewis Spence. LC 77-167199. (Illus.). 414p. 1975. Repr. of 1916 ed. 53.00x (ISBN 0-8103-4089-5). Gale.

Myths & Legends of Bantu. Alice Werner. 289p. 1968. Repr. of 1933 ed. 30.00x (ISBN 0-7146-1735-0, F Cass Co). Biblio Dist.

Myths & Legends of China. E. T. Werner. LC 71-172541. (Illus.). Repr. of 1922 ed. 33.00 (ISBN 0-405-09059-5, Pub. by Blom). Ayer Co Pubs.

Myths & Legends of China. 2nd ed. E. T. Werner. (Illus.). 453p. 1984. pap. 15.00 (ISBN 9971-947-55-2, Pub. by Graham Brash Singapore). Three Continents.

Myths & Legends of Japan. F. Hadland Davis. (Illus.). 1978. Repr. of 1912 ed. lib. bdg. 45.00 (ISBN 0-8495-1008-2). Arden Lib.

Myths & Legends of Many Lands. new ed. Compiled by Harriet Ross. (Illus.). 160p. 1984. PLB 7.95. Lion Bks.

Myths & Legends of the Bantu. Alice Werner. LC 78-63237. (Folktale). (Illus.). Repr. of 1933 ed. 34.00 (ISBN 0-404-16176-6). AMS Pr.

Myths & Legends of the Celtic Race. T. W. Rolleston. (Illus.). 457p. 1985. 14.95 (ISBN 0-8052-3996-0). Schocken.

Myths & Legends of the Great Dismal Swamp. Hubert J. Davis. (Illus.). 112p. 1981. 7.50 (ISBN 0-930230-42-6). Johnson NC.

Myths & Legends of the Indian Southwest. Bertha P. Dutton & Caroline Olin. (Bk 2). (Illus.). 1978. pap. 2.95 (ISBN 0-88388-062-8). Bellerophon Bks.

Myths & Legends of the Indian Southwest, Bk 1. 1st ed. Caroline Olin & D. Caroline Olin. (Illus.). 1978. pap. 2.95 (ISBN 0-88388-049-0). Bellerophon Bks.

Myths & Legends of the Lipan Apache Indians. Morris E. Opler. LC 40-13687. (Amer. Folklore SocietyMemoirs Ser.). Repr. of 1940 ed. 21.00 (ISBN 0-527-01088-X). Kraus Repr.

Myths & Legends of the North American Indian. L. Spence. LC 72-81598. (Illus.). 396p. 1975. pap. cancelled (ISBN 0-8334-1745-2, Steinerbks). Garber Comm.

Myths & Legends of the Polynesians. Johannes C. Andersen. LC 75-35170. (Illus.). Repr. of 1931 ed. 43.50 (ISBN 0-404-14200-1). AMS Pr.

Myths & Legends of the Polynesians. Johannes E. Anderson. LC 69-13509. (Illus.). 1969. Repr. of 1928 ed. 37.50 (ISBN 0-8048-0414-1). C E Tuttle.

Myths & Legends of the Swahili. Jan Knappert. (African Writers Ser.). 1970. pap. text ed. 5.00x (ISBN 0-435-90075-7). Heinemann Ed.

Myths & Legends of the Vikings. John Lindow. (Illus.). 1980. pap. 2.95 (ISBN 0-88388-071-7). Bellerophon Bks.

Myths & Myth-Makers: Old Tales & Superstitions Interpreted by Comparative Mythology. John Fiske. LC 77-85618. 1977. Repr. of 1890 ed. lib. bdg. 30.00 (ISBN 0-89341-304-6). Longwood Pub Group.

Myths & Songs from the South Pacific. William W. Gill. Ed. by Richard M. Dorson. LC 77-70596. (International Folklore Ser.). 1977. Repr. of 1876 ed. lib. bdg. 25.50x (ISBN 0-405-10095-7). Ayer Co Pubs.

Myths & Symbols, or Aboriginal Religions in America. Stephen O. Peet. LC 76-27515. (Illus.). 1976. Repr. of 1905 ed. lib. bdg. 45.00 (ISBN 0-89341-039-X). Longwood Pub Group.

Myths & Tales from the San Carlos Apache. Pliny E. Goddard. LC 76-43715. (AMNH. Anthropological Pap.: Vol. 29, Pt. 1). Repr. of 1918 ed. 16.50 (ISBN 0-404-15548-0). AMS Pr.

Myths & Tales of the Chiricahua Apache Indians. Morris E. Opler. LC 43-2944. (Amer. Folklore Society Memoirs Ser.). Repr. of 1942 ed. 15.00 (ISBN 0-527-01089-8). Kraus Repr.

Myths & Tales of the Jicarilla Apache Indians. Morris E. Opler. LC 38-22477. (American Folklore Society Memoirs). Repr. of 1938 ed. 37.00 (ISBN 0-527-01083-9). Kraus Repr.

Myths & Tales of the Southeastern Indians. John R. Swanton. LC 74-9011. (Smithsonian Institution. Bureau of American Enthnology. Bulletin: 88). Repr. of 1929 ed. 20.00 (ISBN 0-404-11908-5). AMS Pr.

Myths & Tales of the White Mountain Apache. Ed. by Grenville Goodwin. LC 39-33959. (AFS M). Repr. of 1939 ed. 29.00 (ISBN 0-527-01085-5). Kraus Repr.

Myths & Traditions of the Crow Indians. Robert H. Lowie. LC 74-7981. Repr. of 1918 ed. 24.00 (ISBN 0-404-11872-0). AMS Pr.

Myths, Dreams & Mysteries: The Encounter Between Contemporary Faiths & Archaic Realities. Mircea Eliade. pap. 5.95x (ISBN 0-06-131943-0, TB 1943, Torch). Har-Row.

Myths Every Child Should Know: A Selection of the Classic Myths of All Times for Young People. Ed. by Hamilton W. Mabie. (Illus.). 351p. 1986. Repr. of 1914 ed. lib. bdg. 40.00 (ISBN 0-8482-5040-0). Norwood Edns.

Myths: Gods, Heroes & Saviors. Leonard J. Biallas. 304p. (Orig.). 1986. pap. 9.95 (ISBN 0-89622-290-X). Twenty-Third.

Myths in Adventism Education. George R. Knight. Ed. by Gerald Wheeler. 1985. 16.95 (ISBN 0-8280-0277-0). Review & Herald.

Myths, Models, & Paradigms. Ian G. Barbour. LC 73-18690. 1976. pap. text ed. 6.95x (ISBN 0-06-060387-9, RD 183, HarpR). Har-Row.

Myths of Ancient Greece. Compiled by Harriet Ross. (Illus.). 160p. 1984. PLB 7.95 (ISBN 0-87460-383-8). Lion Bks.

Myths of Babylonia & Assyria. Donald A. MacKenzie. LC 77-94601. 1978. Repr. of 1915 ed. lib. bdg. 60.00 (ISBN 0-89341-315-1). Longwood Pub Group.

Myths of China & Japan. Donald A. Mackenzie. LC 77-6878. 1977. Repr. of 1923 ed. lib. bdg. 45.00 (ISBN 0-89341-149-3). Longwood Pub Group.

Myths of Crete & Pre-Hellenic Europe. Donald A. MacKenzie. LC 76-27522. (Illus.). 1976. Repr. of 1918 ed. lib. bdg. 45.00 (ISBN 0-89341-035-7). Longwood Pub Group.

Myths of Greece & Rome. H. A. Gueber. 1986. 27.50x (ISBN 0-245-56918-9, Pub. by Harrap Ltd England). State Mutual Bk.

Myths of Greece & Rome. Jane E. Harrison. LC 76-46570. 1976. Repr. of 1927 ed. lib. bdg. 20.00 (ISBN 0-8414-4907-4). Folcroft.

Myths of Greece & Rome. Holme. 288p. 1981. pap. 18.95 (ISBN 0-14-005643-2). Penguin.

Myths of Greece & Rome: Narrated with Special Reference to Literature & Art. H. A. Guerber. 428p. 1985. Repr. of 1893 ed. 40.00 (ISBN 0-8495-2102-5). Arden Lib.

Myths of Mexico & Peru. Lewis Spence. 1976. lib. bdg. 60.00 (ISBN 0-8490-0700-3). Gordon Pr.

Myths of Mexico & Peru. Lewis Spence. LC 76-27516. (Illus.). 1976. Repr. of 1914 ed. lib. bdg. 45.00 (ISBN 0-89341-031-4). Longwood Pub Group.

Myths of Norsemen. H. A. Guerber. 69.95 (ISBN 0-87968-280-9). Gordon Pr.

Myths of Pre-Columbian America. D. Mackenzie. 75.00 (ISBN 0-8490-0701-1). Gordon Pr.

Myths of Pre-Columbian America. Donald A. MacKenzie. LC 77-94602. 1978. Repr. of 1923 ed. lib. bdg. 40.00 (ISBN 0-89341-314-3). Longwood Pub Group.

Myths of Satan. Bertrand Belisle. 64p. 1982. 6.95 (ISBN 0-89962-284-4). Todd & Honeywell.

Myths of the Atonement. Ralph A. Letch. 1985. 20.00x (ISBN 0-7223-1657-7, Pub. by A H Stockwell England). State Mutual Bk.

Myths of the Cherokee. James Mooney. LC 16-5534. (Landmarks in Anthropology Ser). Repr. of 1900 ed. 37.00 (ISBN 0-384-39920-7). Johnson Repr.

Myths of the Cherokee. James Mooney. LC 70-108513. (American Indian History Sers). 1970. Repr. of 1900 ed. 89.00 (ISBN 0-403-00221-4). Scholarly.

Myths of the Cherokee & Sacred Formulas of the Cherokees. James Mooney. LC 72-188151. (Illus.). 1982. 20.00 (ISBN 0-918450-05-5); pap. 14.00x (ISBN 0-918450-22-5). C Elder.

Myths of the Greeks & Romans. Michael Grant. (Illus.). 1964. pap. 4.95 (ISBN 0-451-62267-7, ME2267, Ment). NAL.

Myths of the Hindus & Buddhists. A. K. Coomaraswamy & M. E. Noble. (Illus.). 15.25 (ISBN 0-8446-1896-9). Peter Smith.

Myths of the Hindus & Buddhists. Ananda K. Coomaraswamy & Sr. Nivedita. (Illus.). 400p. pap. 6.95 (ISBN 0-486-21759-0). Dover.

Myths of the Modocs: Indian Legends from the Northwest. Jeremiah Curtin. LC 74-170711. Repr. of 1912 ed. 20.00 (ISBN 0-405-08415-3, Blom Pubns). Ayer Co Pubs.

Myths of the New World. Daniel G. Brinton. LC 71-144901. 331p. 1972. Repr. of 1876 ed. 10.00 (ISBN 0-403-00839-5). Scholarly.

Myths of the New World: A Treatise on the Symbolism & Mythology of the Red Race of America. D. G. Brinton. LC 68-24972. (American History & Americana Ser., No. 47). 1969. Repr. of 1876 ed. lib. bdg. 75.00x (ISBN 0-8383-0918-6). Haskell.

Myths of the New World: A Treatise on the Symbolism & Mythology of the Red Race in America. Daniel G. Brinton. LC 74-1038. 360p. 1974. Repr. of 1896 ed. 30.00x (ISBN 0-8103-3959-5). Gale.

Myths of the New World: A Treatise on the Symbolism & Mythology of the Red Race of America. 2nd ed. Daniel G. Brinton. LC 69-13839. 1969. Repr. of 1876 ed. lib. bdg. 22.50x (ISBN 0-8371-2040-3, BRMN). Greenwood.

Myths of the New World: A Treatise on the Symbolism & Mythology of the Red Race of America. Daniel G. Brinton. LC 78-31682. 1979. Repr. of 1868 ed. lib. bdg. 30.00 (ISBN 0-89341-326-7). Longwood Pub Group.

Myths of the New World: The Symbolism & Mythology of the Indians of the Americas. Daniel G. Brinton. LC 72-81594. (Illus.). 348p. pap. cancelled (ISBN 0-89345-207-6, Steinerbks). Garber Comm.

Myths of the Orient. Barbara Christesen. LC 77-22199. (Myth, Magic & Superstition). (Illus.). 1977. PLB 14.65 (ISBN 0-8172-1043-1). Raintree Pubs.

Myths of the Toba & Pilaga Indians of the Gran Chaco. Alfred Metraux. LC 46-4565. (Amer. Folklore Society Memoirs Ser.). Repr. of 1946 ed. 15.00 (ISBN 0-527-01092-8). Kraus Repr.

Myths That Every Child Should Know. Hamilton W. Mabie. Repr. of 1905 ed. 20.00 (ISBN 0-89987-175-5). Darby Bks.

Mythus und Kultur: Myth & Culture. Arthur Liebert. Ed. by Kees W. Bolle. (Mythology Ser.). (Ger.). 1978. Repr. of 1925 ed. lib. bdg. 17.00x (ISBN 0-405-10549-5). Ayer Co Pubs.

N

N. Eldon Tanner: His Life & Service. G. Homer Durham. LC 82-9681. (Illus.). 370p. 1982. 9.95 (ISBN 0-87747-913-5). Deseret Bk.

N. F. S. Grundtvig: Selected Writings. Ed. by Johannes Knudsen. LC 76-7873. 192p. 1976. pap. 1.50 (ISBN 0-8006-1238-8, 1-1238). Fortress.

Na Pule Kahiko: Ancient Hawaiian Prayers. June Gutmanis. LC 83-80256. (Illus.). 136p. 1983. 17.50 (ISBN 0-9607938-6-0); deluxe ed. 100.00 (ISBN 0-9607938-7-9). Editions Ltd.

Naam or Word. 4th ed. Kirpal Singh. LC 81-51512. (Illus.). 335p. 1982. pap. 5.50 (ISBN 0-918224-12-8). Sawan Kirpal Pubns.

Naaman & the Little Maid. Lucy Diamond. (Ladybird Ser). (Illus.). 1959. bds. 2.50 (ISBN 0-87508-852-X). Chr Lit.

Naaman & the Little Servant Girl. Illus. by Graham Round. (Illus.). 1982. pap. 0.99 (ISBN 0-86683-660-8, AY8242, HarpR). Har-Row.

Naaman's Dreadful Secret. Penny Frank. Ed. by P. Alexander. (Lion Story Bible Ser.). 24p. 1987. 2.95 (ISBN 0-85648-748-1). Lion USA.

Nacer a Una Nueva Vida. Billy Graham. Tr. by Rhode Ward from Eng. LC 78-52622. Tr. of How to Be Born Again. (Span.). 191p. 1978. pap. 4.95 (ISBN 0-89922-110-6). Edit Caribe.

Nachgelassene Schriften, 5 vols. in 3. Abraham Geiger. Ed. by Steven Katz. LC 79-7132. (Jewish Philosophy, Mysticism & History of Ideas Ser.). 1980. Repr. of 1875 ed. Set. lib. bdg. 172.50x (ISBN 0-405-12255-1); lib. bdg. 57.50x ea. Vol. 1 (ISBN 0-405-12256-X). Vol. 2 (ISBN 0-405-12257-8). Vol. 3 (ISBN 0-405-12228-4). Ayer Co Pubs.

Naci de Nuevo. Charles Colson. Tr. by Rhode Ward from Eng. LC 77-81645. Tr. of Born Again. (Span.). 419p. 1977. pap. 6.50 (ISBN 0-89922-087-8). Edit Caribe.

Nacimiento del Mesias. Ed. by Roberto A. Rivera. (Span.). 172p. 1983. pap. 4.95 (ISBN 0-87148-308-4). Pathway Pr.

Nadie Me Quiere. O. F. Walton. Tr. of Nobody Loves Me. (Span.). 128p. 1984. 3.25 (ISBN 0-8254-1850-X). Kregel.

Nag Hammadi & the Gospel Tradition: Synoptic Tradition in the Nag Hammadi Library. Christopher Tuckett. 190p. 1986. 21.50 (ISBN 0-567-09364-6, Pub. by T & T Clark Ltd UK). Fortress.

Nag Hammadi, Gnosticism & Early Christianity. Dr. Charles W. Hedrick, Sr. & Robert Hodgson, Jr. 296p. 1986. pap. 14.95 (ISBN 0-913573-16-7). Hendrickson MA.

Nag Hammadi Library. James M. Robinson. 1978. 23.03i (ISBN 0-06-066929-2, HarpR); pap. 11.95 (CN4008). Har-Row.

Nag Mahasaya: A Saintly Householder Disciple of Sri Ramakrishna. Sarat C. Chakravarty. 1978. pap. 2.25 (ISBN 0-87481-481-2). Vedanta Pr.

Naga Cult in Orissa. Sadhu C. Panda. xx, 142p. 1986. text ed. 30.00x (ISBN 81-7018-356-1, Pub. by B. R. Pub Corp Delhi). Apt Bks.

Nagarjuna: The Philosophy of the Middle Way. David J. Kalupahana. (Buddhist Studies). 488p. 1986. 49.50x (ISBN 0-88706-148-6); pap. 19.95 (ISBN 0-88706-149-4). State U NY Pr.

Nagarjuna's Letter to King Gautamiputra. Lozang Jamspal et al. 1978. 9.95 (ISBN 0-89684-022-0, Pub. by Motilal Banarsidass India). Orient Bk Dist.

Nahjul Balagha. Ali-Ibne-Abu Talib. Tr. by Syded A. Jafery from Arabic. LC 84-51778. 691p. 1984. text ed. 19.95 (ISBN 0-940368-43-9); pap. 9.00 (ISBN 0-940368-42-0). Tahrike Tarsile Quran.

Nahman of Bratslav, the Tales. Arnold Band. LC 78-53433. (Classics of Western Spirituality). 368p. 1978. pap. 9.95 (ISBN 0-8091-2103-4). Paulist Pr.

Nahum Goldmann: His Missions to the Gentiles. Raphael Patai. LC 85-24518. (Judaic Studies Ser.). (Illus.). 345p. 1987. 29.95 (ISBN 0-8173-0294-8). U of Ala Pr.

Nahum, Habakkuk, Zephaniah & Haggai. J. Boo Heflin. (Bible Study Commentary). 240p. (Orig.). 1986. pap. text ed. 7.95 (ISBN 0-310-27531-8, 18385P). Zondervan.

Nahum in the Light of Northwest Semetic. Kevin J. Cathcart. (Biblica et Orientalia: Vol. 26). 1973. pap. 20.00 (ISBN 88-7653-326-5). Loyola.

Nahum-Malachi. Elizabeth Achtemeier. LC 85-45458. (Interpretation Ser.). 216p. 1986. 17.95 (ISBN 0-8042-3129-X). John Knox.

Nahum, Sofonias, Habacuc (Comentario Biblico Portavoz) Hobart Freeman. Orig. Title: Nahum, Zephaniah & Habakkuk (Everyman's Bible Commentary) (Span.). 112p. 1980. pap. 3.50 (ISBN 0-8254-1246-3). Kregel.

Naikan Psychotherapy: Meditation for Self-Development. David K. Reynolds. LC 82-21862. 184p. 1983. 17.50x (ISBN 0-226-71029-7). U of Chicago Pr.

Naked Church. Wayne Jacobsen. 208p. (Orig.). 1987. pap. 6.95 (ISBN 0-89081-569-0). Harvest Hse.

Naked Public Square: Religion & Democracy in America. Richard J. Neuhaus. LC 84-6017. 288p. 1984. 16.95 (ISBN 0-8028-3588-0). Eerdmans.

Naked Public Square: Religion & Democracy in America. Richard J. Neuhaus. 280p. 1986. pap. 8.95 (ISBN 0-8028-0080-7). Eerdmans.

Nama Japa: Prayer of the Name in the Hindu & Christian Traditions. Vandana. 1985. pap. 10.00 (ISBN 0-8364-1509-4, Pub. by Bharatiya Vidya Bhavan). South Asia Bks.

Namami Krsnasundaram - Salutations to Lord Krsna. Shrii Shrii Anandamurti. 252p. 1981. pap. 4.00 (ISBN 0-686-95432-7). Ananda Marga.

Namaz the Yoga of Islam. Ashraf F. Nizami. (Illus.). xxiii, 46p. 1981. text ed. 5.95x (ISBN 0-86590-052-3, Pub. by Taraporevala India). Apt Bks.

Nambudiri Veda Recitation. J. F. Staal. (Disputationes Rheno-Trajectinae: No. 5). (Illus.). pap. 13.60 (ISBN 90-2790-031-0). Mouton.

Name above Every Name: The Names & Titles of Jesus Christ Beginning with P-S. rev. ed. Charles J. Rolls. LC 65-26585. 1985. pap. 5.95 (ISBN 0-87213-734-1). Loizeaux.

Name Index to the Library of Congress Collection of Mormon Diaries. Meirill Library Staff. (Western Text Society Ser.: Vol. 1, No. 2). 391p. (Orig.). 1971. pap. 12.95 (ISBN 0-87421-045-3). Utah St U Pr.

Name of God. Kevin Conner. (Illus.). 90p. 1975. 8.95 (ISBN 0-914936-15-8). Bible Temple.

Name of God & the Angel of the Lord: Samaritan & Jewish Concepts of Intermeditation & the Origin of Gnosticism. Jarl E. Fossum. 400p. 1985. lib. bdg. 54.00x (ISBN 3-16-144789-1, Pub. by J C B Mohr BRD). Coronet Bks.

Name of Jesus. Kenneth E. Hagin. 1979. pap. 3.50 (ISBN 0-89276-502-X). Hagin Ministries.

Name of Jesus. Irenee Hausherr. Tr. by Charles Cummings. LC 77-10559. (Cistercian Studies: No. 44). 358p. 1978. 15.95 (ISBN 0-87907-844-8); pap. 8.00 (ISBN 0-87907-944-4). Cistercian Pubns.

Names & Name-Days: A Dictionary of Catholic Christian Names in Alphabetical Order with Origins & Meanings. Donald Attwater. LC 68-30595. 1968. Repr. of 1939 ed. 40.00x (ISBN 0-8103-3108-X). Gale.

Names, Dates, & Numbers: A System of Numerology. Roy P. Walton. 80p. 1981. pap. 5.00 (ISBN 0-89540-104-5, SB-104). Sun Pub.

Names of Christ: A Pocket Guide. Francis H. Derk. LC 75-44928. 176p. 1976. pap. 3.95 (ISBN 0-87123-390-8, 210390). Bethany Hse.

Names of God. Nathan Stone. 1944. pap. 3.50 (ISBN 0-8024-5854-8). Moody.

Names of God in Holy Scripture. Andrew Jukes. LC 67-28843. 1976. pap. 7.95 (ISBN 0-8254-2958-7). Kregel.

Names of Quran in Holy Quran. A. Sakr. pap. 2.50 (ISBN 0-317-01599-0). Kazi Pubns.

Namgyal Rinpoche: Unfolding Through Art. The Open Path. Ed. by Karma C. Wongmo. (Illus.). 157p. (Orig.). 1982. text ed. 30.00x (ISBN 0-9602722-2-4). Open Path.

Naming God. Ed. by Robert P. Scharlemann. (Contemporary Discussion Ser.). 224p. (Orig.). 1986. 21.95 (ISBN 0-913757-22-5, Pub. by New Era Bks.); pap. 12.95 (ISBN 0-913757-23-3, Pub. by New Era Bks). Paragon Hse.

Naming Names. Victor Navasky. LC 80-15044. 468p. 1980. 15.95 (ISBN 0-670-50393-2). Viking.

Naming the Powers: The Language of Power in the New Testament. Walter Wink. LC 83-48905. (Power Ser.: Vol. 1). 192p. 1984. pap. 14.95 (ISBN 0-8006-1786-X, 1-1786). Fortress.

Napoleon of Notting Hill. G. K. Chesterton. LC 77-99307. 228p. 1978. pap. 3.45 (ISBN 0-8091-2096-8). Paulist Pr.

Napoleon, the Jews & the Sanhedria. Simon Schwartzfuchs. (Littman Library of Jewish Civilization). 1979. 24.00x (ISBN 0-19-710023-6). Oxford U Pr.

Napoleon's Book of Fate. Richard Deacon. Orig. Title: Book of Fate: Its Origins & Uses. 1977. 10.00 (ISBN 0-8065-0564-8); pap. 4.95 (ISBN 0-8065-0577-X). Citadel Pr.

Narada Bhakti Sutras: The Gospel of Divine Love. Narada. Tr. by Swami Tyagisananda. (Sanskrit & Eng). pap. 4.95 (ISBN 0-87481-427-8). Vedanta Pr.

Narada Purana, Vol. 15. Tr. by G. V. Tagare. write for info. (ISBN 0-89581-539-7). Asian Human Pr.

Narada's Way of Divine Love: The Bhakti Sutras. 1st ed. Narada. Tr. by Swami Prabhavananda from Sansk. LC 75-161488. 1971. pap. 4.95 (ISBN 0-87481-508-8). Vedanta Pr.

Narahari: Prophet of New India. Vinayak K. Gokak. 298p. 1972. pap. 7.95 (ISBN 0-317-20882-9). CSA Pr.

Narrated Bible in Chronological Order. F. LaGard Smith. 1984. text ed. 34.95 (ISBN 0-89081-408-2). Harvest Hse.

Narrative & Morality: A Theological Inquiry. Paul Nelson. LC 86-43034. 192p. 1987. 21.50x (ISBN 0-271-00485-1). Pa St U Pr.

Narrative & the Poetry in the Books of Samuel; Vol. 2: The Crossing Fates. J. P. Fokkelman. (Studia Semitica Neerlandica: No. 20). 744p. 1986. 50.00 (ISBN 90-232-2175-3, Pub. by Van Gorcum Holland). Longwood Pub Group.

Narrative Art & Poetry in the Books of Samuel: A Full Interpretation on Stylistic & Structural Analysis, Volume 1. J. P. Fokkelman. (King David-Studia Semitica Neerlandica: No. 20). 534p. 1981. text ed. 50.00 (ISBN 90-232-1852-3). Longwood Pub Group.

Narrative Elements & Religious Meanings. Wesley A. Kort. LC 75-15257. pap. 32.00 (2026873). Bks Demand UMI.

Narrative of a Mission to Central Africa: 1850-1851, 2 vols. James Richardson. (Illus.). 704p. 1970. Repr. of 1853 ed. 95.00x set (ISBN 0-7146-1848-9, BHA-01848, F Cass Co). Biblio Dist.

Narrative of a Mission to Nova Scotia, New Brunswick & the Somers Islands. Joshua Marsden. Repr. of 1816 ed. 25.00 (ISBN 0-384-35430-0). Johnson Repr.

Narrative of a Visit to the West Indies: In 1840 & 1841. facsimile ed. George Truman et al. LC 71-38027. (Black Heritage Library Collection). Repr. of 1844 ed. 15.25 (ISBN 0-8369-8993-7). Ayer Co Pubs.

Narrative of Sojourner Truth. Sojourner Truth. LC 68-29021. (American Negro: His History & Literature Ser., No. 1). 1968. Repr. of 1878 ed. 15.00 (ISBN 0-405-01841-X). Ayer Co Pubs.

Narrative of the Captivity of Nehemiah How. Nehemiah How. 59.95 (ISBN 0-8490-0708-9). Gordon Pr.

Narrative of the Days of the Reformation, Chiefly from the Manuscripts of John Foxe the Martyrologist. Ed. by John G. Nichols. Repr. of 1859 ed. 37.00 (ISBN 0-384-41460-5). Johnson Repr.

Narrative of the Days of the Reformation. Ed. by John G. Nichols. (Camden Society, London. Publications, First Ser.: No. 77). Repr. of 1859 ed. 37.00 (ISBN 0-404-50177-X). AMS Pr.

Narrative of the Mission of the United Brethren Among the Delaware & Mohegan Indians. John Heckewelder. LC 79-146399. (First American Frontier Ser). 1971. Repr. of 1820 ed. 29.00 (ISBN 0-405-02852-0). Ayer Co Pubs.

Narrative Space & Mythic Meaning in Mark. Elizabeth S. Malbon. 208p. (Orig.). 1986. 24.95 (ISBN 0-06-254540-X, HarpR). Har-Row.

Narrative Style of the Priestly Writer. Sean E. McEvenne. (Analecta Biblica: Vol. 50). 1971. pap. 17.00 (ISBN 88-7653-050-9). Loyola.

Narrative Unity of Luke-Acts: A Literary Interpretation Vol. 1. Robert C. Tannehill. LC 86-45224. (Gospel According to Luke Series). 352p. 1986. 19.95 (ISBN 0-8006-2112-3, 1-2112). Fortress.

Narratives of the Rites & Laws of the Yncas. Ed. & tr. by Clements R. Markham. (Hakluyt Society First Ser.: No. 48). (Illus.). 1964. Repr. of 1873 ed. 26.50 (ISBN 0-8337-2232-8). B Franklin.

Narrow Is the Way. B. D. Hyman & Jeremy Hyman. Ed. by Pat Golbitz. LC 86-28588. 352p. 1987. 17.95 (ISBN 0-688-06345-4). Morrow.

Narrow Lane. Meher Baba. Ed. by William Le Page. 148p. 1979. pap. 3.95 (ISBN 0-913078-39-5). Sheriar Pr.

NAS Thinline Bible. 1983. Brown cloth edition. text ed. 17.95 (ISBN 0-8024-6283-9); Brown. deluxe ed. 29.95 (ISBN 0-8024-6281-2); Burgundy. deluxe ed. 29.95 (ISBN 0-8024-6282-0). Moody.

NASB Handy Concordance. 272p. (Orig.). 1984. pap. text ed. 5.95 (ISBN 0-310-45252-X, 12395P). Zondervan.

NASB Interlinear Greek-English New Testament. Alfred Marshall. 1056p. 1984. text ed. 27.95 (ISBN 0-310-45240-6, 12394). Zondervan.

Nascido para a Batalha. R. Arthur Matthews. Orig. Title: Born for Battle. (Port.). 1986. write for info. (ISBN 0-8297-1606-8). Life Pubs Intl.

Nataraja Temple: History, Art & Architecture. (Illus.). 1977. 12.00x (ISBN 0-686-22668-2). Intl Bk Dist.

Nathaniel A. Urshan: Champion of the Faith & Legend in Our Time. Georgia Smelser. (Illus.). 160p. (Orig.). 1985. pap. 15.00 (ISBN 0-912315-95-4). Word Aflame.

Nathaniel Emmons: Works, 6 vols. Bruce Kuklick. (American Religious Thought of the 18th & 19th Centuries Ser.). 4935p. 1987. Set. lib. bdg. 620.00 (ISBN 0-8240-6952-8). Garland Pub.

National Catholic Rural Life Conference Idea Book for Small Town Churches. Kathleen Rother & Carol A. Gosse. LC 76-2333. 106p. 1976. pap. 2.50x (ISBN 0-914422-05-7). Glenmary Res Ctr.

National Church of Sweden. John Wordsworth. LC 11-35349. 1911. 20.00x (ISBN 0-8401-2821-5). A R Allenson.

National Conference on Catholic School Finance III. 84p. 1977. 3.60 (ISBN 0-686-29258-8). Natl Cath Educ.

National Conference on Catholic School Finance I. 75p. 1974. 3.60 (ISBN 0-686-29260-X). Natl Cath Educ.

National Directory of Christian Artists. Fred Littaur. LC 85-80487. 256p. (Orig.). 1985. pap. 9.95 (ISBN 0-89081-490-2). Harvest Hse.

National Inventory of Parish Catechetical Programs. pap. cancelled (ISBN 0-686-15370-7, V-590). US Catholic.

National Religions & Universal Religions. Abraham Kuenen. LC 77-27169. (Hibbert Lectures Ser.: 1882). Repr. of 1882 ed. 34.00 (ISBN 0-404-60403-X). AMS Pr.

National Sin & the Decline of American Advantages: Loss of the American Edge in War. Ed. by Bernard Pyron. 230p. (Orig.). 1986. pap. text ed. 7.00 (ISBN 0-9615024-1-X). Rebound Pubns.

National Socialism & the Religion of Nature. Robert A. Pois. LC 85-27615. 208p. 1986. 27.50 (ISBN 0-312-55958-5). St Martin.

National Survey of American Jews, 1984: Political & Social Outlooks. Steven M. Cohen. iv, 60p. (Orig.). 1985. pap. 4.00 (ISBN 0-87495-069-4). Am Jewish Comm.

National Trust Book of Christmas & Festive Day Recipes. Sara P. Williams. (Illus.). 192p. 1980. 13.95 (ISBN 0-7153-8100-8). David & Charles.

Nationalism & Religion in America: Concepts of American Identity & Mission. Winthrop S. Hudson. 12.00 (ISBN 0-8446-0711-8). Peter Smith.

Nationalism & Revolution in Egypt: The Role of the Muslim Brotherhood. Christina Harris. LC 79-2861. 276p. 1987. Repr. of 1964 ed. 25.00 (ISBN 0-8305-0034-0). Hyperion Conn.

Nationalism, Islam & Pakistan. A. H. Hashmi. pap. 14.95 (ISBN 0-317-46108-7). Kazi Pubns.

Nationalism, Positivism & Catholicism: The Politics of Charles Maurras & French Catholics, 1890-1914. Michael Sutton. LC 82-4360. (Cambridge Studies in the History & Theory of Politics). 320p. 1983. 47.50 (ISBN 0-521-22868-9). Cambridge U Pr.

Nationalist Muslim & Indian Politics. Ed. by V. N. Datta & B. E. Gleghorn. LC 75-902114. 352p. 1974. 14.00 (ISBN 0-333-90023-5). South Asia Bks.

Nations in Prophecy. John F. Walvoord. 1967. pap. 5.95 (ISBN 0-310-34101-9, 12159P). Zondervan.

Native American Astronomy. Ed. by Anthony F. Aveni. LC 76-53569. (Illus.). 304p. 1977. text ed. 18.95x (ISBN 0-292-75511-2). U of Tex Pr.

Native American Religions. Sam Gill. 208p. 1981. pap. text ed. write for info. (ISBN 0-534-00973-5). Wadsworth Pub.

Native Cemeteries & Forms of Burial East of the Mississippi. David L. Bushnell, Jr. Repr. of 1920 ed. 29.00x (ISBN 0-403-03658-5). Scholarly.

Native Land: Sagas of the Indian Americas. Jamake Highwater. 1986. 24.95 (ISBN 0-316-36087-2). Little.

Native Mesoamerican Spirituality. Ed. by Miguel Leon-Portilla. Tr. by Arthur J. Anderson & Charles E. Dibble. LC 80-80821. (Classics of Western Spirituality Ser.). 320p. 1980. 13.95 (ISBN 0-8091-0293-5); pap. 9.95 (ISBN 0-8091-2231-6). Paulist Pr.

Native North American Spirituality of the Eastern Woodlands: Sacred Myths, Dreams, Vision Speeches, Healing Formulas, Rituals & Ceremonials. Ed. by Elisabeth Tooker. LC 79-66573. (Classics of Western Spirituality Ser.). 320p. 1979. pap. 9.95 (ISBN 0-8091-2256-1). Paulist Pr.

Native Religions of Mexico & Peru: Hibbert Lectures. Albert Reville. Tr. by Phillip H. Wicksteed. LC 77-27167. 224p. 1983. Repr. of 1884 ed. 29.50 (ISBN 0-404-60405-6). Ams Pr.

Native Tongue & the Word: Developments in English Prose Style, 1380-1580. Janel Mueller. LC 83-15817. 512p. 1984. lib. bdg. 27.50x (ISBN 0-226-54562-8). U of Chicago Pr.

Native Use of Fish in Hawaii. 2nd ed. Margaret Titcomb. 185p. 1972. pap. 4.50 (ISBN 0-8248-0592-5). UH Pr.

Nativity. Juliana Bragg. (Golden Storytime Bk.). (Illus.). 24p. 1987. pap. 2.95 (ISBN 0-307-11960-2, Golden Bks.). Western Pub.

Nativity. Notes by Johanna Hecht. LC 81-65400. (Illus.). 1981. pop-up bk. 9.95 (ISBN 0-385-28713-5). Delacorte.

Nativity. Bart Midwood. 56p. 1982. 9.95 (ISBN 0-9607118-0-5). Bel Esprit.

Nativity. (Illus.). 64p. (Orig.). 1983. 19.95 (ISBN 0-86683-852-X, 8464, HarpR); pap. 9.95 (ISBN 0-86683-726-4, 8304). Har-Row.

Nativity. Dory Younger. 1983. pap. 3.75 (ISBN 0-89536-614-2, 1416). CSS of Ohio.

Nativity Play. Nick Butterworth & Mick Inkpen. (Illus.). 32p. 1985. 10.95 (ISBN 0-316-11903-2). Little.

Natural & the Supernatural. John W. Oman. LC 79-39696. (Select Bibliographies Reprint Ser.). 1972. Repr. of 1931 ed. 20.75 (ISBN 0-8369-9941-X). Ayer Co Pubs.

Natural & the Supernatural Jew: An Historical and Theological Introduction. Arthur A. Cohen. LC 79-13038. 1979. pap. text ed. 6.95x (ISBN 0-87441-291-9). Behrman.

Natural Childbirth & the Christian Family. 4th, rev. ed. Helen Wessel. LC 82-48943. (Illus.). 384p. 1985. pap. text ed. 8.95 (ISBN 0-06-069317-7, HarpR). Har-Row.

Natural Depth in Man. Wilson Van Dusen. LC 72-78055. 197p. pap. 2.50 (ISBN 0-87785-165-4). Swedenborg.

Natural Desire for God: Aquinas Lectures. William R. O'Connor. 1948. 7.95 (ISBN 0-87462-113-5). Marquette.

Natural History of Religion. David Hume. Ed. by H. E. Root. 1957. pap. 4.95x (ISBN 0-8047-0333-7). Stanford U Pr.

Natural History of Religion & Dialogues Concerning Natural Religion. David Hume. Ed. by A. Wayne Colver & Vladimir Price. 1976. 49.95x (ISBN 0-19-824379-0). Oxford U Pr.

Natural Law in the Spiritual World. Henry Drummond. 371p. 1981. pap. 20.00 (ISBN 0-89540-082-0, SB-082). Sun Pub.

Natural Motivation in the Pauline Epistles. rev. ed. Robert J. Austgen. 1969. 10.95 (ISBN 0-268-00374-2). U of Notre Dame Pr.

Natural Path to Genuine Lasting Happiness. Rodney Gale. 1976. 6.50 (ISBN 0-533-02131-6). H R Gale.

Natural Reason: A Study of the Notions of Inference, Assent, Intuition, & First Principles in the Philosophy of John Henry Cardinal Newman. Gerard Casey. (American University Studies V Philosophy: Vol. 4). 345p. 1984. 37.00 (ISBN 0-8204-0078-5). P Lang Pubs.

Natural Religion. Friedrich M. Mueller. LC 73-18810. (Gifford Lectures: 1888). Repr. of 1889 ed. 44.50 (ISBN 0-404-11450-4). AMS Pr.

Natural Religion & Christian Theology: First & Second Series, 2 vols. Charles E. Raven. LC 77-27176. (Gifford Lectures: 1951-52). Repr. of 1953 ed. Set. 37.50 (ISBN 0-404-60540-0). AMS Pr.

Natural Religion in American Literature. Arnold Smithline. 1966. 11.95x (ISBN 0-8084-0227-7); pap. 7.95x (ISBN 0-8084-0228-5). New Coll U Pr.

Natural Supernaturalism: Tradition & Revolution in Romantic Literature. M. H. Abrams. 550p. 1973. pap. 11.95 (ISBN 0-393-00609-3). Norton.

Natural Symbols: Explorations in Cosmology. Mary Douglas. 1982. pap. 5.95 (ISBN 0-394-71105-X). Pantheon.

Natural Theology. William Paley. 1986. lib. bdg. 30.00x (ISBN 0-935005-61-7); pap. 15.00x (ISBN 0-935005-62-5). Ibis Pub VA.

Natural Theology. George G. Stokes. LC 77-27232. (Gifford Lectures: 1891). Repr. of 1891 ed. 30.00 (ISBN 0-404-60452-8). AMS Pr.

Natural Theology for Our Time. Charles Hartshorne. LC 66-14722. 145p. 1967. pap. 9.95 (ISBN 0-87548-239-2). Open Court.

Naturaleza de Dios. Fisher Humphreys. Tr. by Arnoldo Canclini from Eng. (Biblioteca de Doctrina Cristiana). Tr. of Nature of God. (Span.). 144p. (Orig.). 1987. pap. 5.95 (ISBN 0-311-09114-8). Casa Bautista.

Naturalism & Agnosticism: The Gifford Lectures Delivered Before the University of Aberdeen in 1896-1898, 2 Vols. in 1. 4th ed. J. Ward. Repr. of 1899 ed. 36.00 (ISBN 0-527-94500-5). Kraus Repr.

Naturalistic Poetry, Selected from Psalms & Hymns of the Last Three Centuries: In Four Essays, Developing the Progress of Nature-Study, in Connection with Sacred Song. Henry Dircks. 1979. Repr. of 1872 ed. lib. bdg. 20.00 (ISBN 0-8482-0622-3). Norwood Edns.

Naturalistic Tradition in Indian Thought. Dale M. Riepe. LC 82-9185. xii, 308p. 1982. Repr. of 1961 ed. lib. bdg. 35.00x (ISBN 0-313-23622-4, RINA). Greenwood.

Naturalists & the Supernatural: Studies in Horizon & an American Philosophy of Religion. William M. Shea. LC 84-14686. xvi, 242p. 1984. 21.50 (ISBN 0-86554-116-7, MUP/H98). Mercer Univ Pr.

Naturalization of Foreign Protestants in the American & West Indian Colonies, Etc. Montague S. Giuseppi. LC 64-19759. 196p. 1979. Repr. of 1921 ed. 14.00 (ISBN 0-8063-0157-0). Genealog Pub.

Nature & Authority of the Bible. R. Abba. 349p. 1958. 8.95 (ISBN 0-227-67539-8). Attic Pr.

Nature & Character of Theology. J. A. Quenstedt. Tr. by Luther Poellet. 208p. 1986. 12.95 (ISBN 0-570-03984-3, 12-3011). Concordia.

Nature & Dignity of Love. William of St. Thierry. Ed. by E. R. Elder. Tr. by Thomas X. Davis from Lat. (Cistercian Fathers Ser.: No. 30). Orig. Title: De natura et dignitate amoris. 1981. 13.95 (ISBN 0-87907-330-6). Cistercian Pubns.

Nature & Function of Faith in the Theology of John Calvin. Victor A. Shepherd. LC 82-24899. vii, 248p. 1983. pap. 17.45 (ISBN 0-86554-066-7, P07). Mercer Univ Pr.

Nature & Function of Faith in the Theology of John Calvin. Victor A. Shepherd. (Dissertation Ser.: No. 2). viii, 248p. 1982. pap. 17.45 (ISBN 0-86554-066-7). NABPR.

Nature & Grace: A Vital Unity. Leon J. Suenens. (Malines Document Ser.: No. V). (Fr.). 80p. (Orig.). 1986. pap. 5.95 (ISBN 0-89283-303-3). Servant.

Nature & Man in the Bible. Yehuda Feliks. 294p. 1981. 25.00 (ISBN 0-900689-19-6). Soncino Pr.

Nature & Man in the Bible: Chapters in Biblical Ecology. Yehuda Felins. 1982. 25.00x (ISBN 0-900689-19-6). Bloch.

Nature & Meaning of Chastity. William E. May. (Synthesis Ser.). 1977. pap. 1.75 (ISBN 0-8199-0710-3). Franciscan Herald.

Nature & Miracle. J. Diemer. 1977. pap. 1.95 (ISBN 0-88906-015-0). Wedge Pub.

Nature & Mission of the Church. Donald G. Miller. LC 57-9443. (Orig.). 1957. pap. 5.95 (ISBN 0-8042-3208-3). John Knox.

Nature & Necessity of Christ's Church. Michael Richards. LC 83-2596. 142p. 1983. pap. 7.95 (ISBN 0-8189-0458-5). Alba.

Nature & Origin of the New Testament. J. Merle Rife. LC 74-80276. 1975. 9.95 (ISBN 0-8022-2148-3). Philos Lib.

Nature & Religious Imagination: From Edwards to Bushnell. Conrad Cherry. LC 79-7374. 256p. 1980. 3.00 (ISBN 0-8006-0550-0, 1-550). Fortress.

Nature & the Effect of the Heresy of the Fraticelli. Decima L. Douie. LC 77-84715. Repr. of 1932 ed. 36.50 (ISBN 0-404-16121-9). AMS Pr.

Nature & the Supernatural As Together Constituting the One System of God. Horace Bushnell. LC 70-39569. Repr. of 1858 ed. 29.50 (ISBN 0-404-01246-9). AMS Pr.

Nature & Truth of the Great Religions: Toward a Philosophy of Religion. August K. Reischauer. LC 65-20612. 1966. 19.50 (ISBN 0-8048-0420-6). C E Tuttle.

Nature & Use of Ritual. Peter R. De Coppens. 1977. pap. text ed. 9.75 (ISBN 0-8191-0341-1). U Pr of Amer.

Nature & Use of Ritual for Spiritual Attainment. Peter Roche de Coppens. Ed. by John Rossner. LC 85-10270. (Llewellyn's Spiritual Perspectives Ser.). (Illus.). 250p. (Orig.). 1985. pap. 9.95 (ISBN 0-87542-675-1, L-675). Llewellyn Pubns.

Nature, Contemplation, & the One: A Study in the Philosophy of Plotinus. John N. Deck. LC 67-98055. pap. 36.30 (ISBN 0-317-08774-6, 2014184). Bks Demand UMI.

Nature, History, God. Xavier Zubiri. Tr. by Thomas B. Fowler, Jr. from Span. LC 80-1355. 441p. 1981. lib. bdg. 31.25; pap. text ed. 17.75. U Pr of Amer.

Nature in Grace: A Study in the Theology of Nature. Claude Y. Stewart, Jr. LC 83-8196. xx, 318p. 1983. pap. 21.50 (ISBN 0-86554-068-3, P08). Mercer Univ Pr.

Nature in the Works of Fray Luis De Granada. Sr. Mary B. Brentano. LC 75-94164. (Catholic University. Studies in Romance Languages & Literatures: No. 15). Repr. of 1936 ed. 21.00 (ISBN 0-404-50315-2). AMS Pr.

Nature Is Lord. English J. Matthews. 80p. 1986. 7.95 (ISBN 0-89962-511-8). Todd & Honeywell.

Nature, Man & God. William Temple. LC 77-27190. (Gifford Lectures Ser.: 1932-33, 1933-34). 1979. Repr. of 1935 ed. 54.50 (ISBN 0-404-60493-5). AMS Pr.

Nature, Man & Woman. Alan W. Watts. LC 58-8266. 1970. pap. 3.95 (ISBN 0-394-70592-0, V592, Vin). Random.

Nature Meditations. Hazrat I. Khan. LC 80-50829. (Collected Works of Hazrat Inayat Khan Ser.). (Illus.). 128p. (Orig.). 1980. pap. 6.95 (ISBN 0-930872-12-6). Omega Pr NM.

Nature, Mind & Death. C. J. Ducasse. (Paul Carus Lecture Ser.). 533p. 1951. 19.95 (ISBN 0-87548-102-7). Open Court.

Nature of Belief. facsimile ed. Martin C. D'Arcy. (Select Bibliographies Reprint Ser). Repr. of 1931 ed. 21.00 (ISBN 0-8369-5930-2). Ayer Co Pubs.

Nature of Christian Belief. Church of England, House of Bishops Staff. 60p. (Orig.). 1986. pap. 2.25 (ISBN 0-88028-062-X). Forward Movement.

Nature of Consciousness in Hindu Philosophy. 2nd ed. S. K. Saksena. 1971. 5.95 (ISBN 0-89684-284-3). Orient Bk Dist.

Nature of Doctrine: Religion & Theology in a Postliberal Age. George A. Lindbeck. LC 83-27332. 142p. 1984. 16.95 (ISBN 0-664-21829-6); pap. 9.95 (ISBN 0-664-24618-4). Westminster.

Nature of Evil: Considered in a Letter to the Rev. Edward Beecher, D.D. Henry James, Sr. LC 72-920. (Selected Works of Henry James, Sr.: Vol. 6). 352p. 1983. Repr. of 1855 ed. 37.50 (ISBN 0-404-10086-4). AMS Pr.

Nature of Faith. Gerhard Ebeling. Ed. by Ronald G. Smith. LC 62-7194. pap. 47.80 (2026871). Bks Demand UMI.

Nature of God. Fisher Humphreys. LC 84-20037. (Layman's Library of Christian Doctrine Ser.). 1985. 5.95 (ISBN 0-8054-1634-X). Broadman.

Nature of Greek Myths. G. S. Kirk. LC 74-21683. 336p. 1975. 27.95 (ISBN 0-87951-031-5). Overlook Pr.

Nature of Greek Myths. G. S. Kirk. 1975. pap. 5.95 (ISBN 0-14-021783-5, Pelican). Penguin.

Nature of Guilt. Jean Kirkpatrick. 16p. 1983. pap. 1.50 (ISBN 0-318-19524-0). WFS.

Nature of Imam Hussein'n Movement. Murtaza Mutahhari. Ed. by Muhammed K. Ali. Tr. by Alaedin Pazargadi. 20p. 1984. pap. 2.95 (ISBN 0-940368-33-1). Tahrike Tarsile Quran.

Nature of Man in Theological & Psychological Perspective. Ed. by Simon Doniger. LC 72-10819. (Essay Index Reprint Ser.). 1973. Repr. of 1962 ed. 18.00 (ISBN 0-8369-7213-9). Ayer Co Pubs.

Nature of Morality: An Introduction to Ethics. Gilbert Harman. 1977. pap. text ed. 10.95x (ISBN 0-19-502143-6). Oxford U Pr.

Nature of Public Philosophy. Richard Bishirjian. LC 82-20170. 62p. 1983. pap. text ed. 4.75 (ISBN 0-8191-2861-9). U Pr of Amer.

Nature of Quakerism. Howard H. Brinton. 1983. pap. 2.50x (ISBN 0-87574-047-2, 047). Pendle Hill.

Nature of Religion. William P. Paterson. LC 77-27202. (Gifford Lectures: 1924-25). Repr. of 1926 ed. 47.50 (ISBN 0-404-60476-5). AMS Pr.

Nature of Religious Experience: Essays in Honor of Douglas Clyde Macintosh. facsimile ed. LC 78-152202. (Essay Index Reprint Ser). Repr. of 1937 ed. 16.00 (ISBN 0-8369-2286-7). Ayer Co Pubs.

Nature of Religious Man. D. B. Fry. 1982. 15.95 (ISBN 0-900860-67-7, Pub. by Octagon Pr England). Ins Study Human.

Nature of Revival. rev. ed. John Wesley. Ed. by Clare Weakley. 256p. 1987. pap. 6.95 (ISBN 0-87123-925-6). Bethany Hse.

Nature of Spiritual Growth. rev. ed. John Wesley & Clare Weakley. 208p. 1986. pap. 5.95 (ISBN 0-87123-876-4). Bethany Hse.

Nature of the Church. Bill J. Leonard. (Orig.). 1986. 5.95 (ISBN 0-8054-1642-0). Broadman.

Nature of the Gods. Cicero. Tr. by Horace C. McGregor. (Classics Ser.). 280p. (Orig.). 1972. pap. 6.95 (ISBN 0-14-044265-0). Penguin.

Nature of the Kingdom. John Wesley. Ed. by Clare Weakley. 288p. 1986. pap. 6.95 (ISBN 0-87123-875-6, 210875). Bethany Hse.

Nature of the Soul & Its Ultimate Goals. Dwane K. Martell. (Science of Man Library). (Illus.). 109p. 1983. 47.25 (ISBN 0-89920-048-6). Am Inst Psych.

Nature of Things to Come. Stanley E. Sayers. 1972. 7.95 (ISBN 0-88027-013-6). Firm Foun Pub.

Nature of True Virtue. Jonathan Edwards. 1960. pap. 5.95 (ISBN 0-472-06037-6, 37, AA). U of Mich Pr.

Nature of Truth, It's Union & Unity with the Soule. Brooke R. Greville. 210p. Repr. of 1640 ed. text ed. 33.12x (ISBN 0-576-02144-X, Pub. by Gregg Intl Pubs England). Gregg Intl.

Nature Sense in the Writings of Ludwig Tieck. George H. Danton. LC 78-163673. (Columbia University. Germanic Studies, Old Ser.: No. 9). Repr. of 1907 ed. 15.00 (ISBN 0-404-50409-4). AMS Pr.

Nature, Spirituality & Science. Sukh R. Tarneja. 240p. 1980. text ed. 27.50x (ISBN 0-7069-1203-9, Pub by Vikas India). Advent NY.

Nature, Structure, & Function of the Church in William of Ockham. John J. Ryan. LC 78-2891. (American Academy of Religion: Studies in Religion, 16). 1979. pap. 9.95 (ISBN 0-89130-230-1, 1010016). Scholars Pr GA.

Nature-Word. R. A Schwaller de Lubicz. Tr. by Deborah Lawlor & Robert Lawlor. LC 82-81069. 160p. 1982. pap. 8.95 (ISBN 0-89281-036-X). Inner Tradit.

Nature Word: Verbe Nature. R. A. Schwaller de Lubicz. Tr. & intro. by Deborah Lawlor. LC 82-81069. (Illus.). 160p. (Orig.). 1982. pap. 6.95 (ISBN 0-940262-00-2, Lindisfarne Pr). Inner Tradit.

Nature's Nation. Perry G. Miller. LC 67-17316. 1967. 20.00x (ISBN 0-674-60550-0, Belknap Pr). Harvard U Pr.

Natures Religion. Jack V. Williamson. 6.95 (ISBN 0-8062-2425-8). Carlton.

Nauvoo: Kingdom on the Mississippi. Robert B. Flanders. LC 65-19110. (Illus.). 374p. 1975. pap. 8.95 (ISBN 0-252-00561-9). U of Ill Pr.

Navaho Classification of Their Song Ceremonials. L. C. Wyman & Clyde Kluckhohn. LC 38-23008. (American Anthro. Association Memoirs). 1938. pap. 15.00 (ISBN 0-527-00549-5). Kraus Repr.

Navaho Religion: A Study of Symbolism. Gladys A. Reichard. LC 83-5082. 804p. 1983. pap. 19.95x (ISBN 0-8165-0834-8). U of Ariz Pr.

Navaho Witchcraft. Clyde Kluckhohn. 1962. pap. 8.95x (ISBN 0-8070-4697-3, BP243). Beacon Pr.

Navajo Bringing-Home Ceremony: The Claus Chee Sonny Version of Deerway Ajilee. Karl W. Luckert. LC 78-59701. (Illus.). 14p. 1978. pap. 14.95x (ISBN 0-89734-027-2). Mus Northern Ariz.

Navajo Creation Myth: The Story of Emergence. Hasteen Klah. LC 76-43762. (Museum of Navajo Ceremonial Art. Religion Ser.: Vol. 1). Repr. of 1942 ed. 24.50 (ISBN 0-404-15615-0). AMS Pr.

Navajo Medicine Man Sand Paintings. Gladys Reichard. (Illus.). 1977. pap. 8.95 (ISBN 0-486-23329-4). Dover.

Navajos in the Catholic Church Records of New Mexico 1694-1875. David M. Brugge. LC 84-60510. 1986. 12.50x (ISBN 0-912586-59-1). Navajo Coll Pr.

Navarre Bible: St. Mark. Ed. by Theological Faculty, University of Navarre. 202p. 1986. 10.00 (ISBN 0-906127-92-0). Lumen Christi.

Naven: A Survey of the Problems Suggested by a Composite Picture of the Culture of a New Guinea Tribe Drawn from Three Points of View. 2nd ed. Gregory Bateson. (Illus.). 1958. 25.00x (ISBN 0-8047-0519-4); pap. 10.95 (ISBN 0-8047-0520-8). Stanford U Pr.

Nave's Study Bible. Orville J. Nave. 24.95 (ISBN 0-8010-6696-4). Baker Bk.

Nave's Topical Bible. Orville J. Nane. 1616p. Date not set. 19.95 (ISBN 0-917006-02-X). Hendrickson MA.

Nave's Topical Bible. condensed ed. Orville Nave. Ed. by Moody Press Staff. pap. 4.95 (ISBN 0-8024-0030-2). Moody.

Nave's Topical Bible. Orville J. Nave. LC 79-14111. 1979. 19.95 (ISBN 0-8407-4992-9). Nelson.

Nave's Topical Bible. enlarged ed. Orville J. Nave & S. Maxwell Coder. 1384p. 1975. 21.95 (ISBN 0-8024-5861-0). Moody.

Navidad. Compiled by L. M. Weatherford De Ruiz. (Span.). 192p. 1981. pap. 2.75 (ISBN 0-311-08207-6). Casa Bautista.

Navidad en Nuestra Familia. Ruth B. Graham. Tr. by Roberto Gama from Eng. Orig. Title: Our Christmas Story. (Span., Illus.). 128p. (Orig.). pap. 5.25 (ISBN 0-311-08225-4). Casa Bautista.

Navigator. Robert D. Foster. LC 83-60287. 240p. 1983. pap. 3.95 (ISBN 0-89109-495-4). NavPress.

Navigator Bible Studies Handbook. x1979 ed. Navigators Staff. LC 79-87654. (Illus.). 132p. 1974. pap. 5.95 (ISBN 0-89109-075-4). Navpress.

Navya Nyaya System of Logic. 3rd enlarged ed. D. C. Guha. 1979. 15.50 (ISBN 0-89684-059-X, Pub. by Motilal Banarsidass India). Orient Bk Dist.

Nay-Saying in Concord: Emerson, Alcott & Thoreau. Taylor Stoehr. LC 78-25580. 179p. 1979. 21.50 (ISBN 0-208-01767-4, Archon). Shoe String.

Nazi Doctors: Medical Killing & the Psychology of Genocide. Robert J. Lifton. LC 85-73874. 576p. 1986. 19.95 (ISBN 0-465-04904-4). Basic.

Nazi State & the New Religions: Five Case Studies in Non-conformity. Christine E. King. LC 82-20910. (Studies in Religion & Society: Vol. 4). 332p. 1982. 59.95x (ISBN 0-88946-865-6). E Mellen.

Nazir, 1 vol. 15.00 (ISBN 0-910218-69-2). Bennet Pub.

NCEA. (Keynote Ser.). 1985. write for info. Natl Cath Educ.

NCEA-GANLEY's Catholic Schools in America. 322p. 33.00 (ISBN 0-686-29255-3). Natl Cath Educ.

NCEA Roman Catholic Theological Seminaries Fact Book: National Summary of Key Issues 1980-1984. 72p. 1985. 6.00 (ISBN 0-318-20614-5). Natl Cath Educ.

Near-Death Experience: A Christian Approach. Brennan Hill. 66p. 1981. pap. 3.50 (ISBN 0-697-01756-7). Wm C Brown.

Near Eastern Mythology. John Gray. LC 84-45599. (Library of the World's Myths & Legends). (Illus.). 144p. 1985. 18.95 (ISBN 0-87226-004-6). P Bedrick Bks.

Near Eastern Religious Texts Relating to the Old Testament. Ed. by Walter Beyerlin. Tr. by John Bowden. LC 77-28284. (Old Testament Library). (Illus.). 324p. 1978. 22.00 (ISBN 0-664-21363-4). Westminster.

Near Eastern Studies: In Honor of William Foxwell Albright. Hans Goedicke. LC 70-142817. 504p. 1971. 42.50x (ISBN 0-8018-1235-6). Johns Hopkins.

Near Hurting People: The Pastoral Ministry of Robert Moffat Fine. Donald Demaray. (Illus.). 1978. pap. 3.50 (ISBN 0-89367-024-3). Light & Life.

Nebuchadrezzar & Babylon. D. J. Wiseman. (British Academy - Schweich Lectures). (Illus.). 144p. 1986. 34.50x (ISBN 0-19-726040-3). Oxford U Pr.

Necessity of Ethical Absolutes: (CFUC) Erwin W. Lutzer. 112p. (Orig.). 1981. pap. 6.95 (ISBN 0-310-35791-8, 12659P). Zondervan.

Necessity of Prayer. E. M. Bounds. (Direction Bks). 144p. 1976. pap. 2.95 (ISBN 0-8010-0659-7). Baker Bk.

Necessity of Prayer. E. M. Bounds. 144p. 1984. pap. 3.50 (ISBN 0-88368-139-0). Whitaker Hse.

Necromancer, Or, Voo-Doo Doctor. Handy N. Brown. LC 77-39544. Repr. of 1904 ed. 13.50 (ISBN 0-404-00008-8). AMS Pr.

Nectar of Chanting. 3rd, rev. ed. SYDA Foundation. LC 78-68854. 216p. 7.95 (ISBN 0-914602-16-0). SYDA Found.

Nectar of Devotion. Swami A. C. Bhaktivedanta. LC 78-118082. (Illus.). 1970. 12.95 (ISBN 0-912776-05-6). Bhaktivedanta.

Nedarim, 1 vol. 18.00 (ISBN 0-910218-68-4). Bennet Pub.

Need for Certainty: A Sociological Study of Conventional Religion. Robert Towler. 180p. 1985. 22.50x (ISBN 0-7100-9973-8). Methuen Inc.

Need for the Magisterium of the Church. K. D. Whitehead. (Synthesis Ser.). 1979. 0.75 (ISBN 0-8199-0747-2). Franciscan Herald.

Need: The New Religion. J. A. Walter. LC 86-184. 173p. 1986. pap. 6.95 (ISBN 0-87784-948-X). Inter-Varsity.

Need to Believe: The Psychology of Religion. Mortimer Ostow & Ben-Ami Scharfstein. 1969. pap. text ed. 19.95 (ISBN 0-8236-8159-9, 23520). Intl Univs Pr.

Neeley Never Said Good-By. Carole G. Page. (Sensitive Issues Ser.). (Orig.). 1984. pap. 3.50 (ISBN 0-8024-0342-5). Moody.

Nefesh Hayah: Commentary & Interpretation on the Passover Haggadah with the Haggadah Text. P. S. Pollak. (Hebrew.). 9.50 (ISBN 0-87559-091-8). Shalom.

Negative Language of the Dionysian School of Mystical Theology: An Approach to the Cloud of Unknowing, 2 vols. Rosemary A. Lees. Ed. by James Hogg. (Analecta Cartusiana Ser.: No. 107). 549p. (Orig.). 1983. pap. 50.00 (ISBN 0-317-42591-9, Pub. by Salzburg Studies). Longwood Pub Group.

Neglected Aspects of Sufi Study. Idries Shah. 83p. 1977. 9.95 (ISBN 0-900860-56-1, Pub. by Octagon Pr England). Ins Study Human.

Negro Baptist Pulpit. facs. ed. Ed. by Edward M. Brawley. LC 74-154072. (Black Heritage Library Collection Ser). 1890. 19.25 (ISBN 0-8369-8783-7). Ayer Co Pubs.

Negro Church in America. E. Franklin Frazier & C. Eric Lincoln. Bd. with Black Church Since Frazier. LC 72-96201. (Sourcebooks in Negro History Ser.). 1973. pap. 4.95 (ISBN 0-8052-0387-7). Schocken.

Negro Freemasonry. D. A. Cass. 11.00x (ISBN 0-685-22057-5). Wehman.

Negro Freemasonry & Segregation. Cass. 11.00 (ISBN 0-685-19494-9). Powner.

Negro-Jewish Relations in the United States. Conference On Jewish Social Studies. 1966. pap. 1.50 (ISBN 0-8065-0092-1, 218). Citadel Pr.

Negro Masonry. William H. Upton. LC 70-144696. Repr. of 1902 ed. 16.00 (ISBN 0-404-00218-8). AMS Pr.

Negro Pew. facs. ed. LC 76-149873. (Black Heritage Library Collection Ser). 1837. 10.00 (ISBN 0-8369-8753-5). Ayer Co Pubs.

Negro Sings a New Heaven. Mary A. Grissom. LC 70-168209. Repr. of 1930 ed. 11.50 (ISBN 0-404-08311-0). AMS Pr.

Negro Spirituals, 2 vols. in 1. Harry T. Burleigh. LC 74-24262. Repr. of 1922 ed. 45.00 (ISBN 0-404-12874-2). AMS Pr.

Negro Spirituals: From Bible to Folk Song. Christa K. Dixon. LC 75-364444. pap. 31.80 (2026874). Bks Demand UMI.

Negro's Church. Benjamin E. Mays & Joseph W. Nicholson. LC 70-83430. (Religion in America, Ser. 1). 1969. Repr. of 1933 ed. 25.50 (ISBN 0-405-00255-6). Ayer Co Pubs.

Negro's God As Reflected in His Literature. Benjamin E. Mays. LC 69-16578. (Illus.). Repr. of 1938 ed. 24.75x (ISBN 0-8371-1139-0, MAG&, Pub. by Negro U Pr). Greenwood.

Nehemiah. rev. ed. G. Michael Cocoris. 37p. 1984. pap. 1.00 (ISBN 0-935729-14-3). Church Open Door.

Nehemiah. rev. ed. G. Michael Cocoris. 37p. 1984. pap. 1.00 (ISBN 0-935729-15-1). Church Open Door.

Nehemiah: A Man of Prayer & Persistence. Gene A. Getz. LC 80-53102. 1981. pap. 4.95 (ISBN 0-8307-0778-6, 5414500). Regal.

Nehemiah & the Dynamics of Effective Leadership: Study Guide. Cyril J. Barber. (Illus.). 56p. 1980. pap. text ed. 3.25 (ISBN 0-87213-022-3). Loizeaux.

Nehemiah & the Dynamics of Effective Leadership. Cyril J. Barber. LC 76-22567. 1976. pap. 3.95 (ISBN 0-87213-021-5). Loizeaux.

Nehemiah Builds a City. Illus. by Graham Round. (Illus.). 16p. 1982. pap. 0.99 (ISBN 0-86683-661-6, AY8241, HarpR). Har-Row.

Nehemiah: Man in Charge. Donald K. Campbell. 1979. pap. 4.95 (ISBN 0-88207-781-3). Victor Bks.

Nehemiah's Greatest Day. (Story Bible Ser.). 1987. pap. 2.95. Lion USA.

Neighborhood of IS, Approaches to the Inner Solitude, A Thematic Anthology: Plotinus, Dionysius the Areopagite, The Cloud of Unknowing, The Book of Privy Counseling, Meister Eckhart. Ed. by Hastings Moore & Gary W. Moore. 108p. (Orig.). 1984. pap. text ed. 9.50 (ISBN 0-8191-3972-6). U Pr of Amer.

Neighbors, Friends, or Madmen: The Puritan Adjustment to Quakerism in Seventeenth-Century Massachusetts Bay. Jonathan M. Chu. LC 84-29035. (Contributions to the Study of Religion Ser.: No. 14). xiii, 207p. 1985. lib. bdg. 29.95 (ISBN 0-313-24809-5, CNE/). Greenwood.

Neither Male nor Female. Q. A. Adams. 4.95 (ISBN 0-89985-104-5). Christ Nations.

Neither This Nor That. Bhagwan Shree Rajneesh. Ed. by Ma Yoga Pratima. LC 83-181238. (Zen Ser.). (Illus.). 280p. (Orig.). 1975. 14.95 (ISBN 0-88050-097-2). Chidvilas Found.

Neither White nor Black: Mormon Scholars Confront the Race Issue in a Universal Church. Ed. by Lester E. Bush & Armand L. Mauss. 250p. 1984. pap. 11.95 (ISBN 0-941214-22-2). Signature Bks.

Nelson Children's Bible. Retold by Pat Alexander. 6.95 (ISBN 0-8407-5238-5). Nelson.

Nelson's Complete Concordance of the New American Bible. LC 77-22170. 1977. 44.95 (ISBN 0-8407-4900-7). Nelson.

Nelson's Complete Concordance of the Revised Standard Version. 2nd ed. John W. Ellison. 1136p. 1985. 29.95 (ISBN 0-8407-4954-6). Nelson.

Nelson's Illustrated Bible Dictionary. Ed. by Herbert Lockyer, Sr. 1088p. 1986. 26.95 (ISBN 0-8407-4955-4). Nelson.

Nelson's New Compact Illustrated Bible Dictionary. (Illus.). 1978. 2.95 (ISBN 0-8407-5636-4). Nelson.

Nennius's "History of the Brittons". Nennius. Tr. by A. W. Wade-Evans. Bd. with Annals of Britons of Court Pedigree of Hywel the Good. (Church Historical Society, London, N. S.: No. 34). pap. 23.00 (ISBN 0-317-15134-7). Kraus Repr.

Nenshu & the Tiger: Parables of Life & Death. Martin Bell. 112p. 1982. pap. 5.95 (ISBN 0-8164-2356-3, HarpR). Har-Row.

Neo-Confucian Orthodoxy & the Learning of the Mind-&-Heart. William T. De Bary. LC 81-3809. (Neo-Confucian Studies). 267p. 1986. pap. 15.00x (ISBN 0-231-05229-4). Columbia U Pr.

Neo-Confucian Terms Explained: The Pei-hsi tzu-i. Tr. by Wing-Tsit Chan from Chinese. LC 86-5427. (Neo-Confucian Studies Ser.). 288p. 1986. 35.00x (ISBN 0-231-06384-9). Columbia U Pr.

Neo-Congregationalism. Hugo R. Pruter. LC 85-13416. 90p. 1985. Repr. lib. bdg. 19.95x (ISBN 0-89370-598-5). Borgo Pr.

Neo-Conservatism: Social & Religious Phenomenon. Ed. by Gregory Baum & John Coleman. (Concilium 1981 Ser.: Vol. 141). 128p. (Orig.). 1981. pap. 6.95 (ISBN 0-8164-2308-3, HarpR). Har-Row.

Neo-Darwinism. R. J. Berry. (Studies in Biology: No. 144). 72p. 1982. pap. text ed. 9.95 (ISBN 0-7131-2849-6). E Arnold.

Neo-Orthodoxy. Charles Ryrie. 1978. pap. 2.50 (ISBN 0-937396-27-3). Walterick Pubs.

Neoevangelicalism Today. Robert P. Lightner. LC 78-11426. (Illus.). 1979. pap. 3.95 (ISBN 0-87227-067-X). Reg Baptist.

Neoplatonism & Christian Thought. Dominic J. O'Meara. LC 81-5272. (Neoplatonism: Ancient & Modern Ser.). 270p. 1981. 44.50x (ISBN 0-87395-492-0); pap. 14.95x (ISBN 0-87395-493-9). State U NY Pr.

Nervous Christians. L. Gilbert Little. 1956. pap. 3.95 (ISBN 0-8024-5878-5). Moody.

Nervous Disorders & Religion: A Study of Souls in the Making. John G. McKenzie. LC 79-8719. 183p. 1981. Repr. of 1951 ed. lib. bdg. 22.50x (ISBN 0-313-22192-8, MCND). Greenwood.

NESFA Hymnal. 2nd ed. Joe Ross. 220p. pap. 10.00 (ISBN 0-915368-69-2). New Eng SF Assoc.

Nesting in the Rock. George Maloney. 6.95 (ISBN 0-87193-002-1). Dimension Bks.

Nestorian Churches. Aubrey R. Vine. LC 78-63173. (Heresies of the Early Christian & Medieval Era: Second Ser.). Repr. of 1937 ed. 31.50 (ISBN 0-404-16188-X). AMS Pr.

Nestorian Collection of Christological Texts, 2 vols. Ed. by Luise Abramowski & Allan E. Goodman. Incl. Vol. 1. Syriac Text. 59.50 (ISBN 0-521-07578-5); Vol. 2. Introduction, Translation & Indexes. 49.50 (ISBN 0-521-08126-2). LC 77-130904. (Oriental Publications Ser.: No. 18, 19). 1972. Cambridge U Pr.

Nestorian Missionary Enterprise. John Stewart. LC 78-63172. (Heresies of the Early Christian & Medieval Era: Second Ser.). Repr. of 1928 ed. 46.50 (ISBN 0-404-16187-1). AMS Pr.

Nestorians & Their Muslim Neighbors, A Study of Western Influence on Their Relations. John B. Joseph. LC 61-7417. (Princeton Studies on the Near East). pap. 74.30 (ISBN 0-317-08465-8, 2000553). Bks Demand UMI.

Nestorius & His Place in the History of the Christian Doctrine. Richard Loofs. LC 75-1225. 1975. Repr. of 1914 ed. 18.50 (ISBN 0-8337-4903-X). B Franklin.

Nestorius & His Teaching. J. F. Bethune-Baker. 1908. 20.00 (ISBN 0-527-07500-0). Kraus Repr.

Nests Above the Abyss. Isobel Kuhn. pap. 3.95 (ISBN 9971-83-817-6). OMF Bks.

Neturei Karta; Voice of Anti-Zionist Judaism: A Study. Ed. by B. Chaim. 1980. 75.00 (ISBN 0-87700-273-8). Revisionist Pr.

Neuf Annees De Bibliographie Erasmienne (1962-1970) Jean-Claude Margolin. 1977. 85.00x (ISBN 0-8020-2276-6). U of Toronto Pr.

Neuplatonische und gnostische Weltablehnung in der Schule Plotins. Christoph Elsas. (Religionsgeschichtliche Versuche und Vorarbeiten Ser., Vol. 34). 1975. 45.60 (ISBN 3-11-003941-9). De Gruyter.

Never A Day Too Much. Daniel Black. (Orig.). 1985. pap. text ed. 4.95 (ISBN 0-87148-631-8). Pathway Pr.

Never Alone. Joan W. Brown. 48p. 1985. 6.95 (ISBN 0-8378-5084-3). Gibson.

Never Alone. pap. 0.45 (ISBN 0-686-23470-7). Rose Pub MI.

Never Born a Hero. Phyllis R. Naylor. LC 82-70950. 128p. pap. 3.95 (ISBN 0-8066-1925-2, 10-4647). Augsburg.

Never Give It up. Sheila Walsh. 1987. pap. 6.95. Revell.

Never Ninkarrak-Text. Johannes S. Nikel. pap. 7.00 (ISBN 0-384-41600-4). Johnson Repr.

Never On Your Own. Gordon Spykman. 125p. 1983. pap. 4.95 (ISBN 0-933140-85-1); Pt. 1, 48pgs. student manual 1.95 (ISBN 0-933140-86-X); Pt. 2, 48pgs. student manual 1.95 (ISBN 0-933140-87-8). CRC Pubns.

Never Say Die: Story of Gladys Aylward. Cyril Davey. 1964. pap. 2.95 (ISBN 0-87508-616-0). Chr Lit.

Never Say Old. Bartlett Hess & Margaret Hess. 156p. 1984. pap. 5.95 (ISBN 0-89693-375-X). Victor Bks.

Never to Forget: The Jews of the Holocaust. Milton Meltzer. 192p. 1977. pap. 3.25 (ISBN 0-440-96070-3, LFL); tchr's. guide by Max Nadel 0.50. Dell.

Never to Forget: The Jews of the Holocaust. Milton Meltzer. LC 75-25409. (YA) 1976. PLB 13.89 (ISBN 0-06-024175-6). HarpJ.

Never Underestimate the Power of God's Woman. Daisy Hepburn. LC 84-3337. (Life with Spice Bible Study Ser.). 1984. 2.95 (ISBN 0-8307-0948-7, 6101856). Regal.

Nevertheless. John H. Yoder. LC 75-170197. (Christian Peace Shelf Ser.). 144p. 1972. pap. 4.95 (ISBN 0-8361-1661-5). Herald Pr.

New Accounts in Contemporary Theology. Roger Hazelton. LC 78-12237. 1979. Repr. of 1960 ed. lib. bdg. cancelled (ISBN 0-313-21181-7, HANA). Greenwood.

New Age. Gertrude C. Carlson. LC 85-90283. 252p. 1986. 13.95 (ISBN 0-533-06790-1). Vantage.

New Age Bible Interpretation, Vol. 1. Corinne Heline. (Illus.). 496p. 1985. Repr. of 1935 ed. lib. bdg. 16.00 (ISBN 0-933963-01-7). New Age Bible.

New Age Bible Interpretation, Vol. 2. Corinne Heline. (Illus.). 469p. Repr. lib. bdg. 16.00 (ISBN 0-933963-02-5). New Age Bible.

New Age Bible Interpretation, Vol. 3. Corinne Heline. (Illus.). 516p. Repr. text ed. 16.00 (ISBN 0-87613-046-5). New Age Bible.

New Age Bible Interpretation, Vol. 4. Corinne Heline. 144p. 1985. Repr. of 1935 ed. lib. bdg. 8.00 (ISBN 0-87613-089-9). New Age Bible.

New Age Bible Interpretation, Vol. 5. Corinne Heline. 230p. Repr. lib. bdg. 11.00 (ISBN 0-933963-05-X). New Age Bible.

New Age Bible Interpretation, Vol. 6. Corinne Heline. (Illus.). 255p. lib. bdg. 12.00 (ISBN 0-933963-06-8). New Age Bible.

New Age Bible Interpretation, Vol. 7. Corinne Heline. (Illus.). 298p. lib. bdg. 14.00 (ISBN 0-933963-07-6). New Age Bible.

New Age Globalism: Humanist Agenda for Building a New World Without God. H. Edward Rowe. 95p. (Orig.). 1985. pap. 4.95 (ISBN 0-931225-11-6). Growth Pub.

New Age Handbook on Death & Dying: Death Is Life Too. Carol W. Parrish-Harra. LC 81-70369. 160p. 1982. pap. 5.95 (ISBN 0-87516-470-6). De Vorss.

New Age Movement. Douglas R. Groothuis. 32p. (Orig.). 1986. pap. 0.75 (ISBN 0-87784-079-2). Inter-Varsity.

New Age-Old Path. Ishwar C. Puri. Ed. by Edward D. Scott. 54p. (Orig.). 1985. pap. 3.00 (ISBN 0-937067-04-0). Inst Study Hum Aware.

New Age Tantra Yoga: The Sexual Gateway to Spiritual Fulfillment. 6th ed. Howard J. Zitko. LC 75-3657. 1985. pap. 7.50 (ISBN 0-941902-00-5). World Univ AZ.

New Alchemy: To Turn You On. Bhagwan Shree Rajneesh. Ed. by Ma Satya Bharti. LC 83-181814. (Western Mystics Ser.). (Illus.). 308p. (Orig.). 1978. 15.50 (ISBN 0-88050-098-0). Chidvilas Found.

New American Justice: A Moral Proposal for the Reconciliation of Personal Freedom & Social Justice. Daniel C. Maguire. 218p. 1982. pap. 9.95 (ISBN 0-86683-636-5, HarpR). Har-Row.

New American Reformation: A Study of Youth Culture & Religion. James F. Drane. (Quality Paperback Ser.: No. 293). 166p. 1974. pap. 2.95 (ISBN 0-8226-0293-8). Littlefield.

New American Standard Exhaustive Concordance of the Bible: Hebrew-Aramaic & Greek Dictionaries. Ed. by Robert L. Thomas. LC 80-39626. 1695p. 1981. 29.95 (ISBN 0-87981-197-8, 4690-98); thumb-indexed 34.95 (ISBN 0-87981-503-5). Holman Bible Pub.

New & Old in God's Revelation. Benedict Engelzakis. (Studies in Relations Between Spirit & Tradition in the Bible). 128p. 1982. text ed. 12.95 (ISBN 0-913836-89-3). St Vladimirs.

New Apocalypse: The Radical Christian Vision of William Blake. Thomas J. Altizer. 1967. 8.50 (ISBN 0-87013-108-7). Mich St U Pr.

New Approach to Buddhism. Dhiravamsa. LC 74-81623. 1974. pap. 3.95 (ISBN 0-913922-08-0). Dawn Horse Pr.

New Approach to Jewish Life. 4.95 (ISBN 0-87677-142-8). Hartmore.

New Approaches in Pastoral Counseling. Steven K. Kaplan & Lynn A. Schoeneberg. 1987. text ed. 19.95 (ISBN 0-8290-1806-9). Irvington.

New Approaches to Family Pastoral Care. Douglas A. Anderson. LC 79-8898. (Creative Pastoral Care & Counseling Ser.). pap. 24.00 (2029614). Bks Demand UMI.

New Art of Living. Norman V. Peale. 160p. 1977. pap. 2.50 (ISBN 0-449-23938-1, Crest). Fawcett.

New Atheism & the Erosion of Freedom. Robert Morey. 180p. (Orig.). 1986. pap. 5.95 (ISBN 0-87123-889-6, 210889). Bethany Hse.

New Bantam-Megiddo Hebrew & English Dictionary. Reuven Sivan & Edward A. Levenston. LC 77-75289. (Hebrew & Eng.). 1977. 24.95 (ISBN 0-8052-3666-X). Schocken.

New Bantam-Megiddo Hebrew Dictionary. Edward A. Levenston & Reuven Sivan. (Hebrew.). 736p. 1975. pap. 4.95 (ISBN 0-553-26387-0). Bantam.

New Beginning: Studies in John's Gospel. John A. Ishee. 35p. (Orig.). 1982. pap. 3.50 (ISBN 0-939298-13-9, 139). J. M. Prods.

New Being. Paul Tillich. 1955. pap. 6.95 (ISBN 0-684-71908-8, ScribT). Scribner.

New Bible Atlas. Ed. by J. H. Paterson & D. J. Wiseman. 128p. 1985. 14.95 (ISBN 0-8423-4675-9). Tyndale.

New Bible Commentary. rev. ed. Donald Guthrie. 1970. 24.95 (ISBN 0-8028-2281-9). Eerdmans.

New Bible Crossword Puzzles, No. 5. Gretchen Whitlow. 128p. (Orig.). 1983. pap. 2.25 (ISBN 0-8007-8471-5, Spire Bks.). Revell.

New Bible Dictionary. Ed. by J. D. Douglas. 1344p. 1982. 24.95 (ISBN 0-8423-4667-8). Tyndale.

New Bible Studies. G. H. Showalter & W. M. Davis. 1949. pap. 1.50 (ISBN 0-88027-027-6). Firm Foun Pub.

New Birth. David K. Bernard. Ed. by Mary H. Wallace. 346p. (Orig.). 1984. pap. 6.95 (ISBN 0-912315-77-6). Word Aflame.

New Birth. Kenneth E. Hagin. 1975. pap. 0.50 mini bk. (ISBN 0-89276-050-8). Hagin Ministries.

New Birth. Arthur W. Pink. pap. 0.50 (ISBN 0-685-00739-1). Reiner.

New Birth. John Wesley. Ed. by Thomas C. Oden. LC 83-48460. 128p. 1984. 10.45 (ISBN 0-06-069312-6, HarpR). Har-Row.

New Birth: A Naturalist View of Religious Conversion. Joe E. Barnhart & Mary A. Barnhart. LC 81-9557. xiv, 174p. 1981. 15.50 (ISBN 0-86554-009-8, MUP-H11). Mercer Univ Pr.

New Birth: A Study Guide. Neil Stegall & David Bernard. 120p. (Orig.). 1987. pap. 5.95 spiral bd. (ISBN 0-932581-15-3). Word Aflame.

New Blueprint for Marriage. Merrily Neill & Joanne Tangedahl. 256p. 1981. pap. 6.50 (ISBN 0-942494-65-2). Coleman Pub.

New Book of Christian Prayers. Tony Castle. 364p. 1986. 17.95 (ISBN 0-8245-0781-9). Crossroad NY.

New Book of Christian Quotations. Ed. by Tony Castle. LC 82-25253. 272p. 1983. pap. 9.95 (ISBN 0-8245-0551-4). Crossroad NY.

New Boy. Reginald Wallis. pap. 1.00 (ISBN 0-87213-910-7). Loizeaux.

New Brown-Driver-Briggs Hebrew - Lexicon of the Old Testament. Ed. by Francis Brown et al. 1200p. 1979. 34.95 (ISBN 0-913573-20-5). Hendrickson MA.

New Call for Peacemakers. Maynard Shelly. (Illus.). 109p. 1980. pap. text ed. 2.00 (ISBN 0-87303-031-1). Faith & Life.

New Canon Law: Perspectives on the Law, Religious Life & the Laity. LC 82-17889. (Orig.). 1983. pap. 11.00 (ISBN 0-87125-076-4). Cath Health.

New Catechism. 1967. 10.00 (ISBN 0-8245-0331-7). Crossroad NY.

New Catechism: Catholic Faith for Adults. 1977. pap. 8.95 (ISBN 0-8245-0332-5). Crossroad NY.

New Categories for Dancing: The Old Testament. Hal Taussig. (Orig.). 1981. pap. 2.50 (ISBN 0-941500-25-X). Sharing Co.

New Catholic Commentary on Holy Scripture. rev. ed. Ed. by Reginald C. Fuller et al. 1378p. 1984. 34.95 (ISBN 0-8407-5017-X). Nelson.

New Catholic Encylopedia, 17 vols. Catholic University of America Staff. LC 66-22292. 712p. 1981. Repr. of 1967 ed. Set. 750.00 (ISBN 0-07-010235-X). Publishers Guild.

New Catholic Study Bible: St. Jerome Edition. 1786p. 1985. 29.95 (ISBN 0-87973-542-2). Our Sunday Visitor.

New Celibacy: Why More Men & Women Are Abstaining from Sex & Enjoying It. Gabrielle Brown. 300p. 1980. 10.95 (ISBN 0-07-008430-0). McGraw.

New Century Bible Commentary on Isaiah 1-39. rev. ed. R. E. Clements. 320p. 1980. pap. 8.95 (ISBN 0-8028-1841-2). Eerdmans.

New Century Bible Commentary on Job. rev. ed. H. H. Rowley. Ed. by Ronald E. Clements. 304p. 1980. pap. 7.95 (ISBN 0-8028-1838-2). Eerdmans.

New Charismatics II: How a Christian Renewal Movement Became a Part of the American Religious Mainstream. Richard Quebedeaux. LC 82-48417. 228p. 1983. pap. 8.95 (ISBN 0-06-066723-0, RD379, HarpR). Har-Row.

New Charter for Monasticism. Ed. by John Moffitt. 1970. 17.95x (ISBN 0-268-00433-1). U of Notre Dame Pr.

New Chinese-Kosher Cookbook. rev. ed. Bob Grossman. LC 77-79248. (Illus.). 1978. 5.95 (ISBN 0-8397-6308-5); pap. 4.95 (ISBN 0-8397-6309-3). Eriksson.

New Christian Communities: Origins, Style, & Survival. Ed. by Michael Zeik. LC 76-181995. pap. 4.95 (ISBN 0-87957-002-4). Roth Pub.

New Christian Politics. David G. Bromley & Anson D. Shupe, Jr. LC 84-6598. xii, 288p. 1984. 23.95 (ISBN 0-86554-115-9, MUP/H108). Mercer Univ Pr.

New Christian Right: Mobilization & Legitimation. Robert C. Liebman & Robert Wuthnow. (Social Institutions & Social Change Ser.). 1983. lib. bdg. 26.95x (ISBN 0-202-30307-1); pap. text ed. 9.95 (ISBN 0-202-30308-X). De Gruyter Aldine.

New Christian Right, Nineteen Eighty-One to Nineteen Eighty-Eight: Prospects for the Next Presidential Election. Erling Jorstad. LC 87-1636. (Studies in American Religion: Vol. 25). 280p. 1987. lib. bdg. 49.95 (ISBN 0-88946-669-6). E Mellen.

New Christianity. Salem Bland. LC 72-95815. (Social History of Canada Ser.). 1973. pap. 6.00 (ISBN 0-8020-6179-6). U of Toronto Pr.

New Christian's Guide to Following Jesus. Terry Miethe. 144p. 1984. pap. 4.95 (ISBN 0-87123-439-4, 210439). Bethany Hse.

New Christmas Treasury: With More Stories for Reading Aloud. Ed. by Robert Lohan & Maria Lohan. LC 54-12862. 14.50 (ISBN 0-8044-2536-1, Pub. by Stephen Daye Pr). Ungar.

New Christology. Karl Rahner & Wilhelm Thusing. 256p. 1980. 12.95 (ISBN 0-8245-0333-3). Crossroad NY.

New Church & the New Germany: A Study of Church & State. Charles S. MacFarland. LC 78-63691. (Studies in Fascism: Ideology & Practice). 224p. Repr. of 1934 ed. 28.00 (ISBN 0-404-16953-8). AMS Pr.

New Church Debate: Issues Facing American Lutheranism. Ed. by Carl E. Braaten. LC 83-48008. 176p. 1984. pap. 7.95 (ISBN 0-8006-1715-0, 1-1715). Fortress.

New Clear Energy: Rudra Abhisekam. Panduranga R. Malyala. (Illus.). 120p. 1983. 5.00 (ISBN 0-938924-11-7). Sri Shirdi Sai.

New Code & the Sacraments. David Q. Liptak. 140p. 1983. pap. 7.95 (ISBN 0-941850-12-9). Sunday Pubns.

New Code: Laity & Deacons. David Q. Liptak & Philip A. Sheridan. 128p. (Orig.). 1986. pap. 7.95 (ISBN 0-941850-20-X). Sunday Pubns.

New Combined Bible Dictionary & Concordance. (Direction Bks). 1973. pap. 5.95 (ISBN 0-8010-6680-8). Baker Bk.

New Commandment: An Inquiry into the Social Precept & Practice of the Ancient Church. Charles S. Phillips. LC 31-31370. (Church Historical Society Ser.: No. 4). 1930. 10.00x (ISBN 0-8401-5004-0). A R Allenson.

New Commandment: An Inquiry into the Social Precept & Practice of the Ancient Church. Charles S. Phillips. (Church Historical Society London Ser.: No. 4). Repr. of 1930 ed. 40.00 (ISBN 0-8115-3128-7). Kraus Repr.

New Commandment: Loving As Jesus Loved. Sharon A. Steele. (Basic Bible Study). 64p. 1986. pap. 2.95 (ISBN 0-932305-21-0, 521021). Aglow Pubns.

New Commentary on Genesis, 2 vols. Franz Delitzsch. 1978. Set. 30.50 (ISBN 0-86524-131-7, 0101). Klock & Klock.

New Communities, New Ministries: The Church Resurgent in Africa, Asia, & Latin America. Michel Bavarel. Tr. by Francis Martin from Fr. LC 82-22318. Orig. Title: Chretienes Du Bout Du Monde. 122p. (Orig.). 1983. pap. 5.95 (ISBN 0-88344-337-6). Orbis Bks.

New Compact Bible Dictionary. T. A. Bryant. 1967. 9.95 (ISBN 0-310-22080-7, 6726P); pap. 5.95 (ISBN 0-310-22082-3). Zondervan.

New Concepts of Bible Mysteries & Eschatologies. Clay C. Fisher. LC 76-96074. 1969. pap. 2.50 (ISBN 0-686-00510-4). C C Fisher.

New Concordance of the Old Testament: Using the Hebrew & Aramaic Text. Ed. by Abraham Even-Shoshan. 1328p. 51.00 (ISBN 0-8010-3417-5). Baker Bk.

New Consciousness Sourcebook, No. 5. LC 84-15040. 256p. 1985. Repr. of 1982 ed. lib. bdg. 19.95x (ISBN 0-89370-887-9). Borgo Pr.

New Consciousness Sourcebook: Spiritual Community Guide, No. 6. 6th ed. Ed. by D. K. Khalsa. 256p. 1985. pap. 8.95 (ISBN 0-89509-055-4). Arcline Pubns.

New Covenant. Robert Coleman. 132p. 1985. pap. 4.95 (ISBN 0-89109-524-1). NavPress.

New Covenant's Power. Douglas R. Behm. 1983. 3.50 (ISBN 0-89536-600-2, 1412). CSS of Ohio.

New Creation. Ronald D. Tucker. (Illus.). 34p. (Orig.). 1983. pap. 1.75 (ISBN 0-933643-11-X). Grace World Outreach.

New Creation: Marxist & Christian? Jose-Maria Gonzalez-Ruiz. Tr. by Mathew J. O'Connell from Spanish. LC 76-10226. Orig. Title: Marxismo y Cristianismo Frente Al Hombre Nuevo. 160p. (Orig.). 1976. 1.74 (ISBN 0-88344-327-9). Orbis Bks.

New Creation People. Richard Reichert. (New Creation Ser.). 96p. 1985. pap. text ed. 4.25 (ISBN 0-697-01997-7); tchr's. ed. 4.50 (ISBN 0-697-01998-5). Wm C Brown.

New Creation Story: The Creative Spirituality of Teilhard de Chardin. Donald P. Gray. (Teilhard Studies). 1979. pap. 2.00 (ISBN 0-89012-014-5). Anima Pubns.

New Creation: Towards a Theology of the Christian Life. August Brunner. 143p. 1956. 10.00 (ISBN 0-8022-0189-X). Philos Lib.

New Creationism. Harold Clark. LC 79-22250. (Horizon Ser.). 1980. pap. 9.95 (ISBN 0-8127-0247-6). Review & Herald.

New Cults. Walter Martin. LC 80-52210. (Orig.). 1980. pap. 8.95 (ISBN 0-88449-016-5, A424378). Vision Hse.

New Day. Rod Vickers. 47p. 1984. pap. 0.95 (ISBN 0-88144-032-9). Christian Pub.

New Day in Church Revivals. Bill V. Cathey. LC 83-70645. 1984. pap. 7.95 (ISBN 0-8054-6244-9). Broadman.

New Design for Family Ministry. Dennis B. Guernsey. LC 82-72793. 126p. 1982. pap. 6.95 (ISBN 0-89191-650-4). Cook.

New Dictionary for Episcopalians. John N. Wall, Jr. 168p. (Orig.). 1985. pap. 7.95 (ISBN 0-86683-787-6, HarpR). Har-Row.

New Dimension in Old Testament Study. Sadie Gregory. 103p. (Orig.). 1980. pap. 5.00 (ISBN 0-917479-05-X). Guild Psy.

New Dimensions in Philosophical Theology. Ed. by Carl A. Raschke. (AAR Thematic Studies). 19.50 (ISBN 0-89130-682-X, 01-24-91). Scholars Pr GA.

New Dimensions in Puppet Ministry. Lee Garsee. 1983. pap. 5.95 (ISBN 0-89137-607-0). Quality Pubns.

New Directions from the Ten Commandments. Arthur F. Sueltz. LC 75-36744. 128p. (Orig.). 1976. pap. 3.95i (ISBN 0-06-067760-0, RD145, HarpR). Har-Row.

New Directions in Biography. Ed. by Anthony M. Friedson. (Biography Monographs: No. 2). 125p. 1982. pap. text ed. 7.95x (ISBN 0-8248-0783-9). UH Pr.

New Directions in Economic Justice. Roger Skurski. LC 83-1254. 304p. 1983. text ed. 20.95x (ISBN 0-268-01460-4, 85-14606); pap. text ed. 10.95x (ISBN 0-268-01461-2, 85-14614). U of Notre Dame Pr.

New Directions in English Teaching. Ed. by Anthony Adams. 245p. 1982. text ed. 29.00x (ISBN 0-905273-37-0, Falmer Pr); pap. 16.00x (ISBN 0-905273-36-2, Falmer Pr). Taylor & Francis.

New Directions in New Testament Study. Patrick Henry. LC 79-16267. 300p. 1979. 19.95 (ISBN 0-664-21376-6); pap. 10.95 (ISBN 0-664-24283-9). Westminster.

New Directions in Primary Education. Ed. by Colin Richards. 310p. 1982. text ed. 30.00x (ISBN 0-905273-27-3, Falmer Pr); pap. 16.00x (ISBN 0-905273-26-5). Taylor & Francis.

New Directions in Religious Education. Ed. by John Hull. 226p. 1982. text ed. 24.50x (ISBN 0-905273-31-1, Falmer Pr); pap. 15.00x (ISBN 0-905273-30-3). Taylor & Francis.

New Disciple: Church Membership Junior-Junior High. Arline J. Ban & Joseph D. Ban. LC 75-35898. 96p. 1976. pap. 1.95 (ISBN 0-8170-0658-3). Judson.

New Disciple, Leader's Guide. Arline J. Ban & Joseph D. Ban. 48p. 1976. pap. 1.50 (ISBN 0-8170-0706-7). Judson.

New Discoveries in St. Catherine's Monastery: A Preliminary Report on the Manuscripts. James H. Charlesworth. Intro. by David N. Freedman. LC 81-10992. (American Schools of Oriental Research Monographs: No. 3). (Illus.). 45p. (Orig.). 1982. pap. text ed. 6.00x (ISBN 0-89757-403-6, Am Sch Orient Res). Eisenbrauns.

New Discoveries into the Realm of Psychic Phenomena. Jay T. Hudson. (Illus.). 129p. 1983. 85.85 (ISBN 0-89920-065-6). Am Inst Psych.

New Discovery. Donald Gee. Orig. Title: Pentecost. 96p. 1932. pap. 1.00 (ISBN 0-88243-569-8, 02-0569). Gospel Pub.

New Dynamic Church. Victor P. Wierwille. LC 70-176281. (Studies in Abundant Living: Vol. 2). 242p. 1971. 6.95 (ISBN 0-910068-03-8). Am Christian.

New Earth: Methods, Exercises, Formulas, Prayers. Omraam M. Aivanhov. (Complete Works: Vol. 13). (Illus.). 232p. (Orig.). 1982. pap. 9.95 (ISBN 2-85566-113-7). Prosveta USA.

New Educational Methods for Increasing Religious Effectiveness. Dean C. Dauw. pap. 0.65 (ISBN 0-8199-0389-2, L38532). Franciscan Herald.

New Encounter Between Christians & Jews. John M. Oesterreicher. LC 85-26033. 472p. 1986. 25.00 (ISBN 0-8022-2496-2). Philos Lib.

New Engagement: Evangelical Political Thought, 1966-1976. Robert B. Fowler. 298p. (Orig.). 1983. pap. 13.95 (ISBN 0-8028-1929-X). Eerdmans.

New Engagement: Evangelical Political Thought, 1966-1976. Robert B. Fowler. LC 82-11389. Repr. of 1982 ed. 77.00 (2027453). Bks Demand UMI.

New England & the Bavarian Illuminati. Vernon Stauffer. LC 66-27153. 1967. Repr. of 1918 ed. 8.50x (ISBN 0-8462-0953-5). Russell.

New England Calvinism & the Disruption of the Presbyterian Church. Earl Pope. Ed. by Bruce Kuklick. (American Religious Thought of the 18th & 19th Centuries Ser.). 400p. 1987. lib. bdg. 50.00 (ISBN 0-8240-6969-2). Garland Pub.

New England Church: Its First Hundred Years. Ina Mansur. LC 74-76868. (Illus.). 256p. 1974. 10.95 (ISBN 0-87027-139-3); pap. 5.95 (ISBN 0-87027-140-7). Cumberland Pr.

New England Dissent, 1630-1833: The Baptists & the Separation of Church & State, 2 vols. William G. McLoughlin. LC 70-131464. (Center for the Study of the History of Liberty in America Ser). (Illus.). 1971. Set. 80.00x (ISBN 0-674-61175-6). Harvard U Pr.

New England Revivals, As They Existed at the Close of the Eighteenth & the Beginning of the Nineteenth Centuries Compiled Principally from Narratives First Pub. in the Conn. Evangelical Magazine Revival Library. Bennet Tyler. 378p. 1980. Repr. of 1846 ed. lib. bdg. 12.95 (ISBN 0-940033-18-6). R O Roberts.

New England Soul: Preaching & Religious Culture in Colonial New England. Harry S. Stout. LC 85-29853. 352p. 1986. 29.95x (ISBN 0-19-503958-0). Oxford U Pr.

New England Transcendentalism & St. Louis Hegelianism. Henry A. Pochmann. LC 68-55163. (Studies in Comparative Literature, No. 35). 1969. Repr. of 1948 ed. lib. bdg. 39.95x (ISBN 0-8383-0610-1). Haskell.

New England Transcendentalists & the DIAL: A History of the Magazine & Its Contributors. Joel Myerson. LC 78-66814. 400p. 1980. 35.00 (ISBN 0-8386-2294-1). Fairleigh Dickinson.

New England's Place in the History of Witchcraft. facsimile ed. George L. Burr. LC 71-164592. (Select Bibliographies Reprint Ser). Repr. of 1911 ed. 15.00 (ISBN 0-8369-5876-4). Ayer Co Pubs.

New English Bible Companion to the New Testament. A. E. Harvey. 1979. 65.00 (ISBN 0-521-07705-2). Cambridge U Pr.

New English Bible Companion to the New Testament: The Gospels. A. E. Harvey. 400p. 1972. pap. 9.95 (ISBN 0-521-09689-8). Cambridge U Pr.

New English Bible Companion to the New Testament: The Gospels. A. E. Harvey. (Orig.). 1972. pap. 13.95x (ISBN 0-19-826168-3). Oxford U Pr.

New Englishmans Greek Concordance & Lexicon. George V. Wigram. 960p. 1982. 34.95 (ISBN 0-913573-23-X). Hendrickson MA.

New Englishman's Hebrew Concordance. 1424p. 1984. 39.95 (ISBN 0-913573-21-3). Hendrickson MA.

New Enthusiasts: And What They Are Doing to the Catholic Church. James Hitchcock. 168p. 1982. pap. 9.95 (ISBN 0-88347-150-7). Thomas More.

New Era Community. (Agni Yoga Ser.). 1978. Repr. of 1951 ed. flexible cover 12.00 (ISBN 0-933574-03-7). Agni Yoga Soc.

New Essays on Paradise Lost. Ed. by Thomas Kranidas. LC 72-82463. 1969. pap. 4.95x (ISBN 0-520-01902-4, CAMPUS51). U of Cal Pr.

New Every Morning: Three Hundred Sixty-Six Daily Meditations from Your Favorite Christian Writers. Ed. by Al Bryant. 224p. 1985. 9.95 (ISBN 0-8499-0507-9, 0507-9). Word Bks.

New Exodus: A Study of Israel in Russia. Harold Frederic. LC 71-115538. (Russia Observed, Series I). 1970. Repr. of 1892 ed. 19.00 (ISBN 0-405-03027-4). Ayer Co Pubs.

New Face of Hinduism: The Swaminarayan Religion. Raymond B. Williams. LC 83-7197. 256p. 1984. 37.50 (ISBN 0-521-25454-X); pap. 13.95 (ISBN 0-521-27473-7). Cambridge U Pr.

New Fire Is Blazing. Peter Popoff. Ed. by Don Tanner. LC 80-67993. (Illus.). 194p. (Orig.). 1980. pap. 4.95 (ISBN 0-938544-02-0). Faith Messenger.

New First Mass Book. (Illus.). black leaherette, hard bd. 2.25 (ISBN 0-89942-808-8, 808/67-B); white leatherette, hard bd. 2.25 (ISBN 0-89942-809-6, 808/67W); black soft simulated lea., colored edges 2.75 (ISBN 0-89942-810-X, 808/42-B); white soft sim. lea., colored edges 2.75 (ISBN 0-89942-811-8, 808/42W); dlx. black sim. pearl, gold edges 8.95 (ISBN 0-89942-812-6, 808/82B); dlx. white sim. pearl, gold edges 8.95 (ISBN 0-89942-813-4, 808/82W). Catholic Bk Pub.

New, Fully Illustrated Book of the Most Dramatic Paintings in the Vatican. John E. Baldassarre. (Illus.). 127p. 1982. 121.45 (ISBN 0-89266-323-5). Am Classical Coll Pr.

New Fun Encyclopedia: Vol. 1: Games. E. O. Harbin. 256p. (Orig.). 1983. pap. 9.95 (ISBN 0-687-27754-X). Abingdon.

New Functional Hebrew-English, English-Hebrew Dictionary. Nathan Goldberg. (Hebrew & Eng.). 1958. 5.00x (ISBN 0-87068-379-9). Ktav.

New Gita. Wesley LaViolette. (Illus.). 1973. pap. 4.95 (ISBN 0-87516-172-3). De Vorss.

New Gnosis: Heidegger, Hillman, & Angels. Roberts Avens. LC 84-5297. 155p. (Orig.). 1984. 18.50 (ISBN 0-88214-328-X); pap. 12.50 (ISBN 0-88214-327-1). Spring Pubns.

New God Cares for Us. 154p. 1980. pap. text ed. 4.20 (ISBN 0-8294-0303-5). Loyola.

New Golden Bough. rev. ed. James Frazer. Ed. by Theodore Gaster. 832p. 1975. pap. 5.95 (ISBN 0-451-62208-1, ME2208, Ment). NAL.

New Gospel Parallels, Vol. 1. Robert W. Funk. LC 84-48727. (Foundations & Facets Ser.). 512p. 1985. 29.95 (ISBN 0-8006-2104-2, 1-2104). Fortress.

New Gospel Parallels, Vol. 2. Robert W. Funk. LC 84-48727. (Foundations & Facets Ser.). 384p. 1986. 24.95 (ISBN 0-8006-2106-9, 1-2106). Fortress.

New Government: Prophecies for Today. K. R. Jones. 1984. 16.95 (ISBN 0-533-05993-3). Vantage.

New Guide to Reading & Studying the Bible. enl. ed. Wilfrid Harrington. pap. 7.95 (ISBN 0-89453-092-5). M Glazier.

New Haggadah. 3rd rev. ed. Jewish Reconstructionist Foundation. Ed. by Mordecai M. Kaplan et al. LC 77-16803. (Illus.). 1978. pap. text ed. 3.95x (ISBN 0-87441-304-4). Behrman.

New Haggadah. Rev. ed. 1978. pap. 4.95 (ISBN 0-935457-31-3). Reconstructionist Pr.

New Harmonia Sacra. 1980. legacy edition 10.00x (ISBN 0-686-91950-5). Park View.

New Harmony of the Gospels. Albert C. Wieand. 1947. 15.95 (ISBN 0-8028-3299-7). Eerdmans.

New Harp of Columbia. M. L. Swan. Ed. by Dorothy D. Horn et al. LC 78-5504. (Tennesseana Editions Ser.). (Facsimile of 1867 Ed.). 1978. 18.95x (ISBN 0-87049-251-9). U of Tenn Pr.

New Heaven? New Earth? Simon Tugwell & Peter Hocken. 1977. pap. 5.95 (ISBN 0-87243-072-3). Templegate.

New Heaven, New Earth: A Study of Millenarian Activities. Kenelm Burridge. (Pavilion Ser.). 198p. 1969. pap. text ed. 12.95x (ISBN 0-631-11950-7). Basil Blackwell.

New Heaven on a New Earth. Philip Bender. LC 85-81579. (Faith & Life Bible Studies). 106p. (Orig.). 1985. pap. 4.95 (ISBN 0-87303-106-7). Faith & Life.

New Heavens & the New Earth. Gordon Lindsay. (Revelation Ser.). 1.25 (ISBN 0-89985-049-9). Christ Nations.

New Hebrew Nation: A Study in Israeli Heresy & Fantasy. Yaacov Shavit. 1987. 29.50 (ISBN 0-7146-3302-X, F Cass Co). Biblio Dist.

New Hope for Divorced Catholics: A Concerned Pastor Offers Alternatives to Annulment. Barry Brunsman. LC 85-42770. 128p. 1986. 12.95 (ISBN 0-06-061147-2, HarpR). Har-Row.

New Hymns for the Lectionary: To Glorify the Maker's Name. Thomas H. Troeger. 144p. (Music by Carol Doran). 1986. 7.95 (ISBN 0-19-385729-4). Oxford U Pr.

New Illustrated Hebrew-English Dictionary for Young Readers. Nathan Goldberg. (Hebrew & Eng., Illus.). 1958. pap. 6.95x (ISBN 0-87068-370-5). Ktav.

New International Commentary on the New Testament: The Epistles of John. I. Howard Marshall. 1978. 14.95 (ISBN 0-8028-2189-8). Eerdmans.

New International Dictionary of Biblical Archaeology. Ed. by E. M. Blaiklock & R. K. Harrison. 1986. 24.95 (ISBN 0-310-21250-2, 9277). Zondervan.

New International Dictionary of New Testament Theology, 3 vols. Colin Brown. Set. 109.95 (ISBN 0-310-21928-0, 11137P). Zondervan.

New International Dictionary of New Testament Theology, 4 vols. Ed. by Colin Brown. 1986. 109.95 (ISBN 0-310-33238-9, 11137). Zondervan.

New International Dictionary of the Christian Church. rev. ed. Ed. by J. D. Douglas & Earle E. Cairns. 1978. 29.95 (ISBN 0-310-23830-7, 11100). Zondervan.

New Interpretive Translation of St. Anselm's Monologion & Proslogion. Jasper Hopkins. LC 86-70086. xiv, 188p. Date not set. text ed. 25.00x (ISBN 0-938060-33-3); pap. text ed. 10.00x (ISBN 0-938060-34-1). Banning Pr.

New Jerusalem. 24p. (Orig.). 1982. pap. 0.95 (ISBN 0-937408-18-2). GMI Pubns Inc.

New Jerusalem. Paul L. Tan. LC 78-73221. 1978. pap. text ed. 1.95 (ISBN 0-932940-05-6). Assurance Pubs.

New Jewish Encyclopedia. rev. ed. Bridger & Wolk. LC 76-15251. (Illus.). 542p. 1976. 14.95 (ISBN 0-87441-120-3). Behrman.

New Jewish Ethics. S. Daniel Breslauer. LC 83-23659. (Symposium Ser.: Vol. 9). 136p. 1983. lib. bdg. 19.95x (ISBN 0-88946-700-5). E Mellen.

New Jewish Homemaker: A Treasury of Tips, Crafts, Foods & Stories. Shirley Bogart. 256p. 16.95t (ISBN 0-940646-20-X). Rossel Bks.

New Jewish Identity in America. Stuart E. Rosenberg. LC 84-10938. 384p. 1985. 19.95 (ISBN 0-88254-997-9). Hippocrene Bks.

New Jewish Songbook. Harry Coopersmith. LC 65-14593. pap. 9.95x (ISBN 0-87441-060-6). Behrman.

New Jewish Wedding. Anita Diamant. LC 84-24102. (Illus.). 1985. 16.95 (ISBN 0-671-49527-5). Summit Bks.

New Jewish Wedding. Anita Diamant. 272p. 1986. 8.95 (ISBN 0-671-62882-8). Summit Bks.

New John G. Lake Sermons. Gordon Lindsay. 1982. 1.75 (ISBN 0-686-79435-4). Christ Nations.

New Joy. Colleen T. Evans. (Orig.). 1975. pap. 1.50 (ISBN 0-89129-015-X). Jove Pubns.

New Judea: Jewish Life in Modern Palestine & Egypt. Benjamin L. Gordon. Ed. by Moshe Davis. LC 77-70697. (America & the Holy Land Ser.). (Illus.). 1977. Repr. of 1919 ed. lib. bdg. 30.00x (ISBN 0-405-10251-8). Ayer Co Pubs.

New Knowledge in the Biomedical Sciences. Ed. by William Bondeson et al. 1982. lib. bdg. 29.50 (ISBN 90-277-1319-7, Pub. by Reidel Holland). Kluwer Academic.

New Land! Conscious Experience Beyond Horizons. Kenneth G. Mills. (Illus.). 77p. 1978. pap. 4.95 (ISBN 0-919842-01-1). Sun-Scape Pubns.

New Law & Life: Sixty Practical Questions & Answers on the New Code of Canon Law. Elissa Rinere. 103p. (Orig.). 1985. pap. 4.50 (ISBN 0-943616-28-X). Canon Law Soc.

New Libertarian Gospel: Pitfalls of the Theology of Liberation. Juan G. Gonzalez. 1977. 7.95 (ISBN 0-8199-0682-4). Franciscan Herald.

New Life. rev. ed. A. R. Knight & Gordon H. Schroeder. 1971. pap. 1.50 (ISBN 0-8170-0120-4); pap. 1.00 spanish ed. (ISBN 0-8170-0696-6). Judson.

New Life, No. 1. Dan Caslow. 1984. pap. 1.95 (ISBN 0-317-30423-2). Pacific Pr Pub Assn.

New "Life after Death" Religion. Charles R. Smith. 1980. pap. 1.00 (ISBN 0-88469-125-X). BMH Bks.

New Life for Men: A Book for Men & the Women Who Care about Them. Joe Vaughn & Ron Klug. LC 84-21685. 144p. 1984. pap. 4.95 (ISBN 0-8066-2114-1, 10-4642). Augsburg.

New Life in Christ. Forest Bivens & David Vallesky. Ed. by William E. Fischer. (Bible Class Course Ser.). 120p. (Orig.). 1986. pap. text ed. 4.95 (ISBN 0-938272-07-1). WELS Board.

New Life in Christ. George B. Eager. LC 86-62669. (Illus.). 163p. 1987. pap. text ed. 4.95 (ISBN 0-9603752-6-0). Mailbox.

New Life in Christ. Donald C. Frisk. 1969. pap. 2.95 (ISBN 0-910452-03-2). Covenant.

New Life in Christ Jesus. C. I. Scofield. 1975. pap. 1.95 (ISBN 0-915374-41-2, 41-2). Rapids Christian.

New Life in Christ: Teacher's Guide. Forest Bivens & David Vallesky. (Bible Class Course Ser.). 40p. (Orig.). 1986. pap. text ed. 2.50 (ISBN 0-938272-03-9). WELS Board.

New Life in the Church. rev. ed. Robert A. Raines. LC 61-5267. (Harper's Ministers Paperback Library). 192p. 1980. pap. 4.50i (ISBN 0-06-066773-7, RD 309, HarpR). Har-Row.

New Life in the Spirit. Leonard I. Sweet. LC 81-23112. (Library of Living Faith: Vol. 4). 120p. (Orig.). 1982. pap. 5.95 (ISBN 0-664-24414-9). Westminster.

New Life: Kirpal Singh. Ed. by Ruth Seader. (Teachings of Kirpal Ser.: Vol. 3). 1976. pap. 3.50 (ISBN 0-89142-030-4). Sant Bani Ash.

New Life, New Lifestyle: A Fresh Look at the World. Michael Green. LC 84-25390. 159p. 1985. pap. 5.95 (ISBN 0-88070-073-4). Multnomah.

New Life: Preparation of Religious for Retirement. Sr. Duchesne Herold. LC 73-76987. 168p. 1973. pap. 5.50 (ISBN 0-87125-007-1). Cath Health.

New Life Principles. Tom Taylor. (Illus.). 1977. tchr's ed. 4.95 (ISBN 0-914936-26-3); wkbk. 1.10 (ISBN 0-914936-30-1). Bible Temple.

New Life: Readings in Christian Theology. Ed. by Millard J. Erickson. LC 79-53903. 1979. pap. 11.95 (ISBN 0-8010-3340-3). Baker Bk.

New Life Studies. 2nd rev. abr. ed. James D. Craig. 174p. 1983. pap. text ed. 15.00 (ISBN 0-88151-023-8). Lay Leadership.

New Life Studies: Group Leader's Guide. 2nd rev. abr. ed. James D. Craig. 48p. 1983. 4.00 (ISBN 0-88151-025-4). Lay Leadership.

New Life Studies: Home Study Guide. 2nd rev. abr. ed. James D. Craig. 64p. 1983. 8.00 (ISBN 0-88151-024-6). Lay Leadership.

New Life: The Sunday Paper's Baptism Book. Gretchen W. Pritchard. (Illus.). 80p. (Orig.). 1986. pap. 5.75x (ISBN 0-9614022-2-9). Sunday Paper.

New Life thru Christ. 1981. pap. 0.95 (ISBN 0-89221-055-9). New Leaf.

New Light Breaks Forth. Lyndon W. Cook & Donald Q. Cannon. pap. 7.95 (ISBN 0-89036-148-7). Hawkes Pub Inc.

New Light on Heredity & Evolution. Hermann Poppelbaum. Tr. by Norman Macbeth. 1977. pap. 6.95 (ISBN 0-916786-15-3). St George Bk Serv.

New Light on the Gospels. Omraam M. Aivanhov. (Izvor Collection: Vol. 217). (Orig.). 1985. pap. 4.95 (ISBN 2-85566-339-3, Pub. by Prosveta France). Prosveta USA.

New Light on the Protocols of Zion. W. Cruetz. 1982. lib. bdg. 69.95 (ISBN 0-87700-366-1). Revisionist Pr.

New Light on the Rapture. Donald Meresco. LC 80-67028. (Orig.). 1980. pap. 6.95 (ISBN 0-937078-00-X). Bible Light.

New Light on the Shepherd Psalm. William S. Deal. 1982. 3.95. Crusade Pubs.

New List of Proverbs. Merle R. Beckwith. LC 79-92430. cancelled (ISBN 0-8022-2361-3). Philos Lib.

New Liturgy & Old Devotions. Walter Kern. LC 78-73623. (Illus., Orig.). 1979. pap. 3.50 (ISBN 0-8189-1151-4, 151, Pub. by Alba Bks). Alba.

New Liturgy, New Laws. R. Kevin Seasoltz. LC 79-27916. 256p. 1980. pap. 7.95 (ISBN 0-8146-1077-3). Liturgical Pr.

New Liturgy, Old Heresy. T. Robert Ingram. LC 81-52116. (Orig.). 1981. pap. 4.50 (ISBN 0-686-75087-X). St Thomas.

New Lives: The Adjustment of Soviet Jewish Immigrants in the United States & Israel. Ed. by Rita J. Simon. 208p. 1985. 19.95 (ISBN 0-669-09767-5). Lexington Bks.

New Look at Biblical Crime. Ralph W. Scott. LC 78-27535. 232p. 1979. 18.95x (ISBN 0-88229-416-4). Nelson-Hall.

New Look at Church Growth. Floyd Bartel. LC 79-53523. 1979. pap. 2.95 (ISBN 0-87303-027-3). Faith & Life.

New Look at Preaching. Ed. by John Burke. (Good News Studies Ser.: Vol. 7). 1983. pap. 6.95 (ISBN 0-89453-336-3). M Glazier.

New Look at Spiritual Life. Franklin Atkinson. (Orig.). 1987. pap. 4.98 (ISBN 0-8054-1235-2). Broadman.

New Look at the Book. Brian L. Harbour. LC 84-27479. 1985. pap. 5.95 (ISBN 0-8054-1535-1). Broadman.

New Look at the Lutheran Confession. Holsten Fagerberg. Tr. by Gene J. Lund. 336p. 1981. 15.50 (ISBN 0-570-03223-7, 15-2121). Concordia.

New Look at the Pilgrims: Why They Came to America. Beatrice Siegel. LC 76-57060. (Illus.). 96p. 1987. Repr. of 1977 ed. o. p. 5.95 (ISBN 0-8027-6291-3); PLB 12.85 (ISBN 0-8027-6292-1). Walker & Co.

New Lottie Moon Story. Catherine Allen. LC 79-52336. 1980. 9.95 (ISBN 0-8054-6319-4). Broadman.

New Man. Thomas Merton. 256p. 1962. pap. 6.95 (ISBN 0-374-51444-5). FS&G.

New Man. Thomas Merton. 1983. 13.50 (ISBN 0-8446-5987-8). Peter Smith.

New Man: An Interpretation of Some Parables & Miracles of Christ. Maurice Nicoll. LC 83-20279. 153p. (Orig.). 1984. pap. 9.95 (ISBN 0-87773-268-X). Shambhala Pubns.

New Manners & Customs of Bible Times. rev. ed. Fred H. Wight & Ralph Gower. 1986. 24.95 (ISBN 0-8024-5954-4). Moody.

New Martyrs of the Turkish Yoke. Ed. by St. Nectarios Press. Tr. by Leonidas Papadopulos et al from Gr. LC 84-50974. 400p. (Orig.). 1985. pap. 12.50x (ISBN 0-913026-57-3); pap. 15.00x after January 1986. St Nectarios.

New Mass. A. M. Roguet. 2.95 (ISBN 0-89942-130-X, 130/05). Catholic Bk Pub.

New Me. Gladys Seashore. 1972. pap. 1.75 (ISBN 0-911802-31-2). Free Church Pubns.

New Meanings of Death. Herman Feifel. (Illus.). 1977. 25.00 (ISBN 0-07-020350-4); pap. 18.95 (ISBN 0-07-020349-0). McGraw.

New Men-New Roles. Perry Yoder & Elizabeth Yoder. 1977. pap. 2.00 (ISBN 0-87303-001-X). Faith & Life.

New Ministries: The Global Context. William R. Burrows. LC 80-17261. 192p. (Orig.). 1980. pap. 7.95 (ISBN 0-88344-329-5). Orbis Bks.

New Missionary Era. Ed. by Padraig Flanagan. LC 81-9595. 192p. (Orig.). 1982. pap. 2.49 (ISBN 0-88344-331-7). Orbis Bks.

New Model Seder. Ed. by Sidney Greenberg. pap. 1.95 (ISBN 0-87677-058-8). Prayer Bk.

New Models for Financing the Local Church. 2nd ed. Raymond B. Knudsen. 157p. 1985. pap. 8.95 (ISBN 0-8192-1369-1). Morehouse.

New Money System. Mary S. Relfe. 271p. 1982. pap. 6.95 (ISBN 0-9607986-1-7). Ministries.

New Morality from Science: Beyondism. Raymond B. Cattell. 1973. 42.00 (ISBN 0-08-016956-2). Pergamon.

New Nations for Old. Kenneth Boulding. 1983. pap. 2.50x (ISBN 0-87574-017-0, 017). Pendle Hill.

New Object Lessons for Children of All Ages. Sheryl Bruinsma. (Object Lesson Ser.). 1980. pap. 4.95 (ISBN 0-8010-0775-5). Baker Bk.

New Old Testament. Tony Hanne. LC 84-90178. 105p. 1986. 8.95 (ISBN 0-533-06228-4). Vantage.

New Options, New Dilemmas: An Interprofessional Approach to Life or Death Decisions. Ed. by Anne S. Allen. LC 85-45436. 144p. 1985. 22.00 (ISBN 0-669-11730-7). Lexington Bks.

New Organon: Bacon. Ed. by Fulton H. Anderson. 1960. pap. text ed. write for info. (ISBN 0-02-303380-0). Macmillan.

New Oxford Book of Christian Verse. Ed. by Donald Davie. 1982. 27.50x (ISBN 0-19-213426-4). Oxford U Pr.

New Oxford History of Music, Vol. 5: Opera & Church Music 1630-1750. Ed. by Nigel Fortune & Anthony Lewis. (Illus.). 1975. 49.95x (ISBN 0-19-316305-5). Oxford U Pr.

New Panorama Bible Study Course. Alfred T. Eade. Incl. No. 1. A Study of Dispensational Truth. (Illus.). 28p (ISBN 0-8007-0221-2); No. 2. The Study of Angelology. 32p (ISBN 0-8007-0222-0); No. 3. The Second Coming of Christ. 36p (ISBN 0-8007-0223-9); No. 4. The Book of Revelation. (Illus.). 28p (ISBN 0-8007-0434-7). pap. 6.95 ea. Revell.

New Parish Ministries. 400p. 1983. pap. 17.50 (ISBN 0-86683-742-6, HarpR). Har-Row.

New Parish Ministries: Series 2. 248p. 1984. pap. 8.95 (ISBN 0-86683-839-2, HarpR). Har-Row.

New Park Street Pulpit Index. C. H. Spurgeon. 1976. pap. 1.50 (ISBN 0-686-16848-8). Pilgrim Pubns.

New Park Street Pulpit 1855-1860, 6 vols. C H. Spurgeon. 1981. Set. 60.00 (ISBN 0-686-16847-X). Pilgrim Pubns.

New Paths in Buddhist Research. Ed. by Anthony K. Warder. LC 82-83594. x, 137p. 1985. 15.95x (ISBN 0-89386-008-5); pap. 9.95 (ISBN 0-89386-009-3). Acorn NC.

New Paths in Muslim Evangelism: Evangelical Approaches to Contextualization. Phil Parshall. 200p. (Orig.). 1980. pap. 8.95 (ISBN 0-8010-7056-2). Baker Bk.

New Pathways: A Dialogue in Christian Higher Education. Ed. by Ben C. Fisher. LC 80-80255. x, 110p. 1980. pap. 4.95 (ISBN 0-86554-000-4, MUP-P01). Mercer Univ Pr.

New Perspectives in Moral Theology. Charles E. Curran. LC 76-13206. 293p. 1976. text ed. 18.95 (ISBN 0-268-01449-3); pap. 6.95 (ISBN 0-268-01450-7). U of Notre Dame Pr.

New Perspectives on Abraham Geiger. Ed. by Jacob Petuchowski. pap. 2.50x (ISBN 0-87820-201-3, Pub. by Hebrew Union College Press). Ktav.

New Platonism & Alchemy. Alexander Wilder. (Secret Doctrine Reference Ser). 1975. pap. 3.00 (ISBN 0-913510-18-1). Wizards.

New Pockets of Jewish Energy: A Study of Adults Who Found Their Way Back to Judaism. 32p. 1982. 2.50 (ISBN 0-87495-046-5). Am Jewish Comm.

New Polytheism. 2nd, rev. ed. David L. Miller. 148p. 1981. pap. 9.50 (ISBN 0-88214-314-X). Spring Pubns.

New Possibilities for Small Churches. Douglas A. Walrath. 120p. (Orig.). 1983. pap. 7.95 (ISBN 0-8298-0668-7). Pilgrim NY.

New Pressures, New Responses in Religious Life. John P. Dondero & Thomas D. Frary. LC 76-26585. 1979. pap. 5.95 (ISBN 0-8189-0332-5). Alba.

New Priests. Michel De Saint Pierre. 209p. 1966. pap. 1.95 (ISBN 0-912414-18-9). Lumen Christi.

New Psalms Fragment. J. W. Barns & G. D. Kilpatrick. 1957. pap. 2.25 (ISBN 0-85672-621-4, Pub. by British Acad). Longwood Pub Group.

New Puritanism: During the Semi-Centennial Celebration of Plymouth Church, N.Y., 1847-1897. Lyman Abbott et al. LC 70-39672. (Essay Index Reprint Ser.). 19.00 (ISBN 0-8369-2732-X). Ayer Co Pubs.

New Quest of the Historical Jesus & Other Essays. James M. Robinson. LC 82-48586. 224p. 1983. pap. 12.95 (ISBN 0-8006-1698-7). Fortress.

New Question Box. rev. ed. John J. Dietzen. 606p. 1987. pap. 9.95 (ISBN 0-940518-01-5). Guildhall Pubs.

New Quests for Corvo: A Collection of Essays. Ed. by Cecil Woolf & Brocard Sewell. 1961. 6.95 (ISBN 0-685-09185-6); pap. 3.00 (ISBN 0-685-09186-4). Dufour.

New Regulations on Indulgences. Winfrid Herbst. 47p. 1970. pap. 1.50 (ISBN 0-89555-103-9). TAN Bks Pubs.

New Relation of Gaspesia: With the Customs & Religion of the Gaspesian Indian. Chretien Le Clercq. Ed. by William F. Ganong. LC 68-28600. 1968. Repr. of 1910 ed. lib. bdg. 33.75x (ISBN 0-8371-5044-2, LERG). Greenwood.

New Religion & Relativity. Dicksen T. Lau. LC 83-62038. 138p. (Orig.). 1983. pap. 5.95 (ISBN 0-9612000-0-6). Magnolia Bks.

New Religions. Ed. by Haralds Biezais. 233p. (Orig.). 1975. pap. text ed. 18.50x (Pub. by Almqvist & Wiksell). Coronet Bks.

New Religions. Jacob Needleman. 276p. 1984. pap. 10.95 (ISBN 0-8245-0635-9). Crossroad NY.

New Religions & Mental Health. Herbert Richardson. 177p. 1980. pap. 11.95. Rose Sharon Pr.

New Religions & Mental Health: Understanding the Issues. Ed. by Herbert W. Richardson. (Symposium Ser.: Vol. 5). 240p. (Orig.). 1980. 39.95x (ISBN 0-88946-910-5). E Mellen.

New Religions of Africa. Ed. by Bennetta Jules-Rosette. LC 78-16925. (Modern Sociology Ser.). (Illus.). 1979. 34.50x (ISBN 0-89391-014-7). Ablex Pub.

New Religions of Japan. Harry Thomsen. LC 77-13846. (Illus.). 1978. Repr. of 1963 ed. lib. bdg. 25.75x (ISBN 0-8371-9878-X, THNR). Greenwood.

New Religious Consciousness. Ed. by Charles Glock & Robert N. Bellah. 391p. 29.50 (ISBN 0-686-95181-6); pap. 6.95 (ISBN 0-686-99471-X). ADL.

New Religious Consciousness. Ed. by Charles Y. Glock & Robert N. Bellah. LC 75-17295. 1976. 36.50x (ISBN 0-520-03083-4); pap. 11.95x (ISBN 0-520-03472-4, CAMPUS 329). U of Cal Pr.

New Religious Movements. Ed. by Gregory Baum & John Coleman. (Concilium Ser. 1983: Vol. 161). 128p. (Orig.). 1983. pap. 6.95 (ISBN 0-8164-2441-1, HarpR); pap. 62.55 10 Volume Subscription (ISBN 0-8164-2453-5). Har-Row.

New Religious Movements: A Perspective for Understanding Society. Ed. by Eileen Barker. LC 82-8263. (Studies in Religion & Society: Vol. 3). 440p. 1982. 69.95x (ISBN 0-88946-864-8). E Mellen.

New Religious Movements in Nigeria. Ed. by Rosalind I. Hackett. LC 86-31080. (African Studies: Vol. 5). 1987. 59.95 (ISBN 0-88946-180-5). E Mellen.

New Religious Movements in the United States & Canada: A Critical Assessment & Annotated Bibliography. Compiled by Diane Choquette. LC 85-9964. (Bibliographies & Indexes in Religious Studies Ser.: No. 5). i, 235p. 1985. lib. bdg. 39.95 (ISBN 0-313-23772-7, CRM/). Greenwood.

New Religious-Political Right in America. Samuel S. Hill & Dennis E. Owen. LC 81-20661. 160p. 1982. 10.95 (ISBN 0-687-27867-8). Abingdon.

New Revised Sixth & Seventh Books of Moses & the Magical Use of the Psalms. Ed. by M. Gonzalez Wippler. pap. 6.95 (ISBN 0-942272-02-1). Original Pubns.

New Right: A Plea for Fair Play Through a More Just Social Order. Samuel M. Jones. LC 75-327. (Radical Tradition in America Ser.). (Illus.). 479p. 1975. Repr. of 1899 ed. 32.45 (ISBN 0-88355-231-0). Hyperion Conn.

New Saint Joseph Baltimore Catechism, 2 bks. (Official Baltimore Catechism Ser.: Nos. 1 & 2). (Illus.). No. 1, Gr. 3-5. 1.80 (ISBN 0-89942-241-1, 241/05); No. 2, Gr. 6-8. 1.95 (ISBN 0-89942-242-X, 242/05). Catholic Bk Pub.

New Saint Joseph First Communion Cathechism. rev. ed. (Official Baltimore Catechism Ser.). (Illus.). 1.60 (ISBN 0-89942-240-3, 240/05). Catholic Bk Pub.

New Saint Joseph Sunday Missal & Hymnal. complete ed. (Illus., References, Calendar, Bold Sense-Lines, Two Color Ordinary, Perpetual). red flexible vinyl 9.25 (ISBN 0-89942-820-7, 820/09); green cloth, colored edges 10.95 (ISBN 0-89942-819-3, 820/22-GN); black cloth hard bdg. 10.95 (ISBN 0-89942-818-5, 820/22-B); brown flexible bdg., colored edges 11.95 (ISBN 0-89942-817-7, 820/10-BN); white durocoat, marriage cert, gold edges 12.95 (ISBN 0-89942-816-9, 820/51W); dlx. white sim. pearl, gold edges 15.00 (ISBN 0-89942-815-0, 820/82W). Catholic Bk Pub.

New Saint Joseph Sunday Missal: Prayer Book & Hymnal. regular, annual 1986 ed. (Two Color Large Type Ordinary, Year "C" Only, Introduction). blue flexible bdg. 1.70 (ISBN 0-89942-886-X, 886/04). Catholic Bk Pub.

New Saint Joseph Weekday Missal, 2 vols. Incl. Vol. 1. Advent to Pentecost (ISBN 0-89942-920-3, 920/09); Vol. 2. Pentecost to Advent (ISBN 0-89942-921-1, 921/09). 9.25 ea.; annual guide o.s.i. 1.00 (ISBN 0-686-14349-3, 920-G). Catholic Bk Pub.

New Scientific Case for God's Existence. Mark Mahin. LC 84-62349. 137p. (Orig.). 1985. pap. 8.95 (ISBN 0-931959-01-2). Mindlifter Pr.

New Seeds of Contemplation. rev. ed. Thomas Merton. LC 61-17869. 1972. pap. 5.50 (ISBN 0-8112-0099-X, NDP337). New Directions.

New Shape of American Religion. Martin E. Marty. LC 78-1576. 1978. Repr. of 1959 ed. lib. bdg. 22.50x (ISBN 0-313-20353-9, MANE). Greenwood.

New Short Grammar of the Greek New Testament. 10th ed. A. T. Robertson & W. Hersey Davis. 1977. pap. 12.95 (ISBN 0-8010-7656-0). Baker Bk.

New Smith's Bible Dictionary. rev. ed. William Smith. LC 78-69668. 1979. pap. 9.95 (ISBN 0-385-14652-3, Galilee). Doubleday.

New Song: Celibate Women in the First Three Christian Centuries. Jo Ann McNamara. LC 83-10852. (Women & History Ser.: Nos. 6 & 7). 154p. 1983. text ed. 29.95 (ISBN 0-86656-249-4, B249). Haworth Pr.

New Song: Celibate Women in the First Three Christian Centuries. Jo Ann McNamara. LC 85-8505. 154p. 1985. pap. 8.95 (ISBN 0-918393-17-5). Harrington Pk.

New Start in Youth Ministry. Eldor Kaiser & Leo Symmank. 1980. pap. 4.95 (ISBN 0-570-03805-7, 12-2914). Concordia.

New State. Victor Pradera. Tr. by B. Malley. LC 79-180421. Repr. of 1939 ed. 29.50 (ISBN 0-404-56196-9). AMS Pr.

New Strong's New Exhaustive Concordance of the Bible. 2nd ed. Ed. by James Strong. 1984. 24.95 (ISBN 0-8407-5360-8); indexed 28.95 (ISBN 0-8407-5442-6). Nelson.

New Studies in Berkeley's Philosophy. Ed. by Warren E. Steinkraus. LC 81-40866. 218p. 1982. lib. bdg. 27.75 (ISBN 0-8191-2006-5); pap. text ed. 12.75 (ISBN 0-8191-2007-3). U Pr of Amer.

New Studies in Bonhoeffer's Ethics. Ed. by William J. Peck. (Toronto Studies in Theology: Vol. 31). 284p. 1987. lib. bdg. 49.95 (ISBN 0-88946-775-7). E Mellen.

New Studies in Deontic Logic: Norms, Actions & the Foundations of Ethics. Ed. by Risto Hilpinen. 272p. 1981. 39.50 (ISBN 90-277-1278-6, Pub. by Reidel Holland). Kluwer Academic.

New Studies in Mystical Religion. Rufus M. Jones. 69.95 (ISBN 0-87968-102-0). Gordon Pr.

New Subversives: Anti-Americanism of the Religious Right. Daniel Maguire. 160p. 1982. 9.95 (ISBN 0-8264-0189-9). Continuum.

New Synoptic Studies: The Cambridge Gospel Conference & Beyond. Ed. by William R. Farmer. LC 83-13396. xii, 533p. 1983. 32.95 (ISBN 0-86554-087-X, MUP/H76). Mercer Univ Pr.

New System of Mental Therapeutics & the Phenomena of Spiritism. T. J. Hudson. (Illus.). 171p. 1986. 187.65 (ISBN 0-89920-138-5). Am Inst Psych.

New System, or, an Analysis of Ancient Mythology, 3 vols. Jacob Bryant. Ed. by Burton Feldman & Robert Richardson. LC 78-60881. (Myth & Romanticism Ser.: Vol. 5). (Illus.). 1979. Set. lib. bdg. 240.00 (ISBN 0-8240-3554-2). Garland Pub.

New Systematics. Ed. by Julian S. Huxley. LC 40-35139. 583p. 1940. Repr. 49.00 (ISBN 0-403-01786-6). Scholarly.

New Technologies of Birth & Death: Medical, Legal & Moral Dimensions. LC 80-83425. xvi, 196p. (Orig.). 1980. pap. 8.95 (ISBN 0-935372-07-5). Pope John Ctr.

New Testament, 3 Vols. Corinne Heline. Vol. 4. 8.00 (ISBN 0-87613-086-4); Vol. 5. 12.00 (ISBN 0-87613-082-1); Vol. 6. 12.00 (ISBN 0-87613-083-X). New Age.

New Testament. James L. Price. 544p. 1986. lib. bdg. write for info. (ISBN 0-02-396610-6). Macmillan.

New Testament: A Bibliography. Daniel J. Harrington. (Theological & Biblical Resources Ser.: Vol. 2). 1985. pap. 8.95 (ISBN 0-89453-535-8). M Glazier.

New Testament: A Guide to Its Writings. Gunther Bornkamm. Tr. by Reginald H. Fuller & Ilse Fuller. LC 73-79009. 176p. (Orig.). 1973. pap. 4.95 (ISBN 0-8006-0168-8, 1-168). Fortress.

New Testament: A Pictorial Archive from Nineteenth-Century Sources. Ed. by Don Rice. (Pictorial Archive Ser.). (Illus.). 192p. (Orig.). 1986. pap. 7.95 (ISBN 0-486-25073-3). Dover.

New Testament: A Study Aid. (Book Notes). (Orig.). 1985. pap. text ed. 2.50 (ISBN 0-8120-3530-5). Barron.

New Testament Age: Essays in Honor of Bo Reicke, 2 vols. Ed. by William C. Weinrich. LC 84-713. 606p. 1984. 44.95x (ISBN 0-86554-097-7, MUP/H89). Mercer Univ Pr.

New Testament: An Expanded Translation. Tr. by Kenneth S. Wuest. 1961. 14.95 (ISBN 0-8028-3306-3); pap. 9.95 (ISBN 0-8028-1229-5). Eerdmans.

New Testament: An Introduction. 2nd ed. Norman Perrin & Dennis C. Duling. (Illus.). 516p. (Orig.). 1982. pap. text ed. 15.95 (ISBN 0-15-565726-7, HC). HarBraceJ.

New Testament: An Introduction for the General Reader. Oscar Cullmann. LC 68-12796. 138p. 1968. pap. 8.95 (ISBN 0-664-24817-9). Westminster.

New Testament: An Introduction to Its History & Literature. J. Gresham Machem. 1976. 11.95 (ISBN 0-85151-240-2). Banner of Truth.

New Testament & Criticism. George E. Ladd. 1966. pap. 6.95 (ISBN 0-8028-1680-0). Eerdmans.

New Testament & Early Christianity. Joseph B. Tyson. 480p. 1984. text ed. write for info. (ISBN 0-02-421890-1). Macmillan.

New Testament & Gnosis. Ed. by A. H. Logan & A. J. Wedderburn. 272p. 1983. 22.95 (ISBN 0-567-09344-1, Pub. by T&T Clark Ltd UK). Fortress.

New Testament & Homosexuality. Robin Scroggs. LC 82-48588. 160p. 1984. pap. 8.95 (ISBN 0-8006-1854-8, 1-1854). Fortress.

New Testament & Mythology & Other Basic Writings. Rudolf Bultmann. Ed. & tr. by Schubert M. Ogden. LC 84-47921. 192p. 1984. 12.95 (ISBN 0-8006-0727-9). Fortress.

New Testament & Rabbinic Judaism. David Daube. LC 73-2191. (Jewish People; History, Religion, Literature Ser.). Repr. of 1956 ed. 38.50 (ISBN 0-405-05257-X). Ayer Co Pubs.

New Testament & Structuralism: A Collection of Essays. Ed. & tr. by Alfred M. Johnson, Jr. LC 76-25447. (Pittsburgh Theological Monographs: No. 11). 1976. pap. text ed. 11.50 (ISBN 0-915138-13-1). Pickwick.

New Testament & the Literary Imagination. David Jasper. 128p. 1987. text ed. 19.95 (ISBN 0-391-03482-0). Humanities.

New Testament & the Mishnah. Charles R. Gianotti. 1983. pap. 3.50 (ISBN 0-8010-3791-3). Baker Bk.

New Testament Apocalyptic. Paul S. Minear. LC 81-4721. (Interpreting Biblical Texts Ser.). 160p. (Orig.). 1981. pap. 8.95 (ISBN 0-687-27890-2). Abingdon.

New Testament Apocrypha, 2 vols. Edgar Hennecke. Incl. Vol. 1. Gospels & Related Writings. 532p. 1963. 18.95 (ISBN 0-664-20385-X); Vol. 2. Writings Relating to the Apostles; Apocalypses & Related Subjects. LC 63-7492. 852p. 1966. 32.50 (ISBN 0-664-20680-8). Westminster.

New Testament Apocrypha & Pseudepigrapha: A Guide to Publications, with Excursueses on Apacalypses. James H. Charlesworth & James R. Mueller. LC 85-18350. (ATLA Bibliographer Ser.: No. 17). 468p. 1987. 42.50 (ISBN 0-8108-1845-0). Scarecrow.

New Testament as Canon: An Introduction. Brevard S. Childs. LC 84-21169. 640p. 1985. 22.95 (ISBN 0-8006-0739-2, 1-739). Fortress.

New Testament as Personal Reading. Ed. by Ronan Drury. 158p. 1983. pap. 7.95 (ISBN 0-87243-122-3). Templegate.

New Testament Background: Selected Documents. Ed. by Charles K. Barrett. pap. 6.95x (ISBN 0-06-130086-1, TB86, Torch). Har-Row.

New Testament Backgrounds. 2nd ed. Wilbur Fields. (Bible Student Study Guides Ser). 1977. pap. 5.95 (ISBN 0-89900-156-4). College Pr Pub.

New Testament Basis of Peacemaking. Richard McSorley. LC 84-25121. 160p. 1985. pap. 7.95 (ISBN 0-8361-3383-8). Herald Pr.

New Testament Blueprint for the Church. John Moore & Kenneth Neff. 1985. pap. 7.95 (ISBN 0-8024-5901-3). Moody.

New Testament Books for Pastor & Teacher. Ralph P. Martin. LC 83-21654. 152p. (Orig.). 1984. pap. 8.95 (ISBN 0-664-24511-0). Westminster.

New Testament Canon: Its Making & Meaning. Harry Y. Gamble. LC 85-4509. (Guides to Biblical Scholarship Ser.). 96p. 1985. pap. 4.50 (ISBN 0-8006-0470-9). Fortress.

New Testament Characters. Raymond O. Corvin. (Alpha & Omega Studies). 94p. (Orig.). 1986. pap. text ed. 5.95 (ISBN 0-89221-137-7). New Leaf.

New Testament Charts. M. Ross Richards & Marie C. Richards. pap. 2.95 (ISBN 0-87747-446-X). Deseret Bk.

New Testament Church. Everett Ferguson. LC 68-55790. (Way of Life Ser: No. 108). 1968. pap. 3.95 (ISBN 0-89112-108-0, Bibl Res Pr). Abilene Christ U.

New Testament Church: A Divine Institution. L. R. Wilson. 1970. pap. 2.7500210895x (ISBN 0-88027-035-7). Firm Foun Pub.

New Testament Church & Its Ministries. Bill Scheidler. (Illus.). 120p. 1980. pap. 8.95 (ISBN 0-914936-43-3). Bible Temple.

New Testament Church & Its Symbols. Fred Pruitt. 131p. 1.00 (ISBN 0-686-29157-3). Faith Pub Hse.

New Testament Church Organization. Don Norbie. pap. 2.50 (ISBN 0-937396-28-1). Walterick Pubs.

New Testament Church Then & Now. LeRoy Lawson. LC 81-50631. 160p. (Orig.). 1981. pap. 3.95 (ISBN 0-87239-443-3, 88585). Standard Pub.

New Testament Church Then & Now Workbook. LeRoy Lawson. 48p. 1983. pap. 1.75 (ISBN 0-87239-609-6, 88586). Standard Pub.

New Testament Commentary, 2 Vols. John A. Bengel. LC 70-155250. 1910p. 1982. Set. 59.95 (ISBN 0-8254-2242-6). Kregel.

New Testament Commentary, 11 vols. Heinrich A. Meyer. 7050p. 250.00 (ISBN 0-913573-04-3). Hendrickson MA.

New Testament Concept of Witness. A. A. Trites. LC 76-11067. (Society for New Testament Studies Monograph: No. 31). 1977. 59.50 (ISBN 0-521-21015-1). Cambridge U Pr.

New Testament Development of Old Testament Themes. Ed. by Frederick F. Bruce. 1969. pap. 6.95 (ISBN 0-8028-1729-7). Eerdmans.

New Testament Digest. John D. Hawkes. 160p. 1968. pap. 3.95 (ISBN 0-89036-014-6). Hawkes Pub Inc.

New Testament Documents: Are They Reliable. Frederick F. Bruce. pap. 3.95 (ISBN 0-87784-691-X). Inter-Varsity.

New Testament Documents: Are They Reliable? Ed. by Frederick F. Bruce. (Orig.). 1959. pap. 2.95 (ISBN 0-8028-1025-X). Eerdmans.

New Testament Environment. Edward Lohse. Tr. by John E. Steely from Ger. LC 75-43618. 320p. 1976. pap. 10.95 (ISBN 0-687-27944-5). Abingdon.

New Testament Era: The World of the Bible from 500 B.C. to A.D. 100. Bo Reicke. LC 68-15864. 352p. 1974. pap. 8.95 (ISBN 0-8006-1080-6, 1-1080). Fortress.

New Testament Ethics. Dale Goldsmith. 196p. (Orig.). 1987. pap. 9.95 (ISBN 0-87178-605-2). Brethren.

New Testament Exegesis: A Handbook for Students & Pastors. Gordon D. Fee. LC 82-24829. (Illus.). 154p. (Orig.). 1983. pap. 8.95 (ISBN 0-664-24469-6). Westminster.

New Testament Experience of Faith. 2nd ed. Leander Keck. LC 76-46491. 160p. 1985. pap. 6.95 (ISBN 0-8272-2508-3). CBP.

New Testament Exposition: From Text to Sermon. Walter L. Liefeld. 176p. 1984. 11.95 (ISBN 0-310-45910-9, 12607P). Zondervan.

New Testament Express. Terry Hall. 160p. 1986. pap. 3.95 (ISBN 0-88207-598-5). Victor Bks.

New Testament Follow-Up. Wayland B. Moore. (Orig.). 1963. pap. 3.95 (ISBN 0-8028-1136-1). Eerdmans.

New Testament for English Readers, 4 vols. Henry Alford. 1983. Repr. of 1976 ed. 54.95 (ISBN 0-8010-0195-1). Baker Bk.

New Testament for Spiritual Reading, 25 vols. Ed. by J. L. McKenzie. Incl. Vol. 1. Gospel According to St. Matthew, Pt. 1 (ISBN 0-8245-0334-1); Vol. 2. Gospel According to St. Matthew, Pt. 2 (ISBN 0-8245-0335-X) (ISBN 0-8245-0111-X); Vol. 3. Gospel According to St. Mark, Pt. 1 (ISBN 0-8245-0336-8) (ISBN 0-8245-0112-8); Vol. 4. Gospel According to St. Mark, Pt. 2 (ISBN 0-8245-0337-6) (ISBN 0-8245-0113-6); Vol. 5. Gospel According to St. Luke, Pt. 1 (ISBN 0-8245-0338-4) (ISBN 0-8245-0114-4); Vol. 6. Gospel According to St. Luke, Pt. 2 (ISBN 0-8245-0339-2) (ISBN 0-8245-0115-2); Vol. 7. Gospel According to St. John, Pt. 1 (ISBN 0-8245-0340-6) (ISBN 0-8245-0116-0); Vol. 8. Gospel According to St. John, Pt. 2 (ISBN 0-8164-1079-8) (ISBN 0-8245-0117-9); Vol. 9. Gospel According to St. John, Pt. 3 (ISBN 0-8245-0342-2) (ISBN 0-8245-0118-7); Vol. 10. Acts of the Apostles, Pt. 1 (ISBN 0-8245-0343-0) (ISBN 0-8245-0119-5); Vol. 11. Acts of the Apostles, Pt. 2 (ISBN 0-8245-0344-9) (ISBN 0-8245-0120-9); Vol. 12. Epistle to the **Romans (ISBN 0-8245-0345-7) (ISBN 0-8245-0121-7); Vol. 13. First Epistle to the Corinthians (ISBN 0-8245-0346-5) (ISBN 0-8245-0122-5); Vol. 14. Second Epistle to the Corinthians (ISBN 0-8245-0347-3) (ISBN 0-8245-0123-3); Vol. 15. Epistle to the Galatians (ISBN 0-8245-0348-1) (ISBN 0-8245-0124-1); Vol. 16. Epistle to the Ephesians (ISBN 0-8245-0349-X) (ISBN 0-8245-0125-X); Vol. 17. Epistle to the Philippians. Epistle to the Colossians (ISBN 0-8164-1088-7) (ISBN 0-8245-0126-8); Vol. 18. First Epistle to the Thessalonians. Second Epistle to the Thessalonians (ISBN 0-8245-0352-X) (ISBN 0-8245-0127-6); Vol. 19. First Epistle to Timothy. Second Epistle to Timothy (ISBN 0-8245-0353-8) (ISBN 0-8245-0128-4); Vol. 20. Epistle to Titus. Epistle to Philemon (ISBN 0-8245-0354-6) (ISBN 0-8245-0129-2); Vol. 21. Epistle to the Hebrews. Epistle to James (ISBN 0-8245-0355-4) (ISBN 0-8245-0130-6); Vol. 22. First Epistle to Peter. Second Epistle to Peter (ISBN 0-8245-0356-2) (ISBN 0-8245-0131-4); Vol. 23. Epistle to Jude. Three Epistles of John (ISBN 0-8245-0357-0) (ISBN 0-8245-0132-2); Vol. 24. Revelation of St. John, Pt. 1 (ISBN 0-8245-0358-9) (ISBN 0-8245-0133-0); Vol. 25. Revelation of St. John, Pt. 2 (ISBN 0-8245-0359-7) (ISBN 0-8245-0134-9). 10.00 ea.; Set. 123.75 (ISBN 0-8245-0135-7); pap. 4.95 ea. Crossroad NY.**

New Testament Foundations: A Guide for Christian Students, Vol. 2. Ralph P. Martin. 1986. pap. 9.95 (ISBN 0-8028-0076-9). Eerdmans.

New Testament Greek for Beginners. J. Gresham Machen. 1923. text ed. write for info. (ISBN 0-02-373480-9). Macmillan.

New Testament Greek Notebook. Benjamin Chapman. 1976. looseleaf 19.95 (ISBN 0-8010-2389-0). Baker Bk.

New Testament: Greek Notebook Exegesis Filler. Benjamin Chapman. 1.00 (ISBN 0-8010-2425-0). Baker Bk.

New Testament Greek Primer. Alfred Marshall. 176p. (Orig.). 1981. leather edition 49.95 (ISBN 0-310-20540-9, 6246). Zondervan.

New Testament Herald. Judy Nickell. 1985. 1.25 (ISBN 0-89536-733-5, 5878). CSS of Ohio.

New Testament History. F. F. Bruce. LC 78-144253. 462p. 1972. pap. 9.95 (ISBN 0-385-02533-5, Anch). Doubleday.

New Testament History-Acts. 5th ed. Gareth Reese. (Bible Study Textbook Ser.). (Illus.). 1976. 19.95 (ISBN 0-89900-055-X). College Pr Pub.

New Testament History: The Story of the Emerging Church. Floyd V. Filson. LC 64-15360. (Illus.). 464p. 1964. 12.95 (ISBN 0-664-20525-9). Westminster.

New Testament Holiness. Cook. 4.95 (ISBN 0-686-12895-8). Schmul Pub Co.

New Testament Hospitality: Partnership with Strangers As Promise & Mission. John Koenig. LC 85-47725. (Overtures to Biblical Theology Ser.). 176p. 1985. pap. 9.95 (ISBN 0-8006-1543-3, 1-1543). Fortress.

New Testament Illustrations. Clifford M. Jones. (Cambridge Bible Commentary on the New English Bible, New Testament Ser.). 27.95 (ISBN 0-521-05446-X); pap. 12.95x (ISBN 0-521-09376-7, 376). Cambridge U Pr.

New Testament in Art. Barbara Shissler. LC 70-84411. (Fine Art Books). (Illus.). 1970. PLB 5.95 (ISBN 0-8225-0169-4). Lerner Pubns.

New Testament in Context: Sources & Documents. Howard C. Kee. (Illus.). 256p. 1984. pap. text ed. 20.33 (ISBN 0-13-615774-2). P-H.

New Testament in Current Study. Reginald H. Fuller. (Hudson River Editions). 1976. 15.00x (ISBN 0-684-14843-9, ScribT). Scribner.

New Testament in Everyday American English (EAE) Julian G. Anderson. LC 84-194786. (Illus.). 896p. 1984. pap. 4.95 (ISBN 0-9602128-4-1). Anderson Publ.

New Testament in Greek: The Gospel According to St. Luke, Vol. 3, Pt. 1. American & British Committee for the International Greek New Testament Project. (New Testament in Greek Ser.). 1983. 98.00x (ISBN 0-19-826167-5). Oxford U Pr.

New Testament in Its Literary Environment. David E. Aune. Ed. by Wayne A. Meeks. (Library of Early Christianity: Vol. 8). 262p. 1987. 22.95 (ISBN 0-664-21912-8). Westminster.

New Testament in Its Social Environment. John E. Stambaugh & David L. Balch. LC 85-15516. (Library of Early Christianity: Vol. 2). (Illus.). 208p. 1986. 16.95 (ISBN 0-664-21906-3). Westminster.

New Testament in Life & Literature. Janet T. Stoddart. 1973. 40.00 (ISBN 0-8274-0860-9). R West.

New Testament in Literary Criticism. Ed. by Leland Ryken. (Library of Literary Criticism). 450p. 1985. 45.00 (ISBN 0-8044-3271-6). Ungar.

New Testament in Modern English. J. B. Phillips. 1973. 8.95 (ISBN 0-02-088490-7). Macmillan.

New Testament in Modern Speech. 3rd ed. R. F. Weymouth. LC 78-9536. 750p. 1978. kivar 14.95 (ISBN 0-8254-4025-4). Kregel.

New Testament in Modern Speech. 6th ed. Richard F. Weymouth. 457p. 1983. 9.50 (ISBN 0-227-67550-9, Pub. by J Clarke UK). Attic Pr.

New Testament in Survey. Paul Southern. pap. 2.70 (ISBN 0-89137-550-3). Quality Pubns.

New Testament in the Life of the Church. Eugene LaVerdiere. LC 80-67403. 192p. (Orig.). 1980. pap. 4.95 (ISBN 0-87793-213-1). Ave Maria.

New Testament Index. Ed. by R. G. Bratcher. 37p. 1963. pap. 1.15x (ISBN 0-8267-0003-9, 08507, Pub. by United Bible). Am Bible.

New Testament Interpretation Through Rhetorical Criticism. George A. Kennedy. LC 83-23577. x, 171p. 1984. 14.00x (ISBN 0-8078-1601-9); pap. 6.95 (ISBN 0-8078-4120-X). U of NC Pr.

New Testament Introduction. rev. ed. Donald Guthrie. 1971. 34.95 (ISBN 0-87784-953-6). Inter-Varsity.

New Testament: Its Background, Growth & Content. enl. ed. Bruce M. Metzger. 310p. 1965. 16.50 (ISBN 0-687-27914-3). Abingdon.

New Testament Living. Norman B. Harrison. 1972. pap. 1.25 (ISBN 0-911802-30-4). Free Church Pubns.

New Testament Logia on Divorce: A Study of their Interpretation from Erasmus to Milton. V. N. Olsen. 167p. (Orig.). 1971. pap. 40.00x (Pub. by J. C. B. Mohr BRD). Coronet Bks.

New Testament Manuscripts in the Freer Collection. Henry A. Sanders. Repr. of 1918 ed. 37.00 (ISBN 0-384-38809-4). Johnson Repr.

New Testament Men of Faith. F. B. Meyer. LC 79-66338. 1979. pap. 4.95 (ISBN 0-89107-171-7). Good News.

New Testament Notes. Charles H. Patterson. (Orig.). 1965. pap. 3.25 (ISBN 0-8220-0880-7). Cliffs.

New Testament of the New Jerusalem Bible. Henry Wansbrough. LC 86-11680. (Illus.). 552p. 1986. pap. 6.95 (ISBN 0-385-23706-5, Im). Doubleday.

New Testament Prophecy. David Hill. LC 79-16707. (New Foundations Theological Library). 260p. (Peter Toon & Ralph Martin series editors). 1980. 6.49 (ISBN 0-8042-3702-6). John Knox.

New Testament Simply Told. Florence E. Waggener. LC 86-90523. 160p. 1986. 11.95x (ISBN 0-9617339-0-X). Waggener Publ Co.

New Testament Social Ethics for Today. Richard N. Longenecker. 128p. (Orig.). 1984. pap. 5.95 (ISBN 0-8028-1992-3). Eerdmans.

New Testament Speaks. William L. Lane et al. 1969. 16.95 (ISBN 0-06-064917-8, HarpR). Har Row.

New Testament Story Sermons for Children's Church. Marianne Radius. 120p. 1984. pap. 5.95 (ISBN 0-8010-7723-0). Baker Bk.

New Testament Student & Bible Translation. John H. Skilton. (New Testament Student Ser.). 1978. pap. 5.00 (ISBN 0-87552-436-2). Presby & Reformed.

New Testament Student & His Field. John H. Skilton. (New Testament Student Ser.). 318p. 1982. pap. 9.95 (ISBN 0-87552-437-0). Presby & Reformed.

New Testament: Student Text. Michael Pennock. LC 82-70088. (Illus.). 256p. (Orig.). 1982. pap. 5.50 (ISBN 0-87793-246-8). Ave Maria.

New Testament Studies: Essays in Honor of Ray Summers in His Sixty-fifth Year. Ed. by Huber L. Drumwright & Curtis Vaughan. LC 75-29815. 195p. 1975. 7.95 (ISBN 0-918954-15-0). Baylor Univ Pr.

New Testament Study Guide. J. W. Malone. kivar 4.95 (ISBN 0-686-12848-6). Schmul Pub Co.

New Testament Study Guide. Chuck Smith. 224p. (YA) 1982. pap. 2.95 (ISBN 0-936728-33-7). Word For Today.

New Testament Survey. Walter M. Dunnett. LC 63-7410. 96p. 1963. pap. text ed. 4.95 (ISBN 0-910566-03-8); Perfect bdg. instr's. guide 5.95 (ISBN 0-910566-19-4). Evang Tchr.

New Testament Survey. Robert G. Gromacki. 16.95 (ISBN 0-8010-3677-1). Baker Bk.

New Testament Survey. Robert G. Gromacki. LC 74-83793. 1974. 9.95 (ISBN 0-87227-018-1). Reg Baptist.

New Testament Survey. Ken Malmin. 1975. 4.25 (ISBN 0-914936-22-0). Bible Temple.

New Testament Survey. rev. ed. Merrill C. Tenney. Rev. by Walter M. Dunnett. 480p. 1985. 19.95 (ISBN 0-8028-3611-9). Eerdmans.

New Testament: Teacher's Manual. Michael Pennock. 112p. (Orig.). 1982. 2.95 (ISBN 0-87793-247-6). Ave Maria.

New Testament Teaching on Tongues. Merrill F. Unger. LC 70-165057. 1971. pap. 5.95 (ISBN 0-8254-3900-0). Kregel.

New Testament Textual Criticism: Its Significance for Exegesis. Ed. by Eldon J. Epp & Fee D. Gordon. (Illus.). 94.00x (ISBN 0-19-826175-6). Oxford U Pr.

New Testament Theology. Donald Guthrie. 1056p. 1981. text ed. 34.95 (ISBN 0-87784-965-X). Inter-Varsity.

New Testament Theology. Gerhard Hasel. pap. 5.95 (ISBN 0-8028-1733-5). Eerdmans.

New Testament Theology. Joachim Jeremias. LC 70-143936. lib. rep. ed. 30.00x (ISBN 0-684-15157-X, ScribT). Scribner.

New Testament Theology. Leon Morris. 448p. 1986. text ed. 19.95 (ISBN 0-310-45570-7, 12391, Pub. by Academie Bks). Zondervan.

New Testament Theology. Frank Stagg. LC 62-15328. 1962. 13.95 (ISBN 0-8054-1613-7). Broadman.

New Testament Times. Michael Rakel & Maryann Bremke. 1984. 9.95 (ISBN 0-89837-100-7, Pub. by Pflaum Press). Peter Li.

New Testament Times. Merrill C. Tenney. 1965. 21.95 (ISBN 0-8028-3250-4). Eerdmans.

New Testament Understanding of Jesus. Megan McKenna & Darryl Ducote. LC 78-71529. (Followers of the Way Ser.: Vol. 2). 1979. 22.50 (ISBN 0-8091-9543-7); cassette 7.50 (ISBN 0-8091-7667-X). Paulist Pr.

New Testament Without Illusion. John L. McKenzie. (Crossroad Paperback Ser.). 256p. 1982. pap. 6.95 (ISBN 0-8245-0451-8). Crossroad NY.

New Testament Witness in Today's World. Allison A. Trites. 144p. 1982. pap. 8.95 (ISBN 0-8170-0988-4). Judson.

New Testament Word Book: A Glossary. facsimile ed. Eric Partridge. LC 70-117907. (Select Bibliographies Reprint Ser). Repr. of 1940 ed. 19.00 (ISBN 0-8369-5359-2). Ayer Co Pubs.

New Testament Word Lists. Clinton D. Morrison & David H. Barnes. 1964. pap. 3.95 (ISBN 0-8028-1141-8). Eerdmans.

New Testament Words. William Barclay. LC 73-12737. 302p. 1976. softcover 5.95 (ISBN 0-664-24761-X). Westminster.

New Testament Words in Today's Language. Wayne Detzler. 408p. 1986. 14.95 (ISBN 0-89693-528-0). Victor Bks.

New Testament World: Insights from Cultural Anthropology. Bruce J. Malina. LC 80-84650. (Illus.). 169p. 1981. pap. 10.95 (ISBN 0-8042-0423-3). John Knox.

New Testament Writings: History, Literature, Interpretation. James M. Efird. LC 79-87750. (Biblical Foundation Ser.). 1980. pap. 7.95 (ISBN 0-8042-0246-X). John Knox.

New Thayer's Greek Lexicon. John Thayer. 784p. 1981. 19.95 (ISBN 0-913573-22-1). Hendrickson MA.

New Themes for the Protestant Clergy. Stephen Colwell. LC 71-83417. (Religion in America, Ser. 1). 1969. Repr. of 1851 ed. 32.00 (ISBN 0-405-00243-2). Ayer Co Pubs.

New Themes in Christian Philosophy. Ed. by Ralph M. McInerny. LC 68-20439. 1968. 17.95 (ISBN 0-8290-1654-6); pap. text ed. 9.50x (ISBN 0-8290-1606-6). Irvington.

New Themes in Christian Philosophy. Ed. by Ralph M. McInerny. LC 68-20439. 1968. 19.95 (ISBN 0-268-00192-8). U of Notre Dame Pr.

New Theory of the Earth: Its Original, to the Consummation of All Things Wherein the Creation of the World in Six Days. William Whiston. Ed. by Claude C. Albritton, Jr. LC 77-6545. (History of Geology Ser.). 1978. lib. bdg. 37.50x (ISBN 0-405-10463-4). Ayer Co Pubs.

New Thought or a Modern Religious Approach: The Philosophy of Health, Happiness & Prosperity. Martin A. Larson. LC 84-7637. 475p. 1985. 19.95 (ISBN 0-8022-2464-4). Philos Lib.

New Thought Religion. 2nd., rev. ed. Martin A. Larson. LC 86-16947. 390p. 1987. 16.95 (ISBN 0-8022-2525-X); pap. 9.95 (ISBN 0-8022-2527-6). Philos Lib.

New Thought: The Revolt Against Orthodoxy. Martin Larson. 352p. cancelled (ISBN 0-8159-6317-3). Devin.

New Thresholds of Faith. 2nd ed. Kenneth E. Hagin. 1972. pap. 2.50 (ISBN 0-89276-070-2). Hagin Ministries.

New Tower of Babel. Dietrich Von Hildebrand. LC 76-998. 1977. Repr. 5.95 (ISBN 0-8199-0600-X). Franciscan Herald.

New Training for Service. rev. ed. C. J. Sharp. (Illus.). 128p. (Orig.). 1942. pap. 2.95 (ISBN 0-87239-334-8, 3059). Standard Pub.

New Translation of Volney's Ruins, 2 vols. C. F. Volney. Ed. by Burton Feldman & Robert D. Richardson. LC 78-60900. (Myth & Romanticism Ser.: Vol. 25). (Illus.). 1979. Set. lib. bdg. 160.00 (ISBN 0-8240-3574-7). Garland Pub.

New Treasury of Judaism. Ed. by Philip Birnbaum. 1977. 15.00 (ISBN 0-88482-410-1, Sanhedrin Pr); pap. 9.95 (ISBN 0-88482-411-X, Sanhedrin Pr). Hebrew Pub.

New Unger's Bible Handbook. rev. ed. Merrill F. Unger. Ed. by Gary N. Larson. (Illus.). 1984. 24.95 (ISBN 0-8024-9049-2). Moody.

New Ventures-Free Methodist Missions Nineteen Sixty to Nineteen Seventy-Nine. Leona K. Fear. (Orig.). 1979. pap. 1.50 (ISBN 0-89367-036-7). Light & Life.

New Views of Mormon History: A Collection of Essays in Honor of Leonard J. Arrington. Ed. by Davis Bitton & Maureen U. Beecher. 1987. 25.00x (ISBN 0-87480-304-7). U of Utah Pr.

New Wars for Old. John H. Holmes. LC 71-147623. (Library of War & Peace; Non-Resis. & Non-Vio.). 1972. lib. bdg. 46.00 (ISBN 0-8240-0398-5). Garland Pub.

New Way of Jesus. Ed. by William Klassen. LC 80-65049. 158p. 1980. pap. 7.95 (ISBN 0-87303-038-9). Faith & Life.

New Way of Thinking. Charles Roth. LC 78-64751. 1979. 5.95 (ISBN 0-87159-113-8). Unity School.

New Way to Live. Neta Jackson. LC 82-83392. 104p. 1983. pap. 4.95 (ISBN 0-8361-3323-4). Herald Pr.

New Ways in Christian Worship. Robert W. Bailey. LC 81-65390. 1981. pap. 6.95 (ISBN 0-8054-2311-7). Broadman.

New Ways to Worship. Church of Scotland, Committee on Public Worship & Aids to Devotion. 1980. pap. 4.95x (ISBN 0-7152-0454-8). Outlook.

New Webster's Bible Dictionary & Concordance. (Deluxe Pocket Editions Ser.). 288p. pap. 2.50 (ISBN 0-8326-0066-0, 6531). World Bible.

New Wedding Service For You. Arthur Homburg. 1985. 5.95 (ISBN 0-89536-731-9, 5815). CSS of Ohio.

New Westminster Dictionary of Liturgy & Worship. Ed. by J. G. Davies. LC 86-9219. (Illus.). 560p. 1986. 29.95 (ISBN 0-664-21270-0). Westminster.

New Westminster Dictionary of the Bible. Ed. by Henry S. Gehman. LC 69-10000. (Illus.). 1064p. 1982. thumb indexed 25.95 (ISBN 0-664-21388-X); 22.95. Westminster.

New Wilson's Old Testament Word Studies: Keyed to Strong's Numbering System & to the Theological Wordbook of Old Testament. rev. ed. William Wilson. LC 86-7210. 584p. 1987. 27.95 (ISBN 0-8254-4030-0); prepub. 24.95 until Oct. 1987. Kregel.

New Wine Is Better. Robert Thom. 1974. pap. 2.95 (ISBN 0-88368-036-X). Whitaker Hse.

New Wine: New Wineskins. James B. Dunning. 128p. (Orig.). 1981. pap. 5.95 (ISBN 0-8215-9807-4). Sadlier.

New Wineskins: A Study of the House Church Movement, Vol. 30. Joyce V. Thurmann. (IC-Studien zur Interkulturellen Geschichte). 109p. 1982. pap. 14.20 (ISBN 3-8204-7172-3). P Lang Pubs.

New Wineskins: Reimagining Religious Life Today. Sandra M. Schneiders. 320p. (Orig.). 1986. pap. 10.95 (ISBN 0-8091-2765-2). Paulist Pr.

New Witness for the Articles of Faith. Bruce R. McConkie. LC 85-12888. 735p. 1985. 17.95 (ISBN 0-87747-872-4). Deseret Bk.

New Woman-New Earth: Sexist Ideologies & Human Liberation. Rosemary R. Ruether. 255p. 1978. pap. 9.95 (ISBN 0-8164-2185-4, HarpR). Har-Row.

New World. Alan T. Dale. (Illus.). 429p. (Orig.). 1973. pap. 9.95 (ISBN 0-8192-1149-4). Morehouse.

New World Dictionary Concordance to the New American Bible. 12.95 (ISBN 0-529-06094-9, 2418); pap. 4.95 (ISBN 0-529-04540-0, 2416). World Bible.

New World Jerusalem: The Swedenborgian Experience in Community Construction. Mary A. Meyers. LC 82-11997. (Contributions in American Studies: No. 65). (Illus.). xiii, 217p. 1983. lib. bdg. 29.95 (ISBN 0-313-23602-X, MNJ/). Greenwood.

New World Jewry, Fourteen Ninety-Three to Eighteen Twenty-Five: Requiem for the Forgotten. Seymour B. Liebman. 25.00x (ISBN 0-87068-277-6). Ktav.

New World Metaphysics: Readings on the Religious Meaning of the American Experience. Ed. by Giles Gunn. 1981. pap. text ed. 10.95x (ISBN 0-19-502874-0). Oxford U Pr.

New Yoga. Leonard Orr. write for info. L Orr.

New York Dictionary Catalog of the Missionary Research Library, 17 vols. Missionary Research Library. 1968. Set. 1680.00 (ISBN 0-8161-0778-5, Hall Library). G K Hall.

New York Jew. Alfred Kazin. LC 77-20359. 1978. 12.95 (ISBN 0-394-49567-5). Knopf.

New York Jews & the Quest for Community. Arthur A. Goren. LC 76-129961. 1979. 34.00x (ISBN 0-231-03422-9); pap. 17.00x (ISBN 0-231-08368-8). Columbia U Pr.

New York Review, 1905-1908. Michael J. De Vito. LC 77-75637. (Monograph Ser.: No. 34). (Illus.). 1977. 13.95x (ISBN 0-930060-14-8). US Cath Hist.

New You. Harold Myra. 1980. pap. 3.95 (ISBN 0-88207-581-0). Victor Bks.

New You. Dede Robertson. 1984. 12.95 (ISBN 0-8407-5408-6). Nelson.

New Zionism & the Foreign Policy System of Israel. Ofira Seliktar. 256p. cancelled (ISBN 0-7099-3341-X, Pub. by Croom Helm Ltd). Methuen Inc.

New Zionism & the Foreign Policy System of Israel. Ofira Seliktar. (Middle East Research Institute Special Studies). 272p. 1986. text ed. 32.50x (ISBN 0-8093-1287-5). S Ill U Pr.

New Zondervan Pictorial Bible Dictionary. rev. ed. Ed. by J. D. Douglas & E. Van der Maas. 1000p. 1987. price not set. Zondervan.

Newborn. Jack Hayford. 96p. 1987. 2.95 (ISBN 0-8423-4677-5). Tyndale.

Newborn: Alive in Christ, the Savior. Jack W. Hayford. (Orig.). 1984. pap. 2.95 (ISBN 0-916847-00-4). Living Way.

Newborn Christian: 114 Readings. J. B. Phillips. 240p. 1984. 5.95 (ISBN 0-02-088270-X, Collier). Macmillan.

Newborn Might & Strength Everlasting: A Christmas Offering. Rudolf Steiner. Ed. by Gilbert Church. (Illus.). 19p. (Orig.). 1977. pap. 2.00 (ISBN 0-88010-100-8). Anthroposophic.

Newes from Italy of a Second Moses or, the Life of Galeacius Carracciolus the Noble Marquese of Vico. Niccolo Balbani. Tr. by W. Crashaw. LC 79-84085. (English Experience Ser.: No. 905). 92p. 1979. Repr. of 1608 ed. lib. bdg. 10.00 (ISBN 90-221-0905-4). Walter J Johnson.

Newly Made Mason: What He & Every Mason Should Know about Masonry. 5th ed. Ed. by H. L. Haywood. (Illus.). 256p. 1978. Repr. of 1973 ed. text ed. 12.50 (ISBN 0-88053-030-8, M-80). Macoy Pub.

Newly Married. Wayne Rickerson. (Family Ministry Ser.). 96p. 1986. pap. 19.95 (ISBN 0-89191-967-8). Cook.

Newman. Owen Chadwick. (Past Masters Ser.). 1983. 13.95x (ISBN 0-19-287568-X); pap. 4.95 (ISBN 0-19-287567-1). Oxford U Pr.

Newman: An Appreciation. Alexander Whyte. 1973. Repr. of 1901 ed. 30.00 (ISBN 0-8274-0570-7). R West.

Newman & Gladstone: The Vatican Decrees. Ed. by Alvan Ryan. 1962. 13.95 (ISBN 0-268-00190-1). U of Notre Dame Pr.

Newman & the Gospel of Christ. Roderick Strange. (Oxford Theological Monographs). 1981. 39.00x (ISBN 0-19-826718-5). Oxford U Pr.

Newman & the Modernists. Ed. by Mary J. Weaver. (Resources in Religion Ser.: Vol. 1). 232p. (Orig.). 1986. lib. bdg. 25.75 (ISBN 0-8191-4687-0, College Theo Soc); pap. text ed. 12.25 (ISBN 0-8191-4688-9). U Pr of Amer.

Newman Anthology. Ed. by W. S. Lilly. 356p. 1981. 25.00x (ISBN 0-234-77060-0, Pub. by Dobson Bks England). State Mutual Bk.

Newman Anthology. Cardinal John H. Newman. Ed. by W. S. Lilly. 1977. lib. bdg. 59.95 (ISBN 0-8490-2341-6). Gordon Pr.

Newman Brothers: An Essay in Comparative Intellectual Biography. William Robbins. LC 66-4976. (Illus.). 1966. 15.00x (ISBN 0-674-62200-6). Harvard U Pr.

Newman Movement. John Whitney Evans. 264p. 1980. 16.95 (ISBN 0-268-01453-1). U of Notre Dame Pr.

Newman's Concept of Faith. John A. Elbert. 59.95 (ISBN 0-8490-0729-1). Gordon Pr.

Newman's Journey. Meriol Trevor. LC 84-62224. 285p. 1985. pap. 9.50 (ISBN 0-87973-627-5, 627). Our Sunday Visitor.

Newman's Vision of Faith. Bouyer Louis C.O. LC 86-81425. 210p. 1986. pap. 10.95 (ISBN 0-89870-113-9). Ignatius Pr.

Newness of Life. rev. ed. Estelle C. Carver. Ed. by Hal M. Helms. (Living Library Ser.). 150p. pap. 4.95 (ISBN 0-941478-19-X). Paraclete Pr.

Newness of Life. Richard Howard. 300p. 1975. 5.95 (ISBN 0-8341-0353-2). Beacon Hill.

Newness of Life: A Modern Introduction to Catholic Ethics. James Gaffney. LC 79-84404. 360p. 1979. pap. 6.95 (ISBN 0-8091-2202-2). Paulist Pr.

News from True Cultivators, Vol. I. Heng Sure & Heng Chau. 128p. (Orig.). 1983. pap. 5.00 (ISBN 0-88139-016-X). Buddhist Text.

News from True Cultivators, Vol. 2. Heng Sure & Heng Chau. 130p. (Orig.). 1983. pap. 5.00 (ISBN 0-88139-024-0). Buddhist Text.

New...Saint Joseph Children's Missal. (Illus.). black leatherette, hard bd. 2.25 (ISBN 0-89942-806-1, 806/67-B); white leatherette, hard bd. 2.25 (ISBN 0-89942-805-3, 806/67-W); black soft simulated lea., colored edges 2.50 (ISBN 0-89942-804-5, 806/42-B); white soft simulated lea., colored edges 2.50 (ISBN 0-89942-803-7, 806/42-W); dlx. black sim. pearl, gold edges 8.95 (ISBN 0-89942-802-9, 806/82B); dlx. white sim. pearl, gold edges 8.95 (ISBN 0-89942-801-0, 806/82W). Catholic Bk Pub.

Next Chapter after the Last. Compiled by Harry Verploegh. (Orig.). Date not set. pap. price not set (ISBN 0-87509-391-4). Chr Pubns.

Next Life: Course XX, Lessons 173-82. (Illus.). 1976. pap. 11.00 (ISBN 0-87887-356-2). Church of Light.

Next Step. Jack T. Chick. (Illus.). 64p. (Orig.). 1978. pap. 1.95 (ISBN 0-937958-04-2). Chick Pubns.

Next Step in Religion: An Essay Toward the Coming Renaissance. Roy W. Sellars. LC 75-3360. Repr. of 1918 ed. 24.50 (ISBN 0-404-59358-5). AMS Pr.

Next to God...Poland: Politics & Religion in Contemporary Poland. Bogdan Szajkowski. LC 83-40151. 258p. 1983. 25.00 (ISBN 0-312-57233-6). St Martin.

Next World-& the Next. Crookall. 7.95 (ISBN 0-8356-5008-1). Theos Pub Hse.

NFCLC Formation Program. NFCLC. 150p. 1975. wkbk. 7.00x (ISBN 0-913605-02-6). NFCLC.

NFCLC Formation Program: Leader's Manual. NFCLC. 80p. (Orig.). 1975. pap. 3.50x wkbk. (ISBN 0-913605-03-4). NFCLC.

Nibble Theory & the Kernel of Power. Kaleel Jamison. LC 83-63112. 74p. (Orig.). 1984. 4.95 (ISBN 0-8091-2621-4); pap. 3.95 (ISBN 0-8091-2621-4). Paulist Pr.

Nibelungen Prosody. Ray M. Wakefield. (De Proprietatibus Litterarum Ser.: No. 112). 1976. pap. 16.00x (ISBN 0-686-22366-7). Mouton.

Nibelungenlied. William N. Lettsom. LC 77-13811. 1977. lib. bdg. 45.00 (ISBN 0-8414-5830-8). Folcroft.

Niccolo Machiavelli. Silvia Ruffo-Fiore. (World Authors Ser.). 1982. lib. bdg. 15.95 (ISBN 0-8057-6499-2, Twayne). G K Hall.

Nice Girls Don't Get Raped. Jennifer Botkin-Mayer. 1987. pap. 5.95. Heres Life.

Nice Place to Live. limited ed. (Illus.). 7.50 (ISBN 0-317-20858-6). Cricketfield Pr.

Nicene Creed, Illumined by Modern Thought. Geddes MacGregor. LC 80-19348. pap. 40.80 (ISBN 0-317-20013-5, 2023220). Bks Demand UMI.

Nicene Creed: Our Common Faith. Metropolitan Emilianos Timiadis. LC 82-71826. 128p. (Orig.). 1983. pap. 7.95 (ISBN 0-8006-1653-7, 1-1653). Fortress.

Nicephori Archiepiscopi Constantinopolitani Opuscula Historica. Nicephorus. Ed. by Carl G. De Boor. LC 75-7311. (Roman History Ser.). (Gr.). 1975. Repr. 25.50x (ISBN 0-405-07193-0). Ayer Co Pubs.

Niceta of Remesiana, Sulp. Severus, Vincent of Lerins, Prosper. LC 50-5703. (Fathers of the Church Ser: Vol. 7). 443p. 1949. 22.95x (ISBN 0-8132-0007-5). Cath U Pr.

Nicetae Choniatae Historiae, 2 vols. Ed. by Ioannes Van Dieten. (Corpus Fontium Historiae Byzantinae Vol. XI: Series Berolinensis). 1975. 242.00x (ISBN 3-11-004528-1). De Gruyter.

Nichiren: The Buddhist Prophet. Masharu Anesaki. 1916. 11.25 (ISBN 0-8446-1029-1). Peter Smith.

Nichiren's Senji-sho: An Essay on the Selection of Proper Time. Kenneth Dollarhide. LC 82-21687. (Studies in Asian Thought & Religion: Vol. 1). 184p. 1983. 39.95x (ISBN 0-88946-051-5). E Mellen.

Nicholas Ferrar of Little Gidding. A. L. Maycock. LC 80-16684. pap. 63.50 (ISBN 0-8357-9131-9, 2019345). Bks Demand UMI.

Nicholas I, Patriarch of Constantinople: Letters. Ed. & tr. by R. J. Jenkins. LC 74-28930. (Dumbarton Oaks Texts: Vol. 2). 668p. 1973. 45.00x (ISBN 0-88402-039-8). Dumbarton Oaks.

Nicholas I, Patriarch of Constantinople: Miscellaneous Writings. Ed. by L. G. Westerink. LC 80-70736. (Dumbarton Oaks Texts: Vol. 6). 160p. 1981. 28.00x (ISBN 0-88402-089-4). Dumbarton Oaks.

Nicholas Love: The Myrrour of the Blessed LYF of Jesu Christ, 2 Vols. Michael Sargent & James Hogg. (Analecta Cartusiana Ser.: No. 91). (Orig.). 1987. pap. 50.00 (ISBN 3-7052-0159-X, Pub. by Salzburg Studies). Longwood Pub Group.

Nicholas of Cusa. Henry Bett. LC 76-1131. (Great Medieval Churchmen Ser). x, 210p. 1976. Repr. of 1932 ed. lib. bdg. 17.50x (ISBN 0-915172-05-4). Richwood Pub.

Nicholas of Cusa on God as Not-other: A Translation & an Appraisal of De Li Non Aliud. 2nd ed. Jasper Hopkins. LC 82-73976. ix, 179p. 1983. text ed. 20.00x (ISBN 0-938060-26-0). Banning Pr.

Nicholas of Cusa on God as Not-other: A Translation & an Appraisal of De li non aliud. Jasper Hopkins. LC 78-22006. pap. 46.30 (ISBN 0-317-39689-7, 2055880). Bks Demand UMI.

Nicholas of Cusa on Learned Ignorance: A Translation & an Appraisal of De Docta Ignorantia. 2nd ed. Jasper Hopkins. LC 80-82907. ix, 205p. 1985. text ed. 23.00x (ISBN 0-938060-30-9); pap. text ed. 10.00x (ISBN 0-938060-27-9). Banning Pr.

Nicholas of Cusa's Debate with John Wenck: A Translation & an Appraisal of De Ignota Litteratura & Apologia Doctae Ignorantiae. 2nd ed. Jasper Hopkins. LC 80-82908. viii, 119p. 1984. text ed. 23.00x (ISBN 0-938060-31-7). Banning Pr.

Nicholas Wiseman & the Transformation of English Catholicism. Richard J. Schiefen. (Illus.). 416p. 1984. 32.50x (ISBN 0-915762-15-3). Patmos Pr.

Nichtov M'aleph V'ad Tav: Spirit Duplicating Primer. Aviva Langsam. text ed. 15.00 (ISBN 0-915152-03-7, A05). Torah Umesorah.

Nichtpriesterliche Josephsgeschichte (Gen 37-50) Hans-Christoph Schmitt. 1979. 34.40 (ISBN 3-11-007834-1). De Gruyter.

Nicolaitanism, the Rise & Growth of the Clergy. F. W. Grant. Ed. by R. P. Daniel. pap. 2.95 (ISBN 0-88172-139-5). Believers Bkshelf.

Nicolas Cotheret's Annals of Citeaux, Outlined from the Original French. Louis J. Lekai. (Cistercian Studies Ser.: 57). 1983. pap. 13.95 (ISBN 0-87907-857-X). Cistercian Pubns.

Nicolas Gueudeville & His Work Sixteen Fifty-Two to Seventeen Twenty-Five. A. Rosenberg. 1982. 49.50 (ISBN 90-247-2533-X, Pub. by Martinus Nijhoff Netherlands). Kluwer Academic.

Nicolas Love's Myrrour of the Blessed Lyf of Jesu Christ. Elizabeth Salter. Ed. by James Hogg. (Analecta Carusiana Ser.: No. 10). (Orig.). 1974. pap. 25.00 (ISBN 3-7052-0011-9, Pub by Salzburg Studies). Longwood Pub Group.

Nicomachean Ethics. Aristotle. Tr. by Martin Ostwald. LC 62-15690. (Orig.). 1962. pap. 6.65 scp (ISBN 0-672-60256-3, LLA75). Bobbs.

Nicomachean Ethics. Aristotle. (Loeb Classical Library: No. 73). 13.95x (ISBN 0-674-99081-1). Harvard U Pr.

Nicomachean Ethics. Aristotle. Tr. by Hippocrates G. Apostle. LC 75-5871. (Synthese Historical Library: No. 13). 372p. 1975. lib. bdg. 71.00 (ISBN 90-277-0569-0, Pub. by Reidel Holland). Kluwer Academic.

Niddah, 2 vols. 30.00 (ISBN 0-910218-87-0). Bennet Pub.

Niebuhr. G. Wurth. (Modern Thinkers Ser.). 1960. pap. 1.50 (ISBN 0-87552-586-5). Presby & Reformed.

Nietzche und Emerson. Stanley Hubbard. LC 80-2538. Repr. of 1958 ed. 25.50 (ISBN 0-404-19264-5). AMS Pr.

Nietzsche. Richard Schacht. (Arguments of the Philosophers Ser.). 560p. 1983. 35.00x (ISBN 0-7100-9191-5); pap. 17.50 (ISBN 0-7102-0544-9). Methuen Inc.

Nietzsche & Buddhism. Freny Mistry. (Monographien und Texte zur Nietzsche-Forschung, Vol. 6). 211p. 1981. 43.25 (ISBN 3-11-008305-1). De Gruyter.

Nietzsche & Christianity, Vol. 145. Ed. by Claude Geffre & Jean-Pierre Jossua. (Concilium 1981). 128p. (Orig.). 1981. pap. 6.95 (ISBN 0-8164-2312-1, HarpR). Har-Row.

Nietzsche & Pascal on Christianity. Charles M. Natoli. LC 83-49020. (American University Studies V (Philosophy): Vol. 3). 200p. (Orig.). 1984. pap. text ed. 24.25 (ISBN 0-8204-0071-8). P Lang Pubs.

Nietzsche en France: L'antichristianisme et la Critique, 1891-1915. Eric H. Deudon. LC 81-43820. 176p. (Orig.). 1982. lib. bdg. 27.50 o. p. (ISBN 0-8191-2339-0); pap. text ed. 11.75 (ISBN 0-8191-2340-4). U Pr of Amer.

Nietzsche Reader. Friedrich Nietzsche. Tr. by R. J. Hollingdale from Ger. (Classics Ser.). (Orig.). 1978. pap. 4.95 (ISBN 0-14-044329-0). Penguin.

Nietzsche und Die Metaphysik. Mihailo Djuric. (Monographien und Texte zur Nietsche-Forschung: Band 16). (Ger.). viii, 326p. 1985. 61.60x (ISBN 3-11-010169-6). De Gruyter.

Nietzsche, Werke, Kritische Gesamtausgabe, Sect. 8, Vol. 1: Nachgelassene Fragmente, Herbst 1885 bis Herbst 1887. Friedrich Nietzsche. Ed. by Giorgio Colli & Mazzino Montinari. (Ger.). viii, 360p. 1974. 28.20x (ISBN 3-11-004741-1). De Gruyter.

Nietzsche's Existential Imperative. Bernd Magnus. LC 77-9864. (Studies in Phenomenology & Existential Philosophy Ser.). 256p. 1978. 20.00x (ISBN 0-253-34062-4). Ind U Pr.

Nietzsche's Moral Philosophy. John A. Bernstein. LC 85-46001. 1987. 32.50 (ISBN 0-8386-3283-1). Fairleigh Dickinson.

Night after: Climatic & Biological Consequences of a Nuclear War. Y. Velikhov et al. 165p. 1985. 8.95 (ISBN 0-8285-3110-2, Pub. by Mir Pubs USSR). Imported Pubns.

Night Before Christmas. Clement C. Moore. (Pictureback Book & Cassette Library Ser.). (Illus.). 32p. 1985. pap. 4.95 incl. cassette (ISBN 0-394-87658-X). Random.

Night Before Christmas-in Texas, that Is. Leon Harris. (Illus.). 1977. Repr. of 1952 ed. 7.95 (ISBN 0-88289-175-8). Pelican.

Night Before Jesus. Herbert Brokering. (Continued Applied Christianity Ser.). 1983. 6.50 (ISBN 0-570-04084-1, 56-1439). Concordia.

Night Chant: A Navaho Ceremony. Washington Matthews. LC 74-7991. Repr. of 1902 ed. 70.00 (ISBN 0-404-11880-1). AMS Pr.

Night Cometh: Two Wealthy Evangelicals Face the Nation. Rebecca J. Winter. LC 77-87594. 1977. pap. 2.95 (ISBN 0-87808-429-0). William Carey Lib.

Night Cries. Patricia Marie. 1981. 4.75 (ISBN 0-8062-1794-4). Carlton.

Night He Was Betrayed: Bible Studies in Our Lord's Preparation for His Passion. Reginald E. White. LC 82-13783. pap. 35.30 (ISBN 0-317-30167-5, 2025349). Bks Demand UMI.

Night Light. 400p. (Orig.). pap. 5.95 (ISBN 0-89486-381-9). Hazelden.

Night Light: A Book of Nightime Meditations. (Hazelden Meditation Ser.). 1986. 5.95 (ISBN 0-06-255437-9). Har-Row.

Night Light: A Book of Nighttime Meditations. (Hazelden Bks.). scp 5.95t (ISBN 0-06-255437-9). Har-Row.

Night of Anguish: Morning of Hope. Jean Mize. LC 79-88497. 1979. pap. 2.95 (ISBN 0-87123-398-3, 200398). Bethany Hse.

Night of Miracles. Georgianna Summers. 1982. pap. 4.95 (ISBN 0-89536-552-9, 1411). CSS of Ohio.

Night of Wonder: Service-Story for Christmas Eve. Mike Sherer & Nathan Aaseng. 1985. 2.75 (ISBN 0-89536-762-9, 5869). CSS of Ohio.

Night Prayer, From the Liturgy of the Hours. 86p. 1976. pap. 2.95 (ISBN 1-55586-480-5). US Catholic.

Night Preacher. Louise A. Vernon. LC 73-94378. (Illus.). 134p. 1969. pap. 4.50 (ISBN 0-8361-1774-3). Herald Pr.

Night Scenes in the Bible. Daniel March. LC 77-189204. 348p. 1977. 12.95 (ISBN 0-8254-3211-1). Kregel.

Night the Animals Talked. Bonnie Bartel. 1982. pap. 3.25 (ISBN 0-89536-551-0, 1410). CSS of Ohio.

Nightfall at Nauvoo. Samuel W. Taylor. 1986. pap. 2.75 (ISBN 0-380-00247-7, 52696-4). Avon.

Nightmare in Israel. Scott Roston. 1987. 14.95 (ISBN 0-533-07157-7). Vantage.

Nightmare of God. Daniel Berrigan. LC 81-51877. (Sunburst Originals Ser.: No. 9). (Illus.). 144p. (Orig.). 1983. pap. 6.00 (ISBN 0-934648-08-5). Sunburst Pr.

Nights with Uncle Remus: Myths & Legends of the Old Plantation. Joel C. Harris. LC 70-164329. 1971. Repr. of 1883 ed. 42.00x (ISBN 0-8103-3866-1). Gale.

Niketas Choniates: Erlaeuterungen Zu Den Reden und Briefen Nebst Einer Biographie. Jan-Louis Van Dieten. (Supplementa Byzantina, 2). 1971. 43.20x (ISBN 3-11-002290-7). De Gruyter.

Nine & One Half Mystics. Herbert Weiner. 1986. pap. 8.95 (ISBN 0-02-068160-7, Collier). Macmillan.

Nine Gates to the Chassidic Mysteries. new ed. Jiri Langer. Ed. by Seymour Rossel. Tr. by Stephen Jolly from Czech, Fr. LC 76-5859. (Jewish Legacy Ser.). 266p. 1976. pap. text ed. 4.95x (ISBN 0-87441-241-2). Behrman.

Nine-Headed Dragon River. Peter Matthiessen. 1987. pap. 9.95 (ISBN 0-87773-401-1). Shambhala Pubns.

Nine-Headed Dragon River: Zen Journals 1969-1982. Peter Matthiessen. LC 85-27918. (Dragons Ser.). 288p. 1987. pap. 9.95 (ISBN 0-87773-401-1). Shambhala Pubns.

Nine Lessons on the Holy Spirit. Don DeWelt. 187p. 1978. cancelled (ISBN 0-89900-116-5). College Pr Pub.

Nine-Month Miracle. Carrie J. Heiman. (Illus.). 144p. (Orig.). 1986. pap. 4.95 (ISBN 0-89243-250-0). Liguori Pubns.

Nine Months Journey: A Christian Mother's Reflections on Pregnancy & Childbirth. Sarah H. O'Connor. 128p. (Orig.). 1984. pap. 6.95 (ISBN 0-687-28017-6). Abingdon.

Nine O'Clock in the Morning: An Episcopal Priest Discovers the Holy Spirit. Dennis J. Bennett. LC 72-85205. 1970. pap. 5.95 (ISBN 0-912106-41-7). Bridge Pub.

Nine Questions People Ask About Judaism. Dennis Prager & Joseph Telushkin. 1981. 14.95 (ISBN 0-671-42593-5). S&S.

Nine Questions People Ask about Judaism. Dennis Prager & Joseph Telushkin. 1986. pap. 7.95 (ISBN 0-671-62261-7, Touchstone Bks). S&S.

Nine Shaker Spirituals. Daniel W. Patterson. (Illus.). 34p. 1981. pap. 2.00 (ISBN 0-937942-10-3). Shaker Mus.

Nine Songs: A Study of Shamanism in Ancient China. 2nd ed. Ch'u Yuan. Tr. by Arthur Waley. LC 73-84228. 1973. pap. 3.95 (ISBN 0-87286-075-2). City Lights.

Nine-Twenty O'Farrell Street. facsimile ed. Harriet L. Levy. LC 74-29501. (Modern Jewish Experience Ser.). (Illus.). 1975. Repr. of 1947 ed. 23.50x (ISBN 0-405-06728-3). Ayer Co Pubs.

Nine Visions: A Book of Fantasies. Ed. by Andrea LaSonde Melrose. 192p. 1983. pap. 8.95 (ISBN 0-8164-2490-X, HarpR). Har-Row.

Nineteen Eighty-Eight Liturgical Calendar & Ordo. (Liturgical Calendar & Ordo Ser.). 120p. (Orig.). 1987. pap. 7.50 (ISBN 1-55586-141-5). US Catholic.

Nineteen Eighty-Eighty-One Collection of Fellowship Readings. 105p. 7.50 (ISBN 0-318-03276-7, 142802). ASHMM.

Nineteen Eighty-Six Take the Crazy out of Christmas Hints & Holiday Planner. 1986. 5.00 (ISBN 0-943786-04-5). Hollyday.

Nineteen Eighty-Three Annual Conference Proceedings. 160p. 25.00 (ISBN 0-318-03308-9, 142805). ASHMM.

Nineteen Eighty-Three Collection of Fellowship Readings. 95p. 18.00 (ISBN 0-318-03298-8, 142804). ASHMM.

Nineteen Eighty-Three Travis Papers in the Integration of Psychology & Theology. Ed. by Christopher H. Rosik & H. Newton Malony. 1986. pap. 10.00 (ISBN 0-9609928-5-5). Integ Pr.

Nineteen Eighty-Two Collection of Fellowship Readings. 127p. 10.00 (ISBN 0-318-03296-1, 142803). ASHMM.

Nineteen Gifts of the Spirit. Leslie B. Flynn. LC 74-91027. 204p. 1974. pap. 6.95 (ISBN 0-88207-701-5). Victor Bks.

Nineteen Letters of Ben Uziel. Samson R. Hirsch. Tr. by Karen Paritzky from Ger. 6.95 (ISBN 0-87306-180-2). Feldheim.

Nineteen Letters of Ben Uziel: A Spiritual Presentation of the Principles of Judaism. Somson R. Hirsch. Tr. by Bernard Drachman. (Eng. & Ger., Heb). 27.50 (ISBN 0-87559-076-4). Shalom.

Nineteen Letters of Ben Uziel on Judaism. Samson R. Hirsch. Tr. by Bermard Drachman. LC 69-131727. 1969. 4.95 (ISBN 0-87306-045-8). Feldheim.

Nineteen Seventeen: Red Banners, White Mantle. Warren H. Carroll. 168p. (Orig.). 1981. pap. 4.95 (ISBN 0-931888-05-0). Christendom Pubns.

Nineteenth-Century American Methodist Itinerant Preacher's Wife. Ed. by Carolyn G. De Swarte. Tr. by Doanald Dayton. (Women in American Protestant Religion Series 1800-1930). 276p. 1987. lib. bdg. 40.00 (ISBN 0-8240-0656-9). Garland Pub.

Nineteenth-Century Emigration of "Old Lutherans" from Eastern Germany (Mainly Pomerania & Lower Silesia) to Australia, Canada, & the United States. Clifford N. Smith. (German-American Genealogical Research Monograph: No. 7). 1979. pap. 14.00 (ISBN 0-915162-06-7). Westland Pubns.

Nineteenth Century Evangelical Theology. Fisher Humphreys. LC 83-71439. (Orig.). 1984. pap. 10.95 (ISBN 0-8054-6579-0). Broadman.

Nineteenth Century Miracles. Emma Britten. 1977. lib. bdg. 59.95 (ISBN 0-8490-2348-3). Gordon Pr.

Nineteenth Century Nonconformity. Ian Sellers. (Foundations of Modern History Ser.). 110p. 1977. pap. text ed. 14.50x (ISBN 0-8419-5802-5). Holmes & Meier.

Nineteenth Century Religious Thought in the West, Vol. 1. Ed. by Ninian Smart et al. 350p. 1985. 49.50 (ISBN 0-521-22831-X). Cambridge U Pr.

Nineteenth Century Religious Thought in the West, Vols. 2 & 3. Ninian Smart et al. 368p. Vol. 2, 08/1985. 49.50 (ISBN 0-521-22832-8); Vol. 3, 10/1985. 49.50 (ISBN 0-521-30114-9). Cambridge U Pr.

Ninety Day Experience. Jim Burns. 112p. 1984. wkbk. 5.95 (ISBN 0-915929-12-0). Merit Bks.

Ninety-Nine Fun Ideas for Teaching Bible Verses. Elizabeth Crisci. (Illus.). 112p. 1985. pap. 3.95 (ISBN 0-87239-869-2, 3072). Standard Pub.

Ninety-Nine Names of Allah. Ira Friedlander. (Orig.). 1978. pap. 6.95 (ISBN 0-06-090621-9, CN 621, PL). Har-Row.

Ninety-Nine Names of Nothingness. Bhagwan Shree Rajneesh. Ed. by Ma Prem Maneesha. (Initiation Talks Ser.). (Illus.). 596p. (Orig.). 1980. pap. 18.95 (ISBN 0-88050-599-0). Chidvilas Found.

Ninety-Nine Questions People Ask Most about the Bible. Don Stewart. 160p. (Orig.). 1987. pap. 5.95 (ISBN 0-8423-5107-8). Tyndale.

Ninety-One Sermon Outlines on Types & Metaphors. Jabez Burns. LC 86-27347. 128p. (Orig.). 1987. pap. 5.95 (ISBN 0-8254-2270-1). Kregel.

Ninety Story Sermons for Children's Church. Marianne Radius. 286p. 1976. pap. 7.95 (ISBN 0-8010-7641-2). Baker Bk.

Ninib, the Determiner of Fates from the Temple Library of Nippur. Hugo Radau. (Publications of the Babylonian Section, Ser. D: Vol. 5-2). (Illus.). x, 73p. 1910. bound 5.00xsoft (ISBN 0-686-11919-3). Univ Mus of U PA.

Ninos de la Biblia. Jean-Francois Bourgeois. Ed. by Alberto Maecha. Orig. Title: Enfants de la Bible. (Span., Illus.). 40p. 1984. pap. write for info. (ISBN 0-942504-11-9). Overcomer Pr.

Ninteenth-Century Churches: The History of a New Catholicism in Wurttemberg, England & France. R. W. Franklin. Ed. by William H. McNeill. 700p. 1987. lib. bdg. 105.00 (ISBN 0-8240-8067-X). Garland Pub.

Ninth Amendment: History, Interpretation & Meaning. Mark N. Goodman. 74p. 1981. 5.00 (ISBN 0-682-49630-8, University). Exposition Pr FL.

Ninth Floor. Paula Kilpatrick & Cliff Dudley. LC 81-80942. 128p. 1981. pap. 4.95 (ISBN 0-89221-085-0). New Leaf.

Ninth Hour. Gilbert Kilpack. 1983. pap. 2.50x (ISBN 0-87574-063-4, 063). Pendle Hill.

Nippur One: Temple of Enlil, Scribal Quarter & Soundings. Donald E. McCown & Richard C. Haines. LC 66-17104. (Illus.). 1967. 10.00 (ISBN 0-226-55688-3, OIP78). U of Chicago Pr.

Nirvana. Arundale. 7.50 (ISBN 0-8356-7537-8). Theos Pub Hse.

Nirvana, a Story of Buddhist Psychology. Paul Carus. LC 78-72395. (Illus.). Repr. of 1902 ed. 22.00 (ISBN 0-404-17254-7). AMS Pr.

Nirvana: A Story of Buddhist Psychology. Paul Carus. 93p. 1913. 1.95 (ISBN 0-317-40415-6). Open Court.

Nirvana-Tao: The Secret Meditation Techniques of the Taoist & Buddhist Masters. Daniel Odier. (Illus.). 208p. (Orig.). 1986. pap. 9.95 (ISBN 0-89281-045-9). Inner Tradit.

Nirvana: The Last Nightmare. Bhagwan Shree Rajneesh. Ed. by Ma Yoga Pratima. LC 77-902717. (Zen Ser.). (Illus.). 290p. (Orig.). 1976. 17.50 (ISBN 0-88050-101-4). Chidvilas Found.

Nirvana: The Last Nightmare. Bhagwan Sri Rajneesh. Ed. by Rajneesh Foundation. (Illus.). 278p. (Orig.). 1981. pap. 8.95 (ISBN 0-914794-37-X). Wisdom Garden Bks.

Nirvanasara. Da Free John. 280p. (Orig.). 1982. pap. 9.95 (ISBN 0-913922-65-X). Dawn Horse Pr.

Nisab Al Ihtisab. Mouel Y. Izzidien. Ed. by Hamid Quinlan. LC 82-70458. (Illus.). 230p. (Orig.). Date not set. pap. 5.00 (ISBN 0-89259-031-9). Am Trust Pubns.

Nishkamakarma. John G. Finch. LC 82-83498. (Orig.). 1982. pap. 8.50 (ISBN 0-9609928-0-4). Integ Pr.

Nissim Ibn Shahin: The Arabic Original of Ibn Shahin's Book of Comfort. Ed. by Julian Obermann. LC 78-63561. (Yale Oriental Ser. Researches: No. 17). Repr. of 1933 ed. 72.50 (ISBN 0-404-60287-8). AMS Pr.

Nitya Sutras: The Revelations of Nityananda from the Chidakash Gita. M. U. Hatengdi & Swami Chetanananda. (Illus.). 224p. (Orig.). 1985. pap. 11.95 (ISBN 0-915801-02-7). Rudra Pr.

Nityananda: The Divine Presence. M. U. Hatengdi. Ed. by Aurelia Navarro. LC 84-60099. (Illus.). 192p. (Orig.). 1984. pap. 10.95 (ISBN 0-915801-00-0). Rudra Pr.

NIV Complete Concordance. Edward W. Goodrick & John P. Kohlenberger. 1056p. 1981. 22.95 (ISBN 0-310-43650-8, 12100). Zondervan.

NIV Handy Concordance. Edward W. Goodrick & John R. Kohlenberger, III. 384p. (Orig.). 1982. pap. 5.95 (ISBN 0-310-43662-1, 12101P). Zondervan.

NIV Interliear Greek-English New Testament. Alfred Marshall. 1976. 21.95 (ISBN 0-310-28680-8). Zondervan.

NIV Interlinear Hebrew-English Old Testament. John R. Kohlenberger, III. 544p. 1980. Vol. 1. 24.95 (ISBN 0-310-38880-5, 6280); Vol. 2. 24.95 (ISBN 0-310-38890-2, 6281); Vol. 3. 24.95 (ISBN 0-310-44200-1, 6282). Zondervan.

NIV Interlinear Hebrew-English Old Testament: Genesis-Malachi, 4 vols. John R. Kohlenberger, III. 1985. Set. text ed. 95.80 (ISBN 0-310-38948-8, 6284). Zondervan.

NIV Interlinear Hebrew-English Old Testament: Isaiah-Malachi, Vol. 4. John Kohlenberger, III. 640p. 1985. 24.95 (ISBN 0-310-44210-9, 6283). Zondervan.

NIV: The Making of a Contemporary Translation. Ed. by Kenneth Barker. 240p. 1986. pap. 8.95 (ISBN 0-310-24181-2). Zondervan.

NIV Vest Pocket Companion for Christian Workers. rev. ed. R. A. Torrey. 96p. 1980. pap. 1.95 saddle-stitch (ISBN 0-310-33331-8, 12152P). Zondervan.

Niyamsara (the Perfect Law) Kundakunda Acharya. Tr. & intro. by Uggar Sain. LC 73-3844. (Sacred Books of the Jainas: No. 9). Repr. of 1931 ed. 18.00 (ISBN 0-404-57709-1). AMS Pr.

Nizari Ismaili Tradition in the Indo-Pakistan Subcontinent. Azim Nanji. LC 78-12990. (Monographs in Islamic Religion & Theology). 1979. 30.00x (ISBN 0-88206-020-1). Caravan Bks.

Njevidimaja Bran' Saint Nicodemos the Hagiorite. Tr. of Unseen Warfare. 288p. 15.00 (ISBN 0-317-28905-5); pap. 10.00 (ISBN 0-317-28906-3). Holy Trinity.

No Abiding City. Bede Jarrett. 1.95 (ISBN 0-87243-012-X). Templegate.

No Alien Power. Benjamin P. Campbell. (Orig.). 1985. pap. 1.75 (ISBN 0-88028-050-6). Forward Movement.

No Appointment Needed. Bernhard Aaen. Ed. by Bobbie J. Van Dolson. 128p. 1981. pap. 5.95 (ISBN 0-8280-0025-5). Review & Herald.

No Black-White Church. Raphael P. Powell. 1984. 7.50 (ISBN 0-8062-2295-6). Carlton.

No Book: No Buddha, No Teaching, No Discipline. Bhagwan Shree Rajneesh. Ed. by Ma Prem Maneesha. (Initation Talks Ser.). (Illus.). 354p. (Orig.). 1981. 26.95 (ISBN 0-88050-102-2). Chidvilas Found.

No Capital Crime. Ed Lipman. 1975. pap. 2.00x (ISBN 0-915016-04-4). Second Coming.

No Church Is an Island. David S. King. LC 79-27113. (Orig.). 1980. pap. 5.95 (ISBN 0-8298-0385-8). Pilgrim NY.

No Church Is an Island: Study Guide. King. 1980. pap. 1.00 (ISBN 0-8298-0389-0). Pilgrim NY.

No Condemnation: Rethinking Guilt Motivation in Counseling, Preaching & Parenting. S. Bruce Narramore. 208p. 1984. pap. 8.95 (ISBN 0-310-30401-6, 11244P). Zondervan.

No Crib for a Bed. Claire Lynn. (Doctrinal Ser.: Bk. 2). (Illus., Orig.). 1983. pap. 1.95 (ISBN 0-89323-029-4). Bible Memory.

No Cross No Crown. Clement H. Crock. 1974. Repr. 3.00 (ISBN 0-8198-0510-6). Dghtrs St Paul.

No Cross No Crown. William Penn & Anna Brinton. 1983. pap. text ed. 2.50x (ISBN 0-87574-030-8, 030). Pendle Hill.

No Crying He Makes. Miriam S. Lind. LC 78-181580. 96p. 1972. pap. 1.50 (ISBN 0-8361-1321-7). Herald Pr.

No Culpe a Dios! Kenneth E. Hagin. (Span.). 1983. pap. 0.50 mini bk. (ISBN 0-89276-156-3). Hagin Ministries.

No Easy Road: Inspirational Thoughts on Prayer. new ed. Dick Eastman. (Direction Bks.). 1973. pap. 2.50 (ISBN 0-8010-3259-8). Baker Bk.

No Easy Salvation. R. E. Glaze, Jr. LC 66-10708. 72p. 1984. pap. 4.00 (ISBN 0-914520-06-7). Insight Pr.

No Empty Phrases. Frank H. Seilhamer. 1985. 4.25 (ISBN 0-89536-732-7, 5816). CSS of Ohio.

No Faith of My Own & Graceful Reason: The Contribution of Reason to Theology. J. V. Langmead Casserley. 408p. 1984. pap. text ed. 16.75 (ISBN 0-8191-3793-6). U Pr of Amer.

No Foot of Land: Folklore of American Methodist Itinerants. Donald E. Byrne. LC 75-1097. (ATLA Monograph: No. 6). (Illus.). 370p. 1975. 22.50 (ISBN 0-8108-0798-X). Scarecrow.

No-Frills Guide to Youth Group Drama. John Duckworth & Liz Duckworth. 64p. 1985. pap. 5.95 (ISBN 0-88207-574-8). Victor Bks.

No Good-byes: My Search Into Life Beyond Death. A. R. St. Johns. 1981. 10.95 (ISBN 0-07-054450-6). McGraw.

No Graven Image. Elisabeth Elliot. LC 81-71346. 256p. 1982. pap. 5.95 (ISBN 0-89107-235-7, Crossway Bks). Good News.

No Graven Images: Studies in Art & the Hebrew Bible. Joseph Gutmann. (Library of Biblical Studies). 1970. 50.00x (ISBN 0-87068-063-3). Ktav.

No Greater Love. Kris Mackay. LC 81-22123. 99p. 1982. 6.95 (ISBN 0-87747-906-2). Deseret Bk.

No Greater Love. (Encounter Ser.). 1979. 3.00 (ISBN 0-8198-0588-2); pap. 2.00 (ISBN 0-8198-0589-0). Dghtrs St Paul.

No Greater Love: Maximilian Kolbe. Boniface Hanley. LC 82-72656. (Illus.). 80p. (Orig.). 1982. pap. 3.95 (ISBN 0-87793-257-3). Ave Maria.

No Greater Sacrifice: The Atonement & Redemption of Christ. Steven L. Shields. LC 80-83864. 140p. 1980. 7.95 (ISBN 0-88290-166-4, 1059). Horizon Utah.

No Handle on the Cross: An Asian Meditation on the Crucified Mind. Kosuke Koyama. LC 76-23160. pap. 32.00 (ISBN 0-317-26647-0, 2025120). Bks Demand UMI.

No Haven for the Oppressed: United States Policy Toward Jewish Refugees, 1938-1945. Saul S. Friedman. LC 72-2271. 315p. 1973. 25.00x (ISBN 0-8143-1474-0). Wayne St U Pr.

No Instant Grapes in God's Vineyard. Louise C. Spiker. 112p. 1982. pap. 5.95 (ISBN 0-8170-0955-8). Judson.

No King But Caesar? William R. Durland. LC 74-30093. (Christian Peace Shelf Ser.). 184p. 1975. o. p. 6.95 (ISBN 0-8361-1757-3); pap. 4.95 (ISBN 0-8361-1927-4). Herald Pr.

No Longer Strangers. Larson. 145p. 1985. pap. 5.95 (ISBN 0-8499-3020-0, 3020-0). Word Bks.

No Longer Strangers: A Biogrpahy of H. Stover Kulp. Mary A. Kulp. LC 68-4439. pap. 47.00 (ISBN 0-317-28389-8, 2022413). Bks Demand UMI.

No Man Ever Spoke As This Man. A. M. Coniaris. 1969. pap. 4.95 (ISBN 0-937032-18-2). Light&Life Pub Co MN.

No Man Is an Island. Thomas Merton. LC 78-7108. 264p. 1978. pap. 5.95 (ISBN 0-15-665962-X, Harv). HarBraceJ.

No Man Is an Island. Thomas Merton. 264p. 1983. Repr. of 1955 ed. lib. bdg. 21.00 (ISBN 0-88254-872-7, Octagon). Hippocrene Bks.

No Man Knows My History: The Life of Joseph Smith. Fawn M. Brodie. (Illus.). 1971. 19.95 (ISBN 0-394-46967-4). Knopf.

No Matter How Dark, the Valley: The Power of Faith in Times of Need. G. Don Gilmore. LC 81-48208. 141p. 1982. pap. 7.64 (ISBN 0-06-063121-X, RD-391, HarpR). Har-Row.

No Matter What, We Still Love You. Neal A. Kuyper. (Illus.). 40p. (Orig.). 1985. pap. 2.95 (ISBN 0-933350-48-1). Morse Pr.

No More Alphabet Soup. Nancy B. Irland. Ed. by Bobbie J. Van Dolson. LC 83-3303. (A Banner Bk.). 128p. (Orig.). 1984. pap. 5.95 (ISBN 0-8280-0165-0). Review & Herald.

No More for the Road: One Man's Journey from Chemical Dependency to Freedom. Duane Mehl. LC 75-22721. 144p. 1976. pap. 7.95 (ISBN 0-8066-1515-X, 10-4665). Augsburg.

No More Mr. Nice Guy: Saying Goodbye to Doormat Christianity. Stephen Brown. 224p. 1986. 14.95 (ISBN 0-8407-5539-2). Nelson.

No More Plastic Jesus: Global Justice & Christian Lifestyle. Adam Corson-Finnerty. LC 76-13174. 223p. (Orig.). 1977. pap. 6.95x (ISBN 0-88344-341-4). Orbis Bks.

No One But Us: Personal Reflections on Public Sanctuary. Ted Loder. LC 86-7516. 224p. (Orig.). 1986. pap. 9.95 (ISBN 0-931055-09-1). LuraMedia.

No One Could Have Known: An Autobiography--The Early Years. Josef Pieper. Tr. by Graham Harrison from Ger. LC 86-72509. Tr. of Noch Wusste es Niemand. (Illus.). 227p. (Orig.). 1987. pap. 9.95 (ISBN 0-89870-131-7). Ignatius Pr.

No One's Perfect. Betty Carlson. LC 76-17669. 1976. pap. 4.95 (ISBN 0-89107-143-1). Good News.

No Other God. Mary J. Tully. 96p. 1984. pap. 3.50 (ISBN 0-697-01942-X). Wm C Brown.

No Other God. Gabriel Vahanian. LC 66-28591. (Orig.). 1966. pap. 2.50 (ISBN 0-8076-0389-9). Braziller.

No Other Gospel. Bill Kaiser. 153p. (Orig.). 1984. pap. 6.95 (ISBN 0-914307-16-9, Dist. by Harrison Hse). Word Faith.

No Other Light. Mary W. Salin. 224p. 1986. 14.95 (ISBN 0-8245-0748-7). Crossroad NY.

No Other Name. Leonard R. Small. 192p. 1966. 12.95 (ISBN 0-567-02257-9, Pub. by T & T Clark Ltd UK). Fortress.

No Other Name? A Critical Survey of Christian Attitudes Toward the World Religions. Paul F. Knitter. LC 84-16491. 304p. (Orig.). 1985. pap. 14.95 (ISBN 0-88344-347-3). Orbis Bks.

No Pain, No Gain: Hope for Those Who Struggle. John R. Wimmer. 71p. 1985. 8.95 (ISBN 0-345-32181-2, Epiphany). Ballantine.

No Pat Answers. Eugenia Price. 144p. 1983. pap. 5.95 (ISBN 0-310-31331-7, 16244P). Zondervan.

No Pope of Rome: Militant Protestantism in Modern Scotland. S. Bruce. 270p. 1985. text ed. 35.00x (ISBN 0-906391-78-4, Pub. by Mainstream Pubs UK). Humanities.

No Popery & Radicalism: Opposition to Roman Catholic Relief in Scotland, 1778-1782. Robert K. Donovan. Ed. by Willaim H. McNeill & Peter Stansky. (Modern European History Ser.). 425p. 1987. lib. bdg. 65.00 (ISBN 0-8240-7804-7). Garland Pub.

No Reason to Die. Eric Hadar. 32p. 1983. pap. 5.00 (ISBN 0-942494-76-8). Coleman Pub.

No Respecter of Persons. Harry Price. 128p. 1981. pap. 4.95 (ISBN 0-8059-2797-2). Dorrance.

No Retirement: Devotions on Christian Discipleship for Older People. Lillian R. Reynolds. LC 83-48916. 96p. 1984. pap. 4.50 (ISBN 0-8006-1779-7, 1-1779). Fortress.

No Rival Love. Dwight H. Small. 201p. (Orig.). 1985. pap. 4.95 (ISBN 0-87508-495-8). Chr Lit.

No Room in the Brotherhood: The Preus-Otten Purge of Missouri. Frederick W. Danker. LC 77-74386. (Illus.). 1977. text ed. 12.95 (ISBN 0-915644-10-X). Clayton Pub Hse.

No Souvenirs, Journal, Nineteen Fifty-Seven to Nineteen Sixty-Nine. Mircea Eliade. 1983. 16.00 (ISBN 0-8446-6030-2). Peter Smith.

No Strangers to Violence, No Strangers to Love. Boniface Hanley. LC 83-71608. (Illus.). 224p. (Orig.). 1983. pap. 6.95 (ISBN 0-87793-302-2). Ave Maria.

No Time for Silence: Evangelical Women in Public Ministry Around the Turn of the Century. Janette Hassey. 176p. 1986. pap. 7.95 (ISBN 0-310-29451-7, 12786P). Zondervan.

No Uncertain Sound: Charges & Addresses. J. C. Ryle. 384p. 1984. pap. 10.95 (ISBN 0-85151-444-8). Banner of Truth.

No Volvera a Mi Vacia. LC 76-55490. (Span.). 365p. (Orig.). 1976. pap. 3.75 (ISBN 0-89922-080-0). Edit Caribe.

No Water, No Moon. 2nd ed. Bhagwan Shree Rajneesh. Ed. by Ma Yoga Anurag. LC 75-907472. (Zen Ser.). (Illus.). 260p. 1978. 14.50 (ISBN 0-88050-105-7). Chidvilas Found.

No Water, No Moon. Bhagwan Shree Rajneesh. Ed. by Swami Krishna Prabhu. LC 84-42871. (Zen Ser.). 320p. 1984. pap. 4.95 (ISBN 0-88050-605-9). Chidvilas Found.

No Wonder They Call Him the Savior: Chronicles of the Cross. Max Lucado. LC 85-31026. 1986. 6.95 (ISBN 0-88070-133-1). Multnomah.

Noah. Rebecca Daniel. (Our Greatest Heritage Ser.). (Illus.). 1983. wkbk. 3.95 (ISBN 0-86653-132-7, SS 801). Good Apple.

Noah. new ed. Louie J. Fant, Jr. (Illus.). 14p. 1973. pap. text ed. 5.00 (ISBN 0-917002-70-9). Joyce Media.

Noah. (Burl Ives Bible-Time Stories). incl. tape 4.95 (ISBN 0-89191-801-9, 98012). Cook.

Noah. Ellen G. Traylor. 256p. 1985. pap. 6.95 (ISBN 0-8423-4703-8). Tyndale.

Noah & God's Promise. Truitt. (Arch Bks.). 24p. (Orig.). 1985. pap. 0.99 (ISBN 0-570-06193-8, 59-1294). Concordia.

Noah & His Ark. Ella K. Lindvall. (People of the Bible Ser.). 4.95 (ISBN 0-8024-0396-4). Moody.

Noah & His Ark. D. M. Prescott. (Very First Bible Stories Ser.). 1984. 1.59 (ISBN 0-87162-273-4, D8502). Warner Pr.

Noah & His Ark. Catherine Storr. Retold by Catherine Storr. LC 82-7712. (People of the Bible Ser.). (Illus.). 32p. 1982. PLB 10.65 (ISBN 0-8172-1975-7). Raintree Pubs.

Noah & His Great Ark. John Simons & Kay Ward. Ed. by Kay Ward. (Bible Stories for Today Ser.). (Illus.). 16p. (Orig.). 1987. pap. text ed. 2.50 (ISBN 0-937039-00-4). Sun Pr FL.

Noah & the Ark. Tomie DePaola. (Illus.). 40p. (Orig.). 1983. 12.95 (ISBN 0-86683-699-3, AY8268, HarpR); pap. 5.95. Har-Row.

Noah & the Ark. Tomie DePaola. (Illus.). 32p. 1983. 12.95 (ISBN 0-86683-819-8, AY8451, HarpR). Har-Row.

Noah & the Ark. Belinda Hollyer. LC 84-50450. (Bible Stories Ser.). (Illus.). 24p. 1984. PLB 6.96 (ISBN 0-382-06793-2); pap. 5.45 (ISBN 0-382-06942-0). Silver.

Noah & the Ark. Retold by Elaine Ife & Rosalind Sutton. (Now You Can Read Stories from the Bible Ser.). (Illus.). 24p. 1985. 2.50 (ISBN 0-8407-5390-X). Nelson.

Noah & the Ark: In Arabic. (MacDonald Educational Ser.). (Illus.). 3.50x (ISBN 0-86685-212-3). Intl Bk Ctr.

Noah & the Flood. Mark E. Petersen. LC 82-14947. 97p. 1982. 6.95 (ISBN 0-87747-935-6). Deseret Bk.

Noah & the Great Flood. Warwick Hutton. LC 77-3217. (Illus.). 32p. 1977. 8.95 (ISBN 0-689-50098-X, McElderry Bk). Macmillan.

Noah & the Rainbow Promise. Frances T. Stewart & Charles P. Stewart. (Stick & L Book Ser.). (Illus.). 1986. pap. 6.95 (ISBN 0-8054-4187-5). Broadman.

Noah-in Sign Language. Ed. by Louie Fant, Jr. pap. 5.00 (ISBN 0-917002-10-5). Joyce Media.

Noah Takes Two. Ellen Abbay. LC 85-80406. 1985. 9.95 (ISBN 0-9615015-0-2). Kudzu.

Noah's Ark. Pamela Broughton. (Golden Bible Stories Ser.). (Illus.). 32p. 1985. 3.95 (ISBN 0-307-11621-2, Pub. by Golden Bks). Western Pub.

Noah's Ark. Jasper Dimond. (Illus.). 48p. 1983. 8.95 (ISBN 0-13-622951-4). P-H.

Noah's Ark. Illus. by Tibor Gergely. (Illus.). 24p. 1983. 3.50 (ISBN 0-307-11482-1, 10391, Golden Bks). Western Pub.

Noah's Ark. Illus. by Hanna-Barbera. (Greatest Adventure: Stories from the Bible). (Illus., Orig.). Date not set. 5.95 (ISBN 0-687-15744-7). Abingdon.

Noah's Ark. Elspeth Murphy. (Tubable Hugable Ser.). (Illus.). 1984. pap. 2.95 (ISBN 0-89191-820-5). Cook.

Noah's Ark. (Illus.). 1986. 2.95 (ISBN 1-55513-177-8, Chariot Bks). Cook.

Noah's Ark. Peter Spier. LC 76-43630. (Illus.). 44p. 1977. 11.95 (ISBN 0-385-09473-6); PLB 11.95 (ISBN 0-385-12730-8). Doubleday.

Noah's Ark. Peter Spier. 48p. 1981. pap. 4.95 (ISBN 0-385-17302-4, Zephyr). Doubleday.

Noah's Ark. Virginia Williams-Ellis. (Board Bks.). (Illus.). 10p. 1984. 2.95 (ISBN 0-8249-8079-4). Ideals.

Noah's Ark. Linda Yeatman. (Press-Out Model Bk.). (Illus.). 12p. 1984. 6.95 (ISBN 0-698-20598-7, Coward). Putnam Pub Group.

Noah's Ark: A Novel. Barbara Trapido. 264p. 1985. 16.95 (ISBN 0-531-09704-8). Watts.

Noah's Ark Found! The End of the Search. Rene Noorbergen. Ed. by Pat Golbitz. LC 86-33162. (Illus.). 192p. 1987. 14.95 (ISBN 0-688-06456-6). Morrow.

Noah's Ark Nonsense. Howard M. Teeple. LC 78-53529. (Truth in Religion Ser.: No. 1). 156p. 1978. 10.00 (ISBN 0-914384-01-5). Religion & Ethics.

Noah's Ark, Pitched & Parked. Nathan M. Meyer. pap. 4.00 (ISBN 0-88469-039-3). BMH Bks.

Noah's Boat. (Read, Show & Tell Ser). (Eng. & Span., Illus.). 1977. Eng. Ed. 2.25 (ISBN 0-8326-2605-8, 3623). Span. Ed (5623). World Bible.

Noah's Flood, Joshua's Long Day, & Lucifer's Fall: What Really Happened? Ralph Woodrow. (Illus.). 1984. 4.95 (ISBN 0-916938-07-7). R Woodrow.

Noble Eightfold Path. Manly P. Hall. pap. 2.50 (ISBN 0-89314-337-5). Philos Res.

Noble Families among the Sephardic Jews. I. DaCosta. 1976. lib. bdg. 134.95 (ISBN 0-8490-2349-1). Gordon Pr.

Noble Heritage: Jerusalem & Christianity - a Portrait of the Church of the Resurrection. Alistair Duncan. 1974. 12.95x (ISBN 0-86685-011-2). Intl Bk Ctr.

Noble Piety & Reformed Monasticism. 166p. pap. 8.95 (ISBN 0-87907-864-2). Cistercian Pubns.

Noble Quran, Vol. 1. M. M. Khan & T. Hilali. 1986. 49.95 (ISBN 0-317-43012-2). Kazi Pubns.

Noble Qur'an, Arabic-English: A Summarized Version of At-Tabari, Al-Qurtubi & Ibn Kathir with comments from Sahih Al-Bukhari, Vol I. M. M. Khan. 49.00 (ISBN 0-317-46109-5). Kazi Pubns.

Noble Romans. Arthur Garrett. LC 86-30240. 550p. 1987. 34.95 (ISBN 0-8022-2528-4). Philos Lib.

Nobody Else Will Listen. Marjorie Holmes. 1976. pap. 2.95 (ISBN 0-553-23457-9). Bantam.

Nobody Has a Prayer. Madalyn M. O'Hair. 105p. (Orig.). 1982. pap. 3.00 (ISBN 0-910309-07-8). Am Atheist.

Nobody Says "Please" in the Psalms. Patricia G. Opatz. 72p. (Orig.). 1984. pap. 2.95 (ISBN 0-8146-1326-8). Liturgical Pr.

Nobody's Perfect. Terry Powell. LC 78-65556. 116p. 1979. pap. 3.95 (ISBN 0-88207-577-2). Victor Bks.

Noches Para la Familia. Terry Reilly & Mimi Reilly. Tr. by Movimiento Familiar Cristiano De Miami. LC 81-65209. (Span., Illus.). 64p. 1981. pap. 2.95 (ISBN 0-87029-175-0, 20249-9). Abbey.

Nociones Esenciales Del Hebreo Biblico. Kyle M. Yates & J. J. Owens. Tr. by S. Daniel Daglio. 308p. 1984. Repr. of 1980 ed. 6.75 (ISBN 0-311-42056-7). Casa Bautista.

Noels: A Collection of Christmas Carols. Marx Oberndorfer & Anne Oberndorfer. 144p. 1932. complete gift edition 8.50 (ISBN 0-912222-05-0, R2582751); pap. 4.00 choral ed., carols only (ISBN 0-912222-06-9). FitzSimons.

Nomad of the Spirit: Reflections of a Young Monastic. Bernadin Schellenberger. 112p. 1981. 8.95 (ISBN 0-8245-0075-X). Crossroad NY.

Nomenclator Litterarius Theologiae Catholicae Theologo Sexhibens Aetate, Natione, Disciplins Distinctos, 5 Vols. in 6. Hugo Hurter. 1903. Set. 294.00 (ISBN 0-8337-1772-3). B Franklin.

Non-Bourgeois Theology: An African Experience of Jesus. Joseph G. Donders. LC 84-16677. 224p. (Orig.). 1985. pap. 10.95 (ISBN 0-88344-352-X). Orbis Bks.

Non-Canonical Psalms from Qumran: A Pseudepigraphic Collection. Eileen M. Schuller. (Harvard Semitic Studies). 1987. 23.95 (ISBN 0-89130-943-8, 04-04-28). Scholars Pr GA.

Non-Catholic in the Catholic School. Reverend James Hawker & Sr. Thea Bowman. 1984. 4.20 (ISBN 0-318-18580-6); member 3.15. Natl Cath Educ.

Non-Christian Quakers: Their Faith & Message. Raquel Wood & Ranan Banerji. Ed. by Kenneth Ives. (Studies in Quakerism Ser.: No. 9). 59p. (Orig.). 1983. pap. 4.00 (ISBN 0-89670-012-7). Progresiv Pub.

Non-Denominational Christianity: Is Unity Possible. Bert Thompson. 29p. (Orig.). 1984. pap. 2.00 (ISBN 0-932859-11-9). Apologetic Pr.

Non-Existence of God: Linguistic Paradox in Tillich's Thought. Robert R. N. Ross. LC 78-65486. (Toronto Studies in Theology: Vol. 1). xiv, 216p. 1978. 39.95x (ISBN 0-88946-905-9). E Mellen.

Non-Jewish Jew. Isaac Deutscher. 170p. 1982. pap. 5.95 (ISBN 0-932870-18-X). Alyson Pubns.

Non-Jewish Zionism: Its Roots in Western History. Regina S. Sharif. 160p. 1983. 18.75x (ISBN 0-86232-151-4, Pub. by Zed Pr England); pap. 8.75 (ISBN 0-86232-152-2). Humanities.

Non-Judgemental Sacred Dance: Simple Ways to Pray Through Dance. Lu Bellamak. 1984. 3.00 (ISBN 0-941500-14-4). Sharing Co.

Non Muslims in the Islamic Society. Yusuf Al-Qaradawl. Tr. by Khalil M. Hamad & Sayed M. Shah. LC 83-72763. 68p. (Orig.). 1985. pap. 3.75 (ISBN 0-89259-049-1). Am Trust Pubns.

Non-Muslims Under Shari'ah. A. R. Doi. 1981. 6.50 (ISBN 0-686-97861-7). Kazi Pubns.

Non-Resistance: Christian or Pagan. Banjamin W. Bacon. 1918. pap. 19.50x (ISBN 0-686-83649-9). Elliots Bks.

Non Role of Religion in Peace or How to Convince a Woman to Kill Her Child or Have It Killed by Others. (Analysis Ser.: No. 6). 1982. pap. 10.00 (ISBN 0-686-42841-2). Inst Analysis.

Non-Violence-Central to Christian Spirituality: Perspectives from Scriptures to the Present. Joseph T. Culliton. LC 82-7964. (Toronto Studies in Theology: Vol. 8). 312p. 1982. 49.95x (ISBN 0-88946-964-4). E Mellen.

Non-Violence in an Aggressive World. A. J. Muste. LC 76-137551. (Peace Movement in America Ser). 220p. 1972. Repr. of 1940 ed. lib. bdg. 15.95x (ISBN 0-89198-081-4). Ozer.

Non-Violent Action: How it Works. George Lakey. 1983. pap. 2.50x (ISBN 0-87574-129-0, 129). Pendle Hill.

Nonconformist Conscience: Chapel & Politics 1870-1914. D. W. Bebbington. 192p. 1982. text ed. 24.95x (ISBN 0-04-942173-5). Allen Unwin.

Nonconformity in Modern British Politics. Stephen Koss. LC 75-8646. 272p. 1975. 26.00 (ISBN 0-208-01553-1, Archon). Shoe String.

Nonconformity in the Nineteenth Century. Ed. by David M. Thompson. (Birth of Modern Britain Ser.). 1972. pap. 9.95x (ISBN 0-7100-7275-9). Methuen Inc.

None But a Child May Enter: Poetry. Fred Moeckel. 80p. 1982. pap. 4.95 (ISBN 0-910452-49-0). Covenant.

None is Too Many: Canada & the Jews of Europe, 1933-1948. Irving Abella & Harold Troper. LC 83-42864. 368p. 1983. 17.95 (ISBN 0-394-53328-3). Random.

None of These Diseases. S. I. McMillen. 160p. 1963. pap. 2.95 (ISBN 0-8007-8030-2, Spire Bks). Revell.

None of These Diseases. rev. ed. S. I. McMillen. Ed. by David E. Stern. 192p. 1984. pap. write for info. (ISBN 0-8007-5233-3). Revell.

Nonresistance & Responsibility, & Other Mennonite Essays. Gordon D. Kaufman. (Institute of Mennonite Studies: No. 5). 1979. pap. 7.95 (ISBN 0-87303-024-9). Faith & Life.

Nonviolent Resistance. Cecil E. Hinshaw. 1983. pap. 2.50x (ISBN 0-87574-088-X, 088). Pendle Hill.

Nonwovens Conference, 1986: Proceedings of TAPPI, Marriott Hotel, Atlanta, GA, April 20-25, 1986. Technical Association of the Pulp & Paper Industry Staff. pap. 67.30 (2029189). Bks Demand UMI.

Norah's Ark. Ann Cartwright & Reg Cartwright. (Illus.). 32p. 1984. PLB 11.97 (ISBN 0-671-52540-9). Messner.

Normal Christian Life. Watchman Nee. 1961-1963. pap. 4.50 (ISBN 0-87508-414-1). Chr Lit.

Normal Christian Life. Watchman Nee. 1977. pap. 4.95 (ISBN 0-8423-4710-0). Tyndale.

Normal Christian Life: Study Guide. rev ed. H. Foster. 52p. 1985. pap. 2.25 (ISBN 0-317-43399-7). Chr Lit.

Normal Christian Life Study Guide. Watchman Nee. Ed. by Foster. 1978. pap. 2.25 (ISBN 0-87508-418-4). Chr Lit.

Norman Anonymous of Eleven Hundred A.D. Toward the Identification & Evaluation of the So-Called Anonymous of York. George H. Williams. (Harvard Theological Studies). 1951. 24.00 (ISBN 0-527-01018-9). Kraus Repr.

Norman Constables in America. Herbert B. Adams. pap. 9.00 (ISBN 0-384-00333-8). Johnson Repr.

Norman Monasteries & Their English Possessions. Donald Matthew. LC 78-26293. (Oxford Historical Ser.). 1979. Repr. of 1962 ed. lib. bdg. 24.75x (ISBN 0-313-20847-6, MANM). Greenwood.

Norman Perrin's Interpretation of the New Testament. Calvin R. Mercer. Ed. by Charles Mabee. (Studies in American Biblical Hermeneutics). 192p. 1986. 19.95 (ISBN 0-86554-219-8, MUP-H197). Mercer Univ Pr.

Norman Splendour: Duiske Abbey, Graignamanagh. Geraldine Carville. (Illus.). 120p. 1979. 11.25 (ISBN 0-85640-171-4, Pub. by Blackstaff Pr). Longwood Pub Group.

Norman Vincent Peale's Treasury of Courage & Confidence. Norman V. Peale. 256p. 1985. pap. 3.50 (ISBN 0-515-08329-1). Jove Pubns.

Norman Vincent Peale's Treasury of Joy & Enthusiasm. Norman V. Peale. 192p. 1982. pap. 2.50 (ISBN 0-8007-8450-2). Revell.

Normas de Interpretacion Biblica. Ernesto Trenchard. (Span.). 150p. 1958. pap. 3.95 (ISBN 0-8254-1749-X). Kregel.

Normative Psychology of Religion. Henry N. Wieman & Regina Westcott-Wieman. 564p. 1986. Repr. of 1935 ed. lib. bdg. 95.00 (ISBN 0-89984-538-X). Century Bookbindery.

Norms & Guidelines for Catechetical Planners. 112p. 1980. pap. 3.75 (ISBN 1-55586-686-7). US Catholic.

Norms for Priestly Formation: A Compendium of Official Documents on Training of Candidates for the Priesthood. 344p. 1982. pap. 17.50 (ISBN 1-55586-838-X). US Catholic.

Norse Gods & Giants. Ingri D'Aulaire & Edgar P. D'Aulaire. LC 67-19109. (Illus.). 160p. 1967. write for info. (ISBN 0-385-04908-0); o. p. 14.95 (ISBN 0-385-07235-X). Doubleday.

Norse Mythology, Legends of Gods & Heroes. Peter A. Munch. Tr. by Sigurd B. Hustvedt. LC 74-112002. 1970. Repr. of 1926 ed. 23.75 (ISBN 0-404-04538-3). AMS Pr.

Norse Mythology or the Religion of Our Forefathers. R. B. Anderson. LC 77-6879. 1977. Repr. of 1891 ed. lib. bdg. 25.00 (ISBN 0-89341-147-7). Longwood Pub Group.

Norse Myths. Kevin Crossley-Holland. 1981. pap. 7.95 (ISBN 0-394-74846-8). Pantheon.

North America Is the Lord's. James W. Lowry. (Christian Day School Ser.). 1980. 17.05x (ISBN 0-87813-916-8). Christian Light.

North American Mythology. Hartley B. Alexander. LC 63-19095. (Mythology of All Races Ser.: Vol. 10). (Illus.). 1964. Repr. of 1932 ed. 30.00x (ISBN 0-8154-0007-1). Cooper Sq.

North American Psalms. Thomas Kretz. LC 81-69454. 166p. 1981. pap. 4.95 (ISBN 0-933402-24-4). Charisma Pr.

North & South Nodes: The Guideposts of the Spirit. Cynthia Bohannon. LC 79-55867. 1979. pap. 4.95 (ISBN 0-932782-02-7). Arthur Pubns.

North Carolina Indian Legends & Myths. F. Roy Johnson. (Illus.). 112p. 1981. 8.50 (ISBN 0-930230-43-4). Johnson NC.

North Country Bishop: A Biography of William Nicolson. Francis G. James. 1956. 59.50x (ISBN 0-686-51425-4). Elliots Bks.

North Italian Church Music in the Age of Monteverdi. Jerome Roche. (Illus.). 1984. 45.00x (ISBN 0-19-316118-4). Oxford U Pr.

Northeast Retreat of 1759 & 1981. Joseph S. Haas. LC 81-90691. (Cathedral of the Beechwoods Ser.: No. 1). (Illus.). 148p. (Orig.). 1981. per copy 7.00 (ISBN 0-9605552-0-X). Haas Ent NH.

Northern Africa: Islam & Modernization. Ed. by Michael Brett. 156p. 1973. 28.50x (ISBN 0-7146-2972-3, F Cass Co). Biblio Dist.

Northern Algonquian Supreme Being. John M. Cooper. LC 76-43682. (Catholic University of America Anthropological Ser.: No. 2). Repr. of 1934 ed. 14.00 (ISBN 0-404-15515-4). AMS Pr.

Northern Arabia, According to the Original Investigations of Alois Musil. Alois Musil. LC 77-87092. (American Geographical Society. Oriental Explorations & Studies: Map Vol.). Repr. of 1928 ed. 30.00 (ISBN 0-404-60237-1). AMS Pr.

Northern California Church Member Study, 1963. Charles Y. Glock & Rodney Stark. LC 79-63206. 1979. codebk. write for info. (ISBN 0-89138-980-6). ICPSR.

Northern Crusades: The Baltic & the Catholic Frontier, 1100-1525. Eric Christiansen. (Illus.). xxii, 265p. 1981. 25.00 (ISBN 0-8166-0994-2); pap. 10.95x (ISBN 0-8166-1018-5). U of Minn Pr.

Northern Ireland: Society under Siege. Rona M. Fields. LC 80-80316. 267p. 1980. pap. 5.95 (ISBN 0-87855-806-3). Transaction Bks.

Northern Methodism & Reconstruction. Ralph E. Morrow. ix, 269p. 1956. 5.00 (ISBN 0-87013-018-8). Mich St U Pr.

Northern Mythology. Friedrich Kauffman. LC 76-5464. 1976. Repr. of 1903 ed. lib. bdg. 17.50 (ISBN 0-8414-5524-4). Folcroft.

Northern Mythology. Friedrich Kauffmann. 1978. Repr. of 1903 ed. lib. bdg. 15.00 (ISBN 0-8495-3022-9). Arden Lib.

Northern Mythology. Friedrich Kauffmann. 106p. 1980. Repr. of 1903 ed. lib. bdg. 15.00 (ISBN 0-89987-450-9). Darby Bks.

Northern Nativity. William Kurelek. (Illus.). 1976. 14.95 (ISBN 0-88776-071-6); pap. 5.95 (ISBN 0-88776-071-6). Tundra Bks.

Northern Passion: Pt. I: Four Parallel Texts. (EETS, OS Ser.: No. 145). Repr. of 1912 ed. 20.00 (ISBN 0-527-00141-4). Kraus Repr.

Northern School of & the Formation of Early Ch'an Buddhism. John R. McRae. LC 86-4062. (Studies in East Asian Buddhism: No. 3). 456p. 1987. 40.00x (ISBN 0-8248-1056-2). UH Pr.

Northumberland County, Virginia 1678-1713, Vol. 1. Lindsay O. Duvall. (Virginia Colonial Abstracts, Series II). 160p. 1979. pap. 20.00 (ISBN 0-89308-062-4). Southern Hist Pr.

Northwest Semetic Grammar & Job. Anton C. Blommerde. (Biblica et Orientalia Ser.: Vol. 22). 1969. pap. 13.00 (ISBN 88-7653-322-2). Loyola.

Norwegian Stave Churches. R. Hauglid. (Illus.). 1977. 22.00x (ISBN 8-2090-0937-0, N497). Vanous.

Norweigian of Gods & Giants. 4th ed. H. Hveberg. (Tanum of Norway Tokens Ser). 86p. pap. 12.75x (ISBN 82-518-0083-8, N430). Vanous.

Nos Amaremos Toda la Vida: Paquete de Hojas para el Dialogo. Robert Ruhnke. Tr. by Olimpia Diaz. (Span.). 96p. 1983. 3.75 (ISBN 0-89243-185-7). Liguori Pubns.

Nos Preparamos Para Recibir a Jesus. (Span. & Eng.). pap. text ed. 1.75 (ISBN 0-317-46869-3); activity bk. 1.00 (ISBN 0-8198-5102-7). Dghtrs St Paul.

Nos Veremos en la Cumbre. Rev ed. Zig Ziglar. Tr. by Sergio Fernandez from Eng. Orig. Title: See You at the Top. (Span., Illus.). 352p. 1985. pap. 9.95 (ISBN 0-311-46100-X). Casa Bautista.

Not a Silent People: Controversies That Have Shaped Southern Baptists. Walter B. Shurden. LC 79-178066. 128p. 1972. 6.50 (ISBN 0-8054-8801-4). Broadman.

Not a Sparrow Shall Fall. Joan P. Glanville. 184p. (Orig.). 1984. pap. 6.35 (ISBN 0-919797-38-5). Kindred Pr.

Not by Accident. Isabel Fleece. 1987. pap. 1.95 (ISBN 0-317-54045-9). Moody.

Not by Bread Alone. Ed. by Cookbook Committee of Holy Trinity Episcopal Church. (Illus.). 304p. 1985. pap. 11.95 (ISBN 0-9615284-0-0). Holy Episcopal.

Not by Bread Alone. Nellie Vandeman. (Outreach Ser.). 1981. pap. 1.25 (ISBN 0-8163-0452-1). Pacific Pr Pub Assn.

Not by Bread Alone: Bible Readings for the Weekdays of Lent. (Illus.). 112p. 1972. pap. 2.45 (ISBN 0-87793-087-2). Ave Maria.

Not by Might. Ed. by Daniel Hertzler. LC 83-10831. 192p. (Orig.). 1983. pap. 9.95 (ISBN 0-8361-3342-0). Herald Pr.

Not by Prescription. Lucile J. Small. 64p. pap. 3.50 (ISBN 0-686-82633-7). Review & Herald.

Not Even God Is Ripe Enough. Bakare Gbadamosi & Ulli Beier. (African Writers Ser.). 1968. pap. text ed. 4.00x (ISBN 0-435-90048-X). Heinemann Ed.

Not for Innocent Ears: Spiritual Traditions of a Desert Cahuilla Medicine Woman. rev. ed. Ruby Modesto & Guy Mount. (Illus.). 128p. 1986. pap. 7.95 (ISBN 0-9604462-0-6). Sweetlight.

Not Healed? Charlotte Collins. LC 82-73707. 1983. pap. text ed. 2.50 (ISBN 0-932050-15-8). New Puritan.

Not I but Christ. Roy Hession. 1980. pap. 3.95 (ISBN 0-87508-198-3). Chr Lit.

Not I, But Christ. Watchman Nee. Tr. by Stephen Kaung. (Basic Lesson Ser.: Vol. 4). 1974. 4.50 (ISBN 0-935008-11-X); pap. 3.25 (ISBN 0-935008-12-8). Christian Fellow Pubs.

Not in Heaven or Beyond the Sea: Explorations in the World of Jewish Tradition. Shmuel Werzberger. 17.95 (ISBN 0-88125-128-3). Ktav.

Not in Heaven: The Nature & Function of Halakha. Eliezer Berkovits. LC 82-23255. 131p. 1983. 12.00x (ISBN 0-88125-003-1). Ktav.

Not in Vain: A Holocaust Documentary. Herbert Druks. 125p. 1984. text ed. 14.95x (ISBN 0-8290-1499-3). Irvington.

Not Just a Job: Serving Christ in Your Work. Judith A. Shelly. LC 84-29676. 140p. (Orig.). 1985. pap. 4.95 (ISBN 0-87784-332-5). Inter-Varsity.

Not Just Yes & Amen: Christians with a Cause. Dorothee Soelle & Fulbert Steffensky. LC 84-48708. 96p. 1985. pap. 3.50 (ISBN 0-8006-1828-9, 1-1828). Fortress.

Not Knowing Whither. Oswald Chambers. 1957. pap. 2.95 (ISBN 0-87508-118-5). Chr Lit.

Not Like the Gentiles: Marriage Rules in the Letters of Paul. Larry O. Yarbrough. (SBL Dissertation Ser.). 1985. 17.95 (ISBN 0-89130-874-1, 06-01-80); pap. 11.95 (ISBN 0-89130-875-X). Scholars Pr GA.

Not Made for Quitting. Dick Hillis. 144p. 1973. pap. 2.95 (ISBN 0-87123-396-7, 200396, Dimension Bks). Bethany Hse.

Not Mixing up Buddhism: Essays on Women & Buddhist Practice. Ed. by The Kahawai Collective Staff. 1987. 10.00 (ISBN 0-934834-71-7). White Pine.

Not My Will. Andrew Murray. Tr. by Marian Schoolland. 1977. pap. 2.95 (ISBN 0-310-29722-2, 10381P). Zondervan.

Not Only Dreamers. David R. Collins. Ed. by David Eller. 160p. (Orig.). 1986. pap. 7.95 (ISBN 0-87178-612-5). Brethren.

Not Quite at Home: How an American Jewish Community Lives with Itself & Its Neighbors. Marshall Sklare et al. LC 77-81092. (Institute of Human Relations Press Paperback Ser). x, 85p. (Orig.). 1969. pap. 1.00 (ISBN 0-87495-017-1). Am Jewish Comm.

Not Quite Puritans: Some Genial Follies & Peculiar Frailities of Our Revered New England Ancestors. Henry W. Lawrence. (Illus.). 1975. Repr. of 1928 ed. 40.00x (ISBN 0-8103-3993-5). Gale.

Not-So-Amazing Mormonism. Charles Beach. (Truthway Ser.). 39p. 1981. pap. text ed. 1.25 (ISBN 0-87148-629-6). Pathway Pr.

Not Without Struggle. C. William Mensendiek. (Illus.). 236p. 1986. 16.95 (ISBN 0-8298-0586-9). Pilgrim NY.

Not Wrath: But Rapture. H. A. Ironside. pap. 1.50 (ISBN 0-87213-380-X). Loizeaux.

Notable Quotables (A Compendium of Quotes by Salvation Army Authors) Allen Satterlee. 1985. 15.95 (ISBN 0-86544-028-X). Salv Army Suppl South.

Notas Sobre el Cantar de los Cantares. Harry Ironside. Orig. Title: Song of Solomon. (Span.). 128p. Date not set. pap. 4.75 (ISBN 0-8254-1328-1). Kregel.

Note on Genesis. Allan Bennett. (Equinox Reprints: Vol. 1, No. 2). 1976. pap. 1.50 (ISBN 0-87728-338-9). Weiser.

Notebook of the Reverand John Fiske: 1644 to 1675. Ed. by Robert G. Pope. LC 74-81447. 256p. 1974. 17.50 (ISBN 0-88389-052-6). Essex Inst.

Notebooks. Jacques Maritain. Tr. by Joseph W. Evans from Fr. LC 83-26743. Tr. of Carnet de Notes. (Illus.). 320p. 1984. 12.95x (ISBN 0-87343-050-6). Magi Bks.

Notebooks of Paul Brunton, Vol. 3: Part 1, Practices for the Quest; Part 2, Relax & Retreat. Paul Brunton. Ed. by Paul Cash & Timothy Smith. LC 86-81030. 392p. 1986. smyth-sewn bdg, acid-free 22.50 (ISBN 0-943914-15-9, Dist. by Kampmann & Co); pap. 12.50 smyth-sewn bdg, acid free (ISBN 0-943914-16-7, Dist. by Kampmann & Co). Larson Pubns Inc.

Notebooks of Paul Brunton, Vol. 4: Pt. 1 - Meditation; Pt. 2 - The Body. Paul Brunton. Ed. by Paul Cash & Timothy Smith. LC 86-81949. 432p. 1986. smyth-sewn bdg, acid free 22.50 (ISBN 0-943914-18-3, Dist. by Kampmann & Co); Pt. 1: Meditation. pap. 10.95 smyth-sewn bdg (ISBN 0-943914-19-1, Dist. by Kampmann & Co); Pt. 2: The Body. pap. 9.95 smyth-sewn bdg (ISBN 0-943914-20-5, Dist. by Kampmann & Co). Larson Pubns Inc.

Notebooks of Paul Brunton, Vol. 7: Healing of the Self; the Negatives, 2 pts. Paul Brunton. Ed. by Paul Cash & Timothy Smith. (Illus.). 320p. 1987. 22.50 (ISBN 0-943914-26-4, Dist. by Kampmann & Co.); pap. 12.50 (ISBN 0-943914-27-2, Dist. by Kampmann & Co.). Larson Pubns Inc.

Notebooks of Paul Brunton, Vol. 8: Reflections on My Life & Writings. Paul Brunton. Ed. by Timothy Smith. (Illus.). 224p. 1987. 22.50 (ISBN 0-943914-28-0); pap. 12.50 (ISBN 0-943914-29-9). Larson Pubns Inc.

Notes & Comments on Scripture, 7 vols. J. N. Darby. Set. 30.00 (ISBN 0-88172-068-2); 4.95 ea. Believers Bkshelf.

Notes & Jottings on Scripture. J. N. Darby. 5.95 (ISBN 0-88172-069-0). Believers Bkshelf.

Notes for a New Mythology: Pittsburgh Memoranda, 2 Vols. in 1. Haniel Long. 1971. Repr. of 1926 ed. 27.00 (ISBN 0-384-33540-3). Johnson Repr.

Notes from the Song of Life. rev. ed. Tolbert McCarroll. LC 77-7135. (Illus.). 144p. (Orig.). 1986. pap. 6.95. Celestial Arts.

Notes from the Song of Life: Spiritual Reflections. Tolbert McCarroll. LC 77-7135. (Illus.). 1977. pap. 6.95 (ISBN 0-89087-200-7). Celestial Arts.

Notes of a Madman. Bhagwan Shree Rajneesh. Ed. by Swami Devaraj Sambuddha & Swami Devageet Mahasattva. LC 85-43071. (Biography Ser.). 140p. (Orig.). 1985. pap. 4.50 (ISBN 0-88050-714-4). Chidvilas Found.

Notes of Some Wanderings. Sr. Nivedita. 3.00 (ISBN 0-87481-185-6). Vedanta Pr.

Notes of the Treaty Carried on at Ripon Between King Charles First & the Covenanters of Scotland, A. D. 1640. John Borough. Ed. by John Bruce. (Camden Society, London. Publications, First Ser.: No. 100). Repr. of 1869 ed. 19.00 (ISBN 0-404-50200-8). AMS Pr.

Notes of the Treaty Carried on at Ripon Between King Charles First & the Covenanters of Scotland, A. D. 1640. John Borough. 1869. 19.00 (ISBN 0-384-05145-6). Johnson Repr.

Notes on Biblical Theology. Geerhardus Vos. 1948. pap. 10.95 (ISBN 0-8028-1209-0). Eerdmans.

Notes on Epistles of Saint Paul. J. B. Lightfoot. Ed. by J. R. Harmer. (Thornapple Commentaries Ser.). 345p. 1980. pap. 8.95 (ISBN 0-8010-5602-0). Baker Bk.

Notes on First Corinthians. W. Kelly. 8.50 (ISBN 0-88172-094-1). Believers Bkshelf.

Notes on Humanity: Faith, Reason, Certainty. R. W. Carstens. 142p. (Orig.). 1985. pap. text ed. 8.50 (ISBN 0-8191-4885-7). U Pr of Amer.

Notes on Islam. A. Jang. pap. 1.50 (ISBN 0-686-18487-4). Kazi Pubns.

Notes on Moral Theology. Richard A. McCormick. LC 80-5682. 902p. 1981. lib. bdg. 33.00 (ISBN 0-8191-1439-1); pap. text ed. 17.75 (ISBN 0-8191-1440-5). U Pr of Amer.

Notes on Moral Theology: Nineteen Eighty-One Through Nineteen Eighty-Four. Richard J. McCormick. 242p. 1985. lib. bdg. 22.00 (ISBN 0-8191-4351-0); pap. text ed. 9.25 (ISBN 0-8191-4352-9). U Pr of Amer.

Notes on Muhammadanism: Being Outlines of the Religious System of Islam. Thomas P. Hughes. LC 74-83164. (Islam & MidEast Ser). 1976. Repr. of 1877 ed. 33.00 (ISBN 0-8420-1756-9). Scholarly Res Inc.

Notes on Prayer. Elisabeth Elliot. 1982. pap. 0.95 (ISBN 0-89107-254-3). Good News.

Notes on Romans. W. Kelly. 8.50 (ISBN 0-88172-107-7). Believers Bkshelf.

Notes on Romans. Arthur Pridham. 1983. 13.95 (ISBN 0-8254-3519-6). Kregel.

Notes on the Bhagavad-Gita. W. Q. Judge. 69.95 (ISBN 0-8490-0739-9). Gordon Pr.

Notes on the Bhagavad-Gita. William Q. Judge & Robert Crosbie. 237p. 1918. Repr. 4.00 (ISBN 0-938998-10-2). Theosophy.

Notes on the Bhagavad-Gita. T. Subba Row. LC 77-88628. 1978. 6.00 (ISBN 0-911500-81-2); pap. 3.50 (ISBN 0-911500-82-0). Theos U Pr.

Notes on the Buffalo-Head Dance of the Bear Gens of the Fox Indians. Truman Michelson. Repr. of 1928 ed. 29.00x (ISBN 0-403-03668-2). Scholarly.

Notes on the Catechism: An Outline of the Faith. James C. Thompson. 1979. pap. 4.95 (ISBN 0-8192-1249-0). Morehouse.

Notes on the Cathedral Libraries of England. Beriah Botfield. LC 68-23138. 1969. Repr. of 1849 ed. 65.00x (ISBN 0-8103-3174-8). Gale.

Notes on the Celebration of the Eucharist: A Supplement to the Ceremonial Directions of the Book of Common Prayer, 1979. Bruce E. Ford. LC 86-21523. 48p. (Orig.). 1986. pap. 7.50 (ISBN 0-942466-10-1). Hymnary Pr.

Notes on the Hebrew Text of Samuel. S. R. Driver. 1986. 24.95 (ISBN 0-88469-163-2). BMH Bks.

Notes on the Lectures. L. Ron Hubbard. 31.00 (ISBN 0-686-30778-X). Church Scient NY.

Notes on the Lectures of L. Ron Hubbard. L. Ron Hubbard. (Illus.). 160p. 1951. 36.44 (ISBN 0-88404-005-4). Bridge Pubns Inc.

Notes on the Miracles. R. C. Trench. (Twin Brooks Ser.). pap. 7.95 (ISBN 0-8010-8776-7). Baker Bk.

Notes on the Parables of Our Lord. R. C. Trench. (Twin Brooks Ser). pap. 5.95 (ISBN 0-8010-8774-0). Baker Bk.

Notes on the Poro in Liberia. George W. Harley. (HU PMP). 1941. 12.00 (ISBN 0-527-01248-3). Kraus Repr.

Notes on the Principles & Practices of Baptist Churches. Francis Wayland. Ed. by Edwin S. Gaustad. LC 79-52610. (Baptist Tradition Ser.). 1980. Repr. of 1857 ed. lib. bdg. 27.50x (ISBN 0-405-12475-9). Ayer Co Pubs.

Notes on the Psalms. G. Campbell Morgan. 288p. 1947. 14.95 (ISBN 0-8007-0241-7). Revell.

Notes to My Children: A Simplified Metaphysics. Ken Carey. 170p. 1987. pap. 8.95 (ISBN 0-913299-36-7, Dist. by NAL). Stillpoint.

Noteworthy: A Believer's Companion. Gregory L. Dixon. 116p. 1986. 9.95 (ISBN 0-9616294-0-1). Joi Prod Enter.

Nothing but a Footprint. Nina T. Pollard. LC 85-29049. 1986. pap. 3.25 (ISBN 0-8054-5716-X). Broadman.

Nothing but Honour: The Story of the Warsaw Uprising, 1944. J. K. Zawodny. LC 76-51880. (Publication Ser: No. 183). (Illus.). 1978. 16.95x (ISBN 0-8179-6831-8). Hoover Inst Pr.

Nothing but the Blood. Bailey E. Smith. (Orig.). 1987. pap. 6.95 (ISBN 0-8054-1537-8). Broadman.

Nothing but the Truth: What It Takes to Be Honest. Margaret L. Furse. LC 81-3501. 128p. 1981. 8.75 (ISBN 0-687-28130-X). Abingdon.

Nothing Can Separate Us. C. W. Bess. 1986. pap. 4.95 (ISBN 0-8054-2263-3). Broadman.

Nothing Is Impossible with God. Kathryn Kuhlman. (Orig.). 1976. pap. 1.75 (ISBN 0-89129-084-2). Jove Pubns.

Nothing to Fear: Unleashing the Power of the Resurrection. Carol Luebering & Robert E. Schmitz. (Illus.). 104p. 1985. pap. text ed. 4.50 (ISBN 0-86716-047-0). St Anthony Mess Pr.

Nothing to Laugh About. Illus. by Len Munnik. (Illus.). 96p. (Orig.). 1983. pap. 6.95 (ISBN 0-8298-0694-6). Pilgrim NY.

Nothing to Lose but Your Head. Bhagwan Shree Rajneesh. Ed. by Ma Prem Maneesha. LC 78-901075. (Initiation Talks Ser.). (Illus.). 408p. (Orig.). 1977. 19.50 (ISBN 0-88050-104-9). Chidvilas Found.

Nothing Without Christ. Dean Freiday. LC 84-70040. (Orig.). 1984. pap. 3.95 (ISBN 0-913342-44-0). Barclay Pr.

Notices of the Jews & Their Country by the Classic Writers of Antiquity. Ed. by John Gill. LC 70-97281. (Judaica Ser). 180p. 1972. Repr. of 1872 ed. lib. bdg. 22.50x (ISBN 0-8371-2603-7, GINJ). Greenwood.

Notion of Tao in Lao Tzu & Chuang Tsu. Giancarlo Finazzo. 240p. 1980. 11.95 (ISBN 0-89955-146-7, Pub. by Mei Ya China). Intl Spec Bk.

Notitia Cestriensis, 2 Vols. in 4. Francis Gastrell. Repr. of 1850 ed. Set. 92.00 (ISBN 0-384-17700-X). Johnson Repr.

Notre-Dame of Noyon in the Twelfth Century: A Study in the Early Development of Gothic Architecture. Charles Seymour, Jr. (Illus.). 1968. pap. 3.95x (ISBN 0-393-00464-3, Norton Lib). Norton.

Notre Seigneur. Charles Peguy. pap. 2.50 (ISBN 0-685-37032-1). French & Eur.

Notwithstanding My Weakness. Neal A. Maxwell. LC 81-65352. 129p. 1981. 6.95 (ISBN 0-87747-855-4). Deseret Bk.

Nourished with Peace: Studies in Hellenistic Judaism in Memory of Samuel Sandmel. Ed. by Frederick E. Greenspahn et al. (Scholars Press Homage Ser.: No. 9). 23.95 (ISBN 0-89130-740-0, 00 16 09). Scholars Pr GA.

Nourishing the Life Force. Mary-Alice Jafolla et al. LC 82-51301. 200p. 1983. 6.95 (ISBN 0-87159-114-6). Unity School.

Nouveau Dictionnaire Hebreu-Francais. Marc M. Cohn. (Fr. & Hebrew.). 792p. 1974. 32.50 (ISBN 0-686-56956-3, M-6078). French & Eur.

Nouveau Testament, 2 Vols. Jacques Lefevre. 1970. Repr. of 1523 ed. 135.00 (ISBN 0-384-32082-1). Johnson Repr.

Nouveau Theologien, M. Laudet. Charles Peguy. pap. 3.95 (ISBN 0-685-37044-5). French & Eur.

Nouvelle Bibliotheque des Auteurs Ecclesiastiques du Premier au 173 Siecle, 36 vols, Ser. I. Louis E. Dupin. 18798p. Date not set. Repr. of 1723 ed. text ed. 3720.00 (ISBN 0-576-72786-5, Pub. by Gregg Intl Pubs England). Gregg Intl.

Nouvelle Encyclopedie Theologique (Second Series, 52 vols. in 53. Ed. by J. P. Migne. 37237p. Repr. of 1862 ed. lib. bdg. 4695.75x (ISBN 0-89241-202-X). Caratzas.

Novalis: German Poet, European Thinker, Christian Mystic. Friedrich Hiebel. LC 54-62201. (North Carolina University Studies in the Germanic Languages & Literatures: No. 10). Repr. of 1953 ed. 27.00 (ISBN 0-404-50910-X). AMS Pr.

Novatian: Writings. LC 73-9872. (Fathers of the Church Ser.: Vol. 67). 223p. 1974. 17.95x (ISBN 0-8132-0067-9). Cath U Pr.

Novels. Charles W. Williams. Incl. War in Heaven. pap. 6.95 (ISBN 0-8028-1219-8); Many Dimensions. pap. 5.95 (ISBN 0-8028-1221-X); Place of the Lion. pap. 7.95 (ISBN 0-8028-1222-8); Shadows of Ecstacy. pap. 4.95 (ISBN 0-8028-1223-6); Descent into Hell. pap. 6.95 (ISBN 0-8028-1220-1); Greater Trumps. pap. 6.95. 1965. Boxed set. pap. 46.95 (ISBN 0-8028-1215-5). Eerdmans.

Novena of Confidence & Thanksgiving to the Sorrowful & Immaculate Heart of Mary. Tr. by Mary E. Hickey from Fr. (Illus.). 20p. 1962. pap. 0.25 (ISBN 0-913382-21-3, 107-2). Prow Bks-Franciscan.

Novgorodian Icon-Painting. V. N. Lazarev. (Illus.). 40.00 (ISBN 0-912729-00-7). Newbury Bks.

Novije Mutcheniki Rossijskije, tom 2, Vol. 2. Protopresbyter Michael Polsky. Tr. of New Martyrs of Russia. 329p. 1957. pap. 11.00 (ISBN 0-317-29207-2). Holy Trinity.

Novios: Conversemos Sobre Cosas Que Apenas Se Hablan. Jose Martinez. (Span.). 80p. 1986. pap. 2.95 (ISBN 0-311-46104-2). Casa Bautista.

Now Abideth Faith. E. Harold Henderson. 120p. 1962. pap. 0.50 (ISBN 0-89114-149-9). Baptist Pub Hse.

Now about Peace. James McKinnell. (Orig.). 1971. pap. 1.50 (ISBN 0-87178-935-3). Brethren.

Now & Future Church. Eugene Kennedy. LC 83-20574. 216p. 1985. pap. 7.95 (ISBN 0-385-23236-5, Im). Doubleday.

Now & Future Church: The Psychology of Being an American Catholic. Eugene Kennedy. LC 83-20574. 216p. 1984. 13.95 (ISBN 0-385-19040-9). Doubleday.

Now & Then. Frederick Buechner. LC 82-48413. 128p. 1983. 12.45 (ISBN 0-06-061161-8, HarpR). Har-Row.

Now Faith Is. Frederick K. Price. 32p. 1984. pap. 0.75 (ISBN 0-89274-302-6). Harrison Hse.

Now I Know Why I'm Depressed. H. Norman Wright. 1984. pap. 4.95 (ISBN 0-89081-423-6). Harvest Hse.

Now Is Eternity. Johann C. Blumhardt & Christoph Blumhardt. LC 76-10251. 1976. 4.00 (ISBN 0-87486-209-4); pap. 3.00 (ISBN 0-87486-219-1). Plough.

Now is the Thing to Praise. Dolores Kendrick. LC 83-82774. 116p. 1984. pap. 7.00 perf. bnd. (ISBN 0-916418-54-5). Lotus.

Now Is the Time. rev. ed. Llewellyn A. Wilcox. 1966. 8.95 (ISBN 0-911080-06-6). Outdoor Pict.

Now Is the Time to Love. John M. Drescher. LC 73-123411. 144p. 1970. pap. 1.50 (ISBN 0-8361-1641-0). Herald Pr.

Now Is Your Time to Win. Dave Dean. Ed. by Vickie De Vries. 1p. 1985. pap. 2.95 (ISBN 0-8423-4727-5). Tyndale.

Now Is Your Time to Win. Dave Dean & Marti Hefley. 1983. 8.95 (ISBN 0-8423-4724-0). Tyndale.

Now It Can Be Told. Lewis H. Morley. Ed. by Mary H. Wallace. LC 84-126606. (Illus.). 251p. (Orig.). 1983. pap. 5.95 (ISBN 0-912315-11-3). Word Aflame.

Now Lord, How Did You Manage That? Lois Beougher. 143p. 1984. 7.95 (ISBN 0-533-05912-7). Vantage.

Now Rings the Bell. Esther Embree. (Illus.). 1978. pap. 2.95 (ISBN 0-89367-023-5). Light & Life.

Now That I Believe: New King James Version. Robert A. Cook. 1986. pap. text ed. 2.95 (ISBN 0-8024-5983-8). Moody.

Now That You Are a Catholic. rev. & enl. ed. John Kenny. LC 73-80417. 108p. (Orig.). 1986. pap. 3.95 (ISBN 0-8091-1743-6). Paulist Pr.

Now That You Are Saved. Lyle Pointer. (Christian Living Ser.). 32p. (Orig.). 1987. pap. 2.50 (ISBN 0-8341-1157-8). Beacon Hill.

Now That You Are Single Again. Gary Chapman. 80p. 1985. wkbk. 3.95 (ISBN 0-89840-087-2). Heres Life.

Now That You Have Believed: An Exploration of the Life & Walk of Faith. Douglas Vickers. 1981. 10.00 (ISBN 0-682-49830-0). Exposition Pr FL.

Now That You're a Christian. J. Glenn Harvey. 127p. (Orig.). 1983. pap. 3.95 (ISBN 0-915059-01-0). Ind Christ Pubns.

Now That You're a Deacon. Howard B. Foshee. LC 74-79488. 128p. 1975. 7.95 (ISBN 0-8054-3506-9). Broadman.

Now That You're Saved. Richard Kennedy. 1977. pap. 0.95 (ISBN 0-89265-046-X). Randall Hse.

Now That You've Been Baptized in the Spirit. Donald Gee. 176p. 1972. pap. 1.50 (ISBN 0-88243-461-6, 02-0461). Gospel Pub.

Now This Day. Elise N. Morgan. 1948. 3.50 (ISBN 0-87516-330-0). De Vorss.

Now We Are Three. Eldon E. Fry et al. (Family Ministry Ser.). (Illus.). 54p. 1985. pap. text ed. 19.95 (ISBN 0-89191-977-5). Cook.

Now We Can Face the Day. Eise F. Green. 1975. 2.25 (ISBN 0-87509-112-1). Chr Pubns.

Now What? A Guidebook for the New Christian. Ralph W. Harris. 24p. 1964. pap. 0.35 (ISBN 0-88243-558-2, 02-0558). Gospel Pub.

Now What Do I Do? Ronald Rehrer. 1982. pap. 4.95 (ISBN 0-570-03854-5, 12-2809). Concordia.

Now What, Lord? Bible Devotions for Girls. Barbara O. Webb. LC 85-22884. (Young Readers Ser.). 112p. (Orig.). 1985. pap. 3.95 (ISBN 0-8066-2182-6, 10-4680). Augsburg.

Now You Can Read Stories from the Bible. Elaine Ife & Rosalind Sutton. (Illus.). 208p. 1984. 9.95 (ISBN 0-8407-5396-9). Nelson.

Noyesism Unveiled. Hubbard Eastman. LC 72-134402. Repr. of 1849 ed. 30.00 (ISBN 0-404-08446-X). AMS Pr.

NPCD Handbook for DREs. 88p. 1983. 6.00 (ISBN 0-318-00786-X). Natl Cath Educ.

NTC-Romans, 1 Vol. William Hendriksen. 1981. 19.95 (ISBN 0-8010-4265-8). Baker Bk.

Nuclear Arms: Two Views on World Peace. Augsburger & Curry. 1987. 14.95 (ISBN 0-8499-0576-1). Word Bks.

Nuclear Deterrence: Ethics & Strategy. Ed. by Russell Hardin et al. LC 85-8423. viii, 396p. 1985. 25.00x (ISBN 0-226-31702-1); pap. 10.95 (ISBN 0-226-31704-8). U of Chicago Pr.

Nuclear Disarmament: Key Statements of Popes, Bishops, Councils & Churches. Ed. by Robert Heyer. 1982. pap. 7.95 (ISBN 0-8091-2456-4). Paulist Pr.

Nuclear Ethics: A Christian Moral Argument. David Hollenbach. 112p. 1983. pap. 3.95 (ISBN 0-8091-2546-3). Paulist Pr.

Nuclear Holocaust & Christian Hope. Ronald J. Sider & Richard K. Taylor. (Illus.). 492p. (Orig.). 1982. pap. 7.95 (ISBN 0-87784-386-4). Inter-Varsity.

Nuclear Holocaust & Christian Hope: A Book for Christian Peacemakers. Ronald J. Sider & Richard K. Taylor. 360p. 1983. pap. 6.95 (ISBN 0-8091-2512-9). Paulist Pr.

Nuclear Power & Public Policy: The Social & Ethical Problems of Fission Technology. K. S. Shrader-Frechette. (Pallas Paperbacks Ser.: No. 15). 220p. 1980. lib. bdg. 20.00 (ISBN 90-277-1054-6, Pub. by Reidel Holland); pap. 10.50 (ISBN 90-277-1080-5). Kluwer Academic.

Nuclear Rights-Nuclear Wrongs. Ed. by Ellen F. Paul et al. LC 85-26711. 248p. 1986. text ed. 24.95x (ISBN 0-631-14964-3). Basil Blackwell.

Nuclear Strategy & the Code of the Warrior: Faces of Mars & Shiva in the Crisis of Human Survival. Ed. by Richard Grossinger & Lindy Hough. (Io Ser.: No. 33). 320p. (Orig.). 1984. 25.00 (ISBN 0-938190-50-4); pap. 12.95 (ISBN 0-938190-49-0). North Atlantic.

Nuclear Voices: A Book of Quotations & Perspectives. Peter D. Bollen. LC 85-60616. (Illus.). 250p. (Orig.). 1985. pap. 6.95x (ISBN 0-9611350-1-8). Hillside Bks.

Nuclear War & the American Churches: Ethical Positions on Modern Warfare. Donald L. Davidson. 200p. 1983. 21.50x (ISBN 0-86531-706-2). Westview.

Nuclear War: The Moral Dimension. James Child. (Studies in Social Philosophy & Policy: No. 6). 150p. 1986. 16.95 (ISBN 0-912051-09-4); pap. 8.95 (ISBN 0-912051-10-8). Soc Phil Pol.

Nuclear War: The Moral Dimension. Ed. by James E. Child. 160p. (Orig.). 1985. 16.95 (ISBN 0-912051-04-3, Dist. by Transaction Bks); pap. 8.95 (ISBN 0-912051-05-1). Soc Phil Pol.

Nuclear Weapons & Christian Conscience. Walter Stein. 165p. (Orig.). 1981. pap. 6.75 (ISBN 0-85036-112-5, Pub. by Merlin Pr UK). Longwood Pub Group.

Nuclear Weapons & Scientific Responsibility. C. G. Weeramantry. 225p. 1986. 25.00 (ISBN 0-89341-542-1, Pub. by Longwood Academic). Longwood Pub Group.

Nucleus: Reconnecting Science & Religion in the Nuclear Age. Scott T. Eastham. LC 86-22265. 223p. (Orig.). 1986. pap. 9.95 (ISBN 0-939680-31-9). Bear & Co.

Nuctemeron of Apollonius Tyana. Jan Van Rijckenborgh. (Dutch.). 125p. (Orig.). 1987. pap. 11.00. Rosycross Pr.

Nuer Religion. Edward E. Evans-Pritchard. (Illus.). 1956. 10.95x (ISBN 0-19-874003-4). Oxford U Pr.

Nuestro Nuevo Testamento. Merrill C. Tenney. Orig. Title: New Testament Survey. (Span.). 492p. 1981. pap. 12.95 (ISBN 0-8254-1716-3). Kregel.

Nueva Llamada. Jan Van Rijckenborgh. (Span.). 1987. pap. 1.50. Rosycross Pr.

Nueva Vida. Andrew Murray. 144p. 1979. 2.95 (ISBN 0-88113-220-9). Edit Betania.

Nuevo Comentario Biblico. Guthrie et al. Orig. Title: New Bible Commentary Revised. 972p. 1986. pap. 39.95 (ISBN 0-311-03001-7). Casa Bautista.

Nuevo Lexico Griego Espanol. McKibben-Stockwell. (Span.). 316p. 1985. pap. 6.95 (ISBN 0-311-42072-9, Edit Mundo). Casa Bautista.

Nuevo Manual Biblico de Unger. Merrill F. Unger. Orig. Title: New Unger's Bible Handbook. (Span.). 720p. 1987. 32.95 (ISBN 0-8254-1779-1). Kregel.

Nuevo Nacimiento. Kenneth E. Hagin. (Span.). 1983. pap. 0.50 mini bk. (ISBN 0-89276-150-4). Hagin Ministries.

Nuevo Testamento. (Span.). 1970. pap. 2.00 (ISBN 0-8198-2301-5). Dghtrs St Paul.

Nuevo Testamento de Nuestro Senor Jesucristo. Tr. by Pablo Besson from Greek. (Span.). 576p. 1981. pap. 6.50 (ISBN 0-311-48710-6, Edit Mundo). Casa Bautista.

Nuevo Testamento: Reina-Valera Actualizada. (Span.). 320p. (Orig.). 1986. pap. 0.95 (ISBN 0-311-48753-X). Casa Bautista.

Nuevo Testamento: "Venid a Mi" Rva. (Span.). 320p. (Orig.). 1986. pap. 0.60 (ISBN 0-311-48752-1). Casa Bautista.

Nuggets for Happiness. Allen Phillips. 1959. 2.95 (ISBN 0-87148-625-3). Pathway Pr.

Nuggets From Numbers. W. G. Heslop. LC 75-13660. (W. G. Heslop Bible Study Aids). 192p. 1975. pap. 4.50 (ISBN 0-8254-2828-9). Kregel.

Nuggets of Truth. Charles Hunter & Frances Hunter. 1975. pap. 3.25 (ISBN 0-917726-01-4). Hunter Bks.

Number One Way to Fight the Devil. Norvel Hayes. 1978. pap. 0.75 (ISBN 0-89274-094-9, HH-094). Harrison Hse.

Number Our Days. Barbara Myerhoff. 1980. 8.95 (ISBN 0-671-25430-8, Touchstone). S&S.

Number Sense. Joanne M. Vannah. 1985. 4.95 (ISBN 0-8062-2451-7). Carlton.

Numbers. George Bush. 1981. 17.95 (ISBN 0-86524-099-X, 0401). Klock & Klock.

Numbers. Brant L. Doty. (Bible Study Textbook Ser.). 1973. 14.30 (ISBN 0-89900-008-8). College Pr Pub.

Numbers. Charles R. Erdman. 144p. 1982. pap. 4.50 (ISBN 0-8010-3378-0). Baker Bk.

Numbers. B. Maarsingh. Ed. by A. S. Van der Woude. Tr. by John Vriend from Dutch. (Text & Interpretation Commentary Ser.). 128p. (Orig.). 1987. pap. 6.95 (ISBN 0-8028-0104-8). Eerdmans.

Numbers. Helen K. Mainelli. (Bible Commentary Ser.). 136p. 1985. pap. 2.50 (ISBN 0-8146-1373-X). Liturgical Pr.

Numbers. Moriarty. (Bible Ser.). Pt. 1. pap. 1.00 (ISBN 0-8091-5101-4); Pt. 2. pap. 1.00 (ISBN 0-8091-5102-2). Paulist Pr.

Numbers. Walter Riggans. LC 83-7007. (Daily Study Bible-Old Testament). 262p. (Orig.). 1983. 14.95 (ISBN 0-664-21393-6); pap. 7.95 (ISBN 0-664-24474-2). Westminster.

Numbers. John Sturdy. LC 75-39373. (Cambridge Bible Commentary on the New English Bible, Old Testament Ser.). 1976. pap. 11.95 (ISBN 0-521-09776-2). Cambridge U Pr.

Numbers. Gordon J. Wenham. Ed. by D. J. Wiseman. LC 81-11806. (Tyndale Old Testament Commentaries Ser.). 240p. 1981. 12.95 (ISBN 0-87784-891-2); pap. 6.95 (ISBN 0-87784-254-X). Inter-Varsity.

Numbers. Westcott. 9.50 (ISBN 0-7229-5027-6). Theos Pub Hse.

Numbers, Vol. 4. James Philip. 300p. 1987. 18.95 (ISBN 0-8499-0409-9). Word Bks.

Numbers & Deuteronomy. Irving L. Jensen. (Bible Self Study Ser.). 1970. pap. 3.25 (ISBN 0-8024-1004-9). Moody.

Numbers: Bible Study Commentary. F. B. Huey, Jr. (Bible Study Commentary Ser.). 144p. (Orig.). 1981. pap. 4.95 (ISBN 0-310-36073-0, 11064P). Zondervan.

Numbers in God's World. Beverly Beckmann. 1983. 5.95 (ISBN 0-570-04083-3, 56-1438). Concordia.

Numbers: Journey to God's Rest-Land. Irving L. Jensen. (Everyman's Bible Commentary Ser.). 1968. pap. 5.95 (ISBN 0-8024-2004-4). Moody.

Numbers of Life. Kevin Quinn Avery. LC 76-45969. 354p. 1977. pap. 8.95 (ISBN 0-385-12629-8, Dolp). Doubleday.

Numerical Bible, 7 vols. Ed. by F. W. Grant. Incl. Vol. 1. Genesis to Deuteronomy (ISBN 0-87213-262-5); Vol. 2. Joshua to Second Samuel (ISBN 0-87213-263-3); Vol. 3. Psalms (ISBN 0-87213-264-1); Vol. 4. Ezekiel (ISBN 0-87213-265-X); Vol. 5. Matthew to John (ISBN 0-87213-266-8); Vol. 6. Acts to Philemon (ISBN 0-87213-267-6); Vol. 7. Hebrews to Revelation (ISBN 0-87213-268-4). 1890-1932. Set. 79.95 (ISBN 0-87213-261-7); 12.95 ea. Loizeaux.

Numerical Distinction of Sins According to the Franciscan School of the Seventeenth & Eighteenth Centuries. Bonaventure A. Brown. 1948. 3.50 (ISBN 0-686-11581-3). Franciscan Inst.

Numerical Structure of Scripture. F. W. Grant. 1956. pap. 4.95 (ISBN 0-87213-269-2). Loizeaux.

Numerology. Eric T. Bell. LC 78-13855. (Illus.). 1985. Repr. of 1933 ed. 19.00 (ISBN 0-88355-774-6). Hyperion Conn.

Numerology. Austin Coates. 128p. 1984. 4.95 (ISBN 0-8065-0892-2). Citadel Pr.

Numerology & the Divine Triangle. Faith Javane & Dusty Bunker. (Illus.). 1979. pap. 13.95 (ISBN 0-914918-10-9). Para Res.

Numerology for the New Age. Lynn M. Buess. (Illus.). 1979. pap. 6.95 (ISBN 0-87516-265-7). De Vorss.

Numerology: Its Facts & Secrets. Ariel Y. Taylor. pap. 3.00 (ISBN 0-87980-109-3). Wilshire.

Numerology: Its Facts & Secrets. Ariel Taylor-Hyler. 1958. 8.95 (ISBN 0-910140-17-0). C & R Anthony.

Numerology Made Easy. M. Mykian. 1979. pap. 5.00 (ISBN 0-87980-376-2). Wilshire.

Numerology Made Plain. Ariel Y. Taylor. 147p. 1973. pap. 5.95 (ISBN 0-87877-012-7, P-12). Newcastle Pub.

Numerology: The Secret Power of Numbers. Mary Anderson. (Paths to Inner Power Ser.). 1972. pap. 3.50 (ISBN 0-85030-183-1). Weiser.

Numeros: Viaje a la Tierra de Reposo (Comentario Biblico Portavoz) Irving L. Jensen. Orig. Title: Numbers(Everyman's Bible Commentary) (Span.). 112p. 1980. pap. 3.50 (ISBN 0-8254-1355-9). Kregel.

Numerous Choirs: A Chronicle of Elizabeth Bayley Seton & Her Spiritual Daughters, Volume 1: the Seton Years 1774-1821. Ed. by Ellin M. Kelly. LC 81-80304. (Illus.). x, 296p. 1981. 15.00 (ISBN 0-9605784-0-4). Mater Dei Provincialate.

Nun: A Memoir. Mary G. Wong. LC 82-47656. 416p. 1983. 15.95 (ISBN 0-15-167739-5). HarBraceJ.

Nun-A Memoir: An Intimate Account of One Women's Years in the Covent & Her Eventual Return to the World. Mary G. Wong. LC 84-47611. 416p. 1984. pap. 8.95 (ISBN 0-06-091188-3, CN 1188, PL). Har-Row.

Nun in the Concentration Camp. C. M. Target. 1974. pap. 1.60 (ISBN 0-08-017611-9). Pergamon.

Nun, the Infidel, & the Superman: The Remarkable Friendships of Dame Laurentia McLachlan. Felicitas Corrigan. LC 84-52822. (Illus.). viii, 152p. 1985. 14.95 (ISBN 0-226-11589-5). U of Chicago Pr.

Nun, Witch, Playmate: The Americanization of Sex. 2nd ed. Herbert W. Richardson. xii, 147p. 1977. Repr. of 1974 ed. 19.95x (ISBN 0-88946-950-4). E Mellen.

Nuns' Rule or the Ancrew Riwle. Tr. by James Morton. LC 66-23314. (Medieval Library). Repr. of 1926 ed. 17.50x (ISBN 0-8154-0155-8). Cooper Sq.

Nuptial Blessing: A Study of Christian Marriage Rites. Ed. by Kenneth Stevenson. 1983. 22.50x (ISBN 0-19-520418-2); pap. 9.95x (ISBN 0-19-520419-0). Oxford U Pr.

Nursery Songbook. Ed. by Katherine Royer. (Illus.). 48p. 1957. pap. 2.95x (ISBN 0-8361-1278-4). Herald Pr.

Nursery Stories of Jesus. Katherine Royer. (Illus.). 48p. 1957. pap. 2.95 (ISBN 0-8361-1276-8). Herald Pr.

Nursing Care of the Terminally Ill. Madalon Amenta & Nancy Rohnet. 1986. pap. text ed. 22.00 (ISBN 0-316-03693-5). Little.

Nursing Father: Moses As a Political Leader. Aaron Wildavsky. LC 83-1099. (Illus.). xi, 262p. 1984. text ed. 25.00 (ISBN 0-8173-0168-2); pap. text ed. 11.95 (ISBN 0-8173-0169-0). U of Ala Pr.

Nursling of Mortality: A Study of the Homeric Hymn to Aphrodite. Peter Smith. (Studien zur klassischen Philologie: Vol. 3). 155p. 1980. pap. 20.65 (ISBN 3-8204-6111-6). P Lang Pubs.

Nurturing Children in the Lord. Jack Fennema. 1978. pap. 4.95 (ISBN 0-87552-266-1). Presby & Reformed.

Nurturing Contemplation. Carol Murphy. 1983. pap. 2.50x (ISBN 0-87574-252-1, 252). Pendle Hill.

Nurturing Faith in the Family. Jan Chartier & Myron Chartier. (Family Life Ser.). 160p. 1986. pap. 6.95 (ISBN 0-8170-1093-9). Judson.

Nurturing My Students. Lawrence O. Richards & Marlene D. LeFever. (Complete Teacher Training Meeting Ser.). 48p. 1985. pap. text ed. 9.95 (ISBN 0-317-38010-9). Cook.

Nurturing Spiritual Development: Stages, Structure, Style. Kenneth H. Ives. (Studies in Quakerism: No. 8). 60p. (Orig.). 1982. pap. 4.00 (ISBN 0-89670-011-9). Progresiv Pub.

Nutrition & Health. Rudolf Steiner. Tr. by Gladys Hahn from Ger. Tr. of Schoepfung der Welt und des Menschen. Erdenleben und Stennenwirken. (Illus.). 35p. 1987. pap. 3.95 (ISBN 0-88010-182-2). Anthroposophic.

Nutrition for the Cancer Patient. Ernest Rosenbaum et al. (Orig.). 1980. pap. 7.95 (ISBN 0-915950-38-3). Bull Pub.

Nuts & Bolts of Church Growth. Paul W. Powell. LC 81-68926. 1982. pap. 5.95 (ISBN 0-8054-2542-X). Broadman.

Nyaya: Gautama's Nyaya Sutra with Vatsyayana's Commentary. Tr. by M. Gangopadhyaya. 1983. 28.50x (ISBN 0-8364-1000-9, Pub. by Indian Stud). South Asia Bks.

Nyaya Sutras of Gotama. Gotama. Tr. by Satisa Chandra Vidyabhusana. LC 73-3795. (Sacred Books of the Hindus: No. 8). Repr. of 1913 ed. 29.00 (ISBN 0-404-57808-X). AMS Pr.

Nyayanukha of Dignaga. Ed. by Giuseppe Tucci. LC 78-72427. Repr. of 1930 ed. 17.50 (ISBN 0-404-17288-1). AMS Pr.

Nyingma Edition of the sDe-dge bKa-gyur & bsTun-gyur, 120 vols. Ed. by Tarthang Tulku. (Tibetan Buddhist Canon). 65000p. 1981. Set. 17250.00 (ISBN 0-89800-129-3). Dharma Pub.

O

O Christian! O Jew! Paul R. Carlson. LC 74-78937. 256p. (Orig.). 1974. pap. 1.95 (ISBN 0-912692-39-1). Cook.

O Come, Let Us Worship: Corporate Worship in the Evangelical Church. Robert G. Rayburn. LC 79-55192. 1980. 11.95 (ISBN 0-8010-7690-0); pap. 8.95 (ISBN 0-8010-7728-1). Baker Bk.

O Come, O Come, Emmanuel. James Schackel. (Candlelight Ser.). 1984. 2.25 (ISBN 0-89536-691-6, 4867). CSS of Ohio.

O God, Guide Me: A Selection of Prayers Revealed. Bahaullah & Bab. (Illus.). 1986. pap. 4.75 (ISBN 0-87743-202-3). Baha'i.

O Happy Day! W. Wangerin, Jr. (Arch Bks.: No. 12). 1981. pap. 0.99 (ISBN 0-570-06093-1, 59-1211). Concordia.

O Holy Mountain: Journal of a Retreat on Mount Athos. Basil Pennington. pap. 6.95 (ISBN 0-89453-382-7). M Glazier.

O Inward Traveller. Carol R. Murphy. LC 77-91637. 31p. (Orig.). 1977. pap. 2.50x (ISBN 0-87574-216-5). Pendle Hill.

O Jerusalem. Larry Collins & Dominique Lapierre. 1980. pap. 3.95 (ISBN 0-671-83684-6). PB.

O Monashestvje. Archpriest John Vostorgov. Tr. of On Monasticism. 48p. 1969. pap. 2.00 (ISBN 0-317-29004-5). Holy Trinity.

O Monashistvje. Archbishop Averky Taushev. Tr. of On Monasticism. 46p. pap. 2.00 (ISBN 0-317-29064-9). Holy Trinity.

O My Pilot Beloved. Sri Chinmoy. 54p. (Orig.). 1980. pap. 2.00 (ISBN 0-88497-502-9). Aum Pubns.

O None Can Be Loved Like Jesus. Basilea Schlink. 1974. pap. 1.00 (ISBN 3-87209-651-6). Evang Sisterhood Mary.

O Pravoslavii s Predestereshenijami ot Pogreshenij Protiv Hego. Theophan the Recluse. Tr. of On Orthodoxy with Warning Against Apostasy from It. 202p. 1962. pap. 7.00 (ISBN 0-317-28919-5). Holy Trinity.

O Reforme v Byte Russkoi Tserkvi: Sbornik Statei. E. E. Golubinskii. 142p. Repr. of 1913 ed. text ed. 33.12x (ISBN 0-576-99237-2, Pub. by Gregg Intl Pubs England). Gregg Intl.

O. T. Books of the Bible. Karen Jessie. 48p. (Orig.). (YA) 1983. 1.95 (ISBN 0-87239-674-6, 2774). Standard Pub.

O Zhizni o Vjere o Tzerkvje, 2 vols. Protopresbyter Michael Pomazansky. Tr. of On Life, Faith & the Church. 650p. 1976. pap. 23.00 (ISBN 0-317-29072-X). Holy Trinity.

O Znamjenii Obnovlenija Svatykh Ikon. Archbishop Metodies. Tr. of On the Signs of the Renewing of Holy Icons. 82p. 1963. pap. 3.00 (ISBN 0-317-29041-X). Holy Trinity.

Oak King, the Holly King, & the Unicorn: The Myths & Symbolism of the Unicorn Tapestries. John Williamson. LC 85-45242. (Illus.). 280p. 1987. pap. 12.95 (ISBN 0-06-096032-9, PL 6032, PL). Har-Row.

Obadiah. G. Michael Cocoris. 19p. (Orig.). 1983. pap. 1.00 (ISBN 0-935729-29-1). Church Open Door.

Obadiah: A Critical & Exegetical Commentary. John D. Watts. 78p. 1981. pap. 4.95x (ISBN 0-686-79148-7). Eisenbrauns.

Obadiah & Habakkuk. Edward Marbury. 1979. 23.95 (ISBN 0-86524-007-8, 7003). Klock & Klock.

Obadiah & Jonah: A Commentary. Hans W. Wolf. Tr. by Margaret Kohl from German. LC 86-22256. Orig. Title: Obadja, Jona. 192p. 1986. text ed. 19.95 (ISBN 0-8066-2244-X, 10-4710). Augsburg.

Obeah, Christ, & Rastaman: Jamaica & Its Religion. Ivor Morrish. 128p. 1982. 17.95 (ISBN 0-227-67831-1). Attic Pr.

Obeah: Witchcraft in the West Indies. Henry H. Bell. LC 78-106879. Repr. of 1889 ed. 22.50x (ISBN 0-8371-3275-4, BEO&, Pub. by Negro U Pr). Greenwood.

Obedience. Archimandrite Chrysostomos & Hieromonk Ambrosios. Ed. by Alexey Young & Vladimir Derugin. (Themes in Orthodox Patristic Psychology Ser.: Vol. 2). 90p. (Orig.). 1984. text ed. write for info. (ISBN 0-916586-88-X); pap. text ed. write for info. (ISBN 0-916586-31-6). Holy Cross Orthodox.

Obedience. S. J. Hulshizer. 69p. pap. 3.95 (ISBN 0-88172-156-5). Believers Bkshelf.

Obedience Brings Happiness. Vera Groomer. (Come Unto Me Ser.). 16p. 1979. pap. 1.65 (ISBN 0-8127-0251-4). Review & Herald.

Obedience Experiments: A Case Study of Controversy in Social Science. Arthur Miller. LC 85-25723. 305p. 1986. 35.00 (ISBN 0-275-92012-7, C2012). Praeger.

Obedience in Church & State: Three Political Tracts. Stephen Gardiner. Ed. by Pierre Janelle. LC 68-19272. 1968. Repr. of 1930 ed. lib. bdg. 22.50x (ISBN 0-8371-0081-X, GABW). Greenwood.

Obedience in Finances. Kenneth Hagin. 1983. pap. 0.50 mini bk. (ISBN 0-89276-259-4). Hagin Ministries.

Obedience of a Christen Man & How Christe Rulers Ought to Governe. William Tyndale. LC 77-7436. (English Experience Ser.: No. 897). 1977. Repr. of 1528 ed. lib. bdg. 24.00 (ISBN 90-221-0897-X). Walter J Johnson.

Obedience of Faith. Morris Venden. Ed. by Gerald Wheeler. LC 83-13934. 96p. (Orig.). 1984. pap. 5.95 (ISBN 0-8280-0203-7). Review & Herald.

Obedience: The Road to Reality. Kathy Hendershot. 176p. (Orig.). 1982. pap. 3.50 (ISBN 0-911567-00-3). Christian Mini.

Oberammergau Passionsspiel Nineteen Eighty-Four. Ed. by Leonard Swidler & Gerard S. Sloyan. 104p. pap. 5.00 (ISBN 0-686-95110-7). ADL.

Oberlin: The Colony & the College. James H. Fairchild. Ed. by Donald W. Dayton. (Higher Christian Life Ser.). 377p. 1985. 45.00 (ISBN 0-8240-6416-X). Garland Pub.

Obikhod Tserkovnago Penija. Tr. of Obikhod of Sacred Music. 167p. 1959. 20.00 (ISBN 0-317-30405-4). Holy Trinity.

Object-Centered Children's Sermons. C. W. Bess. (Object Lesson Ser.). 1978. pap. 3.95 (ISBN 0-8010-0734-8). Baker Bk.

Object Lessons. Charles C. Ryrie. 96p. 1981. pap. 3.95 (ISBN 0-8024-6024-0). Moody.

Object Lessons & Stories for the Children's Church. Jessie P. Sullivan. (Object Lesson Ser.). 160p. 1974. pap. 4.95 (ISBN 0-8010-8037-1). Baker Bk.

Object Lessons for a Year. David J. Classen. 112p. 1986. pap. 4.95 (ISBN 0-8010-2514-1). Baker Bk.

Object Lessons for Children. Luther Cross. (Object Lesson Ser). (Illus., Orig.). 1967. pap. 3.95 (ISBN 0-8010-2315-7). Baker Bk.

Object Lessons for Children's Worship. Mary Foxwell Loeks. (Object Lesson Ser). 1979. pap. 3.50 (ISBN 0-8010-5584-9). Baker Bk.

Object Lessons for Special Days. Sheryl Bruinsma. 80p. 1986. 4.50 (ISBN 0-8010-0920-0). Baker Bk.

Object Lessons from Science Experiments. Richard F. Gebhardt & Mark Armstrong. (Object Lesson Ser.). 128p. 1987. pap. 5.95 (ISBN 0-8010-3811-1). Baker Bk.

Object Lessons from Sports & Games. William C. Hendricks & Merle Den Bleyker. (Object Lessons Ser). 126p. 1975. pap. 3.95 (ISBN 0-8010-4134-1). Baker Bk.

Object Lessons from the Bible. Wesley T. Runk. (Object Lessons Ser.). 96p. 1980. pap. 3.95 (ISBN 0-8010-7698-6). Baker Bk.

Object Lessons That Teach Bible Truths. William C. Hendricks & Merle Den Bleyker. (Object Lessons Ser.). 1977. pap. 3.95 (ISBN 0-8010-4172-4). Baker Bk.

Object Lessons Using Common Things. DeGolia. 1954. 3.50 (ISBN 0-88207-026-6). Victor Bks.

Object Lessons: With Easy-to-Find Objects. Jessie P. Sullivan. (Object Lesson Ser.). 128p. (Orig.). 1981. pap. 3.95 (ISBN 0-8010-8190-4). Baker Bk.

Object of Life According to the Holy Qur'an. T. Nadvi. 1972. 3.50x (ISBN 0-87902-181-0). Orientalia.

Object of Morality. G. J. Warnock. 1971. pap. 10.95x (ISBN 0-416-29900-8, NO. 2575). Methuen Inc.

Object Talks for Special Days. Compiled by Bob Korth. (Illus.). 48p. (Orig.). 1984. pap. 2.95 (ISBN 0-87239-723-8, 2859). Standard Pub.

Object Talks from A to Z. Carol DeWolf. (Illus.). 64p. 1987. 5.95 (ISBN 0-87403-237-7, 2867). Standard Pub.

Object Talks on Christian Living. Compiled by Bob Korth. (Illus.). 48p. (Orig.). 1984. pap. 2.95 (ISBN 0-87239-724-6, 2860). Standard Pub.

Object Talks on the Parables of Jesus. Lois Edstrom. (Illus.). 48p. (Orig.). 1984. pap. 2.95 (ISBN 0-87239-721-1, 2857). Standard Pub.

Object Talks on the Teachings of Jesus. Compiled by Bob Korth. (Illus.). 48p. (Orig.). 1984. pap. 2.95 (ISBN 0-87239-722-X, 2858). Standard Pub.

Objections Answered by Way of Dialogue, Wherein Is Proved That No Man Ought to Be Persecuted for His Religion. Thomas Helwys. LC 73-6139. (English Experience Ser.: No. 603). 80p. 1973. Repr. of 1615 ed. 6.00 (ISBN 90-221-0603-9). Walter J Johnson.

Objections to Humanism. H. J. Blackham et al. LC 73-16796. 128p. 1974. Repr. of 1963 ed. lib. bdg. 22.50x (ISBN 0-8371-7235-7, BLOH). Greenwood.

Objections to Nuclear Defence: Philosophers on Deterrence. Ed. by Nigel Blake & Kay Pole. 208p. (Orig.). 1984. pap. 11.95x (ISBN 0-7102-0249-0). Methuen Inc.

Objetos Que Ensenan de Dios. Cecil McConnell & Mary McConnell. (Span.). 96p. 1986. pap. 3.50 (ISBN 0-311-44007-X). Casa Bautista.

Obligations to Future Generations. Ed. by R. I. Sikora & Brian Barry. LC 78-5495. (Philosophical Monographs: Second Annual Ser.). 272p. 1978. 14.95 (ISBN 0-87722-132-4); pap. 12.95 (ISBN 0-87722-128-6). Temple U Pr.

Obras de Joaquin Garcia Icazbalceta, 10 vols. Joaquin Garcia Icazbalceta. LC 68-58758. (Span). 1969. Repr. of 1898 ed. Set. 225.00 (ISBN 0-8337-1798-7). B Franklin.

Obscure Destinies. Willa Cather. LC 74-5323. 1974. pap. 4.95 (ISBN 0-394-71179-3, V-179, Vin). Random.

Observation-Thinking-the Senses. Eileen Hutchins. 1975. pap. 1.95 (ISBN 0-916786-13-7). St George Bk Serv.

Observations. Ernest Holmes. Ed. by Willis H. Kinnear. 64p. 1968. pap. 5.50 (ISBN 0-911336-12-5). Sci of Mind.

Observations on Some Tendencies of Sentiment & Ethics in 18th Century Poetry. Johannes H. Harder. LC 68-886. (Studies in Poetry, No. 38). 1969. Repr. of 1933 ed. lib. bdg. 49.95x (ISBN 0-8383-0564-4). Haskell.

Observations on the Charter & Conduct of the Society for the Propagation of the Gospel in Foreign Parts; Designed to Show Their Non-Conformity to Each Other. Jonathan Mayhew. LC 72-38456. (Religion in America, Ser. 2). 180p. 1972. Repr. of 1763 ed. 15.00 (ISBN 0-405-04077-6). Ayer Co Pubs.

Observations on the Growth of the Mind Including GENIUS. 5th ed. Sampson Reed. LC 72-4971. (Romantic Tradition in American Literature Ser.). 110p. 1972. Repr. of 1859 ed. 18.00 (ISBN 0-405-04641-3). Ayer Co Pubs.

Observations on the Influence of Religion upon the Health & Physical Welfare of Mankind. Amariah Brigham. LC 73-2389. (Mental Illness & Social Policy; the American Experience Ser.). Repr. of 1835 ed. 21.00 (ISBN 0-405-05197-2). Ayer Co Pubs.

Observations on the Influence of Religion upon the Health & Physical Welfare of Mankind, 1835: Remarks on the Influence of Mental Cultivation & Mental Excitement Upon Health, 2 vols. in 1. Amariah Brigham. LC 73-17271. (History of Psychology Ser.). 1973. 55.00x (ISBN 0-8201-1125-2). Schol Facsimiles.

Observations on the Popular Antiquities of Great Britain: Chiefly Illustrating the Origin of Our Vulgar & Provincial Customs, Ceremonies & Superstitions, 3 vols. John Brand. LC 67-23896. 1969. Repr. of 1849 ed. Set. 68.00x (ISBN 0-8103-3256-6). Gale.

Observatory in Islam. Aydin Sayili. Ed. by I. Bernard Cohen. LC 80-2144. (Development of Science Ser.). (Illus.). 1981. lib. bdg. 45.00x (ISBN 0-405-13951-9). Ayer Co Pubs.

Observe the Sons of Ulster Marching Towards the Somme. Frank McGuinness. (Orig.). 1986. pap. 8.95 (ISBN 0-571-14611-2). Faber & Faber.

Observing National Holidays & Church Festivals: A Weekday Church School Unit in Christian Citizenship Series for Grades Three & Four. Florence Martin. LC 76-174077. 1971. Repr. of 1940 ed. 44.00x (ISBN 0-8103-3804-1). Gale.

Observing Self: Mysticism & Psychotherapy. Arthur J. Deikman. LC 81-70486. 208p. 1983. pap. 8.95 (ISBN 0-8070-2951-3, BP 652). Beacon Pr.

Obsession & Possession. T. K. Oesterreich. 1935. 11.00x (ISBN 0-685-00976-8). Wehman.

Obshchje-zhitel'naya Sarovskaja Pustin' Tr. of Sarov Monastery. (Illus.). 241p. pap. 10.00 (ISBN 0-317-29243-9). Holy Trinity.

Obshchjedostupnija Chtenija o Tserkovnom Peniji. J. Voznesensky. Tr. of Popular Readings in Church Singing. 48p. 1969. pap. 2.00 (ISBN 0-317-30383-X). Holy Trinity.

Obstacles to Mystical Experience. Scott Crom. 1983. pap. 2.50x (ISBN 0-87574-132-0, 132). Pendle Hill.

Obstruction of Justice by Religion: A Treatise on Religious Barbarities of the Common Law, & a Review of Judicial Oppressions of the Non-Religious in the U. S. Frank Swancara. LC 70-139581. (Civil Liberties in American History Ser). (Illus.). 1971. Repr. of 1936 ed. lib. bdg. 32.50 (ISBN 0-306-71964-9). Da Capo.

Obtaining Answers to Prayer. E. M. Bounds. 144p. 1984. pap. 3.50 (ISBN 0-88368-142-0). Whitaker Hse.

Occasional Papers, 2 vols. R. W. Church. 1973. Repr. of 1897 ed. 20.00 set (ISBN 0-8274-1533-8). R West.

Occasional Papers on Catholic Higher Education. Incl. Vol. 1, No. 1. 20p. 1975. 1.20 (ISBN 0-318-18249-1); Vol. I, No. 2. 49p. 1975. 2.40 (ISBN 0-318-18250-5); Vol. II, No. 1. 11p. 1976. 1.20 (ISBN 0-318-18251-3); Vol. II, No. 2. 23p. 1976. 1.20 (ISBN 0-318-18252-1); Vol. III, No. 1. 19p. 1977. 1.20 (ISBN 0-318-18253-X); Vol. III, No. 2. 32p. 1977. 1.20 (ISBN 0-318-18254-8); Vol. IV, No. 1. 35p. 1978. 1.80 (ISBN 0-318-18255-6); Vol. IV, No. 2. 35p. 1978. 2.40 (ISBN 0-318-18256-4); Vol. V, No. 1. 35p. 1979. 2.40 (ISBN 0-318-18257-2). Natl Cath Educ.

Occulation of Imam: A Historical Background. Jassim M. Hussain. 221p. 1986. lib. bdg. 30.00 (ISBN 0-7103-0158-8). Methuen Inc.

Occult Anatomy & the Bible. Corinne Heline. 1985. pap. 9.95 (ISBN 0-87613-093-7). New Age.

Occult & Scientific Mentalities in the Renaissance. Ed. by Brian Vickers. 432p. 1986. pap. 15.95 (ISBN 0-521-33836-0). Cambridge U Pr.

Occult Experience & the New Criticism: Daemonism, Sexuality & the Hidden in Literature. Clive Bloom. LC 86-10963. 160p. 1987. 27.50x (ISBN 0-389-20646-6). B&N Imports.

Occult Glossary. G. De Purucker. LC 53-37086. (A Compendium of Oriental & Theosophical Terms). 1972. 7.50 (ISBN 0-911500-50-2); pap. 4.00 (ISBN 0-911500-51-0). Theos U Pr.

Occult Glossary: A Compendium of Oriental & Theosophical Terms. 69.95 (ISBN 0-8490-0749-6). Gordon Pr.

Occult Japan. Percival Lowell. 59.95 (ISBN 0-8490-0750-X). Gordon Pr.

Occult Power of Numbers. W. Wynn Westcott. LC 84-21740. (Illus.). 128p. 1984. Repr. of 1984 ed. lib. bdg. 15.95x (ISBN 0-89370-675-2). Borgo Pr.

Occult Powers in Nature & in Man. Hodson. 5.50 (ISBN 0-8356-7085-6). Theos Pub Hse.

Occult Symbolism in France: Josephin Peladan & the Salons De la Rose-Croix. Robert Pincus-Witten. LC 75-23809. (Outstanding Dissertations in the Fine Arts-20th Century). (Illus.). 300p. 1976. lib. bdg. 50.00 (ISBN 0-8240-2003-0). Garland Pub.

Occult World. 9th ed. A. P. Sinnett. 1969. 12.95 (ISBN 0-8356-5019-7). Theos Pub Hse.

Occultation of the Twelfth Imam: A Historical Background. J. M. Hussain. 221p. 1982. 35.00x (ISBN 0-317-39132-1, Pub. by Luzac & Co Ltd). State Mutual Bk.

Occultism, Witchcraft, & Cultural Fashion: Essays in Comparative Religions. Mircea Eliade. LC 75-12230. 1978. pap. 9.00 (ISBN 0-226-20392-1, P755, Phoen). U of Chicago Pr.

Occultists & Mystics of All Ages. Ralph Shirley. 176p. 1974. pap. 2.95 (ISBN 0-8065-0419-6). Citadel Pr.

Occupation of Celtic Sites in Medieval Ireland by the Canons Regular of St Augustine & the Cistercians. Geraldine Carville. (Cistercian Studies Ser.: Nbr. 56). (Illus.). 1983. 13.95 (ISBN 0-87907-856-1). Cistercian Pubns.

Occupation of Chios by the Genoese & Their Administration of the Island, 1346-1566, 3 vols. Philip P. Argenti. LC 78-63339. (Crusades & Military Orders: Second Ser.). Repr. of 1958 ed. Set. 120.00 (ISBN 0-404-17000-5); 40.00 ea. AMS Pr.

Ocean of Love: Anurag Sagar of Kabir. Kabir. Ed. by Rusell Perkins. Tr. by Raaj K. Bagga & Pratap Singh. LC 82-50369. (Illus.). 252p. (Orig.). 1982. pap. 15.00 (ISBN 0-89142-039-8). Sant Bani Ash.

Ocean of Theosophy. W. Q. Judge. 69.95 (ISBN 0-8490-0752-6). Gordon Pr.

Ocean of Theosophy. William Q. Judge. LC 73-78147. 1973. 6.00 (ISBN 0-911500-25-1); pap. 3.50 (ISBN 0-911500-26-X). Theos U Pr.

Ocean of Theosophy. William Q. Judge. (Illus.). 153p. 1915. Repr. of 1893 ed. 5.00 (ISBN 0-938998-07-2). Theosophy.

Oceanic, American Indian, & African Myths of Snaring the Sun. K. Luomala. (BMB Ser.). Repr. of 1940 ed. 11.00 (ISBN 0-527-02276-4). Kraus Repr.

Oceanic Feeling: The Origins of Religious Sentiment in Ancient India. J. Moussaieff Masson. (Studies of Classical India: No. 3). 228p. 1980. lib. bdg. 34.00 (ISBN 90-277-1050-3, Pub. by Reidel Holland). Kluwer Academic.

Oceanic Mythology, Vol. 9. Roland B. Dixon. LC 63-19094. (Mythology of All Races Ser). (Illus.). 1964. Repr. of 1932 ed. 30.00x (ISBN 0-8154-0059-4). Cooper Sq.

Oceano de la Teosofia. William Q. Judge. Tr. by Bermudez Y. Polanco from Eng. Tr. of Ocean of Theosophy. (Span.). 128p. 1983. pap. 3.75 (ISBN 0-938998-28-5). Theosophy.

Ochlah W'Ochlah. Salomon Frensdorff. 35.00x (ISBN 0-87068-194-X). Ktav.

Ochre Robe: An Autobiography. 2nd ed. Agahananda Bharati. 300p. 1980. 14.95 (ISBN 0-915520-40-0); pap. 7.95 (ISBN 0-915520-28-1). Ross-Erikson.

Octavius. M. Minucius Felix. pap. 31.00 (ISBN 0-384-39070-6). Johnson Repr.

Octavius of Marcus Minucius Felix. Ed. by Thomas C. Lawler & Johannes Burghart. Tr. by G. W. Clarke from Latin. (Ancient Christian Writers Ser.: Vol. 39). 1974. 14.95 (ISBN 0-8091-0189-0). Paulist Pr.

Ocupate en Ensenar. Crea Ridenour. 48p. 1983. pap. 1.50 (ISBN 0-311-11031-2). Casa Bautista.

Odes of Solomon. Ed. by J. H. Barnard. (Texts & Studies Ser.: No. 1, Vol. 8, Pt. 3). pap. 13.00 (ISBN 0-8115-1710-1). Kraus Repr.

Odes of Solomon. James H. Charlesworth. LC 77-21285. (SBL Texts & Translations). 192p. 1983. pap. 8.95 (ISBN 0-89130-202-6, 06 02 13). Scholars Pr GA.

Odes of Solomon: Original Christianity Revealed. Robert Winterhalter. Ed. by Peter Roche de Coppens et al. LC 85-45288. (Spiritual Perspectives Ser.). 240p. (Orig.). 1985. pap. 9.95 (ISBN 0-87542-875-4, L-875). Llewellyn Pubns.

Odors from Golden Vials. C. E. Orr. 78p. pap. 0.60 (ISBN 0-686-29131-X). Faith Pub Hse.

Odysseus & the Giants. Homer. Adapted by I. M. Richardson. LC 83-14233. (Tales from the Odyssey Ser.). (Illus.). 32p. 1984. PLB 9.79 (ISBN 0-8167-0009-5); pap. text ed. 2.50 (ISBN 0-8167-0010-9). Troll Assocs.

Odyssey. John Bierman. 288p. 1984. 16.95 (ISBN 0-671-50156-9). S&S.

Odyssey of Farah Antun: A Syrian Christian's Quest for Secularism. Donald M. Reid. LC 74-80598. (Studies in Middle Eastern History: No. 2). 1975. 25.00x (ISBN 0-88297-009-7). Bibliotheca.

Odyssey of New Religious Movements: Persecution, Struggle, Legitimation - a Case Study of the Unification Church. John T. Biermans. (Symposium Ser.). 232p. text ed. 49.95 (ISBN 0-88946-710-2). E Mellen.

Oedipus & Akhnaton: Myth & History. Immanuel Velikovsky. LC 60-7886. 1960. 11.95 (ISBN 0-385-00529-6). Doubleday.

Oedipus & Job in West African Religion. Meyer Fortes. 1980. Repr. of 1959 ed. lib. bdg. 15.50x (ISBN 0-374-92820-7, Octagon). Hippocrene Bks.

Oedipus & Job in West African Religion. Meyer Fortes & Robin Horton. LC 83-7587. (Cambridge Studies in Social Anthropology: No. 48). 128p. 1984. 32.50 (ISBN 0-521-26208-9); pap. 9.95 (ISBN 0-521-27719-1). Cambridge U Pr.

Oeuvres, 11 tomes. Rene Descartes. Ed. by Adam & Tannery. Incl. Tome I. Correspondance (Avril 1622-Fevrier 1638) 36.95 (ISBN 0-685-34212-3); Tome II. Correspondance (Mars 1638 - Decembre 1639) 32.95 (ISBN 0-685-34213-1); Tome III. Correspondance (Janvier 1640-Juin 1643) 37.95 (ISBN 0-685-34214-X); Tome IV. Correspondance (Juillet 1643-Avril 1647) 37.95 (ISBN 0-685-34215-8); Tome V. Correspondance (Mai 1647 - Fevrier 1650) 36.95 (ISBN 0-685-34216-6); Tome VI. Discours de la Methode et Essais. 32.95 (ISBN 0-685-34217-4); Tome VII. Meditationes de Prima Philosophia. 27.95 (ISBN 0-685-34218-2); Tome VIII, Pt. 1. Principia Philosophiae. 15.95 (ISBN 0-685-34219-0); Tome VIII, Pt. 2. Epistola ad Voetium, Lettre Apologetique, Notas in Programma. 20.95 (ISBN 0-685-34220-4); Tome IX, Pt. 1. Meditations. 12.95 (ISBN 0-685-34221-2); Tome IX, Pt. 2. Principes. 14.95 (ISBN 0-685-34222-0); Tome X. Physico-Mathematica, Compendium Musicae, Regulea ad Directionem Ingenii, Recherche de la Verite, Supplement a la Correspondance. **37.95 (ISBN 0-685-34223-9); Tome XI. Monde, Description du Corps Humain, Passions de l'Ame, Anatomica, Varia. 37.95 (ISBN 0-685-34224-7). French & Eur.**

Oeuvres en Prose: 1909-1914. Charles Peguy. Ed. by M. Peguy. (Bibl. de la Pleiade). 1957. 42.95 (ISBN 0-685-01987-X). French & Eur.

Oeuvres et Lettres: Avec: Discours de la Methode. Rene Descartes. 1424p. 1937. 42.95 (ISBN 0-686-55676-3). French & Eur.

Oeuvres: Introduction a la Vie Devote & Traite de l'Amour de Dieu, etc. Francois De Sales. (Saint). 2024p. 46.95 (ISBN 0-686-56512-6). French & Eur.

Of Cabbages & Kings. Tillie H. Gandy. 1983. 6.50 (ISBN 0-8062-2138-0). Carlton.

Of Caesar's Household. Mollie Thompson. Ed. by Charles Clanton. 232p. (Orig.). 1978. pap. 4.95 (ISBN 0-912315-29-6). Word Aflame.

Of Course I Love You. Albert J. Nimeth. 1973. 5.00 (ISBN 0-8199-0466-X). Franciscan Herald.

Of Deity & Bones. Nancy Thomas. (Illus.). 90p. (Orig.). 1983. pap. 6.95 (ISBN 0-913342-38-6). Barclay Pr.

Of Divorce for Adulterie & Marrying Againe: That There Is No Sufficient Warrant So to Do. Edmund Bunny. (English Experience Ser.: No. 781). 1977. Repr. of 1612 ed. lib. bdg. 20.00 (ISBN 90-221-0781-7). Walter J Johnson.

Of Domesticall Duties. William Gouge. LC 76-57385. (English Experience Ser.: No. 803). 1977. Repr. of 1622 ed. lib. bdg. 66.00 (ISBN 90-221-0803-1). Walter J Johnson.

Of Errors & Truth. Louis-Claude De Saint-Martin. Tr. by Philip Vadenais & Antoinette Vadenais. LC 86-63353. 435p. (Orig.). 1987. pap. write for info. (ISBN 0-912057-47-5, G-651). AMORC.

Of Everlasting Value, Vol. 1. Ed. by Howard H. Barron. (Orig.). 1978. pap. 5.95 (ISBN 0-89036-129-0). Hawkes Pub Inc.

Of Everlasting Value, Vol. 2. Ed. by Howard H. Barron. (Orig.). pap. 5.95 (ISBN 0-89036-130-4). Hawkes Pub Inc.

Of Fast & Festival: Celebrating Lent & Easter. Barbara O'Dea. 1982. pap. 3.95 (ISBN 0-8091-2426-2). Paulist Pr.

Of God & Man. Martin C. D'Arcy. 1967. pap. 1.25x (ISBN 0-268-00197-9). U of Notre Dame Pr.

Of God & Maxim Guns: Presbyterianism in Nigeria, 1846-1966, Vol. 8. Geoffrey Johnston. 270p. 1987. pap. 17.50 (ISBN 0-88920-180-3, Pub. by Wilfrid Laurier Canada). Humanities.

Of God & Men. Aiden W. Tozer. pap. 4.45 (ISBN 0-87509-193-8); 2.95. Chr Pubns.

Of God, the Devil & the Jews. Dagobert D. Runes. 1952. 5.00 (ISBN 0-8022-1444-4). Philos Lib.

Of Gods & Men: New Religious Movements in the West. Ed. by Eileen Barker. LC 83-23822. xiv, 347p. 1984. 26.50 (ISBN 0-86554-095-0, MUP/H87). Mercer Univ Pr.

Of Heaven & Hell: A Dialogue Between Junius, a Scholar & Theophorus, His Master. Jacob Boehme. 1986. pap. 3.95 (ISBN 0-916411-53-2). Sure Fire.

Of Holy Disobedience. A. J. Muste. LC 52-1568. (Orig.). 1952. pap. 2.50x (ISBN 0-87574-064-2). Pendle Hill.

Of Holy Disobedience. A. J. Muste. 23p. 1952-1964. pap. 1.25 (ISBN 0-934676-09-7). Greenlf Bks.

Of Jewish Law & Lore. Louis Ginzberg. LC 55-6707. (Temple Bks). 1970. pap. 5.95 (ISBN 0-689-70231-0, T12). Atheneum.

Of Life & Hope: Toward Effective Witness in Human Rights. Mia Adjali. (Orig.). 1979. pap. 2.95 (ISBN 0-377-00084-1). Friend Pr.

Of Miracles. David Hume. LC 85-11410. 60p. 1985. pap. 4.95 (ISBN 0-912050-72-1). Open Court.

Of One Body: Renewal Movements in the Church. Joseph W. Trigg & William L. Sachs. LC 86-2788. 168p. (Orig.). 1986. pap. 9.95 (ISBN 0-8042-0677-5). John Knox.

Of Other Gods & Other Spirits. E. H. Wendland. 1977. pap. 4.95 (ISBN 0-8100-0034-2, 12-1711). Northwest Pub.

Of Plymouth Plantation: The Pilgrims in America. William Bradford. 18.00 (ISBN 0-8446-1718-0). Peter Smith.

Of Plymouth Plantation: 1620-1647. William Bradford. Ed. by Samuel E. Morison. (American Past Ser). (Illus.). (YA) 1952. 19.95 (ISBN 0-394-43895-7). Knopf.

Of Prelates & Princes: A Study of the Economic & Social Position of the Tudor Episcopate. Felicity Heal. LC 79-41791. (Illus.). 368p. 1980. 59.50 (ISBN 0-521-22950-2). Cambridge U Pr.

Of Presbyters & Kings: Church & State in the Law of Scotland. Francis Lyall. 220p. 1980. 20.00 (ISBN 0-08-025715-1). Pergamon.

Of Sex & Sin. R. Thomas Dickman. LC 85-91068. 1986. 10.00 (ISBN 0-87212-195-X). Libra.

Of Such Is the Kingdom: Sermons for Children. Robert S. Coombs & Iris Perry. (Object Lesson Ser.). 96p. (Orig.). 1987. pap. 4.95 (ISBN 0-8010-2518-4). Baker Bk.

Of the Imitation of Christ. Thomas a Kempis. (Large Print Christian Classic Ser.). 1982. 14.95 (ISBN 0-87983-288-6). Keats.

Of the Imitation of Christ. Thomas a Kempis. 256p. 1981. pap. 2.95 (ISBN 0-88368-094-7). Whitaker Hse.

Of the Imitation of Christ. Thomas a Kempis. Tr. by Richard Whytford & W. Russell Flint. 264p. 1983. Repr. of 1909 ed. lib. bdg. 95.00 (ISBN 0-89984-921-0). Century Bookbindery.

Of the Lawes of Ecclesiasticall Politie, 2 pts. Richard Hooker. LC 76-171765. (English Experience Ser.: No. 390). 500p. 1971. Repr. of 1594 ed. 46.00 (ISBN 90-221-0390-0). Walter J Johnson.

Of the Laws of Ecclesiastical Polity, Bks. VI-VIII. Richard Hooker. Ed. by P. G. Stanwood. LC 76-24883. (Folger Library Edition of the Works of Richard Hooker). 1980. text ed. 65.00x (ISBN 0-674-63210-9, Belknap). Harvard U Pr.

Of the Laws of Ecclesiastical Polity: Attack & Response, Vol. IV. Ed. by John E. Booty & Richard Hooker. (Folger Library Edition of the Works of Richard Hooker). (Illus.). 320p. 1981. text ed. 45.00 (ISBN 0-674-63216-8). Harvard U Pr.

Of the Laws of Ecclesiastical Polity: Preface & Books I-V, 2 vols. Richard Hooker. Ed. by W. Speed Hill. (Folger Library Edition of the Works of Richard Hooker). 1977. Set. 85.00x (ISBN 0-674-63205-2, Belknap Pr). Harvard U Pr.

Of the Principles & Duties of Natural Religion: Two Books. John Wilkins. Repr. of 1693 ed. 35.00 (ISBN 0-384-68500-5). Johnson Repr.

Of the Supersensual Life. Jacob Boehme. pap. 4.95 (ISBN 0-916411-90-7). Sure Fire.

Of Time & Eternity. James D. Freeman. LC 81-51069. 200p. 1981. 5.95 (ISBN 0-87159-122-7). Unity School.

Of War & Love. Dorothee Solle. Tr. by Robert Kimber & Rita Kimber. LC 83-8252. Orig. Title: Im Hause Des Menschenfressers. 172p. (Orig.). 1983. pap. 7.95 (ISBN 0-88344-350-3). Orbis Bks.

Of Water & the Spirit: A Liturgical Study of Baptism. Alexander Schmemann. LC 74-30061. 170p. 1974. pap. 7.95 (ISBN 0-913836-10-9). St Vladimirs.

Of Whom the World Was Not Worthy. Marie Chapian. LC 78-769. (Illus.). 256p. 1978. pap. 6.95 (ISBN 0-87123-250-2, 210417). Bethany Hse.

Off the Main Road. Jerry W. Mixon. LC 85-19065. 1985. 5.95 (ISBN 0-8054-5015-7). Broadman.

Off the Shelf & Into Your Self. Hall. 1982. 3.95 (ISBN 0-88207-589-6). Victor Bks.

Offenbarung nach dem Lehrbegriffe der Synagoge, 4 vols. Salomon L. Steinheim. Ed. by Steven Katz. LC 79-7151. (Jewish Philosophy, Mysticism & History of Ideas Ser.). 1980. Repr. of 1865 ed. Set. lib. bdg. 160.00x (ISBN 0-405-12286-1); lib. bdg. 40.00x ea. Vol. 2 (ISBN 0-405-12288-8). Vol. 3 (ISBN 0-405-12220-9). Vol. 4 (ISBN 0-405-12221-7). Ayer Co Pubs.

Offense to Reason: The Theology of Sin. Bernard Ramm. LC 84-48777. 288p. 1985. 15.45 (ISBN 0-06-066792-3, HarpR). Har-Row.

Offering Meditations & Prayers. Laurence C. Keene. Ed. by Herbert Lambert. LC 84-266. 64p. (Orig.). 1984. pap. 4.95 (ISBN 0-8272-2706-X). CBP.

Offering of Uncles: The Priesthood of Adam & the Shape of the World. Robert F. Capon. (Crossroad Paperback Ser.). 192p. 1982. pap. 5.95 (ISBN 0-8245-0422-4). Crossroad NY.

Office & Work of the Holy Spirit. James Buchanan. 488p. 1984. Repr. of 1843 ed. 11.95 (ISBN 0-85151-089-2). Banner of Truth.

Office of Peter. Has U. Von Balthasar. Tr. by Andree Emery from German. LC 86-80787. Tr. of Der Antiromische Affekt. 368p. 1986. pap. 12.95 (ISBN 0-89870-020-5). Ignatius Pr.

Office of Readings. 1952p. 1984. 26.95 (ISBN 0-8198-5407-7). Dghtrs St Paul.

Offices from the Service Books of the Holy Eastern Church. Richard F. Littledale. LC 77-133819. 1970. Repr. of 1863 ed. 24.50 (ISBN 0-404-03996-0). AMS Pr.

Offices of the Oriental Church. Orthodox Eastern Church. LC 73-79805. Repr. of 1884 ed. 16.75 (ISBN 0-404-00874-7). AMS Pr.

Official & Popular Religion. Ed. by Peter H. Vrijhof & Jacques Waardenburg. (Religion & Society Ser.). 1979. text ed. 38.00x (ISBN 0-686-27030-4). Mouton.

Official Commentary for Sharing the Light of Faith. Berard L. Marthaler. 119p. 1981. pap. 7.50 (ISBN 1-55586-694-8). US Catholic.

Official History of Free Masonry among the Colored People in North America. William H. Grimshaw. LC 74-91257. (Illus.). Repr. of 1903 ed. 22.50x (ISBN 0-8371-2051-9, GRF&, Pub. by Negro U Pr). Greenwood.

Official History of Freemasonry among the Colored People in North America. facs. ed. William H. Grimshaw. LC 74-157370. (Black Heritage Library Collection). 1903. 22.50 (ISBN 0-8369-8808-6). Ayer Co Pubs.

Official Priests of Rome under the Julio-Claudians: A Study of the Nobility from 44 B. C. to 68 A. D. Martha W. Lewis. LC 56-2111. (American Academy in Rome. Papers & Monographs: Vol. 16). pap. 48.00 (2026730). Bks Demand UMI.

Oglala Religion. William K. Powers. LC 76-30614. (Illus.). xxii, 237p. 1977. pap. 6.95 (ISBN 0-8032-8706-2, BB 802, Bison). U of Nebr Pr.

Oglasytel' Nija i Tajnovodstennija Pouchenija. St. Cyril of Jerusalem. Tr. of Prochatechisis & Mystagogical Catechesis. (Rus.). 376p. (Orig.). 1976. 18.00x (ISBN 0-88465-024-3); pap. 13.00x (ISBN 0-88465-025-1). Holy Trinity.

Oglasytel'nija I Tajnovdstvennija Pouchenija Svjatago Kirilma Jerusalimskago. Tr. of Prochatechisis & Mystagogical Catechesis of St. Cyril of Jerusalem. 366p. 18.00 (ISBN 0-317-28884-9); pap. 13.00 (ISBN 0-317-28885-7). Holy Trinity.

Ogun: An Old God for a New Age. Sandra T. Barnes. LC 79-26577. (ISHI Occasional Papers in Social Change: No. 3). 72p. 1980. pap. text ed. 5.95x (ISBN 0-89727-011-8). ISHI PA.

Oh Angry Sea (a-ab-ba hu-luh-ha) The History of a Sumerian Congregational Lament. Raphael Kutscher. LC 74-77343. (Near Eastern Researches Ser.: No. 6). (Illus.). 208p. 1975. 24.50x (ISBN 0-300-01579-8). Yale U Pr.

Oh, Zalmy! Or, the Tale of the Porcelain Pony, Bk. 1. Gitel Kleinbard. (Oh, Zalmy Ser.). (Illus.). 1976. 4.95 (ISBN 0-917274-04-0); pap. 2.95 (ISBN 0-917274-01-6). Mah Tov Pubns.

O'Hair on Prayer. Madalyn O'Hair. 12p. (Orig.). 1980. saddle stiched 1.00 (ISBN 0-910309-30-2). Am Atheist.

Oikos: A Practical Approach to Family Evangelism. Joseph W. Hinkle et al. LC 81-69328. 1982. pap. 4.95 (ISBN 0-8054-6234-1). Broadman.

Ojos de Dios. Evelyn Ely & Phyllis Hughes. (Illus.). 1972. pap. 2.50 (ISBN 0-89013-056-6). Museum NM Pr.

Okinawan Religion: Belief, Ritual, & Social Structure. William P. Lebra. 256p. 1985. pap. text ed. 8.95x (ISBN 0-87022-450-6). Uh Pr.

Oklahoma Delaware Ceremonies, Feasts & Dances. Frank G. Speck. LC 76-43845. (Memoirs of the American Philosophical Sociey: Vol. 7). Repr. of 1937 ed. 21.50 (ISBN 0-404-15696-7). AMS Pr.

Olavus Petri & the Ecclesiastical Transformation in Sweden (1521-1552) A Study in the Swedish Reformation. Conrad J. Bergendoff. LC 83-45600. Date not set. Repr. of 1928 ed. 32.50 (ISBN 0-404-19868-6). AMS Pr.

Old & New in Southern Shona, Independent Churches, Vol. 1: Background & Rise of the Major Movements. M. L. Daneel. (Change & Continuity in Africa Ser). 1971. text ed. 29.60x (ISBN 0-686-22598-8). Mouton.

Old & New Testaments in Muslim Religious Art. T. W. Arnold. (British Academy, London, Schweidr Lectures in Biblical Archaeology Series, 1928). pap. 19.00 (ISBN 0-8115-1270-3). Kraus Repr.

Old Arts & New Theology: The Beginnings of Theology As an Academic Discipline. G. Rosemary Evans. 1980. text ed. 34.95x (ISBN 0-19-826653-7). Oxford U Pr.

Old Babylonian Omen Texts. Albrecht Goetze. LC 79-3537. (Yale Oriental Series: Babylonian Texts: No. 10). (Illus.). 176p. Repr. of 1966 ed. 37.50 (ISBN 0-404-60265-7). AMS Pr.

Old Babylonian Temple Records. Robert J. Lau. (Columbia University. Oriental Studies: No. 3). Repr. of 1906 ed. 15.50 (ISBN 0-404-50493-0). AMS Pr.

Old Believers & the World of Antichrist: The Vyg Community & the Russian State, 1694-1855. Robert O. Crummey. LC 79-98121. (Illus.). 278p. 1970. 30.00x (ISBN 0-299-05560-4). U of Wis Pr.

Old Brethren. James H. Lehman. LC 76-20274. (Illus.). 1976. pap. 2.45 (ISBN 0-87178-650-8). Brethren.

Old Brewery & the New Mission House at the Five Points. Ladies Of The Mission. LC 72-112563. (Rise of Urban America). (Illus.). 1970. Repr. of 1854 ed. 26.50 (ISBN 0-405-02461-4). Ayer Co Pubs.

Old Burma-Early Pagan, 3 Vols. Gordon H. Luce. 1969. 120.00 set (ISBN 0-686-92654-4). J J Augustin.

Old Calendar Orthodox Church of Greece. Archimandrite Chrysostomos et al. 116p. 1985. pap. 4.50 (ISBN 0-911165-05-3). Ctr Trad Orthodox.

Old Cathedral. 2nd ed. Gregory M. Franzwa. LC 80-15885. (Illus.). 1980. 14.95 (ISBN 0-935284-18-4). Patrice Pr.

Old Catholic Missal & Ritual. Tr. by Arnold H. Mathew. LC 73-84708. Repr. of 1909 ed. 27.45 (ISBN 0-404-01949-8). AMS Pr.

Old Catholic Sourcebook. Karl Pruter & J. Gordon Melton. LC 83-47610. 254p. 1983. 39.00 (ISBN 0-8240-9111-6). Garland Pub.

Old Catholics & Anglicans: 1931-81. Ed. by Gordon Huelin. (Illus.). 1983. text ed. 27.50x (ISBN 0-19-920129-3). Oxford U Pr.

Old Christian Right: The Protestant Far Right from the Great Depression to the Cold War. Leo Ribuffo. 277p. 1983. 29.95 (ISBN 0-87722-297-5). Temple U Pr.

Old Christmas. Washington Irving. LC 77-8465. (Illus.). 208p. 1977. Repr. of 1875 ed. 10.00 (ISBN 0-912882-30-1). Sleepy Hollow.

Old Christmas Carols of the Southern Counties. Alice E. Gillington. LC 76-25121. 1976. Repr. of 1910 ed. lib. bdg. 17.50 (ISBN 0-8414-4534-6). Folcroft.

Old Church Slavonic Grammar. rev. ed. Horace G. Lunt. (Slavistic Printings & Reprintings Ser: No. 3). 1974. text ed. 54.00x (ISBN 90-2793-362-6). Mouton.

Old Church Slavonic Kiev Fragment. G. L. Trager. (LM). 1933. pap. 16.00 (ISBN 0-527-00817-6). Kraus Repr.

Old Church Slavonic Translation of the Andron Hagion Biblos in the Edition of Nikolas Van Wijk. D. Armstrong et al. Ed. by C. H. Van Schooneveld. (Slavistic Printings & Reprintings Ser: No. 1). 310p. 1975. text ed. 67.20x (ISBN 90-2793-196-8). Mouton.

Old Churches, Ministers & Families of Virginia, 2 vols. William Meade. Bd. with Digested Index & Genealogical Guide. Jennings C. Wise. Repr. of 1910 ed. LC 65-28854. 1100p. 1978. Repr. of 1857 ed. Set. 50.00 (ISBN 0-8063-0238-0). Genealog Pub.

Old Colony Mennonites: Dilemmas of Ethnic Minority Life. Calvin W. Redekop. LC 69-13192. (Illus.). 302p. 1969. 22.00x (ISBN 0-8018-1020-5). Johns Hopkins.

Old Colony Mennonites: Dilemmas of Ethnic Minority Life. Calvin W. Redekop. LC 69-13192. pap. 80.50 (ISBN 0-317-08392-9, 2021737). Bks Demand UMI.

Old Cornish Crosses. Arthur G. Langdon. 1977. lib. bdg. 134.95 (ISBN 0-8490-2367-X). Gordon Pr.

Old Diary Leaves. Henry S. Olcott. 1973. 7.50 ea. Vol. I (ISBN 0-8356-7106-2). Vol. II (ISBN 0-8356-7123-2). Vol. III (ISBN 0-8356-7480-0). Vol. IV (ISBN 0-8356-7484-3). Vol. V (ISBN 0-8356-7487-8). Vol. VI (ISBN 0-8356-7491-6). Theos Pub Hse.

Old Dominion Addresses & Ceremonies. Inez P. Meekins. 70p. 1975. Repr. of 1972 ed. softcover 1.00 (ISBN 0-88053-312-9, S-417). Macoy Pub.

Old English Bible & Other Essays. Francis C. Gasquet. LC 68-26209. 1969. Repr. of 1897 ed. 28.50x (ISBN 0-8046-0166-6, Pub. by Kennikat). Assoc Faculty Pr.

Old English Christian Epic. George A. Smithson. LC 75-128192. 128p. 1971. Repr. of 1910 ed. 12.50x (ISBN 0-87753-050-5). Phaeton.

Old English Churches: Their Architecture, Furniture, Decorations & Monuments. George Clinch. 1977. lib. bdg. 59.95 (ISBN 0-8490-2368-8). Gordon Pr.

Old English Churches: Their Architecture, Furniture, Decoration & Monuments. George Clinch. LC 77-94552. 1978. Repr. of 1900 ed. lib. bdg. 30.00 (ISBN 0-89341-221-X). Longwood Pub Group.

Old English Homilies & Homiletic Treatises, Pts. I & II. Ed. by Richard Morris. (EETS. OS Ser. I: No. 29, 31). Repr. of 1868 ed. 25.00 (ISBN 0-527-00029-9). Kraus Repr.

Old English Homilies of the 13th Century. Ed. by Richard Morris. (EETS OS Ser. II: No. 53). Repr. of 1873 ed. 30.00 (ISBN 0-527-00048-5). Kraus Repr.

Old English Metrical Psalter: An Annotated Set of Collation Lists with the Psalter Glosses. Sarah L. Keefer. LC 79-7920. (Garland Reference Library of the Humanities). 200p. 1979. lib. bdg. 36.00 (ISBN 0-8240-9538-3). Garland Pub.

Old English Prudentius Glosses at Boulogne-Sur-Mer. Ed. by Herbert D. Meritt. LC 58-7843. (Stanford University. Stanford Studies in Language & Literature: No. 16). Repr. of 1959 ed. 24.00 (ISBN 0-404-51826-5). AMS Pr.

Old English Version of Bede's Ecclesiastical History, Pt. II, No. 1. Ed. by T. Miller. (EETS OS Ser.: Vol. 110). Repr. of 1898 ed. 21.00 (ISBN 0-8115-3368-9). Kraus Repr.

Old English Vision of St. Paul. Ed. by Antonette DiPaolo-Healey. LC 77-89928. 1978. 11.00x (ISBN 0-910956-76-6, SAM 2); pap. 5.00x (ISBN 0-910956-62-6). Medieval Acad.

Old Estonian Folk Religion. Ivar Paulson. LC 76-63029. (Uralic & Altaic Ser: Vol. 108). (Orig.). 1971. pap. text ed. 19.95x (ISBN 0-87750-154-8). Res Ctr Lang Semiotic.

Old European Jewries. David Philipson. LC 74-178586. Repr. of 1895 ed. 27.50 (ISBN 0-404-56663-4). AMS Pr.

Old Faith & the New Gospels. Albert B. Simpson. pap. 1.25 (ISBN 0-87509-031-1). Chr Pubns.

Old-Fashioned Christmas in Illustration & Decoration. Clarence P. Hornung. (Orig.). 1970. pap. 5.00 (ISBN 0-486-22367-1). Dover.

Old-Fashioned Christmas in Illustration & Decoration. Ed. by Clarence P. Hornung. (Illus.). 15.75 (ISBN 0-8446-0147-0). Peter Smith.

Old Franciscan Missions of California. George W. James. LC 77-91532. 1977. Repr. of 1913 ed. lib. bdg. 25.00 (ISBN 0-89341-321-6). Longwood Pub Group.

Old Indian Temples, Idols & Worship. Eduard F. Herrick. (Illus.). 154p. 1985. Repr. of 1882 ed. 91.45 (ISBN 0-89901-209-4). Found Class Reprints.

Old Jewish Folk Music: The Collections & Writings of Moshe Beregovski. Ed. by Mark Slobin. LC 81-43526. (Illus.). 640p. (Orig.). 1982. 45.00x (ISBN 0-8122-7833-X); pap. 18.95x (ISBN 0-8122-1126-X). U of Pa Pr.

Old John Neptune & Other Maine Indian Shamans. Fannie H. Eckstorm. 209p. 1980. pap. 5.95 (ISBN 0-89101-044-0). U Maine Orono.

Old Landmarkism & the Baptists. Bob L. Ross. 1979. pap. 3.95 (ISBN 0-686-26196-8). Pilgrim Pubns.

Old Law New Life: Ten Commandments & New Testament Faith. Earl F. Palmer. 128p. (Orig.). 1984. pap. 7.95 (ISBN 0-687-28744-8). Abingdon.

Old Log Cabin. (Color-a-Story Bks.). (Illus.). 1985. pap. 0.89 (ISBN 0-89191-993-7). Cook.

Old Low Franconian Psalms & Glosses. Ed. by Robert L. Kyes. LC 69-15843. pap. 42.50 (ISBN 0-317-09363-0, 2051048). Bks Demand UMI.

Old New England Christmas. Kenneth MacIver & William Thomson. (Illus.). 47p. (Orig.). 1980. pap. 3.00 (ISBN 0-88448-019-4). Harpswell Pr.

Old North Trail; or, Life, Legends & Religion of the Blackfeet Indians. Walter McClintock. LC 68-13651. (Illus.). xxvii, 539p. 1968. pap. 11.50 (ISBN 0-8032-5130-0, BB 379, Bison). U of Nebr Pr.

Old Paths: Being Plain Statements on Some of the Weightier Matters of Christianity. John C. Ryle. 553p. 1977. 12.95 (ISBN 0-227-67821-4). Attic Pr.

Old Priest Remembers, Eighteen Ninety-Two to Nineteen Seventy-Eight. 2nd ed. John K. Sharp. 1978. 10.00 (ISBN 0-682-49183-7). Exposition Pr FL.

Old Protestantism & the New: Essays on the Reformation Heritage. B. A. Gerrish. LC 82-2730. 400p. 1983. lib. bdg. 38.00x (ISBN 0-226-28869-2). U of Chicago Pr.

Old Religion in the Brave New World: Reflections on the Relation Between Christendom & the Republic. Sidney Mead. LC 76-24588. (Jefferson Memorial Lectures). 1977. 16.95x (ISBN 0-520-03322-1). U of Cal Pr.

Old St. Andrews Music Book. facsimile ed. James H. Baxter. LC 70-178515. (Medieval Studies Ser.). Repr. of 1931 ed. 34.50 (ISBN 0-404-56525-5). AMS Pr.

Old St. Patrick's: New York's First Cathedral. Mary P. Carthy. (Monograph Ser.: No. 23). (Illus.). 1947. 10.00x (ISBN 0-930060-05-9). US Cath Hist.

Old St. Thomas' at Poplar Neck, Bardstown, Kentucky. William J. Howlett. (Illus.). 200p. 1971. pap. 3.25 (ISBN 0-913228-02-8). R J Liederbach.

Old Salem in Pictures. Frances Griffin. (Illus.). 64p. 1986. pap. 5.95 (ISBN 0-914875-10-8). Bright Mtn Bks.

Old Stories for a New Time. James Limburg. LC 82-49019. 127p. 1983. pap. 8.95 (ISBN 0-8042-0148-X). John Knox.

Old Synagogues of Turkey: A Pictorial Narrative. Don A. Halperin. LC 86-50586. (Illus.). 73p. (Orig.). 1987. pap. text ed. 9.95x (ISBN 0-932269-89-3). Wyndham Hall.

Old Tales for a New Day: Early Answers to Life's Eternal Questions. Sophia L. Fahs & Alice Cobb. LC 80-84076. (Library of Liberal Religion). (Illus.). 1980. 11.95 (ISBN 0-87975-138-X); tchr's manual 9.95 (ISBN 0-87975-131-2). Prometheus Bks.

Old Testament. Stanley A. Cook. 1936. 39.50 (ISBN 0-8274-3060-4). R West.

Old Testament. Melnick. (Book Note). 1985. pap. 2.50 (ISBN 0-8120-3531-3). Barron.

Old Testament: A Beginning Survey. Dane R. Gordon. (Illus.). 400p. 1985. pap. text ed. 23.33 (ISBN 0-13-634031-8). P-H.

Old Testament: A Guide to Its Writings. Hans W. Wolff. Tr. by Keith R. Crim from Gr. LC 73-79010. 160p. (Orig.). 1973. pap. 4.95 (ISBN 0-8006-0169-6, 1-169). Fortress.

Old Testament: An Introduction. Otto Eissfeldt. LC 65-15399. 1965. 14.95xi (ISBN 0-06-062171-0, RD162, HarpR). Har-Row.

Old Testament: An Introduction. Rolf Rendtorff. Tr. by John Bowden. LC 85-47728. (Ger.). 1986. 22.95 (ISBN 0-8006-0750-3). Fortress.

Old Testament & Criticism. Carl E. Armeding. 144p. 1983. pap. 6.95 (ISBN 0-8028-1951-6). Eerdmans.

Old Testament & Related Studies. Hugh Nibley. LC 85-27544. (Collected Works of Hugh Nibley Ser.). 304p. 1986. 15.95 (ISBN 0-87579-032-1). Deseret Bk.

Old Testament & the Archaeologist. H. Darrell Lance. Ed. by Gene M. Tucker. LC 80-2387. (Guides to Biblical Scholarship: Old Testament Ser.). 112p. (Orig.). 1981. pap. 4.50 (ISBN 0-8006-0467-9, 1-467). Fortress.

Old Testament & the Historian. J. Maxwell Miller. Ed. by Gene M. Tucker. LC 75-10881. (Guides to Biblical Scholarship: Old Testament Ser.). 96p. 1976. pap. 4.50 (ISBN 0-8006-0461-X, 1-461). Fortress.

Old Testament Bible History. Alfred Edersheim. 1972. 24.95 (ISBN 0-8028-8028-2). Eerdmans.

Old Testament Books for Pastor and Teacher. Brevard S. Childs. LC 76-52457. 120p. 1977. pap. 4.95 (ISBN 0-664-24120-4). Westminster.

Old Testament Canon of the New Testament Church. Roger Beckwith. 536p. 1986. 35.00 (ISBN 0-8028-3617-8). Eerdmans.

Old Testament Characters. Raymond O. Corvin. (Alpha & Omega Bible Studies). 94p. (Orig.). 1986. pap. text ed. 5.95 (ISBN 0-89221-136-9). New Leaf.

Old Testament Charts. M. Ross Richards & Marie C. Richards. pap. 1.95 (ISBN 0-87747-447-8). Deseret Bk.

Old Testament Commentaries, 10 vols. Carl F. Keil & Franz Delitzsch. Incl. Vol. 1. Pentateuch (ISBN 0-8028-8035-5); Vol. 2. Joshua - Second Samuel (ISBN 0-8028-8036-3); Vol. 3. First Kings - Esther (ISBN 0-8028-8037-1); Vol. 4. Job (ISBN 0-8028-8038-X); Vol. 5. Psalms (ISBN 0-8028-8039-8); Vol. 6. Proverbs - Song of Solomon (ISBN 0-8028-8040-1); Vol. 7. Isaiah (ISBN 0-8028-8041-X); Vol. 8. Jeremiah-Lamentations (ISBN 0-8028-8042-8); Vol. 9. Ezekiel-Daniel (ISBN 0-8028-8043-6); Vol. 10. Minor Prophets (ISBN 0-8028-8044-4). 1971. Repr. Set. 225.00 (ISBN 0-8028-8034-7); 22.50 ea. Eerdmans.

Old Testament Commentary Survey. 2nd ed. John Goldingay. Ed. by Robert Hubbard & Mark L. Branson. 66p. 1981. pap. 3.50 (ISBN 0-8308-5499-1). Inter-Varsity.

Old Testament Criticism in the Nineteenth Century. John W. Rogerson. LC 84-47933. 448p. 1985. 29.95 (ISBN 0-8006-0737-6, 1-737). Fortress.

Old Testament Digest: Gen-Deut, Vol. 1. William MacDonald & Mike Hamel. 1981. pap. 7.50 (ISBN 0-937396-59-1). Walterick Pubs.

Old Testament Digest: Vol. 2, Joshua - Esther. William MacDonald & Mike Hamel. 1982. pap. 8.50 (ISBN 0-937396-61-3). Walterick Pubs.

Old Testament Digest: Vol. 3, Job-Malachi. William MacDonald. 1981. pap. 7.50 (ISBN 0-937396-29-X). Walterick Pubs.

Old Testament Dramas. Hersey E. Spence. LC 74-175994. 1976. Repr. of 1936 ed. 15.50 (ISBN 0-404-06176-1). AMS Pr.

Old Testament Exegesis: A Primer for Students & Pastors. 2nd, rev. & enl. ed. Douglas Stuart. LC 84-10431. 142p. 1984. pap. 7.95 (ISBN 0-664-24559-5). Westminster.

Old Testament Express. Terry Hall. 160p. 1985. pap. 3.95 (ISBN 0-88207-599-3). Victor Bks.

Old Testament Faith. John W. Drane. LC 86-45075. (Illus.). 224p. (Orig.). 1986. pap. 10.95 (ISBN 0-06-062064-1, HarpR). Har-Row.

Old Testament Form Criticism. Ed. by John H. Hayes. LC 72-97351. (Trinity University Monograph Series in Religion: Vol. 2). pap. 77.50 (ISBN 0-317-28182-8, 2022566). Bks Demand UMI.

Old Testament Friends: Men of Courage. Robert G. Fulbright. (BibLearn Ser.). (Illus.). 1979. 5.95 (ISBN 0-8054-4251-0, 4242-51). Broadman.

Old Testament: God's People-Our Story. DeVere Ramsay. LC 84-51829. (Illus.). 1985. 12.95 (ISBN 0-8358-0500-X). Upper Room.

Old Testament Healings. Gordon Lindsay. (Miracles in the Bible Ser.: Vol. 1). 0.95 (ISBN 0-89985-179-7). Christ Nations.

Old Testament Highlights: Survey of the Hebrew Scriptures. Jim Townsend. (Bible Mastery Ser.). 144p. 1987. pap. 5.95 (ISBN 1-55513-847-0). Cook.

Old Testament History. Charles F. Pfeiffer. 1973. 22.95 (ISBN 0-8010-6945-9). Baker Bk.

Old Testament History. William Smith. Ed. by Wilbur Fields. LC 78-1072. (Bible Study Textbook Ser.). (Illus.). 1967. Repr. of 1901 ed. 17.50 (ISBN 0-89900-001-0). College Pr Pub.

Old Testament History. G. W. Wade. 1904. lib. bdg. 20.00 (ISBN 0-8482-9973-6). Norwood Edns.

Old Testament Illustrations. Clifford M. Jones. LC 76-142131. (Cambridge Bible Commentary on the New English Bible, Old Testament Ser.). (Illus.). 1971. 29.95 (ISBN 0-521-08007-X); pap. 12.95 (ISBN 0-521-09646-4). Cambridge U Pr.

Old Testament in Art. Rena N. Coen. LC 77-84410. (Fine Art Books). (Illus.). 1970. PLB 5.95 (ISBN 0-8225-0168-6). Lerner Pubns.

Old Testament in Contemporary Preaching. Walter C. Kaiser, Jr. 1973. pap. 6.95 (ISBN 0-8010-5331-5). Baker Bk.

Old Testament in the Gospel Passion Narratives. Douglas J. Moo. xii, 468p. 1983. text ed. 29.95x (ISBN 0-907459-28-5, Pub. by Almond Pr England); pap. text ed. 17.95x (ISBN 0-907459-29-3). Eisenbrauns.

Old Testament in the New: An Argument for Biblical Inspiration. S. Lewis Johnson. (Contemporary Evangelical Perspectives Ser.). 128p. (Orig.). 1980. pap. 4.95 (ISBN 0-310-41851-8, 18244P). Zondervan.

Old Testament in the New Testament Church. Michael Pomazansky. 40p. (Orig.). 1977. pap. 2.00 (ISBN 0-317-30281-7). Holy Trinity.

Old Testament Journeys in Faith. Megan McKenna & Darryl Ducote. LC 78-71528. (Followers of the Way Ser.: Vol. 1). 1979. 22.50 (ISBN 0-8091-9542-9); 7.50 (ISBN 0-8091-7666-1). Paulist Pr.

Old Testament Law. Dale Patrick. LC 84-4418. 228p. (Orig.). 1984. 15.95 (ISBN 0-8042-0133-1). John Knox.

Old Testament Light. George M. Lamsa. LC 84-48774. 1008p. 1985. 34.95 (ISBN 0-06-064924-0, HarpR); pap. 19.95 (ISBN 0-06-064925-9, HarpR). Har-Row.

Old Testament Made Easy. Julie C. Tatham. LC 85-90957. (Illus.). 720p. 1985. 25.00 (ISBN 0-682-40263-X). Exposition Pr FL.

Old Testament Made Easy. Julie C. Tatham. (Illus.). 540p. (Orig.). 1986. limp leatherette 20.00 (ISBN 0-9617543-0-3). J C Tatham.

Old Testament Manuscripts in the Freer Collection. Henry A. Sanders. Repr. of 1917 ed. 37.00 (ISBN 0-384-38808-6). Johnson Repr.

Old Testament Men of Faith. F. B. Meyer. 1979. pap. 5.95 (ISBN 0-89107-170-9). Good News.

Old Testament Message (Series, 23 vols. 1981. Set. 235.00 (ISBN 0-89453-400-9); Set. pap. text ed. 165.00 (ISBN 0-89453-235-9). M Glazier.

Old Testament Notes. Charles H. Patterson. (Orig.). 1965. pap. 3.25 (ISBN 0-8220-0949-8). Cliffs.

Old Testament of the Early Church: A Study of Canon. A. C. Sundberg, Jr. (Harvard Theological Studies). 1964. 24.00 (ISBN 0-527-01020-0). Kraus Repr.

Old Testament Parsing Guide: Genesis - Esther. Todd Beall & William Banks. (Orig.). 1986. 25.95 (ISBN 0-8024-6315-0). Moody.

Old Testament Priests & the New Priest. Albert Vanhoye. Tr. by Bernard Orchard from Fr. LC 85-2171. (Studies in Scripture: Vol. II). Tr. of Pretres anciens, pretre nouveau selon le nouveau testament. 1986. pap. 24.95 (ISBN 0-932506-38-0). St Bedes Pubns.

Old Testament Prophets Then & Now. James M. Efird. 128p. 1982. pap. 4.95 (ISBN 0-8170-0960-4). Judson.

Old Testament Pseudepigrapha, 2 vols. Ed. by James H. Charlesworth. 1056p. 1986. slipcased set 80.00 (ISBN 0-385-19491-9). Doubleday.

Old Testament Pseudepigrapha & the New Testament. J. Charlesworth. (Society for New Testament Studies Monographs: No. 54). 213p. 1985. 34.50 (ISBN 0-521-30190-4). Cambridge U Pr.

Old Testament Pseudepigrapha: Expansions of the Old Testament & Legends, Wisdom & Philosophical Literature, Prayers, Psalms & Odes, Fragments of Lost Judeo-Hellenistic Words, Vol. II. Ed. by James H. Charlesworth. 1056p. 1985. 40.00 (ISBN 0-385-18813-7). Doubleday.

Old Testament Pseudepigrapha, Vol. I: Apocalyptic Literature & Testaments. Ed. by James H. Charlesworth. LC 80-2443. 1056p. 1983. 40.00 (ISBN 0-385-09630-5). Doubleday.

Old Testament Quotations in the New Testament: A Complete Survey. Gleason L. Archer & G. C. Chirichigno. 1983. 21.95 (ISBN 0-8024-0236-4). Moody.

Old Testament Quotations in the New Testament. 2nd, rev. ed. Ed. by Robert G. Bratcher. LC 84-8493. (Helps for Translators Ser.). xii, 80p. 1984. flexible bdg. 2.60x (ISBN 0-8267-0029-2, 08530, Pub. by United Bible). Am Bible.

Old Testament Roots for New Testament Faith. Robert L. Cate. LC 80-70914. 1982. pap. 7.95 (ISBN 0-8054-1220-4). Broadman.

Old Testament Roots of Our Faith. Paul J. Achtemeier & Elizabeth Achtemeier. LC 78-14659. 160p. 1979. pap. 5.95 (ISBN 0-8006-1348-1, 1-1348). Fortress.

Old Testament Royalty: History of a Nation. Ed. by Gary Wilde. (Basic Bible Ser.). 96p. 1986. pap. 4.95 (ISBN 0-89191-481-1). Cook.

Old Testament Speaks. 3rd ed. Samuel J. Schultz. LC 80-7740. (Illus.). 448p. 1980. 17.95xi (ISBN 0-06-067134-3, HarpR). Har-Row.

Old Testament Stories: For Church & Home. Elaine M. Ward. 70p. (Orig.). 1984. pap. 6.95 (ISBN 0-940754-19-3). Ed Ministries.

Old Testament Story. 2nd ed. John H. Tullock. (Illus.). 432p. 1987. text ed. 28.67 (ISBN 0-13-633892-5). P-H.

Old Testament: Student Text. James Black. LC 82-70087. (Illus.). 160p. (Orig.). 1982. pap. 4.95 (ISBN 0-87793-248-4). Ave Maria.

Old Testament Study Simplified. new ed. James N. Layne. LC 77-23715. 1978. pap. 3.95 (ISBN 0-87148-656-3). Pathway Pr.

Old Testament Survey. Ken Malmin. 1974. 4.25 (ISBN 0-914936-21-2). Bible Temple.

Old Testament Survey: Law & History. rev. ed. Samuel J. Schultz. LC 64-10037. 96p. 1968. pap. text ed. 4.95 (ISBN 0-910566-01-1); Perfect bdg. instr's. guide 5.95 (ISBN 0-910566-20-8). Evang Tchr.

Old Testament Survey: Poetry & Prophecy. rev. ed. Clarence H. Benson. 96p. 1972. pap. text ed. 4.95 (ISBN 0-910566-02-X); Perfect bdg. instr's. guide 5.95 (ISBN 0-910566-21-6). Evang Tchr.

Old Testament Survey: The Message, Form, & Background of the Old Testament. W. S. La Sor & David A. Hubbard. 698p. 1982. 24.95 (ISBN 0-8028-3556-2). Eerdmans.

Old Testament: Teacher's Manual. James Black. 80p. (Orig.). 1982. tchrs. ed. 2.25 (ISBN 0-87793-249-2). Ave Maria.

Old Testament Theology, 2 vols. Gerhard Von Rad. LC 62-7306. Vol. 1. S.D. 17.95 (ISBN 0-06-068930-7, HarpR); Vol. 2. 16.95 (ISBN 0-06-068931-5, HarpR). Har-Row.

Old Testament Theology: Basic Issues in the Current Debate. rev. ed. Gerhard F. Hasel. 168p. 1975. pap. 5.95 (ISBN 0-8028-1478-6). Eerdmans.

Old Testament Theology in a Canonical Context. Brevard S. Childs. LC 85-45503. 272p. 1986. 16.95 (ISBN 0-8006-0772-4, 1-772). Fortress.

Old Testament Theology in Outline. Walther Zimmerli. Tr. by David Green. Tr. of Grundriss der Alttestamentlichen Theologie. 258p. 1978. pap. 12.95 (ISBN 0-567-22353-1, Pub. by T&T Clark Ltd UK). Fortress.

Old Testament Theology: Its History & Development. John H. Hayes & Frederick Prussner. LC 84-47798. 336p. 1984. pap. 15.95 (ISBN 0-8042-0146-3). John Knox.

Old Testament Times. Roland K. Harrison. (Illus.). 1970. 16.95 (ISBN 0-8028-3334-9). Eerdmans.

Old Testament Times. Michael Rakel & Maryann Bremke. 1984. 9.95 (ISBN 0-89837-099-X, Pub. by Pflaum Press). Peter Li.

Old Testament Tithing versus New Testament Giving. James E. Baldwin, Sr. 1984. 6.95 (ISBN 0-317-03291-7). Vantage.

Old Testament Translation. Helen Spurrell. 840p. 1987. 29.95 (ISBN 0-8254-3757-1). Kregel.

Old Testament Truth Sermons by Jesus. Daniel G. Samuels. pap. 12.50 (ISBN 0-686-34378-6). New Age Min Spiritualist.

Old Testament Truth Sermons on Jeremiah by Jesus. Daniel G. Samuels. pap. 5.00 (ISBN 0-686-12713-7). New Age Min Spiritualist.

Old Testament Wisdom: An Introduction. James L. Crenshaw. LC 80-82183. 262p. 1981. 16.95 (ISBN 0-8042-0143-9); pap. 12.95 (ISBN 0-8042-0142-0). John Knox.

Old Testament Writings: History, Literature, Interpretation. James M. Efird. LC 81-82352. (Biblical Foundations Ser.). (Illus.). 324p. 1982. pap. 11.95 (ISBN 0-8042-0145-5). John Knox.

Old Testment & Christian Preaching. Hans W. Wolff. Tr. by Margaret Kohl. LC 85-45477. 112p. 1986. pap. 8.95 (ISBN 0-8006-1905-6, 1-1905). Fortress.

Old Thinking, New Thinking. 2nd ed. F. Inayat-Khan. 256p. 1985. cancelled. Hunter Hse.

Old-Time Parson. P. H. Ditchfield. 342p. 1980. Repr. of 1908 ed. lib. bdg. 35.00 (ISBN 0-89760-130-0). Telegraph Bks.

Old Time Power. Vinson Synan. 6.95 (ISBN 0-911866-67-1). Advocate.

Old Time Religion. Fred Hanson. 1986. pap. 1.00 (ISBN 0-89265-099-0). Randall Hse.

Old Wine in Old Bottles. Joseph R. Narot. pap. 0.75 (ISBN 0-686-15809-1). Rostrum Bks.

Older People Have Choices: Information for Decisions about Health, Home, & Money. Nancy Manser. 32p. (Orig.). 1984. pap. 3.95 (ISBN 0-8066-2098-6, 10-4741). Augsburg.

Oldest Christian People. William C. Emhardt & G. M. Lamsa. LC 71-126651. Repr. of 1926 ed. 14.50 (ISBN 0-404-02339-8). AMS Pr.

Oldest God: Archaic Religion Yesterday & Today. Denise L. Carmody. LC 80-25499. 192p. (Orig.). 1981. pap. 7.50 (ISBN 0-687-28813-4). Abingdon.

Oldest Story in the World. Sekiya Miyoshi. Ed. by Barbara L. Jensh. LC 69-18145. (Illus.). 5.95 (ISBN 0-8170-0436-X). Judson.

Olive Tree Connection: Sharing Israel's Messiah. John Fischer. LC 83-12645. 192p. (Orig.). 1983. pap. 8.95 (ISBN 0-87784-848-3). Inter-Varsity.

Oliver Cromwell. John Buchan. 1957. 25.00 (ISBN 0-8274-3062-0). R West.

Oliver Cromwell. Samuel R. Gardiner. 1977. Repr. of 1909 ed. 25.00x (ISBN 0-7158-1181-9). Charles River Bks.

Oliver Cromwell. Frederic Harrison. 228p. 1980. Repr. of 1915 ed. lib. bdg. 25.00 (ISBN 0-8495-2293-5). Arden Lib.

Oliver Cromwell. Frederic Harrison. LC 78-39196. (Select Bibliographies Reprint Ser.). Repr. of 1888 ed. 18.00 (ISBN 0-8369-6798-4). Ayer Co Pubs.

Oliver Cromwell. Frederic Harrison. 1973. Repr. of 1888 ed. lib. bdg. 25.00 (ISBN 0-8414-5006-4). Folcroft.

Oliver Cromwell. John Morley. 1977. Repr. of 1900 ed. lib. bdg. 25.00 (ISBN 0-8492-1850-0). R West.

Oliver Cromwell & His Times. Hilda Johnstone. 92p. 1981. Repr. lib. bdg. 20.00 (ISBN 0-89987-430-4). Darby Bks.

Oliver Cromwell & the English People. facsimile ed. Ernest Barker. LC 72-37329. (Select Bibliographies Reprint Ser). Repr. of 1937 ed. 12.00 (ISBN 0-8369-6674-0). Ayer Co Pubs.

Oliver Cromwell: Pretender, Puritan, Statesman, Paradox? Ed. by John F. New. LC 76-23190. (European Prob. Studies Ser.). 128p. 1977. pap. text ed. 5.95 (ISBN 0-88275-457-2). Krieger.

Oliver Cromwell: The Man & His Mission. J. Allanson Picton. 1978. Repr. of 1883 ed. lib. bdg. 40.00 (ISBN 0-8482-2126-5). Norwood Edns.

Olmec Religion: A Key to Middle America & Beyond. Karl W. Luckert. LC 75-12869. (The Civilization of the American Indian: Vol. 137). (Illus.). 200p. 1976. 14.95x (ISBN 0-8061-1298-0). U of Okla Pr.

Om: Creative Meditations. Alan Watts. LC 79-54101. 160p. 1984. pap. 6.95 (ISBN 0-89087-257-0). Celestial Arts.

Om! Meditation & Tranquility. 5.95 (ISBN 0-88088-456-8). Peter Pauper.

OMA. Georgia Smelser. LC 85-31579. (Illus.). 254p. (Orig.). 1981. pap. 5.95 (ISBN 0-912315-16-4). Word Aflame.

Omaha Tribal Myths & Tricksters Tales. Roger L. Welsch. LC 80-22636. x, 285p. 1981. 21.95 (ISBN 0-8040-0700-4, SB). Ohio U Pr.

Omens from the Flight of Birds: The First 101 Days of Jimmy Carter. Ed. by Stephen Vincent. (Illus.). 1978. pap. 4.95x (ISBN 0-917672-05-4). Momos.

Omission of the Holy Spirit from Reinhold Niebuhr's Theology. Rachel H. King. LC 64-13324. 209p. 1964. 6.95 (ISBN 0-8022-0865-7). Philos Lib.

Omnipotence & Other Theological Mistakes. Charles Hartshorne. LC 83-6588. 144p. 1983. 34.50 (ISBN 0-87395-770-9); pap. 9.95x (ISBN 0-87395-771-7). State U NY Pr.

Omnipotence, Covenant & Order: An Excursion in the History of Ideas from Abelard to Leibniz. Francis Oakley. LC 83-45945. 168p. 1984. 18.50x (ISBN 0-8014-1631-0). Cornell U Pr.

Omnipotent Light Revealed: Wisdom of the Kabbalah. Levi Krakovsky. 4.00 (ISBN 0-686-13335-8). Yesod Pubs.

Omraam Mikhael Aivanhov: Master of the Great Universal White Brotherhood. Agnes Lejbowicz. (Testimonials Ser.). 115p. (Orig.). 1982. pap. 4.95 (ISBN 2-85566-191-9, Pub. by Prosveta France). Prosveta USA.

On a Wild & Windy Mountain: And 25 other Mediations for the Christian Year. William H. Willimon. 144p. 1984. pap. 8.95 (ISBN 0-687-28846-0). Abingdon.

On Art & Architecture. Paul Tillich. Ed. by John Dillenberger & Jane Dillenberger. (Illus.). 272p. 1987. 14.50 (ISBN 0-8245-0829-7). Crossroad NY.

On Becoming a Catholic: The Challenge of Christian Initiation. Regis A. Duffy. LC 84-47721. 176p. (Orig.). 1984. pap. 7.95 (ISBN 0-06-062106-0, RD 525, HarpR). Har-Row.

On Becoming a Musical Mystical Bear: Spirituality American Style. Matthew Fox. LC 75-34842. 192p. 1976. pap. 4.95 (ISBN 0-8091-1913-7). Paulist Pr.

On Becoming Christian. 2nd ed. Henri Bourgeois. 160p. 1985. pap. 6.95 (ISBN 0-89622-270-5). Twenty-Third.

On Becoming Married: The Art of a Loving Marriage. Gerald Weiss. LC 81-85262. 108p. (Orig.). 1982. pap. 2.95 (ISBN 0-87973-664-X, 664). Our Sunday Visitor.

On Becoming Whole in Christ: An Interpretation of the Spiritual Exercises. John F. Sheehan. 1978. pap. 3.95 (ISBN 0-8294-0278-0). Loyola.

On Behalf of Children. Linda Isham. LC 74-17842. 48p. (Orig.). 1975. pap. 1.95 (ISBN 0-8170-0666-4). Judson.

On Being a Christian & a Lawyer. Thomas L. Shaffer. LC 80-25215. 288p. 1981. 12.95 (ISBN 0-8425-1833-9). Brigham.

On Being a Deacon's Wife. Martha Nelson. LC 72-96150. 96p. 1973. 7.95 (ISBN 0-8054-3505-0). Broadman.

On Being a Deacon's Wife: Study Guide. Martha Nelson. LC 72-96150. 1977. saddlewire 2.25 (ISBN 0-8054-3507-7). Broadman.

On Being Catholics. Charles Connolly. 96p. 1983. pap. 5.00 (ISBN 0-912414-37-5). Lumen Christi.

On Being Family: Essays on a Social Theology of the Family. Ray S. Anderson & Dennis B. Guernsey. 192p. (Orig.). 1986. pap. 9.95 (ISBN 0-8028-1990-7). Eerdmans.

On Being Human. Paul E. More. 1978. Repr. of 1936 ed. lib. bdg. 25.00 (ISBN 0-8414-2308-3). Folcroft.

On Being Human: Essays in Theological Anthropology. Ray S. Anderson. 234p. (Orig.). 1982. pap. 9.95 (ISBN 0-8028-1926-5). Eerdmans.

On Being Human: Principles of Ethics. Andrew C. Varga. LC 78-51589. 160p. 1978. pap. 3.95 (ISBN 0-8091-2111-5). Paulist Pr.

On Being Human Religiously. 2nd ed. James L. Adams. Ed. by Max L. Stackhouse. 1986. pap. 10.95 (ISBN 0-933840-29-2, Skinner Hse Bks). Unitarian Univ.

On Being Involved. Adrian Van Kaam. 2.95 (ISBN 0-87193-039-0). Dimension Bks.

On Being Present Where You Are. Douglas V. Steere. LC 67-12913. (Orig.). 1967. pap. 2.50x (ISBN 0-87574-151-7, 151). Pendle Hill.

On Being Real. Scott Crom. LC 67-29811. (Orig.). 1967. pap. 2.50x (ISBN 0-87574-155-X, 155). Pendle Hill.

On Being Yourself. Adrian Van Kaam. 6.95 (ISBN 0-87193-038-2). Dimension Bks.

On Both Sides of the Wall. Vladka Meed. Tr. by Steven Meed. LC 78-71300. (Illus.). 304p. 1979. 16.95 (ISBN 0-89604-012-7); pap. 10.95 (ISBN 0-89604-013-5). Holocaust Pubns.

On Call. Lois Rowe. 1984. 8.95 (ISBN 0-8010-7724-9). Baker Bk.

On Catechesis in Our Time. 100p. 1976. pap. 3.95 (ISBN 1-55586-654-9). US Catholic.

On Christian Doctrine. Saint Augustine. Tr. by D. W. Robertson, Jr. LC 58-9956. 1958. pap. 7.20 scp (ISBN 0-672-60262-8). Bobbs.

On Christian Doctrine: Augustine. W. Robertson. 1958. pap. text ed. write for info. (ISBN 0-02-402150-4). Macmillan.

On Christian Faith. Edward Schillebeeckx. 128p. 1987. 12.95 (ISBN 0-8245-0827-0). Crossroad NY.

On Christian Faith: The Spiritual, Ethical & Political Dimensions. Edward Schillebeeckx. 1987. 12.95. Crossroad NY.

On Christian Joy. Pope Paul VI. 1975. pap. 0.30 (ISBN 0-8198-0448-7). Dghtrs St Paul.

On Christian Truth. Harry Blamires. 168p. (Orig.). pap. 4.95 (ISBN 0-89283-130-8). Servant.

On Common Ground: The Boston Jewish Community 1649-1980. (Illus.). 1981. 6.00 (ISBN 0-911934-19-7). Am Jewish Hist Soc.

On Death & Dying. Peter Noll. 1987. price not set (ISBN 0-670-80703-6). Viking.

On del Clouds to China (J. Hudson Taylor) Cyril Davey. 1964. pap. 2.95 (ISBN 0-87508-617-9). Chr Lit.

On Divine Predicates & Their Attributes. Al-Ghazzali. 1970. 6.50x (ISBN 0-87902-057-1). Orientalia.

On Divorce. John MacArthur, Jr. (John MacArthur's Bible Studies). 1985. pap. 3.50 (ISBN 0-8024-5111-X). Moody.

On Earth As It Is... Gladys S. Lewis. LC 83-70006. (Orig.). 1983. pap. 6.50 (ISBN 0-8054-6332-1). Broadman.

On Earth As It Is in Heaven: Jews, Christians, & Liberation Theology. Dan Cohn-Sherbok. LC 86-23509. 128p. (Orig.). 1987. pap. 7.95 (ISBN 0-88344-410-0). Orbis Bks.

On Earth Peace. Ed. by Donald F. Durnbaugh. 1978. pap. 9.95 (ISBN 0-87178-660-5). Brethren.

On Equal Terms: Jews in America 1881-1981. Lucy S. Dawidowicz. 1984. pap. 6.95 (ISBN 0-03-071058-8). H Holt & Co.

On Essence. Xavier Zubiri. LC 78-68067. pap. 132.30 (2029514). Bks Demand UMI.

On Evangelization in the Modern World. Pope Paul Sixth. 70p. 1975. pap. 2.95 (ISBN 1-55586-129-6). US Catholic.

On Evangelization in the Modern World. Pope Paul VI. 1976. pap. text ed. 0.40 (ISBN 0-8198-0409-6). Dghtrs St Paul.

On Exodus: An Evangelical & Popular Commentary. George V. Pixley. Tr. by Robert R. Barr from Span. 256p. (Orig.). 1987. 19.95 (ISBN 0-88344-560-3); pap. 9.95 (ISBN 0-88344-559-X). Orbis Bks.

On Fire for God. Darlene Loomis. (Illus.). 53p. (Orig.). 1976. 2.00 (ISBN 0-686-36274-8). Drain Enterprise.

On Fire with the Spirit. John Bertolucci & Fred Lilly. 140p. (Orig.). 1984. pap. 4.95 (ISBN 0-89283-193-6). Servant.

On Free Choice of the Will. Saint Augustine. Tr. by A. S. Benjamin & L. H. Hackstaff. LC 63-16932. (Orig.). 1964. pap. 7.20 scp (ISBN 0-672-60368-3, LLAS150). Bobbs.

On Free Choice of the Will: Augustine. A. Benjamin & L. H. Hackstaff. 1964. pap. text ed. write for info. (ISBN 0-02-308030-2). Macmillan.

On Gide's Promethee: Private Myth & Public Mystification. Kurt Weinberg. LC 70-173760. (Princeton Essays in Literature Ser.). 144p. 1972. 22.50x (ISBN 0-691-06222-6). Princeton U Pr.

On Glory Roads: A Pilgrims Book about Pilgrimages. Eleanor Munro. LC 86-50231. (Illus.). 286p. 1987. pap. 17.95 (ISBN 0-500-24127-9). Thames Hudson.

On God & Man. John Calvin. Ed. by F. W. Strothmann. LC 56-7500. (Milestones of Thought Ser.). 1965. o.p 6.00 (ISBN 0-8044-5214-8); pap. 3.95 (ISBN 0-8044-6073-6). Ungar.

On God & Political Duty: Calvin. John T. McNeil. 1956. pap. text ed. write for info. (ISBN 0-02-379760-6). Macmillan.

On Growing Older. Eugene C. Bianchi. 176p. 1985. pap. 9.95 (ISBN 0-8245-0700-2). Crossroad NY.

On Guilt & Innocence: Essays in Legal Philosophy & Moral Psychology. Herbert Morris. 1976. pap. 3.95 (ISBN 0-520-03944-0, 434). U of Cal Pr.

On Guilt, Responsibility & Punishment. Alf Ross. LC 73-94446. 1974. 33.00x (ISBN 0-520-02717-5). U of Cal Pr.

On Having No Head: Zen & the Rediscovery of the Obvious. rev. ed. D. E. Harding. (Illus.). 96p. 1986. pap. 4.95 (ISBN 0-317-40544-6). Methuen Inc.

On His Way. Larry Powell. 1984. 5.00 (ISBN 0-89536-681-9, 4857). CSS of Ohio.

On Holy Ground. Kirkie Morrissey. 144p. (Orig.). 1983. pap. 4.95 (ISBN 0-89109-051-7). NavPress.

On Holy Images. Damascenus Joannes. Tr. by Mary H. Allies from Greek. 1977. pap. 2.95 (ISBN 0-686-19232-X). Eastern Orthodox.

On Hope. Josef Pieper. Tr. by Mary F. McCarthy from Ger. LC 85-82177. Orig. Title: Uber die Hoffnung. 99p. (Orig.). 1986. pap. 6.95 (ISBN 0-89870-067-1). Ignatius Pr.

On Human Dignity: Political Theology & Ethics. Jurgen Moltmann. Tr. by M. Douglas Meeks from Ger. LC 83-48913. 240p. 1984. 15.95 (ISBN 0-8006-0715-5, 1-715). Fortress.

On Human Work. Pope John Paul II. 62p. 1981. pap. 3.95 (ISBN 1-55586-825-8). US Catholic.

On Jesus' Team. Wesley T. Runk. Ed. by Michael L. Sherer. (Orig.). 1986. pap. 5.25 (ISBN 0-89536-809-9, 6838). CSS of Ohio.

On Jews & Judaism in Crisis: Selected Essays. Gershom Scholem. Ed. by Werner J. Dannhauser. LC 75-37010. 1978. 16.50 (ISBN 0-8052-3613-9). Schocken.

On Job: God-Talk & the Suffering of the Innocent. Gustavo Gutierrez. Tr. by Matthew O'Connell from Span. LC 87-5661. Tr. of Hablar de Dios desde el Sufrimento del Inocente. 144p. (Orig.). 1987. 10.95 (ISBN 0-88344-577-8); pap. 8.95 (ISBN 0-88344-552-2). Orbis Bks.

On Jordan's Stormy Banks: Religion in the South (A Southern Exposure Profile) Ed. by Samuel S. Hill, Jr. LC 82-14524. vi, 160p. 1982. pap. 11.95 (ISBN 0-86554-035-7, MUP-P10). Mercer Univ Pr.

On Judaism. Martin Buber. Ed. by Nahum Glatzer. LC 67-28091. 256p. 1972. pap. 7.50 (ISBN 0-8052-0343-5). Schocken.

On Justifying Moral Judgements. Lawrence C. Becker. (International Library of Philosophy & Scientific Method). 199p. 1973. text ed. 19.95x (ISBN 0-7100-7524-3, Pub. by Routledge UK). Humanities.

On Knowing God. Jerry H. Gill. LC 81-10481. 174p. 1981. pap. 9.95 (ISBN 0-664-24380-0). Westminster.

On Law, Morality, & Politics. St. Thomas Acquinas. Ed. by Richard J. Regan & William P. Baumgarth. (HPC Classics Ser.). 300p. 1987. 27.50 (ISBN 0-87220-032-9); pap. text ed. 7.95 (ISBN 0-87220-031-0). Hackett Pub.

On Liturgical Theology. Aidan Kavanagh. 216p. (Orig.). 1984. pap. 9.95 (ISBN 0-916134-67-9). Pueblo Pub Co.

On Love. Ishwar C. Puri. Ed. by Edward D. Scott. 28p. (Orig.). 1984. pap. 2.00 (ISBN 0-937067-03-2). Inst Study Hum Aware.

On Love & Happiness. Pierre Teilhard de Chardin. LC 83-48979. 96p. 1984. 9.45 (ISBN 0-06-068151-9, HarpR). Har-Row.

On Loving God: Selections from Sermons by St. Bernard of Clairvaux. St. Bernard de Clairvaux. Ed. by Hugh Martin. LC 79-8706. (Treasury of Christian Bks.). 125p. 1981. Repr. of 1959 ed. lib. bdg. 22.50x (ISBN 0-313-20787-9, BEOL). Greenwood.

On Moral Character: A Practical Guide to Aristotle's Virtues & Vices. Jody Palmour. 350p. (Orig.). 1986. 29.00 (ISBN 0-9616203-1-5); pap. 18.00 (ISBN 0-9616203-0-7). Archon Inst Leader Dev.

On Moral Medicine: Theological Perspectives in Medical Ethics. Ed. by Stephen E. Lammers & Allen Verhey. 680p. 1987. 35.00 (ISBN 0-8028-3629-1). Eerdmans.

On Mortality. St. Cyprian. pap. 1.50 (ISBN 0-686-05658-2). Eastern Orthodox.

On My Back, Looking Up! Evelyn Orser. Ed. by Richard W. Coffen. LC 83-13882. (Banner Bk.). (Illus.). 94p. (Orig.). 1984. pap. 5.95 (ISBN 0-8280-0218-5). Review & Herald.

On My Own. Tom Eisenman. (Family Ministry Ser.). (Illus.). 54p. 1985. pap. text ed. 19.95 (ISBN 0-89191-978-3). Cook.

On Nature. Ed. by Leroy S. Rouner. LC 84-7502. (Boston University Studies in Philosophy & Religion: Vol. 6). 224p. 1984. text ed. 20.95 (ISBN 0-268-01499-X, 85-14994). U of Notre Dame Pr.

On New Creation. B. D. Napier. LC 70-134553. (Rockwell Lectures). 1971. 14.95x (ISBN 0-8071-0524-4). La State U Pr.

On Our Father's Knee: Devotions for Times of Illness. Fredrik Wisloff. LC 72-90264. 144p. 1973. pap. 5.95 (ISBN 0-8066-1309-2, 10-4765). Augsburg.

On Our Spiritual Journey: A Creative Shabbat Service. Ed. by Jackie Tolley. (Illus.). 74p. (Orig.). 1984. pap. 5.95 (ISBN 0-9608054-3-5). Womans Inst-Cont Jewish Ed.

On Our Way. Richard Reichert. (New Creation Ser.). 96p. 1985. pap. text ed. 4.25 (ISBN 0-697-01995-0); tchr's. ed. 4.50 (ISBN 0-697-01996-9). Wm C Brown.

On Our Way Rejoicing. Ingrid Trobisch. LC 64-20195. (Harper Jubilee Book). 256p. 1976. pap. 3.95i (ISBN 0-06-068451-8, HJ-25, HarpR). Har-Row.

On Our Way Rejoicing. Ingrid Trobisch. 240p. (Orig.). 1986. pap. 6.95 (ISBN 0-8423-4745-3). Tyndale.

On Our Way to Christmas: A Family Activity Book for Advent. Mary P. Warren. 32p. (Orig.). 1980. pap. 4.95 (ISBN 0-8066-1784-5, 10-4768). Augsburg.

On Pascha & Fragments. Melito. Ed. by Stuart G. Hall. (Oxford Early Christian Texts). 1979. text ed. 34.95x (ISBN 0-19-826811-4). Oxford U Pr.

On Pilgrimage with Father Ralph Diorio: Following the Footpaths of Faith through the Holyland, Rome & Lourdes. Catherine Odell. LC 85-7083. (Illus.). 192p. 1986. 16.95 (ISBN 0-385-19908-2). Doubleday.

On Prayer. St. John of Kronstadt. (Orig.). 1985. pap. 3.00 (ISBN 0-317-30263-9). Holy Trinity.

On Prayer: The Lord's Prayer in Today's World. Gerhard Ebeling. Tr. by James W. Leitch. LC 78-5079. pap. 27.80 (2026853). Bks Demand UMI.

On Preaching. Robert L. Dabney. 1979. 11.95 (ISBN 0-85151-290-9). Banner of Truth.

On Religion. Karl Marx & Friedrich Engels. LC 82-17032. (Classics in Religious Studies). 384p. 1982. Repr. of 1964 ed. 10.50x (ISBN 0-89130-599-8, 01 05 03). Scholars Pr GA.

On Religion: Shi'ism & on Islam, Bk. 1. Ahmad Kasravi. Ed. by Mohammad A. Jazayery. Tr. by M. R. Ghanoonparvar from Persian. 180p. Date not set. lib. bdg. write for info. (ISBN 0-939214-39-3); pap. text ed. write for info. (ISBN 0-939214-42-3). Mazda Pubs.

On Religion: Speeches to Its Cultured Despisers. Friedrich Schleiermacher. pap. 8.95x (ISBN 0-06-130036-5, TB36, Torch). Har-Row.

On Religion: Speeches to Its Cultured Despisers. Friedrich Schleiermacher. 18.25 (ISBN 0-8446-2878-6). Peter Smith.

On Religious Maturity. Merlyn Belanger. LC 61-15238. 1962. 5.95 (ISBN 0-8022-0090-7). Philos Lib.

On St. Basil the Great. LC 79-20045. (Word & Spirit Ser.: Vol. I). 1979. pap. 4.95 (ISBN 0-932506-07-0). St Bedes Pubns.

On St. Benedict. LC 80-25958. (Word & Spirit Ser.: Vol. II). 1980. pap. 6.00 (ISBN 0-932506-09-7). St Bedes Pubns.

On Shumuel Hugo Bergman's Philosophy. Ed. by A. Zvie Bar-On. 134p. 1986. pap. 19.95x (ISBN 90-6203-947-2, Pub. by Rodopi Holland). Humanities.

On Speaking out of the Silence: Vocal Ministry. Douglas V. Steere. LC 72-182983. 24p. (Orig.). 1972. pap. 2.50x (ISBN 0-87574-182-7). Pendle Hill.

On Striving to Be a Muslim. A. Qayyum. pap. 12.50 (ISBN 0-686-63908-1). Kazi Pubns.

On Tangled Paths. George MacDonald. Ed. by Dan Hamilton. 288p. 1987. pap. 5.95 (ISBN 0-89693-791-7). Victor Bks.

On the Anvil. Max Lucado. 128p. 1985. pap. 4.95 (ISBN 0-8423-4738-0). Tyndale.

On the Art of Teaching from the Initiatic Point of View. Omraam M. Aivanhov. (Complete Works: Vol. 29). (Illus.). 245p. 1981. pap. 9.95 (ISBN 2-85566-142-0). Prosveta USA.

On the Basis of Morality. Arthur Schopenhauer. Tr. by E. F. Payne. LC 65-26525. (Orig.). 1965. pap. write for info. (ISBN 0-02-392400-4, LLA203). Macmillan.

On the Bible: Eighteen Studies. Martin Buber. Ed. by Nahum N. Glatzer. LC 81-16555. 288p. 1982. 17.95x (ISBN 0-8052-3796-8); pap. 7.95 (ISBN 0-8052-0691-4). Schocken.

On the Brink of the Absolute. Subramuniya. pap. 1.00 (ISBN 0-87516-359-9). De Vorss.

On the Christian Meaning of Human Suffering. 48p. 1984. pap. 3.95 (ISBN 1-55586-919-X). US Catholic.

On the Church of Christ: The Person of the Church & Her Personnel. Jacques Maritain. Tr. by Joseph W. Evans from Fr. LC 73-11559. Orig. Title: De l'Eglise Du Christ. (Eng. & Fr.). 352p. 1973. text ed. 24.95 (ISBN 0-268-00519-2); pap. text ed. 8.95x (ISBN 0-268-00525-7). U of Notre Dame Pr.

On the Crest of the Wave: Becoming a World Christian. C. Peter Wagner. LC 83-8616. 1983. pap. 5.95 (ISBN 0-8307-0895-2, 5418015). Regal.

On the Crest of the Wave: Leader's Guide. Janet Hermansen. LC 83-8616. 64p. 1985. pap. 3.95 (ISBN 0-8307-1010-8, 6101974). Regal.

On the Diction of Tennyson, Browning & Arnold. Bernard Groom. LC 79-138975. 57p. 1970. Repr. of 1939 ed. 14.50 (ISBN 0-208-01027-0, Archon). Shoe String.

On the Dignity of Man. Giovanni Pico Della Mirandola. Tr. by Charles G. Wallis et al. Bd. with On Being & Unity; Heptaplus. LC 65-26540. 1965. pap. 7.87 scp (ISBN 0-672-60483-3, LLA227). Bobbs.

On the Divine Images: St. John of Damascus. Tr. by David Anderson from Greek. LC 80-13409. 106p. 1980. pap. 4.95 (ISBN 0-913836-62-1). St Vladimirs.

On the Divine Liturgy. St. Germanus of Constantinople. Tr. by Paul Meyendorff from Gr. LC 84-27615. 107p. 1984. pap. text ed. 4.95 (ISBN 0-88141-038-1). St Vladimirs.

On the Divine Liturgy: Orthodox Homilies, Vol. 1. Asterios Gerostergios. Tr. by Augoustinos N. Kantiotes. LC 85-81949. (Illus.). 274p. 1986. 13.95 (ISBN 0-914744-72-0). Inst Byzantine.

On the Divine Liturgy: Orthodox Homilies, Vol. 2. Augoustinos N. Kantiotes. Tr. by Asterios Gerostergios. (Illus.). 285p. 1986. 14.95 (ISBN 0-914744-73-9). Inst Byzantine.

On the Doctrine of the Modernists. Pope Pius X. 1973. pap. 0.50 (ISBN 0-8198-0248-4). Dghtrs St Paul.

On the Duties of Brotherhood. Al-Ghazali. 7.95 (ISBN 0-686-83895-5). Kazi Pubns.

On the Duties of Brotherhood in Islam. Al-Ghazali. Tr. by Muhtar Holland from Arabic. 95p. (Orig.). 1980. pap. 4.95 (ISBN 0-86037-068-2, Pub. by Islamic Found UK). New Era Pubns MI.

On the Edge of a Truth. Ed. & intro. by Nancy Thomas. 112p. (Orig.). pap. 4.50 (ISBN 0-913342-25-4). Barclay Pr.

On the Edge of Destruction: Jews in Poland Between the Two World Wars. Celia Heller. LC 76-22646. (Illus.). 1977. 36.00x (ISBN 0-231-03819-4). Columbia U Pr.

On the Edge of Destruction: Jews of Poland Between the Two World Wars. Celia S. Heller. LC 79-24645. 384p. 1980. pap. 8.95 (ISBN 0-8052-0651-5). Schocken.

On the Edge of Politics: The Roots of Jewish Political Thought in America. William S. Berlin. (Contributions in Political Science Ser.: No. 14). 1978. lib. bdg. 29.95x (ISBN 0-313-20422-5, BEP/). Greenwood.

On the Edge of the Primeval Forest & More from the Primeval Forest: Experiences & Observations of a Doctor in Equatorial Africa. Albert Schweitzer. LC 75-41244. (Illus.). 1976. Repr. of 1948 ed. 18.50 (ISBN 0-404-14598-1). AMS Pr.

On the Elevation of the Poor: A Selection from His Reports As Minister at Large in Boston. Joseph Tuckerman. LC 79-137190. (Poverty U. S. A. Historical Record Ser). 1971. Repr. of 1874 ed. 15.00 (ISBN 0-405-03128-9). Ayer Co Pubs.

On the Eternal in Man. Max F. Scheler. Tr. by Bernard Noble. LC 72-6599. 480p. 1972. Repr. of 1960 ed. 35.00 (ISBN 0-208-01280-X, Archon). Shoe String.

On the Family. 93p. 1981. pap. 3.95 (ISBN 1-55586-833-9). US Catholic.

On the Genealogy of Morals. Friedrich Nietzsche. Tr. by Walter Kaufman. Bd. with Ecce Homo. 1967. pap. 4.76 (ISBN 0-394-70401-0, Vin). Random.

On the Glaubenslehre: Two Letters to Dr. Lucke. Friedrich Schleiermacher. Ed. by James A. Massey. Tr. by James Duke & Francis S. Fiorenza. LC 80-20717. (American Academy of Religion, Texts & Translations Ser.: No. 3). Orig. Title: Sendschreiben Uber Seine Glaubenslehre an Lucke. 1981. pap. 9.95 (ISBN 0-89130-420-7, 01-02-03). Scholars Pr GA.

On the Gleaming Way: Navajos, Eastern Pueblos, Zunis, Hopis, Apaches & Their Land, & Their Meanings to the World. John Collier. LC 62-12407. 163p. (Photos, Orig). 1962. pap. 5.95 (ISBN 0-8040-0232-0, SB). Ohio U Pr.

On the Harmony of Religion & Philosophy. G. F. Hourani. 128p. 1976. 25.00x (ISBN 0-317-39133-X, Pub. by Luzac & Co Ltd). State Mutual Bk.

On the Highroad of Surrender. Frances J. Roberts. 1973. 6.95 (ISBN 0-932814-14-X); pap. 4.95 (ISBN 0-932814-15-8). Kings Farspan.

On the Holy Spirit. St. Basil The Great. Tr. by David Anderson from Gr. LC 80-25502. 118p. (Orig.). 1980. pap. 4.95 (ISBN 0-913836-74-5). St Vladimirs.

On the Holy Spirit & on Prayer. LC 81-9305. (Word & Spirit Ser.: Vol. 3). (Orig.). 1981. pap. 6.00 (ISBN 0-932506-15-1). St Bedes Pubns.

On the Imagination. Giovanni Pico della Mirandola. Tr. & notes by Harry Caplan. LC 72-113063. (Lat. & Eng.). ix, 102p. Repr. of 1930 ed. lib. bdg. 22.50x (ISBN 0-8371-4703-4, PIOI). Greenwood.

On the Impact of Morality in Our Times. Bernard M. Bane. 113p. 1985. pap. 5.00 (ISBN 0-317-20545-5). BMB Pub Co.

On the Incarnation of the Word. Saint Athanasius. pap. 2.95 (ISBN 0-686-25556-9). Eastern Orthodox.

On the Incomprehensible Nature of God. John Chrysostom. Tr. by Paul W. Harkins from Greek. LC 83-1984. (Fathers of the Church Ser.: No. 72). 357p. 1984. 29.95x (ISBN 0-8132-0072-5). Cath U Pr.

On the Independence of Matthew & Mark. J. M. Rist. LC 76-40840. (Society for New Testament Studies Monographs: No. 22). 1978. 24.95 (ISBN 0-521-21476-9). Cambridge U Pr.

On the Invocation of the Name of Jesus. Lev Gillet. 1985. pap. 4.95 (ISBN 0-87243-133-9). Templegate.

On the Job: The Christian Nine to Five. Fred Catherwood. 192p. 1983. pap. 5.95 (ISBN 0-310-37261-5). Zondervan.

On the Kabbalah & Its Symbolism. Gershom Scholem. LC 65-11575. 1969. pap. 6.95 (ISBN 0-8052-0235-8). Schocken.

On the Knowledge of Good & Evil. Philip B. Rice. LC 75-8968. 299p. 1975. Repr. of 1955 ed. lib. bdg. 22.50x (ISBN 0-8371-8124-0, RIGE). Greenwood.

On the Life of the Soul. Rudolf Steiner. Ed. by Gisela O'Neil & Alan Howard. Tr. by Samuel L. Borton. 18p. (Orig.). 1985. pap. 3.50 (ISBN 0-88010-076-1). Anthroposophic.

On the Means Which Conduce to True Philosophy & on the True Philosopher. Emmanuel Swedenborg. Tr. by Augustus Clissold from Lat. 42p. pap. 1.00 (ISBN 0-915221-15-2). Swedenborg Sci Assn.

On the Mormon Frontier: The Diary of Hosea Stout, 2 Vols. Ed. by Juanita Brooks. 832p. 1982. Repr. of 1964 ed. 39.95 (ISBN 0-87480-214-8, SET). U of Utah Pr.

On the Morning of Christ's Nativity: Milton's Hymn with Illustrations by William Blake. John Milton. Ed. by Geoffrey Keynes. LC 77-22296. (Illus.). Repr. of 1923 ed. lib. bdg. 12.50 (ISBN 0-8414-9917-9). Folcroft.

On the Mother: The Chronicle of a Manifestation & Ministry, 2 vols. K. R. Iyengar. 1979. pap. 45.00 (ISBN 0-89744-947-9). Auromere.

On the Move with Jesus. Wesley T. Runk. 1984. 4.50 (ISBN 0-89536-670-3, 1511). CSS of Ohio.

On the Move with the Master: A Daily Devotional Guide on World Mission. Duain W. V. ow. LC 76-57679. 1977. 4.95 (ISBN 0-87808-155-0). William Carey Lib.

On the Mysteries. Iamblichus. Tr. by Thomas Taylor from Greek. LC 81-50200. (Secret Doctrine Reference Ser.). Tr. of Iamblichus on the Mysteries. 400p. 1984. Repr. of 1895 ed. 20.00 (ISBN 0-913510-51-3). Wizards.

On the Nature of Suicide. Ed. by Edwin S. Shneidman. LC 78-92890. (Jossey-Bass Behavioral Science Ser.). pap. 40.00 (ISBN 0-317-08618-9, 2013857). Bks Demand UMI.

On the Original Inhabitants of Bharatavarsa or India. Gustav Oppert. Ed. by Kees W. Bolle. (Mythology Ser.). 1978. Repr. of 1893 ed. lib. bdg. 55.00x (ISBN 0-405-10557-6). Ayer Co Pubs.

On the Philosophy of Religion. Yitzhak J. Guttmann. Tr. by David V. Herman from Hebrew. 134p. 1976. text ed. 25.00x (Pub. by Magnes Pr Israel). Humanities.

On the Poetry of Matthew Arnold: Essays in Critical Reconstruction. William E. Buckler. (Gotham Library). 228p. 1982. 35.00x (ISBN 0-8147-1039-5). NYU Pr.

On the Poetry of Matthew Arnold, Robert Browning & Rabindranath Tagore. Amulyachandra Aikat. 1978. lib. bdg. 37.00 (ISBN 0-8495-0053-2). Arden Lib.

On the Poetry of Matthew Arnold, Robert Browning & Rabindranath Tagore. Amulyachandra Aikat. LC 72-13660. 1972. Repr. of 1921 ed. lib. bdg. 20.00 (ISBN 0-8414-1237-5). Folcroft.

On the Political System of the Islamic State. M. S. El-Awa. pap. 4.50. Am Trust Pubns.

On the Preparation & Delivery of Sermons. 4th ed. John A. Broadus. Rev. by Vernon L. Stanfield. LC 78-20602. 1979. 7.95 (ISBN 0-06-061112-X, HarpR). Har-Row.

On the Relations Between the Physical & Moral Aspects of Man, Vol. I. Pierre J. Cabanis. Tr. by Margaret D. Saidi. LC 80-21694. pap. 112.00 (ISBN 0-317-08229-9, 2019949). Bks Demand UMI.

On the Road with Jesus. Tom Tozer. 1980. 3.95 (ISBN 0-89536-415-8, 1526). CSS of Ohio.

On the Shores of the Infinite. G. Stuart. pap. 4.95 (ISBN 0-910122-34-2). Amherst Pr.

On the Sociology of Islam. 3rd ed. Ali Shari'ati. Tr. by Hamid Algar from Persian. LC 79-83552. 1980. 15.95 (ISBN 0-933782-01-2); pap. 5.95 (ISBN 0-933782-00-4). Mizan Pr.

On the Subject of Tongues: From the New Testament. Don Welborn. 56p. pap. 0.50 (ISBN 0-937396-48-6). Walterick Pubs.

On the Theology of Work: Aspects of the Teaching of the Founder of Opus Dei. Jose L. Illanes. Tr. by Michael Adams from Span. Tr. of La Santification del Trabajo. 107p. (Orig.). 1983. pap. 3.95 (ISBN 0-906127-56-4). Scepter Pubs.

On the Third Day. Georges Chevrot. 208p. 1961. 5.95 (ISBN 0-933932-10-3); pap. 2.95 (ISBN 0-933932-11-1). Scepter Pubs.

On the Threshold of God's Future. John H. Westerhoff, III & Caroline A. Hughes. 160p. (Orig.). 1986. pap. 7.95 (ISBN 0-06-254781-X, HarpR). Har-Row.

On the Trail of Process. Lester Mann. 592p. 1979. 46.00 (ISBN 0-8089-1137-6, 792678). Grune.

On the Trail of the UCC. Goddard. 1981. pap. 8.95 (ISBN 0-8298-0353-X). Pilgrim NY.

On the Trial of Jesus. 2nd ed. Paul Winter. Ed. by T. A. Burkill & G. Vermes. (Studia Judaica, Vol. 1). 1973. 31.00x (ISBN 3-11-002283-4). De Gruyter.

On the Way! David R. Currie. LC 81-69403. 1982. pap. 3.95 (ISBN 0-8054-5336-9, 4253-36). Broadman.

On Theology. Schubert M. Ogden. 180p. 1986. 19.50 (ISBN 0-86683-529-6, HarpR). Har-Row.

On This Day We Will Pray: Prayers for Sunday Through Saturday. Ed. by Bibliotheca Press Research Division Staff. 7p. 1986. pap. 1.75 (ISBN 0-939476-19-3, Pub. by Biblio Pr GA). Prosperity & Profits.

On This Rock I Stand. Vance Havner. 160p. 1986. pap. 5.95 (ISBN 0-8010-4296-8). Baker Bk.

On Tiptoe with Love. John T. Seamands. (Direction Bk). pap. 1.95 (ISBN 0-8010-7991-8). Baker Bk.

On to the World of "Freedom": A Kantian Meditation on Finite Selfhood. Francisco L. Peccorini. LC 82-40233. 370p. (Orig.). 1982. lib. bdg. 30.25 o. p. (ISBN 0-8191-2643-8); pap. text ed. 15.75 (ISBN 0-8191-2644-6). U Pr of Amer.

On Trial: Being a Summary of Eyewitness Reports Concerning the Early Church. Luke the Physician. LC 82-60668. (Illus.). 120p. 1982. pap. 3.25 (ISBN 0-87973-648-8, 648). Our Sunday Visitor.

On Truth: An Ontological Theory. Eliot Deutsch. LC 79-12754. 1979. text ed. 14.00x (ISBN 0-8248-0615-8). UH Pr.

On Understanding Human Sexuality. William May & John Harvey. (Synthesis Ser). 1978. pap. 1.50 (ISBN 0-8199-0720-0). Franciscan Herald.

On Understanding Islam. Wilfred C. Smith. (Religion & Reason Ser.: No. 19). 352p. 1984. 55.50 (ISBN 90-279-3448-7); pap. 19.95 (ISBN 3-11-010020-7). Mouton.

On Value. L. Dumont. (Radcliffe-Brown Lectures on Social Anthropology). 1980. pap. 4.00 (ISBN 0-85672-239-1, Pub. by British Acad). Longwood Pub Group.

On War, Abortion & the Homeless. (Sermon Ser.: No. 1). 18p. 1982. pap. 2.00 (ISBN 0-936384-10-7). Cowley Pubns.

On Wealth & Poverty. St. John Chrysostom. Tr. by Catharine P. Roth from Gr. LC 84-22920. 140p. 1984. pap. text ed. 5.95 (ISBN 0-88141-039-X). St Vladimirs.

On Wings of Healing. Ronald Crabtree. 80p. 1986. 21.00X (ISBN 0-7223-2002-7, Pub. by A H Stockwell England). State Mutual Bk.

On Women. Sri Aurobindo Ashram Publications Department Staff & Sri Aurobindo. 126p. (Orig.). Date not set. pap. 6.00 (ISBN 0-89744-236-9, Pub. by Sri Aurobindo Ashram Trust India). Auromere.

On Women & Judaism: A View from Tradition. Blu Greenberg. LC 81-11779. 192p. 1983. pap. 5.95 (ISBN 0-8276-0195-6, 482). Jewish Pubns.

On Yoga II: Letters on Yoga Tome I. Sri Aurobindo. 1979. 15.00 (ISBN 0-89744-911-8). Auromere.

On Your Mark. William Coleman. LC 79-16458. 112p. 1979. pap. 4.95 (ISBN 0-87123-490-4, 210490). Bethany Hse.

On Yuan Chwang's Travels in India 629-645 A. D. Thomas Watters. LC 74-158213. Repr. of 1905 ed. Set. 45.00 (ISBN 0-404-06878-2). AMS Pr.

On Zen Practice: Foundations of Practice. Ed. by Hakuyu T. Maezumi & Bernard T. Glassman. LC 76-9463. (Zen Writings Ser.: Vol. 1). (Illus.). 1976. pap. 5.00 (ISBN 0-916820-02-5). Center Pubns.

Once a Doctor, Always a Doctor: The Memoirs of a German-Jewish Immigrant Physician. Heinz Hartmann. 130p. Date not set. 18.95 (ISBN 0-87975-342-0). Prometheus Bks.

Once More Astonished: The Parables of Jesus Christ. Jan Lambrecht. 262p. 1981. pap. 9.95 (ISBN 0-8245-0093-8). Crossroad NY.

Once Saved Always Saved. J. E. Elliott. 74p. (Orig.). 1986. pap. 2.25 (ISBN 0-934942-62-5, 4115). White Wing Pub.

Once Saved, Always Saved. R. T. Kendall. (Orig.). 1985. pap. 3.95 (ISBN 0-8024-6064-X). Moody.

Once Saved...Always Saved. new ed. Perry Lassiter. LC 74-15289. 98p. 1975. pap. 3.75 (ISBN 0-8054-1931-4). Broadman.

Once There Was a Hassid. Devorah Omer. (Illus.). 28p. 1987. 9.95 (ISBN 0-915361-73-6, Dist. by Watts). Adama Pubs Inc.

Once to Every Man & Nation: Stories about Becoming a Baha'i. Randie Gotlieb & Steven Gotlieb. 160p. 1985. pap. 5.95 (ISBN 0-85398-211-2). G Ronald Pub.

Once to Sinai. Hilda F. Prescott. LC 78-63358. (Crusades & Military Orders: Second Ser.). Repr. of 1957 ed. 27.00 (ISBN 0-404-17028-5). AMS Pr.

Once upon a Bible Time. Etta B. Degering. Ed. by Bobbie J. Van Dolson. LC 76-14118. (Illus.). 1976. 7.95 (ISBN 0-8280-0052-2). Review & Herald.

Once upon a Christmas. James D. Freeman. LC 78-53345. (Illus.). 1978. 6.95 (ISBN 0-87159-119-7). Unity School.

Once upon a Christmas. Oxtoby & Sandison. 1986. 14.95 (ISBN 0-8120-5755-4). Barron.

Once upon a Christmas Time. Thyra F. Bjorn. 1964. 5.95 (ISBN 0-03-047195-8). H Holt & Co.

Once upon a Christmas Time: Stories for a Family Christmas. John R. Aurelio. (Illus.). 224p. 1986. pap. 8.95 (ISBN 0-8091-2819-5). Paulist Pr.

Once upon a Parable: Dramas for Worship & Religious Education. Michael E. Moynahan. (Orig.). 1984. pap. 8.95 (ISBN 0-8091-2586-2). Paulist Pr.

Once upon a Rainbow. Cecilia Marchand. (Illus.). 128p. 1986. 8.95 (ISBN 0-89962-558-4). Todd & Honeywell.

Once upon a Summer. 1987. 5.95 (210413). Bethany Hse.

Once upon a Tree. Calvin Miller. 1978. pap. 3.95 (ISBN 0-8010-6050-8). Baker Bk.

Once upon an Eternity. David Edman. LC 83-62515. 108p. 1984. pap. 6.95 (ISBN 0-89390-052-4). Resource Pubns.

ONE. Orest. LC 76-47223. (Orig.). 1977. pap. 4.95 (ISBN 0-89407-002-9). Strawberry Hill.

One a Day: An Anthology of Jewish Historical Sketches for Everyday of the Year. 20.00 (ISBN 0-88125-108-9). Ktav.

One & Two Samuel. Robert P. Gordon. (Old Testament Guides Ser.). 102p. 1984. pap. text ed. 3.95x (ISBN 0-905774-64-7, Pub. by JSOT Pr England). Eisenbrauns.

One & Two Thessalonians: Hope of His Coming. Ed. by Gary Wilde. (Basis Bible Ser.). 96p. 1986. pap. 4.95 (ISBN 0-89191-520-6). Cook.

One Body, One Spirit, One Lord. Gordon Lindsay. pap. 3.95 (ISBN 0-89985-991-7). Christ Nations.

One Bread & Cup: Source of Communion. Ernest Falardeau. 1987. pap. 7.95. M Glazier.

One Day in Paradise. Helme Heine. LC 85-72492. (Illus.). 32p. 1986. 12.95 (ISBN 0-689-50394-6, McElderry Bk). Macmillan.

One Day in the Life of Christ. Harry E. Klinger. 96p. 1987. 6.95 (ISBN 0-8059-3042-6). Dorrance.

ONE-drous Light. Ruth M. Bublitz. 128p. (Orig.). 1985. pap. 5.95 (ISBN 0-87516-556-7). De Vorss.

One Faith, One Church, Man, Many Moralities, Vol. 150. Ed. by Jacques Pohier & Dietmar Mieth. (Concilium 1981). 128p. (Orig.). 1981. pap. 6.95 (ISBN 0-8164-2350-4, HarpR). Har-Row.

One Family under God. Ed. by Daughters of St. Paul. (Divine Master Ser.). (Orig.). 1968. 3.00 (ISBN 0-8198-0109-7); pap. 2.00 (ISBN 0-8198-0110-0). Dghtrs St Paul.

One Flesh. Donald L. Kline. 1985. 4.95 (ISBN 0-89536-730-0, 5814). CSS of Ohio.

One Flesh, One Heart: Putting Celestial Love into Your Temple Marriage. Carlfred Broderick. LC 85-29329. 101p. 1986. 8.95 (ISBN 0-87579-010-0). Deseret Bk.

One Followed by Eternity of Zeros. Ali Shariati. Tr. by A. Asghar Ghasemy. 23p. 1980. pap. 1.00 (ISBN 0-941722-15-5). Book-Dist-Ctr.

One God. Jerry Palmer. (Contemporary Poets of Dorrance Ser.). 88p. 1981. 4.95 (ISBN 0-8059-2789-1). Dorrance.

One God or Three. LC 78-51674. 1978. pap. 2.50 (ISBN 0-915540-19-3). Friends Israel-Spearhead Pr.

One God or Three? Stanley Rosenthal. 1978. pap. text ed. 2.25 (ISBN 0-87508-464-8). Chr Lit.

One Gospel: Taken Literally from the Four Gospels in the Authorized King James Version of the Bible. Ed. by R. Louis Pryor. LC 85-42545. 381p. 1985. 29.95x (ISBN 0-89950-184-2); pap. 19.95x (ISBN 0-89950-192-3). McFarland & Co.

One Hand upon Another. Sallie Chesham. (Illus.). 160p. (Orig.). 1978. pap. 1.50 (ISBN 0-89216-016-0). Salvation Army.

One Holy Passion: The Consuming Thirst to Know God. R. C. Sproul. 1987. 13.95. Nelson.

One Home under God. Jack Taylor. LC 73-91609. 8.95 (ISBN 0-8054-5222-2); study guide 1.00 (ISBN 0-8054-5225-7); guide book 5.00 (ISBN 0-8054-5615-5). Broadman.

One Hundred & Eight Rosebushes: Preaching in Germany. Satsvarupa Das Goswami. Ed. by Mandalesvara dasa & Bimala dasi. (Prabupada-lila Ser.). 44p. (Orig.). 1982. pap. text ed. 2.00 (ISBN 0-911233-04-0). Gita-Nagari.

One Hundred & One Questions & Answers on Demon Powers. Lester Sumrall. 145p. (Orig.). 1983. pap. 3.25 (ISBN 0-89274-261-5). Harrison Hse.

One Hundred & One Questions People Ask Most about Jesus. Don Stewart. 224p. (Orig.). 1987. pap. 5.95 (ISBN 0-8423-4748-8). Tyndale.

One Hundred & One Things to Do During a Dull Sermon. Tim Sims & Dan Pegoda. 85p. (Orig.). pap. 6.95 (ISBN 0-910125-05-8). Youth Special.

One Hundred & One Word Puzzles on the Bible. Emily Filipi. LC 84-21445. 1985. pap. 2.95 (ISBN 0-8054-9110-4). Broadman.

One Hundred & Seventy-Five Sermon Outlines. John L. Mayshack. (Sermon Outline Ser.). 1979. pap. 2.50 (ISBN 0-8010-6085-0). Baker Bk.

One Hundred & Three Questions People Ask about God. Don Stewart. 188p. 1987. pap. 5.95 (ISBN 0-8423-4747-X). Tyndale.

One Hundred & Twenty Dramatic Story Sermons for Children's Church. Marianne Radius. 368p. 1985. pap. 8.95 (ISBN 0-8010-7730-3). Baker Bk.

One Hundred Bible Games. Edith B. Allen. (Paperback Program Ser). (YA) 1968. pap. 3.95 (ISBN 0-8010-0033-5). Baker Bk.

One Hundred Bible Quiz Activities for Church School Classes. James H. Robinson & R. Darline. 1981. pap. 3.95 (ISBN 0-570-03829-4, 12-2794). Concordia.
One Hundred Bible Stories. rev. ed. LC 66-10838. (Illus., King James Ed). 1966. 6.95 (ISBN 0-570-03461-2, 56-1063); wkbk. 3.85 (ISBN 0-570-01519-7, 22-1201). Concordia.
One Hundred Fifty-One Sermon Outlines. Jabez Burns. LC 86-27520. 208p. (Orig.). 1987. pap. 7.95 (ISBN 0-8254-2266-3). Kregel.
One Hundred Forty-Four Thousand on Mt. Zion & the First-Fruits. Gordon Lindsay. (Revelation Ser.). 1.25 (ISBN 0-89985-044-8). Christ Nations.
One Hundred Forty-Nine Sermon Outlines. Jabez Burns. LC 86-27436. 208p. (Orig.). 1987. pap. 7.95 (ISBN 0-8254-2265-5). Kregel.
One Hundred Great Religious Poems. Ed. by Randolph Ray. LC 78-80378. (Granger Index Reprint Ser). 1951. 15.00 (ISBN 0-8369-6060-2). Ayer Co Pubs.
One Hundred Handy Ideas for Busy Teachers. Nancy S. Williamson. (Teaching Helps Ser.). 1980. pap. 2.50 (ISBN 0-8010-9630-8). Baker Bk.
One Hundred New Testament Stories. Norman Bull. 160p. (Orig.). 1984. pap. 7.95 (ISBN 0-687-29073-2). Abingdon.
One Hundred Ninety-Nine Sermon Outlines. Jabez Burns. LC 86-27540. 256p. (Orig.). 1987. pap. 8.95 (ISBN 0-8254-2267-1). Kregel.
One Hundred One Bible Action Games. Erma Reynolds. 64p. 1986. pap. 3.95 (ISBN 0-87403-017-X, 2801). Standard Pub.
One Hundred One Bible Activity Sheets. Betty DeVries. 144p. 1983. pap. 5.95 (ISBN 0-8010-2931-7). Baker Bk.
One Hundred One Hymn Stories. Kenneth W. Osbeck. LC 81-17165. 288p. 1982. pap. 8.95 (ISBN 0-8254-3416-5). Kregel.
One Hundred One More Hymn Stories. Kenneth W. Osbeck. LC 84-27847. 328p. (Orig.). 1985. pap. 9.95 (ISBN 0-8254-3420-3). Kregel.
One Hundred One Sermon Outlines. Frank L. Cox. 1971. 3.00 (ISBN 0-88027-028-4). Firm Foun Pub.
One Hundred One Ways to Enrich Your Marriage. William J. Krutza. 144p. 1982. pap. 4.95 (ISBN 0-8010-5452-4). Baker Bk.
One Hundred Percent: Beyond Mediocrity. Fred Hartley. (Illus.). 160p. 1983. pap. 5.95 (ISBN 0-8007-5112-4, Power Bks). Revell.
One Hundred Percent Christian. C. S. Lovett. 1970. pap. 4.25 (ISBN 0-938148-07-9). Personal Christianity.
One Hundred Prison Meditations. Richard Wurmbrand. 1984. pap. 2.95 (ISBN 0-88270-577-6). Bridge Pub.
One Hundred Series Implementation Outline. James D. Craig & Donald E. Hill. 38p. 1980. pap. 9.95 inc. cassettes (ISBN 0-88151-020-3). Lay Leadership.
One Hundred Sermon Outlines from the New Testament. John Phillips. 1979. pap. 4.95 (ISBN 0-8024-7817-4). Moody.
One Hundred Sermon Outlines from the Old Testament. 2nd ed. John Phillips. pap. 4.95 (ISBN 0-8024-7816-6). Moody.
One Hundred Short Prayers. 4th ed. May S. Hilburn. 100p. 1983. pap. 3.50 softcover (ISBN 0-88053-313-7). Macoy Pub.
One Hundred Twenty-Three Questions & Answers: From the Edgar Cayce Readings. rev. ed. Gladys D. Turner & Mae G. St. Clair. 58p. 1974. pap. 3.95 (ISBN 0-87604-073-3). ARE Pr.
One Hundred Ways to Live a Happy & Successful Life. Frank B. Minirth & States Skipper. (Direction Bks.). 1979. pap. 4.95 (ISBN 0-8010-6213-6). Baker Bk.
One Hundred Ways to Obtain Peace: Overcoming Anxiety. Richard L. Flournoy et al. (Life Enrichment Ser.). 1986. pap. 4.95 (ISBN 0-8010-3528-7). Baker Bk.
One Hundred Word Puzzles on the Bible. Emily Filipi. LC 81-68367. 1982. pap. 2.95 (ISBN 0-8054-9107-4). Broadman.
One Hundred Years of Challenge & Change: A History of the Synod of Texas of the United Presbyterian Church in the U. S. A. George H. Paschal, Jr. & Judith A. Benner. LC 68-20488. 259p. 1968. 4.00 (ISBN 0-911536-32-9). Trinity U Pr.
One Hundred Years of Old Testament Interpretation. Ronald E. Clements. LC 76-23236. 160p. 1976. pap. 7.95 (ISBN 0-664-24747-4). Westminster.
One Hundred Years of Oratorio at Augustana: A History of the Handel Oratorio Society, 1881-1980. Conrad Bergendoff. LC 81-52434. (Augustana Historical Society Publication Ser.: No. 29). 54p. 1981. 7.50 (ISBN 0-910184-00-3); pap. 5.00 (ISBN 0-910184-29-1). Augustana.
One Hundred Years of Theosophy. Joy Mills. 245p. (Orig.). 1987. pap. 9.95 (ISBN 0-8356-0235-4). Theos Pub Hse.
One Hundred Years of Thomism: Aeterni Patris & Afterwards - A Symposium. Ed. by Victor B. Brezik. LC 85-14986. 210p. pap. text ed. 9.95 (ISBN 0-9605456-0-3). U of Notre Dame Pr.
One in a Minyan & Other Studies. Max J. Routtenberg. 1979. pap. 6.95x (ISBN 0-87068-342-X). Ktav.
One in Every Other Family. Gordon Lindsay. 1.00 (ISBN 0-89985-016-2). Christ Nations.
One in the Gospel. Friedemann Hebart. 1981. pap. 4.25 (ISBN 0-570-03830-8, 12-2796). Concordia.
One Jesuit's Spiritual Journey: Autobiographical Conversations with Jean-Claude Dietsch, S. J. Pedro Arrupe. Frwd. by George E. Ganss. Tr. by Ruth Bradley. LC 84-81990. Orig. Title: Itineraire d'un Jesuite. Entretiens avec Jean-Claude Dietsch, S. J. 174p. 1986. 10.00 (ISBN 0-912422-69-6); smyth sewn 8.00 (ISBN 0-912422-68-8). Inst Jesuit.
One Life Isn't Enough. Harold W. Roupp. 3.50 (ISBN 0-910924-44-9). Macalester.
One Little Candle. 4th ed. Ruth Adams. 206p. 1981. Repr. of 1966 ed. text ed. 6.50 (ISBN 0-88053-314-5, S-251). Macoy Pub.
One Lives, One Dies. Sri Chinmoy. 81p. 1974. pap. 2.00 (ISBN 0-88497-072-8). Aum Pubns.
One Long War. Netanel Lorch. 1976. 8.00 (ISBN 0-685-82597-3). Herzl Pr.
One Lord, One Church, One Hope, & One God. Ed. by Howard J. Loewen. (Text-Reader Ser.: No. 2). 369p. 1985. pap. text ed. 12.00x (ISBN 0-936273-08-9). Inst Mennonite.
One Man's Destiny. C. R. Dickey. 1942. 8.00 (ISBN 0-685-08811-1). Destiny.
One Man's Journey. Ed. by Kazuo Miyamoto. 120p. (Orig.). 1981. pap. 6.95 (ISBN 0-938474-02-2). Buddhist Study.
One Man's Valor: Leo Baeck & the Holocaust. Anne E. Neimark. (Jewish Biography Ser.). (Illus.). 128p. 1986. 14.95 (ISBN 0-525-67175-7, 01451-440). Lodestar Bks.
One-Minute Bible Stories: New Testament. Shari Lewis & Florence Henderson. LC 86-6401. (Illus.). 48p. 1986. 6.95 (ISBN 0-385-23286-1); PLB 6.95 (ISBN 0-385-23287-X). Doubleday.
One-Minute Bible Stories: Old Testament. Shari Lewis. LC 86-2011. (Illus.). 48p. 1986. 6.95 (ISBN 0-385-19565-6); PLB 6.95 (ISBN 0-385-19566-4). Doubleday.
One-Minute Wisdom. Anthony De Mello. LC 85-29003. 216p. 1986. 14.95 (ISBN 0-385-23585-2). Doubleday.
One More Brown Bag. Jerry M. Jordan. (Illus.). 128p. 1983. pap. 6.95 (ISBN 0-8298-0645-8). Pilgrim NY.
One More River. E. E. Cleveland. Ed. by Gerald Wheeler. 1985. write for info. (ISBN 0-8280-0300-9). Review & Herald.
One Must Die: Six-Week Lenten Drama Series. Ronald Wean. 1986. 6.50 (ISBN 0-89536-794-7, 6812). CSS of Ohio.
One Nation under God. Rus Walton. 240p. 1987. pap. 9.95 (ISBN 0-8407-3093-4). Nelson.
One of a Kind: A Biblical View of Self-Acceptance. M. Blaine Smith. LC 84-574. 140p. 1984. pap. 3.95 (ISBN 0-87784-921-8). Inter-Varsity.
One People. Rev. ed. John Stott. 128p. 1982. pap. 4.95 (ISBN 0-8007-5099-3, Power Bks). Revell.
One People. John R. Stott. LC 84-72468. 127p. pap. 4.95 (ISBN 0-87509-324-8); leader's guide 2.95 (ISBN 0-87509-358-2). Chr Pubns.
One People: A Study in Comparative Judaism. Abraham Segal. Ed. by Bernard M. Zlotowitz. 160p. (Orig.). 1983. pap. text ed. 6.95 (ISBN 0-8074-0169-2, 140025). UAHC.
One Perfect Lover: A Story of the Resurrection. Matthew Ignoffo. LC 86-60171. 200p. 1987. 14.95 (ISBN 0-89390-084-2). Resource Pubns.
One Plus One Equals. Palmer Gedde. Ed. by Mentor Kujath. 1979. pap. 4.95 (ISBN 0-8100-0103-9, 12-1712). Northwest Pub.
One Plus One Equals One. Phyllis J. Le Peau & Andrew T. Le Peau. 96p. (Orig.). 1981. pap. 3.95 (ISBN 0-87784-803-3). Inter-Varsity.
One Season Following Another: A Cycle of Faith. William L. Doty. LC 68-54394. 141p. 1968. 4.50 (ISBN 0-8199-0152-0, L38573). Franciscan Herald.
One Step at a Time. Frances C. Matranga. (Illus.). 1987. pap. 3.95 (ISBN 0-570-03642-9). Concordia.
One Step at a Time. Compiled by Hester Monsma. 86p. 1984. 5.95 (ISBN 0-8010-6177-6). Baker Bk.
One Step Between Death & Me. Victor Houston. (Illus.). 68p. (Orig.). 1986. pap. 9.95 (ISBN 1-55630-019-0). Brentwood Comm.
One Step More, Lord! Opha Bingham & Robert E. Bingham. LC 84-4942. 1984. pap. 7.95 (ISBN 0-8054-5432-2). Broadman.
One Table, Many Laws: Essays on Catholic Eucharistic Discipline. John Huels. 112p. 1986. pap. 5.95 (ISBN 0-8146-1465-5). Liturgical Pr.
One Thousand. Salem Kirban. (Illus.). 1973. pap. 2.95 (ISBN 0-912582-09-X). Kirban.
One Thousand Bible Drill Questions. W. Burgess McCreary. 1980. pap. 1.75 (ISBN 0-87162-263-7, WP#D5899). Warner Pr.
One Thousand Bible Questions in Rhymes, Puzzles, Quizzes & Games. Mildred O. Honors. (Quiz & Puzzle Bks.). pap. 2.95 (ISBN 0-8010-4136-8). Baker Bk.
One Thousand Bible Study Outlines. F. E. Marsh. LC 75-125115. 1970. pap. 12.95 (ISBN 0-8254-3247-2). Kregel.
One Thousand Illustrations for Preaching & Teaching. G. Curtis Jones. 1986. pap. 9.95 (ISBN 0-8054-2249-8). Broadman.
One Thousand Keys to the Truth: Spiritual Guidelines for Latter Days & Second Coming. Mark-Age. LC 75-40976. 156p. 1976. pap. 5.00 (ISBN 0-912322-51-9). Mark-Age.
One Thousand Moons: Krishnamurti at Eighty-Five. Asit Chandmal. (Illus.). 128p. 1985. 25.00 (ISBN 0-8109-1209-0). Abrams.
One Thousand One More Questions on the Bible. Larry Piatt. 96p. 1986. pap. 4.95 (ISBN 0-8010-7094-5). Baker Bk.
One Thousand One Questions on the Bible. Larry Piatt. 50p. 1984. pap. 3.95 (ISBN 0-8010-7085-6). Baker Bk.
One Thousand One Yiddish Proverbs. Fred Kogos. 1970. 5.95 (ISBN 0-8065-0013-1). Citadel Pr.
One Thousand One Yiddish Proverbs. Fred Kogos. 160p. 1974. pap. 3.95 (ISBN 0-8065-0455-2). Citadel Pr.
One Thousand Questions on Genesis. Gussie Lambert. 2.50 (ISBN 0-89315-188-2). Lambert Bk.
One Thousand Years Peace...A Utopia? Wim Malgo. 3.95 (ISBN 0-937422-11-8). Midnight Call.
One Thousand Years: Stories from the History of Christianity in the U. S. S. R., 988-1988. Martin Bailey. 1987. pap. 4.95. Friend Pr.
One-Two Chronicles, Ezra, Nehemiah. Celine Mangan. (Old Testament Message Ser.: Vol. 13). 1982. 12.95 (ISBN 0-89453-413-0); pap. 7.95 (ISBN 0-89453-247-2). M Glazier.
One, Two Samuel: Bible Study Commentary. Howard F. Vos. (Bible Study Commentary Ser.). 1986. pap. 5.95 (ISBN 0-310-33893-X, 11153P). Zondervan.
One, Two, Three, Four, Five, Six, Seven, All Dead Children Go to Heaven. Cora N. Bennett. 32p. 1986. 5.95 (ISBN 0-89962-509-6). Todd & Honeywell.
One, Two, Three, John. R. Alan Culpepper. Ed. by John Hayes. LC 85-42821. (Preaching Guides). 132p. 1985. pap. 6.95 (ISBN 0-8042-3248-2). John Knox.
One, Two, Three John. Curtis Vaughan. (Bible Study Commentary Ser.). 140p. 1984. pap. 4.95 (ISBN 0-310-33563-9). Zondervan.
One Way. Robert L. Brandt. LC 77-75601. (Radiant Life Ser.). 128p. 1977. pap. 2.50 (ISBN 0-88243-909-X, 02-0909); teacher's ed 3.95 (ISBN 0-88243-179-X, 32-0179). Gospel Pub.
One Way Through the Jungle. Ken Nightingale. pap. 2.50 (ISBN 0-85363-107-7). OMF Bks.
One Who Made His Cross. Raymond Council. 1986. 2.95 (ISBN 0-89536-793-9, 6811). CSS of Ohio.
One World: The Interaction of Science & Theology. John Polkinghorne. 128p. 1987. 17.50 (ISBN 0-691-08459-9); pap. 7.95 (ISBN 0-691-02407-3). Princeton U Pr.
One-Year Bible. Kenneth Taylor. 1985. cloth 16.95 (ISBN 0-8423-2431-3); kivar 10.95 (ISBN 0-8423-2428-3). Tyndale.
One Yet Two: Monastic Tradition East & West. Ed. by M. B. Pennington. LC 75-26146. (Cistercian Studies Ser.: No. 29). 1976. 14.95 (ISBN 0-87907-800-6). Cistercian Pubns.
One Young Billion: The Youth For Christ Story-the People, the Promise, & the Hope for Reaching... Dennis E. Hensley & Jim Groen. 224p. Date not set. 10.95 (ISBN 0-8407-5455-8). Nelson.
Oneida Community. A. Eastlake. 69.95 (ISBN 0-8490-0769-0). Gordon Pr.
Oneida Community: A Record of an Attempt to Carry Out the Principles of Christian Unselfishnes & Scientific Race-Improvement. Allan Estlake. LC 72-4179. Repr. of 1900 ed. 11.50 (ISBN 0-404-10758-3). AMS Pr.
Oneida Community Profiles. C. N. Robertson. (Illus.). 1977. 10.00x (ISBN 0-8156-0140-9). Syracuse U Pr.
Oneida Community: The Breakup, 1876 - 1881. Constance N. Robertson. LC 72-38405. (New York State Studies). (Illus.). 330p. 1972. 14.95x (ISBN 0-8156-0086-0). Syracuse U Pr.
Oneness, Vol. III. Sri Donato & Gopi G. Donato. Ed. by Morningland Publications, Inc. 167p. 1981. pap. 7.95 spiral bdg. (ISBN 0-935146-58-X). Morningland.
Oneness, Vol. II. Patricia & Gopi Gyan. (Orig.). 1980. spiral bdg. 7.95 (ISBN 0-935146-24-5). Morningland.
Oneness, Vol. I. Sri Patricia & Gopi Gyan. 1979. pap. 3.95 (ISBN 0-935146-11-3). Morningland.
Oneness Motif in the Fourth Gospel: Motif Analysis & Exegetical Probe into the Theology of John. Mark L. Appold. 322p. 1976. pap. text ed. 38.50x (ISBN 0-89563-577-1, Pub. by J. C. B. Mohr BRD). Coronet Bks.
Oneness of All Life. Marjorie H. Russell. 160p. 1984. 5.95 (ISBN 0-87159-123-5). Unity School.
Oneness of God. David K. Bernard. Ed. by Mary K. Wallace. LC 86-19051. 326p. (Orig.). 1983. pap. 6.95 (ISBN 0-912315-12-1). Word Aflame.
Oneness of Politics & Religion. Nicholas C. Eliopoulos. 126p. (Orig.). 1970. pap. 3.00x (ISBN 0-9605396-1-1). Eliopoulos.
Oneness of Politics & Religion. rev. ed. Nicholas C. Elipoulos. 169p. 1979. text ed. 6.95 (ISBN 0-9605396-3-8). Eliopoulos.
Oneness, the Trinity & Logic. Robert A. Herrmann. Ed. by Mary Wallace. 112p. 1984. pap. 4.95 (ISBN 0-912315-80-6). Word Aflame.
Onesimus. Lance Webb. LC 80-21306. 374p. 1980. pap. 4.95 (ISBN 0-8407-5742-5). Nelson.
Onion Creek Philosophy. Charles B. Hodge, Jr. LC 79-87865. 1979. 6.95 (ISBN 0-89112-054-8, Bibl Res Pr). Abilene Christ U.
Only a Prayer Away. John Guest. 140p. (Orig.). 1985. pap. 6.95 (ISBN 0-89283-273-8, Pub. by Vine Books). Servant.
Only a Prayer Meeting. C. H. Spurgeon. 1976. pap. 4.25 (ISBN 0-686-09106-X). Pilgrim Pubns.
Only a Prophet Could Do It. A. H. Nadvi. pap. 1.00 (ISBN 0-686-18429-7). Kazi Pubns.
Only by Grace: A Candid Look at the Life of a Minister. Tom S. Sampson. Ed. by Herbert Lambert. LC 85-29916. 144p. (Orig.). 1986. pap. 9.95 (ISBN 0-8272-2707-8). CBP.
Only Dance There Is. Ram Dass. LC 73-14054. 295p. 1974. pap. 6.95 (ISBN 0-385-08413-7, Anch). Doubleday.
Only Don't Know: The Teaching Letters of Zen Master Seung Sahn. Seung Sahn. LC 82-17380. (Wheel Ser.: No. 3). 205p. (Orig.). 1982. pap. 7.95 (ISBN 0-87704-054-0). Four Seasons Foun.
Only God Cast out the Anti-Christ. Bertie W. Sharpe. 1983. 4.95 (ISBN 0-8062-2214-X). Carlton.
Only Losers Can Win In This Game. Bhagwan Shree Rajneesh. Ed. by Ma Prem Maneesha. LC 82-229469. (Initation Talks Ser.). 610p. (Orig.). 1981. 23.50 (ISBN 0-88050-107-3). Chidvilas Found.
Only Love. Sri Daya Mata. LC 75-44633. (Illus.). 295p. 1976. 6.50 (ISBN 0-87612-215-2). Self Realization.
Only Love Can Make It Easy, 2 vols. rev. ed. Bill Coleman & Patty Coleman. LC 80-52360. 1981. Couples' Wkbk. pap. 2.95x (ISBN 0-89622-131-8); Leader's Guide. pap. 8.50 (ISBN 0-89622-132-6). Twenty-Third.
Only One Word. Jim McKeever. 1979. 1.00 (ISBN 0-86694-011-1). Omega Pubns OR.
Only the Beginning. Nelson L. Price. LC 79-55662. 1980. 7.95 (ISBN 0-8054-5331-8, 4253-31). Broadman.
Only Way. Lewis Foster. LC 77-83658. 96p. (Orig.). 1978. pap. 2.25 (ISBN 0-87239-193-0, 40048). Standard Pub.
Only Wise God. William L. Craig. 1987. pap. 7.95 (ISBN 0-8010-2519-2). Baker Bk.
Onstage Christ: Studies in the Persistence of a Theme. John Ditsky. (Critical Studies Ser.). 188p. 1980. 28.50x (ISBN 0-389-20059-X). B&N Imports.
Ontological Argument of Charles Hartshorne. George L. Goodwin. LC 78-2821. 1978. pap. 9.95 (ISBN 0-89130-228-X, 01-01-20). Scholars Pr GA.
Ontology of Humor. Bob W. Parrott. LC 81-80239. 96p. 1982. 10.95 (ISBN 0-8022-2387-7). Philos Lib.
Ontology of Paul Tillich. Adrian Thatcher. (Oxford Theological Monographs). 1978. text ed. 29.95x (ISBN 0-19-826715-0). Oxford U Pr.
Onward Christian Soldiers Nineteen Twenty to Nineteen Forty-two: Propaganda, Censorship, & One Man's Struggle to Herald the Truth. Donald Day & Walter Trohan. 1982. lib. bdg. 69.95 (ISBN 0-87700-450-1). Revisionist Pr.
Opacity of Signs: Acts of Interpretation in George Herbert's The Temple. Richard Todd. LC 83-36133. (Illus.). 240p. 1986. text ed. 27.00 (ISBN 0-8262-0609-3). U of Mo Pr.
Open-Air Churches of Sixteenth-Century Mexico: Atrios, Posas, Open Chapels, & Other Studies. LC 63-17205. pap. 160.00 (ISBN 0-317-10003-3, 2003001). Bks Demand UMI.
Open Arms. Norman Rohrer. 256p. (Orig.). 1987. pap. 6.95 (ISBN 0-8423-4754-2). Tyndale.
Open Book to Padre Pio. Adelene Lampson. 160p. 1986. 11.95 (ISBN 0-89962-554-1). Todd & Honeywell.

Open Book to the Christian Divorcee. Roger H. Crook. LC 73-87064. pap. 4.95 (ISBN 0-8054-5217-6). Broadman.

Open Church: History of an Idea. Esther B. McBride. LC 83-91256. (Illus.). 112p. 1983. pap. 10.50 (ISBN 0-9613017-0-8). Esther McBride.

Open Door. Bhagwan Shree Rajneesh. Ed. by Ma Prem Maneesha. LC 83-181263. (Initiation Talks Ser.). (Illus.). 336p. (Orig.). 1980. 18.95 (ISBN 0-88050-608-3). Chidvilas Found.

Open Doors. Samuel F. Pannabecker. LC 75-9417. (Mennonite Historical Ser.). (Illus.). 432p. 1975. 18.50 (ISBN 0-87303-636-0). Faith & Life.

Open Heart. Frederick Buechner. LC 84-47715. (Books of Bebb). 1984. pap. 3.95 (ISBN 0-06-061166-9, P-5008, HarpR). Har-Row.

Open Heart-Open Home. Karen B. Mains. LC 76-1554. 224p. 1976. 5.95 (ISBN 0-89191-111-1). Cook.

Open Heart-Open Home. Karen B. Mains. 1980. pap. 2.95 (ISBN 0-451-14183-0, AE2641, Sig). NAL.

Open Heaven: The Study of Apocalyptic in Judaism & Early Christianity. Christopher Rowland. LC 82-7409. 540p. 1982. 29.50x (ISBN 0-8245-0455-0). Crossroad NY.

Open Lesson to a Bishop. Michael Davies. 1980. pap. 1.00 (ISBN 0-89555-142-X). Tan Bks Pubs.

Open Letter to Moses & Mohammed. Joel Carmichael. LC 68-9705. (Open Letter Ser). (Orig.). 1968. pap. 4.95 (ISBN 0-685-11973-4, 18). Heineman.

Open Letters from a Roman Prison: Philippians, Colossians, Philemon, Leader's Guide. (New Horizons Bible Study Ser.). 48p. 1980. pap. 1.95 (ISBN 0-89367-047-2). Light & Life.

Open Letters from a Roman Prison: Philippians, Colossians, Philemon Study Guide. (New Horizons Bible Study Ser.). 64p. 1980. pap. 2.50 (ISBN 0-89367-046-4). Light & Life.

Open Moment. Barbara Stone. 400p. (Orig.). 1985. pap. 11.95 (ISBN 0-87418-021-X, 158). Coleman Pub.

Open Path: Christian Missionaries, 1515-1914. Jack Beeching. LC 80-21270. (Illus.). 350p. 1982. 19.95 (ISBN 0-915520-37-0); pap. 10.95 (ISBN 0-915520-53-2). Ross-Erikson.

Open Rapture. Sakae Kubo. (Flame Ser.). 1978. pap. 0.99 (ISBN 0-8127-0170-4). Review & Herald.

Open Secret. Bhagwan Shree Rajneesh. Ed. by Ma Prem Maneesha. LC 83-180822. (Initiation Talks Ser.). 382p. (Orig.). 1980. 25.50 (ISBN 0-88050-109-X). Chidvilas Found.

Open Texture of Moral Concepts. John M. Brennan. LC 74-31826. 171p. 1977. text ed. 26.50x (ISBN 0-06-490656-6, 06364). B&N Imports.

Open the Door Wide to Happy Living. Huffman T. Harris. 1985. 12.95 (ISBN 0-8062-2523-8). Carlton.

Open the Frontiers. Leon J. Suenens. 1981. 8.95 (ISBN 0-8164-0489-5, HarpR). Har-Row.

Open the Meeting with Prayer. Alfred Doerffler. LC 55-7442. 1955. 3.50 (ISBN 0-570-03147-8, 12-2531). Concordia.

Open up Your Life: A Woman's Workshop on Christian Hospitality. Latayne C. Scott. 144p. 1983. pap. 2.95 (ISBN 0-310-38901-1, 10451P). Zondervan.

Open Windows. Neal Stanford. 80p. 1984. 8.00 (ISBN 0-682-40172-2). Exposition Pr FL.

Open Your Eyes. Heng Sure et al. (Illus.). 347p. (Orig.). 1979. pap. 7.50 (ISBN 0-917512-32-4). Buddhist Text.

Open Your Mind to Prosperity. rev. ed. Catherine Ponder. LC 70-155720. 184p. 1984. pap. 5.50 (ISBN 0-87516-531-1). De Vorss.

Open Your Mind to Receive. Catherine Ponder. LC 82-74283. 128p. 1983. pap. 4.50 (ISBN 0-87516-507-9). De Vorss.

Opened Heavens. Jessie Penn-Lewis. 1962. pap. 2.95 (ISBN 0-87508-996-8). Chr Lit.

Opened Treasures. Frances R. Havergal. LC 62-21063. 1962. 7.95 (ISBN 0-87213-320-6). Loizeaux.

Opening a Temple in Los Angelos: A Visit to Boston. Satsvarupa D. Goswami. Ed. by Mandalesvara Dasa et al. (Prabhupada-lila Ser.). 72p. 1981. pap. 2.25 (ISBN 0-911233-01-6). Gita Nagari.

Opening Blind Eyes. John R. Claypool. 144p. (Orig.). 1987. pap. 7.95 (ISBN 0-940989-05-0). Meyer Stone Bks.

Opening Devotions for Womens Groups. Deborah Edwards. 96p. 1985. pap. 4.95 (ISBN 0-8010-3428-0). Baker Bk.

Opening of the Way. Isha S. De Lubicz. Tr. by Rupert Gleadow. LC 81-782. 256p. 1981. pap. 9.95 (ISBN 0-89281-015-7). Inner Tradit.

Opening of the Wisdom Eye. Dalai Lama. LC 70-152732. 178p. 1981. pap. 6.95 (ISBN 0-8356-0549-3, Quest). Theos Pub Hse.

Opening of the Wisdom-Eye. Dalai Lama, IV. Tr. by Thubten K. Rinpoche et al from Tibetan. LC 70-152732. (Illus.). 1972. 7.50 (ISBN 0-8356-0202-8). Theos Pub Hse.

Opening the Bible. Thomas Merton. LC 85-24722. 96p. 1986. pap. 4.95 (ISBN 0-8006-1910-2). Fortress.

Opening the Bible with Children: Beginning Bible Skills. Patricia Griggs. 64p. (Orig.). 1986. pap. 7.50 (ISBN 0-687-29210-7). Abingdon.

Opening the Book. Hans Finzel. 352p. 1986. pap. 11.95 (ISBN 0-89693-277-X). Victor Bks.

Opening the New Testament. N. Robert Cowles. LC 84-72468. 158p. (Orig.). 1985. pap. 4.95 (ISBN 0-87509-357-4); leader's guide 2.95 (ISBN 0-87509-358-2). Chr Pubns.

Opening the Old Testament. H. Robert Cowles. LC 80-65149. (Illus.). 158p. (Orig.). 1980. pap. 4.50 (ISBN 0-87509-279-9); Leader's Guide. 2.95 (ISBN 0-87509-283-7). Chr Pubns.

Opening the Treasures: A Book of Daily Homily Meditations. Charles E. Miller. LC 81-19095. (Illus.). 557p. 1982. pap. 16.95 (ISBN 0-8189-0424-0). Alba.

Opening to Channel: How to Connect with Your Guide. Sanaya Roman & Duane Packer. Ed. by Gregory Armstrong. (Birth into Light Ser.). 280p. (Orig.). 1987. pap. 12.95 (ISBN 0-915811-05-7). H J Kramer Inc.

Opening to God. Thomas H. Green. (Religion Ser.). 128p. 1987. pap. 2.95 (ISBN 0-553-26666-7). Bantam.

Opening to God: A Guide to Prayer. Thomas H. Green. LC 77-83197. 144p. 1977. pap. 3.95 (ISBN 0-87793-136-4). Ave Maria.

Opening to God: Guided Imagery Meditation on Scripture. Carolyn Stahl. LC 77-87403. 1977. 3.50x (ISBN 0-8358-0357-0). Upper Room.

Opening Way. Dan Wilson. LC 61-11637. (Orig.). 1961. pap. 2.50x (ISBN 0-87574-113-4, 113). Pendle Hill.

Openings into Ministry. Ed. by Ross Snyder. LC 77-92707. (Studies in Ministry & Parish Life). 1977. 13.95x (ISBN 0-913552-10-0); pap. 5.95x (ISBN 0-913552-11-9). Exploration Pr.

Opera, 3 Vols. Saint Ambrosius. Set. 210.00 (ISBN 0-384-01038-5). Johnson Repr.

Opera. Saint Hilarius. Ed. by A. Feder. (Corpus Scriptorum Ecclesiasticorum Latinorum Ser: Vol. 65). 1916. 50.00 (ISBN 0-384-23110-1). Johnson Repr.

Opera. Claudianus Mamertus. Ed. by A. Engelbrecht. (Corpus Scriptorum Ecclesiasticorum Latinorum Ser: Vol. 11). 1885. 50.00 (ISBN 0-384-09245-4). Johnson Repr.

Opera, 2 Vols. Quintus S. Tertullianus. (Lat). Repr. of 1890 ed. Set. 100.00 (ISBN 0-384-59850-1). Johnson Repr.

Opera. Saint Victorinus. Ed. by I. Haussleiter. (Corpus Scriptorum Ecclesiasticorum Latinorum Ser: Vol. 49). Repr. of 1916 ed. 40.00 (ISBN 0-384-64555-0). Johnson Repr.

Opera, Pt. 2. Johannes Cassianus. Ed. by M. Petschenig. (Corpus Scriptorum Ecclesiasticorum Latinorum Ser: Vol. 13). 1886. 50.00 (ISBN 0-384-07860-5). Johnson Repr.

Opera: Enneades IV-V, Vol II. Plotinus. Ed. by H. R. Schwyzer & Paul Henry. (Oxford Classical Texts). 1977. 24.95x (ISBN 0-19-814582-9). Oxford U Pr.

Opera Omnia. Saint Cyprianus. (Corpus Scriptorum Ecclesiasticorum Latinorum Ser: Vol. 3). 1868-1871. pap. 131.00 (ISBN 0-384-10518-1). Johnson Repr.

Opera Omnia. Magnus F. Ennodius. (Corpus Scriptorum Ecclesiasticorum Latinorum Ser.: Vol. 6). 1882. pap. 60.00 (ISBN 0-384-14370-9). Johnson Repr.

Opera Omnia, 26 vols. Joannes D. Scotus. 18302p. 1895. text ed. 4843.80x (ISBN 0-576-99127-9, Pub. by Gregg Intl Pubs England). Gregg Intl.

Opera Omnia. Sedulius. Ed. by Iohnnes Huemer. (Corpus Scriptorum Ecclesiasticorum Latinorum Ser: Vol. 10). Repr. of 1885 ed. 50.00 (ISBN 0-384-54730-3). Johnson Repr.

Opera Omnia: 1890-97, 4 pts. Lucius C. Lactantius. (Corpus Scriptorum Ecclesiasticorum Latinorum Ser: Vols. 19, 2 Pts.). 1890-97. Set Pts. 1 & 2. Vol 19. pap. 50.00 (ISBN 0-384-30865-1); Pts. 1 & 2 Vol 27. pap. 44.00 ea. Johnson Repr.

Opera Pars 1. Orationum Gregorii Nazianzeni Novem Interpretation. Tyrannius Rufinius. Ed. by A. Engelbrecht. Repr. of 1910 ed. 40.00 (ISBN 0-384-52540-7). Johnson Repr.

Opera Quae Supersunt Omnia, 59 Vols. in 58. Jean Calvin. Ed. by G. Baum et al. 1863-1900. Set. 2600.00 (ISBN 0-384-07195-3); 50.00 ea. Johnson Repr.

Opera Quae Supersunt Omnia, 28 Vols. Philipp Melanchthon. (Corpus Reformatorum). Repr. of 1860 ed. Set. 1650.00 (ISBN 0-384-38050-6); 60.00 ea. Johnson Repr.

Operation Discipleship, Level II. Dollas Messer. 1986. wkbk 12.95 (ISBN 0-317-40165-3). Pathway Pr.

Operation Discipleship: Being in Christ. Dollas Messer. 138p. 1984. pap. text ed. 5.95 student manual (ISBN 0-87148-659-8). Pathway Pr.

Operation Discipleship: Being in Christ. Dollas Messer. 70p. (Orig.). 1984. pap. text ed. 5.95 tchr's guide (ISBN 0-87148-660-1). Pathway Pr.

Operation Manhunt Made Easy. C. S. Lovett. 1961. 2.95 (ISBN 0-938148-17-6). Personal Christianity.

Operation Moses: The Untold Story of the Secret Exodus of the Falasha Jews from Ethiopia. Tudor Parfitt. LC 85-40240. (Illus.). 192p. 1986. 16.95 (ISBN 0-8128-3059-8). Stein & Day.

Operation World: A Day-to-Day Guide to Praying for the World. 4th ed. Patrick Johnstone. 502p. Date not set. pap. 5.95 (ISBN 0-87808-211-5). William Carey Lib.

Opinions on Church Music: Comments & Reports from Four & a Half Centuries. Ed. by Elwyn A. Wienandt. LC 74-75229. 214p. 1974. 14.00 (ISBN 0-918954-12-6). Baylor Univ Pr.

Opponents of Paul in Second Corinthians: A Study of Religious Propaganda in Late Antiquity. Dieter Georgi. LC 84-47917. 464p. 1985. 32.95 (ISBN 0-8006-0729-5, 1-729). Fortress.

Opportunities for Belief & Behavior. Christian Duquoc. LC 67-31523. (Concilium Ser: Vol. 29). 186p. 1967. 7.95 (ISBN 0-8091-0106-8). Paulist Pr.

Opportunities in Religious Service. John O. Nelson. (VGM Career Bks.). (Illus.). 160p. 1983. 9.95 (ISBN 0-8442-6600-0, 6600-0, Passport Bks); pap. 7.95 (ISBN 0-8442-6601-9, 6601-9). Natl Textbk.

Opportunity My Ally. Lewis Cameron. (Illus.). 253p. 1965. 10.95 (ISBN 0-227-67706-4). Attic Pr.

Opposite Book. Illus. by Marc Harrison. (Bible Look-n-Learn Ser.). 1986. 3.95 (ISBN 0-8407-6710-2). Nelson.

OPTAT: Occasional Papers in Translation & Textlinguistics, Studies in Translation, Discourse Analysis, & Related Areas of Biblical Research. Ed. by Robert E. Longacre. 88p. (Orig.). 1986. pap. 5.00 (ISBN 0-88312-668-0). Summer Inst Ling.

Optati Milevitani Libri Septum. Saint Optatus. (Corpus Scriptorum Ecclesiasticorum Latinorum Ser: Vol. 26). (Lat). pap. 50.00 (ISBN 0-384-43390-1). Johnson Repr.

Optimism, the Lesson of Ages. Benjamin P. Blood. LC 75-3055. Repr. of 1860 ed. 18.00 (ISBN 0-404-59053-5). AMS Pr.

Optina Pustin' i jeja vremja. I. M. Kontsevich. Tr. of Optina Hermitage & It's Time. (Illus.). 604p. 1970. 25.00 (ISBN 0-317-29246-3); pap. 20.00 (ISBN 0-317-29247-1). Holy Trinity.

Option for the Poor: A Hundred Years of Vatican Social Teaching. Donal Dorr. 333p. (Orig.). 1983. pap. 11.95 (ISBN 0-88344-365-1). Orbis Bks.

Option for the Poor: Challenge to the Reich. Leonard Boff. Ed. by Virgil Elizondo. (Concilium Nineteen Eighty-Six Ser.). 120p. 1986. pap. 6.95 (ISBN 0-567-30067-6, Pub. by T & T Clark Ltd UK). Fortress.

Optional God. Stephen F. Bayne. LC 80-80876. 134p. 1980. pap. 6.95 (ISBN 0-8192-1268-7). Morehouse.

Options in Contemporary Christian Ethics. Norman L. Geisler. LC 80-69431. 128p. (Orig.). 1981. pap. 4.95 (ISBN 0-8010-3757-3). Baker Bk.

Options in Contemporary Theology. Stanley T. Sutphin. 1978. pap. text ed. 10.75 (ISBN 0-8191-0277-6). U Pr of Amer.

Options in Contemporary Theology. rev. ed. Stanley T. Sutphin. LC 86-28199. 176p. 1987. lib. bdg. 22.50 (ISBN 0-8191-6058-X); pap. text ed. 10.75 (ISBN 0-8191-6059-8). U Pr of Amer.

Options in Roman Catholicism: An Introduction. Ed. by Nathan R. Kollar. LC 82-21823. 224p. (Orig.). 1983. lib. bdg. 27.00 (ISBN 0-8191-2958-5); pap. text ed. 12.50 (ISBN 0-8191-2959-3). U Pr of Amer.

Opus Sanctorum Angelorum: Work of the Holy Angels. Robert J. Fox. 1.50 (ISBN 0-911988-49-1). AMI Pr.

Opvuscula. Lucifer of Cagliari. (Corpus Scriptorum Ecclesiasticorum Latinorum Ser: Vol. 14). (Lat). pap. 40.00 (ISBN 0-384-34090-3). Johnson Repr.

Or Nerev: Hebrew Text. Moses Cordavero. 1980. 10.00 (ISBN 0-943688-17-5). Res Ctr Kabbalah.

Or, Sir Walter Scott's Use of Sacred Scriptures. Nicholas Dickson. 1979. Repr. of 1884 ed. lib. bdg. 30.00 (ISBN 0-8414-3830-7). Folcroft.

Oracion - Clave del Avivamiento. Paul Y. Cho & R. Whitney Manzano. Tr. by Juan S. Araujo from Eng. Tr. of Prayer - Key to Revival. (Span.). 128p. 1987. pap. 3.95 (ISBN 0-88113-241-1). Edit Betania.

Oracion Eficaz. Ed. by Frances Foulks. Tr. of Effectual Prayer. (Span.). 160p. 5.95 (ISBN 0-87159-089-1). Unity School.

Oracion Invade Lo Imposible. Jack W. Hayford. Ed. by Angel Carrodeguas. Tr. by Eliezer Oyola from Span. Orig. Title: Prayer Is Invading the Impossible. 160p. 1985. pap. text ed. 2.95 (ISBN 0-8297-1457-X). Life Pubs Intl.

Oracion Que Prevalece. Kenneth E. Hagin. (Span.). 1986. pap. 2.50 (ISBN 0-89276-186-5). Hagin Ministries.

Oracion y los Cultos de Oracion. 2nd ed. Carlos H. Mackintosh. Ed. by Roger P. Daniel. Tr. by Sara Bautista from Eng. (Serie Diamante). Tr. of Prayer & the Prayer Meeting. (Span., Illus.). 40p. 1982. pap. 0.85 (ISBN 0-942504-08-9). Overcomer Pr.

Oracle of Baalbek: The Tiburtine Sibyl in Greek Dress. Paul J. Alexander. LC 75-27113. (Dumbarton Oaks Studies: Vol. 10). (Illus.). 151p. 1967. 12.00x (ISBN 0-88402-020-7). Dumbarton Oaks.

Oracle of the Lord. Neil J. McEleney. (Bible Ser.: No. 24). (Orig.). 1974. pap. 1.00 (ISBN 0-8091-5174-X). Paulist Pr.

Oracles & Demons of Tibet. Rene De Nebesky-Wojkowitz. 100.00 (ISBN 0-87968-463-1). Gordon Pr.

Oracles of Nostradamus. Charles A. Ward. 400p. 1981. pap. 22.00 (ISBN 0-89540-084-7, SB-084). Sun Pub.

Orad en el Espiritu. Arthur Wallis. LC 82-23203. 144p. 1975. 2.75 (ISBN 0-88113-240-3). Edit Betania.

Orah V'Simchoh. Mandelbaum. cancelled (ISBN 0-87306-117-9). Feldheim.

Oraibi Soyal Ceremony, & Oraibi Powamu Ceremony, & Mishongnovi Ceremonies of the Snake & Antelope Fraternities, & Oraibi Summer Snake Ceremony, 4 wks. in 1 vol. 1901-03. G. A. Dorsey & H. R. Voth. (Chicago Field Museum of Natural History). 70.00 (ISBN 0-527-01863-5). Kraus Repr.

Oraibu Marau Ceremony-Brief Miscellaneous Hopi Papers. H. R. Voth. (Chicago Field Museum of Natural History Fieldiana Anthropology Ser). 1912. 44.00 (ISBN 0-527-01871-6). Kraus Repr.

Oral & the Written Gospel: The Hermeneutics of Speaking & Writing in the Synoptic Tradition, Mark, Paul, & Q. Werner H. Kelber. LC 82-7450. 272p. 1983. 23.95 (ISBN 0-8006-0689-2, 1-689). Fortress.

Oral Communication of the Scripture: Insights from African Oral Art. Herbert V. Klem. LC 81-10052. (Applied Cultural Anthropology Ser.). (Illus.). 280p. (Orig.). 1982. pap. text ed. 9.95x (ISBN 0-87808-332-4). William Carey Lib.

Oral Law. Schimmel. cancelled (ISBN 0-87306-088-1). Feldheim.

Oral Roberts Scrapbook. Warner Hutchinson. LC 78-58611. 1978. pap. 5.95 (ISBN 0-448-16259-8). Brown Bk.

Oral Torah: The Sacred Books of Judaism. Jacob Neusner. LC 85-42788. 256p. 1986. 19.45 (ISBN 0-06-066103-8, HarpR). Har-Row.

Orange Book: The Meditation Techniques of Bhagwan Shree Rajneesh. 2nd ed. Bhagwan Shree Rajneesh. Ed. by Rajneesh Foundation International. LC 82-63117. (Meditation Ser.). 256p. 1983. pap. 3.95 (ISBN 0-88050-697-0). Chidvilas Found.

Orange Morgan's 38, 325 Mornings. Forrest M. Smith. 1978. 7.00 (ISBN 0-918626-10-2); pap. 4.00 (ISBN 0-918626-07-2). Word Serv.

Orations of Mohammad. S. L. Pool. pap. 2.00 (ISBN 0-686-18347-9). Kazi Pubns.

Oratorio ad Graecos & Fragments. Tatian. Ed. & tr. by Molly Whittaker. (Oxford Early Christian Texts). 1982. 27.50x (ISBN 0-19-826809-2). Oxford U Pr.

Orb & the Cross: A Normative Study in the Relations of Church & State, with Reference to Gladstones Early Writings. Alec R. Vidler. LC 46-19947. 1945. text ed. 7.50x (ISBN 0-8401-2544-5). A R Allenson.

Orcherd of Syon & the English Mystical Tradition. P. Hodgson. (Sir Israel Gollancz Memorial Lectures in Old English). 1964. pap. 2.25 (ISBN 0-85672-264-2, Pub. by British Acad). Longwood Pub Group.

Ordained of the Lord: H. A. Ironside. E. Schuyler English. LC 76-13873. (Illus.). 1976. pap. 4.95 (ISBN 0-87213-143-2). Loizeaux.

Ordained to Service: A Theology of the Permanent Diaconate. Norbert Brockman. 1976. 7.50 (ISBN 0-682-48561-6, University). Exposition Pr FL.

Ordeal by Labyrinth: Conversations with Claude-Henri Rocquet. Mircea Eliade. Tr. by Derek Coltman from Fr. LC 81-21796. (Illus.). 1982. 17.50x (ISBN 0-226-20387-5). U of Chicago Pr.

Ordeal of Civility: Freud, Marx, Levi-Strauss, & the Jewish Struggle with Modernity. John M. Cuddihy. LC 86-47757. 272p. 1987. pap. 9.95 (ISBN 0-8070-3609-9, BP-738). Beacon Pr.

Order & History, 4 vols. Eric Voegelin. Incl. Vol. 1. Israel & Revelation. LC 56-11670. xxvi, 534p. 1956 (ISBN 0-8071-0818-9); Vol. 2. World of the Polis. LC 57-11670. xvii, 390p. 1957 (ISBN 0-8071-0819-7); Vol. 3. Plato & Aristotle. LC 57-11670. xviii, 384p. 1957 (ISBN 0-8071-0820-0); Vol. 4. Ecumenic Age. LC 56-11670. 1974 (ISBN 0-8071-0081-1). 19.95 ea. La State U Pr.

Order My Steps in Thy Word. Victor P. Wierwille. LC 70-176281. (Studies in Abundant Living: Vol. V). 300p. 1985. 6.95 (ISBN 0-910068-59-3). Am Christian.

Order of Assassins. Marshall G. Hodgson. LC 78-63343. (Crusades & Military Orders: Second Ser.). Repr. of 1955 ed. 46.50 (ISBN 0-404-17018-8). AMS Pr.

Order of Christian Funerals: General Introduction & Pastoral Notes. (Liturgy Documentary Ser.: No. 8). 72p. (Orig.). Date not set. pap. 5.95 (ISBN 1-55586-990-4). US Catholic.

Order of Future Events. Ray H. Hughes. 1970. pap. 3.50 (ISBN 0-87148-650-4). Pathway Pr.

Order of Minoresses in England. A. F. C. Bourdillon. 115p. Repr. of 1926 ed. text ed. 33.12x (ISBN 0-576-99212-7, Pub. by Gregg Intl Pubs England). Gregg Intl.

Order of St. John of Jerusalem: Past & Present. Rose G. Kingsley. LC 76-29842. Repr. of 1918 ed. 27.50 (ISBN 0-404-15422-0). AMS Pr.

Order of the Synoptics: Why Three Synoptic Gospels? Bernard Orchard & Harold Riley. 384p. 1987. 38.95 (ISBN 0-86554-222-8, MUP H-199). Mercer Univ Pr.

Order or the Hospital of St. John of Jerusalem. William K. Bedford. LC 76-29831. Repr. of 1902 ed. 31.25 (ISBN 0-404-15412-3). AMS Pr.

Ordered Love: Sex Roles & Sexuality in Victorian Utopias--the Shakers, the Mormons, & the Oneida Community. Louis J. Kern. LC 80-10763. xv, 430p. 1981. 27.00x (ISBN 0-8078-1443-1); pap. 9.95x (ISBN 0-8078-4074-2). U of NC Pr.

Ordering Wisdom: The Hierarchy of Philosophical Discourses in Aquinas. Mark D. Jordon. LC 86-40335. (Publications in Medieval Studies: No. 24). 448p. 1986. text ed. 35.00 (ISBN 0-268-01500-7). U of Notre Dame Pr.

Orders of Knighthood, Awards & the Holy See: A Historical Juridical & Practical Compendium. 3rd, rev., enl. ed. H. E. Cardinale. 1985. text ed. 55.00x (ISBN 0-905715-26-8). Humanities.

Orders of the Great Work - Alchemy. Manly P. Hall. 5.95 (ISBN 0-89314-534-3). Philos Res.

Orders of the Quest - the Holy Grail. Manly P. Hall. 5.95 (ISBN 0-89314-533-5). Philos Res.

Ordinals of Christ from Their Origins to the Twelfth Century. Roger E. Reynolds. 1978. 55.00x (ISBN 3-11-007058-8). De Gruyter.

Ordinances of the New Testament. William G. Schell. 67p. pap. 0.50 (ISBN 0-686-29158-1). Faith Pub Hse.

Ordinances: What Are They? David R. Plaster. 1985. pap. 5.95 (ISBN 0-88469-164-0). BMH Bks.

Ordinarily Sacred. Lynda Sexson. LC 82-17145. 144p. 1982. 9.95 (ISBN 0-8245-0530-1). Crossroad NY.

Ordinary Christians in a High-Tech World. Robert Slocum. 224p. 1986. 10.95 (ISBN 0-8499-0490-0, 0490-0); pap. 9.95 (ISBN 0-8499-3046-4). Word Bks.

Ordinary Men Called by God: Abraham, Moses, & David. James M. Boice. 160p. 1982. pap. 5.95 (ISBN 0-88207-224-2). Victor Bks.

Ordinary Saint, John Neumann. Jane F. Hindman. 1977. pap. 1.95 (ISBN 0-88479-004-5). Arena Lettres.

Ordinary Way: A Family Spirituality. Dolores R. Leckey. (Crossroad Paperback Ser.). 192p. 1982. pap. 7.95 (ISBN 0-8245-0442-9). Crossroad NY.

Ordination: A Biblical-Historical View. Marjorie Warkentin. LC 82-8908. pap. 53.00 (ISBN 0-317-30166-7, 2025348). Bks Demand UMI.

Ordination Anointings in the Western Church Before 1000 A. D. G. Ellard. (Med Acad of Amer Pubns). 1932. 18.00 (ISBN 0-527-01688-8). Kraus Repr.

Ordination of Baptist Ministers. J. Wash Watts. pap. 1.50 (ISBN 0-8054-9404-9). Broadman.

Ordination of Women. Paul K. Jewett. LC 80-15644. 160p. (Orig.). 1980. pap. 5.95 (ISBN 0-8028-1850-1). Eerdmans.

Organ Improvisation for Beginners. Jan Bender. LC 75-2934. (Illus.). 71p. 1975. bds. 8.25 (ISBN 0-570-01312-7, 99-1229). Concordia.

Organist & Hymn Playing. rev. ed. Austin C. Lovelace. LC 81-80265. (Illus.). 61p. 1981. pap. 5.95 (ISBN 0-916642-16-X). Hope Pub.

Organization & Leadership in the Local Church. Kenneth Kilinski & Jerry Wolfert. 14.95 (ISBN 0-310-26810-9, 18132). Zondervan.

Organization Executive Course. L. Ron Hubbard. 840.00 (ISBN 0-686-30798-4). Church Scient NY.

Organization Executive Course: An Encyclopedia of Scientology Policy (1950-1951, 1953-1974, 7 vols. L. Ron Hubbard. Incl. Vol. 0. Basic Staff Volume of the Organization Executive Course (ISBN 0-88404-025-9); Vol. 1. Hubbard Communications Office Division One of the Organization Executive Course (ISBN 0-88404-026-7); Vol. 2. Hubbard Communications Office Dissemination Division Two of the Organization Executive Course (ISBN 0-88404-027-5); Vol. 3. Treasury Division Three of the Organization Executive Course (ISBN 0-88404-028-3); Vol. 4. Technical Division Four of the Organization Executive Course (ISBN 0-88404-029-1); Vol. 5. Qualifications Division Five of the Organization Executive Course (ISBN 0-88404-030-5); Vol. 6. Distribution Division Six of the Organization Executive Course. 1971 (ISBN 0-88404-031-3); Vol. 7. Executive Division Seven: The Executive's Handbook of the Organization Executive Course (ISBN 0-88404-032-1). 1974. 836.00 set (ISBN 0-88404-033-X); 107.18 ea. Bridge Pubns Inc.

Organization of Medieval Christianity. Summerfield Baldwin. 1986. 11.25 (ISBN 0-8446-1051-8). Peter Smith.

Organization of the Early Christian Churches: Eight Lectures Delivered Before the University of Oxford in the Year 1880 on the Foundation of the Late Rev. John Bampton, M. A., Canon of Salisbury. Edwin Hatch. LC 77-183696. (Research & Source Works Ser). 222p. 1972. Repr. of 1881 ed. lib. bdg. 18.50 (ISBN 0-8337-4163-2). B Franklin.

Organization of the United Methodist Church. rev. ed. Jack M. Tuell. 176p. 1985. pap. 7.95 (ISBN 0-687-29445-2). Abingdon.

Organizational Communication Nineteen Seventy-Seven: Abstracts, Analysis, & Overview. new ed. Howard H. Greenbaum & Raymond L. Falcione. 1979. pap. 9.00 (ISBN 0-931874-08-4). Assn Busn Comm.

Organized Anti-Semitism in America: The Rise of Group Prejudice During the Decade 1930-1940. Donald S. Strong. LC 78-26198. 1979. Repr. of 1941 ed. lib. bdg. 22.50x (ISBN 0-313-20883-2, STOA). Greenwood.

Organized Miracles: A Study of a Contemporary, Youth, Communal, Fundamentalist Organization. James T. Richardson et al. LC 78-55937. 368p. 1979. 19.95 (ISBN 0-87855-284-7). Transaction Bks.

Organizing a Youth Ministry to Fit Your Needs. Jeffrey D. Jones & Kenneth C. Potts. 64p. 1983. pap. 3.95 (ISBN 0-8170-1004-1). Judson.

Organizing & Developing a Free Will Baptist Sunday School. William Hill. (Sunday School Workers Training Course Ser.: No. 1). 1969. pap. 3.95 (ISBN 0-89265-002-8, Free Will Baptist Dept). Randall Hse.

Organs & Organists of the Cathedral Church of St. Thomas of Canterbury at Portsmouth. Philip Barrett. 1975. Repr. of 1968 ed. 39.00x (ISBN 0-317-43672-4, Pub. by City of Portsmouth). State Mutual Bk.

Orient in American Transcendentalism: A Study of Emerson, Thoreau & Alcott. Arthur Christy. 1963. lib. bdg. 26.00x (ISBN 0-374-91539-3, Octagon). Hippocrene Bks.

Orientacion Sicologica Eficaz. Gary Collins. Tr. by Miguel Blanch from Eng. Tr. of Effective Counseling. (Span.). 206p. 1979. pap. 4.75 (ISBN 0-89922-136-X). Edit Caribe.

Oriental & Biblical Studies: Collected Writings of E. A. Speiser. Ephraim A. Speiser. Ed. by Moshe Greenberg & Jacob J. Finkelstein. LC 65-21779. pap. 154.00 (ISBN 0-317-08338-4, 2003802). Bks Demand UMI.

Oriental Orthodox Churches in the United States. Ed. by Robert F. Taft. 32p. 1986. pap. 2.95 (ISBN 1-55586-987-4). US Catholic.

Oriental Religions & Their Relation to Universal Religion. Samuel Johnson. 999p. Repr. of 1877 ed. text ed. 42.50x (ISBN 0-89644-558-5, Pub. by Chineses Matl Ctr). Coronet Bks.

Oriental Religions in Roman Paganism. Franz Cumont. 1911. pap. 5.95 (ISBN 0-486-20321-2). Dover.

Oriental Religions in Roman Paganism. Franz Cumont. 14.00 (ISBN 0-8446-1925-6). Peter Smith.

Oriental Religious & American Thought: Nineteenth-Century Explorations. Carl T. Jackson. LC 80-25478. (Contributions in American Studies: No. 55). 296p. 1981. lib. bdg. 32.95 (ISBN 0-313-22491-9, JOR/). Greenwood.

Oriental Thought: An Introduction to the Philosophical & Religious Thought of Asia. Yong C. Kim. (Quality Paperback Ser.: No. 365). 144p. 1981. pap. 4.95 (ISBN 0-8226-0365-9). Littlefield.

Oriental Thought: An Introduction to the Philosophical & Religious Thought of Asia. Yong Choon Kim. LC 80-39672. 144p. 1981. Repr. of 1973 ed. 11.50x (ISBN 0-8476-6972-6). Rowman.

Orientalism, Islam & Islamists. Ed. by Asaf Hussain et al. LC 84-72244. 300p. (Orig.). 1985. 17.50 (ISBN 0-915597-15-2); pap. 9.95 (ISBN 0-915597-09-8). Amana Bks.

Orientalisms of the Bible, Vol. II. K. C. Pillai. LC 84-50935. 141p. 1984. 3.95 (ISBN 0-910068-56-9). Am Christian.

Orientalisms of the Bible, Vol. 1. K. C. Pillai. 1969. 4.95x (ISBN 0-912178-02-7). Mor-Mac.

Orientalisms of the Bible, Vol. 2. K. C. Pillai. 1974. 4.95x (ISBN 0-912178-04-3). Mor-Mac.

Orientation by Disorientation: Studies on Literary Criticism & Biblical Literary Criticism Presented in Honor of William A. Beardslee. Ed. by Richard A. Spencer. (Pittsburgh Theological Monograph Ser.: No. 35). 1980. pap. text ed. 15.00 (ISBN 0-915138-44-1). Pickwick.

Orientation for New Adventists. Richard M. Jewett. (Waymark Ser.). 1978. pap. 2.95 (ISBN 0-8127-0184-4). Review & Herald.

Oriflamme, Vol. VI, No. 1: Yoga & Magick. Aleister Crowley & Marcelo Motta. 1984. 8.00 (ISBN 0-913735-02-7). O T O.

Origen: A Critical Reading. Antonia Tripolitis. (American University Studies VII (Theology & Religion): Vol. 8). 208p. 1985. text ed. 21.55 (ISBN 0-8204-0213-3). P Lang Pubs.

Origen & His Work. Eugene De Faye. LC 78-16959. 1926. 27.50 (ISBN 0-8414-3684-3). Folcroft.

Origen & the Doctrine of Grace. Benjamin Drewery. LC 61-19395. 1960. text ed. 17.50x (ISBN 0-8401-0579-7). A R Allenson.

Origen & the Jews. N. R. De Lange. LC 75-36293. (Oriental Publications Ser.: No. 25). 160p. 1977. 39.50 (ISBN 0-521-20542-5). Cambridge U Pr.

Origen: Contra Celsum. Ed. by H. Chadwick. LC 78-73132. 1980. 80.00 (ISBN 0-521-05866-X); pap. 32.50 (ISBN 0-521-29576-9). Cambridge U Pr.

Origen, Prayer, Exhortation to Martyrdom. Ed. by W. J. Burghardt et al. LC 78-62467. (ACW Ser.: No. 19). 261p. 1954. 14.95 (ISBN 0-8091-0256-0). Paulist Pr.

Origen: Selected Writings. Ed. by Rowan A. Greer. LC 79-84886. (Classics of Western Spirituality Ser.). 334p. 1979. 13.95 (ISBN 0-8091-0283-8); pap. 9.95 (ISBN 0-8091-2198-0). Paulist Pr.

Origen: Spirit & Fire: A Thematic Anthology of His Writings by Hans Urs von Balthasar. Hans U. Von Balthasar. Tr. by Robert J. Daly. LC 83-14368. 416p. 1984. 34.95x (ISBN 0-8132-0591-3). Cath U Pr.

Origen: The Bible & Philosophy in the Third Century Church. Joseph W. Trigg. (Illus.). 280p. 1983. pap. 16.95 (ISBN 0-8042-0945-6). John Knox.

Origen, the Song of Songs: Commentary & Homilies. Ed. by W. J. Burghardt et al. LC 57-11826. (ACW Ser.: No. 26). 491p. 1957. 14.95 (ISBN 0-8091-0261-7). Paulist Pr.

Origin & Development of Islam. Asghar A. Engineer. 248p. 1980. 18.95x (ISBN 0-940500-33-7). Asia Bk Corp.

Origin & Development of Islam: An Essay on Its Socio-Economic Growth. Asghar A. Engineer. 248p. 1980. text ed. 18.95x (ISBN 0-86131-174-4, Pub. by Orient Longman Ltd India). Apt Bks.

Origin & Development of Muslim Historiography. M. G. Rasul. 1970. 5.00x (ISBN 0-87902-183-7). Orientalia.

Origin & Development of the Christian Church in Gaul During the First Six Centuries of the Christian Era. T. Scott Holmes. 1977. lib. bdg. 59.95 (ISBN 0-8490-2382-3). Gordon Pr.

Origin & Development of the Moral Ideas, 2 vols. facsimile ed. Edward Westermarck. LC 74-37359. (Select Bibliographies Reprint Ser.). Repr. of 1908 ed. Set. 81.50 (ISBN 0-8369-6706-2). Ayer Co Pubs.

Origin & Development of the Moral Ideas, 2 vols. 2nd ed. Edward A. Westermarck. (Landmarks in Anthropology Ser.). 1621p. Repr. 115.00 (ISBN 0-384-66958-1). Johnson Repr.

Origin & Doctrines of Early Indian Buddhist Schools. Vasu-Mitra. Tr. by Jiryo Masuda. LC 78-70133. Repr. of 1925 ed. 17.00 (ISBN 0-404-17403-5). AMS Pr.

Origin & Evolution of the Priesthood. James A. Mohler. 137p. 1976. pap. 3.95 (ISBN 0-8189-0342-2). Alba.

Origin & Growth of Religion: Facts & Theories. W. Schmidt. Tr. by H. J. Rose from Ger. LC 74-184909. xvi, 302p. 1972. Repr. of 1931 ed. lib. bdg. 22.50x (ISBN 0-8154-0408-5). Cooper Sq.

Origin & History of Hebrew Law. John M. Smith. LC 79-1620. 1980. Repr. of 1960 ed. 23.65 (ISBN 0-88355-924-2). Hyperion Conn.

Origin & Meaning of Hasidism. Martin Buber. LC 60-8161. 256p. 1972. pap. 5.95 (ISBN 0-8180-1315-X). Horizon.

Origin & Operation of Demons. 2nd ed. Kenneth E. Hagin. 1983. pap. 1.00 (ISBN 0-89276-025-7). Hagin Ministries.

Origin & Permanent Value of the Old Testament. Charles F. Kent. 270p. 1981. Repr. of 1906 ed. lib. bdg. 30.00 (ISBN 0-89760-429-6). Telegraph Bks.

Origin & Propagation of Sin: Being the Hulsean Lectures Delivered Before the University of Cambridge, 1901-2. F. R. Tennant. 235p. 1982. Repr. of 1908 ed. lib. bdg. 50.00 (ISBN 0-89987-822-9). Darby Bks.

Origin & Significance of the Great Pyramid. 2nd ed. C. Staniland Wake. LC 73-84047. (Secret Doctrine Reference Ser.). (Illus.). 170p. 1980. pap. 6.00 (ISBN 0-913510-32-7). Wizards.

Origin by Design. Harold G. Coffen. Ed. by Gerald Wheeler. LC 82-21445. (Illus.). 494p. 1983. text ed. 18.95 (ISBN 0-8280-0131-6). Review & Herald.

Origin of All Religious Worship. Charles Dupuis. Ed. by Burton Feldman & Robert D. Richardson. LC 78-60897. (Myth & Romanticism Ser.). 1984. lib. bdg. 80.00 (ISBN 0-8240-3558-5). Garland Pub.

Origin of Biblical Tradition. Albert T. Clay. LC 78-63556. (Yale Oriental Ser. Researches: No. 12). Repr. of 1923 ed. 37.50 (ISBN 0-404-60282-7). AMS Pr.

Origin of Christology. Charles F. Moule. LC 76-11087. 1977. 29.95 (ISBN 0-521-21290-1); pap. 11.95 (ISBN 0-521-29363-4). Cambridge U Pr.

Origin of Death: Studies in African Mythology. Hans Abrahamsson. Ed. by Robert Kastenbaum. LC 76-19555. (Death and Dying Ser.). 1977. Repr. of 1951 ed. lib. bdg. 23.50x (ISBN 0-405-09551-1). Ayer Co Pubs.

Origin of Demons & the Orders, Vol. 5. Gordon Lindsay. (Sorcery & Spirit World Ser.). 0.95 (ISBN 0-89985-088-X). Christ Nations.

Origin of Life. Richard B. Bliss & Gary E. Parker. LC 78-58477. (Illus.). 1978. pap. 4.95 (ISBN 0-89051-053-9). Master Bks.

Origin of Life & Death. Ulli Beier. (African Writers Ser.). 1966. pap. text ed. 4.50x (ISBN 0-435-90023-4). Heinemann Ed.

Origin of Pagan Idolatry, 3 vols. George S. Faber. Ed. by Burton Feldman & Robert D. Richardson. LC 78-60891. (Myth & Romanticism Ser.). 1984. Set. lib. bdg. 240.00 (ISBN 0-8240-3559-3). Garland Pub.

Origin of Paul's Gospel. 2nd., rev., enl. ed. Seyoon Kim. 426p. (Orig.). 1984. pap. 52.00x (ISBN 3-16-144836-7, Pub. by J C B Mohr BRD). Coronet Bks.

Origin of Russian Communism. Nicolas Berdyaev. 1960. pap. 8.95 (ISBN 0-472-06034-1, 34, AA). U of Mich Pr.

Origin of Saivism & Its Development in the Tamil Land. K. R. Subramaniam. 88p. 1986. Repr. 15.00X (ISBN 0-8364-1715-1, Pub. by Usha). South Asia Bks.

Origin of Suffering, The Origin of Evil, Illness & Death. Rudolf Steiner. Tr. by Mabel Cotterell & V. E. Watkin. (Ger.). 31p. 1980. pap. 2.95 (ISBN 0-919924-12-3, Pub. by Steiner Book Centre Canada). Anthroposophic.

Origin of the Idea of Crusade. Carl Erdmann. Tr. by Marshall W. Baldwin & Walter Goffart. 1977. 55.50x (ISBN 0-691-05251-4). Princeton U Pr.

Origin of the Inequality of the Social Classes. Gunnar Landtman. LC 68-56332. (Illus.). 1968. Repr. of 1938 ed. lib. bdg. 22.50x (ISBN 0-8371-0522-6, LASC). Greenwood.

Origin of the Jesuits. James Brodrick. LC 70-138604. 1971. Repr. of 1940 ed. lib. bdg. 22.50x (ISBN 0-8371-5523-1, BROJ). Greenwood.

Origin of the Jesuits. James Brodrick. LC 83-45590. Date not set. Repr. of 1940 ed. 33.50 (ISBN 0-404-19883-X). AMS Pr.

Origin of the Kabbala. M. Gaster. 1976. lib. bdg. 69.95 (ISBN 0-8490-2386-6). Gordon Pr.

Origin of the Solar System. John C. Whitcomb. (Biblical & Theological Studies). pap. 2.50 (ISBN 0-8010-9590-5). Baker Bk.

Origin of the Solar System. John C. Whitcomb, Jr. 1979. pap. 1.75 (ISBN 0-317-53170-0). BMH Bks.

Origin of the Universe, Life, Then Religion. Parker L. Johnstone. 235p. 7.95 (ISBN 0-917802-20-9). Theoscience Found.

Origin of the Young God: Kalidasa's Kumarasambhava. Hank Heifetz. 1985. 30.00x (ISBN 0-520-05304-4). U of Cal Pr.

Origin, Persecutions, & Doctrines of the Waldenses from Documents: Many Now for the First Time Collected & Edited. Pius Melia. LC 77-84716. Repr. of 1870 ed. 27.50 (ISBN 0-404-16122-7). AMS Pr.

Origin, Progress & Prospects of the Catholic Mission to the Rocky Mountains. Pierre-Jean De Smet. 1971. pap. 1.00 (ISBN 0-87770-044-3). Ye Galleon.

Origin Science. Norman L. Geisler & J. Kerby Anderson. 1987. pap. 8.95 (ISBN 0-8010-3808-1). Baker Bk.

Original & Sprynge of All Sectes & Orders by Whome, Wha or Where (Sic) They Beganne. Tr. by M. Coverdale from Dutch. LC 79-84127. (English Experience Ser.: No. 946). (Eng.). 140p. 1979. Repr. of 1537 ed. lib. bdg. 11.50 (ISBN 90-221-0946-1). Walter J Johnson.

Original Anecdotes of Peter the Great, Collected from the Conversation of Several Persons of Distinction at Petersburg & Moscow. Jakob Von Storcksburg Staehlin. LC 74-115587. (Russia Observed, Series I). 1970. Repr. of 1788 ed. 21.00 (ISBN 0-405-03064-9). Ayer Co Pubs.

Original Bulletin Boards on Jewish Themes. Nachama S. Moskowitz. 128p. (Orig.). 1986. pap. text ed. 12.50 (ISBN 0-86705-019-5). AIRE.

Original Commentary on the I Ching. John Stahl. 32p. 1976. 10.00 (ISBN 0-318-21738-4). Evanescent Pr.

Original Face: An Anthology of Rinzai Zen. Ed. by Thomas Cleary. LC 77-91354. 1978. pap. 4.95 (ISBN 0-394-17038-5, E707, Ever). Grove.

Original Feminist Attack on the Bible. Elizabeth C. Stanton. LC 74-9343. 258p. 1974. 6.95 (ISBN 0-405-05997-3). Ayer Co Pubs.

Original Ideas of Jesus That Are Changing the World. George Drew. 45p. (Orig.). 1980. pap. 5.45 (ISBN 0-940754-05-3). Ed Ministries.

Original Letters Relating to the Ecclesiastical Affairs of Scotland, 2 Vols. Ed. by David Laing. LC 73-171637. (Bannatyne Club, Edinburgh. Publications: No. 92). Repr. of 1852 ed. 95.00 (ISBN 0-404-52833-3). AMS Pr.

Original Letters Relative to the English Reformation, 2 Vols. 1846-1847. Set. 61.00 (ISBN 0-384-43680-3). Johnson Repr.

Original Meaning of the Resurrection. William Tregay. 60p. (Orig.). Date not set. pap. price not set. Church Man Pub.

Original Mr. Jacobs: Startling Expose. Telemachus T. Timayenis. Ed. by Gerald Grob. LC 76-46107. (Anti-Movements in America). 1977. Repr. of 1888 ed. lib. bdg. 24.50x (ISBN 0-405-09978-9). Ayer Co Pubs.

Original New Testament: A Radical Translation & Reinterpretation. Ed. & tr. by Hugh J. Schonfield. LC 85-42792. 628p. 1985. 19.45 (ISBN 0-06-250776-1, HarpR). Har-Row.

Original Papers Illustrative of the Life & Writings of John Milton. W. Douglas Hamilton. LC 76-29043. 1859. lib. bdg. 25.00 (ISBN 0-8414-4935-X). Folcroft.

Original Papers Illustrative of the Life & Writings of John Milton. Ed. by William D. Hamilton. (Camden Society, London. Publications, First Ser.: No. 75). Repr. of 1859 ed. 28.00 (ISBN 0-404-50175-3). AMS Pr.

Original Papers Illustrative of the Life & Writings of John Milton. Ed. by William D. Hamilton. 1859. 28.00 (ISBN 0-384-21220-4). Johnson Repr.

Original Revolution. John H. Yoder. LC 76-181577. (Christian Peace Shelf Ser.). 208p. 1972. pap. 6.95 (ISBN 0-8361-1812-X). Herald Pr.

Original Sin. Jonathan Edwards. Ed. by Clyde A. Holbrook. (Works of Jonathan Edwards Ser.: Vol. 3). 1970. 50.00x (ISBN 0-300-01198-9). Yale U Pr.

Original Sin in the Light of Modern Science. Patrick O'Connell. 128p. 1973. pap. 3.00 (ISBN 0-912414-15-4). Lumen Christi.

Original Sin: Two Major Trends in Contemporary Roman Catholic Reinterpretation. G. Vandervelde. LC 81-40000. 364p. 1982. lib. bdg. 32.50 (ISBN 0-8191-1849-4); pap. text ed. 15.75 o. p. (ISBN 0-8191-1850-8). U Pr of Amer.

Original Teachings of Cha'an Buddhism. Chang Chung-Yuan. pap. 9.95 (ISBN 0-394-62417-3, V-333, Vin). Random.

Original Teachings of Ch'an Buddhism. Ed. by Chang Chung-Yuan. LC 82-48003. (Grove Press Eastern Philosophy & Religion Ser.). 320p. 1982. pap. 9.95 (ISBN 0-394-62417-3, E813, Ever). Grove.

Original Unity of Man & Woman. Pope John Paul II. 184p. 1981. 4.00 (ISBN 0-8198-5405-0); pap. 3.00 (ISBN 0-686-78419-7). Dghtrs St Paul.

Original Vision: A Study of the Religious Experience of Childhood. Edward Robinson. 192p. (Orig.). 1983. pap. 7.95 (ISBN 0-8164-2439-X, HarpR). Har-Row.

Origines du Chant Litturgique de l'Eglise Latin. Francois A. Gavaert. 93p. Repr. of 1890 ed. lib. bdg. 30.00x (Pub. by G. Olms BRD). Coronet Bks.

Origines du chant romain: L'antiphonaire Gregorien. Amedee Gastoue. (Fr.). Repr. of 1907 ed. 32.50 (ISBN 0-404-56609-X). AMS Pr.

Origines du Culte des martyrs. 2nd, rev. ed. Hippolyte Delehaye. LC 78-63459. (Crusades & Military Orders: Second Ser.). Repr. of 1933 ed. 40.00 (ISBN 0-404-16518-4). AMS Pr.

Origines et les caracteres de la premiere croisade. Paul Rousset. LC 76-29837. (Fr.). Repr. of 1945 ed. 25.00 (ISBN 0-404-15428-X). AMS Pr.

Origines et Raison De la Liturgie Catholique En Forme De Dictionnaire... Suivies De la Liturgie Armenienne Traduite En Francais. Ed. by J. P. Migne. Tr. by Gabriel Avedichian & E. Pascal. (Encyclopedie Theologique Ser.: Vol. 8). (Fr.). 652p. Repr. of 1833 ed. lib. bdg. 83.00x (ISBN 0-89241-233-X). Caratzas.

Origines Parochiales Scotiae, 2 Vols. in 3. Ed. by Cosmo Innes et al. LC 76-170804. (Bannatyne Club, Edinburgh. Publications: No. 97). Repr. of 1855 ed. 210.00 (ISBN 0-404-52850-3). AMS Pr.

Origins & Characteristics of Anabaptism. M. Lienhard. (International Archives of the History of Ideas Ser: No. 87). 1977. lib. bdg. 53.00 (ISBN 90-247-1896-1, Pub. by Martinus Nijhoff Netherlands). Kluwer Academic.

Origins & Destiny: A Scientist Examines God's Handiwork. Robert Gange. 192p. 1986. 12.95 (ISBN 0-8499-0447-1, 0447-1). Word Bks.

Origins & Development of African Theology. Gwinyai H. Muzorewa. LC 84-14769. 160p. (Orig.). 1985. pap. 9.95 (ISBN 0-88344-351-1). Orbis Bks.

Origins & History of Consciousness. Erich Neumann. Tr. by R. F. Hull. (Bollingen Ser.: Vol. 42). (Illus.). 1954. pap. 9.95 (ISBN 0-691-01761-1). Princeton U Pr.

Origins & Rise of Ethology. W. H. Thorpe. 186p. 1979. 35.95 (ISBN 0-03-053251-5). Praeger.

Origins: Contemporary Vedic Library Series Based on the Teachings of A. C. Bhaktivedanta Swami Prabhupada. 1.50 (ISBN 0-89213-137-3). Bhaktivedanta.

Origins of Agnosticism: Victorian Unbelief & the Limits of Knowledge. Bernard Lightman. LC 86-46288. 272p. 1987. text ed. 29.50x (ISBN 0-8018-3375-2). Johns Hopkins.

Origins of American Transcendentalism. N. Kaplan & T. Katsanos. 1975. pap. 11.95x (ISBN 0-8084-0415-6). New Coll U Pr.

Origins of Certainty: Means & Meanings in Pascal's "Pensees". Hugh M. Davidson. LC 78-12768. 1979. lib. bdg. 16.00x (ISBN 0-226-13716-3). U of Chicago Pr.

Origins of Christianity: A Critical Introduction. Ed. by R. Joseph Hoffmann. 326p. (Orig.). 1985. pap. 15.95 (ISBN 0-87975-308-0). Prometheus Bks.

Origins of Christianity: A Historical Introduction to the New Testament. Schuyler Brown. (Oxford Bible Ser.). (Orig.). 1984. pap. 8.95 (ISBN 0-19-826202-7). Oxford U Pr.

Origins of Christianity: Sources & Documents. Howard C. Kee. LC 73-4830. 320p. 1973. P-H.

Origins of Church Wealth in Mexico: Ecclesiastical Revenues & Church Finances, 1523-1600. John F. Schwaller. LC 85-1122. (Illus.). 241p. 1985. 22.50x (ISBN 0-8263-0813-9). U of NM Pr.

Origins of Early Semitic Ritual. S. H. Hooke. (British Academy, London, Schweich Lectures on Biblical Archeology Series, 1935). pap. 19.00 (ISBN 0-8115-1277-0). Kraus Repr.

Origins of European Dissent. R. I. Moore. 338p. 1985. pap. 12.95x (ISBN 0-631-14404-8). Basil Blackwell.

Origins of Evil in Hindu Mythology Hermeneutics. Wendy D. O'Flaherty. (Studies in the History of Religions). 1977. pap. 6.95 (ISBN 0-520-04098-8, CAL 456). U of Cal Pr.

Origins of Faith & Life: Genesis A. (New Horizons Bible Study Ser.). 1981. pap. 1.95 leader's guide (ISBN 0-89367-052-9); pap. 2.50 study guide (ISBN 0-89367-053-7). Light & Life.

Origins of Greek Religion. B. C. Dietrich. 314p. 1973. 84.00x (ISBN 3-11-003982-6). De Gruyter.

Origins of Islamic Jurisprudence. M. Y. Guraya. 18.00 (ISBN 0-317-46093-5). Kazi Pubns.

Origins of Isma'ilism: A Study of the Historical Background of the Fatimid Caliphate. Bernard Lewis. LC 74-180357. Repr. of 1940 ed. 22.50 (ISBN 0-404-56289-2). AMS Pr.

Origins of Modern Europe: The Medieval Heritage of Western Civilization. R. Allen Brown. LC 72-11597. 1973. pap. 7.95x (ISBN 0-88295-705-8). Harlan Davidson.

Origins of Nativism in the United States, 1800-1844. Ray A. Billington. LC 73-19129. (Politics & People Ser.). (Illus.). 716p. 1974. Repr. 52.00x (ISBN 0-405-05854-3). Ayer Co Pubs.

Origins of Natural Science. Rudolf Steiner. Tr. of Der Entstehungsoment der Naturwissenschaft in der Weltgeschichte und ihre seitherige Entwickelung. 159p. (Orig.). 1985. 20.00 (ISBN 0-317-38883-5); pap. 9.95 (ISBN 0-88010-140-7). Anthroposophic.

Origins of Papal Infallibility 1150-1350. B. Tierney. 1972. 45.00. Heinman.

Origins of Popular Superstitions & Customs. Thomas S. Knowlson. LC 68-30946. 1968. Repr. of 1910 ed. 36.00x (ISBN 0-8103-3357-0). Gale.

Origins of the Christian Doctrine of Sacrifices. Robert J. Daly. LC 77-78628. pap. 40.00 (2026875). Bks Demand UMI.

Origins of the Christian Mystical Tradition: From Plato to Denys. Andrew Louth. 1981. pap. text ed. 9.95x (ISBN 0-19-826668-5). Oxford U Pr.

Origins of the Druze People & Religion, with Extracts from Their Sacred Writings. Philip K. Hitti. LC 30-27674. (Columbia University. Oriental Studies: No. 28). Repr. of 1928 ed. 19.00 (ISBN 0-404-50518-X). AMS Pr.

Origins of the English Civil War: Conspiracy, Crusade, or Class Conflict. Ed. by Philip A. Taylor. (Problems in European Civilization Ser.). 1960. pap. text ed. 5.50 (ISBN 0-669-24174-1). Heath.

Origins of the Gospel Traditions. Birger Gerhardsson. LC 78-19634. pap. 23.80 (2029615). Bks Demand UMI.

Origins of the Holocaust: Christian Anti-Semitism. Ed. by Randolph L. Braham. (East European Monographs: No. 204). 100p. 1986. 18.00 (ISBN 0-88033-953-5). East Eur Quarterly.

Origins of the Islamic State, 2 vols. Al-Baladuri Ahmad Ibn Yahya. Incl. Vol. 1. Tr. by Philip K. Hitti. Repr. of 1916 ed (ISBN 0-404-51694-7); Vol. 2. Tr. by Francis C. Murgotten. Repr. of 1924 ed (ISBN 0-404-51695-5). LC 76-82247. (Columbia University Studies in the Social Sciences: No. 163 & No. 163a). Set. 82.50 (ISBN 0-404-51163-5). AMS Pr.

Origins of the Israeli Polity: Palestine Under the Mandate. Dan Horowitz & Moshe Lissak. Tr. by Charles Hoffman. LC 78-3175. (Illus.). 320p. 1979. lib. bdg. 24.00x (ISBN 0-226-35366-4). U of Chicago Pr.

Origins of the Kabbalah. Gershom Scholem. Ed. by R. J. Werblowsky. Tr. by Allan Arkush. 500p. 1987. 47.50 (ISBN 0-691-07314-7). Princeton U Pr.

Origins of the Liturgical Year. Thomas J. Talley. 300p. (Orig.). 1986. pap. 17.50 (ISBN 0-916134-75-X). Pueblo Pub Co.

Origins of the Medieval World. William C. Bark. 1958. 15.00x (ISBN 0-8047-0513-5); pap. 5.95x (ISBN 0-8047-0514-3). Stanford U Pr.

Origins of the Modern Jew: Jewish Identity & European Culture in Germany, 1749-1824. Michael A. Meyer. LC 67-12384. (Waynebooks Ser: No. 32). 250p. 1972. o. p. 9.95x (ISBN 0-8143-1315-9); pap. 7.95x (ISBN 0-8143-1470-8). Wayne St U Pr.

Origins of the Order of Friars Minor. Cajetan Esser. (Orig.). 1970. 12.50 (ISBN 0-8199-0414-7). Franciscan Herald.

Origins of the Sacred. Anne Bancroft. 240p. 1987. pap. 12.95 (ISBN 1-85063-028-3, 30283, Ark Paperbks). Methuen Inc.

Origins of the Synagogue & the Church. Kaufmann Kohler. Ed. by H. G. Enelow. LC 73-2213. (Jewish People; History, Religion, Literature Ser.). Repr. of 1929 ed. 24.50 (ISBN 0-405-05277-4). Ayer Co Pubs.

Origins of the Synoptic Gospels. Ned B. Stonehouse. (Twin Brooks Ser.). 1979. pap. 5.95 (ISBN 0-8010-8180-7). Baker Bk.

Origins of Zionism. David Vital. (Illus.). 1975. pap. 14.95x (ISBN 0-19-827439-4). Oxford U Pr.

Origins: Today's Science, Tomorrow's Myth. James E. Strickling, Jr. 1986. 11.95 (ISBN 0-317-40170-X). Vantage.

Origins: Two Models. Richard Bliss. Ed. by Duane T. Gish & John N. Moore. LC 76-20178. (Illus.). 1976. 5.95 (ISBN 0-89051-027-X); tchr's. guide avail. Master Bks.

Orlando Gibbons. Ed. by P. C. Buck. (Tudor Church Music Ser.: Vol. 4). 1963. Repr. of 1925 ed. 85.00x (ISBN 0-8450-1854-X). Broude.

Ornamented Bags for Tallit & Tefllin. Ruth Eis. Ed. by Nelda Cassuto. LC 83-83059. (Magnes Museum Collection Ser.). 99p. (Orig.). 1984. pap. text ed. 22.50 (ISBN 0-318-01125-5). Magnes Mus.

Ornamented Jewish Oil Lamps. Varda Sussman. (Illus.). 144p. 1982. pap. text ed. 55.00x (ISBN 0-85668-164-4, Pub. by Aris & Phillips UK). Humanities.

Ornaments for the Daughters of Zion. Cotton Mather. LC 78-8588. 1978. 35.00x (ISBN 0-8201-1311-5). Schol Facsimiles.

Oroz Codex, or Relation of the Description of the Holy Gospel Province in New Spain, & the Lives of the Founders & Other Note-Worthy Men of Said Province Composed by Fray Pedro Oroz: 1584-1586. Ed. by Angelico Chavez. (Documentary Ser.). 1972. 25.00 (ISBN 0-88382-011-0). AAFH.

Orphean Passages: The Drama of Faith. Walter Wangerin, Jr. 305p. 1986. 16.95 (ISBN 0-06-069256-1). Har-Row.

Orpheus Philologus Bachofen versus Mommsen on the Study of Antiquity. Lionel Gossman. 90p. 1983. 8.00 (ISBN 0-87169-735-1). Am Philos.

Orpheus, the Metamorphoses of a Myth. Ed. by John Warden. LC 82-189058. pap. 63.50 (2026404). Bks Demand UMI.

Orrin Porter Rockwell: Man of God, Son of Thunder. 2nd ed. Harold Schindler. (University of Utah Publications in the American West: Vol. 15). (Illus.). 1983. 24.95 (ISBN 0-87480-204-0). U of Utah Pr.

Orrin Porter Rockwell, Mormon Frontier Marshall. Nicholas Van Alfen. 72p. pap. 3.95 (ISBN 0-87747-468-0). Deseret Bk.

Orson Hyde: Missionary, Apostle, Colonizer. Howard H. Barron. LC 77-74490. (Illus.). 336p. 1977. 10.95 (ISBN 0-88290-076-5). Horizon Utah.

Orthodox & Heretical Perfectionism in the Johannine Community As Evident in the First Epistle of John. John L. Bogart. LC 77-5447. (Society of Biblical Literature. Dissertation Ser.). 1977. pap. 9.95 (ISBN 0-89130-138-0, 060133). Scholars Pr GA.

Orthodox Approach to Philosophy. Apostolos Makrakis. Ed. by Orthodox Christian Educational Society. Tr. by Denver Cummings from Hellenic. (Logos & Holy Spirit in the Unity of Christian Thought Ser.: Vol. 1). 82p. 1977. pap. 3.25x (ISBN 0-938366-06-8). Orthodox Chr.

Orthodox Christian Education of Children in Our Days. George Grabbe. 30p. 1976. pap. 1.00x (ISBN 0-913026-17-4). St Nectarios.

Orthodox Christian Meditations (Spiritual Discourses for the Orthodox Christians) Apostolos Makrakis. Ed. by Orthodox Christian Educational Society. Tr. by Denver Cummings from Hellenic. 143p. (Orig.). 1965. pap. 3.50x (ISBN 0-938366-22-X). Orthodox Chr.

Orthodox Church. Timothy Ware. (Orig.). 1963. pap. 5.95 (ISBN 0-14-020592-6, Pelican). Penguin.

Orthodox Church & the Ecumenical Movement During the Period 1920-1969. George P. Macris. (Illus.). 196p. (Orig.). 1986. pap. 12.50 (ISBN 0-913026-74-3). St Nectarios.

Orthodox Church Directory of the United States. Adam S. Eterovich. 1968. softcover 5.00 (ISBN 0-88247-126-0). Ragusan Pr.

Orthodox Church in Independent Greece 1821-52. Charles A. Frazee. LC 69-10488. 1969. 42.50 (ISBN 0-521-07247-6). Cambridge U Pr.

Orthodox Church in the Byzantine Empire. J. M. Hussey. (History of the Christian Church Ser.). 320p. 1986. 59.00x (ISBN 0-19-826901-3). Oxford U Pr.

Orthodox Church: Its Past & Its Role in the World Today. John Meyendorff. LC 81-4978. 258p. 1981. pap. 8.95 (ISBN 0-913836-81-8). St Vladimirs.

Orthodox Church of Russia: A Millennial Celebration. Monseigneur Pitirim et al. LC 82-6933. (Illus.). 320p. 1982. 65.00 (ISBN 0-86565-029-2). Vendome.

Orthodox Church of the East in the Eighteenth Century. Tr. by George Williams. LC 73-131028. Repr. of 1868 ed. 21.00 (ISBN 0-404-06977-0). AMS Pr.

Orthodox Churches & the West. Ed. by Derek Baker. (Studies in Church History Ser.: Vol. 13). 350p. 1976. 45.00x (ISBN 0-631-17180-0). Basil Blackwell.

Orthodox Definition of Political Science. Apostolos Makrakis. Ed. by Orthodox Christian Educational Society. Tr. by Denver Cummings from Hellenic. 163p. 1968. pap. 4.00x (ISBN 0-938366-31-9). Orthodox Chr.

Orthodox Doctrine of the Apostolic Eastern Church. Platon. 1973. 5.00 (ISBN 0-686-05409-1). Eastern Orthodox.

Orthodox Doctrine of the Apostolic Eastern Church: A Compendium of Christian Theology. Platon. LC 70-81772. Repr. of 1857 ed. 18.50 (ISBN 0-404-05058-1). AMS Pr.

Orthodox Eastern Church. 3rd facsimile ed. Adrian Fortescue. LC 70-179520. (Select Bibliographies Reprint Ser). Repr. of 1920 ed. 26.50 (ISBN 0-8369-6649-X). Ayer Co Pubs.

Orthodox Eastern Church. Adrian Fortescue. (Illus.). 1969. 25.50 (ISBN 0-8337-1217-9). B Franklin.

Orthodox Evangelist. John Norton. LC 78-280. (American Puritan Writings Ser.: No. 11). Repr. of 1654 ed. 67.50 (ISBN 0-404-60811-6). AMS Pr.

Orthodox Hymns of Christmas, Easter, & Holy Week. Alexander Bogolepov. LC 65-16177. 78p. 1965. pap. 1.95 (ISBN 0-913836-02-8). St Vladimirs.

Orthodox Iconography. Constantine Cavarnos. LC 77-74606. (Illus.). 76p. 1977. pap. 4.50 (ISBN 0-914744-37-2). Inst Byzantine.

Orthodox Judaism in America. (American Jewish History Ser.: Vol. 69, Pt. 2). 1980. 6.00 (ISBN 0-911934-13-8). Am Jewish Hist Soc.

Orthodox Liturgical Vesture: An Historical Treatment. Archimandrite Chrysostomos. 76p. 1981. 6.95 (ISBN 0-916586-43-X); pap. 3.95 (ISBN 0-916586-44-8). Holy Cross Orthodox.

Orthodox Liturgy. 1984. priest's ed. 29.95 (ISBN 0-19-143495-7); congregational ed. 21.95 (ISBN 0-19-143492-2). Oxford U Pr.

Orthodox-Protestant Debate. Apostolos Makrakis. Tr. by Denver Cummings. 101p. 1949. pap. 3.25x (ISBN 0-938366-37-8). Orthodox Chr.

Orthodox Spirituality. pap. 0.25 (ISBN 0-686-05392-3). Eastern Orthodox.

Orthodox Spirituality: An Outline of the Orthodox Ascetical & Mystical Tradition. A Monk of the Eastern Church. 111p. 1978. pap. 4.95 (ISBN 0-913836-51-6). St Vladimirs.

Orthodox Spirituality & Protestant & Anglican Spirituality. Louis Bouyer. (History of Christian Spirituality Ser.: Vol. 3). 232p. 1982. pap. 9.95 (ISBN 0-8164-2374-1, HarpR). Har-Row.

Orthodox Synthesis: The Unity of Theological Thought. Ed. by Joseph J. Allen. 231p. (Orig.). 1981. pap. 8.95 (ISBN 0-913836-84-2). St Vladimirs.

Orthodox Theology: An Introduction. Vladimir Lossky. LC 78-1853. 137p. 1978. pap. 5.95 (ISBN 0-913836-43-5). St Vladimirs.

Orthodox Theology & Diakonia: Trends & Prospects. Intro. by Demetrios J. Constantelos. 398p. 1981. 24.95 (ISBN 0-916586-79-0); pap. 17.95 (ISBN 0-916586-80-4). Hellenic Coll Pr.

Orthodox-Unification Dialog. Ed. by Constantine N. Tsirpanlis. 139p. (Orig.). pap. 7.95. Rose Sharon Pr.

Orthodox-Unification Dialogue. Ed. by Constantine N. Tsirpanlis. LC 80-54586. (Conference Ser.: No. 8). (Illus.). x, 139p. (Orig.). 1981. pap. text ed. 7.95 (ISBN 0-932894-08-9, Pub. by New Era Bks). Paragon Hse.

Orthodox View on Abortion. John Kowalczyk. pap. 1.95 (ISBN 0-686-27070-3). Light&Life Pub Co MN.

Orthodox Way. Kallistos T. Ware. 196p. 1979. pap. 4.95 (ISBN 0-913836-58-3). St Vladimirs.

Orthodoxy. G. K. Chesterton. 160p. 1973. pap. 3.50 (ISBN 0-385-01536-4, Im). Doubleday.

Orthodoxy. G. K. Chesterton & Thomas More. (Books to Live Ser.). 1985. Repr. of 1908 ed. 10.95 (ISBN 0-88347-184-1). Thomas More.

Orthodoxy. Gilbert K. Chesterton. 297p. 1980. Repr. lib. bdg. 39.50 (ISBN 0-89987-125-9). Darby Bks.

Orthodoxy: A Creed for Today. A. M. Coniaris. 1972. pap. 7.95 (ISBN 0-937032-19-0). Light&Life Pub Co MN.

Orthodoxy & Anglicanism. Vasil T. Istavridis. LC 67-79982. 1966. 15.00x (ISBN 0-8401-1183-5). A R Allenson.

Orthodoxy & Heresy in Earliest Christianity. Walter Bauer. Ed. by Robert A. Kraft & Gerhard Krodel. LC 71-141252. 360p. 1979. pap. 2.50 (ISBN 0-8006-1363-5, 1-1363). Fortress.

Orthodoxy & Heresy in Early Christianity. Walter Bauer. LC 71-141252. pap. 88.00 (2027876). Bks Demand UMI.

Orthodoxy & Papism. Archimandrite Chrysostomos. Ed. by Theodore M. Williams. LC 82-73693. 70p. 1982. pap. 4.50 (ISBN 0-911165-00-2). Ctr Trad Orthodox.

Orthodoxy, Faith & Life: Christ & the Church. Gerasimos Papadopoulos. 151p. 1981. 10.95 (ISBN 0-916586-48-0); pap. 5.95 (ISBN 0-916586-47-2). Holy Cross Orthodox.

Orthodoxy, Faith & Life: Christ in the Gospels, Vol. 1. Gerasimos Papadopoulos. 164p. 1980. 9.50 (ISBN 0-916586-38-3); pap. 4.95 (ISBN 0-916586-37-5). Holy Cross Orthodox.

Orthodoxy, Heterodoxy & Dissent in India. Ed. by S. N. Eisenstadt et al. LC 83-26910. (Religion & Society Ser.: No. 23). viii, 179p. 1984. 42.00x (ISBN 3-11-009659-5). Mouton.

Orwellian World of Jehovah's Witnesses. Heather Botting & Gary Botting. (Illus.). 224p. 1984. pap. 10.95 (ISBN 0-8020-6545-7). U of Toronto Pr.

Osage Mission Baptisms, Marriages, & Interments, 1820-1886. Ed. by Louis F. Burns. (Osage Indian & Eng.). 869p. 1986. 35.00 (ISBN 0-942574-08-7). Ciga Pr.

Osiander in Preussen (1549-1552) Martin Stupperich. (Arbeiten Zur Kirchengeschichte, Vol. 44). 402p. 1973. 30.80x (ISBN 3-11-004221-5). De Gruyter.

Osiris. Cook. 1979. Repr. of 1931 ed. 12.50 (ISBN 0-89005-287-5). Ares.

Osiris & the Egyptian Resurrection, 2 vols. E. Wallis Budge. LC 72-81534. (Illus.). 906p. 1973. Vol. 1. pap. 7.95 (ISBN 0-486-22780-4); Vol. 2. pap. 7.95 (ISBN 0-486-22781-2). Dover.

Osiris & the Egyptian Resurrection, 2 vols. E. Wallis Budge. (Illus.). 30.50 (ISBN 0-8446-4715-2). Peter Smith.

Osterreichische Tauferakten One. Grete Mecenseffy. (Tauferakten Kommision Ser., Vol. 11). 402p. (Ger). 1964. 15.00x (ISBN 0-8361-1171-0). Herald Pr.

Osterreichische Tauferakten Two. Grete Mecenseffy. (Tauferakten Kommission Ser.). 544p. 1973. 40.00x (ISBN 0-8361-1192-3). Herald Pr.

Ostraka & Name Stones from the Tomb of Sen-Mut (No. 71) at Thebes: Metropolitan Museum of Art Publications in Reprint. William C. Hayes. LC 76-168406. (Illus.). 136p. 1972. Repr. of 1942 ed. 22.00 (ISBN 0-405-02239-5). Ayer Co Pubs.

Ostrich Christianity: Self-Deception in Popular Christianity. Van B. Weigel. LC 85-17981. 254p. (Orig.). 1986. lib. bdg. 25.75 (ISBN 0-8191-4974-8); pap. text ed. 12.75 (ISBN 0-8191-4975-6). U Pr of Amer.

Otfrid Von Weissenburg: Narrator or Commentator. Donald A. Mackenzie. (Stanford University. Stanford Studies in Language & Literature: Vol. 6, Pt. 3). Repr. of 1946 ed. 18.00 (ISBN 0-404-51812-5). AMS Pr.

Other Apostolates Today: Selected Letters & Addresses - III. Pedro Arrupe. Ed. by Jerome Aixala. LC 81-80741. 380p. 1981. 9.00 (ISBN 0-912422-81-5); pap. 8.00 smyth sewn (ISBN 0-912422-80-7). Inst Jesuit.

Other Bible. Ed. by Willis Barnstone. LC 83-48416. 768p. 1984. 24.45 (ISBN 0-06-250031-7, HarpR); pap. 14.95 (ISBN 0-06-250030-9, CN 4087). Har-Row.

Other Catholics. Keith P. Dyrud et al. 33.00 (ISBN 0-405-10820-6). Ayer Co Pubs.

Other Gospels: Non-Canonical Gospel Texts. Ed. by Ron Cameron. LC 82-8662. 192p. 1982. pap. 11.95 (ISBN 0-664-24428-9). Westminster.

Other Kingdom. David Rousset. Tr. by Ramon Guthrie from Fr. LC 81-12572. 173p. 1982. Repr. of 1947 ed. lib. bdg. 21.50 (ISBN 0-86527-339-1). Fertig.

Other Kingdom. Hubert Van Zeller. 3.95 (ISBN 0-87243-032-4). Templegate.

Other Nine. Colleen L. Reece. (Orig.). 1981. pap. 7.50 (ISBN 0-8309-0288-0). Herald Hse.

Other People. Mary J. Meadow. LC 84-2315. (Choices; Guides for Today's Woman: Vol. 6). 120p. (Orig.). 1984. pap. 6.95 (ISBN 0-664-24544-7). Westminster.

Other People, Other Places. Marzieh Gail. 288p. 14.95 (ISBN 0-85398-122-1); pap. 8.95 (ISBN 0-85398-123-X). G Ronald Pub.

Other Revelation for Christians. Hulon M. Madeley. (Illus.). 48p. 1985. 7.95 (ISBN 0-89962-434-0). Todd & Honeywell.

Other Shepherd. William S. Deal. 1982. 1.95 (ISBN 0-686-38053-3). Crusade Pubs.

Other Side of Silence: A Guide to Christian Meditation. Morton T. Kelsey. LC 76-9365. 314p. 1976. pap. 9.95 (ISBN 0-8091-1956-0). Paulist Pr.

Other Side of the Sun. Madeleine L'Engle. (Epiphany Bks.). 352p. (Orig.). 1983. pap. 3.50 (ISBN 0-345-30616-3). Ballantine.

Other Side of the Wall: Three Novellas. Nathan Shaham. Tr. by Leonard Gold from Hebrew. 256p. 1983. 13.95 (ISBN 0-8276-0223-5, 607). Jewish Pubns.

Other: Studies in the Social Ontology of Husserl, Heidegger, Sartre & Buber. Michael Theunissen. Tr. by Christopher Macann from Ger. LC 83-16267. (Studies in Contemporary German Social Thought). 429p. 1984. text ed. 45.00x (ISBN 0-262-20048-1). MIT Pr.

Other Text of Jeremiah: A Reconstruction of the Hebrew Text Underlying the Greek Version of the Prose Sections of Jeremiah with English Translation. Louis Stulman. LC 85-20278. 178p. (Orig.). 1986. lib. bdg. 25.75 (ISBN 0-8191-4988-8); pap. text ed. 12.75 (ISBN 0-8191-4989-6). U Pr of Amer.

Other Than That I Have No Opinion. Chuck Snyder. 240p. (Orig.). 1985. pap. 5.95 (ISBN 0-8423-4763-1). Tyndale.

Other Wise Man. Henry Van Dyke. 63p. (Orig.). 1984. pap. 7.95 (ISBN 0-941478-33-5). Paraclete Pr.

Other World, According to Descriptions in Medieval Literature. Howard R. Patch. LC 77-96164. 1970. Repr. of 1950 ed. lib. bdg. 27.50x (ISBN 0-374-96289-8, Octagon). Hippocrene Bks.

Other World: Spiritualism & Physical Research in England, 1850-1914. Janet Oppenheim. (Illus.). 580p. 1985. 44.50 (ISBN 0-521-26505-3). Cambridge U Pr.

Otherworld Journeys: Accounts of Near-Death Experience in Medieval & Modern Times. Carol Zaleski. 288p. 1987. 18.95 (ISBN 0-19-503915-7). Oxford U Pr.

Otjets Ioann Kronshtadtsky. P. M. Tchizhiv. Tr. of Father John of Kronstadt. 192p. 1958. pap. 8.00 (ISBN 0-317-29203-X). Holy Trinity.

Otkuda Proizoshla Vijera v Boga. F. E. Melnikov. Tr. of Where did Faith in God Come from? 48p. 1938. pap. 2.00 (ISBN 0-317-29132-7). Holy Trinity.

Otritsanije vmesto utverzhdenije. George Grabbe. Tr. of Denial Instead of Affirmation. 48p. 1971. pap. 2.00 (ISBN 0-317-30377-5). Holy Trinity.

Otterbein (Philip William) Arthur C. Core. 1968. 4.00 (ISBN 0-687-30917-4); pap. 2.25 (ISBN 0-687-30918-2). Abingdon.

Ottumwa District - A History: The United Methodist Church. Lyle Johnston. (Illus.). 118p. (Orig.). 1986. pap. 6.50 (ISBN 0-9616365-3-X). Grt Plains Emporium.

Otzar Hazmiros. (Heb). 7.50 (ISBN 0-87559-089-6); pap. 5.00 (ISBN 0-87559-088-8). Shalom.

Otzar Leshon Ha-Tannaim-Sifra-Tarat Kohanim, 4 vols. Binyamin Kosovsky. 1967. Set. 75.00x (ISBN 0-685-31426-X, Pub. by Jewish Theol Seminary). Ktav.

Otzar Leshon Ho-Tannaim-Mekilta d'rabi Ishmael, 4 vols. Binyamin Kosovsky. 1965. Set. 75.00x (ISBN 0-685-31425-1, Pub. by Jewish Theol Seminary). Ktav.

Ou-yang Hsiu: An Eleventh-Century Neo-Confucianist. James T. Liu. 1967. 18.50x (ISBN 0-8047-0262-4). Stanford U Pr.

Ounce of Prevention: A Parent's Guide to Moral & Spiritual Growth in Children. S. Bruce Narramore. 160p. 1973. pap. 6.95 (ISBN 0-310-30301-X, 11035P). Zondervan.

Our American Cardinals. J. J. Walsh. 59.95 (ISBN 0-8490-0782-8). Gordon Pr.

Our American Cardinals. facs. ed. James J. Walsh. LC 68-58815. (Essay Index Reprint Ser). 1926. 23.75 (ISBN 0-8369-1072-9). Ayer Co Pubs.

Our Amish Neighbors. William I. Schrieber. LC 62-17137. (Illus.). 1978. pap. 5.95 (ISBN 0-226-74035-8). U of Chicago Pr.

Our Baby: The First Five Years. Marion Stroud. (Illus.). 48p. 1986. 11.95 (ISBN 0-7459-1119-6). Lion USA.

Our Baptist Ministers & Schools. Albert W. Pegues. Repr. of 1892 ed. 44.00 (ISBN 0-384-45660-X). Johnson Repr.

Our Best Kept Secret: The Rich Heritage of Catholic Social Teaching. Michael J. Schultheis et al. (Illus.). 60p. (Orig.). 1985. pap. text ed. 3.50 (ISBN 0-934255-01-6). Center Concern.

Our Best Kept Secret: The Rich Heritage of Catholic Social Teaching. rev. & expanded ed. Michael J. Schultheis et al. 75p. (Orig.). 1987. pap. text ed. 4.50 (ISBN 0-934255-03-2). Center Concern.

Our Bible. Martha Durepo. LC 86-17571. (Bible-&-Me Ser.). 1987. 5.95 (ISBN 0-8054-4175-1). Broadman.

Our Brilliant Heritage. Oswald Chambers. 1965. pap. 2.95 (ISBN 0-87508-120-7). Chr Lit.

Our Caring Fellowship. L. D. Harsin. 1983. pap. 8.50 (ISBN 0-8309-0373-9). Herald Hse.

Our Catholic Heritage in Texas, 1519-1936, 7 vols. Carlos E. Casteneda. LC 76-1471. (Chicano Heritage Ser.). (Illus.). 1976. Repr. Set. 248.00 (ISBN 0-405-09488-4). Ayer Co Pubs.

Our Christian Faith: Answers for the Future. Karl Rahner & Karl-Heinz Weger. 208p. (Orig.). 1980. 10.95 (ISBN 0-8245-0361-9); pap. 4.95 (ISBN 0-8245-0362-7). Crossroad NY.

Our Christian Heritage. Garver. (Illus.). 4.50 (ISBN 0-935120-00-9). Christs Mission.

Our Christian Heritage: Revised & Expanded. 4th ed. Powel M. Dawley. LC 78-62062. 1978. pap. 5.50 (ISBN 0-8192-1243-1); leader's guide 3.95x (ISBN 0-8192-4086-9). Morehouse.

Our Christian Home & Family: An Illustrated Treasury of Inspirational Quotations, Poems & Prayers. Charles Wallis & Betty Wallis. LC 82-47758. (Illus.). 1982. 14.45 (ISBN 0-06-069009-7, HarpR). Har-Row.

Our Christian Symbols. Friedrich Rest. LC 53-9923. (Illus.). 96p. 1954. pap. 3.25 (ISBN 0-8298-0099-9). Pilgrim NY.

Our Christian Wedding. (Illus.). 48p. 1982. padded cover boxed 12.95 (ISBN 0-8007-1309-5). Revell.

Our Christian Wedding Guest Book. (Illus.). 48p. 1983. padded cover 8.50 (ISBN 0-8007-1345-1). Revell.

Our Christian Worship: Advent-Christmas. Friedrich Rest. 1985. 4.75 (ISBN 0-89536-761-0, 5868). CSS of Ohio.

Our Christmas Book. rev. ed. Jane B. Moncure. LC 85-29132. (Special-Day Bks.). (Illus.). 32p. 1986. lib. bdg. 7.45 (ISBN 0-89565-341-9). Childs World.

Our Christmas Handbook. Sandra Ziegler et al. LC 80-14587. (Illus.). 112p. (Orig.). 1980. pap. 6.50 (ISBN 0-89565-180-7). Childs World.

Our Christmas Handbook, No. 4. Marie H. Frost. (Illus.). 112p. 1986. 7.95 (ISBN 0-87403-081-1, 3044). Standard Pub.

Our Church. Gordon G. Johnson & Bob Putman. LC 83-82990. (Foundation Ser.). (Illus.). 147p. (Orig.). 1984. pap. 2.95 (ISBN 0-935797-06-8). Harvest IL.

Our Church & Our Children. Sophie Koulomzin. LC 75-20215. 158p. 1975. pap. 6.95 (ISBN 0-913836-25-7). St Vladimirs.

Our Church Music. Richard S. Willis. LC 72-1662. Repr. of 1856 ed. 11.50 (ISBN 0-404-08336-6). AMS Pr.

Our Church of God Faith for Children. Ralph E. Day. 1961. pap. 1.25 (ISBN 0-87148-652-0). Pathway Pr.

Our Church of God Faith: For Young People & Adults. Ralph E. Day. 1959. pap. 1.95 (ISBN 0-87148-651-2). Pathway Pr.

Our Church Today: What It Is & Can Be. G. Arthur Keough. (Horizon Ser.). 160p. 1980. pap. 5.95 (ISBN 0-8127-0300-6). Review & Herald.

Our City: The Jews of San Francisco. Irena Narrell. LC 80-21216. 1980. 25.00 (ISBN 0-8310-7122-2). Howell-North.

Our Constant Companion. David S. McCarthy. 96p. 1984. pap. 2.95 (ISBN 0-8170-1019-X). Judson.

Our Continuing Yes. Mother Ignatius Balla. 1973. pap. 2.00 (ISBN 0-8198-0243-3). Dghtrs St Paul.

Our Crowd: The Great Jewish Families of New York. Stephen Birmingham. 528p. 1985. pap. 4.50 (ISBN 0-425-07557-5). Berkley Pub.

Our Daily Bread. M. R. DeHaan & Henry G. Bosch. 1986. 13.95 (ISBN 0-310-23410-7, 9505). Zondervan.

Our Daily Bread. Mieczyslaw Malinski. 142p. 1979. 7.95 (ISBN 0-8245-0363-5). Crossroad NY.

Our Daily Bread Favorites. rev. ed. Richard W. DeHaan & Henry G. Bosch. 384p. 1986. pap. 9.95 large print ed. (ISBN 0-310-25877-4, 12587L). Zondervan.

Our Daily Bread Favorites. Ed. by Richard W. De Haan & Henry G. Bosch. 384p. 1971. 10.95 (ISBN 0-310-23590-1). Zondervan.

Our Decentralized Literature: Cultural Mediations in Selected Jewish & Southern Writers. Jules Chametzky. LC 86-1259. 168p. 1986. lib. bdg. 25.00x (ISBN 0-87023-527-3); pap. text ed. 9.95 (ISBN 0-87023-540-0). U of Mass Pr.

Our Destiny: The Influence of Socialism on Morals & Religion; an Essay on Ethics. Laurence Gronlund. LC 75-321. (Radical Tradition in America Ser.). 170p. 1975. Repr. of 1890 ed. 19.25 (ISBN 0-88355-225-6). Hyperion Conn.

Our Dialogue with Rome: The Second Vatican Council & After. G. B. Caird. 7.25 (ISBN 0-8446-1797-0). Peter Smith.

Our English Bible. H. W. Hoare. 1925. 27.00 (ISBN 0-8274-3083-3). R West.

Our Eucharistic Prayers in Worship, Preaching & Study. Raymond Moloney. (Theology & Life Ser.: Vol. 14). 1985. pap. 8.95 (ISBN 0-89453-531-5). M Glazier.

Our Eyes Can Be Opened: Preaching the Miracle Stories of the Synoptic Gospels Today. Ronald J. Allen. LC 81-43679. 146p. 1983. pap. text ed. 9.50 (ISBN 0-8191-2671-3). U Pr of Amer.

Our Faith. Emil Brunner. 1936. pap. text ed. 7.95 (ISBN 0-684-16856-1, SL87, ScribT). Scribner.

Our Faith. Emil Brunner. 153p. 1980. pap. text ed. write for info. (ISBN 0-02-315940-5, Pub. by Scribner). Macmillan.

Our Faith. Casimir Kucharek. Ed. by Jose D. Vinck. LC 82-73784. 350p. 1983. 17.75 (ISBN 0-911726-43-8). Alleluia Pr.

Our Faith & Fellowship. G. Raymond Carlson. LC 77-75023. (Radiant Life Ser.). 128p. 1977. pap. 2.50 (ISBN 0-88243-908-1, 02-0908); teacher's ed. 3.95 (ISBN 0-88243-178-1, 32-0178). Gospel Pub.

Our Faith: Basic Christian Belief. Max Thurian. Tr. by Emily Chisholm from Fr. LC 82-72008. 192p. 1982. 12.95 (ISBN 0-8245-0547-6). Crossroad NY.

Our Faith Speaks. Mrs. Boyd Crooks. 62p. 1962. pap. 0.35 (ISBN 0-89114-147-2). Baptist Pub Hse.

Our Family: A Love Story. Maur Burbach et al. 66p. 1981. 12.50 (ISBN 0-8146-1222-9). Liturgical Pr.

Our Family Christmas Book. Mary Batchelor. 96p. 1984. 9.95 (ISBN 0-687-29587-4). Abingdon.

Our Family Lenten Experience. Amy Shaw. 1983. 4.95 (ISBN 0-89536-590-1, 1506). CSS of Ohio.

Our Family Night In: Workbook of Covenant Living. Lois Seifert. LC 80-54803. 200p. (Orig.). pap. 4.95x (ISBN 0-8358-0420-8). Upper Room.

Our Family Shares Advent: Scripture, Prayer, & Activities for Families. Mary Y. Nilsen. (Illus.). 64p. (Orig.). 1980. pap. 7.95 (ISBN 0-86683-637-3, 8129, HarpR). Har-Row.

Our Father. Ruth Burrows. (Illus.). 96p. 1986. 5.95 (ISBN 0-87193-255-5). Dimension Bks.

Our Father. Joan Hodgson. (Illus.). 1977. pap. 2.95 (ISBN 0-85487-040-7). De Vorss.

Our Father. Joanne L. Kepes. 1982. 9.95 (ISBN 0-89837-060-4, Pub. by Pflaum Pr). Peter Li.

Our Father. (Illus.). 48p. 1983. 7.95 (ISBN 0-86683-745-0, AY8398, HarpR). Har-Row.

Our Father, Friend of Little Children Coloring Book. 1973. 2.50 (ISBN 0-89536-177-9, 1515). CSS of Ohio.

Our Father Saint Benedict. M. Regina Goberna. Tr. by Maurus Green from Catalan. Tr. of El Pare Sant Benet. (Illus.). 128p. (Orig.). 1983. pap. 4.95 (ISBN 0-911782-45-1). New City.

Our Father Who Art in Heaven. Kurt Rommel. Tr. by Edward A. Cooperrider from Ger. LC 80-2373. Tr. of Einladung zum Gesprach mit Gott: Gedanken uber das Vaterunser. 96p. 1981. pap. 4.95 (ISBN 0-8006-1448-8, 1-1448). Fortress.

Our Father's Plan. Boyd K. Packer. LC 84-72516. (Illus.). 64p. 1984. 8.95 (ISBN 0-87747-523-7). Deseret Bk.

Our Fathers World. (Social Studies Ser.). 3.55 (ISBN 0-686-37694-3). Rod & Staff.

Our Favorite Verse. Stuart Briscoe & Jill Briscoe. LC 86-71753. (My Favorite Verse Ser.). 24p. 1987. pap. 4.95 (ISBN 0-89636-224-8). Accent Bks.

Our Favorite Verse. David Mains & Karen Mains. LC 86-73188. (My Favorite Verse Ser.). 24p. 1987. pap. 4.95 (ISBN 0-89636-232-9). Accent Bks.

Our First Communion: A Growing-up Moment. Angela Schrieber. Ed. by Carl Fischer. 1986. dupl. masterbk 9.95 (ISBN 0-89837-107-4). Peter Li.

Our First One Hundred Years. Charles Conn. (Church Training Course Ser.). 1986. cloth 5.75 (ISBN 0-87148-668-7); pap. 4.75 (ISBN 0-87148-669-5). Pathway Pr.

Our First Penance: Celebrating God's Forgiving Love. Kathleen Holmberg. Ed. by Carl Fischer. 1986. dupl. masterbk 9.95 (ISBN 0-89837-108-2). Peter Li.

Our First Song: Evangelism in the Hymns of Charles Wesley. Ellsworth Kalas. LC 84-70133. 64p. (Orig.). 1984. pap. 2.95 (ISBN 0-88177-010-8, DRO10B). Discipleship Res.

Our First Sukkah. Norma Simon. (Festival Series of Picture Story Books). (Illus.). 1959. plastic cover 4.50 (ISBN 0-8381-0703-6). United Syn Bk.

Our Gift: Sunshine. 5.00 (ISBN 0-8198-6830-2); 4.00 (ISBN 0-8198-6831-0). Dghtrs St Paul.

Our God. Russell G. Jones. LC 81-66135. 1981. pap. 4.95 (ISBN 0-89636-069-5). Accent Bks.

Our God: A "Sun & Shield" for Troubled Hearts. Thomas B. Warren. 1963. 10.00 (ISBN 0-934916-38-1). Natl Christian Pr.

Our God Gives Life. Joan Mitchell. 1984. 9.95 (ISBN 0-89837-098-1, Pub. by Pflaum Press). Peter Li.

Our Gospel's Women. Alma E. Blanton. (Illus.). 114p. (Orig.). 1979. pap. 3.00 (ISBN 0-938134-01-9). Loving Pubs.

Our Growing Child. Mary J. Saia & Judith Boyle. 112p. (Orig.). 1985. pap. 5.95 (ISBN 0-89622-221-7). Twenty-Third.

Our Hearts Are Restless. Gilbert Kilpatrick. 1983. pap. 2.50x (ISBN 0-87574-032-4, 032). Pendle Hill.

Our Hearts Are Restless: The Prayer of St. Augustine. F. J. Sheed. 96p. 1976. pap. 4.95 (ISBN 0-8164-2127-7, HarpR). Har-Row.

Our Hearts Wait: Daily Prayer for Advent. Joan Cole. 48p. 1984. pap. 1.50 (ISBN 0-89243-215-2). Liguori Pubns.

Our Heavenly Father. Robert Frost. LC 77-95191. 1978. pap. 3.95 (ISBN 0-88270-266-1). Bridge Pub.

Our Heavenly Father. Daria Sockey. (Faith & Life Ser.: Bk. 1). (Illus.). 125p. 1987. pap. text ed. 4.95; activity book 2.50. Ignatius Pr.

Our Heritage & Our Hope: A History of Pullen Memorial Baptist Church 1884-1984. Roger H. Crook. LC 84-62984. (Illus.). 252p. 1985. 10.00 (ISBN 0-9614485-0-4). Pullen Mem Baptist.

Our Heritage: Brethren Beliefs & Practices. Harold H. Etling. pap. 4.95 (ISBN 0-88469-022-9). BMH Bks.

Our Heritage in Public Worship. D. H. Hislop. 354p. 1935. 12.95 (ISBN 0-567-02138-6, Pub. by T & T Clark Ltd UK). Fortress.

Our Heritage Is the Lord. new ed. John Kirvan. 1980. 5.95 (ISBN 0-03-047661-5, HarpR). Har-Row.

Our Heritage of Hymns: A Swift Survey. Bernard E. Seton. LC 84-71734. 160p. (Orig.). 1984. pap. 10.95 (ISBN 0-943872-89-8). Andrews Univ Pr.

Our Heritage Speaks: Applying Jewish Values to Contempary Issues. National Council of Jewish Women Staff. (Jewish Values Ser.: Choices in Action & Advocacy: Module II). 19p. (Orig.). pap. 3.50 (ISBN 0-941840-28-X). NCJW.

Our Heritage Speaks: Applying Jewish Values to Contemporary Issues. National Council of Jewish Women. (Module I - Care of Aging Parents). (Illus.). 30p. (Orig.). 1985. pap. 3.50 (ISBN 0-941840-23-9). NCJW.

Our Heroes: Four Complete Meetings for Junior High Youth Groups. Kevin Miller. (Best of Young Teen Action Ser.). 32p. 1985. pap. 4.95 (ISBN 0-89191-380-7). Cook.

Our Holidays. Miriam Schlein. (Illus.). 128p. 1983. pap. text ed. 4.95x (ISBN 0-87441-382-6). Behrman.

Our Hymns of Praise. Ed. by J. Mark Stauffer. (Illus.). 168p. 1958. 4.95x (ISBN 0-8361-1126-5). Herald Pr.

Our Idea of God. Juan L. Segundo. Tr. by John Drury from Span. LC 73-77358. (Theology for Artisans of a New Humanity Ser.: Vol. 3). Orig. Title: Nuestra idea de Dios. 212p. (Orig.). 1974. 7.95x (ISBN 0-88344-483-6); pap. 4.95 o. p. (ISBN 0-88344-489-5). Orbis Bks.

Our Infallible Bible. David Nettleton. LC 77-15540. (Illus.). 1978. pap. 1.75 (ISBN 0-87227-055-6); tchr's guide 4.50 (ISBN 0-87227-056-4). Reg Baptist.

Our Inheritance: A Collection of Sermons & Addresses for All the Sabbaths & Festivals. Isaiah Raffalovich. 272p. 32.50 (ISBN 0-87559-146-9). Shalom.

Our Inheritance in the Great Pyramid, Vol. 8. Piazzi Smyth. LC 77-5284. (Illus.). 672p. 1980. Repr. of 1877 ed. lib. bdg. 45.00 (ISBN 0-89345-029-4, Spiritual Sci Lib). Garber Comm.

Our Invaluable Pearl: The Unique Status of Women in Judaism. H. Yedidiah Ghatan. LC 85-73454. 200p. (Orig.). 1986. pap. 9.95x (ISBN 0-8197-0502-0). Bloch.

Our Jerusalem. Yaffa Ganz. (Illus.). 1979. pap. 3.50x (ISBN 0-87441-308-7). Behrman.

Our Jerusalem: An American Family in the Holy City, 1881-1949. Bertha H. Vester. Ed. by Moshe Davis. LC 77-70752. (America & the Holy Land Ser.). 1977. Repr. of 1950 ed. lib. bdg. 30.00x (ISBN 0-405-10296-8). Ayer Co Pubs.

Our Jewish Friends. Rev. ed. Louis Goldberg. 1983. pap. text ed. 4.95 (ISBN 0-87213-239-0). Loizeaux.

Our Lady among Us. Valentino Del Mazza. 1978. 4.00 (ISBN 0-8198-0363-4); pap. 3.00 (ISBN 0-8198-0364-2). Dghtrs St Paul.

Our Lady: Eight Hundred & Sixty-Eight Pronouncements from Benedict Fourteenth to John Twenty-Third. Ed. by Monks Of Solesmes. 5.50 (ISBN 0-8198-0111-9). Dghtrs St Paul.

Our Lady of Fatima. William Thomas Walsh. pap. 4.50 (ISBN 0-385-02869-5, D1, Im). Doubleday.

Our Lady of Fatima's Peace Plan from Heaven. 32p. 1983. pap. 0.40 (ISBN 0-89555-217-5). TAN Bks Pubs.

Our Lady of Guadalupe & the Conquest of Darkness. Warren H. Carroll. 123p. (Orig.). pap. 4.95 (ISBN 0-931888-12-3). Christendom Pubns.

Our Lengthened Shadows. Jackie Corbitt. 110p. 1970. pap. 1.75 (ISBN 0-89114-015-8). Baptist Pub Hse.

Our Liberal Movement in Theology: Chiefly As Shown in Recollections of the History of Unitarianism in New England. 3rd ed. Joseph H. Allen. LC 73-38432. (Religion in America, Ser. 2). 230p. 1972. Repr. of 1892 ed. 20.00 (ISBN 0-405-04053-9). Ayer Co Pubs.

Our Life & Times. Dale Dieleman. 1985. pap. 5.95 (ISBN 0-8010-2951-1). Baker Bk.

Our Life in Christ. Albert L. Schlitzer. (University Theology Ser.: Vols. 1 & 2). 1962. Set. 12.95 (ISBN 0-268-00201-0). U of Notre Dame Pr.

Our Life Together. James Thompson. LC 77-79338. (Journey Bks.). 1977. pap. 3.50 (ISBN 0-8344-0095-2). Sweet.

Our Life with Mister Gurdjieff. Thomas De Hartmann. LC 64-22661. (Illus.). 1964. 17.50x (ISBN 0-8154-0058-6). Cooper Sq.

Our Life with Mr. Gurdjieff. rev. ed. Thomas De Hartmann & Olga De Hartmann. LC 83-47722. 160p. 1983. pap. 7.95 (ISBN 0-06-061865-5, RD 469, HarpR). Har-Row.

Our Lord's Pattern for Prayer. Adolph Saphir. LC 84-9710. (Adolph Saphir Study Ser.). 432p. 1984. pap. 11.95 (ISBN 0-8254-3748-2). Kregel.

Our Lost World. Bertha Smith. LC 80-68537. 1981. pap. 4.95 (ISBN 0-8054-6324-0). Broadman.

Our Many Selves. Elizabeth O'Connor. LC 78-124699. 1971. pap. 4.95 (ISBN 0-06-066336-7, RD-36, HarpR). Har-Row.

Our Masters Taught Rabbinic Stories & Sayings. Jakob J. Petuchowski. LC 82-9999. 160p. 1982. 10.95 (ISBN 0-8245-0521-2). Crossroad NY.

Our Methodist Heritage. Charles W. Keysor. LC 84-80824. 174p. pap. 3.95 (ISBN 0-917851-00-5). Good News KY.

Our Miracle. Benjamin Dolinsky. LC 86-43253. 116p. 1987. pap. 5.95 (ISBN 0-88400-126-1). Shengold.

Our Mission. Gene Edwards. (Orig.). 1984. pap. 7.95 (ISBN 0-940232-11-1). Christian Bks.

Our Moral Nature. James McCosh. LC 75-3260. Repr. of 1892 ed. 18.00 (ISBN 0-404-59247-3). AMS Pr.

Our Mother Church, Her Worship & Offices. 1948 ed. Compiled by Catherine Zvegintzov. LC 78-227697. pap. 6.50x (ISBN 0-281-00849-3). A R Allenson.

Our Name Is Peter. Sean O'Reilly. LC 77-380. 155p. 1977. 5.95 (ISBN 0-8199-0666-2). Franciscan Herald.

Our Nearest Kinsman. Roy Hession. 1976. pap. 2.95 (ISBN 0-87508-229-7). Chr Lit.

Our New Age: Words for the People. 1st ed. Christopher. LC 77-72309. (Illus., Orig.). 1977. pap. 2.95 (ISBN 0-916940-01-2). World Light.

Our Ordered Lives Confess. Irwin T. Hyatt, Jr. (American-East Asian Relations Ser.: No. 8). 1976. 20.00x (ISBN 0-674-64735-1). Harvard U Pr.

Our Own Religion in Ancient Persia. Lawrence H. Mills. LC 74-21262. Repr. of 1913 ed. 45.00 (ISBN 0-404-12811-4). AMS Pr.

Our Own Years. Alice Lake. 244p. 1982. pap. 8.95 (ISBN 0-86683-667-5, HarpR). Har-Row.

Our Pagan Christmas. R. J. Condon. 12p. 1982. pap. 1.00 (ISBN 0-911826-47-5). Am Atheist.

Our Pentecostal Heritage. Frank W. Lemons. 174p. 1963. pap. 4.95 (ISBN 0-87148-653-9). Pathway Pr.

Our People: The Amish & Mennonites of Ohio. Levi Miller. LC 82-84405. (Illus.). 56p. (Orig.). 1983. pap. 2.50 (ISBN 0-8361-3331-5). Herald Pr.

Our Perfecting World: Zarathushtra's Way of Life. Maneckji N. Dhalla. LC 74-21257. Repr. of 1930 ed. 27.50 (ISBN 0-404-12807-6). AMS Pr.

Our Portrait in Genesis. Oswald Chambers. 1973. pap. 2.25 (ISBN 0-87508-135-5). Chr Lit.

Our Presbyterian Belief. Felix B. Gear. LC 79-23421. 90p. (Orig.). 1980. pap. 6.95 (ISBN 0-8042-0676-7). John Knox.

Our Prophet, Vol. II. A. Ghazi. 1981. 3.50 (ISBN 0-686-97846-3). Kazi Pubns.

Our Quaker Friends of Ye Olden Time. James P. Bell. LC 76-22486. (Illus.). 287p. 1976. Repr. of 1905 ed. 17.50 (ISBN 0-8063-0732-3). Genealog Pub.

Our Reasonable Faith: A Survey of Christian Doctrine. Herman Bavinck. Tr. by Henry Zylstra. (Twin Brooks Ser). 1977. pap. 13.95 (ISBN 0-8010-0513-2). Baker Bk.

Our Relationship to Those Who Have Died. Hermann Heisler. 1976. pap. 2.50 (ISBN 0-916786-03-X). St George Bk Serv.

Our Right to Choose: Toward a New Ethic of Abortion. Beverly W. Harrison. LC 81-70488. 256p. 1983. 18.95x (ISBN 0-8070-1508-3). Beacon Pr.

Our Right to Choose: Toward a New Ethic of Abortion. Beverly W. Harrison. LC 81-70488. 356p. 1984. pap. 10.95 (ISBN 0-8070-1509-1, BP673). Beacon Pr.

Our Road to Prayer. Francis Line & Helen Line. 1974. pap. 1.25x (ISBN 0-8358-0305-8). Upper Room.

Our Sages, God & Israel: An Anthology of the Jerusalem Talmud. Ed. by Jacob Neusner. LC 84-23793. 179p. 1985. 19.95 (ISBN 0-940646-18-8). Rossel Bks.

Our Sages Showed the Way, Vol. 1. Yocheved Segal. Tr. by Esther Falk. (Hebrew.). pap. 9.95 (ISBN 0-87306-289-2). Feldheim.

Our Sages Showed the Way, Vol. 2. Yocheved Segal. Tr. by Esther Falk from Hebrew. (Jewish Youth Classics Ser.). (Illus.). 192p. 1982. text ed. 9.95 (ISBN 0-87306-200-0). Feldheim.

Our Savior Is Born. Dan Carr. 1984. 6.50 (ISBN 0-570-04092-2, 56-1460). Concordia.

Our Search for Identity: Humanity in the Image of God. Marianne H. Micks. LC 81-70592. 176p. 1982. pap. 1.00 (ISBN 0-8006-1627-8). Fortress.

Our Search for Serenity. Gigi Tchividjian & Stephan Tchividjian. 168p. 1983. pap. 5.95 (ISBN 0-8007-5151-5, Power Bks). Revell.

Our Share of Morning. James E. Heller. LC 73-5262. 360p. 1974. Repr. of 1961 ed. lib. bdg. 22.50x (ISBN 0-8371-6874-0, BUOS). Greenwood.

Our Sisters in the Bible. Jerrie W. Hurd. LC 83-50986. 168p. 1983. 8.95 (ISBN 0-87747-981-X). Deseret Bk.

Our Sisters in the Latter-Day Scriptures. Jerrie W. Hurd. 1987. 10.95 (ISBN 0-87579-091-7). Deseret Bk.

Our Special Child. rev. ed. Bette M. Ross. 256p. 1984. pap. 8.95 (ISBN 0-8007-1230-7). Revell.

Our Spiritual Resources. Joel S. Goldsmith. LC 78-16010. 192p. 1983. pap. 3.50 (ISBN 0-06-063212-7, RD 478, HarpR). Har-Row.

Our Story According to St. Mark. William H. Barnwell. 288p. (Orig.). 1982. pap. 9.95 (ISBN 0-86683-634-9, HarpR). Har-Row.

Our Story of Bringing a Course in Miracles into Application. Tara Singh. (Orig.). Date not set. price not set (ISBN 1-55531-127-X); pap. price not set (ISBN 1-55531-128-8). Life Action Pr.

Our Synagogue, 3 vols. Raymond A. Zwerin & Audrey Friedman. (Illus.). 1974. pap. text ed. 3.50x (ISBN 0-03-012671-1). Behrman.

Our Time Together: Children's Sermons Based on Lectionary Series A. Jim Morentz & Doris Morentz. 112p. (Orig.). 1983. pap. 8.75 (ISBN 0-687-29775-3). Abingdon.

Our Treasured Heritage. Theresa Scheing & Lou Savary. 176p. 1986. pap. 8.95 (ISBN 0-8245-0731-2). Crossroad NY.

Our Treasured Heritage: Teaching Christian Meditation to Children. Louis M. Savary & Theresa O. Scheihing. LC 81-7818. 176p. 1981. 9.95 (ISBN 0-8245-0078-4). Crossroad NY.

Our Unitarian Heritage: An Introduction to the History of the Unitarian Movement. Earl M. Wilbur. LC 83-45635. Date not set. Repr. of 1925 ed. 49.50 (ISBN 0-404-19877-5). AMS Pr.

Our Visited Planet. William M. Justice. 1978. pap. 4.95 (ISBN 0-918626-03-X). Word Serv.

Our Wonderful Bible. R. K. Campbell. 417p. 12.95 (ISBN 0-88172-009-7); pap. 10.50 (ISBN 0-88172-010-0). Believers Bkshelf.

Our World Belongs to God: A Contemporary Testimony (Study Version) Contemporary Testimony Committee of the Christian Reformed Church. 1984. pap. 1.00 (ISBN 0-933140-91-6). CRC Pubns.

Our World of Wonders. Sterling W. Sill. 96p. 1986. 7.95 (ISBN 0-88290-287-3). Horizon Utah.

Our Yes to God. Chiara Lubich. Tr. by Hugh J. Moran from Ital. LC 81-82064. 112p. (Orig.). 1981. pap. 3.95 (ISBN 0-911782-38-9). New City.

Ouspensky: The Unsung Genius. J. H. Reyner. 115p. 1982. 14.95 (ISBN 0-04-294122-9). Allen Unwin.

Out! In the Name of Jesus. 3rd ed. Pat Brooks. LC 85-72223. 235p. 1986. pap. text ed. 5.00 (ISBN 0-932050-27-1). New Puritan.

Out of Bondage. Arnold Perrin. (Illus.). 52p. 1983. pap. 4.95 (ISBN 0-939736-45-4). Wings ME.

Out of Chaos. Challoner. 6.95 (ISBN 0-8356-5051-0). Theos Pub Hse.

Out of Confusion-into the Light. large print ed. Pearl Brians. 58p. 1984. pap. 9.50 (ISBN 0-914009-12-5). VHI Library.

Out of Curiosity: Spirit of Nyingma in America. 350p. 1987. pap. 12.95 (ISBN 0-89800-135-8). Dharma Pub.

Out of Darkness into Light. Asa Mahan. Ed. by Donald W. Dayton. (Higher Christian Life Ser.). 366p. 1985. 45.00 (ISBN 0-8240-6429-1). Garland Pub.

Out of Easter, the Gospels. Jean Hall. (YA) 1979. pap. text ed. 4.25 (ISBN 0-03-021301-0, 321, HarpR); tchr's ed 2.95 (ISBN 0-03-021306-1, 322). Har-Row.

Out of Mighty Waters. Lois L. Shenk. LC 81-20116. 192p. (Orig.). 1982. 10.95 (ISBN 0-8361-1987-8); pap. 6.95 (ISBN 0-8361-1988-6). Herald Pr.

Out of My Bondage. Marion B. West. LC 76-5297. 128p. 1976. 5.50 (ISBN 0-8054-5144-7). Broadman.

Out of Our People's Past: Sources for the Study of Jewish History. Walter Ackerman. 1978. 7.50x (ISBN 0-8381-0221-2). United Syn Bk.

Out of Solitude. Henri J. Nouwen. (Illus.). 64p. 1974. pap. 1.95 (ISBN 0-87793-072-4). Ave Maria.

Out of the Cloister: A Study of Organizational Dilemmas. Helen R. Ebaugh. 177p. 1977. text ed. 12.50x (ISBN 0-292-76007-8). U of Tex Pr.

Out of the Dark Valley. Gordon Lindsay. 1.25 (ISBN 0-89985-019-7). Christ Nations.

Out of the Depths. John Newton. LC 80-85340. (Shepherd Illustrated Classics Ser.). (Illus.). 1981. pap. 5.95 (ISBN 0-87983-243-6). Keats.

Out of the Depths Have I Cried: Thoughts on Incarnational Theology in the Eastern Christian Experience. Metropolitan Philip Saliba & Joseph J. Allen. LC 79-18611. (Illus., Orig.). 1979. pap. 4.95 (ISBN 0-916586-32-4). Holy Cross Orthodox.

Out of the Depths: The Psalms Speak for Us Today. Revised & Expanded ed. Bernhard W. Anderson. LC 83-19801. 254p. 1983. pap. 11.95 (ISBN 0-664-24504-8). Westminster.

Out of the Ghetto: The Social Background of Jewish Emancipation, 1770-1870. Jacob Katz. LC 72-86386. 1973. 18.50x (ISBN 0-674-64775-0). Harvard U Pr.

Out of the Labyrinth. L. H. Lehmann. 252p. 1983. pap. 6.95 (ISBN 0-937958-13-1). Chick Pubns.

Out of the Saltshaker: Evangelism As a Way of Life. Rebecca M. Pippert. LC 79-1995. 1979. pap. 6.95 (ISBN 0-87784-735-5); study guide 2.95 (ISBN 0-87784-532-8). Inter-Varsity.

Out of the Silence. Ralph Butler. 142p. 1978. pap. 2.95 (ISBN 0-7050-0059-1). Attic Pr.

Out of the Whirlwind. Albert Friedlander. 1968. 10.95 (ISBN 0-8074-0043-2, 959065). UAHC.

Out of the Wilderness: The Brethren & Two Centuries of Life in Central Pennsylvania. Earl C. Kaylor. (Illus.). 384p. 1981. 12.50 (ISBN 0-8453-4716-0, Cornwall Bks). Assoc Univ Prs.

Out of This World: A Guide to the Retreat Houses of Great Britain. George Target. 1985. 35.00x (ISBN 0-900873-67-1, Pub. by Bishopsgate Pr. Ltd); pap. 21.00x (ISBN 0-900873-73-6). State Mutual Bk.

Outbreak of the English Civil War. Anthony Fletcher. 480p. 1985. pap. text ed. 19.95 (ISBN 0-7131-6454-9). E Arnold.

Outcaste: Jewish Life in Southern Iran. Ed. by L. Loeb. (Library of Anthroplogy). 354p. 1977. 42.95 (ISBN 0-677-04530-1). Gordon & Breach.

Outdoor Life in the Menominee Forest. Sylvester Norick. 1979. 7.95 (ISBN 0-8199-0767-7). Franciscan Herald.

Outgrowing the Ingrown Church. C. John Miller. 176p. 1986. pap. 7.95 (ISBN 0-310-28411-2). Zondervan.

Outines of Buddhism: A Historical Sketch. Caroline A. Davids. 126p. 1934. Repr. text ed. 12.50x. Coronet Bks.

Outline for Discipling. rev. ed. G. Michael Cocoris. 9p. 1984. pap. 1.00 (ISBN 0-935729-10-0). Church Open Door.

Outline History of Greek Religion. Lewis R. Farnell. 160p. (Orig.). 1986. 10.00 (ISBN 0-89005-025-2); pap. 10.00 (ISBN 0-89005-442-8). Ares.

Outline of Administrative Responsibilities in a Hebrew Day School. 0.25 (ISBN 0-914131-47-8, C25). Torah Umesorah.

Outline of Bible History & Major Christian Movements. Michael L. Wilson. 1974. pap. 4.95 (ISBN 0-88027-014-4). Firm Foun Pub.

Outline of Classical Mythology. Robert E. Wolverton. (Quality Paperback: No. 97). (Orig.). 1975. pap. 2.95 (ISBN 0-8226-0097-8). Littlefield.

Outline of Confucianism. Don Y. Lee. LC 85-80477. 113p. 1984. 29.50x (ISBN 0-939758-10-5). Eastern Pr.

Outline of Dahomean Religious Belief. Melville J. Herskovits & Frances S. Herskovits. LC 34-5259. (American Anthro. Association Memoirs). 1933. 11.00 (ISBN 0-527-00540-1). Kraus Repr.

Outline of Hinduism. F. H. Smith. 59.95 (ISBN 0-8490-0788-7). Gordon Pr.

Outline of New Testament Survey. Walter Dunnett. (Orig.). 1960. pap. 5.95 (ISBN 0-8024-6245-6). Moody.

Outline of Occult Science. Rudolf Steiner. 352p. 1972. 16.00 (ISBN 0-910142-26-2); pap. 9.95 (ISBN 0-910142-75-0). Anthroposophic.

Outline of Religious Literature of India. J. N. Farquhar. 1984. Repr. 30.00 (ISBN 0-89684-287-8). Orient Bk Dist.

Outline of Swedenborg's Teaching. William F. Wunsch. LC 74-23796. 275p. 1975. pap. 3.95 (ISBN 0-87785-151-4). Swedenborg.

Outline of the Bible: Book by Book. Benson Y. Landis. (Orig.). 1963. pap. 5.95 (ISBN 0-06-463263-6, EH 263, B&N Bks). Har-Row.

Outline of the Book of Nehemiah. H. Smith. pap. 4.25 (ISBN 0-88172-125-5). Believers Bkshelf.

Outline of the History of Christian Literature. George Hurst. 1977. lib. bdg. 69.95 (ISBN 0-8490-2395-5). Gordon Pr.

Outline of Theosophy. Leadbeater. 2.95 (ISBN 0-8356-7185-2). Theos Pub Hse.

Outline Studies in Acts. W. Griffith Thomas. 1956. pap. 10.95 (ISBN 0-8028-1570-7). Eerdmans.

Outline Studies in Christian Doctrine. George P. Pardington. pap. 5.95 (ISBN 0-87509-116-4). Chr Pubns.

Outline Studies in Luke. W. Griffith Thomas. LC 84-784. 408p. 1984. pap. text ed. 11.95 (ISBN 0-8254-3821-7). Kregel.

Outline Study of the Tabernacle. Ada R. Habershon. LC 73-85298. 1974. pap. 2.95 (ISBN 0-8254-2820-3). Kregel.

Outline Talks for Teens. Charles R. Wood. LC 83-25543. 64p. (Orig.). 1984. pap. 2.95 (ISBN 0-8254-4024-6). Kregel.

Outlined Bible. Robert Lee. 1986. pap. 7.95 (ISBN 0-310-44821-2, 10465P). Zondervan.

Outlines for Christian Youth. R. P. Daniel. pap. 5.95 (ISBN 0-88172-019-4). Believers Bkshelf.

Outlines for Christmas Sermons. John S. Meyer. (Sermon Outline Ser.). 48p. 1980. pap. 2.95 (ISBN 0-8010-6107-5). Baker Bk.

Outlines for Evangelistic Preaching. C. W. Keiningham. 80p. 1984. pap. 2.95 (ISBN 0-8010-5461-3). Baker Bk.

Outlines of a Critical Theory of Ethics. John Dewey. LC 71-92299. Repr. of 1957 ed. lib. bdg. 22.50x (ISBN 0-8371-2707-6, DETE). Greenwood.

Outlines of Bible History. Roy Lanier, Sr. 2.50 (ISBN 0-89315-189-0). Lambert Bk.

Outlines of Bible Study: An Easy-to-Follow Guide to Greater Bible Knowledge. Ed. by G. Dallas Smith. 120p. 1986. pap. text ed. 3.95 (ISBN 0-89225-287-1). Gospel Advocate.

Outlines of Ecclesiastical History. B. H. Roberts. LC 79-9744. 1979. 7.95 (ISBN 0-87747-748-5). Deseret Bk.

Outlines of Jainism. Jagmandar L. Jaini. Ed. by F. W. Thomas. LC 78-14128. (Illus.). 1981. Repr. of 1940 ed. 21.00 (ISBN 0-88355-801-7). Hyperion Conn.

Outlines of Medieval History. 2nd ed. C. W. Previte-Orton. LC 64-25837. 1916. 12.00 (ISBN 0-8196-0147-0). Biblo.

Outlines of Muhammadan Law. 5th ed. Asaf A. Fyzee. Ed. by David Pearl. 520p. 1986. pap. 13.95x (ISBN 0-19-561393-7). Oxford U Pr.

Outlines of Mythology. Lewis Spence. LC 77-3223. 1977. Repr. of 1944 ed. lib. bdg. 17.50 (ISBN 0-8414-7803-1). Folcroft.

Outlines of Primitive Belief among the Indo-European Races. Charles F. Keary. LC 77-85620. 1977. Repr. of 1882 ed. lib. bdg. 50.00 (ISBN 0-89341-305-4). Longwood Pub Group.

Outlines of the Moral Philosophy. Dugald Stewart. LC 75-11255. (British Philosophers & Theologians of the 17th & 18th Centuries: Vol. 54). 322p. 1976. Repr. of 1793 ed. lib. bdg. 51.00 (ISBN 0-8240-1805-2). Garland Pub.

Outlines of the Philosophy of Religion: Dictated Portions of the Lectures of Hermann Lotze. H. Lotze. Ed. by G. Ladd. LC 11-24754. Repr. of 1885 ed. 20.00 (ISBN 0-527-58550-5). Kraus Repr.

Outlines of Theology. A. A. Hodge. 1983. 16.95 (ISBN 0-85151-160-0). Banner of Truth.

Outlines of Truth. F. B. Hole. Ed. by R. P. Daniel. 73p. pap. 3.75 (ISBN 0-88172-143-3). Believers Bkshelf.

Outlines of Zuni Creation Myths. Frank H. Cushing. LC 74-7947. Repr. of 1896 ed. 20.00 (ISBN 0-404-11834-8). AMS Pr.

Outlines on Revelation. Croft M Pentz. (Sermon Outline Ser.). 1978. pap. 2.50 (ISBN 0-8010-7030-9). Baker Bk.

Outlines on the Holy Spirit. Croft M Pentz. (Sermon Outline Ser.). 1978. pap. 2.50 (ISBN 0-8010-7029-5). Baker Bk.

Outlines on the Parables of Jesus. Croft M. Pentz. (Sermon Outline Ser.). (Orig.). 1980. pap. 2.50 (ISBN 0-8010-7055-4). Baker Bk.

Outpouring: Jesus in the Feasts of Israel. Elwood McQuaid. (Orig.). 1986. pap. 5.95 (ISBN 0-8024-6101-8). Moody.

Outpouring of the Soul. Nachman of Breslov & Nathan of Breslov. Tr. by Aryeh Kaplan from Hebrew. Tr. of Hishtap'kuth HaNefesh. 96p. (Orig.). 1980. pap. 2.50 (ISBN 0-930213-14-9). Breslov Res Inst.

Outreach Preaching: The Role of Preaching in Evangelism. Elton P. Richards, Jr. 56p. (Orig.). 1986. pap. 4.25 (ISBN 0-8066-2232-6, 10-4859). Augsburg.

Outreach Through Neighborhood Bible Study. Michael L. Roach. 54p. 1986. 3.50 (ISBN 0-317-52739-8). Herald Hse.

Outreach to Youth. Ed. by Ed Stewart. 1978. pap. 1.50 (ISBN 0-8307-0503-1, 9770402). Regal.

Outside the Camp. R. K. Campbell. 16p. pap. 0.30 (ISBN 0-88172-087-9). Believers Bkshelf.

Outside the Old Testament. Marinus De Jonge. (Camridge Commentaries on the Writings of the Jewish & Christian World 200 B.C. to 200 A.D. Ser.: No. 4). 264p. 1985. 49.50 (ISBN 0-521-24249-5); pap. 18.95 (ISBN 0-521-28554-2). Cambridge U Pr.

Outstanding Black Sermons. Ed. by J. Alfred Smith. LC 76-2084. 96p. 1976. pap. 4.95 (ISBN 0-8170-0664-8). Judson.

Outstanding Black Sermons, Vol. 2. Ed. by Walter B. Hoard. 1978. pap. 5.95 (ISBN 0-8170-0832-2). Judson.

Outstanding Black Sermons, Vol. 3. Ed. by Milton E. Owens, Jr. 80p. 1982. pap. 4.95 (ISBN 0-8170-0973-6). Judson.

Outwit the Devil. Roalla McCluney. 160p. (Orig.). 1987. pap. 6.95 (ISBN 0-89896-296-X, Linolean). Larksdale.

Outwitting Tomorrow. Valiant Thor. (Illus.). 64p. (Orig.). pap. 4.50 (ISBN 0-934414-00-9, Co Pub by Intl Evang). Hover.

Over the Bent World. Ed. by Sr. Mary Louise. LC 73-105031. (Essay Index Reprint Ser). 1939. 40.00 (ISBN 0-8369-1676-X). Ayer Co Pubs.

Over the Cliff. Vivian D. Gunderson. 1974. pap. 1.75 (ISBN 0-915374-13-7, 13-7). Rapids Christian.

Over the Mormon Trail. Helen H. Jones. LC 63-9706. (Frontiers of America Ser.). (Illus.). 128p. 1980. PLB 10.60 (ISBN 0-516-03354-9). Childrens.

Over to Home & From Away. Ed. by Jim Brunelle. (Illus.). 340p. (Orig.). 1980. pap. 9.95 (ISBN 0-930096-11-8). G Gannett.

Over Two Hundred Ways to Improve Your Sunday School. Harold A. Malehor. 1982. pap. 5.95 (ISBN 0-570-03857-X, 12-2811). Concordia.

Overcome Any Problem. Carlton Johnson. (Out Ser.). 1985. pap. 1.25 (ISBN 0-8163-0580-3). Pacific Pr Pub Assn.

Overcoming Anxiety. Gary Collins. 1975. pap. 2.25 (ISBN 0-88449-017-3, A324101). Vision Hse.

Overcoming Barriers to Sunday School Growth. Jones R. Wayne. LC 86-23290. (Orig.). 1987. pap. 5.95 (ISBN 0-8054-3238-8). Broadman.

Overcoming Barriers to Witnessing. Delos Miles. LC 83-70641. (Orig.). 1984. pap. 5.50 (ISBN 0-8054-6245-7). Broadman.

Overcoming Depression. Richard K. Mower. LC 85-29228. 160p. 1986. 8.95 (ISBN 0-87579-025-9). Deseret Bk.

Overcoming Discouragement. Elbert Willis. 1976. 1.25 (ISBN 0-89858-000-5). Fill the Gap.

Overcoming Hurts & Anger. Dwight L. Carlson. LC 80-83852. 1981. pap. 4.95 (ISBN 0-89081-277-2). Harvest Hse.

Overcoming Loneliness. David Jeremiah. LC 83-48411. 143p. 1983. pap. 5.95 (ISBN 0-89840-049-X). Heres Life.

Overcoming Materialism. John MacArthur, Jr. (John MacArthur's Bible Studies). (Orig.). 1986. pap. 3.50 (ISBN 0-8024-5099-7). Moody.

Overcoming Power. Shy Mackes. LC 82-73708. 1983. pap. text ed. 5.00 (ISBN 0-932050-17-4). New Puritan.

Overcoming Religion. David Mills. 1980. pap. 3.95 (ISBN 0-8065-0742-X). Citadel Pr.

Overcoming Stress: Everything You Ever Need to Know! Ed. by Horace W. Batson & Gary Batson. 100p. (Orig.). 1987. pap. 9.95 (ISBN 0-938503-00-6). Welstar Pubns.

Overcoming Temptation. Larry M. Arrowood. Ed. by David Bernard. LC 86-24735. (Illus.). 120p. (Orig.). 1986. pap. text ed. 5.50 (ISBN 0-932581-04-8). Word Aflame.

Overcoming the Adversary. Mark I. Bubeck. 1984. pap. 5.95 (ISBN 0-8024-0333-6). Moody.

Overcoming Worry. Elbert Willis. 1976. 1.25 (ISBN 0-89858-001-3). Fill the Gap.

Overcoming Worry & Fear. Paul A. Hauck. LC 74-20629. 112p. 1975. pap. 6.95 (ISBN 0-664-24811-X). Westminster.

Overeaters Feelings & Faith. large print ed. Pearl Brians. 40p. 1985. pap. 5.50 (ISBN 0-914009-31-1). VHI Library.

Overeating: A Common Sin. large print ed. Ellen White. 52p. 1985. pap. 6.50 (ISBN 0-914009-45-1). VHI Library.

Overlook: A Castle in the Kingdom. Vic Cassizzi. (Illus.). 1981. 3.95 (ISBN 0-686-30374-1). Cassizzi.

Ownership: Early Christian Teaching. Charles Avila. LC 83-8330. 256p. (Orig.). 1981. pap. 9.95 (ISBN 0-88344-384-8). Orbis Bks.

Oxford American Prayer Book Commentary. Massey H. Shepherd. 1950. 27.50 (ISBN 0-19-501202-X). Oxford U Pr.

Oxford Annotated Apocrypha: Revised Standard Version. Ed. by Bruce M. Metzger. 1977. text ed. write for info. Oxford U Pr.

Oxford Apostles. Geoffrey Faber. 467p. 1974. 7.95 (ISBN 0-571-10495-9). Faber & Faber.

Oxford Apostles: A Character Study of the Oxford Movement. Geoffrey Faber. 1979. Repr. of 1933 ed. lib. bdg. 35.00 (ISBN 0-8482-3953-9). Norwood Edns.

Oxford Apostles: A Character Study of the Oxford Movement. Geoffrey C. Faber. LC 75-30022. Repr. of 1933 ed. 34.50 (ISBN 0-404-14027-0). AMS Pr.

Oxford Bible Atlas. 3rd. ed. Ed. by Herbert G. May. 1985. 18.95 (ISBN 0-19-143452-3); pap. 10.95x (ISBN 0-19-143451-5). Oxford U Pr.

Oxford Bible Reader's Dictionary & Concordance: Cyclopedic Concordance. (Illus.). 1984. 7.95 (ISBN 0-19-143442-6); pap. 4.95 (ISBN 0-19-143441-8). Oxford U Pr.

Oxford Book of Carols. Ed. by Percy Dearmer et al. 1928. 21.00 (ISBN 0-19-353314-6); pap. 13.95 (ISBN 0-19-353315-4); Words & Melody. pap. 6.95 (ISBN 0-19-313118-8). Oxford U Pr.

Oxford Book of Carols for Schools. Ed. by Percy Dearmer et al. 1956. piano ed. 6.75 (ISBN 0-19-330830-4); melody ed. 2.50 (ISBN 0-19-330831-2). Oxford U Pr.

Oxford Book of Prayer. Ed. by George Appleton. 416p. 1985. 22.95 (ISBN 0-19-213222-9). Oxford U Pr.

Oxford Concise Concordance to the Revised Standard Version of the Holy Bible. Compiled by Bruce M. Metzger. 1962. 7.95 (ISBN 0-19-528388-0). Oxford U Pr.

Oxford Concordance: King James Version. write for info. Oxford U Pr.

Oxford Dictionary of Popes. J. N. Kelly. LC 85-15599. 450p. 1986. 24.95 (ISBN 0-19-213964-9). Oxford U Pr.

Oxford Dictionary of Saints. Ed. by David H. Farmer. 1978. pap. 8.95 (ISBN 0-19-283036-8). Oxford U Pr.

Oxford Dictionary of the Christian Church. F. L. Cross & Elizabeth A. Livingstone. 1974. 60.00 (ISBN 0-19-211545-6). Oxford U Pr.

Oxford Easy Anthem Book. 1957. 12.00 (ISBN 0-19-353320-0); pap. 7.00 (ISBN 0-19-353321-9). Oxford U Pr.

Oxford Movement. Wilfrid Ward. (Victorian Age Ser). 20.00 (ISBN 0-8482-6908-X). Norwood Edns.

Oxford Movement: Being a Selection from the Tracts for the Times. William G. Hutchison. (Victorian Age Ser). 1906. Repr. 20.00 (ISBN 0-8482-4421-4). Norwood Edns.

Oxford Movement in America. Clarence A. Walworth. LC 77-150436. (Monograph Ser.: No. 30). (Illus.). 1974. Repr. of 1895 ed. 12.00x (ISBN 0-930060-10-5). US Cath Hist.

Oxford Movement: Twelve Years 1833-1845. R. W. Church. 1979. Repr. of 1891 ed. lib. bdg. 35.00 (ISBN 0-8482-7569-1). Norwood Edns.

Oxford Reformers. Frederick Seebohm. Incl. Oxford Wit & Humour. 1914. Repr. 20.00 (ISBN 0-8274-3094-9). R West.

Oxford S-A-B Carol Book: Forty Carols. Ed. by Reginald Jacques. (YA) 1960. limp linen 7.25x (ISBN 0-19-330514-3). Oxford U Pr.

Oxford Studies in Ancient Philosophy, Vol. 2. Ed. by Julia Annas. 1984. text ed. 39.95x (ISBN 0-19-824769-9); pap. text ed. 16.95x (ISBN 0-19-824768-0). Oxford U Pr.

Oz & Mary Quick: Taiwan Teammates. William N. McElrath. LC 84-2962. (Meet the Missionary Ser.). 1984. pap. 5.50 (ISBN 0-8054-4287-1, 4242-87). Broadman.

Ozark Parson. Ida B. Bontrager. 1978. 5.55 (ISBN 0-87813-512-X). Christian Light.

Ozark Tales & Superstitions. Phillip W. Steele. LC 82-22425. (Illus.). 96p. 1983. pap. 4.95 (ISBN 0-88289-404-8). Pelican.

P

P-H Encyclopedia of World Proverbs. Wolfgang Mieder. LC 85-12345. 582p. 1986. 34.95 (ISBN 0-13-695586-X). P-H.

P. M. Friesen & His History: Understanding Mennonite Brethren Beginnings. Abraham Friesen. (Perspective on Mennonite Life & Thought Ser.: Vol. 2). 176p. (Orig.). 1979. pap. 5.95 (ISBN 0-318-18906-2). Kindred Pr.

P. T. Forsyth: The Man, the Preacher's Theologian & Prophet for the Twentieth Century. Donald G. Miller et al. (Pittsburgh Theological Monograph Ser.: No. 36). 1981. pap. 18.00 (ISBN 0-915138-48-4). Pickwick.

Pablo, el Lider. J. Oswald Sanders. Tr. of Paul the Leader. (Span.). 208p. 1986. pap. 3.50 (ISBN 0-8297-0760-3). Life Pubs Intl.

Pachomian Koinonia I: The Life of St. Pachomius. Tr. by Armand Veilleux. (Cistercian Studies: No. 45). (Gr.). 524p. 1981. pap. 12.95 (ISBN 0-87907-945-2). Cistercian Pubns.

Pachomian Koinonia II: Chronicles & Rules. (Cistercian Studies: No. 46). 239p. 1981. pap. 10.00 (ISBN 0-87907-946-0). Cistercian Pubns.

Pachomian Koinonia III. Instructions, Letters & Other Writings, No. 47. Armand Veilleux. (Cistercian Studies). 1983. 26.95 (ISBN 0-87907-847-2); pap. 10.00 (ISBN 0-87907-947-9). Cistercian Pubns.

Pacific Coast. Bayard McConnaughey & Evelyn McConnaughey. Ed. by Charles Elliott. LC 84-48673. (Audubon Society Nature Guides Ser.). (Illus.). 633p. 1985. pap. 14.95 (ISBN 0-394-73130-1). Knopf.

Pacific People Sing Out Strong. William L. Coop. (Orig.). 1982. pap. 4.95 (ISBN 0-377-00118-X). Friend Pr.

Pacifist Program. Richard B. Gregg. 1983. pap. 2.50x (ISBN 0-686-43957-0, 005). Pendle Hill.

Pacing the Void: T'ang Approaches to the Stars. Edward H. Schafer. LC 76-48362. 1978. 49.50x (ISBN 0-520-03344-2). U of Cal Pr.

Packet of Letters: A Selection from the Correspondence of John Henry Newman. John H. Newman. Intro. by Joyce Suggs. LC 82-4444. (Illus.). 1983. 19.95x (ISBN 0-19-826442-9). Oxford U Pr.

Padre Martinez & Bishop Lamy. 3rd ed. Ray J. De Aragon. LC 78-70565. (History Ser.). (Illus.). 1978. pap. 7.95 (ISBN 0-932906-00-1). Pan-Am Publishing Co.

Padre on Horseback. Herbert E. Bolton. LC 63-13248. (Illus.). 1963. Repr. of 1962 ed. 3.00 (ISBN 0-8294-0003-6). Loyola.

Padre Pio. Dante Alimenti. (Illus.). 179p. 1987. 49.95 (ISBN 0-87973-491-4). Our Sunday Visitor.

Padre Pio. John A. Capuchin. 1983. 9.50 (ISBN 0-8199-0864-9). Franciscan Herald.

Padre Pio Profile. John A. Schug. (Orig.). 1987. pap. 4.95 (ISBN 0-932506-56-9). St Bedes Pubns.

Padre Pio: The Stigmatist. Charles M. Carty. (Illus.). 1971. pap. 8.50 (ISBN 0-89555-054-7, 115). TAN Bks Pubs.

Padre Pio: The True Story. C. Bernard Ruffin. LC 81-81525. (Illus.). 348p. (Orig.). 1982. pap. 8.95 (ISBN 0-87973-673-9, 673). Our Sunday Visitor.

Padyacudamani of Buddhaghosacarya. Buddhaghosa. LC 78-72387. Repr. of 1921 ed. 32.50 (ISBN 0-404-17248-2). AMS Pr.

Pagan & Christian Anxiety: A Response to E. R. Dodds. Ed. by Robert C. Smith & John Lounibos. LC 83-27345. 248p. 1984. lib. bdg. 25.25 (ISBN 0-8191-3823-1); pap. text ed. 12.25 (ISBN 0-8191-3824-X). U Pr of Amer.

Pagan & Christian Creeds. Edward Carpenter. 59.95 (ISBN 0-8490-0794-1). Gordon Pr.

Pagan & Christian in an Age of Anxiety: Some Aspects of Religious Experience from Marcus Aurelius to Constantine. E. R. Dodds. 1970. pap. 5.95 (ISBN 0-393-00545-3, Norton Lib). Norton.

Pagan & Christian Rome. Rodolfo Lanciani. LC 67-23856. (Illus.). 1968. Repr. of 1892 ed. 27.50 (ISBN 0-405-08728-4, Blom Pubns). Ayer Co Pubs.

Pagan Babies & Other Catholic Memories. Gina Cascone. 160p. 1982. 9.95 (ISBN 0-312-59418-6). St Martin.

Pagan Babies & Other Catholic Memories. Gina Cascone. 160p. 1983. pap. 4.95 (ISBN 0-312-59419-4). St Martin.

Pagan Background of Christianity. W. R. Halliday. 59.95 (ISBN 0-8490-0795-X). Gordon Pr.

Pagan Bible. Melvin Gorham. 296p. 1982. 8.95 (ISBN 0-914752-22-7). Sovereign Pr.

Pagan-Christian Conflict over Miracle in the Second Century. Harold Remus. LC 83-6729. (Patristic Monograph: No. 10). xiii, 371p. 1983. pap. 11.00 (ISBN 0-915646-09-9). Phila Patristic.

Pagan Christs. John M. Robinson. 1967. 5.95 (ISBN 0-8216-0136-9). Univ Bks.

Pagan Divinities & Their Worship As Depicted in the Work of St. Augustine. Sr. Mary Madden. 59.95 (ISBN 0-8490-0796-8). Gordon Pr.

Pagan Meditations: The Worlds of Aphrodite, Artemis, & Hestia. Ginette Paris. Tr. by Gwendolyn Moore from Fr. LC 86-6675. 204p. (Orig.). 1986. pap. 13.50 (ISBN 0-88214-330-1). Spring Pubns.

Pagan Mysteries in the Renaissance. rev. ed. Edgar Wind. (Illus.). 1969. pap. 7.95 (ISBN 0-393-00475-9, Norton Lib). Norton.

Pagan Mysteries in the Renaissance. Edgar Wind. (Illus.). 1958. 75.00x (ISBN 0-686-83672-3). Elliots Bks.

Pagan Myth & Christian Tradition in English Poetry. Douglas Bush. LC 68-8639. (Memoirs Ser.: Vol. 72). 1968. 5.00 (ISBN 0-87169-072-1). Am Philos.

Pagan Papers. Kenneth Grahame. LC 72-3427. (Essay Index Reprint Ser.). Repr. of 1898 ed. 15.00 (ISBN 0-8369-2903-9). Ayer Co Pubs.

Pagan Races of the Malay Peninsula, 2 vols. new ed. Walter W. Skeat & Charles O. Blagden. (Illus.). 1966. 95.00x set (ISBN 0-7146-2027-0, F Cass Co). Biblio Dist.

Pagan Reality. Melvin Gorham. 201p. 1970. pap. 5.00 (ISBN 0-914752-02-2). Sovereign Pr.

Pagan Rome & the Early Christians. Stephen Benko. LC 83-48898. 192p. 1985. 20.00x (ISBN 0-253-34286-4). Ind U Pr.

Pagan Rome & the Early Christians. Stephen Benko. LC 83-48898. (Midland Books Ser.: no. 385). 192p. 1986. pap. 7.95x (ISBN 0-253-20385-6). Ind U Pr.

Pagan Temptation. Thomas Molnar. 208p. (Orig.). 1987. pap. 11.95 (ISBN 0-8028-0262-1). Eerdmans.

Paganism in Our Christianity. Arthur Weigall. 69.95 (ISBN 0-87968-149-7). Gordon Pr.

Paganism in the Roman Empire. Ramsay MacMullen. LC 80-54222. 384p. 1981. 30.00x (ISBN 0-300-02655-2); pap. text ed. 8.95x (ISBN 0-300-02984-5). Yale U Pr.

Pagans & Christians. Robin L. Fox. 1987. 35.00 (ISBN 0-394-55495-7). Knopf.

Page a Day for Lent 1987. Barbara Sullivan. 56p. (Orig.). 1987. pap. 2.95 (ISBN 0-8091-2852-7). Paulist Pr.

Pages in the Life of a Sufi. M. M. Khan. 1979. 14.95 (ISBN 11-1910-334-7, Pub. by Sufi Pub Co England). Hunter Hse.

Pahlavi Texts. Ed. by F. W. West. (Vols. 5, 18, 24, 37, 47). 5 vols. 75.00 (ISBN 0-686-97478-6); 15.00 ea. Asian Human Pr.

Paideia: The Ideals of Greek Culture, 3 vols. Werner Jaeger. Tr. by Gilbert Highet from Ger. Incl. Vol. 1. Archaic Greece; The Mind of Athens. 2nd ed. 1945 (ISBN 0-19-500399-3); Vol. 2. In Search of the Divine Center. 1943 (ISBN 0-19-500592-9); Vol. 3. The Conflict of Cultural Ideals in the Age of Plato. 1944 (ISBN 0-19-500593-7). 35.00x ea. Oxford U Pr.

Pain & Providence. Ladislaus Boros. 132p. 1975. pap. 2.95 (ISBN 0-686-85825-5). Crossroad NY.

Pain & the Possibility. Paula Ripple. LC 78-67745. 144p. 1978. pap. 2.95 (ISBN 0-87793-162-3). Ave Maria.

Pain & the Privilege: Diary of a City Priest. Joseph Gallagher. LC 82-1766. 384p. 1983. pap. 7.95 (ISBN 0-385-19019-0, Im). Doubleday.

Pain, Anxiety & Grief: Pharmacotherapeutic Care of the Dying Patient & the Bereaved. Ed. by Ivan K. Goldberg et al. 224p. 1985. 24.00x (ISBN 0-231-04742-8). Columbia U Pr.

Pain of Being Human. Eugene C. Kennedy. LC 73-83645. 280p. 1974. pap. 4.95 (ISBN 0-385-06888-3, Im). Doubleday.

Pain That Heals: The Place of Suffering in the Growth of the Person. Martin Israel. (Crossroad Paperback Ser.). 192p. 1982. pap. 8.95 (ISBN 0-8245-0437-2). Crossroad NY.

Painful Blessings. Vernon A. Holman. LC 85-8042. (Illus.). 45p. (Orig.). 1985. pap. write for info. (ISBN 0-933315-07-4). Taran House Pub.

Painful Echoes: From the Diary of Luba Krugman Gurdus. Luba K. Gurdus. pap. 12.95 (ISBN 0-89604-059-3). Holocaust Pubns.

Pain's Hidden Purpose: Finding Perspective in the Midst of Suffering. Don Baker. LC 83-22135. 1984. pap. 5.95 (ISBN 0-88070-035-1). Multnomah.

Painted Churches of Romania: A Visitor's Impressions. John Fletcher. (Illus.). 52p. 1971. 22.95 (ISBN 0-88010-062-1, Pub. by Steinerbooks). Anthroposophic.

Painted Queen. Olga Hesky. 1962. 12.95 (ISBN 0-8392-1083-3). Astor-Honor.

Painted Windows. Harold Begbie. LC 77-108696. (Essay & General Literature Index Reprint Ser). 1970. Repr. of 1922 ed. 23.50x (ISBN 0-8046-0918-7, Pub. by Kennikat). Assoc Faculty Pr.

Painting in Florence & Siena after the Black Death: The Arts, Religion & Society in the Mid-Fourteenth-Century. Millard Meiss. 1976. 37.00x (ISBN 0-691-03919-4); pap. 9.95x (ISBN 0-691-00312-2). Princeton U Pr.

Painting in Islam. Thomas W. Arnold. (Illus.). 16.25 (ISBN 0-8446-1553-6). Peter Smith.

Painting of the Life of St. Francis in Assisi, with Notes on the Arena Chapel. Leonetto Tintori & Millard Meiss. LC 62-10308. pap. 55.50 (ISBN 0-317-10175-7, 2050842). Bks Demand UMI.

Paintings of Mysticism & Violence in Full Colours of Dario Anzul. Dario Anzul. (Illus.). 97p. 1983. 225.75x (ISBN 0-86650-073-1). Gloucester Art.

Paiute Sorcery. Beatrice B. Whiting. Repr. of 1950 ed. 19.00 (ISBN 0-384-68180-8). Johnson Repr.

Pakua. R. W. Smith. pap. 8.25x (ISBN 0-685-22068-0). Wehman.

Palabras. Kenneth E. Hagin. (Span.). 1983. pap. 0.50 mini bk. (ISBN 0-89276-157-1). Hagin Ministries.

Palabras Griegas Del Nuevo Testamento. William Barclay. Tr. by Javier J. Marin. 220p. 1985. pap. 4.50 (ISBN 0-311-42052-4). Casa Bautista.

Palatinate-a Full Declaration of the Faith & Ceremonies Professed in the Dominions of Prince Fredericke, 5. Prince Elector Palatine. Tr. by J. Rolte. LC 79-84129. (English Experience Ser.: No. 947). 208p. 1979. Repr. of 1614 ed. lib. bdg. 20.00 (ISBN 90-221-0947-X). Walter J Johnson.

Pale Hecates Team: Examination of the Beliefs on Witchcraft & Magic Among Shakespeare's Contemporaries & His Immediate Succesors. Katherine M. Briggs. Ed. by Richard M. Dorson. LC 77-70582. (International Folklore Ser.). (Illus.). 1977. lib. bdg. 24.50x (ISBN 0-405-10083-3). Ayer Co Pubs.

Paleo-Hebrew Leviticus Scroll. D. N. Freedman & K. A. Mathews. (Illus.). xii, 135p. 1985. text ed. 19.95x (ISBN 0-89757-007-3). Am Sch Orient Res.

Palestine: A Policy. Albert M. Hyamson. LC 75-6438. (Rise of Jewish Nationalism & the Middle East Ser). 214p. 1975. Repr. of 1942 ed. 20.35 (ISBN 0-88355-325-2). Hyperion Conn.

Palestine: A Study of Jewish, Arab, & British Policies, 2 Vols. Esco Foundation For Palestine Inc. LC 47-2569. Repr. of 1947 ed. Set. 192.00 (ISBN 0-527-27750-9). Kraus Repr.

Palestine & Israel in the Nineteenth & Twentieth Centuries. Ed. by Elie Kedourie & Sylvia G. Haim. (Illus.). 286p. 1982. 39.50x (ISBN 0-7146-3121-3, F Cass Co). Biblio Dist.

Palestine & Roumania: A Description of the Holy Land & the Past & Present State of Roumania & the Roumanian Jews. Haym Z. Sneersohn. Ed. by Moshe Davis. LC 77-70745. (America & the Holy Land Ser.). 1977. Repr. of 1872 ed. lib. bdg. 17.00x (ISBN 0-405-10291-7). Ayer Co Pubs.

Palestine & the Bible. Ed. by M. T. Mehdi. LC 71-114557. 1971. pap. 4.00 (ISBN 0-911026-06-1). New World Press NY.

Palestine & the Zionist Threat. Institute for Palestine, Beirut, Lebanon Staff. Date not set. cancelled (ISBN 0-88728-190-7). Inst Palestine.

Palestine Diary. Chaim Chissin. 1976. 10.00 (ISBN 0-685-82598-1). Herzl Pr.

Palestine Diary. Frederick H. Kisch. LC 73-180354. Repr. of 1938 ed. 31.45 (ISBN 0-404-56286-8). AMS Pr.

Palestine Herald, 4 vols. William Coleman. (Palestine Herald Ser.). (Illus.). No. 1. 2.95 (ISBN 0-89191-981-3); No. 2. 2.95 (ISBN 0-89191-982-1); No. 3. 2.95 (ISBN 0-89191-983-X); No. 4. 2.95 (ISBN 0-89191-984-8). Cook.

Palestine: Mohammedan Holy Land. Ibn Al-Firkah & Ibrahim ibn Abd Al-Rahman. Ed. by Charles Matthews. LC 78-63568. (Yale Oriental Ser. Researches: No. 24). Repr. of 1949 ed. 34.50 (ISBN 0-404-60324-6). AMS Pr.

Palestine of Jesus. Bernard R. Youngman. (Background to the Bible Ser.: Vol. 3). pap. 8.95 (ISBN 0-7175-0418-2). Dufour.

Palestine Question in American History. American Jewish Historical Society Staff et al. Ed. by American Historical Association. 14.00 (ISBN 0-405-11521-0). Ayer Co Pubs.

Palestine under the Moslems. Tr. by Guy Le Strange. LC 70-180356. Repr. of 1890 ed. 47.50 (ISBN 0-404-56288-4). AMS Pr.

Palestinian Figurines in Relation to Certain Goddesses Known Through Literature. James B. Pritchard. (American Oriental Ser.: Vol. 24). 1943. 11.00 (ISBN 0-527-02698-0). Kraus Repr.

Palestinian Judaism & the New Testament. Martin McNamara. (Good News Studies: Vol. 4). 1983. pap. 12.95 (ISBN 0-89453-274-X). M Glazier.

Palestinians. Frank H. Epp. LC 76-12976. 240p. 1976. 10.00 (ISBN 0-8361-1338-1). Herald Pr.

Pali Buddhist Texts. Rune E. Johansson. 160p. 1982. 30.00x (ISBN 0-7007-0063-3, Pub. by Curzon England). State Mutual Bk.

Pali Buddhist Texts Explained to the Beginner. Rune E. Johansson. 1981. pap. 12.00 (ISBN 0-8364-0329-0, Pub. by Curzon Pr). South Asia Bks.

Pali Literature of Burma. Mabel H. Bode. LC 77-87008. Repr. of 1909 ed. 15.00 (ISBN 0-404-16796-9). AMS Pr.

Palkhi: An Indian Pilgrimage. D. B. Mokashi. Tr. by Philip C. Engblom. 160p. 1987. 34.50x (ISBN 0-88706-461-2); pap. 10.95x (ISBN 0-88706-462-0). State U NY Pr.

Palladas & Christianity. C. M. Bowra. 1959. pap. 2.25 (ISBN 0-85672-641-9, Pub. by British Acad). Longwood Pub Group.

Palladium of Conscience. Philip Furneaux. LC 74-122161. (Civil Liberties in American History Ser). 267p. 1974. Repr. of 1773 ed. lib. bdg. 35.00 (ISBN 0-306-71972-X). Da Capo.

Palladius: Dialogue on the Life of St. John Chrysostom. Ed. by Robert T. Meyer. (ACW Ser.: No. 45). 1985. text ed. 16.95 (ISBN 0-8091-0358-3). Paulist Pr.

Palm & the Pleiades. S. Hugh-Jones. LC 78-5533. (Studies in Social Anthropology: No. 24). (Illus.). 1979. 37.50 (ISBN 0-521-21952-3). Cambridge U Pr.

Palm Leaves, Peanuts, & Sixty-One Other Children's Sermons. Bill Lampkin. LC 81-3497. 112p. 1981. pap. 6.50 (ISBN 0-687-30000-2). Abingdon.

Palm Tree of Deborah. Moses Cordovero. Tr. by Louis Jacobs from Heb. LC 80-54594. (Judaic Studies Library: No. SPH8). 133p. 1981. pap. 7.95 (ISBN 0-87203-097-0). Hermon.

Palmer's Bible Atlas (Facsimile Edition) Archbishop of York. 84p. 1982. 14.95 (ISBN 0-686-43010-7, Carta Pub Isreal). Hippocrene Bks.

Palmistry. Mary Anderson. (Paths to Inner Power Ser.). 1973. pap. 3.50 (ISBN 0-85030-164-5). Weiser.

Pamjati Igumena Fillimona. Archbishop Konstantine Zaitsev. Tr. of In Memory of Igumen Philimon. 58p. 1954. pap. 2.00 (ISBN 0-317-29287-0). Holy Trinity.

Pan & the Nightmare: Two Essays. Wilhelm Roscher & James Hillman. (Dunquin Ser.: No. 4). lxiii, 88p. 1972. pap. 8.50 (ISBN 0-88214-204-6). Spring Pubns.

Pan-Islam. George W. Bury. LC 80-1938. Repr. of 1919 ed. 30.00 (ISBN 0-404-18956-3). AMS Pr.

Pan-Islamism. B. K. Narayan. 232p. 35.00X (ISBN 0-317-52149-7, Pub. by S Chand Mutual). State Mutual Bk.

Pan-Turkism & Islam in Russia. Serge A. Zenkovsky. LC 60-5399. (Russian Research Center Studies: No. 36). 1960. 25.00x (ISBN 0-674-65350-5). Harvard U Pr.

Pancadasi. Swami Vidyaranya. Tr. by Swami Swahananda. (Sanskrit & Eng). 10.00 (ISBN 0-87481-429-4). Vedanta Pr.

Panchatantra. J. Hertel. lib. bdg. 79.95 (ISBN 0-87968-523-9). Krishna Pr.

Panchikaranam. Shankara. (Sanskrit & English). pap. 2.00 (ISBN 0-87481-068-X). Vedanta Pr.

Pandora's Box. Lisl Weil. LC 85-20128. (Illus.). 40p. 1986. 12.95 (ISBN 0-689-31216-4, Childrens Bk). Macmillan.

Panic among the Phillistines. Bryan F. Griffin. (Christian Activist Ser.). 259p. 1985. pap. 5.95 (ISBN 0-89526-817-5). Regnery Bks.

Panj Sura: Collection of 5 Famous Prayers. 4.50 (ISBN 0-686-18594-3). Kazi Pubns.

Panorama de la Biblia. Alfred T. Eade. Orig. Title: New Panorama Bible Study Course. 32p. 1986. pap. 3.75 (ISBN 0-311-03657-0). Casa Bautista.

Panorama of Judaism, 2 pts. Ed. by Leo Jung. 1974. Pt. 1, 275 pp. 9.50 (ISBN 0-900689-48-X); Pt. 2, 243 pp. 9.50 (ISBN 0-900689-49-8). Soncino Pr.

Pantheism. J. Allanson Picton. 96p. 1914. 0.95 (ISBN 0-317-40425-3). Open Court.

Pantheism & Christianity. John Hunt. LC 78-102573. 1970. Repr. of 1884 ed. 25.50 (ISBN 0-8046-0733-8, Pub. by Kennikat). Assoc Faculty Pr.

Pantheism & the Christian System. Arthur Schopenhauer. (Illus.). 119p. 1987. 117.50 (ISBN 0-89266-588-2). Am Classical Coll Pr.

Pantheism Is Heresy. Parker L. Johnstone. 208p. 1982. cloth 7.95 (ISBN 0-917802-05-5). Theoscience Found.

Pantheistic Monism of Ibn Al-Arabi. S. A. Husaini. 1970. 9.30x (ISBN 0-87902-164-0). Orientalia.

Pantheisticon. John Toland. Ed. by Rene Wellek. LC 75-11260. (British Philosophers & Theologians of the 17th & 18th Centuries: Vol. 59). 1977. Repr. of 1751 ed. lib. bdg. 51.00 (ISBN 0-8240-1810-9). Garland Pub.

Pantheon. Antoine Pomey. LC 75-27879. (Renaissance & the Gods Ser.: Vol. 34). (Illus.). 1976. Repr. of 1694 ed. lib. bdg. 88.00 (ISBN 0-8240-2083-9). Garland Pub.

Pantheon. Andrew Tooke. LC 75-27880. (Renaissance & the Gods Ser.: Vol. 35). (Illus.). 1976. Repr. of 1713 ed. lib. bdg. 88.00 (ISBN 0-8240-2084-7). Garland Pub.

Pantheon: or, Ancient History of the Gods of Greece & Rome. William Godwin. Ed. by Burton Feldman & Robert D. Richardson. LC 78-60886. (Myth & Romanticism Ser.). 1984. lib. bdg. 80.00 (ISBN 0-8240-3560-7). Garland Pub.

Papa Nicholas Planas. Mother Martha. Ed. & tr. by Holy Transfiguration Monastery. (Orig.). 1981. pap. 5.50x (ISBN 0-913026-18-2). St Nectarios.

Papa Was a Preacher. Alyene Porter. 192p. 1979. 3.50 (ISBN 0-8007-8359-X, Spire Bks). Revell.

Papacy. A. L. Maycock. 1928. 10.00 (ISBN 0-8414-6607-6). Folcroft.

Papacy & Fascism: The Crisis of the 20th Century. Francis A. Ridley. LC 72-180422. (Studies in Fascism, Ideology & Practice). Repr. of 1937 ed. 24.50 (ISBN 0-404-56156-X). AMS Pr.

Papacy & the Church: A Study of Praxis & Reception in Ecumenical Perspective. J. Robert Dionne. LC 85-9319. 524p. 1987. 29.95 (ISBN 0-8022-2494-6). Philos Lib.

Papacy & the Levant, Twelve Hundred Four to Fifteen Seventy-One, Vol. Two: The Fifteenth Century. Kenneth M. Setton. LC 75-25476. (Memoirs Ser.: Vol. 127). (Illus.). 1978. 40.00 (ISBN 0-87169-127-2). Am Philos.

Papacy & the Levant Twelve Hundred Four to Fifteen Seventy-One Vol I: The Thirteenth & Fourteenth Centuries. Kenneth M. Setton. LC 75-25476. (Memoirs Ser.: Vol. 114). 1976. 35.00 (ISBN 0-87169-114-0). Am Philos.

Papacy & the Levant, Twelve Hundred Four to Fifteen Seventy-One, Vols. III & IV. Kenneth M. Setton. LC 75-25476. (Memoirs Ser.: Vols. 161 & 162). 1984. Vol. 161. 45.00 (ISBN 0-87169-161-2); Vol. 162. 45.00 (ISBN 0-87169-162-0). Am Philos.

Papacy & the Middle East: The Role of the Holy See in the Arab-Israeli Conflict, 1962-1984. George E. Irani. LC 85-41013. 224p. 1986. text ed. 22.95x (ISBN 0-268-01560-0). U of Notre Dame Pr.

Papacy in the Age of Napoleon & the Restoration: Pius VII, 1800-1823. Margaret M. O'Dwyer. 296p. (Orig.). 1985. lib. bdg. 24.00 (ISBN 0-8191-4825-3); pap. text ed. 12.75 (ISBN 0-8191-4826-1). U Pr of Amer.

Papacy in the Modern World Nineteen Fourteen to Nineteen Seventy. Derek J. Holmes. LC 81-65110. 275p. 1981. 14.95 (ISBN 0-8245-0047-4). Crossroad NY.

Papado Siglo XX. I. Grigulevich. 354p. 1982. 5.95 (ISBN 0-8285-2323-1, Pub. by Progress Pubs USSR). Imported Pubns.

Papago Indian Religion. Ruth M. Underhill. LC 74-82363. (Columbia Univ. Contributions to Anthropology Ser.: Vol. 33). Repr. of 1946 ed. 37.50 (ISBN 0-404-50583-X). AMS Pr.

Papal Conspiracy Exposed & Protestantism Defended. Edward Beecher. LC 76-46066. (Anti-Movements in America). (Illus.). 1977. Repr. of 1885 ed. lib. bdg. 32.00x (ISBN 0-405-09940-1). Ayer Co Pubs.

Papal Crusading Policy, Twelve Hundred Forty-Four to Twelve Hundred Ninety-One. M. Purcell. 1975. 40.00 (ISBN 90-04-04317-9). Heinman.

Papal Documents Relating to the New China, 1937-1984. Elmer P. Wurth. 193p. (Orig.). 1985. pap. 10.00 (ISBN 0-88344-403-8). Orbis Bks.

Papal Enforcement of Some Medieval Marriage Laws. Charles E. Smith. LC 40-12564. pap. 59.30 (ISBN 0-317-28663-3, 2055314). Bks Demand UMI.

Papal Government & England During the Pontificate of Honorius III (1216-1227) Jane E. Sayers. LC 84-1853. (Cambridge Studies in Medieval Life & Thought: 3rd Ser., Vol. 21). 1985. 49.50 (ISBN 0-521-25911-8). Cambridge U Pr.

Papal Ideology of Social Reform: A Study in Historical Development, 1878-1967. R. L. Camp. 1969. 30.00 (ISBN 9-0040-4317-9). Heinman.

Papal Infallibility: An Application of Lonergan's Theological Method. Ed. by Terry J. Tekippe. LC 82-23837. 416p. (Orig.). 1983. lib. bdg. 34.50 (ISBN 0-8191-2995-X); pap. text ed. 17.75 o. p. (ISBN 0-8191-2996-8). U Pr of Amer.

Papal Power: A Study of Vatican Control Over Lay Catholic Elites. Jean-Guy Vaillancourt. 375p. 1980. 24.95x (ISBN 0-520-03733-2). U of Cal Pr.

Papal Primacy & the Universal Church. Ed. by Paul C. Empie et al. LC 74-83329. 1974. pap. 7.95 (ISBN 0-8066-1450-1, 10-4870). Augsburg.

Papal Pronouncements on Marriage & the Family: From Leo XIII to Pius XII (1878-1954) Compiled by Alvin Werth. LC 82-6265. xxi, 189p. 1982. Repr. of 1955 ed. lib. bdg. 27.50x (ISBN 0-313-22521-4, WEPA). Greenwood.

Papal Social Principles: A Guide & Digest. Thomas Harte. 12.00 (ISBN 0-8446-1225-1). Peter Smith.

Papal Thought on the State: Excerpts from Encyclicals & Other Writings of Recent Popes. Ed. by Gerard F. Yates. LC 58-5745. (Crofts Classics Ser.). 1958. pap. text ed. 1.25x (ISBN 0-88295-064-9). Harlan Davidson.

Papancasudani Majjhimanikayatthakatha of Buddhaghosacariya, 5 vols. in 4. Buddhaghosa. LC 78-72388. Repr. of 1938 ed. Set. 165.00 (ISBN 0-404-17560-0). AMS Pr.

Paper Shtetl: A Complete Model of an East European Jewish Town. David Grupper & David G. Klein. LC 83-42714. (Illus., Orig.). 1984. pap. 11.95 (ISBN 0-8052-0749-X). Schocken.

Paper Tearing Bible Talks, No. 4. Arnold C. Westphal. 1970. pap. 4.95 (ISBN 0-915398-03-6). Visual Evangels.

Paper Tearing Evangels, No. 8. Arnold C. Westphal. 1975. pap. 4.95 (ISBN 0-915398-07-9). Visual Evangels.

Paper Tearing Gospel Illustrations, No. 3. Arnold C. Westphal. 1969. pap. 4.95 (ISBN 0-915398-02-8). Visual Evangels.

Paper Tearing Trick Talks, No. 1. Arnold C. Westphal. 1967. pap. 4.95 (ISBN 0-915398-00-1). Visual Evangels.

Papers Connected with the Affairs of Milton & His Family. John F. Marsh. LC 74-22180. 1974. Repr. of 1851 ed. lib. bdg. 15.00 (ISBN 0-8414-5959-2). Folcroft.

Papers in Logic & Ethics. Arthur N. Prior. Ed. by P. T. Geach & A. J. Kenny. LC 76-9376. 238p. 1976. 15.00x (ISBN 0-87023-213-4). U of Mass Pr.

Papers of the American Home Missionary Society, 1816 (1826-1894) 1936: A Guide to the Microfilm Edition. Ed. by David G. Horvath. 94p. 1975. pap. 50.00 (ISBN 0-88455-994-7). Microfilming Corp.

Papers on Godliness. Catherine Booth. (Writings of Catherine Booth Ser.). 1986. Repr. of 1890 ed. deluxe ed. 4.95 (ISBN 0-86544-032-8). Salvation Army.

Papers on Practical Religion. Catherine Booth. (Writings of Catherine Booth Ser.). 1986. Repr. of 1891 ed. deluxe ed. 4.95 (ISBN 0-86544-036-0). Salvation Army.

Papes Du Onzieme Siecle et la Chretiente. 2nd ed. Jules Gay. 1970. 21.00 (ISBN 0-8337-1302-7). B Franklin.

Papist Pamphleteers. Thomas H. Clancy. LC 64-14078. (Jesuit Studies). 1964. 4.95 (ISBN 0-8294-0013-3). Loyola.

Papstlichen Legaten in England Bis Zur Beendigung der Legation Gualas, 1218. Helene Tillman. LC 80-2208. 1981. Repr. of 1926 ed. 29.50 (ISBN 0-404-18795-1). AMS Pr.

Papsttum Und Byzanz: Das Problem Ihrer Wiedervereinigung Bis Zum Untergange Des Byzantinischen Reichs (1453) Walter Norden. 1903. 40.50 (ISBN 0-8337-2571-8). B Franklin.

Para la Futura Mama. Helen G. Brenneman. Tr. of Meditations for the Expectant Mother. (Span.). 80p. 1979. pap. 2.85 (ISBN 0-8361-1216-4). Herald Pr.

Para que Vuestro Gozo Sea colmado. John Catoir. Tr. by Jose Casamada from Eng. (Span.). 158p. (Orig.). 1986. pap. 5.00 (ISBN 0-317-46550-3). Chrstphrs NY.

Para Ser Catolico: Un Catecismo Para Hoy. new, spanish ed. Joseph V. Gallagher. 1976. pap. 1.50 (ISBN 0-8091-1939-0). Paulist Pr.

Parable of Jesus & Santa. Bobbie M. Grimes. LC 84-90331. (Illus.). 40p. 1984. 14.95 (ISBN 0-9613328-0-8). B & D Pub.

Parable of the Father's Heart. G. Campbell Morgan. (Morgan Library). 96p. 1981. pap. 2.95 (ISBN 0-8010-6118-0). Baker Bk.

Parable of the Ninth Hour. George L. Nutting & Ruth S. Nutting. 165p. (Orig.). 1983. pap. 2.95 (ISBN 0-9612266-0-9). Numard Bks.

Parable of the Wicked Tenants: An Inquiry into Parable Interpretation. Klyne Snodgrass. 150p. 1983. pap. 48.00x (Pub. by J. C. B. Mohr BRD). Coronet Bks.

Parable of Willie Juan. Brennan Manning. 1985. 2.95 (ISBN 0-87193-162-1). Dimension Bks.

Parables. Madeleine I. Boucher. (New Testament Message Ser.: Vol. 7). 12.95 (ISBN 0-89453-195-6); pap. 7.95 (ISBN 0-89453-130-1). M Glazier.

Parables, 4 vols. Nick Butterworth. (Illus.). 1986. 6.95 ea. Vol. 1: The House on the Rock (ISBN 0-88070-146-3). Vol. 2: The Lost Sheep (ISBN 0-88070-147-1). The Two Sons (ISBN 0-88070-145-5) (ISBN 0-88070-148-X). Multnomah.

Parables. Lyon Opal. 1984. pap. 1.95 (ISBN 0-317-30409-7). Pacific Pr Pub Assn.

Parables & Metaphors of Our Lord. G. Campbell Morgan. 352p. 1956. 15.95 (ISBN 0-8007-0245-X). Revell.

Parables & Miracles of Jesus. G. L. LeFevre. (Bible Quiz 'N Tattletotals Ser.). 16p. (Orig.). 1982. pap. 0.98 (ISBN 0-87239-580-4, 2807). Standard Pub.

Parables & Presence. Robert W. Funk. LC 82-71827. 224p. 1982. 3.00 (ISBN 0-8006-0688-4, 1-688). Fortress.

Parables & Similes of the Rabbis, Agricultural & Pastoral. Asher Feldman. LC 75-23127. 1975. Repr. of 1927 ed. lib. bdg. 27.50 (ISBN 0-8414-4229-0). Folcroft.

Parables at Work. John C. Purdy. LC 84-17323. 132p. 1986. 10.95 (ISBN 0-664-21268-9); pap. 7.95 (ISBN 0-664-24640-0). Westminster.

Parables by the Sea. Pamela Reeve. LC 77-6209. (Illus.). 1976. gift ed. o.p. 5.95 (ISBN 0-930014-10-3); pap. 5.95 (ISBN 0-930014-11-1). Multnomah.

Parables for Christian Living. Douglas Beyer. 112p. 1985. pap. 5.95 (ISBN 0-8170-1074-2). Judson.

Parables for Little People. Lawrence Castagnola. LC 86-62628. (Illus.). 101p. (Orig.). 1982. pap. 5.56 (ISBN 0-89390-034-6); pap. text ed. 7.95. Resource Pubns.

Parables for Now. Edmund Flood. 4.95 (ISBN 0-87193-186-9). Dimension Bks.

Parables for Young Teens: Twenty-Six Junior High Programs. Susan Titus. 1986. 4.95 (ISBN 0-87403-150-8, 3412). Standard Pub.

Parables from Nature. John C. Reid. 1954. 3.95 (ISBN 0-8028-4025-6). Eerdmans.

Parables from the Cross. Kenneth Rogahn & Walter Schoedel. 1981. pap. 5.95 (ISBN 0-570-03847-2, 12-2950). Concordia.

Parables in Depth. George Drew. 55p. (Orig.). 1982. pap. 6.95 (ISBN 0-940754-18-5). Ed Ministries.

Parables in Gospels. John Drury. LC 84-27652. 192p. 1985. 14.95 (ISBN 0-8245-0655-3). Crossroad NY.

Parables in Matthew's Gospel. R. K. Campbell. 1978. pap. 1.95 (ISBN 0-915374-42-0, 42-0). Rapids Christian.

Parables in Matthew's Gospel: Matthew 13. R. K. Campbell. tchr's lesson outline 3.95 (ISBN 0-88172-011-9). Believers Bkshelf.

Parables of Christ. A. B. Bruce. 1980. 15.50 (ISBN 0-86524-059-0, 9503). Klock & Klock.

Parables of Christ, Vol. 1. Gordon Lindsay. (Span.). 1.50 (ISBN 0-89985-980-1). Christ Nations.

Parables of Jesus. James M. Boice. 1983. pap. 6.95 (ISBN 0-8024-0163-5). Moody.

Parables of Jesus. Julianne Booth. (Arch Bks.). 1982. pap. 0.99 (ISBN 0-570-06163-6, 59-1309). Concordia.

Parables of Jesus. Norman Bull. (Bible Story & Its Background Ser.: Vol. 6). 9.95 (ISBN 0-7175-0452-2). Dufour.

Parables of Jesus. George A. Buttrick. (Minister's Paperback Library Ser). 274p. 1973. pap. 6.95 (ISBN 0-8010-0597-3). Baker Bk.

Parables of Jesus. 2nd ed. Joachim Jeremias. LC 63-22114. (Illus.). 248p. 1972. pap. text ed. 8.95 (ISBN 0-02-360510-3, Pub. by Scribner). Macmillan.

Parables of Jesus. Simon Kistemaker. 264p. 1980. 11.95 (ISBN 0-8010-5462-1). Baker Bk.

Parables of Jesus, 2 vols. Neil R. Lightfoot. (Way of Life Ser.). 1986. pap. 3.95 ea. Vol. 1, 95p; Vol. 2, 95p. Abilene Christ U.

Parables of Jesus. J. Dwight Pentecost. 160p. 1982. 9.95 (ISBN 0-310-30960-3, 17017). Zondervan.

Parables of Jesus. Geraldine Tapia. 144p. 1987. 10.95 (ISBN 0-317-53382-7). Todd & Honeywell.

Parables of Jesus: A History of Interpretation & Bibliography. Warren S. Kissinger. LC 78-23271. (American Theological Library Association (ATLA) Bibliography Ser.: No. 4). 463p. 1979. lib. bdg. 30.00 (ISBN 0-8108-1186-3). Scarecrow.

Parables of Jesus in Matthew 13. Jack D. Kingsbury. LC 76-40850. 1976. pap. text ed. 12.95 (ISBN 0-915644-08-8). Clayton Pub Hse.

Parables of Jesus: Twenty Stories with a Message. Daniel L. Lowery. 64p. 1987. pap. 1.95 (ISBN 0-89243-266-7). Liguori Pubns.

Parables of Our Lord. William Arnot. LC 80-8065. 532p. 1981. 14.95 (ISBN 0-8254-2119-5). Kregel.

Parables of Our Lord & Savior Jesus Christ. John E. Millais. 7.75 (ISBN 0-8446-5225-3). Peter Smith.

Parables of Our Saviour. William M. Taylor. LC 74-79943. 1975. 14.95 (ISBN 0-8254-3805-5). Kregel.

Parables of the Kingdom. Robert F. Capon. 192p. 1985. 10.95 (ISBN 0-310-42670-7, 17040). Zondervan.

Parables of the Kingdom. C. H. Dodd. 176p. 1977. pap. text ed. write for info. (ISBN 0-02-330460-X, Pub. by Scribner). Macmillan.

Parables of the Kingdom. John MacArthur, Jr. (John MacArthur's Bible Studies). (Orig.). 1985. pap. 3.50 (ISBN 0-8024-5112-8). Moody.

Parables, Psalms, Prayers. Sean Freeman. 1985. 10.95 (ISBN 0-88347-185-X). Thomas More.

Parables: Their Literary & Existential Dimension. Dan O. Via, Jr. LC 67-11910. 232p. 1974. pap. 6.95 (ISBN 0-8006-1392-9, 1-1392). Fortress.

Parables Then & Now. Archibald M. Hunter. LC 72-170113. 128p. 1972. pap. 5.95 (ISBN 0-664-24940-X). Westminster.

Parables Told by Jesus: Contemporary Approach. Wilfrid J. Harrington. LC 74-12395. 135p. (Orig.). 1974. pap. 3.95 (ISBN 0-8189-0296-5). Alba.

Parabolas del Evangelio. Charles L. Neal. 144p. 1983. pap. 2.50 (ISBN 0-311-04338-0). Casa Bautista.

Paraclete Power: A Study Guide for the Acts of the Apostles. Joseph J. Faraone & Jane L. Stewart. LC 77-16475. 1978. pap. 3.50 (ISBN 0-8189-0361-9). Alba.

Parade of Plays for Your Church. 96p. pap. 5.95 (ISBN 0-317-47009-4, 33274, Chariot Bks). Cook.

Parade of Plays I. Ed. by L. Townsend et al. 96p. 1986. pap. 5.95 (ISBN 0-89191-322-X). Cook.

Parade of Plays II. Ed. by L. Townsend et al. 96p. 1986. pap. 5.95 (ISBN 0-89191-323-8). Cook.

Parade of Plays III. Ed. by L. Townsend et al. 96p. 1987. pap. 5.95 (ISBN 0-89191-281-9). Cook.

Parade of Saints. Mark J. Twomey. LC 82-202387. (Illus.). 176p. 1983. 10.95 (ISBN 0-8146-1275-X). Liturgical Pr.

Paradigm Shift: Teach the Universal Values. Robert L. Humphrey, J. D., & Associates Staff. LC 83-83386. (Illus.). 100p. 1984. pap. 7.95 (ISBN 0-915761-00-9). Life Values Pr.

Paradise-Abode of the Righteous Dead. Gordon Lindsay. (Sorcery & Spirit World Ser.). 1.25 (ISBN 0-89985-085-5). Christ Nations.

Paradise Found. Arthur R. Charlesworth. LC 72-91109. 1973. 10.00 (ISBN 0-8022-2104-1). Philos Lib.

Paradise Lost. G. K. Hunter. (Critical Library). 232p. 1980. text ed. 24.95x (ISBN 0-04-800004-3). Allen Unwin.

Paradise Lost. John Milton. Ed. by Scott Elledge. (Critical Editions Ser). 546p. 1975. 19.95 (ISBN 0-393-04406-8); pap. 8.95x (ISBN 0-393-09230-5). Norton.

Paradise Lost. John Milton. (Modern Critical Interpretations--Seventeenth & Eighteenth Century British Literature Ser.). 1987. 19.95 (ISBN 0-87754-421-2). Chelsea Hse.

Paradise Lost, Bks. 3 & 4. John Milton. Ed. by L. J. Potter & J. Broadbent. LC 75-36681. (Milton for Schools & Colleges Ser.). 200p. 1976. pap. 8.95x (ISBN 0-521-21150-6). Cambridge U Pr.

Paradise Lost, Bks. 5 & 6. John Milton. Ed. by R. I. Hodge & I. MacCaffrey. LC 75-8314. (Milton for Schools & Colleges Ser). (Illus.). 176p. 1975. pap. text ed. 8.95 (ISBN 0-521-20796-7). Cambridge U Pr.

Paradise Lost, Bks. 7 & 8. John Milton. Ed. by D. Aers & Mary Ann Radzinowics. LC 77-181884. (Milton for Schools & Colleges Ser.). 200p. 1974. pap. text ed. 8.95 (ISBN 0-521-20457-7). Cambridge U Pr.

Paradise Lost, Bks. 9 & 10. John Milton. Ed. by J. M. Evans. LC 72-87438. (Milton for Schools & Colleges). 208p. 1973. 8.95 set (ISBN 0-521-20067-9). Cambridge U Pr.

Paradise Lost: A Tercenenary Tribute. Ed. by Balachandra Rajan. LC 77-429833. pap. 38.50 (ISBN 0-317-27001-X, 2023659). Bks Demand UMI.

Paradise Lost & Its Critics. A. J. Waldock. 11.50 (ISBN 0-8446-1463-7). Peter Smith.

Paradise Lost As Myth. Isabel G. MacCaffrey. LC 59-9282. 1959. 15.00x (ISBN 0-674-65450-1). Harvard U Pr.

Paradise Now & Not Yet. Andrew T. Lincoln. LC 80-41024. (Society for the New Testament Studies Monographs: No. 43). 240p. 1981. 44.50 (ISBN 0-521-22944-8). Cambridge U Pr.

Paradise of the Fathers, 2 vols. Tr. by A. E. Budge from Syriac. (Illus.). 1984. Set. pap. 25.00 (ISBN 0-913026-56-5). Vol. 1, 386 pp. Vol. 2, 352 pp. St Nectarios.

Paradise Regained, A Poem, in Four Books. John Milton. LC 73-9863. Repr. of 1795 ed. lib. bdg. 50.00 (ISBN 0-8414-5950-9). Folcroft.

Paradise to Prison: Studies in Genesis. John J. Davis. LC 74-30753. (Old Testament Studies). 384p. 1975. 14.95 (ISBN 0-8010-2838-8). Baker Bk.

Paradise to Prison: Studies in Genesis. John J. Davis. 14.95 (ISBN 0-88469-050-4). BMH Bks.

Paradisical Universe for Man: Man's Preparation for Sharing. 2nd ed. Reuben L. Katter. 200p. 1984. pap. 5.95 (ISBN 0-911806-03-2). Theotes.

Paradox & Identity in Theology. R. T. Herbert. LC 78-20784. 221p. 1979. 24.50x (ISBN 0-8014-1222-6). Cornell U Pr.

Paradox & Promise in Human Rights. Peggy Billings. (Orig.). 1979. pap. 2.95 (ISBN 0-377-00083-3). Friend Pr.

Paradox of Existentialist Theology: The Dialectics of a Faith-Subsumed Reason-in-Existence. Howard A. Slatte. LC 81-43508. 272p. 1982. lib. bdg. 29.00 (ISBN 0-8191-2187-8); pap. text ed. 13.25 (ISBN 0-8191-2188-6). U Pr of Amer.

Paradox of Instruction: An Introduction to the Esoteric Spiritual Teaching of Da Free John. Da Free John. LC 77-81836. 9.95 (ISBN 0-913922-32-3). Dawn Horse Pr.

Paradox of Preaching. Kring Allen. (Illus.). 104p. (Orig.). 1986. pap. 9.95 (ISBN 1-55630-018-2). Brentwood Comm.

Paradox of Religion. Willard L. Sperry. LC 77-27146. (Hibbert Lectures: 1927). Repr. of 1927 ed. 20.00 (ISBN 0-404-60424-2). AMS Pr.

Paradoxes & Further Paradoxes. Henry De Lubac. Tr. by Paule Simon et al. LC 86-62928. Orig. Title: Paradoxes, Nuveaux Paradoxes. (Fr.). 222p. (Orig.). 1986. pap. 11.95 (ISBN 0-89870-132-5). Ignatius Pr.

Paradoxes of Paradise: Identity & Difference in the Song of Songs. Francis Landy. (Bible & Literature Ser.: No. 7). 1983. text ed. 29.95x (ISBN 0-907459-16-1, Pub. by Almond Pr England); pap. text ed. 16.95x (ISBN 0-907459-17-X, Pub. by Almond Pr England). Eisenbrauns.

Paragon of Human Perfection. H. A. Omar. 85p. 1984. 21.00x (ISBN 0-7212-0566-6, Pub. by Regency Pr). State Mutual Bk.

Paraleipomena Jeremiou. Robert A. Kraft & Ann-Elizabeth Purintun. LC 72-88436. (Society of Biblical Literature. Texts & Translation-Psuedepigrapha Ser.). 49p. 1972. pap. 8.95 (ISBN 0-89130-169-0, 06 02 01). Scholars Pr GA.

Parallelism in Early Biblical Poetry. Stephen A. Geller. LC 78-27255. (Harvard Semitic Monographs: No. 20). 1979. 12.00 (ISBN 0-89130-275-1, 040020). Scholars Pr GA.

Parallels in Dante & Milton. C. L. Barnes. LC 74-3180. 1917. lib. bdg. 12.50 (ISBN 0-8414-9926-8). Folcroft.

Paramahansa Yogananda: In Memoriam. Self-Realization Fellowship. (Illus.). 127p. 1986. pap. 2.50 (ISBN 0-87612-170-9). Self Realization.

Paramartha Katha Prasang: Spiritual Conversations with Swami Muktananda. Swami Muktananda. 356p. 6.95 (ISBN 0-914602-90-X). SYDA Found.

Paramount Doctrines of Orthodoxy-the Tricompositeness of Man, Apology of A. Makrakis & the Trial of A. Makrakis. Apostolos Makrakis. Ed. by Orthodox Christian Educational Society. Tr. by Denver Cummings from Hellenic. 904p. 1954. 15.00x (ISBN 0-938366-17-3). Orthodox Chr.

Paraphrase & Notes on the Epistles of St. Paul, 2 vols. John Locke. (Clarendon edition of the Works of John Locke). (Illus.). 800p. 1986. Set. 125.00x (ISBN 0-19-824801-6). Oxford U Pr.

Paraphrases for Pilgrims. Jean Lanier. 1977. pap. 1.75 (ISBN 0-89192-187-7). Interbk Inc.

Paraphrases on Romans & Galatians. Desiderius Erasmus. Ed. by Robert D. Sider. Tr. by John B. Payne et al. (Collected Works of Erasmus Ser.: Vol. 42). 232p. 1984. 29.50x (ISBN 0-8020-2510-2). U of Toronto Pr.

Pardon My Lenten Smile: Daily Homily-Meditation Themes for the Weekdays of Lent. Michael Manning. 90p. 1976. pap. 5.95 (ISBN 0-8189-0325-2). Alba.

Pardoned: Prayers & Promises for Prisoners. John M. Robertson. 1983. pap. 2.50 (ISBN 0-8423-4831-X). Tyndale.

Pareja Cristiana. Larry Christenson. 1982. 3.75 (ISBN 0-88113-314-0). Edit Betania.

Parent & Child. J. W. Byers. 60p. pap. 0.50 (ISBN 0-686-29132-8). Faith Pub Hse.

Parent-Child Group Therapy: Building Self-Esteem in a Cognitive-Behavioral Group. L. Eugene Arnold & Donna G. Estreicher. LC 84-40723. 288p. 1985. 29.00 (ISBN 0-669-09934-1). Lexington Bks.

Parent, the Parish, & the Catholic School. Ed Weiss. 1986. 6.60 (ISBN 0-318-20566-1). Natl Cath Educ.

Parenthesis in Eternity. Joel S. Goldsmith. LC 64-10368. 1963. pap. 11.95 (ISBN 0-06-063230-5, HarpR). Har-Row.

Parenthesis in Eternity: Living the Mystical Life. Joel S. Goldsmith. LC 85-45354. 1986. pap. 11.95 (ISBN 0-06-063231-3, PL 4125, PL). Har-Row.

Parenthood: A Commitment in Faith. Kathryn W. Orso. LC 75-5219. 64p. (Orig.). 1975. pap. text ed. 2.95 (ISBN 0-8192-1198-2); tchr's ed. 3.75 (ISBN 0-8192-1204-0); wkbk. 3.95 (ISBN 0-8192-1199-0). Morehouse.

Parenthood Without Hassles-Well, Almost. Kevin Leman. LC 78-656211. 144p. 1982. pap. 2.95 (ISBN 0-89081-304-3). Harvest Hse.

Parenting. Ed. by Paul F. Wilczak. LC 78-69758. (Marriage & Family Living in Depth Bk.). 1978. pap. 2.45 (ISBN 0-87029-138-6, 20220-0). Abbey.

Parenting Alone. Ed. by Patricia Roberts. 1980. pap. 4.50 (ISBN 0-8309-0297-X). Herald Hse.

Parenting for Peace & Justice. Kathleen McGinnis & James McGinnis. LC 81-3917. 143p. (Orig.). 1981. pap. 7.95 (ISBN 0-88344-376-7). Orbis Bks.

Parenting Us: How God Does It. Karen Mains & David Mains. 96p. 1986. pap. 3.50 (ISBN 0-87788-669-5). Shaw Pubs.

Parenting with Love & Limits. Bruce Narramore. 312p. 1987. pap. 9.95 (ISBN 0-310-30541-1). Zondervan.

Parenting with Love & Limits. Bruce S. Narramore. 176p. 1982. pap. 5.95 (ISBN 0-310-30351-6, 11240P). Zondervan.

Parenting Your Disabled Child. Bernard Ikeler. LC 86-9118. 138p. (Orig.). 1986. pap. 8.95 (ISBN 0-664-24044-5). Westminster.

Parents & Children. Ed. by Jay Kesler et al. 640p. 1986. 16.95 (ISBN 0-89693-809-3). Victor Bks.

Parents & Discipline. Herbert Wagemaker, Jr. LC 80-14624. (Christian Care Bks.: Vol. 12). 120p. 1980. pap. 7.95 (ISBN 0-664-24328-2). Westminster.

Parents & Teenagers. Ed. by Jay Kesler. 696p. 1984. pap. 16.95 (ISBN 0-88207-817-8). Victor Bks.

Parents As Partners in Youth Ministry. Darrell Pearson. 64p. 1985. 5.95 (ISBN 0-89693-322-9). Victor Bks.

Parents' Guide to Sex Education. Mary A. Mayo. 208p. pap. 6.95 (ISBN 0-310-44581-7, 11357P). Zondervan.

Parents in Pain. John White. LC 78-24760. 1979. pap. 7.95 (ISBN 0-87784-582-4); study guide 1.95 (ISBN 0-87784-492-5). Inter-Varsity.

Parents of the Homosexual, Vol. 11. David K. Switzer & Shirley A. Switzer. LC 80-13748. (Christian Care Bks.). 118p. 1980. pap. 7.95 (ISBN 0-664-24327-4). Westminster.

Parents Talk Love: The Catholic Family Handbook on Sexuality. Susan Sullivan & Matthew Kawiak. LC 84-80361. 164p. (Orig.). 1984. pap. 7.95 (ISBN 0-8091-2639-7). Paulist Pr.

Paris Psalter & Meters of Boethius. Ed. by George P. Krapp. LC 33-2302. 239p. 1932. 30.00 (ISBN 0-231-08769-1). Columbia U Pr.

Parish: A Place for Worship. Ed. by Mark Searle. LC 81-13655. 192p. (Orig.). 1981. pap. 5.95 (ISBN 0-8146-1236-9). Liturgical Pr.

Parish Adult Education in Five Practical Steps. Robert Y. O'Brien. 32p. 1985. pap. text ed. 1.50 (ISBN 0-89243-234-9). Liguori Pubns.

Parish & Democracy in French Canada. Maurice Roy. LC 52-1123. (University of Toronto, Duncan & John Gray Memorial Lecture Ser.). pap. 20.00 (2026546). Bks Demand UMI.

Parish As Learning Community. Thomas Downs. LC 78-70816. 128p. 1979. pap. 3.95 (ISBN 0-8091-2172-7). Paulist Pr.

Parish Celebrations: A Reflective Guide for Liturgy Planning. Dennis J. Geaney & Dolly Sokol. (Orig.). 1983. pap. 5.95 (ISBN 0-89622-190-3). Twenty-Third.

Parish Churches of Medieval England. Colin Platt. 1981. 34.95 (ISBN 0-436-37553-2, Pub. by Secker & Warburg UK); pap. 16.95 (ISBN 0-436-37554-0, Pub. by Secker & Warburg UK). David & Charles.

Parish Churches: Their Architectural Development in England. Hugh Braun. 1970. 12.50 (ISBN 0-571-09045-1). Transatl Arts.

Parish Clergy in Nineteenth-Century Russia: Crisis, Reform, Counter-Reform. Gregory L. Freeze. LC 82-61361. 552p. 1983. 52.50x (ISBN 0-691-05381-2). Princeton U Pr.

Parish Clergy under the Later Stuarts: The Leicestershire Experience. John H. Pruett. LC 78-8174. 203p. 1978. 19.95 (ISBN 0-252-00662-3). U of Ill Pr.

Parish Council Handbook. Robert C. Broderick. 1968. pap. 2.25 (ISBN 0-8199-0083-4, L38623). Franciscan Herald.

Parish Counseling. Edgar Jackson. LC 84-45066. 221p. 1983. 25.00x (ISBN 0-87668-672-2). Aronson.

Parish Education in Colonial Virginia. Guy F. Wells. LC 73-177649. Repr. of 1923 ed. 22.50 (ISBN 0-404-55138-6). AMS Pr.

Parish Education in Colonial Virginia. Guy F. Wells. LC 71-89252. (American Education: Its Men, Institutions & Ideas, Ser. 1). 1969. Repr. of 1923 ed. 11.00 (ISBN 0-405-01490-2). Ayer Co Pubs.

Parish Family Life & Social Action. Joachim O'Brien. LC 77-3573. 1977. pap. 1.50 (ISBN 0-8199-0673-5). Franciscan Herald.

Parish Guide to Adult Initiation. Kenneth Boyak. LC 79-91001. 112p. (Orig.). 1980. pap. 4.95 (ISBN 0-8091-2282-0). Paulist Pr.

Parish Help Book: A Guide to Social Ministry in the Parish. Herbert Weber. LC 83-71894. 112p. 1983. pap. 3.95 (ISBN 0-87793-304-9). Ave Maria.

Parish in Transition: Proceedings of a Conference on the American Catholic Parish. Ed. by David Byers. 120p. 1986. pap. 8.95 (ISBN 1-55586-967-X). US Catholic.

Parish Institutions of Maryland. Edward Ingle. LC 78-63736. (Johns Hopkins University. Studies in Social Sciences. First Ser. 1882-1883: 6). Repr. of 1883 ed. 11.50 (ISBN 0-404-61006-4). AMS Pr.

Parish Institutions of Maryland, with Illustrations from Parish Records. E. Ingle. 1973. pap. 9.00 (ISBN 0-384-25740-2). Johnson Repr.

Parish Life in the United States, Final Report to the Bishops of the United States by the Parish Project, November, 1982. 90p. 1983. pap. 7.50 (ISBN 1-55586-876-2). US Catholic.

Parish Life: Manual for Spiritual Leadership Formation. Nancy Westmeyer. 1983. pap. 8.95 (ISBN 0-8091-2489-0). Paulist Pr.

Parish Lines, Diocese of Southern Virginia. Charles F. Cocke. (Virginia State Library Publications: No. 22). 287p. 1979. Repr. of 1964 ed. 5.00 (ISBN 0-88490-049-5). VA State Lib.

Parish Lines, Diocese of Southwestern Virginia. Charles F. Cocke. (Virginia State Library Publications: No. 14). 196p. 1980. Repr. of 1960 ed. 5.00 (ISBN 0-686-74611-2). VA State Lib.

Parish Lines, Diocese of Virginia. Charles F. Cocke. LC 78-19035. (Virginia State Library Publications: No. 28). xv, 321p. 1978. Repr. of 1967 ed. 5.00 (ISBN 0-88490-062-2). VA State Lib.

Parish of All Hallows, Pt. 1. Ed. by Lilian J. Redstone. LC 74-138273. (London County Council. Survey of London: No. 12). Repr. of 1929 ed. 74.50 (ISBN 0-404-51662-9). AMS Pr.

Parish of Bromley-By-Bow. Ed. by Charles R. Ashbee. LC 73-138270. (London County Council. Survey of London: No. 1). Repr. of 1900 ed. 74.50 (ISBN 0-404-51651-3). AMS Pr.

Parish of Chelsea, Pt. 1. Ed. by Walter H. Godfrey. LC 71-138271. (London County Council. Survey of London: No. 2). Repr. of 1909 ed. 74.50 (ISBN 0-404-51652-1). AMS Pr.

Parish of St. Margaret, Westminster. Ed. by Montagu H. Cox. LC 70-138272. (London County Council. Survey of London: No. 10). (Illus.). Repr. of 1926 ed. 74.50 (ISBN 0-404-51660-2). AMS Pr.

Parish of St. Margaret, Westminster: Neighbourhood of Whitehall, Vol. 1. Montagu H. Cox & G. Topham Forrest. LC 70-138272. (London County Council. Survey of London: No. 13). Repr. of 1930 ed. 74.50 (ISBN 0-404-51663-7). AMS Pr.

Parish of St. Martin-in-the Fields: Trafalgar Square & Neighborhood, Pt. 3. George H. Gater & F. R. Hiorns. LC 70-37852. (London County Council. Survey of London: No. 20). Repr. of 1940 ed. 74.50 (ISBN 0-404-51670-X). AMS Pr.

Parish of St. Pancras, Pt. 2. Ed. by Percy Lovell & William Marcham. LC 70-37855. (London County Council. Survey of London: No. 19). Repr. of 1938 ed. 74.50 (ISBN 0-404-51669-6). AMS Pr.

Parish Priests among the Saints. facs. ed. Walter Gumbley. LC 76-148214. (Biography Index Reprint Ser.). 1947. 15.00 (ISBN 0-8369-8061-1). Ayer Co Pubs.

Parish Priests & Their People in the Middle Ages in England. Edward L. Cutts. LC 74-107457. Repr. of 1898 ed. 32.50 (ISBN 0-404-01898-X). Ams Pr.

Parish Renewal at the Grassroots. David Prior. 1987. 12.95 (ISBN 0-310-38370-6). Zondervan.

Parish Secretary's Handbook. Wayne Paulson. 192p. (Orig.). 1983. pap. 12.95 (ISBN 0-8066-1898-1, 10-4868). Augsburg.

Parish Self-Study Guide. 97p. 1982. pap. 7.95 (ISBN 1-55586-842-8). US Catholic.

Parish the Thought. Vikki Knoche. 1984. pap. 4.95 (ISBN 0-8163-0560-9). Pacific Pr Pub Assn.

Parishes & Families: A Model for Christian Formation Through Liturgy. Ed. by Gabe Huck & Virginia Sloyan. 1973. pap. 5.00 (ISBN 0-918208-11-4). Liturgical Conf.

Parishes of Christ Church & All Saints & the Liberties of Norton Folgate & the Old Artillery Ground. London County Council. LC 74-6547. (London County Council. Survey of London: No. 27). Repr. of 1957 ed. 74.50 (ISBN 0-404-51677-7). AMS Pr.

Parker Lifetime Treasury of Mystic & Occult Powers. Theodor Lawrence. 1982. pap. 4.95 (ISBN 0-13-650747-6, Reward). P-H.

Parker Society Publications, 55 Vols. Parker Society-London. Repr. of 1841 ed. Set. 2200.00 (ISBN 0-384-44880-1). Johnson Repr.

Parliamentary Guide for Church Leaders. C. Barry McCarty. 1987. pap. 6.95 (ISBN 0-8054-3116-0). Broadman.

Parnassus. facsimile ed. Ed. by Ralph Waldo Emerson. LC 73-116400. (Granger Index Reprint Ser). 1874. 25.50 (ISBN 0-8369-6141-2). Ayer Co Pubs.

Parochiaid & the Courts. Dale E. Twomley. (Andrews University Monographs, Studies in Education: Vol. 2). x, 165p. 1979. 3.95 (ISBN 0-943872-51-0). Andrews Univ Pr.

Parochial & Plain Sermons. John H. Newman. LC 86-62927. 1734p. (Orig.). 1987. pap. 49.00 (ISBN 0-89870-136-8). Ignatius Pr.

Parody in Jewish Literature. Israel Davidson. LC 77-163670. (Columbia University. Oriental Studies: No. 2). Repr. of 1907 ed. 24.50 (ISBN 0-404-50492-2). AMS Pr.

Parsing Guide to the Greek New Testament. Nathan E. Han. LC 77-158175. 496p. 1971. pap. 17.95 (ISBN 0-8361-1653-4). Herald Pr.

Parsis. Martin Haug. 427p. 1978. Repr. of 1878 ed. 25.00 (ISBN 0-89684-157-X). Orient Bk Dist.

Parson & the Publican. A. Tindal Hart. 1984. 9.50 (ISBN 0-533-05730-2). Vantage.

Parson Pettigrew of the "Old Church" 1744-1807. Sarah M. Lemmon. (James Sprunt Studies in History & Political Science: No. 52). vii, 168p. 1971. pap. 5.00x (ISBN 0-8078-5052-7). U of NC Pr.

Parson Weems: A Biographical & Critical Study. Lawrence C. Wroth. LC 75-31143. Repr. of 1911 ed. 10.00 (ISBN 0-404-13615-X). AMS Pr.

Parson Weems of the Cherry-Tree. Harold Kellock. LC 75-107137. 1971. Repr. of 1928 ed. 35.00x (ISBN 0-8103-3785-1). Gale.

Partakers of Divine Nature. C. Stavropoulos. 1976. pap. 4.95 (ISBN 0-937032-09-3). Light&Life Pub Co MN.

Parte of a Register, Contayninge Sundrie Memorable Matters, Written by Diuers Godly & Learned in Our Time, Which Stande for the Reformation of Our Church. Church of England Staff. LC 72-5981. (English Experience Ser.: No. 509). 1973. Repr. of 1593 ed. 67.00 (ISBN 90-221-0509-1). Walter J Johnson.

Parthenon. Susan Woodford. (Cambridge Introduction to the History of Mankind Ser.). 1981. pap. 4.95 (ISBN 0-521-22629-5). Cambridge U Pr.

Parthian Period. M. A. Colledge. (Iconography of Religions XIV Ser.: No. 3). (Illus.). xiv, 47p. 1986. pap. 34.25 (ISBN 90-04-07115-6, Pub. by E J Brill). Heinman.

Partial Knowledge: Philosophical Studies in Paul. Paul W. Gooch. LC 86-40589. 224p. 1987. text ed. 22.95x (ISBN 0-268-01567-8, Dist. by Har-Row). U of Notre Dame Pr.

Participant Self, 2 vols. Adrian Van Kaam et al. pap. 4.95 (ISBN 0-87193-045-5). Dimension Bks.

Participant Self, 2 vols. in 1. Adrian Van Kaam et al. 1985. write for info. (ISBN 0-87193-160-5). Dimension Bks.

Participation in Rural Life. Mildred B. Young. 1983. pap. 2.50x (ISBN 0-87574-019-7, 019). Pendle Hill.

Parting Counsels: Exposition of II Peter 1. John Brown. (Banner of Truth Geneva Series Commentaries). 1980. 13.95 (ISBN 0-85151-301-8). Banner of Truth.

Partisan. Yitzhak Arad. LC 78-71299. (Illus.). 288p. 1979. 16.95 (ISBN 0-317-06371-5); pap. 10.95 (ISBN 0-89604-011-9). Holocaust Pubns.

Partisan: From the Valley of Death to Mount Zion. Yitzhak Arad. LC 78-71299. 1979. 16.95 (ISBN 0-8052-5011-5, Pub. by Holocaust Library); pap. 10.95 (ISBN 0-8052-5010-7, Pub. by Holocaust Library). Schocken.

Partisan Guide to the Jewish Problem. Milton Steinberg. LC 86-1509. (Brown Classics in Judaica). 312p. 1986. pap. text ed. 13.50 (ISBN 0-8191-4493-2). U Pr of Amer.

Partly Right. Anthony Campolo. 192p. 1985. 11.95 (ISBN 0-8499-0368-8, 0368-8). Word Bks.

Partners Across the Pacific. Winston Crawley. LC 85-29088. 1986. pap. 4.95 (ISBN 0-8054-6341-0). Broadman.

Partners in Catechesis. Archdiocese of Baltimore Staff. 96p. 1984. pap. 9.95 (ISBN 0-697-02016-9). Wm C Brown.

Partners in Creation. Ronald D. Petry. 126p. (Orig.). 1979. pap. 4.95 (ISBN 0-87178-688-5). Brethren.

Partners in Dialogue: Christianity & Other World Religions. Arnulf Camps. Tr. by John Drury from Dutch. LC 82-18798. Tr. of Christendom en godsidienstein der wereld. 272p. (Orig.). 1983. pap. 10.95 (ISBN 0-88344-378-3). Orbis Bks.

Partners in Ministry. James Garlow. (Illus.). 195p. (Orig.). 1981. pap. 4.95 (ISBN 0-8341-0693-0). Beacon Hill.

Partners in Process. Truman Esau & Beverly Burch. 156p. 1986. pap. 5.95 (ISBN 0-89693-372-5). Victor Bks.

Partners in Service: Toward a Biblical Theology of Christian Marriage. Elisabeth M. Tetlow & Louis M. Tetlow. LC 83-7016. 192p. (Orig.). 1983. lib. bdg. 26.00 (ISBN 0-8191-3206-3); pap. text ed. 11.25 (ISBN 0-8191-3207-1). U Pr of Amer.

Partners in the Impossible. Richard W. Patt. 1984. 4.95 (ISBN 0-89536-678-9, 4854). CSS of Ohio.

Partnership, A Study of the Covenant. Andrew Kuyvenhoven. 80p. 1983. pap. 2.50 (ISBN 0-933140-89-4). CRC Pubns.

Parvitas Materiae in Sexto in Contemporary Catholic Thought. Patrick J. Boyle. 132p. (Orig.). 1987. lib. bdg. 21.50 (ISBN 0-8191-5790-2); pap. text ed. 9.25 (ISBN 0-8191-5791-0). U Pr of Amer.

Pasame Otro Ladrillo. Charles R. Swindoll. 208p. 1980. 3.75 (ISBN 0-88113-315-9). Edit Betania.

Pascal. Viscount St. Cyres. 1909. Repr. 25.00 (ISBN 0-8274-3103-1). R West.

Pascal & Nietzche: Etude Historique & Comparee. James R. Dionne. LC 74-3300. (Fr.). 1976. lib. bdg. 18.00 (ISBN 0-89102-032-2). B Franklin.

Pascal & Theology. Jan Miel. LC 75-93822. 216p. 1970. 19.50x (ISBN 0-8018-1101-5). Johns Hopkins.

PASCAL: Pensees. John Cruickshank. (Critical Guides to French Texts Ser.: No. 23). 79p. 1983. pap. 3.95 (ISBN 0-7293-0154-0, Pub. by Grant & Cutler). Longwood Pub Group.

Pascal's Anguish & Joy. Charles S. MacKenzie. LC 73-77404. 272p. 1973. 12.95 (ISBN 0-8022-2117-3). Philos Lib.

Pascal's Philosophy of Religion. C. J. Webb. Repr. of 1929 ed. 12.00 (ISBN 0-527-94918-3). Kraus Repr.

Pascal's Unfinished Apology. Marie L. Hubert. LC 70-153272. 165p. 1973. Repr. of 1952 ed. 21.50 (ISBN 0-8046-1699-X, Pub. by Kennikat). Assoc Faculty Pr.

Pascal's Wager: A Study of Practical Reasoning in Philosophical Theology. Nicholas Rescher. LC 84-40820. 176p. 1985. text ed. 19.95 (ISBN 0-268-01556-2, 85-15561). U of Notre Dame Pr.

Pascha: The Resurrection of Christ. David Drillock et al. (Music Ser.). 274p. 1980. pap. 15.00 (ISBN 0-913836-50-8); 20.00 (ISBN 0-913836-65-6). St Vladimirs.

Paschal Cycle. Paul Bosch. 1979. pap. 6.75 (ISBN 0-570-03796-4, 12-2778). Concordia.

Paschal Mystery: Ancient Liturgical & Patristic Texts. Adelbert Hamman. Ed. by Thomas Halton. LC 78-77646. Orig. Title: Mystere De Paques. 1969. 5.95 (ISBN 0-8189-0108-X). Alba.

Paschal Mystery: Core Grace in the Life of the Christian. Augustine Hennessey. (Synthesis Ser.). 37p. 1977. pap. 0.75 (ISBN 0-8199-0707-3). Franciscan Herald.

Paschal Mystery in Christian Living. James Alberione. Tr. by Daughters Of St. Paul. LC 68-28102. (St. Paul Editions). (Illus.). 1968. 3.95 (ISBN 0-8198-0114-3); pap. 2.95 (ISBN 0-8198-0115-1). Dghtrs St Paul.

Paschal or Lent Fast. Peter Gunning. LC 70-168214. (Library of Anglo-Catholic Theology: No. 7). Repr. of 1845 ed. 27.50 (ISBN 0-404-52088-X). AMS Pr.

Pasion por las Almas. Oswald J. Smith. Orig. Title: Passion for Souls. (Span.). 208p. 1985. pap. 4.25 (ISBN 0-8254-1672-8). Kregel.

Paslanije Svatago Ignatija Aniokhiskago I Sviatago Polykarpa Smirnskago. Tr. of Letters of St. Ignatius of Anioch & of St.Polycarp of Smyrna. Repr. 2.00 (ISBN 0-317-28881-4). Holy Trinity.

Pass It on. Robert H. Mounce. LC 78-68851. (Bible Commentary for Layman Ser.). 160p. 1979. pap. 3.50 (ISBN 0-8307-0667-4, S332108). Regal.

Pass It on. Larry Richards. LC 77-87260. (Bible Alive Ser.). (Illus.). 1978. pap. text ed. 2.95 (ISBN 0-89191-089-1); tchr's ed. 3.95 (ISBN 0-89191-090-5). Cook.

Passages of Observation: A Guru's Guide to Salvation. Michael Friedman. Ed. by Liz Jacobsen. (Illus.). 1983. pap. 4.95 (ISBN 0-912561-00-9). Counsel & Stress.

Passing of the Gods. V. F. Calverton. 326p. 1982. Repr. of 1934 ed. lib. bdg. 35.00 (ISBN 0-89987-123-2). Darby Bks.

Passing on the Torch. Roger L. Dudley. Ed. by Raymond H. Woolsey. 192p. 1986. 12.95 (ISBN 0-8280-0348-3). Review & Herald.

Passing the Torch. Carol B. Knight. LC 81-82491. 130p. (Orig.). 1985. pap. 7.95 (ISBN 0-913299-16-2). Stillpoint.

Passio Domini Theme in the Works of Richard Rolle: His Personal Contribution in Its Religeous Cultural, & Literary Context. Mary F. Madigan. Ed. by James Hogg. (Elizabethan & Renaissance Studies). 347p. (Orig.). 1978. pap. 15.00 (ISBN 3-7052-0723-7, Pub. by Salzburg Studies). Longwood Pub Group.

Passio XVIII Cartusianorum in Anglia Martyrum a Domo Maurito Chauncy: A Critical Study. James Hogg. (Analecta Cartusiana Ser.: No. 86). (Orig.). 1987. pap. 25.00 (ISBN 3-7052-0143-3, Pub. by Salzburg Studies). Longwood Pub Group.

Passion According to Luke. Jerome Neyrey. 232p. (Orig.). 1985. pap. 8.95 (ISBN 0-8091-2688-5). Paulist Pr.

Passion According to Luke: The Special Material of Luke 22. Marion L. Soards. (JSOT Supplement Ser.: No. 14). 150p. 1987. text ed. 24.50x (ISBN 1-85075-036-X, Pub. by JSOT Pr England); pap. text ed. 11.95x (ISBN 1-85075-037-8, Pub. by JSOT Pr England). Eisenbrauns.

Passion & Compassion: Mga Tula Sa Ingles at Pilipino. Marra P. Lanot. 153p. 1981. pap. 6.50x (ISBN 0-686-32581-8, Pub. by New Day Phillipines). Cellar.

Passion & Perfection. Norman W. Pittenger. 1985. pap. 2.00 (ISBN 0-88028-044-1). Forward Movement.

Passion & Purity. Elisabeth Elliot. 160p. (Orig.). 1984. pap. 6.95 (ISBN 0-8007-5137-X, Power Bks). Revell.

Passion As Story: The Plot of Mark. John Blackwell. LC 85-16209. (Fortress Resources for Preaching Ser.). 96p. 1986. pap. 5.95 (ISBN 0-8006-1144-6, 1-1144). Fortress.

Passion for Jesus: A Passion for Justice. Esther B. Bruland & Stephen C. Mott. 176p. 1983. pap. 9.95 (ISBN 0-8170-0994-9). Judson.

Passion for Living. Danuta Soderman. 1987. 11.95 (ISBN 0-8007-1534-9). Revell.

Passion for Sharing: The Life of Edith Rosenwald Stern. Gerda Weissmann Klein. (Illus.). 448p. 1984. 18.95 (ISBN 0-940646-15-3). Rossel Bks.

Passion for the Divine. Ruth Lambek. 1979. pap. 4.95 (ISBN 0-87516-289-4). De Vorss.

Passion for the Impossible. Leslie T. Lyall. 1965. pap. 2.40 (ISBN 0-85363-115-8). OMF Bks.

Passion for the Impossible. Bhagwan S. Rajneesh. Ed. by Ma P. Maneesha. LC 83-181944. (Initiation Talks Ser.). (Illus.). 464p. (Orig.). 1978. 18.95 (ISBN 0-88050-111-1). Chidvilas Found.

Passion, Knowing How, & Understanding: An Essay on the Concept of Faith. Andrew J. Burgess. LC 75-31550. (American Academy of Religion. Dissertation Ser.). 1975. pap. 9.95 (ISBN 0-89130-044-9, 010109). Scholars Pr GA.

Passion Narratives. Herman Hendrickx. (Commentary on the Synoptic Gospels Ser.). 210p. 1984. pap. 9.95 (ISBN 0-225-66400-3, 8524, HarpR). Har-Row.

Passion Narratives & Gospel Theologies: Interpreting the Synoptics Through Their Passion Stories. Frank J. Matera. 320p. 1986. pap. 12.95 (ISBN 0-8091-2775-X). Paulist Pr.

Passion of Al-Hallaj: Mystic & Martyr of Islam, 4 vols. Louis Massignon. Tr. by Herbert Mason from Fr. LC 80-11085. (Bollingen Ser.: No. XCVIII). 2010p. 1983. Set. 145.00x (ISBN 0-691-09910-3); 24.50x (ISBN 0-691-10203-1). Princeton U Pr.

Passion of Christ. Veselin Kesich. 84p. pap. 1.95 (ISBN 0-913836-80-X). St Vladimirs.

Passion of Christ. Shri Kripalvanandji. LC 83-80214. 51p. 1983. pap. 4.50 (ISBN 0-940258-09-9). Kripalu Pubns.

Passion of Christ, Passion of the World: The Facts, Their Interpretation & Their Meaning Yesterday & Today. Leonardo Boff. Tr. by Robert R. Barr from Port. 160p. (Orig.). 1987. 19.95 (ISBN 0-88344-564-6); pap. 9.95 (ISBN 0-88344-563-8). Orbis Bks.

Passion of God: Divine Suffering in Contemporary Protestant Theology. Warren McWilliams. 208p. 1985. text ed. 16.50 (ISBN 0-86554-158-2, MUP H148). Mercer Univ Pr.

Passion of Jesus in the Gospel of Mark. Donald Senior. (Passion Ser.: Vol. 2). 1984. pap. 8.95 (ISBN 0-89453-436-X). M Glazier.

Passion of Jesus in the Gospel of Matthew. Donald Senior. (Passion Ser.: Vol. 1). 1985. pap. 8.95 (ISBN 0-89453-460-2). M Glazier.

Passion of Our Lord. Tr. by Fiscar Marison. 302p. 1980. pap. 4.50 (ISBN 0-911988-38-6). AMI Pr.

Passion of S. Perpetua. Ed. by J. A. Robinson. (Texts & Studies Ser.: No. 1, Vol. 1,Pt. 2). pap. 13.00 (ISBN 0-8115-1680-6). Kraus Repr.

Passion Paths. William Grimbol. Ed. by Michael L. Sherer. (Orig.). 1987. pap. 3.95 (ISBN 0-89536-842-0, 7801). CSS of Ohio.

Passion Play. Charles Numrich. 1983. 4.95 (ISBN 0-89536-601-0, 1627). CSS of Ohio.

Passionate God. Rosemary Haughton. LC 81-80049. 352p. 1981. pap. 9.95 (ISBN 0-8091-2383-5). Paulist Pr.

Passionate Mind. Joel Kramer. 122p. 1983. pap. 7.95 (ISBN 0-938190-12-1). North Atlantic.

Passionate Necessity. Hugh Shearman. 3.50 (ISBN 0-8356-0200-1). Theos Pub Hse.

Passions. Robert C. Solomon. xxv, 448p. 1983. text ed. 22.95x (ISBN 0-268-01551-1); pap. text ed. 9.95x (ISBN 0-268-01552-X). U of Notre Dame Pr.

Passions. Ellen White. 1985. pap. 6.00 (ISBN 0-914009-55-9). VHI Library.

Passions among God's People. large print ed. Ellen White. 35p. 1985. pap. 6.00 (ISBN 0-914009-46-X). VHI Library.

Passion's Child: The Extraordinary Life of Jane Digby. Margaret F. Schmidt. 5.95 (ISBN 0-7043-3202-7, Pub. by Quartet England). Charles River Bks.

Passover. Howard Greenfeld. LC 77-13910. (Illus.). 32p. 1978. 6.95 (ISBN 0-03-039921-1). H Holt & Co.

Passover. Ed. by Klein Mordell. 128p. pap. 4.50 (ISBN 0-686-95142-5). ADL.

Passover. 64p. (Orig.). 1986. 20.95 (ISBN 0-86683-778-7, HarpR); pap. 10.95 (ISBN 0-86683-778-7). Har-Row.

Passover. Norma Simon. LC 65-11644. (Holiday Ser.). (Illus.). 1965. PLB 12.89 (ISBN 0-690-61094-7, Crowell Jr Bks). HarpJ.

Passover Anthology. Ed. by Philip Goodman. LC 61-11706. (Illus.). 196p. 1961. 14.95 (ISBN 0-8276-0019-4, 250). Jewish Pubns.

Passover Fun Book: Puzzles, Riddles, Magic & More. David A. Adler. (Bonim Fun-to-Do Bk.). (Illus.). 1978. saddlewire bdg. 3.95 (ISBN 0-88482-759-3, Bonim Bks). Hebrew Pub.

Passover Gourmet. Nira Rousso. (Illus.). 192p. 1987. 19.95 (ISBN 0-915361-66-3, Dist. by Watts). Adama Pubs Inc.

Passover Haggadah. Ed. by Herbert Bronstein. (Illus.). 1974. 79.00 set (ISBN 0-916694-66-6); lib. bdg. 27.50 (ISBN 0-916694-06-2); pap. 9.95 (ISBN 0-916694-05-4). Central Conf.

Passover Haggadah. rev. ed. Central Conference of American Rabbis Staff. Ed. & illus. by Leonard Baskin. (Illus.). 124p. 1978. pap. 14.95 (ISBN 0-14-004871-5). Penguin.

Passover Haggadah. Roe Halper. (Illus.). 40p. (Orig.). 1986. pap. 5.00 (ISBN 0-916326-03-9). Bayberry Pr.

Passover Haggadah. Tr. by Aryeh Kaplan. (MeAm Lo'ez Ser.). 288p. sephardic 11.95 (ISBN 0-940118-23-8). Maznaim.

Passover Haggadah. Tr. by Chaim Raphael. LC 78-52362. (Illus.). 1978. pap. 3.95 (ISBN 0-87441-312-5). Behrman.

Passover Haggadah. Ed. by Morris Silverman. pap. 4.95 (ISBN 0-87677-029-4). Hartmore.

Passover Haggadah. rev. ed. Ed. by Morris Silverman. (Illus.). 1986. 10.00 (ISBN 0-87677-025-1); pap. 4.95 (ISBN 0-87677-029-4). Prayer Bk.

Passover Haggadah: A Messianic Celebration. Eric-Peter Lipson. LC 85-82168. (Illus.). 128p. 1986. 10.95 (ISBN 0-9616148-0-3). JFJ Pub.

Passover Haggadah: Including Readings on the Holocaust, with English Translation, Introduction & Commentary. 3rd ed. Ed. by Nahum N. Glatzer. LC 69-10846. (Illus., Bilingual ed). 1979. pap. 3.95 (ISBN 0-8052-0624-8). Schocken.

Passover Haggadah: The Complete Seder. Arthur M. Silver. 1980. 10.95 (ISBN 0-932232-06-X). Menorah Pub.

Passover, Its History & Tradition. Theodor H. Gaster. LC 83-22678. (Illus.). 102p. 1984. Repr. of 1949 ed. lib. bdg. 22.50x (ISBN 0-313-24372-7, GAPA). Greenwood.

Passover Meal. Arleen Hynes. LC 76-187207. 64p. 1972. pap. 2.50 (ISBN 0-8091-1653-7). Paulist Pr.

Passover Plot Exposed. Clifford Wilson. LC 77-73814. 1977. pap. 2.95 (ISBN 0-89051-032-6). Master Bks.

Passover Seder. Ruth G. Fredman. 1982. pap. 5.95 (ISBN 0-452-00606-6, Mer). NAL.

Passover Seder. Arthur Gilbert. (Illus.). 1965. pap. 2.95x (ISBN 0-87068-504-X). Ktav.

Passover Seder: Afikoman in Exile. Ruth G. Fredman. 1981. 22.00x (ISBN 0-8122-7788-0). U of Pa Pr.

Passover Seder: Afikoman in Exile. Ruth G. Fredman. 192p. 19.00 (ISBN 0-686-95143-3). ADL.

Passover Seder for Christian Families. Sam Mackintosh. 32p. 1984. pap. 2.95 (ISBN 0-89390-057-5). Resource Pubns.

Password to Heaven. Susan Davis. (My Church Teaches Ser.). 32p. 1980. pap. 2.50 (ISBN 0-8127-0298-0). Review & Herald.

Past Life Therapy in Action. Dick Sutphen & Lauren L. Taylor. 100p. 1983. pap. 2.95 (ISBN 0-911842-32-2). Valley Sun.

Past Life Visions: A Christian Exploration. William DeArteaga. 256p. 1983. pap. 9.95 (ISBN 0-8164-2414-4, HarpR). Har-Row.

Past Lives Future Growth. Ann Druffel & Armand Marcotte. (Inner Visions Ser.). (Orig.). 1987. pap. 12.95 (ISBN 0-917086-88-0). A C S Pubns Inc.

Past Lives, Future Loves. Dick Sutphen. 1982. pap. 3.50 (ISBN 0-671-54363-6). PB.

Past Lives: The Key to Your Present Relationships: Introducing the Youngs' Past Life Regression Technique. Robert Young & Loy Young. Ed. by Mignonette Pellegrin. LC 85-73214. (Illus.). 344p. (Orig.). 1985. pap. 19.95 (ISBN 0-936121-00-9). Draco Prod Pubns.

Past, Present, & Future of Biblical Theology. James D. Smart. LC 79-16943. 162p. 1979. softcover 8.95 (ISBN 0-664-24284-7). Westminster.

Past, Present & Future of the Church. Fred Pruitt. 72p. pap. 0.60 (ISBN 0-686-29133-6). Faith Pub Hse.

Past Tense of God's Word. Kenneth Hagin, Jr. 1980. pap. 0.50 mini bk. (ISBN 0-89276-706-5). Hagin Ministries.

Pasteur & la Cure d'Ame. Paul Hoff. Tr. of Pastor As a Counselor. (Fr.). 240p. 1986. pap. 4.10 (ISBN 0-8297-0692-5). Life Pubs Intl.

Pastirskoje Bogoslovije, 2 Vols. Konstantine Zaitsev. Tr. of Pastoral Theology. 478p. 1960. pap. text ed. 16.00 (ISBN 0-317-30273-6). Holy Trinity.

Pastirskoje Sovjeshchjanije 1969. Tr. of Pastoral Conference 1969. 95p. 1969. pap. 3.00 (ISBN 0-317-30274-4). Holy Trinity.

Pastor. H. Harvey. Tr. by Alejandro Trevino. Orig. Title: Pastor. (Span.). 232p. 1984. pap. 3.95 (ISBN 0-311-42025-7). Casa Bautista.

Pastor & His Work. Homer A. Kent, Sr. pap. 8.95 (ISBN 0-88469-079-2). BMH Bks.

Pastor & Laity in the Theology of Jean Gerson. D. Catherine Brown. 420p. 1987. 54.50 (ISBN 0-521-33029-7). Cambridge U Pr.

Pastor & Parish: A Systems Approach. E. Mansell Pattison. Ed. by Howard J. Clinebell & Howard W. Stone. LC 76-62619. (Creative Pastoral Care & Counseling Ser.). 96p. 1977. pap. 0.50 (ISBN 0-8006-0559-4, 1-559). Fortress.

Pastor & Patient. Ed. by Richard Dayringer. LC 80-70247. 240p. 1981. 25.00x (ISBN 0-87668-437-1). Aronson.

Pastor & People. R. T. Williams. pap. 2.95 (ISBN 0-686-12898-2). Schmul Pub Co.

Pastor & the Church Musicians: Thoughts on Aspects of a Common Ministry. Carl Schalk. 12p. (Orig.). 1984. pap. 1.50 (ISBN 0-570-01330-5, 99-1256). Concordia.

Pastor & the People: Building a New Partnership for Effective Ministry. Lyle E. Schaller. LC 72-8567. 176p. (Orig.). 1973. pap. 7.95 (ISBN 0-687-30136-X). Abingdon.

Pastor & the Personal Computer: Information Management for Ministers. William R. Johnson. 224p. (Orig.). 1985. pap. 10.50 (ISBN 0-687-30134-3). Abingdon.

Pastor As Evangelist. Richard S. Armstrong. LC 84-10359. 202p. 1984. pap. 9.95 (ISBN 0-664-24556-0). Westminster.

Pastor As God's Minister. Earle G. Griffith. LC 76-50694. 1978. 7.95 (ISBN 0-87227-054-8). Reg Baptist.

Pastor As Person. Gary L. Harbaugh. LC 84-24259. 176p. (Orig.). 1984. pap. 9.95 (ISBN 0-8066-2115-X, 10-4889). Augsburg.

Pastor As Priest. Ed. by Earl E. Shelp & Ronald H. Sunderland. (Pastoral Ministry Ser.). 160p. (Orig.). 1987. pap. 9.95 (ISBN 0-8298-0751-9). Pilgrim NY.

Pastor As Prophet. Ed. by Earl E. Shelp & Ronald H. Sutherland. 172p. 1985. pap. 9.95 (ISBN 0-8298-0547-8). Pilgrim NY.

Pastor As Servant. Earl E. Shelp & Ronald H. Sunderland. 112p. (Orig.). 1986. pap. 8.95 (ISBN 0-8298-0580-X). Pilgrim NY.

Pastor As Shepherd of the School Community. John R. Gilbert. 52p. 1983. 4.80 (ISBN 0-318-00788-6). Natl Cath Educ.

Pastor at Prayer. George Kraus. LC 6-1188. (Continued Applied Christianity Ser.). 1983. 15.95 (ISBN 0-570-03073-0, 6-1188). Concordia.

Pastor at Work. Harold Steindam. (Illus.). 128p. 1985. pap. 7.95 (ISBN 0-8298-0562-1). Pilgrim NY.

Pastor Charles Taze Russell. David Horowitz. LC 85-20511. 159p. 1986. 15.95 (ISBN 0-8022-2503-9); pap. 9.95 (ISBN 0-8022-2504-7). Philos Lib.

Pastor, Church & Law. Richard R. Hammar. LC 83-80245. 448p. 1983. 16.95 (ISBN 0-88243-580-9, 02-0580). Gospel Pub.

Pastor, Church & Law Supplement. Richard R. Hammar. LC 85-82192. 208p. (Orig.). 1986. 6.95 (ISBN 0-88243-582-5, 02-0582). Gospel Pub.

Pastor-Evangelist in Worship. Richard S. Armstrong. LC 85-26380. 216p. (Orig.). 1986. pap. 9.95 (ISBN 0-664-24693-1). Westminster.

Pastor Goode & His Marvelous Micro. Neil B. Houk. 59p. (Orig.). 1984. pap. 5.95 (ISBN 0-9615086-0-4). Church Bytes.

Pastor Goode & His Marvelous Micro. rev. ed. 1986. pap. 6.95 (ISBN 0-9615086-4-7). Church Bytes.

Pastor in a Teaching Church. David M. Evans. 96p. 1983. pap. 4.95 (ISBN 0-317-00688-6). Judson.

Pastor in Prayer. C. H. Spurgeon. 3.75 (ISBN 0-686-09092-6). Pilgrim Pubns.

Pastor in Prayer. C. H. Spurgeon. 192p. Date not set. pap. write for info. Pilgrim Pubns.

Pastor of the Range. R. J. Sherman. (Illus.). 224p. 1985. 13.00 (ISBN 0-682-40225-7). Exposition Pr FL.

Pastor Pete. Duane Hutchinson. (Illus.). pap. write for info (ISBN 0-934988-05-6). Foun Bks.

Pastor Search Committee Planbook. Gerald M. Williamson. LC 81-68923. 1982. pap. 5.50 (ISBN 0-8054-3515-8). Broadman.

Pastor Search Committee Primer. Gerald M. Williamson. LC 81-68924. 1982. pap. 3.50 (ISBN 0-8054-3516-6). Broadman.

Pastor to Pastor. James E. Hamill. LC 85-60248. 192p. 1985. 5.50 (ISBN 0-88243-600-7, 02-0600). Gospel Pub.

Pastor to the Rural Philippines: an Autobiography. Cornelio M. Ferrer. 1974. wrps. 2.50x (ISBN 0-686-18697-4). Cellar.

Pastoral Approach to Atheism. Karl S. Rahner. LC 67-21347. (Concilium Ser.: Vol. 23). 189p. 7.95 (ISBN 0-8091-0107-6). Paulist Pr.

Pastoral Associate & the Lay Pastor. Mary Chandler. 72p. 1986. pap. 3.95 (ISBN 0-8146-1470-1). Liturgical Pr.

Pastoral Care: A Thematic Approach. Donald Capps. LC 78-15093. (Illus.). 162p. 1979. softcover 8.95 (ISBN 0-664-24222-7). Westminster.

Pastoral Care & Counseling in Grief & Separation. Wayne E. Oates. Ed. by Howard J. Clinebell & Howard W. Stone. LC 75-13048. (Creative Pastoral Care & Counseling Ser.). 96p. 1976. pap. 4.50 (ISBN 0-8006-0554-3, 1-554). Fortress.

Pastoral Care & Counseling: Using the Unique Resources of the Christian Tradition. William E. Hulme. LC 80-67806. 160p. (Orig.). 1981. pap. 9.95 (ISBN 0-8066-1869-8, 10-4896). Augsburg.

Pastoral Care & Counselling. James E. Giles. pap. text ed. 10.95 (ISBN 0-311-72535-X). Casa Bautista.

Pastoral Care & Hermeneutics. Donald Capps. LC 84-47909. (Theology & Pastoral Care Ser.). 128p. 1984. pap. 7.95 (ISBN 0-8006-1732-0). Fortress.

Pastoral Care & Liberation Praxis: Studies in Personal & Social Transformation. Ed. by Perry LeFevre & W. Widick Schroeder. (Studies in Ministry & Parish Life). 112p. 1986. text ed. 18.95x (ISBN 0-913552-31-3); pap. text ed. 8.95x (ISBN 0-913552-32-1). Exploration Pr.

Pastoral Care & Process Theology. Gordon E. Jackson. LC 81-40159. 266p. (Orig.). 1981. lib. bdg. 29.75 (ISBN 0-8191-1710-2); pap. text ed. 12.75 (ISBN 0-8191-1711-0). U Pr of Amer.

Pastoral Care & the Jewish Tradition: Empathic Process & Religious Counseling. Robert L. Katz. LC 84-47925. (Theology & Pastoral Care Ser.). 128p. 1984. pap. 7.95 (ISBN 0-8006-1731-2). Fortress.

Pastoral Care & the Parish. Peter Davie. 102p. 1984. 24.95x (ISBN 0-631-13225-2); pap. 8.95x (ISBN 0-631-13226-0). Basil Blackwell.

Pastoral Care for Alcoholism: An Introduction. Conrad L. Bergendoff. 36p. 1981. pap. 1.95 (ISBN 0-89486-123-9). Hazelden.

Pastoral Care for Severe Emotional Disorders: Principles of Diagnosis & Treatment. Paul C. Holinger. LC 83-18670. 145p. 1985. text ed. 24.95x (ISBN 0-8290-1509-4). Irvington.

Pastoral Care for Single Parents. Harold I. Smith. 158p. 1982. pap. 3.95 (ISBN 0-8341-0782-1). Beacon Hill.

Pastoral Care in Historical Perspective. William Clebsch & Charles Jaekle. LC 84-451130. 344p. 1983. Repr. of 1975 ed. 30.00x (ISBN 0-87668-717-6). Aronson.

Pastoral Care in the Church. C. W. Brister. LC 64-19497. 1977. pap. 6.00 (ISBN 0-06-061051-4, RD 222, HarpR). Har-Row.

Pastoral Care in the Modern Hospital. Heije Faber. Tr. by Hugo De Waal. LC 70-168632. 160p. 1972. 10.95 (ISBN 0-664-20922-X). Westminster.

Pastoral Care Issues in the Pulpit. Ed. by Gregory J. Johanson. 1984. 7.50 (ISBN 0-89536-621-5, 1630). CSS of Ohio.

Pastoral Care of Battered Women. Rita-Lou Clarke. LC 86-5604. 132p. (Orig.). 1986. pap. 7.95 (ISBN 0-664-24015-1). Westminster.

Pastoral Care of the Handicapped. Roy E. Hartbauer. LC 82-74357. (Illus.). xvi, 183p. 1983. pap. 11.95 (ISBN 0-943872-87-1). Andrews Univ Pr.

Pastoral Care of the Sick: Rites of Anointing & Viaticum. 1983. deluxe ed. 19.95; text ed. 13.95 (ISBN 0-8146-1287-3). Liturgical Pr.

Pastoral Care to the Cancer Patient. Nancy V. Platt. 100p. 1980. pap. 9.75x (ISBN 0-398-04051-6). C C Thomas.

Pastoral Care with Children in Crisis. Andrew D. Lester. LC 84-21901. 144p. (Orig.). 1985. pap. 9.95 (ISBN 0-664-24598-6). Westminster.

Pastoral Care with Handicapped Persons. Lowell G. Colston. Ed. by Howard J. Clinebell & Howard W. Stone. LC 77-15229. (Creative Pastoral Care & Counseling Ser). 96p. (Orig.). 1978. pap. 4.50 (ISBN 0-8006-0560-8, 1-560). Fortress.

Pastoral Companion. 14th ed. Ed. by Marcian Mathis & Dismas Bonner. 1976. 17.50 (ISBN 0-8199-0084-2, L38625). Franciscan Herald.

Pastoral Companion: A Canon Law Handbook for Catholic Ministry. John M. Huels. LC 85-29316. 1986. 25.00 (ISBN 0-8199-0900-9); pap. 15.00. Franciscan Herald.

Pastoral Companion: A Canon Law Handbook for Pastoral Ministry. John M. Huels. 1986. 25.00 (ISBN 0-8199-0900-9); pap. 15.00. Franciscan Herald.

Pastoral Companionship: Ministry with Seriously Ill Persons & Their Families. Gerald J. Calhoun. 180p. (Orig.). 1986. pap. 8.95 (ISBN 0-8091-2753-9). Paulist Pr.

Pastoral Constitution on the Church in the Modern World (Gaudium et Spes) 138p. 1965. pap. 3.95 (ISBN 1-55586-015-X). US Catholic.

Pastoral Counseling. rev. ed. Seward Hiltner. (Series AF). 1969. pap. 9.95 (ISBN 0-687-30317-6, Apex). Abingdon.

Pastoral Counseling. Loyola College, Pastoral & Counseling Faculty. (Illus.). 352p. 1982. 29.67 (ISBN 0-13-652867-8). P-H.

Pastoral Counseling. Wayne E. Oates. LC 73-19719. 240p. 1982. pap. 8.95 (ISBN 0-664-24405-X). Westminster.

Pastoral Counseling: A Ministry of the Church. John Patton. 240p. (Orig.). 1983. pap. 12.95 (ISBN 0-687-30314-1). Abingdon.

Pastoral Counseling Across Cultures. David W. Augsburger. LC 86-13343. 408p. 1986. 21.95 (ISBN 0-664-21272-7). Westminster.

Pastoral Counseling & Preaching: A Quest for an Integrated Ministry. Donald Capps. LC 80-18502. 156p. 1980. pap. 8.95 (ISBN 0-664-24342-8). Westminster.

Pastoral Counseling & Spiritual Values: A Black Point of View. Edward P. Wimberly. LC 81-10918. 176p. (Orig.). 1982. pap. 7.75 (ISBN 0-687-30336-2). Abingdon.

Pastoral Counseling with People in Distress. Harold I. Haas. LC 77-99316. 1969. pap. 6.95 (ISBN 0-570-03794-8, 12-2776). Concordia.

Pastoral Counselor in Social Action. Speed Leas & Paul Kittlaus. Ed. by Howard J. Clinebell & Howard W. Stone. LC 80-8059. (Creative Pastoral Care & Counseling Ser.). 96p. (Orig.). 1981. pap. 4.50 (ISBN 0-8006-0565-9, 1-565). Fortress.

Pastoral Epistles. E. M. Blaiklock. 128p. 1972. pap. 4.95 (ISBN 0-310-21233-2, 9232). Zondervan.

Pastoral Epistles. Gordon H. Clark. (Trinity Papers: No. 6). 294p. (Orig.). 1983. pap. 9.95 (ISBN 0-940931-06-0). Trinity Found.

Pastoral Epistles. Martin Dibelius & Hans Conzelmann. Ed. by Helmut Koester. Tr. by Philip Buttolph & Adela Yarbro. LC 71-157549. (Hermeneia: a Critical & Historical Commentary on the Bible). 1972. 19.95 (ISBN 0-8006-6002-1, 20-6002). Fortress.

Pastoral Epistles. Patrick Fairbairn. 1980. 17.25 (ISBN 0-86524-053-1, 7107). Klock & Klock.

Pastoral Epistles. Donald Guthrie. (Tyndale Bible Commentary). 1957. pap. 4.95 (ISBN 0-8028-1413-1). Eerdmans.

Pastoral Epistles. Robert J. Karris. (New Testament Message Ser.: Vol. 17). 9.95 (ISBN 0-89453-205-7); pap. 5.95 (ISBN 0-89453-140-9). M Glazier.

Pastoral Epistles. Homer A. Kent, Jr. 320p. 1982. pap. 10.95 (ISBN 0-88469-075-X). BMH Bks.

Pastoral Epistles. rev. ed. Homer Kent, Jr. 1958. 10.95 (ISBN 0-8024-6357-6). Moody.

Pastoral Epistles. (Erdmans Commentaries Ser.). 3.95 (ISBN 0-8010-3403-5). Baker Bk.

Pastoral Epistles: Introduction & Commentary. Irving A. Sparks. LC 85-10925. (Orig.). 1985. pap. 6.00 (ISBN 0-934743-01-0). Inst Biblical.

Pastoral Epistles: Timothy & Titus. J. H. Bernard. (Thornapple Commentaries Ser.). 272p. 1980. pap. 6.95 (ISBN 0-8010-0797-6). Baker Bk.

Pastoral Evangelism. Samuel Southard. LC 80-82196. 192p. 1981. pap. 4.50 (ISBN 0-8042-2037-9). John Knox.

Pastoral Formation & Pastoral Field Edcation in the Catholic Seminary. 84p. 1985. pap. 4.95 (ISBN 1-55586-936-X). US Catholic.

Pastoral Health Care: Understanding the Church's Healing Ministers. Robert Patterson. LC 83-1948. 30p. 1983. pap. 0.90 (ISBN 0-87125-080-2). Cath Health.

Pastoral Letters. Ed. by Anthony T. Hanson. (Cambridge Bible Commentary on the New English Bible, New Testament Ser.). (Orig.). 1966. 17.95 (ISBN 0-521-04214-3); pap. 7.50x (ISBN 0-521-09380-5, 380). Cambridge U Pr.

Pastoral Letters of the United States Catholic Bishops: 1792-1983, 4 vols. Ed. by Hugh J. Nolan. 1890p. 1984. pap. 95.00 (ISBN 1-55586-897-5). US Catholic.

Pastoral Letters of the United States Catholic Bishops, 1975-1983, Vol. IV. Ed. by Hugh J. Nolan. 616p. 1984. pap. 24.95 (ISBN 1-55586-875-4). US Catholic.

Pastoral Letters of the United States Catholic Bishops, 1962-1974, Vol. III. Ed. by Hugh J. Nolan. 511p. 1984. pap. 24.95 (ISBN 1-55586-870-3). US Catholic.

Pastoral Letters of the United States Catholic Bishops, 1941-1961, Vol. II. Ed. by Hugh J. Nolan. 271p. 1984. pap. 24.95 (ISBN 1-55586-885-1). US Catholic.

Pastoral Letters of the United States Catholic Bishops, 1792-1940, Vol. I. Ed. by Hugh J. Nolan. 487p. 1984. pap. 24.95 (ISBN 1-55586-880-0). US Catholic.

Pastoral Life in the Power of the Spirit. Johannes Hofinger. LC 81-1439. (Illus.). 215p. 1982. pap. 6.95 (ISBN 0-8189-0427-5). Alba.

Pastoral: Mediaeval into Renaissance. Helen Cooper. 257p. 1977. 32.50x (ISBN 0-87471-906-2). Rowman.

Pastoral Medicine. Rudolf Steiner. Tr. by Gladys Hahn from Ger. Tr. of Pastoral-Medizinischer Kurs. 1987. 20.00 (ISBN 0-88010-250-0); pap. 9.95 (ISBN 0-88010-253-5). Anthroposophic.

Pastoral Ministry with Disabled Persons. Walter Kern. LC 84-24619. 248p. 1985. pap. 6.95 (ISBN 0-8189-0472-0). Alba.

Pastoral Mission of the Church. Ed. by Karl Rahner. LC 76-57341. (Concilium Ser.: Vol. 3). 192p. 7.95 (ISBN 0-8091-0108-4). Paulist Pr.

Pastoral Pointers: Contribution by Thirteen Church of God Ministers. 1976. pap. 2.95 (ISBN 0-87148-686-5). Pathway Pr.

Pastoral Practice & the Paranormal. Bonaventure Kloppenburg. Tr. by David Smith from Span. 1979. 8.95 (ISBN 0-685-92509-9). Franciscan Herald.

Pastoral Preaching: Timeless Truth for Changing Needs. Gary D. Stratman. 112p. (Orig.). 1983. pap. 8.75 (ISBN 0-687-30139-4). Abingdon.

Pastoral Presence & the Diocesan Priest. Paul T. Keyes. LC 78-22009. 142p. 1978. pap. 4.95 (ISBN 0-89571-004-8). Affirmation.

Pastoral Reform in Church Government. Ed. by Teodoro-J Urresti & Neophytos Edelby. LC 65-28464. (Concilium Ser.: Vol. 8). 192p. 7.95 (ISBN 0-8091-0109-2). Paulist Pr.

Pastoral Role in Caring for the Dying & Bereaved: Pragmatic & Ecumenical. Ed. by Brian P. O'Connor et al. LC 86-545. (Foundation of Thanatology Ser.: Vol. 7). 245p. 1986. lib. bdg. 39.95 (ISBN 0-275-92153-0, C2153). Praeger.

Pastoral Sermons. Ronald Knox. 1960. 12.50 (ISBN 0-8199-0823-1). Franciscan Herald.

Pastoral Statement on the Catholic Charismatic Renewal. 48p. 1984. pap. 2.25 (ISBN 1-55586-931-9). US Catholic.

Pastoral Teaching of Paul. Edward W. Chadwick. LC 84-7123. 416p. 1984. 11.95 (ISBN 0-8254-2325-2). Kregel.

Pastoral Theologian of the Year: Seward Hiltner; Special Issue PP 29, No. 1. Liston M. Mills. LC 80-82467. 112p. 1980. pap. 12.95 (ISBN 0-89885-068-1). Human Sci Pr.

Pastoral Theology. Hills. kivar 6.95 (ISBN 0-686-12899-0). Schmul Pub Co.

Pastoral Theology: Essentials of Ministry. Thomas C. Oden. LC 82-47753. 456p. (Orig.). 1983. 15.95 (ISBN 0-06-066353-7, RD 415, HarpR). Har-Row.

Pastoral Vision of John Paul II. Ed. by Joan Bland. 1982. 7.95 (ISBN 0-8199-0839-8). Franciscan Herald.

Pastorale Dramatique en France a la Fin du Seizieme & Au Commencement du Dix-Septieme Siecle. Jules Marsan. LC 79-159703. (Research & Source Works Ser.: No. 745). (Illus.). 1971. Repr. of 1905 ed. lib. bdg. 32.50 (ISBN 0-8337-4254-X). B Franklin.

Pastoring the Smaller Church. John C. Thiessen. kivar 6.95 (ISBN 0-310-36901-0). Zondervan.

Pastors & Parishes. Robert L. Randall. LC 86-27176. 184p. 1987. text ed. 29.95 (ISBN 0-89885-348-6). Human Sci Pr.

Pastors & People: German & Lutheran Reformed Churches in the Pennsylvania Field, 1717-1793, Vol. II, The History. Charles H. Glatfelter. LC 80-83400. (Penn. German Ser.: Vol. 15). (Illus.). 25.00 (ISBN 0-911122-44-3). Penn German Soc.

Pastors & People: German Lutheran & Reformed Churches in the Pennsylvania Field, 1717-1793. Charles H. Glatfelter. LC 80-83400. (Penn. German Ser.: Vol. 13). (Illus.). 1979. 30.00 (ISBN 0-911122-40-0). Penn German Soc.

Pastors Are People Too. Ed. by David B. Biebel & Howard W. Lawrence. LC 86-3835. 205p. (Orig.). 1986. pap. 5.95 (ISBN 0-8307-1102-3, 5418654). Regal.

Pastors' Barracks. Robert Wise. 192p. 1986. pap. 11.95 (ISBN 0-89693-157-9). Victor Bks.

Pastor's Counseling Manual for Ministry to Those Who Must Sustain a Loved One in Crisis. Theodore W. Schroeder. 1981. pap. 2.75 (ISBN 0-570-08250-1, 12YY2922). Concordia.

Pastor's Guidebook: A Manual for Worship. Marion D. Aldridge. LC 83-70213. 1984. 9.95 (ISBN 0-8054-2312-5). Broadman.

Pastor's Handbook. C & MA Home Department Board Staff. 102p. 3.95 (ISBN 0-87509-118-0). Chr Pubns.

Pastor's Handbook. Jack Dunigan. (Orig.). 1985. pap. 6.95 (ISBN 0-932943-00-4). Life Lines.

Pastor's Handbook. Richard A. Hufton. 47p. (Orig.). 1984. pap. 3.00 (ISBN 0-933643-05-5). Grace World Outreach.

Pastor's Handbook, Vol. II. Wayne E. Oates. LC 79-28639. (Christian Care Bks.). 120p. 1980. pap. 7.95 (ISBN 0-664-24330-4). Westminster.

Pastor's Handbook, Vol. 1. Wayne E. Oates. LC 79-28639. (Christian Care Bks.). 120p. 1980. pap. 7.95 (ISBN 0-664-24300-2). Westminster.

Pastor's Handbook on Interpersonal Relationships. Jard DeVille. 145p. 1986. pap. 8.95 (ISBN 0-8010-2961-9). Baker Bk.

Pastors in Ministry: Guidelines for Seven Critical Issues. Ed. by William E. Hulme et al. LC 85-1213. 176p. (Orig.). 1985. pap. 9.95 (ISBN 0-8066-2159-1, 10-4898). Augsburg.

Pastor's Manual. James R. Hobbs. 1940. 8.95 (ISBN 0-8054-2301-X). Broadman.

Pastor's Primer for Premarital Guidance. Robert L. Hawkins. 1978. pap. 3.95 (ISBN 0-9607764-0-0). R L Hawkins.

Pastor's Problems. Ed. by Cyril S. Rodd. 168p. pap. 11.65 Canada (ISBN 0-317-31449-1); pap. 8.95 (ISBN 0-317-31450-5, 30-29117-1902). Fortress.

Pastor's Wedding & Funeral Record. LC 68-12321. 1968. 11.95 (ISBN 0-8054-2306-0). Broadman.

Pastor's Wife. Sabina Wurmbrand. 1979. pap. 4.95 (ISBN 0-88264-000-3). Diane Bks.

Pastor's Wife Today. Donna M. Sinclair. LC 80-26076. (Creative Leadership Ser.). 128p. (Orig.). 1981. pap. 5.95 (ISBN 0-687-30269-2). Abingdon.

Pat Robertson: A Biography. Neil Eskelin. 192p. (Orig.). 1987. pap. 7.95 (ISBN 0-910311-47-1). Huntington Hse Inc.

Patanjali & Yoga. Mircea Eliade. LC 75-10785. (Illus.). 224p. 1975. pap. 5.95 (ISBN 0-8052-0491-1). Schocken.

Patanjali's Yoga Sutras. 2nd ed. Patanjali. Tr. by Rama Prasada from Sanskrit. 318p. 1981. Repr. of 1912 ed. 28.50 (ISBN 0-89744-220-2, Pub. by Orient Reprint India). Auromere.

Patanjali's Yoga Sutras. (the Aphorisms of Yoga, by Patanjali.) with the Commentary of Vyasa & the Gloss of Vachaspati Misra. Patanjali. Tr. by Rama Prasada. LC 73-3789. Repr. of 1912 ed. 29.00 (ISBN 0-404-57804-7). AMS Pr.

Patches of Joy. Velma S. Daniels. 1979. 7.95 (ISBN 0-88289-101-4); pap. 5.95 (ISBN 0-88289-232-0). Pelican.

Patchwork: Stories, Poems & Meditations for Mothers. Illus. by Dwight Walles. (Illus.). 1987. 6.95. Cook.

Pater Calendar. J. M. Kennedy. LC 73-606. 1973. lib. bdg. 12.50 (ISBN 0-8414-1531-5). Folcroft.

Paterna: The Autobiography of Cotton Mather. Cotton Mather. Ed. by Ronald A. Bosco. LC 76-10595. (Center for Editions of American Authors). 504p. 1976. lib. bdg. 75.00x (ISBN 0-8201-1273-9). Schol Facsimiles.

Path: Autobiography of a Western Yogi. Swami Kriyananda. LC 77-72787. (Illus.). 640p. 1977. 15.00 (ISBN 0-916124-11-8); pap. 4.95 (ISBN 0-916124-12-6). Dawn Pubns CA.

Path Beneath the Sea. Devorah Omer. 192p. 1969. 3.50 (ISBN 0-88482-744-5). Hebrew Pub.

Path of a Pioneer: The Autobiography of Rabbi Leo Jung. Leo Jung. 408p. 1980. 9.50 (ISBN 0-900689-51-X). Soncino Pr.

Path of a Pioneer: The Early Days of Sun Myung Moon & the Unification Church. Ed. by Jonathan G. Gullery. (Illus.). 88p. (Orig.). 1986. pap. 3.95 (ISBN 0-910621-50-0). HSA Pubns.

Path of Action. Jack Schwarz. LC 77-2247. 1977. pap. 8.95 (ISBN 0-525-48231-8, 0869-260). Dutton.

Path of Compassion: Contemporary Writings on Engaged Buddhism. Ed. by Fred Eppsteiner & Dennis Maloney. 1985. 9.95 (ISBN 0-934834-52-0). White Pine.

Path of Compassion: Time-honored Principles of Spiritual & Ethical Conduct. G De Purucker. 84p. 1986. pap. 4.00 (ISBN 0-911500-69-3). Theos U Pr.

Path of Discipleship. Beasant. 4.25 (ISBN 0-8356-7044-9). Theos Pub Hse.

Path of Fire & Light: Advanced Practices of Yoga. Swami Rama. 180p. (Orig.). 1986. pap. 8.95 (ISBN 0-89389-097-9). Himalayan Pubs.

Path of Healing. H. K. Challoner. LC 76-3660. 175p. 1976. pap. 5.25 (ISBN 0-8356-0480-2, Quest). Theos Pub Hse.

Path of Healing. H. K. Challoner. 10.50 (ISBN 0-8356-5227-0). Theos Pub Hse.

Path of Initiation. Inayat Khan. (Sufi Message of Hazrat Inayat Khan Ser.: Vol. 10). 270p. 1979. 14.95 (ISBN 90-6325-098-3, Pub. by Servire BV Netherlands). Hunter Hse.

Path of Light. Regina E. Lorr & Robert W. Crary. LC 83-71354. 180p. (Orig.). 1983. pap. 7.95 (ISBN 0-87516-520-6). De Vorss.

Path of Light. Santideva. LC 78-70117. Repr. of 1909 ed. 20.00 (ISBN 0-404-17374-8). AMS Pr.

Path of Love. Bhagwan Shree Rajneesh. Ed. by Ma Yoga Sudha. LC 83-181255. (Kabir Ser.). (Illus.). 350p. (Orig.). 1978. 16.50 (ISBN 0-88050-112-X); pap. 12.95 358p (ISBN 0-88050-612-1). Chidvilas Found.

Path of Prayer. Samuel Chadwick. 1963. pap. 2.95 (ISBN 0-87508-095-2). Chr Lit.

Path of Purity, 3 vols. Buddhaghosa. Tr. by Pe Maung Tin. LC 78-72389. Repr. of 1931 ed. Set. 95.00 (ISBN 0-404-17570-8). AMS Pr.

Path of Righteousness: Dhammapada-An Introductory Essay, Together with the Pali Text, English Translation with Commentary. David J. Kalupahana. LC 86-9088. (Eng. & Pali.). 234p. (Orig.). 1986. lib. bdg. 24.75 (ISBN 0-8191-5365-6); pap. text ed. 12.50 (ISBN 0-8191-5366-4). U Pr of Amer.

Path of Serenity & Insight. Henepola Gunaratna. 1984. 22.50x (ISBN 0-8364-1149-8). South Asia Bks.

Path of Subud. Husein Rofe. 69.95 (ISBN 0-8490-0805-0). Gordon Pr.

Path of the Buddha: Buddhism Interpreted by Buddhists. Kenneth W. Morgan. 1986. 24.00X (ISBN 81-208-0030-3, Pub. by Motilal Banarsidass). South Asia Bks.

Path of the Just-Mesilath Yesharim. Luzzato. 1982. 10.95 (ISBN 0-87306-114-4); pap. 7.95 (ISBN 0-87306-115-2). Feldheim.

Path of the Kabbalah: An Introduction to the Living Jewish Spiritual Tradition. David Sheinkin. (Patterns of World Spirituality Ser.). 224p. 1986. pap. 9.95 (ISBN 0-913757-69-1, Pub. by New Era Bks). Paragon Hse.

Path of the Phoenix. Kendall K. McCabe. Ed. by Michael L. Sherer. (Orig.). 1986. pap. 7.25 (ISBN 0-89536-818-8, 6827). CSS of Ohio.

Path of the Soul. White Eagle. 1959. 5.95 (ISBN 0-85487-020-2). De Vorss.

Path of Transcendence. Bennett Penn. 144p. 1987. pap. text ed. 10.00 (ISBN 0-682-40332-6). Exposition Pr FL.

Path of Wisdom: Biblical Investigations. Bruce Vawter. (Background Bks.: Vol. 3). 1986. pap. 12.95 (ISBN 0-89453-466-1). M Glazier.
Path Through the Bible. John H. Piet. LC 81-2258. (Illus.). 318p. 1981. pap. 14.95 (ISBN 0-664-24369-X). Westminster.
Path to No-Self: Life at the Center. Bernadette Roberts. LC 84-19340. 224p. (Orig.). 1985. pap. 9.95 (ISBN 0-87773-306-6, 72999-4). Shambhala Pubns.
Path to Transcendence: From Philosophy to Mysticism in Saint Augustine. Paul Henry. Tr. by Francis F. Burch. (Pittsburgh Theological Monographs: No. 37). 1981. pap. 12.50 (ISBN 0-915138-49-2). Pickwick.
Pathetic Fallacy. Llewelyn Powys. LC 77-828. 1977. Repr. of 1930 ed. lib. bdg. 25.00 (ISBN 0-8414-6797-8). Folcroft.
Pathfinders of the World Missionary Crusade. facs. ed. George S. Eddy. LC 76-84304. (Essay Index Reprint Ser). 1945. 20.25 (ISBN 0-8369-1127-X). Ayer Co Pubs.
Paths & Means to Holiness. Constantine Cavarnos. 85p. (Orig.). 1986. pap. 5.00 (ISBN 0-911165-08-8). Ctr Trad Orthodox.
PATHS Numerology-Secret Power. Mary Anderson. pap. 4.95x (ISBN 0-317-07306-0, Regent House). B of A.
Paths of Faith. 3rd ed. John A. Hutchison. (Illus.). 608p. 1981. 31.95x (ISBN 0-07-031532-9). McGraw.
Paths of Leadership. Andrew T. Le Peau. LC 82-23221. 132p. (Orig.). 1983. pap. 3.95 (ISBN 0-87784-806-8). Inter-Varsity.
Paths of Liberation: A Third World Spirituality. Bakole Wa Ilunga. Tr. by Matthew J. O'Connell from Fr. LC 84-5177. Tr. of Chemins de Liberation. 240p. (Orig.). 1984. pap. 12.95 (ISBN 0-88344-401-1). Orbis Bks.
Paths of Life: Preface to a World Religion. Charles W. Morris. LC 72-94732. 228p. 1973. pap. 2.25x (ISBN 0-226-53879-6, P541, Phoen). U of Chicago Pr.
Paths of Meditation. Ed. by Vedanta Kesari Staff. 241p. 1980. pap. 3.25 (ISBN 0-87481-501-0). Vedanta Pr.
Paths to Human Perfection. Robert E. Birdsong. (Aquarian Academy Supplementary Lecture: No. 3). 1979. pap. 0.75 (ISBN 0-917108-26-4). Sirius Bks.
Paths to Power. A. W. Tozer. 64p. pap. 1.75 (ISBN 0-87509-190-3). Chr Pubns.
Paths to the Northwest: A Jesuit History of the Oregon Province. Wilfred Schoenberg. 477p. 1983. 27.50 (ISBN 0-8294-0405-8). Loyola.
Paths to Transformation: A Study of the General Agencies of the United Methodist Church. Kristine M. Rogers & Bruce A. Rogers. LC 81-17565. (Into Our Third Century Ser.). 96p. (Orig.). 1982. pap. 3.50 (ISBN 0-687-30094-0). Abingdon.
Pathway of Discipleship One Hundred One: Group Leader's Guide. 2nd rev. ed. Donald E. Hill. 48p. 1983. 4.00 (ISBN 0-88151-028-9). Lay Leadership.
Pathway of Discipleship One Hundred One: Home Study Guide. 2nd rev. ed. Donald E. Hill. 56p. 1983. 8.00 (ISBN 0-88151-027-0). Lay Leadership.
Pathway of Discipleship One Hundred One. 2nd rev. ed. Donald E. Hill. (Pathway of Discipleship Ser.). 184p. 1983. pap. text ed. 15.00 (ISBN 0-88151-026-2). Lay Leadership.
Pathway of Perfection. Hodson. 2.50 (ISBN 0-8356-7018-X). Theos Pub Hse.
Pathway to Perfection. Thomas S. Monson. LC 73-886344. 328p. 1973. 6.95 (ISBN 0-87747-511-3). Deseret Bk.
Pathway to Prayer & Pietie. Robert Hill. LC 74-28864. (English Experience Ser.: No. 744). 1975. Repr. of 1613 ed. 26.50 (ISBN 90-221-0744-2). Walter J Johnson.
Pathways of Spiritual Living. Susan A. Muto. LC 84-1564. 192p. 1984. pap. 6.95 (ISBN 0-385-19473-0, Im). Doubleday.
Pathways Through Jewish History. rev ed. Ruth Samuels. (Illus.). 1977. pap. 9.00x (ISBN 0-87068-520-1). Ktav.
Pathways Through the Bible. rev. ed. Mortimer J. Cohen. (Illus.). 574p. 1946. 10.95 (ISBN 0-8276-0155-7, 167). Jewish Pubns.
Pathways to Power: Keys That Open Doors. Paul Tassell. LC 83-9576. 1983. pap. 3.95 (ISBN 0-87227-093-9). Reg Baptist.
Pathways to the Gods: The Stones of Kiribati. Erich Von Daniken. Tr. by Michael Heron from Ger. (Illus.). 288p. 1983. 16.95 (ISBN 0-399-12751-8, Putnam). Putnam Pub Group.
Pathways to the Past: A Guide to the Ruins of Mezo-America. Paul R. Cheesman & Barbara W. Hutchins. LC 83-83236. 210p. 1984. pap. 8.95 (ISBN 0-88290-236-9). Horizon Utah.
Patience. Carole MacKenthun & Paulinus Dwyer. (Fruit of the Spirit Ser.). (Illus.). 48p. Date not set. wkbk. 4.95 (ISBN 0-86653-364-8). Good Apple.
Patience & Persistence. Robert Tilton. (Orig.). 1986. mini bk. 0.75 (ISBN 0-89274-413-8). Harrison Hse.
Patience Never Fails. Gary Jones. 45p. 1985. pap. 0.95 (ISBN 0-88144-048-5). Christian Pub.
Patience of God. 4.50 (ISBN 0-8198-5821-8); 3.50 (ISBN 0-8198-5821-8). Dghtrs St Paul.
Patience of Hope. Spiros Zodhiates. (Trilogy Ser.: Vol. 1). pap. 4.95 (ISBN 0-89957-543-9). AMG Pubs.
Patisambhidamagga, 2 vols. in one. Ed. by Arnold C. Taylor. LC 78-70108. Repr. of 1905 ed. 43.50 (ISBN 0-404-17358-6). AMS Pr.
Patmos: When the Heavens Opened. Basilea Schlink. LC 76-24522. 1976. pap. 1.95 (ISBN 0-88419-012-9). Creation Hse.
Patriarch & Patriot: William Grant Broughton 1788-1853: Colonial Statesman & Ecclesiastic. George P. Shaw. 1978. 28.50x (ISBN 0-522-84122-8, Pub. by Melbourne U Pr). Intl Spec Bk.
Patriarch Nicephorus of Constantinople: Ecclesiastical Policy & Image Worship in the Byzantine Empire. Paul J. Alexander. LC 78-63177. (Heresies Ser.: No. II). Repr. of 1958 ed. 42.50 (ISBN 0-404-16195-2). AMS Pr.
Patriarch Nikon on Church & State. Ed. by Valerie A. Tumins & George Vernadsky. 812p. 1982. 99.20 (ISBN 90-279-7676-7). Mouton.
Patriarchs. Behn Boruch. 28p. 1959. 3.95 (ISBN 0-88482-729-1). Hebrew Pub.
Patriarchs. Reed M. Holmes. LC 78-1895. 1978. pap. 7.00 (ISBN 0-8309-0205-8). Herald Hse.
Patriarchs & Politics. Marilyn Warenski. (McGraw-Hill Paperbacks Ser.). 352p. 1980. pap. 6.95 (ISBN 0-07-068271-2). McGraw.
Patriarchs & Politics. Marilyn Warenski. (Illus.). 1978. 10.95 (ISBN 0-07-068270-4). McGraw.
Patriarchs & Prophets. Stanley B. Frost. 232p. 1963. 10.00 (ISBN 0-7735-0010-3). McGill-Queens U Pr.
Patriarchs & Prophets. Ellen G. White. 805p. 1958. deluxe ed. 9.95 (ISBN 0-8163-0038-0, 16082-0); pap. 5.95 (ISBN 0-8163-0039-9, 16083-8). Pacific Pr Pub Assn.
Patriarchs, Judges, & Kings. Bernard R. Youngman. (Background to the Bible Ser.: Vol. 1). pap. 8.95 (ISBN 0-7175-0414-X). Dufour.
Patrologiae Cursus Completus. Jacques P. Migne. Incl. Patrologia Latina, 221 vols. pap. write for info.; Patrologia Graeco Latina, 162 vols. pap. write for info.. 1965-71. pap. Adlers Foreign Bks.
Patrology, 3 vols. Johannes Quasten. 1514p. 1983. Set. pap. 50.00 (ISBN 0-87061-084-8); Vol. 1. pap. 15.00 (ISBN 0-87061-084-8); Vol. 2. pap. 18.00 (ISBN 0-87061-085-6); Vol. 3. pap. 21.00 (ISBN 0-87061-091-0); Set of 4 vols. pap. 85.00. Chr Classics.
Patrology, Vol. IV: The Golden Age of Latin Patristic Literature. Ed. by Johannes Quasten & Angelo Di Berardino. Tr. by Placid Solari. 1986. 48.00 (ISBN 0-87061-126-7); pap. 39.95 (ISBN 0-87061-127-5); Set of 4 vols. pap. 85.00. Chr Classics.
Pattern for Life: An Exposition of the Sermon on the Mount. rev. ed. Archibald M. Hunter. LC 66-11517. 128p. 1966. pap. 5.95 (ISBN 0-664-24687-7). Westminster.
Pattern for Progress. Walter R. Beach & Bert B. Beach. Ed. by Ray Woolsey. 142p. (Orig.). 1985. pap. text ed. 6.95 (ISBN 0-8280-0308-4). Review & Herald.
Pattern of Baha'i Life. 3rd ed. Baha'u'llah et al. 1963. pap. 2.95 (ISBN 0-900125-15-2, 315-030-10). Baha'i.
Pattern of Christian Truth: A Study in the Relations Between Orthodoxy & Heresy in the Early Church. Henry E. Turner. LC 77-84707. (Bampton Lectures: 1954). 1977. Repr. of 1954 ed. 47.50 (ISBN 0-404-16114-6). AMS Pr.
Pattern of God's Truth. Frank E. Gaebelein. LC 54-6908. 1968. pap. 5.95 (ISBN 0-8024-6450-5). Moody.
Pattern of God's Truth. Frank E. Gaebelein. 1985. pap. 5.95 (ISBN 0-88469-170-5). BMH Bks.
Pattern of Judgement in the "Queste" & "Cleanness". Charlotte C. Morse. LC 77-25158. (Illus.). 248p. 1978. 19.00x (ISBN 0-8262-0242-X). U of Mo Pr.
Patterns. Joan K. Hamilton. (Illus.). 1977. tchrs' manual 5.25x (ISBN 0-8192-4078-8); parents' letters & pupils' leaflets package 5.75x (ISBN 0-8192-4077-X). Morehouse.
Patterns & Instructions for a Child's Quiet Book. Joanne Harlow. 27p. 1977. 3.50 (ISBN 0-317-03553-3). Randall Bk Co.
Patterns for Educational Growth. Theodore M. Hesburgh. 1958. 5.95x (ISBN 0-268-00202-9). U of Notre Dame Pr.
Patterns for Living with God. Marilyn Kunz. pap. 2.95 (ISBN 0-87784-409-7). Inter-Varsity.
Patterns for Mature Living. Milton H. Keene. LC 76-27093. Repr. of 1976 ed. 21.30 (ISBN 0-8357-9019-3, 2016389). Bks Demand UMI.
Patterns for Power. D. Stuart Briscoe. LC 78-68850. (Bible Commentary for Laymen Ser.). 160p. 1979. pap. 3.50 (ISBN 0-8307-0701-8, S331101). Regal.
Patterns for Prayer. Hubert Van Zeller. 128p. 1983. pap. 5.95 (ISBN 0-87243-124-X). Templegate.
Patterns in Comparative Religion. Mircea Eliade. pap. 9.95 (ISBN 0-452-00728-3, Mer). NAL.
Patterns in Comparative Religion. Mircea Eliade. 16.00 (ISBN 0-8446-6226-7). Peter Smith.
Patterns in Pluralism: A Portrait of American Religion, 1952-1971. William M. Newman & Peter L. Halvorson. LC 79-55177. 1980. pap. 6.50 (ISBN 0-914422-10-3). Glenmary Res Ctr.
Patterns of Belief, 2 vols. Eric Carlton. Incl. Vol. 1. Peoples & Religion. 130p. pap. 4.95 Vol. 1 (ISBN 0-04-377004-5); Vol. 2. Religions in Society. 140p. pap. 4.95 2 vols. each (ISBN 0-04-377005-3); pap. 4.95 Vol. 2. 1973. pap. 6.95 ea. Attic Pr.
Patterns of Christian Community. Ed. by Stephen B. Clark. 98p. (Orig.). 1984. pap. 4.95 (ISBN 0-89283-186-3). Servant.
Patterns of Creativity Mirrored in Creation Myths. Marie-Louise Von Franz. (Seminar Ser: No. 6). 250p. 1972. pap. 15.00 (ISBN 0-88214-106-6). Spring Pubns.
Patterns of Grace: Human Experience As Word of God. Tom F. Driver. 214p. 1985. pap. text ed. 9.75 (ISBN 0-8191-4637-4). U Pr of Amer.
Patterns of Illusion & Change. John Stahl. (Illus.). 24p. 1984. pap. 3.50 (ISBN 0-318-21732-5). Evanescent Pr.
Patterns of Myth Series. Ed. by Alan W. Watts. Incl. Lord of the Four Quarters. John W. Perry; The Two Hands of God. Alan W. Watts; The Wisdom of the Serpent. Joseph L. Henderson & Maud Oakes. Braziller.
Patterns of Prayer in the Psalms. Laurence Dunlop. 160p. (Orig.). 1982. pap. 9.95 (ISBN 0-8164-2377-6, HarpR). Har-Row.
Patterns of Protestant Church Music. Robert M. Stevenson. LC 53-8271. viii, 219p. 1953. 20.50 (ISBN 0-8223-0168-7). Duke.
Patterns of Protestant Church Music. Robert M. Stevenson. LC 53-8271. pap. 56.80 (ISBN 0-317-26858-9, 2023455). Bks Demand UMI.
Patterns of Renewal. Laurens Van Der Post. LC 62-15859. (Orig.). 1962. pap. 2.50x (ISBN 0-87574-121-5). Pendle Hill.
Paul. Ethel Barrett. LC 81-51740. (Bible Biography Ser.). 128p. 1981. pap. text ed. 1.95 (ISBN 0-8307-0767-0, 5810701). Regal.
Paul. Gunther Bornkamm. Tr. by D. M. Stalker from Ger. LC 70-85068. 1971. short disc 15.95xi (ISBN 0-06-060933-8, HarpR). Har-Row.
Paul. Lucas Grollenberg. Tr. by John Bowden. LC 78-14372. 186p. 1979. pap. 4.50 (ISBN 0-664-24234-0). Westminster.
Paul. F. B. Meyer. 1968. pap. 4.50 (ISBN 0-87508-348-X). Chr Lit.
Paul. (Burl Ives Bible-Time Stories). incl. tape 4.95 (ISBN 0-89191-601-6, 26013). Cook.
Paul. 1979. 0.75 (ISBN 0-8198-0590-4). Dghtrs St Paul.
Paul. Herman N. Ridderbos. Tr. by J. Richard DeWitt. 587p. 1975. 23.95 (ISBN 0-8028-3438-8). Eerdmans.
Paul. Gladys S. Stump. (Books I Can Read). (Illus.). 1978. pap. 1.95 (ISBN 0-8127-0165-8). Review & Herald.
Paul: A Study in Social & Religious History. Adolph Deissman. Tr. by William W. Wilson. 1958. 12.75 (ISBN 0-8446-1965-5). Peter Smith.
Paul: Adventurer for Christ. Gwendolyne Arbuckle & Carolyn Wolcott. (Illus.). 96p. (Orig.). 1984. pap. 5.50 (ISBN 0-687-30487-3). Abingdon.
Paul Against Supernaturalism. William E. Phipps. LC 85-19228. 177p. 1986. 17.95 (ISBN 0-8022-2501-2). Philos Lib.
Paul Among Jews & Gentiles & Other Essays. Krister Stendahl. LC 75-36450. 144p. 1976. pap. 4.95 (ISBN 0-8006-1224-8, 1-1224). Fortress.
Paul: An Example for Christian Teachers. Richard Grunze. 1979. pap. text ed. 3.50 (ISBN 0-8100-0108-X, 07N0740). Northwest Pub.
Paul: An Illustrated Documentary on the Life & Writings. John Drane. LC 76-62918. (Illus.). 1977. pap. text ed. 9.95 (ISBN 0-06-062065-X, RD 208, HarpR). Har-Row.
Paul & Friends. (Story Bible Ser.). 1987. pap. 2.95. Lion USA.
Paul & His Converts. rev. ed. F. F. Bruce. LC 85-19764. 155p. 1985. pap. 5.95 (ISBN 0-87784-593-X). Inter-Varsity.
Paul & His Friends. Penny Frank. Ed. by P. Alexander. (Lion Story Bible Ser.). 24p. 1987. 2.95 (ISBN 0-85648-776-7). Lion USA.
Paul & His Letters. Leander E. Keck. Ed. by Gerhard Krodel. LC 78-54554. (Proclamation Commentaries, The New Testament Witnesses for Preaching). 144p. 1979. pap. 4.95 (ISBN 0-8006-0587-X, 1-587). Fortress.
Paul & His Message for Life's Journey. William Thompson. 160p. 1986. pap. 9.95 (ISBN 0-8091-2824-1). Paulist Pr.
Paul & Palestinian Judaism: A Comparison of Patterns of Religion. E. P. Sanders. LC 76-62612. 648p. 1977. pap. 19.95 (ISBN 0-8006-1899-8, 1-1899). Fortress.
Paul & Power: The Structure of Authority in the Primitive Church Reflected in the Pauline Epistles. Bengt Holmberg. LC 79-8905. 240p. 1980. 3.00 (ISBN 0-8006-0634-5, 1-634). Fortress.
Paul & Rabbinic Judaism: Some Rabbinic Elements in Pauline Theology. W. D. Davies. LC 80-8049. 448p. 1980. pap. 14.95 (ISBN 0-8006-1438-0, 1-1438). Fortress.
Paul & Silas Evangelize Greece. Gordon Lindsay. (Acts in Action Ser.: Vol. 4). pap. 1.25 (ISBN 0-89985-965-8). Christ Nations.
Paul & the Anatomy of Apostolic Authority. J. H. Schutz. LC 74-76573. (Society for New Testament Studies, Monographs: No. 26). 1975. 59.50 (ISBN 0-521-20464-X). Cambridge U Pr.
Paul & the Law. Heikki Raisanen. 332p. 1986. pap. 19.95 (ISBN 0-8006-1915-3, 1-1915). Fortress.
Paul & the Law. Heikki Raisanen. 330p. 1983. lib. bdg. 67.50x (ISBN 3-16-144629-1, Pub. by J C B Mohr BRD). Coronet Bks.
Paul & the Salvation of Mankind. Johannes Munck. LC 60-5412. 1977. pap. 8.95 (ISBN 0-8042-0373-3). John Knox.
Paul & the Thessalonians: The Philosophic Tradition of Pastoral Care. Abraham Malherbe. LC 86-45918. 144p. 1987. 8.95 (ISBN 0-8006-0863-1, 1-863). Fortress.
Paul: Apostle of Steel & Velvet. 3rd. ed. James T. Dyet. LC 76-9579. 1976. pap. 3.50 (ISBN 0-916406-30-X). Accent Bks.
Paul: Apostle of the Heart Set Free. F. F. Bruce. LC 77-26127. 1978. 20.95 (ISBN 0-8028-3501-5). Eerdmans.
Paul, Apostle of Weakness: Astheneia & Its Cognates in the Pauline Literature. David A. Black. LC 83-49515. (American University Studies VII (Theology & Religion): Vol. 3). 340p. (Orig.). 1984. pap. text ed. 27.00 (ISBN 0-8204-0106-4). P Lang Pubs.
Paul, Apostle to the Gentiles: Studies in Chronology. Gerd Luedemann. Tr. by Stanley F. Jones from Ger. LC 83-48919. 320p. 1984. 29.95 (ISBN 0-8006-0714-7, 1-714). Fortress.
Paul at Athens. Cornellius Van Til. 1959. pap. 0.95 (ISBN 0-87552-493-1). Presby & Reformed.
Paul Before the Sanhedrin. Gordon Lindsay. (Acts in Action Ser.: Vol. 5). pap. 1.25 (ISBN 0-89985-966-6). Christ Nations.
Paul Believes in Jesus. Loyal Kolbrek. (Illus.). 24p. 1987. pap. 00.99 (ISBN 0-570-09008-3, 59-1436). Concordia.
Paul Claudel: The Man & the Mystic. Louis Chaigne. LC 78-5951. 1978. Repr. of 1961 ed. lib. bdg. 24.75x (ISBN 0-313-20465-9, CHCL). Greenwood.
Paul: Crisis in Galatia: A Study in Early Christian Theology. George Howard. LC 77-84002. (Society for New Testament Studies Monographs: No. 35). pap. 31.50 (ISBN 0-317-29375-3, 2024478). Bks Demand UMI.
Paul for a New Day. Robin Scroggs. LC 76-9719. 96p. 1977. pap. 3.95 (ISBN 0-8006-1242-6, 1-1242). Fortress.
Paul, God's Special Missionary. Bessie Dean. (Story Books to Color.). 72p. (Orig.). 1980. pap. 2.50 (ISBN 0-88290-152-4). Horizon Utah.
Paul, His Letters & Theology: An Introduction to Paul's Epistles. Stanley B. Marrow. 288p. (Orig.). 1986. pap. 9.95 (ISBN 0-8091-2744-X). Paulist Pr.
Paul: His Life & Work. Walther Von Loewenich. 1960. text ed. 7.50x (ISBN 0-8401-1421-4). A R Allenson.
Paul, Judaism, & the Gentiles: A Sociological Approach. Francis Watson. (Society for New Testament Studies Monographs: No. 56). 266p. Date not set. 32.50 (ISBN 0-521-32573-0). Cambridge U Pr.
Paul: Mystic & Missionary. Bernard T. Smyth. LC 80-14041. 191p. (Orig.). 1980. pap. 3.98 (ISBN 0-88344-380-5). Orbis Bks.
Paul of Pergula: Logica & Tractatus De Sensu Composito et Diviso. Ed. by Sr. Mary A. Brown. (Text Ser). 1961. 11.00 (ISBN 0-686-11558-9). Franciscan Inst.
Paul of Tarsus. Herold Weiss. 175p. (Orig.). 1986. pap. 9.95 (ISBN 0-943872-92-8). Andrews Univ Pr.
Paul of Venice, Logica Magna, Pt. I, Fasc. I. Ed. by Norman Kretzmann. 344p. 1979. 52.50 (ISBN 0-85672-690-7, Pub. by British Acad). Longwood Pub Group.
Paul of Venice, Logica Magna, Part II, Fasc. 6. Ed. by Francesco Del Punta. Tr. by Marilyn M. Adams from Latin. 288p. 1978. 27.00 (ISBN 0-85672-695-8, Pub. by British Acad.). Longwood Pub Group.
Paul of Venice: Logica Magna, Tractatus De Suppositione. Ed. by Alan Perreiah. (Text Ser). 1971. 16.00 (ISBN 0-686-11560-0). Franciscan Inst.

Paul on Trial. John MacArthur, Jr. (John MacArthur's Bible Studies). (Orig.). 1986. pap. 3.95 (ISBN 0-8024-5131-4). Moody.

Paul One. Duncan Macpherson et al. Ed. by Laurence Bright. LC 71-173033. (Scripture Discussion Ser.: Pt. 10). 224p. 1972. pap. text ed. 4.50 (ISBN 0-87946-009-1). ACTA Found.

Paul: Rabbi & Apostle. Pinchas Lapide & Peter Stuhlmacher. Tr. by Lawrence W. Denef. LC 84-23482. 80p. (Orig.). 1984. pap. 5.95 (ISBN 0-8066-2122-2, 10-4903). Augsburg.

Paul, Speak for God. Charlotte Graeber. (Speak for Me Ser.). (Illus.). 24p. 1986. 3.95 (ISBN 0-8407-6700-5). Nelson.

Paul the Apostle. Robert E. Picirilli. (Orig.). 1986. pap. 7.95 (ISBN 0-8024-6325-8). Moody.

Paul the Apostle. Robert E. Picirilli. 1986. pap. 7.95 (ISBN 0-89265-117-2). Randall Hse.

Paul the Apostle. Edward Schillebeeckx. (Illus.). 128p. 1983. 14.95 (ISBN 0-8245-0574-3). Crossroad NY.

Paul the Apostle: The Triumph of God in Life & Thought. J. Christian Beker. LC 79-8904. 468p. 1980. pap. 14.95 (ISBN 0-8006-1811-4). Fortress.

Paul, the Law & the Jewish People. E. P. Sanders. LC 82-17487. 240p. 1983. pap. 9.95 (ISBN 0-8006-1878-5, 1-1878). Fortress.

Paul the Leader. J. O. Sanders. LC 83-62737. 192p. 1984. pap. 5.95 (ISBN 0-89109-515-2). NavPress.

Paul the Missionary. 64p. Date not set. pap. 2.95 (ISBN 0-9609302-0-5). L Imperio.

Paul: The Missionary. Iva J. Tucker. (BibLearn Ser.). (Illus.). 5.95 (ISBN 0-8054-4228-6, 4242-28). Broadman.

Paul the Mystic. James M. Campbell. 1977. lib. bdg. 59.95 (ISBN 0-8490-2415-3). Gordon Pr.

Paul, the Saint Who Ain't. Max Spiegelstein. 1980. 12.50 (ISBN 0-89962-017-5). Todd & Honeywell.

Paul the Teacher: A Resource for Teachers in the Church. Kent L. Johnson. LC 86-17384. 128p. (Orig.). 1986. pap. 6.95 (ISBN 0-8066-2226-1, 10-4905). Augsburg.

Paul: The Theology of the Apostle in the Light of Jewish Religious History. Hans J. Schoeps. Tr. by Harold Knight. LC 61-10284. 304p. 1979. Repr. of 1961 ed. softcover 7.95 (ISBN 0-664-24273-1). Westminster.

Paul the Traveler. Alan T. Dale. (Rainbow Books, Bible Story Books for Children). 1976. pap. 1.00 (ISBN 0-8192-1211-3). Morehouse.

Paul, the World Ascetic: Response to the World & Self-Understanding According to 1 Corinthians 7. Vincent L. Wimbush. 128p. 1987. 18.95 (ISBN 0-86554-263-5, H224). Mercer Univ Pr.

Paul: Thirteenth Apostle. Chuck Christensen & Winnie Christensen. (Fisherman Bible Studyguide Ser.). 64p. (Orig.). 1987. pap. 2.95 (ISBN 0-87788-652-0). Shaw Pubs.

Paul Tillich. John P. Newport. 320p. 1984. 12.95 (ISBN 0-8499-2952-0). Word Bks.

Paul Tillich: A Comprehensive Bibliography & Keyword Index of Primary & Secondary Writings in English. Richard C. Crossman. LC 83-15026. (ATLA Bibliography Ser.: No. 9). 193p. 1983. 17.50 (ISBN 0-8108-1650-4). Scarecrow.

Paul Tillich: His Life & Thought, Vol. 1: Life. Wilhelm Pauck & Marion Pauck. LC 74-25709. (Illus.). 352p. 1976. 15.00 (ISBN 0-06-066474-6, HarpR). Har-Row.

Paul Tillich's Dialectical Humanism: Unmasking the God above God. Leonard F. Wheat. LC 74-105365. (Illus.). 287p. 1970. 26.50x (ISBN 0-8018-1161-9). Johns Hopkins.

Paul Tillich's Philosophy of Art. Michael Palmer. LC 83-15056. (Theologische Bibliothek Toepelmann Ser.: Vol. 41). xxii, 217p. 1983. 49.50x (ISBN 3-11-009681-1). De Gruyter.

Paul Tillich's Radical Social Thought. Ronald H. Stone. 180p. 1986. pap. text ed. 10.75 (ISBN 0-8191-5152-1). U Pr of Amer.

Paul Tillich's Theology of the Church: A Catholic Appraisal. Modras. LC 76-6082. 326p. 1976. 25.95x (ISBN 0-8143-1552-6). Wayne St U Pr.

Paul Two. Laurence Bright et al. LC 71-173033. (Scripture Discussion Commentary Ser.: Pt. 11). 224p. 1971. pap. text ed. 4.50 (ISBN 0-87946-010-5). ACTA Found.

Paul Wrote from the Heart. Tr. & intro. by Raymond V. Schoder. (Gr. & Eng.). 64p. 1987. 24.50 (ISBN 0-86516-181-X). Bolchazy-Carducci.

Paul Young. Philip Kamin. (Illus.). 32p. 1985. pap. 4.95 (ISBN 0-88188-411-1, 00183876, Robus Bks). H Leonard Pub Corp.

Paulician Heresy: A Study of the Origin & Development of Paulicianism in Armenia & the Eastern Provinces of the Byzantine Empire. N. G. Garsoian. (Publications in Near & Middle East Ser.: No. 6). 1967. text ed. 32.80x (ISBN 90-2790-096-5). Mouton.

Pauline & Other Studies in Early Christian History. W. M. Ramsay. 1977. lib. bdg. 59.95 (ISBN 0-8490-2416-1). Gordon Pr.

Pauline Autobiography: Toward a New Understanding. George Lyons. (Society of Biblical Literature Dissertation Ser.). 1985. 23.50 (ISBN 0-89130-730-3, 06-01-73); pap. 15.50 (ISBN 0-89130-765-6). Scholars Pr GA.

Pauline Christianity. John Ziesler. (Oxford Bible Ser.). (Orig.). 1983. pap. 9.95 (ISBN 0-19-213247-4). Oxford U Pr.

Pauline Epistles. William Kelly. (Introductory Lecture Ser.). 551p. 6.95 (ISBN 0-88172-098-4). Believers Bkshelf.

Pauline Idea of Faith in Its Relation to Jewish & Hellenistic Religion. W. H. Hatch. (Harvard Theological Studies). 1917. 11.00 (ISBN 0-527-01002-2). Kraus Repr.

Pauline Letters. Leander Keck et al. 160p. (Orig.). 1984. pap. 9.50 (ISBN 0-687-30494-6). Abingdon.

Pauline Muses. Ed. by Edward Pine. 355p. 1981. Repr. of 1947 ed. lib. bdg. 25.00 (ISBN 0-8495-4395-9). Arden Lib.

Pauline Parallels. rev. ed. Fred O. Francis & J. Paul Sampley. LC 83-48920. (Foundations & Facets: New Testament Ser.). 416p. 1984. 29.95 (ISBN 0-8006-2103-4, 1-2103). Fortress.

Pauline Partnership in Christ: Christian Community & Commitment in Light of Roman Law. J. Paul Sampley. LC 79-8895. 144p. 1980. 2.00 (ISBN 0-8006-0631-0, 1-631). Fortress.

Pauline Studies: Essays Presented to Prof. F. F. Bruce on His 70th Birthday. Ed. by Donald Hagner & Murray Harris. LC 80-16146. 336p. 1981. 19.95 (ISBN 0-8028-3531-7). Eerdmans.

Pauline Theology: A Brief Sketch. Joseph F. Fitzmyer. (Orig.). 1967. pap. text ed. write for info. (ISBN 0-13-654525-4). P-H.

Pauline Theology & Mission Practice. Dean S. Gilliland. 304p. 1983. pap. 12.95 (ISBN 0-8010-3788-3). Baker Bk.

Pauline Theology of Charismata. Siegfried Schatzman. 150p. 1986. pap. 7.95 (ISBN 0-913573-45-0). Hendrickson MA.

Pauline Writings Notes. Robert Picirilli. 1967. pap. 2.95 (ISBN 0-89265-001-X). Randall Hse.

Paulo, o Lider. J. Oswald Sanders. Orig. Title: Paul the Leader. (Port.). 1986. write for info. (ISBN 0-8297-0756-5). Life Pubs Intl.

Paul's Apocalyptic Gospel: The Coming Triumph of God. J. Christiaan Beker. LC 82-8670. 128p. (Orig.). 1982. pap. 7.95 (ISBN 0-8006-1649-9, 1-1649). Fortress.

Paul's Awakening. Frederik Van Eeden. Tr. by H. S. Lake from Dutch. LC 83-81704. 96p. 1985. 6.95 (ISBN 0-86164-156-6, Pub. by Momenta Pub Ltd). Hunter Hse.

Paul's Departure & Crown. John Bunyan. pap. 0.95 (ISBN 0-685-19839-1). Reiner.

Paul's Early Letters: From Hope, Through Faith, to Love. Paul Wrightman. LC 83-7126. 148p. (Orig.). 1983. pap. 6.95 (ISBN 0-8189-0440-2). Alba.

Paul's Epistle to the Galatians. Vladimir M. Gelesnoff. 1977. pap. text ed. 3.00 (ISBN 0-910424-73-X). Concordant.

Paul's Epistle to the Romans. Ernest F. Scott. LC 79-4204. 1979. Repr. of 1947 ed. lib. bdg. 22.50x (ISBN 0-313-20800-X, SCPE). Greenwood.

Paul's Faith & the Power of the Gospel: A Structural Introduction to the Pauline Letters. Daniel Patte. LC 82-7416. 432p. (Orig.). 1983. 21.95 (ISBN 0-8006-0683-3, 1-1682). Fortress.

Paul's First Letter to Corinth. John Ruef. LC 77-24086. (Westminster Pelican Commentaries). 224p. 1978. 10.00 (ISBN 0-664-21348-0); softcover 5.45 (ISBN 0-664-24183-2). Westminster.

Paul's Gospel & Mission: The Outlook from His Letter to the Romans. Arland J. Hultgren. LC 85-45494. 176p. 1985. pap. 9.95 (ISBN 0-8006-1871-8). Fortress.

Paul's Idea of Community: The Early House Churches in the Historical Setting. Robert Banks. 1980. pap. 5.95 (ISBN 0-8028-1830-7). Eerdmans.

Paul's Intercessory Prayers. G. P. Wiles. (Society for New Testament Studies Monographs: No. 24). 360p. 1974. 59.50 (ISBN 0-521-20274-4). Cambridge U Pr.

Paul's Later Letters: From Promise to Fulfillment. Paul Wrightman. LC 84-11039. 238p. (Orig.). 1984. pap. 9.95 (ISBN 0-8189-0441-0). Alba.

Paul's Letter to the Corinthians 55 A.D. Sanford G. Shetler. (Compact Commentary Ser.). 1971. 7.80 (ISBN 0-87813-504-9); pap. 4.65 (ISBN 0-87813-503-0). Christian Light.

Paul's Letter to the Romans. Robert S. Bell. 1970. pap. 2.75 (ISBN 0-88027-036-5). Firm Foun Pub.

Paul's Letters from Prison (Elphesians, Phillipians, Colossians, Philemon) in the Revised Standard Edition. George B. Caird. (New Clarendon Bible). (Orig.). 1976. pap. text ed. 18.95x (ISBN 0-19-836920-4). Oxford U Pr.

Paul's Letters from Prison: Philippians, Colossians, Philemon & Ephesians. Ed. by J. L. Houlden. LC 77-24028. (Westminister Pelican Commentaries). 358p. 1978. 11.50 (ISBN 0-664-21347-2); pap. 6.95 (ISBN 0-664-24182-4). Westminster.

Paul's Letters Made Easy for Devotions. L. S. Cross. 120p. (Orig.). 1982. pap. 4.95 (ISBN 0-89221-090-7, Pub by SonLife). New Leaf.

Paul's Letters to Timothy & Titus. LC 78-1143. (Bible Study Textbook Ser.). (Illus.). 1962. 12.20 (ISBN 0-89900-043-6). College Pr Pub.

Paul's Message of Freedom: What Does It Mean to the Black Church? Amos Jones, Jr. 256p. 1984. 12.95 (ISBN 0-8170-0840-3). Judson.

Paul's Perilous Journey. John MacArthur, Jr. (John MacArthur's Bible Studies). (Orig.). 1987. pap. 3.50 (ISBN 0-8024-5350-3). Moody.

Paul's Prison Prayers. W. Graham Scroggie. LC 80-8077. (W. Graham Scroggie Library). 78p. 1981. pap. 4.50 (ISBN 0-8254-3737-7). Kregel.

Paul's Revelation: The Gospel of Reconciliation. Kenneth Hagin. 1983. pap. 0.50 mini bk. (ISBN 0-89276-261-6). Hagin Ministries.

Paul's Thorn. Don Hughes. (Orig.). 1977. pap. 0.75 (ISBN 0-89274-047-7, HH-047). Harrison Hse.

Paul's Two-Age Construction & Apologetics. William D. Dennison. LC 85-20272. 144p. (Orig.). 1986. lib. bdg. 19.50 (ISBN 0-8191-5011-8); pap. text ed. 8.75 (ISBN 0-8191-5012-6). U Pr of Amer.

Pavel Florensky: A Metaphysics of Love. Robert Slesinski. LC 83-27130. 256p. 1984. pap. text ed. 12.95 (ISBN 0-88141-032-2). St Vladimirs.

Pawnee Ghost Dance Hand Game. Alexander Lesser. LC 79-82340. (Columbia Univ. Contributions to Anthropology Ser.: Vol. 16). 1969. Repr. of 1933 ed. 37.00 (ISBN 0-404-50566-X). AMS Pr.

Paying Attention. Dan Carr. (God I Need to Talk to You About...Ser.). (Illus.). 1984. pap. 0.75 (ISBN 0-570-08729-5, 56-1473). Concordia.

Payson de Garonne: Un Vieux Laic s'Interroge a propos du Temps Present. Jacques Maritain. 19.95 (ISBN 0-685-34274-3). French & Eur.

Paz con Dios. Billy Graham. Tr. by Carrie Muntz from Eng. Orig. Title: Peace with God. 272p. 1981. pap. 3.75 (ISBN 0-311-43037-6). Casa Bautista.

Paz con Dios. rev. & enl. ed. Billy Graham. Tr. of Peace with God. (Span.). 220p. 1987. pap. 7.50 (ISBN 0-311-46109-3). Casa Bautista.

Paz con Dios. 2nd ed. Algernon J. Pollock. Ed. by Alberto Mahecha. Tr. by SAra Bautista from Eng. (Serie Diamante). Tr. of Peace With God. (Span., Illus.). 48p. 1982. pap. 0.85 (ISBN 0-942504-09-7). Overcomer Pr.

Peace. Carole MacKenthun & Paulinus Dwyer. (Fruit of the Spirit Ser.). (Illus.). 48p. 1986. wkbk. 4.95 (ISBN 0-86653-365-6). Good Apple.

Peace & Bread in Time of War. Jane Addams. LC 75-137524. (Peace Movement in America Ser). 269p. 1972. Repr. of 1922 ed. lib. bdg. 18.95x (ISBN 0-89198-051-2). Ozer.

Peace & Conscience Formation. Thomas Matty. (Faith & Justice Issues Ser.). (Illus.). 68p. (Orig.). 1983. tchr's ed. 14.95 (ISBN 0-88489-147-X). St Mary's.

Peace & War. facs. ed. Guglielmo Ferrero. Tr. by B. Pritchard. LC 69-18927. (Essay Index Reprint Ser). 1933. 18.00 (ISBN 0-8369-0041-3). Ayer Co Pubs.

Peace Be with You. Henry Drummond. (Illus.). 1978. 4.95 (ISBN 0-915720-44-2). Brownlow Pub Co.

Peace Be with You. Cornelia Lehn. LC 80-70190. (Illus.). 126p. 1981. 12.95 (ISBN 0-87303-061-3). Faith & Life.

Peace Bishops & the Arms Race: Can Religious Leadership Help in Preventing War? George Weigel. 54p. 1982. 2.00 (ISBN 0-318-18653-5). World Without War.

Peace Child. Don Richardson. LC 75-26356. (Illus.). 288p. 1975. Repr. of 1974 ed. digest 6.95 (ISBN 0-8307-0415-9, 5403006). Regal.

Peace in a Nuclear Age: The Bishops' Pastoral Letter in Perspective. Ed. by Charles J. Reid, Jr. 1986. 44.95 (ISBN 0-8132-0624-3). Cath U Pr.

Peace in Palestine. M. T. Mehdi. LC 75-43266. 1976. pap. 8.00 (ISBN 0-911026-08-8). New World Press NY.

Peace-ing It Together: Peace & Justice Activities for Youth. Pat Fellers. (Learning Connection Ser.). 160p. (Orig.). 1984. pap. 9.95 (ISBN 0-86683-836-8, 8440, HarpR). Har-Row.

Peace Is in the Eye of the Beholder. Raphuel Israeli. xxiv, 389p. 1985. text ed. 62.00 (ISBN 0-89925-077-7). Mouton.

Peace Is Possible: The Politics of the Sermon on the Mount. Franz Alt. Tr. by Joachim Neugroschel from Ger. LC 84-23499. 136p. 1985. 12.95 (ISBN 0-8052-3969-3). Schocken.

Peace is Within Our Reach. Sri Swami Satchidanada. LC 85-14384. 96p. (Orig.). 1985. pap. 4.95 (ISBN 0-932040-29-2). Integral Yoga Pubns.

Peace Like a River. Sallie Chesham. 1981. pap. 5.95 (ISBN 0-86544-014-X). Salv Army Suppl South.

Peace Ministry in Practice. Richard K. Taylor. (YA) 1986. pap. 3.95 (ISBN 0-697-02205-6). Wm C Brown.

Peace My Heart. Bessie Beihl. pap. 1.00 (ISBN 0-87516-133-2). De Vorss.

Peace of Soul. Fulton J. Sheen. 1954. pap. 4.95 (ISBN 0-385-02871-7, D8, Im). Doubleday.

Peace, Politics, & the People of God. Ed. by Paul Peachey. LC 85-45490. 208p. 1986. pap. 12.95 (ISBN 0-8006-1898-X). Fortress.

Peace, Print & Protestantism, Fourteen Fifty to Fifteen Eighty. S. L. Davies. 1976. 24.50x (ISBN 0-8464-0706-X). Beekman Pubs.

Peace, Prosperity & the Coming Holocaust. Dave Hunt. LC 82-84069. 224p. 1983. pap. 6.95 (ISBN 0-89081-331-0). Harvest Hse.

Peace That You Seek. Alan Cohen. (Illus.). 195p. (Orig.). 1985. pap. 5.95 (ISBN 0-910367-35-3, 157). A Cohen.

Peace Thinking in a Warring World. Edward L. Long, Jr. LC 83-14675. 118p. 1983. pap. 6.95 (ISBN 0-664-24503-X). Westminster.

Peace Tradition in the Catholic Church: An Annotated Bibliography. Ronald G. Musto. LC 86-31950. (Garland Reference Library of Social Science). 500p. 1987. lib. bdg. 67.00 (ISBN 0-8240-8584-1). Garland Pub.

Peace Treaty with God. John Hendee. (Ambassadors Training Program Ser.). 16p. (Orig.). 1984. pap. 0.50 (ISBN 0-87239-814-5, 3223). Standard Pub.

Peace Trek: Reclaiming Our Future. Ed. by Don Carlson. Craig Comstock. (Illus.). 300p. (Orig.). 1985. pap. 19.95 (ISBN 0-317-19166-7). Ark Comm Inst.

Peace Where Is It? Annie Gagiati. LC 73-91996. 1974. pap. 1.95 (ISBN 0-8198-0507-6). Dghtrs St Paul.

Peace with God. rev. ed. Billy Graham. 288p. 1985. 10.95 (ISBN 0-8499-0464-1, 0464-1); pap. text ed. 7.95 (ISBN 0-8499-2991-1, 2991-1). Word Bks.

Peace Within Yourself. Joseph Murphy. 300p. 1972. pap. 6.50 (ISBN 0-87516-188-X). De Vorss.

Peaceable Kingdom: A Primer in Christian Ethics. Stanley Hauerwas. LC 83-14711. 224p. 1983. text ed. 17.95x (ISBN 0-268-01553-8, 85-15538); pap. text ed. 7.95x (ISBN 0-268-01554-6, 85-15546). U of Notre Dame Pr.

Peaceful Seed Living, Vols. 1 & 2. 2nd ed. Jerome F. Coniker. LC 78-66369. (Living Meditation & Prayerbook Ser.). (Illus.). 156p. 1981. pap. text ed. 3.00 ea. (ISBN 0-932406-00-9). AFC.

Peacemaker. Myron S. Augsburger. 208p. 1987. pap. 9.95 (ISBN 0-687-30353-2). Abingdon.

Peacemakers: Christian Voices from the New Abolitionist Movement. Jim Wallis. LC 82-48940. 160p. (Orig.). 1983. pap. 5.95 (ISBN 0-06-069244-8, CN-4058, HarpR). Har-Row.

Peacemakers' Dilemma. Bertram Pickard. 1983. pap. 2.50x (ISBN 0-87574-016-2, 016). Pendle Hill.

Peacemaking. Douglas Fisher. homily bk. 1.50 (ISBN 0-8091-9321-3); group discussion guide 2.95 (ISBN 0-8091-9326-4); participants' bks. 1.00 (ISBN 0-8091-9341-8). Paulist Pr.

Peacemaking & the Community of Faith: A Handbook for Congregations. John A. Donaghy. 2.95 (ISBN 0-8091-5181-2). Paulist Pr.

Peacemaking: Family Activities for Peace & Justice. Jacqueline Haessly. 2.95 (ISBN 0-8091-2269-3). Paulist Pr.

Peacemongers. Robert D. Culver. Ed. by Mark Carpenter. 160p. 1985. pap. 5.95 (ISBN 0-8423-4789-5). Tyndale.

Peaceways: Sixteen Christian Perspectives on Security in a Nuclear Age. Charles P. Lutz & Jerry L. Folk. LC 83-70500. 224p. (Orig.). 1983. pap. 10.95 (ISBN 0-8066-2006-4, 10-4904). Augsburg.

Peaceworld. Michael McIntyre et al. (Illus., Orig.). 1976. pap. 2.50 (ISBN 0-377-00054-X). Friend Pr.

Peacock Angel: Being Some Account of Votaries of a Secret Cult & Their Sanctuaries. Ethel S. Drower. LC 77-87643. Repr. of 1941 ed. 20.00 (ISBN 0-404-16425-0). AMS Pr.

Peak of Eloquence-Nahjul Balagha. x ed. Ali B. Abi Talib. Tr. by Askari Jafery. 558p. 1983. Repr. 10.00 (ISBN 0-941724-18-2). Islamic Seminary.

Peake's Commentary on the Bible. Matthew Black & H. H. Rowley. 1962. 39.95 (ISBN 0-8407-5019-6). Nelson.

Peaks & Lamas. Marco Pallis. lib. bdg. 100.00 (ISBN 0-87968-327-9). Gordon Pr.

Peal of Puzzles. A. Newing. 1985. 16.25x (ISBN 0-317-54301-6, Pub. by J Richardson UK). State Mutual Bk.

Pearl: Hymn of the Robe of Glory. Illus. by Nonny Hogrogian. LC 79-66092. (Illus.). 1979. 7.95 (ISBN 0-89756-002-7). Two Rivers.

Pearl, Image of the Ineffable: A Study in Medieval Poetic Symbolism. Theodore Bogdanos. LC 82-42783. 184p. 1983. 22.50x (ISBN 0-271-00339-1). Pa St U Pr.

Pearl of Great Price: The Life of Mother Maria Skobtsova 1891-1945. rev. ed. Sergei Hackel. LC 81-21356. 192p. 1982. pap. 6.95 (ISBN 0-913836-85-0). St Vladimirs.

Pearls from the Prophet Ezekiel. William G. Heslop. LC 76-12081. (W. G. Heslop Bible Study Aids). 160p. 1976. pap. 4.50 (ISBN 0-8254-2832-7). Kregel.

Pearls of Faith. E. Arnold. 319p. 1984. 60.00x (ISBN 0-317-39177-1, Pub. by Luzac & Co Ltd). State Mutual Bk.

Pearls of the Faith: Islam's Rosary. E. Arnold. pap. 3.50x (ISBN 0-87902-044-X). Orientalia.

Pearls of Wisdom. Angelos M. Chattalas. 1986. 9.50 (ISBN 0-8062-2507-6). Carlton.

Pearls of Wisdom: A Prophecy of Karma, to the Earth & Her Evolutions, Vol. 23. Ed. by Elizabeth C. Prophet. LC 81-50418. 540p. 1980. 14.95 (ISBN 0-916766-41-1). Summit Univ.

Pearls of Wisdom, Nineteen Eighty-Two: Kuan Yin Opens the Door to the Golden Age, Vol. 25, Bks. I & II. LC 83-50756. (Illus.). Bk. 1, 322 pgs. 25.00 (ISBN 0-916766-58-6); Bk. 2, 476 pgs. 25.00 (ISBN 0-916766-59-4). Summit Univ.

Pearls of Wisdom 1965: The Mechanization Concept. Ed. by Mark Prophet & Elizabeth Prophet. LC 79-89833. 297p. 1979. 16.95 (ISBN 0-916766-35-7). Summit Univ.

Pearls of Wisdom 1969: Kuthumi-On Selfhood, Vol. 12. Ed. by Mark Prophet & Elizabeth Prophet. LC 79-53229. 314p. 1979. 17.95 (ISBN 0-916766-34-9). Summit Univ.

Pearls of Wisdom 1971: Masters of the Far East-On the Pillars of Eternity, Vol. 14. Ed. by Elizabeth C. Prophet & Elizabeth Prophet. LC 78-60619. 234p. 14.95 (ISBN 0-916766-31-4). Summit Univ.

Pearls of Wisdom 1975: El Morya-On Discipleship East & West, Vol. 18. Ed. by Elizabeth C. Prophet. LC 79-64047. 349p. 1979. 18.95 (ISBN 0-916766-15-2). Summit Univ.

Pearls of Wisdom 1976, Vol. 19. Ed. by Elizabeth C. Prophet. LC 76-52850. 13.95 (ISBN 0-916766-24-1). Summit Univ.

Pearls of Wisdom, 1978: Spoken by Elohim, Vol. 21. Ed. by Mark Prophet & Elizabeth Prophet. LC 79-66985. 513p. 1980. 14.95 (ISBN 0-916766-36-5). Summit Univ.

Peasant Politics & Religious Sectarianism: Peasant & Priest in the Cao Dai in Viet Nam. Jayne S. Werner. LC 81-52078. (Monograph Ser.: No. 23). 123p. 1981. 10.50x (ISBN 0-938692-07-0). Yale U SE Asia.

Peasants' Rising & the Lollards. Ed. by Edgar Powell & G. M. Trevelyan. LC 78-63202. (Heresies of the Early Christian & Medieval Era: Second Ser.). Repr. of 1899 ed. 24.00 (ISBN 0-404-16238-X). AMS Pr.

Pecado Despues de la Conversion. 2nd ed. Algernon J. Pollock & Gordon H. Bennett. Tr. by Sara Bautista from Eng. (Serie Diamante). Tr. of Sin After Conversion. (Span., Illus.). 36p. 1982. pap. 0.85 (ISBN 0-942504-04-6). Overcomer Pr.

Peculiar Forms of Ancient Religious Cults. Rudolf E. Cushman. (Illus.). 1980. deluxe ed. 67.50 (ISBN 0-89266-234-4). Am Classical Coll Pr.

Peculiar Mission of a Friends School. Douglas H. Heath. LC 79-84919. 1979. pap. 2.50x (ISBN 0-87574-225-4). Pendle Hill.

Peculiar Mystical Rites of Ancient Peoples. Alexander Wilder. (Illus.). 269p. 1984. 117.85x (ISBN 0-89266-451-7). AM Classical Coll Pr.

Peculiar People: Iowa's Old Order Amish. facs. ed. Elmer Schwieder & Dorothy Schwieder. (Illus.). 188p. 1975. 9.95x (ISBN 0-8138-0105-2). Iowa St U Pr.

Peculiar Treasures: A Biblical Who's Who. Frederick Buechner. Tr. by Katherine A. Buechner. LC 78-20586. 1979. 12.45 (ISBN 0-06-061157-X, HarpR). Har-Row.

Pedagogia Fructifera. Findley B. Edge. Tr. by Alberto Lopez from Eng. Tr. of Teaching for Results. (Span.). 192p. 1985. pap. 3.95 (ISBN 0-311-11025-8). Casa Bautista.

Pedagogia Ilustrada: Tomo I Principios Generales. Leroy Ford. Orig. Title: Primer for Teachers & Leaders. (Illus.). 144p. 1982. pap. 3.95 (ISBN 0-311-11001-0, Edit Mundo). Casa Bautista.

Pedagogies for the Non-Poor. Alice Frazer Evans & Robert A. Evans. LC 86-21831. 272p. (Orig.). 1987. pap. 13.95 (ISBN 0-88344-409-7). Orbis Bks.

Pedagogue for God's Kingdom: Lyman Beecher & the Second Great Awakening. James W. Fraser. LC 85-17794. 248p. 1985. lib. bdg. 27.50 (ISBN 0-8191-4905-5); pap. text ed. 12.75 (ISBN 0-8191-4906-3). U Pr of Amer.

Pedagogy of God's Image: Essays on Symbol & the Religious Imagination. Ed. by Robert Masson. 214p. 1986. lib. bdg. 23.00 (ISBN 0-8191-5721-X, Pub. by College Theology Society); pap. text ed. 13.00 (ISBN 0-8191-5619-1, Pub. by College Theology Society). U Pr of Amer.

Pedegrewe of Heretiques. John Barthlet. LC 79-76432. (English Experience Ser.: No. 76). 180p. 1969. Repr. of 1566 ed. 21.00 (ISBN 90-221-0076-6). Walter J Johnson.

Pedigree of the Devil. Frederic T. Hall. LC 76-173108. (Illus.). Repr. of 1883 ed. 27.50 (ISBN 0-405-08594-X, Blom Pubns). Ayer Co Pubs.

Pedro Ciruelo's A Treatise Reproving All Superstitions & Forms of Witchcraft: Very Necessary & Useful for All Good Christians Zealous for Their Salvation. Ed. by D'Orsay W. Pearson. Tr. by Eugene Maio & D'Orsay W. Pearson. LC 74-4979. 366p. 1976. 27.50 (ISBN 0-8386-1580-5). Fairleigh Dickinson.

Pedro Moya de Contreras: Catholic Reform & Royal Power in New Spain, 1571-1591. C. M. Stafford Poole. LC 86-1410. 350p. 1987. text ed. 30.00 (ISBN 0-520-05551-9). U of Cal Pr.

Peel, Priests & Politics: Sir Robert Peel's Administration & the Roman Catholic Church in Ireland, 1841-1846. Donal A. Kerr. (Oxford Historical Monographs). 400p. 1982. pap. 15.95x (ISBN 0-19-822932-1). Oxford U Pr.

Peer Counseling in the Church. Paul M. Miller. LC 78-9299. 168p. 1978. pap. 7.95 (ISBN 0-8361-1854-5). Herald Pr.

Pegaluis's Expositions on Thirteen Epistles of St. Paul, 3 pts. in 1 vol. A. Souter. (Texts & Studies Ser. 1: Vol. 9). pap. 83.00 (ISBN 0-8115-1712-8). Pt. 1: Introduction. Kraus Repr.

Pegasus, the Winged Horse. new ed. Adapted by C. J. Naden. LC 80-50069. (Illus.). 32p. 1980. PLB 9.79 (ISBN 0-89375-361-0); pap. 2.50 (ISBN 0-89375-365-3). Troll Assocs.

Peirce-Nichols House. Gerald W. Ward. LC 76-16904. (Historic House Booklet Ser.: No. 4). 1976. 2.00 (ISBN 0-88389-062-3). Essex Inst.

Pelagius: A Historical & Theological Study. John Ferguson. LC 77-84700. Repr. of 1956 ed. 27.00 (ISBN 0-404-16107-3). AMS Pr.

Pelagius & the Fifth Crusade. Joseph P. Donovan. LC 76-29822. Repr. of 1950 ed. 29.00 (ISBN 0-404-15416-6). AMS Pr.

Pele & Hiiaka: A Myth from Hawaii. Nathaniel B. Emerson. LC 75-35190. Repr. of 1915 ed. 29.50 (ISBN 0-404-14218-4). AMS Pr.

Pele, Volcano Goddess of Hawaii. L. R. McBride. (Illus.). 1968. pap. 3.25 (ISBN 0-912180-11-0). Petroglyph.

Peleg Burroughs's Journal, 1778-1798: The Tiverton R. I. Years of the Humbly Bold Baptist Minister. Ed. by Ruth W. Sherman. LC 80-39673. (Illus.). xxvi, 404p. 1981. 19.00x (ISBN 0-9604144-0-1). RI Genealogical.

Pelerinage a la Mekke: Etude D'histoire Religieuse. Maurice Gaudefroy-Demombynes. LC 77-10690. (Studies in Islamic History: No. 7). viii, 332p. 1978. Repr. of 1923 ed. lib. bdg. 35.00x (ISBN 0-87991-456-4). Porcupine Pr.

Pelican History of Medieval Europe. Maurice Keen. 1969. pap. 5.95 (ISBN 0-14-021085-7, Pelican). Penguin.

Pelican History of the Church: A History of the Christian Missions, Vol. 6. Stephen Neill. 512p. 1987. pap. 6.95 (ISBN 0-14-022736-9, Pelican). Penguin.

Peloubet's Sunday School Notes, 1987-1988. Ralph Earle. 1987. pap. 7.95 (ISBN 0-8010-3439-6). Baker Bk.

Pen & the Faith: Eight Modern Muslim Writers & the Qur'an. Kenneth Cragg. 188p. 1985. text ed. 16.00x (ISBN 0-04-297044-X). Allen Unwin.

Penal Law of Islam. M. I. Siddiqui. 1980. 16.50 (ISBN 0-686-64662-2). Kazi Pubns.

Penalty of Eve: John Milton & Divorce. Gladys J. Willis. LC 83-49352. (American University Studies IV (English Language & Literature): Vol. 6). 164p. (Orig.). 1985. text ed. 21.55 (ISBN 0-8204-0094-7). P Lang Pubs.

Penance & Reconciliation. Patrick J. Brennan. (Guidelines for Contemporary Catholics Ser.). (Orig.). 1986. pap. 7.95 (ISBN 0-88347-195-7). Thomas More.

Penance & Reconciliation in the Church. (Liturgy Documentary Ser.: No. 7). 96p. (Orig.). 1986. pap. 5.95 (ISBN 1-55586-104-0). US Catholic.

Penance: God's Gift for Forgiveness. Blanche Twigg. (Illus.). 64p. 1974. pap. 2.50 (ISBN 0-912228-15-6). St Anthony Mess Pr.

Penateuch & Haftorahs. J. H. Hertz. 1067p. 1960. 25.00 (ISBN 0-900689-21-8). Soncino Pr.

Pencils & Sticks: Scripture Word-Searches for LDS Families. Joseph D. Kayne. 32p. (Orig.). 1983. pap. 3.95 (ISBN 0-88290-218-0). Horizon Utah.

Pendle Hill: A Quaker Experiment in Education & Community. new ed. Eleanore P. Mather. 128p. 1980. 7.00 (ISBN 0-87574-954-2). Pendle-Hill.

Pendle Hill Idea. Howard Brinton. LC 50-11234. (Orig.). 1950. pap. 2.50x (ISBN 0-87574-055-3). Pendle Hill.

Pendle Hill Reader. facsimile ed. Ed. by Herrymon Maurer. LC 74-142668. (Essay Index Reprint Ser). Repr. of 1950 ed. 18.00 (ISBN 0-8369-2415-0). Ayer Co Pubs.

Penetrating Laughter: Hakuin's Zen & Art. Kazuaki Tanahashi. LC 83-43155. (Illus.). 144p. 1984. 16.95 (ISBN 0-87951-952-5); pap. 8.95 (ISBN 0-87951-280-6). Overlook Pr.

Penetrating Poets. Gerald H. Twombly. 112p. 1982. pap. 4.95 (ISBN 0-88469-151-9). BMH Bks.

Penguin Book of Hebrew Verse. Ed. by T. Carmi. (Hebrew & Eng.). 448p. (Orig.). 1981. pap. 13.95 (ISBN 0-14-042197-1). Penguin.

Penguin Dictionary of Religions. Ed. by John R. Hinnells. (Reference Ser.). 464p. 1984. pap. 7.95 (ISBN 0-14-051106-7). Penguin.

Penguin Dictionary of Saints. rev. ed. Donald Attwater. Rev. by Catherine R. John. 352p. 1984. pap. 7.95 (ISBN 0-14-051123-7). Penguin.

Penguin Principles. David Belasic & Paul Schmidt. 1986. 5.95 (ISBN 0-89536-799-8, 6817). CSS of Ohio.

Penguin Shorter Atlas of the Bible. Luc H. Grollenberg. Tr. by Mary F. Hedlund. (Reference Ser). (Illus.). 1978. pap. 7.95 (ISBN 0-14-051056-7). Penguin.

Penitence of Adam: (A Study of the Andrius MS., No. 36. Esther C. Quinn. Tr. by Micheline Dufau. LC 79-19056. 192p. 1980. 21.00x (ISBN 84-499-3367-6). Romance.

Penitente Moradas of Abiquiu. Richard E. Ahlborn. LC 85-43242. (Illus.). 52p. 1986. pap. 3.95x (ISBN 0-87474-253-6). Smithsonian.

Penitential Discipline of the Primitive Church. Nathaniel Marshall. LC 74-172846. (Library of Anglo-Catholic Theology: No. 13). Repr. of 1844 ed. 27.50 (ISBN 0-404-52105-3). AMS Pr.

Penitential Rite of the Ancient Mexicans. Zelia Nuttall. (HU PMP Ser.). 1904. pap. 10.00 (ISBN 0-527-01189-4). Kraus Repr.

Penmanship for Christian Writing. Daniel Strubhar. 1981. write for info.; tchr's. ed. avail. Rod & Staff.

Pennies from a Poor Box. Joseph E. Manton. 1962. 6.50 (ISBN 0-8198-0119-4). Dghtrs St Paul.

Pennsylvania Dutch. Eva D. Costabel. LC 86-3334. (Illus.). 48p. 1986. 14.95 (ISBN 0-689-31281-4, Children Bk). Macmillan.

Pennsylvania Tradition of Semitics: A Century of Near Eastern & Biblical Studies at the University of Pennsylvania. Cyrus Gordon. (Biblical Scholarship in North America Ser.). 85p. 1987. 13.95 (ISBN 1-55540-022-1); pap. 11.95 (ISBN 1-55540-023-X). Scholars Pr GA.

Penobscot Shamanism. Frank G. Speck. LC 20-13167. (AAA Memoirs Ser.: No. 25). 1919. pap. 15.00 (ISBN 0-527-00527-4). Kraus Repr.

Pens under the Swastika. Wilhelm W. Schutz. LC 70-118415. 1971. Repr. of 1946 ed. 19.95x (ISBN 0-8046-1192-0, Pub. by Kennikat). Assoc Faculty Pr.

Pensamientos Sobre la Cultura Intelectual y Moral. Enrique Aguilar. Tr. of Thoughts on Intellectual & Moral Culture. 1967. 7.00 (ISBN 0-686-27936-0). Franciscan Inst.

Pensando con Dios. Norman Camp. Orig. Title: Thinking with God. (Span.). 128p. 1981. pap. 3.25 (ISBN 0-8254-1100-9). Kregel.

Pensar Bien y Mal. 2nd ed. Kenneth E. Hagin. (Span.). 1983. pap. 1.00 (ISBN 0-89276-104-0). Hagin Ministries.

Pensees. Blaise Pascal. (Univers des Lettres). pap. 2.50 (ISBN 0-685-34246-8). French & Eur.

Pensees, 2 vols. Blaise Pascal. (Folios 936 & 937). 4.50 ea. French & Eur.

Pensees. Blaise Pascal. Ed. by Desgranges. 1962. pap. 9.95 (ISBN 0-685-11485-6). French & Eur.

Pensees. Blaise Pascal. Ed. by Desgranges. (Coll. Prestige). 16.95 (ISBN 0-685-34245-X). French & Eur.

Pensees. Blaise Pascal. Tr. by A. J. Krailsheimer. (Classics Ser.). (Orig.). 1966. pap. 3.95 (ISBN 0-14-044171-9). Penguin.

Pensees of Pascal: A Study in Baroque Style. Sr. M. Julie Maggioni. LC 79-94181. (Catholic University of America Studies in Romance Languages & Literature Ser: No. 39). Repr. of 1950 ed. 25.00 (ISBN 0-404-50339-X). AMS Pr.

Penseurs de l'Islam, 5 vols. Bernard Carra de Vaux. LC 80-2197. Repr. of 1926 ed. Set. 200.00 (ISBN 0-404-18990-3). AMS Pr.

Pensive Mans Practise. John Norden. LC 77-171776. (English Experience Ser.: No. 401). 192p. 1971. Repr. of 1584 ed. 18.50 (ISBN 90-221-0401-X). Walter J Johnson.

Pentacostal Light. A. M. Hills. 2.95 (ISBN 0-686-27775-9). Schmul Pub Co.

Pentateuch. Lloyd R. Bailey. LC 81-4495. (Interpreting Biblical Texts Ser.). 160p. (Orig.). 1981. pap. 8.95 (ISBN 0-687-30610-8). Abingdon.

Pentateuch. Joseph Blenkinsopp & John Challenor. Ed. by Laurence Bright. LC 71-173033. (Scripture Discussion Commentary Ser.: Pt. 1). 248p. 1971. pap. text ed. 4.50 (ISBN 0-87946-000-8). ACTA Found.

Pentateuch. William Kelly. (Introductory Lecture Ser.). 524p. 6.95 (ISBN 0-88172-099-2). Believers Bkshelf.

Pentateuch-Haftaroth & Sabeth Prayers: Hebrew with English. Isaac Lesser. 22.50 (ISBN 0-317-00457-3). Shalom.

Pentateuch in Its Cultural Environment. G. Herbert Livingston. pap. 12.95 (ISBN 0-8010-5630-6). Baker Bk.

Pentateuch with Rashi, 5 vols. A. M. Silbermann & M. Rosenbaum. LC 30-11064. 1973. 44.95 (ISBN 0-87306-019-9); slipcased ed. 46.95. Feldheim.

Pentateuco. Charles Erdman. Tr. by Humberto Casanova & Viviana Casanova. Tr. of Pentateuch. 396p. 1986. 12.95 (ISBN 0-939125-14-5). Evangelical Lit.

Pentecost. Joseph Brice. 6.95 (ISBN 0-686-12901-6). Schmul Pub Co.

Pentecost & the Chosen One. W. J. Corbett. 240p. 1987. 14.95 (ISBN 0-385-29549-9). Delacorte.

Pentecost & Tongues. William H. Turner. pap. 3.50 (ISBN 0-911866-83-3). Advocate.

Pentecost Cycle. R. W. Kemper. LC 12-2965. 1982. pap. 7.95 (ISBN 0-570-03872-3). Concordia.

Pentecost: God's Answer for the Occult. pap. 2.00 (ISBN 0-911866-77-9). Advocate.

Pentecost One. Frederick H. Borsch. LC 84-18756. (Proclamation Three C Ser.). 64p. 1986. pap. 3.75 (ISBN 0-8006-4130-2, 1-4130). Fortress.

Pentecost One. Leander E. Keck & Francis W. Hobbie. LC 79-7377. (Proclamation 2: Aids for Interpreting the Lessons of the Church Year, Series B). 64p. 1982. pap. 3.75 (ISBN 0-8006-4089-6, 1-4089). Fortress.

Pentecost One. Howard C. Kee & Peter J. Gomes. Ed. by Elizabeth Achtemeier et al. LC 79-7377. (Proclamation 2: Aids for Interpreting the Lessons of the Church Year, Ser. C). 64p. 1980. pap. 3.75 (ISBN 0-8006-4081-0, 1-4081). Fortress.

Pentecost One: Proclamation 3B. David A. Hubbard. LC 84-18756. (Proclamation Ser.). 64p. 1985. pap. 3.75 (ISBN 0-8006-4106-X, 1-4106). Fortress.

Pentecost Or Pretense. Arthur J. Clement. 1981. pap. 7.95 (ISBN 0-8100-0118-7, 12N1718). Northwest Pub.

Pentecost Project. Thierry Breton. LC 86-33730. 1987. 17.95 (ISBN 0-8050-0380-0). H Holt & Co.

Pentecost: The Christian Student Movement from Howard University. Stephen N. Short. (Illus., Orig.). 1987. pap. 6.95 (ISBN 0-9616056-2-6). Mid Atl Reg Pr.

Pentecost Three. Paul J. Achtemeier. LC 84-18756. (Proclamation Three C Ser.). 64p. 1986. pap. 3.75 (1-4132). Fortress.

Pentecost Three. Schuyler Brown & Don E. Saliers. Ed. by Elizabeth Actemeier et al. LC 79-7377. (Proclamation Ser.: No. 2). 64p. 1982. pap. 3.75 (ISBN 0-8006-4099-3, 1-4099). Fortress.

Pentecost Three: Proclamation 3B. John B. Rogers, Jr. LC 84-18756. (Proclamation Ser.). 64p. 1985. pap. 3.75 (ISBN 0-8006-4108-6, 1-4108). Fortress.

Pentecost Two. Adela Y. Collins & Charles Rice. LC 79-7377. (Proclamation 2: Aids for Interpreting the Lessons of the Church Year, Series B). 64p. 1982. pap. 3.75 (ISBN 0-8006-4090-X, 1-4090). Fortress.

Pentecost Two. R. Alan Culpepper. LC 84-18756. (Proclamation Three C Ser.). 64p. 1986. pap. 3.75 (ISBN 0-8006-4131-0, 1-4131). Fortress.

Pentecost Two: Proclamation 3B. Daniel J. Harrington. LC 84-18756. (Proclamation Ser.). 64p. 1985. pap. 3.75 (ISBN 0-8006-4107-8, 1-4107). Fortress.

Pentecost Yesterday & Today. Wade H. Horton. 1972. 7.25 (ISBN 0-87148-676-8). Pathway Pr.

Pentecost 1. Virgil P. Howard. LC 84-18756. (Proclamation 3 A). 64p. 1987. pap. 3.75 (ISBN 0-8006-4122-1, 1-4122). Fortress.

Pentecost 1. David L. Tiede & Aidan Kavanagh. Ed. by Elizabeth Achtemeier et al. LC 79-7377. (Proclamation 2: Aids for Interpreting the Lessons of the Church Year, Ser. A). 64p. (Orig.). 1981. pap. 3.75 (ISBN 0-8006-4096-9, 1-4096). Fortress.

Pentecost 2. Donald H. Juel & David Buttrick. Ed. by Elizabeth Achtemeier et al. LC 79-7377. (Proclamation 2: Aids for Interpreting the Lessons of the Church Year, Ser. C). 64p. 1980. pap. 3.75 (ISBN 0-8006-4083-7, 1-4083). Fortress.

Pentecost 2. Patrick D. Miller, Jr. LC 84-18756. (Proclamation 3 A). 64p. 1987. pap. 3.75 (ISBN 0-8006-4123-X). Fortress.

Pentecost 2. Paul S. Minear & Harry B. Adams. Ed. by Elizabeth Achtemeier et al. LC 79-7377. (Proclamation 2: Aids for Interpreting the Lessons of the Church Year, Ser. A). 64p. (Orig.). 1981. pap. 3.75 (ISBN 0-8006-4097-7, 1-4097). Fortress.

Pentecost 3. O. C. Edwards, Jr. & Gardner C. Taylor. Ed. by Elizabeth Achtemeier et al. LC 79-7377. (Proclamation 2: Aids for Interpreting the Lessons of the Church Year, Ser. C). 64p. (Orig.). 1980. pap. 3.75 (ISBN 0-8006-4084-5, 1-4084). Fortress.

Pentecost 3. Victor P. Furnish & Richard L. Thulin. Ed. by Elizabeth Achtemeier et al. LC 79-7377. (Proclamation 2: Aids for Interpreting the Lessons of the Church Year, Ser. A). 64p. (Orig.). 1981. pap. 3.75 (ISBN 0-8006-4098-5, 1-4098). Fortress.

Pentecost 3. George Peck. LC 84-18756. (Proclamation 3 A). 64p. 1987. pap. 3.75 (ISBN 0-8006-4124-8, 1-4124). Fortress.

Pentecostal Catholics: Power, Charisma, & Order in a Religious Movement. Meredith B. McGuire. 270p. 1982. 29.95 (ISBN 0-87722-235-5). Temple U Pr.

Pentecostal Experience. J. Massyngberd Ford. LC 72-116869. 64p. (Orig.). 1970. pap. 1.95 (ISBN 0-8091-1655-3). Paulist Pr.

Pentecostal Grace. Laurence W. Wood. Ed. by Harold Burgess. 1980. pap. 8.95 (ISBN 0-310-75041-5, 17028P). Zondervan.

Pentecostal Holiness Church. Joe E. Campbell. pap. 6.00 (ISBN 0-911866-55-8). Advocate.

Pentecostal Home: Study Guide. A. L. Clanton. 80p. (Orig.). 1978. pap. 1.00 (ISBN 0-912315-43-1). Word Aflame.

Pentecostal Origins & Trends Early & Modern. 3rd, rev. ed. Karl Roebling. LC 85-63631. 112p. 8.95 (ISBN 0-942910-12-5). Paragon-Dynapress.

Pentecostal Preaching. Ray H. Hughes. LC 81-84606. 159p. (Orig.). 1981. pap. text ed. 5.95 (ISBN 0-87148-711-X). Pathway Pr.

Pentecostal Promise. Robert L. Brandt. (Charismatic Bks.). 47p. 1972. pap. 0.69 (ISBN 0-88243-920-0, 02-0920). Gospel Pub.

Pentecostal Worship. Cecil B. Knight. 1974. pap. 3.95 (ISBN 0-87148-684-9). Pathway Pr.

Pentecostalism in Colombia: Baptism by Fire & Spirit. Cornelia B. Flora. LC 74-4974. 288p. 1976. 26.50 (ISBN 0-8386-1578-3). Fairleigh Dickinson.

Pentecostalism in the Church. James D. Bales. pap. 2.95 (ISBN 0-89315-204-8). Lambert Bk.

Penthos. I. Hausherr. 24.95 (ISBN 0-87907-853-7); pap. 7.95 (ISBN 0-87907-953-3). Cistercian Pubns.

Penuel; or Face to Face with God. A. McLean & J. W. Easton. Ed. by Donald W. Dayton. (Higher Christian Life Ser.). 483p. 1985. 60.00 (ISBN 0-8240-6427-5). Garland Pub.

People among Peoples: Quaker Benevolence in Eighteenth Century America. Sydney V. James. LC 62-20248. (Center for the Study of the History of Liberty in America Ser). 1963. 27.50x (ISBN 0-674-66050-1). Harvard U Pr.

People & the Faith of the Bible. Andre Chouraqui. Tr. by William V. Gugli. LC 74-21237. 224p. 1975. 15.00x (ISBN 0-87023-172-3). U of Mass Pr.

People & the Promise. Ursula Synge. LC 74-10661. 192p. 1974. 12.95 (ISBN 0-87599-208-0). S G Phillips.

People & Their Religions, Part One. Thomas J. Clarke. (Literacy Volunteers of America Readers Ser.). 48p. (Orig.). 1983. pap. 1.95 (ISBN 0-8428-9609-0). Cambridge Bk.

People & Their Religions, Part Two. Thomas J. Clarke. (Literacy Volunteers of America Readers Ser.). 48p. (Orig.). 1983. pap. 1.95 (ISBN 0-8428-9610-4). Cambridge Bk.

People Are Different, People Are the Same. Marge Passamaneck. 1983. pap. 3.10 (ISBN 0-89536-615-0, 1629). CSS of Ohio.

People Called Methodist. Gordon Rupp et al. LC 84-72360. (Pan-Methodist Lectures). 96p. (Orig.). 1985. DR016B. pap. 3.95 (ISBN 0-88177-016-7). Discipleship Res.

People Called Nazarenes. Gene Van Note. 120p. 1983. pap. 2.95 (ISBN 0-8341-0894-1). Beacon Hill.

People Called Quakers. facsimile ed. Doris N. Dalglish. LC 78-90628. (Essay Index Reprint Ser). 1938. 15.00 (ISBN 0-8369-1254-3). Ayer Co Pubs.

People Called Quakers. D. Elton Trueblood. LC 66-15046. 1971. pap. 9.95 (ISBN 0-913408-02-6). Friends United.

People Called Shakers. new & enl. ed. Edward D. Andrews. 15.50 (ISBN 0-8446-1535-8). Peter Smith.

People Called Shakers: A Search for the Perfect Society. Edward D. Andrews. (Illus.). 1953. pap. 6.95 (ISBN 0-486-21081-2). Dover.

People Called: The Growth of Community in the Bible. Paul D. Hanson. LC 84-47725. 448p. 1986. 29.45 (ISBN 0-06-063700-5, HarpR). Har-Row.

People, Church & State in Modern Russia. Paul B. Anderson. LC 79-5204. 240p. 1980. Repr. of 1944 ed. 23.00 (ISBN 0-8305-0058-8). Hyperion Conn.

People for His Name: A Church-Based Mission Strategy. Paul A. Beals. LC 84-73488. (Illus.). 248p. (Orig.). 1985. pap. text ed. 9.95X (ISBN 0-87808-336-7). William Carey Lib.

People Helper Growthbook. Gary Collins. LC 76-25752. 1976. pap. 5.95 (ISBN 0-88449-056-4, A424084). Vision Hse.

People Ideology-People Theology: New Perspectives on Religious Dogma. Dario Lisiero. 226p. 1980. 10.95 (ISBN 0-682-49664-2, Banner). Exposition Pr FL.

People in Pain: Guidelines for Pastoral Care. Wayne E. Oates & Charles E. Oates. LC 85-5403. 152p. 1985. pap. 8.95 (ISBN 0-664-24674-5). Westminster.

People in Turmoil: A Woman's Workshop on First Corinthians. Carolyn Nystrom & Margaret Fromer. (Woman's Workshop Ser.). 128p. (Orig.). 1985. pap. 3.95 (ISBN 0-310-41891-7, 11278P). Zondervan.

People of Ancient Israel: An Introduction to the Old Testament Literature, History & Thought. J. Kenneth Kuntz. (Illus.). 1974. pap. text ed. 21.95 scp (ISBN 0-06-043822-3, HarpC). Har-Row.

People of God. Markus Barth. (Journal for the Study of the New Testament, Supplement Ser.: No. 5). 100p. 1983. text ed. 15.95x (ISBN 0-905774-54-X, Pub. by JSOT Pr England); pap. text ed. 7.95x (ISBN 0-905774-55-8, Pub. by JSOT Pr England). Eisenbrauns.

People of God: A Plea for the Church. Anton Houtepen. Tr. by John Bowden from Dutch. Orig. Title: Mensen Van God. 224p. (Orig.). 1985. pap. 10.95 (ISBN 0-88344-402-X). Orbis Bks.

People of God in Ministry. William K. McElvaney. LC 80-26077. 176p. (Orig.). 1981. pap. 7.75 (ISBN 0-687-30660-4). Abingdon.

People of God in the Night. Eloi Leclerc. Tr. by Paul Lachance & Paul Schwartz. (Tau Ser.). 1979. 5.95 (ISBN 0-8199-0768-5). Franciscan Herald.

People of Mission: A History of General Conference Mennonite Overseas Missions. James C. Juhnke. LC 78-74809. 1979. pap. 5.95 (ISBN 0-87303-019-2). Faith & Life.

People of Our Parish. Leila H. Bugg. 20.00 (ISBN 0-405-10811-7). Ayer Co Pubs.

People of That Book. Mary Willis. Ed. by Bobbie J. Van Dolson. 128p. 1981. pap. 4.95 (ISBN 0-8280-0033-6). Review & Herald.

People of the Book: Drama, Felloship, & Religion. Samuel C. Heilman. LC 82-13369. x, 338p. 1987. pap. text ed. price not set (ISBN 0-226-32493-1). U of Chicago Pr.

People of the Book: Drama, Fellowship, & Religion. Samuel C. Heilman. LC 82-13369. 264p. 1983. lib. bdg. 25.00x (ISBN 0-226-32492-3). U of Chicago Pr.

People of the Book: The Story Behind the Old Testament. Anthony E. Gilles. (Illus.). 178p. (Orig.). 1983. pap. text ed. 5.95 (ISBN 0-86716-026-8). St Anthony Mess Pr.

People of the Creed: The Story Behind the Early Church. Anthony E. Gilles. (People Ser.: Vol. 3). (Illus., Orig.). 1985. pap. text ed. 5.95 (ISBN 0-86716-046-2). St Anthony Mess Pr.

People of the Lie: The Hope for Healing Human Evil. M. Scott Peck. LC 83-13631. 269p. 1983. 15.95 (ISBN 0-671-45492-7). S&S.

People of the Lie: The Hope for Healing Human Evil. M. Scott Peck. 1985. pap. 7.95 (ISBN 0-671-52816-5, Touchstone Bks). S&S.

People of the New Testament: Arch Book Supplement. Gloria Truitt. LC 59-1311. 1983. pap. 0.99 (ISBN 0-570-06173-3). Concordia.

People of the Old Testament: Arch Book Supplement. Gloria Truitt. LC 59-1310. 1983. pap. 0.99 (ISBN 0-570-06172-5). Concordia.

People of the Saints. George Mills. (Illus.). 1967. 5.00 (ISBN 0-916537-30-7, Taylor Museum). CO Springs Fine Arts.

People of the Secret. Ernest Scott. 1983. 16.95 (ISBN 0-86304-027-6, Pub. by Octagon Pr England); pap. 8.95 (ISBN 0-86304-038-1). Ins Study Human.

People of the Way. John A. Toews. Ed. by A. J. Dueck et al. 256p. 1981. 10.95 (ISBN 0-919797-15-6); pap. 7.95 (ISBN 0-919797-16-4). Kindred Pr.

People of the Way: Biblical Ecumenism. Henry Johnsen. 5.95 (ISBN 0-685-00743-X). Reiner.

People of the Way: The Story Behind the New Testament. Anthony E. Gilles. (Illus.). 142p. (Orig.). 1984. pap. 5.95 (ISBN 0-86716-036-5). St Anthony Mess Pr.

People of Two Kingdoms. new ed. James C. Juhnke. LC 74-84697. (Mennonite Historical Ser.). (Illus.). 221p. 1975. 7.95 (ISBN 0-87303-662-X). Faith & Life.

People Parish: A Model of Church Where People Flourish. Gerald J. Kleba. LC 86-82035. 136p. (Orig.). 1986. pap. 4.95 (ISBN 0-87793-346-4). Ave Maria.

People Power. Roger W. Thomas. LC 80-53675. 96p. (Orig.). 1982. pap. 2.25 (ISBN 0-87239-442-5, 40096). Standard Pub.

People, Power, Change: Movements of Social Transformation. Luther P. Gerlach & Virginia H. Hine. LC 70-109434. 1970. pap. 9.63 scp (ISBN 0-672-60613-5). Bobbs.

People, Priests, & Prelates: Ecclesiastical Democracy & the Tensions of Trusteeism. Patrick W. Carey. LC 86-40243. (Studies in American Catholicism: Vol. 8). 392p. 1987. text ed. 26.95x (ISBN 0-268-01563-5). U of Notre Dame Pr.

People Set Apart. Jean J. Gietzen. LC 83-61452. 1983. pap. 6.95 (ISBN 0-89390-047-8). Resource Pubns.

People That Dwells Alone. Yaacov Herzog. Ed. by Misha Louvish. 282p. 1975. 10.95 (ISBN 0-88482-895-6, Sanhedrin Pr). Hebrew Pub.

People That Love. Heritage Village Church & Missionary Fellowship, Inc. Staff. Ed. by Roger H. Boulton. (Illus.). 128p. (Orig.). 1986. text ed. write for info. (ISBN 0-912275-05-7); pap. text ed. write for info. (ISBN 0-912275-06-5). PTL Enterprises.

People Walk on Their Heads: Moses Weinberger's Jews & Judaism in New York. Ed. by Jonathan D. Sarna. 137p. 1982. text ed. 24.50x (ISBN 0-8419-0707-2); pap. text ed. 12.95x (ISBN 0-8419-0731-5). Holmes & Meier.

People Who Couldn't Be Stopped. Ethel Barrett. LC 70-96703. (Illus., Orig.). 1970. pap. 1.95 (ISBN 0-8307-0007-2, S063107). Regal.

People Who Knew Paul. Wesley T. Runk. 1985. 2.00 (ISBN 0-89536-185-X, 1610). CSS of Ohio.

People's Christmas. Gerald O'Collins. (Orig.). 1984. pap. 3.50 (ISBN 0-8091-2660-5). Paulist Pr.

People's Church. Bonaventure Kloppenburg. 1978. 8.95 (ISBN 0-8199-0692-1). Franciscan Herald.

People's Idea of God, Christian Healings No & Yes. Mary B. Eddy. pap. 4.50 (ISBN 0-87952-042-6). First Church.

People's New Testament with Notes, 1 vol. Ed. by B. W. Johnson. 1971. 14.95 (ISBN 0-89225-141-7). Gospel Advocate.

Peoples of Israel: Fifty-Seven Centuries of Presence. rev. & enl. ed. Herbert A. Klein. Ed. by Joseph Simon. Orig. Title: Israel - Land of the Jews. (Illus.). 240p. 1986. Repr. of 1972 ed. 23.50 (ISBN 0-934710-13-9). J Simon.

People's Reformation: Magistrates, Clergy & Commons in Strasbourg, 1500-1598. Lorna J. Abray. LC 84-45805. 288p. 1985. text ed. 27.50x (ISBN 0-8014-1776-7). Cornell U Pr.

People's Theology. Ed. by Adolf Exeler & Norbert Mette. 192p. pap. 9.95 cancelled (ISBN 0-8245-0477-1). Crossroad NY.

Peopling of the Earth. Geoffrey Barborka. LC 75-4243. (Illus.). 240p. 1975. 10.00 (ISBN 0-8356-0221-4). Theos Pub Hse.

Pepper & Salt. Vance Havner. (Pulpit Library). 128p. 1983. pap. 4.95 (ISBN 0-8010-4276-3). Baker Bk.

Pequena Gran Mujer en la China. Gladys Aylward. Orig. Title: Little Woman in China. (Span.). 160p. 1974. pap. 3.50 (ISBN 0-8254-1048-7). Kregel.

Perce Judd: Man of Peace. Winifred Sarre. (Illus.). 176p. 1983. pap. 10.00 (ISBN 0-8309-0377-1). Herald Hse.

Perception & Inference: An Essay on Classical Indian Theories of Knowledge. Bimal K. Matilal. 350p. 1986. 65.00x (ISBN 0-19-824625-0). Oxford U Pr.

Perceval: The Story of the Grail. Chretien De Troyes. Tr. by Nigel Bryant. 320p. 1986. pap. 16.25 (ISBN 0-85991-224-8, Pub. by Boydell & Brewer). Longwood Pub Group.

Perder Para Ganar. Evelyn Christenson. 1983. 3.75 (ISBN 0-88113-243-8). Edit Betania.

Perdon de los Pecados. 2nd ed. Carlos H. Mackintosh. Ed. by Gordon H. Bennett. Tr. by Sara Bautista from Eng. (Serie Diamante). Tr. of Forgiveness of Sins. (Span.). 36p. 1982. pap. 0.85 (ISBN 0-942504-02-X). Overcomer Pr.

Perdonado. John M. Robertson. Tr. by Luis B. Lumpuy from Eng. Orig. Title: Pardoned. (Span., Illus.). 64p. 1985. pap. 0.95 (ISBN 0-8297-0909-6). Life Pubs Intl.

Perdonar para Ser Libre. David Augsburger. Orig. Title: Freedom of Forgiveness. (Span.). 160p. 1977. pap. 3.50 (ISBN 0-8254-1046-0). Kregel.

Pere Lamy. Paul Biver. Tr. by John O'Connor from Fr. 1973. pap. 5.50 (ISBN 0-89555-055-5). TAN Bks Pubs.

Peregrinaje Esde Roma. Bartholomew F. Brewer & Alfred W. Furrell. Tr. by Jose M. Vargas-Caba from Eng. (Span., Illus.). 194p. 1986. pap. 5.95 (ISBN 0-89084-328-7). Bob Jones Univ Pr.

Perek Shira & Zemirot. Ed. by Baruch Chait. 100p. (Orig.). 1986. text ed. 4.95 (ISBN 0-88125-095-3). Ktav.

Perennial Pentecost. Frank W. Lemons. 1971. pap. 2.95 (ISBN 0-87148-679-2). Pathway Pr.

Perennial Philosophy. Aldous Huxley. 1970. pap. 7.95 (ISBN 0-06-090191-8, CN191, PL). Har-Row.

Perennial Philosophy. Aldous L. Huxley. LC 76-167362. (Essay Index Reprint Ser.). Repr. of 1945 ed. 25.50 (ISBN 0-8369-2773-7). Ayer Co Pubs.

Perennial Wisdom. Elda Hartley. (Chrysalis Bk). (Illus.). 80p. (Orig.). 1986. pap. 4.95 (ISBN 0-916349-09-8). Amity Hous Inc.

Perfect Christmas. Rose H. Heaton. Repr. of 1932 ed. 20.00 (ISBN 0-686-20659-2). Lib Serv Inc.

Perfect Church. Donald L. Roberts. LC 79-56331. 95p. (Orig.). 1980. pap. 2.95 (ISBN 0-87509-267-5). Chr Pubns.

Perfect Church. Roger Thomas. LC 81-14544. 96p. (Orig.). 1982. pap. 2.25 (ISBN 0-87239-479-4, 41012). Standard Pub.

Perfect Fools. John Saward. 1980. text ed. 29.95x (ISBN 0-19-213230-X). Oxford U Pr.

Perfect Friend. Frances C. Matranga. 80p. (Orig.). 1985. pap. 3.95 (ISBN 0-570-04112-0, 56-1523). Concordia.

Perfect Gift. Spiros Zodhiates. (Illus.). 1973. pap. 1.75 (ISBN 0-89957-511-0). AMG Pubs.

Perfect Joy of St. Francis. Felix Timmermans. 280p. 1974. pap. 4.95 (ISBN 0-385-02378-2, Im). Doubleday.

Perfect Life: The Shakers in America. Doris Faber. LC 73-90968. (Illus.). 224p. 1974. 10.95 (ISBN 0-374-35819-2). FS&G.

Perfect Love. John MacArthur, Jr. (John MacArthur's Bible Studies). 1985. pap. 3.50 (ISBN 0-8024-5110-1). Moody.

Perfect Master. C. B. Purdom. (Illus.). 330p. 1976. pap. 3.95 (ISBN 0-913078-24-7). Sheriar Pr.

Perfect Master, 2 vols. Bhagwan Shree Rajneesh. Ed. by Ma Yoga Anurag. LC 83-172954. (Sufi Ser.). (Illus.). 1980. Vol. I, 380 pgs. 19.95 ea. (ISBN 0-88050-113-8). Vol. II, 368 pgs. 1981 (ISBN 0-88050-114-6). Chidvilas Found.

Perfect Power Within You. new ed. Jack Addington & Cornelia Addington. LC 73-87712. 167p. 1973. pap. 4.95 (ISBN 0-87516-179-0). De Vorss.

Perfect Relationship. Swami Muktananda. LC 80-54457. 240p. 1980. pap. 6.95 (ISBN 0-914602-53-5). SYDA Found.

Perfect Relationship. Doric Wilson. LC 83-61708. 98p. (Orig.). 1983. pap. 5.95 (ISBN 0-933322-12-7). Sea Horse.

Perfect Shepherd. John J. Davis. (Illus., Orig.). 1980. pap. 4.50 (ISBN 0-8010-2905-8). Baker Bk.

Perfect Shepherd: Studies in the Twenty-Third Psalm. John J. Davis. pap. 5.50 (ISBN 0-88469-110-1). BMH Bks.

Perfect Way. Bhagwan Shree Rajneesh. Ed. by Mahasattva Swami Krishna Prem. LC 84-42808. (Early Writings & Discourses Ser.). 208p. 1984. pap. 3.95 (ISBN 0-88050-707-1). Chidvilas Found.

Perfect "10". Brent D. Earles. 112p. 1986. 5.95 (ISBN 0-8010-3431-0). Baker Bk.

Perfectability of Man. John Passmore. LC 77-129625. 1970. 25.00x (ISBN 0-684-15521-4, ScribT). Scribner.

Perfected Millenial Kingdom. Robert Millet. 1974. pap. 2.00 (ISBN 0-89036-034-0). Hawkes Pub Inc.

Perfection & Perfectionism: A Dogmatic-Ethical Study of Biblical Perfection & Phenomenal Perfectionism. Hans K. LaRondelle. (Andrews University Monographs, Studies in Religion: Vol. III). vii, 364p. pap. 9.95 (ISBN 0-943872-02-2). Andrews Univ Pr.

Perfection in the Head World. Sri Chinmoy. 55p. (Orig.). 1980. pap. 2.00 (ISBN 0-88497-492-8). Aum Pubns.

Perfection of Wisdom in Eight Thousand Lines & Its Verse Summary. Tr. & pref. by Edward Conze. LC 72-76540. (Wheel Ser.: No. 1). 348p. 1973. 15.00 (ISBN 0-87704-048-6); pap. 8.95 (ISBN 0-87704-049-4). Four Seasons Foun.

Perfection of Wisdom: The Career of the Predestined Buddhas. Tr. by E. J. Thomas from Sanskrit. LC 78-12005. 1979. Repr. of 1952 ed. lib. bdg. 22.50x (ISBN 0-313-20646-5, MAPWI). Greenwood.

Perfection of Yoga. Swami A. C. Bhaktivedanta. LC 72-76302. (Illus.). 1972. pap. 1.95 (ISBN 0-912776-36-6). Bhaktivedanta.

Perfectionism. B. B. Warfield. 12.95 (ISBN 0-8010-9587-5). Baker Bk.

Perfectionist Persuasion: The Holiness Movement & American Methodism, 1867-1936. Charles E. Jones. LC 74-13766. (ATLA Monograph: No. 5). (Illus.). 262p. 1974. 22.50 (ISBN 0-8108-0747-5). Scarecrow.

Performative Approach to Ritual. J. Tambiah. (Radcliffe-Brown Lectures in Social Anthropology). 1978. pap. 3.75 (ISBN 0-85672-197-2, Pub. by British Acad). Longwood Pub Group.

Performing Arts Information, Nineteen Seventy-Five to Nineteen Eighty: A Bibliography of Reference Works. Paula Elliot. 1982. pap. 4.00. KSU.

Perfumed Scorpion. Idries Shah. 193p. 1982. 14.95 (ISBN 0-900860-62-6, Pub. by Octagon Pr England). Ins Study Human.

Peril of Faith. Martin L. Bard. 155p. (Orig.). 1982. pap. 5.00 (ISBN 0-910309-05-1). Am Atheist.

Perilous Vision of John Wyclif. Louis B. Hall. LC 82-18890. 288p. 1983. lib. bdg. 23.95X (ISBN 0-8304-1006-6). Nelson-Hall.

Perils of Professionalism. Donald B. Kraybill & Phyllis P. Good. LC 82-3052. 240p. (Orig.). 1982. pap. 9.95 (ISBN 0-8361-1997-5). Herald Pr.

Periodical & Monographic Index to the Literature on the Gospels & Acts Based on the Files of Ecole Biblique in Jerusalem. LC 78-27276. (Bibliographia Tripotamopolitana: No.3). 1971. 12.00x (ISBN 0-931222-02-8). Pitts Theolog.

Periodicals of American Transcendentalism. Clarence Gohdes. LC 77-136380. Repr. of 1931 ed. 16.00 (ISBN 0-404-02854-3). AMS Pr.

Periodicals of American Transcendentalism. Clarence L. Gohdes. LC 76-107803. (Select Bibliographies Reprint Ser). 1931. 19.00 (ISBN 0-8369-5206-5). Ayer Co Pubs.

Peripatetic Saying: The Problem of the Thrice-Told Tale in the Canon of Talmudic Literature. Jacob Neusner. (Brown Judaic Studies: No. 89). 208p. 1985. 18.95 (ISBN 0-89130-830-X, 14 00 89); pap. 15.95 (ISBN 0-89130-831-8). Scholars Pr GA.

Periya Puranam. Sekkizhaar. Ed. by N. Mahalingam. Tr. by G. Vanmikanathan from Tamil. 612p. 1985. text ed. 11.95x (ISBN 0-87481-534-7, Pub. by RamaKrishna Math). Vedanta Pr.

Permanent Deacons. rev. ed. Russell Shaw. 40p. 1986. pap. 1.95 (ISBN 1-55586-989-0). US Catholic.

Permanent Deacons in the United States: Guidelines on Their Formation & Ministry. rev. ed. 60p. 1985. pap. 3.95 (ISBN 1-55586-974-2). US Catholic.

Permanent Horizon. Ludwig Lewisohn. LC 73-117818. (Essay Index Reprint Ser). 1934. 19.00 (ISBN 0-8369-1811-8). Ayer Co Pubs.

Perpetual Chantries in Britain. Kathleen Wood-Legh. LC 65-28505. pap. 93.30 (ISBN 0-317-26370-6, 2024564). Bks Demand UMI.

Perpetual Dilemma: Jewish Religion in the Jewish State. S. Zalman Abramov. 1979. pap. 7.50 (ISBN 0-8074-0088-2, 382500, WUPJ). UAHC.

Perpetual Help Story. A Redemptorist Publication. 64p. 1977. pap. 1.95 (ISBN 0-89243-066-4, 29230). Liguori Pubns.

Perpetual Peace. Immanuel Kant. Tr. by Lewis W. Beck. LC 57-3588. 1957. pap. 3.56 scp (ISBN 0-672-60227-X, LLA54). Bobbs.

Perpetual Peace. Immanuel Kant. 59.95 (ISBN 0-8490-0815-8). Gordon Pr.

Perplexing Scriptures. Wade H. Phillips. 135p. (Orig.). 1984. pap. 4.50 (ISBN 0-934942-44-7, 2034). White Wing Pub.

Persatuan Islam: Islamic Reform in Twentieth Century Indonesia. Howard Federspiel. (Monograph Ser.). (Orig.). 1970. pap. 7.50 (ISBN 0-87763-013-5). Cornell Mod Indo.

Persecution & Liberty: Essays in Honor of George Lincoln Burr. facs. ed. George L. Burr. LC 68-26467. (Essay Index Reprint Ser). 1968. Repr. of 1931 ed. 17.50 (ISBN 0-8369-0783-3). Ayer Co Pubs.

Persecution & Martyrdom: From Experience to Theology in Paul. John S. Pobee. (JSNT Supplement Ser.: No. 6). 150p. 1984. text ed. 28.50x (ISBN 0-905774-52-3, Pub. by JSOT Pr. England); pap. text ed. 13.50x (ISBN 0-905774-53-1, Pub. by JSOT Pr. England). Eisenbrauns.

Persecution & the Art of Writing. Leo Strauss. LC 73-1407. 204p. 1973. Repr. of 1952 ed. lib. bdg. 19.75 (ISBN 0-8371-6801-5, STPA). Greenwood.

Persecution & Toleration. Ed. by W. J. Sheils. (Studies in Church History: Vol. 21). 500p. 1984. 45.00x (ISBN 0-631-13601-0). Basil Blackwell.

Persecutor. Sergei Kourdakov. (Illus.). 256p. 1974. pap. 3.50 (ISBN 0-8007-8177-5, Spire Bks). Revell.

Persepolis & Ancient Iran. Oriental Institute Staff. LC 76-7942. 1976. 55.00 (ISBN 0-226-69493-3, Chicago Visual Lib); 1 color & 11 black-&-white fiches incl. U of Chicago Pr.

Perseus & Medusa. Adapted by C. J. Naden. LC 80-50083. (Illus.). 32p. 1980. PLB 9.79 (ISBN 0-89375-362-9); pap. 2.50 (ISBN 0-89375-366-1). Troll Assocs.

Perseverance. Robert E. Picirilli. 28p. 1973. pap. 0.95 (ISBN 0-89265-108-3). Randall Hse.

Perseverance for People under Pressure. Neva Coyle. 64p. (Orig.). 1986. pap. 2.50 saddle stitched (ISBN 0-87123-888-8). Bethany Hse.

Perseverance in Preservation. Ralph Staten. 36p. 1975. pap. 0.95 (ISBN 0-89265-109-1). Randall Hse.

Persian Life & Customs. 3rd ed. Samuel G. Wilson. LC 76-178305. Repr. of 1900 ed. 24.50 (ISBN 0-404-06996-7). AMS Pr.

Persian Literature (Comprising of the Shan Nameth, the Rubaiyat, the Divan & the Gulistan, 2 vols. Intro. by Richard J. Gottheil. 1986. Repr. of 1900 ed. Set. PLB 150.00 (ISBN 0-89760-246-3). Telegraph Bks.

Persian Mythology. John R. Hinnells. LC 85-70554. (Library of the World's Myths & Legends). (Illus.). 144p. 1985. 18.95 (ISBN 0-87226-017-8). P Bedrick Bks.

Persistent Pastoralists: Nomadic Societies in Transition. Peter Rigby. 208p. 1985. 26.25x (ISBN 0-86232-226-X, Pub. by Zed Pr England); pap. 9.95 (ISBN 0-86232-227-8, Pub. by Zed Pr England). Humanities.

Persistent Prejudice: Anti-Catholicism in America. Michael Schwartz. LC 84-60746. 240p. 1984. pap. 6.95 (ISBN 0-87973-715-8, 715). Our Sunday Visitor.

Person & Myth: Maurice Leenhardt in the Melanesian World. James Clifford. LC 81-4509. (Illus.). 320p. 1982. 35.00x (ISBN 0-520-04247-6). U of Cal Pr.

Person & the Work of the Holy Spirit. 2nd ed. R. A. Torrey. 1985. pap. text ed. 7.95 (ISBN 0-310-33301-6, 10902P). Zondervan.

Person & Work of Christ. B. B. Warfield. 12.95 (ISBN 0-8010-9588-3). Baker Bk.

Person & Work of Christ. Benjamin B. Warfield. 1950. 12.95 (ISBN 0-87552-529-6). Presby & Reformed.

Person & Work of the Holy Spirit. Rene Pache. 1960. pap. 7.50 (ISBN 0-8024-6471-8). Moody.

Person & Work of the Holy Spirit. Reuben A. Torrey. 1968. 7.95 (ISBN 0-310-33300-8, 10902P). Zondervan.

Person in the Pulpit: Preaching as Caring. Willard F. Jabusch. LC 79-28812. (Abingdon Preacher's Library). (Orig.). 1980. pap. 5.95 (ISBN 0-687-30784-8). Abingdon.

Person of Christ: A Biblical & Historical Analysis of the Incarnation. David F. Wells. LC 84-70979. (Foundations for Faith Ser.). 224p. 1984. pap. 8.95 (ISBN 0-89107-315-9, Crossway Bks). Good News.

Person of Christ: Covenant Between God & Man. Jean Galot. Tr. by Angeline Bouchard. LC 84-5982. 102p. 1983. 7.50 (ISBN 0-8199-0832-0). Franciscan Herald.

Person Reborn. Paul Tournier. LC 75-12283. 256p. 1975. (HarpR); pap. 1.95 (ISBN 0-06-068377-5, RD-327). Har-Row.

Person to Person Evangelism. new ed. R. Edward Davenport. LC 77-23716. 1978. pap. 2.95 (ISBN 0-87148-691-1). Pathway Pr.

Person to Person: How to Be Effective in Evangelism. Jim Berlucchi. 144p. (Orig.). 1984. pap. 3.50 (ISBN 0-89283-164-2). Servant.

Personal Becoming: In Honor of Karl Rahner. Andrew Tallon. 188p. pap. 19.95 (ISBN 0-686-65691-1). Marquette.

Personal Bible Study. William C. Lincoln. LC 75-2345. 160p. 1975. pap. 4.95 (ISBN 0-87123-458-0, 210458). Bethany Hse.

Personal Bible Study. Jim Townsend. (Complete Teacher Training Meeting Ser.). 48p. 1986. tchr's ed 9.95 (ISBN 0-89191-320-3). Cook.

Personal Computer: A New Tool for Ministers. Russell H. Dilday, Jr. LC 84-20360. 1985. pap. 8.95 (ISBN 0-8054-3111-X). Broadman.

Personal Decisions. H. Paul LeMaire. LC 81-43668. 220p. (Orig.). 1982. lib. bdg. 28.25 (ISBN 0-8191-2329-3); pap. text ed. 11.75 (ISBN 0-8191-2330-7). U Pr of Amer.

Personal Declension & Revival of Religion in the Soul. Octavius Winslow. 1978. pap. 3.95 (ISBN 0-85151-261-5). Banner of Truth.

Personal Destinies: A Philosophy of Ethical Individualism. David L. Norton. 1976. 47.50x (ISBN 0-691-07215-9); pap. 10.95x (ISBN 0-691-01975-4). Princeton U Pr.

Personal Devotions. Randal E. Denny. (Christian Living Ser.). 32p. (Orig.). 1987. pap. write for info. (ISBN 0-8341-1186-1). Beacon Hill.

Personal Discernment Inventory: An Instrument for Spiritual Guides. Brian P. Hall. pap. 5.95 (ISBN 0-8091-2312-6). Paulist Pr.

Personal Evangelism among Roman Catholics. Aniceto Sparagna. (Orig.). 1978. pap. 3.95 (ISBN 0-89900-122-X). College Pr Pub.

Personal Evangelism for Today. G. William Schweer. LC 83-70003. 1984. 10.95 (ISBN 0-8054-6241-4). Broadman.

Personal Experiences of S. O. Susag. S. O. Susag. 191p. pap. 1.75 (ISBN 0-686-29134-4). Faith Pub Hse.

Personal Faith of Jesus as Revealed in the Lord's Prayer. J. Neville Ward. 128p. 1982. pap. 6.95 (ISBN 0-86683-678-0, HarpR). Har-Row.

Personal Finances for Ministers. Darold H. Morgan. LC 85-17443. (Broadman Leadership Ser.). 1985. pap. 5.95 (ISBN 0-8054-6405-0). Broadman.

Personal Life Notebook. David Gustaveson. 192p. 1980. pap. 8.95 spiral bdg. (ISBN 0-87123-467-X, 210467). Bethany Hse.

Personal Life of David Livingstone. William G. Blaikie. LC 69-19353. (Illus.). 1880. 22.50x (ISBN 0-8371-0518-8, BLL&). Greenwood.

Personal Life of the Christian. Arthur W. Robinson. 1981. pap. 7.95X (ISBN 0-19-213427-2). Oxford U Pr.

Personal Ministry, No. 3. Dan Caslow. 1984. pap. 1.95 (ISBN 0-8163-0498-X). Pacific Pr Pub Assn.

Personal Ministry Handbook. Larry Richards. 224p. 1986. pap. 9.95 (ISBN 0-8010-7736-2). Baker Bk.

Personal Narrative of a Pilgrimage to Al-Madinah & Meccah, 2 Vols. Richard F. Burton. (Illus.). 1893. Vol. 1. pap. 8.95 (ISBN 0-486-21217-3). Vol. 2. pap. 8.95 (ISBN 0-486-21218-1). Dover.

Personal Narrative of a Pilgrimage to Al-Madinah & Meccah, 2 Vols. Richard F. Burton. Ed. by Isabel Burton. Set. 28.50 (ISBN 0-8446-1781-4). Peter Smith.

Personal Pathway to Prayer. Dorothea H. McHugh. LC 85-51408. 104p. 1985. 6.95 (ISBN 0-938232-90-8, Dist. by Baker & Taylor). Winston-Derek.

Personal Presence: Its Effects on Honesty & Truthfulness. Joseph T. Culliton. LC 85-6218. 202p. (Orig.). 1985. 24.50 (ISBN 0-8191-4661-7); pap. text ed. 10.75 (ISBN 0-8191-4662-5). U Pr of Amer.

Personal Promise Pocketbook. (Pocketpac Ser.). 128p. 1984. deluxe ed. 3.95 leatherette gift (ISBN 0-87788-677-6). Shaw Pubs.

Personal Recollections of Joan of Arc by the Sieur Louis De Conte. Samuel L. Clemens. LC 80-23663. (Illus.). xiv, 461p. 1980. Repr. of 1906 ed. lib. bdg. 60.50x (ISBN 0-313-22373-4, CLPR). Greenwood.

Personal Relevance of Truth. Thomas S. Brown. 1983. pap. 2.50x (ISBN 0-87574-081-2, 081). Pendle Hill.

Personal Religion among the Greeks. Andre-Jean Festugiere. (Sather Classical Lecture Ser.: No. 26). 186p. 1984. Repr. of 1954 ed. lib. bdg. 25.00 (ISBN 0-313-23209-1, FERG). Greenwood.

Personal Responsibility & Christian Morality. Josef Fuchs. Tr. by William Cleves et al from Ger. LC 83-1548. 240p. (Orig.). 1983. pap. 10.95 (ISBN 0-87840-405-8). Georgetown U Pr.

Personal Talks with Jesus. Marnie Koski. (Orig.). 1979. pap. 4.95 (ISBN 0-917200-25-X). ESPress.

Personal Values in Public Policy. John Haughey. LC 79-84401. (Woodstock Studies: No. 3). 288p. (Orig.). 1979. pap. 6.95 (ISBN 0-8091-2201-4). Paulist Pr.

Personal Witness. John Navone. LC 67-13761. 1967. 4.95 (ISBN 0-685-42652-1, Pub-by Sheed). Guild Bks.

Personal Work. Milo Kauffman. 1940. pap. 2.00 (ISBN 0-87813-951-6). Christian Light.

Personal Work. Reuben A. Torrey. 180p. 1956. 10.95 (ISBN 0-8007-0251-4). Revell.

Personalidades Quebrantadas. Gary Collins. Tr. by Jose Flores from Eng. LC 78-62403. Tr. of Fractured Personalities. (Span.). 215p. 1978. pap. 4.95 (ISBN 0-89922-116-5). Edit Caribe.

Personalism in Theology. Ed. by Edgar S. Brightman. LC 75-3088. (Philosophy in America Ser.). Repr. of 1943 ed. 24.50 (ISBN 0-404-59086-1). AMS Pr.

Personality & Configuration with Christ. James J. Alberione. (Orig.). 3.50 (ISBN 0-8198-0120-8); pap. 2.50 (ISBN 0-8198-0121-6). Dghtrs St Paul.

Personality & Religion. Edgar S. Brightman. LC 75-3084. (Philosophy in America Ser.). Repr. of 1934 ed. 20.00 (ISBN 0-404-59083-7). AMS Pr.

Personality & Sexual Problems in Pastoral Psychology. Ed. by W. C. Bier. LC 62-16224. (Pastoral Psychology Ser: No. 1). xvi, 256p. 1964. 20.00 (ISBN 0-8232-0585-1). Fordham.

Personality Fulfillment in the Spiritual Life. Adrian Van Kaam. 4.95 (ISBN 0-87193-043-9). Dimension Bks.

Personality of St. Paul. Cornelius A. Lapide. 1959. 3.50 (ISBN 0-8198-5802-1); pap. 2.25 (ISBN 0-8198-5803-X). Dghtrs St Paul.

Personality of the Holy Ghost. C. H. Spurgeon. 1977. pap. 0.95 (ISBN 0-686-23222-4). Pilgrim Pubns.

Personality Plus. Florence Littauer. (Illus.). 192p. 1982. 5.95 (Power Ed.); pap. 9.95 (ISBN 0-8007-1323-0). Revell.

Personas Escogidas de Dios. Margaret Ralph. (Serie Jirafa). Orig. Title: God's Special People. 28p. 1979. 3.95 (ISBN 0-311-38535-4, Edit Mundo). Casa Bautista.

Personnel Administration in the Christian School. J. Lester Brubaker. 168p. (Orig.). 1980. pap. 6.95 (ISBN 0-88469-130-6). BMH Bks.

Personnel Inventory & Employment Application. 1979. 25 copies 3.60 (ISBN 0-686-39902-1). Natl Cath Educ.

Personnel Management in the Church: Developing Personnel Policies & Practices. Alvin Rueter. (Church Administration Ser.). 56p. (Orig.). 1984. pap. 3.95 (ISBN 0-8066-2072-2, 10-4920). Augsburg.

Persons & Institutions in Early Rabbinic Judaism. Ed. by William S. Green. LC 79-20712. (Brown University, Brown Judaic Studies: No. 3). 1977. pap. 13.50 (ISBN 0-89130-131-3, 14 00 03). Scholars Pr GA.

Perspectives for Moral Decisions. John Howie. LC 80-6102. 192p. 1981. lib. bdg. 25.00 (ISBN 0-8191-1375-1); pap. text ed. 11.25 (ISBN 0-8191-1376-X). U Pr of Amer.

Perspectives in Churchmanship: Essays in Honor of Robert G. Torbet. Ed. by David M. Scholer. (Festschriften Ser.: No. 3). vi, 108p. 1986. write for info. (ISBN 0-86554-268-6, MUP/H231). NABPR.

Perspectives in Education, Religion, & the Arts. Ed. by Howard Keifer & Milton Munitz. LC 69-14641. Repr. of 1970 ed. 82.70 (ISBN 0-8357-9596-9, 2010111). Bks Demand UMI.

Perspectives in Jewish Population Research. Ed. by Steven M. Cohen et al. LC 84-50660. (Replica Edition). 275p. 1984. 22.50x (ISBN 0-86531-853-0). Westview.

Perspectives in Medieval History. Ed. by Katherine F. Drew & Floyd S. Lear. LC 63-20902. Repr. of 1963 ed. 26.30 (ISBN 0-8357-9653-1, 2015753). Bks Demand UMI.

Perspectives in the History of Religions. Jan De Vries. Tr. & intro. by Kees W. Bolle. LC 76-20154. 1977. pap. 3.65 (ISBN 0-520-03300-0, CAL 352). U of Cal Pr.

Perspectives of Truth in Literature. John D. Martin & Lester E. Showalter. (Christian Day School Ser.). 1982. 15.05 (ISBN 0-87813-921-4); tchr's. guide 10.95x (ISBN 0-87813-922-2). Christian Light.

Perspectives on Applied Christianity: Essays in Honor of Thomas Buford Maston. Ed. by William M. Tillman, Jr. (National Association of Baptist Professors of Religion (NABPR) Festschrift Ser.). vi, 108p. 1986. 10.50 (ISBN 0-86554-196-5, MUP-H180). Mercer Univ Pr.

Perspectives on Bereavement. Ed. by Irwin Gerber et al. (Thanatology Ser.). 1978. 14.95x (ISBN 0-8422-7304-2); pap. text ed. 7.95x (ISBN 0-8290-1878-6). Irvington.

Perspectives on First Peter. Ed. by Charles H. Talbert. LC 86-8772. (NABPR (National Association of Baptist Professors of Religion0 Special Studies: No. 9). 151p. (Orig.). 1986. pap. 15.95 (ISBN 0-86554-198-1, MUP-M11). Mercer Univ Pr.

Perspectives on God: Sociological, Theological & Philosophical. Charles Curtis et al. LC 78-62943. 1978. pap. text ed. 11.50 (ISBN 0-8191-0605-4). U Pr of Amer.

Perspectives on Guru Amardas. Ed. by Fauja Singh. 1985. 8.50x (ISBN 0-8364-1518-3, Pub. by Punjabi U India). South Asia Bks.

Perspectives on Indian Religion. Karel Werner. Ed. by Peter Connolly. 253p. 1986. lib. bdg. 56.00 (ISBN 0-85424-021-7, Pub. by Sri Satguru Pubns India). Orient Bk Dist.

Perspectives on Jews & Judaism: Essays in Honor of Wolfe Kelman. Ed. by Arthur A. Chiel. 25.00x (ISBN 0-87068-683-6). Ktav.

Perspectives on Living the Orthodox Faith. A. M. Coniaris. 1985. pap. 7.95 (ISBN 0-937032-36-0). Light&Life Pub Co MN.

Perspectives on Luke-Acts. Ed. by Charles Talbert. LC 78-51610. (Special Studies: No. 5). ix, 269p. 1978. pap. 10.00 (ISBN 0-932180-04-3). NABPR.

Perspectives on Old Testament Literature. Woodrow Ohlsen. LC 77-91012. (Illus.). 450p. 1978. 14.95 (ISBN 0-15-570484-2, HC). HarBraceJ.

Perspectives on Our Age: Jacques Ellul Speaks on His Life & Work. Jacques Ellul. Ed. by William H. Vanderburg. Tr. by Joachim Neugroschel. 1981. 10.95 (ISBN 0-8164-0485-2, HarpR). Har-Row.

Perspectives on Paul. Ernst Kasemann. LC 79-157540. pap. 45.80 (2029296). Bks Demand UMI.

Perspectives on Pentecost. Richard B Gaffin. 1979. pap. 3.95 (ISBN 0-87552-269-6). Presby & Reformed.

Perspectives on Pentecostalism: Case Studies from the Caribbean & Latin America. Ed. by Stephen D. Glazier. LC 80-7815. 207p. 1980. lib. bdg. 25.25 (ISBN 0-8191-1071-X); pap. text ed. 12.25 (ISBN 0-8191-1072-8). U Pr of Amer.

Perspectives on Political Ethics: An Ecumenical Inquiry. Koson Srisang. 196p. 1983. pap. 8.95 (ISBN 0-87840-407-4). Georgetown U Pr.

Perspectives on Soviet Jewry. Anti-Defamation League Staff. 150p. pap. 2.50 (ISBN 0-686-95144-1). ADL.

Perspectives on the Christian Reformed Church. Ed. by Peter DeKlerk & Richard R. DeRidder. 1983. 14.95 (ISBN 0-8010-2934-1). Baker Bk.

Perspectives on the Cross. Jon L. Joyce. (Orig.). 1982. pap. 3.25 (ISBN 0-937172-33-2). JLJ Pubs.

Perspectives on the Holocaust. Randolph L. Braham. (Holocaust Studies). 1983. lib. bdg. 20.00 (ISBN 0-89838-124-X). Kluwer Nijhoff.

Perspectives on the New Testament: Essays in Honor of Frank Stagg. Malcolm Tolbert et al. Ed. by Charles H. Talbert. vi, 108p. 1985. lib. bdg. 9.95x (ISBN 0-86554-152-3, MUP-H121). Mercer Univ Pr.

Perspectives on the Parables: An Approach to Multiple Interpretations. Mary Ann Tolbert. LC 78-54563. 144p. 1978. 9.95 (ISBN 0-8006-0527-6, 1-527). Fortress.

Perspectives on the Passion. William Grimbol. 1984. 5.95 (ISBN 0-89536-665-7, 1645). CSS of Ohio.

Perspectives on the World Christian Movement: A Reader. Ed. by Ralph D. Winter & Steven C. Hawthorne. LC 81-69924. (Illus.). 864p. (Orig.). 1981. pap. 14.95x (ISBN 0-87808-189-5). William Carey Lib.

Persuasive Preaching. Ronald E. Sleeth. LC 55-8527. viii, 96p. 1981. pap. 4.95 (ISBN 0-943872-81-2). Andrews Univ Pr.

Persuasive Preaching Today. Ralph L. Lewis. 276p. 1982. Repr. of 1979 ed. 6.95 (ISBN 0-9608180-0-6). Asbury Theological.

Pesach: A Holiday Funtext. Judy Bin-Nun & Nancy Cooper. (Illus.). 32p. (Orig.). 1983. pap. text ed. 5.00 (ISBN 0-8074-0161-7, 101310). UAHC.

Pesah Is Coming. Hyman Chanover & Alice Chanover. (Holiday Series of Picture Story Books). (Illus.). 1956. 5.95 (ISBN 0-8381-0713-3, 10-713). United Syn Bk.

Pesah Is Here. Hyman Chanover & Alice Chanover. (Holiday Series of Picture Story Books). (Illus.). 1956. 5.95 (ISBN 0-8381-0714-1). United Syn Bk.

Pesahim, 2 vols. 30.00 (ISBN 0-910218-55-2). Bennet Pub.

Peshitta of the Twelve Prophets. A. Gelston. 272p. 1985. 34.50x (ISBN 0-19-826179-9). Oxford U Pr.

Petaled Sun. Mary A. Seguin. 48p. (Orig.). 1986. pap. 3.25 (ISBN 0-9616951-0-2). M A Seguin.

Peter. Ethel Barrett. LC 81-52942. (Bible Biography Ser.). 128p. (Orig.). 1982. pap. text ed. 1.95 (ISBN 0-8307-0768-9, 5810809). Regal.

Peter. William Coleman. LC 81-85894. 160p. (Orig.). 1982. pap. 4.95 (ISBN 0-89081-305-1). Harvest Hse.

Peter. F. B. Meyer. 1968. pap. 4.50 (ISBN 0-87508-349-8). Chr Lit.

Peter: A Journey in Faith. R. Scott Sullender. 47p. (Orig.). 1986. pap. 6.95 (ISBN 0-940754-37-1). Ed Ministries.

Peter Abelard. facsimile ed. Joseph McCabe. LC 74-148889. (Select Bibliographies Reprint Ser). Repr. of 1901 ed. 22.00 (ISBN 0-8369-5655-9). Ayer Co Pubs.

Peter Abelard, Letters IX-XIV. Edme R. Smits. xii, 315p. (Orig.). 1983. pap. 18.00x (ISBN 90-6088-085-4, Pub. by Boumas Boekhuis Netherlands). Benjamins North AM.

Peter Abelard (1079-1142) Joseph McCabe. LC 72-85102. ix, 402p. 1972. Repr. of 1901 ed. lib. bdg. 23.50 (ISBN 0-8337-4244-2). B Franklin.

Peter & Susie Find a Family. Edith Hess & Jacqueline Blass. Tr. of Peter & Susi Finden eine Familie. (Illus.). 28p. 1985. Repr. of 1981 ed. 10.95 (ISBN 0-687-30848-8). Abingdon.

Peter & the First Christians. Laurent Lalo. LC 84-42946. (Illus.). 24p. 1985. 4.95 (ISBN 0-88070-084-X). Multnomah.

Peter Calvay -- Hermit: A Personal Rediscovery of Prayer. Rayner Torkington. LC 80-13188. 107p. (Orig.). 1980. pap. 3.95 (ISBN 0-8189-0404-6). Alba.

Peter De Vries. J. H. Bowden. (United States Authors Ser.). 1983. lib. bdg. 16.95 (ISBN 0-8057-7388-6, Twayne). G K Hall.

Peter Escapes From Prison. Gordon Lindsay. (Acts in Action Ser.: Vol. 3). pap. 1.25 (ISBN 0-89985-964-X). Christ Nations.

Peter Fjellstedt: Missionary Mentor to Three Continents. Emmet E. Eklund. LC 83-71472. (Augustana Historical Society Publication Ser.: No. 30). 197p. 1983. 20.00x (ISBN 0-910184-30-5). Augustana.

Peter in the New Testament. Raymond E. Brown et al. LC 73-83787. 1973. 7.95 (ISBN 0-8066-1401-3, 10-4930). Augsburg.

Peter in the New Testament. Raymond E. Brown et al. LC 73-84424. (Orig.). 1973. pap. 5.95 (ISBN 0-8091-1790-8). Paulist Pr.

Peter Lombard & the Sacramental System. Elizabeth F. Rogers. 250p. 1976. Repr. of 1927 ed. lib. bdg. 19.50x (ISBN 0-915172-22-4). Richwood Pub.

Peter Martyr Vermigli & Italian Reform. Ed. by Joseph C. McLelland. 155p. 1980. text ed. 17.95x (ISBN 0-88920-092-0, Pub. by Wilfrid Laurier Canada). Humanities.

Peter, One & Two. Marilyn Kunz & Catherine Schell. (Neighnborhood Bible Studies). 1973. pap. 2.95 (ISBN 0-8423-4820-4). Tyndale.

Peter One, Estrangement & Community. John Elliot. (Herald Biblical). 1979. 1.25 (ISBN 0-8199-0728-6). Franciscan Herald.

Peter Parker & the Opening of China. Edward V. Gulick. LC 73-82628. (Harvard Studies in American-East Asian Relations: No. 3). 228p. 1974. text ed. 17.50x (ISBN 0-674-66326-8). Harvard U Pr.

Peter Sinks in the Water. Joyce Morse. (Books I Can Read). 32p. (Orig.). 1980. pap. 1.95 (ISBN 0-8127-0281-6). Review & Herald.

Peter, Speak for God. Charlotte Graeber. (Speak for Me Ser.). (Illus.). 24p. 1986. 3.95 (ISBN 0-8407-6701-3). Nelson.

Peter Spier's Little Bible Storybooks. Peter Seymour. (Illus.). 1983. 7.95 (ISBN 0-385-19061-1). Doubleday.

Peter, Stephen, James & John: Studies in Non-Pauline Christianity. F. F. Bruce. (Orig.). 1980. 8.95 (ISBN 0-8028-3532-5). Eerdmans.

Peter the Great. Nina B. Baker. (Illus.). 310p. 1943. 10.95 (ISBN 0-8149-0263-4). Vanguard.

Peter the Great: A Life of Peter I of Russia. Stephen Graham. LC 75-138241. (Illus.). 1971. Repr. of 1950 ed. lib. bdg. 39.75x (ISBN 0-8371-5598-3, GRPG). Greenwood.

Peter: The Prince of Apostles. Muriel Blackwell. (BibLearn Ser.). (Illus.). 5.95 (ISBN 0-8054-4227-8, 4242-27). Broadman.

Peter the Rock: Extraordinary Lessons from an Ordinary Man. David Gill. LC 86-7383. 192p. (Orig.). 1986. pap. 6.95 (ISBN 0-87784-609-X). Inter-Varsity.

Peter Tudebode: Historia De Hierosolymitano Itinere. John H. Hill & Laurita L. Hill. LC 74-78091. (Memoirs Ser.: Vol. 101). 1974. 6.50 (ISBN 0-87169-101-9). Am Philos.

Peterborough Psalter in Brussells & Other Fenland Manuscripts. Lucy F. Sandler. (Illus.). 1974. 49.00x (ISBN 0-19-921005-5). Oxford U Pr.

Peter's Kingdom: Inside the Papal City. Jerrold M. Packard. (Illus.). 352p. 1985. 17.95 (ISBN 0-684-18430-3, ScribT). Scribner.

Peter's Portrait of Jesus. J. B. Phillips. (Festival Ser.). 192p. 1981. pap. 1.95 (ISBN 0-687-30850-X). Abingdon.

Petition Against God: The Full Story Behind RM-2493. A. W. Allworthy. LC 75-43375. (Illus.). 150p. 1976. pap. 3.95 (ISBN 0-686-16824-0, Pub. by Christ the Light). Mho & Mho.

Petri Pictaviensis Allegoriae Super Tabernaculum Moysi. Ed. by James A. Corbett & Philip S. Moore. (Mediaeval Studies Ser.: No. 3). 1938. 17.95 (ISBN 0-268-00207-X). U of Notre Dame Pr.

Petri Riage Biblia Versificato: Petri Rigue Biblia Versificato, a Verse Commentary on the Bible, 2 vols. Paul E. Beichner. (Mediaeval Studies Ser.: No. 19). 1965. 50.00 set (ISBN 0-268-00016-6). U of Notre Dame Pr.

Petrine Controversies in Early Christianity: Attitudes Towards Peter in Christian Writings for the First Two Centuries. Terrence V. Smith. 259p. (Orig.). 1985. pap. 52.50x (ISBN 3-16-144876-6, Pub. by J C B Mohr BRD). Coronet Bks.

Petrograd Codex of the Hebrew Bible: The Latter Prophets, Prophetarum Posteriorum. rev. ed. Hermann L. Strack. (Library of Biblical Studies Ser). 1970. 50.00x (ISBN 0-87068-111-7). Ktav.

Petrus Thomae, O. F. M. Quodlibet. Ed. by Sr. M. Rachel Hooper & Eligius M. Buytaert. (Text Ser). 1957. 10.00 (ISBN 0-686-11556-2). Franciscan Inst.

Pets, People, Plagues. Allan Magie. LC 79-19321. (Better Living Ser.). 1979. pap. 0.99 (ISBN 0-8127-0233-6). Review & Herald.

Pew for One, Please. William Lyon. LC 76-41976. 1977. 6.95 (ISBN 0-8164-0374-0, HarpR). Har-Row.

Peyote Cult. 4th ed. Weston LaBarre. LC 75-19425. (Illus.). xix, 296p. 1975. 27.50 (ISBN 0-208-01456-X, Archon). Shoe String.

Peyote Hunt: The Sacred Journey of the Huichol Indians. Barbara G. Myerhoff. LC 73-16923. (Symbol, Myth & Ritual Ser.). (Illus.). 288p. 1976. pap. 9.95x (ISBN 0-8014-9137-1). Cornell U Pr.

Peyote Music. David P. McAllester. pap. 19.00 (ISBN 0-384-36490-X). Johnson Repr.

Peyote Religion among the Navaho. 2nd ed. David F. Aberle. LC 82-2562. (Illus.). 454p. 1982. lib. bdg. 35.00x (ISBN 0-226-00082-6); pap. text ed. 15.00x (ISBN 0-226-00083-4). U of Chicago Pr.

Peyote: The Divine Cactus. Edward F. Anderson. LC 79-20173. 248p. 1980. pap. 9.95 (ISBN 0-8165-0613-2). U of Ariz Pr.

Peyotism in the West: A Historical & Cultural Perspective. Ed. by Omer C. Stewart. (Anthropological Papers: No. 108). (Illus.). 168p. (Orig.). 1984. pap. 17.50x (ISBN 0-87480-235-0). U of Utah Pr.

Phaedo. Plato. Tr. by F. J. Church. LC 51-10496. 1951. pap. 4.24 scp (ISBN 0-672-60192-3, LLA30). Bobbs.

Phaedo. Plato. Tr. by G. M. Grube. LC 76-49565. 72p. 1977. pap. 2.50 (ISBN 0-915144-18-2). Hackett Pub.

Phallism in Ancient Worships: Ancient Symbol Worship. 2nd ed. Hodder M. Westropp & Wake C. Staniland. (Illus.). 111p. pap. 8.95 (ISBN 0-88697-017-2). Life Science.

Phallos: A Symbol & Its History in the Male World. Thorkil Vanggaard. LC 72-80553. (Illus.). 266p. 1972. text ed. 22.50 (ISBN 0-8236-4135-X); pap. text ed. 17.95 (ISBN 0-8236-8192-0, 24135). Intl Univs Pr.

Phantom Church. Arlon Stubbe. 1986. 7.95 (ISBN 0-89536-802-1, 6820). CSS of Ohio.

Pharaoh's Counsellors: Job, Jethro, & Balaam in Rabbinic & Patristic Tradition. Judith R. Baskin. LC 83-11535. (Brown Judaic Studies). 200p. 1983. pap. 18.00 (ISBN 0-89130-637-4, 14 00 47). Scholars Pr GA.

Pharisaic Judaism in Transition. Ben Z. Bokser. LC 73-2189. (Jewish People; History, Religion, Literature Ser.). Repr. of 1935 ed. 18.00 (ISBN 0-405-05255-3). Ayer Co Pubs.

Pharisaism & Jesus. Samuel Umen. LC 62-20875. 1962. 5.00 (ISBN 0-8022-1752-4). Philos Lib.

Pharisee Among Philistines: The Diary of Judge Matthew P. Deady, 1871-1892, 2 vols. Matthew P. Deady. Intro. by Malcolm Clark, Jr. LC 74-75363. (Illus.). 702p. 1975. 27.95 (ISBN 0-87595-046-9); deluxe ed. 30.00 (ISBN 0-686-96825-5); pap. 19.95 (ISBN 0-87595-080-9). Oregon Hist.

Pharisee & the Publican. John Bunyan. pap. 3.95 (ISBN 0-685-19840-5). Reiner.

Pharisees' Guide To Total Holiness. William Coleman. LC 82-4551. 147p. 1982. 8.95 (ISBN 0-87123-473-4, 210473); pap. 4.95 (ISBN 0-87123-472-6, 210472). Bethany Hse.

Pharisees: Rabbinic Perspectives. Jacob Neusner. LC 85-5783. (Studies in Ancient Judaism). 300p. (Orig.). 1985. pap. text ed. 19.95x (ISBN 0-88125-067-8). Ktav.

Phases in the Religion of Ancient Rome. Cyril Bailey. LC 75-114460. 340p. 1972. Repr. of 1932 ed. lib. bdg. 22.50x (ISBN 0-8371-4759-X, BARA). Greenwood.

Phases of American Culture. facs. ed. Jesuit Philosophical Association Of The Eastern States. LC 69-17579. (Essay Index Reprint Ser). 1942. 14.00 (ISBN 0-8369-0021-9). Ayer Co Pubs.

Phenomena of Life. Ed. by Mystic Jhamom Staff. (Conversations with a Mystic Ser.: No. 4). (Illus.). 1986. pap. write for info. (ISBN 0-933961-09-X). Mystic Jhamom.

Phenomena of Life Illustrations Booklet: Supplement. Ed. by Mystic Jhamom Staff. (Conversations with a Mystic Ser.: No. 4). (Illus.). 24p. 1986. pap. write for info. (ISBN 0-933961-10-3). Mystic Jhamom.

Phenomene Humain. Pierre Teilhard De Chardin. (Coll. Points). 1955. pap. 6.25 (ISBN 0-685-11491-0). French & Eur.

Phenomene Humain. Pierre Teilhard De Chardin. 15.95 (ISBN 0-685-36581-6). French & Eur.

Phenomenological Transformation of the Social Scientific Study of Religion. Anthony J. Blasi. LC 85-13303. (American University Studies VII: Theology & Religion: Vol. 10). 195p. 1985. text ed. 27.85 (ISBN 0-8204-0235-4). P Lang Pubs.

Phenomenology & Religion: Structures of the Christian Institution. Henry Dumery. Tr. by Paul Barrett. LC 73-94443. (Hermeneutics Series: Studies in the History of Religion). 1975. 27.50x (ISBN 0-520-02714-0). U of Cal Pr.

Phenomenology of Moral Experience. Maurice Mandelbaum. 336p. 1969. pap. 8.95x (ISBN 0-8018-1095-7). Johns Hopkins.

Phenomenon of Man. Pierre Teilhard De Chardin. pap. 7.95 (ISBN 0-06-090495-X, CN495, PL). Har-Row.

Phenomenon of Man Revisited: A Biological Viewpoint on Teilhard de Chardin. E. O. Dodson. LC 83-20959. (Illus.). 288p. 1984. 26.50x (ISBN 0-231-05850-0). Columbia U Pr.

Phenomenon of Pentecost. Frank J. Ewart. 208p. (Orig.). 1947. pap. 4.95 (ISBN 0-912315-32-6). Word Aflame.

Philadelphia Church. 27p. (Orig.). pap. 0.95 (ISBN 0-937408-19-0). GMI Pubns Inc.

Philadelphia Quakers in the Industrial Age, 1865-1920. Philip S. Benjamin. LC 75-22967. 309p. 1976. 19.95 (ISBN 0-87722-086-7). Temple U Pr.

Philanthropy of God: Described & Illustrated in a Series of Sermons. Hugh P. Hughes. 1978. Repr. of 1892 ed. lib. bdg. 12.50 (ISBN 0-8482-4402-8). Norwood Edns.

Philemon. G. Michael Cocoris. 22p. (Orig.). 1985. pap. 1.00 (ISBN 0-935729-08-9). Church Open Door.

Philemon: Timothy, Titus. H. A. Ironside. 9.95 (ISBN 0-87213-391-5). Loizeaux.

Philemon's Problem: The Daily Dilemma of the Christian. James T. Burtchaell. LC 73-88935. 1973. pap. 2.95 (ISBN 0-914070-05-3). ACTA Found.

Philip Melanchthon, the Protestant Preceptor of Germany. James W. Richard. LC 72-82414. 1974. Repr. of 1898 ed. lib. bdg. 25.50 (ISBN 0-8337-4341-4). B Franklin.

Philip of Spain & the Netherlands: An Essay on Moral Judgments in History. Cecil J. Cadoux. LC 69-15788. xv, 251p. 1969. Repr. of 1947 ed. 27.50 (ISBN 0-208-00735-0, Archon). Shoe String.

Philip Schaff: Christian Scholar & Ecumenical Prophet. George H. Shriver. xii, 136p. 1987. 19.95 (ISBN 0-86554-234-1). Mercer Univ Pr.

Philip the Fair & Boniface VIII: State vs. Papacy. C. T. Wood. LC 76-23207. (European Problem Ser.). 124p. 1976. pap. 5.95 (ISBN 0-88275-454-8). Krieger.

Philippian Fragment. Calvin Miller. LC 82-15. (Illus.). 175p. 1982. pap. 5.95 (ISBN 0-87784-805-X). Inter-Varsity.

Philippians. Don Baker. (Lifebuilder Bible Studies). 60p. (Orig.). 1985. pap. text ed. 2.95 (ISBN 0-8308-1013-7). Inter-Varsity.

Philippians. Irving L. Jensen. (Bible Self-Study Ser.). 80p. 1973. pap. 3.25 (ISBN 0-8024-1051-0). Moody.

Philippians. Roy L. Laurin. 208p. 1987. pap. 8.95 (ISBN 0-8254-3134-4). Kregel.

Philippians. Handley Moule. 1975. pap. 4.95 (ISBN 0-87508-364-1). Chr Lit.

Philippians. (Erdmans Commentaries Ser.). 3.95 (ISBN 0-8010-3404-3). Baker Bk.

Philippians. Geoffrey B. Wilson. 109p. (Orig.). 1983. pap. 4.95 (ISBN 0-85151-363-8). Banner of Truth.

Philippians: A Bible Study Commentary. Howard F. Vos. (Study Guide Commentary Ser.). 96p. (Orig.). 1980. pap. 3.95 (ISBN 0-310-33863-8, 10967P). Zondervan.

Philippians: A Good News Commentary. F. F. Bruce. LC 82-48919. 176p. (Orig.). 1983. pap. 7.95 (ISBN 0-06-061138-3, RD/446, HarpR). Har-Row.

Philippians: A Study Guide. Roger Van Horn. (Revelation Series for Adults). 1983. pap. text ed. 2.50 (ISBN 0-933140-84-3). CRC Pubns.

Philippians: A Translation with Notes. R. Paul Caudill. LC 80-70403. (Orig.). 1981. pap. 2.25 (ISBN 0-938980-00-9). Blue Ridge.

Philippians: An Expositional Commentary. James M. Boice. 320p. 1982. pap. 10.95 (ISBN 0-310-21501-3, 10310). Zondervan.

Philippians & Colossians. Marilyn Kunz & Catherine Schell. (Neighborhood Bible Studies). 1974. pap. 2.95 (ISBN 0-8423-4825-5). Tyndale.

Philippians & Philemon. Mary A. Getty. (New Testament Message Ser.: Vol. 14). 10.95 (ISBN 0-89453-202-2); pap. 5.95 (ISBN 0-89453-137-9). M Glazier.

Philippians & Thessalonians. Kenneth Grayston. (Cambridge Bible Commentary on the New English Bible, New Testament Ser.). 1967. 16.95 (ISBN 0-521-04224-0); pap. 8.95 (ISBN 0-521-09409-7, 409). Cambridge U Pr.

Philippians, Colossians, & Philemon. William Hendriksen. (New Testament Commentary). 243p. 1979. 17.95 (ISBN 0-8010-4212-7). Baker Bk.

Philippians, Colossians, Philemon. Wilbur Fields. LC 78-8763. (Bible Study Textbook Ser.). (Illus.). 1969. 10.60 (ISBN 0-89900-041-X). College Pr Pub.

Philippians, Colossians, Thessalonians. H. A. Ironside. 433p. 11.95 (ISBN 0-87213-398-2). Loizeaux.

Philippians: Interpretation: A Bible Commentary for Teaching & Preaching. Fred Craddock. Ed. by James L. Mays & Patrick D. Miller. LC 84-47797. 96p. 1984. 12.95 (ISBN 0-8042-3140-0). John Knox.

Philippians: Joy & Peace. John F. Walvoord. (Everyman's Bible Commentary). 1971. pap. 5.95 (ISBN 0-8024-2050-8). Moody.

Philippians: Joy in the Lord. Ed. by Gary Wilde. (Basic Bible Ser.). 96p. 1986. pap. 4.95 (ISBN 0-89191-482-X). Cook.

Philippians: Living Joyfully. Ron Klug. (Young Fisherman Bible Studyguide Ser.). (Illus.). 64p. 1983. tchr's ed. 4.95 (ISBN 0-87788-682-2); saddle-stitched student's ed. 2.95 (ISBN 0-87788-681-4). Shaw Pubs.

Philippians: Our High Calling. Richard A. Hufton. LC 85-70134. 116p. (Orig.). 1985. pap. 4.00 (ISBN 0-933643-01-2). Grace World Outreach.

Philippians: Studies. Lehman Strauss. 1959. 7.50 (ISBN 0-87213-823-2). Loizeaux.

Philippians, The Epistle of Christian Joy. Keith L. Brooks. (Teach Yourself the Bible Ser.). 1964. pap. 2.75 (ISBN 0-8024-6506-4). Moody.

Philippians: The Joyful Life. William W. Menzies. LC 81-80302. (Radiant Life Ser.). 128p. (Orig.). 1981. pap. 2.50 (ISBN 0-88243-880-8, 02-0880); tchr's ed. 3.95 (ISBN 0-88243-191-9, 32-0191). Gospel Pub.

Philippians: Twenty-Six Daily Bible Studies. David Jeremiah. (Steps to Higher Ground Ser.). 1983. pap. 1.95 (ISBN 0-86508-208-1). BCM Intl Inc.

Philippine Pagans: The Autobiographies of Three Ifugaos. Roy F. Barton. LC 76-44686. Repr. of 1938 ed. 30.00 (ISBN 0-404-15903-6). AMS Pr.

Philip's Cousin Jesus: The Untold Story. Fenwicke Holmes & Margaret McEathron. LC 81-65247. 425p. 1982. pap. 9.95. Reading Hse.

Philistines & the Old Testament. Edward E. Hindson. (Baker Studies in Biblical Archaeology). pap. 6.95 (ISBN 0-8010-4034-5). Baker Bk.

Phillip Brooks: The Man, the Preacher, & the Author. Newell Dunbar. 1978. Repr. of 1893 ed. lib. bdg. 35.00 (ISBN 0-8492-0668-5). R West.

Philo & the Oral Law: The Philonic Interpretation of Biblical Law. Samuel Belkin. (Harvard Semitic Ser.: Vol. 11). Repr. of 1940 ed. 25.00 (ISBN 0-384-03795-X). Johnson Repr.

Philo: Foundations of Religious Philosophy in Judaism, Christianity & Islam, 2 vols. rev. ed. Harry A. Wolfson. LC 47-30635. 1962. Set. 55.00x (ISBN 0-674-66450-7). Harvard U Pr.

Philo of Alexandria: An Introduction. Samuel Sandmel. 1979. pap. 9.95 (ISBN 0-19-502515-6). Oxford U Pr.

Philo of Alexandria: The Contemplative Life, Giants & Selections. Tr. by David Winston. LC 80-84499. (Classics of Western Spirituality Ser.). 448p. 13.95 (ISBN 0-8091-0315-X); pap. 9.95 (ISBN 0-8091-2333-9). Paulist Pr.

Philokalia, Vol. 3. Tr. by Philip Sherrard & Kallistos Ware. LC 82-202671. 432p. 1984. 29.95 (ISBN 0-571-11726-0). Faber & Faber.

Philokalia, Vol. 1: The Complete Text Compiled By St. Nikodimos of the Holy Mountain & St. Markarios of Corinth, Vol. 1. Tr. by G. E. Palmer & Philip Sherrard. 384p. 1983. pap. 10.95 (ISBN 0-571-13013-5). Faber & Faber.

Philokalia, Vol. 2: The Complete Text. Ed. by G. E. Palmer et al. 408p. 1981. 30.00 (ISBN 0-571-11725-2). Faber & Faber.

Philonis Alexandrini in Flaccum. Philo. Ed. by W. R. Connor. LC 78-18570. (Greek Texts & Commentaries Ser.). 1979. Repr. of 1939 ed. lib. bdg. 17.00x (ISBN 0-405-11414-1). Ayer Co Pubs.

Philosophers of Greece. Robert S. Brumbaugh. LC 81-9120. (Illus.). 274p. 1981. 34.50x (ISBN 0-87395-550-1); pap. 8.95x (ISBN 0-87395-551-X). State U NY Pr.

Philosopher's Search for the Infinite. Jules M. Brady. 96p. 1983. 10.00 (ISBN 0-8022-2410-5). Philos Lib.

Philosophers Speak of God. Charles Hartshorne & William L. Reese. LC 53-10041. (Midway Reprint Ser.). 1976. 24.00x (ISBN 0-226-31862-1). U of Chicago Pr.

Philosophia Perennis, Vol. 1. Bhagwan Shree Rajneesh. Ed. by Ma Yoga Anurag. (Western Mystics Ser.). (Illus.). 392p. (Orig.). 1981. 19.95 (ISBN 0-88050-115-4); pap. 15.95 428p (ISBN 0-88050-615-6). Chidvilas Found.

Philosophia Perennis, Vol. 2. Bhagwan Shree Rajneesh. Ed. by Ma Yoga Anurag. (Western Mystics Ser.). (Illus.). 436p. (Orig.). 1981. pap. 15.95 (ISBN 0-88050-616-4). Chidvilas Found.

Philosophia Ultima. Bhagwan Shree Rajneesh. Ed. by Ma Yoga Anurag. LC 83-43216. (Upanishads Ser.). 384p. (Orig.). 1983. pap. 4.95 (ISBN 0-88050-617-2). Chidvilas Found.

Philosophical Assessment of Theology: Essays in Honor of F. C. Copleston. Ed. by Gerard J. Hughes. (Orig.). 1987. pap. price not set (ISBN 0-87840-449-X). Georgetown U Pr.

Philosophical Bases of Theism. George D. Hicks. LC 77-27142. (Hibbert Lectures: 1931). Repr. of 1937 ed. 31.00 (ISBN 0-404-60427-7). AMS Pr.

Philosophical Essays: Discourse on Method; Meditations; Rules for the Direction of the Mind. Rene Descartes. Tr. by Laurence J. Lafleur. LC 63-16951. (Orig.). 1964. pap. 7.87 scp (ISBN 0-672-60292-X, LLA99). Bobbs.

Philosophical Essence of Islam. Mohamed. (Essential Library of the Great Philosophies). (Illus.). 143p. 1985. 117.50 (ISBN 0-317-19583-2). Am Inst Psych.

Philosophical Foundations of Faith. Marion J. Bradshaw. LC 78-99248. Repr. of 1941 ed. 10.00 (ISBN 0-404-00968-9). AMS Pr.

Philosophical Foundations of Mormon Theology. Sterling M. McMurrin. 1959. pap. 4.95 (ISBN 0-87480-169-9). U of Utah Pr.

Philosophical Fragments, or a Fragment of Philosophy-Johannes Climacus, or De Omnibus Dubitandum Est, 2 bks. in 1 vol. Soren Kierkegaard. Ed. by Howard V. Hong & Edna H. Hong. LC 85-3420. (No. VII). 386p. 1985. text ed. 35.00x (ISBN 0-691-07273-6); pap. 7.95x (ISBN 0-691-02036-1). Princeton U Pr.

Philosophical Frontiers of Christian Theology: Essays Presented to D. M. Mackinnon. Ed. by Brian L. Hebblethwaite. Stewart Sutherland. LC 81-10132. (Illus.). 230p. 1982. 29.50 (ISBN 0-521-24012-3). Cambridge U Pr.

Philosophical Ideas of Swami Abhenananda: A Critical Study (A Guide to the Complete Works of Swami Abhedananda) Swami Prajnananda. (Illus.). 7.95 (ISBN 0-87481-623-8). Vedanta Pr.

Philosophical Interpretation of History. A. H. Siddiqui. 14.95 (ISBN 0-686-83884-X). Kazi Pubns.

Philosophical Radicals & Other Essays. Andrew Seth Pringle Pattison. 1907. 23.50 (ISBN 0-8337-4388-0). B Franklin.

Philosophical Studies by Heinrich Gomperz. Heinrich Gomperz. Ed. by Daniel S. Robinson. 1953. 9.50 (ISBN 0-8158-0100-9). Chris Mass.

Philosophical Study of the Mysticism of Sankara. G. Sundara Ramaiah. 1983. 12.00x (ISBN 0-686-88924-X, Pub. by KP Bagchi India). South Asia Bks.

Philosophical Teachings in the Upanisats. Mohan L. Sandal. LC 73-3831. (Sacred Books of the Hindus: Extra Vol. 5). Repr. of 1926 ed. 17.00 (ISBN 0-404-57849-7). AMS Pr.

Philosophical Terms in the Moreh Nebukim. Israel I. Efros. LC 73-164764. (Columbia University. Oriental Studies: No. 22). Repr. of 1924 ed. 17.00 (ISBN 0-404-50512-0). AMS Pr.

Philosophical Theology. James F. Ross. 366p. 1982. 15.50 (ISBN 0-8290-0335-5). Irvington.

Philosophical Theology. James F. Ross. 366p. 1982. pap. 7.95 (ISBN 0-8290-1764-X). Irvington.

Philosophical Understanding & Religious Truth. Erich Frank. LC 82-8476. 220p. 1982. pap. text ed. 11.75 (ISBN 0-8191-2510-5). U Pr of Amer.

Philosophical Works, 5 vols. Henry Viscount Bolingbroke. Ed. by Rene Wellek. LC 75-11198. (British Philosophers & Theologians of the 17th & 18th Centuries: Vol. 5). 1976. Repr. of 1777 ed. Set. lib. bdg. 231.00 (ISBN 0-8240-1754-4); lib. bdg. 254.00. Garland Pub.

Philosophical Works, 2 Vols. Rene Descartes. Ed. by E. S. Haldane & G. R. Ross. 1967. Vol. 2. 57.50 (ISBN 0-521-06944-0); Vol. 1. pap. 14.95 (ISBN 0-521-09416-X); Vol. 2. pap. 14.95 (ISBN 0-521-09417-8). Cambridge U Pr.

Philosophical Writings. George Berkeley. Ed. by T. E. Jessop. LC 69-13823. Repr. of 1953 ed. lib. bdg. 22.50x (ISBN 0-8371-1056-4, BEPW). Greenwood.

Philosophical Writings. Rene Descartes. Ed. by Elizabeth Anscombe & Peter T. Geach. Tr. by Elizabeth Anscombe & Peter T. Geach. LC 79-171798. 1971. pap. 7.20 scp (ISBN 0-672-61274-7, LLA198). Bobbs.

Philosophie De Jacob Boehme. Alexandre Koyre. 1929. 32.00 (ISBN 0-8337-1953-X). B Franklin.

Philosophie und Mythos. Hans Poser. 1979. text ed. 35.20x (ISBN 3-11-007601-2). De Gruyter.

Philosophies & Religions of India. Yogi Ramacharaka. 8.00 (ISBN 0-911662-05-7). Yoga.

Philosophies of Judaism: The History of Jewish Philosophy from Biblical Times to Franz Rosenzweig. Julius Guttman. LC 63-11875. 560p. 1973. pap. 13.50 (ISBN 0-8052-0402-4). Schocken.

Philosophische Theologie im Schatten des Nihilismus. Wilhelm Weischedel et al. Ed. by Joerg Salaquarda. (Ger). 1971. pap. 9.60x (ISBN 3-11-001604-4). De Gruyter.

Philosophy: An Orthodox Christian Understanding. Apostolos Makrakis. Ed. by Orthodox Christian Educational Society. Tr. by Denver Cummings from Hellenic. (Logos & Holy Spirit in the Unity of Christian Thought Ser.: Vol. 5). 279p. 1977. pap. 5.50x (ISBN 0-938366-02-5). Orthodox Chr.

Philosophy & Atheism. Kai Nielsen. (Skeptic's Bookshelf Ser.). 231p. 1985. 20.95 (ISBN 0-87975-289-0). Prometheus Bks.

Philosophy & Christian Theology. Ed. by George F. McLean & Jude P. Dougherty. (Proceedings of the American Catholic Philosophical Association: Vol. 44). 1970. pap. 15.00 (ISBN 0-918090-04-0). Am Cath Philo.

Philosophy & Development of Religion, 2 vols. Otto Pfleiderer. LC 77-27229. (Gifford Lectures: 1894). Repr. of 1894 ed. Set. 65.00 (ISBN 0-404-60470-6). AMS Pr.

Philosophy & Education: An Introduction in Christian Perspective. George R. Knight. LC 81-117900. (Illus.). xii, 244p. 1980. pap. text ed. 10.95 (ISBN 0-943872-79-0). Andrews Univ Pr.

Philosophy & Humanism: Renaissance Essays in Honor of Paul Oskar Kristeller. Ed. by Edward P. Mahoney. LC 75-42285. 624p. 1976. 65.00 (ISBN 0-231-03904-2). Columbia U Pr.

Philosophy & Law: Essays Toward the Understanding of Maimonides His Predecessors. Leo Strauss. Tr. by Fred Baumann from Ger. Tr. of Philosophie und Gesetz. 120p. 1987. 18.95 (ISBN 0-8276-0273-1). Jewish Pubns.

Philosophy & Miracle: The Contemporary Debate. David Basinger & Randall Basinger. LC 86-12766. (Problems in Contemporary Philosophy Ser.: No. 2). 130p. 1986. 39.95 (ISBN 0-88946-327-1). E Mellen.

Philosophy & Mysticism. Ed. by Herbert Guerry. Dell.

Philosophy & Philosophical Authors of the Jews: A Historical Sketch with Explanatory Notes. S. Munk. Tr. by Isidor Kalisch. (Reprints in Philosophy Ser.). Repr. of 1881 ed. lib. bdg. 26.50 (ISBN 0-697-00012-5). Irvington.

Philosophy & Philosophical Authors of the Jews: A Historical Sketch With Explanatory Notes. S. Munk. Tr. by Isidor Kalisch. (Reprints in Philosophy Ser.). 1986. pap. text ed. 6.95x (ISBN 0-8290-1881-6). Irvington.

Philosophy & Practice of Yoga. Roy E. Davis. 192p. 1983. pap. 4.95 (ISBN 0-317-20862-4). CSA Pr.

Philosophy & Psychology in the Abhidharma. 2nd rev. ed. H. V. Guenther. 1974. 18.00 (ISBN 0-87773-048-2). Orient Bk Dist.

Philosophy & Religion in Colonial America. Claude M. Newlin. LC 68-23317. 1968. Repr. of 1962 ed. lib. bdg. cancelled (ISBN 0-8371-0184-0, NEPR). Greenwood.

Philosophy & Religion: Six Lectures Delivered at Cambridge. Hastings Rashdall. Repr. of 1910 ed. lib. bdg. 22.50x (ISBN 0-8371-3025-5, RAPR). Greenwood.

Philosophy & Religion: Some Contemporary Perspectives. Jerry H. Gill. LC 68-54894. pap. 95.50 (ISBN 0-317-08950-1, 2003459). Bks Demand UMI.

Philosophy & Religion: The Logic of Religious Belief. John Wilson. LC 78-14000. 1979. Repr. of 1961 ed. lib. bdg. 24.75x (ISBN 0-313-20738-0, WIPH). Greenwood.

Philosophy & the Christian Faith. Colin Brown. LC 68-58083. (Orig.). 1969. pap. 9.95 (ISBN 0-87784-712-6). Inter-Varsity.

Philosophy & the Experimental Sciences: Proceedings, Vol. 26. American Catholic Philosophical Association Staff. 1952. 18.00 (ISBN 0-384-46400-9). Johnson Repr.

Philosophy & Theology. James H. Stirling. LC 77-27233. (Gifford Lectures: 1890). 1978. Repr. of 1890 ed. 39.00 (ISBN 0-404-60451-X). AMS Pr.

Philosophy & Unified Science. George Talbot. 1435p. 1982. Repr. of 1978 ed. 36.50 (ISBN 0-941524-18-3). Lotus Light.

Philosophy As Metanoetics. Tanabe Hasime. 224p. 1987. text ed. 40.00 (ISBN 0-520-05490-3). U of Cal Pr.

Philosophy: Basic Judaism. (Home Study Program Ser.: No. 601). 5.00 (ISBN 0-686-96129-3). United Syn Bk.

Philosophy Beyond the Classroom. Vergilius Ferm. 411p. 1974. 12.95 (ISBN 0-8158-0314-1). Chris Mass.

Philosophy, Cosmology & Religion: Ten Lectures. Rudolf Steiner. Ed. by Stewart C. Easton et al. 180p. (Orig.). 1984. 16.00 (ISBN 0-88010-109-1); pap. 9.95 (ISBN 0-88010-110-5). Anthroposophic.

Philosophy East-Philosophy West: A Critical Comparison of Indian, Chinese, Islamic & European Philosophy. Ed. by Ben-Ami Scharfstein. 1978. 25.00x (ISBN 0-19-520064-0). Oxford U Pr.

Philosophy for Understanding Theology. Diogenes Allen. LC 84-48510. 252p. 1985. pap. 14.95 (ISBN 0-8042-0688-0). John Knox.

Philosophy in Literature: Metaphysical Darkness & Ethical Light. Konstantin Kolenda. LC 81-7979. 250p. 1982. 28.75x (ISBN 0-389-20224-X). B&N Imports.

Philosophy in the Middle Ages: The Christian, Islamic & Jewish Traditions. 2nd ed. Ed. by Arthur Hyman & James J. Walsh. LC 82-23337. 816p. (Orig.). 1983. lib. bdg. 30.00 (ISBN 0-915145-81-2); pap. text ed. 15.00x (ISBN 0-915145-80-4). Hackett Pub.

Philosophy of Bhedabheda. P. N. Srinivasachari. 6.95 (ISBN 0-8356-7253-0). Theos Pub Hse.

Philosophy of Buddhism: A "Totalistic" Synthesis. A. Verdu. 264p. 1981. 34.50 (ISBN 90-247-2224-1, Pub. by Martinus Nijhoff Netherlands). Kluwer Academic.

Philosophy of Christ. D. Rayford Bell. LC 80-67408. 104p. 1980. 6.95 (ISBN 0-9604820-0-8); pap. 4.95 (ISBN 0-9604820-1-6). D R Bell.

Philosophy of Christian Education. Pierre J. Marique. Repr. of 1939 ed. lib. bdg. 22.50x (ISBN 0-8371-4271-7, MAED). Greenwood.

Philosophy of Church Music. Robert Berglund. (Orig.). 1985. pap. 9.95 (ISBN 0-8024-0279-8). Moody.

Philosophy of Conduct: A Treatise of the Facts, Principles, & Ideals of Ethics. George T. Ladd. LC 75-3222. Repr. of 1902 ed. 46.50 (ISBN 0-404-59218-X). AMS Pr.

Philosophy of Existence: Introduction to Weltanschauugslehre. Wilthelm Dilthey. LC 78-5673. 1978. Repr. of 1957 ed. lib. bdg. 22.50x (ISBN 0-313-20460-8, DIPH). Greenwood.

Philosophy of Faqirs. Ahmed Hussain. 126p. (Orig.). 1981. pap. 5.25 (ISBN 0-88004-006-8). Sunwise Turn.

Philosophy of Freedom. Rudolf Steiner. Tr. by Michael Wilson from Ger. 226p. 1973. pap. 7.95 (ISBN 0-910142-52-1). Anthroposophic.

Philosophy of Good Life. Charles Gore. 1963. Repr. of 1935 ed. 12.95x (ISBN 0-460-00924-9, Evman). Biblio Dist.

Philosophy of Hatha Yoga. 2nd ed. Pandit U. Arya. 95p. pap. 5.95 (ISBN 0-89389-088-X). Himalayan Pubs.

Philosophy of Hope. C. C. Brown. 1972. 2.95 (ISBN 0-9600378-0-2); pap. 2.00 (ISBN 0-9600378-3-7). C C Brown Pub.

Philosophy of Human Nature. Chu Hsi. 1976. lib. bdg. 59.95 (ISBN 0-8490-2432-3). Gordon Pr.

Philosophy of Humanism. 6th ed. Corliss Lamont. LC 81-70127. 340p. 1982. 15.95 (ISBN 0-8044-5997-5); pap. 9.95 (ISBN 0-8044-6379-4). Ungar.

Philosophy of Humanism. 5th ed. Corliss Lamont. LC 65-16612. 10.50 (ISBN 0-8044-5595-3); pap. 10.95 (ISBN 0-8044-6378-6). Ungar.

Philosophy of Immortality. R. Swinburne Clymer. 208p. 1960. 6.95 (ISBN 0-932785-39-5). Philos Pub.

Philosophy of Indian Monotheism. M. Christanand. 1979. 12.00x (ISBN 0-8364-0558-7, Pub. by Macmillan India). South Asia Bks.

Philosophy of J. Krishnamurti: A Systematic Study. R. K. Shringy. LC 78-670076. 1977. 24.00x (ISBN 0-89684-442-0). Orient Bk Dist.

Philosophy of Jacques Maritain. Charles A. Fecher. LC 70-90705. Repr. of 1953 ed. lib. bdg. 22.50x (ISBN 0-8371-2287-2, FEJM). Greenwood.

Philosophy of Jesus. Ernest Holmes. Ed. by Willis Kinnear. 94p. 1973. pap. 4.50 (ISBN 0-911336-51-6). Sci of Mind.

Philosophy of Jesus: Real Love. Jules A. Delanghe. LC 72-96805. 1973. 4.95 (ISBN 0-8059-1821-3). Dorrance.

Philosophy of Justice Between God & Man. Benjamin P. Blood. LC 75-3056. Repr. of 1851 ed. 20.50 (ISBN 0-404-59054-3). AMS Pr.

Philosophy of Life & the Philosophy of Death: Considerations & Anticipations of the Future Universe & of Man's Existence in It. 2nd ed. (Illus.). 1977. 47.25 (ISBN 0-89266-058-9). Am Classical Coll Pr.

Philosophy of Life & the Philosophy of Death. C. M. Flumiani. 89p. 1987. pap. 8.50 (ISBN 0-86650-223-8). Gloucester Art.

Philosophy of Light: An Introductory Treatise. Floyd I. Lorbeer. 259p. 1981. pap. 15.00 (ISBN 0-89540-102-9, SB-102). Sun Pub.

Philosophy of Magic. large type ed. Eusebe Salverte. pap. 6.95 (ISBN 0-910122-41-5). Amherst Pr.

Philosophy of Martin Buber. Ed. by Paul A. Schilpp & Maurice Friedman. LC 65-14535. (Library of Living Philosophers: Vol. XII). 831p. 1967. 37.95 (ISBN 0-87548-129-9). Open Court.

Philosophy of Mental Healing. Leander E. Whipple. 234p. 1981. pap. 13.50 (ISBN 0-89540-110-X, SB-110). Sun Pub.

Philosophy of Mizvot. Gersion Appel. pap. 11.95x (ISBN 0-87068-250-4). Ktav.

Philosophy of Mulla Sadra Shirazi. Fazlur Rahman. LC 75-31693. 1976. 39.50x (ISBN 0-87395-300-2). State U NY Pr.

Philosophy of Mysticism, 2vols. in 1. Carl Du Prel. Tr. by C. C. Massey. LC 75-36838. (Occult Ser.). 1976. Repr. of 1889 ed. 51.00x (ISBN 0-405-07951-6). Ayer Co Pubs.

Philosophy of Mysticism, 2 vols. Carl Du Prel. 1977. lib. bdg. 250.00 (ISBN 0-8490-2434-X). Gordon Pr.

Philosophy of Pancharatra: An Advaitic Approach. S. R. Bhatt. 137p. pap. 4.25 (ISBN 0-89744-122-2, Pub. by Ganesh & Co. India). Auromere.

Philosophy of Paul Ricoeur: An Anthology of His Work. Ed. by Charles E. Reagan & David Stewart. LC 77-75444. 1978. pap. 11.95x (ISBN 0-8070-1517-2, BPA15, Pub. by Ariadne Bks). Beacon Pr.

Philosophy of Personalism: A Study in the Metaphysics of Religion. Albert C. Knudson. LC 27-21477. 1968. Repr. of 1927 ed. 26.00 (ISBN 0-527-51600-7). Kraus Repr.

Philosophy of Plotinus: The Gifford Lectures at St. Andrews, 1917-1918, 2 Vols. 3rd ed. William R. Inge. LC 68-8740. (Illus.). 1968. Repr. of 1929 ed. Set. lib. bdg. 67.50x (ISBN 0-8371-0113-1, INPP). Greenwood.

Philosophy of Religion. Christopher J. Bostrom. 1962. 42.50x (ISBN 0-685-69791-6). Elliots Bks.

Philosophy of Religion. Edgar S. Brightman. LC 72-95112. Repr. of 1940 ed. lib. bdg. 29.75x (ISBN 0-8371-2468-9, BRPR). Greenwood.

Philosophy of Religion. William H. Davis. LC 75-92048. (Way of Life Ser: No. 114). (Orig.). 1969. pap. 3.95 (ISBN 0-89112-114-5, Bibl Res Pr). Abilene Christ U.

Philosophy of Religion. C. Stephen Evans. LC 84-25198. (Contours of Christian Philosophy Ser.). 180p. (Orig.). 1985. pap. 6.95 (ISBN 0-87784-343-0). Inter-Varsity.

Philosophy of Religion. 3rd ed. John Hick. 160p. 1983. pap. write for info. (ISBN 0-13-663906-2). P-H.

Philosophy of Religion. H. Hoffding. 1977. lib. bdg. 59.95 (ISBN 0-8490-2435-8). Gordon Pr.

Philosophy of Religion. facsimile ed. Harald Hoffding. Tr. by B. E. Meyer from Ger. LC 71-152987. (Select Bibliographies Reprint Ser). Repr. of 1906 ed. 24.50 (ISBN 0-8369-5739-3). Ayer Co Pubs.

Philosophy of Religion. S. Kanal. 480p. 1984. text ed. 45.00x (ISBN 0-86590-272-0, Sterling Pubs India). Apt Bks.

Philosophy of Religion, 2 vols. George T. Ladd. LC 75-3225. 1976. Repr. of 1905 ed. 82.50 set (ISBN 0-404-59221-X). AMS Pr.

Philosophy of Religion. Ed. by Basil Mitchell. (Oxford Readings in Philosophy Ser). (Orig.). 1971. pap. text ed. 9.95x (ISBN 0-19-875018-8). Oxford U Pr.

Philosophy of Religion. Robert L. Patterson. LC 74-101130. 1970. 31.75 (ISBN 0-8223-0223-3). Duke.

Philosophy of Religion. Ninian Smart. 1979. pap. 7.95x (ISBN 0-19-520139-6). Oxford U Pr.

Philosophy of Religion. David E. Trueblood. LC 75-31446. 324p. 1976. Repr. of 1957 ed. lib. bdg. 29.25x (ISBN 0-8371-8514-9, TRPHR). Greenwood.

Philosophy of Religion. Elton Trueblood. (Twin Brooks Ser.). 1973. 12.95 (ISBN 0-8010-8813-5). Baker Bk.

Philosophy of Religion: A Book of Readings. 2nd ed. Ed. by George L. Abernethy & Thomas A. Langford. 1968. write for info. (ISBN 0-02-300150-X, 30015). Macmillan.

Philosophy of Religion: An Annotated Bibliography of Twentieth-Century Writings in English. William J. Wainwright. LC 77-83374. (Library of Humanities Reference Bks.: No. 111). lib. bdg. 83.00 (ISBN 0-8240-9849-8). Garland Pub.

Philosophy of Religion: An Anthology. Louis P. Pojman. Ed. by Ken King. (Orig.). 1986. write for info. (ISBN 0-534-06672-0). Wadsworth Pub.

Philosophy of Religion: An Approach to World Religions. A. R. Mohapatra. 208p. 1986. text ed. 27.50x (ISBN 81-207-0110-0, Pub. by Sterling Pubs India). Apt Bks.

Philosophy of Religion: An Introduction. William Rowe. 207p. 1985. pap. text ed. write for info. (ISBN 0-8221-0208-0). Wadsworth Pub.

Philosophy of Religion from the Standpoint of Protestant Theology. Heinrich E. Brunner. LC 78-14106. 1979. Repr. of 1937 ed. 20.35 (ISBN 0-88355-779-7). Hyperion Conn.

Philosophy of Religion: Lectures Written for the Elliott Lectureship at the Western Theological Seminary. Alexander T. Ormond. 195p. 1982. Repr. of 1922 ed. lib. bdg. 50.00 (ISBN 0-8495-4219-7). Arden Lib.

Philosophy of Religion on the Basis of Its History, 4 vols. in 2. O. Pfleiderer. Repr. of 1886 ed. Set. 72.00 (ISBN 0-527-03238-7). Kraus Repr.

Philosophy of Religion: Or, the Rational Grounds of Religious Belief. John Bascom. LC 75-3037. Repr. of 1876 ed. 57.50 (ISBN 0-404-59035-7). AMS Pr.

Philosophy of Religion: Selected Readings. Ed. by William L. Rowe & William J. Wainwright. 489p. 1973. pap. text ed. 16.95 (ISBN 0-15-570580-6, HC). HarBraceJ.

Philosophy of Revelation. Herman Bavinck. (Twin Brooks Ser.). 1980. pap. 7.95 (ISBN 0-8010-0767-4). Baker Bk.

Philosophy of Revelation: According to Karl Rahner. Richard J. Rolwing. LC 78-63067. 1978. pap. text ed. 8.50 (ISBN 0-8191-0609-7). U Pr of Amer.

Philosophy of Right. G. W. Hegel. Tr. by T. M. Knox. 1942. 37.50x (ISBN 0-19-824128-3); pap. 10.95x (ISBN 0-19-500276-8). Oxford U Pr.

Philosophy of Right & Wrong. Bernard Mayo. 176p. 1986. 22.95 (ISBN 0-7102-0851-0, 08510); pap. 12.95 (ISBN 0-7102-0859-6, 08596). Methuen Inc.

Philosophy of Robert Grosseteste. James McEvoy. 450p. 1986. pap. 19.95x (ISBN 0-19-824939-X). Oxford U Pr.

Philosophy of St. Bonaventure. Etienne Gilson. 1965. 7.50 (ISBN 0-8199-0526-7). Franciscan Herald.

Philosophy of St. Thomas Aquinas. facsimile ed. Etienne H. Gilson. Ed. by G. A. Elrington. Tr. by Edward Bullough from Fr. LC 70-157337. (Select Bibliographies Reprint Ser). Repr. of 1937 ed. 26.50 (ISBN 0-8369-5797-0). Ayer Co Pubs.

Philosophy of Schleiermacher: The Development of His Theory of Scientific & Religious Knowledge. Richard B. Brandt. LC 68-19265. 1968. Repr. of 1941 ed. lib. bdg. 27.00x (ISBN 0-8371-0027-5, BRPS). Greenwood.

Philosophy of Science. Del Ratzsch. Ed. by C. Stephen Evans. LC 86-178. (Contours of Christian Philosophy Ser.). 128p. (Orig.). 1986. pap. 6.95 (ISBN 0-87784-344-9). Inter-Varsity.

Philosophy of Science & Belief in God. 2nd rev. ed. Gordon H. Clark. 125p. pap. 5.95 (ISBN 0-940931-18-4). Trinity Found.

Philosophy of Sikh Religion. Wazir Singh. 127p. 1981. 13.95x (ISBN 0-940500-09-4, Pub. by Ess Ess Pubns India). Asia Bk Corp.

Philosophy of Sin. Oswald Chambers. 1961. pap. 2.25 (ISBN 0-87508-122-3). Chr Lit.

Philosophy of Spiritual Activity, Vol. 2. 2nd ed. Rudolf Steiner. LC 80-65627. (Spiritual Science Library). 304p. 1980. lib. bdg. 16.00 (ISBN 0-89345-030-8, Spiritual Sci Lib); pap. 9.50 (ISBN 0-89345-208-4). Garber Comm.

Philosophy of Symbolic Forms, Vol. 2, Mythical Thought. Ernst Cassirer. Tr. by Ralph Manheim. 1955. pap. 11.95x (ISBN 0-300-00038-3, Y147). Yale U Pr.

Philosophy of the Christian Religion. Edward J. Carnell. (Twin Brooks Ser.). 525p. 1981. pap. 10.95 (ISBN 0-8010-2464-1). Baker Bk.

Philosophy of the Church Fathers: Faith, Trinity, Incarnation. 3rd rev. ed. Harry A. Wolfson. LC 70-119077. 1970. 32.50x (ISBN 0-674-66551-1). Harvard U Pr.

Philosophy of the Enlightenment: The Burgess & the Enlightenment. Lucien Goldmann. Tr. by Henry Maas from Fr. 1973. 17.50x (ISBN 0-262-07060-X). MIT Pr.

Philosophy of the Good Life. Charles Gore. LC 77-27197. (Gifford Lectures: 1929-30). Repr. of 1930 ed. 24.00 (ISBN 0-404-60484-6). AMS Pr.

Philosophy of the I Ching. Carol K. Anthony. LC 81-69537. 160p. 1981. pap. 6.50 (ISBN 0-9603832-1-2). Anthony Pub Co.

Philosophy of the Inner Light. Michael Marsh. LC 76-50674. (Orig.). 1976. pap. 2.50x (ISBN 0-87574-209-2). Pendle-Hill.

Philosophy of the Kalam. Harry A. Wolfson. LC 74-78718. 864p. 1976. 40.00x (ISBN 0-674-66580-5). Harvard U Pr.

Philosophy of the Quran. H. G. Sarwar. 4.50 (ISBN 0-686-18604-4). Kazi Pubns.

Philosophy of the Qur'an. H. G. Sarwar. 1969. 7.25x (ISBN 0-87902-187-X). Orientalia.

Philosophy of the Religions of Ancient Greeks & Israelites. Ben Kimpel. LC 83-6512. 362p. (Orig.). 1983. lib. bdg. 30.00 (ISBN 0-8191-3225-X); pap. text ed. 15.50 (ISBN 0-8191-3226-8). U Pr of Amer.

Philosophy of the Second Advent. Howard Redmond. Ed. by Leonard G. Goss. 160p. 1985. write for info. (ISBN 0-88062-070-6); pap. write for info. (ISBN 0-88062-067-6). Mott Media.

Philosophy of the Second Advent. Howard A. Redmond. 1986. text ed. 12.95 (ISBN 0-8010-7740-0). Baker Bk.

Philosophy of the Self. Ghanshamdas R. Malkani. 15.00 (ISBN 0-384-35112-3); pap. 10.00 (ISBN 0-685-13549-7). Johnson Repr.

Philosophy of the Upanishads. Paul Deussen. Tr. by A. S. Geden. (Orig.). 1966. pap. 8.50 (ISBN 0-486-21616-0). Dover.

Philosophy of the Upanishads. Edward Gough. 268p. 1979. Repr. of 1882 ed. 19.95 (ISBN 0-89684-158-8). Orient Bk Dist.

Philosophy of Theism. Alexander C. Fraser. LC 77-27228. (Gifford Lectures: 1894-95). Repr. of 1895 ed. 24.50 (ISBN 0-404-60453-6). AMS Pr.

Philosophy of Theism: Second Series. Alexander C. Fraser. LC 77-27227. (Gifford Lectures: 1895-96). Repr. of 1896 ed. 30.00 (ISBN 0-404-60454-4). AMS Pr.

Philosophy of Upanishads. B. Singh. 160p. 1983. text ed. 10.50x (ISBN 0-391-02935-5). Humanities.

Philosophy of Vaisnava Religion. G. N. Mallik. 59.95 (ISBN 0-8490-0829-8). Gordon Pr.

Philosophy of Worship in Islam. F. R. Ansari. pap. 1.00 (ISBN 0-686-18603-6). Kazi Pubns.

Philosophy, Psychology & Mysticism. Inayat Khan. (Sufi Message of Hazrat Inayat Khan Ser.: Vol. 11). 256p. 1979. 14.95 (ISBN 90-6325-099-1, Pub. by Servire BV Netherlands). Hunter Hse.

Philosophy, Psychology & Spirituality. Ed. by James W. Kidd. LC 83-80836. 87p. (Orig.). 1984. pap. text ed. 9.95 (ISBN 0-910727-05-8). Golden Phoenix.

Philosophy, Religion & Psychotherapy: Essays in the Philosophical Foundations of Psychotherapy. Ed. by Paul W. Sharkey. LC 81-40828. 242p. (Orig.). 1982. lib. bdg. 29.00 (ISBN 0-8191-2331-5); pap. text ed. 12.50 (ISBN 0-8191-2332-3). U Pr of Amer.

Philosophy: Ritual-Shabbat & Kashrut. (Home Study Program Ser.: No. 602). 6.00 (ISBN 0-686-96133-1). United Syn Bk.

Philosophy, Science & the Sociology of Knowledge. Irving L. Horowitz. LC 76-27756. 1976. Repr. of 1961 ed. lib. bdg. 22.50x (ISBN 0-8371-9051-7, HOPS). Greenwood.

Philosophy, the Bible & the Supernatural. Derek Prince. 1969. pap. 0.10 (ISBN 0-934920-22-2, B71). Derek Prince.

Phineas F. Bresse: A Prince in Israel. E. A. Girvin. Ed. by Donald W. Dayton. (Higher Christian Life Ser.). 464p. 55.00 (ISBN 0-8240-6407-0). Garland Pub.

Phoebe Palmer: Her Life & Thought. Harold E. Raser. LC 86-31251. (Studies in Women & Religion: Vol. 22). 392p. 1987. 59.95 (ISBN 0-88946-527-4). E Mellen.

Phoenix & the Ashes. Geoffrey Nash. 160p. 1985. pap. 6.95 (ISBN 0-85398-199-X). G Ronald Pub.

Phoenix Lectures. L. Ron Hubbard. 31.00 (ISBN 0-686-13925-9). Church Scient NY.

Phoenix of His Age: Interpretations of Erasmus, Fifteen Fifty to Seventeen Fifty. Bruce Mansfield. LC 79-14960. (Erasmus Studies). (Illus.). 1979. 30.00x (ISBN 0-8020-5457-9). U of Toronto Pr.

Phoenix of the Western World: Quetzalcoatl & the Sky Religion. Burr C. Brundage. LC 81-40278. (Civilization of the American Indian Ser.: Vol. 160). (Illus.). 320p. 1982. 22.50x (ISBN 0-8061-1773-7). U of Okla Pr.

Phoenix Trip: Notes on a Quaker Mission to Haiphong. Elizabeth J. Boardman. LC 84-72319. (Illus.). 192p. 1985. pap. 9.95 (ISBN 0-914064-22-3). Celo Pr.

Photo Directory of the United States Catholic Hierarchy. pap. cancelled (ISBN 0-686-15371-5, V-576). US Catholic.

Phrase Concordance of the Bible. 736p. 1986. 17.95 (ISBN 0-8407-4948-1). Nelson.

Physical & Ethereal Spaces. George Adams. (Illus.). 71p. 1978. pap. 5.00 (ISBN 0-85440-328-0, Pub. by Steinerbooks). Anthroposophic.

Physical & Transcendental Analysis of the Soul. The School of Philosophy Editorial Committee. 74p. 1986. 47.50 (ISBN 0-89266-565-3). Am Classical Coll Pr.

Physical Cosmology. R. Balian & J. Adouse. (Houches Summer School Ser.: Vol. 32). 668p. 1980. 115.00 (ISBN 0-444-85433-9). Elsevier.

Physical Education in the Colleges of the United Lutheran Church of America: A Survey & Program. Carl P. Schott. (Columbia University. Teachers College. Contributions to Education: No. 379). Repr. of 1929 ed. 22.50 (ISBN 0-404-55379-6). AMS Pr.

Physical Experience & Karmic Liability. Robert E. Birdsong. (Aquarian Academy Monograph: Ser. A, Lecture No. 6). 38p. 1977. pap. 1.50 (ISBN 0-917108-20-5). Sirius Bks.

Physical Fitness & the Christian. Diehl & Morris. 212p. 1986. pap. text ed. 14.95 (ISBN 0-8403-4200-4). Kendall-Hunt.

Physical Manifestations & Philosophy of Christ. Thomson J. Hudson. 1978. pap. 4.50 deluxe (ISBN 0-87852-003-1). Inst Human Growth.

Physical Religion. Friedrich M. Mueller. LC 73-18811. (Gifford Lectures: 1890). Repr. of 1891 ed. 34.00 (ISBN 0-404-11451-2). AMS Pr.

Physical, the Mental, the Spiritual. Joel Jessen. 185p. 1978. pap. 10.00 (ISBN 0-942958-05-5). Kappeler Inst Pub.

Physician of the Dance of Death: A Historical Study of the Evolution of the Dance of Death Mythus in Art. Alfred S. Warthin. Ed. by Robert Kastenbaum. LC 76-19592. (Death & Dying Ser.). (Illus.). 1977. Repr. of 1931 ed. lib. bdg. 17.00x (ISBN 0-405-09587-2). Ayer Co Pubs.

Physician's Covenant: Images of the Healer in Medical Ethics. William F. May. LC 83-16992. 204p. 1983. pap. 10.95 (ISBN 0-664-24497-1). Westminster.

Physico-Theology: A Demonstration of the Being & Attributes of God, from His Works of Creation. William Derham. Ed. by Frank N. Egerton, 3rd. LC 77-74212. (History of Ecology Ser.). 1978. Repr. of 1716 ed. lib. bdg. 37.50 (ISBN 0-405-10383-2). Ayer Co Pubs.

Physics of William of Ockham. A. Goddu. (Studies und Texte zur Geistesgeschichte des Mittelalters: No. 16). 310p. 1984. text ed. 50.00x (ISBN 90-04-06912-7, Pub. by EJ Brill Holland). Humanities.

Physikkommentar Hugolins von Orvieto Oesa: Ein Beitrag zur Erkenntnislehre des spaetmittelalterlichen Augustinismus. Willigis Eckermann. (Spaetmittelalter und Reformation, Vol. 5). 160p. 1972. 23.60x (ISBN 3-11-003714-9). De Gruyter.

Physiology of the Soul. Hugo Matrisian. (Illus.). 129p. 1980. deluxe ed. 49.75 (ISBN 0-89266-261-1). Am Classical Coll Pr.

Physyke of the Soule. Thomas Becon. LC 74-28831. (English Experience Ser.: No. 713). 1975. Repr. of 1549 ed. 3.50 (ISBN 90-221-0713-2). Walter J Johnson.

Pia Desideria. Philip J. Spener. Ed. & tr. by Theodore G. Tappert. LC 64-12995. 1964. pap. 5.95 (ISBN 0-8006-1953-6, 1-1953). Fortress.

Pia Dictamina, 7 Vols. Ed. by Guido M. Dreves. 1893-1905. 60.00 ea. (ISBN 0-384-12950-1). Johnson Repr.

Piano Man's Christmas & Other Stories for Christmas. Ira Williams, Jr. 80p. (Orig.). 1986. pap. 4.95 (ISBN 0-687-30920-4). Abingdon.

Picking a Partner. William S. Deal. 2.95 (ISBN 0-686-13716-7). Crusade Pubs.

Pictorial Bible Atlas. J. Catling Allen. 14.95 (ISBN 0-7175-0991-5); pap. 9.95 (ISBN 0-7175-0857-9). Dufour.

Pictorial Biography of C. H. Spurgeon. Bob L. Ross. 1981. 5.95 (ISBN 0-686-16830-5); pap. 3.95 (ISBN 0-686-16831-3). Pilgrim Pubns.

Pictorial Biography of the Venerable Master Hsu Yun, Vol. 1. Tr. by Buddhist Text Translation Society Staff. (Illus.). 236p. (Orig.). 1983. pap. 8.00 (ISBN 0-88139-008-9). Buddhist Text.

Pictorial Biography of the Venerable Master Hsu Yun, Vol. 2. Tr. by Buddhist Text Translation Society Staff. (Illus.). 236p. (Orig.). 1985. pap. 8.00 (ISBN 0-88139-116-6). Buddhist Text.

Pictorial History of Our English Bible. David Beale. (Illus.). 79p. (Orig.). 1982. pap. 2.95 (ISBN 0-89084-149-7). Bob Jones Univ Pr.

Pictorial History of Self-Realization Fellowship. (Illus.). 80p. 1982. pap. 5.50 (ISBN 0-87612-196-2). Self Realization.

Pictorial History of the Jewish People: From Biblical Times to Our Own Day Throughout the World. rev ed. Nathan Ausubel. (Illus.). 1984. 19.95 (ISBN 0-517-55283-3). Crown.

Pictorial History of the Jewish People. Nathan Ausubel. (Illus.). 1953. 19.95 (ISBN 0-517-09757-5). Crown.

Pictorial Introduction to the Bible. William S. Deal. (Baker's Paperback Reference Library). 440p. 1982. pap. 12.95 (ISBN 0-8010-2926-0). Baker Bk.

Pictorial Introduction to the Bible. William S. Deal. large print 12.95 (ISBN 0-686-13725-6); pap. 7.95. Crusade Pubs.

Pictorial Introduction to the Bible. William S. Deal. LC 67-20517. 438p. 1982. pap. 12.95 (ISBN 0-89081-363-9). Harvest Hse.

Pictorial Pilgrim's Progress. John Bunyan. 1960. pap. 3.95 (ISBN 0-8024-0019-1). Moody.

Picture-Book for Proud Lovers of Danville, Montour County & Riverside, PA. Arthur T. Foulke. LC 75-32061. (Illus.). 320p. 1976. 15.00 (ISBN 0-8158-0334-6). Chris Mass.

Picture Book History of the Jews. Howard Fast & Bette Fast. 60p. 1942. 5.95 (ISBN 0-88482-771-2). Hebrew Pub.

Picture Book of Devils, Demons, & Witchcraft. Ernst Lehner & Johanna Lehner. LC 72-137002. 1972. pap. 6.50 (ISBN 0-486-22751-0). Dover.

Picture Book of Devils, Demons & Witchcraft. Ernst Lehner & Johanna Lehner. (Illus.). 15.50 (ISBN 0-8446-5830-8). Peter Smith.

Picture Book of Hanukkah. David A. Adler. LC 82-2942. (Illus.). 32p. 1982. reinforced bdg. 12.95 (ISBN 0-8234-0458-7). Holiday.

Picture Book of Hanukkah. David A. Adler. LC 82-2942. (Illus.). 1985. pap. 5.95 (ISBN 0-8234-0574-5). Holiday.

Picture Book of Jewish Holidays. David A. Adler. LC 81-2765. (Illus.). 32p. 1981. reinforced bdg. 12.95 (ISBN 0-8234-0396-3). Holiday.

Picture Book of Passover. David A. Adler. LC 81-6983. (Illus.). 32p. 1982. reinforced bdg. 10.95 (ISBN 0-8234-0439-0); pap. 5.95 (ISBN 0-8234-0609-1). Holiday.

Picture Book of Saints. Lawrence G. Lovasik. (Illus.). 4.95 (ISBN 0-89942-235-7, 235-22). Catholic Bk Pub.

Picture Life of Pope John Paul II. Bonic. Date not set. lib. bdg. 9.90 (ISBN 0-531-04806-3). Watts.

Picture of a Papist: Whereunto Is Annexed a Certain Treatise, Intituled Pagano-Papismus. Oliver Ormerod. LC 74-28878. (English Experience Ser.: No. 756). 1975. Repr. of 1606 ed. 18.50 (ISBN 90-221-0756-6). Walter J Johnson.

Picture of a Puritane: Or, a Relation of the Opinions - of the Anabaptists in Germanie, & of the Puritanes in England. Oliver Ormerod. LC 74-28879. (English Experience Ser.: No. 757). 1975. Repr. of 1605 ed. 9.50 (ISBN 90-221-0757-4). Walter J Johnson.

Picture Parade of Jewish History. Morris Epstein. 1977. pap. 4.95 (ISBN 0-8197-0024-X). Bloch.

Picture Stories from the Bible. pap. 5.00 (ISBN 0-87068-598-8). Ktav.

Picture Stories from the Bible: The Old Testament in Full-Color Comic-Strip Form. Ed. by M. C. Gaines. LC 79-66064. (Illus.). 224p. 1979. Repr. of 1943 ed. 9.95 (ISBN 0-934386-01-3). Scarf Pr.

Picture Story Bible ABC Book. rev. ed. Elsie E. Egermeier. (Illus.). 1963. 5.95 (ISBN 0-87162-262-9, D1703). Warner Pr.

Picture Windows on the Christ. Charles C. Wise, Jr. LC 78-69928. (Illus.). 354p. 1979. 11.95 (ISBN 0-917023-03-X); pap. 5.95 (ISBN 0-917023-04-8). Magian Pr.

Pictures & Biographies of Brigham Young & His Wives. J. H. Crockwell. 1980. lib. bdg. 59.95 (ISBN 0-8490-3158-3). Gordon Pr.

Pictures of Truth. Ralph W. Harris. LC 76-58081. (Radiant Life Ser.). 128p. 1977. pap. 2.50 (ISBN 0-88243-905-7, 02-0905); teacher's ed 3.95 (ISBN 0-88243-175-7, 32-0175). Gospel Pub.

Picturesque Ideas on the Flight into Egypt. Colta Ives. LC 82-4405. (Illus.). 72p. 1982. Repr. 20.00 (ISBN 0-8076-1047-X). Braziller.

Piebald Standard. Edith Simon. LC 76-29836. Repr. of 1959 ed. 40.00 (ISBN 0-404-15419-0). AMS Pr.

Pieces of White Shell. Terry T. Williams. (Illus.). 176p. 1987. pap. 8.95 (ISBN 0-8263-0969-0). U of NM Pr.

Pierce Penilesse, His Supplication to the Divell. Thomas Nash. Repr. of 1924 ed. lib. bdg. 22.50x (ISBN 0-8371-2919-2, NAPP). Greenwood.

Pierre d'Ailly & the Council of Constance. John P. McGowan. 110p. 1984. Repr. of 1936 ed. 22.00x (ISBN 0-939738-34-1). Zubal Inc.

Pierre-Gibault, Missionary, Seventeen Thirty-Seven to Eighteen Hundred Two. Joseph P. Donnelly. LC 77-156371. 1971. 8.95 (ISBN 0-8294-0203-9). Loyola.

Pierre Leroux & the Birth of Democratic Socialism. Jack Bakunin. 1976. lib. bdg. 79.95 (ISBN 0-87700-221-5). Revisionist Pr.

Pierre Teilhard De Chardin's Philosophy of Evolution. H. James Birx. 192p. 1972. 21.50x (ISBN 0-398-02466-9). C C Thomas.

Piers Plowman & Contemporary Religious Thought. Greta Hort. LC 72-193685. lib. bdg. 15.00 (ISBN 0-8414-5129-X). Folcroft.

Piers Plowman & Contemporary Religious Thought. Greta Hort. (Church Historical Society, London, New Ser.: No. 29). Repr. of 1938 ed. 40.00 (ISBN 0-8115-3153-8). Kraus Repr.

Pietas et Societas, New Trends in Reformation Social History: Essays in Memory of Harold J. Grimm. Kyle Sessions & Phillip Bebb. (Sixteenth Century Essays & Studies: Vol. IV). (Illus.). 240p. 1985. Smyth Sewn 25.00x (ISBN 0-940474-04-2). Sixteenth Cent.

Pietists: Selected Writings. Ed. by Peter C. Erb. (Classics of Western Spirituality Ser.). 1983. 13.95 (ISBN 0-8091-0334-6); pap. 9.95 (ISBN 0-8091-2509-9). Paulist Pr.

Piety. S. R. Bourghei et al. Tr. by Amir Tavakoli from Persian. 1980. pap. 1.00 (ISBN 0-318-03827-7). Book-Dist-Ctr.

Piety & Patriotism. James W. Van Hoeven. 1976. pap. 4.95 (ISBN 0-8028-1663-0). Eerdmans.

Piety & Patronage in Renaissance Venice: Bellini, Titian, & Franciscans. Rona Goffen. LC 85-91280. 320p. 1986. 40.00 (ISBN 0-300-03455-5). Yale U Pr.

Piety & Politics: Catholic Revival & the Generation of 1905-1914 in France. Paul M. Cohen. Ed. by William H. McNeill & David H. Pinkney. (Modern European History Ser.). 348p. 1987. lib. bdg. 50.00 (ISBN 0-8240-8034-3). Garland Pub.

Piety & Politics: Religion & the Rise of Absolutism in England, Wurttemberg & Prussia. Mary Fulbrook. LC 83-5316. 224p. 1984. 37.50 (ISBN 0-521-25612-7); pap. 13.95 (ISBN 0-521-27633-0). Cambridge U Pr.

Piety & Power: The Role of Italian Parishes in the New York Metropolitan Area (1889-1930) Silvano M. Tomasi. LC 74-79913. 201p. 1975. 14.95x (ISBN 0-913256-16-1). Ctr Migration.

Piety & the Princeton Theologians. W. Andrew Hoffecker. (Orig.). 1981. pap. 5.95 (ISBN 0-8010-4253-4). Baker Bk.

Piety & the Princeton Theologians: Archibald Alexander, Charles Hodge, & Benjamin Warfield. W. Andrew Hoffecker. 1981. pap. 5.95 (ISBN 0-87552-280-7). Presby & Reformed.

Piety, Politics, & Ethics: Reformation Studies in Honor of George Wolfgang Forell. Ed. by Carter Lindberg. (Sixteenth Century Essays & Studies: Vol. III). (Illus.). 200p. 1984. smythe sewn 25.00x (ISBN 0-940474-03-4). Sixteenth Cent.

Piggyback Songs in Praise of God. Compiled by Jean Warren. (Piggyback Songs Ser.). (Illus.). 80p. (Orig.). 1986. pap. 6.95 (ISBN 0-911019-10-3). Warren Pub Hse.

Pigs in the Parlor. Frank Hammond & Ida M. Hammond. 153p. (Orig.). 1973. pap. 4.95 (ISBN 0-89228-027-1). Impact Bks MO.

Pilgerreise der Aetheria. August Bludau. pap. 22.00 (ISBN 0-384-04760-2). Johnson Repr.

Pilgrim Aflame. Myron S. Augsburger. LC 67-15993. (Illus.). 288p. 1967. pap. 2.25 (ISBN 0-8361-1840-5). Herald Pr.

Pilgrim & Dreamer: John Bunyan: His Life & Work. Ernest W. Bacon. 176p. pap. text ed. 8.95 cancelled (ISBN 0-85364-309-1). Attic Pr.

Pilgrim & the Book: A Study of Dante, Langland & Chaucer. Julia B. Holloway. (American University Studies IV- English Language & Literature: Vol. 42). 343p. 1987. text ed. 30.75 (ISBN 0-8204-0345-8). P Lang Pubs.

Pilgrim Church. William J. Bausch. LC 73-6608. 560p. 1980. pap. 9.95 (ISBN 0-89622-140-7). Twenty-Third.

Pilgrim Church & the Easter People. Norman Pittenger. LC 86-45327. 112p. (Orig.). 1987. pap. 8.95 (ISBN 0-89453-598-6). M Glazier.

Pilgrim Courage. E. Brooks Smith & Robert Meredith. (Illus.). 1962. 6.95 (ISBN 0-316-80045-7). Little.

Pilgrim Experiences the World's Religions: Discovering the Human Faces of the Hidden God. Aaron Milavec. (Mellen Lives Ser.: Vol. 1). 96p. 1984. pap. 9.95x (ISBN 0-88946-010-8). E Mellen.

Pilgrim Fathers from a Dutch Point of View. D. Plooij. LC 71-100509. Repr. of 1932 ed. 8.50 (ISBN 0-404-05065-4). AMS Pr.

Pilgrim Fathers from a Dutch Point of View. Daniel Plooij. LC 79-131801. 1970. Repr. of 1932 ed. 7.00x (ISBN 0-403-00688-0). Scholarly.

Pilgrim Fathers of New England. John Brown. 352p. 1970. 4.95 (ISBN 0-686-09112-4). Pilgrim Pubns.

Pilgrim Fathers of New England & Their Puritan Successors. 4th ed. J. Brown. (Illus.). Repr. of 1920 ed. 39.00 (ISBN 0-527-12050-2). Kraus Repr.

Pilgrim from a Red Land. Quentin K. Y. Huang. 1981. 8.00 (ISBN 0-682-49669-3). Exposition Pr FL.

Pilgrim God: A Biblical Journey. Brother John of Taize. (Orig.). 1985. pap. 12.95 (ISBN 0-912405-18-X). Pastoral Pr.

Pilgrim Hymnal. Blue. 1958. 9.95x (ISBN 0-8298-0460-9). Pilgrim NY.

Pilgrim Hymnal. Red. 1958. 9.95x (ISBN 0-8298-0107-3). Pilgrim NY.

Pilgrim Hymnal: Organist's Edition. UCC. 1981. 15.00 (ISBN 0-8298-0454-4). Pilgrim NY.

Pilgrim in Love: An Introduction to Dante & His Spirituality. James Collins. 312p. 1984. 12.95 (ISBN 0-8294-0453-8). Loyola.

Pilgrim in the Parish: Spirituality for Lay Ministers. Virginia S. Finn. 208p. (Orig.). 1986. pap. 8.95 (ISBN 0-8091-2742-3). Paulist Pr.

Pilgrim of the Clear Light: The Biography of Dr. Walter Y. Evans-Wentz. Kenneth D. Winkler. Intro. by Lama Govinda A. LC 81-70193. (Illus.). 140p. (Orig.). 1982. pap. 4.95 (ISBN 0-942058-00-3). Dawnfire.

Pilgrim of the Himalayas. Edmond B. Szekely. (Illus.). 32p. 1974. pap. 2.95 (ISBN 0-89564-061-9). IBS Intl.

Pilgrim on a Bicycle. Barbara M. Johnson. LC 81-68637. 144p. 1982. write for info. (ISBN 0-86693-001-9). B M Johnson.

Pilgrim People: Learning Through the Church Year. John H. Westerhoff, III. 128p. (Orig.). 1984. pap. 7.95 (ISBN 0-86683-884-8, 7462, HarpR). Har-Row.

Pilgrim Psalms: An Exposition of the Songs of Degrees. Samuel Cox. 255p. 1983. lib. bdg. 9.50 (ISBN 0-86524-159-7, 1903). Klock & Klock.

Pilgrim Study Bible. 1984. write for info. Oxford U Pr.

Pilgrim to Poland: Pope John Paul II. 1979. 5.00 (ISBN 0-686-63640-6); pap. 3.50 (ISBN 0-8198-0627-7). Dghtrs St Paul.

Pilgrim Way. Robert M. Bartlett. LC 70-172790. 384p. 1971. 15.00 (ISBN 0-8298-0222-3). Pilgrim NY.

Pilgrimage. J. Ellsworth Kalas. Ed. by Michael L. Sherer. (Orig.). 1987. pap. 3.95 (ISBN 0-89536-845-5, 7804). CSS of Ohio.

Pilgrimage. Kinnara Inc. (Illus., Orig.). 1977. pap. 4.95 (ISBN 0-89346-011-7). Heian Intl.

Pilgrimage: A Workbook on Christian Growth. Richard Peace. 1985. pap. 6.95 (ISBN 0-8010-7087-2). Baker Bk.

Pilgrimage & Service. Joseph Krimsky. Ed. by Moshe Davis. LC 77-70712. (America & the Holy Land Ser.). 1977. Repr. of 1919 ed. lib. bdg. 17.00x (ISBN 0-405-10261-5). Ayer Co Pubs.

Pilgrimage from Rome. rev. ed. Bartholomew F. Brewer & Alfred W. Furrell. (Illus.). 1986. pap. 5.95 (ISBN 0-89084-327-9). Bob Jones Univ Pr.

Pilgrimage Home. Gerald May. LC 78-61720. 196p. 1979. pap. 6.95 (ISBN 0-8091-2143-3). Paulist Pr.

Pilgrimage in Faith: An Introduction to the Episcopal Church. rev. ed. Franklin C. Ferguson. LC 75-5220. 180p. (Orig.). 1979. pap. 6.95 (ISBN 0-8192-1277-6). Morehouse.

Pilgrimage in Mission. Donald R. Jacobs. LC 83-306. 168p. 1983. pap. 6.50 (ISBN 0-8361-3324-2). Herald Pr.

Pilgrimage in Mission: Leader's Guide. Richard A. Kauffman. 60p. 1983. pap. 4.95x (ISBN 0-8361-1260-1). Herald Pr.

Pilgrimage in the Hindu Tradition: A Case Study of West Bengal. Ed. by E. Alan Morinis. (Illus.). 1984. 34.95x (ISBN 0-19-561412-7). Oxford U Pr.

Pilgrimage of Buddhism & a Buddhist Pilgrimage. James B. Pratt. LC 75-3325. (Philosophy of America Ser.). Repr. of 1928 ed. 57.50 (ISBN 0-404-59320-8). AMS Pr.

Pilgrimage of Buddhism & a Buddhist Pilgrimage. James B. Pratt. 758p. 1982. Repr. of 1928 ed. lib. bdg. 45.00 (ISBN 0-89984-828-1). Century Bookbindery.

Pilgrimage of Faith of Tanzania Mennonite Church, 1934-83. Mahlon M. Hess. (Illus.). 176p. 1985. 5.00 (ISBN 0-9613368-2-X). E Mennonite Bd.

Pilgrimage of Faith: The Legacy of the Otterbeins. J. Steven O'Malley. LC 73-5684. (ATLA Monograph: No. 4). 226p. 1973. 18.00 (ISBN 0-8108-0626-6). Scarecrow.

Pilgrimage of Love, Book I. Shri Kripalvanandaji. LC 81-82015. 86p. (Orig.). 1981. pap. 4.50 (ISBN 0-940258-02-1). Kripalu Pubns.

Pilgrimage of Love, Book II. Swami Shri Kripalvandji. LC 81-82015. 416p. (Orig.). 1982. pap. 7.50 (ISBN 0-940258-05-6). Kripalu Pubns.

Pilgrimage of Love: Premyatra, Bk. III. Shri Kripalvanandji. LC 81-82015. (Illus.). 136p. (Orig.). 1984. pap. 5.50 (ISBN 0-940258-12-9). Kripalu Pubns.

Pilgrimage of Peace: John Paul II in Ireland & the United States. Pope John Paul II. (Illus.). 175p. 1980. 17.50 (ISBN 0-374-23307-1); pap. 9.95 (ISBN 0-374-51578-6). FS&G.

Pilgrimage of Sudhana. J. Fontein. 1967. text ed. 35.60x (ISBN 90-2796-387-8). Mouton.

Pilgrimage of the Heart. Thomas McGuiness. LC 83-63477. 74p. (Orig.). 1984. pap. text ed. 2.95 (ISBN 0-911905-19-7). Past & Mat Rene Ctr.

Pilgrimage of the Life of Man, Pts. 1-3. Guillaume De Deguilleville. Ed. by F. J. Furnivall & K. B. Locock. (EETS, ES Ser.: Nos. 77, 83, & 92). Repr. of 1904 ed. 90.00 (ISBN 0-527-00279-8). Kraus Repr.

Pilgrimage Project: Leader's Guide. John & Adrienne Carr. 64p. (Orig.). 1987. pap. 4.95 (ISBN 0-8358-0550-6). Upper Room.

Pilgrimage Project: Participant's Notebook. John Carr & Adrienne Carr. 48p. (Orig.). 1987. pap. 2.95 (ISBN 0-8358-0549-2). Upper Room.

Pilgrimage to Luther's Germany. Herb Brokering & Roland Bainton. 80p. 1983. 14.95 (ISBN 0-86683-629-2, HarpR). Har-Row.

Pilgrimage to Nejd, 2 vols. Anne Blunt. (Illus.). 1968. Repr. of 1881 ed. 85.00x (ISBN 0-7146-1979-5, F Cass Co). Biblio Dist.

Pilgrimage to Palestine. Harry E. Fosdick. Ed. by Moshe Davis. LC 77-70688. (America & the Holy Land Ser.). 1977. Repr. of 1927 ed. lib. bdg. 30.00x (ISBN 0-405-10247-X). Ayer Co Pubs.

Pilgrimage to Priesthood. Elizabeth Canham. 128p. (Orig.). 1985. pap. 9.95 (ISBN 0-8164-2492-6, 8603, HarpR). Har-Row.

Pilgrimage to Rebirth. Erlo Van Waveren. 125p. 1978. 7.95 (ISBN 0-87728-420-2); pap. 3.95. Weiser.

Pilgrimage to Renewal. Herbert F. Brokering. 96p. (Orig.). 1979. pap. 1.95 (ISBN 0-03-053791-6, HarpR). Har-Row.

Pilgrimage to the Holy Land. Alphonse de Lamartine. LC 78-14368. 1978. Repr. of 1838 ed. 75.00x (ISBN 0-8201-1323-9). Schol Facsimiles.

Pilgrimages: A Guide to the Holy Places of Europe for Today's Traveler. Paul L. Higgins. 146p. 1984. 12.95 (ISBN 0-13-676163-1); pap. 5.95 (ISBN 0-13-676155-0). P-H.

Pilgrimages to Rome & Beyond: A Guide to the Holy Places of Southern Europe for Today's Traveler. Paul L. Higgins. (Illus.). 156p. 1985. 17.95 (ISBN 0-13-676073-2); pap. 7.95 (ISBN 0-13-676065-1). P-H.

Pilgrimages to Rome & Beyond: A Guide to the Holy Places of Southern Europe for Today's Traveler. 1985. pap. 7.95. S&S.

Pilgrims & Strangers: Essays in Mennonite Brethren History. Paul Toews. (Perspective on Mennonite Life & Thought Ser.: Vol. 1). 183p. (Orig.). 1977. pap. 5.95 (ISBN 0-919797-36-9). Kindred Pr.

Pilgrims & Thanksgiving. Rae Bains. LC 84-2686. (Illus.). 32p. 1985. PLB 7.59 (ISBN 0-8167-0222-5); pap. text ed. 1.95 (ISBN 0-8167-0223-3). Troll Assocs.

Pilgrims & Their History. Roland G. Usher. (Illus.). 310p. 1977. Repr. of 1918 ed. 20.00 (ISBN 0-87928-082-4). Corner Hse.

Pilgrims & Their Times. rev. ed. Ed. by Elizabeth M. Brown et al. (Illus.). 32p. 1973. pap. 2.50 (ISBN 0-87534-121-7). Highlights.

Pilgrim's Guide to Forty-Six Temples. Shiro Usui. (Illus.). 336p. (Orig.). 1986. pap. 12.50 (ISBN 0-8348-0211-2). Weatherhill.

Pilgrim's Guide to Planet Earth. LC 85-11046. 320p. 1985. Repr. of 1981 ed. lib. bdg. 19.95x (ISBN 0-89370-888-7). Borgo Pr.

Pilgrim's Guide to Prayer. Edward C. Briggs. (Orig.). 1987. pap. 3.25 (ISBN 0-8054-8156-7). Broadman.

Pilgrims in a New Land. Lee M. Friedman. LC 78-26208. (Illus.). 1979. Repr. of 1948 ed. lib. bdg. 32.50x (ISBN 0-313-20877-8, FRPI). Greenwood.

Pilgrims in a Strange Land: Hausa Communities in Chad. John A. Works, Jr. LC 76-23138. 1976. 32.00x (ISBN 0-231-03976-X). Columbia U Pr.

Pilgrims in Their Own Land. Martin E. Marty. 512p. 1985. pap. 7.95 (ISBN 0-14-008268-9). Penguin.

Pilgrims in Their Own Land: Five Hundred Years of Religion in America. Martin E. Marty. (Illus.). 416p. 1984. 25.00 (ISBN 0-316-54867-7). Little.

Pilgrim's Interfaith Guide to the Holy Land. Franklin H. Littell. (Illus.). 84p. 1982. 7.95 (ISBN 9-65220-030-1, Carta Pub Israel). Hippocrene Bks.

Pilgrim's Journey: The Autobiography of Ignatius of Loyola. Tr. & intro. by Joseph N. Tylenda. 1985. pap. 8.95 (ISBN 0-89453-468-8). M Glazier.

Pilgrim's New Guide to the Holy Land. Stephen Doyle. 1985. pap. 7.95 (ISBN 0-89453-440-8). M Glazier.

Pilgrims of a Common Life. Trevor J. Saxby. LC 86-27043. 208p. (Orig.). 1987. pap. 17.95 (ISBN 0-8361-3426-5). Herald Pr.

Pilgrims of Forty-Eight. facsimile ed. Josephine Goldmark. LC 74-27989. (Modern Jewish Experience Ser.). (Illus.). 1975. Repr. of 1930 ed. 29.00x (ISBN 0-405-06716-X). Ayer Co Pubs.

Pilgrims of Russian-Town: The Community of Spiritual Christian Jumpers in America. Pauline V. Young. LC 66-27375. (Illus.). 1967. Repr. of 1932 ed. 9.00x (ISBN 0-8462-1001-0). Russell.

Pilgrims of the Lonely Road. facs. ed. Gaius G. Atkins. LC 67-28741. (Essay Index Reprint Ser). 1913. 18.00 (ISBN 0-8369-0162-2). Ayer Co Pubs.

Pilgrims of the Prairie: Pioneer Ukrainian Baptists in North Dakota. Andrew Dubovy. Ed. by Marie H. Bloch. (Illus.). 72p. (Orig.). 1983. lib. bdg. 8.50; pap. 4.50. Ukrainian Cult Inst.

Pilgrims of the Stars. 2nd ed. Indira Devi & Dilip K. Roy. (Illus.). 406p. 1985. pap. 14.95 (ISBN 0-931454-10-7). Timeless Bks.

Pilgrims on the Earth. Richard D. Scheuerman. 165p. 1976. 12.00 (ISBN 0-87770-128-8). Ye Galleon.

Pilgrim's Progress. John Bunyan. (Giant Summit Bks). pap. 8.95 (ISBN 0-8010-0732-1). Baker Bk.

Pilgrim's Progress. John Bunyan. 1979. Repr. 19.95 (ISBN 0-85151-259-3). Banner of Truth.

Pilgrim's Progress. John Bunyan. (Moody Classics Ser.). 1984. pap. 3.95 (ISBN 0-8024-0012-4). Moody.

Pilgrim's Progress. John Bunyan. 1975. 14.95 (ISBN 0-685-52821-9). Reiner.

Pilgrim's Progress. John Bunyan. 288p. 1965. pap. 3.50 (ISBN 0-8007-8032-9, Spire Bks). Revell.

Pilgrim's Progress. John Bunyan. 416p. 1981. pap. 3.95 (ISBN 0-88368-096-3). Whitaker Hse.

Pilgrim's Progress. John Bunyan. 256p. 1973. pap. 3.95 (ISBN 0-310-22142-0, 6610P). Zondervan.

Pilgrim's Progress. John Bunyan. Ed. by Hal M. Helms. LC 81-85770. (Living Library Ser.). (Illus.). 270p. 1982. 6.95 (ISBN 0-941478-02-5). Paraclete Pr.

Pilgrim's Progress. John Bunyan. Ed. by Hal M. Helms. (Illus.). 268p. pap. 6.95 (ISBN 0-941478-02-5, Pub. by Paraclete Pr). Upper Room.

Pilgrim's Progress: Critical & Historical Views. Ed. by Vincent Newey. (English Texts & Studies). 302p. 1980. 30.00x (ISBN 0-389-20016-6). B&N Imports.

Pilgrim's Progress Guides. Ed. by Diane Zimmerman. (LifeView: a Christian Approachto Literature Studies). 1977. pap. 0.85 student guide (ISBN 0-915134-32-2); tchrs. ed. 1.50 (ISBN 0-915134-36-5). Mott Media.

Pilgrim's Progress in Today's English. John Bunyan. LC 64-25255. 1964. pap. 6.95 (ISBN 0-8024-6520-X). Moody.

Pilgrims Progress, Sixteen Seventy-Eight. John Bunyan. 288p. 1984. 30.00x (ISBN 0-905418-29-8, Pub. by Gresham England). State Mutual Bk.

Pilgrims, Puritans & Patriots: Our Christian Heritage. Don Boys. 1983. pap. 9.00x (ISBN 0-686-40717-2). Freedom Univ-FSP.

Pilgrim's Regress. C. S. Lewis. 224p. 1981. pap. 3.50 (ISBN 0-553-26063-4). Bantam.

Pilgrim's Regress: An Allegorical Apology for Christianity, Reason, & Romanticism. C. S. Lewis. LC 82-101595. pap. 55.30 (ISBN 0-317-30149-7, 2025332). Bks Demand UMI.

Pilgrims' Road. Mike Wood. 1976. pap. 2.95 (ISBN 0-89390-015-X). Resource Pubns.

Pilgrim's Staff or Daily Steps Heavenward by the Pathway of Faith. 1979. Repr. of 1897 ed. lib. bdg. 20.00 (ISBN 0-8495-4332-0). Arden Lib.

Pilgrim's Way: Shrines & Saints in Britain & Ireland. John Adair. (Illus.). 1978. 12.98 (ISBN 0-500-25061-8). Thames Hudson.

Pillar in the Twilight. (Encounter Bk.). 3.00 (ISBN 0-8198-0591-2); pap. 2.00 (ISBN 0-8198-0592-0). Dghtrs St Paul.

Pillars of Faith. Herman O. Wilson & Morris M. Womack. 6.95 (ISBN 0-8010-9540-9); pap. 4.95 (ISBN 0-8010-9538-7). Baker Bk.

Pillars of Pentecost. Charles W. Conn. 148p. 1979. 6.95 (ISBN 0-87148-681-4). Pathway Pr.

Pillars of the Church. Theodore Maynard. LC 76-136763. (Essay Index Reprint Ser). 1945. 19.00 (ISBN 0-8369-1990-8). Ayer Co Pubs.

Pilot's Voice. Isabel Byrum. (Illus.). 146p. pap. 1.50 (ISBN 0-686-29159-X). Faith Pub Hse.

Piman Shamanism & Staying Sickness: Ka: cim Mumkidag. Donald M. Bahr et al. LC 72-92103. 332p. 1974. pap. 9.95 (ISBN 0-8165-0303-6). U of Ariz Pr.

Pink & Green Church & Other Missionary Stories for Children. Illus. by Janis Timyan. (Illus.). Date not set. pap. price not set (ISBN 0-87509-393-0). Chr Pubns.

Pinnacles of India's Past: Selections from the Rgveda. Walter Maurer. LC 85-30784. (University of Pennsylvania Studies on South Asia: No. 2). 350p. 1986. 44.00x (ISBN 0-915027-62-3); pap. 20.00x (ISBN 0-915027-83-6). Benjamins North Am.

Pinstripe Prayers: Or How to Talk to God While Pursuing Mammon. John Chervokas. 48p. (Orig.). 1984. pap. 2.95 (ISBN 0-86683-874-0, 7457, HarpR). Har-Row.

Pintura Cristiana En los Tres Primeros Siglos. Miguel Figueroa Y Miranda. (UPREX, Humanidades: No. 12). pap. 1.85 (ISBN 0-8477-0012-7). U of PR Pr.

Pioneer Churches of Florida. Ed. by Elizabeth Chase. LC 77-72276. (Illus.). 74p. 1977. pap. 6.00 (ISBN 0-913122-11-4). Mickler Hse.

Pioneer Churchman: J. W. C. Dietrichson in Wisconsin, 1844-1850. Ed. by E. Clifford Nelson. Tr. by Malcolm Rosholt & Harris Kaasa. 1973. lib. bdg. 11.50 (ISBN 0-8057-5443-1, Twayne). G K Hall.

Pioneer Churchman: The Narrative & Journal of J. W. C. Dietrichson, 1844-1850. Tr. by Harris Kaasa & Malcolm Rosholt. Ed. by Clifford Nelson. 265p. 1973. 9.00 (ISBN 0-87732-053-5). Norwegian-Am Hist Assn.

Pioneer Colored Christians. facsimile ed. Harriet P. Miller. LC 73-37313. (Black Heritage Library Collection). Repr. of 1911 ed. 13.50 (ISBN 0-8369-8950-3). Ayer Co Pubs.

Pioneer Evangelists of the Church of God in the Pacific Northwest. John L. Green. 164p. pap. 2.00 (ISBN 0-686-29135-2). Faith Pub Hse.

Pioneer Experiences. Ed. by Phoebe Palmer & Donald W. Dayton. (Higher Christian Life Ser.). 368p. 1985. 45.00 (ISBN 0-8240-6433-X). Garland Pub.

Pioneer Jesuits in Northern Mexico. Peter M. Dunner. LC 78-10566. (Illus.). 1979. Repr. of 1944 ed. lib. bdg. 24.75x (ISBN 0-313-20653-8, DUPJ). Greenwood.

Pioneer Jews: A New Life in the Far West. Harriett Rochlin. LC 83-12647. (Illus.). 1984. 17.95 (ISBN 0-395-31832-7). HM.

Pioneer Pentecostal Women. Mary H. Wallace. (Pioneer Pentecostal Women Ser.: Vol. 1). (Illus.). 272p. (Orig.). 1983. pap. 5.95 (ISBN 0-912315-18-0). Word Aflame.

Pioneer Pentecostal Women. Mary H. Wallace. LC 85-20981. (Pioneer Pentecostal Women: Vol. II). (Illus.). 288p. (Orig.). 1981. pap. 5.95 (ISBN 0-912315-19-9). Word Aflame.

Pioneer Publisher: The Life & Times of J. F. Harms. Orlando Harms. LC 84-82050. 116p. (Orig.). 1984. pap. 5.95 (ISBN 0-919797-33-4). Kindred Pr.

Pioneer Settlement in the Twenties: An Original Anthology. Ed. by Moshe Davis. LC 77-70699. (America & the Holy Land Ser.). 1977. lib. bdg. 20.00x (ISBN 0-405-10250-X). Ayer Co Pubs.

Pioneer Swedish Settlements & Swedish Lutheran Churches in America 1845-1860. Eric Norelius. Tr. by Conrad Bergendoff from Swedish. LC 84-71391. (Publication Ser.: No. 31). Orig. Title: De Svenska Luterska Forsamlingarnas och Svenska Historia i Amerika. 419p. 1984. 15.00 (ISBN 0-910184-31-3). Augustana.

Pioneering on the Congo, 2 Vols. W. Holman Bently. (Landmarks in Anthropology Ser). 1970. Repr. of 1900 ed. Set. lib. bdg. 85.00 (ISBN 0-384-03943-X). Johnson Repr.

Pioneers in the Arab World. Dorothy Van Ess. 1974. pap. 4.95 (ISBN 0-8028-1585-5). Eerdmans.

Pioneers of a Peaceable Kingdom: The Quaker Peace Testimony from the Colonial Era to the First World War. Peter Brock. 1970. pap. 12.95x (ISBN 0-691-00573-7). Princeton U Pr.

Pioneers of Catholic Europe. Frederick J. Cowie. LC 84-62160. 190p. 1985. pap. 6.95 (ISBN 0-87973-713-1, 713). Our Sunday Visitor.

Pioneers of Christian Thought. facs. ed. Frederick D. Kershner. LC 68-57327. (Essay Index Reprint Ser). 1930. 20.00 (ISBN 0-8369-0594-6). Ayer Co Pubs.

Pioneers of Faith. Marian W. Bloxton. 80p. 1984. pap. 7.95 (ISBN 0-8170-1036-X). Judson.

Pioneers of Religious Education. facs. ed. Tom F. Kinlock. LC 69-18929. (Essay Index Reprint Ser). 1939. 14.00 (ISBN 0-8369-0045-6). Ayer Co Pubs.

Pioneers, Peddlers, & Tsadikim: The Story of the Jews in Colorado. 2nd ed. Ida L. Uchill. LC 57-57817. 327p. 1979. pap. 9.95 (ISBN 0-9604468-0-X). Uchill.

Pious & Secular America. Reinhold Niebuhr. LC 79-128063. 1977. Repr. of 1958 ed. 17.50x (ISBN 0-678-02756-0). Kelley.

Pious Prentice, or, the Prentices Piety. Abraham Jackson. LC 74-28866. (English Experience Ser.: No. 746). 1975. Repr. of 1640 ed. 7.00 (ISBN 90-221-0746-9). Walter J Johnson.

Pirke Aboth: Sayings of the Fathers. Joseph H. Hertz. 1945. pap. 3.95x (ISBN 0-87441-155-6). Behrman.

Pirke De Rabbi Eliezer (The Chapters of Rabbi Eliezer the Great) Tr. by Gerald Friedlander from Heb. LC 80-545920. (Judaic Studies Library: No. SPH6). 552p. 1981. pap. 14.95 (ISBN 0-87203-095-4). Hermon.

Pisoma Arkhiepiskopa Theophana Poltavskago i Perejaslavskago. Tr. of Letters of Archbishop Theophan of Poltava & Pereyeslav. 76p. 1974. pap. 4.00 (ISBN 0-317-29047-9). Holy Trinity.

Pisoma Tsarskoj Semji iz Zatotchenija. Ed. by E. E. Alferirff. LC 73-91829. Tr. of Letters of the Tsar's Family from Captivity. (Illus.). 544p. 1974. 25.00 (ISBN 0-317-29225-0). Holy Trinity.

Pistis Sophia: A Gnostic Gospel, Vol. 21. 3rd ed. G. R. Mead. LC 83-83170. (Spiritual Science Library). 408p. 1984. Repr. of 1921 ed. lib. bdg. 25.00 (ISBN 0-89345-041-3, Spiritual Sci Lib). Garber Comm.

Pit & the Trap: Leyb Rochman. Ed. by Sheila Friedling. Tr. by Moshe Kohn. (Yiddish., Illus.). 288p. (Orig.). 1983. 16.95 (ISBN 0-8052-5044-1); pap. 10.95 (ISBN 0-8052-5045-X). Holocaust Pubns.

Pitcairn's Island. Thomas Murray. LC 72-281. (World History Ser., No. 48). 1972. Repr. of 1860 ed. lib. bdg. 52.95x (ISBN 0-8383-1410-4). Haskell.

Pitzel Holiday Book. Leonard Jaffe. (Illus.). 1962. 7.95x (ISBN 0-87068-359-4). Ktav.

Pius XII & the Third Reich. Saul Friedlander. LC 80-12830. 238p. 1980. Repr. of 1966 ed. lib. bdg. 21.50x (ISBN 0-374-92930-0, Octagon). Hippocrene Bks.

Pius XII: Greatness Dishonoured. Michael O'Carroll. 252p. 1980. 10.00 (ISBN 0-912414-41-3). Lumen Christi.

Pjatidesjatnitsa. M. Skaballanovitch. Tr. of Pentacost. 176p. pap. 6.00 (ISBN 0-317-29163-7). Holy Trinity.

Place Apart: Monastic Prayer & Practice for Everyone. M. Basil Pennington. LC 81-43566. 168p. 1985. pap. 5.95 (ISBN 0-385-19706-3, Im). Doubleday.

Place Called Community. Parker J. Palmer. LC 77-75909. (Orig.). 1977. pap. 2.50x (ISBN 0-87574-212-2). Pendle Hill.

Place de L'homme dans la Nature. Pierre Teilhard De Chardin. 15.95 (ISBN 0-685-36584-0). French & Eur.

Place in the Sun: Liberation Theology in the Third World. Theo Witvliet. Tr. by John Bowden from Dutch. LC 84-27229. Tr. of Fen Plaats onder de zon Bevrijdingstheologie in de Derde Wereld. 208p. (Orig.). 1985. pap. 8.95 (ISBN 0-88344-404-6). Orbis Bks.

Place of Faith & Grace in Judaism. David R. Blumenthal. 29p. (Orig.). 1985. pap. 3.50 (ISBN 0-918873-03-7). Ctr Judaic-Christ Studies.

Place of Help. Oswald Chambers. 1973. pap. 2.95 (ISBN 0-87508-139-8). Chr Lit.

Place of Pride: The Role of the Bishops in the Development of Catechesis in the United States. Mary C. Bryce. LC 84-17065. 227p. 1985. 25.95x (ISBN 0-8132-0595-6). Cath U Pr.

Place of St. Patrick in History & His Life. J. B. Burg. 59.95 (ISBN 0-8490-0839-5). Gordon Pr.

Place of Saint Thomas More in English Literature & History. R. W. Chambers. LC 65-15870. (English Biography Ser., No. 31). 1969. Repr. of 1937 ed. lib. bdg. 75.00x (ISBN 0-8383-0523-7). Haskell.

Place of Suffering. John Ferguson. 137p. 1972. 7.95 (ISBN 0-227-67803-6). Attic Pr.

Place of Wesley in the Christian Tradition: Essays Delevered at Drew University in Celebration of the Commencement of the Publication of the Oxford Edition of the Works of John Wesley. Ed. by Kenneth E. Rowe. LC 76-27659. 168p. 1976. 16.50 (ISBN 0-8108-0981-8). Scarecrow.

Place to Dig In. William H. Hinson. 1987. 10.95t (ISBN 0-687-31549-2). Abingdon.

Place to Stand: A Reformed Study of Creeds & Confessions. Cornelius Plantinga, Jr. LC 79-371. (Illus.). 1979. pap. text ed. 8.95 (ISBN 0-933140-01-0). CRC Pubns.

Place to Stand: When Life Throws You Off Balance. Mark Littleton. (Christian Living Ser.). 1986. pap. 6.95 (ISBN 0-88070-141-2). Multnomah.

Place to Start: The Bible As a Guide for Today. R. T. Brooks. 120p. 1983. pap. 4.95 (ISBN 0-86683-708-6, HarpR). Har-Row.

Placer De Estudiar la Biblia. Miguel Berg. (Span.). 127p. (Orig.). 1973. pap. 2.95 (ISBN 0-89922-026-6). Edit Caribe.

Placer Sexual Ordenado por Dios. Ed Wheat & Gaye De Wheat. 224p. 1980. 4.25 (ISBN 0-88113-320-5). Edit Betania.

Places & Visions Shared: The Collected Poems of Lawrence V. Jowers. Lawrence V. Jowers. Ed. by John E. Westburg. 64p. pap. 10.00 (ISBN 0-87423-032-2). Westburg.

Places I Like to Be. Evelyn M. Andre. LC 79-23964. (Illus.). 1980. 7.75g (ISBN 0-687-31540-9). Abingdon.

Places of the Bible. Gloria A. Truit. 1984. pap. 0.99 (59-1313). Concordia.

Places of Worship-Milwaukee. Mary E. Young & Wayne Attoe. (Publications in Architecture & Urban Planning Ser.). (Illus.). viii, 112p. 1977. 10.00 (ISBN 0-938744-46-1, R77-1). U of Wis Ctr Arch Urban.

Plain & Precious Things. Neal A. Maxwell. LC 83-72478. 103p. 1983. 6.95 (ISBN 0-87747-979-8). Deseret Bk.

Plain Dealing: Or News from New England. Thomas Lechford. 1969. Repr. of 1867 ed. 19.00 (ISBN 0-384-31985-8). Johnson Repr.

Plain People: An Ethnography of the Holdeman Mennonites. Linda L. Boynton. (Illus.). 222p. (Orig.). 1986. pap. text ed. 9.95x (ISBN 0-88133-198-8). Sheffield Wisc.

Plain Pine Box: A Return to Simple Jewish Funerals & Eternal Traditions. Arnold M. Goodman. 7.95x (ISBN 0-87068-895-2). Ktav.

Plain Prayers for a Complicated World. Avery Brooke. 124p. 1983. 5.95 (ISBN 0-8164-0501-8, HarpR); pap. 2.95 (ISBN 0-8164-2428-4). Har-Row.

Plain Talk on Acts. Manford G. Gutzke. 224p. 1972. pap. 7.95 (ISBN 0-310-25501-5, 9725P). Zondervan.

Plain Talk on Corinthians. Manford G. Gutzke. 1978. pap. 7.95 (ISBN 0-310-25641-0, 9858P). Zondervan.

Plain Talk on Ephesians. Manford G. Gutzke. 224p. 1973. pap. 6.95 (ISBN 0-310-25511-2, 9729P). Zondervan.

Plain Talk on Hebrews. Manford G. Gutzke. 160p. 1976. pap. 5.95 (ISBN 0-310-25541-4, 9852P). Zondervan.

Plain Talk on Isaiah. Manford G. Gutzke. 1977. pap. 6.95 (ISBN 0-310-25551-1, 9854P). Zondervan.

Plain Talk on James. Manford G. Gutzke. 1969. pap. 5.95 (ISBN 0-310-25561-9, 9728P). Zondervan.

Plain Talk on John. Manford G. Gutzke. LC 69-11646. (Prog. Bk.). 1969. pap. 7.95 (ISBN 0-310-25571-6, 9726P). Zondervan.

Plain Talk on Luke. Manford G. Gutzke. 1966. pap. 5.95 (ISBN 0-310-25581-3, 9097P). Zondervan.

Plain Talk on Mark. Manford G. Gutzke. 295p. 1975. pap. 6.95 (ISBN 0-310-25591-0, 9762P). Zondervan.

Plain Talk on Matthew. Manford G. Gutzke. pap. 6.95 (ISBN 0-310-25601-1, 9727P). Zondervan.

Plain Talk on Revelation. Manford G. Gutzke. (Orig.). 1979. pap. 5.95 (ISBN 0-310-25681-X, 9863P). Zondervan.

Plain Talk on the Epistles of John. Manford G. Gutzke. 1977. pap. 5.95 (ISBN 0-310-25631-3, 9857P). Zondervan.

Plain Talk on Timothy, Titus, & Philemon. Manford G. Gutzke. (Plain Talk Ser.). 1978. pap. 6.95 (ISBN 0-310-25661-5, 9861P). Zondervan.

Plain Talks on Parenting. William S. Deal. 1984. pap. 3.95 (ISBN 0-318-18715-9). Crusade Pubs.

Plain Truth About the Plain Truth. Salem Kirban. (Illus.). 1972. pap. 4.95 (ISBN 0-912582-12-X). Kirban.

Plaine Declaration That Our Brownists Be Full Donatists. George Gifford. LC 74-80180. (English Experience Ser.: No. 661). 1974. Repr. of 1590 ed. 14.00 (ISBN 90-221-0661-6). Walter J Johnson.

Plaine Mans Path-Way to Heaven. Arthur Dent. LC 74-80173. (English Experience Ser.: No. 652). 430p. 1974. Repr. of 1601 ed. 29.00 (ISBN 90-221-0652-7). Walter J Johnson.

Plainer Translation: Joseph Smith's Translation of the Bible, a History & Commentary. Robert J. Matthews. LC 75-5937. 1975. 15.95 (ISBN 0-8425-1411-2). Brigham.

Plains Cree Texts. Leonard Bloomfield. LC 73-3552. (American Ethnological Society. Publications Ser.: No. 16). Repr. of 1934 ed. 36.00 (ISBN 0-404-58166-8). AMS Pr.

Plains Indian Mythology. Rachlin & Marriott. 224p. 1977. pap. 3.95 (ISBN 0-452-00766-6, Mer). NAL.

Plan of Salvation. Ostis B. Wilson. 64p. pap. 0.50 (ISBN 0-686-29160-3). Faith Pub Hse.

Plan of Salvation & the Future in Prophecy. Duane S. Crowther. LC 72-173391. (Scripture Guide Ser.). 228p. 1971. pap. 5.95 (ISBN 0-88290-005-6). Horizon Utah.

Plan Para Memorizar las Escrituras. J. W. Alexander. Orig. Title: Fire in My Bones. 48p. 1981. Repr. of 1979 ed. 1.75 (ISBN 0-311-03660-0). Casa Bautista.

Plan to Win. Bill Glass & James E. McEachern. 160p. 1984. 8.95 (ISBN 0-8499-0431-5, 0431-5). Word Bks.

Planetary Influences Upon Plants: Cosmological Botany. Ernst M. Kranich. 184p. (Orig.). pap. 12.50 (ISBN 0-938250-20-5). Anthroposophic.

Planetary Theology. Tissa Balasuriya. LC 83-19339. 352p. (Orig.). 1984. pap. 10.95 (ISBN 0-88344-400-3). Orbis Bks.

Planets in Houses: Experiencing Your Environment Planets. Robert Pelletier. Ed. by Margaret Anderson. (Planets Ser.). (Illus.). 1978. pap. 19.95 (ISBN 0-914918-27-3). Para Res.

Planning a Christian Funeral: A Minister's Guide. Ed. by W. A. Poovey. LC 78-52198. 1978. pap. 7.95 (ISBN 0-8066-1668-7, 10-4990). Augsburg.

Planning a Christian Wedding. Paul M. Krause. 1963. pap. 0.95 (ISBN 0-570-03504-X, 14-2010). Concordia.

Planning a Christian Wedding. Don Talafous. 36p. 1985. pap. 1.00 (ISBN 0-8146-1407-8). Liturgical Pr.

Planning Bulletin Boards for Church & Synagogue Libraries. Janelle A. Paris. LC 83-7331. (CSLA Guide Two Ser. No. 11). (Orig.). 1983. pap. 6.95 (ISBN 0-915324-20-2); pap. 5.50 members. CSLA.

Planning Christian Education in Your Church. Kenneth D. Blazier & Evelyn M. Huber. LC 73-19585. 32p. (Orig.). 1974. pap. 1.00 (ISBN 0-8170-0633-8); pap. 2.95 spanish ed (ISBN 0-8170-0685-0). Judson.

Planning Family Ministry: A Guide for the Teaching Church. Joe Leonard, Jr. 64p. 1982. pap. 3.95 (ISBN 0-8170-0971-X). Judson.

Planning for Church Growth: A Comprehensive Guide: Developing a Total Program for Ministry. 299p. (Orig.). 1983. wkbk. 150.00 (ISBN 0-914307-42-8). Word Faith.

Planning for Single Young Adult Ministry: Directions for Ministerial Outreach. 65p. 1981. pap. 4.95 (ISBN 1-55586-738-3). US Catholic.

Planning for Stewardship: Developing a Giving Program for Congregations. Thomas Heyd. (Administration for Churches Ser.). 40p. (Orig.). 1980. pap. 3.95 (ISBN 0-8066-1782-9, 10-4992). Augsburg.

Planning for Sunday School Progress. Ray H. Hughes & Bernice Stout Woodard. 5.25 (ISBN 0-87148-682-2). Pathway Pr.

Planning for Teaching Church School. Donald L. Griggs. LC 85-12588. 64p. 1985. pap. 5.95 (ISBN 0-8170-1079-3). Judson.

Planning Growth in Your Church. Duncan McIntosh & Richard E. Rusbuldt. 224p. 1983. pap. 16.95 (ISBN 0-8170-1007-6). Judson.

Planning to Stay Together. Ed. by Terry R. Armstrong. Anne Armstrong. 1980. pap. 1.99 (ISBN 0-8309-0308-9). Herald Hse.

Planning Your Preaching. J. Winston Pearce. LC 78-73135. 1979. pap. 6.25 (ISBN 0-8054-2108-4). Broadman.

Plano de Deus para a Familia. Elvin Irwin. Orig. Title: Living on God's Family Plan. (Port.). 1986. write for info. (ISBN 0-8297-0708-5). Life Pubs Intl.

Planting & Development of Missionary Churches. John Nevius. 1974. pap. 2.45 (ISBN 0-87552-346-3). Presby & Reformed.

Planting & Growing a Fundamental Church. Roy Thomas. 1979. pap. 5.95 (ISBN 0-89265-070-2). Randall Hse.

Planting Churches Cross-Culturally. David J. Hesselgrave. 1980. pap. 12.95 (ISBN 0-8010-4219-4). Baker Bk.

Planting New Churches. F. J. Redford. LC 78-55694. 1979. 8.50 (ISBN 0-8054-6314-3). Broadman.

Planting of the Presbyterian Church in Northern Virginia Prior to the Organization of Winchester Presbytery, December Fourth, Seventeen Ninenty Four. James R. Graham. LC 26-22114. 168p. 1904. 15.00x (ISBN 0-685-65067-7). Va Bk.

Planting of the Swedish Church in America: Graduation Dissertation of Tobias Eric Biorck. Ed. & tr. by Ira O. Nothstein. LC 43-18182. (Augustana College Library Publication Ser.: No. 19). 39p. 1943. pap. 3.00x (ISBN 0-910182-14-0). Augustana Coll.

Plants of Hope. Robert Muller. (Chrysalis Bk). (Illus.). 128p. 1986. pap. 7.95 (ISBN 0-916349-04-7). Amity Hous Inc.

Plants of the Bible. Nancy Peelman. LC 75-14607. (Illus.). 40p. (Orig.). 1975. pap. 4.50 (ISBN 0-8192-1196-6). Morehouse.

Plants of the Bible: A Complete Handbook to all the Plants with 200 Full-Color Plates taken in the Natural Habitat. Michael Zohary. LC 82-4535. (Illus.). 224p. 1982. 17.95 (ISBN 0-521-24926-0). Cambridge U Pr.

Plastic Flowers in the Holy Water. George M. Bass. 1981. 4.35 (ISBN 0-89536-480-8, 1605). CSS of Ohio.

Plate of Hot Toast. Jeanette Lockerbie. (Quiet Time Bks.). 128p. (Orig.). 1971. pap. 3.50 (ISBN 0-8024-6625-7). Moody.

Platform Sutra of the Sixth Patriarch. Tr. by Philip B. Yampolsky. LC 67-11847. (Records of Civilization, Studies & Sources: No. 76). 1967. pap. 15.00x (ISBN 0-231-08361-0). Columbia U Pr.

Plato & Augustine: Taken from Vol. 1 of the Great Philosophers. Karl Jaspers. Tr. by Karl Manheim. LC 67-38117. Orig. Title: Great Philosophers, Vol. 1 (Pt. 2) 1966. pap. 4.95 (ISBN 0-15-672035-3, Harv). HarBraceJ.

Plato & Vedic Idealism. Swami Paramananda. (Orig.). 1924. 4.50 (ISBN 0-911564-15-2). Vedanta Ctr.

Plato Two: Ethics, Politics, & Philosophy of Art & Religion; a Collection of Critical Essays. Ed. by Gregory Vlastos. LC 77-19103. (Modern Studies in Philosophy). 1978. text ed. 16.95 (ISBN 0-268-01530-9); pap. text ed. 8.95x (ISBN 0-268-01531-7). U of Notre Dame Pr.

Platonic Bearings in Rabindranath. Bhaktivenode Chakraborty. 1986. 9.00x (ISBN 0-8364-1580-9, Pub. by KP Bagchi India). South Asia Bks.

Platonic Renaissance in England. Ernst Cassirer. LC 71-128186. 207p. 1970. Repr. of 1954 ed. 19.50x (ISBN 0-87752-128-X). Gordian.

Platonic Theology, Vol. II: Bks IV-VI. rev. ed. Proclus. Ed. by Robert Navon. Tr. by Thomas Taylor from Gr. LC 84-52789. (Great Works of Philosophy: Vol. II). Tr. of Six Books of Proclus on the Theology of Plato. 292p. 1986. text ed. 35.00 (ISBN 0-933601-05-0); pap. text ed. 22.50 (ISBN 0-933601-06-9). Selene Bks.

Platonic Theology: Vol. 1 - Books I-III. Rev. ed. Proclus. Ed. by Robert Navon. Tr. by Thomas Taylor from Greek. (Great Works of Philosophy Ser.: Vol. I). xxvi, 222p. 1985. text ed. 35.00 (ISBN 0-9609866-7-7); pap. text ed. 22.50 (ISBN 0-9609866-6-9). Selene Bks.

Platonic Tradition in English Religious Thought. William R. Inge. LC 77-8095. 1977. Repr. of 1926 ed. lib. bdg. 15.00 (ISBN 0-8414-5055-2). Folcroft.

Platonism & Cartesianism in the Philosophy of Ralph Cudworth. Lydia Gysi. 163p. 1962. 14.35 (ISBN 3-261-00648-X). P Lang Pubs.

Platonism of Gregory of Nyssa. Harold F. Cherniss. 1971. Repr. of 1930 ed. lib. bdg. 18.50 (ISBN 0-8337-0556-3). B Franklin.

Plato's "Parmenides" The "Conversion" of the Soul. Mitchell H. Miller, Jr. LC 85-43301. 264p. 1986. 30.00x (ISBN 0-691-07303-1). Princeton U PR.

Plato's Phaedo. Plato. Tr. by R. S. Bluck. 1955. pap. 7.87 scp (ISBN 0-672-60308-X, LLA110). Bobbs.

Plato's Theology. Friedrich Solmsen. 1942. 24.00 (ISBN 0-384-56600-6). Johnson Repr.

Platy: The Child in Us. Grady B. Brittain. LC 81-6503. (Illus.). 53p. (Orig.). 1981. pap. 0.50 (ISBN 0-86663-761-3). Ide Hse.

Play Called Corpus Christi. V. A. Kolve. LC 66-15301. 1966. 27.50x (ISBN 0-8047-0277-2); pap. 8.95 (ISBN 0-8047-0278-0, SP126). Stanford U Pr.

Play It: Team Games for Groups. Wayne Rice & Mike Yaconelli. 256p. 1986. pap. 10.95 (ISBN 0-310-35191-X, 10799). Zondervan.

Play of Consciousness. Swami Muktananda. LC 78-15841. (Illus.). 1979. pap. 7.64 (ISBN 0-06-066044-9, RD 223, HarpR). Har-Row.

Play of Consciousness. Swami Muktananda. LC 78-62769. 322p. 1978. 9.95 (ISBN 0-914602-36-5); pap. 6.95 (ISBN 0-914602-37-3). SYDA Found.

Play of Consciousness in the Web of the Universe. Edward L. Gardner. LC 86-30006. (Illus.). 224p. 1987. pap. 7.25 (ISBN 0-8356-0236-2). Theos Pub Hse.

Play of Daniel, a Thirteenth-Century Musical Drama. Ed. by Noah Greenberg & W. H. Auden. (Illus.). 1959. pap. 5.95 (ISBN 0-19-385195-4). Oxford U Pr.

Play of Herod: A Twelfth-Century Musical Drama. Ed. by Noah Greenberg & W. L. Smoldon. (Illus.). 1965. pap. 4.25 (ISBN 0-19-385196-2). Oxford U Pr.

Playboy Comes Home. C. M. Ward. LC 75-32603. 112p. (Orig.). 1976. pap. 1.25 (ISBN 0-88243-572-8, 02-0572). Gospel Pub.

Playboy to Priest. Kenneth J. Roberts. LC 78-169145. 304p. 1974. pap. 4.95 (ISBN 0-87973-782-4). Our Sunday Visitor.

Played by Ear. Daniel A. Lord. LC 56-7099. (Illus.). 1956. 11.95 (ISBN 0-8294-0049-4). Loyola.

Playing Dirty: The Secret War Against Beliefs. Omar V. Garrison. 13.95 (ISBN 0-931116-04-X). Church of Scient Info.

Playing Dirty: The Secret War Against Beliefs. Omar V. Garrison. LC 80-51315. (Illus.). 288p. 1980. 10.50 (ISBN 0-931116-04-X); pap. 4.95 (ISBN 0-931116-05-8). Ralston-Pilot.

Playing His Game. Vincent Bove. LC 84-70985. 1984. pap. 5.95 (ISBN 0-88270-570-9). Bridge Pub.

Playing Marbles with Diamonds: And Other Messages for America. Vance Havner. 80p. 1985. text ed. 7.95 (ISBN 0-8010-4290-9). Baker Bk.

Plays That'll Preach. Robert D. Huges. LC 85-365. 1985. pap. 4.95 (ISBN 0-8054-6812-9). Broadman.

Playwriters, Preachers & Politicians: A Study of Testament Dramas. Naomi E. Pasachoff. Ed. by James Hogg. (Elizabethan & Renaissance Studies). 162p. (Orig.). 1975. pap. 15.00 (ISBN 3-7052-0691-5, Pub. by Salzburg Studies). Longwood Pub Group.

Plead Your Case. Kenneth E. Hagin. 1979. pap. 0.50 mini bk. (ISBN 0-89276-058-3). Hagin Ministries.

Pleaders & Protesters: The Future of Citizens' Organizations in Israel. Eliezer D. Jaffe. LC 80-68431. 40p. 1980. pap. 2.50 (ISBN 0-87495-028-7). Am Jewish Comm.

Pleading the Case of the Fatherless. Dick Benjamin. 1982. pap. 0.95 (ISBN 0-911739-09-2). Abbott Loop.

Pleading with the Father. large print ed. Pearl Brians. 27p. 1985. pap. 4.50 (ISBN 0-914009-36-2). VHI Library.

Pleas for the West. Lyman Beecher. Ed. by Gerald Grob. LC 76-46067. (Anti-Movements in America). 1977. lib. bdg. 17.00x (ISBN 0-405-09941-X). Ayer Co Pubs.

Pleasant Paths. Vance Havner. (Direction Bks.). 96p. 1983. pap. 2.95 (ISBN 0-8010-4268-2). Baker Bk.

Please Don't Hurt Me. Grant Martin. 180p. 1987. pap. 6.95 (ISBN 0-89693-743-7). Victor Bks.

Please Don't Squeeze the Christian. Scott Sernau. 150p. (Orig.). 1987. pap. 4.95 (ISBN 0-87784-571-9). Inter Varsity.

Please Give a Devotion. Amy Bolding. 1963. 3.95 (ISBN 0-8010-0819-0). Baker Bk.

Please Give a Devotion for Active Teens. Amy Bolding. (Direction Bks). 1974. pap. 3.95 (ISBN 0-8010-0827-1). Baker Bk.

Please Give a Devotion for All Occasions. Amy Bolding. 1967. pap. 4.45 (ISBN 0-8010-0519-1). Baker Bk.

Please Give a Devotion for Church Groups. Amy Bolding. (Paperback Program Ser.). pap. 3.95 (ISBN 0-8010-0623-6). Baker Bk.

Please Give a Devotion: For Women's Groups. Amy Bolding. (Paperback Program Ser.). 108p. 1976. pap. 3.95 (ISBN 0-8010-0583-3). Baker Bk.

Please God. Gordon Stowell. (Little Fish Books About You & Me: III). 14p. 1984. mini-bk 0.59 (ISBN 0-8307-0954-1, 5608381). Regal.

Please, God, Help Me Get Well in Your Spare Time. Evelyn Kliewer. LC 79-17683. 128p. 1979. pap. 3.95 (ISBN 0-87123-027-5, 210027). Bethany Hse.

Please, Lord, Don't Put Me on Hold! Jane Graver. 1979. pap. 2.25 (ISBN 0-570-03790-5, 12-2753). Concordia.

Please, Lord, Untie My Tongue. K. Erickson. LC 12-2816. 1983. pap. 2.50 (ISBN 0-570-03881-2). Concordia.

Please Make Me Cry! Cookie Rodriguez. 1974. pap. 2.95 (ISBN 0-88368-042-4). Whitaker Hse.

Please Plan a Program. Amy Bolding. (Paperback Program Ser). (Orig.). 1971. pap. 3.95 (ISBN 0-8010-0527-2). Baker Bk.

Please Talk to Me, God! Donald Deffner. (Continued Applied Christianity). 1983. pap. 4.95 (ISBN 0-570-03899-5, 12-2981). Concordia.

Please Tell Me How You Feel. Marion Stroud. LC 83-22410. 160p. 1984. pap. 4.95 (ISBN 0-87123-427-0, 210427). Bethany Hse.

Pleasing God. David Hocking. 144p. 1985. pap. 5.95 (ISBN 0-89840-101-1). Heres Life.

Pleasing God. David L. Hocking. LC 84-47802. 144p. 1984. Heres Life.

Pleasure & Business in Western Pennsylvania: The Journal of Joshua Gilpin, 1809. Ed. by Joseph E. Walker. LC 75-623536. (Illus.). 156p. 1975. 9.00 (ISBN 0-911124-78-0). Pa Hist & Mus.

Pleasure of God's Company. Patrica G. Opatz. 96p. 1985. pap. 3.95 (ISBN 0-8146-1437-X). Liturgical Pr.

Pleasures Forevermore: The Theology of C. S. Lewis. John R. Willis. 157p. 1983. 12.95 (ISBN 0-8294-0446-5). Loyola.

Pleasures of Being a Catholic. new ed. Leo Panzion. (Human Development Library Bk.). (Illus.). 1979. Set. 49.75 (ISBN 0-89266-155-0). Am Classical Coll Pr.

Plenty for Everyone. Corrie ten Boom. 1967. pap. 2.95 (ISBN 0-87508-023-5). Chr Lit.

Pleroma: An Essay on the Origin of Christianity. Paul Carus. 163p. 1921. pap. 4.95 (ISBN 0-317-40408-3). Open Court.

Pleroma Trinitatis: Die Trinitaetstheologie bei Matthias Joseph Scheeben. Karl-Heinz Minz. (Disputationes Theologicae Ser.: Vol. 10). 404p. 1982. 40.55 (ISBN 3-8204-6182-5). P Lang Pubs.

Pletzl of Paris: Jewish Immigrant Workers in the Belle Epoque. Nancy L Green. 278p. 1985. 39.55 (ISBN 0-8419-0995-4). Holmes & Meier.

Plight of Man & the Power of God. D. Martyn Lloyd-Jones. (Summit Bks.). 96p. 1982. pap. 2.95 (ISBN 0-8010-5621-7). Baker Bk.

Plot Against Christianity. Elizabeth Dilling. 310p. 12.00 (ISBN 0-913022-33-0). Angriff Pr.

Plot Against Christianity: A Study of the Talmud. E. Dilling. 1982. lib. bdg. 69.95 (ISBN 0-87700-359-9). Revisionist Pr.

Plot Against the Catholic Church: Communism, Free Masonry & the Jewish Fifth Column in the Clergy. M. Pinay. 1979. lib. bdg. 69.95 (ISBN 0-8490-2984-8). Gordon Pr.

Plot Against the Church. Maurice Pinay. 1978. 15.00x (ISBN 0-911038-39-6). Noontide.

Plot to Kill the Pope. Paul Henze. 224p. 1985. pap. 4.50 rack size (ISBN 0-684-18357-9). Scribner.

Plotin & l'Occident: Firmicus Maternus, Marius Victorinus, Saint Augustin, et Macrobe. P. Henry. (Classical Studies Ser.). (Fr.). Repr. of 1934 ed. lib. bdg. 39.50x (ISBN 0-697-00039-7). Irvington.

Plotinus. G. R. Mead. 1983. pap. 5.95 (ISBN 0-916411-01-X, Pub. by Alexandrian Pr). Holmes Pub.

Plotinus: Essay on the Beautiful. Plotinus. Tr. by Thomas Taylor. 1984. pap. 5.95 (ISBN 0-916411-86-9, Pub. by Alexandrian Pr). Holmes Pub.

Plug into a Rainbow. Joyce Ellis. 144p. (Orig.). 1984. pap. 3.95 (ISBN 0-310-47192-3, 12495P). Zondervan.

Plum Jelly & Stained Glass & Other Prayers. Jo Carr & Imogene Sorley. 1981. pap. 2.50 (ISBN 0-687-31660-X, Festival). Abingdon.

Pluralism & Truth in Religion. John F. Kane. Ed. by Wendell Dietrich. LC 80-20659. (American Academy of Religion Dissertation Ser.). 1981. 13.95 (ISBN 0-89130-413-4, 01-01-33); pap. 9.95 (ISBN 0-89130-414-2). Scholars Pr GA.

Pluralism: Challenge to World Religions. Harold Coward. LC 84-14737. 144p. (Orig.). 1985. pap. 8.95 (ISBN 0-88344-710-X). Orbis Bks.

Plurality & Ambiguity: Religion As Test Case for Hermeneutics. David Tracy. 175p. 1985. 14.95 (ISBN 0-86683-983-6, 8567, HarpR). Har-Row.

Plymouth Colony Probate Guide: Where to Find Wills & Related Data for 800 People of Plymouth Colony, 1620-1691. Ruth W. Sherman & Robert S. Wakefield. LC 83-2362. (Plymouth Colony Research Group Ser.: No.2). xxi, 167p. 1983. 21.00x (ISBN 0-910233-01-2). Plymouth Col.

Plymouth Rock & the Pilgrims: And Other Salutary Opinions. Mark Twain. Ed. by Charles Neider. LC 84-47603. 320p. 1984. 19.45i (ISBN 0-06-015353-9, HarpT). Har-Row.

Pneumatikos-Psychikos Terminology in First Corinthians. Birger A. Pearson. LC 73-92202. (Society of Biblical Literature. Dissertation Ser.). 1975. pap. 8.95 (ISBN 0-88414-034-2, 060112). Scholars Pr GA.

Pocket Bible Ready Reference for Personal Workers. Ernest A. Clevenger, Jr. (Bible Ready Reference Ser.). 24p. (Orig.). 1982. pap. 0.50 (ISBN 0-88428-011-X). Parchment Pr.

Pocket Book of Bible Prayers. David E. Rosage. 224p. (Orig.). 1987. compact ed. 5.95 (ISBN 0-89283-320-3). Servant.

Pocket Book of Prayers. M. Basil Pennington. LC 85-12936. 192p. 1986. pap. 4.50 (ISBN 0-385-23298-5, Im). Doubleday.

Pocket Catholic Dictionary. John A. Hardon. LC 85-5790. 528p. 1985. pap. 6.95 (ISBN 0-385-23238-1, Im). Doubleday.

Pocket Concordance to the New Testament. Charles J. Hazelton. 1984. leather flex 4.95 (ISBN 0-8407-5824-3). Nelson.

Pocket Dictionary of Irish Myth & Legend. Ronan Coghlan. (Pocket Bk.). (Illus.). 96p. (Orig.). 1985. pap. 3.95 (ISBN 0-86281-152-X, Pub. by Appletree Pr). Irish Bks Media.

Pocket Dictionary of Saints. John J. Delaney. LC 82-45479. 528p. 1983. pap. 6.95 (ISBN 0-385-18274-0, Im). Doubleday.

Pocket Guide for the Church Choir Member. Kenneth W. Osbeck. 48p. 1984. pap. 1.25 (ISBN 0-8254-3408-4); Per Dozen. pap. 12.95 (ISBN 0-8254-3417-3). Kregel.

Pocket Guide to the New Testament. Francis Foulkes. LC 77-27742. 1978. pap. 2.95 (ISBN 0-87784-580-8). Inter-Varsity.

Pocket Interlinear New Testament. Ed. by Jay P. Green. 1981. pap. 5.95 (ISBN 0-8010-3777-8). Baker Bk.

Pocket Lexicon of Freemasonry. 3.50 (ISBN 0-685-19495-7). Powner.

Pocket Lexicon to the Greek New Testament. Ed. by Alexander Souter. 1916. 17.95x (ISBN 0-19-864203-2). Oxford U Pr.

Pocket Parables. Carl G. Carlozzi & Ellen Parkes. 80p. (Orig.). 1985. pap. 2.95 (ISBN 0-8423-4919-7). Tyndale.

Pocket Praise. Robert C. Savage. (Pocket Ser.). 176p. 1985. pap. 2.95 (ISBN 0-8423-4931-6). Tyndale.

Pocket Prayer Book: Large-Type Edition. Compiled by Ralph S. Cushman. 1977. 5.00x (ISBN 0-8358-0361-9). Upper Room.

Pocket Prayers: Seven Hundred & Seventy-Seven Bible Ways to Pray. Robert C. Savage. 1982. pap. 2.95 (ISBN 0-8423-4849-2). Tyndale.

Pocket Promise Book. gift ed. David Wilkerson. LC 72-86208. 96p. 1981. imitation leather 3.95 (ISBN 0-8307-0789-1, 5007953). Regal.

Pocket Treasury of Daily Devotions. Al Bryant. LC 77-82183. 112p. 1978. pap. 3.50 (ISBN 0-87123-464-5, 200464). Bethany Hse.

Pocket Treasury of Devotional Verse. Compiled by Al Bryant. 160p. (Orig.). 1980. pap. 3.50 (ISBN 0-87123-466-1, 200466). Bethany Hse.

Pocketful of Hope. Mary C. Crowley. 352p. 1981. 12.50 (ISBN 0-8007-1272-2). Revell.

Pocketful of Puppets: Poems for Church School. Lynn Irving. Ed. by Merily H. Keller. (Puppetry in Education ser.). (Illus.). 48p. (Orig.). 1982. 11.50; pap. 7.50 (ISBN 0-931044-05-7). Renfro Studios.

Poder De la Oracion Tenaz. Juan Bisagno. Tr. by Olivia S. D. De Lerin from Eng. Orig. Title: Power of Positive Praying. (Span.). 96p. 1983. pap. 2.15 (ISBN 0-311-40029-9). Casa Bautista.

Poder para Vencer. Michael Harper. 1982. 2.95 (ISBN 0-88113-245-4). Edit Betania.

Poder Sanador de la Gracia. William P. Wilson & Kathryn Slattery. Ed. by Mario Llerena. Tr. by Luis Bernal from Span. Orig. Title: Grace to Grow. 176p. 1985. pap. text ed. 2.95 (ISBN 0-8297-0744-1). Life Pubs Intl.

Poderes Tecnologicos y la Persona. 370p. 1984. pap. cancelled (ISBN 0-935372-16-4). Pope John Ctr.

Poeme Babylonien de la Creation. Enuma Elish. LC 78-72734. (Ancient Mesopotamian Texts & Studies). Repr. of 1935 ed. 24.50 (ISBN 0-404-18173-2). AMS Pr.

Poems, Vol. 1. Prudentius. LC 63-5499. (Fathers of the Church Ser: Vol. 43). 343p. 1962. 16.95x (ISBN 0-8132-0043-1). Cath U Pr.

Poems, Vol. 2. Prudentius. LC 63-5499. (Fathers of the Church Ser: Vol. 52). 224p. 1965. 15.95x (ISBN 0-8132-0052-0). Cath U Pr.

Poems & Hymn Tunes As Songs: Metrical Partners. Joseph Jones. 84p. 1983. with 2 audio cassettes 24.50, (ISBN 0-88432-119-3, S1560). J Norton Pubs.

Poems in One Part Harmony. T. J. Reddy. 60p. 1980. pap. 4.00 (ISBN 0-932112-07-2). Carolina Wren.

Poems of Cloister & Jungle, a Buddhist Anthology. Rhys Davids. 59.95 (ISBN 0-8490-0849-2). Gordon Pr.

Poems of St. John of the Cross. St. John Of The Cross. Tr. & intro. by Willis Barnstone. LC 68-14597. (Eng. & Span.). 144p. 1972. pap. 4.95 (ISBN 0-8112-0449-9, NDP341). New Directions.

Poems of St. Paulinus of Nola. Ed. by J. Quasten. Tr. by P. G. Walsh. (Ancient Christian Writers Ser.: Vol. 40). 1975. 14.95 (ISBN 0-8091-0197-1). Paulist Pr.

Poems of the Holocaust: From the Diary of Luba Krugman Gurdus. bilingual ed. (Illus.). 1985. 12.95 (ISBN 0-8052-5059-X, Dist. by Schocken). Holocaust Pubns.

Poems, Prayers & Graces. Sally Gregory. (Illus.). 28p. 1987. 12.95 (ISBN 0-340-34873-9, Pub. by Hodder & Stoughton UK). David & Charles.

Poems to the Child-God: Structures & Strategies in the Poetry of Surdas. Kenneth E. Bryant. LC 77-80467. (Center for South & Southeast Asia Studies, UC Berkeley). 1978. 33.00x (ISBN 0-520-03540-2). U of Cal Pr.

Poesia y Profecia del Antiquo Testamento. C. H. Benson. Tr. by Fernando P. Villalobos from Eng. (Curso Para Maestros Cristianos: No. 2). (Span.). 122p. 1972. pap. 3.50 (ISBN 0-89922-010-X). Edit Caribe.

Poet & the Historian: Essays in Literary & Historical Biblical Criticism. Richard E. Friedman. LC 83-9035. (Harvard Semitic Studies). 172p. 1983. 13.50 (ISBN 0-89130-629-3, 04 04 26). Scholars Pr GA.

Poet Philosophers of the Rig Veda. C. Kunhan Raja. (Sanskrit & eng.). 10.00 (ISBN 0-89744-121-4, Pub. by Ganesh & Co. India). Auromere.

Poet Pope. Ed. by Diana Kwiatkowski. 67p. 1981. 9.50 (ISBN 0-933906-16-1); pap. 4.50 (ISBN 0-933906-15-3). Gusto Pr.

Poetae Christiani Minores, Pt. 1. (Corpus Scriptorum Ecclesiasticorum Latinorum Ser: Vol. 16). 1888. 50.00 (ISBN 0-384-47060-2). Johnson Repr.

Poetic Drama of Paul Claudel. Joseph Chiari. LC 71-90365. 1969. Repr. of 1954 ed. 15.00x (ISBN 0-87752-018-6). Gordian.

Poetic Edda. rev. ed. Tr. by Lee M. Hollander from Norse. 375p. 1986. pap. 12.95 (ISBN 0-292-76499-5). U of Tex Pr.

Poetics & Interpretation of Biblical Narrative. Adele Berlin. (Bible & Literature Ser.: No. 9). 180p. 1983. text ed. 22.95x (ISBN 0-907459-23-4, Pub. by Almond Pr England); pap. text ed. 10.95x (ISBN 0-907459-24-2). Eisenbrauns.

Poetics of Biblical Narrative. Meir Sternberg. (Literary Biblical Ser.). 380p. cancelled (ISBN 0-8245-0640-5). Crossroad NY.

Poetics of Biblical Narrative: Ideological Literature & the Drama of Reading. Meir Sternberg. LC 85-42752. (Indiana Studies in Biblical Literature). 596p. 1985. 57.50x (ISBN 0-253-34521-9). Ind U Pr.

Poetics of Conversion: Number Symbolism & Alchemy in Gottfried's "Tristan". Susan L. Clark & Julian N. Wasserman. (Utah Studies in Literature & Linguistics: Vol. 7). 168p. 1977. pap. 20.90 (ISBN 3-261-02085-7). P Lang Pubs.

Poetics of Love: Meditations with John of the Cross. Mary E. Giles. (American University Studies VII-Theology & Religion). 177p. 1987. text ed. 20.00 (ISBN 0-8204-0321-0). P Lang Pubs.

Poetics of Reverie: Childhood, Language & the Cosmos. Gaston Bachelard. 1971. pap. 8.95x (ISBN 0-8070-6413-0, BP375). Beacon Pr.

Poetry & Dogma. Malcolm M. Ross. LC 78-86284. 1969. Repr. of 1954 ed. lib. bdg. 18.50x (ISBN 0-374-96973-6, Octagon). Hippocrene Bks.

Poetry & Drama in the York Corpus Christi Play. Richard Collier. LC 77-21348. 303p. 1977. 27.50 (ISBN 0-208-01611-2, Archon). Shoe String.

Poetry & Faith. Augustus Ralli. LC 76-16831. 1976. Repr. of 1951 ed. lib. bdg. 20.00 (ISBN 0-8414-7316-1). Folcroft.

Poetry & Religion As Drama. Prabodh C. Ghosh. 1979. Repr. of 1965 ed. lib. bdg. 25.00 (ISBN 0-8492-4940-6). R West.

Poetry & Speculation of the Rg Veda. Willard Johnson, Jr. LC 80-14040. (Hermaneutics: Studies in the History of Religions). 175p. 1980. 25.95x (ISBN 0-520-02560-1). U of Cal Pr.

Poetry & the Fountain of Light: Observations on the Conflict Between Christian & Classical Traditions in Seventeenth-Century Poetry. Harold R. Swardson. LC 62-9993. 1962. 4.50x (ISBN 0-8262-0015-X). U of Mo Pr.

Poetry from the Bible. Ed. by Lincoln MacVeagh. 180p. 1981. Repr. of 1925 ed. lib. bdg. 30.00 (ISBN 0-8495-3531-X). Arden Lib.

Poetry of Baruch: A Reconstruction & Analysis of the Original Hebrew Text of Baruch 3: 9-5: 9. Ed. by David G. Burke. LC 80-10271. (Society of Biblical Literature, Septuagint & Cognate Studies: No. 10). pap. 15.95 (ISBN 0-89130-382-0, 06-04-10). Scholars Pr GA.

Poetry of Sacred Song. John M. Shaw. 1972. 3.00 (ISBN 0-9607778-6-5). Friends Fla St.

Poetry of the Old Testament. Theodore H. Robinson. LC 75-41233. Repr. of 1947 ed. 15.00 (ISBN 0-404-14593-0). AMS Pr.

Poetry of the Old Testament. Sanford C. Yoder. 426p. 1948. pap. 9.95 (ISBN 0-8361-1709-3). Herald Pr.

Poetry of the Passion: Studies in Twelve Centuries of English Verse. J. A. Bennett. 1982. 37.50x (ISBN 0-19-812804-5); pap. 16.95x (ISBN 0-19-812832-0). Oxford U Pr.

Poets & Mystics. facs. ed. Edward I. Watkin. LC 68-55862. (Essay Index Reprint Ser). 1953. 19.00 (ISBN 0-8369-0979-8). Ayer Co Pubs.

Poets & Prophets of Israel. Charles W. Conn. 1981. 5.25 (ISBN 0-87148-707-1); pap. 4.25 (ISBN 0-87148-708-X). Pathway Pr.

Poets & Their Critics: Langland & Milton. R. W. Chambers. 1942. lib. bdg. 10.00 (ISBN 0-685-10478-8). Folcroft.

Poets Chantry. Katherine Bregy. LC 70-105766. 1970. Repr. of 1912 ed. 21.50x (ISBN 0-8046-1043-6, Pub. by Kennikat). Assoc Faculty Pr.

Poets' Life of Christ. Norman Ault. 30.00 (ISBN 0-686-17669-3). Quaker City.

Poets of the Church. Edwin F. Hatfield. LC 77-91533. 1977. Repr. of 1884 ed. lib. bdg. 45.00 (ISBN 0-89341-195-7). Longwood Pub Group.

Poets of the Church: A Series of Biographical Sketches of Hymn-Writers, with Notes on Their Hymns. Edwin F. Hatfield. 1979. Repr. of 1884 ed. 110.00x (ISBN 0-8103-4291-X). Gale.

Poets of Transcendentalism: An Anthology. George W. Cooke. 59.95 (ISBN 0-8490-0868-9). Gordon Pr.

Poets of Transcendentalism: An Anthology. Ed. by George W. Cooke. LC 72-126410. (Literature & Criticism Ser). 1971. Repr. of 1903 ed. lib. bdg. 21.00 (ISBN 0-8337-0652-7). B Franklin.

Poets on Christmas. Ed. by William Knight. Repr. of 1907 ed. lib. bdg. 25.00 (ISBN 0-8495-3016-4). Arden Lib.

Poets, Prophets & Pragmatists: A New Challenge to Religious Life. Evelyn Woodward. LC 86-72375. 248p. (Orig.). 1987. pap. 6.95 (ISBN 0-87793-349-9). Ave Maria.

Poets, Prophets, & Sages: Essays in Biblical Interpretation. Robert Gordis. LC 79-98984. pap. 111.50 (ISBN 0-317-37273-4, 2055498). Bks Demand UMI.

Poet's Time: Politics & Religion in the Work of Andrew Marvell. Warren L. Chernaik. LC 82-4395. 250p. 1983. 37.50 (ISBN 0-521-24773-X). Cambridge U Pr.

Poets Walk In. Anna P. Broomell. 1983. pap. 2.50x (ISBN 0-87574-077-4, 077). Pendle Hill.

Poets's Life of Christ. Norman Ault. LC 72-2513. (Select Bibliographies Reprint Ser). 1972. Repr. of 1922 ed. 22.00 (ISBN 0-8369-6847-6). Ayer Co Pubs.

Poimandres As Myth: Scholarly Theory & Gnostic Meaning. Robert A. Segal. (Religion & Reason Ser.: No. 33). 216p. 1986. lib. bdg. 58.00x (ISBN 0-89925-146-3). Mouton.

Point After: Advice from God's Athletes. Elliot Johnson. 128p. 1987. pap. 5.95 (ISBN 0-310-26171-6, 12416P). Zondervan.

Point Loma Community in California, 1897-1942: A Theosophical Experiment. Emmett A. Greenwalt. LC 76-42802. Repr. of 1955 ed. 22.00 (ISBN 0-404-60068-9). AMS Pr.

Point Loma Theosophical Society: A List of Publications, 1898 - 1942. Loren R. Brown. LC 81-187499. (Illus.). 136p. 1977. pap. 10.00 (ISBN 0-913510-46-7). Wizards.

Point of Christology. Schubert M. Ogden. LC 81-47842. 224p. 1982. 14.00i (ISBN 0-06-066352-9, HarpR). Har-Row.

Point of View. Paul Carus. Ed. by Catherine E. Cook. (Illus.). 227p. 1927. 16.95 (ISBN 0-87548-268-6). Open Court.

Pointed Tales. William C. Dixon. LC 80-81102. 98p. (Orig.). 1980. pap. 5.95 (ISBN 0-8192-1270-9). Morehouse.

Pointers from Nisargadatta Maharaj. Ramesh s. Balsekar. LC 82-71505. xiv, 223p. 1983. Repr. of 1984 ed. 13.50 (ISBN 0-89386-004-2). Acorn NC.

Pointing the Way. Rajneesh. 1979. text ed. 10.95 (ISBN 0-89684-070-0, Pub. by Motilal Banarsidass Delhi). Orient Bk Dist.

Pointing the Way with Puppets. Pat Zabriskie. LC 81-81240. 80p. 1981. pap. 3.95 (ISBN 0-88243-574-4, 02-0574). Gospel Pub.

Points for Emphasis, Nineteen Eighty-Seven to Eighty-Eight. William J. Fallis. (Orig.). 1987. pap. 3.95 (ISBN 0-8054-1560-2). Broadman.

Points for Emphasis, Nineteen Eighty-Seven to Eighty-Eight. William J. Fallis. 1987. pap. 2.95 (ISBN 0-8054-1559-9). Broadman.

Points with Punch. Dennis Fakes. 1982. pap. 5.00 (ISBN 0-89536-534-0, 1616). CSS of Ohio.

Poland's Millenium of Christianity. Canadian Polish Millenium Fund Staff. (Eng. & Fr.). 50p. 1966. 1.00 (ISBN 0-940962-29-2). Polish Inst Art & Sci.

Polar Structures in the Book of Qohelet. Jamer A. Loader. (Beihefte aur Zeitschrift fuer die alttestamentliche Wissenschaft). 150p. 1979. text ed. 32.75x (ISBN 3-11-007636-5). De Gruyter.

Policies & Procedures for the Pastoral Care Department. Robert D. Wheelock. LC 76-9660. 1977. pap. 4.00 (ISBN 0-87125-036-5). Cath Health.

Policies of Genocide: Jews & Soviet Prisoners of War in Nazi Germany. Ed. by Gerhard Hirschfeld. (Illus.). 176p. 1986. text ed. 24.95x (ISBN 0-04-943045-9); pap. text ed. 9.95x (ISBN 0-04-943046-7). Allen Unwin.

Policy & Police: The Enforcement of the Reformation in the Age of Thomas Cromwell. G. R. Elton. 458p. 1985. pap. 14.95 (ISBN 0-521-31309-0). Cambridge U Pr.

Polish Catholics in Chicago, 1850-1920: A Religious History. Joseph J. Parot. LC 81-11297. 298p. 22.50 (ISBN 0-87580-081-5); pap. 10.00 (ISBN 0-87580-527-2). N Ill U Pr.

Polish Jew. B. C. Baskerville. 75.00 (ISBN 0-8490-0870-0). Gordon Pr.

Polish-Jewish Relations During the Second World War. Emmanuel Ringelblum. Tr. by Dafna Allon et al. LC 76-1394. 330p. 1976. 35.00x (ISBN 0-86527-155-0). Fertig.

Polish Jews: A Pictorial Record. Roman Vishniac. LC 65-25413. (Illus.). 1968. pap. 7.95 (ISBN 0-8052-0360-5). Schocken.

Polish Jews: The Final Chapter. Earl Vinecour. LC 77-83266. (Illus.). 1977. 17.50x (ISBN 0-8147-8756-8). NYU Pr.

Polish Jews: The Final Chapter. Earl Vinecour & Charles Fishman. (Paperbacks Ser). (Orig.). 1977. pap. 5.95 (ISBN 0-07-067490-6). McGraw.

Polish Jews, 1914-1939. Ed. by Nachman Tamir. LC 85-47709. (Illus.). 216p. 1986. 19.95 (ISBN 0-8453-4791-8, Cornwall Bks). Assoc Univ Prs.

Polish Love Story. Ron Manske. LC 79-84322. (Illus.). 1979. pap. 2.50 (ISBN 0-89221-060-5). New Leaf.

Polite Escape: On the Myth of Secularization. Harry J. Ausmus. xii, 189p. 1982. lib. bdg. 22.95x (ISBN 0-8214-0650-7, 82-84192). Ohio U Pr.

Political Activities of the Baptists & the Fifth Monarchy Men in England During the Interregnum. Louise F. Brown. 1964. Repr. of 1911 ed. 20.50 (ISBN 0-8337-0399-4). B Franklin.

Political & Ecclesiastical Allegory of First Book of the Faerie Queen. Frederick M. Padelford. 1911. lib. bdg. 10.00 (ISBN 0-8414-9237-9). Folcroft.

Political & Ecclesiastical Allegory of the First Book of the Fairie Queen. Frederick M. Padelford. LC 70-111785. Repr. of 1911 ed. 5.00 (ISBN 0-404-04856-0). AMS Pr.

Political & Economic Activities of the Jesuits in the Plata Region. Magnus Morner. 1976. lib. bdg. 59.95 (ISBN 0-8490-2451-X). Gordon Pr.

Political & Social Ideas of St. Augustine. Herbert A. Deane. LC 63-9809. 356p. 1963. pap. 14.00x (ISBN 0-231-08569-9). Columbia U Pr.

Political & Social Rights & Human Dignity. Canadian Christian Movement for Peace Staff. (People Living for Justice Ser.). 208p. 1984. pap. text ed. 29.95 (ISBN 0-317-19703-7). Wm C Brown.

Political Anti-Semitism in England 1918-1939. Gisela C. Lebzelter. LC 78-16795. 222p. 1979. text ed. 49.50x (ISBN 0-8419-0426-X). Holmes & Meier.

Political Babylon. 32p. (Orig.). 1982. pap. 0.95 (ISBN 0-937408-16-6). GMI Pubns Inc.

Political Buddhism in Southeast Asia: The Role of the Sangha in the Modernization of Thailand. Somboon Suksamran. LC 77-77606. (Illus.). 1977. 20.00x (ISBN 0-312-62137-X). St Martin.

Political Expectation. Paul Tillich. Ed. by James L. Adams. LC 83-10294. 208p. 1983. pap. text ed. 11.25 (ISBN 0-8191-3320-5). U Pr of Amer.

Political Ideas of St. Thomas Aquinas: A Selection from His Writings. St. Thomas Aquinas. 1973. pap. 9.95x (ISBN 0-317-30522-0). Free Pr.

Political Ideas of St. Thomas Aquinas. St. Thomas Aquinas. Ed. by Dino Bigongiari. (Library of Classics Ser.: No. 15). 1973. pap. text ed. 7.95x (ISBN 0-02-840380-0). Hafner.

Political Intrigue in the Establishment of the Identity of Jesus & Mary. James H. Boykin. LC 86-90957. 286p. 1986. pap. 15.00x (ISBN 0-9603342-6-2). Boykin.

Political Issues in Luke-Acts. Ed. by Richard J. Cassidy & Philip J. Scharper. LC 82-19060. 192p. (Orig.). 1983. 16.95 (ISBN 0-88344-390-2); pap. 9.95 (ISBN 0-88344-385-6). Orbis Bks.

Political Personality of Islam. Fida E. Islam. 280p. 1985. pap. 6.95 (ISBN 0-940368-37-4). Tahrike Tarsile Quran.

Political Philosophy of Modern Shinto: A Study of the State Religion of Japan. Daniel C. Holtom. LC 84-3072. (BCC Ser.). 338p. 1984. Repr. of 1922 ed. 37.50 (ISBN 0-404-15937-0). AMS Pr.

Political Philosophy of Sri Aurobindo. 2nd rev. ed. V. P. Varma. 1976. 12.50 (ISBN 0-8426-0873-7). Orient Bk Dist.

Political Philosophy of the Orthodox Church. Apostolos Makrakis. Ed. by Orthodox Christian Educational Society. Tr. by Denver Cummings from Hellenic. Orig. Title: Orthodox Definition of Political Science. 163p. (Orig.). 1965. pap. 4.00x (ISBN 0-938366-11-4). Orthodox Chr.

Political Pulpit. Roderick P. Hart. LC 76-12290. 160p. 1977. 7.95 (ISBN 0-911198-44-X). Purdue U Pr.

Political Religions. Erich Voegelin. (TST Ser.: No. 23). 1986. 39.95x (ISBN 0-88946-767-6). E Mellen.

Political, Religious & Love Poems. Ed. by Frederick J. Furnivall. 348p. 1981. Repr. of 1866 ed. lib. bdg. 75.00 (ISBN 0-89987-276-X). Darby Bks.

Political Role of Mongol Buddhism. Larry W. Moses. LC 81-622859. (Indiana University Uralic & Altaic Ser.: Vol. 133). x, 299p. 1977. 15.00 (ISBN 0-933070-01-2). Ind U Res Inst.

Political Role of Religion on the U. S. Ed. by John E. Rouse, Jr. et al. (Special Study Ser.). 300p. 1985. pap. text ed. 24.50x (ISBN 0-8133-7030-2). Westview.

Political Struggle of Active Homosexuals to Gain Social Acceptance. George A. Kelly. 106p. 1975. pap. 1.50 (ISBN 0-8199-0365-5). Franciscan Herald.

Political System of the Anuak of the Anglo-Egyptian Sudan. Edward E. Evans-Pritchard. LC 74-15036. (London School of Economics & Political Science Monographs on Social Anthropology: No. 4). Repr. of 1940 ed. 27.50 (ISBN 0-404-12041-5). AMS Pr.

Political Testament of Cardinal Richelieu: The Significant Chapters & Supporting Selections. Tr. by Henry B. Hill. (Illus.). 148p. 1961. 15.00x (ISBN 0-299-02420-2); pap. 8.95x (ISBN 0-299-02424-5). U of Wis Pr.

Political Theology: Four Chapters on the Concept of Sovereignity. Carl Schmitt. Tr. by George Schwab from Ger. (German Social Thought Ser.). 75p. 1985. 15.00x (ISBN 0-262-19244-6). MIT Pr.

Political Theories of Martin Luther. Luther H. Waring. LC 68-15837. 1968. Repr. of 1910 ed. 21.50x (ISBN 0-8046-0488-6, Pub. by Kennikat). Assoc Faculty Pr.

Political Theory & Institutions of the Khawarij. Elie A. Salem. LC 78-64226. (Johns Hopkins University. Studies in the Social Sciences. Seventy-Fourth Ser. 1956: 2). Repr. of 1956 ed. 15.50 (ISBN 0-404-61328-4). AMS Pr.

Political Theory As Public Confession. Peter D. Bathory. LC 80-15667. 180p. 1981. 24.95 (ISBN 0-87855-405-X). Transaction Bks.

Political Theory of Eric Voegelin. Barry Cooper. LC 86-23517. (Toronto Studies in Theology: Vol. 21). 256p. 1986. text ed. 49.95 (ISBN 0-88946-771-4). E Mellen.

Political Theory of Islam. A. A. Maududi. pap. 1.00 (ISBN 0-686-18547-1). Kazi Pubns.

Political Theory of John Wyclif. Lowrie J. Daly. LC 62-20515. (Jesuit Studies). 1962. 4.95 (ISBN 0-8294-0020-6). Loyola.

Political Thought in Medieval Islam: An Introductory Outline. Erwin I. Rosenthal. LC 85-21909. ix, 345p. 1985. Repr. of 1958 ed. lib. bdg. 47.50x (ISBN 0-313-25094-4, JA82). Greenwood.

Political Thought of Martin Luther. W. D. Cargill-Thompson. Ed. by Philip Broadhead. LC 83-27521. 204p. 1984. 27.50x (ISBN 0-389-20468-4, 08029). B&N Imports.

Political Transformation of the Brazilian Catholic Church. Thomas C. Bruneau. LC 73-79318. (Perspective on Development Ser.: Vol. 2). pap. 71.00 (ISBN 0-317-28009-0, 2025579). Bks Demand UMI.

Political Uses of Symbols. Charles D. Elder & Roger W. Cobb. Ed. by Irving Rockwood. LC 82-12722. (Professional Studies in Political Communication). (Illus.). 192p. 1983. text ed. 22.50x (ISBN 0-582-28392-2); pap. text ed. 10.95 (ISBN 0-582-28393-0). Longman.

Political World of American Zionism. LC 61-10126. pap. 112.30 (ISBN 0-317-08433-X, 2001332). Bks Demand UMI.

Political Writings of St. Augustine. Saint Augustine. Ed. by Henry Paolucci. 358p. pap. 5.95 (ISBN 0-89526-941-4). Regnery Bks.

Politics & Christianity in Malawi 1875-1940. J. McCracken. LC 76-27905. (Cambridge Commonwealth Ser.). (Illus.). 1977. 49.50 (ISBN 0-521-21444-0). Cambridge U Pr.

Politics & Exegesis: Origen & the Two Swords. Gerard E. Caspary. LC 77-71058. 1979. 42.00x (ISBN 0-520-03445-7). U of Cal Pr.

Politics & Jewish Purpose. Michael Selzer. 45p. 1972. pap. 2.50 (ISBN 0-934676-12-7). Greenlf Bks.

Politics & Protestant Theology: An Interpretation of Tillich, Barth, Bonhoeffer, & Brunner. Rene De Visme Williamson. LC 76-20817. 1976. 20.00x (ISBN 0-8071-0193-1). La State U Pr.

Politics & Religion in Seventeenth-Century France. W. J. Stankiewicz. LC 76-2075. 269p. 1976. Repr. of 1960 ed. lib. bdg. 22.50x (ISBN 0-8371-8770-2, STPR). Greenwood.

Politics & Religion in Sixteenth-Century France: A Study of the Career of Henry of Montmorency-Damville, Uncrowned King of the South. Franklin C. Palm. 13.25 (ISBN 0-8446-0835-1). Peter Smith.

Politics & the Biblical Drama. Richard J. Mouw. 1983. pap. 5.95 (ISBN 0-8010-6153-9). Baker Bk.

Politics & the Churches in Great Britain, 1832-1868. G. I. Machin. 1977. 57.00x (ISBN 0-19-826436-4). Oxford U Pr.

Politics & the State: The Catholic View. Thomas Molnar. 1980. 7.50 (ISBN 0-317-46875-8). Franciscan Herald.

Politics at God's Funeral: The Spiritual Crisis of Western Civilization. Michael Harrington. (Penguin Nonfiction Ser.). 320p. 1985. pap. 7.95 (ISBN 0-14-007689-1). Penguin.

Politics, Finance & the Church in the Reign of Edward II: Walter Stapeldon, Treasurer of England. Mark Buck. LC 82-17695. (Cambridge Studies in Medieval Life & Thought 19). 248p. 1983. 52.50 (ISBN 0-521-25025-0). Cambridge U Pr.

Politics of Accommodation: German Social Democracy & the Catholic Church, 1945-1959. Paul R. Waibel. (European University Studies: No. 31, Vol. 35). 161p. 1983. pap. 23.15 (ISBN 3-8204-7270-3). P Lang Pubs.

Politics of Belief in Nineteenth-Century France. Philip Spencer. LC 77-80592. 284p. 1973. Repr. of 1954 ed. 24.50x (ISBN 0-86527-156-9). Fertig.

Politics of Compassion: A Biblical Perspective on World Hunger, the Arms Race & U. S. Policy in Central America. Jack Nelson-Pallmeyer. LC 85-25809. 128p. (Orig.). 1986. pap. 8.95 (ISBN 0-88344-356-2). Orbis Bks.

Politics of Compromise: State & Religion in Israel. Ervin Birnbaum. LC 70-92557. 348p. 1970. 27.50 (ISBN 0-8386-7567-0). Fairleigh Dickinson.

Politics of Erasmus: A Pacifist Intellectual & His Political Milieu. James D. Tracy. LC 77-20697. (Erasmus Studies). 1978. 22.50x (ISBN 0-8020-5393-9). U of Toronto Pr.

Politics of German Protestantism: The Rise of the Protestant Church Elite in Prussia, 1815-1848. Robert M. Bigler. LC 77-142055. 1972. 38.50x (ISBN 0-520-01881-8). U of Cal Pr.

Politics of God. 2nd ed. Hugh J. Schonfield. LC 78-9024. (Illus.). 264p. 1978. pap. 9.95 (ISBN 0-916438-14-7). Univ of Trees.

Politics of Heaven & Hell: Christian Themes from Classical, Medieval & Modern Political Philosophy. James V. Schall. LC 84-7409. 360p. (Orig.). 1984. lib. bdg. 26.00 (ISBN 0-8191-3991-2); pap. text ed. 13.50 (ISBN 0-8191-3992-0). U Pr of Amer.

Politics of Heresy: The Modernist Crisis in Roman Catholicism. Lester R. Kurtz. LC 85-1179. 256p. 1986. text ed. 32.50x (ISBN 0-520-05537-3). U of Cal Pr.

Politics of Jesus. John H. Yoder. 176p. 1972. pap. 7.95 (ISBN 0-8028-1485-9). Eerdmans.

Politics of Mirth: Jonson, Herrick, Milton, Marvell, & the Defense of Old Holiday Pastimes. Leah S. Marcus. LC 86-7133. (Illus.). 328p. 1986. lib. bdg. 29.00x (ISBN 0-226-50451-4). U of Chicago Pr.

Politics of Moralism: The New Christian Right in American Life. Erling Jorstad. LC 81-65641. 128p. (Orig.). 1981. pap. 6.95 (ISBN 0-8066-1877-9, 10-5011). Augsburg.

Politics of Obedience: The Discourse of Voluntary Servitude. Etienne La Boetie. Tr. by Harry Kurz from Fr. Tr. of De la Servitude Volontaire. 88p. 1975. 19.95 (ISBN 0-919618-58-8, Dist. by U of Toronto Pr); pap. 9.95 (ISBN 0-919618-57-X, Dist. by U of Toronto Pr). Black Rose Bks.

Politics of Reproductive Ritual. Karen E. Paige & Jeffrey M. Paige. 392p. 1981. 31.00x (ISBN 0-520-03071-0); pap. 8.95 (ISBN 0-520-04782-6, CAL 572). U of Cal Pr.

Politics of Rescue. Henry L. Feingold. LC 80-81713. (Illus.). 432p. (Orig.). 1970. pap. 12.95 (ISBN 0-89604-019-4). Holocaust Pubns.

Politics of Rescue: The Roosevelt Administration & the Holocaust, 1938-1945. Henry L. Feingold. LC 75-127049. 1970. 40.00 (ISBN 0-8135-0664-6). Rutgers U Pr.

Politics of Sex & Religion: A Case History in the Development of Doctrine, 1962-1984. Robert B. Kaiser. LC 84-82552. 200p. (Orig.). 1985. pap. 10.95 (ISBN 0-934134-16-2, Leaven Pr). Sheed & Ward MO.

Politics of Sikhs. Jitender Kaur. 280p. 1986. 24.00x (ISBN 0-8364-1795-X, Pub. by Manohar India). South Asia Bks.

Politics of Spirituality. William Stringfellow. LC 84-10434. (Spirituality & the Christian Life Ser.: Vol. 4). 90p. 1984. pap. 7.95 (ISBN 0-664-24633-8). Westminster.

Politics of the Miraculous in Peru: Haya de la Torre & the Spiritualist Tradition. Fredrick B. Pike. LC 85-1162. (Illus.). xviii, 391p. 1986. 32.50x (ISBN 0-8032-3672-7). U of Nebr Pr.

Politics of Women's Spirituality: Essays on the Rise of Spiritualist Power Within the Feminist Movement. Charlene Spretnak. LC 80-2876. 624p. 1982. pap. 14.95 (ISBN 0-385-17241-9, Anch). Doubleday.

Polity & Praxis: A Program for American Practical Theology. Dennis P. McCann & Charles R. Strain. 176p. 1985. 15.95 (ISBN 0-86683-986-0, AY8571, HarpR). Har-Row.

Pollen Path: A Collection of Navajo Myths. Retold by Margaret S. Link. LC 56-7272. (Illus.). 1956. 17.50x (ISBN 0-8047-0473-2). Stanford U Pr.

Polnij Russkij Orthograficheskij Slovar' Ed. by P. A. Romashkevitch. Tr. of Complete Russian Orthographic Dictionary. 264p. pap. 10.00 (ISBN 0-317-29290-0). Holy Trinity.

Polychrome Historical Prayerbook: Siddur 'Bet Yosef' Jacob Freedman. (Illus.). 400p. 1984. 125.00x (ISBN 0-686-12113-9). J Freedman Liturgy.

Polydoxy: Explorations in a Philosophy of Liberal Religion. Alvin J. Reines. 200p. 1987. 29.95 (ISBN 0-87975-399-4). Prometheus Bks.

Polygamy in Islamic Law. G. A. Badawi. pap. 1.00 (ISBN 0-686-18440-8). Kazi Pubns.

Polyglot of Foreign Proverbs. Henry G. Bohn. LC 68-55796. (Bohn's Antiquarian Library Ser.). Repr. of 1857 ed. 12.50 (ISBN 0-404-50004-8). AMS Pr.

Polyglot of Foreign Proverbs - with English Translations. Ed. by Henry G. Bohn. LC 67-23915. (Polyglot Ser.). 1968. Repr. of 1857 ed. 40.00x (ISBN 0-8103-3197-7). Gale.

Polymetis. Joseph Spence. LC 75-27886. (Renaissance & the Gods Ser.: Vol. 41). (Illus.). 1976. Repr. of 1747 ed. lib. bdg. 88.00 (ISBN 0-8240-2090-1). Garland Pub.

Polynesian Mythology & Ancient Traditional History of the New Zealanders As Furnished by Their Priests & Chiefs. George Grey. LC 75-35253. Repr. of 1906 ed. 20.50 (ISBN 0-404-14425-X). AMS Pr.

Polynesian Religion. E. S. Handy. (Bayard Dominick Expedition Publication Ser: No. 12). Repr. of 1927 ed. 56.00 (ISBN 0-527-02137-7). Kraus Repr.

Polynj Pravoslavnyj Bogoslavskij Enciklopedíceskij. Ed. by Variorum. 1240p. 1971. 75.00x (ISBN 0-902089-08-0). State Mutual Bk.

Polytyque Churche: Religion & Early Tudor Political Culture. Peter I. Kaufman. 208p. 1986. 24.95 (ISBN 0-86554-211-2, MUP-H191). Mercer Univ Pr.

Pondering the Proverbs. Donald Hunt. (Bible Study Textbook Ser.). (Illus.). 1974. 14.30 (ISBN 0-89900-018-5). College Pr Pub.

Ponderings. Kenneth Grant. 48p. 1986. 6.95 (ISBN 0-8378-5087-8). Gibson.

Pontifes de L'Ancienne Rome: Etudes Historique sur les Institutions Religieuses de Rome. facsimile ed. Auguste Bouche-Leclercq. LC 75-10630. (Ancient Religion & Mythology Ser.). (Fr.). 1976. Repr. of 1871 ed. 33.00x (ISBN 0-405-07006-3). Ayer Co Pubs.

Pontius Pilate. Paul L. Maier. 1981. pap. 3.95 (ISBN 0-8423-4852-2). Tyndale.

Poor in Spirit: Awaiting All from God. Gabriel-Marie Garrone. 1978. pap. 2.95 (ISBN 0-232-51337-6). Living Flame Pr.

Poor Jews: An American Awakening. Ed. by Naomi Levine & Martin Hochbaum. LC 73-85097. 206p. 1974. 19.95 (ISBN 0-87855-073-9); pap. 8.95x (ISBN 0-87855-570-6). Transaction Bks.

Poor Man Called Jesus: Reflections on the Gospel of Mark. Jose C. Pallares. Tr. by Robert R. Barr from Span. LC 85-15339. 144p. (Orig.). 1986. pap. 8.95 (ISBN 0-88344-398-8). Orbis Bks.

Poor Ralph. Kurt Mitchell. (Illus.). 32p. 1982. 8.95 (ISBN 0-89107-273-X, Crossway Bks). Good News.

Poorhouse Waif & His Divine Teacher. Isabel Byrum. 223p. pap. 2.00 (ISBN 0-686-29161-1). Faith Pub Hse.

Pope Alexander III & the Council of Tours (1163) A Study of Ecclesiastical Politics & Institutions in the Twelfth Century. Robert Somerville. (Center for Medieval & Renaissance Studies, UCLA: Publications No. 12). 1978. 24.50x (ISBN 0-520-03184-9). U of Cal Pr.

Pope Alexander the Seventh & the College of Cardinals. John Bargrave. Ed. by James C. Robertson. LC 78-160001. (Camden Society, London. Publications, First Ser.: No. 92). Repr. of 1867 ed. 19.00 (ISBN 0-404-50192-3). AMS Pr.

Pope Alexander the Seventh & the College of Cardinals. John Bargrave. 19.00 (ISBN 0-384-03435-7). Johnson Repr.

Pope: An Analysis of the Office of the Pope & the Roman Church & City. Jean Carrere. 1977. lib. bdg. 59.95 (ISBN 0-8490-2453-6). Gordon Pr.

Pope & Bishops: A Study of the Papal Monarchy in the Twelfth & Thirteenth Centuries. Kenneth Pennington. LC 83-21799. (Middle Ages Ser.). 227p. 1984. 31.50x (ISBN 0-8122-7918-2). U of Pa Pr.

Pope & Revolution: John Paul II Confronts Liberation Theology. Ed. by Quentin L. Quade. LC 82-4971. 205p. 1982. 12.00 (ISBN 0-89633-059-1); pap. 7.00 (ISBN 0-89633-054-0). Ethics & Public Policy.

Pope & the Duce. Peter Kent. 1981. 26.00 (ISBN 0-312-63024-7). St Martin.

Pope & the Italian Jackal. Joseph McCabe. 31p. pap. cancelled (ISBN 0-911826-88-2). Am Atheist.

Pope & the New Apocalypse: The Holy War Against Family Planning. Stephen D. Mumford. (Illus.). 82p. (Orig.). 1986. 6.95 (ISBN 0-937307-00-9); pap. 3.95 (ISBN 0-937307-01-7). CRPS.

Pope from the Ghetto: The Legend of the Family of Pier Leone. Gertrud Von Le Fort. Tr. by Conrad R. Bonacina. 330p. 1981. Repr. of 1935 ed. lib. bdg. 15.00 (ISBN 0-89984-205-4). Century Bookbindery.

Pope Gregory XI: The Failure of Tradition. Paul R. Thibault. 252p. 1986. lib. bdg. 26.50 (ISBN 0-8191-5462-8); pap. text ed. 12.75 (ISBN 0-8191-5463-6). U Pr of Amer.

Pope Helps Hitler to World Power. Joseph McCabe. 30p. pap. cancelled (ISBN 0-911826-87-4). Am Atheist.

Pope, His Banker & Venice. Felix Gilbert. LC 80-13062. (Illus.). 167p. 1980. text ed. 12.50x (ISBN 0-674-68975-5). Harvard U Pr.

Pope Innocent III. H. Tillmann. (Europe in the Middle Ages Selected Studies: Vol. 12). 374p. 1980. 64.00 (ISBN 0-444-85137-2, North-Holland). Elsevier.

Pope John Paul II. Mary Craig. (Profiles Ser.). (Illus.). 64p. 1982. 8.95 (ISBN 0-241-10711-3, Pub. by Hamish Hamilton England). David & Charles.

Pope John Paul II: An Authorized Biography. Lord Longford. LC 82-8001. (Illus.). 208p. 1982. 20.50 (ISBN 0-688-01393-7). Morrow.

Pope John Paul II & the Catholic Restoration. Paul Johnson. 224p. 1982. 11.95 (ISBN 0-312-63032-8). St Martin.

Pope John Paul II & the Family & Text. Pope Paul II. LC 82-13308. 416p. 1983. 15.00 (ISBN 0-8199-0851-7). Franciscan Herald.

Pope John Paul II At the United Nations. pap. 4.95 (E. 80.1.8); pap. 4.95 (ISBN 92-1-100166-8). UN.

Pope John Paul II: Bringing Love to a Troubled World. Anthony DiFranco. LC 82-23618. (Taking Part Ser.). (Illus.). 48p. 1983. PLB 8.95 (ISBN 0-87518-241-0). Dillon.

Pope John Paul II: Catechist. 1980. 4.50 (ISBN 0-317-46877-4). Franciscan Herald.

Pope John Paul II: He Came to Us As a Father. (Illus.). 1979. gift edition 14.95 (ISBN 0-8198-0628-5). Dghtrs St Paul.

Pope John Paul II in America. Lucius Annese. LC 79-56497. 1980. 50.00 (ISBN 0-933402-10-4). Charisma Pr.

Pope John Paul II: On Jews & Judiasm, 1979-1986. Pope John Paul, II. (Orig.). Date not set. pap. price not set (ISBN 1-55586-151-2). US Catholic.

Pope John Paul II: Pilgrim of Peace. John Paul II. 1987. 25.00 (ISBN 0-517-56423-8, Harmony). Crown.

Pope John Paul II: The People's Pope. George Sullivan. LC 83-40395. (Illus.). 120p. 1984. 11.95 (ISBN 0-8027-6523-8). Walker & Co.

Pope John the Twenty-Third & Master John Hus of Bohemia. Eustace J. Kitts. LC 77-84726. Repr. of 1910 ed. 47.00 (ISBN 0-404-16127-8). AMS Pr.

Pope John Twenty-Third: A Clever, Pastoral Leader. Bernard R. Bonnot. LC 79-1770. 1980. 9.95 (ISBN 0-8189-0388-0). Alba.

Pope John XXIII. Ed. by William P. Hansen & John Haney. (World Leaders--Past & Present Ser.). (Illus.). 112p. 1987. lib. bdg. 16.95 (ISBN 0-87754-535-9). Chelsea Hse.

Pope John XXIII: Shepherd of the Modern World. Peter Hebblethwaite. LC 82-45484. (Illus.). 576p. 1985. 19.95 (ISBN 0-385-17298-2). Doubleday.

Pope of AntiSemitism: The Career & Legacy of Edouard-Adolphe Drumont. Frederick Busi. 242p. (Orig.). 1986. text ed. 26.50 (ISBN 0-8191-5594-2); pap. text ed. 12.50 (ISBN 0-8191-5595-0). U Pr of Amer.

Pope, or President? Startling Disclosures of Romanism As Revealed by Its Own Writers: Facts for Americans. Ed. by Gerald Grob. LC 76-46094. (Anti-Movements in America). 1977. lib. bdg. 27.50x (ISBN 0-405-09967-3). Ayer Co Pubs.

Pope Paul II. Mary Craig. (Illus.). 80p. 1982. pap. 2.50 (ISBN 0-686-40828-4, Pub by Penguin England). Irish Bk Ctr.

Pope Pius IX. Frank J. Coppa. (World Leaders Ser.). 1979. lib. bdg. 15.95 (ISBN 0-8057-7727-X, Twayne). G K Hall.

Pope, the Council, & the Mass. James Likoudis & K. D. Whitehead. 1981. 13.95 (ISBN 0-8158-0400-8). Chris Mass.

Pope, the Protestants, & the Irish: Papal Aggression & Anti-Catholicism in Mid-Nineteenth Century England. Robert J. Klaus. Ed. by William H. McNeill & Peter Stansky. (Modern European History Ser.). 400p. 1987. lib. bdg. 60.00 (ISBN 0-8240-7820-9). Garland Pub.

Popery & Politics in England, 1660-1688. J. Miller. LC 73-79306. (Illus.). 278p. 1973. 44.50 (ISBN 0-521-20236-1). Cambridge U Pr.

Popes & European Revolution. Owen Chadwick. (Oxford History of the Christian Church Ser.). 1981. 84.00x (ISBN 0-19-826919-6). Oxford U Pr.

Popes & Heresy in the Thirteenth Century. Albert C. Shannon. LC 78-63192. (Heresies of the Early Christian & Medieval Era: Second Ser.). Repr. of 1949 ed. 31.00 (ISBN 0-404-16228-2). AMS Pr.

Popes & Princes Fourteen Seventeen to Fifteen Seventeen: Politics & Polity in Late Medieval Church. J. A. Thomson. (Early Modern Europe Today Ser.). 256p. 1980. text ed. 10.00 (ISBN 0-04-901027-1). Allen Unwin.

Popes & Science. James J. Walsh. 1977. lib. bdg. 59.95 (ISBN 0-8490-2454-4). Gordon Pr.

Pope's Divisions. Peter Nichols. 16.95 (ISBN 0-03-047576-7). Brown Bk.

Pope's Dunciad & the Queen of Night: A Study in Emotional Jacobitism. Douglas Brooks-Davies. LC 84-17135. 190p. 1985. 35.00 (ISBN 0-7190-1735-1, Pub. by Manchester Univ Pr); pap. write for info. Longwood Pub Group.

Pope's Jews. Sam Waagenaar. (Illus.). 500p. 1974. 9.95 (ISBN 0-912050-49-7, Library Pr). Open Court.

Popes, Monks & Crusaders. H. E. Cowdrey. (No. 27). 400p. 1983. 40.00 (ISBN 0-907628-34-6). Hambledon Press.

Popes of the 20th Century. 2.50 (ISBN 0-8198-5811-0); 1.50 (ISBN 0-8198-5812-9). Dghtrs St Paul.

Popes of Vatican Council II. Peter Wigginton. 329p. 1983. 15.00 (ISBN 0-8199-0828-2). Franciscan Herald.

Pope's Plan for Social Reconstruction. Charles P. Bruehl. 10.00 (ISBN 0-8159-6507-9). Devin.

Popessa. Paul I. Murphy & R. Rene Arlington. LC 82-61880. (Illus.). 296p. (Orig.). 1983. 16.50 (ISBN 0-446-51258-3). Warner Bks.

Popessa. Paul I. Murphy & R. Rene Arlington. 432p. 1985. pap. 3.95 (ISBN 0-446-32817-0). Warner Bks.

Popol Vuh: Mythic & Heroic Sagas of the Kiches of Central America. Lewis Spence. LC 75-139178. (Popular Studies in Mythology, Romance & Folklore: No. 16). Repr. of 1908 ed. 5.50 (ISBN 0-404-53516-X). AMS Pr.

Popol Vuh: The Sacred Book of the Ancient Quiche Maya: Spanish Version of the Original Maya. Tr. by Adrian Recinos & Delia Goetz. (Civilization of the American Indian Ser.: No. 29). (Eng). 1983. Repr. of 1950 ed. 16.95 (ISBN 0-8061-0205-5). U of Okla Pr.

Popular Beliefs & Folklore Tradition in Siberia. Ed. by V. Dioszegi. (Uralic & Altaic Ser.: No. 57). 1968. text ed. 40.80x (ISBN 0-686-22621-6). Mouton.

Popular Beliefs & Superstitions from Utah. Ed. by Anthon S. Cannon et al. 526p. 1984. 45.00x (ISBN 0-87480-236-9). U of Utah Pr.

Popular Buddhism in China. Shao-ch'Ang Li. lib. bdg. 79.95 (ISBN 0-87968-539-5). Krishna Pr.

Popular Catholicism in Nineteenth-Century Germany. Johnathan Sperber. LC 84-42559. 552p. 1984. text ed. 45.00x (ISBN 0-691-05432-0). Princeton U Pr.

Popular Christianity. Catherine Booth. (Writings of Catherine Booth Ser.). 1986. Repr. of 1888 ed. deluxe ed. 4.95 (ISBN 0-86544-035-2). Salvation Army.

Popular Commentary of the Bible, 4 Vols. 2 Pts. Paul E. Kretzmann. Set. 70.95 (ISBN 0-570-06735-9, 15-1201). Concordia.

Popular Dictionary of Buddhism. Christmas Humphreys. 224p. 1984. pap. 8.95 (ISBN 0-7007-0184-2). Salem Hse Pubs.

Popular Dictionary of Judaism. Hugh J. Schonfield. 1966. pap. 1.75 (ISBN 0-8065-0075-1, 232). Citadel Pr.

Popular Ethics in Ancient Greece. Lionel Pearson. 1962. 20.00x (ISBN 0-8047-0102-4). Stanford U Pr.

Popular Guide to New Testament Criticism. H. P. Hamann. 1977. pap. 4.75 (ISBN 0-570-03760-3, 12-2671). Concordia.

Popular Hinduism & Hindu Mythology: An Annotated Bibliography. Compiled by Barron Holland. LC 79-7188. 1979. lib. bdg. 45.00 (ISBN 0-313-21358-5, HPH/). Greenwood.

Popular Hinduism: The Religion of the Masses. Lewis S. O'Malley. LC 70-142072. 1971. Repr. of 1935 ed. 24.00 (ISBN 0-384-43305-7). Johnson Repr.

Popular Islam South of the Sahara. Ed. by J. D. Peel & Charles C. Stewart. (African Studies). 128p. 1986. pap. 15.00 (ISBN 0-7190-1975-3, Pub. by Manchester Univ Pr). Longwood Pub Group.

Popular Religion. Ed. by Norbert Greinacher & Norbert Mette. (Concilium Nineteen Eighty-Six Ser.). 120p. 1986. pap. 6.95 (ISBN 0-567-30066-8, Pub. by T & T Clark Ltd UK). Fortress.

Popular Religion in Restoration England. C. John Sommerville. LC 77-7618. (University of Florida Social Sciences Monographs: No. 59). 1977. pap. 4.50 (ISBN 0-8130-0564-7). U Presses Fla.

Popular Religion in the Middle Ages. Rosalind Brooke & Christopher Brooke. (Illus.). 1985. pap. 10.95 (ISBN 0-500-27381-2). Thames Hudson.

Popular Religion: Inspirational Books in America. Louis Schneider & Sanford M. Dornbusch. LC 58-11958. (Midway Reprint Ser.). pap. 46.50 (2026741). Bks Demand UMI.

Popular Studies in Mythology, Romance & Folklore, 15 vols. Repr. of 1908 ed. write for info. (ISBN 0-404-53500-3). AMS Pr.

Popular Superstitions. Charles Platt. LC 70-167114. 244p. 1973. Repr. of 1925 ed. 46.00x (ISBN 0-8103-3170-5). Gale.

Popular Superstitions & Festive Amusements of the Highlanders of Scotland. W. Grant Stewart. 1978. Repr. of 1851 ed. lib. bdg. 37.50 (ISBN 0-8492-8007-9). R West.

Popular Survey of the Old Testament. Norman L. Geisler. LC 77-78578. 1977. pap. 8.95 (ISBN 0-8010-3684-4). Baker Bk.

Popular Witchcraft. John Fritscher. 224p. 1973. 6.95 (ISBN 0-8065-0380-7). Citadel Pr.

Popular Yoga Asanas. Swami Kuvalayananda. LC 76-130420. (Illus.). (YA) 1972. Repr. of 1931 ed. 12.50 (ISBN 0-8048-0673-X). C E Tuttle.

Population. Colin Clark. 30p. 1974. pap. 0.50 (ISBN 0-912414-19-7). Lumen Christi.

Population Crisis & Moral Responsibility. Ed. by Philip J. Wogaman. 1973. 15.00 (ISBN 0-8183-0146-5). Pub Aff Pr.

Population: Dynamics, Ethics & Policy. Ed. by Priscilla Reining & Irene Tinker. 1975. pap. 19.00 (ISBN 0-12-586751-4). Acad Pr.

Population, Evolution, & Birth Control: A Collage of Controversial Ideas. 2nd ed. Ed. by Garrett Hardin. LC 69-16921. (Biology Ser.). (Illus.). 386p. 1969. pap. text ed. 13.95x (ISBN 0-7167-0670-9). W H Freeman.

Population of Israel: Growth, Policy & Implications. Dov Friedlander & Calvin Goldscheider. LC 78-13139. 264p. 1979. 31.00x (ISBN 0-231-04572-7). Columbia U Pr.

Por Que Guardamos el Domingo? Domingo Fernandez. 87p. 1984. pap. 2.00 (ISBN 0-311-05603-2). Casa Bautista.

Por Sendas Biblicas. T. E. Quiros. (Span.). 162p. 1985. pap. 3.25 (ISBN 0-311-08753-1). Casa Bautista.

Porno Plague. Neil Gallagher. LC 77-21992. (Illus.). 256p. 1977. pap. 5.95 (ISBN 0-87123-231-6, 210231). Bethany Hse.

Pornography: A Human Tragedy. Ed. by Tom Minnery. 350p. 1986. pap. 14.95 (ISBN 0-8423-4947-2). Tyndale.

Porque De Las Lenguas. Kenneth E. Hagin. (Span.). 1983. pap. 0.50 (ISBN 0-89276-151-2). Hagin Ministries.

Porque No Llega el Avivamiento. Leonard Ravenhill. 144p. 1980. 2.75 (ISBN 0-88113-250-0). Edit Betania.

Port-Royal, 3 tomes. Charles-Augustin De Sainte-Beuve. 1953-1955. Set. 79.95 (ISBN 0-685-11502-X). French & Eur.

Port Royal, 3 vols. Saint-Beuve. Vol. 1. 37.50 (ISBN 0-686-56564-9); Vol. 2. 37.50 (ISBN 0-686-56565-7); Vol. 3. 35.95 (ISBN 0-686-56566-5). French & Eur.

Portable Emerson. Ralph Waldo Emerson. Ed. by Carl Bode & Malcolm Cowley. 664p. 1981. pap. 7.95 (ISBN 0-14-015094-3). Penguin.

Portals to Freedom. Howard C. Ives. 256p. 1937. pap. 8.95 (ISBN 0-87743-013-6). G Ronald Pub.

Portavoces del Eterno. Harold Ellison. Orig. Title: Old Testament Prophets. (Span.). 214p. 1982. pap. 7.50 (ISBN 0-8254-1201-3). Kregel.

Portrait of a Builder: William A. McIntyre. Clarence W. Hall. 1983. pap. 5.95 (ISBN 0-86544-020-4). Salv Army Suppl South.

Portrait of a Fulfilled Woman. Virginia Leih. 1979. pap. 4.95 (ISBN 0-8423-4860-3). Tyndale.

Portrait of a Place: San Luis Obispo. Barbara Seymour. (Illus.). 120p. (Orig.). 1986. pap. 12.95 (ISBN 0-9617522-0-3). Garden Creek Pubns.

Portrait of a Preacher. John Fletcher. 8.95 (ISBN 0-686-12902-4). Schmul Pub Co.

Portrait of a Quaker. Donald McNichols. LC 80-66654. (Illus.). 180p. 1980. 12.50 (ISBN 0-913342-24-6). Barclay Pr.

Portrait of a Woman. Herbert O'Driscoll. 96p. (Orig.). 1981. pap. 4.95 (ISBN 0-8164-2332-6, HarpR). Har-Row.

Portrait of Andre Gide. Justin O'Brien. 390p. 1976. Repr. of 1953 ed. lib. bdg. 29.00x (ISBN 0-374-96139-5, Octagon). Hippocrene Bks.

Portrait of Christ in Poetry. Georgia M. Cottrell. (Contemporary Poets of Dorrance Ser.). 100p. 1983. 5.95 (ISBN 0-8059-2888-X). Dorrance.

Portrait of Jesus. Alan T. Dale. (Illus.). 1979. 6.95 (ISBN 0-8317-7091-0, Mayflower Bks). Smith Pubs.

Portrait of Jesus? The Illustrated Story of the Shroud of Turin. Frank C. Tribbe. 176p. 1983. 19.95 (ISBN 0-8128-2904-2). Stein & Day.

Portrait of John Milton at Princeton. John R. Martin. LC 61-14263. (Illus.). 42p. 1961. 7.50 (ISBN 0-87811-006-2). Princeton Lib.

Portrait of My Father: The Wonder of Knowing God. Peter Law. LC 85-15458. (Living Theology Ser.). 1985. pap. 7.95 (ISBN 0-88070-107-2). Multnomah.

Portrait of Pascal. Mary Duclaux. 1927. Repr. 25.00 (ISBN 0-8274-3188-0). R West.

Portrait of Youth Ministry. Maria Harris. LC 80-84512. 232p. (Orig.). 1981. pap. 8.95 (ISBN 0-8091-2354-1). Paulist Pr.

Portraits in American Sanctity. Ed. by Joseph N. Tylenda. 1983. 18.00 (ISBN 0-686-45830-3). Franciscan Herald.

Portraits: O Those I Love. Daniel Berrigan. (Crossroad Paperback Ser.). 160p. 1982. pap. 6.95 (ISBN 0-8245-0416-X). Crossroad NY.

Portraits of a Hasidic Master: Levi Yitzhak of Berditchev. Samuel H. Dresner. 1986. pap. 8.95 (ISBN 0-933503-59-8). Shapolsky Pubs.

Portraits of Bible Men. George Matheson. LC 86-7428. (First Series (Adam to Job)). Orig. Title: Representative Men of the Bible. 384p. 1986. pap. 8.95 (ISBN 0-8254-3251-0). Kregel.

Portraits of Bible Men. George Matheson. LC 86-27221. (Ishmael to David, Second Ser.). 368p. 1987. pap. 8.95 (ISBN 0-8254-3252-9). Kregel.

Portraits of Bible Women. George Matheson. LC 86-7429. Orig. Title: Representative Women of the Bible (Eve to Mary Magdalene) 304p. 1986. pap. 7.95 (ISBN 0-8254-3250-2). Kregel.

Portraits of Christ. Ernst Kitzinger & Elizabeth Senior. (Illus.). 62p. 1983. Repr. of 1940 ed. lib. bdg. 25.00 (ISBN 0-89987-459-2). Darby Bks.

Portraits of Christ in Genesis. M. R. DeHaan. 1978. pap. 6.95 (ISBN 0-310-23431-X, 9516P). Zondervan.

Portraits of Customs & Carols. Norma Leary. 1983. pap. 2.95 (ISBN 0-937172-54-5). JLJ Pubs.

Portraits of Faith. Albert J. Lown. 155p. (Orig.). 1981. pap. 3.95 (ISBN 0-8341-0695-7). Beacon Hill.

Portraits of God: Word Pictures of the Deity from the Earliest Times Through Today. Louis Baldwin. LC 85-43571. 192p. 1986. lib. bdg. 18.95x (ISBN 0-89950-198-2). McFarland & Co.

Portraits of Jews by Gilbert Stuart & Other Early American Artists. Hannah R. London. LC 69-19613. (Illus.). 1969. Repr. 13.75 (ISBN 0-8048-0459-1). C E Tuttle.

Portraits of Septimus Severus, A.D. 193-211. A. M. McCann. 222p. 1968. 48.00x (ISBN 0-271-00452-5). Pa St U Pr.

Portraits of the Passion. Paul G. Hansen. 1983. 6.25 (ISBN 0-89536-582-0, 1624). CSS of Ohio.

Portraits, Prints & Writings of John Milton. John Milton. LC 73-15855. 1908. lib. bdg. 17.50 (ISBN 0-8414-6060-4). Folcroft.

Portraiture of Shakerism. Mary Marshall. LC 70-134420. Repr. of 1822 ed. 28.45 (ISBN 0-404-08461-3). AMS Pr.

Portsea Island Churches. Rodney Hubbuck. 1969. 39.00x (ISBN 0-317-43678-3, Pub. by City of Portsmouth). State Mutual Bk.

Portugal: Message of Fatima. 3.50 (ISBN 0-8198-5809-9); 2.50 (ISBN 0-8198-5810-2). Dghtrs St Paul.

Portuguese Letters: Love Letters of a Nun to a French Officer. 2nd ed. Ed. Donald E. Ericson. LC 86-71957. 78p. 1986. pap. 5.95 (ISBN 0-9617271-0-1). Bennett-Edwards.

Position of Christianity in the United States, in Its Relations with Our Political Institutions, & Specially with Reference to Religious Instruction in the Public Schools. Stephen Colwell. LC 78-38444. (Religion in America, Ser. 2). 180p. 1972. Repr. of 1854 ed. 17.00 (ISBN 0-405-04063-6). Ayer Co Pubs.

Positive Background of Hindu Sociology, 2 vols. Benoy K. Sarkar. LC 73-3807. (Sacred Books of the Hindus: Nos. 16 & 25). Repr. of 1926 ed. Set. 74.50 (ISBN 0-404-57839-X). AMS Pr.

Positive Background of Hindu Sociology: Introduction to Hindu Positivism. Benoy K. Sarkar. LC 74-17338. (Sacred Books of the Hindus: 32). Repr. of 1937 ed. 74.50 (ISBN 0-404-57850-0). AMS Pr.

Positive Christian Living. J. J. Turner. pap. 4.25 (ISBN 0-89137-316-0). Quality Pubns.

Positive Evolution of Religion. facs. ed. Frederic Harrison. LC 74-142641. (Essay Index Reprint Ser). 1913. 18.00 (ISBN 0-8369-2053-8). Ayer Co Pubs.

Positive Family. Arvella Schuller. 1983. pap. 2.75 (ISBN 0-8007-8474-X, Spire Bks). Revell.

Positive Imaging: The Powerful Way to Change Your Life. Norman V. Peale. 192p. 1981. pap. 2.95 (ISBN 0-8007-8484-7). Revell.

Positive Power of Christian Partnership. Richard Andersen. 1982. pap. 1.95 (ISBN 0-570-03844-8, 12-2947). Concordia.

Positive Power of Jesus Christ. Norman V. Peale. 1980. pap. 6.95 1981o. p. (ISBN 0-8423-4875-1); pap. 3.95 (ISBN 0-8423-4914-6). Tyndale.

Positive Power of the Ten Commandments. Phyllis S. Prokop. LC 86-31043. (Orig.). 1987. 7.95 (ISBN 0-8054-5037-8). Broadman.

Positive Sciences of the Ancient Hindus. Brajendranath Seal. 313p. 1986. Repr. 19.00x (ISBN 0-8364-1575-2, Pub. by Motilal Banarsidass). South Asia Bks.

Positive Thinkers: Religion As Pop Psychology from Mary Baker Eddy to Oral Roberts. Donald Meyer. 1980. 15.95 (ISBN 0-394-51029-1); pap. 5.95 (ISBN 0-394-73899-3). Pantheon.

Positive Thoughts for Successful Living. Jim Lewis. LC 80-50277. 138p. (Orig.). 1979. pap. 7.95 (ISBN 0-942482-00-X). Unity Church Denver.

Positive Values of Chastity. Eugene Diamond & Rosemary Diamond. 1983. 7.50 (ISBN 0-8199-0829-0). Franciscan Herald.

Positive Vision for Family Life: A Resource Guide for Pope John Paul II's Apostolic Exhortation Familiaris Consortio. Ed. by Valerie V. Dillon. 56p. 1985. pap. 3.95 (ISBN 1-55586-938-6). US Catholic.

Poslanije Saviatago Ignatija Antiokhiskago i Sviatago Polykarpa Smirnskago. St. Ignatius of Antioch & St. Polycarp of Simirna. Tr. of Letters of St. Ignatius of Antioch & of St. Polycarp of Smirna. (Rus.). 80p. (Orig.). 1975. pap. 2.00x (ISBN 0-88465-023-5). Holy Trinity.

Possess the Land. Valarie Owen. 193p. (Orig.). 1984. pap. text ed. 6.95 (ISBN 0-914307-17-7, Dist. by Harrison Hse). Word Faith.

Possessing the Mind of Christ. Frances Hunter. 1984. pap. 4.95 (ISBN 0-917726-64-2). Hunter Bks.

Possession. Traugott K. Oesterreich. 1966. 10.00 (ISBN 0-8216-0138-5). Univ Bks.

Possession: Demoniacal & Other. T. K. Oesterreich. 400p. 1974. pap. 4.95 (ISBN 0-8065-0436-6). Citadel Pr.

Possessions, Projections & Entities. John-Roger. 1976. pap. 5.00 (ISBN 0-914829-17-3). Baraka Bk.

Possibilities of Prayer. E. M. Bounds. (Direction Bks). 1979. pap. 3.95 (ISBN 0-8010-0757-7). Baker Bk.

Possibility of an All-Knowing God. Jonathan L. Kvanvig. LC 86-6465. 224p. 1986. 27.50 (ISBN 0-312-63195-2). St Martin.

Possibility of God. James F. Drane. (Quality Paperback Ser.: No. 321). 194p. 1976. pap. 3.50 (ISBN 0-8226-0321-7). Littlefield.

Possibility of Universal Moral Judgement in Existential Ethics: A Critical Analysis of the Phenomenology of Moral Experience According to Jean-Paul Sartre. Joseph Kariuki. (European University Studies: Series 20, Philosophy: Vol. 87). 363p. 1981. 37.95 (ISBN 3-261-04962-6). P Lang Pubs.

Possibility of Weakness of Will. Robert Dunn. LC 85-24784. 192p. 1986. lib. bdg. 25.00 (ISBN 0-915145-99-5); pap. 14.50 (ISBN 0-915145-98-7). Hackett Pub.

Possible Worlds: And Other Papers. facsimile ed. John B. Haldane. LC 75-167351. (Essay Index Reprint Ser). Repr. of 1928 ed. 18.00 (ISBN 0-8369-2452-5). Ayer Co Pubs.

Post-Byzantine Ecclesiastical Personalities. Ed. by Nomikos M. Vaporis. LC 78-11037. 111p. 1978. pap. 3.95 (ISBN 0-916586-30-8). Holy Cross Orthodox.

Post Charismatic Experience: The New Wave of the Spirit. Robert Wild. 136p. (Orig.). 1984. pap. text ed. 4.50 (ISBN 0-914544-50-0). Living Flame Pr.

Post Darwinian Controversies. J. R. Moore. LC 77-94372. 1979. 57.50 (ISBN 0-521-21989-2); pap. 24.95 (ISBN 0-521-28517-8). Cambridge U Pr.

Post-Holocaust Dialogues: Critcal Studies in Modern Jewish Thought. Steven T. Katz. 416p. 1983. 45.00x (ISBN 0-8147-4583-0). NYU Pr.

Post-Holocaust Dialogues: Critical Studies in Modern Jewish Thought. Steven T. Katz. 1985. pap. 15.00 (ISBN 0-8147-4587-3). NYU Pr.

Post Mishnaic Judaism in Transition: Samuel in Berakhot & the Beginnings of Gemara. Baruch M. Bokser. LC 80-19702. (Brown Judaic Studies). 543p. 1980. 19.50 (ISBN 0-89130-432-0, 14 00 17); pap. 15.00 (ISBN 0-89130-433-9). Scholars Pr GA.

Post-Theistic Thinking: The Marxist-Christian Dialogue in Radical Perspective. Thomas Dean. LC 74-83202. 300p. 1975. 29.95 (ISBN 0-87722-037-9). Temple U Pr.

Post Victorians. Williiam R. Inge. 1933. Repr. lib. bdg. 21.45 (ISBN 0-8414-5059-5). Folcroft.

Posthumous Theological Works, 2 vols. Emanuel Swedenborg. LC 38-24293. 634p. Vol. 1. Set. cancelled (ISBN 0-87785-078-X); student ed. 12.00 ea. Vol. 1 (ISBN 0-87785-073-9). Vol. 2 (ISBN 0-87785-074-7). Set. 24.00 (ISBN 0-87785-075-5). Swedenborg.

Postscript to Preaching: After Forty Years, How Will I Preach Today? Gene E. Bartlett. 88p. 1981. pap. 3.95 (ISBN 0-8170-0909-4). Judson.

Posture of Contemplation. Frederick C. Lyman. LC 68-54973. 123p. 1969. 5.00 (ISBN 0-8022-2258-7). Philos Lib.

Pot of Gold. Jessie M. Von Eschen. 1983. 7.95 (ISBN 0-8062-2135-6). Carlton.

Potato Man. Sophia Marcus. Ed. by Gerald Wheeler. (Banner Ser.). 128p. (Orig.). 1986. pap. 6.50 (ISBN 0-8280-0309-2). Review & Herald.

Potent Prayers. Harriete Curtiss & F. Homer. 1976p. pap. 1.00 (ISBN 0-87516-362-9). De Vorss.

Potential for Spiritual Direction in the New Rite of Penance. Frederick Schroeder & Craig Meyers. 1.85 (ISBN 0-89942-530-5, 530/04). Catholic Bk Pub.

Potential Principle. Edwin L. Cole. 144p. (Orig.). 1984. pap. 3.95 (ISBN 0-88368-144-7). Whitaker Hse.

Potentials: Ed. by Wayne E. Oates. (Guides for Productive Living Ser.). 1984. pap. 7.95 ea. Westminster.

Potestas Clavium. Lev Shestov. Tr. by Bernard Martin. LC 67-24282. 1968. 15.00x (ISBN 0-8214-0040-1). Ohio U Pr.

Potter & the Clay. Glenna Cadram & Sylvia Grubbs. 1986. pap. 9.95 (ISBN 0-87162-446-X). Warner Pr.

Potter's Clay. Frieda H. Mild. 160p. 1984. 10.50 (ISBN 0-89962-356-5). Todd & Honeywell.

Pottery, Poetry & Prophecy: Studies in Early Hebrew Poetry. D. N. Freedman. 1980. text ed. 20.00 (ISBN 0-931464-04-8). Eisenbrauns.

Potts' Discovery of Witches in the County of Lancaster. Thomas Potts. Repr. of 1745 ed. 31.00 (ISBN 0-384-47430-6). Johnson Repr.

Poustinia. Catherine D. Doherty. LC 74-19961. 216p. 1975. pap. 3.95 (ISBN 0-87793-083-X). Ave Maria.

Poverello: St. Francis of Assisi. Mark Hegener. pap. 2.00 (ISBN 0-8199-0358-2). Franciscan Herald.

Poverty & Economic Justice: A Philosophical Approach. Ed. by Robert H. Hartman. 1984. pap. 10.95 (ISBN 0-8091-2597-8). Paulist Pr.

Poverty & Wealth in James. Pedrito U. Maynard-Reid. LC 86-23506. 128p. (Orig.). 1987. pap. 8.95 (ISBN 0-88344-417-8). Orbis Bks.

Poverty & Wealth: The Christian Debate over Capitalism. Ronald H. Nash. LC 86-70291. 256p. (Orig.). 1986. pap. 8.95 (ISBN 0-89107-402-3, Crossway Bks). Good News.

Poverty of Spirit. Johannes B. Metz. LC 68-31045. 56p. 1968. 2.95 (ISBN 0-8091-1924-2). Paulist Pr.

Poverty, Revolution & the Church. Wilkes M. Paget. 142p. (Orig.). 1982. pap. text ed. 10.95 (ISBN 0-85364-285-0). Attic Pr.

Power & Authority in the Catholic Church: Cardinal Cody in Chicago. Charles Dahm & Robert Ghelardi. LC 81-40453. 334p. 1982. text ed. 22.95 (ISBN 0-268-01546-5). U of Notre Dame Pr.

Power & Peace in Prayer. R. A. Torrey. (One Evening Christmas Classic Ser.). 1976. pap. 2.50 (ISBN 0-89107-019-2). Good News.

Power & Polity among the Brethren. S. Loren Bowman. (Orig.). 1987. pap. 5.95. Brethren.

Power & Powerlessness in Jewish History. David Biale. 1986. 18.95 (ISBN 0-8052-4015-2). Schocken.

Power & Secret of the Jesuits. Rene Fulop-Miller. 1930. 29.50 (ISBN 0-8414-4288-6). Folcroft.

Power & Sexuality: The Emergence of Canon Law at the Synod of Elvira. Samuel Laeuchli. LC 72-83671. 143p. 1972. 9.95 (ISBN 0-87722-015-8). Temple U Pr.

Power & the Pulpit in Puritan New England. Emory Elliott. 256p. 1975. 27.00x (ISBN 0-691-07206-X). Princeton U Pr.

Power Delusion. Anthony Campolo, Jr. 168p. 1983. pap. 5.95 (ISBN 0-88207-292-7). Victor Bks.

Power Evangelism. John Wimber & Kevin Springer. 224p. 1986. 13.45 (ISBN 0-06-069532-3). Har-Row.

Power Filled Christian: The Work of the Holy Spirit in Man. LC 83-6658. 144p. 1984. pap. 4.95 (ISBN 0-310-33471-3, 6658P, Clarion Class). Zondervan.

Power for a Finished Work. J. L. Shuler. LC 78-53212. (Stories That Win Ser.). 1978. pap. 0.99 (ISBN 0-8163-0208-1, 16416-0). Pacific Pr Pub Assn.

Power for Living. Horace Ward. (International Correspondence Program Ser.). (Orig.). 1986. pap. text ed. 6.95 (ISBN 0-87148-718-7). Pathway Pr.

Power for the Day: 108 Meditations from Matthew. John T. Seamands. LC 75-45044. Repr. of 1976 ed. 28.00 (ISBN 0-8357-9020-7, 2016391). Bks Demand UMI.

Power from on High. L. D. Wilcox. 1.50 (ISBN 0-686-27776-7). Schmul Pub Co.

Power Ideas for a Happy Family. Robert Schuller. 1982. pap. 1.95 (ISBN 0-515-06499-8). Jove Pubns.

Power Ideas for a Happy Family. Robert H. Schuller. 1987. 8.95 (ISBN 0-8007-1528-4). Revell.

Power in Penance. Michael Scanlan. 64p. 1972. pap. 0.95 (ISBN 0-87793-092-9). Ave Maria.

Power in Praise. Merlin R. Carothers. 143p. 1972. pap. 4.95 (ISBN 0-943026-01-6). Carothers.

Power in Weakness: New Hearing for Gospel Stories of Healing & Discipleship. Frederick H. Borsh. LC 82-15997. 160p. 1983. pap. 8.95 (ISBN 0-8006-1703-7, 1-1703). Fortress.

Power of Affirmation. Subramuniya. pap. 1.00 (ISBN 0-87516-357-2). De Vorss.

Power of Affirmations. Jerry Fankhauser. 56p. 1979. pap. 8.00 (ISBN 0-9617006-1-0). J Fankhauser.

Power of Affirming Touch. Wilson W. Grant. LC 86-10830. (Christian Growth Bks). 128p. (Orig.). 1986. pap. 6.95 (ISBN 0-8066-2210-5, 10-5028). Augsburg.

Power of an Idea. Ernest Holmes. Ed. by Willis H. Kinnear. 96p. 1965. pap. 4.50 (ISBN 0-911336-31-1). Sci of Mind.

Power of Belief. Ernest Holmes. Ed. by Willis H. Kinnear. 96p. 1970. pap. 5.50 (ISBN 0-911336-13-3). Sci of Mind.

Power of Commitment. Jerry White. (Christian Character Library). 176p. 1985. 8.95 (ISBN 0-89109-532-2). NavPress.

Power of Commitment. Jerry White. Date not set. pap. price not set. NavPress.

Power of Communication. Kenneth A. Erickson. 112p. (Orig.). 1986. pap. 4.95 (ISBN 0-570-04435-9). Concordia.

Power of Compassion. James McNamara. 1984. pap. 4.95 (ISBN 0-8091-2567-6). Paulist Pr.

Power of Creativity. Patricia Metten. LC 81-50863. (Power Tales Ser.). pap. write for info. (ISBN 0-911712-89-5). Promised Land.

Power of Darkness. Durwood Buchheim. 1985. 6.95 (ISBN 0-89536-746-7, 5852). CSS of Ohio.

Power of Encouragement. Jeanne Doering. 176p. (Orig.). 1983. pap. 5.95 (ISBN 0-8024-0146-5). Moody.

Power of Faith Exemplified in the Life & Writings of the Late Mrs. Isabella Graham. Joanna Bethune. Ed. by Carolyn G. De Swarte & Donald Dayton. (Women in American Protestant Religion Series 1800-1930). 440p. 1987. lib. bdg. 65.00 (ISBN 0-8240-0659-3). Garland Pub.

Power of God. Daniel L. Migliore. LC 82-20037. (Library of Living Faith Ser.: Vol. 8). 116p. (Orig.). 1983. pap. 5.95 (ISBN 0-664-24454-8). Westminster.

Power of God's Character. Don Clowers. 230p. (Orig.). 1983. pap. text ed. 5.50 (ISBN 0-914307-14-2, Dist. by Harrison Hse). Word Faith.

Power of God's Word. Perry A. Gaspard. 60p. 1981. pap. 2.00 (ISBN 0-931867-05-3). Abundant Life Pubns.

Power of Goodness. Cesare Zappulli. 1980. 3.00 (ISBN 0-8198-5800-5); pap. 2.00 (ISBN 0-8198-5801-3). Dghtrs St Paul.

Power of Intecession. Peter Grant. 108p. (Orig.). 1984. pap. 4.95 (ISBN 0-89283-132-4). Servant.

Power of Knowing Who I Am in Christ. J. R. Reinhart. LC 82-73254. 220p. 1983. pap. 7.95 (ISBN 0-918060-04-4). Burn-Hart.

Power of Light: Eight Stories for Hanukkah. Isaac B. Singer. LC 80-20263. (Illus.). 87p. 1980. 10.95 (ISBN 0-374-36099-5). FS&G.

Power of Love. Fulton J. Sheen. 1968. pap. 2.95 (ISBN 0-385-01090-7, D235, Im). Doubleday.

Power of Numbers. Mary Valla. 1972. pap. 5.95 (ISBN 0-87516-108-1). De Vorss.

Power of Poetry. Sterling W. Sill. LC 83-83267. 141p. 1984. 7.95 (ISBN 0-88290-238-5). Horizon Utah.

Power of Positive Evangelism: How to Hold a Revival. John R. Bisagno. LC 68-26912. 1968. pap. 3.95 (ISBN 0-8054-2503-9). Broadman.

Power of Positive Living. John R. Bisagno. LC 70-93913. (Orig.). 1970. pap. 3.95 (ISBN 0-8054-1910-1). Broadman.

Power of Positive Praying. John Bisagno. 1965. pap. 3.50 (ISBN 0-310-21212-X, 9238). Zondervan.

Power of Positive Resistance. Roy H. Hicks. 128p. 1983. pap. 2.95 (ISBN 0-89274-294-1). Harrison Hse.

Power of Positive Thinking. Norman V. Peale. 1954. pap. 9.95 (ISBN 0-13-686402-3). P-H.

Power of Positive Thinking. Norman V. Peale. 224p. 1966. pap. 3.50 (ISBN 0-8007-8033-7, Spire Bks). Revell.

Power of Positive Thinking. Norman V. Peale. 552p. 1985. pap. 15.95 large print ed. (ISBN 0-8027-2465-5). Walker & Co.

Power of Praise. Kenneth Erickson. 1984. pap. 4.95 (ISBN 0-570-03925-8, 12-2859). Concordia.

Power of Praise & Worship. Terry Law. (Illus.). 256p. (Orig.). 1985. pap. 6.95 (ISBN 0-932081-01-0). Victory Hse.

Power of Prayer. Reuben A. Torrey. 192p. 1971. pap. 3.95 (ISBN 0-310-33312-1, 10907P). Zondervan.

Power of Prayer & Fasting. Marlin A. Hoffman. 2.50 (ISBN 0-89137-535-X). Quality Pubns.

Power of Receiving. Landon B. Saunders. (Twentieth Century Sermons Ser.). 1979. 11.95 (ISBN 0-89112-312-1, Bibl Res Pr). Abilene Christ U.

Power of Symbols in Religion & Culture. F. W. Dillistone. 176p. 1986. 14.95 (ISBN 0-8245-0784-3). Crossroad NY.

Power of the Aleph Beth, Vol. II. Phillip S. Berg. 1987. 14.95 (ISBN 0-943688-56-6); pap. 9.95 (ISBN 0-943688-57-4). Res Ctr Kabbalah.

Power of the Aleph Beth, Vol. 1. Philip S. Berg. 288p. 1986. 14.95 (ISBN 0-943688-11-6); pap. 9.95 (ISBN 0-943688-10-8). Res Ctr Kabbalah.

Power of the Blood. Andrew Murray. 1984. pap. 3.50 (ISBN 0-87508-428-1). Chr Lit.

Power of the Blood. H. A. Whyte. 1973. pap. 3.50 (ISBN 0-88368-027-0). Whitaker Hse.

Power of the Blood of Jesus. Andrew Murray. LC 85-62802. 1985. pap. 3.50 (ISBN 0-88270-597-0). Bridge Pub.

Power of the Holy Spirit, Vol. III. 3rd ed. Don Dewelt. 1972. pap. 3.95 (ISBN 0-89900-125-4). College Pr Pub.

Power of the Holy Spirit, Vol. IV. 2nd ed. Don DeWelt. (Orig.). 1976. pap. 6.95 (ISBN 0-89900-126-2). College Pr Pub.

Power of the Holy Spirit, Vol. II. 5th ed. Don DeWelt. (Orig.). 1971. pap. 3.95 (ISBN 0-89900-124-6). College Pr Pub.

Power of the Holy Spirit, Vol. I. 8th ed. Don DeWelt. (Orig.). 1963. pap. 3.95 (ISBN 0-89900-123-8). College Pr Pub.

Power of the Mind in the Philosophy of William of Ockham. William of Ockham. (Illus.). 137p. 1986. 117.50 (ISBN 0-89920-132-6). Am Inst Psych.

Power of the Plus Factor. Norman V. Peale. 1987. 14.95 (ISBN 0-8007-1526-8). Revell.

Power of the Spirit. William Law. Ed. by Andrew Murray. LC 76-57110. (Classics of Devotions Ser). 224p. 1977. pap. 4.95 (ISBN 0-87123-463-7, 200463). Bethany Hse.

Power of the Spirit. William Law. Ed. by D. Hunt. 1971. pap. 2.95 (ISBN 0-87508-247-5). Chr Lit.

Power of the Tongue. Perry A. Gaspard. 1983. pap. 1.50 (ISBN 0-931867-04-5). Abundant Life Pubns.

Power of Total Living. Marcus Bach. 1978. pap. 2.50 (ISBN 0-449-23747-8, Crest). Fawcett.

Power of Truth. Herrymon Maurer. 1983. pap. 2.50x (ISBN 0-87574-053-7, 053). Pendle Hill.

Power of Your Perceptions. William V. Arnold. LC 83-26089. (Potentials: Guides for Productive Living Ser.,: Vol. 6). 118p. (Orig.). 1984. pap. 7.95 (ISBN 0-664-24524-2). Westminster.

Power Pack. Bob Bartlett. LC 85-16841. 100p. 1985. pap. 4.95 (ISBN 0-89221-124-5). New Leaf.

Power Picture. Estelle McCarthy & Charles McCarthy. (Orig.). 1973. pap. 1.95 (ISBN 0-377-03031-7). Friend Pr.

Power Struggle. Richard L. Rubenstein. LC 86-16000. 214p. 1986. pap. text ed. 12.75 (ISBN 0-8191-5428-8). U Pr of Amer.

Power Tactics of Jesus Christ, & Other Essays. 2nd ed. Jay Haley. 160p. 1986. 14.95 (ISBN 0-931513-04-9, Dist. by W. W. Norton, Inc). Triang Pr.

Power That Worketh in Us. F. Henry Edwards. 1987. pap. 16.00 (ISBN 0-8309-0481-6). Herald Hse.

Power Through Constructive Thinking. Emmet Fox. 1940. 12.45 (ISBN 0-06-062930-4, HarpR). Har-Row.

Power Through Prayer. E. M. Bounds. 112p. 1983. pap. text ed. 2.95 (ISBN 0-88368-117-X). Whitaker Hse.

Power Through Prayer. E. M. Bounds. (Moody Classics Ser.). 1985. pap. text ed. 3.50 (ISBN 0-8024-6729-6). Moody.

Power Through Prayer. Edward M. Bounds. (Direction Bks). 1972. pap. 3.95 (ISBN 0-8010-0584-1). Baker Bk.

Power Through Prayer. Edward M. Bounds. pap. 2.95 (ISBN 0-310-21612-5, 9237). Zondervan.

Power Through Release. Ruth Stapleton. pap. 0.50 (ISBN 0-910924-39-2); 3 for 1.00 (ISBN 0-685-04195-6). Macalester.

Power to Be. Thomas Olbricht. LC 79-67136. (Journey Bks.). 1979. pap. 3.50 (ISBN 0-8344-0108-8). Sweet.

Power to Change: How to Stay Slim, Sober, & Smokeless. Harold Hill & Liz Rogers. (Orig.). 1987. pap. 4.95 (ISBN 0-88270-625-X, P625-X). Bridge Pub.

Power to Dissolve: Lawyers & Marriages in the Courts of the Roman Curia. John T. Noonan, Jr. LC 75-176044. (Illus.). 464p. 1972. 30.00x (ISBN 0-674-69575-5, Belknap Pr). Harvard U Pr.

Power to Heal. Francis MacNutt. LC 77-77845. 256p. 1977. pap. 3.95 (ISBN 0-87793-133-X). Ave Maria.

Power Trio. Mae Wilson-Ludlam. 152p. 1981. Repr. of 1976 ed. soft cover 6.95 (ISBN 0-88053-765-5). Macoy Pub.

Power with Purpose. John Sims. 1985. text ed. 8.95 (ISBN 0-87148-717-9); pap. text ed. 7.95 (ISBN 0-87148-716-0). Pathway Pr.

Power Within Us. facs. ed. Charles Baudouin. LC 68-16905. (Essay Index Reprint Ser). 1923. 15.00 (ISBN 0-8369-0176-2). Ayer Co Pubs.

Power Within You. Pat Williams & Jerry Jenkins. LC 82-24825. 180p. 1983. 12.95 (ISBN 0-664-27008-5, A Bridgebooks Publication). Westminster.

Power Words for Prosperous Living! 120p. 1984. pap. 4.95 (ISBN 0-9602166-1-8). Golden Key.

Powerful Petite Prayers. 3rd ed. Anna Cook. LC 85-52398. (Illus.). 112p. 1986. pap. 4.95 (ISBN 0-936029-02-1). Western Bk Journ.

Powerful Points for Preaching. John R. Terry. 150p. 1982. pap. 4.95 (ISBN 0-933704-44-5). Dawn Pr.

Powerhouse. Robert L. Sumner. 1978. pap. 3.95 (ISBN 0-914012-18-5, Pub. by Bibl Evang Pr). Sword of Lord.

Powerhouse for God: Sacred Speech, Chant & Song in an Appalachian Baptist Church. Jeff T. Titon. (American Folklore Recordings Ser.). 26p. 1982. pap. 20.00x incl. records (ISBN 0-8078-4084-X). U of NC Pr.

Powers of Imagining: Ignatius de Loyola: A Philosophical Hermeneutic of Imagining through the Collected Works of Ignatius de Loyola with a Translation of These Works. Antonio De Nicolas. 416p. 1986. 44.50x (ISBN 0-88706-109-5); pap. 19.95x (ISBN 0-88706-110-9). State U NY Pr.

Powers of Prophecy: The Cedar of Lebanon Vision from the Mongol Onslaught to the Dawn of the Enlightenment. Robert E. Lerner. LC 82-4824. 256p. 1983. text ed. 38.50x (ISBN 0-520-04461-4). U of Cal Pr.

Powers of the Psalms. Anna Riva. 128p. (Orig.). 1982. pap. 3.95 (ISBN 0-943832-07-1). Intl Imports.

Powers That Be: Earthly Rulers & Demonic Powers in Romans, Chapter 13, 1-7. Clinton D. Morrison. LC 60-4219. (Studies in Biblical Theology: No. 29). 1960. pap. 10.00x (ISBN 0-8401-3029-5). A R Allenson.

Powers That Make Us Human: The Foundations of Medical Ethics. Ed. by Kenneth Vaux. LC 84-28028. 152p. 1986. 16.95 (ISBN 0-252-01187-2). U of Ill Pr.

Prabhakara School of Purva Mimamsa. 2nd, rev. ed. Ganganatha Jha. 1978. 12.50 (ISBN 0-89684-016-6, Pub. by Motilal Banarsidass India). Orient Bk Dist.

Prabhupada: He Built a House in Which the Whole World Could Live. Satsvarupa Das Goswami. 7.95 (ISBN 0-89213-133-0). Bhaktivedanta.

Prabhupada Nectar, Bk. 2. Satsvarupa Das Goswami. Ed. by Bimala Dasi. 145p. pap. 4.99 (ISBN 0-911233-23-7). Gita Nagari.

Prabhupada Nectar, Vol. 3. Satvarupa Dasa Goswami. Ed. by Bimala dasi. 160p. 1985. pap. text ed. 2.00 (ISBN 0-911233-24-5). Gita Nagari.

Prabhupada Nectar, Vol. 4. Satsvarupa Das Goswami. Ed. by Bimala dasi. 160p. 1985. pap. text ed. 2.00 (ISBN 0-911233-29-6). Gita Nagari.

Prabhupada Nectar, Vol. 5. Satvarupa Das Goswami. Ed. by Bimala dasi. 160p. 1986. pap. text ed. 4.00 (ISBN 0-911233-31-8). Gita Nagari.

Practical Application of Science of Mind. Ernest Holmes & Willis Kinnear. 96p. 1958. pap. 4.50 (ISBN 0-911336-24-9). Sci of Mind.

Practical Bible Doctrine. Keith L. Brooks. (Teach Yourself the Bible Ser.). 1962. pap. 2.75 (ISBN 0-8024-6733-4). Moody.

Practical Candle-Burning Rituals. Raymond Buckland. (Illus.). 189p. 1984. pap. 5.95 (ISBN 0-87542-048-6). Llewellyn Pubns.

Practical Catechism, 3 Vols. Henry Hammond. LC 79-168238. (Library of Anglo-Catholic Theology: No. 8). Repr. of 1850 ed. Set. 87.50 (ISBN 0-404-52090-1). AMS Pr.

Practical Christian Socialism. Adin Ballou. LC 72-2936. (Communal Societies in America Ser.). Repr. of 1854 ed. 37.50 (ISBN 0-404-10702-8). AMS Pr.

Practical Christian Socialism, 2 vols. Adin Ballou. 655p. 1985. Repr. of 1854 ed. Set. lib. bdg. 69.00 (ISBN 0-932051-86-3, Pub. by Am Repr Serv). Am Biog Serv.

Practical Christianity. Arthur W. Pink. pap. 6.95 (ISBN 0-8010-6990-4). Baker Bk.

Practical Christianity. 500p. 1987. 14.95 (ISBN 0-8423-4957-X). Tyndale.

Practical Christianity of Malcolm Muggeridge. David Porter. LC 83-26442. 132p. 1984. pap. 4.95 (ISBN 0-87784-971-4). Inter-Varsity.

Practical Church Financing. Frederick Harrison. 128p. 1970. pap. 5.95 (ISBN 0-912522-58-5). Aero Medical.

Practical Divinity: Theology in the Wesleyan Tradition. Thomas A. Langford. 304p. (Orig.). 1983. pap. 9.95 (ISBN 0-687-33326-1). Abingdon.

Practical Dreamer: Israel Friedlaender & the Shaping of American Judaism. Baila R. Shargel. (Illus.). 1985. text ed. 20.00 (ISBN 0-87334-025-6, Pub. by Jewish Theol Seminary). Ktav.

Practical Encyclopedia of Natural Healing. rev. ed. Mark Bricklin. (Illus.). 592p. 1983. 21.95 (ISBN 0-87857-480-8). Rodale Pr Inc.

Practical Ethics. Peter Singer. LC 79-52328. 1980. 37.50 (ISBN 0-521-22920-0); pap. 10.95 (ISBN 0-521-29720-6). Cambridge U Pr.

Practical Grammar for Classical Hebrew. 2nd ed. Jacob Weingreen. 1959. 15.95x (ISBN 0-19-815422-4). Oxford U Pr.

Practical Guide for Altar Guilds. A. E. Bockelman. LC 62-16936. (Illus., Orig.). 1962. pap. 4.95 (ISBN 0-8066-0223-6, 10-5050). Augsburg.

Practical Guide for the Christian Writer. David S. McCarthy. 112p. 1983. pap. 5.95 (ISBN 0-8170-0979-5). Judson.

Practical Guide to Christian Living. Michael Scrogin. 144p. 1985. pap. 6.95 (ISBN 0-8170-1053-X). Judson.

Practical Guide to Finding & Using Your Spiritual Gifts. Tim Blanchard. 1983. pap. 6.95 (ISBN 0-8423-4898-0). Tyndale.

Practical Guide to Holistic Health. Swami Rama. 152p. 8.95 (ISBN 0-89389-066-9); pap. 6.95 (ISBN 0-89389-065-0). Himalayan Pubs.

Practical Guide to Integral Yoga. 7th ed. Sri Aurobindo. Ed. by Manibhai. 1979. pap. 9.00 (ISBN 0-89744-942-8). Auromere.

Practical Guide to Integral Yoga. Sri Aurobindo. (Illus.). 1985. 9.00 (ISBN 0-89071-217-4); pap. 6.95. Matagiri.

Practical Guide to Kashruth. 1982. 7.50 (ISBN 0-686-76247-9); pap. 6.00. Feldheim.

Practical Guide to Preaching. George Fitzgerald. LC 79-67742. 160p. (Orig.). 1980. pap. 5.95 (ISBN 0-8091-2281-2). Paulist Pr.

Practical Guide to Qabalistic Symbolism. Gareth Knight. 1978. 22.50 (ISBN 0-87728-397-4). Weiser.

Practical Guide to Sermon Preparation. Jerry Vines. 1985. 9.95 (ISBN 0-8024-6744-X). Moody.

Practical Guide to Spiritual Reading. Susan Muto. 9.95 (ISBN 0-87193-046-3). Dimension Bks.

Practical Holiness: A Second Look. David K. Bernard. 336p. (Orig.). 1985. pap. 6.95 (ISBN 0-912315-91-1). Word Aflame.

Practical Hymnology. Hubert M. Poteat. LC 72-1693. Repr. of 1921 ed. 14.50 (ISBN 0-404-09912-2). AMS Pr.

Practical Implications of Calvinism. Albert N. Martin. 1979. pap. 1.00 (ISBN 0-85151-296-8). Banner of Truth.

Practical Intelligence: Origins of Competence in the Everyday World. Ed. by Robert J. Sternberg & Richard K. Wagner. (Illus.). 240p. 1986. 49.50 (ISBN 0-521-30253-6); pap. 15.95 (ISBN 0-521-31797-5). Cambridge U Pr.

Practical Issues of This Life. Watchman Nee. Tr. by Stephen Kaung. 1975. pap. 3.25 (ISBN 0-935008-29-2). Christian Fellow Pubs.

Practical Jung: Nuts & Bolts of Jungian Psychotherapy. Harry A. Wilmer. 250p. 1987. 17.95 (ISBN 0-933029-16-0). Chiron Pubns.

Practical Laws of Islam. Imam Khomeini. LC 83-50077. 1983. pap. 9.00 (ISBN 0-940368-25-0). Tahrike Tarsile Quran.

Practical Medical Halacha. 1982. 5.00 (ISBN 0-87306-221-3). Feldheim.

Practical Meditator. Harry C. Meserve. LC 80-15631. 137p. 1981. 19.95 (ISBN 0-87705-506-8); professional 16.95. Human Sci Pr.

Practical Mysticism. Evelyn Underhill. 160p. 1986. pap. 5.95 (ISBN 0-89804-143-0). Ariel OH.

Practical Pointers for Training Your Child. Lloy A. Kniss. 1975. pap. 2.75 (ISBN 0-87813-509-X). Christian Light.

Practical Psychology for Pastors. William R. Miller & Kathleen A. Jackson-Miller. (Illus.). 400p. 1985. 30.95 (ISBN 0-13-692807-2). P-H.

Practical Reasoning: ACPA Proceedings, 1984, Vol. 58. Ed. by Daniel O. Dahlstrom. 250p. 1985. pap. 12.00 (ISBN 0-918090-18-0). Am Cath Philo.

Practical Religion: Being Plain Papers on Daily Duties, Experience Dangers, & Privileges of Professing Christianity. J. C. Ryle. 334p. 1977. Repr. of 1959 ed. 12.95 (ISBN 0-227-67569-X). Attic Pr.

Practical Sermon Outlines. Russell E. Spray. 80p. 1984. pap. 3.95 (ISBN 0-8010-8240-4). Baker Bk.

Practical Sermons: New York, 1858. Nathaniel W. Taylor. Ed. by Bruce Kuklick. (American Religious Thought of the 18th & 19th Centuries Ser.). 455p. 1987. lib. bdg. 60.00 (ISBN 0-8240-6959-5). Garland Pub.

Practical Sermons That Motivate. J. J. Turner. pap. 2.95 (ISBN 0-89315-211-0). Lambert Bk.

Practical Spirituality. John R. Price. 160p. (Orig.). 1985. pap. 6.95 (ISBN 0-942082-06-0). Quartus Bks.

Practical Theology: The Emerging Field in Theology, Church & World. Ed. by Don S. Browning. LC 82-47739. 128p. (Orig.). 1982. pap. 7.95 (ISBN 0-06-061153-7, RD-410, HarpR). Har-Row.

Practical Truth Series, 6 Vols. Alfred Edersheim et al. Incl. Elisha; Jonah; Thessalonians; Pastoral Epistles; Israel's Wanderings; Judges. 1940p. 1986. Set. 74.70 (ISBN 0-8254-3529-3). Kregel.

Practical Truths from Elisha. Alfred Edersheim. LC 82-18702. 368p. 1983. 14.95 (ISBN 0-8254-2511-5). Kregel.

Practical Truths from First Thessalonians. F. E. Marsh. LC 86-2742. Orig. Title: Flashes from the Lighthouse of Truth. 272p. 1986. Repr. 12.95 (ISBN 0-8254-3234-0). Kregel.

Practical Truths from Israel's Wanderings. George Wagner. LC 82-18706. 384p. 1983. 14.95 (ISBN 0-8254-4017-3). Kregel.

Practical Truths from Jonah. Joseph S. Exell. LC 82-18671. 240p. 1983. 11.95 (ISBN 0-8254-2525-5). Kregel.

Practical Truths From Judges. Luke H. Wiseman. LC 85-8096. 354p. 1985. 14.95 (ISBN 0-8254-4034-3). Kregel.

Practical Truths from the Pastoral Epistles. Eugene Stock. LC 83-6113. 352p. 1983. 14.95 (ISBN 0-8254-3746-6). Kregel.

Practical Use of the Greek New Testament. Kenneth Wuest. Rev. by Donald Wise. 160p. 1982. text ed. 11.95 (ISBN 0-8024-6737-7). Moody.

Practical Vedanta. Swami Vivekananda. pap. 2.00 (ISBN 0-87481-124-4). Vedanta Pr.

Practical Vedanta: Of Swami Rama Tirtha. Ed. by Brandt Dayton. LC 78-10567. 350p. 8.95 (ISBN 0-89389-038-3). Himalayan Pubs.

Practical Vision of Christian Unity. Jean C. Lyles. LC 81-15032. (Into Our Third Century Ser.). 96p. (Orig.). 1982. pap. 3.95 (ISBN 0-687-33330-X). Abingdon.

Practical Water Cure. Yogi Ramacharaka. leatherette 3.00 (ISBN 0-911662-12-X). Yoga.

Practical Works of Richard Baxter. Richard Baxter. (Giant Summit Bks.). 1000p. 1981. pap. 14.95 (ISBN 0-8010-0804-2). Baker Bk.

Practical Yoga: Thoroughly Practical Lessons upon the Philosophy & Practice of Yoga. 6th ed. O. Hashnu Hara. 79p. 1970. pap. 4.95 (ISBN 0-88697-032-6). Life Science.

Practicando la Presencia de Dios. Lawrence. LC 82-50949. Tr. of Practice of the Presence of God. (Span.). 72p. (Orig.). 1983. pap. 1.35 (ISBN 0-8358-0456-9). Upper Room.

Practice & Preaching of Liberation. William J. Nottingham. Ed. by Herbert Lambert. LC 85-18997. 96p. (Orig.). 1986. pap. 9.95 (ISBN 0-8272-2931-3). CBP.

Practice & Realization. Nathan Rotenstreich. 1979. lib. bdg. 29.00 (ISBN 90-247-2112-1, Pub. by Martinus Nijhoff Netherlands). Kluwer Academic.

Practice & Theory of Tibetan Buddhism. Geshe Lhundup Sopa & Jeffrey Hopkins. LC 75-42898. 1976. pap. 4.95 (ISBN 0-394-17905-6, E672, Ever). Grove.

Practice of Chinese Buddhism, 1900-1950. Holmes H. Welch. LC 67-13256. pap. 9.95x (ISBN 0-674-69701-4). Harvard U Pr.

Practice of Faith: A Handbook of Contemporary Spirituality. Karl Rahner. 354p. 1983. 19.50 (ISBN 0-8245-0603-0); pap. 14.95. Crossroad NY.

Practice of Faith: A Handbook of Contemporary Spirituality. rev. ed. Karl Rahner. 336p. 1986. pap. 14.95 (ISBN 0-8245-0779-7). Crossroad NY.

Practice of Godliness. Jerry Bridges. LC 83-61499. 272p. 1983. pap. 3.95 (ISBN 0-89109-497-0). NavPress.

Practice of Godliness. Jerry Bridges. (Christian Character Library). 272p. 1985. hdbk. 8.95 (ISBN 0-89109-466-0). NavPress.

Practice of Humility. Pope Leo. Tr. by John F. O'Connor. 1976. lib. bdg. 59.95 (ISBN 0-8490-2462-5). Gordon Pr.

Practice of Humility. Pope Leo. Tr. by John F. O'Conor. 1980. lib. bdg. 59.95 (ISBN 0-8490-3177-X). Gordon Pr.

Practice of Humilty. 1978. 2.50 (ISBN 0-8198-0546-7); pap. 1.50 (ISBN 0-8198-0547-5). Dghtrs St Paul.

Practice of Jesus. Hugo Echegaray. Tr. by Matthew J. O'Connell from Span. LC 83-19341. Orig. Title: Practica de Jesus. 176p. (Orig.). 1984. pap. 7.95 (ISBN 0-88344-397-X). Orbis Bks.

Practice of Karma Yoga. Swami Sivananda. 1974. 7.95 (ISBN 0-8426-0675-0); pap. 3.50 (ISBN 0-686-67764-1). Orient Bk Dist.

Practice of Meditation 1971. rev. ed. Charles Bowness. (Paths to Inner Power Ser.). 1979. pap. 3.50 (ISBN 0-85030-182-3). Weiser.

Practice of Piety: Directing a Christian How to Walk, That He May Please God. Lewis Bayly. LC 75-31081. Repr. of 1718 ed. 34.50 (ISBN 0-404-13500-5). AMS Pr.

Practice of Piety: Puritan Devotional Disciplines in Seventeenth Century New England. Charles E. Hambrick-Stowe. LC 81-19806. (Published for the Institute of Early American History & Culture, Williamsburg, Virginia Ser.). xvi, 298p. 1986. pap. 10.95x (ISBN 0-8078-4145-5). U of Nc Pr.

Practice of Prayer. David A. Hubbard. 91p. 1983. pap. 2.95 (ISBN 0-87784-393-7). Inter-Varsity.

Practice of Prayer. G. Campbell Morgan. (Morgan Library). pap. 3.95 (ISBN 0-8010-5896-1). Baker Bk.

Practice of Process Meditation: The Intensive Journal Way to Spiritual Experience. Ira Progoff. LC 80-68847. 343p. 1980. 18.95 (ISBN 0-87941-008-6); pap. 9.95, 1980 (ISBN 0-87941-008-6). Dialogue Hse.

Practice of Spiritual Direction. William A. Barry & William J. Connolly. 224p. (Orig.). 1982. pap. 11.95 (ISBN 0-8164-2357-1, AY7870, HarpR). Har-Row.

Practice of the Presence of God. Brother Lawrence. 64p. pap. 2.75 (ISBN 0-8007-8034-5, Spire Bks). Revell.

Practice of the Presence of God. Tr. by John J. Delaney. LC 77-70896. 1977. pap. 2.95 (ISBN 0-385-12861-4, Im). Doubleday.

Practice of the Presence of God. Ed. by Donald E. Demaray & Bro. Lawrence. (Devotional Classics Ser). 64p. 1975. pap. 2.45 (ISBN 0-8010-2844-2). Baker Bk.

Practice of the Presence of God. Lawrence. 128p. 1981. pap. 6.95 (ISBN 0-87243-129-0). Templegate.

Practice of the Presence of God. Lawrence. Ed. by Hal H. Helms. LC 84-61019. (Living Library Ser.). 161p. (Orig.). 1984. pap. 5.95 (ISBN 0-941478-29-7). Paraclete Pr.

Practice of the Presence of God. Brother Lawrence. Tr. by E. M. Blaiklock. 96p. 1982. pap. 4.95 (ISBN 0-8407-5803-0). Nelson.

Practice of the Presence of God. Brother Lawrence. 96p. 1982. pap. 3.50 (ISBN 0-88368-105-6). Whitaker Hse.

Practice of Zen. Chang Cheng-Chi. LC 78-618. 1978. Repr. of 1959 ed. lib. bdg. 29.75x (ISBN 0-313-20264-8, CHPZ). Greenwood.

Practice to Win. Larry Jones. 1982. pap. 4.95 (ISBN 0-8423-4887-5). Tyndale.

Practicing Church. Donald L. Roberts. LC 1-67318. 100p. (Orig.). 1981. pap. 2.95 (ISBN 0-87509-303-5). Chr Pubns.

Practicing His Presence. 3rd ed. Brother Lawrence & Frank Laubach. Ed. by Gene Edwards. 1973. pap. 5.95 (ISBN 0-940232-01-4). Christian Bks.

Practicing the Prayer of Presence. Adrian van Kaam & Susan Muto. 7.95 (ISBN 0-87193-174-5). Dimension Bks.

Practicing the Presence. Joel S. Goldsmith. LC 58-7474. 1958. 11.95 (ISBN 0-06-063250-X, HarpR). Har-Row.

Practicing the Presence of the Spirit. Myron S. Augsburger. LC 81-20170. 200p. (Orig.). 1982. pap. 7.95 (ISBN 0-8361-1990-8). Herald Pr.

Practiquemos la Visitacion. J. T. Sisemore. Ed. by Ananias Gonzalez. Tr. by Josue Grijalva. Orig. Title: Ministry of Visitation. 1981. Repr. of 1979 ed. 2.50 (ISBN 0-311-11034-7). Casa Bautista.

Praeter Sermones Pseudo-Eusebianos Opera. Saint Faustus. Ed. by A. Engelbrecht. (Corpus Scriptorum Ecclesiasticorum Latinorum Ser: Vol. 21). 1891. unbound 50.00 (ISBN 0-384-15200-7). Johnson Repr.

Pragmatic Meaning of God. Robert O. Johann. (Aquinas Lecture). 1966. 7.95 (ISBN 0-87462-131-3). Marquette.

Prahlad, Picture & Story Book. Swami A. C. Bhaktivedanta. LC 72-2032. (Illus.). 1973. pap. 2.95 (ISBN 0-685-47513-1). Bhaktivedanta.

Praise: A Matter of Life & Breath. R. Allen. Tr. by Silas Chan. (Chinese.). 204p. 1982. pap. write for info. (ISBN 0-941598-04-7). Living Spring Pubns.

Praise! A Matter of Life & Breath. Ronald B. Allen. LC 80-23894. 248p. 1980. pap. 5.95 (ISBN 0-8407-5733-6). Nelson.

Praise & Lament in the Psalms. rev. enl. ed. Claus Westermann. Tr. by Keith Crim & Richard Soulen. LC 65-10553. 1981. 12.95 (ISBN 0-8042-1791-2); pap. 9.95 (ISBN 0-8042-1792-0). John Knox.

Praise & Prayer. Gary P. Colton. 1978. 7.95 (ISBN 0-8198-0593-9). Dghtrs St Paul.

Praise & Thanksgiving. James Weekley. 1986. 6.95 (ISBN 0-89536-792-0, 6810). CSS of Ohio.

Praise Avenue. Don Gossett. 128p. 1976. pap. 3.50 (ISBN 0-88368-059-9). Whitaker Hse.

Praise Book. Compiled by Dale Dieleman. 1984. pap. 5.95 (ISBN 0-8010-2947-3). Baker Bk.

Praise Every Day. Muriel Larson. 135p. 1984. 10.95 (ISBN 0-910311-11-0). Huntington Hse Inc.

Praise Faith in Action. Charles Trombley. (Orig.). 1976. pap. 3.95 (ISBN 0-89350-009-7). Fountain Pr.

Praise God: Common Prayer at Taize. Ed. by Members of Community at Taize, France. LC 76-47437. 1977. 16.95x (ISBN 0-19-519915-4). Oxford U Pr.

Praise Him: A Prayerbook for Today's Christian. William G. Storey. 224p. (Orig.). 1973. pap. 2.95 (ISBN 0-87793-056-2). Ave Maria.

Praise Him, Praise Him! Jennie Davis. 1982. pap. text ed. 4.95 (ISBN 0-89693-208-7, Sonflower Bks). SP Pubns.

Praise in St. Augustine: Readings & Reflections. John M. Quinn. 220p. pap. 8.95 (ISBN 0-8158-0430-X). Chris Mass.

Praise of Folly. Desiderius Erasmus. Intro. by Clarence H. Miller. LC 78-13575. 1979. text ed. 25.00 (ISBN 0-300-02279-4); pap. 7.95x (ISBN 0-300-02373-1). Yale U Pr.

Praise the Lord. Nesta De Robeck. 1967. 4.50 (ISBN 0-8199-0086-9, L38643). Franciscan Herald.

Praise the Lord! James E. Haas. LC 74-80388. 1974. pap. 3.95 (ISBN 0-8192-1176-1). Morehouse.

Praise the Lord & Rub It Out. Ralph Gross. (Illus.). 30p. (Orig.). 1981. pap. 5.00 (ISBN 0-686-32010-7). Karma Pub.

Praise the Lord Anyway. Frances Hunter. 1978. pap. 3.25 (ISBN 0-87162-131-2). Hunter Bks.

Praise the Lord with Psalms: Metrical Paraphrases of Selected Psalms. Laura B. Lane. 1986. 5.95 (ISBN 0-533-06823-1). Vantage.

Praise with Understanding. David Wright & Jill Wright. 64p. 1983. pap. 3.50 (ISBN 0-85364-355-5, Pub. by Paternoster UK). Attic Pr.

Praise Works. Merlin R. Carothers. 161p. (Orig.). 1973. pap. 4.95. Carothers.

Praises We Sing. Elmina Yoder & Lula Miller. 1980. 5.45 (ISBN 0-87813-515-4). Christian Light.

Praising & Knowing God. Daniel W. Hardy & David F. Ford. LC 84-25756. 226p. (Orig.). 1985. pap. 12.95 (ISBN 0-664-24624-9). Westminster.

Prakrit Dhammapada. Suttapitaka. LC 78-70127. Repr. of 1921 ed. 31.50 (ISBN 0-404-17386-1). AMS Pr.

Praktische Theologie nach den Grundsatzen. Friedrich Schleiermacher. (Ger.). 845p. 1983. 96.00 (ISBN 3-11-009699-4). De Gruyter.

Pranayama: The Yoga of Breathing. Andre Van Lysebeth. (Unwin Paperbacks). (Illus.). 1979. pap. 6.95 (ISBN 0-04-149050-9). Allen Unwin.

Prapanchasara Tantra. Ed. by Arthur Avalon, pseud. (Sanskrit.). 617p. 1982. text ed. 48.00 (ISBN 0-89744-239-3). Auromere.

Prasna Upanishad. Tr. by Swami Gambhirananda from Sanskrit. (Upanishads with Shankara's Commentary Ser.). 104p. 1980. pap. 2.25 (ISBN 0-87481-204-6). Vedanta Pr.

Prasnopanisad. Tr. by Swami Sarvananda. (Sanskrit & English). pap. 1.00 (ISBN 0-87481-459-6). Vedanta Pr.

Pratical Yoga. Harvey Day. pap. cancelled (ISBN 0-7225-0351-2). Thorsons Pubs.

Pravda o Russkoj Tserkvi na Rodinje i za Rubjezhom. George Grabbe. Tr. of Truth of the Russian Church at Home & Abroad. 216p. 1961. pap. 8.00 (ISBN 0-317-30359-7). Holy Trinity.

Pravda ob Ubijstvje Tsarskoj Semji. P. Paganuzzi. LC 80-84594. Tr. of Truth About the Murder of the Royal Family. 234p. 1981. 15.00 (ISBN 0-317-29234-X); pap. 10.00 (ISBN 0-317-29235-8). Holy Trinity.

Pravosavnoje Dogmaticheskoje Bogoslovije. Protopresbyter Michael Pomazansky. Tr. of Orthodox Dogmatic Theology. 280p. 1963. pap. text ed. 20.00 (ISBN 0-317-29309-5). Holy Trinity.

Pravoslavije i Inoslavnija Khristijanskija Ispovjedanija. Metropolitan Panteleimon. Tr. of Orthodoxy & Other Christian Faiths. 1950. pap. 0.55 (ISBN 0-317-30259-0). Holy Trinity.

Pravoslavije, Rimo-Katolichestvo, Protenstatizm i Sektantstvo. Mitrophan Znoskovo-Borovsky. Tr. of Orthodoxy, Roman-Catholicism, Protenstatism & Sectarianism. 156p. 1972. pap. text ed. 5.00 (ISBN 0-317-30254-X). Holy Trinity.

Pravoslavno-Khristijanskaja Apologetika. I. M. Andreyev. Tr. of Orthodox-Christian Apologetics. 92p. 1965. pap. text ed. 5.00 (ISBN 0-317-30249-3). Holy Trinity.

Pravoslavno-Khristijanskoe Nravstvennoje Bogoslovije. I. M. Andreyev. Tr. of Orthodox-Christian Moral Theology. 148p. 1966. pap. text ed. 5.00 (ISBN 0-317-30264-7). Holy Trinity.

Praxis of Suffering: An Interpretation of Liberation & Political Theologies. Rebecca S. Chopp. LC 86-824. 192p. (Orig.). 1986. pap. 12.95 (ISBN 0-88344-256-6). Orbis Bks.

Pray All Ways. Edward Hays. LC 81-69329. (Illus.). 164p. (Orig.). 1981. pap. 7.95 (ISBN 0-939516-01-2). Forest Peace.

Pray Always. James Alberione. 1966. 4.00 (ISBN 0-8198-0126-7); pap. 3.00 (ISBN 0-8198-0127-5). Dghtrs St Paul.

Pray: An Introduction to the Spiritual Life for Busy People. Richard J. Huelsman. LC 76-24449. (Participants Handbook). 136p. 1976. pap. 4.95 (ISBN 0-8091-1976-5). Paulist Pr.

Pray: God Is Listening. Richard W. DeHaan. 80p. (Orig.). 1980. pap. 2.50 (ISBN 0-310-23542-1). Zondervan.

Pray: How to Be Effective in Prayer. Warren Myers & Ruth Myers. LC 83-61679. 204p. 1984. pap. 5.95 (ISBN 0-89109-510-1). NavPress.

Pray in the Spirit. Arthur Wallis. 1970. pap. 2.95 (ISBN 0-87508-561-X). Chr Lit.

Pray It Again, Sam. Kenneth J. Roberts. Ed. by Anna Marie Ruskin. LC 83-61243. 116p. (Orig.). 1983. pap. 3.95 (ISBN 0-9610984-0-6). Pax Tapes.

Pray Like This: Pray with Saint Paul. Leonard Sheil. 1963. 3.00 (ISBN 0-8198-0128-3). Dghtrs St Paul.

Pray: Moderator's Manual: An Introduction to the Spiritual Life for Busy People. Huelsman. LC 76-2449. 168p. 1976. pap. 7.95 (ISBN 0-8091-1975-7). Paulist Pr.

Pray the Rosary. J. M. Lelen. (Illus., Purse-Size). blue bdg. 0.60 (ISBN 0-89942-040-0, 40/05). Catholic Bk Pub.

Pray to Win! A Blueprint for Success. Alfred A. Montapert. LC 86-73037. 235p. 1986. perfect bdg. 4.95 (ISBN 0-9603174-4-9). Bks of Value.

Pray to Win: A Blueprint for Success. Alfred A. Montapert. pap. 4.95 (ISBN 0-9603174-4-9, Pub. by Bks of Value). Borden.

Pray Today's Gospel: Reflections on the Day's Good News. Bernard C. Mischke & Fritz Mischke. LC 80-14186. 358p. (Orig.). 1980. pap. 9.95 (ISBN 0-8189-0403-8). Alba.

Pray Your Way Through It. Joseph Murphy. 171p. 1973. pap. 4.00 (ISBN 0-87516-190-1). De Vorss.

Prayer. Abhishiktananda. LC 73-600. 88p. 1973. pap. 3.95 (ISBN 0-664-24973-6). Westminster.

Prayer. 2nd ed. Karl Barth. Ed. by Don E. Saliers. Tr. by Sara F. Terrien from German. LC 84-25782. 96p. 1985. pap. 7.95 (ISBN 0-664-24626-5). Westminster.

Prayer. Gaynell Cronin & Jim Cronin. 1980. pap. 7.55 (ISBN 0-88479-032-0). Arena Lettres.

Prayer. O. Hallesby. LC 75-2846. 176p. 1975. pap. 3.95 (ISBN 0-8066-1473-0, 10-5067). Augsburg.

Prayer. Spencer W. Kimball et al. LC 77-15521. 1977. 8.95 (ISBN 0-87747-657-8). Deseret Bk.

Prayer. Spencer W. Kimball et al. 1977. pap. 1.95 (ISBN 0-87747-739-6). Deseret Bk.

Prayer. Abraham Kon. 12.95x (ISBN 0-900689-05-6). Bloch.

Prayer. Abraham Kon. 277p. 1971. 9.95 (ISBN 0-900689-05-6). Soncino Pr.

Prayer. Karen D. Merrell. 23p. 4.95 (ISBN 0-87747-562-8). Deseret Bk.

Prayer. Rudolf Steiner. 1966. pap. 2.00 (ISBN 0-910142-30-0). Anthroposophic.

Prayer. Hans U. Von Balthasar. Tr. by Graham Harrison from Ger. LC 85-82172. Orig. Title: Das Betrachtende Gebet. 311p. 1986. pap. 10.95 (ISBN 0-89870-074-4). Ignatius Pr.

Prayer. John White. 1984. pap. 0.75 (ISBN 0-87784-067-9). Inter-Varsity.

Prayer, a Baha'i Approach. Incl. Part I. Man's Link with God. William Hellaby; Part II. Prayer as a Living Reality. William Hellaby & Madeline Hellaby. 1985. 9.95 (ISBN 0-85398-212-0); pap. 4.95 (ISBN 0-85398-213-9). G Ronald Pub.

Prayer: A Discovery of Life. Alexandra Kovats. (Nazareth Bks). 128p. 1983. pap. 4.95 (ISBN 0-86683-714-0, AY8361, HarpR). Har-Row.

Prayer: A Guide When Troubled. Martin C. Helldorfer. LC 85-13561. (Illus.). 88p. (Orig.). 1985. pap. 7.95 (ISBN 0-89571-024-2). Affirmation.

Prayer after Nine Rainy Days & Other Family Prayers. Pat C. Hinton. 1978. pap. 4.95 (ISBN 0-86683-626-8, HarpR). Har-Row.

Prayer: An Adventure in Living. B. C. Butler. (Ways of Prayer Ser.: Vol. 10). 8.95 (ISBN 0-89453-431-9); pap. 4.95 (ISBN 0-89453-302-9). M Glazier.

Prayer: An Invitation from God. Charles Nieman. 140p. (Orig.). 1983. pap. text ed. 4.95 (ISBN 0-914307-03-7, Dist. by Harrison Hse). Word Faith.

Prayer & Action. Tom Boone & Edna Boone. 1974. pap. 1.25x (ISBN 0-8358-0309-0). Upper Room.

Prayer & Evangelism. Jessie Penn-Lewis. 1962. pap. 2.95 (ISBN 0-87508-952-6). Chr Lit.

Prayer & Fasting. Gordon Lindsay. (School of Prayer Ser.). 1.75 (ISBN 0-89985-076-6). Christ Nations.

Prayer & Meditation. Intro. by Elizabeth C. Prophet. LC 76-28086. (Illus.). 306p. (Orig.). 1978. pap. 9.95 (ISBN 0-916766-19-5). Summit Univ.

Prayer & Meditation for Middle School Kids. John B. Hesch. 144p. (Orig.). 1985. pap. 7.95 (ISBN 0-8091-2723-7). Paulist Pr.

Prayer & Modern Man. Jacques Ellul. Tr. by C. Edward Hopkins from Fr. 192p. 1973. pap. 6.95 (ISBN 0-8164-2081-5, HarpR). Har-Row.

Prayer & Personal Religion. John B. Coburn. LC 57-5397. (Layman's Theological Library). 96p. 1957. pap. 4.95 (ISBN 0-664-24005-4). Westminster.

Prayer & Personal Religion. John B. Coburn. LC 85-10477. 160p. 1985. pap. 8.95 (ISBN 0-8027-2509-0). Walker & Co.

Prayer & Poetry: Contribution to Poetical Theory. Henri Bremond. LC 72-188148. 1927. lib. bdg. 25.00 (ISBN 0-8414-9825-3). Folcroft.

Prayer & Power in the Capital: With Prayers of the Presidents. Ed. by Pauline Innis. LC 82-156801. (Illus.). 120p. 1982. 10.00 (ISBN 0-941402-02-9). Devon Pub.

Prayer & Praying Men. E. M. Bounds. (Direction Bks). 1977. pap. 3.95 (ISBN 0-8010-0721-6). Baker Bk.

Prayer & Revival. Wim Malgo. 4.95 (ISBN 0-937422-12-6). Midnight Call.

Prayer & Temperament: Different Prayer Forms for Different Personality Types. Chester P. Michael & Marie C. Norrisey. 192p. (Orig.). 1984. pap. 5.95 (ISBN 0-940136-01-5). Open Door Inc.

Prayer & the Christian Life: C-4 Devotional Journal II. Ed. by Steve Clapp. (C-4 Journals Ser.). 126p. (Orig.). 1982. pap. 6.00 (ISBN 0-317-11522-7). C-Four Res.

Prayer & the Christian's Devotional Life. G. Raymond Carlson. LC 80-83522. (Radiant Life Ser.). 128p. (Orig.). 1981. 2.50 (ISBN 0-88243-878-6, 02-0878); teacher's ed. 3.95 (ISBN 0-88243-190-0, 32-0190). Gospel Pub.

Prayer & the Common Life. Thomas Langford. LC 83-51396. 96p. (Orig.). 1984. pap. 3.95 (ISBN 0-8358-0473-9). Upper Room.

Prayer & the Pursuit of Happiness. Richard Harries. 160p. (Orig.). 1985. pap. 6.95 (ISBN 0-8028-0089-0). Eerdmans.

Prayer & the Will of God. Hubert Van Zeller. 1978. 4.95 (ISBN 0-87243-084-7). Templegate.

Prayer & Worship. Douglas V. Steere. LC 78-70480. 1978. pap. 3.95 (ISBN 0-913408-44-1). Friends United.

Prayer & You. Michael Pennock. LC 85-70162. (Illus., Orig.). 1985. pap. text ed. 5.50 student ed., 160 pg. (ISBN 0-87793-284-0); tchr's. ed., 144 pg. 7.95 (ISBN 0-87793-285-9). Ave Maria.

Prayer As a Political Problem. Jean Danielou. Ed. by J. R. Kirwan. 1967. 3.50 (ISBN 0-8362-0278-3, Pub. by Sheed). Guild Bks.

Prayer Attitude in the Eastern Church. Gabriele Winkler. 1978. pap. 1.45 (ISBN 0-937032-01-8). Light&Life Pub Co MN.

Prayer Book. Tr. by Ben Z. Bokser from Hebrew. 430p. 1983. pap. text ed. 11.95 (ISBN 0-87441-372-9). Behrman.

Prayer Book. 368p. (Orig.). 1979. 10.00 (ISBN 0-317-30304-X). Holy Trinity.

Prayer Book. S. Singer. Repr. of 1962 ed. 10.95x (ISBN 0-8197-0057-6). Bloch.

Prayer Book & the Lord's Prayer. Frederick D. Maurice. 416p. 1977. Repr. of 1880 ed. 12.50 (ISBN 0-87921-038-9). Attic Pr.

Prayer Book for Young Catholics. Robert J. Fox. LC 82-81318. 168p. 1982. pap. 5.50 Leatherette (ISBN 0-87973-370-5, 370). Our Sunday Visitor.

Prayer Book Guide to Christian Education. Episcopal Church. 224p. 1983. pap. 9.95 (ISBN 0-8164-2422-5, HarpR). Har-Row.

Prayer Book of Michelino Da Besozzo. Colin Eisler & Patricia Corbett. LC 81-68186. (Illus.). 1981. 50.00 (ISBN 0-8076-1016-X). Braziller.

Prayer Book of the Bible: Reflection on the Old Testament. Peter M. Stravinskas. LC 83-63171. 160p. 1984. pap. 5.95 (ISBN 0-87973-606-2, 606). Our Sunday Visitor.

Prayer Book of the Saints. Charles Dollen. LC 84-60749. 1984. pap. 6.95 (ISBN 0-87973-717-4, 717). Our Sunday Visitor.

Prayer Book Office. Ed. by Howard Galley. 800p. 1980. 39.95 (ISBN 0-8164-0370-8, HarpR). Har-Row.

Prayer Can Change Your Life. W. Parker & E. St. Johns. 1974. pap. 2.95 (ISBN 0-346-12137-X). Cornerstone.

Prayer Can Change Your Life. William Parker & Elaine St. Johns. 270p. 1983. pap. 4.95 (ISBN 0-13-694786-7, Reward). P-H.

Prayer Changes My Life. large print ed. Pearl Brians. 23p. 1985. pap. 4.00 (ISBN 0-914009-35-4). VHI Library.

Prayer: Conversing with God. Rosalind Rinker. pap. 3.50 (ISBN 0-310-32092-5, 10716P). Zondervan.

Prayer Course for Healing Life's Hurts: Book. Matthew Linn & Dennis Linn. 128p. 1983. pap. 5.95 (ISBN 0-8091-2522-6). Paulist Pr.

Prayer Flags: The Spiritual Life & Songs of Jigten Sumgon. Khenpo K. Gyalsten. 96p. (Orig.). 1986. pap. 6.95 (ISBN 0-937938-37-8). Snow Lion.

Prayer for a Child. Rachel Field. LC 44-47191. (Illus.). 32p. 1968. 8.95 (ISBN 0-02-735190-4). Macmillan.

Prayer for All Times. Pierre Charles. Tr. by Robin Waterfield from Fr. Tr. of La Priere du Toutes Les Heures. 157p. 1983. pap. 5.95 (ISBN 0-87061-090-2). Chr Classics.

Prayer for Guidance. Elbert Willis. 1977. 1.25 (ISBN 0-89858-012-9). Fill the Gap.

Prayer for Our Day. E. Lee Phillips. LC 81-82349. 156p. 1982. pap. 4.95 (ISBN 0-8042-2583-4). John Knox.

Prayer for Patient Waiting. Elbert Willis. 1977. 1.25 (ISBN 0-89858-002-1). Fill the Gap.

Prayer for Pilgrims: A Book about Prayer for Ordinary People. Sheila A. Cassidy. (Crossroad Paperback Ser.). 192p. 1982. pap. 6.95 (ISBN 0-8245-0420-8). Crossroad NY.

Prayer for Today's People: Sermons on Prayer by Carl Michalson (1915-1965) Ed. by Edward J. Wynne, Jr. & Henry O. Thompson. LC 82-17583. 88p. (Orig.). 1983. lib. bdg. 23.50 (ISBN 0-8191-2771-X); pap. text ed. 8.75 (ISBN 0-8191-2772-8). U Pr of Amer.

Prayer: God's Time & Ours! Warren F. Groff. 144p. (Orig.). 1984. pap. 6.95 (ISBN 0-87178-714-8). Brethren.

Prayer: How to Talk to God. (Teaching Bks.). (Illus.). 1970. pap. text ed. 2.95 (ISBN 0-86508-153-0). BCM Intl Inc.

Prayer, Humility & Compassion. Samuel Dresner. 4.95 (ISBN 0-87677-006-5). Hartmore.

Prayer in Baptist Life. Charles W. Deweese. LC 85-21301. 1986. pap. 4.95 (ISBN 0-8054-6941-9). Broadman.

Prayer in Life: Life in Prayer. George A. Buttrick. 1976. pap. 0.85x (ISBN 0-8358-0346-5). Upper Room.

Prayer in Practice. Simon Tugwell. 1980. pap. 7.95 (ISBN 0-87243-099-5). Templegate.

Prayer in Sixteenth Century England. Faye L. Kelly. LC 66-64090. (U of Fla. Humanities Monographs: No. 22). 1966. pap. 3.50 (ISBN 0-8130-0127-7). U Presses Fla.

Prayer in the Black Tradition. O. R. Bowyer et al. 112p. 1986. pap. 5.95 (ISBN 0-8358-0538-7, ICN 609100, Dist. by Abingdon Press). Upper Room.

Prayer in the Contemporary World. Douglas V. Steere. LC 80-82942. 32p. pap. 2.50x (ISBN 0-87574-907-0). Pendle Hill.

Prayer in the Home. Ed. by David M. Thomas. LC 81-69503. (Marriage & Family Living in Depth Bk.). 1981. pap. 2.45 (ISBN 0-87029-180-7, 20250-7). Abbey.

Prayer in the Life of Jesus. Paris Donehoo. (Orig.). 1984. pap. 3.95 (ISBN 0-8054-5101-3). Broadman.

Prayer in the New Age. White Eagle. 1957. 3.95 (ISBN 0-85487-041-5). De Vorss.

Prayer in the New Age. White Eagle. 112p. 1984. Repr. of 1957 ed. 5.95 (ISBN 0-85487-064-4, Pub. by White Eagle Pub). De Vorss.

Prayer in the Public Schools: Law & Attitude Change. William K. Muir, Jr. LC 67-28851. 1967. U of Chicago Pr.

Prayer in the Religious Traditions of Africa. Aylward Shorter. 1975. pap. 7.95 (ISBN 0-19-519848-4). Oxford U Pr.

Prayer in the Talmud: Forms & Patterns. Joseph Heinemann. (Studia Judaica: Vol. 9). 1977. 61.00 (ISBN 3-11-004289-4). De Gruyter.

Prayer Is... Furn F. Kelling. (Illus.). 1979. 5.95 (ISBN 0-8054-4256-1, 4242-56). Broadman.

Prayer Is a Hunger. Edward Farrell. 4.95 (ISBN 0-87193-031-5). Dimension Bks.

Prayer Is Invading the Impossible. Jack Hayford. LC 77-71684. 1977. pap. 4.95 (ISBN 0-88270-218-1). Bridge Pub.

Prayer Is Invading the Impossible. Jack Hayford. (Epiphany Bks.). 160p. 1983. pap. 2.50 (ISBN 0-345-30467-5). Ballantine.

Prayer Is the Answer. Joseph Murphy. 190p. 1973. pap. 5.00 (ISBN 0-87516-189-8). De Vorss.

Prayer: Its Nature & Technique. 4th ed. Kirpal Singh. LC 81-50727. (Illus.). 149p. 1982. pap. 5.95 (ISBN 0-918224-10-1). Sawan Kirpal Pubns.

Prayer, Its Significance & Benefits. A. Rahman. pap. 12.50 (ISBN 0-317-46106-0). Kazi Pubns.

Prayer: Key to Revival. Paul Y. Cho & R. Whitney Manzano. 224p. 1984. 9.95 (ISBN 0-8499-0453-6, 0453-6). Word Bks.

Prayer: Learning How to Talk to God. J. L. Groth. LC 56-1395. (Concept Books Series Four). 1983. pap. 3.95 (ISBN 0-570-07799-0). Concordia.

Prayer Life. Agape Ministries Staff. (Orig.). 1984. pap. 3.50 (ISBN 0-89274-346-8). Harrison Hse.

Prayer Life. Andrew Murray. (Andrew Murray Ser.). pap. 3.50 (ISBN 0-8024-6806-3). Moody.

Prayer Life. Andrew Murray. 160p. 1981. pap. 3.50 (ISBN 0-88368-102-1). Whitaker Hse.

Prayer Life. Charles H. Usher. 1967. pap. 1.50 (ISBN 0-87508-545-8). Chr Lit.

Prayer: Life's Limitless Reach. Jack R. Taylor. LC 77-73984. 1977. 8.95 (ISBN 0-8054-5258-3). Broadman.

Prayer: Living with God. Simon Tugwell. 1980. pap. 7.95 (ISBN 0-87243-100-2). Templegate.

Prayer Meeting at Our House. large print ed. Pearl Brians. 25p. 1985. pap. 4.00 (ISBN 0-914009-33-8). VHI Library.

Prayer Meetings. Harry Doty. LC 78-10622. 1979. pap. 6.00 (ISBN 0-8309-0228-7). Herald Hse.

Prayer Ministry of the Church. Watchman Nee. Tr. by Stephen Kaung. 1973. pap. 2.75 (ISBN 0-935008-30-6). Christian Fellow Pubs.

Prayer: More Than Words. LeRoy Eims. LC 82-61301. 162p. 1983. pap. 3.95 (ISBN 0-89109-493-8). NavPress.

Prayer Movements: An International Directory. International Partners in Prayer Staff. 20p. Date not set. pap. 3.00 (ISBN 0-917593-00-6, Pub. by Intl Partners). Prosperity & Profits.

Prayer of Cosa: Praying in the Way of Francis of Assisi. Cornelia Jessey. (Orig.). 1985. pap. 5.95 (ISBN 0-86683-936-4, AY8512, HarpR). Har-Row.

Prayer of Faith. Leonard S. Boase. 1985. Repr. 5.95 (ISBN 0-8294-0493-7). Loyola.

Prayer of Faith. Ed. by J. O. Fraser & Mary E. Allbutt. pap. 1.00 (ISBN 0-85363-106-9). OMF Bks.

Prayer of Faith. Quentin Hakenewerth. 76p. (Orig.). 1969. pap. 1.75 (ISBN 0-9608124-3-1). Marianist Com Ctr.

Prayer of Love: The Art of Aspiration. Venard Poslusney. 128p. (Orig.). 1975. pap. 2.95 (ISBN 0-914544-06-3). Living Flame Pr.

Prayer of Recollection: St. Teresa of Avila. 1983. 1.95 (ISBN 0-87193-208-3). Dimension Bks.

Prayer of St. Patrick. pap. 1.00 (ISBN 0-686-18721-0). Eastern Orthodox.

Prayer of the Faithful: Understanding & Creatively Using the Prayer of the Church. Walter Huffman. 80p. (Orig.). 1986. pap. 5.95 (ISBN 0-8066-2230-X, 10-5079). Augsburg.

Prayer of the Heart. George A. Maloney. LC 80-69095. 208p. (Orig.). 1981. pap. 3.95 (ISBN 0-87793-216-6). Ave Maria.

Prayer, Patronage, & Power: The Abbey of la Trinite, Vendome, 1032-1187. Penelope Johnson. (Illus.). 224p. 1981. 30.00x (ISBN 0-8147-4162-2). NYU Pr.

Prayer: Personal & Liturgical. Agnes Cunningham. (Message of the Fathers of the Church Ser.: Vol. 16). 1985. 12.95 (ISBN 0-89453-356-8); pap. 8.95 (ISBN 0-89453-327-4). M Glazier.

Prayer Perspectives. Ed. by Edward Carter. LC 86-28675. 108p. (Orig.). 1987. pap. 5.95 (ISBN 0-8189-0513-1). Alba.

Prayer Pilgrimage Through Scripture. Rea McDonnell. LC 83-82025. (Orig.). 1984. pap. 6.95 (ISBN 0-8091-2601-X). Paulist Pr.

Prayer Pilgrimage with Paul. Rea McDonnell. 112p. 1986. pap. 4.95 (ISBN 0-8091-2746-6). Paulist Pr.

Prayer Poems. facsimile ed. Ed. by O. V. Armstrong & Helen Armstrong. LC 72-86793. (Granger Index Reprint Ser). 1942. 16.00 (ISBN 0-8369-6094-7). Ayer Co Pubs.

Prayer Power & Stress Management. Stewart Bedford. pap. 6.95 (ISBN 0-935930-05-1). A & S Pr.

Prayer Power Unlimited. J. Oswald Sanders. (Moody Press Electives Ser.). (Orig.). 1984. pap. 3.95 (ISBN 0-8024-6675-3); pap. 2.50 leader's guide (ISBN 0-8024-6676-1). Moody.

Prayer Primer. Erwin Kolb. 1982. pap. 4.25 (ISBN 0-570-03843-X, 12-2946). Concordia.

Prayer Primer: A Philosophy Book. Patty Jo Cornish. Ed. by Roberto Quintero. LC 84-81741. 68p. (Orig.). pap. 5.95 (ISBN 0-9613717-0-6). Hilltop Hse.

Prayer, Responding to God. Robert B. Hall & Marjorie W. Hall. 1985. pap. 5.95 (ISBN 0-318-04676-8). Episcopal Ctr.

Prayer Room Counselor's Handbook. Cathy Jakobcic. 47p. 1983. pap. 2.25 (ISBN 0-88144-015-9). Christian Pub.

Prayer, Saints, Scripture & Ourselves. Chuck Gallagher & Oliver Crilly. LC 83-60189. 162p. (Orig.). 1983. pap. text ed. 6.95 (ISBN 0-911905-03-0). Past & Mat Rene Ctr.

Prayer Secrets. 2nd ed. Kenneth E. Hagin. 1983. pap. 1.00 (ISBN 0-89276-005-2). Hagin Ministries.

Prayer: Selections from the Writings of the Holy Fathers. pap. 2.95 (ISBN 0-317-11391-7). Eastern Orthodox.

Prayer Seminar-Workshop Workbook. International Partners in Prayer. 11p. 1984. pap. 2.50 (ISBN 0-917593-02-2, Pub. by Intl Partners). Prosperity & Profits.

Prayer Services for Parish Meetings. Debra T. Hintz. (Illus.). 96p. (Orig.). 1983. pap. 9.95 (ISBN 0-89622-170-9). Twenty-Third.

Prayer Services for the Christian Educator. Johannes Hofinger. 1983. 5.35 (ISBN 0-686-40164-6). Natl Cath Educ.

Prayer, Stress & Our Inner Wounds. Flora S. Wuellner. 94p. (Orig.). 1985. pap. 4.95 (ISBN 0-8358-0501-8). Upper Room.

Prayer Support System: A Plan to Strengthen the Local Church. Rick Blumenberg. LC 86-42933. 40p. (Orig.). 1986. pap. 4.00 (ISBN 0-937021-04-0). Sagamore Bks MI.

Prayer-Talk: Casual Conversations with God. William V. Coleman. LC 82-74085. 112p. (Orig.). 1983. pap. 3.95 (ISBN 0-87793-265-4). Ave Maria.

Prayer That Heals. Francis MacNutt. LC 80-69770. 120p. (Orig.). 1981. pap. 2.95 (ISBN 0-87793-219-0). Ave Maria.

Prayer That Moves Mountains. Gordon Lindsay. (School of Prayer Ser.). 2.50 (ISBN 0-89985-078-2). Christ Nations.

Prayer That Spans the World. Helmut Thielicke. Tr. by J. W. Doberstein from Ger. 160p. 1978. Repr. 13.95 (ISBN 0-227-67671-8). Attic Pr.

Prayer That Teaches to Pray. Marcus Dods. LC 80-82323. (Shepherd Illustrated Classics Ser.). (Illus.). 1980. pap. 5.95 (ISBN 0-87983-232-0). Keats.

Prayer: The Cornerstone. Helen G. Hole. LC 62-19073. (Orig.). 1962. pap. 2.50x (ISBN 0-87574-123-1). Pendle Hill.

Prayer: The Divine Dialog. Carroll E. Simcox. LC 84-28930. 108p. (Orig.). 1985. pap. 4.95 (ISBN 0-87784-527-1). Inter-Varsity.

Prayer: The Eastern Tradition. Andrew Ryder. (Orig.). 1983. pap. 2.95 (ISBN 0-914544-47-0). Living Flame Pr.

Prayer: The Great Conversation-Straight Answers to Tough Questions about Prayer. Peter Kreeft. 164p. (Orig.). 1985. pap. 6.95 (ISBN 0-89283-218-5). Servant.

Prayer-the Key to Salvation. Michael Muller. LC 85-52207. 226p. 1985. pap. 5.00 (ISBN 0-89555-287-6). Tan Bks Pubs.

Prayer: The Master Key. James D. Freeman. 1975. 5.95 (ISBN 0-87159-128-6). Unity School.

Prayer: The Vital Link. William J. Krutza. 96p. 1983. pap. 3.95 (ISBN 0-8170-0986-8). Judson.

Prayer Times for Primary Grades. Marilyn Brokamp. 1987. pap. 4.95. St Anthony Mess Pr.

Prayer Transparencies. Stuart Kelman. 32p. (Orig.). 1982. 29.95x (ISBN 0-686-81835-0). Arbit.

Prayer Veil in Scripture & History. J. C. Wenger. 31p. 1964. pap. 1.50 (ISBN 0-8361-1501-5). Herald Pr.

Prayer Works. Robert Collier. 1950. pap. 3.95 (ISBN 0-910140-04-9). C & R Anthony.

Prayer Works! Robert Collier. 4.95 (ISBN 0-912576-01-4). R Collier.

Prayerable a Day. Irene B. Harrell. (Orig.). 1987. pap. 7.00 (ISBN 0-915541-15-7). Star Bks Inc.

Prayerbook. Laurence Mancuso. (New Skete). (Illus.). 720p. 1976. 35.00x (ISBN 0-9607924-3-0). Monks of New Skete.

Prayerbook for Catholics. Robert J. Fox. 112p. (Orig.). 1982. 6.00 (ISBN 0-931888-08-5); pap. 3.95. Christendom Pubns.

Prayerbook Hebrew Teacher's Guide. Joseph Anderson. Ed. by Ethelyn Simon & Victoria Kelman. (Orig.). 1985. pap. text ed. 4.95 (ISBN 0-939144-10-7). EKS Pub Co.

Prayerbook Hebrew the Easy Way. 2nd ed. Joseph Anderson et al. Ed. by Ethelyn Simon. 1985. pap. text ed. 14.95 (ISBN 0-939144-12-3). EKS Pub Co.

Prayerbook of Favorite Litanies: 116 Favorite Catholic Litanies & Responsory Prayers. Compiled by Albert Hebert. LC 84-51818. 192p. 1985. pap. 7.50 (ISBN 0-89555-252-3). Tan Bks Pubs.

Prayerbook Reform in Europe: The Liturgy of European Liberal & Reform Judaism. Jakob J. Petuchowski. LC 68-8262. (Illus.). 1969. 13.50 (ISBN 0-8074-0091-2, 387580, Pub. by World Union). UAHC.

Prayerbook: Service of the Heart. (Home Study Program Ser.: No. 302). 6.00 (ISBN 0-686-96123-4). United Syn Bk.

Prayerful Heart. Charles L. Allen & Helen S. Rice. 160p. (Orig.). 1981. pap. 5.95 (ISBN 0-8007-5073-X, Power Bks). Revell.

Prayerful Pauses with Jesus & Mary. Bill Peffley. (Illus.). 96p. (Orig.). 1985. pap. 5.95 (ISBN 0-89622-251-9). Twenty-Third.

Prayerlife of the Church. Albert L. Schlitzer. 1962. 7.95x (ISBN 0-268-00214-2). U of Notre Dame Pr.

Prayerpath. Jack Hayford. 80p. (Orig.). 1987. mass 2.95, (ISBN 0-8423-4964-2). Tyndale.

Prayers. Theodore P. Ferris. 1981. 6.95 (ISBN 0-8164-0483-6, HarpR). Har-Row.

Prayers. Michael Quoist. 1975. pap. 5.95 (ISBN 0-380-00406-2, 60244-X). Avon.

Prayers Alleged to Be Jewish: An Examination of the Constitutiones Apostolorum. David A. Fiensy. (Brown Judaic Studies). 1985. 29.95 (ISBN 0-89130-795-8, 14-00-65); pap. 21.95 (ISBN 0-89130-796-6). Scholars Pr GA.

Prayers & Devotions from Pope John Paul II. Ed. by Peter C. Van Lierde. 472p. 1984. 10.95 (ISBN 0-89526-601-6). Regnery Bks.

Prayers & Graces. Alice J. Davidson. (Alice in Bibleland Ser.). 32p. 1986. 4.95 (ISBN 0-8378-5078-9). Gibson.

Prayers & Inspiration for Senior Children of God. Anne Kunath & Lillian Riegert. 1979. pap. 1.75. De Vorss.

Prayers & Meditations. rev. ed. Tr. by Aurobindo from Fr. 380p. (Orig.). 1979. pap. 16.00 (ISBN 0-89744-998-3, Sri Aurobindo Ashram Trust India); text ed. 21.00 (ISBN 0-89744-219-9). Auromere.

Prayers & Meditations. Bahaullah. Tr. by Shoghi Effendi. 1978. 14.95 (ISBN 0-900125-39-X). Baha'i.

Prayers & Meditations: An Anthology of the Spiritual Writings of Karl Rahner. Karl Rahner. Ed. by John Griffiths. 128p. 1980. pap. 4.95 (ISBN 0-8245-0053-9). Crossroad NY.

Prayers & Meditations of St. Anselm. Tr. by Benedicta Ward. (Classics Ser.). 1979. pap. 5.95 (ISBN 0-14-044278-2). Penguin.

Prayers & Others Pieces of Thomas Becon, Chaplain to Archbishop Cranmer. Thomas Becon. Repr. of 1844 ed. 55.00 (ISBN 0-384-03730-5). Johnson Repr.

Prayers & Praises. Nathaniel Micklem. 1982. pap. 3.95x (ISBN 0-7152-0541-2). Outlook.

Prayers & Promises for Every Day from the Living Bible. Corrie ten Boom. 272p. 1985. pap. 9.95 (ISBN 0-8027-2505-8). Walker & Co.

Prayers & Promises for Every Day: With Corrie Ten Boom. Corrie ten Boom. Ed. by Luci Shaw. LC 77-92352. (Day Star Devotional). 144p. 1977. pap. 2.95 (ISBN 0-87788-689-X). Shaw Pubs.

Prayers & Reading for Worship. Ed. by Judy Judd. 1987. pap. 12.50 (ISBN 0-8309-0478-6). Herald Hse.

Prayers & Recommended Practices. 2nd ed. Jerome F. Coniker. LC 78-66374. (Living Meditation & Prayerbook Ser.). (Illus.). 91p. pap. text ed. 3.00 (ISBN 0-932406-01-7). AFC.

Prayers at Meals. Michael Kwatera & Dietrich Reinhart. 48p. 1983. pap. 0.50 (ISBN 0-8146-1318-7). Liturgical Pr.

Prayers at Midpoint: Conversations with God for Those in Life's Second Half. William A. Miller. LC 83-72110. 96p. 1984. pap. 5.95 (ISBN 0-8066-2054-4, 10-5081). Augsburg.

Prayers Before & after Communion. Paschal Botz et al. 24p. 1981. pap. 0.50 (ISBN 0-8146-1213-X). Liturgical Pr.

Prayers for a Lifetime. Karl Rahner. 256p. 1984. 12.95 (ISBN 0-8245-0678-2). Crossroad NY.

Prayers for a Lifetime. Karl Rahner. 256p. 1986. pap. 8.95 (ISBN 0-317-42453-X). Crossroad NY.

Prayers for a Small Child. LC 83-16050. (Knee-High Bks.). (Illus.). 24p. 1984. PLB 4.99 (ISBN 0-394-96281-8, BYR); 3.95 (ISBN 0-394-86281-3). Random.

Prayers for All Occasions. Andrew W. Blackwood. (Pocket Pulpit Library). pap. 3.95 (ISBN 0-8010-0923-5). Baker Bk.

Prayers for All Occasions. Stuart R. Oglesby. 180p. 1983. pap. 5.95 (ISBN 0-8042-2485-4). John Knox.

Prayers for All Occasions. 1951. 0.95 (ISBN 0-88028-006-9). Forward Movement.

Prayers, for All People, for All Occasions. Leander M. Zimmerman. pap. 2.00 (2027877). Bks Demand UMI.

Prayers for All Reasons. Roy D. Fauth. 1980. 3.50 (ISBN 0-89536-448-4, 1642). CSS of Ohio.

Prayers for Boys. Herman C. Alleman. LC 81-142145. pap. 3.95 (ISBN 0-8407-5241-5). Nelson.

Prayers for Boys. Ruth Odor. 1985. pap. 0.69 pocket size (ISBN 0-87239-825-0, 2815). Standard Pub.

Prayers for Boys & Prayers for Girls. Herman Alleman & Elizabeth R. Scovil. 3.95x. Nelson.

Prayers for Children. 32p. 1981. pap. 3.95 (ISBN 0-8249-8023-9). Ideals.

Prayers for College Students. J. T. Cummings & H. Moll. LC 12-2962. 1982. pap. 4.95 (ISBN 0-570-03869-3). Concordia.

Prayers for Contemporary Worship. Church of Scotland - Committee on Public Worship & Aids to Devotion. 1977. pap. 4.95x (ISBN 0-7152-0351-7). Outlook.

Prayers: For Daily & Occasional Use. Victor Hoagland. pap. 1.45 (ISBN 0-8091-5158-8). Paulist Pr.

Prayers for Dark People. W. E. B. Dubois. Ed. by Herbert Aptheker. LC 80-12234. 88p. 1980. lib. bdg. 12.00x (ISBN 0-87023-302-5); pap. 6.95 (ISBN 0-87023-303-3). U of Mass Pr.

Prayers for Every Need. William H. Kadel. pap. 4.95 (ISBN 0-8042-2496-X). John Knox.

Prayers for Every Occasion. Ed. by Frank Colquhoun. Orig. Title: Parish Prayers. 445p. 1974. Repr. of 1967 ed. kivar 14.95 (ISBN 0-8192-1280-6). Morehouse.

Prayers for Everyone. (Illus.). 16p. 1982. pap. 0.99 (ISBN 0-86683-653-5, AY8232, HarpR). Har-Row.

Prayers for Girls. Herman C. Alleman. 3.95 (ISBN 0-8407-5242-3). Nelson.

Prayers for Girls. Ruth Odor. 1985. pap. 0.69 pocket size (ISBN 0-87239-826-9, 2816). Standard Pub.

Prayers for Holy Communion. Holy Transfiguration Monastery Staff. 120p. (Orig.). 1986. pap. 3.00x (ISBN 0-913026-60-3, Holy Transfiguration). St Nectarios.

Prayers for Home & School. (Illus.). 16p. 1982. pap. 0.99 (ISBN 0-86683-652-7, AY8231, HarpR). Har-Row.

Prayers for Impossible Days. Paul Geres. Tr. by Ingalill H. Hjelm from Fr. LC 75-36442. 64p. 1976. pap. 2.95 (ISBN 0-8006-1214-0, 1-1214). Fortress.

Prayers for Inner Strength. Ed. by John Beilenson. (Illus.). 64p. 1986. 5.95 (ISBN 0-88088-468-1, 884681). Peter Pauper.

Prayers for Mothers. Caroline G. Blair. 1980. pap. 1.95 (ISBN 0-8170-0864-0). Judson.

Prayers for Mothers & Children. 3rd. ed. Rudolf Steiner. Tr. by Eileen V. Hersey & Christian Von Arnim. 76p. 1983. pap. 5.00 (ISBN 0-85440-195-4, Pub. by Steinerbooks). Anthroposophic.

Prayers for Our Times. Ed. by John Cumming & Paul Burns. 144p. 1983. 10.95 (ISBN 0-8245-0071-7); pap. 6.95 (ISBN 0-8245-0107-1). Crossroad NY.

Prayers for Public Worship. Edward K. Ziegler. Ed. by David Eller. 1986. pap. 3.95. Brethren.

Prayers for Sunday. Madeleine L'Engle. (Illus.). 1974. pap. 1.95 (ISBN 0-8192-1153-2). Morehouse.

Prayers for Sunday Services. Church of Scotland - Committee on Public Worship & Aids to Devotion. 1980. pap. 6.95x (ISBN 0-7152-0456-4). Outlook.

Prayers for the Christian Year. 2nd ed. Church of Scotland - General Assembly - Committee On Public Worship And Aids To Devotion. 172p. 1952. 10.95x (ISBN 0-19-145602-0). Oxford U Pr.

Prayers for the Domestic Church: A Handbook for Worship in the Home. rev. ed. Edward Hays. LC 82-72077. (Illus.). 216p. 1979. pap. 8.95 (ISBN 0-939516-02-0); pap. 10.95 spiral bound (ISBN 0-939516-08-X); leather 17.95 (ISBN 0-939516-09-8). Forest Peace.

Prayers for the Newly Single. Lois S. Hertzler. 32p. 1981. pap. 1.95 (ISBN 0-8170-0914-0). Judson.

Prayers for the Seasons. Lois Kikkert. 1.50 (ISBN 0-8091-9306-X). Paulist Pr.

Prayers for the Servants of God. Edward Hays. (Illus.). 144p. (Orig.). 1980. pap. 6.95 (ISBN 0-939516-03-9). Forest Peace.

Prayers for the Sickroom. William A. Lauterbach. 1953. 1.10 (ISBN 0-570-03524-4, 14-1236). Concordia.

Prayers for the Third Age: A Devotion for Mature Catholics. Charles Dollen. LC 85-60889. 200p. (Orig.). 1985. pap. 7.95 (ISBN 0-87973-837-5, 837). Our Sunday Visitor.

Prayers for the Young Child. Don Roberts. 1981. pap. 7.95 (ISBN 0-570-04051-5, 56-1717). Concordia.

Prayers for Troubled Times. Jay E. Adams. 1979. pap. 1.50 (ISBN 0-87552-067-7). Presby & Reformed.

Prayers for Worship. E. Lee Phillips. 148p. 1985. pap. 4.95 (ISBN 0-8010-7090-2). Baker Bk.

Prayers for Worship Leaders. Arnold Kenseth & Richard P. Unsworth. LC 77-15249. 132p. (Orig.). 1978. pap. 5.95 (ISBN 0-8006-1331-7, 1-1331). Fortress.

Prayers for Young Adults. Daughters of St. Paul. 1985. 4.00 (ISBN 0-8198-5822-6). Dghtrs St Paul.

Prayers from a Mother's Heart. Judith Mattison. LC 74-14177. (Illus.). 96p. (Orig.). 1975. pap. 5.95 (ISBN 0-8066-1460-9, 10-5095). Augsburg.

Prayers from a Troubled Heart. George Appleton. LC 83-48010. 64p. 1983. pap. 3.50 (ISBN 0-8006-1711-8, 1-1711). Fortress.

Prayers from Prison. Dietrich Bonhoeffer. Tr. by Johann C. Hampe from Ger. LC 77-15228. Tr. of Von guten Machten. 1978. pap. 4.95 (ISBN 0-8006-1334-1, 1-1334). Fortress.

Prayers from Riverside. Leo S. Thorne. 120p. (Orig.). 1983. pap. 5.95 (ISBN 0-8298-0643-1). Pilgrim NY.

Prayers from the Mount. J. Barrie Shepherd. LC 85-26400. 144p. 1986. pap. 8.95 (ISBN 0-664-24699-0). Westminster.

Prayers I Love. David A. Redding et al. LC 78-17798. (Illus., Orig.). 1978. pap. 6.95 (ISBN 0-89407-025-8). Strawberry Hill.

Prayers in Dialogue. C. David Godshall. (Common & Lutheran Ser. C). 1985. 7.95 (ISBN 0-89536-759-9, 5866). CSS of Ohio.

Prayers in Dialogue B: (Con-Luth) C. David Godshall. 1984. 7.95 (ISBN 0-89536-692-4, 4869). CSS of Ohio.

Prayers in Dialogue: Series A. rev. ed. C. David Godshall. Ed. by Michael L. Sherer. 1986. pap. 7.95 (ISBN 0-89536-813-7, 6842). CSS of Ohio.

Prayers in Later Life. Rita Snowden. 1981. pap. 3.50 (ISBN 0-8358-0435-6). Upper Room.

Prayers New & Old. 1937. 1.25 (ISBN 0-88028-005-0). Forward Movement.

Prayers of a Christian Educator. Mobby Larson. (Greeting Book Line Ser.). 32p. (Orig.). 1985. pap. 1.50 (ISBN 0-89622-277-2). Twenty-Third.

Prayers of a Mystic. Flower A. Newhouse. Compiled by & intro. by Pamela Boult. LC 86-71083. 100p. (Orig.). 1986. pap. 6.00 (ISBN 0-910378-21-5). Christward.

Prayers of a New Mother. Mobby Larson. (Greeting Book Line Ser.). 48p. (Orig.). 1985. pap. 1.50 (ISBN 0-89622-230-6). Twenty Third.

Prayers of a Woman. rev. 3rd ed. Tracy Voigt. 55p. 1982. Repr. of 1976 ed. spiral bdg. 4.00 (ISBN 0-686-37419-3). T Voigt.

Prayers of a Working Mother. Judy Esway. (Getting Book Line Ser.). 32p. (Orig.). 1985. pap. 1.50 (ISBN 0-89622-269-1). Twenty-Third.

Prayers of Blessing & Praise for All Occasions. Humberto Porto & Hugo Schlesinger. Tr. by Michael Leipsiger from Port. Tr. of Dialogando com Deus. 128p. 1987. 9.95 (ISBN 0-89622-311-6). Twenty-Third.

Prayers of Catherine of Siena. Ed. by Suzanne Noffke. LC 82-60746. 288p. 1983. pap. 9.95 (ISBN 0-8091-2508-0). Paulist Pr.

Prayers of Christ. Elton Trueblood. LC 65-10706. Orig. Title: Lord's Prayers. 1982. pap. 3.95 (ISBN 0-932970-24-9). Prinit Pr.

Prayers of Confession: Series B. David L. Wade. (Orig.). 1987. pap. price not set (ISBN 0-89536-885-4, 7871). CSS of Ohio.

Prayers of Consolation. Morris Silverman. 1972. 8.95x (ISBN 0-87677-062-6); pap. 6.95x (ISBN 0-87677-063-4). Prayer BK.

Prayers of Father Killian. Killian Speckner. 384p. 1986. pap. 8.95 (ISBN 0-941478-56-4). Paraclete Pr.

Prayers of Jesus. Joachim Jeremias. Tr. by John Bowden et al from Ger. LC 77-10427. 132p. 1978. pap. 4.95 (ISBN 0-8006-1322-8, 1-1322). Fortress.

Prayers of John Donne. John Donne. Ed. by Herbert H. Umbach. (Orig.). 1962. 11.95x; pap. 7.95x (ISBN 0-8084-0252-8). New Coll U Pr.

Prayers of John Paul II. Pope John Paul II. Ed. by John F. McDonald. LC 82-72495. 108p. 1982. pap. 6.95 (ISBN 0-8245-0537-9). Crossroad NY.

Prayers of Kierkegaard. Ed. by Perry D. LeFevre. LC 56-11000. (Midway Reprint Ser.). 1956. pap. 14.00x (ISBN 0-226-47059-8). U of Chicago Pr.

Prayers of Man. Ed. by Alfonso Di Nola. 1960. 27.95 (ISBN 0-8392-1152-X). Astor-Honor.

Prayers of Mohammad. (With arabic text). pap. 16.50 (ISBN 0-686-18346-0). Kazi Pubns.

Prayers of Muhammad. A. H. Farid. 1969. 10.75x (ISBN 0-87902-050-4). Orientalia.

Prayers of St. Augustine: A Contemporary Anthology. Tr. by Barry Ulanov from Lat. 160p. (Orig.). 1984. pap. 7.95 (ISBN 0-86683-881-3, 7460, HarpR). Har-Row.

Prayers of Susanna Wesley. Ed. by W. L. Doughty. 80p. 1984. pap. 3.95 (ISBN 0-310-36351-9, 12368P, Clarion Class). Zondervan.

Prayers of the Eucharist: Early & Reformed. 2nd ed. Ed. by R. C. Jasper & G. J. Cuming. 1980. 17.95x (ISBN 0-19-520140-X); pap. 5.95 (ISBN 0-19-520141-8). Oxford U Pr.

Prayers of the Faithful. Liturgical Prayer Magazine. Ed. by Henry Fehren. 1977. pap. 11.50 (ISBN 0-916134-29-6). Pueblo Pub Co.

Prayers of the Orthodox Church. pap. 1.00 (ISBN 0-317-11389-5). Eastern Orthodox.

Prayers of the Prophet with Arabic Text. A. H. Siddiqui. pap. 2.00 (ISBN 0-686-18345-2). Kazi Pubns.

Prayers of the Social Awakening. Walter Rauschenbusch. LC 77-8615. 1909. 22.00 (ISBN 0-8414-7332-3). Folcroft.

Prayers of the World. Compiled by Richard Polese. 62p. 1987. pap. 5.00 (ISBN 0-943734-00-2). Ocean Tree Bks.

Prayers or Medytacions, Wherin the Mynde Is Styrred Patiently to Suffre All Afflictions Here. Catharine Parr. LC 76-57370. (English Experience Ser.: No. 788). 1977. Repr. of 1545 ed. PLB 6.00 (ISBN 90-221-0788-4). Walter J Johnson.

Prayers Responsively: Responsive Prayers for the Three-Year Lectionary. Theodore P. Bornhoeft. 1984. pap. 8.95 (ISBN 0-570-03922-3, 12-2861). Concordia.

Prayers That Are Answered. Betty Malz. 1981. pap. 3.50 (ISBN 0-451-14948-3, Sig). NAL.

Prayers That Avail Much. Word Ministries, Inc. 110p. (Orig.). 1980. pap. 3.95 (ISBN 0-89274-116-3). Harrison Hse.

Prayers That Avail Much for Children. Angela Brown. (Illus.). 32p. (Orig.). 1983. pap. 3.98 (ISBN 0-89274-296-8). Harrison Hse.

Prayers That Make a Difference. rev. ed. Marjorie Soderholm. Orig. Title: Study Guide to Bible Prayers. 96p. 1980. pap. 2.50 (ISBN 0-911802-49-5). Free Church Pubns.

Prayers to a God of Surprises. Lois Kikkert. 1.50 (ISBN 0-8091-9327-2). Paulist Pr.

Prayers Written at Vailima. Robert Louis Stevenson. xi, 61p. 1973. 40.00 (ISBN 0-317-11648-7). Dawsons.

Prayertimes: Morning-Midday-Evening. M. Basil Pennington. LC 87-4212. 168p. 1987. pap. 3.95 (ISBN 0-385-24061-9, Im). Doubleday.

Prayerways: For Those Who Feel Discouraged or Distraught, Frightened or Frustrated, Angry or Anxious, Powerless or Purposeless, Over-Extended or Under-Appreciated, Burned Out or Just Plain Worn Out. Louis M. Savary & Patricia H. Berne. LC 80-7737. 176p. 1984. pap. 7.95 (ISBN 0-06-067064-9, RD 526, HarpR). Har-Row.

Praying. Robert S. J. Faricy. 120p. 1980. pap. 3.50 (ISBN 0-03-056661-4, HarpR). Har-Row.

Praying & Doing the Stations of the Cross with Children. Diane Abajian. (Illus.). 24p. 1980. pap. 1.50 (ISBN 0-89622-118-0). Twenty-Third.

Praying Beyond God's Ability. Roy H. Hicks. 96p. 1977. 2.95 (ISBN 0-89274-052-3). Harrison Hse.

Praying for Inner Healing. Robert Faricy. LC 79-92857. 94p. (Orig.). 1979. pap. 3.95 (ISBN 0-8091-2250-2). Paulist Pr.

Praying for One Another. Gene Getz. 132p. 1982. pap. 5.50 (ISBN 0-88207-351-6). Victor Bks.

Praying for Others. Thomas D. Elliff. LC 79-52341. 1979. pap. 3.95 (ISBN 0-8054-5273-7). Broadman.

Praying for the Government. Derek Prince. 1970. pap. 1.50 (ISBN 0-934920-11-7, B-20). Derek Prince.

Praying for Your Unborn Child. Francis MacNutt. (Illus.). 144p. 1987. 12.95 (ISBN 0-385-23281-0). Doubleday.

Praying God's Word. Ed Dufresne. 96p. (Orig.). 1983. pap. 2.75 (ISBN 0-89274-276-3). Harrison Hse.

Praying God's Word. Ed Dufresne Ministries. 1979. pap. 1.50 (ISBN 0-89274-126-0). Harrison Hse.

Praying: How to Start & Keep Going. Bobb Biehl & James W. Hagelganz. LC 80-54003. 128p. 1981. pap. 2.50 (ISBN 0-8307-0781-6, 5016900). Regal.

Praying Hyde. E. G. Carre. LC 82-73972. 183p. 1983. pap. 4.95 (ISBN 0-88270-541-5). Bridge Pub.

Praying Hyde. Francis A. McGaw. 80p. 1970. pap. 2.95 (ISBN 0-87123-454-8, 200454). Bethany Hse.

Praying in the Holy Ghost. Jim Richardson. 1983. pap. 1.75 (ISBN 0-911739-02-5). Abbott Loop.

Praying in the Home. 2nd. ed. John Doherty. LC 83-61212. 54p. 1984. pap. text ed. 1.95 (ISBN 0-911905-04-9). Past & Mat Rene Ctr.

Praying in the Spirit. Theo Wolmarans. 56p. (Orig.). 1985. 4.95 (ISBN 0-914307-50-9). Word Faith.

Praying Jesus' Way. Curtis C. Mitchell. 160p. 1977. 10.95 (ISBN 0-8007-0843-1). Revell.

Praying More Effectively. David Mains. (Chapel Talks Ser.). 64p. 1.75 (ISBN 0-89191-261-4, 52613). Cook.

Praying Our Experience. Joseph Schmidt. (Illus.). 56p. (Orig.). 1980. pap. 1.95 (ISBN 0-88489-113-5). St Mary's.

Praying Our Prayers. H. P. Lyons. 1976. 4.95 (ISBN 0-8199-0598-4). Franciscan Herald.

Praying Our Way Through Life. Basilea Schlink. 32p. 1970. pap. 0.95 (ISBN 0-87123-455-6, 260455). Bethany Hse.

Praying Shapes Believing: A Theological Commentary on the Book of Common Prayer. Leonel L. Mitchell. 220p. 1985. 17.95 (ISBN 0-86683-494-X, HarpR). Har-Row.

Praying the Bible: A Parish Life Sourcebook. Elizabeth Canham. LC 86-32976. 98p. (Orig.). 1987. pap. 6.95 (ISBN 0-936384-46-8). Cowley Pubns.

Praying the Daily Gospels: A Guide to Meditation. Philip St. Romain. LC 84-71186. 248p. (Orig.). 1984. pap. 5.95 (ISBN 0-87793-314-6). Ave Maria.

Praying the Kingdom: Towards A Political Spirituality. Charles Elliott. 160p. (Orig.). 1986. pap. 6.95 (ISBN 0-8091-2820-9). Paulist Pr.

Praying the Life of Christ. Mary I. Bodenstedt. Ed. by James Hogg. (Analecta Cartusiana Ser.: No. 15). 184p. (Orig.). 1983. pap. 25.00 (ISBN 3-7052-0017-8, Pub by Salzburg Studies). Longwood Pub Group.

Praying the Name of Jesus. Robert V. Dodd. 96p. (Orig.). 1985. pap. 4.95 (ISBN 0-8358-0514-X). Upper Room.

Praying the Psalms. Walter Brueggemann. LC 81-86045. (Illus.). 90p. (Orig.). 1982. pap. 6.95 (ISBN 0-88489-143-7). St Mary's.

Praying the Right Way. Elbert Willis. 1977. 1.25 (ISBN 0-89858-011-0). Fill the Gap.

Praying to Change the World, 2 vols. Gordon Lindsay. (School of Prayer Ser.). 2.95 ea. Vol. 1 (ISBN 0-89985-956-9). Vol. 2 (ISBN 0-89985-957-7). Christ Nations.

Praying to Get Results. 2nd ed. 1983. pap. 1.00 (ISBN 0-89276-013-3). Hagin Ministries.

Praying to God As a Friend. Alphonsus Liguori. 48p. 1987. pap. text ed. 1.50 (ISBN 0-89243-264-0). Liguori Pubns.

Praying Together. Peter Gilmour. LC 77-91623. (Illus.). 1978. pap. 1.95 (ISBN 0-88489-097-X); leader's manual 1.00 (ISBN 0-88489-120-8). St Mary's.

Praying Together: Making Marriage Last. Charlie Shedd & Martha Shedd. 128p. 1987. pap. 5.95 (ISBN 0-310-43291-X). Zondervan.

Praying with Christ: A Holy Hour. 128p. 1981. pap. 1.95 (ISBN 0-8146-1244-X). Liturgical Pr.

Praying with One Another for Healing. Dennis M. Linn et al. 1984. pap. 4.95 (ISBN 0-8091-2619-2). Paulist Pr.

Praying with Power. LLoyd J. Ogilvie. LC 83-17742. 1983. 8.95 (ISBN 0-8307-0854-5, 5110309). Regal.

Praying with Scripture Handbook. Maureen Gallagher et al. LC 82-62923. 176p. (Orig.). 1984. pap. 7.95 (ISBN 0-8091-2544-7); leader's manual with slides 22.95 (ISBN 0-8091-7751-X). Paulist Pr.

Praying with Scripture in the Holy Land: Daily Meditations with the Risen Jesus. David E. Rosage. 184p. (Orig.). 1977. pap. 3.95 (ISBN 0-914544-14-4). Living Flame Pr.

Praying with the Family of God: Leader Guide. Urban T. Holmes. 1980. pap. 3.95 (ISBN 0-03-049551-2, HarpR). Har-Row.

Pre-Conquest Church in England. 2nd ed. Margaret Deanesly. (Ecclesiastical History of England Ser.). 376p. 1963. text ed. 30.00x (ISBN 0-06-491638-3). B&N Imports.

Pre-Dinnaga Buddhist Texts on Logic from Chinese Sources. Tr. by Giuseppe Tucci. 368p. 1929. Repr. text ed. 32.00 (ISBN 0-89644-478-3, Pub. by Chinese Matl Ctr). Coronet Bks.

Pre-Earthly Deeds of Christ. Rudolf Steiner. 16p. 1976. pap. 2.75 (ISBN 0-919924-01-8, Pub. by Steiner Book Centre Canada). Anthroposophic.

Pre-Eternal Rest. Frank E. Stranges. 12p. 1985. pap. text ed. 2.00 (ISBN 0-933470-07-X). Intl Evang.

Pre-Marital Assessment Skills Training Program Leader Guide. Kenneth Metz & John Trokan. 144p. 1986. pap. 12.95 (ISBN 0-8091-2809-8). Paulist Pr.

Pre-Marital Assessment Skills Training Program: Team Couple Workbook. Kenneth Metz & John Trokan. 96p. 1986. pap. 9.95 (ISBN 0-8091-2810-1). Paulist Pr.

Pre-Reformation English Spirituality. Ed. by James Walsh. LC 65-12885. 1966. 20.00 (ISBN 0-8232-0655-6). Fordham.

Pre-Service Formation of Teachers for Catholic Schools. Alfred McBride & O. Praem. 24p. 1982. 2.40 (ISBN 0-686-39890-4). Natl Cath Educ.

Pre-Tribulation Rapture. Allen Beechick. LC 79-53291. 256p. (Orig.). 1980. pap. 4.95 (ISBN 0-89636-040-7). Accent Bks.

Preach On! J. Alfred Smith. LC 84-8439. 1984. pap. 4.95 (ISBN 0-8054-2112-2). Broadman.

Preach the Gospel. Joel Gerlach & Richard Bolge. 1982. 8.95 (ISBN 0-8100-0153-5, 15NO387). Northwest Pub.

Preach the Word. Billy Apostolon. (Sermon Outline Ser.). 1978. pap. 2.50 (ISBN 0-8010-0039-4). Baker Bk.

Preach the Word. Charles R. Gresham. LC 83-71917. 200p. (Orig.). 1983. pap. 3.95 (ISBN 0-89900-198-X). College Pr Pub.

Preach the Word. Russel Mast. LC 68-28782. 1968. pap. 1.25 (ISBN 0-87303-680-8). Faith & Life.

Preacher among the Prophets. George B. Duncan. 176p. 1985. pap. 5.95 (ISBN 0-930577-00-0). N Burleson.

Preacher & His Preaching. A. P. Gibbs. 16.95 (ISBN 0-937396-31-1); pap. 10.95 (ISBN 0-937396-30-3). Walterick Pubs.

Preacher & His Preaching. J. D. O'Donnell. 1974. pap. 3.95 (ISBN 0-89265-018-4). Randall Hse.

Preacher & Preaching: Reviving the Art in the Twentieth Century. Ed. by Samuel T. Logan, Jr. 480p. 1986. 16.95 (ISBN 0-87552-294-7). Presby & Reformed.

Preacher as Jacob: A Paradigm for Pulpit Ministry. Kenneth L. Gibble. 144p. (Orig.). 1985. pap. 8.95 (ISBN 0-8164-2633-3, AY8587, HarpR). Har-Row.

Preacher Had Ten Kids. Frances Bradsher. 1980. pap. 3.50 (ISBN 0-8423-4886-7). Tyndale.

Preacher of the People. Sanford G. Shetler. LC 81-13387. 288p. 1982. 16.95x (ISBN 0-8361-1247-4); pap. 13.95x (ISBN 0-8361-1248-2). Herald Pr.

Preacher: The Wit & Wisdom of Reverend Will B. Dunn. Doug Marlette. 128p. 1984. pap. 4.95 (ISBN 0-8407-5895-2). Nelson.

Preacher's Homiletic Commentary, 31 vols. 1978. 450.00 (ISBN 0-8010-6962-9). Baker Bk.

Preacher's Homiletic Library, 14 vols. Set. 189.50 (ISBN 0-8010-6916-5). Baker Bk.

Preacher's Notebook on Isaiah. Joe H. Cothen & John O. Strange. LC 82-24596. 96p. 1983. pap. 6.95 (ISBN 0-88289-365-3). Pelican.

Preacher's Portrait in the New Testament. John R. Stott. 1964. pap. 4.95 (ISBN 0-8028-1191-4). Eerdmans.

Preachers: You Asked for It. Oscar Moore. pap. 2.00 (ISBN 0-911866-79-5). Advocate.

Preaching. Fred B Craddock. 224p. 1985. 16.95 (ISBN 0-687-33636-8). Abingdon.

Preaching: A Comprehensive Approach to the Design & Delivery of Sermons. James W. Cox. LC 84-48214. 320p. 1985. 18.45 (ISBN 0-06-061600-8, HarpR). Har-Row.

Preaching: A Kind of Folly. Ian Pitt-Watson. LC 77-21983. 120p. 1978. pap. 3.95 (ISBN 0-664-24181-6). Westminster.

Preaching about Death: Eighteen Sermons Dealing with the Experience of Death from the Christian Perspective. Ed. by Alton M. Motter. LC 74-26336. pap. 23.50 (2026862). Bks Demand UMI.

Preaching & Biblical Theology. Edmund P. Clowney. 1956. pap. 3.95 (ISBN 0-87552-145-2). Presby & Reformed.

Preaching & Leading Worship. William H. Willimon. LC 83-26021. (Pastor's Handbooks Ser.: Vol. 1). 116p. (Orig.). 1984. pap. 7.95 (ISBN 0-664-24616-8). Westminster.

Preaching & Pastoral Care. Arthur L. Teikmanis. LC 64-23551. pap. 36.00 (2026863). Bks Demand UMI.

Preaching & Preachers. D. Martyn Lloyd-Jones. 325p. 1972. 15.95 (ISBN 0-310-27870-8, 10573). Zondervan.

Preaching & the Non-Ordained: An Interdisciplinary Study. Intro. by N. Nadine Foley. 1983. pap. 6.95 (ISBN 0-8146-1291-1). Liturgical Pr.

Preaching & Worship in the Small Church. William H. Willimon & Robert L. Wilson. LC 79-24529. (Creative Leadership Ser.). (Orig.). 1980. pap. 6.95 (ISBN 0-687-33820-4). Abingdon.

Preaching As Communication: An Interpersonal Perspective. Myron R. Chartier. LC 80-21304. (Abingdon Preacher Library). 128p. (Orig.). 1981. pap. 6.95 (ISBN 0-687-33826-3). Abingdon.

Preaching As Theology & Art. Elizabeth Achtemeier. 144p. 1984. pap. 8.75 (ISBN 0-687-33828-X). Abingdon.

Preaching Better. Frank J. McNulty. 1985. pap. 8.95 (ISBN 0-8091-2682-6). Paulist Pr.

Preaching Biblically. Ed. by Don M. Wardlaw. LC 83-1276. 174p. (Orig.). 1983. pap. 10.95 (ISBN 0-664-24478-5). Westminster.

Preaching Biblically: Exegesis & Interpretation. William D. Thompson. (Abingdon Preacher's Library). (Orig.). 1981. pap. 6.95 (ISBN 0-687-33840-9). Abingdon.

Preaching Christian Doctrine. William J. Carl, II. LC 83-48923. pap. 8.95 (ISBN 0-8006-1788-6). Fortress.

Preaching for Today. Clyde Fant. 1977. pap. 8.95 (ISBN 0-06-062332-2, RD-204, HarpR). Har-Row.

Preaching from the Bible. J. Solomon Benn, III. (Resources for Black Ministries Ser.). 80p. (Orig.). 1981. pap. 2.45 (ISBN 0-8010-0801-8). Baker Bk.

Preaching from the Prophets. Kyle M. Yates. 1953. text ed. 12.50 (ISBN 0-8054-1502-5). Broadman.

Preaching from the Types & Metaphors of the Bible. Benjamin Keach. LC 78-165059. (Kregel Reprint Library). 1038p. 1975. 31.95 (ISBN 0-8254-3008-9). Kregel.

Preaching Holiness Effectively. Mel-Thomas Rothwell. 160p. 1982. pap. 4.95 (ISBN 0-8341-0784-8). Beacon Hill.

Preaching in a New Key. Clement Welsh. LC 74-5268. 192p. 1974. 5.95 (ISBN 0-8298-0273-8). Pilgrim NY.

Preaching in a Revolutionary Age. facsimile ed. Garfield B. Oxnam. LC 75-142687. (Essay Index Reprint Ser). Repr. of 1944 ed. 18.00 (ISBN 0-8369-2421-5). Ayer Co Pubs.

Preaching in England in the Late Fifteenth & Sixteenth Centuries. J. W. Blench. 378p. 1981. Repr. of 1964 ed. lib. bdg. 50.00 (ISBN 0-8495-0604-2). Arden Lib.

Preaching in the Spanish Golden Age: A Study of Some Preachers of the Reign of Philip III. Hilary D. Smith. (Modern Language & Literature Monographs). 1979. 29.95x (ISBN 0-19-815532-8). Oxford U Pr.

Preaching in the Spirit. Dennis F. Kinlaw. 1985. pap. 6.95 (ISBN 0-310-75091-1, 17036P). Zondervan.

Preaching in Today's World. Ed. by James C. Barry. LC 83-24021. (Orig.). 1984. pap. 6.50 (ISBN 0-8054-2113-0). Broadman.

Preaching Is Dialogue. Henry J. Eggold. 144p. 1980. pap. 5.95 (ISBN 0-8010-3358-6). Baker Bk.

Preaching Ladies. Sallie Chesham. (Illus.). 179p. (Orig.). 1983. pap. 3.50 (ISBN 0-89216-045-4). Salvation Army.

Preaching Moment: A Guide to Sermon Delivery. Charles L. Bartow. LC 80-12370. (Abingdon Preacher's Library). (Orig.). 1980. pap. 5.95 (ISBN 0-687-33907-3). Abingdon.

Preaching of Islam. T. Arnold. 1968. 27.50x (ISBN 0-87902-045-8). Orientalia.

Preaching of Islam. T. W. Arnold. 32.50 (ISBN 0-686-18455-6). Kazi Pubns.

Preaching of Islam: A History of Propagation of the Muslim Faith. Thomas W. Arnold. LC 72-180319. (Mid-East Studies). Repr. of 1913 ed. 27.50 (ISBN 0-404-56214-0). AMS Pr.

Preaching on Peace. Ed. by Ronald J. Sider & Darrel J. Brubaker. LC 82-10958. 96p. 1982. pap. 0.50 (ISBN 0-8006-1681-2). Fortress.

Preaching Paul. Daniel Patte. LC 84-47931. (Fortress Resources for Preaching Ser.). 96p. 1984. pap. 4.95 (ISBN 0-8006-1140-3). Fortress.

Preaching the Bible. Solomon B. Freehof. 1974. 12.50x (ISBN 0-87068-244-X). Ktav.

Preaching the Christmas Story. Hugh Lichtfield. LC 83-71689. 1984. pap. 5.50 (ISBN 0-8054-2101-7). Broadman.

Preaching the Creative Gospel Creatively. Francis Rossow. 1983. pap. 8.95 (ISBN 0-570-03917-7, 12-2856). Concordia.

Preaching the Easter Story. Hugh Litchfield. (Orig.). 1987. pap. 5.95 (ISBN 0-8054-2117-3). Broadman.

Preaching the Good News. George E. Sweazey. 368p. 1976. 24.95 (ISBN 0-13-694802-2). P-H.

Preaching the Gospel. Norman Pittenger. LC 83-62716. 108p. (Orig.). 1984. pap. 5.95 (ISBN 0-8192-1340-3). Morehouse.

Preaching the Gospel. Ed. by Henry J. Young. LC 75-36449. pap. 23.80 (2026828). Bks Demand UMI.

Preaching the Gospel of Jesus Christ. Clarke E. Goodman. LC 84-90077. 101p. 1985. 8.95 (ISBN 0-533-06156-3). Vantage.

Preaching the Great Themes of the Bible. Chevis F. Horne. (Orig.). 1986. pap. 7.95 (ISBN 0-8054-2262-5). Broadman.

Preaching the Lectionary: The Word of God for the Church Today. rev. ed. Reginald H. Fuller. 672p. 1984. pap. 16.95 (ISBN 0-8146-1351-9). Liturgical Pr.

Preaching the New Common Lectionary. Fred B. Craddock et al. 176p. (Orig.). 1984. pap. 8.50 (ISBN 0-687-33845-X). Abingdon.

Preaching the New Common Lectionary: Year B: Lent, Holy Week, Easter, 2 vols. Fred B. Craddock et al. 256p. (Orig.). 1984. Vol. 2, 256 pgs. pap. 9.95 (ISBN 0-687-33846-8); Vol. 3, 304 pgs. pap. 11.95 (ISBN 0-687-33847-6). Abingdon.

Preaching the New Common Lectionary: Year C-Advent, Christmas, Epiphany. Fred B. Craddock et al. 176p. (Orig.). 1985. pap. 9.50 (ISBN 0-687-33848-4). Abingdon.

Preaching the New Common Lectionary: Year C, Lent, Holy Week, Easter. Ed. by Fred B. Craddock et al. 240p. (Orig.). 1986. pap. 9.95 (ISBN 0-687-33849-2). Abingdon.

Preaching the New Testament. Archibald M. Hunter. LC 81-19482. pap. 39.00 (ISBN 0-317-30145-4, 2025328). Bks Demand UMI.

Preaching the Parables: Series B. John Brokhoff. (Orig.). 1987. pap. price not set (ISBN 0-89536-880-3, 7866). CSS of Ohio.

Preaching the Saints As Models. David Q. Liptak. 1983. pap. 8.95 (ISBN 0-941850-10-2). Sunday Pubns.

Preaching the Story. Edmund A. Steimle et al. LC 78-14675. 208p. 1980. 9.95 (ISBN 0-8006-0538-1, 1-538). Fortress.

Preaching the Theology of the Cross: Sermons & Worship Ideas for Lent & Easter. Peter L. Steinke. LC 82-72638. 128p. (Orig.). 1983. pap. 6.95 (ISBN 0-8066-1944-9, 10-5144). Augsburg.

Preaching the Word. Thomas K. Carroll. (Message of the Fathers of the Church Ser.: Vol. 11). 15.95 (ISBN 0-89453-351-7); pap. 9.95 (ISBN 0-89453-322-3). M Glazier.

Preaching Through the Bible. 2nd ed. Edwin V. Hayden. LC 81-82987. 557p. 1981. pap. 8.95 (ISBN 0-89900-145-9). College Pr Pub.

Preaching Through the Bible, 14 vols. Joseph Parker. 189.50 (ISBN 0-8010-7032-5). Baker Bk.

Preaching Through the Life of Christ. D. W. Cleverly. Ed. by Herbert Lambert. LC 85-19002. 112p. 1986. pap. 7.95 (ISBN 0-8272-2930-5). CBP.

Preaching Through the Prophets. John B. Taylor. LC 84-23773. 110p. 1985. pap. 7.95 (ISBN 0-8272-2929-1). CBP.

Preaching Through the Saints. James A. Wallace. LC 82-7745. 80p. 1982. pap. 2.50 (ISBN 0-8146-1271-7). Liturgical Pr.

Preaching Through the Year. David Steel. LC 80-82191. 168p. 1980. pap. 1.79 (ISBN 0-8042-1801-3). John Knox.

Preaching to Convince. James D. Berkley. 192p. 1986. 9.95 (ISBN 0-8499-0577-X). Word Bks.

Preaching to Convince. Ed. by Jim Berkley. (Leadership Library). 175p. 1986. 9.95 (ISBN 0-917463-11-0). Chr Today.

Preaching to Modern Man. Frank Pack & Prentice A. Meador, Jr. Ed. by J. D. Thomas. LC 73-75928. 1969. 10.95 (ISBN 0-89112-060-2, Bibl Res Pr). Abilene Christ U.

Preaching to the Heart. Jay E. Adams. 40p. 1983. pap. 1.75 (ISBN 0-87552-080-4). Presby & Reformed.

Preaching to the Spirits in Prison. W. Kelly. pap. 4.75 (ISBN 0-88172-105-0). Believers Bkshelf.

Preaching Tradition: A Brief History. DeWitte T. Holland. LC 80-16339. (Abingdon Preacher's Library). 128p. (Orig.). 1980. pap. 6.95 (ISBN 0-687-33875-1). Abingdon.

Preaching with Power. Edward Fudge. pap. 2.00 (ISBN 0-686-12680-7). E Fudge.

Preaching with Purpose. Jay E. Adams. 1983. pap. 6.95 (ISBN 0-87552-078-2). Presby & Reformed.

Preaching with Purpose & Power: Selected E. Y. Mullins Lectures on Preaching. Ed. by Don Aycock. LC 81-22388. vi, 314p. 1982. 15.95 (ISBN 0-86554-027-6, MUP-H27). Mercer Univ Pr.

Preaching with Purpose: The Urgent Task of Homiletics. Jay E. Adams. (Jay Adams Library). 160p. 1986. pap. 7.95 (ISBN 0-310-51091-0, 12121P). Zondervan.

Preachings of Islam. T. W. Arnold. 467p. 1984. Repr. of 1913 ed. text ed. 50.00x (ISBN 0-86590-250-X, Pub. by Renaissance New Delhi). Apt Bks.

Precarious Organisation: Sociological Explorations of the Church's Mission & Structure. Mady A. Thung. (Religion & Society Ser.: No. 5). 1976. text ed. 22.00 (ISBN 0-686-22627-5). Mouton.

Precarious Vision. Peter L. Berger. LC 76-1981. 238p. 1976. Repr. of 1961 ed. lib. bdg. 22.50x (ISBN 0-8371-8657-9, BEPV). Greenwood.

Precepts for Practice. Malcolm C. Fry. (Way of Life Ser.). 1971. pap. 3.95 (ISBN 0-89265-004-4, Free Will Baptist Dept); tchrs' guide 4.95 (ISBN 0-89265-005-2). Randall Hse.

Precepts for the Young. Ann R. Colton. 66p. 1959. pap. 2.50 (ISBN 0-917187-15-6). A R C Pub.

Precious Bible Promises: From the King James Version. 384p. 1984. 16.95 (ISBN 0-8407-5354-3). Nelson.

Precious Bible Promises: From the New American Bible. 384p. 1985. 17.95 (ISBN 0-8407-5456-6). Nelson.

Precious Blood of Jesus. Kenneth E. Hagin. 1984. pap. 0.50 mini bk. (ISBN 0-89276-263-2). Hagin Ministries.

Precious in the Sight of God. Lea Fowler. 1983. pap. 4.95 (ISBN 0-89137-428-0). Quality Pubns.

Precious Legacy: Judaic Treasures from the Czechoslavak State Collection. Ed. by David Altschuler. (Illus.). 256p. (Orig.). 1983. 40.00 (ISBN 0-671-49448-1); pap. 17.50 (ISBN 0-671-49498-8). Summit Bks.

Precious Pearl: A Translation from the Arabic. Ed. by Jane I. Smith. LC 79-140. (Studies in World Religions: No. 1). 1979. 15.00 (ISBN 0-89130-278-6, 030001); pap. 8.95 05539067x (ISBN 0-89130-305-7). Scholars Pr GA.

Precious Pearl: Al-Durrah Al-Fakhirah. Abd al-Rahman al Jami. Tr. by Nicholas L. Heer from Arabic. LC 78-126071. 1979. 29.50 (ISBN 0-87395-379-7). State U NY Pr.

Precious Remedies Against Satan's Devices. Thomas Brooks. 253p. 1984. pap. 5.95x (ISBN 0-85151-002-7). Banner of Truth.

Predestination. George Fletcher. pap. 0.50 (ISBN 0-686-64389-5). Reiner.

Predestination & Free Will. David Basinger & Randall Basinger. LC 85-23887. 180p. 1986. pap. 6.95 (ISBN 0-87784-567-0). Inter-Varsity.

Predestination, God's Foreknowledge & Future Contingents. 2nd ed. William Of Ockham. Tr. by Norman Kretzmann & Marilyn M. Adams. LC 82-23317. 146p. 1983. 19.50 (ISBN 0-915144-14-X); pap. text ed. 4.95x (ISBN 0-915144-13-1). Hackett Pub.

Predestination Primer. John H. Gerstner. 1981. pap. 2.50 (ISBN 0-88469-145-4). BMH Bks.

Predicacion Biblica para el Mundo Actual. Lloyd M. Perry. Tr. by Angel A. Carrodeguas from Eng. Orig. Title: Biblical Preaching for Today's World. (Span.). 176p. 1986. pap. 4.95 (ISBN 0-8297-0957-6). Life Pubs Intl.

Predicacion Expositiva. D. M. White. Tr. by Francisco E. Estrello. Orig. Title: Excellence of Exposition. 160p. 1982. Repr. of 1980 ed. 3.75 (ISBN 0-311-42061-3). Casa Bautista.

Predicador: Platicas a Mis Estudiantes. Alejandro Trevino. 155p. 1984. pap. 2.95 (ISBN 0-311-42016-8). Casa Bautista.

Predicament of the Prosperous. Bruce C. Birch & Larry L. Rasmussen. LC 78-18412. (Biblical Perspectives on Current Issues). 212p. 1978. pap. 7.95 (ISBN 0-664-24211-1). Westminster.

Predicar Al Corazon-Bosquejos Selectos. Jay E. Adams & Lyle A. Thompson. Tr. by Angel A. Carrodeguas from English. (Span.). 175p. 1986. pap. 2.95 (ISBN 0-8297-0699-2). Life Pubs Intl.

Preface to Bonhoeffer: The Man & Two of His Shorter Writings. John D. Godsey. LC 79-7378. 80p. 1979. pap. 3.50 (ISBN 0-8006-1367-8, 1-1367). Fortress.

Preface to Paradise Lost. Clive S. Lewis. 1942. pap. 7.95x (ISBN 0-19-500345-4). Oxford U Pr.

Preface to Paul. Morna Hooker. 1980. pap. 4.95 (ISBN 0-19-520188-4). Oxford U Pr.

Preface to Well Being. Joseph R. Narot. pap. 1.00 (ISBN 0-686-15806-7). Rostrum Bks.

Prefigurations in Meistergesang. Clarence W. Friedman. LC 75-140020. (Catholic University of America Studies in German Ser.: No. 18). Repr. of 1943 ed. 22.00 (ISBN 0-404-50238-5). AMS Pr.

Pregare in Certosa Oggi. Mario Giacometti. Ed. by James Hogg. (Analecta Cartusiana Ser.: No. 97). 141p. (Orig.). 1980. pap. 25.00 (ISBN 3-7052-0168-9, Pub. by Salzburg Studies). Longwood Pub Group.

Preguntas Practicas y Dificiles Contestadas. R. A. Torrey. Orig. Title: Practical & Perplexing Questions Answered. (Span.). 128p. 1980. pap. 3.25 (ISBN 0-8254-1722-8). Kregel.

Preguntas y Respuestas Rosacruces: Con la historia completa de la Orden. 8th ed. H. Spencer Lewis. Tr. by AMORC Staff. (Span., Illus.). 231p. 1982. pap. 8.00 (ISBN 0-912057-61-0, GS-501). AMORC.

Preguntas y Respuestas sobre la Biblia. Juan Alfaro. (Span.). 64p. 1982. pap. 1.50 (ISBN 0-89243-162-8). Liguori Pubns.

Prehistoric Religion in Greece. J. V. Leuven. (Illus.). 280p. 1987. lib. bdg. 72.00 (Pub. by A. M. Hakkert). Coronet Bks.

Preliminary & Interim Report on the Hebrew Old Testament Text Project, Vols. 1-5. Ed. by UBS Committee. Incl. Vol. 1. (Pentateuch). xxxiii, 317p. 1973. pap. 4.00x (ISBN 0-8267-0008-X, 08520); Vol. 2. (Historical Bks.). xxxiv, 556p. 1976. pap. 6.60x (ISBN 0-8267-0009-8, 08521); Vol. 3. (Poetical Books). xxxiii, 620p. 1977. pap. 7.00x (ISBN 0-8267-0010-1, 08522); Vol. 4. (Prophetical Books: No. 1). xxxiii, 335p. 1979. pap. 4.50x (ISBN 0-8267-0011-X, 08523); (Prophetical Books: No. 2). xxxiii, 443p. 1980. pap. 5.00x (ISBN 0-8267-0012-8, 08559). (Eng. & Fr., Pub. by United Bible). Am Bible.

Preliminary & Interim Report on the Hebrew Old Testament Text Project, Vol. 2. Ed. by UBS Committee. (Historical Bks.). (Eng. & Fr.). xxiv, 556p. 1976. pap. 6.60x (ISBN 0-8267-0009-8, 08521, Pub. by United Bible). Am Bible.

Preliminary & Interim Report on the Hebrew Old Testament Text Project, Vol. 3. Ed. by UBS Committee. (Poetical Books). (Eng. & Fr.). xxxiii, 620p. 1977. pap. 7.00x (ISBN 0-8267-0010-1, 08522, Pub. by United Bible). Am Bible.

Preliminary & Interim Report on the Hebrew Old Testament Text Project, Vol. 5. Ed. by UBS Committee. (Prophetical Bks.: No. II). (Eng. & Fr.). xxxiii, 443p. 1980. pap. 5.00x (ISBN 0-8267-0012-8, 08559, Pub. by United Bible). Am Bible.

Preliminary Report on the Synagogue at Dura-Europos. H. F. Pearson et al. (Illus.). 1936. pap. 49.50x (ISBN 0-686-51290-1). Elliots Bks.

Prelude to Israel: An Analysis of Zionist Diplomacy, 1897-1947. rev. ed. Alan Taylor. 126p. 1970. Repr. of 1961 ed. 3.50 (ISBN 0-88728-093-5). Inst Palestine.

Prelude to Pentecost. R. L. Speaks. 200p. 1985. 11.95 (ISBN 0-682-40229-X). Exposition Pr FL.

Prelude to the Kingdom: Mormon Desert Conquest, a Chapter in American Cooperative Experience. Gustave O. Larson. LC 78-5694. 19??. Repr. of 1947 ed. lib. bdg. 25.75x (ISBN 0-313-20452-7, LAPK). Greenwood.

Prelude to the Reformation: A Study of English Church Life from the Age of Wycliffe to the Breach with Rome. Richard S. Arrowsmith. LC 83-45573. Date not set. Repr. of 1923 ed. 30.00 (ISBN 0-404-19891-0). AMS Pr.

Premarital Counseling: A Manual for Clergy & Counselors. John L. Mitman. 128p. (Orig.). 1984. pap. 6.95 (ISBN 0-86683-879-1, 7874, HarpR). Har-Row.

Premarital Counseling Handbook for Ministers. Theodore K. Pitt. 192p. 1985. pap. 9.95 (ISBN 0-8170-1071-8). Judson.

Premarital Guide for Couples & Their Counselors. David A. Thompson. 80p. 1979. pap. 4.95 (ISBN 0-87123-465-3, 210465). Bethany Hse.

Prematurely Saved. John Garvey. 1986. pap. 8.95 (ISBN 0-87243-150-9). Templegate.

Premchand: His Life & Work. V. S. Naravane. 280p. 1980. text ed. 25.00x (ISBN 0-7069-1091-5, Pub. by Vikas India). Advent NY.

Prenatal Yoga & Natural Birth. rev. ed. Jeannine Parvati. (Illus.). 64p. 1986. pap. 7.95 (ISBN 0-938190-89-X). North Atlantic.

Preobrazhenije Gospodnje. Ed. by Moscow Synod. Staff. Tr. of Rransfiguration of the Lord. 128p. pap. 6.00 (ISBN 0-317-29169-6). Holy Trinity.

Preparacion de Sermones Biblicos. A. W. Blackwood. Tr. by Santiago D. Crane. (Span.). 255p. 1985. pap. 3.95 (ISBN 0-311-42030-3). Casa Bautista.

Preparation for Covenant Life. Frank R. Keller. LC 79-53522. 1979. pap. 4.95x (ISBN 0-87303-018-4). Faith & Life.

Preparation for Death. abr. ed. Alphonsus Liguori. 1982. pap. 5.00 (ISBN 0-89555-174-8). TAN Bks Pubs.

Preparation for Ordination. Herman Hersey. 1981. pap. 1.95 (ISBN 0-89265-069-9). Randall Hse.

Preparation for the Final Crisis. Fernando Chaij. LC 66-29118. 1966. pap. 6.95 (ISBN 0-8163-0137-9, 16510-0). Pacific Pr Pub Assn.

Preparation for the Gospel, 2 vols. Eusebius. Tr. by Edwin H. Gifford from Gr. (Twin Brooks Ser.). 948p. 1982. pap. 24.95 (ISBN 0-8010-3369-1). Baker Bk.

Preparation for Total Consecration. pap. 2.00 (ISBN 0-910984-10-7). Montfort Pubns.

Preparation to Deathe: A Boke As Devout As Eloquent. Desiderius Erasmus. LC 74-28852. (English Experience Ser.: No. 733). 1975. Repr. of 1538 ed. 6.00 (ISBN 90-221-0762-0). Walter J Johnson.

Preparation to the Psalter. George Wither. 1884. Repr. of 1619 ed. 30.50 (ISBN 0-8337-3850-X). B Franklin.

Preparative to Mariage: Whereunto Is Annexed a Treatise of the Lords Supper, & Another of Usurie. Henry Smith. LC 74-28885. (English Experience Ser.: No. 762). 1975. Repr. of 1591 ed. 16.00 (ISBN 90-221-0762-0). Walter J Johnson.

Prepare for Peace, Pt. I. Ruth Obold. (Illus.). 40p. 1986. 6.25 (ISBN 0-87303-116-4). Faith & Life.

Prepare for Peace, Pt. II. Ruth Obold. (Illus.). 48p. 1986. 6.25 (ISBN 0-87303-117-2). Faith & Life.

Prepare for Peace, Pt. III. Ruth Obold. (Illus.). 55p. (YA) 1986. 6.25 (ISBN 0-87303-118-0). Faith & Life.

Prepare in the Wilderness. Richard Eslinger. 1984. 5.25 (ISBN 0-89536-680-0, 4856). CSS of Ohio.

Prepare My People. Vincent M. Walsh. 100p. (Orig.). (YA) 1986. pap. text ed. 5.00 (ISBN 0-943374-13-8). Key of David.

Prepare Our Hearts: Advent & Christmas Traditions for Families. Muriel T. Kurtz. 144p. (Orig.). 1986. pap. 6.95 spiral bdg. (ISBN 0-8358-0544-1). Upper Room.

Preparemonos para la Adolescencia. James Dobson. 192p. 1981. 3.25 (ISBN 0-88113-253-5). Edit Betania.

Preparese Para Evangelizar: Un Programa De Evangelizacion Personal. Richard Sisson et al. Tr. by David Powell & Esteban Ditmore. Tr. of Training for Evangelism - A Program for Personal Evangelism. (Span.). 224p. (Orig.). 1984. pap. 5.95. Casa Bautista.

Preparing for Adolescence. James Dobson. LC 78-57673. 192p. 1980. 5.95 (ISBN 0-88449-111-0, A424717); pap. 2.95 (ISBN 0-88449-045-9, A324551). Vision Hse.

Preparing for Baptism. Sandy Halverson. 48p. 1983. pap. 3.95 (ISBN 0-88290-233-4). Horizon-Utah.

Preparing for Christian Marriage: Couples. Joan A. Hunt & Richard A. Hunt. LC 81-1770. 96p. 1982. 6.95 (ISBN 0-687-33919-7). Abingdon.

Preparing for Christian Marriage: Pastor's Edition. Antoinette Smith & Leon Smith. LC 80-28001. 112p. 1982. 7.75 (ISBN 0-687-33918-9). Abingdon.

Preparing for Church Ministry: A Practical Guide to Spiritual Formation. Alfred C. Hughes. 6.95 (ISBN 0-87193-167-2). Dimension Bks.

Preparing for God's Gift: Devotions for Families Using the Advent Wreath. Heather Hammond. 40p. (Orig.). 1986. pap. 2.50 (ISBN 0-8066-2260-1, 23-1809). Augsburg.

Preparing for Liturgy: A Theology & Sprituality. Austin H. Fleming. (Orig.). 1985. pap. 6.95 (ISBN 0-912405-16-3). Pastoral Pr.

Preparing for Marriage. Larry Hard & Mark P. Watts. 1984. 2.95 (ISBN 0-89536-673-8, 1638). CSS of Ohio.

Preparing for Marriage Handbook. Ed. by Jean M. Hiesberger. LC 80-80386. (Paths of Life Ser.). 112p. 1980. 2.95 (ISBN 0-8091-2260-X). Paulist Pr.

Preparing for Spiritual Direction. Jean LaPlace. 196p. 1975. 6.95 (ISBN 0-8199-0558-5). Franciscan Herald.

Preparing for the Greatest Two Years of Your Life. Mark A. Dennison. pap. 3.95 (ISBN 0-89036-128-2). Hawkes Pub Inc.

Preparing for the Messiah. Doris Williams & Patricia Griggs. (Griggs Educational Resources Ser.). 1979. pap. 5.95 (ISBN 0-687-33920-0). Abingdon.

Preparing for the Sacrament of Marriage. Anthony Del Vecchio & Mary Del Vecchio. LC 80-67721. (Illus.). 144p. (Orig.). 1980. pap. 3.95 (ISBN 0-87793-208-5). Ave Maria.

Preparing for the Sixth Epoch. Rudolf Steiner. Orig. Title: How Anthroposophic Groups Prepare for the Sixth Epoch. 1976. pap. 2.00 (ISBN 0-910142-72-6). Anthroposophic.

Preparing for the Storm. Kenneth D. Barney. LC 74-21021. 96p. 1975. pap. 1.25 (ISBN 0-88243-576-0, 02-0576). Gospel Pub.

Preparing for Your Marriage. William J. McRae. 160p. (Orig.). 1980. pap. 5.95 (ISBN 0-310-42761-4, 9366P). Zondervan.

Preparing Missionaries for Intercultural Communication. Lyman E. Reed. LC 84-23060. (Illus.). 224p. (Orig.). 1985. pap. text ed. 6.95x (ISBN 0-87808-438-X). William Carey Lib.

Preparing to Receive Holy Communion. Tom Avramis. 1986. pap. 1.95 (ISBN 0-937032-43-3). Light&Life Pub Co MN.

Preparing to Receive Jesus Christ. Daughters of St. Paul. (Way, Truth & Life Ser.). 1978. 1.75 (ISBN 0-8198-0548-3); tchr's manual 3.50 (ISBN 0-8198-0549-1); activity book 1.00 (ISBN 0-8198-0550-5). Dghtrs St Paul.

Preparing to Serve As a God Parent. William S. Chiganos. 1986. pap. 1.25 (ISBN 0-937032-44-1). Light&Life Pub Co MN.

Preparing to Teach God's Word. G. Raymond Carlson. LC 75-5221. (Illus.). 128p. 1975. pap. 1.25 (ISBN 0-88243-579-5, 02-0579). Gospel Pub.

Preparing Your Children for Greatness. Jessie R. Sandberg. (Joyful Living Ser.). 1987. pap. 1.50 (ISBN 0-912623-05-5). Joyful Woman.

Preparing Your Church for Ministry to Alcoholics & Their Families. Thomas H. Cairns. 136p. 1986. 19.75x (ISBN 0-398-05230-1). C C Thomas.

Preparing Your Own Chapel Talks for Children. Dolores E. Hermann. 1987. pap. 3.95 (ISBN 0-570-04466-9). Concordia.

Preparing Youth for Dating, Courtship & Marriage-Teacher's Guide. Norman Wright & Marvin Inmon. LC 78-56879. (Orig.). 1978. pap. 9.95 (ISBN 0-89081-147-4); transparencies & repro masters incl. Harvest Hse.

Presbyterian Bibliography. Compiled by Harold B. Prince. LC 83-10116. (ATLA Bibliography Ser.: No. 8). 466p. 1983. pap. 35.00 (ISBN 0-8108-1639-3). Scarecrow.

Presbyterian Churches & the Federal Union 1861-1869. Lewis G. Vander-Velde. LC 32-30007. (Historical Studies: No. 33). 1932. 35.00x (ISBN 0-674-70151-8). Harvard U Pr.

Presbyterian Churches in Alabama 1811-1936: Sketches of Churches, Outposts, & Preaching Points in the Synod of Alabama, Pt. I: Abbeville-Butler, & Megargel. James W. Marshall. Ed. by Kenneth J. Foreman, Jr. (Illus.). 519p. (Orig.). 1985. 29.95 (ISBN 0-935883-01-0); pap. 14.95 (ISBN 0-935883-00-2); With computer-readable disk. 69.95 (ISBN 0-935883-02-9). Cooling Spring.

Presbyterian Creeds: A Guide to the Book of Confessions. Jack Rogers. LC 84-22001. 252p. (Orig.). 1985. pap. 8.95 (ISBN 0-664-24627-3). Westminster.

Presbyterian Elder. rev. ed. Paul S. Wright. 64p. (Orig.). 1986. pap. 4.95 saddle stapled (ISBN 0-664-24014-3). Westminster.

Presbyterian in the South. Ernest T. Thompson. LC 63-19121. (Presbyterian Historical Society. Publication Ser.: Vol. 13). Vol. 1. pap. 157.30 (2027295); Vol. 2. pap. 132.00; Vol. 3. pap. 159.00. Bks Demand UMI.

Presbyterian Missionary Attitudes Toward American Indians, 1837-1893. Michael C. Coleman. LC 85-7496. (Illus.). 1985. 25.00x (ISBN 0-87805-278-X). U Pr of Miss.

Presbyterian Parochial Schools, 1846-1870. Lewis J. Sherrill. LC 74-89234. (American Education: Its Men, Institutions & Ideas, Ser. 1). 1969. Repr. of 1932 ed. 11.50 (ISBN 0-405-01471-6). Ayer Co Pubs.

Presbyterian Polity for Church Officers. Joan S. Gray & Joyce C. Tucker. LC 86-2797. 228p. (Orig.). 1986. pap. 7.95 (ISBN 0-8042-1406-9). John Knox.

Presbyterian Women in America: Two Centuries of a Quest for Status. Lois A. Boyd & R. Douglas Brackenridge. LC 82-15845. (Contributions to the Study of Religion: No. 9). 416p. 1983. lib. bdg. 35.00 (ISBN 0-313-23678-X, BOY/). Greenwood.

Presbyterians, Their History & Beliefs. Walter L. Lingle & John W. Kuykendall. LC 77-15750. 1978. pap. 5.95 (ISBN 0-8042-0985-5). John Knox.

Presbyteries & Profits: Calvinism & the Development of Capitalism in Scotland, 1560 - 1707. Gordon Marshall. 1980. 54.00x (ISBN 0-19-827246-4). Oxford U Pr.

Preschool Bible Activities, 4 vols. Jean Baxendale. (Illus.). 24p. (Orig.). 1982. No. 1. pap. 1.50 (ISBN 0-87239-487-5, 2459); No. 2. pap. 1.50 (ISBN 0-87239-488-3, 2460); No. 3. pap. 1.25 (ISBN 0-87239-489-1, 2461); No. 4. pap. 1.50 (ISBN 0-87239-490-5, 2462). Standard Pub.

Preschool Pattern Book. Marian Bennett. (Illus.). 48p. (Orig.). 1973. pap. 4.95 (ISBN 0-87239-339-9, 2145). Standard Pub.

Preschool Teacher Survival Kit. Robert Klausmeier. 80p. 1986. tchr's ed 9.95 (ISBN 0-89191-362-9). Cook.

Preschoolers Sing & Say. Ed. by Valerie Wilson & Shirley Hull. 1976. wire spiral 2.50 (ISBN 0-87227-045-9). Reg Baptist.

Prescribed Islamic Prayers. A. R. Shad. pap. 5.50 (ISBN 0-686-18593-5). Kazi Pubns.

Prescription for Anxiety: How You Can Overcome Fear & Despair. Leslie D. Weatherhead. LC 57-5284. (Festival Bks.). 1979. pap. 1.95 (ISBN 0-687-33987-1). Abingdon.

Prescription for Living. 2nd, rev. ed. Ruhiyyih Rabbani. 272p. 4.75 (ISBN 0-85398-002-0). G Ronald Pub.

Prescription for Preaching. Woodrow M. Kroll. 1980. 11.95 (ISBN 0-8010-5409-5). Baker Bk.

Prescription for Troubled Hearts. Jim Mankin. 1984. pap. 5.95 (ISBN 0-89225-273-1). Gospel Advocate.

Prescriptions from the Beloved Physician. James Henry. 108p. 1972. pap. 1.00 (ISBN 0-89114-055-7). Baptist Pub Hse.

Presdestinacion of Saintes. Saint Augustine. Bd. with Perserveraunce Unto Thende. LC 68-54611. (English Experience Ser.: No. 32). Repr. of 1556 ed. 20.00 (ISBN 90-221-0032-4). Walter J Johnson.

Presence & Absence of God. Ed. by Christopher F. Mooney. LC 68-8748. 1969. 20.00 (ISBN 0-8232-0810-9). Fordham.

Presence of God. Roland Murphy et al. LC 78-107214. (Concilium Ser.: Vol. 50). 215p. 7.95 (ISBN 0-8091-0116-5). Paulist Pr.

Presence of Other Worlds. Wilson Van Dusen. LC 73-18684. 240p. pap. 5.95 (ISBN 0-87785-166-2). Swedenborg.

Presence of Siva. Stella Kramrisch. LC 80-8558. (Illus.). 550p. 1981. 50.00x (ISBN 0-691-03964-X); pap. 18.95x (ISBN 0-691-10115-9). Princeton U Pr.

Presence of the Future: The Eschatology of Biblical Realism. George E. Ladd. 1973. pap. 7.95 (ISBN 0-8028-1531-6). Eerdmans.

Presence, Power, Praise; Documents on Charismatic Renewal: International Documents, Vol. 3. Ed. by Kilian McDonnell. LC 79-26080. 306p. 1980. 15.00 (ISBN 0-8146-1065-X). Liturgical Pr.

Presence, Power, Praise: Documents on Charismatic Renewal: National Documents, Vol. 1. Ed. by Kilian McDonnell. LC 79-26080. 696p. 1980. 20.00 (ISBN 0-8146-1066-8). Liturgical Pr.

Presence, Power, Praise: Documents on Charismatic Renewal: National Documents, Vol. 2. Kilian McDonnell. LC 79-26080. 568p. 1980. 20.00 (ISBN 0-8146-1189-3). Liturgical Pr.

Presence Through the Word. Evelyn Ann Schumacher, Sr. 144p. (Orig.). 1983. pap. 2.95 (ISBN 0-914544-46-2). Living Flame Pr.
Presences of Jesus. 2nd ed. Carl J. Pfeifer. 112p. 1984. pap. 4.95 (ISBN 0-89622-193-8). Twenty-Third.
Present Age. Soren Kierkegaard. Ed. & tr. by Alexander Dru. pap. 5.95x (ISBN 0-06-130094-2, TB94, Torch). Har-Row.
Present & Future: Modern Aspects of New Testament Theology. Rudolf Schnackenburg. 1966. 11.95x (ISBN 0-268-00215-0). U of Notre Dame Pr.
Present & Future of Religion. Cyril E. Joad. LC 77-109756. 310p. 1974. Repr. of 1930 ed. lib. bdg. 22.50x (ISBN 0-8371-4246-6, JOPF). Greenwood.
Present Christ. John Main. 128p. (Orig.). 1986. pap. 7.95 (ISBN 0-8245-0740-1). Crossroad NY.
Present-Day Christological Debate. Klaus Runia. Ed. by I. Howard Marshall. LC 84-6554. (Issues in Contemporary Theology Ser.). 120p. 1984. pap. 7.95 (ISBN 0-87784-937-4). Inter-Varsity.
Present-Day Ministry of Jesus Christ. 2nd ed. Kenneth E. Hagin. 1983. pap. 1.00 (ISBN 0-89276-014-1). Hagin Ministries.
Present for Jessica. Teddi Doleski. (Illus.). 48p. (Orig.). 1986. pap. 2.50 (ISBN 0-8091-6557-0). Paulist Pr.
Present State of Hayti: Saint Domingo-with Remarks on Its Agriculture, Commerce, Laws, Religion, Finance & Population. James Franklin. LC 79-109325. Repr. of 1828 ed. 25.00x (ISBN 0-8371-3591-5, FRH&). Greenwood.
Present State of the Greek & Armenian Churches. Paul Rycaut. LC 75-13321. Repr. of 1679 ed. 32.50 (ISBN 0-404-05476-5). AMS Pr.
Present State of the Greek Church in Russia. Platon. LC 75-131031. Repr. of 1815 ed. 21.50 (ISBN 0-404-05059-X). AMS Pr.
Presenting Belief in an Age of Unbelief. Charles Colson. 48p. 1986. 1.95 (ISBN 0-89693-158-7). Victor Bks.
Preservative, or Triacle, Agaynst the Poyson of Pelagius. William Turner. LC 78-171795. (English Experience Ser.: No. 418). 208p. 1971. Repr. of 1551 ed. 20.00 (ISBN 90-221-0418-4). Walter J Johnson.
Preserving Life: Public Policy & the Life Not Worth Living. Richard Sherlock. LC 86-21347. 1987. 15.95 (ISBN 0-8294-0526-7). Loyola.
Preserving One's Own Life. Valdemar Paradise. 160p. 1986. 9.95 (ISBN 0-8059-3035-3). Dorrance.
Preserving the Pentecostal Lady. Nell Morgan & Catherine Chambers. Ed. by Mary H. Wallace. LC 86-28067. (Illus.). 134p. 1980. pap. 4.95 (ISBN 0-912315-50-4). Word Aflame.
President Kimball Speaks Out. Spencer W. Kimball. LC 81-68861. 103p. 1981. 5.95 (ISBN 0-87747-881-3). Deseret Bk.
President Witherspoon. Varnum L. Collins. LC 78-83416. (Religion in America, Ser. 1). 1969. Repr. of 1925 ed. 30.00 (ISBN 0-405-00242-4). Ayer Co Pubs.
Presidential Biblical Scoreboard, 1980. write for info. (ISBN 0-89921-008-2). Biblical News Serv.
Presidential Biblical Scoreboard, 1984, No. 1. 1984. write for info. (ISBN 0-89921-009-0). Biblical News Serv.
Presidential Biblical Scoreboard, 1984, No. 2. write for info. (ISBN 0-89921-010-4). Biblical News Serv.
Presidential Biblical Scoreboard, 1984, No. 3. write for info. (ISBN 0-89921-011-2). Biblical News Serv.
Presidential Biblical Scoreboard, 1984, No. 5. write for info. (ISBN 0-89921-013-9). Biblical News Serv.
Presidential Biblical Scoreboard, 1984, No. 5. write for info. (ISBN 0-89921-014-7). Biblical News Serv.
Presidents of the Church. Ed. by Leonard J. Arrington. LC 85-31117. 468p. 1986. 15.95 (ISBN 0-87579-026-7). Deseret Bk.
Press View the FBI Raid. (Illus.). 1977. pap. 3.00 (ISBN 0-915598-17-5). Church of Scient Info.
Pressing on When You'd Rather Turn Back: Philippians. rev. ed. Gene A. Getz. (Biblical Renewal Ser.). 200p. 1985. pap. 5.95 (ISBN 0-8307-1089-2, 5418561). Regal.
Pressing Toward the Mark. Ed. by Robert Fisher. LC 83-63384. 176p. 1983. pap. text ed. 8.95 (ISBN 0-87148-714-4). Pathway Pr.
Pressings from the Vine. Jim Hall. (Orig.). 1987. pap. 7.00 (ISBN 0-915541-18-1). Star Bks Inc.
Presupposition & Transcendental Inference. Humphrey Palmer. LC 84-18384. 108p. 1985. 27.50 (ISBN 0-312-64173-7). St Martin.
Preteen Bible Exploration. Leslie H. Stobbe. 1987. pap. 4.95 (ISBN 0-8010-8273-0). Baker Bk.
Pretre. Pierre Teilhard De Chardin. pap. 4.95 (ISBN 0-685-36600-6). French & Eur.
Pretribulation Rapture & the Bible. Charles R. Taylor. (Illus.). 40p. (Orig.). 1980. pap. 1.50 (ISBN 0-937682-03-9). Today Bible.
Pretty-shield: Medicine Woman of the Crows. Frank B. Linderman. LC 72-3273. (Illus.). 256p. 1974. pap. 6.95 (ISBN 0-8032-5791-0, BB 580, Bison). U of Nebr Pr.
Prevail: A Handbook for the Overcomer. K. H. Varner. 172p. 1982. pap. 3.95 (ISBN 0-938612-06-9). Revival Press.
Prevailing Prayer. Charles G. Finney. LC 65-25846. (Charles G. Finney Memorial Library). 1975. pap. 3.50 (ISBN 0-8254-2603-0). Kregel.
Prevailing Prayer. D. L. Moody. pap. 3.50 (ISBN 0-8024-6814-4). Moody.
Prevailing Prayer to Peace. 2nd ed. Kenneth E. Hagin. 1973. pap. 2.50 (ISBN 0-89276-071-0). Hagin Ministries.
Prevent Doomsday! Anti-Nuclear Anthology. new ed. Vinson Brown et al. (Illus.). 96p. 1983. pap. 4.95 (ISBN 0-8283-1875-1). Branden Pub Co.
Preventing a Church Split. Gene Edwards. 1987. 8.95 (ISBN 0-940232-26-X). Christian Bks.
Price & the Prize. Culbert G. Rutenber. LC 81-65392. 1981. 6.95 (ISBN 0-8054-6230-9). Broadman.
Price of Success: An Autobiography. J. B. Phillips. 288p. (Orig.). 1985. pap. 7.95 (ISBN 0-87788-659-8). Shaw Pubs.
Price Tags of Life. C. Roy Angell. LC 59-9692. 1959. 6.95 (ISBN 0-8054-5108-0). Broadman.
Priceless Pearl. Ruhiyyih Rabbani. (Illus.). 1969. pap. 8.95 (ISBN 0-900125-03-9, 331-048). Baha'i.
Pride According to Gregory the Great: A Study of the Moralia. Matthew Baasten. LC 86-18057. (Studies in the Bible & Early Christianity: Vol. 7). 216p. 1986. lib. bdg. 49.95 (ISBN 0-88946-606-8). E Mellen.
Pride's Purge: Politics in the Puritan Revolution. David Underdown. 440p. 1985. pap. text ed. 13.50x (ISBN 0-04-822045-0). Allen Unwin.
Prieres en Ancien Francais. Keith V. Sinclair. LC 78-137. 208p. 1978. 35.00 (ISBN 0-208-01741-0, Archon). Shoe String.
Priest & A Dead Priestess Speaks. H. D. Doolittle. (Illus.). 38p. 1983. 90.00x (ISBN 0-914742-79-5). Copper Canyon.
Priest & Bishop. Raymond E. Brown. LC 78-139594. 96p. 1970. pap. 4.95 (ISBN 0-8091-1661-8). Paulist Pr.
Priest & Parish in Eighteenth-Century France. T. Tackett. 1977. 38.00 (ISBN 0-691-05243-3). Princeton U Pr.
Priest & Parish in Eighteenth-Century France. Timothy Tackett. LC 76-29801. 368p. 1986. 19.50x (ISBN 0-691-10199-X). Princeton U Pr.
Priest & Sacred Scripture. Ed. by Ernest Larkin & Gerald T. Broccolo. cancelled (ISBN 0-686-18989-2, V-226). US Catholic.
Priest & Stress. 26p. 1982. pap. 2.25 (ISBN 1-55586-832-0). US Catholic.
Priest as a Person: A Philosophy of Priestly Existence. Robert E. Lauder. LC 81-3665. 144p. (Orig.). 1981. pap. 5.00 (ISBN 0-89571-013-7). Affirmation.
Priest as Type of Christ: The Leader of the Eucharist in Salvation History According to Cyprian of Carthage. John D. Laurance. LC 84-47539. (American University Studies VII (Theology & Religion): Vol. 5). 245p. (Orig.). 1984. 37.25 (ISBN 0-8204-0117-X). P Lang Pubs.
Priest for All Reason: William B. Faherty 50 Years a Jesuit. Ed. by Angela Harris & Dick Friedrich. LC 81-52127. (Illus., Orig.). 1981. pap. 6.95 (ISBN 0-933150-27-X). River City MO.
Priest for Now: Masculine & Celibate. Conrad W. Baars. LC 72-87091. (Synthesis Ser). 1972. pap. 1.25 (ISBN 0-8199-0375-2). Franciscan Herald.
Priest in Public Service: Francis J. Haas & the New Deal. Thomas E. Blantz. LC 81-40452. 384p. 1982. 25.00 (ISBN 0-268-01547-3). U of Notre Dame Pr.
Priest the Man of God: His Dignity & Duties. St. Joseph Cafasso. Tr. by Patrick O'Connell from It. LC 79-112472. 1971. Repr. of 1892 ed. 7.00 (ISBN 0-89555-041-5). TAN Bks Pubs.
Priest, the Woman, & the Confessional. Charles Chiniquy. 144p. 1979. pap. 4.50 (ISBN 0-937958-03-4). Chick Pubns.
Priester und Beamtentum der Altbabylonischen Kontrakte. Ernest Lindl. Repr. of 1913 ed. 37.00 (ISBN 0-384-32780-X). Johnson Repr.
Priester und Tempel Im Hellenistischen Agypten: Ein Beitrag Zur Kulturgeschichte Des Hellenismus, 2 vols. in 1. facsimile ed. Walter G. Otto. LC 75-10645. (Ancient Religion & Mythology Ser.). (Ger.). 1976. Repr. 62.00x (ISBN 0-405-07278-3). Ayer Co Pubs.
Priesthood. Spencer W. Kimball et al. LC 81-5394. 170p. 1981. 8.95 (ISBN 0-87747-859-7). Deseret Bk.
Priesthood. Wilhelm Stockums. 242p. 1982. pap. 7.00 (ISBN 0-89555-170-5). TAN Bks Pubs.
Priesthood & Humanity. Sylvester L. DiNunzio. 1984. 8.50 (ISBN 0-8062-2379-0). Carlton.
Priesthood Manual. rev. ed. Ed. by Clifford A. Cole. LC 81-7220. 1985. 15.00 (ISBN 0-8309-0420-4). Herald Hse.
Priesthood, Old & New. Edward Laity. 1980. 2.25 (ISBN 0-86544-012-3). Salv Army Suppl South.
Priesthoods & Apostasies of Pierce Connally: A Study of Victorian Conversion & Anticatholicism. D. G. Paz. (Studies in American Religion: Vol. 18). 418p. 1986. lib. bdg. 69.95x (ISBN 0-88946-662-9). E Mellen.
Priestly Celibacy: Recurrent Battle & Lasting Values. Albert J. Hebert. 198p. 1971. 6.00 (ISBN 0-912414-01-4). Lumen Christi.
Priestly Gift in Mishnah: A Study of Tractate Terumot. Alan Peck. LC 81-2764. (Brown BJS Ser.). 1981. pap. 16.50 (ISBN 0-89130-488-6, 140020). Scholars Pr GA.
Priestly Heart. James A. Griffin. LC 83-26611. 149p. (Orig.). 1984. pap. 6.95 (ISBN 0-8189-0460-7). Alba.
Priestly Kingdom: Social Ethics As Gospel. John H. Yoder. LC 84-40358. 208p. 1986. text ed. 16.95 (ISBN 0-268-01627-5, 85-16270); pap. text ed. 8.95 (ISBN 0-268-01628-3, 85-16288). U of Notre Dame Pr.
Priestly People. Edward O'Donnell. 64p. 1982. pap. 1.50 (ISBN 0-89243-168-7). Liguori Pubns.
Priests & Kings. H. F. Fleure & Harold Peake. (Corridors of Time Ser.: No. 4). 1927. 29.50x (ISBN 0-686-83710-X). Elliots Bks.
Priests & Power: The Case of the Dente Shrine in Nineteenth-Century Ghana. D. J. E. Maier. LC 82-48582. (Illus.). 272p. 1983. 22.50X (ISBN 0-253-34602-9). Ind U Pr.
Priests Are Only Human. John C. Tormey. LC 73-15083. (Illus.). 128p. 1974. pap. 1.25 (ISBN 0-8189-1114-X, Pub. by Alba Bks). Alba.
Priest's Handbook: The Ceremonies of the Church. Dennis G. Michno. LC 81-84716. (Illus.). 304p. 1983. 32.50 (ISBN 0-8192-1300-4). Morehouse.
Priests in Working Class Blue: The History of the Worker-Priests, (1943-1954) Oscar L. Arnal. 248p. (Orig.). 1986. pap. 11.95 (ISBN 0-8091-2831-4). Paulist Pr.
Priests of Ancient Egypt. Serge Sauneron. LC 59-10792. (Illus.). 192p. 1980. pap. 3.50 (ISBN 0-394-17410-0, B433, BC). Grove.
Priests, Philosophers & Prophets. Thomas Whittaker. LC 77-102589. 1970. Repr. of 1911 ed. 22.50x (ISBN 0-8046-0748-6, Pub. by Kennikat). Assoc Faculty Pr.
Priests to Each Other. Carlyle Marney. 125p. 1985. pap. 6.95 (ISBN 0-913029-06-8). Stevens Bk Pr.
Priests, Warriors & Cattle: A Study in the Ecology of Religions. Bruce Lincoln. LC 78-68826. (Hermeneutics: Studies in the History of Religions Ser.). 240p. 1981. 37.95x (ISBN 0-520-03880-0). U of Cal Pr.
Prigotovlenije k Ispovjedi i Blagogvejnomy Prithashcheniju Svijatikh Khristvikh Tajin. Archpriest Michael Bogoslovsky. Tr. of Preporation for Confession & the Receiving of the Holy Mysteries. 169p. pap. 8.00 (ISBN 0-317-29105-X). Holy Trinity.
Primacy of Christ. Michael D. Meilach. 1964. 4.95 (ISBN 0-8199-0087-7, L38655). Franciscan Herald.
Primacy of Faith. Richard Kroner. LC 77-27184. (Gifford Lectures: 1939-40). Repr. of 1943 ed. 26.25 (ISBN 0-404-60497-8). AMS Pr.
Primacy of Peter. Meyendorff et al. 134p. 1963. 7.95 (ISBN 0-913836-20-6). St Vladimirs.
Primal Myths: Creating the World. Barbara C. Sproul. LC 78-4429. 1979. pap. 9.95x (ISBN 0-06-067501-2, HarpR, RD 230, HarpR). Har-Row.
Primal Power in Man: The Kundalini Shakti Yoga. Swami Narayananda. 155p. 1971. pap. 11.95 (ISBN 0-88697-027-X). Life Science.
Primal Scenes: Literature, Philosophy, Psychoanalysis. Ned Lukacher. LC 85-25513. 368p. 1986. text ed. 24.95x (ISBN 0-8014-1886-0). Cornell U Pr.
Primary Speech: A Psychology of Prayer. Ann Ulanov & Barry Ulanov. LC 81-85328. 192p. 1982. 10.95 (ISBN 0-8042-1134-5). John Knox.
Prime Rib & Apple. Jill Briscoe. 1976. 5.95 (ISBN 0-310-21810-1, 9257P); pap. 4.95 (ISBN 0-310-21811-X). Zondervan.
Primer for Angry Christians. Steve Clapp & Sue I. Mauck. (Illus.). 138p. (Orig.). 1981. pap. 6.00 (ISBN 0-914527-09-6). C-Four Res.
Primer for Church Worship. Hoyt Hickman. 112p. (Orig.). 1984. pap. 7.95 (ISBN 0-687-34033-0). Abingdon.
Primer for Preachers. Pitt-Watson. 112p. 1987. 5.95 (ISBN 0-8010-7096-1). Baker Bk.
Primer for Temple Life. Joseph R. Narot. pap. 1.00 (ISBN 0-686-15808-3). Rostrum Bks.
Primer of Christianity & Ethics. Douglas Young. Ed. by Constance Hunting. 200p. (Orig.). (YA) 1985. pap. 12.95 (ISBN 0-913006-34-3). Puckerbrush.
Primer of Ecclesiastical Latin. John F. Collins. LC 84-22957. 250p. 1985. 24.95x (ISBN 0-8132-0610-3). Cath U Pr.
Primer of Hinduism. D. S. Sarma. 170p. 1987. pap. 3.25 (ISBN 0-87481-532-0, Pub. by Ramakrishna Math Madras India). Vedanta Pr.
Primer of Prayer Gesture. Kay Irwin. 43p. 1977. pap. 3.00 (ISBN 0-941500-21-7). Sharing Co.
Primer of Soto Zen: A Translation of Dogen's Shobogenzo Zuimonki. Dogen. Tr. by Reiho Masunaga from Japanese. LC 76-126044. 128p. 1975. pap. text ed. 5.95x (ISBN 0-8248-0357-4, Eastwest Ctr). UH Pr.
Primer on Dispensationalism. John H. Gerstner. 1982. pap. 1.75 (ISBN 0-87552-273-4). Presby & Reformed.
Primer on Free Will. John H. Gerstner. 1982. pap. 1.50 (ISBN 0-87552-272-6). Presby & Reformed.
Primer on Justification. John H. Gerstner. 32p. 1983. pap. 1.50 (ISBN 0-87552-276-9). Presby & Reformed.
Primer on Prayer. W. T. Purkiser. (Christian Living Ser.). 32p. (Orig.). 1987. pap. write for info. (ISBN 0-8341-1191-8). Beacon Hill.
Primer on the Deity of Christ. John H. Gerstner. 40p. 1984. pap. 1.75 (ISBN 0-87552-277-7). Presby & Reformed.
Primera Epistola a los Corintios. Ernesto Trenchard. (Span.). 348p. 1970. 9.95 (ISBN 0-8254-1728-7); pap. 8.95 (ISBN 0-8254-1727-9). Kregel.
Primera y Segunda Pedro, Comentario Biblico Portavoz. Louis A. Barbieri. Orig. Title: First & Second Peter, Everyman's Bible Commentary. (Span.). 1981. pap. 3.95 (ISBN 0-8254-1051-7). Kregel.
Primera y Segunda Tesalonicenses (Comentario Biblico Portavoz) Charles C. Ryrie. Orig. Title: First & Second Thessalonians (Everyman's Bible Commentary) (Span.). 104p. 1981. pap. 2.95 (ISBN 0-8254-1634-5). Kregel.
Primers for the Age of Innerspace - I Beyond the Present Prospect: The Impact of the Twentieth Century Revolutions in Science on the Varieties of Ethical & Religious Experience. John E. Whiteford Boyle. LC 76-44888. 9.95 (ISBN 0-917888-00-6). Wheat Forders.
Primitive Baptist Hymns of the Blue Ridge. Brett Sutton. (American Folklore Recordings Ser.). 28p. 1982. pap. 15.00x incl. records (ISBN 0-8078-4083-1). U of NC Pr.
Primitive Beliefs in the North-East of Scotland. Joseph M. McPherson. Ed. by Richard M. Dorson. LC 77-70605. (International Folklore Ser.). 1977. Repr. of 1929 ed. lib. bdg. 24.50x (ISBN 0-405-10109-0). Ayer Co Pubs.
Primitive Christianity, 4 vols. Otto Pfleiderer. Ed. by W. D. Morrison. Tr. by W. Montgomery. LC 65-22085. (Library of Religious & Philosophical Thought). 1966. Repr. of 1906 ed. lib. bdg. 150.00x (ISBN 0-678-09954-5, Reference Bk Pubs). Kelley.
Primitive Christianity & Its Non-Jewish Sources. D. D. Clemen. 1977. lib. bdg. 59.95 (ISBN 0-8490-2472-2). Gordon Pr.
Primitive Christianity: In Its Contemporary Setting. Rudolf Bultmann. Tr. by Reginald H. Fuller from Ger. LC 80-8043. 256p. 1980. pap. 8.95 (ISBN 0-8006-1408-9, 1-1408). Fortress.
Primitive Church. D. I. Lanslots. LC 79-67862. 295p. 1980. pap. 5.50 (ISBN 0-89555-134-9). TAN Bks Pubs.
Primitive Church: Studies in the Origin of the Christian Ministry. B. H. Streeter. 1977. lib. bdg. 59.95 (ISBN 0-8490-2473-0). Gordon Pr.
Primitive Conceptions of Death & the Nether World in the Old Testament. Nicholas J. Tromp. (Biblica et Orientalia: Vol. 21). 1969. pap. 18.00 (ISBN 88-7653-321-4). Loyola.
Primitive Methodist Connexion: Its Background & Early History. Julia S. Werner. LC 84-40161. (Illus.). 352p. 1985. text ed. 35.00x (ISBN 0-299-09910-5). U of Wis Pr.
Primitive Mythology: The Mythic World of the Australian & Papuan Natives. Lucien Levy-Bruel. Tr. by Brian Elliott. LC 82-17332. 332p. 1984. text ed. 32.50 (ISBN 0-7022-1667-4). U of Queensland Pr.
Primitive Reader: An Anthology of Myths, Tales, Songs, Riddles, & Proverbs of Aboriginal Peoples Around the World. John Greenway. LC 65-21986. viii, 211p. Repr. of 1965 ed. 35.00x (ISBN 0-8103-5014-9). Gale.
Primitive Religion. John J. Collins. (Quality Paperback Ser.: No. 342). 256p. 1978. pap. 4.95 (ISBN 0-8226-0342-X). Littlefield.
Primitive Religion. new ed. Robert H. Lowie. LC 75-114373. 1970. pap. 5.95 (ISBN 0-87140-209-2). Liveright.
Primitive Religion. Pual Radin. 15.25 (ISBN 0-8446-2775-5). Peter Smith.

Primitive Religion: Its Nature & Origin. Paul Radin. 1937. pap. text ed. 5.95 (ISBN 0-486-20393-X). Dover.

Primitive Traits in Religious Revivals: A Study in Mental & Social Evolution. F. M. Davenport. 1977. lib. bdg. 59.95 (ISBN 0-8490-2478-1). Gordon Pr.

Primitive Traits in Religious Revivals. Frederick M. Davenport. LC 72-163669. Repr. of 1905 ed. 15.00 (ISBN 0-404-01929-3). AMS Pr.

Primitive Traits in Religious Revivals. Frederick M. Davenport. LC 68-58053. Repr. of 1905 ed. cancelled (ISBN 0-8371-0378-9, DAR&). Greenwood.

Primitives & the Supernatural. J. Levy-Bruhl. LC 73-4358. (Studies in Comparative Literature, No. 35). 1972. Repr. of 1935 ed. lib. bdg. 58.95x (ISBN 0-8383-1589-5). Haskell.

Primogenesis. Howard B. Rand. 1953. 15.00 (ISBN 0-685-08813-8). Destiny.

Primordial Experience: An Introduction to Dzogchen Meditation. Manjusrimitra. Tr. by Kennard Lipman & Namkhai Norbu. LC 86-11842. Tr. of Rdo La Gser Zhun. 140p. 1986. pap. 11.95 (ISBN 0-87773-372-4). Shambhala Pubns.

Prince Charles's Puritan Chaplain, John Preston. Irvonwy Morgan. LC 58-3992. 1957. 10.00x (ISBN 0-8401-1648-9). A R Allenson.

Prince George County, Virginia, Vol. 6. Lindsay O. Duvall. (Virginia Colonial Abstracts, Series II). 80p. 1978. pap. 20.00 (ISBN 0-89308-067-5). Southern Hist Pr.

Prince Hall & His Followers. George W. Crawford. LC 74-144591. Repr. of 1914 ed. 16.00 (ISBN 0-404-00145-9). AMS Pr.

Prince of Ayodhya. Hansa Mehta. (Nehru Library for Children). (Illus.). 1979. pap. 2.00 (ISBN 0-89744-178-8). Auromere.

Prince of Darkness: A Witchcraft Anthology. Gerald Verner et al. 1978. Repr. of 1946 ed. lib. bdg. 25.00 (ISBN 0-8492-2816-6). R West.

Prince of Martyrs: A Brief Account of Imam Husayn. A. Q. Faizi. 74p. 1977. pap. 3.50 (ISBN 0-85398-073-X). G Ronald Pub.

Prince of Peace. Alban Goodier. 152p. 1982. 3.25 (ISBN 0-8198-5807-2, SP0585); pap. 2.25 (ISBN 0-8198-5808-0). Dghtrs St Paul.

Prince of Peace. Carl G. Nelson. LC 79-63954. (Illus., Ltd. ed-600copies). 1979. 10.00 (ISBN 0-930954-11-4). Tidal Pr.

Prince of Peace: Returns to Fulfill All Prophecy. Shirley Telford. (Illus.). 56p. (Orig.). 1984. 5.50 (ISBN 0-9600202-0-9); Audio-Video Cassette. 12.00 (ISBN 0-9613706-1-0). William & Rich.

Prince of the Church: Schleiermacher & the Beginnings of Modern Theology. B. A. Gerrish. LC 83-48924. 80p. 1984. pap. 4.95 (ISBN 0-8006-1787-8, 1-1787). Fortress.

Prince of the House of David. F. Ingraham & Eric Anderson. Orig. Title: Three Years in the Holy City. 363p. 1980. Repr. text ed. 15.95 (ISBN 0-89841-003-7). Zoe Pubns.

Prince Siddhartha. Jonathan Landaw. (Illus.). 144p. 1984. 15.95 (ISBN 0-318-04415-3, Wisdom Pubns). Great Traditions.

Princeps a Diis Electus: The Divine Election of the Emperor as a Political Concept at Rome. J. R. Fears. 353p. 1977. 38.00x (ISBN 0-271-00474-6). Pa St U Pr.

Princes & Paupers in the English Church: 1500-1800. Ed. by Rosemary O'Day & Felicity Heal. 294p. 1981. 28.50x (ISBN 0-389-20200-2, 06982). B&N Imports.

Princes, Politics & Religion, 1547-1589. N. M. Sutherland. (No. 31). 240p. 1984. 30.00 (ISBN 0-907628-44-3). Hambledon Press.

Princess & the Baby. Janice Kramer. (Arch Bks: Set 6). 1969. laminated bdg 0.99 (ISBN 0-570-06043-5, 59-1158). Concordia.

Princeton Pulpit Prayers. Donald Macleod. 112p. (Orig.). 1987. prayerbook 9.95 (ISBN 0-941850-21-8). Sunday Pubns.

Princeton Sermons. Charles Hodge. 1979. 13.95 (ISBN 0-85151-285-2). Banner of Truth.

Princeton Theology: An Anthology. Compiled by Mark A. Noll. 432p. (Orig.). 1983. pap. 14.95 (ISBN 0-8010-6737-5). Baker Bk.

Principal Ecclesiastical Judgments Delivered in the Court of Arches 1867 to 1875. Robert Phillimore. xiii, 420p. 1981. Repr. of 1876 ed. lib. bdg. 35.00x (ISBN 0-8377-2504-6). Rothman.

Principes de la Philosophie, Vol. 1. 3rd ed. Rene Descartes. 158p. 1970. 9.95 (ISBN 0-686-55678-X). French & Eur.

Principia Ethica. George E. Moore. 1959. 37.50 (ISBN 0-521-05753-1); pap. 12.95 (ISBN 0-521-09114-4). Cambridge U Pr.

Principia: Or the First Princples of Natural Things, Vols. I & II. Emmanuel Swedenborg. Tr. & intro. by Augustus Clissold. (Illus.). 1976. Repr. of 1846 ed. Set. 15.00 (ISBN 0-915221-20-9). Vol. I, 380p (ISBN 0-915221-37-3). Vol. II, 413p (ISBN 0-915221-38-1). Swedenborg Sci Assn.

Principios Rosacruces para el Hogar y los Negocios. 4th ed. H. Spencer Lewis. Tr. by AMORC Staff. (Span.). 210p. (Orig.). 1980. pap. 8.00 (ISBN 0-912057-76-9, GS-502). AMORC.

Principle & Practicality: Essays in Neo-Confucianism & Practical Learning. Ed. by W. Theodore De Bary & Irene Bloom. LC 78-11530. (Neo-Confucian Series & Studies in Oriental Culture). 1979. 38.00x (ISBN 0-231-04612-X); pap. 19.00x (ISBN 0-231-04613-8). Columbia U Pr.

Principle & Practice of Mahayana Buddhism: An Interpretation of Professor Suzuki's Translation of Ashvaghosa's Awakening of Faith. Asvaghosa. Ed. by Dwight Goodard. LC 78-72373. Repr. of 1933 ed. 18.00 (ISBN 0-404-17223-7). AMS Pr.

Principle of Creation. Ed. by Chung H. Kwak. (Home Study Course Ser.). 60p. 1980. pap. 4.00. HSA Pubns.

Principle of Non-Resistance As Held by the Mennonite Church. John Horsch. Bd. with Hutterian Brethren, Fifteen Twenty-Eight to Nineteen Thirty-One. John Horsch. LC 74-147672. (Library of War & Peace; Relig. & Ethical Positions on War). lib. bdg. 46.00 (ISBN 0-8240-0430-2). Garland Pub.

Principle of Protestantism: Chambersburg, PA 1845. Philip Schaff. Ed. by Bruce Kuklick. Bd. with What Is Church History? Philadelphia, PA 1846. 215p. (American Religious Thought of the 18th & 19th Centuries Ser.). 343p. 1987. lib. bdg. 50.00. Garland Pub.

Principle of Reincarnation. Walter J. Stein. 1986. pap. 2.50 (ISBN 0-916786-85-4). St George Bk Serv.

Principle of Spiritual Economy. Rudolf Steiner. Tr. by Peter Mollenhauer. Tr. of Prinzip der Spirituellen Okonomie im Zusammenhang mit Wiederverkorperungsfragen. 220p. 1986. 20.00 (ISBN 0-88010-163-6); pap. 9.95 (ISBN 0-88010-162-8). Anthroposophic.

Principles & Development of Jewish Law. Mendell Lewittes. 200p. Date not set. 19.95x (ISBN 0-8197-0512-8); pap. 10.95x (ISBN 0-8197-0506-3). Bloch.

Principles & Practice of Indigenous Church Planting. Charles Brock. 1981. pap. 4.25 (ISBN 0-8054-6328-3). Broadman.

Principles & Practice of Past Life Therapy. Ruth Norman & Charles Spaegel. (Illus.). 500p. 1984. 10.95 (ISBN 0-932642-79-9). Unarius Pubns.

Principles & Practice of Preaching. Ilion T. Jones. LC 56-7761. 1974. pap. 7.75 (ISBN 0-687-34061-6). Abingdon.

Principles & Practices for Baptist Churches. Edward T. Hiscox. LC 80-8083. 598p. (Orig.). 1985. pap. 11.95 (ISBN 0-8254-2860-2). Kregel.

Principles & Purposes of Vedanta. 8th ed. Swami Paramananda. 1937. pap. 1.00 (ISBN 0-911564-30-6). Vedanta Ctr.

Principles for a Catholic Morality. Timothy E. O'Connell. 1978. (HarpR); pap. 9.95 (ISBN 0-86683-885-6). Har-Row.

Principles of Biblical Hermeneutics. J. Edwin Hartill. 13.95 (ISBN 0-310-25900-2, 9774). Zondervan.

Principles of Biblical Interpretation. Louis Berkhof. 1950. 9.95 (ISBN 0-8010-0549-3). Baker Bk.

Principles of Buddhist Psychology. David J. Kalupahana. (Buddhist Studies). 256p. 1987. 39.50 (ISBN 0-88706-404-3); pap. 12.95 (ISBN 0-88706-403-5). State U NY Pr.

Principles of Canon Law. Hubert S. Box. LC 86-3163. 1986. Repr. of 1949 ed. 32.75x (ISBN 0-313-25204-1, BPRC/). Greenwood.

Principles of Catholic Moral Life. Ed. by William E. May. LC 80-10969. 456p. 1981. 10.50 (ISBN 0-8199-0793-6). Franciscan Herald.

Principles of Catholic Theology: A Synthesis of Dogma & Morals. Edward Gratsch et al. LC 80-26272. 401p. (Orig.). 1981. pap. 12.95 (ISBN 0-8189-0407-0). Alba.

Principles of Catholic Theology: Building Stones for Fundamental Theology. Joseph C. Ratzinger. Tr. by Mary F. McCarthy from Ger. LC 86-83133. Tr. of Theologische Prinzipienlehre. 320p. (Orig.). 1986. 24.95 (ISBN 0-89870-133-3). Ignatius Pr.

Principles of Christian Art. Percy Gardner. 1977. lib. bdg. 59.95 (ISBN 0-8490-2479-X). Gordon Pr.

Principles of Christian Morality. Joseph Ratzinger et al. Tr. by Graham Harrison from Ger. LC 85-82176. Orig. Title: Prinzipien Chrislicher Moral. 104p. (Orig.). 1986. pap. 6.95 (ISBN 0-89870-086-8). Ignatius Pr.

Principles of Christian Religion. Thomas Becon. LC 76-57355. (English Experience Ser.: No. 774). 1977. Repr. of 1552 ed. lib. bdg. 14.00 (ISBN 90-221-0774-4). Walter J Johnson.

Principles of Christian Theology. 2nd ed. John Macquarrie. LC 76-23182. 544p. 1977. pap. text ed. write for info. (ISBN 0-02-374510-X, Pub. by Scribner). Macmillan.

Principles of Conduct. John Murray. 1957. pap. 7.95 (ISBN 0-8028-1144-2). Eerdmans.

Principles of Devotion. rev. ed. Charles Finney. Ed. by Louis Parkhurst. 288p. 1987. pap. 6.95 (ISBN 0-87123-873-X). Bethany Hse.

Principles of Discipleship. Debbie Crinzi. 102p. 1984. pap. text ed. 5.00 (ISBN 0-8309-0394-1). Herald Hse.

Principles of Ethics. Borden P. Bowne. LC 75-3073. (Philosophy in America Ser.). Repr. of 1892 ed. 28.00 (ISBN 0-404-59074-8). AMS Pr.

Principles of Ethics, 2 vols. Herbert Spencer. LC 77-71453. 550p. 1980. Set. pap. 8.00 (ISBN 0-913966-34-7, Liberty Clas); Vol. I. pap. (ISBN 0-913966-77-0); Vol. II. pap. (ISBN 0-913966-75-4). Liberty Fund.

Principles of Ethics, 2 vols. Herbert Spencer. LC 77-71453. 1978. Repr. Set. 20.00 (ISBN 0-913966-33-9, Liberty Clas); Vol. I. (ISBN 0-913966-76-2); Vol. II. (ISBN 0-913966-74-6). Liberty Fund.

Principles of Faith (Rosh Amanah) Isaac Abravanal. (Littman Library of Jewish Civilization). 272p. 1982. 26.00x (ISBN 0-19-710045-7). Oxford U Pr.

Principles of Holiness. Charles G. Finney. LC 83-25769. 274p. 1984. pap. 5.95 (ISBN 0-87123-403-3, 210403). Bethany Hse.

Principles of Integral Science of Religion. Georg Schmid. (Religion & Reason Ser.). 1979. text ed. 33.75 (ISBN 90-279-7864-6). Mouton.

Principles of Jewish Law. Ed. by Menachem Elon. 866p. 1975. 50.00 (ISBN 0-87855-188-3). Transaction Bks.

Principles of Leadership. Don Clowers. 40p. (Orig.). 1985. wkbk. 4.95 (ISBN 0-914307-49-5). Word Faith.

Principles of Liberty. rev. ed. Charles G. Finney & L. B. Parkhurst. LC 82-20705. (Finney's Sermons on Romans Ser.). 194p. (Orig.). 1983. pap. 5.95 (ISBN 0-87123-475-0, 210475). Bethany Hse.

Principles of Love. Charles G. Finney. Ed. by Louis G. Parkhurst. 200p. 1986. pap. 5.95 (ISBN 0-87123-866-7, 210866). Bethany Hse.

Principles of Lutheran Theology. Carl E. Braaten. LC 82-16542. 160p. 1983. pap. 8.95 (ISBN 0-8006-1689-8). Fortress.

Principles of Moral & Political Philosophy. William Paley. Ed. by Rene Wellek. LC 75-11246. (British Philosophers & Theologians of the 17th & 18th Centuries Ser.: Vol. 45). 1977. Repr. of 1785 ed. lib. bdg. 51.00 (ISBN 0-8240-1797-8). Garland Pub.

Principles of Moral & Political Science, 2 Vols. Adam Ferguson. LC 71-147970. Repr. of 1792 ed. Set. 85.00 (ISBN 0-404-08222-X). AMS Pr.

Principles of Moral & Political Science, 2 vols. Adam Ferguson. Ed. by Rene Wellek. LC 75-11218. (British Philosophers & Theologians of the 17th & 18th Centuries Ser.: Vol. 21). 1978. Repr. of 1792 ed. Set. lib. bdg. 101.00 (ISBN 0-8240-1772-2). Garland Pub.

Principles of Muhammadan Jurisprudence According to the Hanali, Maliki, Shafi'i & Hanbali Schools. Abdur Rahim. LC 79-2879. 443p. 1981. Repr. of 1911 ed. 34.50 (ISBN 0-8305-0047-2). Hyperion Conn.

Principles of Muhammadan Law. William H. Macnauhten. 140p. (Orig.). 1981. pap. 6.50 (ISBN 0-88004-010-6). Sunwise Turn.

Principles of Musik, in Singing & Setting. Charles Butler. LC 68-13273. (Music Ser.). 1970. Repr. of 1636 ed. lib. bdg. 23.50 (ISBN 0-306-70939-2). Da Capo.

Principles of Musik, in Singing & Setting. Charles Butler. LC 74-25439. (English Experience Ser.: No. 284). 136p. 1971. Repr. of 1636 ed. 14.00 (ISBN 90-221-0284-X). Walter J Johnson.

Principles of Natural Theology. George H. Joyce. LC 79-170829. Repr. of 1923 ed. 37.45 (ISBN 0-404-03609-0). AMS Pr.

Principles of New Testament Christianity. Charles E. Crouch. 1985. pap. 5.50 (ISBN 0-89137-546-5). Quality Pubns.

Principles of Patristic Exegesis: Romans 9-11 in Origen, John Chrysostom & Augustine. Peter Gorday. LC 83-20588. (Studies in the Bible & Early Christianity: Vol. 4). 424p. 1984. 69.95x (ISBN 0-88946-602-5). E Mellen.

Principles of Peace: Exemplified by the Conduct of the Society of Friends in Ireland, 1798. Thomas Hancock. LC 70-147620. (Library of War & Peace; Non-Resis. & Non-Vio.). lib. bdg. 46.00 (ISBN 0-8240-0377-2). Garland Pub.

Principles of Philosophy of Religion. H. G. Hubbeling. (Philosophia Religionis Ser.: Vol. 25). 280p. 1987. pap. 22.95 (ISBN 90-232-2272-5, Pub. by Van Gorcum Holland). Longwood Pub Group.

Principles of Prayer. Charles G. Finney. Ed. by L. G. Parkhurst. LC 80-17856. 112p. (Orig.). 1980. pap. 3.95 (ISBN 0-87123-468-8, 210468). Bethany Hse.

Principles of Preaching. Robert F. Morneau. 1983. pap. 6.95 (ISBN 0-941850-11-0). Sunday Pubns.

Principles of Protestantism. Philip Schaff. Ed. by Bard Thompson & George H. Bricker. 1964. pap. 6.95 (ISBN 0-8298-0348-3). Pilgrim NY.

Principles of Religious Education. Henry C Potter. (Educational Ser.). 1900. Repr. 10.00 (ISBN 0-8482-5585-2). Norwood Edns.

Principles of Sacred Theology. Abraham Kuyper. Tr. by J. Hendrick DeVries from Dutch. (Twin Brooks Ser.). 712p. 1980. pap. 12.95 (ISBN 0-8010-5420-6). Baker Bk.

Principles of Sanctification. rev. ed. Charles Finney & Louis Parkhurst. 240p. 1986. pap. 5.95 (ISBN 0-87123-859-4). Bethany Hse.

Principles of Tantra, 2 vols. John Woodroffe. 1979. Set. 42.00 (ISBN 0-89744-129-X, Pub. by Ganesh & Co India). Auromere.

Principles of the Gospel in Practice. Ed. by Sperry Symposium Staff. 257p. Date not set. 10.95 (ISBN 0-934126-75-5). Randall Bk Co.

Principles of the Liturgy. A. G. Martimort et al. Ed. by A. G. Martimort. Tr. by Matthew J. O'Connell. (Church at Prayer: Vol. 1). 300p. 1987. pap. 14.95 (ISBN 0-8146-1363-2). Liturgical Pr.

Principles of the Most Ancient & Modern Philosophy. Anne Conway. 1982. 35.00 (ISBN 90-247-2671-9, Pub. by Martinus Nijhoff Netherlands). Kluwer Academic.

Principles of Union with Christ. Charles G. Finney. Ed. by Louis G. Parkhurst. 128p. 1985. pap. 4.95 (ISBN 0-87123-447-5, 210447). Bethany Hse.

Principles of Victory. Charles G. Finney. Ed. by G. Parkhurst. LC 81-15464. 201p. (Orig.). 1981. pap. 5.95 (ISBN 0-87123-471-8, 210471). Bethany Hse.

Principles, Origin & Establishment of the Catholic School System in the United States. J. A. Burns. LC 74-89155. (American Education: Its Men, Institutions & Ideas Ser). 1969. Repr. of 1908 ed. 21.00 (ISBN 0-405-01393-0). Ayer Co Pubs.

Prinoshenije Sovremennomu Monashestvu, Vol. 5. Ignatius Brianchianinov. Tr. of Offering to Contemporary Monasticism. 354p. 20.00 (ISBN 0-317-28966-7); pap. 15.00 (ISBN 0-317-28967-5). Holy Trinity.

Printed Circuit Board Basics. Ed. by Donna J. Esposito. 92p. (Orig.). 1986. 14.95 (ISBN 0-931463-00-9). PMS Indus.

Printed Italian Vernacular Religious Books 1465-1550: A Finding List. A. J. Shutte. 484p. (Orig.). 1983. pap. text ed. 65.00x (Pub. by Droz Switzerland). Coronet Bks.

Printed Writings of Jonathan Edwards 1703-1758: A Bibliography. Thomas H. Johnson. 1970. Repr. of 1940 ed. text ed. 21.50 (ISBN 0-8337-1854-1). B Franklin.

Prinzipieproblem in der Philosophie des Thomas von Aquin. Wilfried Kuhn. (Bochum Studies in Philosophy Ser.: No. 1). 531p. 1982. 40.00x (ISBN 90-6032-227-4, Pub by B R Gruener Amsterdam). Benjamins North Am.

Prior to Consciousness: Talks with Sri Nisargadatta Maharaj. Nisargadatta Maharaj. Ed. by Jean Dunn. LC 85-71544. ix, 159p. (Orig.). pap. 9.95 (ISBN 0-317-19710-X). Acorn NC.

Priorities in Biomedical Ethics. James F. Childress. LC 81-3. 144p. 1981. pap. 8.95 (ISBN 0-664-24368-1). Westminster.

Priorities in Praying: Learning from the Lord's Prayer. Merlin Davies. 104p. (Orig.). 1984. pap. 10.95 (ISBN 0-86474-002-6, Pub. by Interface Press). ANZ Religious Pubns.

Priority: Jesus' Life in Sixty Drawings. Annie Vallotton. (Illus.). 64p. 1969. pap. 0.95 (ISBN 0-8361-1901-0). Herald Pr.

Priority of John. John A. Robinson. 464p. 1987. pap. 19.95 (ISBN 0-940989-01-8). Meyer Stone Bks.

Priority of Labor: A Commentary on "Laborem Exercens", Encyclical Letter of Pope John Paul II. Gregory Baum. 112p. 1982. pap. 5.95 (ISBN 0-8091-2479-3). Paulist Pr.

Priscilla Principle: Making Your Life a Ministry. Jo Berry. 256p. 1984. pap. 6.95 (ISBN 0-310-42631-6, 11218P). Zondervan.

Prism of Scripture: Studies on History & Historicity in the Work of Jonathan Edwards, Vol. 1. Karl D. Pfisterer. (Anglo-American Forum Ser.: Vol. 1). 381p. 1975. pap. 31.55 (ISBN 3-261-00965-9). P Lang Pubs.

Prison & Pastoral Letters. W. G. MacDonald. 96p. 1967. pap. 0.75 (ISBN 0-88243-792-5, 02-0792). Gospel Pub.

Prison Chaplain: Memoirs of the Rev. John Clay with Selections from His Reports & Correspondence & a Sketch of Prison Discipline in England. Walter L. Clay. LC 69-16232. (Criminology, Law Enforcement, & Social Problems Ser.: No. 90). (Index added). 1969. Repr. of 1861 ed. 25.00 (ISBN 0-87585-090-1). Patterson Smith.

Prison Door Is Open: What Are You Still Doing Inside? Kenneth Hagin, Jr. 1982. pap. 0.50 mini bk (ISBN 0-89276-710-3). Hagin Ministries.

Prison Ministry Training Manual. Tay Wallace. (Illus.). 44p. (Orig.). 1981. pap. 3.00 (ISBN 0-933643-08-X). Grace World Outreach.

Prison or Paradise? The New Religious Cults? A. James Rudin & Marcia R. Rudin. LC 80-10210. 168p. 1980. 4.95 (ISBN 0-8006-1937-4, 1-1937). Fortress.

Prison to Praise. Merlin R. Carothers. 106p. (Orig.). 1970. pap. 2.95 (ISBN 0-943026-02-4). Carothers.

Prison to Praise: Giant Print. Merlin R. Carothers. 106p. (Orig.). 1970. pap. 3.95 (ISBN 0-943026-08-3). Carothers.

Prisoner & Other Tales of Faith. 1980. pap. 5.95 (ISBN 0-87306-243-4). Feldheim.

Prisoner Rejoice. Nicole Valery. 238p. 1980. pap. 4.95 (ISBN 0-88264-179-4). Diane Bks.

Prisoners of Hope. James Hefley & Marti Hefley. LC 76-28840. 1976. 6.95 (ISBN 0-87509-122-9); pap. 3.95 (ISBN 0-87509-123-7). Chr Pubns.

Prisoners of Hope: The Silver Age of the Italian Jews, 1924-1974. H. Stuart Hughes. 184p. 1983. text ed. 15.00x (ISBN 0-674-70727-3). Harvard U Pr.

Privacy: A Vanishing Value? Ed. by W. C. Bier. LC 79-56138. (Pastoral Psychology Ser.: No. 10). xiv, 398p. 1980. 25.00 (ISBN 0-8232-1044-8). Fordham.

Private Churches & Public Money: Church-Government Fiscal Relations. Paul J. Weber & Dennis A. Gilbert. LC 80-1793. (Contributions to the Study of Religion: No. 1). (Illus.). xx, 260p. 1981. lib. bdg. 29.95 (ISBN 0-313-22484-6, WCM/). Greenwood.

Private Devotions of Lancelot Andrewes. Lancelot Andrewes. Tr. & intro. by F. E. Brightman. 15.25 (ISBN 0-8446-1534-X). Peter Smith.

Private Diary of Ananda Ranga Pillai in 12 Volumes. Ananda R. Pillai et al. Ed. by J. F. Price & Rangachari. Tr. by Joseph F. Dupleix. 1986. Repr. per Set 420.00X (PUb. by Abhinav by India). South Asia Bks.

Private House of Prayer. Leslie D. Weatherhead. (Festival Bks). 1979. pap. 2.95 (ISBN 0-687-34220-1). Abingdon.

Private Life of the Minister's Wife. Betty J. Coble. LC 81-65385. 1981. pap. 5.95 (ISBN 0-8054-6935-4). Broadman.

Private Praise. Elbert Willis. 1977. 1.25 (ISBN 0-89858-009-9). Fill the Gap.

Private Prayers, Put Forth by Authority During the Reign of Queen Elizabeth. 1851. 51.00 (ISBN 0-384-47970-7). Johnson Repr.

Private Testimony & Public Policy. Phillips Ruopp. 1983. pap. 2.50x (ISBN 0-87574-105-3, 105). Pendle Hill.

Privileges des Clercs Au Moyen-Age. Rene Poncet. (Fr.). 230p. Repr. of 1901 ed. lib. bdg. 42.50x. Coronet Bks.

Pro-Life Catechism. 3.25 (ISBN 0-8198-5818-8); 2.00 (ISBN 0-8198-5819-6). Dghtrs St Paul.

Pro-Life, Pro-Peace: Life Affirming Alternatives to Abortion, War, Mercy Killing, & the Death Penalty. Lowell O. Erdahl. LC 86-3552. 160p. (Orig.). 1986. pap. 8.95 (ISBN 0-8066-2209-1, 10-5240). Augsburg.

Probability & Statistical Inference in Ancient & Medieval Jewish Literature. Nachum L. Rabinovitch. LC 79-187394. pap. 54.80 (ISBN 0-317-08544-1, 2014349). Bks Demand UMI.

Probe into the History of Ashura. Ibrahim Ayati. Tr. of Barasi Tarkh-i-Ashura. 234p. 1985. pap. 9.00 (ISBN 0-941724-41-7). Islamic Seminary.

Probing Our Problems. R. O. Covey. 176p. (Orig.). 1986. pap. 5.95 (ISBN 0-934942-59-5, 3950). White Wing Pub.

Problem Clergymen Don't Talk About. Charles L. Rassieur. LC 75-40306. 156p. 1976. pap. 5.95 (ISBN 0-664-24790-3). Westminster.

Problem de L'acte de Foi: Donnees Traditionnelles et Resultants des Controverses Recentes. Roger Aubert. 1978. Repr. of 1958 ed. lib. bdg. 85.00 (ISBN 0-8492-0092-X). R West.

Problem der Parusieverzoegerung in den Synoptischen Evangelien und in der Apostelgeschichte. 3rd ed. Erich Graesser. (Beihefte zur Zeitschrift fuer die Alttestamentliche Wissenschaft 22). 1977. 36.40x (ISBN 3-11-007512-1). De Gruyter.

Problem in Greek Ethics. John A. Symonds. LC 71-163126. (Studies in Philosophy, No. 40). 1971. lib. bdg. 31.95x (ISBN 0-8383-1253-5). Haskell.

Problem Is God: The Selection & Care of Your Personal God. C. Alan Anderson. LC 84-50108. (Illus.). 304p. (Orig.). 1985. pap. 9.95 (ISBN 0-913299-02-2). Stillpoint.

Problem of Christianity. Josiah Royce. LC 68-16716. 1968. 25.00x (ISBN 0-226-73058-1). U of Chicago Pr.

Problem of Eschatology. Ed. by Edward Schillebeeckx & Boniface Willems. LC 79-76195. (Concilium Ser.: Vol. 41). 175p. 1969. 7.95 (ISBN 0-8091-0117-3). Paulist Pr.

Problem of Etiological Narrative in the Old Testament. Burke O. Long. (Beiheft 108 zur Zeitschrift fuer die alttestamentliche Wissenschaft). 1968. 15.50x (ISBN 3-11-005590-2). De Gruyter.

Problem of Evil. Cornelius Hagerty. LC 77-3022. 1978. 9.95 (ISBN 0-8158-0352-4). Chris Mass.

Problem of Evil. Errol E. Harris & D. Litt. LC 77-72325. (Aquinas Lecture Ser.). 1977. 7.95 (ISBN 0-87462-142-9). Marquette.

Problem of Evil & Indian Thought. A. L. Herman. 1976. 13.95 (ISBN 0-8426-0991-1). Orient Bk Dist.

Problem of Evil & the Judgments of God. A. E. Knoch. 351p. 1976. pap. text ed. 4.00 (ISBN 0-910424-59-4). Concordant.

Problem of God. Edgar S. Brightman. LC 75-3085. (Philosophy in America Ser.). Repr. of 1930 ed. 27.50 (ISBN 0-404-59084-5). AMS Pr.

Problem of God. Edgare S. Brightman. 1979. Repr. of 1930 ed. lib. bdg. 30.00 (ISBN 0-8482-7365-6). Norwood Edns.

Problem of God: A Short Introduction. rev. ed. Peter A. Angeles. LC 73-85469. 156p. 1981. pap. text ed. 11.95 (ISBN 0-87975-216-5). Prometheus Bks.

Problem of God & the Emotional Equilibrium of Man. Bonaventura. (Illus.). 78p. 1984. pap. 23.75 (ISBN 0-89266-490-8). Am Classical Coll Pr.

Problem of God in Philosophy of Religion: A Critical Examination of the Category of the Absolute & the Scheme of Transcendence. Henry Dumery. Tr. by Charles Courtney. (Studies in Phenomenology & Existential Philosophy). 135p. 1964. 14.95 (ISBN 0-8101-0083-5); pap. 8.95 (ISBN 0-8101-0606-X). Northwestern U Pr.

Problem of God: Yesterday & Today. John C. Murray. (St. Thomas More Lectures Ser.: No. 1). (Orig.). 1964. pap. 5.95x (ISBN 0-300-00171-1, Y138). Yale U Pr.

Problem of Pain. C. S. Lewis. 1978. pap. 3.95 (ISBN 0-02-086850-2, Collier). Macmillan.

Problem of Pleasure. John H. Gerstner. 1983. pap. 1.50 (ISBN 0-87552-275-0). Presby & Reformed.

Problem of Rebirth. Sri Aurobindo. 186p. 1983. 7.50 (ISBN 0-89071-305-7, Pub. by Sri Aurobindo Ashram India); pap. 5.50 (ISBN 0-89071-304-9, Pub. by Sri Aurobindo Ashram India). Matagiri.

Problem of Rebirth. Sri Aurobindo. 1979. pap. 15.00 (ISBN 0-89744-913-4). Auromere.

Problem of Religious Knowledge. Margaret L. Furse et al. (Rice University Studies: Vol. 60, No. 1). 129p. 1974. pap. 10.00x (ISBN 0-89263-219-4). Rice Univ.

Problem of Self-Love in Saint Augustine. Oliver O'Donovan. LC 80-5397. 208p. 1980. text ed. 23.50x (ISBN 0-300-02468-1). Yale U Pr.

Problem of Sovereignty in the Later Middle Ages: The Papal Monarchy with Augustinus Triumphus & the Publicists. Michael Wilks. (Cambridge Studies in Medieval Life & Thought New: Vol. 9). pap. 158.30 (ISBN 0-317-09407-6, 2013890). Bks Demand UMI.

Problem of Space in Jewish Medieval Philosophy. Israel I. Efros. LC 77-164765. (Columbia University. Oriental Studies: No. 11). Repr. of 1917 ed. 14.75 (ISBN 0-404-50501-5). AMS Pr.

Problem of Space in Jewish Medieval Philosophy. facsimile ed. Israel I. Efros. lib. bdg. 37.50x (ISBN 0-697-00037-0); pap. 7.95 (ISBN 0-89197-904-2). Irvington.

Problem of the Beginning of Dogma in Recent Theology: Theology. Paul Schrodt. (European University Studies: Ser. 23, Vol. 103). xxvi, 339p. 1978. pap. 40.40 (ISBN 3-261-02464-X). P Lang Pubs.

Problem of the Day. Shrii Prabhat Rainjain Sarkar. 64p. 1968. pap. 1.00 (ISBN 0-686-95454-8). Ananda Marga.

Problem of the Hexateuch & Other Essays. Gerhard Von Rad. 352p. pap. 15.95 (ISBN 0-317-31485-8, 30-1310-259). Fortress.

Problem of the Lord's Supper. Albert Schweitzer & Mattill A. J. LC 81-22590. xiv, 144p. 1982. 10.95 (ISBN 0-86554-025-X, MUP-H25). Mercer Univ Pr.

Problem of Unbelief in the Sixteenth Century: The Religion of Rabelais. Lucien Febvre. Tr. by Beatrice Gottlieb from Fr. (Illus.). 528p. 1982. text ed. 40.00x (ISBN 0-674-70825-3). Harvard U Pr.

Problem of Unbelief in the Sixteenth Century: The Religion of Rabelais. Lucien Febvre. Tr. by Beatrice Gottlieb. 552p. 1985. pap. 9.95x (ISBN 0-674-70826-1). Harvard U Pr.

Problem of War in the Old Testament. Peter C. Craigie. LC 78-17698. 1979. pap. 5.95 (ISBN 0-8028-1742-4). Eerdmans.

Problem of Wineskins: Church Renewal in Technological Age. Howard A. Snyder. LC 74-31842. (Illus.). 216p. 1975. pap. text ed. 6.95 (ISBN 0-87784-769-X). Inter-Varsity.

Problem-Play. R. Balmforth. LC 76-52915. (Studies in Drama, No. 39). 1977. lib. bdg. 41.95x (ISBN 0-8383-2129-1). Haskell.

Problema de Liberalismo. 2nd ed. Francisco Ayala. pap. 4.35 (ISBN 0-8477-2402-6). U of PR Pr.

Problema del Dolor. C. S. Lewis. Tr. by Ernesto S. Vilela from Eng. LC 77-16715. Tr. of Problem of Pain. (Span.). 156p. 1977. pap. 3.95 (ISBN 0-89922-097-5). Edit Caribe.

Problemas De Actualidad. Foy Valentine. Tr. by Ana M. Swenson. 38p. 1983. Repr. of 1981 ed. 1.50 (ISBN 0-311-46039-9). Casa Bautista.

Probleme de Dieu dans la Pensee de Karl Barth. Sebastian A. Matczak. (Philosophical Questions Ser.: No. 1). 1968. pap. 19.50 (ISBN 0-912116-00-5). Learned Pubns.

Problems & Perspectives of Fundamental Theology. Ed. by Rene Latourelle & Gerald O'Collins. 416p. 1982. pap. 12.95 (ISBN 0-8091-2466-1). Paulist Pr.

Problems in Conducting. rev. ed. Daniel Moe. 1968. pap. 4.50 (ISBN 0-8066-0834-X, 11-9369). Augsburg.

Problems of Authority in the Continental Reformers: A Study of Luther, Zwingli, & Calvin. Rupert E. Davies. LC 78-5871. 1978. Repr. of 1946 ed. lib. bdg. cancelled (ISBN 0-313-20487-X, DAPA). Greenwood.

Problems of Biblical Theology in the 20th Century. Henning G. Reventlow. LC 86-4722. 1986. pap. 14.95 (ISBN 0-8006-1935-8, 1-1935). Fortress.

Problems of Old Testament Theology in the Twentieth Century. Henning G. Reventlow. Tr. by John Bowden. LC 84-21178. 96p. 1985. 14.95 (ISBN 0-8006-1875-0, 1-1875). Fortress.

Problems of Religion: An Introductory Survey. Durant Drake. LC 68-19268. Repr. of 1916 ed. lib. bdg. 22.50x (ISBN 0-8371-0062-3, DRPR). Greenwood.

Problems of Religious Experience. C. R. Brakenhelm. 158p. 1985. pap. 23.50x (ISBN 91-554-1657-8, Pub. by Almqvist & Wiksell). Coronet Bks.

Problems of Religious Faith. James P. Mackey. 344p. 1975. 12.95 (ISBN 0-8199-0454-6). Franciscan Herald.

Problems of Religious Pluralism. John Hick. LC 85-2505. 144p. 1985. 19.95 (ISBN 0-312-65154-6). St Martin.

Problems of Suffering in the Religions of the World. John Bowker. LC 77-73706. 1975. 47.50 (ISBN 0-521-07412-6); pap. 12.95x (ISBN 0-521-09903-X). Cambridge U Pr.

Problems of the Spirit-Filled Life. William S. Deal. 2.95 (ISBN 0-686-13724-8). Crusade Pubs.

Problems of Theology. Brian L. Hebblethwaite. LC 79-41812. 176p. 1980. o. p. 29.95 (ISBN 0-521-23104-3); pap. 9.95 (ISBN 0-521-29811-3). Cambridge U Pr.

Problems of Two Truths in Buddhism & Vedanta. Ed. by G. M. Sprung. LC 73-83570. 1973. lib. bdg. 26.00 (ISBN 90-277-0335-3, Pub. by Reidel Holland). Kluwer Academic.

"Problems" of Verbal Inspiration. Alva J. McClain. 1968. pap. write for info. (ISBN 0-88469-116-0). BMH Bks.

Problems of Work. L. Ron Hubbard. 20.00 (ISBN 0-686-30789-5). Church Scient NY.

Problems of Work: Scientology Applied to the Work-a-Day World. L. Ron Hubbard. 106p. 1956. 21.44 (ISBN 0-88404-007-0). Bridge Pubns Inc.

Procatechesis, Catacheses One - Twelve. St. Cyril Of Jerusalem. LC 68-55980. (Fathers of the Church Ser.: Vol. 61). 279p. 1969. 15.95x (ISBN 0-8132-0061-X). Cath U Pr.

Proceedings. Association of Orthodox Jewish Scientists. Set. cancelled (ISBN 0-87306-072-5); Vol. 1. 5.95 (ISBN 0-87306-018-3); Vol. 2. 6.95 (ISBN 0-87306-073-3). Feldheim.

Proceedings, Vol. 3 & 4. Associations of Orthodox Jewish Scientists Staff. Ed. by Fred Rosner. 248p. 1976. pap. 9.95 (ISBN 0-87306-074-1). Feldheim.

Proceedings, Vol. 5. Association of Orthodox Jewish Scientists. Ed. by Fred Rosner. 1978. pap. 8.95 (ISBN 0-87306-150-0). Feldheim.

Proceedings of Holiness Conferences Held at Cincinnati, November 26th, 1877 & at New York, December 17th, 1877. (Higher Christian Life Ser.). 255p. 1985. lib. bdg. 30.00 (ISBN 0-8240-6438-0). Garland Pub.

Proceedings of the Anti-Sabbath Convention, Melodeon, Boston. Anti-Sabbath Convention Staff. Ed. by Henry M. Parkhurst. LC 79-122662. 1971. Repr. of 1848 ed. 16.50x (ISBN 0-8046-1311-7, Pub. by Kennikat). Assoc Faculty Pr.

Proceedings of the Association of Orthodox Jewish Scientists, Vol. 6. 1982. pap. 9.95 (ISBN 0-87306-225-6). Feldheim.

Proceedings of the Association of Orthodox Jewish Scientists, Vol. 7. Ed. by Paul Kahn. 240p. 1984. pap. 9.95. Hermon.

Proceedings of the Associations of the Associations of Orthodox Jewish Scientists, Vols. 8-9. Ed. by Charles S. Naiman. (Illus.). 304p. (Orig.). 1987. pap. 14.95 (ISBN 0-87203-125-X). Hermon.

Proceedings of the Cosma de Koros Memorial Symposium. Louis Ligeti. 586p. 1978. 142.50x (ISBN 0-569-08468-7, Pub. by Collets (UK)). State Mutual Bk.

Proceedings of the First Italian International Congress on Spinoza. Ed. by Emilia Giancotti. (Illus.). 556p. 1985. 60.00x (ISBN 88-7088-121-0, Pub. by Bibliopolis Italy). Humanities.

Proceedings of the Forty-Sixth Annual Convention. Canon Law Society of America Staff. 308p. (Orig.). 1985. pap. 8.00 (ISBN 0-943616-29-8). Canon Law Soc.

Proceedings of the Grisons in the Year 1618. LC 78-171760. (English Experience Ser.: No. 383). 94p. Repr. of 1619 ed. 14.00 (ISBN 90-221-0383-8). Walter J Johnson.

Proceedings of the Nineteen Seventy-Seven United States Conference of Research on the Shroud of Turin. Ed. by Kenneth Stevenson. (Illus.). 244p. (Orig.). 1980. pap. 10.00 (ISBN 0-9605516-0-3). Shroud of Turin.

Proceedings of the Third Symposium on the Psychology of Religion in Europe: Current Issues in the Psychology of Religion. Ed. by J. A. Van Belzen & J. M. Van Der Lans. (Amsterdam Studies in Theology Ser.). 292p. 1986. pap. text ed. 65.00 (ISBN 90-6203-758-5, Pub. by Rodopi Holland). Humanities.

Proceedings of the Virgin Islands' Seminar on Unification Theology. Ed. by Darrol Bryant. LC 80-52594. (Conference Ser.: No. 6). (Illus.). xv, 323p. (Orig.). 1980. pap. text ed. 9.95 (ISBN 0-932894-06-2). Unif Theol Sem.

Proceedings Principally in the County of Kent, in Connection with the Parliaments Called in 1640, & Especially with the Committee of Religion Appointed in That Year. Ed. by Lambert B. Larking. (Camden Society, London. Publications, First Series: No. 80a). Repr. of 1862 ed. 37.00 (ISBN 0-404-50180-X). Ams Pr.

Proceedings, Principally in the County of Kent, in Connection with the Parliaments Called in 1640. Ed. by Lambert B. Larking. Repr. of 1862 ed. 37.00 (ISBN 0-384-31380-9). Johnson Repr.

Proceedings, World Zionist Organization. Jerusalem Ideological Conference Hebrew University. Repr. of 1959 ed. lib. bdg. 23.00x (ISBN 0-8371-4120-6, WOZO). Greenwood.

Proces De Condamnation et De Rehabilitation De Jeanne D'Arc, 5 Vols. Saint Jeanne D'Arc. Ed. by Jules Quicherat. 1841-1849. Set. 230.00 (ISBN 0-384-27070-0); Set. pap. 200.00 (ISBN 0-384-27071-9). Johnson Repr.

Process & Conscience: Toward a Theology of Human Emergence. Linda L. Stinson. 202p. (Orig.). 1986. lib. bdg. 22.50 (ISBN 0-8191-5206-4); pap. text ed. 11.50 (ISBN 0-8191-5207-2). U Pr of Amer.

Process & Divinity: The Hartshorne Festschrift. Ed. by William L. Reese & Eugene Freeman. LC 64-13547. 644p. 1964. 32.95 (ISBN 0-87548-054-3). Open Court.

Process Ethics: A Constructive System. Kenneth Cauthen. LC 84-16662. (Toronto Studies in Theology: Vol. 18). 365p. 1985. 59.95x (ISBN 0-88946-764-1). E Mellen.

Process Metaphysics & Hua-Yen Buddhism: A Critical Study of Cumulative Penetration vs. Interpretation. Steve Odin. LC 81-9388. 256p. 1982. 44.50 (ISBN 0-87395-568-4); pap. 16.95 (ISBN 0-87395-569-2). State U NY Pr.

Process of Islamic Revolution. A. A. Maududi. pap. 1.50 (ISBN 0-686-18546-3). Kazi Pubns.

Process of Religion: Essays in Honor of Dean Shailer Mathews. facsimile ed. Ed. by Miles H. Krumbine. LC 71-38776. (Essay Index Reprint Ser). Repr. of 1933 ed. 18.00 (ISBN 0-8369-2667-6). Ayer Co Pubs.

Process of Speech: Puritan Religious Writing & Paradise Lost. Boyd M. Berry. LC 75-36933. pap. 80.00 (ISBN 0-317-41618-9, 2025830). Bks Demand UMI.

Process Theology: An Introductory Exposition. John B. Cobb, Jr. & David R. Griffin. LC 76-10352. 192p. 1976. pap. 8.95 (ISBN 0-664-24743-1). Westminster.

Process Theology & Secularization. Edwin C. Garvey. 21p. 1972. pap. 0.75 (ISBN 0-912414-14-6). Lumen Christi.

Process Theology & the Christian Tradition. Illtyd Trethowan. LC 84-26240. (Studies in Historical Theology). 122p. 1985. 11.95 (ISBN 0-932506-36-4). St Bedes Pubns.

Process Theology As Political Theology. John B. Cobb, Jr. LC 82-1845. 174p. (Orig.). 1982. pap. 8.95 (ISBN 0-664-24417-3). Westminster.

Process Thought on the Eve of the Twenty-First Century. Ewert H. Cousins. 50p. (Orig.). 1985. pap. 3.95x (ISBN 0-932269-25-7). Wyndham Hall.

Procession of Friends. Daisy Newman. 484p. 1980. pap. 11.95 (ISBN 0-913408-59-X). Friends United.
Procession of Saints. James Brodrick. LC 72-5436. (Biography Index Reprint Ser). 1972. Repr. of 1949 ed. 20.50 (ISBN 0-8369-8134-0). Ayer Co Pubs.
Processive World View for Pragmatic Christians. Joseph T. Culliton. LC 75-3781. 302p. 1975. 13.95 (ISBN 0-8022-2170-X). Philos Lib.
Proclaim His Word: Homiletic Themes for Sundays & Holy Days - Cycle C, Vol. 1. new ed. Joseph Fichtner. LC 73-5726. 238p. (Orig.). 1973. pap. 3.95 (ISBN 0-8189-0274-4). Alba.
Proclaim His Word: Homiletic Themes for Sundays & Holy Days-Cycle A, Vol. 2. new ed. Joseph Fichtner. LC 73-5726. 239p. (Orig.). 1974. pap. 4.95 (ISBN 0-8189-0292-2). Alba.
Proclaim the Good News: Essays in Honor of Gordon G. Johnson. Carl Lundquist et al. Ed. by Norris Magnuson. LC 86-80862. 244p. (Orig.). 1986. pap. 4.95 (ISBN 0-935797-24-6). Harvest IL.
Proclaim the Word. Eugene E. Hall & James L. Heflin. LC 84-17458. 1985. 9.95 (ISBN 0-8054-2102-5). Broadman.
Proclaim Your God. Herbert L. Beierle. 1.00 (ISBN 0-940480-09-3). U of Healing.
Proclaiming Grace & Freedom: The Story of United Methodism in America. John G. McEllhenney. (Orig.). 1982. pap. 7.95 (ISBN 0-687-34323-2). Abingdon.
Proclaiming Justice & Peace: Documents from John XXIII to John Paul II. Ed. by Michael Walsh & Brian Davies. 370p. 1985. 16.95 (ISBN 0-89622-239-X); pap. 12.95 (ISBN 0-89622-236-5). Twenty Third.
Proclaiming the Good News: Homilies for the A Cycle. John J. Hughes. LC 82-62554. 156p. 1983. pap. 14.95 (ISBN 0-87973-722-0, 722). Our Sunday Visitor.
Proclaiming the Good News: Homilies for the "B" Cycle. John J. Hughes. LC 84-60750. 156p. 1984. 14.95 (ISBN 0-87973-723-9, 723). Our Sunday Visitor.
Proclaiming the Good News: Homilies for the "C" Cycle, No. 724. John J. Hughes. 1985. 14.95 (ISBN 0-87973-724-7). Our Sunday Visitor.
Proclaiming the Promise: Christian Preaching from the Old Testament. Foster R. McCurley, Jr. LC 74-76921. 176p. (Orig.). 1974. pap. 5.75 (ISBN 0-8006-1083-0, 1-1083). Fortress.
Proclaiming the Truth. Donald E. Demaray. 1980. pap. 6.95 (ISBN 0-8010-2898-1). Baker Bk.
Proclaiming the Word. 2nd ed. G. B. Harrison & John McCabe. 1976. pap. 4.95 (ISBN 0-916134-00-8). Pueblo Pub Co.
Proclaiming the Word: The Concept of Preaching in the Thought of Ellen G. White. R. Edward Turner. (Andrews University Monographs, Studies in Religion: Vol. XII). x, 183p. 1980. pap. 3.95 (ISBN 0-943872-12-X). Andrews Univ Pr.
Proclamation & Presence: Old Testament Essays in Honor of Gwynne Henton Davies. Ed. by John I. Durham & J. R. Porter. LC 83-17445. xx, 315p. 1983. 17.95 (ISBN 0-86554-101-9, MUP/H93). Mercer Univ Pr.
Proclamation: Eighteen Forty-Five. William Smith. (Orig.). 1983. pap. 1.50 (ISBN 0-942284-03-8). Restoration Re.
Proclamation from Prophecy & Pattern: Lucan Old Testament Christiology. Darrell L. Bock. (JSOT Supplement Ser.: No. 12). 350p. 1986. text ed. 28.50x (ISBN 1-85075-000-9, Pub. by JSOT Pr England); pap. text ed. 13.50x (ISBN 1-85075-001-7). Eisenbrauns.
Proclamation of Baha'u'llah. Baha'u'llah. LC 72-237435. 1967. 8.95 (ISBN 0-87743-064-0, 103-012); pap. 4.95 (ISBN 0-87743-065-9, 103-013). Baha'i.
Proclemation of the Gospel in a Pluralistic World: Essays on Christianity & Culture. George W. Forell. LC 73-79354. pap. 36.00 (2026865). Bks Demand UMI.
Proclus' Commentary on Plato's "Parmenides". Glenn R. Morrow & John M. Dillion. LC 85-43302. 712p. 1986. text ed. 80.00x (ISBN 0-691-07305-8). Princeton U Pr.
Prodigal. Henry Moorehouse et al. (Moody Classics Ser.). 1984. pap. 3.50 (ISBN 0-8024-0494-4). Moody.
Prodigal Son. Retold by Pamela Broughton. (Golden Bible Stories Ser.). (Illus.). 32p. 1986. 3.95 (ISBN 0-307-11623-9, Pub. by Golden Bks). Western Pub.
Prodigal Son. Retold by Catherine Storr. LC 82-23011. (People of the Bible). (Illus.). 32p. 1983. PLB 10.65 (ISBN 0-8172-1982-X). Raintree Pubs.
Prodigal Sons: The New York Intellectuals & Their World. Alexander Bloom. 461p. 1986. 24.95 (ISBN 0-19-503662-X). Oxford U Pr.
Prodigals & Publicans: Dramas & Meditations on Six Parables. W. A. Poovey. LC 79-54111. 100p. 1979. pap. 5.95 (ISBN 0-8066-1763-2, 10-5247). Augsburg.
Production of Medieval Church Music-Drama. Fletcher Collins, Jr. LC 78-168610. (Illus.). xiii, 356p. 1972. 25.00x (ISBN 0-8139-0373-4). U Pr of Va.
Productions of Time: Tradition History in the Old Testament Scholarship. Ed. by Knud Jeppesen & Benedikt Otzen. 169p. 1984. 24.95x (ISBN 0-907459-36-6, Pub. by Almond Pr England); pap. text ed. 10.95x (ISBN 0-907459-37-4). Eisenbrauns.
Productive Christians in An Age of Guilt Manipulators. 3rd ed. David Chilton. 480p. 1985. pap. 12.50 (ISBN 0-930464-04-4). Inst Christian.
Profecia Simbolica de la Gran Piramide. 4th ed. H. Spencer Lewis. Tr. by AMORC Staff. (Span., Illus.). 167p. (Orig.). 1982. pap. 7.00 (ISBN 0-912057-70-X, GS-514). AMORC.
Profecia y Carisma, Que de las Lenguas? Jose Flores. Orig. Title: Prophecy & Charisma. (Span.). 68p. 1974. pap. 2.25 (ISBN 0-8254-1238-2). Kregel.
Profession: Minister. James D. Glasse. LC 68-17447. Repr. of 1968 ed. 33.50 (ISBN 0-8357-9021-5, 2011670). Bks Demand UMI.
Professional Care: Its Meaning & Practice. Alastair W. Campbell. LC 84-4081. 160p. 1984. pap. 7.95 (ISBN 0-8006-1812-2). Fortress.
Professional Ethics. Michael D. Bayles. 176p. 1981. pap. text ed. write for info. (ISBN 0-534-00998-0). Wadsworth Pub.
Professional Ethics: Power & Paradox. Karen Labacqz. 192p. (Orig.). 1985. pap. 11.95 (ISBN 0-687-34325-9). Abingdon.
Professionalism & Pastoral Care. Alastair V. Campbell. LC 84-48710. (Theology & Pastoral Care Ser.). 128p. 1985. pap. 7.95 (ISBN 0-8006-1733-9, 1-1733). Fortress.
Professionalization & Professionalism of Catholic Priests. Hernan Vera. LC 82-6886. (University of Florida Social Sciences Monographs: No. 68). xii, 116p. 1982. pap. 7.00x (ISBN 0-8130-0713-5). U Presses Fla.
Profeta da Esperanca. F. B. Meyer. Orig. Title: Prophet of Hope. (Port.). 1986. write for info. (ISBN 0-8297-1607-6). Life Pubs Intl.
Profetas Del Antiguo Testamento. K. M. Yates. Tr. by Simon Corona from Eng. Orig. Title: Preaching from the Prophets. (Span.). 336p. 1985. pap. 4.95 (ISBN 0-311-04026-8). Casa Bautista.
Profile Method for Classifying & Evaluating Manuscript Evidence. Frederik Wisse. 140p. 1982. pap. 17.00x (ISBN 0-8028-1918-4). Eerdmans.
Profile of Faith. Charles E. Bradshaw. 9.95 (ISBN 0-911866-01-9). Advocate.
Profile of Three Theories: Erikson, Maslow, Piaget. Carol Tribe. 120p. 1982. pap. text ed. 8.95 (ISBN 0-8403-2800-1). Kendall-Hunt.
Profiles in American Judaism: The Reform, Conservative, Orthodox & Reconstructionist Traditions in Historical Perspective. Marc L. Raphael. LC 84-47734. 288p. 1985. 20.45 (ISBN 0-06-066801-6, HarpR). Har-Row.
Profiles in Belief: the Religious Bodies of North America, Vol. 1: Roman Catholic, Old Catholic & Eastern Orthodox. Arthur C. Piepkorn. LC 76-9971. 1977. 20.00 (ISBN 0-06-066580-7, HarpR). Har-Row.
Profiles in Belief: The Religious Bodies of the United States & Canada, Vols. 3 & 4. Arthur C. Piepkorn. Incl. Vol. 3. Holiness & Pentecostal Bodies; Vol. 4. Evangelical, Fundamental, & Other Christian Bodies. 1979. Set. 25.45i (ISBN 0-06-066581-5, HarpR). Har-Row.
Profiles in Belief, Vol. 2: Protestantism. Arthur C. Piepkorn. LC 76-9971. 1978. 30.00 (ISBN 0-06-066582-3, HarpR). Har-Row.
Profiles in Faith. William D. Mounce. LC 84-9961. 1984. pap. 3.95 (ISBN 0-8307-0984-3, S382102). Regal.
Profiles of a Leader. Judson Cornwall. LC 80-85161. (Orig.). 1980. pap. 4.95 (ISBN 0-88270-503-2). Bridge Pub.
Profiles of Black Georgia Baptists. Clarence M. Wagner. Ed. by Bennett Brother's Printing. (Illus.). 268p. 1981. pap. 12.95 (ISBN 0-686-30456-X). Tru-Faith.
Profiles of Faith. Frank W. Lemons. 1971. pap. 2.95 (ISBN 0-87148-683-0). Pathway Pr.
Profiles of Our Heritage. Jon L. Joyce. (Orig.). 1983. pap. 3.00 (ISBN 0-937172-51-0). JLJ Pubs.
Profiles of Pentecostal Missionaries. Mary H. Wallace. LC 86-15919. (Illus.). 352p. (Orig.). 1986. pap. 6.95 (ISBN 0-932581-00-5). Word Aflame.
Profiles of Pentecostal Preachers, Vol. II. Mary H. Wallace. LC 84-51290. (Illus.). 398p. (Orig.). 1984. pap. 6.95 (ISBN 0-912315-71-7). Word Aflame.
Profiles of Pentecostal Preachers, Vol. I. Ed. by Mary H. Wallace. LC 84-51290. (Illus.). 281p. (Orig.). 1983. pap. 5.95 (ISBN 0-912315-63-6). Word Aflame.
Profiles of Protestant Saints. Howard V. Harper. LC 67-24071. 1968. 9.95 (ISBN 0-8303-0037-6). Fleet.
Profiles of Radical Reformers. Hans J. Goertz. Tr. of Radikale Reformatoren. 228p. 1982. pap. 9.95x (ISBN 0-8361-1250-4). Herald Pr.
Profit. Kehlog Albran. 108p. (Orig.). 1973. pap. 2.95 (ISBN 0-8431-0260-8). Price Stern.
Profit & Loss of Dying. Clyde Irion. 4.95 (ISBN 0-87516-030-1). De Vorss.
Profit with Delight: The Literary Genre of the Acts of the Apostles. Richard I. Pervo. LC 86-45220. 224p. 1987. 16.95 (ISBN 0-8006-0782-1). Fortress.
Profiting from the Word. A. W. Pink. 1977. pap. 3.45 (ISBN 0-85151-032-9). Banner of Truth.
Profits of Religion. Upton B. Sinclair. LC 73-120566. 1970. Repr. of 1918 ed. 22.50 (ISBN 0-404-06093-5). AMS Pr.
Profundas Verdades de la Biblia. Kay H. Friederichsen. Orig. Title: God's World Made Plain. (Span.). 256p. 1958. pap. 4.75 (ISBN 0-8254-1248-X). Kregel.
Program Evaluation in Church Organization. M. James Gardiner. LC 77-80070. (Management Ser.). (Illus.). 1977. pap. 4.50 (ISBN 0-89305-017-2). Anna Pub.
Program for a New Man. J. W. Sire. pap. 0.75 (ISBN 0-87784-146-2). Inter-Varsity.
Program for Higher Education in the Church of the Brethren. John S. Noffsinger. LC 78-177711. (Columbia University. Teachers College. Contributions to Education: No. 172). Repr. of 1925 ed. 22.50 (ISBN 0-404-55172-6). AMS Pr.
Program of Priestly Formation, NCCB. 3rd ed. 174p. 1982. pap. 14.95 (ISBN 1-55586-837-1). US Catholic.
Program Planning for Youth Ministry. John E. Forliti. LC 75-143. 1975. pap. 4.50 (ISBN 0-88489-061-9). St Marys.
Program Your Own Life. Michael H. Greene. 230p. 1982. 10.00 (ISBN 0-9610136-0-5). Behavorial Sys Inc.
Programa del Espiritu Santo. George A. Hilgeman. 174p. 1982. pap. 4.50 (ISBN 0-89922-216-1). Edit Caribe.
Programas Para Dias Especiales Tomo I. A. Lopez Munoz. 107p. 1984. pap. 1.95 (ISBN 0-311-07005-1). Casa Bautista.
Programas Para Dias Especiales Tomo II. A. Lopez Munoz. 64p. 1984. pap. 1.95 (ISBN 0-311-07006-X). Casa Bautista.
Programmed Guide to Increasing Church Attendance. Jimmie Gentle & Dwight Peter Richard. 1980. 10.75 (ISBN 0-89536-446-8, 1641). CSS of Ohio.
Programmed Hebrew Series, 2 vols. David Bridger. Incl. Vol. 1. 1971. pap. text ed. 3.50x (ISBN 0-87441-079-7); Vol. 2. 1971. pap. text ed. 3.50x (ISBN 0-87441-080-0). (Reshit Tefillah V'lashon). 62p. (Prog. Bk.). (YA) pap. Behrman.
Programming to Build Disciples. Duffy Robbins. 64p. 1987. pap. 4.95 (ISBN 0-89693-573-6). Victor Bks.
Programs & Parties for Christmas. Helen Eisenberg & Larry Eisenberg. 160p. 1980. pap. 4.50 (ISBN 0-8010-3359-4). Baker Bk.
Programs & Promises: Reflections on the Beatitudes. Wallace H. Kirby. 1980. 3.50 (ISBN 0-89536-414-X, 1640). CSS of Ohio.
Programs for Advent & Christmas. Ed. by Vincie Alessi. 1978. pap. 4.95 (ISBN 0-8170-0808-X). Judson.
Programs for Advent & Christmas, Vol. 2. Ed. by Vincie Alessi. 64p. 1981. pap. 4.95 (ISBN 0-8170-0930-2). Judson.
Programs for Lent & Easter. Ed. by Vincie Alessi. 1979. pap. 3.95 (ISBN 0-8170-0861-6). Judson.
Programs for Lent & Easter, Vol. 2. Vincie Alessi. 64p. 1983. pap. 5.95 (ISBN 0-8170-1016-5). Judson.
Programs for Special Occasions. Matilda Nordtvedt & Pearl Steinkuehler. (Orig.). 1984. pap. 4.95 (ISBN 0-8024-1218-1). Moody.
Progreso del Peregrino Ilustrado. John Bunyan. Orig. Title: Pilgrim's Progress Illustrated. (Span.). 254p. pap. 4.75 (ISBN 0-8254-1096-7). Kregel.
Progress & Decline in the History of Church Renewal. Ed. by Roger Aubert. LC 67-30136. (Concilium Ser.: Vol. 27). 191p. 1967. 7.95 (ISBN 0-8091-0119-X). Paulist Pr.
Progress & Intelligence of Americans: Collateral Proof of Slavery, from the First to the Eleventh Chapter of Genesis, As Founded on Organic Law. facs. ed. M. T. Wheat. LC 77-83882. (Black Heritage Library Collection Ser.). 1862. 21.75 (ISBN 0-8369-8684-9). Ayer Co Pubs.
Progress & Nostalgia: Silvester-Klausen in Urnasch, Switzerland. Regina Bendix. LC 84-28128. (UC Publications in Folklore & Mythology: Vol. 33). 1985. 21.00 (ISBN 0-520-09959-1). U of Cal Pr.
Progress & Pessimism: Religion, Politics & History in Late Nineteenth Century Britain. Jeffrey P. Von Arx. (Harvard Historical Studies: No. 104). 256p. 1985. text ed. 25.00x (ISBN 0-674-71375-3). Harvard U Pr.
Progress & Problems in Moral Education. Ed. by Monica Taylor. 240p. 1975. 16.00x (ISBN 0-85633-069-8, Pub. by NFER Nelson UK). Taylor & Francis.
Progress & Religion, an Historical Enquiry. Christopher H. Dawson. LC 79-104266. Repr. of 1929 ed. lib. bdg. 27.50x (ISBN 0-8371-3917-1, DAPR). Greenwood.
Progress of a Biographer. Hugh Kingsmill. 1973. lib. bdg. 25.00 (ISBN 0-8414-5588-0). Folcroft.
Progress of Another Pilgrim. Frances J. Roberts. 1970. 6.95 (ISBN 0-932814-10-7); pap. 4.95 (ISBN 0-932814-11-5). Kings Farspan.
Progress of God's People. M. J. Evans. (Discovering the Bible Ser.). pap. 8.95 (ISBN 0-7175-1161-8). Dufour.
Progress of Piety. John Norden. Repr. of 1847 ed. 21.00 (ISBN 0-384-41910-0). Johnson Repr.
Progress(?) of Woman. Elijah H. Munn. 84p. 6.95 (ISBN 0-9609828-0-9). EHM Pub.
Progress Through Mental Prayer. Edward Leen. 1978. pap. 2.45 (ISBN 0-88479-012-6). Arena Lettres.
Progress Through Pioneer Evangelism. Dan Beller. pap. 2.00 (ISBN 0-911866-80-9). Advocate.
Prolegomena to a Grammar of New Testament, Vol. I. James H. Moulton. (Moulton's Grammar of New Testament Greek Ser.). 320p. 1906. 19.95 (ISBN 0-567-01011-2, Pub. by T & T Clark Ltd UK). Fortress.
Prolegomena to Ethics. 5th ed. Thomas H. Green. Ed. by A. C. Bradley. LC 32-3225. 1968. Repr. of 1929 ed. 42.00 (ISBN 0-527-35800-2). Kraus Repr.
Prolegomena to the History of Ancient Israel. Julius Wellhausen. 14.25 (ISBN 0-8446-3147-7). Peter Smith.
Prolegomena to the Study of Greek Religion. Jane Harrison. 682p. 1981. text ed. 27.50x (ISBN 0-85036-262-8, Pub. by Merlin Pr UK); pap. 17.50x. Humanities.
Prolegomena to the Study of Greek Religion. facsimile ed. Jane E. Harrison. LC 75-10639. (Ancient Religion & Mythology Ser.). (Illus.). 1976. Repr. of 1922 ed. 57.50x (ISBN 0-405-07018-7). Ayer Co Pubs.
Prolegomena zur Altesten Geschichte des Islam: Verschiedenes (Unveraenderter Photomechanischer Nachdruck der 1. Auflage 1899) Julius Wellhausen. (Skizzen und Vorarbeiten: 6 Heft). (Ger.). viii, 260p. 1985. 61.00x (ISBN 3-11-002215-X). De Gruyter.
Prologue: A Drama of John Hus. Bob Jones. (Illus.). 85p. 1968. pap. 3.95 (ISBN 0-89084-195-0). Bob Jones Univ Pr.
Prologue in the Old French & Provencal Mystery. David H. Carnahan. LC 68-55160. (Studies in French Literature, No. 45). 1969. Repr. of 1905 ed. lib. bdg. 46.95x (ISBN 0-8383-0519-9). Haskell.
Prologue of the Gospel of St. John: Esoteric Studies. E. C. Marion-Wild. Tr. by Helga Roboz & Steven Roboz. 19p. 1984. pap. 3.75 (ISBN 0-919924-22-0). Anthroposophic.
Promesas de Jesus. David Wilkerson. (Span.). 95p. 1974. pap. 2.50 (ISBN 0-89922-027-4). Edit Caribe.
Promesas Personales de la Biblia. (Span.). 128p. 1982. pap. 2.50 (ISBN 0-87788-692-X). Shaw Pubs.
Promethean Ethics: Living with Death, Competition, & Triage. Garrett Hardin. LC 79-56592. (Jesse & John Danz Lecture Ser.). 92p. 1980. 10.00x (ISBN 0-295-95717-4). U of Wash Pr.
Prometheus & the Story of Fire. I. M. Richardson. LC 82-15979. (Illus.). 32p. 1983. PLB 9.79 (ISBN 0-89375-859-0); pap. text ed. 2.50 (ISBN 0-89375-860-4). Troll Assocs.
Prometheus: Archetypal Image of Human Existence. C. Kerenyi. 1963. 50.00 (ISBN 0-8274-3210-0). R West.
Prometheus Reborn. Michael J. Johnson. LC 76-52144. 1977. 7.95 (ISBN 0-87212-073-2). Libra.
Prometheus Rising. Robert A. Wilson. LC 83-81665. 280p. 1983. pap. 7.95 (ISBN 0-941404-19-6). Falcon Pr Az.
Promise. Hal Lindsey. 208p. 1984. pap. 5.95 (ISBN 0-89081-424-4). Harvest Hse.
Promise & Fulfilment. Ed. by F. F. Bruce. 216p. 1963. 15.95 (ISBN 0-567-02055-X, Pub. by T & T Clark Ltd UK). Fortress.
Promise & Present: Adventist Eschatology & Ethics. John C. Brunt. Ed. by Richard W. Coffen. 96p. 1987. pap. 5.95 (ISBN 0-8280-0386-6). Review & Herald.

Promise & the Power. Ed. by Donald N. Bowdle. 332p. 1980. 14.95 (ISBN 0-87148-706-3). Pathway Pr.

Promise Deferred. Siegfried Horn. Ed. by Gerald Wheeler. 96p. 1987. pap. price not set (ISBN 0-8280-0380-7). Review & Herald.

Promise Is to Keep. Nan H. Agle. 160p. (Orig.). 1985. pap. 6.95 (ISBN 0-310-41591-8, 9290P). Zondervan.

Promise Me Life: Evolution & Creation As a Dynamic Unity. Anna Van Gogh. (Illus.). 424p. (Orig.). Date not set. PLB price not set (ISBN 0-913829-34-X); pap. price not set (ISBN 0-913829-35-8). Lucy Mary Bks.

Promise of a New Day. Karen Casey & Martha Vanceburg. 400p. (Orig.). 1985. pap. 5.95 (ISBN 0-86683-502-4, HarpR). Har-Row.

Promise of a New Day. Karen Casey & Martha Vanceburg. (Meditation Ser.). 400p. (Orig.). 1983. text ed. 7.95 (ISBN 0-89486-308-8). Hazelden.

Promise of a New Spring: The Holocaust & Renewal. Gerda W. Klein. (Illus.). 64p. 1981. 10.95 (ISBN 0-940646-50-1); pap. 5.95 (ISBN 0-940646-51-X). Rossel Bks.

Promise of All Ages. 3rd, rev. ed. George Townshend. 192p. 1972. 10.95 (ISBN 0-85398-044-6); pap. 3.50 (ISBN 0-85398-006-3). G Ronald Pub.

Promise of Deliverance. Dan Wilson. 1983. pap. 2.50x (ISBN 0-87574-060-X, 060). Pendle Hill.

Promise of Deliverance in Time of Trouble. 1978. 1.25 (ISBN 0-89858-023-4). Fill the Gap.

Promise of Eternal Life: Biblical Witness to Christian Hope. Janis Rozentals. LC 86-26456. 112p. (Orig.). 1987. pap. 6.50 (ISBN 0-8066-2254-7, 10-5257). Augsburg.

Promise of His Coming. John I. Snyder. LC 85-52310. 192p. 1986. pap. text ed. 12.50 (ISBN 0-936029-01-3). Western Bk Journ.

Promise of Life. Roger Prescott. 1984. 4.75 (ISBN 0-89536-683-5, 4859). CSS of Ohio.

Promise of Narrative Theology: Recovering the Gospel in the Church. George W. Stroup. LC 80-84654. 216p. (Orig.). 1982. pap. 9.95 (ISBN 0-8042-0683-X). John Knox.

Promise of Paradox. Parker J. Palmer. LC 80-68134. 128p. (Orig.). 1980. pap. 3.95 (ISBN 0-87793-210-7). Ave Maria.

Promise of Peace, Call for Justice. Thomas E. Ridenhour, Sr. Ed. by Michael L. Sherer. (Orig.). 1986. pap. 6.75 (ISBN 0-89536-822-6, 6831). CSS of Ohio.

Promise of Power to Serve. 1978. 1.25 (ISBN 0-89858-024-2). Fill the Gap.

Promise of the Father. Phoebe Palmer. Ed. by Donald W. Dayton. (Higher Christian Life Ser.). 421p. 1985. 50.00 (ISBN 0-8240-6434-8). Garland Pub.

Promise of the Spirit. William Barclay. LC 60-11200. 120p. 1978. pap. 6.95 (ISBN 0-664-24205-7). Westminster.

Promise of the Spirit. Charles G. Finney. Ed. by Timothy L. Smith. LC 79-26286. 272p. (Orig.). 1980. pap. 6.95 (ISBN 0-87123-207-3, 210207). Bethany Hse.

Promise of Total Protection. 1978. 1.25 (ISBN 0-89858-022-6). Fill the Gap.

Promise to Keep: A Narrative of the American Encounter with Anti-Semitism. Nathan C. Belth. LC 81-40403. (Illus.). 1981. pap. 7.95 (ISBN 0-8052-0682-5). Schocken.

Promise to Keep: The American Encounter with Anti-Semitism. Nathan C. Belth. 305p. Repr. 6.95 (ISBN 0-686-95111-5). ADL.

Promised City: New York's Jews, 1870-1914. Moses Rischin. (Illus.). 342p. 1977. pap. 8.95x (ISBN 0-674-71501-2); text ed. 22.50x (ISBN 0-674-71502-0). Harvard U Pr.

Promised Day Is Come. rev. ed. Shoghi Effendi. 1980. 10.95 (ISBN 0-87743-132-9, 108-017); pap. 5.50 (ISBN 0-87743-138-8, 108-018). Baha'i.

Promised Land for a Chosen People. Gordon Ceperley. LC 79-65616. (Illus., Orig.). 1979. pap. 2.50 (ISBN 0-915540-25-8). Friends Israel-Spearhead Pr.

Promised-Land Living. J. Oswald Sanders. 1984. pap. 5.95 (ISBN 0-8024-0372-7). Moody.

Promised Messiah. Bruce R. McConkie. LC 78-3478. 1978. 17.95 (ISBN 0-87747-702-7). Deseret Bk.

Promised One. Louis W. Coscia, pseud. 192p. 1983. 10.95. Todd & Honeywell.

Promised Ones Are Alive & Well on Planet Earth. 1986. write for info. Port Love Intl.

Promises, 3 bks. Anita L. Wheatcroft. (Illus.). 80p. (Orig.). 1973. Set. pap. 2.95x (ISBN 0-8192-4043-5); tchrs'. guide 4.50x (ISBN 0-8192-4044-3). Morehouse.

Promises: A Daily Guide to Supernatural Living. Bill Bright. LC 82-72302. 365p. 1983. 9.95 (ISBN 0-317-00638-X). Campus Crusade.

Promises: A Guide to Christian Commitment. Frances L. Carroll. 228p. 1985. 14.95 (ISBN 0-13-731076-5); pap. 7.95 (ISBN 0-13-731068-4). P H.

Promises & Prayers for Healing: Hope for the Future. Carl G. Carlozzi. (Pocketpac Books). 128p. (Orig.). 1985. pap. 2.50 (ISBN 0-87788-336-X). Shaw Pubs.

Promises & Turtle Shells: And Forty-Nine Other Object Lessons for Children. Dorothy B. Francis. 112p. (Orig.). 1984. pap. 7.50 (ISBN 0-687-34337-2). Abingdon.

Promises for the Golden Years. Pocketpac Bks. 96p. 1983. pap. 2.50 (ISBN 0-87788-320-3). Shaw Pubs.

Promises from Proverbs. David Carder. 1986. pap. 2.50 (ISBN 0-310-36782-4, 12732P). Zondervan.

Promises of Jesus from the Bibles: Puzzle Book. Ruby Maschke. (Illus.). 48p. 1983. pap. 2.50 (ISBN 0-87239-591-X, 2789). Standard Pub.

Promises, Promises, Promises. Joel Nederhood. LC 79-18889. (Orig.). 1979. pap. text ed. 4.50 (ISBN 0-933140-09-6). CRC Pubns.

Promises to Keep: A Workbook of Experiences for Covenant Living. Dennis C. Benson & Marilyn J. Benson. (Orig.). 1978. pap. 3.95 (ISBN 0-377-00077-9). Friend Pr.

Promises to Keep: Reading & Writing about Values. J. Dahlstrom & D. Ryel. 1977. pap. text ed. write for info (ISBN 0-13-731059-5). P-H.

Promises to Live by. David Wilkerson. LC 72-86208. 96p. (Orig.). 1972. pap. 2.50 (ISBN 0-8307-0197-4, 5007305). Regal.

Promises to the Fathers: Studies on the Patriarchal Narratives. Claus Westermann. Tr. by David E. Green from Ger. LC 79-7395. 208p. 1980. 13.95 (ISBN 0-8006-0580-2, 1-580). Fortress.

Promises to the Fathers: Studies on the Patriarchal Narratives. Claus Westermann. LC 79-7395. pap. 51.80 (2027191). Bks Demand UMI.

Promoting Social & Moral Development in Young Children: Creative Approaches for the Classroom. Carolyn P. Edwards. (Early Childhood Education Ser.). 192p. 1986. text ed. 25.95x (ISBN 0-8077-2831-4); pap. text ed. 13.95x (ISBN 0-8077-2820-9). Tchrs Coll.

Promotion & Publicity for Churches. W. David Crockett. LC 74-80382. 48p. (Orig.). 1974. pap. 3.95 (ISBN 0-8192-1181-8). Morehouse.

Promptorium Parvulorum Sive Clericorum, Dictionarius Anglolatinus Princeps, 3 Pts. Galfridus Anglicus. Repr. of 1865 ed. 37.00 ea. Johnson Repr.

Promus & Cassandra, Pts. 1 & 2. George Whetstone. (Tudor Facsimile Texts. Old English Plays: No. 52). Repr. of 1910 ed. 49.50 (ISBN 0-404-53352-3). AMS Pr.

Pronouncing Bible Names. rev. ed. W. Murray Severance. 96p. 5.95 (ISBN 0-87981-657-0, 4691-03). Holman Bible Pub.

Proof of the Accuracy of the Bible. Elihu A. Schatz. LC 73-10726. (Illus.). xxvi, 740p. 1973. 15.00x (ISBN 0-8246-0161-0). Jonathan David.

Proofs for Eternity, Creation, & the Existence of God in Medieval Islamic & Jewish Philosophy. Herbert Davidson. (Studies in Northeast Culture & Society: Vol. 7). 500p. 1985. write for info. (ISBN 0-89003-180-0); pap. 62.00x (ISBN 0-89003-181-9). Undena Pubns.

Proofs of a Conspiracy. John Robison. 1967. pap. 4.95 (ISBN 0-88279-121-4). Western Islands.

Proofs of Christianity. Charles Harris. LC 77-77215. (Radiant Life Ser.). 128p. 1977. pap. 2.50 (ISBN 0-88243-911-1, 02-0911); teacher's ed 3.95 (ISBN 0-88243-181-1, 32-0181). Gospel Pub.

Propaganda & Aryanization, 1938-1944. John Mendelsohn. LC 81-80312. (Holocaust Ser.). 255p. 1982. lib. bdg. 61.00 (ISBN 0-8240-4878-4). Garland Pub.

Propago Sacri Ordinis Cartusienses per Germaniam Pars 2, 2 Vols. Georgius Schwengel. Ed. by James Hogg. (Analecta Cartusiana Ser.: No. 90/4). 378p. 1982. pap. 50.00 (ISBN 3-7052-0151-4, Pub. by Salzburg Studies). Longwood Pub Group.

Propago Sacri Ordinis Cartusiensis-Apparatus ad Annales Carytusiae Paradisi B.M.V, 2 Vols. (Analecta Cartusianae Ser.: No. 90/10). 454p. 1982. pap. 50.00 (ISBN 3-7052-0157-3, Pub. by Salzburg Studies). Longwood Pub Group.

Propago Sacri Ordinis Cartusiensis-Appartus Annales Sacri Ordinis Cartusiensis, 3 Vols. Georgius Schwengel. Ed. by James Hogg. (Analecta Cartusiana Ser.: No. 90/9). 534p. (Orig.). 1983. pap. 85.00 (ISBN 3-7052-0156-5, Pub. by Salzburg Studies). Longwood Pub Group.

Propago Sacri Ordinis Cartusiensis: Appendix ad Tom I, 2 Vols. Georgius Schwengel. Ed. by James Hogg. (Analecta Cartusiana Ser.: No. 90/5). 440p. (Orig.). 1983. pap. 50.00 (ISBN 3-7052-0152-2, Pub. by Salzburg Studies). Longwood Pub Group.

Propago Sacri Ordinis Cartusiensis: Appendis ad Tom II, 2 Vols. Georgius Schwengel. Ed. by James Hogg. (Analecta Cartusiana: No. 90/6). 397p. (Orig.). 1983. pap. 50.00 (ISBN 0-317-42583-8, Pub. by Salzburg Studies). Longwood Pub Group.

Propago Sacri Ordinis Cartusiensis: Appendix ad Tom III, 2 vols. Georgius Schwengel. Ed. by James Hogg. (Analecta Cartusiana Ser.: No. 90/7). 357p. (Orig.). 1983. pap. 50.00 (ISBN 3-7052-0154-9, Pub. by Salzburg Studies). Longwood Pub Group.

Propago Sacri Ordinis Cartusiensis: Appendix ad Tom IV, 2 Vols. Georgius Schwengel. Ed. by James Hogg. (Analecta Cartusiana: No. 90/8). 412p. (Orig.). 1983. pap. 50.00 (ISBN 3-7052-0155-7, Pub. by Salzburg Studies). Longwood Pub Group.

Propago Sacri Ordinis Cartusiensis de Provinciis Burgundiae, Franciae, Picardiae, Teutoniae et Angliae. Georgius Schwengel. Ed. by James Hogg. (Analecta Cartusiana Ser.: No. 90/2). 276p. (Orig.). 1981. pap. 25.00 (ISBN 3-7052-0149-2, Pub. by Salzburg Studies). Longwood Pub Group.

Propago Sacri Ordinis Cartusiensis-Diplomata Poloniae et Prussiae, 2 Vols. Georgius Schwengel. Ed. by James Hogg. (Analecta Cartusiana Ser.: No. 90/11). 256p. (Orig.). 1982. pap. 50.00 (ISBN 3-7052-0158-1, Pub. by Salzburg Studies). Longwood Pub Group.

Propago Sacri Ordinis Cartusiensis per Franciam, 2 Vols. Georgius Schwengel. Ed. by James Hogg. (Analecta Cartusiana Ser.: No. 90/1). 300p. (Orig.). 1984. pap. 50.00 (ISBN 3-7052-0148-4, Pub. by Salzburg Studies). Longwood Pub Group.

Propago Sacri Ordinis Cartusiensis per Germaniam. Georgius Schwengel. Ed. by James Hogg. (Analecta Cartusiana Ser.: No. 90/3). 480p. (Orig.). 1981. pap. 25.00 (ISBN 3-7052-0150-6, Pub. by Salzburg Studies). Longwood Pub Group.

Proper Balance. Joseph M. Champlin. LC 81-68000. 144p. (Orig.). 1981. pap. 3.95 (ISBN 0-87793-233-6). Ave Maria.

Proper Distinction Between Law & Gospel. Carl F. Walther. Tr. by W. H. Dau. 1929. 15.50 (ISBN 0-570-03248-2, 15-1601). Concordia.

Proper Way to Study the Bible. W. B. Searcy. 1982. 6.75 (ISBN 0-8062-1943-2). Carlton.

Property & Riches in the Early Church: Aspects of a Social History of Early Christianity. Martin Hengel. Tr. by John Bowden from Ger. LC 75-305658. pap. 26.00 (2026856). Bks Demand UMI.

Prophecies & Revelations about the Jesuits. Tr. by James S. Terrien. 143p. pap. 3.98 (ISBN 0-913452-27-0). Jesuit Bks.

Prophecies of Daniel. Gordon Lindsay. (Daniel Ser.). 4.00 (ISBN 0-89985-052-9). Christ Nations.

Prophecies of Jeremiah. Hans C. von Orelli. 1977. 15.25 (ISBN 0-86524-102-3, 2401). Klock & Klock.

Prophecies of Joseph Smith. Duane S. Crowther. LC 83-80664. 413p. 1873. 10.95 (ISBN 0-88290-221-0). Horizon-Utah.

Prophecies of St. Malachy. Peter Bander. LC 74-125419. (Illus.). 1973. pap. 3.00 (ISBN 0-89555-038-5). TAN Bks Pubs.

Prophecies of St. Malachy & St. Columbkille. 3rd ed. Peter Bander. 1979. pap. text ed. 6.95x (ISBN 0-901072-10-9). Humanities.

Prophecies of the Holy Quran. Hingora. pap. 4.50 (ISBN 0-686-18509-9). Kazi Pubns.

Prophecy. Frank Gularte & Jim Richardson. pap. 2.95 (ISBN 0-911739-23-8). Abbott Loop.

Prophecy. Bruce Yocum. (Orig.). 1976. pap. 4.95 (ISBN 0-89283-029-8). Servant.

Prophecy & Canon: A Contribution to the Study of Jewish Origins. Joseph Blenkinsopp. LC 76-22411. 1977. text ed. 14.95 (ISBN 0-268-01522-8). U of Notre Dame Pr.

Prophecy & Canon: A Contribution to the Study of Jewish Origins. Joseph Blenkinsopp. LC 76-22411. 206p. 1986. pap. 9.95 (ISBN 0-268-01559-7). U of Notre Dame Pr.

Prophecy & Ethics: Isaiah & the Ethical Traditions of Israel. Eryl Davies. (Journal for the Study of the Old Testament, Supplement: No. 16). 1981. 19.95 (ISBN 0-905774-26-4, Pub. by JSOT Pr England). Eisenbrauns.

Prophecy & Hermeneutics in Early Christianity: New Testament Essays. E. Earle Ellis. 306p. 1978. lib. bdg. 54.00x. Coronet Bks.

Prophecy & History in Luke-Acts. David L. Tiede. LC 79-8897. 180p. 1980. 2.00 (ISBN 0-8006-0632-9, 1-632). Fortress.

Prophecy & History in Luke-Acts. David L. Tiede. LC 79-8897. pap. 44.00 (2029616). Bks Demand UMI.

Prophecy & Politics: Militant Evangelists on the Road to Nuclear War. Grace Halsell. (Illus.). 256p. 1986. 14.95 (ISBN 0-88208-210-8). Lawrence Hill.

Prophecy & Politics: Socialism, Nationalism, & the Russian Jews, 1862-1917. Jonathan Frankel. LC 80-14414. 686p. 1984. pap. 19.95 (ISBN 0-521-26919-9). Cambridge U Pr.

Prophecy & Prediction. Dewey M. Beegle. 274p. 1978. write for info. (ISBN 0-933462-00-X); pap. text ed. 8.95 (ISBN 0-933462-01-8). Pryor Pettengill.

Prophecy & Prophets of the Old Testament. John F. Sawyer. 1987. pap. 8.95. Oxford U Pr.

Prophecy & Religion in Ancient China & Israel. Harold H. Rowley. LC 56-12074. 1956. 12.00x (ISBN 0-8401-2059-1). A R Allenson.

Prophecy & Society in Ancient Israel. Robert R. Wilson. LC 78-14677. 336p. 1980. 11.95 (ISBN 0-8006-1814-9, 1-1814). Fortress.

Prophecy & the Church. Oswald T. Allis. 1977. pap. 5.95 (ISBN 0-8010-0110-2). Baker Bk.

Prophecy & the Church. Oswald T. Allis. 1945. pap. 5.95 (ISBN 0-87552-104-5). Presby & Reformed.

Prophecy Continuous: Aspects of Ahmadi Religious Thoughts & Its Medieval Background. Yohanan Friedmann. 370p. 1987. text ed. 35.00x. U of Cal Pr.

Prophecy for Today. J. Dwight Pentecost. 224p. 1984. pap. 5.95 (ISBN 0-310-30981-6, 17018P). Zondervan.

Prophecy Foretold-Fulfilled: Puzzle Book. Irene Johnson. (Illus.). 48p. 1983. pap. 2.50 (ISBN 0-87239-590-1, 2788). Standard Pub.

Prophecy from Here to Two Thousand. Karl Roebling. 144p. 1983. pap. 4.95 (ISBN 0-942910-06-0). Paragon DynaPress.

Prophecy in Ancient Israel. J. Lindblom. LC 63-907. 480p. 1962. 17.95 (ISBN 0-8006-0916-6, 1-916). Fortress.

Prophecy in Ancient Israel. Johannes Lindblom. LC 63-907. pap. 120.00 (2029298). Bks Demand UMI.

Prophecy in Cross Cultural Perspective: A Sourcebook for Biblical Researchers. Thomas W. Overholt. (Society of Biblical Literature Ser.). 1985. pap. 26.95 (ISBN 0-89130-901-2, 06-03-17). Scholars Pr GA.

Prophecy in Early Christianity & the Ancient Mediterranean World. David E. Aune. 490p. 1983. 29.95 (ISBN 0-8028-3584-8). Eerdmans.

Prophecy in Islam: Philosophy & Orthodoxy. Fazlur Rahman. LC 78-66082. (Midway Reprints Ser.). 1979. pap. text ed. 9.00x (ISBN 0-226-70282-0). U of Chicago Pr.

Prophecy in Israel: Search for an Identity. Ed. by David L. Petersen. LC 85-45584. (Issues in Religion & Theology Ser.). 176p. 1986. pap. 7.95 (ISBN 0-8006-1773-8, 1-773). Fortress.

Prophecy Library. C. R. Moore & K. W. Moore. 957p. 1972. spiral bdg 19.80 (ISBN 0-914674-01-3). Freelandia.

Prophecy of Ezekiel. Charles L. Feinberg. 1984. 11.95 (ISBN 0-8024-6908-6). Moody.

Prophecy on Trial. James Stephenson. 1984. 10.50 (ISBN 0-317-03380-8). Lucis.

Prophecy, Things to Come. James L. Boyer. pap. 4.95 (ISBN 0-88469-006-7). BMH Bks.

Prophesy Deliverance! An Afro-American Revolutionary Christianity. Cornel West. LC 82-13483. 186p. 1982. pap. 11.95 (ISBN 0-664-24447-5). Westminster.

Prophet & a Pilgrim. Herbert Schneider & George Lawton. LC 78-134433. (Illus.). Repr. of 1942 ed. 36.50 (ISBN 0-404-05610-5). AMS Pr.

Prophet & His Message. K. A. Hakim. 8.50 (ISBN 0-686-18422-X). Kazi Pubns.

Prophet & Peacemaker: The Life of Adolphe Monod. James L. Osen. (Illus.). 420p. 1984. lib. bdg. 32.25 (ISBN 0-8191-3825-8); pap. text ed. 17.75 (ISBN 0-8191-3826-6). U Pr of Amer.

Prophet & Poet: The Bible & the Growth of Romanticism. Murray Roston. 1979. Repr. of 1965 ed. lib. bdg. 27.50 (ISBN 0-8495-4610-9). Arden Lib.

Prophet Crying in the Wilderness. Bonnie L. Wright et al. Ed. by John Donohue & Diane Turowski. 164p. 1986. pap. 6.98 (ISBN 0-9616309-0-6). Mountain Movers.

Prophet Dance of the Northwest & Its Derivatives: The Source of the Ghost Dance. Leslie Spier. LC 76-43853. Repr. of 1935 ed. 18.00 (ISBN 0-404-15708-4). AMS Pr.

Prophet Daniel. Arno C. Gaebelein. LC 55-9465. 218p. 1968. pap. 5.95 (ISBN 0-8254-2701-0). Kregel.

Prophet Elijah in the Development of Judaism. Aharon Wiener. (Littman Library of Jewish Civilization). 250p. 1978. 24.00x (ISBN 0-19-710010-4). Oxford U Pr.

Prophet for the Archangels. Ann R. Colton & Jonathan Murro. (Illus.). 289p. 1964. 8.95 (ISBN 0-917187-06-7). A R C Pub.

Prophet Jakob Lorber Predicts Coming Catastrophes & the True Christianity. Kurt Eggstein. Ed. by Marjorie M. Schuck. Tr. by A. R. Meuss from Ger. LC 85-51354. 480p. 1985. pap. 12.00 (ISBN 0-934616-40-X). Valkyrie Pub Hse.

Prophet of Hope. F. B. Meyer. 157p. 1983. pap. 3.95 (ISBN 0-317-43398-9). Chr Lit.

Prophet of Joy. facsimile ed. Gamaliel Bradford. LC 77-179506. (Select Bibliographies Reprint Ser.). Repr. of 1920 ed. 17.00 (ISBN 0-8369-6635-X). Ayer Co Pubs.

Prophet of the Dead Sea Scrolls. Upton C. Ewing. 148p. pap. 6.95 (ISBN 0-317-07628-0). Edenite.

Prophet of the New Hindu Age: The Life & Times of Archarya Pranavananda. Ninian Smart & Swami Purnananda. (Illus.). 256p. 1985. 15.00 (ISBN 0-04-922032-2); pap. 9.50 (ISBN 0-04-922033-0). Allen Unwin.

Prophet of the Pacific. Margaret Kabell. (Stories of Faith, Fame Ser.). (YA) 1976. pap. 2.95 (ISBN 0-87508-619-5). Chr Lit.

Prophet of the People: A Biography of Padre Pio. Dorothy Gaudiose. LC 74-7123. 1977. pap. 5.95 (ISBN 0-8189-0351-1). Alba.

Prophet, Pastor, Protestant: The Work of Huldrych Zwingli after Five Hundred Years. Ed. by E. J. Furchs & H. Wayne Pipkin. LC 84-14723. (Pittsburgh Theological Monographs (New Series): No. 11). (Orig.). 1984. pap. 15.00 (ISBN 0-915138-64-6). Pickwick.

Prophet Potpourri: H. B. & His-Her Bible Adventures, Vol. 6. H. B. Harper. LC 86-81422. 216p. (Orig.). 1986. pap. 5.95 (ISBN 0-934318-91-3). Falcon Pr MT.

Prophet Sulaiman. Da'i Al-Islam. 32p. 1985. pap. 3.95 (ISBN 0-940368-53-6). Tahrike Tarsile Quran.

Prophet to the Nations: Essays in Jeremiah Studies. Ed. by Leo G. Perdue & Brian W. Kovacs. xii, 391p. 1984. text ed. 25.00x (ISBN 0-931464-20-X). Eisenbrauns.

Prophethood in Islam. A. H. Siddiqui. pap. 4.95 (ISBN 0-686-18344-4). Kazi Pubns.

Prophethood of All Believers. James L. Adams. Ed. by George K. Beach. LC 85-73368. 324p. 1986. 25.00 (ISBN 0-8070-1602-0). Beacon Pr.

Prophetic Anointing: God's Call to the Sick, the Elderly, & the Dying. James L. Empereur. (Message of the Sacraments Ser.: Vol. 7). 1982. text ed. 15.95 (ISBN 0-89453-397-5); pap. 10.95 (ISBN 0-89453-233-2). M Glazier.

Prophetic Books of William Blake: Jerusalem. Ed. by E. R. MacLagan & A. G. Russell. 1979. Repr. of 1904 ed. lib. bdg. 35.00 (ISBN 0-8495-3510-7). Arden Lib.

Prophetic Conflict: Its Effect upon Israelite Religion. James L. Crenshaw. (Beiheft 124 zur Zeitschrift fuer die alttestamentliche Wissenschaft). 134p. 1971. 33.00x (ISBN 3-11-003363-1, 3-11-003363-1). De Gruyter.

Prophetic Element in Modern Art. Dorothea Blom. 1983. pap. 2.50x (ISBN 0-87574-148-7, 148). Pendle Hill.

Prophetic Events. E. C. Hadley. 74p. pap. 4.25 (ISBN 0-88172-146-8). Believers Bkshelf.

Prophetic Faith. Martin Buber. 15.75 (ISBN 0-8446-6206-2). Peter Smith.

Prophetic Faith & the Secular Age. Levi A. Olan. LC 82-2903. 168p. 1982. 15.00x (ISBN 0-87068-888-X). Ktav.

Prophetic Gatherings in the Church. David K. Blomgren. (Illus.). 100p. 1979. pap. 8.95 (ISBN 0-914936-36-0). Bible Temple.

Prophetic History of Christendom. R. K. Campbell. 6.95 (ISBN 0-88172-012-7). Believers Bkshelf.

Prophetic Imagination. Walter Brueggemann. LC 78-54546. 128p. 1978. pap. 5.95 (ISBN 0-8006-1337-6, 1-1337). Fortress.

Prophetic Imperative. Richard Gilbert. 1980. pap. 6.75 (ISBN 0-933840-16-0). Unitarian Univ.

Prophetic Lectures on Daniel & Revelations. F. G. Smith. 260p. pap. 3.50 (ISBN 0-686-29136-0). Faith Pub Hse.

Prophetic Milton. William Kerrigan. LC 74-6118. Repr. of 1974 ed. 74.30 (ISBN 0-8357-9813-5, 2016964). Bks Demand UMI.

Prophetic Ministry. Howard H. Brinton. 1983. pap. 2.50x (ISBN 0-87574-054-5, 054). Pendle Hill.

Prophetic Ministry. Morton Kelsey. 224p. 1984. pap. 9.95 (ISBN 0-8245-0631-6). Crossroad NY.

Prophetic Ministry: The Psychology & Spirituality of Pastoral Care. Morton T. Kelsey. 258p. 1982. 12.95 (ISBN 0-8245-0441-0). Crossroad NY.

Prophetic Moment: An Essay on Spenser. Angus Fletcher. LC 73-130587. 1971. 20.00x (ISBN 0-226-25332-5). U of Chicago Pr.

Prophetic Mysteries Revealed: The Prophetic Significance of the Parables of Matthew 13 & the Letters of Revelation 2-3. Lehman Strauss. LC 80-17540. 256p. 1980. 9.95 (ISBN 0-87213-832-1). Loizeaux.

Prophetic Parish: A Center for Peace & Justice. Dennis J. Geaney. 144p. (Orig.). 1983. pap. 6.95 (ISBN 0-86683-807-4, HarpR). Har-Row.

Prophetic Persona: The Language of Self-Reference in Jeremiah. Timothy Polk. (JSOT Supplement Ser.: No. 32). 240p. 1985. text ed. 28.50x (ISBN 0-905774-70-1, Pub. by JSOT Pr England); pap. text ed. 13.50x (ISBN 0-905774-71-X, Pub. by JSOT Pr England). Eisenbrauns.

Prophetic Religions & Politics: Religion & the Political Order. Ed. by Jeffrey K. Hadden & Anson Shupe. 408p. 1986. 24.95 (ISBN 0-913757-63-2, Pub. by New Era Bks); pap. 12.95 (ISBN 0-913757-53-5, Pub. by New Era Bks). Paragon Hse.

Prophetic Song. LaMar Boschman. (Orig.). 1986. pap. 3.95 (ISBN 0-938612-12-3). Revival Press.

Prophetic Sons & Daughters: Female Preaching & Popular Religion in Industrial England. Deborah M. Valenze. LC 85-42755. (Illus.). 344p. 1985. 38.50x (ISBN 0-691-05455-X). Princeton U Pr.

Prophetic Stream. William Taber. LC 84-61291. (Orig.). 1984. pap. 2.50x (ISBN 0-87574-256-4). Pendle Hill.

Prophetic Thought: Essays & Addresses. S. H. Blank. (Jewish Perspectives Ser: Vol. 2). 15.00x (ISBN 0-87820-501-2, HUC Pr). Ktav.

Prophetic Trilogy: The Nations in Prophecy, the Church in Prophecy, Israel in Prophecy. John F. Walvoord. pap. 15.85 (ISBN 0-310-34148-5, 17051P00687415X). Zondervan.

Prophetic Voice for the Kingdom. Gregory L. Jackson. Ed. by Ross E. Paulson. LC 86-71907. (Augustana Historical Society Pub. Ser.: No. 35). 239p. 1986. text ed. 19.95 (ISBN 0-910184-35-6). Augustana.

Prophetic Warnings to Modern America. Duane S. Crowther. LC 77-87431. 415p. 1977. 12.95 (ISBN 0-88290-016-1). Horizon Utah.

Prophetic Words of Hosea: A Morphological Study. Martin J. Buss. (Beiheft 111 Zur Zeitschrift Fuer Die alttestamentliche Wissenschaft). 1969. 30.00- (ISBN 3-11-002579-5). De Gruyter.

Prophetical Walk Through the Holy Land. Hal Lindsey. LC 83-80121. 200p. 1983. text ed. 29.95 (ISBN 0-89081-381-7). Harvest Hse.

Prophets, 2 vols. Abraham J. Heschel. Vol. 1, 1969. pap. 6.95x (ISBN 0-06-131421-8, TB1421, Torch); Vol. 2, 1971. pap. 7.95x (ISBN 0-06-131557-5, TB1557, Torch). Har-Row.

Prophets. James M. Ward. LC 81-20575. (Interpreting Biblical Texts). 160p. (Orig.). 1982. pap. 8.95 (ISBN 0-687-34370-4). Abingdon.

Prophets--Nevi'im: A New Translation of the Holy Scriptures According to the Traditional Hebrew Text. LC 77-87245. 930p. 1978. 10.95 (ISBN 0-8276-0096-8, 55). Jewish Pubns.

Prophets & Kings. Ellen G. White. 752p. deluxe ed. 9.95 (ISBN 0-8163-0040-2, 16642-1); pap. 5.95 (ISBN 0-8163-0041-0, 16643-9). Pacific Pr Pub Assn.

Prophets & Lovers: In Search of the Holy Spirit. Brennan Manning. 1985. 4.95 (ISBN 0-87193-013-7). Dimension Bks.

Prophets & Our Times. R. Gerald Culleton. 1974. pap. 6.00 (ISBN 0-89555-050-4). TAN Bks Pubs.

Prophets & Prophecies of the Old Testament. 2nd ed. Duane S. Crowther. LC 66-25508. (Comprehensive Bible Ser.). (Illus.). 644p. 1973. Repr. of 1967 ed. 12.95 (ISBN 0-88290-022-6). Horizon Utah.

Prophets & Prophecy: Seven Key Messengers. Frank H. Seilhamer. LC 76-62603. pap. 23.80 (2027878). Bks Demand UMI.

Prophets & Rulers. Bernard R. Youngman. (Background to the Bible Ser.: Vol. 2). pap. 8.95 (ISBN 0-7175-0416-6). Dufour.

Prophets & the Law. Victor Bergren. 15.00x (ISBN 0-87820-403-2, Pub. by Hebrew Union College Press). Ktav.

Prophets & the Powerless. James Limburg. LC 76-12397. 1976. pap. 6.95 (ISBN 0-8042-0156-0). John Knox.

Prophets & the Rise of Judaism. Adolphe Lods. Tr. by S. H. Hooke. LC 77-109772. (Illus.). 1971. Repr. of 1937 ed. lib. bdg. 25.75x (ISBN 0-8371-4262-8, LOPR). Greenwood.

Prophets & Their Times. rev ed. John M. Smith. Ed. by William A. Irwin. LC 25-6864. 1941. 20.00x (ISBN 0-226-76356-0). U of Chicago Pr.

Prophets Denied Honor: An Anthology on the Hispanic Church in the U. S. Ed. by Antonio Stevens-Arroyo. LC 79-26847. 397p. (Orig.). 1982. pap. 12.95 (ISBN 0-88344-395-3). Orbis Bks.

Prophets for a Day of Judgment. facsimile ed. Albert E. Baker. LC 72-90605. (Essay Index Reprint Ser). 1944. 17.00 (ISBN 0-8369-1390-6). Ayer Co Pubs.

Prophets in Combat: The Nicaraguan Journal of Bishop Pedro Casaldaliga. Pedro Casaldaliga. Tr. by Phillip Berryman from Span. 128p. (Orig.). 1987. pap. 8.95 (ISBN 0-940989-02-6). Meyer Stone Bks.

Prophets in the Church. Roger Aubert. LC 68-57877. (Concilium Ser.: Vol. 37). 160p. 1964. 7.95 (ISBN 0-8091-0120-3). Paulist Pr.

Prophets Now. Leslie F. Brandt. 1979. 8.50 (ISBN 0-570-03278-4, 15-2722). Concordia.

Prophets of Deceit. J. L. Davidson. 1960. 5.25 (ISBN 0-88027-016-0). Firm Foun Pub.

Prophets of Doom in an Age of Optimism. V. Kerry Inman. (Orig.). 1981. pap. 4.95 (ISBN 0-934688-02-8). Great Comm Pubns.

Prophets of Hope. Marilyn Kunz & Catherine Schell. (Neighborhood Bible Studies). 48p. (Orig.). 1984. pap. 2.50 (ISBN 0-8423-4908-1). Tyndale.

Prophets of Israel. William R. Smith. (Social Science Classics Ser.). 446p. text ed. cancelled (ISBN 0-87855-700-8); pap. text ed. cancelled (ISBN 0-686-68060-X). Transaction Bks.

Prophets of Israel. Leon J. Wood. LC 79-50172. 1979. 16.95 (ISBN 0-8010-9607-3). Baker Bk.

Prophets of Israel & Their Place in History to the Close of the Eighth Century B. C. W. Robertson Smith. 1979. Repr. of 1895 ed. lib. bdg. 50.00 (ISBN 0-8495-4905-1). Arden Lib.

Prophets of Israel: And Their Place in History to the Close of the Eighth Century, B.C. William R. Smith. LC 77-87666. 504p. Repr. of 1907 ed. 47.50 (ISBN 0-404-16403-X). AMS Pr.

Prophets of Israel: Popular Sketches from Old Testament History. Carl H. Cornhill. 1977. Repr. of 1913 ed. lib. bdg. 30.00 (ISBN 0-8482-3453-7). Norwood Edns.

Prophets of the Jews. Norman Bull. (Bible Story & Its Background Ser.: Vol. 3). pap. 9.95 (ISBN 0-7175-0979-6). Dufour.

Prophets of the Nineteenth Century: Carlyle, Ruskin, Tolstoi. May A. Ward. LC 76-7949. 1978. Repr. of 1900 ed. lib. bdg. 20.00 (ISBN 0-8414-9437-1). Folcroft.

Prophets of Yesterday & Their Message for Today. facs. ed. John Kelman. LC 74-152181. (Essay Index Reprint Ser). 1924. 17.00 (ISBN 0-8369-2193-3). Ayer Co Pubs.

Prophets One. Ann Macpherson et al. Ed. by Laurence Bright. LC 71-173033. (Scripture Discussion Commentary Ser.: Pt. 2). 214p. 1971. pap. text ed. 4.50 (ISBN 0-87946-001-6). ACTA Found.

Prophets, Poets, Priests, & Kings: The Old Testament Story. F. Washington Jarvis. 288p. 1975. pap. 6.95 (ISBN 0-8164-2089-0, HarpR). Har-Row.

Prophets: Preachers for God. Tom McMinn. (BibLearn Ser.). (Illus.). 1979. 5.95 (ISBN 0-8054-4250-2, 4242-50). Broadman.

Prophets' Report on Religion in North America. rev. ed. Peter J. Ediger. LC 78-150650. 1978. pap. 2.00 (ISBN 0-87303-686-7). Faith & Life.

Prophets Speak to Our Time. George Drew. 62p. (Orig.). 1981. pap. 6.95 (ISBN 0-940754-09-6). Ed Ministries.

Prophet's Speech at Tabuk. abr. ed. Abdullah. 16p. (Orig.). 1984. pap. 1.00 (ISBN 0-916157-02-4). African Islam Miss Pubns.

Prophet's Stories. Abul H. Ali-Nadawi. Ed. by Hamid Quinlan. Tr. by Kamal El-Helbawy from Arabic. LC 82-70453. Tr. of Qasas An Nabiyin. (Illus.). 200p. (Orig.). Date not set. pap. 5.00 (ISBN 0-89259-038-6). Am Trust Pubns.

Prophets Two. Francis McDonagh et al. LC 71-173033. (Scripture Discussion Commentary Ser.: Pt. 4). 184p. 1972. pap. text ed. 4.50 (ISBN 0-87946-003-2). ACTA Found.

Prophets, Volume One. Klaus Koch. Tr. by Margaret Kohl from Ger. LC 79-8894. 224p. 1982. pap. 10.95 (ISBN 0-8006-1648-0, 1-1648). Vol. 1, The Assyrian Age. Fortress.

Prophets, Volume Two: The Babylonian & Persian Period. Klaus Koch. LC 79-8894. 224p. 1984. pap. 10.95 (ISBN 0-8006-1756-8, 1-1756). Fortress.

Propitious Speech from the Beginning, Middle & End. Patrul Rinpoche. Tr. by Thinley Norbu from Tibetan. 46p. (Orig.). 1984. pap. 7.00 (ISBN 0-9607000-6-4). Jewel Pub Hse.

Propositions on the Dignity & Rights of the Human Person. Tr. by Miceal Ledwith from Lat. (International Theological Commission Ser.). 28p. (Orig.). 1986. pap. 1.95 (ISBN 1-55586-997-1). US Catholic.

Prosareden des Jeremiabuches. Helga Weippert. LC 72-76045. (Beiheft 132 zur Zeitschrift fuer die alttestamentliche Wissenschaft). (Ger.). 1973. 55.00x (ISBN 3-11-003867-6). De Gruyter.

Prose Edda. S. Sturluson. Tr. by A. G. Brodeur. 1916. 12.50x (ISBN 0-89067-000-5). Am Scandinavian.

Prose Edda of Snorri Sturluson: Tales from Norse Mythology. Snorri Sturluson. Tr. by Jean I. Young. 1964. pap. 5.95x (ISBN 0-520-01232-1, CAMPUS55). U of Cal Pr.

Prose Lives of Women Saints of Our Contrie of England. Ed. by C. Horstmann. (EETS, OS Ser.: No.86). Repr. of 1886 ed. 45.00 (ISBN 0-527-00082-5). Kraus Repr.

Prose of Milton. Richard Garnett. 1894. Repr. 20.00 (ISBN 0-8274-3214-3). R West.

Prose Sermons of the Book of Jeremiah: A Redescription of the Correspondence with Deuteronomistic Literature in Light of Recent Text-Critical Research. Louis Stulman. (Society of Biblical Literature Dissertation Ser.). 166p. 1987. 17.25 (ISBN 0-89130-960-8, 06-01-83); pap. 13.25 (ISBN 0-89130-961-6). Scholars Pr GA.

Prose Studies in Newman. Gilbert J. Garraghan. 1915. Repr. 25.00 (ISBN 0-8274-3216-X). R West.

Prose Style of John Jewel. David K. Weiser. Ed. by James Hogg. (Elizabethan & Renaissance Studies). 194p. (Orig.). 1973. pap. 15.00 (ISBN 3-7052-0658-3, Pub. by Salzburg Studies). Longwood Pub Group.

Prose Works. Mary B. Eddy. new type ed. 32.50 (ISBN 0-87952-074-4); brown new type ed. o.p. 70.00 (ISBN 0-87952-076-0); standard ed. 25.00 (ISBN 0-87952-070-1); new type bonded lea. ed. o.p. 47.00 (ISBN 0-87952-075-2). First Church.

Prosecution of John Wyclyf. Joseph H. Dahmus. xi, 167p. 1970. Repr. of 1952 ed. 22.50 (ISBN 0-208-00953-1, Archon). Shoe String.

Prosopographia Cartuaiana Belgica: 1314-1796. Jan De Grauwe. Ed. by James Hogg. (Analecta Cartusiana Ser.: No. 28). (Flemish & Fr.). 360p. (Orig.). 1976. pap. 25.00 (ISBN 3-7052-0029-1, Pub by Salzburg Studies). Longwood Pub Group.

Prospering Power of Love. rev. ed. Catherine Ponder. LC 66-25849. 126p. 1984. pap. 3.50 (ISBN 0-87516-525-7). De Vorss.

Prospering Power of Prayer. Catherine Ponder. 80p. 1983. pap. 3.00 (ISBN 0-87516-516-8). De Vorss.

Prosperity & the Healing Power of Prayer. F. Bernadette Turner. LC 83-21276. (Illus.). 166p. 1984. pap. 6.95 (ISBN 0-13-731324-1). P-H.

Prosperity in the End Time. Roger F. Campbell. 1983. pap. 2.95 (ISBN 0-87508-055-3). Chr Lit.

Prosperity Is God's Idea. Margaret M. Stevens. (Illus.). 1978. pap. 4.50 (ISBN 0-87516-264-9). De Vorss.

Prostitution & Prejudice: The Jewish Fight Against White Slavery 1870-1939. Edward J. Bristow. 368p. 1983. 21.95 (ISBN 0-8052-3866-2). Schocken.

Prostrannij Khristijanskij Katekhisis. Metropolitan Philaret Drozdov. Tr. of Complete Christian Catechism. 170p. pap. text ed. 6.00 (ISBN 0-317-29305-2). Holy Trinity.

Protection by Angles. 1982. 3.50 (ISBN 0-89858-041-2). Fill the Gap.

Protection of Corporate Names: A Country by Country Survey. United States Trademark Association. LC 82-4235. 1982. looseleaf 85.00 (ISBN 0-87632-404-9). Boardman.

Protection of the Weak in the Talmud. Mordecai Katz. LC 26-5707. (Columbia University. Oriental Studies: No. 24). Repr. of 1925 ed. 12.50 (ISBN 0-404-50514-7). AMS Pr.

Protest & Politics: Christianity & Contemporary Affairs. Ed. by Robert G. Clouse et al. 277p. 1968. 5.95 (ISBN 0-87921-000-1). Attic Pr.

Protestant & Catholic. Kenneth W. Underwood. LC 72-9051. (Illus.). 484p. 1973. Repr. of 1957 ed. lib. bdg. 22.50x (ISBN 0-8371-6567-9, UNPC). Greenwood.

Protestant & Catholic Reform. Enzo Bellini et al. Ed. & tr. by John Drury. (Illustrated History of the Church). (Illus.). 124p. (Orig.). 1981. 12.95 (ISBN 0-03-056831-5, HarpR). Har-Row.

Protestant & Roman Catholic Ethics: Prospects for Rapprochement. James M. Gustafson. LC 77-21421. 1980. pap. 8.00x (ISBN 0-226-31108-2, P868); 15.00 (ISBN 0-226-31107-4). U of Chicago Pr.

Protestant Biblical Interpretation. Bernard Ramm. 9.95 (ISBN 0-8010-7600-5). Baker Bk.

Protestant Biblical Interpretation. Bernard Ramm. Tr. by Silas Chan from Eng. (Chinese.). 1984. pap. write for info. (ISBN 0-941598-10-1). Living Spring Pubns.

Protestant, Catholic, Jew: An Essay in American Religious Sociology. Will Herberg. LC 83-9120. xvi, 310p. 1983. pap. 11.00x (ISBN 0-226-32734-5). U of Chicago Pr.

Protestant Cemetery of Rome. Revalee R. Stevens & Robert K. Steven. LC 81-84484. (North American Records in Italy). (Illus.). 110p. (Orig.). 1982. pap. 9.00 (ISBN 0-88127-003-2). Oracle Pr LA.

Protestant Challenge to Corporate America: Issues of Social Responsibility. Roy W. Morano. Ed. by Richard Farmer. LC 84-8514. (Research for Business Decisions Ser.: No. 69). 256p. 1984. 44.95 (ISBN 0-8357-1592-2). UMI Res Pr.

Protestant Christian Churches. Marcus Ward. 1985. 13.00x (ISBN 0-7062-3597-5, Pub. by Ward Lock Educ Co Ltd). State Mutual Bk.

Protestant Christianity. John Dillenberger & Claude Welch. 340p. 1976. pap. text ed. write for info. (ISBN 0-02-330470-7, Pub. by Scribner). Macmillan.

Protestant Christianity & People's Movements in Kerala, 1850-1936. J. W. Gladstone. 470p. 1986. 12.50x (ISBN 0-8364-1821-2, Pub. by Somaiya). South Asia Bks.

Protestant Church & the Negro, a Pattern of Segregation. Frank S. Loescher. LC 76-135601. 159p. 1972. Repr. of 1948 ed. text ed. cancelled (ISBN 0-8371-5193-7, LPC&, Pub. by Negro U Pr). Greenwood.

Protestant Church Music in America. Archibald Davison. 59.95 (ISBN 0-8490-0905-7). Gordon Pr.

Protestant Clergy & Public Issues, Eighteen Twelve to Eighteen Forty-Eight. John R. Bodo. LC 79-12849. (Perspectives in American History Ser: No. 52). 1980. Repr. of 1954 ed. lib. bdg. 27.50x (ISBN 0-87991-854-3). Porcupine Pr.

Protestant Concepts of Church & State. Thomas G. Sanders. 19.50 (ISBN 0-8446-6185-6). Peter Smith.

Protestant Credo. Virgiulius Ferm. 1953. 5.95 (ISBN 0-8022-0494-5). Philos Lib.

Protestant Dictionary: Containing Articles on the History, Doctrines, & Practices of the Christian Church. Ed. by Charles Wright & Charles Neil. LC 73-155436. 1971. Repr. of 1933 ed. 65.00x (ISBN 0-8103-3388-0). Gale.

Protestant Era. abr ed. Paul Tillich. Tr. by James L. Adams. 1957. pap. 7.00x (ISBN 0-226-80342-2, P19, Phoen). U of Chicago Pr.

Protestant Ethic & the Spirit of Capitalism. rev. ed. Max Weber. 1977. pap. 8.95 (ISBN 0-684-16489-2, ScribT). Scribner.

Protestant Ethic & the Spirit of Capitalism. Max Weber. 1984. 15.50 (ISBN 0-8446-6118-X). Peter Smith.

Protestant Evangelism among Italians in America. Ed. by Francesco Cordasco. LC 74-17943. (Italian American Experience Ser.). (Illus.). 276p. 1975. Repr. 21.00x (ISBN 0-405-06414-4). Ayer Co Pubs.

Protestant Faith. George W. Forell. LC 74-26341. 320p. 1975. pap. 9.95 (ISBN 0-8006-1095-4, 1-1095). Fortress.

Protestant in Purgatory: Richard Whately, Archbishop of Dublin. Donald H. Akenson. LC 81-3522. (Conference on British Studies (CBS) Biography: Vol. II). xiii, 276p. 1981. 25.00 (ISBN 0-208-01917-0, Archon). Shoe String.

Protestant Leadership Education Schools. Floy Hyde. LC 70-176892. (Columbia University. Teachers College. Contributions to Education: No. 965). Repr. of 1950 ed. 22.50 (ISBN 0-404-55965-4). AMS Pr.

Protestant Mind of the English Reformation, 1570-1640. Charles George & Katherine George. LC 77-130746. pap. 116.00 (ISBN 0-317-08472-0, 2000986). Bks Demand UMI.

Protestant Mission Education in Zambia: Eighteen Eighty to Nineteen Fifty-Four. John P. Ragsdale. LC 85-40505. 192p. 1986. 26.50x (ISBN 0-941664-09-0). Susquehanna U Pr.

Protestant Parish Minister: A Behavioral Science Interpretation. Samuel Blizzard. LC 85-50402. (SSSR Monography: No. 5). 1985. pap. 8.00 (ISBN 0-932566-04-9). Soc Sci Stud Rel.

Protestant Poetics & the Seventeenth Century Religious Lyric. Barbara K. Lewalski. LC 78-70305. (Illus.). 536p. 1984. 47.50x (ISBN 0-691-06395-8); pap. 14.50x (ISBN 0-691-01415-9). Princeton U Pr.

Protestant Reformation. Ed. by Hans J. Hillerbrand. (Documentary History of Western Civilization Ser). (Orig.). 1968. pap. 7.95x (ISBN 0-06-131342-4, TB 1342, Torch). Har-Row.

Protestant Reformation. Lewis W. Spitz. (Orig.). 1966. pap. 3.95x (ISBN 0-13-731638-0, Spec). P-H.

Protestant Reformation, Fifteen Seventeen to Fifteen Fifty-Nine: The Rise of Modern Europe. Lewis W. Spitz. LC 83-48805. (Illus.). 448p. 1986. pap. 8.95 (ISBN 0-06-091277-4, PL 1277, PL). Har-Row.

Protestant Reformation 1517-1559. Lewis W. Spitz. LC 83-48805. (Rise of Modern Europe Ser.). (Illus.). 444p. 1984. 22.45i (ISBN 0-06-013958-7, HarpT). Har-Row.

Protestant Reformers in Elizabethan England. C. M. Dent. (Oxford Theological Monographs). 1985. 39.95x (ISBN 0-19-826723-1). Oxford U Pr.

Protestant Spiritual Traditions. Ed. by Frank C. Senn. 288p. (Orig.). 1986. pap. 9.95 (ISBN 0-8091-2761-X). Paulist Pr.

Protestant Succession in International Politics, 1710-1716. Edward Gregg. (Outstanding Theses from the London School of Economics & Political Science Ser.). 475p. 1987. lib. bdg. 75.00 (ISBN 0-8240-1918-0). Garland Pub.

Protestant Theological Education in America: A Bibliography. Heather F. Day. LC 85-18300. (ATLA Biobliography Ser.: No. 15). 523p. 1985. 42.50 (ISBN 0-8108-1842-6). Scarecrow.

Protestant Thought. facs. ed. Karl Barth. LC 73-142606. (Essay Index Reprint Ser). 1959. 23.50 (ISBN 0-8369-2102-X). Ayer Co Pubs.

Protestant Thought & Natural Science: A Historical Interpretation. John Dillenberger. LC 77-7200. 1977. Repr. of 1960 ed. lib. bdg. 22.75x (ISBN 0-8371-9670-1, DIPT). Greenwood.

Protestant Thought Before Kant. A. C. McGiffert. 11.25 (ISBN 0-8446-0204-3). Peter Smith.

Protestant Thought in the Nineteenth Century, Vol. 1: 1799 to 1870. Claude Welch. LC 72-75211. Repr. of 1972 ed. 84.00 (ISBN 0-8357-9459-8, 2013200). Bks Demand UMI.

Protestant Thought in the Nineteenth Century: Volume 1, 1799-1870. Claude Welch. LC 72-75211. 335p. 1986. Repr. 25.00x (ISBN 0-300-01535-6). Yale U Pr.

Protestant Thought in the Nineteenth Century: Volume 2, 1870-1914. Claude Welch. LC 72-75211. 328p. 1985. 25.00x (ISBN 0-300-03369-9). Yale U Pr.

Protestant Thought in the Twentieth Century: Whence & Whither? Ed. by Arnold S. Nash. LC 78-5860. 1978. Repr. of 1951 ed. lib. bdg. 22.50x (ISBN 0-313-20484-5, NAPT). Greenwood.

Protestant vs. Catholic in Mid-Victorian England: Mr. Newdegate & the Nuns. Walter L. Arnstein. LC 81-11451. 272p. text ed. 20.00x (ISBN 0-8262-0354-X). U of Mo Pr.

Protestant Worship Music: Its History & Practice. Charles L. Etherington. LC 77-15990. (Illus.). 1978. Repr. of 1962 ed. lib. bdg. 35.00x (ISBN 0-313-20024-6, ETPW). Greenwood.

Protestantism. facs. ed. Ed. by William K. Anderson. LC 69-18918. (Essay Index Reprint Ser). 1944. 17.50 (ISBN 0-8369-1018-4). Ayer Co Pubs.

Protestantism. Ed. by J. Leslie Dunstan. LC 61-15497. (Great Religions of Modern Man Ser). 1961. 8.95 (ISBN 0-8076-0161-6). Braziller.

Protestantism. Hugh Kerr. LC 76-16065. (World Religions Ser.). 1979. pap. text ed. 6.95 (ISBN 0-8120-0665-8). Barron.

Protestantism & Capitalism & Social Science: The Webster Thesis Controversy. 2nd ed. Ed. by Robert W. Green. (Problems in American Civilization Ser). 1973. pap. text ed. 5.50 (ISBN 0-669-81737-6). Heath.

Protestantism & Latinos in the United States: An Original Anthology. Ed. by Carlos E. Cortes. LC 79-6266. (Hispanics in the United States Ser.). (Illus.). 1981. lib. bdg. 51.50x (ISBN 0-405-13173-9). Ayer Co Pubs.

Protestantism & Progress: The Significance of Protestantism for the Rise of the Modern World. Ernst Troeltsch. LC 86-45221. (Fortress Texts in Modern Theology Ser.). 112p. 1986. pap. 8.95 (ISBN 0-8006-3200-1). Fortress.

Protestantism & Repression: A Brazilian Case Study. Rubem Alves. Tr. by John Drury from Portuguese. LC 82-3594. Tr. of Protestantismo e repressao. 256p. (Orig.). 1985. pap. 11.95 (ISBN 0-88344-098-9). Orbis Bks.

Protestantism & Social Reform in New South Wales 1890-1910. J. D. Bollen. (Illus.). 200p. 1972. 20.00x (ISBN 0-522-84023-X, Pub. by Melbourne U Pr). Intl Spec Bk.

Protestantism & the American University: An Intellectual Biography of William Warren Sweet. James L. Ash, Jr. LC 82-10629. (Illus.). 180p. 1982. 15.95x (ISBN 0-87074-183-7). SMU Press.

Protestantism & the New South: North Carolina Baptists & Methodists in Political Crisis, 1894-1903. Frederick A. Bode. LC 75-1289. 171p. 1975. 15.00x (ISBN 0-8139-0597-4). U Pr of Va.

Protestantism in America: A Narrative History. rev. ed. Jerald C. Brauer. LC 66-12686. 320p. 1972. Westminster.

Protestantism in Central America. Wilton M. Nelson. 96p. (Orig.). 1984. pap. 4.95 (ISBN 0-8028-0024-6). Eerdmans.

Protestantism in Latin America: A Bibliographical Guide. rev. ed. Ed. by John H. Sinclair. LC 73-12837. 1976. pap. text ed. 8.95x (ISBN 0-87808-126-7). William Carey Lib.

Protestantism in the United States: Righteous Empire. 2nd ed. Martin E. Marty. 320p. 1986. text ed. write for info. (ISBN 0-02-376500-3). Macmillan.

Protestantismo en Centro America. Wilton M. Nelson. (Span.). 102p. (Orig.). 1982. pap. 2.50 (ISBN 0-89922-211-0). Edit Caribe.

Protestants Against Poverty: Boston's Charities, 1870-1900. Nathan I. Huggins. (Contributions in American History: No. 9). 1970. lib. bdg. 29.95 (ISBN 0-8371-3307-6, HUP/). Greenwood.

Protestants & Catholics: A Guide to Understanding the Differences. Peter Toon. 160p. (Orig.). 1984. pap. 5.95 (ISBN 0-89283-188-X). Servant.

Protestants in a Catholic State: Ireland's Privileged Minority. Kurt Bowen. 240p. 1983. 27.50x (ISBN 0-7735-0412-5). McGill-Queens U Pr.

Protestants in an Age of Science: The Baconian Ideal & Antebellum Religious Thought. Theodore D. Bozeman. LC 76-25962. xv, 240p. 1977. 22.50x (ISBN 0-8078-1299-4). U of NC Pr.

Protestants in Russia. J. A. Hebly. Tr. by John Pott. LC 76-149. pap. 48.00 (ISBN 0-317-08445-3, 2012741). Bks Demand UMI.

Protestation of the Generall Assemblie Made in the High Kirk, & at the Mercate Crosse of Glasgow. LC 79-26239. (English Experience Ser.: No. 343). 1971. Repr. of 1638 ed. 7.00 (ISBN 90-221-0525-3). Walter J Johnson.

Protocols of the Learned Elders of Zion. Nilus. Ed. & tr. by Victor E. Marsden. 1977. lib. bdg. 59.95 (ISBN 0-8490-1388-7). Gordon Pr.

Protocols of the Learned Elders of Zion. 299p. 1986. pap. 7.00 (ISBN 0-317-53280-4). Noontide.

Protocols of the Meetings of the Learned Elders of Zion. Tr. by Victor E. Marsden from Russian. 1978. pap. 4.00x (ISBN 0-911038-42-6). Noontide.

Proverbs. Kenneth T. Aitken. LC 86-15660. (Daily Study Bible-Old Testament). 276p. 1986. 15.95 (ISBN 0-664-21837-7); pap. 8.95 (ISBN 0-664-24586-2). Westminster.

Proverbs. Charles Bridges. (Geneva Commentaries Ser.). 1979. 15.95 (ISBN 0-85151-088-4). Banner of Truth.

Proverbs. A. Cohen. 223p. 1946. 10.95 (ISBN 0-900689-33-1). Soncino Pr.

Proverbs. J. Terrence Forestell. (Bible Ser.). 1.00 (ISBN 0-8091-5122-7). Paulist Pr.

Proverbs. Irving L. Jensen. (Bible Self-Study Guide Ser.). (Illus.). 96p. 1976. pap. 3.25 (ISBN 0-8024-1020-0). Moody.

Proverbs. F. Derek Kidner. LC 75-23850. (Tyndale Old Testament Commentary Ser.). 12.95 (ISBN 0-87784-861-0); pap. 6.95 (ISBN 0-87784-266-3). Inter-Varsity.

Proverbs. Bob Yandian. 1985. pap. 6.95 (ISBN 0-89274-386-7). Harrison Hse.

Proverbs: A Commentary on an Ancient Book of Timeless Advice. Robert L. Alden. 222p. 1984. 12.95 (ISBN 0-8010-0194-3). Baker Bk.

Proverbs: A New Approach. William McKane. LC 75-108185. (Old Testament Library). 692p. 1970. Westminster.

Proverbs & Ecclesiastes. John J. Collins. LC 79-92067. (Knox Preaching Guides Ser.). 117p. (Orig., John Hayes series editor). 1980. pap. 4.95 (ISBN 0-8042-3218-0). John Knox.

Proverbs & Ecclesiastes. Ed. by R. B. Scott. LC 65-13988. (Anchor Bible Ser.: No. 18). 1965. 14.00 (ISBN 0-385-02177-1, Anch). Doubleday.

Proverbs & How to Collect Them. Margaret M. Bryant. (Publications of the American Dialect Society: No. 4). 25p. 1945. pap. 2.35 (ISBN 0-8173-0604-8). U of Ala Pr.

Proverbs & Parables: God's Wisdom for Living. Dee Brestin & Steve Brestin. (Fisherman Bible Studyguide Ser.). 75p. 1975. saddle-stitch 2.95 (ISBN 0-87788-694-6). Shaw Pubs.

Proverbs, Ecclesiastes, Song of Solomon. J. Coert Rylaarsdam. LC 59-10454. (Layman's Bible Commentary Ser: Vol. 10). 1964. pap. 4.95 (ISBN 0-8042-3070-6). John Knox.

Proverbs-Ezekiel. Albert Barnes. 10.95 (ISBN 0-8010-0839-5). Baker Bk.

Proverbs for Graduates. Brent D. Earles. 1984. 5.95 (ISBN 0-8010-3415-9). Baker Bk.

Proverbs For People. Vern McLellan. LC 82-83841. (Illus.). 1983. pap. 3.25 (ISBN 0-89081-326-4). Harvest Hse.

Proverbs, God's Powerhouse of Wisdom. Chuck Colclasure. 1981. pap. 2.50 (ISBN 0-8423-4928-6). Tyndale.

Proverbs: Good Advice for Good Living. John H. Scammon. LC 78-24505. 1979. pap. 3.95 (ISBN 0-8170-0819-5). Judson.

Proverbs II. Barbara J. Thomas. 56p. (Orig.). 1985. pap. 5.95 (ISBN 0-9616788-0-1). Landsberry Pr.

Proverbs-Important Things to Know. Carol Greene. 1980. pap. 0.99 (ISBN 0-570-06140-7, 59-1303, Arch Bk). Concordia.

Proverbs in the Earlier English Drama. B. J. Whiting. LC 70-86290. 1969. Repr. of 1938 ed. lib. bdg. 34.50x (ISBN 0-374-98513-8, Octagon). Hippocrene Bks.

Proverbs-Isaiah 39. Christopher Wright. 1983. pap. 4.95 (ISBN 0-87508-158-4). Chr Lit.

Proverbs or Adages. Desiderius Erasmus. Tr. by Richard Taverner. LC 55-11634. 1977. Repr. of 1569 ed. 35.00x (ISBN 0-8201-1232-1). Schol Facsimiles.

Proverbs or Adagies with Newe Addicions, Gathered Out of the Chiliades of Erasmus. Desiderius Erasmus. LC 73-264117. (English Experience Ser.: No. 124). 1969. Repr. of 1539 ed. 13.00 (ISBN 90-221-0124-X). Walter J Johnson.

Proverbs: Practical Directions for Living. James T. Draper, Jr. (Living Studies). pap. 4.95 (ISBN 0-8423-4922-7); leader's guide 2.95 (ISBN 0-8423-4923-5). Tyndale.

Proverbs, Promises & Principles. pap. 3.25 (ISBN 0-89081-460-0). Harvest Hse.

Proverbs Puzzle. Fannie L. Houck. 48p. 1986. pap. 2.50 (ISBN 0-87403-048-X, 2692). Standard Pub.

Proverbs, Song of Solomon. H. A. Ironside. 12.95 (ISBN 0-87213-395-8). Loizeaux.

Proverbs Thirty-One Lady & Other Impossible Dreams. Marsha Drake. LC 84-6453. 192p. (Orig.). 1984. pap. 5.95 (ISBN 0-87123-595-1, 210595). Bethany Hse.

Proverbs: Wisdom for All Ages. Thomas L. Seals. 5.50 (ISBN 0-89137-529-5). Quality Pubns.

Proverbs, with Introduction to Sapiential Books. Dermot Cox. (Old Testament Ser.: Vol. 17). 1982. 12.95 (ISBN 0-89453-417-3); pap. 9.95 (ISBN 0-89453-251-0). M Glazier.

Providence & Evil. P. T. Geach. LC 76-28005. 1977. 24.95 (ISBN 0-521-21477-7). Cambridge U Pr.

Providence & Free Will in Human Actions. Daniel W. Goodenough. 132p. 1986. pap. 5.95 (ISBN 0-915221-63-2). Swedenborg Sci Assn.

Providence & Predestination: Questions 5 & 6 of "Truth". St. Thomas Aquinas. Tr. by Robert W. Mulligan. 154p. 1961. pap. 5.95 (ISBN 0-89526-937-6). Regnery Bks.

Providence As "Idee-Maitresse" in the Works of Bossuet. Georgiana Terstegge. LC 73-128931. (Catholic University of America. Studies in Romance Languages & Literature: No. 43). 1970. Repr. of 1948 ed. 29.00 (ISBN 0-404-50334-9). AMS Pr.

Providential Order of the World. Alexander B. Bruce. LC 77-27225. (Gifford Lectures: 1897). 1978. Repr. of 1897 ed. 37.50 (ISBN 0-404-60455-2). AMS Pr.

Province Beyond the River: The Diary of a Protestant at a Trappist Monastery. W. Paul Jones. 160p. (Orig.). 1986. pap. 6.95 (ISBN 0-8358-0546-8). Upper Room.

Province into Being. Skip Baldwin. Ed. by Douglas Anderson. (Illus.). 80p. (Orig.). 1984. pap. 6.95 (ISBN 0-912549-04-1). Bread and Butter.

Provincial Cemetery of the Pyramid Age, Naga-Ed-Der, Pt. 3. George A. Reisner. (Publications in Egyptian Archaeology: Vol. 6). 1932. 110.00x (ISBN 0-520-01060-4). U of Cal Pr.

Provinciales. Blaise Pascal. 1966. 4.95 (ISBN 0-686-54852-3). French & Eur.

Proving Yourself: A Study of James. Anna M. Orr. (Basic Bible Study Ser.). 64p. pap. 2.95 (ISBN 0-930756-75-4, 521015). Aglow Pubns.

Provo, Pioneer Mormon City. Writers Program, Utah. LC 73-3654. (American Guide Ser.). 1942. Repr. 11.50 (ISBN 0-404-57954-X). AMS Pr.

Provoker. Earl Paulk. Ed. by Trisha Weeks. 400p. (Orig.). 1986. pap. 9.95 (ISBN 0-917595-09-2). K-Dimension.

Provozvjestnik Karl Bozhijej Russkomy Narodu. Archbishop Averky Taushev. Tr. of Prophet of the Wrath of God upon the Russian People. 30p. 1968. pap. 1.00 (ISBN 0-317-29066-5). Holy Trinity.

Prudentius 'Psychomachia' A Re-examination. Macklin Smith. LC 75-37192. 1976. 30.50x (ISBN 0-691-06299-4). Princeton U Pr.

Prymer, or Lay Folks Prayer Book, Pts. 1 & 2. Ed. by H. Littlehales. (EETS, OS Ser.: No. 109). Repr. of 1897 ed. Set. 18.00 (ISBN 0-527-00108-2). Kraus Repr.

Psalm for the Frightened & Frustrated Sheep. James D. Bales. 1977. pap. 1.50 (ISBN 0-89315-216-1). Lambert Bk.

Psalm Journal. Joan Chittister & Mary L. Kownacki. LC 85-50308. 104p. (Orig.). 1985. pap. 6.95 (ISBN 0-934134-28-6, Leaven Pr). Sheed & Ward MO.

Psalm Locator. 2nd ed. Anthony Lawrence. (Orig.). 1985. pap. 10.95 (ISBN 0-89390-063-X). Resource Pubns.

Psalm of Christ: Forty Poems on the Twenty-Second Psalm. Chad Walsh. LC 82-5566. (Wheaton Literary Ser.). 74p. 1982. pap. 5.95 (ISBN 0-87788-700-4). Shaw Pubs.

Psalm of Saiva-being. T. Isaac Tamby. 506p. 1986. Repr. of 1925 ed. 30.00X (ISBN 0-8364-1682-1, PUb. by Abhinav India). South Asia Bks.

Psalm One Hundred Four. Dorsey Alexander & Joyce Alexander. 32p. (Calligraphy & Illus.). 1978. pap. 5.00 (ISBN 0-912020-19-9). Turtles Quill.

Psalm One Hundred Nineteen. Charles Bridges. 1977. 13.95 (ISBN 0-85151-176-7). Banner of Truth.

Psalm Sampler. Office of Worship for the Presbyterian Church (U. S. A.) & Cumberland Presbyterian Church. LC 85-753089. (Illus.). 48p. 1986. pap. 4.95 ea. (ISBN 0-664-24681-8). Westminster.

Psalm Singer's Amusement. William Billings. LC 73-5100. (Earlier American Music Ser.: Vol. 20). 104p. 1974. Repr. of 1781 ed. lib. bdg. 25.00 (ISBN 0-306-70587-7). Da Capo.

Psalmen der Vulgata: Ihre Eigenart. Arthur Allgeier. 22.00 (ISBN 0-384-00870-4). Johnson Repr.

Psalmen Des Koniglichen Propheten Davids. Johann P. Von Schonborn. xl, 872p. Repr. of 1658 ed. 62.00. Johnson Repr.
Psalmen: Stilistische Verfahren und Aufbau mit besonderer Beruecksichtigung von Ps. 1-41. N. H. Ridderbos. Tr. by Karl E. Mittring from Dutch. (Beiheft 117 zur Zeitschrift fuer die alttestamentliche Wissenschaft). 305p. 1972. 41.60x (ISBN 3-11-001834-9). De Gruyter.
Psalmenkommentare aus der Katenenueberlieferung, Vol. 1. Ekkehard Muehlenberg. LC 73-91808. (Patristische Texte und Studien, Band 15). (Ger.). 1974. 58.40x (ISBN 3-11-004182-0). De Gruyter.
Psalmenkommentare aus der Katenenueberlieferung: Untersuchungen zu den Psalmenkatenen, Vol. 3. Ekkehard Muehlenberg. (Patristische Texte und Studien: No. 19). 1978. 41.20x (ISBN 3-11-006959-8). De Gruyter.
Psalmenkommentware aus Katenenveberlieferung, Vol. 2. Ekkehard Muehlenberg. (Patristische Texte und Studien: Vol. 16). 1977. 59.60x (ISBN 3-11-005717-4). De Gruyter.
Psalmes of David, 2 vols. in 1. George Wither. 1967. Repr. of 1632 ed. 89.00 (ISBN 0-8337-3838-0). B Franklin.
Psalmist with a Camera. Gail Rubin. LC 79-5086. (Illus.). 116p. 1979. 19.95 (ISBN 0-89659-076-3); pap. 14.95 (ISBN 0-89659-071-2). Abbeville Pr.
Psalmnary: Gradual Psalms for Cantor & Congregation. James E. Barrett. 196p. 1982. incl. binder 24.00 (ISBN 0-942466-04-7); 21.00 (ISBN 0-942466-03-9). Hymnary Pr.
Psalmody & Prophecy. W. H. Bellinger. (JSOT Supplement Ser.: No. 27). 146p. 1984. text ed. 28.50x (ISBN 0-905774-60-4, Pub. by JSOT Pr England); pap. text ed. 11.95x (ISBN 0-905774-61-2, Pub. by JSOT England). Eisenbrauns.
Psalmody in Seventeenth Century America: Series 1, the Ainsworth Psalter. Ed. by Carleton S. Smith. price on application (ISBN 0-685-18958-9, Dist. by C. F. Peters Corp). NY Pub Lib.
Psalms. Albert Barnes. 29.95 (ISBN 0-8010-0838-7). Baker Bk.
Psalms. Ernesto Cardenal. 96p. 1981. pap. 3.95 (ISBN 0-8245-0044-X). Crossroad NY.
Psalms. A. Cohen. 488p. 1945. 10.95 (ISBN 0-900689-32-3). Soncino Pr.
Psalms. David Dickson. (Geneva Commentary Ser.). 1064p. 1985. Repr. of 1653 ed. 21.95 (ISBN 0-85151-481-2). Banner of Truth.
Psalms. Arno C. Gaebelein. 1939. 10.95 (ISBN 0-87213-222-6). Loizeaux.
Psalms, 2 vols. Hirsch. 1975. 26.95 (ISBN 0-87306-025-3). Feldheim.
Psalms. Irving L. Jensen. (Bible Self-Study Guides). 1968. pap. 3.25 (ISBN 0-8024-1019-7). Moody.
Psalms. A. F. Kirkpatrick. (Thornapple Commentaries Ser.). 964p. 1982. pap. 19.95 (ISBN 0-8010-5453-2). Baker Bk.
Psalms, 3 Vols. Alexander MacLarsen. 1981. smythe sewn 45.00 (ISBN 0-86524-038-8, 1902). Klock & Klock.
Psalms. Robert North. (Bible Ser.). Pt. 3. pap. 1.00 (ISBN 0-8091-5125-1); Pt. 4. pap. 1.00 (ISBN 0-8091-5126-X); Pt. 5. pap. 1.00 (ISBN 0-8091-5127-8); Pt. 6. pap. 1.00 (ISBN 0-8091-5128-6). Paulist Pr.
Psalms. W. S. Plumer. (Geneva Commentaries Ser.). 1978. 32.95 (ISBN 0-85151-209-7). Banner of Truth.
Psalms. Arnold B. Rhodes. LC 59-10454. (Layman's Bible Commentary Ser: Vol. 9). 1960. 4.25 (ISBN 0-8042-3009-9); pap. 4.95 (ISBN 0-8042-3069-2). John Knox.
Psalms. Charles H. Spurgeon. Ed. by David O. Fuller. LC 76-12085. 704p. 1977. kivar 14.95 (ISBN 0-8254-3714-8). Kregel.
Psalms. Carroll Stuhlmueller. (Read & Pray Ser.). 1979. 1.75 (ISBN 0-8199-0631-X). Franciscan Herald.
Psalms. Stafford Wright. (Bible Study Commentaries Ser.). 152p. 1982. pap. 4.95 (ISBN 0-317-43374-1). Chr Lit.
Psalms: A Commentary. Artur Weiser. LC 62-16760. (Old Testament Library). 842p. 1962. 29.50 (ISBN 0-664-20418-X). Westminster.
Psalms: A Form-Critical Introduction. Hermann Gunkel. Ed. by John Reumann. Tr. by Thomas M. Horner from Ger. LC 67-22983. (Facet Bks.). 64p. (Orig.). 1967. pap. 2.50 (ISBN 0-8006-3043-2, 1-3043). Fortress.
Psalms: A Matchless Treasury. Richard A. Hufton. LC 84-82058. 106p. (Orig.). 1984. pap. 4.00 (ISBN 0-933643-02-0). Grace World Outreach.
Psalms: A New Translation. Bonaventure Zerr. 8.95 (ISBN 0-8091-2218-9). Paulist Pr.
Psalms: A New Translation for Prayer & Worship. Tr. by Gary Chamberlain. LC 84-50842. 192p. (Orig.). 1984. pap. 6.95 (ISBN 0-8358-0485-2). Upper Room.
Psalms: A New Version. Roy E. Koeblitz. LC 85-63357. 208p. 1986. 12.95 (ISBN 0-936187-11-5). Palm Pub Co.
Psalms: A Singing Version. Joseph Gelineau. 256p. 1968. pap. 3.95 (ISBN 0-8091-1669-3, Deus). Paulist Pr.
Psalms: A Study Guide. Dale J. Cooper. (Revelation Series for Adults). 1979. pap. text ed. 2.50 (ISBN 0-933140-08-8). CRC Pubns.
Psalms & Prayers for Congregational Participation: Series A. B. David Hostetter. 1983. 7.75 (ISBN 0-89536-639-8, 1633). CSS of Ohio.
Psalms & Prayers for Congregational Participation: Series B (Common Consensus Lectionary) B. David Hostetter. 1984. 7.75 (ISBN 0-89536-694-0, 4871). CSS of Ohio.
Psalms & Prayers for Congregational Participation: Series C (Common Consensus Lectionary) B. David Hostetter. 1985. 7.75 (ISBN 0-89536-770-X, 5865). CSS of Ohio.
Psalms & Proverbs. Alice J. Davidson. (Alice in Bibleland Ser.). (Illus.). 32p. 1984. 4.95 (ISBN 0-8378-5069-X). Gibson.
Psalms & Proverbs, Neighborhood Bible Study. Marilyn Kunz & Catherine Schell. 1971. pap. 2.95 (ISBN 0-8423-4991-X). Tyndale.
Psalms & Wisdom. Leonard Johnston & Michael Smith. Ed. by Laurence Bright. LC 71-173033. (Scripture Discussion Commentary Ser.: Pt. 6). 256p. 1972. pap. text ed. 4.50. ACTA Found.
Psalms Anew. Nancy Schreck & Maureen Leach. 208p. (Orig.). 1986. pap. 6.95 (ISBN 0-88489-174-7). St Mary's.
Psalms (CC, Vol. 13. Donald Williams. 448p. 1986. 23.95 (ISBN 0-8499-0419-6). Word Bks.
Psalms: Chronologically Treated with a New Translation. rev. ed. Moses Buttenwieser. (Library of Biblical Studies Ser.). 1969. 59.50x (ISBN 0-87068-044-7). Ktav.
Psalms Come Alive: Capturing the Voice & the Art of Israel's Songs. John H. Eaton. LC 86-20115. (Illus.). 180p. 1986. pap. 6.95 (ISBN 0-87784-387-2). Inter-Varsity.
Psalms: Faith Songs for the Faith-Filled. Mary Jo Tully. 96p. 1982. pap. 3.50 (ISBN 0-697-01824-5). Wm C Brown.
Psalms for Children: Series B. Eldon Weisheit. LC 84-18562. 128p. (Orig.). 1984. pap. 6.95 (ISBN 0-8066-2096-X, 10-5304). Augsburg.
Psalms for Children: Series C. Eldon Weisheit. LC 85-11154. 128p. (Orig.). 1985. pap. 6.95 (ISBN 0-8066-2169-9, 10-5305). Augsburg.
Psalms for Children: Sixty Object Lessons. Eldon Weisheit. LC 83-70510. (Series A). 128p. (Orig.). 1983. pap. 6.95 (ISBN 0-8066-2016-1, 10-5303). Augsburg.
Psalms for God's People. Robert Johnston. LC 82-5344. (Bible Commentary for Laymen Ser.). 160p. 1982. pap. 3.50 (ISBN 0-8307-0820-0, S362105). Regal.
Psalms for Graduates. Brent D. Earles. 5.95 (ISBN 0-8010-3426-4). Baker Bk.
Psalms for Singing: Twenty-Six Psalms with Musical Settings for Congregation & Choir. Tr. by Gary Chamberlain. LC 84-50778. 141p. (Orig.). 1984. pap. 7.50 (ISBN 0-8358-0495-X). Upper Room.
Psalms for Sojourners. James Limburg. LC 86-2621. (Illus.). 112p. (Orig.). 1986. pap. 5.95 (ISBN 0-8066-2206-7, 10-5306). Augsburg.
Psalms from Prison. Benjamin F. Chavis, Jr. 192p. 1983. 10.95 (ISBN 0-8298-0661-X); pap. 7.95 (ISBN 0-8298-0666-0). Pilgrim NY.
Psalms in Rhyme, Vol. I. Diana L. Berry. LC 86-80658. 104p. (Orig.). 1986. pap. 6.95 (ISBN 0-931637-01-5). Ferndale Hse.
Psalms in Song for the White Cavalry. 3rd ed. Frank M. Wakeman. (Illus.). 1979. 5.00 (ISBN 0-910840-19-9). Kingdom.
Psalms, Job. Roland E. Murphy. LC 77-78637. (Proclamation Commentaries: the Old Testament Witnesses for Preaching). (Orig.). 1977. pap. 4.95 (ISBN 0-8006-0588-8, 1-588). Fortress.
Psalms, Meditations in the Psalms. Erling C. Olsen. 1050p. 1975. Repr. 19.95 (ISBN 0-87213-680-9). Loizeaux.
Psalms: Nos. 1-72, Vol. 1. George A. Knight. LC 82-20134. (Daily Study Bible Old Testament Ser.). 350p. 1982. 12.95 (ISBN 0-664-21805-9); pap. 7.95 (ISBN 0-664-24572-2). Westminster.
Psalms: Nos. 73-150, Vol. 2. George A. Knight. LC 82-20134. (Daily Study Bible Old Testament Ser.). 384p. 1983. 15.95 (ISBN 0-664-21808-3); pap. 8.95 (ISBN 0-664-24575-7). Westminster.
Psalms-Now. Leslie Brandt. LC 73-78108. 1973. 8.50 (ISBN 0-570-03230-X, 15-2125). Concordia.
Psalms of Joy & Faith. Kyle M. Yates. 216p. 1984. pap. 7.95 (ISBN 0-913029-03-3). Stevens Bk Pr.
Psalms of My Life. Joseph Bayly. 1969. pap. 0.95 pock. pap. (ISBN 0-8423-5002-0). Tyndale.
Psalms of the Rabbi Physician. Eric R. Braverman. (Illus.). 112p. (Orig.). 1986. pap. 9.95 (ISBN 1-55630-003-4). Brentwood Comm.
Psalms of the Sons of Korah. Michael D. Goulder. (Journal for the Study of the Old Testament, Supplement Ser.: No. 20). xiv, 302p. 1983. 27.50x (ISBN 0-905774-40-X, Pub. by JSOT Pr England); pap. text ed. 14.95x (ISBN 0-905774-41-8). Eisenbrauns.
Psalms One. Carroll Stuhlmueller. (Old Testament Message Ser.: Vol. 21). 16.95 (ISBN 0-89453-421-1); pap. 12.95 (ISBN 0-89453-255-3). M Glazier.
Psalms One - Seventy-Two. D. Kidner. LC 75-23852. 1973. 12.95 (ISBN 0-87784-868-8); pap. 6.95 (ISBN 0-87784-264-7). Inter-Varsity.
Psalms One, One - Fifty. Ed. by Mitchell Dahood. (Anchor Bible Ser.: Vol. 16). 1966. 16.00 (ISBN 0-385-02765-6, Anchor Pr). Doubleday.
Psalms: Prayer Power for Your Problems. Carrie Pevarnik & Robert Chaney. LC 78-58146. (Illus.). 1978. pap. 9.95 (ISBN 0-918936-05-5). Astara.
Psalms: Prayers for the Ups, Downs & In-Betweens of Life: A Literary Experiential Approach. John Craghan. (Background Bks.: Vol. 2). 1985. pap. 7.95 (ISBN 0-89453-439-4). M Glazier.
Psalms: Prayers of the Heart. Eugene Peterson. (LifeGuide Bible Studies). 64p. (Orig.). 1987. pap. 2.95. Inter-Varsity.
Psalms: Songs of Discipleship, 3 vols. Robert L. Alden. (Everyman's Bible Commentary Ser.). 1975. pap. 5.95 ea. Vol. 1 (ISBN 0-8024-2018-4). Vol. 2 (ISBN 0-8024-2019-2). Vol. 3 (ISBN 0-8024-2020-6). Moody.
Psalms: Structure, Content, & Message. Claus Westermann. Tr. by Ralph D. Gehrke from Ger. LC 79-54127. Tr. of Psalter. 136p. (Orig.). 1980. pap. 7.95 (ISBN 0-8066-1762-4, 10-5300). Augsburg.
Psalms, Studies on Book One. H. A. Ironside. 8.95 (ISBN 0-87213-383-4). Loizeaux.
Psalms That Touch Us Where We Live. David Mains. (Chapel Talks Ser.). 64p. 0.95 (ISBN 0-89191-265-7, 52654). Cook.
Psalms: The Poetry of Palestine. Woodrow M. Kroll. 464p. (Orig.). 1987. lib. bdg. 37.50 (ISBN 0-8191-5750-3); pap. text ed. 24.75 (ISBN 0-8191-5751-1). U Pr of Amer.
Psalms: The Prayer Book of the Bible. 2nd ed. Dietrich Bonhoeffer. Tr. by James H. Burtness from Ger. LC 73-101111. Tr. of Gebetbuch der Bibel. 88p. 1974. 4.95 (ISBN 0-8066-1439-0, 10-5321). Augsburg.
Psalms: Their Origin & Meaning. Leopold Sabourin. LC 73-16459. 560p. (Orig.). 1974. pap. 12.95 (ISBN 0-8189-0121-7). Alba.
Psalms Three, One Hundred One - One Hundred Fifty. Ed. by Mitchell Dahood. LC 66-11766. (Anchor Bible Ser.: Vol. 17A). 18.00 (ISBN 0-385-00607-1, Anchor Pr). Doubleday.
Psalms: Translation & Commentary by Rabbi Samson Raphael Hirsch. Tr. by Gertrude Hirschler from German. (Compact Ser.). 1978. 16.95 (ISBN 0-87306-135-7). Feldheim.
Psalms Two. Carroll Stuhlmueller. (Old Testament Message Ser.: Vol. 22). 15.95 (ISBN 0-89453-422-X); pap. 10.95 (ISBN 0-89453-257-X). M Glazier.
Psalms Two, Fifty-One to One Hundred. Ed. by Mitchell Dahood. LC 66-11766. (Anchor Bible Ser.: Vol. 17). 1966. 16.00 (ISBN 0-385-03759-7, Anchor Pr). Doubleday.
Psalms: With Introduction to Cultic Poetry, Prt. I. Ed. by Erhard Gerstenberger. (Forms of the Old Testament Literature Ser.: Vol. XIV). 224p. (Orig.). 1987. pap. 21.95 (ISBN 0-8028-0255-9). Eerdmans.
Psalms, 1-50. John W. Rogerson. LC 76-27911. (Cambridge Bible Commentary on the New English Bible, Old Testament Ser.). 1977. 37.50 (ISBN 0-521-21463-7); pap. 11.95 (ISBN 0-521-29160-7). Cambridge U Pr.
Psalms 1-72. Richard J. Clifford. (Collegeville Bible Commentary: Old Testament Ser.: Vol. 22). 80p. 1986. pap. 2.95. Liturgical Pr.
Psalms, 101-150. John W. Rogerson. LC 76-27911. (Cambridge Bible Commentary on the New English Bible, Old Testament Ser.). 1977. 37.50 (ISBN 0-521-21465-3); pap. 11.95 (ISBN 0-521-29162-3). Cambridge U Pr.
Psalms, 51-100. John W. Rogerson. LC 76-27911. (Cambridge Bible Commentary on the New English Bible, Old Testament Ser.). 1977. 37.50 (ISBN 0-521-21464-5); pap. 11.95 (ISBN 0-521-29161-5). Cambridge U Pr.
Psalms 73-150. Richard J. Clifford. (Collegeville Bible Commentary: Old Testament Ser.: Vol. 23). 88p. 1986. pap. 2.95 (ISBN 0-8146-1479-5). Liturgical Pr.
Psalom 118. Theophan the Recluse. Tr. of Psalm 118. 496p. 22.00 (ISBN 0-317-28925-X); pap. 17.00 (ISBN 0-317-28926-8). Holy Trinity.
Psalter. Tr. by The Monks of New Skete. 286p. 1984. 39.50x (ISBN 0-9607924-5-7). Monks of New Skete.
Psalter. 3.50 (ISBN 0-8164-0311-2, HarpR). Har-Row.
Psalter & Hours of Yolande of Soissons. Karen Gould. LC 78-55888. 1978. 11.00x (ISBN 0-910956-78-2, SAM4); pap. 5.00x (ISBN 0-910956-64-2). Medieval Acad.
Psalter of Robert de Lisle. Lucy F. Sandler. (Harvey Miller Publication Ser.). (Illus.). 1983. 105.00x (ISBN 0-19-921028-4). Oxford U Pr.
Psalteria Rhythmica, 2 Vols. Ed. by Guido M. Dreves. 1900-01. 60.00 ea. (ISBN 0-384-12960-9) (ISBN 0-384-12961-7). Johnson Repr.
Psalteria Wessofontana. Ulrich V. Stocklin. Ed. by Guido M. Dreves. Repr. of 1902 ed. 60.00 (ISBN 0-384-58320-2). Johnson Repr.
Psaumes Choisis. Henry Morris. Tr. of Sampling the Psalms. (Fr.). 192p. 1986. pap. 3.50 (ISBN 0-8297-0697-6). Life Pubs Intl.
Pseudepigrapha & Modern Research, with a Supplement. James H. Charlesworth. LC 76-25921. (Society Biblical Literature Septuagint & Cognate Studies). 344p. 1981. pap. 12.75 (ISBN 0-89130-440-1, 06 0707S). Scholars Pr GA.
Pseudo-Dionysius Aeropagite: The Divine Names & Mystical Theology. Tr. by John D. Jones. (Mediaeval Philosophical Texts in Translation: No. 21). 320p. 24.95 (ISBN 0-87462-221-2). Marquette.
Pseudo Discipleship. George Verwer. (YA) 1970. pap. 1.50 (ISBN 0-87508-548-2). Chr Lit.
Pseudo-Epiphanius Testimony Book. Robert V. Hotchkiss. LC 74-15203. (Society of Biblical Literature. Texts & Translation-Early Christian Literature Ser.). 1974. pap. 8.95 (060204). Scholars Pr GA.
Pseudo-Ezekiel & the Original Prophecy. Charles C. Torrey. LC 78-63562. (Yale Oriental Ser. Researches: No. 18). Repr. of 1930 ed. 15.00 (ISBN 0-404-60288-6). AMS Pr.
Pseudo-Martyr. John Donne. LC 74-16215. 450p. 1974. 60.00x (ISBN 0-8201-1140-6). Schol Facsimiles.
Pseudoepigraphy & Ethical Arguments in the Pastoral Epistles. Lewis R. Donelson. 260p. 1986. lib. bdg. 52.50x (ISBN 3-16-145009-4, Pub. by J C B Mohr BRD). Coronet Bks.
Psicologia de Jesus y la Salud Mental. Raymond L. Cramer. Tr. by Carlos A. Vargas from Eng. LC 76-16438. Tr. of Psychology of Jesus & Mental Health. (Span.). 191p. 1976. pap. 5.95 (ISBN 0-89922-074-6). Edit Caribe.
Psicologia Pastoral de la Iglesia. Jorge A. Leon. LC 77-43121. (Span.). 192p. (Orig.). pap. 5.95 (ISBN 0-89922-113-0). Edit Caribe.
Psicologia Pastoral para Todos los Cristianos. Jorge A. Leon. LC 76-43121. (Span.). 181p. (Orig.). 1976. pap. 5.95 (ISBN 0-89922-020-7). Edit Caribe.
Psicologia y el Ministerio Cristiano. James E. Giles. 384p. 1982. Repr. of 1978 ed. 3.20 (ISBN 0-311-42059-1). Casa Bautista.
Psicologia y Religion. J. W. Drakeford. 384p. 1980. pap. 8.95 (ISBN 0-311-46035-6, Edit Mundo). Casa Bautista.
Psychanodia I: A Survey of the Evidence Concerning the Ascension of the Soul & its Relevance. Ioan P. Culianu. (Etudes Prelimminaires aux Religions Orientales dans l'Empire Romain Ser.: No. 99). 81p. 1983. pap. text ed. 19.95x (ISBN 90-04-06903-8, Pub. by EJ Brill Holland). Humanities.
Psyche & History. Marvin Goldwert. 85p. (Orig.). 1985. pap. 6.95x (ISBN 0-932269-41-9). Wyndham Hall.
Psyche & Psychism, 2 vols. Torkom Saraydarian. LC 80-67684. 1981. Set. 60.00 (ISBN 0-911794-06-9). Aqua Educ.
Psyche & Spirit. rev. ed. John J. Heaney. 1984. pap. 10.95 (ISBN 0-8091-2610-9). Paulist Pr.
Psyche Reborn: The Emergence of H. D. Susan S. Friedman. LC 80-8378. (Illus.). 352p. 1981. 22.50x (ISBN 0-253-37826-5). Ind U Pr.
Psyche: The Cult of Souls & Belief in Immortality Among the Greeks. facsimile ed. Erwin Rohde. LC 75-37911. (Select Bibliographies Reprint Ser). Repr. of 1920 ed. 32.00 (ISBN 0-8369-6749-6). Ayer Co Pubs.
Psychedelic Experience: A Manual Based on the Tibetan Book of the Dead. Timothy Leary & Ralph Metzner. 1976. pap. 4.95 (ISBN 0-8065-0552-4). Citadel Pr.
Psyche's Task: A Discourse Concerning the Influence of Superstition on the Growth of Institutions. 2nd ed. J. G. Frazer. 1979. Repr. of 1913 ed. lib. bdg. 27.50 (ISBN 0-8495-1636-6). Arden Lib.
Psychiatric Study of Jesus. Albert Schweitzer. 14.75 (ISBN 0-8446-2894-8). Peter Smith.
Psychiatric Study of Myths & Fairy Tales: Their Origins, Meaning & Usefulness. 2nd ed. Julius E. Heuscher. (Illus.). 440p. 1974. 23.75x (ISBN 0-398-02851-6). C C Thomas.
Psychiatry & Ethics. Maurice Levine. LC 72-18354. 384p. 1972. 12.50 (ISBN 0-8076-0642-1). Braziller.
Psychiatry & Mysticism. Stanley R. Dean. LC 75-8771. (Illus.). 446p. 1975. 30.95x (ISBN 0-88229-189-0). Nelson-Hall.

Psychiatry & Pastoral Care. Edgar Draper. LC 65-23861. (Successful Pastoral Counseling Series). pap. 34.50 (2026894). Bks Demand UMI.

Psychiatry & Religion: Overlapping Concerns (Clinical Insights Monograph) Lillian H. Robinson. LC 85-28728. 192p. 1986. pap. text ed. 12.00x (ISBN 0-88048-099-8, 48-099-8). Am Psychiatric.

Psychiatry, Ministry, & Pastoral Counseling. rev ed. Ed. by A. W. Sipe & Clarence J. Rowe. Orig. Title: Psychiatry, the Clergy, & Pastoral Counseling. 384p. 1984. pap. 12.95 (ISBN 0-8146-1324-1). Liturgical Pr.

Psychic Conversion & Theological Foundations: Toward a Reorientation of the Human Sciences. Robert M. Doran. LC 81-9360. (American Academy of Religion Studies in Religion Ser.). 1981. pap. 9.95 (ISBN 0-89130-522-X, 01-00-25). Scholars Pr GA.

Psychic Function of Religion in Mental Illness & Health, Vol. 6. GAP Committee on Psychiatry & Religion. LC 62-2872. (Report: No. 67). 1968. pap. 5.00 (ISBN 0-87318-092-5, Pub. by GAP). Brunner-Mazel.

Psychic Healing. John Weldon & Zola Levitt. 1982. pap. 5.95 (ISBN 0-8024-6446-7). Moody.

Psychic Life of Jesus. Maurice Elliott. 69.95 (ISBN 0-87968-185-3). Gordon Pr.

Psychic Philosophy & the Awakening of Spiritual Consciousness, 2 vols. Charles B. Newcomb. (Illus.). 1985. Set. 187.65 (ISBN 0-89920-090-7). Am Inst Psych.

Psychic Wholeness & Healing: Using All the Powers of the Human Psyche. Conrad W. Baars & Anna A. Terruwe. LC 81-4964. 245p. (Orig.). 1981. pap. 8.95 (ISBN 0-8189-0410-0). Alba.

Psychical Research & Spiritualism. Sanford E. Coates. (Illus.). 1980. deluxe ed. 69.75 (ISBN 0-89920-006-0). Am Classical Coll Pr.

Psycho-Cosmic Symbolism of the Buddhist Stupa. Lama A. Govinda. LC 76-797. (Illus.). 144p. 1976. pap. 6.95 (ISBN 0-913546-36-4). Dharma Pub.

Psycho-Cosmic Symbolism of the Buddhist Stupa. Lama A. Govinda. 102p. 1976. 20.00x (ISBN 0-317-39141-0, Pub. by Luzac & Co Ltd). State Mutual Bk.

Psychoanalysis & Ethics. Lewis S. Feuer. LC 73-1433. 134p. 1973. Repr. of 1955 ed. lib. bdg. 45.00x (ISBN 0-8371-6795-7, FEPE). Greenwood.

Psychoanalysis & Judaism. Mortimer Ostow. 1982. 25.00x (ISBN 0-87068-713-1). Ktav.

Psychoanalysis & Moral Values. Heinz Hartmann. LC 58-9230. (New York Psychoanalytic Institute Freud Anniversary Lecture Ser.). 121p. 1960. text ed. 17.50 (ISBN 0-8236-5240-8). Intl Univs Pr.

Psychoanalysis & Religion. Benjamin Beit-Hallahmi. 1978. lib. bdg. 27.50 (ISBN 0-8482-7374-5). Norwood Edns.

Psychoanalysis & Religion. Erich Fromm. (Terry Lectures Ser.). 1950. pap. 5.95 (ISBN 0-300-00089-8, Y12). Yale U Pr.

Psychoanalysis & Religious Experience. W. W. Meissner. 1984. 27.50 (ISBN 0-317-13715-8). Yale U Pr.

Psychoanalysis & Religious Experience. W. W. Meissner. LC 83-51296. 272p. 1986. pap. 9.95x (ISBN 0-300-03751-1, Y-599). Yale U Pr.

Psychoanalysis & Religious Mysticism. David C. McMlelland. 1983. pap. 2.50x (ISBN 0-87574-104-5, 104). Pendle Hill.

Psychoanalysis & the Bible: A Study in Depth of Seven Leaders. Dorothy F. Zeligs. LC 73-85071. 1973. 15.95x (ISBN 0-8197-0360-5). Bloch.

Psychoanalytic Object Relations Theory & the Study of Religion: On Faith & the Imaging of God. John McDargh. 296p. 1983. lib. bdg. 28.50 (ISBN 0-8191-3510-0); pap. text ed. 12.75 (ISBN 0-8191-3511-9). U Pr of Amer.

Psychoanalytic Reflections on the Holocaust: Selected Essays. Steven Luel & Paul Marcus. 1985. 25.00 (ISBN 0-88125-041-4). Ktav.

Psychodynamic Perspectives on Religion, Sect & Cult. D. A. Halperin. 416p. 1983. pap. text ed. 46.50 (ISBN 0-7236-7029-3). PSG Pub Co.

Psychodynamics of Yoga. H. L. Sharma. 160p. 1981. 16.95x (ISBN 0-317-12326-2, Pub. by G D K Pubns India). Asia Bk Corp.

Psychogenesis: Everything Begins in the Mind. Jack E. Addington. LC 79-145391. 1971. 10.95 (ISBN 0-396-06334-9). Dodd.

Psychogenesis: Everything Begins in the Mind. Jack E. Addington. 1987. pap. 8.95 (ISBN 0-396-09021-4). Dodd.

Psychohistory & Religion: The Case of Young Man Luther. Roger A. Johnson et al. LC 76-7870. pap. 51.50 (2026895). Bks Demand UMI.

Psychological & Ethical Aspects of Mormon Group Life. Ephraim E. Ericksen. LC 75-310523. (Bonneville Books Reprint Edition). pap. 30.80 (ISBN 0-317-41838-6, 2025900). Bks Demand UMI.

Psychological & Religious Development: Maturity & Maturation. Charles C. Kao. LC 80-5852. 382p. (Orig.). 1981. lib. bdg. 30.00 (ISBN 0-8191-1759-5); pap. text ed. 15.25 (ISBN 0-8191-1760-9). U Pr of Amer.

Psychological Aspects of Pauline Theology. Gerd Theissen. Tr. by John P. Galvin from Ger. LC 86-45196. 512p. 1986. 34.95 (ISBN 0-8006-0789-9). Fortress.

Psychological Assessment of Candidates for a Religious Order. Charles A. Weisgerber. LC 77-91649. 1969. pap. 2.95 (ISBN 0-8294-0019-2). Loyola.

Psychological Basis of Morality: An Essay on Value & Desire. F. C. T. Moore. LC 77-22632. (Library of Philosophy & Religion Ser). 106p. 1978. text ed. 28.50x (ISBN 0-06-494933-8). B&N Imports.

Psychological Commentaries on the Teaching of Gurdjieff & Ouspensky, Vol. 1. Maurice Nicoll. LC 83-25194. 371p. (Orig.). 1984. pap. 15.95 (ISBN 0-87773-269-8). Shambhala Pubns.

Psychological Commentaries on the Teachings of Gurdjieff & Ouspensky, Vol. 2. Maurice Nicoll. LC 83-25194. 404p. (Orig.). 1984. pap. 18.95 (ISBN 0-87773-270-1). Shambhala Pubns.

Psychological Commentaries on the Teachings of Gurdjieff & Ouspensky, Vol. 3. Maurice Nicoll. LC 83-25194. 447p. (Orig.). 1984. pap. 11.95 (ISBN 0-87773-271-X). Shambhala Pubns.

Psychological Commentaries on the Teaching of Gurdjieff & Ouspensky, Vol. 4. Maurice Nicoll. LC 83-25194. 268p. 1984. pap. 11.95 (ISBN 0-87773-287-6, 72695-2). Shambhala Pubns.

Psychological Commentaries on the Teaching of Gurdjieff & Ouspensky, Vol. 5. Maurice Nicoll. LC 83-25194. 253p. 1984. pap. 11.95 (ISBN 0-87773-288-4, 72694-4). Shambhala Pubns.

Psychological Foundations of Moral Education & Character Development: An Integrated Theory of Moral Development. Ed. by Richard T. Knowles & George F. McLean. 374p. (Orig.). 1986. lib. bdg. 26.75 (ISBN 0-8191-5406-7, Pub. by The Council for Research in Values & Philosophy); pap. 14.50 (ISBN 0-8191-5407-5, Pub by The Council for Research in Values & Philosophy). U Pr of Amer.

Psychological Meaning of the Sacred Symbols in Art, 2 vols. E. E. Goldsmith. (Illus.). 311p. 1987. Set. 167.50 (ISBN 0-89920-149-0). Am Inst Psych.

Psychological Origin & the Nature of Religion. James H. Leuba. LC 78-1577. 17.00 (ISBN 0-8414-5837-5). Folcroft.

Psychological Origin & the Nature of Religion. James H. Leuba. 94p. 1980. Repr. of 1909 ed. lib. bdg. 17.50 (ISBN 0-8482-1622-9). Norwood Edns.

Psychological Patterns of Jesus Christ. Frank Jakubowsky. 342p. (Orig.). 1982. pap. 14.95 (ISBN 0-932588-02-6). Jakubowsky.

Psychological Search for God. Roy V. Rowland. (Illus.). 1980. 44.75 (ISBN 0-89920-003-6). Am Inst Psych.

Psychological Seduction: The Failure of Modern Psychology. William K. Kilpatrick. LC 83-12151. 228p. 1983. pap. 5.95 (ISBN 0-8407-5843-X). Nelson.

Psychological Studies on Religious Man. T. Kallstad. 252p. 1978. pap. text ed. 22.00x (ISBN 91-554-0801-X, Pub. by Almqvist & Wiksell). Coronet Bks.

Psychological Testing for Ministerial Selection: Proceedings of the Seventh Academy Symposium. Academy of Religion & Mental Health Staff. Ed. by W. C. Bier. LC 73-79568. 1970. 25.00 (ISBN 0-8232-0850-8). Fordham.

Psychological Themes in the Golden Epistle of William Saint-Thierry to the Carthusians of Mont-Dieu. Louis M. Savary. Ed. by James Hogg. (Analecta Cartusiana Ser.: No. 8). 198p. (Orig.). 1973. pap. 25.00 (ISBN 3-7052-0009-7, Pub by Salzburg Studies). Longwood Pub Group.

Psychological Way: the Spiritual Way. Martin Bobgan & Deidre Bobgan. LC 79-17884. 224p. 1979. pap. 6.95 (ISBN 0-87123-026-7, 210026). Bethany Hse.

Psychological Wisdom from the Sanskrit, 2 Vols. (Illus.). 301p. 1985. 167.85 (ISBN 0-89920-080-X). Am Inst Psych.

Psychologie und Erkenntnisslehre D. Johannes Bonaventura. Karl Werner. (Ger.). 70p. 1973. Repr. of 1876 ed. lib. bdg. 18.50 (ISBN 0-8337-3739-2). B Franklin.

Psychology: An Orthodox Christian Perspective. Apostolos Makrakis. Ed. by Orthodox Christian Educational Society. Tr. by Denver Cummings from Hellenic. (Logos & Holy Spirit in the Unity of Christian Thought Ser.: Vol. 2). 151p. 1977. pap. 4.25x (ISBN 0-938366-05-X). Orthodox Chr.

Psychology & Christianity: Integrative Readings. Ed. by J. Roland Fleck & John D. Carter. LC 81-7911. 400p. (Orig.). 1981. pap. 15.95 (ISBN 0-687-34740-8). Abingdon.

Psychology & Morals. J. A. Hadfield. 245p. 1980. Repr. of 1926 ed. lib. bdg. 30.00 (ISBN 0-8492-5282-2). R West.

Psychology & Religion. Carl G. Jung. (Terry Lecture Ser.). 1938. pap. 5.95 (ISBN 0-300-00137-1, Y14). Yale U Pr.

Psychology & Religion: A Reader. Ed. by Margaret Gorman. pap. 11.95 (ISBN 0-8091-2684-2). Paulist Pr.

Psychology & Religion: Eight Points of View. Andrew R. Fuller. 143p. 1977. pap. text ed. 8.75 (ISBN 0-8191-0143-5). U Pr of Amer.

Psychology & Religion: Eight Points of View. 2nd ed. Andrew R. Fuller. 286p. 1986. pap. text ed. 9.75 (ISBN 0-8191-5336-2). U Pr of Amer.

Psychology & Religious Education. 3rd ed. John L. Elias. LC 83-7061. 154p. 1984. text ed. 11.50 (ISBN 0-89874-615-9). Krieger.

Psychology & Silence. Stanislaw Zielinski. Ed. by Daniel Bassuk. LC 75-7413. (Illus.). 32p. (Orig.). 1975. pap. 2.50x (ISBN 0-87574-201-7). Pendle Hill.

Psychology & the Christian Faith: An Introductory Reader. Ed. by Stanton L. Jones. 1986. pap. 11.95 (ISBN 0-8010-5217-3). Baker Bk.

Psychology & Theology. Gary R. Collins. LC 81-588. 160p. (Orig.). 1981. pap. 7.50 (ISBN 0-687-34830-7). Abingdon.

Psychology & Theology in Western Thought, 1672-1965: A Historical & Annotated Bibliography. Hendrika Vande Kemp. LC 82-49045. (Bibliographies in the History of Psychology & Psychiatry Ser.). (Orig.). 1984. lib. bdg. 75.00 (ISBN 0-527-92779-1). Kraus Intl.

Psychology & Western Religion. C. G. Jung. LC 84-42548. (Bollingen Ser.). (Illus.). 312p. (Orig.). 1984. pap. 8.95x (ISBN 0-691-01862-6). Princeton U Pr.

Psychology As Religion: The Cult of Self-Worship. Paul C. Vitz. 192p. 1977. pap. 5.95 (ISBN 0-8028-1696-7). Eerdmans.

Psychology in Search of a Soul. John W. Drakeford. LC 64-15096. 1964. 11.95 (ISBN 0-8054-6701-7). Broadman.

Psychology-Judaism Reader. Reuven P. Bulka & Moshe H. Spero. (Illus.). 338p. 1982. pap. 27.00x (ISBN 0-398-04582-8). C C Thomas.

Psychology of a Fairy Tale. David Hart. Ed. by Harriett Crosby. LC 76-56563. (Orig.). 1976. pap. 2.50x (ISBN 0-87574-210-6). Pendle-Hill.

Psychology of C. G. Jung. C. A. Meier. Tr. by Eugene Rolfe. (Unconscious in Its Empirical Manifestations Ser.: Vol. I). (Illus.). 256p. 1985. 25.50 (ISBN 0-938434-10-1). Sigo Pr.

Psychology of Christian Personality. Ernest M. Ligon. LC 35-22951. 1975. 7.00 (ISBN 0-915744-00-7); pap. 4.00 (ISBN 0-915744-01-5). Character Res.

Psychology of Conviction: A Study of Beliefs & Attitudes. Joseph Jastrow. 1979. Repr. of 1918 ed. lib. bdg. 40.00 (ISBN 0-8495-2744-9). Arden Lib.

Psychology of Counseling. Clyde M. Narramore. 13.95 (ISBN 0-310-29930-6, 10409). Zondervan.

Psychology of Ethics. John M. Dorsey. 261p. 1974. 18.95 (ISBN 0-8143-1639-5). Wayne St U Pr.

Psychology of Fate & of Free Will. Socrates & Plato. (Illus.). 121p. 1983. 75.85 (ISBN 0-89920-067-2). Am Inst Psych.

Psychology of Funeral Service. 6th ed. Edward A. Martin. text ed. 12.50 (ISBN 0-686-20530-8). E A Martin.

Psychology of Love According to St. Bonaventure. Robert P. Prentice. (Philosophy Ser). 1957. 8.00 (ISBN 0-686-11536-8). Franciscan Inst.

Psychology of Mysticism, 2 Vols. Max Nordau. 271p. 1985. Set. 249.50 (ISBN 0-89920-099-0). Am Inst Psych.

Psychology of Myth, Folklore & Religion. Leo Schneiderman. LC 81-9471. 232p. 1981. text ed. 21.95x (ISBN 0-88229-659-0); pap. text ed. 10.95x (ISBN 0-88229-783-X). Nelson-Hall.

Psychology of Redemption. Oswald Chambers. 1955. pap. 2.95 (ISBN 0-87508-124-X). Chr Lit.

Psychology of Religion. Joseph F. Byrnes. LC 84-47854. 320p. 1984. 24.95x (ISBN 0-02-903580-5). Free Pr.

Psychology of Religion. George A. Coe. LC 75-3113. Repr. of 1916 ed. 40.00 (ISBN 0-404-59109-4). AMS Pr.

Psychology of Religion. George A. Coe. Repr. of 1916 ed. 25.00 (ISBN 0-89987-046-5). Darby Bks.

Psychology of Religion. Heije Faber. LC 75-43721. 348p. 1976. 13.95 (ISBN 0-664-20748-0). Westminster.

Psychology of Religion: A Guide to Information Sources. Ed. by Donald Capps et al. LC 73-17530. (Philosophy & Religion Information Guide Ser.: Vol. 1). vii, 380p. 1976. 62.00x (ISBN 0-8103-1356-1). Gale.

Psychology of Religion: An Empirical Approach. Bernard Spilka et al. (Illus.). 400p. 1985. text ed. write for info. (ISBN 0-13-736398-2). P-H.

Psychology of Religion: Religion in Individual Lives. Mary J. Meadow & Richard D. Kahoe. 488p. 1984. text ed. 22.50 scp (ISBN 0-06-044411-8, HarpC). Har-Row.

Psychology of Religious Belief. L. B. Brown. 1987. 48.00 (ISBN 0-12-136355-4); pap. 24.00 (ISBN 0-12-136356-2). Acad Pr.

Psychology of Religious Belief. James B. Pratt. LC 75-3326. (Philosophy of America Ser.). Repr. of 1907 ed. 34.00 (ISBN 0-404-59321-6). AMS Pr.

Psychology of Religious Experiences. Erwin R. Goodenough. (Brown Classics in Judaica Ser.). 214p. 1986. pap. text ed. 10.75 (ISBN 0-8191-4489-4). U Pr of Amer.

Psychology of Religious Ritual. Manly P. Hall. pap. 2.50 (ISBN 0-89314-347-2). Philos Res.

Psychology of Religious Sects. Henry C. McComas. LC 70-172763. Repr. of 1912 ed. 20.00 (ISBN 0-404-04107-8). AMS Pr.

Psychology of Religious Vocations: Problems of the Religious Life. Andre Godin. Ed. by LeRoy A. Wauck. LC 82-24708. 136p. (Orig.). 1983. lib. bdg. 24.00 (ISBN 0-8191-3007-9); pap. text ed. 9.50 (ISBN 0-8191-3008-7). U Pr of Amer.

Psychology of Spiritual Growth. Mary E. Carreiro. 160p. 1987. 24.95 (ISBN 0-89789-123-6); pap. 8.95 (ISBN 0-89789-124-4). Bergin & Garvey.

Psychology of Superstition. Gustav Jahoda. LC 74-9667. 158p. 1974. Repr. 20.00x (ISBN 0-87668-185-2). Aronson.

Psychology of the Catholic Intellectual. Ed. by Fintan McNamee. (Synthesis Ser.). 1967. pap. 0.75 (ISBN 0-8199-0241-1, L38669). Franciscan Herald.

Psychology of the Soul. James H. Quitoriano. (Illus.). 1979. 47.50 (ISBN 0-89266-204-2). Am Classical Coll Pr.

Psychology of the Soul, 2 vols. Otto Rank. (Illus.). 201p. 1986. Set. 147.55 (ISBN 0-89920-127-X). Am Inst Psych.

Psychology's Occult Doubles: Psychology & the Problem of Pseudoscience. Thomas H. Leahey & Grace E. Leahey. LC 82-24635. 296p. 1983. lib. bdg. 25.95x (ISBN 0-88229-717-1). Nelson-Hall.

Psychomental Complex of the Tungus. Sergei M. Shirokogorov. LC 76-44788. 488p. Repr. of 1935 ed. 120.00 (ISBN 0-404-15879-X). AMS Pr.

Psychosomatic Yoga. J. Mumford. (Paths to Inner Power Ser.). 96p. 1974. 1.25 (ISBN 0-85030-208-0). Weiser.

Psychotherapy & Religion. Josef Rudin. Tr. by Paul C. Bailey & Elisabeth Reinecke. LC 68-12291. 1968. pap. 7.95x (ISBN 0-268-00226-6). U of Notre Dame Pr.

Psychotherapy & the Religiously Committed Patient. Ed. by E. Mark Stern. LC 84-25276. (Psychotherapy Patient Ser.: Vol. 1, No. 3). 158p. 1985. text ed. 19.95 (ISBN 0-86656-394-6); pap. text ed. 14.95 (ISBN 0-86656-396-2). Haworth Pr.

Psychotherapy Based on Human Longing. Robert Murphy, Jr. LC 60-14173. (Orig.). 1960. pap. 2.50x (ISBN 0-87574-111-8, 111). Pendle Hill.

Psychotherapy in a Religious Framework. Rebecca L. Propst. LC 86-27582. 208p. 1987. text ed. 29.95 (ISBN 0-89885-350-8). Human Sci Pr.

Psychotherapy in Christian Perspective. Ed. by David G. Benner. 300p. 1987. pap. price not set (ISBN 0-8010-0942-1). Baker Bk.

Psychotherapy of the Religious Patient. Ed. by Moshe H. Spero. 250p. 1985. 32.75 (ISBN 0-398-05058-9). C C Thomas.

Psycological Dynamics of Religious Experience. Andre Godin. Tr. by Mary Turton from Fr. Orig. Title: Psychologie des Experiences Religieuses. 279p. 1985. pap. 13.95 (ISBN 0-89135-039-X). Religious Educ.

PTA with a Purpose. 2.00 (ISBN 0-914131-49-4, L01). Torah Umesorah.

Public Career of Sir Thomas More. J. A. Guy. LC 80-5391. 224p. 1980. 34.00x (ISBN 0-300-02546-7). Yale U Pr.

Public Church: Mainline-Evangelical-Catholic. Martin E. Marty. 192p. 1981. 10.95 (ISBN 0-8245-0019-9). Crossroad NY.

Public Duties in Islam: The Institution of the Hisba. Ibn Taymiya. Tr. by Muhtar Holland from Arabic. 159p. (Orig.). 1982. pap. 6.95x (ISBN 0-86037-113-1, Pub by Islamic Found UK). New Era Pubns MI.

Public Education Religion Studies: An Overview. N. Piediscalzi et al. Ed. by B. Swyhart. LC 76-26670. (American Academy of Religion. Section Papers). 1976. pap. 12.00 (ISBN 0-89130-082-1, 01-09-18). Scholars Pr GA.

Public Education Religion Studies: An Overview. Paul J. Will et al. LC 80-12237. (Aids for the Study of Religion Ser.). 1981. write for info. (ISBN 0-89130-401-0); pap. 12.00 (ISBN 0-89130-402-9, 01-03-07). Scholars Pr GA.

Public Life in Bible Times. Ed. by James I. Packer et al. 224p. 1985. pap. 6.95 (ISBN 0-8407-5984-3). Nelson.

Public Life of Our Lord Jesus Christ, 2 vols. A. Goodier. 1978. Set. 15.95 (ISBN 0-8198-0551-3); Set. pap. 13.95 (ISBN 0-8198-0552-1). Dghtrs St Paul.

Public Ministry of Christ. William G. Blaikie. 356p. 1984. lib. bdg. 13.25 (ISBN 0-86524-167-8, 9517). Klock & Klock.

Public Money & Parochial Education: Bishop Hughes, Governor Seward & the New York School Controversy. Vincent Lannie. 294p. (Pub. by Press of Case Western University). 1968. 16.95 (ISBN 0-268-00565-6). U of Notre Dame Pr.

Public Prayer & the Constitution: A Case Study in Constitutional Interpretation. Rodney K. Smith. 320p. 1987. 35.00 (ISBN 0-8420-2260-0). Scholarly Res Inc.

Public Prayers. Arthur C. McGiffert, Jr. LC 83-83269. (Studies in Ministry & Parish Life). 44p. 1984. pap. 2.50x (ISBN 0-913552-24-0). Exploration Pr.

Public Relations. Cathy Campbell. 1985. 4.80 (ISBN 0-318-18572-5). Natl Cath Educ.

Public Relations Are an Asset for Archives & Museums. Ed. by Rowland P. Gill. (No. 6). 32p. (Orig.). 1985. pap. text ed. 5.15 (ISBN 0-910653-12-7, 8101-L). Archival Servs.

Public Relations Handbook for Your Church. Barbara Williams. 112p. 1985. pap. 5.95 (ISBN 0-8170-1050-5). Judson.

Public Religion in American Culture. John F. Wilson. 240p. 1981. pap. 9.95 (ISBN 0-87722-226-6). Temple U Pr.

Public Religion in American Culture. John F. Wilson. 240p. 1979. lib. bdg. 24.95 (ISBN 0-87722-159-6). Temple U Pr.

Public School & Moral Education. Henry C. Johnson, Jr. LC 80-20768. (Education of the Public & the Public School Ser.). 96p. (Orig.). 1981. pap. 5.95 (ISBN 0-8298-0420-X). Pilgrim NY.

Public Side of Learning: The Political Consequences of Scholorship in the Context of Judaism. Jacob Neusner. (Studies in Religion). 1985. 17.95 (ISBN 0-89130-860-1); pap. 11.95 (ISBN 0-89130-861-X, 01-00-40). Scholars Pr GA.

Public Speaking: A Handbook for Christians. Duane Litfin. LC 81-65993. 400p. (Orig.). 1981. pap. 13.95 (ISBN 0-8010-5605-5). Baker Bk.

Public Style: A Study of the Community Participation of Protestant Ministers. Walter M. Stuhr, Jr. LC 72-89687. (Studies in Religion & Society Ser.). 1972. 14.95x (ISBN 0-913348-12-0); pap. 8.95x (ISBN 0-913348-02-3). Ctr Sci Study.

Public Theology & Political Economy: Christian Stewardship in Modern Society. Max L. Stackhouse. 192p. (Orig.). 1987. pap. 8.95 (ISBN 0-8028-0267-2). Eerdmans.

Public Virtue: Law & the Social Character of Religion. Christopher F. Mooney. LC 85-41014. 192p. 1986. text ed. 22.95x (ISBN 0-268-01561-9). U of Notre Dame Pr.

Public Vocation of Christian Ethics. Beverly W. Harrison et al. 400p. (Orig.). 1987. pap. 12.95 (ISBN 0-8298-0582-6). Pilgrim NY.

Public Worship of God: A Source Book. Henry S. Coffin. 16.00 (ISBN 0-8369-7272-4, 8071). Ayer Co Pubs.

Publish Good News: A Resource Guide for Self-Publishing Church Groups. Gerald L. Hastings. (Illus.). 80p. (Orig.). 1986. pap. 6.50 (ISBN 0-937641-01-4). Stone Canyon Pr.

Puebla: A Pilgrimage of Faith. Pope John Paul. 1979. pap. 2.00 (ISBN 0-8198-0629-3). Dghtrs St Paul.

Puebla & Beyond. Ed. by John Eagleson & Philip J. Scharper. LC 79-24098. 370p. (Orig.). 1979. pap. 9.95 (ISBN 0-88344-399-6). Orbis Bks.

Pueblo Cultures. B. Wright. (Iconography of Religions X Ser.: No. 4). (Illus.). xii, 29p. 1986. pap. 26.25 (ISBN 90-04-07106-7, Pub. by E J Brill). Heinman.

Pueblo God & Myths. Hamilton A. Tyler. LC 64-11317. (Civilization of the American Indians Ser.: Vol. 71). (Illus.). 336p. 1984. pap. 8.95 (ISBN 0-8061-1112-7). U of Okla Pr.

Puerto Rican Neighbor. Roy Schuckman. 1983. pap. 2.50x (ISBN 0-87574-075-8, 075). Pendle Hill.

Puggala-Pannatti. Ed. by Richard Morris. LC 78-70109. Repr. of 1883 ed. 20.00 (ISBN 0-404-17359-4). AMS Pr.

Pulpit & Press. Mary B. Eddy. pap. 4.50 (ISBN 0-87952-046-9). First Church.

Pulpit & the Pew. Charles H. Parkhurst. 1913. 39.50x (ISBN 0-686-83717-7). Elliots Bks.

Pulpit Commentary, 23 vols. H. D. Spence & T. S. Exell. Incl. Old Testament only, 14 Vols. 320.00 (ISBN 0-8028-8056-8, 2209); New Testament only, 8 Vols. 200.00 (ISBN 0-8028-8057-6, 2210). 1959. Repr. Set. 520.00 (ISBN 0-8028-8055-X); 0er vol 22.95. Eerdmans.

Pulpit Commentary, 23 vols. Ed. by H. D. Spence & Joseph S. Exell. 26612p. Date not set. Set. 520.00 (ISBN 0-917006-32-1). Hendrickson MA.

Pulpit of the American Revolution: Political Sermons of the Period of 1776. Ed. by John W. Thornton. LC 71-109611. (Era of the American Revolution Ser). 1970. Repr. of 1860 ed. lib. bdg. 49.50 (ISBN 0-306-71907-X). Da Capo.

Pulpit Preparation. Paul Hamsher. (Orig.). 1981. pap. 5.95 (ISBN 0-937172-29-4). JLJ Pubs.

Pulpit under the Sky: A Life of Hans Nielson Hauge. Joseph M. Shaw. LC 78-12391. 1979. Repr. of 1955 ed. lib. bdg. 24.75x (ISBN 0-313-21123-X, SHPU). Greenwood.

Pulpit Words Translated for Pew People. Charles W. Turner. pap. 4.95 (ISBN 0-88469-046-6). BMH Bks.

Pumpkin Personalities. Ruth Katz. (Illus.). 1979. 5.95 (ISBN 0-8027-6364-2); PLB 5.85 (ISBN 0-8027-6365-0). Walker & Co.

Punishing the Perpetrators of the Holocaust: The Ohlendorf & Von Weizsaecker Cases. John Mendelsohn. LC 81-80326. (Holocaust Ser.). 310p. 1982. lib. bdg. 61.00 (ISBN 0-8240-4892-X). Garland Pub.

Punishment in Islamic Law. M. S. El Awa. 162p. Date not set. pap. 6.00 (ISBN 0-89259-015-7). Am Trust Pubns.

Punishment of Apostasy in Islam. S. A. Rahman. pap. 7.50 (ISBN 0-686-18551-X). Kazi Pubns.

Punjab Problem: The Muslim Connection. Balraj Madhok. 1985. 14.00x (ISBN 0-8364-1519-1, Pub. by Vision). South Asia Bks.

Punjab Story. Amarjit Kaur et al. 1985. 12.50x (ISBN 0-8364-1319-9, Pub. by Roli Books). South Asia Bks.

Pupil Profiles. Roger C. Reeds. (Sunday School Workers Training Course Ser.: No. 3). 1973. pap. 3.95 (ISBN 0-89265-010-9). Randall Hse.

Pupil Profiles: Teacher's Guide. Larry D. Hampton. 1978. pap. 1.50 (ISBN 0-89265-057-5). Randall Hse.

Puppet & the Word. R. Sylwester. LC 12-2966. 1982. pap. 4.95 (ISBN 0-570-03873-1). Concordia.

Puppet Animals Tell Bible Stories. Marie M. Chapman. LC 77-75134. (Illus.). 1977. tchr's ed. spiral bdg. 4.95 (ISBN 0-916406-74-1). Accent Bks.

Puppet Dialogues. Charles E. Magnet. LC 78-53323. 1978. spiral bdg. 4.95 (ISBN 0-916406-99-7). Accent Bks.

Puppet Ministry. James Christy. 78p. 1978. 2.50 (ISBN 0-8341-0532-2). Beacon Hill.

Puppet People. Pat Zabriskie. LC 79-53725. 80p. (Orig.). 1979. pap. 2.95 (ISBN 0-88243-753-4, 02-0753). Gospel Pub.

Puppet People Scripts. Violet Whittaker. 1984. pap. 8.95 (ISBN 0-8010-9666-9). Baker Bk.

Puppet Plays with a Point. rev. ed. David Faust & Candy Faust. 160p. 1979. pap. 7.95 (ISBN 0-87239-248-1, 3364). Standard Pub.

Puppet Scripts by the Month. Margaret Cheasebro. 1985. pap. 4.95 (ISBN 0-8054-7524-9). Broadman.

Puppet Scripts for Children's Church. Jessie P. Sullivan. (Paperback Program Ser.). 1978. pap. 4.50 (ISBN 0-8010-8124-6). Baker Bk.

Puppet Scripts for Use at Church. Ed. by Everett Robertson. LC 78-72843. 1979. pap. 6.95 (ISBN 0-8054-7516-8). Broadman.

Puppet Scripts for Use at Church, No. 2. Ed. by Everett Robertson. LC 78-72843. 1980. saddle-wire 6.95 (ISBN 0-8054-7519-2). Broadman.

Puppet Shows That Reach & Teach Children, 3 vols. Joyce Reynolds. LC 73-185586. (Illus.). 1974. Vol. 1. pap. 3.50 (ISBN 0-88243-740-2, 02-0740); Vol. 2. pap. 3.50 (ISBN 0-88243-741-0, 02-0741); Vol. 3. pap. 3.50 (ISBN 0-88243-744-5, 02-0744). Gospel Pub.

Puppets Go to Church. Earl Perry & Wilma Perry. 85p. 1975. pap. 2.50 (ISBN 0-8341-0385-0). Beacon Hill.

Puranas: Ancient Indian Tradition & Mythology. J. L. Shastri. 1978-82. Shiva Purana: 4 Vols. 60.00 (ISBN 0-89581-343-2); Bhagavata Purana: 5 Vols. 75.00 (ISBN 0-89581-536-2); Linga Purana: 2 Vols. 45.00 (ISBN 0-89581-537-0); Garuda Purana: 3 Vols. 45.00 (ISBN 0-89581-538-9); Narada Purana: 5 Vols. 75.00 (ISBN 0-89581-539-7). Asian Human Pr.

Purchas His Pilgrim Microcosmus: Or The Historie of Man. Samuel Purchas. LC 76-25513. (English Experience Ser.: No. 146). 820p. 1969. Repr. of 1619 ed. 69.00 (ISBN 90-221-0146-0). Walter J Johnson.

Purdah & the Status of Women in Islam. A. A. Maududi. pap. 9.50 (ISBN 0-686-18464-5). Kazi Pubns.

Pure Grace. Bro. Stanley. 96p. 1984. 6.95 (ISBN 0-89962-414-6). Todd & Honeywell.

Pure Land. Lonnie C. Mings. (Orig.). 1979. pap. 4.95 (ISBN 0-8024-5989-7). Moody.

Pure Lust: Elemental Feminist Philosophy. Mary Daly. LC 83-71944. 488p. 1984. 18.95 (ISBN 0-8070-1504-0); pap. 11.95 (ISBN 0-8070-1505-9, BP 692). Beacon Pr.

Pure Thoughts. Eileen C. Wood. 1985. 5.95 (ISBN 0-533-06662-X). Vantage.

Purgatory--Explained by the Lives & Legends of the Saints. F. X. Schouppe. LC 86-50579. 427p. (Orig.). 1986. pap. 5.00 (Pulp Pocketbook (ISBN 0-89555-301-5). Tan Bks Pubs.

Purgatory & Heaven. J. P. Arendzen. (Canterbury Ser.). 1972. pap. 2.00 (ISBN 0-89555-045-8). TAN Bks Pubs.

Purgatory: Explained by the Lives & Legends of the Saints. F. X. Shouppe. LC 79-112489. 1973. pap. 8.50 (ISBN 0-89555-042-3). TAN Bks Pubs.

Purged. Gerald F. Mundfrom. 175p. Date not set. 5.00 (ISBN 0-318-19336-1). Mercy & Truth.

Purim. Howard Greenfeld. LC 82-3058. (Illus.). 32p. 1983. 9.95 (ISBN 0-03-061478-3). H Holt & Co.

Purim Anthology. Ed. by Philip Goodman. (Illus.). 525p. 1949. 7.50 (ISBN 0-8276-0022-4, 248). Jewish Pubns.

Purim Party. Norma Simon. (Festival Series of Picture Story Books). (Illus.). 1959. plastic cover 4.50 (ISBN 0-8381-0707-9). United Syn Bk.

Puritan Age & Rule in the Colony of the Massachusetts Bay, 1629-1685. George E. Ellis. LC 75-122838. (Research & Source Ser.: No. 522). 1970. Repr. of 1888 ed. lib. bdg. 32.00 (ISBN 0-8337-1054-0). B Franklin.

Puritan & the Cynic: Moralists & Theorists in French Letters. Jefferson Humphries. 144p. 1986. 15.95 (ISBN 0-19-504180-1). Oxford U Pr.

Puritan As a Colonist & Reformer. Ezra H. Byington. LC 75-31115. Repr. of 1899 ed. 34.50 (ISBN 0-404-13601-X). AMS Pr.

Puritan Attitudes Towards Recreation in Early Seventeenth-Century New England, Vol. 17. Hans-Peter Wagner. (Mainzer Studien zur Internationalen Entwecklung). 273p. 1982. pap. 33.15 (ISBN 3-8204-7286-X). P Lang Pubs.

Puritan Boston & Quaker Philadelphia. E. Digby Baltzell. LC 81-70494. 585p. 1982. pap. 12.95x (ISBN 0-8070-5415-1, BP 638). Beacon Pr.

Puritan Colony in Maryland. Daniel R. Randall. LC 78-63763. (Johns Hopkins University. Studies in the Social Sciences. Fourth Ser. 1886: 6). Repr. of 1886 ed. 11.50 (ISBN 0-404-61031-5). AMS Pr.

Puritan Colony in Maryland. Daniel R. Randall. 1973. pap. 9.00 (ISBN 0-384-49568-0). Johnson Repr.

Puritan Commonwealth. Peter Oliver. LC 75-31127. Repr. of 1856 ed. 41.50 (ISBN 0-404-13606-0). AMS Pr.

Puritan Conscience & Modern Sexuality. Edmund Leites. LC 85-20198. 208p. 1986. 17.50 (ISBN 0-300-03490-3). Yale U Pr.

Puritan Conversion Narrative: The Beginnings of American Expression. Patricia Caldwell. LC 82-22772. (Cambridge Studies in American Literature & Culture). 192p. 1983. 21.95 (ISBN 0-521-25460-4). Cambridge U Pr.

Puritan Conversion Narrative: The Beginnings of American Expression. Patricia Caldwell. 224p. 1985. pap. 12.95 (ISBN 0-521-31147-0). Cambridge U Pr.

Puritan Dilemma: The Story of John Winthrop. Edmund S. Morgan. (Library of American Biography). 224p. 1962. pap. 8.75 (ISBN 0-316-58286-7). Little.

Puritan Element in Victorian Fiction. Florence Maly-Schlatter. LC 72-195449. 1940. lib. bdg. 20.00 (ISBN 0-8414-5974-6). Folcroft.

Puritan Family. E. S. Morgan. 14.75 (ISBN 0-8446-2609-0). Peter Smith.

Puritan Family: Religion & Domestic Relations in Seventeenth-Century New England. Edmund S. Morgan. LC 80-18819. x, 196p. 1980. Repr. of 1966 ed. lib. bdg. 29.75x (ISBN 0-313-22703-9, MOPFA). Greenwood.

Puritan Family: Religion & Domestic Relations in 17th-Century New England. rev. ed. Ed. by Edmund S. Morgan. pap. 6.95x (ISBN 0-06-131227-4, TB1227, Torch). Har-Row.

Puritan Gentry: The Great Puritan Families of Early Stuart England. J. T. Cliffe. 300p. 1984. 25.00x (ISBN 0-7102-0007-2). Methuen Inc.

Puritan Heritage. George M. Stephenson. LC 78-10512. 1978. Repr. of 1952 ed. lib. bdg. 22.50x (ISBN 0-313-20733-X, STPU). Greenwood.

Puritan Hope. Iain H. Murray. 1975. pap. 5.95 (ISBN 0-85151-037-X). Banner of Truth.

Puritan in England & New England: With a Chapter on Witchcraft in New England. 4th & enl. ed. Ezra H. Byington. LC 70-183241. (Research & Source Works Ser). (Illus.). 457p. 1972. Repr. of 1900 ed. lib. bdg. 29.50 (ISBN 0-8337-4017-2). B Franklin.

Puritan in Voodoo-Land. Edna Taft. LC 73-174115. (Tower Bks). (Illus.). 1971. Repr. of 1938 ed. 43.00x (ISBN 0-8103-3919-6). Gale.

Puritan Justice & the Indian: White Man's Law in Massachusetts, 1630-1763. Yasuhide Kawashima. (Illus.). xii, 258p. 1984. 35.00x (ISBN 0-8195-5068-X). Wesleyan U Pr.

Puritan Lectureships: The Politics of Religious Dissent, 1560-1662. Paul S. Seaver. LC 71-93497. 1970. 30.00x (ISBN 0-8047-0711-1). Stanford U Pr.

Puritan London: A Study of Religion & Society in the City Parishes. Tai Liu. LC 85-40534. 256p. 1986. 38.50x (ISBN 0-87413-283-5, Pub. by U Delaware Pr). Assoc Univ Prs.

Puritan Manifestoes. Walter H. Frere. 1907. 20.50 (ISBN 0-8337-4119-5). B Franklin.

Puritan Migration to Connecticut: The Saga of the Seymour Family, 1129-1746. Malcolm Seymour. LC 82-548. (Illus.). 136p. 1982. 29.50 (ISBN 0-914016-85-7). Phoenix Pub.

Puritan Moment: The Coming of Revolution in an English County. William Hunt. (Harvard Historical Studies: No. 102). (Illus.). 384p. 1983. text ed. 36.00x (ISBN 0-674-73903-5). Harvard U Pr.

Puritan Moment: The Coming of Revolution in an English County. William Hunt. (Harvard Historical Studies: No. 102). 384p. 1985. pap. text ed. 8.95x (ISBN 0-674-73904-3). Harvard U Pr.

Puritan Origins of the American Self. Sacvan Bercovitch. LC 74-29713. 272p. 1975. pap. 9.95x (ISBN 0-300-02117-8). Yale U Pr.

Puritan Personal Writings: Autobiographies & Other Writings, Vol. 8. LC 78-270. (American Puritan Writings Ser.). 240p. 1982. 67.50 (ISBN 0-404-60808-6). AMS Pr.

Puritan Personal Writings: Diaries, Vol. 7. LC 78-269. (American Puritan Writings Ser.). 1982. 67.50 (ISBN 0-404-60807-8). AMS Pr.

Puritan Protagonist: President Thomas Clap of Yale College. Louis L. Tucker. xviii, 283p. 1962. 25.00x (ISBN 0-8078-0841-5). U of NC Pr.

Puritan Rhetoric: The Issue of Emotion in Religion. Eugene E. White. LC 76-181987. (Landmarks in Rhetoric & Public Address Ser.). 229p. 1972. 10.95x (ISBN 0-8093-0563-1). S Ill U Pr.

Puritan Sermon in America, 1630-1750, 4 vols. Ed. by Ronald A. Bosco. LC 78-114749. (Sermon in America Ser.). 1978. Repr. 200.00x set (ISBN 0-8201-1320-4). Schol Facsimiles.

Puritan Sermons, Sixteen Fifty-Nine To Sixteen Eighty-Nine Being the Morning Exercises at Cripplegate, St. Giles in the Fields & in Southwark: By 75 Ministers of the Gospel in or Near London, with Notes & Translations by James Nichols, 6 vols. Samuel Annesley. Ed. by James Nichols. 4200p. 1981. Set. lib. bdg. 120.00 (ISBN 0-940033-19-4). R O Roberts.

Puritan Sermons, 1659-1689, 6 vols. Samuel Annesley et al. Ed. by James Nichols. 4220p. 1981. Repr. of 1845 ed. lib. bdg. 120.00 set (ISBN 0-939464-07-1). Labyrinth Pr.

Puritan Treasury of Quotations. pap. 6.45 (ISBN 0-85151-249-6). Banner of Truth.

Puritan Village Evolves: A History of Wayland, Massachusetts. Helen F. Emery. LC 81-5185. (Illus.). 384p. 1981. 15.00x (ISBN 0-914016-78-4). Phoenix Pub.

Puritan Way of Death: A Study in Religion, Culture & Social Change. David E. Stannard. LC 76-42647. (Illus.). 1977. 19.95x (ISBN 0-19-502226-2). Oxford U Pr.

Puritan Way of Death: A Study in Religion, Culture, & Social Change. David E. Stannard. LC 76-42647. (Illus.). 1977. pap. 8.95 (ISBN 0-19-502521-0). Oxford U Pr.

Puritanism & Democracy. Ralph B. Perry. 688p. 1944. 19.50 (ISBN 0-8149-0180-8). Vanguard.

Puritanism & Liberty: Being the Army Debates (1647-9) from the Clarke Manuscripts with Supplementary Documents. Ed. & intro. by A. S. Woodhouse. 634p. 1986. pap. 11.95x (ISBN 0-460-01057-3, Pub. by Evman England). Biblio Dist.

Puritanism & Richard Bancroft. Stuart B. Babbage. LC 63-2799. (Church Historical Society Ser.: No. 84). 1962. 20.00x (ISBN 0-8401-5084-9). A R Allenson.

Puritanism & Theatre: Thomas Middleton & Opposition Drama Under the Early Stuarts. Margot Heinemann. LC 79-14991. (Past & Present Publications Ser.). 309p. 1982. 34.50 (ISBN 0-521-22602-3); pap. 13.95 (ISBN 0-521-27052-9). Cambridge U Pr.

Puritanism in America. Everett Emerson. (World Leaders Ser.). 1977. lib. bdg. 12.50 (ISBN 0-8057-7692-3, Twayne). G K Hall.

Puritanism in Early America. 2nd ed. Ed. by George M. Waller. (Problems in American Civilization Ser). 1973. pap. text ed. 5.95 (ISBN 0-669-82719-3). Heath.

Puritanism in England. Herbert H. Henson. LC 70-185944. 294p. 1973. Repr. of 1912 ed. 23.50 (ISBN 0-8337-4177-2). B Franklin.

Puritanism in Old & New England. Alan Simpson. LC 55-13637. (Walgreen Foundation Lecture Ser). 1961. pap. 4.00x (ISBN 0-226-75929-6, P66, Phoen). U of Chicago Pr.

Puritanism in the Period of the Great Persecution, 1660-1688. Gerald R. Cragg. LC 76-143557. 1971. Repr. of 1957 ed. 16.00x (ISBN 0-8462-1578-0). Russell.

Puritanism in Tudor England. Ed. by H. C. Porter. LC 75-145532. (History in Depth Ser). xvi, 312p. 1971. 17.95x (ISBN 0-87249-222-2); pap. 7.95x (ISBN 0-87249-223-0). U of SC Pr.

Puritans: A Sourcebook of Their Writings, 2 Vols. Perry Miller & T. H. Johnson. Set. 38.50 (ISBN 0-8446-2593-0). Vol. 2. Peter Smith.

Puritans: A Sourcebook of Their Writings, 2 vols. Ed. by Perry Miller & Thomas H. Johnson. (Orig.). Vol. 1. pap. 8.95x (ISBN 0-06-131093-X, TB1093, Torch); Vol. 2. pap. 8.95x (ISBN 0-06-131094-8, TB1094, Torch). Har-Row.

Puritans among the Indians: Accounts of Captivity & Redemption, 1676-1724. Ed. by Alden T. Vaughan & Edward W. Clark. (John Harvard Library). 288p. 1986. pap. text ed. 7.95x (ISBN 0-674-73899-3, Belknap Pr). Harvard U Pr.

Puritans & Libertines: Anglo-French Literary Relations in the Reformation. Hugh M. Richmond. 400p. 1981. 35.95x (ISBN 0-520-04179-8). U of Cal Pr.

Puritans & Pragmatists: Eight Eminent American Thinkers. Paul K. Conkin. LC 75-34730. (Midland Bks.: No. 197). 512p. 1976. 20.00x (ISBN 0-253-34720-3); pap. 6.95x (ISBN 0-253-20197-7). Ind U Pr.

Puritans & Predestination: Grace in English Protestant Theology, 1525 to 1695. Dewey D. Wallace, Jr. LC 81-11563. (Studies in Religion). xiii, 289p. 1982. 29.95x (ISBN 0-8078-1499-7). U of NC Pr.

Puritans & Radicals in North England: Essays on the English Revolution. Roger Howell, Jr. LC 84-10411. 226p. (Orig.). 1984. lib. bdg. 24.25 (ISBN 0-8191-4013-9); pap. text ed. 12.25 (ISBN 0-8191-4014-7). U Pr of Amer.

Puritans in America: A Narrative Anthology. Ed. by Alan Heimert & Nicholas Delbanco. 456p. 1985. text ed. 25.00x (ISBN 0-674-74065-3); pap. text ed. 7.95x (ISBN 0-674-74066-1). Harvard U Pr.

Purity & Danger: An Analysis of the Concepts of Pollution & Taboo. Mary Douglas. 196p. 1984. pap. 6.95 (ISBN 0-7448-0011-0, Ark Paperbks). Methuen Inc.

Purity Crusade: Sexual Morality & Social Control, 1868-1900. David J. Pivar. LC 70-179650. (Contributions in American History Ser.: No. 23). 308p. 1973. lib. bdg. 29.95 (ISBN 0-8371-6319-6, PPC/). Greenwood.

Purity in the Christian Home. Paul M. Landis. 1978. 0.95 (ISBN 0-686-25260-8). Rod & Staff.

Purity of Heart. Vaughn J. Featherstone. LC 82-72728. 103p. 1982. 8.95 (ISBN 0-87747-914-3). Deseret Bk.

Purity of Heart. Soren Kierkegaard. Tr. by Douglas Steere. pap. 7.95x (ISBN 0-06-130004-7, TB4, Torch). Har-Row.

Purpose. Gene Edwards. 1987. pap. 5.95 (ISBN 0-940232-27-8). Christian Bks.

Purpose: A Little Gift in the Adventure of Life. Buddy Sears. 169p. (Orig.). 1986. pap. 6.95 (ISBN 0-87418-023-6, 160). Coleman Pub.

Purpose in Prayer. Edward M. Bounds. (Direction Bks). 1978. pap. 3.95 (ISBN 0-8010-0738-0). Baker Bk.

Purpose of a Christian School. Ed. by David Cummings. 1979. pap. 4.50 (ISBN 0-87552-157-6). Presby & Reformed.

Purpose of Authority? Lucius Annese. LC 78-72295. (Orig.). 1978. 50.00 (ISBN 0-933402-12-0). Charisma Pr.

Purpose of Church-Related Colleges. Leslie K. Patton. LC 78-177145. (Columbia University. Studies in the Social Sciences: No. 783). Repr. of 1940 ed. 22.50 (ISBN 0-404-55783-X). AMS Pr.

Purpose of Genesis. Stephen D. Eckstein, Jr. 1976. pap. 2.75 (ISBN 0-88027-037-3). Firm Foun Pub.

Purpose of Islam. M. Yameen Zubairi. LC 84-90999. 100p. (Orig.). 1984. pap. text ed. write for info. (ISBN 0-930895-02-9). Byron Daven Pub.

Purpose of Life. Satguru S. Keshavadas. LC 78-50754. (Illus.). 112p. 1978. 5.95 (ISBN 0-533-03147-8). Vishwa.

Purpose of Luke-Acts. Robert Maddox. Ed. by John Riches. 220p. 1982. 26.95 (ISBN 0-567-09312-3, Pub. by T&T Clark Ltd UK). Fortress.

Purpose of Physical Reality: The Kingdom of Names. John S. Hatcher. Ed. by Betty J. Fisher & Richard A. Hill. 250p. 1987. pap. 12.00 (ISBN 0-87743-208-2). Baha'i.

Purpose of Suffering: Knowing the God Who Comforts. H. Edwin Young. LC 85-80488. 144p. (Orig.). 1985. pap. 4.95 (ISBN 0-89081-496-1). Harvest Hse.

Purpose of the Church & Its Ministry. H. Richard Niebuhr. LC 76-62925. (Orig.). 1977. pap. 3.00i (ISBN 0-06-066174-7, RD 211, HarpR). Har-Row.

Purposes of Pentecost. Derek Prince. (Foundation Ser.: Bk. IV). 1965-66. pap. 3.95 (ISBN 0-934920-03-6). Derek Prince.

Pursued. rev. ed. J. Vera Schlamm & Bob Friedman. LC 86-600. 189p. 1986. pap. 3.95 (ISBN 0-8307-1146-5, 5018631). Regal.

Pursuing Life's Adventures. Dorothy M. Schmidt. LC 85-40650. 168p. 1985. pap. 5.95 (ISBN 0-938232-84-3, Dist. by Baker & Taylor Co.). Winston-Derek.

Pursuit of a Just Social Order: Policy Statements of the U. S. Catholic Bishops, 1966-80. Brian J. Benestad. LC 82-18326. 220p. 1982. 12.00 (ISBN 0-89633-060-5); pap. 7.00 (ISBN 0-89633-061-3). Ethics & Public Policy.

Pursuit of Death. Howard K. Congdon. LC 76-44308. Repr. of 1977 ed. 36.30 (ISBN 0-8357-9022-3, 2016395). Bks Demand UMI.

Pursuit of God. Aiden W. Tozer. LC 82-70768. 128p. 1982. 4.95 (ISBN 0-87509-191-1); pap. 3.95 (ISBN 0-87509-192-X); 3.25 (ISBN 0-87509-223-3); legacy ed. 5.95 (ISBN 0-87509-366-3). Chr Pubns.

Pursuit of Happiness. Florence Littauer. LC 80-85333. 1981. pap. 4.95 (ISBN 0-89081-284-5). Harvest Hse.

Pursuit of Happiness. 2nd ed. Spiros Zodhiates. 665p. 1982. pap. 9.95 (ISBN 0-89957-508-0). AMG Pubs.

Pursuit of Holiness. Jerry Bridges. LC 78-18109. 158p. 1978. pap. 3.95 (ISBN 0-89109-430-X). NavPress.

Pursuit of Holiness. Jerry Bridges. (Christian Character Library). 158p. 1985. hdbk. 8.95 (ISBN 0-89109-467-9). NavPress.

Pursuit of Holiness. Jerry Bridges. 192p. 1985. pap. 9.95 (ISBN 0-8027-2507-4). Walker & Co.

Pursuit of Purity: A History of American Fundamentalism since 1850. David O. Beale. 1986. 15.95 (ISBN 0-89084-351-1); pap. 12.95 (ISBN 0-89084-350-3). Bob Jones Univ Pr.

Pursuit of the Millennium. rev ed. Norman Cohn. 1970. pap. 11.95 (ISBN 0-19-500456-6). Oxford U Pr.

Purushartha-Siddhyupaya (Jaina-Pravachana-Rahasya-Kosha) Amritachandra. Ed. & tr. by Ajit Prasada. LC 73-3838. (Sacred Books of the Jainas: No. 4). Repr. of 1933 ed. 22.50 (ISBN 0-404-57704-0). AMS Pr.

Purva-Mimamsa-Sutras of Jaimini. Jaimini. Tr. & commentary by Ganganath Jha. LC 73-3797. (Sacred Books of the Hindus: No. 10). Repr. of 1916 ed. 55.00 (ISBN 0-404-57810-1). AMS Pr.

Push Me Gently, Lord. Marilyn Moravec et al. LC 85-80100. 186p. (Orig.). 1985. pap. 4.95 (ISBN 0-935797-21-1). Harvest IL.

Push-Pull Marriage. Les Carter. 1984. 7.95 (ISBN 0-8010-2497-8); pap. 5.95 (ISBN 0-8010-2490-0). Baker Bk.

Pusillum, 4 vols. Athanasius Bierbaum. 7.50 (ISBN 0-685-10971-2, L38675). Franciscan Herald.

Put a Little Starch in Your Faith. Otis Bernard. 150p. 1980. pap. 4.95 (ISBN 0-89221-095-8). New Leaf.

Put Your Arms Around the World. Marcus V. Hand. LC 78-66976. 112p. (Orig.). 1978. pap. text ed. 1.25 (ISBN 0-87148-698-9). Pathway Pr.

Put Your Mind at Ease. Joyce S. Hifler. 128p. (Orig.). 1983. pap. 7.75 (ISBN 0-687-34929-X). Abingdon.

Putting Away Childish Things. David A. Seamands. 144p. 1982. pap. 5.95 (ISBN 0-88207-308-7). Victor Bks.

Putting Christ First: A Woman's Workshop on Colossians. Margaret Fromer & Paul Fromer. Ed. by Janet Kobobel. (Woman's Workshop Ser.). 128p. 1986. pap. 5.95 (ISBN 0-310-44801-8, 11313P). Zondervan.

Putting Forgiveness into Practice. Doris Donnelly. LC 82-71967. 192p. 1982. 5.95 (ISBN 0-89505-087-0). Argus Comm.

Putting God First. Jim Burns. (Illus.). 64p. 1983. wkbk. 3.95 (ISBN 0-89081-366-3). Harvest Hse.

Putting It All Together in a Puppet Ministry. Fredda Marsh. LC 77-91674. 144p. 1978. pap. text ed. 6.95 (ISBN 0-88243-578-7, 02-0578). Gospel Pub.

Putting Life Back Together. Marion R. Brown. 96p. 1986. 5.95 (ISBN 0-87159-132-4). Unity School.

Putting on the New Self: A Guide to Personal Development & Community Living. David Sanderlin. 1986. pap. 12.95 (ISBN 0-87061-125-9). Chr Classics.

Putting the Pieces Together: Advent Christians Interpret Prophecy. Ed. by Freeman Barton. 80p. (Orig.). 1983. pap. 3.00 (ISBN 0-913439-02-9). Henceforth.

Putting the Pieces Together: Guidance from a Pastoral Psychologist. Robert L. Randall. 80p. (Orig.). 1986. pap. 4.95 (ISBN 0-8298-0583-4). Pilgrim NY.

Putting up with Your Put Downs. Clark B. McCall. (Uplook Ser.). 1978. pap. 0.79 (ISBN 0-8163-0093-3, 16970-6). Pacific Pr Pub Assn.

Putting Your Faith on the Line. Hubert Mitchell. (Orig.). 1981. pap. 5.95 (ISBN 0-89840-027-9). Heres Life.

Puyallup-Nisqually. Marian W. Smith. LC 73-82360. (Columbia Univ. Contributions to Anthropology Ser.: Vol. 32). 1969. Repr. of 1940 ed. 34.50 (ISBN 0-404-50582-1). AMS Pr.

Puzzled! The Jewish Word Search. Norma A. Orovitz. LC 77-83177. 1977. pap. 3.95 (ISBN 0-8197-0022-3). Bloch.

Puzzling Gospels. Joseph Dahmus. (Basics of Christian Thought Ser.). 1985. 10.95 (ISBN 0-88347-182-5). Thomas More.

Pylgrymage of Sir Richard Guylforde to the Holy Land, A. D. 1506. Ed. by Henry Ellis. LC 75-166023. (Camden Society, London. Publications, First Ser.: No. 51). Repr. of 1851 ed. 19.00 (ISBN 0-404-50151-6). AMS Pr.

Pylgrymage of Sir Richard Guylforde to the Holy Land A. D. 1506. 1851. 19.00 (ISBN 0-384-48440-9). Johnson Repr.

Pyramid Builders of Ancient Egypt: A Modern Investigation of Pharoah's Workforce. A. R. David. 258p. 1986. text ed. 34.95 (ISBN 0-7100-9909-6). Methuen Inc.

Pyramid Power. Max Toth & Greg Nielson. (Illus.). 207p. 1985. pap. 4.95 (ISBN 0-89281-106-4). Inner Tradit.

Pyramids. 2nd ed. Ahmed Fakhry. LC 61-8645. 272p. 1974. pap. 9.95 (ISBN 0-226-23473-8, P571, Phoen). U of Chicago Pr.

Pyramids. John Weeks. (Cambridge Introduction to the History of Mankind Ser.). (Illus.). 1971. 5.95 (ISBN 0-521-07240-9). Cambridge U Pr.

Pyramids. John Weeks. LC 76-22457. (Cambridge Topic Bks.). (Illus.). 1977. PLB 8.95 (ISBN 0-8225-1209-2). Lerner Pubns.

Pyramids & the Second Reality. Bill Schul & Ed Pettit. 1979. pap. 4.95 (ISBN 0-449-90008-8, Columbine). Fawcett.

Pyramids of Egypt. I. E. S. Edwards. 368p. 1987. 25.00 (ISBN 0-670-80153-4). Viking.

Pyramids: Tombs for Eternity. Mildred M. Pace. (Illus.). 192p. 1981. 10.95 (ISBN 0-07-048054-0). McGraw.

Python. Joseph Fontenrose. 1959. 25.00 (ISBN 0-8196-0285-X). Biblo.

Python: A Study of Delphic Myth & Its Origins. Joseph Fontenrose. (California Library Reprint Ser.: No. 108). 637p. 1981. 40.00x (ISBN 0-520-04106-2); pap. 8.95 (ISBN 0-520-04091-0, CAL 449). U of Cal Pr.

Q

Qabala Trilogy. Carlo Suares. Tr. by Micheline Stuart & Vincent Stuart. LC 85-8179. 565p. 1985. pap. 17.95 (ISBN 0-87773-337-6, 74220-6). Shambhala Pubns.

Qabalah. Papus. 1977. pap. 12.95 (ISBN 0-85030-340-0). Weiser.

Qabalism. Henry B. Pullen-Burry. 167p. 1972. Repr. of 1925 ed. 10.00 (ISBN 0-911662-45-6). Yoga.

Qabbalah: The Philosophical Writings of Solomon Ben Yehudah Ibn Gabirol. Isaac Myer. 69.95 (ISBN 0-8490-0922-7). Gordon Pr.

Quaestionum in Heptateuchum Libri 7, Adnotationum in Iob Liber Unus. Saint Aurelius Augustinus. (Corpus Scriptorum Ecclesiasticorum Latinorum Ser: Vol. 38, Pt. 2). 50.00 (ISBN 0-384-02515-3). Johnson Repr.

Quaker: A Study in Costume. Amelia M. Gummere. LC 68-56494. (Illus.). 1968. Repr. of 1901 ed. 20.00 (ISBN 0-405-08585-0, Blom Pubns). Ayer Co Pubs.

Quaker Anecdotes. Irvin C. Poley & Ruth V. Poley. 1983. pap. 2.50x (ISBN 0-87574-033-2, 033). Pendle Hill.

Quaker Approach to Contemporary Problems. Ed. by John Kavanaugh. Repr. of 1953 ed. lib. bdg. 22.50x (ISBN 0-8371-4432-9, KAGA). Greenwood.

Quaker Cavalier: William Penn. Joyce Reason. 1971. pap. 2.95 (ISBN 0-87508-618-7). Chr Lit.

Quaker Colonies. Sidney G. Fisher. 1919. 8.50x (ISBN 0-686-83720-7). Elliots Bks.

Quaker Doctrine of Inward Peace. Howard H. Brinton. LC 64-23230. (Orig.). 1948. pap. 2.50x (ISBN 0-87574-044-8). Pendle Hill.

Quaker Education in the Colony & State of New Jersey. Thomas Woody. LC 76-89256. (American Education: Its Men, Institutions & Ideas, Ser. 1). 1969. Repr. of 1923 ed. 32.00 (ISBN 0-405-01494-5). Ayer Co Pubs.

Quaker Education in Theory & Practice. rev. ed. Howard H. Brinton. LC 58-12843. (Orig.). 1940. pap. 15.00x (ISBN 0-87574-009-X). Pendle Hill.

Quaker Experiences in International Conciliation. C. H. Yarrow. LC 78-7415. 1978. 25.00x (ISBN 0-300-02260-3). Yale U Pr.

Quaker Heritage in Medicine. Russell J. Elkinton & Robert A. Clark. (Illus.). 1978. pap. 3.95 (ISBN 0-910286-68-X). Boxwood.

Quaker Influence in American Literature. Howard W. Hintz. Repr. of 1940 ed. lib. bdg. 18.75 (ISBN 0-8371-3945-7, HIGA). Greenwood.

Quaker Invasion of Massachusetts. Richard P. Hallowell. 13.50 (ISBN 0-8369-7139-6, 7972). Ayer Co Pubs.

Quaker Journals: Varieties of Religious Experience among Friends. Howard H. Brinton. LC 78-188399. (Illus., Orig.). 1983. 7.00 (ISBN 0-87574-952-6). Pendle Hill.

Quaker Looks at Yoga. Dorothy Ackerman. LC 76-23909. (Orig.). 1976. pap. 2.50x (ISBN 0-87574-207-6, 207). Pendle Hill.

Quaker Meeting. Howard E. Collier. 1983. pap. 2.50x (ISBN 0-87574-026-X, 026). Pendle Hill.

Quaker Message. Sidney Lucas. 1983. pap. 2.50x (ISBN 0-87574-040-5, 040). Pendle Hill.

Quaker Message: A Personal Affirmation. Hugh L. Doncaster. 1983. pap. 2.50x (ISBN 0-87574-181-9, 181). Pendle Hill.

Quaker Mutation. Gerald Heard. 1983. pap. 2.50x (ISBN 0-87574-007-3, 007). Pendle Hill.

Quaker Poets Past & Present. Mary H. Jones. LC 75-7414. 32p. (Orig.). 1975. pap. 2.50x (ISBN 0-87574-202-5). Pendle Hill.

Quaker Relief During the Siege of Boston. Henry J. Cadbury. 1983. pap. 2.50x (ISBN 0-686-43965-1, 004). Pendle Hill.

Quaker Sloopers: From the Fjords to the Prairies. Wilmer L. Tjossem. LC 84-80195. 80p. 1984. pap. 8.95 (ISBN 0-913408-85-9). Friends United.

Quaker Social History: Sixteen Sixty-Nine to Seventeen Thirty-Eight. Arnold Lloyd. LC 79-4398. 1979. Repr. of 1950 ed. lib. bdg. 22.50x (ISBN 0-313-20943-X, LLQU). Greenwood.

Quaker Spirituality: Selected Writings. Ed. by Douglas V. Steere. (Classics of Western Spirituality Ser.). 384p. 1984. 12.95 (ISBN 0-8091-0335-4); pap. 9.95 (ISBN 0-8091-2510-2). Paulist Pr.

Quaker Strongholds. Caroline Stephen. Ed. by Mary G. Ogilvie. LC 51-4625. 32p. (Orig.). 1951. pap. 2.50x (ISBN 0-87574-059-6, 059). Pendle Hill.

Quaker Struggle for the Rights of Women. pap. 0.70 (ISBN 0-686-95360-6). Am Fr Serv Comm.

Quaker Testimonies & Economic Alternatives. Severyn Broyn. LC 80-80915. 35p. pap. 2.50x (ISBN 0-87574-231-9). Pendle Hill.

Quaker Worship & Techniques of Meditation. Scott Crom. 1983. pap. 2.50x (ISBN 0-87574-195-9, 195). Pendle Hill.

Quakerism: A Study Guide on the Religious Society of Friends. Leonard S. Kenworthy. LC 81-80656. 224p. 1981. pap. 5.00 (ISBN 0-932970-21-4). Prinit Pr.

Quakerism & Christianity. Edwin B. Bronner. LC 67-18689. (Orig.). 1967. pap. 2.50x (ISBN 0-87574-152-5, 152). Pendle Hill.

Quakerism & Other Religions. Howard H. Brinton. 1983. pap. 2.50x (ISBN 0-87574-093-6, 093). Pendle Hill.

Quakerism in India. Horace Alexander. 1983. pap. 2.50x (ISBN 0-87574-031-6, 031). Pendle Hill.

Quakerism of the Future: Mystical, Prophetic & Evangelical. John Yungblut. LC 74-81830. (Orig.). 1974. pap. 2.50x (ISBN 0-87574-194-0). Pendle Hill.

Quakerism on the Eastern Shore. Kenneth Carroll. LC 70-112986. (Illus.). 328p. 1970. 15.00x (ISBN 0-938420-15-1). Md Hist.

Quakers. Hope Hay. 1985. 13.00x (ISBN 0-7062-4025-1, Pub. by Ward Lock Educ Co Ltd). State Mutual Bk.

Quakers & Education. W. A. Stewart. LC 76-115330. 1971. Repr. of 1953 ed. 32.50x (ISBN 0-8046-1121-1, Pub. by Kennikat). Assoc Faculty Pr.

Quakers & Slavery: A Divided Spirit. Jean R. Soderlund. LC 85-42707. (Illus.). 240p. 1985. text ed. 27.50x (ISBN 0-691-04732-4). Princeton U Pr.

Quakers & the Atlantic Culture. Frederick Tolles. 1980. Repr. of 1960 ed. lib. bdg. 16.00x (ISBN 0-374-97949-9, Octagon). Hippocrene Bks.

Quakers & the English Revolution. Barry Reay. LC 84-22355. 200p. 1985. 22.50 (ISBN 0-312-65808-7). St Martin.

Quakers & the Use of Power. Paul Lacey. LC 81-85558. (Pendle Hill Pamphlets Ser.). 32p. (Orig.). 1982. pap. 2.50x (ISBN 0-87574-241-6, 241). Pendle Hill.

Quakers As Pioneers in Social Work. Auguste Jorns. LC 68-8232. 1969. Repr. of 1931 ed. 26.50x (ISBN 0-8046-0244-1, Pub. by Kennikat). Assoc Faculty Pr.

Quakers As Pioneers in Social Work. Auguste Jorns. Tr. by Thomas K. Brown. LC 69-14934. (Criminology, Law Enforcement, & Social Problems Ser.: No. 27). 1969. Repr. of 1931 ed. 8.50x (ISBN 0-87585-027-8). Patterson Smith.

Quakers in Conflict: The Hicksite Reformation. H. Larry Ingle. LC 86-1528. 330p. 1986. text ed. 29.95x (ISBN 0-87049-501-1). U of Tenn Pr.

Quakers in Nazi Germany. Michael Seadle. (Studies in Quakerism: No. 5). 44p. (Orig.). 1978. pap. 2.00 (ISBN 0-89670-006-2). Progresiv Pub.

Quakers in Peace & War. Margaret E. Hirst. LC 70-147671. (Library of War & Peace; Relig. & Ethical Positions on War Ser.). lib. bdg. 46.00 (ISBN 0-8240-0429-9). Garland Pub.

Quakers in Peace & War: An Account of Their Peace Principles & Practice. Margaret E. Hirst. LC 73-137545. (Peace Movement in America Ser). 560p. 1972. Repr. of 1923 ed. lib. bdg. 32.95x (ISBN 0-89198-073-3). Ozer.

Quakers in Pennsylvania. Albert C. Applegarth. LC 78-63813. (Johns Hopkins University. Studies in the Social Sciences. Tenth Ser. 1892: 8-9). Repr. of 1892 ed. 11.50 (ISBN 0-404-61076-5). AMS Pr.

Quakers in Pennsylvania. Albert C. Applegarth. pap. 9.00 (ISBN 0-384-01765-7). Johnson Repr.

Quakers in Puritan England. Hugh Barbour. LC 85-6963. 300p. 1985. pap. 14.95 (ISBN 0-913408-87-5). Friends United.

Quakers in Science & Industry. Arthur Raistrick. LC 68-18641. (Illus.). 1968. Repr. of 1950 ed. 35.00x (ISBN 0-678-05622-6). Kelley.

Quakers in the Colonial Northeast. Arthur J. Worrall. LC 79-63086. 248p. 1980. 20.00x (ISBN 0-87451-174-7). U Pr of New Eng.

Qualities & Competencies of the Catechist. rev. ed. 1983. 4.80 (ISBN 0-318-00789-4). Natl Cath Educ.

Qualities of Holy Quran. M. I. Siddiqui. 1981. 2.50 (ISBN 0-686-97854-4). Kazi Pubns.

Quality Friendship. Gary Inrig. LC 81-38379. 192p. (Orig.). 1981. pap. 5.95 (ISBN 0-8024-2891-6). Moody.

Quality Living. rev. ed. Walter C. Kaiser, Jr. (MP Electives Ser.). 1986. pap. text ed. 3.95 (ISBN 0-8024-7069-6); tchr's ed. 4.95 (ISBN 0-8024-7070-X). Moody.

Quality of Life in a Global Society. Paul McCleary & J. Philip Wogaman. (Orig.). 1978. pap. 2.50 (ISBN 0-377-00070-1). Friend Pr.

Quality of Witness: A Romanian Diary, 1937-1944. Emil Dorian. Ed. by Marguerite Dorian. Tr. by Mara S. Vamos from Romanian. 352p. 1983. 19.95 (ISBN 0-8276-0211-1). Jewish Pubns.

Quality of Work Life: Health Care Applications. Ed. by Kenneth A. Buback & Mary K. Grant. LC 82-12766. 300p. 1985. pap. 24.00 (ISBN 0-87125-074-8). Cath Health.

Quandary of Life, Science & Religion. Parker L. Johnstone. LC 82-83297. 212p. 1982. cloth 7.95 (ISBN 0-917802-04-7). Theoscience Found.

Quantum Questions: Mystical Writings of the Great Physicists. Ed. by Ken Wilber. LC 83-20332. (New Science Library). 200p. 1984. pap. 9.95 (ISBN 0-87773-266-3). Shambhala Pubns.

Quarterback Speaks to His God. Herbert Wilner. 288p. 1987. 17.95 (ISBN 0-933529-04-X); pap. 8.95 (ISBN 0-933529-03-1). Cayuse Pr.

Quarternary of Israel. Aharon Horowitz. LC 78-8855. 1979. 45.00 (ISBN 0-12-356170-1). Acad Pr.

Quartet in Heaven. facs. ed. Sheila Kaye-Smith. LC 75-136649. (Biography Index Reprint Ser.). 1952. 18.00 (ISBN 0-8369-8044-1). Ayer Co Pubs.

Quasi-Dramatic St. John Passions from Scandinavia & Their Medieval Background. Audrey E. Davidson. (Early Drama, Art & Music Monograph: No. 3). (Illus.). viii, 135p. 1981. pap. 8.95 (ISBN 0-918720-14-1). Medieval Inst.

Que Creen los Menonitas. J. C. Wenger. Ed. by Arnoldo J. Casas. Tr. by Ernesto S. Vilela from Eng. LC 79-89307. (Mennonite Faith Ser.: No. 2). (Span.). 72p. 1979. pap. 1.50x (ISBN 0-8361-1223-7). Herald Pr.

Que es la Doctrina Cristiana? Su Valor, Necesidad y Base. (Biblioteca de Doctrina Cristiana Ser.). Tr. of What is Christian Doctrine? (Span.). 1985. pap. 5.95 (ISBN 0-311-09111-3). Casa Bautista.

Que Mi Pueblo Adore. Edward W. Nelson. Tr. by Salomon C. Mussiett from Eng. Tr. of Music & Worship. (Span.). 184p. 1986. pap. 5.00 (ISBN 0-311-17029-3). Casa Bautista.

Que Pasa Despues de la Muerte? 2nd ed. H. Rossier. Ed. by Gordon H. Bennett. Tr. by Sara Bautista from Eng. (Serie Diamante). Tr. of What Happens After Death? (Span., Illus.). 36p. 1982. pap. 0.85 (ISBN 0-942504-07-0). Overcomer Pr.

Que Paso con Estos Pecados? P. A. Deiros. 144p. 1979. pap. 2.50 (ISBN 0-311-42063-X). Casa Bautista.

Queen Anne Churches: A Catalogue of the Papers in Lambeth Palace Library of the Commission for Building Fifty New Churches in London & Westminster, 1711-1759. Compiled by E. G. Bill. 280p. 1979. 53.00x (ISBN 0-7201-0919-1). Mansell.

Queen Esther. Illus. by Tomie DePaola. (Bible Story Cutout Bks.). (Illus., Orig.). 1984. 32p 12.95, (ISBN 0-86683-822-8, 8454, HarpR); pap. 4.95, 40p (ISBN 0-86683-702-7, 8271). Har-Row.

Queen of Apostles Prayerbook. James Alberione. 7.50 (ISBN 0-8198-0266-2); plastic bdg. 6.00 (ISBN 0-8198-0267-0). Dghtrs St Paul.

Queen of Peace, Echo of the Eternal Word. Tomislav Pervan. (Illus.). 58p. (Orig.). 1986. pap. 3.50 (ISBN 0-940535-05-X). Franciscan U Pr.

Queen of the Air: A Study of the Greek Myths of Cloud & Storm. John Ruskin. LC 78-58190. 1978. Repr. of 1869 ed. lib. bdg. 25.00 (ISBN 0-89341-322-4). Longwood Pub Group.

Queener: The Man Behind the Preaching. Foster Bell & Darlene Bell. 1976. pap. 2.95 (ISBN 0-934942-13-7). White Wing Pub.

Queening of Ceridwen. Esther Elias. 1982. 6.95 (ISBN 0-8158-0409-1). Chris Mass.

Queen's Heart of Gold: The Complete Story of Our Lady of Beauraing. Sr. Mary Amatora. LC 78-188443. 1972. 7.50 (ISBN 0-682-47467-3, Banner); pap. 5.00 (ISBN 0-682-47480-0, Banner). Exposition Pr FL.

Queen's Portrait: The Story of Guadalupe. Sr. Mary Amatora. LC 74-188442. 1972. 7.50 (ISBN 0-682-47468-1, Lochinvar); (Lochinvar). Exposition Pr FL.

Quellen und Forschungen zur Reformationsgeschichte, Vols. 1-23, Lacking Vols. 3 & 7. Set. 895.00 (ISBN 0-384-49010-7); Set. pap. 775.00 (ISBN 0-685-02139-4). Johnson Repr.

Quellen zur Ethik Theophrasts. William Fortenbaugh. 380p. 1983. 48.00x (ISBN 90-6032-218-5, Pub by B R Gruener Amsterdam). Benjamins North Am.

Quellen zur Geschichte der Taufer, Band IV. Manfred Krebs. 61.00 (ISBN 0-384-30425-7); pap. 55.00 (ISBN 0-384-30424-9). Johnson Repr.

Quellen zur Geschichte der Taufer. Karl Schornbaum. 34.00 (ISBN 0-384-54246-8); pap. 28.00 (ISBN 0-384-54245-X). Johnson Repr.

Quellen zur Geschichte der Taufer in der Schweiz, Vol 1: Zurich. Walter Schmid & Leonhard Von Murat. 428p. 1952. PLB 9.00x (ISBN 0-8361-1152-4). Herald Pr.

Quellen zur Geschichte der Taufer in der Schweiz, Vol. 2: Ostschweiz. Heinhold Fast. (Ger.). 1974. 59.00x (ISBN 0-8361-1197-4). Herald Pr.

Quellen zur Geschichte der Wiedertaufer. Karl Schornbaum. 34.00 (ISBN 0-384-54249-2); pap. 28.00 (ISBN 0-384-54248-4). Johnson Repr.

Quellen zur Geshichte der Wiedertaufer. Gustav Bossert. 90.00 (ISBN 0-384-05276-2); pap. 84.00 (ISBN 0-384-05275-4). Johnson Repr.

Quench Not the Spirit. rev. ed. Myron S. Augsburger. LC 62-7330. 1975. pap. 2.95 (ISBN 0-8361-1477-9). Herald Pr.

Querelle des Images Huitieme-Neuvieme Siecle. Louis Brehier. 1969. 14.00 (ISBN 0-8337-0362-5). B Franklin.

Quest. Stephen Carman & Robert Owen. 160p. (Orig.). 1986. pap. 5.95 (ISBN 0-8423-5112-4). Tyndale.

Quest Anthology. Ed. by James Webb. LC 75-36916. (Occult Ser.). 1976. Repr. of 1976 ed. 46.50x (ISBN 0-405-07971-0). Ayer Co Pubs.

Quest for a Black Theology. Ed. by James J. Gardiner & J. Deotis Roberts. LC 76-151250. 128p. 1971. 6.95 (ISBN 0-8298-0196-0). Pilgrim NY.

Quest for a Philosophical Jesus: Christianity & Philosophy in Rousseau, Kant, Hegel, & Schelling. Vincent A. McCarthy. xv, 240p. 1986. 28.95 (ISBN 0-86554-210-4, MUP-H190). Mercer Univ Pr.

Quest for Better Preaching: Resources for Renewal in the Pulpit. Edward F. Markquart. LC 85-13500. 240p. (Orig.). 1985. pap. 10.95 (ISBN 0-8066-2170-2, 10-5349). Augsburg.

Quest for Church Unity: From John Calvin to Isaac d'Huisseau. Richard Stauffer. (Pittsburgh Theological Monographs: No. 19). (Orig.). 1986. pap. 14.00 (ISBN 0-915138-63-8). Pickwick.

Quest for Eastern Christians: Travels & Rumor in the Age of Discovery. Francis M. Rogers. LC 62-18138. pap. 58.30 (ISBN 0-317-41750-9, 2055901). Bks Demand UMI.

Quest for Eden. Elena M. Marsella. LC 66-16172. 275p. 1966. 8.95 (ISBN 0-8022-1063-5). Philos Lib.

Quest for Eternity: An Outline of the Philosophy of Religion. J. C. Gaskin. (Pelican Ser.). 192p. 1984. pap. 5.95 (ISBN 0-14-022538-2). Penguin.

Quest for Eternity: Manners & Morals in the Age of Chivalry. Charles T. Wood. LC 82-40476. (Illus.). 172p. 1983. pap. 8.00x (ISBN 0-87451-259-X). U Pr of New Eng.

Quest for Faith. C. Stephens Evans. LC 86-7436. 144p. (Orig.). 1986. pap. 4.95 (ISBN 0-87784-511-5). Inter-Varsity.

Quest for Faith, Quest for Freedom: Aspects of Pennsylvania's Religious Experience. Ed. by Otto Reimherr. LC 86-61790. (Illus.). 208p. 1987. 28.50x (ISBN 0-941664-26-0). Susquehanna U Pr.

Quest for God: A Journey into Prayer & Symbolism. Abraham J. Heschel. (Crossroad Paperback Ser.). 176p. 1982. pap. 7.95 (ISBN 0-8245-0436-4). Crossroad NY.

Quest for Justice. Ed. by J. Brian Benestace & Frances J. Butler. 487p. (Orig.). 1981. pap. 17.95 (ISBN 1-55586-649-2). US Catholic.

Quest for Love & Self-Esteem: New Insights from Psychology & Religion. Virginia Bourgeous. LC 76-29301. (Illus.). 80p. (Orig.). 1976. pap. 5.95 (ISBN 0-88290-070-6). Horizon Utah.

Quest for Moral Law. facsimile ed. Louise S. Eby. LC 78-37849. (Essay Index Reprint Ser). Repr. of 1944 ed. 20.00 (ISBN 0-8369-2588-2). Ayer Co Pubs.

Quest for Noah's Ark. John W. Montgomery. LC 74-21993. (Illus.). 384p. 1972. pap. 4.95 (ISBN 0-87123-477-7, 200477). Bethany Hse.

Quest for Past & Future: Essays in Jewish Theology. Emil. L. Fackenheim. LC 83-12692. 336p. 1983. Repr. of 1968 ed. lib. bdg. 39.75x (ISBN 0-313-22738-1, FAQP). Greenwood.

Quest for Piety & Obedience: The Story of the Brethren in Christ. Carlton O. Wittlinger. LC 77-94894. 1978. 12.95 (ISBN 0-916035-05-0). Evangel Indiana.

Quest for Political & Spiritual Liberation: A Study in the Thought of Sri Aurobindo Ghose. June O'Connor. LC 75-5249. 153p. 1976. 16.50 (ISBN 0-8386-1734-4). Fairleigh Dickinson.

Quest for Renewal: Personal Revival in the Old Testament. Walter C. Kaiser, Jr. (Orig.). 1986. pap. 6.95 (ISBN 0-8024-7050-5). Moody.

Quest for the Historical Israel. George W. Ramsey. LC 80-82188. 208p. (Orig.). 1981. pap. 13.95 (ISBN 0-8042-0187-0). John Knox.

Quest for the Holy Grail. Ellen Cooney. LC 80-67333. 85p. (Orig.). 1981. pap. 5.95 (ISBN 0-9602912-3-7). Duir Press.

Quest for the Holy Grail. Frederick W. Locke. LC 70-181948. (Stanford University. Stanford Studies in Language & Literature: No. 21). Repr. of 1960 ed. 22.50 (ISBN 0-404-51831-1). AMS Pr.

Quest for the Kingdom of God: Essays in Honor of George E. Mendenhall. Ed. by H. B. Huffmon et al. 1983. text ed. 20.00x (ISBN 0-931464-15-3). Eisenbrauns.

Quest for the Liberated Christian. Mary Hall. (IC-Studies in the Intercultural History of Christianity: Vol. 19). 341p. 1978. pap. 37.25 (ISBN 3-261-02668-5). P Lang Pubs.

Quest for Unity in the New Teatament Church: A Study in Paul & Acts. Paul J. Achtemeier. LC 86-45911. 128p. 1987. pap. 7.95 (ISBN 0-8006-1972-2, 1-1972). Fortress.

Quest for Unity in the New Testament Church: A Study in Paul & Acts. Paul J. Achtemeier. 1987. pap. 7.95. Fortress.

Quest for Wholeness. Carl G. Vaught. LC 81-18365. 224p. 1982. 44.50 (ISBN 0-87395-593-5); pap. 14.95 (ISBN 0-87395-594-3). State U NY Pr.

Quest: History & Meaning in Religion. Mircea Eliade. LC 68-19059. (Midway Reprint Ser.). xii, 180p. 1984. pap. text ed. 10.00x (ISBN 0-226-20386-7). U of Chicago Pr.

Quest of Enlightenment. Tripitaka. Tr. by E. J. Thomas from Sanskrit. LC 85-24863. (Wisdom of the East Ser.). 95p. 1986. Repr. of 1950 ed. lib. bdg. 29.75x (ISBN 0-313-22185-5, TRQE). Greenwood.

Quest of Enlightenment: A Selection of the Buddhist Scriptures. Tr. by E. J. Thomas from Sanskrit. LC 78-70130. Repr. of 1950 ed. 17.50 (ISBN 0-404-17389-6). AMS Pr.

Quest of the Holy Grail. Tr. by P. M. Matarasso. (Classics Ser.). 304p. 1969. pap. 4.95 (ISBN 0-14-044220-0). Penguin.

Quest of the Holy Grail. Jessie L. Weston. LC 72-10823. (Arthurian Legend & Literature Ser., No. 1). 1973. Repr. of 1913 ed. lib. bdg. 75.00x (ISBN 0-8383-0642-X). Haskell.

Quest There Is. Elizabeth G. Vining. 1983. pap. 2.50x (ISBN 0-87574-246-7, 246). Pendle Hill.

Question & Answer Catholic Catechism. John A. Hardon. LC 80-2961. 408p. 1981. (Im); pap. 9.95 (ISBN 0-385-13664-1). Doubleday.

Question in Baptist History: Whether the Anabaptists in England Practiced Immersion Before the Year 1641? William H. Whitsitt. Ed. by Edwin S. Gaustad. LC 79-52611. (Baptist Tradition Ser.). 1980. Repr. of 1896 ed. lib. bdg. 14.00x (ISBN 0-405-12476-7). Ayer Co Pubs.

Question in Search of an Answer: Understanding Learning Disability in Jewish Education. Roberta M. Greene & Elaine Heavenrich. LC 8-18059. (Illus.). 262p. 1981. pap. 5.00 (ISBN 0-8074-0029-7). UAHC.

Question Is the Answer. Siegmund Frost. cancelled (ISBN 0-87306-075-X). Feldheim.

Question of Elites: An Essay on the Cultural Elitism of Nietzche, George & Hesse. Stanley J. Antosik. (New York University Ottendorfer Series, Neue Folge: Vol. 11). 204p. 1978. 22.75 (ISBN 3-261-03102-6). P Lang Pubs.

Question of Survival: Quakers in Australia in the Nineteenth Century. William N. Oats. LC 84-2351. (Illus.). 409p. 1985. text ed. 35.00x (ISBN 0-7022-1708-5). U of Queensland Pr.

Questioning Back: The Overcoming of Metaphysics in Christian Tradition. Joseph S. O'Leary. 224p. 1985. cancelled (ISBN 0-8245-0675-8). Crossroad NY.

Questioning Christianity. G. Michael Cocoris. 67p. (Orig.). 1985. pap. text ed. 1.00 (ISBN 0-935729-00-3). Church Open Door.

Questioning Traveller & Karma. Torkom Saraydarian. 1979. pap. 2.50 (ISBN 0-911794-45-X). Aqua Educ.

Questions about the Beginning of Life. Ed. by Edward D. Schneider. LC 85-15617. 192p. (Orig.). 1985. pap. 8.95 (ISBN 0-8066-2167-2, 10-5360). Augsburg.

Questions about Your Faith, Bk. IV. David Q. Liptak. pap. 3.95 (ISBN 0-941850-09-9). Sunday Pubns.

Questions & Answers, Vol. II. Guy N. Woods. 1986. 16.95 (ISBN 0-89225-277-4). Gospel Advocate.

Questions & Answers, Biblical. Corinne Heline. pap. 2.50 (ISBN 0-87613-026-0). New Age.

Questions & Answers on Creation-Evolution. John N. Moore. 128p. 1976. pap. 3.95 (ISBN 0-8010-5997-6). Baker Bk.

Questions & Answers on Guru & Disciple. Herbert Guenther et al. (Illus.). 1978. pap. text ed. 3.00 (ISBN 0-931454-02-6). Timeless Bks.

Questions & Answers on Moral Education. Kevin Ryan. LC 81-80011. (Fastback Ser.: No. 153). 1981. pap. 0.90 (ISBN 0-87367-153-8). Phi Delta Kappa.

Questions & Answers on Reincarnation & Karma. Rene Querido. 1977. pap. 3.50 (ISBN 0-916786-18-8). St George Bk Serv.

Questions & Answers on Spiritual Gifts. Howard Carter. 127p. 1976. pocket bk. 2.95 (ISBN 0-89274-007-8). Harrison Hse.

Questions & Answers on T'ai Chi Ch'uan. Chen Wei-Ming. Tr. by Benjamin Pang Jeng Lo & Robert Smith. Tr. of T'ai Chi Ch'uan Ta Wen. 64p. (Orig.). 1985. 20.00 (ISBN 0-938190-77-6). North Atlantic.

Questions & Answers: Sermon Outlines & Bible Study Notes. H. Leo Boles. 1985. pap. 8.95 (ISBN 0-89225-274-X). Gospel Advocate.

Questions & Answers: The Gospel of Matthew. Mike Freze. 144p. 1987. pap. 4.95 (ISBN 0-8010-3534-1). Baker Bk.

Questions? Answers! Verne Becker et al. (Campus Life Ser.). 158p. 1986. pap. 5.95 (ISBN 0-8423-5117-5). Tyndale.

Questions Are the Answer. Wayne Robinson. LC 80-36780. 110p. 1980. pap. 5.95 (ISBN 0-8298-0409-9). Pilgrim NY.

Questions Catholics Ask. Father Sheedy. LC 78-58466. 1978. pap. 4.95 (ISBN 0-87973-738-7). Our Sunday Visitor.

Questions Christians Ask about Prayer & Intercession. Barry Wood. 160p. (Orig.). 1984. pap. 5.95 (ISBN 0-8007-5177-9, Power Bks). Revell.

Questions for Jehovah's Witnesses. William Cetnar & Jean Cetnar. 1983. pap. 3.95 (ISBN 0-87552-162-2). Presby & Reformed.

Questions for Living. Dom H. Camara. Tr. by Robert R. Barr from Fr. Tr. of Des Questions pour Vivre. (Illus.). 112p. (Orig.). 1987. pap. 7.95 (ISBN 0-88344-558-1). Orbis Bks.

Questions Frequently Asked Me on Prophecy. Salem Kirban. (Illus.). 1981. pap. 4.95 (ISBN 0-912582-01-4). Kirban.

Questions from Text of Old Testament. Stanley Outlaw. 1977. pap. 2.95 (ISBN 0-89265-049-4). Randall Hse.

Questions from the Text of the New Testament. Stanley Outlaw. 36p. 1977. pap. 2.95 (ISBN 0-89265-050-8). Randall Hse.

Questions I'd Like to Ask. Stephen Bly & Janet Bly. LC 82-2252. 1982. 3.50 (ISBN 0-8024-7058-0). Moody.

Questions I'd Like to Ask God. Fred Unruh. LC 80-67504. (Illus.). 64p. 1980. tchr's. guide 3.95 (ISBN 0-87303-041-9). Faith & Life.

Questions Jesus Raised. Roger Lovette. LC 85-15137. 1986. 4.95 (ISBN 0-8054-2259-5). Broadman.
Questions Jews Ask. Rev ed. Mordecai M. Kaplan. LC 56-8577. 532p. 1956. pap. 10.50 (ISBN 0-935457-21-6). Reconstructionist Pr.
Questions New Christians Ask. Barry Wood. 160p. 1979. pap. 5.95 (ISBN 0-8007-5044-6, Power Bks). Revell.
Questions Non-Christians Ask. Barry Wood. 160p. 1980. pap. 5.95 (ISBN 0-8007-5047-0, Power Bks). Revell.
Questions of Christians: Mark's Response, Vol. 1. J. C. Massion & H. R. Lambin. LC 80-68045. 1980. pap. 2.75 (ISBN 0-914070-16-9). ACTA Found.
Questions of Dress. A. A. Maududi. pap. 1.50 (ISBN 0-686-63910-3). Kazi Pubns.
Questions of Special Urgency: The Church in the Modern World Twenty Years after Vatican II. Ed. by Judith A. Dwyer. 200p. (Orig.). 1986. 17.95 (ISBN 0-87840-434-1); pap. 9.95 (ISBN 0-87840-425-2). Georgetown U Pr.
Questions of the Day. facs. ed. John A. Ryan. LC 67-26779. (Essay Index Reprint Ser). 1931. 20.00 (ISBN 0-8369-0846-5). Ayer Co Pubs.
Questions of the Heart. Edward Chinn. (Orig.). 1987. pap. price not set (ISBN 0-89536-877-3, 7863). CSS of Ohio.
Questions on the Way. Beverley D. Tucker. 160p. (Orig.). 1987. pap. price not set (ISBN 0-88028-056-5). Forward Movement.
Questions Pentecostals Ask. David F. Gray. Ed. by David Bernard. LC 86-26784. 304p. (Orig.). 1986. pap. 6.95 (ISBN 0-932581-07-2). Word Aflame.
Questions People Ask Ministers Most. Harold Hazelip. 1986. pap. 3.95 (ISBN 0-8010-4302-6). Baker Bk.
Questions Teens Are Asking Today. Theodore W. Schroeder & Dean Nadasdy. 1987. pap. 5.95 (ISBN 0-570-04454-5). Concordia.
Questions to a Zen Master. Taisen Deshimaru. Tr. by Nancy Amphoux. 160p. 1985. pap. 8.95 (ISBN 0-525-48141-9, 0869-260). Dutton.
Questions You Have Always Wanted to Ask about Tongues, but... William Banks. (Illus.). 1979. pap. 2.25 (ISBN 0-89957-526-9). AMG Pubs.
Quete de Paul Gadenne: Une Morale pour Notre Epoque. James B. Davis. (Fr.). 96p. 1979. 9.95 (ISBN 0-917786-18-1). Summa Pubns.
Quetzalcoatl & Guadalupe: The Formation of Mexican National Consciousness, 1531-1813. Jacques Lafaye. Tr. by Benjamin Keen from Fr. LC 75-20889. 1976. lib. bdg. 26.00x (ISBN 0-226-46794-5). U of Chicago Pr.
Quick-Line Stories for Young Children. Judith B. Kaiser. 1975. spiral bdg. 3.95 (ISBN 0-916406-12-1). Accent Bks.
Quick Reference Scripture Handbook. Dick Mills. 50p. (Orig.). 1984. pap. 1.95 (ISBN 0-89274-323-9). Harrison Hse.
Quick Scripture Reference for Counseling. John G. Kruis. 80p. 1987. pap. price not set (ISBN 0-8010-5488-5). Baker Bk.
Quickening Flame: A Scriptural Study of Revival. Winifred Ascroft. (Basic Bible Study). 64p. 1985. pap. 2.95 (ISBN 0-932305-20-2, 521020). Aglow Pubns.
Quickening Seed: Death in the Sermons of John. Bettie A. Doebler. (Elizabethan & Renaissance Studies). 297p. (Orig.). 1974. pap. 15.00 (ISBN 3-7052-0678-8, Pub. by Salzburg Studies). Longwood Pub Group.
Quickie Quizzes from the Bible. Charles Vander Meer. (Quiz & Puzzles Bks.). 48p. 1976. pap. 2.50 (ISBN 0-8010-9252-3). Baker Bk.
Quickie Quizzes No. 2. Charles Vander Meer. (Quiz & Puzzle Bks.). pap. 1.95 (ISBN 0-8010-9266-3). Baker Bk.
Quien es Jesuscristo? William Hendricks. Tr. by Jose L. Martinez from Eng. (Biblioteca de Doctrina Cristiana Ser.). Tr. of Who is Jesus Christ? (Span.). 164p. 1986. pap. 5.95 (ISBN 0-311-09112-1). Casa Bautista.
Quien Movio la Piedra? Frank Morison. Tr. by Rhode Ward from Eng. LC 77-11752. Tr. of Who Moved the Stone? (Span.). 206p. 1977. pap. 4.95 (ISBN 0-89922-100-9). Edit Caribe.
Quiet & Peaceable Life. rev. ed. John L. Ruth. LC 85-70284. (People's Place Booklet: No. 2). (Illus.). 96p. (Orig.). 1985. pap. 4.50 (ISBN 0-934672-25-3). Good Bks PA.
Quiet Because. Vera Groomer. (Come Unto Me Ser.). 1979. pap. 1.65 (ISBN 0-8127-0253-0). Review & Herald.
Quiet Companion: Peter Favre S. J., 1506-1546. Mary Purcell. vi, 198p. 1981. 8.95 (ISBN 0-8294-0377-9). Loyola.
Quiet Healing Zone. Herbert L. Beierle. 1980. 10.00 (ISBN 0-940480-10-7). U of Healing.
Quiet Heart: Prayers & Meditations for Each Day of the Year. George Appleton. LC 84-6019. 480p. 1984. pap. 7.95 (ISBN 0-8006-1789-4). Fortress.
Quiet Imperative: Meditations on Justice & Peace Based on Readings from the New Testament. John Carmody. 176p. (Orig.). 1986. pap. 6.95 (ISBN 0-8358-0518-2). Upper Room.
Quiet Mind. White Eagle. 1972. 3.95 (ISBN 0-85487-009-1). De Vorss.
Quiet Moment: Devotions for the Golden Years. Jeanette Lockerbie. LC 82-7344. (Illus.). 96p. (Orig.). 1982. pap. 4.95 (ISBN 0-87239-606-1, 3009). Standard Pub.
Quiet Moments for Women: A Daily Devotional. June M. Bacher. LC 79-84722. 1979. pap. 7.95 (ISBN 0-89081-187-3). Harvest Hse.
Quiet Moments with God. Joseph Murphy. pap. 2.00 (ISBN 0-87516-276-2). De Vorss.
Quiet Night: A Play for Christmas. Thomas J. Hatton. 24p. (Orig.). 1980. pap. text ed. 5.25 (ISBN 0-89536-438-7, 1703). CSS of Ohio.
Quiet Places with Jesus. Isaias Powers. LC 78-64452. 128p. 1978. pap. 4.95 (ISBN 0-89622-086-9). Twenty-Third.
Quiet Places with Mary. Isaias Powers. 160p. (Orig.). 1986. pap. 4.95 (ISBN 0-89622-297-7). Twenty-THird.
Quiet Power: Words of Faith, Hope, & Love. Helen L. Marshall. 64p. 1985. pap. 3.95 (ISBN 0-8010-6197-0). Baker Bk.
Quiet Rebels: The Story of the Quakers in America. Margaret H. Bacon. 250p. 1985. lib. bdg. 24.95 (ISBN 0-86571-058-9); pap. 8.95 (ISBN 0-86571-057-0). New Soc Pubs.
Quiet Talks on Prayer. S. D. Gordon. (S. D. Gordon Library). 1980. pap. 4.95 (ISBN 0-8010-3754-9). Baker Bk.
Quiet Talks with the Master. Eva B. Werber. 1936. pap. 3.25 (ISBN 0-87516-104-9). De Vorss.
Quiet Time. Inter-Varsity Staff. pap. 1.95 (ISBN 0-87784-250-7). Inter Varsity.
Quiet Time with God. Kristen Ingram. 96p. 1984. pap. 3.95 (ISBN 0-8170-1026-2). Judson.
Quincentennial Essays on St. Thomas More: Selected Papers from the Thomas More College Conference. LC 78-67288. 14.95 (ISBN 0-932530-00-1). Albion NC.
Quinientas Ilustraciones. Compiled by Alfredo Lerin. (Span.). 324p. 1984. pap. 5.95 (ISBN 0-311-42037-0). Casa Bautista.
Quintessence of Islamic History & Culture. S. P. Gulati. 225p. 1986. 23.00X (ISBN 81-85061-44-0, Pub. by Manohar India). South Asia Bks.
Quintessence of the Animate & Inanimate: A Discourse on the Holy Dharma. Venerable Larma Lodo. Ed. by Nancy Clark & Caroline Parke. LC 85-2290. (Illus.). 238p. 1985. pap. 11.95 (ISBN 0-910165-01-7). KDK Pubns.
Quips & Quotes for Church Bulletins. E. C. McKenzie. (Direction Bks). 1978. pap. 2.95 (ISBN 0-8010-6059-1). Baker Bk.
Quiz for Christian Wives. Mae Erickson. 32p. 1976. pap. 0.95 (ISBN 0-930756-20-7, 541003). Aglow Pubns.
Qumran. Philip R. Davies. (Cities of the Biblical World Ser.). 1983. pap. 6.95 (ISBN 0-8028-1034-9). Eerdmans.
Qumran & Corinth. Martin H. Scharlemann. 1962. pap. 5.95x (ISBN 0-8084-0358-3). New Coll U Pr.
Qumran & Corinth. Martin H. Scharlemann. 78p. 1962. write for info. Concordia Schl Grad Studies.
Qumran & History: The Place of the Teachers in Religion. Olive Gilliam. 3.95 (ISBN 0-533-01167-1). Vantage.
Qumran & the History of the Biblical Text. Ed. by Frank M. Cross & Shemaryahu Talmon. LC 75-12529. 415p. 1975. text ed. 25.00x (ISBN 0-674-74360-1); pap. text ed. 9.95x (ISBN 0-674-74362-8). Harvard U Pr.
Qumran Community: Its History & Scrolls. Charles T. Fritsch. 1973. Repr. of 1956 ed. 18.00 (ISBN 0-8196-0279-5). Biblo.
Qumran Grotte Four, No. III. Ed. by Maurice Baillet. (Discoveries in the Judean Desert Ser.: Vol. 7). (Illus.). 1982. 140.00x (ISBN 0-19-826321-X). Oxford U Pr.
Qumran Studies. Chaim Rabin. LC 76-40116. (Scripta Judaica: No. 2). 1976. Repr. of 1957 ed. lib. bdg. 22.50x (ISBN 0-8371-9060-6, RAQS). Greenwood.
Qumran Text of Samuel & Josephus. Eugene C. Ulrich, Jr. LC 78-15254. (Harvard Semitic Museum. Harvard Semitic Monographs: No. 19). 1978. 15.00 (ISBN 0-89130-256-5, 040019). Scholars Pr GA.
Quo Vadis. Henryk Sienkiewicz. (Classics Ser). 1968. pap. 2.50 (ISBN 0-8049-0188-0, CL-188). Airmont.
Quotable Bresee. Compiled by Harold I. Smith. 280p. (Orig.). 1983. pap. 5.95 (ISBN 0-8341-0835-6). Beacon Hill.
Quotable Chesterton. Ed. by G. Marlin et al. LC 86-80788. 391p. 1986. 24.95 (ISBN 0-89870-102-3); pap. 16.95 (ISBN 0-89870-122-8). Ignatius Pr.
Quotable Quotations. Compiled by Lloyd Cory. 400p. 1985. pap. 12.95 (ISBN 0-88207-823-2). Victor Bks.
Quoted Direct Speech. George Savran. (Studies in Biblical Literature). Date not set. price not set. Ind U Pr.
Quotes & Notes to Share. Paul J. Molnar. Ed. by Patrice Goebel. (Orig.). 1982. pap. 4.95 (ISBN 0-938736-06-X). Life Enrich.
Quran. Ed. by Mashef Al-Esman. (Arabic.). 25.00x (ISBN 0-86685-135-6). Intl Bk Ctr.
Quran. Ed. by M. Baydun. (Arabic.). medium sized. 25.00x (ISBN 0-86685-134-8). Intl Bk Ctr.
Quran. Ed. by E. H. Palmer. (Sacred Books of the East: Vols. 6, 9). both vols. 30.00 (ISBN 0-686-97479-4); 15.00 ea. Asian Human Pr.
Quran: A New English Translation, with the Arabic Text. 736p. 1985. 17.00 (ISBN 0-7007-0148-6). Salem Hse Pubs.
Qur'an: A New Translation with a Critical Rearrangement of the Surahs, 2 vols. Muhammad. Tr. by Richard Bell. 14.95 ea. (Pub. by T & T Clark Ltd UK). Vol. 1, 348 pgs (ISBN 0-567-02027-4). Vol. 2, 352 pgs (ISBN 0-567-02028-2). Fortress.
Quran, an Introduction. A. R. Doi. pap. 5.50 (ISBN 0-686-63911-1). Kazi Pubns.
Qur'an & Bible: Studies in Interpretation & Dialogue. M. S. Seale. 124p. 1978. 23.50 (ISBN 0-85664-818-3, Pub. by Croom Helm Ltd). Methuen Inc.
Qur'an & Its Interpreters, Vol. 1. Mahmoud M. Ayoub. LC 82-21713. 290p. 1984. 29.50x (ISBN 0-87395-727-X). State U NY Pr.
Qur'an and Slavery. Hafiz M. Qureshi. Tr. by Kaukab Siddique from Urdu. 39p. (Orig.). 1984. pap. 2.00 (ISBN 0-942978-07-2). Am Soc Ed & Rel.
Qur'An & the World Today. K. N. Siddigi. 295p. 1971. 7.25x (ISBN 0-87902-249-3). Orientalia.
Quran: Arabic Text with English Translation. Tr. by Muhammed Z. Khan. 736p. 1981. 40.00x (ISBN 0-7007-0148-6, Pub. by Curzon England). State Mutual Bk.
Qur'an As Scripture. Arthur Jeffery. LC 80-1924. Repr. of 1952 ed. 18.00 (ISBN 0-404-18970-9). AMS Pr.
Quran: Basic Teachings. T. B. Irving et al. 278p. (Orig.). 1979. pap. 10.00 (ISBN 0-86037-021-6, Pub by Islamic Found UK). New Era Pubns MI.
Quran for Children. Omar Farook & A. Rauf. pap. 5.95 (ISBN 0-686-63912-X). Kazi Pubns.
Qur'an Made Easy. Revealed Book. 132p. 1983. pap. 6.00 (ISBN 0-941724-09-3). Islamic Seminary.
Quran Made Easy (Yassar nal Quran) S. A. Behlim. Date not set. pap. 7.50 (ISBN 0-317-43010-6). Kazi Pubns.
Quran, Sh. Tabarsi's Commentary. M. A. Abdul. 15.95 (ISBN 0-317-01596-6). Kazi Pubns.
Qur'an: The First American Version. Tr. by T. B. Irving. LC 84-72242. 500p. (Orig.). 1985. 17.50 (ISBN 0-915597-08-X). Amana Bks.
Qur'an: The Glorious. Tr. by Muhammad Pickthall. 767p. 1983. pap. 8.00 (ISBN 0-940368-30-7). Tahrike Tarsile Quran.
Qur'an: The Holy. Tr. by A. Yusuf Ali. (Eng. & Arabic.). 1862p. 1983. text ed. 20.00 (ISBN 0-940368-32-3); pap. 10.00 (ISBN 0-940368-31-5). Tahrike Tarsile Quran.
Quran, the Ultimate Miracle. A. Deedat. pap. 2.95 (ISBN 0-686-63913-8). Kazi Pubns.
Quranic Ethics. B. A. Dar. pap. 3.50 (ISBN 0-686-18602-8). Kazi Pubns.
Qur'anic Ethics. B. A. Dar. 1970. 5.00x (ISBN 0-87902-160-8). Orientalia.
Qur'anic Laws. M. V. Merchant. 1971. 8.50x (ISBN 0-87902-177-2). Orientalia.
Quranic Phenomenon. Malik B. Nabi. Tr. by Abu B. Kirkari from Fr. LC 82-70460. (Illus.). 187p. (Orig.). 1982. pap. 6.00 (ISBN 0-89259-023-8). Am Trust Pubns.
Quranic Sciences. A. Rahaman. pap. 14.95 (ISBN 0-317-46103-6). Kazi Pubns.
Quranic Studies: Sources & Methods of Scriptural Interpretations, Vol. 31. J. Wansbrough. (London Oriental Ser). 1977. 55.00x (ISBN 0-19-713588-9). Oxford U Pr.
Quranic Sufism. 2nd rev. ed. Mir Valiuddin. 1977. 16.95 (ISBN 0-89684-300-9, Pub. by Motilal Banarsidass India). Orient Bk Dist.
Quranic Sufism. Mir Valiuddin. 221p. 1981. pap. 13.25 (ISBN 0-88004-007-6). Sunwise Turn.

R

R. C. I. A. A Practical Approach to Christian Initiation. Rosalie Curtin et al. 136p. (Orig.). 1981. pap. 10.95 (ISBN 0-697-01759-1). Wm C Brown.
R. C. I. A. Foundations of Christian Initiation. Archdiocese of Dubuque Staff. 96p. 1982. wire coil 7.95 (ISBN 0-697-01781-8). Wm C Brown.
R. C. I. A: The Rites Revisited. Sandra DeGidio. 144p. (Orig.). 1984. pap. 7.95 (ISBN 0-86683-837-6, 8436, HarpR). Har-Row.
R. H. Hutton, Critic & Theologian: The Writings of R. H. Hutton on Newman, Arnold, Tennyson, Wordsworth & George Eliot. Ed. by Malcom Woodfield. 240p. 42.00 (ISBN 0-19-818564-2). Oxford U Pr.
R. S. Thomas: Poet of the Hidden God. D. Z. Phillips. (Princeton Theolographical Monograph Ser.: No. 2). 192p. (Orig.). 1986. pap. 18.00 (ISBN 0-915138-83-2). Pickwick.
R. V. H. Manual on Palliative-Hospice Care: A Resource Book. Ed. by Ina Ajemian & Balfour M. Mount. pap. 34.00 (ISBN 0-405-13934-9). Ayer Co Pubs.
Rab Saadia Gaon: Studies in His Honor. Ed. by Louis Finkelstein & Steven Katz. LC 79-7169. (Jewish Philosophy, Mysticism & History of Ideas Ser.). 1980. Repr. of 1944 ed. lib. bdg. 19.00x (ISBN 0-405-12250-0). Ayer Co Pubs.
Rabad of Posquieres: A Twelfth-Century Talmudist. Isadore Twersky. LC 62-7192. (Semitic Ser: No. 18). 1962. 22.50x (ISBN 0-674-74550-7). Harvard U Pr.
Rabban Gamaliel II: The Legal Traditions. Shamai Kanter. LC 80-12229. (Brown Judaic Studies: No. 8). 15.00x (ISBN 0-89130-403-7, 14 00 08); pap. 10.50x (ISBN 0-89130-404-5). Scholars Pr GA.
Rabbi & Minister: The Friendship of Stephen S. Wise & John Haynes Holmes. Carl H. Voss. LC 80-7453. (Library of Liberal Religion). 384p. 1980. pap. 11.95 (ISBN 0-87975-130-4). Prometheus Bks.
Rabbi Emil G. Hirsch: The Reform Advocate. David E. Hirsch. LC 68-24717. 1968. pap. 3.00x (ISBN 0-87655-502-4). Collage Inc.
Rabbi Isaac Jacob Reines: His Life & Thought. Joseph Wanefsky. LC 79-118314. 181p. 1970. 6.95 (ISBN 0-8022-2349-4). Philos Lib.
Rabbi Jonah of Gerona. cancelled (ISBN 0-686-76524-9). Feldheim.
Rabbi Joseph H. Lookstein Memorial Volume. Leo Landman. 1979. 35.00x (ISBN 0-87068-705-0). Ktav.
Rabbi Letters, No. 1. Lillian M. Rossini. (Illus.). 32p. 1986. 5.95 (ISBN 0-89962-506-1). Todd & Honeywell.
Rabbi Moses Nahmanides: Explorations in His Religious & Literary Virtuosity. Ed. by Isadore Twersky. (Center for Jewish Studies Ser.). 110p. (Orig.). 1983. pap. text ed. 9.50x (ISBN 0-674-74560-4). Harvard U Pr.
Rabbi Nachman De Breslov. Rabbi Nachman of Breslov & Rabbi Nathan of Breslov. Ed. by Alon Dimermanas. (Illus.). 442p. 1986. text ed. 18.00 (ISBN 0-930213-19-X); pap. 15.00 (ISBN 0-930213-20-3). Breslov Res Inst.
Rabbi Nachman's Stories. Nachman of Breslov. Tr. by Aryeh Kaplan from Hebrew. LC 83-70201. Tr. of Sippurey Ma'asioth. 552p. 1983. 15.00 (ISBN 0-930213-02-5). Breslov Res Inst.
Rabbi Nachman's Stories: Skazocnniji Histori Rabbi Nechman iz Bratzlav. Nachman of Breslov. Tr. by Baruch Avni from Hebrew & Rus. Tr. of Sippurey Maasiot. (Illus.). 332p. (Orig.). 1987. pap. 10.00 (ISBN 0-930213-29-7). Breslov Res Inst.
Rabbi Nachman's Tikkun: The Comprehensive Remedy. Nachman of Breslov. Tr. by Avraham Greenbaum from Hebrew. 240p. 1984. 10.00 (ISBN 0-930213-06-8). Breslov Res Inst.
Rabbi Nachman's Wisdom. Nachman of Breslov. Ed. by Zvi A. Rosenfeld. Tr. by Aryeh Kaplan from Hebrew. Tr. of Shevachay HaRan-Sichos HaRan. (Illus.). 510p. 1984. 14.00 (ISBN 0-930213-00-9); pap. 11.00 (ISBN 0-930213-01-7). Breslov Res Inst.
Rabbi Tarfon: The Tradition, the Man & Early Rabbinic Judaism. Joel Gereboff. LC 78-15220. (Brown Judaic Studies: No. 7). 1979. 16.50 (ISBN 0-89130-257-3, 140007); pap. 12.00 (ISBN 0-89130-299-9). Scholars Pr GA.
Rabbi Yisroel Baal Shem Tov. Moshe Prager. (Hebrew., Illus.). 1.75 (ISBN 0-914131-51-6, D50). Torah Umesorah.
Rabbinic Anthology. Ed. by C. G. Montefiore & H. Loewe. LC 73-91340. 1970. pap. 16.95 (ISBN 0-8052-0442-3). Schocken.
Rabbinic Authority. Elliot Stevens. 1982. 15.00x (ISBN 0-916694-88-7). Ktav.
Rabbinic Authority. Ed. by Elliot L. Stevens. 184p. 1982. 15.00 (ISBN 0-317-01466-8). Central Conf.
Rabbinic Commentary on the New Testament: The Gospels of Matthew, Mark & Luke. Samuel T. Lachs. 600p. 1987. 39.50 (ISBN 0-88125-089-9); pap. 19.95. Ktav.
Rabbinic Essays. Jacob Z. Lauterbach. LC 52-18170. pap. 146.50 (ISBN 0-317-42031-3, 2025693). Bks Demand UMI.
Rabbinic Mind. 3rd ed. Max Kadushin. LC 75-189016. 1972. 12.50 (ISBN 0-8197-0007-X). Bloch.
Rabbinic Psychology. W. Hirsch. LC 73-2208. (Jewish People; History, Religion, Literature Ser.). Repr. of 1947 ed. 24.50 (ISBN 0-405-05272-3). Ayer Co Pubs.
Rabbinic Responsa of the Holocaust Era. Ed. by Robert S. Kirschner. LC 84-23509. 204p. 1985. 17.95 (ISBN 0-8052-3978-2). Schocken.

Rabbinical Assembly Mahzor. 12.00 (ISBN 0-686-96025-4). United Syn Bk.

Rabbinical Seminary of Budapest, 1877-1977: A Centennial Volume. Ed. by Moshe Carmilly-Weinberger. (Illus.). 420p. 1986. 35.00 (ISBN 0-87203-148-9). Hermon.

Rabbis & Wives. Chaim Grade. LC 83-5855. 320p. 1983. pap. 5.95 (ISBN 0-394-71647-7, Vin). Random.

Rabbi's Blessing. 1982. 7.50 (ISBN 0-686-76249-5). Feldheim.

Rabbi's Manual. rev. ed. 1961. 7.50 (ISBN 0-916694-26-7). Central Conf.

Rabbi's Rovings. Israel Mowshowitz. 385p. 1985. 20.00 (ISBN 0-88125-069-4). Ktav.

Rabbit Christmas. Thomas J. Hatton. (Orig.). 1982. pap. 2.95 (ISBN 0-937172-40-5). JLJ Pubs.

Rabboni. W. Phillip Keller. 256p. 1980. pap. 6.95 (ISBN 0-8007-5053-5, Power Bks). Revell.

Rabi'a the Mystic & Her Fellow-Saints in Islam. 2nd ed. Margaret Smith. 256p. 1984. 37.50 (ISBN 0-521-26779-X); pap. 13.95 (ISBN 0-521-31863-7). Cambridge U Pr.

Raccoon John Smith. Daniel D. Schantz. (Restoration Booklets). (Illus.). 16p. (Orig.). 1984. pap. 0.75 (ISBN 0-87239-778-5, 3298). Standard Pub.

Race & Reich: The Story of an Epoch. Joseph Tenenbaum. LC 76-8503. (Illus.). 1976. Repr. of 1956 ed. lib. bdg. 35.25x (ISBN 0-8371-8857-1, TERR). Greenwood.

Race: Challenge to Religion. National Conference on Religion & Race. Ed. by Mathew Ahmann. LC 78-24276. 1979. Repr. of 1963 ed. lib. bdg. 22.50x (ISBN 0-313-20796-8, NCRA). Greenwood.

Race: Discipleship for the Long Run. John White. LC 84-6695. 216p. 1984. pap. 5.95 (ISBN 0-87784-976-5). Inter-Varsity.

Race Horse. Bob Buess. 1978. pap. 2.50 (ISBN 0-934244-08-1). Sweeter Than Honey.

Race, Nation, Person: Total Aspects of the Race Problem. facs. ed. LC 70-128291. (Essay Index Reprint Ser). 1944. 25.50 (ISBN 0-8369-2019-8). Ayer Co Pubs.

Race, Religion, & the Continuing American Dilemma. C. Eric Lincoln. 304p. 1984. 17.95 (ISBN 0-8090-8016-8). Hill & Wang.

Race, Religion, & the Continuing American Dilemma. Eric Lincoln. (American Century Ser.). 304p. 1985. 17.95 (ISBN 0-8090-8016-8). FS&G.

Race Riot at East St. Louis, July 2, 1917. Elliot Rudwick. LC 64-13634. (Studies in American Negro Life). 1972. pap. text ed. 3.95x (ISBN 0-689-70336-8, NL31). Atheneum.

Race to Grace. George Harper. (H. B. Bible Adventures Ser.). 216p. (Orig.). 1986. pap. 5.95 (ISBN 0-934318-74-3). Falcon Pr MT.

Rachel Weeping: The Case Against Abortion. James T. Burtchaell. LC 83-48986. 400p. 1984. pap. 10.95 (ISBN 0-06-061251-7, RD 517, HarpR). Har-Row.

Racial Biology of the Jews. Otmar Von Verschuer. (Illus.). 1984. lib. bdg. 79.95 (ISBN 0-87700-560-5). Revisionist Pr.

Racial Biology of the Jews. Otmar Von Verschuer. 1987. lib. bdg. 75.00 (ISBN 0-8490-3945-2). Gordon Pr.

Racial Strife in the U. S. Military: Toward the Elimination of Discrimination. Richard O. Hope. LC 79-65932. 144p. 1979. 35.95 (ISBN 0-03-046146-4). Praeger.

Racing Toward Judgment. David Wilkerson. 160p. 1976. pap. 2.50 (ISBN 0-8007-8276-3, Spire Bks). Revell.

Radha: Diary of a Woman's Search. Swami Sivananda Radha. LC 80-26470. (Illus.). 230p. (Orig.). 1981. pap. 7.95 (ISBN 0-931454-06-9). Timeless Bks.

Radhakrishna on Hindu Moral Life & Action. Aloysius Michael. 1979. 17.50x (ISBN 0-8364-0334-7). South Asia Bks.

Radhakrishna: Profile of a Universalist. Ishwar C. Harris. 1982. 17.50x (ISBN 0-8364-0778-4). South Asia Bks.

Radhakrishnan: A Religious Biography. Robert N. Minor. 178p. 1987. text ed. 34.50x (ISBN 0-88706-554-6); pap. 10.95x (ISBN 0-88706-555-4). State U NY Pr.

Radhasoami Faith: A Historical Study. A. P. Mathur. 1974. 9.00 (ISBN 0-686-20296-1). Intl Bk Dist.

Radiance of the Inner Splendor. Lloyd J. Ogilvie. LC 80-51524. 144p. 1980. pap. text ed. 4.95x (ISBN 0-8358-0405-4). Upper Room.

Radiant Faith. Rudolph F. Norden. Ed. by Oscar E. Feucht. 1966. pap. 1.60 study guide (ISBN 0-570-03527-9, 14-1330); pap. 1.95 leader's manual (ISBN 0-570-03528-7, 14-1331). Concordia.

Radiant Heart. Linda Sabbath. 1986. Repr. of 1985 ed. 4.95 (ISBN 0-87193-003-X). Dimension Bks.

Radiant Science, Dark Politics: A Memoir of the Nuclear Age. Martin D. Kamen. 1987. pap. 8.95 (ISBN 0-520-05897-6). U of Cal Pr.

Radical Abolitionism: Anarchy & the Government of God in Anti-Slavery Thought. Lewis Perry. 328p. 1973. 27.50x (ISBN 0-8014-0754-0). Cornell U Pr.

Radical Bible. 1972. pap. 1.95 (ISBN 0-377-02141-5). Friend Pr.

Radical Brethren. Irvin B. Horst. 216p. 1972. 30.00x (ISBN 0-8361-1193-1). Herald Pr.

Radical Christian. Arthur Wallis. 160p. 1982. pap. 5.95 (ISBN 0-8007-5081-0, Power Bks). Revell.

Radical Christian Living. Richard Booker. LC 84-90103. (Illus.). 124p. (Orig.). 1985. pap. 4.95 (ISBN 0-932081-03-7). Victory Hse.

Radical Christianity. Tim Timmons. 144p. 1986. pap. 4.95 (ISBN 0-89693-531-0). Victor Bks.

Radical Commitment: Getting Serious about Christian Growth. Vernon Grounds. LC 84-3344. 1984. pap. 5.95 (ISBN 0-88070-051-3). Multnomah.

Radical Discontinuities: American Romanticism & Christian Consciousness. Harold P. Simonson. LC 81-72051. 180p. 1983. 24.50 (ISBN 0-8386-3159-2). Fairleigh Dickinson.

Radical Hospitality. David Rupprecht & Ruth Rupprecht. 110p. 1983. 7.95 (ISBN 0-87552-421-4); pap. 4.95 (ISBN 0-87552-420-6). Presby & Reformed.

Radical Humanism: Selected Essays. Jean Amery. Ed. by Sidney Rosenfeld & Stella P. Rosenfeld. Tr. by Stella Rosenfeld & Sidney Rosenfeld. LC 83-49525. 160p. 1984. 22.50x (ISBN 0-253-34770-X). Ind U Pr.

Radical Imperative: From Theology to Social Ethics. John C. Bennett. LC 75-15538. 208p. 1975. 8.50 (ISBN 0-664-20824-X). Westminster.

Radical Islam. Emmanuel Sivan. LC 84-20999. 224p. 1987. pap. 9.95x (ISBN 0-300-03888-7). Yale U Pr.

Radical Islam: Medieval Theology & Modern Politics. Emmanuel Sivan. LC 84-20999. 224p. 1985. 20.00x (ISBN 0-300-03263-3). Yale U Pr.

Radical Kingdom: The Western Experience of Messianic Hope. Rosemary R. Ruether. LC 70-109080. 324p. 1975. pap. 5.95 (ISBN 0-8091-1860-2). Paulist Pr.

Radical Love for a Broken World. George Moore. 175p. (Orig.). 1987. pap. price not set (ISBN 0-89109-139-4). NavPress.

Radical Love: Toward a Sexual Spirituality. Dorothy H. Donnelly. 144p. 1984. pap. 6.95 (ISBN 0-86683-817-1, AY8407, HarpR). Har-Row.

Radical Monotheism in Western Culture. H. Richard Niebuhr. pap. 5.95x (ISBN 0-06-131491-9, TB1491, Torch). Har-Row.

Radical Nature of Christianity: Church Growth Eyes Look at the Supernatural Mission of the Christian & the Church. Waldo J. Werning. LC 76-8359. 1976. pap. 5.85 (ISBN 0-87808-730-3, Pub. by Mandate Pr). William Carey Lib.

Radical Pietists. Delburn Carpenter. LC 72-13586. (Illus.). 19.00 (ISBN 0-404-11008-8). AMS Pr.

Radical Prayer. David J. Hassel. 160p. 1983. 5.95 (ISBN 0-8091-2649-4). Paulist Pr.

Radical Prayer: Contemporary Interpretations. Perry LeFevre. LC 82-72097. 100p. 1982. text ed. 13.95x (ISBN 0-913552-18-6); pap. text ed. 5.95x (ISBN 0-913552-19-4). Exploration Pr.

Radical Preacher's Sermon Book. Ed. by Kathleen Schultz et al. (Illus.). 96p. 1983. pap. 4.00 (ISBN 0-9612114-0-7). Inst People's Church.

Radical Reactionaries: The Political Thought of the French Catholic League. F. J. Baumgartner. 320p. (Orig.). 1976. pap. text ed. 37.50x (Pub. by Droz Switzerland). Coronet Bks.

Radical Reformation. George H. Williams. LC 62-7066. (Illus.). 960p. 1962. 24.95 (ISBN 0-664-20372-8). Westminster.

Radical Religion in the English Revolution. J. F. McGregor. Ed. by B. Reay. 219p. 1984. 34.95x (ISBN 0-19-873044-6); pap. 14.95x (ISBN 0-19-873045-4). Oxford U Pr.

Radical Religious Movements in Early Modern Europe. Michael Mullett. (Early Modern Europe Today Ser.). 208p. 1980. text ed. 9.95 (ISBN 0-04-901028-X). Allen Unwin.

Radical Sects of Revolutionary New England. Stephen A. Marini. LC 81-6913. 224p. 1982. text ed. 16.50x (ISBN 0-674-74625-2). Harvard U Pr.

Radical Spinoza. Paul Wienpahl. LC 78-65448. 1979. 32.50 (ISBN 0-8147-9186-7). NYU Pr.

Radical Vision of Saul Alinsky. P. David Finks. (Orig.). 1984. pap. 9.95 (ISBN 0-8091-2608-7). Paulist Pr.

Radical Wesley. Howard Snyder. LC 80-18197. 180p. (Orig.). 1980. pap. 5.95 (ISBN 0-87784-625-1). Inter-Varsity.

Radicalism & Conservatism Toward Conventional Religion: A Psychological Study Based on a Group of Jewish College Students. P. M. Kitay. LC 72-176953. (Columbia University. Teachers College. Contributions to Education: No. 919). Repr. of 1947 ed. 22.50 (ISBN 0-404-55919-0). AMS Pr.

Radicalism in Religion, Philosophy, & Social Life: Four Papers from the Boston Courier for 1858. LC 72-1804. (Black Heritage Library Collection Ser.). Repr. of 1858 ed. 10.50 (ISBN 0-8369-9052-8). Ayer Co Pubs.

Radio Replies, 3 vols. Leslie Rumble & Charles M. Carty. LC 79-51938. 1979. Set. pap. 27.00 (ISBN 0-89555-159-4). Vol. 1 (ISBN 0-89555-089-X). Vol. 2 (ISBN 0-89555-090-3). Vol. 3 (ISBN 0-89555-091-1). TAN Bks Pubs.

Rafael: Cardinal Merry del Val. Marie C. Buehrle. 308p. (Orig.). 1980. pap. 7.00 (ISBN 0-912414-28-6). Lumen Christi.

Raft of Mohammed: Social & Human Consequences of the Return to Traditional Religion in the Arab World. Jean-Pierre Peroncel-Hugoz. 304p. 1987. 18.95 (ISBN 0-913729-31-0). Paragon Hse.

Rage! Reflect. Rejoice! Praying with the Psalmists. Thomas H. Troeger. LC 77-22755. 96p. 1977. pap. 3.95 (ISBN 0-664-24293-6). Westminster.

Ragman & Other Cries of Faith. Walter Wangerin, Jr. LC 83-48980. 176p. 1984. 12.45 (ISBN 0-06-069253-7, HarpT). Har-Row.

Rahel Varnagen. Ellen S. Key. LC 75-7680. (Pioneers of the Woman's Movement: an International Perspective Ser.). (Illus.). xix, 312p. 1976. Repr. of 1913 ed. 23.10 (ISBN 0-88355-351-1). Hyperion Conn.

Rahel Varnhagen: The Life of a Jewish Woman. Hannah Arendt. Tr. by Richard Winston & Clara Winston. LC 74-6478. (Illus.). 236p. 1974. pap. 7.95 (ISBN 0-15-676100-9, Harv). HarBraceJ.

Rahner Handbook. Robert Kress. LC 81-85333. 118p. 1982. pap. 10.95 (ISBN 0-8042-0652-X). John Knox.

Rahner Reader. Ed. by Gerald McCool. (Orig.). 1975. pap. 10.95 (ISBN 0-8245-0370-8). Crossroad NY.

Raid on the Inarticulate: An Invitation to Adult Religion. Michael G. Lawler. LC 80-1438. 168p. 1980. pap. text ed. 9.50 (ISBN 0-8191-1186-4). U Pr of Amer.

Rain in the Desert Music Book. 5.95 (ISBN 0-8198-0727-3). Dghtrs St Paul.

Rain of Wisdom. Chogyam Trungpa. Tr. by Nalanda Translation Committee. LC 80-51130. Tr. of Bka'-Rgyud Mgur-Mtsho. 384p. 1985. pap. 18.95 (ISBN 0-87773-345-7, 73972-8). Shambhala Pubns.

Rainbow. Fitzgerald. (Dear God Kids Ser.). Date not set. 3.95 (ISBN 0-671-50681-1). S&S.

Rainbow. Nancy Lecourt. (Books I Can Read). 32p. 1980. pap. 1.95 (ISBN 0-8127-0290-5). Review & Herald.

Rainbow. G. F. Taylor. pap. 2.00 (ISBN 0-911866-61-2). Advocate.

Rainbow Book of Poems. Ruth Baker. 1984. 3.95 (ISBN 0-89536-993-1, 7544). CSS of Ohio.

Rainbow Bridge. Bhagwan Shree Rajneesh. Ed. by Krishna Prabhu. LC 85-42535. (Initiation Talks Ser.). 368p. (Orig.). 1985. pap. 3.95 (ISBN 0-88050-618-0). Chidvilas Found.

Rainbow Bridge II: Link with the Soul Purification. 1981. pap. 8.50 (ISBN 0-87613-078-3). New Age.

Rainbow Bridge: Two Disciples. 1981. casebound 10.00 (ISBN 0-87613-069-4); pap. 8.50 (ISBN 0-87613-068-6); pap. text ed. Write for info. (ISBN 0-87613-078-3). New Age.

Rainbow Connection. Rebecca Clark. LC 82-84590. 192p. 1983. 4.95 (ISBN 0-87159-136-7). Unity School.

Rainbow Songs. James E. Haas. 40p. (Orig.). 1975. pap. 3.95 (ISBN 0-8192-1201-6). Morehouse.

Rainbows for the Fallen World. C. Seerveld. 1980. pap. 9.95x (ISBN 0-919071-01-5). Radix Bks.

Rainbows of Promise. Ivy D. Doherty. Ed. by Gerald Wheeler. (Banner Bk.). (Illus.). 92p. (Orig.). 1984. pap. 5.95 (ISBN 0-8280-0213-4). Review & Herald.

Rainhouse & Ocean: Speeches for the Papago Year. Ruth M. Underhill et al. LC 79-66733. (American Tribal Religions Ser.: Vol. 4). (Illus.). vi, 154p. 1979. pap. 12.95x (ISBN 0-89734-029-9, Pub by Mus Northern Ariz). U of Nebr Pr.

Raised Immortal: Resurrection & Immortality in the New Testament. Murray J. Harris. 320p. (Orig.). 1985. pap. 10.95 (ISBN 0-8028-0053-X). Eerdmans.

Raising a Child Conservatively in a Sexually Permissive World. Sol Gordon & Judith Gordon. 224p. 1986. pap. 7.95 (ISBN 0-671-62797-X, Fireside). S&S.

Raising of Lazarus. John Cornish. 1979. pap. 2.95 (ISBN 0-916786-36-6). St George Bk Serv.

Raising PG Kids in an X-Rated Society. Tipper Gore. 240p. 1987. 12.95 (ISBN 0-687-35283-5); pap. 8.95 (ISBN 0-687-35282-7). Abingdon.

Raising Your Child, Not by Force But by Love. Sidney D. Craig. LC 72-10436. 192p. 1982. pap. 6.95 (ISBN 0-664-24413-0). Westminster.

Raising Your Child, Not Your Voice. Duane Cuthbertson. 168p. 1986. pap. 5.95 (ISBN 0-89693-342-3). Victor Bks.

Raising Your Jewish-Christian Child: Wise Choices for Interfaith Parents. Lee F. Gruzen. 1987. 16.95 (ISBN 0-396-08551-2). Dodd.

Raissa's Journal. Raissa Maritain. LC 72-95648. 1974. 12.95x (ISBN 0-87343-041-7). Magi Bks.

Raja-Vidya: The King of Knowledge. Swami A. C. Bhaktivedanta. LC 72-84845. (Illus.). 1973. pap. 1.95 (ISBN 0-912776-40-4). Bhaktivedanta.

Raja Yoga. Yogi Ramacharaka. 8.00 (ISBN 0-911662-03-0). Yoga.

Raja Yoga. Subramuniya. (Illus.). 193p. 1973. 7.00 (ISBN 0-87516-348-3). De Vorss.

Raja-Yoga. Swami Vivekananda. LC 55-12231. 320p. pocket ed. 6.95 (ISBN 0-911206-06-X); pap. 6.95 large size (ISBN 0-911206-23-X). Ramakrishna.

Raja Yoga. Selvarajan Yesudian & Elisabeth Haich. (Unwin Paperbacks). (Illus.). 1980. pap. 5.95 (ISBN 0-04-149056-8). Allen Unwin.

Raja Yoga: A Simplified & Practical Course. Wallace Slater. LC 71-3051. 1969. pap. 4.50 (ISBN 0-8356-0131-5, Quest). Theos Pub Hse.

Raja Yoga Sutras. Patanjali. Tr. by Swami Jyotir Maya Nanda from Sanskrit. (Illus.). 1978. pap. 2.99 (ISBN 0-934664-38-2). Yoga Res Foun.

Raja Yoga (The Study of the Mind) Swami Jyotir Maya Nanda. (Illus.). 1970. 5.99 (ISBN 0-934664-09-9). Yoga Res Foun.

Raja-Yoga: The Yoga Aphorisms of Patanjali. Tr. by Swami Vivekananda. pap. 3.25 (ISBN 0-87481-160-0). Vedanta Pr.

Rajarsi Janakananda: A Great Western Yogi. (Illus.). 95p. 1984. pap. 1.95 (ISBN 0-87612-181-4). Self Realization.

Rajneesh Bible, Vol. II. Bhagwan S. Rajneesh. Ed. by Rajneesh Academy Staff. LC 85-42539. 839p. (Orig.). 1985. pap. 7.95x (ISBN 0-88050-201-0, 201-0). Chidvilas Found.

Rajneesh Bible, Vol. III. Bhagwan S. Rajneesh. Ed. by Rajneesh Academy Staff. LC 85-42539. 1072p. (Orig.). 1985. pap. 6.95 (ISBN 0-88050-202-9). Chidvilas Found.

Rajneesh Bible, Vol. IV. Bhagwan Shree Rajneesh. LC 85-42539. (Illus.). 800p. (Orig.). 1987. pap. 9.95x (ISBN 3-907757-02-5). Chidvilas Found.

Rajneesh Bible, Vol. 1. Baghwan S. Rajneesh. Ed. by Rajneesh Academy Staff. LC 85-42539. 800p. (Orig.). 1985. pap. 6.95 (ISBN 0-88050-200-2). Chidvilas Found.

Rajneesh: The Mystic of Feeling. 2nrev. ed. Ram Chandra Prasad. 1978. 10.95 (ISBN 0-89684-023-9, Pub. by Motilal Banarsidass India). Orient Bk Dist.

Rajneesh Upanishad. Bhagwan S. Rajneesh. Ed. by Ma Deva Sarito. 1032p. 1986. pap. 9.95 (ISBN 3-907757-00-9). Rajneesh Neo-Sannyas Intl.

Ralliement in French Politics, Eighteen Ninety to Eighteen Ninety-Eight. Alexander C. Sedgwick. LC 65-12828. (Historical Studies: No. 74). 1965. 14.00x (ISBN 0-674-74751-8). Harvard U Pr.

Ralph Waldo Emerson. Amos B. Alcott. LC 68-24930. (American Biography Ser., No. 32). 1969. Repr. of 1881 ed. lib. bdg. 49.95x (ISBN 0-8383-0908-9). Haskell.

Ralph Waldo Emerson. Sarah K. Bolton. LC 73-15752. 1973. lib. bdg. 10.00 (ISBN 0-8414-3304-6). Folcroft.

Ralph Waldo Emerson. Joseph H. Choate. 1978. Repr. of 1903 ed. lib. bdg. 8.50 (ISBN 0-8495-0818-5). Arden Lib.

Ralph Waldo Emerson. Joseph H. Choate. LC 73-4034. 1973. lib. bdg. 7.50 (ISBN 0-8414-1831-4). Folcroft.

Ralph Waldo Emerson. George W. Cooke. LC 74-8996. 1882. lib. bdg. 30.00 (ISBN 0-8414-3367-4). Folcroft.

Ralph Waldo Emerson. Oscar W. Firkins. LC 80-2532. Repr. of 1915 ed. 44.50 (ISBN 0-404-19258-0). AMS Pr.

Ralph Waldo Emerson. Alfred H. Guernsey. 1978. Repr. of 1901 ed. lib. bdg. 30.00 (ISBN 0-8492-0969-2). R West.

Ralph Waldo Emerson. Edward E. Hale. LC 72-8439. 1972. Repr. of 1902 ed. lib. bdg. 20.00 (ISBN 0-8414-0295-7). Folcroft.

Ralph Waldo Emerson. David G. Haskins. LC 76-122656. 1971. Repr. of 1887 ed. 26.50x (ISBN 0-8046-1305-2, Pub. by Kennikat). Assoc Faculty Pr.

Ralph Waldo Emerson. Franklin B. Sanborn. LC 72-7220. Repr. of 1901 ed. lib. bdg. 15.00 (ISBN 0-8414-0262-0). Folcroft.

Ralph Waldo Emerson. Warren Staebler. (World Leaders Ser.). 1973. lib. bdg. 12.50 (ISBN 0-8057-3674-3, Twayne). G K Hall.

Ralph Waldo Emerson. George Woodberry. LC 68-24947. (American Biography Ser., No. 32). 1969. Repr. of 1907 ed. lib. bdg. 49.95x (ISBN 0-8383-0262-9). Haskell.

Ralph Waldo Emerson. George E. Woodberry. 1973. lib. bdg. 12.75 (ISBN 0-8414-9790-7). Folcroft.

Ralph Waldo Emerson Eighteen Hundred Three to Eighteen Eighty-Two. John D. Gordon. LC 73-16267. 1973. lib. bdg. 10.00 (ISBN 0-8414-4481-1). Folcroft.

Ralph Waldo Emerson: Man & Teacher. Henry B. Baildon. LC 72-14362. Repr. of 1884 ed. lib. bdg. 10.00 (ISBN 0-8414-1340-1). Folcroft.

Ralph Waldo Emerson: Sa Vie et Son Oeuvre. Marie Dugard. LC 76-100530. (Illus.). Repr. of 1907 ed. 37.50 (ISBN 0-404-02215-4). AMS Pr.

Ralph Waldo Emerson: Sa Vie et Son Oeuvre. Marie Dugard. 1973. 16.45 (ISBN 0-8274-0066-7). R West.

Ram Mohan Roy: Social, Political & Religious Reform in 19th Century India. S. Cromwell Crawford. 288p. 1986. 22.95 (ISBN 0-913729-15-9). Paragon Hse.

Rama & the Bards: Epic Memory in the Ramayana. Robert Antoine. (Greybird Book). 114p. 1975. 12.00 (ISBN 0-88253-821-7); pap. 6.75 (ISBN 0-88253-822-5). Ind-US Inc.

Ramakien: The Thai Epic. J. M. Cadet. LC 70-128685. (Illus.). 256p. 1970. 35.00 (ISBN 0-87011-134-5). Kodansha.

Ramakrishna: A Biography in Pictures. Ed. by Advaita Ashrama Staff. (Illus.). 1976. 30.00x (ISBN 0-87481-167-8). Vedanta Pr.

Ramakrishna & His Disciples. Christopher Isherwood. LC 65-17100. 384p. 1980. pap. 8.95 (ISBN 0-87481-037-X). Vedanta Pr.

Ramakrishna & His Message. Swami Vivekananda. (Orig.). 1971. pap. 2.00 (ISBN 0-87481-126-0). Vedanta Pr.

Ramakrishna & the Vitality of Hinduism. Solange LeMaitre. Tr. by Charles L. Markmann from Fr. LC 68-54059. (Overlook Spiritual Masters Ser.). (Illus.). 244p. 1986. pap. 9.95 (ISBN 0-87951-241-5). Overlook Pr.

Ramakrishna As Swamiji Saw Him. Swami Vivekananda. (Orig.). 1970. pap. 1.00 (ISBN 0-87481-452-9). Vedanta Pr.

Ramakrishna, His Life & Sayings. Friedrich M. Mueller. LC 73-18812. Repr. of 1899 ed. 22.00 (ISBN 0-404-11452-0). AMS Pr.

Ramakrishna Math & Mission: Its Ideals & Activities. Swami Ranganathananda. (Illus.). pap. 1.00 (ISBN 0-87481-448-0). Vedanta Pr.

Ramakrishna Movement: Its Ideal & Activities. Swami Tejasananda. (Illus.). pap. 3.95 (ISBN 0-87481-117-1). Vedanta Pr.

Ramakrishna, Sri: Sahasra-Nama-Stotram. T. A. Bhandarkar. (Illus.). 200p. (Orig.). pap. 7.95x (ISBN 0-87481-509-6). Vedanta Pr.

Ramakrishna, Sri: The Great Master, Pts. 1 & 2. rev. ed. Swami Saradananda. Tr. by Swami Jagadananda. (Illus.). 1980. Pt. 1, 563p. pap. 8.50x ea. (ISBN 0-87481-495-2). Pt. 2 (ISBN 0-87481-496-0). Vedanta Pr.

Ramakrishna: The Power & the Glory. 303p. (Orig.). 1987. pap. 3.50 (ISBN 0-87481-544-4, Pub. by Ramakrishna Math Madras India). Vedanta Pr.

Ramakrishna Upanishad. C. Rajagopalachari. pap. 1.95 (ISBN 0-87481-430-8). Vedanta Pr.

Ramakrishna-Vedanta Wordbook: A Brief Dictionary of Hinduism. Ed. by Brahmacharini Usha. (Orig.). pap. 3.25 (ISBN 0-87481-017-5). Vedanta Pr.

Ramayana. Tr. by Romesh C. Dutt. Bd. with Mahabharata. 1972. 12.95x (ISBN 0-460-00403-4, Evman). Biblio Dist.

Ramayana. C. Rajagopalachari. 1979. pap. 5.95 (ISBN 0-89744-930-4). Auromere.

Ramayana. 3rd ed. Valmiki. Ed. & tr. by Chakravarti Rajagopalachari. 320p. (Orig.). 1980. pap. 4.25 (ISBN 0-934676-17-8). Greenlf Bks.

Ramayana at a Glance. Satguru S. Keshavadas. (Illus.). 184p. (Orig.). 1978. pap. 3.50 (ISBN 0-942508-11-4). Vishwa.

Ramayana in Historical Perspective. H. D. Sankalia. 1983. 18.50x (ISBN 0-8364-0997-3, Pub. by Macmillan India). South Asia Bks.

Ramayana of R. K. Narayan: A Shortened Modern Prose Version of the Indian Epic, Suggested by the Tamil Version of Kamban. R. K. Narayan. LC 79-189514. (Illus.). 192p. 1972. 13.95 (ISBN 0-670-58950-0). Viking.

Ramayana Tradition in Asia. Ed. by V. Raghavan. 1982. 18.00x (ISBN 0-8364-0899-3, Pub. by National Sahitya Akademi). South Asia Bks.

Ramban: His Life & Teachings. Charles B. Chavel. LC 63-1543. pap. 5.95 (ISBN 0-87306-037-7). Feldheim.

Ramban (Nachmanides) Commentary on the Torah, 5 vols. Charles B. Chavel. 2575p. 1971. 84.75 set (ISBN 0-686-86743-2); Vol. I, Book Of Genesis. 16.95 ea. (ISBN 0-88328-006-X). Vol. II, Book Of Exodus (ISBN 0-88328-007-8). Vol. III, Book Of Leviticus (ISBN 0-88328-008-6). Vol. IV, Book Of Numbers (ISBN 0-88328-009-4). Vol. V, Book Of Deuteronomy (ISBN 0-88328-010-8). Shilo Pub Hse.

Ramban (Nachmanides) Writings & Discourses, 2 vols. Charles B. Chavel. 768p. 1978. Set. slipcase 33.00 (ISBN 0-88328-013-2). Shilo Pub Hse.

Rambles in Vedanta. B. R. Iyer. 1974. Repr. 22.50 (ISBN 0-8426-0601-7). Orient Bk Dist.

Ramblings in the Elucidation of the Autograph of Milton. S. L. Sotheby. 1974. Repr. of 1861 ed. lib. bdg. 100.00 limited ed. (ISBN 0-8414-8008-7). Folcroft.

Ramblings of an Ascetic. Yuacharya Shri Mahaprajna. xvi, 127p. 1979. 9.00 (ISBN 0-88065-212-8, Pub. by Messers Today & Tomorrows Printers & Publishers India). Scholarly Pubns.

Ramesses II: A Chronological Structure of His Reign. John D. Schmidt. LC 72-6558. (Near Eastern Studies). Repr. of 1973 ed. 56.00 (ISBN 0-8357-9282-X, 2011503). Bks Demand UMI.

Rampa Story. T. Lobsang Rampa. pap. 2.95 (ISBN 0-552-11413-8). Weiser.

Ramprasad: The Melodius Mystic. Ramprasad. Tr. by Buddhananda. 72p. 1985. pap. 2.00 (ISBN 0-87481-568-1, Pub. by Ramakrishna Math Madras India). Vedanta Pr.

Ramtha. Ramtha. Ed. by Steven L. Weinberg. LC 85-61768. 224p. 1986. 19.95 (ISBN 0-932201-11-3). Sovereignty.

Ramtha: A Treasure Chest of Wisdom. Ramtha. Ed. by Sue A. Fazio & Randall Weischedel. 250p. 1987. 16.95 (ISBN 0-932201-23-7). Sovereignty.

Ramtha in Audience. Ramtha. 300p. 1987. 15.95 (ISBN 0-932201-90-3); pap. 9.95 (ISBN 0-932201-82-2). Sovereignty.

Ramtha: Select Teachings. Ramtha. Ed. by Steven L. Weinberg. 150p. 1987. pap. 8.95 (ISBN 0-932201-19-9). Sovereignty.

Rance & the Trappist Legacy. A. J. Krailsheimer. 16.95 (ISBN 0-87907-886-3); pap. 6.95. Cistercian Pubns.

Ranchos De Taos: San Francisco De Asis Church. Wolfgang Pogzeba & Joy Overbeck. LC 81-82257. (Illus.). 68p. (Orig.). 1981. pap. 7.95 (ISBN 0-913504-66-1). Lowell Pr.

Rand McNally Book of Favorite Christmas Stories. (Illus.). 112p. 1985. 8.95 (ISBN 0-528-82678-6). Macmillan.

Randall House Bible Commentary: Romans. F. Leroy Forlines. (Bible Commentary Ser.). 350p. 1986. 19.95 (ISBN 0-89265-116-4). Randall Hse.

Randall House Bible Commentary Series. Ed. by Robert E. Picirilli & H. D. Harrison. Date not set. price not set (ISBN 0-89265-115-6). Randall Hse.

Randall House Bible Commentary (1, 2 Corinthians) Robert E. Picirilli. Ed. by H. D. Harrison. (Bible Commentary Ser.). 350p. 1986. 19.95 (ISBN 0-89265-118-0). Randall Hse.

Random Sampler: Helpful Hints for Latter-day Living from the Ensign. LC 86-1465. 220p. 1986. 7.95 (ISBN 0-87747-977-1). Deseret Bk.

Random Talks with the Living Christ. Francis L. L'Estrange. 107p. 1986. 30.00X (ISBN 0-7223-2038-8, Pub. by A H Stockwell England). State Mutual Bk.

Rangoon, Burma, Thathana Yeiktha Meditation Course. E. H. Shattock. 175p. 1985. 137.50 (ISBN 0-89920-094-X). Am Inst Psych.

Rank among the Canaanite Gods: El, Baal, & the Raphaim. Conrad E. L'Heureux. LC 79-15582. (Harvard Semitic Monographs: No. 21). 1979. 10.50 (ISBN 0-89130-326-X, 040021). Scholars Pr GA.

Ransoming Captives in Crusader Spain: The Order of Merced on the Christian-Islamic Frontier. James W. Brodman. LC 85-20362. (Middle Ages Ser.). (Illus.). 216p. 1986. text ed. 21.95 (ISBN 0-8122-8001-6). U of PA Pr.

Ransoming the Mind: An Integration of Yoga & Modern Therapy. Charles Bates. LC 86-50084. (Illus.). 352p. (Orig.). 1986. pap. 11.95 (ISBN 0-936663-00-6). Yes Intl.

Ransoming the Time. Jacques Maritain. Tr. by Harry L. Binsse. LC 70-165665. 322p. 1972. Repr. of 1941 ed. 25.00x (ISBN 0-87752-153-0). Gordian.

Rape of a Noble Ideology. Aslam Munjee. 487p. 1986. write for info. (ISBN 0-9617573-0-2). First Amend Pubs.

Rape of Palestine. William B. Ziff. LC 73-97310. (Illus.). 612p. 1975. Repr. of 1938 ed. lib. bdg. 29.25x (ISBN 0-8371-2639-8, ZIRP). Greenwood.

Rape of the Sabine Women. Janemarie Luecke. 1978. 5.95 (ISBN 0-87482-097-9). Wake-Brook.

Raphael's Bible: A Study of the Vatican Logge. Bernice F. Davidson. LC 84-43088. (College Art Association Monographs: Vol. 39). (Illus.). 198p. 1985. 30.00 (ISBN 0-271-00388-X). Pa St U Pr.

Rappaccini's Children: American Writers in a Calvinist World. William H. Shurr. LC 79-57573. 176p. 1981. 16.00x (ISBN 0-8131-1427-6). U Pr of Ky.

Rapture. E. Schuyler English. 1954. pap. 5.95 (ISBN 0-87213-144-0). Loizeaux.

Rapture. Gordon Lindsay. (Prophecy Ser.). 1.50 (ISBN 0-89985-063-4). Christ Nations.

Rapture: A Question of Timing. William R. Kimball. 200p. (Orig.). pap. 5.95 (ISBN 0-89900-205-6). College Pr Pub.

Rapture: A Question of Timing. William R. Kimball. 1985. pap. 6.95 (ISBN 0-8010-5468-0). Baker Bk.

Rapture & Its Mystery. Wim Malgo. pap. 1.95 (ISBN 0-937422-13-4). Midnight Call.

Rapture & the Second Coming of Christ. Gordon Lindsay. (Revelation Ser.). 1.25 (ISBN 0-89985-041-3). Christ Nations.

Rapture Question. rev. enlarged ed. John F. Walvoord. 1970. pap. 8.95 (ISBN 0-310-34151-5, 10978P). Zondervan.

Rapture: Truth or Consequences. Hal Lindsey. 224p. (Orig.). 1985. pap. 3.95 (ISBN 0-553-26692-6). Bantam.

Raptured. Zola Levitt & Tom McCall. LC 75-15481. 1975. pap. 4.95 (ISBN 0-89081-014-1). Harvest Hse.

Rare Jewel of Christian Contentment. Jeremiah Burroughs. 1979. pap. 5.45 (ISBN 0-85151-091-4). Banner of Truth.

Rarest of These Is Hope. Harold C. Warlick, Jr. 1985. 7.50 (ISBN 0-89536-743-2, 5826). CSS of Ohio.

Ras Shamra & the Bible. Charles F. Pfeiffer. (Baker Studies in Biblical Archaeology). 1976. pap. 2.95 (ISBN 0-8010-7003-1). Baker Bk.

Ras Shamra Mythological Texts. James A. Montgomery & Zellig S. Harris. LC 36-2726. (American Philosophical Society. Philadelphia. Memoirs: Vol. 4). pap. 34.80 (ISBN 0-317-09878-0, 2000354). Bks Demand UMI.

Rasa Tantra: Blood Marriage, The Sacred Initiation, A Marriage of the Faiths of East & West. Tsampa Yeshe Norbu. (Illus.). 36p. 1980. pap. 6.95 (ISBN 0-9609802-2-9). Life Science.

Rashi Vocalized for Beginners. text ed. 2.50 (ISBN 0-914131-52-4, B01). Torah Umesorah.

Raspberry Kingdom. Renee Hermanson. LC 78-62985. 1978. pap. 4.50 (ISBN 0-8358-0374-0). Upper Room.

Rasputin the Holy Devil. Rene Fulop-Miller. 1977. Repr. of 1928 ed. lib. bdg. 30.00 (ISBN 0-8414-4308-4). Folcroft.

Rasta & Resistance: From Marcus Garvey to Walter Rodney. Horace Campbell. LC 85-73332. 240p. (Orig.). 1987. 32.95 (ISBN 0-86543-034-9); pap. 10.95 (ISBN 0-86543-035-7). Africa World.

Rastafari: A Way of Life. Tracy Nicholas. LC 77-76285. (Illus.). 1979. pap. 9.95 (ISBN 0-385-11575-X, Anch). Doubleday.

Rastafarians. Kathy Williams. 1985. 13.00x (ISBN 0-7062-4063-4, Pub. by Ward Lock Educ Co Ltd). State Mutual Bk.

Rastafarians: Sounds of Cultural Dissonance. Leonard E. Barrett. LC 76-48491. (Illus.). 1977. pap. 9.95 (ISBN 0-8070-1115-0, BP559). Beacon Pr.

Rastaman: The Rastafarian Movement in England. Ernest Cashmore. (Illus.). 272p. 1980. pap. text ed. 9.95x (ISBN 0-04-301116-0). Allen Unwin.

Rastaman: The Rastafarian Movement in England. Ernest Cashmore. (Counterpoint Ser.). 263p. 1983. pap. 9.95 (ISBN 0-04-301164-0). Allen Unwin.

Ratio Disciplinae Fratrum Novanglorum: A Faithful Account of the Discipline Professed & Practised, in the Churches of New-England. Cotton Mather. LC 71-141114. (Research Library of Colonial Americana). 1971. Repr. of 1726 ed. 23.50 (ISBN 0-405-03327-3). Ayer Co Pubs.

Rational Faith: Essays in Honor of Levi A. Olan. Ed. by J. Bemporad. 15.00x (ISBN 0-87068-448-5). Ktav.

Rational Irrational Man: Torah Psychology. Avrohom Amsel. 1976. pap. 7.95 (ISBN 0-87306-129-2). Feldheim.

Rational Man: A Modern Interpretation of Aristotelian Ethics. Henry B. Veatch. LC 62-16161. (Midland Bks.: No. 71). 228p. 1962. pap. 8.95x (ISBN 0-253-20071-7). Ind U Pr.

Rational Theology & the Creativity of God. Keith Ward. LC 82-81888. 256p. 1982. 17.95 (ISBN 0-8298-0618-0). Pilgrim NY.

Rationalist Encyclopaedia: A Book of Reference on Religion, Philosophy, Ethics, & Science. Joseph McCabe. LC 79-164054. 1971. Repr. of 1948 ed. 51.00x (ISBN 0-8103-3754-1). Gale.

Rationality & Religious Belief. Ed. by C. F. Delaney. LC 79-63359. (Studies in the Philosophy of Religion: No. 1). 1979. text ed. 12.95x (ISBN 0-268-01602-X, 85-16023); pap. text ed. 5.95x (ISBN 0-268-01603-8, 85-16031). U of Notre Dame Pr.

Rationality in the Calvinian Tradition. Ed. by Hendrik Hart & Johan Van Der Hoeven. LC 83-19672. (Christian Studies Today). 420p. (Orig.). 1984. lib. bdg. 32.25 (ISBN 0-8191-3616-6); pap. text ed. 16.75 (ISBN 0-8191-3617-4). U Pr of Amer.

Rationality of Islam. Murtaza Mutahhery. Tr. by M. A. Ansari. 170p. 1983. pap. 6.00 (ISBN 0-941724-17-4). Islamic Seminary.

Rationality, Religious Belief, & Moral Commitment: New Essays in the Philosophy of Religion. Ed. by Robert Audi & William J. Wainwright. LC 85-48200. 352p. 1986. text ed. 42.50x (ISBN 0-8014-1856-9); pap. text ed. 12.95x (ISBN 0-8014-9381-1). Cornell U Pr.

Ratis Raving, & Other Moral & Religious Pieces. Joseph R. Lumby. (EETS, OS Ser.: No. 43). Repr. of 1870 ed. 12.00 (ISBN 0-527-00038-8). Kraus Repr.

Rats in the Sacristy. facs. ed. Llewelyn Powys. LC 67-30226. (Essay Index Reprint Ser.). 1937. 17.00 (ISBN 0-8369-0798-1). Ayer Co Pubs.

Ratzinger Report. Joseph Ratzinger & Vittorio Messori. Tr. by Salvator Attanasio & Graham Harrison. LC 85-81218. Tr. of Rapporto sulla Fede. (Ger. & Ital.). 197p. (Orig.). 1985. pap. 9.95 (ISBN 0-89870-080-9). Ignatius Pr.

Rav. Naftali H. Ehrmann. Tr. by Karen Paritzky from Ger. Tr. of Rav. (Illus.). 1978. 7.95 (ISBN 0-87306-137-3); pap. 5.95. Feldheim.

Ravalette: The Rosicrucian's Story. Paschal B. Randolph. 283p. 1939. 7.95 (ISBN 0-932785-40-9). Philos Pub.

Ravished by the Spirit: Religious Revivals, Baptists, & Henry Alline. G. A. Rawlyk. 190p. 1984. 19.95x (ISBN 0-7735-0439-7); pap. 7.95 (ISBN 0-7735-0440-0). McGill-Queens U Pr.

Raw & the Cooked. Claude Levi-Strauss. (Science of Mythology Ser.). 1979. Repr. of 1970 ed. lib. bdg. 29.00x (ISBN 0-374-94953-0, Octagon). Hippocrene Bks.

Raw & the Cooked: Introduction to a Science of Mythology, Vol. 1. Claude Levi-Strauss. Tr. by John Weightman & Doreen Weightman. LC 82-15895. (Illus.). xiv, 388p. 1969. pap. 11.00x (ISBN 0-226-47487-9). U of Chicago Pr.

Ray Buckland's Complete Book of Witchcraft. Raymond Buckland. Ed. by Carl L. Weschcke. LC 85-45280. (Sourcebook Ser.). (Illus.). 320p. (Orig.). 1986. wkbk. 12.95 (ISBN 0-87542-050-8). Llewellyn Pubns.

Raymond III of Tripolis & the Fall of Jerusalem: 1140-1187. Marshall W. Baldwin. LC 76-29830. Repr. of 1936 ed. 28.50 (ISBN 0-404-15411-5). AMS Pr.

Raymund Lully: Christian Mystic. Arthur E. Waite. 69.95 (ISBN 0-87968-100-4). Gordon Pr.

Rays of Hope. D. O. Teasley. 95p. pap. 0.75 (ISBN 0-686-29137-9). Faith Pub Hse.

Rays of Light. Mary Light. pap. 1.00 (ISBN 0-910924-59-7). Macalester.

Razmishljenije o Bozhestvennoj Liturgii. Nikolai Gogol. Tr. of Meditations on the Divine Liturgy. 48p. pap. 2.00 (ISBN 0-317-29135-1). Holy Trinity.

RB Nineteen Eighty. Ed. by Timothy Fry et al. LC 81-1013. 627p. 1981. 24.95 (ISBN 0-8146-1211-3); pap. 17.50 (ISBN 0-8146-1220-2). Liturgical Pr.

RB Nineteen-Eighty: The Rule of St. Benedict in Latin & English with Notes & Thematic Index. abr. ed. Ed. by Timothy Fry et al. LC 81-12434. xii, 198p. 1981. pap. 8.95 (ISBN 0-8146-1243-1). Liturgical Pr.

RCIA: A Total Parish Process. William A. Anderson. 1986. pap. 12.95 (ISBN 0-697-02200-5). Wm C Brown.

RCIA Team Manual: How to Implement the Rite of Christian Initiation of Adults in Your Parish. Patricia Barbernitz. 88p. 1986. pap. 7.95 (ISBN 0-8091-2814-4). Paulist Pr.

RCIA: The Rite of Christian Initiation of Adults. Patricia Barbernitz. 48p. 1983. pap. 2.95 (ISBN 0-89243-190-3). Liguori Pubns.

Re-Conciliation: The Hidden Hyphen. Mary Morrison. LC 74-24007. 24p. (Orig.). 1974. pap. 2.50x (ISBN 0-87574-198-3, 198). Pendle Hill.

Re-Creation of Eve. Rosemary Haughton. 1985. pap. 8.95 (ISBN 0-87243-135-5). Templegate.

Re-Discovery of the Old Testament. facs. ed. Harold H. Rowley. LC 75-76912. (Essay Index Reprint Ser). 1946. 19.00 (ISBN 0-8369-1154-7). Ayer Co Pubs.

Re-Entry II. John W. White. 1986. pap. 4.95 (ISBN 0-8010-9680-4). Baker Bk.

Re-Establishment of the Church of England, 1660-1663. I. M. Green. (Oxford Historical Monographs). 1978. 42.00x (ISBN 0-19-821867-2). Oxford U Pr.

Re-Evaluation of the Eldership. Dayton Keese. pap. 2.50 (ISBN 0-89137-552-X). Quality Pubns.

Re-Treat Your Family to Lent. Sandra De Gidio. 50p. (Orig.). 1983. pap. text ed. 1.95 (ISBN 0-86716-022-5). St Anthony Mess Pr.

Reach for Your Spiritual Potential. Doris Black. 1986. pap. 4.95 (ISBN 0-89137-438-8). Quality Pubns.

Reach Out. Paul Foust & Richard Kortals. 1984. pap. 3.95 (ISBN 0-570-03933-9, 12-2868). Concordia.

Reach Out & Touch. Thomas R. Haney. 1980. pap. 3.95 (ISBN 0-88479-027-4). Arena Lettres.

Reach Out for New Life. Robert H. Schuller. 1979. pap. 3.50 (ISBN 0-553-25222-4). Bantam.

Reach Out to Singles: A Challenge to Ministry. Raymond K. Brown. LC 79-15495. 192p. 1979. pap. 7.95 (ISBN 0-664-24270-7). Westminster.

Reaching Decisions. Howard H. Brinton. 1983. pap. 2.50x (ISBN 0-87574-065-0, 065). Pendle Hill.

Reaching for Excellence. Tannis Duncan. 67p. (Orig.). 1982. pap. text ed. 2.50 (ISBN 0-87148-737-3). Pathway Pr.

Reaching for Joy. Stephanie C. Oda. 48p. 1985. 4.95 (ISBN 0-8378-5402-4). Gibson.

Reaching for More. Pascal Foresi. Tr. by Hugh J. Moran from Ital. Tr. of Conversazioni con i Focolarini. 128p. (Orig.). 1982. pap. 4.95 (ISBN 0-911782-40-0). New City.

Reaching for Rainbows: Resources for Creative Worship. Ann Weems. LC 80-19330. 156p. 1980. pap. 8.95 (ISBN 0-664-24355-X). Westminster.

Reaching for the Sky. Thomas B. Pittman, 3rd. 1976. pap. 3.95 (ISBN 0-87148-731-4). Pathway Pr.

Reaching High: The Psychology of Spiritual Living. Marvin Gawryn. LC 80-24306. 200p. 1981. 11.95 (ISBN 0-938380-00-1); pap. 7.95 (ISBN 0-938380-01-X). Highreach Colorado.

Reaching Our Jewish Friends. Lee Belcher & Carol Belcher. (Truthway Ser.). 79p. (Orig.). 1981. pap. text ed. 1.50 (ISBN 0-87148-735-7). Pathway Pr.

Reaching Out for Life's Best. William J. Krutza. (Contemporary Discussion Ser.). 96p. (Orig.). 1982. pap. 2.95 (ISBN 0-8010-5444-3). Baker Bk.

Reaching Out in Love. Randolph J. Klassen. 144p. (Orig.). 1981. pap. 5.95 (ISBN 0-910452-47-4). Covenant.

Reaching Out: The Three Movements of the Spiritual Life. Henri J. Nouwen. LC 86-2901. (Illus.). 168p. 1986. pap. 5.95 (ISBN 0-385-23682-4, Im). Doubleday.

Reaching Out: The Three Movements of the Spiritual Life. Henri J. M. Nouwen. LC 74-9460. 120p. 1975. 9.95 (ISBN 0-385-03212-9). Doubleday.

Reaching Out to People. Talmadge R. Amberson. LC 79-55435. 1979. pap. 5.95 (ISBN 0-8054-6321-6). Broadman.

Reaching Out to the Baptists with Heart & Mind. William J. Whalen. (Reaching Out to...Ser.). 32p. 1984. pap. 1.50 (ISBN 0-89243-209-8). Liguori Pubns.

Reaching Out to the Episcopalians with Heart & Mind. William J. Whalen. (Reaching Out to...Ser.). 32p. 1984. pap. 1.50 (ISBN 0-89243-210-1). Liguori Pubns.

Reaching Out to the Lutherans with Heart & Mind. William J. Whalen. (Reaching Out to...Ser.). 32p. 1984. pap. 1.50 (ISBN 0-89243-206-3). Liguori Pubns.

Reaching Out to the Presbyterians & the Reformed with Heart & Mind. William J. Whalen. (Reaching Out to...Ser.). 32p. 1984. pap. 1.50 (ISBN 0-89243-208-X). Liguori Pubns.

Reaching Out to Troubled Youth. Dwight Spotts & David Veerman. 204p. 1987. pap. 11.95 (ISBN 0-89693-296-6). Victor Bks.

Reaching People from the Pulpit: A Guide to Effective Sermon Delivery. Dwight E. Stevenson & Charles F. Diehl. (Notable Books on Preaching). 1978. pap. 4.50 (ISBN 0-8010-8133-5). Baker Bk.

Reaching the Inactive Member. John H. Krahn. 1982. 5.25 (ISBN 0-89536-570-7, 1815). CSS of Ohio.

Reaching the Unreached. Ed. by Harvie M. Conn. (Orig.). 1985. pap. 8.95 (ISBN 0-87552-209-2). Presby & Reformed.

Reaching the Unreached: The Old-New Challenge. Ed. by Harvie M. Conn. 192p. 1985. 8.95 (ISBN 0-8010-2508-7). Baker Bk.

Reaching, Touching, Teaching: How to Run Successful Days of Retreat. Randy Cooney. 1986. pap. 15.95 (ISBN 0-697-02199-8). Wm C Brown.

Reaching Toward God. Michael Marsh. LC 81-81683. 27p. 1981. pap. 2.50x (ISBN 0-87574-237-8, 237). Pendle Hill.

Reaching Toward the Heights. Richard Wurmbrand. 1979. pap. 7.95x (ISBN 0-88264-142-5). Diane Bks.

Reaching Up, Reaching Out. Leland E. Pulley. LC 85-90071. (Orig.). 1985. pap. 5.95 (ISBN 0-9611282-1-6). Stewardship Enters.

Reaching Your Full Potential. Richard Furman. 1984. pap. 6.95 (ISBN 0-89081-443-0). Harvest Hse.

Reaching Your World. Beth Mainhood. 118p. 1986. pap. 4.95 (ISBN 0-89109-537-3). NavPress.

Reaching Youth Today: Heirs to the Whirlwind. Barbara Hargrove & Stephen D. Jones. 1983. pap. 5.95 (ISBN 0-8170-0977-9). Judson.

Reactions Between Dogma & Philosophy Illustrated from the Works of St. Thomas Aquinas. Philip H. Wicksteed. LC 77-27153. (Hibbert Lectures: 1916). Repr. of 1920 ed. 57.50 (ISBN 0-404-60418-8). AMS Pr.

Read-Aloud Bible Stories, Vol. 1. Ella K. Lindvall. LC 82-2114. 160p. 1982. 16.95 (ISBN 0-8024-7163-3). Moody.

Read-Aloud Bible Stories, Vol. 2. Ella K. Lindvall. (Illus.). 1985. text ed. 16.95 (ISBN 0-8024-7164-1). Moody.

Read 'n Grow Picture Bible. Ed. by Libby Weed. LC 84-51093. (Illus.). 319p. 1984. 14.95 (ISBN 0-8344-0124-X, BB200C). Sweet.

Read Through the Bible in a Year. John R. Kohlenberger, III. (Orig.). 1986. pap. 1.95 (ISBN 0-8024-7168-4). Moody.

Reader in Comparative Religion: An Anthropological Approach. 4th ed. William A. Lessa & Evon Z. Vogt. 1979. pap. text ed. 27.50 scp (ISBN 0-06-043991-2, HarpC). Har-Row.

Reader's Bible, A Narrative: Selections from the King James Version. Ed. by Roland M. Frye. LC 77-311. 638p. 1979. pap. 13.50 (ISBN 0-691-01995-9). Princeton U Pr.

Reader's Greek-English Lexicon of the New Testament & a Beginner's Guide for the Translation of New Testament Greek. Sakae Kubo. (Andrews University Monographs, Studies in Religion: Vol. IV). x, 327p. 1975. text ed. 14.95 (ISBN 0-943872-04-9). Andrews Univ Pr.

Reader's Greek-English Lexicon of the New Testament & Benjamin's Guide. Sakae Kubo. 1975. text ed. 15.95 (ISBN 0-310-26920-2, 6269). Zondervan.

Reader's Guide: The Development of Baha'i Literature in English. Eunice Braun. 176p. 1986. 14.95 (ISBN 0-85398-228-7); pap. 8.95 (ISBN 0-85398-229-5). G Ronald Pub.

Reader's Guide to Proclamation: For Sundays & Major Feasts in Cycle A. Jerome J. DuCharme. 160p. 1974. pap. 2.95 (ISBN 0-8199-0577-1). Franciscan Herald.

Reader's Guide to the Best Evangelical Books. Ed. by Mark L. Branson. LC 82-48205. 208p. (Orig.). 1982. pap. 5.95 (ISBN 0-06-061046-8, RD-388, HarpR). Har-Row.

Reader's Guide to the Great Religions. 2nd ed. Ed. by Charles J. Adams. LC 76-10496. 1977. 24.95 (ISBN 0-02-900240-0). Free Pr.

Reader's Hebrew-English Lexicon of the Old Testament: Genesis-II Kings. Ed. by Terry Armstrong et al. (Hebrew & Eng.). 1982. 16.95 (ISBN 0-310-37040-X, 6291). Zondervan.

Reader's Hebrew-English Lexicon of the Old Testament: Isaiah-Malachi, Vol. 3. Terry A. Armstrong et al. 208p. 1985. 14.95 (ISBN 0-310-37010-8, 6293). Zondervan.

Reader's Theatre Comes to Church. 2nd ed. Gordon C. Bennett. LC 85-61999. 128p. 1985. pap. 7.95 (ISBN 0-916260-33-X, B-191). Meriwether Pub.

Readiness for Reconciliation. Lynn Buzzard & Juanita Buzzard. 36p. (Orig.). 1982. wkbk 3.00 (ISBN 0-686-39857-2). Chr Concil Serv.

Readiness for Religion. Ronald Goldman. 1970. pap. 4.95 (ISBN 0-8164-2060-2, SP70, HarpR). Har-Row.

Readiness for Religion. Harold Loukes. LC 63-11818. (Orig.). 1963. pap. 2.50x (ISBN 0-87574-126-6). Pendle Hill.

Reading & Believing. Jacob Neuser. (Brown Judaic Studies). 138p. 1986. 25.50 (ISBN 0-89130-976-4, 14-01-13); pap. 20.50 (ISBN 0-89130-977-2). Scholars Pr GA.

Reading & Preaching the Bible: A New Approach. Walter Vogels. (Background Bks.: Vol. 4). 1986. pap. 7.95 (ISBN 0-89453-472-6). M Glazier.

Reading Corinthians: A Literary & Theological Commentary on 1 and 2 Corinthians. Charles H. Talbert. 224p. 1987. 15.95 (ISBN 0-8245-0804-1). Crossroad NY.

Reading Freud: Psychology, Neurosis, & Religion. Volney P. Gay. LC 83-2917. (AAR Studies in Religion). 142p. 1983. pap. 8.25 (ISBN 0-89130-613-7, 01 00 32). Scholars Pr GA.

Reading Guide to the Book of Mormon: A Simplified Program Featuring Brief Outlines & Doctrinal Summaries. Duane S. Crowther. LC 75-5322. 169p. 1975. 7.95 (ISBN 0-88290-045-5). Horizon Utah.

Reading Hebrew. L. W. Adler & C. Castberg. 1972. pap. 3.95x (ISBN 0-87441-042-8). Behrman.

Reading Jung: Science, Psychology, & Religion. Volney P. Gay. LC 84-1322. (AAR-Studies in Religion). 166p. 1984. pap. 8.25 (ISBN 0-89130-731-1, 01 00 34). Scholars Pr GA.

Reading Luke: A Literary & Theological Commentary on the Third Gospel. Charles H. Talbert. LC 82-12737. 288p. 1982. 17.95 (ISBN 0-8245-0532-8). Crossroad NY.

Reading Luke: A Literary & Theological Commentary on the Third Gospel. Charles H. Talbert. 256p. 1984. pap. 10.95 (ISBN 0-8245-0668-5). Crossroad NY.

Reading My Bible in Fall. Lou Heath & Beth Taylor. LC 85-30947. (Orig.). 1986. pap. 4.50 (ISBN 0-8054-4322-3). Broadman.

Reading My Bible in Spring. Lou Heath & Beth Taylor. (Orig.). 1987. pap. 4.50 (ISBN 0-8054-4320-7). Broadman.

Reading My Bible in Summer. Lou Heath & Beth Taylor. (Orig.). 1987. pap. 4.50 (ISBN 0-8054-4321-5). Broadman.

Reading My Bible in Winter. Lou Heath & Beth Taylor. LC 85-30940. (Orig.). 1986. pap. 4.50 (ISBN 0-8054-4323-1). Broadman.

Reading of I Samuel. Peter D. Miscall. (Literary Bible Ser.). 256p. 1985. cancelled (ISBN 0-8245-0662-6). Crossroad NY.

Reading of Vergil's "Georgics". J. Seaton. 222p. 1983. lib. bdg. 33.00x (Pub. by A M Hakkert). Coronet Bks.

Reading, Preaching & Celebrating the Word. Ed. by Paul Marcoux & Joseph P. LoCigno. pap. 9.95 (ISBN 0-941850-00-5). Sunday Pubns.

Reading Reform. Satsvar upa Das Goswami. Ed. by Dattatreya dasa. 120p. 1985. pap. text ed. 4.00 (ISBN 0-911233-28-8). Gita Nagari.

Reading Scripture As the Word of God. Rev. ed. George Martin. 200p. 1982. pap. 4.95 (ISBN 0-89283-152-9). Servant.

Reading the Acts, Epistles & Revelations. J. Kingsley Dalpadado. 1977. 6.95 (ISBN 0-8198-0450-9); pap. 5.95 (ISBN 0-8198-0451-7). Dghtrs St Paul.

Reading the Bible. J. Kingsley Dalpadado. 1973. 5.95 (ISBN 0-8198-0338-3); pap. 4.95 (ISBN 0-8198-0339-1). Dghtrs St Paul.

Reading the Bible As History. James W. Dixon. 605p. 1986. 21.90 (ISBN 0-533-06192-X). Vantage.

Reading the Bible As History. Theodore Plantinga. 110p. (Orig.). 1980. pap. 4.25 (ISBN 0-932914-04-7). Dordt Coll Pr.

Reading the Gospels. J. Kinglsey Dalpadado. 1975. pap. 4.00 (ISBN 0-8198-0454-1). Dghtrs St Paul.

Reading the New Testament. Ronald J. Wilkins. (To Live Is Christ Ser.). 160p. 1983. pap. 5.50 extended study (ISBN 0-697-01810-5); tchr's. manual 4.00 (ISBN 0-697-01811-3); spirit masters 12.95 (ISBN 0-697-01674-9); pap. 3.95 short ed. (ISBN 0-697-01673-0); tchr's. manual 3.75 (ISBN 0-697-01680-3). Wm C Brown.

Reading the New Testament: An Introduction. Pheme Perkins. LC 78-51892. 352p. 1978. pap. 5.95 (ISBN 0-8091-9535-6). Paulist Pr.

Reading the New Testament for Understanding. Robert G. Hoerber. 192p. 1986. pap. 7.50 (ISBN 0-570-03988-6, 12-3016). Concordia.

Reading the Old Testament: An Introduction. Lawrence Boadt. LC 84-60723. 416p. (Orig.). 1984. pap. 7.95 (ISBN 0-8091-2631-1). Paulist Pr.

Reading the Old Testament: Method in Biblical Study. John Barton. LC 84-3640. 272p. 1984. pap. 12.95 (ISBN 0-664-24555-2). Westminster.

Reading the Ramayana: A Bibliographic Guide for Students & College Teachers. Indian Variants on the Rama Theme in English Translations. H. Daniel Smith. (Foreign & Comparative Studies Program, South Asian Special Publications: No. 4). (Orig.). 1983. pap. text ed. 6.50x (ISBN 0-915984-87-3). Syracuse U Foreign Comp.

Reading Through Romans. C. K. Barrett. LC 76-55828. 96p. 1977. pap. 3.95 (ISBN 0-8006-1250-7, 1-1250). Fortress.

Readings, Cases, Materials in Canon Law: A Textbook for Ministerial Students. Jordan F. Hite et al. LC 79-24977. 370p. (Orig.). 1980. pap. text ed. 8.50 (ISBN 0-8146-1081-1). Liturgical Pr.

Readings for Town & Country Church Workers: An Annotated Bibliography. David M. Byers & Bernard Quinn. LC 74-77445. 120p. 1974. pap. 2.00x (ISBN 0-914422-00-6). Glenmary Res Ctr.

Readings from the History of the Episcopal Church. Ed. by Robert W. Prichard. 192p. (Orig.). 1986. pap. 14.95 (ISBN 0-8192-1383-7). Morehouse.

Readings in California Catholic History. Francis J. Weber. 10.00 (ISBN 0-87026-000-6). Westernlore.

Readings in Calvin's Theology. Donald K. McKim. 304p. (Orig.). 1984. pap. 15.95 (ISBN 0-8010-6150-4). Baker Bk.

Readings in Christian Humanism. Ed. by Joseph M. Shaw et al. LC 82-70963. (Orig.). 1982. pap. 24.95 (ISBN 0-8066-1938-4, 10-5400). Augsburg.

Readings In Christian Theology. Ed. by Millard J. Erickson. 1973. pap. 12.95 (ISBN 0-8010-3305-5). Baker Bk.

Readings in Christian Theology. Ed. by Peter C. Hodgson & Robert H. King. LC 84-48721. 432p. 1985. pap. 19.95 Kivar (ISBN 0-8006-1849-1, 1-1849). Fortress.

Readings in Christian Thought. Ed. by Hugh T. Kerr. LC 66-14992. 1966. 25.95 (ISBN 0-687-35549-4). Abingdon.

Readings in Church History, 3 vols. in 1. Ed. by Colman J. Barry. 1985. pap. 50.00 (ISBN 0-87061-104-6). Chr Classics.

Readings in Dynamic Indigeneity. Ed. by Charles H. Kraft & Thomas N. Wisley. LC 79-24160. (Applied Cultural Anthropology Ser). 1979. pap. 12.95x (ISBN 0-87808-739-7). William Carey Lib.

Readings in Eastern Religious Thought, 3 vols. Ed. by Allie M. Frazier. Incl. Vol. 1. Hinduism; Vol. 2. Buddhism; Vol. 3. Chinese & Japanese Religions. (ISBN 0-664-24848-9). LC 69-14197. 1969. Westminster.

Readings in Interpretation: Holderlin, Hegel, Heidegger. Andrzej Warminski. (Theory & History of Literature Ser.: Vol. 26). 272p. (Orig.). 1987. 29.50 (ISBN 0-8166-1239-0); pap. 12.95 (ISBN 0-8166-1240-4). U of Minn Pr.

Readings in Jewish History: From the American Revolution to the Present. E. L. Ehrmann. 9.95x (ISBN 0-87068-447-7). Ktav.

Readings in Missionary Anthropology II. 2nd rev. enl. ed. Ed. by William A. Smalley. LC 78-6009. (Applied Cultural Anthropology Ser.). 1978. pap. text ed. 13.95x (ISBN 0-87808-731-1). William Carey.

Readings in Moral Theology: No. 1, Moral Norms & Catholic Tradition. Charles E. Curran & Richard McCormick. LC 79-84237. 1979. pap. 9.95 (ISBN 0-8091-2203-0). Paulist Pr.

Readings in Moral Theology, No. 2: The Distinctiveness of Christian Ethics. Ed. by Charles E. Curran & Richard A. McCormick. LC 79-84237. 360p. 1980. pap. 7.95 (ISBN 0-8091-2303-7). Paulist Pr.

Readings in Moral Theology, No. 3: The Magisterium & Morality. Ed. by Charles E. Curran & Richard A. McCormick. LC 81-82436. (Orig.). 1981. pap. 7.95 (ISBN 0-8091-2407-6). Paulist Pr.

Readings in Moral Theology, No. 4: The Use of Scripture in Moral Theology. Charles E. Curran & Richard A. McCormick. 1984. pap. 9.95 (ISBN 0-8091-2563-3). Paulist Pr.

Readings in Moral Theology, No. 5: Official Catholic Social Teaching. Ed. by Richard A. McCormick & Charles Curran. 400p. (Orig.). 1986. pap. 9.95 (ISBN 0-8091-2738-5). Paulist Pr.

Readings in St. John's Gospel. William Temple. 391p. 1985. pap. 8.95 (ISBN 0-8192-1360-8). Morehouse.

Readings in the Philosophy of Religion: An Analytic Approach. Ed. by Baruch Brody. LC 73-20485. 608p. 1974. text ed. write for info. (ISBN 0-13-759340-6). P-H.

Readings in Third World Missions: A Collection of Essential Documents. Ed. by Marlin L. Nelson. LC 76-45803. 1976. pap. 6.95x (ISBN 0-87808-319-7). William Carey Lib.

Readings in Value Development. Brian Hall et al. 1982. pap. 11.95 (ISBN 0-8091-2448-3). Paulist Pr.

Readings in Vedic Literature. Satsvarupa Das Gosvami. 1985. 7.95 (ISBN 0-912776-88-9). Bhaktivedanta.

Readings: "John at Patmos" & "A Book of Hours". Catherine D. Vinck. LC 78-55341. 68p. 1978. 5.75 (ISBN 0-911726-32-2); pap. 3.75 (ISBN 0-911726-33-0). Alleluia Pr.

Readings on Religion: From Inside & Outside. Ed. by Robert S. Ellwood, Jr. 1978. pap. text ed. write for info. (ISBN 0-13-760942-6). P-H.

Ready or Not. Charles Dollen. LC 67-29164. 1969. 3.00 (ISBN 0-8198-0130-5). Dghtrs St Paul.

Ready to Minister. William M. Pinson, Jr. LC 84-3052. (Broadman Leadership Ser.). 1984. pap. 4.95 (ISBN 0-8054-3109-8). Broadman.

Ready to Restore. Jay E. Adams. (Orig.). 1981. pap. 3.50 (ISBN 0-8010-0171-4). Baker Bk.

Ready to Restore. Jay E. Adams. 1981. pap. 3.50 (ISBN 0-87552-070-7). Presby & Reformed.

Ready to Use Cartoons for Church Publications. Phil Jackson. 160p. 1987. pap. price not set (ISBN 0-8010-5221-1). Baker Bk.

Ready-to-Use Christmas Designs. Ed Sibbett, Jr. (Clip Art Ser.). (Illus.). 1979. pap. 3.50 (ISBN 0-486-23900-4). Dover.

Ready-to-Use Christmas Silhouettes. Bob Censoni. 64p. (Orig.). 1985. pap. 3.50 (ISBN 0-486-24954-9). Dover.
Ready to Use Sermon Outlines. Russell E. Spray. 80p. 1987. pap. 3.95 (ISBN 0-8010-8268-4). Baker Bk.
Reagan, God & the Bomb. F. H. Knelman. 350p. 1985. 19.95 (ISBN 0-87975-310-2). Prometheus Bks.
Real Caruja de Jesus Nazareno de Valldemossa. James Hogg. (Analecta Cartusiana Ser.: No. 41-9). (Span., Illus.). 66p. (Orig.). 1983. pap. 25.00 (ISBN 3-7052-0057-7, Pub by Salzburg Studies). Longwood Pub Group.
Real Christianity. Bailey E. Smith. LC 79-50336. 1980. 9.95 (ISBN 0-8054-5168-4). Broadman.
Real Christianity: Contrasted with the Prevailing Religious System. William Wilberforce. Ed. by James M. Houston. LC 82-8061. (Classics of Faith & Devotion Ser.). 1982. casebound 10.95 (ISBN 0-930014-90-1). Multnomah.
Real Christmas Tree. Ardith Dorrough. 48p. (Orig.). 1983. pap. 2.50 (ISBN 0-88144-020-5, CPS/020). Christian Pub.
Real Evangelism. Bailey E. Smith. LC 77-92283. 1978. 8.95 (ISBN 0-8054-6220-1). Broadman.
Real Faith. Kenneth E. Hagin. 1970. pap. 1.00 (ISBN 0-89276-017-6). Hagin Ministries.
Real Faith: One of the Classic Faith-Builders. Charles S. Price. 1972. pap. 4.95 (ISBN 0-88270-000-6). Bridge Pub.
Real History of the Rosicrucians, Vol. 20. Arthur E. Waite. LC 76-53632. (Spiritual Science Library). (Illus.). 456p. 1982. lib. bdg. 22.00 (ISBN 0-89345-018-9); pap. 14.00 (ISBN 0-89345-019-7). Garber Comm.
Real Is Not the Rational. Joan Stambaugh. (Buddhist Studies). 142p. (Orig.). 1986. 34.50 (ISBN 0-88706-166-4); pap. 10.95 (ISBN 0-88706-167-2). State U NY Pr.
Real Jesus. Garner T. Armstrong. 1983. pap. 2.25 (ISBN 0-380-40055-3, 40055-3). Avon.
Real Jesus. 128p. pap. 2.95 (ISBN 0-89191-066-2, 08243). Cook.
Real Jewish World: A Rabbi's Second Thoughts. Stuart E. Rosenberg. LC 83-17455. 434p. 1984. 19.95 (ISBN 0-8022-2439-3). Philos Lib.
Real Living: A Small-Group Life Experience with the Gospel of Luke, Pt. 1. Mary Nilsen. (Illus.). 1977. pap. text ed. 5.65 (ISBN 0-03-021856-X, HarpR); tchr's. ed. 7.95 (ISBN 0-03-021861-6). Har-Row.
Real Living: A Small Group Life Experience with the Gospel of Luke, Pt. 2. Mary Y. Nilsen. (Illus.). 1978. pap. text ed. 5.65 (ISBN 0-03-022141-2, HarpR); tchr's. guide 7.95 (ISBN 0-03-022146-3). Har-Row.
Real Living: A Small-Group Life Experience with the Gospel of Luke, Pt. 3. Mary Y. Nilsen. (Illus.). 1978. pap. text ed. 5.65 (ISBN 0-03-045696-7, HarpR); tchr's. guide 7.95 (ISBN 0-03-045701-7). Har-Row.
Real Living: A Small-Group Life Experience with the Gospel of Luke, Pt. 4. Mary Y. Nilsen. Ed. by Winston Press Editorial Staff. (Illus.). 1979. pap. text ed. 5.65 (ISBN 0-03-045706-8, HarpR); tchr's. guide 7.95 (ISBN 0-03-045711-4). Har-Row.
Real Mormonism. Robert C. Webb. LC 72-2971. Repr. of 1916 ed. 29.00 (ISBN 0-404-10736-2). AMS Pr.
Real People. rev. ed. Martha Denlinger. LC 74-16966. (Illus.). 96p. 1975. pap. 3.95 (ISBN 0-8361-1960-6). Herald Pr.
Real Presence: The Holy Spirit in the Works of C. S. Lewis. Leanne Payne. LC 78-71945. 183p. 1979. pap. 6.95 (ISBN 0-89107-164-4, Crossway Bks). Good News.
Real Presence: Worship, Sacraments, & Commitment. Regis Duffy. LC 81-47877. 192p. 1982. pap. 8.95 (ISBN 0-06-062105-2, RD 383, HarpR). Har-Row.
Real Questions: Searching the Psalms for Answers. Ron Klug. (Young Fisherman Bible Studyguide Ser.). 64p. 1984. saddle-stitched tchr's. ed. 4.95 (ISBN 0-87788-702-0); saddle-stitched student ed. 2.95 (ISBN 0-87788-701-2). Shaw Pubs.
Real Race. Skip Wilkins & Joseph Dunn. 240p. 1987. pap. 6.95 (ISBN 0-8423-5283-X). Tyndale.
Real Reason Why Christians Are Sick. Gordon Lindsay. (Divine Healing & Health Ser.). 3.50 (ISBN 0-89985-029-4). Christ Nations.
Real Revival Preaching. Bailey E. Smith. LC 81-86667. 1982. 8.50 (ISBN 0-8054-6235-X). Broadman.
Real Truth Concerning Apostolos Makrakis. Themistocles Livadeas & Minas Charitos. Ed. by Orthodox Christian Educational Society. Tr. by Denver Cummings from Hellenic. 230p. (Orig.). 1952. pap. 4.50x (ISBN 0-938366-30-0). Orthodox Chr.
Real Worship. Warren W. Wiersbe. 192p. 1986. 12.95 (ISBN 0-8407-9045-7). Oliver-Nelson.
Realism. Ed. by Daniel O. Dahlstrom. (ACPA Proceedings: Vol. 59). 250p. 1985. 15.00 (ISBN 0-918090-19-9). Am Cath Philo.
Realism & Hope. Ronald H. Stone. 1977. pap. text ed. 11.75 (ISBN 0-8191-0128-1). U Pr of Amer.
Realism & Illusionism in Hinduism. Bharatan Kumarappa. xvi, 356p. 1986. Repr. text ed. 40.00x (ISBN 81-7047-012-9, Pub. by Mayur Pubns India). Apt Bks.
Realistic Theology. Walter M. Horton. 207p. 1982. Repr. of 1934 ed. lib. bdg. 30.00 (ISBN 0-89760-362-1). Telegraph Bks.
Realities of Faith. Bernard E. Meland. 1962. pap. 2.25x (ISBN 0-912182-03-2). Seminary Co-Op.
Realities of Faith. Mother Basilea Schlink. 144p. (Orig.). 1983. pap. 3.95 (ISBN 0-87123-299-5). Bethany Hse.
Reality & Evangelical Theology. T. F. Torrance. LC 81-19811. 174p. 1982. pap. 8.95 (ISBN 0-664-24401-7). Westminster.
Reality & Radiance: Selected Autobiographical Works of Emilia Fogelklou. Emilia Fogelklou. Ed. & tr. by Howard T. Lutz. 196p. (Orig.). 1986. pap. 10.95 (ISBN 0-913408-89-1). Friends United.
Reality & Scientific Theology. T. F. Torrance. (Theology & Science at the Frontiers of Knowledge Ser.: Vol. 1). 212p. 1985. 15.50 (ISBN 0-7073-0429-6, Pub. by Scottish Academic Pr Scotland). Longwood Pub Group.
Reality, Myths & Illusions. Peter D. Francuch. LC 83-51193. 513p. 1984. 9.95 (ISBN 0-939386-06-2). TMH Pub.
Reality of Christian Learning: Strategies for Faith-Discipline Integration. Ed. by Harold Heie & David L. Wolfe. 448p. 1987. pap. 19.95 (ISBN 0-8028-0233-8). Eerdmans.
Reality of God. Schubert M. Ogden. LC 66-20783. 1977. pap. 4.95xi (ISBN 0-06-066351-0, RD 241, HarpR). Har-Row.
Reality of God: Thoughts on the Death of God Controversy. Alexander Purdy. LC 67-23314. (Orig.). pap. 2.50x (ISBN 0-87574-154-1). Pendle Hill.
Reality of Hell & the Goodness of God. Harold T. Bryson. LC 83-51674. 192p. 1984. pap. 4.95 (ISBN 0-8423-5279-1). Tyndale.
Reality of Jesus. Dermont A. Lane. LC 77-70635. (Exploration Book Ser.). 180p. 1977. pap. 6.95 (ISBN 0-8091-2020-8). Paulist Pr.
Reality of Living Yoga. 212p. 1978. pap. 6.95x (ISBN 0-933740-01-8). Mindbody Inc.
Reality of Prayer. E. M. Bounds. (Direction Bks). 1978. pap. 3.50 (ISBN 0-8010-0739-9). Baker Bk.
Reality of the Historical Past. Paul Ricoeur. LC 84-60012. (Aquinas Lecture Ser.). 51p. 1984. 7.95 (ISBN 0-87462-152-6). Marquette.
Reality of the Spiritual World. Thomas Kelly. LC 76-9644. (Orig.). 1942. pap. 2.50x (ISBN 0-87574-021-9). Pendle Hill.
Realization of Neter Nu: A Kabalistical Guide to the Realization of Self. R. A. Straughn. 1975. pap. 8.00 (ISBN 0-917650-01-8). Maat Pub.
Realization of Oneness: The Practice of Spiritual Healing. Joel S. Goldsmith. 200p. 1974. pap. 5.95 (ISBN 0-8065-0453-6). Citadel Pr.
Realization: The Anthropology of Pastoral Care. Josef Goldbrunner. 1966. 18.95 (ISBN 0-268-00227-4). U of Notre Dame Pr.
Realize & Rejoice. Richard C. Hoefler. 1981. 4.00 (ISBN 0-89536-468-9, 1803). CSS of Ohio.
Reallexikon der aegyptischen Religionsgeschichte. 2nd ed. Hans Bonnet. (Ger., Illus.). 1981. 71.20x (ISBN 3-11-003365-8). De Gruyter.
Really Living. Daughters of St. Paul. LC 68-59042. (Divine Master Ser.). pap. 3.00 (ISBN 0-8198-0350-2); rev. tchr's. manual 3.95 (ISBN 0-8198-0351-0). Dghtrs St Paul.
Realm of Ends: Or, Pluralism & Theism. James Ward. LC 77-27173. (Gifford Lectures: 1907-10). Repr. of 1911 ed. 34.50 (ISBN 0-404-60464-1). AMS Pr.
Realm of Spirit & the Realm of Caesar. Nicolaii Berdiaer. Tr. by Donald A. Luurie from Rus. LC 74-1554. 182p. 1975. Repr. of 1953 ed. lib. bdg. 55.00x (ISBN 0-8371-7395-7, BESC). Greenwood.
Realm of Totality. Kevin O'Neil. 49p. (Orig.). 1984. pap. 6.00 (ISBN 0-86627-011-6). Crises Res Pr.
Realms of Healing. Stanley Krippner & Alberto Villoldo. LC 75-7858. 320p. (Orig.). 1986. pap. 9.95 (ISBN 0-89087-474-3). Celestial Arts.
Reaping the Whirlwind: A Christian Interpretation of History. Langdon Gilkey. 1977. (HarpR); pap. 12.95 (ISBN 0-8164-2317-2). Har-Row.
Reappearance of Christ in the Etheric. rev. ed. Rudolf Steiner. 190p. (Orig.). 1983. 14.00 (ISBN 0-88010-017-6); pap. 8.95 (ISBN 0-88010-016-8). Anthroposophic.
Reappearance of the Christ. Alice A. Bailey. 1978. 18.00 (ISBN 0-85330-014-3); pap. 7.00 (ISBN 0-85330-114-X). Lucis.
Reappearance of the Christ & the Masters of Wisdom. Benjamin Creme. LC 80-50639. 253p. 1980. pap. 6.00 (ISBN 0-936604-00-X). Tara Ctr.
Reappearance of the Dove. Helena E. Ruhnau. LC 75-27625. (Illus.). 1978. 12.95 (ISBN 0-941036-03-0). Colleasius Pr.
Reason & Conduct: New Bearings in Moral Philosophy. Henry D. Aiken. LC 77-26079. 1978. Repr. of 1962 ed. lib. bdg. 28.50 (ISBN 0-313-20083-1, AIRD). Greenwood.
Reason & Dignity. Raymond Dennehy. LC 81-40364. 152p. 1982. lib. bdg. 25.00 (ISBN 0-8191-1898-2); pap. text ed. 9.75 (ISBN 0-8191-1899-0). U Pr of Amer.
Reason & Eros: The Social Theory of Herbert Marcuse. Vincent Geoghegan. 122p. 1981. pap. 6.75 (ISBN 0-86104-335-9, Pub. by Pluto Pr). Longwood Pub Group.
Reason & Faith Revisited. Francis H. Parker. (Aquinas Lecture 1971). 7.95 (ISBN 0-87462-136-4). Marquette.
Reason & God: Encounters of Philosophy with Religion. John E. Smith. LC 77-13887. 1978. Repr. of 1961 ed. lib. bdg. 22.50x (ISBN 0-8371-9867-4, SMRG). Greenwood.
Reason & Morality. Alan Gewirth. LC 77-13911. 1978. pap. text ed. 9.95x (ISBN 0-226-28876-5). U. of Chicago Pr.
Reason & Religion. Ed. by Stuart Brown. LC 77-3115. 336p. 1977. pap. 12.95x (ISBN 0-8014-9166-5). Cornell U Pr.
Reason & Religion: An Introduction to the Philosophy of Religion. Rem B. Edwards. LC 78-66278. 1979. pap. text ed. 12.50 (ISBN 0-8191-0690-9). U Pr of Amer.
Reason & Revelation: John Duns Scotus on Natural Theology. Cecil B. Currey. LC 77-9614. (Synthesis Ser.). 1977. pap. 0.75 (ISBN 0-8199-0717-0). Franciscan Herald.
Reason & Tradition in Islamic Ethics. G. F. Hourani. 282p. 1985. 39.50 (ISBN 0-521-26712-9). Cambridge U Pr.
Reason & Value. E. J. Bond. LC 82-4564. (Cambridge Studies in Philosophy). 220p. 1983. 32.50 (ISBN 0-521-24571-0); pap. 11.95 (ISBN 0-521-27079-0). Cambridge U Pr.
Reason, Emotion & Habit in the Training of a Torah Personality. Nachman Bulman. (Annual Fryer Memorial Lecture Ser.). 0.75 (ISBN 0-914131-53-2, I34). Torah Umesorah.
Reason Enough: A Case for the Christian Faith. Clark H. Pinnock. 126p. 1986. pap. 4.95 (ISBN 0-85364-296-6, Pub. by Paternoster UK). Attic Pr.
Reason for Our Hope: A Introduction to Anthropology. Richard Viladesau. LC 83-82019. 1984. pap. 10.95 (ISBN 0-8091-2574-9). Paulist Pr.
Reason for the Hope Within: Sermons on the Theory of Religious Belief. John H. Newman. 368p. 1985. pap. 14.95 (ISBN 0-87193-219-9). Dimension Bks.
Reason in Faith. Ralph T. Flewelling. LC 75-3148. Repr. of 1924 ed. 24.00 (ISBN 0-404-59155-8). AMS Pr.
Reason in Religion. George Santayana. 1983. 14.50 (ISBN 0-8446-5927-4). Peter Smith.
Reason of the Laws of Moses. Moses Maimonides. Ed. by James Townley. LC 78-97294. 451p. 1975. Repr. of 1827 ed. lib. bdg. 22.50x (ISBN 0-8371-2618-5, MARL). Greenwood.
Reason, Relativism & God. Joseph Runzo. LC 85-27893. 308p. 1986. 29.95x (ISBN 0-312-66538-5). St Martin.
Reason, Religion, & Kindness. 3rd, rev. ed. Paul Avallone. LC 77-83952. 1977. pap. 4.75 (ISBN 0-89944-030-4). Don Bosco Multimedia.
Reason Revisited: The Philosophy of Karl Jaspers. Sebastian Samay. LC 72-160423. pap. 79.50 (ISBN 0-317-26140-1, 2024371). Bks Demand UMI.
Reason, Ridicule & Religion. John Redwood. 1976. 16.50x (ISBN 0-674-74953-7). Harvard U Pr.
Reason to Believe. R. C. Sproul. 160p. 1982. pap. 5.95 (ISBN 0-310-44911-1, 12370P). Zondervan.
Reason to Hope: A Synthesis of Teilhard de Chardin's Vision & Systems Thinking. R. Wayne Kraft. (Systems Inquiry Ser.). 292p. 1983. pap. 12.95x (ISBN 0-914105-14-0). Intersystems Pubns.
Reason to Live, a Reason to Die. rev. ed. John Powell. LC 75-24848. (Illus.). 208p. 1972. pap. 3.95 (ISBN 0-913592-61-7). Argus Comm.
Reason, Truth & God. Renford Bambrough. (Library Reprints Ser.). 174p. 1979. 45.00x (ISBN 0-416-72530-9, NO. 2823). Methuen Inc.
Reason Why. Robert A. Laidlaw. 48p. 1975. pap. 1.95 (ISBN 0-310-27112-6, 18243P). Zondervan.
Reason Within the Bounds of Religion. 2nd ed. Nicholas Wolterstorff. 168p. 1984. pap. 4.95 (ISBN 0-8028-1604-5). Eerdmans.
Reasonable Belief: A Funny of the Christian Faith. Anthony Hanson & Richard Hanson. 1980. pap. 11.95x (ISBN 0-19-213238-5). Oxford U Pr.
Reasonable Faith. Anthony Campolo. 208p. 1985. 8.95 (ISBN 0-8499-3040-5, 3040-5). Word Bks.
Reasonable Reason to Wait. Jacob Aranza & Theresa Lamson. 101p. (Orig.). 1984. pap. 4.95 (ISBN 0-910311-21-8). Huntington Hse Inc.
Reasonable Religion: A Commonsense Approach. Robert E. Romig. LC 84-42823. 200p. 1984. 18.95 (ISBN 0-87975-252-1). Prometheus Bks.
Reasonableness of Christianity & a Discourse of Miracles. John Locke. Ed. by I. T. Ramsey. 1958. pap. 6.95x (ISBN 0-8047-0341-8). Stanford U Pr.
Reasonableness of Scripture-Belief. Charles Wolseley. LC 73-2618. 488p. 1973. Repr. of 1672 ed. lib. bdg. 75.00x (ISBN 0-8201-1113-9). Schol Facsimiles.
Reasoned Look at Asian Religions. David L. Johnson. 150p. 1985. pap. 5.95 (ISBN 0-87123-798-9, 210798). Bethany Hse.
Reasoning Heart: Toward a North American Theology. Ed. by Frank M. Oppenheim. 160p. (Orig.). 1986. pap. 9.95 (ISBN 0-87840-433-3); 17.95 (ISBN 0-87840-439-2). Georgetown U Pr.
Reasoning with Juniors for Christs Sake. Lance Colkmire. 1982. pap. 5.95 (ISBN 0-87148-736-5). Pathway Pr.
Reasons. Josh McDowell & Don Stewart. LC 80-67432. (Answers to Tough Questions Ser.: Vol.II). 160p. (Orig.). 1981. pap. 6.95 (ISBN 0-918956-98-6). Campus Crusade.
Reasons. Josh McDowell & Don Stewart. (Living Bks.). 256p. 1986. 3.95 (ISBN 0-8423-5287-2). Tyndale.
Reasons for Hope. rev. ed. W. H. Carroll et al. 254p. 1982. pap. 6.95 (ISBN 0-931888-07-7, Chris. Coll. Pr.). Christendom Pubns.
Reasons for Jewish Customs & Traditions. Abraham I. Sperling. Tr. by Abraham Matts. LC 68-31711. cancelled. (ISBN 0-8197-0184-X); pap. cancelled (ISBN 0-8197-0008-8). Bloch.
Reasons for Rejoicing: Readings in Christian Hope. Kenneth Zanca. (Orig.). 1976. pap. 2.95 (ISBN 0-914544-12-8). Living Flame Pr.
Reasons Four, Explaining the Reformed Perspective. 120p. (Orig.). 1981. pap. text ed. 4.10 (ISBN 0-933140-29-0); tchr's manual, 60pgs 4.10 (ISBN 0-933140-30-4). CRC Pubns.
Reasons of the Heart: A Journey into Solitude & Back Again into the Human Circle. John S. Dunne. 1979. pap. 5.95 (ISBN 0-268-01606-2). U of Notre Dame Pr.
Reasons One, Sects & Cults with Non-Christian Roots. Bill Evenhouse. 120p. (Orig.). 1981. pap. text ed. 4.10 (ISBN 0-933140-23-1); tchr's manual, 61 pgs. 4.10 (ISBN 0-933140-24-X). CRC Pubns.
Reasons Two, Sects & Cults with Christian Roots. Bill Evenhouse. (Orig.). 1981. pap. text ed. 4.10 (ISBN 0-933140-25-8); tchr's manual, 67 pgs. 4.10 (ISBN 0-933140-26-6). CRC Pubns.
Reawakening. Primo Levi. 224p. 1987. 4.95 (ISBN 0-02-022370-6, Collier). Macmillan.
Reawakening of Christian Faith. facsimile ed. Bernard E. Meland. LC 72-142670. (Essay Index Reprint Ser). Repr. of 1949 ed. 15.00 (ISBN 0-8369-2663-3). Ayer Co Pubs.
Rebbe's Treasure. Beth Jacob Hebrew Teachers College Staff. write for info. (ISBN 0-934390-01-0); pap. write for info. (ISBN 0-934390-02-9). B J Hebrew Tchrs.
Rebecca's Children: Judaism & Christianity in the Roman World. Alan F. Segal. LC 85-17656. 216p. 1986. text ed. 20.00x (ISBN 0-674-75075-6). Harvard U Pr.
Rebel for God. Harold G. Sager. 1983. 5.75 (ISBN 0-8062-1868-1). Carlton.
Rebel in the Soul. Bika Reed. LC 78-15791. (Illus.). 1979. pap. 9.95 (ISBN 0-89281-004-1). Inner Tradit.
Rebel Lands: An Investigation into the Origins of Early Mesopotamian Mythology. J. V. Kinnier-Wilson & Herman Vanstiphout. LC 77-1272. (Oriental Publications Ser.: No. 29). (Illus.). 1979. 39.00 (ISBN 0-521-21469-6). Cambridge U Pr.
Rebel, Priest & Prophet: A Biography of Dr. Edward McGlynn. Stephen Bell. LC 75-301. (Radical Tradition in America Ser). 303p. 1975. Repr. of 1937 ed. 24.75 (ISBN 0-88355-206-X). Hyperion Conn.
Rebel Saints. facs. ed. Mary A. Best. LC 68-55839. (Essay Index Reprint Ser). 1925. 18.00 (ISBN 0-8369-0205-X). Ayer Co Pubs.
Rebellion, Creativity & Revelation. S. Giora Shoham. Intro. by Albert Cherns. 320p. 1986. 29.95 (ISBN 0-905927-61-3). Transaction Bks.
Rebellious Prophet: A Life of Nicolai Berdgaev. Donald A. Lowrie. LC 73-11867. (Illus.). 310p. 1974. Repr. of 1960 ed. lib. bdg. 35.00x (ISBN 0-8371-7095-8, LORP). Greenwood.

Rebirth for Christianity. Alvin B. Kuhn. LC 76-104032. 1970. 6.50 (ISBN 0-8356-0015-7). Theos Pub Hse.

Rebirth of Cosmology. Jacques Merleau-Ponty & Bruno Morando. LC 82-60404. (Illus.). xvi, 302p. 1982. pap. text ed. 9.95x (ISBN 0-8214-0606-X). Ohio U Pr.

Rebirth of Hindu Music. Dane Rudhyar. 112p. 1980. pap. 4.95 (ISBN 0-87728-448-2). Weiser.

Rebirth of Images: The Making of St. John's Apocalypse. Austin Farrar. 13.25 (ISBN 0-8446-0617-0). Peter Smith.

Rebirth of Images: The Making of St. John's Apocalypse. Austin Farrer. 352p. (Orig.). 1986. 39.50 (ISBN 0-88706-271-7); pap. 12.95 (ISBN 0-88706-272-5). State U NY Pr.

Rebirth of Israel. Ed. by Israel Cohen. LC 75-6427. (Rise of Jewish Nationalism & the Middle East Ser.). 338p. 1975. Repr. of 1952 ed. 25.85 (ISBN 0-88355-314-7). Hyperion Conn.

Rebirth of Ministry: A Study of the Biblical Character of the Church's Ministry. James D. Smart. LC 60-6189. 192p. 1978. pap. 4.95 (ISBN 0-664-24206-5). Westminster.

Rebirth of Music: Training Course. Carolyn Smith. 76p. 1985. pap. 4.95 (ISBN 0-938612-10-7). Revival Press.

Rebirth of the Congregation. Richard Bieber. 1973. pap. 1.25 (ISBN 0-87508-012-X). Chr Lit.

Rebirthing in the New Age. Leonard Orr & Sondra Ray. LC 76-53337. 1978. pap. 9.95 (ISBN 0-89087-134-5). Celestial Arts.

Rebonding: Preventing & Restoring Damaged Relationships. Donald Joy. 192p. 1986. 11.95 (ISBN 0-8499-0519-2, 0519-2). Word Bks.

Reborn Again in the Kingdom. Jacques Sollov. LC 81-71382. (Temple of Love Ser.). (Illus.). 128p. (Orig.). 1982. pap. 10.95 (ISBN 0-941804-04-6). White Eagle Pub.

Reborn to Multiply. Paul Foust. LC 73-9110. 1973. pap. 2.75 (ISBN 0-570-03170-2, 12-2573). Concordia.

Rebuild My Church. Luke Chiampi. LC 72-87090. 105p. 1972. pap. 0.95 (ISBN 0-8199-0502-X). Franciscan Herald.

Rebuild Your Life. Dale Galloway. 1981. pap. 4.95 (ISBN 0-8423-5323-2). Tyndale.

Rebuilding of Psychology. Gary Collins. 1976. pap. 7.95 (ISBN 0-8423-5315-1). Tyndale.

Rebuilding the Christian Commonwealth: New England Congregationalists & Foreign Missions, 1800-1830. John A. Andrew, III. LC 75-38214. 240p. 1976. 22.00x (ISBN 0-8131-1333-4). U Pr of Ky.

Rebuilding the Real You. Jack W. Hayford. 195p. (Orig.). 1986. pap. 7.95 (ISBN 0-8307-1156-2, 5418849). Regal.

Rebuke & Challenge: The Point of Jesus' Parables. Norman Young. Ed. by Richard W. Coffen. 96p. (Orig.). 1985. pap. 6.95 (ISBN 0-8280-0286-X). Review & Herald.

Recapturing Wisdom's Valley: The Watervliet Shaker Heritage, 1775-1975. Dorothy M. Filley. Ed. by Mary L. Richmond. LC 75-27133. (Illus.). 128p. 1975. 10.00 (ISBN 0-89062-010-5, Pub. by Town of Colonie); pap. 5.00 (ISBN 0-89062-029-6). Pub Ctr Cult Res.

Receive All God Has to Give. Katie Fortune. 1971. pap. write for info. color booklet (ISBN 0-930756-01-0, 541001); pap. 0.95 color booklet (ISBN 0-317-03288-7). Aglow Pubns.

Receive Miracle Healing. T. L. Osborn. 1983. pap. 4.95 (ISBN 0-89274-221-6, HH221). Harrison Hse.

Receive the Holy Spirit. Arlo F. Newell. 1984. pap. 2.95 (ISBN 0-87162-409-5, D6431). Warner Pr.

Receive Your Healing. Colin Urquhart. 312p. 1987. pap. 10.95 (ISBN 0-8245-0807-6). Crossroad NY.

Receiving the Holy Spirit. Robert B. Hall. 1964. pap. 1.00 (ISBN 0-686-14948-3). Episcopal Ctr.

Receiving the Holy Spirit Today. Victor P. Wierwille. LC 82-71185. 298p. 1983. 5.95 (ISBN 0-910068-49-6). Am Christian.

Receiving the Promise: The Spirit's Work of Conversion. Thomas Weinandy. 128p. 1985. pap. 3.95 (ISBN 0-932085-01-6). Word Among Us.

Receiving the Spirit at Old First Church. Arthur A. Rouner, Jr. LC 81-19959. 96p. (Orig.). 1982. pap. 5.95 (ISBN 0-8298-0492-7). Pilgrim NY.

Receiving Woman: Studies in the Psychology & Theology of the Feminine. Ann B. Ulanov. LC 80-26813. 186p. 1981. pap. 9.95 (ISBN 0-664-24360-6). Westminster.

Recent Advances in Leather Conservation: Proceedings of a Refresher Course Sponsored by FAIC, June,1984. Ferry W. Harpers & Sonja Fogle. 15.00 (ISBN 0-318-18700-0). Am Inst Conser Hist.

Recent Developments in the Textual Criticism of the Greek Bible. F. G. Kenyon. (British Academy of London Ser.). pap. 19.00 (ISBN 0-8115-1274-6). Kraus Repr.

Recent Discoveries & the Biblical World. Raymond E. Brown. (Background Books Ser.: Vol. 1). 4.95 (ISBN 0-89453-363-0). M Glazier.

Recent Homiletical Thought: A Bibliography, 1966-1979. Ed. by Duane Litfin & Haddon Robinson. LC 82-72135. 296p. 1983. 16.95 (ISBN 0-8010-5613-6). Baker Bk.

Recent Problems in Admiralty Jurisdiction. Edgar T. Fell. LC 78-63977. (Johns Hopkins University. Studies in the Social Sciences. Fortieth Ser. 1922: 3). Repr. of 1922 ed. 16.50 (ISBN 0-404-61222-9). AMS Pr.

Recent Revelation. Jim Rosemergy. LC 81-50146. 137p. 1981. 5.95 (ISBN 0-87159-002-6). Unity School.

Receptive Prayer: A Christian Approach to Meditation. Grace A. Brame. Ed. by Herbert Lambert. LC 84-29302. 144p. (Orig.). 1985. pap. 9.95 (ISBN 0-8272-3211-X). CBP.

Receptivity. Francis K. Nemeck. 135p. 1985. 10.00 (ISBN 0-533-06057-5). Vantage.

Receuil Arien de Verone. R. Gryson. 1983. 46.00 (ISBN 90-247-2705-7, Pub. by Martinus Nijhoff Netherlands). Kluwer Academic.

Recherches sur la Communaute Juive De Manosque Au Moyen Age (1241-1329) Joseph Shatzmiller. (Etudes Juives: No. 15). 1973. pap. 14.00x (ISBN 90-2797-188-9). Mouton.

Recherches sur le Symbolisme Funeraire des Romains. facsimile ed. Franz Cumont. LC 75-10632. (Ancient Religion & Mythology Ser.). (Fr., Illus.). 1976. Repr. of 1942 ed. 57.50x (ISBN 0-405-07007-1). Ayer Co Pubs.

Rechtfertigung und zukuenftiges Heil. Untersuchungen zu Roemer 5, 1-11. Michael Wolter. (Beihefte zur Zeitschrift fuer die Neutestamentliche Wissenschaft: No. 43). 1978. 29.20x (ISBN 3-11-007579-2). De Gruyter.

Rechtssaetze in gebundener Sprache und Rechtssatzreihen im israelitischen Recht: Ein Beitrag zur Gattungsforschung. Volker Wagner. (Beiheft 127 zur Zeitschrift fuer die alttestamentliche Wissenschaft). 1972. 16.80x (ISBN 3-11-003945-1). De Gruyter.

Recipe for Holiness. Pope Pius Tenth. 125p. 1971. 4.00 (ISBN 0-912414-04-9). Lumen Christi.

Recital Concerning the Sweet Land of Cyprus, 2 vols. Leontios Machairas. Ed. by R. M. Dawkins. LC 78-63351. (Crusades & Military Orders: Second Ser.). Repr. of 1932 ed. Set. 92.50 (ISBN 0-404-17030-7). AMS Pr.

Recitation & Interpretation of the Qur'an. Muhammad A. Quasem. 1979. 12.00 (ISBN 0-318-00410-0). Quasem.

Recited Koran: A History of the First Recorded Version. Labib As-Said. Ed. by Bernard Weiss. LC 73-20717. (Illus.). 156p. 1975. 10.00 (ISBN 0-87850-024-3). Darwin Pr.

Recits de Resurrection des Morts dans le Nouveau Testament. G. Rochais. LC 79-41615. (Society for New Testament Studies Monographs: No. 40). (Fr.). 240p. 1981. 39.50 (ISBN 0-521-22381-4). Cambridge U Pr.

Reckless Heart: Meleager & Atalanta. Daniel R. Butterly. 64p. (Orig.). 1986. 25.00 (ISBN 0-86516-172-0); pap. 15.00 (ISBN 0-86516-173-9). Bolchazy-Carducci.

Reclaiming the Dream: Marriage Counseling in the Parish Context. Brian W. Grant. 176p. (Orig.). 1986. pap. 9.95 (ISBN 0-687-35729-2). Abingdon.

Reclaiming the Humanities: The Roots of Self-Knowledge in the Greek & Biblical Worlds. R. Thomas Simone & Richard I. Sugarman. 226p. (Orig.). 1986. lib. bdg. 25.75 (ISBN 0-8191-5093-2); pap. text ed. 9.75 (ISBN 0-8191-5094-0). U Pr of Amer.

Reclaiming the Old Testament for the Christian Pulpit. Donald E. Gowan. 176p. Date not set. pap. 10.95 (ISBN 0-567-29106-5, Pub. by T & T Clark Ltd UK). Fortress.

Recognizing & Helping the Learning Disabled Child in Your Classroom. Mary J. Rolando. 24p. 1978. 2.40 (ISBN 0-686-39949-8). Natl Cath Educ.

Recollections of a Long Life. Jeremiah B. Jeter. Ed. by Edwin S. Gaustad. LC 79-52595. (Baptist Tradition Ser.). 1980. Repr. of 1891 ed. lib. bdg. 24.00x (ISBN 0-405-12462-7). Ayer Co Pubs.

Recollections of an Excursion. William Beckford. 1983. 60.00x (ISBN 0-900000-78-3, Pub. by Centaur Bks). State Mutual Bk.

Recollections of an Excursion to the Monasteries of Alcobaca & Batalha. William Beckford. 27.50 (ISBN 0-87556-541-7). Saifer.

Recollections of Eminent Men with Other Papers. Edwin P. Whipple. 397p. 1982. Repr. of 1886 ed. lib. bdg. 45.00 (ISBN 0-8495-5840-9). Arden Lib.

Recollections of Seventy Years. Daniel A. Payne. LC 68-29015. (American Negro: His History & Literature Ser., No. 1). (Illus.). 1968. Repr. of 1888 ed. 14.00 (ISBN 0-405-01834-7). Ayer Co Pubs.

Recollections of the Flathead Mission. Gregory Mengarini. Ed. by Gloria Lothrop. LC 74-27573. (Illus.). 1977. 16.95 (ISBN 0-87062-111-4). A H Clark.

Recollective Resolve: A Phenomenological Understanding of Time & Myth. Sanford Krolick. 160p. 1987. 24.95 (ISBN 0-86554-248-1, MUP H-214). Mercer Univ Pr.

Reconciled Sinners: Healing Human Brokenness. Bernard Cooke. 128p. (Orig.). 1986. pap. 4.95 (ISBN 0-89622-284-5). Twenty-Third.

Reconciliation. John E. Jones. 164p. 1984. 8.95 (ISBN 0-87123-438-6); pap. 4.95 (ISBN 0-87123-862-4). Bethany Hse.

Reconciliation: A Biblical Call. Carroll Stuhlmueller. (Biblical Booklets Ser). 68p. 1975. pap. 1.25 (ISBN 0-8199-0522-4). Franciscan Herald.

Reconciliation: A Study of Paul's Theology. Ed. by Ralph Martin & Peter Toon. LC 80-16340. (New Foundations Theological Library). 272p. 1981. 12.95 (ISBN 0-8042-3709-3); pap. 11.95 (ISBN 0-8042-3729-8). John Knox.

Reconciliation & Penance. 144p. 1984. pap. 3.95 (ISBN 1-55586-951-3). US Catholic.

Reconciliation & Renewal. James O'Reilly. (Synthesis Ser). 36p. 1974. pap. 0.75 (ISBN 0-8199-0361-2). Franciscan Herald.

Reconciliation: Celebrating God's Healing Forgiveness. Chris Aridas. LC 87-5344. 160p. 1987. pap. 3.95 (ISBN 0-385-24022-8, Im). Doubleday.

Reconciliation in the Church. Leonce Hamelin. Tr. by Matthew J. O'Connell from Fr. LC 80-29328. Orig. Title: Reconciliation en Eglise. 111p. 1980. pap. text ed. 5.50 (ISBN 0-8146-1215-6). Liturgical Pr.

Reconciliation, Law & Righteousness: Essays in Biblical Theology. Peter Stuhlmacher. Tr. by Everett R. Kalin. LC 85-45482. 240p. 1986. 24.95 (ISBN 0-8006-0770-8, 1-770). Fortress.

Reconciliation: Preparing for Confession in the Episcopal Church. Martin L. Smith. LC 85-21271. 121p. (Orig.). 1985. pap. 8.95 (ISBN 0-936384-30-1). Cowley Pubns.

Reconciliation: The Sacramental Path to Peace. David E. Rosage. 144p. (Orig.). 1984. pap. 5.95 (ISBN 0-914544-56-X). Living Flame Pr.

Reconciliation with God & Family. Joseph L. Kellermann. 16p. 1981. pap. 0.95 (ISBN 0-89486-146-8). Hazelden.

Reconciliations: Inner Peace in an Age of Anxiety. Theodore I. Rubin. 1983. pap. 3.50 (ISBN 0-425-06312-7). Berkley Pub.

Reconciling. Francis J. Buckley. LC 81-68699. 96p. (Orig.). 1981. pap. 2.95 (ISBN 0-87793-237-9). Ave Maria.

Reconciling Community: The Rite of Penance. James Dallen. (Reformed Rites of the Catholic Church Ser.: Vol. III). 400p. (Orig.). 1986. pap. 17.50 (ISBN 0-916134-76-8). Pueblo Pub Co.

Reconciling Heaven & Earth: The Transcendental Enthusiasm & Growth of an Urban Protestant Community, Bogota, Colombia. Karl-Wilhelm Westmeier. (Studies in the Intercultural History of Christianity: Vol. 41). 462p. 1986. text ed. 34.00 (ISBN 3-261-03547-1). P Lang Pubs.

Reconsecrating America. George Goldberg. 160p. 1984. 9.95 (ISBN 0-8028-3607-0). Eerdmans.

Reconstructing Judaism: An Autobiography. Ira Eisenstein. 1986. 17.95 (ISBN 0-935457-37-2). Reconstructionist Pr.

Reconstruction in Schematic Representations of Kant's Psychological Theory of God. Immanuel Kant. (Illus.). 110p. 1983. 87.45x (ISBN 0-89266-430-4). Am Classical Coll Pr.

Reconstruction of Religious Thoughts in Islam. M. Iqbal. 15.50 (ISBN 0-686-18482-3). Kazi Pubns.

Reconstruction of the Christian Revelation Claim: A Philosophical & Critical Apologetic. Stuart C. Hackett. 560p. 1984. pap. 19.95 (ISBN 0-8010-4283-6). Baker Bk.

Reconstruction of the Church. Ed. by James B. Jordan. LC 86-80570. (Christianity & Civilization Ser.: No. 4). xiv, 338p. (Orig.). 1986. pap. 12.95 (ISBN 0-939404-11-7). Geneva Ministr.

Reconstruction of the Spiritual Ideal. Felix Adler. LC 77-27148. (Hibbert Lectures: 1923). Repr. of 1924 ed. 25.00 (ISBN 0-404-60422-6). AMS Pr.

Reconstructions of Early Christian Documents. Herbert J. Bardsley. 1977. lib. bdg. 59.95 (ISBN 0-8490-2504-4). Gordon Pr.

Record of Hawksbill Church 1788-1850, Page County, Virginia. Klaus Wust. 1979. pap. 5.50 (ISBN 0-917968-06-9). Shenandoah Hist.

Record of the Buddhist Religion as Practised in India & the Malay Archipelago. I. Tsing. Tr. by J. Takakusu. Repr. of 1896 ed. text ed. 22.50x (ISBN 0-89644-178-4). Coronet Bks.

Record of the Convention for the Promotion of Scriptural Holiness Held at Brighton May 29th, to June 7th, 1875. (Higher Christian Life Ser.). 496p. 1985. lib. bdg. 60.00 (ISBN 0-8240-6439-9). Garland Pub.

Record of Tung Shan. William F. Powell. LC 86-4305. (Classics in East Asian Buddism: No. 1). 112p. 1986. pap. text ed. 8.50x (ISBN 0-8248-1070-8). UH Pr.

Recordar Es Vivir. Eutimio Topete. LC 78-71069. 1978. pap. 6.00 (ISBN 0-915808-32-3). Editorial Justa.

Recording Locator. Orig. Title: MusiCatalog. 858p. 1986. pap. 160.00 (ISBN 0-89390-098-2). Resource Pubns.

Records of High Sanghans, Vol. I. Tripitaka Master Hua. Tr. by Buddhist Text Translation Society. 160p. (Orig.). 1983. pap. 7.00 (ISBN 0-88139-012-7). Buddhist Text.

Records of Ming Scholars. Huang Tsung-Hsi. Ed. by Julia Ching & Chaoying Fang. LC 86-27257. 688p. 1987. text ed. 27.00x (ISBN 0-8248-1028-7). UH Pr.

Records of Pastoral Acts at Emanual Lutheran Church (Known in the Eighteen Century as the Warwick Congregation, Near Brickerville, Elizabeth Township, Lancaster County) 1743-1799. Tr. by Frederick S. Weiser. (Sources & Documents Ser.: No. 8). 229p. 1983. pap. 15.00 (ISBN 0-911122-47-8). Penn German Soc.

Records of Salem Lutheran Church, Brenham, Texas 1850-1940. Jack A. Dabbs & Edward C. Breitenkamp. LC 86-72575. (Illus.). 501p. 1986. 35.00 (ISBN 0-911494-10-3). Dabbs.

Records of Salem Witchcraft, 2 vols. in 1. (Woodward's Historical Ser.: Nos. 1 & 2). 1968. Repr. of 1864 ed. 40.50 (ISBN 0-8337-2916-0). B Franklin.

Records of Salem Witchcraft, Copied from the Original Documents, 2 Vols. LC 78-75274. (Law, Politics & History Ser.). 1969. Repr. of 1864 ed. lib. bdg. 45.00 (ISBN 0-306-71309-8). Da Capo.

Records of the Dutch Reformed Church in New Amsterdam & New York. Samuel S. Purple. 50.00 (ISBN 0-8490-0936-7). Gordon Pr.

Records of the English Province of the Society of Jesus, 7 Vols. in 8. Henry Foley. (Illus.). Repr. of 1883 ed. Set. 690.00 (ISBN 0-384-16310-6). Johnson Repr.

Records of the First Church in Salem, Massachusetts, 1629-1736. Ed. by Richard D. Pierce. LC 73-93302. 1974. 30.00 (ISBN 0-88389-050-X). Essex Inst.

Records of the Life of Tripitaka Master Hua, Vol. 1. Biography of Master Hsuan Hua Publication Committee. (Illus.). 90p. (Orig.). 1981. pap. 5.00 (ISBN 0-917512-78-2). Buddhist Text.

Records of the Life of Tripitaka Master Hua, Vol. 2. Biography of Master Hsuan Hua Publication Committee. (Illus.). 229p. (Orig.). 1976. pap. 8.00 (ISBN 0-917512-10-3). Buddhist Text.

Records of the Moravians in North Carolina, 11 vols. Incl. Vol. 1, 1752-1771. 511p. 1968. Repr. of 1925 ed; Vol. 2, 1752-1775. viii, 460p. 1968. Repr. of 1925 ed; Vol. 3, 1776-1779. viii, 513p. 1968. Repr. of 1926 ed; Vol. 4, 1780-1783. v, 471p. 1968. Repr. of 1930 ed; Vol. 5, 1784-1792. ix, 487p. 1970. Repr. of 1943 ed. 15.00x (ISBN 0-86526-060-5); Vol. 6, 1793-1808. x, 566p. 1970. Repr. of 1943 ed. 15.00x (ISBN 0-86526-061-3); Vol. 7, 1809-1822. x, 593p. 1970. Repr. of 1947 ed. 15.00x (ISBN 0-86526-062-1); Vol. 8, 1823-1837. Ed. by Minnie J. Smith. xi, 756p. 1954. 15.00x (ISBN 0-86526-063-X); Vol. 9, 1838-1847. Ed. by Kenneth G. Hamilton. xiii, 685p. 1964; Vol. 10, 1841-1851. Ed. by Kenneth G. Hamilton. xviii, 626p. 1966; Vol. 11, 1852-1879. Ed. by Kenneth G. Hamilton. xvi, 524p. 1969. 15.00x (ISBN 0-86526-066-4). (Illus.). NC Archives.

Records of the Past: Being English Translations of the Ancient Monuments of Egypt & Western Asia, 6 vols. in 2. Ed. by A. H. Sayce. LC 72-83175. Repr. of 1888 ed. Set. 71.00 (ISBN 0-405-08918-X); 35.75 ea. Vol. 1 (ISBN 0-405-08919-8). Vol. 2 (ISBN 0-405-08922-8). Ayer Co Pubs.

Records of the Presbyterian Church in the United States of America, 1706-1788. Presbyterian Church In The United States Of America. LC 75-83434. (Religion in America, Ser. 1). 1969. Repr. of 1904 ed. 30.00 (ISBN 0-405-00259-9). Ayer Co Pubs.

Records of the Reformed Dutch Church of Albany, New York, 1683-1809. Holland Society of New York. LC 78-54063. 922p. (Repr. of the 1904-1927 eds.). 1978. 38.50 (ISBN 0-8063-0808-7). Genealog Pub.

Records of the Reformed Dutch Church of New Paltz, New York. Tr. by Dingman Versteeg. LC 77-77266. 269p. 1977. Repr. of 1896 ed. 15.00 (ISBN 0-8063-0772-2). Genealog Pub.

Records of the Templars in England in the 1185 with Illustrative Charters & Documents. (British Academy, London, Records of the Social & Economic History Of England & Wales Ser.: Vol. 9). pap. 70.00 (ISBN 0-8115-1249-5). Kraus Repr.

Records of Trinity Church, Boston: Vol. II - 1728-1830. Andrew Oliver & James B. Peabody. LC 80-68230. 571p. 1982. 30.00x (ISBN 0-8139-0982-1, Colonial Soc MA). U Pr of Va.

Records of Trinity Church, Boston, 1728-1830. Ed. by Andrew Oliver & James B. Peabody. LC 80-68230. 519p. 1980. 30.00x (ISBN 0-8139-0950-3, Colonial Soc Ma). U Pr of Va.

Recovering from Divorce. David A. Thompson. (Counseling Guides Ser.). 94p. (Orig.). 1982. pap. 5.95 Oversize (ISBN 0-87123-476-9, 210476). Bethany Hse.

Recovery from Compulsive Overeating. large print ed. Pearl Brians. 31p. 1985. pap. 5.00 (ISBN 0-914009-29-X). VHI Library.

Recovery of Faith. Sarvepalli Radhakrishnan. Repr. of 1955 ed. lib. bdg. 22.50x (ISBN 0-8371-0197-2, RARF). Greenwood.

Recovery of Innocence. Pico Iyer. (Illus.). 1984. 8.75 (ISBN 0-88695-019-8). Concord Grove.

Recovery of Man in Childhood. 2nd ed. A. C. Harwood. (Illus.). 212p. 1981. pap. 8.95 (ISBN 0-88010-001-X). Anthroposophic.

Recovery of Reality: Overcoming Chemical Dependency. George A. Mann. LC 78-19496. (Illus.). 1979. 14.45 (ISBN 0-06-250560-2, HarpR). Har-Row.

Recovery of Spirit in Higher Education. Myron B. Bloy, Jr. et al. Ed. by Robert Rankin. 1980. 17.50 (ISBN 0-8164-0469-0, HarpR). Har-Row.

Recovery of the Anabaptist Vision: A Sixtieth Anniversary Tribute to Harold S. Bender. Ed. by Guy F. Hershberger. LC 57-10214. pap. 92.00 (ISBN 0-317-26605-5, 2025419). Bks Demand UMI.

Recreation & the Local Church. Ed. by Frances Clemens & Robert Tully. LC 57-18412. pap. 47.80 (ISBN 0-317-28391-X, 2022409). Bks Demand UMI.

Recreation Cristiana. Viola D. Campbell. (Span., Illus.). 160p. 1986. pap. 4.25 (ISBN 0-311-11037-1). Casa Bautista.

Recreation Leadership Today. Richard Kraus. 1985. text ed. write for info. (ISBN 0-673-18140-5); instr's. manual & test items incl. Scott F.

Recruiting Evangelism Callers: Enlisting & Coordinating Workers. Walter A. Schmidt. 64p. (Orig.). 1984. pap. 3.95 (ISBN 0-8066-2069-2, 23-1830). Augsburg.

Recueil de Plans d'Eglises Cisterciennes, 2 tomes. Dimier. Set. 100.75 (ISBN 0-685-34012-0). French & Eur.

Recueil des Historiens des Croisades: Lois, 2 vols. (Fr.). Repr. of 1906 ed. text ed. 258.76x ea. vol. (ISBN 0-576-78858-9, Pub. by Gregg Intl Pubs England). Gregg Intl.

Recueil des Historiens des Croisades: Documents Armeniens, 2 vols. (Fr.). Repr. of 1906 ed. text ed. 310.50x ea. vol. (ISBN 0-576-78860-0, Pub. by Gregg Intl Pubs England). Gregg Intl.

Recueil des Historiens des Croisades: Historiens Grecs, 2 vols. (Fr.). Repr. of 1906 ed. text ed. 207.00x ea. vol. (ISBN 0-576-78859-7, Pub. by Gregg Intl Pubs England). Gregg Intl.

Recueil des Historiens des Croisades: Historiens Occidentaux, 6 vols. (Fr.). Repr. of 1906 ed. text ed. 258.76x ea. vol. (ISBN 0-576-78857-0, Pub. by Gregg Intl Pubs England). Gregg Intl.

Recueil des Historiens des Croisades: Historiens Orientaux, 4 vols. (Fr.). Repr. of 1906 ed. text ed. 258.76x ea. vol. (ISBN 0-576-78861-9, Pub. by Gregg Intl Pubs England). Gregg Intl.

Recycled Hallelujahs. James Weekley. 1982. pap. 4.95 (ISBN 0-89536-532-4, 1814). CSS of Ohio.

Red China in Prophecy. Gordon Lindsay. (Prophecy Ser.). 2.25 (ISBN 0-89985-059-6). Christ Nations.

Red Man's Religion: Beliefs & Practices of the Indians North of Mexico. Ruth M. Underhill. LC 65-24985. 1972. pap. 10.00 (ISBN 0-226-84167-7, P481, Phoen). U of Chicago Pr.

Red Sea Is Your Blood. Alvin B. Kuhn. 66p. 1976. pap. 5.95 (ISBN 0-88697-007-5). Life Science.

Red Sea Waters. Sisters of the Community of Jesus. LC 82-61465. (Illus.). 72p. (Orig.). 1983. pap. 7.95 incl. cassette (ISBN 0-941478-08-4). Paraclete Pr.

Red Shi'ism. Ali Shariati. Tr. by Habib Shirazi from Persian. 1980. pap. 1.00 (ISBN 0-941722-17-1). Book-Dist-Ctr.

Red Swan: Myths and Tales of the American Indians. Ed. by John Bierhorst. LC 76-196. 368p. 1976. pap. 7.95 (ISBN 0-374-51393-7). FS&G.

Redaction of Genesis. Gary A. Rendsburg. xii, 132p. 1986. text ed. 12.50x (ISBN 0-931464-25-0). Eisenbrauns.

Redactional Style in the Marcan Gospel. E. J. Pryke. LC 76-52184. (Society for New Testament Studies Monographs: No. 33). 1978. 44.50 (ISBN 0-521-21430-0). Cambridge U Pr.

Redating the Exodus & Conquest. 2nd ed. John J. Bimson. 288p. 1981. pap. text ed. 14.95x (ISBN 0-907459-04-8, Pub. by Almond Pr England). Eisenbrauns.

Redating the New Testament. John A. T. Robinson. LC 76-17554. 384p. 1976. 15.00 (ISBN 0-664-21336-7). Westminster.

Rede Me & Be Nott Wrothe for I Say No Thynge but Trothe. William Roy. LC 76-38221. (English Experience Ser.: No. 485). 144p. 1972. Repr. of 1528 ed. 13.00 (ISBN 90-221-0485-0). Walter J Johnson.

Redeem the Time: The Puritan Sabbath in Early America. Winton U. Solberg. (Illus.). 1977. 25.00x (ISBN 0-674-75130-2). Harvard U Pr.

Redeemed Creation: The Sacramentals Today. Laurence Brett. (Message of the Sacraments Ser.: Vol. 8). 10.95 (ISBN 0-89453-398-3); pap. 6.95 (ISBN 0-89453-234-0). M Glazier.

Redeemed from Poverty, Sickness, & Death. Kenneth E. Hagin. 1966. pap. 1.00 (ISBN 0-89276-001-X). Hagin Ministries.

Redeemed from the Curse. Perry A. Gaspard. 64p. 1983. pap. 2.00 (ISBN 0-931867-03-7). Abundant Life Pubns.

Redeemer of Man. Pope John Paul II. 103p. (Orig.). 1979. pap. 3.95 (ISBN 1-55586-003-6). US Catholic.

Redeeming Creation: A Christian World Evolving. John Morton. (Illus.). 84p. (Orig.). 1984. pap. 9.95 (ISBN 0-318-20036-8, Pub. by Zealandia Pubns). ANZ Religious Pubns.

Redeeming State: A Handbook-Leader's Guide for Couples Planning Remarriage in the Church. Judith T. O'Brien & Gene O'Brien. 1984. leader's guide pamphlet 2.95 (ISBN 0-8091-5183-9); pap. 3.95 handbook-pamphlet (ISBN 0-8091-5182-0). Paulist Pr.

Redeeming the City: Theology, Politics & Urban Policy. Ed. by Ronald D. Pasquariello et al. 224p. 1982. pap. 11.00 (ISBN 0-317-02300-4). Schalkenbach.

Redemption Accomplished & Applied. Donald W. Bowdle. 1972. 5.25 (ISBN 0-87148-726-8); pap. 4.25 (ISBN 0-87148-727-6). Pathway Pr.

Redemption: Accomplished & Applied. John Murray. 1961. pap. 5.95 (ISBN 0-8028-1143-4). Eerdmans.

Redemption, Conceived & Revealed. H. P. Robinson. 3.95 (ISBN 0-911866-59-0); pap. 2.95 (ISBN 0-911866-89-2). Advocate.

Redemption, Hindu & Christian: The Religious Quest of India. facsimile ed. Sydney Cave. LC 73-102230. (Select Bibliographies Reprint Ser). 1919. 24.50 (ISBN 0-8369-5115-8). Ayer Co Pubs.

Redemption in Black Theology. Olin P. Moyd. LC 78-23816. 1979. soft cover 8.95 (ISBN 0-8170-0806-3). Judson.

Redemption of God: A Theology of Mutual Relation. Isabel C. Heyward. LC 81-43706. 266p. (Orig.). 1982. lib. bdg. 29.25 (ISBN 0-8191-2389-7); pap. text ed. 12.25 (ISBN 0-8191-2390-0). U Pr of Amer.

Redemption of Howard Gray. C. W. Naylor. 72p. pap. 0.50 (ISBN 0-686-29162-X). Faith Pub Hse.

Redemption of Man. T. B. Kilpatrick. (Short Course Ser.). 200p. 1940. 6.95 (ISBN 0-567-08320-9, Pub. by T & T Clark Ltd UK). Fortress.

Redemption of Matter: Towards the Rapprochment of Science & Religion. James W. Jones. 154p. (Orig.). 1984. lib. bdg. 23.00 (ISBN 0-8191-3675-1); pap. text ed. 9.25 (ISBN 0-8191-3676-X). U Pr of Amer.

Redemption of Ruth. Leslie Madison. 96p. (Orig.). 1982. pap. 2.50 (ISBN 0-89323-038-3). Bible Memory.

Redemption of the Unwanted: From the Liberation of the Death Camps to the Founding of Israel. Abram L. Sachar. LC 83-3025. (Illus.). 320p. 1983. 19.95 (ISBN 0-312-66729-9, Pub. by Marek). St Martin.

Redemption of the Unwanted: The Post-Holocaust Years. Abram Sachar. 334p. 1985. pap. 9.95 (ISBN 0-312-66730-2, Pub. by Marek). St Martin.

Redemption of Thinking: A Study in the Philosophy of Thomas Aquinas. Rudolf Steiner. Tr. by A. P. Sheperd & Mildred R. Nicoll. Orig. Title: Philosophie des Thomas von Aquino. 191p. 1983. pap. text ed. 8.95 (ISBN 0-88010-044-3). Anthroposophic.

Redemption: Three Sermons, 1637-1656. Thomas Hooker. LC 56-9145. 1977. Repr. 30.00x (ISBN 0-8201-1234-8). Schol Facsimiles.

Redemption Truths. Robert Anderson. LC 80-16161. (Sir Robert Anderson Library). Orig. Title: For Us Men. 192p. 1980. pap. 4.95 (ISBN 0-8254-2131-4). Kregel.

Redemptive Dancing: Prayer Dance & Congregational Dance in the Life of the Contemporary Church. Janet Skidmore. Ed. by Doug Adams. pap. 2.50 (ISBN 0-941500-46-2). Sharing Co.

Redemptive History & Biblical Interpretation. Geerhardus Vos. Ed. by Richard B. Gaffin, Jr. 584p. 1981. 17.50 (ISBN 0-8010-9286-8). Baker Bk.

Redemptive History & Biblical Interpretation: The Shorter Writings of Geerhardus Vos. Ed. by Richard B. Gaffin, Jr. 1980. 17.50 (ISBN 0-87552-270-X). Presby & Reformed.

Redemptive Intimacy. Dick Westley. LC 80-54810. 176p. 1981. pap. 5.95 (ISBN 0-89622-123-7). Twenty-Third.

Redemptive Responses of Jesus. Howard W. Roberts. (Orig.). 1987. pap. 5.95 (ISBN 0-8054-5715-1). Broadman.

Redemptive Suffering in Islam. Mahmoud Ayoub. (Religion & Society Ser.: No. 10). 1978. 35.25 (ISBN 90-279-7948-0). Mouton.

Redemptorama. Carol Flake. LC 82-45356. 288p. 1984. 15.95 (ISBN 0-385-18241-4, Anchor Pr). Doubleday.

Redemptorama: Culture, Politics & the New Evangelicalism. Carol Flake. (Nonfiction Ser.). 320p. 1985. pap. 7.95 (ISBN 0-14-008265-4). Penguin.

Redemptorist on the American Missions, 3 vols. In 2. Joseph Wissel. 115.00 (ISBN 0-405-10867-2). Ayer Co Pubs.

Redencion Lograda y Aplicada. Ed. by Donald N. Bowdle. (Span.). 126p. 1979. pap. 3.95 (ISBN 0-87148-521-4). Pathway Pr.

Redimido De La Pobreza, La Enfermedad, La Muerte. 2nd ed. Kenneth E. Hagin. 1982. pap. 1.00 (ISBN 0-89276-101-6). Hagin Ministries.

Rediscovering Fatima. Robert J. Fox. LC 82-60667. (Illus.). 144p. (Orig.). 1982. pap. 4.50 (ISBN 0-87973-657-7, 657). Our Sunday Visitor.

Rediscovering Jesus: Challenge of Discipleship. Eamonn Bredin. 300p. 1986. pap. 9.95 (ISBN 0-89622-300-0). Twenty-Third.

Rediscovering Pastoral Care. Alastair V. Campbell. LC 81-7547. 132p. 1981. pap. 7.95 (ISBN 0-664-24381-9). Westminster.

Rediscovering Paul: Philemon & the Sociology of Paul's Narrative World. Norman Petersen. LC 84-48730. 320p. 1985. 24.95 (ISBN 0-8006-0741-4, 1-741). Fortress.

Rediscovering Prophecy: A New Song for a New Kingdom. Ronald B. Allen. 1987. pap. 7.95. Multnomah.

Rediscovering the Angels & Natives of Eternity. 7th ed. Flower A. Newhouse. (Illus.). 11.00 (ISBN 0-910378-02-9). Christward.

Rediscovering the Charismata: Building up the Body of Christ Through Spiritual Gifts. Charles Bryant. 192p. 1986. 11.95 (ISBN 0-8499-0539-7). Word Bks.

Rediscovering the Gift of Healing. 2nd ed. Lawrence Althouse. 144p. 1983. pap. 5.95 (ISBN 0-87728-604-3). Weiser.

Rediscovering the Power of the Gospel: Jesus' Theology of the Kingdom. J. Arthur Baird. LC 82-83623. 1982. pap. 9.95 (ISBN 0-910789-00-2). Iona Pr.

Rediscovering the Sacraments: Approaches to the Sacrament. Brennan Hill. 126p. (Orig.). 1982. 3.95 (ISBN 0-8215-9882-1). Sadlier.

Rediscovering the Teachings of Jesus. Norman Perrin. LC 67-11510. 1976. pap. 6.95xi (ISBN 0-06-066493-2, RD 151, HarpR). Har-Row.

Rediscovering the Traditions of Israel. Douglas A. Knight. LC 75-6868. (Society of Biblical Literature. Dissertation Ser.: No. 9). pap. 86.50 (ISBN 0-317-07884-4, 2017515). Bks Demand UMI.

Rediscovery of Jesus' Eschatological Discourse: Studies in the History of Gospel Traditions. David Wenham. (Gospel Perspectives Ser.: Vol. IV). 406p. 1984. text ed. 24.50x (ISBN 0-905774-72-8, Pub. by JSOT Pr England); pap. text ed. 13.50x (ISBN 0-905774-73-6, Pub. by JSOT England). Eisenbrauns.

Rediscovery of John Wesley. George C. Cell. LC 83-6505. 438p. 1983. pap. text ed. 15.50 (ISBN 0-8191-3222-5). U Pr of Amer.

Rediscovery of Newman: An Oxford Symposium. Ed. by John Coulson & Arthur M. Allchin. LC 68-84451. 1967. text ed. 15.00x (ISBN 0-8401-0458-8). A R Allenson.

Rediscovery of the Family & Other Lectures: Sister Marie Hilda Memorial Lectures 1954-1973. 112p. 1981. pap. 12.00 (ISBN 0-08-025754-2). Pergamon.

Rediscovery of the Old Testament. H. H. Rowley. 224p. 1946. 14.00 (ISBN 0-227-67576-2). Attic Pr.

Redland Park Recorded. Peggy Thomas. 240p. 1986. pap. 30.00x (ISBN 0-947939-03-2, Pub. by Elmcrest Uk). State Mutual Bk.

Reducing the Storm to a Whisper: The Story of a Breakdown. Patrick Howell. 228p. 1985. 15.95 (ISBN 0-88347-183-3). Thomas More.

Reed of God. Caryll Houselander. 128p. 1978. pap. 3.95 (ISBN 0-88479-013-4). Arena Lettres.

Reel Index to the Microfilm Edition of Utah & the Mormons. 13p. 1982. 15.00. Res Pubns CT.

Reenacting the Heavenly Vision: The Role of Religion in the Taping Rebellion. Rudolf G. Wagner. (China Research Monograph: No. 25). (Illus.). 146p. 1984. pap. 12.00x (ISBN 0-912966-60-2). IEAS.

Reese Chronological Bible. Compiled by Edward Reese. 1620p. 1980. Repr. of 1977 ed. 26.95 (ISBN 0-87123-115-8, 230115). Bethany Hse.

Reexamining Conscience. John Carmody. 144p. (Orig.). 1982. pap. 8.95 (ISBN 0-8164-2405-5, HarpR). Har-Row.

Reference Passage Bible, New Testament: With Old Testament References. LC 78-56146. 1978. 9.95 (ISBN 0-88270-275-0). Bridge Pub.

Reference Works for Theological Research: An Annotated Selective Bibliographical Guide. 2nd ed. Robert J. Kepple. LC 81-40350. 298p. 1981. lib. bdg. 29.00 (ISBN 0-8191-1679-3); pap. text ed. 13.75 (ISBN 0-8191-1680-7). U Pr of Amer.

Reference Works in the Field of Religion 1977-1985. Elsie Freudenberger. (Orig.). 1986. pap. 15.00 (ISBN 0-87507-037-X). Cath Lib Assn.

Refiner's Fire. Alvin R. Dyer. 8.95 (ISBN 0-87747-222-X). Deseret Bk.

Refining Your Life: From the Zen Kitchen to Enlightenment. Kosho Uchiyama & Kosho Uchiyama. Tr. by Tom Wright. LC 82-20295. 136p. 1983. pap. 9.95 (ISBN 0-8348-0179-5). Weatherhill.

Reflecting Christ. Ellen G. White. Ed. by Raymond H. Woolsey. (Devotional Ser.). 384p. 1985. 7.95 (ISBN 0-8280-0305-X). Review & Herald.

Reflecting the Lord's Radiance. Clair Cosby. (Orig.). 1987. pap. 5.95 (ISBN 0-8054-5916-2). Broadman.

Reflection & Doubt in the Thought of Paul Tillich. Robert P. Scharlemann. LC 79-81430. Repr. of 1969 ed. 45.60 (ISBN 0-8357-9481-4, 2013185). Bks Demand UMI.

Reflection: Diary of a German Jew in Hiding. Julian C. Stanford. 1965. 4.50 (ISBN 0-943376-00-9). Magnes Mus.

Reflection Guide on Human Sexuality & the Ordained Priesthood. 72p. 1983. pap. 2.95 (ISBN 1-55586-865-7). US Catholic.

Reflection of a Soul. Mary S. Eyer. 83p. 1986. 7.95 (ISBN 0-934126-66-6). Randall Bk Co.

Reflection of Humanity. 2nd ed. Ali Shariati. Tr. by Fathollah Marjani from Persian. 37p. 1984. pap. 2.00 (ISBN 0-941722-11-2). Book-Dist-Ctr.

Reflection of the Awakened. Sadraddin Al-Qunawi. Tr. by Hasan Askari. 112p. 1987. pap. 12.95 (ISBN 0-7103-0217-7, Pub. by Routledge UK). Methuen Inc.

Reflection of Theology in Literature: A Case Study in Theology & Culture. William Mallard. LC 76-14036. (Trinity University Monograph Series in Religion). 271p. 1977. 10.00 (ISBN 0-911536-64-7). Trinity U Pr.

Reflection on the Holocaust. Irene G. Shur & Franklin H. Littell. Ed. by Richard D. Lambert. LC 80-66618. (Annals of the American Academy of Political & Social Science: No. 450). 272p. 1980. pap. text ed. 7.95 (ISBN 0-87761-253-6). Am Acad Pol Soc Sci.

Reflections. Charles J. Dertinger. 1983. write for info. (ISBN 0-8062-2043-0). Carlton.

Reflections. Subramuniya. (On the Path Ser.). (Illus.). 72p. 1969. pap. 2.00 (ISBN 0-87516-354-8). De Vorss.

Reflections & Prayers for Visits with Our Eucharistic King. John Carberry. pap. 0.50 (ISBN 0-8198-0315-4). Dghtrs St Paul.

Reflections Books, 4 vols. Daniel Overduin. 1980. Set. pap. 6.95 (ISBN 0-570-03817-0, 12-2785). Concordia.

Reflections: Fifty Years of Pastoral Ministry. Charles F. Kemp. (Orig.). pap. 9.95 (ISBN 0-937689-04-1). Chisum Pub.

Reflections from the Light of Christ: 5 Quaker Classics. James R. Newby. LC 80-7477. 126p. 1980. 7.95 (ISBN 0-913408-55-7). Friends United.

Reflections from the Son: For Men. Harrison Forbes. (Orig.). 1986. pap. 5.00 (ISBN 0-915541-07-6). Star Bks Inc.

Reflections in a Shop Window. Joan P. Berry. 1983. 4.25 (ISBN 0-89536-605-3, 1817). CSS of Ohio.

Reflections in Righteousness. Jackie Banas. (Illus.). 56p. (Orig.). 1985. 5.00 (ISBN 0-9614014-2-7). Know Him Pr.

Reflections of a Catholic Theologian on Visiting an Abortion Clinic. Daniel C. Maguire. 11p. pap. 1.50 (ISBN 0-915365-10-3). Cath Free Choice.

Reflections of a Scientist. Henry Eyring. LC 83-7109. (Illus.). 101p. 1983. 7.95 (ISBN 0-87747-944-5). Deseret Bk.

Reflections of Faith. Harold G. Bennett. LC 81-67326. 1983. pap. 5.95 (ISBN 0-8054-6565-0). Broadman.

Reflections of Him. Dorothy Eker. LC 75-393402. 1976. 4.95 (ISBN 0-87212-053-8). Libra.

Reflections of Love. Alice J. Davidson. (Illus.). 128p. 1982. 12.95 (ISBN 0-8007-1327-3). Revell.

Reflections of Mind: Western Psychology Meets Tibetan Buddhism. Tarthang Tulku. LC 75-5254. (Illus.). 1975. 14.95 (ISBN 0-913546-15-1); pap. 7.95 (ISBN 0-913546-14-3). Dharma Pub.

Reflections of My Life: The Apology of John the Baptist. Dennis Dallison. Ed. by Ruth Norman. 77p. (Orig.). 1982. pap. text ed. 2.50 (ISBN 0-932642-75-6). Unarius Pubns.

Reflections of Social Life in the Navaho Origin Myth. Katherine Spencer. LC 76-43850. (Univ. of New Mexico. Publications in Anthropology: No. 3). 1983. Repr. of 1947 ed. 20.00 (ISBN 0-404-15705-X). AMS Pr.

Reflections of Southern Jewry: The Letters of Charles Wessolowsky. Ed. by Louis Schmier. LC 81-16995. viii, 184p. 1982. 12.95 (ISBN 0-86554-020-9, MUP-H15). Mercer Univ Pr.

Reflections of Success. Janet Trout & Diane Walter. 1984. pap. 5.95 (ISBN 0-912315-81-4). Word Aflame.

Reflections of the Inward Silence. Ed. by Salvatore S. Buttaci & Susan L. Gerstle. LC 76-19240. 1976. 9.95 (ISBN 0-917398-03-3); pap. 7.95 (ISBN 0-917398-04-1). New Worlds.

Reflections of the Self: Poems of Spiritual Life. Swami Muktananda. LC 80-50391. (Illus.). 205p. (Orig.). 1980. pap. 5.95 (ISBN 0-914602-50-0). SYDA Found.

Reflections on Community Building. Marjorie Spock. 1984. pap. 3.25 (ISBN 0-916786-67-6). St George Bk Serv.

Reflections on Deacon Spirituality. Steve Landregan. (Orig.). Date not set. pap. price not set (ISBN 1-55586-150-4). US Catholic.

Reflections on Death & Grief. Albert J. Walsh. 96p. 1986. 4.50 (ISBN 0-8010-9673-1). Baker Bk.

Reflections on Francis Schaeffer. Ed. by Ronald W. Ruegsegger. 336p. 1986. pap. 12.95 (ISBN 0-310-37091-4, 12355P). Zondervan.

Reflections on Humanae Vitae. Pope John Paul II. 96p. 1984. 3.76 (ISBN 0-8198-6409-9); pap. 2.75 (ISBN 0-8198-6410-2). Dghtrs St Paul.

Reflections on Liberation. Daryl R. Grigsby. LC 84-72421. (Illus.). 176p. (Orig.). 1985. pap. 5.95 (ISBN 0-9614210-0-2). Asante Pubns.

Reflections on Life & Death. Joseph Chiari. LC 77-4054. 141p. 1977. 12.50x (ISBN 0-87752-212-X). Gordian.

Reflections on Religion & Public Policy. Richard Rubenstein. (Monographs). 1984. 1.95 (ISBN 0-88702-002-X, Pub. by Wash Inst DC). Paragon Hse.

Reflections on Revival. Charles G. Finney. LC 78-26527. 160p. 1979. pap. 4.95 (ISBN 0-87123-157-3, 210157). Bethany Hse.

Reflections on St. Paul. Burns K. Seeley. Ed. by Jerome F. Coniker. LC 82-72202. (Living Meditation & Prayerbook Ser.). (Illus.). 270p. (Orig.). 1982. pap. text ed. 5.00 (ISBN 0-932406-07-6). AFC.

Reflections on Shamanism: The Tribal Healer & the Technological Trance. John Grim. (Teilhard Studies: No. 6). 20p. (Orig.). 1981. pap. 2.00 (ISBN 0-89012-029-3). Anima Pubns.

Reflections on Simplicity. Elaine Prevallet. LC 82-80439. 31p. 1982. pap. 2.50x (ISBN 0-87574-244-0). Pendle Hill.

Reflections on the Creed. Daniel Overduin. 1980. pap. 1.95 (ISBN 0-570-03814-6, 12-2782). Concordia.

Reflections on the Gospel of John, Vol. 2. Leon Morris. 208p. 1987. pap. 8.95 (ISBN 0-8010-6215-2). Baker Bk.

Reflections on the Gospels, 3 vols, Vol. 2. John M. Talbot. 196p. (Orig.). 1987. pap. 5.95 (ISBN 0-89283-349-1). Servant.

Reflections on the Gospels: Daily Devotions for Radical Christian Living. John M. Talbot. 196p. (Orig.). 1986. pap. 5.95 (ISBN 0-89283-306-8). Servant.

Reflections on the Jesus Prayer. 1985. 3.95 (ISBN 0-87193-070-6). Dimension Bks.

Reflections on the Lord's Prayer. Daniel Overduin. 1980. pap. 1.95 (ISBN 0-570-03815-4, 12-2783). Concordia.

Reflections on the Path. Herbert B. Puryear. 224p. 1986. pap. 3.50 (ISBN 0-553-25659-9). Bantam.

Reflections on the Psalms. C. S. Lewis. LC 58-10910. 1964. pap. 3.95 (ISBN 0-15-676248-X, Harv). HarBraceJ.

Reflections on the Psalms. C. S. Lewis. 224p. 1985. pap. 9.95 (ISBN 0-8027-2512-0). Walker & Co.

Reflections on the Sacraments. Daniel Overduin. 1980. pap. 1.95 (ISBN 0-570-03816-2, 12-2784). Concordia.

Reflections on the Study of Religion. Jacques Waardenburg. (Religion & Reason Ser.: No. 15). 1978. text ed. 32.00 (ISBN 0-686-27034-7). Mouton.

Reflections on the Ten Commandments. Daniel Overduin. 1980. pap. 1.95 (ISBN 0-570-03813-8, 12-2781). Concordia.

Reflections on Things at Hand: The Neo-Confucian Anthology. Tr. by Wing Tstit Chan. LC 65-22548. (Records of Civilization Sources Studies). 441p. 1967. 38.00x (ISBN 0-231-02819-9); pap. 16.00x (ISBN 0-231-06037-8). Columbia U Pr.

Reflections: 50 Years of Pastoral Ministry. Charles F. Kemp. 150p. (Orig.). 1986. pap. 9.95 (ISBN 0-318-20075-9). Chisum Pub.

Reflective Living: A Spiritual Approach to Everyday Life. Claire M. Brisette. LC 83-21369. (Illus.). 136p. (Orig.). 1983. pap. 8.00 (ISBN 0-89571-019-6). Affirmation.

Reflective Meditation. Kay Mouradian. LC 82-50163. 175p. (Orig.). 1982. pap. 4.50 (ISBN 0-8356-0565-5, Quest). Theos Pub Hse.

Reflexion Pastoral: El Pastor y Su Ministerio. Emilio A. Nunez. Orig. Title: Pastoral Reflection. (Span.). Date not set. pap. 6.50 (ISBN 0-8254-1515-2). Kregel.

Reflexions et Prieres dans L'espace-temps. Pierre Teilhard De Chardin. 13.95 (ISBN 0-685-36601-4). French & Eur.

Reflexions Sur la Question Juive. Jean-Paul Sartre. 1962. pap. 3.95 (ISBN 0-685-11523-2). French & Eur.

Reform & Authority in the Medieval & Reformation Church. Ed. by Guy F. Lytle. LC 79-17380. pap. 87.80 (2029496). Bks Demand UMI.

Reform & Reformation: England & the Continent c.1500-c.1750. Ed. by Derek Baker. (Studies in Church History: Subsidia 2). (Illus.). 336p. 1980. 45.00x (ISBN 0-631-19270-0). Basil Blackwell.

Reform & Reformation: England, 1509-1558. G. R. Elton. LC 77-6464. (Harvard Paperback Ser.: No. 146, The New History of England). 1979. 27.50x (ISBN 0-674-75245-7); pap. 8.95x (ISBN 0-674-75248-1). Harvard U Pr.

Reform & Renewal, Thomas Cromwell & the Common Weal. Geoffrey R. Elton. (Wiles Lectures, 1972). 230p. 1973. pap. 11.95 (ISBN 0-521-09809-2). Cambridge U Pr.

Reform Jewish Practice. S. Freehof. 9.95x (ISBN 0-685-55600-X). Ktav.

Reform Judaism Today. Eugene B. Borowitz. 800p. 1983. pap. text ed. 9.95x (ISBN 0-87441-364-8). Behrman.

Reform, Rebellion & the Heavenly Way. Benjamin Weems. LC 64-17267. (Association for Asian Studies Monograph: No. 15). 122p. 1964. 7.95x (ISBN 0-8165-0144-0). U of Ariz Pr.

Reform Responsa for Our Time. S. B. Freehof. 15.00x (ISBN 0-87820-111-4, HUC Pr). Ktav.

Reform Thought in Sixteenth Century Italy. Elisabeth G. Gleason. Ed. by James A. Massey. LC 81-5648. (American Academy of Religion Texts & Translations Ser.). 1981. pap. text ed. 10.95 (ISBN 0-89130-498-3, 01-02-04). Scholars Pr GA.

Reformatio Perennis: Essays on Calvin & the Reformation in Honor of Ford Lewis Battles. Ed. by Brian Gerrish. (Pittsburgh Theological Monograph Ser.: No. 32). 1981. pap. 15.00 (ISBN 0-915138-41-7). Pickwick.

Reformation. J. A. Babington. LC 71-118513. 1971. Repr. of 1901 ed. 28.75x (ISBN 0-8046-1135-1, Pub. by Kennikat). Assoc Faculty Pr.

Reformation. Will Durant. (Story of Civilization: Vol. 6). (Illus.). 1957. 29.95 (ISBN 0-671-61050-3). S&S.

Reformation. George P. Fisher. LC 83-45660. Date not set. Repr. of 1906 ed. 54.50 (ISBN 0-404-19810-4). AMS Pr.

Reformation. Harold J. Grimm. LC 72-76717. (AHA Pamphlets: No. 403). 1972. pap. text ed. 1.50 (ISBN 0-87229-003-4). Am Hist Assn.

Reformation. Peter Klassen. LC 79-54030. (Problems in Civilization Ser.). (Orig.). 1980. pap. text ed. 6.95x (ISBN 0-88273-408-3). Forum Pr IL.

Reformation. Thomas M. Lindsay. Ed. by A. Whyte & J. Moffatt. (Handbooks for Bible Classes & Private Students Ser.). 228p. 1889. pap. 6.95 (ISBN 0-686-70864-4, Pub. by T & T Clark Ltd UK). Fortress.

Reformation. rev. ed. George L. Mosse. LC 63-11339. (Berkshire Studies in History). 1969. pap. text ed. 10.95 (ISBN 0-03-082836-8, HoltE). H Holt & Co.

Reformation, Vol. 3. Owen Chadwick. (History of the Church Ser.). (Orig.). 1964. pap. 5.95 (ISBN 0-14-020504-7, Pelican). Penguin.

Reformation: A Narrative History Related by Contemporary Observers & Participants. Ed. by Hans J. Hillerbrand. (Twin Brooks Ser). (Illus.). 1978. pap. 11.95 (ISBN 0-8010-4185-6). Baker Bk.

Reformation: A Picture Story of Martin Luther. Dietrich Steinwede. Tr. by Edward A. Cooperrider from German. LC 82-49055. (Illus.). 56p. 1983. pap. 6.95 (ISBN 0-8006-1710-X, 1-1710). Fortress.

Reformation & Catholicity. Gustaf E. Aulen. Tr. by Eric H. Wahlstrom from Swedish. LC 78-25981. 1979. Repr. of 1961 ed. lib. bdg. 22.50x (ISBN 0-313-20809-3, AURC). Greenwood.

Reformation & Counter-Reformation. Ed. by Hubert Jedin & John Dolan. 1980. 59.50x (ISBN 0-686-95526-9). Crossroad NY.

Reformation & Reaction in Tudor Cambridge. H. C. Porter. LC 77-179573. (Illus.). xv, 462p. 1972. Repr. of 1958 ed. 35.00 (ISBN 0-208-01228-1, Archon). Shoe String.

Reformation & Renaissance. Jean M. Stone. LC 83-45670. (Illus.). Date not set. Repr. of 1904 ed. 76.50 (ISBN 0-404-19820-1). AMS Pr.

Reformation & Society in Sixteenth Century Europe. A. G. Dickens. (History of European Civilization Library). (Illus., Orig.). 1966. pap. text ed. 11.95 (ISBN 0-15-576455-1, HC). HarBraceJ.

Reformation & the Advent Movement. Walter L. Emmerson. 224p. pap. 9.95 (ISBN 0-8280-0168-5). Review & Herald.

Reformation & the English People. J. J. Scarisbrick. 214p. 1986. pap. text ed. 12.95x (ISBN 0-631-14755-1). Basil Blackwell.

Reformation & the Irish Episcopate. 2nd ed. Hugh J. Lawlor. (Church Historical Society, London, Ser.: No. 11). Repr. of 1932 ed. 20.00 (ISBN 0-8115-3135-X). Kraus Repr.

Reformation & the People. Thomas A. Lacey. LC 83-45583. Date not set. Repr. of 1929 ed. 22.00 (ISBN 0-404-19901-1). AMS Pr.

Reformation: Basic Interpretations. 2nd ed. Ed. by Lewis W. Spitz. (Problems in European Civilization Ser.). 1972. pap. text ed. 5.95 (ISBN 0-669-81620-5). Heath.

Reformation Debate. Ed. by John Calvin & Jacopo Sadoleto. 1976. pap. 4.95 (ISBN 0-8010-2390-4). Baker Bk.

Reformation Era: 1500-1650. 2nd ed. Harold J. Grimm. (Illus.). 700p. 1973. text ed. write for info. (ISBN 0-02-347270-7, 34727). Macmillan.

Reformation Essays. James P. Whitney. (Church Historical Society London N. S. Ser.: No. 38). Repr. of 1939 ed. 40.00 (ISBN 0-8115-3161-9). Kraus Repr.

Reformation Europe: A Guide to Research. Ed. by Steven E. Ozment. 390p. 1982. 18.50x (ISBN 0-910345-01-5); pap. 13.50x (ISBN 0-686-82436-9). Center Reform.

Reformation Europe: Age of Reform & Revolution. De Lamar Jensen. 480p. 1981. pap. text ed. 12.95 (ISBN 0-669-03626-9). Heath.

Reformation in England. Gustave L. Constant. Tr. by R. E. Scantlebury. LC 83-45576. Date not set. Repr. of 1934 ed. 85.00 (ISBN 0-404-19895-3). AMS Pr.

Reformation in England, 2 vols. Merle D'Aubigne. 1977. Vol. 1. pap. 13.95 (ISBN 0-85151-486-3); Vol. 2. pap. 13.95 (ISBN 0-85151-487-1); Set. o. p. 25.95 (ISBN 0-85151-488-X). Banner of Truth.

Reformation in England to the Accession of Elizabeth 1. Arthur G. Dickens & Dorothy Carr. (Documents of Modern History Ser). (Orig.). 1968. pap. 11.95 (ISBN 0-312-66815-5). St Martin.

Reformation in Germany. H. C. Vedder. 1977. lib. bdg. 59.95 (ISBN 0-8490-2506-0). Gordon Pr.

Reformation in Historical Thought. A. G. Dickens et al. 456p. 1985. text ed. 33.50x (ISBN 0-674-75311-9). Harvard U Pr.

Reformation in Northern England. J. S. Fletcher. LC 71-118469. 1971. Repr. of 1925 ed. 23.50x (ISBN 0-8046-1218-8, Pub. by Kennikat). Assoc Faculty Pr.

Reformation in Poland. Paul Fox. LC 72-136395. Repr. of 1924 ed. 24.50 (ISBN 0-404-02544-7). AMS Pr.

Reformation in Poland, Some Social & Economic Aspects. Paul Fox. LC 71-104272. Repr. of 1924 ed. lib. bdg. 22.50x (ISBN 0-8371-3924-4, FORP). Greenwood.

Reformation in Scotland, Causes, Characteristics, Consequences: Stone Lectures at Princeton Theological Seminary, 1907-1908. Ed. by David H. Fleming. LC 83-45579. Date not set. Repr. of 1910 ed. 67.50 (ISBN 0-404-19897-X). AMS Pr.

Reformation in the Cities: The Appeal of Protestantism to Sixteenth-Century Germany & Switzerland. Steven E. Ozment. LC 75-8444. 228p. 1975. 28.50x (ISBN 0-300-01898-3); pap. 7.95x (ISBN 0-300-02496-7). Yale U Pr.

Reformation of American Quakerism, 1748-1783. Jack D. Marietta. LC 83-23502. 352p. 1984. 28.95 (ISBN 0-8122-7922-0). U of Pa Pr.

Reformation of the Heretics: The Waldenses of the Alps, 1480-1580. Euan Cameron. (Oxford Historical Monographs). (Illus.). 291p. 1984. 48.00x (ISBN 0-19-822930-5). Oxford U Pr.

Reformation of the Sixteenth Century. Roland Bainton. 18.50 (ISBN 0-8446-1581-1). Peter Smith.

Reformation of the Sixteenth Century. enl. ed. Roland H. Bainton. LC 85-47516. (Illus.). 290p. 1985. pap. 9.95 (ISBN 0-8070-1301-3, BP697). Beacon Pr.

Reformation of the Sixteenth Century in Its Relations to Modern Thought & Knowledge. new ed. Charles Beard. LC 77-27168. (Hibbert Lectures: 1883). Repr. of 1927 ed. 47.50 (ISBN 0-404-60404-8). AMS Pr.

Reformation of the Sixteenth Century in Its Relation to Modern Thought & Knowledge. Charles Beard. LC 80-12915. xxviii, 450p. 1980. Repr. of 1962 ed. lib. bdg. 37.50x (ISBN 0-313-22410-2, BERF). Greenwood.

Reformation Spirituality: The Religion of George Herbert. Gene E. Veith, Jr. LC 83-46176. 288p. 1985. 34.50 (ISBN 0-8387-5071-0). Bucknell U Pr.

Reformation Studies. A. G. Dickens. 624p. 1983. 40.00 (ISBN 0-907628-04-4). Hambledon Press.

Reformation und Spanische Andachtsliteratur. Maria Hagedorn. 1934. 12.00 (ISBN 0-384-20770-7). Johnson Repr.

Reforme et Contre-Reforme Catholiques Recherches Sur la Chartreuse de Cologne au XVI Siecle. Gerald Chaix. Ed. by James Hogg. (Analecta Cartusiana Ser.: No. 80,1-3). (Fr.). 1119p. (Orig.). 1981. pap. 85.00 (ISBN 3-7052-0117-4, Pub. by Salzburg Studies). Longwood Pub Group.

Reformed America: The Middle & Southern States, Seventeen Eighty-Three to Eighteen Thirty-Seven. Fred J. Hood. LC 79-28834. 304p. 1980. 21.50 (ISBN 0-8173-0034-1). U of Ala Pr.

Reformed & Catholic: Selected Theological Writings of Phillip Schaff. Ed. by Charles Yrigoyen, Jr. & George H Bricker. LC 79-17391. (Pittsburgh Original Texts & Translations Ser: No. 4). 1979. pap. text ed. 15.75 (ISBN 0-915138-40-9). Pickwick.

Reformed Church Roots. Arie R. Brouwer. write for info. (ISBN 0-685-62275-4). Reformed Church.

Reformed Doctrine of Predestination. Loraine Boettner. 1932. 7.95x (ISBN 0-87552-129-0). Presby & Reformed.

Reformed Dogmatics. Heinrich Heppe. Ed. by Ernst Bizer. Tr. by G. T. Thomson. (Twin Brooks Ser.). 1978. pap. 19.95 (ISBN 0-8010-4207-0). Baker Bk.

Reformed Faith & Politics: Essays Prepared for the Advisory Council on Church & Society of the United Presbyterian Church in the U. S. A. & the Council on Theology & Culture of the Presbyterian Church in the U. S. Ed. by Ronald H. Stone. LC 83-10513. 210p. (Orig.). 1983. lib. bdg. 22.00 (ISBN 0-8191-3295-0); pap. text ed. 8.50 (ISBN 0-8191-3296-9). U Pr of Amer.

Reformed Pastor. Richard Baxter. 1979. pap. 4.95 (ISBN 0-85151-191-0). Banner of Truth.

Reformed Pastor: A Pattern for Personal Growth & Ministry. rev. ed. Richard Baxter. Ed. by James M. Houston. LC 82-18825. (Classics of Faith & Devotion Ser.). 150p. 1983. 10.95 (ISBN 0-88070-003-3). Multnomah.

Reformed Pulpit. 2.50 (ISBN 0-686-23482-0). Rose Pub MI.

Reformed Roots of the English New Testament: The Influence of Theodore Beza on the English New Testament. Irena Backus. (Pittsburgh Theological Monographs: No. 28). 1980. pap. 10.00 (ISBN 0-915138-36-0). Pickwick.

Reformed Theology: Essays in Its Modern Expression in America. Ed. by David F. Wells. 296p. (Orig.). 1985. pap. 19.95 (ISBN 0-8028-0096-3). Eerdmans.

Reformers & the Theology of Reformation. William Cunningham. 1979. 19.95 (ISBN 0-85151-013-2). Banner of Truth.

Reformers Before the Reformation. Emile de Bonnechose. Tr. by Campbell Mackenzie. LC 78-63194. (Heresies of the Early Christian & Medieval Era: Second Ser.). Repr. of 1844 ed. 36.50 set (ISBN 0-404-16190-1). AMS Pr.

Reformers Before the Reformation in Germany & the Netherlands, 2 vols. C. Ullmann. 1977. lib. bdg. 200.00 (ISBN 0-8490-2507-9). Gordon Pr.

Reformers in India, 1793-1833: An Account of the Work of Christian Missionaries on Behalf of Social Reform. Kenneth Ingham. LC 73-16425. xi, 150p. 1973. Repr. of 1956 ed. lib. bdg. 17.00x (ISBN 0-374-94112-2, Octagon). Hippocrene Bks.

Reformers in the Wings. David C. Steinmetz. (Twin Brooks Ser.). 240p. 1981. pap. 7.95 (ISBN 0-8010-8208-0). Baker Bk.

Reforming the Rites of Death. Ed. by Johannes Wagner. LC 68-20845. (Concilium Ser.: Vol. 32). 189p. 7.95. Paulist Pr.

Refreshment in the Desert: Spiritual Connections in Daily Life. Gilbert Padilla. 144p. (Orig.). 1985. pap. 7.95 (ISBN 0-89622-228-4). Twenty-Third.

Refuge from Darkness: Wilfrid Israel & the Rescue of the Jews. Naomi Shepherd. LC 83-22000. 18.45 (ISBN 0-394-52503-5). Pantheon.

Refugee Scholars in America: Their Impact & Their Experiences. Lewis A. Coser. LC 84-40193. 384p. 1984. 27.50x (ISBN 0-300-03193-9). Yale U Pr.

Refusenik: Voices of Struggle & Hope. Albert S. Axelrad. 75p. (Orig.). 1986. pap. text ed. 9.95x (ISBN 0-932269-56-7). Wyndham Hall.

Refutation of Scepticism. Anthony C. Grayling. LC 85-5032. 150p. 1985. cloth 22.95 (ISBN 0-87548-314-3). Open Court.

Refutation of the Sects. Yeznik Koghbatsi. Ed. by Thomas J. Samuelian. (Armenian Church Classics Ser.). (Illus.). 1986. pap. write for info (ISBN 0-934728-13-5). D O A C.

Regard the Lilies, Regard the Blood: Poems to the Blessed Virgin. John Hart. 79p. 1983. pap. 6.00 (ISBN 0-682-49941-2). Exposition Pr FL.

Regarding Religious Education. Mary K. Cove & Mary L. Mueller. LC 77-10873. 181p. (Orig.). 1977. pap. 8.95 (ISBN 0-89135-011-X). Religious Educ.

Regeneration. Arthur W. Pink. pap. 0.75 (ISBN 0-685-00735-9). Reiner.

Regents of Seven Spheres. Challoner. 8.75 (ISBN 0-8356-5009-X). Theos Pub Hse.

Region, Race & Reconstruction: Essays in Honor of C. Vann Woodward. J. Morgan Kousser & James M. McPherson. 1982. 25.00x (ISBN 0-19-503075-3). Oxford U Pr.

Regional Cults & Rural Traditions: An Interacting Pattern of Divinity & Humanity in Rural Bengal. R. M. Sarkar. (Illus.). xx, 351p. 1986. text ed. 50.00x (ISBN 81-210-0095-5, Pub. by Inter India Pubns N Delhi). Apt Bks.

Register Innocenz' 3rd Uber Die Reichsfrage, 1198-1209. Pope Innocent Third. Ed. by Georgine Tangl. 1923. 23.00 (ISBN 0-384-07885-0). Johnson Repr.

Register of Baptisms of the French Protestant Refugees Settled at Thorney, Cambridgeshire, 1654-1727. Ed. by Henry Peet. Bd. with Letters of Denization. Ed. by William A. Shaw. Repr. of 1911 ed; Registers of the French Church of Portarlington, Ireland. Ed. by Thomas P. Le Fanu. Repr. of 1908 ed; Registers of the French Churches of Bristol. Ed. by Charles E. Lart. Repr. of 1912 ed; Register of the French Church at Thorpe-le-Spoken. Ed. by William C. Waller. Repr. of 1912 ed. (Huguenot Society of London Publications Ser.: Vols. 17 & 20). Repr. of 1903 ed. 144.00 (ISBN 0-317-17885-7). Kraus Repr.

Register of Ministers, Exhorters & Readers & of Their Stipends. Church of Scotland Staff. LC 71-174310. (Maitland Club, Glasgow. Publications: No. 5). Repr. of 1830 ed. 15.00 (ISBN 0-404-52929-1). AMS Pr.

Register of St. Augustine's Abbey, Canterbury: Commonly Called the Black Book, 2 pts. Ed. by G. J. Turner & H. E. Salter. (British Academy, London, Record of the Social & Economic History of England & Wales Ser.: Vol. 2). Pt. 1, Reprint of 1915 Edition. pap. 45.00 (ISBN 0-8115-1242-8); Pt. 2, Reprint of 1924 Ed. pap. 36.00 (ISBN 0-8115-1243-6). Kraus Repr.

Register of the Charterhouse of London: Land Rev. Misc Book 61 of the London Public Record Office. James Hogg. (Analecta Cartusiana Ser.: No. 89). (Orig.). 1987. 25.00 (ISBN 3-7052-0146-8, Pub. by Salzburg Studies). Longwood Pub Group.

Registers of the Church Known As La Patente in Spittlefields from 1689-1785. Ed. by William Minet & William C. Waller. Bd. with Register of Baptisms in the Dutch Church at Colchester from 1645-1728. Ed. by William J. Moens. Repr. of 1905 ed; Pt. 2. Registers of the French Church. Ed. by W. J. Moens. Repr. of 1899 ed. (Hugenot Society of London Publications Ser.: Vols. 11-13). Repr. of 1898 ed. 135.00 (ISBN 0-8115-1648-2). Kraus Repr.

Registers of the French Non-Conformist Churches of Lucy Lane & Peter Street, Dublin. Ed. by Thomas P. Le Fanu. Bd. with History of the Walloon & Huguenot Church at Canterbury. F. W. Cross. Repr. of 1898 ed; Pt. 3. Registers of the French Church. Ed. by T. C. Colyer-Fergusson. Repr. of 1906 ed. (Hugenot Society of London Publication Ser.: Vols. 14-16). Repr. of 1901 ed. 135.00 (ISBN 0-8115-1649-0). Kraus Repr.

Registers of the Walloon or Strangers' Church in Canterbury, 3 pts. Ed. by Robert Hovenden. (Huguenot Society of London Publications Ser.: Vol. 5). Repr. of 1891 ed. Set. 107.00 (ISBN 0-8115-1644-X). Kraus Repr.

Registrum Cartarum Ecclesie Sancti Egidii De Edinburgh. Ed. by David Laing. LC 76-174803. (Bannatyne Club, Edinburgh. Publications: No. 105). Repr. of 1859 ed. 47.50 (ISBN 0-404-52860-0). AMS Pr.

Registrum De Dunfermelyn. Ed. by Cosmo Innes. LC 70-164810. (Bannatyne Club, Edinburgh. Publications: No. 74). Repr. of 1842 ed. 55.00 (ISBN 0-404-52793-0). AMS Pr.

Registrum Domus De Soltre. Ed. by David Laing. LC 77-171638. (Bannatyne Club, Edinburgh. Publications: No. 109). Repr. of 1861 ed. 42.50 (ISBN 0-404-52863-5). AMS Pr.

Registrum Episcopatus Brechinensis, 2 Vols. Ed. by Patrick Chalmers & John I. Chalmers. LC 72-39524. (Bannatyne Club, Edinburgh. Publications: No. 102). Repr. of 1856 ed. Set. 110.00 (ISBN 0-404-52855-4). AMS Pr.

Registrum Episcopatus Glasguensis, 2 Vols. Ed. by Cosmo Innes. LC 70-168151. (Maitland Club, Glasgow. Publications: No. 61). Repr. of 1843 ed. Set. 95.00 (ISBN 0-685-05956-1). AMS Pr.

Registrum Episcopatus Moraviensis. Moray Scotland. Ed. by Cosmo N. Innes. LC 71-172742. (Bannatyne Club, Edinburgh. Publications: No. 58). Repr. of 1837 ed. 47.50 (ISBN 0-404-52768-X). AMS Pr.

Registrum Monasterii De Passelet. Paisley Abbey. Ed. by Cosmo Innes. LC 75-174311. (Maitland Club. Glasgow. Publications: No. 17). Repr. of 1832 ed. 52.50 (ISBN 0-404-52954-2). AMS Pr.

Registrum S. Marie De Neubotle. Newbattle Abbey. Ed. by Cosmo Innes. LC 74-173074. (Bannatyne Club, Edinburgh. Publications: No. 89). Repr. of 1849 ed. 42.50 (ISBN 0-404-52819-8). AMS Pr.

Registry of Women in Religious Studies, 1981-1982. Compiled by Carol Bohn & Lorine Getz. (Bohn Ser.). 1981. 9.95 (ISBN 0-88946-277-1). E Mellen.

Regla Kimbisa del Santo Cristo del Buen Viaje. 2nd ed. Lydia Cabrera. (Coleccion del Chichereku en el Exilio Ser.). (Span.). 85p. 1986. pap. 6.95 (ISBN 0-89729-396-7). Ediciones.

Regulating Society: Beguines, Bohemians, & Other Marginals. Ephraim H. Mizruchi. LC 82-48161. xvi, 208p. 1987. pap. 10.95 (ISBN 0-226-53284-4). U of Chicago Pr.

Rehabilitation Exercises for the Cancer Patient. Ernest H. Rosenbaum et al. (Illus., Orig.). 1980. pap. 4.95 (ISBN 0-915950-37-5). Bull Pub.

Rehabilitation of Clergy Alcoholics: Ardent Spirits Subdued. Joseph H. Fichter. LC 80-28447. 203p. 1982. 26.95 (ISBN 0-89885-009-6). Human Sci Pr.

Reich & Nation: The Holy Roman Empire As Idea & Reality, 1763-1806. John G. Gagliardo. LC 79-2170. 384p. 1980. 25.00x (ISBN 0-253-16773-6). Ind U Pr.

Reichstag Fire Trial: The Second Brown Book of the Hitler Terror. World Committee For The Relief Of The Victims Of German Fascism. LC 68-9605. 1969. Repr. of 1934 ed. 32.50 (ISBN 0-86527-165-8). Fertig.

Reign of AntiChrist. R. Gerald Culleton. 1974. pap. 6.00 (ISBN 0-89555-047-4). TAN Bks Pubs.

Reign of Conscience: Individual, Church & State in Lord Acton's History of Liberty. John Nurser. Ed. by William H. McNeill & Peter Stansky. (Modern European History Ser.). 225p. 1987. lib. bdg. 40.00 (ISBN 0-8240-7826-8). Garland Pub.

Reign of Elizabeth, Fifteen Fifty-Eight to Sixteen Three. 2nd ed. J. B. Black. (Oxford History of England Ser.). 1959. 45.00x (ISBN 0-19-821701-3). Oxford U Pr.

Reign of God: An Introduction to Christian Theology from a Seventh-Day Adventist Perspective. Richard Rice. LC 85-70344. 400p. 1985. text ed. 23.95 (ISBN 0-943872-90-1). Andrews Univ Pr.

Reign of Grace. Abrh Booth. 5.95 (ISBN 0-685-88390-6). Reiner.

Reign of Jesus Thru Mary. Gabriel Denis. 5.50 (ISBN 0-910984-03-4). Montfort Pubns.

Reign of Law (Buddhist Essays) Curuppumullage Jinarajadasa. LC 78-72902. Repr. of 1923 ed. 22.50 (ISBN 0-404-17314-4). AMS Pr.

Reimagining America: A Theological Critique of the American Mythos & Biblical Hermeneutics. Charles Mabee. LC 84-27335. xvi, 156p. 1985. 13.95 (ISBN 0-86554-148-5, MUP/H139). Mercer Univ Pr.

Reimarus: Fragments. Ed. by Charles H. Talbert. Tr. by Ralph S. Fraser. (Reprints & Translations). 1985. pap. 13.95 (ISBN 0-89130-858-X, 00-07-07). Scholars Pr Ga.

Reincarnation. Swami Abhedananda. 2.95 (ISBN 0-87481-604-1). Vedanta Pr.

Reincarnation. 11th ed. Annie Besant. 1975. 5.25 (ISBN 0-8356-7019-8). Theos Pub Hse.

Reincarnation. George B. Brownell. 153p. 1981. pap. 9.00 (ISBN 0-89540-107-X, SB-107). Sun Pub.

Reincarnation. Katherine Tingley. 72p. 1981. pap. 4.50 (ISBN 0-89540-111-8, SB-111). Sun Pub.

Reincarnation. Leoline L. Wright. LC 74-18350. pap. 3.25 (ISBN 0-8356-0453-5, Quest). Theos Pub Hse.

Reincarnation: A Hope of the World. Irving S. Cooper. LC 79-11475. 1979. pap. 3.95 (ISBN 0-8356-0528-0, Quest). Theos Pub Hse.

Reincarnation: A Lost Chord in Modern Thought. Leoline L. Wright et al. Ed. by Emmett Small & Helen Todd. (Theosophical Manual). 122p. 1975. pap. 3.25 (ISBN 0-8356-0453-5). Point Loma Pub.

Reincarnation: A New Horizon in Science, Religion & Society. Sylvia Cranston & Carey Williams. 1984. 16.95 (ISBN 0-517-55496-8, Harmony). Crown.

Reincarnation: An East-West Anthology. Joseph Head & S. L. Cranston. LC 68-146. 1968. pap. 5.50 (ISBN 0-8356-0035-1, Quest). Theos Pub Hse.

Reincarnation & Christianity. Robert A. Morey. LC 80-24497. 60p. 1980. pap. 2.95 (ISBN 0-87123-493-9, 210493). Bethany Hse.

Reincarnation & Immortality. 2nd ed. Swami Paramananda. 1961. 4.50 (ISBN 0-911564-05-5). Vedanta Ctr.

Reincarnation & Immortality. 3rd ed. Rudolf Steiner. LC 77-130817. 224p. 1970. pap. 5.00 (ISBN 0-89345-221-1, Steinerbks). Garber Comm.

Reincarnation & Karma: Their Significance in Modern Culture. Rudolf Steiner. Tr. by D. S. Osmond & Charles Davy. (Ger.). 95p. 1977. pap. 6.50 (ISBN 0-919924-06-9, Pub. by Steiner Book Centre Canada). Anthroposophic.

Reincarnation & Law of Karma. William W. Atkinson. 8.00 (ISBN 0-911662-26-X). Yoga.

Reincarnation & Translation. Jim Lewis. 31p. (Orig.). 1981. pap. 3.00 (ISBN 0-942482-02-6). Unity Church Denver.

Reincarnation As a Christian Hope. Geddes MacGregor. LC 81-8013. (Library of Philosophy & Religion). 174p. 1982. 28.50x (ISBN 0-389-20220-7). B&N Imports.

Reincarnation: Cycle of Opportunity. Robert G. Chaney. LC 84-72387. (Adventures in Esoteric Learning Ser.). (Illus.). 56p. 1984. pap. 4.25 (ISBN 0-918936-13-6). Astara.

Reincarnation Explained. Chris Butler. LC 83-61000. 288p. 1984. 12.95 (ISBN 0-88187-000-5). Science Identity.

Reincarnation, Fact or Fallacy. rev. ed. Geoffrey Hodson. LC 67-4405. 1967. pap. 2.95 (ISBN 0-8356-0046-7, Quest). Theos Pub Hse.

Reincarnation Five Keys to Past Lives. J. H. Brennan. (Paths to Inner Power Ser.). 1981. pap. 3.50 (ISBN 0-85030-275-7). Weiser.

Reincarnation: Illusion or Reality. Edmond Robillard. LC 82-1638. 182p. (Orig.). 1982. pap. 5.95 (ISBN 0-8189-0432-1). Alba.

Reincarnation in Christianity. Geddes MacGregor. LC 77-20925. (Orig.). 1978. 9.75 (ISBN 0-8356-0504-3). Theos Pub Hse.

Reincarnation, Key to Immortality. Marcia Moore & Mark Douglas. LC 67-19603. 1968. 10.00 (ISBN 0-912240-02-4). Arcane Pubns.

Reincarnation Sensation. Norman L. Geisler & J. Yutaka Amano. 224p. 1986. pap. 6.95 (ISBN 0-8423-5404-2). Tyndale.

Reincarnation: The Cycle of Necessity. Manly P. Hall. 1978. 8.50 (ISBN 0-89314-519-X); pap. 4.95 (ISBN 0-89314-387-1). Philos Res.

Reincarnation: the Phoenix Fire Mystery. Joseph Head & S. L. Cranston. 1977. 10.95 (ISBN 0-517-52893-2). Crown.

Reincarnation-The Unanswered Questions. Dick Sutphen. 100p. 1983. pap. 2.95 (ISBN 0-686-47947-5). Valley Sun.

Reincarnation Unnecessary. Violet M. Shelley. 1979. pap. 5.95 (ISBN 0-87604-112-8). ARE Pr.

Reincarnation vs Resurrection. John Snyder. (Orig.). 1984. pap. 4.95 (ISBN 0-8024-0321-2). Moody.

Reincarnations. Richard Kostelanetz. 1981. pap. 5.00 (ISBN 0-686-84602-8); signed 50.00 (ISBN 0-686-84603-6). Future Pr.

Reinhold Niebuhr. Bob E. Patterson. LC 76-46783. (Makers of the Modern Theological Mind Series). 1977. 8.95 (ISBN 0-87680-508-X). Word Bks.

Reinhold Niebuhr. Nathan A. Scott, Jr. (Pamphlets on American Writers Ser: No. 31). (Orig.). 1963. pap. 1.25x (ISBN 0-8166-0305-7, MPAW31). U of Minn Pr.

Reinhold Niebuhr: A Prophetic Voice in Our Time. Ed. by Harold R. Landon. (Essay Index Reprint Ser.). Repr. of 1962 ed. 11.00 (ISBN 0-518-10150-9). Ayer Co Pubs.

Reinhold Niebuhr & the Issues of Our Time. Ed. by Richard Harries. 216p. (Orig.). 1986. pap. 9.95 (ISBN 0-8028-0232-X). Eerdmans.

Reinhold Niebuhr: His Religious, Social & Political Thought. rev. ed. Ed. by Charles W. Kegley. LC 82-22531. 448p. (Orig.). 1984. pap. 11.95 (ISBN 0-8298-0616-4). Pilgrim NY.

Reinhold Niebuhr: Prophet from America. facs. ed. D. R. Davies. (Select Bibliographies Reprint Ser). 1945. 13.00 (ISBN 0-8369-5324-X). Ayer Co Pubs.

Reinhold Niebuhr's Works: A Bibliography. D. B. Robertson. LC 83-16840. 282p. 1984. lib. bdg. 25.50 (ISBN 0-8191-3592-5); pap. text ed. 12.75 (ISBN 0-8191-3593-3). U Pr of Amer.

Reino de Dios y el Ministerio Educativo de la Iglesia. Daniel S. Schipani. (Span.). 213p. 1984. pap. 5.50 (ISBN 0-89922-232-3). Edit Caribe.

Reino Inconmovible. David Gooding. Orig. Title: Unshakeable Kingdom. (Span.). 196p. 1983. pap. 4.95 (ISBN 0-8254-1275-7). Kregel.

Reishis Chochmah. Nacha Rivkin. (Illus.). 64p. text ed. 3.50 (ISBN 0-914131-54-0, A01); wkbk. 3.00 (ISBN 0-914131-55-9). Torah Umesorah.

Reishis Chochmah, Vol. II. Nacha Rivkin. (Illus.). 100p. 4.75 (ISBN 0-914131-56-7, A03). Torah Umesorah.

Rejected Avatar. Samuel L. Lewis. (Illus.). 24p. (Orig.). 1968. pap. 1.25 saddlestitched (ISBN 0-915424-00-2, Prophecy Pressworks). Sufi Islamia-Prophecy.

Rejection Syndrome. Charles R. Solomon. 144p. 1982. pap. 5.95 (ISBN 0-8423-5417-4). Tyndale.

Rejoice. Fulton J. Sheen. LC 84-45271. (Illus.). 80p. 1984. pap. 8.95 (ISBN 0-385-19164-2, Im). Doubleday.

Rejoice: A Biblical Study of the Dance. Debbie Roberts. 98p. 1982. pap. 3.95 (ISBN 0-938612-02-6). Revival Press.

Rejoice & Be Exceeding Glad. Mary Light. pap. 1.00 (ISBN 0-910924-60-0). Macalester.

Rejoice & Sing. Reid Lancaster. 1984. pap. 2.95 (ISBN 0-8344-0126-6). Sweet.

Rejoice & Sing Praise: A Collection of Songs & Materials to Be Used with Elementary Boys & Girls. Compiled by Evelyn Andre. LC 77-1604. 1977. pap. 9.95 (ISBN 0-687-35930-9). Abingdon.

Rejoice & Take It Away: Sunday Preaching from the Scriptures, 2 vols. Gerard Sloyan. 1984. 15.00 (ISBN 0-89453-381-9). M Glazier.

Rejoice in Me: A Pocket Guide to Daily Scriptural Prayer. David Rosage. 256p. 1986. pocket-size 3.95 (ISBN 0-89283-298-3). Servant.

Rejoice in the Lord. James D. Craig. 32p. 1981. pap. 2.49 (ISBN 0-88151-018-1). Lay Leadership.

Rejoice in the Lord: A Hymn Companion to the Scriptures. The Reformed Church in America. Ed. by Erik Routley. 608p. 1985. 12.95x (ISBN 0-8028-9009-1). Eerdmans.

Rejoice with Jerusalem. Ed. by Dov P. Elkins. 1972. pap. 1.95 (ISBN 0-87677-065-0). Prayer BK.

Rejoice, You're a Sunday School Teacher. John T. Sisemore. LC 76-20053. 1977. 9.50 (ISBN 0-8054-5147-1). Broadman.

Rejoicing Heart. Joyce M. Smith. 1979. pap. 2.95 (ISBN 0-8423-5418-2). Tyndale.

Rejoicing with Creation. Tom Malone. pap. 6.95 (ISBN 0-8042-1420-4). John Knox.

Rekindling the Flame: Strategies for a Vital United Methodism. William H. Willimon & Robert L. Wilson. 128p. 1987. 9.95 (ISBN 0-687-35932-5). Abingdon.

Relacion Perfecta. Swami Muktananda. LC 81-84261. 218p. 1982. pap. 6.95 (ISBN 0-914602-84-5). SYDA Found.

Relaciones. Geronimo Zarate Salmeron. LC 66-27660. 122p. 1982. lib. bdg. 29.95x (ISBN 0-89370-728-7). Borgo Pr.

Relatedness: Essays in Metaphysics & Theology. Harold H. Oliver. LC 84-1152. xvi, 178p. 1984. 14.50 (ISBN 0-86554-141-8, MUP/H132). Mercer Univ Pr.

Relating. Michele McCarty. (Fullness of Life Ser.). 128p. (Orig.). 1979. pap. text ed. 5.50 (ISBN 0-697-01710-9); tchr's manual 8.00 (ISBN 0-697-01711-7). Wm C Brown.

Relation of Diu Krone to La Mule Sanz Frain. Lawrence L. Boll. LC 77-140018. (Catholic University Studies in German Ser.: No. 2). Repr. of 1929 ed. 18.00 (ISBN 0-404-50222-9). AMS Pr.

Relation of Proceedings Concerning the Affairs of the Kirk of Scotland. John L. Rothes. LC 79-174966. (Bannatyne Club, Edinburgh. Publications: No. 37). Repr. of 1830 ed. 28.00 (ISBN 0-404-52743-4). AMS Pr.

Relation of Religion to Civil Government in the United States. Isaac J. Cornelison. LC 75-107409. (Civil Liberties in American History Ser). 1970. Repr. of 1895 ed. lib. bdg. 45.00 (ISBN 0-306-71890-1). Da Capo.

Relation of the Bible to Learning. E. H. Runner. 1974. pap. 4.95 (ISBN 0-686-11988-6). Wedge Pub.

Relational Self: Ethics & Therapy from a Black Church Perspective. John Smith, Jr. 256p. (Orig.). 1982. pap. 11.95 (ISBN 0-687-35945-7). Abingdon.

Relations Between Arabs & Israelis Prior to the Rise of Islam. D. S. Margoliouth. (British Academy, London, Schweich Lectures on Biblical Archaeology Series, 1921). pap. 19.00 (ISBN 0-8115-1263-0). Kraus Repr.

Relations Between Northern & Southern Baptists. rev. ed. Robert A. Baker. Ed. by Edwin S. Gaustad. LC 79-52590. (Baptist Tradition Ser.). 1980. Repr. of 1954 ed. lib. bdg. 23.00x (ISBN 0-405-12457-0). Ayer Co Pubs.

Relations Between Religion & Science: Eight Lectures Preached Before the University of Oxford in Eighteen Eighty-Four on the Foundation of the Late Reverend John Bampton Ma. Frederick Temple. 264p. Repr. of 1884 ed. text ed. 41.40x (ISBN 0-576-29206-0, Pub. by Gregg Intl Pubs England). Gregg Intl.

Relations Between the Laws of Babylonia & the Laws of the Hebrew Peoples. C. H. Johns. (British Academy, London, Schweich Lectures on Biblical Archaeology Series, 1912). pap. 19.00 (ISBN 0-8115-1254-1). Kraus Repr.

Relations of Religious Training & Life Patterns to the Adult Religious Life. Luther E. Woodward. LC 71-177627. (Columbia University. Teachers College. Contributions to Education: No. 527). Repr. of 1932 ed. 22.50 (ISBN 0-404-55527-6). AMS Pr.

Relationship of Renaissance Concepts of Honour to Shakespeares Problem Plays. Alice Shalvi. Ed. by James Hogg. (Jacobean Drama Studies). 362p. (Orig.). 1972. pap. 15.00 (ISBN 3-7052-0306-1, Pub. by Salzburg Studies). Longwood Pub Group.

Relationship of the Library to Instructional Systems. James Brown et al. Ed. by John T. Corrigan. (Catholic Library Association Studies in Librarianship: No. 2). 1978. pap. 3.00 (ISBN 0-87507-006-X). Cath Lib Assn.

Relationships. Gladys Hunt. (Fisherman Bible Studyguide Ser.). 64p. 1983. saddle stitched 2.95 (ISBN 0-87788-721-7). Shaw Pubs.

Relationships Among the Gospels: An Interdisciplinary Dialogue. Albert C. Outler et al. Ed. by William O. Walker, Jr. LC 78-52845. (Monograph Series in Religion). 359p. 1978. text ed. 15.00 (ISBN 0-911536-73-6). Trinity U Pr.

Relationships: Face to Face. Carolyn Nystrom & Matthew Floding. (Young Fisherman Bible Studyguide Ser.). 64p. (Orig.). (YA) 1986. pap. 2.95 student ed. (ISBN 0-87788-722-5); tchr's ed. 4.95 (ISBN 0-87788-723-3). Shaw Pubs.

Relationships: Issues of Emotional Living in an Age of Stress for Clergy & Religious. Martin C. Helldorfer & Anna Polcino. Ed. by Sean D. Sammon. LC 83-2706. 144p. (Orig.). 1983. pap. 8.00 (ISBN 0-89571-015-3). Affirmation.

Relatives. Tracy Voigt. (Orig.). 1982. pap. write for info. T Voigt.

Relatives in Orbit. Corine Holschbach. (Illus.). 64p. 1986. 7.95 (ISBN 0-89962-514-2). Todd & Honeywell.

Relativism, Knowledge, & Faith. Gordon D. Kaufman. LC 59-11620. pap. 38.80 (2026778). Bks Demand UMI.

Relativity, Logic & Mysticism: Proceedings, Supplementary Vol. 3. Aristotelian Society for the Systematic Study of Philosophy Staff. 14.00 (ISBN 0-384-50269-5); pap. 9.00. Johnson Repr.

Relaxation & Meditation Techniques: A Complete Stress-Proofing System. Leon Chaitow. 128p. 1983. pap. cancelled (ISBN 0-7225-0737-2). Thorsons Pubs.

Relaxation Sensation: The Number One Success Factor in Life. Lorenzo. (Illus.). 128p. (Orig.). 1981. pap. 9.95 (ISBN 0-941122-00-X). Prema Bks.

Released to Reign. Charles Trombley. LC 79-90266. 1979. pap. 4.95 (ISBN 0-89221-064-8). New Leaf.

Releasement: Spirituality for Ministry. Barbara Fiand. 112p. 1987. 11.95 (ISBN 0-8245-0813-0). Crossroad NY.

Releasing the Ability of God Through Prayer. Charles Capps. 159p. 1978. pocketbook 3.50 (ISBN 0-89274-075-2). Harrison Hse.

Releasing the Power of the Holy Spirit. Brick Bradford. 32p. 1983. 1.95x (ISBN 0-934421-00-5). Presby Renewal Pubns.

Relevance of Apocalyptic. 3rd, rev. ed. H. H. Rowley. LC 64-12221. 240p. 1980. pap. text ed. 7.95 (ISBN 0-87921-061-3). Attic Pr.

Relevance of Bliss. Nona Coxhead. 192p. 1986. pap. 6.95 (ISBN 0-312-67055-9). St Martin.

Relevance of Education. Jerome S. Bruner. LC 74-139376. 192p. 1971. 5.95x (ISBN 0-393-04334-7, Norton Lib.); pap. 4.95x (ISBN 0-393-00690-5, Norton Lib). Norton.

Relevance of Natural Science to Theology. William H. Austin. LC 75-43222. (Library of Philosophy & Religion). 132p. 1976. text ed. 28.50x (ISBN 0-06-490240-4, 06321). B&N Imports.

Relevance of Preaching. Pierre Ch. Marcel. (Notable Books on Preaching). 1977. pap. 2.95 (ISBN 0-8010-6037-0). Baker Bk.

Relevance of the Bible for Today. D. Coggan. 1967. pap. 1.75x (ISBN 0-85564-005-7, Pub. by U of W Austral Pr). Intl Spec Bk.

Relevance of the Old Testament for the Christian Faith: Biblical Theology & Interpretive Methodology. S. M. Mayo. 220p. (Orig.). 1982. lib. bdg. 27.75 (ISBN 0-8191-2656-X); pap. text ed. 12.50 (ISBN 0-8191-2657-8). U Pr of Amer.

Relevancy of Torah to the Social & Ethical Issues of Our Time. Dovid Cohen. (Annual Fryer Memorial Lecture Ser.). 0.50 (ISBN 0-914131-57-5, I36). Torah Umesorah.

Relevant Record. Charles P. Conn & Charles W. Conn. LC 76-2969. (Illus.). 1976. pap. 1.99 (ISBN 0-87148-732-2). Pathway Pr.

Relics. Joan C. Cruz. LC 84-60744. (Illus.). 352p. 1984. pap. 10.95 (ISBN 0-87973-701-8, 701). Our Sunday Visitor.

Relief & Reconstruction. Roger Wilson. 1983. pap. 2.50x (ISBN 0-87574-022-7, 022). Pendle Hill.

Relief & Rescue of Jews from Nazi Oppression, 1943-1945. J. Mendelsohn. LC 81-80322. (Holocaust Ser.). 264p. 1982. lib. bdg. 61.00 (ISBN 0-8240-4888-1). Garland Pub.

Relief in Hungary & the Failure of the Joel Brand Mission. J. Mendelsohn. LC 81-80323. (Holocaust Ser.). 256p. 1982. lib. bdg. 61.00 (ISBN 0-8240-4889-X). Garland Pub.

Religioese Existenz und Literarische Produktion. Albrecht Willert. (Ger.). 316p. 1982. 43.70 (ISBN 3-8204-5994-4). P Lang Pubs.

Religion. Gilda Berger. (Reference First Bk.). 96p. 1983. PLB 9.40 (ISBN 0-531-04538-2). Watts.

Religion. Leszek Kolakowski. LC 81-85135. 1982. 22.50x (ISBN 0-19-520372-0). Oxford U Pr.

Religion. Desmond Painter & John Shepard. Ed. by Malcolm Yapp & Margaret Killinger. (World History Ser.). (Illus.). 32p. 1980. lib. bdg. 6.95 (ISBN 0-89908-145-2); pap. text ed. 2.45 (ISBN 0-89908-120-7). Greenhaven.

Religion, 3 vols. (British Parliamentary Papers Ser.). 1971. Set. 284.00x (ISBN 0-7165-1498-2, Pub. by Irish Academic Pr Ireland). Biblio Dist.

Religion, Vol. 1 (incl. 1978-1980 Supplements) Ed. by Eleanor C. Goldstein. (Social Issues Resources Ser.). 1981. 70.00 (ISBN 0-89777-021-8). Soc Issues.

Religion, Vol. 2 (incl. 1981-1985 Supplements) Ed. by Eleanor C. Goldstein. 1986. 70.00 (ISBN 0-89777-053-6). Soc Issues.

Religion: A Dialogue, & Other Essays. 3rd ed. Arthur Schopenhauer. Tr. by T. Bailey Saunders. LC 72-488. (Essay Index Reprint Ser.). Repr. of 1891 ed. 13.00 (ISBN 0-8369-2820-2). Ayer Co Pubs.

Religion: A Dialogue, & Other Essays. Arthur Schopenhauer. Tr. by T. Bailey Saunders. LC 72-11305. 140p. 1973. Repr. of 1899 ed. lib. bdg. 25.00x (ISBN 0-8371-6652-7, SCRE). Greenwood.

Religion: A Preface. John F. Wilson. (Illus.). 240p. 1982. pap. text ed. write for info. (ISBN 0-13-773192-2). P-H.

Religion: A Secular Theory. Andrew M. Greeley. 144p. 1982. text ed. 19.95 (ISBN 0-02-912870-6); pap. text ed. 8.95x (ISBN 0-02-912880-3). Free Pr.

Religion: A Sociological View. Elizabeth K. Nottingham. LC 81-40769. 348p. 1981. pap. text ed. 13.50 (ISBN 0-8191-1813-3). U Pr of Amer.

Religion Across Cultures. Eugene A. Nida. LC 68-11733. (Applied Cultural Anthropology Ser). 1979. pap. text ed. 3.95x (ISBN 0-87808-738-9). William Carey Lib.

Religion, Altered States of Consciousness, & Social Change. Ed. by Erika Bourguignon. LC 72-8448. (Illus.). 399p. 1973. 12.50 (ISBN 0-8142-0167-9). Ohio St U Pr.

Religion: An Anthropological View. Anthony F. Wallace. 1966. text ed. 16.00 (ISBN 0-394-30543-4, RanC). Random.

Religion: An Introduction. T. William Hall et al. LC 85-42777. 288p. (Orig.). 1986. pap. 14.45 (ISBN 0-06-063573-8, HarpR). Har-Row.

Religion & Aging: An Annotated Bibliography. Vincent J. Fecher. LC 82-81019. 119p. 1982. 16.00 (ISBN 0-911536-96-5); pap. 9.00 (ISBN 0-911536-97-3). Trinity U Pr.

Religion & Aging: The Behavioral & Social Sciences Look at Religion & Aging. Ed. by Richard H. Davis. 84p. 1967. pap. 3.00 (ISBN 0-88474-009-9). U of S Cal Pr.

Religion & Alienation: A Theological Reading of Sociology. Ed. by Gregory Baum. LC 75-28652. 304p. 1976. pap. 9.95 (ISBN 0-8091-1917-X). Paulist Pr.

Religion & America: Spirituality in a Secular Age. Ed. by Mary Douglas & Steven M. Tipton. LC 82-72500. 256p. 1983. 25.00x (ISBN 0-8070-1106-1); pap. 13.95x (ISBN 0-8070-1107-X, BP648). Beacon Pr.

Religion & Art. Paul Weiss. (Aquinas Lecture). 1963. 7.95 (ISBN 0-87462-128-3). Marquette.

Religion & Art of William Hale White (Mark Rutherford) Wilfred Stone. 1979. Repr. of 1954 ed. lib. bdg. 30.00 (ISBN 0-8492-8233-0). R West.

Religion & Art of William Hale White. Wilfred H. Stone. LC 79-176447. Repr. of 1954 ed. 28.00 (ISBN 0-404-51822-2). AMS Pr.

Religion & Atheism. William A. Luijpen & H. J. Koren. 200p. 1982. pap. 10.95 (ISBN 0-391-02801-4). Humanities.

Religion & Ceremonies of the Lenape. Mark R. Harrington. LC 76-43731. (MAI Indian Notes & Monographs. Miscellaneous). Repr. of 1921 ed. 31.50 (ISBN 0-404-15572-3). AMS Pr.

Religion & Churches in Eastern Europe. Ed. by Virgil Elizondo & Norbert Greinacher. (Concilium Ser.: Vol. 154). 128p. (Orig.). 1982. pap. 6.95 (ISBN 0-8164-2385-7, HarpR). Har-Row.

Religion & Civilization. A. H. Nadvi. 4.00 (ISBN 0-686-18566-8). Kazi Pubns.

Religion & Communism. Julius F. Hecker. LC 73-842. (Russian Studies: Perspectives on the Revolution Ser.). 302p. 1987. Repr. of 1934 ed. 26.75 (ISBN 0-88355-037-7). Hyperion Conn.

Religion & Communist Society: Selected Papers from the Second World Congress for Soviet & East European Studies. Ed. by Dennis J. Dunn. 165p. (Orig.). 1983. pap. 14.00 (ISBN 0-933884-29-X). Berkeley Slavic.

Religion & Conscience in Ancient Egypt. William F. Petrie. LC 72-83176. Repr. of 1898 ed. 24.50 (ISBN 0-405-08854-X). Ayer Co Pubs.

Religion & Constitutional Government in the United States: A Historical Overview with Sources. John E. Semonche. (Constitutional Bookshelf Ser.). 250p. (Orig.). 1985. pap. 14.95 (ISBN 0-930095-09-X). Signal Bks.

Religion & Cult. John Sheehan. 240p. pap. 6.95 (ISBN 0-87462-446-0). Marquette.

Religion & Culture. Christopher H. Dawson. LC 77-27183. (Gifford Lectures Ser.: 1947). 232p. Repr. of 1948 ed. 27.50 (ISBN 0-404-60498-6). AMS Pr.

Religion & Culture: An Introduction to Anthropology of Religion. Anne M. Malefijt. 1968. text ed. write for info. (ISBN 0-02-374920-2). Macmillan.

Religion & Culture: Essays in Honor of Bernard Lonergan, S.J. Ed. by Timothy P. Fallon & Philip B. Riley. 512p. 1987. 44.50x (ISBN 0-88706-289-X). State U NY Pr.

Religion & Culture: Essays in Honor of Paul Tillich. facsimile ed. Walter Leibrecht. LC 78-167376. (Essay Index Reprint Ser). Repr. of 1959 ed. 24.50 (ISBN 0-8369-2558-0). Ayer Co Pubs.

Religion & Culture in Canada. Ed. by Peter Slater. 568p. pap. text ed. 9.75x (ISBN 0-919812-06-6, Pub. by Wilfrid Laurier Canada). Humanities.

Religion & Dance. Ed. by Dennis J. Fallon & Mary J. Wolbers. LC 83-189712. (Focus on Dance Ser.: No. 10). pap. 24.00 (2029558). Bks Demand UMI.

Religion & Doubt: Toward a Faith of Your Own. Richard Creel. 1977. write for info. (ISBN 0-13-771931-0). P-H.

Religion & Education Under the Constitution. James Milton O'Neill. LC 72-171389. (Civil Liberties in American History Ser). 338p. 1972. Repr. of 1949 ed. lib. bdg. 39.50 (ISBN 0-306-70228-2). Da Capo.

Religion & Empire. Louis B. Wright. 1965. lib. bdg. 18.50x (ISBN 0-374-98816-1, Octagon). Hippocrene Bks.

Religion & Empire: The Dynamics of Aztec & Inca Expansionism. Geoffrey W. Conrad & Arthur A. Demarest. LC 83-14414. (New Studies in Archaeology). 256p. 1984. 52.50 (ISBN 0-521-24357-2); pap. 17.95 (ISBN 0-521-31896-3). Cambridge U Pr.

Religion & Empiricism. John E. Smith. (Aquinas Lecture Ser.). 1967. 7.95 (ISBN 0-87462-132-1). Marquette.

Religion & Environmental Crisis. Ed. by Eugene C. Hargrove. LC 86-7019. 248p. 1986. 25.00x (ISBN 0-8203-0845-5); pap. 12.00x (ISBN 0-8203-0846-3). U of GA Pr.

Religion & Ethnicity. Ed. by Harold Coward & Leslie Kawamura. 181p. 1978. pap. text ed. 9.95 (ISBN 0-88920-064-5, Pub. by Wilfrid Laurier Canada). Humanities.

Religion & Fertility: Arab Christian-Muslim Differentials. Joseph Chamie. LC 80-19787. (ASA Rose Monograph). (Illus.). 176p. 1981. 29.95 (ISBN 0-521-23677-0); pap. 9.95 (ISBN 0-521-28147-4). Cambridge U Pr.

Religion & Freedom in the Modern World. Herbert J. Muller. LC 63-20911. 1963. pap. 1.50x (ISBN 0-226-54815-5, P193, Phoen). U of Chicago Pr.

Religion & Freedom of Thought. facs. ed. Perry Miller et al. LC 78-128296. (Essay Index Reprint Ser). 1954. 10.00 (ISBN 0-8369-2199-2). Ayer Co Pubs.

Religion & Human Experience. Andrew Panzarella. LC 73-87024. 1974. pap. 5.20x (ISBN 0-88489-058-9); tchr's. guide 3.00x (ISBN 0-88489-080-5). St Marys.

Religion & Human Experience: Opposing Viewpoints. Ed. by David L. Bender & Bruno Leone. LC 85-7660. 1981. 11.95 (ISBN 0-89908-333-1); pap. text ed. 6.95 (ISBN 0-89908-308-0). Greenhaven.

Religion & Human Purpose. Ed. by William Horosz & Tad Clements. 1987. lib. bdg. 64.50 (ISBN 90-247-3000-7, Pub. by Martinus Nijhoff Netherlands). Kluwer Academic.

Religion & Humanism: Papers Read at the Eighteenth Summer Meeting & the Nineteenth Winter Meeting of the Ecclesiastical History Society. Ed. by Keith Robbins. (Studies in Church History: Vol. 17). (Illus.). 378p. 1981. 45.00x (ISBN 0-631-18050-8). Basil Blackwell.

Religion & Imagination. John Coulson. 1981. 39.95x (ISBN 0-19-826656-1). Oxford U Pr.

Religion & Industrial Society: The Protestant Social Congress in Wilhelmine Germany. Harry Liebersohn. LC 86-71421. (Transaction Ser.: Vol. 76, Pt. 6). 1986. 15.00 (ISBN 0-87169-766-1). Am Philos.

Religion & Judgment: An Essay on the Method & Meaning of Religion. Willard E. Arnett. LC 66-11680. (Century Philosophy Ser.). 1966. 39.50x (ISBN 0-89197-377-X). Irvington.

Religion & Law in American History. John E. Semonche. LC 85-201489. (Church, State, & the First Amendment, a North Carolina Dialogue: No. 2). 125p. Date not set. price not set. U of NC Pr.

Religion & Learning at Yale: Church of Christ in the College & University, 1757-1957. Ralph H. Gabriel. 1958. 39.50x (ISBN 0-685-69820-3). Elliots Bks.

Religion & Legitimation of Power in Sri Lanka. Ed. by Bardwell L. Smith. LC 77-7449. 1978. pap. 7.95 (ISBN 0-89012-008-0). Anima Pubns.

Religion & Legitimation of Power in Thailand, Laos & Burma. Ed. by Bardwell L. Smith. LC 77-7444. 1978. pap. 7.95 (ISBN 0-89012-009-9). Anima Pubns.

Religion & Life: The Foundations of Personal Religion. facs. ed. W. R. Inge et al. LC 68-22940. (Essay Index Reprint Ser). 1923. 13.00 (ISBN 0-8369-0819-8). Ayer Co Pubs.

Religion & Literature. Dame H. Gardner. 1983. pap. text ed. 9.95x (ISBN 0-19-812824-X). Oxford U Pr.

Religion & Literature: The Convergence of Approaches. Ed. by John R. Mulder. (AAR Thematic Studies). pap. 8.95_o.s. (ISBN 0-89130-676-5, 01-24-72). Scholars Pr GA.

Religion & Man: Indian & Far Eastern Religious Traditions. Robert D. Baird & Alfred Bloom. (Religion & Man: An Introduction, Pts. 2 & 3). 1972. pap. text ed. 14.95 scp (ISBN 0-06-040448-5, HarpC). Har-Row.

Religion & Medicine: A Medical Subject Analysis & Research Index with Bibliography. Patricia S. Hurley. LC 83-71656. 148p. 1985. 34.50 (ISBN 0-88164-032-8); pap. 26.50 (ISBN 0-88164-033-6). ABBE Pubs Assn.

Religion & Medicine of the Ga People. Margaret J. Field. LC 76-44718. 1977. Repr. of 1937 ed. 37.50 (ISBN 0-404-15923-0). AMS Pr.

Religion & Mental Illness. Carol Murphy. 1983. pap. 2.50x (ISBN 0-87574-082-0, 082). Pendle Hill.

Religion & Modern Life. Harvard University, Phillips Brooks House Association. LC 75-39104. (Essay Index Reprint Ser.). Repr. of 1927 ed. 21.00 (ISBN 0-8369-2713-3). Ayer Co Pubs.

Religion & Modernization in Southeast Asia. Fred Von Der Mehden. 232p. 1986. text ed. 29.95x (ISBN 0-8156-2360-7); pap. text ed. 14.95x (ISBN 0-8156-2361-5). Syracuse U Pr.

Religion & Morality in American Schooling. Ed. by Thomas C. Hunt & Marilyn M. Maxson. LC 81-40154. 297p. (Orig.). 1981. lib. bdg. 25.75 (ISBN 0-8191-1584-3); pap. text ed. 12.50 (ISBN 0-8191-1585-1). U Pr of Amer.

Religion & Morality: Their Nature & Mutual Relations. James J. Fox. 334p. 1983. Repr. of 1899 ed. 20.00x (ISBN 0-939738-09-0). Zubal Inc.

Religion & Myth. James MacDonald. LC 74-82059. Repr. of 1893 ed. 22.50x (ISBN 0-8371-1550-7, MAR&, Pub. by Negro U Pr). Greenwood.

Religion & National Identity. Ed. by Stuart Mews. (Studies in Church History: Vol. 18). 500p. 1982. 45.00x (ISBN 0-631-18060-5). Basil Blackwell.

Religion & Nationalism in Southeast Asia: Burma, Indonesia, & the Philippines. Fred R. Von der Mehden. (Illus.). 272p. 1963. pap. 7.95 (ISBN 0-299-02944-1). U of Wis Pr.

Religion & Nationalism in Soviet & East European Politics. Ed. by Pedro Ramet. (Policy Studies). v, 282p. 1985. text ed. 35.00 (ISBN 0-8223-0608-5). Duke.

Religion & Nothingness. Keiji Nishitani. Tr. by Jan Van Bragt from Japanese. LC 81-4084. 366p. 1982. 35.95x (ISBN 0-520-04329-4); pap. 10.95x (ISBN 0-520-04946-2, CAL 634). U of Cal Pr.

Religion & Our Divided Denominations. facs. ed. Ed. by Willard L. Sperry. LC 74-128315. (Essay Index Reprint Ser). 1945. 14.00 (ISBN 0-8369-2201-8). Ayer Co Pubs.

Religion & Pain: The Spiritual Dimensions of Health Care. Joseph H. Fichter. 128p. 1981. 9.95 (ISBN 0-8245-0102-0). Crossroad NY.

Religion & Personality in the Spiral of Life. David Belgum. LC 79-66478. 1979. pap. text ed. 14.25 (ISBN 0-8191-0832-4). U Pr of Amer.

Religion & Philosophy in Germany. Heinrich Heine. Tr. by John Snodgrass from Ger. 210p. (Orig.). 1986. 29.50x (ISBN 0-88706-282-2); pap. 9.95 (ISBN 0-88706-283-0). State U NY Pr.

Religion & Philosophy of the Veda & Upanishads, 2 vols. A. B. Keith. 1976. Repr. Set. 42.00 (ISBN 0-89684-304-1). Orient Bk Dist.

Religion & Philosophy of the Veda & Upanishads, 2 vols. Arthur B. Keith. LC 71-109969. Repr. of 1925 ed. lib. bdg. 34.00x (ISBN 0-8371-4475-2, KEVU). Greenwood.

Religion & Political Conflict in Latin America. Ed. by Daniel H. Levine. LC 85-24525. xiii, 266p. 1986. 24.95x (ISBN 0-8078-1689-2); pap. 9.95x (ISBN 0-8078-4150-1). U of NC Pr.

Religion & Political Culture in Kano. John N. Paden. LC 74-153548. 1973. 46.50x (ISBN 0-520-02020-0). U of Cal Pr.

Religion & Political Modernization. Ed. by Donald E. Smith. LC 73-86917. pap. 87.50 (ISBN 0-317-29714-7, 2022041). Bks Demand UMI.

Religion & Political Society. Jurgen Moltmann et al. LC 73-18424. (Symposium Ser.: Vol. 1). xi, 209p. 1976. Repr. of 1974 ed. 19.95x (ISBN 0-88946-953-9). E Mellen.

Religion & Politics. Ed. by Myron J. Aronoff. (Political Anthropology Ser.: Vol. III). 145p. 1983. 24.95 (ISBN 0-87855-459-9); pap. 12.95 (ISBN 0-87855-977-9). Transaction Bks.

Religion & Politics. F. W. Sollmann. 1983. pap. 2.50x (ISBN 0-87574-014-6, 014). Pendle Hill.

Religion & Politics: Bishop Valerian Trifa & His Times. Gerald J. Bobango. (East European Monograph: No. 92). 299p. 1981. 25.00x (ISBN 0-914710-86-9). East Eur Quarterly.

Religion & Politics in America. Robert Booth Fowler. LC 84-20237. (Atla Monograph: No. 21). 365p. 1984. 25.00 (ISBN 0-8108-1752-7). Scarecrow.

Religion & Politics in Chile: An Analysis of Religious Models. Orlando Mella. (Illus.). 202p. (Orig.). 1986. pap. text ed. 22.00x. Coronet Bks.

Religion & Politics in Contemporary Iran. Shahrough Akhavi. LC 79-22084. 1980. 44.50 (ISBN 0-87395-408-4); pap. 16.95 (ISBN 0-87395-456-4). State U NY Pr.

Religion & Politics in Haiti. Harold Courlander & Remy Bastien. LC 66-26633. (Illus.). 1970. 3.95 (ISBN 0-911976-00-0). ICR.

Religion & Politics in Iran: Shi'ism from Quiestism to Revolution. Nikki R. Keddie. LC 82-17351. 288p. 1983. text ed. 28.50x (ISBN 0-300-02874-1). Yale U Pr.

Religion & Politics in Iran: Shi'ism from Quietism to Revolution. Ed. by Nikki R. Keddie. LC 82-17351. 288p. 1984. pap. 9.95x (ISBN 0-300-03245-5, Y-504). Yale U Pr.

Religion & Politics in Israel. Charles S. Liebman & Eliezer Don-Yehiya. LC 83-48172. (Jewish Political & Social Studies Ser.). 160p. 1984. 17.50x (ISBN 0-253-34497-2). Ind U pr.

Religion & Politics in Israel: The Interplay of Judaism & Zionism. Daniel J. Elazar & Janet Aviad. 32p. 1981. pap. 2.50 (ISBN 0-87495-033-3). Am Jewish Comm.

Religion & Politics in Mid-Eighteenth Century Anglesey. G. Nesta Evans. 251p. 1953. text ed. 17.50x (ISBN 0-7083-0071-5, Pub. by U of Wales). Humanities.

Religion & Politics in Muslim Society: Order & Conflict in Pakistan. Abkar S. Ahmed. LC 82-14774. (Illus.). 225p. 1983. 44.50 (ISBN 0-521-24635-0). Cambridge U Pr.

Religion & Politics in the Age of the Counterreformation: Emperor Ferdinand II, William Lamormaini, S.J., & the Formation of Imperial Policy. Robert S. J. Bireley. LC 80-27334. xiii, 311p. 1981. 30.00x (ISBN 0-8078-1470-9). U of NC Pr.

Religion & Politics in the Middle East. Ed. by Michael Curtis. LC 81-52445. (Westview Special Studies on the Middle East). 406p. 1982. pap. 14.95x (ISBN 0-86531-388-1). Westview.

Religion & Politics in the Modern World. Ed. by Peter H. Merkl. Ninian Smart. 296p. 1983. 37.50 (ISBN 0-8147-5389-2); pap. 12.50 (ISBN 0-8147-5393-0). NYU Pr.

Religion & Politics in the Punjab in the 1920's. Prem R. Uprety. 1981. 20.00x (ISBN 0-8364-0757-1, Pub. by Sterling). South Asia Bks.

Religion & Politics in the South: Mass & Elite Perspectives. Ed. by Tod A. Baker & Robert P. Steed. LC 83-21155. 208p. 1983. 29.95 (ISBN 0-03-069558-9, C0940). Praeger.

Religion & Politics in the United States. Kenneth D. Wald. LC 86-60659. 304p. 1986. 29.95 (ISBN 0-312-67058-3); pap. 10.00 (ISBN 0-312-67056-7). St Martin.

Religion & Politics in Tibet. Bina R. Burman. 1979. text ed. 17.50x (ISBN 0-7069-0801-5, Pub. by Vikas India). Advent NY.

Religion & Politics: The Intentions of the Authors of the First Amendment. Michael J. Malbin. 40p. 1978. pap. 3.25 (ISBN 0-8447-3302-4). Am Enterprise.

Religion & Power: The Case of Methodism in Norway. Arne Hassing. (Jesse Lee Prize Ser.). (Illus.). 300p. 1980. 15.00 (ISBN 0-915466-03-1). United Meth Archives.

Religion & Psychology: A Medical Subject Analysis & Research Index with Bibliography. Nancy L. Alpert. LC 83-71657. 150p. 1985. 34.50 (ISBN 0-88164-034-4); pap. 26.50 (ISBN 0-88164-035-2). ABBE Pubs Assn.

Religion & Public Doctrine in Modern England: Assaults, Vol. 2. Maurice Cowling. (Cambridge Studies in the History & Theory of Politics). 403p. 1985. 49.50 (ISBN 0-521-25959-2). Cambridge U Pr.

Religion & Public Doctrine in Modern England. Maurice Cowling. (Cambridge Studies in the History & Theory of Politics). 498p. 1981. 59.50 (ISBN 0-521-23289-9). Cambridge U Pr.

Religion & Rational Choice. Shivesh C. Thakur. (Library of Philosophy & Religion). 132p. 1981. 29.50x (ISBN 0-389-20047-6). B&N Imports.

Religion & Rational Outlook. S. N. Dasgupta. 1974. Repr. 9.95 (ISBN 0-8426-0661-0). Orient Bk Dist.

Religion & Reality. James H. Tuckwell. LC 77-118552. 1971. Repr. of 1915 ed. 25.00x (ISBN 0-8046-1177-7, Pub. by Kennikat). Assoc Faculty Pr.

Religion & Rebellion in Iran: The Iranian Tobacco Protest of 1891-1892. Nikki R. Keddie. 163p. 1966. 27.50x (ISBN 0-7146-1971-X, F Cass Co). Biblio Dist.

Religion & Religiosity in America. Ed. by Jeffrey K. Hadden & Theodore E. Long. LC 82-23605. (Studies in Honor of Joseph H. Fichter). 192p. 1983. 15.95 (ISBN 0-8245-0555-7). Crossroad NY.

Religion & Religious Education. Ed. by Christian W. Troll. (Islam in India: Studies & Commentaries: Vol. 2). xxi, 315p. 1985. text ed. 40.00x (ISBN 0-7069-2751-6, Pub. by Vikas India). Advent NY.

Religion & Republic: The American Circumstance. Martin E. Marty. LC 86-47755. 320p. 1987. 25.00 (ISBN 0-8070-1206-8). Beacon Pr.

Religion & Respectability: Sunday Schools & English Working Class Culture, 1780-1850. Thomas W. Laqueur. LC 74-29728. 1976. 38.50x (ISBN 0-300-01859-2). Yale U Pr.

Religion & Revolution in Peru, 1824-1976. Jeffrey L. Klaiber. LC 76-51616. 1977. text ed. 22.95x (ISBN 0-268-01599-6). U of Notre Dame Pr.

Religion & Ritual in Chinese Society. Ed. by Arthur P. Wolf. LC 73-89863. (Studies in Chinese Society). xiv, 378p. 1974. 27.50x (ISBN 0-8047-0858-4). Stanford U Pr.

Religion & Ritual in Korean Society. Ed. by Laurel Kendall & Griffin Dix. LC 86-82390. (Korea Research Monograph Ser.: No. 12). xii, 240p. 1987. pap. 15.00x. IEAS.

Religion & Ritual in Society: Lamaist Buddhism in Late 19th-Century Mongolia. Aleksei M. Pozdneyev. Ed. by John R. Krueger. Tr. by Alo Raun & Linda Raun. (Occasional Papers Ser.: No. 10). Orig. Title: Ocherki Byta Buddiiskikh Monastyrei. pap. 15.00x (ISBN 0-910980-50-0). Mongolia.

Religion & Rural Life: A Mission Statement for the Religion & Rural Life Council of Rural America. Patrick J. Ronan. 1982. 1.90 (ISBN 0-318-01734-2). Rural America.

Religion & Science. Joseph Le Conte. LC 75-3239. Repr. of 1874 ed. 21.50 (ISBN 0-404-59231-7). AMS Pr.

Religion & Science. Bertrand Russell. 1961. pap. 8.95 (ISBN 0-19-500228-8). Oxford U Pr.

Religion & Science. F. V. Verbitsky. 1959. pap. 1.00 (ISBN 0-317-30432-1). Holy Trinity.

Religion & Science: Considered in Their Historical Relations. Charles Singer. 78p. 1980. Repr. lib. bdg. 15.00 (ISBN 0-89987-756-7). Darby Bks.

Religion & Scientific Method. G. Schlesinger. 1977. lib. bdg. 29.00 (ISBN 90-277-0815-0, Pub. by Reidel Holland); pap. 10.50 (ISBN 90-277-0816-9, Pub. by Reidel Holland). Kluwer Academic.

Religion & Self-Acceptance: A Study of the Relationship Between Belief in God & the Desire to Know. John F. Haught. LC 80-5872. 195p. 1980. lib. bdg. 24.75 (ISBN 0-8191-1296-8); pap. text ed. 10.50 (ISBN 0-8191-1297-6). U Pr of Amer.

Religion & Sex. Chapman Cohen. LC 72-9631. Repr. of 1919 ed. 40.00 (ISBN 0-404-57430-0). AMS Pr.

Religion & Sexism. Rosemary R. Ruether. 1974. pap. 10.95 (ISBN 0-671-21693-7, Touchstone Bks). S&S.

Religion & Sexuality: Judaic-Christian Viewpoints in the U. S. A. John M. Holland et al. LC 81-66867. (Association of Sexologists Monographs: No. 1). 80p. 1981. pap. 5.95 (ISBN 0-939902-00-1). Assn Sexologists.

Religion & Sexuality: Three American Communal Experiments of the Nineteenth Century. Lawrence Foster. 1981. 24.95x (ISBN 0-19-502794-9). Oxford U Pr.

Religion & Social Conflicts. Otto Maduro. Tr. by Robert R. Barr from Span. LC 82-3439. Orig. Title: Religion y Lucha de Clase. 192p. (Orig.). 1982. pap. 8.95 (ISBN 0-88344-428-3). Orbis Bks.

Religion & Social Conflicts in the U. S. A. D. Furman. 254p. 1985. 7.95 (ISBN 0-8285-2975-2, Pub. by Progress Pubs USSR). Imported Pubns.

Religion & Social Organization in Central Polynesia. Robert W. Williamson. Ed. by Ralph Piddington. LC 75-35218. Repr. of 1937 ed. 38.00 (ISBN 0-404-14241-9). AMS Pr.

Religion & Social Responsibility. T. B. Irving. pap. 1.00 (ISBN 0-686-18445-9). Kazi Pubns.

Religion & Societies: Asia & the Middle East. Ed. by Carlo Caldarola. (Religion & Society: No. 22). 688p. 1982. text ed. 73.75 (ISBN 90-279-3259-X); Pub. 1984. pap. 29.50 (ISBN 3-11-010021-5). Mouton.

Religion & Society in Central Africa: The BaKongo of Lower Zaire. Wyatt MacGaffey. LC 85-31805. (Illus.). xii, 296p. 1986. lib. bdg. 45.00x (ISBN 0-226-50029-2); pap. text ed. 16.95 (ISBN 0-226-50030-6). U of Chicago Pr.

Religion & Society in Modern Japan. Edward Norbeck. (Rice University Studies: Vol. 56, No. 1). 232p. 1970. pap. 10.00x (ISBN 0-89263-203-8). Rice Univ.

Religion & Society in North America: An Annotated Bibliography. Ed. by Robert de V. Brunkow. LC 82-24304. (Clio Bibliography Ser.: No. 12). 515p. 1983. lib. bdg. 68.25 (ISBN 0-87436-042-0). ABC-Clio.

Religion & Society in Transition: The Church & Social Change in England, 1560-1850. Ernest E. Best. LC 82-21699. (Texts & Studies in Religion: Vol. 15). 353p. 1983. 59.95x (ISBN 0-88946-804-4). E Mellen.

Religion & Society of North-East India. Sujata Miri. 128p. 1980. text ed. 13.95x (ISBN 0-7069-1136-9, Pub. by Vikas India). Advent NY.

Religion & State in Iran, 1785-1906: The Role of the 'Ulama in the Qajar Period. Hamid Algar. LC 72-79959. (Near Eastern Center, UCLA; Ca. Library Reprint Ser.: No. 106). 1980. 34.50x (ISBN 0-520-04100-3). U of Cal Pr.

Religion & State in the Kingdom of Saudi Arabia. Ayman Al-Yassini. (WVSS on the Middle East Ser.). 190p. 1985. 30.00x (ISBN 0-8133-0058-4). Westview.

Religion & Statecraft among the Romans. Alan Wardman. LC 82-47928. pap. 55.80 (2026708). Bks Demand UMI.

Religion & Superstition in the Plays of Ben Johnson & Thomas Middleton. B. Johansson. (Essays & Studies on English Language & Literature: Vol. 7). pap. 28.00 (ISBN 0-8115-0205-8). Kraus Repr.

Religion & the American Revolution. Jerald Brauer. LC 76-9718. pap. 22.30 (2026888). Bks Demand UMI.

Religion & the Challenge of Philosophy. J. E. Barnhart. (Quality Paperback Ser.: No. 291). 400p. (Orig.). 1975. pap. 5.95 (ISBN 0-8226-0291-1). Littlefield.

Religion & the Constitution. Paul G. Kauper. LC 64-7898. (Edward Douglass White Lectures). 1964. pap. 6.95x (ISBN 0-8071-0114-1). La State U Pr.

Religion & the Constitution. Paul G. Kauper. LC 64-7898. pap. 36.80 (ISBN 0-317-29869-0, 2051881). Bks Demand UMI.

Religion & the Decline of Magic. Keith Thomas. 716p. 1975. pap. text ed. write for info. (ISBN 0-02-420200-2, Pub. by Scribner). Macmillan.

Religion & the Decline of Magic. Keith Thomas. 736p. 1986. pap. 17.95 (ISBN 0-684-14542-1). Scribner.

Religion & the Law. 64p. 1975. pap. 1.00 (ISBN 0-686-47944-0). Amer Bar Assn.

Religion & the Law: Religious Liberty in Modern English Law. St. John A. Robillard. LC 83-197990. 224p. 1984. pap. 42.50 (ISBN 0-7190-0956-1, Pub. by Manchester Univ Pr). Longwood Pub Group.

Religion & the Modern Mind. Walter T. Stace. LC 80-24093. 285p. 1980. Repr. of 1952 ed. lib. bdg. 24.75x (ISBN 0-313-22662-8, STRM). Greenwood.

Religion & the Modern State. Christopher Dawson. 1977. Repr. lib. bdg. 20.00 (ISBN 0-8482-0547-2). Norwood Edns.

Religion & the Modern World. Pennsylvania University Bicentennial Conference. Ed. by Jacques Maritain & Joseph Hromadka. LC 68-26204. Repr. of 1941 ed. 22.50x (ISBN 0-8046-0360-X, Pub. by Kennikat). Assoc Faculty Pr.

Religion & the Northern Ireland Problem. John Hickey. LC 83-26612. 162p. 1984. 23.50x (ISBN 0-389-20448-X, 08012). B&N Imports.

Religion & the One: Philosophies East & West. Frederick Copleston. LC 81-5372. (Gifford Lectures, 1980 Ser.). 320p. 1981. 24.50x (ISBN 0-8245-0092-X). Crossroad NY.

Religion & the People of Western Europe, 1789-1970. Hugh McLeod. (Oxford Paperbacks University Ser.). 1981. 17.95x (ISBN 0-19-215832-5); pap. 8.95x (ISBN 0-19-289101-4). Oxford U Pr.

Religion & the People, 800-1700. Ed. by James Obelkevich. LC 78-7847. v, 336p. 1979. 30.00x (ISBN 0-8078-1332-X). U of NC Pr.

Religion & the Presidential Election. Paul Lopatto. LC 84-26281. (American Political Parties & Elections Ser.). 192p. 1985. 34.95 (ISBN 0-03-001474-3, C0138). Praeger.

Religion & the Public Order: An Annual Review of Church & State & of Religion, Law, & Society. Ed. by Donald A. Giannella. LC 64-17164. pap. 72.00 (ISBN 0-317-20699-0, 2024114). Bks Demand UMI.

Religion & the Public Schools. Incl. The Legal Issue. Paul A. Freund. (Burton Lectures Ser: 1965); The Educational Issue. Robert Ulich. (Inglis Lectures Ser: 1965). LC 65-26011. vi, 56p. 1965. 2.00x (ISBN 0-674-75600-2). Harvard U Pr.

Religion & the Rebel. Colin Wilson. LC 74-9134. 338p. 1974. Repr. of 1957 ed. lib. bdg. 27.50x (ISBN 0-8371-7596-8, WIRA). Greenwood.

Religion & the Rebel. Rev. ed. Colin Wilson. 352p. 1984. pap. 9.95 (ISBN 0-88162-050-5). Salem Hse Pubs.

Religion & the Rise of Capitalism. Richard H. Tawney. 12.75 (ISBN 0-8446-1446-7). Peter Smith.

Religion & the Rise of Western Culture. Christopher H. Dawson. LC 77-27181. (Gifford Lectures: 1948-49). Repr. of 1950 ed. 26.50 (ISBN 0-404-60499-4). AMS Pr.

Religion & the Sciences of Life: With Other Essays on Allied Topics. William McDougall. LC 70-39108. (Essay Index Reprint Ser.). Repr. of 1934 ed. 20.00 (ISBN 0-8369-2700-1). Ayer Co Pubs.

Religion & the Scientific Future. Langdon Gilkey. LC 81-18934. (Reprints of Scholarly Excellence (ROSE)). xii, 193p. Repr. of 1970 ed. text ed. 13.95 (ISBN 0-86554-030-6, MUP-H21). Mercer Univ Pr.

Religion & the Sociology of Knowledge: Modernization & Pluralism in Christian Thought & Structure. Ed. by Barbara Hargrove. LC 83-22149. (Studies in Religion & Society: Vol. 8). 412p. 1984. 59.95x (ISBN 0-88946-872-9). E Mellen.

Religion & the State: Essays in Honor of Leo Pfeffer. Ed. by James E. Wood, Jr. 596p. 1985. 39.95x (ISBN 0-918954-29-0). Baylor Univ Pr.

Religion & the State in Georgia in the Eighteenth Century. Reba C. Strickland. LC 40-4840. (Columbia University Studies in the Social Sciences: No. 460). Repr. of 1939 ed. 18.50 (ISBN 0-404-51460-X). AMS Pr.

Religion & the State: The Making & Testing of an American Tradition. Evarts B. Greene. LC 75-41122. Repr. of 1941 ed. 17.25 (ISBN 0-404-14548-5). AMS Pr.

Religion & the State: The Struggle for Legitimacy & Power. Ed. by Robert J. Myers. LC 85-72100. (Annals of the American Academy of Political & Social Science Ser.: Vol. 483). 1986. text ed. 15.00 (ISBN 0-8039-2538-7); pap. text ed. 7.95 (ISBN 0-8039-2539-5). Sage.

Religion & the Transformation of Society: A Study in Social Change in Africa. Monica H. Wilson. LC 73-134622. (Scott Holland Memorial Lectures: 15; 1969). pap. 43.30 (ISBN 0-317-27081-8, 2024562). Bks Demand UMI.

Religion & the Unconscious. Ann Ulanov & Barry Ulanov. LC 75-16302. 288p. 1975. 13.95 (ISBN 0-664-20799-5). Westminster.

Religion & the Unconscious. 2nd ed. Ann Ulanov & Barry Ulanov. LC 75-16302. 288p. 1985. pap. 14.95 (ISBN 0-664-24657-5). Westminster.

Religion & the Western Mind. Ninian Smart. 1986. 39.50 (ISBN 0-88706-382-9); pap. 12.95 (ISBN 0-88706-383-7). State U NY Pr.

Religion & the Working Class in Nineteenth Century Britain. H. McLeod. (Studies in Economic & Social History). 72p. 1984. pap. text ed. 7.95x (ISBN 0-333-28115-2, Pub. by Macmillan UK). Humanities.

Religion & the World. Morteza Mutahhari. Tr. by Mohammad S. Tawheedi. 44p. 1984. pap. 3.95 (ISBN 0-940368-34-X). Tahrike Tarsile Quran.

Religion & the World Order. Ed. by F. Ernest Johnson. LC 68-26189. (Essay & General Literature Index Reprint Ser). 1969. Repr. of 1944 ed. 22.50x (ISBN 0-8046-0221-2, Pub. by Kennikat). Assoc Faculty Pr.

Religion & Theatre. M. L. Varadpande. 100p. 1982. text ed. 15.00x (ISBN 0-391-02794-8). Humanities.

Religion & Theology of Paul. W. Morgan. 272p. 1917. 9.95 (ISBN 0-567-02200-5, Pub. by T & T Clark Ltd UK). Fortress.

Religion & Truth. Donald Wiche. 295p. 1981. text ed. 44.50 (ISBN 90-279-3149-6). Mouton.

Religion & Ultimate Well-Being: An Explanatory Theory. Martin Prozesky. LC 84-3340. 224p. 1984. 22.50 (ISBN 0-312-67057-5). St Martin.

Religion & Welsh Literature in the Age of the Reformation. Glanmor Williams. (Sir John Rhys Memorial Lectures in Celtic Studies). 1985. pap. 4.25 (ISBN 0-85672-497-1, Pub. by British Acad). Longwood Pub Group.

Religion As an Occupation. Joseph H. Fichter. (Orig.). 1966. pap. 3.95x (ISBN 0-268-00229-0). U of Notre Dame Pr.

Religion As Anxiety & Tranquillity: An Essay in Comparative Phenomenology of the Spirit. J. G. Arapura. (Religion & Reason Ser.: No. 5). 1973. 19.00x (ISBN 90-2797-180-3). Mouton.

Religion As Art. T. R. Martland. LC 80-27104. (Series in Philosophy). 265p. 1981. 49.50x (ISBN 0-87395-520-X); pap. 16.95 (ISBN 0-87395-521-8). State U NY Pr.

Religion As Creative Insecurity. Peter A. Bertocci. LC 73-1836. 128p. 1973. Repr. of 1958 ed. lib. bdg. 22.50x (ISBN 0-8371-6803-1, BECI). Greenwood.

Religion as Critique. Robert J. Ackermann. LC 84-16471. 184p. 1985. lib. bdg. 20.00x (ISBN 0-87023-462-5); pap. 8.95x (ISBN 0-87023-463-3). U of Mass Pr.

Religion As Story. Ed. by James B. Wiggins. 218p. 1985. pap. text ed. 9.75 (ISBN 0-8191-4682-X). U Pr of Amer.

Religion at Bowdoin College: A History. Ernst C. Helmreich. LC 81-71331. (Illus.). 1981. pap. 7.50 (ISBN 0-916606-03-1). Bowdoin Coll.

Religion Behind the Iron Curtain. George N. Shuster. LC 78-13547. 1978. Repr. of 1954 ed. lib. bdg. 22.50x (ISBN 0-313-20634-1, SHRB). Greenwood.

Religion, BL-BX. Ed. by James Larrabee. LC 85-6863. (LC Cumulative Classification Ser.). 1000p. 1985. loose-leaf set 105.00 (ISBN 0-933949-11-1); vol. 1 0.00 (ISBN 0-933949-12-X); vol. 2 0.00 (ISBN 0-933949-13-8); fiche set 0.00 (ISBN 0-933949-15-4); fiche vol. 1 0.00 (ISBN 0-933949-16-2); fiche vol. 2 0.00 (ISBN 0-933949-17-0). Livia Pr.

Religion: Classic Sociological Approaches. R. O'Toole. 1984. text ed. 12.95 (ISBN 0-07-548560-5). McGraw.

Religion Coming of Age. Roy W. Sellars. LC 75-3362. Repr. of 1928 ed. 20.50 (ISBN 0-404-59359-3). AMS Pr.

Religion Cristiana En Su Expresion Doctrinal. Edgar Y. Mullins. Tr. by Sara A. Hale. Orig. Title: Christian Religion in Its Doctrinal Expression. 522p. 1980. pap. 10.95 (ISBN 0-311-09042-7). Casa Bautista.

Religion, Cults & the Law. 2nd ed. A. Burstein. (Legal Almanac Ser.: No. 23). 128p. 1980. 6.95 (ISBN 0-379-11133-0). Oceana.

Religion, Culture & Methodology: Papers of the Groningen Working-Group for the Study of Fundamental Problems & Methods of Science of Religion. Ed. by T. P. Van Baaren & H. J. Driljvers. 1973. text ed. 14.00x (ISBN 90-2797-249-4). Mouton.

Religion, Culture & Values: A Cross-Cultural Analysis of Motivational Factors in Native Irish & American Irish Catholicism. Bruce F. Biever. LC 76-6322. (Irish Americans Ser). 1976. 62.00 (ISBN 0-405-09319-5). Ayer Co Pubs.

Religion der Aegypter. Erman Adolf. (Illus.). 1978. Repr. of 1934 ed. 19.20x (ISBN 3-11-005187-7). De Gruyter.

Religion des Geistes. Salomon Formstecher. Ed. by Steven Katz. LC 79-7129. (Jewish Philosophy, Mysticism & History of Ideas Ser.). 1980. Repr. of 1841 ed. lib. bdg. 40.00x (ISBN 0-405-12251-9). Ayer Co Pubs.

Religion Des Romischen Heeres. facsimile ed. Alfred Von Domaszewski. LC 75-10634. (Ancient Religion & Mythology Ser.). (Ger., Illus.). 1976. Repr. of 1895 ed. 12.00 (ISBN 0-405-07012-8). Ayer Co Pubs.

Religion, Dynamique Sociale et Dependance: Les Mouvements Protestants En Argentine et Au Chili. Christian Lalive D'Epinay. (Interaction Ser: L'homme et Son Environnementsocial, No. 4). (Fr., Illus.). 368p. 1976. pap. text ed. 36.40x (ISBN 90-2797-922-7). Mouton.

Religion et Culture. Jacques Maritain. 176p. 1968. 3.95 (ISBN 0-686-56366-2). French & Eur.

Religion Faces the World Crisis. Leroy Waterman. 1943. 3.75x (ISBN 0-685-21800-7). Wahr.

Religion for a New Generation. 2nd ed. Jacob Needleman et al. Ed. by Kenneth Scott. 576p. 1977. pap. text ed. write for info. (ISBN 0-02-385990-3). Macmillan.

Religion for Free Minds. Julius S. Bixler. LC 75-3048. (Philosophy in America Ser.). 1976. Repr. of 1939 ed. 18.00 (ISBN 0-404-59045-4). AMS Pr.

Religion for Little Children: A Parent's Guide. Christiane Brusselmans & Edward Wakin. LC 76-140110. 1977. pap. 6.95 (ISBN 0-87973-825-1). Our Sunday Visitor.

Religion for Mankind. Horace Holley. 248p. 1956. 12.95 (ISBN 0-87743-011-X); pap. 5.95 (ISBN 0-85398-000-4). G Ronald Pub.

Religion for the People of Today. Daughters of St. Paul. LC 78-160576. (Illus.). 1971. pap. 1.25 (ISBN 0-8198-0345-6). Dghtrs St Paul.

Religion for Tomorrow. Theron D. Wilson. LC 62-9776. 148p. 1963. 5.95 (ISBN 0-8022-1897-0). Philos Lib.

Religion Game, American Style. Edward Stevens. LC 76-9367. 168p. 1976. pap. 5.95 (ISBN 0-8091-1951-X). Paulist Pr.

Religion, Government & Education. Ed. by William W. Brickman & Stanley Lehrer. LC 77-24684. 1977. Repr. of 1961 ed. lib. bdg. 22.50x (ISBN 0-8371-9749-X, BRRG). Greenwood.

Religion: If There Is No God.. On God, the Devil, Sin & Other Worries of the So-Called Philosophy of Religion. Leszek Kolakowski. Ed. by Frank Kermode. 1982. pap. 7.95 (ISBN 0-19-520429-8). Oxford U Pr.

Religion in a Free Society. Sidney Hook. LC 67-11242. xii, 120p. 1967. 10.95x (ISBN 0-8032-0077-3). U of Nebr Pr.

Religion in a Religious Age. Ed. by S. D. Goitein. 10.00x (ISBN 0-87068-268-7, Pub. by an Academic Inst); pap. 8.95. Ktav.

Religion in a Revolutionary Society. Peter L. Berger. (Bicentennial Lecture Ser.). 16p. 1974. pap. 1.00 (ISBN 0-8447-1306-6). Am Enterprise.

Religion in a Technical Age. Samuel H. Miller. LC 68-17628. 1968. 8.95x (ISBN 0-674-75650-9). Harvard U Pr.

Religion in a Tswana Chiefdom. Berthold A. Pauw. LC 85-21881. (Illus.). xii, 274p. 1985. Repr. of 1960 ed. lib. bdg. 75.00x (ISBN 0-313-24974-1, PRTC). Greenwood.

Religion in Aboriginal Australia: An Anthology. Ed. by Max Charlesworth et al. LC 83-23437. (Illus.). 458p. 1984. text ed. 39.50x (ISBN 0-7022-1754-9). U of Queensland Pr.

Religion in America. 2nd ed. George C. Bedell et al. LC 81-8239. 1982. text ed. write for info. (ISBN 0-02-307810-3). Macmillan.

Religion in America, 38 vols. Ed. by Edwin S. Gaustad. 1969. Repr. Set. 2510.50 (ISBN 0-405-00229-7). Ayer Co Pubs.

Religion in America. James Geisendorfer. 175p. 1983. pap. text ed. 19.95x (ISBN 90-04-06910-0, Pub. by Magnes Pr Israel). Humanities.

Religion in America. Ed. by Gillian Lindt. LC 75-54571. (Great Contemporary Issues Ser.). 1977. lib. bdg. 35.00x (ISBN 0-405-09865-0). Ayer Co Pubs.

Religion in America: A Critical Abridgment. Robert Baird. 11.25 (ISBN 0-8446-0471-2). Peter Smith.

Religion in America: An Historical Account of the Development of American Religious Life. 4th ed. Winthrop Hudson. 512p. 1987. text ed. write for info. (ISBN 0-02-357280-9). Macmillan.

Religion in America: History & Historiography. Edwin S. Gaustad. LC 73-91240. (AHA Pamphlets: No. 260). 60p. 1974. pap. text ed. 1.50 (ISBN 0-87229-016-6). Am Hist Assn.

Religion in America: Ser. 2, 40 vols. Ed. by Edwin S. Gaustad. 1972. Repr. 830.00 set (ISBN 0-405-04050-4). Ayer Co Pubs.

Religion in American History: Interpretive Essays. John F. Wilson & John M. Mulder. 448p. 1978. pap. text ed. write for info. (ISBN 0-13-771980-9). P-H.

Religion in American Life. Compiled by Nelson R. Burr. LC 70-136219. (Goldentree Bibliographies in American History Ser.). (Orig.). 1971. 15.95x (ISBN 0-88295-507-1). Harlan Davidson.

Religion in American Public Life. A. James Reichley. LC 85-21312. 402p. 1985. 31.95 (ISBN 0-8157-7378-1); pap. 11.95 (ISBN 0-8157-7377-3). Brookings.

Religion in an African City. Geoffrey Parrinder. LC 74-142921. (Illus.). Repr. of 1953 ed. 22.50x (ISBN 0-8371-5947-4, PAC&, Pub. by Negro U Pr). Greenwood.

Religion in Antebellum Kentucky. John B. Boles. LC 76-4434. (Kentucky Bicentennial Bookshelf Ser.). 160p. 1976. 6.95 (ISBN 0-8131-0227-8). U Pr of Ky.

Religion in Appalachia. Ed. by John D. Photiadis. 1979. 10.75 (ISBN 0-686-26337-5). W Va U Ctr Exten.

Religion in Changing Japanese Society. Kiyomi Morioka. 231p. 1975. 29.50 (ISBN 0-86008-131-1, Pub. by U of Tokyo Japan). Columbia U Pr.

Religion in China. Robert G. Orr. (Orig.). 1980. pap. 4.95 (ISBN 0-377-00103-1). Friend Pr.

Religion in Contemporary Society. H. Paul Chalfant & Robert E. Beckley. 500p. 1986. text ed. 28.95 (ISBN 0-87484-691-9). Mayfield Pub.

Religion in Contemporary Society. Paul H. Chalfant & Robert E. Beckley. Ed. by C. Eddie Palmer. 592p. 1981. Repr. text ed. 28.95 (ISBN 0-87484-691-9). Mayfield Pub.

Religion in Context: Cults & Charisma. I. M. Lewis. (Essays in Social Anthropology Ser.). (Illus.). 160p. 1986. 37.50 (ISBN 0-521-30616-7); pap. 9.95 (ISBN 0-521-31596-4). Cambridge U Pr.

Religion in Crisis & Custom: A Sociological & Psychological Study. Anton T. Boisen & John Leary. LC 72-10977. 271p. 1973. Repr. of 1955 ed. lib. bdg. 22.50x (ISBN 0-8371-6642-X, BORC). Greenwood.

Religion in Dialogue: East & West Meet. Ed. by Zacharias P. Thundy et al. 336p. (Orig.). 1985. lib. bdg. 29.75 (ISBN 0-8191-4466-5); pap. text ed. 14.75 (ISBN 0-8191-4467-3). U Pr of Amer.

Religion in Economics: A Study of John B. Clark, Richard T. Ely & Simon N. Patten. J. Rutherford Everett. 1982. Repr. of 1946 ed. lib. bdg. 22.50x (ISBN 0-87991-866-7). Porcupine Pr.

Religion in England: 1688-1781. Gordon Rupp. (History of the Christian Church Ser.). 520p. 1987. 79.00x (ISBN 0-19-826918-8). Oxford U Pr.

Religion in Essence & Manifestation, 2 vols. Gerardus Van Der Leeuw. 26.50 set (ISBN 0-8446-1457-2). Peter Smith.

Religion in Film. Ed. by John R. May & Michael Bird. LC 81-23983. (Illus.). 232p. 1982. text ed. 17.95x (ISBN 0-87049-352-3); pap. text ed. 8.95x (ISBN 0-87049-368-X). U of Tenn Pr.

Religion in Greek Literature: A Sketch in Outline. facsimile ed. Lewis Campbell. LC 79-148874. (Select Bibliographies Reprint Ser). Repr. of 1898 ed. 22.00 (ISBN 0-8369-5645-1). Ayer Co Pubs.

Religion in Higher Education among Negroes. Richard I. McKinney. LC 75-38785. (Religion in America, Ser. 2). 186p. 1972. Repr. of 1945 ed. 15.00 (ISBN 0-405-04075-X). Ayer Co Pubs.

Religion in Higher Education among Negroes. Richard I. McKinney. 1945. 13.50x (ISBN 0-686-51299-5). Elliots Bks.

Religion in Human Life: Anthropological Views. E. Norbeck. LC 73-7862. (Basic Anthropology Unit Ser.). 1974. pap. text ed. 9.95 (ISBN 0-03-091284-9, HoltC). H HOlt & Co.

Religion in Indiana: A Guide to Historical Resources. L. C. Rudolph & Judith E. Endelman. LC 84-43186. 224p. 1986. 22.50x (ISBN 0-253-34960-5). Ind U Pr.

Religion in Japanese History. Joseph M. Kitagawa. LC 65-23669. 475p. 1966. 35.00x (ISBN 0-231-02834-2). Columbia U Pr.

Religion in Judah under the Assyrians. John McKay. LC 72-97460. (Studies in Biblical Theology, 2nd Ser.: No. 26). 1973. pap. text ed. 10.00x (ISBN 0-8401-3076-7). A R Allenson.

Religion in Life at Louisbourg, 1713-1758. A. J. Johnston. 288p. 1984. 30.00x (ISBN 0-7735-0427-3). McGill-Queens U pr.

Religion in Modern English Drama. Gerald C. Weales. LC 75-45367. 317p. 1976. Repr. of 1961 ed. lib. bdg. 24.75x (ISBN 0-8371-8735-4, WEME). Greenwood.

Religion in New Zealand Society. Ed. by Brian Colless & Peter Donovan. 216p. 1980. 17.95 (ISBN 0-567-09303-4, Pub. by T & T Clark Uk). Fortress.

Religion in North America. Ronald J. Wilkins. (To Live Is Christ Ser.). 208p. 1984. pap. 5.75 (ISBN 0-697-01930-6); tchr's manual 4.95 (ISBN 0-697-01931-4); spirit masters 10.95 (ISBN 0-697-01735-4). Wm C Brown.

Religion in Overalls. William Johnsson. LC 77-22464. (Anvil Ser.). 1977. pap. 8.95 (ISBN 0-8127-0143-7). Review & Herald.

Religion in Plato & Cicero. John E. Rexine. LC 68-28581. 72p. Repr. of 1959 ed. lib. bdg. 22.50x (ISBN 0-8371-0198-0, RERP). Greenwood.

Religion in Practice. Swami Prabhavananda. 6.95 (ISBN 0-87481-016-7). Vedanta Pr.

Religion in Primitive Culture. Edward Tylor. (Primitive Culture - Part 2). 18.75 (ISBN 0-8446-0946-3). Peter Smith.

Religion in Primitive Cultures: A Study in Ethnophilosophy. Wilhelm Dupre. (Religion & Reason: No. 9). 366p. 1975. text ed. 39.00x (ISBN 0-686-22610-0). Mouton.

Religion in Public Education. Vivian T. Thayer. LC 78-12385. 1979. Repr. of 1947 ed. lib. bdg. 22.50x (ISBN 0-313-21212-0, THRP). Greenwood.

Religion in Radical Transition. Ed. by Jeffrey K. Hadden. 166p. 1973. 9.95 (ISBN 0-87855-070-4); pap. 3.95x (ISBN 0-87855-567-6). Transaction Bks.

Religion in Recent Art. 3rd ed. Peter T. Forsyth. LC 73-148780. Repr. of 1905 ed. 24.50 (ISBN 0-404-02515-3). AMS Pr.

Religion in Roman Britain. Martin Henig. LC 84-6914. 256p. 1984. 29.95 (ISBN 0-312-67059-1). St Martin.

Religion in Shreds. C. Brandon Rimmer. LC 73-82861. pap. 1.25 (ISBN 0-88419-046-3, Co-Pub by Crection Hse). Aragorn Bks.

Religion in Society: A Sociology of Religion. 2nd ed. Ronald L. Johnstone. (Illus.). 320p. 1983. text ed. write for info. (ISBN 0-13-773077-2). P-H.

Religion in Sociological Perspective. Keith A. Roberts. 466p. 1984. 31.00x (ISBN 0-256-03127-4). Dorsey.

Religion in Sociological Perspective. Bryan Wilson. 1982. pap. 7.95x (ISBN 0-19-826664-2). Oxford U Pr.

Religion in Soviet Russia, Nineteen Seventeen to Nineteen Forty-Two. Nicholas S. Timasheff. LC 78-23615. 1979. Repr. of 1942 ed. lib. bdg. 22.50x (ISBN 0-313-21040-3, TIRS). Greenwood.

Religion in Tennessee, Seventeen Seventy-Seven to Nineteen Forty-Five. Herman A. Norton. LC 81-1562. (Tennessee Three Star Ser.). (Illus.). 136p. 1981. pap. 3.50 (ISBN 0-87049-318-3). U of Tenn Pr.

Religion in the Age of Romanticism: Studies in Early Nineteenth Century Thought. Bernard M. Reardon. 320p. 1985. 39.50 (ISBN 0-521-30088-6); pap. 14.95 (ISBN 0-521-31745-2). Cambridge U Pr.

Religion in the American Novel: The Search for Belief, 1860-1920. Leo F. O'Connor. LC 83-21842. 364p. (Orig.). 1984. lib. bdg. 31.00 (ISBN 0-8191-3683-2); pap. text ed. 14.50 (ISBN 0-8191-3684-0). U Pr of Amer.

Religion in the Eighteenth Century. John Browning & Richard Morton. LC 79-17715. (McMaster University Eighteenth Century Studies). 145p. 1979. lib. bdg. 22.00 (ISBN 0-8240-4005-8). Garland Pub.

Religion in the Lives of English Women, 1760-1930. Ed. by Gail Malmgreen. LC 86-45172. 224p. 1986. 29.95x (ISBN 0-253-34973-7). Ind U Pr.

Religion in the Making. Alfred N. Whitehead. pap. 5.95 (ISBN 0-452-00723-2, Mer). NAL.

Religion in the Medieval West. Bernard Hamilton. 224p. 1986. pap. text ed. 14.95 (ISBN 0-7131-6461-1). E Arnold.

Religion in the Middle East, 2 Vols. Arthur J. Arberry. LC 68-21187. (Illus.). 1969. Set. 105.00 (ISBN 0-521-07400-2). Vol. 1. 62.50 (ISBN 0-521-20543-3); Vol. 2. 59.50 (ISBN 0-521-20544-1). Cambridge U Pr.

Religion in the New Netherland, 1623-1664. Frederick K. Zwierlein. LC 72-120851. (Civil Liberties in American History Ser.). 1971. Repr. of 1910 ed. lib. bdg. 39.50 (ISBN 0-306-71960-6). Da Capo.

Religion in the Old South. Donald G. Mathews. LC 77-587. 1979. pap. 11.00x (ISBN 0-226-51002-6, P819, Phoen). U of Chicago Pr.

Religion in the Pacific Era. Ed. by Frank K. Flinn & Tyler Hendricks. 244p. (Orig.). 1985. (Pub. by New Era Bks.); pap. text ed. 12.95 (ISBN 0-913757-19-5, Pub. by New Era Bks.). Paragon Hse.

Religion in the Philosophy of William James. Julius S. Bixler. LC 75-3049. Repr. of 1926 ed. 24.50 (ISBN 0-404-59046-2). AMS Pr.

Religion in the Post-War World. facsimile ed. Ed. by Willard L. Sperry et al. LC 76-142698. (Essay Index Reprints - Religion & Education Ser.: Vol. 4). Repr. of 1945 ed. 14.00 (ISBN 0-8369-2202-6). Ayer Co Pubs.

Religion in the Public Realm. David Tracy. 176p. 1987. 12.95 (ISBN 0-8245-0666-9). Crossroad NY.

Religion in the Public Schools. Kris Amundson. 80p. (Orig.). 1986. pap. write for info. Am Assn Sch Admin.

Religion in the Public Schools: An Introduction. Richard C. McMillan. LC 84-9147. x, 301p. 1984. 21.95 (ISBN 0-86554-093-4, H85). Mercer Univ Pr.

Religion in the Rebel Ranks. Sidney J. Romero. (Illus.). 226p. (Orig.). 1983. lib. bdg. 27.00 (ISBN 0-8191-3327-2); pap. text ed. 12.50 (ISBN 0-8191-3328-0). U Pr of Amer.

Religion in the Reich. Michael Power. LC 78-63706. (Studies in Fascism: Ideology & Practice). 1979. Repr. of 1939 ed. 28.00 (ISBN 0-404-16976-7). AMS Pr.

Religion in the Secular City: Toward a Post-Modern Theology. Harvey Cox. 320p. 1984. 16.95 (ISBN 0-671-45344-0). S&S.

Religion in the Secular City: Toward a Postmodern Theology. Harvey Cox. 304p. 1985. pap. 7.95 (ISBN 0-671-52805-X, Touchstone Bks). S&S.

Religion in the South. Ed. by Charles R. Wilson. LC 85-5361. (Chancellor's Symposium Ser.). (Orig.). 1985. 15.00x (ISBN 0-87805-256-9); pap. 8.95 (ISBN 0-87805-257-7). U Pr of Miss.

Religion in the Soviet Union. Albert Boiter. (Washington Papers: Vol. VIII, No. 78). 88p. (Orig.). 1980. pap. text ed. 7.95 (ISBN 0-8191-6022-9, Pub. by CSIS). U Pr of Amer.

Religion in the Struggle for Power: A Study in the Sociological Study of Religion. Milton J. Yinger. Ed. by Harriet Zuckerman & Robert K. Merton. LC 79-9040. (Dissertations in Sociology Ser.). 1980. Repr. of 1946 ed. lib. bdg. 26.50x (ISBN 0-405-13007-4). Ayer Co Pubs.

Religion in the Struggle for World Community: Unabridged Proceedings. World Conference on Religion & Peace, 3rd Assembly. Ed. by Homer A. Jack. (Orig.). 1980. pap. 6.95 (ISBN 0-935934-05-7). World Confer Rel & Peace.

Religion in the Twentieth Century. Ed. by Vergilius T. Ferm. Repr. of 1948 ed. lib. bdg. 22.50x (ISBN 0-8371-2290-2, FERT). Greenwood.

Religion in the U. S. A, 2 vols. Robert Baird. (Works of Rev. Robert Baird Ser.). 1985. Repr. Set. lib. bdg. 79.00 (ISBN 0-932051-57-X, Pub. by Am Repr Serv). Am Biog Serv.

Religion in the United States of America. Robert Baird. LC 70-83411. (Religion in America, Ser. 1). 1969. Repr. of 1844 ed. 38.50 (ISBN 0-405-00232-7). Ayer Co Pubs.

Religion in Transition. facs. ed. Ed. by Vergilius T. Ferm. LC 68-29204. (Essay Index Reprint Ser). 1937. 15.50 (ISBN 0-8369-0074-X). Ayer Co Pubs.

Religion in Twentieth Century America. Herbert W. Schneider. LC 52-8219. (Library of Congress Ser. in American Civilization). (Illus.). 1952. 16.50x (ISBN 0-674-75700-9). Harvard U Pr.

Religion in Various Cultures. Horace L. Friess & Herbert W. Schneider. (Illus.). Repr. of 1932 ed. 24.00 (ISBN 0-384-16990-2). Johnson Repr.

Religion in Victorian Society: A Sourcebook of Documents. Ed. by Richard J. Helmstadter & Paul T. Phillips. 484p. (Orig.). 1986. lib. bdg. 36.00 (ISBN 0-8191-4994-2); pap. text ed. 17.75 (ISBN 0-8191-4995-0). U Pr of Amer.

Religion in West European Politics. Ed. by Suzanne Berger. (Illus.). 200p. 1982. text ed. 29.50x (ISBN 0-7146-3218-X, F Cass Co). Biblio Dist.

Religion in Western Civilization Since the Reformation: Select Readings. Ed. by Jon Alexander & Giles Dimock. 184p. 1983. pap. text ed. 6.75 (ISBN 0-8191-3391-4). U Pr of Amer.

Religion in Wood: A Book of Shaker Furniture. Edward D. Andrews & Faith Andrews. LC 66-12722. (Midland Bks Ser.: No. 286). (Illus.). 128p. 1966. 20.00 (ISBN 0-253-17360-4); pap. 7.95x (ISBN 0-253-20286-8). Ind U Pr.

Religion Inc. S. Lamont. 1986. 49.75X (ISBN 0-245-54334-1, Pub. by Harrap Ltd England). State Mutual Bk.

Religion: Innocent or Guilty. Ron Yerman. LC 85-90019. 180p. 1985. 11.95 (ISBN 0-533-06540-2). Vantage.

Religion, Law & the Growth of Constitutional Thought, 1150-1650. Brian Tierney. LC 81-12265. 128p. 1982. 24.95 (ISBN 0-521-23495-6). Cambridge U Pr.

Religion Lessings. Gottfried Fittbogen. 1967. 36.00; pap. 31.00 (ISBN 0-685-13575-6). Johnson Repr.

Religion, Morality & "the New Right". Ed. by Melinda Maidens. 224p. 1982. 24.95x (ISBN 0-87196-639-5). Facts on File.

Religion Nature: With Charles Birch & Others. Ed. by K. J. Sharpe & J. M. Ker. (Illus.). 116p. (Orig.). 1984. pap. 11.95 (ISBN 0-9597672-0-7, Pub. by Auckland Univ Chaplaincy). ANZ Religious Pubns.

Religion o Cristo? Martin R. DeHaan. Orig. Title: Religion or Christ. (Span.). 64p. 1970. pap. 2.25 (ISBN 0-8254-1153-X). Kregel.

Religion of Ancient Greece. Jane E. Harrison. 1979. Repr. of 1905 ed. lib. bdg. 27.00 (ISBN 0-8495-2325-7). Arden Lib.

Religion of Ancient Greece. Jane E. Harrison. 66p. 1921. 0.95 (ISBN 0-317-40433-4). Open Court.

Religion of Ancient Greece. T. Zielinski. x, 235p. pap. 10.00 (ISBN 0-89005-090-2). Ares.

Religion of Ancient Greece. facsimile ed. Thaddeus Zielinski. Tr. by George R. Noyes. LC 76-107838. (Select Bibliographies Reprint Ser). 1926. 17.00 (ISBN 0-8369-5222-7). Ayer Co Pubs.

Religion of Ancient Palestine. Stanley A. Cook. 122p. 1921. 0.95 (ISBN 0-317-40429-6). Open Court.

Religion of Ancient Palestine in the Light of Archaeology. S. A Cook. (British Academy, London, Schweich Lectures on Biblical Archaeology Series, 1925). pap. 28.00 (ISBN 0-8115-1267-3). Kraus Repr.

Religion of Ancient Scandinavia. W. A. Craigie. 59.95 (ISBN 0-8490-0939-1). Gordon Pr.

Religion of Ancient Scandinavia. facsimile ed. William A. Craigie. LC 74-99657. (Select Bibliographies Reprint Ser). 1906. 14.50 (ISBN 0-8369-5086-0). Ayer Co Pubs.

Religion of Burma & Other Papers. Ananda-Maitreya. LC 77-87482. Repr. of 1929 ed. 31.50 (ISBN 0-404-16790-X). AMS Pr.

Religion of China. Max Weber. 1968. 14.95 (ISBN 0-02-934440-9); text ed. 14.95 (ISBN 0-02-934450-6). Free Pr.

Religion of Dr. Johnson. facsimile ed. William T. Cairns. LC 71-93324. (Essay Index Reprint Ser). 1946. 17.00 (ISBN 0-8369-1279-9). Ayer Co Pubs.

Religion of Dostoevsky. Boyce Gibson. 214p. 6.95 (ISBN 0-664-20989-0). Brown Bk.

Religion of Ethical Nationhood. Mordecai M. Kaplan. 1970. pap. 11.50 (ISBN 0-935457-22-4). Reconstructionist Pr.

Religion of George Fox: As Revealed in His Epistles. Howard H. Brinton. LC 68-57978. (Orig.). 1968. pap. 2.50x (ISBN 0-87574-161-4). Pendle Hill.

Religion of Humanity: The Impact of Comtean Positivism on Victorian Britain. T. R. Wright. (Illus.). 325p. 1986. 44.50 (ISBN 0-521-30671-X). Cambridge U Pr.

Religion of Islam. F. A. Klein. 248p. 1985. text ed. 17.95x (ISBN 0-7007-0010-2, Pub. by Curzon Pr England); pap. text ed. 8.95 (ISBN 0-7007-0190-7). Apt Bks.

Religion of Islam. F. A. Klein. 241p. 1978. Repr. of 1906 ed. 16.50 (ISBN 0-89684-153-7). Orient Bk Dist.

Religion of Islam. F. A. Klein. 8.95x (ISBN 0-317-20253-7). Intl Bk Ctr.

Religion of Islam. F. A. Klein. 248p. 1985. pap. text ed. 12.50x (ISBN 0-7007-0190-7, Pub by Curzon Pr UK). Humanities.

Religion of Islam. Maulana-Muhammad-Ali. 1978. 42.50x (ISBN 0-89684-447-1). Orient Bk Dist.

Religion of Israel. Yehezkel Kaufmann. Tr. by Moshe Greenberg. LC 60-5466. 1960. 36.00x (ISBN 0-226-42728-5). U of Chicago Pr.

Religion of Israel: From Its Beginnings to the Babylonian Exile. Yehezkel Kaufmann. Tr. by Moshe Greenberg. LC 60-5466. 304p. 1972. pap. 10.95 (ISBN 0-8052-0364-8). Schocken.

Religion of Japan's Korean Minority: The Preservation of Ethnic Identity. Helen Hardacre. (Korea Research Monographs: No. 9). (Illus.). 155p. (Orig.). 1984. pap. text ed. 12.00x (ISBN 0-912966-67-X). IEAS.

Religion of Jesus: Christianity's Unclaimed Heritage of Prophetic Religion. Leroy Waterman. LC 78-16405. 1978. Repr. of 1952 ed. lib. bdg. 22.50x (ISBN 0-313-20586-8, WARJ). Greenwood.

Religion of Love. Swami Vivekananda. 114p. pap. 2.50 (ISBN 0-87481-129-5). Vedanta Pr.

Religion of Man. Rabindranath Tagore. LC 77-27145. (Hibbert Lectures: 1930). 248p. Repr. of 1931 ed. 27.50 (ISBN 0-404-60426-9). AMS Pr.

Religion of Manipur. Saroj Nalini Parratt. 1980. 13.00x (ISBN 0-8364-0594-3, Pub. by Mukhopadhyaya India). South Asia Bks.

Religion of Nature. Basil Willey. LC 76-40105. 1957. lib. bdg. 12.50 (ISBN 0-8414-9506-8). Folcroft.

Religion of Nature Delineated. William Wollaston. Ed. by Rene Wellek. LC 75-11267. (British Philosophers & Theologians of the 17th & 18th Centuries Ser.). 1978. Repr. of 1722 ed. lib. bdg. 51.00 (ISBN 0-8240-1816-8). Garland Pub.

Religion of Nature Delineated, 1724 & Related Commentaries. William Wollaston. LC 74-1469. 1974. 45.00x (ISBN 0-8201-1127-9). Schol Facsimiles.

Religion of Philosophers. facs. ed. James H. Dunham. LC 78-80386. (Essay Index Reprint Ser). 1947. 21.50 (ISBN 0-8369-1059-1). Ayer Co Pubs.

Religion of Plato. P. E. More. (Greek Tradition: Vol. 1). Repr. of 1921 ed. 22.00 (ISBN 0-527-64950-3). Kraus Repr.

Religion of Power. Cheryl Forbes. 176p. 1983. 9.95 (ISBN 0-310-45770-X, 12396). Zondervan.

Religion of Protestants: The Church in English Society 1559-1625. Patrick Collinson. 1982. pap. 15.95x (ISBN 0-19-820053-6). Oxford U Pr.

Religion of Science. 3rd ed. Paul Carus. 145p. 1913. 6.95 (ISBN 0-912050-68-3). Open Court.

Religion of Shakespeare. Richard Simpson. Ed. by Henry S. Bowden. LC 74-176025. Repr. of 1899 ed. 17.50 (ISBN 0-404-00961-1). AMS Pr.

Religion of Shakespeare. Richard Simpson. 1973. Repr. of 1899 ed. 17.45 (ISBN 0-8274-1094-8). R West.

Religion of Soldier & Sailor. Moody. LC 45-3352. 1945. 8.50x (ISBN 0-674-75750-5). Harvard U Pr.

Religion of the Ancient Celts. John A. MacCulloch. LC 77-4127. 1977. lib. bdg. 52.50 (ISBN 0-8414-5998-3). Folcroft.

Religion of the Chinese. Jan J. Groot. LC 79-2824. 230p. 1981. Repr. of 1910 ed. 21.50 (ISBN 0-8305-0004-9). Hyperion Conn.

Religion of the Chinese People. Marcel Granet. Tr. by Maurice Freedman from Fr. 1977. pap. 5.95x (ISBN 0-06-131905-8, TB 1905, Torch). Har-Row.

Religion of the Crow Indians. Robert H. Lowie. LC 74-7986. Repr. of 1922 ed. 15.00 (ISBN 0-404-11876-3). AMS Pr.

Religion of the Greeks & Romans. Karoly Kerenyi. LC 72-9823. (Illus.). 303p. 1973. Repr. of 1962 ed. lib. bdg. 24.75x (ISBN 0-8371-6605-5, KERG). Greenwood.

Religion of the Heart: Anglican Evangelicalism & the Nineteenth-Century Novel. Elisabeth Jay. 1979. 49.00x (ISBN 0-19-812092-3). Oxford U Pr.

Religion of the Hindus. H. H. Wilson. 416p. 1978. Repr. of 1862 ed. 13.95x (ISBN 0-89684-135-9). Orient Bk Dist.

Religion of the Hindus: Interpreted by Hindus. Ed. by Kenneth W. Morgan. LC 53-10466. Repr. of 1953 ed. 112.00 (ISBN 0-8357-9975-1, 2015620). Bks Demand UMI.

Religion of the Ifugaos. R. F. Barton. LC 48-3664. (American Anthropological Association Memoirs Ser). Repr. of 1946 ed. 21.00 (ISBN 0-527-00564-9). Kraus Repr.

Religion of the Kwakiutl Indians, 2 Vols. Franz Boas. LC 72-82368. (Columbia Univ. Contributions to Anthropology Ser.: No. 10). Repr. of 1930 ed. Set. 60.00 (ISBN 0-404-50560-0); 30.00 ea. AMS Pr.

Religion of the Machine Age. Dora Russell. 232p. 1985. 27.95 (ISBN 0-7100-9547-3). Methuen Inc.

Religion of the Manichees: Donnellan Lectures for 1924. Francis C. Burkitt. LC 77-84698. Repr. of 1925 ed. 29.00 (ISBN 0-404-16105-7). AMS Pr.

Religion of the Primitives. Alexander Le Roy. Tr. by Newton Thompson. LC 72-78769. Repr. of 1922 ed. cancelled (ISBN 0-8371-1400-4). Greenwood.

Religion of the Republic. Elwyn A. Smith. LC 70-130326. pap. 76.00 (2026890). Bks Demand UMI.

Religion of the Rigveda. H. D. Griswold. 1971. 8.50 (ISBN 0-89684-305-X). Orient Bk Dist.

Religion of the Samurai: A Study of Zen Philosophy & Discipline in China & Japan. K. Nukariva. 253p. 1973. 30.00x (ISBN 0-317-39142-9, Pub. by Luzac & Co Ltd); pap. 20.00x (ISBN 0-317-39143-7). State Mutual Bk.

Religion of the Sufis. David Shea & Anthony Troyer. 1979. 11.95 (ISBN 0-900860-65-0). Ins Study Human.

Religion of the Tempusak Dusuns of North Borneo. Ivor H. Evans. LC 77-86972. Repr. of 1953 ed. 40.00 (ISBN 0-404-16707-1). AMS Pr.

Religion of the Teutons. P. Chantepie De La Saussaye. LC 76-27519. 1976. Repr. of 1902 ed. lib. bdg. 50.00 (ISBN 0-89341-030-6). Longwood Pub Group.

Religion of the Veda. Maurice Bloomfield. LC 70-94310. (BCL Ser. II). Repr. of 1908 ed. 18.00 (ISBN 0-404-00912-3). AMS Pr.

Religion of Tibet. Charles A. Bell. lib. bdg. 79.95 (ISBN 0-87968-482-8). Krishna Pr.

Religion of Tibet: Study of Lamaism. J. E. Ellam. 59.95 (ISBN 0-8490-0940-5). Gordon Pr.

Religion of Tomorrow. John E. Boodin. LC 75-3062. Repr. of 1943 ed. 14.00 (ISBN 0-404-59061-6). AMS Pr.

Religion of Truth. A. A. Maududi. pap. 1.00 (ISBN 0-686-18537-4). Kazi Pubns.

Religion on Capitol Hill: Myths & Realities. Peter L. Benson & Dorothy Hill. LC 86-16434. (Illus.). 223p. 1986. pap. 8.95x (ISBN 0-19-504168-2). Oxford U Pr.

Religion on the American Frontier. William W. Sweet. Incl. Vol. 1. Baptists, 1783-1830. 652p. Repr. of 1931 ed; Vol. 2. Presbyterians, 1783-1840. (Illus.). 939p. 1964. Repr. of 1936 ed. 37.50x (ISBN 0-8154-0223-6); Vol. 3. Congregationalists, 1783-1850. (Illus.). 435p. 1964. Repr. of 1934 ed. 37.50x (ISBN 0-8154-0224-4); Vol. 4. Methodists, 1783-1840. (Illus.). 800p. 1964. Repr. of 1946 ed. 37.50x (ISBN 0-8154-0225-2). LC 63-21092. 1964. Repr. of 1946 ed. Cooper Sq.

Religion, Order, & Law: A Study in Pre-Revolutionary England. David Little. LC 84-2611. 270p. 1984. pap. text ed. 11.00x (ISBN 0-226-48546-3). U of Chicago Pr.

Religion, Politics & Social Change in the Third World. Donald E. Smith. LC 73-143516. 1951. 14.95 (ISBN 0-02-929490-8); pap. text ed. 6.95 (ISBN 0-02-929460-6). Free Pr.

Religion, Politics, & the Higher Learning: A Collection of Essays. Morton G. White. LC 82-1013. x, 140p. 1982. Repr. of 1959 ed. lib. bdg. 22.50x (ISBN 0-313-23480-9, WHRE). Greenwood.

Religion Power & Protest in Local Communities: The Northern Shore of the Mediterranean. Ed. by Eric R. Wolf. LC 84-8407. (Religion & Society Ser.: No. 24). 287p. 1984. 65.00 (ISBN 3-11-009777-X). Mouton.

Religion, Reason & Man. Fritz Marti. LC 74-9353. 127p. 1974. 7.50 (ISBN 0-87527-141-3). Green.

Religion, Reason & Revelation, No. 13. 2nd, rev. ed. Gordon H. Clark. (Trinity Papers). 251p. 1986. pap. 7.95 (ISBN 0-940931-13-3). Trinity Found.

Religion, Reason, & Truth: Historical Essays in the Philosophy of Religion. Sterling M. McMurrin. 1982. 24.95 (ISBN 0-87480-203-2). U of Utah Pr.

Religion, Rebellion, Revolution: An Interdisciplinary & Cross-Cultural Collection of Essays. Ed. by Bruce Lincoln. LC 85-1992. 312p. 1985. 27.50 (ISBN 0-312-67061-3). St Martin.

Religion, Revelation & Reason. Eric C. Rust. LC 81-2760. vi, 192p. 1981. 14.50x (ISBN 0-86554-006-3). Mercer Univ Pr.

Religion, Science & Human Crises. Francis L. Hsu. LC 73-7308. (Illus.). 142p. 1973. Repr. of 1952 ed. lib. bdg. 22.50x (ISBN 0-8371-6921-6, HSRS). Greenwood.

Religion, Science, & Society in the Modern World. facsimile ed. Alexander D. Lindsay. LC 70-37847. (Essay Index Reprint Ser). Repr. of 1943 ed. 12.00 (ISBN 0-8369-2604-8). Ayer Co Pubs.

Religion, Science & Worldview: Essays in Honor of Richard S. Westfall. Ed. by Margaret J. Osler & Paul L. Farber. 320p. 1985. 49.50 (ISBN 0-521-30452-0). Cambridge U Pr.

Religion, Society, & Utopia in Nineteenth-Century America. Ira L. Mandelker. LC 84-47. 200p. 1984. lib. bdg. 22.00x (ISBN 0-87023-436-6). U of Mass Pr.

Religion Southern Style: Southern Baptists & Society in Historical Perspective. Norman A. Yance. LC 78-61185. (Special Studies: No. 4). vi, 66p. 1978. pap. 3.95 (ISBN 0-932180-03-5). NABPR.

Religion, Spirituality, & Thought of Traditional Africa. Dominique Zahan. Tr. by Kate E. Martin & Lawrence M. Martin. LC 78-23525. 1979. Repr. of 1970 ed. lib. bdg. 17.00x (ISBN 0-226-97777-3). U of Chicago Pr.

Religion, Spirituality, & Thought of Traditional Africa. Dominique Zahan. Tr. by Kate Ezra & Lawrence M. Martin. vi, 180p. 1979. pap. 6.50x (ISBN 0-226-97778-1). U of Chicago Pr.

Religion, State & the Burger Court. Leo Pfeffer. LC 84-43056. 310p. 1985. 23.95 (ISBN 0-87975-275-0). Prometheus Bks.

Religion, the Courts, & Public Policy. Robert F. Drinan. LC 78-6124. 261p. 1978. Repr. of 1963 ed. lib. bdg. 22.50x (ISBN 0-313-20444-6, DRRE). Greenwood.

Religion: The Great Questions. Denise L. Carmody & John Carmody. 176p. 1983. pap. 11.95 (ISBN 0-8164-2476-4, HarpR). Har-Row.

Religion: The Social Context. 2nd ed. McGuire. Ed. by Sheryl Fullerton. 1986. pap. text ed. write for info. (ISBN 0-534-07242-9). Wadsworth Pub.

Religion, the State, & Education. Ed. by James E. Wood, Jr. LC 84-81477. (Institute of Church-State Studies). 151p. 1984. 10.95 (ISBN 0-918954-31-2); pap. 6.95 (ISBN 0-918954-32-0). Baylor Univ Pr.

Religion und Sittlichkeit Bei Luther Bis Zum Sermon Von Den Guten Werken 1520. Martin Ludwig. (Ger). 34.00 (ISBN 0-384-34151-9); pap. 28.00 (ISBN 0-384-34150-0). Johnson Repr.

Religion: What Is It? 2nd ed. William C. Tremmel. 1984. pap. text ed. 17.95 (ISBN 0-03-062834-2). HR&W.

Religion Within Limits or Reason Alone. Immanuel Kant. pap. 8.95x (ISBN 0-06-130067-5, TB67, Torch). Har-Row.

Religion Without God. Konstantin Kolenda. LC 76-19349. (Skeptic's Bookshelf Ser.). 125p. 1976. 13.95 (ISBN 0-87975-066-9). Prometheus Bks.

Religion Without Revelation. Julian S. Huxley. LC 78-12065. 1979. Repr. of 1967 ed. lib. bdg. 24.75x (ISBN 0-313-21225-2, HURR). Greenwood.

Religion y Revolucion en Cuba. Manuel Fernandez. (Realidades Ser.). (Span., Illus.). 250p. 1984. pap. 14.95 (ISBN 0-917049-00-4). Saeta.

Religion Yesterday & Today. facs. ed. Henry S. Coffin. LC 75-117769. (Essay Index Reprint Ser). 1940. 18.00 (ISBN 0-8369-1790-1). Ayer Co Pubs.

Religiones Vivas. Roberto E. Hume. Tr. by Manuel Beltroy from Eng. Orig. Title: Living Religions of the World. (Span.). 320p. 1981. pap. 5.25 (ISBN 0-311-05758-6, Edit Mundo). Casa Bautista.

Religions. Myrtle Langley. (Book of Beliefs Ser.). 1981. 9.95 (ISBN 0-89191-478-1, 54783). Cook.

Religions: A Select, Classified Bibliography. Joseph F. Mitros. Intro. by Sebastian A. Matczak. LC 77-183042. (Philosophical Questions Ser.: No. 8). 350p. 1973. 45.00x (ISBN 0-912116-08-0). Learned Pubns.

Religions & Communities of India. Ed. by P. N. Chopra. 1982. 59.00x (ISBN 0-85692-081-9, Pub. by E-W Pubns England). State Mutual Bk.

Religions & Hidden Cults of India. George MacMunn. (Illus.). xii, 244p. 1983. text ed. 30.00x (ISBN 0-86590-107-4). Apt Bks.

Religions & History: A Textbook for the Enlightenment of 12th Graders in our Tax-Supported Public High Schools. Leslie R. Severinghaus. 1985. 13.95 (ISBN 0-533-06577-1). Vantage.

Religions East & West. Ward J. Fellows. LC 78-27721. 1979. text ed. 31.95 (ISBN 0-03-019441-5, HoltC). H Holt & Co.

Religions for Human Dignity & World Peace: Unabridged Proceedings of the World Conference on Religion & Peace, 4th. World Conference on Religion & Peace Staff. Ed. by John B. Taylor & Gunther Gebhardt. 469p. 1986. pap. write for info. (ISBN 2-88235-000-7). World Confer Rel & Peace.

Religions in America. Ed. by Herbert L. Marx. (Reference Shelf Ser.). 1977. 8.00 (ISBN 0-8242-0608-8). Wilson.

Religions in Coastal Karnataka: 1500-1763. K. G. Madhava. (Illus.). 206p. 1985. text ed. 37.50x (ISBN 0-86590-585-1, Inter India Pubns Delhi). Apt Bks.

Religions in Japan. Ed. by William K. Bunce. LC 59-9234. 216p. 1981. pap. 5.25 (ISBN 0-8048-0500-8). C E Tuttle.

Religions in Japan: Buddhism, Shinto, Christianity. Supreme Commander for the Allied Powers. Civil Information & Education Section. LC 77-13855. 1978. Repr. of 1955 ed. lib. bdg. 22.50x (ISBN 0-8371-9874-7, SURJ). Greenwood.

Religions in Modern India. Ed. by Giri Raj Gupta. (Main Currents in Indian Sociology Ser.: Vol. 5). 368p. 1983. text ed. 37.50x (ISBN 0-7069-0793-0, Pub. by Vikas India). Advent NY.

Religions of Africa. Thomas E. Lawson. LC 84-47729. (Religious Traditions of the World Ser.). (Illus.). 128p. (Orig.). 1984. pap. 6.95 (ISBN 0-06-065211-X, HarpR). Har-Row.

Religions of America. Ed. by Leo Rosten. LC 74-11705. 1975. pap. 11.95 (ISBN 0-671-21971-5, Touchstone Bks). S&S.

Religions of Ancient China. H. A. Giles. 59.95 (ISBN 0-8490-0941-3). Gordon Pr.

Religions of Ancient China. Herbert A. Giles. LC 79-95067. (Select Bibliographies Reprint Ser). 1905. 17.00 (ISBN 0-8369-5069-0). Ayer Co Pubs.

Religions of Ancient China. Herbert A. Giles. LC 76-20524. 1976. Repr. of 1905 ed. lib. bdg. 17.00 (ISBN 0-8414-4518-4). Folcroft.

Religions of Ancient Egypt & Babylonia. Archibald H. Sayce. LC 77-27223. (Gifford Lectures: 1902). Repr. of 1903 ed. 46.50 (ISBN 0-404-60457-9). AMS Pr.

Religions of Ancient India. Louis Renou. 147p. Repr. of 1953 ed. text ed. 19.95x. Coronet Bks.

Religions of Asia. Ed. by Niels Nielsen et al. LC 82-60477. 384p. 1983. pap. text ed. 17.95 (ISBN 0-312-67096-6). St Martin.

Religions of China. James Legge. LC 78-2685. 1979. Repr. of 1880 ed. lib. bdg. 45.00 (ISBN 0-8495-3313-9). Arden Lib.

Religions of China. James Legge. LC 76-28535. 1976. Repr. of 1880 ed. lib. bdg. 40.00 (ISBN 0-8414-5809-X). Folcroft.

Religions of China. Daniel Overmyer. LC 85-42789. 128p. (Orig.). 1986. pap. 6.95 (ISBN 0-06-066401-0, HarpR). Har-Row.

Religions of Democracy. Finkelstein et al. 1941. 9.50 (ISBN 0-8159-6708-X). Devin.

Religions of India. 6th ed. A. Barth. Tr. by J. Wood from Fr. 309p. 1980. Repr. of 1880 ed. 23.95x (ISBN 0-940500-64-7). Asia Bk Corp.

Religions of India. A. Barth. 1980. text ed. 22.00x (ISBN 0-89563-630-1). Coronet Bks.

Religions of India. A. Barth. 332p. 25.00X (ISBN 0-317-52150-0, Pub. by S Chand India). State Mutual Bk.

Religions of India. Edward W. Hopkins. LC 77-94585. 1979. Repr. of 1895 ed. lib. bdg. 65.00 (ISBN 0-89341-312-7). Longwood Pub Group.

Religions of Japan: From the Dawn of History to the Era of Meiji. facsimile ed. William E. Griffis. LC 70-37469. (Essay Index Reprint Ser). Repr. of 1895 ed. 21.00 (ISBN 0-8369-2550-5). Ayer Co Pubs.

Religions of Man. Huston Smith. pap. 7.95 (ISBN 0-06-090043-1, CN43, PL). Har-Row.

Religions of Man. Huston Smith. 1965. pap. 5.95 (ISBN 0-06-080021-6, P21, PL). Har-Row.

Religions of Modern Syria & Palestine. Frederick J. Bliss. LC 76-39454. Repr. of 1912 ed. 20.00 (ISBN 0-404-00897-6). AMS Pr.

Religions of Mongolia. Walther Heissig. Tr. by Geoffrey Samuel from Ger. LC 80-146381. 1980. 31.00x (ISBN 0-520-03857-6). U of Cal Pr.

Religions of Primitive Peoples. Daniel G. Brinton. LC 79-88423. Repr. of 1897 ed. 22.50x (ISBN 0-8371-1763-1, BRR&). Greenwood.

Religions of the American Indians. Ake Hultkrantz. LC 73-90661. (Hermeneutics: Studies in the History of Religions). 1979. 20.95x (ISBN 0-520-02653-5); pap. 7.95 (ISBN 0-520-04239-5, CAL 463). U of Cal Pr.

Religions of the Ancient Near East. Helmer Ringgren. Tr. by John Sturdy. LC 72-8587. (Illus.). 208p. 1972. 7.50 (ISBN 0-664-20953-X). Westminster.

Religions of the East. enl. ed. Joseph M. Kitagawa. LC 60-7742. 352p. 1968. pap. 7.95 (ISBN 0-664-24837-3). Westminster.

Religions of the Hindukush, Vol. 1: The Religion of the Kafirs: The Pre-Islamic Heritage of Afghan Nuristan. Karl Jettmar. Tr. by Adam Nayyar from Ger. (Illus.). 184p. 1986. text ed. 35.00 (ISBN 0-85668-163-6, Pub. by Aris & Phillips UK). Humanities.

Religions of the Hindukush Volume III: The Religions of the Chitralis. Karl Jettmar. Tr. by Adam Nayyar from Ger. (Central Asian Studies). 1989. pap. text ed. 45.00 (ISBN 0-85668-368-X, Pub. by Aris & Phillips UK). Humanities.

Religions of the Hindukush Volume II: The Religion of the Dards. Karl Jettmar. Tr. by Adam Nayyar from Ger. (Central Asian Studies). 200p. 1987. text ed. 45.00 (ISBN 0-85668-291-8, Pub. by Aris & Phillips UK). Humanities.

Religions of the Orient: A Christian View. John A. Hardon. LC 71-108377. pap. 55.30 (ISBN 0-317-30169-1, 2025351). Bks Demand UMI.

Religions of the People in Sixteenth Century Champagne. A. N. Galpern. (Historical Studies: No. 92). 1976. 22.50x (ISBN 0-674-75836-6). Harvard U Pr.

Religions of the Roman Empire. John Ferguson. LC 71-110992. (Aspects of Greek & Roman Life Ser.). (Illus.). 296p. (Orig.). 1985. 29.95x (ISBN 0-8014-0567-X); pap. text ed. 8.95x (ISBN 0-8014-9311-0). Cornell U Pr.

Religions of the World. George A. Barton. LC 74-90469. Repr. of 1929 ed. lib. bdg. 22.50x (ISBN 0-8371-2216-3, BARW). Greenwood.

Religions of the World. facs. ed. Carl C. Clemen et al. LC 69-17570. (Essay Index Reprint Ser). 1931. 35.50 (ISBN 0-8369-0011-1). Ayer Co Pubs.

Religions of the World. 4th ed. Lewis M. Hopfe. 522p. 1987. pap. write for info. (ISBN 0-02-356930-1). Macmillan.

Religions of the World. F. H. Meade et al. 97p. 1985. 32.00x (ISBN 0-7157-2355-3, Pub by Holmes McDougall Ltd). State Mutual Bk.

Religions of the World. Ed. by Niels Nielsen et al. LC 81-51859. 688p. 1982. text ed. 28.95 (ISBN 0-312-67121-0); write for info. instructors manual. St Martin.

Religions of the World. rev. ed. Ronald J. Wilkins. (To Live Is Christ Ser.). 240p. 1984. pap. 5.95 (ISBN 0-697-01928-4); tchr's manual 5.00 (ISBN 0-697-01929-2); spirit masters 10.95 (ISBN 0-697-01730-3). Wm C Brown.

Religions of the World Made Simple. rev. ed. John Lewis. (Made Simple Ser.). 1958. pap. 4.95 (ISBN 0-385-02276-X). Doubleday.

Religions of Tibet. Helmut Hoffmann. LC 78-11420. (Illus.). 1979. Repr. of 1961 ed. lib. bdg. 24.75x (ISBN 0-313-21120-5, HORT). Greenwood.

Religion's Rebel Son: Fanaticism in Our Time. Lloyd Billingsley. LC 86-16311. 1986. 11.95 (ISBN 0-88070-139-0). Multnomah.

Religions, Values, & Peak-Experiences. Abraham H. Maslow. 1976. pap. 4.95 (ISBN 0-14-004262-8). Penguin.

Religions: Values & Peak Experiences. Abraham H. Maslow. 1983. 13.25 (ISBN 0-8446-6070-1). Peter Smith.

Religionsgeschichtliche Erklaerung des Neuen Testamentes: Die Abhaengigkeit des aeltesten Christentums von nichtjuedischen Religionen und philosophischen Systemen. Carl Clemen. 440p. 1973. Repr. of 1924 ed. text ed. 59.20x (ISBN 3-11-002412-8). De Gruyter.

Religionsgespraech Als Mittel Der Konfessionellen Und Politischen Auseinandersetzung Im Deutschland Des 16. Jahrhunderts. Marion Hollerbach. (European University Studies: No. 3, Vol. 165). (Ger.). 1982. 36.85 (ISBN 3-8204-7015-8). P Lang Pubs.

Religionsphilosophie. rev. ed. Heinrich Scholz. (Ger.). xi, 332p. 1974. Repr. of 1922 ed. 36.80x (ISBN 3-11-002217-6). De Gruyter.

Religionsphilosophie. Wolfgang Trillhaas. 278p. 1972. 19.20x (ISBN 3-11-003868-4). De Gruyter.

Religionsphilosophie der Juden. Samuel Hirsch. Ed. by Steven Katz. LC 79-7136. (Jewish Philosophy, Mysticism & History of Ideas Ser.). 1980. Repr. of 1842 ed. lib. bdg. 74.50x (ISBN 0-405-12262-4). Ayer Co Pubs.

Religionsphilosophie des Sohar und Ihr Verhaltnis zur Allgemeinen Judischen Theologie. David H. Joel. Ed. by Steven Katz. LC 79-7139. (Jewish Philosophy, Mysticism & History of Ideas Ser.). 1980. Repr. of 1923 ed. lib. bdg. 34.50x (ISBN 0-405-12265-9). Ayer Co Pubs.

Religionsphilosophischen Lehren des Isaak Abravanel. Jacob Guttmann. Ed. by Steven Katz. LC 79-7134. (Jewish Philosophy, Mysticism & History of Ideas Ser.). 1980. Repr. of 1916 ed. lib. bdg. 14.00x (ISBN 0-405-12260-8). Ayer Co Pubs.

Religionswissenschaft Joachim Wachs. Rainer Flasche. (Theologische Bibliothek Toeelmann: Vol. 35). 1978. 35.20x (ISBN 3-11-007238-6). De Gruyter.

Religiose Poesie der Juden in Spanien. Michael Sachs. Ed. by Steven Katz. LC 79-7150. (Jewish Philosophy, Mysticism & History of Ideas Ser.). 1980. Repr. of 1901 ed. lib. bdg. 37.00x (ISBN 0-405-12285-3). Ayer Co Pubs.

Religiose Stromungen Judentum: Mit besondered Berucksichtigung des Chassidismus. Samuel A. Horodezky. Ed. by Steven Katz. LC 79-7137. (Jewish Philosophy, Mysticism & History of Ideas Ser.). 1980. Repr. of 1920 ed. lib. bdg. 23.00x (ISBN 0-405-12263-2). Ayer Co Pubs.

Religious Affections. Jonathan Edwards. Ed. by John E. Smith. LC 59-12702. (Works of Jonathan Edwards Ser.: Vol. 2). (Illus.). 1959. 50.00x (ISBN 0-300-00966-6). Yale U Pr.

Religious Affections. Jonathan Edwards. Ed. by James M. Houston. LC 84-14863. (Classics of Faith & Devotion Ser.). 1984. 11.95 (ISBN 0-88070-064-5). Multnomah.

Religious Affections. Jonathan Edwards. 382p. 1986. pap. 9.45 (ISBN 0-85151-485-5). Banner of Truth.

Religious & Anti-Religious Thought in Russia. George L. Kline. LC 68-54484. (Weil Lectures). Repr. of 1968 ed. 47.30 (ISBN 0-317-09813-6, 2020097). Bks Demand UMI.

Religious & Cosmic Beliefs of Central Polynesia, 2 vols. Robert W. Williamson. LC 75-35220. Repr. of 1933 ed. Set. 87.50 (ISBN 0-404-14300-8). AMS Pr.

Religious & Educational Philosophy of the Young Women's Christian Association. Grace H. Wilson. LC 70-177632. (Columbia University. Teachers College. Contributions to Education: No. 554). Repr. of 1933 ed. 22.50 (ISBN 0-404-55554-3). AMS Pr.

Religious & Historical Paintings of Jan Steen. (Illus.). 1977. 42.50 (ISBN 0-8390-0170-3, Allanheld & Schram). Abner Schram Ltd.

Religious & Inspirational Books & Serials in Print 1987. Ed. by R. R. Bowker Co. Staff. 1700p. 1987. 89.00 (ISBN 0-8352-2320-5). Bowker.

Religious & Inspirational Books & Serials in Print, 1985. 1648p. 1985. 79.95x (ISBN 0-8352-2052-4). Bowker.

Religious & Moral Wisdom of Thomas Jefferson: An Anthology. Allen Jayne. 1984. 12.95 (ISBN 0-533-05800-7). Vantage.

Religious & Spiritual Groups in Modern America. Robert S. Ellwood, Jr. 352p. 1973. pap. 24.33 (ISBN 0-13-773309-7). P-H.

Religious Archives, a Complete Technical Look for the Layman. Kevin Sandifer. Ed. by Rowland P. Gill. 96p. (Orig.). 1985. pap. text ed. 5.50 (ISBN 0-910653-03-8, 8101-C). Archival Servs.

Religious Archives: An Introduction. August R. Suelflow. LC 80-17159. (SAA Basic Archival Manual Ser.). 1980. pap. text ed. 7.00 (ISBN 0-931828-20-1). Soc Am Archivists.

Religious Art: A Workbook for Artists & Designers. Robin Landa. 272p. 1985. 29.95 (ISBN 0-13-773037-3); pap. 16.95 (ISBN 0-13-773029-2). P-H.

Religious Art from the Twelfth to the Eighteenth Century. Emile Male. LC 82-47903. (Illus.). 256p. 1982. 31.50x (ISBN 0-691-04000-1); pap. 10.50x (ISBN 0-691-00347-5). Princeton U Pr.

Religious Art in France: The Late Middle Ages: A Study of Medieval Iconography & Its Sources. Emile Male. Ed. by Harry Bober. Tr. by Marthiel Mathews. (Bollingen Ser. XC: No. 3). 600p. 1987. text ed. 85.00x (ISBN 0-691-09914-6). Princeton U Pr.

Religious Art in France: The Twelfth Century. Emile Male. LC 72-14029. (Bollingen Ser.: No. 90). 1978. 73.50x (ISBN 0-691-09912-X). Princeton U Pr.

Religious Aspects of Swedish Immigration: A Study of Immigrant Churches. George M. Stephenson. LC 69-18790. (American Immigration Collection Ser., No. 1). (Illus.). 1969. Repr. of 1932 ed. 22.50 (ISBN 0-405-00539-3). Ayer Co Pubs.

Religious Aspects of Swedish Immigration. George M. Stephenson. LC 71-137294. Repr. of 1932 ed. 14.00 (ISBN 0-404-06257-1). AMS Pr.

Religious Aspects of the Conquest of Mexico. C. S. Braden. 1976. lib. bdg. 59.95 (ISBN 0-8490-2510-9). Gordon Pr.

Religious Aspects of the Conquest of Mexico. Charles S. Braden. LC 74-181914. Repr. of 1930 ed. 37.50 (ISBN 0-404-00925-5). AMS Pr.

Religious Attitude & Life in Islam. Duncan B. Macdonald. LC 70-121277. Repr. of 1909 ed. 20.50 (ISBN 0-404-04125-6). AMS Pr.

Religious Attitudes of Japanese Men. Fernando M. Basabe. LC 68-57415. 1969. bds. 15.00 (ISBN 0-8048-0651-9). C E Tuttle.

Religious Belief & Character among Jewish Adolescents. Abraham N. Franzblau. LC 78-176783. (Columbia University. Teachers College. Contributions to Education: No. 634). Repr. of 1934 ed. 22.50 (ISBN 0-404-55634-5). AMS Pr.

Religious Belief & Religious Skepticism. Gary Gutting. LC 82-50287. 192p. 1982. text ed. 15.95 (ISBN 0-268-01613-5). U of Notre Dame Pr.

Religious Belief & Religious Skepticism. Gary Gutting. LC 82-50287. xi, 192p. 1983. pap. text ed. 9.95x (ISBN 0-268-01618-6, 85-16189). U of Notre Dame Pr.

Religious Belief & the Will. Louis P. Pojman. (Problems of Philosophy Ser.). 256p. 1986. text ed. 32.50 (ISBN 0-7102-0399-3). Methuen Inc.

Religious Beliefs & White Prejudice. Robert Buis. 71p. 1975. pap. text ed. 7.95x (ISBN 0-86975-044-5, Pub. by Ravan Pr). Ohio U Pr.

Religious Books for Children: An Annotated Bibliography. Patricia Pearl. (Orig.). 1983. pap. 5.95 (ISBN 0-915324-21-0); pap. 4.75 members. CSLA.

Religious Books, 1876-1982, 4 vol. set. 4389p. 1983. 225.00x (ISBN 0-8352-1602-0). Bowker.

Religious Broadcast Management Handbook. Thomas C. Durfey & James A. Ferrier. 1986. pap. 14.95 (ISBN 0-310-39741-3). Zondervan.

Religious Broadcasting, Nineteen Twenty to Nineteen Eighty-Three: A Selectively Annotated Bibliography. Lenwood Davis & George H. Hill. (Reference Library of Social Science). 1984. lib. bdg. 40.00 (ISBN 0-8240-9015-2). Garland Pub.

Religious Buildings. Architectural Record Magazine Staff. 1980. 43.50 (ISBN 0-07-002342-5). McGraw.

Religious Care of the Psychiatric Patient. Wayne E. Oates. LC 78-18454. 252p. 1978. 13.95 (ISBN 0-664-21365-0). Westminster.

Religious Case for Abortion. Ed. by Hamilton Gregory. LC 82-61786. 96p. (Orig.). 1983. pap. 9.95 (ISBN 0-910915-00-8). Madison Polk.

Religious Change & Continuity: Sociological Perspectives. Ed. by Harry M. Johnson. LC 79-83574. (Jossey-Bass Social & Behavioral Science Ser.). pap. 94.80 (2027756). Bks Demand UMI.

Religious Change in an African Town: A Sociological Study of God's Town, Liberia. Richard Stakeman. 1987. 49.95. E Mellen.

Religious Change in Zambia: Exploratory Studies. Wim M. Van Binsbergen. 424p. 1984. pap. 14.95x (ISBN 0-7103-0012-3, Kegan Paul). Methuen Inc.

Religious Change in Zambia: Exploratory Studies. Wim M. J. Van Binsbergen. (Monographs from the African Studies Centre, Leiden). (Illus.). 416p. 1981. 50.00x (ISBN 0-7103-0000-X). Methuen Inc.

Religious Changes in Contemporary Poland: Secularization & Politics. Maciej Pomian-Srzednicki. (International Library of Sociology). 227p. 1982. 27.95x (ISBN 0-7100-9245-8). Methuen Inc.

Religious Chastity: An Ethnological Study, by John Main (Pseud.) Elsie W. Parsons. LC 72-9672. Repr. of 1913 ed. 52.00 (ISBN 0-404-57489-0). AMS Pr.

Religious Concerns in Contemporary Education. Philip H. Phenix. LC 59-11329. Repr. of 1959 ed. 29.50 (ISBN 0-8357-9605-1, 2016949). Bks Demand UMI.

Religious Confessions & Confessants. Anna R. Burr. 1977. lib. bdg. 59.95 (ISBN 0-8490-2511-7). Gordon Pr.
Religious Conflict in America: A Bibliography. Albert J. Menendez. LC 84-48078. (Reference Library of Social Science). 500p. 1984. lib. bdg. 20.00 (ISBN 0-8240-8904-9). Garland Pub.
Religious Conflict in Fourth Century Rome. B. F. Croke & J. D. Harris. (Sources in Ancient History Ser.). 139p. (Orig.). 1982. pap. 21.00x (ISBN 0-424-00091-1, Pub. by Sydney U Pr Australia). Intl Spec Bk.
Religious Conflict in Social Context: The Resurgence of Orthodox Judaism in Frankfurt Am Main, 1838-1877. Robert Liberles. LC 84-27981. (Contributions to the Study of Religion Ser.: No. 13). xvi, 297p. 1985. lib. bdg. 29.95 (ISBN 0-313-24806-0, LRX/). Greenwood.
Religious Congregations & Health Care Facilities: Accountability & Adaptation. LC 83-5228. 86p. (Orig.). 1983. pap. 7.00 (ISBN 0-87125-083-7). Cath Health.
Religious Congregations & Health Care Facilities: Commitment & Collaboration. LC 81-18064. 100p. 1982. pap. 6.00 (ISBN 0-87125-073-X). Cath Health.
Religious Congregations & Health Facilities: Tradition & Transition. LC 84-7692. 100p. (Orig.). 1984. pap. 9.00 (ISBN 0-87125-095-0). Cath Health.
Religious Consciousness: A Psychological Study. James B. Pratt. 1971. Repr. of 1920 ed. 21.95x (ISBN 0-02-850350-3). Hafner.
Religious Controversies of the Elizabethan Age: A Survey of Printed Sources. Peter Milward. LC 77-80038. xvi, 202p. 1977. 21.00x (ISBN 0-8032-0923-1). U of Nebr Pr.
Religious Controversies of the Nineteenth Century: Selected Documents. Ed. by A. O. Cockshut. LC 66-18225. vi, 265p. 1966. 19.95x (ISBN 0-8032-0019-6). U of Nebr Pr.
Religious Conversions in India. Brojendra N. Bannerjee. 384p. 1982. 29.95x (ISBN 0-940500-28-0, Pub. by Harnam Pub India). Asia Bk Corp.
Religious Crises in Modern America. Martin E. Marty. LC 81-80740. (Charles Edmondson Historical Lectures Ser.). 40p. (Orig.). 1981. pap. 4.50 (ISBN 0-918954-26-6). Baylor Univ Pr.
Religious Cults Associated with the Amazons. Florence M. Anderson. LC 73-158253. Repr. of 1912 ed. 16.00 (ISBN 0-404-00749-X). AMS Pr.
Religious Cults Associated with the Amazons. F. M. Bennett. v, 79p. 1985. Repr. of 1912 ed. lib. bdg. 25.00x (ISBN 0-89241-204-6). Caratzas.
Religious Cults Today: A Challenge to Christian Families. John A. Saliba. 48p. 1983. pap. 1.50 (ISBN 0-89243-189-X). Liguori Pubns.
Religious Currents in the Nineteenth Century. Vilhelm Gronbech. Tr. by P. M. Mitchell & W. D. Paden. LC 72-11829. (Arcturus Bks. Paperbacks). 206p. 1973. lib. bdg. 7.00x (ISBN 0-8093-0629-8); pap. 2.45x (ISBN 0-8093-0630-1). S Ill U Pr.
Religious Dances in the Christian & in Popular Medicine. Eugene L. Backman. Ed. by E. Classen. LC 77-8069. 1977. Repr. of 1952 ed. 32.00x (ISBN 0-8371-9678-7, BARD). Greenwood.
Religious Data: Recurrent Christian Sources, Non-Recurrent Christian Data, Judaism, Other Religions. L. M. Barley et al. (Reviews of U. K. Statistical Sources Ser.: No. 20). 635p. 1987. 86.50 (ISBN 0-08-034778-9). Pergamon.
Religious Denominations in the United States: Their Past History, Present Condition, & Doctrines. Israel D. Rupp. LC 72-2943. Repr. of 1861 ed. 67.50 (ISBN 0-404-10709-5). AMS Pr.
Religious Development in the Province of North Carolina. Stephen B. Weeks. LC 78-63811. (Johns Hopkins University. Studies in the Social Sciences. Tenth Ser. 1892: 5-6). Repr. of 1892 ed. 11.50 (ISBN 0-404-61074-9). AMS Pr.
Religious Dimension in Hispanic Los Angeles: A Protestant Case Study. Clifton L. Holland. LC 74-5123. 542p. (Orig.). 1974. pap. 10.95 (ISBN 0-87808-309-X). William Carey Lib.
Religious Dimension: New Directions in Quantitative Research. Ed. by Robert Wuthnow. LC 79-6948. 1979. 29.95 (ISBN 0-12-766050-X). Acad Pr.
Religious Discourse: Thanksgiving Day Sermon, November 26, 1789. Gershom M. Seixas. LC 77-7298. (Illus.). 1977. pap. 2.00 (ISBN 0-916790-00-2). Jewish Hist.
Religious Diversity. Wilfred C. Smith. (Crossroad Paperback Ser.). 224p. 1982. pap. 7.95 (ISBN 0-8245-0458-5). Crossroad NY.
Religious Dogmatics & the Evolution of Societies. Niklas Luhmann. Tr. by Peter Beyer. LC 84-8976. (Studies in Religion & Society: Vol. 9). 192p. 1984. 49.95x (ISBN 0-88946-866-4). E Mellen.
Religious Doubt: Its Nature, Treatment, Causes, Difficulties, Consequences & Dissolution. John W. Diggle. 1978. Repr. of 1895 ed. lib. bdg. 25.00 (ISBN 0-8495-1030-9). Arden Lib.
Religious Drama: Ends & Means. Harold A. Ehrensperger & Stanley Lehrer. LC 77-22986. (Illus.). 1977. Repr. of 1962 ed. lib. bdg. 32.50x (ISBN 0-8371-9744-9, EHRD). Greenwood.
Religious Drama, Vol. 1: Five Plays. Ed. by Marvin Halverson. 11.25 (ISBN 0-8446-2792-5). Peter Smith.
Religious Drama, Vol. 2: 21 Medieval Mystery & Morality Plays. Ed. by E. Martin Browne. 17.75 (ISBN 0-8446-2793-3). Peter Smith.
Religious Drama, Vol. 3. Ed. by Marvin Halverson. 11.25 (ISBN 0-8446-2794-1). Peter Smith.
Religious Ecstasy. Ed. by Nils G. Holm. (Scripta Instituti Donnerain Aboensis: No. XI). 306p. 1982. pap. text ed. 25.00x (ISBN 91-22-00574-9, Pub. by Almqvist & Wiksell Sweden). Humanities.
Religious Education & Our Ultimate Committment: An Application of Henry Nelson Wieman's Philosophy of Creative Interchange. Harold Rosen. LC 84-19651. 196p. (Orig.). 1985. lib. bdg. 24.25 (ISBN 0-8191-4341-3, Unitarian Univ Assn); pap. text ed. 10.75 (ISBN 0-8191-4342-1, Unitarian Univ. Assn.). U Pr of Amer.
Religious Education & the Future. Ed. by Dermot Lane. 240p. (Orig.). 1987. pap. 9.95 (ISBN 0-8091-2877-2). Paulist Pr.
Religious Education & Theology. Ed. by Norma H. Thompson. LC 81-17852. 254p. 1982. pap. 12.95 (ISBN 0-89135-029-2). Religious Educ.
Religious Education, Catechesis & Freedom. Kenneth Barker. LC 81-13962. 255p. (Orig.). 1981. pap. 12.95 (ISBN 0-89135-028-4). Religious Educ.
Religious Education: Chicago, 1906-1955, Vols. 1-50. Repr. of 1955 ed. Set. lib. bdg. 2250.00 (ISBN 0-685-77259-4); lib. bdg. 45.00 ea. AMS Pr.
Religious Education Development. Gabriel Moran. (Images for the Future). 204p. 1983. pap. 12.95 (ISBN 0-86683-692-6, AY8272, HarpR). Har-Row.
Religious Education Five-Twelve. Derek Bastide. 27.00 (ISBN 1-85000-149-9, Falmer Press); pap. 14.00 (ISBN 1-85000-150-2). Taylor & Francis.
Religious Education Handbook: A Practical Parish Guide. James P. Enswiler. LC 79-26008. 108p. (Orig.). 1980. pap. 4.95 (ISBN 0-8189-0398-8). Alba.
Religious Education in a Pluralistic Society. M. C. Felderhof. 160p. 1985. pap. text ed. 18.95 (ISBN 0-340-35413-5). Princeton Bk Co.
Religious Education in a Psychological Key. John H. Peatling. LC 81-8678. 439p. (Orig.). 1981. pap. 14.95 (ISBN 0-89135-027-6). Religious Educ.
Religious Education in German Schools: An Historical Approach. Ernst C. Helmreich. LC 59-11509. 1959. 22.50x (ISBN 0-674-75850-1). Harvard U Pr.
Religious Education: Its Effects, Its Challenges Today. Robert J. Fox. 1972. pap. 0.95 (ISBN 0-8198-0344-8). Dghtrs St Paul.
Religious Education Ministry with Youth. Ed. by D. Campbell Wyckoff & Don Richter. LC 81-19239. 257p. (Orig.). 1982. pap. 12.95 (ISBN 0-89135-030-6). Religious Educ.
Religious Education, Nineteen Forty-Four to Nineteen Eighty-Four. Ed. by A. G. Wedderspoon. 238p. 1968. 3.95 (ISBN 0-87921-063-X); pap. 1.95 (ISBN 0-87921-064-8). Attic Pr.
Religious Education of Adults. Leon McKenzie. LC 81-19926. 256p. 1982. pap. 12.95 (ISBN 0-89135-031-4). Religious Educ.
Religious Education of Older Adults. Linda J. Vogel. LC 83-21109. 217p. (Orig.). 1984. pap. 12.95 (ISBN 0-89135-040-3). Religious Educ.
Religious Education of Preschool Children. Lucie W. Barber. LC 80-27623. 196p. (Orig.). 1981. pap. 12.95 (ISBN 0-89135-026-8). Religious Educ.
Religious Education of the Deaf. Ed. by J. Van Eijndhoven. (Modern Approaches to the Diagnosis & Instruction of Multi-Handicapped Children Ser.: Vol. 11). 168p. 1973. text ed. 14.75 (ISBN 90-237-4111-0, Pub. by Swets & Zeitlinger Netherlands). Hogrefe Intl.
Religious Education: Philosophical Perspectives. John Sealey. Ed. by Philip Snelders & Colin Wringe. (Introductory Studies in the Philosophy of Education). 120p. 1985. text ed. 19.95x (ISBN 0-04-370130-2); pap. text ed. 7.95x (ISBN 0-04-370131-0). Allen Unwin.
Religious Education We Need: Toward the Renewal of Christian Education. Ed. by James M. Lee. LC 76-55587. 174p. (Orig.). 1977. pap. 7.95 (ISBN 0-89135-005-5). Religious Educ.
Religious Enthusiasm in the New World: Heresy to Revolution. David S. Lovejoy. 336p. 1985. text ed. 25.00x (ISBN 0-674-75864-1). Harvard U Pr.
Religious Ethics & Pastoral Care. Don S. Browning. LC 83-5589. (Theology & Pastoral Care Ser.). 128p. 1983. pap. 7.95 (ISBN 0-8006-1725-8, 1-1725). Fortress.
Religious Experience. Wayne Proudfoot. LC 84-23928. 1985. 30.00x (ISBN 0-520-05143-2). U of Cal Pr.
Religious Experience: A Social-Psychological Perspective. Daniel C. Batson & W. Larry Ventis. (Illus.). 1982. text ed. 29.95x (ISBN 0-19-503030-3); pap. text ed. 15.95x (ISBN 0-19-503031-1). Oxford U Pr.
Religious Experience & Other Essays & Addresses. William Temple. Ed. by A. E. Baker. 270p. 1959. 10.95 (ISBN 0-227-67579-7). Attic Pr.
Religious Experience & Religious Belief: Essays in the Epistemology of Religion. Ed. by Joseph Runzo & Graig K. Ihara. LC 86-1614. 160p. 1986. lib. bdg. 23.50 (ISBN 0-8191-5292-7); pap. text ed. 10.75 (ISBN 0-8191-5293-5). U Pr of Amer.
Religious Experience & Scientific Method. Henry N. Wieman. Repr. of 1926 ed. lib. bdg. 22.50x (ISBN 0-8371-4368-3, WIRE). Greenwood.
Religious Experience & Scientific Method. Henry N. Wieman. 387p. 1971. Repr. of 1927 ed. lib. bdg. 11.95x (ISBN 0-8093-0537-2). S Ill U Pr.
Religious Experience & Scientific Method. Henry N. Wieman. (Arcturus Books Paperbacks). 387p. 1971. pap. 9.95x (ISBN 0-8093-0530-5). S Ill U Pr.
Religious Experience: Its Nature & Function in the Human Psyche. Walter H. Clark et al. (Illus.). 168p. 1973. 13.00x (ISBN 0-398-02550-9). C C Thomas.
Religious Experience: Its Nature, Types, & Validity. Alan C. Bouquet. LC 75-40997. 140p. 1976. Repr. of 1968 ed. lib. bdg. 22.50x (ISBN 0-8371-8714-1, BORL). Greenwood.
Religious Experience of John Humphrey Noyes, Founder of the Oneida Community. facsimile ed. John H. Noyes. Ed. by George W. Noyes. (Select Bibliographies Reprint Ser). Repr. of 1923 ed. 26.50 (ISBN 0-8369-5750-4). Ayer Co Pubs.
Religious Experience of John Humphrey Noyes. Ed. by George W. Noyes. 1923. 15.00x (ISBN 0-8156-8060-0). Syracuse U Pr.
Religious Experience of Mankind. 3rd ed. Ninian Smart. (Scribner Press Ser.). (Illus.). 656p. 1984. 30.00 (ISBN 0-684-18077-4, ScribT). Scribner.
Religious Experience of Mankind. 3rd ed. Ninian Smart. LC 83-20169. (Illus.). 634p. 1984. pap. text ed. 17.95 (ISBN 0-02-412130-4, Pub. by Scribner). Macmillan.
Religious Experience of the Primitive Church Proir to the Influence of Paul. P. G. Hopwood. 1977. lib. bdg. 59.95 (ISBN 0-8490-2512-5). Gordon Pr.
Religious Experiencing: William James & Eugene Gendlin. John J. Shea. 156p. (Orig.). 1987. lib. bdg. 22.50 (ISBN 0-8191-6136-5); pap. text ed. 10.75 (ISBN 0-8191-6137-3). U Pr of Amer.
Religious Explanations: A Model from the Sciences. Edward L. Schoen. LC 84-24237. xiv, 226p. 1985. text ed. 24.75 (ISBN 0-8223-0616-6). Duke.
Religious Factor: A Sociological Study of Religion's Impact on Politics, Economics, & Family Life. Gerhard E. Lenski. LC 77-1275. 1977. Repr. of 1961 ed. lib. bdg. 27.50x (ISBN 0-8371-9506-3, LERF). Greenwood.
Religious Faith & Twentieth Century Man. F. C. Happold. 192p. 1981. 6.95 (ISBN 0-8245-0046-6). Crossroad NY.
Religious Faith & World Culture. Ed. by Amandus W. Loos. LC 71-128270. (Essay Index Reprint Ser). 1951. 20.00 (ISBN 0-8369-1976-9). Ayer Co Pubs.
Religious Faith of Great Men. facs. ed. Archer Wallace. LC 67-26792. (Essay Index Reprint Ser). 1934. 17.00 (ISBN 0-8369-0968-2). Ayer Co Pubs.
Religious Fanaticism. Hannah Smith. Ed. & intro. by Ray Strachey. LC 72-8252. Orig. Title: Group Movements of the Past & Experiments in Guidance. Repr. of 1928 ed. 21.50 (ISBN 0-404-11005-3). AMS Pr.
Religious Ferment in Asia. Ed. by Robert J. Miller. LC 73-11401. xii, 196p. 1974. 22.50x (ISBN 0-7006-0111-2). U Pr of KS.
Religious Ferment in Modern India. Hal W. French & Arvind Sharma. 1982. 19.95x (ISBN 0-312-67134-2). St Martin.
Religious Folk Art in America: Reflections of Faith. C. Kurt Dewhurst et al. (Illus.). 163p. 1983. 29.95 (ISBN 0-525-93300-X, 02908-870). Dutton.
Religious Foundation of Human Relations: Beyond Games. George Henderson. LC 76-62510. 1977. 15.95x (ISBN 0-8061-1398-7). U of Okla Pr.
Religious Foundations of the Jewish State: The Concept & Practice of Jewish Statehood from Biblical Times to the Modern State of Israel. M. Lewittes. 25.00x (ISBN 0-87068-433-7). Ktav.
Religious Freedom. Ed. by Neophytos Edelby & Teodoro-J. Urresti. LC 66-29260. (Concilium Ser.: Vol. 18). 191p. 7.95 (ISBN 0-8091-0124-6). Paulist Pr.
Religious Freedom. L. Pfeffer. Ed. by Franklyn S. Haiman. (To Protect These Rights Ser.). 192p. 1983. pap. 12.95 (ISBN 0-8442-6001-0, 6001-0, Passport Bks.). Natl Textbk.
Religious Freedom in Spain: Its Ebb & Flow. facsimile ed. John D. Hughey. LC 77-119935. (Select Bibliographies Reprint Ser). Repr. of 1955 ed. 21.50 (ISBN 0-8369-5378-9). Ayer Co Pubs.
Religious Freedom, Nineteen Sixty-Five to Nineteen Seventy-Five: A Symposium on a Historic Document. Ed. by Walter J. Burghardt. LC 76-45938. 1977. pap. 2.95 (ISBN 0-8091-1993-5). Paulist Pr.
Religious Freedom under Indian Constitution. Krishna Prasad. 1976. 9.00x (ISBN 0-88386-839-3). South Asia Bks.
Religious Healing in the Veda. Kenneth G. Zysk. LC 84-45899. (Transaction Ser.: Vol. 75 Pt. 7). 300p. 1986. 30.00 (ISBN 0-87169-757-2). Am Philos.
Religious Heritage of America. Albert M. Shulman. LC 81-3594. (Illus.). 480p. 1982. 25.00 (ISBN 0-498-02162-9). A S Barnes.
Religious History of America. Edwin S. Gaustad. 1974. pap. 10.95 (ISBN 0-06-063093-0, RD/66, HarpR). Har-Row.
Religious History of the American People. S. E. Ahlstrom. LC 72-151564. (Illus.). 1120p. 1972. 50.00x (ISBN 0-300-01475-9); pap. 18.95x (ISBN 0-300-01762-6). Yale U Pr.
Religious Humanism. Eugene Kohn. LC 53-10661. 154p. 1953. pap. 8.95 (ISBN 0-935457-24-0). Reconstructionist Pr.
Religious Ideas of Harriet Beecher Stowe: Her Gospel of Womanhood. Gayle Kimball. LC 82-80377. (Studies in Women & Religion: Vol. 8). 216p. 1982. 49.95x (ISBN 0-88946-544-4). E Mellen.
Religious Imagination. James Mackey. 256p. 1986. 17.50x (ISBN 0-85224-512-2, Pub. by Edinburgh U Pr Scotland). Columbia U Pr.
Religious Imagination: A Study in Psychonalysis & Jewish Theology. Richard L. Rubenstein. LC 85-15825. (Brown Classics in Judaica Ser.). 276p. 1985. pap. text ed. 12.50 (ISBN 0-8191-4539-4). U Pr of Amer.
Religious Imagination & the Sense of God. John Bowker. 1978. text ed. 32.50x (ISBN 0-19-826646-4). Oxford U Pr.
Religious Imagination: God's Gift to Prophets & Preachers. Robert D. Young. LC 78-26843. 176p. 1979. pap. 6.95 (ISBN 0-664-24239-1). Westminster.
Religious in the Nineteen Eighty-Three Code. 1985. 5.50 (ISBN 0-8199-0884-3). Franciscan Herald.
Religious Innovation in Africa: Collected Essays on New Religious Movements. Harold W. Turner. 1979. lib. bdg. 32.50 (ISBN 0-8161-8303-1, Hall Reference). G K Hall.
Religious Inquiry: An Introduction to the Why & How. Samuel Southard. LC 76-20449. Repr. of 1976 ed. 24.20 (ISBN 0-8357-9024-X, 2016398). Bks Demand UMI.
Religious Inquiry: Participation & Detachment. Holmes Rolston, III. LC 83-24602. 323p. 1985. 22.50 (ISBN 0-8022-2450-4). Philos Lib.
Religious Institutes, Secular Institutes, Societies of the Apostolic Life. Ed. by Jordan Hite et al. (Handbook on Canons Ser.: Nos. 573-746). 400p. 1985. pap. 22.50 (ISBN 0-8146-1403-5). Liturgical Pr.
Religious Institutions. Joan Brothers. (Aspects of Modern Sociology Ser.). 1971. pap. text ed. 6.95 (ISBN 0-582-48120-1). Humanities.
Religious Institutions & Cults in the Deccan. R. N. Nandi. 1973. 8.50 (ISBN 0-8426-0564-9). Orient Bk Dist.
Religious Instruction of the Negroes in the United States. C. C. Jones. 1842. 23.00 (ISBN 0-527-46700-6). Kraus Repr.
Religious Instruction of the Negroes in the United States. facs. ed. Charles C. Jones. LC 70-149869. (Black Heritage Library Collection). 1842. 16.50 (ISBN 0-8369-8718-7). Ayer Co Pubs.
Religious Instruction of the Negroes in the United States. Charles C. Jones. LC 73-82466. Repr. of 1842 ed. 22.50x (ISBN 0-8371-1645-7, JOI&). Greenwood.
Religious Investigations of William James. Henry S. Levinson & Ralph Levering. LC 80-26109. (Studies in Religion). xii, 316p. 1981. 27.50x (ISBN 0-8078-1468-7). U of NC Pr.
Religious Issues in Nineteenth Century Feminism. Donna A. Behnke. LC 80-52544. 300p. 1982. 22.50x (ISBN 0-87875-203-X). Whitston Pub.

Religious Knowledge. Paul F. Schmidt. LC 79-8726. ix, 147p. 1981. Repr. of 1961 ed. lib. bdg. 22.50x (ISBN 0-313-22188-X, SCRK). Greenwood.
Religious Language & the Problem of Religious Knowledge. Ed. by Ronald E. Santoni. LC 68-27352. Repr. of 1968 ed. 95.50 (ISBN 0-8357-9238-2, 2017640). Bks Demand UMI.
Religious Language of Nicholas of Cusa. James E. Biechler. LC 75-23096. (American Academy of Religion, Dissertation Ser.). 240p. 1975. pap. 10.25 (ISBN 0-89130-021-X, 01 01 08). Scholars Pr GA.
Religious Language of Thomas Traherne's Centuries. Kenneth J. Ames. (Religion & Literature Ser.). 1979. lib. bdg. 59.95 (ISBN 0-87700-260-6). Revisionist Pr.
Religious Liberals & Conservatives: A Comparison of Those Who Are Liberal in Their Religious Thinking & Those Who Are Conservative. Thomas A. Symington. LC 70-177727. (Columbia University. Teachers College. Contributions to Education: No. 640). Repr. of 1935 ed. 22.50 (ISBN 0-404-55640-X). AMS Pr.
Religious Liberty: An Inquiry. M. Searle Bates. LC 77-166096. (Civil Liberties in American History Ser.). 1972. Repr. of 1945 ed. lib. bdg. 59.50 (ISBN 0-306-70235-5). Da Capo.
Religious Liberty & Human Rights in Nations & in Religions. Ed. by Leonard Swidler. 255p. (Orig.). 1986. pap. 9.95 (ISBN 0-931214-06-8). Ecumenical Phila.
Religious Liberty & the Secular State. John M. Swomley. 140p. 1987. 16.95x (ISBN 0-87975-373-0); pap. 10.95 (ISBN 0-87975-398-6). Prometheus Bks.
Religious Liberty in Eastern Europe: A Test Case for Human Rights. pap. cancelled (ISBN 0-686-15372-3, B-122). US Catholic.
Religious Life. Elio Gambaci. 25.00 (ISBN 0-8198-6416-1). Dghtrs St Paul.
Religious Life & the Poor: Liberation Theology Perspectives. Alejandro Cussianovich. Tr. by John Drury from Sp. LC 78-16740. Orig. Title: Desde los Pobres de la Tiera. 168p. (Orig.). 1979. pap. 1.74 (ISBN 0-88344-429-1). Orbis Bks.
Religious Life at the Crossroads. Ed. by David A. Fleming. 200p. (Orig.). 1985. pap. 8.95 (ISBN 0-8091-2709-1). Paulist Pr.
Religious Life in the Light of Vatican 2. Daughters Of St. Paul. (Orig.). 4.00 (ISBN 0-8198-0132-1). Dghtrs St Paul.
Religious Life of Ancient Rome. Jesse B. Carter. 270p. 1972. Repr. of 1911 ed. lib. bdg. 27.50x (ISBN 0-8154-0429-8). Cooper Sq.
Religious Life of Fugitive Slaves & Rise of the Coloured Baptist Churches, 1820-1865, in What Is Now Ontario. James K. Lewis. Ed. by Edwin S. Gaustad. LC 79-52574. (Baptist Tradition Ser.). 1980. lib. bdg. 21.00x (ISBN 0-405-12442-2). Ayer Co Pubs.
Religious Life of Oliver Cromwell. H. Lovell Cocks. LC 61-47823. 1961. text ed. 6.00x (ISBN 0-8401-0443-X). A R Allenson.
Religious Life of Samuel Johnson. Charles R. Pierce, Jr. LC 82-13938. 184p. 1982. lib. bdg. 21.50 (ISBN 0-208-01992-8, Archon). Shoe String.
Religious Life of Theological Students. Benjamin B. Warfield. 1983. pap. 0.95 (ISBN 0-87552-524-5). Presby & Reformed.
Religious Life of Thomas Jefferson. Charles B. Sanford. LC 83-21649. 246p. 1984. 13.95x (ISBN 0-8139-0996-1). U Pr of Va.
Religious Life or Secular Institute. Jean Beyer. 1970. pap. 2.75 (ISBN 0-8294-0319-1, Pub. by Gregorian U Pr). Loyola.
Religious Life Today. John A. Hardon. 1977. 3.00 (ISBN 0-8198-0452-5). Dghtrs St Paul.
Religious Life Today. Karl Rahner. 1976. 5.95 (ISBN 0-8245-0371-6). Crossroad NY.
Religious Lyrics of the Thirteenth, Fourteenth, & Fifteenth Centuries, 3 vols. Carleton Brown. 300.00 (ISBN 0-8490-0942-1). Gordon Pr.
Religious Melancholy or Psychological Depression: Some Issues Involved in Relating Psychology & Religion As Illustrated in a Study of Elie Wiesel. Christopher J. Frost. 274p. (Orig.). 1985. lib. bdg. 27.75 (ISBN 0-8191-4496-7); pap. text ed. 13.50 (ISBN 0-8191-4497-5). U Pr of Amer.
Religious Ministry in a Transcendentless Culture. Ronald B. Mayers. LC 79-3424. 1980. pap. text ed. 10.75 (ISBN 0-8191-0889-8). U Pr of Amer.
Religious Minorities in Australia. Gregory Tillett. 1985. 27.95x (ISBN 0-19-554555-9). Oxford U Pr.
Religious Mission of the Irish People & Catholic Colonization. John L. Spalding. 17.00 (ISBN 0-405-10859-1, 11857). Ayer Co Pubs.
Religious Motivation: Biographical & Sociological Problems for the Church Historian. Derek Baker. (Studies in Church History: Vol. 15). 516p. 1978. 45.00x (ISBN 0-631-19250-6). Basil Blackwell.
Religious Motive in Philanthropy. Henry B. Washburn. LC 72-105047. (Essay Index Reprint Ser). 1931. 18.00 (ISBN 0-8369-1634-4). Ayer Co Pubs.
Religious Movements: Genesis, Exodus, & Numbers. Ed. by Rodney Stark. LC 85-9539. (Sociology of Religion Ser.). 369p. 1986. 24.95 (ISBN 0-913757-43-8, Pub by New Era Bks); pap. 12.95 (ISBN 0-913757-44-6, Pub. by New Era Bks). Paragon Hse.
Religious Movements in Contemporary America. Ed. by Irving I. Zaretsky & Mark P. Leone. LC 73-39054. 900p. 1974. 71.00 (ISBN 0-691-07186-1); pap. 18.50x (ISBN 0-691-01993-2). Princeton U Pr.
Religious Movements of Bengal, 1800-1850. Aparna Bhattacharya. 1984. pap. 9.00x (ISBN 0-8364-1118-8, Pub. by New Times). South Asia Bks.
Religious Mythology & the Art of War: Comparative Religious Symbolisms of Military Violence. James A. Aho. LC 80-23465. (Contributions to the Study of Religion Ser.: No. 3). 264p. 1981. lib. bdg. 29.95 (ISBN 0-313-22564-8, ARM/). Greenwood.
Religious Newspapers in the Old Northwest to 1861: A History, Bibliography, & Record of Opinion. Wesley Norton. LC 75-36983. xi, 196p. 1977. 12.50x (ISBN 0-8214-0193-9). Ohio U Pr.
Religious Opinions & Example of Milton, Locke, & Newton. Henry Acton. LC 71-158223. Repr. of 1833 ed. 11.50 (ISBN 0-404-00283-8). AMS Pr.
Religious Opinions of Milton, Locke & Newton. Herbert McLachlan. LC 74-20740. 1974. Repr. of 1941 ed. lib. bdg. 35.00 (ISBN 0-8414-5930-4). Folcroft.
Religious Opinions of Milton, Locke & Newton. Herbert McLachlan. LC 74-173539. 1972. Repr. of 1941 ed. 12.00x (ISBN 0-8462-1623-X). Russell.
Religious Orders in England. David Knowles. Incl. Vol. 1. The Old Orders. 1948. 57.50 (ISBN 0-521-05480-X); Vol. 2. End of the Middle Ages. 1955. 67.50 (ISBN 0-521-05481-8); pap. 22.95 (ISBN 0-521-29567-X); Vol. 3. The Tudor Age. David Knowles. 1979. 72.50 (ISBN 0-521-05482-6); pap. 24.95 (ISBN 0-521-29568-8). Cambridge U Pr.
Religious Organization: A Trend Report & Bibliography Prepared for the International Sociological Association Under the Auspices of the International Committee for Social Science Documentation. James A. Beckford. (La Sociologie Contemporaine: Vol. 21, No. 2). 1973. pap. 11.60x (ISBN 90-2797-851-4). Mouton.
Religious Organization & Religious Experience. Ed. by J. Davis. (ASA Monograph). 1982. 42.00 (ISBN 0-12-206580-8). Acad Pr.
Religious Origins of Modern Science: Belief in Creation in Seventeenth-Century Thought. Eugene M. Klaaren. LC 85-17804. 256p. 1985. pap. text ed. 12.75 (ISBN 0-8191-4922-5). U Pr of Amer.
Religious Origins of the American Revolution. Page Smith. LC 76-13157. (American Academy of Religion, Aids for the Study of Religion). 1976. pap. 8.95 (ISBN 0-89130-121-6, 010303). Scholars Pr GA.
Religious Outsiders & the Making of Americans. R. Laurence Moore. 288p. 1986. text ed. 24.95x (ISBN 0-19-503663-8). Oxford U Pr.
Religious Painting. Stephanie Brown. LC 78-24454. (Mayflower Gallery). (Illus.). 1979. 12.50 (ISBN 0-8317-7370-7, Mayflower Bks); pap. 6.95 (ISBN 0-8317-7371-5). Smith Pubs.
Religious Periodical Press in China, 2 vols. Rudolph Lownethal. (Illus.). 300p. Repr. of 1940 ed. Set. text ed. 45.50x (ISBN 0-89644-569-0, Pub. by Chinese Matl Ctr). Coronet Bks.
Religious Periodicals Directory. Graham Cornish. (Clio Periodicals Directories Ser.). 250p. 1986. lib. bdg. 89.00 (ISBN 0-87436-365-9). ABC-Clio.
Religious Periodicals of the United States: Academic & Scholarly Journals. Ed. by Charles H. Lippy. LC 85-9861. (Historical Guides to the World's Periodicals & Newspapers Ser.). 626p. 1986. lib. bdg. 65.00 (ISBN 0-313-23420-5, LRP/). Greenwood.
Religious Perplexities. 3rd ed. Lawrence P. Jacks. LC 77-27149. (Hibbert Lectures: 1922). Repr. of 1923 ed. 20.00 (ISBN 0-404-60421-8). AMS Pr.
Religious Perspectives & Problems: An Introduction to the Philosophy of Religion. Ed. by Allen V. Eikner. LC 80-67265. 368p. 1980. lib. bdg. 29.75 (ISBN 0-8191-1215-1); pap. text ed. 15.25 (ISBN 0-8191-1216-X). U Pr of Amer.
Religious Philanthropy & Colonial Slavery: The American Correspondence of the Associates of Dr. Bray, 1717-1777. Ed. & intro. by John C. Van Horne. LC 84-2766. (Blacks in the New World Ser.). 400p. 1985. 29.95 (ISBN 0-252-01142-2). U of Ill Pr.
Religious Philosophy: A Group of Essays. Harry A. Wolfson. LC 61-16696. 1961. 17.50x (ISBN 0-674-75900-1, Belknap Pr). Harvard U Pr.
Religious Philosophy of Josiah Royce. Josiah Royce. Ed. by Stuart G. Brown. LC 76-4496. 239p. 1976. Repr. of 1952 ed. lib. bdg. 22.50x (ISBN 0-8371-8810-5, RORP). Greenwood.
Religious Philosophy of Plotinus & Some Modern Philosophies of Religion. W. R. Inge. 1977. lib. bdg. 59.95 (ISBN 0-8490-2513-3). Gordon Pr.
Religious Philosophy of William James. R. R. Sahay. 1980. text ed. 18.95x. Coronet Bks.
Religious Philosophy of William James. Robert J. Vanden Burgt. LC 80-22936. 176p. 1981. text ed. 19.95x (ISBN 0-88229-594-2); pap. text ed. 9.95x (ISBN 0-88229-767-8). Nelson-Hall.
Religious Platonism. James K. Feibleman. LC 78-161628. 236p. Repr. of 1959 ed. lib. bdg. 22.50x (ISBN 0-8371-6184-3, FERP). Greenwood.
Religious Pluralism. Ed. by Leroy S. Rouner. LC 84-7431. (Boston University Studies in Philosphy & Religion: Vol. 5). 256p. 1984. text ed. 22.95 (ISBN 0-268-01626-7, 85-16262). U of Notre Dame Pr.
Religious Poems of Richard Crashaw with an Introductory Study. R. A. Shepherd. 1979. Repr. of 1914 ed. lib. bdg. 35.00 (ISBN 0-8495-4942-6). Arden Lib.
Religious Policy of the Bavarian Government During the Napoleonic Period. Chester P. Higby. LC 19-12150. (Columbia University. Studies in the Social Sciences: No. 196). Repr. of 1919 ed. 36.00 (ISBN 0-404-51196-1). AMS Pr.
Religious Potential of the Child. Sofia Cavalletti. 224p. 1982. pap. 10.95 (ISBN 0-8091-2389-4). Paulist Pr.
Religious Poverty & the Profit Economy in Medieval Europe. Lester K. Little. LC 78-58630. 278p. (Orig.). 1983. pap. 10.95x (ISBN 0-8014-9247-5). Cornell U Pr.
Religious Practices of Primitive Peoples. Norman P. Mayfair. (Illus.). 139p. 1980. deluxe ed. 67.75 (ISBN 0-89266-241-7). Am Classical Coll.
Religious Press in America. Martin E. Marty et al. LC 72-6844. 184p. 1973. Repr. of 1963 ed. lib. bdg. 22.50x (ISBN 0-8371-6500-8, MARP). Greenwood.
Religious Press in the South Atlantic States, 1802-1865. Henry S. Stroupe. (Duke University. Trinity College Historical Socity. Historical Papers: No. 32). Repr. of 1956 ed. 24.50 (ISBN 0-404-51782-X). AMS Pr.
Religious Progress on the Pacific Slope: Addresses & Papers at the Celebration of the Semi-Centennial Anniversary of Pacific School of Religion, Berkeley, California. facs. ed. Pacific School Of Religion. LC 68-22941. (Essay Index Reprint Ser). 1968. Repr. of 1917 ed. 19.00 (ISBN 0-8369-0820-1). Ayer Co Pubs.
Religious Quests of the Graeco-Roman World. S. Angus. 1929. 30.00 (ISBN 0-686-20108-6). Quality Lib.
Religious Quests of the Graeco-Roman World: A Study in the Historical Background of Early Christianity. Samuel Angus. LC 66-30791. 1929. 18.00 (ISBN 0-8196-0196-9). Biblo.
Religious Reason: The Rational & Moral Basis of Religious Belief. Ronald M. Green. 1978. text ed. 18.95x (ISBN 0-19-502388-9); pap. text ed. 7.95x (ISBN 0-19-502389-7). Oxford U Pr.
Religious Repression in Cuba. Juan Clark. 115p. (Orig.). 1986. pap. 8.95 (ISBN 0-935501-04-5). U Miami N-S Ctr.
Religious Revolt in the Seventeenth Century: The Schism of the Russian Church. Nickolas B. Lupinin. 220p. 1984. 24.00 (ISBN 0-940670-12-7). Kingston Pr.
Religious Revolution in the Ivory Coast: The Prophet Harris & the Harris Church. Sheila S. Walker. LC 81-13010. (Studies in Religion). xvii, 206p. 1983. 29.95x (ISBN 0-8078-1503-9). U of NC Pr.
Religious Right & the Christian Faith. Gabriel Fackre. 1982. 8.95 (ISBN 0-8028-3566-X); pap. 4.95 (ISBN 0-8028-1983-4). Eerdmans.
Religious Roots of Rebellion: Christians in Central American Revolutions. Philip Berryman. LC 83-19343. 480p. (Orig.). 1984. pap. 19.95 (ISBN 0-88344-105-5). Orbis Bks.
Religious School Board: A Manual. Louis Lister & Rebecca Lister. 1978. pap. 5.00 (ISBN 0-8074-0014-9, 243870). UAHC.
Religious Schools in America: A Selected Bibliography. Thomas C. Hunt et al. LC 86-12118. (Reference Library of Social Science: Vol. 338). 416p. 1986. lib. bdg. 47.00 (ISBN 0-8240-8583-3). Garland Pub.
Religious Science Book. Parker L. Johnstone. 212p. 1984. 7.95 (ISBN 0-917802-13-6). Theoscience Found.
Religious Science for Youth. Docia W. Norris. pap. 1.50 (ISBN 0-87516-153-7). De Vorss.
Religious Science Hymnal. 3rd ed. Ed. by Irma Glen. 225p. 1982. Repr. of 1956 ed. 8.00 (ISBN 0-87516-489-7). De Vorss.
Religious Significance of Atheism. Alasdair MacIntyre & Paul Ricoeur. LC 68-28398. (Bampton Lectures in America Ser.: No. 18). 98p. 1969. 20.00 (ISBN 0-231-03139-4). Columbia U Pr.
Religious Significance of Atheism. Alasdair MacIntyre & Paul Ricoeur. LC 68-28398. (Bampton Lectures in America: No. 18). 98p. 1986. pap. 10.00 (ISBN 0-231-06367-9). Columbia U Pr.
Religious Signing. Elaine Costello. (Illus.). 176p. 1986. pap. 9.95 (ISBN 0-553-34244-4). Bantam.
Religious Solution to the Social Problem. Howard H. Brinton. 1983. pap. 2.50x (ISBN 0-87574-002-2, 002). Pendle Hill.
Religious Spectrum. Margaret Chatterjee. (Studies in an Indian Context). 196p. 1984. 23.95x (ISBN 0-317-39860-1, Pub. by Allied Pubs India). Asia Bk Corp.
Religious Speeches of Bernard Shaw. Ed. by Warren S. Smith. LC 63-18890. 1963. 19.95x (ISBN 0-271-73095-1). Pa St U Pr.
Religious Strife in Egypt: Crisis & Ideological Conflict in the Seventies. Nadia R. Farah. 144p. 1986. text ed. 42.00 (ISBN 2-88124-092-5). Gordon & Breach.
Religious Studies in Alberta: A State-of-the-Art Review. Ronald Neufeldt. (Study of Religion in Canada Ser.). 145p. 1983. pap. text ed. 10.00x (ISBN 0-317-03613-0, Pub. by Wilfrid Laurier Canada). Humanities.
Religious Study of Judaism: Context, Text, Circumstance, Vol. 3. Jacob Neusner. (Studies in Judaism). 234p. (Orig.). 1987. lib. bdg. 25.50 (ISBN 0-8191-6047-4, Pub. by Studies in Judaism); pap. 13.75 (ISBN 0-8191-6048-2, Pub. by Studies in Judaism). U Pr of Amer.
Religious Study of Judaism: Description, Analysis & Interpretation. Jacob Neusner. LC 85-30411. (Studies in Judaism Ser.: Vol. 1). 188p. (Orig.). 1986. lib. bdg. 22.50 (ISBN 0-8191-5393-1, Pub. by Studies in Judaism); pap. text ed. 9.75 (ISBN 0-8191-5394-X). U Pr of Amer.
Religious Study of Judaism: Description, Analysis, Interpretation-The Centrality of Context. Jacob Neusner. LC 85-30411. (Studies in Judaism: Vol. 2). 230p. (Orig.). 1986. lib. bdg. 24.50 (ISBN 0-8191-5450-4, Pub. by Studies in Judaism); pap. text ed. 12.75 (ISBN 0-8191-5451-2). U Pr of Amer.
Religious Symbols & Their Functions. Ed. by Haralds Biezais. 178p. (Orig.). 1979. pap. text ed. 22.50 (ISBN 91-22-00199-9, Pub. by Almqvist & Wiksell). Coronet Bks.
Religious System of China, 6 vols. J. J. DeGroot. 1982. Repr. of 1892 ed. 130.00 (ISBN 0-89986-346-9). Oriental Bk Store.
Religious Systems of the Mahanubhava Sect. Anne Feldhaus. 1983. 26.00x (ISBN 0-8364-1005-X). South Asia Bks.
Religious Teachers of Greece. James Adam. LC 72-2565. (Select Bibliographies Reprint Ser). 1972. Repr. of 1908 ed. 26.00 (ISBN 0-8369-6843-3). Ayer Co Pubs.
Religious Teachers of Greece. James Adam. LC 65-22806. (Library of Religious & Philosophical Thought). 1966. Repr. of 1908 ed. lib. bdg. 35.00x (ISBN 0-678-09950-2, Reference Bk Pubs). Kelley.
Religious Teachings for Children, Bk. 1. Shaikh M. Sarwar. 44p. pap. 5.00 (ISBN 0-941724-03-4). Islamic Seminary.
Religious Teachings for Children, Bk. 2. Shaikh M. Sarwar. 66p. pap. 5.00 (ISBN 0-941724-04-2). Islamic Seminary.
Religious Teachings for Children, Bk. 3. Shaikh M. Sarwar. 80p. pap. 5.00 (ISBN 0-941724-05-0). Islamic Seminary.
Religious Teachings for Children, Bk. 4. Shaikh M. Sarwar. 72p. 1981. pap. 5.00 (ISBN 0-941724-06-9). Islamic Seminary.
Religious Television: The Experience in America. Peter Horsfield. LC 83-11313. (Communication & Human Values Ser.). (Illus.). 192p. 1984. text ed. 15.00 (ISBN 0-582-28432-5). Longman.
Religious Thinking from Childhood to Adolescence. Ronald Goldman. 1968. pap. text ed. 6.95 (ISBN 0-8164-2061-0, SP53, HarpR). Har-Row.
Religious Thought & Economic Society: Four Chapters of an Unfinished Work. Jacob Viner. Ed. by Jacques Melitz & Donald Winch. LC 77-93857. 1978. 19.75 (ISBN 0-8223-0398-1). Duke.
Religious Thought & the Modern Psychologies: A Critical Conversation in the Theology of Culture. Don S. Browning. LC 86-45205. 288p. 1986. 22.50 (ISBN 0-8006-0784-8). Fortress.
Religious Thought in England from the Reformation to the End of the Last Century, 3 Vols. John Hunt. LC 72-153593. Repr. of 1873 ed. Set. 125.00 (ISBN 0-404-09480-5). AMS Pr.

Religious Thought in England in the Nineteenth Century. John Hunt. 424p. Repr. of 1896 ed. text ed. 62.10x (ISBN 0-576-29211-7, Pub. by Gregg Intl Pubs England). Gregg Intl.

Religious Thought in India. T. N. Sharma. 1980. 11.00x (ISBN 0-8364-0619-2, Pub. by Ramneek). South Asia Bks.

Religious Thought in the Greater American Poets. facs. ed. Elmer J. Bailey. LC 68-8436. (Essay Index Reprint Ser). 1968. Repr. of 1922 ed. 16.00 (ISBN 0-8369-0167-3). Ayer Co Pubs.

Religious Thought in the Last Quarter-Century. Ed. by Gerald B. Smith. LC 71-107739. (Essay Index Reprint Ser). 1927. 12.00 (ISBN 0-8369-1583-6). Ayer Co Pubs.

Religious Thought in the Nineteenth Century. Bernard M. Reardon. (Orig.). 1966. 49.50 (ISBN 0-521-06049-4); pap. 16.95x (ISBN 0-521-09386-4). Cambridge U Pr.

Religious Thought in the Victorian Age: A Survey from Coleridge to Gore. Bernard M. Reardon. (Illus.). 512p. 1980. pap. text ed. 15.95x (ISBN 0-582-49126-6). Longman.

Religious Thought of H. Richard Niebuhr. Jerry A. Irish. LC 83-6202. pap. 32.30 (2027155). Bks Demand UMI.

Religious Thought of Jose Rizal. rev. ed. Eugene A. Hessel. 354p. (Orig.). 1984. pap. 12.25x (ISBN 0-318-01161-1, Pub. by New Day Philippines). Cellar.

Religious Thoughts in the Reformation. Bernard Reardon. 1981. pap. text ed. 14.95 (ISBN 0-582-49031-6). Longman.

Religious Thoughts of Some of Our Poets. Alfred C. Fryer. 1911. Repr. 17.50 (ISBN 0-8274-3263-1). R West.

Religious Toleration & Persecution in Ancient Rome. Simeon L. Guterman. LC 70-104269. 160p. Repr. of 1951 ed. lib. bdg. 22.50x (ISBN 0-8371-3936-8, GURT). Greenwood.

Religious Toleration & Social Change in Hamburg, 1529-1819. Joachim Whaley. (Cambridge Studies in Early Modern History). 290p. 1985. 49.50 (ISBN 0-521-26189-9). Cambridge U Pr.

Religious Trends in English Poetry, 6 vols. Hoxie N. Fairchild. Incl. Vol. 1. Protestantism & the Cult of Sentiment: 1700-1740 (ISBN 0-231-08821-3); Vol. 2. Religious Sentimentalism in the Age of Johnson: 1740-1780. 1942 (ISBN 0-231-08822-1); Vol. 3. Romantic Faith: 1780-1830. 1949 (ISBN 0-231-08823-X); Vol. 4. Christianity & Romanticism in the Victorian Era: 1830-1880. 1957 (ISBN 0-231-08824-8); Vol. 5. Gods of a Changing Poetry: 1880-1920. 1962 (ISBN 0-231-08825-6); Vol. 6. Valley of Dry Bones: 1920-1965. 1968 (ISBN 0-231-08826-4). LC 39-12839. 45.00x ea. Columbia U Pr.

Religious Values. Edgar S. Brightman. Repr. of 1925 ed. 29.00 (ISBN 0-527-11010-8). Kraus Repr.

Religious Values & Development. Ed. by Kenneth P. Jameson & Charles K. Wilber. (Illus.). 154p. 1981. 44.00 (ISBN 0-08-026107-8). Pergamon.

Religious Values in an Age of Violence. Marc H. Tanenbaum. (Pere Marquette Theology Lectures). 1976. 7.95 (ISBN 0-87462-508-4). Marquette.

Religious Values in Education. John A. Stoops. LC 67-25689. 1967. text ed. 4.95x (ISBN 0-8134-0950-0, 950). Inter Print Pubs.

Religious Vocation: An Unnecessary Mystery. Richard O. Butler. LC 78-14365. 1979. Repr. of 1961 ed. lib. bdg. cancelled (ISBN 0-313-21018-7, BURV). Greenwood.

Religious Woman Minister of Faith: A Compilation of Addresses Given at First International Assembly, Consotium Perfecte Caritatis. LC 74-16745. 1974. pap. 2.50 (ISBN 0-8198-0508-4). Dghtrs St Paul.

Religious Women in the United States: A Survey of the Literature from 1950 to 1983. Elizabeth Kolmer. (Consecrated Life Studies Ser.: Vol. 4). 1984. pap. 6.95 (ISBN 0-89453-445-9). M Glazier.

Religious Word. Richard C. Bush et al. 1982. text ed. write for info. (ISBN 0-02-317480-3). Macmillan.

Religious Writer's Marketplace: The Definitive Sourcebook. rev. ed. Ed. by William H. Gentz. LC 84-27691. 221p. 1985. pap. 17.95 (ISBN 0-89471-305-1). Running Pr.

Religious Writers of England. Pearson M. Muir. 1901. 20.00 (ISBN 0-8274-3264-X). R West.

Religiously Mixed Marriage. Gary Beauchamp & Deanna Beauchamp. 4.95 (ISBN 0-89137-528-7). Quality Pubns.

Religiousness in Yoga: Lectures on Theory & Practice. T. K. Desikachar. Ed. by Mary L. Skelton & J. R. Carter. LC 79-9643. (Illus.). 314p. 1980. text ed. 27.00 (ISBN 0-8191-0966-5); pap. text ed. 11.75 (ISBN 0-8191-0967-3). U Pr of Amer.

Religioznaya Tchuvstvo, Promisl Bozhil i Dukovnoje Prizvanije. Archbishop Athanasius Martos. Tr. of Religious Feeling, the Providence of God & Spiritual Calling. 30p. 1983. pap. 2.00 (ISBN 0-317-29069-X). Holy Trinity.

Religya i Literatura: Religion & Literature. Sergei Averintsev. LC 81-4115. (Rus.). 140p. 1981. pap. 7.00 (ISBN 0-938920-02-2). Hermitage.

Reliquienkult im Altertum, 2 vols. in 1. Friedrich Pfister. Incl. Vol. 1. Das Objekt des Reliquienkultes; Vol. 2. Reliquien als Kultobjekt: Geschichte des Reliquienkultes. (Ger.). xii, 686p. 1974. Repr. of 1909 ed. 76.00x (ISBN 3-11-002453-5). De Gruyter.

Reluctant Followers: A Chosen People? Ronald R. Hamilton. Ed. by Michael L. Sherer. (Orig.). 1986. pap. 6.25 (ISBN 0-89536-824-2, 6833). CSS of Ohio.

Reluctant Naturalist: A Study of G.E. Moore's Principia Ethica. Dennis Rohatyn. 150p. (Orig.). 1987. lib. bdg. 22.50 (ISBN 0-8191-5767-8); pap. text ed. 9.75 (ISBN 0-8191-5768-6). U Pr of Amer.

Reluctant Vision: An Essay in the Philosophy of Religion. Thomas P. Burke. LC 73-88354. pap. 35.50 (2026883). Bks Demand UMI.

Reluctant Witness. Kenneth L. Chaffin. LC 74-84548. 1975. 6.95 (ISBN 0-8054-5550-7). Broadman.

Remaines of Gentilisme & Judaisme, Sixteen Hundred Eighty-Six to Eighty-Seven. John Aubrey. Ed. by James Britten. (Folk-Lore Society, London, Monograph Ser.: Vol. 4). pap. 29.00 (ISBN 0-8115-0501-4). Kraus Repr.

Remains of Myles Coverdale, Bishop of Exeter. Myles Coverdale. 1846. 51.00 (ISBN 0-384-09950-5). Johnson Repr.

Remarkable Birth of Planet Earth. Henry M. Morris. 124p. 1973. pap. 2.50 (ISBN 0-89051-000-8). Master Bks.

Remarkable World of John Wesley: Pioneer in Mental Health. Franklin Wilder. (Illus.). 1978. 7.00 (ISBN 0-682-49129-2). Exposition Pr FL.

Remarks on the Character & Writings of John Milton. 3rd ed. William E. Channing. LC 72-966. Repr. of 1828 ed. 12.50 (ISBN 0-404-01448-8). AMS Pr.

Remarks upon Milton's Paradise Lost. William Massey. LC 77-4961. 1751. lib. bdg. 30.00 (ISBN 0-8414-6194-5). Folcroft.

Remarriage & God's Renewing Grace. Dwight H. Small. 184p. 1986. pap. 7.95 (ISBN 0-8010-8264-1). Baker Bk.

Remarried Divorcees & Eucharistic Communion. Bertrand De Margerie. 1980. pap. 1.95 (ISBN 0-8198-6401-3). Dghtrs St Paul.

Rembrandt. J. G. De Lint. Repr. 20.00 (ISBN 0-8482-3695-5). Norwood Edns.

Rembrandt, 2 vols. Emile Michel. 200.00 (ISBN 0-8490-0943-X). Gordon Pr.

Rembrandt: All the Etchings. Rembrandt Van Rijn. LC 77-87012. (Illus.). 1977. (Pub. by Two Continents). Hippocrene Bks.

Rembrandt Bible Drawings. Rembrandt Van Rijn. LC 79-52975. (Fine Art Library). (Illus.). 64p. (Orig.). 1980. pap. 3.50 (ISBN 0-486-23878-4). Dover.

Rembrandt Drawings. B. Haak. Tr. by Elizabeth Willems-Treeman. LC 76-10073. (Illus.). 1976. 22.50 (ISBN 0-87951-047-1). Overlook Pr.

Rembrandt Drawings. B. Haak. Tr. by Elizabeth Willems-Treeman. LC 76-10073. (Illus.). 1977. pap. 10.95 (ISBN 0-87951-051-X). Overlook Pr.

Rembrandt Van Ryn. Hope Rea. Repr. of 1903 ed. 20.00 (ISBN 0-8482-5893-2). Norwood Edns.

Rembrandt: Werk und Forschung. Otto Benesch. Repr. 17.00 (ISBN 0-384-03899-9). Johnson Repr.

Remediarium Conversorum: A Synthesis in Latin of "Moralia in Job". Gregory the Great. Compiled by Peter of Waltham & Joseph Gildea. LC 84-3693. 504p. 1984. 25.00 (ISBN 0-8453-4507-9). Assoc Univ Prs.

Remember the Days of Old. Isidore Fishman. LC 79-100058. 1969. 4.95 (ISBN 0-87677-000-6). Hartmore.

Remember the Poor. Dick Benjamin & Jim Richardson. 1982. pap. 1.75 (ISBN 0-911739-26-2). Abbott Loop.

Remember the Prisoners: Current Accounts of Believers in Russia. Ed. by Peter Masters. pap. 6.95 (ISBN 0-8024-7388-1). Moody.

Remember the Promise. Alvin N. Rogness. LC 76-27082. 1977. kivar 2.95 (ISBN 0-8066-1567-2, 10-5480). Augsburg.

Remember the Promise. Alvin N. Rogness. LC 76-27082. 1978. gift ed. 7.50 (ISBN 0-8066-1619-9, 10-5481). Augsburg.

Remember Who You Are: Baptism, a Model for Christian Life. William H. Willimon. LC 79-93359. (Illus.). 128p. (Orig.). 1980. pap. 4.95x (ISBN 0-8358-0399-6). Upper Room.

Remember Your Confirmation. 1977. pap. 2.10 (ISBN 0-570-03751-4, 12-2655). Concordia.

Remembered Future: A Study in Literary Mythology. Harold Fisch. LC 83-48899. 208p. 1985. 22.50x (ISBN 0-253-35003-4). Ind U Pr.

Remembering God in Youth. Robert Taylor. 2.50 (ISBN 0-89315-238-2). Lambert Bk.

Remembrance of Christ. C. H. Spurgeon. 1977. pap. 0.95 (ISBN 0-686-23223-2). Pilgrim Pubns.

Reminded of His Goodness Songbook. Gary L. Johnson. 32p. 1981. pap. 2.50 (ISBN 0-87123-779-2, 280779). Bethany Hse.

Reminiscences. Isaac Wise. Ed. by David Philipson. LC 73-2233. (Jewish People; History, Religion, Literature Ser.). Repr. of 1901 ed. 30.00 (ISBN 0-405-05294-4). Ayer Co Pubs.

Reminiscences: A Lifetime of Spiritualism. Ursula Roberts. 115p. 1985. 20.00x (ISBN 0-7212-0726-X, Pub. by Regency Pr). State Mutual Bk.

Reminiscences & Gospel Hymn Stories. George C. Stebbins. LC 74-144689. Repr. of 1924 ed. 24.50 (ISBN 0-404-07203-8). AMS Pr.

Reminiscences, Biographical & Historical. Randolph Clark. LC 86-1286. 96p. 1986. Repr. of 1919 ed. 25.00x (ISBN 0-87565-064-3). Tex Christian.

Reminiscences of an Army Chaplain. Horace M. Taylor. LC 86-1472. Date not set. price not set. (ISBN 0-9617424-0-2). H M Taylor.

Reminiscences of H. P. Blavatsky. rev. new ed. Constance Wachtmeister. LC 76-44810. 1977. pap. 3.75 (ISBN 0-8356-0488-8, Quest). Theos Pub Hse.

Reminiscences of Present-Day Saints. facsimile ed. Francis G. Peabody. LC 74-37525. (Essay Index Reprint Ser). Repr. of 1927 ed. 23.50 (ISBN 0-8369-2576-9). Ayer Co Pubs.

Reminiscences of School Life & Hints On Teaching. Fanny J. Coppin. Ed. by Carolyn G. De Swarte & Donald Dayton. (Women in American Protestant Religion Series 1800-1930). 191p. 1987. lib. bdg. 30.00 (ISBN 0-8240-0662-3). Garland Pub.

Remnant: The History & Theology of the Remnant Idea from Genesis to Isaiah. 3rd ed. Gerhard F. Hasel. (Andrews University Monographs, Studies in Religion: Vol. V). x, 474p. 1980. pap. 10.95 (ISBN 0-943872-05-7). Andrews Univ Pr.

Remnants: The Last Jews of Poland. Malgorzata Niezabitowska. Tr. by William Brand & Hanna Dobosiewicz. LC 86-1468. (Illus.). 272p. 1986. 35.00 (ISBN 0-914919-05-9). Friendly Pr NY.

Remodelling God. Ed. by William W. Emilsen & A. D. Irvine. 125p. (Orig.). 1983. pap. 7.95 (ISBN 0-85819-418-X, Pub. by JBCE). ANZ Religious Pubns.

Removing the Stones. Mary Hajos. 1976. pap. 2.95 (ISBN 0-87508-264-5). Chr Lit.

Renaissance & Reform: The Italian Contribution. Frances A. Yates. Ed. by J. Trapp. (Collected Essays Ser.: Vol. II). (Illus.). 288p. 1983. 31.50 (ISBN 0-7100-9530-9). Methuen Inc.

Renaissance & Reformation. William R. Estep. 320p. (Orig.). pap. text ed. 21.95 (ISBN 0-8028-0050-5). Eerdmans.

Renaissance & Reformation. 2nd ed. Vivian H. Green. (Illus.). 1974. pap. text ed. 16.95 (ISBN 0-312-67305-1). St Martin.

Renaissance & Reformation, 2 vols. Lewis W. Spitz. Incl. Vol. 1. Renaissance. LC 12-2759 (ISBN 0-570-03818-9); Vol. 2. Reformation. LC 12-2760 (ISBN 0-570-03819-7). 1980. pap. 15.50 ea. Concordia.

Renaissance & Reformation. Bard Thompson. (Texts & Studies in Religion). (Orig.). write for info. (ISBN 0-88946-915-6). E Mellen.

Renaissance & Reformation: A Short History. 2nd ed. John F. New. 201p. 1977. pap. text ed. 11.00 (ISBN 0-394-34199-6, RanC). Random.

Renaissance & Reformation: A Survey of European History Between 1450 & 1660. 2nd ed. V. H. Green. 462p. 1964. pap. text ed. 17.95 (ISBN 0-7131-5617-1). E Arnold.

Renaissance & Reformation in Germany: An Introduction. Gerhart Hoffmeister. LC 77-5429. 1977. 25.00 (ISBN 0-8044-1391-6); pap. 9.95 (ISBN 0-8044-6272-0). Ungar.

Renaissance & Reformation in Scotland. Ed. by Ian B. Cowan & Duncan Shaw. 220p. 1983. 20.00x (ISBN 0-7073-0261-7, Scot Acad Pr). Longwood Pub Group.

Renaissance & Reformation, Thirteen Hundred to Sixteen Forty-Eight. 3rd ed. Gelffrey R. Elton. (Ideas & Institutions in Western Civilization: Vol. 3). 1976. pap. text ed. write for info. (ISBN 0-02-332840-1). Macmillan.

Renaissance & Reformation Times. Dorothy Mills. LC 83-45667. Date not set. Repr. of 1939 ed. 55.00 (ISBN 0-404-19817-1). AMS Pr.

Renaissance & Renewal in Christian History. Derek Baker. (Studies in Church History: Vol. 14). 428p. 1977. 45.00x (ISBN 0-631-17780-9). Basil Blackwell.

Renaissance & the Reformation. Henry S. Lucas. LC 83-45665. Date not set. Repr. of 1934 ed. 67.50 (ISBN 0-404-19815-5). AMS Pr.

Renaissance Drama & the English Church Year. R. Chris Hassel, Jr. LC 78-24233. (Illus.). xii, 215p. 1979. 18.95x (ISBN 0-8032-2304-8). U of Nebr Pr.

Renaissance English Translations of Erasmus: A Bibliography to 1700. E. J. Devereux. (Erasmus Ser.). 256p. 1983. 35.00x (ISBN 0-8020-2411-4). U of Toronto Pr.

Renaissance Humanism in Papal Rome: Humanists & Churchmen on the Eve of the Reformation. John F. D'Amico. LC 82-49059. (Studies in Historical & Political Science). 352p. 1983. text ed. 32.50x (ISBN 0-8018-2860-0). Johns Hopkins.

Renaissance Influences & Religious Reforms in Russia: Western & Post-Byzantine Impacts on Culture & Education, (16th-17th Centuries) W. K. Medlin & C. G. Patrinelis. 184p. (Orig.). 1970. pap. text ed. 22.00x (Pub. by Droz Switzerland). Coronet Bks.

Renaissance New Testament, Vols. 1-9. Randolph O. Yaeger. Incl. Vol. 1. 25.00 (ISBN 0-88289-957-0); Vol. 2 (ISBN 0-88289-657-1); Vol. 3 (ISBN 0-88289-357-2); Vol. 4 (ISBN 0-88289-857-4); Vol. 5 (ISBN 0-88289-257-6); Vol. 6 (ISBN 0-88289-757-8); Vol. 7. 1982. 22.50 (ISBN 0-88289-457-9); Vol. 8. 1982. 22.50 (ISBN 0-88289-358-0); Vol. 9. 1982. 22.50 (ISBN 0-88289-858-2). 590p. 1980. each 22.50 (ISBN 0-686-77622-4). Pelican.

Renaissance New Testament, Vol. 10. Randolph O. Yeager. LC 79-28652. 660p. 1982. 22.50 (ISBN 0-88289-258-4). Pelican.

Renaissance New Testament, Vol. 11. Randolph O. Yeager. 660p. 22.50 (ISBN 0-88289-758-6). Pelican.

Renaissance New Testament, Vol. 14. Randolph Yaeger. 660p. 1983. 22.50 (ISBN 0-88289-859-0). Pelican.

Renaissance of Islam. S. K. Bukhsh. 1981. 29.00 (ISBN 0-686-97863-3). Kazi Pubns.

Renaissance of Islam. Adam Mez. Tr. by Salahuddin K Bukhsl & D. S. Margoliovth. LC 70-180361. Repr. of 1937 ed. 27.00 (ISBN 0-404-56293-0). AMS Pr.

Renaissance of the Torah Jew. Saul Bernstein. 1986. text ed. 20.00x (ISBN 0-88125-090-2). Ktav.

Renaissance, Reformation, & Absolutism: 1450 to 1650. 2nd ed. Ed. by Norman F. Cantor & Michael S. Werthman. LC 72-76355. (Structure of European History Ser.: Vol. 3). 319p. 1972. pap. text ed. 7.95x (ISBN 0-88295-712-0). Harlan Davidson.

Renaissance Savonarola. Arthur Count Gobineau. Ed. by Oscar Levy. Tr. by Paul V. Cohen. (Fr., Illus.). 349p. 1986. Repr. of 1913 ed. lib. bdg. 75.00 (ISBN 0-89760-264-1). Telegraph Bks.

Renaissance, Savonarola - Cesare - Borgia -Julius II - Leo X - Michael Angelo. Arthur Gobineau. Ed. by Oscar Levy. 349p. 1981. Repr. of 1903 ed. lib. bdg. 50.00 (ISBN 0-89984-235-6). Century Bookbindery.

Renaissance, the Protestant Revolution & the Catholic Reformation in Continental Europe. Edward M. Hulme. LC 83-45662. Date not set. Repr. of 1915 ed. 62.50 (ISBN 0-404-19812-0). AMS Pr.

Renaissance Thought: The Classic, Scholastic & Humanistic Strains. Paul O. Kristeller. 15.50 (ISBN 0-8446-2405-5). Peter Smith.

Renegade, Outcast & Maverick: Three Pioneer California Clergy 1847-1893. Lionel J. Ridout. 1973. 7.95x (ISBN 0-916304-10-8). SDSU Press.

Renegade Saint: A Story of Hope by a Child Abuse Survivor. Phil E. Quinn. 1986. 12.95 (ISBN 0-687-36130-3). Abingdon.

Renew, Leadership Book. Archdiocese of Newark, Office of Pastoral Renewal Staff. 1980. write for info. (ISBN 0-8091-9195-4). Paulist Pr.

Renew, Parish Book. Archdiocese of Newark, Office of Pastoral Renewal Staff. 1980. write for info. (ISBN 0-8091-9191-1). Paulist Pr.

Renew, Participant Book: Empowerment by the Spirit. Archdiocese of Newark, Office of Pastoral Renewal Staff. 1980. write for info. (ISBN 0-8091-9194-6). Paulist Pr.

Renew, Participant Book: Our Response. Archdiocese of Newark, Office of Pastoral Renewal Staff. 1980. write for info. (ISBN 0-8091-9193-8). Paulist Pr.

Renew, Participant Book: The Lord's Call. Archdiocese of Newark, Office of Pastoral Renewal Staff. 1980. write for info. (ISBN 0-8091-9192-X). Paulist Pr.

Renew, Pastoral Staff Book. Archdiocese of Newark, Office of Pastoral Renewal Staff. 1980. write for info. (ISBN 0-8091-9196-2). Paulist Pr.

Renew the Earth: A Guide to the Second Draft of the U. S. Bishops' Pastoral Letter on Catholic Social Teachings & the U. S. Economy. James E. Hug. (Illus.). 32p. (Orig.). 1985. pap. text ed. 1.50 (ISBN 0-934255-02-4). Center Concern.

Renewal & Reform of Canon Law. Teodoro J. Urresti et al. Ed. by Neophytos Edelby. LC 67-30868. (Concilium Ser.: Vol. 28). 191p. 1967. 7.95 (ISBN 0-8091-0125-4). Paulist Pr.
Renewal As a Way of Life. Richard F. Lovelace. LC 85-10029. 216p. 1985. pap. 7.95 (ISBN 0-87784-594-8). Inter-Varsity.
Renewal in the Spirit. Pius R. Regamey. 1980. 5.95 (ISBN 0-8198-6402-1); pap. 4.95 (ISBN 0-8198-6403-X). Dghtrs St Paul.
Renewal in Worship. rev. ed. Michael E. Marshall. 120p. 1985. pap. 6.95 (ISBN 0-8192-1374-8). Morehouse.
Renewal of American Catholicism. David J. O'Brien. LC 72-85825. 320p. 1974. pap. 4.95 (ISBN 0-8091-1828-9). Paulist Pr.
Renewal of Buddhism in China: Chu-Hung & the Late Ming Synthesis. Chun-fang Yu. LC 79-28073. (Buddhist Studies). (Illus.). 1981. 34.00x (ISBN 0-231-04972-2). Columbia U Pr.
Renewal of Faith. Thomas White & Desmond O'Donnell. LC 74-76320. 240p. 1974. pap. 2.95 (ISBN 0-87793-068-6). Ave Maria.
Renewal of Our Salesian Life, 2 vols. Joseph Aubry. Tr. by Paul Bedard & Kenneth Whitehead. LC 84-70210. Orig. Title: Rinnovare la Nostra Vita Salesiana. 426p. 1984. pap. text ed. write for info. (ISBN 0-89944-071-1); Vol. I:The Active Apostolate. pap. 5.00; Vol. II:The Salesian Community & Family. pap. 5.50 (ISBN 0-89944-077-0). Don Bosco Multimedia.
Renewal of Preaching. Ed. by Karl Rahner. LC 68-22795. (Concilium Ser.: Vol. 33). 204p. 7.95 (ISBN 0-8091-0126-2). Paulist Pr.
Renewed at Each Awakening: The Formative Power of Sacred Words. Susan Muto. 1985. pap. 4.95 (ISBN 0-87193-147-8). Dimension Bks.
Renewed Church of the United Brethren, 1722-1930. William G. Addison. (Church Historical Society London Ser.: No. 9). Repr. of 1932 ed. 40.00 (ISBN 0-8115-3133-3). Kraus Repr.
Renewed Day by Day. A. W. Tozer. Ed. by Gerald B. Smith. 384p. kivar binding 7.95 (ISBN 0-8007-5064-0, Power Bks). Revell.
Renewed Day by Day. Aiden W. Tozer. LC 80-69301. 380p. 12.95 (ISBN 0-87509-252-7); pap. 7.95 kivar (ISBN 0-87509-292-6). Chr Pubns.
Renewed Mind. Larry Cristenson. LC 74-12770. 144p. (Orig.). 1974. pap. 4.95 (ISBN 0-87123-479-3, 210479). Bethany Hse.
Renewed Power for Preaching. Glenn H. Asquith. 128p. 1983. pap. 3.95 (ISBN 0-8170-1003-3). Judson.
Renewing Family Life. Abraham Schmitt & Dorothy Schmitt. LC 84-22504. (Orig.). 1985. pap. 6.95 (ISBN 0-8361-3384-6). Herald Pr.
Renewing the Earth: Catholic Documents on Peace, Justice & Liberation. Ed. by David J. O'Brien & Thomas A. Shannon. LC 76-52008. 1977. pap. 6.95 (ISBN 0-385-12954-8, Im). Doubleday.
Renewing the Sunday School & the CCD. Ed. by D. Campbell Wyckoff. LC 85-19419. 254p. (Orig.). 1986. pap. 14.95 (ISBN 0-89135-053-5). Religious Educ.
Renewing the World: Northern Plains Indian Religion. Howard L. Harrod. LC 87-5010. 210p. 1987. 22.50x (ISBN 0-8165-0958-1). U of Ariz Pr.
Renewing Your Mind. Mona Johnian. (Orig.). 1986. pap. text ed. 3.95 (ISBN 0-88368-182-X). Whitaker Hse.
Renewing Your Mind in a Secular World. Ed. by John Woodbridge et al. (Orig.). 1985. pap. 6.95 (ISBN 0-8024-0384-0). Moody.
Renueva Mi Iglesia. David Haney. Ed. by Jose Luis Martinez. Tr. by Guillermo Kratzig. Orig. Title: Renew My Church. (Span.). 104p. 1983. pap. 3.75 (ISBN 0-311-17025-0). Casa Bautista.
Renunciation & Reformulation: A Study of Conversion in an American Sect. Harriet Whitehead. LC 86-16211. (Anthropology of Contemporary Issues Ser.). (Illus.). 304p. 1987. text ed. 32.50x (ISBN 0-8014-1849-6). Cornell U Pr.
Repairing Christian Lifestyles. 2nd ed. Steve Clapp & Sue I. Mauck. (Repairing Christian Lifestyles Ser.). (Illus.). 174p. (YA) 1983. pap. 6.00 (ISBN 0-914527-26-6); pap. 5.00 leader's guide (ISBN 0-914527-27-4). C-Four Res.
Repairing the Breach: Ministering in Community Conflict. Ronald S. Kraybill. LC 82-80586. 95p. 1982. pap. 3.95 (ISBN 0-8361-3302-1). Herald Pr.
Repent & Believe. Derek Prince. (Foundation Ser.: Bk. II). 1965-66. pap. 2.95 (ISBN 0-934920-01-X, B-11). Derek Prince.
Repentance. Bishop Chrysostomos. (Themes in Orthodox Patristic Psychology Ser.: Vol. III). 75p. (Orig.). 1986. pap. 5.00 (ISBN 0-911165-09-6). Ctr Trad Orthodox.
Repentance. Saint Ephraem. pap. 1.95 (ISBN 0-686-18718-0). Eastern Orthodox.
Repentance & Twentieth Century Man. C. John Miller. (Orig.). 1980. pap. 2.95 (ISBN 0-87508-334-X). Chr Lit.
Repentance of Mary Magdalene. Lewis Wager. LC 70-133754. (Tudor Facsimile Texts. Old English Plays: No. 36). Repr. of 1908 ed. 49.50 (ISBN 0-404-53336-1). AMS Pr.
Repentance: The Joy Filled Life. Basilea Schlink. LC 83-23774. 96p. 1984. pap. 3.95 (ISBN 0-87123-592-7, 210592). Bethany Hse.
Repercussions of the Kalam in Jewish Philosophy. Harry A. Wolfson. LC 78-9798. 1979. 18.50x (ISBN 0-674-76175-8). Harvard U Pr.
Repertoire des Articles Relatifs a l'Histoire et a la Litterature Juives Parus dans les Periodiques De 1665 a 1900. rev. ed. Moise Schwab. (Fr.). 1971. 79.50 (ISBN 0-87068-163-X). Ktav.
Repertorio de Navidad. Francisco Ordonez. 80p. 1986. pap. 1.75 (ISBN 0-311-08211-4). Casa Bautista.
Repertorium der Griechischen Christlichen Papyri, Pt.1: Biblische Papyri, Altes Testament, Neues Testament, Varia, Apokryphen. Ed. by Kurt Aland. (Patristische Texte und Studien, Vol. 18). 473p. 1976. 63.20x (ISBN 3-11-004674-1). De Gruyter.
Repertory of Tropes at Winchester, 2 vols. Alejandro Planchart. LC 76-3033. 1976. text ed. 63.00x (ISBN 0-691-09121-8). Princeton U Pr.
Reply of the Orthodox Church to Roman Catholic Overtures on Reunion. rev., enl. ed. Anthimos. 64p. 1986. pap. 2.00 (ISBN 0-913026-62-X). St Nectarios.
Report from Israel. Arnold Forster. 72p. pap. 1.25 (ISBN 0-686-74976-6). ADL.
Report of Mr. S. Hoofien to the Joint Distribution Committee of the American Funds for Jewish War Sufferers,New York. Sigfried Hoofien. Ed. by Moshe Davis. LC 77-70702. (America & the Holy Land Ser.). (Illus.). 1977. Repr. of 1918 ed. lib. bdg. 17.00x (ISBN 0-405-10254-2). Ayer Co Pubs.
Report of the Bishops' Ad Hoc Committee for Priestly Life & Ministry: Authority, Maturity, Ministry, Scholarship. pap. cancelled (ISBN 0-686-18990-6, V-295). US Catholic.
Report on the Shroud of Turin. John Heller. 1984. pap. 8.95 (ISBN 0-395-36568-6). HM.
Report on the Shroud of Turin. John H. Heller. LC 83-127. 1983. 15.95 (ISBN 0-395-33967-7). HM.
Report on Theosophical Society. Society for Psychical Report. LC 75-36920. (Occult Ser.). (Illus.). 1976. 26.50x (ISBN 0-405-07975-3). Ayer Co Pubs.
Report on United States Catholic Schools, 1972-73. 98p. 1973. 2.40 (ISBN 0-686-29263-4). Natl Cath Educ.
Reporte of a Discourse Concerning Supreme Power in Affaires of Religion. John Hayward. LC 79-84116. (English Experience Ser.: No. 935). 64p. 1979. Repr. of 1606 ed. lib. bdg. 8.00 (ISBN 90-221-0935-6). Walter J Johnson.
Reports on the State of Certain Parishes in Scotland. Ed. by Alexander Macdonald. LC 79-175588. (Maitland Club, Glasgow. Publications: No. 34). Repr. of 1835 ed. 24.50 (ISBN 0-404-53003-6). AMS Pr.
Representation & Misrepresentation of the Puritan in Elizabethan Drama. Aaron M. Myers. LC 76-20654. 1976. Repr. of 1931 ed. lib. bdg. 27.50 (ISBN 0-8414-6141-4). Folcroft.
Representation of Deities of the Maya Manuscripts. P. Schellhas. (Hupmaen Ser.: Vol. 4, No. 1). (Illus.). 1904. pap. 15.00 (ISBN 0-527-01198-3). Kraus Repr.
Representational Outline of the Philosophy of Buddhism. Nicholas S. Graumann. (Illus.). 151p. 1982. 77.85 (ISBN 0-89266-331-6). Am Classical Coll Pr.
Representative Medieval & Tudor Plays. Ed. by Roger S. Loomis & Henry W. Wells. LC 77-111109. (Play Anthology Reprint Ser). 1942. 22.50 (ISBN 0-8369-8202-9). Ayer Co Pubs.
Representative Modern Preachers. facs. ed. Lewis O. Brastow. LC 68-57306. (Essay Index Reprint Ser). 1904. 20.00 (ISBN 0-8369-0101-0). Ayer Co Pubs.
Representatives: The Real Nature & Function of Papal Legates. Mario Oliveri. LC 81-108272. 192p. (Orig.). 1981. pap. 4.95 (ISBN 0-905715-20-9). Wanderer Pr.
Represion Religiosa en Cuba. Juan Clark. (Span.). 124p. (Orig.). Date not set. pap. cancelled (ISBN 0-917049-05-5). Saeta.
Reproach of the Gospel: An Inquiry into the Apparent Failure of Christianity As a General Rule of Life & Conduct. James H. Peile. 1977. lib. bdg. 59.95 (ISBN 0-8490-2516-8). Gordon Pr.
Reprobation Asserted. John Bunyan. pap. 1.25 (ISBN 0-685-19841-3). Reiner.
Republic of God: An Institute of Theology. Elisha Mulford. LC 75-3291. Repr. of 1881 ed. 18.00 (ISBN 0-404-59277-5). AMS Pr.
Republic of St. Peter: The Birth of the Papal State, 680-825. Thomas F. X. Noble. LC 83-21870. (The Middle Ages Ser.). (Illus.). 416p. 1984. 36.95x (ISBN 0-8122-7917-4); pap. 14.95. U of Pa Pr.
Republican Protestantism in Aztlan. E. C. Orozco. LC 80-82906. 261p. 1980. 24.00x (ISBN 0-9606102-1-9); pap. 14.50x (ISBN 0-9606102-2-7). Petereins Pr.
Request Presented to the King of Spayn by the Inhabitants of the Lowe Countreyes, Protesting That They Will Live According to the Reformation of the Gospell. LC 71-26044. (English Experience Ser.: No. 266). 1970. Repr. of 1578 ed. 7.00 (ISBN 90-221-0266-1). Walter J Johnson.
Requirements for Faithfulness. 1981. 1.25 (ISBN 0-89858-030-7). Fill the Gap.
Rescue Attempts During the Holocaust. Ed. by Y. Gutman & E. Zuroff. 25.00x (ISBN 0-87068-345-4). Ktav.
Rescue in Denmark. Harold Flender. LC 80-81716. (Illus.). 281p. (Orig.). 1963. pap. 10.95 (ISBN 0-89604-018-6). Holocaust Pubns.
Rescue of Danish Jewry. Leni Yahil. Tr. by Morris Gradel from Hebrew. (Illus.). 538p. 1983. pap. 9.95 (ISBN 0-8276-0232-4). Jewish Pubns.
Rescue of the Eighteen Fifty-Six Handcart Companies. Rebecca Cornwall & Leonard J. Arrington. Ed. by Thomas G. Alexander. (Charles Redd Monographs in Western History: No. 11). (Illus.). 59p. pap. 4.95 (ISBN 0-941214-04-4, Signature Bks). C Redd Ctr.
Rescue the Perishing. James L. Slay. 1961. 6.95 (ISBN 0-87148-729-2). Pathway Pr.
Rescue to Switzerland: The Mussy & Saly Mayer Affair. J. Mendelsohn. LC 81-80324. (Holocaust Ser.). 280p. 1982. lib. bdg. 61.00 (ISBN 0-8240-4890-3). Garland Pub.
Rescued from the Dragon. Alice H. Taylor. 199p. (Orig.). 1982. pap. 5.25 (ISBN 0-89367-078-2). Light & Life.
Research & Discovery Series, 8 vols. L. Ron Hubbard. Set. write for info. (ISBN 0-686-30030-0); Vol. 1, June 1950. 100.00 (ISBN 0-686-30031-9); Vol. 2, July 1950. 100.00 (ISBN 0-686-30032-7); Vol. 3. 100.00; Vol. 4. 100.00. Church Scient NY.
Research Guide to Religious Studies. Ed. by John F. Wilson & Thomas P. Slavens. LC 81-22862. (Sources of Information in the Humanities Ser.). 199p. 1982. lib. bdg. 22.50x (ISBN 0-8389-0330-4). ALA.
Research in Ritual Studies: A Programmatic Essay & Bibliography. Ronald L. Grimes. LC 84-23474. (ATLA Bibliography Ser.: No. 14). 177p. 1985. 15.00 (ISBN 0-8108-1762-4). Scarecrow.
Research Memorandum on Religion in the Depression. Samuel C. Kincheloe. LC 71-162843. (Studies in the Social Aspects of the Depression). 1971. Repr. of 1937 ed. 17.00 (ISBN 0-405-00846-5). Ayer Co Pubs.
Research on Men's Vocations to the Priesthood & the Religious Life. Dean R. Hoge et al. 104p. 1984. pap. 6.50 (ISBN 1-55586-904-1). US Catholic.
Research on Reincarnation. Manly P. Hall. pap. 2.50 (ISBN 0-89314-349-9). Philos Res.
Researches in Manichaeism with Special Reference to the Turfan Fragments. Abraham V. Jackson. LC 32-9567. (Columbia University. Indo-Iranian Ser.: No. 13). Repr. of 1932 ed. 31.00 (ISBN 0-404-50483-3). AMS Pr.
Researches in South Africa, 2 vols. John Philip. LC 77-82065. (Illus.). Repr. of 1828 ed. 33.00x (ISBN 0-8371-3855-8, PHR&). Greenwood.
Researches into Chinese Superstitions, 5 vols. (vols. I-X & XIII) Henri Dore. Repr. of 1914 ed. Set. text ed. 97.00x (ISBN 0-89644-108-3, Pub. by Chinese Matl Ctr). Coronet Bks.
Resena Critica De Una Introduccion al Antiguo Testament (Survey of Old Testament Introduction) Gleason L. Archer. (Span.). 507p. 1982. pap. 14.95 (ISBN 0-8254-1033-9). Kregel.
Resist Not Evil. Clarence S. Darrow. LC 77-137538. (Peace Movement in America Ser). 179p. 1972. Repr. of 1903 ed. lib. bdg. 14.95x (ISBN 0-89198-065-2). Ozer.
Resistance & Compromise: The Political Thought of the Elizabethan Catholics. Peter Holmes. LC 81-17990. (Cambridge Studies in the History & Theory of Politics). 296p. 1982. 44.50 (ISBN 0-521-24343-2). Cambridge U Pr.
Resolves, a Duple Century. 3rd ed. Owen Feltham. LC 74-28853. (English Experience Ser.: No. 734). 1975. Repr. of 1628 ed. 35.00 (ISBN 90-221-0734-5). Walter J Johnson.
Resolving Church Conflicts: A Case Study Approach for Local Congregations. Douglass Lewis. LC 80-8347. 192p. (Orig.). 1981. pap. 7.95 (ISBN 0-06-065244-6, RD 342, HarpR). Har-Row.
Resonance of Dust: Essays on Holocaust Literature & Jewish Fate. Edward Alexander. LC 79-15515. 276p. 1979. 20.00 (ISBN 0-8142-0303-5). Ohio St U Pr.
Resource Directory for Youth Workers 1986. rev. ed. Ed. by Jim Hancock. 128p. pap. 9.95 (ISBN 0-310-35161-8, 10785P). Zondervan.
Resource Directory for Youth Workers, 1985. Ed. by Tic Long. 128p. (Orig.). 1985. pap. 8.95 (ISBN 0-687-36167-2). Abingdon.
Resource Kit for Your Church's History. Ed. by Charles W. Deweese. 1984. 11.95 (ISBN 0-939804-12-3). Hist Comm S Baptist.
Resources for Christian Leaders. 8th ed. E. Dayton. 40p. 1982. pap. 3.95 (ISBN 0-912552-16-6). Missions Adv Res Com Ctr.
Resources for Christian Leaders. 1982. 1982. 2.50 (ISBN 0-912552-23-9). World Vision Intl.
Resources for Development. Robert J. Yeager. (How to Ser.). 46p. 1986. 8.95. Natl Cath Educ.
Resources for Latin American Jewish Studies: Essays on Using Jewish Reference Sources for the Study of Latin American Jewry; U. S. Library Collections on L. A. Jews; & U. S. Archival Resources for the Study of Jews in L. A. Thomas Niehaus et al. Ed. by Judith L. Elkin. LC 84-80219. (LAJSA Publication Ser.: No. 1). 59p. (Orig.). 1984. pap. text ed. 10.00 (ISBN 0-916921-00-X). Lat Am Jewish Assn.
Resources for Renewal (Romans) Leader's Guide. 48p. (Orig.). 1982. pap. 1.95 (ISBN 0-89367-080-4). Light & Life.
Resources for Renewal (Romans) Student Guide. 64p. (Orig.). 1982. pap. 2.50 (ISBN 0-89367-079-0). Light & Life.
Resources for Women's Ministries. (Women's Ministries Commission Ser.). 1975. 4.00 (ISBN 0-8309-0258-9). Herald Hse.
Respectable Folly: Millenarians and the French Revolution in France and England. Clarke Garrett. LC 74-24378. 252p. 1975. 26.00x (ISBN 0-8018-1618-1). Johns Hopkins.
Respecting Life: An Activity Guide. Jane B. Katenkamp. (Illus.). 144p. (Orig.). 1985. pap 14.95 (ISBN 1-55586-964-5). US Catholic.
Resplendent Themes. Billy E. Simmons. 70p. 1983. pap. 4.00 (ISBN 0-914520-19-9). Insight Pr.
Responding to God: The Life of Stewardship. Turner N. Clinard. LC 79-24762. 118p. 1980. Westminster.
Responding to Worldwide Needs. Cornelius J. Dyck. LC 80-10975. (MCC Story Ser.: Vol. 2). 168p. 1980. pap. 3.95x (ISBN 0-8361-1230-X). Herald Pr.
Responsa & Halakhic Studies. Isaac Klein. 15.00x. Ktav.
Responsa of Solomon Luria (Marharshal) Legal Decisions of the Famous Sixteenth-Century Sage. 2nd ed. Simon Hurwitz. LC 68-31710. 1969. 10.00 (ISBN 0-8197-0096-7). Bloch.
Responsa of the Babylonian Geonim As a Source of Jewish History. Jacob Mann. LC 73-2215. (Jewish People; History, Religion, Literature Ser.). Repr. of 1921 ed. 23.50 (ISBN 0-405-05279-0). Ayer Co Pubs.
Response. Bahiyyih Nakhjavani. 144p. pap. 4.95 (ISBN 0-85398-107-8). G Ronald Pub.
Response in American Catholic Periodicals to the Crises of the Great Depression, 1930-1935. Lawrence B. DeSaulniers. LC 83-23603. 198p. (Orig.). 1984. lib. bdg. 24.75 (ISBN 0-8191-3786-3); pap. text ed. 11.75 (ISBN 0-8191-3787-1). U Pr of Amer.
Response to God's Love: A View of the Spiritual Life. Edward Carter. 184p. 1984. 9.95 (ISBN 0-317-14585-1). Loyola.
Responses to Elie Wiesel. Ed. by Harry J. Cargas. LC 77-94055. 1978. o. p. 15.00 (ISBN 0-89255-031-7); pap. 5.95 (ISBN 0-89255-032-5). Persea Bks.
Responses to Religion: Studies in the Social Psychology of Religious Belief. Gary M. Maranell. LC 73-19860. (Illus.). xviii, 314p. 1974. 25.00x (ISBN 0-7006-0114-7). U Pr of KS.
Responsibility & Morality: Helping Children Become Responsible & Morally Mature. Larry C. Jensen & Karen M. Hughston. LC 79-10727. (Illus.). 1979. pap. 7.95x (ISBN 0-8425-1679-4). Brigham.
Responsibility for Evil in the Theodicy of IV Ezra: A Study Illustrating the Significance of Form & Structure for the Meaning of the Book. Alden Thompson. LC 76-40915. (Society of Biblical Literature. Dissertation Ser.). 1977. pap. 9.95 (ISBN 0-89130-091-0, 060129). Scholars Pr GA.
Responsibility of Hermeneutics. Clarence Walhout et al. 160p. (Orig.). 1985. pap. 8.95x (ISBN 0-8028-0029-7). Eerdmans.
Responsible Christian: A Guide for Moral Decision Making According to Classical Tradition. Vincent E. Rush. 288p. 1984. 9.95 (ISBN 0-8294-0448-1). Loyola.

Responsible Faith: Christian Theology in the Light of 20th-Century Questions. Hans Scwarz. LC 85-26657. 448p. 1986. text ed. 23.95 (ISBN 0-8066-2188-5, 10-5483). Augsburg.
Responsible Self. H. Richard Niebuhr. LC 63-15955. 1978. pap. 6.95xi (ISBN 0-06-066211-5, RD 266, HarpR). Har-Row.
Responsible Technology: A Christian Perspective. Stephen Monsma et al. 248p. (Orig.). 1986. pap. 12.95 (ISBN 0-8028-0175-7). Eerdmans.
Responsio Ad Lutherum, 2 Vols. St. Thomas More. Ed. by John M. Headley. LC 63-7949. (Complete Works of St. Thomas More Ser.: No. 5). 1969. Set. 85.00x (ISBN 0-300-01123-7). Yale U Pr.
Responsive Singing: Sabbath Morning Service. Robert Segal. 184p. 1972. 4.50x (ISBN 0-8381-0218-2). United Syn Bk.
Respuesta a La Guerra. Millard Lind. Orig. Title: Answer to War. 188p. 1963. pap. 1.50x (ISBN 0-8361-1149-4). Herald Pr.
Rest & Redemption: A Study of the Biblical Sabbath. Neils-Erik Andreason. (Andrews University Monographs, Studies in Religion: Vol. XI). vii, 137p. 1978. pap. 3.95 (ISBN 0-943872-11-1). Andrews Univ Pr.
Rest Days, the Christian Sunday, the Jewish Sabbath & Their Historical & Anthropological Prototypes. Hutton Webster. LC 68-58165. 1968. Repr. of 1916 ed. 48.00x (ISBN 0-8103-3342-2). Gale.
Rest of Us: The Rise of America's Eastern European Jews. Stephen Birmingham. 384p. 1984. 19.95 (ISBN 0-316-09647-4). Little.
Rest of Us: The Rise of America's Eastern European Jews. Stephen Birmingham. 432p. 1985. pap. 4.50 (ISBN 0-425-08074-9). Berkley Pub.
Resting in the Lord. Stephen S. Wilburn. 48p. 1985. 4.95 (ISBN 0-8378-5404-0). Gibson.
Restitution of All Things. Andrew Jukes. 194p. 1976. pap. text ed. 4.00 (ISBN 0-910424-65-9). Concordant.
Restless Heart: The Life & Influence of St. Augustine. Michael Marshall. (Illus.). 192p. 1987. 19.95 (ISBN 0-8028-3632-1). Eerdmans.
Restless Memories: Recollections of the Holocaust Years. rev., 2nd ed. Samuel P. Oliner. LC 85-82084. 215p. (Orig.). 1986. pap. 9.95 (ISBN 0-943376-28-9). Magnes Mus.
Restless Woman. Beverly LaHaye. 176p. 1984. pap. 5.95 (ISBN 0-310-27091-X, 18337P). Zondervan.
Restoration. Neva Coyle. 50p. (Orig.). 1985. saddlestitched 2.50 (ISBN 0-87123-851-9). Bethany Hse.
Restoration: A Political & Religious History of England & Wales 1658-1667. Ronald Hutton. (Illus.). 379p. 1985. 29.95x (ISBN 0-19-822698-5). Oxford U Pr.
Restoration of All Things. Victor P. Abram. LC 62-18059. 1962. 4.00 (ISBN 0-910840-07-5). Kingdom.
Restoration of Christian Culture. John Senior. LC 82-83497. 244p. (Orig.). 1983. pap. 9.95 (ISBN 0-89870-024-8). Ignatius Pr.
Restoration: Our Philosophy Through Inspired Poems. Ed. by Rosa M. Williams. LC 79-66586. 1980. (ISBN 0-9602366-1-9); pap. 6.50x. Sooty-Face.
Restoration Studies, Vol. II. Maurice L. Draper. 1983. pap. 13.00 (ISBN 0-8309-0362-3). Herald Hse.
Restoration Studies III. Ed. by Maurice L. Draper. 1986. pap. 15.00 (ISBN 0-8309-0432-8, Pub. by Reidel Holland). Kluwer Academic.
Restoration Studies, Vol.1. Ed. by Maurice L. Draper. 1980. pap. 13.00 (ISBN 0-8309-0292-9). Herald Hse.
Restore My Soul. Nachman of Breslov & Nathan of Breslov. Tr. by Avraham Greenbaum from Hebrew. Tr. of Meshivat Nefesh. 128p. (Orig.). 1980. pap. 3.00 (ISBN 0-930213-13-0). Breslov Res Inst.
Restored Church. Steven L. Shields. 16p. (Orig.). 1982. pap. 1.00 (ISBN 0-942284-01-1). Restoration Re.
Restored Value: A Woman's Status in Christ. JoAnne Sekowsky. (Encourager Ser.). 32p. 1985. pap. 2.25 (ISBN 0-932305-01-6, 523001). Aglow Pubns.
Restoring Father. William Richardson. 64p. 1987. pap. price not set (ISBN 0-87403-257-1, 39966). Standard Pub.
Restoring Fellowship: Judgement & Church Discipline. Ken Gage & Joy Gage. (Orig.). 1984. pap. 4.50 (ISBN 0-8024-4440-7). Moody.
Restoring Persons in World Community. J. Andrew Bolton. 1986. pap. 9.00 (ISBN 0-8309-0461-1). Herald Hse.
Restoring the Christian Family. John Sandford & Paula Sandford. LC 79-64977. 336p. 1986. pap. 6.95 (ISBN 0-932081-12-6). Victory Hse.
Restoring the Church. Kevin J. Conner & K. R. Iverson. (Illus.). 92p. 1977. Answer key. pap. 8.95 (ISBN 0-914936-23-9). Bible Temple.
Restoring the Family. 3rd ed. Elders of Bible Temple & Dick Iverson. 143p. Date not set. pap. price not set. Bible Temple.
Restoring the Image: An Introduction to Christian Caring & Counselling. Roger F. Hurding. 128p. 1986. pap. 6.50 (ISBN 0-85364-268-0). Attic Pr.
Restoring the Kingdom. Ed. by Deane W. Ferme. LC 83-82671. 226p. 1984. pap. 11.95 (ISBN 0-913757-06-3). Rose Sharon Pr.
Restoring the Kingdom. Ed. by Deane W. Fern. 240p. (Orig.). 1984. pap. text ed. 10.95 (ISBN 0-913757-06-3, Pub. by New Era Bks). Paragon Hse.
Restoring Your Spiritual Passion. Gordon MacDonald. 192p. 1986. 12.95 (ISBN 0-8407-9069-4). Oliver-Nelson.
Resurrection. Florence DeGroat. LC 81-67782. (Universal Man Ser.: Vol. 2). (Illus.). 168p. (Orig.). 1981. pap. text ed. 6.50 (ISBN 0-87516-456-0). De Vorss.
Resurrection According to Matthew, Mark, & Luke. Norman Perrin. LC 76-47913. 96p. (Orig.). 1977. pap. 3.95 (ISBN 0-8006-1248-5, 1-1248). Fortress.
Resurrection & Moral Order: An Outline for an Evangelical Ethics. Oliver O'Donovan. 320p. 1986. 18.95 (ISBN 0-8028-3610-0). Eerdmans.
Resurrection & the Life. John MacArthur, Jr. (John MacArthur's Bible Studies). 1986. pap. 3.50 (ISBN 0-8024-5091-1). Moody.
Resurrection Evidences. Kent Fishel & John Rayds. (Cornerstone Ser.). 1985. pap. 2.95 (ISBN 0-310-46102-2, 12675P). Zondervan.
Resurrection Factor. Josh McDowell. 180p. (Orig.). 1981. (ISBN 0-918956-71-4, Dist. by Here's Life Publishers Inc.); pap. 6.95 (ISBN 0-918956-72-2). Campus Crusade.
Resurrection (Five) Ed. by Chung H. Kwak. (Home Study Course Ser.). 40p. (Orig.). 1980. pap. 4.00 (ISBN 0-910621-14-4). HSA Pubns.
Resurrection Gospel. Robley E. Whitson. LC 85-51481. (Illus.). 48p. (Orig.). 1985. pap. text ed. 4.95x (ISBN 0-932269-55-9). Wyndham Hall.
Resurrection: Interpreting the Easter Gospel. Rowan Williams. 144p. (Orig.). 1985. pap. 5.95 (ISBN 0-8298-0727-6). Pilgrim NY.
Resurrection Is Not a Fairy Tale. George Nutting. 1981. 5.75 (ISBN 0-8062-1649-2). Carlton.
Resurrection Life & Power. Samuel L. Brengle. 1978. Repr. of 1925 ed. 3.95 (ISBN 0-86544-005-0). Salv Army Suppl South.
Resurrection Narratives. Herman Hendrickx. (Commentary on the Synoptic Gospels Ser.). 168p. 1984. pap. 9.95 (ISBN 0-225-66401-1, 8525, HarpR). Har-Row.
Resurrection Narratives: A Redactional Study. Grant R. Osborne. 288p. 1984. pap. 11.95 (ISBN 0-8010-6708-1). Baker Bk.
Resurrection: New Testament Witness & Contemporary Reflection. Pheme Perkins. LC 83-25473. 564p. 1984. 19.95 (ISBN 0-385-17256-7). Doubleday.
Resurrection of Christ. H. C. Moule & J. Orr. 1980. 20.00 (ISBN 0-86524-062-0, 9506). Klock & Klock.
Resurrection of Christ. John M. Shaw. 218p. 1920. 10.95 (ISBN 0-567-02252-8, Pub. by T & T Clark Ltd UK). Fortress.
Resurrection of Jesus: A Jewish Perspective. Pinchas Lapide. Tr. by Wilhelm C. Linss. LC 83-70514. 160p. (Orig.). 1983. pap. 8.95 (ISBN 0-8066-2020-X, 10-5485). Augsburg.
Resurrection of Jesus: An Apologetic. Gary R. Habermas. 188p. 1984. pap. text ed. 11.50 (ISBN 0-8191-3750-2). U Pr of Amer.
Resurrection of Jesus Christ. Gerald O'Collins. LC 73-2613. 160p. 1973. pap. 3.50 (ISBN 0-8170-0614-1). Judson.
Resurrection of Jesus Christ in New Testament Theology. John F. Jansen. LC 80-231. 188p. 1980. pap. 9.95 (ISBN 0-664-24309-6). Westminster.
Resurrection of Jesus of Nazareth. Willi Marxsen. Tr. by Margaret Kohl from Ger. LC 76-120083. 192p. (Orig.). 1970. pap. 4.95 (ISBN 0-8006-0001-0, 1-1). Fortress.
Resurrection of Life. John Brown. 1978. 15.50 (ISBN 0-86524-962-8, 4601). Klock & Klock.
Resurrection of the Dead. Karl Barth. Ed. by Robert Kastenbaum. LC 76-19559. (Death and Dying Ser.). 1977. Repr. of 1933 ed. lib. bdg. 23.50x (ISBN 0-405-09555-4). Ayer Co Pubs.
Resurrection of the Dead. Derek Prince. (Foundation Ser.: Bk. VI). 1965-66. pap. 2.95 (ISBN 0-934920-05-2, B-15). Derek Prince.
Resurrection of Theism: Prolegomena to Christian Apology. Stuart C. Hackett. (Twin Brooks Ser.). 381p. 1982. pap. 11.95 (ISBN 0-8010-4263-1). Baker Bk.
Resurrection of Value. John Walchars. 176p. (Orig.). 1986. pap. 8.95 (ISBN 0-8245-0746-0). Crossroad NY.
Resurrection Promise: An Interpretation of the Easter Narratives. Charles A. Perry. 152p. (Orig.). 1987. pap. 8.95 (ISBN 0-8028-0249-4). Eerdmans.
Resurrection Promises. Leonard H. Budd & Roger G. Talbott. Ed. by Michael L. Sherer. (Orig.). 1987. pap. 6.25 (ISBN 0-89536-850-1, 7809). CSS of Ohio.
Resurrection: Release from Oppression. Morton T. Kelsey. LC 84-62150. 201p. 1985. pap. 8.95 (ISBN 0-8091-2673-7). Paulist Pr.
Resurrection: True or False? Spiros Zodhiates. (Illus.). 1978. pap. 3.95 (ISBN 0-89957-524-2). AMG Pubs.
Retelling the Biblical Story. H. Stephen Shoemaker. LC 85-16650. 1985. pap. 6.95 (ISBN 0-8054-2114-9). Broadman.
Retention of Religious Experiences. T. Pettersson. (Illus.). 158p. (Orig.). 1975. pap. text ed. 18.50x (Pub. Almqvist & Wiksell). Coronet Bks.
Rethinking Adult Religious Education: A Practical Parish Guide. Jeanne Tighe & Karen Szentkeresti. 144p. (Orig.). 1986. pap. 9.95 (ISBN 0-8091-2829-2). Paulist Pr.
Rethinking Church Music. rev. ed. Paul W. Wohlgemuth. LC 80-85254. 112p. 1981. pap. 5.95 (ISBN 0-916642-15-1). Hope Pub.
Rethinking Congregational Development. George E. Morris. LC 84-71366. 144p. (Orig.). 1984. pap. 5.25 (ISBN 0-88177-012-4, DRO12B). Discipleship Res.
Rethinking Evangelism: A Theological Approach. Ben C. Johnson. LC 86-26787. 142p. (Orig.). 1987. pap. 9.95 (ISBN 0-664-24060-7). Westminster.
Rethinking Quaker Principles. Rufus M. Jones. 1983. pap. 2.50x (ISBN 0-87574-008-1, 008). Pendle Hill.
Retractations. St. Augustine. (Fathers of the Church Ser.: Vol. 60). 451p. 1968. 17.95x (ISBN 0-8132-0060-1). Cath U Pr.
Retrato de la Reina: La Historia de Nuestra Senora de Guadalupe. Sr. Mary Amatora. 1972. 7.50 (ISBN 0-682-47542-4, Lochinvar); pap. 5.00 (ISBN 0-682-47548-3, Lochinvar). Exposition Pr FL.
Retratos del Salvador. Herbert Lockyer. Tr. of Portraits of the Savior. (Span.). 192p. 1986. pap. 3.50 (ISBN 0-8297-0741-7). Life Pubs Intl.
Retreat Guide I. Steve Clapp. 20p. (Orig.). 1981. pap. 2.00 (ISBN 0-914527-04-5). C-Four Res.
Retreat Guide II. Steve Clapp. (C-4 Journals). 29p. (Orig.). 1982. pap. 2.00 (ISBN 0-914527-13-4). C-Four Res.
Retreat Handbook. Virgil Nelson & Lynn Nelson. LC 75-23468. 128p. 1976. pap. 7.95 (ISBN 0-8170-0694-X). Judson.
Retreat Handbook. Sandy Reimer & Larry Reimer. 192p. 1987. pap. 9.95. Morehouse.
Retreat into Eternity: An Upanishad-Book of Aphorisms. Swami Amar Jyoti. LC 80-54236. (Illus.). 128p. (Orig.). 1981. pap. 12.95 (ISBN 0-933572-03-4). Truth Consciousness.
Retreat Planning Made Easy: A Resource for Christian Retreats. Shirley Harman. 40p. (Orig.). pap. 4.95 (ISBN 0-8066-2155-9, 10-5488). Augsburg.
Retrospect of Fifty Years, 2 vols. in 1. James C. Gibbons. LC 79-38447. (Religion in America, Ser. 2). 720p. 1972. Repr. of 1916 ed. 47.50 (ISBN 0-405-04066-0). Ayer Co Pubs.
Retrospection & Introspection. Mary B. Eddy. pap. 4.50 (ISBN 0-87952-044-2). First Church.
Retrospection & Introspection. Mary B. Eddy. French 12.50 (ISBN 0-87952-122-8); German 12.50 (ISBN 0-87952-157-0); Italian 12.50 (ISBN 0-87952-182-1); Portugese 12.50 (ISBN 0-87952-207-0); Spanish 7.50 (ISBN 0-87952-231-3); Swedish 12.50 (ISBN 0-87952-252-6). First Church.
Return from Tomorrow. George G. Ritchie & Elizabeth Sherrill. 128p. 1981. pap. 2.95 (ISBN 0-8007-8412-X, Spire Bks). Revell.
Return of Arthur Conan Doyle. Grace Cooke & Ivan Cooke. (Illus.). 1963. 9.95 (ISBN 0-85487-037-7). De Vorss.
Return of Astraea: An Astral-Imperial Myth in Calderon. Frederick A. De Armas. LC 86-7758. (Studies in Romance Languages: No. 32). 272p. 1986. 27.00 (ISBN 0-8131-1570-1). U Pr of Ky.
Return of Eden: Five Essays on Milton's Epics. Northrop Frye. 1975. 15.00x (ISBN 0-8020-1353-8). U of Toronto Pr.
Return of Elijah. Morris Venden. (Harv Ser.). 1983. pap. 4.50 (ISBN 0-8163-0453-X). Pacific Pr Pub Assn.
Return of the Ancients. F. Edward Butterworth. (Orig.). 1987. pap. 10.00 (ISBN 0-941227-00-6). Cosmic Pr Chico.
Return of the Goddess. Edward C. Whitmont. 288p. 1986. pap. 9.50 (ISBN 0-8334-1002-4, Freedeeds Bks). Garber Comm.
Return of the Jesuits. Francis X. Curran. LC 66-29559. 1966. 3.00 (ISBN 0-8294-0018-4). Loyola.
Return of the Lord. Ralph Martin. 118p. (Orig.). 1983. pap. 4.95 (ISBN 0-89283-145-6). Servant.
Return of the Millenium. Ed. by Joseph Bettis & Stanley Johannesen. LC 83-82671. 232p. (Orig.). pap. 11.95 (ISBN 0-913757-02-0, Pub. by New Era Bks.). Paragon Hse.
Return of the Millennium. Ed. by Joseph Bettis & S. K. Johannesen. LC 83-82671. 247p. 1984. pap. 11.95 (ISBN 0-913757-02-0). Rose Sharon Pr.
Return of the Star of Bethlehem. Kenneth Boa & William Proctor. 224p. (Orig.). 1985. pap. 7.95 (ISBN 0-310-33631-7, 12770P). Zondervan.
Return of the Wolf. Martin Bell. 128p. 1983. 12.50 (ISBN 0-8164-0545-X, HarpR); pap. 7.95 (ISBN 0-8164-2470-5). Har-Row.
Return to Center. Bobbie Probstein. LC 85-70723. (Illus.). 256p. (Orig.). 1985. pap. 9.95 (ISBN 0-87516-554-0). De Vorss.
Return to Judaism: Religious Renewal in Israel. Janet Aviad. LC 82-17663. xiv, 194p. 1985. pap. 8.95 (ISBN 0-226-03235-3). U of Chicago Pr.
Return to Life: Two Imaginings of the Lazarus Theme. an original anthology ed. Ed. by Robert Kastenbaum. LC 76-19587. (Death & Dying Ser.). 1977. Repr. of 1976 ed. lib. bdg. 19.00x (ISBN 0-405-09582-1). Ayer Co Pubs.
Return to Natural Theology. F. H. Cleobury. 246p. 1967. 17.95 (ISBN 0-227-67722-6). Attic Pr.
Return to Reality: Some Essays on Contemporary Christianity. Ed. by Stanley G. Evans. 1954. 39.50x (ISBN 0-317-07644-2). Elliots Bks.
Return to Religion. Henry C. Link. LC 77-17291. 1977. Repr. of 1937 ed. lib. bdg. 16.50 (ISBN 0-8414-5846-4). Folcroft.
Return to Shiva. Valmiki. (Sacred Texts Ser.). viii, 88p. 1983. pap. 8.75 (ISBN 0-88695-006-6). Concord Grove.
Return to the Center. Bede Griffiths. 1976. pap. 7.95 (ISBN 0-87243-112-6). Templegate.
Return Unto Me. R. F. DeHaan. pap. 2.00 (ISBN 0-686-14199-7). Rose Pub MI.
Returning Sun: Hope for a Broken World. George A. Maloney. 63p. (Orig.). 1982. pap. 2.50 (ISBN 0-914544-42-X). Living Flame Pr.
Returning to the Source. Bhagwan Shree Rajneesh. Ed. by Ma Yoga Sudha. LC 83-182149. (Zen Ser.). (Illus.). 402p. (Orig.). 1976. 15.95 (ISBN 0-88050-120-0). Chidvilas Found.
Reunion of Christendom: A Survey of Present Position. James Marchant. 329p. 1980. Repr. of 1929 ed. lib. bdg. 30.00 (ISBN 0-8495-3771-1). Arden Lib.
Reunion of the Church: A Defence of the South India Scheme. James E. Newbigin. LC 79-4205. 1979. Repr. of 1960 ed. lib. bdg. cancelled (ISBN 0-313-20797-6, NERU). Greenwood.
Revealing Word. Charles Fillmore. 1959. 5.95 (ISBN 0-87159-137-5). Unity School.
Revelacion e Inspiracion de las Escrituras. John M. Lewis & Pablo A. Deiros. (Biblioteca de Doctrina Cristiana). (Span.). 162p. 1986. pap. 5.95 (ISBN 0-311-09113-X). Casa Bautista.
Revelation. Albert Barnes. 12.95 (ISBN 0-8010-0849-2). Baker Bk.
Revelation. Bert Beagle. 160p. 1986. 11.95 (ISBN 0-89962-568-1). Todd & Honeywell.
Revelation. Siegbert W. Becker. 1985. 16.95 (ISBN 0-8100-0190-X, 15N0410). Northwest Pub.
Revelation. James L. Blevins. Ed. by John Hayes. LC 84-4387. (Preaching Guides Ser.). 132p. (Orig.). 1984. pap. 6.95 (ISBN 0-8042-3250-4). John Knox.
Revelation. M. R. De Haan. 1956. 13.95 (ISBN 0-310-23440-9, 9498P). Zondervan.
Revelation. Charles L. Feinberg. 1985. 9.95 (ISBN 0-88469-162-4). BMH Bks.
Revelation. Alger M. Fitch, Jr. (Standard Bible Studies). 112p. 1986. pap. 5.95 (ISBN 0-87403-173-7, 40113). Standard Pub.
Revelation. Tr. by J. Massyngberde Ford. LC 74-18796. (Anchor Bible Ser.: Vol. 38). (Illus.). 504p. 1975. 18.00 (ISBN 0-385-00895-3). Doubleday.
Revelation. Arno C. Gaebelein. LC 61-17225. 1960. 7.95 (ISBN 0-87213-223-4). Loizeaux.
Revelation. Homer Hailey. LC 78-62441. 1979. 14.95 (ISBN 0-8010-4201-1). Baker Bk.
Revelation. Timothy A. Heck. (Standard Bible Study Workbooks Ser.). 64p. 1986. pap. text ed. 1.95 (ISBN 0-87403-193-1, 40213). Standard Pub.
Revelation. H. A. Ironside. 9.95 (ISBN 0-87213-384-2). Loizeaux.
Revelation. Irving L. Jensen. (Bible Self-Study Ser.). 124p. (Orig.). 1971. pap. 3.25 (ISBN 0-8024-1066-9). Moody.
Revelation. Irving L. Jensen. (Irving Jensen's Do-It-Yourself Bible Study Ser.). 110p. (Orig.). 1985. wkbk. 5.95 (ISBN 0-89840-081-3). Heres Life.
Revelation. (Erdmans Commentaries Ser.). 4.50 (ISBN 0-8010-3405-1). Baker Bk.
Revelation. Charles C. Ryrie. (Everyman's Bible Commentary Ser.). (Orig.). 1968. pap. 5.95 (ISBN 0-8024-2066-4). Moody.

Revelation. Lehman Strauss. LC 64-8641. Orig. Title: Book of the Revelation. 9.95 (ISBN 0-87213-825-9). Loizeaux.

Revelation. J. P. Sweet. LC 78-26383. (Westminster Pelican Commentaries). 378p. 1979. 14.95 (ISBN 0-664-21375-8); softcover 9.95 (ISBN 0-664-24262-6). Westminster.

Revelation. Frederick A. Tatford. 656p. 1985. Repr. lib. bdg. 23.00 (ISBN 0-86524-186-4, 6602). Klock & Klock.

Revelation - the Last Book of the Bible. Edwin A. Schick. LC 76-62602. pap. 20.00 (2029617). Bks Demand UMI.

Revelation - the Seer, the Saviour, & the Saved. rev. ed. James D. Strauss. (Bible Study Textbook Ser.). (Illus.). 1972. 15.90 (ISBN 0-89900-048-7). College Pr Pub.

Revelation: A Commentary on the Book, Based on the Study of Twenty Four Psychic Discourses of Edgar Cayce. Edgar Cayce. (Twenty-Six Interpretive Readings). 1969. pap. 8.95 (ISBN 0-87604-003-2). ARE Pr.

Revelation: A Study Guide. Edwin Walhout. (Revelation Series for Adults). 1978. pap. text ed. 2.50 (ISBN 0-933140-07-X). CRC Pubns.

Revelation: An Exposition of the First Eleven Chapters. James B. Ramsey. (Geneva Commentary Ser.). 1977. 17.95 (ISBN 0-85151-256-9). Banner of Truth.

Revelation: An Expositional Commentary. Donald G. Barnhouse. 1971. 14.95 (ISBN 0-310-20490-9); pap. 11.95 (ISBN 0-310-20491-7, 9760P). Zondervan.

Revelation & Experience. Carol R. Murphy. LC 64-22765. (Orig.). pap. 2.50x (ISBN 0-87574-137-1). Pendle Hill.

Revelation & Faith: Theological Reflections on the Knowing & Doing of Faith. Theron D. Price. 192p. 1987. 29.95 (ISBN 0-86554-260-0, MUP H-221); pap. 14.95 (ISBN 0-86554-261-9, MUP P-45). Mercer Univ Pr.

Revelation & Its Interpretation. Aylward Shorter. 280p. 1984. pap. text ed. 14.95 (ISBN 0-225-66356-2, AY8482, HarpR). Har-Row.

Revelation & Love's Architecture. Martin C. D'Arcy. 90p. 1976. 8.00 (ISBN 0-89182-010-8). Charles River Bks.

Revelation & Reason. Emil Brunner. 448p. 1984. pap. 14.95 (ISBN 0-913029-01-7). Stevens Bk Pr.

Revelation & Reason in Advaita Vedanta. K. S. Murty. 1974. Repr. 11.25 (ISBN 0-8426-0662-9). Orient Bk Dist.

Revelation & Reason in Islam. Arthur J. Arberry. LC 80-1936. (BCL: Series I & II). Repr. of 1957 ed. 20.00 (ISBN 0-404-18952-0). AMS Pr.

Revelation & Redemption. George W. Buchanan. 1978. text ed. 29.50 (ISBN 0-915948-04-4). Bks Distinction.

Revelation & Religion: Studies in the Theological Interpretation of Religious Types. Herbert H. Farmer. LC 77-27177. (Gifford Lectures: 1950). (Illus.). 256p. Repr. of 1954 ed. 31.00 (ISBN 0-404-60505-2). AMS Pr.

Revelation & Response in the Old Testament. Cuthbert A. Simpson. LC 73-76022. Repr. of 1947 ed. 15.00 (ISBN 0-404-06056-0). AMS Pr.

Revelation & Theology: The Gospel As Narrated Promise. Ronald F. Thiemann. LC 84-40822. 208p. 1985. text ed. 23.95 (ISBN 0-268-01629-1, 85-16296). U of Notre Dame Pr.

Revelation & Theology: The Gospel As Narrated Promise. Ronald F. Thiemann. LC 84-40822. 198p. 1987. pap. text ed. 9.95 (ISBN 0-268-01632-1, Dist. by Har-Row). U of Notre Dame Pr.

Revelation & Violence: A Study in Contextualization. Walter Brueggemann. LC 86-60473. (Pere Marquette Ser.). 72p. 1986. 7.95 (ISBN 0-87462-541-6). Marquette.

Revelation As Drama. James L. Blevins. LC 84-4986. 1984. pap. 6.95 (ISBN 0-8054-1393-6). Broadman.

Revelation: Bible Study Commentary. Alan F. Johnson. (Bible Study Commentary Ser.). 1986. pap. 7.95 (ISBN 0-310-45173-6, 12386P). Zondervan.

Revelation Explained. F. G. Smith. 464p. Repr. 5.50 (ISBN 0-686-29163-8). Faith Pub Hse.

Revelation Expounded. W. Kelly. 5.95 (ISBN 0-88172-106-9). Believers Bkshelf.

Revelation: For a New Age. Dorothy Elder. LC 81-65477. 320p. (Orig.). 1981. pap. 11.50 (ISBN 0-87516-446-3). De Vorss.

Revelation for Layman. Jim McKeever. 1980. 10.95 (ISBN 0-931608-07-4); pap. 5.95 (ISBN 0-931608-08-2). Omega Pubns OR.

Revelation for Today: Images of Hope. Richard L. Jeske. LC 82-16079. 144p. 1983. pap. 6.95 (ISBN 0-8006-1693-6). Fortress.

Revelation: God & Satan in the Apocalypse. James Kallas. LC 73-78268. 128p. 1973. pap. 6.95 (ISBN 0-8066-1332-7, 10-5490). Augsburg.

Revelation: God's Grand Finale. Hilton Sutton. 280p. (Orig.). 1984. pap. 6.95 (ISBN 0-89274-298-4). Harrison Hse.

Revelation: God's Stamp of Sovereignty. R. Hollis Gause. LC 83-63383. 286p. 1983. pap. text ed. 9.95 (ISBN 0-87148-740-3). Pathway Pr.

Revelation-Illustrated & Made Plain. rev. ed. Tim Lahaye. 456p. 1975. 7.95 (ISBN 0-310-26991-1, 18073P). Zondervan.

Revelation in Christianity & Other Religions. Mariasusai Dhavamony et al. (Studia Missionalia: Vol. 20). (Eng., Fr., & Ital.). 1971. pap. 15.00 (ISBN 0-8294-0324-8, Pub. by Gregorian U Pr). Loyola.

Revelation in Indian Thought: A Festschrift in Honor of Professor T. R. V. Murti. Ed. by Harold Coward. LC 77-71192. 1977. 25.00 (ISBN 0-913546-52-6). Dharma Pub.

Revelation in Jewish Wisdom Literature. John C. Rylaarsdam. (Midway Reprint Ser.). pap. 35.00 (ISBN 0-317-26582-2, 2024065). Bks Demand UMI.

Revelation in the Fourth Gospel: Narrative Mode & Theological Claim. Gail R. O'Day. LC 86-45217. 160p. 1986. pap. 9.95 (ISBN 0-8006-1933-1). Fortress.

Revelation, Inspiration, Scripture. John M. Lewis. LC 83-71822. (Layman's Library of Christian Doctrine Ser.). 1985. 5.95 (ISBN 0-8054-1633-1). Broadman.

Revelation of Baha'u'llah, Vol. I: Baghdad 1853-1863. Adib Taherzadeh. (Illus.). 384p. 1974. 18.95 (ISBN 0-85398-052-7); pap. 11.95 (ISBN 0-85398-057-8). G Ronald Pub.

Revelation of Baha'u'llah, Vol. II: Adrianople, 1863-1868. Adib Taherzadeh. (Illus.). 492p. 1977. 17.95 (ISBN 0-85398-070-5). G Ronald Pub.

Revelation of Baha'u'llah Vol. III: Akka',the Early Years 1868-77. Ad. Taherzaden. (Illus.). 544p. 19.95 (ISBN 0-85398-143-4). G Ronald Pub.

Revelation of Bethlehem. Two Hermits. 1985. pap. 3.50 (ISBN 0-932506-41-0). St Bedes Pubns.

Revelation of Deity. J. E. Turner. Repr. of 1931 ed. 20.00 (ISBN 0-527-91170-4). Kraus Repr.

Revelation of Elchasai: Investigations into the Evidence for a Mesopotamian Jewish Apocalypse of the Second Century & Its Reception by Judeo-Christian Propagandists. Gerard P. Luttikhuizen. 263p. 1985. lib. bdg. 60.00x (ISBN 3-16-144935-5, Pub. by J C B Mohr BRD). Coronet Bks.

Revelation of God in Nature. Bert Thompson & Wayne Jackson. (That You May Believe Ser.). 22p. (Orig.). 1985. pap. 1.50 (ISBN 0-932859-04-6). Apologetic Pr.

Revelation of Jesus Christ. Ray F. Robbins. LC 75-1739. 240p. 1976. bds. 6.50 (ISBN 0-8054-1354-5). Broadman.

Revelation of Jesus Christ. John F. Walvoord. LC 66-16227. 1966. 15.95 (ISBN 0-8024-7310-5). Moody.

Revelation of John. Ed. by Thomas F. Glasson. (Cambridge Bible Commentary on the New English Bible, New Testament Ser.). (Orig.). 1965. 16.95 (ISBN 0-521-04208-9); pap. 9.95x (ISBN 0-521-09256-6). Cambridge U Pr.

Revelation of Life Eternal: An Introduction to the Christian Message. Nicholas Arseniev. 144p. 1964. pap. 5.95 (ISBN 0-913836-00-1). St Vladimirs.

Revelation of Purgatory by an Unknown, 15th Century Woman Visionary: Introduction, Critical Text & Translation. Marta P. Harley. (Studies in Women & Religion: Vol. 18). 160p. 1986. lib. bdg. 49.95x (ISBN 0-88946-531-2). E Mellen.

Revelation of St. John, Vol. I. Eduard Schick. Ed. by John L. McKenzie. LC 81-605. (New Testament for Spiritual Reading Ser.). 112p. 1981. pap. 4.95 (ISBN 0-8245-0133-0). Crossroad NY.

Revelation of St. John, Vol. II. Eduard Schick. Ed. by John L. McKenzie. LC 81-605. (New Testament for Spiritual Reading Ser.). 112p. 1981. 10.00 (ISBN 0-8245-0359-7); pap. 4.95 (ISBN 0-8245-0134-9). Crossroad NY.

Revelation of St. John the Divine. G. B. Caird. LC 66-20774. (New Testament Commentaries Ser.). 1966. 17.95 (ISBN 0-06-061296-7, HarpR). Har-Row.

Revelation of Saint John the Divine. (Modern Critical Interpretations--Ancient, Medieval, & Renaissance Ser.). 1987. 19.95 (ISBN 0-87754-916-8). Chelsea Hse.

Revelation of Treasure Hid--Concerning Freedom, Concerning the Motherland, Concerning Justice, Apostolical Canons Respecting Baptism. Apostolos Makrakis. Ed. by Orthodox Christian Educational Society. Tr. by Denver Cummings from Hellenic. 80p. (Orig.). 1952. pap. 2.00x (ISBN 0-938366-23-8). Orthodox Chr.

Revelation Record. Henry M. Morris. 1983. 18.95 (ISBN 0-8423-5511-1). Tyndale.

Revelation Revealed. Jack Van Impe. 282p. 1982. pap. 6.95 (ISBN 0-934803-09-9); 8-cassette set 29.95 (ISBN 0-934803-35-8). J Van Impe.

Revelation, Systematically Studied. Parnell C. Coward. 1983. pap. 6.95 (ISBN 0-87148-739-X). Pathway Pr.

Revelation Taught: The Paraclete in the Gospel of John. Eskil Franck. (New Testament Ser.: No. 14). 168p. (Orig.). 1985. pap. text ed. 27.50x (ISBN 91-40-05114-5, Pub. by Liber Utbildning (Stockholm Sweden)). Coronet Bks.

Revelation Teaching Syllabus. Hilton Sutton. 1985. 10.00 (ISBN 0-89274-318-2). Harrison Hse.

Revelation, the Future Foretold. Keith L. Brooks. (Teach Yourself the Bible Ser.). 1962. pap. 2.75 (ISBN 0-8024-7308-3). Moody.

Revelation: The Lamb Who Is the Lion. Gladys Hunt. (Fisherman Bible Studyguide). 73p. 1973. saddle-stitched 2.95 (ISBN 0-87788-486-2). Shaw Pubs.

Revelation: The Triumph of God. Paul Stevens. (LifeBuilder Bible Studies). 64p. (Orig.). 1987. pap. 2.95 (ISBN 0-8308-1021-8). Inter-Varsity.

Revelation: Three Viewpoints. LC 77-74512. 1977. pap. 9.95 (ISBN 0-8054-1363-4). Broadman.

Revelation Through Reason: Religion in the Light of Science & Philosophy. Errol E. Harris. 1958. 39.50x (ISBN 0-317-27547-X). Elliots Bks.

Revelation to John. Martin H. Franzmann. 148p. 1986. pap. 7.95 (ISBN 0-570-03728-X, 12-2630). Concordia.

Revelation Unfolded. Jack B. Scott. pap. 2.95 (ISBN 0-8423-5510-3). Tyndale.

Revelation Visualized. Salem Kirban & Gary Cohen. 1971. pap. 14.95 (ISBN 0-912582-08-1). Kirban.

Revelation: Your Future Prophesied. Marjorie H. Russell. (Illus.). 60p. (Orig.). 1985. pap. 7.98 (ISBN 0-9614745-0-5). Arcadia Corp.

Revelations: As It Is. Patricia Sri. Ed. by Moringland Publications Inc. (Illus.). 635p. (Orig.). 1979. pap. 10.00 (ISBN 0-935146-08-3). Morningland.

Revelations of Antichrist. W. H. Burris. 59.95 (ISBN 0-8490-0950-2). Gordon Pr.

Revelations of Antichrist: Concerning Christ & Christianity. William H. Burr. LC 79-161340. (Atheist Viewpoint Ser). 448p. 1972. Repr. of 1879 ed. 29.00 (ISBN 0-405-03801-1). Ayer Co Pubs.

Revelations of Brimstone: Ominous Portents of the Parousia of Christ. R. Henry Hall. (Illus.). 374p. (Orig.). 1984. pap. 6.95 (ISBN 0-930351-00-2). Spirit Prophecy.

Revelations of Divine Love. Julian of Norwich. Ed. by Roger L. Roberts. LC 82-80471. (Treasures from the Spiritual Classics Ser.). 64p. 1982. pap. 2.95 (ISBN 0-8192-1308-X). Morehouse.

Revelations of Divine Love: Juliana of Norwich. Tr. by M. L. Del Mastro. LC 76-52004. 1977. pap. 4.95 (ISBN 0-385-12297-7, Im). Doubleday.

Revelations of Margaret of Cortona. Ange-Marie Hiral. (Spirit &Life Ser). 1952. 3.00 (ISBN 0-686-11562-7). Franciscan Inst.

Revelations of Saint Birgitta. Ed. by W. P. Cumming. (EETS, OS Ser.: No. 178). Repr. of 1929 ed. 38.00 (ISBN 0-527-00175-9). Kraus Repr.

Revelations of Things to Come. Earlyne C. Chaney. (Illus.). 156p. 1982. pap. 13.95 (ISBN 0-918936-12-8). Astara.

Revenant Christ. Friend Stuart. 1983. pap. 4.95 (ISBN 0-912132-15-9). Dominion Pr.

Reverence for Life. Albert Schweitzer. Tr. by Reginald H. Fuller. LC 71-85052. 1980. Repr. of 1969 ed. 14.95 (ISBN 0-89197-920-4). Irvington.

Reverence for Life & Family Program: Parent-Teacher Resource. John E. Forliti. 1981. pap. 4.50 176 pp (ISBN 0-697-01789-3); tchr. training tape 9.95 (ISBN 0-697-01837-7). Wm C Brown.

Reverend Colonel Finch. Elizabeth Nitchie. LC 40-33650. Repr. of 1940 ed. 12.50 (ISBN 0-404-04777-7). AMS Pr.

Reverend Elhanan Winchester: Biography & Letters. LC 72-38464. (Religion in America, Ser. 2). 358p. 1972. Repr. of 1972 ed. 26.50 (ISBN 0-405-04090-3). Ayer Co Pubs.

Reverend John Clayton: A Parson with a Scientific Mind. John Clayton. Ed. by Edmund Berkeley & Dorothy S. Berkeley. LC 65-23459. (Virginia Historical Document: No. 6). (Illus.). 1965. 15.00x (ISBN 0-8139-0067-0). U Pr of Va.

Reverend Sun Myung Moon. Chong Sun Kim. LC 78-52115. 1978. pap. text ed. 9.50 (ISBN 0-8191-0494-9). U Pr of Amer.

Reverend Thomas Bray: His Life & Selected Works Relating to Maryland. Thomas Bray. Ed. by Bernard C. Steiner. LC 72-14420. (Maryland Historical Society. Fund-Publications Ser.: No. 37). Repr. of 1901 ed. 15.00 (ISBN 0-404-57637-0). AMS Pr.

Reverent Discipline: Essays in Literary Criticism & Culture. George A. Panichas. LC 73-15749. 488p. 1974. 29.95x (ISBN 0-87049-149-0). U of Tenn Pr.

Reverent Skeptic. J. Wesley Robb. LC 79-83609. 238p. 1979. 12.50 (ISBN 0-8022-2245-5). Philos Lib.

Reverse Side of the Cross. Rufus Moseley. pap. 0.65 ea. 2 for 1.00 (ISBN 0-910924-83-X). Macalester.

Review of "Shall We Splinter?". Robert R. Taylor, Jr. 1985. pap. 3.00 (ISBN 0-934916-08-X). Natl Christian Pr.

Review of the Mexican War on Christian Principles: And an Essay on the Means of Preventing War. Philip A. Berry. LC 76-143427. (Peace Movement in America Ser). ix, 87p. 1972. Repr. of 1849 ed. lib. bdg. 11.95x (ISBN 0-89198-057-1). Ozer.

Review of the Principal Questions in Morals. Richard Price. LC 73-179398. 516p. 1974. Repr. of 1787 ed. lib. bdg. 32.50 (ISBN 0-8337-2831-8). B Franklin.

Revised Code of Canon Law: A Missed Opportunity, Vol. 147. Ed. by Peter Huizing & Knut Walf. (Concilium 1981). 128p. (Orig.). 1981. pap. 6.95 (ISBN 0-8164-2347-4, HarpR). Har-Row.

Revised Handful of Ideas. Becky T. Holbrook. 5.95 (ISBN 0-89137-611-9). Quality Pubns.

Revisions: Changing Perspectives in Moral Philosophy. Ed. by Stanley Hauerwas & Alasdair MacIntyre. (Revisions Ser.). 320p. 1983. text ed. 24.95 (ISBN 0-268-01614-3); pap. text ed. 9.95 (ISBN 0-268-01617-8). U of Notre Dame Pr.

Revitalizing the Church. Bill Hull. 1986. pap. cancelled (ISBN 0-89109-539-X). NavPress.

Revitalizing the Twentieth Century Church. Lloyd M. Perry & Norman Shawchuck. LC 81-16974. Date not set. pap. 7.95 (ISBN 0-8024-7318-0). Moody.

Revival. D. Martyn Lloyd-Jones. LC 86-72057. 320p. (Orig.). 1987. pap. 9.95 (ISBN 0-89107-415-5, Crossway Bks). Good News.

Revival! Richard O. Roberts. 186p. 1982. pap. 6.95 (ISBN 0-8423-5575-8). Tyndale.

Revival! Ed. by Wayne E. Warner. (Illus.). 163p. (Orig.). 1978. pap. 4.95 (ISBN 0-89274-303-4). Harrison Hse.

Revival Addresses. R. A. Torrey. 282p. 1974. Repr. of 1903 ed. 10.95 (ISBN 0-227-67808-7). Attic Pr.

Revival & Local Church Evangelism. Charles Kempf. (Orig.). 1987. pap. price not set (ISBN 0-89084-369-4). Bob Jones Univ Pr.

Revival Fires in Canada. Kurt E. Koch. LC 72-93352. 96p. 1975. pap. 2.95 (ISBN 0-8254-3015-1). Kregel.

Revival God's Way. Leonard Ravenhill. LC 83-15589. 128p. 1983. text ed. 7.95 (ISBN 0-87123-580-3). Bethany Hse.

Revival God's Way. Leonard Ravenhill. 128p. (Orig.). 1983. pap. 7.95 (210620). Bethany Hse.

Revival Lectures. Charles G. Finney. 544p. 15.95 (ISBN 0-8007-0272-7). Revell.

Revival of Religion. Burns et al. 449p. 1984. Repr. of 1840 ed. 13.95 (ISBN 0-85151-435-9). Banner of Truth.

Revival of Scholastic Philosophy in the Nineteenth Century. Joseph L. Perrier. LC 9-10966. Repr. of 1909 ed. 17.50 (ISBN 0-404-04994-X). AMS Pr.

Revival of the Griesbach Hypothesis: An Analysis & Appraisal. C. M. Tuckett. LC 81-6128. (Society for New Testament Studies Monographs: No. 44). 230p. 1983. 37.50 (ISBN 0-521-23803-X). Cambridge U Pr.

Revival Praying. Leonard Ravenhill. 176p. 1962. pap. 4.95 (ISBN 0-87123-482-3, 210482). Bethany Hse.

Revival: Principles to Change the World. Winkie Pratney. 320p. (Orig.). 1983. pap. 3.95 (ISBN 0-88368-124-2). Whitaker Hse.

Revival Sermon Outlines. Ed. by Charles R. Wood. 64p. 1975. pap. 2.95 (ISBN 0-8254-4005-X). Kregel.

Revival Sermons. William C. Burns. 205p. 1981. pap. 4.95 (ISBN 0-85151-316-6). Banner of Truth.

Revivalism & Social Reform: American Protestantism on the Eve of the Civil War. Timothy Smith. LC 80-8114. 272p. 1980. pap. text ed. 8.95x (ISBN 0-8018-2477-X). Johns Hopkins.

Revivalism & Social Reform: American Protestantism on the Eve of the Civil War. Timothy L. Smith. 11.25 (ISBN 0-8446-2960-X). Peter Smith.

Revivalism in America. William W. Sweet. 1944. 12.75 (ISBN 0-8446-1430-0). Peter Smith.

Revivalism, Social Conscience, & Community in the Burned-Over District: The Trial of Rhoda Bement. Glenn C. Altschuler & Jan M. Saltzgaber. (Illus.). 184p. 1983. 27.95x (ISBN 0-8014-1541-1); pap. 8.95x (ISBN 0-8014-9246-7). Cornell U Pr.

Revivals, Awakening, & Reform: An Essay on Religion & Social Change in America, 1607 to 1977. William G. McLoughlin. LC 77-27830. xvi, 240p. 1980. pap. 9.00x (ISBN 0-226-56092-9, P891, Phoen). U of Chicago Pr.

Revivals of the Eighteenth Century, Particulary at Cambuslang: With Three Sermons by the Rev. George Whitefield. Duncan Macfarlan. (Revival Library). (Illus.). 263p. 1980. Repr. of 1847 ed. lib. bdg. 12.95 (ISBN 0-940033-14-3). R O Roberts.

Revived Life. Lewis A. Drummond. LC 82-71217. 1982. pap. 6.50 (ISBN 0-8054-5205-2). Broadman.

Revnitel' Blagotchestija 19-go vjeka, Episkop Theofan Zatvornik. Priest Nikolai Deputatov. Tr. of Zealot for Piety in the 19th Century Bishop Theophan the Recluse. 71p. 1971. pap. 3.00 (ISBN 0-317-29261-7). Holy Trinity.

Revolt Against Dualism. 2nd ed. Arthur O. Lovejoy. (Paul Carus Lecture Ser.). 420p. 1960. 21.95 (ISBN 0-87548-106-X); pap. 8.95 (ISBN 0-87548-107-8). Open Court.

Revolt Against Reason. Arnold H. Lunn. LC 72-108396. xiv, 273p. Repr. of 1951 ed. lib. bdg. 22.50x (ISBN 0-8371-3819-1, LURA). Greenwood.

Revolt Against the Dead: The Modernization of a Mayan Community in the Highlands of Guatemala. D. E. Brintnall. (Library of Anthropology). 224p. 1979. 29.00x (ISBN 0-677-05170-0). Gordon & Breach.

Revolt of the Widows: The Social World of the Apocryphal Acts. Stevan L. Davies. LC 80-11331. 150p. 1980. 12.95x (ISBN 0-8093-0958-0). S Ill U Pr.

Revolution. Bhagwan Shree Rajneesh. Ed. by Ma Ananda Vandana. LC 83-181203. (Kabir Ser.). (Illus.). 424p. (Orig.). 1979. 16.95 (ISBN 0-88050-121-9). Chidvilas Found.

Revolution & After. Gordon Lindsay. (Old Testament Ser.). 1.25 (ISBN 0-89985-152-5). Christ Nations.

Revolution & Church: The Early History of Christian Democracy, 1789-1901. Hans Maier. Tr. by Emily M. Schossberger. LC 68-27577. 1969. 7.95 (ISBN 0-268-00319-X). U of Notre Dame Pr.

Revolution Gottes. Eberhard Arnold. 110p. 1984. pap. 7.00 (ISBN 3-87173-689-9). Plough.

Revolution in Judaea: Jesus & the Jewish Resistance. Hyam Maccoby. LC 80-16752. 256p. 1980. 9.95 (ISBN 0-8008-6784-X). Taplinger.

Revolution of the Latin American Church. Hugo Latorre Cabal. Tr. by Frances K. Hendricks & Beatrice Berler. LC 77-9117. 1978. 14.95x (ISBN 0-8061-1449-5). U of Okla Pr.

Revolution Underway: An Aging Church in an Aging Society. Cedric W. Tilberg. LC 84-8122. 128p. 1984. pap. 5.95 (ISBN 0-8006-1817-3). Fortress.

Revolutionaries for the Gospel: Testimonies of Fifteen Christians in the Nicaraguan Government. Teofilo Cabestrero. Tr. by Phillip Berryman from Spanish. LC 85-25865. Tr. of Revolucionarios por el Evangelico. 176p. (Orig.). 1986. pap. 9.95 (ISBN 0-88344-406-2). Orbis Bks.

Revolutionary Bishop: Who Saw God at Work in Africa. Ralph E. Dodge. LC 85-29092. (Illus.). 216p. (Orig.). 1986. pap. 7.95 (ISBN 0-87808-203-4, WCL203-4). William Carey Lib.

Revolutionary Clergy: The Filipino Clergy & the Nationalist Movement, 1850-1903. John N. Schumacher. 306p. 1982. (Pub. by Ateneo De Manila U Pr Philippines); pap. 17.50. Cellar.

Revolutionary Mystery. Spiros Zodhiates. (I Corinthians). (Illus.). 1974. pap. 6.95 (ISBN 0-89957-507-2). AMG Pubs.

Revolutionary Religion: Christianity, Fascism, & Communism. Roger B. Lloyd. LC 78-63686. (Studies in Fascism: Ideology & Practice). Repr. of 1938 ed. 24.50 (ISBN 0-404-16903-1). AMS Pr.

Revolutionary War & Issachar Bates. John S. Williams. 14p. 1960. 0.50 (ISBN 0-937942-02-2). Shaker Mus.

Rev'rund, Get Your Gun. Robert Opie. LC 77-78851. 1978. pap. 3.50 (ISBN 0-88419-141-9). Creation Hse.

Rhea's World. Rhea Tauber. LC 86-16989. (Paperback Ser.). 217p. 1987. pap. 7.95 (ISBN 0-8022-2499-7). Philos Lib.

Rhetoric & Reform: Erasmus' Civil Dispute with Luther. Marjorie O. Boyle. (Harvard Historical Monographs: No. 71). 240p. 1983. text ed. 24.00x (ISBN 0-674-76870-1). Harvard U Pr.

Rhetoric of Christian Socialism. Paul H. Boase. 9.00 (ISBN 0-8446-0501-8). Peter Smith.

Rhetoric of Menachem Begin: The Myth of Redemption Through Return. Robert C. Rowland. 330p. (Orig.). 1985. lib. bdg. 29.50 (ISBN 0-8191-4735-4); pap. text ed. 14.75 (ISBN 0-8191-4736-2). U Pr of Amer.

Rhetoric of Religion: Studies in Logology. Kenneth Burke. 1970. pap. 9.95x (ISBN 0-520-01610-6, CAMPUS 341). U of Cal Pr.

Rhetorical Criticism: Essays in Honor of James Muilenburg. Ed. by Jared J. Jackson & Martin Kessler. LC 74-22493. (Pittsburgh Theological Monographs: No. 1). 1974. pap. 9.50 (ISBN 0-915138-00-X). Pickwick.

Rhetorical World of Augustan Humanism: Ethics & Imagery from Swift to Burke. Paul Fussell. LC 66-1724. pap. 80.80 (ISBN 0-317-29155-6, 2055599). Bks Demand UMI.

Rhine Flows into the Tiber: A History of Vatican II. Ralph M. Wiltgen. LC 82-50583. 304p. pap. 8.00 (ISBN 0-89555-186-1). Tan Bks Pubs.

Rhinoceros Bound: Cluny in the Tenth Century. Barbara H. Rosenwein. LC 81-43525. (Middle Ages Ser.). 192p. 1982. 24.00x (ISBN 0-8122-7830-5). U of Pa Pr.

Rhode Island Catholicism: A Historical Guide. Patrick T. Conley. 24p. (Orig.). 1984. pap. 2.95 (ISBN 0-917012-56-9). RI Pubns Soc.

Rhode Island Chaplain in the Revolution. Ebenezer David. Ed. by Jeannette D. Black & W. Greene Roelker. LC 73-159068. 1971. Repr. of 1949 ed. 21.50x (ISBN 0-8046-1662-0, Pub. by Kennikat). Assoc Faculty Pr.

Rhyme & Reason. Ed. by Bob Jones. (Illus.). 222p. (Orig.). 1981. pap. 9.95 (ISBN 0-89084-142-X). Bob Jones Univ Pr.

Rhyme & Reason: St. Thomas & Modes of Discourse. Ralph McInerny. LC 81-80234. (Aquinas Lecture Ser.). 84p. 1981. 7.95 (ISBN 0-87462-148-8). Marquette.

Rhythm of Life. Leo Jung. 742p. 32.50 (ISBN 0-87559-145-0). Shalom.

Rhythms of Jewish Living: The Sephardic Approach. Marc D. Angel. LC 86-25993. 208p. 1987. 14.95 (ISBN 0-87203-125-X). Hermon.

Rhythms of the Ecosystem. Janette Shetter. LC 76-26392. (Illus., Orig.). 1976. pap. 2.50x (ISBN 0-87574-208-4). Pendle Hill.

Riadh-us-Salihin. A. R. Shad. (Eng. & Arabic.). 29.00 (ISBN 0-317-01590-7). Kazi Pubns.

Rib. Amy Sit. LC 76-22278. 1977. pap. 3.95 (ISBN 0-89221-026-5). New Leaf.

Ribbing Him Rightly. Beneth P. Jones. (Orig.). 1987. pap. write for info. (ISBN 0-89084-381-3). Bob Jones Univ Pr.

Ribbon of Lies, Knife of Truth. Jean Sheldon. Ed. by Ken McFarland. (Harvest Ser.). 96p. 1982. pap. 3.95 (ISBN 0-8163-0449-1). Pacific Pr Pub Assn.

Rich & Poor in the Shepherd of Hermas: An Exegetical-Social Investigation. Carolyn Osiek. Ed. by Bruce Vawter. LC 83-7385. (Catholic Biblical Quarterly Monographs: No. 15). xi, 184p. (Orig.). 1983. pap. 6.00x (ISBN 0-915170-14-0). Catholic Biblical.

Rich & the Poor. Henry Parker. LC 77-7419. (English Experience Ser.: No. 882). 1977. Repr. of 1493 ed. lib. bdg. 69.00 (ISBN 90-221-0882-1). Walter J Johnson.

Rich Christian in the Church of the Early Empire: Contradictions & Accomodations. L. Wm. Countryman. LC 80-81884. (Texts & Studies in Religion: Vol. 7). viii, 248p. 1980. 49.95x (ISBN 0-88946-970-9). E Mellen.

Rich Christians in an Age of Hunger: A Biblical Study. Ronald J. Sider. LC 76-45106. 254p. 1977. pap. 5.95 (ISBN 0-8091-2015-1). Paulist Pr.

Rich Christians in an Age of Hunger: A Biblical Study. 2nd, rev. ed. Ronald J. Sider. LC 84-4549. (Illus.). 257p. 1984. pap. 7.95 (ISBN 0-87784-977-3). Inter-Varsity.

Rich Church-Poor Church? Enzo Gatti. Tr. by Matthew O'Connell from It. LC 74-77432. Orig. Title: Couli che Sa Il Dolore Dell'uomo. 138p. (Orig.). 1974. 4.95 (ISBN 0-88344-437-2). Orbis Bks.

Rich in Mercy. 61p. 1980. pap. 3.95 (ISBN 1-55586-734-0). US Catholic.

Rich Man & Lazarus. Brownlow North. 1979. pap. 2.95 (ISBN 0-85151-121-X). Banner of Truth.

Rich, the Poor & the Bible. rev. ed. Conrad Boerma. Tr. by John Bowden from Dutch. LC 80-15337. 120p. 1980. pap. 5.95 (ISBN 0-664-24349-5). Westminster.

Rich World, Poor World: A Curriculum Resource on Youth & Development. Christian Movement for Peace Staff. (YA) 1986. pap. text ed. 29.95 (ISBN 0-697-02203-X). Wm C Brown.

Richard Baxter: Puritan Man of Letters. N. H. Keeble. 1982. 45.00x (ISBN 0-19-811716-7). Oxford U Pr.

Richard Crashaw. Basil Willey. LC 76-26647. 1949. lib. bdg. 12.50 (ISBN 0-8414-9386-3). Folcroft.

Richard Crashaw Poet & Saint. Thomas Foy. LC 74-9797. 1933. lib. bdg. 10.00 (ISBN 0-8414-4204-5). Folcroft.

Richard Furman: Life & Legacy. James A. Rogers. (Illus.). xxxii, 336p. 1985. 24.95 (ISBN 0-86554-151-5, MUP/H142). Mercer Univ Pr.

Richard Hooker & the Politics of a Christian England. Robert K. Faulkner. LC 79-65776. 195p. 1981. 31.00x (ISBN 0-520-03993-9). U of Cal Pr.

Richard Mather. B. Richard Burg. (United States Authors Ser.). 1982. lib. bdg. 16.50 (ISBN 0-8057-7364-9, Twayne). G K Hall.

Richard Mather of Dorchester. B. R. Burg. LC 75-41987. 224p. 1976. 21.00x (ISBN 0-8131-1343-1). U Pr of Ky.

Richard of St. Victor: The Twelve Patriarchs, the Mystical Ark Book, Three of the Trinity. Ed. by Grover A. Zinn. LC 79-83834. (Classics of Western Spirituality Ser.). 448p. 1979. 13.95 (ISBN 0-8091-0241-2); pap. 7.95 (ISBN 0-8091-2122-0). Paulist Pr.

Richard R. Niebuhr on Christ & Religion: The Four-Stage Development of His Thought. Patrick Primeaux. (Toronto Studies in Theology: Vol. 4). (Illus.). xiv, 288p. 1981. 49.95x (ISBN 0-88946-973-3). E Mellen.

Richard Rolle & de Holy Boke Gratia Dei: An Edition with Commentary. Mary Luke Arntz. Ed. by James Hogg. (Elizabethan & Renaissance Studies). 207p. (Orig.). 1981. pap. 15.00 (ISBN 3-7052-0743-1, Pub. by Salzburg Studies). Longwood Pub Group.

Richard Rolle's Expositio Super Novem Lectiones Mortuorum. Malcolm Moyes. Ed. by James Hogg. (Elizabethan & Renaissance Studies). (Orig.). 1984. pap. 15.00 (ISBN 3-7052-0753-9, Pub. by Salzburg Studies). Longwood Pub Group.

Richard the Lionheart & the Crusades. Christopher Gibb. (Life & Times Ser.). (Illus.). 64p. 1985. s&l 11.40 (ISBN 0-531-18011-5, Pub. by Bookwright Pr). Watts.

Richard Upjohn, Architect & Churchman. Everard M. Upjohn. LC 68-26119. (Architecture & Decorative Art Ser). (Illus.). 1968. Repr. of 1939 ed. lib. bdg. 45.00 (ISBN 0-306-71043-9). Da Capo.

Richelieu. Hilarie Belloc. 1935. Repr. 17.50 (ISBN 0-8274-3281-X). R West.

Richelieu. Karl Federn. LC 72-132440. (World History Ser., No. 48). 1970. Repr. of 1928 ed. lib. bdg. 38.95x (ISBN 0-8383-1222-5). Haskell.

Richelieu. Richard Lodge. LC 77-112812. 1970. Repr. of 1896 ed. 23.00x (ISBN 0-8046-1079-7, Pub. by Kennikat). Assoc Faculty Pr.

Richelieu: A Study. Hilaire Belloc. 1978. Repr. of 1929 ed. lib. bdg. 20.00 (ISBN 0-8495-0383-3). Arden Lib.

Richelieu & Reason of State. William F. Church. LC 76-181518. 582p. 1972. 49.00x (ISBN 0-691-05199-2). Princeton U Pr.

Richelieu & Reason of State. William F. Church. LC 76-181518. pap. 140.50 (ISBN 0-317-42020-8, 2025688). Bks Demand UMI.

Richelieu & the French Monarchy. Cicely V. Wedgwood. 1962. pap. 4.95 (ISBN 0-02-038240-5, Collier). Macmillan.

Richelieu & the Growth of French Power. James B. Perkins. 359p. 1982. Repr. of 1900 ed. lib. bdg. 40.00 (ISBN 0-89984-826-5). Century Bookbindery.

Richer Life: I Corinthians. Spiros Zodhiates. Orig. Title: Richer Life for You in Christ. 1972. 8.95 (ISBN 0-89957-501-3); kivar 5.95 (ISBN 0-89957-502-1). AMG Pubs.

Richer Living. Ernest Holmes & Raymond C. Barker. 372p. 1973. pap. 9.50 (ISBN 0-911336-48-6). Sci of Mind.

Riches of Grace. James E. Davey. pap. 0.95 (ISBN 0-87509-127-X). Chr Pubns.

Riches of Prayer. Olavi Kaukola. Tr. by Bernhard Hillila. LC 85-47716. 80p. 1986. pap. 3.95 (ISBN 0-8006-1861-0). Fortress.

Richest Lady in Town. Joyce Landorf. 1979. pap. 2.95 (ISBN 0-310-27142-8, 10123P). Zondervan.

Richest Man in Babylon. George Clason. 160p. 1985. pap. 3.50 (ISBN 0-553-25345-X). Bantam.

Richmond Eighteen Eighty-Seven: A Quaker Drama Unfolds. Mark Minear. 150p. 1987. pap. 5.95 (ISBN 0-913408-98-0). Friends United.

Richmond's Jewry, Seventeen Sixty-Nine to Nineteen Seventy-Six. Myron Berman. LC 78-6377. 438p. 1979. 20.00x (ISBN 0-8139-0743-8). U Pr of Va.

Riddle of Genesis. R. Koch. pap. 0.75 (ISBN 0-8199-0395-7). Franciscan Herald.

Riddle of Life. Beasant. 4.50 (ISBN 0-8356-0231-1). Theos Pub Hse.

Riddle of Pyramids. Kurt Mendelssohn. (Illus.). 1986. 24.95f (ISBN 0-500-05015-5); pap. 12.95f (ISBN 0-500-27388-X). Thames Hudson.

Riddle of the Didache: Fact or Fiction, Heresy or Catholicism? Frederick E. Vokes. (Church Historical Society London N. S.: No. 32). Repr. of 1938 ed. 40.00 (ISBN 0-8115-3156-2). Kraus Repr.

Riddle of the Outlaw Bear & Other Faith-Building Stories. John H. Leeper. (Illus.). 1984. pap. 4.95 (ISBN 0-8024-7352-0). Moody.

Riddle of the Sphinx, or Human Origins. Geza Roheim. Tr. by R. Money-Kryle. 10.75 (ISBN 0-8446-5238-5). Peter Smith.

Riddle of the Universe at the Close of the 19th Century. Ernst Haeckel. LC 6403. 1900. 18.00x (ISBN 0-403-00117-X). Scholarly.

Riddle of This World. Sri Aurobindo. 98p. 1984. pap. 1.25 (ISBN 0-89071-306-5, Pub. by Sri Aurobindo Ashram India). Matagiri.

Ride the Hot Wind. Mark Fackler. LC 77-78850. 1978. pap. 2.95 (ISBN 0-88419-126-5). Creation Hse.

Riding High. Ben Leach. (Uplook Ser.). 32p. 1982. pap. 0.79 (ISBN 0-8163-0514-5). Pacific Pr Pub Assn.

Riding the Ox Home: A History of Meditation from Shamanism to Science. Willard Johnson. LC 86-47752. (Illus.). 262p. 1987. pap. 8.95 (ISBN 0-8070-1305-6, BP-735). Beacon Pr.

Rifts in the Universe: A Study of the Historic Dichotomies & Modalities of Being. Jared S. Moore. 1927. 29.50x (ISBN 0-686-51303-7). Elliots Bks.

Rig Veda. Wendy O'Flaherty. (Pengiun Classic Ser.). 1982. pap. 5.95 (ISBN 0-14-044402-5). Penguin.

Rig Veda, 4 pts. Vedas. Ed. by Daniel H. Ingalls. LC 54-10046. (Oriental Ser: No. 33-35). Pts. 1-3. 1952 65.00x (ISBN 0-674-76965-1); Pt. 4. 1957 16.50x (ISBN 0-674-76967-8). Harvard U Pr.

Rig Veda Americanus. Ed. by Daniel G. Brinton. LC 73-83463. (Library of Aboriginal American Literature Ser.: No. 8). Repr. of 1890 ed. 30.00 (ISBN 0-404-52188-6). AMS Pr.

Rig-Veda-Samhita: The Sacred Hymns of the Brahmans, 4 vols. 2nd ed. Friedrich M. Mueller. LC 73-18831. 1892. Set. 176.00 (ISBN 0-404-11461-X); Vol. 1. (ISBN 0-404-11462-8); Vol. 2. (ISBN 0-404-11463-6); Vol. 3. (ISBN 0-404-11464-4); Vol. 4. (ISBN 0-404-11465-2). AMS Pr.

Rig-Veda Sanhita, 7 vols. H. H. Wilson. Incl. Vol. I. 348p. Repr. of 1850 ed (ISBN 0-89684-125-1); Vol. II. 346p. Repr. of 1854 ed (ISBN 0-89684-126-X); Vol. III. 249p. Repr. of 1857 ed (ISBN 0-89684-127-8); Vol. IV. 179p. Repr. of 1857 ed (ISBN 0-89684-128-6); Vol. V. 314p. Repr. of 1866 ed (ISBN 0-89684-129-4); Vol VI. 443p. Repr. of 1888 ed (ISBN 0-89684-130-8); Vol. VII. 436p. Repr. of 1888 ed (ISBN 0-89684-131-6). 1977. 120.00 set (ISBN 0-686-77518-X, Pub. by Cosmo Pubns India). Orient Bk Dist.

Rig-Veda (Summary) Date not set. 5.00 (ISBN 0-938924-29-X). Sri Shirdi Sai.

Right & Wrong: A Philosophical Dialogue Between Father & Son. Paul Weiss & Jonathan Weiss. LC 73-12702. (Arcturus Books Paperbacks). 222p. 1974. pap. 5.95x (ISBN 0-8093-0658-1). S Ill U Pr.

Right & Wrong Thinking. 2nd ed. Kenneth E. Hagin. 1966. pap. 1.00 (ISBN 0-89276-004-4). Hagin Ministries.

Right Here, Right Now: Spiritual Exercises for Busy Christians. Christopher Carstens & William Mahedy. 1985. 9.95 (ISBN 0-345-31801-3, Pub. by Ballantine Epiphany). Ballantine.

Right Here, Right Now: Spiritual Exercises for Busy Christians. Christopher Carstens & William Mahedy. 1987. pap. 2.95 (ISBN 0-345-34018-3, Pub. by Ballantine Epiphany). Ballantine.

Right Human Relations: The Only Way to World Peace. Gene H. Lawrence. 110p. 1980. pap. 3.00 (ISBN 0-682-49627-8). Exposition Pr FL.

Right Mental Attitude. Jerry Savelle. 138p. (Orig.). 1981. pap. 3.25 (ISBN 0-89274-159-7). Harrison Hse.

Right of the Catechized to the Truth. Silvie C. Oddi. 102p. 1983. pap. 2.00 (ISBN 0-8198-6407-2). Dghtrs St Paul.

Right of the Community to a Priest: New Concilium 1980, No. 133. Ed. by Edward Schillebeeckx & Johann B. Metz. 128p. 1980. pap. 5.95 (ISBN 0-8164-2275-3, HarpR). Har-Row.

Right-on Ideas for Youth Groups. Wayne Rice & Mike Yaconelli. (Illus.). 96p. 1973. pap. 6.95 (ISBN 0-310-34951-6, 10796P). Zondervan.

Right Resolutions. 2nd ed. Swami Paramananda. 1981. pap. 1.00 (ISBN 0-911564-29-2). Vedanta Ctr.

Right Thinking: Insights for Spiritual Growth. Bill Hull. LC 84-63115. 144p. 1985. pap. 4.95 (ISBN 0-89109-531-4). NavPress.

Right Time: The Best of Kairos. Ed. by David Parke. 1982. pap. 7.95 (ISBN 0-933840-13-6). Unitarian Univ.

Right to Be Here. Eddie Ruth. (Illus.). 28p. (Orig.). 1981. pap. 2.00 (ISBN 0-911826-27-0). Am Atheist.

Right to Be Merry. Sr. Mary Francis. LC 73-6850. 1973. pap. 6.50 (ISBN 0-8199-0506-2). Franciscan Herald.

Right to Heresay-Castellio Against Calvin. 2nd ed. Stefan Zweig. LC 84-40514. (History & Biography Ser.). (Illus.). 300p. 1985. pap. cancelled (ISBN 0-910129-27-4). Wiener Pub Inc.

Right to Know One's Human Rights: A Road Toward Marriage & Family. Vratislav Pechota. LC 83-72868. 52p. 1983. pap. 2.50 (ISBN 0-87495-056-2). Am Jewish Comm.

Right to Live: the Right to Die. C. Everett Koop. 1980. pap. 3.95 (ISBN 0-8423-5594-4). Tyndale.
Right to Silence: Privileged Clergy Communication & the Law. William H. Tiemann & John C. Bush. 256p. (Orig.). 1983. pap. 11.95 (ISBN 0-687-36315-2). Abingdon.
Right Usefulness. Thomas Hora. 35p. 1987. pap. 4.00 (ISBN 0-913105-12-0). PAGL Pr.
Right with God. John Blanchard. LC 78-6809. 1978. pap. 3.50 (ISBN 0-8024-7357-1). Moody.
Right with God. rev. ed. John Blanchard. 126p. 1985. pap. 2.95 (ISBN 0-85151-045-0). Banner of Truth.
Righte Merrie Christmasse. John Ashton. LC 68-56543. (Illus.). 1968. Repr. of 1894 ed. 15.00 (ISBN 0-405-08225-8, Pub. by Blom). Ayer Co Pubs.
Righteous Struggle. Mahadev Desai. 105p. 1983. pap. 1.25 (ISBN 0-934676-34-8). Greenlf Bks.
Righteousness. Ronald D. Tucker. (Illus.). 48p. (Orig.). 1983. pap. 2.00 (ISBN 0-933643-09-8). Grace World Outreach.
Righteousness in Matthew & His World of Thought. Benno Przybylski. LC 79-41371. (Society for New Testament Studies Monographs: No. 41). 240p. 1981. 32.50 (ISBN 0-521-22566-3). Cambridge U Pr.
Righteousness in the New Testament: Justification in Lutheran-Catholic Dialogue. John Reumann. LC 81-43086. 320p. 1982. pap. 13.95 (ISBN 0-8006-1616-2, 1-1616). Fortress.
Righteousness in the New Testament: Justification in Lutheran-Catholic Dialogue. John Reumann. LC 81-85385. 320p. (Orig.). 1982. pap. 13.95 (ISBN 0-8091-2436-X). Paulist Pr.
Righteousness in the Septuagint of Isaiah: A Contextual Study. John W. Olley. LC 78-3425. (Society of Biblical Literature, Septuagint & Cognate Studies: No. 8). 1979. pap. 9.95 (ISBN 0-89130-226-3, 06-04-08). Scholars Pr GA.
Righteousness Which Is of Faith. Charles Capps. (Orig.). 1986. mini bk. 0.75 (ISBN 0-89274-411-1). Harrison Hse.
Rightly Dividing. Truman H. Etheridge. 1955. 6.00 (ISBN 0-88027-017-9). Firm Foun Pub.
Rightly Dividing the Word of Truth. C. I. Scofield. pap. 1.50 (ISBN 0-87213-770-8). Loizeaux.
Rightly Dividing the Word of Truth. C. I. Scofield. 72p. (Orig.). 1974. pap. 2.95 (ISBN 0-310-32662-1, 6364P). Zondervan.
Rights & Responsibilities. Thomas P. Doyle. 64p. (Orig.). 1983. pap. 2.50 (ISBN 0-916134-58-X). Pueblo Pub Co.
Rights & Wrongs of Anger. H. Norman Wright. 176p. (Orig.). 1985. pap. 4.95 (ISBN 0-89081-457-0). Harvest Hse.
Rights of Allah & Human Rights. M. I. Siddiqui. 1981. 15.95 (ISBN 0-686-97876-5). Kazi Pubns.
Rights of Man & Natural Law. Jacques Maritain. LC 74-150416. 120p. 1971. Repr. of 1943 ed. 17.50x (ISBN 0-87752-146-8). Gordian.
Rights of Racial Minorities. E. Richard Larson & Laughlin McDonald. 1979. pap. 1.95 (ISBN 0-380-75077-5, 75077-5, Discus). Avon.
Rights of Reason: A Study of Kant's Philosophy & Politics. Susan M. Shell. LC 79-19801. 1979. 23.50x (ISBN 0-8020-5462-5). U of Toronto Pr.
Rights, Restitution, & Risk: Essays in Moral Theory. Judith J. Thomson. Ed. & pref. by William Parent. (Illus.). 288p. 1986. text ed. 29.95x (ISBN 0-674-76980-5); pap. text ed. 9.95x (ISBN 0-674-76981-3). Harvard U Pr.
Rights, Wrongs, & In-Betweens: Guiding Our Children to Christian Maturity. Jim Larson. LC 83-72121. 144p. (Orig.). 1984. pap. 6.95 (ISBN 0-8066-2065-X, 10-5518). Augsburg.
Rigid Scrutiny: Critical Essays on the Old Testament. Ivan Engnell. Tr. by John T. Willis. LC 70-76166. 1969. 15.00x (ISBN 0-8265-1133-3). Vanderbilt U Pr.
Rigid Scrutiny: Critical Essays on the Old Testament. Ivan Engnell. Ed. by John T. Willis. (Vanderbilt University Press Bks.). 303p. 1969. 15.00 (ISBN 0-8265-1133-3). U of Ill Pr.
Rigveda. Edward V. Arnold. LC 73-139172. (Popular Studies in Mythology, Romance & Folklore: No. 9). Repr. of 1900 ed. 5.50 (ISBN 0-404-53509-7). AMS Pr.
Rigveda Brahmanas. Ed. by Arthur Keith. lib. bdg. 100.00 (ISBN 0-87968-440-2). Krishna Pr.
Rigveda Samhita, 10 vols. Swami S. Prakash & Pandit S. Vidyalankar. (Eng.). vol. 17.00 ea. (Pub. by S Chand India). State Mutual Bk.
Rim of Christendom: A Biography of Eusebio Francisco Kino, Pacific Coast Pioneer. Herbert E. Bolton. LC 84-8814. 644p. 1984. Repr. of 1960 ed. 40.00x (ISBN 0-8165-0863-1). U of Ariz Pr.
Rimas del Pesebre. Luis Salem. LC 77-82265. (Span.). 86p. (Orig.). 1978. pap. 2.50 (ISBN 0-89922-118-1). Edit Caribe.
Ringing in Hertfordshire. L. Goodman. 1985. 15.00x (ISBN 0-317-54314-8, Pub. by J Richardson UK). State Mutual Bk.
Ringship of God in Crisis: A Close Reading of 1 Samuel 1-12. Lyle Eslinger. (Bible & Literature Ser.: No. 35). 515p. 1985. text ed. 29.95x (ISBN 0-907459-40-4, Pub. by Almond Pr England); pap. text ed. 15.95 (ISBN 0-907459-41-2). Eisenbrauns.
Rios De Agua Viva. Ruth Paxson. 96p. 1983. pap. 1.95 (ISBN 0-311-46065-8). Casa Bautista.
Rios De Tinta: Historia y Ministerio De la Casa Bautista De Publicaciones. Tomas Hill. Tr. by Josie Smith from Eng. Orig. Title: Rivers of Ink. 64p. 1980. pap. 2.50 (ISBN 0-311-29009-4). Casa Bautista.
Ripples of Stillness. Ralph Wright. 1978. 5.95 (ISBN 0-8198-0365-0). Dghtrs St Paul.
Rise & Decline of the Program for Black Education in the United Presbyterian Church, U. S. A. 1865-1970. Inez M. Parker. LC 76-49248. (Presbyterian Historical Ser.). 320p. 1977. 10.00 (ISBN 0-911536-66-3). Trinity U Pr.
Rise & Destiny of the German Jew. rev. ed. Jacob R. Marcus. 1971. 15.00x (ISBN 0-87068-148-6). Ktav.
Rise & Fall of Superwoman. Carole Sheron. LC 79-26704. (Orion Ser.). 96p. 1980. pap. 3.50 (ISBN 0-8127-1270-6). Review & Herald.
Rise & Fall of the Anabaptists. E. Belfort Bax. 59.95 (ISBN 0-8490-0958-8). Gordon Pr.
Rise & Fall of the Bulgarian Connection. Edward S. Herman & Frank Brodhead. 270p. (Orig.). 1986. 19.95 (ISBN 0-940380-07-2); pap. text ed. 9.95 (ISBN 0-940380-06-4). Sheridan Square Pubns.
Rise & Fall of the Judaean State, 3 vols. Solomon Zeitlin. LC 61-11708. 1978. Vol. 3, 66-120 C. E. 534 Pgs. 12.50 (ISBN 0-686-91516-X). Jewish Pubns.
Rise & Fall the of Party-Kings: Politics & Society in Islamic Spain, 1002-1086. David Wasserstein. LC 94-16072. (Illus.). 344p. 1985. text ed. 35.00x (ISBN 0-691-05436-3). Princeton U Pr.
Rise & Progress of the People Called Quakers. William Penn. 1977. pap. 2.95 (ISBN 0-913408-32-8). Friends United.
Rise of Afrikanerdom: Power, Apartheid, & the Afrikaner Civil Religion. T. Dunbar Moodie. LC 72-85512. (Perspectives on Southern Africa Ser). 1975. pap. 5.95 (ISBN 0-520-03943-2, CAL 433). U of Cal Pr.
Rise of Christianity. W. H. Frend. LC 83-48909. (Illus.). 1042p. 1984. pap. 24.95 (ISBN 0-8006-1931-5, 1-1931). Fortress.
Rise of Ecclesiastical Control in Quebec. Walter A. Riddell. (Columbia University. Studies in the Social Sciences: No. 174). Repr. of 1916 ed. 17.50 (ISBN 0-404-51174-0). AMS Pr.
Rise of Esoteric Buddhism in the Tibet. Eva Darqyay. 272p. 1979. pap. 5.95 (ISBN 0-87728-432-6). Weiser.
Rise of Esoteric Buddhism in Tibet. Eva M. Dargyay. 1977. 14.00 (ISBN 0-8426-0915-6, Pub by Molilal Banarsidass India). Orient Bk Dist.
Rise of Fernando Cortes. H. R. Wagner. (Cortes Society). 1944. 51.00 (ISBN 0-527-19733-5). Kraus Repr.
Rise of Modern Judaism: An Intellectual History of German Jewry 1650-1942. Heinz M. Graupe. LC 77-9059. 344p. 1979. lib. bdg. 24.00 (ISBN 0-88275-395-9); pap. text ed. 10.50 (ISBN 0-89874-562-4). Krieger.
Rise of Modern Mythology, Sixteen Hundred Eighty to Eighteen Hundred Sixty. Burton Feldman & Robert D. Richardson. LC 71-135005. pap. 147.80 (2056249). Bks Demand UMI.
Rise of Neo-Confucianism in Korea. Ed. by William T. De Bary & Jahyun K. Haboush. 512p. 1985. 40.00x (ISBN 0-231-06052-1). Columbia U pr.
Rise of Puritanism. William Haller. LC 57-10117. 479p. 1972. pap. 14.95x (ISBN 0-8122-1048-4, Pa Paperbks). U of Pa Pr.
Rise of Reform Judaism: A Sourcebook of Its European Origins. W. Gunther Plaut. Incl. Growth of Reform Judaism: American & European Sources to 1948. 1965. 1963. 10.00 (ISBN 0-8074-0089-0, 382770, Pub. by World Union). UAHC.
Rise of Religious Liberty in America. Sanford H. Cobb. 1978. pap. write for info. (ISBN 0-89102-115-9, Artemis). B Franklin.
Rise of Religious Liberty in America: A History. Sanford H. Cobb. LC 68-27517. 541p. 1968. Repr. of 1902 ed. 32.50x (ISBN 0-8154-0051-9). Cooper Sq.
Rise of Religious Liberty in America: A History. Sanford H. Cobb. (American Studies). 1970. Repr. of 1902 ed. 30.00 (ISBN 0-384-09445-7). Johnson Repr.
Rise of the Anti-Mission Baptists: Sources & Leaders, 1800-1840. Byron C. Lambert. Ed. by Edwin S. Gaustad. LC 79-52573. (Baptist Tradition Ser.). 1980. lib. bdg. 39.00x (ISBN 0-405-12441-4). Ayer Co Pubs.
Rise of the Antichrist. Gordon Lindsay. (Revelation Ser.). 1.25 (ISBN 0-89985-042-1). Christ Nations.
Rise of the Black Magus in Western Art. Paul H. Kaplan. Ed. by Linda Seidel. LC 85-8461. (Studies in the Fine Arts: Iconography: No. 10). 344p. 1985. 49.95 (ISBN 0-8357-1667-8). UMI Res Pr.
Rise of the Evolution Fraud. Malcolm Bowden. 1982. pap. 8.95 (ISBN 0-89051-085-7). Master Bks.
Rise of the Jew in the Western World. Uriah Z. Engelman. LC 73-2194. (Jewish People; History, Religion, Literature Ser.). Repr. of 1944 ed. 22.00 (ISBN 0-405-05260-X). Ayer Co Pubs.
Rise of the Medieval Church & Its Influence on the Civilization of Western Europe from the 1st to the 13th Century. Alexander C. Flick. 636p. 1973. Repr. of 1909 ed. lib. bdg. 33.50 (ISBN 0-8337-1159-8). B Franklin.
Rise of the Missionary Spirit in America 1790-1815. Oliver W. Elsbree. LC 79-13028. (Perspectives in American History Ser.: No. 55). 1980. Repr. of 1928 ed. 22.50x (ISBN 0-87991-376-2). Porcupine Pr.
Rise of the Monophysite Movement: Chapters in the History of the Church in the Fifth & Sixth Centuries. W. H. Frend. LC 72-75302. (Illus.). 400p. 1972. 74.50 (ISBN 0-521-08130-0). Cambridge U Pr.
Rise of the Phoenix: Universal Government by Nature's Laws. new ed. Christopher Hills. Ed. by Ann Ray & Deborah Rozman. LC 76-53176. (Illus.). 1024p. (Orig.). 1979. 24.95 (ISBN 0-916438-04-X). Univ of Trees.
Rise of the Religion of Anti-Christism. David R. Mains. Ed. by Judith Markham. 1985. 9.95 (ISBN 0-310-34830-7, Pub. by Zondervan Bks). Zondervan.
Rise of the Religious Significance of Rama. Frank Whaling. 392p. 1980. text ed. 10.00 (ISBN 0-8426-1758-2). Verry.
Rise of the Social Gospel in American Protestantism, 1865-1895. Charles H. Hopkins. LC 75-41141. (BCL Ser.: Vol. II). 368p. Repr. of 1940 ed. 30.00 (ISBN 0-404-14771-2). AMS Pr.
Rise of Western Rationalism: Max Weber's Developmental History. Wolfgang Schluchter. Tr. by Guenther Roth from Ger. LC 81-2763. 300p. 1981. 24.50x (ISBN 0-520-04060-0); pap. 9.95 (ISBN 0-520-05464-4, CAL 747). U of Cal Pr.
Risen & with You Always: Daily Meditations for the Easter Season Masses. Emeric Lawrence. 140p. 1986. pap. 5.95 (ISBN 0-8146-1448-5). Liturgical Pr.
Risen Indeed: Lessons of Faith from the U. S. S. R. Michael Boudeaux. (Orig.). 1983. pap. text ed. 5.95 (ISBN 0-88141-021-7). St Vladimirs.
Risen Jesus. 4.00 (ISBN 0-8198-6411-0); 3.00 (ISBN 0-8198-6412-9). Dghtrs St Paul.
Rising above Strife. Ed. by Nancy I. Witte. pap. 4.95 (ISBN 0-89137-424-8). Quality Pubns.
Rising from History: U. S. Catholic Theology Looks to the future. Ed. by Robert J. Daly. LC 87-2011. (Annual Publication of the College Theology Society, 1984: Vol. 30). 234p. (Orig.). 1987. lib. bdg. 24.50 (ISBN 0-8191-6155-1, Pub. by College Theology Society); pap. text ed. 12.75 (ISBN 0-8191-6156-X, Pub. by College Theology Society). U Pr of Amer.
Rising Generation. 1987. pap. 5.95 (ISBN 0-87579-088-7). Deseret Bk.
Rising of al-Husayn: Its Impact on the Consciousness of Muslim Society. Shaykh M. Al-Din. Tr. by I. K. Howard. Date not set. pap. 15.95 (ISBN 0-7103-0191-X, Kegan Paul). Methuen Inc.
Rising Storm: An Analysis of the Growing Conflict Over the Political Dilemma of Roman Catholics in America. Hiram W. Evans. Ed. by Gerald Grob. LC 76-46075. (Anti-Movements in America). 1977. lib. bdg. 27.50x (ISBN 0-405-09948-7). Ayer Co Pubs.
Risk & Retoric in Religion: Whitehead's Theory of language. Lyman T. Lundeen. LC 71-171501. pap. 72.00 (202868). Bks Demand UMI.
Risk of Love. W. H. Vanstone. 1978. 11.95x (ISBN 0-19-520053-5). Oxford U Pr.
Risk of the Cross: Christian Discipleship in the Nuclear Age. J. Christopher Grannis et al. 128p. (Orig.). 1981. pap. 5.95 (ISBN 0-8164-2305-9, HarpR). Har-Row.
Risky Living: The Key to Inner Healing. Jamie Buckingham. LC 76-12033. 1976. (Pub. by Logos); pap. 4.95 (ISBN 0-88270-177-0). Bridge Pub.
Rite & Man: Natural Sacredness & Christian Liturgy. Louis Bouyer. Tr. by Joseph Costelloe. 224p. 1985. pap. text ed. 12.25 (ISBN 0-8191-4340-5). U Pr of Amer.
Rite of Anointing & Pastoral Care of the Sick. pocket ed. 6.95 (ISBN 0-89942-156-3, 156/04). Catholic Bk Pub.
Rite of Baptism for Children. green cloth 8.50 (ISBN 0-89942-136-9, 136/22). Catholic Bk Pub.
Rite of Funerals. Tr. by International Committee on English in the Liturgy. blue cloth 8.50 (ISBN 0-89942-350-7, 350/22). Catholic Bk Pub.
Rite of Marriage. (Large Type, Two Colors, Homiletic Notes). red cloth 8.50 (ISBN 0-89942-238-1, 238/22). Catholic Bk Pub.
Rite of Penance. pocket ed. 3.95 (ISBN 0-89942-128-8, 128/04). Catholic Bk Pub.
Rite of Penance. large ed. 160p. (Large, Two-Color Type). 8.50 (ISBN 0-89942-528-3, 528/22). Catholic Bk Pub.
Rites & Ceremonies of the Greek Church in Russia. John G. King. LC 73-126673. Repr. of 1772 ed. 34.50 (ISBN 0-404-03692-9). AMS Pr.
Rites & Symbols of Initiation: The Mysteries of Birth & Rebirth. Mircea Eliade. Orig. Title: Birth & Rebirth. pap. 5.95x (ISBN 0-06-131236-3, TB1236, Torch). Har-Row.
Rites & Symbols of Initiation: The Mysteries of Birth & Rebirth. Mircea Eliade. 16.75 (ISBN 0-8446-2027-0). Peter Smith.
Rites of Birth, Marriage, Death, & Kindred Occasions Among the Semites. Julian Morgenstern. 1966. 20.00x (ISBN 0-87068-230-X). Ktav.
Rites of Christian Initiation. Michel Dujarier. 244p. 1982. pap. 5.95 (ISBN 0-8215-9328-5). Sadlier.
Rites of Eastern Christendom, 2 Vols. Archdale A. King. LC 70-142246. Repr. of 1948 ed. Set. 125.00 (ISBN 0-404-03677-5). Vol. 1 (ISBN 0-404-03678-3). Vol. 2 (ISBN 0-404-03679-1). AMS Pr.
Rites of Passage. Ed. by John Duckworth et al. (Pacesetter Ser.). 64p. 1987. tchr's. ed. 7.95. Cook.
Rites of Rulers: Ritual in Industrial Society-the Soviet Case. Christel Lane. LC 80-41747. (Illus.). 338p. 1981. 57.50 (ISBN 0-521-22608-2); pap. 18.95 (ISBN 0-521-28347-7). Cambridge U Pr.
Rites of the Catholic Church, Vol. 1. rev. ed. Sacred Congregation for Divine Worship. Tr. by International Committee on English in the Liturgy. 1983. 14.50 (ISBN 0-916134-15-6). Pueblo Pub Co.
Rites of the Catholic Church, Vol. 2. Sacred Congregation for Divine Worship. Tr. by International Commission on English in the Liturgy. 1980. pap. 11.50 (ISBN 0-916134-37-7). Pueblo Pub Co.
Rites of the Gods. Aubrey Burl. (Illus.). 272p. 1981. text ed. 26.50x (ISBN 0-460-04313-7, BKA 04660, Pub. by J M Dent England). Biblio Dist.
Ritual. Theodore Reik. pap. text ed. 19.95 (ISBN 0-8236-8269-2, 025840). Intl Univs Pr.
Ritual & Knowledge among the Baktaman of New Guinea. Fredrik Barth. LC 74-19572. (Illus.). pap. 74.00 (ISBN 0-317-11336-4, 2021979). Bks Demand UMI.
Ritual & Pastoral Care. Elaine Ramshaw. LC 85-45487. (Theology and Pastoral Care Ser.). 128p. 1987. pap. 7.95 (ISBN 0-8006-1738-X). Fortress.
Ritual & Religion among Muslims in India. Ed. by Imtiaz Ahmad. 1982. 20.00x (ISBN 0-8364-0852-7, Pub. by Manohar India). South Asia Bks.
Ritual Cosmos: The Sanctification of Life in African Religions. Evan Zuesse. LC 79-13454. 256p. 1985. pap. 12.95x (ISBN 0-8214-0814-3). Ohio U Pr.
Ritual Cosmos: The Sanctification of Life in African Religions. Evan M. Zuesse. LC 79-13454. x, 256p. 1980. 21.95x (ISBN 0-8214-0398-2). Ohio U Pr.
Ritual Human Sacrifice in Mesoamerica: A Conference at Dumbarton Oaks, October 13 & 14, 1979. Ed. by Elizabeth H. Boone. LC 83-14059. (Illus.). 256p. 1984. 18.50x (ISBN 0-88402-120-3). Dumbarton Oaks.
Ritual, Myth & Magic in Early Modern Europe. William Monter. LC 83-43136. (Illus.). viii, 184p. 1984. cloth 24.95x (ISBN 0-8214-0762-7). Ohio U Pr.
Ritual of Music. Ed. by Doris H. Cooley. 12p. 1968. pap. text ed. 1.00 (ISBN 0-88053-318-8, S-79). Macoy Pub.
Ritualism & Politics in Victorian Britain. James Bentley. (Oxford Theological Monographs). (Illus.). 1978. 37.00x (ISBN 0-19-826714-2). Oxford U Pr.
Rituals & Power: The Roman Imperial Cult in Asia Minor. S. R. Price. (Illus.). 316p. 1986. pap. 14.95 (ISBN 0-521-31268-X). Cambridge U Pr.
Rituals of Manhood: Male Initiation in Papua New Guinea. Ed. by Gilbert H. Herdt. 392p. 1982. 38.50x (ISBN 0-520-04448-7); pap. 10.95 (ISBN 0-520-04454-1, CAL 564). U of Cal Pr.

Rituals of the Kandyan State. H. L. Seneviratne. LC 77-80842. (Cambridge Studies in Social Anthropology: No. 22). (Illus.). 1978. 37.50 (ISBN 0-521-21736-9). Cambridge U Pr.

Rivalitaet zwischen Engeln und Menschen: Untersuchungen zur rabbinischen Engelvorstellung. Peter Schaefer. (Studia Judaica, Vol. 8). xiv, 280p. 1975. 38.80x (ISBN 3-11-004632-6). De Gruyter.

Rivayat-i Hemit-i Asawahistan: A Study in Zoroastrian Law. Nezhat Safa-Isfahani. (Harvard Iranian Ser.: No. 2). 304p. 1981. text ed. 25.00x (ISBN 0-674-77305-5). Harvard U Pr.

River of Compassion. Bede Griffiths. (Wellspring Bk.). 224p. (Orig.). pap. 11.95 (ISBN 0-916349-08-X). Amity Hous Inc.

River of Life. Subramuniya. pap. 1.00 (ISBN 0-87516-360-2). De Vorss.

River of Light: Spirituality, Judaism, & the Evolution of Consciousness. Lawrence Kushner. LC 80-7738. 192p. (Orig.). 1981. pap. 7.95 (ISBN 0-06-064902-X, RD 370, HarpR). Har-Row.

River of Light: Spirituality, Judaism, & the Evolution of Consciousness. Lawrence Kushner. LC 80-7738. 192p. 1981. 12.95 (ISBN 0-940646-00-5). Rossel Bks.

River Remembers. S. L. Shneiderman. LC 77-93935. (Illus.). 1978. 8.95 (ISBN 0-8180-0821-0). Horizon.

River Within: The Search for God in Depth. Christopher Bryant. 160p. 1983. pap. 5.50 (ISBN 0-8358-0468-2). Upper Room.

Rivers of Living Water. Ruth Paxson. (Moody Classics Ser.). 1984. pap. 3.50 (ISBN 0-8024-7367-9). Moody.

Rivers of Living Water. Kenneth V. Reeves. (Illus.). 78p. (Orig.). 1980. pap. 3.00 (ISBN 0-912315-65-2). Word Aflame.

Road: A Study of John Bunyan's Pilgrim's Progress, 2 Vols. John Kelman. LC 77-113339. 1970. Repr. of 1912 ed. Set. 50.00x (ISBN 0-8046-1025-8, Pub. by Kennikat). Assoc Faculty Pr.

Road Back. 1981. pap. 6.95 (ISBN 0-87306-264-7). Feldheim.

Road Back: A Discovery of Judaism Without Embellishments. new ed. Mayer Schiller. 1978. 9.95 (ISBN 0-87306-164-0). Feldheim.

Road from Babylon: The Story of the Sephardic & Oriental Jews. Chaim Raphael. LC 85-42587. (Illus.). 320p. 1986. 22.45i (ISBN 0-06-039048-4, C&M Bessie Bks). Har-Row.

Road Less Traveled. M. Scott Peck. 448p. 1985. pap. 16.95 (ISBN 0-8027-2498-1). Walker & Co.

Road of Life & Death. Paul Radin. (Bollingen Ser.: Vol. 5). 1945. 33.00 (ISBN 0-691-09819-0). Princeton U Pr.

Road of Science & the Ways to God. Stanley L. Jaki. LC 77-21667. 1978. lib. bdg. 14.95x (ISBN 0-226-39144-2). U of Chicago Pr.

Road to Damascus. Ralph Carnes & Valerie Carnes. 336p. 1986. 16.95 (ISBN 0-312-68517-3, Thomas Dunne Bks). St Martin.

Road to Daulis: Psychoanalysis, Psychology & Classical Mythology. Robert Eisner. 284p. 1987. 32.50 (ISBN 0-8156-0210-3). Syracuse U Pr.

Road to Freedom. Lev S. Pinsker. LC 70-162734. 142p. 1975. Repr. of 1944 ed. lib. bdg. 22.50x (ISBN 0-8371-6195-9, PIRF). Greenwood.

Road to Hell: A Study of the Conception of the Dead in Old Norse Literature. Hilda R. Ellis. LC 68-23286. (Illus.). 1968. Repr. of 1943 ed. lib. bdg. 22.50x (ISBN 0-8371-0070-4, ELRH). Greenwood.

Road to Mecca. Muhammad Asad. 380p. (Orig.). 1981. 14.95 (ISBN 0-317-52460-7, Pub. by Dar Al Andalus). New Era Pubns MI.

Road to Nazareth: Through Palestine Today. John Gibbons. LC 77-180339. Repr. of 1936 ed. 26.00 (ISBN 0-404-56264-7). AMS Pr.

Road to Now. John Moffitt. LC 82-4650. 176p. 1982. pap. 7.95 (ISBN 0-8245-0514-X). Crossroad NY.

Road to Peace. facsimile ed. James J. Daly. LC 78-107691. (Essay Index Reprint Ser.). 1936. 17.00 (ISBN 0-8369-1495-3). Ayer Co Pubs.

Road to Reality: The Spiritual Path for Everyone. Ed. by Iris M. Turner. 124p. 1986. 29.00x (ISBN 0-7212-0732-4, Pub. by Regency Pr). State Mutual Bk.

Road to Salvation. A. A. Maududi. pap. 1.00 (ISBN 0-686-18583-8). Kazi Pubns.

Road to San Luis Rey. Thelma H. Jones. LC 73-87882. (Illus.). 1974. text ed. 5.00 (ISBN 0-912472-18-9). Miller Bks.

Road to Self Knowledge. Rudolf Steiner. 1975. 10.95 (ISBN 0-85440-290-X, Pub by Steinerbooks); pap. 6.95 o. p. (ISBN 0-85440-291-8). Anthroposophic.

Road to Total Freedom. Roy Wallis. LC 76-27273. 1977. 32.00x (ISBN 0-231-04200-0). Columbia U Pr.

Road to Wholeness. Laura Mathis. 240p. 1986. pap. 6.95 (ISBN 0-8423-5674-6). Tyndale.

Road Unseen. Peter Jenkins & Barbara Jenkins. (General Ser.). 406p. 1986. lib. bdg. 18.95 (ISBN 0-317-46368-3, Large Print Bks). G K Hall.

Roads to Extinction: Essays on the Holocaust. Philip Friedman. Ed. by Ada J. Friedman. LC 79-89818. 616p. 1980. 27.50 (ISBN 0-8276-0170-0, 446). Jewish Pubns.

Roads to Paradise: Reading the Lives of the Early Saints. Alison G. Elliott. LC 86-40384. 272p. 1987. 27.50 (ISBN 0-87451-389-8). U Pr of New Eng.

Robe. Lloyd C. Douglas. 1942. 12.95 (ISBN 0-395-07635-8). HM.

Robert Applegarth: Trade Unionist, Educationist, Reformer. A. W. Humphrey. Ed. by F. M. Leventhal. LC 83-48484. (World of Labour - English Workers 1850-1890 Ser.). 328p. 1984. lib. bdg. 44.00 (ISBN 0-8240-5711-2). Garland Pub.

Robert Browning As a Religious Poet: An Annotated Bibliography of the Crticism. Vincent P. Anderson. LC 82-50407. 350p. 1984. 25.00X (ISBN 0-87875-221-8). Whitston Pub.

Robert Curthose, Duke of Normandy. Charles W. David. LC 78-63356. (Crusades & Military Orders: Second Ser.). (Illus.). 296p. Repr. of 1920 ed. 32.50 (ISBN 0-404-17007-2). AMS Pr.

Robert Graves & the White Goddess. John B. Vickery. LC 70-183363. Repr. of 1972 ed. 29.50 (ISBN 0-8357-9713-9, 2011899). Bks Demand UMI.

Robert Grosseteste, Bishop of Lincoln: A Contribution to the Religious, Political & Intellectual History of the Thirteenth Century. F. S. Stevenson. (Medieval Studies Ser.). Repr. of 1899 ed. lib. bdg. 39.50 (ISBN 0-697-00018-4). Irvington.

Robert Grosseteste: The Growth of an English Mind in Medieval Europe. Richard Southern. 300p. 1986. 55.00x (ISBN 0-19-826450-X). Oxford U Pr.

Robert H. Schuller Tells You How to Be an Extraordinary Person in an Ordinary World. Robert H. Schuller. Ed. by Robert A. Schuller. 1987. 16.95 (Large Print Bks). G K Hall.

Robert Mackintosh: Theologian of Integrity. Alan P. Sell. (European University Studies: Ser. 23, Vol. 95). 107p. 1977. pap. 16.95 (ISBN 3-261-03008-9). P Lang Pubs.

Robert Schuller's Life Changers. Ed. by Robert A. Schuller. 192p. 1981. 2.75 (ISBN 0-8007-8476-6, Spire Bks). Revell.

Robert Southwell the Writer. Pierre Janelle. LC 72-162495. 347p. 1971. Repr. of 1935 ed. 12.00x (ISBN 0-911858-18-0). Appel.

Robert White. Ed. by P. C. Buck et al. (Tudor Church Music Ser.: Vol. 5). 1963. Repr. of 1926 ed. 85.00x (ISBN 0-8450-1855-8). Broude.

Robin MacNaughton's Sun Sign Personality Guide. Robin MacNaughton. 1978. pap. 4.50 (ISBN 0-553-25747-1). Bantam.

Rock in a Weary Land: The African Methodist Episcopal Church During the Civil War & Reconstruction. Clarence E. Walker. LC 81-11743. 188p. 1981. 22.50x (ISBN 0-8071-0883-9). La State U Pr.

Rock: Making Musical Choices. Richard Peck. 174p. (Orig.). 1985. pap. 4.95 (ISBN 0-89084-297-3). Bob Jones Univ Pr.

Rock's Hidden Persuader: The Truth about Back Masking. Dan Peters et al. 128p. 1985. pap. 3.95 (ISBN 0-87123-857-8, 200857). Bethany Hse.

Roemische Tempel in Syrien: Nach Aufnahmen und Untersuchungen von Mitgliedern der Deutschen Baalbekexpedition, 1901-1904, 2 pts. Daniel Krencker & Willy Zschietzschmann. (Denkmaeler antiker Architektur, Vol. 5). (Ger., Illus.). 298p. 1978. Repr. of 1938 ed. Pt. 1. 132.00x (ISBN 3-11-004989-9); Pt. 2. 84.00 (ISBN 3-11-004990-2). De Gruyter.

Roemischen Mosaiken in Deutschland. Klans Parlasca. (Illus.). 156p. 1970. Repr. of 1959 ed. 64.00x (ISBN 3-11-001212-X). De Gruyter.

Roemischen Titelkirchen Im Altertum. Johann P. Kirsch. 1918. 19.00 (ISBN 0-384-29614-9). Johnson Repr.

Roger, Bishop of Worcestor Eleven Sixty Four to Eleven Seventy Nine: An English Bishop of the Age of Becket. Mary G. Cheney. (Oxford Historical Monographs). (Illus.). 1980. 63.00x (ISBN 0-19-821879-6). Oxford U Pr.

Roger Williams: New England Firebrand. James E. Ernst. LC 76-90097. (BCL Ser.: I). Repr. of 1932 ed. 24.50 (ISBN 0-404-02355-X). AMS Pr.

Roger Williams, Prophet & Pioneer. Emily Easton. LC 76-101266. Repr. of 1930 ed. 40.00 (ISBN 0-404-02236-7). AMS Pr.

Roger Williams, Prophet & Pioneer. Emily Easton. LC 71-102235. (Select Bibliographies Reprint Ser). 1930. 32.00 (ISBN 0-8369-5120-4). Ayer Co Pubs.

Roger Williams: Prophet & Pioneer. Emily Easton. LC 78-144994. 399p. 1972. Repr. of 1930 ed. 17.00x (ISBN 0-403-00793-3). Scholarly.

Roger Williams: The Church & the State. Edmund S. Morgan. 176p. 1987. pap. 5.95 (ISBN 0-393-30403-5). Norton.

Roger Williams, the Pioneer of Religious Liberty. facs. ed. Oscar S. Straus. LC 76-137385. (Select Bibliographies Reprint Ser). 1936. 20.00 (ISBN 0-8369-5586-2). Ayer Co Pubs.

Rol' Pravoslavnoi Tserkvi V Istorii Rosii: The Role of the Orthodox Church in Russian History. Sergei Pushkarev. Pref. by Protoierei. LC 85-80831. (Rus.). 125p. 1985. 9.50 (ISBN 0-911971-13-0). Effect Pub.

Roland H. Bainton: An Examination of His Reformation Historiography. Steven Simpler. LC 85-21567. (Texts & Studies in Religion: Vol. 24). 266p. 1985. PLB 49.95x (ISBN 0-88946-812-5). E Mellen.

Role & Responsibility of the Moral Philosopher: Proceedings, Vol. 56. Ed. by John T. Noonan, Jr. et al. LC 81-69068. 214p. 1983. pap. 15.00 (ISBN 0-918090-16-4). Am Cath Philo.

Role of Computers in Religious Education. Kenneth Bedell. 144p. 1986. pap. 7.95 (ISBN 0-687-36540-6). Abingdon.

Role of Faith in the Process of Healing. Edgar N. Jackson. 216p. 1982. pap. 9.95 (ISBN 0-86683-679-9, HarpR). Har-Row.

Role of Feelings in Morals. William Neblett. LC 81-40105. 114p. (Orig.). 1981. lib. bdg. 24.75 (ISBN 0-8191-1752-8); pap. text ed. 9.75 (ISBN 0-8191-1753-6). U Pr of Amer.

Role of Ideology in Church Participation. Phillip E. Hammond. Ed. by Harriet Zuckerman & Robert K. Merton. LC 79-9003. (Dissertations on Sociology Ser.). 1980. lib. bdg. 27.50x (ISBN 0-405-12972-6). Ayer Co Pubs.

Role of Knowledge in Western Religion. John H. Randall, Jr. 160p. 1986. pap. text ed. 10.75 (ISBN 0-8191-5167-X). U Pr of Amer.

Role of Music in the New Roman Liturgy. William Herring. LC 75-14548. 1971. pap. 0.50 (ISBN 0-915866-01-3). Am Cath Pr.

Role of Muslims in Indian Politics, 1857-1947. Kamalesh Sharma. 295p. 1986. text ed. 45.00x (ISBN 81-210-0028 9, Pub. by Inter India Pubns N Delhi). Apt Bks.

Role of New Testament Examples As Related to Biblical Authority. M. R. Hadwin. 1974. pap. 2.75 (ISBN 0-88027-038-1). Firm Foun Pub.

Role of Religion in American Life: An Interpretive Historical Anthology. Ed. by Robert R. Mathisen. LC 80-6246. 420p. (Orig.). 1982. pap. text ed. 14.75 (ISBN 0-8191-2514-8). U Pr of Amer.

Role of the Aged in Primitive Society. Leo W. Simmons. LC 78-103998. (Illus.). 317p. 1970. Repr. of 1945 ed. 28.00 (ISBN 0-208-00824-1, Archon). Shoe String.

Role of the Augsburg Confession: Catholic & Lutheran Views. Ed. by Joseph A. Burgess. LC 79-7373. 224p. 1980. 14.95 (ISBN 0-8006-0549-7, 1-549). Fortress.

Role of the Christian Philosopher: Proceedings. American Catholic Philosophical Association Staff. 1958. 18.00. Johnson Repr.

Role of the Church in Aging: Implications for Policy & Action. Ed. by Michael C. Hendrickson. LC 85-17564. (Journal of Religion & Aging: Vol. 2, Nos. 1-2). 178p. 1986. text ed. 29.95 (ISBN 0-86656-482-9, B482); pap. text ed. 19.95 (ISBN 0-86656-483-7, B483). Haworth Pr.

Role of the Church in Society. Charles Colson. 48p. 1986. 1.95 (ISBN 0-89693-167-6). Victor Bks.

Role of the Community Hospital in the Care of the Dying Patient, & the Bereaved. Elias Gerchick. 16.50 (ISBN 0-405-12506-2). Ayer Co Pubs.

Role of the Faith Mission: A Brazilian Case Study. Fred E. Edwards. LC 79-152406. (Illus.). 76p. 1971. pap. 3.45 (ISBN 0-87808-406-1). William Carey Lib.

Role of the Minister in Caring for the Dying Patient & the Bereaved. Brian O'Connor et al. 16.50 (ISBN 0-405-12504-6). Ayer Co Pubs.

Role of the Nun in Nineteenth Century America. Mary Ewens. 36.50 (ISBN 0-405-10828-1). Ayer Co Pubs.

Role of the Priest & the Apostolate of the Laity. L. J. Patsavos & G. J. Charles. Ed. by N. M. Vaporis. (Clergy Seminar Lectures Ser.). 63p. (Orig.). 1983. pap. 3.00 (ISBN 0-916586-57-X). Holy Cross Orthodox.

Role of the Volunteer Director in the Care of the Terminal Patient & the Family. Harriet H. Naylor. 17.00 (ISBN 0-405-13092-9). Ayer Co Pubs.

Role of Women in Early Christianity. Jean LaPorte. LC 82-8281. (Studies in Women & Religion: Vol. 7). 196p. 1982. 39.95x (ISBN 0-88946-545-2). E Mellen.

Role of Women in the Church. Charles C. Ryrie. LC 58-8329. 1979. pap. 5.95 (ISBN 0-8024-7371-7). Moody.

Role of Women: New Testament Perspectives. Neil R. Lightfoot. (Orig.). 1978. pap. 2.95 (ISBN 0-931118-00-X). Student Assn.

Roles. Brunetta R. Wolfman. LC 83-12441. (Choices: Guides for Today's Woman: Vol. 3). 118p. (Orig.). 1983. pap. 6.95 (ISBN 0-664-24542-0). Westminster.

Roles in the Liturgical Assembly. Von Allmen et al. Tr. by Matthew J. O'Connell from Fr. (Orig.). 1981. pap. 17.50 (ISBN 0-916134-44-X). Pueblo Pub Co.

Roles of Israel's Prophets. David L. Peterson. (Journal for the Study of the Old Testament: Supplement Ser. 17). 131p. 1982. text ed. 14.95 (ISBN 0-905774-32-9, Pub. by JSOT Pr England); (Pub. by JSOT Pr England). Eisenbrauns.

Rolin-Madonna of Jan Van Eyck. Heinz Roosen-Runge. (Illus.). 56p. 1973. pap. 9.75 (ISBN 0-8390-0125-8). Abner Schram Ltd.

Roll of the Household Expenses of Richard De Swinfield, Bishop of Hereford, 1289-1290, 2 Vols. Johannes De Kemeseye. 1854-1855. 65.00 (ISBN 0-384-29130-9). Johnson Repr.

Rolling Files: A Study of the Bible. Cuthbert Melville. 1980. 7.95 (ISBN 0-682-48165-3). Exposition Pr FL.

Rolling Thunder. Doug Boyd. 273p. 1986. pap. 9.95 (ISBN 0-385-28859-X, Delta). Dell.

Roma Sacra: Essays on Christian Rome. facs. ed. William F. Barry. LC 68-14896. (Essay Index Reprint Ser). 1927. 18.00 (ISBN 0-8369-0174-6). Ayer Co Pubs.

Roman & British Martyrology. Catholic Church Staff. 1980. lib. bdg. 79.95 (ISBN 0-8490-3128-1). Gordon Pr.

Roman & Christian Imperialism. John Westbury-Jones. LC 78-118555. 1971. Repr. of 1939 ed. 28.00x (ISBN 0-8046-1180-7, Pub. by Kennikat). Assoc Faculty Pr.

Roman Canon Law in the Church of England. Frederic W. Maitland. 1969. Repr. of 1898 ed. 21.00 (ISBN 0-8337-2186-0). B Franklin.

Roman Catechism. 15.00 (ISBN 0-8198-6408-0); 14.00 (ISBN 0-8198-6413-7). Dghtrs St Paul.

Roman Catholic Church & the Creation of the Modern Irish State, 1878-1886. Emmet J. Larkin. LC 75-7169. (American Philosophical Society Memoirs Ser.: Vol. 108). pap. 109.00 (ISBN 0-317-29437-7, 2024293). Bks Demand UMI.

Roman Catholic Church & the North-West School Question: A Study in Church-State Relations in Western Canada, 1875-1905. M. R. Lupul. LC 73-89844. 1974. 27.50x (ISBN 0-8020-5301-7). U of Toronto Pr.

Roman Catholic Church in Colonial Latin America. Richard E. Greenleaf. LC 77-76836. 284p. 1977. pap. 6.50x (ISBN 0-87918-034-X). ASU Lat Am St.

Roman Catholic Church in England 1780-1850: A Study in Internal Politics. Joan Connell. 215p. 1984. 14.00 (ISBN 0-87169-158-2). Am Philos.

Roman Catholic Church in Ireland & the Fall of Parnell, 1888-1891. Emmet Larkin. LC 78-22056. xxi, 316p. 1979. 30.00x (ISBN 0-8078-1352-4). U of NC Pr.

Roman Catholic Church Index of Prohibited Books As Issued by Pope Leo XIII. 201p. 1985. Repr. of 1907 ed. 127.55 (ISBN 0-89901-199-3). Found Class Reprints.

Roman Catholic Hierarchy. Thomas E. Watson. (Studies in Populism). 1980. lib. bdg. 69.95 (ISBN 0-686-68883-X). Revisionist Pr.

Roman Catholic Modernism. Ed. by Bernard M. Reardon. 1970. 20.00x (ISBN 0-8047-0750-2). Stanford U Pr.

Roman Catholic Theology of Pastoral Care. Regis A. Duffy. LC 83-48006. (Theology & Pastoral Care Ser.). 128p. 1983. pap. 7.95 (ISBN 0-8006-1727-4, 1-1727). Fortress.

Roman Catholicism. Loraine Boettner. 8.95 (ISBN 0-8010-0685-6). Baker Bk.

Roman Catholicism. Loraine Boettner. 1962. 8.95 (ISBN 0-87552-130-4). Presby & Reformed.

Roman Catholicism. Peter Kelly. 1985. 13.00x (ISBN 0-7062-3601-7, Pub. by Ward Lock Educ Co Ltd). State Mutual Bk.

Roman Catholicism & Freemasonry. Dudley Wright. 1977. lib. bdg. 69.95 (ISBN 0-8490-2531-1). Gordon Pr.

Roman Catholicism & the American Way of Life. Ed. by Thomas T. McAvoy. LC 72-13177. (Essay Index Reprint Ser.). Repr. of 1960 ed. 14.75 (ISBN 0-8369-8167-7). Ayer Co Pubs.

Roman Catholicism & the Right to Work. Edward B. McLean. 186p. (Orig.). 1986. lib. bdg. 25.50 (ISBN 0-8191-5009-6); pap. text ed. 11.25 (ISBN 0-8191-5010-X). U Pr of Amer.

Roman Catholicism in England from the Elizabethan Settlement to the Second Vatican Council. Edward Norman. (OPUS). 160p. 1985. 18.95x (ISBN 0-19-219181-0); pap. 9.95 (ISBN 0-19-281935-6). Oxford U Pr.

Roman Catholicism: The Search for Relevance. William McSweeney. 1980. 25.00 (ISBN 0-312-68969-1). St Martin.

Roman Catholics in England: Studies in Social Structure Since the Second World War. Michael P. Hornsby-Smith. (Illus.). 288p. 1987. 29.50 (ISBN 0-521-30313-3). Cambridge U Pr.

Roman Converts. facs. ed. Arnold H. Lunn. LC 67-22102. (Essay Index Reprint Ser). 1923. 18.00 (ISBN 0-8369-0636-5). Ayer Co Pubs.

Roman Dogma vs. Bible Doctrine. E. Harold Henderson. 152p. 1964. pap. 1.00 (ISBN 0-89114-060-3). Baptist Pub Hse.

Roman Group Portraiture: The Funerary Reliefs of the Late Republic & Early Empire. Diana E. Kleiner. LC 76-23634. (Outstanding Dissertations in the Fine Arts - 2nd Series - Ancient). (Illus.). 1977. Repr. lib. bdg. 76.00 (ISBN 0-8240-2703-5). Garland Pub.

Roman History & Mythology. Ed. by Henry A. Sanders. Repr. of 1910 ed. 37.00 (ISBN 0-384-38804-3). Johnson Repr.

Roman Ideas of Deity in the Last Century Before the Christian Era. William W. Fowler. LC 75-102236. (Select Bibliographies Reprint Ser). 1914. 19.00 (ISBN 0-8369-5121-2). Ayer Co Pubs.

Roman Inquisition & the Venetian Press, 1540-1605. Paul F. Grendler. LC 76-45900. 1978. text ed. 42.00x (ISBN 0-691-05245-X). Princeton U Pr.

Roman Mould of the Australian Catholic Church. J. N. Molony. 1969. 17.50x (ISBN 0-522-83934-7, Pub by Melbourne U Pr). Intl Spec Bk.

Roman Mythology. Stewart Perowne. LC 84-6446. (Library of the World's Myths & Legends). (Illus.). 144p. 1984. 18.95 (ISBN 0-911745-56-4). P Bedrick Bks.

Roman, Provincial & Islamic Law: The Origins of the Islamic Patronate. Patricia Crone. (Cambridge Studies in Islamic Civilization). 200p. Date not set. price not set (ISBN 0-521-32253-7). Cambridge U Pr.

Roman Questions of Plutarch. facsimile ed. Plutarch. Ed. by Herbert J. Rose. LC 75-14267. (Ancient Religion & Mythology Ser.). 1976. Repr. of 1924 ed. 17.00x (ISBN 0-405-07272-4). Ayer Co Pubs.

Roman Religion. Michael Massey. Ed. by Peter Hodge. (Aspects of Roman Life Ser.). 48p. (Orig.). 1979. pap. text ed. 4.40 (ISBN 0-582-21573-0). Longman.

Roman Religion & Roman Empire: Five Essays. Robert E. Palmer. LC 73-89289. (Haney Foundation Ser.: No. 15). Repr. of 1974 ed. 36.40 (2055281). Bks Demand UMI.

Roman Replies & CLSA Advisory Opinions, 1985. Ed. by William A. Schumacher & J. James Cuneo. 68p. (Orig.). 1985. pap. 5.50 (ISBN 0-943616-30-1). Canon Law Soc.

Roman Replies, 1982. William A. Shumacher. 42p. (Orig.). 1982. pap. 3.00 (ISBN 0-943616-13-1). Canon Law Soc.

Roman Replies, 1983. William A. Schumacher. 24p. (Orig.). 1983. pap. 3.00 (ISBN 0-943616-21-2). Canon Law Soc.

Roman Rite in Orthodoxy, Part I: Additional Testimonies, Pt. II. Chrysostomos H. Stratman & Apostolos Makrakis. 62p. 1957. pap. 1.00x (ISBN 0-938366-38-6). Orthodox Chr.

Roman Society & Roman Law in the New Testament. A. N. Sherwin-White. (Twin Brooks Ser.). 1978. pap. 7.95 (ISBN 0-8010-8148-3). Baker Bk.

Roman Society in the Last Century of Western Empire. S. Dill. 75.00 (ISBN 0-87968-060-1). Gordon Pr.

Roman Sources of Christian Art. Emerson H. Swift. (Illus.). Repr. of 1951 ed. lib. bdg. 22.50x (ISBN 0-8371-3430-7, SWCA). Greenwood.

Roman Spirit in Religion, Thought & Art. Albert Grenier. Tr. by M. R. Dobie. LC 76-118639. (Illus.). 423p. 1970. Repr. of 1926 ed. lib. bdg. 32.50x (ISBN 0-8154-0330-5). Cooper Sq.

Roman Spirit in Religion, Thought & Art. Albert Grenier. (Illus.). 423p. 1986. Repr. of 1926 ed. lib. bdg. 100.00 (ISBN 0-89760-448-2). Telegraph Bks.

Roman Theater-Temples. John A. Hanson. LC 78-5510. (Illus.). 1978. Repr. of 1959 ed. lib. bdg. 27.50x (ISBN 0-313-20477-2, HATT). Greenwood.

Romance of Symbolism & Its Relation to Church Ornament & Architecture. Sidney Heath. LC 70-174054. (Illus.). 1976. Repr. of 1909 ed. 40.00x (ISBN 0-8103-4302-9). Gale.

Romance of the English Bible. Laura H. Wild. 1929. 15.00 (ISBN 0-8274-3303-4). R West.

Romance of the Episcopal Church in West Tennessee. Ellen Davies-Rodgers. 12.00 (ISBN 0-685-84991-0). Plantation.

Romance of the Floridas. Michael Kenny. LC 70-120573. (Illus.). Repr. of 1934 ed. 15.00 (ISBN 0-404-03656-2). AMS Pr.

Romance of the Hebrew Language. William H. Saulex. 243p. 1983. Repr. of 1913 ed. lib. bdg. 30.00 (ISBN 0-8482-6303-0). Norwood Edns.

Romance of the Hebrew Language. William H. Saulez. 1979. Repr. of 1913 ed. lib. bdg. 27.50 (ISBN 0-8414-8013-3). Folcroft.

Romance with Reality. Russell L. Reid. 1983. 5.75 (ISBN 0-8062-2185-2). Carlton.

Romanesque Bible Illumination. Walter Cahn. LC 82-71593. (Illus.). 308p. 1982. 95.00x (ISBN 0-8014-1446-6). Cornell U Pr.

Romanesque Church Facade in Britain. J. Phillip McAleer. LC 83-48699. (Theses from the Courtauld Institute of Art Ser.). (Illus.). 785p. 1984. lib. bdg. 80.00 (ISBN 0-8240-5979-4). Garland Pub.

Romanesque Sculpture from the Cathedral of Saint-Etienne, Toulouse. Linda Seidel. LC 76-23646. (Outstanding Dissertations in the Fine Arts). (Illus.). 1977. Repr. of 1965 ed. lib. bdg. 63.00 (ISBN 0-8240-2729-9). Garland Pub.

Romanesque Sculpture of the Pilgrimage Roads, 10 Vols. in 3. A. Kingsley Porter. LC 67-4262. (Illus.). 1986. Repr. of 1923 ed. 250.00 set (ISBN 0-87817-020-0). Hacker.

Romanesque Wooden Doors of Auvergne. Walter Cahn. LC 74-15391. (College Art Association Monograph Ser.: Vol. 30). (Illus.). 225p. 1985. Repr. of 1974 ed. 30.00x (ISBN 0-271-00400-2). Pa St U Pr.

Romania: The Jewries of the Levant After the Fourth Crusade. Joshua Starr. 1943. 10.00x (ISBN 0-87068-108-7). Ktav.

Romanian Icons Painted on Glass. Cornel Irimie & Marcela Focsa. (Illus.). 1971. 75.00 (ISBN 0-393-04309-6). Norton.

Romanist, No. 4-5. Ed. by John C. Moran et al. 1981. 10.00 (ISBN 0-318-20641-2). F M Crawford.

Romanist, No. 6-8. Ed. by John C. Moran et al. 1984. 10.00 (ISBN 0-318-20642-0). F M Crawford.

Romans. James Bales. 2.50 (ISBN 0-89315-241-2). Lambert Bk.

Romans, Vol. VI. Beacon Bible Commentary Staff. 8.95 (ISBN 0-8010-0680-5). Baker Bk.

Romans. Matthew Black. (New Century Bible Series). 191p. 1973. 7.50 (ISBN 0-551-00447-9). Attic Pr.

Romans. rev. ed. Matthew Black. (New Century Bible Commentary Ser.). 192p. 1981. pap. 6.95 (ISBN 0-8028-1905-2). Eerdmans.

Romans. Martin H. Franzmann. 288p. 1986. pap. 8.95 (ISBN 0-570-04426-X, 12-3036). Concordia.

Romans. Charles Hodge. (Geneva Commentaries Ser.). 1975. 13.95 (ISBN 0-85151-213-5). Banner of Truth.

Romans. H. A. Ironside. 7.95 (ISBN 0-87213-386-9). Loizeaux.

Romans. Irving Jensen. (Irving Jensen's Do-It Yourself Bible Study). 114p. (Orig.). 1983. pap. 5.95 wkbk. (ISBN 0-89840-036-8). Heres Life.

Romans. Irving L. Jensen. (Bible Self-Study Ser.). 1970. pap. 3.25 (ISBN 0-8024-1045-6). Moody.

Romans, 2 vols. Don J. Kenyon. Incl. Vol. 1. Triumph of Truth. pap. text ed. 4.95 (ISBN 0-87509-147-4); leader's guide 2.95 (ISBN 0-87509-265-9); student's manual 1.00 (ISBN 0-87509-262-4); Vol 2. Glory of Grace. pap. text ed. 4.95 (ISBN 0-87509-148-2); leader's guide 2.95 (ISBN 0-87509-266-7); student's manual 1.00 (ISBN 0-87509-263-2). 1978. pap. Chr Pubns.

Romans. Roy L. Laurin. Orig. Title: Romans: Where Life Begins. 540p. 1988. Repr. of 1955 ed. 12.95 (ISBN 0-8254-3130-1). Kregel.

Romans. Martin Luther. Tr. by J. Theodore Mueller. LC 76-12077. Orig. Title: Commentary on the Epistle to the Romans. 1976. kivar 8.95 (ISBN 0-8254-3119-0). Kregel.

Romans. Eugene H. Maly. (New Testament Message Ser.: Vol. 9). 160p. 1980. 12.95 (ISBN 0-89453-197-2); pap. 7.95 (ISBN 0-89453-132-8). M Glazier.

Romans. H. C. Moule. 1982. lib. bdg. 16.25 (ISBN 0-86524-086-8, 4502). Klock & Klock.

Romans. Handley Moule. 1975. pap. 4.95 (ISBN 0-87508-362-5). Chr Lit.

Romans. (Erdmans Commentaries Ser.). 3.95 (ISBN 0-8010-3407-8). Baker Bk.

Romans. David N. Steele & Curtis C. Thomas. pap. 5.95 (ISBN 0-8010-8018-5). Baker Bk.

Romans. Geoffrey Wilson. 254p. 1977. pap. 5.45 (ISBN 0-85151-238-0). Banner of Truth.

Romans. Paul Zilonka. (Read & Pray Ser.). 1979. 1.75 (ISBN 0-8199-0633-6). Franciscan Herald.

Romans, Vol. 1. rev. ed. Alan Johnson. (Everyman's Bible Commentary Ser.). 1984. pap. 5.95 (ISBN 0-8024-0446-4). Moody.

Romans- The Gospel of God: An Exposition of Chapter 1. D. Martyn Lloyd-Jones. 416p. 1986. 16.95 (ISBN 0-310-27950-X, 10571). Zondervan.

Romans: A Daily Dialogue With God. James Reapsome. (Personal Bible Studyguide Ser.). 120p. pap. 4.95 (ISBN 0-87788-731-4). Shaw Pubs.

Romans, a Devotional Commentary. C. O. Rosenius. 1978. pap. 5.45 (ISBN 0-910452-42-3). Covenant.

Romans: A Study Guide. Andrew Kuyvenhoven. (Revelation Series for Adults). 1976. pap. text ed. 2.50 (ISBN 0-933140-04-5). CRC Pubns.

Romans: A Study Guide Commentary. Curtis Vaughan & Bruce Corley. 1976. pap. 4.95 (ISBN 0-310-33573-6, 10960P). Zondervan.

Romans: Assurance, Vol. 2. D. Martyn Lloyd-Jones. 272p. 1972. 14.95 (ISBN 0-310-27890-2, 10542). Zondervan.

Romans: Atonement & Justification; an Exposition of Chapters 3: 20 - 4: 35, Vol. 1. D. Martyn Lloyd-Jones. 13.95 (ISBN 0-310-27880-5, 10561). Zondervan.

Romans: Christianity on Trial. Carolyn Nystrom. (Young Fisherman Bible Studyguide Ser.). (Illus.). 124p. 1980. pap. 4.95 tchr's ed. (ISBN 0-87788-899-X); student ed. 3.95 (ISBN 0-87788-898-1). Shaw Pubs.

Romans Debate: Essays on the Origin & Purpose on the Epistle. Ed. by Karl P. Donfried. LC 77-84082. 1977. pap. 10.95 (ISBN 0-8066-1607-5, 10-5542). Augsburg.

Romans Dou Lis. Frederick C. Ostrander. Repr. of 1915 ed. 16.50 (ISBN 0-404-50616-X). AMS Pr.

Romans, First & Second Corinthians. Kenneth J. Foreman. LC 59-10454. (Layman's Bible Commentary Ser: Vol. 21). 1961. pap. 4.95 (ISBN 0-8042-3081-1). John Knox.

Romans Five: Sons of God - Chapter 8: 17 - 39. D. Martyn Lloyd-Jones. 448p. 1975. 15.95 (ISBN 0-310-27920-8, 10592). Zondervan.

Romans, II-Corinthians, Vol. VIII. Beacon Bible Commentary Staff. 13.95 (ISBN 0-8010-0695-3). Baker Bk.

Romans: Interpretation: A Bible Commentary for Teaching & Preaching. Paul J. Achtemeier. Ed. by James L. Mays. LC 84-47796. 240p. 1985. 17.95 (ISBN 0-8042-3137-0). John Knox.

Romans: Justification by Faith. William MacDonald. (Orig.). 1981. pap. 5.95 (ISBN 0-937396-36-2). Walterick Pubs.

Romans, Neighborhood Bible Study. Marilyn Kunz & Catherine Schell. 1970. pap. 2.95 (ISBN 0-8423-5701-7). Tyndale.

Romans Outlined & Summarized. Alva J. McClain. 1979. pap. 1.95 (ISBN 0-88469-015-6). BMH Bks.

Romans Realized. Don DeWelt. LC 72-1068. (Bible Study Textbook Ser.). (Illus.). 1959. 12.20 (ISBN 0-89900-037-1). College Pr Pub.

Romans: The Final Perseverance of the Saints (8: 17-39) D. Martin Lloyd-Jones. 458p. 1976. text ed. 15.95 (ISBN 0-310-27930-5, 10592). Zondervan.

Romans: The Freedom Letter, Vol. 2. rev. ed. Alan F. Johnson. (Everyman's Bible Commentary Ser.). Date not set. pap. 5.95 (ISBN 0-8024-2079-6). Moody.

Romans: The Gift of Righteousness. Jack Kuhatschek. (Lifebuilder Bible Studies). 96p. (Orig.). 1986. pap. 2.95 (ISBN 0-8308-1008-0). Inter-Varsity.

Romans: The Gospel According to Paul. Arden E. Gilmer. LC 85-72274. 1985. pap. 4.50x (ISBN 0-934970-05-X). Brethren Ohio.

Romans: The Gospel for All. Keith L. Brooks. (Teach Yourself the Bible Ser.). 1962. pap. 2.75 (ISBN 0-8024-7372-5). Moody.

Romans, the Gospel of God's Grace. Alva J. McClain. 11.95 (ISBN 0-88469-080-6). BMH Bks.

Romans: The Gospel of God's Grace. Alva J. McClain. 1979. 11.95 (ISBN 0-8024-7373-3). BMH Bks.

Romans: The Law-Chapter 7: 1 to 8: 4. D. Martyn Lloyd-Jones. 368p. 1974. 14.95 (ISBN 0-310-27910-0, 10574); Six-volume Set. text ed. 87.70 (ISBN 0-310-27948-8, 10575). Zondervan.

Romans: The New Man, Vol. 3. D. Martyn Lloyd-Jones. 1973. text ed. 14.95 (ISBN 0-310-27900-3, 10534). Zondervan.

Romans Verse by Verse. William R. Newell. 1938. 19.95 (ISBN 0-8024-7385-7). Moody.

Romantic Hero & His Biblical Sources. Wolf Z. Hirst. Ed. by James Hogg. (Romantic Reassessment ser.). (Orig.). 1985. pap. 15.00 (ISBN 3-7052-0573-0, Pub. by Salzburg Studies). Longwood Pub Group.

Romantic Idealism & Roman Catholicism: Schelling & the Theologians. Thomas F. O'Meara. LC 81-40449. 240p. 1982. 25.00 (ISBN 0-268-01610-0). U of Notre Dame Pr.

Romantic Movement & Methodism: A Study of English Romanticism & the Evangelical Revival. Frederick C. Gill. 1978. Repr. of 1937 ed. lib. bdg. 25.00 (ISBN 0-8492-4910-4). R West.

Romanticism & Religion. Stephen Prickett. LC 75-2254. 320p. 1976. 49.50 (ISBN 0-521-21072-0). Cambridge U Pr.

Romanticism & the Gothic Revival. Agnes Addison. 204p. 1967. Repr. of 1938 ed. 17.50x (ISBN 0-87752-000-3). Gordian.

Rome & Reform, 2 Vols. Thomas L. Kington-Oliphant. LC 76-118541. 1971. Repr. of 1902 ed. Set. 47.50x (ISBN 0-8046-1165-3, Pub. by Kennikat). Assoc Faculty Pr.

Rome & The Anglicans: Historical & Doctrinal Aspects of Anglican-Roman Catholic Relations. J. C. Aveling et al. Ed. by Wolfgang Haase. 301p. 1982. 81.50 (ISBN 3-11-008267-5). De Gruyter.

Rome & the Political Theory of History with Cogent Applications to the Rivalries Between the United States & Soviet Russia. Donald Hoagland. (Illus.). 166p. 1985. 167.95 (ISBN 0-86722-103-8). Inst Econ Pol.

Rome & the Vatican in Color. (Sterling Travel Guide in Color Ser.). (Illus.). 140p. (Orig.). 1983. pap. 4.95 (ISBN 0-8069-1372-X). Sterling.

Rome in the Age of Bernini, Vol. II: From the Election of Innocent X to the Death of Innocent XI. Torgil Magnuson. Tr. by Nancy Adler from Swedish. (Illus.). 420p. 1986. 39.95 (ISBN 0-391-03448-0, Pub. by Humanities Press & Almgrist & Wiksell). Humanities.

Rome in the High Renaissance: The Age of Leo X. Bonner Mitchell. LC 72-9277. (Centers of Civilization Ser.: Vol. 33). 1973. 11.95x (ISBN 0-8061-1052-X). U of Okla Pr.

Rome, Judea & Christianity: The Crucifixion. James P. Jacobs. 300p. 1987. pap. 7.95 (ISBN 0-9617280-0-0). James Pr Inc.

Rome of Alexander VII, 1655-1667. Richard Krautheimer. LC 84-26553. (Illus.). 214p. 1987. 34.50 (ISBN 0-691-04032-X); pap. 12.95 (ISBN 0-691-00277-0). Princeton U Pr.

Romische Mythologie: Roman Mythology. Ludwig Preller. Ed. by Kees W. Bolle. LC 77-79154. (Mythology Ser.). (Ger.). 1978. Repr. of 1865 ed. lib. bdg. 53.00x (ISBN 0-405-10563-0). Ayer Co Pubs.

Romischen Grabaltare der Kaiserzeit. facsimile ed. Walter Altmann. LC 75-10626. (Ancient Religion & Mythology Ser.). (Ger., Illus.). 1975. Repr. of 1905 ed. 26.50x (ISBN 0-405-07002-0). Ayer Co Pubs.

Ronald Reagan: In God I Trust. 1984. pap. 3.95 (ISBN 0-8423-5704-1). Tyndale.

Ronsard & Biblical Tradition. Joyce M. Hanks. (Etudes litteraires francaises: 17). 199p. (Orig.). 1982. pap. 19.00x (ISBN 3-87808-896-5). Benjamins North Am.

Room Called Remember: Uncollected Pieces. Frederick Buechner. LC 83-48457. 192p. 1984. 13.45 (ISBN 0-06-061163-4, HarpR). Har-Row.

Room to Be People: An Interpretation of the Message of the Bible for Today's World. Jose M. Bonino. Tr. by Vickie Leach from Span. LC 78-14662. 80p. 1979. pap. 4.50 (ISBN 0-8006-1349-X, 1-1349). Fortress.

Roosevelt & Romanism: Catholics & American Diplomacy, 1937-1945. George Q. Flynn. LC 75-35343. (Contributions in American History: No. 47). 272p. 1976. lib. bdg. 29.95 (ISBN 0-8371-8581-5, FRR/). Greenwood.

Root & Branch: The Jewish Christian Dialogue. Ed. by Michael Zeik & Martin Siegel. LC 70-181996. pap. 4.95 (ISBN 0-87957-001-6). Roth Pub.

Root & the Branch: Judaism & the Free Society. Robert Gordis. LC 62-17133. 1962. 20.00x (ISBN 0-226-30411-6). U of Chicago Pr.

Root of the Righteous. Aiden W. Tozer. 5.95 (ISBN 0-87509-194-6); pap. 4.45 (ISBN 0-87509-195-4); mass market 3.25 (ISBN 0-87509-224-1). Chr Pubns.

Roots & Boots: From Crypto-Jew in New Spain to Community Leader in the American Southwest. Floyd S. Fierman. 1987. 20.00 (ISBN 0-88125-114-3). KTAV.

Roots & Fruits. Jamie S. Lash. Date not set. pap. 3.00 (ISBN 0-915775-04-2). Love Song Mess Assn.

Roots & Fruits of the Camp Farthest Out. Camp Farthest Out Staff. 1980. 3.95 (ISBN 0-910924-89-9). Macalester.

Roots & Wings. James Angell. 80p. 1983. text ed. 7.95 (ISBN 0-687-36585-6). Abingdon.

Roots & Wings. Helen R. Bateman. LC 83-1868. (Illus.). 160p. 1983. 7.95 (ISBN 0-87747-950-X). Deseret Bk.

Roots & Wings: Prayers & Promises for Parents. John M. Robertson. 84p. 1983. pap. 2.50 (ISBN 0-8423-5712-2). Tyndale.

Roots & Wings: Talks on Zen. Bhagwan S. Rajneesh. (Orig.). 1979. pap. 9.95 (ISBN 0-7100-0420-6). Methuen Inc.

Roots in the Void: Baul Songs of Bengal. Dasgupta Alokeranjan. 1983. 5.00x (ISBN 0-8364-0972-8, Pub. by KP Bagchi India). South Asia Bks.

Roots of a Black Future: Family & Church. J. Deotis Roberts. LC 80-16788. 152p. 1980. pap. 8.95 (ISBN 0-664-24333-9). Westminster.

Roots of Anti-Semitism. Ernest L. Abel. LC 73-8286. 264p. 1975. 25.00 (ISBN 0-8386-1406-X). Fairleigh Dickinson.

Roots of Anti-Semitism: In the Age of Renaissance & Reformation. Heiko A. Oberman. Tr. by James I. Porter from Ger. LC 83-5695. 163p. 1983. 13.95 (ISBN 0-8006-0709-0, 1-709). Fortress.
Roots of Christian Anti-Semitism. Malcolm Hay. 356p. 10.00 (ISBN 0-686-95112-3). ADL.
Roots of Christian Joy. Adrian Van Kaam. 1985. 8.95 (ISBN 0-87193-241-5). Dimension Bks.
Roots of Egyptian Christianity. Ed. by Birger A. Pearson & James E. Goehring. LC 85-47736. (Studies in Antiquity & Christianity). 336p. 1986. 39.95 (ISBN 0-8006-3100-5, 1-3100). Fortress.
Roots of Ethics. Ed. by Daniel Callahan & H. Tristram Engelhardt, Jr. (Hasting Center Series in Ethics). 464p. 1981. 35.00 (ISBN 0-306-40796-5, Plenum Pr). Plenum Pub.
Roots of Evil. Norman L. Geisler. (Christian Free University Curriculum Ser.). 1978. pap. 4.95 (ISBN 0-310-35751-9, 12655P). Zondervan.
Roots of Ghana Methodism. Francis L. Bartels. LC 64-21525. pap. 95.50 (ISBN 0-317-08427-5, 2050799). Bks Demand UMI.
Roots of Jewish Nonviolence. Ed. by Jewish Peace Fellowship. 1984. lib. bdg. 79.95 (ISBN 0-87700-628-8). Revisionist Pr.
Roots of Modern Mormonism. Mark P. Leone. LC 78-25965. 1979. 17.50x (ISBN 0-674-77970-3). Harvard U Pr.
Roots of North Indian Shi'ism in Iran & Iraq: Religion & State in Awadh, 1722-1859. J. R. Cole. 340p. 1987. text ed. 38.00x (ISBN 0-520-05641-8). U of Cal Pr.
Roots of Peace. Viva Emmons. LC 73-78911. (Orig.). 1969. pap. 1.75 (ISBN 0-8356-0505-1, Quest). Theos Pub Hse.
Roots of Pendle Hill. Carol R. Murphy. LC 78-1768. (Orig.). pap. 2.50x (ISBN 0-87574-223-8). Pendle Hill.
Roots of St. Francis. Raphael Brown. 9.50 (ISBN 0-686-45828-1). Franciscan Herald.
Roots of the Modern Christian Tradition. Ed. by E. R. Elder. 1984. 24.95 (ISBN 0-87907-855-3); pap. 10.00. Cistercian Pubns.
Roots of the Reorganization: French Polynesia. F. Edward Butterworth. LC 77-944. (Illus.). 1977. pap. 8.00 (ISBN 0-8309-0176-0). Herald Hse.
Roots of the Synoptic Gospels. Bo Reicke. LC 85-45485. 224p. 1986. 22.95 (ISBN 0-8006-0766-X, 1-766). Fortress.
Roots of Unbelief: In Defense of Everything. William J. O'Malley. LC 75-34840. 96p. 1976. pap. 2.95 (ISBN 0-8091-1915-3). Paulist Pr.
Roots of Witchcraft. Michael Harrison. 280p. 1974. 7.95 (ISBN 0-8065-0444-7). Citadel Pr.
Roots out of Dry Ground. Reuben J. Swanson. 1979. 8.50 (ISBN 0-915948-06-0); pap. 6.50 (ISBN 0-686-57420-6). Bks Distinction.
Roots, Renewal & the Brethren. Nathan D. Smith. 152p. (Orig.). 1986. text ed. 12.95 (ISBN 0-932727-09-3); pap. 6.95 (ISBN 0-932727-08-5). Hope Pub Hse.
Rope of God. James T. Siegel. LC 69-15942. (Center for South & Southeast Asia Studies, California Library Reprint Ser.: No. 96). 1978. Repr. of 1969 ed. 35.00x (ISBN 0-520-03714-6). U of Cal Pr.
Rosa: A Story of Two Survivals. Rosa Strygler. 190p. 15.95 (ISBN 0-88400-125-3). Shengold.
Rosanna of the Amish. rev. ed. Joseph W. Yoder. 256p. 1973. pap. 3.95 (ISBN 0-8361-1714-X). Herald Pr.
Rosario Biblico. Christianica Center Staff. (Illus.). 1980. 5.95 (ISBN 0-911346-04-X). Christianica.
Rosary. Gaynell Cronin & Jim Gaynell. 1978. 7.55 (ISBN 0-88479-018-5). Arena Lettres.
Rosary. Joanne L. Kepes. 1982. 9.95 (ISBN 0-89837-061-2, Pub. by Pflaum Pr). Peter Li.
Rosary: A Gospel Prayer. Wilfrid J. Harrington. LC 75-44676. (Illus.). 160p. 1976. pap. 2.95 (ISBN 0-8189-1129-8, Pub. by Alba Bks). Alba.
Rosary in Action. John S. Johnson. 1977. pap. 5.00 (ISBN 0-89555-023-7). TAN Bks Pubs.
Rosary Novenas. C. Lacy. 1974. pap. 1.00 (ISBN 0-02-645810-1). Macmillan.
Rosary Novenas. 1.80. Benziger Pub Co.
Rosa's Song: The Life & Ministry of Rosa Page Welch. Rosa P. Welch & Oma L. Myers. LC 84-1882. 224p. 1984. pap. 8.95x (ISBN 0-8272-3210-1). CBP.
Rose Is a Rose Is a Rose. Bhagwan Shree Rajneesh. Ed. by Ma Yoga Pratima. (Initiation Talks Ser.). (Illus.). 428p. (Orig.). 1978. 18.95 (ISBN 0-88050-123-5). Chidvilas Found.
Rosegger's Religion. Henry C. Sorg. LC 78-140029. (Catholic University Studies in German Ser.: No. 11). 1970. Repr. of 1938 ed. 24.00 (ISBN 0-404-50231-8). AMS Pr.
Rosenbaums of Zell. Strauss. cancelled (ISBN 0-685-48598-6). Feldheim.
Roses in December: Finding Strength Within Grief. Marilyn W. Heavilin. 1987. pap. 6.95. Heres Life.
Rosey: The Gentle Giant. Rosey Grier. 1986. 17.95 (ISBN 0-89274-406-5). Harrison Hse.
Rosh Hashana: A Holiday Funtext. Judy Bin-Nun & Franne Einhorn. (Illus.). 1978. pap. 5.00 (ISBN 0-8074-0010-6, 101300). UAHC.
Rosh Hashanah, 1 vol. 15.00 (ISBN 0-910218-56-0). Bennet Pub.
Rosh Hashanah. Norma Simon. (Festival Series of Picture Story Books). (Illus.). 1961. plastic cover 4.50 (ISBN 0-8381-0700-1). United Syn Bk.
Rosh Hashanah & Yom Kippur. Howard Greenfeld. LC 79-4818. (Illus.). 1979. 6.95 (ISBN 0-03-044756-9). H Holt & Co.
Rosh Hashanah Anthology. Ed. by Philip Goodman. LC 74-105069. (Illus.). 379p. 1970. 10.95 (ISBN 0-8276-0023-2, 246). Jewish Pubns.
Rosicrucian Enlightenment. Frances A. Yates. (Illus.). 320p. 1986. pap. 7.95 (ISBN 0-7448-0051-X, 0051W, Ark Paperbks). Methuen Inc.
Rosicrucian Esotericism. Rudolf Steiner. Tr. by Dorothy S. Osmond from Ger. 122p. 1978. 14.00 (ISBN 0-910142-78-5). Anthroposophic.
Rosicrucian Fraternity in America, 2 vols. R. Swinborne Clymer. 1935. 75.00 (ISBN 0-686-10446-3). Philos Pub.
Rosicrucian Manual. 28th ed. H. Spencer Lewis. LC 78-104932. (Illus.). 214p. 1987. 8.95 (ISBN 0-912057-39-4, G-508). AMORC.
Rosicrucian Principles for the Home & Business. 21st ed. H. Spencer Lewis. LC 54-21694. 241p. 1981. 11.95 (ISBN 0-912057-04-1, G-502). AMORC.
Rosicrucian Questions & Answers with Complete History. 16th ed. H. Spencer Lewis. LC 65-14964. 358p. 1984. 12.50 (ISBN 0-912057-37-8, G-501). AMORC.
Rosicrucian Symbols. Franz Hartman. 1983. 2.95 (ISBN 0-916411-15-X). Sure Fire.
Rosicrucian Thoughts on the Ever-Burning Lamps of the Ancients. W. W. Westcott. 1986. pap. 2.95 (ISBN 0-916411-56-7). Sure Fire.
Rosicrucianism & Modern Initiation: Mystery Centres of the Middle Ages. 3rd. ed. Rudolf Steiner. Tr. by Mary Adams. 98p. 1982. pap. 9.95 (ISBN 0-85440-381-7, Pub by Steinerbooks). Anthroposophic.
Rosicrucians: Their Rites & Mysteries. 4th ed. Hargrave Jennings. LC 75-36845. (Occult Ser.). (Illus.). 1976. Repr. of 1907 ed. 36.50x (ISBN 0-405-07957-5). Ayer Co Pubs.
Ross Hannas: Living, Laughing, Loving. Wayne Grinstead. LC 86-6807. (Meet the Missionary Ser.). 1986. 5.50 (ISBN 0-8054-4325-8). Broadman.
Rosy Cross: Its Teachings. R. Swinburne Clymer. 287p. 1965. 7.95 (ISBN 0-932785-43-3). Philos Pub.
Rouault. Pierre Courthion. (Library of Great Painters). (Illus.). 1977. 45.00 (ISBN 0-8109-0459-4). Abrams.
Rough Edges of the Christian Life. Inter-Varsity Staff. pap. 2.50 (ISBN 0-87784-442-9). Inter-Varsity.
Rouleaux Des Morts Du IXe Au XVe Siecle. Ed. by Leopold V. Delisle. 1866. 43.00 (ISBN 0-384-11361-3); pap. 37.00 (ISBN 0-384-11360-5). Johnson Repr.
Roy Rogers-Dale Evans: Happy Trails. Roy Rogers et al. 1979. 2.50 (ISBN 0-8499-0086-7); 13.95. Word Bks.
Royal Abbey of Saint-Denis from Its Beginnings to the Death of Suger 475-1151. Sumner M. Crosby. LC 85-26464. 570p. 1987. text ed. 55.00 (ISBN 0-300-03143-2). Yale U Pr.
Royal Abbey of Saint-Denis in the Time of Abbot Suger (1122-1151) Sumner M. Crosby et al. Ed. by Ellen Shultz. LC 80-28849. (Illus.). 128p. 1981. pap. 12.95 (ISBN 0-87099-261-9). Metro Mus Art.
Royal Arch: Its Hidden Meaning. George H. Steinmetz. (Illus.). 145p. 1979. Repr. of 1946 ed. text ed. 9.50 (M-302). Macoy Pub.
Royal Bounty. F. R. Havergal. pap. 1.95 (ISBN 0-685-88391-4). Reiner.
Royal Dynasties in Ancient Israel. Tomoo Ishida. 1977. 45.25 (ISBN 3-1100-6519-3). De Gruyter.
Royal Funeral Ceremony in Renaissance France. R. E. Giesey. viii, 240p. (Orig.). 1960. pap. text ed. 40.00x (Pub. by Droz Switzerland). Coronet Bks.
Royal Hymns of Shulgi, King of Ur: Man's Quest for Immortal Fame. Jacob Klein. LC 81-65929. (Transactions Ser.: Vol. 71, Pt. 7.). 1981. 6.00 (ISBN 0-87169-717-3). Am Philos.
Royal Matron's Treasury of Addresses & Ceremonies, No. 2. Geraldine Boldt Maxwell. 1975. pap. 2.00 29 selections (ISBN 0-88053-320-X). Macoy Pub.
Royal Patronage of Buddhism in Ancient India. Hazra Kanai Lal. 1984. text ed. 55.00x (ISBN 0-86590-167-8). Apt Bks.
Royal Priesthood. Nolan P. Howington. LC 85-22376. 1986. pap. 4.95 (ISBN 0-8054-1622-6). Broadman.
Royal Reach. Lamm. 11.95 (ISBN 0-87306-133-0). Feldheim.
Royal Resident. Marcus Lehmann. 1981. 6.95 (ISBN 0-686-76251-7). Feldheim.
Royal Route to Heaven: Studies in First Corinthians. Alan Redpath. 256p. 1960. 12.95 (ISBN 0-8007-0279-4). Revell.
Royal Way of the Cross. Archbishop Fenelon. Ed. by Hal M. Helms. LC 80-67874. (Living Library Ser.). 1982. 5.95 (ISBN 0-941478-00-9). Paraclete Pr.
Royalty of the Pulpit. Edgar D. Jones. LC 79-134105. (Essay Index Reprint Ser). 1951. 27.50 (ISBN 0-8369-1979-3). Ayer Co Pubs.
Royaume Latin de Jerusalem. Jean Richard. LC 78-63359. (Crusades & Military Orders: Second Ser.). Repr. of 1953 ed. 28.50 (ISBN 0-404-17029-3). AMS Pr.
Royaume Secret. Pat Robertson. Ed. by Annie L. Cosson. Tr. by Anne Gimenez. Tr. of Secret Kingdom. (Fr.). 261p. 1985. pap. 2.75 (ISBN 0-8297-1277-1). Life Pubs Intl.
Royte Pomerantsen or How to Laugh in Yiddish. Ed. by Immanuel Olsvanger. 1979. pap. 6.95 (ISBN 0-8052-0099-1). Schocken.
Rozhdestvo Khristovo. M. Skaballanovitch. Tr. of Nativity of Christ. 195p. pap. 7.00 (ISBN 0-317-29162-9). Holy Trinity.
Rozhdestvo Presvjatia Bogoroditsi. M. Skaballanovitch. Tr. of Nativity of the Holy Mother of God. 134p. pap. 5.00 (ISBN 0-317-29149-1). Holy Trinity.
RSV Handy Concordance. 192p. 1972. pap. 5.95 (ISBN 0-310-32391-6, 6765P). Zondervan.
RSV Interlinear Greek, New Testament. Alfred Marshall. 24.95 (ISBN 0-310-20410-0, 10108). Zondervan.
Rubbish Theory: The Creation & Destruction of Value. Michael Thompson. 1979. text ed. 24.00x (ISBN 0-19-217658-7). Oxford U Pr.
Rubens & the Counter Reformation: Studies in His Religious Paintings Between 1609 & 1620. Thomas L. Glen. LC 76-23621. (Outstanding Dissertations in the Fine Arts Ser.). 1977. lib. bdg. 68.00 (ISBN 0-8240-2692-6). Garland Pub.
Rubens: Landscapes. Wolfgang Adler. (Harvey Miller Publication Ser.). (Illus.). 320p. 1982. 74.00x (ISBN 0-19-921027-6). Oxford U Pr.
Rubens: The Life of Christ after the Passion, Pt. VII. David Freedberg. (Corpus Rubenianum Ludwig Burchand). (Illus.). 1983. 74.00 (ISBN 0-19-921032-2). Oxford U Pr.
Rubies from Ruth. William G. Heslop. LC 76-12078. (W. G. Heslop Bible Study Aids Ser.). 116p. 1976. pap. 4.50 (ISBN 0-8254-2830-0). Kregel.
Rudder & the Rock. Charles W. Conn. 1976. pap. 4.25 (ISBN 0-87148-733-0). Pathway Pr.
Rudimental Divine Science & No & Yes. Mary B. Eddy. Danish 12.50 (ISBN 0-87952-105-8); German 12.50 (ISBN 0-87952-158-9); Italian 12.50 (ISBN 0-87952-183-X); Portugese 12.50 (ISBN 0-87952-208-9); Swedish 12.50 (ISBN 0-87952-253-4); Spanish 12.50 (ISBN 0-87952-232-1). First Church.
Rudimental Divine Science: No & Yes. Mary B. Eddy. 1976. lib. bdg. 69.95 (ISBN 0-8490-2546-X). Gordon Pr.
Rudolf Otto: An Introduction to His Philosophical Theology. Philip C. Almond. LC 83-19865. (Studies in Religion). x, 172p. 1984. 23.00x (ISBN 0-8078-1589-6). U of NC Pr.
Rudolf Steiner: A Documentary Biography. Johannes Hemleben. Tr. by Leo Twyman. (Illus.). 1975. (Pub by Henry Goulden, Ltd); pap. 10.95 (ISBN 0-904822-03-6). St George Bk Serv.
Rudolf Steiner: An Autobiography, Vol. 1. 2nd ed. Rudolf Steiner. LC 72-95242. (Spiritual Science Library). (Illus.). 560p. 1980. lib. bdg. 25.00 (ISBN 0-89345-031-6); pap. 17.00 (ISBN 0-89345-210-6). Garber Comm.
Rudolf Steiner: Herald of a New Epoch. Stewart C. Easton. LC 80-67026. (Illus.). 1980. pap. 10.95 (ISBN 0-910142-93-9). Anthroposophic.
Rudolf Steiner on His Book, The Philosophy of Freedom. Otto Palmer. Tr. by Marjorie Spock from Ger. 1975. 4.50 (ISBN 0-910142-68-8). Anthroposophic.
Rufinus: A Commentary of the Apostles' Creed. Ed. by W. J. Burghardt et al. LC 78-62468. (ACW Ser.: No. 20). 167p. 1955. 10.95 (ISBN 0-8091-0257-9). Paulist Pr.
Rufus Jones, Master Quaker. facsimile ed. David Hinshaw. LC 74-133522. (Select Bibliographies Reprint Ser.). Repr. of 1951 ed. 19.00 (ISBN 0-8369-5554-4). Ayer Co Pubs.
Ruin of Antichrist. John Bunyan. pap. 1.95 (ISBN 0-685-19842-1). Reiner.
Rukovodstvo k Izucheniju Svijashchennago Pisanija Vjetkhago Zavjeta, 3 vols. Archpriest Michael Kheraskov & D. Athanasiev. Tr. of Guide for Study of the Holy Scriptures of the Old Testament. 942p. pap. text ed. 32.00 (ISBN 0-317-29295-1). Holy Trinity.
Rukovodstvo k Izuchjeniju Svjashchennago Pisanija Novago Zavjeta-Tchetvjerojevangelija. Archbishop Averky Taushev. Tr. of Guide for Study of the Holy Scriptures of the New Testament-The Four Gospels. 345p. 1974. pap. text ed. 12.00 (ISBN 0-317-29299-4). Holy Trinity.
Rukovodstvo po Gomiletikje. Archbishop Averky Taushev. Tr. of Handbook for Homiletics. 110p. 1961. pap. text ed. 5.00 (ISBN 0-317-30276-0). Holy Trinity.
Rule & Exercises of Holy Dying: Means & Instruments of Preparing Ourselves & Others Respectively for a Blessed Death. Jeremy Taylor. Ed. by Robert Kastenbaum & Thomas Thirlwall. LC 76-19590. (Death & Dying Ser.). 1977. Repr. of 1819 ed. lib. bdg. 25.50x (ISBN 0-405-09585-6). Ayer Co Pubs.
Rule & Exercises of Holy Living. Jeremy Taylor. 295p. 1982. Repr. of 1982 ed. lib. bdg. 35.00 (ISBN 0-89984-468-5). Century Bookbindery.
Rule & Exercises of Holy Living & the Rule & Exercises of Holy Dying. Jeremy Taylor. LC 82-80478. (Treasures from the Spiritual Classics Ser.). 64p. 1982. pap. 2.95 (ISBN 0-8192-1309-8). Morehouse.
Rule for a New Brother. H. Van der Looy. 1985. pap. 4.95 (ISBN 0-87243-138-X). Templegate.
Rule of Iosif of Volokolamsk. D. Goldfrank. (Cistercian Studies: No. 36). pap. 14.95 (ISBN 0-87907-836-7). Cistercian Pubns.
Rule of Saint Augustine. Saint Augustine. Tr. by Raymond Canning. LC 85-20760. 128p. 1986. pap. 3.95 (ISBN 0-385-23241-1, Im). Doubleday.
Rule of Saint Benedict. Saint Benedict. Tr. by Cardinal Gasquet. LC 66-30730. (Medieval Library). (Illus.). 130p. 1966. Repr. of 1926 ed. 18.50x (ISBN 0-8154-0022-5). Cooper Sq.
Rule of St. Benedict. Tr. by Anthony C. Meisel & M. L. Del Mastro. LC 74-33611. 120p. 1975. pap. 2.95 (ISBN 0-385-00948-8, Im). Doubleday.
Rule of Saint Benedict: A Doctrinal & Spiritual Commentary. Adalbert De Vogue. Tr. by John B. Hasbrouck from Fr. (Cistercian Studies: No. 54). Tr. of Regle de saint Benoit, VII, Commentaire doctrinal et spirituel. 1983. pap. 25.95 (ISBN 0-87907-845-6). Cistercian Pubns.
Rule of St. Benedict in English. Ed. by Timothy Fry & Imogene Baker. 96p. (Orig.). 1982. pap. 2.25 (ISBN 0-8146-1272-5). Liturgical Pr.
Rule of St. Cormac: Irish Monastic Rules. St. Cormac, Bishop of Munster. (Vol. III). pap. 1.50 (ISBN 0-317-11386-0). Eastern Orthodox.
Rule of St. Pachomius. Saint Pachomius. Tr. by E. A. Budge from Coptic. 1975. pap. 1.95 (ISBN 0-686-10939-2). Eastern Orthodox.
Rule of the Master: Regula Magistri. Tr. & Luke Eberle. LC 77-3986. (Cistercian Studies Ser: No. 6). 1977. 12.95 (ISBN 0-87907-806-5). Cistercian Pubns.
Rule Statutes & Customs of the Hospitallers, 1099-1310. Knights of Malta. LC 78-63347. (Crusades & Military Orders: Second Ser.). 272p. Repr. of 1934 ed. 29.00 (ISBN 0-404-16246-0). AMS Pr.
Ruled by the Spirit. Basilea Schlink. 144p. 1970. pap. 3.50 (ISBN 0-87123-483-1, 200483). Bethany Hse.
Ruler of the Kings on the Earth: A Clear Look at Amillennialism for the Lay Person. R. G. Currell & E. P. Hurlbut. 126p. 1983. pap. 4.95 (ISBN 0-87552-211-4). Presby & Reformed.
Rulers of Mecca. Gerald De Gaury. LC 78-63458. (Pilgrimages Ser.). (Illus.). 1982. Repr. of 1954 ed. 34.50 (ISBN 0-404-16517-6). AMS Pr.
Rules & Precepts of the Jesuit Missions of Northwestern New Spain. Charles Polzer. LC 75-8456. 141p. 1976. pap. 4.50 (ISBN 0-8165-0488-1). U of Ariz Pr.
Rules & Racial Equality. Edwin Dorn. LC 79-64228. 1979. 24.50x (ISBN 0-300-02362-6). Yale U Pr.
Rules & Resolutions, Nineteen Eighty. Ed. by Paul A. Wellington. LC 74-84765. 1980. 10.00 (ISBN 0-8309-0136-1). Includes Supplements 1982, 1984 & 1986. Herald Hse.
Rules Mean Happiness. Bonita Kraemer. (Come Unto Me Ser.). 1979. pap. 1.65 (ISBN 0-8127-0254-9). Review & Herald.
Rules of HAJJ. Ayatullah Al-Khu'i. Tr. by Shaikh Muhammad Sarwar from Arabic. 50p. 1981. pap. 3.00 (ISBN 0-941724-02-6). Islamic Seminary.
Ruling Ideas of the Present Age. Washington Gladden. 1971. Repr. of 1895 ed. 23.00 (ISBN 0-384-18865-6). Johnson Repr.
Ruling Trinity: A Community Study of Chruch, State & Business in Ireland. Chris Eipper. 1986. text ed. 42.00 (ISBN 0-566-05173-7, Pub. by Gower Pub England). Gower Pub Co.
Rumbuli. Frida Michelson. Tr. by Wolf Goodman from Rus. 224p. 1981. 16.95 (ISBN 0-89604-029-1); pap. 10.95 (ISBN 0-89604-030-5). Holocaust Pubns.
Rumi the Persian Mystic. 1970. 15.00 (ISBN 0-87902-185-3). Orientalia.
Rumi the Persian: Rebirth in Creativity & Love. A. R. Arasteh. 1970. 6.50x (ISBN 0-87902-043-1). Orientalia.

Rumor of Trumpets: The Return of God to Secular Society. Jerry D. Cardwell. 118p. (Orig.). 1985. lib. bdg. 22.00 (ISBN 0-8191-4791-5); pap. text ed. 8.75 (ISBN 0-8191-4792-3). U Pr of Amer.

Rumors of War: A Moral & Theological Perspective on the Arms Race. Ed. by Charles A. Cesaretti & Joseph T. Vitale. 128p. (Orig.). 1982. pap. 6.95 (ISBN 0-8164-2365-2, HarpR). Har-Row.

Run Baby Run: The Story of a Gang-Lord Turned Crusader. Nicky Cruz. LC 68-23446. 240p. 1968. pap. 3.50 (ISBN 0-912106-58-1, Pub. by Logos). Bridge Pub.

Run Devil Run. Hugh Van Eaton. (Illus.). 1975. pap. 3.95 (ISBN 0-89957-513-7). AMG Pubs.

Run to the Roar. Tammy Bakker & Cliff Dudley. LC 80-80656. 142p. 1980. 7.95 (ISBN 0-89221-073-7). New Leaf.

Run to Win: Training for the Overcoming Life. Glenyce Coffin. (Cornerstone Ser.). 40p. 1984. pap. 2.50 (ISBN 0-930756-87-8, 533010). Aglow Pubns.

Run Toward the Nightland: Magic of the Oklahoma Cherokees. Jack F. Kilpatrick & Anna G. Kilpatrick. LC 67-19814. (Illus.). 1967. pap. 9.95 (ISBN 0-87074-084-9). SMU Press.

Run with the Horses. Eugene Peterson. LC 83-13005. 216p. (Orig.). 1983. pap. 6.95 (ISBN 0-87784-905-6). Inter-Varsity.

Run with the Winners. Warren W. Wiersbe. Ed. by Wightman Weese. 160p. (Orig.). 1985. pap. 4.95 (ISBN 0-8423-5798-X); study guide 2.95 (ISBN 0-8423-5799-8). Tyndale.

Runaway. Patricia St. John. 1985. pap. 3.95 (ISBN 0-8024-9159-6). Moody.

Runaway Jonah & Other Biblical Adventures Including Little Joseph, Singing David & Captain Noah. Retold by Jan Wahl. (Illus.). 96p. 1985. 13.95 (ISBN 0-89845-421-2). Caedmon.

Runners' World Yoga, Bk. II. DeBarra Mayo. 180p. (Orig.). 1983. pap. 9.95 (ISBN 0-89037-274-8). Anderson World.

Running a Library: Managing the Congregation's Library with Care, Confidence, & Common Sense. Ruth S. Smith. 144p. (Orig.). 1982. pap. 7.95 (ISBN 0-8164-2413-6, HarpR). Har-Row.

Running Around in Spiritual Circles. Fay Angus. LC 85-42768. 192p. 1986. 13.45 (ISBN 0-06-060238-4, HarpR). Har-Row.

Running Free: Conquering Fear & Shyness. Nathanael Pugh. Ed. by Mary H. Wallace. 96p. (Orig.). 1984. pap. 4.50 (ISBN 0-912315-69-5). Word Aflame.

Running God's Plan. Foster Bailey. 190p. (Orig.). 1972. pap. 5.00 (ISBN 0-85330-128-X). Lucis.

Running Red Lights. Charles Mylander. LC 86-444. 250p. (Orig.). 1986. pap. 6.95 (ISBN 0-8307-1103-1, 5418666). Regal.

Running Register: Recording the State of the English Colledges in All Forraine Parts. Lewis Owen. LC 68-54654. (English Experience Ser.: No. 19). 118p. 1968. Repr. of 1626 ed. 13.00 (ISBN 90-221-0019-7). Walter J Johnson.

Running the Race. Judson Edwards. LC 85-4700. 1985. pap. 5.95 (ISBN 0-8054-5711-9). Broadman.

Running the Race: Keeping the Faith. Sandy Larsen. (Young Fisherman Bible Studyguide Ser.). 64p. (Orig.). 1986. pap. 2.95 (ISBN 0-87788-740-3); tchr's. ed. 4.95 (ISBN 0-87788-741-1). Shaw Pubs.

Runways to God. Paschal Botz. LC 79-24756. 346p. (Orig.). 1979. pap. 3.50 (ISBN 0-8146-1059-5). Liturgical Pr.

Rupert of Deutz. John Van Engen. LC 82-40089. (Center for Medieval & Renaissance Studies, UCLA: Publication: No. 18). 1983. text ed. 34.50x (ISBN 0-520-04577-7). U of Cal Pr.

Rush Hour of the Gods. H. Neill McFarland. 1967. 11.95x (ISBN 0-02-583200-X). Macmillan.

Rush to Armaggedon. Texe W. Marrs. (Living Bk.). 128p. (Orig.). 1987. 3.95 (ISBN 0-8423-5796-3). Tyndale.

Rush to Resurrection. Donald X. Burt. 112p. 1985. pap. 5.95 (ISBN 0-8146-1440-X). Liturgical Pr.

Ruskin & Gandhi. Elizabeth T. McLaughlin. LC 72-3260. 202p. 1974. 20.00 (ISBN 0-8387-1086-7). Bucknell U Pr.

Ruskin & the Rhetoric of Infallibility. Gary Wihl. LC 85-5310. (Yale Studies in English: No. 194). 256p. 1985. 17.50x (ISBN 0-300-03321-4). Yale U Pr.

Ruskin As a Religious Teacher. Dean Farrar. 1978. Repr. of 1904 ed. lib. bdg. 15.00 (ISBN 0-8495-1616-1). Arden Lib.

Ruskin As a Religious Teacher. Dean Farrar. LC 73-2834. 1973. lib. bdg. 8.50 (ISBN 0-8414-1957-4). Folcroft.

Ruskin: Prophet of the Good Life. John Howard Whitehouse. LC 73-16263. 1948. lib. bdg. 12.50 (ISBN 0-8414-9491-6). Folcroft.

Ruskin the Prophet & Other Centenary Studies. John Howard Whitehouse. LC 73-11306. 1920. lib. bdg. 25.00 (ISBN 0-8414-9368-5). Folcroft.

Ruskin's Landscape of Beatitude. David A. Downes. LC 83-48767. (American University Studies IV (English Language & Literature): Vol. 4). 247p. 1984. pap. text ed. 24.75 (ISBN 0-8204-0049-1). P Lang Pubs.

Russellism Unveiled. O. C. Lambert. 1940. pap. 3.50 (ISBN 0-88027-090-X). Firm Foun Pub.

Russia under Peter the Great. Voltaire. Tr. by M. F. Jenkins. LC 81-72050. 340p. 1983. 35.00 (ISBN 0-8386-3148-7). Fairleigh Dickinson.

Russian Azerbaijan, Nineteen Five to Nineteen Twenty. T. Swietochowski. 255p. 1985. 125.00 (ISBN 0-317-40712-0, Pub. by Collets UK). State Mutual Bk.

Russian Church & Russian Dissent. Albert F. Heard. LC 70-127907. Repr. of 1887 ed. 24.50 (ISBN 0-404-03198-6). AMS Pr.

Russian Church & the Soviet State, 1917-1950. John S. Curtiss. 1953. 11.75 (ISBN 0-8446-1141-7). Peter Smith.

Russian Church Singing: Orthodox Worship & Hymnography, Vol. I. Johann Von Gardner. LC 79-27480. 146p. 1980. pap. 7.95 (ISBN 0-913836-59-1). St Vladimirs.

Russian Church under the Soviet Regime. Dimitry Pospielovsky. 533p. Set. 18.95 (ISBN 0-88141-033-0); Vol. I, 248 pgs. 9.95 (ISBN 0-88141-015-2); Vol. II, 285 pgs. 9.95 (ISBN 0-88141-016-0). St Vladimirs.

Russian Clergy. Jean X. Gagarin. LC 70-131035. Repr. of 1872 ed. 21.00 (ISBN 0-404-02666-4). AMS Pr.

Russian Ecclestiastical Mission in Peking During the Eighteenth Century. Eric Widmer. (East Asian Monographs: No. 69). 1976. 21.00x (ISBN 0-674-78129-5). Harvard U Pr.

Russian Emigre Authors: A Biographical Index & Bibliography of Their Works on Theology, Religious Philosophy, Church History & Orthodox Culture, 1921-1972. Compiled by Nicholas Zernov. 1973. lib. bdg. 23.50 (ISBN 0-8161-1005-0). G K Hall.

Russian Government & the Massacres. E. P. Semenov. LC 70-97304. (Judaica Ser.). 265p. 1972. Repr. of 1907 ed. lib. bdg. 29.75 (ISBN 0-8371-2632-0, SERG). Greenwood.

Russian Icons in the Santa Barbara Museum of Art. A. Dean McKenzie. LC 82-62426. (Illus.). 54p. (Orig.). 1982. pap. 8.25 (ISBN 0-89951-049-3). Santa Barb Mus Art.

Russian Idea. Nikolai A. Berdiaev. Tr. by R. M. French. LC 78-32021. 1979. Repr. of 1948 ed. lib. bdg. 37.50x (ISBN 0-313-20968-5, BERN). Greenwood.

Russian Jewry Reader. Evan R. Chesler. 147p. pap. 2.45 (ISBN 0-686-95145-X). ADL.

Russian Letters of Direction. Staretz Macarius. LC 75-1064. 115p. 1975. pap. 4.95 (ISBN 0-913836-23-0). St Vladimirs.

Russian Levites: Parish Clergy in the Eighteenth Century. Gregory L. Freeze. (Russian Research Center Studies: 78). 1977. 22.50x (ISBN 0-674-78175-9). Harvard U Pr.

Russian Martyr. Ivan V. Moiseyev. 0.95 (ISBN 0-89985-107-X). Christ Nations.

Russian Missions in China & Japan. Charles Hale. 1974. pap. 1.50 (ISBN 0-686-10198-7). Eastern Orthodox.

Russian Mystics. Sergius Bolshakoff. (Cistercian Studies: No. 26). Orig. Title: I Mistici Russi. 303p. 1981. pap. 6.95 (ISBN 0-87907-926-6). Cistercian Pubns.

Russian Nonconformity: The Story of Unofficial Religion in Russia. Serge Bolshakoff. Repr. of 1950 ed. 10.00 (ISBN 0-404-00933-6). AMS Pr.

Russian Orthodox Church: A Contemporary History. Jane Ellis. LC 85-45884. 700p. 1986. 39.95x (ISBN 0-253-35029-8). Ind U Pr.

Russian Orthodox Missions. Eugene Smirnoff. pap. 8.95 (ISBN 0-686-01299-2). Eastern Orthodox.

Russian Orthodoxy under the Old Regime. Ed. by Robert L. Nichols & Theofanis G. Stavrou. LC 78-3196. 1978. 16.50 (ISBN 0-8166-0846-6); pap. text ed. 8.95x (ISBN 0-8166-0847-4). U of Minn Pr.

Russian Piety. Nicholas Arseniev. 143p. 1964. pap. 5.95 (ISBN 0-913836-21-4). St Vladimirs.

Russian Protestants: Evangelicals in the Soviet Union. Steve Durasoff. LC 72-76843. (Illus.). 312p. 1969. 27.50 (ISBN 0-8386-7465-8). Fairleigh Dickinson.

Russians & Their Church. Nicolas Zernov. 196p. 1977. pap. 6.95 (ISBN 0-913836-36-2). St Vladimirs.

Russia's Attitude Towards Union with Rome: 9th-16th Centuries. Joseph B. Kincevicious. 208p. 1983. Repr. of 1927 ed. 24.95x (ISBN 0-939738-10-4). Zubal Inc.

Russia's Last Invasion. Wim Malgo. 1980. 3.95 (ISBN 0-937422-01-0). Midnight Call.

Russia's New Religion. Parker L. Johnstone. 208p. 1984. 7.95 (ISBN 0-917802-11-X). Theoscience Found.

Russkaja Pravoslavnaja Tserkov' v Severnoj Ameriki. N. D. Talberg. Tr. of Russian Orthodox Church in North America. 224p. 1955. pap. 8.00 (ISBN 0-317-30366-X). Holy Trinity.

Russkii Arkhierei iz Vizantii i Pravo Ego Naznacheniia do Nachala XV Veka. P. Sokolov. 582p. 1913. text ed. 74.52x (ISBN 0-576-99187-2, Pub. by Gregg Intl Pubs England). Gregg Intl.

Ruta de Escape. Don Wilkerson & David Manuel. Tr. by Juan S. Araujo from Eng. Tr. of Hellbound. (Span.). 224p. 1986. pap. 4.75 (ISBN 0-88113-266-7). Edit Betania.

Ruth. Marlee Alex. (Women of the Bible Ser.). (Illus.). 32p. 1987. 8.95 (ISBN 0-8028-5017-0). Eerdmans.

Ruth. Ethel Barrett. LC 80-52961. (Bible Biography Ser.). 128p. 1980. pap. 1.95 (ISBN 0-8307-0764-6, 5810418). Regal.

Ruth. Edward F. Campbell. LC 74-18785. (Anchor Bible Ser.: Vol. 7). (Illus.). 216p. 1975. 14.00 (ISBN 0-385-05316-9). Doubleday.

Ruth. R. H. Munce. 117p. 1971. spral bdg 3.95x (ISBN 0-914674-00-5). Freelandia.

Ruth: A Bible Study Commentary. Paul P. Enns. 96p. (Orig.). 1982. pap. 3.95 (ISBN 0-310-44061-0, 11832P). Zondervan.

Ruth: A Woman of Worth. Joyce M. Smith. 1979. pap. 2.50 (ISBN 0-8423-5810-2). Tyndale.

Ruth & Daniel: God's People in an Alien Society. Penelope Stokes. (Fisherman Bible Studyguide Ser.). 64p. (Orig.). 1986. pap. 2.95 (ISBN 0-87788-735-7). Shaw Pubs.

Ruth & Jonah: People in Process. Bob & Win Couchman. (Carpenter Studyguide). 80p. 1983. saddle-stiched member's handbk. 1.95 (ISBN 0-87788-736-5); leader's handbook 2.95 (ISBN 0-87788-737-3). Shaw Pubs.

Ruth & Naomi. (Arch Book Ser.: No. 21). 1984. pap. 0.99 (ISBN 0-570-06188-1, 59-1289). Concordia.

Ruth, Esther, Ecclesiastes, the Song of Songs, Lamentations. W. J. Fuerst. LC 74-82589. (Cambridge Bible Commentary on the New English Bible, Old Testament Ser.). 250p. 1975. 32.50 (ISBN 0-521-20651-0); pap. 11.95 (ISBN 0-521-09920-X). Cambridge U Pr.

Ruth, Esther, Jonah. Johanna W. Bos. LC 85-45793. (Preaching Guides Ser.). 108p. 1986. pap. 4.95 (ISBN 0-8042-3227-X). John Knox.

Ruth Montgomery: Herald of the New Age. Ruth Montgomery. LC 85-25424. 288p. 1986. 16.95 (ISBN 0-385-23311-6, Dolp). Doubleday.

Ruth, The Gleaner, & the Boy Samuel. Gordon Lindsay. (Old Testament Ser.). 1.25 (ISBN 0-89985-137-1). Christ Nations.

Ruth: Woman of Courage. Paula Parris. (BibLearn Ser.). (Illus.). 1977. bds. 5.95 (ISBN 0-8054-4229-4, 4242-29). Broadman.

Ruth's Story. As told by Catherine Storr. (Peoples of the Bible Ser.). (Illus.). 32p. 1985. PLB 10.65 (ISBN 0-8172-2043-7). Raintree Pubs.

Rx for Living: Take as Needed. Max L. Foreman. 1982. 20.00x (ISBN 0-8197-0490-3). Bloch.

Ryrie's Concise Guide to the Bible. Charles Ryrie. LC 83-71924. 163p. (Orig.). 1983. pap. 5.95 (ISBN 0-86605-121-X). Heres Life.

S

S. A. Rachinskij i jego Shkola. Tr. of S. A. Rachinsky & His School. 84p. 1956. pap. 2.00 (ISBN 0-317-30334-1). Holy Trinity.

S. Andrea in Mantua: The Building. Eugene J. Johnson. LC 74-30085. (Illus.). 220p. 1975. 42.50x (ISBN 0-271-01186-6). Pa St U Pr.

S. Aureli Augustini: De Beata Vita: A Translation with an Introduction & Commentary, Vol. 72. Ruth A. Brown. (Patristic Studies). 211p. 1984. Repr. of 1944 ed. 30.00x (ISBN 0-939738-30-9). Zubal Inc.

S. B. C.: House on the Sand? David O. Beale. 246p. (Orig.). 1985. pap. 4.95 (ISBN 0-89084-281-7). Bob Jones Univ Pr.

S. Ephraim's Quotations from the Gospel. F. C. Burkitt. (Texts & Studies Ser.: No. 1, Vol. 7, Pt. 2). pap. 13.00 (ISBN 0-8115-1704-7). Kraus Repr.

S. Thomas of Canterbury. W. H. Hutton. 59.95 (ISBN 0-8490-0983-9). Gordon Pr.

Saadia Anniversary Volume. Ed. by Boaz Cohen & Steven Katz. LC 79-7168. (Jewish Philosophy, Mysticism & History of Ideas Ser.). 1980. Repr. of 1943 ed. lib. bdg. 28.50x (ISBN 0-405-12244-6). Ayer Co Pubs.

Saadia Gaon Book of Beliefs & Opinions. Tr. by Samuel Rosenblatt. (Judaica Ser.: No. 1). 1948. 55.00x (ISBN 0-300-00865-1). Yale U Pr.

Saadiah Gaon: Selected Essays: An Original Anthology. Ed. by Steven Katz. LC 79-7171. (Jewish Philosophy, Mysticism & History of Ideas Ser.). 1980. lib. bdg. 34.50x (ISBN 0-405-12230-6). Ayer Co Pubs.

Saadya Studies: In Commemoration of the One Thousandth Anniversary of the Death of R. Saadya Gaon. Ed. by Erwin I. Rosenthal & Steven Katz. LC 79-7170. (Jewish Philosophy, Mysticism & History of Ideas Ser.). 1980. Repr. of 1943 ed. lib. bdg. 25.50x (ISBN 0-405-12284-5). Ayer Co Pubs.

Saal-Buch Des Benedictiner-Stiftes Gottweig (Benedictine Abbey) Repr. of 1855 ed. 23.00 (ISBN 0-384-19080-4). Johnson Repr.

Saama-Veda (Summary) Date not set. 5.00 (ISBN 0-938924-31-1). Sri Shirdi Sai.

Sabbaath in England. Max Levy. Repr. of 1933 ed. 24.00 (ISBN 0-384-32425-8). Johnson Repr.

Sabbatai Sevi: The Mystical Messiah. Gershom Scholem. Tr. by R. Zwi Werblowski from Hebrew. LC 75-166389. (Bollingen Series, Vol. 93). (Illus.). 1040p. 1973. 71.00x (ISBN 0-691-09916-2); pap. 22.50x (ISBN 0-691-01809-X). Princeton U Pr.

Sabbath. Samuel H. Dresner. 1970. pap. 2.95 (ISBN 0-8381-2114-4). United Syn Bk.

Sabbath. Abraham J. Heschel. 118p. 1975. pap. 4.50 (ISBN 0-374-51267-1). FS&G.

Sabbath. Charles Wengrove. (Illus.). 1960. pap. 0.99 (ISBN 0-914080-65-2). Shulsinger Sales.

Sabbath: A Guide to Its Understanding & Observance. I. Grunfeld. 6.95; pap. 4.95 (ISBN 0-87306-099-7). Feldheim.

Sabbath & Festival Praybook. 9.85 (ISBN 0-686-96035-1). United Syn Bk.

Sabbath & the Lord's Day. H. M. Riggle. 160p. pap. 1.50 (ISBN 0-686-29165-4). Faith Pub Hse.

Sabbath at Sea. Michael L. Roland. (Destiny II Ser.). 108p. 1984. pap. 6.50 (ISBN 0-8163-0547-1). Pacific Pr Pub Assn.

Sabbath Breaking & the Death Penalty: A Theological Investigation. James B. Jordan. LC 86-80679. 109p. (Orig.). 1986. pap. 9.95 (ISBN 0-939404-13-3). Geneva Ministr.

Sabbath in Puritan New England. Alice M. Earle. 335p. 1969. Repr. of 1891 ed. 20.00 (ISBN 0-87928-005-0). Corner Hse.

Sabbath-Law of R. Meir. Robert Goldenberg. LC 78-14370. (Brown University. Brown Judaic Studies: No. 6). 1978. pap. 9.00 (ISBN 0-89130-249-2, 140006). Scholars Pr GA.

Sabbath Prayerbook. Ed. by Mordecai M. Kaplan & Eugene Kohn. LC 57-9678. 573p. 1979. 11.50 (ISBN 0-935457-32-1). Reconstructionist Pr.

Sabbath School Manual. rev. ed. General Conference Sabbath School Department. 1982. pap. 5.50 (ISBN 0-8127-0228-X). Review & Herald.

Sabbath Service. 1982. 15.00 (ISBN 0-686-76253-3). Feldheim.

Sabbath Service: Shaharit L'Shabbat. Abraham Shumsky. Date not set. pap. 3.95x (ISBN 0-940646-35-8). Rossel Bks.

Sabbath Shiurim. Miller. 1979. Vol. I. 12.00 (ISBN 0-87306-993-5); Vol. II. 12.00 (ISBN 0-686-67019-1). Feldheim.

Sabbath: The Day of Delight. Ed. by Abraham E. Millgram. (Illus.). 495p. 1944. 12.95 (ISBN 0-8276-0157-3, 247). Jewish Pubns.

Sabbath Time: Understanding & Practice for Contemporary Christians. Tilden Edwards. 144p. 1984. pap. 8.95 (ISBN 0-8164-0526-3, AY7883, HarpR). Har-Row.

Sabbathday Lake Shakers: An Introduction to the Shaker Heritage. 2nd ed. Sr. R. Mildred Barker. (Illus.). 26p. 1985. pap. 3.00 (ISBN 0-915836-04-1). Shaker Pr ME.

Sackcloth & Ashes. Jacqueline K. Bridges. LC 84-91345. 99p. 1985. 8.95 (ISBN 0-533-06442-2). Vantage.

Sackcloth & Ashes: Liturgical Reflections for Lenten Weekdays. James A. Griffin. LC 74-44463. 1976. pap. 4.00 (ISBN 0-8189-0336-8). Alba.

Sacral Treasure of the Guelphs. Patrick M. De Winter. LC 85-3820. (Illus.). 160p. 1985. pap. 14.95X (ISBN 0-910386-81-1, Pub. by The Cleveland Museum of Art). Ind U Pr.

Sacralization & Secularization. Roger Aubert. LC 76-96949. (Concilium Ser.: Vol. 47). 190p. 7.95 (ISBN 0-8091-0128-9). Paulist Pr.

Sacrament of Confirmation in the Early - Middle Scholastic Period: Texts, Vol. 1. Kilian F. Lynch. (Theology Ser). 1957. 17.00 (ISBN 0-686-11589-9). Franciscan Inst.

Sacrament of Love: The Nuptial Mystery in the Light of the Orthodox Tradition. Paul Evdokimov. Tr. by Anthony P. Gythiel & Victoria Steadman. LC 85-2261. 192p. (Orig.). 1985. pap. 8.95 (ISBN 0-88141-042-X). St Vladimirs.

Sacrament of Matrimony According to the Doctrine & Ritual of the Eastern Orthodox Church. F. Basaroff. Tr. by N. Bjerring from Russian. pap. 1.95 (ISBN 0-686-16370-2). Eastern Orthodox.

Sacrament of Peace. Francoise D. Berube & John-Paul Berube. Ages 7-8. childs bk. 2.95 (ISBN 0-8091-9166-0); Ages 9-12. childs bk. 2.95 (ISBN 0-8091-9167-9); director's guide 4.95 (ISBN 0-8091-9169-5). Paulist Pr.

Sacrament of Penance & Reconciliation. George Kelly. (Synthesis Ser). 96p. 1976. 0.75 (ISBN 0-8199-0701-4). Franciscan Herald.
Sacrament of Penance in Our Time. Ed. by George Kelly. 1976. 4.00 (ISBN 0-8198-0455-X). Dghtrs St Paul.
Sacrament of Penance: Its Past & Its Meaning for Today. Eamon Tobin. 32p. (Orig.). 1984. pap. 1.50 (ISBN 0-89243-199-7). Liguori Pubns.
Sacrament of Salvation. Kevin McNamara. 1981. 9.50 (ISBN 0-8199-0806-1). Franciscan Herald.
Sacrament of the Eucharist in Our Time. George A. Kelly. 1978. 3.75 (ISBN 0-8198-0553-X); pap. 2.25 (ISBN 0-8198-0554-8). Dghtrs St Paul.
Sacramental & Occasional Homilies. David Q. Liptak. LC 80-29287. 96p. (Orig.). 1981. pap. 5.95 (ISBN 0-8189-0408-9). Alba.
Sacramental & Spiritual Communion. Dietrich V. Asten. Ed. by Werner Glas. (Orig.). 1984. pap. 2.50 (ISBN 0-88010-121-0). Anthroposophic.
Sacramental Ethics: Paschal Identity & the Christian Life. Timothy F. Sedgwick. LC 86-45925. 128p. 1987. pap. text ed. 7.95 (ISBN 0-8006-1965-X, 1-1965). Fortress.
Sacramental Mysteries: A Byzantine Approach. Casimir Kucharek. 416p. 1976. 15.75 (ISBN 0-911726-17-9); pap. 12.75 laminated (ISBN 0-911726-25-X). Alleluia Pr.
Sacramental Realism: A General Theory of the Sacraments. Colman O'Neill. (Theology & Life Ser.: Vol. 2). 1983. 9.95 (ISBN 0-89453-297-9). M Glazier.
Sacramentary. rev. ed. red cloth, colored edges 35.00 (ISBN 0-89942-022-2, 22/22). Catholic Bk Pub.
Sacramentary. large size ed. (Large Type). red cloth 59.00 (ISBN 0-89942-044-3, 44-02); lea., gold design, gold edges 85.00 (ISBN 0-89942-045-1, 44/13); protective jacket o.s.i. 1.50 (ISBN 0-686-14323-X, 44-CJ). Catholic Bk Pub.
Sacramentary for Sundays & Feastdays. (Extra Large Type). 25.00 (ISBN 0-89942-054-0, 54/02). Catholic Bk Pub.
Sacraments. Maureen Curley. (Children of the Kingdom Activities Ser.). 1975. 9.95 (ISBN 0-89837-019-1, Pub. by Pflaum Pr). Peter Li.
Sacraments. Peter A. Judd. LC 78-12776. 1978. pap. 7.00 (ISBN 0-8309-0225-2). Herald Hse.
Sacraments & Liturgy. Louis Weil. 116p. 1984. 24.95x (ISBN 0-631-13192-2); pap. 6.95 (ISBN 0-631-13229-5). Basil Blackwell.
Sacraments & Passages: Celebrating the Tensions of Modern Life. Gerard Fourez. LC 83-71164. 168p. (Orig.). 1983. pap. 4.95 (ISBN 0-87793-301-4). Ave Maria.
Sacraments & Their Celebration. Nicholas Halligan. LC 85-23031. 284p. (Orig.). 1986. pap. 14.95 (ISBN 0-8189-0489-5). Alba.
Sacraments & You. Michael Pennock. LC 81-65227. (Illus.). 272p. 1981. pap. 5.50 (ISBN 0-87793-221-2); teachers ed. 2.95 (ISBN 0-87793-222-0). Ave Maria.
Sacraments & You. 2.50 (ISBN 0-8198-6866-3). Dghtrs St Paul.
Sacraments As Encasement: Jesus Is with Us. Michael J. Taylor. 80p. 1986. pap. 4.95 (ISBN 0-8146-1469-8). Liturgical Pr.
Sacraments: Encountering the Risen Lord. Paul A. Feider. LC 85-73569. 128p. (Orig.). 1986. pap. 4.95 (ISBN 0-87793-327-8). Ave Maria.
Sacraments in Religious Education & Liturgy: An Ecumenical Model. Robert L. Browning & Roy A. Reed. LC 84-27536. 313p. (Orig.). 1985. pap. 14.95 (ISBN 0-89135-044-6). Religious Educ.
Sacraments in Theology & Canon Law. Ed. by Neophytos Edelby et al. LC 68-58308. (Concilium Ser.: Vol. 38). 191p. 1968. 7.95 (ISBN 0-8091-0132-7). Paulist Pr.
Sacraments, Liturgy & Prayer. Megan McKenna & Darryl Ducote. LC 78-71531. (Followers of the Way Ser.: Vol. 5). 221p. 1979. 22.50 (ISBN 0-8091-9546-1); cassette 7.50 (ISBN 0-8091-7670-X). Paulist Pr.
Sacraments of Simple Folk. Robert R. Marett. LC 77-27192. (Gifford Lectures: 1932-33). Repr. of 1933 ed. 28.00 (ISBN 0-404-60488-9). AMS Pr.
Sacraments: Readings in Contemporary Theology. Ed. by Michael J. Taylor. LC 80-9534. 274p. (Orig.). 1981. pap. 8.95 (ISBN 0-8189-0406-2). Alba.
Sacraments Today. 1979. leader's guide 2.95 (ISBN 0-89243-116-4); worksheets o.p. 1.50 (ISBN 0-89243-115-6). Liguori Pubns.
Sacraments Today. Juan L. Segundo. Tr. by John Drury from Span. LC 73-77359. (Theology for Artisans of a New Humanity Ser: Vol. 4). Orig. Title: Sacramentos Hay y. 192p. (Orig.). 1974. pap. 4.95x (ISBN 0-88344-490-9). Orbis Bks.
Sacraments Today: Their Meaning & Celebration. Christopher Farrell & Thomas Artz. LC 78-69750. 1978. pap. 3.95 (ISBN 0-89243-087-7). Liguori Pubns.
Sacraments: Twenty-Eight Family Times to Celebrate Life. Kathryn Fitzpatrick. (Family Time - Faith Time: A Home-Based Approach to Religious Education Ser.). (Illus.). 70p. (Orig.). 1982. pap. 3.50 (ISBN 0-86716-010-1). St Anthony Mess Pr.
Sacred Adventure. El Morya. LC 81-85464. 148p. 1981. 7.95 (ISBN 0-916766-53-5). Summit Univ.
Sacred & Legendary Art, 2 Vols. Anna B. Jameson. LC 71-124594. Repr. of 1896 ed. 18.50 (ISBN 0-404-03551-5). AMS Pr.
Sacred & the Feminine: Toward a Theology of Housework. Kathryn A. Rabuzzi. 224p. 1982. 15.95 (ISBN 0-8164-0509-3, HarpR). Har-Row.
Sacred & the Profane: The Nature of Religion. Mircea Eliade. Tr. by Willard Trask. LC 58-10904. 1968. pap. 4.95 (ISBN 0-15-679201-X, Harv). HarBraceJ.
Sacred & the Profane: The Nature of Religion. Mircea Eliade. 1983. 13.75 (ISBN 0-8446-6080-9). Peter Smith.
Sacred & the Subversive: Political Witch-Hunts as National Rituals. Albert Bergessen. LC 84-61370. (Society for Scientific Study of Religion Monograph: No. 4). 1984. pap. 5.50 (ISBN 0-932566-03-0). Soc Sci Stud Rel.
Sacred Book of the East: Vedic Hymns, 2 vols. Ed. by Max Muller. 250.00 (ISBN 0-87968-438-0). Krishna Pr.
Sacred Books of China, 6 vols. James Legge. 600.00. Krishna Pr.
Sacred Books of China. James Legge. (Sacred Bks. of the East: Vols. 3, 16, 27, 28, 39, 40). 6 vols. 90.00 (ISBN 0-686-97476-X); 15.00 ea. Asian Human Pr.
Sacred Books of China: Text of Taoism, 2 vols. Ed. by Max Muller. lib. bdg. 250.00 (ISBN 0-87968-298-1). Krishna Pr.
Sacred Books of the East, 50 vols. Ed. by Max Muller. 1977-1980. Repr. of 1975 ed. Set. 630.00; 16.80 ea. (ISBN 0-89684-310-6). Orient Bk Dist.
Sacred Books of the East. 457p. 1986. Repr. of 1900 ed. lib. bdg. 150.00 (ISBN 0-8495-5928-6). Arden Lib.
Sacred Books of the East. Epiphanius Wilson. 464p. 1986. Repr. 25.00X (ISBN 0-8364-1764-X, Pub. by Usha). South Asia Bks.
Sacred Books of the Hindus, 47 vols. Ed. by Baman Das Basu. Repr. of 1937 ed. 1251.50 (ISBN 0-404-19548-2). AMS Pr.
Sacred Books of the Jainas (Bibliotheca Jainica, 11 vols. Ed. by Sarat C. Ghoshal. Repr. of 1940 ed. 324.00 (ISBN 0-404-19549-0). AMS Pr.
Sacred Books of the Jews. Harry Gersh. LC 68-17320. 1972. pap. 4.95 (ISBN 0-8128-1528-9). Stein & Day.
Sacred Bridge. Eric Werner. (Music Reprint Ser.). 1979. Repr. of 1959 ed. lib. bdg. 65.00 (ISBN 0-306-79581-7). Da Capo.
Sacred Bridge. Eric Werner. 640p. 1981. 60.00x (ISBN 0-234-77352-9, Pub. by Dobson Bks England). State Mutual Bk.
Sacred Bridge: Supplementary Volume. Ed. by Dobson Books Ltd. 256p. 1981. 75.00x (ISBN 0-234-77038-4, Pub. by Dobson Bks England). State Mutual Bk.
Sacred Bundles of the Sac & Fox Indians. M. R. Harrington. (Anthropological Publications Ser.: Vol. 4-2). (Illus.). 142p. 1914. 10.50x (ISBN 0-686-24093-6). Univ Mus of U.
Sacred Bundles of the Sac & Fox Indians. Mark R. Harrington. LC 76-43732. (Univivesity of Pennsylvania Museum Anthropological Publications: Vol. 4, No. 1). (Illus.). 192p. Repr. of 1914 ed. 30.00 (ISBN 0-404-15573-1). AMS Pr.
Sacred Canopy: Elements of a Sociological Theory of Religion. Peter L. Berger. LC 67-19805. 1969. pap. 4.50 (ISBN 0-385-07305-4, Anch). Doubleday.
Sacred Choral Music in Print, 2 vols. 2nd ed. Ed. by Gary S. Eslinger & F. Mark Daugherty. LC 85-15368. (Music in Print Ser.: Vol. 1). 1312p. 1985. lib. bdg. 180.00 (ISBN 0-88478-017-1). Musicdata.
Sacred Chow. Adell Harvey & Mari Gonzalez. 176p. 1987. pap. 9.95 (ISBN 0-687-36713-1). Abingdon.
Sacred City of Anuradhapura. Chandra B. Charish. (Illus.). 132p. 1986. Repr. 26.00X (ISBN 0-8364-1746-1, Pub. by Abhinav India). South Asia Bks.
Sacred Dance with Physically & Mentally Handicapped. Ann M. Blessin. Ed. by Doug Adams. 1982. pap. 3.00 (ISBN 0-941500-28-4). Sharing Co.
Sacred Dance with Senior Citizens in Churches, Convalescent Homes, & Retirement Homes. Doug Adams. 1982. pap. 3.00 (ISBN 0-941500-27-6). Sharing Co.
Sacred Executioner: Human Sacrifice & the Legacy of Guilt. Hyam Maccoby. LC 82-80492. (Illus.). 208p. 1983. 19.95 (ISBN 0-500-01281-4). Thames Hudson.
Sacred Fire. B. Z. Goldberg. 285p. 1974. pap. 3.95 (ISBN 0-8065-0456-0). Citadel Pr.
Sacred Fire. B. Z. Goldberg. (Illus.). 1958. 7.50 (ISBN 0-8216-0146-6). Univ Bks.
Sacred Fire Christian Marriage Through the Ages. David Mace & Vera Mace. 1986. 16.95 (ISBN 0-687-36712-3). Abingdon.
Sacred Geometry: Philosophy & Practice. Robert Lawlor. Ed. by Jill Purce. LC 81-67703. (Illustrated Library of Sacred Imagination Ser.). (Illus.). 96p. 1982. pap. 9.95 (ISBN 0-8245-0067-9). Crossroad NY.
Sacred Harp: A Tradition & Its Music. Buell E. Cobb, Jr. LC 76-12680. 256p. 1978. 15.00x (ISBN 0-8203-0426-3). U of Ga Pr.
Sacred Heart & the Priesthood. Louise M. De La Touche. LC 79-90487. 1979. pap. 5.00 (ISBN 0-89555-128-4). TAN Bks Pubs.
Sacred Heart of Christmas. 2nd ed. Flower A. Newhouse. Ed. by Athene Bengtson. LC 78-74956. (Illus.). 1978. pap. 7.00 (ISBN 0-910378-14-2). Christward.
Sacred in a Secular Age: Toward Revision in the Scientific Study of Religion. Philip E. Hammond. LC 84-16470. 380p. 1985. 37.50x (ISBN 0-520-05342-7); pap. 8.95 (ISBN 0-520-05343-5, CAL 726). U of Cal Pr.
Sacred in All Its Forms. Pope John Paul II. 482p. 1984. 7.50 (ISBN 0-8198-6845-0); pap. 6.50 (ISBN 0-8198-6846-9). Dghtrs St Paul.
Sacred India: Hinduism, Buddhism, Jainism. Ann C. Boger & Joellen K. DeOreo. LC 85-19559. (Illus.). 60p. 1986. pap. 7.95 (ISBN 0-910386-84-6, Pub. by Cleveland Mus Art). Ind U Pr.
Sacred Journey. Frederick Buechner. LC 81-47843. 128p. 1982. 12.45 (ISBN 0-06-061158-8, HarpR). Har-Row.
Sacred Journey. Frederick Buechner. 224p. 1984. pap. 8.95 large print ed. (ISBN 0-8027-2479-5). Walker & Co.
Sacred Knowledge: The Altaf Al-Quds of Shah Waliullah. Shah Waliullah. Tr. by G. N. Jalbani & D. L. Pendlebury. 1982. 13.95 (ISBN 0-900860-93-6, Pub. by Octagon Pr England). Ins Study Human.
Sacred Kural. 2nd. ed. Ed. & tr. by H. A. Popley. Orig. Title: Tamil Veda of Tiruvalluvar. 159p. pap. 2.80 (ISBN 0-88253-386-X). Ind-US Inc.
Sacred Language: The Nature of Supernatural Discourse in Lakota. William Powers. LC 86-40079. (Civilization of the American Indians Ser.: Vol. 179). (Illus.). 320p. 1986. 24.95x (ISBN 0-8061-2009-6). U of Okla Pr.
Sacred Laws of the Aryas. Ed. by Georg Buhler. (Sacred Bks. of the East: Vols. 2 & 14). both vols. 30.00 (ISBN 0-686-97474-3); 15.00 ea. Asian Human Pr.
Sacred Meadows: A Structural Analysis of Religious Symbolism in an East African Town. Abdul H. El-Zein. LC 73-91310. (Studies in African Religion). 1974. text ed. 19.95x (ISBN 0-8101-0443-1). Northwestern U Pr.
Sacred Mirror: A Spiritual Diary. Margery Eyre. 94p. 9.95 (ISBN 0-86140-068-2). Dufour.
Sacred Mysteries among the Mayas & the Quiches. Augustus Le Plongeon. LC 73-76094. (Secret Doctrine Reference Ser). (Illus.). 200p. 1985. Repr. of 1886 ed. 12.00 (ISBN 0-913510-02-5). Wizards.
Sacred Narrative: Reading in the Theory of Myth. Ed. by Alan Dundes. LC 83-17921. (Illus.). ix, 352p. 1984. 42.00x (ISBN 0-520-05156-4); pap. 11.95x (ISBN 0-520-05192-0, CAL 362). U of Cal Pr.
Sacred Officials of the Eleusinian Mysteries. Kevin Clinton. LC 73-79573. (Transaction Ser.: Vol. 64, Pt. 3). (Illus.). 1974. pap. 16.00 (ISBN 0-87169-643-6). Am Philos.
Sacred Path: Spells, Prayers & Power Songs of the American Indians. Ed. by John Bierhorst. LC 82-14118. (Illus.). 191p. 1983. PLB 10.25 (ISBN 0-688-01699-5). Morrow.
Sacred Path: Spells, Prayers, & Power Songs of the American Indians. Ed. by John Bierhorst. LC 83-19460. (Illus.). 192p. 1984. pap. 8.20 (ISBN 0-688-02647-8, Quill). Morrow.
Sacred Pipe: Black Elk's Account of the Seven Rites of Oglala Sioux. Ed. by Joseph E. Brown. LC 53-8810. (Civilization of the American Indian Ser.: No. 36). (Illus.). 1981. 17.95 (ISBN 0-8061-0272-1). U of Okla Pr.
Sacred Places: Religious Architecture of the 18th & 19th Centuries in British Columbia. Barry Downs. LC 81-670050. (Illus.). 160p. 1980. 29.95 (ISBN 0-295-95774-3, Pub. by Douglas & McIntyre Canada). U of Wash Pr.
Sacred Play of Children. Ed. by Diane Apostolos-Cappadona. 160p. 1983. pap. 9.95 (ISBN 0-8164-2427-6, HarpR). Har-Row.
Sacred Poetry of the Seventeenth Century: Including the Whole of Giles Fletcher's Christ's Victory & Triumph, 2 vols. Ed. by Richard Cattermole. (Research & Source Works Ser.: No. 346). 1969. Repr. of 1835 ed. Set. 44.50 (ISBN 0-8337-0499-0). B Franklin.
Sacred Portal: A Primary Symbol in Ancient Judaic Art. Bernard Goldman. LC 86-10983. (Brown Classics in Judaica Ser.). (Illus.). 260p. 1986. pap. text ed. 15.75 (ISBN 0-8191-5269-2). U Pr of Amer.
Sacred Rage: The Wrath of Militant Islam. Robin Wright. 336p. 1986. pap. 7.95 (ISBN 0-671-62811-9, Touchstone Bks). S&S.
Sacred Readings: The Gathas. Inayat Khan. (Sufi Message of Hazrat Inayat Khan Ser.: Vol. 13). 304p. 1982. 14.95 (ISBN 90-6325-021-5, Pub. by Servire BV Netherlands). Hunter Hse.
Sacred Rose Tarot. Johanna Sherman. 56p. 1982. pap. 12.00 incl. card deck (ISBN 0-88079-012-1). US Games Syst.
Sacred Science of Numbers. Corinne Heline. 140p. 1981. pap. 4.00 (ISBN 0-87516-442-0). De Vorss.
Sacred Science of Numbers. Corinne Heline. 33p. pap. 4.00 (ISBN 0-87613-027-9). New Age.
Sacred Scrolls of the Southern Ojibway. Selwyn Dewdney. LC 73-90150. 1974. 27.50x (ISBN 0-8020-3321-0). U of Toronto Pr.
Sacred Sex. Twenty-Four Magazine Editors & John Burns. Ed. by Thomas R. White. LC 74-84538. (Illus.). 150p. (Orig.). 1975. pap. 1.95 (ISBN 0-914896-01-6, Strength). East Ridge Pr.
Sacred Sound: Music in Religious Thought & Practice. Ed. by Joyce Irwin. LC 83-15390. (AAR Thematic Studies). 180p. 1984. 22.50 (ISBN 0-89130-655-2, 01 25 01). Scholars Pr GA.
Sacred Space: An Aesthetic for the Liturgical Environment. Dennis McNally. 215p. (Orig.). 1985. pap. 8.95x (ISBN 0-932269-45-1). Wyndham Hall.
Sacred Stories of the Sweet Grass Cree. Leonard Bloomfield. LC 74-7933. Repr. of 1930 ed. 34.50 (ISBN 0-404-11821-6). AMS Pr.
Sacred Survival: The Civil Religion of American Jews. Jonathan S. Woocher. LC 85-45790. (Jewish Political & Social Studies). (Illus.). 224p. 1986. 25.00x (ISBN 0-253-35041-7). Ind U Pr.
Sacred Symbols That Speak, Vol. I. A. Coniaris. 1986. pap. 7.95 (ISBN 0-937032-39-5). Light&Life Pub Co MN.
Sacred Texts of the World. Ninian Smart & Richard Hecht. 496p. 1984. pap. 16.95 (ISBN 0-8245-0639-1). Crossroad NY.
Sacred Texts of the World: A Universal Anthology. Ed. by Ninian Smart & Richard Hecht. LC 82-7375. 1982. 27.50x (ISBN 0-8245-0483-6). Crossroad NY.
Sacred Texts of the World: A Universal Anthology. Ed. by Ninian Smart & Richard B. Hecht. (Illus.). 496p. 1987. pap. 17.00 (ISBN 0-8334-1001-6, Freedeeds Bks). Garber Comm.
Sacred Theory of the Earth. Thomas Burnet. LC 65-10027. (Centaur Classics Ser.). (Illus.). 414p. 1965. 22.50x (ISBN 0-8093-0186-5). S Ill U Pr.
Sacred Thread: Hinduism in Continuity & Diversity. J. L. Brockington. 222p. 1981. pap. 10.50x (ISBN 0-85224-393-6, Pub. by Edinburgh U Pr Scotland). Columbia U Pr.
Sacred Times, Timeless Seasons. Gary J. Boelhower. (Illus.). 76p. 1986. pap. 6.95 (ISBN 0-937997-05-6). Hi-Time Pub.
Sacred Tradition in the Orthodox Church. Lazarus Moore. 1984. pap. 2.95 (ISBN 0-937032-34-4). Light&Life Pub Co MN.
Sacred Tree: The Tree in Religion & Myth. J. H. Philpot. 1977. lib. bdg. 69.95 (ISBN 0-8490-2553-2). Gordon Pr.
Sacred Tunes for the Consecration of Life. Paul Carus. 48p. 1899. 0.95 (ISBN 0-317-40427-X). Open Court.
Sacred Vision: Native American Religion & Its Practice Today. Michael Steltenkamp. LC 82-60594. 1983. pap. 5.95 (ISBN 0-8091-2481-5). Paulist Pr.
Sacred: Ways of Knowledge, Sources of Life. Peggy V. Beck & Anna L. Walters. (Illus.). 384p. 1977. 16.00x (ISBN 0-912586-24-9). Navajo Coll Pr.
Sacred Words: A Study of Navajo Religion & Prayer. Sam D. Gill. LC 80-659. (Contributions in Intercultural & Comparative Studies: No. 4). (Illus.). xxvi, 257p. 1981. lib. bdg. 29.95 (ISBN 0-313-22165-0, GSW/). Greenwood.
Sacred Writings of the Worlds Great Religions. Ed. by S. E. Frost, Jr. 416p. 1972. pap. 6.95 (ISBN 0-07-022520-6). McGraw.
Sacred Writings of the World's Great Religions. Ed. by S. E. Frost, Jr. 410p. 1983. Repr. of 1951 ed. lib. bdg. 40.00 (ISBN 0-89760-241-2). Telegraph Bks.
Sacred Yes. Bhagwan Shree Rajneesh. Ed. by Ma Prem Maneesha. LC 83-17665. (Initiation Talks Ser.). 448p. (Orig.). 1983. pap. 4.95 (ISBN 0-88050-624-5). Chidvilas Found.
Sacrifice. Marvin Moore. LC 78-21712. (Flame Ser.). 1979. pap. 0.99 (ISBN 0-8127-0214-X). Review & Herald.
Sacrifice: Its Nature & Function. Henri Hubert & Marcel Mauss. Tr. by W. D. Halls. LC 64-12260. 1964. pap. 11.00x (ISBN 0-226-35679-5). U of Chicago Pr.

Sacrifice We Offer: Tridentine Dogma & Its Reinterpretation. David N. Power. 240p. 1987. 16.95 (ISBN 0-8245-0743-6). Crossroad NY.

Sacrifices. M. F. C. Bourdillon & M. Fortes. 1980. 54.50 (ISBN 0-12-119040-4). Acad Pr.

Sacrificial Ideas in Greek Christian Writers. Frances M. Young. LC 78-61400. (Patristic Monograph: No. 5). 1979. pap. 10.00 (ISBN 0-915646-04-8). Phila Patristic.

Sacrificial Interpretation of Jesus' Achievement in the New Testament. Tibor Horvath. 1980. 9.95 (ISBN 0-8022-2240-4). Philos Lib.

Sacrificial Ritual in the Satapatha Brahmana. Naama Drury. 137p. 1981. text ed. 8.25 (ISBN 0-8426-1759-0). Verry.

Sacrificial Worship of the Old Testament. J. H. Kurtz. Tr. by James Martin. (Twin Brooks Ser.). 454p. 1980. pap. 8.95 (ISBN 0-8010-5419-2). Baker Bk.

Sacrificial Worship of the Old Testament. John H. Kurtz. 1979. 16.50 (ISBN 0-86524-012-4, 8703). Klock & Klock.

Sacrorum Emblematum Centuria Una. Andrew Willet. LC 84-5360. 1984. Repr. of 1592 ed. 35.00x (ISBN 0-8201-1395-6). Schol Facsimiles.

Saddharma-Pundarika: Lotus of True Law. Tr. by H. Kern. lib. bdg. 79.95 (ISBN 0-87968-530-1). Krishna Pr.

Saddharma-Pundarika or the Lotus of the Good Law. H. Kern. (Sacred Bks. of the East: Vol. 21). 15.00 (ISBN 0-89581-524-9). Asian Human Pr.

Sadguru Speaks. Satguru S. Keshavadas. (Illus.). 96p. (Orig.). 1975. pap. 3.50 (ISBN 0-942508-06-8). Vishwa.

Sadhak's Companion. Svami Kripalvananda. Ed. by Darshana Shakti Ma. Tr. by Gauri Modi from Gujarati. Orig. Title: Guru Vachanamrit. (Illus., Orig.). 1977. pap. text ed. 2.95 (ISBN 0-933116-04-7). Sanatana.

Sadhana: A Way to God. Anthony DeMello. LC 84-6735. 144p. 1984. pap. 5.50 (ISBN 0-385-19614-8, Im). Doubleday.

Sadhana: A Way to God, Christian Exercises in Eastern Form. Anthony De Mello. LC 78-70521. (Study Aids on Jesuit Topics: No. 9). 146p. 1978. pap. 4.95 (ISBN 0-912422-46-7). Inst Jesuit.

Sadhana Guidelines. (Illus.). 122p. 9.95 (ISBN 0-89509-004-X). Arcline Pubns.

Sadhana in Our Daily Lives: A Handbook for the Awakening of the Spiritual Self. John Ernst. LC 81-51360. 320p. (Orig.). 1981. pap. 9.95 (ISBN 0-9606482-0-8). Valley Lights.

Sadhana in Sri Aurobindo's Yoga. M. P. Pandit. LC 78-59851. 1978. pap. 3.95 (ISBN 0-89744-000-5, Pub. by Atmaniketan Ashram). Auromere.

Sadhanas for Spiritual Life. Ed. by Ramakrishna Math Staff. 166p. pap. 2.75 (ISBN 0-87481-507-X). Vedanta Pr.

Sadi: The Rose Garden. Edward Eastwick. 1979. 16.95 (ISBN 0-900860-65-0). Ins Study Human.

Saducismus Triumphatus: Or, Full & Plain Evidence Concerning Witches & Apparitions. Joseph Glanvill. LC 66-60009. 1966. Repr. of 1689 ed. 75.00x (ISBN 0-8201-1021-3). Schol Facsimiles.

Saeculum: History & Society in the Theology of St Augustine. R. A. Markus. LC 71-87136. 1970. 54.50 (ISBN 0-521-07621-8). Cambridge U Pr.

Safarnama & Zafarnama. I. S. Nara. 327p. 1986. 25.00x (ISBN 0-8364-1793-3, Pub. by Minerva India). South Asia Bks.

Safed Spirituality: Rules of Mystical Piety, the Beginning of Wisdom. Safed. Tr. by Lawrence Fine. (Classics of Western Spirituality Ser.). 1984. 12.95 (ISBN 0-8091-0349-4); pap. 9.95 (ISBN 0-8091-2612-5). Paulist Pr.

Safety Zones: Finding Refuge in Times of Turmoil. Elizabeth Skoglund. 220p. 1987. 12.95 (ISBN 0-8499-0555-9). Word Bks.

Saga & Myth of Sir Thomas More. Raymond W. Chambers. 1926. lib. bdg. 10.00 (ISBN 0-8414-3642-8). Folcroft.

Saga & the Myth of Sir Thomas More. R. W. Chambers. 1978. Repr. of 1927 ed. lib. bdg. 15.00 (ISBN 0-8495-0744-8). Arden Lib.

Saga, Legend, Tale, Novella, Fable. George W. Coats. (JSOT Supplement Ser.). 159p. 1985. text ed. 18.50x (ISBN 0-905774-84-1, Pub by JSOT Pr England); pap. text ed. 8.95x (ISBN 0-905774-85-X). Eisenbrauns.

Saga of an Ordinary Man. Goldie Down. (Dest Two Ser.). 1984. pap. 4.95 (ISBN 0-8163-0554-4). Pacific Pr Pub Assn.

Saga of God Incarnate. Robert G. Crawford. 120p. 1985. 13.95 (ISBN 0-86981-309-9, Pub. by T&T Clark Ltd UK). Fortress.

Saga of Saints. facs. ed. Sigrid Undset. Tr. by E. C. Ramsden. LC 68-22952. (Essay Index Reprint Ser). 1968. Repr. of 1934 ed. 20.00 (ISBN 0-8369-0959-3). Ayer Co Pubs.

Saga of Seven Sisters. Hazel S. McCartney. 1985. 12.00 (ISBN 0-533-06270-5). Vantage.

Saga of the American Soul. Richard E. Wentz. LC 80-5598. 163p. 1980. pap. text ed. 9.50 (ISBN 0-8191-1150-3). U Pr of Amer.

Saga of the Spirit. Morris A. Inch. 12.95 (ISBN 0-8010-5037-5). Baker Bk.

Saga of Tristram & Isond. Tr. by Paul Schach from Old Norse. LC 73-76351. (Illus.). xxiv, 148p. 1973. 14.95x (ISBN 0-8032-0832-4); pap. 3.95x (ISBN 0-8032-5847-X, BB 608, Bison). U of Nebr Pr.

Sage & the Way: Spinoza's Ethics of Freedom. Jon Wetlesen. (Philosophia Spinozae Perennis Ser.: No. 4). 474p. 1979. text ed. 50.00 (ISBN 90-232-1596-6, Pub. by Van Gorcum Holland). Longwood Pub Group.

Sage & the Way: Studies in Spinoza's Ethics of Freedom. Jon Wetlesen. (Philosophia Spinozae Perennis Ser.: No. 4). 1979. text ed. 55.00x (ISBN 90-232-1596-6). Humanities.

Sage Ninomiya's Evening Talks. Sontoku Ninomiya. Tr. by Isoh Yamagata. Repr. of 1953 ed. lib. bdg. 22.50x (ISBN 0-8371-3134-0, NIEV). Greenwood.

Sages & Saints. Leo Jung. (Jewish Library: Vol. X). 1987. pap. 20.00. Ktav.

Saguaro Forest. Peter Wild & Hal Coss. LC 86-60514. (Western Horizons Ser.). (Illus.). 96p. (Orig.). 1986. pap. 11.95 (ISBN 0-87358-405-8). Northland.

Sahih Al-Bukhari: The Early Years. Muhammad Asad. 306p. (Orig.). 1981. 24.95 (ISBN 0-317-52458-5, Pub. by Dar Al Andalus). New Era Pubns MI.

Sai Baba Avatar: A New Journey into Power & Glory. Howard Murphet. LC 77-83643. 1977. 10.25 (ISBN 0-9600958-2-9); pap. 5.40 (ISBN 0-9600958-3-7). Birth Day.

Sai Baba: The Holy Man & the Psychiatrist. Samuel H. Sandweiss. LC 75-28784. 1975. 10.25 (ISBN 0-9600958-0-2); pap. 6.30 (ISBN 0-9600958-1-0). Birth Day.

Sai Baba, the Saint of Shirdi. Mani Sahukar. LC 75-29273. 1977. 3.95 (ISBN 0-913922-11-0). Dawn Horse Pr.

Sai Baba the Ultimate Experience. Phyllis Kaystal. (Illus.). 277p. (Orig.). 1985. pap. 7.95. Aura Bks.

Sai Krishna Lila. William J. Jackson. LC 80-67137. 1980. pap. 4.50 (ISBN 0-9600958-7-X). Birth Day.

Sailing with Paul. H. A. Ironside. pap. 1.35 (ISBN 0-87213-387-7). Loizeaux.

Saint-Adventurers of the Virginia Frontier. Klaus Wust. LC 76-48566. (Illus.). 1977. 8.50 (ISBN 0-917968-29-8). Shenandoah Hist.

St. Alban's College, Valladolid: Four Centuries of English Catholic Presence in Spain. Michael C. Williams. LC 86-17787. 278p. 1986. 35.00 (ISBN 0-312-69736-8). St Martin.

St. Alexander Nevsky. pap. 0.50 (ISBN 0-686-05660-4). Eastern Orthodox.

Saint Ambrose: His Life & Times. Angela Paredi. LC 63-19325. pap. 123.80 (ISBN 0-317-26143-6, 2024372). Bks Demand UMI.

Saint & a Half. Denis Meadows. 1963. 5.00 (ISBN 0-8159-6803-5). Devin.

Saint & His Savior. C. H. Spurgeon. Date not set. pap. write for info. Pilgrim Pubns.

Saint & Sufi in Modern Egypt: An Essay in the Sociology of Religion. Michael Gilsenan. (Monographs in Social Anthropology). (Illus.). 1973. 42.00x (ISBN 0-19-823181-4). Oxford U Pr.

Saint & Symbol: Images of Saint Jerome in Early Italian Art. Bernhard Ridderbos. (Illus.). xv, 126p. 1984. pap. 18.00x (ISBN 90-6088-087-0, Pub. by Boumas Boekhuis Netherlands). Benjamins North AM.

Saint & the Skeptics: Joan of Arc in the World of Mark Twain, Anatole France, & Bernard Shaw. William Searle. LC 75-26709. 178p. 1976. text ed. 22.50x (ISBN 0-8143-1541-0). Wayne St U Pr.

Saint & Thought for Every Day. James Alberione. 1976. 4.50 (ISBN 0-8198-0471-1); pap. 3.50 (ISBN 0-8198-6800-0). Dghtrs St Paul.

St. Andrews Seven. Scotish Missions Promotion. (Orig.). 1985. pap. 5.95 (ISBN 0-85151-428-6). Banner of Truth.

Saint Anselm & His Biographer: A Study of Monastic Life & Thought, 1059c-1130. Richard W. Southern. (Birkbeck Lectures: 1959). pap. 101.30 (ISBN 0-317-09510-2, 2022473). Bks Demand UMI.

St. Anselm, Archbishop of Canterbury: A Concordance to the Works of St. Anselm, 4 vols. Ed. by Gillian Evans. LC 82-48973. (Orig.). 1985. Set. lib. bdg. 400.00 (ISBN 0-527-03661-7). Kraus Intl.

Saint Anselm: Basic Writings. 2nd ed. St. Anselm. Tr. by Sidney M. Deane. Incl. Proslogium; Monologium; Gaunilo's "In Behalf of the Fool"; Cur Deus Homo. LC 74-3309. 371p. 1974. 19.95 (ISBN 0-87548-108-6); pap. 8.95 (ISBN 0-87548-109-4). Open Court.

St. Anselm's Proslogion. Tr. by M. J. Charlesworth. LC 78-63300. 1979. text ed. 17.95x (ISBN 0-268-01696-8); pap. text ed. 6.95x (ISBN 0-268-01697-6). U of Notre Dame Pr.

St. Anthony: Doctor of the Gospel. Sophronius Clausen. Tr. by Ignatius Brady from Ger. LC 61-11200. Orig. Title: Antonius. 140p. pap. 2.50 (ISBN 0-8199-0458-9). Franciscan Herald.

St. Anthony of Padua. Isidore O'Brien. 1976. 5.00 (ISBN 0-8198-0472-X). Dghtrs St Paul.

St. Anthony, the Wonder-Worker of Padua. 2nd ed. Charles W. Stoddard. 1971. pap. 2.50 (ISBN 0-89555-039-3). TAN Bks Pubs.

St. Athanasius on the Incarnation. St. Anthanasius. 120p. 1977. pap. 4.95 (ISBN 0-913836-40-0). St Vladimirs.

St. Athanasius: The Life of St. Antony. Ed. by W. J. Burghardt et al. LC 78-62454. (ACW Ser.: No. 10). 155p. 1950. 12.95 (ISBN 0-8091-0250-1). Paulist Pr.

Saint Augustine. Adolphe Hatzfeld. LC 71-168252. 155p. 1975. Repr. of 1903 ed. 16.00 (ISBN 0-404-03155-2). AMS Pr.

St. Augustine. Rebecca West. 174p. 1979. Repr. of 1938 ed. lib. bdg. 22.50 (ISBN 0-89987-853-9). Darby Bks.

St. Augustine, Against the Academics. Ed. by W. J. Burghardt et al. LC 78-62461. (ACW Ser.: No. 12). 220p. 1950. 10.95 (ISBN 0-8091-0252-8). Paulist Pr.

St. Augustine: Aspects of His Life & Thought. W. Montgomery. 1977. lib. bdg. 34.95 (ISBN 0-8490-2556-7). Gordon Pr.

St. Augustine: Being & Nothingness in the Dialogs & Confessions. Emilie Z. Brunn. 210p. 1987. 21.95 (ISBN 0-913729-17-5). Paragon Hse.

St. Augustine, Faith, Hope & Charity. Ed. by J. Kuasten & J. Plumpe. Tr. by Louis A. Arand. LC 78-62450. (Ancient Christian Writers Ser.: No. 3). 165p. 1947. 10.95 (ISBN 0-8091-0045-2). Paulist Pr.

Saint Augustine: Man, Pastor, Mystic. Augustine Trape. (Orig.). 1985. pap. 6.95 (ISBN 0-89942-172-5, 172/02). Catholic BK Pub.

St. Augustine of Hippo: Life & Controversies. Geraldian Bonner. LC 82-45807. 1985. Repr. of 1963 ed. 42.50 (ISBN 0-404-62376-X). AMS Pr.

St. Augustine on Nature, Sex & Marriage. John Hugo. 249p. 1969. pap. 8.95 (ISBN 0-933932-23-5). Scepter Pubs.

Saint Augustine on the End of the World. Ed. by George N. Thompson. 55p. (Orig.). pap. text ed. 5.95 (ISBN 0-940564-15-7). Directions Pr.

St. Augustine on the Psalms, Vol. 1. St. Augustine. Ed. by J. Quasten & W. J. Burghardt. Tr. by Scholastica Hebgin & Felicitas Corrigan. LC 60-10722. (Ancient Christian Writers Ser.: No. 29). 360p. 1960. 12.95 (ISBN 0-8091-0104-1). Paulist Pr.

St. Augustine on the Psalms: Vol. 2. St. Augustine. Ed. by J. Quasten & W. J. Burghardt. Tr. by D. Scholastica Hebgin & D. Felicitas Corrigan. LC 60-10722. (Ancient Christian Writers Ser.: No. 30). 425p. 1961. 14.95 (ISBN 0-8091-0105-X). Paulist Pr.

St. Augustine, Sermons for Christmas & Epiphany. St. Augustine. Ed. by J. Quasten & J. Plumpe. Tr. by Thomas Lawler. LC 78-62464. (Ancient Christian Writers Ser.: No. 15). 250p. 1952. 10.95 (ISBN 0-8091-0137-8). Paulist Pr.

St. Augustine, the First Catechetical Instruction. St. Augustine. Ed. by J. Quasten & J. Plumpe. Tr. by Joseph P. Christopher. LC 78-62449. (Ancient Christian Writers Ser.: No. 2). 170p. 1946. 10.95 (ISBN 0-8091-0047-9). Paulist Pr.

St. Augustine: The Greatness of the Soul, Vol. 9. St. Augustine. Ed. by J. Quasten & J. Plumpe. Tr. by Joseph M. Colleran. LC 78-62455. (Ancient Christian Writers Ser.). 255p. 1950. 14.95 (ISBN 0-8091-0060-6). Paulist Pr.

St. Augustine: The Literal Meaning of Genesis, Vol. 1. Tr. & annotations by John H. Taylor. (Ancient Christian Writers Ser.: Vol. 41). 292p. 1983. 19.95 (ISBN 0-8091-0326-5). Paulist Pr.

St. Augustine: The Literal Meaning of Genesis, Vol. 2. Tr. & annotations by John H. Taylor. (Ancient Christian Writers Ser.: Vol. 42). 358p. 1983. 22.95 (ISBN 0-8091-0327-3). Paulist Pr.

St. Augustine, the Lord's Sermon on the Mount. Ed. by W. J. Burghardt et al. LC 78-62451. (ACW Ser.: No. 5). 227p. 1948. 13.95 (ISBN 0-8091-0246-3). Paulist Pr.

St. Augustine, the Problem of Free Choice. Ed. by W. J. Burghardt et al. LC 78-62469. (ACW Ser.: No. 22). 298p. 1955. 11.95 (ISBN 0-8091-0259-5). Paulist Pr.

St. Augustine's Comments on Imago Dei. Joseph Heijke. 3.00 (ISBN 0-686-23375-1). Classical Folia.

Saint Augustine's Early Theory of Man, A. D. 386-391. Robert J. O'Connell. LC 68-21981. 1968. text ed. 20.00x (ISBN 0-674-78520-7, Belknap Pr). Harvard U Pr.

St. Augustine's Theory of Knowledge: A Contemporary Analysis. Bruce Bubacz. LC 81-18754. (Texts & Studies in Religion: Vol. 11). 248p. 1982. 39.95x (ISBN 0-88946-959-8). E Mellen.

Saint Basil & Monasticism. Sr. M. Gertrude Murphy. LC 70-144661. Repr. of 1930 ed. 14.75 (ISBN 0-404-04543-X). AMS Pr.

St. Basil the Great on The Forty Martyrs of Sebaste, Paradise, & the Catholic Faith. Saint Basil. 1979. pap. 3.95 (ISBN 0-686-25227-6). Eastern Orthodox.

St. Bede: A Tribute. Jean Leclercq et al. LC 85-8214. (Word & Spirit Ser.: Vol. VII). 1985. pap. 7.00. St Bedes Pubns.

Saint Benedict & the Sixth Century. John Chapman. LC 79-109719. 239p. 1972. Repr. of 1929 ed. lib. bdg. 22.50x (ISBN 0-8371-4209-1, CHSB). Greenwood.

St. Benedict: Blessed by God. Guy-Marie Oury. Tr. by John A. Otto from Fr. LC 80-13253. Orig. Title: Ce que croyait Benoit. 92p. (Orig.). 1980. pap. text ed. 4.50 (ISBN 0-8146-1181-8). Liturgical Pr.

Saint Bernadette. Leon Cristiani. LC 65-15727. (Illus.). 181p. 1981. pap. 3.95 (ISBN 0-8189-0421-6). Alba.

Saint Bernadette Soubirous. Francois Trochu. LC 84-51819. 432p. 1985. pap. 12.00 (ISBN 0-89555-253-1). Tan Bks Pubs.

St. Bernard of Clairvaux. Leon Cristiani. 1977. 3.95 (ISBN 0-8198-0463-0); pap. 2.95 (ISBN 0-8198-0464-9). Dghtrs St Paul.

Saint Bernard of Clairvaux: Essays Commemorating the Eighth Centenary of His Canonization. Ed. by M. Basil Pennington. LC 77-4487. (Cistercian Studies: No. 28). 1977. 14.95 (ISBN 0-87907-828-6). Cistercian Pubns.

Saint Bernward of Hildesheim, 3 vols. Francis J. Tschan. Incl. His Life & Times. 242p. 1942; His Works of Art. 503p. 1951. 30.00 (ISBN 0-268-00242-8); Album of All Extant Works. 1952. 30.00 (ISBN 0-268-00240-1). (Mediaeval Studies Ser.: Vols. 6, 12, 13). U of Notre Dame Pr.

Saint Bonaventure. Efrem Bettoni. Tr. by La Scuola, Editrice, Brescia, Italy. LC 81-13371. (Notre Dame Pocket Library). Tr. of Santa Bonaventura. 127p. 1982. Repr. of 1964 ed. lib. bdg. 22.50x (ISBN 0-313-23271-7, BESB). Greenwood.

Saint Bonaventure As a Biblical Commentator: A Translation & Analysis of His "Commentary on Luke," XVIII,34-XIX,42. Thomas Reist. 284p. (Orig.). 1985. lib. bdg. 24.00 (ISBN 0-8191-4578-5); pap. text ed. 12.75 (ISBN 0-8191-4579-3). U Pr of Amer.

Saint Bonaventure's Disputed Questions on the Mystery of the Trinity. Tr. by Zachary Hayes. (Works of Saint Bonaventure Ser.). 1980. 11.00 (ISBN 0-686-28123-3). Franciscan Inst.

St. Boniface & His World. David Keep. (Illus.). 64p. 1979. pap. 4.50 (ISBN 0-85364-276-1). Attic Pr.

Saint Book: For Parents, Teachers, Homilists, Storytellers & Children. Mary R. Newland. (Illus.). 206p. 1979. pap. 8.95 (ISBN 0-8164-0210-8, 7480, HarpR). Har-Row.

Saint Book: For Parents, Teachers, Homilists, Storytellers & Children. Mary R. Newland. 206p. (Orig.). 1985. pap. 8.95 (ISBN 0-86683-979-8, 7480, HarpR). Har-Row.

St. Catherine Laboure of the Miraculous Medal. Joseph I. Dirvin. LC 84-50466. 245p. 1984. pap. 7.50 (ISBN 0-89555-242-6). TAN Bks Pubs.

St. Catherine of Siena. Alice Curtayne. LC 80-53745. 1980. pap. 7.50 (ISBN 0-89555-162-4). Tan Bks Pubs.

Saint Catherine of Siena. Igino Giordani. 1981. 8.00 (ISBN 0-8198-0493-2); pap. 7.00 (ISBN 0-8198-6809-4). Dghtrs St Paul.

Saint Catherine of Siena. Raymond of Cupua. 30.00 (ISBN 0-89453-151-4). M Glazier.

Saint Catherine of Siena: A Study in the Religion, Literature & History of the Fourteenth Century in Italy. E. Gardner. 1976. lib. bdg. 59.95 (ISBN 0-8490-2557-5). Gordon Pr.

St. Clair Papers: The Life & Public Services of Arthur St. Clair, 2 Vols. facs. ed. William H. Smith. LC 77-117894. (Select Bibliographies Reprint Ser). 1881. Set. 62.00 (ISBN 0-8369-5347-9). Ayer Co Pubs.

Saint Clotilda. Godefried J. Kurth. Tr. by M. V. Crawford. LC 72-171634. Repr. of 1906 ed. 7.00 (ISBN 0-404-03788-7). AMS Pr.

St. Columbanus in His Own Words. Tomas O'Fiaich. pap. 4.95 (ISBN 0-686-05661-2). Eastern Orthodox.

St. Cyprian, the Lapsed, the Unity of the Catholic Church. Ed. by W. J. Burghardt et al. LC 57-7364. (Ancient Christian Writers Ser.: No. 25). 132p. 1957. 10.95 (ISBN 0-8091-0260-9). Paulist Pr.

St. Cyril of Jerusalem on the Sacraments. Saint Cyril Of Jerusalem. 83p. 1977. pap. 4.95 (ISBN 0-913836-39-7). St Vladimirs.

Saint David-Patron Saint of Wales. E. G. Dewi Sant Bowen. (St. David's Day Bilingual). 90p. 1983. pap. text ed. 6.95x (ISBN 0-7083-0839-2, Pub. by U of Wales). Humanities.

Saint-Denis, Noyon & the Early Gothic Choir: Methodological Considerations for the History of Early Gothic Architecture, Vol. 4. Thomas E. Polk, II. (Sanctuaries of the Gallic-Frankish Church Ser.). (Illus.). 220p. 1982. pap. 32.10 (ISBN 3-8204-6177-9). P Lang Pubs.

Saint Dominic. Mary J. Dorcy. LC 82-50978. 173p. 1982. pap. 5.00 (ISBN 0-89555-195-0). TAN Bks Pubs.

St. Dominic Savio. rev. ed. St. John Bosco. Tr. by Paul Aronica from Ital. LC 78-67221. (Illus.). 1979. pap. 2.95 (ISBN 0-89944-037-1). Don Bosco Multimedia.

Saint Dominic: The Grace of the Word. Guy Bedouelle. (Illus.). 290p. (Orig.). 1987. pap. 11.95 (ISBN 0-89870-140-6). Ignatius Pr.

St. Dominic's Family. Mary J. Dorcy. LC 83-70219. 631p. 1983. pap. 20.00 (ISBN 0-89555-208-6). TAN Bks Pubs.

Saint Erkenwald. new ed. Ed. by Clifford Peterson. LC 76-53197. (Haney Foundation Ser). 1977. 16.00x (ISBN 0-8122-7723-6). U of Pa Pr.

Saint for Your Name: Saints for Boys. Albert J. Nevins. LC 79-92504. (Illus.). 120p. (YA) 1980. pap. 5.95 (ISBN 0-87973-320-9, 320). Our Sunday Visitor.

Saint for Your Name: Saints for Girls. Albert J. Nevins. LC 79-92502. (Illus.). 104p. (YA) 1980. pap. 5.95 (ISBN 0-87973-321-7, 321). Our Sunday Visitor.

Saint Francis. Nikos Kazantzakis. 1963. Translation 1971. pap. 9.95 (ISBN 0-671-21247-8, Touchstone Bks). S&S.

Saint Francis: A Model for Human Liberation. Leonardo Boff. 192p. 1984. pap. 9.95 (ISBN 0-8245-0671-5). Crossroad NY.

Saint Francis & His Four Ladies. Joan M. Erikson. LC 71-127178. (Illus.). 1970. 6.95 (ISBN 0-393-05427-6). Norton.

Saint Francis & the Song of Brotherhood. Eric Doyle. 1981. pap. 5.95 (ISBN 0-8164-2300-8, HarpR). Har-Row.

St. Francis De Sales. Henry Covannier. 1973. Repr. 5.00 (ISBN 0-8198-0512-2). Dghtrs St Paul.

St. Francis, Nature Mystic: The Derivation & Significance of the Nature Stories in the Franciscan Legend. Edward A. Armstrong. LC 74-149949. (Hermeneutics: Studies in the History of Religions). 1973. pap. 5.95 (ISBN 0-520-03040-0, CAL 314). U of Cal Pr.

St. Francis of Assisi. Nina Bawden. LC 82-13105. (Illus.). 32p. 1983. PLB 10.88 (ISBN 0-688-01653-7). Lothrop.

St. Francis of Assisi. Thomas Celano. 1963. pap. 10.50 (ISBN 0-8199-0098-2). Franciscan Herald.

St. Francis of Assisi. G. K. Chesterton. 1979. Repr. lib. bdg. 25.00 (ISBN 0-8495-0933-5). Arden Lib.

Saint Francis of Assisi. G. K. Chesterton. LC 57-1230. 1957. pap. 3.95 (ISBN 0-385-02900-4, Im). Doubleday.

St. Francis of Assisi. Leon Christiani. LC 74-79802. 1975. 4.95 (ISBN 0-8198-0494-0). Dghtrs St Paul.

Saint Francis of Assisi. Lawrence Cunningham. LC 81-47419. (Illus.). 128p. 1981. 5.00 (ISBN 0-06-061651-2, HarpR). Har-Row.

Saint Francis of Assisi. Johannes Jorgensen. pap. 4.95 (ISBN 0-385-02875-X, D22, Im). Doubleday.

St. Francis of Assisi. John R. H. Moorman. 1986. 4.95 (ISBN 0-8199-0904-1). Franciscan Herald.

Saint Francis of Assisi: A Biography. abr. ed. Omer Englebert. 1979. pap. 3.95 (ISBN 0-89283-071-9). Servant.

St. Francis of Assisi & Nature. cancelled (ISBN 0-8199-0882-7). Franciscan Herald.

St. Francis of Assisi: Essays in Commemoration, 1982. Ed. by Maurice W. Sheehan. 10.00. Franciscan Inst.

St. Francis of Assisi: Omnibus of Sources of the Life of St.Francis. Ed. by Marion A. Habig. Tr. by Raphael Brown & B. Fahy. (Illus.). 1828p. 1975. 35.00 (ISBN 0-8199-0440-6). Franciscan Herald.

St. Francis of Paola: God's Miracle Worker Supreme. Gino J. Simi & Mario M. Segreti. LC 77-78097. 1977. pap. 4.50 (ISBN 0-89555-065-2). TAN Bks Pubs.

St. Francis: Poet of Creation. 1985. 7.50 (ISBN 0-8199-0877-0). Franciscan Herald.

Saint Francis Prayer Book. Auspicius Van Corstanje. 1978. pap. 2.50 (ISBN 0-8199-0693-X). Franciscan Herald.

Saint George: The Saint with Three Faces. David Fox. (Illus.). 188p. 1986. 42.00 (ISBN 0-946041-13-X). Salem Hse Pubs.

St. George's Episcopal Church, Germantown, Tennessee: The First Twenty Years. Leonard V. Hughes, Jr. Ed. by James D. Russell. LC 83-50804. (Illus.). 224p. 1984. 6.00 (ISBN 0-9613533-0-9). St Georges Episcopal.

St. Germaine. rev. ed. Louise Cantoni. 1973. 1.75 (ISBN 0-8198-0262-X). Dghtrs St Paul.

St. Gertrude the Great: Herald of Divine Love. Benedictine Sisters of Clyde, Missouri Staff. 1977. pap. 0.75 (ISBN 0-89555-026-1). TAN Bks Pubs.

St. Gregory of Nyssa on the Origin & Destiny of the Soul. John P. Cavarnos. 12p. 1982. pap. 0.90 (ISBN 0-914744-60-7). Inst Byzantine.

St. Gregory of Nyssa, the Lord's Prayer, the Beatitudes. Ed. by W. J. Burghardt & T. C. Lawler. LC 78-62466. (ACW Ser.: No. 18). 216p. 1954. 14.95 (ISBN 0-8091-0255-2). Paulist Pr.

St. Gregory Palamas & Orthodox Spirituality. John Meyendorff. (Illus.). 184p. pap. 7.95 (ISBN 0-913836-11-7). St Vladimirs.

St. Gregory the Great: Pastoral Care. Ed. by W. J. Burghardt et al. (ACW Ser.: No. 11). 282p. 1950. 13.95 (ISBN 0-8091-0251-X). Paulist Pr.

St. Herman Calendar of Orthodox Saints. Brotherhood of St. Herman of Alaska Staff. pap. 5.00 (ISBN 0-686-05410-5). Eastern Orthodox.

Saint Hugh of Lincoln. David H. Farmer. (Cistercian Studies: No. 87). xi, 114p. 1987. pap. 7.95 (ISBN 0-87907-887-1). Cistercian Pubns.

Saint Ignatius' Idea of a Jesuit University. 2nd ed. George E. Ganss. (Illus.). 1956. pap. 16.95 (ISBN 0-87462-437-1). Marquette.

St. Ignatius of Loyola. Paul Dudon. Tr. by William J. Young. LC 83-45591. Date not set. Repr. of 1949 ed. 49.50 (ISBN 0-404-19884-8). AMS Pr.

Saint Ignatius of Loyola. Henri Joly. LC 70-170821. Repr. of 1899 ed. 21.00 (ISBN 0-404-03597-3). AMS Pr.

St. Ignatius's Own Story. Tr. by William Young. 1980. Repr. 3.95 (ISBN 0-8294-0359-0). Loyola.

Saint in the Slums (Kagawa of Japan) Cyril Davey. 1968. pap. 2.95 (ISBN 0-87508-620-9). Chr Lit.

St. Innocent: Apostle to America. Paul D. Garrett. LC 79-19634. 345p. 1979. pap. 8.95 (ISBN 0-913836-60-5). St Vladimirs.

St. Irenaeus: Proof of the Apostolic Preaching. Ed. by W. J. Burghardt & T. C. Lawler. LC 78-62503. (ACW Ser.: No. 16). 242p. 1952. 12.95 (ISBN 0-8091-0254-4). Paulist Pr.

Saint Jean De Crevecoeur. Julia P. Mitchell. LC 71-181959. Repr. of 1916 ed. 20.00 (ISBN 0-404-04347-X). AMS Pr.

Saint Jerome in the Renaissance. Eugene F. Rice, Jr. LC 84-21321. (Symposia in Comparative History Ser.: No. 13). (Illus.). 272p. 1985. text ed. 24.00x (ISBN 0-8018-2381-1). Johns Hopkins.

St. Joan. George B. Shaw. (Modern Critical Interpretations--Modern British Literature Ser.). 1987. 19.95 (ISBN 1-55546-030-5). Chelsea Hse.

Saint Joan. George Bernard Shaw. (Penguin Plays Ser.). (YA) 1950. pap. 2.95 (ISBN 0-14-048005-6). Penguin.

Saint Joan, a Screenplay. Bernard Shaw. Ed. by Bernard F. Dukore. LC 68-11039. (Illus.). 224p. 1968. 15.00x (ISBN 0-295-97885-6); pap. 5.95x (ISBN 0-295-95072-2, WP56). U of Wash Pr.

Saint Joan, Major Barbara, Androcles. Bernard Shaw. Bd. with Major Barbara; Androcles & the Lion. LC 56-5413. 6.95 (ISBN 0-394-60480-6). Modern Lib.

St. Joan of Arc. John Beevers. 1974. pap. 5.00 (ISBN 0-89555-043-1). TAN Bks Pubs.

Saint Joan of Arc. V. Sackville-West. LC 84-9125. 416p. 1984. pap. 7.95 (ISBN 0-8398-2856-X, Gregg). G K Hall.

St. Joan of Arc, Virgin-Soldier. Leon Cristiani. 1977. 3.95 (ISBN 0-8198-0465-7); pap. 2.95 (ISBN 0-8198-0466-5). Dghtrs St Paul.

St. John, 2 vols, Vol. I & 2. George Reith. Ed. by A. Whyte & J. Moffatt. (Handbooks for Bible Classes & Private Students Ser.). 1889. 8.95 ea. (Pub. by T & T Clark Ltd UK). Vol. 1, 200 pgs (ISBN 0-567-08114-1). Vol. 2, 180 pgs (ISBN 0-567-08115-X). Fortress.

Saint John Bosco. A. Auffray. 393p. (Orig.). 1983. pap. 12.95 (ISBN 0-89944-060-6). Don Bosco Multimedia.

Saint John Chrysostom: A Scripture Index. R. A. Krupp. LC 84-21028. 270p. 1985. lib. bdg. 27.50 (ISBN 0-8191-4380-4). U Pr of Amer.

St. John Chrysostom, Baptismal Instructions. Ed. by W. J. Burghardt et al. LC 62-21489. (Ancient Christian Writers Ser.: No. 31). 381p. 1963. 14.95 (ISBN 0-8091-0262-5). Paulist Pr.

St. John Chrysostom on the Priesthood. John Chrysostom. 160p. 1977. pap. 4.95 (ISBN 0-913836-38-9). St Vladimirs.

Saint John Damascene: De Fide Orthodoxa, Versions of Burgundio & Cerbanus. Ed. by Eligius M. Buytaert. (Text Ser). 1955. 23.00 (ISBN 0-686-11554-6). Franciscan Inst.

Saint John Damascene: Dialectica, Version of Robert Grosseteste. Ed. by Owen A. Colligan. (Text Ser.). 1953. 3.50 (ISBN 0-686-11552-X). Franciscan Inst.

St. John of Patmos & the Seven Churches of the Apocalypse. Otto F. Meinardus. LC 78-51245. (In the Footsteps of the Saints Ser.). (Illus.). 160p. 1979. 17.50 (ISBN 0-89241-070-1); pap. 6.95 (ISBN 0-89241-043-4). Caratzas.

St. John of the Cross & Dr. C. G. Jung: Christian Mysticism in the Light of Jungian Psychology. James Arraj. LC 86-11315. 200p. (Orig.). 1986. pap. 11.95 (ISBN 0-914073-02-8). Tools for Inner.

St. John of the Cross & Other Lectures & Addresses. E. Allison Peers. 1977. lib. bdg. 59.95 (ISBN 0-8490-2558-3). Gordon Pr.

St. John of the Cross, & Other Lectures & Addresses, 1920-1945. facs. ed. Edgar A. Peers. LC 70-136650. (Biography Index Reprint Ser.). 1946. 16.00 (ISBN 0-8369-8045-X). Ayer Co Pubs.

Saint John of the Cross: Doctor of Divine Love, an Introduction to His Philosophy, Theology & Spirituality. Bede Frost. 1977. lib. bdg. 59.95 (ISBN 0-8490-2559-1). Gordon Pr.

St. John of the Cross: His Life & Poetry. Gerald Brenan. LC 72-83577. pap. 61.30 (ISBN 0-317-26068-5, 2024428). Bks Demand UMI.

St. John Ogilvie S.J., 1579-1615. 68p. 1979. 30.00x (Pub. by Third Eye Centre). State Mutual Bk.

Saint John the Evangelist Church, Indianapolis, Indiana: A Photographic Essay of the Oldest Catholic Church in Indianapolis & Marion County. William F. Stineman & Jack W. Porter. LC 85-63564. (Illus.). 80p. 1986. 39.95 (ISBN 0-9616134-0-8). ST John Evang.

St. Joseph Cafasso: Priest of the Gallows. Saint John Bosco. LC 82-50979. Orig. Title: Saint Speaks for Another Saint. 80p. 1983. pap. 2.00 (ISBN 0-89555-194-2). TAN Bks Pubs.

Saint Joseph Commentary on the Sunday Readings, 3 vols. Achille Degeest. 3.95 ea. Year A (ISBN 0-89942-341-8, 341/04). Year B (ISBN 0-89942-342-6, 342/04). Year C (ISBN 0-89942-343-4, 343/04). Catholic Bk Pub.

Saint Joseph Concise Bible History. (Capsule Comments, Catechetical Aids). flexible bdg. 2.25 (ISBN 0-89942-770-7, 770). Catholic Bk Pub.

St. Joseph: His Life As He Might Tell It. Robert J. Fox. 1983. pap. 1.00 (ISBN 0-911988-55-6). AMI Pr.

Saint Joseph New American Catechism. Lawrence Lovasik. (Illus.). flexible bdg. 3.00 (ISBN 0-89942-253-5, 253/05). Catholic Bk Pub.

St. Joseph of Arimathea at Glastonbury. Lionel S. Lewis. (Illus.). 212p. 1983. pap. 8.95 (ISBN 0-227-67868-0). Attic Pr.

Saint Joseph of Copertino. Angelo Pastrovicchi. LC 79-91298. 135p. 1980. pap. 3.00 (ISBN 0-89555-135-7). TAN Bks Pubs.

St. Jude & "His People". Antoinette Ancona. LC 85-90095. 124p. 1985. 10.95 (ISBN 0-533-06604-2). Vantage.

St. Leon: A Tale of the Sixteenth Century. William Godwin. LC 74-162884. (Illus.). Repr. of 1835 ed. 32.50 (ISBN 0-404-54405-3). AMS Pr.

Saint Louis: Louis IX of France, the Most Christian King. Frederick Perry. LC 73-14462. Repr. of 1901 ed. 30.00 (ISBN 0-404-58280-X). AMS Pr.

St. Louis Marie Grignon de Montfort: His Life As He Might Tell It. Robert J. Fox. 20p. 1983. 1.00 (ISBN 0-911988-62-9). Ami Pr.

St. Louise de Marillac: Servant of the Poor. Sr. Vincent Regnault. LC 83-50058. 136p. 1984. pap. 3.50 (ISBN 0-89555-215-9). TAN Bks Pubs.

Saint Luke. G. B. Caird. LC 77-81622. (Westminster Pelican Commentaries Ser.). 272p. 1978. 10.95 (ISBN 0-664-21345-6). Westminster.

Saint Luke's Life of Christ. W. M. Wightman. pap. 1.00x (ISBN 0-685-02586-1). Outlook.

St. Margaret Mary Alacoque. Leon Cristiani. 1976. 5.00 (ISBN 0-8198-0456-8). Dghtrs St Paul.

St. Martin & His Hagiographer: History & Miracle in Sulpicius Severus. Clare Stancliffe. (Oxford Historical Monographs). (Illus.). 1983. 45.00x (ISBN 0-19-821895-8). Oxford U Pr.

St. Martin de Porres. Richard C. Cushing. LC 62-20203. (Illus.). 75p. 1981. 4.00 (ISBN 0-8198-6818-3, STO280); pap. 2.00 (ISBN 0-8198-6819-1). Dghtrs St Paul.

St. Martin de Porres-Apostle of Charity. Giuliana Cavallini. Tr. by Caroline Holland from It. LC 79-65530. (Cross & Crown Series of Spirituality). 1979. pap. 7.00 (ISBN 0-89555-092-X). TAN Bks Pubs.

St. Mary at Hill Church: The Medieval Records of a London City Church A.D. 1420-1559, Pts. 1 & 2. Ed. by H. Littlehales. (EETS, OS Ser.: Nos. 125, 128). Repr. of 1905 ed. Set. 77.00 (ISBN 0-527-00121-X). Kraus Repr.

Saint Mary Magdalene in Medieval Literature. Helen M. Garth. LC 78-64210. (Johns Hopkins University. Studies in the Social Sciences. Sixty-Seventh Ser. 1949: 3). Repr. of 1950 ed. 15.50 (ISBN 0-404-61315-2). AMS Pr.

Saint Matthew. J. C. Fenton. LC 77-81620. (Westminster Pelican Commentaries Ser.). 488p. 1978. Westminster.

Saint Mawr. David H. Lawrence. Bd. with Man Who Died. 1959. pap. 3.95 (ISBN 0-394-70071-6, Vin). Random.

St. Maximilian Kolbe. Antonio Ricciardi. Tr. by Daughters of St. Paul. (Illus.). 314p. 1982. 7.95 (ISBN 0-8198-6838-8, ST0283); pap. 6.50 (ISBN 0-8198-6837-X). Dghtrs St Paul.

St. Maximus the Confessor: The Ascetic Life, the Four Centuries on Charity. Ed. by W. J. Burghardt et al. LC 55-8642. (ACW Ser.: No. 21). 293p. 1955. 13.95 (ISBN 0-8091-0258-7). Paulist Pr.

St. Methodius, the Symposium: A Treatise on Chastity. Ed. by W. J. Burghardt et al. (Ancient Christian Writers Ser.: No. 27). 256p. 1958. 11.95 (ISBN 0-8091-0143-2). Paulist Pr.

St. Michael & the Angels. LC 82-62040. Orig. Title: Precious Blood & the Angels. 133p. 1983. pap. 3.50 (ISBN 0-89555-196-9). TAN Bks Pubs.

St. Nectarios Orthodox Conference. Ed. by Neketas S. Palassis. LC 80-53258. 176p. (Orig.). 1981. pap. 15.00x (ISBN 0-913026-14-X). St Nectarios.

St. Nicholas Book. Martin Greif. LC 76-5089. (Illus.). 60p. 1976. 5.95 (ISBN 0-87663-554-0). Universe.

Saint Nicholas Book: A Celebration of Christmas Past. 3rd, rev. ed. Ed. by Martin Greif. LC 86-21706. (Illus.). 96p. (Orig.). 1986. pap. 7.95 (ISBN 1-55562-006-X). Main Street.

Saint Nicholas: His Legend & His Role in the Christmas Celebration & Other Popular Customs. George H. McKnight. (Illus.). 153p. 1974. Repr. of 1917 ed. 15.95 (ISBN 0-87928-051-4). Corner Hse.

Saint Nicholas of Myra, Bari & Manhattan: Biography of a Legend. Charles W. Jones. LC 77-51487. 1978. lib. bdg. 36.00x (ISBN 0-226-40699-7). U of Chicago Pr.

Saint of Auschwitz: The Story of Maximilian Kolbe. Diana Dewar. LC 82-48926. (Illus.). 160p. (Orig.). 1983. pap. 5.95 (ISBN 0-06-061901-5, RD/460, HarpR). Har-Row.

Saint of the Day. Ed. by Leonard Foley. (Illus.). 354p. 1981. text ed. 10.95 (ISBN 0-912228-96-2). St Anthony Mess Pr.

Saint of the Day: A Life & Lesson for Each of the 173 Saints of the New Missal, Vol. 1. Ed. by Leonard Foley. (Illus.). 1974. pap. 3.50 (ISBN 0-912228-16-4). St Anthony Mess Pr.

Saint of the Day: A Life & Lesson for Each of the 173 Saints of the New Missal, Vol. 2. Leonard Foley. (Illus.). 160p. 1975. pap. 3.50 (ISBN 0-912228-20-2). St Anthony Mess Pr.

St. Paisios the Great. 71p. 1983. pap. 3.00 (ISBN 0-317-30439-9). Holy Trinity.

St. Panteleimon. Sebastian Dabovich. pap. 0.25 (ISBN 0-686-01298-4). Eastern Orthodox.

St. Patrick & Irish Christianity. T. Corfe. LC 73-75862. (Cambridge Introduction to the Hoistory of Mankind Ser.). 48p. 1973. 4.95 (ISBN 0-521-20228-0). Cambridge U Pr.

St. Patrick & Irish Christianity. Tom Corfe. LC 78-56811. (Cambridge Topic Bks). (Illus.). 1978. PLB 8.95 (ISBN 0-8225-1217-3). Lerner Pubns.

St. Patrick & the Irish. Richard C. Cushing. 1963. 3.50 (ISBN 0-8198-6824-8); pap. 2.00 (ISBN 0-8198-6827-2). Dghtrs St Paul.

Saint Patrick's Day. Mary Cantwell. LC 67-10070. (Holiday Ser.). (Illus.). 1967. PLB 12.89 (ISBN 0-690-71673-7, Crowell Jr Bks). HarpJ.

Saint Patrick's Purgatory. J. M. Picard & Y. De Pontlarcy. 78p. 1985. pap. 7.00 (ISBN 0-912414-44-8). Lumen Christi.

St. Patrick's Summer. Marigold Hunt. 273p. 1950. 6.00 (ISBN 0-912414-24-3). Lumen Christi.

St. Paul. George Drew. 60p. (Orig.). 1984. pap. 6.95 (ISBN 0-940754-22-3). Ed Ministries.

Saint Paul. Michael Grant. (Crossroad Paperback Ser.). 256p. pap. 7.95 (ISBN 0-686-85826-3). Crossroad NY.

Saint Paul. Michael Grant. 272p. 1976. 5.95 (ISBN 0-684-14682-7, ScribT); pap. 5.95 (ISBN 0-684-17746-3). Scribner.

St. Paul: A Good Friend of Jesus. Daughters of St. Paul. 1980. 2.50 (ISBN 0-8198-6811-6); pap. 1.75 (ISBN 0-8198-6810-8). Dghtrs St Paul.

Saint Paul & His Gospel. G. P. Tasker. 87p. 1982. pap. 1.00 (ISBN 0-686-36256-X). Faith Pub Hse.

St. Paul & Paganism. Thomas Wilson. 1977. lib. bdg. 59.95 (ISBN 0-8490-2560-5). Gordon Pr.

St. Paul & the Mystery Religions. H. A. Kennedy. 1977. lib. bdg. 59.95 (ISBN 0-8490-2561-3). Gordon Pr.

St. Paul Apostle & Martyr. Igino Giordani. (Obelisk Ser.). 1961. 8.00 (ISBN 0-8198-0138-0); pap. 7.00 (ISBN 0-8198-0139-9). Dghtrs St Paul.

St. Paul Family Catechism. 5.95 (ISBN 0-8198-7329-2); 4.50 (ISBN 0-8198-7330-6). Dghtrs St Paul.

Saint Paul for Every Day of the Year. Daughters of St Paul. 1979. 6.00 (ISBN 0-686-63641-4); pap. 4.50 (ISBN 0-8198-0646-3). Dghtrs St Paul.

St. Paul in Britain. R. W. Morgan. LC 83-73168. 128p. 1984. pap. 4.50 (ISBN 0-934666-12-1). Artisan Sales.

St. Paul in Ephesus & the Cities of Galatia & Cyprus. Otto F. Meinardus. LC 78-51246. (In the Footsteps of the Saints Ser.). (Illus.). 160p. 1979. 17.50 (ISBN 0-89241-071-X); pap. 6.95 (ISBN 0-89241-044-2). Caratzas.

St. Paul in Greece. Otto F. Meinardus. LC 78-51244. (In the Footsteps of the Saints Ser.). 160p. 1979. 17.50 (ISBN 0-89241-072-8); pap. 6.95 (ISBN 0-89241-045-0). Caratzas.

St. Paul Mass Book for Children. Daughters of St. Paul. (Illus.). 1973. 1.75 (ISBN 0-8198-0336-7); pap. 1.00 (ISBN 0-8198-0337-5). Dghtrs St Paul.

St. Paul of the Cross: A Source-Workbook in Paulacrucian Studies. Jude C. Mead. 560p. 1983. pap. 12.95 (ISBN 0-89944-070-3). Don Bosco Multimedia.

St. Paul: The Apostle & His Letters. Norman P. Madsen. LC 85-62816. 165p. (Orig.). 1986. pap. 6.95 (ISBN 0-87973-589-9, 598). Our Sunday Visitor.

St. Paul the First Hermit: His Life by St. Jerome. St Jerome. Ed. by Walter Shewring. Tr. by Hawkins from Lat. 48p. 1987. 1.50 (ISBN 0-916375-07-2). Press Alley.

St. Paul the Traveller & Roman Citizen. William M. Ramsay. (William M. Ramsay Library Ser.). 1979. pap. 14.95 (ISBN 0-8010-7613-7). Baker Bk.

St. Paul's Cathedral. Peter Burman. (New Bell's Cathedral Guides Ser.). 1986. cancelled 24.95 (ISBN 0-918678-15-3). Historical Times.

St. Paul's Corinth: Texts & Archaeology. Jerome Murphy-O'Connor. (Good News Studies: Vol. 6). 1983. pap. 9.95 (ISBN 0-89453-303-7). M Glazier.

St. Paul's Epistle to the Ephesians. Brooke F. Westcott. 281p. 1983. lib. bdg. 10.50 (ISBN 0-86524-171-6, 4901). Klock & Klock.

St. Paul's Epistle to the Romans. W. Griffith Thomas. 1946. pap. 9.95 (ISBN 0-8028-1582-0). Eerdmans.

St. Paul's Epistle to the Thessalonians. George Milligan. 144p. 1980. 12.95 (ISBN 0-8007-1098-3). Revell.

St. Paul's Epistles to the Thessalonians. George Milligan. 1980. 12.00 (ISBN 0-86524-022-1, 7104). Klock & Klock.

St. Paul's Last Journey. Otto F. Meinardus. LC 78-51247. (In the Footsteps of the Saints Ser.). (Illus.). 160p. 1979. 17.50 (ISBN 0-686-85764-X); pap. 6.95 (ISBN 0-89241-073-6). Caratzas.

St. Peter & St. Paul. Catherine Storr. LC 84-18078. (People of the Bible Ser.). (Illus.). 32p. 1985. PLB 10.65 (ISBN 0-8172-1998-6). Raintree Pubs.

Saint Peter & the Popes. Michael M. Winter. LC 78-21507. 1979. Repr. of 1960 ed. lib. bdg. cancelled (ISBN 0-313-21158-2, WISP). Greenwood.

Saint Peter Canisius. James Brodrick. (Request Reprint). (Illus.). 1962. 19.95 (ISBN 0-8294-0008-7). Loyola.

Saint Peter Canisius, S. J., 1521-1597. James Brodrick. LC 83-45589. Date not set. Repr. of 1935 ed. 65.00 (ISBN 0-404-19882-1). AMS Pr.

Saint Peter Principle. Paul W. Powell. LC 81-67372. 1982. 5.50 (ISBN 0-8054-5299-0). Broadman.

Saint Peter's. E. M. Jung-Inglesis. (Illus.). 64p. (Orig.). 1980. pap. 12.50 (ISBN 0-935748-15-6). Scala Books.

St. Philip Neri. V. J. Matthews. LC 84-50406. 120p. 1984. pap. 3.00 (ISBN 0-89555-237-X). TAN Bks Pubs.

St. Photios the Great. Asterios Gerostergios. LC 80-82285. (Illus.). 125p. 1980. 8.50 (ISBN 0-914744-50-X); pap. 5.50 (ISBN 0-914744-51-8). Inst Byzantine.

Saint Pius the Tenth. John Smit. 1965. 4.00 (ISBN 0-8198-0140-2); pap. 3.00 (ISBN 0-8198-0141-0). Dghtrs St Paul.

St. Pius V - A Brief Account of His Life, Times, Virtues & Miracles. Robin Anderson. LC 78-55637. 1978. pap. 2.50 (ISBN 0-89555-068-7). TAN Bks Pubs.

St. Prosper of Aquitaine, Defense of St. Augustine. Ed. by W. J. Burghardt et al. LC 78-62463. (Ancient Christian Writers Ser.: No. 32). 235p. 1963. 10.95 (ISBN 0-8091-0263-3). Paulist Pr.

St. Prosper of Aquitaine, the Call of All Nations. Ed. by W. J. Burghardt et al. (Ancient Christian Writers Ser.: No. 14). 250p. 1952. 10.95 (ISBN 0-8091-0253-6). Paulist Pr.

St. Rita of Cascia: Saint of the Impossible. Daughters of St. Paul. LC 73-91992. 1973. 3.95 (ISBN 0-8198-0335-9). Dghtrs St Paul.

St. Rose of Lima. Mary Alphonsus. LC 81-86444. 304p. 1982. pap. 8.00 (ISBN 0-89555-172-1). TAN Bks Pubs.

St. Seraphim of Sarov. Valentine Zander. LC 75-24136. Orig. Title: Seraphim of Sarov. 150p. 1975. pap. 6.95 (ISBN 0-913836-28-1). St Vladimirs.

St. Sergius & Russian Spirituality. Pierre Kovalevsky. LC 76-13018. (Illus.). 190p. 1976. 7.95 (ISBN 0-913836-24-9). St Vladimirs.

St. Sharbel, Mystic of the East. Clare M. Benedict. 1977. 6.95 (ISBN 0-911218-11-4); pap. 3.45 (ISBN 0-911218-12-2). Ravengate Pr.

Saint-Simonian Religion in Germany. E. M. Butler. 1968. Repr. of 1926 ed. 45.00x (ISBN 0-86527-177-1). Fertig.

Saint-Simonism in the Radicalism of Thomas Carlyle. David B. Cofer. (English Literature Ser., No. 33). 1970. pap. 39.95x (ISBN 0-8383-0017-0). Haskell.

St. Symeon, the New Theologian: Theological & Practical Discourses & Three Theological Discourses. St. Symeon. Ed. by David N. Bell. Tr. by Paul McGuckin from Greek. (Cistercian Studies: No. 41). 1982. write for info. (ISBN 0-87907-841-3); pap. 8.00 (ISBN 0-87907-941-X). Cistercian Pubns.

St. Teresa of Avila. Stephen Clissold. 288p. (Orig.). 1982. pap. 8.95 (ISBN 0-8164-2621-X, HarpR). Har-Row.

St. Teresa of Avila. Giorgio Papasogli. LC 58-12223. 1973. Repr. 5.00 (ISBN 0-8198-0511-4). Dghtrs St Paul.

St. Theodore the Studite on the Holy Icons. Tr. by Catherine Roth. LC 81-18319. 115p. (Orig.). pap. 4.95 (ISBN 0-913836-76-1). St Vladimirs.

Saint Theresa, the Little Flower. Sr. Gesualda Of The Holy Spirit. (Illus.). 1960. 4.95 (ISBN 0-8198-0142-9); pap. 3.95. Dghtrs St Paul.

Saint Therese of Lisieux General Correspondence: Vol. I, 1877-1890. Tr. by John Clarke. LC 81-6474. 700p. (Orig.). 1982. pap. 9.95x (ISBN 0-9600876-9-9). ICS Pubns.

St. Therese of Lisieux: Her Last Conversations. Tr. by John Clarke from Fr. LC 76-27207. (Illus.). 1977. pap. 6.95x (ISBN 0-9600876-3-X). ICS Pubns.

St. Therese of Lisieux: Her Life As She Might Tell It. Robert J. Fox. 20p. 1982. pap. 1.00 (ISBN 0-911988-54-8). AMI Pr.

Saint Therese, the Little Flower: The Making of a Saint. John Beevers. LC 73-80147. (Orig.). 1976. pap. 3.50 (ISBN 0-89555-035-0). TAN Bks Pubs.

Saint Thomas & Analogy. Gerald B. Phelan. (Aquinas Lecture). 1941. 7.95 (ISBN 0-87462-105-4). Marquette.

Saint Thomas & Epistemology. Louis-Marie Regis. (Aquinas Lecture Ser.). 1946. 7.95 (ISBN 0-87462-110-0). Marquette.

St. Thomas & Historicity. Armand A. Maurer. LC 79-84278. (Aquinas Lecture Ser.). 1979. 7.95 (ISBN 0-87462-144-5). Marquette.

Saint Thomas & Philosophy. Anton C. Pegis. (Aquinas Lecture). 1964. 7.95 (ISBN 0-87462-129-1). Marquette.

Saint Thomas & the Future of Metaphysics. Joseph C. Owens. (Aquinas Lecture). 1957. 7.95 (ISBN 0-87462-122-4). Marquette.

Saint Thomas & the Gentiles. Mortimer J. Adler. (Aquinas Lecture). 1938. 7.95 (ISBN 0-87462-102-X). Marquette.

Saint Thomas & the Greek Moralists. Vernon J. Bourke. (Aquinas Lecture). 1947. 7.95 (ISBN 0-87462-111-9). Marquette.

Saint Thomas & the Greeks. Anton C. Pegis. (Aquinas Lecture). 1939. 7.95 (ISBN 0-87462-103-8). Marquette.

Saint Thomas & the Life of Learning. John F. McCormick. (Aquinas Lecture). 1937. 7.95 (ISBN 0-87462-101-1). Marquette.

Saint Thomas & the Problem of Evil. Jacques Maritain. (Aquinas Lecture). 1942. 7.95 (ISBN 0-87462-106-2). Marquette.

Saint Thomas & the World State. Robert M. Hutchins. (Aquinas Lecture). 1949. 7.95 (ISBN 0-87462-114-3). Marquette.

Saint Thomas Aquinas. G. K. Chesterton. 200p. 1974. pap. 3.95 (ISBN 0-385-09002-1, Im). Doubleday.

St. Thomas Aquinas. Ralph McInerny. LC 81-16293. 197p. 1982. pap. text ed. 5.95 (ISBN 0-268-01707-7). U of Notre Dame Pr.

St. Thomas Aquinas on Analogy: A Textual Analysis & Systematic Synthesis. George P. Klubertanz. LC 60-9602. (Jesuit Studies). pap. 81.80 (ISBN 0-317-09004-6, 2000813). Bks Demand UMI.

Saint Thomas Aquinas: On Charity. St. Thomas Aquinas. Tr. by Lotti H. Kendzierski. (Medieval Philosophical Texts in Translation: No. 10). 1960. pap. 7.95 (ISBN 0-87462-210-7). Marquette.

Saint Thomas Aquinas: On Spiritual Creatures. St. Thomas Aquinas. Tr. by Mary C. Fitzpatrick. (Medieval Philosophical Texts in Translation: No. 5). 1949. pap. 7.95 (ISBN 0-87462-205-0). Marquette.

St. Thomas Aquinas on the Existence of God: Collected Papers of Joseph Owens. Joseph Owens. Ed. by John R. Catan. LC 79-13885. 1980. 44.50x (ISBN 0-87395-401-7); pap. 16.95x (ISBN 0-87395-446-7). State U NY Pr.

Saint Thomas Aquinas: On the Unity of the Intellect Against the Averroists. Ed. by Beatrice H. Zedler. (Medieval Philosophical Texts in Translation: No. 19). 1968. pap. 7.95 (ISBN 0-87462-219-0). Marquette.

St. Thomas Aquinas: Philosophical Texts. St. Thomas Aquinas. Ed. by Thomas Gilby. xxiv, 406p. 1982. pap. 12.50x (ISBN 0-939464-06-3). Labyrinth Pr.

Saint Thomas Aquinas: Questions on the Soul. James H. Robb. (Medieval Philosophical Texts in Translation: N0. 27). 1984. 24.95 (ISBN 0-87462-226-3). Marquette.

St. Thomas Aquinas: Theological Texts. St. Thomas Aquinas. Ed. by Thomas Gilby. 444p. 1982. pap. 12.50x (ISBN 0-939464-01-2). Labyrinth Pr.

Saint Thomas et le Pseudo-Denis. J. Durantel. (Medieval Studies Ser.). (Fr.). Repr. of 1919 ed. lib. bdg. 45.00x (ISBN 0-697-00036-2). Irvington.

St. Thomas More: Vol. 3, Pt. 2-Latin Poems. St. Thomas More. Ed. by Clarence H. Miller et al. LC 63-7949. (Yale Edition of the Complete Works of St. Thomas More). 800p. 1984. text ed. 62.00x (ISBN 0-300-02591-2). Yale U Pr.

St. Thomas of Canterbury: His Death & Miracles, 2 vols. in 1. Edwin A. Abbott. LC 80-18216. (Crusades & Military Orders: Second Ser.). Repr. of 1898 ed. 55.00 (ISBN 0-404-16366-1). AMS Pr.

Saint Thomas, Sieger De Brabant, St. Bonaventure: On the Eternity of the World. Tr. by Cyril Vollert et al. (Medieval Philosophical Texts in Translation: No. 16). 1965. pap. 7.95 (ISBN 0-87462-216-6). Marquette.

Saint Tikhon of Zadonsk: Inspirer of Dostoevsky. Nadejda Gorodetzky. LC 76-49919. 320p. 1977. pap. 8.95 (ISBN 0-913836-32-X). St Vladimirs.

Saint Valentine's Day. Clyde R. Bulla. LC 65-11643. (Holiday Ser.). (Illus.). 1965. PLB 12.89 (ISBN 0-690-71744-X, Crowell Jr Bks). HarpJ.

Saint Watching. Phyllis McGinley. (Crossroad Paperback Ser.). 256p. 1982. pap. 6.95 (ISBN 0-8245-0450-X). Crossroad NY.

Saint Wulstan, Prelate & Patriot: A Study of His Life & Times. John W. Lamb. (Church Historical Society, London, New Ser.: No. 16). Repr. of 1933 ed. 40.00 (ISBN 0-8115-3139-2). Kraus Repr.

Sainte Marguerite de Cortone. Francois Mauriac. pap. 5.95 (ISBN 0-685-34304-9). French & Eur.

Sainte Vierge: Etudes Archeologiques et Iconographiques, 2 vols. C. Rohault De Fleury. (Fr., Illus.). Repr. of 1878 ed. Set. 325.00x (ISBN 0-89241-154-6). Caratzas.

Saints. Jean Pedrick. (Chapbook Ser.: No. 1). 40p. (Orig.). 1980. pap. 4.95 (ISBN 0-937672-00-9). Rowan Tree.

Saints Alive. facsimile ed. James R. Adair. LC 76-117319. (Biography Index Reprint Ser). 1951. 18.00 (ISBN 0-8369-8011-5). Ayer Co Pubs.

Saints Alive! the Book. Ed. by Hal M. Helms. (Orig.). 1985. pap. 9.95 (ISBN 0-941478-44-0). Paraclete Pr.

Saints Always Belong to the Present. John Wright. Pref. by Stephen Almagno. LC 84-80016. 221p. 1984. pap. 8.95 (ISBN 0-89870-047-7). Ignatius Pr.

Saints & Festivals of the Christian Church. Harold P. Brewster. LC 73-159869. (Illus.). xiv, 558p. 1975. Repr. of 1904 ed. 48.00x (ISBN 0-8103-3992-7). Gale.

Saints & Heroes Since the Middle Ages. George Hodges. LC 75-107713. (Essay Index Reprint Ser.). 1912. 21.50 (ISBN 0-8369-1515-1). Ayer Co Pubs.

Saints & Heroes Speak. Robert J. Fox. 512p. 1983. 7.95 (ISBN 0-911988-43-2). Ami Pr.

Saints & Heroes to the End of the Middle Ages. facs. ed. George Hodges. LC 67-26749. (Essay Index Reprint Ser). 1911. 20.00 (ISBN 0-8369-0544-X). Ayer Co Pubs.

Saints & Heroes to the End of the Middle Ages. facsimile ed. George Hodges. LC 67-26749. (Essay Index Reprint Ser.). (Illus.). 268p. 1982. Repr. of 1911 ed. lib. bdg. 19.00 (ISBN 0-8290-0526-9). Irvington.

Saints & Innocents. Barbara Rex. 1972. 6.95 (ISBN 0-393-08664-X). Norton.

Saints & Martyrs of Ireland: Feast Days Calendar. H. Patrick Montague. (Illus.). 138p. Date not set. 15.95 (ISBN 0-86140-106-9); pap. 5.95 (ISBN 0-86140-107-7). Dufour.

Saints & Rebels. facsimile ed. Eloise Lownsbery. LC 72-156682. (Essay Index Reprint Ser). Repr. of 1937 ed. 22.00 (ISBN 0-8369-2322-7). Ayer Co Pubs.

Saints & Sinners. Bill J. Cook. 64p. 1981. pap. 3.95 (ISBN 0-938400-05-3). Donahoe Pubs.

Saints & Sinners in the Early Church: Differing & Conflicting Traditions in the First Six Centuries. W. H. Frend. (Theology & Life Ser.: Vol. 11). 1985. pap. 8.95 (ISBN 0-89453-451-3). M Glazier.

Saints & Sinners: The Planting of New England Congregationalism in Portland, Oregon, 1851-1876. Egbert S. Oliver. Ed. by Joe E. Pierce. (Illus.). 250p. 1987. pap. 4.95 (ISBN 0-913244-66-X). Hapi Pr.

Saints & Society: The Two Worlds of Western Christendom, 1000 to 1700. Donald Weinstein & Rudolph M. Bell. LC 82-7972. (Illus.). xii, 314p. 1986. 25.00x (ISBN 0-226-89055-4); pap. 11.95 (ISBN 0-226-89056-2). U of Chicago Pr.

Saints & the Union: Utah Territory During the Civil War. E. B. Long. LC 80-16775. (Illus.). 292p. 1981. 22.50 (ISBN 0-252-00821-9). U of Ill Pr.

Saints & Their Cults: Studies in Religious Sociology, Folklore & History. Ed. by Stephen Wilson. LC 82-25296. 416p. 1984. 62.50 (ISBN 0-521-24978-3). Cambridge U Pr.

Saints & Their Cults: Studies in Religious Sociology, Folklore & History. Ed. by Stephen Wilson. 447p. 1986. pap. 19.95 (ISBN 0-521-31181-0). Cambridge U Pr.

Saints & Their Emblems. Maurice Drake. (Illus.). 1971. Repr. of 1916 ed. lib. bdg. 24.50 (ISBN 0-8337-0902-X). B Franklin.

Saints Are Now: Eight Portraits of Modern Sanctity. John J. Delaney. LC 82-45866. 224p. 1983. pap. 4.50 (ISBN 0-385-17356-3, Im). Doubleday.

Saints Are People: Church History Through the Saints. Alfred McBride. 144p. (Orig.). 1981. pap. 4.50 (ISBN 0-697-01785-0). Wm C Brown.

Saints Beyond the White Cliffs: Stories of English Saints. facs. ed. Margaret Gibbs. LC 75-148211. (Biography Index Reprint Ser.). (Illus.). 1947. 20.00 (ISBN 0-8369-8058-1). Ayer Co Pubs.

Saints Book: Stories for Children. Kate Dooley. LC 80-82814. 48p. (Orig.). 1981. pap. 2.95 (ISBN 0-8091-6547-3). Paulist Pr.

Saints Daily Exercise. John Preston. LC 76-57409. (English Experience Ser.: No. 824). 1977. Repr. of 1629 ed. lib. bdg. 16.00 (ISBN 90-221-0824-4). Walter J Johnson.

Saints for All Seasons. Ed. by John J. Delaney. LC 77-81438. 1978. pap. 3.95 (ISBN 0-385-12909-2, Im). Doubleday.

Saints for Kids by Kids. Robert Charlebois et al. 80p. 1984. pap. 2.95 (ISBN 0-89243-223-3). Liguori Pubns.

Saints for Sinners. Alban Goodier. LC 70-99637. (Essay Index Reprint Ser.). 1930. 18.00 (ISBN 0-8369-1504-6). Ayer Co Pubs.

Saints for This Age. A. J. Muste. LC 62-21962. (Orig.). 1962. pap. 2.50x (ISBN 0-87574-124-X, 124). Pendle Hill.

Saints for Today's Women. Mary H. Valentine. 1987. 11.95 (ISBN 0-88347-210-4). Thomas More.

Saints for Young Christians. Ed Curley. 1983. 9.95 (ISBN 0-89837-088-4, Pub. by Pflaum Pr). Peter Li.

Saints for Young People for Every Day of the Year, Vol. 2. Daughters of St Paul. (Illus.). 6.00 (ISBN 0-8198-0647-1); pap. 4.50 (ISBN 0-8198-0648-X). Dghtrs St Paul.

Saints Galore. David L. Veal. 160p. (Orig.). 1972. pap. 1.75 (ISBN 0-88028-009-3, 405). Forward Movement.

Saints Go Marching In. rev. ed. Robert F. Holtzclaw. LC 84-52751. (Illus.). 194p. (Orig.). 1984. write for info.; pap. 10.00 (ISBN 0-933144-00-8). Keeble Pr.

Saints in Action. facs. ed. Dumas Malone. LC 70-142664. (Essay Index Reprint Ser). 1939. 15.00 (ISBN 0-8369-2062-7). Ayer Co Pubs.

Saints in Arms. Leo F. Solt. LC 74-153355. (Stanford University. Stanford Studies in History, Economics & Political Science: No. 18). Repr. of 1959 ed. 19.00 (ISBN 0-404-50976-2). AMS Pr.

Saints in Art. Clara E. Clement. LC 77-89303. 1976. Repr. of 1899 ed. 46.00x (ISBN 0-8103-3030-X). Gale.

Saints in Due Season. Thomas P. McDonnell. LC 83-60742. 196p. (Orig.). 1983. pap. 5.95 (ISBN 0-87973-623-2, 623). Our Sunday Visitor.

Saints Knowledge of Christ's Love. John Bunyan. pap. 1.50 (ISBN 0-685-19843-X). Reiner.

Saints' Legends. G. H. Gerould. 59.95 (ISBN 0-8490-0987-1). Gordon Pr.

Saints' Legends. Gordon H. Gerould. 1980. Repr. of 1916 ed. lib. bdg. 37.00 (ISBN 0-8414-4627-X). Folcroft.

Saints of Chaos. facs. ed. Peter Oliver. LC 67-23255. (Essay Index Reprint Ser). 1934. 17.00 (ISBN 0-8369-0752-3). Ayer Co Pubs.

Saints of Egypt. De Lacy E. O'Leary. (Church Historical Society, London, News Ser.: No. 27). Repr. of 1937 ed. 55.00 (ISBN 0-8115-3151-1). Kraus Repr.

Saints of Gwynedd. Molly Miller. (Studies in Celtic History). 132p. 1979. 21.50x (ISBN 0-8476-6186-5). Rowman.

Saints of India. Satguru S. Keshavadas. 100p. (Orig.). 1975. pap. 3.50 (ISBN 0-942508-05-X). Vishwa.

Saints of India. Anna A. Subramanian. (Illus.). 1978. pap. 3.25 (ISBN 0-87481-479-0). Vedanta Pr.

Saints of Ireland. Mary R. D'Arcy. 241p. 1985. pap. 9.95 (ISBN 0-9614900-0-4). Irish Am Cult.

Saints of Qumran: Stories & Essays on Jewish Themes. Rudolf Kayser. Ed. by Harry Zohn. LC 76-20273. 188p. 1977. 18.00 (ISBN 0-8386-2024-8). Fairleigh Dickinson.

Saints of Sage & Saddle: Folklore Among the Mormons. Austin Fife & Alta Fife. 375p. 1980. pap. 14.95 (ISBN 0-87480-180-X). U of Utah Pr.

Saint's Revelation. LC 84-90117. 51p. 1985. 6.95 (ISBN 0-533-06193-8). Vantage.

Saints, Signs & Symbols. W. Ellwood Post. (Illus.). 96p. 1974. pap. 6.50 (ISBN 0-8192-1171-0). Morehouse.

Saints, Slaves, & Blacks: The Changing Place of Black People Within Mormonism. Newell G. Bringhurst. LC 81-1093. (Contributions to the Study of Religion Ser.: No. 4). (Illus.). 256p. 1981. lib. bdg. 29.95 (ISBN 0-313-22752-7, BSB/). Greenwood.

Saints That Moved the World: Anthony, Augustine, Francis, Ignatius, Theresa. Rene Fulop-Miller. LC 72-13293. (Essay Index Reprint Ser.). Repr. of 1945 ed. 32.00 (ISBN 0-8369-8159-6). Ayer Co Pubs.

Saints: Visible, Orderly & Catholic: The Congregational Idea of the Church. Alan P. Sell. (Princeton Theological Monograph Ser.: No. 7). (Orig.). 1986. pap. 15.00 (ISBN 0-915138-89-1). Pickwick.

Saints Who Shaped the Church. Jerry Schmalenberger. Ed. by Michael L. Sherer. (Orig.). 1987. pap. 6.50 (ISBN 0-89536-856-0, 7815). CSS of Ohio.

Saints Without Halos: The Human Side of Mormon History. Leonard J. Arrington & Davis Bitton. 168p. 1981. 10.95 (ISBN 0-941214-01-X). Signature Bks.

Saintspeak. Orson S. Card. 64p. (Orig.). 1981. pap. 3.95 (ISBN 0-941214-00-1). Signature Bks.

Saiva Art & Architecture in South India. C. Krishna Murthy. 1985. 48.00x (ISBN 0-8364-1417-9, Pub. by Sundeep). South Asia Bks.

Saivism in Philosophical Perspective. K. Sivaraman. 1973. 17.95 (ISBN 0-8426-0538-X). Orient Bk Dist.

Sakta Upanisads. A. Krishna Warrier. 3.50 (ISBN 0-8356-7318-9). Theos Pub Hse.

Sakti & Sakta. John Woodroffe. 24.50 (ISBN 0-89744-116-8, Pub. by Ganesh & Co. India). Auromere.

Sakya of Buddhist Origins. Rhys Davids. lib. bdg. 79.95 (ISBN 0-87968-512-3). Krishna Pr.

Sakya or Buddhist Origins. Caroline A. Davids. 444p. 1931. Repr. text ed. 32.50x. Coronet Bks.

Salem in the Eighteenth Century. James D. Phillips. LC 37-36381. (Illus.). 533p. 1969. Repr. of 1937 ed. 25.00 (ISBN 0-88389-017-8). Essex Inst.

Salem Kirban Reference Bible. (Illus.). 1979. skivertex flexible bdg. 49.95 (ISBN 0-912582-31-6); leather ed. 69.95 (ISBN 0-686-52197-8). Kirban.

Salem Light Guard. Lester L. Kempfer. LC 73-76068. (Illus.). 128p. 1973. 5.95 (ISBN 0-686-04916-0); pap. 3.95 (ISBN 0-686-04917-9). L Kempfer.

Salem, Massachusetts, Sixteen Twenty-Six to Sixteen Eighty-Three: A Covenant Community. Richard P. Gildrie. LC 74-20841. (Illus.). 187p. 1975. 20.00x (ISBN 0-8139-0532-X). U Pr of Va.

Salem Possessed: The Social Origins of Witchcraft. Paul Boyer & Stephen Nissenbaum. LC 73-84399. 320p. 1974. pap. 6.95x (ISBN 0-674-78526-6). Harvard U Pr.

Salem Witchcraft, 2 vols. C. Upham. 1022p. 1971. Repr. of 1867 ed. Set. 48.00 (ISBN 0-87928-024-7). Corner Hse.

Salem Witchcraft, 2 Vols. Charles W. Upham. LC 59-10887. (American Classics Ser.). (Illus.). 1959. 40.00 (ISBN 0-8044-1947-7). Ungar.

Salem Witchcraft Papers: Verbatim Transcripts, 3 vols. Ed. by Paul Boyer & Stephen Nissenbaum. (Civil Liberties in American History Ser.). 1977. Set. lib. bdg. 145.00 (ISBN 0-306-70655-5). Da Capo.

Salesian Cooperators: A Practical Way of Life. Enzo Bianco. Tr. by Peter Swain. (Salesian Family Ser.). 40p. 1983. pap. 3.25 (ISBN 0-89944-073-8). Don Bosco Multimedia.

Salient Characteristics of Ancient Christian Architecture. Harold Lowrie. (Illus.). 142p. 1982. Repr. of 1880 ed. 84.55 (ISBN 0-89901-053-9). Found Class Reprints.

Sallee. Sallee Moses. 140p. 1985. 5.95 (ISBN 0-89221-120-2). New Leaf.

Sallust on the Gods & the World & Other Works. Thomas Taylor. 12.50 (ISBN 0-89314-401-0). Philos Res.

Sally & Tommy John Story. Tommy John & Sally John. 288p. 1985. pap. 3.50 (ISBN 0-425-07304-1). Berkley Pub.

Sally Wister's Journal: A True Narrative Being a Quaker Maiden's Account of Her Experiences with Officers of the Continental Army, 1777-1778. Sally Wister. Ed. by Albert C. Myers. LC 73-78039. (Eyewitness Accounts of the American Revolution Ser., No. 2). 1969. Repr. of 1902 ed. 16.00 (ISBN 0-405-01169-5). Ayer Co Pubs.

Sally's Calendar Book. Gloria G. Morrell. 1986. pap. 3.95 (ISBN 0-8054-4337-1). Broadman.

Salman el-Farsi. Sayed A. Razwy. 1985. pap. 3.95 (ISBN 0-933543-02-6). Aza Khana.

Salmos. Mary J. Tully. Tr. by Angelina Marquez. 1986. pap. 3.95 (ISBN 0-697-02202-1). Wm C Brown.

Salmos: Cantos de Vida. Fred M. Wood. Tr. by Edna L. De Gutierrez from Span. Tr. of Psalms: Songs From Life. 160p. 1984. pap. 2.75 (ISBN 0-311-04032-2). Casa Bautista.

Salo Wittmayer Baron Jubilee Volume: On the Occasion of His Eightieth Birthday, 3 vols. new ed. Ed. by Saul Lieberman & Arthur Hyman. LC 74-82633. 1533p. 1975. 112.00x set (ISBN 0-685-51945-7); Vol. 1. (ISBN 0-231-03911-5); Vol. 2. (ISBN 0-231-03912-3); Vol. 3. (ISBN 0-231-03913-1). Columbia U Pr.

Salomo Gabirol und seine Dichtungen. Abraham Geiger. Ed. by Steven Katz. LC 79-7130. (Jewish Philosophy, Mysticism & History of Ideas Ser.). 1980. Repr. of 1867 ed. lib. bdg. 14.00x (ISBN 0-405-12254-3). Ayer Co Pubs.

Saloon Keeper's Daughter Saved. Bertha Mackey. 15p. 1982. pap. 0.15 (ISBN 0-686-36264-0); pap. 0.25 2 copies (ISBN 0-686-37285-9). Faith Pub HSe.

Salt & Light. Matthew De Brincat. 56p. 1983. pap. 3.00 (ISBN 0-911423-00-1). Bible-Speak.

Salt & Light: Talks & Writings of the Sermon on the Mount. Eberhard Arnold. LC 77-1204. 1977. pap. 6.00 (ISBN 0-87486-170-5). Plough.

Salt & Light: Talks & Writings on the Sermon on the Mount. Eberhard Arnold. LC 67-18009. 1967. 8.00 (ISBN 0-87486-105-5). Plough.

Salt & Light: Talks & Writings on the Sermon on the Mount. rev. ed. Eberhard Arnold. Ed. & tr. by Hutterian Brethren. 338p. 1986. pap. 6.00 (ISBN 0-87486-174-8). Plough.

Salt-Cellars. C. H. Spurgeon. 1976. pap. 7.75 (ISBN 0-686-16837-2). Pilgrim Pubns.

Salt for Society. Phillip Keller. 1986. 5.95 (ISBN 0-8499-3059-6). Word Bks.

Salt for Society. W. Phillip Keller. 160p. 1981. 8.95 (ISBN 0-8499-0290-8). Word Bks.

Salt from the Psalter. Mary F. Owens. LC 80-67147. 1981. pap. 4.95 (ISBN 0-8054-1218-2). Broadman.

Salt in My Kitchen. Jeanette W. Lockerbie. (Quiet Time Books). 1967. pap. 3.50 (ISBN 0-8024-7500-0). Moody.

Salt Lake Temple: A Monument to a People. Ed. by Charles M. Hamilton & C. Nina Cutrubus. (Illus.). 208p. 1983. write for info. (ISBN 0-913535-01-X); pap. write for info. (ISBN 0-913535-02-8); Ltd. Ed. 250.00 (ISBN 0-913535-00-1). Univ Servs Inc.

Salt of the Earth. Clarence M. Wagner. Ed. by Tru-Faith Pub. 80p. (Orig.). 1981. pap. 3.50x (ISBN 0-937498-01-7). Tru-Faith.

Salvacion: Su Seguridad, Creteza y Gozo. 2nd ed. Jorge Cutting. Ed. by Roger P. Daniel. Tr. by Sara Bautista from Eng. (Serie Diamante). Tr. of Safety, Certainity & Enjoyment. (Span., Illus.). 48p. 1982. pap. 0.85 (ISBN 0-942504-05-4). Overcomer Pr.

Salvacion y las Dudas de Algunas Personas. 2nd ed. Alejandro Marshall & Gordon H. Bennett. Tr. by Sara Bautista from Span. (Serie Diamante). Tr. of God's Way of Salvation. (Eng., Illus.). 36p. 1982. pap. 0.85 (ISBN 0-942504-01-1). Overcomer Pr.

Salvado Memoirs: Historical Memoirs of Australia & Particularly of the Benedictine Mission of New Norcia & of the Habits & Customs of the Australian Natives. Rosendo Salvado. Tr. by E. J. Stormon. 1978. pap. 10.95x (ISBN 0-85564-114-2, Pub. by U of W Austral Pr). Intl Spec Bk.

Salvador Witness: The Life & Calling of Jean Donovan. Ana Carrigan. 320p. 1984. 16.95 (ISBN 0-671-47992-X). S&S.

Salvador Witness: The Life & Calling of Jean Donvan. Ana Carrigan. 320p. 1986. pap. 3.95 (ISBN 0-345-32984-8). Ballantine.

Salvados por Su Vida. Harold J. Brokke. 224p. 1978. 2.50 (ISBN 0-88113-317-5). Edit Betania.

Salvation. Lewis S. Chafer. 160p. 1972. pap. 5.95 (ISBN 0-310-22351-2, 6309P). Zondervan.

Salvation. Perry A. Gaspard. 1983. pap. 1.00 (ISBN 0-931867-00-2). Abundant Life Pubns.

Salvation. Richard L. Grossman. (Literary Chapbook Ser.). 48p. 1977. pap. 3.00 (ISBN 0-916300-05-6). Gallimaufry.

Salvation. Ed. by John E. Hartley & R. L. Shelton. (Wesleyan Theological Perspectives Ser.: Vol. I). 1981. 14.95 (ISBN 0-87162-240-8, D4850). Warner Pr.

Salvation. Robert Hicks & Richard Bewes. (Understanding Bible Truth Ser.). (Orig.). 1981. pap. 0.95 (ISBN 0-89840-019-8). Heres Life.

Salvation & Atonement in the Qumran Scrolls. Paul Garnett. 160p. 1977. pap. 24.00x (Pub. by J C B Mohr BRD). Coronet Bks.

Salvation & Liberation: In Search of a Balance Between Faith & Politics. Clodovis Boff & Leonardo Boff. Tr. by Robert R. Barr from Port. LC 84-7220. Tr. of Da Liberatacas. 128p. (Orig.). 1984. pap. 6.95 (ISBN 0-88344-451-8). Orbis Bks.

Salvation & Nurture of the Child of God. G. Temp Sparkman. 1983. 9.95 (ISBN 0-8170-0985-X). Judson.

Salvation & Protest: Studies of Social & Religious Movements. Roy Wallis. 1979. 26.00x (ISBN 0-312-69834-8). St Martin.

Salvation & Santification. John A. Hardon. 1978. 3.50 (ISBN 0-8198-0366-9); pap. 2.50 (ISBN 0-8198-0367-7). Dghtrs St Paul.

Salvation & the Perfect Society: The Eternal Quest. Alfred Braunthal. LC 79-4705. 448p. 1979. lib. bdg. 25.00x (ISBN 0-87023-273-8). U of Mass Pr.

Salvation & the Savage: An Analysis of Protestant Missions & American Indian Response, 1787-1862. Robert F. Berkhofer. LC 77-22857. 1977. Repr. of 1965 ed. lib. bdg. 22.50x (ISBN 0-8371-9745-7, BESSA). Greenwood.

Salvation & the Savage: An Analysis of Protestant Missions & American Indian Response, 1787-1862. Robert F. Berkhofer, Jr. LC 65-11826. 1972. pap. text ed. 4.95x (ISBN 0-689-70290-6, 184). Atheneum.

Salvation Army & the Children. John D. Waldron. 135p. (Orig.). 1985. pap. 3.00 (ISBN 0-89216-060-8). Salvation Army.

Salvation Army & the Churches. John D. Waldron. 142p. (Orig.). 1986. pap. 3.95 (ISBN 0-89216-064-0). Salvation Army.

Salvation Army Farm Colonies. Clark C. Spence. LC 85-8763. 151p. 1985. 19.95x (ISBN 0-8165-0897-6). U of Ariz Pr.

Salvation Army in America: Selected Reports, 1899-1903. Frederick Booth-Tucker. LC 79-38439. (Religion in America, Ser. 2). 212p. 1972. Repr. of 1972 ed. 19.00 (ISBN 0-405-04060-1). Ayer Co Pubs.

Salvation Army Word Search Puzzles. David Cedervall. 75p. (Orig.). 1985. pap. 1.65 (ISBN 0-89216-061-6). Salvation Army.

Salvation by Faith & Your Will. Morris L. Venden. LC 78-7597. (Horizon Ser.). 1978. pap. 5.95 (ISBN 0-8127-0190-9). Review & Herald.

Salvation by Grace Through Faith in Contrast to the Restorationist Doctrine. Bob L. Ross. 1979. pap. 1.00 (ISBN 0-686-35836-8). Pilgrim Pubns.

Salvation Comes from the Lord. Arnold V. Wallenkampf. Ed. by Gerald Wheeler. LC 83-3297. 128p. (Orig.). 1983. pap. 5.95 (ISBN 0-8280-0210-X). Review & Herald.

Salvation, Entire Sanctification. Jernigan. pap. 1.95 (ISBN 0-686-12907-5). Schmul Pub Co.

Salvation for Sale: An Insider's View of Pat Robertson's Ministry. Gerald T. Straub. (Illus.). 300p. 1986. 18.95 (ISBN 0-87975-357-9). Prometheus Bks.

Salvation from Sin. John H. Noyes. 59.95 (ISBN 0-8490-0990-1). Gordon Pr.

Salvation, Learning about God's Plan. (Teaching Bks.). (Illus.). 19p. (Orig.). 1974. pap. text ed. 2.95 (ISBN 0-86508-151-4). BCM Intl Inc.

Salvation of the Nations. Jean Danielou. 1962. pap. 1.25x (ISBN 0-268-00244-4). U of Notre Dame Pr.

Salvation of the Soul. Watchman Nee. Tr. by Stephen Kaung. 1978. pap. 2.75 (ISBN 0-935008-31-4). Christian Fellow Pubs.

Salvation of the Soul & Islamic Devotion. M. A. Quasem. 200p. (Orig.). 1984. pap. 12.95 (ISBN 0-7103-0033-6, Kegan Paul). Methuen Inc.

Salvation, Present, Perfect, Now or Never. D. S. Warner. 63p. pap. 0.40 (ISBN 0-686-29138-7); pap. 1.00 3 copies (ISBN 0-686-29139-5). Faith Pub Hse.

Salvation: The Way Made Plain. James H. Brookes. pap. 4.50 (ISBN 0-685-61831-5). Reiner.

Salvation, Then What. Marjorie Soderholm. 1968. pap. 1.75 (ISBN 0-911802-14-2). Free Church Pubns.

Salz und Licht. Ed. & tr. by Hutterian Society of Brothers. (Ger.). 186p. 1982. pap. 4.95 (ISBN 3-87067-166-1, Pub. by Brendow-Verlag, West Germany). Plough.

Salzburgs Weideraofgebaute Synagogue. cancelled (ISBN 0-686-76252-5). Feldheim.

Sam Ellis's Island. Beatrice Siegel. LC 85-42799. (Illus.). 128p. 1985. PLB 11.95 (ISBN 0-02-782720-8, Four Winds). Macmillan.

Sam Pollard of Yunnan. pap. 3.95 (ISBN 0-686-23584-3). Schmul Pub Co.

Sam-Veda Sanhita. Tr. by Ralph T. Griffith from Sanskrit. 338p. 1978. Repr. of 1907 ed. 22.00 (ISBN 0-89684-160-X). Orient Bk Dist.

Samadhi & Beyond. Sri S. Chakravarti. LC 74-79444. 1974. pap. 3.50 (ISBN 0-87707-135-7). Ranney Pubns.

Samadhi: Self Development in Zen, Swordsmanship, & Psychotherapy. Mike Sayama. (Transpersonal & Humanistic Psychology). 147p. 1985. 34.50x (ISBN 0-88706-146-X); pap. 10.95 (ISBN 0-88706-147-8). State U NY Pr.

Samadhi: The Superconsciousness of the Future. Mouni Sadha. (Unwin Paperbacks). 1977. pap. 5.95 (ISBN 0-04-149039-8). Allen Unwin.

Samantha among the Brethren, By Josiah Allen's Wife. Marietta Holley. Ed. by Carolyn Gifford & Donald Dayton. (Women in American Protestan Religion 1800-1930 Ser.). 437p. 1987. lib. bdg. 60.00 (ISBN 0-8240-0664-X). Garland Pub.

Samaritan Chronicle No. 2 (or, Sepher Ha-Yamim) from Joshua to Nebuchadnezzar. John Macdonald. (Beiheft 107 zur Zeitschrift fuer die alttestamentliche Wissenschaft). 1969. 34.80 (ISBN 3-11-002582-5). De Gruyter.

Samaritan Oral Law & Ancient Traditions. Moses Gaster. LC 77-87609. Repr. of 1932 ed. 22.00 (ISBN 0-404-16433-1). AMS Pr.

Samaritan Problem: Studies in the Relationship of Samaritanism, Judaism, & Early Christianity. John Bowman. Tr. by Alfred M. Johnson, Jr. from Ger. LC 75-20042. (Pittsburgh Theological Monographs: No. 4). 1975. pap. 8.75 (ISBN 0-915138-04-2). Pickwick.

Samaritans Documents Relating to Their History, Religion & Life. Ed. & tr. by John Bowman. LC 77-4949. (Pittsburgh Original Texts & Translations Ser.: No. 2). 1977. pap. 11.50 (ISBN 0-915138-27-1). Pickwick.

Samaritans: History, Doctrine & Literature. M. Gaster. 1976. lib. bdg. 134.95 (ISBN 0-8490-2563-X). Gordon Pr.

Samaritans of Molokai. facsimile ed. Charles J. Dutton. (Select Bibliographies Reprint Ser). Repr. of 1932 ed. 23.50 (ISBN 0-8369-5733-4). Ayer Co Pubs.

Samaritans: Their History, Doctrines & Literature. M. Gaster. (British Academy, London, Schweich Lectures on Biblical Archaeology Series, 1923). pap. 28.00 (ISBN 0-8115-1265-7). Kraus Repr.

Samaritans: Their Testimony to the Religion of Israel. J. Thomson. 1976. lib. bdg. 59.95 (ISBN 0-8490-2564-8). Gordon Pr.

Samas Religious Texts Classified in the British Museum Catalogue As Hymns, Prayers, & Incantations. Ed. by Clifton D. Gray. LC 78-72728. (Ancient Mesopotamian Texts & Studies). Repr. of 1901 ed. 17.50 (ISBN 0-404-18176-7). AMS Pr.

Samavedic Chant. Wayne Howard. LC 76-49854. (Illus.). 1977. 50.00x (ISBN 0-300-01956-4). Yale U Pr.

Samayasara (the Soul Essence) Kundakunda Acharya. Tr. & commentaries by Rai B. Jaini. LC 73-3843. (Sacred Books of the Jainas: No. 8). Repr. of 1930 ed. 25.00 (ISBN 0-404-57708-3). AMS Pr.

Same Jesus. Clarence M. Wagner. Ed. by Tru-Faith Publishers. 72p. (Orig.). 1981. pap. 3.50x (ISBN 0-937498-00-9). Tru-Faith.

Same Jesus: A Contemporary Christology. Ed. by Daniel A. Helminiak. 368p. 1986. 15.95 (ISBN 0-8294-0521-6). Loyola.

Same Sex: An Appraisal of Homosexuality. Ed. by Ralph Weltge. LC 71-88184. 1969. pap. 3.95 (ISBN 0-8298-0118-9). Pilgrim NY.

Samed. Raja Shehaden. 172p. 1984. pap. 9.95 (ISBN 0-531-09839-7). Watts.

Samgraha-Cudamani of Govinda. S. Subrahmanya Sastri. 4.75 (ISBN 0-8356-7354-5). Theos Pub Hse.

Samkhya: A Dualist Tradition in Indian Philosophy. Ed. by Gerald J. Larson & Ram Shankar Bhattacharya. LC 85-43199. (Encyclopedia of Indian Philosophies: Vol. 4). 800p. 1987. 75.00x (ISBN 0-691-07301-5). Princeton U Pr.

Samkhya-Sutras of Pancasikha & the Samkhyatattvalcka. Hariharananda Aranya. 1977. 11.25 (ISBN 0-89684-313-0, Pub. by Motilal Banarsidass India); pap. 6.95 (ISBN 0-89684-346-7). Orient Bk Dist.

Samkyha-Yoga: Proceedings of the IASWR Conference, 1981. Ed. by Christopher Chapple. 181p. 1983. pap. text ed. 10.00 (ISBN 0-915078-04-X). Inst Adv Stud Wld.

Sammy Morris: Believing in God's Power. Fern N. Stocker. (Guessing Bks.). (Orig.). 1986. pap. 3.95 (ISBN 0-8024-5443-7). Moody.

Samples from the Love of King David & Fair Bethsabe: With Reference Portions of the Bible. George Peele. Ed. by G. K. Dreher. LC 79-56834. 71p. (Orig.). 1980. pap. 4.95 (ISBN 0-9601000-2-4). Longshanks Bk.

Sampling the Psalms. Henry M. Morris. LC 78-55613. 1978. pap. 5.95 (ISBN 0-89051-049-0). Master Bks.

Samson. Rebecca Daniel. (Our Greatest Heritage Ser.). (Illus.). 32p. 1983. wkbk. 3.95 (ISBN 0-86653-137-8, SS 806). Good Apple.

Samson. (Read, Show & Tell Ser.). (Eng. & Span., Illus.). 1977. Eng. Ed. 2.25 (ISBN 0-8326-2607-4, 3625). Span. Ed (5625). World Bible.

Samson: A Secret Betrayed, A Vow Ignored. James L. Crenshaw. LC 77-15748. 173p. 1981. text ed. 9.95 (ISBN 0-86554-042-X, MUP-H01). Mercer Univ Pr.

Samson Agonistes. John Milton. Ed. by F. T. Prince. 1957. pap. 7.95x (ISBN 0-19-831910-X). Oxford U Pr.

Samson & Delilah. Illus. by Hanna-Barbera. (Greatest Adventure: Stories from the Bible). (Illus., Orig.). Date not set. 5.95 (ISBN 0-687-15745-5). Abingdon.

Samson & Delilah. As told by Catherine Storr. (People of the Bible). (Illus.). 32p. 1985. PLB 10.65 (ISBN 0-8172-2044-5). Raintree Pubs.

Samson Saga & Its Place in Comparative Religion. A. Smythe Palmer. 1977. lib. bdg. 59.95 (ISBN 0-8490-2565-6). Gordon Pr.

Samson-Saga & Its Place in Comparative Religion. Abram S. Palmer. Ed. by Richard Dorson. LC 77-70613. (International Folklore Ser.). 1977. Repr. of 1913 ed. lib. bdg. 23.50x (ISBN 0-405-10112-0). Ayer Co Pubs.

Samson's Secret. Loyal Kolbrek & Chris Larsen. (Arch Bks.: Set 8). (Orig.). 1970. pap. 0.99 (ISBN 0-570-06052-4, 59-1168). Concordia.

Samtliche Werke: Anbind-oder Fangbriefe. Gelegenheitsdichtungen. Beschreibung des Gluckhafens, Vol. 4, Pt. 1. Wolfhart Spangenberg. Ed. by Vizkelety & Bircher. (Ger.). iv, 393p. 1981. 120.00 (ISBN 3-11-008030-3). De Gruyter.

Samuel. Ed. by A. Cohen. 361p. 1949. 10.95 (ISBN 0-900689-26-9). Soncino Pr.

Samuel. Retold by Elaine Ife & Rosalind Sutton. (Now You Can Read Stories from the Bible Ser.). (Illus.). 24p. 1985. 2.50 (ISBN 0-8407-5449-3). Nelson.

Samuel. F. B. Meyer. 1978. pap. 4.50 (ISBN 0-87508-339-0). Chr Lit.

Samuel Beckett's Real Silence. Helene L. Baldwin. LC 80-21465. 184p. 1981. 19.95x (ISBN 0-271-00301-4). Pa St U Pr.

Samuel Butler on the Resurrection. Ed. by Robert Johnstone. 64p. Date not set. 9.95 (ISBN 0-901072-59-1). Dufour.

Samuel Hopkins & the New Divinity Movement: Calvinism, the Congregational Ministry, & Reform in New England Between the Great Awakenings. Joseph A. Conforti. LC 80-28268. pap. 62.30 (ISBN 0-317-08398-8, 2020840). Bks Demand UMI.

Samuel Hopkins Works, 3 vols. Bruce Kuklick. (American Religious Thought of the 18th & 19th Centuries Ser.). 1838p. 1987. Set. lib. bdg. 240.00 (ISBN 0-8240-6951-X). Garland Pub.

Samuel II. Ed. by P. Kyle McCarter, Jr. LC 81-43919. (Anchor Bible Ser.: No. 9). (Illus.). 576p. 1984. 18.00 (ISBN 0-385-06808-5, Anchor Pr). Doubleday.

Samuel Johnson & the Problem of Evil. Richard B. Schwartz. LC 74-27314. 128p. 1975. 27.50x (ISBN 0-299-06790-4). U of Wis Pr.

Samuel K. Mirsky Memorial Volume. Gersion Appel. 1970. 25.00x (ISBN 0-87068-084-6). Ktav.

Samuel Logan Brengle: Portrait of a Prophet. Clarence W. Hall. 1978. Repr. of 1933 ed. 3.95 (ISBN 0-86544-006-9). Salv Army Suppl South.

Samuel Morris. Lindley Baldwin. 74p. 1980. 1.50 (ISBN 0-88113-319-1). Edit Betania.

Samuel Morris. Lindley Baldwin. 96p. 1987. pap. 3.50 (ISBN 0-87123-950-7). Bethany Hse.

Samuel One & Two. James D. Nawsome. Ed. by James D. Hayes. (Knox Preaching Guide Ser.). 1983. pap. 5.95 (ISBN 0-8042-3211-3). John Knox.

Samuel One: Volume Eight, a New Translation with Introduction & Commentary. P. Kyle McCarter, Jr. LC 79-7201. (Anchor Bible Ser.). 1980. 20.00 (ISBN 0-385-06760-7). Doubleday.

Samuel: Prophet & Judge. Richie Whaley. (BibLearn Ser.). (Illus.). 1979. 5.95 (ISBN 0-8054-4242-1, 4242-42). Broadman.

Samuel Seabury: A Bicentennial Biography. Anne Rowthorn. 160p. 1983. 14.95 (ISBN 0-8164-0517-4, HarpR). Har-Row.

Samuel Sewall: A Puritan Portrait. T. B. Strandness. viii, 250p. 1967. 7.50 (ISBN 0-87013-119-2). Mich St U Pr.

Samuel, the Judge. Louise Ulmer. (Arch Bks.). (Illus.). 24p. 1986. pap. 0.99 saddlestitched (ISBN 0-570-06200-4, 59-1423). Concordia.

Samuel the Prophet. C. Knapp. 6.95 (ISBN 0-88172-113-1). Believers Bkshelf.

Samuel, the Prophet. Gordon Lindsay. (Old Testament Ser.). 1.25 (ISBN 0-89985-138-X). Christ Nations.

San Antonio Missions: Edward Everett & the American Occupation, 1847. Richard E. Ahlborn. LC 85-71971. (Illus.). 62p. 1985. pap. 6.95 (ISBN 0-88360-076-5). Amon Carter.

San Cipriano: Life in a Puerto Rican Community. Anthony L. LaRuffa. LC 73-136765. (Library of Anthropology Ser.). (Illus.). 166p. 1971. 44.00 (ISBN 0-677-03470-9). Gordon & Breach.

San Diego Women's Haggadah. rev. ed. Ed. by Jane S. Zones. LC 85-51376. (Illus.). 80p. 1986. pap. 7.50 (ISBN 0-9608054-5-1). Womans Inst-Cont Jewish Ed.

San Juan Bautista: Gateway to Spanish Texas. Robert S. Weddle. (Illus.). 485p. 1968. 24.50x (ISBN 0-292-73306-2). U of Tex Pr.

Sancti Filastrii Episcopi Brixiensis Diversarum Hereseon Liber. St. Philastrius Bishop of Brescia. Repr. of 1898 ed. 50.00 (ISBN 0-384-46225-1). Johnson Repr.

Sancti Pontii Meropii Paulini Nolani Epistulae. Saint Paulinus of Nola. (Corpus Scriptorum Ecclesiasticorum Latinorum Ser: Vol. 29). (Lat). Repr. of 1894 ed. 50.00 (ISBN 0-384-45195-0). Johnson Repr.

Sancti Pontii Meropii Paulini Nolani Carmina. Saint Paulinus of Nola. (Corpus Scriptorum Ecclesiasticorum Latinorum Ser: Vol. 30). Repr. of 1894 ed. 46.00 (ISBN 0-384-45185-3). Johnson Repr.

Sanctification. William Baker. 160p. 1986. pap. 6.95 (ISBN 0-310-35301-7, 11140P). Zondervan.

Sanctification. J. W. Byers. 96p. 0.75 (ISBN 0-686-29140-9). Faith Pub Hse.

Sanctification. Charles G. Finney. Ed. by W. E. Allen. 1963. pap. 2.50 (ISBN 0-87508-191-6). Chr Lit.

Sanctification. C. H. Spurgeon. 1976. pap. 1.50 (ISBN 0-686-16844-5). Pilgrim Pubns.

Sanctification & the Christian. Jeanette Key. 1979. pap. 2.95 (ISBN 0-88027-049-7). Firm Foun Pub.

Sanctified Church. Zora N. Hurston. 107p. 1983. pap. 6.95 (ISBN 0-913666-44-0). Turtle Isl Foun.

Sanctifier. Luis M. Martinez. 1981. 7.50 (ISBN 0-8198-6803-5); pap. 6.00 (ISBN 0-8198-6804-3). Dghtrs St Paul.

Sanctifying Life, Time & Space: An Introduction to Liturgical Study. Marion J. Hatchett. 1976. (HarpR); pap. 8.95 (ISBN 0-8164-2396-2). Har-Row.

Sanctity of the Seventh Year: A Study of Mishnah Tractate Shebiit. Louis E. Newman. LC 83-8683. (Brown Judaic Studies). 276p. 1983. pap. 12.00 (ISBN 0-89130-630-7, 14 00 44). Scholars Pr GA.

Sanctity of the Synagogue. Baruch Litvin & Jeanne Litvin. 1987. 19.95 (ISBN 0-88125-113-5). KTAV.

Sanctuary Doctrine: Three Approaches in the Seventh-Day Adventist Church. Roy Adams. (Andrews University Seminary Doctoral Dissertation Ser.: Vol. 1). viii, 327p. (Orig.). 1981. pap. 9.95 (ISBN 0-943872-33-2). Andrews Univ Pr.

Sanctuary, Eighteen Forty-Four & the Pioneers. Paul A. Gordon. Ed. by Gerald Wheeler. LC 83-17611. 160p. (Orig.). 1984. pap. 9.95 (ISBN 0-8280-0217-7). Review & Herald.

Sanctuary for Lent, 1985. Maxie Dunnam. 48p. (Orig.). 1985. pap. 30.00 per 100 (ISBN 0-687-36847-2). Abingdon.

Sand & Foam. Kahlil Gibran. (Illus.). 1926. 9.95 (ISBN 0-394-44369-1). Knopf.

Sand & Pebbles: The Tales of Muju Ichien, a Voice for Pluralism in Kamakura Buddhism. Robert E. Morrell. (Series in Buddhist Studies). 337p. 1985. 44.50 (ISBN 0-88706-059-5); pap. 16.95x (ISBN 0-88706-060-9). State U NY Pr.

Sand in the Cloud: Voices of Old Testament Witnesses. Ted Loder. Ed. by Marcia Broucek. 180p. (Orig.). 1987. pap. 9.95 (ISBN 0-931055-42-3). LuraMedia.

Sandarbh-MulAK Shabd-Kosh: Hindi-English-Hindi Dictionary of Phrase & Fable Including Symbolic & Idiomatic Expressions. Om P. Gauba. viii, 258p. 1986. text ed. 35.00x (ISBN 81-7018-363-4, Pub. by B. R. Pub Corp Delhi). Apt Bks.

Sane Occultism. Dion Fortune. 192p. 1973. pap. 7.95 (ISBN 0-85030-105-X). Weiser.

Sangha & State in Burma: A Study of Monastic Sectarianism & Leadership. E. Michael Mendelson. Ed. by John P. Ferguson. LC 75-13398. (Illus.). 416p. 1975. 42.50x (ISBN 0-8014-0875-X). Cornell U Pr.

Sangha, State, & Society: Thai Buddhism in History. Yoneo Ishii. Tr. by Peter Hawkes from Japanese. (Monographs, Center for Southeast Asian Studies, Kyoto University). 224p. 1985. text ed. 25.00x (ISBN 0-8248-0993-9); pap. text ed. 16.00x (ISBN 0-8248-0994-7). UH Pr.

Sangreal Sacrament. William G. Gray. LC 82-62847. (Sangreal Sodality Ser.: Vol. 2). 224p. 1983. pap. 8.95 (ISBN 0-87728-562-4). Weiser.

Sanhedrin, 2 vols. 30.00 (ISBN 0-910218-74-9). Bennet Pub.

Sanity of Mysticism. Geraldine E. Hodgson. LC 76-11826. 1976. Repr. of 1926 ed. lib. bdg. 20.00 (ISBN 0-8414-4845-0). Folcroft.

Sankara-Dig-Vijaya: The Traditional Life of Sri Sankaracharya. Madhava-Vidyaranya. Tr. by Swami Tapasyananda. 1979. pap. 6.95 (ISBN 0-87481-484-7). Vedanta Pr.

Sanskrit & Its Kindred Literatures. Laura E. Poor. LC 76-27525. 1976. Repr. of 1880 ed. lib. bdg. 35.00 (ISBN 0-89341-038-1). Longwood Pub Group.

Sanskrit Buddhism in Burma. Nihar-Ranjan Ray. LC 78-70112. Repr. of 1936 ed. 22.00 (ISBN 0-404-17367-5). AMS Pr.

Sanskrit Keys to the Wisdom-Religion. Judith M. Tyberg. 180p. 1976. pap. 5.00 (ISBN 0-913004-29-4). Point Loma Pub.

Sanskrit Mantras. 1977. 10.00x (ISBN 0-930736-03-6); cassett tape recording incl. (ISBN 0-685-32618-7). E W Cultural Ctr.

Santa, Are You for Real? Harold Myra. LC 77-23023. (Illus.). 6.95 (ISBN 0-8407-5122-2). Nelson.

Santa Biblia Dios Habla Hoy. 1504p. 1980. pap. 15.95 (ISBN 0-311-48716-5, Edit Mundo). Casa Bautista.

Santa Biblia: Edicion Bilingue Espanol-Ingles. 1812p. bonded leather 39.95 (ISBN 0-311-48748-3). Casa Bautista.

Santa Claus Stories: Broadcast on 1927 from Palais Royal Department Store, Washington DC. 1987. write for info. Interspace Bks.

Santa Claus: The Tooth Fairy & Other Stories - A Child's Introduction to Religion. Ronald Gestwicki. Ed. by Sylvia Ashton. LC 77-80276. 1977. 15.95 (ISBN 0-87949-108-6). Ashley Bks.

Santa Eucarista y Otros Servicios. (Span.). 44p. 1983. pap. 1.50 (ISBN 0-935461-05-1). St Alban Pr CA.

Santa Is Coming. (Christmas Ser.). 2.95 (ISBN 0-86112-229-1, Pub. by Brimax Bks). Borden.

Santa Maria de Guadalupe. Jose Chavez. (Span.). 1963. pap. 2.00 (ISBN 0-8198-6825-6). Dghtrs St Paul.

Santan Dharma Ka Mahatva: (Uttarpara Speech) Sri Aurobindo. 14p. 3.00 (ISBN 0-317-17480-0). Auromere.

Santa's Christmas Journey. Roger Brooke. LC 85-61188. (Illus.). 32p. 1985. 5.95 (ISBN 0-528-82688-3). Macmillan.

Santiago, St. Denis, & St. Peter: The Reception of the Roman Liturgy in Leon-Castile in 1080. Bernard F. Reilly. (Illus.). xvi, 216p. 1985. 37.50 (ISBN 0-8232-1125-8). Fordham.

Santiago: Una Fe en Accion. Evis L. Carballosa. Orig. Title: James: Faith in Action. (Span.). 352p. (Orig.). 1986. pap. 10.95 (ISBN 0-8254-1112-2). Kregel.

Santificados por Completo-Wholly Sanctified. A. B. Simpson. (Eng., Illus.). 136p. 1981. 2.50 (ISBN 0-87509-307-8). Chr Pubns.

Santification & Liberation: Liberation Theologies in Light of the Wesleyan Tradition. Ed. by Theodore H. Runyon. LC 80-20287. 1981. pap. 6.95 (ISBN 0-687-36810-3). Abingdon.

Santo Rosario en la Cartuja. James Hogg. (Analecta Cartusiana Ser.: No. 103). 134p. (Orig.). 1983. pap. 25.00 (ISBN 0-317-42593-5, Pub. by Salzburg Studies). Longwood Pub Group.

Sarada Devi, Sri: The Great Wonder. 508p. 1985. pap. 8.95 (ISBN 0-87481-569-X, Pub. by Ramakrishna Mission India). Vedanta Pr.

Sarada Devi, Sri the Holy Mother, 2 bks. rev. ed. Incl. Bk. 1. Life. Swami Tapasyananda. pap. 4.95 (ISBN 0-87481-485-5); Bk. 2. Conversations. Tr. by Swami Nikhilananda from Bengali. pap. 3.95 (ISBN 0-87481-486-3). 1978. pap. Vedanta Pr.

Sarada Devi, the Holy Mother: Her Life & Conversations. Swami Tapasyananda & Swami Nikhilananda. (Illus.). 12.95 (ISBN 0-87481-435-9). Vedanta Pr.

Sarah. Marlee Alex. (Outstanding Women of the Bible Ser.). 32p. 1987. 8.95 (ISBN 0-8028-5015-4). Eerdmans.

Sarah the Priestess: The First Matriarch of Genesis. Savina J. Teubal. LC 84-96. xx, 201p. 1984. 16.95 (ISBN 0-8040-0843-4, Swallow); pap. 8.95 (ISBN 0-8040-0844-2, Swallow). Ohio U Pr.

Sarah's Story. Lillian Cantleberry. (Continued Applied Christianity Ser.). 1983. pap. 7.95 (ISBN 0-570-03898-7, 12-2980). Concordia.

Sarajevo Haggadah. Intro. by C. Roth. 50.00 (ISBN 0-87068-761-1). Ktav.

Sarapis & Isis: Collected Essays. Thomas A. Brady. Ed. by Fordyce Mitchel. 129p. 1978. 25.00 (ISBN 0-89005-253-0). Ares.

Sarca Ainda Arde. Lloyd J. Ogilvie. Orig. Title: Bush Is Still Burning. (Port.). 1986. write for info. (ISBN 0-8297-1093-0). Life Pubs Intl.

Sartre & Flaubert. Hazel E. Barnes. LC 80-26872. x, 450p. 1982. pap. 10.95 (ISBN 0-226-03721-5, PHOEN). U of Chicago Pr.

Sartre & the Sacred. Thomas M. King. LC 73-87304. xii, 196p. 1974. 17.00x (ISBN 0-226-43612-8). U of Chicago Pr.

Satan. Lewis S. Chafer. 1977. pap. 5.95 (ISBN 0-310-22361-X, 6308P). Zondervan.

Satan. C. H. Spurgeon. 1978. pap. 1.95 (ISBN 0-686-23026-4). Pilgrim Pubns.

Satan: A Defeated Foe. Charles H. Usher. 1964. pap. 1.95 (ISBN 0-87508-546-6). Chr Lit.

Satan, A Portrait: A Study of the Character of Satan Through All the Ages. Edward Langton. LC 74-2434. 1973. lib. bdg. 35.00 (ISBN 0-8414-5716-6). Folcroft.

Satan, a Portrait: A Study of the Character of Satan Through All the Ages. Edward Langton. 1976. lib. bdg. 59.95 (ISBN 0-8490-2568-0). Gordon Pr.

Satan & Israel. Date not set. pap. 0.95 (ISBN 0-937408-13-1). GMI Pubns Inc.

Satan Exposed. B. D. Voarhis. 1975. pap. 2.25 (ISBN 0-87148-735-3). Pathway Pr.

Satan, Fallen Angels & Demons. Gordon Lindsay. (Satan Ser.: Vol. 2). pap. 1.25 (ISBN 0-89985-954-2). Christ Nations.

Satan, God & Saint Teresa. Robert O. Reddish, Jr. (Illus.). 1967. soft cover 5.00 (ISBN 0-686-08728-3). Rorge Pub Co.

Satan: His Personality, Power & Overthrow. E. M. Bounds. (Direction Bks). 1972. pap. 2.95 (ISBN 0-8010-0586-8). Baker Bk.

Satan in the Pulpit. Staunton E. Smith-Perkins. (Illus.). 104p. (Orig.). 1982. pap. 4.95 (ISBN 0-943982-00-6, Dis. by Book Carrier). SES Development.

Satan in the Woods. Moses J. Steiner. LC 78-54567. 1978. 10.95 (ISBN 0-88400-057-5). Shengold.

Satan Is Alive & Well on Planet Earth. Hal Lindsey. 256p. 1985. pap. 3.95 (ISBN 0-553-24406-X). Bantam.

Satan Is Alive & Well on Planet Earth. Hal Lindsey & C. C. Carlson. 256p. (Orig.). 1974. pap. 4.95 (ISBN 0-310-27792-2, 18195P00687079X). Zondervan.

Satan Is No Myth. J. Oswald Sanders. LC 74-15358. 1983. pap. 5.95 (ISBN 0-8024-7525-6). Moody.

Satan of Milton. R. H. Anstice. LC 72-191957. 1910. lib. bdg. 10.00 (ISBN 0-8414-0289-2). Folcroft.

Satan, Rebellion & Fall, 3 vols. Gordon Lindsay. (Sorcery & Spirit World Ser.: Vol. 3). 1.25 ea. (ISBN 0-89985-953-4). Christ Nations.

Satan-Seller. Mike Warnke et al. LC 79-94042. 204p. 1972. (Pub. by Logos); pap. 3.50 (ISBN 0-88270-096-0). Bridge Pub.

Satan Unmasked: Principles & Practice of Christian Exorcism. G. M. Farley & Robert W. Pelton. LC 78-70632. (Illus.). 1979. 7.50 (ISBN 0-916620-24-7). Portals Pr.

Satanic Mass. H. T. Rhodes. 256p. 1974. 7.95 (ISBN 0-8065-0405-6). Citadel Pr.

Satanic Mass. H. T. Rhodes. 254p. 1975. pap. 3.95 (ISBN 0-8065-0484-6). Citadel Pr.

Satanic Rituals. Anton S. LaVey. 1972. pap. 4.50 (ISBN 0-380-01392-4). Avon.

Satanism & Witchcraft. Jules Michelet. 352p. 1983. pap. 5.95 (ISBN 0-8065-0059-X, 89). Citadel Pr.

Satan's Angels Exposed. Salem Kirban. 1980. pap. 5.95 (ISBN 0-912582-32-4). Kirban.

Satan's Demon Manifestations & Delusions. Gordon Lindsay. (Satan Ser.: Vol. 3). pap. 1.25 (ISBN 0-89985-955-0). Christ Nations.

Satan's Invisible World Discovered. George Sinclair. LC 68-17017. 1969. Repr. of 1685 ed. 45.00x (ISBN 0-8201-1068-X). Schol Facsimiles.

Satan's Music Exposed. Salem Kirban. 1980. pap. 5.95 (ISBN 0-912582-35-9). Kirban.

Satan's Power: A Deviant Psychotherapy Cult. William S. Bainbridge. LC 77-80466. 1978. 33.00x (ISBN 0-520-03546-1). U of Cal Pr.

Satan's Secret Revealed: From the Files of a Christian Exorcist. Frank M. Brim. 176p. 1983. pap. 5.00 (ISBN 0-9612676-0-7). World Wide Mini.

Satan's Ten Most Believable Lies. 2nd ed. David Breese. 1987. pap. 6.95 (ISBN 0-8024-7675-9). Moody.
Satapatha Brahmana. Julius Eggeling. (Sacred Bks. of the East: Vols. 12, 26, 41, 43, 44). 5 vols. 75.00 (ISBN 0-686-97483-2); 15.00 ea. Asian Human Pr.
Satapatha Brahmana, 5 vols. Ed. by Julius Eggeling. 1974. lib. bdg. 500.00 (ISBN 0-8490-0994-4). Gordon Pr.
Satin Principle. Roy Masters. LC 78-78158. 1978. pap. 6.50 (ISBN 0-933900-05-8). Foun Human Under.
Satisfaction of Interest & the Concept of Morality. Steven A. Smith. LC 73-8305. 165p. 1975. 18.00 (ISBN 0-8387-1383-1). Bucknell U Pr.
Satisfied...A Promise of Peace in a Troubled World. Rexella Van Impe. 142p. 1984. pap. 4.95 (ISBN 0-934803-15-3). J Van Impe.
Satsang. M. P. Pandit. Ed. by Vasanti R. Golikhere. (Vol. I). 298p. (Orig.). 1979. pap. 11.00 (ISBN 0-941524-10-8). Lotus Light.
Satsang Notes of Swami Amar Jyoti. Kessler Frey. LC 77-89524. (Illus.). 1977. 4.95 (ISBN 0-933572-01-8); pap. 2.95 (ISBN 0-933572-02-6). Truth Consciousness.
Saturday Evening Post Christmas Book. Saturday Evening Post Editors. LC 76-24034. (Illus.). 160p. 1976. 14.95 (ISBN 0-89387-001-3, Co-Pub by Sat Eve Post). Curtis Pub Co.
Saturday Evening Post Christmas Stories. Saturday Evening Post Editors. LC 80-67058. (Illus.). 144p. 1980. 14.95 (ISBN 0-89387-046-3, Co-Pub by Sat Eve Post). Curtis Pub Co.
Saturday Night, Sunday Morning: Singles & the Church. Nicholas B. Christoff. LC 77-7841. 160p. 1980. pap. 4.95 (ISBN 0-06-061381-5, RD 341, HarpR). Har-Row.
Saturn: The Reaper. Alan Leo. LC 75-16450. 1975. pap. 3.95 (ISBN 0-87728-019-3). Weiser.
Saudaryalahari or, Flood of Beauty. Sankaracarya. Ed. by William N. Brown. LC 57-9072. (Oriental Ser: No. 43). (Illus.). 1958. 16.50x (ISBN 0-674-78990-3). Harvard U Pr.
Saul & Jonathan. Gordon Lindsay. (Old Testament Ser.). 1.25 (ISBN 0-89985-140-1). Christ Nations.
Saul, Israel's First King. Gordon Lindsay. (Old Testament Ser.). 1.25 (ISBN 0-89985-139-8). Christ Nations.
Savage & His Totem. Percival Hadfield. LC 75-32825. Repr. of 1938 ed. 20.00 (ISBN 0-404-14129-3). AMS Pr.
Savage My Kinsman. Elisabeth Elliot. (Illus.). 149p. 1981. pap. 5.95 (ISBN 0-89283-099-9, Pub. by Vine Books). Servant.
Savage Rock: Inniskeen, the History of a Parish. Peter Kavanagh. LC 78-58360. 1978. 20.00. Kavanagh.
Savage Sacrament: A Theology of Marriage after American Feminism. Eileen Z. Silbermann. 128p. (Orig.). 1983. pap. 5.95 (ISBN 0-89622-165-2). Twenty-Third.
Savannah's Old Jewish Community Cemeteries. B. H. Levy. LC 83-1045. vii, 118p. 1983. 10.95 (ISBN 0-86554-076-4, H68). Mercer Univ Pr.
Save America to Save the World. James Robison & Jim Cox. 1980. pap. 1.95 (ISBN 0-8423-5823-4). Tyndale.
Saved & Certain. Thomas G. Davis. (Orig.). 1955. pap. 3.95 (ISBN 0-8054-1611-0). Broadman.
Saved & Kept. F. B. Meyer. 1970. pap. 4.50 (ISBN 0-87508-350-1). Chr Lit.
Saved by Grace. John Bunyan. pap. 2.25 (ISBN 0-685-88393-0). Reiner.
Saved by Grace...for Service. Robert L. Sumner. 1979. 8.95 (ISBN 0-87398-797-7, Pub. by Bibl Evang Pr). Sword of Lord.
Saved by Hope: Essays in Honor of Richard C. Oudersluys. Ed. by James I. Cook. LC 78-5416. Repr. of 1978 ed. 49.50 (ISBN 0-8357-9132-7, 2016060). Bks Demand UMI.
Saved on Monday. Vivian D. Gunderson. 1964. pap. 1.75 (ISBN 0-915374-14-5, 14-5). Rapids Christian.
Saved? What Do You Mean Saved? A Journalist's Report on Salvation. Joe Ortiz. Ed. by Mark D. Feldstein. (Illus.). 95p. (Orig.). 1983. pap. 4.95 (ISBN 0-912695-00-5). GBM Bks.
Saving Challenge of Religion. Budhananda. 272p. (Orig.). 1982. pap. 9.50 (ISBN 0-87481-567-3). Vedanta Pr.
Saving Life of Christ. W. Ian Thomas. 1961. pap. 3.95 (ISBN 0-310-33262-1, 10908S). Zondervan.
Saving Presence: The Ministry & Mystery of the Church. David M. Knight. 1983. 6.95 (ISBN 0-87193-205-9). Dimension Bks.
Saving the Appearances: A Study in Idolatry. Owen Barfield. LC 65-23538. 190p. 1965. pap. 4.95 (ISBN 0-15-679490-X, Harv). HarBraceJ.
Saving Word, Years A, B & C. W. Harrington et al. 370p. 1982. pap. 12.00 ea. (ISBN 0-89453-266-9); Set. pap. 30.00. M Glazier.
Savio: A Study Guide. Joseph Aubry. Tr. by Joe Boenzi from Ital. LC 79-50460. (Orig.). 1979. pap. 2.75 (ISBN 0-89944-038-X). Don Bosco Multimedia.
Saviors of Islamic Spirit, 3 Vols. Nadvi. 60.00 set (ISBN 0-686-18312-6); 20.00 ea. Kazi Pubns.
Saviors of Mankind. William R. Van Buskirk. LC 71-86790. (Essay Index Reprint Ser.). 1929. 32.00 (ISBN 0-8369-1432-5). Ayer Co Pubs.
Saviour God: Comparative Studies in the Concept of Salvation Presented to Edwin Oliver James. Ed. by Samuel G. Brandon. LC 80-14924. xxii, 242p. 1980. Repr. of 1963 ed. lib. bdg. 24.75x (ISBN 0-313-22416-1, BRSG). Greenwood.
Savonarola & Florence: Prophecy & Patriotism in the Renaissance. Donald Weinstein. LC 76-113013. Repr. of 1970 ed. 102.80 (ISBN 0-8357-9511-X, 2015484). Bks Demand UMI.
Savonarola, Protestantism & the Church of Rome, 2 vols. Peter Miscitelli. (Illus.). 247p. 1985. Set. 187.50 (ISBN 0-89901-230-2). Found Class Reprints.
Savoring the Sabbath. Janet Watkins. LC 80-83865. 80p. (Orig.). 1980. pap. 4.95 (ISBN 0-88290-165-6, 1058). Horizon Utah.
Say Amen Brother, Old-Time Negro Preaching: A Study in American Frustration. William H. Pipes. LC 73-111585. Repr. of 1951 ed. 22.50x (ISBN 0-8371-4611-9, PSA&, Pub. by Negro U Pr). Greenwood.
Say-It-Faith. Elmer L. Towns. 1983. pap. 5.95 (ISBN 0-8423-5825-0). Tyndale.
Say It with Love. Howard G. Hendricks. LC 72-77011. 143p. 1972. pap. 5.95 (ISBN 0-88207-050-9). Victor Bks.
Say Jesus & Come to Me. Ann Shockley. 288p. 1985. pap. 2.95 (ISBN 0-380-79657-0, 79657-0, Bard). Avon.
Say Jesus & Come to Me. Ann A. Shockley. 288p. 1986. pap. 8.95 (ISBN 0-930044-98-3). Naiad Pr.
Say No, Say Yes to Change. Elaine Dickson. LC 81-67375. 1982. 6.95 (ISBN 0-8054-5210-9). Broadman.
Say Uncle. Dick Jewett. (Quest Ser.). 32p. 1982. pap. 0.99 (ISBN 0-8163-0489-0). Pacific Pr Pub Assn.
Saying "No" When You'd Rather Say "Yes". Gene A. Getz. LC 83-2939. (Measure of...Ser.). 200p. 1983. pap. 5.95 (ISBN 0-8307-0882-0, 5419099). Regal.
Saying of Buddha. K. R. Moore. 159p. 1982. 15.95x. Coronet Bks.
Saying Thank You Makes Me Happy. Wanda Hayes. (Happy Day Book). (Illus.). 24p. 1979. 1.59 (ISBN 0-87239-353-4, 3623). Standard Pub.
Saying Yes & Saying No: On Rendering to God & Caesar. Robert McAfee Brown. LC 85-29575. 144p. (Orig.). 1986. pap. 7.95 (ISBN 0-664-24695-8). Westminster.
Sayings & Doings of Pai-Chang. Tr. by Thomas Cleary. LC 78-21228. (Zen Writings Ser.: Vol. 6). 1979. pap. 5.95 (ISBN 0-916820-10-6). Center Pubns.
Sayings of Buddha: The Iti-Vuttaka. Itivuttaka. LC 9-4569. (Columbia University. Indo-Iranian Ser.: No. 5). Repr. of 1908 ed. 16.50 (ISBN 0-404-50475-2). AMS Pr.
Sayings of Confucius. Confucius. Tr. by James R. Ware. (Orig.). pap. 2.95 (ISBN 0-451-62168-9, Ment). NAL.
Sayings of Jesus. 5.95 (ISBN 0-88088-351-0). Peter Pauper.
Sayings of Jesus in the Pseudo-Clementine Homilies. Leslie L. Kline. LC 75-1645. (Society of Biblical Literature. Dissertation Ser.: No. 14). Repr. of 1975 ed. 52.00 (ISBN 0-8357-9579-9, 2017517). Bks Demand UMI.
Sayings of Muhammad. G. Ahmad. 8.25 (ISBN 0-87902-036-9). Orientalia.
Sayings of Muhammad. Ghazi Ahmad. pap. 2.00 (ISBN 0-686-18342-8). Kazi Pubns.
Sayings of Muhammad, the Last Prophet. S. A. Hussain. pap. 1.25 (ISBN 0-686-18340-1). Kazi Pubns.
Sayings of Paramahansa Yogananda. Paramahansa Yogananda & Self-Realization Fellowship Editorial Staff. LC 79-66287. (Illus.). 136p. 1980. 4.95 (ISBN 0-87612-115-6); Italian ed. 4.00x (ISBN 0-87612-113-X); German ed. 7.50x (ISBN 0-87612-114-8); Spanish ed. 2.25x (ISBN 0-87612-111-3); Icelandic ed. 9.00x (ISBN 0-87612-112-1). Self Realization.
Sayings of Sri Ramakrishna. Sri Ramakrishna. 5.50 (ISBN 0-87481-431-6). Vedanta Pr.
Sayings of the Ancient One. Patrick G. Bowen. lib. bdg. 79.95 (ISBN 0-87968-490-9). Krishna Pr.
Sayings of the Desert Fathers. (Cistercian Studies: No. 59). pap. 7.95 (ISBN 0-87907-859-6). Cistercian Pubns.
Sayings of the Fathers. E. A. Budge. 1975. pap. 5.95 (ISBN 0-686-10941-4). Eastern Orthodox.
Sayings of the Jewish Fathers, 2 Vols. in 1. rev. ed. Charles Taylor. (Library of Jewish Classics). 1969. 25.00x (ISBN 0-87068-114-1). Ktav.
Sayings of the Jewish Fathers. Charles W. Taylor. 59.95 (ISBN 0-8490-0995-2). Gordon Pr.
Sayings of the Risen Jesus: Christian Prophecy in the Synoptic Tradition. M. Eugene Boring. LC 81-18022. (Society for New Testament Studies Monograph: No. 46). (Illus.). 310p. 1981. 44.50 (ISBN 0-521-24117-0). Cambridge U Pr.
Sayings Parallels: A Workbook for the Jesus Tradition. John D. Crossan. LC 85-16220. (Foundations & Facets Ser.). 256p. 1986. 24.95 (ISBN 0-8006-2109-3, 1-2109); pap. 14.95 (ISBN 0-8006-1909-9, 1-1909). Fortress.
Sayings Traditions in the Apocryphon of James. Ron Cameron. LC 84-45189. (Harvard Theological Studies). 160p. 1984. pap. 12.95 (ISBN 0-8006-7015-9). Fortress.
Sborniki Dukhovno-Muzikal'nikh Proizvjedenij Borisa Mikhajlovicha Ledkovskago, 3 Vols. Tr. of Collections of Sacred Hymns Composed by Boris M. Ledkovsky. 1972. Vol. 1, 47p. 5.00 (ISBN 0-317-30399-6); Vol. 2, 88p. 8.00 (ISBN 0-317-30400-3); Vol. 3, 185p. 15.00 (ISBN 0-317-30401-1). Holy Trinity.
Scale of Perfection & the English Mystical Tradition. Joseph E. Milosh. LC 66-22857. pap. 56.50 (ISBN 0-317-07863-1, 2010975). Bks Demand UMI.
Scalp Ceremonial of Zuni. Elsie C. Parsons. LC 25-1663. (American Anthro. Association Memoirs). 1924. pap. 15.00 (ISBN 0-527-00530-4). Kraus Repr.
Scandal of Christianity: The Gospel as Stumbling Block to Modern Man. Emil Brunner. LC 65-12729. 1965. pap. 5.95 (ISBN 0-8042-0708-9). John Knox.
Scandinavian Mythology. H. R. Davidson. LC 85-22895. (Library of the World's Myths & Legends). (Illus.). 144p. 1986. 18.95 (ISBN 0-87226-041-0). P Bedrick Bks.
Scandinavian Mythology: An Annotated Bibliography. John Lindow. LC 82-49170. (Folklore Ser.). 200p. 1986. lib. bdg. 25.00 (ISBN 0-8240-9173-6). Garland Pub.
Scapegoats: The Exodus of the Remnants of Polish Jewry. Josef Banas. Tr. by Tadeusz Szafar. 221p. 1979. text ed. 34.50 (ISBN 0-8419-6303-7). Holmes & Meier.
Scared & the Doomed: The Jewish Establishment vs. the Six Million. M. J. Nurenberger. (Illus.). 320p. (Orig.). 1986. pap. 12.95 (ISBN 0-88962-289-2). Riverrun NY.
Scared Woman: True Expose, Vol. I. Beulah S. Kershaw. (Illus.). 44p. (Orig.). 1981. pap. 3.00x (ISBN 0-911870-03-2). Beulah.
Scarlet Feather. Joan Cerart. 290p. 1988. pap. 7.95 (ISBN 0-89804-148-1). Ariel OH.
Scarlet Sin, Vol. 4. Gordon Lindsay. (Sorcery & Spirit World Ser.). 3.00 (ISBN 0-89985-087-1). Christ Nations.
Scattering & Oneing: A Study of Conflict in the Works of the Author of the Cloud of Unknowing. Robert W. Englert. Ed. by James Hogg. (Analecta Cartusiana Ser.: No. 105). 184p. (Orig.). 1983. pap. 25.00 (ISBN 0-317-42594-3, Pub. by Salzburg Studies). Longwood Pub Group.
Scenarios of the Imaginary: Theorizing the French Enlightenment. Josue V. Harari. LC 86-24247. 240p. 1987. text ed. 24.95x (ISBN 0-8014-1842-9). Cornell U Pr.
Scenes & Characters of the Middle Ages. Edward L. Cutts. LC 77-23575. 1977. Repr. of 1922 ed. lib. bdg. 45.00 (ISBN 0-89341-160-4). Longwood Pub Group.
Scenes Beyond the Grave. Gordon Lindsay. (Sorcery & Spirit World Ser.). 2.95 (ISBN 0-89985-091-X). Christ Nations.
Scenes from Indian Mythology. 2nd ed. S. M. Imam. 1975. pap. 1.50 (ISBN 0-89684-347-5). Orient Bk Dist.
Scenes of Clerical Life. George Eliot. Ed. by David Lodge. (English Library). (Orig.). 1973. pap. 4.95 (ISBN 0-14-043087-3). Penguin.
Scenes with the Savior. Warner E. Fusselle. LC 84-11389. 1984. pap. 3.75 (ISBN 0-8054-1532-7). Broadman.
Scepsis Scientifica: Or Confest Ignorance, the Way to Science, 2 vols. in 1. Joseph Glanvill. Ed. by Rene Wellek. LC 75-11222. (British Philosophers & Theologians of the 17th & 18th Centuries Ser.). 330p. 1978. lib. bdg. 51.00 (ISBN 0-8240-1776-5). Garland Pub.
Scepticism. Kai E. Nielsen. LC 72-77776. (New Studies in the Philosophy of Religion Ser.). 96p. 1973. 18.95 (ISBN 0-312-70070-9). St Martin.
Scepticism: A Critical Reappraisal. Nicholas Rescher. LC 79-22990. 265p. 1980. 30.00x (ISBN 0-8476-6240-3). Rowman.
Scepticism & Animal Faith. George Santayana. 14.75 (ISBN 0-8446-2863-8). Peter Smith.
Scepticism & Animal Faith: Introduction to a System of Philosophy. George Santayana. 1955. pap. text ed. 6.00 (ISBN 0-486-20236-4). Dover.
Scepticism, Man & God: Selections from the Major Writings Of Sextus Empiricus. Sextus Empiricus. Ed. by Philip P. Hallie. Tr. by Sanford G. Etheridge. LC 64-22377. pap. 62.00 (ISBN 0-317-08988-9, 2001959). Bks Demand UMI.
Scepticism or Platonism: The Philosophy of the Fourth Academy. Harold Tarrant. (Cambridge Classical Studies). 192p. 1985. 39.50 (ISBN 0-521-30191-2). Cambridge U Pr.
Sceptics of the Old Testament. E. J. Dillon. LC 73-16064. (Studies in Comparative Literature, No. 35). 1974. Repr. of 1895 ed. lib. bdg. 51.95x (ISBN 0-8383-1723-5). Haskell.
Scharansky: Hero of our Time. Martin Gilbert. 512p. 1986. 24.95 (ISBN 0-317-46605-4). Viking.
Schelling's Treatise on "the Deities of Samothrace" A Translation & an Interpretation. Robert F. Brown. LC 76-42239. (American Academy of Religion. Studies in Religion). 1977. pap. 9.95 (ISBN 0-89130-087-2, 010012). Scholars Pr GA.
Schemer & the Dreamer: God's Way to the Top. Luis Palau. LC 77-4589. 1976. pap. 3.50 (ISBN 0-930014-12-X). Multnomah.
Schillebeeckx Case. Ed. by Ted Schoof. (Orig.). 1984. pap. 7.95 (ISBN 0-8091-2607-9). Paulist Pr.
Schillebeeckx Reader. Edward Schillebeeckx. Ed. by Robert Schreiter. 1987. pap. 16.95 (ISBN 0-8245-0828-9). Crossroad NY.
Schism in the Methodist Episcopal Church, 1844. John H. Norwood. LC 76-10284. (Perspectives in American Hist. Ser.: No. 33). 255p. 1976. Repr. of 1923 ed. lib. bdg. 25.00x (ISBN 0-87991-357-6). Porcupine Pr.
Schisme orientale du onzieme siecle. Louis Brehier. 1969. Repr. of 1899 ed. 25.50 (ISBN 0-8337-0363-3). B Franklin.
Schleiermacher the Theologian: The Construction of the Doctrine of God. Robert R. Williams. LC 77-78650. pap. 54.50 (2026892). Bks Demand UMI.
Schleiermachers Predigt. 2nd ed. Wolfgang Trillhaas. (Theologische Bibliothek Toepelmann, Vol. 28). 1975. 20.80x (ISBN 3-11-005739-5). De Gruyter.
Schleiermacher's Soliloques. Friedrich E. Schleiermacher. Tr. by Horace L. Friess. LC 78-59040. 1984. Repr. of 1926 ed. 23.00 (ISBN 0-88355-712-6). Hyperion Conn.
Schleitheim Confession. Tr. by John H. Yoder. 32p. 1977. pap. 1.95 (ISBN 0-8361-1831-6). Herald Pr.
Schlemiel As Metaphor: Studies in the Yiddish & American Jewish Novel. Sanford Pinsker. LC 77-132487. (Crosscurrents-Modern Critiques Ser.). 185p. 1971. 6.95x (ISBN 0-8093-0480-5). S Ill U Pr.
Schlemiel Comes to America. Ezra Greenspan. LC 83-14399. 258p. 1983. 20.00 (ISBN 0-8108-1646-6). Scarecrow.
Schoepfung aus dem Nichts: Die Entstehung der Lehre von der Creatio Ex Nihilo. Gerhard May. (Arbeiten zur Kirchengeschichte: Vol. 48). 1978. 34.40 (ISBN 3-11-007204-1). De Gruyter.
Scholars, Saints & Sufis: Muslim Religious Institutions Since 1500. Ed. by Nikki R. Keddie. LC 77-153546. (Near Eastern Center, UCLA). 350p. 1972. pap. 9.95x (ISBN 0-520-03644-1, CAMPUS 210). U of Cal Pr.
Scholars, Saints & Sufis: Muslim Religious Institutions since 1500. Ed. by Nikki R. Keddie. 1983. 14.50 (ISBN 0-8446-5970-3). Peter Smith.
Scholarship of Dr. Samuel Belkin. pap. cancelled (ISBN 0-686-76254-1). Feldheim.
Scholastic Culture of the Middle Ages: 1000-1300. John W. Baldwin. LC 70-120060. (Civilization & Society Ser). 192p. 1971. pap. 8.95x (ISBN 0-669-62059-9). Heath.
Scholastic Miscellany: Anselm to Ockham. Ed. by Eugene R. Fairweather et al. LC 56-5104. (Library of Christian Classics). 454p. 1982. pap. 11.95 (ISBN 0-664-24418-1). Westminster.
Scholastic Rabbinism: A Literary Study of the Fathers According to Rabbi Nathan. Anthony J. Saldarini. LC 81-13564. (Brown Judaic Studies). 1982. pap. text ed. 12.00 (ISBN 0-89130-523-8, 14-00-14). Scholars Pr GA.
Scholastica Commentaria in Primam Partem Summae Theologicae S. Thomae Aquinatis, De Deo Uno. F. Dominico Banes. Ed. by Luis Urbano. (Medieval Studies Reprint Ser.). (Lat. & Span.). Repr. of 1934 ed. lib. bdg. 45.00x (ISBN 0-697-00028-1). Irvington.
Scholasticism & Politics. Jacques Maritain. LC 72-353. (Essay Index Reprint Ser.). Repr. of 1940 ed. 15.00 (ISBN 0-8369-2805-9). Ayer Co Pubs.
Scholasticism & Welfare Economics. Stephen T. Worland. 1967. 17.95 (ISBN 0-268-00246-0). U of Notre Dame Pr.

Scholasticism in the Modern World. Ed. by George F. McLean. (Proceedings of the American Catholic Philosophical Association: Vol. 40). 1966. pap. 15.00 (ISBN 0-918090-00-8). Am Cath Philo.

Scholia Bembina in Terentium. J. F. Mountford. 140p. 1934. text ed. 41.40x (ISBN 0-576-72270-7, Pub. by Gregg Intl Pubs England). Gregg Intl.

School Board Study Programs: Board Members Manual, Series I. Daniel Brent & Carolyn Jurkowitz. 1983. 6.00 (ISBN 0-318-00790-8). Natl Cath Educ.

School Controversy Eighteen Ninety-One to Eighteen Ninety-Three. Daniel F. Reilly. LC 76-89221. (American Education: Its Men, Institutions & Ideas, Ser. 1). 1969. Repr. of 1943 ed. 24.00 (ISBN 0-405-01460-0). Ayer Co Pubs.

School Evaluation for the Catholic Elementary School: An Overview. Carleen Reck & Judith Coreil. 56p. 1983. 3.00 (ISBN 0-318-00791-6). Natl Cath Educ.

School for Masters. Herbert L. Beierle. 1979. 1.00 (ISBN 0-940480-11-5). U of Healing.

School of Jesus. new ed. James A. Mohler. LC 72-11835. 280p. 1973. 5.95 (ISBN 0-8189-0262-0). Alba.

School of Kabbalah. Z'ev ben Shimon Halevi. LC 85-50635. (Illus.). 288p. (Orig.). 1985. pap. 8.95 (ISBN 0-87728-648-5). Weiser.

School of Obedience. Andrew Murray. (Andrew Murray Ser.). pap. 3.50 (ISBN 0-8024-7627-9). Moody.

School Prayer & Other Religious Issues in American Public Education: A Bibliography. Albert J. Menendez. LC 84-48756. (Reference Library of Social Science). 178p. 1985. lib. bdg. 20.00 (ISBN 0-8240-8775-5). Garland Pub.

School Prayer Decisions: From Court Policy to Local Practice. Kenneth M. Dolbeare & Philip E. Hammond. LC 70-140461. 1971. 8.00x (ISBN 0-226-15515-3). U of Chicago Pr.

School Prayers. John H. Laubach. 1969. 9.00 (ISBN 0-8183-0206-2). Pub Aff Pr.

School Year Liturgies. William DeAngelis. (Illus.). 64p. (Orig.). 1985. pap. 9.95 (ISBN 0-89622-218-7). Twenty-Third.

Schools & Churches in American Democracy: In Defense of Public Schools. H. Leo Eddleman. 135p. 1983. pap. 4.00 (ISBN 0-682-40144-7). Exposition Pr FL.

Schools & the Cloister: The Life & the Writings of Alexander Nequam, 1157-1217. R. W. Hunt & Margaret Gibson. 1984. 49.00x (ISBN 0-19-822398-6). Oxford U Pr.

Schools of Thought in the Christian Tradition. Ed. by Patrick Henry. LC 84-47924. 208p. 1984. 19.95 (ISBN 0-8006-0730-9, 1-730). Fortress.

Schopenhauer As Transmitter of Buddhist Ideas. Dorothea W. Dauer. (European University Studies: Series 1, German Language & Literature: Vol. 15). 39p. 1969. 6.55 (ISBN 3-261-00014-7). P Lang Pubs.

Schriften des Johannes von Damaskos, Vol. 3: Contra imaginum columniatores orationes tres. Ed. by P. Bonifatius Kotter. (Patristische Texte und Studien: Vol. 17). (Ger. & Lat.). xvi, 224p. 1975. 51.20x (ISBN 3-11-005971-1). De Gruyter.

Schriftwort in der Rabbinischen Literatur. rev. ed. Victor Aptowitzer. (Library of Biblical Studies Ser). 1970. 45.00x (ISBN 0-87068-005-6). Ktav.

Schurer's History of the Jewish People in the Age of Jesus Christ, 2 vols. Emil Schurer. Ed. by Geza Vermes et al. 42.95 ea. (Pub. by T & T Clark Ltd UK). Vol. 1, 1973, 608 pgs (ISBN 0-567-02242-0). Vol. 2, 1979, 608 pgs (ISBN 0-567-02243-9). Fortress.

Schwenckfeld & Early Schwenkfeldianism. Peter C. Erb. 428p. (Orig.). 1986. pap. 10.00 (ISBN 0-935980-05-9). Schwenkfelder Lib.

Schwenkfelder Hymnology. A. A. Seipt. LC 77-134414. Repr. of 1909 ed. 14.50 (ISBN 0-404-09908-4). AMS Pr.

Schwenkfelders in Silesia. Horst Weigelt. Tr. by Peter C. Erb from Ger. Tr. of Spiritualistische Tradition im Protestantismus. 1985. pap. 10.00 (ISBN 0-935980-04-0). Schwenkfelder Lib.

Science - The False Messiah. C. E. Ayres. Bd. with Holier Than Thou; Way of the Righteous. LC 71-130660. 1973. Repr. of 1927 ed. 37.50x (ISBN 0-678-00774-8). Kelley.

Science, Action, & Fundamental Theology: Toward a Theology of Communicative Action. Helmut Peukert. Tr. by James Bohman from Ger. (German Social Thought Ser.). 364p. 1984. text ed. 37.50x (ISBN 0-262-16095-1). MIT Pr.

Science, Action, & Fundamental Theology: Toward a Theology of Communicative Action. Helmut Peukert. Tr. by James Bohman. (Studies in Contemporary German Social Thought Ser.). 360p. 1986. pap. text ed. 12.50x (ISBN 0-262-66060-1). MIT Pr.

Science Activities for Christian Children. rev. ed. Clifton Keller & Jeanette Appel. 112p. 1986. pap. 5.50 (ISBN 0-930192-15-X). Gazelle Pubns.

Science & Absolute Values: Ten Addresses by Sun Myung Moon. Sun M. Moon. (Illus.). 139p. 1982. casebound 9.95 (ISBN 0-89226-023-8, Pub. by ICF Pr); pap. 5.95 (ISBN 0-89226-019-X). Paragon Hse.

Science & Christian Faith. William H. Davis. LC 68-21524. (Way of Life Ser: No. 104). 1968. pap. 3.95 (ISBN 0-89112-104-8, Bibl Res Pr). Abilene Christ U.

Science & Christian Tradition. Thomas H. Huxley. 419p. 1981. Repr. of 1894 ed. lib. bdg. 45.00 (ISBN 0-89984-285-2). Century Bookbindery.

Science & Christianity. 2nd ed. John D. Callahan. (Illus.). 120p. 1986. pap. 5.95 (ISBN 0-9615767-0-7). Callahan CA.

Science & Creation: Geological, Theological & Educational Perspectives. Ed. by Robert W. Hanson. LC 83-50822. (AAAS Ser. on Issues in Science & Technology). 288p. 1985. text ed. 24.95x (ISBN 0-02-949870-8). Macmillan.

Science & Creationism. Ed. by Ashley Montagu. LC 82-14173. 434p. 1984. 24.95 (ISBN 0-19-503252-7); pap. 11.95x (ISBN 0-19-503253-5). Oxford U Pr.

Science & Creationism: A View from the National Academy of Sciences. National Research Council. 28p. 1984. pap. 4.00 (ISBN 0-309-03440-X). Natl Acad Pr.

Science & Ethical Values. Hiram B. Glass. LC 81-13170. ix, 101p. 1981. Repr. of 1965 ed. lib. bdg. 22.50x (ISBN 0-313-23141-9, GLSE). Greenwood.

Science & Health with Key to the Scriptures. Mary B. Eddy. (Pol.). 25.00 (ISBN 0-87952-200-3). First Church.

Science & Health with Key to the Scriptures. Mary B. Eddy. pap. 10.50 Spanish ed. (ISBN 0-87952-225-9); pap. 10.50 German ed. (ISBN 0-87952-150-3); pap. 10.50 French ed. (ISBN 0-87952-116-3). First Church.

Science & Health with Key to the Scriptures. Mary B. Eddy. Indonesian 25.00 (ISBN 0-87952-175-9); Japanese 25.00 (ISBN 0-87952-190-2). First Church.

Science & Health with Key to the Scriptures. Mary B. Eddy. Incl. Vol. 1. Danish Ed. 25.00 (ISBN 0-87952-103-1); Vol. 2. Dutch Ed. 25.00 (ISBN 0-87952-109-0); Vol. 3. French Ed. 25.00 (ISBN 0-87952-117-1); Vol. 4. German Ed. 25.00 (ISBN 0-87952-151-1); Vol. 5. Norwegian Ed. 25.00 (ISBN 0-87952-195-3); Vol. 6. Swedish Ed. 25.00 (ISBN 0-87952-250-X); Vol. 7. Russian Ed. 25.00 (ISBN 0-87952-220-8); Vol. 8. Greek Ed. 25.00 (ISBN 0-87952-170-8); Vol. 9. Italian Ed. 25.00 (ISBN 0-87952-180-5); Vol. 10. Spanish Ed. 25.00 (ISBN 0-87952-226-7). First Church.

Science & Hebrew Tradition: Essays. Thomas H. Huxley. 1979. Repr. of 1894 ed. lib. bdg. 30.00 (ISBN 0-8495-2263-3). Arden Lib.

Science & Human Values. rev. & enl. ed. Jacob Bronowski. Bd. with Abacus & the Rose. (Illus.). 142p. 1972. pap. 3.50 (ISBN 0-06-080269-3, P269, PL). Har-Row.

Science & Immortality. Manly P. Hall. pap. 2.50 (ISBN 0-89314-351-0). Philos Res.

Science & Justice: The Massachusetts Witchcraft Trials. Sanford J. Fox. LC 68-18771. (Illus.). Repr. of 1968 ed. 27.40 (ISBN 0-8357-9285-4, 2016570). Bks Demand UMI.

Science & Morality: New Directions in Bioethics. Doris Teichler-Zallen & Colleen D. Clements. LC 80-8926. 320p. 1982. 29.00x (ISBN 0-669-04406-7); pap. text ed. 12.00x (ISBN 0-669-09808-6). Lexington Bks.

Science & Morals, & Other Essays. facsimile ed. Bertram C. Windle. LC 70-156731. (Essay Index Reprint Ser). Repr. of 1919 ed. 17.00 (ISBN 0-8369-2301-4). Ayer Co Pubs.

Science & Mysticism: A Comparative Study of Western Natural Science, Theravada Buddhism, & Advaita Vedanta. Richard H. Jones. LC 84-46098. 272p. 1986. 35.00x (ISBN 0-8387-5093-1, Pub. by Bucknell U Pr). Assoc Univ Prs.

Science & Occultism. Taimni. 6.95 (ISBN 0-8356-7501-7). Theos Pub Hse.

Science & Philosophy in the Light of the New Church. (Words for the New Church Ser.: Vols. IV-VI). 289p. 1976. Repr. of 1879 ed. 7.00 (ISBN 0-915221-24-1). Swedenborg Sci Assn.

Science & Practice of Yoga. Swami Paramananda. 1918. pap. 0.50 (ISBN 0-911564-31-4). Vedanta Ctr.

Science & Religion. Elsa M. Glover. 1987. 8.95 (ISBN 0-533-07048-1). Vantage.

Science & Religion. facs. ed. Julian Huxley et al. LC 75-84336. (Essay Index Reprint Ser). 1931. 14.25 (ISBN 0-8369-1106-7). Ayer Co Pubs.

Science & Religion. Swami Ranganathananda. 1979. pap. 3.75 (ISBN 0-87481-190-2). Vedanta Pr.

Science & Religion. 1982. pap. 3.95 (ISBN 0-686-76255-X). Feldheim.

Science & Religion: A Critical Survey. Holmes Rolston, III. 368p. 1986. 34.95 (ISBN 0-87722-437-4). Temple U Pr.

Science & Religion: An Annotated Bibliography. Barker. 1986. lib. bdg. 40.00 (ISBN 0-8240-8762-3). Garland Pub.

Science & Religion: An Introduction. Holmes Rolston, III. 200p. 1987. pap. text ed. 11.50 (ISBN 0-394-36327-2, RanC). Random.

Science and Religion-Convergence or Collision. R. H. Twining. 136p. pap. 2.95 (ISBN 0-686-12939-3). Hiawatha Bondurant.

Science & Religion in America, 1800-1860. Herbert Hovenkamp. LC 78-53332. 1978. 26.00x (ISBN 0-8122-7748-1). U of Pa Pr.

Science & Religion in American Thought. Edward A. White. LC 68-54307. (Stanford University. Stanford Studies in History, Economics, & Poltical Science: No. 8). Repr. of 1952 ed. 17.50 (ISBN 0-404-50972-X). AMS Pr.

Science & Religion in Contemporary Philosophy. Emile Boutroux. Tr. by Jonathan Nield. 1979. Repr. of 1909 ed. lib. bdg. 35.00 (ISBN 0-8495-0540-2). Arden Lib.

Science & Religion in Contemporary Philosophy. Emile Boutroux. LC 70-102563. 1970. Repr. of 1909 ed. 33.50x (ISBN 0-8046-0723-0, Pub. by Kennikat). Assoc Faculty Pr.

Science & Religion in the Nineteenth Century. Tess Cosslett. LC 83-7505. (Cambridge English Prose Texts Ser.). 225p. 1984. 42.50 (ISBN 0-521-24402-1); pap. 14.95 (ISBN 0-521-28668-9). Cambridge U Pr.

Science & Religion in the Thought of Nicolas Malebranche. Michael E. Hobart. LC 81-7419. x, 196p. 1982. 19.95x (ISBN 0-8078-1487-3). U of NC Pr.

Science & Religion: Opposing Viewpoints. Ed. by David L. Bender & Bruno Leone. LC 85-7641. 1981. 11.95 (ISBN 0-89908-334-X); pap. 6.95 (ISBN 0-89908-309-9). Greenhaven.

Science & Religious Thought: A Darwinism Case Study. Walter J. Wilkins. Ed. by Margaret R. Miles. LC 86-24946. (Studies in Religion: No. 3). 224p. 1986. 39.95 (ISBN 0-8357-1778-X). UMI Res Pr.

Science & Sentiment in America: Philosophical Thought from Jonathan Edwards to John Dewey. Morton White. 1972. 25.00x (ISBN 0-19-501519-3). Oxford U Pr.

Science & Superstition in the Eighteenth Century: A Study of the Treatment of Science in Two Encyclopedias of 1725-1750. Philip Shorr. LC 33-3916. (Columbia University. Studies in the Social Sciences: No. 364). Repr. of 1932 ed. 10.00 (ISBN 0-404-51364-6). AMS Pr.

Science & Synthesis: An International Colloquium Organized by UNESCO on the Tenth Anniversary of the Death of Albert Einstein & Teilhard De Chardin. UNESCO Colloqium, 10th Anniversary of the Death of Albert Einstein & Teilhard De Charden. Tr. by B. M. Crook. LC 77-143044. 1971. 29.00 (ISBN 0-387-05344-1). Springer-Verlag.

Science & the Bible. rev., expanded ed. Henry M. Morris. 1986. pap. 5.95 (ISBN 0-8024-0656-4). Moody.

Science & the Bible in a Troubled World. W. W. Crouch. LC 84-90294. 102p. 1985. 8.95 (ISBN 0-533-06326-4). Vantage.

Science & the Business of Living. James G. Vail. 1983. pap. 2.50x (ISBN 0-87574-070-7, 070). Pendle Hill.

Science & the Christian Experiment. A. R. Peacocke. 1971. pap. 8.95x (ISBN 0-19-213956-8). Oxford U Pr.

Science & the Religious Life. Carl Rahn. 1928. 39.50x (ISBN 0-685-69853-X). Elliots Bks.

Science & Ultimate Truth. W. R. Inge. 1978. lib. bdg. 12.50 (ISBN 0-8495-2603-5). Arden Lib.

Science & Ultimate Truth. W. R. Inge. LC 73-7513. 1926. Repr. lib. bdg. 8.50 (ISBN 0-8414-2109-9). Folcroft.

Science & Values. Joseph Grunfeld. 210p. (Orig.). 1973. pap. 22.00x (ISBN 90-6032-016-6, Pub. by B R Gruener). Benjamins North AM.

Science, Democracy, & Islam: And Other Essays. Kabir Humayun. LC 80-2195. Repr. of 1955 ed. 20.00 (ISBN 0-404-18967-9). AMS Pr.

Science et Christ. Pierre Teilhard De Chardin. 1965. 14.50 (ISBN 0-685-11556-9). French & Eur.

Science for Democracy. facs. ed. Conference On The Scientific Spirit And Democratic Faith - 3rd. LC 70-121459. (Essay Index Reprint Ser.). 1946. 18.00 (ISBN 0-8369-1793-6). Ayer Co Pubs.

Science, History & Faith. Alan Richardson. LC 86-22863. 216p. 1986. Repr. of 1950 ed. lib. bdg. 39.75x (ISBN 0-313-25325-0, RISHF). Greenwood.

Science, History & the Shroud of Turin. Robert W. Maher. 1986. 8.95 (ISBN 0-533-06641-7). Vantage.

Science History & Theology: Proceedings, Suppl. 14. Aristotelian Society for the Systematic Study of Philosophy Staff. 13.00 (ISBN 0-384-54410-X); pap. 8.00 (ISBN 0-384-54411-8). Johnson Repr.

Science, Metaphysics, & the Chance of Salvation: An Interpretation of the Thought of William James. Henry S. Levinson. LC 78-7383. 1978. pap. 9.95 (ISBN 0-89130-234-4, 01-01-24). Scholars Pr GA.

Science of Kriya Yoga. Roy E. Davis. 192p. 1984. 7.95 (ISBN 0-317-20860-8). CSA Pr.

Science of Meditation. Rohit Mehta. 1978. 11.95 (ISBN 0-89684-007-7, Pub. by Motilal Banarsidass India). Orient Bk Dist.

Science of Meditation. Haroutiun Saraydarian. LC 77-158995. 1971. 11.00 (ISBN 0-911794-29-8); pap. 9.00 (ISBN 0-911794-30-1). Aqua Educ.

Science of Mind. rev. & enl. ed. Ernest Holmes. 17.95 (ISBN 0-396-02069-0). Dodd.

Science of Mind Hymnal. Thomas L. McClellan. 9.50 (ISBN 0-87516-343-2). De Vorss.

Science of Natural Theology. Asa Mahan. LC 75-3273. Repr. of 1867 ed. 27.50 (ISBN 0-404-59261-9). AMS Pr.

Science of Numbers. Gopi Sharma. 1984. 11.50x (ISBN 0-8364-1133-1, Pub. by Ajanta). South Asia Bks.

Science of Religion. pap. 9.95 (ISBN 0-937134-16-3). Amrita Found.

Science of Religion. Paramahansa Yogananda. LC 81-52892. (Illus.). 102p. 1982. 6.00 (ISBN 0-87612-004-4); Span. ed. 1.50x (ISBN 0-87612-001-X); pap. 5.00x German ed. (ISBN 3-87041-225-9); pap. 3.50 English ed. (ISBN 0-87612-005-2). Self Realization.

Science of Religion. Paramahansa Yogananda. (Dutch.). 1974. 6.50x (ISBN 90-202-45-465). Self Realization.

Science of Religion & the Sociology of Knowledge: Some Methodological Questions. Ninian Smart. LC 72-12115. 176p. 1973. 20.00x (ISBN 0-691-07191-8); pap. 8.50x (ISBN 0-691-01997-5). Princeton U Pr.

Science of Religion, Studies in Methodology. Ed. by Lauro Honko. (Religion & Reason Ser.). 1979. text ed. 50.50x (ISBN 90-279-7854-9). Mouton.

Science of Self Realization. Swami Bhaktivedanta. (Illus.). 1977. 3.95 (ISBN 0-89213-101-2). Bhaktivedanta.

Science of Spiritual Alchemy. R. Swinburne Clymer. 235p. 1959. 9.95 (ISBN 0-932785-44-1). Philos Pub.

Science of Spirituality. M. K. Khan. 135p. 1983. text ed. 15.00x (ISBN 0-86590-164-3). Apt Bks.

Science of Successful Living. Raymond C. Barker. LC 57-11392. 145p. 1984. pap. 5.50 (ISBN 0-87516-536-2). De Vorss.

Science of Survival. L. Ron Hubbard. 31.00 (ISBN 0-686-30779-8). Church Scient NY.

Science of Survival: Prediction of Human Behavior. L. Ron Hubbard. LC 51-5566. (Illus.). 550p. 1951. 47.16 (ISBN 0-88404-001-1). Bridge Pubns Inc.

Science of the Sacraments. Leadbeater. 18.95 (ISBN 0-8356-7126-7). Theos Pub Hse.

Science of Yoga. Taimni. 10.95 (ISBN 0-8356-7140-2). Theos Pub Hse.

Science of Yoga. I. K. Taimni. LC 67-4112. pap. 6.95 (ISBN 0-8356-0023-8, Quest). Theos Pub Hse.

Science, Philosophy & Religion. John Bascom. LC 75-3041. Repr. of 1871 ed. 36.00 (ISBN 0-404-59039-X). AMS Pr.

Science, Philosophy & Religion. 559p. 1985. Repr. of 1942 ed. lib. bdg. 85.00 (ISBN 0-8492-3208-2). R West.

Science, Philosophy, & Religion: Proceedings. Conference on Science, Philosophy & Religion in Their Relation to the Democratic Way of Life, 3rd. 1943. 37.00 (ISBN 0-527-00650-5). Kraus Repr.

Science, Philosophy, & Religion: Proceedings. Conference on Science, Philosophy & Religion in Their Relation to the Democratic Way of Life, 2nd. 1942. 37.00 (ISBN 0-527-00649-1). Kraus Repr.

Science, Philosophy, & Religion: Proceedings. Conference on Science, Philosophy & Religion & Their Relation to the Democratic Way of Life, 1st. 1941. 37.00 (ISBN 0-527-00648-3). Kraus Repr.

Science, Politics & Gnosticism. Eric Voegelin. LC 68-14367. 128p. 4.95 (ISBN 0-89526-964-3). Regnery Bks.

Science, Politics & the Great Deception, Religion. Ruth Norman. 530p. (Orig.). 1987. text ed. 14.95 (ISBN 0-932642-93-4). Unarius Pubns.

Science Proves the Bible. George Carman. Ed. by Mason De Witt. 190p. 1986. 12.00 (ISBN 0-936749-00-8). Zytech Western Pub.

Science, Reason & Religion. Derek Stanesby. 210p. 1985. 34.50 (ISBN 0-7099-3360-6, Pub. by Croom Helm Ltd). Methuen Inc.

Science, Religion & Tradition. Charles R. Cantonwine. 1986. 7.95 (ISBN 0-533-06727-8). Vantage.
Science, Sin & Scholarship: The Politics of Reverend Moon & the Unification Church. Ed. by Irving L. Horowitz. 312p. 1978. pap. 7.95x (ISBN 0-262-58042-X). MIT Pr.
Science, Society & Philosophy: A New Radical Humanist Approach. Oroon K. Ghosh. 1986. 28.00x (ISBN 0-8364-1563-9, Pub. by Ajanta). South Asia Bks.
Science Studies Yoga. James Funderburk. 270p. (Orig.). pap. 8.95 (ISBN 0-89389-026-X). Himalayan Pubs.
Science, Theology & Einstein. Iain Paul. (Theology & Scientific Culture Ser.). 1982. 16.95x (ISBN 0-19-520378-X). Oxford U Pr.
Sciences & the Vedas. Ed. by Ishwarbhai Patel. 1986. 12.50X (ISBN 0-8364-1663-5, Pub. by Somaiya). South Asia Bks.
Sciences & Theology in the Twentieth Century. Ed. by A. R. Peacocke. LC 81-14771. 309p. 1982. 25.00 (ISBN 0-268-01704-2). U of Notre Dame Pr.
Sciences & Theology in the Twentieth Century. Ed. by Arthur R. Peacocke. LC 81-14771. 327p. 1986. pap. 12.95 (ISBN 0-268-01725-5). U of Notre Dame Pr.
Scientific & Humorous Revelations of God. 2nd rev. ed. Paul J. Raabe. 1981. 4.00 (ISBN 0-682-49415-1). Exposition Pr FL.
Scientific Basis of National Progress, Including That of Morality. G. Gore. 218p. 1970. Repr. of 1882 ed. 26.00x (ISBN 0-7146-2407-1, BHA-02407, F Cass Co). Biblio Dist.
Scientific Case for Creation. Henry M. Morris. LC 77-78019. (Illus.). 1977. pap. 2.95 (ISBN 0-89051-037-7). Master Bks.
Scientific Case for Creation. Bert Thompson. (That You May Believe Ser.). 47p. (Orig.). 1985. pap. 1.50 (ISBN 0-932859-03-8). Apologetic Pr.
Scientific Christian Mental Practice. Emma C. Hopkins. 1974. pap. 7.95 (ISBN 0-87516-199-5). De Vorss.
Scientific Creationism. Ed. by Henry M. Morris et al. LC 74-14160. 1974. pap. 8.95 (ISBN 0-89051-003-2). Master Bks.
Scientific Demonstration of the Future Life. Thomas Hudson. 1979. pap. 2.50 (ISBN 0-89083-464-4). Zebra.
Scientific Evidence of the Existence of the Soul. rev. ed. Benito F. Reyes. LC 70-122432. 1970. (Quest); pap. 7.50 (ISBN 0-8356-0404-7, Dist. by World Univ Amer). Theos Pub Hse.
Scientific Healing Affirmations. pap. 7.95 (ISBN 0-937134-15-5). Amrita Found.
Scientific Insights into Yoruba Traditional Medicine. James I. Durodola. (Traditional Healing Ser.). 1985. 27.50 (ISBN 0-686-85813-1). Conch Mag.
Scientific Proof of the Existence of Reincarnation & Transmigration. Richard Van Den Tak. (Illus.). 1981. 16.50 (ISBN 0-89962-015-9). Todd & Honeywell.
Scientific Spirit & Democratic Faith. facs. ed. Conference On The Scientific Spirit And Democratic Faith-1st-New York-1943. LC 72-121457. (Essay Index Reprint Ser). 1944. 14.00 (ISBN 0-8369-1872-X). Ayer Co Pubs.
Scientific Study of Religion. J. Milton Yinger. (Illus.). 1970. text ed. write for info. (ISBN 0-02-430900-1). Macmillan.
Scientific Theism. Francis E. Abbot. LC 75-3012. (Philosophy in America Ser.). Repr. of 1885 ed. 27.50 (ISBN 0-404-59004-7). AMS Pr.
Scientific Theism. Arvid Reuterdahl. 1926. 10.00 (ISBN 0-8159-6805-1). Devin.
Scientific Theist: A Life of Francis Ellingwood Abbot. Sydney E. Ahlstrom & Robert B. Mullin. 208p. 1987. 29.95 (ISBN 0-86554-236-8). Mercer Univ Pr.
Scientific Theory & Religion. Ernest W. Barnes. LC 77-27198. (Gifford Lectures: 1927-29). Repr. of 1933 ed. 42.50 (ISBN 0-404-60483-8). AMS Pr.
Scientific Vedanta. Kashinath. LC 73-900893. 129p. 1974. 7.50x (ISBN 0-89684-451-X). Orient Bk Dist.
Scientific Yoga for the Man of Today. Sri S. Chakravarti. 1971. pap. 3.50 (ISBN 0-685-58385-6). Ranney Pubns.
Scientism in Chinese Thought, Nineteen Hundred to Nineteen Fifty. D. W. Kwok. LC 73-162297. 231p. 1972. Repr. of 1965 ed. 18.00 (ISBN 0-8196-0275-2). Biblo.
Scientists Confront Creationism. Ed. by Laurie R. Godfrey. 352p. 1984. pap. 8.95 (ISBN 0-393-30154-0). Norton.
Scientists Who Believe: Twenty-One Tell Their Own Stories. Ed. by Eric C. Barrett & David Fisher. 1984. pap. 4.50 (ISBN 0-8024-7634-1). Moody.
Scientology: A History of Man. L. Ron Hubbard. 31.00 (ISBN 0-686-30784-4). Church Scient NY.
Scientology: A History of Man. L. Ron Hubbard. 1952. 13.00 (ISBN 0-88404-024-0). Bridge Pubns Inc.
Scientology: A New Slant on Life. L. Ron Hubbard. 20.00 (ISBN 0-686-13918-6). Church Scient NY.
Scientology: A New Slant on Life. L. Ron Hubbard. 160p. 1965. 21.44 (ISBN 0-88404-013-5). Bridge Pubns Inc.
Scientology: A Religion Helping Others. Information Ser. (Illus.). 1978. pap. 4.00 (ISBN 0-915598-21-3). Church of Scient Info.
Scientology & Dianetics. (Illus.). 1971. pap. 4.00 (ISBN 0-915598-03-5). Church of Scient Info.
Scientology: Clear Procedure. L. Ron Hubbard. 8.75 (ISBN 0-686-30791-7). Church Scient NY.
Scientology: Clear Procedure Issue One. L. Ron Hubbard. 1957. pap. 9.50 (ISBN 0-88404-069-0). Bridge Pubns Inc.
Scientology Documenting the Truth. pap. 7.00 (ISBN 0-915598-24-8). Church of Scient Info.
Scientology Eight to Eight Thousand Eight. L. Ron Hubbard. 152p. 1953. 32.16 (ISBN 0-88404-008-9). Bridge Pubns Inc.
Scientology: Eight to Eights. L. Ron Hubbard. 31.00 (ISBN 0-686-30785-2). Church Scient NY.
Scientology Eight to Eighty: The Discovery & Increase of Life Energy in the Genus Homo Sapiens. L. Ron Hubbard. 1952. 27.85 (ISBN 0-88404-020-8). Bridge Pubns Inc.
Scientology: The Fundamentals of Thought. L. Ron Hubbard. 20.00 (ISBN 0-686-30788-7). Church Scient NY.
Scientology: The Fundamentals of Thought. L. Ron Hubbard. 128p. 1956. 21.44 (ISBN 0-88404-018-6). Bridge Pubns Inc.
Scientology Zero-Eight, the Book of Basics. L. Ron Hubbard. 31.00 (ISBN 0-686-30808-5). Church Scient NY.
Scientology Zero to Eight: The Book of Basics. L. Ron Hubbard. 159p. 1950. 32.16 (ISBN 0-88404-009-7). Bridge Pubns Inc.
Scientology: 8-8008. L. Ron Hubbard. 31.00 (ISBN 0-686-13924-0). Church Scient NY.
Scope & Authority of the Bible. James Barr. LC 80-21394. 164p. 1981. pap. 7.95 (ISBN 0-664-24361-4). Westminster.
Scope of Morality. Peter French. 1980. 25.00 (ISBN 0-8166-0837-7); pap. 9.95 (ISBN 0-8166-0900-4). U of Minn Pr.
Scorpio. Paula Harris. (Sun Signs). (Illus.). 1978. pap. 3.95 (ISBN 0-89812-078-0). Creative Ed.
Scot of the Eighteenth Century. John Watson. LC 76-47571. 1976. Repr. of 1907 ed. lib. bdg. 39.50 (ISBN 0-8414-9459-2). Folcroft.
Scotia Pontificia: Papal Letters to Scotland Before the Pontificate of Innocent III, 1198 to 1216. Ed. by Robert Somerville. 1981. 65.00x (ISBN 0-19-822433-8). Oxford U Pr.
Scotland of Queen Mary & the Religious Wars, 1513-1638. Agnes M. Mackenzie. LC 75-41506. (Illus.). 404p. 1976. Repr. of 1957 ed. lib. bdg. 24.00x (ISBN 0-8371-8704-4, MASQ). Greenwood.
Scots Gospel. Jamie Stuart. LC 86-45544. 87p. (Orig.). 1986. pap. 4.95 (ISBN 0-8042-0421-7); 60 min. cassette 7.95 (ISBN 0-8042-0424-1). John Knox.
Scott. new ed. Christopher. (Orig.). 1978. pap. 3.95 (ISBN 0-87243-078-2). Templegate.
Scottish Abbeys & Social Life. G. G. Coulton. 1977. lib. bdg. 59.95 (ISBN 0-8490-2573-7). Gordon Pr.
Scottish Churchmen & the Council of Basle. J. H. Burns. LC 64-7472. 1962. 15.00 (ISBN 0-8023-9034-X). Dufour.
Scottish Methodism in the Early Victorian Period: The Scottish Correspondence of the Reverend Jabez Bunting, 1800-1857. A. J. Hayes & D. A. Gowland. 143p. 1981. 20.00x (ISBN 0-85224-412-6, Pub. by Edinburgh U Pr Scotland). Columbia U Pr.
Scottish Methodism in the Early Victorian Period: The Scottish Correspondence of the Rev. Jabez Bunting 1800-57. Ed. by A. J. Hayes & D. A. Gowland. 1981. 40.00x (ISBN 0-85224-412-6, Pub. by Edinburgh Univ England). State Mutual Bk.
Scottish Reformation. Ian B. Cowan. LC 82-5834. 256p. 1982. 25.00x (ISBN 0-312-70519-0). St Martin.
Scottish Reformation. G. Donaldson. 49.50 (ISBN 0-521-08675-2). Cambridge U Pr.
Scottish Rite Masonry, 2 vols. E. A. Cook. Set. 20.00x (ISBN 0-685-22097-4). Wehman.
Scottish Rite Masonry, 2 vols. Set. 20.00 (ISBN 0-685-19498-1). Powner.
Scottish Visitors: A Story about 'Abdu'l-Baha in Britain. Anthony A. Lee. (Stories About 'Abdu'l-Baha Ser.). (Illus.). 24p. (Orig.). 1981. pap. 2.50 (ISBN 0-933770-05-7). Kalimat.
Scourge of the Clergy: Peter of Dreux, Duke of Brittany. Sidney Painter. LC 76-96188. 1970. Repr. of 1937 ed. lib. bdg. 16.00x (ISBN 0-374-96175-1, Octagon). Hippocrene Bks.
Scrap Saver's Christmas Stitchery. Sandra L. Foose. (Illus.). 160p. 1986. 19.95 (ISBN 0-8487-0646-3). Oxmoor Hse.
Screening Candidates for the Priesthood & Religious Life. Vincent V. Herr et al. (Illus.). 1964. 2.80 (ISBN 0-8294-0038-9). Loyola.
Screwtape Letters. C. S. Lewis. Bd. with Screwtape Proposes a Toast. 1964-67. 9.95 (ISBN 0-02-571240-3). Macmillan.
Screwtape Letters. C. S. Lewis. (Illus.). 144p. 1978. pap. 2.95 (ISBN 0-8007-8336-0, Spire Bks); pap. 4.95 (ISBN 0-8007-5014-4, Power Bks). Revell.
Scribes, Scrolls, & Scripture: A Layperson's Guide to Textual Criticism. J. Harold Greenlee. 112p. (Orig.). 1985. pap. 6.95 (ISBN 0-8028-0082-3). Eerdmans.
Scripta Contra Donatistas, 3 Vols, Pts. 3. Saint Augustinus. (Corpus Scriptorum Ecclesiasticorum Latinorum Ser: Vols. 51, 52, 53). Set. 130.00 (ISBN 0-384-02553-6). Johnson Repr.
Scriptores Ecclesiastici Minores Saeculorum, Nos. IV, V, VI. (Corpus Scriptorum Ecclesiasticorum Latinorum Ser: Vol. 45). (Lat). 1904. unbound 50.00 (ISBN 0-384-54490-8). Johnson Repr.
Scriptores Historiae Augustae, 3 vols. Ed. by E. H. Warmington. Tr. by D. Magie. (Loeb Classical Library: No. 139-140, 263). (Lat. & Eng.). 13.95x ea.; Vol. 1. (ISBN 0-674-99154-0); Vol. 2. (ISBN 0-674-99155-9); Vol. 3. (ISBN 0-674-99290-3). Harvard U Pr.
Scriptores Originum Constantino-Politanarum. Ed. by Theodorus Preger. LC 75-7335. (Roman History Ser.). (Gr.). 1975. Repr. 32.00x (ISBN 0-405-07054-3). Ayer Co Pubs.
Scriptorium of Bury St. Edmunds in the Twelfth Century. Elizabeth P. McLachlan. LC 83-48695. (Theses from the Courtauld Institute of Art Ser.). (Illus.). 515p. 1984. lib. bdg. 60.00 (ISBN 0-8240-5983-2). Garland Pub.
Scriptual Dramas for Children. Denis O'Gorman. LC 77-70632. 232p. 1977. pap. 8.95 (ISBN 0-8091-2021-6). Paulist Pr.
Scriptural & Allegorical Glossary to Milton's Paradise Lost. Christian Cann. 1978. Repr. of 1828 ed. lib. bdg. 35.00 (ISBN 0-8495-0807-X). Arden Lib.
Scriptural & Allegorical Glossary to Milton's Paradise Lost. Christian Cann. Repr. of 1828 ed. 32.50 (ISBN 0-8414-0566-2). Folcroft.
Scriptural Choreography: Biblical Dance Forms in Shaping Contemporary Worship. Linda K. Seaton. 1979. 2.50 (ISBN 0-941500-15-2). Sharing Co.
Scriptural Guide to a Fulfilling Marriage: Two Shall Become One. Gary K. Harley. 168p. (Orig.). 1987. cancelled (ISBN 0-932990-01-0). Ideals.
Scriptural Holiness. Noel Brooks. 3.95 (ISBN 0-911866-53-1); pap. 2.95 (ISBN 0-911866-54-X). Advocate.
Scriptural Light on Speaking in Tongues. Wesley Bouterse. 1980. pap. 1.25 (ISBN 0-86544-010-7). Salv Army Suppl South.
Scriptural Meditations for the Rosary. Peter H. Huyck. (Greeting Book Line Ser.). (Illus.). 48p. 1982. pap. 1.50 (ISBN 0-89622-157-1). Twenty-Third.
Scriptural Meditations on the Rosary. Compiled by Daughters of St. Paul. 1981. 3.50 (ISBN 0-8198-6814-0). Dghtrs St Paul.
Scriptural Outline of the Baptism of the Holy Spirit. George Gillies & Harriet Gillies. 32p. 1972. pap. 1.50 (ISBN 0-88368-062-9). Whitaker Hse.
Scriptural Prayer Journal. David E. Rosage. 150p. (Orig.). 1987. pap. 4.95 (ISBN 0-89283-341-6). Servant.
Scriptural Principles of Gathering. A. P. Gibbs. pap. 1.95 (ISBN 0-937396-37-0). Walterick Pubs.
Scriptural Refutation of the Pope's Primacy. Apostolos Makrakis. Tr. by Denver Cummings from Hellenic. 171p. (Orig.). 1952. pap. 3.75x (ISBN 0-938366-40-8). Orthodox Chr.
Scriptural Religion & Political Task. E. H. Runner. 1974. pap. 2.95 (ISBN 0-686-11989-4). Wedge Pub.
Scriptural Rosary. Christianica Center Staff. LC 64-66463. (Illus.). 1961. 5.95 (ISBN 0-911346-01-5). Christianica.
Scriptural Sermon Outlines. Russell E. Spray. 64p. 1987. pap. price not set (ISBN 0-8010-8277-3). Baker Bk.
Scriptural Signs of the Second Coming. James J. Unopolus. 1979. pap. 1.50 (ISBN 0-89036-072-3). Hawkes Pub Inc.
Scriptural Treasury of Eternal Life. Mary E. Mathis. 1981. pap. 0.40 (ISBN 0-570-08357-5, 12-2937). Concordia.
Scriptural Treasury of Forgiveness. Mary E. Mathis. 1981. pap. 0.40 (12-2935). Concordia.
Scriptural Treasury of Guidance. Mary E. Mathis. 1981. pap. 0.40 (ISBN 0-570-08350-8, 12-2930). Concordia.
Scriptural Treasury of Hope. Mary E. Mathis. LC 12-2931. 1981. pap. 0.40 (ISBN 0-570-08351-6). Concordia.
Scriptural Treasury of Joy. Mary E. Mathis. 1981. pap. 0.40 (ISBN 0-570-08353-2, 12-2933). Concordia.
Scriptural Treasury of Love. Mary E. Mathis. 1981. pap. 0.40 (ISBN 0-570-08356-7, 12-2936). Concordia.
Scriptural Treasury of Peace. Mary E. Mathis. 1981. pap. 0.40 (ISBN 0-570-08352-4, 12-2932). Concordia.
Scriptural Worship Aids. LeRoy Koopman. (Illus.). 1978. pap. 2.95 (ISBN 0-8010-5392-7). Baker Bk.
Scripture & Tradition. Archimandrite Chrysostomos & Hieromonk Auxentios. 96p. 1984. pap. 5.00 (ISBN 0-911165-04-5). Ctr Trad Orthodox.
Scripture & Tradition in Judaism. 2nd rev. ed. Geza Vermes. (Studia Post Biblica: No. 4). 1973. text ed. 9.95x (ISBN 90-040-3626-1). Humanities.
Scripture & Truth. Ed. by D. A. Carson & John D. Woodbridge. 1986. pap. 11.95 (ISBN 0-310-43791-1, 12643P). Zondervan.
Scripture Birthday Book. 128p. 1986. 9.95 (ISBN 0-529-06363-8). World Bible.
Scripture Facts the Easy Way. Emily Filipi. (Quiz & Puzzle Books). 1980. pap. 1.95 (ISBN 0-8010-3491-4). Baker Bk.
Scripture Handbook on Business & Finance. Don Lasley & Kay Lasley. 1985. pap. 6.95 (ISBN 0-89274-317-4). Harrison Hse.
Scripture in Context: Essays on the Comparative Method. Ed. by Carl D. Evans et al. LC 80-10211. (Pittsburgh Theological Monograph Ser.: No. 34). 1980. pap. 15.00 (ISBN 0-915138-43-3). Pickwick.
Scripture in Context II: More Essays on the Comparative Method. Ed. by W. W. Hallo et al. 1983. text ed. 17.50 (ISBN 0-931464-14-5). Eisenbrauns.
Scripture in History & Theology: Essays in Honor of J. Coert Rylaarsdam. Ed. by Arthur L. Merrill & Thomas W. Overholt. LC 77-12106. (Pittsburgh Theological Monographs: No. 17). 1977. pap. 10.00 (ISBN 0-915138-32-8). Pickwick.
Scripture in the Jewish & Christian Traditions: Authority, Interpretation, Relevance. Ed. by Frederick E. Greenspahn. 240p. 1982. pap. 11.95 (ISBN 0-687-37065-5). Abingdon.
Scripture Index to the New International Dictionary of New Testament Theology: And Index to Selected Extrabiblical Literature. David Townsley & Russell Bjork. Ed. by Brown & Colin. 208p. 1985. pap. 10.95 (ISBN 0-310-44501-9, 11315P). Zondervan.
Scripture Memory One Hundred One. John W. Alexander. 1975. pap. 0.75 (ISBN 0-87784-153-5). Inter-Varsity.
Scripture Notes A. rev. ed. Norman Beck. Ed. by Michael L. Sherer. 1986. pap. 9.95 (ISBN 0-89536-808-0, 6837). CSS of Ohio.
Scripture Notes: Series B (Common Consensus Lectionary) Norman A. Beck. 1984. 7.25 (ISBN 0-89536-687-8, 4863). CSS of Ohio.
Scripture Notes: Series C (Common Consensus Lectionary) Norman A. Beck. 1985. 9.95 (ISBN 0-89536-755-6, 5861). CSS of Ohio.
Scripture of the Lotus Blossom of the Fine Dharma: The Lotus Sutra. Tr. by Leon Hurvitz from Chin & Sanskrit. LC 75-45381. 1976. pap. 16.00x (ISBN 0-231-03920-4). Columbia U Pr.
Scripture of Truth. George S. Syme & Charlotte U. Syme. 121p. 1983. pap. 5.95 (ISBN 0-88062-019-6). Mott Media.
Scripture of Truth. George S. Syme & Charlotte U. Syme. 1986. pap. 5.95 (ISBN 0-8010-8274-9). Baker Bk.
Scripture Principle. Clark H. Pinnock. LC 84-37732. 288p. 1985. 15.45i (ISBN 0-06-066620-X); 15.95. Har-Row.
Scripture Readings in Orthodox Worship. Georges A. Barrois. 197p. 1977. pap. 6.95 (ISBN 0-913836-41-9). St Vladimirs.
Scripture Scrambles. George A. Dawson. 48p. 1987. pap. 2.50 (ISBN 0-87403-235-0, 2685). Standard Pub.
Scripture Stories for Tiny Tots: Read-Aloud Stories from the Bible for Children 1 to 6. Louise A. Randall. LC 83-83429. 38p. (Orig.). 1983. pap. 3.95 (ISBN 0-88290-209-1). Horizon Utah.
Scripture Stories for Today. Ruth A. Matheny. 1983. 9.95 (ISBN 0-89837-089-2, Pub. by Pflaum Pr). Peter Li.
Scripture Themes & Texts for Meditation & Study. Chester P. Michael. 1981. pap. 2.00. Open Door Inc.
Scripture, Tradition & Infallibility. Dewey M. Beegle. LC 79-84557. Orig. Title: Inspiration of Scripture. 332p. pap. text ed. 8.95 (ISBN 0-933462-04-2). Pryor Pettengill.
Scripture Twisting in the Seminaries, Part 1: Feminism. John W. Robbins. (Trinity Papers: No. 10). 116p. (Orig.). 1985. pap. 5.95 (ISBN 0-940931-10-9). Trinity Found.
Scripture Twisting: Twenty Ways the Cults Misread the Bible. James W. Sire. LC 80-19309. 216p. (Orig.). 1980. pap. 6.95 (ISBN 0-87784-611-1). Inter-Varsity.
Scripture Word Search. Wenonah S. Deffner. (Quiz & Puzzle Bks.). 1980. pap. 2.45 (ISBN 0-8010-2897-3). Baker Bk.
Scriptures. C. H. Spurgeon. 1978. pap. 1.95 (ISBN 0-686-23027-2). Pilgrim Pubns.

Scriptures for Living Free. Compiled by Neva Coyle. 58p. (Orig.). 1982. pap. 5.95 (ISBN 0-87123-576-5, 210576). Bethany Hse.
Scriptures from Ancient America. Roy A. Cheville. LC 64-12944. 1964. pap. 10.00 (ISBN 0-8309-0252-X). Herald Hse.
Scriptures: How Shall I Read Them? 1970. pap. 2.25 (ISBN 0-8100-0025-3, 12-0338). Northwest Pub.
Scriptures: Inspired of God. Siegbert W. Becker. 1971. pap. 2.25 (ISBN 0-8100-0027-X, 12-0340). Northwest Pub.
Scriptures: Sacred Fact or Pious Fiction? Robert G. Johnston. 1970. pap. 2.25 (ISBN 0-8100-0024-5, 12-0337). Northwest Pub.
Scriptures, Sects & Visions: A Profile of Judaism from Ezra to the Jewish Revolts. Michael E. Stone. LC 78-54151. 160p. 1980. 11.95 (ISBN 0-8006-0641-8, 1-641). Fortress.
Scriptures to Success. Lionel Kendrick. 99p. 1983. 3.95 (ISBN 0-934126-42-9). Randall Bk Co.
Scroll of Remembrance. Dale A. Howard. (Illus.). 48p. 1987. pap. 5.00 (ISBN 0-940517-02-7). JCMC Louisiana.
Scrolls & Christian Origins: Studies in the Jewish Background of the New Testament. Matthew Black. LC 83-11519. (Brown Judaic Studies). 232p. 1983. pap. 14.00 (ISBN 0-89130-639-0, 14 00 48). Scholars Pr GA.
Scrolls from Qumran Cave I: The Great Isaiah Scroll the Order of the Community, the Pesher to Habakkuk (color) John C. Trever. 163p. 1972. text ed. 30.00x (ISBN 0-89757-002-2, Am Sch Orient Res); pap. 6.00x. Eisenbrauns.
Scrolls from Qumran Cave I: The Great Isaiah Scroll the Order of the Community, the Pesher to Habakkuk. John C. Trever. 82p. 1974. pap. text ed. 6.00x (ISBN 0-89757-001-4). Am Sch Orient Res.
Scuffy Sandals: A Guide for Church Visitation in the Community. Mary M. Eakin. LC 81-15824. 96p. (Orig.). 1982. pap. 5.95 (ISBN 0-8298-0490-0). Pilgrim NY.
Sculpted Saints of a Borderland Mission. Richard Ahlborn. LC 74-18171. (Illus.). 124p. 1974. pap. 7.50 (ISBN 0-915076-03-9). SW Mission.
Sculptural Programs of Chartres Cathedral: Christ, Mary, Ecclesia. Adolf E. Katzenellenbogen. LC 59-14894. pap. 57.50 (ISBN 0-317-10764-X, 2007368). Bks Demand UMI.
Sculptural Programs of Chartres Cathedral. Adolf Katzenellenbogen. (Illus.). 1964. pap. 6.95x (ISBN 0-393-00233-0, Norton Lib). Norton.
Sculpture of Nancy Graves: A Catalogue Raisonne. E. A. Carmean, Jr. et al. LC 86-29970. (Illus.). 192p. 1987. 50.00 (ISBN 0-933920-77-6, Dist. by Rizzoli); Museum Distribution Only. pap. 25.00 (ISBN 0-933920-78-4). Hudson Hills.
S.D.N. Theory of Music. Dean & Acuff. pap. 1.95 (ISBN 0-88027-058-6). Firm Foun Pub.
Sea Breezes: Thoughts of God from a Summer Beach. John Killinger. 96p. (Orig.). 1985. pap. 6.95 (ISBN 0-687-37088-4). Abingdon.
Sea Edge. W. Phillip Keller. 120p. 1985. 9.95 (ISBN 0-8499-0457-9, 0457-9). Word Bks.
Seadog. William K. Tinsley. 270p. 1986. 9.95 (ISBN 0-936637-00-5); pap. 6.95 (ISBN 0-936637-01-3). Living Stone Pubs.
Sealed Orders: The Autobiography of a Christian Mystic. Agnes Sanford. LC 72-76592. 312p. 1972. (Pub. by Logos); pap. 7.95 (ISBN 0-88270-048-0). Bridge Pub.
Seals of Wisdom. Muhyiddin Al-Arabi. (Sacred Texts Ser.). (Illus., Orig.). 1983. pap. 8.75 (ISBN 0-88695-010-4). Concord Grove.
Seamen's Missions: Their Origins & Early Growth. Roald Kverndal. LC 85-25508. (Illus.). 936p. 1987. text ed. 29.95x (ISBN 0-87808-440-1, WCL440-1); pap. text ed. cancelled (ISBN 0-87808-439-8, WCL439-8). William Carey Lib.
Search. Ruth Domino. 1983. pap. 2.50x (ISBN 0-87574-052-9, 052). Pendle Hill.
Search. Bobby Griffin. pap. 1.75 (ISBN 0-686-12739-0). Grace Pub Co.
Search: A Guide for Those Who Dare Ask of Life Everything Good & Beautiful. James Kavanaugh. LC 85-42781. 224p. 1985. 14.95 (ISBN 0-06-250448-7, HarpR). Har-Row.
Search & Find: Theosophical Reference Index. Elsie Benjamin. Ed. by W. Emmett Small & Helen Todd. (Study: No. 1). 1978. pap. 3.95 (ISBN 0-913004-32-4). Point Loma Pub.
Search for a Civic Religion: A History of the Character Education Movement in America, Eighteen Ninety to Nineteen Thirty-Five. Stephen M. Yulish. LC 80-5619. 318p. 1980. lib. bdg. 27.75 (ISBN 0-8191-1173-2); pap. text ed. 13.75 (ISBN 0-8191-1174-0). U Pr of Amer.
Search for Certainty. P. Porterfield & W. W. Spradlin. 290p. 1983. pap. 28.50 (ISBN 0-387-90889-7). Springer-Verlag.
Search for Certainty. Emma Smiley. 1972. pap. 2.50 (ISBN 0-87516-159-6). De Vorss.
Search for Charismatic Reality: One Man's Pilgrimage. Neil Babcox. LC 84-25506. 160p. 1985. pap. 5.95 (ISBN 0-88070-085-8). Multnomah.
Search for Christian America. Mark A. Noll et al. LC 83-71239. 168p. 1983. pap. 6.95 (ISBN 0-89107-285-3, Crossway Bks). Good News.
Search for Common Ground. Howard Thurman. 108p. 1986. pap. 7.95 (ISBN 0-913408-94-8). Friends United.
Search for Concreteness-Reflections on Hegel & Whitehead: A Treatise on Self-Evidence & Critical Method in Philosophy. Darrel E. Christensen. LC 85-63421. 516p. 1986. 45.00x (ISBN 0-941664-22-8, Pub. by Susquehanna U Pr). Assoc Univ Prs.
Search for Excellence: The Christian College in an Age of Educational Competition. Robert T. Sandin. LC 82-12482. vi, 242p. 1982. text ed. 13.50x (ISBN 0-86554-037-3, MUP-H39). Mercer Univ Pr.
Search for God. David M. White. 448p. 1983. 24.95 (ISBN 0-02-627110-9). Macmillan.
Search for God: An Encounter with the Peoples & Religions of Asia. Walbert Buhlmann. Tr. by B. Krokosz & A. P. Dolan. LC 80-15732. Orig. Title: Alle haben denselben Gott. 221p. (Orig.). 1980. pap. 3.98 (ISBN 0-88344-450-X). Orbis Bks.
Search for God in Time & Memory. John S. Dunne. LC 76-20165. 1977. text ed. 15.95x (ISBN 0-268-01689-5); pap. 6.95 (ISBN 0-268-01673-9). U of Notre Dame Pr.
Search for God: Nineteen Forty-Two to Nineteen Fifty, 2 Bks. Ed. by Association for Research & Enlightenment, Inc. Virginia Beach, Va. Study Groups et al. 1942-1950. 4.95 ea. Bk. 1 (ISBN 0-87604-000-8). Bk. 2 (ISBN 0-87604-001-6). ARE Pr.
Search for Human Values. Cornelius J. Van Der Poel. LC 75-161445. 192p. 1973. pap. 3.95 (ISBN 0-8091-1781-9, Deus). Paulist Pr.
Search for Identity. Ed. by Arnold T. Olson. LC 80-66030. (Heritage Ser.: Vol. 1). 160p. 1980. 8.95 (ISBN 0-911802-46-0). Free Church Pubns.
Search for Identity: Youth, Religion, & Culture. Joseph Damrell. LC 78-5887. (Sage Library of Social Research: No. 64). 232p. 24.50 (ISBN 0-8039-0987-X); pap. 14.50 (ISBN 0-8039-0988-8). Sage.
Search for Jewish Theology. new ed. Bernard J. Bamberger. LC 77-28457. 1978. pap. 4.95x (ISBN 0-87441-300-1). Behrman.
Search for Nirvana. Kwan-Jo Lee. (Illus.). 124p. 1984. 24.00 (ISBN 0-8048-1417-1, Pub. by Seoul Intl Publishing House). C E Tuttle.
Search for Nothing: Life of John of the Cross. Richard P. Hardy. 160p. 1987. pap. 8.95 (ISBN 0-8245-0815-7). Crossroad NY.
Search for Nothing: The Life of John of the Cross. Richard P. Hardy. LC 82-13081. 160p. 1982. 10.95 (ISBN 0-8245-0499-2). Crossroad NY.
Search for Sanctuary: Brigham Young & the White Mountain Expedition. Clifford L. Stott. (American West Ser.: Vol. 19). (Illus.). 272p. 1984. 19.95 (ISBN 0-87480-237-7). U of Utah Pr.
Search for Silence. rev. ed. Elizabeth O'Connor. Ed. by Marcia Broucek. LC 86-114. 192p. 1986. pap. 8.95 (ISBN 0-931055-08-3). LuraMedia.
Search for the Absolute in Neo-Vedanta. K. C. Bhattacharrya. Ed. by George B. Burch. LC 75-17740. 202p. 1976. text ed. 14.00x (ISBN 0-8248-0296-9). UH Pr.
Search for the Real Jesus. David Winter. 160p. (Orig.). 1982. pap. 6.95 (ISBN 0-8192-1318-7). Morehouse.
Search for the True Meaning of Christmas. Joyce Reynolds. (Illus.). 1977. pap. text ed. 2.25 (ISBN 0-88243-100-5, 30-0100). Gospel Pub.
Search for the Truth. Ruth Montgomery. 256p. (Orig.). 1986. pap. 3.50 (ISBN 0-449-21085-5, Crest). Fawcett.
Search for the Twelve Apostles. William S. McBirnie. 1979. pap. 4.50 (ISBN 0-8423-5839-0). Tyndale.
Search For the Word of God: A Defense of King James Version. Daniel Segraves. Ed. by Mary Wallace. 328p. (Orig.). 1984. pap. 7.95 (ISBN 0-912315-70-9). Word Aflame.
Search for the Word of God: A Defense of the King James Versions. Daniel L. Segraves. 1982. pap. 6.00x (ISBN 0-912315-70-9). Freedom Univ-FSP.
Search for Truth. Anas Khalid. Ed. by Aliyah F. Abdal-aziz. LC 86-51061. 56p. 1986. pap. 5.00 (ISBN 0-9617422-0-8). A Khalid.
Search for Truth. Natasha Rawson. LC 80-85047. 150p. 1981. 14.95 (ISBN 0-89896-149-1, Pub. by the Linolean Press). Larksdale.
Search for Truth. A. T. Ronk. LC 73-82191. 1973. pap. 1.00x (ISBN 0-934970-04-1). Brethren Ohio.
Search for Yesterday: A Critical Examination of the Evidence for Reincarnation. D. Scott Rogo. 288p. 1985. 22.95 (ISBN 0-13-797036-6); pap. 10.95 (ISBN 0-13-797028-5). P H.
Search Heaven & Hell. Mark Donnelly & Nina Fenton. Ed. by Jon Rappaport. LC 86-81968. 500p. 1986. pap. 10.95 (ISBN 1-55666-001-4). Authors Unltd.
Search Is Within. Subramuniya. (On the Path Ser.). (Illus.). 1973. pap. 2.00 (ISBN 0-87516-349-1). De Vorss.
Search the Scriptures. Clarence Hyde. (Illus.). 112p. (Orig.). 1986. pap. 9.95 (ISBN 1-55630-014-X). Brentwood Comm.
Search the Scriptures. rev. ed. Ed. by Alan M. Stibbs. 9.95 (ISBN 0-87784-856-4). Inter-Varsity.
Search the Word Bible Puzzles. Alice Bostrom. (Illus.). 48p. 1983. pap. 2.50 (ISBN 0-87239-589-8, 2787). Standard Pub.
Search Within. Humphreys. pap. 8.95 (ISBN 0-8356-5143-6). Theos Pub Hse.
Searcher for God (Isabel Kuhn) Joyce Reason. 1963. pap. 2.95 (ISBN 0-87508-621-7). Chr Lit.
Searching for a Better Way. Monroe E. Hawley. 1980. pap. 5.50 (ISBN 0-89137-525-2). Quality Pubns.
Searching for Answers. Wayne T. Gise. LC 85-14993. (Orig.). 1985. pap. 2.95 (ISBN 0-8054-9111-2). Broadman.
Searching Heart. Ralph W. Neighbour, Sr. 1986. pap. 5.95 (ISBN 0-937931-05-5). Global TN.
Searching in God's Word-New Testament. Richard Grunze. (Lutheran Elementary Schools' Religion Curriculum Ser.). 142p. 1986. 4.95 (ISBN 0-938272-41-1). WELS Board.
Searching in God's Word-Old Testament. Richard Grunze. (Lutheran Elementary Schools' Religion Curriculum Ser.). 140p. 1986. 4.95 (ISBN 0-938272-40-3). WELS Board.
Searching in the Syntax of Things: Experiments in the Study of Religion. Maurice S. Friedman & T. Patrick Burke. LC 70-171494. pap. 40.00 (2026864). Bks Demand UMI.
Searching Mind: An Introduction to a Philosophy of God. Joseph F. Donceel. LC 79-18166. 1979. text ed. 6.95 (ISBN 0-268-01700-X). U of Notre Dame Pr.
Searching: Practices & Beliefs of the Religious Cults & Human Potential Movements. Harriet S. Mosatche. LC 83-4829. (Illus.). 437p. 1984. 14.95 (ISBN 0-87396-092-0). Stravon.
Searching the Prophets for Values. Balfour Brickner & Albert Vorspan. 1981. 6.95 (ISBN 0-8074-0047-5). UAHC.
Searching the Scriptures: A History of the Society of Biblical Literature 1880-1980. Ernest W. Saunders. LC 82-10818. (Society of Biblical Literature - Biblical Scholarship in North America Ser.). 15.00 (ISBN 0-89130-591-2, 06-11-08). Scholars Pr GA.
Searchlight. rev. ed. Roger E. Van Harn. 84p. 1980. pap. 3.25 (ISBN 0-933140-16-9). CRC Pubns.
Searchlight on Spurgeon: Spurgeon Speaks for Himself. Eric W. Hayden. 1973. pap. 3.50 (ISBN 0-686-09108-6). Pilgrim Pubns.
Searchlights from the Word. G. Campbell Morgan. 384p. 1956. 14.95 (ISBN 0-8007-0854-7). Revell.
Searchlights from the Word. G. Campbell Morgan. 1984. pap. 11.95 (ISBN 0-8010-6174-1). Baker Bk.
Season for Glory. Gloria Gage. 144p. (Orig.). 1984. pap. 4.95 (ISBN 0-89636-143-8). Accent Bks.
Season of Singleness. Ray Larson. LC 83-81762. 128p. (Orig.). 1984. 2.50 (ISBN 0-88243-584-1, 02-0584). Gospel Pub.
Season Sarcophagus in Dumbarton Oaks. George M. Hanfmann. LC 71-146800. (Dumbarton Oaks Studies: Vol. 2). (Illus.). 518p. 1951. Repr. 35.00x (ISBN 0-88402-001-0). Dumbarton Oaks.
Season Sarcophagus in Dumbarton Oaks, 2 Vols. George M. Hanfmann. Repr. of 1951 ed. Set. 60.00 (ISBN 0-384-21290-5); 30.00 ea. Johnson Repr.
Season with Love. Ed. by Kay W. Wilder. 288p. 1985. pap. 10.95 (ISBN 0-8341-1061-X). Beacon Hill.
Season with the Savior: Meditations on Mark. Edward R. Sims. 1979. 6.95 (ISBN 0-8164-0413-5, HarpR); pap. 3.95 (ISBN 0-8164-2195-1). Har-Row.
Seasonable Revolutionary: The Mind of Charles Chauncy. Charles H. Lippy. LC 81-9560. 176p. 1981. text ed. 19.95x (ISBN 0-88229-625-6). Nelson-Hall.
Seasonal Sermon Outlines. LeRoy Koopman. (Sermon Outlines Ser.). 1979. pap. 2.50 (ISBN 0-8010-5405-2). Baker Bk.
Seasonal Subjects. Buford Johnson. 1981. pap. 3.95 (ISBN 0-934942-25-0). White Wing Pub.
Seasonings for Sermons. Phillip H. Barnhart. 88p. (Orig.). 1980. pap. text ed. 6.25 (ISBN 0-89536-451-4, 1967). CSS of Ohio.
Seasonings for Sermons, Vol. 2. Lynn Ridenhour. 1982. 4.75 (ISBN 0-89536-577-4, 1916). CSS of Ohio.
Seasonings for Sermons, Vol. 3. John H. Krahn. 1983. 4.50 (ISBN 0-89536-585-5, 1922). CSS of Ohio.
Seasons & Saints. Anita L. Wheatcroft. (Illus.). 112p. (Orig.). 1974. pap. text ed. 4.25x (ISBN 0-8192-4050-8); tchrs'. ed. 4.75x (ISBN 0-8192-4049-4). Morehouse.
Seasons & Symbols. Robert Wetzler & Helen Huntington. LC 62-9094. (Illus., Orig.). 1962. pap. 6.95 (ISBN 0-8066-0221-X, 10-5625). Augsburg.
Seasons in God's World. Beverly Beckmann. (In God's World Ser.). (Illus.). 24p. 1985. 5.95 (ISBN 0-570-04127-9, 56-1538). Concordia.
Seasons of a Marriage. H. Norman Wright. LC 82-80010. 1983. pap. 4.95 (ISBN 0-8307-0912-6, 5418058). Regal.
Seasons of Celebration. Thomas Merton. 1983. 13.50 (ISBN 0-8446-5990-8). Peter Smith.
Seasons of Friendship: A Search for Intimacy. Ruth Senter. 160p. 1982. 9.95 (ISBN 0-310-38830-9, 11226). Zondervan.
Seasons of Friendship: Naomi & Ruth As a Pattern. Marjory Z. Bankson. Ed. by Marcia Broucek. 200p. (Orig.). 1987. pap. 9.95 (ISBN 0-931055-41-5). LuraMedia.
Seasons of Inspiration. Ed. by Clinton T. Howell. 160p. 1984. Repr. 10.95 (ISBN 0-8407-5345-4). Nelson.
Seasons of Our Joy: A Handbook of Jewish Festivals. Arthur I. Waskow. 1986. 17.95 (ISBN 0-671-61865-2). Summit Bks.
Seasons of Peace. Ed. by Beth Richardson. 72p. (Orig.). 1986. pap. 3.95 (ISBN 0-8358-0548-4). Upper Room.
Seasons of Strength: New Visions of Adult Christian Maturing. Evelyn E. Eaton & James Whitehead. LC 84-4199. 240p. 1986. pap. 7.95 (ISBN 0-385-19680-6, Im). Doubleday.
Seasons of Success. Valerie Sokolosky. 1985. pap. 3.95 (ISBN 0-89274-382-4). Harrison Hse.
Seasons of the Heart. Judy Miller. 1984. pap. 5.95 (ISBN 0-89225-272-3). Gospel Advocate.
Seasons of the Heart. Ed. by Stephanie C. Oda. (Reader's Digest-C. R. Gibson Bk.). (Illus.). 96p. 1984. 8.00 (ISBN 0-8378-1806-0). Gibson.
Seasons of the Spirit: The Archbishop of Canterbury at Home & Abroad. Robert A. Runcie. LC 83-1734. pap. 68.00 (ISBN 0-317-30160-8, 2025342). Bks Demand UMI.
Seasons of Woman: Song, Poetry, Ritual, Prayer, Myth, Story. Ed. by Penelope Washbourn. LC 78-3359. (Illus.). 128p. (Orig.). 1982. pap. 7.95 (ISBN 0-06-250930-6, CN4042, HarpR). Har-Row.
Seasons That Laugh or Weep: Musings on the Human Journey. Walter J. Burghardt. LC 83-60655. 144p. (Orig.). 1983. 4.95 (ISBN 0-8091-2533-1). Paulist Pr.
Seasons: Women's Search for Self Through Life's Stages. Anita Spencer. LC 81-85379. 128p. (Orig.). 1982. pap. 4.95 (ISBN 0-8091-2437-8). Paulist Pr.
Seated in Heavenly Places. Richard Booker. LC 85-72460. 1986. pap. 5.95 (ISBN 0-88270-600-4). Bridge Pub.
Sebastian Franck: Two Hundred Eighty Paradoxes or Wondrous Sayings. Sebastian Franck. Tr. by E. J. Furcha. (Texts & Studies in Religion: 26). 562p. 1986. lib. bdg. 79.95 (ISBN 0-88946-814-1). E Mellen.
Sebastian: The Essence of My Soul. John H. Hausner. (Illus.). 1982. 5.95 (ISBN 0-533-05510-5). Vantage.
Seceders. J. H. Philpot. pap. 2.95 (ISBN 0-85151-132-5). Banner of Truth.
Second Advent (6) Ed. by Chung H. Kwak. (Home Study Course Ser.). 50p. (Orig.). 1980. pap. 4.00 (ISBN 0-910621-15-2). HSA Pubns.
Second & Third Epistles of John. Judith Lieu. 280p. 1987. 19.95 (ISBN 0-567-09443-X, Pub. by T & T Clark Ltd UK). Fortress.
Second Ark Book of Riddles. Myra Shofner. (Illus.). 1981. pap. 2.50 (ISBN 0-89191-531-1, 55319). Cook.
Second Birth. Omraam M. Aivanhov. (Complete Works of O. M. Aivanhov: Vol. 1). 210p. 1981. pap. 9.50 (ISBN 0-87516-418-8). De Vorss.
Second Book of Chronicles. John A. Grindel. (Bible Ser.: Vol. 18). (Orig.). 1974. pap. 1.00 (ISBN 0-8091-5171-5). Paulist Pr.
Second Book of Irish Myths & Legends. Eoin Neeson. 128p. 1981. pap. 5.95 (ISBN 0-85342-131-5, Pub. by Mercier Pr Ireland). Irish Bks Media.
Second Book of Kings. Ed. by J. Robinson. LC 75-39371. (Cambridge Bible Commentary on the New English Bible, Old Testament Ser.). (Illus.). 1976. pap. 12.95x (ISBN 0-521-09774-6). Cambridge U Pr.
Second Book of Kings. Geoffrey Wood. (Bible Ser.: Vol. 16). (Orig.). 1974. pap. 1.00 (ISBN 0-8091-5169-3). Paulist Pr.

Second Book of Maccabees. Neil J. McEleney. (Bible Ser.: Vol. 23). (Orig.). 1974. pap. 1.00 (ISBN 0-8091-5167-7). Paulist Pr.

Second Book of Samuel. William G. Blaikie. 400p. 1983. lib. bdg. 15.00 (ISBN 0-86524-175-9, 0903). Klock & Klock.

Second Book of Samuel. Frederick Moriarty. (Bible Ser.). pap. 1.00 (ISBN 0-8091-5136-7). Paulist Pr.

Second Book of Samuel: Cambridge Bible Commentary on the New English Bible. Peter R. Ackroyd. LC 76-58074. (Old Testament Ser.). (Illus.). 1977. 32.50 (ISBN 0-521-08633-7); pap. 11.95 (ISBN 0-521-09754-1). Cambridge U Pr.

Second Book of the Bible: Exodus. Walter Jacob. 1983. 59.50x (ISBN 0-88125-028-7). Ktav.

Second Book of the Lamb. Peter C. Stone. 233p. 1987. 22.00 (ISBN 0-934469-02-4). Gabriel Pr CA.

Second Chance. Nancy L. Way. 1985. 5.95 (ISBN 0-8062-2444-4). Carlton.

Second Collection. Bernard J. Lonergan. LC 74-14798. 314p. 1975. 12.00 (ISBN 0-664-20721-9). Westminster.

Second Coming. William Kelly. 375p. 6.25 (ISBN 0-88172-108-5). Believers Bkshelf.

Second Coming Bible Commentary. William E. Biederwolf. (Paperback Reference Library). 728p. 1985. pap. 17.95 (ISBN 0-8010-0887-5). Baker Bk.

Second Coming Bible Study Guide, No. 2. William J. Krutza. (Contemporary Discussion Ser.). (Orig.). 1973. pap. 0.95 (ISBN 0-8010-5330-7). Baker Bk.

Second Coming of Christ. I. M. Haldeman. 326p. 1986. 12.95 (ISBN 0-8254-2844-0). Kregel.

Second Coming of Christ. Gordon Lindsay. (Prophecy Ser.). 0.95 (ISBN 0-89985-061-8). Christ Nations.

Second Coming of Christ, Vol. II. Paramhansa Yogananda. LC 79-50352. 1984. pap. 12.95 (ISBN 0-937134-05-8). Amrita Found.

Second Coming of Jesus. Martin R. DeHaan. 1978. pap. 6.95 (ISBN 0-310-23461-1, 9498P). Zondervan.

Second Coming of Jesus. G. F. Taylor. 3.95 (ISBN 0-911866-63-9); pap. 2.00 (ISBN 0-911866-62-0). Advocate.

Second Coming: Popular Millenarianism 1780-1850. John F. Harrison. 1979. 32.00x (ISBN 0-8135-0879-7). Rutgers U Pr.

Second Coming: Why Jesus Christ Became a Carpenter Instead of an Electrician. Judy L. Bacci. 110p. (Orig.). 1981. pap. 5.95 (ISBN 0-940002-00-0). Studio J Pub.

Second Corinthians. Ernest Best. Ed. by James L. Mays & Paul J. Achtemeier. LC 86-45404. (Interpretation: A Bible Commentary for Teaching & Preaching Ser.). 156p. 1987. 15.95 (ISBN 0-8042-3135-4). John Knox.

Second Corinthians. Francis T. Fallon. (New Testament Message Ser.: Vol. 11). 12.95 (ISBN 0-89453-199-9); pap. 7.95 (ISBN 0-89453-134-4). M Glazier.

Second Corinthians. Robert B. Hughes. (Everyman's Bible Commentary Ser.). 1983. pap. 5.95 (ISBN 0-8024-0241-0). Moody.

Second Corinthians. Irving Jensen. (Bible Self-Study Ser). (Illus.). 108p. 1972. pap. 3.25 (ISBN 0-8024-1047-2). Moody.

Second Corinthians. (Erdmans Commentaries Ser.). 3.50 (ISBN 0-8010-3395-0). Baker Bk.

Second Corinthians. Geoffrey Wilson. 1979. pap. 4.95 (ISBN 0-85151-295-X). Banner of Truth.

Second Corinthians, Vol. 40, WBC. Ralph P. Martin. 380p. 1985. 25.95 (ISBN 0-8499-0239-8, 0239-8). Word Bks.

Second Corinthians Eight & Nine: A Commentary on Two Administrative Letters of the Apostle Paul. Hans D. Betz. LC 84-48904. (Hermeneia Ser.). 288p. 1985. 27.95 (ISBN 0-8006-6014-5, 20-6014). Fortress.

Second Corinthians: Keys to Triumphant Living. Edgar C. James. (Teach Yourself the Bible Ser.). 1964. pap. 2.75 (ISBN 0-8024-7680-5). Moody.

Second Corinthians: Message of the New Testament. J. D. Thomas. (Way of Life Ser.). 60p. 1986. pap. text ed. 3.95 (ISBN 0-915547-92-9, 929). Abilene Christ U.

Second Corinthians: Where Life Endures. Roy L. Laurin. LC 85-8154. 248p. 1985. pap. 9.95 (ISBN 0-8254-3129-8). Kregel.

Second Cup of Coffee: Proverbs for Today's Woman. Jean Shaw. 192p. (Orig.). 1981. pap. 3.95 (ISBN 0-310-43542-0, 9609P). Zondervan.

Second Epistle of Paul to the Corinthians. Randolph V. Tasker. (Tyndale Bible Commentaries). 1958. pap. 4.95 (ISBN 0-8028-1407-7). Eerdmans.

Second Epistle Peter & Epistle of Jude. M. Green. (Tyndale Bible Commentaries: Vol. 18). 1968. pap. 4.95 (ISBN 0-8028-1417-4). Eerdmans.

Second Epistle to the Corinthians. Charles K. Barrett. LC 73-18682. 366p. 1974. 17.95 (ISBN 0-06-060552-9, HarpR). Har-Row.

Second Great Awakening in Connecticut. Charles R. Keller. LC 68-26923. ix, 275p. 1968. Repr. of 1942 ed. 25.00 (ISBN 0-208-00662-1, Archon). Shoe String.

Second Greatest Commandment. William Fletcher. LC 83-62501. 156p. 1983. pap. 4.95 (ISBN 0-89109-502-0). NavPress.

Second Hand Life: Discussions with Bill Barber. Bill Barber. 144p. (Orig.). 1986. pap. 8.95 (ISBN 0-87418-025-2, 163). Coleman Pub.

Second Isaiah. R. N. Whybray. (Old Testament Guides Ser.). xiv, 84p. 1984. pap. text ed. 3.95x (ISBN 0-905774-59-0, Pub. by JSOT Pr England). Eisenbrauns.

Second Jewish Book of Why. A. J. Kolatch. LC 84-21477. 432p. 1985. 13.95 (ISBN 0-8246-0305-2). Jonathan David.

Second Jewish Catalog: Sources & Resources. Ed. by Michael Strassfeld & Sharon Strassfeld. LC 73-11759. (Illus.). 464p. 1976. 8.95 (ISBN 0-8276-0084-4, 391). Jewish Pubns.

Second Jewish Trivia & Information Book. Ian Shapolsky. (Illus.). 400p. 1986. pap. 6.95 (ISBN 0-933503-45-8). Shapolsky Pubs.

Second Journey. Gerald O'Collins. LC 77-99303. 96p. 1978. pap. 3.95 (ISBN 0-8091-2209-X). Paulist Pr.

Second Kings. G. H. Jones. (New Century Bible Commentary Ser.). 352p. 1984. pap. 8.95 (ISBN 0-8028-0040-8). Eerdmans.

Second Kings with Chronicles. rev. ed. Ed. by Irving L. Jensen. (Bible Self-Study Ser.). (Illus., Orig.). 1968. pap. 3.25 (ISBN 0-8024-1012-X). Moody.

Second Letter to the Corinthians. Rudolf Bultmann. Tr. by Wilhelm C. Linss. LC 83-70517. 272p. 1985. pap. 17.95 (ISBN 0-8066-2023-4, 10-5633). Augsburg.

Second Look. Gerhard E. Frost. (Orig.). 1984. pap. 6.95 (ISBN 0-86683-935-6, 8513, HarpR). Har-Row.

Second Man: Monster, Myth, or Minister. Blaine Hughes. 20p. 1976. pap. text ed. 0.95 (ISBN 0-89265-110-5). Randall Hse.

Second Marriage: The Promise & the Challenge. Darlene McRoberts. LC 77-84087. 1978. pap. 6.95 (ISBN 0-8066-1612-1, 10-5635). Augsburg.

Second Mile. Roger Prescott. 1985. 4.95 (ISBN 0-89536-739-4, 5823). CSS of Ohio.

Second-Mile People. Isobel Kuhn. 1982. pap. 3.50 (ISBN 0-85363-145-X). OMF Bks.

Second Person. Lehman Strauss. 1951. 7.95 (ISBN 0-87213-826-7). Loizeaux.

Second Peter & Jude. rev. ed. Michael Green. (Tyndale New Testament Commentaries Ser.). 1987. pap. 5.95 (ISBN 0-8028-0078-5). Eerdmans.

Second Peter: Living Faithfully. J. Allen Blair. LC 61-14600. 1961. pap. 4.95 (ISBN 0-87213-047-9). Loizeaux.

Second Season: Lent, Easter, Ascension. Wayne Saffen. LC 72-87064. pap. 24.00 (2026827). Bks Demand UMI.

Second Thoughts on Missions. W. C. Lees. 1965. pap. 0.95 (ISBN 0-87508-908-9). Chr Lit.

Second Thoughts on the Dead Sea Scrolls. F. F. Bruce. 157p. 1986. pap. 7.95 (ISBN 0-85364-017-3, Pub. by Paternoster UK). Attic Pr.

Second Timothy. D. Edmond Hiebert. (Everyman's Bible Commentary Ser). 1958. pap. 5.95 (ISBN 0-8024-2055-9). Moody.

Second Touch. Keith Miller. LC 67-31340. 1982. 7.95 (ISBN 0-8499-0338-6, 80036). Word Bks.

Second Treasury of Christmas Music. Ed. by Will L. Reed. LC 68-16193. 1968. 12.95 (ISBN 0-87523-165-9). Emerson.

Second United Order among the Mormons. Edward J. Allen. LC 73-38483. (Columbia University Studies in the Social Sciences: No. 419). Repr. of 1936 ed. 15.00 (ISBN 0-404-51419-7). AMS Pr.

Second Vatican Council: Studies by Eight Anglican Observers. B. Pawley. 12.00 (ISBN 0-8446-2713-5). Peter Smith.

Second Zen Reader. Trevor Leggett. Ed. by Florence Sakade. (Illus.). 192p. (Orig.). 1987. pap. 7.95 (ISBN 0-8048-1525-9). C E Tuttle.

Secret. Bhagwan S. Rajneesh. Ed. by Swami P. Chinmaya. LC 83-185068. (Sufi Ser.). (Illus.). 760p. (Orig.). 1980. 23.95 (ISBN 0-88050-127-8). Chidvilas Found.

Secret Abiding Presence. Andrew Murray. (Secret Ser.). (Orig.). 1979. pap. 1.95 (ISBN 0-87508-382-X). Chr Lit.

Secret Bible Prophecies. DeWitt B. Lucas. 1965. pap. 2.50 (ISBN 0-910140-10-3). C & R Anthony.

Secret Books of the Egyptian Gnostics. Jean Doresse. (Illus.). 446p. 1986. pap. 14.95 (ISBN 0-89281-107-2). Inner Tradit.

Secret Code: The Lost & Hidden Language of the Bible, Vol. 1. Thierry Gaudin. LC 85-70031. 300p. (Orig.). 1985. pap. 12.95 (ISBN 0-933357-05-2). Bret Pubns.

Secret Cult of the Order. Anthony C. Sutton. 140p. (Orig.). 1984. pap. text ed. 9.95 (ISBN 0-914981-09-9). Res Pubns AZ.

Secret Doctrine, 3 vols. 7th ed. Helena P. Blavatsky. Ed. by Boris De Zirkoff. (Illus.). 1980. 45.00 ea. (ISBN 0-8356-7525-4). Theos Pub Hse.

Secret Doctrine of H. P. Blavatsky: First International Symposium, July 1984. Ed. by Richard I. Robb. 112p. 1984. pap. 7.00 (ISBN 0-913510-52-1). Wizards.

Secret Doctrine of the Rosicrucians. Magnus Incognito. 8.00 (ISBN 0-911662-30-8). Yoga.

Secret Doctrine: The Synthesis of Science, Religion, & Philosophy, 2 vols. in 1. Helena P. Blavatsky. xci, 1474p. 1925. Repr. of 1888 ed. 18.50 (ISBN 0-938998-00-5). Theosophy.

Secret Doctrines of Jesus. 19th ed. H. Spencer Lewis. LC 37-22922. 237p. 1981. 10.95 (ISBN 0-912057-14-9, G-504). AMORC.

Secret Door to Success. Florence S. Shinn. 1978. pap. 2.50 (ISBN 0-87516-258-4). De Vorss.

Secret Forces of the Pyramids. Warren Smith. 220p. 1975. pap. 1.75 (ISBN 0-89083-114-9). Zebra.

Secret Garden. Mahmud Shabistari. 1969. 10.95 (ISBN 0-900860-38-3). Ins Study Human.

Secret Gospel: The Discovery & Interpretation of the Secret Gospel According to Mark. Morton Smith. LC 82-73215. 157p. pap. 7.95 (ISBN 0-913922-55-2). Dawn Horse Pr.

Secret History: An Eyewitness Expose of the Rise of Mormonism. John Ahmanson. Tr. by Gleason L. Archer from Danish. 1984. 9.95 (ISBN 0-8024-0277-1). Moody.

Secret History of the Jesuits. rev. ed. Edmond Paris. 208p. 1982. pap. 5.95 (ISBN 0-937958-10-7). Chick Pubns.

Secret History of the Oxford Movement. Walter Walsh. LC 73-101915. Repr. of 1898 ed. 25.00 (ISBN 0-404-06819-7). AMS Pr.

Secret History of the Oxford Movement. Walter Walsh. 1977. lib. bdg. 59.95 (ISBN 0-8490-2583-4). Gordon Pr.

Secret Invasion. Dave Hunt & Hans Kristian. 224p. 1987. pap. 5.95 (ISBN 0-89081-560-7). Harvest Hse.

Secret Joy of Repentance. 3.50 (ISBN 0-8198-6863-9); 2.25 (ISBN 0-8198-6864-7). Dghtrs St Paul.

Secret Kingdom: A Promise of Hope & Freedom in a World of Turmoil. Pat Robertson & Bob Slosser. LC 83-14268. 96p. 1983. 13.95 (ISBN 0-8407-5272-5). Nelson.

Secret of a Happy Home. Richard W. DeHaan. (Direction Bks.). 88p. 1982. pap. 2.95 (ISBN 0-8010-2916-3). Baker Bk.

Secret of Abundant Living. Charles L. Allen. 160p. 1980. 8.95 (ISBN 0-8007-1123-8); Spire Bks. pap. 3.50 (ISBN 0-8007-8479-0). Revell.

Secret of Adoration. Andrew Murray. (Secret Ser.). (Orig.). 1979. pap. 1.95 (ISBN 0-87508-384-6). Chr Lit.

Secret of Believing Prayer. Andrew Murray. LC 80-69320. 80p. 1980. pap. 3.50 (ISBN 0-87123-528-5, 200528). Bethany Hse.

Secret of Brotherly Love. Andrew Murray. (Secret Ser.). (Orig.). 1980. pap. 1.95 (ISBN 0-87508-390-0). Chr Lit.

Secret of Christ Our Life. Andrew Murray. (Secret Ser.). (Orig.). 1980. pap. 1.95 (ISBN 0-87508-385-4). Chr Lit.

Secret of Communion with God. Matthew Henry. LC 79-93431. (Shepherd Illustrated Classics Ser.). (Illus.). 144p. 1981. pap. 5.95 (ISBN 0-87983-220-7). Keats.

Secret of Divine Civilization. 2nd ed. Abdu'l-Baha. Tr. by Marzieh Gail. LC 56-12427. 1970. 15.95 (ISBN 0-87743-008-X, 106-006). Baha'i.

Secret of Effective Prayer. Helen S. Shoemaker. LC 67-19306. 1976. pap. 1.95 (ISBN 0-87680-869-0, 91004, Key Word Bks). Word Bks.

Secret of Fatima Fact & Legend. Joaquin M. Alonso. Tr. by Dominican Nuns of the Perpetual Rosary. LC 79-13182. (Illus.). 1979. 8.95 (ISBN 0-911218-14-9); pap. 3.95 (ISBN 0-911218-15-7). Ravengate Pr.

Secret of Fellowship. Andrew Murray. (Secret Ser.). (Orig.). 1980. pap. 1.95 (ISBN 0-87508-388-9). Chr Lit.

Secret of Guidance. F. B. Meyer. LC 77-93177. 96p. 1978. pap. 2.95 (ISBN 0-87123-501-3, 200501). Bethany Hse.

Secret of Guidance. F. B. Meyer. Tr. by Ruth Taniguchi from Eng. (Chinese.). 1984. pap. write for info. (ISBN 0-941598-07-1). Living Spring Pubns.

Secret of Happiness. Irving S. Cooper. LC 75-26815. 75p. 1976. pap. 1.75 (ISBN 0-8356-0469-1, Quest). Theos Pub Hse.

Secret of Happiness. rev. & enl. ed. Billy Graham. 160p. 1985. 11.95 (ISBN 0-8499-0508-7, 0508-7); pap. 9.95 (ISBN 0-8499-3034-0, 3034-0). Word Bks.

Secret of Happiness: Matthew 5, the Beatitudes. 7.95 (ISBN 0-86683-850-3, HarpR). Har-Row.

Secret of Healing. Jack E. Addington. 204p. 1979. pap. 7.95 (ISBN 0-911336-80-X). Sci of Mind.

Secret of Hind's Feet. Sue H. Boggs. 2.95 (ISBN 0-89137-537-6). Quality Pubns.

Secret of Inspiration. Andrew Murray. (Secret Ser.). (Orig.). 1979. pap. 1.95 (ISBN 0-87508-386-2). Chr Lit.

Secret of Instantaneous Healing. Harry D. Smith. 1965. 8.95 (ISBN 0-13-797951-7, Reward); pap. 4.95 (ISBN 0-13-797936-3). P-H.

Secret of Intercession. Andrew Murray. (Secret Ser.). (Orig.). 1980. pap. 1.95 (ISBN 0-87508-391-9). Chr Lit.

Secret of John Milton. H. Mutschmann. LC 72-194771. 1925. lib. bdg. 15.00 (ISBN 0-8414-6694-7). Folcroft.

Secret of Jonestown: The Reason Why. Ed Dieckmann, Jr. 176p. (Orig.). 1982. pap. 6.00 (ISBN 0-939482-02-9). Noontide.

Secret of Loving. Josh McDowell. 200p. 1985. 11.95 (ISBN 0-86605-157-0). Campus Crusade.

Secret of Loving. Josh McDowell. (Living Bks.). 240p. Repr. 3.95 (ISBN 0-8423-5845-5). Tyndale.

Secret of Positive Praying. John Bisagno. Ed. by Jim Ruark. 128p. 1986. pap. 3.95 (ISBN 0-310-21152-2, 9239). Zondervan.

Secret of Power from on High. Andrew Murray. (Secret Ser.). (Orig.). 1980. pap. 1.95 (ISBN 0-87508-392-7). Chr Lit.

Secret of Regeneration. Hilton Hotema. Orig. Title: Science of Human Regeneration (Postgraduate Orthopathy) (Illus.). 900p. 1963. pap. 59.95 (ISBN 0-88697-019-9). Life Science.

Secret of Salvation. E. E. Byrum. 264p. pap. 2.50 (ISBN 0-686-29166-2). Faith Pub Hse.

Secret of Secrets. Uell S. Andersen. pap. 7.00 (ISBN 0-87980-134-4). Wilshire.

Secret of Secrets, Vol. 1. Bhagwan S. Rajneesh. Ed. by Rajneesh Foundation International. LC 82-50464. (Tao Ser.). 588p. (Orig.). 1982. pap. 16.95 (ISBN 0-88050-628-8). Chidvilas Found.

Secret of Secrets, Vol. 2. Bhagwan S. Rajneesh. Ed. by Ma Y. Sudha. LC 82-50464. (Tao Ser.). 528p. (Orig.). 1983. pap. 4.95 (ISBN 0-88050-629-6). Chidvilas Found.

Secret of Self-Realization. Taimni. 4.50 (ISBN 0-8356-7640-4). Theos Pub Hse.

Secret of Soul-Winning. Stephen O. Olford. 1978. pap. 5.95 (ISBN 0-8024-7684-8). Moody.

Secret of Staying in Love. John Powell. LC 74-84712. (Illus.). 1974. pap. 3.95 (ISBN 0-913592-29-3). Argus Comm.

Secret of Stonehenge. I. L. Cohen. Ed. by G. Murphy. LC 82-19107. (Illus.). 310p. 1982. 16.95 (ISBN 0-910891-01-X). New Research.

Secret of Swedenborg: Being an Elucidation of His Doctrine of the Divine Humanity. Henry James, Sr. LC 72-914. (Selected Works of Henry James, Sr.: Vol. 7). 264p. 1983. Repr. of 1869 ed. 30.00 (ISBN 0-404-10087-2). AMS Pr.

Secret of the Cross. Andrew Murray. (Secret Ser.). (Orig.). 1980. pap. 1.95 (ISBN 0-87508-389-7). Chr Lit.

Secret of the Faith Life. Andrew Murray. (Secret Ser.). (Orig.). 1979. pap. 1.95 (ISBN 0-87508-387-0). Chr Lit.

Secret of the Golden Hours. Ed. by Regency Press Ltd. Staff. 112p. 1984. 40.00 (ISBN 0-7212-0656-5, Pub. by Regency Pr). State Mutual Bk.

Secret of the Rosary. St. Louis De Monfort. Tr. by Mary Barbour from Fr. 1976. pap. 1.00 (ISBN 0-89555-056-3). TAN Bks Pubs.

Secret of the Rosary. St. Louis De Montfort. pap. 1.00 (ISBN 0-910984-04-2). Montfort Pubns.

Secret of the Rosicrucian Brotherhood, 4 vols. Jan Van Rijckenborgh. Incl. Vol. 1. Call of Rosicrucian Brotherhood; Vol. 2. Confession of the Rosicrucian Brotherhood; Vol. 3. Alchemical Wedding of Christian Rosycross; Vol. 4. Alchemical Wedding of Christian Rosycross. Date not set. price not set. Rosycross Pr.

Secret of the Sabbath Fish. Ben Aronin. LC 78-63437. (Illus.). 1979. 5.95 (ISBN 0-8276-0110-7, 433). Jewish Pubns.

Secret of the Siddhas. Swami Muktananda. LC 80-53590. 256p. 1980. pap. 6.95 (ISBN 0-914602-52-7). SYDA Found.

Secret of the Throne of Grace. Andrew Murray. (Secret Ser.). (Orig.). 1980. pap. 1.95 (ISBN 0-87508-393-5). Chr Lit.

Secret of the Totem. Andrew Lang. LC 70-115094. 1970. Repr. of 1905 ed. 16.75 (ISBN 0-404-03866-2). AMS Pr.

Secret of the Twenty-Third Psalm. Joel S. Goldsmith. 1972. pap. 1.50 (ISBN 0-87516-140-5). De Vorss.

Secret of the Universe: New Discoveries on God, Man & the Eternity of Life. William S. Brandall. (Illus.). 119p. 1985. 127.45 (ISBN 0-89266-535-1). Am Classical Coll Pr.

Secret of the Veda. Sri Aurobindo. (Sanskrit & Eng.). 1979. oversize ed. 40.00 (ISBN 0-89744-975-4, Pub. by Sri Aurobindo Ashram Trust India); pap. 30.00. Auromere.

Secret of the Veda. Sri Aurobindo. 581p. 1982. 15.00 (ISBN 0-89071-303-0, Pub. by Sri Aurobindo Ashram India); pap. 10.00 (ISBN 0-89071-302-2, Pub. by Sri Aurobindo Ashram India). Matagiri.

Secret of United Prayer. Andrew Murray. (Secret Ser.). (Orig.). 1980. pap. 1.95 (ISBN 0-87508-394-3). Chr Lit.

Secret Oral Teachings in Tibetan Buddhist Sects. Alexandra David-Neel. 1967. pap. 4.95 (ISBN 0-87286-012-4). City Lights.

Secret Place of the Most High. Frank E. Stranges. 12p. 1985. pap. text ed. 2.00 (ISBN 0-933470-09-6). Intl Evang.

Secret Places of the Lion. George H. Williamson. LC 82-2374. 230p. 1983. pap. 7.95 (ISBN 0-89281-039-4, Destiny Bks). Inner Tradit.

Secret Power. rev. ed. Dwight L. Moody & Walter Martin. 1987. pap. 7.95 (ISBN 0-8307-1219-4). Regal.

Secret Power of Pyramids. Bill Schul & Ed Pettit. 1987. pap. 3.50 (ISBN 0-449-13986-7, GM). Fawcett.

Secret Power of Tantrik Breathing. S. Sivapriyananda. 80p. 1983. text ed. 15.00 (ISBN 0-391-02899-5, Pub. by Abhinav Pubs India). Humanities.

Secret Power of the Pyramids. U. S. Andersen. 1977. pap. 7.00 (ISBN 0-87980-343-6). Wilshire.

Secret Self. Orlo Strunk, Jr. LC 76-14780. Repr. of 1976 ed. 27.50 (ISBN 0-8357-9025-8, 2016404). Bks Demand UMI.

Secret Societies. Arkon Daraul. 1983. Repr. of 1961 ed. 14.95 (ISBN 0-86304-024-1, Pub. by Octagon Pr England). Ins Study Human.

Secret Societies: Can a Christian Belong to Them & Still Honor Christ? George L. Hunt. pap. 1.50 (ISBN 0-87213-338-9). Loizeaux.

Secret Symbols of the Rosicrucians of the 16th & 17th Centuries. 1967. 20.00 (ISBN 0-912057-44-0). AMORC.

Secret Talks with Mr. G. LC 78-54137. (Illus.). 1978. pap. 5.95 (ISBN 0-89556-001-1). Gateways Bks & Tapes.

Secret Teachings of All Ages: An Encyclopedic Outlines of Masonic, Hermetic, Quabbalistic & Rosicrucian Symbolical Philosophy. Manly P. Hall. (Illus.). 1978. pap. 24.95 (ISBN 0-89314-540-8). Philos Res.

Secret Teachings of Jesus: Four Gnostic Gospels. Tr. by Marvin W. Meyer. LC 84-42528. 224p. 1984. 15.45 (ISBN 0-394-52959-6). Random.

Secret Teachings of the Vedas: The Ancient Knowledge of the East. Sri Nanda-Nandana. LC 86-51209. 320p. (Orig.). 1987. pap. 14.95 (ISBN 0-9617410-0-7). World Relief.

Secret Temple. Robert Wang. 1980. 15.00 (ISBN 0-87728-490-3); pap. 7.95 (ISBN 0-87728-518-7). Weiser.

Secret Wisdom of Qabalah. J. F. C. Fuller. 1976. Repr. 7.00 (ISBN 0-911662-63-4). Yoga.

Secret World of Interpol. Omar V. Garrison. 13.95 (ISBN 0-686-74638-4). Church of Scient Info.

Secretaries of Death: Accounts by Former Prisoners Who Worked in the Administrative Offices of Auschwitz. Ed. by Lore Shelley. LC 85-43608. 450p. 1986. 20.00 (ISBN 0-88400-123-7). Shengold.

Secretary's Guide to Church Office Management. 128p. (Orig.). 1985. pap. 9.95 (ISBN 0-687-37131-7). Abingdon.

Secreto de la Felicidad. Billy Graham. Orig. Title: Secret of Happiness. (Span.). 192p. 1981. pap. 2.75 (ISBN 0-311-04352-6). Casa Bautista.

Secreto de la Oracion Diaria. Basilea Schlink. 96p. 2.50 (ISBN 0-88113-201-2). Edit Betania.

Secreto de una Vida Feliz. Hannah W. Smith. 224p. 1980. 2.75 (ISBN 0-88113-270-5). Edit Betania.

Secretos de la Oracion. F. J. Huegel. Orig. Title: Secrets of Prayer. (Span.). 1984. pap. 3.25 (ISBN 0-8254-1323-0). Kregel.

Secrets. Frances Wilshire. pap. 1.95 (ISBN 0-87516-318-1). De Vorss.

Secrets for Growing Churches. Charles Mylander. LC 79-1764. 1979. pap. 4.95i (ISBN 0-06-066055-4, RD 302, HarpR). Har-Row.

Secrets of a Nun: My Own Story. Elizabeth Upton. LC 84-14828. 264p. 1985. 16.95 (ISBN 0-688-04187-6). Morrow.

Secrets of a Nun: My Own Story. Elizabeth Upton. 1987. pap. write for info. (ISBN 0-449-21127-4, Crest). Fawcett.

Secrets of Anal-Haqq. K. Khan. 1981. 12.50 (ISBN 0-686-97864-1). Kazi Pubns.

Secrets of Chinese Meditation. Charles Luk. (Illus.). 1969. pap. 6.95 (ISBN 0-87728-066-5). Weiser.

Secrets of Eternity. Annalee Skarin. 1960. pap. 5.95 (ISBN 0-87516-092-1). De Vorss.

Secrets of Numbers. large type ed. Vera Johnson & Thomas Wommack. LC 81-70270. 272p. 1982. pap. 12.50 (ISBN 0-87728-541-1). Weiser.

Secrets of Romanism. Joseph Zacchello. 232p. 1981. pap. 4.95 (ISBN 0-87213-981-6). Loizeaux.

Secrets of Shaolin Temple Boxing. Robert W. Smith. LC 64-22002. (Illus.). 1964. 7.95 (ISBN 0-8048-0518-0). C E Tuttle.

Secrets of Spirulina. Ed. by C. Hills. LC 80-22087. 224p. 1980. 6.95 (ISBN 0-916438-38-4). Univ of Trees.

Secrets of Staying in Love. Ruth S. Peale. 272p. 1984. pap. 5.95 (ISBN 0-8407-5910-X). Nelson.

Secrets of the Bible Seas: An Underwater Archaeologist in the Holy Land. Alexander Flinder. (Illus.). 192p. 1986. 17.95 (ISBN 0-7278-2047-8). Salem Hse Pubs.

Secrets of the Blessed Man. Paul Tassell. 1971. pap. 2.95 (ISBN 0-87227-033-5). Reg Baptist.

Secrets of the Ninja. Ashida Kim. (Illus.). 168p. 1981. 16.95 (ISBN 0-87364-234-1). Paladin Pr.

Secrets of the Self. Mohammad Iqbal. Tr. by Nicholson. (Orig.). 1979. pap. 3.95 (ISBN 0-89684-083-2, Pub. by Arnold Heinemann India). Orient Bk Dist.

Secrets of the Tarot: Origins, History, & Symbolism. Barbara G. Walker. LC 84-47737. (Illus.). 256p. (Orig.). 1984. pap. 12.95 (ISBN 0-06-250927-6, CN 4102, HarpR). Har-Row.

Secrets of Tut's Tomb & the Pyramids. Stephanie A. Reiff. LC 77-22770. (Great Unsolved Mysteries). (Illus.). 1977. PLB 14.65 (ISBN 0-8172-1051-2). Raintree Pubs.

Secrets of Voodoo. Milo Rigaud. Tr. by Robert B. Cross from Fr. (Illus.). 256p. 1985. pap. 7.95 (ISBN 0-87286-171-6). City Lights.

Secrets to Inner Beauty. Joseph C. Aldrich. LC 84-9970. 142p. 1984. pap. 5.95 (ISBN 0-88070-069-6). Multnomah.

Sect, Cult & Church in Alberta. rev. ed. William E. Mann. LC 56-2838. 1972. 20.00x (ISBN 0-8020-5036-0). U of Toronto Pr.

Sect Ideologies & Social Status. Gary Schwartz. LC 72-120598. 1970. 18.00x (ISBN 0-226-74216-4). U of Chicago Pr.

Sectarian College & the Public Purse: Fordham: a Case Study. Walter Gellhorn & R. Kent Greenawalt. LC 74-111415. 212p. 1970. 10.00 (ISBN 0-379-00456-9). Oceana.

Sectarian Laws in the Dead Sea Scrolls: Courts, Testimony & the Penal Code. Lawrence Schiffman. LC 82-837. (Brown Judaic Studies). 294p. 1983. pap. 27.50 (ISBN 0-89130-569-6). Scholars Pr GA.

Sectarianism & Religious Persecution in China: A Page in the History of Religions, 2 vols. J. J. De Groot. 872p. 1972. Repr. of 1903 ed. 60.00x (ISBN 0-7165-2034-6, Pub. by Irish Academic Pr Ireland). Biblio Dist.

Sectional Crisis & Northern Methodism: A Study in Piety, Political Ethics & Civil Religion. Donald G. Jones. LC 78-9978. 349p. 1979. lib. bdg. 22.50 (ISBN 0-8108-1175-8). Scarecrow.

Sects & Society: A Sociological Study of Three Religious Groups in Britain. Bryan R. Wilson. LC 78-5993. 1978. Repr. of 1961 ed. lib. bdg. 31.00x (ISBN 0-313-20439-X, WISA). Greenwood.

Sects or New Religious Movements: Pastoral Challenge. Vatican Secretariat for Promoting Christian Unity Staff. 24p. 1986. pap. 2.95 (ISBN 1-55586-100-8). US Catholic.

Secular Consciousness & National Conscience: The Church & Political Alternatives in Southern Europe. Thomas G. Sanders. Ed. by Manon Spitzer. LC 77-6457. 144p. 1977. pap. text ed. 6.50 (ISBN 0-910116-90-3). U Field Staff Intl.

Secular Humanism. Ern Baxter et al. 1986. pap. 2.95 (ISBN 0-8010-0936-7). Baker Bk.

Secular Humanism. Robert E. Webber. 144p. 1985. pap. 5.95 (ISBN 0-310-36671-2, 12208P). Zondervan.

Secular Humanist Declaration. Paul Kurtz. 40p. 1981. pap. 2.95 (ISBN 0-87975-149-5). Prometheus Bks.

Secular Journal. Thomas Merton. 1983. 16.00 (ISBN 0-8446-5985-1). Peter Smith.

Secular Magi: Marx, Nietzsche, & Freud on Religion. William L. Newell. 264p. (Orig.). 1986. pap. 13.95 (ISBN 0-8298-0579-6). Pilgrim NY.

Secular Marriage, Christian Sacrament. Michael Lawler. 192p. (Orig.). 1985. pap. text ed. 8.95 (ISBN 0-89622-273-X). Twenty-Third.

Secular Mind: Transformations of Faith in Modern Europe. Ed. by W. Warren Wagar. LC 81-20019. 275p. 1982. text ed. 42.50x (ISBN 0-8419-0766-8). Holmes & Meier.

Secular Ritual: A Working Definition of Ritual. Ed. by Sally F. Moore & Barbara G. Myerhoff. 306p. 1977. text ed. 32.00 (ISBN 90-232-1457-9, Pub. by Van Gorcum Holland). Longwood Pub Group.

Secular Sanctity. rev. ed. Edward Hays. LC 84-81954. (Illus.). 176p. 1984. pap. 7.95 (ISBN 0-939516-05-5). Forest Peace.

Secular Scripture: A Study of the Structure of Romance. Northrop Frye. (Charles Eliot Norton Lectures Ser.). 192p. 1976. 15.00x (ISBN 0-674-79675-6); pap. 5.95x (ISBN 0-674-79676-4, HP 127). Harvard U Pr.

Secular Word Is Full-Time Service Study Guide. Larry Peabody. 1976. pap. 1.50 (ISBN 0-87508-449-4). Chr Lit.

Secular Work Is Full Time Service. Larry Peabody. 1974. pap. 2.95 (ISBN 0-87508-448-6). Chr Lit.

Secularism in India. V. K. Sinha. 1968. 6.25 (ISBN 0-89684-521-4). Orient Bk Dist.

Secularization & Spirituality. Christian Duquoc. LC 76-103390. (Concilium Ser.: Vol. 49). 187p. 7.95 (ISBN 0-8091-0136-X). Paulist Pr.

Secularization of American Education As Shown by State Legislation, State Constitutional Provisions & State Supreme Court Decisions. S. W. Brown. LC 70-176600. (Columbia University. Teachers College. Contributions to Education: No. 49). Repr. of 1912 ed. 22.50 (ISBN 0-404-55049-5). AMS Pr.

Secularization of the California Missions (1810-1846) Gerald J. Geary. LC 73-3572. (Catholic University of America. Studies in American Church History: No. 17). Repr. of 1934 ed. 26.00 (ISBN 0-404-57767-9). AMS Pr.

Secure & Rejoicing. George E. Failing. 1980. 0.95 (ISBN 0-937296-03-1, 223-A). Presence Inc.

Secure the Blessings of Liberty: American Constitutional Law & the New Religious Movement. William C. Shepherd. LC 84-1347. (American Academy of Religion Studies in Religion: No. 35). 1984. 16.95 (ISBN 0-89130-733-8, 01-00-35); pap. 9.95 (ISBN 0-89130-824-5). Scholars Pr GA.

Security. C. H. Spurgeon. 1976. pap. 1.50 (ISBN 0-686-16846-1). Pilgrim Pubns.

Security of Salvation. Richard C. Nies. LC 78-17523. (Waymark Ser.). 1978. pap. 2.50 (ISBN 0-8127-0187-9). Review & Herald.

Sed Llenos del Espiritu Santo. rev. ed. John R. Stott. Tr. by David A. Cook from Eng. LC 77-162. Tr. of Be Filled with the Holy Spirit. (Span.). 112p. 1977. pap. 3.50 (ISBN 0-89922-084-3). Edit Caribe.

Seder Mincha U'Maariv. 1982. pap. 0.99 (ISBN 0-686-76256-8). Feldheim.

Sedra Scenes: Skits for Every Torah Portion. Stan J. Beiner. LC 82-71282. 225p. (Orig.). 1982. pap. text ed. 8.75 (ISBN 0-86705-007-1). AIRE.

Seduction?? A Biblical Response. rev. ed. Thomas F. Reid et al. Ed. by Florence K. Biros & Carole Williams. (Illus.). 1986. pap. 6.95 (ISBN 0-936369-02-7). Son-Rise Pubns.

Seduction of Christianity. Dave Hunt & T. A. McMahon. LC 84-81211. 242p. 1985. pap. 7.95 (ISBN 0-89081-441-4, 4414). Harvest Hse.

See & Know. Lois Whitaker. 87p. (Orig.). 1980. pap. text ed. 3.95 (ISBN 0-931097-02-9). Sentinel Pub.

See & Share Stories about Jesus, 4 bks. Robert Kingston. Orig. Title: Bible Stories. (Illus.). 40p. Repr. Set. 7.95 (ISBN 0-687-37132-5). Abingdon.

See His Banner Go: A Centennial History of the First Baptist Church, Paragould, Arkansas. Kenneth M. Startup. LC 84-73475. (Illus.). 100p. 1985. write for info. (ISBN 0-935304-93-2). August Hse.

See It! Do It! Your Faith in Action. David Ng. (Orig.). 1972. pap. 2.50 (ISBN 0-377-02401-5). Friend Pr.

See of Peter. Ed. by James T. Shotwell & Louis R. Loomis. 1965. lib. bdg. 49.00x (ISBN 0-374-97391-1, Octagon). Hippocrene Bks.

Seed & the Tree: Reflections on Non-Violence. Daniel A. Seeger. (Orig.). 1986. pap. 2.50x (ISBN 0-87574-269-6). Pendle Hill.

Seed Money in Action. Jon P. Speller. LC 65-26790. 1965. pap. 3.00 (ISBN 0-8315-0007-7). Speller.

Seed of Abraham: Jews & Arabs in Contact & Conflict. Raphael Patai. 384p. 1986. 29.95 (ISBN 0-87480-251-2). U of Utah Pr.

Seeds for Sermons. Hyman Appelman. (Sermon Outline Ser.). 1980. pap. 2.50 (ISBN 0-8010-0026-2). Baker Bk.

Seeds of Contemplation. Thomas Merton. LC 78-10255. 1979. Repr. of 1949 ed. lib. bdg. 27.50x (ISBN 0-313-20756-9, MESC). Greenwood.

Seeds of Destruction. Thomas Merton. 1983. 14.00 (ISBN 0-8446-5988-6). Peter Smith.

Seeds of Faith. Clarence M. Wagner. (Vol. 11). 100p. 1981. pap. 4.00x (ISBN 0-937498-02-5). Tru-Faith.

Seeds of Greatness. Denis E. Waitley. 224p. 1983. 14.95 (ISBN 0-8007-1361-3); pap. 3.95 (ISBN 0-8007-8560-6). Revell.

Seeds of Light. Swami Radha Sivananda. LC 76-67719. (Illus.). 116p. 1985. pap. 9.95 (ISBN 0-931454-11-5). Timeless Bks.

Seeds of Paradise: A Garland of Holiday Projects. Mary V. Reilly & Margaret K. Wetterer. (Illus.). 44p. (Orig.). 1982. pap. 4.95 (ISBN 0-8192-1298-9). Morehouse.

Seeds of Promise: World Consultation on Frontier Missions, Edinburgh '80. Ed. by Allan Starling. LC 81-69488. (Illus.). 272p. (Orig.). 1981. pap. 8.95 (ISBN 0-87808-186-0). William Carey Lib.

Seeds of Secularization: Calvinism, Culture, & Pluralism in America, 1870-1915. Gary S. Smith. 248p. (Orig.). 1985. pap. 14.95x (ISBN 0-8028-0058-0). Eerdmans.

Seeing Eye & Other Selected Essays from Christian Reflections. C. S. Lewis. 256p. 1986. pap. 3.50 (ISBN 0-345-32866-3). Ballantine.

Seeing Eye: Hermeneutical Phenomenology in the Study of Religion. Walter L. Brenneman, Jr. et al. LC 81-47174. 168p. 1982. 22.50x (ISBN 0-271-00291-3). Pa St U Pr.

Seeing Is Above All: Sant Darshan Singh's First Indian Tour. Ed. by H. C. Chadda. (Illus.). 1977. pap. 3.00 (ISBN 0-918224-04-7). Sawan Kirpal Pubns.

Seeing the Story of the Bible. Myer Pearlman. 128p. 1930. pap. 2.95 (ISBN 0-88243-581-7, 02-0581). Gospel Pub.

Seeing with a Native Eye: Contributions to the Study of Native American Religion. Ed. by Walter H. Capps. LC 76-9980. 1976. pap. 6.95xi (ISBN 0-06-061312-2, RD-177, HarpR). Har-Row.

Seek First His Kingdom. Roger Thomas. 144p. 1987. pap. price not set (ISBN 0-87403-210-5, 39960). Standard Pub.

Seek Good, Not Evil (That You May Live) Paul Harms. 1985. 6.25 (ISBN 0-89536-754-8, 5860). CSS of Ohio.

Seek His Face. Anthony J. Pfarr. LC 73-86211. 1973. 4.95 (ISBN 0-8198-0353-7); pap. 3.95 (ISBN 0-8198-0354-5). Dghtrs St Paul.

Seek It Lovingly. James W. Angell. (Illus.). 1974. pap. 3.95 (ISBN 0-87516-184-7). De Vorss.

Seek That Which Is Above. Cardinal J. Ratzinger. Tr. by Graham Harrison from German. LC 86-81553. Tr. of Suchen was Droben Ist. 132p. 1986. 9.95 (ISBN 0-89870-101-5). Ignatius Pr.

Seek-the-Verses Bible Puzzles. David Gasperson. 48p. 1986. pap. 2.50 (ISBN 0-87403-045-5, 2689). Standard Pub.

Seek Ye First. Elva Martin. 1973. pap. 1.65 (ISBN 0-915374-32-3, 32-3). Rapids Christian.

Seek Ye First: Song of Solomon. Maggie Chandler. 128p. 1979. pap. 2.50 (ISBN 0-89114-089-1). Baptist Pub Hse.

Seek Ye First the Kingdom of God. Valerie Porter. 1984. 6.75 (ISBN 0-8062-2258-1). Carlton.

Seeker after Truth. Idries Shah. 1982. 16.95 (ISBN 0-900860-91-X, Pub. by Octagon Pr England). Ins Study Human.

Seeker after Truth: A Handbook of Sufi Tales & Teachings. Adries Shah. LC 82-48401. 232p. (Orig.). 1982. pap. 7.64 (ISBN 0-06-067257-9, CN-4049, HarpR). Har-Row.

Seeking a Just Society: An Educational Design. Edward Van Merrienboer et al. Incl. Elementary Edition. 42.00 (ISBN 0-318-00795-9); Secondary Edition. 42.00 (ISBN 0-318-00796-7). Total Edition. 72.00 (ISBN 0-318-00793-2); faculty unit 4.00 (ISBN 0-318-00794-0). Natl Cath Educ.

Seeking First the Kingdom. Robert A. Yoder. LC 83-16618. 104p. (Orig.). 1983. pap. 4.50 (ISBN 0-8361-3349-8). Herald Pr.

Seeking for the Kingdom of God: Origins of the Bruderhof Communities. Eberhard Arnold & Emmy Arnold. LC 74-6317. 200p. 1974. 6.50 (ISBN 0-87486-133-0). Plough.

Seeking Foundation Grants. Barbara S. Gary. 1985. 5.65 (ISBN 0-318-18574-1). Natl Cath Educ.

Seeking God: The Way of St. Benedict. Esther De Waal. 160p. 1984. pap. 4.95 (ISBN 0-8146-1388-8). Liturgical Pr.

Seeking God's Face. Joseph Cardinal Ratzinger. 1982. 6.95 (ISBN 0-317-46880-4). Franciscan Herald.

Seeking God's Peace in a Nuclear Age. Leaders of the Christian Church Staff & Kenneth L. Teegarden. Ed. by Ronald Osborn. LC 85-7836. 96p. (Orig.). 1985. pap. 2.50 (ISBN 0-8272-3422-8). CBP.

Seeking Heart: Prayer Journal of Mae Yoho Ward. Mae Y. Ward. Ed. by Don Ward. LC 84-23836. 144p. (Orig.). 1985. pap. 7.95 (ISBN 0-8272-3420-1). CBP.

Seeking Light in the Darkness of the Unconscious. John Yungblut. LC 77-71933. (Orig.). 1977. pap. 2.50x (ISBN 0-87574-211-4). Pendle Hill.

Seeking Purity of Heart: The Gift of Ourselves to God. Joseph Breault. (Illus.). 96p. (Orig.). 1975. pap. 3.95 (ISBN 0-914544-07-1). Living Flame Pr.

Seeking Spiritual Meaning: The World of Vedanta. Joseph D. Damrell. LC 77-9145. (Sociological Observations Ser.: No. 2). pap. 63.00 (ISBN 0-317-08760-6, 2021885). Bks Demand UMI.

Seeking the Spirit. Joseph F. McConkie. LC 78-13372. 122p. 1985. pap. 4.95 (ISBN 0-87747-818-X). Deseret Bk.

Seeking the Spirit. John Mahoney. 11.95 (ISBN 0-87193-187-7). Dimension Bks.

Seeking Wisdom: The Sufi Path. Stuart Litvak. LC 82-60163. 128p. (Orig.). 1984. pap. 6.95 (ISBN 0-87728-543-8). Weiser.

Seer: Joseph Smith. Ron Jackson. Orig. Title: Joseph Smith: the Seer. 1977. 5.95 (ISBN 0-89036-088-X). Hawkes Pub Inc.

Sefer Ha'hinnuch, the Book of Education: Genesis-Exodus. Tr. by Charles Wengrov from Hebrew. (Anonymous Attributed to R. Aharon Halevi). 1978. Vol. 1. 14.95 (ISBN 0-87306-179-9). Feldheim.

Sefer Ha'hinnuch: The Book of Education, Vols. 2 & 3. Leviticus. 1985. 29.95 (ISBN 0-87306-145-4). Feldheim.

Sefer Hahinnuch, Vol. IV: Numbers & Part I. of Deuteronomy. (Hebrew & Eng.). 500p. 1987. 17.95 (ISBN 0-317-42725-3). Feldheim.

Sefer lekarth tov: Perush le-megilat Ester, Tsfat, 1577. Yom-Tov B. Zahalon. 31.00 (ISBN 0-405-11952-6). Ayer Co Pubs.

Segunda Epistola a los Corintos. Pablo Wickham. (Span.). 320p. 1985. pap. 9.95 (ISBN 0-8254-1870-4). Kregel.

Segundo de los Grandes Mandamientos. William M. Fletcher. Ed. by Angel Carrodeguas. Tr. by Elsie R. Romanenghi de Powell from Eng. Tr. of Second Greatest Commandment. (Span.). 192p. Date not set. pap. text ed. 2.95 (ISBN 0-8297-0722-0). Life Pubs Intl.

Sein und Gnade: Die Ontologie in Karl Barths Kirchlicher Dogmatik. Wilfried Haerle. (Theologische Bibliothek Toepelmann, Vol. 27). (Ger.). 428p. 1975. 45.60x (ISBN 3-11-005706-9). De Gruyter.

Seizing the Apple: A Feminist Spirituality of Personal Growth. Denise L. Carmody. 176p. (Orig.). 1984. pap. 10.95 (ISBN 0-8245-0652-9). Crossroad NY.

Sejatel. Claudia Loukashevitch. Tr. of Sower. (Illus.). 462p. 1966. 20.00 (ISBN 0-317-30416-X); pap. 15.00 (ISBN 0-317-30417-8). Holy Trinity.

Seldom-Told Bible Tales. James McKarns. 1985. 4.95 (ISBN 0-89536-738-6, 5821). CSS of Ohio.

Selecciones Teologias Anabautista. Walter Klaassen. Tr. by C. Arnoldo Snyder from Eng. LC 85-81079. (Span.). 280p. (Orig.). 1985. pap. 4.50 (ISBN 0-8361-1281-4). Herald Pr.

Select Discourses. John Smith. Ed. by Rene Wellek. LC 75-11252. (British Philosophers & Theologians of the 17th & 18th Centuries Ser.). 1978. Repr. of 1660 ed. lib. bdg. 51.00 (ISBN 0-8240-1803-6). Garland Pub.

Select Guide to California Catholic History. Francis J. Weber. 12.50 (ISBN 0-87026-001-4). Westernlore.

Select Letters. St. Aurelius Augustine. Tr. by James H. Baxter. LC 75-41012. Repr. of 1930 ed. 37.50 (ISBN 0-404-14503-5). AMS Pr.

Select Medieval Documents & Other Material Illustrative in the History of Church & Empire, 754 A.D.-1254 A.D. Shailer Mathews. LC 70-178566. (Lat.). Repr. of 1900 ed. 21.00 (ISBN 0-404-56628-6). AMS Pr.

Select Poetry, Chiefly Devotional, of the Reign of Queen Elizabeth, 2 Vols. Ed. by Edward Farr. 1845. Vol. 1. 41.00 (ISBN 0-384-15165-5); Vol. 2. 41.00 (ISBN 0-384-15166-3). Johnson Repr.

Select Sermons of Benjamin Whichcote. Benjamin Whichcote. LC 77-16025. 1977. Repr. of 1742 ed. 50.00x (ISBN 0-8201-1306-9). Schol Facsimiles.

Select Sermons of George Whitefield. George Whitefield. 200p. 1985. pap. 3.95 (ISBN 0-85151-454-5). Banner of Truth.

Select Treatises of St. Athanasius in Controversy with the Arians, 2 vols. 5th ed. St. Athanasius. Tr. by John H. Newman. LC 77-84694. (Heresies of the Early Christian & Medieval Era Ser.). Repr. of 1890 ed. 72.00 set (ISBN 0-404-16100-6). AMS Pr.

Select Works of John Bale, Bishop of Ossory. John Bale. 51.00 (ISBN 0-384-03135-8). Johnson Repr.

Selected & Annotated Resource List of Materials on the Holocaust. Pref. by Elie Wiesel. 65p. 5.00 (ISBN 0-686-74934-0). ADL.

Selected Bible Readings. 1962. pap. 2.95 (ISBN 0-686-24354-4); spiral bdg. 3.95 (ISBN 0-686-24355-2); Fabrikoid 4.95 (ISBN 0-686-28567-0). Divine Sci Fed.

Selected Byzantine Hymns. 2nd ed. Holy Transfiguration Monastery Staff. 120p. (Orig.). 1987. pap. 10.00x (ISBN 0-913026-59-X, Holy Transfiguration). St Nectarios.

Selected Chapters from the Writings of the Maya Indians. Ed. by Yuri V. Knorozov & Tatiana Proskouriakoff. Tr. by Sophie Coe. LC 70-38502. (Harvard University. Peabody Museum of Archaeology & Ethnology. Russian Translation Ser.: No. 4). Repr. of 1967 ed. 28.00 (ISBN 0-404-52647-0). AMS Pr.

Selected Conjurations from the Lemegeton (& Other Sources) large type ed. Nelson White & Anne White. LC 81-51403. 50p. (Orig.). 1981. pap. 10.00 (ISBN 0-939856-16-6). Tech Group.

Selected Essays. A. D. Gordon. LC 73-2201. (Jewish People; History, Religion, Literature Ser.). Repr. of 1938 ed. 25.50 (ISBN 0-405-05266-9). Ayer Co Pubs.

Selected Essays. Edwards A. Park. Ed. by Bruce Kuklick. (American Religious Thought of the 18th & 19th Centuries Ser.). 367p. 1987. lib. bdg. 55.00 (ISBN 0-8240-6957-9). Garland Pub.

Selected Essays. F. Lyman Windolph. LC 72-186116. 1972. 7.50 (ISBN 0-685-36105-5). Franklin & Marsh.

Selected Essays on Atheism. Percy Bysshe Shelley. LC 72-161341. (Atheist Viewpoint Ser). 100p. 1972. Repr. 13.00 (ISBN 0-405-03794-5). Ayer Co Pubs.

Selected Essays on Language, Mythology & Religion, 2 vols. Friedrich M. Mueller. LC 73-18814. Repr. of 1881 ed. 87.50 set (ISBN 0-404-11456-3). AMS Pr.

Selected Garlands. Philipa Jones. 160p. 1986. pap. 30.00x (ISBN 0-947939-02-4, Pub. by Elmcrest UK). State Mutual Bk.

Selected Letters. St. Leo The Great. LC 63-18826. (Fathers of the Church Ser: Vol. 34). 312p. 1957. 15.95x (ISBN 0-8132-0034-2). Cath U Pr.

Selected Letters of Cotton Mather. Cotton Mather. Ed. by Kenneth Silverman. LC 78-142338. pap. 118.00 (ISBN 0-317-29860-7, 2019565). Bks Demand UMI.

Selected Messages, Vol. III. Ellen G. White. 1980. Christian Home Library Ed. 8.95 (ISBN 0-8280-0055-7, 19275-7); Shield Ser. Ed. 4.95 (ISBN 0-8280-0056-5, 19276-5); Special Ed. pap. 4.50 (ISBN 0-8280-0057-3, 19277-3). Review & Herald.

Selected Messages, 3 vols. Ellen G. White. 1980. Set. pap. 11.95 (ISBN 0-8280-0059-X, 19269-0). Review & Herald.

Selected Papers & Addresses. Nathaniel D. Pendleton. 251p. 1985. 7.00 (ISBN 0-910557-09-8). Acad New Church.

Selected Papers of Lionel Pearson. Ed. by Donald Lateiner & Susan Stephens. LC 83-16485. (Homage Ser.). 282p. 1983. 14.95 (ISBN 0-89130-646-3, 00 16 04). Scholars Pr GA.

Selected Prayers by Robert Louis Stevenson. Robert Louis Stevenson. (Illus.). 1980. Repr. of 1904 ed. 39.75 (ISBN 0-89901-004-0). Found Class Reprints.

Selected Prose Writings of John Milton. Ed. by Ernest Myers. 1973. Repr. of 1904 ed. lib. bdg. 20.00 (ISBN 0-8414-6695-5). Folcroft.

Selected Sermons. facs. ed. Phillips Brooks. Ed. by William Scarlett. LC 79-142610. (Essay Index Reprint Ser). 1949. 19.50 (ISBN 0-8369-2146-1). Ayer Co Pubs.

Selected Sermons. C. F. Walther. Tr. by Herbert J. Bouman. (Selected Writings of C. F. W. Walther Ser.). 1981. 12.95 (ISBN 0-570-08276-5, 15-2734). Concordia.

Selected Sermons of Hugh Latimer. Hugh Latimer. Ed. by Allan G. Chester. (Documents Ser). 1978. 16.00x (ISBN 0-918016-43-6). Folger Bks.

Selected Temple Documents of the Ur Dynasty. Clarence E. Keiser. LC 78-63533. (Yale Oriental Series: Babylonian Texts: No. 4). (Illus.). 240p. Repr. of 1919 ed. 42.50 (ISBN 0-404-60254-1). AMS Pr.

Selected Texts on Prayer. Nilus of Sinai. pap. 0.25 (ISBN 0-317-11390-9). Eastern Orthodox.

Selected Treatises. St. Cyprian. LC 77-81349. (Fathers of the Church Ser.: Vol. 36). 372p. 1958. 19.95x (ISBN 0-8132-0036-9). Cath U Pr.

Selected Women of the Scriptures of Stamina & Courage. Dolores S. Gilliland. (Illus.). 1978. pap. 3.95 (ISBN 0-931446-02-3). Honor Bks.

Selected Works. Pierre Gassendi. Tr. by Craig B. Brush. 1972. Repr. 45.00 (ISBN 0-384-17685-2). Johnson Repr.

Selected Works. St. John Of Damascus. LC 56-792. (Fathers of the Church Ser: Vol. 37). 426p. 1958. 23.95x (ISBN 0-8132-0037-7). Cath U Pr.

Selected Works. St. Peter Chrysologos & St. Valerian. LC 65-27500. (Fathers of the Church Ser.: Vol. 17). 454p. 1953. 29.95x (ISBN 0-8132-0017-2). Cath U Pr.

Selected Works of Miguel de Unamuno, Vol. 5: The Agony of Christianity & Essays on Faith. Ed. by Anthony Kerrigan & Martin Nozick. LC 67-22341. (Bollingen Ser.: Vol. 85). 313p. 1974. 34.00x (ISBN 0-691-09933-2). Princeton U Pr.

Selected Works of the Dalai Lama I: Bridging the Sutras & Tantras. Rev. ed. Glenn Mullin et al. LC 85-8333. (Teachings of the Dalai Lamas Ser.). Orig. Title: Bridging the Sutras & Tantras. (Tibetan., Illus.). 288p. (Orig.). 1985. pap. 12.95 (ISBN 0-937938-27-0). Snow Lion.

Selected Works of the Dalai Lama II: The Tantric Yogas of the Sister Niguma. Glenn H. Mullin et al. LC 85-40081. (Teachings of the Dalai Lamas Ser.). (Tibetan., Illus.). 240p. (Orig.). 1985. pap. 10.95 (ISBN 0-937938-28-9). Snow Lion.

Selected Works of the Dalai Lama III: Essence of Refined Gold. Rev. ed. Glenn H. Mullin et al. LC 85-8359. (Teachings of the Dalai Lamas Ser.). Orig. Title: Essence of Refined Gold. (Tibetan.). 264p. 1985. pap. 10.95 (ISBN 0-937938-29-7). Snow Lion.

Selected Works of the Dalai Lama VII: Songs of Spiritual Change. Rev. ed. Glenn H. Mullin. LC 85-8332. (Teachings of the Dalai Lamas Ser.). Orig. Title: Songs of Spiritual Change. (Tibetan., Illus.). 225p. 1985. pap. 10.95 (ISBN 0-937938-30-0). Snow Lion.

Selected Writings. Philipp Melanchthon. Ed. by Elmer E. Flack & Lowell J. Satre. Tr. by Charles L. Hill. LC 78-5175. 1978. Repr. of 1962 ed. lib. bdg. cancelled (ISBN 0-313-20384-9, MESW). Greenwood.

Selected Writings. Zwingli. 1972. 9.95x (ISBN 0-8122-1049-2). U of Pa Pr.

Selected Writings by Cardinal Mercier. Desire Mercier. (Illus.). 128p. 1984. 57.85 (ISBN 0-89901-136-5). Found Class Reprints.

Selected Writings of Baha'u'llah. Baha'u'llah. LC 79-15136. 1979. 10.95 (ISBN 0-87743-133-7, 303-024); pap. 1.00 (ISBN 0-87743-077-2, 303-023). Baha'i.

Selected Writings of Hans Denck. Ed. & tr. by E. J. Furcha. LC 76-7057. (Pittsburgh Original Texts & Translations Ser.: No. 1). 1976. 5.50 (ISBN 0-915138-15-8). Pickwick.

Selected Writings of Jonathan Edwards. Jonathan Edwards. Ed. by Harold P. Simonson. LC 78-115064. (Milestones of Thought Ser.). 1970. pap. 7.95 (ISBN 0-8044-6132-5). Ungar.

Selected Writings of Julius Guttmann: An Original Anthology. Ed. by Steven Katz. LC 79-7175. (Jewish Philosophy, Mysticism & History of Ideas Ser.). 1980. lib. bdg. 34.50x (ISBN 0-405-12232-2). Ayer Co Pubs.

Selected Writings of St. Thomas Aquinas. St. Thomas Aquinas. Tr. by Robert P. Goodwin. Incl. Principles of Nature; On Being & Essence; On the Virtues in General; On Free Choice. LC 65-26529. (Orig.). 1965. pap. 4.24 scp (ISBN 0-672-60469-8, LLA217). Bobbs.

Selected Writings of Shoghi Effendi. rev. ed. Shoghi Effendi. 1975. pap. 1.95 (ISBN 0-87743-079-9, 308-043). Baha'i.

Selected Writings on Philosophy, Religion & Politics. J. Bodin. Ed. by Paul L. Rose. xiv, 94p. (Orig.). 1980. pap. text ed. 18.50x (Pub. by Droz Switzerland). Coronet Bks.

Selected Writings on Religion & Society. Edward Bellamy. Ed. by Joseph Schiffman. LC 74-40. (American Heritage Ser.: No. 11). 139p. 1974. Repr. of 1955 ed. lib. bdg. 22.50 (ISBN 0-8371-7359-0, BEWR). Greenwood.

Selecting a Translation of the Bible. Lewis Foster & Jon Stedman. LC 83-4689. (Illus.). 128p. (Orig.). 1983. pap. 3.95 (ISBN 0-87239-645-2, 39975). Standard Pub.

Selecting Computers for Ministry. Robert H. Iles & William L. Callison. LC 84-62333. (Illus.). 160p. (Orig.). 1985. pap. 13.95 (ISBN 0-932489-00-1). New Begin Co.

Selecting the Church Computer. William R. Johnson. 160p. (Orig.). 1984. pap. 8.95 (ISBN 0-687-37135-X). Abingdon.

Selection & Election. Ali Shariati. Tr. by Ali A. Ghasemy from Persian. 12p. 1980. pap. 0.75 (ISBN 0-941722-13-9). Book-Dist-Ctr.

Selection of English Carols. Ed. by Richard L. Greene. LC 77-13760. 1978. Repr. of 1962 ed. lib. bdg. 24.75x (ISBN 0-313-20002-5, GREC). Greenwood.

Selections from Quran & Hadith. A. H. Siddiqui. pap. 22.50 ea. (ISBN 0-686-63914-6). Kazi Pubns.

Selections from Sanskrit Inscriptions. D. B. Diskalkar. 1977. 18.00x (ISBN 0-686-22673-9). Intl Bk Dist.

Selections from Swami Vivekananda. Swami Vivekananda. 10.00x (ISBN 0-87481-094-9); pap. 6.95 (ISBN 0-87481-174-0). Vedanta Pr.

Selections from the Koran. Sirdar Ikbal Ali Shah. 1980. 10.85 (ISBN 0-900860-85-5, Pub. by Octagon Pr England). Ins Study Human.

Selections from the Latin Fathers. Ed. by Peter E. Hebert. (College Classical Ser.). xvii, 186p. 1982. lib. bdg. 25.00x (ISBN 0-89241-357-3); pap. text ed. 12.50x (ISBN 0-89241-370-0). Caratzas.

Selections from the Literature of Theism. Alfred Caldecott & H. R. MacKintosh. 1979. Repr. of 1909 ed. lib. bdg. 65.00 (ISBN 0-8495-0932-7). Arden Lib.

Selections from the New Testament in Chinese. John W. Chu. 6.00 (ISBN 0-88710-083-X); tapes avail. (ISBN 0-88710-084-8). Far Eastern Pubns.

Selections from the Quran. Tr. by Arthur Wormhoudt from Classical Arabic. (Arab Translation Ser.: No. 51). 175p. 1981. pap. 6.50x (ISBN 0-916358-03-8). Wormhoudt.

Selections from the Septuagint. Ed. by F. C. Conybeare & George Stock. (College Classical Ser.). vi, 313p. 1981. lib. bdg. 25.00x (ISBN 0-89241-366-2); pap. 12.50 (ISBN 0-89241-114-7). Caratzas.

Selections from the Upanishads & The Tao Te King. Tr. by Charles Johnston & Lionel Giles. 142p. 1951. Repr. of 1897 ed. 3.00 (ISBN 0-938998-15-3). Cunningham Pr.

Selections from the Upanishads & the Tao Te King. Tr. by Charles Johnston & Lionel Giles. 142p. 1951. 3.00 (ISBN 0-938998-15-3). Theosophy.

Selections from the Works of Jeremy Taylor: With Some Account of the Author & His Writings. 306p. 1983. Repr. of 1865 ed. lib. bdg. 40.00 (ISBN 0-89760-853-4). Telegraph Bks.

Selections from the Writings of Abdu'l-Baha. Abdu'l-Baha. Tr. by Shoghi Effendi & Marzieh Gail. 1978. 14.95 (ISBN 0-85398-081-0, 106-025); pap. 7.95 (ISBN 0-85398-084-5, 106-026); Lightweight. pap. 6.00 (ISBN 0-85398-136-1). Baha'i.

Selections from the Writings of E. G. Browne on the Babi & Baha'i Religions. Moojan Momen. 528p. 1987. 29.50 (ISBN 0-85398-246-5); pap. 16.95 (ISBN 0-85398-247-3). G Ronald Pub.

Selections from the Writings of the Bab. Bab. LC 79-670141. 1976. 14.95 (ISBN 0-85398-066-7, 105-050); pap. 7.95 (ISBN 0-85398-135-3). Baha'i.

Self Analysis. L. Ron Hubbard. 20.00 (ISBN 0-686-30780-1). Church Scient NY.

Self Analysis. L. Ron Hubbard. 254p. 1983. pap. 8.95 (ISBN 0-88404-109-3). Bridge Pubns Inc.

Self & Family. Jane C. Peck. LC 84-13166. (Choices: Guides for Today's Woman Ser.: Vol. 11). 118p. 1984. pap. 6.95 (ISBN 0-664-24547-1). Westminster.

Self & Non-Self in Early Buddhism. Joacquin Perez-Ramon. (Religon & Society Ser.: No. 17). 1980. 58.00x (ISBN 90-279-7987-1). Mouton.

Self & the Other in the Ontologies of Sartre & Buber. Sylvain Boni. LC 82-20130. 202p. (Orig.). 1983. lib. bdg. 27.50 (ISBN 0-8191-2852-X); pap. text ed. 12.50 (ISBN 0-8191-2853-8). U Pr of Amer.

Self As Agent. John MacMurray. 1978. pap. text ed. 5.95x (ISBN 0-391-02043-9). Humanities.

Self-Awareness Through Huna-Hawaii's Ancient Wisdom. Erika S. Nau. Ed. by Stefan Grunwald. LC 80-27842. (Orig.). 1981. pap. 5.95 (ISBN 0-89865-099-2, Unilaw). Donning Co.

Self-Control. Russell Kelfer. (Living Studies). 240p. 1985. pap. 5.95 (ISBN 0-8423-5859-5); leader's guide 2.95 (ISBN 0-8423-5860-9). Tyndale.

Self-Control. Carole MacKenthun & Paulinus Dwyer. (Fruit of the Spirit Ser.). (Illus.). 48p. 1987. pap. 5.95 (ISBN 0-86653-396-6, SS878). Good Apple.

Self-Deceit. Frederick Faber. 1983. pap. 2.50x (ISBN 0-87574-050-2, 050). Pendle Hill.

Self-Destructive Tendencies of Christian Women. Pamela Urfer & Judie Jones. 109p. (Orig.). 1983. pap. text ed. 7.95 (ISBN 0-912801-04-2). Creat Arts Dev.

Self Development Through Meditative Practice. Donald Melcer. 1983. pap. 2.95 (ISBN 0-916786-70-6). St George Bk Serv.

Self-Discovery in Recovery. Abraham J Twerski. 128p. (Orig.). 1984. pap. 3.95 (ISBN 0-89486-238-3). Hazelden.

Self Esteem: A Gift from God. Ruth M. Ward. 1984. pap. 7.95 (ISBN 0-8010-9664-2). Baker Bk.

Self-Esteem for the Latter-Day Saint Woman. 2nd ed. Anita Canfield. 135p. 1983. 7.95 (ISBN 0-934126-15-1). Randall Bk Co.

Self-Esteem: The New Reformation. Robert H. Schuller. 144p. 1982. 3.95 (ISBN 0-8499-4172-5). Word Bks.

Self Esteem: You're Better Than You Think. Ray Burwick. 1983. pap. 5.95 (ISBN 0-8423-5865-X). Tyndale.

Self-Fulfilling Prophecy: Exile & Return As the History of Judaism. Jacob Neusner. LC 86-47756. 320p. 1987. 25.00 (ISBN 0-8070-3606-4). Beacon Pr.

Self-Fulfillment Through Zionism: A Study in Jewish Adjustment. Ed. by Shlomo Bardin. LC 70-142605. (Biography Index Reprint Ser). Repr. of 1943 ed. 17.00 (ISBN 0-8369-8076-X). Ayer Co Pubs.

Self God. Subramuniya. (On the Path Ser.). 72p. 1959. pap. 2.00 (ISBN 0-87516-353-X). De Vorss.

Self, God & Immortality: A Jamesian Investigation. Eugene Fontinell. 320p. 1986. 34.95 (ISBN 0-87722-428-5). Temple U Pr.

Self Healing Yoga & Destiny. 1983. 4.95 (ISBN 0-943358-06-X). Aurora Press.

Self-Help. Samuel Sailes. Ed. by George Bull & Keith Joseph. 240p. 1986. pap. 6.95 (ISBN 0-14-009100-9). Penguin.

Self Help for Seniors. National Council of Jewish Women. 30p. (Orig.). 1983. pap. text ed. 4.00 (ISBN 0-941840-14-X). NCJW.

Self-Image of a Christian: Humility & Self-Esteem. Mark Kinzer. (Living As a Christian Ser.). 106p. (Orig.). 1980. pap. 2.95 (ISBN 0-89283-088-3). Servant.

Self Imagined: Philosophical Reflections on the Social Character of Psyche. Karen Hanson. 160p. 1986. 26.95 (ISBN 0-7102-0559-7, 05597). Methuen Inc.

Self in Secularism. Badi-Ud Din Tyabji. 1971. 21.50x (ISBN 0-8046-8832-X, Pub. by Kennikat). Assoc Faculty Pr.

Self-Incrimination in Jewish Law. Aaron Kirschenbaum. 1970. 8.00x (ISBN 0-8381-3111-5). United Syn Bk.

Self Interpretation of All Religions. Fraymond Jones, Jr. & Kashaf Abdul Haq. 80p. 1983. 8.95 (ISBN 0-89962-293-3). Todd & Honeywell.

Self Knowledge: A Yoga for the West. Laurence J. Bendit. LC 67-7871. (Orig.). 1967. pap. 1.25 (ISBN 0-8356-0032-7, Quest). Theos Pub Hse.

Self Knowledge & Spiritual Yearning. Abdul Fattah Rashid Hamid. Ed. by Hamid Quinlan. LC 82-70348. (Illus.). 116p. 1982. pap. 4.00 (ISBN 0-89259-027-0). Am Trust Pubns.

Self-Knowledge in Plato's Phaedrus. Charles L. Griswold, Jr. LC 86-5506. 328p. 1986. text ed. 29.50x (ISBN 0-300-03594-2). Yale U Pr.

Self-Knowledge: Sankara's "Atmabodha". Tr. by Swami Nikhilananda. LC 50-36440. 248p. with notes 7.00 (ISBN 0-911206-11-6). Ramakrishna.

Self Life & the Christ Life. Albert B. Simpson. pap. 1.95 (ISBN 0-87509-034-6). Chr Pubns.

Self-Love. Robert H. Schuller. 160p. 1975. pap. 2.95 (ISBN 0-8007-8195-3, Spire Bks). Revell.

Self Made by Magic. William G. Gray. LC 76-15547. 198p. (Orig.). 1984. pap. 8.95 (ISBN 0-87728-556-X). Weiser.

Self Mastery & Fate with the Cycles of Life. 33rd ed. H. Spencer Lewis. LC 55-16785. 253p. 1982. 11.95 (ISBN 0-912057-05-X, G-507). AMORC.

Self Mastery & Fate with the Cycles of Life. H. Spencer Lewis. LC 55-16785. (Illus.). 253p. 1986. pap. 8.95 (ISBN 0-912057-45-9, G-657). AMORC.

Self Power. Paul H. Skinner. 194p. pap. 7.95 (ISBN 0-942494-44-X). Coleman Pub.

Self Profile: The Me Nobody Knows. Lyman Coleman. (Free University - Lay Academy in Christian Discipleship Ser.). (Orig.). 1981. pap. 4.95 leader's guide (ISBN 0-687-37346-8); pap. 1.25 (ISBN 0-687-37347-6). Abingdon.

Self-Purification. Jaina Sutra. (Illus.). 8.75 (ISBN 0-88695-020-1). Concord Grove.

Self-Realization. Satguru S. Keshavadas. (Illus.). 131p. (Orig.). 1976. pap. 3.50 (ISBN 0-942508-11-4). Vishwa.

Self-Realization Through Love. Taimni. 4.75 (ISBN 0-8356-7522-X). Theos Pub Hse.

Self-Reliance Through Yoga. 3rd ed. Selvarajan Yesudian. (Unwin Paperbacks). 1979. pap. 7.50 (ISBN 0-04-149054-1). Allen Unwin.

Self, Society, Existence: Human Nature & Dialogue in the Thought of George Herbert Mead & Martin Buber. Paul Pfuetze. 400p. 1973. Repr. of 1961 ed. lib. bdg. 22.50x (ISBN 0-8371-6708-6, PFSS). Greenwood.

Self Study Bible Course. Derek Prince. 1969. pap. 5.95 (ISBN 0-934920-08-7, B-90). Derek Prince.

Self-Study Guide for Catholic High Schools. 76p. 1981. 9.00 (ISBN 0-318-00792-4). Natl Cath Educ.

Self-Study Guide for Catholic High Schools. 76p. 1981. 9.00 (ISBN 0-318-20605-6). Natl Cath Educ.

Self-Study Guide to Galatians & Romans. rev. ed. J. D. Thomas. (Way of Life Ser: No. 122). Orig. Title: Self-Study Guide to Romans. (Orig.). 1971. pap. text ed. 3.95 (ISBN 0-89112-122-6, Bibl Res Pr). Abilene Christ U.

Self-Study Guide to the Corinthian Letters. J. D. Thomas. (Way of Life Ser: No. 123). (Orig.). 1972. pap. text ed. 3.95 (ISBN 0-89112-123-4, Bibl Res Pr). Abilene Christ U.

Self Talk. David Stoop. 160p. 1981. pap. 5.95 (ISBN 0-8007-5074-8, Power Bks). Revell.

Self-Talk, Prayer & Imagery in Counseling (RCC) Norman Wright. 192p. 1986. 12.95 (ISBN 0-8499-0585-0). Word Bks.

Self to the Self. Dora Wilson. 1983. pap. 2.50x (ISBN 0-87574-035-9, 035). Pendle Hill.

Selfcare-Wellcare. Keith W. Sehnert. LC 85-15622. 240p. (Orig.). 1985. text ed. 12.95 (ISBN 0-8066-2179-6, 10-5644); pap. 3.95 (ISBN 0-8066-2180-X, 10-5645). Augsburg.

Selfless Persons: Imagery & Thought in Theravada Buddhism. Steven Collins. LC 81-16998. 1982. 47.50 (ISBN 0-521-24081-6). Cambridge U Pr.

Selichot for the Whole Year. Abraham Rosenfield. 832p. 1956. 13.95 (ISBN 0-910818-10-X). Judaica Pr.

Selichot Reader. pap. 0.75 (ISBN 0-686-96114-5). United Syn Bk.

Selihot. Tr. by Philip Birnbaum. 61p. 1952. pap. 1.95 (ISBN 0-88482-344-X). Hebrew Pub.

Selihot Service. rev. ed. Morris Silverman & Max Arzt. pap. 2.95x (ISBN 0-87677-066-9). Prayer Bk.

Selling of Jesus. Victor V. Brydítzki. (Illus.). 128p. (Orig.). 1985. pap. 3.95 (ISBN 0-937958-22-0). Chick Pubns.

Selma: The Gospel at Work. F. Wilbur Helmbold. 1983. 12.50; pap. 8.50. Banner Pr AL.

Sema-Kanda: Threshold Memories. Coulson Turnbul. 254p. Date not set. pap. 15.00 (ISBN 0-89540-131-2, SB-131). Sun Pub.

Semantics in Biblical Research: New Methods of Defining Hebrew Words for Salvation. John F. Sawyer. LC 72-75901. (Studies in Biblical Theology, Second Ser.: No. 24). 1972. pap. text ed. 12.00x (ISBN 0-8401-3074-0). A R Allenson.

Semantics of Metaphor. Samuel R. Levin. LC 77-4550. pap. 44.00 (ISBN 0-317-41827-0, 2025626). Bks Demand UMI.

Semantics of New Testament Greek. J. P. Louw. LC 81-67308. (Semeia Studies). 176p. 1982. pap. 12.95 (ISBN 0-8006-1511-5). Fortress.

Semantics of New Testament Greek. J. P. Louw. (Semeia Studies). pap. 12.95 (ISBN 0-89130-693-5, 06 06 11). Scholars Pr GA.

Semeia Nineteen: The Book of Job & Ricoeur's Hermeneutics. Ed. by John D. Crossan. (Semeia Ser.). pap. 9.95 (06 20 19). Scholars Pr GA.

SEMEIA: Social Scientific Criticism of the Hebrew Bible & Its Social World: The Israelite Monarchy. Ed. by Norman K. Gottwald. 152p. 1986. pap. 9.95 (ISBN 0-317-52980-3, 06-20-37). Scholars Pr GA.

Semeia Thirty, Christology & Exegesis: New Approaches. Robert Jewett. (SBL-Semeia Ser.). 1985. pap. 9.95 (ISBN 0-317-38906-8, 06-20-30). Scholars Pr Ga.

Semeia Thirty-One: Reader Response Approaches to Biblical & Secular Texts. Ed. by Robert Detweiler. (Semeia Ser.). 1985. pap. 9.95 (ISBN 0-317-38640-9, 06-20-31). Scholars Pr GA.

Semeia Twenty-One: Anthropological Perspectives on Old Testament Prophecy. Ed. by Robert C. Culley & Thomas W. Overholt. pap. 9.95 (06 20 21). Scholars Pr GA.

Semeia Twenty-Three: Derrida & Biblical Studies. Ed. by Robert Detweiler. (Semeia Ser.). pap. 9.95 (06 20 23). Scholars Pr GA.

Semetic Influence in Hellenic Mythology. Robert Brown. LC 65-27053. (Library of Religious & Philosophical Thought). 1966. Repr. of 1898 ed. lib. bdg. 25.00x (ISBN 0-678-09952-9, Reference Bk Pubs). Kelley.

Semi-Centenary & the Retrospection of the African Methodist Episcopal Church. facsimile ed. Daniel A. Payne. LC 76-37598. (Black Heritage Library Collection). Repr. of 1866 ed. 16.50 (ISBN 0-8369-8974-0). Ayer Co Pubs.

Semi-Centenary Discourse. facs. ed. William T. Catto. LC 78-154073. (Black Heritage Library Collection). 1857. 14.25 (ISBN 0-8369-8784-5). Ayer Co Pubs.

Seminar on Jewish Art: Proceedings. Ed. by Vivian B. Mann & Gordon Tucker. 37p. (Orig.). 1985. pap. 6.00 (ISBN 0-87334-029-9). Jewish Sem.

Seminar on Time. A. G. Blake. LC 79-52756. 1980. 5.95 (ISBN 0-934254-00-1). Claymont Comm.

Seminarians in Theology: A National Profile. Eugene F. Hemrick et al. 128p. 1986. pap. 8.95 (ISBN 1-55586-978-5). US Catholic.

Seminarians of the Eighties: A National Survey. Raymond H. Potvin. 64p. 1986. 5.65 (ISBN 0-318-20579-3). Natl Cath Educ.

Seminaries in Dialogue, No. 1. 1980. 2.40 (ISBN 0-318-20625-0). Natl Cath Educ.

Seminaries in Dialogue, No. 2. 24p. 1981. 2.40 (ISBN 0-318-20624-2). Natl Cath Educ.

Seminaries in Dialogue, No. 3. 20p. 1982. 2.40 (ISBN 0-318-20623-4). Natl Cath Educ.

Seminaries in Dialogue, No. 4. 1982. 2.40 (ISBN 0-318-20622-6). Natl Cath Educ.

Seminaries in Dialogue, No. 5. 20p. 1983. 2.40 (ISBN 0-318-20621-8). Natl Cath Educ.

Seminaries in Dialogue, No. 6. 24p. 1984. 2.40 (ISBN 0-318-20620-X). Natl Cath Educ.

Seminaries in Dialogue, No. 7. 24p. 1984. 2.40 (ISBN 0-318-20619-6). Natl Cath Educ.

Seminaries in Dialogue, No. 8. 24p. 1984. 2.40 (ISBN 0-318-20618-8). Natl Cath Educ.

Seminaries in Dialogue, No. 9. 24p. 1985. 2.40 (ISBN 0-318-20617-X). Natl Cath Educ.

Seminaries in Dialogue, No. 10. 24p. 1985. 2.40 (ISBN 0-318-20616-1). Natl Cath Educ.

Seminary: A Search. Paul Hendrickson. 320p. 1987. pap. 6.95 (ISBN 0-671-63586-7). Summit Bks.

Seminary Addresses. Solomon Schechter. 1959. pap. 2.45 (ISBN 0-8381-2109-8). United Syn Bk.

Seminary Addresses & Other Papers. Solomon Schechter. LC 79-83435. (Religion in America, Ser. 1). 1969. Repr. of 1915 ed. 19.00 (ISBN 0-405-00260-2). Ayer Co Pubs.

Seminary Addresses & Other Papers. Solomon Schechter. 270p. Date not set. Repr. of 1915 ed. text ed. 62.10x (ISBN 0-576-80119-4, Pub by Gregg Intl Pubs England). Gregg Intl.

Seminary Education & Christian-Jewish Relationss. Eugene J. Fisher. 100p. 1983. 4.80 (ISBN 0-318-20615-3). Natl Cath Educ.

Seminary Libraries & University Extension. Herbert B. Adams. LC 78-63777. (Johns Hopkins University. Studies in the Social Sciences. Fifth Ser. 1887: 11). Repr. of 1887 ed. 11.50 (ISBN 0-404-61043-9). AMS Pr.

Seminary Notes & Historical Literature. Herbert B. Adams et al. LC 78-63798. (Johns Hopkins University. Studies in the Social Sciences. Eighth Ser. 1890: 11-12). Repr. of 1890 ed. 11.50 (ISBN 0-404-61063-3). AMS Pr.

Seminary Priests: A Dictionary of the Secular Clergy of England & Wales, 1558-1850, 4 vols. Godfrey Anstruther. Incl. Vol. 1. Elizabethan, 1558-1603. 1968 (ISBN 0-87921-059-1); Vol. 2. Early Stuarts 1603-1659. 1975 (ISBN 0-85597-082-0); Vol. 3 Paperback. 660-1715. 1976 (ISBN 0-85597-116-9); Vol. 4 Paperback. 1716-1800. 1977 (ISBN 0-85597-118-5). text ed. 18.50x ea. Attic Pr.

Seminary Priests: A Dictionary of the Secular Clery of England & Wales, 1558 to 1800, Vols. 1-4. Godfrey Anstruther. Incl. Vol. 1. Elizabethan 1558-1603. 1969. text ed. 21.50x (ISBN 0-8401-0071-X); Vol. 2. Early Stuarts 1603-1659. 1975. text ed. 21.50x (ISBN 0-8401-0072-8); Vol. 3. 1660-1715. 1976. text ed. 27.50x (ISBN 0-8401-0073-6); Vol. 4. 1716-1800. 1977. text ed. 27.50x (ISBN 0-8401-0074-4). LC 76-441910. A R Allenson.

Semiology & Parables: Exploration of the Possibilities Offered by Structuralism for Exegesis. Papers of the Vanderbilt University Conference, May 15-17, 1975. Ed. by Daniel Patte. LC 76-20686. (Pittsburgh Theological Monographs: No. 9). 1976. pap. 9.95 (ISBN 0-915138-11-5). Pickwick.

Semiotics & Thematics in Hermeneutics. T. K. Seung. LC 82-4345. 256p. 1982. 27.50 (ISBN 0-231-05410-6). Columbia U Pr.

Semiotics of the Passion Narratives. Louis Marin. Tr. by Alfred M. Johnson, Jr. (Pittsburgh Theological Monographs: No. 25). 1980. 12.95 (ISBN 0-915138-23-9). Pickwick.

Semitic Influence in Hellenic Mythology. R. Brown. xvi, 228p. Repr. of 1898 ed. lib. bdg. 35.00x (ISBN 0-89241-206-2). Caratzas.

Semitic Influence in Hellenic Mythology. Robert Brown. 1977. 19.00 (ISBN 0-405-10084-1, 14709). Ayer Co Pubs.

Semitic Interference in Marcan Syntax. Elliott C. Maloney. LC 80-13016. (Society of Biblical Literature Dissertation Ser.: No. 51). pap. 15.00 (ISBN 0-89130-406-1, 06-01-51). Scholars Pr GA.

Semitic Magic: Its Origins & Development. Reginald C. Thompson. LC 73-18858. Repr. of 1908 ed. 24.50 (ISBN 0-404-11361-3). AMS Pr.

Semitic Mythology. Stephen H. Langdon. LC 63-19090. (Mythology of All Races Ser.: Vol. 5). (Illus.). Repr. of 1932 ed. 30.00x (ISBN 0-8154-0133-7). Cooper Sq.

Semja Pravoslavnago Khristjanina. Tr. of Family of an Orthodox Christian. 569p. 1958. Repr. 15.00 (ISBN 0-317-30248-5). Holy Trinity.

Send in His Clowns. Stephen P. Perrone & James P. Spata. Ed. by Arthur L. Zapel & Kathy Pijanowski. (Illus.). 79p. (Orig.). 1985. pap. 7.95 (ISBN 0-916260-32-1). Meriwether Pub.

Sendbrief from the Alm Bruderhof to the Rhoen Bruderhof. Eberhard Arnold. LC 74-23145. 1974. pap. 2.50 (ISBN 0-87486-148-9). Plough.

Senderos de Comunion. Francisco E. Estrello. 1.75 (ISBN 0-8358-0416-X). Upper Room.

Senderos de Navidad. Juan R. Picasso. 24p. 1980. pap. 0.80 (ISBN 0-311-08218-1). Casa Bautista.

Seneca Myths & Folk Tales. Arthur C. Parker. LC 76-43803. (Buffalo Historical Society. Publication: Vol. 27). Repr. of 1923 ed. 35.00 (ISBN 0-404-15659-2). AMS Pr.

Senior Adult Family Life. John C. Howell. LC 79-51139. 1979. pap. 4.95 large type (ISBN 0-8054-5423-3). Broadman.

Senior Adult Years. Carroll B. Freeman. LC 79-51137. 1979. 7.95 (ISBN 0-8054-5421-7). Broadman.

Senior Field Representative (Human Rights) Jack Rudman. (Career Examination Ser.: C-2563). (Cloth bdg. avail. on request). pap. 14.00 (ISBN 0-8373-2563-3). Natl Learning.

Sennacherib's Invasion of Palestine. Leo L. Honor. LC 26-20926. (Columbia University. Contributions to Oriental History & Philology: No. 12). Repr. of 1926 ed. 15.00 (ISBN 0-404-50542-2). AMS Pr.

Senor: No Me Dejes Rodar. Josie De Smith. (Illus.). 96p. 1986. pap. 2.50 (ISBN 0-311-40042-6). Casa Bautista.

Senor y Sus Laicos. David Haney. Ed. by Jose Luis Martinez. (Span.). 84p. 1986. pap. 2.50 (ISBN 0-311-09095-8). Casa Bautista.

Sensacion de Ser Alguien. Maurice Wagner. Tr. by David A. Cook from Eng. LC 77-16714. Tr. of Sensation of Being Somebody. (Span.). 300p. 1977. pap. 6.50 (ISBN 0-89922-104-1). Edit Caribe.

Sensation & Perception: An Integrated Approach. 2nd ed. Harvey R. Schiffman. LC 81-19770. 540p. 1982. write for info. (ISBN 0-471-08208-2). Wiley.

Sensation of Being Somebody. Maurice Wagner. 256p. 1975. 8.95 (ISBN 0-310-33970-7, 15603P). Zondervan.

Sensation of Being Somebody. Maurice E. Wagner. 251p. 1985. pap. 8.95 (ISBN 0-310-33971-5). Zondervan.

Sense & Absence. Lee Magness. (Semeia Studies). 1986. text ed. 14.95 (ISBN 1-55540-006-X, 06-06-15); pap. 10.95 (ISBN 1-55540-007-8). Scholars Pr GA.

Sense & Nonsense: A Word for Teens. Rolf E. Aaseng. 64p. 1976. pap. 2.50 (ISBN 0-8010-0090-4). Baker Bk.

Sense & Nonsense about Prayer. Lehman Strauss. 128p. 1974. 4.95 (ISBN 0-8024-7700-3). Moody.

Sense & Nonsense about Prayer. Lehman Strauss. 1976. pap. 3.95 (ISBN 0-8024-7702-X). Moody.

Sense of Biblical Narrative II: Stuctural Analyses in the Hebrew Bible. David Jobling. (JSOT Supplement Ser.: No. 39). 120p. 1986. text ed. 21.00x (ISBN 1-85075-010-6, Pub. by JSOT Pr England); pap. text ed. 8.95x (ISBN 1-85075-011-4, Pub. by JSOT Pr England). Eisenbrauns.

Sense of Life, a Sense of Sin. Eugene C. Kennedy. 200p. 1976. pap. 3.50 (ISBN 0-385-12070-2, Im). Doubleday.

Sense of Living. Mildred Tonge. 1983. pap. 2.50x (ISBN 0-87574-079-0, 079). Pendle Hill.

Sense of Mission: Guidance from the Gospel of John. Albert C. Winn. LC 80-28000. 118p. 1981. pap. 6.95 (ISBN 0-664-24365-7). Westminster.

Sense of Text: The Art of Language in the Study of Biblical Literature. Stephen A. Geller et al. 113p. 1983. pap. text ed. 12.50 (ISBN 0-9602686-1-8). Dropsie Coll.

Sense of Unity: The Sufi Tradition in Persian Architecture. Nader Ardalan & Ialeh Bakhtiar. LC 72-92278. (Illus.). xx, 152p. 1986. pap. 29.95 (ISBN 0-226-02560-8). U of Chicago Pr.

Sense of Values. Lewis Chase. LC 79-92431. 67p. 1980. 8.95 (ISBN 0-8022-2362-1). Philos Lib.

Senses in God's World. Beverly Beckman. 24p. 1986. 5.95 (ISBN 0-570-04150-3). Concordia.

Sensing the Spirit. Richard H. Bell. LC 84-5158. (Spirituality & the Christian Life Ser.: Vol. 6). 120p. 1984. pap. 7.95 (ISBN 0-664-24632-X). Westminster.

Sensing Your Hidden Presence: Toward Intimacy With God. Ignacio Larranaga & John Diercksmeier. LC 87-5232. 264p. 1987. pap. 7.95 (ISBN 0-385-24021-X, Im). Doubleday.

Sensitive Leader. Dennis L. Lythgoe. 1986. text ed. 9.95 (ISBN 0-87579-061-5). Deseret Bk.

Sent Free: Mission & Unity in the Perspective of the Kingdom. Emilio Castro. 112p. (Orig.). 1985. pap. 5.95 (ISBN 0-8028-0068-8). Eerdmans.

Sent from the Father: Meditations on the Fourth Gospel. Jose Comblin. Tr. by Carl Kabat from Port. LC 78-16750. Orig. Title: O Enviado do Pai. 115p. (Orig.). 1979. pap. 2.48 (ISBN 0-88344-453-4). Orbis Bks.

Sentence in Biblical Hebrew. Francis I. Andersen. (Janua Linguarum, Ser. Practica: No. 231). 209p. 1974. pap. text ed. 23.20x (ISBN 90-2792-673-5). Mouton.

Sentences of Sextus. Richard Edwards & Robert Wild. LC 81-13770. (Society of Biblical Literature Texts & Translations Ser.). 1981. pap. text ed. 12.00 (ISBN 0-89130-528-9, 06-02-22). Scholars Pr GA.

Sententiae Petri Pictaviensis 1. Philip S. Moore & Marthe Dulong. (Mediaeval Studies Ser.: No. 7). (Lat). 1943. 21.95 (ISBN 0-268-00250-9). U of Notre Dame Pr.

Separated Brethren. rev. ed. William J. Whalen. LC 79-83874. 1979. pap. 7.50 (ISBN 0-87973-829-4). Our Sunday Visitor.

Separation of Church & Freedom: A War Manual for Christian Soldiers. Kent Kelly et al. LC 80-80341. (Illus.). 308p. 1980. 7.95 (ISBN 0-9604138-0-4). Calvary Pr.

Separation of Church & State. Frank Swancara. 346p. pap. 3.00. Truth Seeker.

Separation of Church & State: Dina de-Malkhuta Dina in Jewish Law, 1750-1848. Gil Graff. LC 84-24061. (Judaic Studies Ser.). ix, 224p. 1985. 29.50 (ISBN 0-8173-0264-6). U of Ala Pr.

Separation of Church & State: Historical Fact & Current Fiction. Robert L. Cord. 307p. 1982. 19.95x (ISBN 0-931186-03-X). Lambeth Pr.

Separation of Church & State in Italian Thought from Cavour to Mussolini. S. William Halperin. LC 71-120623. 1970. Repr. lib. bdg. 15.00x (ISBN 0-374-93412-6, Octagon). Hippocrene Bks.

Separation of Church & State in the United States. Alvin W. Johnson & Frank H. Yost. 279p. Repr. of 1948 ed. lib. bdg. 22.50x (ISBN 0-8371-2436-0, JOCS). Greenwood.

Separation of Church & State in Virginia. Hamilton J. Eckenrode. LC 75-122164. (Civil Liberties in American History Ser). 1971. Repr. of 1910 ed. lib. bdg. 22.50 (ISBN 0-306-71969-X). Da Capo.

Separation Without Hope? Ed. by Julio De Santa Ana. LC 80-12831. 198p. (Orig.). 1980. pap. 2.24 (ISBN 0-88344-456-9). Orbis Bks.

Separatism among Indian Muslims: The Politics of the United Provinces' Muslims, 1860-1923. Francis Robinson. LC 73-93393. (Cambridge South Asian Studies: No. 16). pap. 121.80 (ISBN 0-317-26379-X, 2024521). Bks Demand UMI.

Sephardic Home: Ethnic Homogeneity & Cultural Traditions in a Total Institution. Giselle Hendel-Sebestyen. LC 83-45356. (Immigrant Communities & Ethnic Minorities in the United States & Canada Ser.). 1986. 67.50 (ISBN 0-404-19409-5). AMS Pr.

Sephardic Jewish Community of Los Angeles: A Study in Folklore & Ethnic Identity. Stephen Stern. Ed. by Richard M. Dorson. LC 80-734. (Folklore of the World Ser.). 1980. lib. bdg. 40.00x (ISBN 0-405-13324-3). Ayer Co Pubs.

Sephardic Jews of Bordeaux: Assimilation & Emancipation in Revolutionary & Napoleonic France. Frances Malino. LC 77-22659. (Judaic Studies: Vol. 7). 200p. 1978. 15.75 (ISBN 0-8173-6903-1). U of Ala Pr.

Sephardic Kosher Kitchen. Ed. by Suzy David. LC 84-8150. (Illus.). 228p. 1985. 14.95 (ISBN 0-8246-0303-6). Jonathan David.

Sephardim of England. cancelled (ISBN 0-686-76257-6). Feldheim.

Sepher Ha-Razim: The Book of Mysteries. Michael A. Morgan. LC 82-25181. (Society of Biblical Literature Texts & Translations Ser.). 108p. 1983. pap. 10.95 (ISBN 0-89130-615-3, 06 02 25). Scholars Pr GA.

Sepher Yezirah. Isidor Kalisch. 1984. write for info (ISBN 0-686-21219-3). Heptangle.

September Morning: A Practical Guide for the Middle Years. Mildred Tengbom. Ed. by David Eller. 1985. pap. 9.95 (ISBN 0-87178-776-8). Brethren.

Septuagint & Apocrypha in Greek & English. Charles Brenton. 1390p. 1972. 39.95 (ISBN 0-310-20430-5, 6234). Zondervan.

Septuagint & Modern Study. Sidney Jellicoe. 1978. Repr. of 1968 ed. 12.50x (ISBN 0-931464-00-5). Eisenbrauns.

Septuagint of Jewish Worship. H. St. J. Thackeray. (British Academy of London Ser.). pap. 19.00 (ISBN 0-8115-1262-2). Kraus Repr.

Septuagint Translation of the Hebrew Terms in Relation to God in the Book of Jeremiah. Bernard M. Zlotowitz. 1981. 25.00x (ISBN 0-87068-704-2). Ktav.

Septuagintal Lexicography. Robert A. Kraft. LC 75-15894. (Society of Biblical Literature. Septuagint & Cognate Studies). 1975. pap. 9.95 (ISBN 0-89130-008-2, 060401). Scholars Pr GA.

Sepulchre of Christ in Art & Liturgy. Neil C. Brooks. pap. 9.00 (ISBN 0-384-05925-2). Johnson Repr.

Sequence of the Supernatural. J. Robert Ashcroft. 80p. 1972. pap. 1.00 (ISBN 0-88243-748-8, 02-0748). Gospel Pub.

Serendipity Group Study Book. Ed. by Lyman Coleman et al. 496p. 1986. kivar 9.95 (ISBN 0-310-25081-1, 12032P). Zondervan.

Serendipity New Testament for Groups: New International Version. Lyman Coleman. 9.95 (ISBN 0-8091-2863-2). Paulist Pr.

Serenity. (Pocket Power Ser.). 16p. (Orig.). 1986. pap. 0.50 (ISBN 0-89486-355-X). Hazelden.

Serious Call to a Devout & Holy Life. William Law. 1967. Repr. of 1906 ed. 12.95x (ISBN 0-460-00091-8, Evman). Biblio Dist.

Serious Call to a Devout & Holy Life. William Law. Ed. by John Meister et al. LC 55-5330. 156p. 1968. pap. 6.95 (ISBN 0-664-24833-0). Westminster.

Serious Call to a Devout & Holy Life. William Law. LC 82-80470. (Treasures from the Spiritual Classics Ser.). 64p. 1982. pap. 2.95 (ISBN 0-8192-1306-3). Morehouse.

Serious Call to Holy Living. Abriged by ed. William Law. 96p. 1985. pap. 3.95 (ISBN 0-8423-5861-7). Tyndale.

Serious Reflections on the Scandalous Abuse & Effects of the Stage. Arthur Bedford. Bd. with Second Advertisement Concerning the Profaneness of the Play-House; Sermon Preached in the Parish-Church of St. Butolph's Algate, in the City of London: Occasioned by the Erecting of a Play-House in the Neighborhood. (English Stage Ser.: Vol. 41). 1974. lib. bdg. 61.00 (ISBN 0-8240-0624-0). Garland Pub.

Serious Remonstrance in Behalf of the Christian Religion Against English Play-Houses. Arthur Bedfrod. LC 79-170478. (English Stage Ser.: Vol. 42). lib. bdg. 61.00 (ISBN 0-8240-0625-9). Garland Pub.

Serious Season. Ed. by Roger Swenson. LC 86-25876. 116p. (Orig.). 1987. pap. 7.95 (ISBN 0-8189-0512-3). Alba.

Sermon a Day Keeps the Devil Away. Bob Jones, III. 208p. (Orig.). 1980. pap. 2.95 (ISBN 0-89084-114-4). Bob Jones Univ Pr.

Sermon Analysis. Jay Adams. LC 85-73072. (Pastor's Library). 224p. 1986. 17.95 (ISBN 0-89636-193-4). Accent Bks.

Sermon As God's Word: Theologies for Preaching. Robert W. Duke. LC 80-18094. (Abingdon Preacher's Library). 128p. (Orig.). 1980. pap. 6.95 (ISBN 0-687-37520-7). Abingdon.

Sermon Classics by Great Preachers. Ed. by Peter F. Gunther. LC 81-16899. 1982. pap. 4.95 (ISBN 0-8024-3328-6). Moody.

Sermon del Monte. Emmet Fox. Tr. of Sermon on the Mount. 1984. 5.95 (ISBN 0-87159-034-4). Unity School.

Sermon del Monte. J. Dwight Pentecost. Orig. Title: Sermon on the Mount. (Span.). 1981. pap. 4.75 (ISBN 0-8254-1556-X). Kregel.

Sermon del Monte, Vol. 1. D. M. Lloyd-Jones. 1978. 4.75 (ISBN 0-85151-414-6). Banner of Truth.

Sermon Eficaz. James D. Crane. 308p. 1986. pap. 4.50. Casa Bautista.

Sermon Illustrations for the Gospel Lessons. LC 12-2968. 1983. pap. 5.75 (ISBN 0-570-03875-8). Concordia.

Sermon Notes on the Psalms. David Thomas. Ed. by Herbert Lockyer. Tr. of Homilist. 320p. (Orig.). Date not set. pap. 10.95 (ISBN 0-8254-3116-6). Kregel.

Sermon of Repentance. John Bradford. LC 74-28835. (English Experience Ser.: No. 716). 1975. Repr. of 1553 ed. 6.00 (ISBN 90-221-0716-7). Walter J Johnson.

Sermon on the Decollation of St. John the Baptist, & on Herodias, & on Good & Evil Women. St. John Chrysostom. (Early Slavic Literatures, Studies, Texts, & Seminar Materials: Vol. 3). Orig. Title: V 29 den' mesiatsa avgusta slovo Ioanna Zlatoustogo na useknovenie glavy. (Slavic & Gr.). 45p. 1982. pap. 4.00 (ISBN 0-933884-23-0). Berkeley Slavic.

Sermon on the Mount. James M. Boice. LC 72-83882. 256p. 1972. 14.95 (ISBN 0-310-21510-2). Zondervan.

Sermon on the Mount. Clovis G. Chappell. (Pulpit Libarary Ser). 1979. pap. 4.95 (ISBN 0-8010-2363-7). Baker Bk.

Sermon on the Mount. William D. Davies. (Orig.). 1966. pap. 9.95 (ISBN 0-521-09384-8, 384). Cambridge U Pr.

Sermon on the Mount. Emmet Fox. 1934. 12.45 (ISBN 0-06-062950-9, HarpR). Har-Row.

Sermon on the Mount. Robert Guelich. 448p. 1982. 19.95 (ISBN 0-8499-0110-3). Word Bks.

Sermon on the Mount. Manly P. Hall. pap. 2.50 (ISBN 0-89314-353-7). Philos Res.

Sermon on the Mount. Herman Hendrickx. (Commentary on the Synoptic Gospels Ser.). 228p. 1984. pap. 9.95 (ISBN 0-225-66399-6, 8526, HarpR). Har-Row.

Sermon on the Mount. Joachim Jeremias. Ed. by John Reumann. Tr. by Norman Perrin from Ger. LC 63-17882. (Facet Bks.). (Orig.). 1963. pap. 2.50 (ISBN 0-8006-3002-5, 1-3002). Fortress.

Sermon on the Mount. Clarence Jordan. 1970. pap. 4.95 (ISBN 0-8170-0501-3). Judson.

Sermon on the Mount. Roger L. Shinn. LC 62-19785. 112p. (Orig.). 1984. pap. 3.95 (ISBN 0-8298-0120-0). Pilgrim NY.

Sermon on the Mount. John R. Stott. (LifeGuide Bible Studies). 64p. 1987. pap. 2.95. Inter-Varsity.

Sermon on the Mount. Richard Teed. 91p. pap. 2.75 (ISBN 0-87785-124-7). Swedenborg.

Sermon on the Mount. Ed. by Thomas B. Warren & Garland Elkins. 1982. 15.00 (ISBN 0-934916-00-4). Natl Christian Pr.

Sermon on the Mount: A History of Interpretation & Bibliography. Warren S. Kissinger. LC 75-29031. (ATLA Bibliography Ser.: No. 3). 309p. 1975. 22.50 (ISBN 0-8108-0843-9). Scarecrow.

Sermon on the Mount: A Study Guide. Dale Cooper. (Revelation Series for Adults). 1981. pap. text ed. 2.50 (ISBN 0-933140-22-3). CRC Pubns.

Sermon on the Mount: A Theological Interpretation. Carl G. Vaught. (Religious Studies). 192p. (Orig.). 1986. 34.50x (ISBN 0-88706-364-0); pap. 9.95x (ISBN 0-88706-365-9). State U NY Pr.

Sermon on the Mount According to Vedanta. Swami Prabhavananda. 1972. pap. 3.95 (ISBN 0-451-62509-9, ME2338, Ment). NAL.

Sermon on the Mount According to Vedanta. Swami Prabhavananda. LC 64-8660. 6.95 (ISBN 0-87481-002-7). Vedanta Pr.

Sermon on the Mount: An Evangelical Exposition of Matthew 5-7. D. A. Carson. LC 77-93260. 1978. 4.95 (ISBN 0-8010-2480-3). Baker Bk.

Sermon on the Mount As an Ideological Intervention: A Reconstruction of Meaning. Sjef Van Tilborg. 324p. 1986. 30.00 (ISBN 90-232-2243-1, Pub. by Van Gorcum Holland). Longwood Pub Group.

Sermon on the Mount: Authentic Human Values. Oscar S. Brooks. 124p. (Orig.). 1985. lib. bdg. 22.00 (ISBN 0-8191-4740-0); pap. text ed. 8.75 (ISBN 0-8191-4741-9). U Pr of Amer.

Sermon on the Mount for Today. Thomas Coates. LC 77-184. 1979. pap. 2.95x (ISBN 0-915644-13-4). Clayton Pub Hse.

Sermon on the Mount: From the Translation Prepared at Cambridge in 1611 for King James I. Illus. by Judith A. Duncan. LC 81-211201. (Illus.). 1978. 15.00 (ISBN 0-9606844-0-9). Mac Col MN.

Sermon on the Mount Interpreted by Paramhansa Yogananda. Yogananda Paramhansa. LC 79-91531. 1980. pap. 8.95 (ISBN 0-937134-01-5). Amrita Found.

Sermon on the Mount: Proclamation & Exhortation. Jan Lambrecht. (Good News Studies: Vol. 14). 1985. pap. 12.95 (ISBN 0-89453-467-X). M Glazier.

Sermon on the Mount: The Modern Quest for Its Meaning. Clarence Bauman. x, 440p. 1985. 41.95 (ISBN 0-86554-113-2, MUP/H107). Mercer Univ Pr.

Sermon on the Mount: Utopia or Program for Action? Pinchas Lapide. Tr. by Arlene Swindler from Ger. Tr. of DieBergpre digt-Utopie oder Program? 160p. (Orig.). 1986. pap. 9.95 (ISBN 0-88344-248-5, 85-29810). Orbis Bks.

Sermon on the Mount: Wisdom of the Kingdom. Ed. by Gary Wilde. (Basic Bible Ser.). 96p. 1986. pap. 4.95 (ISBN 0-89191-521-4). Cook.

Sermon on the Mountain. Carol Gonsalves. (Arch Bk. Supplement Ser.). 1981. pap. 0.99 (ISBN 0-570-06149-0, 59-1304). Concordia.

Sermon Outlines. W. A. Schultz. 3.95 (ISBN 0-88027-092-6). Firm Foun Pub.

Sermon Outlines for Evangelism. H. Lee Mason. (Sermon Outline Ser.). (Orig.). 1981. pap. 2.50 (ISBN 0-8010-6120-2). Baker Bk.

Sermon Outlines for Funeral Services. Ed. by Charles R. Wood. 64p. 1970. pap. 2.95 (ISBN 0-8254-4007-6). Kregel.

Sermon Outlines for Funerals. C. W. Keiningham. (Sermon Outline Ser.). (Orig.). 1981. pap. 2.50 (ISBN 0-8010-5427-3). Baker Bk.

Sermon Outlines for Revival Preaching. James H. Bolick. (Pulpit Library). 106p. 1986. pap. 2.95 (ISBN 0-8010-0922-7). Baker Bk.

Sermon Outlines for Special Days. Croft M. Pentz. (Sermon Outline Ser.). 1979. pap. 2.50 (ISBN 0-8010-7046-5). Baker Bk.

Sermon Outlines for Special Days & Occasions. Ed. by Charles R. Wood. 64p. 1970. pap. 2.95 (ISBN 0-8254-4006-8). Kregel.

Sermon Outlines from Acts. Croft M. Pentz. (Sermon Outline Ser.). 1978. pap. 2.50 (ISBN 0-8010-7039-2). Baker Bk.

Sermon Outlines from Proverbs. Charles R. Wood. LC 83-25569. 88p. (Orig.). 1984. pap. 3.95 (ISBN 0-8254-4023-8). Kregel.

Sermon Outlines from Pulpit Masters. Ian MacPherson. (Pulpit Library). 224p. 1984. pap. 4.95 (ISBN 0-8010-6180-6). Baker Bk.

Sermon Outlines from the Sermon on the Mount. Charles R. Wood. LC 85-23734. 64p. (Orig.). 1986. pap. 2.95 (ISBN 0-8254-4032-7). Kregel.

Sermon Outlines from the Word. James H. Bolick. (Sermon Outline Ser.). (Orig.). 1980. pap. 2.50 (ISBN 0-8010-0528-0). Baker Bk.

Sermon Outlines on Christian Living. George W. Lockaby. LC 81-68536. 1981. pap. 2.95 (ISBN 0-8054-2244-7). Broadman.

Sermon Outlines on Key Bible Themes. Hyman Appelman. (Sermon Outline Ser.). pap. 1.95 (ISBN 0-8010-0003-3). Baker Bk.

Sermon Outlines on the Person & Work of Christ. George W. Lockaby. LC 80-67916. 1981. pap. 2.95 (ISBN 0-8054-2238-2). Broadman.

Sermon Outlines on the Psalms. Charles R. Wood. LC 85-23735. 64p. (Orig.). 1986. pap. 2.95 (ISBN 0-8254-4033-5). Kregel.

Sermon Preached at Pauls Crosse Touching the Supposed Apostasie of J. King, Late Bishop of London. Henry King. LC 76-57392. (English Experience Ser.: No. 809). 1977. Repr. of 1621 ed. lib. bdg. 9.50 (ISBN 90-221-0809-0). Walter J Johnson.

Sermon Preached at the Cross, February 14, 1607. William Crashaw. Repr. of 1608 ed. 27.00 (ISBN 0-384-10125-9). Johnson Repr.

Sermon Seeds from Psalms. William G. Heslop. LC 76-12080. (W. G. Heslop Bible Study Aids Ser.). 144p. 1976. pap. 4.50 (ISBN 0-8254-2831-9). Kregel.

Sermon Starters for Fifty-Two Sundays. Charles W. Koller. 160p. (Orig.). 1982. pap. 6.95 (ISBN 0-8010-5440-0). Baker Bk.

Sermon Starters from the Greek New Testament. Gerald Cowen. LC 84-27448. 1985. pap. 5.95 (ISBN 0-8054-1397-9). Broadman.

Sermon Struggles: Four Methods of Sermon Preparation. Ernest E. Hunt, III. 160p. (Orig.). 1982. pap. 8.95 (ISBN 0-8164-2375-X, HarpR). Har-Row.

Sermon Studies on the Gospels. Ed. by E. H. Wendland. (Series C). 1982. 12.95 (ISBN 0-8100-0149-7, 15N0378). Northwest Pub.

Sermon Studies on the Old Testament. Ed. by E. H. Wendland. (Series B). 1984. 12.95 (ISBN 0-8100-0192-6, 15N0412). Northwest Pub.

Sermon Texts. Ed. by E. H. Wendland. 1984. 9.95 (ISBN 0-8100-0186-1, 15NO409). Northwest Pub.

Sermones para Dias Especiales, Tomo II. Adolfo Robleto. 96p. 1985. Repr. of 1984 ed. 2.75 (ISBN 0-311-07011-6). Casa Bautista.

Sermones para Dias Especiales, Tomo I. Adolfo Robleto. (Span.). 112p. 1986. Repr. of 1983 ed. 2.50 (ISBN 0-311-07009-4). Casa Bautista.

Sermones Ratherii Episcopi Veronensis. Benny R. Reece. 5.00 (ISBN 0-686-23377-8). Classical Folia.

Sermonic Pictures of a Preacher's Soul. 1981. pap. 4.95 (ISBN 0-933184-32-8). Flame Intl.

Sermons. B. H. Carroll. 1986. Repr. of 1893 ed. 19.50 (ISBN 0-317-47643-2). Church History.

Sermons, 2 vols. Charles E. Coughlin. Set. 250.00 (ISBN 0-8490-1025-X). Gordon Pr.

Sermons. Hugh Latimer. LC 76-172301. Repr. of 1906 ed. 23.50 (ISBN 0-404-03886-7). AMS Pr.

Sermons. Hugh Latimer. 379p. 1985. Repr. of 1984 ed. lib. bdg. 35.00 (ISBN 0-8482-4878-3). Norwood Edns.

Sermons. Thomas Lever. 143p. pap. 15.00 (ISBN 0-87556-200-0). Saifer.

Sermons. Jonathan Mayhew. LC 76-83429. (Religion in America, Ser. 1). 1969. Repr. of 1749 ed. 19.00 (ISBN 0-405-00254-8). Ayer Co Pubs.

Sermons, Nos. 81-186. St. Caesarius Of Arles. LC 56-3628. (Fathers of the Church Ser.: Vol. 47). 495p. 1964. 25.95x (ISBN 0-8132-0047-4). Cath U Pr.

Sermons, Addresses & Reminiscences & Important Correspondence, with a Picture Gallery of Eminent Ministers & Scholars. Elias C. Morris. Ed. by Edwin S. Gaustad. LC 79-52598. (Baptist Tradition Ser.). (Illus.). 1980. Repr. of 1901 ed. lib. bdg. 27.50x (ISBN 0-405-12465-1). Ayer Co Pubs.

Sermons & Addresses, 1853-1891. Daniel A. Payne. LC 70-38458. (Religion in America, Ser. 2). 1972. 19.00 (ISBN 0-405-04079-2). Ayer Co Pubs.

Sermons & Memoirs of Christmas Evans. Christmas Evans. LC 86-7108. 320p. 1986. Repr. 12.95 (ISBN 0-8254-2522-0). Kregel.

Sermons & Speeches of Gerrit Smith. Gerrit Smith. LC 73-82222. (Anti-Slavery Crusade in America Ser). 1969. Repr. of 1861 ed. 11.50 (ISBN 0-405-00660-8). Ayer Co Pubs.

Sermons Capitulaires de la Chartreuse de Mayence du Debut du XV Siecle. Dom P. Dupont. Ed. by James Hogg. (Analecta Cartusiana Ser.: No. 46). (Fr.). 193p. (Orig.). 1978. pap. 25.00 (ISBN 3-7052-0062-3, Pub by Salzburg Studies). Longwood Pub Group.

Sermons for Celebrating. Landrum P. Leavell. LC 77-90220. 1978. pap. 3.75 (ISBN 0-8054-2231-5). Broadman.

Sermons for Christians Seasons. Merle A. Johnson. LC 75-44210. Repr. of 1976 ed. 21.10 (ISBN 0-8357-9026-6, 2016406). Bks Demand UMI.

Sermons for Eighteen Special Occasions. LC 12-2963. 1982. pap. 5.75 (ISBN 0-570-03870-7). Concordia.

Sermons for Funeral Occasions. B. L. Bedwell. 1960. pap. 2.00 (ISBN 0-88027-029-2). Firm Foun Pub.

Sermons for Special Days & Occasions. Charles H. Spurgeon. 160p. 1984. pap. 4.95 (ISBN 0-8010-8247-1). Baker Bk.

Sermons for Special Occasions. 1981. pap. 5.95 (ISBN 0-570-03825-1, 12-2790). Concordia.

Sermons for Special Occasions. Charles H. Spurgeon. Ed. by Charles T Cook. 256p. 1977. Repr. of 1958 ed. limp bk. 5.95 (ISBN 0-551-05573-1). Attic Pr.

Sermons for the Seasons. C. W. Bess. LC 84-23226. 1985. pap. 4.95 (ISBN 0-8054-2256-0). Broadman.
Sermons for the Seventies. Alfred J. Kolatch. LC 75-164518. 1971. 7.95x (ISBN 0-8246-0122-X). Jonathan David.
Sermons for Today. Gary R. Beauchamp. LC 80-70788. 1981. 11.95 (ISBN 0-89112-403-9, Bibl Res Pr). Abilene Christ U.
Sermons for Today. Prentice A. Meador, Jr. LC 80-70788. 1981. 11.95 (ISBN 0-89112-402-0, Bibl Res Pr). Abilene Christ U.
Sermons for Today, No. 1. Rex P. Kyker. LC 80-50106. 196p. 1980. 11.95 (ISBN 0-89112-401-2, Bibl Res Pr). Abilene Christ U.
Sermons from Early America. 2nd ed. 1974. 6.00 (ISBN 0-9606952-0-6). PBBC Pr.
Sermons from Luke. C. M. Ward. 96p. (Orig.). 1983. pap. 2.25 (ISBN 0-89274-260-7). Harrison Hse.
Sermons from the Black Pulpit. Samuel D. Proctor & William D. Watley. 128p. 1984. pap. 7.95 (ISBN 0-8170-1034-3). Judson.
Sermons from the Parables. James Bailey. 128p. (Orig.). 1981. pap. 2.95 (ISBN 0-8341-0730-9). Beacon Hill.
Sermons in a Monastery: Chapter Talks by Matthew Kelty Ocso, No. 59. Ed. by William O. Paulsell. (Cistercian Studies Series). 1983. 14.95 (ISBN 0-87907-858-8); pap. 6.00 (ISBN 0-87907-958-4). Cistercian Pubns.
Sermons, Nos. 187-238. St. Caesarius Of Arles. LC 56-3628. (Fathers of the Church Ser.: Vol. 66). 303p. 1973. 17.95x (ISBN 0-8132-0066-0). Cath U Pr.
Sermons of a Buddhist Abbot. Soyen Shaku. 35.00 (ISBN 0-8490-1026-8). Gordon Pr.
Sermons of Athens Clay Pullias. Athens C. Pullias. Ed. by J. D. Thomas. (Great Preachers Ser). 1962. 11.95 (ISBN 0-89112-203-6, Bibl Res Pr). Abilene Christ U.
Sermons of Batsell Barrett Baxter. Ed. by J. D. Thomas. (Great Preachers Ser). 1960. 11.95 (ISBN 0-89112-201-X, Bibl Res Pr). Abilene Christ U.
Sermons of Charles F. Parham. Ed. by Donald W. Dayton. (Higher Christian Life Ser.). 261p. 1985. lib. bdg. 35.00 (ISBN 0-8240-6413-5). Garland Pub.
Sermons of Edwin Sandys D. D. Edwin Sandys. Repr. of 1841 ed. 41.00 (ISBN 0-384-53200-4). Johnson Repr.
Sermons of Frank Pack. Ed. by J. D. Thomas. (Great Preachers Ser). 1963. 11.95 (ISBN 0-89112-205-2, Bibl Res Pr). Abilene Christ U.
Sermons of George W. Bailey. Ed. by J. D. Thomas. (Great Preachers Ser). 1961. 11.95 (ISBN 0-89112-202-8, Bibl Res Pr). Abilene Christ U.
Sermons of Gus Nichols. Ed. by J. D. Thomas. (Great Preachers Ser). 1966. 11.95 (ISBN 0-89112-209-5, Bibl Res Pr). Abilene Christ U.
Sermons of John Alexander Dowie. Gordon Lindsay. (Champion of the Faith Ser.). 2.50 (ISBN 0-89985-193-2). Christ Nations.
Sermons of John Donne: In Ten Volumes. John Donne. Ed. by Evelyn M. Simpson & George R. Potter. LC 52-7179. 4365p. 1984. lib. bdg. 450.00x set (ISBN 0-520-05255-2). U of Cal Pr.
Sermons of John H. Banister. Ed. by J. D. Thomas. (Great Preachers Ser). 1965. 11.95 (ISBN 0-89112-208-7, Bibl Res Pr). Abilene Christ U.
Sermons of Joseph R. Narot. Joseph R. Narot. 6.00 (ISBN 0-686-15812-1). Rostrum Bks.
Sermons of M. Norvel Young. Ed. by J. D. Thomas. (Great Preachers Ser). 1963. 11.95 (ISBN 0-89112-204-4, Bibl Res Pr). Abilene Christ U.
Sermons of Martin Luther: On the New Testament, 8 vols. Martin Luther. Ed. by John N. Lenker. 1983. Repr. of 1904 ed. 95.00 (ISBN 0-8010-5626-8). Baker Bk.
Sermons of R. M. M'Cheyne. R. M. M'Cheyne. 1985. pap. 4.95 (ISBN 0-85151-165-1). Banner of Truth.
Sermons of St. Alphonsus Liguori for All the Sundays of the Year. Alphonsus de Liguori. LC 82-50894. 408p. 1982. pap. 10.00 (ISBN 0-89555-193-4). TAN Bks Pubs.
Sermons of St. Francis de Sales on Our Lady. St. Francis of Sales. Ed. by Lewis S. Fiorelli. LC 85-51662. 197p. 1985. pap. 7.00 (ISBN 0-89555-259-0). Tan Bks Pubs.
Sermons of St. Francis de Sales on Prayer. Francis De Sales. Ed. by Lewis Fiorelli. Tr. by Visitation Nuns. LC 84-52310. 51p. 1985. pap. 3.00 (ISBN 0-89555-258-2). Tan Bks Pubs.
Sermons of William S. Banowsky. Ed. by J. D. Thomas. (Great Preachers Ser). 1967. 11.95 (ISBN 0-89112-211-7, Bibl Res Pr). Abilene Christ U.
Sermons on Biblical Characters. Clovis G. Chappell. (Pocket Pulpit Lib.). 192p. 1981. pap. 3.95 (ISBN 0-8010-2330-0). Baker Bk.
Sermons on Ephesians. John Calvin. 1979. 19.95 (ISBN 0-85151-170-8). Banner of Truth.
Sermons on Prayer. Ronald E. Wall. (Pulpit Library). 144p. 1986. pap. 6.95 (ISBN 0-8010-9672-3). Baker Bk.
Sermons on Religion & Life. Frederick W. Robertson. 332p. 1981. Repr. of 1906 ed. lib. bdg. 15.00 (ISBN 0-89984-437-5). Century Bookbindery.
Sermons on Religion & Life. Frederick W. Robertson. 332p. 1983. Repr. of 1982 ed. lib. bdg. 20.00 (ISBN 0-89987-731-1). Darby Bks.
Sermons on Revival: Kelvedon. Charles H. Spurgeon. Ed. by Charles T. Cook. 256p. 1977. Repr. of 1958 ed. limp bk. 5.95 (ISBN 0-551-05575-8). Attic Pr.
Sermons on Shalom. Steve Clapp. 79p. (Orig.). 1982. pap. 8.00 (ISBN 0-914527-37-1). C-Four Res.
Sermons on Special Days: Preaching Through the Year in the Black Church. William D. Watley. 128p. 1987. pap. 6.95 (ISBN 0-8170-1089-0). Judson.
Sermons on the Bible. Frederick W. Robertson. 1978. Repr. of 1906 ed. lib. bdg. 35.00 (ISBN 0-8482-2315-2). Norwood Edns.
Sermons on the Final Verses of the Song of Songs. (Cistercian Fathers Ser.: Nbr. 43). 1982. 21.95 (ISBN 0-87907-643-7). Cistercian Pubns.
Sermons on the Final Verses of the Song of Songs, Vol. 1. John of Ford. (Cistercian Fathers Ser.: No. 29). 14.95 (ISBN 0-87907-629-1). Cistercian Pubns.
Sermons on the Final Verses of the Song of Songs, Vol. 2. John Of Ford. Tr. by Wendy M. Beckett from Latin. (Cistercian Fathers Ser.: No. 39). 1982. 21.95 (ISBN 0-87907-639-9). Cistercian Pubns.
Sermons on the Final Verses of the Song of Songs, Vol. 4. John of Ford. (Cistercian Fathers Ser.: No. 44). 24.95 (ISBN 0-87907-644-5). Cistercian Pubns.
Sermons on the Final Verses of the Song of Songs, Vol. 5. John of Ford. (Cistercian Fathers Ser.: No. 45). 24.95 (ISBN 0-87907-645-3). Cistercian Pubns.
Sermons on the Final Verses of the Song of Songs, Vol. 6. John of Ford. 24.95 (ISBN 0-87907-646-1). Cistercian Pubns.
Sermons on the Final Verses of the Song of Songs, Vol. 7. John of Ford. 24.95. Cistercian Pubns.
Sermons on the Liturgical Seasons. St. Augustine. (Fathers of the Church Ser.: Vol. 38). 1959. 29.95x (ISBN 0-8132-0038-5). Cath U Pr.
Sermons on the Miracles. Charles H. Spurgeon. Ed. by Charles T Cook. 256p. 1977. Repr. of 1958 ed. limp bk. 5.95 (ISBN 0-551-05576-6). Attic Pr.
Sermons on the Parables. Charles H. Spurgeon. Ed. by Charles T Cook. 256p. 1977. Repr. of 1958 ed. limp bk. 5.95 (ISBN 0-551-05574-X). Attic Pr.
Sermons on the Song of Songs, Vol. 1. Bernard of Clairvaux. (Cistercian Fathers Ser.: No. 4). pap. 5.00 (ISBN 0-87907-704-2). Cistercian Pubns.
Sermons on the Song of Songs, 3 vols, Vols. 1-3. Gilbert of Hoyland. Set. 30.00. Cistercian Pubns.
Sermons on the Song of Songs, Vol. 4. Bernard of Clairvaux. (Cistercian Fathers Ser.: No. 40). 15.95. Cistercian Pubns.
Sermons on Timothy & Titus. John Calvin. 1983. 37.95 (ISBN 0-85151-374-3). Banner of Truth.
Sermons on Unusual Occasions. C. H. Spurgeon. 1978. pap. 6.25 (ISBN 0-686-00494-9). Pilgrim Pubns.
Sermons on War by Theodore Parker. Blanche Cook et al. LC 70-149546. (Library of War & Peace; Relig. & Ethical Positions on War). 1973. lib. bdg. 46.00 (ISBN 0-8240-0499-X). Garland Pub.
Sermons-One to Eighty. St. Caesarius Of Arles. (Fathers of the Church Ser.: Vol. 31). 1956. 34.95x (ISBN 0-8132-0031-8). Cath U Pr.
Sermons Preached at the Church of St. Paul the Apostle, New York, During the Year, 1863. Church of St. Paul the Apostle, New York Staff. 32.00 (ISBN 0-405-10851-6, 11854). Ayer Co Pubs.
Sermons Preached in the African Protestant Episcopal Church of St. Thomas' Philadelphia. facs. ed. William Douglass. LC 79-157366. (Black Heritage Library Collection Ser). 1854. 20.00 (ISBN 0-8369-8804-3). Ayer Co Pubs.
Sermons Preached on Plantations to Congregations of Negroes. facsimile ed. Alexander Glennie. LC 75-161260. (Black Heritage Library Collection). Repr. of 1844 ed. 16.25 (ISBN 0-8369-8819-1). Ayer Co Pubs.
Sermons Preached upon Various Occasions, 8 vols. Robert South. LC 73-175991. Repr. of 1842 ed. Set. 155.00 (ISBN 0-404-06180-X). AMS Pr.
Sermons, Speeches, Letters on Slavery & Its War 1850-1868. Gilbert Haven. LC 74-82197. (Anti-Slavery Crusade in America Ser). 1969. Repr. of 1869 ed. 26.00 (ISBN 0-405-00637-3). Ayer Co Pubs.
Sermons That Demand a Decision. Edward Fudge. pap. 2.00 (ISBN 0-686-12681-5). E Fudge.
Sermons That Save. Robert R. Taylor. 1984. 10.95 (ISBN 0-317-16702-2). Firm Foun Pub.
Sermons That Should Be in Print. John Stacy. (Illus.). 104p. (Orig.). 1986. pap. 9.95. Brentwood Comm.
Sermons That Strengthen. Edward Fudge. pap. 2.00 (ISBN 0-686-12682-3). E Fudge.
Sermons: The Yale Edition of the Works of Samuel Johnson, Vol. 14. Samuel Johnson. Ed. by Jean H. Hagstrum & James Gray. LC 57-918. (Illus.). 1978. 42.00x (ISBN 0-300-02104-6). Yale U Pr.
Sermons to Grow on. Edward Fudge. pap. 2.00 (ISBN 0-686-12683-1). E Fudge.
Sermons to the Natural Man. W. G. Shedd. 1977. 13.95 (ISBN 0-85151-260-7). Banner of Truth.
Sermons You Can Preach. W. Herschel Ford. (Simple Sermon Ser.). 384p. 1983. pap. 10.95 (ISBN 0-310-46971-6). Zondervan.
Sermons You Can Preach on Acts. W. Herschel Ford. 352p. Date not set. pap. 10.95 (ISBN 0-310-38461-3). Zondervan.
Sermons You Can Preach on John: Simple Sermons. W. Herschel Ford. 432p. pap. 12.95 (ISBN 0-310-38451-6, 9835P). Zondervan.
Sermons You Can Preach on Matthew. W. Herschel Ford. 240p. (Orig.). 1985. pap. 8.95 (ISBN 0-310-45521-9, 9834P). Zondervan.
Sermons You Should Preach. J. J. Turner. 1984. pap. 3.95 (ISBN 0-89137-547-3). Quality Pubns.
Serpent & the Rainbow: A Harvard Scientist Uncovers the Startling Truth about the Secret World of Haitian Voodoo & Zombis. Wade Davis. 384p. (Orig.). 1987. pap. 4.95 (ISBN 0-446-34387-0). Warner Bks.
Serpent Beguiled Me & I Ate: A Heavenly Diet for Saints & Sinners. Edward J. Dumke. LC 86-4445. (Illus.). 1986. pap. 8.95 (ISBN 0-385-23671-9). Doubleday.
Serpent Imagery & Symbolism. Lura Pedrini & Duilio T. Pedrini. 1966. 10.95 (ISBN 0-8084-0274-9); pap. 6.95x (ISBN 0-8084-0275-7). New Coll U Pr.
Serpent Power. Arthur Avalon. LC 74-75259. (Illus.). 1974. pap. 8.95 (ISBN 0-486-23058-9). Dover.
Serpent Power (Sat-Chakra-Nirupana & Paduka-Panchaka) Tr. by John Woodroffe from Sanskrit. (Illus.). 512p. (Eng. only). 1973. 24.00 (ISBN 0-89744-117-6, Pub. by Ganesh & Co. India). Auromere.
Serpent Symbol & the Worship of the Reciprocal Principles of Nature in America. Ephraim G. Squier. LC 17-25223. 1975. Repr. of 1851 ed. 21.00 (ISBN 0-527-03228-X). Kraus Repr.
Serpent Worship in Africa - the Ovimbundu of Angola: Culture Areas of Nigeria. W. D. Hambly. (Chicago Field Museum of Natural History Fieldiana Anthropology Ser). Repr. of 1935 ed. 51.00 (ISBN 0-527-01881-3). Kraus Repr.
Servant & Son: Jesus in Parable & Gospel. J. Ramsey Michaels. LC 80-84651. 322p. 1982. pap. 9.95 (ISBN 0-8042-0409-8). John Knox.
Servant As His Lord. Oswald Chambers. 1973. pap. 2.95 (ISBN 0-87508-137-1). Chr Lit.
Servant Church: Diaconal Ministry & the Episcopal Church. John E. Booty. LC 82-81429. (Orig.). 1982. pap. 7.95 (ISBN 0-8192-1316-0). Morehouse.
Servant Leadership: A Journey into the Nature of Legitimate Power & Greatness. Robert K. Greenleaf. LC 76-45678. 348p. 1977. 9.95 (ISBN 0-8091-2527-7). Paulist Pr.
Servant of God's Servants: The Work of a Christian Minister. Paul M. Miller. LC 63-15499. (Conrad Grebel Lectures: 1963). pap. 59.00 (ISBN 0-317-26613-6, 2025423). Bks Demand UMI.
Servant of Jehovah. H. L. Ellison. 32p. 1983. pap. 2.50 (ISBN 0-85364-254-0, Pub. by Paternoster UK). Attic Pr.
Servant of Love: Mother Teresa & Her Missionaries of Charity. Edward Le Joly. LC 77-15874. (Illus.). 1978. 4.95 (ISBN 0-06-065215-2, HarpR). Har-Row.
Servant of the Word. Dawn De Vries. LC 86-45902. 240p. 1987. pap. 14.95 (ISBN 0-8006-3203-6). Fortress.
Servant of the Word. Herbert H. Farmer. LC 64-20405. 128p. (Orig.). 1964. pap. 3.95 (ISBN 0-8006-4001-2, 1-4001). Fortress.
Servant Songs: A Study in Isaiah. F. Duane Lindsey. 1985. pap. 7.95 (ISBN 0-8024-4093-2). Moody.
Servant Story (Mark) Leader's Guide. (New Horizons Bible Study Ser.). 48p. 1980. pap. 1.95 (ISBN 0-89367-050-2). Light & Life.
Servant Story (Mark) Study Guide. (New Horizons Bible Study Ser.). 64p. 1980. pap. 2.50 (ISBN 0-89367-049-9). Light & Life.
Servant's Call. Knofel Staton. LC 75-7462. (Illus.). 96p. 1976. pap. 2.25 (ISBN 0-87239-051-9, 40024). Standard Pub.
Servants for Christ: The Adventist Church Facing the 80's. Gottfried Oosterwal & Russell L. Staples. vi, 162p. 1980. pap. 3.95 (ISBN 0-943872-78-2). Andrews Univ Pr.
Servants in Charge. Keith M. Bailey. 123p. 1979. pap. 3.95 (ISBN 0-87509-160-1); Leader's Guide. 0.95 (ISBN 0-87509-261-6). Chr Pubns.
Servants of All. Chiara Lubich. Tr. by Hugh Moran from It. LC 78-59470. 176p. 1978. pap. 3.50 (ISBN 0-911782-05-2). New City.
Servants of God: The Lives of the 10 Gurus of the Sikhs. Jon Engle. LC 79-63457. (Illus.). 192p. 1980. pap. 6.00 (ISBN 0-89142-035-5). Sant Bani Ash.
Servants of Satan: The Age of the Witch Hunts. Joseph Klaits. LC 84-48252. (Illus.). 224p. 1987. 24.95X (ISBN 0-253-35182-0); pap. 7.95 (ISBN 0-253-20422-4). Ind U Pr.
Serve Together: With Generosity & Love. Department of Education, USCC Staff. 1987. pap. 4.95. US Catholic.
Server's Book of the Mass. Kenneth Guentert. LC 86-60894. 64p. 1985. pap. 4.95 (ISBN 0-89390-078-8). Resource Pubns.
Service & Spirituality. Swami Swahananda. 211p. (Orig.). 1980. pap. 4.95 (ISBN 0-87481-500-2). Vedanta Pr.
Service Book. Tr. by Laurence Mancuso from Slavonic & Gr. (New Skete). (Illus.). 214p. 1978. 20.00x (ISBN 0-9607924-4-9). Monks of New Skete.
Service Book: Heidelberg Catechism, Pt. No. 5. Liturgical Committee of the Christian Reformed Church. 64p. (Orig.). 1981. pap. text ed. 2.25 (ISBN 0-933140-35-5). CRC Pubns.
Service Book: Liturgical Forms for Baptism & the Lord's Supper, Pt. No. 1. Liturgical Committee of the Christian Reformed Church. 30p. (Orig.). 1981. pap. text ed. 1.50 (ISBN 0-933140-31-2). CRC Pubns.
Service Book: Liturgical Forms (Non-Sacramental, Pt. No. 2. Liturgical Committee of the Christian Reformed Church. 30p. (Orig.). 1981. pap. text ed. 1.50 (ISBN 0-933140-32-0). CRC Pubns.
Service Book, Part Six: Belgic Confession. Belgic Confession Translation Committee. 45p. (Orig.). 1984. pap. 1.25 (ISBN 0-933140-92-4). CRC Pubns.
Service Book: Prayers & Responsive Readings of the Law, Pt. No. 4. Liturgical Committee of the Christian Reformed Church. 37p. (Orig.). 1981. pap. text ed. 1.50 (ISBN 0-933140-34-7). CRC Pubns.
Service Book: Service of Word & Sacrament, Pt. No. 3. Liturgical Committee of the Christian Reformed Church. 64p. (Orig.). 1981. pap. text ed. 1.95 (ISBN 0-933140-33-9). CRC Pubns.
Service Evangelism. Richard S. Armstrong. LC 78-26701. 198p. 1979. pap. 8.95 (ISBN 0-664-24252-9). Westminster.
Service for the Hanging of the Greens. 1984. 2.25 (ISBN 0-89536-709-2, 4890). CSS of Ohio.
Service for the High Holy Days Adapted for Youth. new ed. Adapted by Hyman Chanover. LC 72-2058. 192p. 1972. pap. 3.95x (ISBN 0-87441-123-8). Behrman.
Service for the Lord's Day: The Worship of God. LC 84-5220. (Supplemental Liturgical Resource Ser.: No. 1). 192p. 1984. text ed. 7.95 kivar (ISBN 0-664-24643-5); pap. 14.75 pack of five, pew edition (ISBN 0-664-24641-9). Westminster.
Service Music for the Adult Choir. Ed. by W. Lawrence Curry. 3.50 ea. (ISBN 0-664-10059-7). Westminster.
Service of God. William H. Willimon. 240p. 1983. pap. 11.50 (ISBN 0-687-38094-4). Abingdon.
Service of Humanity. Damodar K. Mavalankar. (Sangam Texts). 132p. 1986. pap. 8.75 (ISBN 0-88695-025-2). Concord Grove.
Service Project Ideas. Sandra Ziegler. (Ideas Ser.). (Illus.). 48p. 1977. pap. text ed. 1.95 (ISBN 0-87239-122-1, 7962). Standard Pub.
Service to a Fool for Christ Sake. Orthodox Eastern Church. pap. 0.75 (ISBN 0-686-05663-9). Eastern Orthodox.
Service to St. Tikhon of Kaluga. (Slavic.). pap. 5.00 (ISBN 0-686-16368-0). Eastern Orthodox.
Services, Pt. 1. Thomas Tomkins. Ed. by P. C. Buck. (Tudor Music Ser.: Vol.8). 1963. Repr. of 1928 ed. 85.00x (ISBN 0-8450-1858-2). Broude.
Services of Our Lady. Ed. by Sten Von Krusenstierna. 70p. 1982. pap. text ed. 2.75 (ISBN 0-918980-11-9). St Alban Pr.
Servile State. Hilaire Belloc. LC 77-2914. 1977. 8.00 (ISBN 0-913966-31-2, Liberty Clas); pap. 3.00 (ISBN 0-913966-32-0). Liberty Fund.

Serving Church. 2nd ed. L. T. Johnson. LC 83-80609. (Enabling Ser.). (Illus.). 104p. (Orig.). 1984. pap. 5.95 (ISBN 0-935797-01-7). Harvest IL.

Serving God. Z. W. Swafford. (God & Us Ser.). 32p. 1981. pap. 2.00 (ISBN 0-89114-097-2); pap. 0.69 coloring bk. (ISBN 0-89114-098-0). Baptist Pub Hse.

Serving God Always. Arnold G. Kuntz. 1966. pap. text ed. 2.75 (ISBN 0-570-06645-X, 22-2014); pap. 5.85 manual (ISBN 0-570-06646-8, 22-2015). Concordia.

Serving God & Mammon: William Juxon, 1582-1663. Thomas Mason. LC 83-40507. (Illus.). 208p. 1985. 29.50 (ISBN 0-87413-251-7). U Delaware Pr.

Serving God First. Sighard Kleiner. 1985. 14.95 (ISBN 0-87907-883-9). Cistercian Pubns.

Serving in the City: Nurturing the Poor to Independence. Monroe Ballard & JoeAnn Ballard. 88p. 1986. 3 ring binder 10.95 (ISBN 0-8341-1125-X, S-350). Beacon Hill.

Serving Life & Faith: Adult Religious Education & the American Catholic Community. Ed. by Neil A. Parent. 72p. 1986. pap. 6.95 (ISBN 1-55586-982-3). US Catholic.

Serving Mentally Impaired People. Gerald Oosterveen & Bruce L. Cook. 52p. 1983. pap. 5.95 (ISBN 0-89191-764-0). Cook.

Serving One Another. Gene Getz. 156p. 1984. pap. 5.95 (ISBN 0-88207-612-4). Victor Bks.

Serving Sunday School. Wayne Goodwin & Gregory D. Cook. (Complete Teacher Training Meeting Ser.). 48p. 1986. tchr's ed 9.95 (ISBN 0-89191-315-7). Cook.

Serving the Jewish Family. Ed. by G. B. Bubis. 25.00x (ISBN 0-87068-439-6). Ktav.

Serving the Salesian Family: A Resource Manual for Salesians. (Salesian Family Ser.). 88p. 1983. pap. 3.50 (ISBN 0-89944-076-2). Don Bosco Multimedia.

Serving with Joy: A Study in Philippians. Stephen A. Grunlan. LC 85-71352. 107p. (Orig.). 1985. pap. 4.95 (ISBN 0-87509-371-X); leader's guide 2.95 (ISBN 0-87509-372-8). Chr Pubns.

Sesshu's Long Scroll: A Zen Landscape Journey. Reiko Chiba. LC 54-14085. (Illus.). 1959. 14.50 (ISBN 0-8048-0677-2). C E Tuttle.

Set Apart for Service. Alton H. McEachern. LC 79-5114. 1980. 7.50 (ISBN 0-8054-2537-3). Broadman.

Set Apart for Service. 4.00 (ISBN 0-8198-6832-9); 3.00 (ISBN 0-8198-6833-7). Dghtrs St Paul.

Set Free. Marilyn Kunz & Catherine Schell. 1982. pap. 2.95 (ISBN 0-8423-5867-6). Tyndale.

Set Free. Betty Tapscott. 1978. pap. 4.95 (ISBN 0-917726-24-3). Hunter Bks.

Set Free from Satan's Slavery. Peter Popoff. Ed. by Don Tanner. LC 82-83455. 64p. 1982. pap. 2.00 (ISBN 0-938544-17-9). Faith Messenger.

Set Free to Serve (Galatians-I, II Thessalonians) Leader's Guide. (New Horizons Bible Study). 47p. (Orig.). 1985. pap. 1.95 (ISBN 0-317-37972-0). Light & Life.

Set Free to Serve (Galatians-I, II Thessalonians) Student Guide. (New Horizons Bible Study). 64p. (Orig.). 1985. pap. 2.50 (ISBN 0-89367-106-1). Light & Life.

Set My Heart Free. Rita J. Carmack. 144p. 1984. pap. 5.00 (ISBN 0-88144-031-0). Jewel Pr.

Set My Spirit Free. Robert Frost. LC 73-84475. 234p. 1973. pap. 4.95 (ISBN 0-88270-058-8). Bridge Pub.

Set of Four Trauma Books. LC 12-2823. (Trauma Bks.: No. 2). 1983. Set. pap. 9.95 (ISBN 0-570-08260-9). Concordia.

Set of the Sail. A. W. Tozer. Ed. by Harry Verploegh. LC 86-70772. 90p. (Orig.). 1986. pap. 5.95 (ISBN 0-87509-379-5). Chr Pubns.

Setting Free the Ministry of the People of God. Ed. by Gerald C. Davis. 120p. (Orig.). 1984. pap. 1.75 (ISBN 0-88028-038-7). Forward Movement.

Setting of the Sermon on the Mount. William Davies. LC 64-630. pap. 140.80 (ISBN 0-317-26320-X, 2024449). Bks Demand UMI.

Setting the Captives Free. Bob Buess. LC 42-1127. 1975. pap. 2.50 (ISBN 0-934244-02-2). Sweeter Than Honey.

Setting the Captives Free! A Practical Guide to Breaking the Power of Satan over Your Life. Marc W. Farschman. LC 85-61138. 146p. (Orig.). 1985. pap. 4.95 (ISBN 0-934285-00-4). New Life Faith.

Settlement of the Israelite Tribes in Palestine. Manfred Weippert. Tr. by James Martin from Ger. LC 74-131587. (Studies in Biblical Theology, 2nd Ser.: No. 21). (Orig.). 1970. pap. 12.00x (ISBN 0-8401-3071-6). A R Allenson.

Settlement of the Jews in North America. C. P. Daly. 59.95 (ISBN 0-8490-1027-6). Gordon Pr.

Seven Archbishops. Sidney Dark. Repr. of 1944 ed. 25.00 (ISBN 0-686-19840-9). Ridgeway Bks.

Seven Beginnings. Walker Knight & Ken Touchton. LC 75-44496. (Human Torch Ser.: 2nd). (Illus.). 1976. 5.95 (ISBN 0-937170-17-8). Home Mission.

Seven Bible Ways to Properly Relate to Your Pastor. Mark Barclay. 32p. 1982. pap. 2.25 (ISBN 0-88144-024-8). Christian Pub.

Seven Books of History Against the Pagans. Paulus Orosius. LC 64-8670. (Fathers of the Church Ser: Vol. 50). 414p. 1964. 22.95x (ISBN 0-8132-0050-4). Cath U Pr.

Seven Centuries of the Problem of Church & State. Frank Gavin. 1938. 22.50x (ISBN 0-86527-180-1). Fertig.

Seven Churches. Marshall Neal. (Illus.). 108p. (Orig.). 1977. pap. 2.95 (ISBN 0-89084-062-8). Bob Jones Univ Pr.

Seven Churches. 36p. (Orig.). pap. 0.95 (ISBN 0-937408-20-4). GMI Pubns Inc.

Seven Churches of Prophecy, 2 vols. Gordon Lindsay. (Revelation Ser.). 1.25 ea. Vol. 1 (ISBN 0-89985-977-1). Vol. 2 (ISBN 0-89985-978-X). Christ Nations.

Seven Daily Sins & What to Do about Them. Cecil Murphey. 112p. (Orig.). 1981. pap. 2.95 (ISBN 0-89283-101-4). Servant.

Seven Day Mystery. John H. Tiner. (Voyager Ser.). 176p. (Orig.). 1981. pap. 3.50 (ISBN 0-8010-8856-9). Baker Bk.

Seven Days a Week. Lion The Printer. (Illus.). 1977. spiral 2.00 (ISBN 0-914080-62-8). Shulsinger Sales.

Seven Days a Week: Faith in Action. Nelvin Vos. LC 84-47937. 144p. 1985. pap. 5.95 (ISBN 0-8006-1658-8, 1-1658). Fortress.

Seven Days & Prayer. Coleen Baird. (Illus.). 1980. pap. 2.95 (ISBN 0-87747-802-3). Deseret Bk.

Seven Days of Creation. Sara Aronow. (Bible Stories in Rhymes Ser.: Vol. 1). (Illus.). 32p. 1985. 4.95 (ISBN 0-87203-119-5). Hermon.

Seven Days of the Beginning. Eli Munk. 8.95 (ISBN 0-87306-028-8). Feldheim.

Seven Deadly Sins. Anthony Campolo. 156p. Date not set. 9.95 (ISBN 0-89693-533-7). Victor Bks.

Seven Deadly Sins. Jon L. Joyce. 1973. pap. 3.50 (ISBN 0-89536-210-4, 1912). CSS of Ohio.

Seven Deadly Sins. Sunday Times, London. LC 75-117848. (Essay Index Reprint Ser). 1962. 14.00 (ISBN 0-8369-1722-7). Ayer Co Pubs.

Seven Deadly Sins Today. Henry Fairlie. LC 79-893. (Illus.). 1979. pap. 5.95 (ISBN 0-268-01698-4, 85-16981). U of Notre Dame Pr.

Seven Delivery Systems for God's Healing Power. Peter Popoff. Ed. by Don Tanner. LC 81-69730. (Illus.). 70p. 1981. pap. 1.50 (ISBN 0-938544-07-1). Faith Messenger.

Seven Ecumenical Councils. Howard A. Slaatte. LC 80-5755. 55p. 1980. pap. text ed. 7.25 (ISBN 0-8191-1204-6). U Pr of Amer.

Seven Exegetical Works: Isaac, or the Soul, Death As a Good, Jacob & the Happy Life, Joseph, the Patriarchs, Flight from the World, the Prayer of Job & David. St. Ambrose. (Fathers of the Church Ser.: Vol. 65). 447p. 1972. 34.95x (ISBN 0-8132-0065-2). Cath U Pr.

Seven Gifts of the Holy Spirit. 1980. plastic 1.75 (ISBN 0-8198-6807-8); pap. 1.00 (ISBN 0-8198-6808-6). Dghtrs St Paul.

Seven Golden Chapters of Hermes. Hermes Trismegistus. 1984. pap. 2.95 (ISBN 0-916411-82-6, Pub by Alchemical Pr). Holmes Pub.

Seven Great Religions. Besant. 6.75 (ISBN 0-8356-7218-2). Theos Pub Hse.

Seven Hindrances to Healing. Kenneth Hagin, Jr. 1980. pap. 0.50 mini bk. (ISBN 0-89276-705-7). Hagin Ministries.

Seven Human Temperaments. 6th ed. Geoffrey Hodson. 1977. 3.25 (ISBN 0-8356-7222-0). Theos Pub Hse.

Seven "Jesus Only" Tracts. Ed. by Donald W. Dayton. (Higher Christian Life Ser.). 379p. 1985. lib. bdg. 45.00 (ISBN 0-8240-6414-3). Garland Pub.

Seven Keys to Color Healing: Successful Treatment Through Color. Roland Hunt. LC 81-47849. (Library of Spiritual Wisdom). 128p. 1982. pap. 7.95 (ISBN 0-06-064080-4, CN 4028, HarpR). Har-Row.

Seven Keys to Triumphant Christian Living. Gordon Lindsay. 1.25 (ISBN 0-89985-006-5). Christ Nations.

Seven Last Words. Fulton J. Sheen. 1982. pap. 2.95 (ISBN 0-8189-0438-0). Alba.

Seven Last Words of the Church. Ralph W. Neighbour, Jr. LC 79-51937. 1979. pap. 4.95 (ISBN 0-8054-5527-2). Broadman.

Seven Last Words of the Risen Christ. Joe E. Trull. (Pulpit Library). 96p. 1985. pap. 4.95 (ISBN 0-8010-8879-8). Baker Bk.

Seven Laws of Teaching. John M. Gregory. 1954. 7.95 (ISBN 0-8010-3652-6). Baker Bk.

Seven Laws of Teaching. John M. Gregory. (Orig.). 1886. 1.95x (ISBN 0-9606952-1-4). PBBC Pr.

Seven Levels of Healing. Lilla Bek & Philippa Pullar. 160p. 1987. pap. 11.95 (ISBN 0-7126-9473-0, Pub. by Century Hutchinson). David & Charles.

Seven Lucky Gods of Japan. Reiko Chiba. LC 65-25467. (Illus.). 1966. 12.95 (ISBN 0-8048-0521-0). C E Tuttle.

Seven Magic Orders. Shan Mui. Ed. by Ruth Tabrah. LC 72-86743. (Illus.). 1973. 5.95 (ISBN 0-89610-011-1). Island Heritage.

Seven Mansions of Color. Alex Jones. LC 82-73248. (Illus.). 152p. 1983. pap. 7.95 (ISBN 0-87516-500-1). De Vorss.

Seven Martyrs of Hurmuzak. Muhammad Labib. Tr. & frwd. by Moojan Momen. (Illus.). 80p. 9.95 (ISBN 0-85398-105-1); pap. 4.95 (ISBN 0-85398-104-3). G Ronald Pub.

Seven Messages to the Mother Church. Mary B. Eddy. pap. 4.50 (ISBN 0-87952-045-0). First Church.

Seven Miracle Plays. Alexander Franklin. 1963. pap. 8.95x (ISBN 0-19-831391-8). Oxford U Pr.

Seven Mountains of Thomas Merton. Michael Mott. LC 84-10944. 1984. 24.95 (ISBN 0-395-31324-4). HM.

Seven Mountains of Thomas Merton. Michael Mott. 1986. pap. 12.95 (ISBN 0-395-40451-7). HM.

Seven Pauline Letters. Peter F. Ellis. LC 82-15252. (Orig.). 1982. pap. 8.95 (ISBN 0-8146-1245-8). Liturgical Pr.

Seven Pentecostal Pioneers. Colin C. Whittaker. LC 84-73310. 224p. 1985. Repr. of 1983 ed. 5.95 (ISBN 0-88243-545-0, 02-0545). Gospel Pub.

Seven Principles of Man. Besant. 3.25 (ISBN 0-8356-7321-9). Theos Pub Hse.

Seven Rays. Ernest Wood. LC 76-4909. 191p. 1976. pap. 4.95 (ISBN 0-8356-0481-0, Quest). Theos Pub Hse.

Seven Sacraments. Lawrence G. Lovasik. (Saint Joseph Picture Bks.). (Illus.). flexible bdg 0.95 (ISBN 0-89942-278-0, 278). Catholic Bk Pub.

Seven Sacrements. 20p. 1980. pap. 7.55 (ISBN 0-88479-025-8). Arena Lettres.

Seven Sayings of Our Saviour on the Cross. Arthur W. Pink. (Summit Bks). 1977. pap. 4.95 (ISBN 0-8010-7084-8). Baker Bk.

Seven Schools of Yoga: An Introduction. Ernest Wood. LC 72-13120. Orig. Title: Occult Training of the Hindus. 120p. 1973. pap. 2.25 (ISBN 0-8356-0435-7, Quest). Theos Pub Hse.

Seven Seal Judgements. Date not set. pap. 0.95 (ISBN 0-686-88510-4). GMI Pubns Inc.

Seven Sermons & One Eulogy As Preached in the Chapel of Princeton University from 1965 to 1980. Frederic E. Fox. Ed. by Donald H. Fox. LC 82-90693. 88p. (Orig.). 1982. pap. 5.95 (ISBN 0-910521-02-6). Fox Head.

Seven Sermons Before Edward VI, Fifteen Forty-Nine. Hugh Latimer. Ed. by Edward Arber. 1985. pap. 17.50. Saifer.

Seven Seven Seven: A Study of the Kabbalah. Aleister Crowley. 1973. lib. bdg. 80.00 (ISBN 0-87968-105-5). Krishna Pr.

Seven Seven Seven & Other Qabalistic Writings. rev. ed. Aleister Crowley. LC 73-80056. 336p. 1977. 12.50 (ISBN 0-87728-222-6). Weiser.

Seven Signs of a Born Again Person. Wim Malgo. 1.45 (ISBN 0-937422-14-2). Midnight Call.

Seven Special Days. Henrietta D. Gambill. (Happy Day Bks.). (Illus.). 32p. 1987. 1.59 (ISBN 0-87403-281-4, 3781). Standard Pub.

Seven Spirits. William Booth. 128p. 1984. Repr. of 1890 ed. 3.95 (ISBN 0-86544-026-3). Salv Army Suppl South.

Seven Spiritual Works of Mercy. Daughters of St. Paul. 1979. 1.75 (ISBN 0-8198-6805-1); pap. 1.00 (ISBN 0-8198-6806-X). Dghtrs St Paul.

Seven Steps along the Way. F. Dale Simpson. 1981. pap. 7.45 (ISBN 0-89137-527-9). Quality Pubns.

Seven Steps for Judging Prophecy. Kenneth E. Hagin. 1982. pap. 1.00 (ISBN 0-89276-024-9). Hagin Ministries.

Seven Steps on How to Become a Mystic & Enjoy the Most Exhilirating Pleasure Available to Man on This Earth. Gilbert J. Malfitano. (Illus.). 1979. deluxe ed. 47.50 (ISBN 0-930582-37-3). Gloucester Art.

Seven Steps to Freedom. Derin Carmack. 31p. 1986. pap. 3.00 (ISBN 0-937093-25-4). Jewel Pr.

Seven Steps to God's Healing Power. Shy Mackes. pap. 0.95 (ISBN 0-910924-28-7). Macalester.

Seven Steps to Peace. Paul R. Caudill. LC 81-71254. 1982. pap. 3.95 (ISBN 0-8054-1527-0). Broadman.

Seven Steps to the New Age. Paul Richard. 1979. pap. 3.95 (ISBN 0-89744-131-1, Pub. by Ganesh & Co India). Auromere.

Seven Steps Toward God. Bill Beatty. LC 85-82315. 102p. (Orig.). 1986. pap. 5.95 (ISBN 0-937779-01-6). Greenlawn Pr.

Seven Storey Mountain. Thomas Merton. LC 78-7109. 429p. 1978. pap. 7.95 (ISBN 0-15-680679-7, Harv). HarBraceJ.

Seven Storey Mountain. Thomas Merton. 1978. Repr. lib. bdg. 32.00x (ISBN 0-88254-843-3, Octagon). Hippocrene Bks.

Seven Storey Mountain. Thomas Merton. LC 85-6375. 784p. 1985. pap. 19.95 (ISBN 0-8027-2497-3). Walker & Co.

Seven Synonyms for God. Max Kappeler. Tr. by Kathleen Lee from Ger. LC 83-83266. Tr. of sieben Synonyme fur Gott. 400p. 35.00 (ISBN 0-942958-09-8). Kappeler Inst Pub.

Seven Tablets of Creation, 2 vols. Enuma Elish. LC 73-18850. (Luzac's Semitic Text & Translation Ser.: Nos. 12 & 13). (Illus.). Repr. of 1902 ed. Set. 45.00 (ISBN 0-404-11344-3). AMS Pr.

Seven Things You Should Know about Divine Healing. Kenneth E. Hagin. 1979. pap. 2.50 (ISBN 0-89276-400-7). Hagin Ministries.

Seven Thunderers Utter Their Voices: History & Verse by Verse Study in the Book of Revelation of the Bible. 2nd ed. E. Warren Anglin. 176p. (Orig.). pap. 7.95 (ISBN 0-318-04199-5). Total Comm Ministries.

Seven Veils over Consciousness. C. Jinarajadasa. 2.50 (ISBN 0-8356-7231-X). Theos Pub Hse.

Seven Vital Steps to Receiving the Holy Spirit. 2nd ed. Kenneth E. Hagin. 1980. pap. 1.00 (ISBN 0-89276-003-6). Hagin Ministries.

Seven Voices Speak. Catharose De Petri. Ed. by Lectorium Rosicrucianum. Orig. Title: Zeven Stemmen Spreken. (Dutch.). 79p. Date not set. pap. 8.00. Rosycross Pr.

Seven Ways Jesus Heals. Norvel Hayes. 142p. (Orig.). 1982. pap. 4.95 (ISBN 0-89274-235-6, HH-235). Harrison Hse.

Seven Words from the Cross: A Commentary. Charles E. Wolfe. 1980. pap. 4.65 (ISBN 0-89536-420-4, 1962). CSS of Ohio.

Seven Words: The Words of Jesus on the Cross Reveal the Heart of the Christian Faith. Clovis G. Chappell. (Pocket Pulpit Library). 80p. 1976. pap. 2.95 (ISBN 0-8010-2387-4). Baker Bk.

Seven Years Conversing with Spirits. Paul Lojnikov. 1987. 6.95 (ISBN 0-533-07213-1). Vantage.

Sevenfold Path to Peace. Alan Bond. 1986. 4.50 (ISBN 0-89536-774-2, 6801). CSS of Ohio.

Seventeen Papal Documents on the Rosary. 1967. pap. 2.00 (ISBN 0-8198-0147-X). Dghtrs St Paul.

Seventeenth Century Background: Studies in the Thought of the Age in Relation to Poetry & Religion. Basil Willey. LC 34-21849. 1942. 31.00x (ISBN 0-231-01395-7). Columbia U Pr.

Seventeenth Century Critics & Biographers of Milton. M. Manuel. LC 77-23430. 1962. lib. bdg. 19.50 (ISBN 0-8414-6184-8). Folcroft.

Seventeenth Century Life in the Country Parish. E. Trotter. 242p. 1968. Repr. of 1919 ed. 28.50x (ISBN 0-7146-1363-0, F Cass Co). Biblio Dist.

Seventh Candle & Other Folk Tales of Eastern Europe. David Einhorn. Tr. by Gertrude Pashin. LC 68-10968. (Illus.). 1968. 7.95x (ISBN 0-87068-369-1). Ktav.

Seventh Day. Gordon Lindsay. 1.25 (ISBN 0-89985-116-9). Christ Nations.

Seventh-Day Adventism. Anthony A. Hoekema. 1974. pap. 3.95 (ISBN 0-8028-1490-5). Eerdmans.

Seventh-Day Adventism in a Nutshell. D. M. Canright. 2.75 (ISBN 0-89225-162-X). Gospel Advocate.

Seventh-Day Adventism Renounced. D. M. Canright. 1982. pap. 5.95. Gospel Advocate.

Seventh-Day Adventist Family: An Empirical Study. Charles C. Crider & Robert C. Kistler. 296p. 1979. pap. 3.95 (ISBN 0-943872-77-4). Andrews Univ Pr.

Seventh-Day Baptists in Europe & America: A Series of Historical Papers Written in Commemoration of the One Hundred Anniversary of the Organization, 2 vols. Seventh-Day Baptist General Conference. Ed. by Edwin S. Gaustad. LC 79-52605. (Baptist Tradition Ser.). (Illus.). 1980. Repr. of 1910 ed. lib. bdg. 160.00x set (ISBN 0-405-12470-8). Ayer Co Pubs.

Seventh-Day Baptists in Europe & America, Vol. 1. Seventh-Day Baptists General Conference. 80.00 (ISBN 0-405-12478-3). Ayer Co Pubs.

Seventh-Day Baptists in Europe & America, Vol. 2. Seventh-Day Baptists General Conference. 80.00 (ISBN 0-405-12479-1). Ayer Co Pubs.

Seventh Day: The Story of the Jewish Sabbath. Miriam Chaikin & David Frampton. LC 82-16987. (Illus.). 48p. (Orig.). 1983. pap. 4.95 (ISBN 0-8052-0743-0). Schocken.

Seventh Day: The Story of the Seventh-Day Adventists. Booton Herndon. LC 78-11705. 1979. Repr. of 1960 ed. lib. bdg. 24.75x (ISBN 0-313-21054-3, HESD). Greenwood.

Seventh Trumpet. Mark Link. LC 78-53943. 1978. 7.95 (ISBN 0-89505-014-5). Argus Comm.

Seventy-First Came to Gunskirchen Lager. Seventy First Infantry Division, U.S. Army. Intro. by Fred R. Crawford. LC 79-51047. (Witness to the Holocaust Ser.: No. 1). (Illus.). 28p. 1983. pap. 1.50 (ISBN 0-89937-036-5). Witness Holocaust.

Seventy-Five Bible Questions Your Instructors Pray You Won't Ask. Gary North. 280p. (Orig.). 1984. pap. 4.95 (ISBN 0-930462-03-3). Am Bur Eco Res.

Seventy-Five Years, Central Park Baptist Church, Birmingham, Alabama, 1910-1985. Ed. by F. Wilbur Helmbold. (Illus., Orig.). 1985. 25.00 (ISBN 0-87121-447-4). Banner Pr AL.

Seventy Negro Spirituals, for High Voice. William A. Fisher. LC 72-1637. Repr. of 1926 ed. 29.00 (ISBN 0-404-09921-1). AMS Pr.

Seventy-One Creative Bible Story Projects: Patterns for Crafts, Visuals, & Learning Centers. Helen Gramelsbach. (Illus.). 64p. 1983. pap. 4.95 (ISBN 0-87239-607-X, 2103). Standard Pub.

Seventy-Seven Sermon Outlines. Frank L. Cox. 1958. pap. 1.75 (ISBN 0-88027-052-7). Firm Foun Pub.

Seventy-Seven Ways of Involving Youth in the Church. Richard Bimler. (Illus.). 1976. pap. 4.50 (ISBN 0-570-03737-9, 12-2641). Concordia.

Seventy Weeks & the Great Tribulation. Philip Mauro. 285p. 1975. pap. 5.95 (ISBN 0-685-53619-X). Reiner.

Seventy Years on Hope Street: A History of the Church of the Open Door 1915-1985. G. Michael Cocoris. (Illus.). 151p. 1985. text ed. 35.00 (ISBN 0-935729-09-7). Church Open Door.

Seventy Years on Hope Street: A History of the Church of the Open Door 1915-1985. G. Michael Cocoris. (Illus.). 151p. 1985. deluxe ed. 195.95 (ISBN 0-935729-30-5). Church Open Door.

Several Israels. Samuel Sandmel. 1971. 12.50x. Ktav.

Severe Mercy. Sheldon Vanuken. 1979. pap. 3.95 (ISBN 0-553-25155-4). Bantam.

Severus Scroll & 1Q1SA. Jonathan P. Siegel. LC 75-28372. (Society of Biblical Literature, Masoretic Studies). 1975. pap. 8.95 (ISBN 0-89130-028-7, 060502). Scholars Pr GA.

Sex--Our Myth Theology? Harlan C. Musser. 196p. 1981. pap. 7.95 (ISBN 0-8059-2768-9). Dorrance.

Sex & Gender: A Theological & Scientific Inquiry. Ed. by Mark F. Schwartz et al. 385p. (Orig.). 1984. pap. 19.95 (ISBN 0-935372-13-X). Pope John Ctr.

Sex & Marriage in the Unification Movement: A Sociological Study. James H. Grace. LC 85-2961. (Studies in Religion & Society: Vol. 13). 304p. 1985. 49.95x (ISBN 0-88946-861-3). E Mellen.

Sex & Religion. Clifford Howard. LC 72-9654. Repr. of 1925 ed. 34.50 (ISBN 0-404-57463-7). AMS Pr.

Sex & Sanity: A Christian View of Sexual Morality. rev. ed. Stuart B. Babbage. LC 67-11492. 1967. Westminster.

Sex & Society in Islam: Birth Control Before the Nineteenth Century. Basim Musallam. LC 82-23539. (Cambridge Studies in Islamic Civilization). 240p. 1983. 34.50 (ISBN 0-521-24874-4). Cambridge U Pr.

Sex & Society in Islam: Birth Control Before the Nineteenth Century. Basim F. Musallam. (Cambridge Studies in Islamic Civilization). 176p. 1986. pap. 12.95 (ISBN 0-521-33858-1). Cambridge U Pr.

Sex & Spirit: God, Woman, & the Ministry. Victoria B. Demarest. LC 76-42915. (Illus.). 1977. 6.95 (ISBN 0-912760-38-9); pap. 4.95 (ISBN 0-912760-29-X). Valkyrie Pub Hse.

Sex & the Bible. Gerald Larue. LC 83-60201. 212p. 1983. 19.95 (ISBN 0-87975-206-8); pap. 11.95 (ISBN 0-87975-229-7). Prometheus Bks.

Sex & the Bible. Frank L. Perry, Jr. LC 82-72143. (Orig.). 1982. pap. 7.95 (ISBN 0-943708-00-1). Chr Educ Res Inst.

Sex & the Confessional. Norberto Valentini & Clara Di Meglio. LC 73-91861. 1975. pap. 1.95 (ISBN 0-8128-1862-8). Stein & Day.

Sex & the Human Psyche. John Yungblut. LC 75-19951. 32p. (Orig.). 1975. pap. 2.50x (ISBN 0-87574-203-3, 203). Pendle Hill.

Sex & the Modern Jewish Woman: Annotated Bibliography - Essays. Compiled by Joan S. Brewer. 128p. 1986. pap. 9.25 (ISBN 0-930395-01-8). Biblio NY.

Sex & the Single Christian. Audrey Beslow. 1987. pap. 9.95 (ISBN 0-687-38197-5). Abingdon.

Sex & the Single Christian. Ed. by Barry Colman. LC 85-30138. 120p. (Orig.). 1986. pap. 6.95 (ISBN 0-8307-1107-4, 5418696). Regal.

Sex & the Spiritual Path. Herbert B. Puryear. 256p. 1986. pap. 3.50 (ISBN 0-553-25635-1). Bantam.

Sex & Violence under God. Ed Hertzog. LC 81-84292. 212p. 1982. 12.00 (ISBN 0-937894-02-8); pap. 7.00 (ISBN 0-937894-03-6). Life Arts.

Sex Begins in the Kitchen. Kevin Leman. LC 80-54004. 1983. pap. 5.95 (ISBN 0-8307-1190-2, 5419017). Regal.

Sex, Dating, & Love: Seventy-Seven Questions Most Often Asked. Ray E. Short. LC 83-72122. 144p. (Orig.). 1984. pap. 3.95 (ISBN 0-8066-2066-8, 10-5648). Augsburg.

Sex Education in a Church Setting: The OCTOPUS Training Manual. Fred Isberner et al. 128p. (Orig.). 1986. pap. text ed. 8.95x (ISBN 0-8093-1315-4). S Ill U Pr.

Sex Education Within the Family. Ed. by David M. Thomas. LC 80-69136. (Marriage & Family Living in Depth Bk.). 80p. 1980. pap. 2.45 (ISBN 0-87029-171-8, 20248-1). Abbey.

Sex, Eros & Marital Love. Gerhard Gollwitzer. pap. 0.75 (ISBN 0-87785-104-2). Swedenborg.

Sex Ethics in the Writings of Moses Maimonides. Fred Rosner. LC 74-75479. 225p. 1974. 7.95x (ISBN 0-8197-0365-6). Bloch.

Sex for Christians. Lewis B. Smedes. 176p. 1976. pap. 5.95 (ISBN 0-8028-1618-5). Eerdmans.

Sex, Ideology & Religion: The Representation of Women in the Bible. Kevin Harris. LC 84-12413. 144p. 1984. 22.50x (ISBN 0-389-20509-5, BNB08067). B&N Imports.

Sex in the Bible. Tom Horner. LC 73-87676. 1974. 8.50 (ISBN 0-8048-1124-5). C E Tuttle.

Sex in the Bible: An Introduction to What the Scriptures Teach Us about Sexuality. Michael Cosby. LC 83-16090. 182p. 1984. 12.95 (ISBN 0-13-807280-9); pap. 5.95 (ISBN 0-13-807272-8). P-H.

Sex in the Light of Reincarnation & Freedom. Alan Howard. 1980. pap. 5.95 (ISBN 0-916786-48-X). St George Bk Serv.

Sex in the Talmud. Reuven P. Bulka. (Illus.). 64p. 1979. 5.95 (ISBN 0-88088-488-6). Peter Pauper.

Sex in the World's Religions. Geoffrey Parrinder. 1980. pap. 9.95x (ISBN 0-19-520202-3). Oxford U Pr.

Sex Is Holy. Mary Rousseau & Chuck Gallagner. (Chrysalis Bk). 160p. (Orig.). 1986. pap. 9.95 (ISBN 0-916349-11-X). Amity Hous Inc.

Sex Isn't That Simple: The New Sexuality on Campus. Richard Hettlinger. LC 73-17876. 256p. 1974. 6.95 (ISBN 0-8264-0155-4); pap. 3.95 (ISBN 0-8264-0156-2). Continuum.

Sex, Love & Procreation: Synthesis Ser. William E. May. 1976. pap. 0.75 (ISBN 0-8199-0711-1). Franciscan Herald.

Sex, Love, or Infatuation: How Can I Really Know? Ray E. Short. LC 78-52180. 1978. pap. 3.95 (ISBN 0-8066-1653-9, 10-5650). Augsburg.

Sex, Marriage & Chastity: Reflections of a Catholic Layman, Spouse & Parent. William E. May. 1981. 6.95 (ISBN 0-8199-0821-5). Franciscan Herald.

Sex, Money & Power: An Essay on Christian Social Ethics. Philip Turner. LC 84-72481. 135p. (Orig.). 1985. pap. 7.95 (ISBN 0-936384-22-0). Cowley Pubns.

Sex Mythology. Sha Rocco. (Illus.). 55p. 1982. Repr. of 1874 ed. 3.00. Am Atheist.

Sex Positive. Larry Uhrig. 160p. (Orig.). 1985. pap. 6.95 (ISBN 0-932870-82-1). Alyson Pubns.

Sex Problem: Its Cause, Its Curse & Its Cure. William T. Bruner. 1977. 3.00 (ISBN 0-9606566-0-X). Bruner.

Sex Roles & the Christian Family. W. Peter Blitchington. 1983. pap. 5.95 (ISBN 0-8423-5896-X); leader's guide 2.95 (ISBN 0-8423-5897-8). Tyndale.

Sex, Sexuality, & You: A Handbook for Growing Christians. Nancy H. Cooney. 100p. (Orig.). 1980. pap. text ed. 3.50 (ISBN 0-697-01741-9); tchrs.' resource guide 1.00 (ISBN 0-697-01742-7). Wm C Brown.

Sex, Sin & Grace: Women's Experience & the Theologies of Reinhold Niebuhr & Paul Tillich. Judith Plaskow. LC 79-5434. 1980. pap. text ed. 11.25 (ISBN 0-8191-0882-0). U Pr of Amer.

Sex, Sin & Salvation. Roy Masters. LC 77-78040. 267p. 1977. pap. 6.50 (ISBN 0-933900-06-6). Foun Human Under.

Sex, Spirit & You. John-Roger. LC 77-81389. 1977. pap. 5.00 (ISBN 0-914829-18-1). Baraka Bk.

Sex Tenets of the Catholic Church & the Ultimate Destinies of Man. Alexander Mantle. 1979. 41.75 (ISBN 0-89266-146-1). Am Classical Coll Pr.

Sex, Woman & Religion. Arthur F. Ide. (Illus.). xi, 212p. (Orig.). 1984. 14.95 (ISBN 0-930383-00-1). Monument Pr.

Sex Worship & Symbolism: An Interpretation. Sanger Brown. LC 72-9624. Repr. of 1922 ed. 27.50 (ISBN 0-404-57419-X). AMS Pr.

Sexism & God-Talk: Toward a Feminist Theology. Rosemary R. Ruether. LC 82-72502. 300p. (Orig.). 1984. pap. 9.95 (ISBN 0-8070-1105-3, BP680); 18.95x (ISBN 0-8070-1104-5). Beacon Pr.

Sexologia para Cristianos. Lewis Smedes. Tr. by Jorge Sanchez from Eng. Tr. of Sex for Christians. 288p. 1982. pap. 5.95 (ISBN 0-89922-175-0). Edit Caribe.

Sextus Empiricus: Selections from the Major Writings on Scepticism, Man, & God. rev. ed. Sextus Empiricus Staff. Ed. by Phillip P. Hallie. Tr. by Sanford G. Etheridge from Gr. LC 85-27059. 256p. 1985. lib. bdg. 27.50 (ISBN 0-87220-007-8); pap. 6.95 (ISBN 0-87220-006-X). Hackett Pub.

Sexual Archetypes: East & West. Ed. by Bina Gupta. (God: The Contemporary Discussion Ser.). (Illus.). 344p. 1986. 22.95 (ISBN 0-913757-59-4, Pub. by New Era Bks); pap. 12.95 (ISBN 0-913757-68-3, Pub. by New Era Bks). Paragon Hse.

Sexual Celibate. Don Goergen. 272p. 1975. 5.00 (ISBN 0-8164-0268-X, HarpR). Har-Row.

Sexual Creators: An Ethical Proposal for Concerned Christians. Andre Guindon. 256p. (Orig.). 1986. lib. bdg. 28.00 (ISBN 0-8191-5239-0); pap. text ed. 13.00 (ISBN 0-8191-5240-4). U Pr of Amer.

Sexual Energy & Yoga. Elisabeth Haich. 160p. 1983. 7.95 (ISBN 0-943358-03-5). Aurora Press.

Sexual Freedom. V. Mary Stewart. pap. 0.75 (ISBN 0-87784-111-X). Inter-Varsity.

Sexual Happiness in Marriage. 2nd rev. ed. Herbert J. Miles. 208p. 1982. pap. 3.95 (ISBN 0-310-29222-0). Zondervan.

Sexual Inversion: The Questions-with Catholic Answers. Herbert F. Smith. 1979. 2.95 (ISBN 0-8198-0612-9); pap. 1.95 (ISBN 0-8198-0613-7). Dghtrs St Paul.

Sexual Morality: A Catholic Perspective. Philip Keane. LC 77-83536. 252p. 1978. pap. 8.95 (ISBN 0-8091-2070-4). Paulist Pr.

Sexual Practices & the Medieval Church. Ed. by Vern Bullough & James Brundage. LC 80-85227. 289p. 1984. pap. 15.95 (ISBN 0-87975-268-8). Prometheus Bks.

Sexual Problems in Marriage: Help from a Christian Counselor. F. Philip Rice. LC 77-27443. 252p. 1978. softcover 6.95 (ISBN 0-664-24194-8). Westminster.

Sexual Revolution, Vol 173. Ed. by Gregory Baum & John Coleman. (Concilium Ser.). 128p. pap. 6.95 (ISBN 0-317-31462-9, Pub. by T & T Clark Ltd UK). Fortress.

Sexual Sanity. Earl D. Wilson. LC 83-22753. 156p. 1984. pap. 5.95 (ISBN 0-87784-919-6). Inter-Varsity.

Sexual Violence: The Unmentionable Sin: An Ethical & Pastoral Perspective. Marie M. Fortune. 256p. (Orig.). 1983. pap. 9.95 (ISBN 0-8298-0652-0). Pilgrim NY.

Sexuality. Mary Durkin. (Guidelines for Contemporary Catholics Ser.). (Orig.). 1987. pap. 7.95 (ISBN 0-88347-211-2). Thomas More.

Sexuality. Letha D. Scanzoni. LC 83-27375. (Choices: Guides for Today's Woman: Vol. 8). 114p. (Orig.). 1984. pap. 6.95 (ISBN 0-664-24548-X). Westminster.

Sexuality & Cancer. Ernest H. Rosenbaum et al. (Orig.). 1980. pap. 2.95 (ISBN 0-915950-39-1). Bull Pub.

Sexuality & Dating. Richard Reichert. LC 81-51011. (Illus.). 160p. 1981. pap. 5.00x (ISBN 0-88489-133-X); tchrs' guide 9.00x (ISBN 0-88489-138-0); student workbook 2.00 (ISBN 0-88489-139-9). St Mary's.

Sexuality & the Counseling Pastor. Herbert W. Stroup & Norma S. Wood. LC 73-88344. pap. 33.50 (2027176). Bks Demand UMI.

Sexuality in Islam. Abdelwahab Bouhdiba. 288p. 1985. 42.50x (ISBN 0-7100-9608-9). Methuen Inc.

Sexuality, Magic & Perversion. Francis King. (Illus.). 1972. 6.95 (ISBN 0-8065-0289-4). Citadel Pr.

Sexuality, the Bible & Science. Stephen Sapp. LC 76-62617. pap. 38.00 (2026976). Bks Demand UMI.

Shaare Rahmin: Sermon Material for the High Holidays in Hebrew. P. S. Pollak. 7.50 (ISBN 0-87559-104-3). Shalom.

Shaarei Mitzvah: Gates of Mitzvah. Ed. by Simeon J. Maslin. (Illus.). 1979. 9.95 (ISBN 0-916694-37-2); pap. 7.95 (ISBN 0-916694-53-4). Central Conf.

Shabbat: A Peaceful Island (a Jewish Holidays Book) Malka Drucker. LC 83-7900. (Illus.). 96p. 1983. reinforced bdg. 11.95 (ISBN 0-8234-0500-1). Holiday.

Shabbat Can Be. Audrey F. Marcus & Raymond A. Zwerin. Ed. by Daniel B. Syme. (Illus.). 1979. pap. text ed. 7.95 (ISBN 0-8074-0023-8, 102560); tchrs'. guide 3.00 (ISBN 0-8074-0024-6, 208025). UAHC.

Shabbat Catalogue. Ruth Brin. 1971. 5.00x (ISBN 0-87068-636-4). Ktav.

Shabbat Haggadah for Celebration & Study. Michael Strassfeld. LC 80-83430. 124p. 1980. pap. 5.50 (ISBN 0-87495-025-2). Am Jewish Comm.

Shabbat Manual. 1972. pap. 5.95 (ISBN 0-916694-54-2). Central Conf.

Shabbat Shalom: A Renewed Encounter with the Sabbath. Pinchas Peli. 120p. 1986. pap. 7.95 (ISBN 0-940646-37-4). Rossel Bks.

Shabbath, 3 vols. 45.00 (ISBN 0-317-39580-7). Bennet Pub.

Shade of His Hand. Oswald Chambers. 1961. pap. 2.95 (ISBN 0-87508-127-4). Chr Lit.

Shadow of a Man. Rick Bundschuh. LC 86-22048. (Light Force Ser.). 120p. (Orig.). (YA) 1986. pap. 4.95 (ISBN 0-8307-1143-0, S185116). Regal.

Shadow of Calvary. Hugh Martin. 1983. pap. 5.95 (ISBN 0-85151-373-5). Banner of Truth.

Shadow of Death. Lilli Schultze. 1981. 3.50 (ISBN 0-87813-516-2). Christian Light.

Shadow of God. Versa H. Davidson. 320p. 1980. 7.95 (ISBN 0-89962-026-4). Todd & Honeywell.

Shadow of God & the Hidden Iman: Religion, Political Order & Societal Change in Shi'ite Iran from the Beginning to 1890. Said A. Arjomand. LC 83-27196. (Publications of the Center for the Middle Eastern Studies: No. 17). (Illus.). xii, 356p. 1984. lib. bdg. 28.00x (ISBN 0-226-02782-1). U of Chicago Pr.

Shadow of God & the Hidden Inam: Religion, Political Order, & Societal Change in Shl'ite Iran from the Beginning to 1890. Said A. Arjomand. LC 83-27196. (Publications of the Center for Middle Eastern Studies: No. 117). (Illus.). 344p. 1987. lib. bdg. price not set; pap. text ed. price not set (ISBN 0-226-02784-8). U of Chicago Pr.

Shadow of the Almighty: The Life & Testament of Jim Elliot. Elizabeth Elliot. LC 58-10365. 1979. pap. 6.95 (ISBN 0-06-062211-3, RD 488, HarpR). Har-Row.

Shadow of the Bamboo. Bhagwan Shree Rajneesh. Ed. by Ma Prem Maneesha. LC 84-42807. (Initiation Talks Ser.). 240p. (Orig.). 1984. pap. 3.95 (ISBN 0-88050-630-X). Chidvilas found.

Shadow of the Cross. Morton F. Rose. LC 86-9630. (Orig.). 1986. pap. 3.25 (ISBN 0-8054-5030-0). Broadman.

Shadow of the Cross: Studies in Self-denial. Walter J. Chantry. 79p. (Orig.). 1981. pap. 3.45 (ISBN 0-85151-331-X). Banner of Truth.

Shadow of the Whip. Bhagwan S. Rajneesh. Ed. by Ma Prem Maneesha. LC 82-230735. (Initiation Talks Ser.). (Illus.). 554p. (Orig.). 1978. 18.95 (ISBN 0-88050-131-6). Chidvilas Found.

Shadow on the Church: Southwestern Evangelical Religion & the Issue of Slavery, 1783-1860. David T. Bailey. LC 84-45795. 264p. 1985. text ed. 26.95x (ISBN 0-8014-1763-5). Cornell U Pr.

Shadowed by the Great Wall: The Story of Kimmer Mennonite Brethren Missions in Inner Mongolia (1922-1949) A. K. Wiens & Gertrude Wiens. LC 79-55686. 120p. (Orig.). 1979. pap. 3.95 (ISBN 0-935196-01-3). Kindred Pr.

Shadows & Symbols. Carl Jech. 1985. 6.25 (ISBN 0-89536-751-3, 5857). CSS of Ohio.

Shadows of Armageddon. Wim Malgo. 4.95 (ISBN 0-937422-15-0). Midnight Call.

Shadows of Good Things, or the Gospel in Type. R. R. Byrum. (Illus.). 144p. pap. 1.50 (ISBN 0-686-29141-7). Faith Pub Hse.

Shadows of Heaven: Religion & Fantasy in the Writing of C. S. Lewis, Charles Williams & J. R. R. Tolkien. Gunnar Urang. LC 73-153998. 208p. 1971. 7.95 (ISBN 0-8298-0197-9). Pilgrim NY.

Shadows of the Holocaust. Harriet Steinhorn. LC 83-14887. 80p. 1983. pap. text ed. 8.95 (ISBN 0-930494-25-3). Kar Ben.

Shaira Devotional Songs of Kashmir: A Translation & Study of Utpaladeva's Shivastotravali. Constantina R. Bailly. (Kashmir Shaivism Ser.). 224p. 1987. 39.50x (ISBN 0-88706-492-2); pap. 12.95x (ISBN 0-88706-493-0). State U NY Pr.

Shai's Shabbat Walk. Ellie Gellman. LC 85-80780. (Illus.). 12p. 1985. bds. 4.95 (ISBN 0-930494-49-0). Kar Ben.

Shake a Palm Branch: The Story & Meaning of Sukkot. Miriam Chaikin. LC 84-5022. (Illus.). 80p. 1984. PLB 12.95 (ISBN 0-89919-254-8, Clarion). HM.

Shake a Palm Branch: The Story & Meaning of Sukkot. Miriam Chaikin. LC 84-5022. (Illus.). 88p. 1986. pap. 4.95 (ISBN 0-89919-428-1, Pub. by Clarion). Ticknor & Fields.

Shaker Adventure. Marguerite F. Melcher. 319p. 1986. pap. 9.95 (ISBN 0-937942-08-1). Shaker Mus.

Shaker Collection of the Western Reserve Historical Society. Ed. by Jack T. Ericson. 77p. 1977. pap. 7.50 (ISBN 0-667-00522-6). Microfilming Corp.

Shaker Communism: Or, Tests of Divine Inspiration. Frederick W. Evans. LC 72-2987. Repr. of 1871 ed. 14.50 (ISBN 0-404-10749-4). AMS Pr.

Shaker Dance Service Reconstucted. J. G. Davies & P. Van Zyl. 1984. pap. 3.00 (ISBN 0-941500-34-9). Sharing Co.

Shaker Days Remembered. Martha Hulings. pap. 5.00 (ISBN 0-317-17252-2). Shaker Her Soc.

Shaker Herbs & Their Medicinal Uses. Dee Herbrandson. (Illus.). 28p. 1985. pap. 4.00. Shaker Her Soc.

Shaker Holy Land: A Community Portrait. Edward R. Horgan. LC 81-20214. (Illus.). 272p. 1982. 15.95 (ISBN 0-916782-22-0). Harvard Common Pr.

Shaker Literature: A Bibliography, 2 vols. Compiled by Mary L. Richmond. LC 75-41908. 656p. 1976. Set. 60.00x (ISBN 0-87451-117-8). U Pr of New Eng.

Shaker Music: Inspirational Hymns & Melodies Illustrative of the Resurection, Life & Testimony of the Shakers. Frederick W. Evans. LC 72-2988. Repr. of 1875 ed. 27.50 (ISBN 0-404-10750-8). AMS Pr.

Shaker Religious Concept. John S. Williams. (Illus.). 32p. 1959. pap. 2.50 (ISBN 0-937942-04-9). Shaker Mus.

Shaker Spiritual. Daniel W. Patterson. LC 77-85557. (Illus.). 1979. text ed. 90.00x (ISBN 0-691-09124-2). Princeton U Pr.

Shaker Village. Edmund Gillon. (Illus.). 56p. 1986. pap. 5.95 (ISBN 0-88740-077-9). Schiffer.

Shaker Your Plate: Of Shaker Cooks & Cooking. Francis A. Carr. LC 85-51982. (Illus.). 156p. (Orig.). 1985. pap. 10.95 (ISBN 0-915836-02-5). Shaker Pr ME.

Shakerism, Its Meaning & Message. Anna White & Lelia S. Taylor. LC 73-134421. Repr. of 1904 ed. 31.50 (ISBN 0-404-08462-1). AMS Pr.

Shakers & the World's People. Flo Morse. LC 79-27271. 1981. 17.95 (ISBN 0-396-07809-5). Dodd.

Shaker's Answer. R. W. Pelham. 32p. 1981. pap. 1.50 (ISBN 0-937942-09-X). Shaker Mus.

Shakers: Compendium of the Origin, History, Principles, Rules & Regulations, Government & Doctrines of the United Society of Believers in Christ's Second Appearing. 4th ed. Frederick W. Evans. LC 72-2985. (Communal Societies in America). Repr. of 1867 ed. 14.00 (ISBN 0-404-10747-8). AMS Pr.

Shakers: Two Centuries of Spiritual Reflection. Ed. by Robley E. Whitson. (Classics of Western Spirituality Ser.). 200p. 1983. 13.95 (ISBN 0-8091-0343-5); pap. 9.95 (ISBN 0-8091-2373-8). Paulist Pr.

Shaker's Viewpoint. Facsimile ed. Eldress E. King. 4p. 1957. pap. 0.25 (ISBN 0-937942-15-4). Shaker Mus.

Shakespeare & Astrology, from a Student's Point of View. William Wilson. LC 77-178308. Repr. of 1903 ed. 16.00 (ISBN 0-404-06998-3). AMS Pr.

Shakespeare & Catholicism. Heinrich Mutschmann & Karl Wentersdorf. LC 71-105107. 1970. Repr. of 1952 ed. 31.50 (ISBN 0-404-04547-2). AMS Pr.

Shakespeare & Holy Scripture. Thomas Carter. LC 74-113574. Repr. of 1905 ed. 22.50 (ISBN 0-404-01398-8). AMS Pr.

Shakespeare & Spiritual Life. John Masefield. LC 77-1449. 1973. lib. bdg. 10.00 (ISBN 0-8414-2315-6). Folcroft.

Shakespeare & the Allegory of Evil: The History of a Metaphor in Relation to His Major Villains. Bernard Spivack. LC 57-12758. pap. 130.30 (ISBN 0-317-28960-8, 2017840). Bks Demand UMI.

Shakespeare & the Bible. G. Q. Colton. LC 74-8569. 1888. lib. bdg. 20.00 (ISBN 0-685-45608-0). Folcroft.

Shakespeare & the Bible. Thomas R. Eaton. LC 77-144601. Repr. of 1860 ed. 19.00 (ISBN 0-404-02237-5). AMS Pr.

Shakespeare & the Bible. James Rees. LC 70-174307. Repr. of 1876 ed. 16.00 (ISBN 0-404-05235-5). AMS Pr.

Shakespeare & the Bible. James Rees. LC 72-14367. 1973. lib. bdg. 15.50 (ISBN 0-8414-1348-7). Folcroft.

Shakespeare & the Influence of the Stars. D. Fraser-Harris. 69.95 (ISBN 0-8490-1031-4). Gordon Pr.

Shakespeare & the Jew. G. Friedlander. 59.95 (ISBN 0-8490-1032-2). Gordon Pr.

Shakespeare & the Jew. Gerald Friedlander. LC 74-168084. Repr. of 1921 ed. 18.00 (ISBN 0-404-02579-X). AMS Pr.

Shakespeare & the Mystery of God's Judgments. Robert G. Hunter. LC 75-11449. 224p. 1976. 17.00x (ISBN 0-8203-0388-7). U of Ga Pr.

Shakespeare & the Supernatural. C. Clark. LC 72-92957. (Studies in Shakespeare, No. 24). 1970. Repr. of 1931 ed. lib. bdg. 75.00x (ISBN 0-8383-0966-6). Haskell.

Shakespeare & the Supernatural. Cumberland Clark. LC 72-186985. 1931. lib. bdg. 37.50 (ISBN 0-8414-0341-4). Folcroft.

Shakespeare & the Supernatural. Cumberland Clark. 346p. Repr. of 1931 ed. 29.00 (ISBN 0-403-04266-6). Somerset Pub.

Shakespeare & the Supernatural. Margaret Lucy. LC 70-144653. Repr. of 1906 ed. 6.50 (ISBN 0-404-04065-9). AMS Pr.

Shakespeare & the Supernatural. Margaret Lucy. LC 73-16087. 1906. lib. bdg. 15.00 (ISBN 0-8414-5699-2). Folcroft.

Shakespeare, Puritan & Recusant. Thomas Carter. LC 70-129386. Repr. of 1897 ed. 16.00 (ISBN 0-404-01397-X). AMS Pr.

Shakespeare, Shylock & Kabbalah. Daniel Banes. LC 78-58912. 1978. 9.99 (ISBN 0-686-10284-3); pap. 3.60 (ISBN 0-686-10285-1). Malcolm Hse.

Shakespeare's Biblical Knowledge. R. Noble. 59.95 (ISBN 0-8490-1039-X). Gordon Pr.

Shakespeare's Biblical Knowledge & Use of the Book of Common Prayer. Richmond Noble. 1970. lib. bdg. 20.00x (ISBN 0-374-96115-8, Octagon). Hippocrene Bks.

Shakespeare's Biblical Knowledge & Use of the Book of Common Prayer: As Exemplified in the Plays of the First Folio. Richmond S. Noble. 303p. 1980. Repr. of 1935 ed. lib. bdg. 37.50 (ISBN 0-8492-1971-X). R West.

Shakespeare's Books. Henry R. Anders. LC 76-158251. Repr. of 1904 ed. 12.50 (ISBN 0-404-00355-9). AMS Pr.

Shakespeare's Church. James H. Bloom. LC 73-116790. (Studies in Shakespeare, No. 24). 1971. Repr. of 1902 ed. lib. bdg. 49.95x (ISBN 0-8383-1032-X). Haskell.

Shakespeare's Debt to the Bible. Charles Bullock. LC 72-187918. 1870. lib. bdg. 10.00 (ISBN 0-8414-2521-3). Folcroft.

Shakespeare's Jew. H. B. Charlton. 1934. lib. bdg. 12.50 (ISBN 0-8414-3560-X). Folcroft.

Shakespeare's Knowledge & Use of the Bible. 3rd ed. Charles Wordsworth. LC 73-144706. Repr. of 1880 ed. 27.50 (ISBN 0-404-07039-6). AMS Pr.

Shakespeare's Religious Background. Ed. by Peter Milward. 312p. 1985. Repr. of 1973 ed. 8.95 (ISBN 0-8294-0508-9). Loyola.

Shakespeare's Religious Frontier. Robert Stevenson. LC 73-16102. 1974. Repr. of 1958 ed. lib. bdg. 25.00 (ISBN 0-8414-7699-3). Folcroft.

Shakespeares-'The Old Faith.' facs. ed. John H. De Groot. LC 68-57315. (Essay Index Reprint Ser.). 1946. 18.00 (ISBN 0-8369-0368-4). Ayer Co Pubs.

Shakespeare's Use of the Supernatural. J. Paul Gibson. LC 79-144615. Repr. of 1908 ed. 15.00 (ISBN 0-404-02719-9). AMS Pr.

Shaking of the Foundations. Paul Tillich. 1948. pap. 8.95 (ISBN 0-684-71910-X, ScribT). Scribner.

Shakti. E. J. Gold. (Illus.). 1973. pap. 4.95 (ISBN 0-89556-005-4). Gateways Bks & Tapes.

Shakti & Shakta. Arthur Avalon. 1978. pap. 8.95 (ISBN 0-486-23645-5). Dover.

Shakti: Power in the Conceptual Structure of Karimpur Religion. Susan S. Wadley. LC 76-37612. (Univ. of Chicago Studies in Anthropology Ser. in Social, Cultural, & Linguistic Anthropology: No. 2). 222p. 1975. pap. 6.00 (ISBN 0-916256-01-4). U Chi Dept Anthro.

Shakyamuni Buddha: A Narrative Biography. rev. ed. Nikkyo Niwano. Ed. by Rebecca M. Davis. Tr. by Kojiro Miyazaki from Japanese. LC 80-154779. Orig. Title: Bukkyo No Inochi Hokeyo. (Illus.). 128p. 1980. pap. 3.50 (ISBN 4-333-01001-2, Pub. by Kosei Publishing Co). C E Tuttle.

Shall We Take Down the Steeple? Helen L. Snyder. (Orig.). 1982. pap. 2.95 (ISBN 0-937172-42-1). JLJ Pubs.

Shalom Aleichem. Noah Golinkin. 77p. 1978. pap. 4.95x (ISBN 0-88482-696-1). Hebrew Pub.

Shalom: Essays in Honor of Dr. Charles H. Shaw. Ed. by Eugene J. Mayhew. 231p. 1983. pap. 11.95 (ISBN 0-912407-01-8). William Tyndale Col Pr.

Shalom: Hope for the World. Steve Clapp. 178p. (Orig.). 1982. pap. 8.00 (ISBN 0-914527-35-5). C-Four Res.

Shalom Seders. Ed. by New Jewish Agenda. 128p. 1984. pap. 12.95 (ISBN 0-531-09840-0). Watts.

Shalom Seders: Three Passover Haggadahs. Compiled by New Jewish Agenda. LC 83-25857. (Illus.). 128p. 1984. pap. 12.95 (ISBN 0-915361-03-5, 09747-1, Dist. by Watts). Adama Pubs Inc.

Shalom: The Bible's Word for Salvation, Justice & Peace. Perry B. Yoder. LC 86-82879. 161p. 1987. pap. 14.95 (ISBN 0-87303-120-2). Faith & Life.

Shalom Woman. Margaret Wold. LC 75-2828. 128p. 1975. pap. 6.95 (ISBN 0-8066-1475-7, 10-5740). Augsburg.

Shamail Tirmidhi. M. Hussain. 22.50 (ISBN 0-317-01594-X). Kazi Pubns.

Shaman: Patterns of Siberian & Ojibway Healing. John A. Grim. LC 83-47834. (Civilization of the American Indian Ser.: Vol. 165). (Illus.). 264p. 1983. pap. 19.95 (ISBN 0-8061-1809-1). U of Okla Pr.

Shaman: The Wounded Healer. Joan Halifax. Ed. by Jill Purce. LC 81-67705. (Illustrated Library of Sacred Imagination Ser.). (Illus.). 96p. 1982. pap. 9.95 (ISBN 0-8245-0066-0). Crossroad NY.

Shamanic Voices: A Survey of Visionary Narratives. Joan Halifax. 1979. pap. 11.95 (ISBN 0-525-47525-7, 01160-350). Dutton.

Shamanism. Compiled by Shirley Nicholson. LC 86-40405. 402p. (Orig.). 1987. pap. 7.50 (ISBN 0-8356-0617-1). Theos Pub Hse.

Shamanism: Archaic Techniques of Ectasy. Mircea Eliade. Tr. by Willard R. Trask. (Bollingen Ser.: Vol. 76). 1964. 50.00x (ISBN 0-691-09827-1); pap. 11.95x (ISBN 0-691-01779-4). Princeton U Pr.

Shamanism, Colonialism, & the Wild Man: A Study in Terror & Healing. Michael Taussig. LC 86-11410. (Illus.). 544p. 1987. lib. bdg. 29.95 (ISBN 0-226-79012-6). U of Chicago Pr.

Shamanism in Western North America. Willard Z. Park. LC 74-12553. 166p. 1975. Repr. of 1938 ed. lib. bdg. 22.50x (ISBN 0-8154-0497-2). Cooper Sq.

Shamans Healing Way. Spencer Rogers. 1976. pap. 4.95 (ISBN 0-916552-06-3). Acoma Bks.

Shamans, Lamas & Evangelicals: The English Missionaries in Siberia. C. R. Bawden. (Illus.). 400p. 1985. 50.00x (ISBN 0-7102-0064-1). Methuen Inc.

Shamans, Mystics, & Doctors: A Psychological Inquiry into India & Its Healing Traditions. Sudhir Kakar. LC 83-70654. 324p. 1983. pap. 10.95x (ISBN 0-8070-2903-3, BP 660). Beacon Pr.

Shamans, Prophets & Sages: A Concise Intro to World Religion. Carmody & Carmody. 1984. write for info. (ISBN 0-534-04263-5). Wadsworth Pub.

Shaman's Touch: Otomi Indian Symbolic Healing. James Dow. (Illus.). 180p. (Orig.). 1986. 13.95 (ISBN 0-87480-257-1). U of Utah Pr.

Shambhala. Nicholas Roerich. softcover 12.00 (ISBN 0-686-79666-7); 16.00. Agni Yoga Soc.

Shambhala: The Sacred Path of the Warrior. Chogyam Trungpa. LC 83-20401. (Illus.). 199p. 1984. pap. 7.95 (ISBN 0-87773-264-7). Shambhala Pubns.

Shambhala: The Sacred Path of the Warriors. Chogyam Trungpa. 176p. 1986. pap. 3.95 (ISBN 0-553-26172-X). Bantam.

Shame & Guilt: Characteristics of the Dependency Cycle. Ernest Kurtz. 68p. 4.95 (ISBN 0-89486-132-8, 1940A). Hazelden.

Shamrocks, Harps, & Shillelaghs: The Story of the St. Patrick's Day Symbols. Edna Barth. LC 77-369. (Illus.). 96p. 1977. 9.95 (ISBN 0-395-28845-2, Clarion). HM.

Shankara on the Yoga Sutras. Trevor Leggett. (Vol. 1). 140p. 1981. 30.00 (ISBN 0-7100-0826-0). Methuen Inc.

Shaolin Temple Boxing Secrets. Robert W. Smith. 7.95x (ISBN 0-685-22107-5). Wehman.

Shape Book. Illus. by Marc Harrison. (Bible Look-n-Learn Ser.). 1986. 3.95 (ISBN 0-8407-6709-9). Nelson.

Shape of Baptism: The Rite of Christian Initiation. Aidan Kavanagh. (Studies in the Reformed Rites of the Catholic Church: Vol. 1). 1978. pap. 9.95 (ISBN 0-916134-36-9). Pueblo Pub Co.

Shape of Death: Life, Death, & Immortality in the Early Fathers. Jaroslav J. Pelikan. LC 78-6030. 1978. Repr. of 1961 ed. lib. bdg. 22.50x (ISBN 0-313-20458-6, PESD). Greenwood.

Shape of Growth. Gale D. Webbe. 110p. (Orig.). 1985. pap. 9.95 (ISBN 0-8192-1356-X). Morehouse.

Shape of Religious Instruction: A Social-Science Approach. James Michael Lee. LC 74-29823. 330p. (Orig.). 1971. lib. bdg. 16.95 (ISBN 0-89135-000-4); pap. 14.95 (ISBN 0-89135-002-0). Religious Educ.

Shape of Sacred Space: Four Biblical Studies. Robert L. Cohn. LC 80-11086. (Studies in Religion: No. 23). pap. 8.50 (ISBN 0-89130-384-7, 01-00-23). Scholars Pr GA.

Shape of Scriptural Authority. David L. Bartlett. LC 83-48009. 176p. 1983. pap. 8.95 (ISBN 0-8006-1713-4, 1-1713). Fortress.

Shape of the Church to Come. Karl Rahner. 1974. 10.95 (ISBN 0-8245-0372-4). Crossroad NY.

Shape of the Liturgy. Dom G. Dix. 816p. 1982. 24.50 (ISBN 0-8164-2418-7, HarpR). Har-Row.

Shape of the Past. John W. Montgomery. LC 75-26651. 400p. 1975. pap. 9.95 (ISBN 0-87123-535-8, 210535). Bethany Hse.

Shape of Things to Come. Joseph A. Synan. 1969. 3.95 (ISBN 0-911866-52-3); pap. 2.95 (ISBN 0-911866-90-6). Advocate.

Shape Up. rev. & updated ed. O. Quentin Hyder. (Illus.). 160p. 1984. pap. 4.95 (ISBN 0-8007-5158-2, Power Bks). Revell.

Shaped by the Word. M. Robert Mulholland. (Orig.). 1985. pap. 7.95 (ISBN 0-8358-0519-0). Upper Room.

Shapers of Baptist Thought. James E. Tull. LC 84-6545. (Reprints of Scholarly Excellence Ser.: No. 8). 255p. 1984. Repr. of 1972 ed. 14.50 (ISBN 0-86554-125-6, MUP-H116). Mercer Univ Pr.

Shapers of Religious Traditions in Germany, Switzerland, & Poland, Fifteen Sixty to Sixteen Hundred. Ed. by Jill Raitt. LC 80-23287. 256p. 1981. text ed. 28.50x (ISBN 0-300-02457-6). Yale U Pr.

Shapes in God's World. Beverly Beckman. LC 56-1462. 1984. 5.95 (ISBN 0-570-04094-9). Concordia.

Shaping a Healthy Religion. Thomas Aldworth. 132p. 1985. pap. 8.95 (ISBN 0-88347-200-7). Thomas More.

Shaping Faith Through Involvement. Sonjia L. Hunt. 72p. (Orig.). 1981. pap. text ed. 2.50 (ISBN 0-87148-796-9). Pathway Pr.

Shaping History Through Prayer & Fasting. Derek Prince. 1973. 9.95 (ISBN 0-934920-23-0, B-24); pap. 5.95 (ISBN 0-686-12766-8, B-25). Derek Prince.

Shaping of Religion in America. Norman W. Harrington. (Illus.). 168p. 1980. 29.95 (ISBN 0-937692-01-8). Queen Anne Pr.

Shaping of the Foundations: Being at Home in the Transcendental Method. Philip McShane. 12.25 (ISBN 0-8191-0209-1). U Pr of Amer.

Shaping of the United Church of Christ: An Essay in the History of American Christianity. Louis H. Gunnemann. LC 77-4900. 1977. 6.95 (ISBN 0-8298-0335-1). Pilgrim NY.

Shaping the Church from the Mind of Christ: A Study of Paul's Letter to the Philippians. Edward L. Tullis. LC 84-50837. 80p. (Orig.). 1984. pap. 3.95 (ISBN 0-8358-0494-1). Upper Room.

Shaping the Church's Educational Ministry. Kenneth L. Cober. LC 75-139502. (Illus.). 1971. pap. 3.95 (ISBN 0-8170-0519-6); pap. 1.95 spanish ed (ISBN 0-8170-0603-6). Judson.

Shaping the Church's Ministry with Youth. David M. Evans. (Orig.). pap. 2.95 (ISBN 0-8170-0342-8). Judson.

Shaping the Coming Age of Religious Life. 2nd ed. Lawrence Cada et al. LC 78-25987. 208p. 1985. pap. 7.95 (ISBN 0-89571-023-4). Affirmation.

Shaping the Congregation. Robert L. Wilson. LC 80-22228. (Into Our Third Century Ser.). 144p. (Orig.). 1981. pap. 3.95 (ISBN 0-687-38334-X). Abingdon.

Shaping the Future: Gaston Berger & the Concept of Prospective. Andre Cournand & Maurice Levy. LC 72-78388. (Current Topics of Contemporary Thought Ser.). 314p. 1973. 72.75 (ISBN 0-677-12550-X). Gordon & Breach.

Shaping the Future: The Ethics of Dietrich Bonhoeffer. James Burtness. LC 85-47723. 208p. 1985. pap. 16.95 (ISBN 0-8006-1869-6, 1-1869). Fortress.

Sharafuddin Maneri: The Hundred Letters. Ed. by Paul Jackson. LC 79-56754. (Classics of Western Spirituality Ser.). 480p. 1980. 13.95 (ISBN 0-8091-0291-9); pap. 9.95 (ISBN 0-8091-2229-4). Paulist Pr.

Shards from the Heart: A Spiritual Odyssey in Twentieth Century America. Bernard J. Garber. LC 64-13358. (Freedeeds Library). 160p. 1965. 8.00 (ISBN 0-89345-004-9, Freedeeds Bks). Garber Comm.

Share the Gospel. Sandy Grant. 80p. 1987. pap. 5.95 (ISBN 1-55513-825-X). Cook.

Share the New Life with a Jew. Moishe Rosen. LC 76-7627. 1976. pap. 3.95 (ISBN 0-8024-7898-0). Moody.

Share Your Bread. rev. ed. Joan Jungerman. 1.25 (ISBN 0-8091-9313-2). Paulist Pr.

Share Your Faith. Leith Samuel. (Contemporary Discussion Ser.). 104p. 1981. pap. 2.95 (ISBN 0-8010-8187-4). Baker Bk.

Share Your Faith with a Muslim. C. R. Marsh. LC 75-15883. 1975. pap. 4.50 (ISBN 0-8024-7900-6). Moody.

Shared Adventure. James R. Tozer. 1985. 5.50 (ISBN 0-89536-736-X, 5820). CSS of Ohio.

Shared Heart: Relationship Initiations & Celebrations. Barry Vissell & Joyce Vissell. LC 85-10981. 192p. 1985. Repr. lib. bdg. 19.95x (ISBN 0-89370-883-6). Borgo Pr.

Shared Ministry: An Integrated Approach to Leadership & Service. Dolore Rocker & Kenneth J. Pierre. (Illus.). 245p. (Orig.). 1984. pap. 18.95 (ISBN 0-88489-158-5). St Mary's.

Sharifa. Cornelia Dalenburg & David De Groot. (Historical Series of the Reformed Church in America: Vol. 11). (Orig.). 1983. pap. 11.95 (ISBN 0-8028-1973-7). Eerdmans.

Sharing. Dan Carr. (God I Need to Talk to You About...Ser.). (Illus.). 1984. pap. 0.75 (ISBN 0-570-08728-7, 56-1472). Concordia.

Sharing: A Manual for Program Directors. Thomas Zanzig. (Sharing Program Ser.). 214p. 1985. pap. 54.00 (ISBN 0-88489-167-4). St Mary's.

Sharing a Vision. Phoebe Willetts. 116p. 1978. pap. 4.95 (ISBN 0-227-67842-7). Attic Pr.

Sharing Care: The Christian Ministry of Respite Care. Judith K. Murphy. (Illus.). 64p. (Orig.). 1986. pap. 3.95 (ISBN 0-8298-0575-3). Pilgrim NY.

Sharing Faith at Home. Jan Hartley. (SPAN Ser.). (Illus.). 31p. (Orig.). 1983. pap. 3.95 (ISBN 0-85819-450-3, Pub. by JBCE). ANZ Religious Pubns.

Sharing from the Psalms. Nelle A. Vander Ark. 64p. 1984. pap. 2.95 (ISBN 0-8010-9295-7). Baker Bk.

Sharing God's Feelings. B. J. Whitley, Jr. LC 84-51661. 201p. (Orig.). 1985. pap. 9.95 (ISBN 0-9615536-0-X). Spirit Christ.

Sharing God's Love. John F. Marshall. LC 81-11794. 108p. 1981. pap. 5.95 (ISBN 0-8146-1068-4). Liturgical Pr.

Sharing His Life. Joan Thiry. 1981. 3.75 (ISBN 0-89837-056-6, Pub. by Pflaum Pr); pap. 1.50 (ISBN 0-89837-084-1). Peter Li.

Sharing His Love. Joan Thiry. 1981. 3.75 (ISBN 0-89837-066-3, Pub. by Pflaum Pr). Peter Li.

Sharing Jesus Effectively. Jerry Savelle. 125p. (Orig.). 1982. pap. 3.95 (ISBN 0-89274-251-8). Harrison Hse.

Sharing Jesus in the "Two Thirds" World. Ed. by Vinay Samuel & Chris Sugden. 432p. (Orig.). 1984. pap. 10.95 (ISBN 0-8028-1997-4). Eerdmans.

Sharing Possessions: Mandate & Symbol of Faith. Luke T. Johnson. Ed. by Walter Brueggemann & John R. Donahue. LC 80-2390. (Overtures to Biblical Theology Ser.: No. 9). 176p. (Orig.). 1981. pap. 8.95 (ISBN 0-8006-1534-4, 1-1534). Fortress.

Sharing the Christian Message: A Program Manual for Volunteer Catechists, Tenth Grade. Thomas Zanzig. 1977. pap. 9.95 (ISBN 0-88489-089-9); duplicating masters 6.95 (ISBN 0-88489-129-1). St Marys.

Sharing the Christian Message: A Program Manual for Volunteer Catechists, 11th & 12th Grade. Thomas Zanzig. (Illus.). 1979. pap. 38.00 (ISBN 0-88489-110-0); spiritmasters 9.95 (ISBN 0-88489-130-5). St Marys.

Sharing the Christian Message: A Program Manual for Volunteer Catechists, Ninth Grade. Thomas Zanzig. 1977. pap. 9.95 (ISBN 0-88489-086-4); duplicating masters 5.95 (ISBN 0-88489-128-3). St Mary's.

Sharing the Eucharistic Bread: The Witness of the New Testament. Xavier Leon-Dufour. 368p. (Orig.). 1987. pap. 12.95 (ISBN 0-8091-2865-9). Paulist Pr.

Sharing the Faith: The Beliefs & Values of Catholic High School Teachers. Peter L. Benson & Michael J. Guerra. 85p. 1985. 11.40 (ISBN 0-318-18578-4); member 8.55. Natl Cath Educ.

Sharing the Faith with Your Child: From Birth to Age Six. Phyllis Chandler & Joan Burney. 96p. 1984. pap. 2.25 (ISBN 0-89243-205-5). Liguori Pubns.

Sharing the Journey. Ellen Cook. 1986. pap. 6.95 (ISBN 0-697-02208-0). Wm C Brown.

Sharing the Light of Faith: National Catechetical Directory for Catholics of the United States. (Illus.). 182p. (Orig.). 1979. pap. 6.50 (ISBN 1-55586-001-X). US Catholic.

Sharing the Light of Faith: National Catechetical Directory for Catholics of the United States. United States Catholic Conference, Conference of Catholic Bishops, Department of Education. (Illus., Orig.). 1979. pap. 6.50 (ISBN 1-55586-001-X). US Catholic.

Sharing the Old, Old Story: Educational Ministry in the Black Community. Nathan Jones. LC 81-86046. (Illus.). 104p. (Orig.). 1982. pap. 8.95 (ISBN 0-88489-144-5). St Mary's.

Sharing Treasure, Time, & Talent: A Parish Manual for Sacrificial Giving or Tithing. Joseph M. Champlin. LC 82-16178. 88p. (Orig.). 1982. pap. 4.95 (ISBN 0-8146-1277-6). Liturgical Pr.

Sharing Your Faith. Robert B. Hall. 1981. pap. 4.95 (ISBN 0-686-14949-1). Episcopal Ctr.

Sharing Your Faith. Harold Odor & Ruth Odor. (Illus.). 16p. 1985. 0.75 (ISBN 0-87239-902-8, 3302). Standard Pub.

Sharing Your Faith with a Muslim. Adiyah Akbar Abdul-Haqq. 192p. (Orig.). 1980. pap. 5.95 (ISBN 0-87123-553-6, 210553). Bethany Hse.

Sharing 1: A Manual for Volunteer Teachers. Thomas Zanzig. (Sharing Program Ser.). (Illus.). 199p. 1985. pap. 18.95 (ISBN 0-88489-163-1). St Mary's.

Sharing 4: A Manual for Volunteer Teachers. Thomas Zanzig. (Sharing Program Ser.). 200p. 1987. pap. 18.95 (ISBN 0-88489-166-6). St Mary's.

Shariyat-Ki-Sugmad. Paul Twitchell. 1971. Vol. 1 1970. kivar bdg. 7.95 (ISBN 0-914766-13-9); Vol. 2 1971. 7.95 (ISBN 0-914766-14-7). IWP Pub.

Shariyat-Ki-Sugmad, Vol. 2. Paul Twitchell. (Fr.). 189p. 1983. pap. 7.95 (ISBN 0-914766-72-4). IWP Pub.

Sharpening the Focus of the Church. Gene A. Getz. 360p. 1984. pap. 8.95 (ISBN 0-89693-393-8). Victor Bks.

Shattered Spectrum: A Survey of Contemporary Theology. Lonnie D. Kliever. LC 80-82184. 276p. (Orig.). 1981. pap. 10.95 (ISBN 0-8042-0707-0). John Knox.

Shavuot Anthology. Ed. by Philip Goodman. LC 74-25802. (Illus.). 369p. 1975. 9.95 (ISBN 0-8276-0057-7, 366). Jewish Pubns.

Shaw & Chesterton: The Metaphysical Jesters. William B. Furlong. LC 77-114616. 1970. 21.95 (ISBN 0-271-00110-0). Pa St U Pr.

Shaw & Religion. Ed. by Charles A. Berst. LC 81-956. (Shaw: the Annual of Bernard Shaw Studies: Vol 1). 264p. 1981. 25.00x (ISBN 0-271-00280-8). Pa St U Pr.

Shaw Pocket Bible Handbook. Ed. by Walter A. Elwell. 400p. 1984. 9.95 (ISBN 0-87788-683-0). Shaw Pubs.

Shcharansky Chronicles: A Complete Documentary. Ed. by Felix Roziner. 1986. 18.95 (ISBN 0-318-21399-0); pap. 11.95. Shapolsky Pubs.

Shcharansky: Hero of Our Time. Martin Gilbert. (Illus.). 512p. 1986. 24.95 (ISBN 0-670-81418-0). Viking.

Shcharansky: The Man. Felix Roziner. 1986. 16.95 (ISBN 0-318-21401-6); pap. 10.95. Shapolsky Pubs.

She Died, She Lives: In Search of Maria Orsola. George Francis. 176p. 1977. pap. 3.95 (ISBN 0-232-51392-9). Attic Pr.

She Hath Done What She Could. Pamela Brubaker. 224p. (Orig.). 1985. pap. 7.95 (ISBN 0-87178-942-6). Brethren.

She-rab Dong-bu, or Prajnya Danda: A Metrical Translation in Tibetan of a Sanskirt Ethical Work. Nagarjuna. Ed. by W. L. Campbell. LC 78-70103. Repr. of 1919 ed. 22.00 (ISBN 0-404-17354-3). AMS Pr.

She Wanted to Read: The Story of Mary Macleod Bethune. Ella K. Carruth. (Illus.). 1966. 6.75 (ISBN 0-687-38353-6). Abingdon.

Shebu'oth, 1 vol. 18.00 (ISBN 0-910218-75-7). Bennet Pub.

Shechem I: Middle Bronze IIB Pottery. Dan P. Cole. (Excavation Reports of the American Schools of Oriental Research). xiv, 203p. 1984. text ed. 30.00 (ISBN 0-89757-047-2, Dist.by Eisenbrauns). Am Sch Orient Res.

Shechita: Religious & Historical Research on the Method of Slaughter. Ed. by Michael L. Munk & Eli Munk. (Illus.). 1976. 9.95 (ISBN 0-87306-992-7). Feldheim.

Sheep among Wolves. Don R. Pegram. 1982. pap. 1.25 (ISBN 0-89265-084-2). Randall Hse.

Sheep of His Pasture: A Study of the Hebrew Noun 'AM(M) & its Semitic Cognates. Robert M. Good. LC 83-90934. (Harvard Semitic Monographs). 214p. 1984. 15.00 (ISBN 0-89130-628-5, 04 00 29). Scholars Pr GA.

She'erit Yoseph. Yoseph Katz. Ed. by Asher Siev. LC 83-50567. 350p. 1984. 15.00 (ISBN 0-87203-116-0). Hermon.

Sheikh & Disciple. M. R. Bawa Muhaiyaddeen. LC 83-1565. (Illus.). 120p. 1983. 7.95 (ISBN 0-914390-26-0). Fellowship Pr PA.

Sheila. John Benton. 192p. 1982. pap. 2.95 (ISBN 0-8007-8419-7, New Hope Bks.). Revell.

Shelf List of the Union Theological Seminary Library (New York), 10 vols. Union Theological Seminary Library. 1960. Set. lib. bdg. 990.00 (ISBN 0-8161-0499-9, Hall Library). G K Hall.

Shelter: A Work of Ministry. Bobbie Gerber. 160p. 1983. pap. 8.95 (ISBN 0-8164-2622-8, HarpR). Har-Row.

Shelter from Compassion. Ruth E. Durr. LC 56-6375. (Orig.). 1956. pap. 2.50x (ISBN 0-87574-087-1). Pendle Hill.

Shelter in the Fury: A Prophet's Stunning Picture of God. Ronald B. Allen. (Living Theology Ser.). (Orig.). 1986. pap. 6.95 (ISBN 0-88070-158-7). Multnomah.

Sheltering Branch. Marzieh Gail. 101p. 1959. 7.95 (ISBN 0-87743-022-5). G Ronald Pub.

Shem Tov: His World & His Words. Sanford Shepard. LC 76-62685. (Coleccion De Estudios Hispanicos). 1978. pap. 10.00 (ISBN 0-89729-189-1). Ediciones.

Shemirath Sabbath. Rabbi Yehoshja Y. Neuwirth. Tr. by W. Grangewood from Hebrew. Tr. of Shemirath Sabbath Kehilchathah. 360p. 1984. 11.95 (ISBN 0-87306-298-1); pap. 8.95 (ISBN 0-87306-375-9). Feldheim.

Shemuel Hanagid. 1982. 7.95 (ISBN 0-87306-220-5); pap. 5.95. Feldheim.

Shepard's Look at Psalm 23. Phillip Keller. 1976. 8.95 (ISBN 0-310-26790-0, 6780); large print 6.95 (ISBN 0-310-26797-8, 12553L). Zondervan.

Shepherd Boy. Mrs. Marvin Good. 1978. pap. 1.95 (ISBN 0-686-24054-5). Rod & Staff.

Shepherd Looks at Psalm 23. Phillip Keller. (Illus.). 160p. 1987. padded gift ed. 19.95 (ISBN 0-310-35670-9). Zondervan.

Shepherd Looks at the Good Shepherd & His Sheep. Phillip Keller. 1979. 9.95 (ISBN 0-310-26800-1, 6784); large print kivar 7.95 (ISBN 0-310-26807-9, 12568L). Zondervan.

Shepherd of My Soul. 1981. 4.95 (ISBN 0-8198-6801-9); pap. 3.50 (ISBN 0-8198-6802-7). Dghtrs St Paul.

Shepherd Psalm. F. B. Meyer. 1972. pap. 2.95 (ISBN 0-87508-351-X). Chr Lit.

Shepherd Psalm. Frederick B. Meyer. (Large Print Christian Classics Ser.). (Illus.). 1984. large print 9.95 (ISBN 0-87983-361-0). Keats.

Shepherd Under Christ. Armin W. Schuetze & Irwin J. Habezk. LC 74-81794. 1974. text ed. 14.95 (ISBN 0-8100-0046-6, 15N0351). Northwest Pub.

Shepherding God's Flock. Jay E Adams. 1979. pap. 10.95 (ISBN 0-87552-058-8). Presby & Reformed.

Shepherding God's Flock: A Handbook on Pastoral Ministry, Counseling, & Leadership. Jay E. Adams. (Jay Adams Library). 544p. 1986. pap. 14.95 (ISBN 0-310-51071-6, 12119P). Zondervan.

Shepherding God's Flock: Pastoral Leadership, Vol. III. Jay E. Adams. 1975. pap. 4.75 (ISBN 0-87552-057-X). Presby & Reformed.

Shepherding the Sheep. Benjamin S. Baker. LC 82-73531. 1983. 8.95 (ISBN 0-8054-2543-8). Broadman.

Shepherds & Bathrobes. Thomas Long. (Orig.). 1987. pap. price not set (ISBN 0-89536-869-2, 7855). CSS of Ohio.

Shepherds & Lovers. Brian Hall. LC 81-84352. 144p. (Orig.). 1982. pap. 6.95 (ISBN 0-8091-2425-4). Paulist Pr.

Shepherd's Care. William Goulooze. pap. 0.45 (ISBN 0-686-23475-8). Rose Pub MI.

Shepherds Find a King. Stephanie Caffrey & Timothy Kenslea. (Rainbow Books (Bible Story Books for Children)). 16p. 1978. pap. 1.00 (ISBN 0-8192-1232-6). Morehouse.

Shepherd's Pipe Songs from the Holy Night: A Christmas Cantata for Children's Voices or Youth Choir. Choral ed. Georg J. Gick & Marlys Swinger. LC 71-85805. (Illus.). 64p. 1969. pap. 2.50 choral ed. (ISBN 0-87486-011-3); cassette 6.00 (ISBN 0-686-66331-4). Plough.

Shepherds Speak: American Bishops Confront the Social & Moral Issues That Challenge Christians Today. Ed. by James F. Hinchey & Dennis Corrado. 240p. (Orig.). 1986. pap. 11.95 (ISBN 0-8245-0737-1). Crossroad NY.

Sherpas of Nepal Buddhist Highlanders. Christoph Von Furer-Haimendorf. 298p. 1982. 49.00x (ISBN 0-85692-020-7, Pub. by E-W Pubns England). State Mutual Bk.

Shetaroth, Hebrew Deeds of English Jews Before 1290. Myer D. Davis. 410p. 1888. text ed. 74.52x (ISBN 0-576-80111-9, Pub. by Gregg Intl Pubs England). Gregg Intl.

Shevilei Hahagadah. 1980. 5.00 (ISBN 0-686-46793-0). T Black.

Shi, Its Religion: A History of Islam in Persia & Iraq. Dwight M. Donaldson. 1976. lib. bdg. 59.95 (ISBN 0-8490-2598-2). Gordon Pr.

Shia Origin & Faith. Ed. by Kashif Al-Gita. Tr. by M. Fazal Haq from Arabic. 284p. 1984. pap. 7.50 (ISBN 0-941724-23-9). Islamic Seminary.

Shield, 5 vols. in 1. Incl. Vol. 1. Russia & the Jews. Maxim Gorky; Vol. 2. First Step. Leonid Andreyev; Vol. 3. Jewish Question in Russia. Paul Milyukov; Vol. 4. Jewish Question As a Russian Question. Dmitry Merezhovsky; Vol. 5. Jew, A Story. Michael Artzibashef. (Eng.). Repr. of 1917 ed. lib. bdg. 15.00 (ISBN 0-8371-2633-9, GOSH). Greenwood.

Shield & Hiding Place: The Religious Life of the Civil War Armies. Gardiner H. Shattuck, Jr. (Illus.). 192p. 1987. 24.95 (ISBN 0-86554-273-2, H236). Mercer Univ Pr.

Shield of Faith. Martyria Madauss. 1974. gift edition 0.95 (ISBN 3-87209-659-1). Evang Sisterhood Mary.

Shi'ism & Social Protest. Juan R. Cole & Nikki R. Keddie. LC 85-22780. 352p. 1986. text ed. 40.00 (ISBN 0-300-03550-0); pap. 12.95 (ISBN 0-300-03553-5, Y-584). Yale U Pr.

Shi'ism, Resistance & Revolution. Ed. by Milton Kramer. 350p. 1986. 39.85 (ISBN 0-8133-0453-9). Westview.

Shi'ite Anthology. Ed. by W. C. Chittick & Allamah Tabataba'i. Tr. by W. C. Chittick. 152p. 1980. 40.00x (ISBN 0-317-39150-X, Pub. by Luzac & Co Ltd); pap. 29.00x (ISBN 0-317-39151-8). State Mutual Bk.

Shi'ite Anthology. Allamah Tabataba'I. Ed. by William C. Chittick. 152p. 1986. text ed. 25.00 (ISBN 0-7103-0159-6); pap. text ed. 12.95 (ISBN 0-317-40555-1). Methuen Inc.

Shi'ite Islam. Muhammad Tabatabai. Tr. by Sayyed H. Nasr from Persian. 253p. 1979. pap. 4.95 (ISBN 0-941722-19-8). Book-Dist-Ctr.

Shi'ite Religion: A History of Islam in Persia & Irak. Dwight M. Donaldson. LC 80-1933. 49.50 (ISBN 0-404-18959-8). AMS Pr.

Shikwa & Jawab-I-Shikwa (Answer) Iqbal's Dialogue with Allah. Mohammed Iqbal. Tr. by Krushwant Singh from Urdu. 96p. (Orig.). 1981. pap. 7.95x (ISBN 0-19-561324-4). Oxford U Pr.

Shimon Peres: A Biography. Matti Golan. Tr. by Ina Friedman. LC 82-7354. (Hebrew., Illus.). 275p. 1982. 25.00 (ISBN 0-312-71736-9). St Martin.

Shingon Buddhism. Minoru Kiyota. LC 77-27894. 1978. text ed. 9.95x (ISBN 0-914910-09-4); pap. 7.95x (ISBN 0-914910-10-8). Buddhist Bks.

Shining Light. Ralph W. Neighbour, Sr. 1986. pap. 5.95 (ISBN 0-937931-03-9). Global TN.

Shining Moments: Stories for Latter-day Saint Children. Lucile C. Reading. LC 85-1655. 158p. 1985. 6.95 (ISBN 0-87747-687-X). Deseret Bk.

Shinran: His Life & Thought. Norihiko Kikumura. LC 70-172538. 192p. 1972. 9.95 (ISBN 0-685-65548-2). Nembutsu Pr.

Shinran's Gospel of Pure Grace. Alfred Bloom. LC 64-8757. (Association for Asian Studies Monograph: No. 20). 97p. 1965. pap. 4.50x (ISBN 0-8165-0405-9). U of Ariz Pr.

Shinto, 2 vols. J. W. Mason. 200.00 (ISBN 0-8490-1050-0). Gordon Pr.

Shinto: Japan's Spiritual Roots. Stuart D. Picken. LC 79-91520. (Illus.). 80p. 1980. 19.95 (ISBN 0-87011-410-7). Kodansha.

Shinto: The Ancient Religion of Japan. W. G. Ashton. 83p. 1921. 0.95 (ISBN 0-317-40426-1). Open Court.

Shinto: The Kami Way. Sokyo Ono. LC 61-14033. 1962. 8.50 (ISBN 0-8048-0525-3). C E Tuttle.

Shinto, the Way of Japan. Floyd H. Ross. LC 83-12970. (Illus.). xvii, 187p. 1983. Repr. of 1965 ed. lib. bdg. 35.00x (ISBN 0-313-24240-2, RSHI). Greenwood.

Shinto, the Way of the Gods. W. G. Aston. lib. bdg. 75.00 (ISBN 0-87968-076-8). Krishna Pr.

Shiny New Lives. Wesley T. Runk. 108p. (Orig.). 1975. pap. 4.50 (ISBN 0-89536-224-4, 1938). CSS of Ohio.

Shinzo: Hachiman Imagery & Its Development. Christine G. Kanda. (Harvard East Asian Monographs: No. 119). 1985. text ed. 30.00x (ISBN 0-674-80650-6, Pub. by Coun East Asian Stud). Harvard U Pr.

Shiokari Pass. Ayako Muira. 1968. 4.95 (ISBN 9971-972-23-9). OMF Bks.

Ships, Saints, & Mariners: A Maritime Encyclopedia of Mormon Migration, 1830-1890. Conway B. Sonne. 256p. 1987. 19.50x (ISBN 0-87480-270-9). U of Utah Pr.

Shir Hashirim-Song of Songs. Meir Zlotowitz. (Art Scroll Tanach Ser.). 224p. 1977. 11.95 (ISBN 0-89906-008-0); pap. 8.95 (ISBN 0-89906-009-9). Mesorah Pubns.

Shirkutu of Babylonian Deities. Raymond P. Dougherty. LC 78-63548. (Yale Oriental Ser. Researches: 5, Pt. 2). Repr. of 1923 ed. 25.00 (ISBN 0-404-60295-9). AMS Pr.

Shirley Jackson Case & the Chicago School: The Socio-Historical Method. William J. Hynes. Ed. by Kent Richards. LC 81-8973. (Society of Biblical Literature Biblical Scholarship in North America Ser.). 1981. pap. text ed. 15.00 (ISBN 0-89130-510-6, 06-11-05). Scholars Pr GA.

Shirot Bialik: A New & Annotated Translation of Chaim Nachman Bialik's Epic Poems. Steven L. Jacobs. (Hebraica-Judaica Bookshelf Ser.). Date not set. price not set (ISBN 0-933771-03-7). Alpha Pub Co.

Shiur Qomah: Liturgy & Theurgy in Pre-Kabbalistic Jewish Mysticism. Martin S. Cohen. 300p. (Orig.). 1983. lib. bdg. 27.50 (ISBN 0-8191-3272-1). U Pr of Amer.

Shiva & Dionysus. Alain Danielou. 250p. (Orig.). 1984. pap. 8.95 (ISBN 0-89281-057-2). Inner Tradit.

Shivering Babe, Victorious Lord: The Nativity in Poetry & Art. Linda C. Sledge. LC 81-9728. pap. 49.80 (ISBN 0-317-30162-4, 2025344). Bks Demand UMI.

Shiv'im: Essays & Studies in Honor of Ira Eisenstein. Ed. by R. A. Brauner. 20.00x (ISBN 0-87068-442-6). Ktav.

Shmittah: What It's All About. Eliezer Gevirtz. (Orig.). 1987. write for info. Torah Umesorah.

Shmueli Family, 2 bks. Incl. Bk. 1. Cartoon Adventure. 5.00x (ISBN 0-685-55046-X, 405310); Bk. 2. More Cartoon Adventures. 5.00x (ISBN 0-685-55047-8, 405311). 1975. 6.00. UAHC.

Sho King, or the Book of Historical Documents, 4 vols, Vol. 2. Tr. by James Legge. (Chinese Classics Ser.). (Chinese & Eng.). 1983. Repr. of 1893 ed. 25.00x (ISBN 0-89986-354-X); Set. 95.00x (ISBN 0-89986-352-3). Oriental Bk Store.

Shobogenzo: Zen Essays by Dogen. Dogen. Tr. by Thomas Cleary. LC 85-20979. 136p. 1986. 14.00x (ISBN 0-8248-1014-7). UH Pr.

Shoemakes: God's Helpers. Elsie Rives. LC 86-4148. (Meet the Missionary Ser.). 1986. pap. 5.50 (ISBN 0-8054-4328-2). Broadman.

Shoghi Effendi: Recollections. Ugo Giachery. (Illus.). 248p. 1973. 16.95 (ISBN 0-85398-050-0). G Ronald Pub.

Sholem Aleykhem: Person, Persona, Presence. Dan Miron. LC 73-161969. (Uriel Weinreich Memorial Lecture Ser.: No.1). 45p. 1972. pap. 2.00 (ISBN 0-914512-02-1). Yivo Inst.

Sholom Aleichem: A Non-Critical Introduction. Sol Gittleman. (De Proprietatibus Litterarum Ser. Didactica: No. 3). 1974. pap. text ed. 13.60x (ISBN 90-2792-606-9). Mouton.

Shop Drawings of Shaker Furniture & Woodenware, Vol. 2. Ejner Handberg. LC 73-83797. 1975. pap. 5.95 (ISBN 0-912944-29-3). Berkshire Traveller.

Shopping for a God. John Allan. 218p. 1987. pap. price not set (ISBN 0-8010-0212-5). Baker Bk.

Shores of Darkness. Edward B. Hungerford. 10.75 (ISBN 0-8446-2285-0). Peter Smith.

Short Account of Early Muslim Architecture. K. Creswell. 1968. 18.00x (ISBN 0-86685-010-4). Intl Bk Ctr.

Short Baptist Manual of Polity & Practice. Norman H. Maring & Winthrop S. Hudson. 1965. pap. 4.95 (ISBN 0-8170-0338-X). Judson.

Short Bible Reference System. Ed. by R. G. Bratcher. 148p. 1961. 4.80x (ISBN 0-8267-0030-6, 08506, Pub. by United Bible). Am Bible.

Short Commentary on Kant's "Critique of Pure Reason". A. C. Ewing. viii, 278p. Date not set. pap. text ed. 16.00 (ISBN 0-226-22779-0, Midway Reprint). U of Chicago Pr.

Short Cut to Divine Love. Martial Lekeux. LC 61-11203. 332p. 1961. pap. 2.50 (ISBN 0-8199-0131-8, L38796). Franciscan Herald.

Short Dictionary of the New Testament. Albert Rouet. (Illus.). 128p. 1982. pap. 6.95 (ISBN 0-8091-2400-9). Paulist Pr.

Short Dramas for the Church. Dorcas D. Shaner. 224p. 1980. pap. 10.95 (ISBN -08170-0883-7). Judson.

Short Grammar of Biblical Aramaic. rev. ed. Alger F. Johns. (Andrews University Monographs, Studies in Religion: Vol. 1). xii, 108p. 1972. pap. text ed. 7.95 (ISBN 0-943872-01-4). Andrews Univ Pr.

Short Guide to Classical Mythology. G. M. Kirkwood. 1960. pap. text ed. 10.95 (ISBN 0-03-008865-8, HoltC). H Holt & Co.

Short History of Christian Doctrine: From the First Century to the Present. rev American ed. Bernhard Lohse. Tr. by F. Ernest Stoeffer from Ger. LC 66-21732. 320p. 1978. pap. 9.95 (ISBN 0-8006-1341-4, 1-1341). Fortress.

Short History of Christian Missions. Frank W. Patterson. 176p. 1985. pap. 15.95 (ISBN 0-311-72663-1). Casa Bautista.

Short History of Christian Theophagy. Preserved Smith. 223p. 1922. 16.95 (ISBN 0-87548-241-4). Open Court.

Short History of Christian Thought. Linwood Urban. LC 85-10654. 1986. text ed. 29.95x (ISBN 0-19-503716-2); pap. text ed. 10.95x (ISBN 0-19-503717-0). Oxford U Pr.

Short History of Christianity. Ed. by Archibald G. Baker. LC 40-34185. (Midway Reprints Ser.). 1983. Repr. of 1940 ed. 11.00x (ISBN 0-226-03527-1). U of Chicago Pr.

Short History of Christianity. Martin E. Marty. LC 80-8042. 384p. 1980. pap. 9.95 (ISBN 0-8006-1427-5, 1-1427). Fortress.

Short History of Confucian Philosophy. Wu-Chi Liu. LC 78-20480. 1983. Repr. of 1955 ed. 20.50 (ISBN 0-88355-857-2). Hyperion Conn.

Short History of Ilum1 Usul. Muhhammad B. Sadr. Tr. by M. A. Ansari from Arabic. 130p. 1985. pap. 5.00 (ISBN 0-941724-37-9). Islamic Seminary.

Short History of Jewish Literature. Israel Abrahams. 1906. Repr. 20.00 (ISBN 0-8274-3400-6). R West.

Short History of Religion in America. Lester B. Scherer. (Illus.). 145p. (Orig.). 1980. pap. 8,95x (ISBN 0-89894-011-7). Advocate Pub Group.

Short History of Religions. facsimile ed. Ernest E. Kellett. LC 71-156671. (Essay Index Reprint Ser). Repr. of 1934 ed. 30.00 (ISBN 0-8369-2281-6). Ayer Co Pubs.

Short History of Syriac Christianity to the Rise of Islam. W. Stewart McCullough. LC 80-29297. (Scholars Press Polebridge Bks.). 1981. 21.95 (ISBN 0-89130-454-1, 00-03-04). Scholars Pr GA.

Short History of Syriac Literature. William Wright. LC 78-14330. 1978. Repr. of 1894 ed. lib. bdg. 42.50 (ISBN 0-8414-9709-5). Folcroft.

Short History of the Baptists. Henry C. Vedder. 12.95 (ISBN 0-8170-0162-X). Judson.

Short History of the Catholic Church. Derek J. Holmes & Bernard W. Bickers. LC 83-63193. 315p. 1984. pap. 8.95 (ISBN 0-8091-2623-0). Paulist Pr.

Short History of the Catholic Church. Denis Meadows. 1959. 12.95 (ISBN 0-8159-6813-2). Devin.

Short History of the Catholic Church. Jose Orlandis. 163p. 1985. pap. 7.50 (ISBN 0-912414-43-X). Lumen Christi.

Short History of the Catholic Church. Jose Orlandis. Tr. by Michael Adams from Span. Tr. of Historia breve del Cristianismo. 163p. (Orig.). 1985. pap. 7.95 (ISBN 0-906127-86-6, Pub. by Four Courts Pr Ireland). Scepter Pubs.

Short History of the Early Church. Harry R. Boer. LC 75-25742. pap. 6.95 (ISBN 0-8028-1339-9). Eerdmans.

Short History of the Georgian Church. Platon Ioseliani. 208p. 1983. pap. 6.00 (ISBN 0-317-30451-8). Holy Trinity.

Short History of the Hebrews: From the Patriarchs to Herod the Great. 3rd ed. B. K. Rattey. (Illus.). 1976. pap. 11.50x (ISBN 0-19-832121-X). Oxford U Pr.

Short History of the Interpretation of the Bible. 2nd, rev. & enlarged ed. Robert M. Grant & David Tracy. LC 83-18485. 224p. 1984. pap. 10.95 (ISBN 0-8006-1762-2, 1-1762). Fortress.

Short History of the Jewish People. rev. ed. Cecil Roth. 1969. 14.95; pap. 6.95 (ISBN 0-87677-183-5). Hartmore.

Short History of the Jews in the United States. Hyman Grinstein. 208p. 1980. 20.00 (ISBN 0-900689-50-1). Soncino Pr.

Short History of the Papacy in the Middle Ages. Walter Ullmann. 1974. pap. 16.95x (ISBN 0-416-74970-4, NO. 2562). Methuen Inc.

Short History of the Twelve Buddhist Sects. Tr. by Bunyiu Nanjio from Japanese. (Studies in Japanese History & Civilization). 1979. Repr. of 1886 ed. 19.75 (ISBN 0-89093-252-2). U Pubns Amer.

Short History of the Twelve Japanese Buddhist Sects. Compiled by Bunyiu Nanjio. LC 78-70104. Repr. of 1886 ed. 23.00 (ISBN 0-404-17355-1). AMS Pr.

Short History of the Western Liturgy. 2nd ed. Theodor Klauser. Tr. by John Halliburton from Ger. 1979. pap. text ed. 10.95x (ISBN 0-19-213223-7). Oxford U Pr.

Short Introduction to the Literature of the Bible. Richard G. Moulton. 1978. Repr. of 1900 ed. lib. bdg. 25.00 (ISBN 0-8495-3729-0). Arden Lib.

Short Introduction to the Literature of the Bible. Richard G. Moulton. 1901. 25.00 (ISBN 0-8274-3404-9). R West.

Short Life of Christ. Everett Harrison. (Highlights in the Life of Christ). 1968. pap. 8.95 (ISBN 0-8028-1824-2). Eerdmans.

Short Life of Kierkegaard. Walter Lowrie. 1942. pap. 9.50x (ISBN 0-691-01957-6). Princeton U Pr.

Short Life of the Holy Mother. Swami Pavitrananandа. pap. 1.75 (ISBN 0-87481-122-8). Vedanta Pr.

Short Meditations, 3 vols. J. G. Bellett. pap. 13.95 set (ISBN 0-88172-003-8); pap. 4.95 ea. Believers Bkshelf.

Short Papers on Scriptural Subjects, 2 vols. C. H. MacKintosh. Set. 15.95 (ISBN 0-88172-115-8). Believers Bkshelf.

Short Pathwaye to the Ryghte & True Understanding of the Holye & Sacred Scriptures. Ulrich Zwingli. Tr. by J. Veron. LC 77-7443. (English Experience Ser.: No. 901). 1977. Repr. of 1550 ed. lib. bdg. 15.00 (ISBN 90-221-0901-1). Walter J Johnson.

Short Prajnaparamita Texts. Edward Conze. 217p. 1973. 35.00x (ISBN 0-317-39153-4, Pub. by Luzac & Co Ltd). State Mutual Bk.

Short Stops with the Lord. Len Kageler. 104p. 1984. 5.95 (ISBN 0-87509-348-5). Chr Pubns.

Short Survey of the Literature of Rabbinical & Medieval Judaism. William O. Oesterley. LC 72-82352. 328p. 1973. Repr. of 1920 ed. lib. bdg. 24.50 (ISBN 0-8337-3944-1). B Franklin.

Short Syntax of New Testament Greek. 5th ed. Henry P. Nunn. 1931. text ed. 10.95 (ISBN 0-521-09941-2). Cambridge U Pr.

Short Talks for Special Occasions, Bk. 1. Mildred Dennis. 64p. 1987. pap. 2.95 (ISBN 0-87403-069-2, 2880). Standard Pub.

Short Talks for Special Occasions, Bk. 2. Mildred Dennis. 64p. 1987. pap. 2.95 (ISBN 0-87403-070-6, 2881). Standard Pub.

Short Talks on Masonry. Joseph F. Newton. 255p. 1979. Repr. of 1969 ed. text ed. 6.95 (ISBN 0-88053-036-7, M-85). Macoy Pub.

Short Titles of Books Relating to or Illustrating the History & Practice of Psalmody in the U. S., 1620-1820. James Warrington. LC 77-178095. (American Classics in History & Social Science Ser.: No. 218). 102p. 1972. Repr. of 1898 ed. lib. bdg. 19.00 (ISBN 0-8337-5357-6). B Franklin.

Short Treatise of Lawfull & Unlawfull Recreations. Dudley Fenner. LC 77-6740. (English Experience Ser.: No. 870). 1977. Repr. of 1590 ed. lib. bdg. 3.50 (ISBN 90-221-0870-8). Walter J Johnson.

Short View of the Immorality, & Profaneness of the English Stage. 3rd ed. Jeremy Collier. LC 74-3401. Repr. of 1698 ed. 21.50 (ISBN 0-404-01619-7). AMS Pr.

Short View of the Profaneness & Immorality of the English Stage. Jeremy Collier. 1969. Repr. of 1730 ed. cancelled (ISBN 3-4870-2589-2). Adlers Foreign Bks.

Shortened Path: Autobiography of a Western Yogi. abr. ed. Swami Kriyananda. 240p. 1980. pap. 6.95 (ISBN 0-916124-19-3). Dawn Pubns CA.

Shorter Books of the Apochrypha: Cambridge Bible Commentary on the New English Bible. J. C. Dancy. LC 72-76358. (Old Testament Ser.). 224p. (Orig.). 1972. pap. 9.95 (ISBN 0-521-09729-0). Cambridge U Pr.

Shorter Cambridge Medieval History, 2 vols. Ed. by C. W. Previte-Orton. Incl. Vol. 1. The Later Roman Empire to the Twelfth Century. (Illus.). 644p. 74.50 (ISBN 0-521-20962-5); pap. 23.95 (ISBN 0-521-09976-5); Vol. 2. The Twelfth Century to the Renaissance. (Illus.). 558p. 74.50 (ISBN 0-521-20963-3); pap. 23.95 (ISBN 0-521-09977-3). (Medieval History Ser). 1975. pap. 18.95 ea. Set. 135.00 (ISBN 0-521-05993-3); Set. pap. 39.50 (ISBN 0-521-08758-9). Cambridge U Pr.

Shorter Catechism: A Study Manual, 2 vols. G. I. Williamson. Vol. 1. pap. 4.50 (ISBN 0-87552-539-3); Vol. 2. pap. 4.50 (ISBN 0-87552-540-7). Presby & Reformed.

Shorter Catechism Explained from Scripture. Thomas Vincent. (Puritan Paperbacks). 282p. (Orig.). 1980. pap. 4.95 (ISBN 0-85151-314-X). Banner of Truth.

Shorter Catechism of the Orthodox Church. pap. 0.50 (ISBN 0-686-05664-7). Eastern Orthodox.

Shorter Catechism with Scripture Proofs. Westminster Assembly. 0.75 (ISBN 0-85151-265-8). Banner of Truth.

Shorter Encyclopaedia of Islam. Ed. by H. A. Gibb & J. H. Kramers. (Illus.). 678p. 1957. 85.00x (ISBN 0-8014-0150-X). Cornell U Pr.

Shorter Lexicon of the Greek New Testament. 2nd, rev. ed. Frederick W. Danker. Rev. by F. Wilbur Gingrich. LC 82-10933. 256p. 1983. lib. bdg. 22.00x (ISBN 0-226-13613-2). U of Chicago Pr.

Shorter Lexicon of the Greek New Testament. 2nd ed. F. Wilbur Gingrich. 256p. 1983. 22.00 (ISBN 0-310-25030-7, 18075). Zondervan.

Shorter Life of Christ. Donald Guthrie. LC 71-120039. (Contemporary Evangelical Perspectives Ser). 1970. kivar 8.95 (ISBN 0-310-25441-8, 6500P). Zondervan.

Shoshinge: The Heart of Shin Buddhism. Alred Bloom. Tr. by T. Nagatani & Ruth Tabrah. 108p. (Orig.). 1986. pap. 6.95 (ISBN 0-938474-06-5). Buddhist Study.

Should a Christian Be a Mason? E. M. Storms. LC 80-83598. (Orig.). 1980. pap. text ed. 2.50 (ISBN 0-932050-08-5). New Puritan.

Should Christians Attend Movies? Gordon Lindsay. 0.95 (ISBN 0-89985-007-3). Christ Nations.

Should Evolution Be Taught? John N. Moore. 1977. pap. 1.00 (ISBN 0-89051-043-1). Master Bks.

Should I Keep My Baby? Martha Zimmerman. 112p. (Orig.). 1983. pap. 3.95 (ISBN 0-87123-578-1, 210578). Bethany Hse.

Should I Tithe? Dick Benjamin. 1977. pap. 1.75 (ISBN 0-911739-11-4). Abbott Loop.

Should War Be Eliminated? Philosophical & Theological Investigations. Stanley Hauerwas. LC 84-60236. (Pere Marquette Lecture Ser.). 75p. 1984. 7.95 (ISBN 0-87462-539-4). Marquette.

Should You Become a Brother? Leo Kirby. 1979. pap. 1.95 (ISBN 0-89243-102-4). Liguori Pubns.

Should You Become a Priest? Terence Tierney. 64p. (Orig.). (YA) 1975. pap. 1.50 (ISBN 0-89243-020-6, 29530). Liguori Pubns.

Should You Become a Sister? Marcella Holloway. 1978. pap. 1.50 (ISBN 0-89243-073-7, 29553). Liguori Pubns.

Shout It from the Housetops: The Story of the Founder of the Christian Broadcasting Network. Pat Robertson & Jamie Buckingham. LC 72-76591. 248p. 1972. pap. 3.95 (ISBN 0-88270-097-9). Bridge Pub.

Shoutin' on the Hills. Nona Freeman. LC 85-22521. (Illus.). 320p. (Orig.). 1985. pap. 6.95 (ISBN 0-912315-94-6). Word Aflame.

Show Me, Lord. Evelyn Ramsey. 178p. 1982. pap. 4.95 (ISBN 0-8341-0781-3). Beacon Hill.

Showdown in the Middle East. G. Vandeman. (Stories That Win Ser.). pap. 1.25 (ISBN 0-8163-0392-4). Pacific Pr Pub Assn.

Showdown with the Devil. Kenneth Hagin, Jr. 1983. pap. 0.50 mini bk. (ISBN 0-89276-715-4). Hagin Ministries.

Showers of Blessings: Hymns for the Shower. Ed. by Nat Wofford. 16p. 1986. pap. 4.95 (ISBN 0-942820-18-5). Steam Pr MA.

Showing the Spirit: A Theological Exposition of 1 Corinthians 12-14. D. A. Carson. 256p. 1987. pap. 12.95 (ISBN 0-8010-2521-4). Baker Bk.

Shpeter: Book One. Meir U. Gottesman. (Judaica Youth Ser.). (Illus.). 1981. 5.95 (ISBN 0-910818-35-5); pap. 4.95 (ISBN 0-910818-36-3). Judaica Pr.

Shpeter: Book Two. Meir U. Gottesman. (Judaica Youth Ser.). (Illus.). 1981. 5.95 (ISBN 0-910818-39-8); pap. 4.95 (ISBN 0-910818-40-1). Judaica Pr.

Shraman Mahavir: His Life & Teachings. Yuvacharya Shri Mahaprajna. 334p. 1980. 12.00 (ISBN 0-88065-213-6, Pub. by Messers Today & Tomorows Printers & Publishers India). Scholarly Pubns.

Shree Guru Gita. Tr. by Swami Muktananda from Sanskrit. LC 81-51183. 128p. (Orig.). 1981. pap. 3.95 (ISBN 0-914602-73-X). SYDA Found.

Shree Rudram: Namakam & Chamakam. 96p. (Orig.). 1978. pap. 3.50 (ISBN 0-914602-64-0). SYDA Found.

Shrichakrasambhara Tantra: A Buddhist Tantra. Tr. by Kazi Dawa-Samdup from Tibetan. 255p. 1984. Repr. of 1919 ed. lib. bdg. 22.50x (ISBN 0-88181-000-2). Canon Pubns.

Shrine of St. Peter & the Vatican Excavations. Jocelyn M. Toynbee. LC 78-63482. Repr. of 1956 ed. 32.00 (ISBN 0-404-16548-6). AMS Pr.

Shroud of Turin: The Burial Cloth of Jesus Christ. Ian Wilson. LC 77-81551. (Illus.). 1979. pap. 5.50 (ISBN 0-385-15042-3, Im). Doubleday.

Shtetl Book. rev ed. Diane K. Roskies & David G Roskies. pap. 9.95x (ISBN 0-87068-455-8). Ktav.

Shtetl Memoirs: Jewish Life in Galicia under the Austro-Hungarian Empire & in the Polish Republic, 1898-1939. Joachim Schoenfeld. 400p. 1985. text ed. 17.50x (ISBN 0-88125-075-9). Ktav.

Shtudies Vegn Yidisher Folksshafung. Judah L. Cahan. Ed. by Weinreich. 1952. 5.00 (ISBN 0-914512-05-6). Yivo Inst.

Shubuhat Haul al-Islam. Muhammad Qutb. (Arabic.). 203p. (Orig.). 1977. pap. 4.75x (ISBN 0-939830-15-9, Pub. by IIFSO Kuwait). New Era Pubns MI.

Shuramana Mantra: A Commentary, Vol. IV. Tripitaka Master Hua. Tr. by Buddhist Text Translation Society. 140p. (Orig.). pap. 6.50 (ISBN 0-88139-022-4). Buddhist Text.

Shurangama Mantra: A Commentary, Vol. III. Tripitaka Master Hua. Tr. by Buddhist Text Translation Society. (Illus.). 156p. (Orig.). 1982. pap. 6.50 (ISBN 0-917512-36-7). Buddhist Text.

Shurangama Mantra: A Commentary, Vol. I. Tripitaka Master Hua. Tr. by Buddhist Text Translation Society. (Illus.). 296p. (Orig.). 1981. pap. 8.50 (ISBN 0-917512-69-3). Buddhist Text.

Shurangama Mantra: A Commentary, Vol. II. Tripitaka Master Hua. Tr. by Buddhist Text Translation Society. (Illus.). 210p. (Orig.). 1982. pap. 7.50 (ISBN 0-917512-82-0). Buddhist Text.

Shurangama Sutra, Vol. 1. Commentary by Tripitaka Master Hua. Tr. by Buddhist Text Translation Society. (Illus.). 289p. (Orig.). 1977. pap. 9.00 (ISBN 0-917512-17-0). Buddhist Text.

Shurangama Sutra, Vol. 2. Commentary by Tripitaka Master Hua. Tr. by Buddhist Text Translation Society. (Illus.). 212p. (Orig.). 1979. pap. 8.00 (ISBN 0-917512-25-1). Buddhist Text.

Shurangama Sutra, Vol. 3. Commentary by Tripitaka Master Hua. Tr. by Buddhist Text Translation Society. (Illus.). 240p. (Orig.). 1980. pap. 8.50 (ISBN 0-917512-94-4). Buddhist Text.

Shurangama Sutra, Vol. 4. Commentary by Tripitaka Master Hua. Tr. by Buddhist Text Translation Society. (Illus.). 285p. (Orig.). 1980. pap. 8.50 (ISBN 0-917512-90-1). Buddhist Text.

Shurangama Sutra, Vol. 5. Commentary by Tripitaka Master Hua. Tr. by Buddhist Text Translation Society. (Illus.). 250p. (Orig.). 1980. pap. 8.50 (ISBN 0-917512-91-X). Buddhist Text.

Shurangama Sutra, Vol. 6. Commentary by Tripitaka Master Hua. Tr. by Buddhist Text Translation Society. (Illus.). 220p. (Orig.). 1981. pap. 8.50 (ISBN 0-917512-37-5). Buddhist Text.

Shurangama Sutra, Vol. 7. Tripitaka Master Hua. Tr. by Buddhist Text Translation Society. (Illus.). 270p. (Orig.). 1982. pap. 8.50 (ISBN 0-917512-97-9). Buddhist Text.

Shylock: The History of a Character. Hermann Sinsheimer. LC 63-23188. (Illus.). Repr. of 1947 ed. 15.00 (ISBN 0-405-08977-5, Pub. by Blom). Ayer Co Pubs.

Si Amas a Tu Adolescente. Ross Campbell. Tr. by Juan S. Araujo from Eng. Tr. of How To Really Love Your Teenager. (Span.). 144p. 1986. pap. 3.95 (ISBN 0-88113-030-3). Edit Betania.

Si-Yu-Ki, Buddhist Records of th Western World, 2 vol. in 1. Hiuen Tsiang. Tr. by Samuel Beal. 618p. Repr. of 1884 ed. 38.50x (ISBN 0-89644-454-6, Pub. by Chinese Matl Ctr). Coronet Bks.

Siberian Stories. S. Sartakov. 607p. 1979. 9.45 (ISBN 0-8285-1621-9, Pub. by Progress Pubs USSR). Imported Pubns.

Sibton Abbey Cartularies & Charters: II. Ed. by Philippa Brown. (Suffolk Charters VIII). 192p. 1986. 28.95 (ISBN 0-85115-443-3, Pub. by Boydell & Brewer). Longwood Pub Group.

Sibylline Oracles. new ed. Tr. by Milton S. Terry from Gr. LC 72-176141. Repr. of 1899 ed. 21.45 (ISBN 0-404-06362-4). AMS Pr.

Sibyls & Seers. Edwyn R. Bevan. 1979. Repr. of 1928 ed. lib. bdg. 39.50 (ISBN 0-8495-0510-0). Arden Lib.

Sic et Non: A Critical Edition, 7 fascicles. P. Abailard. Ed. by Blanche Boyer & Richard McKeon. Incl. Fascicle 1. (ISBN 0-226-00058-3);;; Fascicle 4. (ISBN 0-226-00061-3); Fascicle 5. (ISBN 0-226-00062-1); (ISBN 0-226-00064-8);. LC 74-7567. 1978. pap. text ed. 16.00x ea. O. P.; fascicles 1-7 complete in one clothbound vol. 130.00x (ISBN 0-226-00066-4). U of Chicago Pr.

Sicily: The Fabulous Island. Edith L. Hough. (Illus.). 1949. 4.00 (ISBN 0-8338-0027-2). M Jones.

Sickness & Healing. Klaus Seybold & Ulrich B. Mueller. Tr. by Douglas W. Stott from Ger. LC 81-3663. (Biblical Encounter Ser.). 208p. (Orig.). 1981. pap. 9.95 (ISBN 0-687-38444-3). Abingdon.

Sickness & Sectarianism: Exploratory Studies in Medical & Religious Sectarianism. Ed. by Kenneth Jones. 517p. 1985. text ed. 28.95x (ISBN 0-566-00662-6). Gower Pub Co.

Sickness Unto Death: A Christian Psychological Exposition for Upbuilding & Awakening. Soren Kierkegaard. Tr. by Howard V. Hong & Edna H. Hong. LC 79-3218. (Kierkegaard's Writings Ser.: Vol. XIX). 216p. 1980. 27.50x (ISBN 0-691-07247-7); pap. 9.50x (ISBN 0-691-02028-0). Princeton U Pr.

Siddur Leshabbat Veyom Tov: Prayer Book for Sabbath & Festivals with Torah Readings. Philip Birnbaum. 724p. 1950. 14.50 (ISBN 0-88482-062-9). Hebrew Pub.

Siddur Program, II to Hebrew & Heritage. Pearl Tarnor & Norman Tarnor. (Illus.). 128p. 1982. pap. text ed. 3.95x (ISBN 0-87441-330-3). Behrman.

Siddur Program III to Hebrew & Heritage. Pearl Tarnor & Norman Tarnor. (Illus.). 128p. 1983. pap. text ed. 3.95x (ISBN 0-87441-359-1). Behrman.

Siddur: Sabbath Eve Service. Nosson Scherman. 1980. 10.95 (ISBN 0-686-68764-7); pap. 7.95 (ISBN 0-686-68765-5). Mesorah Pubns.

Side Trips. Keith Knoche. (FRD Ser.). 1985. pap. 4.95 (ISBN 0-8163-0596-X). Pacific Pr Pub Assn.

Sidelights on the Catholic Revival. facs. ed. Francis J. Sheed. LC 74-99649. (Essay Index Reprint Ser). 1940. 18.00 (ISBN 0-8369-2176-3). Ayer Co Pubs.

Sidelong Glance: Politics, Conflict & the Church. Richard Holloway. LC 86-13473. 86p. 1986. pap. 6.95 (ISBN 0-936384-40-9). Cowley Pubns.

Sidewalk Contemplatives: A Spirituality for Concerned Christians. Susan B. Anthony. 160p. (Orig.). 1987. pap. 8.95 (ISBN 0-8245-0795-9). Crossroad NY.

Sidewalk Psalms... & Some from Country Lanes. Wilma Burton. LC 79-92015. 119p. 1980. 8.95 (ISBN 0-89107-165-2). Good News.

Sidgwick's Ethics & Victorian Moral Philosophy. J. B. Schneewind. 1977. 49.95x (ISBN 0-19-824552-1). Oxford U Pr.

Sidonius Apollinaris & His Age. Courtenay E. Stevens. LC 78-21112. 1979. Repr. of 1933 ed. lib. bdg. 24.75x (ISBN 0-313-20850-6, STSA). Greenwood.

Siecus Circle. Claire Chambers. LC 75-41650. 1977. pap. 6.95 (ISBN 0-88279-119-2). Western Islands.

Siege. Thurman Petty, Jr. (Orion Ser.). 144p. 1980. pap. 3.95 (ISBN 0-8127-0302-2). Review & Herald.

Siege: The Saga of Israel & Zionism. Conor C. O'Brien. 800p. 1986. 24.95 (ISBN 0-671-60044-3). S&S.

Sienese Altarpieces 1215-1460 Form, Content, Function: Vol. I 1215-1344. Henk Van Os. Contrib. by Kees Van Der Ploeg. (Mediaevalia Groningana IV: Bk. IV). (Illus.). 163p. 1984. 28.00x (ISBN 90-6088-083-8, Pub. by Boumas Boekhuis Netherlands). Benjamins North AM.

Siete Impedimentos Para Recibir Sanidad. Kenneth Hagin, Jr. (Span.). 1983. pap. 0.50 mini bk. (ISBN 0-89276-175-X). Hagin Ministries.

Siete Pasos Para Recibir El Espiritu Santo. 2nd ed. Kenneth E. Hagin. 1983. pap. 1.00 (ISBN 0-89276-103-2). Hagin Ministries.

Sievers' Law & the Evidence of the Rigveda. Franklin E. Horowitz. LC 73-81807. (Janua Linguarum, Ser. Practica: No. 216). 74p. (Orig.). 1974. pap. text ed. 18.00x (ISBN 90-2792-706-5). Mouton.

Sifra: The Rabbinic Commentary on Leviticus. Tr. by Jacob Neusner & Roger Brooks. (Brown Judaic Studies). 1985. 22.95 (ISBN 0-89130-913-6, 14-01-02); pap. 18.25 (ISBN 0-89130-914-4). Scholars Pr Ga.

Sifre: A Tannaitic Commentary on the Book of Deuteronomy. Tr. & Reuven Hammer. LC 85-29556. (Yale Judaica Ser.: No. 24). 560p. 1986. text ed. 45.00x (ISBN 0-300-03345-1). Yale U Pr.

Sifre on Deuteronomy. Louis Finkelstein. 1969. 25.00x (ISBN 0-685-31422-7, Pub. by Jewish Theol Seminary). Ktav.

Sifre to Numbers, Part I. Jacob Neuser. (Brown Judaic Studies). 1986. text ed. 27.95 (ISBN 1-55540-008-6, 14-01-18); pap. 22.95 (ISBN 1-55540-009-4). Scholars Pr GA.

Sifre to Numbers, Part II. Jacob Neuser. (Brown Judaic Studies). 1986. text ed. 24.95 (ISBN 1-55540-010-8, 14-01-19); pap. 19.95 (ISBN 1-55540-011-6). Scholars Pr GA.

Sigena: Romanesque Paintings in Spain & the Winchester Bible Artists. Walter Oakeshott. (Illus.). 1972. 49.00x (ISBN 0-19-921006-3). Oxford U Pr.

Sighing for Eden: Sin, Evil & the Christian Faith. William H. Willimon. 208p. 1985. pap. 8.95 (ISBN 0-687-38447-8). Abingdon.

Sighting. Luci Shaw. LC 81-9342. (Wheaton Literary Ser.). (Illus.). 95p. 1981. pap. 5.95 (ISBN 0-87788-768-3). Shaw Pubs.

Sign & Glory. cancelled (ISBN 0-686-76258-4). Feldheim.

Sign in the Straw. Richard C. Hoefler. 128p. (Orig.). 1980. pap. text ed. 6.95 (ISBN 0-89536-465-4, 1969). CSS of Ohio.

Sign of Contradiction. Karol Wojtyla. 1980. pap. 3.95 (ISBN 0-686-85827-1). Crossroad NY.

Sign of Jonah in the Theology of the Evangelists & Q. Richard A. Edwards. LC 74-153931. (Studies in Biblical Theology, 2nd Ser.: No. 18). 1971. pap. text ed. 10.00x (ISBN 0-8401-3068-6). A R Allenson.

Sign of Jonas. Thomas Merton. LC 79-10283. 362p. 1979. pap. 6.95 (ISBN 0-15-682529-5, Harv). HarBraceJ.

Sign of Jonas. Thomas Merton. 362p. 1983. Repr. of 1953 ed. lib. bdg. 30.00 (ISBN 0-88254-871-9, Octagon). Hippocrene Bks.

Sign of Reconciliation & Conversion: The Sacrament of Penance for Our Times. Monika Hellwig. (Message of the Sacraments Ser.: Vol. 4). 1982. 13.95 (ISBN 0-89453-394-0); pap. 8.95 (ISBN 0-89453-272-3). M Glazier.

"Sign" of the Last Days--When? Carl O. Jonsson & Wolfgang Herbst. LC 86-72140. (Illus.). 288p. 1987. pap. 7.95 (ISBN 0-914675-09-5). Comment Pr.

Sign of the Times. Kenneth E. Hagin. 1986. pap. 0.50 (ISBN 0-89276-269-1). Hagin Ministries.

Signature of All Things: & Other Writings. Jacob Boehme. 307p. 1969. pap. 12.95 (ISBN 0-227-67733-1). Attic Pr.

Signature of God. Dr. Velma Ruch. 1986. pap. 25.00 (ISBN 0-8309-0428-X). Herald Hse.

Signature of God: A Positive Identification of Christ & His Prophets by Computer Wordprints. Robert L. Hamson. LC 81-51809. (Illus.). 111p. 1982. 8.95 (ISBN 0-940356-01-5). Sandpiper CA.

Significance of a Smile. Sri Chinmoy. 52p. (Orig.). 1977. pap. 2.00 (ISBN 0-88497-367-0). Aum Pubns.

Significance of Jesus. Joyce Marie Smith. 1976. pap. 2.95 (ISBN 0-8423-5887-0). Tyndale.

Significance of Silence. Arnold T. Olson. LC 80-70698. (Heritage Ser.: Vol. 2). 208p. 1981. 8.95 (ISBN 0-911802-49-5). Free Church Pubns.

Significance of Spiritual Research for Moral Action. Rudolf Steiner. Tr. by Alan P. Cottrell from Ger. 17p. 1981. pap. 2.00 (ISBN 0-88010-101-6). Anthroposophic.

Significance of the Church. Robert M. Brown. LC 56-6172. (Layman's Theological Library). 96p. 1956. pap. 2.45 (ISBN 0-664-24001-1). Westminster.

Significations: Signs, Symbols & Images in the Interpretation of Religion. Charles H. Long. LC 85-45495. 208p. 1986. pap. 12.95 (ISBN 0-8006-1892-0, 1-1892). Fortress.

Signifying Nothing: Truth's True Contents in Shakespeare's Text. Malcolm Evans. LC 85-28945. 256p. 1986. 25.00x (ISBN 0-8203-0837-4). U of GA Pr.

Signpost: Questions About the Church & Religion You Always Wanted Answered. Cronan Regan. LC 70-169056. (Illus.). 340p. 1972. 7.50 (ISBN 0-8199-0432-5). Franciscan Herald.

Signposts to Freedom: The Ten Commandments of Christian Ethics. Jan M. Lochman. Tr. by David Lewis. LC 81-52283. 192p. (Orig.). 1982. pap. 10.95 (ISBN 0-8066-1915-5, 10-5767). Augsburg.

Signs Along Our Way: Biblical Reflections for Charting Life's Journey. Karen Berry. 1987. pap. 4.95. St Anthony Mess Pr.

Signs & Emblems. Erhardt D. Stiebner & Dieter Urban. LC 83-14793. (Illus.). 352p. 1984. 17.95 (ISBN 0-442-28059-9). Van Nos Reinhold.

Signs & Omens. Bruce Forester. 256p. 1984. 15.95 (ISBN 0-396-08392-7). Dodd.

Signs & Parables: Semiotics & Gospel Texts. The Entreverses Group. Tr. by Gary Phillips from Fr. LC 78-12840. (Pittsburgh Theological Monographs: No. 23). Orig. Title: Signes et Paraboles. 1978. pap. 10.00 (ISBN 0-915138-35-2). Pickwick.

Signs & Symbols in Christian Art. George Ferguson. (Illus.). 1966. pap. 7.95 (ISBN 0-19-501432-4). Oxford U Pr.

Signs & Wonders. Mary Light. 1968. pap. 1.00 (ISBN 0-910924-66-X). Macalester.

Signs & Wonders. Dr. G. Wasserzug. 1.95 (ISBN 0-686-12836-2). Midnight Call.

Signs & Wonders: Tales from the Old Testament. Bernard Evslin. (Illus.). 352p. 1982. 17.95 (ISBN 0-02-734100-3, Four Winds). Macmillan.

Signs & Wonders Today. Christian Life Magazine Staff & C. Peter Wagner. 1986. write for info. (ISBN 0-8297-0709-3). Life Pubs Intl.

Signs & Wonders Today. 1983. Repr. 4.95 (ISBN 0-88419-189-3). Creation Hse.

Signs in Contemporary Culture. Arthur A. Berger. (Annenberg Communication Ser.). (Illus.). 224p. 1984. text ed. 29.95 (ISBN 0-582-28487-2). Longman.

Signs in Judaism: A Resource Book for the Jewish Deaf Community. Adele K. Shuart. 196p. 1986. pap. 16.95x (ISBN 0-8197-0505-5). Bloch.

Signs of a Lively Congregation. Richard D. Campbell. 1984. 3.95 (ISBN 0-89536-701-7, 4886). CSS of Ohio.

Signs of Celebration. Edie Lauckner. 1978. 3.50 (ISBN 0-570-03770-0, 12-2706). Concordia.

Signs of Christ. Harold Balyoz. LC 79-64608. 1979. 18.00 (ISBN 0-9609710-0-9). Altai Pub.

Signs of Christ's Return: Matthew Twenty-Four Through Twenty-Five. John MacArthur, Jr. (John MacArthur Bible Studies Ser.). 1987. pap. 5.95 (ISBN 0-8024-5311-2). Moody.

Signs of Christ's Second Coming. V. R. Erdman. 29p. pap. 0.95 (ISBN 0-87509-130-X). Chr Pubns.

Signs of Glory. Richard Holloway. 96p. 1983. pap. 5.95 (ISBN 0-8164-2412-8, HarpR). Har-Row.

Signs of God's Love. Jeanne S. Fogle. pap. 4.50. Westminster.

Signs of God's Love: Baptism & Communion. Jeanne S. Fogle. Ed. by Mary J. Duckert & W. Ben Lane. (Illus.). 32p. (Orig.). 1984. pap. 4.50 (ISBN 0-664-24636-2). Geneva Pr.

Signs of His Coming. Arthur E. Bloomfield. LC 57-8724. 160p. 1962. pap. 4.95 (ISBN 0-87123-513-7, 210513). Bethany Hse.

Signs of Life: Jews from Wuerttemberg-Reports for the Period after 1933 in Letters & Descriptions. Ed. by Walter Strauss. 25.00x. Ktav.

Signs of Love: The Sacraments of Christ. Leonard Foley. (Illus.). 1976. pap. 1.95 (ISBN 0-912228-32-6). St Anthony Mess Pr.

Signs of the Apostles. Walter Chantry. 1979. pap. 3.95 (ISBN 0-85151-175-9). Banner of Truth.

Signs of the Coming of the Antichrist. Gordon Lindsay. (End of the Age Ser.: Vol. 1). 1.25 (ISBN 0-89985-067-7). Christ Nations.

Signs of the Judgement, Onomastica Sacra & the Generations from Adam. Michael Stone. LC 80-28371. (University of Pennsylvania Armenian Texts & Studies). 1981. text ed. 16.50 (ISBN 0-89130-460-6, 21-02-03); pap. 12.00 (ISBN 0-89130-461-4). Scholars Pr GA.

Signs of the Times. Marvin L. Johnson. 1983. 6.95 (ISBN 0-8062-2021-X). Carlton.

Signs of the Times in the Heavens. Gordon Lindsay. (Prophecy Ser.). 1.25 (ISBN 0-89985-062-6). Christ Nations.

Signs of the Times: Questions Catholics Ask Today. Russell Shaw. (Orig.). 1985. pap. 8.95 (ISBN 0-87061-133-X). Chr Classics.

Signs of These Times: The Ayer Lectures of the Colgate Rochester Divinity School for 1929. facs. ed. Willard L. Sperry. LC 68-29247. (Essay Index Reprint Ser). 1968. Repr. of 1929 ed. 15.00 (ISBN 0-8369-0897-X). Ayer Co Pubs.

Signs, Songs & Stories. Ed. by Virginia Sloyan. (Illus.). 160p. 1982. pap. 8.50 (ISBN 0-8146-1285-7). Liturgical Pr.

Signs, Words & Gestures. Balthasar Fischer. Tr. by Matthew J. O'Connell from Ger. 1981. pap. 5.95 (ISBN 0-916134-48-2). Pueblo Pub Co.

Sigrid Undset: A Study in Christian Realism. Andreas H. Winsnes. Tr. by P. G. Foote. LC 74-110276. (Illus.). ix, 258p. Repr. of 1953 ed. lib. bdg. 22.50x (ISBN 0-8371-4502-3, WISU). Greenwood.

Sigueme. Ralph W. Neighbour, Jr. 128p. 1986. Repr. of 1983 ed. reader ed. 2.75 (ISBN 0-311-13837-3); student ed. 2.65 (ISBN 0-311-13836-5). Casa Bautista.

Sikh Concept of the Divine. Ed. by Pritam Singh. 1986. 15.00x (ISBN 0-8364-1607-4, Pub. by Nanak Dev Univ India). South Asia Bks.

Sikh Concept of the Divine. Ed. by Pritam Singh. 223p. 1986. 15.00X (ISBN 0-8364-1670-8, Pub. by Abhinav India). South Asia Bks.

Sikh Religion, 6 vols. in 3. Max A. Mcauliffe. 1963. text ed. 100.00. Coronet Bks.

Sikh Religion, 6 vols. Max A. Maculiffe. 1270p. 200.00X set (ISBN 0-317-52153-5, Pub. by S Chand India). State Mutual Bk.

Sikh Religion & Philosophy. Nirmal K. Jain. 1979. text ed. 12.50 (ISBN 0-89684-077-8, Pub. by Sterling New Delhi). Orient Bk Dist.

Sikh Separatism: The Politics of Faith. Rajiv A. Kapur. 240p. 1986. text ed. 29.95x (ISBN 0-04-320179-2). Allen Unwin.

Sikh Studies: Comparative Perspectives of a Changing Tradition. Ed. by Mark Juergensmeyer & Gerald Barrier. 1980. 16.00 (ISBN 0-89581-100-6). Asian Human Pr.

Sikh Symposium 1985. Jarnail Singh. 121p. 1986. 8.00 (ISBN 0-8364-1840-9). South Asia Bks.

Sikh World. Daljit Singh & Angela Smith. (Religions of the World Ser.). (Illus.). 48p. 1985. PLB 14.96 (ISBN 0-382-09158-2); pap. 9.25 (ISBN 0-382-09159-0). Silver.

Sikhism. Ranjit Arora. (Religions of the World Ser.). (Illus.). 48p. 1987. lib. bdg. 11.40 (ISBN 0-531-18067-0, Pub. by Bookwright Pr). Watts.

Sikhism. W. Owen Cole & Piara S. Sambhi. 1985. 13.00x (ISBN 0-7062-3147-3, Pub. by Ward Lock Educ Co Ltd). State Mutual Bk.

Sikhism. Beryl Danjhal. (World Religions Ser.). (Illus.). 72p. 1987. 16.95 (ISBN 0-7134-5202-1, Pub. by Batsford England). David & Charles.

Sikhism. Ed. by H. W. McLeod. (Textual Sources for the Study of Religion). 224p. 1987. pap. 11.75 (ISBN 0-389-20718-7). B&N Imports.

Sikhism. Ed. by W. H. McLeod. LC 84-410. (Textual Sources for the Study of Religion Ser.). 208p. 1984. 23.50x (ISBN 0-389-20479-X, 08041). B&N Imports.

Sikhism. Daljeet Singh. 1979. text ed. 17.95 (ISBN 0-89684-074-3, Pub. by Sterling New Delhi). Orient Bk Dist.

Sikhs. W. Owen Cole & Piara S. Sambhi. (Library of Religious Beliefs & Practices). 210p. 1986. pap. text ed. 14.95 (ISBN 0-7100-8843-4). Methuen Inc.

Sikhs. Khushwant Singh & Raghu Rai. LC 85-22359. 300p. 1985. Repr. lib. bdg. 44.95x (ISBN 0-89370-891-7). Borgo Pr.

Sikhs in Britain. Allan De Souza. (Communities in Britain Ser.). (Illus.). 72p. 1986. 16.95 (ISBN 0-7134-5100-9, Pub. by Batsford England). David & Charles.

Sikhs We Are Not Hindus. Kahan S. Nabha. Tr. by Jarnail Singh. 152p. 1986. pap. 12.00x (ISBN 0-8364-1839-5). South Asia Bks.

Siksa Samuccaya: A Compendium of Buddhist Doctrine. Ed. by Cecil Bendall & W. H. Rouse. 1981. 18.50x (ISBN 0-8364-0793-8, Pub. by Motilal Banarsidass). South Asia Bks.

Siksha-Samuccaya, a Compendium of Buddhist Doctrine. Compiled by Santideva. Tr. by Cecil Bendall & W. D. Rouse. LC 78-70114. Repr. of 1922 ed. 33.50 (ISBN 0-404-17368-3). AMS Pr.

Silence as Yoga. 4th ed. Swami Paramananda. 1974. pap. 3.50 (ISBN 0-911564-11-X). Vedanta Ctr.

Silence of Death. Sri Chinmoy. (Illus.). 46p. (Orig.). 1973. pap. 2.00 (ISBN 0-88497-035-3). Aum Pubns.

Silence of God. Robert Anderson. LC 78-9528. (Sir Robert Anderson Library). 232p. 1978. pap. 5.95 (ISBN 0-8254-2128-4). Kregel.

Silence of God: Creative Response to the Films of Ingmar Bergman. Arthur Gibson. LC 81-18754. 171p. 1978. soft cover 9.95x (ISBN 0-88946-951-2). E Mellen.

Silence of God: Meditations on Prayer. James P. Carse. 128p. 1985. 11.95 (ISBN 0-02-521490-X). Macmillan.

Silence of God: Meditations on Prayer. James P. Carse. 120p. 1987. pap. 4.95 (ISBN 0-02-084270-8, Collier). Macmillan.
Silence of Jesus: The Authentic Voice of the Historical Man. James Breech. LC 82-71825. 192p. 1983. 14.95 (ISBN 0-8006-0691-4, 1-691). Fortress.
Silence of Surrendering Love: Body, Soul, Spirit Integration. George A. Maloney. LC 85-28636. 189p. 1986. pap. 7.95 (ISBN 0-8189-0494-1). Alba.
Silence Speaks--from the Chalkboard of Baba Hari Dass. Baba Hari Dass et al. LC 76-53902. (Illus.). 224p. (Orig.). 1977. pap. 5.95 (ISBN 0-918100-01-1). SRI Rama.
Silencio de Dios. Robert Anderson. Orig. Title: Silence of God. (Span.). 192p. 1981. pap. 3.95 (ISBN 0-8254-1022-3). Kregel.
Silent Churches: Persecution of Religions in Soviet Dominated Areas. Peter J. Babris. LC 78-52811. (Illus.). 1978. 19.50 (ISBN 0-911252-02-9). Res Publs.
Silent Encounter. Ed. by Virginia Hanson. LC 74-4168. 240p. (Orig.). 1974. pap. 4.75 (ISBN 0-8356-0448-9, Quest). Theos Pub Hse.
Silent Fire. Ed. by Walter H. Capps & Wendy M. Wright. LC 78-3366. (Forum Bk.). 1978. pap. 7.95x (ISBN 0-06-061314-9, RD 290, HarpR). Har-Row.
Silent Issues of the Church. Carl H. Lundquist. 156p. 1985. pap. 5.95 (ISBN 0-89693-721-6). Victor Bks.
Silent Life. Thomas Merton. 178p. 1975. pap. 6.95 (ISBN 0-374-51281-7). FS&G.
Silent Life. Thomas Merton. 1983. 12.75 (ISBN 0-8446-5986-X). Peter Smith.
Silent Music: The Science of Meditation. William Johnston. LC 73-18688. 1979. pap. 7.95 (ISBN 0-06-064196-7, RD 293, HarpR). Har-Row.
Silent Night, Holy Night. Paul Rosel. (Illus.). 1969. 3.25 (ISBN 0-8066-0928-1, 11-9388). Augsburg.
Silent Path to God. James E. Griffiss. LC 79-8903. pap. 27.50 (2029620). Bks Demand UMI.
Silent Pilgrimage to God: The Spirituality of Charles deFoucauld. Ed. by Rene Voillaume. Tr. by Jeremy Moiser from Fr. LC 74-32516. Orig. Title: Ce Sue Crojart Charles de Foucauld. 100p. (Orig.). 1977. pap. 4.95 (ISBN 0-88344-461-5). Orbis Bks.
Silent Presence. Ernest Larkin. 4.95 (ISBN 0-87193-172-9). Dimension Bks.
Silent Revolution: The Effects of Modernization on Australian Aboriginal Religion. Erich Kolig. LC 81-6430. (Illus.). 224p. 1981. text ed. 27.50 (ISBN 0-89727-020-7). ISHI PA.
Silent River: A Pastoral Elegy in the Form of a Recollection of Arctic Adventure. Charles R. Metzger. (Illus.). xi, 161p. (Orig.). 1984. pap. 7.95x (ISBN 0-9613094-0-7). Omega LA.
Silent September. Joyce Landorf. 1984. pap. 10.00 (ISBN 0-317-14051-5). Word Bks.
Silent Storm. Marion M. Brown et al. 1985. Repr. of 1963 ed. 6.95 (ISBN 0-8010-0884-0). Baker Bk.
Silhouette Crafts. Romilda Dilley. (Illus.). 24p. (YA) 1987. wkbk. 2.95 (ISBN 0-87403-238-5, 2148). Standard Pub.
Silhouette of a Saint: Albert Pepper. Danny R. Morrow. 1985. 4.95 (ISBN 0-86544-027-1). Salv Army Suppl South.
Silver Christmas Ornaments: A Collector's Guide. Clara J. Scroggins. LC 79-15323. (Illus.). 208p. 1980. 25.00 (ISBN 0-498-02385-0). A S Barnes.
Silver Pen for Cloudy Days. Susan Lenzkes. 144p. 1987. pap. 7.95 (ISBN 0-310-43671-0). Zondervan.
Simeon & the Baby Jesus. Evelyn Marxhausen. (Arch Bks.). (Illus.). 24p. 1986. pap. 0.99 saddlestitched (ISBN 0-570-06202-0, 59-1425). Concordia.
Simhat Torah. Norma Simon. (Festival Series of Picture Story Books). (Illus.). 1960. bds. 4.50 lam. (ISBN 0-8381-0704-4). United Syn Bk.
Simon Magus. G. R. S. Mead. 1978. Repr. of 1892 ed. 10.00 (ISBN 0-89005-258-1). Ares.
Simon Peter. Georges Chevrot. 223p. 1980. pap. 4.95x (ISBN 0-933932-43-X). Scepter Pubs.
Simon Peter. Hugh Martin. 1984. pap. 5.45 (ISBN 0-85151-427-8). Banner of Truth.
Simon Tyssot de Patot & the Seventeenth-Century Background of Critical Deism. David R. McKee. (Johns Hopkins University Studies in Romance Literatures & Languages: Vol. 40). 105p. pap. 14.00 (ISBN 0-384-34885-8). Johnson Repr.
Simon Wiesenthal Center Annual, Vol. 1. Ed. by Alex Grobman. (Illus.). 256p. 1984. text ed. 17.95x (ISBN 0-940646-30-7). Rossel Bks.
Simon Wiesenthal Center Annual, Vol. 2. Ed. by Sybil Milton et al. 1985. lib. bdg. 30.00 (ISBN 0-527-96489-1). Kraus Intl.
Simon Wiesenthal Center Annual, Vol. 3. Ed. by Sybil Milton & Henry Friedlander. 1986. lib. bdg. 35.00 (ISBN 0-527-96490-5). Kraus Intl.
Simone Weil & the Suffering of Love. Eric O. Springsted. 131p. (Orig.). 1986. pap. 8.95 (ISBN 0-936384-33-6). Cowley Pubns.
Simoniacal Entry into Religious Life, 1000 to 1260: A Social, Economic, & Legal Study. Joseph H. Lynch. LC 76-22670. (Illus.). 286p. 1976. 15.00x (ISBN 0-8142-0222-5). Ohio St U Pr.
Simple & Profound. David Du Plessis. 1986. pap. 7.95 (ISBN 0-941478-51-3). Paraclete Pr.
Simple as A, B, C. Charles Hunter & Frances Hunter. 1982. pap. 0.75 (ISBN 0-917726-51-0). Hunter Bks.
Simple Cobler of Aggawam in America. Nathaniel Ward. Ed. by Paul M. Zall. LC 69-19107. xviii, 81p. 1969. 7.50x (ISBN 0-8032-0188-5). U of Nebr Pr.
Simple Gifts, Vols. 1&2. Ed. by Gabe Huck. 1974. pap. 6.50 (ISBN 0-918208-65-3). Liturgical Conf.
Simple Life Coloring Book. Craig Sandberg. 1983. 2.25 (ISBN 0-87813-519-7). Christian Light.
Simple Living. new ed. Edward K. Ziegler. 128p. 1974. pap. 1.25 (ISBN 0-87178-791-1). Brethren.
Simple Matter of Justice: The Phyllis Wheatly YWCA Story. Florence J. Radcliffe. 304p. 1985. 13.00 (ISBN 0-682-40199-4). Exposition Pr FL.
Simple Object Lessons for Children. Tom A. Biller & Martie Biller. (Object Lesson Ser.). 160p. 1980. pap. 4.95 (ISBN 0-8010-0793-3). Baker Bk.
Simple Outlines on the Christian Faith. Russell E. Spray. (Dollar Sermon Library). 1977. pap. 1.95 (ISBN 0-8010-8120-3). Baker Bk.
Simple Prayer. John Dalrymple. (Ways of Prayer Ser.: Vol. 9). 118p. 1984. pap. 4.95 (ISBN 0-89453-301-0). M Glazier.
Simple Sermons for Funeral Services. Herschel W. Ford. 54p. 1985. pap. 2.95 (ISBN 0-8010-3514-7). Baker Bk.
Simple Sermons for Saints & Sinners. W. Herschel Ford. 152p. 1986. pap. 3.95 (ISBN 0-8010-3522-8). Baker Bk.
Simple Sermons for Special Days & Occasions. W. Herschel Ford. 140p. 1985. pap. 4.50 (ISBN 0-8010-3515-5). Baker Bk.
Simple Sermons for Sunday Morning. W. Herschel Ford. 128p. 1986. pap. 3.95 (ISBN 0-8010-3523-6). Baker Bk.
Simple Sermons for Time & Eternity. W. Herschel Ford. 120p. 1985. pap. 3.95 (ISBN 0-8010-3516-3). Baker Bk.
Simple Sermons of Great Christian Doctrines. W. Herschel Ford. 138p. 1985. pap. 4.50 (ISBN 0-8010-3519-8). Baker Bk.
Simple Sermons on Conversion & Commitment. W. Herschel Ford. (W. Herschel Ford Sermon Library). 128p. 1986. pap. 3.95 (ISBN 0-8010-3524-4). Baker Bk.
Simple Sermons on Evangelistic Themes. W. Herschel Ford. 128p. 1986. pap. 3.95 (ISBN 0-8010-3525-2). Baker Bk.
Simple Sermons on Grace & Glory. W. Herschel Ford. 92p. 1986. pap. 3.50 (ISBN 0-8010-3526-0). Baker Bk.
Simple Sermons on Prayer. W. Herschel Ford. 88p. 1985. pap. 3.50 (ISBN 0-8010-3520-1). Baker Bk.
Simple Sermons on Salvation & Service. W. Herschel Ford. 136p. 1986. pap. 4.50 (ISBN 0-8010-3527-9). Baker Bk.
Simple Sermons on the New Testament Texts. W. Herschel Ford. 112p. 1985. pap. 3.95 (ISBN 0-8010-3517-1). Baker Bk.
Simple Sermons That Demand a Decision. Edward Fudge. 2.00 (ISBN 0-686-12689-0). E Fudge.
Simple Sermons That Say Something. Edward Fudge. pap. 2.00 (ISBN 0-686-12684-X). E Fudge.
Simple Story. S. Y. Agnon. Tr. & afterword by Hillel Halkin. LC 85-2481. 256p. 1985. 14.95 (ISBN 0-8052-3999-5). Schocken.
Simple Things of the Christian Life. G. Campbell Morgan. 1984. pap. 2.25 (ISBN 0-915374-40-4). Rapids Christian.
Simple Truth. Mary-Alice Jafolla. 90p. 1982. 5.95 (ISBN 0-87159-146-4). Unity School.
Simple Welcome Speeches & Other Helps. Amy Bolding. (Pocket Pulpit Library). 1973. pap. 4.50 (ISBN 0-8010-0612-0). Baker Bk.
Simplest Explanation of God Ever Explained. Nam U. Detacuden. 230p. 1983. 13.50 (ISBN 0-682-49951-X). Exposition Pr FL.
Simplicity: A Rich Quaker's View. George Peck. LC 72-97851. (Orig.). 1973. pap. 2.50x (ISBN 0-87574-189-4). Pendle Hill.
Simplicity & Ordinariness: Studies in Medieval Cistercian History, Vol. IV. Ed. by John R. Sommerdfeldt. (Cistercian Studies: No. 61). (Orig.). 1980. pap. text ed. 8.95 (ISBN 0-87907-861-8). Cistercian Pubns.
Simplicity of Life As Lived in the Everyday. Kathleen Storms. LC 83-16812. 322p. (Orig.). 1984. lib. bdg. 27.75 (ISBN 0-8191-3601-8); pap. text ed. 13.75 (ISBN 0-8191-3602-6). U Pr of Amer.
Simplified Bible Lessons on the Old & New Testaments. G. H. Showalter & W. M. Davis. 1944. pap. 2.75 (ISBN 0-88027-039-X). Firm Foun Pub.
Simplified Course in Hatha Yoga. Wallace Slater. 1967. pap. 2.75 (ISBN 0-8356-0138-2, Quest). Theos Pub Hse.
Simplified Introduction to the Wisdom of St. Thomas. Peter A. Redpath. LC 80-5230. 180p. 1980. lib. bdg. 24.00 (ISBN 0-8191-1058-2); pap. text ed. 10.50 (ISBN 0-8191-1059-0). U Pr of Amer.
Simplified Techniques of Counseling. Ralph Brand. 132p. 1972. pap. 2.50 (ISBN 0-89114-049-2). Baptist Pub Hse.
Simply Christmas. Noel Pax. (Illus.). 72p. (Orig.). 1980. pap. 3.95 (ISBN 0-8027-7168-8); 5.95 (ISBN 0-8027-0672-X). Walker & Co.
Simply Sane: The Spirituality of Mental Health. Gerald May. (Crossroad Paperback Ser.). 144p. 1982. pap. 8.95 (ISBN 0-8245-0448-8). Crossroad NY.
Simulation Games for Religious Education. Richard Reichert. LC 75-142. 1975. pap. 4.50 (ISBN 0-88489-060-0). St Marys.
Simulations on Brethren History. Dale Brown. pap. 6.95 (ISBN 0-87178-794-6). Brethren.
Sin: A Christian View for Today. Xavier Thevenot. Ed. by Roger Marchand. Tr. by Simone Inkel from Fr. 80p. 1984. pap. 2.95 (ISBN 0-89243-218-7). Liguori Pubns.
Sin & Confession on the Eve of the Reformation. T. Tentler. 1977. 46.50x (ISBN 0-691-07219-1). Princeton U Pr.
Sin & Judgment in the Prophets. Patrick D. Miller. LC 81-8950. (SBL Monograph Ser.). 1982. 19.50 (ISBN 0-89130-514-9, 06-00-27); pap. 16.00 (ISBN 0-89130-515-7). Scholars Pr GA.
Sin & Sanction in Israel & Mesopotamia: A Comparative Study. K. Van der Toorn. (Studia Semitica Neerlandica: No. 22). 213p. 1985. pap. 20.00 (ISBN 90-232-2166-4, Pub. by Van Gorcum Holland). Longwood Pub Group.
Sin & Temptation. John Owen. Ed. by James M. Houston. LC 83-791. (Classics of Faith & Devotion). 1983. 10.95 (ISBN 0-88070-013-0). Multnomah.
Sin: Its Reality & Nature. Ed. by Pietro Palazzini. 238p. 1964. 9.95 (ISBN 0-933932-25-1). Scepter Pubs.
Sin of Obedience. Willard Beecher & Marguerite Beecher. 88p. (Orig.). 1982. pap. 4.75 (ISBN 0-942350-00-6). Beecher Found.
Sin of Unbelief. C. H. Spurgeon. 1977. pap. 0.95 (ISBN 0-686-23224-0). Pilgrim Pubns.
Sin Reconsidered. James Gaffney. LC 82-61424. 96p. (Orig.). 1983. pap. 3.95 (ISBN 0-8091-2516-1). Paulist Pr.
Sin Redemption & Sacrifice: A Biblical & Patristic Study. Stanislas Lyonnet & Leopold Sabarin. (Analecta Biblica: Vol. 48). (Eng.). 1971. pap. 22.00 (ISBN 88-7653-048-7, Biblical Inst. Press). Loyola.
Sin, Salvation & Service. Henry Stob. (Orig.). 1984. pap. 2.95 (ISBN 0-933140-98-3). CRC Pubns.
Sin, Salvation, & the Spirit. Ed. & pref. by Daniel Durken. LC 79-20371. (Illus.). 368p. 1979. text ed. 6.00 (ISBN 0-8146-1078-1); pap. text ed. 10.00 (ISBN 0-8146-1079-X). Liturgical Pr.
Sin, Sex & Self-Control. Norman V. Peale. 1978. pap. 2.50 (ISBN 0-449-23921-7, Crest). Fawcett.
Sin, Suffering & God. Thomas B. Warren. 1980. pap. 15.00 (ISBN 0-934916-25-X). Natl Christian Pr.
Sinai & the Monastery of St. Catherine. John Galey. 191p. 1986. 45.00 (ISBN 977-424-118-5, Pub. by Am Univ Cairo Pr); pap. 24.00x (ISBN 977-424-118-5). Columbia U Pr.
Sinai & Zion: An Entry into the Jewish Bible. Jon D. Levenson. 240p. (Orig.). 1985. 16.95 (ISBN 0-86683-961-5, AY8551, HarpR). Har-Row.
Since Cumorah. Hugh C. Nibley. 11.95 (ISBN 0-87747-240-8). Deseret Bk.
Since Jesus Passed By. Frances Hunter & Charles Hunter. 1973. pap. 3.95 (ISBN 0-917726-38-3). Hunter Bks.
Sincerely. Gigi G. Tchividjian. 144p. 1984. 11.95 (ISBN 0-310-44850-6, 18272). Zondervan.
Sindon: A Layman's Guide to the Shroud of Turin. Frank O. Adams. Ed. by John A. DeSalvo. LC 82-90138. (Illus.). 1982. 12.50 (ISBN 0-86700-008-2, Synergy Bks). P Walsh Pr.
Sinews of the Spirit: The Ideal of Christian Manlines in Victorian Literature & Religious Thought. Norman Vance. 256p. 1985. 34.50 (ISBN 0-521-30387-7). Cambridge U Pr.
Sinful Tunes & Spirituals: Black Folk Music to the Civil War. Dena J Epstein. LC 77-6315. (Music in American Life Ser.). (Illus.). 1981. pap. 10.95 (ISBN 0-252-00875-8). U of Ill Pr.
Sing a New Song. Andrea J. Shepard. 96p. (Orig.). 1986. pap. 4.95 (ISBN 0-310-34302-X, 12352P). Zondervan.
Sing a New Song. H. Lynn Stone. LC 81-85596. 123p. (Orig.). 1981. pap. text ed. 3.00 (ISBN 0-87148-798-5). Pathway Pr.
Sing a New Song! Worship Renewal for Adventists Today. C. Raymond Holmes. LC 84-70077. xii, 190p. 1984. pap. 9.95 (ISBN 0-943872-88-X). Andrews Univ Pr.
Sing & Be Happy: Songs for the Young Child. Clara B. Baker. LC 80-13421. (Illus.). 96p. 1980. pap. 7.95 spiral (ISBN 0-687-38547-4). Abingdon.
Sing & Be Joyful: Enjoying Music with Young Children. Compiled by Evelyn Andre. LC 79-14787. 1979. pap. 8.95 (ISBN 0-687-38550-4). Abingdon.
Sing & Pray & Shout Hurray. Roger Ortmayer. 1974. pap. 2.75 (ISBN 0-377-00004-3). Friend Pr.
Sing & Rejoice! Orlando Schmidt. LC 79-84367. 192p. 1979. 6.95x (ISBN 0-8361-1210-5); pap. 5.95x (ISBN 0-8361-1211-3). Herald Pr.
Sing & Rejoice! Introductory Kit. with cassette 8.25 (ISBN 0-8361-1219-9). Herald Pr.
Sing for Peace. Lois Lenski. 16p. 1985. pap. 1.50 (ISBN 0-8361-3396-X). Herald Pr.
Sing It! Amy Sit. 1979. pap. 3.50 (ISBN 0-917726-39-1). Hunter Bks.
Sing It Again! J. Irving Erickson. 1985. 12.95 (ISBN 0-910452-58-X). Covenant.
Sing Like a Whippoorwill. Stafford Betty. (Illus., Orig.). 1987. pap. 6.95 (ISBN 0-89622-324-8). Twenty-Third.
Sing of Life & Faith. Ed. by Max B. Miller & Louise C. Drew. LC 68-22233. (Illus.). 1969. 5.95 (ISBN 0-8298-0123-5). Pilgrim NY.
Sing Praises! Management of Church Hymns. Dale E. Ramsey. 30p. (Orig.). 1983. pap. 3.50 (ISBN 0-8272-3300-0). CBP.
Sing Praises to His Name. Louis Pratt. Ed. by Michael L. Sherer. (Orig.). 1986. pap. 6.75 (ISBN 0-89536-831-5, 6845). CSS of Ohio.
Sing! Sing! Sing! Music Book for Children. 1.50 (ISBN 0-8198-6836-1). Dghtrs St Paul.
Sing the Joys of Mary. Ed. by Costante Berselli & Georges Gharib. Tr. by Phil Jenkins from Italian. Tr. of Lodi alla Madonna. (Eng.). 136p. (Orig.). 1983. pap. 7.95 (ISBN 0-8192-1329-2). Morehouse.
Sing the Lord's Song in a Strange Land: The Life of Justin Morgan. Betty Bandel. LC 78-73309. 264p. 1981. 24.50 (ISBN 0-8386-2411-1). Fairleigh Dickinson.
Sing to God: Songs & Hymns for Christian Education. (Orig.). 1984. pap. 9.95 leader's ed. (ISBN 0-8298-0688-1); student's ed. 4.95 (ISBN 0-8298-0689-X); spiral bd. leaders guide 12.95 (ISBN 0-8298-0716-0). Pilgrim NY.
Sing to Me of Heaven: A Study of Folk & Early American Materials in Three Old Harp Books. Dorothy D. Horn. LC 74-99122. (Illus.). 1970. 10.00 (ISBN 0-8130-0293-1). U Presses Fla.
Sing Unto God. Compiled by Roy A. Strubhar. 1972. pap. 1.00x (ISBN 0-87813-108-6). Park View.
Sing with Me. 5.50 (ISBN 0-87747-362-5). Deseret Bk.
Singers of the New Song: A Mystical Interpretation of the Song of Songs. George A. Maloney. LC 85-71639. 176p. (Orig.). 1985. pap. 4.95 (ISBN 0-87793-292-1). Ave Maria.
Singing Black. Homer A. Rodeheaver. LC 72-1681. Repr. of 1936 ed. 12.50 (ISBN 0-404-08330-7). AMS Pr.
Singing Campaign for Ten Thousand Pounds. rev. ed. Gustavus D. Pike. LC 75-164392. (Black Heritage Library Collection). Repr. of 1875 ed. 18.25 (ISBN 0-8369-8851-5). Ayer Co Pubs.
Singing Church. 623p. 1985. 7.95x (ISBN 0-916642-25-9). Hope Pub.
Singing Faith. Jane P. Huber. LC 86-753277. 144p. (Orig.). 1987. pap. 7.95 (ISBN 0-664-24055-0); spiral bound 10.95 (ISBN 0-664-24056-9). Westminster.
Singing in Signs. Cathy Rice. LC 81-18830. 160p. 1982. 7.95 (ISBN 0-8407-9006-6). Nelson.
Singing Penguins & Puffed-up Toads. William L. Coleman. 125p. 1981. pap. 4.95 (ISBN 0-87123-554-4, 210554). Bethany Hse.
Singing Pope: The Story of Pope John Paul II. Rinna Wolfe. (Illus.). 128p. 1980. 8.95 (ISBN 0-8164-0472-0, HarpR). Har-Row.
Singing Psalms of Joy & Praise. Fred R. Anderson. LC 86-1550. 78p. (Orig.). 1986. pap. 5.95 ea. (ISBN 0-664-24696-6). Westminster.
Singing the Glory of Lord Krishna Baru Candidasa's Srikrsnakirtana: Baru Candidasa's Srikrsnakirtana. Tr. by M. H. Klaiman. LC 84-3905. (AAR Classics in Religious Studies). 1984. 28.75 (ISBN 0-89130-736-2, 01 05 05); pap. 20.75 (ISBN 0-89130-737-0). Scholars Pr GA.

Singing with Understanding: Including 101 Beloved Hymn Backgrounds. Kenneth W. Osbeck. LC 78-19960. 324p. 1979. 14.95 (ISBN 0-8254-3414-9). Kregel.

Singing Word: Youth with a Mission Songbook. enl &rev. 2nd ed. Youth with a Mission. (Illus.). 288p. 1974. plastic spiral bd. 5.95 (ISBN 0-87123-505-6, 280505). Bethany Hse.

Single Adults: Resource & Recipients for Revival. Dan R. Crawford. LC 85-7889. 1985. pap. 5.95 (ISBN 0-8054-3236-1). Broadman.

Single Adults Want to Be the Church, Too. Britton Wood. LC 77-78411. 1977. 9.50 (ISBN 0-8054-3221-3). Broadman.

Single Again. Wesley Haystead. (Study & Grow Electives). 64p. 1985. pap. 3.95 (ISBN 0-8307-1042-6, 6102111). Regal.

Single Again--This Time with Children: A Christian Guide for the Single Parent. Alice S. Peppler. LC 81-52278. 128p. (Orig.). 1982. pap. 6.95 (ISBN 0-8066-1910-4, 10-5802). Augsburg.

Single & Feeling Good. Harold I. Smith. 160p. 1987. pap. 9.95 (ISBN 0-687-38552-0). Abingdon.

Single & Pregnant. Ruth I. Pierce. LC 72-119678. 1970. pap. 3.95 (ISBN 0-8070-2779-0, BP407). Beacon Pr.

Single & Whole. Rhena Taylor. LC 85-8345. Orig. Title: Every Single Blessing. 96p. 1985. pap. 2.95 (ISBN 0-87784-510-7). Inter-Varsity.

Single But Not Alone. Jane Graver. LC 12-2815. 1983. pap. 2.50 (ISBN 0-570-03880-4). Concordia.

Single, but Not Sorry. rev. ed. Joyce Parks. 235p. 1986. pap. 3.95 (ISBN 0-89084-307-4). Bob Jones Univ Pr.

Single Life: A Christian Challenge. Martha M. Niemann. 144p. 1986. pap. 4.25 (ISBN 0-89243-254-3). Liguori Pubns.

Single on Sunday: A Manual for Successful Single Adult Ministries. Bobbie Reed. 1979. pap. 5.95 (ISBN 0-570-03781-6, 12-2735). Concordia.

Single-Parent Families at Camp: The Essence of an Experience. Bernard Reisman & Gladys Rosen. LC 84-70480. 54p. 1984. pap. 2.50 (ISBN 0-87495-061-9). Am Jewish Comm.

Single Parent: Revised, Updated & Expanded. Virginia W. Smith. 192p. 1983. pap. 5.95 (ISBN 0-8007-5105-1, Power Bks). Revell.

Single Parenting: A Wilderness Journey. Robert G. Barnes, Jr. 176p. 1984. pap. 5.95 (ISBN 0-8423-5892-7). Tyndale.

Single? Single Again? A Handbook for Living. Hugh Binford & Helaina Binford. 120p. (Orig.). 1986. pap. 7.00 (ISBN 0-939313-22-7). Joshua-I-Minist.

Single Truth. Bob E. Lyons. 1982. text ed. 5.25 (ISBN 0-87148-801-9); pap. 4.25 (ISBN 0-87148-802-7); instr's. manual 6.95 (ISBN 0-87148-804-3). Pathway Pr.

Singleness. Dorothy Payne. LC 83-10174. (Choices: Guides for Today's Woman Ser.: Vol. 4). 112p. 1983. pap. 7.95 (ISBN 0-664-24541-2). Westminster.

Singleness: An Opportunity for Growth & Fulfillment. Edward F. Weising & Gwen Weising. LC 82-80197. (Radiant Life Ser.). 128p. (Orig.). 1982. pap. 2.50 (ISBN 0-88243-901-4, 02-0901); teacher's ed. 3.95 (ISBN 0-88243-196-X, 32-0196). Gospel Pub.

Singleness of Purpose. Jeffries Tula. LC 85-19525. (Orig.). 1986. pap. 3.25 (ISBN 0-8054-5029-7). Broadman.

Singular Problem of the Epistle to the Galatians. James H. Ropes. (Harvard Theological Studies). 1929. pap. 15.00 (ISBN 0-527-01014-6). Kraus Repr.

Singular Problems of the Single Jewish Parent. Shlomo D. Levine. 39p. (Orig.). 1981. pap. text ed. 1.25 (ISBN 0-8381-2115-2). United Synagogue.

Sinne: Beitrage Zur Geschichte der Physiologie und Psychologie Im Ittelalter Aus Hebraischen und Arabisch En Quellen. David Kaufmann. Ed. by Steven Katz. LC 79-7141. (Jewish Philosophy, Mysticism & History of Ideas Ser.). 1980. Repr. of 1884 ed. lib. bdg. 17.00x (ISBN 0-405-12267-5). Ayer Co Pubs.

Sinners & Saints. Philip S. Robinson. LC 75-134400. Repr. of 1883 ed. 25.00 (ISBN 0-404-08444-3). AMS Pr.

Sinner's Guide. Venerable Louis of Granada. LC 84-51820. 395p. 1985. pap. 8.00 (ISBN 0-89555-254-X). Tan Bks Pubs.

Sinners in the Hands of an Angry God. Jonathan Edwards. pap. 0.50 (ISBN 0-685-00746-4). Reiner.

Sinner's Return to God: Or, the Prodigal Son. Michael Mueller. LC 82-74244. 224p. 1983. pap. 6.00 (ISBN 0-89555-205-1). TAN Bks Pubs.

Sinnfrage in Psychotherapie und Theologie: Die Existenzanalyse und Logotherapie Viktor E. Frankls aus theologischer Sicht. Uwe Boeschemeyer. (Theologische Bibliothek Toepelmann Ser.: Vol. 32). 1977. 22.80x (ISBN 3-11-006727-7). De Gruyter.

Sinning Against the Holy Spirit. Don R. Pegram. 1982. pap. 1.25 (ISBN 0-89265-085-0). Randall Hse.

Sins of Omission: The Neglected Child. 1982. pap. 5.95 (ISBN 0-686-76259-2). Feldheim.

Sins of Saints. Herbert Lockyer. LC 75-108378. 1970. pap. 5.95 (ISBN 0-87213-532-2). Loizeaux.

Sintesis de Doctrina Biblica. Charles C. Ryrie. Orig. Title: Survey of Bible Doctrine. (Span.). 208p. 1979. pap. 4.95 (ISBN 0-8254-1637-X). Kregel.

Sintesis del Nuevo Testamento. W. M. Dunnett. Tr. by Jose M. Blanch from Eng. (Curso Para Maestros Cristianos: No. 3). (Span.). 128p. 1972. pap. 3.50 (ISBN 0-89922-012-6). Edit Caribe.

Sioux City District - A History: The United Methodist Church. Lyle Johnston. (Illus.). 90p. (Orig.). 1978. pap. 1.95 (ISBN 0-9616365-0-5). Grt Plains Emporium.

Siphre Zutta. Saul Lieberman. 1968. 10.00x (ISBN 0-685-31431-6, Pub. by Jewish Theol Seminary). Ktav.

Sipping Saints. David Wilkerson. 128p. 1979. pap. 2.95 (ISBN 0-8007-8339-5, Spire Bks). Revell.

Siquiatria de Dios. Charles L. Allen. 176p. 1975. 2.95 (ISBN 0-88113-280-2). Edit Betania.

Sir Edwyn Hoskyns As a Biblical Theologian. Richard E. Parsons. LC 85-25038. 152p. 1986. 25.00 (ISBN 0-312-72647-3). St Martin.

Sir, I Represent Christian Salesmanship. William E. Cox. pap. 1.50 (ISBN 0-686-64392-5). Reiner.

Sir Sayyid Ahmad Khan's History of Bijnor Rebellion. Syed A. Khan. Tr. by Hafeez Malik. 1983. 13.50x (ISBN 0-8364-1080-7, Pub. by Idarah). South Asia Bks.

Sir Thomas More. Claude Jenkins. 1935. Repr. 20.00 (ISBN 0-8274-3431-6). R West.

Sir Thomas More. Anthony Munday & William Shakespeare. LC 74-133715. (Tudor Facsimile Texts. Old English Plays: No. 65). Repr. of 1910 ed. 49.50 (ISBN 0-404-53365-5). AMS Pr.

Sir Thomas More. facsimile ed. Leslie Paul. LC 75-128882. (Select Bibliographies Ser). Repr. of 1953 ed. 16.00 (ISBN 0-8369-5502-1). Ayer Co Pubs.

Sir Thomas More Circle: A Program of Ideas & Their Impact on Secular Drama. Pearl Hogrefe. LC 59-10553. 366p. 1959. 29.95 (ISBN 0-252-72653-7). U of Ill Pr.

Sir Thomas More: Selected Letters. Thomas More. LC 61-14944. (Yale Edition of the Works of St. Thomas More: Modernized Ser.). pap. 74.00 (ISBN 0-317-28285-9, 2022022). Bks Demand UMI.

Sir, We Would Like to See Jesus: Homilies from a Hilltop. Walter J. Burghardt. LC 82-60589. 1983. pap. 8.95 (ISBN 0-8091-2490-4). Paulist Pr.

Sir William Dawson: A Life in Science & Religion. Charles F. O'Brien. LC 71-153381. (American Philosophical Society, Memoirs: Vol. 84). pap. 54.30 (ISBN 0-317-20673-7, 2025140). Bks Demand UMI.

Sirach. R. A. MacKenzie. (Old Testament Message Ser.: Vol. 19). 12.95 (ISBN 0-89453-419-X); pap. 8.95 (ISBN 0-89453-253-7). M Glazier.

Sirach. Bruce Vawter. (Bible Ser.). Pt. 1. pap. 1.00 (ISBN 0-8091-5138-3); Pt. 2. pap. 1.00 (ISBN 0-8091-5139-1). Paulist Pr.

Sistema de Evidencias Christianas. Ed. by L. D. Keyser. (Span.). 172p. pap. 4.95 (ISBN 0-87148-885-X). Pathway Pr.

Sister Anna: God's Captive to Set Others Free. Dorothy G. Murray. 175p. (Orig.). 1983. pap. 7.95 (ISBN 0-87178-796-2). Brethren.

Sister of Wisdom: St. Hildegard's Theology of the Feminine. Barbara Newman. 1987. 30.00. U of Cal Pr.

Sister of Wisdom: St. Hildegard's Theology of the Feminine. Barbara Newman. 288p. 1987. 18.95 (ISBN 0-520-05810-0). U of Cal Pr.

Sisters in Spirit: Mormon Women in Historical & Cultural Perspective. Ed. by Maureen U. Beecher & Lavina F. Anderson. 350p. 1987. 21.95 (ISBN 0-252-01411-1). U of Ill Pr.

Sisters of Maryknoll: Through Troubled Waters. Sr. Mary De Paul Cogan. LC 72-167329. (Essay Index Reprint Ser.). Repr. of 1947 ed. 18.00 (ISBN 0-8369-2764-8). Ayer Co Pubs.

Sisters of the Spirit: Three Black Women's Autobiographies of the Nineteenth Century. Ed. by William L. Andrews. LC 85-42544. (Religion in North America Ser.). 256p. 1986. 29.50x (ISBN 0-253-35260-6); pap. 8.95x (ISBN 0-253-28704-9). Ind U Pr.

Sistine Chapel. Lutz Heuzinger & Fabrizio Mancinelli. LC 84-50553. (Illus.). 96p. (Orig.). 1984. pap. 13.95 (ISBN 0-935748-58-X). Scala Books.

Sistine Chapel: The Art, the History, & the Restoration. Carlo Pietrangeli et al. (Illus.). 272p. 1986. 60.00 (ISBN 0-517-56274-X, Harmony). Crown.

Sit, Walk, Stand. Watchman Nee. 1964. pap. 2.50 (ISBN 0-87508-419-2). Chr Lit.

Sit, Walk, Stand. Watchman Nee. 1977. pap. 2.95 (ISBN 0-8423-5893-5). Tyndale.

Sitting at His Feet. Martha Borth. (Illus.). 85p. (Orig.). 1985. pap. 5.95 (ISBN 0-935993-00-2). Clar Call Bks.

Sitting by My Laughing Fire. Ruth B. Graham. LC 77-75457. 1977. 10.95 (ISBN 0-8499-2933-4). Word Bks.

Sitting for the Psalms: A Historical Study. (Church Historical Society, London, New Ser.: No. 6). Repr. of 1931 ed. 20.00 (ISBN 0-8115-3130-9). Kraus Repr.

Situation & Theology: Old Testament Interpretations of the Syro-Ephraimite War. Michael E. W. Thompson. (Prophets & Historians Ser.: No. 1). 1983. text ed. 25.95x (ISBN 0-907459-14-5, Pub. by Almond Pr England); pap. text ed. 12.95x (ISBN 0-907459-15-3, Pub. by Almond Pr England). Eisenbrauns.

Situation Ethics: The New Morality. Joseph Fletcher. LC 66-11917. 176p. 1966. pap. 6.95 (ISBN 0-664-24691-5). Westminster.

Situation Ethics: True or False. Joseph Fletcher & John W. Montgomery. 90p. (Orig.). 1972. pap. 2.95 (ISBN 0-87123-525-0, 200525). Bethany Hse.

Siva & Buddha. Sr. Nivedita. pap. 0.50 (ISBN 0-87481-116-3). Vedanta Pr.

Siva in Dance, Myth & Iconography. Anne-Marie Gaston. (Illus.). 1982. 45.00x (ISBN 0-19-561354-6). Oxford U Pr.

Siva-Mahimna Stotram (the Hymn on the Greatness of Siva) Pushpadanta. Tr. by Swami Pavitrananda. pap. 1.50 (ISBN 0-87481-148-1). Vedanta Pr.

Siva Purana, Vol. 1. Tr. by J. L. Shastri. cancelled (ISBN 0-89581-343-2). Asian Human Pr.

Siva Purana, Vol. 2. Tr. by J. L. Shastri. cancelled (ISBN 0-89581-475-7). Asian Human Pr.

Siva Purana, Vol. 3. Tr. by J. L. Shastri. cancelled (ISBN 0-89581-476-5). Asian Human Pr.

Siva Purana, Vol. 4. Tr. by J. L. Shastri. cancelled (ISBN 0-89581-476-5). Asian Human Pr.

Siva! Siva! Cresent & Heart: Selected Poetry of Murshid Samuel L. Lewis. Samuel L. Lewis. (Bismillah Bks.: No. 1). (Illus.). 112p. (Orig.). 1980. pap. 3.50 (ISBN 0-915424-04-5). Sufi Islamia-Prophecy.

Siva Sutras: The Yoga of Supreme Identity. Jaideva Singh. 1979. 16.95 (ISBN 0-89684-057-3, Pub. by Motilal Banarsidass India); pap. 12.50 (ISBN 0-89684-063-8, Pub. by Motilal Banarsidass India). Orient Bk Dist.

Siva: The Erotic Ascetic. Wendy D. O'Flaherty. (Illus.). 1981. pap. 9.95 (ISBN 0-19-520250-3). Oxford U Pr.

Sivananda: Biography of a Modern Sage. Ed. by Swami Venkatesananda. (Life & Works of Swami Sivananda). (Illus.). 448p. (Orig.). 1985. pap. 9.95 (ISBN 0-949027-01-4). Integral Yoga Pubns.

Sivananda Companion to Yoga. The Sivananda Yoga Center. 1983. pap. 9.95 (ISBN 0-671-47088-4). S&S.

Sivananda Lahari of Sri Sankara. Shankara. Tr. by Tapasyananda from Sanskrit. 87p. 1987. pap. 2.25 (ISBN 0-87481-545-2, Pub. by Ramakrishna Math Madras India). Vedanta Pr.

Six by Lewis, 6 vols. C. S. Lewis. 1978. pap. 18.95 (ISBN 0-02-086770-0, Collier). Macmillan.

Six Collations of New Testament Manuscripts. Ed. by Kirsopp Lake & Silva New. (Harvard Theol Studies). 1932. 24.00 (ISBN 0-527-01017-0). Kraus Repr.

Six Days & the Seven Gates. Yitzhak Navon. 1980. 6.00 (ISBN 0-930832-57-4); pap. 4.00 (ISBN 0-686-70336-7). Herzl Pr.

Six Essays on Erasmus & a Translation of Erasmus' Letter to Carondelet 1523. John C. Olin. LC 76-18467. (Illus.). xiv, 125p. 1977. 17.50 (ISBN 0-8232-1023-5); pap. 8.00 (ISBN 0-8232-1024-3). Fordham.

Six Existential Heroes: The Politics of Faith. Lucio P. Ruotolo. LC 72-86386. 192p. 1973. 12.50x (ISBN 0-674-81025-2). Harvard U Pr.

Six Hundred Bible Gems & Outlines. S. R. Briggs & J. H. Elliott. LC 75-42955. 200p. 1976. pap. 5.95 (ISBN 0-8254-2255-8). Kregel.

Six Hundred Sixty-Six: Pictoral Format. Salem Kirban. 1980. pap. 4.95 (ISBN 0-912582-33-2). Kirban.

Six Keys to a Happy Marriage. Tim LaHaye. 1978. pap. 1.95 (ISBN 0-8423-5895-1). Tyndale.

Six Kings of the American Pulpit. facsimile ed. Clarence E. Macartney. LC 75-152192. (Essay Index Reprint Ser). Repr. of 1942 ed. 16.00 (ISBN 0-8369-2323-5). Ayer Co Pubs.

Six Major Prophets. facsimile ed. Edwin E. Slosson. LC 71-167421. (Essay Index Reprint Ser). Repr. of 1917 ed. 23.00 (ISBN 0-8369-2571-8). Ayer Co Pubs.

Six Makers of English Religion, Fifteen Hundred to Seventeen Hundred. Ernest G. Rupp. (Essay Index Reprint Ser.). Repr. of 1957 ed. 16.75 (ISBN 0-518-10159-2). Ayer Co Pubs.

Six Masters in Disillusion. Algar Thorold. LC 75-113325. 1971. Repr. of 1909 ed. 21.50x (ISBN 0-8046-1364-8, Pub. by Kennikat). Assoc Faculty Pr.

Six Men of Yale. facsimile ed. Francis Parsons. LC 72-156702. (Essay Index Reprint Ser). Repr. of 1939 ed. 18.00 (ISBN 0-8369-2329-4). Ayer Co Pubs.

Six Million Reconsidered. Truth in History Committee. Ed. by William N. Grimstad. (Illus.). 1979. pap. 8.00 (ISBN 0-911038-50-7). Noontide.

Six Miracles of Calvary. William R. Nicholson. (Moody Classics Ser.). 1928. pap. 3.50 (ISBN 0-8024-7834-4). Moody.

Six Missions of Texas. (Illus.). 1965. 15.95 (ISBN 0-87244-002-8). Texian.

Six Modern Authors & Problems of Belief. Patrick Grant. LC 79-14511. 175p. 1979. text ed. 28.50x (ISBN 0-06-492515-3). B&N Imports.

Six Perspectives on New Religions: A Case Study Approach. Anson D. Shupe, Jr. LC 81-9464. (Studies in Religion & Society: Vol. 1). 246p. 1981. 49.95x (ISBN 0-88946-983-0). E Mellen.

Six Pillars: Introduction to the Major Works of Sri Aurobindo. Robert A. McDermott et al. Ed. by Robert A. McDermott. LC 74-77411. 300p. 1974. pap. 5.95 (ISBN 0-89012-001-3). Anima Pubns.

Six Records of a Floating Life. Shen Fu. Tr. by Leonard Pratt. 176p. 1983. pap. 3.95 (ISBN 0-14-044429-7). Penguin.

Six Short Plays about Jesus. Pamela Urfer. 35p. (Orig.). pap. text ed. 3.95 (ISBN 0-912801-07-7). Creat Arts Dev.

Six Spanish Missions in Texas: A Portfolio of Paintings. Memorial ed. E. M. Schiwetz. (Illus.). 1984. 60.00 (ISBN 0-292-77597-0). U of Tex Pr.

Six Stories of Jesus. Peter Enns & Glen Forsberg. (Stories that Live Ser.: Bk. 5). (Illus.). 24p. 1985. 4.95 (ISBN 0-936215-05-4); cassette incl. STL Intl.

Six Theories of Justice: Perspectives from Philosophical & Theological Ethics. Karen Lebacqz. LC 86-26457. 144p. (Orig.). 1986. pap. 9.95 (ISBN 0-8066-2245-8, 10-5820). Augsburg.

Six Things Satan Uses to Rob You of God's Abundant Blessings. Peter Popoff. Ed. by Don Tanner. LC 81-86521. (Illus.). 96p. 1982. pap. 2.00 (ISBN 0-938544-11-X). Faith Messenger.

Six Ways to Pray from Six Great Saints. Gloria Hutchinson. (Illus.). 152p. 1982. pap. text ed. 4.95 (ISBN 0-86716-007-1). St Anthony Mess Pr.

Six Who Dared. Michael L. Sherer. 1984. 6.50 (ISBN 0-89536-663-0, 1971). CSS of Ohio.

Six Yogas of Naropa & Mahamudra. 2nd ed. Garma C. Chang. LC 86-10020. 128p. 1986. pap. 9.95 (ISBN 0-937938-33-5). Snow Lion.

Sixteen & Away from Home. Arleta Richardson. (Grandma's Attic Ser.). 1985. pap. 3.50 (ISBN 0-89191-933-3, 59337). Cook.

Sixteen Documents of Vatican Two. Daughters Of St. Paul. pap. 3.25 (ISBN 0-8198-0146-1). Dghtrs St Paul.

Sixteenth-Century Anthem Book: Twenty Anthems for Four Voices. 1960. 5.00 (ISBN 0-19-353406-1). Oxford U Pr.

Sixth Century Monastery at Beth-Shan (Scythopolis) G. M. FitzGerald. (Publications of the Palestine Section Ser.: Vol. 4). (Illus.). xiv, 66p. 1939. 18.75 (ISBN 0-686-24094-4). Univ Mus of U.

Sixth Day. Tom Noe. LC 79-55296. (Illus.). 80p. (Orig.). 1979. pap. 2.95 (ISBN 0-87793-190-9). Ave Maria.

Sixth Day of Creation: A Discourse on Post Biblical, Post Modern Thought. Roberta Kalechofsky. (Illus.). 24p. 1986. 10.00 (ISBN 0-916288-20-X). Micah Pubns.

Sixth Patriarch's Sutra: Great Master Hui Neng. Commentary by Tripitaka Master Hua. Tr. by Buddhist Text Translation Society Staff. (Illus.). 235p. (Orig.). 1977. 15.00 (ISBN 0-917512-19-7); pap. 10.00 (ISBN 0-917512-33-2). Buddhist Text.

Sixty Dramatic Illustrations in Full Colours of the Cathedral Cities of England. George Gilbert. (Promotion of the Arts Library). (Illus.). 99p. 1983. 297.85 (ISBN 0-86650-046-4). Gloucester Art.

Sixty-Eight Communion Meditations & Prayers. Robert Shannon et al. 120p. (Orig.). 1984. pap. 3.95 (ISBN 0-87239-770-X, 3033). Standard Pub.

Sixty-Five Ways to Give Evangelistic Invitations. Faris D. Whitesell. LC 84-11269. 128p. 1984. pap. 5.95 (ISBN 0-8254-4021-1). Kregel.

Sixty Nine Ways to Start a Study Group & Keep It Growing. 2nd ed. Lawrence O. Richards. 144p. 1980. pap. 3.95 (ISBN 0-310-31981-1, 18138P). Zondervan.

Sixty-One Gospel Talks for Children: With Suggested Objects for Illustration. Eldon Weisheit. LC 70-96217. 1969. pap. 4.95 (ISBN 0-570-03713-1, 12-2615). Concordia.

Sixty-One Worship Talks for Children. rev. ed. E. Weisheit. LC 68-20728. 1975. pap. 4.95 (ISBN 0-570-03714-X, 12-2616). Concordia.

Sixty-Second Christian. Gary R. Collins. 64p. 1984. 5.95 (ISBN 0-8499-0450-1, 0450-1). Word Bks.

Sixty-Two Arguments That Justify a Bold New Creed. Mark Mahin. LC 85-71756. 225p. (Orig.). 1986. 17.95 (ISBN 0-931959-03-9); pap. 9.95 (ISBN 0-931959-04-7). Mindlifter Pr.

Sixty Ways to Let Yourself Grow. Martha M. McGaw. 64p. 1984. pap. 1.50 (ISBN 0-89243-211-X). Liguori Pubns.

Size of God: The Theology of Bernard Loomer in Context. Ed. by William Dean & Larry E. Axel. 96p. 1987. 16.95 (ISBN 0-86554-255-4, MUP H-223). Mercer Univ Pr.

Sizes in God's World. Beverly Beckman. 1984. 5.95 (ISBN 0-570-04095-7, 56-1463). Concordia.

Sjem' Vsjeljenskikh Soborov. Tr. of Seven Ecumenical Councils. 143p. 1968. pap. 5.00 (ISBN 0-317-30292-2). Holy Trinity.

Skanda Purana. Tr. by G. V. Tagare. Date not set. cancelled. Asian Human Pr.

Skazanije o Khrista Radi Jurodivoj - Pelagiji Ivanovna Serebrennikva. Tr. of Life of the Fool for Christ-Pelagia Ivanovna Serebrennikova. 183p. pap. 7.00 (ISBN 0-317-29280-3). Holy Trinity.

Skazanije o zhizni i Podvigakh Ieroskimanakha Parthenija, startsa Kievo-Petcherskoj-Lavri. Tr. of Life & Labours of Hieroschemamonk Parthenius, Elder of the Kiev-Caves Monastery. 104p. pap. 4.00 (ISBN 0-317-29270-6). Holy Trinity.

Skeptic & the Ten Commandmants. H. M. Richard. (Uplook Ser.). 1981. pap. 0.99 (ISBN 0-686-79998-4). Pacific Pr Pub Assn.

Skepticism & Moral Principles: Modern Ethics in Review. Ed. by Curtis I. Carter & Anthony Flew. 14.95 (ISBN 0-89044-017-4); pap. 8.95. Precedent Pub.

Skepticism & Moral Principles: Modern Ethics in Review. Ed. by Curtis L. Carter. LC 73-79477. (Studies in Ethics & Society Ser.: Vol. 1). 1973. 9.95 (ISBN 0-89044-017-4); pap. 4.95 (ISBN 0-89044-018-2). New Univ Pr.

Skeptics Quest. Joe Musser. 224p. (Orig.). 1984. pap. 6.95 (ISBN 0-86605-151-1). Campus Crusade.

Sketch of the Life & Times of Sydney Smith. Stuart J. Reid. 59.95 (ISBN 0-8490-1060-8). Gordon Pr.

Sketch of the Life & Times of the Rev. Sydney Smith. Stuart J. Reid. 1977. Repr. of 1885 ed. lib. bdg. 30.00 (ISBN 0-8495-4512-9). Arden Lib.

Sketch of the Sikhs. Malcolm. 202p. 1986. Repr. of 1812 ed. 20.00X (ISBN 0-8364-1755-0, PUb. by Abhinav India). South Asia Bks.

Sketchbook of the American Episcopate, During One Hundred Years, 1783-1883. Herman G. Batterson. 1980. Repr. cancelled (ISBN 0-87921-047-8). Attic Pr.

Sketches from Church History. S. M. Houghton. Ed. by Iain Murray. (Illus.). 256p. (Orig.). 1981. pap. 12.45 (ISBN 0-85151-317-4). Banner of Truth.

Sketches of Mission Life among the Indians of Oregon. Zachariah A. Mudge. 1983. 12.50 (ISBN 0-87770-308-6). Ye Galleon.

Sketches of North Carolina. 3rd ed. William H. Foote. 593p. 1965. 12.00. Synod NC Church.

Sketches of Tennessee's Pioneer Baptist Preachers: History of Baptist Beginnings in the Several Associations in the State. J. J. Burnett. (Illus.). 576p. 1985. Repr. of 1919 ed. 21.95 (ISBN 0-932807-11-9). Overmountain Pr.

Sketches of the Christian Life & Public Labors of William Miller. James White. LC 70-134376. Repr. of 1875 ed. 27.50 (ISBN 0-404-08424-9). AMS Pr.

Sketches of the Early Catholic Missions of Kentucky; from Their Commencement in 1787 to the Jubilee of 1826-7. Martin Spalding. LC 70-38548. (Religion in America, Ser. 2). 328p. 1972. Repr. of 1844 ed. 22.00 (ISBN 0-405-04087-3). Ayer Co Pubs.

Sketches of the Life, Times, - Character of Right Reverend Benedict Joseph Flaget, First Bishop of Louisville. Martin J. Spalding. LC 71-83441. (Religion in America, Ser. 1). 1969. Repr. of 1852 ed. 21.00 (ISBN 0-405-00266-1). Ayer Co Pubs.

Sketches of the Pioneers of Methodism in North Carolina & Virginia. M. H. Moore. 314p. 1977. Repr. of 1884 ed. 8.95 (ISBN 0-87921-039-7). Attic Pr.

Sketches of Western Methodism: Biographical, Historical & Miscellaneous Illustrative of Pioneer Life. James B. Finley. LC 79-83419. (Religion in America, Ser. 1). 1969. Repr. of 1954 ed. 30.00 (ISBN 0-405-00244-0). Ayer Co Pubs.

Skilful Means: A Concept in Mahayana Buddhism. Michael Pye. 211p. 1978. 75.00 (ISBN 0-7156-1266-2, Pub. by Duckworth London). Longwood Pub Group.

Skillful Shepherds: An Introduction to Pastoral Theology. Derek J. Tidball. 1986. pap. 12.95 (ISBN 0-310-44631-7). Zondervan.

Skits, 2 vols. Set. 8.95 (ISBN 0-685-61260-0). Young Life.

Skits That Teach. Colleen Ison. (Illus.). 112p. 1985. pap. 4.95 (ISBN 0-87239-848-X, 3356). Standard Pub.

Skits That Win. Ruth Vaughn. (Orig.). (YA) 1968. pap. 2.95 (ISBN 0-310-33661-9, 10941P). Zondervan.

Sklaverei, Staatskirche und Freikirche. Adolf Lotz. pap. 10.00 (ISBN 0-384-33770-8). Johnson Repr.

Sky Is My Tipi. Ed. by Mody C. Boatright. LC 49-1690. (Texas Folklore Society Publications: No. 22). (Illus.). 1966. Repr. of 1949 ed. 13.95 (ISBN 0-87074-010-5). SMU Press.

Skywatchers of Ancient Mexico. Anthony F. Aveni. (Texas Pan American Ser.). (Illus.). 369p. 1980. text ed. 30.00x (ISBN 0-292-77557-1). U of Tex Pr.

Slain in the Spirit. Ezra M. Coppin. LC 75-36001. 96p. 1976. pap. 2.50 (ISBN 0-89221-010-9). New Leaf.

Slaughter of the Innocents. John W. Montgomery. LC 81-65469. (Orig.). 1981. pap. 4.95 (ISBN 0-89107-216-0, Crossway Bks). Good News.

Slaveholding Not Sinful. facs. ed. Samuel B. How. LC 70-152922. (Black Heritage Library Collection Ser). 1855. 15.25 (ISBN 0-8369-8766-7). Ayer Co Pubs.

Slavery & Methodism: A Chapter in American Morality, 1780-1845. Donald G. Mathews. LC 78-13249. 1978. Repr. of 1965 ed. lib. bdg. 27.75 (ISBN 0-313-21045-4, MASAM). Greenwood.

Slavery & the Church. facs. ed. William Hosmer. LC 78-133156. (Black Heritage Library Collection Ser). 1853. 14.25 (ISBN 0-8369-8711-X). Ayer Co Pubs.

Slavery & the Church. William Hosmer. LC 70-82465. Repr. of 1853 ed. 22.50 (ISBN 0-8371-1646-5, HOS&). Greenwood.

Slavery Examined in the Light of the Bible. Luther Lee. LC 76-92434. 185p. 1855. Repr. 39.00x (ISBN 0-403-00166-8). Scholarly.

Slavery Ordained by God. facs. ed. Frederick A. Ross. LC 74-83876. (Black Heritage Library Collection Ser). 1857. 14.25 (ISBN 0-8369-8647-4). Ayer Co Pubs.

Slavery Ordained of God. Frederick Ross. LC 70-95445. (Studies in Black History & Culture, No. 54). 1970. Repr. of 1959 ed. lib. bdg. 48.95x (ISBN 0-8383-1202-0). Haskell.

Slavery, Sabbath, War & Women: Case Issues in Biblical Interpretation. Willard Swartley. LC 82-23417. (Conrad Grebel Lecture Ser.). 320p. (Orig.). 1983. pap. 15.95 (ISBN 0-8361-3330-7). Herald Pr.

Slaves & Missionaries: The Disintegration of Jamaican Slave Society, 1787-1834. Mary Turner. LC 82-6983. (Blacks in the New World Ser.). (Illus.). 240p. 1982. 25.95 (ISBN 0-252-00961-4). U of Ill Pr.

Slaves, Citizens, Sons: Legal Metaphors in the Epistles. Francis Lyall. 320p. 1984. pap. 9.95 (ISBN 0-310-45191-4, 12452P). Zondervan.

Slayers of Moses: The Emergence of Rabbinic Interpretation in Modern Literary Theory. Susan A. Handelman. LC 81-16522. (Modern Jewish Literature & Culture Ser.). 284p. 1982. 49.50x (ISBN 0-87395-576-5); pap. 18.95 (ISBN 0-87395-577-3). State U NY Pr.

Slayers of Superstition. Edgar R. Pike. LC 78-102581. 1970. Repr. of 1931 ed. 16.50x (ISBN 0-8046-0741-9, Pub.by Kennikat). Assoc Faculty Pr.

Sleep, Divine & Human, in the Old Testament. Thomas H. McAlpine. (JSOT Supplement Ser.: No. 38). 232p. 1986. text ed. 32.50x (ISBN 0-317-46791-3, Pub. by JSOT Pr England); pap. text ed. 14.95x (ISBN 0-317-46792-1). Eisenbrauns.

Sleep Tight Book. William L. Coleman. LC 82-12953. (Devotionals for Young Children Ser.). 125p. (Orig.). 1982. pap. 4.95 (ISBN 0-87123-577-3, 210577). Bethany Hse.

Slices of Life. Linda Andersen. 112p. 1986. pap. 6.95 (ISBN 0-8010-0205-2). Baker Bk.

Slim for Him. Patricia B. Kreml. LC 78-53422. 1978. pap. 4.95 (ISBN 0-88270-300-5). Bridge Pub.

Slovenian Letters by Missionaries in America, 1851-1874. Intro. by John A. Arnez. (Studia Slovenica Special Ser.: No.4). 230p. 1984. pap. 11.00 (ISBN 0-318-01454-8). Studia Slovenica.

Slow & Certain Light: Thoughts on the Guidance of God. Elisabeth Elliot. (Festival Ser.). 128p. 1982. pap. 1.95 (ISBN 0-687-38700-0). Abingdon.

Small Catechism in Contemporary English. Martin Luther. LC 15-6732. 1963. pap. 8.25 (ISBN 0-8066-0324-0, 15-6732). Augsburg.

Small Church is Different. Lyle E. Schaller. LC 82-1830. 192p. (Orig.). 1982. pap. 7.95 (ISBN 0-687-38717-5). Abingdon.

Small Churches Are the Right Size. David R. Ray. LC 82-11256. 224p. (Orig.). 1982. pap. 7.95 (ISBN 0-8298-0620-2). Pilgrim NY.

Small Golden Key to the Treasure of the Various Essential Necessities of General & Extraordinary Buddhist Dharma. rev. ed. Thinley Norbu. LC 84-29724. 111p. 1985. pap. 10.00 (ISBN 0-9607000-2-1). Jewel Pub Hse.

Small Group Evangelism. rev. ed. Richard Peace. 225p. 1983. pap. 6.95 (ISBN 0-87784-329-5). Inter-Varsity.

Small Groups: Timber to Build up God's House. Bob Couchman & Win Couchman. LC 82-798. (Carpenter Studyguide). 83p. 1982. pap. 2.95 (ISBN 0-87788-097-2). Shaw Pubs.

Small Net in a Big Sea: The Redemptorists in the Philippines, 1905-1929. Michael Baily. (Illus.). 8.00x (ISBN 0-686-24529-6, San Carlos Pubns); pap. 5.00x (ISBN 0-686-24530-X). Cellar.

Small Prayers for Small Children. Paul A. Schreivogel. LC 76-135226. (Illus.). 32p. 1980. pap. 3.95 (ISBN 0-8066-1804-3, 10-5836). Augsburg.

Small Rural Parish. Bernard Quinn. LC 79-56508. (Orig.). 1980. pap. 3.50x (ISBN 0-914422-11-1). Glenmary Res Ctr.

Small Sects in America. Elmer T. Clark. 11.75 (ISBN 0-8446-1862-4). Peter Smith.

Small Town Church. Peter J. Surrey. LC 81-622. (Creative Leadership Ser.). 128p. (Orig.). 1981. pap. 6.95 (ISBN 0-687-38720-5). Abingdon.

Small Woman: The Story of Gladys Aylward of China. Alan Burgess. 266p. 1985. pap. 5.95 (ISBN 0-89283-232-0, Pub. by Vine Books). Servant.

Smaller Church in a Super Church Era. Ed. by Jon Johnston & Bill M. Sullivan. 152p. 1983. pap. 5.95 (ISBN 0-8341-0895-X). Beacon Hill.

Smaller Religious School: A Manual. Rebecca Lister & Louis Lister. 1977. pap. text ed. 5.00 (ISBN 0-685-88426-0, 241850). UAHC.

Smallest Witch. Helen R. Sattler. LC 81-2202. (Illus.). 32p. 1982. 6.75 (ISBN 0-525-66747-4). Dandelion Pr.

Smart Girls Don't & Guys Don't Either. Kevin Leman. LC 82-7686. 1982. 8.95 (ISBN 0-8307-0824-3, 5419026). Regal.

Smashing the Idols: A Jewish Inquiry into the Cults. Gary Eisenberg. 325p. 1987. 25.00 (ISBN 0-87668-974-8). Aronson.

Smells in God's World. Kathryn Lutz. Ed. by Patricia H. Lemon. (Christian Storybooks). 24p. (Orig.). 1986. pap. 5.95 packaged with audio cassette (ISBN 0-939697-01-7); audio cassette incl. Graded Pr.

Smiles. David Kaplan & Marcia Kaplan. (Inspirational Ser.). (Illus.). 100p. 1982. pap. 4.95 (ISBN 0-939944-05-7). M & L Sales.

Smith of Smiths Being the Life, Wit & Humor of Sydney Smith. Hesketh Pearson. LC 73-145230. (Literature Ser.). (Illus.). 338p. 1972. Repr. of 1934 ed. 39.00x (ISBN 0-403-01146-9). Scholarly.

Smith Wigglesworth: Apostle of Faith. Stanley H. Frodsham. 160p. 1948. pap. 2.50 (ISBN 0-88243-586-8, 02-0586). Gospel Pub.

Smith Wigglesworth Remembered. W. Hacking. 107p. 1981. pap. 3.95 (ISBN 0-89274-203-8). Harrison Hse.

Smith Wigglesworth: The Secret of His Power. Albert Hibbert. 112p. 1982. pap. 4.95 (ISBN 0-89274-211-9, HH-211). Harrison Hse.

Smith's Bible Dictionary. rev. ed. William Smith. 9.95 (ISBN 0-87981-033-5); thumb-indexed 14.95 (ISBN 0-87981-035-1); pap. 6.95 (ISBN 0-87981-489-6). Holman Bible Pub.

Smith's Bible Dictionary. William Smith. (Family Library). (YA) 1984. pap. 5.95 (ISBN 0-515-08507-3). Jove Pubns.

Smith's Bible Dictionary. William Smith. Ed. by F. N. Peloubet & M. A. Peloubet. 1979. 8.95 (ISBN 0-8407-5542-2); pap. 5.95 (ISBN 0-8407-3085-3). Nelson.

Smith's Bible Dictionary. William Smith. 800p. pap. 4.95 (ISBN 0-8007-8039-6, Spire Bks). Revell.

Smith's Bible Dictionary. William Smith. (Illus.). 818p. 1981. pap. 7.95 (ISBN 0-310-32871-3, 10820P). Zondervan.

Smith's Bible Dictionary. William Smith. (Illus.). 1955. 10.95 (ISBN 0-310-32870-5, 10820). Zondervan.

Smith's Bible Dictionary. William Smith. 912p. Date not set. 10.95 (ISBN 0-917006-24-0). Hendrickson MA.

Smoke on the Mountain: An Interpretation of the Ten Commandments. Joy Davidman. LC 85-7622. 144p. 1985. pap. 7.95 (ISBN 0-664-24680-X). Westminster.

Smokescreens. Jack T. Chick. (Illus.). 93p. 1982. pap. 2.50 (ISBN 0-937958-14-X). Chick Pubns.

Smoking Gods: Tobacco in Maya Art, History, & Religion. Francis Robicsek. LC 78-64904. (Illus.). 1978. 39.50 (ISBN 0-8061-1511-4). U of Okla Pr.

Smouldering Fire. Martin Israel. 192p. 1986. pap. 8.95 (ISBN 0-8245-0728-2). Crossroad NY.

Smouldering Fire: The Work of the Holy Spirit. Martin Israel. LC 81-9794. 192p. 1981. 10.95 (ISBN 0-8245-0072-5). Crossroad NY.

Smudgkin Elves & Other Lame Excuses. Dotsey Welliver. 81p. 1981. pap. 3.95 (ISBN 0-89367-058-8). Light & Life.

Snake Ceremonials at Walpi. Jesse W. Fewkes et al. LC 76-17497. (Journal of American Ethnology & Archaeology: Vol. 4). Repr. of 1894 ed. 25.00 (ISBN 0-404-58044-0). AMS Pr.

Snake Dance of the Hopi Indians. Earle R. Forrest. LC 61-15835. (Illus.). 9.25 (ISBN 0-87026-018-9). Westernlore.

Snap Your Fingers, Slap Your Face & Wake Up! Bhagwan Shree Rajneesh. Ed. by Ma Deva Sarito. LC 84-43011. (Initiation Talks Ser.). 256p. (Orig.). 1984. pap. 3.95 (ISBN 0-88050-632-6). Chidvilas Found.

Snapdragon: The Story of John Henry Newman. Joyce Sugg. LC 81-85242. (Illus.). 192p. 1982. pap. 3.95 (ISBN 0-87973-653-4, 653). Our Sunday Visitor.

Snappy Bulletin Bits. Paul E. Holdcraft. LC 72-109673. pap. 20.00 (ISBN 0-8357-9027-4, 2016076). Bks Demand UMI.

Snappy Steeple Stories. Oren Arnold. LC 79-128150. (Church Humor Series). 80p. 1970. pap. 1.95 (ISBN 0-8254-2107-1). Kregel.

Snatched Before the Storm! Richard Mayhue. 1980. pap. 1.00 (ISBN 0-88469-124-1). BMH Bks.

So Beloved Cousins: The Life & Times of Solon B. Cousins, Jr. Joseph E. Nettles. LC 82-23986. x, 178p. 1983. 12.95x (ISBN 0-86554-070-5, H53). Mercer Univ Pr.

So Dear to Me. Winifred A. Mole. 1985. 11.95 (ISBN 0-533-06486-4). Vantage.

So Dreadful a Judgment: Puritan Responses to King Philip's War, 1676-1677. Ed. by Richard Slotkin & James K. Folsom. LC 77-14847. 1978. 27.00x (ISBN 0-8195-5027-2); pap. 13.00x (ISBN 0-8195-6058-8). Wesleyan U Pr.

So Great Salvation. Charles G. Finney. LC 65-25844. (Charles G. Finney Memorial Library). 128p. 1975. pap. 4.50 (ISBN 0-8254-2621-9). Kregel.

So Great Salvation. W. W. Hammel. 1972. pap. 2.95 (ISBN 0-87148-751-9). Pathway Pr.

So Great Salvation. 26th ed. J. F. Strombeck. LC 81-85530. 160p. 1982. pap. 3.95 (ISBN 0-89081-215-2). Harvest Hse.

So Great Salvation: The Meaning & Message of the Letter to the Hebrews. Alan M. Stibbs. 118p. 1970. pap. 4.95 (ISBN 0-85364-102-1). Attic Pr.

So High the Price. P. J. Kelley. LC 68-28104. (St. Paul Editions). 1968. 3.00 (ISBN 0-8198-0148-8). Dghtrs St Paul.

So I'm Not Perfect: A Psychology of Humility. Robert J. Furey. 131p. (Orig.). 1986. pap. 6.95 (ISBN 0-8189-0499-2). Alba.

So It Was True: The American Protestant Press & the Nazi Persecution of the Jews. Robert W. Ross. LC 80-196. 1980. 20.00 (ISBN 0-8166-0948-9); pap. 9.95 (ISBN 0-8166-0951-9). U of Minn Pr.

So It Was True: The American Protestant Press & the Nazi Persecution of the Jews. Robert W. Ross. 374p. pap. 9.95 (ISBN 0-686-95052-6). ADL.

So Let's Hear the Applause: The Story of the Jewish Entertainer. Michael Freedland. (Illus.). 250p. 1986. 16.50x (ISBN 0-85303-215-7, Pu. by Valentine Mitchell England). Biblio Dist.

So Many Versions? rev. enlarged ed. Sakae Kubo & Walter Specht. 320p. 1983. pap. 9.95 (ISBN 0-310-45691-6, 12458P). Zondervan.

So Moses Was Born. Joan Cerart. 312p. 1988. pap. 7.95 (ISBN 0-89804-149-X). Ariel OH.

So Moses Was Born. Joan M. Grant. 21.00 (ISBN 0-405-11791-4). Ayer Co Pubs.

So Send I You. Oswald Chambers. 1973. pap. 2.95 (ISBN 0-87508-138-X). Chr Lit.

So Send I You. Ralph M. Riggs. 130p. 1965. 1.25 (ISBN 0-88243-587-6, 02-0587). Gospel Pub.

So Strange My Path. Abraham Carmel. LC 64-17487. 1977. pap. 5.95 (ISBN 0-8197-0066-5). Bloch.

So We're Growing Older. Biegert. (Looking Up Ser.). 1982. pap. 1.25 booklet (ISBN 0-8298-0436-6). Pilgrim NY.

So What Is Peace. Angilee Beery. 1971. pap. 1.50 (ISBN 0-87178-934-5). Brethren.

So What's the Difference? rev. ed. Fritz Ridenour. LC 67-31426. 1979. 5.95 (ISBN 0-8307-0721-2, 5414008). Regal.

So Who's Perfect! Dhyan Cassie. LC 84-12948. 248p. (Orig.). 1984. pap. 12.95 (ISBN 0-8361-3372-2). Herald Pr.

So Who's Perfect? Richard E. Howard. 140p. (Orig.). 1985. pap. 5.95 (ISBN 0-8341-1070-9). Beacon Hill.

So You Think You've Got Problems: Twelve Stubborn Saints & Their Pushy Parents. Sharon Nastick. LC 81-85454. (Illus.). 96p. (Orig.). 1982. pap. 3.95 (ISBN 0-87973-661-5, 661). Our Sunday Visitor.

So You Want Solutions. Chuck Klein. 1979. pap. 4.95 (ISBN 0-8423-6161-8). Tyndale.

So You Want to Be a Leader. Kenneth O. Gangel. pap. 2.95 (ISBN 0-87509-131-8); leaders guide 2.00 (ISBN 0-87509-298-5). Chr Pubns.

So You Want to Get into the Race. Chuck Klein. 1980. concordance study guide 4.95 (ISBN 0-8423-6082-4). Tyndale.

So You Want to Lead Students. Chuck Klein. 96p. 1982. pap. 4.95 leader's guide (ISBN 0-8423-6084-0). Tyndale.

So You Want to Set the Pace. Chuck Klein. 96p. 1982. pap. 4.95 (ISBN 0-8423-6083-2). Tyndale.

So You're a Woman. Vynomma Clark. LC 70-180790. 4.95 (ISBN 0-89112-050-5, Bibl Res Pr). Abilene Christ U.

So You're Getting Married! Carol Benjamin. 1982. pap. 3.95 (ISBN 0-911739-15-7). Abbott Loop.

So You're Going to Heaven. M. R. Keith. 1965. 4.95 (ISBN 0-910122-22-9). Amherst Pr.

So You're the Pastor's Wife. Ruth Senter. 1979. pap. 4.95 (ISBN 0-310-38821-X). Zondervan.

Soaring Beyond Problems: Meditations for Difficult Times. Lois B. Swartz. (Illus.). 72p. (Orig.). 1987. pap. 6.95 (ISBN 0-940045-00-1). Walnut Knoll Assocs.

Soberania De Dios. A. W. Pink. 3.50 (ISBN 0-85151-416-2). Banner of Truth.

Sobibor: Martyrdom & Revolt. Ed. by Miriam Novitch. (Illus.). 168p. pap. 4.95 (ISBN 0-686-95087-9). ADL.

Sociable God. Ken Wilbur. LC 82-15241. (New Press Ser.). 176p. 1982. 12.95 (ISBN 0-07-070185-7). McGraw.

Sociable God: Toward a New Understanding of Religion. Ken Wilber. LC 84-5499. (New Science Library). 160p. 1984. pap. 8.95 (ISBN 0-87773-290-6, 72692-8). Shambhala Pubns.

Social Adjustment in Methodism. John P. Williams. LC 76-177639. (Columbia University. Teachers College. Contributions to Education: No. 765). Repr. of 1938 ed. 22.50 (ISBN 0-404-55765-1). AMS Pr.

Social & Historical Change: An Islamic Perspective. Ayatullah M. Mutahhari. Ed. by Hamid Algar. Tr. by R. Campbell from Persian. (Contemporary Islamic Thought, Persian Ser.). 156p. 1986. 18.95 (ISBN 0-933782-18-7); pap. 7.95 (ISBN 0-933782-19-5). Mizan Pr.

Social & Political History of the Jews in Poland, 1919-1939. Joseph Marcus. LC 82-22420. (New Babylon, Studies in the Social Sciences: No. 37). xviii, 569p. 1983. 88.50x (ISBN 90-279-3239-5). Mouton.

Social & Political Ideas of Some Great Thinkers of the Renaissance & the Reformation. Ed. by F. J. Hearnshaw. LC 85-7662. 216p. 1985. lib. bdg. 39.75x (ISBN 0-313-23862-6, HREN). Greenwood.

Social & Religious Heretics in Five Centuries. Carl Heath. LC 78-147622. (Library of War & Peace; Non-Resis. & Non-Vio.). 1972. lib. bdg. 46.00 (ISBN 0-8240-0397-7). Garland Pub.

Social & Religious History of the Jews, 18 vols. 2nd, rev. & enl. ed. Salo W. Baron. Incl. Vol. 1. Ancient Times to the Beginning of the Christian Era. 1952 (ISBN 0-231-08838-8); Vol. 2. Ancient Times: Christian Era: the First Five Centuries. 1952 (ISBN 0-231-08839-6); Vol. 3. High Middle Ages: Heirs of Rome & Persia. 1957 (ISBN 0-231-08840-X); Vol. 4. High Middle Ages: Meeting of the East & West. 1957 (ISBN 0-231-08841-8); Vol. 5. High Middle Ages: Religious Controls & Dissensions. 1957 (ISBN 0-231-08842-6); Vol. 6. High Middle Ages: Laws, Homilies & the Bible. 1958 (ISBN 0-231-08843-4); Vol. 7. High Middle Ages: Hebrew Language & Letters. 1958 (ISBN 0-231-08844-2); Vol. 8. High Middle Ages: Philosophy & Science. 1958 (ISBN 0-231-08845-0); Vol. 9. Late Middle Ages & Era of European Expansion, 1200-1650: Under Church & Empire. 1965 (ISBN 0-231-08846-9); Vol. 10. Late Middle Ages & Era of European Expansion, 1200-1650: On the Empire's Periphery. 1965 (ISBN 0-231-08847-7); Vol. 11. Late Middle Ages & Era of European **Expansion, 1200-1650: Citizen or Alien Conjurer. 1967 (ISBN 0-231-08848-5); Vol. 12. Late Middle Ages & Era of European Expansion, 1200-1650: Economic Catalyst. 1967 (ISBN 0-231-08849-3); Vol. 13. Late Middle Ages & Era of European Expansion, 1200-1650: Inquisition, Renaissance & Reformation. 1969 (ISBN 0-231-08850-7); Vol. 14. Late Middle Ages & Era of European Expansion, 1200-1650: Catholic Restoration & Wars of Religion. 1969 (ISBN 0-231-08851-5); Vol. 15. Late Middle Ages & Era of European Expansion, 1200-1650: Resettlement & Exploration. 1973 (ISBN 0-231-08852-3); Index. 32.00x (ISBN 0-231-08877-9). LC 52-404. 45.00x ea. Columbia U Pr.**

Social & Religious Life of Italians in the United States. Enrico C. Sartorio. LC 73-13520. 1974. Repr. of 1918 ed. 19.50x (ISBN 0-678-01364-0). Kelley.

Social Aspects of Early Christianity. 2nd, rev. ed. Abraham J. Malherbe. LC 83-5602. 144p. 1983. pap. 7.95 (ISBN 0-8006-1748-7, 1-1748). Fortress.

Social Basis of Religion. Simon Patten. (Neglected American Economists Ser.). 1974. lib. bdg. 61.00 (ISBN 0-8240-1028-0). Garland Pub.

Social Basis of the German Reformation: Martin Luther & His Times. Roy Pascal. LC 68-30539. 1971. Repr. of 1933 ed. 25.00x (ISBN 0-678-00549-4). Kelley.

Social Bond, an Investigation into the Bases of Law-Abidingness, Vol. IV: Safeguards of the Social Bond: Ethos & Religion. Werner Stark. viii, 288p. 1983. 25.00 (ISBN 0-8232-1083-9); pap. 12.50 (ISBN 0-8232-1084-7). Fordham.

Social Change & Prejudice. Bruno Bettelheim & Morris B. Janowitz. LC 64-11214. 1964. 18.95 (ISBN 0-02-903480-9). Free Pr.

Social Change in a Hostile Environment: The Crusaders' Kingdom of Jerusalem. Aharon Ben-Ami. (Princeton Studies on the Near East Ser.). (Illus.). 1969. 25.50x (ISBN 0-691-09344-X). Princeton U Pr.

Social Class & Church Participation. Erich Goode. Ed. by Harriet Zuckerman & Robert K. Merton. LC 79-9001. (Dissertations on Sociology Ser.). 1980. lib. bdg. 22.00x (ISBN 0-405-12970-X). Ayer Co Pubs.

Social Concern in Calvin's Geneva. William C. Innes. (Pittsburgh Theological Monographs: New Series 7). 1983. pap. 22.50 (ISBN 0-915138-33-6). Pickwick.

Social Context & Proclamation: A Socio-Cognitive Study in Proclaiming the Gospel Cross-Culturally. David Filbeck. LC 84-28539. (Illus.). 192p. 1985. pap. text ed. 8.95X (ISBN 0-87808-199-2). William Carey Lib.

Social Context of Paul's Ministry: Tentmaking & Apostleship. Ronald F. Hock. LC 79-7381. 112p. 1980. 8.95 (ISBN 0-8006-0577-2, 1-577). Fortress.

Social Context of Religiosity. Jerry D. Cardwell. LC 80-67216. 174p. 1980. pap. text ed. 10.75 (ISBN 0-8191-1136-8). U Pr of Amer.

Social Context of the New Testament: A Sociological Analysis. Derek Tidball. 160p. 1984. pap. 7.95 (ISBN 0-310-45391-7, 12602P). Zondervan.

Social Credit & Catholicism. George H. Levesque. 1979. lib. bdg. 39.95 (ISBN 0-8490-3006-4). Gordon Pr.

Social Crisis Preaching. Kelly M. Smith. LC 84-6656. x, 125p. 1984. 9.95x (ISBN 0-86554-111-6, MUP/H106); pap. 9.95 (ISBN 0-86554-246-5, MUP-P38). Mercer Univ Pr.

Social Criticism in Popular Religious Literature of the Sixteenth-Century. Helen C. White. 1965. lib. bdg. 20.50x (ISBN 0-374-98455-7, Octagon). Hippocrene Bks.

Social Doctrine of the Sermon on the Mount. Charles Gore. 59.95 (ISBN 0-8490-1063-2). Gordon Pr.

Social Ethics & the Christian: Towards Freedom in Communion. E. McDonagh. 96p. 1979. pap. 8.00 (ISBN 0-7190-0739-9, Pub. by Manchester Univ Pr). Longwood Pub Group.

Social Ethics: Morality & Social Policy. 3rd ed. T. A. Mappes & J. S. Zembathy. 528p. 1987. 22.95 (ISBN 0-07-040125-X). McGraw.

Social Ethics of Islam: Classical Islamic Political Theory & Practice. Abdul M. Al-Sayed. 1982. 14.95 (ISBN 0-533-04671-8). Vantage.

Social Future. new rev. ed. Rudolf Steiner. Tr. by Henry B. Monges from Ger. LC 72-87742. 151p. 1972. pap. text ed. 7.95 (ISBN 0-910142-34-3). Anthroposophic.

Social Gospel in the South: The Woman's Home Mission Movement in the Methodist Episcopal Church, South, 1886-1939. John P. McDowell. LC 82-15292. 167p. 1982. text ed. 20.00x (ISBN 0-8071-1022-1). La State U Pr.

Social Gospel: Religion & Reform in Changing America. Ronald C. White, Jr. & C. Howard Hopkins. LC 75-34745. (Illus.). 326p. 1975. 29.95 (ISBN 0-87722-083-2); pap. 9.95x (ISBN 0-87722-084-0). Temple U Pr.

Social Groups & Religious Ideas in the Sixteenth-Century. Ed. by Miriam Chrisman & Otto Grundler. (Studies in Medieval Culture: No. XIII). 1978. pap. 4.95x (ISBN 0-918720-02-8). Medieval Inst.

Social History & Evolution in the Interrelationship of Adat & Islam in Rembau, Negeri Sembilan. Michael G. Peletz. 59p. (Orig.). 1981. pap. text ed. 9.50x (ISBN 9971-902-28-1, Pub. by Inst Southeast Asian Stud). Gower Pub Co.

Social Ideals of St. Francis. James Meyer. 2.75 (ISBN 0-8199-0296-9, L38825). Franciscan Herald.

Social Ideas of Religious Leaders, Sixteen Sixty to Sixteen Sixty-Eight. Richard B. Schlatter. LC 77-120663. 1970. Repr. lib. bdg. 18.50x (ISBN 0-374-97102-1, Octagon). Hippocrene Bks.

Social Ideas of the Northern Evangelists, Eighteen Twenty-Six to Eighteen Sixty. Charles C. Cole, Jr. 1966. lib. bdg. 20.50x (ISBN 0-374-91843-0, Octagon). Hippocrene Bks.

Social Justice & Church Authority: The Public Life of Archbishop Robert E. Lucey. Saul E. Bronder. 215p. 1982. 29.95 (ISBN 0-87722-239-8). Temple U Pr.

Social Justice & the Christian Church. Ronald H. Nash. 175p. 1983. 12.95 (ISBN 0-88062-008-0). Mott Media.

Social Justice & the Christian Church. Ed. by Ronald H. Nash. 1986. pap. 7.95 (ISBN 0-8010-6746-4). Baker Bk.

Social Justice in Islam. Sayed Kotb. LC 75-96205. 1969. Repr. of 1953 ed. lib. bdg. 20.00x (ISBN 0-374-94617-5, Octagon). Hippocrene Bks.

Social Law in the Spirtual World. Rufus M. Jones. (Studies in Human & Divine Inter-Relationship Ser.). 1978. Repr. of 1904 ed. lib. bdg. 25.00 (ISBN 0-8495-2731-7). Arden Lib.

Social Laws of the Qoran. Robert Roberts. 136p. 1982. text ed. 11.95x (ISBN 0-7007-0009-9, Pub. by Curzon Pr England). Apt Bks.

Social Legislation of the Primitive Semites. Henry Schaeffer. LC 70-174369. Repr. of 1915 ed. 16.00 (ISBN 0-405-08929-5). Ayer Co Pubs.

Social Meanings of Religious Experiences. George D. Herron. (American Studies Ser.). 1969. Repr. of 1896 ed. 18.00 (ISBN 0-384-22660-4). Johnson Repr.

Social Message of Jesus. Igino Giordani. 1977. 4.50 (ISBN 0-8198-0467-3); pap. 3.50 (ISBN 0-8198-0468-1). Dghtrs St Paul.

Social Message of the Early Church Fathers. Igino Giordani. 1977. 3.95 (ISBN 0-8198-0469-X); pap. 2.95 (ISBN 0-8198-0470-3). Dghtrs St Paul.

Social Message of the Gospels. Ed. by Franz Bockle. LC 68-31249. (Concilium Ser.: Vol. 35). 188p. 7.95 (ISBN 0-8091-0138-6). Paulist Pr.

Social Ministry. Dieter T. Hessel. LC 82-6960. 228p. 1982. pap. 10.95 (ISBN 0-664-24422-X). Westminster.

Social Organization & Ritualistic Ceremonies of the Blackfoot Indians, 2 parts in 1 vol. Clark Wissler. LC 74-9020. (Anthropological Papers of the American Museum of Natural History: Vol. 7). (Illus.). Repr. of 1912 ed. 24.00 (ISBN 0-404-11917-4). AMS Pr.

Social Organization & Secret Societies of the Kwakiutl Indians. Based on Personal Observations Notes Made by Mr. George Hunt. Franz Boas. (Landmarks in Anthropology Ser). Repr. of 1897 ed. 60.00 (ISBN 0-384-04872-2). Johnson Repr.

Social Philosophy of Martin Buber: The Social World as a Human Dimension. John W. Murphy. LC 82-21779. 176p. (Orig.). 1983. lib. bdg. 26.25 (ISBN 0-8191-2940-2); pap. text ed. 11.50 (ISBN 0-8191-2941-0). U Pr of Amer.

Social Philosophy of the St. Louis Hegelians. Frances A. Harmon. LC 75-3159. 1976. Repr. of 1943 ed. 20.00 (ISBN 0-404-59164-7). AMS Pr.

Social, Political & Religious Thought of Alfred Rosenberg: An Interpretive Essay. James B. Whisker. LC 81-40652. 150p. (Orig.). 1982. lib. bdg. 25.50 (ISBN 0-8191-2023-5); pap. text ed. 9.75 (ISBN 0-8191-2024-3). U Pr of Amer.

Social Principles of Jesus. Walter Rauschenbusch. LC 76-50566. 1976. Repr. of 1916 ed. lib. bdg. 22.00 (ISBN 0-8414-7308-0). Folcroft.

Social Protest in India: British Protestant Missionaries & Social Reforms, Eighteen Fifty to Nineteen Hundred. G. A. Oddie. 1979. 17.50x (ISBN 0-8364-0195-6). South Asia Bks.

Social Psychology of Religion. Michael Argyle & Benjamin Beit-Hallahmi. 1975. 25.00x (ISBN 0-7100-7997-4); pap. 10.95X (ISBN 0-7100-8043-3). Methuen Inc.

Social Reform & the Church. John R. Commons. LC 66-21663. (Illus.). 1967. Repr. of 1894 ed. 22.50x (ISBN 0-678-00286-X). Kelley.

Social Reform & the Reformation. Jacob S. Schapiro. LC 74-127456. (Columbia University Studies in the Social Sciences: No. 90). 1970. Repr. of 1909 ed. 16.50 (ISBN 0-404-51090-6). AMS Pr.

Social Reformers in Urban China: The Chinese Y. M. C. A., Eighteen Ninety-Five to Nineteen Twenty-Six. Shirley Garrett. LC 74-133218. (East Asian Ser.: No. 56). 1970. 16.50x (ISBN 0-674-81220-4). Harvard U Pr.

Social Relations in the Urban Parish. Joseph H. Fichter. LC 54-11207. pap. 68.00 (ISBN 0-317-07856-9, 2020061). Bks Demand UMI.

Social Relations of Physics, Mysticism & Mathematics. Sal Restivo. 1983. lib. bdg. 49.50 (ISBN 90-277-1536-X, Pub. by Reidel Holland). Kluwer Academic.

Social Relations of Physics, Mysticism & Mathematics. Sal Restivo. (Pallas Paperbacks Ser.). 1985. pap. 14.95 (ISBN 90-277-2084-3, Pub. by Reidel Holland). Kluwer Academic.

Social Responsibility in an Age of Revolution. Louis Finkelstein. 1971. 10.00x (ISBN 0-685-31421-9, Pub. by Jewish Theol Seminary). Ktav.

Social-Scientific Criticism of the New Testament. Ed. by John H. Elliott. (Semeia Ser.: No. 35). pap. 9.95 (06 20 35). Scholars Pr GA.

Social Setting of Pauline Christianity: Essays on Corinth. Gerd Theissen. Tr. by John H. Schutz. LC 81-43087. 1982. 19.95 (ISBN 0-8006-0669-8). Fortress.

Social Sources of Denominationalism. Richard H. Niebuhr. 1984. 17.50 (ISBN 0-8446-6150-3). Peter Smith.

Social Structure & the German Reformation. Norman Birnbaum. Ed. by Harriet Zuckerman & Robert K. Merton. LC 79-8976. (Dissertation on Sociology Ser.). 1980. lib. bdg. 40.00x (ISBN 0-405-12952-1). Ayer Co Pubs.

Social Structure of Islam. Reuben Levy. 1957. 70.00 (ISBN 0-521-05544-X). Cambridge U Pr.

Social Teaching of the Black Churches. Peter J. Paris. LC 84-47930. 176p. 1985. pap. 8.95 (ISBN 0-8006-1805-X, 1-1805). Fortress.

Social Teaching of the Christian Churches, 2 vols. Ernst Troeltsch. Tr. by Olive Wyon. LC 81-10443. 1981. Vol. 1, 446p. pap. 17.00X (ISBN 0-226-81298-7); Vol. II, 569p. pap. 17.00 (ISBN 0-226-81299-5). U of Chicago Pr.

Social Teaching of the Christian Churches, 2 vols. Ernst Troeltsch. 44.00 set (ISBN 0-8446-6134-1). Peter Smith.

Social Teaching of Vatican II: Its Origin & Development. Catholic Social Ethics-an Historical & Comparative Study. Rodger Charles. LC 81-83567. (Illus.). 597p. 1982. 30.00 (ISBN 0-89870-013-2). Ignatius Pr.

Social Themes of the Christian Year: A Commentary on the Lectionary. Ed. by Dieter T. Hessel. LC 83-1504. 284p. (Orig.). 1983. pap. 10.95 (ISBN 0-664-24472-6, A Geneva Press Publication). Westminster.

Social Theories of the Middle Ages, Twelve Hundred to Twelve-Fifty. Bede Bartlett. 1976. lib. bdg. 59.95 (ISBN 0-8490-2619-9). Gordon Pr.

Social Theory of Religious Education. George A. Coe. LC 78-89164. (American Education: Its Men, Institutions & Ideas, Ser. 1). 1969. Repr. of 1917 ed. 24.50 (ISBN 0-405-01402-3). Ayer Co Pubs.

Social Thought. Peter C. Phan. (Message of the Fathers of the Church Ser.: Vol. 20). 15.95 (ISBN 0-89453-360-6); pap. 9.95 (ISBN 0-89453-331-2). M Glazier.

Social Thought of John Twenty-Third: Mater et Magistra. Jean Y. Calvez. Tr. by George J. McKenzie. LC 75-40992. 1977. Repr. of 1965 ed. lib. bdg. 22.50x (ISBN 0-8371-8711-7, CASCJ). Greenwood.

Social Thought of Saint Bonaventure: A Study in Social Philosophy. Matthew M. DeBenedictis. LC 73-138108. 276p. 1946. Repr. lib. bdg. 22.50x (ISBN 0-8371-5684-X, DESB). Greenwood.

Social Triumph of the Ancient Church. facsimile ed. Shirley J. Case. LC 76-164596. (Select Bibliographies Reprint Ser). Repr. of 1933 ed. 18.00 (ISBN 0-8369-5880-2). Ayer Co Pubs.

Social Understanding Through Spiritual Scientific Knowledge. Rudolf Steiner. 20p. 1982. pap. 2.00 (ISBN 0-88010-075-3). Anthroposophic.

Socialism & the American Spirit. facsimile ed. Nicholas P. Gilman. LC 70-150183. (Select Bibliographies Reprint Ser). Repr. of 1893 ed. 23.50 (ISBN 0-8369-5696-6). Ayer Co Pubs.

Socialism & the Jews: The Dilemmas of Assimilation in Germany & Austria-Hungary. Robert S. Wistrich. (Littman Library of Jewish Civilization). 1982. 37.50x (ISBN 0-19-710053-8). Oxford U Pr.

Socialism in Theological Perspective: A Study of Paul Tillich, Nineteen Eighteen to Nineteen Thirty-Three. John R. Stumme. LC 78-3675. (American Academy of Religion. Dissertation Ser.: No. 21). 1978. pap. 9.95 (ISBN 0-89130-232-8, 010121). Scholars Pr GA.

Socialist Democracy. G. Shakhnazarov. 150p. 1974. pap. 2.95 (ISBN 0-8285-0412-1, Pub. by Progress Pubs USSR). Imported Pubns.

Socialist Humanism: The Outcome of Classical European Morality. Donald C. Hodges. LC 73-96983. 384p. 1974. 19.75 (ISBN 0-87527-042-5). Green.

Socialist Zionism: Theory & Issues in Contemporary Jewish Nationalism. Allon Gal. 225p. 1973. pap. 5.50 (ISBN 0-87073-669-8). Transaction Bks.

Sociality, Ethics, & Social Change: A Critical Appraisal of Reinhold Niebuhr's Ethics in the Light of Rosemary Radford Ruether's Works. annual Judith Vaughan. LC 83-1293. 228p. (Orig.). 1983. text ed. 26.00 (ISBN 0-8191-3100-8); pap. text ed. 12.50 (ISBN 0-8191-3101-6). U Pr of Amer.

Socialization of the New England Clergy Eighteen Hundred to Eighteen Sixty. Gordon A. Riegler. LC 79-13027. (Perspectives in American History Ser.: No. 37). 187p. 1980. Repr. of 1945 ed. lib. bdg. 25.00x (ISBN 0-87991-361-4). Porcupine Pr.

Socially Responsible Believers: Puritans, Pietists, & Unionists in the History of the United Church of Christ. Lowell H. Zuck. 164p. (Orig.). 1987. pap. 8.95 (ISBN 0-8298-0744-6). Pilgrim NY.

Socials for All Occasions. Mildred Wade. LC 79-55492. (Orig.). 1980. pap. 4.95 (ISBN 0-8054-7518-4). Broadman.

Society & Economics in Islam. Sayyid M. Taleghani. Tr. by R. Campbell from Persian. LC 82-2115. (Contemporary Islamic Thought Ser.). 225p. 1983. 17.95 (ISBN 0-933782-08-X). Mizan Pr.

Society & Original Sin: Ecumenical Essays on the Impact of the Fall. Ed. by Paul Mojzes & Durwood Foster. LC 84-25406. (Interreligious Explorations Ser.). 216p. (Orig.). 1985. pap. 11.95 (ISBN 0-913757-15-2, Pub. by New Era Bks). Paragon Hse.

Society & Religion in Early Ottoman Egypt. Michael Winter. LC 81-3042. 350p. 1981. 39.95 (ISBN 0-87855-351-7). Transaction Bks.

Society & Religion in Elizabethan England. Richard L. Greaves. LC 81-2530. pap. 160.00 (2056201). Bks Demand UMI.

Society & Religion in Munster. R. Po-chia Hsia. LC 83-14819. (Yale Historical Publications Ser.: No. 131). 320p. 1984. text ed. 27.50x (ISBN 0-300-03005-3). Yale U Pr.

Society & Social Change in the Writings of St. Thomas, Ward, Sumner, & Cooley. Mary E. Healy. LC 75-156191. 159p. 1972. Repr. of 1948 ed. lib. bdg. 22.50x (ISBN 0-8371-6140-1, HESC). Greenwood.

Society & the Sacred: Toward a Theology of Culture in Decline. Langdon Gilkey. LC 81-9775. 225p. 1981. 14.95 (ISBN 0-8245-0089-X). Crossroad NY.

Society & the Sexes in Medieval Islam. Ed. by A. L. Al-Sayyid-Marsot. LC 79-63268. (Giorgio Levi Della Vida Biennial Conference Ser.: Vol. 6). 149p. 1979. pap. 18.50x (ISBN 0-89003-033-2). Undena Pubns.

Society for the Propagation of the Faith: Its Foundation, Organization & Success (1822-1922) Edward J. Hickey. LC 73-3557. (Catholic University of America. Studies in American Church History: No. 3). Repr. of 1922 ed. 25.00 (ISBN 0-404-57753-9). AMS Pr.

Society of Biblical Literature Nineteen Eighty-One: Seminar Papers. Ed. by Kent Richards. (SBL Seminar Papers & Abstracts). pap. 9.00 (ISBN 0-89130-548-3, 06-09-20). Scholars Pr GA.

Society of Biblical Literature: Seminar Papers Nineteen Eighty. Paul J. Achtemeier. (SBL Seminar Papers & Abstracts). pap. 9.00 (ISBN 0-89130-357-X, 06-09-19). Scholars Pr GA.

Society of Biblical Literature: Seminar Papers Nineteen Eighty-Four. Ed. by Kent H. Richards. 412p. 1984. pap. 15.00 (ISBN 0-89130-810-5, 06 09 23). Scholars Pr GA.

Society of Biblical Literature: Seminar Papers Nineteen Eighty-Three. Ed. by Kent H. Richards. (SBL Seminar Papers). 490p. 1983. pap. 15.00 (ISBN 0-89130-607-2, 06 09 22). Scholars Pr GA.

Society of Friends. Howard H. Brinton. 1983. pap. 2.50x (ISBN 0-87574-048-0, 048). Pendle Hill.

Society of Friends. George Gorman. 1978. pap. 3.15 (ISBN 0-08-021412-6). Pergamon.

Society of the Future. Raghavan Iyer. 84. 8.75 (ISBN 0-88695-018-X). Concord Grove.

Society of the Sacred Heart: History of a Spirit 1800-1975. Margaret Williams. 406p. 1978. pap. 12.50 (ISBN 0-232-51395-3). Attic Pr.

Society, State, & Schools: A Case for Structural & Confessional Pluralism. Gordon Spykman et al. 224p. (Orig.). 1981. pap. 9.95 (ISBN 0-8028-1880-3). Eerdmans.

Society, the Redeemed Form of Man, & the Earnest of God's Omnipotence in Human Nature: Affirmed in Letters to a Friend. Henry James. 1971. Repr. of 1879 ed. 35.00 (ISBN 0-384-26735-1). Johnson Repr.

Sociocultural Changes in American Jewish Life As Reflected in Selected Jewish Literature. Bernard Cohen. LC 75-146162. 282p. 1972. 24.50 (ISBN 0-8386-7848-3). Fairleigh Dickinson.

Sociological Approaches to the Old Testament. Robert R. Wilson. LC 83-16607. (Guides to Biblical Scholarship). 96p. 1984. pap. 4.50 (ISBN 0-8006-0469-5, 1-469). Fortress.

Sociological Role of the Yoruba Cult-Group. W. R. Bascom. LC 44-47266. (American Anthro. Association Memoirs). Repr. of 1944 ed. 15.00 (ISBN 0-527-00562-2). Kraus Repr.

Sociological Value of Christianity. Georges Chatterton-Hill. LC 83-45605. Date not set. Repr. of 1912 ed. 36.00 (ISBN 0-404-19873-2). AMS Pr.

Sociology & Human Destiny: Studies in Sociology, Religion & Society. Ed. by Gregory Baum. 224p. 1980. 14.50 (ISBN 0-8164-0110-1, HarpR). Har-Row.

Sociology & Pastoral Work. Francois Houtart. pap. 1.50 (ISBN 0-8199-0133-4, L38828). Franciscan Herald.

Sociology & the Human Image. David Lyon. LC 83-22644. 220p. 1983. pap. 9.95 (ISBN 0-87784-843-2). Inter-Varsity.

Sociology & Theology. Ed. by David Martin et al. 170p. 1980. 26.00x (ISBN 0-312-74007-7). St Martin.

Sociology of Early Palestinian Christianity. Gerd Theissen. Tr. by John Bowden from Ger. LC 77-15248. Tr. of Soziologie der Jesusbewegung. 144p. 1978. pap. 5.95 (ISBN 0-8006-1330-9, 1-1330). Fortress.

Sociology of Religion. Georg Simmel. Ed. by Lewis A. Coser & Walter W. Powell. Tr. by Curt Rosenthal from Ger. LC 79-7021. (Perennial Works in Sociology Ser.). 1979. Repr. of 1959 ed. lib. bdg. 15.00x (ISBN 0-405-12120-2). Ayer Co Pubs.

Sociology of Religion. Joachim Wach. 1944. 12.00x (ISBN 0-226-86707-2). U of Chicago Pr.

Sociology of Religion. Max Weber. Tr. by Ephraim Fischoff. 1964. pap. 10.95x (ISBN 0-8070-4193-9, BP189). Beacon Pr.

Sociology of Religion: A Bibliographical Survey. Compiled by Roger Homan. LC 86-18471. (Bibliographies & Indexes in Religious Studies: No. 9). 309p. 1986. lib. bdg. 45.00 (ISBN 0-313-24710-2, HOS/). Greenwood.

Sociology of Religion: A Study of Christendom, 5 vols. Werner Stark. Incl. Vol. 1. Established Religion. xii, 235p. 1967. 20.00 (ISBN 0-8232-0720-X); Vol. 2. Sectarian Religion. viii, 357p. 1967. 22.50 (ISBN 0-8232-0735-8); Vol. 3. Universal Church. x, 454p. 1967. 25.00 (ISBN 0-8232-0760-9); Vol. 4. Types of Religious Man. xii, 340p. 1970. 22.50 (ISBN 0-8232-0855-9); Vol. 5. Types of Religious Culture. x, 453p. 1972. 25.00 (ISBN 0-8232-0935-0). LC 66-27652. Set (ISBN 0-8232-0719-6). Fordham.

Sociology of Religion: Classical & Contemporary Approaches. Barbara Hargrove. LC 79-50879. 1979. pap. text ed. 16.95x (ISBN 0-88295-211-0). Harlan Davidson.

Sociology of the Church: Essays in Reconstruction. James B. Jordan. LC 86-80571. 320p. (Orig.). 1986. pap. 12.95 (ISBN 0-939404-12-5). Geneva Ministr.

Socioreligious Factors in Fertility Decline. Leon Bouvier & Sethu Rao. LC 75-26602. 224p. 1975. text ed. 25.00x prof ref (ISBN 0-88410-352-8). Ballinger Pub.

Sock Bunnies: Christmas & Spring Edition. Date not set. pap. 4.98 (ISBN 0-317-03192-9). Gick.

Socrates. Gerasimos X. Santas. 1982. pap. 10.95 (ISBN 0-7100-9327-6). Methuen Inc.

Socrates & Christ. R. M. Wenley. 1977. 59.95 (ISBN 0-8490-2621-0). Gordon Pr.

Socrates, Buddha, Confucius & Jesus: Taken from Vol. 1 of the Great Philosophers. Karl Jaspers. Tr. by Ralph Manheim. 1966. pap. 3.95 (ISBN 0-15-683580-0, Harv). HarBraceJ.

Socrates Meets Jesus. Peter Kreeft. 180p. (Orig.). 1987. pap. 5.95 (ISBN 0-87784-999-4). Inter-Varsity.

Sodom Had No Bible. Leonard Ravenhill. 208p. 1979. pap. 4.95 (ISBN 0-87123-496-3, 210496). Bethany Hse.

Sofer: The Story of a Torah Scroll. Eric Ray. LC 85-52420. (Illus.). 32p. (Orig.). 1986. pap. text ed. 4.95 (ISBN 0-933873-04-2). Torah Aura.

Soils & Seeds of Sectarianism. James D. Bales. 1977. pap. 4.50 (ISBN 0-89315-264-1). Lambert Bk.

Sojourner Truth. Victoria Ortiz. LC 73-22290. (Illus.). 160p. (YA) 1974. PLB 10.89 (ISBN 0-397-31504-X, Lipp Jr Bks). HarpJ.

Sol Ecce Surgit Igneus: A Commentary on the Morning & Evening Hymns of Prudentius. Marion M. Van Assendelft. vii, 275p. 1976. 30.00x (ISBN 90-6088-060-9, Pub. by Boumas Boekhuis Netherlands). Benjamins North AM.

Solamente Por Gracia. Charles H. Spurgeon. (Span.). 128p. 1982. pap. 3.25 (ISBN 0-8254-1678-7). Kregel.

Solar Church. Jennifer A. Adams. Ed. by Douglas R. Hoffman. LC 82-11281. 288p. (Orig.). 1982. pap. 9.95 (ISBN 0-8298-0482-X). Pilgrim NY.

Solar Revolution & the Prophet. Pierre Renard. (Testimonials Ser.). (Illus.). 193p. (Orig.). 1980. pap. 9.95 (ISBN 2-85566-135-8, Pub. by Prosveta France). Prosveta USA.

Sold on Sunday School. O. D. Robertson. (Orig.). 1984. pap. text ed. 3.95 (ISBN 0-87148-808-6). Pathway Pr.

Soldier for Jesus. Patricia Maxwell. (Trailblazers Ser.). 1981. pap. 5.95 (ISBN 0-8163-0374-6). Pacific Pr Pub Assn.

Soldier of God. 1.00. Paulist Pr.

Soldier of God. Patricia Treece. 32p. 1982. pap. 1.00 (ISBN 0-913382-22-1, 111-1). Prow Bks-Franciscan.

Soldier of the Church: The Life of Ignatius Loyola. Ludwig Marcuse. LC 70-172842. Repr. of 1939 ed. 23.00 (ISBN 0-404-04187-6). AMS Pr.

Soldier of the Cross. 2nd ed. John Leyburn. 339p. 1986. Repr. of 1851 ed. lib. bdg. 27.50 (ISBN 0-89941-509-1). W S Hein.

Soldier, Sage, Saint. Robert C. Neville. LC 77-75798. 1978. 20.00 (ISBN 0-8232-1035-9); pap. 8.00 (ISBN 0-8232-1036-7). Fordham.

Soldiers of the Cross. J. B. Salpointe. 1977. Repr. of 1898 ed. lib. bdg. 24.95x (ISBN 0-89712-063-9). Documentary Pubns.

Soldiers of the Cross: Notes on the Ecclesiastical History of New Mexico, Arizona, & Colorado. J. B. Salpointe. LC 67-29317. 299p. 1982. lib. bdg. 44.95x (ISBN 0-89370-733-3). Borgo Pr.

Soldiers of the Faith: Crusaders & Moslems at War. Ronald C. Finucane. (Illus.). 256p. 1984. 19.95 (ISBN 0-312-74256-8). St Martin.

Sole Spokesman: Jinnah, the Muslim League & the Demand for Pakistan. Ayesha Jalal. (South Asian Studies: No. 31). (Illus.). 336p. 1985. 49.50 (ISBN 0-521-24462-5). Cambridge U Pr.

Solid Ground: Facts of the Faith for Young Christians. David Schroeder. Frwd. by Paul Bubna. 255p. 1982. pap. 4.95 (ISBN 0-87509-323-X); Leader's guide 2.95 (ISBN 0-87509-326-4). Chr Pubns.

Solid Living in a Shattered World. William H. Hinson. 160p. 1985. 8.95 (ISBN 0-687-39048-6). Abingdon.

Solidaritaet mit den Leidenden im Judentum. Rachel Rosenzweig. (Studia Judaica: Vol. 10). 1978. 46.40x (ISBN 3-11-005939-8). De Gruyter.

Solidarity & Kinship: Essays on American Zionism. Ed. by Nathan M. Kaganoff. (Illus.). 1980. 5.00 (ISBN 0-911934-14-6). Am Jewish Hist Soc.

Solidarity with the People of Nicaragua. James McGinnis. LC 84-27202. (Illus.). 192p. (Orig.). 1985. pap. 7.95 (ISBN 0-88344-448-8). Orbis Bks.

Solidarity with Victims: Toward a Theology of Social Transformation. Matthew L. Lamb. LC 81-22145. 176p. 1982. 12.95 (ISBN 0-8245-0471-2). Crossroad NY.

Solitude in the Thought of Thomas Merton. Richard A. Cashen. (Cistercian Studies: No. 40). 208p. 1981. 15.50 (ISBN 0-87907-840-5); pap. 5.50 (ISBN 0-87907-940-1). Cistercian Pubns.

Solitude to Sacrament. Katherine M. Dyckman & L. Patrick Carroll. LC 82-252. 128p. (Orig.). 1982. pap. 2.95 (ISBN 0-8146-1255-5). Liturgical Pr.

Solo. Sarah Jepson. LC 72-131443. 1970. pap. 1.95 (ISBN 0-88419-134-6). Creation Hse.

Solo para Muchachos. Frank H. Richardson. 112p. 1986. pap. 1.95 (ISBN 0-311-46929-9). Casa Bautista.

Solomon. Rebecca Daniel. (Our Greatest Heritage Ser.). (Illus.). 32p. 1983. wkbk. 3.95 (ISBN 0-86653-139-4, SS 808). Good Apple.

Solomon & Rehoboam. Gordon Lindsay. (Old Testament Ser.). 1.25 (ISBN 0-89985-145-2). Christ Nations.

Solomon & Sheba. Faye Levine. 240p. 1986. pap. 9.95 (ISBN 0-312-74283-5). St Martin.

Solomon & Solomonic Literature. Moncure D. Conway. LC 72-2032. (Studies in Comparative Literature, No. 35). 1972. Repr. of 1899 ed. lib. bdg. 49.95x (ISBN 0-8383-1478-3). Haskell.

Solomon to the Exile: Studies in Kings & Chronicles. John C. Whitcomb, Jr. pap. 4.95 (ISBN 0-88469-054-7). BMH Bks.

Solomon's New Men. E. W. Heaton. LC 74-13412. (Illus.). 216p. 1975. 15.00x (ISBN 0-87663-714-4, Pica Pr). Universe.

Solomon's Secret: Enjoying Life, God's Good Gift. Ray C. Stedman. LC 85-8967. (Authentic Christianity Bks.). 1985. pap. 6.95 (ISBN 0-88070-076-9). Multnomah.

Solomon's Sword: Clarifying Values in the Church. Robert Meyners & Claire Wooster. LC 77-9391. Repr. of 1977 ed. 27.40 (ISBN 0-8357-9028-2, 2016408). Bks Demand UMI.

Soloveitchik on Repentance. Joseph D. Soloveitchik. Tr. by Pinchas Peli. 320p. 1984. 11.95 (ISBN 0-8091-2604-4). Paulist Pr.

Solution of Doctor Resolutus, His Resolutions for Kneeling. David Calderwood. LC 79-84093. (English Experience Ser.: No. 913). 60p. 1979. Repr. of 1619 ed. lib. bdg. 8.00 (ISBN 90-221-0913-5). Walter J Johnson.

Solving Ethical Problems. Murray Friedman. 0.50 (ISBN 0-914131-58-3, 138). Torah Umesorah.

Solving Life's Problems. Paul Y. Cho. LC 80-82787. (Orig.). 1980. pap. 4.95 (ISBN 0-88270-450-8). Bridge Pub.

Solving Marriage Problems. Jay E. Adams. 1983. pap. 4.50 (ISBN 0-8010-0197-8). Baker Bk.

Solving Marriage Problems. Jay E. Adams. 132p. 1983. pap. 5.95 (ISBN 0-87552-081-2). Presby & Reformed.

Solving Marriage Problems: Biblical Solutions for Christian Counselors. Jay E. Adams. (Jay Adams Library). 144p. 1986. pap. 6.95 (ISBN 0-310-51081-3, 12120P). Zondervan.

Solving the Ministry's Toughest Problems, 2 vols. Ed. by Stephen Strang et al. 432p. 1984. Vol. I. 24.95 (ISBN 0-930525-00-0); Vol. II. write for info. (ISBN 0-930525-01-9). Strang Comms Co.

Soma, in Biblical Theology, with Emphasis on Pauline Anthropology. R. Gundry. LC 75-22927. (Society for New Testament Studies: No. 29). 300p. 1976. o. p. 54.50 (ISBN 0-521-20788-6). Cambridge U Pr.

Soma in Biblical Theology: With Emphasis on Pauline Anthropology. Robert H. Gundry. LC 75-22975. (Society for New Testament Studies. Monograph: 29). pap. 69.50 (ISBN 0-317-41736-3, 2025584). Bks Demand UMI.

Somain Biblical Theology: With Emphasis on Pauline Anthropology. Robert H. Gundry. LC 75-22975. (Society for New Testament Studies: No. 29). pap. 69.50 (ISBN 0-317-28002-3, 2025584). Bks Demand UMI.

Some Account of the Alien Priories, & of Such Lands As They Are Known to Have Possessed in England & Wales, 2 Vols. in 1. John Nichols. LC 72-173079. Repr. of 1786 ed. 47.50 (ISBN 0-404-04689-4). AMS Pr.

Some Account of the Life & Writings of John Milton. H. J. Todd. LC 77-22935. 1826. lib. bdg. 49.50 (ISBN 0-8414-8637-9). Folcroft.

Some Ancient Christmas Carols with the Tunes to Which They Were Formally Sung in the West of England. David Gilbert. LC 72-6976. 1972. lib. bdg. 12.50 (ISBN 0-88305-249-0). Norwood Edns.

Some Answered Questions. Abdu'l-Baha. Tr. by Laura C. Barney from Persian. LC 81-2467. xviii, 324p. 1981. 17.95 (ISBN 0-87743-162-0). Baha'i.

Some Answered Questions. Abdu'l-Baha. Tr. by Laura C. Barney from Persian. LC 83-21353. xviii, 324p. 1984. Pocket sized. pap. 5.95 (ISBN 0-87743-190-6). Baha'i.

Some Arval Brethren. Ronald Syme. 1980. 36.00x (ISBN 0-19-814831-3). Oxford U Pr.

Some Aspects of Contemporary Greek Orthodox Thought. Frank S. Gavin. LC 73-133818. Repr. of 1923 ed. 29.00 (ISBN 0-404-02687-7). AMS Pr.

Some Aspects of Hittite Religion. O. R. Gurney. (Schweich Lectures on Biblical Archaeology). (Illus.). 80p. 1976. 10.25 (ISBN 0-85672-740-7, Pub. by British Acad). Longwood Pub Group.

Some Aspects of Islamic Culture. 3.00 (ISBN 0-686-83584-0). Kazi Pubns.

Some Aspects of Orthodox Spirituality. pap. 0.25 (ISBN 0-686-02578-4). Eastern Orthodox.

Some Aspects of Prophet Muhammad's Life. Ed. by M. Tariq Quaraishi. LC 83-71409. 89p. (Orig.). Date not set. pap. 4.50 (ISBN 0-89259-045-9). Am Trust Pubns.

Some Aspects of the Religious Music of the United States Negro. George R. Ricks. Ed. by Richard M. Dorson. LC 77-70621. (International Folklore Ser.). 1977. Repr. of 1977 ed. lib. bdg. 36.50x (ISBN 0-405-10123-6). Ayer Co Pubs.

Some Aspects of Vedanta Philosophy. Swami Siddheswarananda. Tr. by Krishna Bhakti & K. Narayana Marar. 318p. (Orig.). 1976. pap. 4.50 (ISBN 0-87481-471-5). Vedanta Pr.

Some Baha'is to Remember. O. Z. Whitehead. (Illus.). 304p. 14.95 (ISBN 0-85398-147-7); pap. 8.95 (ISBN 0-85398-148-5). G Ronald Pub.

Some Call It Heresy. Martin Weber. Ed. by Raymond Woolsey. 128p. (Orig.). 1985. pap. 6.95 (ISBN 0-8280-0248-7). Review & Herald.

Some Catholic Novelists. facs. ed. Patrick Braybrooke. LC 67-22078. (Essay Index Reprint Ser.). 1931. 19.00 (ISBN 0-8369-1323-X). Ayer Co Pubs.

Some Catholic Novelists: Their Art & Outlook. P. Braybrooke. 59.95 (ISBN 0-8490-1075-6). Gordon Pr.

Some Christian Convictions: A Practical Restatement in Terms of Present-Day Thinking. Henry S. Coffin. LC 79-167328. (Essay Index Reprint Ser.). Repr. of 1915 ed. 17.00 (ISBN 0-8369-2763-X). Ayer Co Pubs.

Some Correspondence Between the Governors & Treasurers of the New England Company in London & the Commissioners of the United Colonies in America, the Missionaries of the Company & Others Between the Years 1657 & 1712. Company for the Propagation of the Gospel in New England & the Parts Adjacent in America, London. Ed. by John W. Ford. LC 73-126413. (Research & Source Works: No. 524). 1970. Repr. of 1896 ed. lib. bdg. 29.50 (ISBN 0-8337-1185-7). B Franklin.

Some Day Peace Will Return: Notes on War & Peace. Arthur Schnitzler. Tr. by Robert O. Weiss from Ger. LC 78-15807. 1971. 8.50 (ISBN 0-8044-2803-4). Ungar.

Some Discourse, Sermons & Remains. Joseph Glanville. Ed. by Rene Wellek. LC 75-11221. (British Philosophers & Theologians of the 17th & 18th Centuries Ser.). 1979. lib. bdg. 51.00 (ISBN 0-8240-1775-7). Garland Pub.

Some Dogmas of Religion. John McTaggart. LC 7-7484. 1968. Repr. of 1906 ed. 23.00 (ISBN 0-527-60000-8). Kraus Repr.

Some Early Alabama Churches. Mabel P. Wilson et al. 316p. 1973. 14.95x (ISBN 0-88428-029-2). Parchment Pr.

Some Early Baha'is of the West. O. Z. Whitehead. (Illus.). 240p. 1976. 14.95 (ISBN 0-85398-065-9). G Ronald Pub.

Some Elements of the Religious Teaching of Jesus According to the Synoptic Gospels. Claude G. Montefiore. LC 73-2223. (Jewish People; History, Religion, Literature Ser.). Repr. of 1910 ed. 17.00 (ISBN 0-405-05285-5). Ayer Co Pubs.

Some English Dictators. Milton Waldman. LC 77-112820. 1970. Repr. of 1940 ed. 24.50x (ISBN 0-8046-1087-8, Pub.by Kennikat). Assoc Faculty Pr.

Some Great Leaders in the World Movement. facs. ed. Robert E. Speer. LC 67-26786. (Essay Index Reprint Ser). 1911. 18.00 (ISBN 0-8369-0895-3). Ayer Co Pubs.

Some Hard Blessings: Meditations on the Beatitudes in Matthew. Luke T. Johnson. LC 81-69108. 96p. 1981. pap. 3.95 (ISBN 0-89505-058-7, 21053). Argus Comm.

Some Hellenistic Elements in Primitive Christianity. W. L. Knox. (British Academy, London, Schweich Lectures on Biblical Archaeology Series, 1942). pap. 19.00 (ISBN 0-8115-1284-3). Kraus Repr.

Some Heretics of Yesterday. Samuel E. Herrick. LC 83-45614. Date not set. Repr. of 1885 ed. 37.50 (ISBN 0-404-19832-5). AMS Pr.

Some Inscriptions of the Safaitic Bedouin. Willard B. Oxtoby. (American Oriental Ser.: Vol. 50). (Illus.). 1968. pap. 8.00x (ISBN 0-940490-50-1). Am Orient Soc.

Some Light on Christian Education. Ed. by James W. Deuink. (Illus.). 195p. (Orig.). 1984. pap. 4.95 (ISBN 0-89084-262-0). Bob Jones Univ Pr.

Some Living Masters of the Pulpit: Studies in Religious Personality. facsimile ed. Joseph F. Newton. LC 71-152203. (Essay Index Reprint Ser). Repr. of 1923 ed. 18.00 (ISBN 0-8369-2287-5). Ayer Co Pubs.

Some Loves of the Seraphic Saint. Father Augustine. 1979. 5.95 (ISBN 0-8199-0776-6). Franciscan Herald.

Some Makers of the Modern Spirit: A Symposium. facs. ed. Ed. by John Macmurray. LC 68-22926. (Essay Index Reprint Ser). Repr. of 1933 ed. 16.25 (ISBN 0-8369-0658-6). Ayer Co Pubs.

Some Mistakes of Moses. Robert G. Ingersoll. 270p. 1986. pap. 12.95 (ISBN 0-87975-361-7). Prometheus Bks.

Some Modern Sects, Cults, Movements & World Religions. Ed. by Thomas B. Warren & Garland Elkins. 1981. 13.00 (ISBN 0-934916-46-2). Natl Christian Pr.

Some Moral & Religious Teachings. Al-Ghazzali. 4.50x (ISBN 0-87902-056-3). Orientalia.

Some New Sources for the Life of Blessed Agnes of Bohemia. W. W. Seton. 184p. 1815. text ed. 33.12 (ISBN 0-576-99207-0, Pub. by Gregg Intl Pubs England). Gregg Intl.

Some Observations on the Relations Between Gods & Powers in the Veda, a Propos of the Phrase, Sunah Sahasah. Jan Gonda. (Disputationes Rheno-Trajectinae Ser.: No. 1). (Orig.). 1957. pap. text ed. 12.80x (ISBN 90-2790-027-2). Mouton.

Some of My Best Friends Are Christians. Paul Blanshard. LC 74-744. 200p. 1974. 14.95 (ISBN 0-87548-149-3). Open Court.

Some People Are Throwing You Into Confusion. Pierre Widmer. LC 83-82879. (Mennonite Faith Ser.: No. 14). 80p. 1984. pap. 1.50 (ISBN 0-8361-3358-7). Herald Pr.

Some Practical Suggestions on the Conduct of a Rescue Home: Including Life of Dr. Kate Waller Barrett. facsimile ed. Kate W. Barrett. LC 74-3928. (Women in America Ser.). Orig. Title: Fifty Years Work with Girls. 186p. 1974. Repr. of 1903 ed. 20.00x (ISBN 0-405-06075-0). Ayer Co Pubs.

Some Qualities Associated with Success in the Christian Ministry. Mary E. Moxcey. LC 76-177095. (Columbia University. Teachers College. Contributions to Education: No. 122). Repr. of 1922 ed. 22.50 (ISBN 0-404-55122-X). AMS Pr.

Some Reasons Why I Am a Freethinker. Robert Ingersoll. 38p. 1983. pap. 3.00 (ISBN 0-911826-67-X). Am Atheist.

Some Recently Discovered Franciscan Documents & Their Relation to the Second Life by Celano & the "Speculum Perfections". A. G. Little. 1926. pap. 2.25 (ISBN 0-85672-691-5, Pub. by British Acad). Longwood Pub Group.

Some Run with Feet of Clay. Jeannette Clift. 127p. Repr. of 1978 ed. 7.95 (ISBN 0-318-20047-3). Manor of Grace.

Some Sayings of the Buddha. F. L. Woodeward. 69.95 (ISBN 0-8490-2629-6). Gordon Pr.

Some Secrets of Christian Living. F. B. Meyer. Ed. by Joseph D. Allison. 144p. (Orig.). 1985. pap. 4.95 (ISBN 0-310-38721-3, 17076P). Zondervan.

Some Taoist Alchemical Legends. Gustav Meyrink. 1986. pap. 3.95 (ISBN 0-916411-52-4, Pub. by Alchemical Pr). Holmes Pub.

Some Thoughts Concerning the Several Causes & Occasions of Atheism, Especially in the Present Age. John Edwards. LC 80-48568. (Philosophy of John Locke Ser.). 268p. 1984. lib. bdg. 35.00 (ISBN 0-8240-5603-5). Garland Pub.

Some Thoughts on Hilaire Belloc: Ten Studies. Patrick Braybrook. 1973. 17.50 (ISBN 0-8274-1717-9). R West.

Some Thoughts on Hilaire Belloc: Ten Studies. Patrick Braybrooke. LC 68-1140. (Studies in Irish Literature, No. 16). 1969. Repr. lib. bdg. 48.95x (ISBN 0-8383-0649-7). Haskell.

Some Thoughts on Marriage. Margaret Ruhe. 36p. 1982. pap. 1.95 (ISBN 0-933770-23-5). Kalimat.

Some Traces of the Pre-Olympian World in Greek Literature & Myth. E. A Butterworth. LC 85-21959. (Illus.). 1966. 44.25x (ISBN 3-11-005010-2). De Gruyter.

Some Versions of the Fall: The Myth of the Fall of Man in English Literature. Eric Smith. LC 75-185025. (Illus.). 1973. 22.95x (ISBN 0-8229-1107-8). U of Pittsburgh Pr.

Some Victorian & Georgian Catholics. facs. ed. Patrick Braybrooke. LC 67-22080. (Essay Index Reprint Ser.). 1932. 18.00 (ISBN 0-8369-1325-6). Ayer Co Pubs.

Somebody Cares. Earl C. Davis. LC 81-71255. 1983. 7.95 (ISBN 0-8054-5211-7). Broadman.

Somebody Lives Inside: The Holy Spirit. Sharon L. Roberts. (Concept Ser.). (Illus.). 24p. (Orig.). 1986. pap. 3.95 saddlestitched (ISBN 0-570-08530-6, 56-1557). Concordia.

Somebody Loves You. Helen S. Rice. 128p. 1976. 12.95 (ISBN 0-8007-0818-0); large-print ed. 10.95 (ISBN 0-8007-1120-3). Revell.

Somebody's Brother: A History of the Salvation Army Men's Social Service Department 1891-1985. E. H. McKinley. LC 86-8604. (Studies in American Religion Ser.: Vol. 21). 264p. 1986. 9.95 (ISBN 0-88946-665-3). E Mellen.

Someday Syndrome. Rod Parsley. 37p. 1986. pap. 2.95 (ISBN 0-88144-069-8). Christian Pub.

Somehow Inside of Eternity. Richard C. Halverson. LC 80-21687. (Illus., Orig.). 1981. pap. 8.95 (ISBN 0-930014-51-0). Multnomah.

Someone Cares: The Collected Poems of Helen Steiner Rice. Helen S. Rice. 128p. 1972. 12.95 (ISBN 0-8007-0524-6); large-print ed. 12.95 (ISBN 0-8007-0959-4). Revell.

Someone Special. Sr. Augustine Weillert. (Illus.). 1979. 4.95 (ISBN 0-89962-005-1). Todd & Honeywell.

Someone Who Beckons. Timothy Dudley-Smith. LC 78-18548. 1978. pap. 3.95 (ISBN 0-87784-731-2). Inter-Varsity.

Someone's There: Paths to Prayer for Young People. Francoise Darcy-Berube & John P. Berube. LC 86-82055. (Illus.). 80p. (Orig.). 1987. pap. 4.95 (ISBN 0-87793-350-2). Ave Maria.

Something Beautiful. Linda Strasheim & Evelyn Bence. 160p. (Orig.). 1985. pap. 5.95 (ISBN 0-310-29391-X, 10467P). Zondervan.

Something Beautiful for God. Malcolm Muggeridge. 312p. 1985. pap. 8.95 (ISBN 0-8027-2474-4). Walker & Co.

Something Beautiful for God: Mother Teresa of Calcutta. Malcolm Muggeridge. 1977. pap. 3.50 (ISBN 0-385-12639-5, Im). Doubleday.

Something for Everyone, Something for You: Essays in Memoriam Albert Franklin Buffington, Vol. 14. Albert F. Buffington et al. (Illus.). 1980. 25.00 (ISBN 0-911122-41-9). Penn German Soc.

Something Good for Those Who Feel Bad: Positive Solutions for Negative Emotions. Louis O. Caldwell. 96p. 1985. pap. 6.95 (ISBN 0-8010-2505-2). Baker Bk.

Something Is Stirring in World Orthodoxy. S. Harakas. 1978. pap. 3.25 (ISBN 0-937032-04-2). Light&Life Pub Co MN.

Something Meaningful for God. Ed. by C. J. Dyck. LC 80-10975. (MCC Story Ser.: Vol. 4). 408p. (Orig.). 1981. pap. 7.95x (ISBN 0-8361-1244-X). Herald Pr.

Something More. Catherine Marshall. 1976. pap. 3.50 (ISBN 0-380-00601-4, 60104-4). Avon.

Something More. Catherine Marshall. 276p. 1976. pap. 3.50 (ISBN 0-8007-8266-6, Spire Bks). Revell.

Something More Than Human: Biographies of Leaders in American Methodist Higher Education. Ed. by Charles E. Cole. LC 85-51267. (Illus.). 256p. 1986. 7.95 (ISBN 0-938162-04-7). United Meth Educ.

Something, Somehow, Somewhere, Someday. Sri Chinmoy. 70p. (Orig.). 1973. pap. 2.00 (ISBN 0-88497-025-6). Aum Pubns.

Something Special. Associated Women's Organization, Mars Hill Bible School. Ed. by Peggy Simpson & Linda Stanley. 1977. pap. 4.95 (ISBN 0-89137-408-6). Quality Pubns.

Something Special Within. 2nd ed. Betts Richter. (Illus.). 48p. 1982. pap. 4.50 (ISBN 0-87516-488-9). De Vorss.

Something Supernatural. Janet McReynolds. 103p. 1986. pap. 3.95 (ISBN 0-88144-038-8). Christian Pub.

Something to Believe in. Robert L. Short. LC 75-36754. (Illus.). 1977. pap. 5.95i (ISBN 0-06-067381-8, RD 169, HarpR). Har-Row.

Something to Live For. Lissa H. Johnson. 1986. 5.95 (ISBN 0-8007-5228-7). Revell.

Something to Think about. Hennie Bristow. pap. 2.50 (ISBN 0-89315-292-7). Lambert Bk.

Something Worse Than Hell & Better Than Heaven. Jerry Barnard. 1979. pap. 3.25 (ISBN 0-917726-31-6). Hunter Bks.

Something's Got to Help-& Yoga Can. Joy F. Herrick & Nancy Schraffenberger. LC 73-80177. (Illus.). 128p. 1974. 5.95 (ISBN 0-87131-126-7). M Evans.

Sometime Before the Dawn. Richard M. Cromie. 111p. (Orig.). 1982. 10.00 (ISBN 0-914733-07-9); pap. 6.95 (ISBN 0-914733-08-7). Desert Min.

Sometimes Everything Feels Just Right. Elspeth C. Murphy. (David & I Talk to God Ser.). (Illus.). 1987. pap. 2.95 (ISBN 1-55513-038-0, Chariot Bks). Cook.

Sometimes I Feel. Rochelle Barsuhn. LC 85-10351. (Illus.). 32p. 1985. PLB 4.95 (ISBN 0-89693-228-1). Dandelion Hse.

Sometimes I Get Lonely. Elspeth Murphy. LC 80-70251. (David & I Talk to God Ser.). (Illus.). 24p. 1981. pap. 2.95 (ISBN 0-89191-367-X, 53678). Cook.

Sometimes I Get Mad. Elspeth C. Murphy. (David & I Talk to God Ser.). 1981. pap. 2.95 (ISBN 0-89191-493-5, 54932). Cook.

Sometimes I Get Scared. Elspeth Murphy. (David & I Talk to God Ser.). (Illus.). 1980. pap. 2.95 (ISBN 0-89191-275-4). Cook.

Sometimes I Have to Cry. Elspeth C. Murphy. (David & I Talk to God Ser.). (Illus.). 1981. pap. 2.95 (ISBN 0-89191-494-3, 54940). Cook.

Sometimes I Hurt: Reflections on the Book of Job. Mildred Tengbom. 192p. (Orig.). 1986. pap. 7.95 (ISBN 0-570-03981-9, 12-2897). Concordia.

Sometimes I Need to Be Hugged. Elspeth C. Murphy. (David & I Talk to God Ser.). (Illus.). 1981. pap. 2.95 (ISBN 0-89191-492-7, 54924). Cook.

Sometimes I'm Good, Sometimes I'm Bad. Elspeth Murphy. (David & I Talk to God Ser.). (Illus.). 24p. 1981. pap. 2.95 (ISBN 0-89191-368-8, 53686). Cook.

Sometimes I'm Small, Sometime's I'm Tall. Elizabeth E. Watson. 1984. pap. 5.99 (ISBN 0-570-04091-4, 56-1459). Concordia.

Somewhere a Master: Further Tales of the Hasidic Masters. Elie Wiesel. 336p. 1982. 13.95 (ISBN 0-671-44170-1). Summit Bks.

Son of a Duck is a Floater: An Illustrated Book of Arab Proverbs. Primose Arnander & Ashkain Skipwith. (Illus.). 90p. 1985. 7.95 (ISBN 0-905743-41-5, Pub. by Stacey Intl UK). Humanities.

Son of God: The Origin of Christology & the History of Jewish-Hellenistic Religion. Martin Hengel. Tr. by John Bowden from Ger. LC 75-37151. 112p. 1976. pap. 5.50 (ISBN 0-8006-1227-2, 1-1227). Fortress.

Son of His Love. W. J. Hocking. 6.25 (ISBN 0-88172-088-7). Believers Bkshelf.

Son of Man. John E. Buckner. 1981. 4.95 (ISBN 0-8062-1796-0). Carlton.

Son of Man & Son of God: A New Language for Faith. John C. Dwyer. 160p. 1983. pap. 7.95 (ISBN 0-8091-2505-6). Paulist Pr.

Son of Man As the Son of God. Seyoon Kim. 128p. (Orig.). 1985. pap. 12.95x (ISBN 0-8028-0056-4). Eerdmans.

Son of Man in Daniel Seven. Arthur J. Ferch. (Andrews University Seminary Doctoral Dissertation Ser.: Vol. 6). x, 237p. 1983. pap. 9.95 (ISBN 0-943872-38-3). Andrews Univ Pr.

Son of Man in Mark. Morna D. Hooker. 1967. 12.50 (ISBN 0-7735-0049-9). McGill-Queens U Pr.

Son of Man in Mark: A Study of the Background of the Term "Son of Man" & Its Use in St. Mark's Gospel. Morna Hooker. LC 67-4912. pap. 60.00 (ISBN 0-317-26028-6, 2023832). Bks Demand UMI.

Son of Man in the Teaching of Jesus. A. J. Higgins. LC 79-42824. (Society for New Testament Studies Monographs: No. 39). 186p. 1981. 32.50 (ISBN 0-521-22363-6). Cambridge U Pr.

Son of Man, Son of God. E. G. Jay. 1965. 4.95c (ISBN 0-7735-0029-4). McGill-Queens U Pr.

Son of the Passion. Godfrey Poage. 1977. 3.50 (ISBN 0-8198-0458-4); pap. 2.25 (ISBN 0-8198-0459-2). Dghtrs St Paul.

Son-Ripened Fruit: Living Out the Fruit of the Spirit. (Orig.). 1986. pap. 1.95 (ISBN 0-8024-2551-8). Moody.

Son Songs for Christian Folk, 2 vols. Gary L. Johnson. Incl. Vol. I. pap. 1.25 (ISBN 0-87123-509-9, 280509); Vol. II. pap. 1.50 (ISBN 0-87123-532-3, 280532). 1975. pap. Bethany Hse.

Son to Susanna: The Private Life of John Wesley. G. Elsie Harrison. 1937. Repr. 35.00 (ISBN 0-8274-3468-5). R West.

Soncino Books of the Bible, 14 vols. Incl. Chumash. 22.50 (ISBN 0-900689-24-2); Daniel. 10.95 (ISBN 0-900689-36-6); Hoshua & Judges. 10.95 (ISBN 0-900689-25-0); Samuel I-II. 10.95 (ISBN 0-900689-26-9); Chronicles. 10.95 (ISBN 0-900689-37-4); King I-II. 10.95 (ISBN 0-900689-27-7); Isaiah. 10.95 (ISBN 0-900689-28-5); Jeremiah. 10.95 (ISBN 0-900689-29-3); Ezekiel. 10.95 (ISBN 0-900689-30-7); Twelve Prophets. 10.95 (ISBN 0-900689-31-5); Psalms. 10.95 (ISBN 0-900689-32-3); Proverbs. 10.95; Job. 10.95; Five Meeillah. 10.95 (ISBN 0-900689-35-8). Set. 149.95x (ISBN 0-900689-23-4). Bloch.

Soncino Haggadah. Cecil Roth. 4.95x (ISBN 0-685-01039-2). Bloch.

Soncino Hebrew-English Talmud. Incl. Tractate Berakoth. 22.95x (ISBN 0-685-23064-3); Tractate Baba Mezia. 22.95x (ISBN 0-685-23065-1); Tractate Gittin. 22.95x (ISBN 0-685-23066-X); Tractate Baba Kamma. 22.95x (ISBN 0-685-23067-8); Tractate Kiddushin. 22.95x (ISBN 0-685-23068-6); Tractate Pesahim. 22.95x (ISBN 0-685-23069-4); Tractate Sanhedrin. 22.95x (ISBN 0-685-23070-8); Tractate Kethuboth. 22.95x (ISBN 0-685-23071-6); Tractate Shabbath, 2 vols. Set. 45.95x (ISBN 0-685-23072-4); Tractate Yoma. 22.95x (ISBN 0-685-23073-2); Baba Bathra, 2 vols. 45.95x (ISBN 0-686-85719-4); Hullin. 22.95x (ISBN 0-686-85720-8). Bloch.

Song & the Story. George M. Bass. 1984. 7.00 (ISBN 0-89536-652-5, 1970). CSS of Ohio.

Song at the Scaffold. rev. ed. Gertrud Von Le Fort. Ed. by Martin McMurtrey & Robert Knopp. (Illus., Orig.). 1954. pap. text ed. 3.95 (ISBN 0-910334-24-2). Cath Authors.

Song Called Hope. Arthur Gordon. 48p. 1985. 6.95 (ISBN 0-8378-5081-9). Gibson.

Song Celestial. Edwin Arnold. 1971. pap. 1.50 (ISBN 0-8356-0418-7, Quest). Theos Pub Hse.

Song Celestial: Bhagavad-Gita. Tr. by Edwin Arnold from Sanskrit. 176p. 1985. Repr. 3.50 (ISBN 0-87612-210-1). Self Realization.

Song Celestial or Bhaggvad-Gita: From the Mahabharata, Being a Discourse Between Arjuna, Prince of India, & the Supreme Being under the Form of Krishna. Tr. by Edwin Arnold. 1967. pap. 5.00 (ISBN 0-7100-6268-0). Methuen Inc.

Song for Lovers. S. Craig Glickman. LC 75-21454. 204p. (Orig.). 1976. pap. 6.95 (ISBN 0-87784-768-1). Inter-Varsity.

Song for Sarah: A Young Mother's Journey Through Grief, & Beyond. Paula D'Arcy. LC 79-14684. 124p. 1979. 6.95 (ISBN 0-87788-778-0); pap. 2.50 (ISBN 0-87788-780-2). Shaw Pubs.

Song of Abraham. Ellen G. Traylor. 1981. pap. 4.50 (ISBN 0-8423-6071-9). Tyndale.

Song of Ascents: A Spiritual Autobiography. E. Stanley Jones. LC 68-17451. (Festival Bks). 1979. pap. 2.25 (ISBN 0-687-39100-8). Abingdon.

Song of Creation. Cyril A. Reilly. 64p. 1983. pap. 9.95 (ISBN 0-86683-710-8, HarpR). Har-Row.

Song of Creation: Selections from the First Article. H. Boone Porter. 120p. (Orig.). 1986. pap. 6.95 (ISBN 0-936384-34-4). Cowley Pubns.

Song of Fourteen Songs. Michael D. Goulder. (JSOT Supplement Ser.: No. 36). viii, 94p. 1986. text ed. 18.00x (ISBN 0-905774-86-8, Pub. by JSOT Pr England); pap. text ed. 7.50x (ISBN 0-905774-87-6). Eisenbrauns.

Song of God. Bhagavad-Gita. Tr. by Swami Prabhavananda & C. Isherwood. pap. 2.95 (ISBN 0-451-62576-5, Ment). NAL.

Song of Jesus. Ron O'Grady. (Illus.). 80p. (Orig.). 1984. pap. 9.95 (ISBN 0-85819-470-8, Pub. by JBCE). ANZ Religious Pubns.

Song of Love. Tr. by George Keyt. Orig. Title: Gita Govinda. 123p. 1969. pap. 2.00 (ISBN 0-88253-048-8). Ind-US Inc.

Song of Peace. Frances G. Nachant. 1969. cancelled (ISBN 0-8233-0126-5). Golden Quill.

Song of Solomon. Bernard of Clairvaux. 560p. 1984. smythe sewn 21.00 (ISBN 0-86524-177-5, 2202). Klock & Klock.

Song of Solomon. G. Lloyd Carr & D. J. Wiseman. LC 83-22651. (Tyndale Old Testament Commentaries Ser.). 240p. 1984. 12.95 (ISBN 0-87784-918-8); pap. 6.95 (ISBN 0-87784-268-X). Inter-Varsity.

Song of Solomon. James Durham. 1981. lib. bdg. 17.25 (ISBN 0-86524-075-2, 2201). Klock & Klock.

Song of Solomon. James Durham. (Geneva Ser.). 460p. 1982. Repr. of 1840 ed. 13.95 (ISBN 0-85151-352-2). Banner of Truth.

Song of Solomon. E. C. Hadley. pap. 3.95 (ISBN 0-88172-080-1). Believers Bkshelf.

Song of Solomon. Paige Patterson. (Everyman's Bible Commentary Ser.). (Orig.). 1986. pap. 5.95 (ISBN 0-8024-2057-5). Moody.

Song of Songs. Jeanne Guyon. 1983. pap. 5.95 (ISBN 0-940232-16-2). Christian Bks.

Song of Songs. Dan T. Muse. 5.95 (ISBN 0-911866-78-7). Advocate.

Song of Songs. Watchman Nee. 1965-1967. pap. 2.95 (ISBN 0-87508-420-6). Chr Lit.

Song of Songs. Tr. by Marvin H. Pope. LC 72-79417. (Anchor Bible Ser.: Vol. 7C). (Illus.). 1977. 18.00 (ISBN 0-385-00569-5, Anchor Pr). Doubleday.

Song of Songs. (Modern Critical Interpretations--Ancient, Medieval, & Renaissance Ser.). 1987. 19.95 (ISBN 0-87754-917-6). Chelsea Hse.

Song of Songs & Lamentations: A Commentary & Translation. Robert Gordis. 1974. 25.00x (ISBN 0-87068-256-3). Ktav.

Song of Songs, Ruth, Lamentations, Ecclesiastes, Esther. James A. Fischer. (Collegeville Bible Commentary Ser.). 112p. 1986. pap. 2.95 (ISBN 0-8146-1480-9). Liturgical pr.

Song of Souls of Men. Glenn Clark. pap. 0.95 (ISBN 0-910924-14-7). Macalester.

Song of the Bird. Anthony DeMello. LC 84-10105. (Illus.). 192p. 1984. pap. 6.95 (ISBN 0-385-19615-6, Im). Doubleday.

Song of the Lord. David K. Blomgren. 70p. Date not set. pap. 6.95. Bible Temple.

Song of the Self Supreme: Astavakra Gita. Tr. by Radhakamal Mukerjee. LC 74-24308. 293p. 1981. 9.95 (ISBN 0-913922-14-5). Dawn Horse Pr.

Song of the Soul Set Free. Caroline Gilroy. 103p. (Orig.). 1986. pap. 3.95 (ISBN 0-8341-1138-1). Beacon Hill.

Song of the Sparrow: Meditations & Poems to Pray by. Murray Bodo. (Illus.). 187p. (Orig.). 1976. pap. 3.95 (ISBN 0-912228-26-1). St Anthony Mess Pr.

Song of the Spirit. Herbert L. Beierle. 1978. 20.00 (ISBN 0-940480-01-8). U of Healing.

Song of the Three Holy Children. Illus. by Pauline Baynes. LC 86-11952. (Illus.). 32p. 1986. 12.95 (ISBN 0-8050-0134-4). H Holt & Co.

Song of the Vineyard: A Guide Through the Old Testament. rev. ed. Davie Napier. LC 78-14672. 360p. 1981. pap. 12.95 (ISBN 0-8006-1352-X, 1-1352). Fortress.

Song of the Virgin. Spiros Zodhiates. LC 82-71643. (Illus.). 1974. pap. 3.95 (ISBN 0-89957-510-2). AMG Pubs.

Song to Creation: A Dialogue with a Text. E. Mihaly. (Jewish Perspectives Ser.: Vol. 1). 7.50x (ISBN 0-87820-500-4, HUC Pr). Ktav.

Song to Creation: A Dialogue with a Text. Eugene Mihaly. LC 75-35761. pap. 27.00 (ISBN 0-317-42034-8, 2025694). Bks Demand UMI.

Song to Demeter. Cynthia Birrer & William Birrer. LC 86-20895. (Illus.). 32p. 1987. 11.75 (ISBN 0-688-04040-3); PLB 11.88 (ISBN 0-688-04041-1). Lothrop.

Songs & Hymns for Primary Children. Ed. by W. Lawrence Curry. 1978. softcover 3.95 (ISBN 0-664-10117-8). Westminster.

Songs & Prayers of Victory. Basilea Schlink. 1978. pap. 1.50 (ISBN 3-87209-652-4). Evang Sisterhood Mary.

Songs Divine. Abhendananda. Tr. by P. S. Aiyer from Sanskrit. 69p. 1985. 6.50 (ISBN 0-87481-653-X, Pub. by Ramakrishna Math Madras India). Vedanta Pr.

Songs for Awakening. Heng Yin et al. (Illus.). 112p. (Orig.). 1979. pap. 8.00 (ISBN 0-917512-31-6). Buddhist Text.

Songs for Early Childhood. 1958. 3.25 ea. (ISBN 0-664-10058-9). Westminster.

Songs for My Fathers. Gary Smith. LC 83-82775. 78p. 1984. pap. 5.00 perf. bnd. (ISBN 0-916418-55-3). Lotus.

Songs for Preschool Children. Ed. by Marian Bennett. LC 80-25091. 96p. (Orig.). 1981. pap. 7.95 (ISBN 0-87239-429-8, 5754). Standard Pub.

Songs for Silent Moments: Prayers for Daily Living. Lois W. Johnson. LC 79-54115. 128p. (Orig.). 1980. pap. 4.95 (ISBN 0-8066-1765-9, 10-5851). Augsburg.

Songs for the Bride: Wedding Rites of Rural India. William G. Archer. Ed. by Barbara S. Miller & Mildred Archer. (Studies in Oriental Culture). 224p. 1985. 22.50x (ISBN 0-317-18769-4). Brooklyn Coll Pr.

Songs for the Joy of Living. Illus. by Children at Sunrise Ranch. (Illus.). 50p. 1985. ring-bound 11.95 (ISBN 0-932869-01-7). Eden Valley.

Songs for Young Children. LC 75-40910. (Illus.). 1976. spiral bdg. 3.50 (ISBN 0-916406-31-8). Accent Bks.

Songs from the House of Pilgrimage. Stephen Isaac. LC 77-169595. 1971. 9.50 (ISBN 0-8283-1334-2). Christward.

Songs from the Land of Dawn. facs. ed. Tr. by Lois J. Erickson. LC 68-58828. (Granger Index Reprint Ser). 1949. 14.00 (ISBN 0-8369-6014-9). Ayer Co Pubs.

Songs of Cheer. Ed. by Carol Ferntheil. (Illus.). 16p. (Orig.). 1979. pap. 0.85 (ISBN 0-87239-345-3, 7948). Standard Pub.

Songs of Degrees. Stephen Kaung. Ed. by Herbert L. Fader. 1970. 4.00 (ISBN 0-935008-32-2); pap. 2.75 (ISBN 0-935008-33-0). Christian Fellow Pubs.

Songs of Deliverance. Flower A. Newhouse. LC 72-94582. 250p. 1972. 9.50 (ISBN 0-910378-08-8). Christward.

Songs of Eternal Faith: Artistic Piano Arrangements of Best-Loved Hymns. Lynn S. Lund. LC 81-80954. 56p. (Orig.). 1982. pap. 5.95 (ISBN 0-88290-184-2, 2901). Horizon Utah.

Songs of Freedom: The Psalter As a School of Prayer. Charles Cummings. 1986. pap. 6.95 (ISBN 0-87193-245-8). Dimension Bks.

Songs of God. Joseph Murphy. LC 79-52353. (Orig.). 1979. pap. 6.00 (ISBN 0-87516-379-3). De Vorss.

Songs of God's Grace. M. R. Bawa Muhaiyaddeen. LC 73-91016. (Illus.). 154p. 1974. pap. 4.95 (ISBN 0-914390-02-3). Fellowship Pr PA.

Songs of Heaven. Robert E. Coleman. 160p. 1982. pap. 5.95 (ISBN 0-8007-5097-7, Power Bks). Revell.

Songs of Hope. Ed. by Holland Boring. 1979. pap. 2.75 (ISBN 0-88027-059-4). Firm Foun Pub.

Songs of Inspiration: Artistic Piano Arrangements of New Latter-day Saint Hymns. Lynn S. Lund. 40p. 1986. pap. text ed. 7.95 (ISBN 0-88290-276-8). Horizon Utah.

Songs of Joyful Praise. Ed. by Frank Roberts. 1975. pap. 2.00x (ISBN 0-88027-060-8). Firm Foun Pub.

Songs of Praise. Percy Dearmer. Ed. by Ralph Vaughan Williams & Martin Shaw. Incl. Music Ed. rev. & enl. ed. 1932. 19.95x (ISBN 0-19-231207-3). Oxford U Pr.

Songs of Submission: On the Practice of Subud. Hurbert Bissing. 180p. (Orig.). 1982. pap. 9.50 (ISBN 0-227-67852-4, Pub. by J Clarke UK). Attic Pr.

Songs of Suffering. Nathan R. Kollar. 160p. (Orig.). 1982. pap. 7.95 (ISBN 0-86683-672-1, HarpR). Har-Row.

Songs of the Ages (Psalms) Leader's Guide. (New Horizons Bible Study). 48p. (Orig.). 1984. pap. 1.95 (ISBN 0-89367-091-X). Light & Life.

Songs of the Ages (Psalms) Student Guide. (New Horizon Bible Study). 68p. (Orig.). 1984. pap. 2.50 (ISBN 0-89367-090-1). Light & Life.

Songs of the Good Earth. Margaret Phillips. LC 79-10731. 62p. 1980. pap. 4.95 (ISBN 0-88289-221-5). Pelican.

Songs of the Martyrs: Hassidic Melodies of Maramures. Max Eisikovits. LC 79-67624. 1980. pap. 7.95 (ISBN 0-87203-089-X). Hermon.

Songs of the Nativity. William A. Husk. LC 73-9861. (Folklore Ser). 32.50 (ISBN 0-88305-258-X). Norwood Edns.

Songs of the Russian People: As Illustrative of Slavonic Mythology & Russian Social Life. W. R. Ralston. LC 77-132444. (Studies in Music, No. 42). 1970. Repr. of 1872 ed. lib. bdg. 69.95x (ISBN 0-8383-1224-1). Haskell.

Songs of the Sabbath Sacrifice: Edition, Translation, & Commentary. Carol Newsom. (Harvard Semitic Museum Ser.). 1985. 34.95 (ISBN 0-89130-837-7, 04-04-27). Scholars Pr GA.

Songs of the Soul. Sri Chinmoy. 96p. (Orig.). 1983. pap. 5.00 (ISBN 0-88497-738-2). Aum Pubns.

Songs of the Soul. Paramahansa Yogananda. LC 83-60701. (Illus.). 200p. 1983. 6.50 (ISBN 0-87612-025-7). Self-Realization.

Songs of the Soul. Paramhansa Yogananda. LC 80-69786. 1980. pap. 9.95 (ISBN 0-937134-02-3). Amrita Found.

Songs of the Synagogue of Florence, 2 vols. Ed. by Fernando D. Belgrado. Incl. Vol. 1. The Three Festivals (ISBN 0-87203-108-X); Vol. 2. The High Holy Days. 0p (ISBN 0-87203-109-8). (Illus.). 60p. 1982. 32.95 ea. Hermon.

Songs of the Vaisnava Acaryas. Ed. by Swami Acyutananda. 1979. pap. 6.95 (ISBN 0-912776-56-0). Bhaktivedanta.

Songs of Zion. Ed. by Verolga Nix & Jefferson Cleveland. LC 81-8039. 352p. (Orig.). 1981. pap. 7.95 accompanist ed. (ISBN 0-687-39121-0); pap. 7.95 (ISBN 0-687-39120-2). Abingdon.

Songs We Sing. Harry Coopersmith. (Illus.). 1950. 22.50x (ISBN 0-8381-0723-0). United Syn Bk.

Sonia: Survival in War & Peace. Sonia Milner. LC 83-50758. 1983. pap. 4.95 (ISBN 0-88400-102-4). Shengold.

Sonnet-No Me Mueve, Mi Dios-Its Theme in Spanish Tradition. Sr. M. Cyria Huff. LC 73-94177. (Catholic University of America Studies in Romance Languages & Literatures Ser: No. 33). Repr. of 1948 ed. 20.00 (ISBN 0-404-50333-0). AMS Pr.

Sonnets Anglais et Italians De Milton. E. Saillens. LC 74-12230. 1930. lib. bdg. 28.50 (ISBN 0-8414-7784-1). Folcroft.

Sonnets for a Christian Year. David R. Wones. (Illus.). 80p. (Orig.). 1987. pap. 4.95 (ISBN 0-936015-06-3). Pocahontas Pr.

Sons & Daughters of God: Our New Identity in Christ. Ken Wilson. (Living As a Christian Ser.). 80p. (Orig.). 1981. pap. 2.50 (ISBN 0-89283-097-2). Servant.

Sons of Africa. Elmer Schmelzenbach & Leslie Parrott. 217p. 1979. 8.95 (ISBN 0-8341-0601-9). Beacon Hill.

Sons of Mosiah. Mark E. Petersen. 125p. 1984. 6.95 (ISBN 0-87747-297-1). Deseret Bk.

Sons of the Gods & Daughters of Men: An Afro-Asiatic Interpretation of Genesis 1-11. Modupe Oduyoye. LC 83-6308. 126p. (Orig.). 1983. pap. 12.95 (ISBN 0-88344-467-4). Orbis Bks.

Sons of the Prophets: Leaders in Protestantism from Princeton Seminary. Ed. by Hugh T. Kerr. 1963. 26.50x (ISBN 0-691-07136-5). Princeton U Pr.

Soon Coming of Our Lord. Dale Crowley. 1958. pap. 2.95 (ISBN 0-87213-091-6). Loizeaux.

Soon Coming World Emperor. Kenneth Hannah. 48p. (Orig.). pap. 2.95 (CPS-012). Christian Pub.

Sophia: The Future of Feminist Spirituality. Susan A. Cady et al. 120p. 1986. 14.95 (ISBN 0-06-254200-1, HarpR). Har-Row.

Sorcerer's Apprentice: A Christian Looks at the Changing Face of Psychology. Mary S. Van Leeuwen. 144p. (Orig.). 1982. pap. 7.95 (ISBN 0-87784-398-8). Inter-Varsity.

Sorcerer's Handbook. Wade Baskin. (Illus.). 640p. 1974. pap. 4.95 (ISBN 0-8065-0399-8). Citadel Pr.

Soren Kierkegaard. Elmer H. Duncan. Ed. by Bob E. Patterson. LC 76-2862. (Markers of the Modern Theological Mind Ser.). 1976. 8.95 (ISBN 0-87680-463-6, 80463). Word Bks.

Sorrel Horse. Ruth N. Moore. LC 82-3136. 144p. (Orig.). 1982. pap. 3.95 (ISBN 0-8361-3303-X). Herald Pr.

Sorrow & Joy. J. D. Thomas et al. 1963. 11.95 (ISBN 0-89112-025-4, Bibl Res Pr). Abilene Christ U.

Sorrow of the Lonely & the Burning of the Dancers. Edward L. Schieffelin. LC 75-10999. (Illus.). 256p. 1975. pap. text ed. 9.95 (ISBN 0-312-74550-8). St Martin.

Sorrow Speaks. Mary L. Williams. 1968. pap. 2.95 (ISBN 0-8272-3405-8). CBP.

Sorrowful & Immaculate Heart of Mary: Message of Berthe Petit, Franciscan Tertiary (1870-1943) Pref. by T. Cadoux. 110p. 1966. pap. 3.00 (ISBN 0-913382-02-7, 101-2). Prow Bks-Franciscan.

Sorting It Out with God. Jim Auer. 64p. 1982. pap. 1.95 (ISBN 0-89243-163-6). Liguori Pubns.

Sorting Life Out. Purgraski. LC 60-9573. 1978. 24.00x (ISBN 0-930004-00-0); free student packet, 36 pgs. C E M Comp.

Soslasno li c Evangelijem Dejstvoval i uchil Ljuter? N. I. Florinsky. Tr. of Were the Actions & Teachings of Luther in Accord with the Gospel? 166p. 1975. pap. text ed. 6.00 (ISBN 0-317-30257-4). Holy Trinity.

Sotah, 1 vol. 15.00 (ISBN 0-910218-70-6). Bennet Pub.

Souffrances et Bonheur du Chretien. Francois Mauriac. pap. 7.50 (ISBN 0-685-34305-7). French & Eur.

Soul Afire: Revelations of the Mystics. H. A. Reinhold. 1977. Repr. of 1944 ed. 30.00 (ISBN 0-89984-099-X). Century Bookbindery.

Soul & Its Mechanism. Alice A. Bailey. 1971. 15.00 (ISBN 0-85330-015-1); pap. 7.00 (ISBN 0-85330-115-8). Lucis.

Soul & Its Vestures. C. W. Leadbeater. 24p. 1983. pap. 1.50 (ISBN 0-918980-12-7). St Alban Pr.

Soul & the Ethic. Ann R. Colton. 262p. 1965. 7.95 (ISBN 0-917187-07-5). A R C Pub.

Soul As Sphere & Androgyne. Keith Critchlow. (Illus., Orig.). 1985. pap. 4.95 (ISBN 0-933999-28-3). Phanes Pr.

Soul Building Sermon Outlines. Russell E. Spray. (Dollar Sermon Library). 1977. pap. 1.95 (ISBN 0-8010-8118-1). Baker Bk.

Soul Economy & Waldorf Education. Rudolf Steiner. Tr. of Die gesunde Entwicklung des Leiblich-Physischen als Grundlage der freien Enfaltung. 320p. (Orig.). pap. 20.00 (ISBN 0-88010-138-5); 30.00 (ISBN 0-88010-139-3). Anthroposophic.

Soul Friend: The Practice of Christian Spirituality. Kenneth Leech. LC 79-2994. 272p. 1980. 14.45 (ISBN 0-06-065225-X, HarpR). Har-Row.

Soul in Egyptian Metaphysics. Manly P. Hall. pap. 2.50 (ISBN 0-89314-355-3). Philos Res.

Soul in Paraphrase: Prayer & the Religious Affections. Don E. Saliers. 160p. 1980. 8.95 (ISBN 0-8164-0121-7, HarpR). Har-Row.

Soul Making: The Desert Way of Spirituality. Alan Jones. LC 84-48222. 192p. 1985. 14.45 (ISBN 0-06-064182-7, HarpR). Har-Row.

Soul Mates. Tomval-Valtom. 96p. (Orig.). 1985. pap. 5.95 (ISBN 0-9615048-0-3). St Thomas Pub.

Soul Mates: The Facts & the Fallacies. Robert E. Birdsong. (Aquarian Academy Supplementary Lecture Ser.: No. 9). 22p. (Orig.). 1980. pap. 1.25 (ISBN 0-917108-32-9). Sirius Bks.

Soul Mending: Letters to Friends in Crisis. Joseph P. Bishop. 160p. 1986. pap. 8.95 (ISBN 0-8192-1379-9). Morehouse.

Soul of John Brown. Stephen Graham. LC 70-109915. Repr. of 1920 ed. 25.00 (ISBN 0-404-00162-9). AMS Pr.

Soul of Man. Paul Carus. 59.95 (ISBN 0-8490-1090-X). Gordon Pr.

Soul of Mbira: Music & Traditions of the Shona People of Zimbabwe. Paul F. Berliner. LC 76-24578. (Perspectives on Southern Africa Ser.: No. 26). 1978. 36.50x (ISBN 0-520-03315-9); pap. 6.95 (ISBN 0-520-04268-9, CAL 466). U of Cal Pr.

Soul of My Soul: Reflections from a Life of Prayer. Catherine De Hueck Doherty. LC 85-72271. 128p. (Orig.). 1985. pap. 4.95 (ISBN 0-87793-298-0). Ave Maria.

Soul of the Apostolate. Jean-Baptiste Chautard. 1977. pap. 6.00 (ISBN 0-89555-031-8). TAN Bks Pubs.

Soul of the Bantu: A Sympathetic Study of the Magico-Religious Practices & Beliefs of the Bantu Tribes of Africa. William C. Willoughby. LC 77-107526. Repr. of 1928 ed. cancelled (ISBN 0-8371-3773-X, WBA&, Pub. by Negro U Pr). Greenwood.

Soul of the Black Preacher. Joseph A. Johnson, Jr. LC 70-162411. 176p. 1971. 4.95 (ISBN 0-8298-0193-6). Pilgrim NY.

Soul of the Indian: An Interpretation. Charles A. Eastman. LC 79-26355. xvi, 170p. 1980. pap. 5.95 (ISBN 0-8032-6701-0, BB 735, Bison). U of Nebr Pr.

Soul So Rebellious. Mary F. Sturlaugson. 88p. 1980. 8.95 (ISBN 0-87747-841-4). Deseret Bk.

Soul Surgery: The Ultimate Self-Healing. Richard Jafolla. LC 81-71018. 176p. (Orig.). 1982. pap. 5.95 (ISBN 0-87516-473-0). De Vorss.

Soul Talk-How to Rejuvenate Your Life. James R. Jacobson. Ed. by Sylvia Ashton. LC 78-54160. 1979. 14.95 (ISBN 0-87949-107-8). Ashley Bks.

Soul! The Soul World! Paschal B. Randolph. Ed. by R. Swinburne Clymer. 246p. 1932. 9.95 (ISBN 0-932785-45-X). Philos Pub.

Soul Touching Sermons. John Stacy. (Illus.). 114p. (Orig.). 1986. pap. 9.95 (ISBN 1-55630-015-8). Brentwood Comm.

Soul Whence & Whither. Hazrat I. Khan. LC 77-15697. (Collected Works of Hazrat Inayat Khan Ser.). 190p. 1977. 7.95 (ISBN 0-930872-00-2). Omega Pr NM.

Soul Winner. C. H Spurgeon. 1978. pap. 2.50 (ISBN 0-686-02430-3). Pilgrim Pubns.

Soul Winner's Secret. Samuel L. Brengle. 1978. pap. 3.95 (ISBN 0-86544-007-7). Salv Army Suppl South.

Soul Winning. David Shofner. (Illus.). 96p. (Orig.). 1980. pap. 2.95 (ISBN 0-89957-051-8). AMG Pubs.

Soul-Winning Classes Made Easy. C. S. Lovett. 1962. pap. 2.95 tchr's. guide (ISBN 0-938148-12-5). Personal Christianity.

Soul-Winning Made Easy. C. S. Lovett. 1978. pap. 4.25 (ISBN 0-938148-10-9). Personal Christianity.

Souldiery Spiritualized: Seven Sermons Preached Before the Artillery Companies of New England, 1674-1774. LC 79-9727. 1979. 60.00x (ISBN 0-8201-1325-5). Schol Facsimiles.

Soules Exaltation. Thomas Hooker. LC 78-298. (American Puritan Writings Ser.: No. 18). Repr. of 1638 ed. 67.50 (ISBN 0-404-60818-3). AMS Pr.

Soules Humiliation. Thomas Hooker. LC 78-293. (American Puritan Writings Ser.: No. 16). 232p. Repr. of 1640 ed. 67.50 (ISBN 0-404-60816-7). AMS Pr.

Soules Implantation. Thomas Hooker. LC 78-297. (American Puritan Writings Ser.: No. 17). 328p. Repr. of 1640 ed. 57.50 (ISBN 0-404-60817-5). AMS Pr.

Soules Preparation for Christ: Or, a Treatise of Contrition. Thomas Hooker. LC 78-291. (American Puritan Writings Ser.). (Illus.). 256p. 1981. Repr. of 1638 ed. 67.50 (ISBN 0-404-60815-9). AMS Pr.

Soulful Cry Versus a Fruitful Smile. Sri Chinmoy. (Orig.). 1977. pap. 10.00 (ISBN 0-88497-402-2). Aum Pubns.

Soulful Tribute to the Secretary-General: The Pilot Supreme of the United Nations. Sri Chinmoy. (Illus.). 1978. pap. 4.95 (ISBN 0-88497-443-X). Aum Pubns.

Souls of Black Folk. W. E. B. Dubois. (Great Illustrated Classics). 1979. 10.95 (ISBN 0-396-07757-9). Dodd.

Souls of Black Folk. W. E. B. Dubois. (Classic Ser). (Orig.). 1969. pap. 3.95 (ISBN 0-451-51953-1, CE1820, Sig Classics). NAL.

Souls of Black Folk. W. E. B. Dubois. (Illus.). 1970. pap. 1.25 (ISBN 0-671-47833-8). WSP.

Soulsearch: Hope for Twenty-First Century Living from Ecclesiastes. rev. ed. Robert S. Ricker & Ron Pitkin. LC 85-21594. (Bible Commentary for Laymen Ser.). 168p. 1985. pap. 4.25 (ISBN 0-8307-1100-7, S393118). Regal.

Soulshine. Georgann Bennett. 1978. pap. cancelled (ISBN 0-89900-133-5). College Pr Pub.

Soulwinner. Charles H. Spurgeon. (Orig.). 1963. pap. 4.95 (ISBN 0-8028-8081-9). Eerdmans.

Soulwinning: A Way of Life. Mark Mensendiek. LC 86-80315. 64p. (Orig.). 1986. pap. 3.50 (ISBN 0-933643-28-4). Grace World Outreach.

Soulwinning: Out Where the People Are. rev. ed. T. L. Osborn. (Illus.). 218p. (Orig.). 1982. pap. 3.95 (ISBN 0-317-44699-1). Harrison Hse.

Soun Tetoken: Nez Perce Boy. Kenneth Thomasma. (Voyager Ser.). 144p. 1984. 8.95 (ISBN 0-8010-8874-7); pap. 5.95 (ISBN 0-8010-8873-9). Baker Bk.

Sound Becomes, Silence Is. Sri Chinmoy. 200p. (Orig.). 1975. pap. 3.00 (ISBN 0-88497-118-X). Aum Pubns.

Sound Mind. Albert L. Meiburg. LC 84-10356. (Potentials: Guides for Productive Living Ser.: Vol. 9). 112p. 1984. pap. 7.95 (ISBN 0-664-24532-3). Westminster.

Sound of Bells: The Episcopal Church in South Florida, 1892-1969. Joseph D. Cushman, Jr. LC 75-30946. (Illus.). 1976. 15.00 (ISBN 0-8130-0518-3). U Presses Fla.

Sound of Light. Irina Starr. LC 69-20335. 1977. pap. 3.50 (ISBN 0-87516-220-7). De Vorss.

Sound of One Hand Clapping. Bhagwan Shree Rajneesh. Ed. by Ma Yoga Pratima. (Initiation Talks Ser.). (Illus.). 632p. (Orig.). 1981. pap. 22.50 (ISBN 0-88050-633-4). Chidvilas Found.

Sound of Running Water. Bhagwan Shree Rajneesh. Ed. by Ma Prem Asha. LC 83-180798. (Photobiography Ser.). (Illus.). 564p. 1980. 100.00 (ISBN 0-88050-134-0). Chidvilas Found.

Sound of Silence: Moving with T'ai Chi. Carol R. Murphy. LC 75-41548. (Orig.). 1976. pap. 2.50x (ISBN 0-87574-205-X, 205). Pendle Hill.

Sound Scriptual Sermon Outlines, No. 2. Wade H. Horton. 1974. 7.25 (ISBN 0-87148-769-1); pap. 6.25 (ISBN 0-87148-770-5). Pathway Pr.

Sound Scriptural Outlines, No. 3. Wade H. Horton. 1977. 7.25 (ISBN 0-87148-781-0); pap. 6.25 (ISBN 0-87148-780-2). Pathway Pr.

Sound Scriptural Sermon Outlines, No. 4. Wade H. Horton. 1979. 7.95 (ISBN 0-87148-783-7); pap. 6.95 (ISBN 0-87148-784-5). Pathway Pr.

Sound Scriptural Sermon Outlines, No. 5. Wade H. Horton. (YA) 1982. text ed. 7.95 (ISBN 0-87148-799-3); pap. 6.95 (ISBN 0-87148-800-0). Pathway Pr.

Sound Scriptural Sermon Outlines, No. 6. Wade H. Horton. 1984. text ed. 7.95 (ISBN 0-87148-806-X); pap. text ed. 6.95 (ISBN 0-87148-807-8). Pathway Pr.

Sound the Shofar: The Story & Meaning of Rosh HaShanah & Yom Kippur. Miriam Chaikin. LC 86-2651. (Illus.). 96p. 1986. 13.95 (ISBN 0-89919-373-0, Pub. by Clarion); pap. 4.95 (ISBN 0-89919-427-3, Pub. by Clarion). Ticknor & Fields.

Sounding of the Trumpet. Frances J. Roberts. 1966. 2.95 (ISBN 0-932814-24-7). Kings Farspan.

Soundings: A Thematic Guide for Daily Scripture Prayer. Christopher Aridas. LC 83-16509. 224p. 1984. pap. 4.50 (ISBN 0-385-19157-X, Im). Doubleday.

Soundings in Tibetan Civilization. Barbara N. Aziz & M. Kapstein. 1986. 32.00x (ISBN 0-8364-1587-6, Pub. by Manohar India). South Asia Bks.

Soundless Music of Life. Thomas Hora. (Discourses in Metapsychiatry Ser.). 48p. 1983. pap. 3.95 (ISBN 0-913105-04-X). PAGL Pr.

Sounds of Joy & Praise: Accompaniment. write for info. (ISBN 0-8198-6873-6). Dghtrs St Paul.

Sounds of Joy & Praise: Singers Edition. 0.50 (ISBN 0-8198-6872-8). Dghtrs St Paul.

Sounds of Stillness. Allen J. Weenink. 1984. 3.95 (ISBN 0-89536-686-X, 4862). CSS of Ohio.

Sounds of the Passion. Wallace H. Kirby. 1984. 4.25 (ISBN 0-89536-647-9, 1944). CSS of Ohio.

Sounion: The Temple of Poseidon. A. B. Tataki. (Illustrated Travel Guides Ser.). (Illus.). 1979. pap. 9.95 (ISBN 0-89241-104-X). Caratzas.

Source Book & Bibliographical Guide to American Church History. Peter G. Mode. 1964. Repr. of 1921 ed. 17.50x (ISBN 0-910324-06-9). Canner.

Source Book of Advaita Vedeanta. Eliot Deutsch & J. A. Van Buitenen. LC 75-148944. pap. 65.60 (ISBN 0-317-12996-1, 2017216). Bks Demand UMI.

Source Book of Modern Hinduism. Ed. by Glyn Richards. 220p. 1985. 20.00 (ISBN 0-7007-0173-7). Salem Hse Pubs.

Source of Life: The Eucharist & Christian Living. Rene Voillaume. Tr. by Dinah Livingstone from Fr. 1977. pap. 2.95 (ISBN 0-914544-17-9). Living Flame Pr.

Source: What the Bible Says about the Problems of Contemporary Life. John L. McKenzie. (Basics of Christian Thought Ser.). 228p. 1984. 14.95 (ISBN 0-88347-172-8). Thomas More.

Sourcebook for Modern Catechetics. Ed. by Michael Warren. LC 83-50246. 496p. (Orig.). 1983. pap. 15.95 (ISBN 0-88489-152-6). St Mary's.

Sourcebook for Stewardship Sermons. James E. Carter. LC 78-74768. 1979. pap. 5.95 (ISBN 0-8054-6403-4). Broadman.

Sourcebook of American Methodism. Ed. by Frederick A. Norwood. 683p. (Orig.). 1982. 20.95 (ISBN 0-687-39140-7). Abingdon.

Sourcebook of Ancient Church History. Joseph C. Ayer. LC 70-113536. Repr. of 1913 ed. lib. bdg. 64.50 (ISBN 0-404-00436-9). AMS Pr.

Sources & Literature of Scottish Church History. Malcolm B. MacGregor. LC 76-1125. 260p. 1977. Repr. of 1934 ed. lib. bdg. 20.00x (ISBN 0-915172-10-0). Richwood Pub.

Sources & Shapes of Power. John R. Sherwood & John C. Wagner. LC 80-28125. (Into Our Third Century Ser.). (Orig.). 1981. pap. 3.95 (ISBN 0-687-39142-3). Abingdon.

Sources de l'Histoire du Montanisme. Pierre C. Labriolle. LC 80-13175. (Heresies of the Early Christian & Medieval Era: Second Ser.). Repr. of 1913 ed. 42.00 (ISBN 0-404-16184-7). AMS Pr.

Sources for the Study of Greek Religion. David G. Rice & John E. Stambaugh. LC 79-18389. (Society of Biblical Literature. Sources for Biblical Study Ser.: No. 14). 1979. pap. 9.95 (ISBN 0-89130-347-2, 060314). Scholars Pr GA.

Sources of Modern Atheism: One Hundred Years of Debate over God. Marcel Neusch. LC 82-60596. 1983. pap. 9.95 (ISBN 0-8091-2488-2). Paulist Pr.

Sources of Power of the Apostolic Witness. Robert Shank. 125p. 1982. pap. 3.95 (ISBN 0-911620-05-2). Westcott.

Sources of Religious Insight. Josiah Royce. LC 76-56454. 1977. Repr. lib. bdg. 20.00x (ISBN 0-374-96989-2, Octagon). Hippocrene Bks.

Sources of Renewal: The Fulfillment of Vatican II. Pope John Paul II. LC 79-1780. 448p. 1980. 15.00 (ISBN 0-06-064188-6, HarpR). Har-Row.

Sources of Spenser's Classical Mythology. Alice E. Randall. 1896. Repr. 10.00 (ISBN 0-8274-3476-6). R West.

Sources of Swiss Anabaptism. Ed. by Leland Harder. LC 85-5520. (Classics of the Radical Reformation: No. 4). 816p. 1985. 69.00x (ISBN 0-8361-1251-2). Herald Pr.

Sources of the Quaker Peace Testimony. Howard H. Brinton. 1983. pap. 2.50x (ISBN 0-87574-027-8, 027). Pendle Hill.

Sources of the Synoptic Gospels. Carl S. Patton. 263p. 1980. Repr. of 1915 ed. lib. bdg. 50.00 (ISBN 0-89984-385-9). Century Bookbindery.

Sources of the Synoptic Gospels. Carl S. Patton. Repr. of 1915 ed. 37.00 (ISBN 0-384-38805-1). Johnson Repr.

Sources of Vitality in American Church Life. Ed. by Robert L. Moore. LC 78-71065. (Studies in Ministry & Parish Life). 1978. text ed. 13.95x (ISBN 0-913552-14-3). Exploration Pr.

Sous-Caste de L'Inde du Sud: Organisation Sociale et Religion des Pramalai Kallar. Louis Dumont. (Le Monde D'outre Mer Passe et Present Etudes: No. 1). (Fr.). 1957. pap. text ed. 21.60x (ISBN 0-686-22530-9). Mouton.

South African Churches in a Revolutionary Situation. Marjorie Hope & James Young. LC 81-9584. 288p. (Orig.). 1981. pap. 9.95 (ISBN 0-88344-466-6). Orbis Bks.

South African Jewish Voices. Ed. by Roberta Kalechofsky. LC 81-83903. (Echad 2: a Global Anthology Ser.). 280p. 1982. pap. text ed. 10.00 (ISBN 0-916288-10-2). Micah Pubns.

South African Testament: From Personal Encounter to Theological Challenge. H. Paul Santmire. 266p. (Orig.). 1987. pap. 7.95 (ISBN 0-8028-0266-4). Eerdmans.

South American Mythology. Harold Osborne. LC 85-28567. (Library of the World's Myths & Legends). (Illus.). 144p. 1986. 18.95 (ISBN 0-87226-043-7). P Bedrick Bks.

South & the North in American Religion. Samuel S. Hill. LC 80-234. (Mercer University Lamar Memorial Lecture Ser.: No. 23). 168p. 1980. 14.00x (ISBN 0-8203-0516-2). U of Ga Pr.

South Asian Religion & Society. Ed. by Asko Parpola & Bent S. Hansen. (Studies on Asian Topics (Scandinavian Institute of Asian Studies): No. 11). 262p. (Orig.). 1986. pap. 18.00 (ISBN 0-913215-16-3). Riverdale Co.

South Carolina Baptists: 1670-1805. Leah Townsend. LC 74-6312. (Illus.). 391p. 1978. Repr. of 1935 ed. 20.00 (ISBN 0-8063-0621-1). Genealog Pub.

South Central Frontiers. Paul Erb. LC 74-12108. (Studies in Anabaptist & Mennonite History, No. 17). (Illus.). 448p. 1974. 19.95x (ISBN 0-8361-1196-6). Herald Pr.

South County Studies: Of Some Eighteenth Century Persons, Places & Conditions. in That Portion of Rhode Island Called Narragansett. facsimile ed. Esther B. Carpenter. LC 75-160961. (Select Bibliographies Reprint Ser). Repr. of 1924 ed. 21.00 (ISBN 0-8369-5829-2). Ayer Co Pubs.

South Indian Images of Gods & Goddesses. H. Krishna Sastri. 308p. 1986. Repr. 37.50X (ISBN 0-8364-1710-0, Pub. by Chanakya India). South Asia Bks.

South Indian Shrines. P. V. Ayyar. 648p. 1986. Repr. 14.00X (ISBN 0-8364-1721-6, Pub. by Usha). South Asia Bks.

Southeast Building, the Twin Basilicas, the Mosaic House. Saul S. Weinberg. LC 75-25699. (Corinth Ser: Vol. 1, Pt. 5). (Illus.). 1971. Repr. of 1960 ed. 25.00x (ISBN 0-87661-015-7). Am Sch Athens.

Southeastern Studies: Toward A.D. 2000. Ed. by John I. Durham. LC 77-80400. (Emerging Directions in Christian Ministry Ser.: Vol. 1). viii, 146p. 1981. 8.95 (ISBN 0-86554-026-8, MUP-H004). Mercer Univ Pr.

Southern Anglicanism: The Church of England in Colonial South Carolina. Charles S. Bolton. LC 81-6669. (Contributions to the Study of Religion: No. 5). (Illus.). 248p. 1982. lib. bdg. 29.95 (ISBN 0-313-23090-0, BOS/). Greenwood.

Southern Baptist Convention & Its People. Robert A. Baker. 18.95 (ISBN 0-8054-6516-2). Broadman.

Southern Baptist Holy War. Joe E. Barnhart. LC 86-5988. 256p. 1986. pap. 16.95 (ISBN 0-87719-037-2). Texas Month Pr.

Southern Baptist Preaching Today. R. Earl Allen & Joel Gregory. 1987. pap. 11.95 (ISBN 0-8054-5714-3). Broadman.

Southern Enterprize: The Work of National Evangelical Societies in the Antebellum South. John W. Kuykendall. LC 81-23723. (Contributions to the Study of Religion Ser.: No. 7). xv, 188p. 1982. lib. bdg. 29.95 (ISBN 0-313-23212-1, KSE/). Greenwood.

Southern Evangelicals & the Social Order, 1800-1860. Anne C. Loveland. LC 80-11200. 354p. 1980. 32.50x (ISBN 0-8071-0690-9); pap. 9.95x (ISBN 0-8071-0783-2). La State U Pr.

Southern Heroes, or the Friends in Wartime. Fernando G. Cartland. Bd. with Conscript Quakers. Ethan Foster. (Library of War & Peace; Conscrip. & Cons. Object.). 1972. lib. bdg. 42.00 (ISBN 0-8240-0424-8). Garland Pub.

Southern Indian Myths & Legends. Ed. by Virginia P. Brown & Laurella Owens. (Illus.). 160p. 1985. 15.95 (ISBN 0-912221-02-X). Beechwood.

Southern Methodist University: Founding & Early Years. Mary M. Thomas. LC 74-80248. (Illus.). 1974. 15.00 (ISBN 0-87074-138-1). SMU Press.

Southern Passion. Beatrice Brown. LC 74-10772. 1927. 20.00 (ISBN 0-8414-3122-1). Folcroft.

Southern Quakers & Slavery: A Study in Institutional History. Stephen B. Weeks. LC 78-64260. (Johns Hopkins University. Studies in the Social Sciences. Extra Volumes: 15). Repr. of 1896 ed. 31.00 (ISBN 0-404-61363-2). AMS Pr.

Southern Tradition in Theology & Social Criticism, 1830-1930: The Religious Liberalism & Social Conservatism of James Warley Miles, William Porcher Dubose & Edgar Gardner Murphy. Ralph Luker. LC 84-8954. (Studies in American Religion: Vol. 11). 476p. 1984. 69.95x (ISBN 0-88946-655-6). E Mellen.

Southern White Protestantism in the Twentieth Century. Kenneth K. Bailey. 15.50 (ISBN 0-8446-1035-6). Peter Smith.

Southerners All. F. N. Boney. LC 84-9127. x, 218p. 1984. 17.95 (ISBN 0-86554-114-0, MUP-P19); 12.95 (ISBN 0-86554-189-2). Mercer Univ Pr.

Southwestern Indian Ritual Drama. Ed. by Charlotte J. Frisbie. LC 79-2308. (School of American Research Advanced Seminar Ser.). (Illus.). 384p. 1980. 30.00x (ISBN 0-8263-0521-0). U of NM Pr.

Souvenir Book of the Ephrata Cloister: Complete History from Its Settlement in 1728 to the Present Time. Samuel G. Zerfass. LC 72-2960. Repr. of 1921 ed. 14.25 (ISBN 0-404-10724-9). AMS Pr.

Sovereign Adventure: The Grail of Mankind. Anna Morduch. 196p. 1970. 11.95 (ISBN 0-227-67754-4). Attic Pr.

Sovereign God. James M. Boice. LC 77-14879. (Foundations of the Christian Faith: Vol. 1). 1978. pap. 7.95 (ISBN 0-87784-743-6). Inter-Varsity.

Sovereign Spirit: Discerning His Gifts. Martyn Lloyd-Jones. 160p. 1986. pap. 7.95 (ISBN 0-87788-697-0). Shaw Pubs.

Sovereignty & Freedom: A Struggle for Balance. Ed. by Freeman Barton. 92p. (Orig.). 1978. pap. 2.50 (ISBN 0-913439-00-2). Henceforth.

Sovereignty of God. A. W. Pink. 1976. pap. 3.95 (ISBN 0-85151-133-3). Banner of Truth.

Sovereignty of God. Arthur W. Pink. pap. 6.95 (ISBN 0-8010-7088-0). Baker Bk.

Sovereignty of Good. Iris Murdoch. 116p. 1985. pap. 5.95 (ISBN 0-7448-0028-5, Ark Paperbks). Methuen Inc.

Sovereignty of Grace. Arthur C. Custance. 1979. 12.95 (ISBN 0-87552-160-6). Presby & Reformed.

Soviet Believers: The Religious Sector of the Population. William Fletcher. LC 80-25495. 276p. 1981. 27.50x (ISBN 0-7006-0211-9). U Pr of KS.

Soviet Charismatics: The Pentecostals in the U. S. S. R. William c. Fletcher. (American University Studies VII (Theology & Religion): Vol. 9). 287p. 1985. text ed. 25.15 (ISBN 0-8204-0226-5). P Lang Pubs.

Soviet Dissent: Contemporary Movements for National, Religious & Human Rights. Ludmilla Alexeyeva. Tr. by John Glad & Carol Pearce. LC 84-11811. 1985. 35.00 (ISBN 0-8195-5124-4, Dist. by Harper). Wesleyan U Pr.

Soviet Evangelicals: Since World War II. Walter Sawatsky. LC 81-94121. 560p. 1981. 19.95x (ISBN 0-8361-1238-5); pap. 14.95x (ISBN 0-8361-1239-3). Herald Pr.

Soviet Government & the Jews, Nineteen Forty-Eight to Nineteen Sixty-Seven: A Documented Study. Benjamin Pinkus. 675p. 1984. 62.50 (ISBN 0-521-24713-6). Cambridge U Pr.

Soviet Human Rights Movement: A Memoir. Valery Chalidze. LC 84-72146. xii, 50p. 1984. pap. 2.50 (ISBN 0-87495-064-3). AM Jewish Comm.

Soviet-Jewish Emigration & Soviet Nationality Policy. Victor Zaslavsky & Robert J. Brym. LC 83-3160. 172p. 1983. 22.50 (ISBN 0-312-74844-2). St Martin.

Soviet Jewry since the Second World War: Population & Social Structure. Mordechai Altshuler. LC 86-12139. (Studies in Population & Urban Demography: No. 5). (Illus.). 296p. 1987. lib. bdg. 37.95 (ISBN 0-313-24494-4, ASO). Greenwood.

Soviets Are Coming. Edmund Heit. LC 80-18836. 160p. 1980. pap. 2.95 (ISBN 0-88243-585-X, 02-0585). Gospel Pub.

Sovremennost' v svjetje Slova Bozhija - Slove i Rechi Arkiepiskopa Averkija, 4 vols. Ed. by Archimandrite Anthony Yamshcikov. Tr. of Comtemporaneity in Light of the Word of God - the Works & Writings of Archbishop Averky. 2100p. 1976. 89.00 (ISBN 0-317-29057-6); pap. 69.00 (ISBN 0-317-29058-4). Holy Trinity.

Soweto: The Fruit of Fear. Peter Magubane. 1986. pap. 14.95 (ISBN 0-8028-0248-6). Eerdmans.

Sowing & Reaping. Lilian Hance. 1981. 14.00x (ISBN 0-7223-1418-3, Pub. by A H Stockwell England). State Mutual Bk.

Sowing in Famine. Jerry Savelle. 32p. (Orig.). 1982. pap. 1.50 (ISBN 0-686-83911-0). Harrison Hse.

Soziale Herkunft Der Schweizer Taufer in Der Feformationszeit. Ed. by Paul Peachey. (Ger.). 157p. (Orig.). 1954. pap. 4.50x (ISBN 0-8361-1160-5). Herald Pr.

Sozialismus und Religion. Franz Linden. Repr. of 1932 ed. 16.00 (ISBN 0-384-32740-0). Johnson Repr.

Space Age Science. 2nd ed. Edward F. Hills. (Illus.). 50p. pap. 1.50 (ISBN 0-915923-02-5). Christian Res Pr.

Space for God: Leader's Guide. Donald H. Postema. 120p. 1983. pap. 3.95 (ISBN 0-933140-47-9). CRC Pubns.

Space for God, Study & Practice of Spirituality & Prayer. Donald H. Postema. LC 83-15504. 180p. 1983. pap. 9.95 (ISBN 0-933140-46-0). CRC Pubns.

Space into Light: The Churches of Balthasar Neumann. Christian F. Otto. (Illus.). 1979. 55.00x (ISBN 0-262-15019-0). MIT Pr.

Space, Time & Creation: Philosophical Aspects of Scientific Cosmology. 2nd ed. Milton K. Munitz. 11.75 (ISBN 0-8446-5908-8). Peter Smith.

Space, Time & Deity: The Gifford Lectures at Glasgow 1916-1918, 2 Vols. S. Alexander. Set. 32.00 (ISBN 0-8446-1521-8). Peter Smith.

Space, Time & Incarnation. Thomas F. Torrance. 1969. pap. 4.95 (ISBN 0-19-520082-9). Oxford U Pr.

Space Time & Self. rev. ed. E. Norman Pearson. LC 71-1546. (Illus.). pap. 5.95 (ISBN 0-8356-0409-8, Quest). Theos Pub Hse.

Spaetbronzezeitliche Seevoelkersturm: Ein Forschungsueberblick mit Folgerungen zur biblischen Exodusthematik. August Strobel. (Beiheft 145 Zur Zeitschrift fuer die Alttestamentliche Wissenschaft Ser). 1976. 61.00x (ISBN 3-11-006761-7). De Gruyter.

Spaghetti from the Chandelier: And Other Humorous Adventures of a Minister's Family. Ruth Truman. 160p. 1984. pap. 7.95 (ISBN 0-687-39146-6). Abingdon.

Spain, the Jews & Franco. Haim Avni. Tr. by Emanuel Shimoni from Hebrew. LC 80-39777. 320p. 1981. 19.95 (ISBN 0-8276-0188-3, 469). Jewish Pubns.

Spanish Cathedral Music in the Golden Age. Robert Stevenson. LC 76-1013. (Illus.). 523p. 1976. Repr. of 1961 ed. lib. bdg. 39.50x (ISBN 0-8371-8744-3, STSP). Greenwood.

Spanish Civil War As a Religious Tragedy. Jose M. Sanchez. LC 86-40581. 272p. 1987. text ed. 22.95x (ISBN 0-268-01726-3, Dist. by Har-Row). U of Notre Dame Pr.

Spanish Inquisition. Cecil Roth. (Illus., Orig.). 1964. pap. 7.95 (ISBN 0-393-00255-1, Norton Lib). Norton.

Spanish Inquisition & the Inquisitional Mind. Ed. by Angel Alcala. (Atlantic Studies: No. 49). write for info (ISBN 0-88033-952-7). Brooklyn Coll Pr.

Spanish Islam: History of the Moslems in Spain. Reinhart Dozy. 770p. 1972. Repr. of 1913 ed. 45.00x (ISBN 0-7146-2128-5, F Cass Co). Biblio Dist.

Spanish Jesuit Churches in Mexico's Tarahumara. Paul M. Roca. LC 78-14467. 369p. 1979. pap. 11.50x (ISBN 0-8165-0572-1). U of Ariz Pr.

Spanish Missions of Georgia. John T. Lanning. (Illus.). 1971. Repr. of 1935 ed. 39.00 (ISBN 0-403-00803-4). Scholarly.

Spanish Pilgrime, or: An Admirable Discovery of a Romish Catholike. Jose Teixeira. LC 72-6033. (English Experience Ser.: No. 560). 148p. 1973. Repr. of 1625 ed. 15.00 (ISBN 90-221-0560-1). Walter J Johnson.

Spanish Protestants & Reformers in the Sixteenth Century: A Bibliography. A. Gordon Kinder. (Research Bibliographies & Checklists Ser.: No. 39). 108p. (Orig.). 1983. pap. 11.95 (ISBN 0-7293-0146-X, Pub. by Grant & Cutler). Longwood Pub Group.

Spanish Story of the Armada & Other Essays. James A. Froude. LC 71-144613. Repr. of 1892 ed. 24.50 (ISBN 0-404-02628-1). AMS Pr.

Spanish Texas Pilgrimage: The Old Franciscan Missions & Other Spanish Settlements of Texas, 1632-1821. Marion A. Habig. 1985. 12.50 (ISBN 0-8199-0883-5). Franciscan Herald.

Spanking: Why? When? How? Roy Lessin. LC 79-54028. 96p. 1979. pap. 2.95 (ISBN 0-87123-494-7, 200494). Bethany Hse.

Spanning the Decades: A Spiritual Pilgrimage. Bertha P. Wyker. (Illus.). 224p. 1981. 8.50 (ISBN 0-682-49746-0). Exposition Pr FL.

Spare No Exertions: One Hundred Seventy-Five Years of the Reformed Presbyterian Theological Seminary. Robert M. Copeland. LC 86-60501. (Illus.). 144p. 1986. 7.95x (ISBN 0-9616417-0-3). Ref Presby Theo.

Spare Your People! Richard Swanson. LC 85-73213. 1986. pap. 3.50 (ISBN 0-88270-596-2). Bridge Pub.

Sparke Towards the Kindling of Sorrow for Zion. Thomas Gataker. LC 76-57382. (English Experience Ser.: No. 800). 1977. Repr. of 1621 ed. lib. bdg. 7.00 (ISBN 90-221-0800-7). Walter J Johnson.

Sparkling Devotions for Women's Groups. Mary A. Vandermey. 144p. 1985. pap. 4.95 (ISBN 0-8010-9300-7). Baker Bk.

Sparkling Object Sermons for Children. C. W. Bess. (Object Lesson Ser.). 120p. (Orig.). 1982. pap. 4.95 (ISBN 0-8010-0824-7). Baker Bk.

Sparks of Light: Counseling in the Hasidic Tradition. Zalman M. Schachter & Edward Hoffman. LC 83-42804. 208p. (Orig.). 1983. pap. 9.95 (ISBN 0-87773-240-X). Shambhala Pubns.

Sparks of Spirit: A Handbook for Personal Happiness. Rolf Gompertz. LC 83-50870. 168p. 1983. velo binding 10.00 (ISBN 0-918248-04-3). Word Doctor.

Sparks of the Holy Tongue. 1982. pap. 4.95 (ISBN 0-87306-240-X). Feldheim.

Sparks of the Truth: From the Dissertations of Meher Baba. Meher Baba. Ed. by C. D. Deshmukh. (Illus.). 96p. (Orig.). 1971. pap. 2.95 (ISBN 0-913078-02-6). Sheriar Pr.

Sparrow's Song. Eleanor Gamblin & Joyce M. Morehouse. Ed. by Mary H. Wallace. 192p. (Orig.). 1984. pap. 5.95 (ISBN 0-912315-68-7). Word Aflame.

Spartans. L. F. Fitzhardinge. LC 79-66136. (Ancient Peoples & Places Ser.). (Illus.). 180p. 1985. pap. 10.95f (ISBN 0-500-27364-2). Thames Hudson.

Spatmittelalterliche Geistliche Literatur in der Nationalsprache, Vol. 1. Ed. by James Hogg. (Analecta Cartusiana Ser.: No. 106/1). 236p. (Orig.). 1983. pap. 25.00 (ISBN 0-317-42595-1, Pub. by Salzburg Studies). Longwood Pub Group.

Spatmittelalterliche Geistliche Literatur in der Nationalsprache, Vol. 2. Ed. by James Hogg. (Analecta Cartusiana Ser.: No. 106/2). 190p. (Orig.). 1984. pap. 25.00 (ISBN 0-317-42596-X, Pub. by Salzburg Studies). Longwood Pub Group.

Speak, Lord, Your Servant Is Listening. David E. Rosage. 1977. pap. 2.95 (ISBN 0-89283-046-8). Servant.

Speak the Thought: How to Read & Speak in Public, with Bible-Lesson Applications. 2nd, exp. ed. Muriel F. Reid. 64p. 1984. 7.00 (ISBN 0-915878-05-4). Joseph Pub Co.

Speak to Me Lord--I'm Listening. Virginia Thompson. LC 78-55479. 1981. pap. 2.25 (ISBN 0-89081-117-2, 1172). Harvest Hse.

Speak up! Christian Assertiveness. Randolph K. Sanders & H. Newton Malony. LC 84-20806. 118p. (Orig.). 1985. pap. 7.95 (ISBN 0-664-24551-X). Westminster.

Speak up! Christian Assertiveness. Randolph K. Sanders & H. Newton Malony. 1986. pap. 2.95 (Pub. by Ballantine-Epiphany). Ballantine.

Speaker's Bible, 18 vols. Ed. by James Hastings & Edward Hastings. 1979. 275.00 (ISBN 0-8010-4036-1). Baker Bk.

Speaker's Bible. 2nd ed. Jacob W. Spatz. 288p. 1986. pap. 10.00 (ISBN 0-938033-00-X). Alert Pubs.

Speaking As One Friend to Another. John Yungblut. (Orig.). 1983. pap. 2.50x (ISBN 0-87574-249-1, 249). Pendle Hill.

Speaking Blood: Speaking Faith. Bob Lamb. 1983. pap. 2.95 (ISBN 0-910709-09-2). PTL Repro.

Speaking for the Master. Batsell B. Baxter. pap. 4.95 (ISBN 0-8010-0588-4). Baker Bk.

Speaking from the Heart. Ken Durham. LC 86-61523. 1986. 10.95 (ISBN 0-8344-0136-3, BA120H). Sweet.

Speaking His Peace. Laura I. Crowell. 160p. 1985. pap. 8.95 (ISBN 0-8192-1359-4). Morehouse.

Speaking in Church Made Simple. Carnell C. Mitchell, Jr. 1985. pap. 3.95 (ISBN 0-8054-3431-3). Broadman.

Speaking in Other Tongues: A Scholarly Defense. Donald L. Barnett & Jeffrey P. McGregor. 840p. 1986. 25.00 (ISBN 0-934287-23-6). Comm Chapel Pubns.

Speaking in Parables: A Study in Metaphor & Theology. Sallie McFague. LC 74-26338. 192p. 1975. pap. 5.95 (ISBN 0-8006-1097-0, 1-1097). Fortress.

Speaking in Stories: Resources for Christian Storytellers. William R. White. LC 82-70954. 128p. (Orig.). 1982. pap. 6.95 (ISBN 0-8066-1929-5, 10-5886). Augsburg.

Speaking in Tongues. Larry Christenson. LC 97-5595. 1968. pap. 3.95 (ISBN 0-87123-518-8, 200518). Bethany Hse.

Speaking in Tongues. Fisher Humphreys & Malcolm Tolbert. LC 73-86749. 94p. (Orig.). 1973. pap. 3.00 (ISBN 0-914520-05-9). Insight Pr.

Speaking in Tongues. Philip Mauro. 1978. pap. 0.50 (ISBN 0-685-36793-2). Reiner.

Speaking in Tongues: A Guide to Research on Glossolalia. Ed. by Watson E. Mills. 552p. (Orig.). 1986. pap. 24.95 (ISBN 0-8028-0183-8). Eerdmans.

Speaking in Tongues & Divine Healing. Robert P. Lightner. LC 65-5805. 1978. pap. 1.95 (ISBN 0-87227-059-9). Reg Baptist.

Speaking in Tongues: Is That All There Is? Bob Cook. (Discovery Bks.). (Illus.). 48p. (YA) 1982. pap. text ed. 1.50 (ISBN 0-88243-932-4, 02-0932); tchr's ed. 3.95 (02-0935). Gospel Pub.

Speaking of Cardinals. facs. ed. Thomas B. Morgan. LC 70-134119. (Essay Index Reprint Ser). 1946. 18.00 (ISBN 0-8369-2002-3). Ayer Co Pubs.

Speaking of Jesus: Finding the Words for Witness. Richard Lischer. LC 81-70556. 144p. 1982. pap. 6.95 (ISBN 0-8006-1631-6, 1-1631). Fortress.

Speaking of My Life. Far West Editions. 149p. 1979. pap. 4.95 (ISBN 0-686-47084-2). Far West Edns.

Speaking of Silence: Christians & Buddhists on the Contemplative Way. Ed. by Susan Walker. 1987. pap. 14.95. Paulist Pr.

Speaking of Siva. Tr. by A. K. Ramanujan. (Classics Ser.). 200p. 1973. pap. 5.95 (ISBN 0-14-044270-7). Penguin.

Speaking the Gospel Through the Ages: A History of Evangelism. Milton L. Rudnick. 1984. 24.95 (ISBN 0-570-04204-6, 15-2172). Concordia.

Speaking the Gospel Today: A Theology for Evangelism. Robert A. Kolb. 1984. 16.95 (ISBN 0-570-04205-4, 15-2173). Concordia.

Speaking the Truth: Ecumenism, Liberation, & Black Theology. James H. Cone. 176p. (Orig.). 1986. pap. 8.95 (ISBN 0-8028-0226-5). Eerdmans.

Speaking to Life's Problems. Lloyd Perry & Charles Sell. 1983. pap. 12.95 (ISBN 0-8024-0170-8). Moody.

Speaking Tree: A Study of Indian Culture & Society. Richard Lannoy. 1971. 32.50x (ISBN 0-19-501469-3). Oxford U Pr.

Speaking Well of God. Edward Vick. LC 79-9336. (Anvil Ser.). 1979. pap. 8.95 (ISBN 0-8127-0245-X). Review & Herald.

Speaking with Signs. Wesley T. Runk. 1975. 2.50 (ISBN 0-89536-216-3, 1920). CSS of Ohio.

Spear of Destiny: The Occult Power Behind the Spear Which Pierced the Side of Christ... & How Hitler Inverted the Force in a Bid to Conquer the World. Trevor Ravenscroft. LC 82-60165. 384p. 1982. pap. 9.95 (ISBN 0-87728-547-0). Weiser.

Special Day Prayers for the Very Young Child. M. Grenier. LC 56-1719. 1983. 7.95 (ISBN 0-570-04076-0). Concordia.

Special Day Sermon Outlines. Russell E. Spray. 80p. 1984. pap. 3.95 (ISBN 0-8010-8241-2). Baker Bk.

Special Day Sermons. W. H. Compton. 1972. 3.25 (ISBN 0-87148-752-7). Pathway Pr.

Special Days & Occasions. Billy Apostolon. (Sermon Outline Ser). 1978. pap. 2.50 (ISBN 0-8010-0007-6). Baker Bk.

Special Days: The Book of Anniversaries & Holidays. Ruth W. Gregory. 1978. pap. 5.95 (ISBN 0-8065-0659-8). Citadel Pr.

Special Education in the Jewish Community. 3.00 (N03). Torah Umesorah.

Special Friends of Jesus: New Testament Stories. Francine M. O'Connor. 64p. 1986. pap. 3.95 (ISBN 0-89243-255-1). Liguori Pubns.

Special Gift. G. Clifton Wisler. (Voyager Ser.). 80p. 1983. pap. 3.50 (ISBN 0-8010-9661-8). Baker Bk.

Special Illumination: The Sufi Use of Humour. Idries Shah. 64p. 1977. 9.95 (ISBN 0-900860-57-X, Pub. by Octagon Pr England). Ins Study Human.

Special Legacy: An Oral History of Soviet Jewish Emigres in the United States. Sylvia Rothchild. 336p. 1986. pap. 8.95 (ISBN 0-671-62817-8, Touchstone). S&S.

Special Meditations for Health, Wealth, Love. Joseph Murphy. pap. 1.50 (ISBN 0-87516-336-X). De Vorss.

Special Messenger. Ruth A. LaVigne. 1978. 3.50 (ISBN 0-8198-0555-6); pap. 2.50 (ISBN 0-8198-0556-4). Dghtrs St Paul.

Special Ministers of the Eucharist. William J. Belford. 1979. pap. 1.95 (ISBN 0-916134-39-3). Pueblo Pub Co.

Special Ministries for Caring Churches. Compiled by Robert E. Korth. 128p. 1986. pap. 5.95 (ISBN 0-87403-145-1, 3183). Standard Pub.

Special Occasion Helps. C. M. O'Guin. (Pulpit Library). 88p. 1983. pap. 2.95 (ISBN 0-8010-6650-6). Baker bk.

Special Occasion Sermon Outlines. Carl G. Johnson. (Pocket Pulpit Library). 112p. 1980. pap. 3.50 (ISBN 0-8010-5126-6). Baker Bk.

Special Problems in the Study of Sufi Ideas. Idries Shah. 45p. 1978. pap. 5.95 (ISBN 0-900860-21-9, Pub by Octagon Pr England). Ins Study Human.

Special Sermons by George Sweeting. George Sweeting. 1985. pap. 11.95 (ISBN 0-8024-8211-2). Moody.

Special Signs of Grace: The Seven Sacraments & Sacramentals. Joseph Champlin. (Illus.). 160p. 1986. pap. 6.95 (ISBN 0-8146-1466-3). Liturgical Pr.

Special Times with God. David Shibley & Naomi Shibley. LC 81-14116. 160p. 1981. 5.95 (ISBN 0-8407-5780-8). Nelson.

Special Treatment: The Untold Story of the Survival of Thousands of Jews in Hitler's Third Reich. Alan Abrams. (Illus.). 261p. 1985. 14.95 (ISBN 0-8184-0364-0). Lyle-Stuart.

Special You. (Benziger Family Life Program Ser.). 6p. 1978. 2.45 (ISBN 0-02-651750-7); tchrs. ed. 4.00 (ISBN 0-02-651760-4); family handbook 1.00 (ISBN 0-02-651790-6). Benziger Pub Co.

Specimens of the Pre-Shakespearean Drama, 2 Vols. John M. Manly. LC 67-18432. 1897. 20.00 (ISBN 0-8196-0200-0). Biblo.

Speck in Your Brother's Eye: How to Be a More Loving Christian. Ron Hembree. 192p. 1985. 9.95 (ISBN 0-8007-1426-1). Revell.

Spectacle of Death. K. M. Islam. pap. 16.50 (ISBN 0-686-63915-4). Kazi Pubns.

Spectrum of Consciousness. Ken Wilber. LC 76-39690. (Illus.). 1977. 12.00 (ISBN 0-8356-0495-0). Theos Pub Hse.

Spectrum of Ritual: A Biogenetic Structural Analysis. Eugene G. D'Aquili et al. LC 78-19015. 408p. 1979. 35.00x (ISBN 0-231-04514-X). Columbia U Pr.

Speculations & Experiments Related to the Origin of Life: A Critique. Duane T. Gish. (ICR Technical Monograph: No. 1). (Illus.). 41p. 1972. pap. 5.95 (ISBN 0-89051-010-5). Master Bks.

Speculative Freemasonary. John Yarker. 1987. pap. 3.95 (ISBN 0-916411-66-4, Pub. by Sure Fire). Holmes Pub.

Speculative Masonry Its Mission, Its Evolution & Its Landmarks. A. S. Macbride. 264p. 1971. Repr. of 1924 ed. text ed. 6.00 (ISBN 0-88053-040-5, M-89). Macoy Pub.

Speculum Christiani: A Middle English Religious Treatise of the 14th Century. (EETS OS: No. 182). Repr. of 1933 ed. 34.00 (ISBN 0-527-00179-1). Kraus Repr.

Speculum Devotorum of an Anonymous Carhusian of Sheen: From the manuscripts Cambridge University Library (Gg. I.6 & Foyle Vol.2) James Hogg. (Analecta Carusiana Ser.: No. 12). (Eng.). 173p. (Orig.). 1973. pap. 25.00 (ISBN 3-7052-0013-5, Pub by Salzburg Studies). Longwood Pub Group.

Speculum Devotorum of an Anonymous Carhusian of Sheen: From the Manuscripts Cambridge University Library (Gg. I.6 & Foyle Vol.3, Pt. 2) Ed. by james Hogg. (Analecta Carusiana Ser.: No. 13). (Eng.). 174p. (Orig.). 1974. pap. 25.00 (ISBN 3-7052-0014-3, Pub by Salzburg Studies). Longwood Pub Group.

Speculum Devotorum of an Anonymous Carthusian of Sheen: Introduction. James Hogg. (Analceta Cartusiana Ser.: No. 11). (Orig.). 1985. pap. 25.00 (ISBN 3-7052-0012-7, Pub by Salzburg Studies). Longwood Pub Group.

'Speculum Inclusorum' MS. British Library London Harley 2372: A Critical Edition, Vol. 1. James Hogg. (Analecta Cartusiana Ser.: No. 59-1). (Orig.). 1985. pap. 25.00 (ISBN 3-7052-0086-0, Pub. by Salzburg Studies). Longwood Pub Group.

'Speculum Incusorum' MS. British Library London Harley 2372. James Hogg. (Analecta Cartusiana Ser.: No. 59-2). (Lat.). 139p. (Orig.). 1981. pap. 25.00 (ISBN 3-7052-0087-9, Pub. by Salzburg Studies). Longwood Pub Group.

Speculum Sacerdotale. (EETS, OS Ser.: No. 200). Repr. of 1936 ed. 21.00 (ISBN 0-527-00200-3). Kraus Repr.

Speech Delivered in the Starr-Chamber, at the Censure of J. Bastwick. William Laud. LC 79-171771. (English Experience Ser.: No. 396). 92p. 1971. Repr. of 1637 ed. 14.00 (ISBN 90-221-0396-X). Walter J Johnson.

Speech of Elder Orson Hyde: 1845. Orson Hyde. 16p. (Orig.). 1986. pap. 1.95 (ISBN 0-942284-07-0). Restoration Re.

Speeches at Home & Abroad. C. H. Spurgeon. 1974. 3.50 (ISBN 0-686-09111-6). Pilgrim Pubns.

Speed of Love: An Exploration of Christian Faithfulness in a Technological World. David P. Young. 150p. (Orig.). 1986. pap. 6.95 (ISBN 0-377-00159-7). Friend Pr.

Spellcraft, Hexcraft & Witchcraft. Anna Riva. (Illus.). 64p. 1977. pap. 3.50 (ISBN 0-943832-00-4). Intl Imports.

Spelling the Word: George Herbert & the Bible. Chana Bloch. LC 84-123. 375p. 1985. 37.50x (ISBN 0-520-05121-1). U of Cal Pr.

Spending Time Alone with God. Barry St. Clair. 144p. 1984. pap. 4.95 (ISBN 0-88207-302-8). Victor Bks.

Spenser, Marvell, & Renaissance Pastoral. Patrick Cullen. LC 76-123566. pap. 42.60 (2014653). Bks Demand UMI.

Spenserian Poetics: Idolatry, Iconoclasm & Magic. Kenneth Gross. LC 85-47701. 256p. 1986. text ed. 24.95x (ISBN 0-8014-1805-4). Cornell U Pr.

Spenser's Cosmic Philosophy of Religion. E. M. Albright. LC 72-100730. 1970. Repr. of 1929 ed. 39.95 (ISBN 0-8383-0001-4). Haskell.

Sperling. Jane T. Clement. 154p. 1986. pap. 6.00 (ISBN 3-922819-36-2). Plough.

Sphota Theory of Language. Harold G. Coward. 1981. 12.00x (ISBN 0-8364-0692-3). South Asia Bks.

Spice & Spirit of Kosher-Passover Cooking. Ed. by Esther Blau & Cyrel Deitsch. LC 77-72116. (Lubavitch Women's Organization Ser.). 1981. 7.95 (ISBN 0-317-14690-4). Lubavitch Women.

Spicer: Leader with the Common Touch. Godfrey T. Anderson. Ed. by Gerald Wheeler. LC 83-3279. (Illus.). 128p. (Orig.). 1983. pap. 5.95 (ISBN 0-8280-0150-2). Review & Herald.

Spicilegium Syriacum: Containing Remains of Bardesan, Meliton, Ambrose & Mara Bar Serapion, 1855. Ed. by William Cureton. 1965. 10.00x (ISBN 0-8401-0493-6). A R Allenson.

Spies Among Us: Agents Provocateurs. Information Service. 1978. pap. 3.00 (ISBN 0-915598-19-1). Church of Scient Info.

Spinning a Sacred Yarn: Women Speak from the Pulpit. LC 82-569. 230p. (Orig.). 1982. pap. 8.95 (ISBN 0-8298-0604-0). Pilgrim NY.

Spinning Straw into Gold. C. C. Cribb. LC 79-84880. (If God Has It I Want It! Ser.). pap. 2.95 (ISBN 0-932046-15-0). Manhattan Ltd NC.

Spinoza. Stuart Hampshire. (Orig.). 1952. pap. 4.95 (ISBN 0-14-020253-6, Pelican). Penguin.

Spinoza. Karl Jaspers. Ed. by Hannah Arendt. Tr. by Ralph Manheim from Ger. LC 74-4336. (From the Great Philosophers Ser.). 120p. 1974. pap. 2.95 (ISBN 0-15-684730-2, Harv). HarBraceJ.

Spinoza. Leon Roth. LC 78-14139. 1986. Repr. of 1954 ed. 23.75 (ISBN 0-88355-813-0). Hyperion Conn.

Spinoza & Moral Freedom. S. Paul Kashap. (SUNY Series in Philosophy). 130p. 1987. text ed. 32.50x (ISBN 0-88706-529-5); pap. 10.95x. State U NY Pr.

Spinoza & the Sciences. Ed. by Nails Grene. 1986. lib. bdg. 54.50 (ISBN 90-277-1976-4, Pub. by Reidel Holland). Kluwer-Academic.

Spinoza Bibliography. Columbia University. Compiled by Adolph S. Oko. 1964. lib. bdg. 79.00 (ISBN 0-8161-0699-1, Hall Library). G K Hall.

Spinoza: His Life & Philosophy. Frederick Pollock. (Reprints in Philosophy Ser.). (Illus.). Repr. of 1880 ed. lib. bdg. 47.00x (ISBN 0-697-00055-9). Irvington.

Spinoza: New Perspectives. Ed. by Robert W. Shahan & J. I. Biro. LC 77-18541. 1980. 16.50x (ISBN 0-8061-1459-2); pap. text ed. 8.95x (ISBN 0-8061-1647-1). U of Okla Pr.

Spinoza: The Man & His Thought. Edward J. Schaub. 61p. 1933. pap. 0.95 (ISBN 0-317-40400-8). Open Court.

Spinoza's Critique of Religion. Leo Strauss. Tr. by E. M. Sinclair from Ger. LC 65-10948. 364p. 1982. pap. 8.50 (ISBN 0-8052-0704-X). Schocken.

Spinoza's Earliest Publication? Ed. by Richard H. Popkin & Michael Signer. 100p. 1987. 17.50 (ISBN 90-232-2223-7, Pub. by Van Gorcum Holland). Longwood Pub Group.

Spinoza's Metaphysics: Essays in Critical Appreciation. James B. Wilbur. (Philosophia Spinozae Perennis Ser.: No. 1). 170p. 1976. pap. text ed. 19.00 (ISBN 90-232-1361-0, Pub. by Van Gorcum Holland). Longwood Pub Group.

Spinoza's Political & Ethical Philosophy. Robert A. Duff. LC 71-108858. 1920. Repr. of 1903 ed. lib. bdg. 37.50x (ISBN 0-678-00615-6). Kelley.

Spinoza's Political & Ethical Philosophy. Robert A. Duff. 1973. Repr. of 1903 ed. 14.00 (ISBN 0-8274-1391-2). R West.

Spiral Dance: Rebirth of the Ancient Religion of the Goddess. Starhawk. (Orig.). 1979. pap. 10.95 (ISBN 0-06-067535-7, RD 301, HarpR). Har-Row.

Spires of Forms: A Study of Emerson's Aesthetic Theory. Vivian C. Hopkins. LC 80-2537. Repr. of 1951 ed. 33.50 (ISBN 0-404-19263-7). AMS Pr.

Spirit Aflame: Luis Palau's Mission to London. Susan Holton & David L. Jones. 258p. 1985. 7.95 (ISBN 0-8010-4293-3). Baker Bk.

Spirit Alive in Liturgy: Spirit Masters. Religous Education Staff. 1981. 9.95 (ISBN 0-686-84105-0). Wm C Brown.

Spirit Alive in Prayer: Spirit Masters. Religious Education Staff. 1979. 9.95 (ISBN 0-697-01699-4). Wm C Brown.

Spirit Alive in Service: Spirit Masters. Religious Education Staff. 1979. 9.95 (ISBN 0-697-01712-5). Wm C Brown.

Spirit Alive in Vocations: Spirit Masters. Religious Education Staff. 1980. 9.95 (ISBN 0-697-01755-9). Wm C Brown.

Spirit Alive in You: Spirit Masters. Religous Education Staff. 1982. 9.95 (ISBN 0-697-01805-9). Wm C Brown.

Spirit & His Gifts. George T. Montague. LC 74-77425. 72p. (Orig.). 1974. pap. 1.95 (ISBN 0-8091-1829-7, Deus). Paulist Pr.

Spirit & Intellect: Thomas Upham's Holiness Theology. Darius L. Salter. LC 86-10048. (Studies in Evangelicalism: No. 7). 283p. 1986. 27.50 (ISBN 0-8108-1899-X). Scarecrow.

Spirit & Life, Book of the Sun. Ed. by Daniel H. Shubin. Tr. by John W. Volkov from Russian. 768p. 1984. 40.00 (ISBN 0-318-20027-9). D H Shubin.

Spirit & Power of Christian Secularity. Ed. by Albert L. Schlitzer. LC 75-75154. 1969. 12.95 (ISBN 0-268-00321-1). U of Notre Dame Pr.

Spirit & Science: Reality & Imagination. Ed. by Jean E. Charon. (Illus.). 440p. 1987. 24.95 (ISBN 0-89226-027-0, Pub. by ICUS). Paragon Hse.

Spirit & Struggle in Southern Asia. Ed. by Barbara H. Chase & Martha L. Man. 105p. (Orig.). 1986. pap. 5.95 (ISBN 0-377-00157-0). Friend Pr.

Spirit & the Bride Say, "Come!" Mary's Role in the New Pentecost. George W. Kosicki & Gerald J. Farrell. 112p. pap. 3.95 (ISBN 0-911988-41-6). AMI Pr.

Spirit & the Bride: Woman in the Bible. Karl H. Schelkle. Ed. by John Schneider. Tr. by Matthew J. O'Connell from Ger. LC 79-16976. 191p. (Orig.). 1979. pap. 3.50 (ISBN 0-8146-1008-0). Liturgical Pr.

Spirit & the Congregation: Studies in I Corinthians 12-15. Ralph P. Martin. 160p. (Orig.). 1984. 11.95 (ISBN 0-8028-3608-9). Eerdmans.

Spirit & the Forms of Love. Daniel D. Williams. LC 81-40368. 316p. 1981. lib. bdg. 27.75 (ISBN 0-8191-1691-2); pap. text ed. 12.25 (ISBN 0-8191-1692-0). U Pr of Amer.

Spirit & the Future of Islam, 2 vols. Abdullah Ali. 155p. 1983. Set. 187.50x (ISBN 0-86722-051-1). Inst Econ Pol.

Spirit & the Mind. Samuel H. Sandweiss. 1985. pap. 6.30 (ISBN 0-9600958-9-6). Birth Day.

Spirit & the Word. Z. T. Sweeny. 1982. pap. 3.95 (ISBN 0-89225-264-2). Gospel Advocate.

Spirit as Lord. Philip Rosato. 240p. 1981. 20.95 (ISBN 0-567-09305-0, Pub. by T&T Clark Ltd UK). Fortress.

Spirit-Baptism: A Pentecostal Alternative. Harold D. Hunter. LC 83-10500. 322p. (Orig.). 1983. lib. bdg. 28.50 (ISBN 0-8191-3323-X); pap. text ed. 14.50 (ISBN 0-8191-3324-8). U Pr of Amer.

Spirit, Being & Self. P. T. Raju. (Studies in Indian & Western Philosophy). 285p. 1982. 29.95 (ISBN 0-940500-98-1, Pub. by S. Asian Pubs India). Asia Bk Corp.

Spirit Bible. Compiled by Eugene S. Geissler. LC 73-88004. 272p. 1973. pap. 2.25 (ISBN 0-87793-062-7). Ave Maria.

Spirit-Controlled Family Living. Tim LaHaye & Beverly LaHaye. 224p. pap. 6.95 (ISBN 0-8007-5026-8, Power Bks). Revell.

Spirit-Controlled Woman. Beverly LaHaye. LC 76-5562. 1976. pap. 4.95 (ISBN 0-89081-020-6, 0206). Harvest Hse.

Spirit-Filled. Jack Hayford. 112p. (Orig.). 1987. mass 2.95, (ISBN 0-8423-6407-2). Tyndale.

Spirit-Filled: Anointed by Christ the King. Jack W. Hayford. LC 84-80747. (Orig.). 1984. pap. 2.95 (ISBN 0-916847-04-7). Living Way.

Spirit-Filled Christian. rev. ed. Navigators Staff. (Design for Discipleship Ser.: Bk. 2). 1980. pap. text ed. cancelled (ISBN 0-934396-17-5). Churches Alive.

Spirit-Filled Church. John Lancaster. LC 75-22584. 112p. 1975. pap. 1.25 (ISBN 0-88243-601-5, 02-0601, Radiant Bks). Gospel Pub.

Spirit Filled Church in Action. A. B. Simpson. 112p. 1975. 2.00 (ISBN 0-87509-037-0). Chr Pubns.

Spirit Filled Family, No. 11. John F. Stephens. 48p. (Orig.). 1980. pap. 1.95 (ISBN 0-89841-008-8). Zoe Pubns.

Spirit-Filled Life. John MacNeil. (Moody Classics Ser.). 1984. pap. 3.50 (ISBN 0-8024-0493-6). Moody.

Spirit-Filled Life. Verla A. Mooth. 1978. 6.00 (ISBN 0-682-49113-6). Exposition Pr FL.

Spirit-Filled Pastor's Guide. Ralph M. Riggs. 1948. pap. 5.95 (ISBN 0-88243-588-4, 02-0588). Gospel Pub.

Spirit Fruit. rev. ed. John M. Drescher. LC 73-21660. 352p. 1978. pap. 8.95 (ISBN 0-8361-1867-7). Herald Pr.

Spirit Guides: You Are Not Alone. Iris Belhayes. (Inner Visions Ser.). (Orig.). 1986. pap. 12.95 (ISBN 0-917086-80-5). A C S Pubns Inc.

Spirit Healing & Spirit Universe. 1985. 6.50 (ISBN 0-8062-2518-1). Carlton.

Spirit Himself. Ralph M. Riggs. 210p. 1949. 5.50 (ISBN 0-88243-590-6, 02-0590). Gospel Pub.

Spirit in Galatia: Paul's Interpretation of Pneuma As Divine Power. David J. Lull. LC 79-26094. (Society of Biblical Literature Dissertation: No. 49). 15.95 (ISBN 0-89130-367-7, 06-01-49); pap. 10.95 (ISBN 0-89130-368-5). Scholars Pr GA.

Spirit in Matter: A Scientist's Answer to the Bishop Quevies. 1948. 10.00 (ISBN 0-906492-16-5, Pub. by Kolisko Archives). St George Bk Serv.

Spirit in My Life. James Alberione. 1977. pap. 0.95 (ISBN 0-8198-0460-6). Dghtrs St Paul.

Spirit in the Church. Megan McKenna & Darryl Ducote. LC 78-71531. (Followers of the Way Ser.: Vol. 4). 1979. 22.50 (ISBN 0-8091-9545-3); cassette 7.50 (ISBN 0-8091-7669-6). Paulist Pr.

Spirit in the Church. Karl Rahner. 1979. pap. 3.95 (ISBN 0-8245-0399-6). Crossroad NY.

Spirit Life. D. Stuart Briscoe. 160p. 1983. pap. 5.95 (ISBN 0-8007-5185-X). Revell.

Spirit Mediumship & Society in Africa. John Beattie & John Middleton. LC 70-80849. 310p. 1969. 35.00x (ISBN 0-8419-0009-4, Africana). Holmes & Meier.

Spirit Moves: A Handbook of Dance & Prayer. Carla De Sola. Ed. & intro. by Doug Adams. LC 77-89743. (Illus.). 152p. 1986. pap. 9.95 (ISBN 0-941500-38-1). Sharing Co.

Spirit of Buddhism. Hari S. Gour. LC 78-72432. Repr. of 1929 ed. 57.50 (ISBN 0-404-17299-7). AMS Pr.

Spirit of Buddhism Today. Koin Takada. Tr. by Philip Yampolsky. (Illus.). 1973. 9.95 (ISBN 0-89346-095-8, Pub. by Tokuma Shoten); pap. 2.95 (ISBN 0-89346-043-5). Heian Intl.

Spirit of Calvary. J. C. Metcalfe. 1970. pap. 3.25 (ISBN 0-87508-921-6). Chr Lit.

Spirit of Catholicism. Karl Adam. Tr. by Dom J. McCann from German. 237p. 1981. Repr. of 1929 ed. lib. bdg. 30.00 (ISBN 0-89987-028-7). Darby Bks.

Spirit of Christ. rev. ed. Andrew Murray. LC 79-51335. 288p. 1979. pap. 4.95 (ISBN 0-87123-589-7, 210589). Bethany Hse.

Spirit of Christ. Andrew Murray. 1970. pap. 4.50 (ISBN 0-87508-395-1). Chr Lit.

Spirit of Christ. 2nd ed. Andrew Murray. 240p. 1984. pap. 3.50 (ISBN 0-88368-126-9). Whitaker Hse.

Spirit of Christmas. Henry Van Dyke. LC 84-19389. 64p. 1984. pap. 2.95 (ISBN 0-89783-033-4). Larlin Corp.

Spirit of Findhorn. Eileen Caddy. LC 75-36747. (Illus.). 1979. pap. 7.95 (ISBN 0-06-061291-6, RD 296, HarpR). Har-Row.

Spirit of God. G. Campbell Morgan. (Morgan Library). 240p. 1981. pap. 4.95 (ISBN 0-8010-6119-9). Baker Bk.

Spirit of Grace. 1979. 2.50 (ISBN 0-681-98059-1); pap. 1.25 (ISBN 0-8198-0598-X). Dghtrs St Paul.

Spirit of Himalaya: The Story of a Truth Seeker. Swami Amar Jyoti. LC 78-73995. (Illus.). 1979. 7.95 (ISBN 0-933572-00-X). Truth Consciousness.

Spirit of Himalaya: The Story of a Truth Seeker. 2nd rev. ed. Swami Amar Jyoti. LC 85-50206. (Illus.). 128p. 1985. pap. 5.95 (ISBN 0-933572-06-9). Truth Consciousness.

Spirit of Indian Culture: Saints of India. Vivek Bhattacharya. 622p. 1980. 29.95 (ISBN 0-940500-40-X). Asia Bk Corp.

Spirit of Islam. Afif Tabbarah. 20.00x (ISBN 0-86685-029-5). Intl Bk Ctr.

Spirit of Jesus. Vincent M. Walsh. 1984. pap. 5.00 (ISBN 0-943374-10-3). Key of David.

Spirit of Jewish Law. George Horowitz. LC 53-7535. 1979. Repr. of 1953 ed. text ed. 40.00x (ISBN 0-87632-167-8). Bloch.

Spirit of Judaism. facsimile ed. Josephine Lazarus. LC 77-38031. (Essay Index Reprint Ser). Repr. of 1895 ed. 16.00 (ISBN 0-8369-2602-1). Ayer Co Pubs.

Spirit of Judgment. Watchman Nee. Ed. by Herbert L. Fader et al. Tr. by Stephen Kaung from Chinese. 158p. (Orig.). 1984. pap. 3.25 (ISBN 0-935008-63-2). Christian Fellow Pubs.

Spirit of Masonry. rev. ed. Foster Bailey. 143p. 1979. pap. 6.00 (ISBN 0-85330-135-2). Lucis.

Spirit of Might. Jerry Savelle. 77p. (Orig.). 1982. pap. 2.50 (ISBN 0-89274-242-9, HH-242). Harrison Hse.

Spirit of Mornese. Carlo Colli. 198p. (Orig.). 1982. pap. 4.95 (ISBN 0-89944-064-9, P-064-9). Don Bosco Multimedia.

Spirit of Prayer & Spirit of Love. William Law. Ed. by Sydney Spencer. 301p. 1969. 17.50 (ISBN 0-227-67720-X). Attic Pr.

Spirit of Prayer: From the Works of Hannah More. Hannah More. Ed. by Julie Link. 144p. 1986. pap. 5.95 (ISBN 0-310-43641-9, 10272, Clarion Class). Zondervan.

Spirit of Prophecy, Vol. I & II. large print ed. Ed. by Charline Brians. 27p. 1984. pap. 5.00 (ISBN 0-9608650-3-9). VHI Library.

Spirit of Protestantism. Robert M. Brown. (YA) 1961. pap. 8.95 (ISBN 0-19-500724-7). Oxford U Pr.

Spirit of Revelation. Joseph F. McConkie. LC 84-1705. 144p. 1984. 6.95 (ISBN 0-87747-990-9). Deseret Bk.

Spirit of Revolt: Anarchism & the Cult of Authority. Richard K. Fenn. LC 86-15430. 192p. 1986. 27.95x (ISBN 0-8476-7522-X). Rowman.

Spirit of the Age or Contemporary Portaits. Tr. by William Hazlitt. 271p. 1979. Repr. lib. bdg. 25.00 (ISBN 0-89987-353-7). Darby Bks.

Spirit of the Counter-Reformation. H. Outram Evennett. LC 68-11282. 1970. pap. 4.95x (ISBN 0-268-00425-0). U of Notre Dame Pr.

Spirit of the Disciplines: Understanding How God Changes Lives. Dallas Willard. 240p. 1986. 13.95 (ISBN 0-06-069441-6, HarpR). Har-Row.

Spirit of the Earth. John Hart. 1984. pap. 8.95 (ISBN 0-8091-2581-1). Paulist Pr.

Spirit of the Ghetto. facsimile ed. Hutchins Hapgood. Ed. by Moses Rischin. LC 67-12099. (John Harvard Library). (Illus.). 1967. 22.50x (ISBN 0-674-83265-5). Harvard U Pr.

Spirit of the Gospel. Watchman Nee. Ed. by Herbert L. Fader. Tr. by Stephen Kaung from Chinese. 100p. (Orig.). 1986. pap. 3.50 (ISBN 0-935008-67-5). Christian Fellow Pubs.

Spirit of the Old Testament. Sidney B. Sperry. LC 70-119330. (Classics in Mormon Literature Ser.). 246p. 1980. Repr. 6.95 (ISBN 0-87747-832-5). Deseret Bk.

Spirit of the Oxford Movement. Christopher H. Dawson. LC 75-30020. Repr. of 1934 ed. 16.50 (ISBN 0-404-14025-4). AMS Pr.

Spirit of the Sikhs, 3 vols. Puran Singh. 1984. Repr. of 1920 ed. Pt.1. 7.50x (ISBN 0-8364-1115-3, Pub. by Punjabi); Pt.2, v.1. 7.50x (ISBN 0-8364-1116-1); Pt.2, Vol.2. 7.50x (ISBN 0-8364-1117-X). South Asia Bks.

Spirit of Wisdom & Revelation. Watchman Nee. Tr. by Stephen Kaung. 1980. pap. 3.25 (ISBN 0-935008-48-9). Christian Fellow Pubs.

Spirit of Your Marriage. David Ludwig. LC 79-50088. 1979. pap. 6.95 (ISBN 0-8066-1721-7, 10-5890). Augsburg.

Spirit of Zen: A Way of Life, Work & Art in the Far East. Alan W. Watts. 1958. pap. 2.95 (ISBN 0-394-17418-6, E219, Ever). Grove.

Spirit Possession & Popular Religion: From the Camisards to the Shakers. Clarke Garrett. LC 86-46284. 288p. 1987. text ed. 29.50x (ISBN 0-8018-3486-4). Johns Hopkins.

Spirit River to Angels' Roost: Religions I Have Loved & Left. Patricia Joudry. LC 76-22996. 1977. 12.95 (ISBN 0-912766-46-8). Tundra Bks.

Spirit, Saints & Immortality. Patrick Sherry. 200p. 1984. 39.50x (ISBN 0-87395-755-5); pap. 14.95x (ISBN 0-87395-756-3). State U NY Pr.

Spirit Soars. Tom Pinkston. 34p. pap. 3.00 (ISBN 0-942494-47-4). Coleman Pub.

Spirit Song. Mary Summer Rain. Ed. by Robert Friedman. LC 85-15894. 200p. (Orig.). 1985. pap. 7.95 (ISBN 0-89865-405-X, Unilaw). Donning Co.

Spirit, Soul, Consciousness, Realization. Yusuf H. Ali. 1975. pap. 3.50 (ISBN 0-913358-10-X). El-Shabazz Pr.

Spirit Speaks in Us. John Sheets. 210p. 1986. 8.95 (ISBN 0-87193-250-4). Dimension Bks.

Spirit, Spirits & Spirituality. Adolph E. Knoch. 157p. 1977. pap. text ed. 3.00 (ISBN 0-910424-69-1). Concordant.

Spirit Touching Spirit, A Contemporary Hymnal. Handt Hanson. 240p. 1986. 10.95 (ISBN 0-933173-01-6). Prince Peace Pub.

Spirit within Structure: Essays in Honor of George Jonhston on the Occasion of His Seventieth Birthday. Ed. by E. J. Furcha. (Pittsburgh Theological Monographs: New Ser.: No. 3). xvi, 194p. 1983. pap. 12.50 (ISBN 0-915138-53-0). Pickwick.

Spiritism in Ghana: A Study of New Religious Movements. Robert W. Wyllie. Ed. by Conrad Cherry. LC 79-20486. (Studies in Religion: No. 21). 139p. 14.00 (ISBN 0-89130-355-3, 01-00-21); pap. 9.95 (ISBN 0-89130-356-1). Scholars Pr GA.

Spirits & Seasons. Mary A. Napoleone & E. Jane Johanson. (Illus.). 83p. 1982. pap. 3.95 (ISBN 0-9610038-0-4). Heatherdown Pr.

Spirits, Heroes & Hunters from North American Indian Mythology. Marion Wood. LC 81-14572. (World Mythologies Ser.). (Illus.). 156p. 1982. 16.95 (ISBN 0-8052-3792-5). Schocken.

Spirits in Bondage: A Cycle of Lyrics. C. S. Lewis. 1984. pap. 3.95 (ISBN 0-15-684748-5, Harv). HarBraceJ.

Spirits in His Parlor. Gail Walker. LC 79-87733. (Destiny Ser.). 1980. pap. 4.95 (ISBN 0-8163-0387-8, 19499-3). Pacific Pr Pub Assn.

Spirits of Protest. P. Fry. LC 75-20832. (Cambridge Studies in Social Anthropology: No. 14). 134p. 1976. 27.95 (ISBN 0-521-21052-6). Cambridge U Pr.

Spirits of Seventy-Six: A Catholic Inquiry. Donald D'Elia. 182p. (Orig.). pap. 6.95 (ISBN 0-931888-10-7). Christendom Pubns.

Spirits, Shamans, & Stars: Perspectives from South America. Ed. by David L. Browman. Ronald A. Scwartz. (World Anthropology Ser.). 1979. text ed. 28.50x (ISBN 90-279-7890-5). Mouton.

Spirit's Sword: God's Infallible Book. B. E. Underwood. 1969. 3.95 (ISBN 0-911866-50-7); pap. 2.95 (ISBN 0-911866-91-4). Advocate.

Spiritual Aids for Those in Renew: Ponderings, Poems & Promises. Robert F. Morneau. LC 84-12299. 111p. (Orig.). 1984. pap. 4.50 (ISBN 0-8189-0473-9). Alba.

Spiritual Alchemy. rev. ed. Omraam M. Aivanhov. (Complete Works: Vol. 2). (Illus.). 205p. 1986. pap. 9.95 (ISBN 2-85566-371-7, Pub. by Prosveta France). Prosveta USA.

Spiritual Almanac: Guidelines for Better Living Each Month of the Year. Don Jennings. 240p. 1984. pap. 5.95 (ISBN 0-13-834748-4). P-H.

Spiritual & Anabaptist Writers. Ed. by George H. Williams & Angel M. Mergal. LC 57-5003. (Library of Christian Classics). 418p. 1977. pap. 11.95 (ISBN 0-664-24150-6). Westminster.

Spiritual Approach to Male-Female Relations. Scott Miners. LC 83-40326. 220p. (Orig.). 1984. pap. 6.50 (ISBN 0-8356-0583-3, Quest). Theos Pub Hse.

Spiritual Aspects of Indian Music. Simon R. Leopold. 1985. 22.50x (ISBN 0-8364-1258-3, Pub. by Sundeep). South Asia Bks.

Spiritual Aspects of the Healing Art. Compiled by Dora Kunz. LC 85-40410. 294p. (Orig.). 1985. pap. 6.50 (ISBN 0-8356-0601-5, Quest). Theos Pub Hse.

Spiritual Aspects of the New Poetry. facs. ed. Amos N. Wilder. LC 68-16988. (Essay Index Reprint Ser). 1940. 16.25 (ISBN 0-8369-0995-X). Ayer Co Pubs.

Spiritual Authority. Watchman Nee. Tr. by Stephen Kaung. 1972. 4.75 (ISBN 0-935008-34-9); pap. 3.75 (ISBN 0-935008-35-7). Christian Fellow Pubs.

Spiritual Authority & Temporal Power in the Indian Theory of Government. Ananda K. Coomaraswamy. (Amer Oriental Soc Ser.). 1942. pap. 16.00 (ISBN 0-527-02696-4). Kraus Repr.

Spiritual Automobile. James W. Cuffee. Ed. by Charles Knickerbocker. 44p. 1980. 4.75 (ISBN 0-682-48997-2). Exposition Pr FL.

Spiritual Awakening. Darshan Singh. LC 81-50726. (Illus.). 338p. (Orig.). 1982. pap. 6.50 (ISBN 0-918224-11-X). Sawan Kirpal Pubns.

Spiritual Awakening: Classic Writings of the Eighteenth Century to Inspire the Twentieth Century Reader. Ed. by Sherwood E. Wirt. LC 86-70283. 256p. (Orig.). 1986. pap. 8.95 (ISBN 0-89107-394-9, Crossway Bks). Good News.

Spiritual Awareness. Ernest Holmes. Ed. by Willis H. Kinnear. 96p. 1972. pap. 5.50 (ISBN 0-911336-41-9). Sci of Mind.

Spiritual Basics: New Life in Christ. Lyman Coleman. (Free University - Lay Academy in Christian Discipleship Ser.). (Orig.). 1981. pap. 1.25 student's bk. (ISBN 0-687-37355-7); pap. 4.95 tchr's bk. (ISBN 0-687-37354-9). Abingdon.

Spiritual Being in the Heavenly Bodies & in the Kingdoms of Nature. Rudolf Steiner. (Ger.). 210p. 1981. pap. 9.95 (ISBN 0-919924-14-X, Pub. by Steiner Book Centre Canada). Anthroposophic.

Spiritual Body & Celestial Earth: From Mazdean Iran to Shi Ite Iran. Henry Corbin. Tr. by Nancy Pearson. (Bollingen Ser: No. 91). 1977. text ed. 40.00x (ISBN 0-691-09937-5). Princeton U Pr.

Spiritual Breakthrough to the Next Millennium. Max Kappeler. LC 85-82058. 75p. 1986. pap. 7.00 (ISBN 0-942958-12-8). Kappeler Inst Pub.

Spiritual Cannibalism. Swami Rudrananda. 208p. (Orig.). 1987. pap. 9.95 (ISBN 0-915801-07-8). Rudra Pr.

Spiritual Care. Dietrich Bonhoeffer. Tr. by Jay C. Rochelle. LC 85-47711. 128p. 1985. pap. 4.95 (ISBN 0-8006-1874-2). Fortress.

Spiritual Care: The Nurse's Role. 2nd ed. Sharon Fish & Judith A. Shelly. LC 83-12604. (Illus.). 192p. 1983. pap. 7.95 (ISBN 0-87784-878-5). Inter-Varsity.

Spiritual Care Workbook. Judith Allen Shelly. 1978. pap. 5.95 (ISBN 0-87784-507-7). Inter-Varsity.

Spiritual Choices, the Problem of Recognizing Authentic Paths to Inner Transformation: The Problem of Recognizing Authentic Paths to Inner Transformation. Ed. by Dick Anthony et al. 448p. 1986. 24.95 (ISBN 0-913729-14-0); pap. 12.95 (ISBN 0-913729-19-1). Paragon Hse.

Spiritual Cleansing. Draja Mickaharic. pap. 5.95 (ISBN 0-942272-09-9). Original Pubns.

Spiritual Combat. Lawrence Scupoli. LC 78-61668. (Spiritual Masters Ser.). 256p. 1978. pap. 4.95 (ISBN 0-8091-2158-1). Paulist Pr.

Spiritual Conferences. Frederick W. Faber. LC 78-66304. 1978. pap. 9.00 (ISBN 0-89555-079-2). TAN Bks Pubs.

Spiritual Conferences. John Tauler. Tr. by Eric Colledge & M. Jane. LC 78-74568. 1979. pap. 7.00 (ISBN 0-89555-082-2). TAN Bks Pubs.

Spiritual Conquest of Mexico: An Essay on the Apostolate & the Evangelizing Methods of the Mendicant Orders in New Spain, 1523-1572. Robert Ricard. Tr. by Lesley B. Simpson from Sp. (California Library Reprint Ser.: No. 57). (Illus.). 435p. 1974. pap. 9.95 (ISBN 0-520-04784-2, CAL 593). U of Cal Pr.

Spiritual Considerations in the Preventive Treatment & Cure of Disease. Jane H. Thompson. 128p. 1984. cancelled (ISBN 0-85362-211-6, Oriel). Methuen Inc.

Spiritual Counsels of Father John of Kronstadt. W. Jardine Grisbrooke. 230p. (Orig.). 1982. pap. 8.95 (ISBN 0-913836-92-3). St Vladimirs.

Spiritual Counsels of Father John of Kronstadt: Select Passages from "My Life in Christ". Ed. by Jardine W. Grisbrooke. 256p. 1983. pap. 10.95 (ISBN 0-227-67856-7, Pub. by J Clarke UK). Attic Pr.

Spiritual Crisis of Man. rev ed. Paul Brunton. LC 83-60829. 224p. 1984. pap. 7.95 (ISBN 0-87728-593-4). Weiser.

Spiritual Crisis of the Gilded Age. Paul A. Carter. LC 72-156938. (Illus.). 295p. 1971. 10.00 (ISBN 0-87580-026-2). N Ill U Pr.

Spiritual Dance & Walk: An Introduction from the Work of Murshid Samuel L. Lewis. 2nd, rev. ed. Samuel L. Lewis. Ed. by Moineddin Jablonski. (Illus.). 64p. (Orig.). 1978. pap. 4.50 (ISBN 0-915424-05-3, Prophecy Pressworks). Sufi Islamia-Prophecy.

Spiritual Depression: Its Causes & Cure. D. Martyn Lloyd-Jones. 1965. pap. 5.95 (ISBN 0-8028-1387-9). Eerdmans.

Spiritual Development: An Interdisciplinary Study. Daniel A. Helminiak. 256p. 1987. 15.95 (ISBN 0-8294-0530-5). Loyola.

Spiritual Diary. 1962. 5.50 (ISBN 0-8198-6823-X); pap. 4.50 (ISBN 0-8198-6824-8). Dghtrs St Paul.

Spiritual Diary. 375p. (Orig.). pap. 7.95 (ISBN 0-89389-073-1). Himalayan Pubs.

Spiritual Diary. 380p. 1982. 2.95 (ISBN 0-87612-021-4). Self Realization.

Spiritual Diary of Emanuel Swedenborg, 6 vols. Emanuel Swedenborg. lib. bdg. 700.00 (ISBN 0-87968-560-3). Krishna Pr.

Spiritual Dilemma of the Jewish People. Arthur W. Kac. 5.95 (ISBN 0-8010-5456-7). Baker Bk.

Spiritual Dimension of Green Politics. Charlene Spretnak. LC 86-70255. 96p. (Orig.). 1986. pap. 4.95 (ISBN 0-939680-29-7). Bear & Co.

Spiritual Dimensions of Pastoral Care: Witness to the Ministry of Wayne E. Oates. Ed. by Gerald L. Borchert & Andrew D. Lester. LC 84-19581. 152p. (Orig.). 1985. pap. 11.95 (ISBN 0-664-24562-5). Westminster.

Spiritual Dimensions of Psychology. Hazrat Inayat Khan. LC 80-54830. (Collected Works of Hazrat Inayat Khan Ser.). 256p. (Orig.). 1981. 7.95 (ISBN 0-930872-24-X, 1012P). Omega Pr NM.

Spiritual Direction. Martin Thornton. LC 83-73658. 145p. (Orig.). 1984. pap. 6.95 (ISBN 0-936384-17-4). Cowley Pubns.

Spiritual Direction: An Invitation to Abundant Life. Francis W. Vanderwall. LC 81-83185. 128p. (Orig.). 1982. pap. 4.95 (ISBN 0-8091-2399-1). Paulist Pr.

Spiritual Direction & Mid-Life Development. Raymond Studzinski. 1985. 12.95 (ISBN 0-8294-0480-5). Loyola.

Spiritual Direction: Contemporary Readings. Intro. by Kevin Cullingan. 237p. (Orig.). 1983. pap. 5.95 (ISBN 0-914544-43-8). Living Flame Pr.

Spiritual Direction: Letters of Starets Macarius of Optina Monastery. pap. 1.95 (ISBN 0-686-00254-7). Eastern Orthodox.

Spiritual Director. Damien Isabel. (Synthesis Ser.). 1976. pap. 2.00 (ISBN 0-8199-0712-X). Franciscan Herald.

Spiritual Directory of St. Francis de Sales. 3.50 (ISBN 0-8198-6860-4); 2.25 (ISBN 0-8198-6861-2). Dghtrs St Paul.

Spiritual Discernment & Politics: Guidelines for Religious Communities. J. B. Libanio. Tr. by Theodore Morrow from Port. LC 82-2257. Orig. Title: Discernment E politica. 144p. (Orig.). 1982. pap. 1.74 (ISBN 0-88344-463-1). Orbis Bks.

Spiritual Discipline in Hinduism, Buddhism, & the West. Harry M. Buck. LC 81-12812. (Focus on Hinduism & Buddhism Ser.). 64p. 1981. pap. 4.95x (ISBN 0-89012-022-6). Anima Pubns.

Spiritual Disciplines: Growth Through the Practice of Prayer, Fasting, Dialogue, & Worship. rev. ed. James E. Massey. Ed. by Joseph D. Allison. 112p. 1985. pap. 4.95 (ISBN 0-310-37151-1, 12410P). Zondervan.

Spiritual Discourses. Ayatollah Morteza Motahhari. Ed. by M. Salman Tawhidi. Tr. by Aluddin Pazargadi. 139p. (Orig.). 1986. pap. 4.95 (ISBN 0-9616897-0-6). MSA Inc.

Spiritual Dryness. Walter Trobisch. pap. 0.75 (ISBN 0-87784-138-1). Inter-Varsity.

Spiritual Dynamics. G. Raymond Carlson. LC 76-5633. (Radiant Life Ser.). 128p. 1976. pap. 2.50 (ISBN 0-88243-894-8, 02-0894); teacher's ed 3.95 (ISBN 0-88243-168-4, 32-0168). Gospel Pub.

Spiritual Economics--the Prosperity Process. Eric Butterworth. 220p. 1983. 5.95 (ISBN 0-87159-142-1). Unity School.

Spiritual Encounter with the Holy One. Jean Koberlein. LC 84-8938. (Mellen Lives Ser.: Vol. 2). 200p. 1984. pap. 9.95x (ISBN 0-88946-012-4). E Mellen.

Spiritual Exercise for New Parents. Elwyn A. Smith. LC 85-47714. 64p. 1985. pap. 3.50 (ISBN 0-8006-1863-7, 1-1863). Fortress.

Spiritual Exercise for the Grieving. Elwyn A. Smith. LC 84-47935. 64p. 1984. pap. 3.50 (ISBN 0-8006-1807-6, 1-1807). Fortress.

Spiritual Exercise for the Sick. Elwyn A. Smith. LC 83-48141. 64p. 1983. pap. 3.50 (ISBN 0-8006-1751-7, 1-1751). Fortress.

Spiritual Exercises According to Saint Bonaventure. Dominic Faccin. Tr. by Owen A. Colligan. (Spirit & Life Ser). 1955. 3.00 (ISBN 0-686-11568-6). Franciscan Inst.

Spiritual Exercises & CLC: The Role of the Exercises in Today's CLC's. Thomas A. Bausch. 24p. 1973. pap. text ed. 1.50x (ISBN 0-913605-00-X). NFCLC.

Spiritual Exercises & the Ignatian Mystical Horizon. Harvey D. Egan. LC 76-5742. (Study Aids on Jesuit Topics, Series 4: No. 5). xii, 216p. 1976. smyth sewn 7.00 (ISBN 0-912422-18-1); pap. 6.00 (ISBN 0-912422-14-9). Inst Jesuit.

Spiritual Exercises & Today's CLC: Making the Exercises Come to Life. Thomas Bausch. 24p. 1973. pap. text ed. 1.50x (ISBN 0-913605-01-8). NFCLC.

Spiritual Exercises of St. Ignatius: A Literal Translation & a Contemporary Reading. David L. Fleming. Ed. by George E. Ganss. LC 77-93429. (Study Aids on Jesuit Topics Ser.: No. 7). 290p. 1978. smyth sewn 9.00 (ISBN 0-912422-31-9). Inst Jesuit.

Spiritual Exercises of St. Ignatius Based on Studies in the Language of the Autograph. Louis J. Puhl. (Request Reprint). 1968. pap. 4.00 (ISBN 0-8294-0065-6). Loyola.

Spiritual Exercises of St. Ignatius. St. Ignatius. Tr. by Anthony Mottola. pap. 3.95 (ISBN 0-385-02436-3, D170, Im). Doubleday.

Spiritual Exercises of St. Ignatius of Loyola. Saint Ignatius. Tr. by Lewis Delmage. 1978. 4.00 (ISBN 0-8198-0557-2); pap. 2.25 (ISBN 0-8198-0558-0). Dghtrs St Paul.

Spiritual Family. John-Roger. 1976. pap. text ed. 5.00 (ISBN 0-914829-21-1, 978-5). Baraka Bk.

Spiritual First Aid from A to Z. Robert S. Mazeroni. 176p. (Orig.). 1987. pap. 2.95 (ISBN 0-345-33824-3, Pub. by Ballantine Epiphany). Ballantine.

Spiritual Folk-Songs of Early America. Ed. by George P. Jackson. 11.25 (ISBN 0-8446-2297-4). Peter Smith.

Spiritual Formation in the Catholic Seminary. 64p. 1984. pap. 4.95 (ISBN 1-55586-920-3). US Catholic.

Spiritual Foundation of Morality. Rudolf Steiner. Tr. by Mabel Cotterell. 90p. 1979. pap. 4.75 (ISBN 0-919924-09-3, Pub. by Steiner Book Centre Canada). Anthroposophic.

Spiritual Franciscans. D. S. Muzzey. 59.95 (ISBN 0-8490-1113-2). Gordon Pr.

Spiritual Friend: Reclaiming the Gift of Spiritual Direction. Tilden Edwards. LC 79-91408. 272p. 1980. pap. 9.95 (ISBN 0-8091-2288-X). Paulist Pr.

Spiritual Friendship. Aelred of Rievaulx. (Cistercian Fathers Ser.: No. 5). 144p. pap. 5.00 (ISBN 0-87907-705-0). Cistercian Pubns.

Spiritual Gifts. John MacArthur, Jr. (John MacArthur's Bible Studies). 1985. pap. 5.95 (ISBN 0-8024-5121-7). Moody.

Spiritual Gifts. George Shalm. 131p. 1983. pap. 4.95 (ISBN 0-912315-04-0). Word Aflame.

Spiritual Gifts & Their Operation. Howard Carter. 96p. 1968. pap. 1.95 (ISBN 0-88243-593-0, 02-0593). Gospel Pub.

Spiritual Gifts for Christians Today. Knofel Staton. 118p. (Orig.). 1973. pap. 3.50 (ISBN 0-89900-134-3). College Pr Pub.

Spiritual Gifts in the Work of the Ministry Today. Donald Gee. 102p. 1963. pap. 1.25 (ISBN 0-88243-592-2, 02-0592). Gospel Pub.

Spiritual Gifts-Ministries & Manifestations. B. E. Underwood. pap. 6.95 (ISBN 0-911866-03-5). Advocate.

Spiritual Gifts: Ministries & Manifestations. B. E. Underwood. pap. 3.95 student wkbk. (ISBN 0-911866-04-3); pap. 6.95 tchr's. guide (ISBN 0-911866-05-1). Advocate.

Spiritual Gospel. Jim Lewis. LC 82-51231. 145p. (Orig.). 1982. pap. 8.95 (ISBN 0-942482-05-0). Unity Church Denver.

Spiritual Greatness: Studies in Exodus. Tom Julien. (Orig.). 1979. pap. 4.95 (ISBN 0-88469-121-7). BMH Bks.

Spiritual Growth: I Am the Way, the Truth, & the Life. rev. ed. Joan Jungerman. 1.17 (ISBN 0-8091-9314-0). Paulist Pr.

Spiritual Growth in Youth Ministry. J. David Stone. LC 85-12623. 213p. 1985. 12.95 (ISBN 0-931529-04-2). Group Bks.

Spiritual Growth Through Creative Drama. Pam Barragar. 128p. 1981. pap. 5.95 (ISBN 0-8170-0923-X). Judson.

Spiritual Guidance. Josef Sudbrack. 1984. pap. 3.95 (ISBN 0-8091-2571-4). Paulist Pr.

Spiritual Guidance for the Separated & Divorced. Medard Laz. 64p. 1982. pap. 1.95 (ISBN 0-89243-158-X). Liguori Pubns.

Spiritual Guidance of Man. Rudolf Steiner. 1983. pap. 5.95 (ISBN 0-910142-35-1). Anthroposophic.

Spiritual Guide. Michael Molinos. Ed. by Gene Edwards. 110p. pap. 5.95 (ISBN 0-940232-08-1). Christian Bks.

Spiritual Guide to Eternal Life. Alex La Perchia. LC 77-75258. 89p. 1977. 6.95 (ISBN 0-8022-2203-X). Philos Lib.

Spiritual Handbook for Women. Dandi D. Knorr. 192p. 1984. 13.95 (ISBN 0-13-834796-4, Spec); pap. 6.95 (ISBN 0-13-834788-3). P-H.

Spiritual Harvest: Reflections on the Fruits of the Spirit. Mary L. Carney. 112p. 1987. pap. 6.95 (ISBN 0-687-39231-4). Abingdon.

Spiritual Healing. Dudley Blades. 128p. (Orig.). 1980. pap. 4.95 (ISBN 0-85030-130-0). Newcastle Pub.

Spiritual Healing. Ed. by Willis H. Kinnear. 110p. (Orig.). 1973. pap. 4.95 (ISBN 0-911336-50-8). Sci of Mind.

Spiritual Healing. 4th ed. Swami Paramananda. 1975. pap. 3.50 (ISBN 0-911564-10-1). Vedanta Ctr.

Spiritual Healing. Nelson White & Anne White. LC 85-50745. (Illus.). 65p. (Orig.). 1985. pap. text ed. 10.00 (ISBN 0-939856-42-5). Tech Group.

Spiritual Healing: Miracle or Mirage? Alan Young. LC 81-82932. 280p. (Orig.). 1982. pap. 7.95 (ISBN 0-87516-460-9). De Vorss.

Spiritual Heritage of India. Swami Prabhavananda. LC 63-10517. 1979. pap. 8.95 (ISBN 0-87481-035-3). Vedanta Pr.

Spiritual Heritage of Tyagaraja. Tyagaraja. Tr. by C. Ramanujachari. (Sanskrit, Telegu & Eng.). 15.00 (ISBN 0-87481-440-5). Vedanta Pr.

Spiritual Hunger. Gordon Lindsay. 2.50 (ISBN 0-89985-020-0). Christ Nations.

Spiritual Hunger of the Modern Child. J. G. Bennett & Mario Montessori. Ed. by Wendy Addison. LC 87-71204. 220p. 1985. pap. 8.95 (ISBN 0-934254-06-0). Claymont Comm.

Spiritual Import of Society. John S. Connor. LC 85-91374. 208p. 1987. 10.95 (ISBN 0-533-06881-9). Vantage.

Spiritual Insights for Daily Living: A Daybook of Reflections on Ancient Spiritual Truths of Relevance for Our Contemporary Lives. Ed. by Elizabeth W. Fenske. (Illus.). 416p. (Orig.). pap. 7.50 (ISBN 0-914071-09-2). Spirit Front Fellow.

Spiritual Instructions of Saint Seraphim of Sarov. Ed. by Franklin Jones. LC 73-89308. 1973. pap. 3.95 (ISBN 0-913922-05-6). Dawn Horse Pr.

Spiritual Interpretation of History. Shailer Mathews. 1977. lib. bdg. 59.95 (ISBN 0-8490-2661-X). Gordon Pr.

Spiritual Intimidation. Nelson White & Anne White. LC 84-51476. 65p. (Orig.). 1984. pap. 10.00 (ISBN 0-939856-39-5). Tech Group.

Spiritual Knowledge. Watchman Nee. Tr. by Stephen Kaung. 1973. 4.00 (ISBN 0-935008-36-5); pap. 2.75 (ISBN 0-935008-37-3). Christian Fellow Pubs.

Spiritual Leadership. rev. ed. J. Oswald Sanders. LC 67-14387. (J. Oswald Sanders Ser.). 160p. 1974. pap. 3.95 (ISBN 0-8024-8221-X). Moody.

Spiritual Leadership. 5th ed. J. Oswald Sanders. 1986. text ed. 9.95 (ISBN 0-8024-8246-5). Moody.

Spiritual Leadership: Leader's Guide. J. Oswald Sanders & Dana Gould. (Orig.). 1987. pap. 4.95 (ISBN 0-8024-8226-0). Moody.

Spiritual Legacies: Holiday Sermons. Isaac Klein. 15.00x (ISBN 0-87068-276-8). Ktav.

Spiritual Legacy of American Indian. Joseph E. Brown. 160p. 1984. pap. 8.95 (ISBN 0-8245-0618-9). Crossroad NY.

Spiritual Legacy of Sister Mary of the Holy Trinity. Ed. by Silvere Van den Broek. LC 81-82830. 364p. 1981. pap. 6.00 (ISBN 0-89555-165-9). TAN Bks Pubs.

Spiritual Legacy of the American Indian. Joseph E. Brown. LC 64-17425. (Illus., Orig.). 1964. pap. 2.50x (ISBN 0-87574-135-5). Pendle Hill.

Spiritual Letters of Madame Guyon. 1983. pap. 6.95 (ISBN 0-940232-14-6). Christian Bks.

Spiritual Letters to Women. Francois Fenelon. 224p. 1984. pap. 5.95 (ISBN 0-310-36371-3, 12366P, Clarion Class). Zondervan.

Spiritual Letters to Women. Francois D. Fenelon. LC 80-82327. (Shepherd Illustrated Classics Ser.). 1980. pap. 5.95 (ISBN 0-87983-233-9). Keats.

Spiritual Liberty. Inayat Khan. (Sufi Message of Hazrat Inayat Khan Ser.: Vol. 5). 256p. 1979. 14.95 (ISBN 90-6325-095-9, Pub. by Servire BV Netherlands). Hunter Hse.

Spiritual Liberty. C. H. Spurgeon. 1978. pap. 0.95 (ISBN 0-686-26197-6). Pilgrim Pubns.

Spiritual Life. Edgar S. Brightman. LC 75-3086. (Philosophy in America Ser.). Repr. of 1942 ed. 27.50 (ISBN 0-404-59085-3). AMS Pr.

Spiritual Life. Evelyn Underhill. LC 84-60646. 128p. 1984. pap. 4.95 (ISBN 0-8192-1350-0). Morehouse.

Spiritual Life - the Word of God. Emanuel Swedenborg. pap. 1.95 (ISBN 0-87785-083-6). Swedenborg.

Spiritual Life, a Guide for Those Seeking Perfection. Joannes Cassianus. 1977. pap. 4.95 (ISBN 0-686-19234-6). Eastern Orthodox.

Spiritual Life for the Overbusy. David M. Bauman. 96p. (Orig.). 1987. pap. price not set (ISBN 0-88028-065-4). Forward Movement.

Spiritual Life in the Bible. Daughters of St. Paul. 1980. 5.95 (ISBN 0-686-76825-6); pap. 4.00 (ISBN 0-8198-6813-2). Dghtrs St Paul.

Spiritual Life in the Modern World. John Hardon. 1982. 3.50 (ISBN 0-8198-6839-6, SP0708); pap. 2.50 (ISBN 0-8198-6840-X). Dghtrs St Paul.

Spiritual Life: Learning East & West. John H. Westerhoff & John Eusden. 172p. 1982. 10.95 (ISBN 0-8164-0516-6, HarpR). Har-Row.

Spiritual Life Songs. 19.41 (ISBN 0-687-39228-4); 2.00 ea. Abingdon.

Spiritual Living. Smith. 1978. pap. 2.95 (ISBN 0-8423-6410-2). Tyndale.

Spiritual Man. Watchman Nee. Tr. by Stephen Kaung. 1968. 12.50 (ISBN 0-935008-38-1); pap. 7.50 (ISBN 0-935008-39-X). Christian Fellow Pubs.

Spiritual Maturity. J. Oswald Sanders. Tr. by Samuel Chao & Lorna Chao. (Chinese.). 1983. pap. write for info. (ISBN 0-941598-08-X). Living Spring Pubns.

Spiritual Meadow: The Pratum Spirituale. Saint John Moschus. pap. 1.25 (ISBN 0-686-16371-0). Eastern Orthodox.

Spiritual Nature of Man. Alister Hardy. 1979. 27.00x (ISBN 0-19-824618-8); pap. 12.95x (ISBN 0-19-824732-X). Oxford U Pr.

Spiritual Needs of Children. Judith A. Shelly. LC 82-7223. (Orig.). 1982. pap. 5.95 (ISBN 0-87784-381-3). Inter-Varsity.

Spiritual Notebook. Paul Twitchell. LC 74-178996. 218p. 1971. pap. 5.95 (ISBN 0-914766-94-5). IWP Pub.

Spiritual Notes. pap. 2.95 (ISBN 0-317-11388-7). Eastern Orthodox.

Spiritual Nurture & Congregational Development. Ed. by Perry Lefevre & W. Widick Schroeder. (Studies in Ministry & Parish Life). 186p. 1984. text ed. 19.95x (ISBN 0-913552-20-8); pap. text ed. 8.95x (ISBN 0-913552-23-2). Exploration Pr.

Spiritual Nutrition. Gabriel Cousens. 232p. 1986. 9.95 (ISBN 0-9615875-2-0). Cassandra Pr.

Spiritual Passages. Benedict J. Groeschel. LC 82-17139. 176p. 1983. 12.95 (ISBN 0-8245-0497-6). Crossroad NY.

Spiritual Perspective II: The Spiritual Dimension & Implications of Love, Sex, & Marriage. Peter R. De Coppens. LC 80-6302. 175p. (Orig.). 1981. pap. text ed. 10.75 (ISBN 0-8191-1512-6). U Pr of Amer.

Spiritual Perspectives: Essays in Mysticism & Metaphysics. Ed. by T. M. Mahadevan. 303p. 1975. lib. bdg. 12.00 (ISBN 0-89253-021-9). Ind-US Inc.

Spiritual Pilgrims: Carl Jung & Teresa of Avila. John Welch. LC 82-80164. 208p. 1982. 8.95 (ISBN 0-8091-2454-8). Paulist Pr.

Spiritual Poverty in Sufism. Nurbakhsh Javad. Tr. by Leonard Lewishon. 1984. pap. 6.00x (ISBN 0-933546-11-4). KhaniQahi-Nimatullahi-Sufi.

Spiritual Power. rev ed. Don Basham. 92p. 1976. pap. 2.25 (ISBN 0-88368-075-0). Whitaker Hse.

Spiritual Power: Great Single Sermons. J. D. Thomas et al. LC 74-170920. 1972. 13.95 (ISBN 0-89112-026-2, Bibl Res Pr). Abilene Christ U.

Spiritual Practice. Ananda. pap. 3.00 (ISBN 0-87481-155-4). Vedanta Pr.

Spiritual Practices. Swami Akhilananda. LC 78-175140. 1972. 12.00 (ISBN 0-8283-1350-4). Branden Pub Co.

Spiritual Practices of India. pap. 1.25 (ISBN 0-8065-0057-3). Citadel Pr.

Spiritual Principle of Prayer. Max Kappeler. 26p. 1969. pap. 3.50 (ISBN 0-85241-077-8). Kappeler Inst Pub.

Spiritual Privileges You Didn't Know Were Yours. Donald G. Mostrom. LC 86-11383. 192p. (Orig.). 1986. pap. 5.95 (ISBN 0-87784-982-X). Inter-Varsity.

Spiritual Psychic Healing: A Comparative Psychological & Biblical Study. Joseph B. Gandolfo. 1986. 6.95 (ISBN 0-533-06839-8). Vantage.

Spiritual Psychology: A New Age Course for Body, Mind & Spirit. 2nd ed. Jim Morningstar. (Illus.). 119p. 1981. pap. 10.00 (ISBN 0-9604856-0-0). Transform Inc.

Spiritual Quest of Albert Camus. Richard H. Akeroyd. LC 76-3324. 1976. 7.50 (ISBN 0-916620-03-4). Portals Pr.

Spiritual Quest: Variations on a Theme. Donald Pelton. (Illus., Orig.). 1986. pap. 7.95 (ISBN 0-933169-02-7). Heldon Pr.

Spiritual Reality or Obsession. Watchman Nee. Tr. by Stephen Kaung. 1970. pap. 2.25 (ISBN 0-935008-41-1). Christian Fellow Pubs.

Spiritual Reflections for the Recovering Alcoholic. S. Jack. LC 84-18590. (Illus.). 90p. 1985. pap. 5.95 (ISBN 0-8189-0477-1). Alba.

Spiritual Reformers of the Sixteenth & Seventeenth Centuries. Rufus M. Jones. 1959. 11.25 (ISBN 0-8446-0161-6). Peter Smith.

Spiritual Regulation of Peter the Great. Ed. & tr. by Alexander V. Muller. LC 74-4590. (Publications on Russia & Eastern Europe of the School of International Studies: No. 3). 188p. 1972. 16.50x (ISBN 0-295-95237-7); pap. 6.95x (ISBN 0-295-95282-2). U of Wash Pr.

Spiritual Renewal of the American Priesthood. Ed. by Ernest E. Larkin & Gerald T. Broccolo. 1973. pap. 2.75 (ISBN 1-55586-230-6, V-230). US Catholic.

Spiritual Renewal: Tapping Your Inner Resources. Lura J. Geiger. (Orig.). 1987. pap. 34.50 (ISBN 0-931055-37-7); cassette incl. LuraMedia.

Spiritual Resistance: Art from the Concentration Camps 1940-1945. Union of American Hebrew Congregations. LC 78-1169. (Illus.). 354p. 1981. 35.00 (ISBN 0-8276-0109-3, 421). Jewish Pubns.

Spiritual Roots of Human Relations. Stephen R. Covey. LC 72-119477. 9.95 (ISBN 0-87747-315-3). Deseret Bk.

Spiritual Science & the New Nature Forces: The Nuclear Dilemma. Georg Unger. Tr. by Nick Thomas. 28p. 1981. pap. 2.95 (ISBN 0-88925-063-4, Pub. by Steiner Book Centre Canada). Anthroposophic.

Spiritual Science As a Foundation for Social Forms. Rudolf Steiner. Ed. by Alan Howard. Tr. by Maria St. Goar from Ger. Tr. of Geisteswissenschaft als Erkenntnis der Grundimpulse sozialer Gestaltung. 300p. 1986. 30.00 (ISBN 0-88010-153-9); pap. 20.00 (ISBN 0-88010-152-0). Anthroposophic.

Spiritual Science, Electricity & Michael Faraday. Ernst Lehrs. 30p. 1975. pap. 3.00 (ISBN 0-85440-296-9, Pub. by Steinerbooks). Anthroposophic.

Spiritual Science of Kriya Yoga. 2nd ed. Goswami Kriyananda. (Illus.). pap. text ed. 16.95 (ISBN 0-9613099-1-1). Temple Kriya Yoga.

Spiritual Secrets of George Muller. 2nd ed. Selected by Roger Steer. 126p. 1987. pap. 5.95 (ISBN 0-87788-782-9). Shaw Pubs.

Spiritual Seekers' Guidebook: And Hidden Threats to Mental & Spiritual Freedom. Richard Kieninger. 1986. 12.95 (ISBN 0-9600308-6-7). Stelle.

Spiritual Sense in Sacred Legend. Edward J. Brailsford. 288p. 1983. Repr. of 1910 ed. lib. bdg. 47.50 (ISBN 0-89987-957-8). Darby Bks.

Spiritual Sex Manual. Christ Foundation Staff. LC 82-72079. (Illus.). 176p. 1982. pap. 9.95 (ISBN 0-910315-01-9). Christ Found.

Spiritual Survival in the Last Days. Greg Laurie. LC 82-81919. Orig. Title: Occupy Till I Come. 144p. (Orig.). 1985. pap. 3.95. Harvest Hse.

Spiritual Talks. Ramakrishna's Disciples. 5.95 (ISBN 0-87481-103-1). Vedanta Pr.

Spiritual Teaching of Ramana Maharshi. Ramana Maharshi. (Clear Light Ser). 112p. (Orig.). 1972. pap. 7.95 (ISBN 0-87773-024-5). Shambhala Pubns.

Spiritual Teachings of Teresa of Avila & Adrian Van Kaam: Formative Spirituality. James Whalen. LC 83-3628. 334p. (Orig.). 1984. lib. bdg. 27.50 (ISBN 0-8191-3864-9); pap. text ed. 15.75 (ISBN 0-8191-3865-7). U Pr of Amer.

Spiritual Thoughts & Prayers. Thomas W. Wersell. LC 74-76920. pap. 20.00 (2026829). Bks Demand UMI.

Spiritual Treasure: Paraphrases of Spiritual Classics. Bernard K. Bangley. LC 84-61026. 144p. (Orig.). 1985. pap. 6.95 (ISBN 0-8091-2646-X). Paulist Pr.

Spiritual Treasures of St. Ramadasa. V. H. Date. 1975. 13.50 (ISBN 0-8426-0805-2). Orient Bk Dist.

Spiritual Unfoldment One. White Eagle. 1942. 6.95 (ISBN 0-85487-012-1). De Vorss.

Spiritual Unfoldment Two. White Eagle. 1969. 6.95 (ISBN 0-85487-001-6). De Vorss.

Spiritual Universe & You. Ernest Holmes. Ed. by Willis Kinnear. 96p. 1971. pap. 4.50 (ISBN 0-911336-37-0). Sci of Mind.

Spiritual Value of Gem Stones. Wally G. Richardson & Lenora Huett. LC 79-54728. 168p. 1980. pap. 6.50 (ISBN 0-87516-383-1). De Vorss.

Spiritual View of Life. Victor Mohr. Tr. by Violet Ozols from Ger. 364p. 1985. pap. cancelled (ISBN 0-934616-15-9). Valkyrie Pub Hse.

Spiritual Warfare. Michael Harper. 120p. 1984. pap. 4.95 (ISBN 0-89283-175-8). Servant.

Spiritual Warfare. Jessie Penn-Lewis. 1962. pap. 2.95 (ISBN 0-87508-997-6). Chr Lit.

Spiritual Warfare. Ed. by Ras Robinson. (Illus.). 72p. 1982. pap. 3.00 (ISBN 0-937778-05-2). Fulness Hse.

Spiritual Warfare: Winning the Daily Battle with Satan. Ray C. Stedman. LC 85-2893. (Authentic Christianity Ser.). 145p. 1985. pap. 6.95 (ISBN 0-88070-094-7). Multnomah.

Spiritual Warfare...Strategy for Winning. Joanne Sekowsky. (Workbook Ser.). 80p. pap. 4.95 (ISBN 0-930756-74-6, 581004). Aglow Pubns.

Spiritual Worker's Handbook. Tarostar. (Illus.). 80p. (Orig.). 1985. pap. 3.95 (ISBN 0-943832-12-8). Intl Imports.

Spiritual World Laid Open. Emanuel Swedenborg. lib. bdg. 79.95 (ISBN 0-87968-561-1). Krishna Pr.

Spiritual Writings of St. John Bosco. Ed. by Joseph Aubry. Tr. by Joseph Caselli from Italian. LC 83-71820. Tr. of Giovanni Bosco, Scritti Spirituali. 412p. 1984. pap. 12.95 (ISBN 0-89944-049-5). Don Bosco Multimedia.

Spiritualism & Mysticism. M. P. Lakhani. x, 119p. 1984. text ed. 20.00x (ISBN 0-86590-381-6, Pub. by Inter Pubns N Delhi). Apt Bks.

Spiritualism in the Bible. E. W. Wallis. 59.95 (ISBN 0-8490-1116-7). Gordon Pr.

Spiritualism in the Old Testament. Maurice Elliott. 59.95 (ISBN 0-8490-1117-5). Gordon Pr.

Spiritualist Healers in Mexico: Successes & Failures of Alternative Therapies. Kaja Finker. 256p. 1984. 29.95 (ISBN 0-03-063912-3, C1156). Praeger.

Spiritualist Healers in Mexico: Successes & Failures of Alternative Therapeutics. Kaja Finkler. (Illus.). 272p. 1983. text ed. 29.95x (ISBN 0-03-063912-3); pap. text ed. 14.95 (ISBN 0-89789-092-2). Bergin & Garvey.

Spiritualitat Heute und Gestern, Vol. 1. Ed. by James Hogg. (Analceta Carusiana Ser.: No. 35). (Eng, Ger, & Fr.). 236p. (Orig.). 1982. pap. 25.00 (ISBN 3-7052-0037-2, Pub by Salzburg Studies). Longwood Pub Group.

Spiritualitat Heute und Gestern, Vol. 3. Ed. by James Hogg. (Analecta Carusiana Ser.: No. 35). (Ital, Ger, & Eng.). 174p. (Orig.). 1983. pap. 25.00 (ISBN 3-7052-0039-9, Pub by Salzburg Studies). Longwood Pub Group.

Spiritualitat Heute und Gestern, Vol. 4. Ed. by James Hogg. (Analecta Cartusiana Ser.: No. 35). (Fr, Ital, Ger, & Eng., Illus.). 131p. (Orig.). 1984. pap. 25.00 (ISBN 3-7052-0040-2, Pub by Salzburg Studies). Longwood Pub Group.

Spiritualitat Heute und Gestern, Vol. 5. Ed. by James Hogg. (Analecta Cartusiana Ser.: No. 35). (Orig.). 1984. pap. 25.00 (ISBN 3-7052-0041-0, Pub by Salzburg Studies). Longwood Pub Group.

Spiritualite de l'Heresie: le Catharisme. Rene Nelli. LC 78-63189. (Heresies of the Early Christian & Medieval Era: Second Ser.). Repr. of 1953 ed. 31.00 (ISBN 0-404-16226-6). AMS Pr.

Spiritualitiat Heute und Gestern, Vol. 2. Ed. by James Hogg. (Analecta Cartusiana Ser.: No. 35). (Ger. & Eng.). 200p. (Orig.). 1983. pap. 25.00 (ISBN 3-7052-0038-0, Pub by Salzburg Studies). Longwood Pub Group.

Spirituality & Administration: The Role of the Bishop in Twelfth-Century Auxerre. Constance B. Bouchard. LC 78-55889. 1979. 11.00x (ISBN 0-910956-79-0, SAM5); pap. 5.00x (ISBN 0-910956-67-7). Medieval Acad.

Spirituality & Analogia Entis According to Erich Przywara, S. J. Metaphysics & Religious Experience, the Ignation Exercises, the Balance in 'Similarity' & 'Greater Dissimilarity' According to Lateran IV. James V. Zeitz. LC 82-17588. 358p. (Orig.). 1983. lib. bdg. 33.00 (ISBN 0-8191-2783-3); pap. text ed. 15.75 (ISBN 0-8191-2784-1). U Pr of Amer.

Spirituality & Human Emotion. Robert C. Roberts. 134p. 1983. pap. 5.95 (ISBN 0-8028-1939-7). Eerdmans.

Spirituality & Justice. Donal Dorr. 264p. (Orig.). 1985. pap. 10.95 (ISBN 0-88344-449-6). Orbis Bks.

Spirituality & Pastoral Care. Nelson S. Thayer. LC 84-48716. (Theology & Pastoral Care Ser.). 128p. 1985. pap. 7.95 (ISBN 0-8006-1734-7, 1-1734). Fortress.

Spirituality & Prayer, Jewish & Christian Understandings (Stimulus Bk.) Ed. by Gabe Huck & Leon Klenicki. LC 82-62966. 200p. (Orig.). 1983. pap. 7.95 (ISBN 0-8091-2538-2). Paulist Pr.

Spirituality & the Desert Experience. Charles Cummings. 1976. cancelled (ISBN 0-87193-166-4). Dimension Bks.

Spirituality & the Gentle Life. Adrian Van Kaam. 6.95 (ISBN 0-87193-037-4). Dimension Bks.

Spirituality & Total Health. Ishwar C. Puri. Ed. by Edward D. Scott. 29p. (Orig.). 1986. pap. 2.00 (ISBN 0-937067-08-3). Inst Study Hum Aware.

Spirituality for an Anxious Age. Patrick Brennan. 151p. 1985. pap. 7.95 (ISBN 0-88347-194-9). Thomas More.

Spirituality for Ministry. Urban T. Holmes, III. LC 81-47839. 244p. 1982. 14.45 (ISBN 0-06-064008-1, HarpR). Har-Row.

Spirituality for the Long Haul: Biblical Risk & Moral Stand. Robert S. Bilheimer. LC 83-48918. 176p. 1984. pap. 8.95 (ISBN 0-8006-1760-6, 1-1760). Fortress.

Spirituality in Church & World. Ed. by Christian Duquoc. LC 65-28868. (Concilium Ser.: Vol. 9). 174p. 7.95 (ISBN 0-8091-0139-4). Paulist Pr.

Spirituality in the Secular City. Ed. by Christian Duquoc. LC 66-30386. (Concilium Ser.: Vol. 19). 192p. 7.95 (ISBN 0-8091-0140-8). Paulist Pr.

Spirituality Named Compassion, & the Healing of the Global Village, Humpty Dumpty, & Us. Matthew Fox. 1979. pap. 7.95 (ISBN 0-86683-751-5, HarpR). Har-Row.

Spirituality of Cornelia Connelly: In God, For God, With God. Caritas McCarthy. LC 86-21718. (Studies in Women & Religion Ser.). 280p. 1986. text ed. 49.95 (ISBN 0-88946-530-4). E Mellen.

Spirituality of St. Ignatius Loyola: An Account of Its Historical Development. Hugo Rahner. Tr. by Francis J. Smith. LC 53-5586. (Request Reprint). 1968. 3.50 (ISBN 0-8294-0066-4). Loyola.

Spirituality of Teilhard de Chardin. Robert S. Faricy. 128p. (Orig.). 1981. pap. 5.95 (ISBN 0-86683-608-X, HarpR). Har-Row.

Spirituality of the Beatitudes: Matthew's Challenge for First World Christians. Michael H. Crosby. LC 80-24755. 254p. (Orig.). 1981. pap. 7.95 (ISBN 0-88344-465-8). Orbis Bks.

Spirituality of the Catholic Church. William A. Kaschmitter. 980p. 1982. 20.00 (ISBN 0-912414-33-2). Lumen Christi.

Spirituality of the Christian East: A Systematic Handbook. Tomas Spidlik. Tr. by Anthony P. Gythiel from Fr. (Cistercian Studies Ser.: No. 79). Tr. of La Spritiualite de l'Orient Chritienne. 1986. 48.95 (ISBN 0-87907-879-0); pap. 17.00 (ISBN 0-87907-979-7). Cistercian Pubns.

Spirituality of the Future: A Search Apropos of R. C. Zaehner's Study in Sri-Aurobindo & Teilhard de Chardin. K. D. Sethna. LC 76-14764. 320p. 1981. 32.50 (ISBN 0-8386-2028-0). Fairleigh Dickinson.

Spirituality of the Middle Ages. Jean LeClercq et al. (History of Christian Spirituality Ser.: Vol. 2). 616p. 1982. pap. 14.95 (ISBN 0-8164-2373-3, HarpR). Har-Row.

Spirituality of the New Testament & the Fathers. Louis Bouyer. (History of Christian Spirituality Ser.: Vol. 1). 560p. 1982. pap. 13.95 (ISBN 0-8164-2372-5, HarpR). Har-Row.

Spirituality of the Religious Educator. Ed. by James M. Lee. 209p. (Orig.). 1985. pap. 12.95 (ISBN 0-89135-045-4). Religious Educ.

Spirituality of the Road. David J. Bosch. LC 79-10856. (Mennonite Missionary Fellowship: No. 6). 104p. 1979. pap. 4.95 (ISBN 0-8361-1889-8). Herald Pr.

Spirituality of Western Christendom. Ed. by E. Rozanne Elder. LC 76-22615. (Cistercian Studies Ser.: No. 30). (Illus.). 1976. pap. 6.95 (ISBN 0-87907-987-8). Cistercian Pubns.

Spirituality of Western Christendom II: The Roots of Modern Christian Spirituality. Ed. by Rozanne E. Elder. (Cistercian Studies: Nbr. 55). pap. write for info. (ISBN 0-87907-855-3). Cistercian Pubns.

Spirituality Recharted. Hubert Van Zeller. 1985. pap. 4.95 (ISBN 0-932506-39-9). St Bedes Pubns.

Spirituality Through the Ages. Tablet Of London Editors. pap. 0.75 (ISBN 0-8199-0240-3, L38838). Franciscan Herald.

Spirituality: What It Is. 3rd ed. Kirpal Singh. LC 81-52000. (Illus.). 112p. 1982. pap. 3.50 (ISBN 0-918224-16-0). Sawan Kirpal Pubns.

Spiritually Single. Marcia Mitchell. LC 83-15754. 112p. 1984. pap. 3.95 (ISBN 0-87123-591-9, 210591). Bethany Hse.

Spiritually Yours: Applying Gospel Principles for Personal Progression. S. Brent Farley. LC 81-82054. 160p. 1982. 6.95 (ISBN 0-88290-192-3, 1068). Horizon Utah.

Spirituals & the Blues. James H. Cone. pap. 5.95 (ISBN 0-8164-2073-4, SP74, HarpR). Har-Row.

Spirituals Reborn: Melody. M. Paget. LC 74-76574. 96p. 1976. Pt. 1. pap. text ed. 5.95 (ISBN 0-521-08714-7); Pt. 2. pap. text ed. 5.95 (ISBN 0-521-21332-0); choral 13.95 (ISBN 0-521-08713-9). Cambridge U Pr.

Spitural Growth. Don Clowers. 164p. (Orig.). 1984. pap. text ed. 3.95 (ISBN 0-914307-31-2). Word Faith.

Splendid Risk. Bernard Mullahy. LC 81-40445. 256p. 1982. text ed. 12.95 (ISBN 0-268-01705-0). U of Notre Dame Pr.

Splendor of His Way. Stephen Kaung. Tr. by Lily Hsu from Eng. (Chinese.). 1984. pap. write for info. (ISBN 0-941598-14-4). Living Spring Pubns.

Splendor of His Ways. Stephen Kaung. Ed. by Herbert L. Fader. 1974. 5.00 (ISBN 0-935008-42-X); pap. 3.25 (ISBN 0-935008-43-8). Christian Fellow Pubs.

Splendor of the Church. De Lubac Henri. LC 86-82080. 382p. 1986. pap. 12.95 (ISBN 0-89870-120-1). Ignatius Pr.

Splendor of the Faith: Meditations on the Credo of the People of God. Anton Morgenroth. 206p. (Orig.). 1983. pap. 7.95 (ISBN 0-931888-14-X). Christendom Pubns.

Splendor of the Holy Land. Ed. by Marwan Buhiery. LC 77-5503. 1979. deluxe ed. 500.00x (ISBN 0-88206-019-8). Caravan Bks.

Splendours of the Vijayanagara. 1981. 30.00x (ISBN 0-8364-0792-X, Pub. by Marg India). South Asia Bks.

Spoken by the Spirit. Ralph W. Harris. LC 73-87106. 128p. 1973. pap. 2.50 (ISBN 0-88243-725-9, 02-0725). Gospel Pub.

Spoken Modern Hebrew. Joseph A. Reif & Hanna Levinson. (Spoken Language Ser.). 590p. 1980. pap. 15.00x (ISBN 0-87950-683-0); cassettes, 31 dual track 180.00x (ISBN 0-87950-684-9); text & cassettes 190.00x (ISBN 0-87950-685-7). Spoken Lang Serv.

Spoken Pangasinan. Richard A. Benton. LC 79-152457. (University of Hawaii, Honolulu. Pacific & Asian Linguistics Institute). pap. 160.00 (ISBN 0-317-10118-8, 2017214). Bks Demand UMI.

Spoken Words of Love. Ruth Wingard. 1986. 6.95 (ISBN 0-533-06768-5). Vantage.

Spokesman for the Devil. Albert F. Fugett. (Illus.). 165p. 1985. 14.95 (ISBN 0-9614870-0-3). Triple Seven.

Spokesmen for God. Edith Hamilton. 1962. pap. 3.95 (ISBN 0-393-00169-5, Norton Lib). Norton.

Spontaneous Expansion of the Church. Roland Allen. 1962. pap. 4.95 (ISBN 0-8028-1002-0). Eerdmans.

Spontaneous You. Norman P. Grubb. 1970. pap. 3.50 (ISBN 0-87508-224-6). Chr Lit.

Sportscape. John R. Gleeson, III. LC 84-52105. (Illus.). 176p. (Orig.). 1984. pap. 12.95 (ISBN 0-912661-04-6). Woodsong Graph.

Spotlight on Stress: Study Guide. Gary Collins. 32p. 1983. 1.50 (ISBN 0-88449-100-5, A424650). Vision Hse.

Spousage of a Virgin to Christ. John Alcock. LC 74-80158. (English Experience Ser.: No. 638). (Illus.). 19p. 1974. Repr. of 1496 ed. 3.50 (ISBN 90-221-0638-1). Walter J Johnson.

Sprache Huldrych Zwinglis im Kontrast zur Sprache Luthers. Walter Schenker. (Studia Linguistica Germanica: Vol. 14). (Illus.). 1977. 66.00x (ISBN 3-11-006605-X). De Gruyter.

Sprachphilosophie Des Hl, Thomas Von Aquin. F. Manthey. (Philosophy Reprints Ser.). (Ger.). Repr. of 1937 ed. lib. bdg. 45.00x (ISBN 0-697-00042-7). Irvington.

Spreading Flame: The Rise & Progress of Christianity from Its Beginnings to the Conversion of the English. F. F. Bruce. 432p. 1980. pap. 14.95 (ISBN 0-8028-1805-6). Eerdmans.

Spreading the Gospel. Bernard R. Youngman. (Background to the Bible Ser.). pap. 8.95 (ISBN 0-7175-0420-4). Dufour.

Spreading Truth. Joe Dennis. 64p. 1979. pap. text ed. 1.95 (ISBN 0-89114-086-7); P. 78. tchrs. ed. 1.95 (ISBN 0-89114-087-5). Baptist Pub Hse.

Sprig of Holly. new ed. Halford E. Luccock. Ed. & intro. by Charles S. Hartman. LC 78-17096. 64p. 1978. text ed. 3.50 (ISBN 0-8298-0354-8). Pilgrim NY.

Sprig of Hope. Robert T. Young. LC 79-20946. 1980. pap. 6.50 (ISBN 0-687-39260-8). Abingdon.

Spring Activity Book. Susan Vesey. Ed. by P. Alexander. (Illus.). 32p. 1987. pap. 3.95 (ISBN 0-7459-1015-7). Lion USA.

Spring Wind of the Silent Administrator. Myrna L Etheridge. 80p. (Orig.). Date not set. pap. 4.00 (ISBN 0-937417-02-5). Etheridge Minist.

Spring 1982: An Annual of Archetypal Psychology & Jungian Thought. Ed. by James Hillman. 316p. (Orig.). 1982. pap. 15.00 (ISBN 0-88214-017-5). Spring Pubns.

Springs in the Valley. Mrs. Charles E. Cowman. 1977. large-print ed. kivar 9.95 (ISBN 0-310-22517-5, 12562L). Zondervan.

Springs in the Valley. 2nd ed. Ed. by Mrs. Charles E. Cowman. 384p. 1980. pap. 4.95 (ISBN 0-310-22511-6, 6806P). Zondervan.

Springs of Hellas. Terrot R. Glover. LC 74-122878. (Essay & General Literature Index Reprint Ser). 1971. Repr. of 1945 ed. 21.00x (ISBN 0-8046-1333-8, Pub. by Kennikat). Assoc Faculty Pr.

Springs of Jewish Life. Chaim Raphael. LC 82-70853. 1982. 16.50 (ISBN 0-465-08192-4). Basic.

Springs of Joy. Penny Dant. (Orig.). 1987. pap. 7.00 (ISBN 0-915541-11-4). Star Bks Inc.

Springs of Love. Anna B. Mow. LC 79-11186. 1979. pap. 1.95 (ISBN 0-87178-810-1). Brethren.

Springtime of Love & Marriage. James R. Hine. (Family Life Ser.). 160p. 1985. pap. 6.95 (ISBN 0-317-38064-8). Judson.

Springtime of the Liturgy: Liturgical Texts of the First Four Centuries. rev. ed. Lucien Deiss. Tr. by Matthew J. O'Connell from Fr. LC 79-15603. 307p. 1979. pap. 10.00 (ISBN 0-8146-1023-4). Liturgical Pr.

Sprung Time: Seasons of the Christian Year. Robert G. Hamerton-Kelly. LC 79-56162. 144p. (Orig.). 1980. pap. 4.50 (ISBN 0-8358-0397-X). Upper Room.

Spur-Of-The-Cock. Ed. by J. Frank Dobie. LC 34-1434. (Texas Folklore Society Publications: No. 11). 1965. Repr. of 1933 ed. 11.95 (ISBN 0-87074-043-1). SMU Press.

Spurgeon. Ernest W. Bacon. (Christian Biography Ser.). 184p. 1982. pap. 3.95 (ISBN 0-8010-0823-9). Baker Bk.

Spurgeon un Principe Olividado. 2nd ed. Iain Murray. (Span.). 156p. 1984. pap. 3.95 (ISBN 0-85151-439-1). Banner of Truth.

Spurgeon's Devotional Bible. Charles H. Spurgeon. 1974. Repr. 19.95 (ISBN 0-8010-8043-6). Baker Bk.

Spurgeon's Expository Encyclopedia, 15 vols. Charles H. Spurgeon. 1977. 195.00 (ISBN 0-8010-8104-1). Baker Bk.

Spurgeon's Sermons, 10 vols. Charles H. Spurgeon. (Charles H. Spurgeon Library). 1983. pap. 99.95 (ISBN 0-8010-8231-5). Baker Bk.

Spurgeon's Sermons on Christ's Names & Titles. Charles H. Spurgeon. Ed. by Charles T. Cook. 1965. Repr. of 1961 ed. 7.95 (ISBN 0-87921-033-8). Attic Pr.

Spurious & Doubtful Works, Pseudo-Augustini Quaestiones Veteris et Novi Testamenti CXXVII. Saint Aurelius Augustinus. Ed. by A. Souter. (Corpus Scriptorum Ecclesiasticorum Latinorum Ser: Vol. 50). 40.00 (ISBN 0-384-02575-7). Johnson Repr.

Sputnik Psalomtschika-odnogolosnij obikhod. Tr. of Psalm-Readers Companion, Unison & Obikhod. 624p. 1959. pap. 30.00 (ISBN 0-317-30389-9). Holy Trinity.

Square Sun Square Moon: A Collection of Prose Essays. Paul Reps. LC 67-14277. (Illus., Orig.). 1967. pap. 6.50 (ISBN 0-8048-0544-X). C E Tuttle.

Sramana Bhagavan Mahavira: Life & Doctrine. K. C. Lalwani. LC 75-904150. 1975. 10.00x (ISBN 0-88386-533-5). South Asia Bks.

Sri Aurobindo. 3rd ed. Manoj Das. 1982. pap. 4.00x (ISBN 0-8364-1585-X, Pub. by National Sahitya Akademi). South Asia Bks.

Sri Aurobindo. G. H. Langley. 59.95 (ISBN 0-8490-1119-1). Gordon Pr.

Sri Aurobindo Album. 55p. Date not set. 15.00 (ISBN 0-317-17482-7). Auromere.

Sri Aurobindo: An Interpretation. Ed. by V. C. Joshi. 1973. 7.50 (ISBN 0-686-20308-9). Intl Bk Dist.

Sri Aurobindo & the Mother on Collective Yoga. Ed. by Eric Hughes. 75p. 1974. pap. 1.25 (ISBN 0-89071-000-7). Matagiri.

Sri Aurobindo & the Mother on Education. 6th, Special ed. Sri Aurobindo. 1978. pap. 16.00 (ISBN 0-89744-955-X). Auromere.

Sri Aurobindo & the Mother on Education. Sri Aurobindo & The Mother. 168p. 1973. pap. 3.50 (ISBN 0-89071-249-2). Matagiri.

Sri Aurobindo & the Mother on Love. Sri Aurobindo & The Mother. Ed. & intro. by P. B. Saint-Hilaire. 49p. 1973. pap. 2.00 (ISBN 0-89071-275-1). Matagiri.

Sri Aurobindo Birth Centenary Library: Complete Writings of Sri Aurobindo, 30 vols. Sri Aurobindo. 1979. Set. 300.00x (ISBN 0-89744-964-9); lib. bdg. 400.00x (ISBN 0-89744-965-7). Auromere.

Sri Aurobindo: His Life Unique. Rishabchand. (Illus.). 427p. 1981. 20.00 (ISBN 0-89071-326-X, Pub. by Sri Aurobindo Ashram India); pap. 15.00 (ISBN 0-89071-325-1, Pub. by Sri Aurobindo Ashram India). Matagiri.

Sri Aurobindo Life Companion Library. Aurobindo. (Life Companion Ser.). 4522p. 1984. Repr. of 1979 ed. 111.85 (ISBN 0-317-19956-0, Pub. by Mandanlal Himatsinghlea). Auromere.

Sri Aurobindo on Himself. Sri Aurobindo. 513p. 1985. 14.95 (ISBN 0-89071-317-0, Pub. by Sri Aurobindo Ashram India); pap. 11.75 (ISBN 0-89071-316-2, Pub. by Sri Aurobindo Ashram India). Matagiri.

Sri Aurobindo on Himself. Sri Aurobindo. 1979. 20.00 (ISBN 0-89744-917-7). Auromere.

Sri Aurobindo-Seer & Poet. Vinayak K. Gokak. LC 73-900907. 185p. 1974. 8.00x (ISBN 0-89684-454-4). Orient Bk Dist.

Sri Aurobindo: The Perfect & the Good. Robert N. Minor. 1978. 15.00x (ISBN 0-8364-0033-X). South Asia Bks.

Sri Aurobindo: The Story of His Life. Themi. 95p. 1983. pap. 2.95 (ISBN 0-89071-327-8, Pub. by Sri Aurobindo Ashram India). Matagiri.

Sri Aurobindo's Concept of the Superman. Chitta R. Goswami. 260p. 1976. 8.00 (ISBN 0-89071-211-5). Matagiri.

Sri Aurobindo's Treatment of Hindu Myth. J. Feys. 1984. 7.50x (ISBN 0-8364-1109-9, Pub. by Mukhopadhyay India). South Asia Bks.

Sri Caitanya Caritamrta: Antya-Lila, 5 vols. Swami A. C. Bhaktivedanta. (Illus.). 1975. 12.95 ea. Vol. 1 (ISBN 0-912776-72-2). Vol. 2 (ISBN 0-912776-73-0). Vol. 3 (ISBN 0-912776-74-9). Vol. 4 (ISBN 0-912776-76-5). Vol. 5 (ISBN 0-912776-77-3). Bhaktivedanta.

Sri Caitanya-Caritamrta: Madhya-Lila, 9 vols. Swami A. C. Bhaktivedanta. (Illus.). 1975. 12.95 ea. Vol. 1 (ISBN 0-912776-63-3). Vol. 2 (ISBN 0-912776-64-1). Vol. 3 (ISBN 0-912776-65-X). Vol. 4 (ISBN 0-912776-66-8). Vol. 5 (ISBN 0-912776-67-6). Vol. 6 (ISBN 0-912776-68-4). Vol. 7 (ISBN 0-912776-69-2). Vol. 8, (ISBN 0-912776-70-6), Vol. 9 (ISBN 0-912776-71-4). Bhaktivedanta.

Sri Chakra. S. Shankaranarayanan. 1979. 14.95 (ISBN 0-941524-11-6). Lotus Light.

Sri Chinmoy Speaks, 10 pts. Sri Chinmoy. Incl. Pt. 1. 55p (ISBN 0-88497-282-8); Pt. 2. 58p (ISBN 0-88497-285-2); Pt. 3. 65p (ISBN 0-88497-286-0); Pt. 4. 62p (ISBN 0-88497-288-7); Pt. 5. 56p (ISBN 0-88497-289-5); Pt. 6. 57p (ISBN 0-88497-290-9); Pt. 7. 58p (ISBN 0-88497-294-1); Pt. 8. 56p (ISBN 0-88497-295-X); Pt. 9. 51p (ISBN 0-88497-296-8); Pt. 10. 62p (ISBN 0-88497-335-2). 1976-77. pap. 2.00 ea. Aum Pubns.

Sri Ganesh Puja (Worship of God of Obstacles) Panduranga R. Malyala. (Illus.). 56p. 1982. 2.00 (ISBN 0-938924-03-6). Sri Shirdi Sai.

Sri Guru Granth Sahib in English Translation, Vol. 1. Tr. by Gurbachan S. Talib. 1985. 30.00x (ISBN 0-8364-1507-8, Pub. by Punjabi U India). South Asia Bks.

Sri Hanumaan Chaaleesa. 2.00 (ISBN 0-938924-22-2). Sri Shirdi Sai.

Sri Isopanisad: Discovering the Original Person. Swami Bhaktivedanta. 1985. 7.95; pap. 2.95 (ISBN 0-89213-138-1). Bhaktivedanta.

Sri Krishna: A Socio-Political & Philosophical Study. Ram C. Gupta. xiv, 188p. 1984. text ed. 30.00x (ISBN 0-86590-376-X, Pub. by B R Pub Corp Delhi). Apt Bks.

Sri Krsna Caitanya: A Historical Study of Gaudiya Vaisnavism. A. N. Chatterjee. 1985. 22.00x (ISBN 0-8364-1321-0, Pub. by Assoc Bks India). South Asia Bks.

Sri Lankan Monastic Architecture. H. T. Basnayake. (Studies on Sri Lanka Ser.: No. 2). (Illus.). 186p. 1986. 85.00x (ISBN 81-7030-009-6, Pub. by SRI SATGURU Pubns India). Orient Bk Dist.

Sri Mad Devi Bhagavatam. Vijnanananda. LC 73-3819. (Sacred Books of the Hindus: No. 26, Bks. 1-12). Repr. of 1921 ed. 79.50 (ISBN 0-404-57826-8). AMS Pr.

Sri Namamrta: The Holy Nectar of the Holy Name. A. C. Bhaktivedanta Prabhupada. (Illus.). 586p. 1982. pap. 12.95 (ISBN 0-89213-113-6). Bhaktivedanta.

Sri Pancaratra-Raksha of Vedanta Desika. 2nd ed. Pandit M. Duraiswami. 1967. 6.00 (ISBN 0-8356-7482-7, ALS 36). Theos Pub Hse.

Sri Ramakrishna in the Eyes of Brahma & Christian Admirers. Ed. by Nanda Mookerjee. LC 76-904430. 1976. 6.50x (ISBN 0-88386-791-5). South Asia Bks.

Sri Ramakrishna's Life & Message in the Present Age: With the Author's Reminiscences of Holy Mother & Some Direct Disciples. Swami Satprakashananda. LC 75-46386. 208p. 1976. 6.00 (ISBN 0-916356-54-X). Vedanta Soc St Louis.

Sri Sankara Vijayam. Ramachandran. 1977. pap. 2.25 (ISBN 0-89744-123-0, Pub. by Ganesh & Co. India). Auromere.

Sri Sarada Devi: Consort of Sri Ramakrishna. Ed. by Nanda Mookerjee. 1978. 6.00x (ISBN 0-8364-0173-5). South Asia Bks.

Sri Sarasvati Puja: Goddess of Knowledge & Education. Panduranga Malyala. (Illus.). 28p. 1982. 2.00 (ISBN 0-938924-10-9). Sri Shirdi Sai.

Sri Shirdi Sai Baba. Date not set. 5.00 (ISBN 0-938924-34-6). Sri Shirdi Sai.

Sri Swami Satchidananda: Apostle of Peace. Sita Bordow et al. LC 86-10533. (Illus.). 454p. (Orig.). 1986. pap. 14.95 (ISBN 0-932040-31-4). Integral Yoga Pubns.

Sriharicarita Mahakavya of Srihari Padmanabhasastrin. Ed. by T. Venkatacharaya. 11.50 (ISBN 0-8356-7322-7). Theos Pub Hse.

Srila Prbhupada in Latin America. Satsvarupa Das Goswami. Ed. by Mandalesvara Dasa & Bimala Dasi. (Prabhupada-lila). (Orig.). Vol. 7. pap. text ed. 2.00 (ISBN 0-911233-05-9). Gita-Nagari.

Srimad-Bhagavad-Gita. 7th ed. Swami Paramananda. Orig. Title: Bhagavad-Gita, Srimad. 1981. 5.75 (ISBN 0-911564-03-9); lexitone bdg. 3.50. Vedanta Ctr.

Srimad Bhagavad Gita: Pocket Book Edition. Swami Jyotir Maya Nanda. (Illus.). 384p. 1986. pap. 3.00 (ISBN 0-934664-44-7). Yoga Res Foun.

Srimad Bhagavatam. Hridayananda Das Goswami. 12.95 (ISBN 0-89213-129-2). Bhaktivedanta.

Srimad Bhagavatam: Eleventh Canto, 4 Vols. Bhakivedanta Swami. (Illus.). 416p. 1983. 12.95 ea. (ISBN 0-89213-125-X). Bhaktivedanta.

Srimad-Bhagavatam: Eleventh Canto, Vol. 1. Hridayananda dasa Goswami Acaryadeva. (Illus.). 450p. 1982. 12.95 (ISBN 0-89213-112-8); text ed. 9.95 (ISBN 0-686-98021-2). Bhaktivedanta.

Srimad Bhagavatam: First Canto, 3 vols. Swami A. C. Bhaktivedanta. LC 73-169353. (Illus.). 1972. 12.95 ea. Vol. 1 (ISBN 0-912776-27-7). Vol. 2 (ISBN 0-912776-29-3). Vol. 3 (ISBN 0-912776-34-X). Bhaktivedanta.

Srimad Bhagavatam: Fourth Canto, 4 vols. Swami A. C. Bhaktivedanta. LC 73-169353. (Illus.). 1974. 12.95 ea. Vol. 1 (ISBN 0-912776-38-2). Vol. 2 (ISBN 0-912776-47-1). Vol. 3 (ISBN 0-912776-48-X). Vol. 4 (ISBN 0-912776-49-8). Bhaktivedanta.

Srimad Bhagavatam: Ninth Canto, 3 vols. Swami A. C. Bhaktivendanta. LC 73-169353. (Sanskrit & Eng., Illus.). 1977. 12.95 ea. Vol. 1 (ISBN 0-912776-94-3). Vol. 2 (ISBN 0-912776-95-1). Vol. 3 (ISBN 0-912776-96-X). Bhaktivedanta.

Srimad Bhagavatam: Second Canto, 2 vols. Swami A. C. Bhaktivedanta. LC 73-169353. (Illus.). 1972. 12.95 ea. Vol. 1 (ISBN 0-912776-28-5). Vol. 2 (ISBN 0-912776-35-8). Bhaktivedanta.

Srimad-Bhagavatam: Tenth Canto, Vol. 3. Swami Prabhupada A. C. Bhaktivedanta. (Illus.). 112p. 1980. 12.95 (ISBN 0-89213-107-1). Bhaktivedanta.

Srimad Bhagavatam: Third Canto, 4 vols. Swami A. C. Bhaktivedanta. LC 73-169353. (Illus.). 1974. 12.95 ea. Vol. 1 (ISBN 0-912776-37-4). Vol. 2 (ISBN 0-912776-44-7). Vol. 3 (ISBN 0-912776-46-3). Vol. 4 (ISBN 0-912776-75-7). Bhaktivedanta.

Srimad Bhagavatam: 11th Canto, Vol. 5. Bhaktivedanta Swami. 1985. 12.95 (ISBN 0-89213-126-8). Bhaktivedanta.

Srimad Bhagavatam: 12th Canto, Vol. 1. Bhaktivedanta Swami. 1985. 12.95 (ISBN 0-89213-129-2). Bhaktivedanta.

Srimad Bhagavatam: 12th Canto, Vol. 2. Bhaktivedanta Swami. 1985. 12.95 (ISBN 0-89213-130-6). Bhaktivedanta.
Srimad Devi Bhagawatam, Pts. I & II. Tr. by Swami Vijnanananda from Sanskrit. LC 75-985029. 1977. 55.00x (ISBN 0-89684-455-2). Orient Bk Dist.
Sruti Gita: The Song of the Srutis. Tr. by Gambhirananda from Sanskrit. 99p. 1982. pap. 4.95 (ISBN 0-87481-510-X). Vedanta Pr.
Ssabier und der Ssabismus, 2 Vols. D. Chwolsohn. 1856. 85.00 (ISBN 0-384-09053-2). Johnson Repr.
Stadt und Eidgenossenschaft im Alten Testament: Eine Auseinandersetzung mit Max Webers Studie "Das Antike Judentum". Christa Schaefer-Lichtenberger. (Ger.). 485p. 1983. 43.20 (ISBN 3-11-008591-7). De Gruyter.
Stage Condemn'd. George Ridpath. LC 79-170443. (English Stage Ser.: Vol. 29). 1973. lib. bdg. 61.00 (ISBN 0-8240-0612-7). Garland Pub.
Stages of Consciousness: Meditations on the Boundaries of the Soul. Georg Kuhlewind. Tr. by Maria St. Goar from Ger. 144p. (Orig.). 1985. pap. 8.95 (ISBN 0-89281-065-3, Lindisfarne Pr). Inner Tradit.
Stages of Faith: The Psychology of Human Development & the Quest for Meaning. James W. Fowler. LC 80-7757. 224p. 1981. 18.45 (ISBN 0-06-062840-5, HarpR). Har-Row.
Stages of Higher Knowledge. Rudolf Steiner. 64p. 1974. pap. 4.50 (ISBN 0-910142-37-8). Anthroposophic.
Stages on the Road. facs. ed. Sigrid Undset. Tr. by A. G. Chater. LC 70-80404. (Essay Index Reprint Ser). 1934. 16.50 (ISBN 0-8369-1068-0). Ayer Co Pubs.
Stages: Understanding How You Make Your Moral Decisions. Nathaniel Lande & Afton Slade. LC 78-195000. 1979. 10.00 (ISBN 0-06-250510-6, HarpR). Har-Row.
Staging of Religious Drama in Europe in the Middle Ages. Ed. by Peter Meredith & John Tailby. Tr. by Margaret Sleeman & Raffaella Ferrari. (Early Drama, Art & Music Ser.). (Illus.). 301p. 1983. 24.95x (ISBN 0-918720-23-0). Medieval Inst.
Staging of Religious Drama in Europe in the Middle Ages. Ed. by Peter Meredith & John Tailby. Tr. by Margaret Sleeman & Raffaella Ferrari. (Early Drama, Art & Music Ser.). (Illus.). 301p. 1983. pap. 14.95x (ISBN 0-918720-24-9). Medieval Inst.
Stained Glass Hours: Modern Pilgrimage. Tom Davies & John Hodder. (Illus.). 161p. 1985. 29.95 (ISBN 0-450-06053-5, New Eng Lib). David & Charles.
Stained Glass of Saint-Pere de Chartres. Meredith P. Lillich. LC 77-13926. (Illus.). 1978. 50.00x (ISBN 0-8195-5023-X). Wesleyan U Pr.
Stained Glass Religion: Who Needs It. Daniel Malachuck. 100p. pap. 4.95 (ISBN 0-89221-127-X, Pub. by SonLife). New Leaf.
Staircase for Silence. Alan Ecclestone. 158p. 1977. pap. 6.50 (ISBN 0-232-51364-3). Attic Pr.
Stairway of Perfection. Walter Hilton. LC 78-60288. 1979. pap. 4.95 (ISBN 0-385-14059-2, Im). Doubleday.
Stairway to Heaven: The Spiritual Roots of Rock & Roll. Davin Seay & Mary Neely. 384p. 1986. pap. 9.95 (ISBN 0-345-33022-6, Pub. by Ballantine Epiphany). Ballantine.
Stake Your Claim. Emmet Fox. LC 52-11683. 1952. 8.95 (ISBN 0-06-062970-3, HarpR). Har-Row.
Staking Your Claim on Healing. C. C. Cribb. LC 79-83919. (If God Has It I Want It!). 1979. pap. 2.95 (ISBN 0-932046-14-2). Manhattan Ltd NC.
Stalwart for the Truth: The Life & Legacy of A. H. Unruh. David Ewert. (Trailblazer Ser.). 148p. (Orig.). 1975. pap. 6.95 (ISBN 0-919797-18-0). Kindred Pr.
Stamm Awad in Alten Testament. Ingrid Riesener. (Beiheft zur Zeitschrift Fuer die Alttestamentliche Wissenschaft: Vol. 149). 1979. 62.00x (ISBN 3-11-007260-2). De Gruyter.
Stand Fast in Liberty. James E. Bristol. 1983. pap. 2.50x (ISBN 0-87574-119-3, 119). Pendle Hill.
Stand in the Door. W. Darryl Goldman. LC 80-65309. 176p. 1980. pap. 2.95 (ISBN 0-88243-599-X, 02-0599). Gospel Pub.
Stand Perfect in Wisdom: Colossians & Ephesians. Robert G. Gromacki. 1981. pap. 5.95 (ISBN 0-8010-3767-0). Baker Bk.
Stand Tough. Powell. 1983. 3.95 (ISBN 0-88207-592-6). Victor Bks.
Stand up & Be Counted: Calling for Public Confession of Faith. R. T. Kendall. 128p. (Orig.). 1985. pap. 5.95 (ISBN 0-310-38351-X, 9281P). Zondervan.
Standard, Vols. 11-26. Ed. by Frank S. Murray. Incl. Vol. 11, o.s.i; Vol. 12; Vol. 13. 1961; Vol. 14. 1962 (ISBN 0-910840-62-8); Vol. 15. 1963 (ISBN 0-910840-63-6); Vol. 16. 1964 (ISBN 0-910840-64-4); Vol. 17. 1965 (ISBN 0-910840-65-2); Vol. 18. 1966 (ISBN 0-910840-66-0); Vol. 19. 1967 (ISBN 0-910840-67-9); Vol. 20. 1968 (ISBN 0-910840-68-7); Vol. 21. 1969 (ISBN 0-910840-69-5); Vol. 22. 1970 (ISBN 0-910840-70-9); Vol. 23. 1971 (ISBN 0-910840-71-7); Vol. 24. 1972 (ISBN 0-910840-72-5); Vol.25. 1973 (ISBN 0-910840-73-3); Vol. 26. 1974 (ISBN 0-910840-74-1). 2.00x ea. Kingdom.
Standard, Vol. 30. Ed. by Frank S. Murray. 1978. 3.00x (ISBN 0-910840-78-4). Kingdom.
Standard Accounting System for Lutheran Congregations. Neal D. Meitler & Linda M. La Porte. 1981. 4.95 (ISBN 0-8100-0129-2, 21N2001). Northwest Pub.
Standard Bible Atlas. Orrin Root. (Illus.). 32p. 1973. pap. 3.50 (ISBN 0-87239-251-1, 3169). Standard Pub.
Standard Christmas Program Book, No. 45. Ed. by Judith Sparks. 48p. 1984. pap. 1.95 (ISBN 0-87239-749-1, 8645). Standard Pub.
Standard Christmas Program Book, No. 46. Laurie Hoard. 48p. 1985. pap. 1.95 (ISBN 0-87239-850-1, 8646). Standard Pub.
Standard Christmas Program Book, No. 47. Compiled by Laurie Hoard. 48p. 1986. pap. 1.95 (ISBN 0-87239-935-4, 8647). Standard Pub.
Standard Easter Program Book, No. 35. Ed. by Laurie Hoard. 48p. (Orig.). 1984. pap. 1.95 (ISBN 0-87239-768-8, 8705). Standard Pub.
Standard Easter Program Book, No. 36. Compiled by Laurie Hoard. 48p. 1985. pap. 1.95 (ISBN 0-87239-870-6, 8706). Standard Pub.
Standard Easter Program Book, No. 37. Compiled by Pat Fittro. 48p. 1986. pap. 1.95 (ISBN 0-87403-083-8, 8707). Standard Pub.
Standard Freemasonry. J. Blanchard. 9.00x (ISBN 0-685-22116-4). Wehman.
Standard Freemasonry. (Illus.). 9.00 (ISBN 0-685-19501-5). Powner.
Standard Lesson Commentary, 1986-87. Ed. by Jim Fehl. 450p. 1986. text ed. 9.50 (ISBN 0-87403-010-2, 74017); pap. text ed. 7.95 (ISBN 0-87403-009-9, 1987). Standard Pub.
Standard Masonic Monitor. George E. Simons. 248p. 1984. pap. 7.50 enlarged type (ISBN 0-88053-010-3). Macoy Pub.
Standard Monitor. George E. Simons. 7.50 (ISBN 0-685-19502-3). Powner.
Standard Nineteen Seventy-Nine. Ed. by Frank S. Murray. 192p. 1979. 3.00x (ISBN 0-910840-79-2). Kingdom.
Standard of Living. Mildred B. Young. 1983. pap. 2.50x (ISBN 0-87574-012-X, 012). Pendle Hill.
Standard Siddur-Prayerbook. 1974. 8.95 (ISBN 0-87306-990-0). Feldheim.
Standard 1982. Ed. by Frank S. Murray. (Sermons Ser.). 192p. 1982. 3.00x (ISBN 0-910840-82-2). Kingdom.
Standard 1983 Termination. Ed. by Frank S. Murray. (Sermons Ser.). 192p. 1983. 3.00x (ISBN 0-910840-83-0). Kingdom.
Standards for Church & Synagogue Libraries. LC 77-6634. (Guide Ser.: No. 6). 1977. pap. 4.95x (ISBN 0-915324-12-1); pap. 3.95 members. CSLA.
Standards for Living. Larry L. Benz. LC 77-70791. 1977. pap. 1.99 (ISBN 0-87148-779-9). Pathway Pr.
Standards of Success. Teresina R. Havens. 1983. pap. 2.50x (ISBN 0-87574-043-X, 043). Pendle Hill.
Standing & Understanding: A Re-Appraisal of the Christian Faith. Stanley B. Frost. LC 68-59095. pap. 46.80 (ISBN 0-317-26033-2, 2023834). Bks Demand UMI.
Standing Before God: Studies on Prayer in Scripture & in Essays in Honor of John M. Oesterreicher. Asher Finkel & Lawrence Frizzell. 1981. 39.50x (ISBN 0-87068-708-5). Ktav.
Standing Firm When You'd Rather Retreat. Gene A. Getz. LC 86-429. (Biblical Renewal Ser.). 168p. (Orig.). 1986. pap. 5.95 (ISBN 0-8307-1093-0, 5418594). Regal.
Standing for Their Faith. William Woodson. 1979. 8.95 (ISBN 0-317-39803-2). Gospel Advocate.
Standing on the Rock: The Importance of Biblical Inerrancy. James M. Boice. (Orig.). 1984. leader's guide 2.95 (ISBN 0-8423-6604-0); pap. 4.95 (ISBN 0-8423-6603-2). Tyndale.
Standing Out: Being Real in an Unreal World. Charles R. Swindoll. LC 82-24595. Orig. Title: Home: Where Life Makes Up Its Mind. 105p. 1983. pap. 9.95 (ISBN 0-88070-014-9). Multnomah.
Standing Strong: Notes from Joseph's Journal. Sandy Larsen. (Bible Discovery Guides for Teen Campers Ser.). (Illus.). 32p. (Orig.). (YA) 1986. pap. 1.50 camper (ISBN 0-87788-784-5); pap. 1.50 counselor (ISBN 0-87788-785-3). Shaw Pubs.
Standing Up for Jesus. Wesley T. Runk. 1985. 4.50 (ISBN 0-89536-725-4, 5809). CSS of Ohio.
Standing Up to Preach. Alan Walker. LC 83-72736. 84p. (Orig.). 1983. pap. 3.95 (ISBN 0-88177-005-1, DR005B). Discipleship Res.
Stanley Frodsham: Prophet with a Pen. Faith F. Campbell. LC 74-77406. 1974. pap. 1.25 (ISBN 0-88243-603-1, 02-0603). Gospel Pub.
Stanley Marcus Collection of Christmas Books. Compiled by Mary Hirth. (Illus., Orig.). 1968. pap. 6.00 (ISBN 0-87959-029-7). U of Tex H Ransom Ctr.
Stapleton's Fortress Overthrown: A Rejoinder to Martiall's Reply. William Fulke. Repr. of 1848 ed. 31.00 (ISBN 0-384-17240-7). Johnson Repr.
Star Beams. Etta M. Gibbany. 24p. 1958. pap. 1.50 (ISBN 0-88053-323-4, S-304). Macoy Pub.
Star Book for Ministers. rev. ed. Edward T. Hiscox. 1967. 7.95 (ISBN 0-8170-0167-0). Judson.
Star Gates. Corinne Heline. 7.95 (ISBN 0-933963-09-2). New Age.
Star in the West: A Humble Attempt to Discover the Long Lost Ten Tribes of Israel. facs. ed. Elias Boudinot. LC 79-121499. (Select Bibliographies Reprint Ser). 1816. 17.00 (ISBN 0-8369-5457-2). Ayer Co Pubs.
Star Is Born. Dale Bringman. (Orig.). 1987. pap. price not set (ISBN 0-89536-881-1, 7867). CSS of Ohio.
Star Myths & Stories: From Andromeda to Virgo. Percy M. Proctor. (Illus.). 1972. 8.50 (ISBN 0-682-47470-3, Banner). Exposition Pr FL.
Star of Bethlehem. Frank E. Stranges. 20p. (Orig.). 1985. pap. text ed. 2.00 (ISBN 0-933470-06-1). Intl Evang.
Star of Bethlehem: An Astronomer's Confirmation. David Hughes. (Illus.). 1979. 14.95 (ISBN 0-8027-0644-4). Walker & Co.
Star of Redemption. Franz Rosenzweig. Tr. by William W. Hallo from Ger. LC 84-40833. 464p. 1985. text ed. 30.00 (ISBN 0-268-01717-4, 85-17179); pap. text ed. 12.95 (ISBN 0-268-01718-2, 85-17187). U of Notre Dame Pr.
Star of the West, 8 vols. (Illus.). 544p. Set. 125.00x (ISBN 0-85398-078-0). G Ronald Pub.
Star Wars & the State of Our Souls: Deciding the Future of Planet Earth. Patricia M. Mische. 122p. (Orig.). 1985. pap. 4.95 (ISBN 0-86683-450-8, HarpR). Har-Row.
Star Wheel Technique. Thyrza Escobar. pap. 12.00 (ISBN 0-912368-04-7). Golden Seal.
Star Woman: We Are Made from Stars & to the Stars We Must Return. Lynn V. Andrews. LC 86-40038. 256p. 1986. 16.95 (ISBN 0-446-51316-4). Warner Bks.
Starlore among the Navaho. Berard Haile. LC 76-53085. 1977. lib. bdg. 15.00x (ISBN 0-88307-532-6). Gannon.
Stars & Tears. Chiara Lubich. LC 85-72399. 153p. 1986. pap. 5.25 (ISBN 0-911782-54-0). New City.
Stars for Your Sky. Leonard W. Mann. 1982. pap. 4.95 (ISBN 0-89536-520-0, 1901). CSS of Ohio.
Stars in the Night. Garver. pap. 2.50 (ISBN 0-935120-01-7). Christs Mission.
Stars Speak: Astronomy in the Bible. Stewart Custer. (Illus.). 203p. (Orig.). 1977. pap. 6.95 (ISBN 0-89084-059-8). Bob Jones Univ Pr.
Starseed Transmissions. Ken Carey. 95p. 1986. pap. 6.95 (ISBN 0-913299-29-4, Dist. by NAL). Stillpoint.
Start Digging! Dan Herr. 1987. 9.95 (ISBN 0-88347-204-X). Thomas More.
Starting a Church-Sponsored Weekday Preschool Program: A Manual of Guidance. Ed. by Thomas H. Sauerman & Linda Schomaker. LC 80-14160. 128p. (Orig.). 1980. pap. 6.95 (ISBN 0-8006-1377-5, 1-1377). Fortress.
Starting a Prayer Bank: Deposits & Withdrawals. International Partners to Prayer. 1985. pap. text ed. 1.00 (ISBN 0-917593-09-X, Pub. by Intl Partners). Prosperity & Profits.
Starting on Monday: Christian Living in the Workplace. Christopher Carstens & William P. Mahedy. 176p. 1987. 11.95 (ISBN 0-345-32910-4). Ballantine.
Starting Over. Ernest A. Hirsch. 1977. 8.95 (ISBN 0-8158-0350-8). Chris Mass.
Starting over: Fresh Hope for the Road Ahead. Charles R. Swindoll. LC 82-24636. 1983. pap. 5.95 (ISBN 0-88070-015-7). Multnomah.
Starting over Single: Life & Hope after the Death of a Marriage. Mervin E. Thompson. 160p. 1985. 10.95 (ISBN 0-933173-00-8). Prince Peace Pub.
Starting Right, Staying Strong: A Guide to Effective Ministry. Daniel L. Johnson. LC 82-22383. 108p. (Orig.). 1983. pap. 5.95 (ISBN 0-8298-0648-2). Pilgrim NY.
Startled by Silence. Ruth Senter. 160p. 1985. 10.95 (ISBN 0-310-38840-6, 11227). Zondervan.
State & the Church in a Free Society. Albert V. Murray. LC 77-27134. (Hibbert Lectures: 1957). Repr. of 1958 ed. 27.50 (ISBN 0-404-60433-1). AMS Pr.
State in Catholic Thought: A Treatise in Political Philosophy. Heinrich A. Rommen. Repr. of 1945 ed. lib. bdg. 26.25x (ISBN 0-8371-2437-9, ROCT). Greenwood.
State in Its Relations with the Church. William E. Gladstone. 1196p. Repr. of 1841 ed. text ed. 62.10x (ISBN 0-576-02192-X, Pub. by Gregg Intl Pubs England). Gregg Intl.
State in the Making. David Horowitz. Tr. by Julian Meltzer from Hebrew. LC 81-6649. viii, 349p. 1981. Repr. of 1953 ed. lib. bdg. 28.75x (ISBN 0-313-23011-0, HOSI). Greenwood.
State of Christianity in India - During the Early Nineteenth Century. Abee J. Dabois. 1977. 11.00x (ISBN 0-686-12059-0). Intl Bk Dist.
State of Israel. Israel T. Naamani. LC 79-12757. (Illus.). 1980. pap. 6.95x (ISBN 0-87441-278-1). Behrman.
State of North Carolina vs Christian Liberty. Kent Kelly. 112p. (Orig.). 1978. pap. 2.95 (ISBN 0-9604138-3-9). Calvary Pr.
State of the Church. Andrew Murray. 1983. pap. 2.95 (ISBN 0-87508-407-9). Chr Lit.
State, Religion, & Ethnic Politics: Afghanistan, Iran, & Pakistan. Ed. by Ali Banuazizi & Myron Weiner. (Contemporary Issues in the Middle East Ser.). (Illus.). 464p. 1986. text ed. 35.00x (ISBN 0-8156-2385-2). Syracuse U Pr.
State Without Stakes: Religious Toleration in Reformation Poland. Janusz Tazbir. Tr. by A. T. Jordan. (Library of Polish Studies: Vol. 3). text ed. 4.00 (ISBN 0-917004-05-1). Kosciuszko.
Statement on American Indians. pap. cancelled (ISBN 0-686-15373-1, B-124). US Catholic.
Stations of the Cross. Laurel Rooney. 1984. 9.95 (ISBN 0-89837-094-9, Pub. by Pflaum Press). Peter Li.
Stations of the Cross of Our Lord & Master Jesus Christ. Ermenegildo Panciatichi. (Illus.). 156p. 1987. 88.85 (ISBN 0-86650-211-4). Gloucester Art.
Stature of Waiting. W. H. Vanstone. 128p. (Orig.). 1983. pap. 8.95 (ISBN 0-8164-2478-0, HarpR). Har-Row.
Status of Animals in the Christian Religion. C. W. Hume. 1980. 20.00x (ISBN 0-317-43856-5, Pub. by Univ Federation Animal). State Mutual Bk.
Status of Muslim Women in North India. Roy Shibany. 1979. 21.00x (ISBN 0-8364-0353-3). South Asia Bks.
Status of Woman in Islam. Gamal Badawi. Ed. by Abussamad Al-Jarrahi. Tr. by Muhammad Bekkari from English. (Illus.). 20p. (Orig.). 1982. pap. 2.00 (ISBN 0-89259-036-X). Am Trust Pubns.
Status of Woman in Islam: (French Edition) Gamal A. Badawi. Ed. by Hamid Quinlan. LC 82-74127. (Illus.). 28p. 1983. pap. 0.75 (ISBN 0-89259-039-4). Am Trust Pubns.
Statuta Jancelini Twelve Twenty-Two & the De Reformatione of Prior Bernard Twelve Forty-Eight. James Hogg. (Analecta Cartusiana Ser.: No. 65-2). 162p. (Orig.). 1978. pap. 25.00 (ISBN 3-7052-0096-8, Pub. by Salzburg Studies). Longwood Pub Group.
'Statuta Jancelini' Twelve Twenty-Two & The 'De Reformatione of Prior Bernard Twelve Forty-Eight: A Critical Edition, Vol. 1. James Hogg. (Analecta Cartusiana Ser.: No. 65-1). (Orig.). 1985. pap. 25.00 (ISBN 3-7052-0095-X, Pub. by Salzburg Studies). Longwood Pub Group.
Staupitz Und Luther. Ernst Wolf. (Ger). 34.00 (ISBN 0-384-69019-X); pap. 28.00 (ISBN 0-384-69018-1). Johnson Repr.
Stave Churches in Norway. Roggenkamp. 17.95 (ISBN 0-85440-205-5). Anthroposophic.
Stavronikita Monastery: History-Icons-Embroideries. Christos Patrinelis et al. (Illus.). 241p. 1974. 75.00 (ISBN 0-89241-076-0). Caratzas.
Stay Alive All Your Life. Norman V. Peale. 256p. 1978. pap. 2.25 (ISBN 0-449-23513-0, Crest). Fawcett.
Staying in... John E. Biegert. (Looking Up Ser.). 1985. pap. 1.25 (ISBN 0-8298-0567-2). Pilgrim NY.
Staying on Top When Things Go Wrong. Linda R. Wright. 120p. 1983. pap. 2.95 (ISBN 0-8423-6623-7). Tyndale.
Staying Positive in a Negative World. Roger Campbell. 132p. 1984. pap. 4.95 (ISBN 0-89693-377-6). Victor Bks.
Steadfastness of the Saints: A Journal of Peace & War in Central & North America. Daniel Berrigan. LC 85-5120. 160p. 1985. pap. 7.95 (ISBN 0-88344-447-X). Orbis Bks.

Steady in an Unsteady World. Ed. by Stephen A. Odom. 144p. 1986. pap. 7.95 (ISBN 0-8170-1097-1). Judson.

Stealing. Dan Carr. (God I Need to Talk to You About...Ser.). (Illus.). 1984. pap. 0.75 (ISBN 0-570-08731-7, 56-1475). Concordia.

Stealing of America. John W. Whitehead. LC 83-70320. 180p. 1983. pap. 6.95 (ISBN 0-89107-286-1, Crossway Bks). Good News.

Steel in His Soul: The Dick Hillis Story. Jan Winebrenner. (Orig.). 1985. pap. 7.95 (ISBN 0-8024-2202-0). Moody.

Steeled in Adversity. Salo W. Baron. (Texts & Studies). (Hebrew.). 1977. 15.00 (ISBN 0-911934-15-4). Am Jewish Hist Soc.

Steele's Answers. D. Steele. 6.95 (ISBN 0-686-27781-3). Schmul Pub Co.

Steeple People & the World: Planning for Mission Through the Church. John Killinger. (Orig.). 1977. pap. 2.50 (ISBN 0-377-00059-0). Friend Pr.

Steeple's Shadow: On the Myths & Realities of Secularization. David Lyon. 176p. (Orig.). 1987. pap. 9.95 (ISBN 0-8028-0261-3). Eerdmans.

Stefanesti: Portrait of a Romanian Shtetl. G. Sternberg. (Illus.). 320p. 1984. 30.00 (ISBN 0-08-030840-6). Pergamon.

Steigende Ruhm Miltons. Alfred Gertsch. Repr. of 1927 ed. 54.00 (ISBN 0-384-18230-5). Johnson Repr.

Steiner's Theosophy: Notes on the Book "Theosophy". Carl Unger. 1982. Repr. 5.95 (ISBN 0-916786-64-1). St George Bk Serv.

Step-by-Step: A Cathechetical Handbook for the RCIA. Mary T. Malone. 1986. pap. 19.95 (ISBN 0-697-02204-8). Wm C Brown.

Step by Step in the Jewish Religion. Isadore Epstein. 143p. 1958. pap. 4.95 (ISBN 0-900689-12-9). Soncino Pr.

Step by Step in the Jewish Religion. Isidore Epstein. PLB 4.95x. Bloch.

Step-by-Step Through the Bible: Puzzles, Quizzes & Writing Experiences for Teaching Important Biblical Passages. J. Louise Gustafson & Christine L. Poziemski. (Learning Connections Ser.). 160p. (Orig.). 1984. pap. 9.95 (ISBN 0-86683-835-X, 8442, HarpR). Har-Row.

Step by Step Through the Parables. John W. Miller. LC 81-80046. 176p. (Orig.). 1981. pap. 7.95 (ISBN 0-8091-2379-7). Paulist Pr.

Step Further. 2nd ed. Joni Eareckson & Steve Estes. (Illus.). 192p. 1980. pap. 5.95 (ISBN 0-310-23971-0, 12007P). Zondervan.

Step Further. Joni Eareckson & Steve Estes. 192p. 1982. pap. 3.95 (ISBN 0-310-23972-9, 12008P). Zondervan.

Step I Have Taken. E. Dennett. Ed. by R. P. Daniel. 53p. pap. 3.50 (ISBN 0-88172-140-9). Believers Bkshelf.

Step into Heaven, Here & Now: The Acrobatics of Soul. Ron Kurz. 48p. (Orig.). 1986. pap. 4.95 (ISBN 0-939829-00-2). R Kurz.

Step One: The Gospel & the Ghetto. Harv Oostdyk. 342p. 1983. pap. 8.95 (ISBN 0-89221-094-X). New Leaf.

Step out in Ministry! Carol Crook. LC 86-71831. 203p. (Orig.). 1986. pap. 9.95 (ISBN 0-939399-07-5). Bks of Truth.

Stephanie. John Benton. 1983. pap. 2.95 (ISBN 0-8007-8472-3, Spire Bks). Revell.

Stephen: A Singular Saint. Martin N. Scharkemann. 207p. 1968. write for info. Concordia Schl Grad Studies.

Stephen of Sawley: Treatises. Ed. by Bede K. Lackner. Tr. by Jeremiah F. O'Sullivan. 1984. 24.95 (ISBN 0-87907-636-4). Cistercian Pubns.

Stephen's Defense & Martyrdom. Gordon Lindsay. (Acts in Action Ser.: Vol. 2). pap. 1.25 (ISBN 0-89985-963-1). Christ Nations.

Stepping Heavenward. Elizabeth Prentiss. pap. 6.95 (ISBN 0-685-99369-8). Reiner.

Stepping Heavenward. 1967. 0.50 (ISBN 0-686-05837-2). Crusade Pubs.

Stepping Out on Faith. Elmer Towns & Jerry Falwell. 192p. 1984. pap. 6.95 (ISBN 0-8423-6626-1). Tyndale.

Stepping Out, Sharing Christ in Everyday Circumstances. Margaret Rockwell. LC 84-47804. 134p. 1984. pap. 5.95 (ISBN 0-89840-072-4). Heres Life.

Stepping Stones. Dorothy E. Watts. Ed. by Raymond Woolsey. (Morning Watch Ser.). 384p. 1987. text ed. price not set (ISBN 0-8280-0384-X). Review & Herald.

Stepping Stones for Boys & Girls. Margaret M. Stevens. (Illus.). 1977. pap. 3.00 (ISBN 0-87516-248-7). De Vorss.

Stepping Stones: Meditations in a Garden. Lillian Marshall. (Illus.). 64p. 1984. 4.95 (ISBN 0-88088-506-8). Peter Pauper.

Stepping Stones of Faith. rev. ed. Donald R. Gilmore. 88p. 1987. price not set (ISBN 0-9617810-0-9). D R Gilmore.

Stepping Stones to Further Jewish-Christian Relations: An Unabridged Collection of Christian Documents. Helga Croner. 157p. pap. 10.00 (ISBN 0-686-95183-2). ADL.

Stepping Stones to Further Jewish Relations. Ed. by Helga Croner. 7.95. Paulist Pr.

Stepping Up in Faith. Jack W. Hayford. LC 84-80748. (Orig.). 1984. pap. 2.95 (ISBN 0-916847-02-0). Living Way.

Steps Along the Way: The Path of Spiritual Reading. Susan Muto. 4.95 (ISBN 0-87193-048-X). Dimension Bks.

Steps Heavenward. R. L. Berry. 123p. pap. 1.00 (ISBN 0-686-29142-5). Faith Pub Hse.

Steps in Self-Knowledge. Leddy Schmelig & Randolph Schmelig. LC 79-64038. 1979. 5.95 (ISBN 0-87159-144-8). Unity School.

Steps into the Mission Field. Sao Paulo, Brazil Mission Team. 1978. 5.95 (ISBN 0-88027-019-5). Firm Foun Pub.

Steps on the Stairway. Ralph Ransom. LC 81-66408. 96p. 1981. 8.95 (ISBN 0-8119-0424-5). Fell.

Steps to Christ. Ellen G. White. LC 56-7169. 134p. 1956. 6.95 (ISBN 0-8163-0045-3, 19543-8); pap. 1.25 (ISBN 0-8163-0046-1, 19547-9). Pacific Pr Pub Assn.

Steps to Getting Overseas. John Gration. 38p. (Orig.). 1986. pap. 1.95 (ISBN 0-87784-203-5). Inter-Varsity.

Steps to Jesus. Ellen G. White. 128p. 1980. 6.95 (ISBN 0-8127-0316-2); pap. 3.25 (ISBN 0-8127-0318-9). Review & Herald.

Steps to Life. Lynn Anderson. (Twentieth Century Sermons Ser.). 1977. 11.95 (ISBN 0-89112-310-5, Bibl Res Pr). Abilene Christ U.

Steps to Prayer Power. Jo Kimmel. (Festival Bks.). 1976. pap. 5.95 (ISBN 0-687-39339-6). Abingdon.

Steps to the Sermon. Henry C. Brown, Jr. et al. LC 63-19068. 1963. 12.95 (ISBN 0-8054-2103-3). Broadman.

Steps Toward Inner Peace: Suggested Uses of Harmonious Principles for Human Living. Peace Pilgrim. (Illus.). 36p. 1987. pap. 2.50 leatherette (ISBN 0-943734-07-X). Ocean Tree Bks.

Steve Bartkowski: Intercepted: A Game Plan for Spiritual Growth. Dan DeHaan. (Illus.). 160p. 1981. pap. 5.95 (ISBN 0-8007-5075-6, Power Bks). Revell.

Steve Paxon: Can't Lose for Winning. Ethel Barrett. LC 84-26238. 1985. pap. 4.95 (ISBN 0-8307-1022-1, 5418424). Regal.

Stewards of Creation. Jerry Schmalenberger. (Orig.). 1987. pap. price not set (ISBN 0-89536-894-3, 7880). CSS of Ohio.

Stewards of God. Edward J. Higgins. 1984. 3.25 (ISBN 0-86544-022-0). Salv Army Suppl South.

Stewards of God. Milo Kauffman. LC 74-13130. 264p. 1975. 9.95 (ISBN 0-8361-1747-6). Herald Pr.

Stewards of God's Grace. Siegfried Grossman. 192p. (Orig.). 1981. pap. text ed. 8.95 (ISBN 0-85364-287-7). Attic Pr.

Stewards of the Mysteries of God: Group Leader's Guide. Michael L. Sherer. 1985. 2.50 (ISBN 0-89536-780-7, 5831). CSS of Ohio.

Stewards of the Mysteries of God: Master Planning Guide. Michael L. Sherer. 1985. 1.75 (ISBN 0-89536-779-3, 5830). CSS of Ohio.

Stewards of the Mysteries of God: Worship Resources. Michael L. Sherer. 1985. 2.75 (ISBN 0-89536-781-5, 5832). CSS of Ohio.

Stewardship Enlistment & Commitment. Raymond B. Knudsen. 130p. 1985. pap. 8.95 (ISBN 0-8192-1371-3). Morehouse.

Stewardship: Lessons from the Bible. Gerald Oliver. LC 84-62421. write for info. (ISBN 0-9614316-0-1). Natl Inst Phil.

Stewardship of Creation: Basic Resource Guide. 96p. pap. 6.45 (ISBN 0-664-24489-0). Westminster.

Stewardship of Creation: Guide for Older Youth. 32p. Pack of 10. pap. 31.50 (ISBN 0-664-24492-0). Westminster.

Stewardship of Creation: Guide for Younger Youth. 32p. Pack of 10. pap. 31.50 (ISBN 0-664-24491-2). Westminster.

Stewardship of Creation: Introductory Kit. Set of Four Guides. pap. 14.50 (ISBN 0-664-24560-9). Westminster.

Stewardship Preaching. Mark Gravrock. (Ser. B). 56p. (Orig.). 1984. pap. 4.95 (ISBN 0-8066-2076-5, 10-6002). Augsburg.

Stewardship Preaching: Series C. Richard H. Foege. 56p. (Orig.). 1985. pap. 4.95 (ISBN 0-8066-2152-4, 10-6003). Augsburg.

Stewardship Source Book. Robert Shannon & Michael Shannon. 160p. 1987. pap. price not set (ISBN 0-87403-250-4, 3180). Standard Pub.

Stewardship: Taking Care of God's World. Sarah Fletcher. (Illus.). 1984. pap. 3.95 (ISBN 0-570-04106-6, 56-1498). Concordia.

Stewardship, the Divine Order. Genieve DeHoyos. LC 81-82055. 200p. 1982. 6.95 (ISBN 0-88290-191-5, 1065). Horizon Utah.

Stewardship: Total Life Commitment. R. Leonard Carroll. 144p. 1967. pap. 4.25 (ISBN 0-87148-755-1). Pathway Pr.

Stickhandling & Passing. Paul J. Deegan. LC 76-8444. (Sports Instruction Ser.). (Illus.). 1976. PLB 8.95 (ISBN 0-87191-520-0); pap. 3.95 (ISBN 0-686-67437-5). Creative Ed.

Sticking Together: Friendships for Life. Sandy Larsen. (Bible Discovery Guides for Teen Campers Ser.). 32p. (Orig.). (YA) 1987. pap. 1.50 camper (ISBN 0-87788-787-X); pap. 1.50 counselor (ISBN 0-87788-788-8). Shaw Pubs.

Stiftungen-Buch der Cistercienser-Klosters Zwetl. Zwetl, Austria (Cistercian Monastery) xvi, 736p. Repr. of 1851 ed. 62.00 (ISBN 0-384-71300-9). Johnson Repr.

Stigmata & Modern Science. Charles M. Carty. 31p. 1974. pap. 0.65 (ISBN 0-89555-104-7). TAN Bks Pubs.

Still Forest Pool. Jack Kornfield & Paul Breiter. LC 85-40411. (Illus.). 225p. (Orig.). 1985. pap. 6.50 (ISBN 0-8356-0597-3, Quest). Theos Pub Hse.

Still Full of Sap, Still Green. Alfred H. Deutsch. LC 79-21558. 130p. 1979. pap. 2.50 (ISBN 0-8146-1051-X). Liturgical Pr.

Still Higher for His Highest. Oswald Chambers. 192p. 1970. 6.95 (ISBN 0-87508-142-8). Chr Lit.

Still Higher for His Highest. Oswald Chambers. LC 75-120048. 1970. Repr. of 1970 ed. 8.95 (ISBN 0-310-22410-1, 6494); large print 6.95 (ISBN 0-310-22417-9, 12565L). Zondervan.

Still Hour. Austin Phelps. 1979. pap. 3.45 (ISBN 0-85151-202-X). Banner of Truth.

Still in the Image: Essays in Biblical Theology & Anthrpology. Waldemar Janzen. LC 82-83886. (Institute of Mennonite Studies: No.6). 226p. (Orig.). 1982. pap. 10.95 (ISBN 0-87303-076-1). Faith & Life.

Still More Seasonings for Sermons, Vol. 3. Phil Barnhart. 1986. 7.50 (ISBN 0-89536-787-4, 6805). CSS of Ohio.

Still Point: Reflections on Zen & Christian Mysticism. William Johnston. LC 75-95713. 1986. pap. 9.00 (ISBN 0-8232-0861-3). Fordham.

Still Proclaiming Your Wonders: Homilies for the Eighties. Walter J. Burghardt. 256p. (Orig.). 1984. pap. 9.95 (ISBN 0-8091-2632-X). Paulist Pr.

Stilmittel Bei Afrath, Dem Perischen Weisen. Leo Haefeli. (Ger). 1932. 19.00 (ISBN 0-384-20710-3). Johnson Repr.

Stimulating Devotions for Church Groups. Amy Bolding. 144p. 1986. pap. 4.95 (ISBN 0-8010-0921-9). Baker Bk.

Stoic, Christian & Humanist. Gilbert Murray. LC 75-99712. (Essay Index Reprint Ser.). 1940. 17.00 (ISBN 0-8369-1363-9). Ayer Co Pubs.

Stoic Creed. William L. Davidson. Ed. by Gregory Vlastos. LC 78-19341. (Morals & Law in Ancient Greece Ser.). 1979. Repr. of 1907 ed. lib. bdg. 23.00x (ISBN 0-405-11535-0). Ayer Co Pubs.

Stoic Philosophy of Life. Keith Campbell. LC 86-13351. 216p. (Orig.). 1986. lib. bdg. 22.50 (ISBN 0-8191-5529-2); pap. text ed. 12.25 (ISBN 0-8191-5530-6). U Pr of Amer.

Stoics & Sceptics. Edwyn Bevan. Ed. by Gregory Vlastos. LC 78-15852. (Morals & Law in Ancient Greece Ser.). 1979. Repr. of 1913 ed. lib. bdg. 14.00x (ISBN 0-405-11530-X). Ayer Co Pubs.

Stolen Church. A. Ratiu. 192p. 1982. pap. 4.95 (ISBN 0-88264-155-7). Diane Bks.

Stone-Campbell Movement. Leroy Garrett. LC 80-65965. 739p. 1981. 21.95 (ISBN 0-89900-059-2). College Pr Pub.

Stone Circles of the British Isles. Burl. 1976. 46.00x (ISBN 0-300-01972-6); pap. 22.50x (ISBN 0-300-02398-7, Y-341). Yale U Pr.

Stone Cried Out. Shigeo Shimada. 208p. 1986. pap. 7.95 (ISBN 0-8170-1111-0). Judson.

Stone for a Pillow: Journeys with Jacob. Madeleine L'Engle. (Wheaton Literary Ser.). 240p. (Orig.). 1986. 11.95 (ISBN 0-87788-789-6); pap. cancelled. Shaw Pubs.

Stone Made Smooth. Wong Ming Dao. 1982. pap. 5.95 (ISBN 0-907821-00-6). OMF Bks.

Stone Power II: The Legendary & Practical Use of Gems & Stones. Dorothee I. Mella. Orig. Title: Stone Power, The Legendary & Practical Use of Gems & Stones. (Illus.). 164p. (Orig.). 1986. pap. 11.95 (ISBN 0-914732-18-8). Bro Life Inc.

Stone Soup. Marcia Brown. (Illus.). 1947. 12.95 (ISBN 0-684-92296-7, Pub. by Scribner); pap. 5.95 (ISBN 0-684-16217-2, Pub. by Scribner). Macmillan.

Stone Turning into Star: Prayer & Meditations for Lent. Joan A. Shelton. 168p. (Orig.). 1986. pap. 5.95 (ISBN 0-8091-2736-9). Paulist Pr.

Stonehenge, a Temple Restored to the British Druids; Abury, a Temple of the British Druids. William Stukeley. Ed. by Burton Feldman & Robert D. Richardson. LC 78-60898. (Myth & Romanticism Ser.). 1984. lib. bdg. 80.00 (ISBN 0-8240-3572-0). Garland Pub.

Stonehenge: An Ancient Masonic Temple. rev., enl. ed. Russell A. Herner. LC 83-63526. (Illus.). 160p. 1984. text ed. 15.95 (ISBN 0-88053-077-4). Macoy Pub.

Stonehenge & Druidism. rev. ed. E. Raymond Capt. LC 79-54773. (Illus.). 96p. 1979. pap. 3.00 (ISBN 0-934666-04-0). Artisan Sales.

Stonehenge Complete: Archaeology, History, Heritage. Christopher Chippindale. LC 83-70803. (Illus.). 300p. 1983. 32.50 (ISBN 0-8014-1639-6). Cornell U Pr.

Stones & the Scriptures. Edwin Yamauchi. 1981. pap. 5.95 (ISBN 0-8010-9916-1). Baker Bk.

Stones Cry Out: Sweden's Response to Persecution of the Jews 1933-1945. Steven Koblik. 1987. 20.95 (ISBN 0-89604-118-2); pap. 13.95 (ISBN 0-89604-119-0). Holocaust Pubns.

Stones of Fire. Isobel Kuhn. 1951. pap. 3.95 (ISBN 9971-972-00-X). OMF Bks.

Stop Making Yourself Sick. Harold Adolph & David L. Bourne. 132p. 1986. pap. 4.95 (ISBN 0-89693-325-3). Victor Bks.

Storia Critico Chronologica Diplomatica del Patriarca S. Brunone e del Suo Ordine Cartusiano, 2 pts, Vol. 1. Benedetto Tromby. Ed. by James Hogg. (Analecta Cartusiana Ser.: No. 84-1). 523p. (Orig.). 1981. pap. 50.00 (ISBN 3-7052-0131-X, Pub. by Salzburg Stiudies). Longwood Pub Group.

Storia Critico Chronologica Diplomatica del Patriarca S. Brunone e del Suo Ordine Cartusiano, 2 pts, Vol. 3. Benedetto Tromby. Ed. by James Hogg. (Analecta Cartusiana Ser.: No. 84-3). 522p. 1982. pap. 50.00 (ISBN 3-7052-0133-6, Pub. by Salzburg Studies). Longwood Pub Group.

Storia Critico-Chronologica-Diplomatica del Patriarca S. Brunone E Del Suo Ordine Cartusiano, Vol. 4 (2 pts.) Benedetto Tromby. Ed. by James Hogg. (Analecta Cartusiana Ser.: No. 84-4). 632p. (Orig.). 1982. pap. 50.00 (ISBN 3-7052-0134-4, Pub. by Salzburg Studies). Longwood Pub Group.

Storia Critico-Chronologica-Diplomatica del Patriarca S. Brunone E. del Suo Ordine Cartusiano, 2 pts, Vol. 6. Benedetto Tromby. Ed. by James Hogg. (Analecta Cartusiana Ser.: No. 84/6). 632p. (Orig.). 1982. pap. 50.00 (ISBN 3-7052-0136-0, Pub. by Salzburg Studies). Longwood Pub Group.

Storia Critico-Chronologica-Diplomatica del Patriarca S. Brunone E del Suo Ordine Cartusiano, 2 pts, Vol. 7. Benedetto Tromby. Ed. by James Hogg. (Analecta Cartusiana Ser.: No. 84/7). 637p. (Orig.). 1982. pap. 50.00 (ISBN 3-7052-0137-9, Pub. by Salzburg Studies). Longwood Pub Group.

Storia Critico-Chronologica-Diplomatica del Patriarca S. Brunone E del Suo Ordine Carusiano, 2 pts, Vol. 8. Benedetto Tromby. Ed. by James Hogg. (Analecta Cartusiana: No. 84-8). 574p. (Orig.). 1982. pap. 50.00 (ISBN 3-7052-0138-7, Pub. by Salzburg Studies). Longwood Pub Group.

Storia-Critico-Chronologica-Diplomatica del Patriarca S. Brunone E. del Suo Cartusiano, 2 pts, Vol. 9. Benedetto Tromby. Ed. by James Hogg. (Analecta Cartusiana: No. 84-9). 638p. (Orig.). 1982. pap. 50.00 (ISBN 3-7052-0139-5, Pub. by Salzburg Studies). Longwood Pub Group.

Storia Critico-Chronologica-Diplomatica del Patriarca S. Brunone E. del Suo Ordine Cartusiano, 3 pts, Vol. 10. Benedetto Tromby. Ed. by James Hogg. (Analecta Cartusiana Ser.: No. 84-10). 730p. (Orig.). 1982. pap. 85.00 (ISBN 3-7052-0140-9, Pub. by Salzburg Studies). Longwood Pub Group.

Storia Critico-Chronologica-Diplomatica del Patriarca S. Brunone E. del Suo Ordine Cartusiano, Vol. 11. Benedetto Tromby. Ed. by James Hogg. (Analecta Cartusiana Ser.: No. 84-11). 31p. (Orig.). 1981. pap. 7.50 (ISBN 3-7052-0141-7, Pub. by Salzburg Studies). Longwood Pub Group.

Stories. Meir Blinkin. Tr. by Max Rosenfeld from Yiddish. (Modern Jewish Literature & Culture Ser.). 166p. 1984. 10.95x (ISBN 0-87395-818-7). State U NY Pr.

Stories About Children of the Bible. Hilda L. Rostron. (Ladybird Ser). (Illus.). 1962. bds. 2.50 (ISBN 0-87508-860-0). Chr Lit.

Stories About Jesus the Friend. Hilda L. Rostron. (Ladybird Ser). (Illus.). 1961. bds. 2.50 (ISBN 0-87508-862-7). Chr Lit.

Stories About Jesus the Helper. Hilda L. Rostron. (Ladybird Ser). (Illus.). 1961. bds. 2.50 (ISBN 0-87508-864-3). Chr Lit.

Stories & Parables. Satguru S. Keshavadas. (Illus.). 100p. 1979. 6.50 (ISBN 0-533-03818-9). Vishwa.

Stories & Parables of the Hafetz Hayyim. David Zaretsky & Charles Wengrov. Orig. Title: Hayyim. 1976. 8.95 (ISBN 0-87306-132-2). Feldheim.

Stories for Communication. Kathy C. Patterson & Phyllis M. Niklaus. Ed. by Communication & Learning Innovators, Ltd. Staff et al. (Bible Ser.). (Illus.). 13p. 1985. 6.00 (ISBN 0-932361-01-3). Comm & Learning.

Stories for Seasonal Festivals. Armandine Kelly. LC 86-62627. 100p. (Orig.). 1987. pap. 7.95 (ISBN 0-89390-096-6). Resource Pubns.

Stories for Telling: A Treasury for Christian Storytellers. William R. White. LC 85-28980. 144p. (Orig.). 1986. pap. 6.95 (10-6023). Augsburg.

Stories from Acts. G. L. LeFevre. (Bible Quiz 'N Tattletotals Ser.). 16p. (Orig.). 1982. pap. 0.98 (ISBN 0-87239-581-2, 2808). Standard Pub.

Stories from Greek Mythology. E. Canstantopoulos. (Illus.). 3.20 (ISBN 0-686-79632-2). Divry.

Stories from Holy Writ. Helen Waddell. LC 74-25538. 280p. 1975. Repr. of 1949 ed. lib. bdg. 22.50x (ISBN 0-8371-7872-X, WAHW). Greenwood.

Stories from Our Living Past. new ed. Francine Prose. Ed. by Jules Harlow. LC 74-8514. (Illus.). 128p. 1974. 6.95x (ISBN 0-87441-081-9). Behrman.

Stories from the Bible. Walter De la Mare. (Illus.). 418p. 1985. pap. 6.95 (ISBN 0-571-11086-X). Faber & Faber.

Stories from the Bible-Newly Retold. Sipke van der Land. LC 79-10049. pap. 51.30 (ISBN 0-317-39654-4, 2023224). Bks Demand UMI.

Stories from The Delight of Hearts: The Memoirs of Haji Mirza Haydar-'Ali. A. Q. Faizi. LC 79-91219. (Illus.). 176p. 1980. 11.95 (ISBN 0-933770-11-1). Kalimat.

Stories from the New Testament. G Polyzoides. (Illus.). 112p. 3.20 (ISBN 0-686-83966-8). Divry.

Stories from the Old Testament. David M. Harralson. (Literacy Volunteers of America Readers Ser.). 48p. (Orig.). 1983. pap. 1.95 (ISBN 0-8428-9607-4). Cambridge Bk.

Stories from the Old Testament. G. Polyzoides. (Gr., Illus.). 71p. 3.20 (ISBN 0-686-80434-1). Divry.

Stories from the Rabbis. Abram S. Isaacs. LC 79-175868. Repr. of 1911 ed. 20.00 (ISBN 0-405-08661-X, Blom Pubns). Ayer Co Pubs.

Stories Jesus Told. Heather Dyer. Incl. The Good Samaritan (ISBN 0-89191-286-X); The Good Shepherd (ISBN 0-89191-283-5); The Great Feast (ISBN 0-89191-284-3); The House Built on Sand (ISBN 0-89191-288-6); The Prodigal Son (ISBN 0-89191-285-1); The Rich Man (ISBN 0-89191-287-8). (Illus.). 1980. Repr. 2.50 ea. Cook.

Stories Jesus Told. Arthur W. Gross. 1981. 6.95 (ISBN 0-570-04059-0, 56YY1352). Concordia.

Stories Jesus Told. Gladys Hunt. (Fisherman Bible Studyguide Ser.). 96p. (Orig.). pap. 2.95 (ISBN 0-87788-791-8). Shaw Pubs.

Stories Jesus Told. Retold by Elaine Ife & Rosalind Sutton. (Now You Can Read Stories from the Bible Ser.). (Illus.). 24p. 1984. 2.50 (ISBN 0-8407-5395-0). Nelson.

Stories Jesus Told. Rawson Lloyd. (Children's Picture Bible Ser.). 1982. 7.95 (ISBN 0-86020-516-9, Usborne-Hayes); PLB 12.96 (ISBN 0-88110-097-8); pap. 4.95 (ISBN 0-86020-521-5). EDC.

Stories Jesus Told. Patricia Mahany. (Coloring Bks.). (Illus.). 16p. (Orig.). 1982. pap. 0.89 (ISBN 0-87239-601-0, 2390). Standard Pub.

Stories Made of Bible Stories. Abraham Cronbach. 1961. 17.95x (ISBN 0-8084-0386-9). New Coll U Pr.

Stories of Baha'u'llah. Ali-Akbar Furutan. 128p. 1986. 12.95; pap. 5.95. G Ronald Pub.

Stories of Christmas Carols. Ernest K. Emurian. (Paperback Program Ser.). 1969. pap. 4.95 (ISBN 0-8010-3265-2). Baker Bk.

Stories of Don Bosco. 2nd ed. Peter Lappin. LC 78-72525. (Illus.). 1979. pap. 2.95 (ISBN 0-89944-036-3). Don Bosco Multimedia.

Stories of Faith. John Shea. 1980. pap. 9.95 (ISBN 0-88347-112-4). Thomas More.

Stories of God: An Unauthorized Biography. John Shea. 1978. pap. 8.95 (ISBN 0-88347-085-3). Thomas More.

Stories of Great Muslims. K. H. Hayes. 4.75 (ISBN 0-686-18389-4). Kazi Pubns.

Stories of Great Muslims. Date not set. 4.00 (ISBN 0-89259-020-3). Am Trust Pubns.

Stories of Home Folks. Mabel Hale. 160p. pap. 1.50 (ISBN 0-686-29143-3). Faith Pub Hse.

Stories of Jesus. Vera R. Jones. 1983. 6.95 (ISBN 0-8062-2242-5). Carlton.

Stories of Jesus, Stories of Now. Alexander Campbell. 80p. (Orig.). 1980. pap. 12.95 (ISBN 0-940754-04-5). Ed Ministries.

Stories of Jesus, Tell Them to Me. P. Gwyn Filby. 200p. 1986. 45.00x (ISBN 0-947939-01-6, Pub. by Elmcrest UK). State Mutual Bk.

Stories of King David. Lillian S. Freehof. (Illus.). 1952. 5.95 (ISBN 0-8276-0162-X, 263). Jewish Pubns.

Stories of Lost Israel in Folklore. James A. Haggart. LC 80-65735. 144p. 1981. pap. 5.00 (ISBN 0-934666-08-3). Artisan Sales.

Stories of Love that Lasts. Don W. Hillis. 80p. 1980. pap. 1.25 (ISBN 0-89323-015-4). Bible Memory.

Stories of Maasaw, a Hopi God. Ekkehart Malotki & Michael Lomatuway'ma. LC 87-164. (American Tribal Religions Ser.: Vol. 10). (Illus.). vi, 388p. 1987. 23.95x (ISBN 0-8032-3117-2); pap. 13.95x (ISBN 0-8032-8147-1). U of Nebr Pr.

Stories of Mother Teresa: Her Smile & Her Words. Jose L. Balado. Tr. by Olimpia Diaz from Span. 96p. 1983. pap. 2.95 (ISBN 0-89243-181-4). Liguori Pubns.

Stories of Our Favorite Hymns. Christopher Idle. (Illus.). 80p. 1980. 12.95 (ISBN 0-8028-3535-X). Eerdmans.

Stories of Some of the Prophets, Vol. I. A. S. Hashim. (Islamic Books for Children: Bk. 8). pap. 4.95 (ISBN 0-686-18402-5); pap. 45.00 entire series (ISBN 0-686-18403-3). Kazi Pubns.

Stories of Some of the Prophets, Vol II. A. S. Hashim. (Islamic Books for Children: Bk. 9). pap. 4.95 (ISBN 0-686-18400-9); pap. 45.00 entire series (ISBN 0-686-18401-7). Kazi Pubns.

Stories of the Buddha. Intro. by C. Rhys Davids. LC 78-72444. Repr. of 1929 ed. 30.00 (ISBN 0-404-17316-0). AMS Pr.

Stories of the Gods & Heroes. Sally Benson. (Illus.). 1940. 12.95 (ISBN 0-8037-8291-8, 01258-370). Dial Bks Young.

Stories of the Greeks. Rex Warner. 480p. 1978. 15.00 (ISBN 0-374-27056-2); pap. 9.95 (ISBN 0-374-50728-7). FS&G.

Stories of the Holy Fathers, 2 vols. Anan Isho. Tr. by E. A. Budge. 1980. Set. lib. bdg. 125.00 (ISBN 0-8490-3195-8). Gordon Pr.

Stories That Live, 6 vols. Peter Enns & Glen Forsberg. (Series I). (Illus.). 144p. 1985. books & cassettes 29.70 (ISBN 0-936215-00-3). STL Intl.

Stories to Learn by. John Koenig. (Illus.). 5.00 (ISBN 0-8198-0333-2); pap. 4.00 (ISBN 0-8198-0334-0). Dghtrs St Paul.

Stories to See & Share. Maline C. Crockett. 80p. 1980. pap. 4.50 (ISBN 0-87747-828-7). Deseret Bk.

Stories to Tell in Children's Church. Velma B. Kiefer. (Paperback Program Ser.). Orig. Title: Please Tell Me a Story. 1976. pap. 5.95 (ISBN 0-8010-5371-4). Baker Bk.

Stories We Love, Vol. 2. Jon L. Joyce. (Orig.). 1983. pap. 14.95 (ISBN 0-937172-52-9). JLJ Pubs.

Storm over the Sutlej: The Sikhs & Akali Politics. A. S. Narang. 1983. 24.00x (ISBN 0-8364-1079-3, Gitanjali). South Asia Bks.

Stormie. Stormie Omartian. 224p. (Orig.). 1986. pap. 6.95 (ISBN 0-89081-556-9). Harvest Hse.

Storming Eastern Temples. Lucindi F. Mooney. LC 76-4903. 1976. 9.75x (ISBN 0-8356-0482-9). Theos Pub Hse.

Story. Catherine Booth. pap. 3.95 (ISBN 0-686-27773-2). Schmul Pub Co.

Story. Ed. by Ted Miller. 400p. 1986. 4.95 (ISBN 0-8423-6677-6). Tyndale.

Story About Light. Maxine C. Wight. LC 79-14691. 1979. 1.99 (ISBN 0-8309-0236-8). Herald Hse.

Story & Faith: A Guide to the Old Testament. James L. Crenshaw. 539p. 1986. text ed. write for info. (ISBN 0-02-325600-1). Macmillan.

Story As Told. rev. ed. Jalil Mahmoudi. LC 79-65925. (Illus.). 80p. (Orig.). 1980. pap. 4.95 (ISBN 0-933770-10-3). Kalimat.

Story Bible for Young Children. Anne De Vries. (Illus.). 1986. pap. 9.95 (ISBN 0-8010-2963-5). Baker Bk.

Story Bible: New Testament, Vol. 2. Pearl S. Buck. 1972. pap. 3.95 (ISBN 0-451-14639-5, AE2694, Sig). NAL.

Story Bible: Old Testament, Vol. 1. Pearl S. Buck. 1972. pap. 3.95 (ISBN 0-451-13458-3, Sig). NAL.

Story, Myth & Celebration in Old French Narrative Poetry 1050-1200. Karl D. Uitti. LC 72-4048. 272p. 1973. 30.50x (ISBN 0-691-06242-0). Princeton U Pr.

Story of a Soul: The Autobiography of St. Therese of Lisieux. Tr. by John Clarke from Fr. LC 76-43620. 1976. pap. 6.95x (ISBN 0-9600876-4-8). ICS Pubns.

Story of Adam & Eve. Gordon Lindsay. (Old Testament Ser.). 1.25 (ISBN 0-89985-124-X). Christ Nations.

Story of Albert J. Iva Hamilton. (Illus., Orig.). 1985. pap. 6.95 (ISBN 0-87418-028-7, 162). Coleman Pub.

Story of Ancient Egypt. George Rawlinson. 1887. Repr. 50.00 (ISBN 0-8482-5897-5). Norwood Edns.

Story of Atlantis & the Lost Lemuria. Scott Elliott. 8.95 (ISBN 0-8356-5509-1). Theos Pub Hse.

Story of Baby Jesus. Marian Bennett. (Illus.). 24p. (Orig.). 1983. pap. 0.49 (ISBN 0-87239-654-1, 2124). Standard Pub.

Story of Baby Jesus. Alice J. Davidson. (Alice in Bibleland Ser.). (Illus.). 32p. 1985. 4.95 (ISBN 0-8378-5072-X). Gibson.

Story of Baby Moses. Alice J. Davidson. (Alice in Bibleland Ser.). (Illus.). 32p. 1985. 4.95 (ISBN 0-8378-5071-1). Gibson.

Story of Baucis & Philemon. Pamela Espeland. LC 80-27674. (Myth for Modern Children Ser.). (Illus.). 32p. 1981. PLB 6.95 (ISBN 0-87614-140-8). Carolrhoda Bks.

Story of Billy McCarrell. Dorothy Martin. 160p. (Orig.). 1983. pap. 3.95 (ISBN 0-8024-0519-3). Moody.

Story of Birthright: The Alternative to Abortion. Louise Summerhill. LC 72-96117. 1973. pap. 3.50 (ISBN 0-913382-06-X, 101-4). Prow Bks-Franciscan.

Story of Brother Francis. Lene Mayer-Skumanz. Tr. by Hildegard Bomer from Ger. LC 83-71779. (Illus.). 48p. (Orig.). 1983. pap. 6.95 (ISBN 0-87793-307-3). Ave Maria.

Story of Buddha. Jonathan Landaw. (Illus.). 1979. 7.50 (ISBN 0-89744-140-0). Auromere.

Story of Buddhism. K. J. Saunders. 69.95 (ISBN 0-8490-1129-9). Gordon Pr.

Story of Cadmus. Pamela Espeland. LC 80-66795. (Myths for Modern Children Ser.). (Illus.). 32p. 1980. PLB 6.95 (ISBN 0-87614-128-9). Carolrhoda Bks.

Story of Canterbury. George R. Taylor. LC 78-63479. (Illus.). Repr. of 1912 ed. 38.50 (ISBN 0-404-16545-1). AMS Pr.

Story of Catholics in America. Ed. by Don Brophy & Edythe Westenhaver. 3.95 (ISBN 0-8091-2087-9). Paulist Pr.

Story of Chanukah for Children. 2.95 (ISBN 0-8249-8020-4). Ideals.

Story of Christian Origins. Martin A. Larson. LC 76-40842. 1977. 12.50 (ISBN 0-88331-090-2). J J Binns.

Story of Christianity. Justo Gonzalez. LC 83-49187. (Reformation to the Present Day Ser.: Vol. II). (Illus.). 448p. (Orig.). 1984. pap. 13.95 kivar cover (ISBN 0-06-063316-6, RD 511, HarpR). Har-Row.

Story of Christianity, Volume 1: The Early Church to the Reformation. Justo L. Gonzalez. LC 83-48430. (Illus.). 448p. (Orig.). 1983. pap. 13.95 (ISBN 0-317-01107-3, RD 510, HarpR). Har-Row.

Story of Christmas. R. J. Campbell. 1977. lib. bdg. 59.95 (ISBN 0-8490-2677-6). Gordon Pr.

Story of Christmas. Manly P. Hall. pap. 2.50 (ISBN 0-89314-379-0). Philos Res.

Story of Christmas. Felix Hoffman. LC 75-6921. (Illus.). 32p. 1975. 6.95 (ISBN 0-689-50031-9, McElderry Bk). Macmillan.

Story of Christmas for Children. Catharine Brandt. LC 74-79366. (Illus.). 20p. (Orig.). 1974. pap. 5.95 (ISBN 0-8066-2030-7, 10-6041). Augsburg.

Story of Christmas for Children. 32p. pap. 2.95 (ISBN 0-89542-454-1). Ideals.

Story of Church Unity: The Lambeth Conference of Anglican Bishops & the Congregational-Episcopal Approaches. Norman Smyth. 1923. 29.50x (ISBN 0-686-83788-6). Elliots Bks.

Story of Confucius & of the Other Great Chinese Mystics, 3 vols. L. A. Beck. (Illus.). 241p. 1986. Set. 187.75 (ISBN 0-89901-274-4). Found Class Reprints.

Story of Creation. Alice J. Davidson. (Alice in Bibleland Storybooks). (Illus.). 32p. 1984. 4.95 (ISBN 0-8378-5066-5). Gibson.

Story of Daniel. Lucy Diamond. (Ladybird Ser). (Illus.). 1958. bds. 2.50 (ISBN 0-87508-866-X). Chr Lit.

Story of Daniel & the Lions. Alice J. Davidson. (Alice in Bibleland Ser.). 32p. 1986. 4.95 (ISBN 0-8378-5079-7). Gibson.

Story of David & Goliath. Alice J. Davidson. (Alice in Bibleland Ser.). (Illus.). 32p. 1985. 4.95 (ISBN 0-8378-5070-3). Gibson.

Story of Deborah. Constance Head. (Arch Bk Ser.: No. 15). (Illus.). 1978. 0.99 (ISBN 0-570-06116-4, 59-1234). Concordia.

Story of Easter for Children. Beverly Wiersum. Ed. by James A. Kuse. (Illus.). 1979. pap. 2.95 (ISBN 0-89542-452-5). Ideals.

Story of God's Love. Elizabeth Friedrich. 144p. 1985. 9.95 (ISBN 0-570-04122-8, 56-1533). Concordia.

Story of God's People. Clarence Y. Fretz. (Christian Day School Ser). pap. 5.90x (ISBN 0-87813-900-1); tchrs. guide 6.95x (ISBN 0-87813-901-X). Christian Light.

Story of Guru Nanak. Mala Singh. (Illus.). 1979. 6.25 (ISBN 0-89744-138-9). Auromere.

Story of Hanukkah. Charles Wengrov. (Holiday Ser.). (Illus.). 1965. pap. 1.50 (ISBN 0-914080-52-0). Shulsinger Sales.

Story of Human Evolution. Barborka. 8.95 (ISBN 0-8356-7550-5). Theos Pub Hse.

Story of Hymns & Tunes. Hezekiah Butterworth. 1981. Repr. lib. bdg. 79.00x (ISBN 0-403-00107-2). Scholarly.

Story of Islamic Culture. A. Rauf. 1981. 2.50 (ISBN 0-686-97868-4). Kazi Pubns.

Story of Jacob, Rachel & Leah. Yvonne H. McCall. (Arch Bks.). (Illus.). 24p. 1986. pap. 0.99 saddlestitched (ISBN 0-570-06205-5, 59-1428). Concordia.

Story of Jesus. Mary P. Smith. (Illus.). 32p. (Orig.). 1980. pap. 1.95 (ISBN 0-87516-420-X). De Vorss.

Story of Jesus Pop-Up Book. (Pop-Up Bks.). (Illus.). 1.98 (ISBN 0-517-43888-7). Outlet Bk Co.

Story of Jesus the Messiah: Acts & Letters. Julian G. Anderson. (New Testament Wkbk.). (Illus.). 1979. pap. text ed. 3.95 (ISBN 0-9602128-3-3). Anderson Publ.

Story of Jesus the Messiah, Four Gospels. Julian G. Anderson. LC 76-52054. (Life of Christ Wkbk). (Illus.). 1977. pap. 3.95 (ISBN 0-9602128-1-7). Anderson Publ.

Story of Jesus the Messiah, Old Testament. Julian G. Anderson. (Old Testament Wkbk). (Illus.). 1977. pap. 3.95 (ISBN 0-9602128-2-5). Anderson Publ.

Story of Jewish Philosophy. Joseph L. Blau. 8.95x (ISBN 0-87068-174-5). Ktav.

Story of Job. Adapted by & illus. by Beverley Brodsky. LC 85-24303. (Illus.). 40p. 14.95 (ISBN 0-8076-1142-5). Braziller.

Story of Job. Jessie Penn-Lewis. 1965. pap. 4.95 (ISBN 0-87508-954-2). Chr Lit.

Story of Job's Beginning. Meir Weiss. 84p. 1983. text ed. 15.00x (ISBN 9-652-23438-9, Pub. by Magnes Pr Israel). Humanities.

Story of Jonah. Alice J. Davidson. (Alice in Bibleland Storybooks). (Illus.). 32p. 1984. 4.95 (ISBN 0-8378-5068-1). Gibson.

Story of Joseph. Lucy Diamond. (Ladybird Ser). (Illus.). 1954. bds. 2.50 (ISBN 0-87508-868-6). Chr Lit.

Story of Joseph. 79p. pap. 0.50 (ISBN 0-686-29167-0). Faith Pub Hse.

Story of Joy. Sophia Karuna Jemal. (Illus.). 1978. pap. 3.00 (ISBN 0-932286-00-3). Suratao.

Story of Judaism. rev. 3rd ed. Bernard J. Bamberger. LC 64-16463. 1964. pap. 12.95 (ISBN 0-8052-0077-0). Schocken.

Story of Judaism. rev. ed. Bernard J. Bamberger. 1970. 9.95 (ISBN 0-8074-0193-5, 959291). UAHC.

Story of King David: Genre & Interpretation. D. M. Gunn. (Journal for the Study of the Old Testament Supplement Ser.: No. 6). 164p. 1978. (Pub. by JSOT Pr England); pap. text ed. 16.95x (ISBN 0-905774-05-1, Pub. by JSOT Pr England). Eisenbrauns.

Story of King Midas. Pamela Espeland. LC 80-66794. (Myths for Modern Children Ser.). (Illus.). 32p. 1980. PLB 6.95 (ISBN 0-87614-129-7). Carolrhoda Bks.

Story of Krishna. Bani R. Choudhary. (Illus.). 1979. 7.25 (ISBN 0-89744-134-6). Auromere.

Story of Krishna. Bhagat Singh. (Illus.). 20p. (Orig.). 1976. pap. 1.75 (ISBN 0-89744-135-4, Pub. by Hemkunt India). Auromere.

Story of Masada. Raphael Rothstein. (Illus.). 296p. 1983. cancelled (ISBN 0-89961-012-9). SBS Pub.

Story of Milton's Paradise. George Carter. 1909. lib. bdg. 15.00 (ISBN 0-8414-1590-0). Folcroft.

Story of Mohammad the Prophet. Bilzik Alladin. (Illus.). 1979. 7.25 (ISBN 0-89744-139-7). Auromere.

Story of Moody Church. Bob Flood. (Orig.). 1985. pap. 5.95 (ISBN 0-8024-0539-8). Moody.

Story of My Heart. Ali A. Furutan. (Illus.). 272p. 14.95 (ISBN 0-85398-114-0); pap. 8.95 (ISBN 0-85398-115-9). G Ronald Pub.

Story of Myths. Ernst E. Kellett. (Folklore & Society Ser). 1969. Repr. of 1927 ed. 20.00 (ISBN 0-384-29025-6). Johnson Repr.

Story of Noah. Alice J. Davidson. (Alice in Bibleland Storybooks). (Illus.). 32p. 1984. 4.95 (ISBN 0-8378-5067-3). Gibson.

Story of Our Calendar. Ruth Brindze. (Illus.). 1949. 9.95 (ISBN 0-8149-0278-2). Vanguard.

Story of Passover. Charles Wengrov. (Holiday Ser.). (Illus.). 1965. pap. 1.50 (ISBN 0-914080-54-7). Shulsinger Sales.

Story of Passover for Children. Naomi Galbreath. (Illus.). 32p. pap. 2.95 (ISBN 0-8249-8084-0). Ideals.

Story of "Patria". Erich G. Steiner. LC 81-85302. 224p. 1982. 16.95 (ISBN 0-8052-5036-0); pap. 10.95 (ISBN 0-8052-5037-9). Holocaust Pubns.

Story of Paul. James Kallas. LC 66-19206. (Orig.). 1966. pap. 6.95 (ISBN 0-8066-0608-8, 10-6055). Augsburg.

Story of Peter Donders. Costanzo J. Antonellis. 115p. 3.50 (ISBN 0-8198-6834-5, BI0217); pap. 2.50 (ISBN 0-8198-6835-3). Dghtrs St Paul.

Story of Peter the Fisherman. D. S. Hare. (Ladybird Ser). 1970. 2.50 (ISBN 0-87508-867-8). Chr Lit.

Story of Phallicism, with Other Essays on Related Subjects by Eminent Authorities. Lee A. Stone. LC 72-9682. Repr. of 1927 ed. 49.50 (ISBN 0-404-57500-5). AMS Pr.

Story of Prophecy. Hannah G. Goodman. LC 65-24925. 1965. 5.95x (ISBN 0-87441-017-7). Behrman.

Story of Purim. Charles Wengrov. (Holiday Ser.). (Illus.). 1965. pap. 1.50 (ISBN 0-914080-53-9). Shulsinger Sales.

Story of Quakerism. rev. ed. Elfrida Vipont. LC 77-71638. (Illus.). 1977. pap. 9.95 (ISBN 0-913408-31-X). Friends United.

Story of Rabbi Yisroel Salanter. Zalman F. Ury. 3.75 (ISBN 0-914131-60-5, D54). Torah Umesorah.

Story of Ramakrishna. Swami Smaranananda. (Illus., Orig.). 1976. pap. 2.25 (ISBN 0-87481-168-6). Vedanta Pr.

Story of Ramayan. Bani R. Choudhary. (Illus.). 1979. 7.50 (ISBN 0-89744-133-8). Auromere.

Story of Redemption. large print ed. 1980. pap. 7.95 (ISBN 0-8280-0058-1, 19654-3). Review & Herald.

Story of Saint Francis de Sales: Patron of Catholic Writers. Katherine Bregy. 108p. 1982. Repr. of 1958 ed. lib. bdg. 35.00 (ISBN 0-89984-015-9). Century Bookbindery.

Story of St. Paul. D. S. Hare. (Ladybird Ser.). (YA) 1969. pap. 2.50 (ISBN 0-87508-869-4). Chr Lit.

Story of Samson, & Its Place in the Religious Development of Mankind. Paul Carus. 183p. 1907. 1.95 (ISBN 0-317-40420-2). Open Court.

Story of Samuel. Joan Kendall. (Very First Bible Stories Ser.). 1984. 1.59 (ISBN 0-87162-271-8, D8500). Warner Pr.

Story of Shavuot. Charles Wengrov. (Holiday Ser.). (Illus.). 1965. pap. 1.50 (ISBN 0-914080-55-5). Shulsinger Sales.

Story of Silent Night. John Travers Moore. LC 65-19252. 1965. 5.95 (ISBN 0-570-03430-2, 56-1056). Concordia.

Story of Singing Waters. Kay Colbeck & Irene B. Harrell. (Orig.). 1987. pap. 7.00 (ISBN 0-915541-21-1). Star Bks Inc.

Story of Southern Hymnology. Arthur L. Stevenson. LC 72-1676. Repr. of 1931 ed. 17.50 (ISBN 0-404-08334-X). AMS Pr.

Story of Superstition. Philip F. Waterman. LC 78-107770. Repr. of 1929 ed. 15.00 (ISBN 0-404-06849-9). AMS Pr.

Story of Taize. J. L. Balado. (Illus.). 144p. (Orig.). 1981. pap. 4.95 (ISBN 0-8164-2321-0, HarpR). Har-Row.

Story of the American Board: An Account of the First Hundred Years of the American Board for Foreign Missions. William E. Strong. LC 79-83443. (Religion in America Ser.). 1969. Repr. of 1910 ed. 26.50 (ISBN 0-405-00277-7). Ayer Co Pubs.

Story of the American Hymn. Edward S. Ninde. LC 72-1708. (Illus.). Repr. of 1921 ed. 29.75 (ISBN 0-404-09914-9). AMS Pr.

Story of the Bible. Edgar J. Goodspeed. LC 36-21666. Repr. of 1967 ed. 44.00 (ISBN 0-8357-9657-4, 2013612). Bks Demand UMI.

Story of the Bible. Ed. by Johnny Ramsey. pap. 3.95 (ISBN 0-89137-543-0). Quality Pubns.

Story of the Chasam Sofer. Shubert Spero. (Illus.). 80p. 2.00 (ISBN 0-914131-61-3, D53). Torah Umesorah.

Story of the Chofetz Chaim. (Illus.). 160p. 9.85 (ISBN 0-317-53891-8); pap. 7.15. Torah Umesorah.

Story of the Christian Church. rev. ed. Jesse L. Hurlbut. 192p. 1986. 11.95 (ISBN 0-310-26510-X, 6527). Zondervan.

Story of the Christian Year. Amy Boudreau. 1971. 4.50 (ISBN 0-685-27196-X). Claitors.

Story of the Christian Year. George M. Gibson. LC 71-142635. (Essay Index Reprint Ser.). (Illus.). Repr. of 1945 ed. 25.00 (ISBN 0-8369-2770-2). Ayer Co Pubs.

Story of the Christians. Jennifer Rye. (Cambridge Books for Children). (Illus.). 32p. 1987. 7.95 (ISBN 0-521-30118-1); pap. 3.95 (ISBN 0-521-31748-7). Cambridge U Pr.

Story of the Christians & Moors of Roman Spain. Charlotte M. Yonge. 1893. 30.00 (ISBN 0-89984-238-0). Century Bookbindery.

Story of the Church. new ed. Inez S. Davis. 1981. pap. 18.00 (ISBN 0-8309-0188-4). Herald Hse.

Story of the Church. George Johnson et al. LC 80-51329. 521p. 1980. pap. 12.50 (ISBN 0-89555-156-X). Tan Bks Pubs.

Story of the Church. 2nd. enl. ed. A. M. Renwick & A. M. Harman. 272p. (Orig.). 1985. pap. 8.95 (ISBN 0-8028-0092-0). Eerdmans.

Story of the Church of Egypt, 2 vols. Edith L. Butcher. LC 75-41459. Repr. of 1897 ed. Set. 87.50 (ISBN 0-404-56231-0). AMS Pr.

Story of the Church: Peak Moments from Pentecost to the Year 2000. Alfred McBride & O. Praem. (Illus.). 168p. 1984. pap. text ed. 7.95 (ISBN 0-86716-029-2). St Anthony Mess Pr.

Story of the Eucharist. Inos Biffi. Tr. by John Drury from Ital. LC 85-82173. (Illustrated History of Christian Culture Ser.). Orig. Title: Storia dell' eucaristia. (Illus.). 125p. 1986. 11.95 (ISBN 0-89870-089-2). Ignatius Pr.

Story of the Falashas: "Black Jews" of Ethiopia. Simon D. Messing. (Illus.). 134p. 1982. pap. 7.50 (ISBN 0-9615946-9-1). Messing Pub.

Story of the Future. Ralph M. Riggs. LC 67-31330. 1968. 2.95 (ISBN 0-88243-742-9, 02-0742). Gospel Pub.

Story of the Hymns. H. Butterworth. 59.95 (ISBN 0-8490-1139-6). Gordon Pr.

Story of the Jesus People: A Factual Survey. Ronald M. Enroth et al. (Illus.). 256p. 1972. pap. 3.95 (ISBN 0-85364-131-5). Attic Pr.

Story of the Jew. rev. ed. Harry Gersh et al. LC 64-22514. (Illus.). 1965. 5.95x (ISBN 0-87441-019-3). Behrman.

Story of the Jewish People, 4 vols. Gilbert Klaperman & Libby Klaperman. Incl. Vol. 1. From Creation to the Second Temple. pap. text ed. 4.50x (ISBN 0-87441-207-2); Vol. 2. From the Building of the Second Temple Through the Age of the Rabbis. pap. text ed. 4.50x (ISBN 0-87441-208-0); Vol. 3. From the Golden Age in Spain Through the European Emancipation. pap. text ed. 5.50x (ISBN 0-87441-209-9); Vol. 4. From the Settlement of America Through Israel Today. pap. text ed. 5.50x (ISBN 0-87441-210-2). LC 56-12175. (Illus.). 1974. pap. Behrman.

Story of the Jewish Way of Life. Meyer Levin & Toby Kurzband. LC 59-13487. (Jewish Heritage Ser: Vol. 3). 1959. 5.95x (ISBN 0-87441-003-7). Behrman.

Story of the Jews. Julia Neuberger. (Cambridge Books for Children). (Illus.). 32p. 1987. 7.95 (ISBN 0-521-30601-9); pap. 3.95 (ISBN 0-521-31580-8). Cambridge U Pr.

Story of the Jubilee Singers with Their Songs. rev. ed. J. B. Marsh. LC 72-165509. (Illus.). Repr. of 1880 ed. 14.00 (ISBN 0-404-04189-2). AMS Pr.

Story of the Jubilee Singers, with Their Songs. rev. ed. J. B. Marsh. LC 79-78583. (Illus.). Repr. of 1881 ed. 22.50x (ISBN 0-8371-1424-1, MAJ&, Pub. by Negro U Pr). Greenwood.

Story of the Kimmer Mennonite Brethren Church. C. F. Plett. pap. 12.00 (ISBN 0-919797-51-2). Herald Pr.

Story of the Loaves & Fishes. Alice J. Davidson. (Alice in Bibleland Ser.). (Illus.). 32p. 1985. 4.95 (ISBN 0-8378-5073-8). Gibson.

Story of the Mass. 1.00. Paulist Pr.

Story of the Mass: From the Last Supper to the Present Day. Pierre Loret. LC 82-83984. 144p. 1983. pap. 3.50 (ISBN 0-89243-171-7). Liguori Pubns.

Story of the Mennonites. C. Henry Smith. Ed. by Cornelius Krahn. LC 81-65130. (Illus.). 589p. 1981. pap. 17.95 (ISBN 0-87303-069-9). Faith & Life.

Story of the Old Testament Simply Told. Florence E. Waggener. (Illus.). 1979. 5.50 (ISBN 0-682-49375-9). Exposition Pr FL.

Story of the Other Wise Man. Henry Van Dyke. 96p. 1986. pap. 2.95 (ISBN 0-345-31882-X, Pub. by Ballantine Epiphany). Ballantine.

Story of the People of God. F. Burton Nelson. (Illus.). 436p. 1971. pap. 5.50 (ISBN 0-910452-17-2). Covenant.

Story of the Prayer Book. Azriel Eisenberg & Philip Arian. pap. 5.95x (ISBN 0-87677-017-0). Hartmore.

Story of the Psalters. Henry A. Glass. LC 72-1635. Repr. of 1888 ed. 18.50 (ISBN 0-404-08308-0). AMS Pr.

Story of the Shakers. Flo Morse. (Illus.). 96p. 1986. pap. 6.95 (ISBN 0-88150-062-3). Countryman.

Story of the Synagogue. Meyer Levin & Toby Kurzband. LC 57-13093. (Jewish Heritage Ser: Vol. 2). 1957. pap. 5.95x (ISBN 0-87441-006-1). Behrman.

Story of the Two Brothers. Penny Frank. Ed. by P. Alexamder. (Lion Story Bible Ser.). 24p. 1987. 2.95 (ISBN 0-85648-765-1). Lion USA.

Story of the Vilna Gaon. Leonard Oschry. 1.50 (ISBN 0-914131-62-1, D52). Torah Umesorah.

Story of the Woman's Foreign Missionary Society of the Methodist Episcopal Church, 1869-1895. Frances J. Baker. Ed. by Carolyn G. De Swarte & Donald Dayton. (Women in American Protestant Religion Series 1800-1930). 438p. 1987. lib. bdg. 65.00 (ISBN 0-8240-0658-5). Garland Pub.

Story of Tisha B'Av. Aryeh Kaplan. 160p. (Orig.). 1981. pap. 2.95 (ISBN 0-940118-32-7). Maznaim.

Story of Unity. rev. ed. James D. Freeman. (Illus.). 1978. 5.95 (ISBN 0-87159-145-6). Unity School.

Story of Vivekananda. Irene R. Ray & Mallika C. Gupta. (Illus.). 1971. pap. 3.00 (ISBN 0-87481-125-2). Vedanta Pr.

Story of Westminster Abbey. Violet Brooke-Hunt. 1977. lib. bdg. 59.95 (ISBN 0-8490-2692-X). Gordon Pr.

Story of Yiddish Literature. A. A. Roback. 75.00 (ISBN 0-87968-084-9). Gordon Pr.

Story of Your Bible. H. G. Mackay. 1985. pap. 2.95 (ISBN 0-937396-65-6). Walterick Pubs.

Story Sermons for Children. Luther S. Cross. (Object Lesson Ser.). (Orig.). 1966. pap. 3.50 (ISBN 0-8010-2328-9). Baker Bk.

Story, Sign, & Self: Phenomenology & Structuralism As Literary-Critical Methods. Robert Detweiler. Ed. by William A. Beardslee. LC 76-9713. (Semeia Studies). 240p. 1978. pap. 9.95 (ISBN 0-8006-1505-0, 1-1505). Fortress.

Story Sunday: Christian Fairy Tales for Children, Parents & Educators. John R. Aurelio. LC 78-51587. 104p. 1978. pap. 3.95 (ISBN 0-8091-2115-8). Paulist Pr.

Story Theology. Terrence Tilley. (Theology & Life Ser.: Vol. 12). 1985. pap. 10.95 (ISBN 0-89453-464-5). M Glazier.

Story Time with Grandma. Mary E. Yoder. 1979. 2.50 (ISBN 0-87813-514-6). Christian Light.

Story Weaving. Peter Morgan. Ed. by Herbert Lambert. LC 86-6079. 128p. (Orig.). 1986. pap. 8.95 (ISBN 0-8272-3423-6). CBP.

Storytelling, Imagination & Faith. William J. Bausch. 240p. (Orig.). 1984. pap. 7.95 (ISBN 0-89622-199-7). Twenty-Third.

Storytelling in the Bible. Jacob Licht. 154p. 1978. text ed. 18.50x (ISBN 965-223-301-3, Pub. by Magnes Pr Israel). Humanities.

Storytelling in the Bible. 2nd ed. Jacob Licht. 156p. 1986. Repr. of 1978 ed. text ed. 22.50 (ISBN 965-223-542-3, Pub. by Magnes Pr Israel). Humanities.

Storytelling: Study Guide, The Enchantment of Theology Cassette Tapes. Belden C. Lane. LC 86-6079. 24p. (Orig.). 1982. pap. 2.50 (ISBN 0-8272-3419-8, 10S2113). CBP.

Stoughton Musical Society's Centennial Collection of Sacred Music. Roger L. Hall. (Earlier American Music Ser.: No. 23). 304p. 1980. Repr. of 1878 ed. lib. bdg. 37.50 (ISBN 0-306-79618-X). Da Capo.

Stow Affair: Anti-Semitism in the California Legislature. Budd Westreich. (Illus.). 84p. 1981. 10.00 (ISBN 0-936300-02-7). Pr Arden Park.

Stowe Psalter. Ed. by A. C. Kimmens. LC 78-23622. (Toronto Old English Ser.). 1979. 47.50x (ISBN 0-8020-2201-4). U of Toronto Pr.

Straight from the Heart: A Call to the New Generation. John Bertolucci. 126p. 1986. pap. 4.95 (ISBN 0-89283-290-8). Servant.

Straight Talk to Men & Their Wives. James C. Dobson. 1980. 12.95 (ISBN 0-8499-0260-6). Word Bks.

Straightforward. Larry Tomczak. LC 78-59856. 1978. pap. 4.95 (ISBN 0-88270-311-0). Bridge Pub.

Strait Gate. John Bunyan. pap. 2.25 (ISBN 0-685-88394-9). Reiner.

Strange Contrarieties: Pascal in England During the Age of Reason. John C. Barker. (Illus.). 352p. 1976. 20.00x (ISBN 0-7735-0188-6). McGill-Queens U Pr.

Strange Fibonacci Discoveries in Numerology for Greater Living Achievement. Thomas Calvert. (Illus.). 245p. 1976. 99.15 (ISBN 0-89266-009-0). Am Classical Coll Pr.

Strange Gifts: A Guide to Charismatic Renewal. Ed. by David Martin & Peter Mullen. 208p. 1984. 24.95x (ISBN 0-631-13357-7); pap. 9.95x (ISBN 0-631-13592-8). Basil Blackwell.

Strange Gods: Contemporary Religious Cults in America. William J. Whalen. LC 80-81451. 1981. pap. 4.95 (ISBN 0-87973-666-6, 666). Our Sunday Visitor.

Strange Gods: The Great American Cult Scare. David Bromley & Anson Shupe. LC 81-65763. 192p. 1982. 21.95x (ISBN 0-8070-3256-5); pap. 8.95 (ISBN 0-8070-1109-6, BP641). Beacon Pr.

Strange New Gospels. Edgar J. Goodspeed. 1979. Repr. of 1931 ed. lib. bdg. 22.50 (ISBN 0-8495-2000-2). Arden Lib.

Strange New Gospels. facsimile ed. Edgar J. Goodspeed. LC 70-156652. (Essay Index Reprint Ser). Repr. of 1931 ed. 12.00 (ISBN 0-8369-2364-2). Ayer Co Pubs.

Strange New Religions. Leon McBeth. LC 76-47780. 1977. pap. 4.25 (ISBN 0-8054-1806-7). Broadman.

Strange Parallel: Zebulun a Tribe of Israel. Rev. ed. Helene Koppejan. LC 83-73689. (Illus.). 96p. 1984. pap. 4.00 (ISBN 0-934666-13-X). Artisan Sales.

Strange Scriptures That Perplex the Western Mind. Barbara M. Bowen. 1940. pap. 3.95 (ISBN 0-8028-1511-1). Eerdmans.

Strange Silence of the Bible in the Church: A Study in Hermeneutics. James D. Smart. LC 72-118323. 184p. 1970. pap. 8.95 (ISBN 0-664-24894-2). Westminster.

Strange Tales About Jesus: A Survey of Unfamiliar Gospels. Per Beskow. LC 82-16001. 144p. 1983. pap. 9.95 (ISBN 0-8006-1686-3, 1-1686). Fortress.

Stranger at Home: "The Holocaust," Zionism, & American Judaism. Jacob Neusner. LC 80-19455. x, 214p. 1985. pap. 8.95 (ISBN 0-226-57629-9). U of Chicago Pr.

Stranger by the River. Paul Twitchell. 176p. 1970. pap. 5.95 (ISBN 0-914766-16-3). IWP Pub.

Stranger in My Home. C. Raymond Holmes. LC 73-9253. (Crown Ser.). 128p. 1974. pap. 5.95 (ISBN 0-8127-0075-9). Review & Herald.

Stranger in Tomorrow's Land. Doreen Kirban & Diane Kirban. 1970. 4.95 (ISBN 0-912582-40-5). Kirban.

Stranger of Galilee. Reginald E. White. LC 60-10096. (Pivot Family Reader Ser). 240p. 1975. pap. 2.25 (ISBN 0-87983-108-1). Keats.

Stranger to Self-Hatred. Brennan Manning. 6.95 (ISBN 0-87193-156-7). Dimension Bks.

Strangers. Bill Van Horn. 1983. 4.00 (ISBN 0-89536-587-1, 1926). CSS of Ohio.

Strangers, All Strangers. Robert A. Yereance. LC 79-27016. 1981. 14.95 (ISBN 0-87949-151-5). Ashley Bks.

Strangers & Pilgrims. Geoffrey F. Spencer. 221p. (Orig.). 1984. pap. text ed. 12.50 (ISBN 0-8309-0399-2). Herald Hse.

Strangers & Sojourners at Port Royal. Ruth Clark. 1972. lib. bdg. 26.00x (ISBN 0-374-91664-0, Octagon). Hippocrene Bks.

Strangers Become Neighbors. Calvin Redekop. LC 80-13887. (Studies in Anabaptist & Mennonite History Ser.: No. 22). (Illus.). 312p. 1980. 24.95x (ISBN 0-8361-1228-8). Herald Pr.

Strangers in Their Midst: Small-Town Jews & Their Neighbors. Peter I. Rose. 1977. lib. bdg. 12.95 (ISBN 0-915172-32-1). Richwood Pub.

Strangers in Their Own Land: Young Jews in Germany & Austria Today. Peter Sichrovsky. Tr. by Jean Steinberg. LC 85-43108. 208p. 1986. 14.95 (ISBN 0-465-08211-4). Basic.

Strangers, Lovers, Friends. Urban G. Steinmetz. LC 80-69479. (Illus.). 176p. (Orig.). 1981. pap. 3.95 (ISBN 0-87793-217-4). Ave Maria.

Strangest Thing Happened. Ethel Barrett. LC 76-84599. 144p. 1971. pap. 1.95 (ISBN 0-8307-0005-6, S061104). Regal.

Stratagems. Julia Lorusso & Joel Glick. 108p. (Orig.). 1985. pap. 7.95 (ISBN 0-914732-15-3). Bro Life Inc.

Strategic Planning Management. Thomas H. Naylor. 156p. 1980. pap. 13.00 (ISBN 0-912841-15-X, 03). Planning Forum.

Strategies for Church Growth. Peter C. Wagner. 1987. 12.95 (ISBN 0-8307-1245-3, 5111756). Regal.

Strategies for Growing Your Church. C. Wayne Zunkel. 112p. 1986. pap. 12.95 (ISBN 0-89191-344-0). Cook.

Strategies for Growth in Religious Life. Gerald A. Arbuckle. LC 86-17359. 240p. (Orig.). 1986. pap. 11.95 (ISBN 0-8189-0505-0). Alba.

Strategies for New Churches. Ezra E. Jones. LC 75-36731. 1979. pap. 7.95 (ISBN 0-06-064184-3, RD 276, HarpR). Har-Row.

Strategies for Sunday School Growth. George A. Edgerly & Harold E. Crosby. LC 83-80404. (Worker's Training Ser.). 128p. (Orig.). 1983. pap. 2.50 (ISBN 0-88243-591-4, 02-0591). Gospel Pub.

Strategies Teaching Christian Adults. Warren N. Wilbert. 280p. 1980. 12.95 (ISBN 0-8010-9668-5). Baker Bk.

Strategy for Leadership. Edward R. Dayton & Ted W. Engstrom. 240p. 1979. 13.95 (ISBN 0-8007-0994-2). Revell.

Strategy for Living. Edward R. Dayton & Ted W. Engstrom. LC 76-3935. (Orig.). 1976. pap. 6.95 (ISBN 0-8307-0424-8, 5403405); wkbk. 4.95 (ISBN 0-8307-0476-0, 5202000). Regal.

Strategy for Survival. James Thompson. LC 79-67274. (Journey Bks). 144p. 1980. pap. 3.50 (ISBN 0-8344-0113-4). Sweet.

Strategy of Satan. Warren W. Wiersbe. 1979. 3.95 (ISBN 0-8423-6665-2). Tyndale.

Strategy of Service. June A. Williams. 112p. (Orig.). 1984. pap. 5.95 (ISBN 0-310-45761-0, 12046P). Zondervan.

Straws from the Crib. Joseph Manton. (Orig.). 1964. 5.95 (ISBN 0-8198-0150-X); pap. 4.95 (ISBN 0-8198-0151-8). Dghtrs St Paul.

Stream of Light. Conrad Wright. 1975. pap. 5.75 (ISBN 0-933840-14-4). Unitarian Univ.

Streams in the Desert. Mrs. Charles E. Cowman. 1974. large print kiver 9.95 (ISBN 0-310-22527-2, 12555L). Zondervan.

Streams in the Desert. Ajaib Singh. Ed. by Russell Perkins & Judith Perkins. LC 81-85843. (Illus.). 468p. (Orig.). 1982. pap. 12.00 (ISBN 0-89142-038-X). Sant Bani Ash.

Streams in the Desert, Vol. 1. Mrs. Charles E. Cowman. 9.95 (ISBN 0-310-22520-5, 6901, Pub. by Cowman). Zondervan.

Streams in the Desert, Vol. 2. Mrs. Charles E. Cowman. 1986. 9.95 (ISBN 0-310-22430-6, 6902, Pub. by Cowman). Zondervan.

Streams in the Desert, Vol. 2. large print ed. Mrs. Charles E. Cowman. 384p. 1976. 9.95 (ISBN 0-310-22537-X, 12557L). Zondervan.

Streams in the Desert Sampler. Charles E. Cowman. 128p. 1983. pap. 3.95 (ISBN 0-310-37651-3, 6881P). Zondervan.

Streams of Renewal. Peter Hocken. 288p. (Orig.). 1986. pap. 11.95 (ISBN 0-932085-03-2). Word Among Us.

Street or Pulpit? The Witness of Activist Monsignor Charles Owen Rice of Pittsburgh. Kenneth K. McNulty, Sr. (Answers Ser.). 288p. (Orig.). 1985. pap. 9.95 (ISBN 0-935025-00-6). Data & Res Tech.

Street Walkin' Ronal Charles. (Illus.). 120p. (Orig.). 1986. pap. 9.95 (ISBN 1-55630-020-4). Brentwood Comm.

Strenghtening Your Grip. Charles R. Swindoll. 272p. 1986. pap. 3.50 (ISBN 0-553-25923-7). Bantam.

Strength from Above. E. J. Saleska. 1946. 0.95 (ISBN 0-570-03677-1, 74-1002). Concordia.

Strength of the Weak: Towards a Christian Feminist Identity. Dorothee Soelle. Tr. by Rita Kimber & Robert Kimber. LC 83-27348. 184p. (Orig.). 1984. pap. 9.95 (ISBN 0-664-24623-0). Westminster.

Strength Through Struggle. Frederick E. Kinzie & Vera D. Kinzie. Ed. & intro. by James Stewart. LC 86-1645. (Illus.). 350p. (Orig.). 1986. pap. 6.95 (ISBN 0-912315-98-9). Word Aflame.

Strength to Love. Martin Luther King, Jr. LC 80-2374. 160p. 1981. pap. 4.95 (ISBN 0-8006-1441-0, 1-1441). Fortress.

Strength to Love. Martin Luther King, Jr. 208p. 1985. pap. 11.95 (ISBN 0-8027-2472-8). Walker & Co.

Strength Under Control: Meekness & Zeal in the Christian Life. John Keating. (Living As a Christian Ser.). 152p. (Orig.). 1981. pap. 3.50 (ISBN 0-89283-104-9). Servant.

Strengthened by Struggle: The Stress Factor in 2 Corinthians. Michael Baughen. 128p. 1984. pap. 5.95 (ISBN 0-87788-792-6). Shaw Pubs.

Strengthening the Adult Sunday School Class. Dick Murray. LC 81-3667. (Creative Leadership Ser.). 128p. (Orig.). 1981. pap. 6.95 (ISBN 0-687-39989-0). Abingdon.

Strengthening the Family. Wayne Rickerson. 128p. 1987. pap. 5.95 (ISBN 0-87403-206-7, 3186). Standard Pub.

Strengthening Your Grip. Charles Swindoll. 1986. deluxe ed. 9.95 (ISBN 0-8499-3852-X). Word Bks.

Strengthening Your Grip. Charles R. Swindoll. 236p. 1982. 12.95 (ISBN 0-8499-0312-2). Word Bks.

Strengthening Your Grip. Charles R. Swindoll. 1986. 3.50 (ISBN 0-8499-4176-8). Word Bks.

Strengths of a Christian. Robert C. Roberts. LC 84-3498. (Spirituality & the Christian Life Ser.: Vol. 2). 118p. 1984. pap. 7.95 (ISBN 0-664-24613-3). Westminster.

Stress. Charles G. Edwards. (Outreach Ser.). 32p. 1982. pap. 1.25 (ISBN 0-8163-0468-8). Pacific Pr Pub Assn.

Stress & Its Management by Yoga. K. N. Udupa. 400p. 1986. 25.00X (ISBN 81-208-0000-1, Pub. by Motilal Banarsidass). South Asia Bks.

Stress! How Christian Parents Cope. Georgianna Summers. LC 86-71746. 80p. (Orig.). 1986. pap. 5.95 (ISBN 0-88177-032-9, DR032B). Discipleship Res.

Stress in the Family: How to Live Through It. Tim Timmons. LC 87-81649. 160p. (Orig.). 1982. pap. 4.95 (ISBN 0-89081-359-0). Harvest Hse.

Stress Management for Ministers. Charles L. Rassieur. LC 81-16458. 168p. 1982. pap. 8.95 (ISBN 0-664-24397-5). Westminster.

Stretch. Edythe Draper. 1983. kivar, girls' ed. 5.95 (ISBN 0-8423-6673-3). Tyndale.

Stretch. Edythe Draper. 1983. kivar, boys' ed. 5.95 (ISBN 0-8423-6668-7). Tyndale.

Stretcher Bearers. Michael Slater. LC 85-8389. 168p. 1985. pap. write for info. (ISBN 0-8307-1044-2, 5418505). Regal.

Stretcher Bearers. Michael Slater & Eric Nachtrieb. 64p. 1985. pap. 3.95 (ISBN 0-8307-1056-6, 6102137). Regal.

Stretching Your Faith. William Deerfield. 48p. 1985. 4.95 (ISBN 0-8378-5401-6). Gibson.

Strike the Original Match. Charles R. Swindoll. LC 80-15639. 1980. pap. 6.95 (ISBN 0-930014-37-5); study guide 2.95 (ISBN 0-930014-49-9). Multnomah.

Striking Sails: A Pastoral View of Growing Older in Our Society. Heije Faber. Tr. by Kenneth R. Mitchell. 160p. 1984. pap. 10.95 (ISBN 0-687-39941-6). Abingdon.

Strings & Things: Poems & Other Messages for Children. Christy Kenneally. (Orig.). 1984. pap. 3.50 (ISBN 0-8091-6555-4). Paulist Pr.

Strive for the Truth: The World of Rav Dessler. E. E. Dessler. Tr. by Aryeh Carmell from Hebrew. Tr. of Michtav M'Eliyahu. 1978. 9.95 (ISBN 0-87306-139-X); pap. 7.95 (ISBN 0-87306-177-2). Feldheim.

Strive for Truth, Vol. 2. Eliyahu Dessler. 1985. 12.95 (ISBN 0-87306-395-3); pap. 9.95 (ISBN 0-87306-396-1). Feldheim.

Striving for Holiness. Bobbie C. Jobe. 2.70 (ISBN 0-89137-423-X). Quality Pubns.

Stroll Through Historic Salem. Samuel Chamberlain. LC 78-79738. (Illus.). 1969. student ed. 9.95 (ISBN 0-8038-6689-5). Hastings.

Strong & the Weak. Paul Tournier. LC 63-8898. 252p. 1976. pap. 6.95 (ISBN 0-664-24745-8). Westminster.

Strong, Loving & Wise: Presiding in Liturgy. 5th ed. Robert W. Hovda. (Illus.). 96p. 1983. pap. 5.95 (ISBN 0-8146-1253-9). Liturgical Pr.

Strong Name. James S. Stewart. (Scholar As Preacher Ser.). 268p. 1940. 12.95 (ISBN 0-567-04427-0, Pub. by T & T Clark Ltd UK). Fortress.

Strong Place. Marion Duckworth. 1983. pap. 4.95 (ISBN 0-8423-6663-6). Tyndale.

Strong Sunday Schools-Strong Churches: The Pastor's Role. Roy Ryan. LC 86-71810. 72p. (Orig.). 1987. pap. 4.95 (ISBN 0-88177-035-3, DR035B). Discipleship Res.

Strong-Willed Child. James C. Dobson. 1978. 10.95 (ISBN 0-8423-0664-1). Tyndale.

Strong's Exhaustive Concordance. James Strong. LC 78-73138. 1978. pap. 15.95 (ISBN 0-8054-1134-8). Broadman.

Strong's Exhaustive Concordance of the Bible with the Exclusive Key-Word Comparison. rev. ed. James Strong. 1980. 23.95 (ISBN 0-687-40030-9); thumb-indexed 28.95 (ISBN 0-687-40031-7). Abingdon.

Strong's Exhaustive Concordance of the Bible. James Strong. 1552p. Date not set. 20.95 (ISBN 0-917006-01-1). Hendrickson MA.

Strong's Exhaustive Concordance of the Bible. Ed. by James Strong. 1552p. 1986. text ed. 10.95 (ISBN 0-529-06334-4); Thumb indexed ed. text ed. 13.95 (ISBN 0-529-06335-2). World Bible.

Strong's New Concordance of the Bible: Popular Edition. James Strong. 784p. 1985. text ed. 10.95 (ISBN 0-8407-4951-1). Nelson.

Structural Analysis & Biblical Exegesis. R. Barthes et al. Tr. by Alfred M. Johnson, Jr. LC 74-31334. (Pittsburgh Theological Monographs: No. 3). 1974. pap. 9.95 (ISBN 0-915138-02-6). Pickwick.

Structural Analysis of the Sermon on the Mount. Andreij Kodjak. (Religion & Reasons Ser.: No. 34). (Illus.). x, 234p. 1986. lib. bdg. 54.50x (ISBN 0-89925-159-5). Mouton.

Structural Depths of Indian Thought. P. T. Raju. (Philosophy Ser.). 600p. 1985. 49.50x (ISBN 0-88706-139-7); pap. 24.50x (ISBN 0-88706-140-0). State U NY Pr.

Structural Study of Myth & Totenism. Ed. by Edmund Leach. (Orig.). 1968. pap. 12.95 (ISBN 0-422-72530-7, NO.2287, Pub by Tavistock England). Methuen Inc.

Structuralism & Biblical Hermeneutics. Ed. & tr. by Alfred M. Johnson, Jr. LC 79-9411. (Pittsburgh Theological Monographs: No. 22). 1979. pap. 12.95 (ISBN 0-915138-18-2). Pickwick.

Structuralism & the Biblical Text. David C. Greenwood. (Religion & Reason Ser.: No. 32). xi, 155p. 1985. 37.75x (ISBN 0-89925-103-X). Mouton.

Structuralist Interpretations of Biblical Myth. Edmund Leach & Alan Aycock. LC 82-25263. (Illus.). 176p. 1983. 34.50 (ISBN 0-521-25491-4); pap. 11.95 (ISBN 0-521-27492-3). Cambridge U Pr.

Structure & Cognition: Aspects of Hindu Caste & Ritual. 2nd ed. Veena Das. 1982. 24.95x (ISBN 0-19-561395-3). Oxford U Pr.

Structure & Creativity in Religion. Douglas Allen. (Religion & Reason Ser.: No. 14). 1978. 20.40x (ISBN 90-279-7594-9). Mouton.

Structure & History in Greek Mythology & Ritual. Walter Burkert. LC 78-62856. (Sather Classical Lectures Ser.: Vol. 47). 1980. 30.00x (ISBN 0-520-03771-5); pap. 9.95 (ISBN 0-520-04770-2, CAL 581). U of Cal Pr.

Structure & Meaning of Second Baruch. Frederick J. Murphy. 1985. 16.50 (ISBN 0-89130-844-X, 06-01-78); pap. 10.95 (ISBN 0-89130-845-8). Scholars Pr GA.

Structure d'un Mythe Vedique: Le Mythe Cosmogonique dans le Rgveda. B. L. Ogibenin. (Approaches to Semiotics: No. 30). 1973. 27.20x (ISBN 0-686-21821-3). Mouton.

Structure of Biblical Myths: The Ontogenesis of the Psyche. Heinz Westman. LC 83-19132. (Seminar Ser.: No. 16). v, 477p. (Orig.). 1983. pap. 18.50 (ISBN 0-88214-116-3). Spring Pubns.

Structure of Christian Existence. John B. Cobb, Jr. 1979. pap. 6.95 (ISBN 0-8164-2229-X, HarpR). Har-Row.

Structure of Jewish History & Other Essays. Heinrich Graetz. 20.00x (ISBN 0-87068-466-3); pap. 14.95x (ISBN 0-685-56206-9). Ktav.

Structure of John Webster's Play. Anthony E. Courtade. Ed. by James Hogg. (Jacobean Drama Studies). 172p. (Orig.). 1980. pap. 15.00 (ISBN 0-317-40036-3, Salzburg Studies). Longwood Pub Group.

Structure of Lutheranism: The Theology & Philosophy of Life of Lutheranism, 16th & 17th Centuries, Vol. 1. Werner Elert. Tr. by Walter A. Hansen. LC 62-19955. 1974. pap. 15.95 (ISBN 0-570-03192-3, 12-2588). Concordia.

Structure of Religious Experience. John MacMurray. LC 73-122406. xi, 77p. 1971. Repr. of 1936 ed. 15.00 (ISBN 0-208-00958-2, Archon). Shoe String.

Structure of the Book of Job: A Form-Critical Analysis. Claus Westermann. Tr. by Charles A. Muenchow from Ger. LC 80-2379. Tr. of Aufbau des Buches Hiob. 160p. 1981. 14.95 (ISBN 0-8006-0651-5, 1-651). Fortress.

Structure of the Book of Job: A Form-Critical Analysis. Claus Westermann. LC 80-2379. pap. 40.00 (2029297). Bks Demand UMI.

Structure of the Christian Science Textbook: Our Way of Life. Max Kappeler. LC 58-26857. 206p. 1954. 14.00 (ISBN 0-85241-071-9). Kappeler Inst Pub.

Structures & Patterns of Religion. G. Mensching. Tr. by V. S. Sharma & H. M. Klimkeit. 1976. 21.00 (ISBN 0-8426-0958-X). Orient Bk Dist.

Structures of the Church. Hans Kung. LC 82-4706. 350p. 1982. pap. 12.95 (ISBN 0-8245-0508-5). Crossroad NY.

Struggle & Submission: R. C. Zaehner on Mysticisms. William L. Newell. LC 80-6295. 402p. 1981. lib. bdg. 29.25 (ISBN 0-8191-1696-3); pap. text ed. 15.25 (ISBN 0-8191-1697-1). U Pr of Amer.

Struggle for Freedom. Knofel Staton. LC 76-18381. 96p. 1977. pap. 2.25 (ISBN 0-87239-063-2, 40034). Standard Pub.

Struggle for Inner Peace. rev. ed. Henry R. Brandt. 136p. 1984. pap. 4.95 (ISBN 0-88207-245-5). Victor Bks.

Struggle for Men's Hearts & Minds. Charles Colson. 48p. 1986. 1.95 (ISBN 0-89693-166-8). Victor Bks.

Struggle for Religious Freedom in Germany. Arthur S. Duncan-Jones. LC 78-63664. (Studies in Fascism: Ideology & Practice). Repr. of 1938 ed. 34.00 (ISBN 0-404-16927-9). AMS Pr.

Struggle for Religious Freedom in Virginia. William T. Thom. LC 78-63877. (Johns Hopkins University. Studies in the Social Sciences. Eighteenth Ser. 1900: 10-12). Repr. of 1900 ed. 11.50 (ISBN 0-404-61133-8). AMS Pr.

Struggle for Religious Freedom in Virginia: The Baptists. W. T. Thom. Repr. of 1900 ed. 13.00 (ISBN 0-384-60163-4). Johnson Repr.

Struggle for Religious Survival in the Soviet Union. Intro. by A. James Rudin & Ann Gillen. LC 86-72630. 76p. 1986. pap. 5.00 (ISBN 0-87495-085-6). Am Jewish Comm.

Struggle of Love. Cheryl Stoesz & Gilbert Brandt. 110p. (Orig.). 1983. pap. 4.95 (ISBN 0-919797-08-3). Kindred Pr.

Struggle of Muslim Women. Kaukab Siddique. LC 86-70641. 152p. (Orig.). 1986. pap. 9.95 (ISBN 0-942978-10-2). Am Soc Ed & Rel.

Struggle of Protestant Dissenters for Religious Toleration in Virginia. H. R. McIlwaine. pap. 9.00 (ISBN 0-384-34893-9). Johnson Repr.

Struggle of Protestant Dissenters for Religious Toleration in Virginia. Henry R. McIlwaine. LC 78-63830. (Johns Hopkins University. Studies in the Social Sciences. Twelfth Ser. 1894: 4). Repr. of 1894 ed. 11.50 (ISBN 0-404-61090-0). AMS Pr.

Struggle over Reform in Rabbinic Literature. Alexander Guttman. LC 75-45046. 1977. 13.50 (ISBN 0-8074-0005-X, 382790). UAHC.

Struggle to Be Free: My Story & Your Story. Wayne E. Oates. LC 83-5904. 164p. 1983. pap. 7.95 (ISBN 0-664-24500-5). Westminster.

Struggles of Gods. Ed. by Hans G. Kippenberg. LC 84-11501. (Religion & Reason Ser.: No. 31). vii, 296p. 1984. 34.95 (ISBN 90-279-3460-6). Mouton.

Struggling With Sex: Serious Call to Marriage-Centered Sexual Life. Arthur A. Rouner, Jr. LC 86-32028. 128p. (Orig.). (YA) 1986. pap. 6.50 (ISBN 0-8066-2243-1, 10-6096). Augsburg.

Sts. Cyril & Methodius. 1966. pap. 0.50 (ISBN 0-317-30441-0). Holy Trinity.

Stubborn Faith: Papers on Old Testament & Related Subjects Presented to Honor William Andrew Irwin. Ed. by Edward C. Hobbs. LC 56-12567. 1956. 13.95x (ISBN 0-87074-079-2). SMU Press.

Stubbs: Portraits in Detail. Intro. by Judy Egenton. (Illus.). 48p. 1985. pap. 8.95 (ISBN 0-946590-17-6). Salem Hse Pubs.

Student. W. P. Stanley. 1957. 4.95 (ISBN 0-87148-756-X). Pathway Pr.

Student Atlas of the Bible. American Map Corp. Staff. (Series 9500: No. 9559). (Illus.). 1978. 2.95 (ISBN 0-8416-9559-8); Span. lang. ed. write for info. Am Map.

Student Guide to Catholic Colleges & Universities. John R. Crocker. LC 82-48923. 468p. (Orig.). 1983. pap. 9.95 (ISBN 0-06-061602-4, RD/459, HarpR). Har-Row.

Student Life in Ave Maria College, Medieval Paris. Astrik L. Gabriel. (Mediaeval Studies Ser.: No. 14). (Illus.). 1955. 26.95 (ISBN 0-268-00265-7). U of Notre Dame Pr.

Student Marriage. Denise George. LC 82-72230. (Orig.). 1983. pap. 4.95 (ISBN 0-8054-6939-7, 4269-39). Broadman.

Student Mission Power: Report of the First International Convention of the Student Volunteer Movement for Foreign Missions, 1891. John R. Mott et al. LC 79-92013. 1979. pap. 6.95 (ISBN 0-87808-736-2). William Carey Lib.

Student Moral Development in the Catholic School. Mary P. Traviss. 96p. 1986. 6.60 (ISBN 0-318-20565-3). Natl Cath Educ.

Student's Bible Atlas. Ed. by H. H. Rowley. 40p. 1984. pap. 3.95 (ISBN 0-8170-1022-X). Judson.

Students, Churches & Higher Education. R. T. Gribbon. 128p. 1981. pap. 6.95 (ISBN 0-8170-0931-0). Judson.

Student's Commentary - Genesis, 2 vols. C. C. Aalders. Set. 29.95 (ISBN 0-310-43968-X, 11755). Zondervan.

Student's Commentary on the Holy Scriptures. George Williams. LC 75-13929. 1971. 29.95 (ISBN 0-8254-4001-7). Kregel.

Student's Dictionary for Biblical & Theological Studies. F. B. Huey, Jr. & Bruce Corley. 1986. pap. 6.96 (ISBN 0-310-45951-6, 12726P). Zondervan.

Student's Guide Through the Talmud. Chajes. 13.95 (ISBN 0-87306-089-X). Feldheim.

Students Guide to the Doctrine & Covenants. F. Henry Edwards. 1980. pap. 9.00 (ISBN 0-8309-0267-8). Herald Hse.

Student's New Testament: The Greek Text & the American Translation. Edgar J. Goodspeed. pap. 160.00 (ISBN 0-317-20700-8, 2024115). Bks Demand UMI.

Student's New Testament: The Greek Text & the American Translation, 2 vols. Edgar J. Goodspeed. (Midway Reprint Ser.). Vol. 1. pap. 121.80 (2026775); Vol. 2. pap. 146.00. Bks Demand UMI.

Students Scholars & Saints. Louis Ginzberg. LC 85-9089. (Brown Classics in Judaica Ser.). 312p. 1985. pap. text ed. 12.75 (ISBN 0-8191-4490-8). U Pr of Amer.

Student's Values in Drugs & Drug Abuse. Mary V. Sztorc. 1976. pap. 2.00 (ISBN 0-87507-000-0). Cath Lib Assn.

Student's Vocabulary for Biblical Hebrew & Aramaic. Larry A. Mitchel. 128p. 1984. pap. 5.95 (ISBN 0-310-45461-1, 11607P). Zondervan.

Student's Vocabulary of Biblical Hebrew. George M. Landes. 56p. (Orig.). 1961. pap. text ed. write for info. (ISBN 0-02-367410-5, Pub. by Scribner). Macmillan.

Studia Biblica Nineteen Seventy-Eight, III: Papers on Paul & Other New Testament Authors. International Congress on Biblical Studies, 6th, Oxford, 3-7 April,1978. Ed. by E. A. Livingstone. (Journal for the Study of the New Testament, Supplement Ser.: No. 3). 468p. 1981. text ed. 37.50x (ISBN 0-905774-27-2, Pub. by JSOT Pr England). Eisenbrauns.

Studia Biblica Nineteen Seventy-Eight II: Papers on the Gospels. International Congress on Biblical Studies. Ed. by E. A. Livingston. (Journal for the Study of the New Testament Supplement Ser.: No. 2). 350p. 1980. text ed. 37.50x (ISBN 0-905774-22-1, Pub. by JSOT Pr England). Eisenbrauns.

Studia Patristica XVIII: Papers of the 1983 Oxford International Patristics Conference, Vol. 1. pap. 40.00 (ISBN 0-87907-350-0). Cistercian Pubns.

Studia Semitica, 2 vols. Erwin I. Rosenthal. Incl. Vol. 1. Jewish Themes. 59.50 (ISBN 0-521-07958-6); Vol. 2. Islamic Themes. 49.50 (ISBN 0-521-07959-4). (Oriental Publications Ser.: Nos. 16 & 17). Cambridge U Pr.

Studien uber Salomon Ibn Gabirol. David Kaufmann. Ed. by Steven Katz. LC 79-7144. (Jewish Philosophy, Mysticism & the History of Ideas Ser.). (Ger. & Hebrew.). 1980. Repr. of 1899 ed. lib. bdg. 14.00x (ISBN 0-405-12272-1). Ayer Co Pubs.

Studien Zum Altenglischen Computus. Heinrich Henel. 1934. pap. 8.00 (ISBN 0-384-22300-1). Johnson Repr.

Studien zum juedischen Neuplatonismus: Die Religionsphilosophie des Abraham Ibn Ezra. Hermann Greive. (Studia Judaica Vol. 7). 225p. 1973. 35.60x (ISBN 3-11-004116-2). De Gruyter.

Studies & Documents Relating to the History of the Greek Church & People Under Turkish Domination. Theodore H. Papadopoullos. LC 78-38759. Repr. of 1952 ed. 27.50 (ISBN 0-404-56314-7). AMS Pr.

Studies & Texts in Folklore, Magic, Medieval Romance, Hebrew Apocrypha & Samaritan Archaeology, 3 Vols. rev. ed. Moses Gaster. 1970. Set. 45.00x (ISBN 0-87068-056-0). Ktav.

Studies by a Recluse in Cloister, Town & Country. 3rd ed. Augustus Jessopp. 1969. Repr. of 1883 ed. lib. bdg. 20.50 (ISBN 0-8337-1841-X). B Franklin.

Studies by Samuel Horodezky: An Original Anthology. Ed. by Steven Katz. LC 79-51391. (Jewish Philosophy, Mysticism & History of Ideas Ser.). 1980. lib. bdg. 17.00x (ISBN 0-405-12233-0). Ayer Co Pubs.

Studies Concerning the Origins of Milton's Paradise Lost. Heinrich Mutschmann. LC 79-163459. (Studies in Milton, No. 22). 1971. Repr. of 1924 ed. lib. bdg. 39.95x (ISBN 0-8383-1324-8). Haskell.

Studies Concerning the Origins of Milton's Paradise Lost. Heinrich Mutschmann. 1924. Repr. 15.00 (ISBN 0-8274-3532-0). R West.

Studies, Historical & Critical. facs. ed. Pasquale Villari. Tr. by L. Villari. LC 68-16983. (Essay Index Reprint Ser). 1968. Repr. of 1907 ed. 18.00 (ISBN 0-8369-0960-7). Ayer Co Pubs.

Studies Honoring Ignatius Charles Brady O. F. M. Ed. by Romano S. Almagno & Conrad L. Harkins. (Theology Ser). 1976. 25.00 (ISBN 0-686-17960-9). Franciscan Inst.

Studies in Acts, Vol. II. Frances Easter. (Bible Study Ser.). 1986. pap. 3.50 (ISBN 0-8309-0442-5). Herald Hse.

Studies in Acts, Vol. II. Wallace Wartick. (Bible Student Study Guides Ser). 1978. pap. 2.95 (ISBN 0-89900-154-8). College Pr Pub.

Studies in Acts, Vol. I. Wallace Wartick. (Bible Student Study Guides Ser). 1977. pap. 2.95 (ISBN 0-89900-153-X). College Pr Pub.

Studies in Acts: The Church in the House. William Arnot. LC 78-59141. 464p. 1978. 12.95 (ISBN 0-8254-2120-9). Kregel.

Studies in American Church History, 25 vols. Catholic University of America Staff. Repr. of 1942 ed. 662.50 (ISBN 0-404-57750-4). AMS Pr.

Studies in American Jewish History. Jacob R. Marcus. 1969. 15.00x (ISBN 0-87820-003-7, Pub. by Hebrew Union). Ktav.

Studies in American Jewish Literature: Isaac Bashevis Singer, 3 Vols. Ed. by Daniel Walden. Incl. Vol. 1. A Mosaic of Jewish Writers; Vol. 3. Jewish Women Writers & Women in Jewish Literature; Vol. 2. From Marginality to Mainstream: A Mosaic of Jewish Writers; Vol. 4. World of Chaim Potok. 1982. 12.95 ea. (ISBN 0-686-97287-2). State U NY Pr.

Studies in Ancient Israelite Wisdom. James L. Crenshaw. 1974. 59.50x (ISBN 0-87068-255-5). Ktav.

Studies in Australian Totemism. Adolphus P. Elkin. LC 76-44712. Repr. of 1933 ed. 31.50 (ISBN 0-404-15857-9). AMS Pr.

Studies in Babi & Baha'i History, Vol. 1. Ed. by Moojan Momen. (Illus.). 1983. text ed. 19.95 (ISBN 0-933770-16-2). Kalimat.

Studies in Babi & Baha'i History: Vol. 2: From Iran East & West. Ed. by Juan R. Cole & Moojan Momen. (Illus.). 205p. 1984. 19.95 (ISBN 0-933770-40-5). Kalimat.

Studies in Babi & Baha'i History Volume 3: In Iran. Ed. & intro. by Peter Smith. (Illus.). 1986. 19.95 (ISBN 0-933770-46-4). Kalimat.

Studies in Babi & Baha'i History, Vol. 5: A Survey of Sources for Early Babi History & Doctorine. Denis MacEoin. 1987. 19.95 (ISBN 0-933770-63-4). Kalimat.

Studies in Babi & Baha'i History, Vol. 6: Baha'is in the West. Ed. by Peter Smith. Date not set. 19.95 (ISBN 0-933770-64-2). Kalimat.

Studies in Bamidbor (Numbers) 1982. 12.95 (ISBN 0-686-76263-0). Feldheim.

Studies in Bereshis (Genesis) 1982. 12.95 (ISBN 0-686-76261-4). Feldheim.

Studies in Biblical & Jewish Folklore. Raphael Patai et al. LC 72-6871. (Studies in Comparitive Literature: No. 35). 1972. Repr. of 1960 ed. lib. bdg. 49.95x (ISBN 0-8383-1665-4). Haskell.

Studies in Biblical & Semitic Symbolism. Maurice H. Fairbridge. 1977. lib. bdg. 59.95 (ISBN 0-8490-2700-4). Gordon Pr.

Studies in Biblical Eschatology. H. A. Ironside & F. Ottman. 426p. 1983. lib. bdg. 16.00 Smythe Sewn (ISBN 0-86524-143-0, 9806). Klock & Klock.

Studies in Biblical Holiness. Donald Metz. 284p. 1971. 10.95 (ISBN 0-8341-0117-3). Beacon Hill.

Studies in Buddhist Iconography. Dipak C. Bhattacharya. 1978. 22.50x (ISBN 0-8364-0016-X). South Asia Bks.

Studies in Catholic History. Ed. by Nelson H. Minnich. 1985. 35.00 (ISBN 0-89453-530-7). M Glazier.

Studies in Ch'an & Hua-Yen. Ed. by Robert M. Gimello & Peter N. Gregory. (Studies in East Asian Buddhism: No. 1). 406p. 1983. pap. text ed. 14.95x (ISBN 0-8248-0835-5). UH Pr.

Studies in Christian Antiquity. Richard Hanson. 376p. 1986. 32.95 (ISBN 0-567-09363-8, Pub. by T & T Clark Ltd UK). Fortress.

Studies in Christian Doctrine, 4 Vols. G. P. Pardington. Rev. by H. M. Freligh & E. H. Schroeder. 312p. 1964. pap. 1.95 ea. Vol. 1 (ISBN 0-87509-135-0). Vol. 2 (ISBN 0-87509-136-9). Vol. 3 (ISBN 0-87509-137-7). Vol. 4 (ISBN 0-87509-138-5). Chr Pubns.

Studies in Christian Enthusiasm. Geoffrey F. Nuttall. 1983. pap. 2.50x (ISBN 0-87574-041-3, 041). Pendle Hill.

Studies in Christian Mysticism. W. H. Dyson. 1977. lib. bdg. 69.95 (ISBN 0-8490-2702-0). Gordon Pr.

Studies in Christianity. Borden P. Bowne. LC 75-3074. Repr. of 1909 ed. 28.50 (ISBN 0-404-59075-6). AMS Pr.

Studies in Cistercian Art & Architecture, I. Ed. by Meredith Lillich et al. (Cistercian Studies: No. 66). (Illus., Orig.). 1982. pap. 12.95 (ISBN 0-87907-866-9). Cistercian Pubns.

Studies in Cistercian Art & Architecture, II. Ed. by Meredith P. Lillich. (Cistercian Studies: No. 69). (Illus.). pap. 14.95 (ISBN 0-87907-869-3). Cistercian Pubns.

Studies in Cistercian Art & Architecture, III. Ed. by Meredith P. Lillich. (Cistercian Studies: No. 89). (Orig.). 1987. pap. write for info. (ISBN 0-87907-889-8). Cistercian Pubns.

Studies in Cistercian Medieval History: Presented to Jeremiah F. O'Sullivan. Ed. by J. F. O'Callahan. LC 77-152486. (Cistercian Studies: No. 13). 1971. 7.95 (ISBN 0-87907-813-8). Cistercian Pubns.

Studies in Classics & Jewish Hellenism. Ed. by Richard Koebner. (Scripts Hierosolymitana Ser.: Vol. 1). pap. 39.00 (ISBN 0-317-28711-7, 2051594). Bks Demand UMI.

Studies in Colossiani. John Kackelman, Jr. 1986. pap. 5.50 (ISBN 0-89137-562-7). Quality Pubns.

Studies in Colossians & Philemon. H. C. G. Moule. LC 77-79185. (Kregel Popular Commentary Ser.). 196p. 1977. kivar 6.95 (ISBN 0-8254-3217-0). Kregel.

Studies in Colossians to Philemon. W. H. Thomas. LC 86-7178. 192p. 1986. pap. 6.95 (ISBN 0-8254-3834-9). Kregel.

Studies in Contemporary Jewry, Vol.I. Institute of Contemporary Jewry of The Hebrew University of Jerusalem. (Illus.). 608p. 1984. 22.50X (ISBN 0-253-39511-9). Ind U Pr.

Studies in Contemporary Superstition. W. H. Mallock. 1973. Repr. of 1895 ed. 25.00 (ISBN 0-8274-1566-4). R West.

Studies in Creation: A General Introduction to the Creation-Evolution Debate. John Klotz. 224p. (Orig.). 1985. pap. 9.95 (ISBN 0-570-03969-X, 12-3004). Concordia.

Studies in Daniel's Prophecy. Charles H. Wright. 368p. 1983. lib. bdg. 13.95 (ISBN 0-86524-162-7, 2703). Klock & Klock.

Studies in Dante, First Series: Scriptures & Classical Authors in Dante. Edward Moore. LC 68-57627. (Illus.). 1969. Repr. of 1896 ed. lib. bdg. 22.50x (ISBN 0-8371-0909-4, MODF). Greenwood.

Studies in Dante, Second Series: Miscellaneous Essays. Edward Moore. LC 68-57628. (Illus.). 1969. Repr. of 1899 ed. lib. bdg. 22.50x (ISBN 0-8371-0908-6, MOSD). Greenwood.

Studies in Dante, Third Series: Miscellaneous Essays. Edward Moore. LC 68-57629. (Illus.). 1969. Repr. of 1903 ed. lib. bdg. 22.50x (ISBN 0-8371-0917-5, MODT). Greenwood.

Studies in Devorim (Deuteronomy) 1982. 12.95 (ISBN 0-686-76264-9). Feldheim.

Studies in Discipleship. Charles P. Conn & Donald S. Aultman. LC 75-14887. 1975. pap. 1.99 (ISBN 0-87148-772-1). Pathway Pr.

Studies in Divine Science. Mrs. C. L. Baum. 1964. 6.50 (ISBN 0-686-24362-5). Divine Sci Fed.

Studies in Dogmatics: Theology. Gerrit C. Berkouwer. Incl. Vol. 1. Faith & Sanctification; Vol. 2. Providence of God. 10.95 (ISBN 0-8028-3029-3); Vol. 3. Faith & Justification. 8.95 (ISBN 0-8028-3030-7); Vol. 4. Person of Christ. 9.95 (ISBN 0-8028-3031-5); Vol. 5. General Revelation. 10.95 (ISBN 0-8028-3032-3); Vol. 6. Faith & Perseverance. 8.95 (ISBN 0-8028-3033-1); Vol. 7. Divine Election. 9.95 (ISBN 0-8028-3034-X); Vol. 8. Man-The Image of God. 12.95 (ISBN 0-8028-3035-8); Vol. 9. Work of Christ. 9.95 (ISBN 0-8028-3036-6); Vol. 10. Sacraments. 12.95 (ISBN 0-8028-3037-4); Vol. 11. Sin. 17.95 (ISBN 0-8028-3027-7); Vol. 12. Return of Christ. 13.95 (ISBN 0-8028-3393-4); The Church. 9.95 (ISBN 0-8028-3433-7); Holy Scripture. 11.95 (ISBN 0-8028-3394-2). 1952. Eerdmans.

Studies in Early Buddhist Architecture of India. H. Sarkar. (Illus.). 1966. 16.00x. Coronet Bks.

Studies in East European Jewish Mysticism. Joseph Weiss. Ed. by David Goldstein. (Littman Libray of Jewish Civilazation). 1985. 29.95x (ISBN 0-19-710034-1). Oxford U Pr.

Studies in Eastern Chant, Vol. IV. Ed. by Milos Velimirovic. 248p. 1979. pap. text ed. 10.95 (ISBN 0-913836-57-5). St Vladimirs.

Studies in Eighteenth-Century Islamic History. Ed. by Thomas Naff & Roger Owen. LC 77-22012. 462p. 1977. 24.95x (ISBN 0-8093-0819-3). S Ill U Pr.

Studies in English Puritanism from the Restoration to the Revolution, 1660-1688. Charles E. Whiting. LC 68-56060. 1968. Repr. of 1931 ed. 37.50x (ISBN 0-678-05203-4). Kelley.

Studies in English Puritanism from the Restoration to the Revolution, 1660-1688. Charles E. Whiting. (Church Historical Society London, N. S. Ser.: No. 5). Repr. of 1931 ed. 95.00 (ISBN 0-8115-3129-5). Kraus Repr.

Studies in Ephesians. R. C. Bell. 1971. pap. 2.75 (ISBN 0-88027-041-1). Firm Foun Pub.

Studies in Ephesians. H. C. G. Moule. LC 77-79179. (Kregel Popular Commentary Ser.). 176p. 1977. kivar 7.95 (ISBN 0-8254-3218-9). Kregel.

Studies in Ephesians. W. Leon Tucker. LC 83-6115. 136p. 1983. pap. 4.95 (ISBN 0-8254-3828-4). Kregel.

Studies in Ethical Theory. Ed. by Peter A. French et al. (Midwest Studies in Philosophy: Vol. 3). 1980. 25.00x (ISBN 0-8166-0968-3); pap. 12.95 (ISBN 0-8166-0971-3). U of Minn Pr.

Studies in Exodus, Vol. 1. Clifford Cole. (Bible Studies Ser.). 1986. pap. 3.50 (ISBN 0-8309-0460-3). Herald Hse.

Studies in Exodus, Vol. 2. Clifford A. Cole. (Bible Study Ser.). 1986. pap. 3.50 (ISBN 0-8309-0462-X). Herald Hse.

Studies in First & Second Samuel. Willard W. Winter. LC 70-1508. (Bible Study Textbook Ser.). 1967. 15.90 (ISBN 0-89900-011-8). College Pr Pub.

Studies in First & Second Thessalonians. Robert R. Taylor, Jr. 1977. pap. 2.50 (ISBN 0-89315-285-4). Lambert Bk.

Studies in First & Second Timothy. Robert Taylor, Jr. 2.50 (ISBN 0-89315-286-2). Lambert Bk.

Studies in First Corinthians. Paul T. Butler. (Bible Study Textbook Ser.). 416p. text ed. 14.30 (ISBN 0-89900-063-0). College Pr Pub.

Studies in First Corinthians. Don Compier. (Bible Study Ser.). 1987. pap. 3.50 (ISBN 0-8309-0448-4). Herald Hse.

Studies in First, Second Peter. Robert R. Taylor, Jr. pap. 2.50 (ISBN 0-89315-294-3). Lambert Bk.

Studies in First, Second, Third John. Robert R. Taylor, Jr. pap. 2.50 (ISBN 0-89315-295-1). Lambert Bk.

Studies in First Timothy. Alfred Rowland. 302p. 1985. smythe sewn 12.00 (ISBN 0-86524-194-5, 5402). Klock & Klock.

Studies in Galatians. R. C. Bell. 1954. pap. 2.75 (ISBN 0-88027-042-X). Firm Foun Pub.

Studies in Genesis. John B. Burke. 1979. pap. 4.95 (ISBN 0-88469-048-2). BMH Bks.

Studies in Genesis, 2 vols. in one. Robert S. Candlish. LC 79-14084. (Kregel Bible Study Classics Ser.). 854p. 1979. 22.95 (ISBN 0-8254-2315-5). Kregel.

Studies in Genesis, Vol. 1. F Henry Edwards. 1987. pap. 3.50 (ISBN 0-8309-0482-4). Herald Hse.

Studies in Genesis, Vol. 2. Wayne Ham. (Bible Study Ser.). 1987. pap. 3.50 (ISBN 0-8309-0483-2). Herald Hse.

Studies in Genesis One. Edward J. Young. pap. 4.95 (ISBN 0-87552-550-4). Presby & Reformed.

Studies in Hadith Methodology & Literature. Mustafa Azami. Ed. by Anwer Beg. LC 77-90335. 1978. pap. 5.50 (ISBN 0-89259-011-4); pap. text ed. 5.50. Am Trust Pubns.

Studies in Hebrews. H. C. G. Moule. LC 77-79181. (Kregel Popular Commentary Ser.). 120p. 1977. kivar 5.95 (ISBN 0-8254-3223-5). Kregel.

Studies in Hegelian Cosmology. 2nd ed. John M. McTaggart. 1986. lib. bdg. 25.00x (ISBN 0-935005-59-5); pap. text ed. 13.00x (ISBN 0-935005-60-9). Ibis Pub VA.

Studies in Hinduism. Rene Guenon. 1986. 18.50x (ISBN 0-8364-1548-5, Pub. by Navrang). South Asia Bks.

Studies in Humanism. facs. ed. John W. Mackail. LC 73-84322. (Essay Index Reprint Ser). 1938. 17.75 (ISBN 0-8369-1092-3). Ayer Co Pubs.

Studies in Idealism. High I. Fausset. 278p. 1982. Repr. of 1923 ed. lib. bdg. 30.00 (ISBN 0-89760-230-7). Telegraph Bks.

Studies in Indian Temple Architecture. Pramod Chandra. LC 75-904089. 1975. 40.00x (ISBN 0-88386-649-8). South Asia Bks.

Studies in Islamic & Judaic Traditions. Ed. by William M. Brinner & Stephen D. Ricks. (Brown Judaic Studies). 287p. 1986. 29.95 (ISBN 1-55540-047-7, 14-01-10); pap. 24.95 (ISBN 1-55540-048-5). Scholars Pr GA.

Studies in Islamic Economics. Ed. by Khurshid Ahmad. 390p. (Orig.). 1980. 31.50x (ISBN 0-86037-066-6, Pub. by Islamic Found UK); pap. 15.95 (ISBN 0-86037-067-4). New Era Pubns MI.

Studies in Islamic History & Civilization. Ed. by Uriel Heyd. (Scripta Hierosolymitana Ser.: Vol. 9). pap. 60.00 (ISBN 0-317-08597-2, 2051596). Bks Demand UMI.

Studies in Islamic Mysticism. Reynold A. Nicholson. LC 78-73958. 1979. pap. 16.95 (ISBN 0-521-29546-7). Cambridge U Pr.

Studies in Jainism. Ed. by M. P. Marathe et al. 267p. 1986. pap. 9.50X (ISBN 0-8364-1665-1, Pub. by Abhinav India). South Asia Bks.

Studies in James & Jude. Robert Taylor. 2.50 (ISBN 0-89315-293-5). Lambert Bk.

Studies in Japanese Buddhism. A. K. Reischauer. LC 73-107769. Repr. of 1917 ed. 24.50 (ISBN 0-404-05237-1). AMS Pr.

Studies in Japanese Buddhism. August Reischauer. 75.00 (ISBN 0-8490-1147-7). Gordon Pr.

Studies in Jewish & Christian History, Pt. 3. Elias Bickerman. (Arbeiten zur Geschichte des antiken Judentums und des Urchristentums Ser.: Band 9). xvi, 392p. 1986. 93.50 (ISBN 90-04-07480-5, Pub. by E J Brill). Heinman.

Studies in Jewish & World Folklore. Haim Schwarzbaum. (Fabula Supplement Ser., No. B 3). 1968. 97.50x (ISBN 3-11-000393-7). De Gruyter.

Studies in Jewish Bibliography & Related Subjects in Memory of Abraham Solomon Freidus (1867-1923) Georg Schweinfurth. 814p. 1929. Repr. text ed. 124.20x (ISBN 0-576-80130-5, Pub. by Gregg Intl Pubs England). Gregg Intl.

Studies in Jewish Bibliography, History & Literature: In Honor of I. Edward Kiev. Charles Berlin. 1971. 50.00x (ISBN 0-87068-143-5). Ktav.

Studies in Jewish Demography. U. O. Schmelz. 1983. 25.00x (ISBN 0-88125-013-9). Ktav.

Studies in Jewish Education & Judaica in Honor of Louis Newman. Alexander M. Shapiro & Burton I. Cohen. 1984. 20.00 (ISBN 0-317-13172-9). Ktav.

Studies in Jewish Folklore. Dov Noy. 1981. 25.00x (ISBN 0-915938-02-2). Ktav.

Studies in Jewish History & Booklore. A. Marx. 472p. 1944. text ed. 49.68x (ISBN 0-576-80136-4, Pub. by Gregg Intl Pubs England). Gregg Intl.

Studies in Jewish Jurisprudence. Ed. by Abraham Fuss. (Studies in Jewish Jurisprudence Ser.: Vol. 4). 320p. 1975. 14.50 (ISBN 0-87203-058-X). Hermon.

Studies in Jewish Law & Philosophy. I. Twersky. 39.50x (ISBN 0-87068-335-7). Ktav.

Studies in Jewish Law I: The Touro Conference Volume. Bernard S. Jackson & Jewish Law Association, International Congress Staff. LC 84-1329. (SP Occasional Papers & Proceedings: No. 3). 1985. 26.75 (ISBN 0-89130-732-X, 15-00-01); pap. 17.75 (ISBN 0-89130-868-7). Scholars Pr GA.

Studies in Jewish Literature Issued in Honor of Professor Kaufmann Kohler, Ph.D. David Philipson et al. Ed. by Steven Katz. LC 79-7167. (Jewish Philosophy, Mysticism & History of Ideas Ser.). 1980. Repr. of 1913 ed. lib. bdg. 26.50x (ISBN 0-405-12283-7). Ayer Co Pubs.

Studies in Jewish Mysticism. Ed. by Joseph Dan & Frank Talmage. 25.00x (ISBN 0-915938-03-0). Ktav.

Studies in Jewish Nationalism. Leon Simon. LC 75-6458. (Rise of Jewish Nationalism & the Middle East Ser.). xi, 174p. 1975. Repr. of 1920 ed. 19.80 (ISBN 0-88355-343-0). Hyperion Conn.

Studies in Jewish Theology. A. Marmorstein. 376p. Repr. of 1950 ed. text ed. 49.68x (ISBN 0-576-80153-4, Pub. by Gregg Intl Pubs England). Gregg Intl.

Studies in Jewish Theology: The Arthur Marmorstein Memorial Volume. Arthur Marmorstein. Ed. by Joseph Rabbinowitz & Meyer S. Lew. LC 76-39174. (Essay Index Reprint Ser.). Repr. of 1950 ed. 21.00 (ISBN 0-8369-2702-8). Ayer Co Pubs.

Studies in Jonah. John L. Kachelman. pap. 5.50 (ISBN 0-89137-319-5). Quality Pubns.

Studies in Joshua-Job. William R. Newell. LC 83-19899. (Old Testament Studies). 224p. 1983. kivar 7.95 (ISBN 0-8254-3314-2). Kregel.

Studies in Joshua, Judges, Ruth. Willard W. Winter. (Bible Study Textbook Ser.). (Illus.). 1969. 15.90 (ISBN 0-89900-010-X). College Pr Pub.

Studies in Judaism. facsimile ed. Solomon Schechter. LC 78-38775. (Essay Index Reprint Ser). Repr. of 1896 ed. 19.50 (ISBN 0-8369-2670-6). Ayer Co Pubs.

Studies in Judges. John Kackelman, Jr. 1986. pap. 5.95 (ISBN 0-89137-564-3). Quality Pubns.

Studies in Late Medieval & Renaissance Painting in Honor of Millard Meiss. Ed. by Irving Lavin & John Plummer. LC 75-27118. 550p. 1978. 200.00x set (ISBN 0-8147-4963-1); Vol. I (ISBN 0-8147-5001-X); Vol. II (ISBN 0-8147-4978-X). NYU Pr.

Studies in Literature & Belief. facsimile ed. Martin Jarrett-Kerr. LC 74-134101. (Essay Index Reprint Ser). Repr. of 1954 ed. 18.00 (ISBN 0-8369-1978-5). Ayer Co Pubs.

Studies in Literature & History. facs. ed. Alfred C. Lyall. LC 68-29227. (Essay Index Reprint Ser). 1968. Repr. of 1915 ed. 21.50 (ISBN 0-8369-0637-3). Ayer Co Pubs.

Studies in Luke-Acts. Ed. by Leander E. Keck & J. Louis Martyn. LC 79-8886. 324p. 1980. pap. 9.95 (ISBN 0-8006-1379-1, 1-1379). Fortress.

Studies in Lutheran Doctrine. Paul F. Keller. LC 60-15574. (YA) 1959. pap. 5.50 (ISBN 0-570-03517-1, 14-1265); correction & profile chart 0.40 (ISBN 0-570-03526-0, 14-1267); tests 0.45 (ISBN 0-570-03525-2, 14-1266). Concordia.

Studies in Lutheran Hermeneutics. Ed. by John Reumann et al. LC 78-14673. 352p. 1979. 15.95 (ISBN 0-8006-0534-9, 1-534). Fortress.

Studies in Maimonidean Medicine. Ed. by J. I. Dienstag. (Texts, Studies & Translations in Maimonidean Thought & Scholarship: Vol.2). 35.00x (ISBN 0-87068-449-3). Ktav.

Studies in Maimonides & Spinoza. Ed. by J. I. Dienstag. (Texts, Studies & Translations in Maimonidean Thought & Scholarship: Vol. 3). 35.00x (ISBN 0-87068-330-6). Ktav.

Studies in Marriage & Funerals of Taiwan Aborigines. Ch'en Kou-Chun. (Asian Folklore & Social Life Monograph: No. 4). (Chinese.). 1970. 14.00 (ISBN 0-89986-007-9). Oriental Bk Store.

Studies in Medieval Cistercian History, Vol. 2. Ed. by J. R. Sommerfeldt. (Studies Ser.: No. 24). 1977. pap. 10.95 (ISBN 0-87907-824-3). Cistercian Pubns.

Studies in Medieval Jewish History & Literature. Ed. by Isadore Twersky. LC 79-11588. (Judaic Monographs: No. 2). 1979. text ed. 25.00x (ISBN 0-674-85192-7). Harvard U Pr.

Studies in Medieval Jewish History & Literature, Vol. 2. Ed. by Isadore Twersky. (Harvard Judaic Monographs: No. V). 460p. 1985. text ed. 25.00x (ISBN 0-674-85193-5). Harvard U Ctr Jewish.

Studies in Medieval Painting. Bernard Berenson. LC 73-153884. (Graphic Art Ser.). (Illus.). 148p. 1971. Repr. of 1930 ed. lib. bdg. 39.50 (ISBN 0-306-70292-4). Da Capo.

Studies in Medieval Thought & Learning from Abelard to Wyclif. Beryl Smalley. (Illus.). 455p. 1982. 45.00 (ISBN 0-9506882-6-6). Hambledon Press.

Studies in Milton. Sten Lijegren. LC 67-30816. (Studies in Milton, No. 22). 1969. Repr. of 1918 ed. lib. bdg. 75.00x (ISBN 0-8383-0718-3). Haskell.

Studies in Milton. Sten B. Liljegren. 1918. lib. bdg. 20.00 (ISBN 0-8414-5707-7). Folcroft.

Studies in Milton & an Essay on Poetry. Alden Sampson. LC 71-126686. 1970. Repr. of 1913 ed. 24.00 (ISBN 0-404-05555-9). AMS Pr.

Studies in Mo-So Tribal Stories. Li Lin-Tsan. (Asian Folklore & Social Life Monograph: No. 3). (Chinese.). 1970. 17.00 (ISBN 0-89986-006-0). Oriental Bk Store.

Studies in Monastic Theology. Odo Brooke. (Cistercian Studies Ser.: No. 37). 1980. 8.95 (ISBN 0-87907-837-5). Cistercian Pubns.

Studies in Muslim Philosophy. M. Saeed. 12.00 (ISBN 0-686-18601-X). Kazi Pubns.

Studies in Muslim Philosophy. M. Saeed Sheikh. 248p. (Orig.). 1981. pap. 11.75 (ISBN 0-88004-008-4). Sunwise Turn.

Studies in Mystical Religion. Jones M. Rufus. 1978. Repr. of 1919 ed. lib. bdg. 45.00 (ISBN 0-8492-1257-X). R West.

Studies in Mysticism & Religion. cancelled (ISBN 0-686-76265-7). Feldheim.

Studies in New England Puritanism. Ed. by Winfried Herget. 240p. 1983. 28.95. P Lang Pubs.

Studies in New England Transcendentalism. H. C. Goddard. 1978. Repr. of 1960 ed. lib. bdg. 30.00 (ISBN 0-8492-4906-6). R West.

Studies in Paul. Nils A. Dahl. LC 77-84083. 1977. pap. 10.95 (ISBN 0-8066-1608-3, 10-6100). Augsburg.

Studies in Paul's Epistles. Frederic L. Godet. LC 84-7138. 352p. 1984. 14.95 (ISBN 0-8254-2723-1). Kregel.

Studies in Perfectionism. Benjamin B. Warfield. 1958. 12.95 (ISBN 0-87552-528-8). Presby & Reformed.

Studies in Personalism. Edgar S. Brightman. Ed. by Warren Steinkraus & Robert Beck. (Signature Series of Philosophy & Religion). Date not set. 16.00 (ISBN 0-86610-067-9). Meridian Pub.

Studies in Philemon. W. Graham Scroggie. LC 77-79186. (W. Graham Scroggie Library). 136p. 1982. pap. 4.50 (ISBN 0-8254-3739-3). Kregel.

Studies in Philippians. R. C. Bell. 1956. pap. 2.75 (ISBN 0-88027-043-8). Firm Foun Pub.

Studies in Philippians. H. C. G. Moule. LC 77-79184. (Kregel Popular Commentary Ser.). 136p. 1977. kivar 6.95 (ISBN 0-8254-3216-2). Kregel.

Studies in Philosophy & the History of Philosophy, Vol. 4. Ed. by John K. Ryan. LC 61-66336. Repr. of 1969 ed. 59.50 (ISBN 0-8357-9057-6, 2017279). Bks Demand UMI.

Studies in Philosophy & Theology. Ed. by Emil C. Wilm. LC 75-3078. Repr. of 1922 ed. 17.00 (ISBN 0-404-59079-9). AMS Pr.

Studies in Proverbs. William Arnot. LC 78-6014. (Reprint Library). Orig. Title: Laws From Heaven for Life on Earth. 584p. 1986. pap. 14.95 (ISBN 0-8254-2123-3). Kregel.

Studies in Proverbs. Maurice Meredith. pap. 2.50 (ISBN 0-89315-261-7). Lambert Bk.

Studies in Proverbs: Wise Words in a Wicked World. Charles W. Turner. (Contemporary Discussion Ser.). 1977. pap. 3.50 (ISBN 0-8010-8815-1). Baker Bk.

Studies in Psalms, Vol. I. Joseph B. Rotherham. Ed. by Don DeWelt. (Bible Study Textbook Ser.). (Illus.). 1970. Repr. 14.30 (ISBN 0-89900-016-9). College Pr Pub.

Studies in Psalms, Vol. II. rev. ed. Joseph B. Rotherham. Ed. by Don DeWelt. (Bible Study Textbook Ser.). (Illus.). 1971. Repr. of 1901 ed. 14.30 (ISBN 0-89900-017-7). College Pr Pub.

Studies in Qur'an & Hadith: The Formation of the Islamic Law of Inheritance. David S. Powers. 1986. text ed. 30.00x (ISBN 0-520-05558-6). U of Cal Pr.

Studies in Religion & Education. J. Hull. 292p. 1984. 29.00x (ISBN 0-905273-52-4, Falmer Pr); pap. 17.00x (ISBN 0-905273-51-6). Taylor & Francis.

Studies in Religion in Early American Literature: Edwards, Poe, Channing, Emerson, Some Minor Transcendentalists, Hawthorne & Thoreau. David Lyttle. 262p. (Orig.). 1984. lib. bdg. 28.50 (ISBN 0-8191-3499-6). U Pr of Amer.

Studies in Religious Fundamentalism. Ed. by Lionel Caplan. 240p. 1987. 39.50 (ISBN 0-88706-518-X); pap. 14.95 (ISBN 0-88706-519-8). State U NY Pr.

Studies in Religious Philosophy & Mysticism. Alexander Altmann. (New Reprints in Essay & General Literature Index Ser.). 1975. Repr. of 1969 ed. 24.25 (ISBN 0-518-10194-0). Ayer Co Pubs.

Studies in Religious Poetry of the Seventeenth Century: Essays on Henry Vaughn, Francis Quarles, Richard Crawshaw, John Davies, Henry More & Thomas Traherne. W. L. Doughty. LC 68-26278. Repr. of 1946 ed. 21.00x (ISBN 0-8046-0113-5, Pub. by Kennikat). Assoc Faculty Pr.

Studies in Revelation. W. M. Davis. 1976. pap. 2.75 (ISBN 0-88027-044-6). Firm Foun Pub.

Studies in Revelation, 4 Vols. H. M. Freligh. Ed. by E. H. Schroeder. 327p. 1969. pap. text ed. 2.50 ea.; Vol. 1. (ISBN 0-87509-140-7); Vol. 2. (ISBN 0-87509-141-5); Vol. 3. (ISBN 0-87509-142-3); Vol. 4. (ISBN 0-87509-143-1). Chr Pubns.

Studies in Revelation. Herman A. Hoyt. pap. 5.95 (ISBN 0-88469-118-7). BMH Bks.

Studies in Revelation. W. Leon Tucker. LC 80-16206. (Kregel Bible Study Classics Ser.). 400p. 1980. 14.95 (ISBN 0-8254-3826-8). Kregel.

Studies in Roman Literature, Culture & Religion. Hendrik Wagenvoort. Ed. by Steele Commager. LC 77-70817. (Latin Poetry Ser.: Vol. 31). 1978. lib. bdg. 40.00 (ISBN 0-8240-2981-X). Garland Pub.

Studies in Romans. R. C. Bell. 1957. pap. 2.75 (ISBN 0-88027-025-X). Firm Foun Pub.

Studies in Romans. H. C. G. Moule. LC 77-79180. (Kregel Popular Commentary Ser.). 270p. 1977. kivar 8.95 (ISBN 0-8254-3215-4). Kregel.

Studies in Romans. W. Leon Tucker. LC 83-6114. 112p. 1983. pap. 4.95 (ISBN 0-8254-3827-6). Kregel.

Studies in Romans, Vol. 1. Richard Brown. (Bible Study Ser.). 1986. pap. 3.50 (ISBN 0-8309-0452-2). Herald Hse.

Studies in Romans, Vol. 2. Richard A. Brown. (Bible Study Ser.). 1986. pap. 3.50 (ISBN 0-8309-0454-9). Herald Hse.

Studies in Romans: A Suggestive Commentary on Paul's Epistle to the Romans, 2 vols. in 1. Thomas Robinson. LC 82-7795. (Kregel Bible Study Classics Ser.). 912p. 1982. 24.95 (ISBN 0-8254-3625-7). Kregel.

Studies in Scripture: The Gospels, Vol. 5. Compiled by Kent P. Jackson & Robert Millet. 1986. text ed. 15.95 (ISBN 0-87579-064-X). Deseret Bk.

Studies in Scripture: The Old Testament, Vol. III. Robert Millett & Kent Jackson. 345p. 1985. 13.95 (ISBN 0-934126-81-X). Randall Bk Co.

Studies in Scripture, Vol. Six: Acts to Revelation. Ed. by Robert L. Millet. 1987. 15.95 (ISBN 0-87579-084-4). Deseret Bk.

Studies in Second Corinthians. Don Compier. (Bible Study Ser.). 1987. pap. 3.50 (ISBN 0-8309-0479-4). Herald Hse.

Studies in Second Corinthians. Wallace Wartick. (Bible Student Study Guides Ser.). 1977. pap. 2.95 (ISBN 0-89900-155-6). College Pr Pub.

Studies in Second Timothy. H. C. G. Moule. LC 77-79182. (Kregel Popular Commentary Ser.). 180p. 1977. kivar 6.95 (ISBN 0-8254-3219-7). Kregel.

Studies in Sephardic Culture: The David N. Barocas Memorial Volume. Ed. by Marc D. Angel. LC 79-92737. (Illus.). 190p. 1980. 15.00 (ISBN 0-87203-090-3). Hermon.

Studies in Sexual Inversion. John A. Symonds. LC 72-9683. Repr. of 1928 ed. 32.50 (ISBN 0-404-57503-X). AMS Pr.

Studies in Shakespeare, Milton & Donne. Oscar J. Campbell et al. Ed. by Eugene S. McCartney. LC 78-93244. (University of Michigan Publications: Vol. 1). 235p. 1970. Repr. of 1925 ed. 20.00x (ISBN 0-87753-020-3). Phaeton.

Studies in Spinoza: Critical & Interpretative Essays. Ed. by S. Paul Kashap. LC 71-174459. 360p. 1973. pap. 10.95x (ISBN 0-520-02590-3, CAMPUS 109). U of Cal Pr.

Studies in Statecraft. Geoffrey Butler. LC 79-110899. 1970. Repr. of 1920 ed. 17.00x (ISBN 0-8046-0882-2, Pub. by Kennikat). Assoc Faculty Pr.

Studies in Sublime Failure. Shane Leslie. LC 70-117817. (Essay Index Reprint Ser). 1932. 20.00 (ISBN 0-8369-1670-0). Ayer Co Pubs.

Studies in Targum Jonathan to the Prophets. Pinchas Churgin & Leivy Smolar. 59.50x (ISBN 0-87068-109-5). Ktav.

Studies in Tertullian & Augustine. Benjamin B. Warfield. Repr. of 1930 ed. lib. bdg. 29.00x (ISBN 0-8371-4490-6, WATT). Greenwood.

Studies in the American Jewish Experience II: Contributions from the Fellowship Programs of the American Jewish Archives. Ed. by Jacob R. Marcus & Abraham J. Peck. 228p. (Orig.). 1984. lib. bdg. 25.25 (ISBN 0-8191-3714-6); pap. text ed. 12.25 (ISBN 0-8191-3715-4). U Pr of Amer.

Studies in the Book of Acts. Charles J. Vaughan. 620p. 1985. smythe sewn 24.95 (ISBN 0-86524-189-9, 4404). Klock & Klock.

Studies in the Book of Esther. Carey A. Moore. 1982. 59.50x (ISBN 0-87068-718-2). Ktav.

Studies in the Book of Job. Ed. by Walter Aufrecht. (SR Supplements Ser.: No. 16). 104p. 1985. pap. text ed. 8.95x (ISBN 0-88920-179-X, Pub. by Wilfrid Laurier Canada). Humanities.

Studies in the Book of Judges. John M. Lang. 473p. 1983. Repr. lib. bdg. 17.75 Smythe Sewn (ISBN 0-86524-151-1, 0603). Klock & Klock.

Studies in the Books of Kings. T. Kirk & G. Rawlinson. 556p. 1983. lib. bdg. 20.75 Smythe Sewn (ISBN 0-86524-155-4, 1301). Klock & Klock.

Studies in the Buddhistic Culture of India. 2nd rev. ed. Lalman Joshi. 1977. 28.00 (ISBN 0-89684-325-4, Pub. by Motilal Banarsidass India). Orient Bk Dist.

Studies in the Buddhistic Culture of India (During the 7th & 8th Centuries A.D.) Lal M. Joshi. 1977. text ed. 35.00x (ISBN 0-8426-1056-1). Verry.

Studies in the Covenant of Grace. David L. Neilands. 1981. pap. 5.75 (ISBN 0-87552-365-X). Presby & Reformed.

Studies in the Early British Church. Nora K. Chadwick et al. LC 73-673. vii, 374p. 1973. Repr. of 1958 ed. 32.50 (ISBN 0-208-01315-6, Archon). Shoe String.

Studies in the Early History of Judaism. Solomon Zeitlin. Vol. 3. 49.50x (ISBN 0-87068-278-4); Vol. 4. 49.50x (ISBN 0-87068-454-X). Ktav.

Studies in the Early History of Judaism, Vol. 1. Solomon Zeitlin. 1973. 59.50x (ISBN 0-87068-208-3). Ktav.

Studies in the Early History of Judaism, Vol. 2. Solomon Zeitlin. 1973. 59.50x (ISBN 0-87068-209-1). Ktav.

Studies in the English Mystery Plays. Charles Davidson. LC 68-752. (Studies in Drama, No. 39). 1969. Repr. of 1892 ed. lib. bdg. 49.95x (ISBN 0-8383-0536-9). Haskell.

Studies in the English Mystics: Book to a Mother, No. 1. Adrian J. McCarthy. Ed. by James Hogg. (Elizabethan & Renaissance Studies). 275p. (Orig.). 1981. pap. 15.00 (ISBN 3-7052-0742-3, Pub. by Salzburg Studies). Longwood Pub Group.

Studies in the Epistle to the Romans. Hermann Olshausen. 438p. 1983. lib. bdg. 16.50 (ISBN 0-86524-163-5, 4503). Klock & Klock.

Studies in the First Book of Samuel. W. J. Deane & T. Kirt. 509p. 1983. lib. bdg. 19.00 Smythe Sewn (ISBN 0-86524-150-3, 0902). Klock & Klock.

Studies in the First Six Upanisads, & the Isa & Kena Upanisads with the Commentary of Sankara. Srisa Chandra Vasu. Tr. by Srisa Chandra Vidyarnava. LC 73-3814. (Sacred Books of the Hindus: No. 22, Pt. 1). Repr. of 1919 ed. 14.50 (ISBN 0-404-57822-5). AMS Pr.

Studies in the form of Sirach 44-50. Thomas R. Lee. (Dissertation Ser.). 284p. 1986. 17.95 (ISBN 0-89130-834-2, 06-01-75); pap. 13.95 (ISBN 0-89130-835-0). Scholars Pr GA.

Studies in the Four Gospels, 4 vols. G. Campbell Morgan. Incl. The Gospel According to Matthew. 320p (ISBN 0-8007-0122-4); The Gospel According to Mark. 352p (ISBN 0-8007-0121-6); The Gospel According to Luke. 288p (ISBN 0-8007-0120-8); The Gospel According to John. 336p (ISBN 0-8007-0119-4). Set. 49.95 (ISBN 0-8007-0373-1); one-volume ed. 27.95 (ISBN 0-8007-0297-2); 13.95 ea. Revell.

Studies in the Gospel of Mark. Martin Hengel. Tr. by John Bowden. LC 85-4508. 216p. 1985. pap. 12.95 (ISBN 0-8006-1881-5). Fortress.

Studies in the History of Philosophy & Religion, Vol. I. Harry A. Wolfson. Ed. by Isadore Twersky & George H. Williams. LC 72-86385. 640p. 1973. 40.00x (ISBN 0-674-84765-2). Harvard U Pr.

Studies in the History of Philosophy & Religion, Vol. II. Harry A. Wolfson. Ed. by Isadore Twersky & George H. Williams. 1977. 40.00x (ISBN 0-674-84766-0). Harvard U Pr.

Studies in the History of Worship in Scotland. Ed. by Duncan B. Forrester & Douglas M. Murray. 190p. 1984. pap. 15.95 (ISBN 0-567-29349-1, Pub. by T&T Clark Ltd UK). Fortress.

Studies in the Inner Life of Jesus. A. E. Garvie. 1977. lib. bdg. 69.95 (ISBN 0-8490-2705-5). Gordon Pr.

Studies in the Lankavatara Sutra: An Elucidation & Analysis of One of the Most Important Texts of Mahayana Buddhism, in Which Almost All Its Principal Tenets Are Presented Including the Teaching of Zen. Daisetz T. Suzuki. 1968. Repr. of 1930 ed. 31.00 (ISBN 0-7100-6330-X). Methuen Inc.

Studies in the Life of Christ. R. C. Foster. 1979. Repr. 29.95 (ISBN 0-8010-3452-3). Baker Bk.

Studies in the Milton Tradition. John W. Good. LC 73-144619. Repr. of 1915 ed. 16.00 (ISBN 0-404-02862-4). AMS Pr.

Studies in the Milton Tradition. John W. Good. Repr. of 1915 ed. 22.00 (ISBN 0-384-19150-9). Johnson Repr.

Studies in the Miracles of Our Lord. John Laidlaw. 390p. 1984. lib. bdg. 14.75 (ISBN 0-86524-168-6, 9518). Klock & Klock.

Studies in the Origin of Buddhism. 2nd rev. ed. G. C. Pande. 1974. 30.00 (ISBN 0-8426-0547-9). Orient Bk Dist.

Studies in the Parables of Our Lord. John Laidlaw. 352p. 1984. 13.25 (ISBN 0-86524-183-X, 9521). Klock & Klock.

Studies in the Pentateuch. William R. Newell. LC 83-19903. (Old Testament Studies). 272p. 1983. kivar 7.95 (ISBN 0-8254-3313-4). Kregel.

Studies in the Period of David & Solomon & Other Essays: Papers Read at the International Symposium for Biblical Studies, 6-7 December 1979. Ed. by T. Ishida. LC 82-11183. 409p. 1982. text ed. 35.00x (ISBN 0-931464-16-1). Eisenbrauns.

Studies in the Philosophy of Kierkegaard. Klemke. 1976. pap. 16.00 (ISBN 90-247-1852-X, Pub. by Martinus Nijhoff Netherlands). Kluwer Academic.

Studies in the Philosophy of Religion. A. Seth Pringle-Pattison. LC 77-27204. (Gifford Lectures: 1923). Repr. of 1930 ed. 30.00 (ISBN 0-404-60474-9). AMS Pr.

Studies in the Posthumous Works of Spinoza: On Style, Earliest Translation & Reception, Earliest & Modern Edition of Some Texts. Fokke Akkerman. vi, 285p. (Orig.). 1980. pap. 17.00x (ISBN 0-317-19838-6, Pub. by Boumas Boekhuis Netherlands). Benjamins North AM.

Studies in the Problem of Sovereignty. Harold J. Laski. 1968. Repr. 29.50x (ISBN 0-86527-191-7). Fertig.

Studies in the Prophecy of Jeremiah. G. Campbell & Morgan. 288p. 13.95 (ISBN 0-8007-0298-0). Revell.

Studies in the Psychology of the Mystics. Joseph Marechal. LC 65-1694. 1964. lib. bdg. 12.95x (ISBN 0-87343-044-1). Magi Bks.

Studies in the Puranic Records on Hindu Rites & Customs. 2nd ed. R. C. Hazra. 1975. 28.00 (ISBN 0-8426-0965-2). Orient Bk Dist.

Studies in the Religious Life of Ancient & Medieval India. D. C. Sircar. 1971. 9.95 (ISBN 0-89684-326-2). Orient Bk Dist.

Studies in the Scriptures, 1946. A. W. Pink. pap. 9.45 (ISBN 0-85151-346-8). Banner of Truth.

Studies in the Scriptures, 1947. A. W. Pink. 298p. pap. 9.45 (ISBN 0-85151-347-6). Banner of Truth.

Studies in the Sermon on the Mount. Oswald Chambers. 1973. pap. 2.95 (ISBN 0-87508-136-3). Chr Lit.

Studies in the Sermon on the Mount. D. Martyn Lloyd-Jones. 1984. 12.95 (ISBN 0-8028-0036-X). Eerdmans.

Studies in the Shemoth, 2 vols. Leibowitz. 1976. 17.50 (ISBN 0-685-71930-8). Feldheim.

Studies in the Tantras & the Veda. M. P. Pandit. 1973. 3.95 (ISBN 0-89744-110-9, Pub. by Ganesh & Co India). Auromere.

Studies in the Text of Jeremiah. John G. Janzen. LC 73-81265. (Harvard Semitic Monographs: Vol. 6). pap. 64.00 (ISBN 0-317-09145-X, 2021591). Bks Demand UMI.

Studies in the Use of Fire in the Ancient Greek Religion. rev. ed. William D. Furley. Ed. by W. R. Connor. LC 80-2650. (Monographs in Clasical Studies). (Illus.). 1981. lib. bdg. 29.00 (ISBN 0-405-14037-1). Ayer Co Pubs.

Studies in Theism. Borden P. Bowne. LC 7-25071. 1968. Repr. of 1907 ed. 28.00 (ISBN 0-527-10450-7). Kraus Repr.

Studies in Theology. Loraine Boettner. 1947. 7.95 (ISBN 0-87552-131-2). Presby & Reformed.

Studies in Titus & Philemon. Robert Taylor, Jr. 2.50 (ISBN 0-89315-287-0). Lambert Bk.

Studies in Vayikra. 1982. 8.95 (ISBN 0-686-76262-2). Feldheim.

Studies in West African Islamic History: The Cultivators of Islam, Vol. 1. Ed. by John R. Willis. (Illus.). 325p. 1979. 39.50x (ISBN 0-7146-1737-7, F Cass Co). Biblio Dist.

Studies of A. J. Wensinck: An Original Arno Press Anthology. Ed. by Kees W. Bolle. LC 77-82275. (Mythology Ser.). 1978. lib. bdg. 17.00x (ISBN 0-405-10567-3). Ayer Co Pubs.

Studies of Arianism: Chiefly Referring to the Character & Chronology of the Reaction Which Followed the Council of Nicaea. 2nd ed. Henry M. Gwatkin. LC 77-84703. Repr. of 1900 ed. 38.00 (ISBN 0-404-16110-3). AMS Pr.

Studies of Contemporary Superstition. William H. Mallock. LC 72-333. (Essay Index Reprint Ser.). Repr. of 1895 ed. 20.00 (ISBN 0-8369-2804-0). Ayer Co Pubs.

Studies of English Mystics. facs. ed. William R. Inge. LC 69-17578. (Essay Index Reprint Ser). 1906. 15.00 (ISBN 0-8369-0081-2). Ayer Co Pubs.

Studies of the Book of Mormon. B. H. Roberts. Ed. by Brigham D. Madsen. LC 84-236. (Illus.). 412p. 1985. 21.95 (ISBN 0-252-01043-4). U of Ill Pr.

Studies of the Church in History: Essays Honoring Robert S. Paul on His Sixty-Fifth Birthday, Vol. X. Ed. by Horton Davies. (Pittsburgh Theological Monographs. New Series: No. 5). 276p. (Orig.). 1983. pap. 16.95 (ISBN 0-686-45571-1). Pickwick.

Studies of the Spanish Mystics, 3 vols. E. A. Peers. 1977. lib. bdg. 300.00 (ISBN 0-8490-2706-3). Gordon Pr.

Studies of Type-Images in Poetry, Religion & Philosophy. Maud Bodkin. LC 74-14665. 1951. lib. bdg. 15.00 (ISBN 0-8414-3273-2). Folcroft.

Studies on Islam. Merlin L. Swartz et al. 1981. 22.50x (ISBN 0-19-502716-7); pap. 10.95x (ISBN 0-19-502717-5). Oxford U Pr.

Studies on Palestine During the Ottoman Period. Ed. by Moshe Ma'Oz. 582p. 1975. text ed. 40.00x (Pub. by Magnes Pr Israel). Humanities.

Studies on Religion & Politics. Ed. by Jerome J. Hanus & James V. Schall. LC 86-9166. 120p. (Orig.). 1986. lib. bdg. 28.50 (ISBN 0-8191-5391-5); pap. text ed. 12.75 (ISBN 0-8191-5392-3). U Pr of Amer.

Studies on the Early Papacy. H. John Chapman. LC 76-118517. 1971. Repr. of 1928 ed. 23.00x (ISBN 0-8046-1139-4, Pub. by Kennikat). Assoc Faculty Pr.

Studies on the Iconography of Cosmic Kingship in the Ancient World. H. P. L'Orange. (Illus.). 206p. 1982. Repr. of 1953 ed. lib. bdg. 50.00X (ISBN 0-89241-150-3). Caratzas.

Studies on the Legend of the Holy Grail with Special Reference to the Hypothesis of Its Celtic Origin. Alfred Nutt. (Folk-Lore Society, London, Monographs: Vol. 23). pap. 29.00 (ISBN 0-8115-0510-3). Kraus Repr.

Studies on the Testament of Abraham. Ed. by George W. Nickelsburg, Jr. LC 76-44205. (Society of Biblical Literature. Septuagint & Cognate Studies). 1976. pap. 13.50 (ISBN 0-89130-117-8, 060406). Scholars Pr GA.

Studies on the Testament of Joseph. Ed. by George W. Nicklesburg. LC 75-26923. (Society of Biblical Literature. Septurgint & Cognate Studies). 153p. 1975. pap. 13.50 (ISBN 0-89130-027-9, 060405). Scholars Pr GA.

Study Adventure in Trial by Fire. Anne S. White & Don Vanzant. 56p. (Orig.). 1985. pap. 1.95 (ISBN 0-89228-102-2). Impact Bks MO.

Study Edition (Lectors' Guide) of the Lectionary for Mass, Cycle A Sundays & Solemnities. Catholic Church, Sacred Congregation of Divine Worship Staff. Tr. by International Committee on English in the Liturgy, Confraternity of Christian Doctrine for the New American Bible. (The Study Edition (Lector's Guide) of the Lectionary for Mass Ser.: Texts from the New American Bible). 1977. pap. 6.95 (ISBN 0-916134-04-0). Pueblo Pub Co.

Study Edition (Lectors' Guide) of the Lectionary for Mass, Cycle B Sundays & Solemnities. Catholic Church, Sacred Congregation of Divine Worship Staff. 1978. pap. 6.95 (ISBN 0-916134-05-9). Pueblo Pub Co.

Study Edition (Lectors' Guide) of the Lectionary for Mass, Cycle C, Sunday & Solemnities. Tr. by International Committee on English in the Liturgy. (Study Edition (Lectors' Guide) of the Lectionary for Mass Ser.: Texts from the New American Bible). 1976. pap. 6.95 (ISBN 0-916134-06-7). Pueblo Pub Co.

Study Guide for Archbishop Hunthausen's Pastoral on Matrimony. rev. ed. Thomas L. Vandenberg. LC 82-62716. 59p. 1984. pap. text ed. 2.95 (ISBN 0-911905-02-2). Past & Mat Rene Ctr.

Study Guide for Ezra, Nehemiah, Esther. John F. Brug. (Study Guide for People's Bible Ser.). 60p. (Orig.). 1985. pap. 1.50 (ISBN 0-938272-53-5). Wels Board.

Study Guide for Genesis. Hagen Staack. 1984. pap. 3.95 (ISBN 0-9613270-0-6). G McBride.

Study Guide for Hebrews. Richard E. Lauersdorf. Ed. by William E. Fischer. (Study Guide for People's Bible Ser.). 48p. (Orig.). 1986. pap. 1.50 (ISBN 0-938272-56-X). WELS Board.

Study Guide for Paul's Letters to the Thessalonians. David P. Kuske. 41p. (Orig.). 1984. pap. 1.50 (ISBN 0-938272-51-9). WELS Board.

Study Guide for Philippians-Colossians & Philemon. Harlyn J. Kuschel. Ed. by William E. Fischer. (Study Guide for People's Bible Ser.). 48p. (Orig.). 1987. pap. text ed. 1.50 (ISBN 0-938272-57-8). Wels Board.

Study Guide to Greater Bible Knowledge. Wayne Jackson. 156p. (Orig.). 1986. pap. 5.00 (ISBN 0-932859-12-7). Apologetic Pr.

Study in Anti-Gnostic Polemics: Irenaeus, Hippolytus & Epiphanius. Gerard Vallee. 128p. 1981. pap. text ed. 8.95x (ISBN 0-919812-14-7, Pub. by Wilfrid Laurier Canada). Humanities.

Study in Austrian Intellectual History from Late Baroque to Romanticism. Robert A. Kann. LC 73-16356. 367p. 1973. Repr. lib. bdg. 27.50x (ISBN 0-374-94504-7, Octagon). Hippocrene Bks.

Study in Consciousness. 6th ed. Annie Besant. 1972. 7.50 (ISBN 0-8356-7287-5). Theos Pub Hse.

Study in Creative History. O. E. Burton. LC 71-105821. (Classics Ser). 1971. Repr. of 1932 ed. 26.00x (ISBN 0-8046-1197-1, Pub. by Kennikat). Assoc Faculty Pr.

Study in Daniel. Howard B. Rand. 1948. 12.00 (ISBN 0-685-08814-6). Destiny.

Study in Hosea. Howard B. Rand. 1955. 8.00 (ISBN 0-685-08815-4). Destiny.

Study in Jeremiah. Howard B. Rand. 1947. 12.00 (ISBN 0-685-08816-2). Destiny.

Study in Karma. Besant. 2.25 (ISBN 0-8356-7292-1). Theos Pub Hse.

Study in Metaphysics. Henri Bergson. LC 61-10604. 1961. pap. 5.00 (ISBN 0-8022-0107-5). Philos Lib.

Study in Milton's Christian Doctrine. Arthur Sewell. LC 72-193159. 1939. lib. bdg. 25.00 (ISBN 0-8414-8118-0). Folcroft.

Study in Milton's Christian Doctrine. Arthur Sewell. LC 67-26661. xiii, 214p. 1967. Repr. of 1939 ed. 22.50 (ISBN 0-208-00416-5, Archon). Shoe String.

Study in Revelation. Howard B. Rand. 1941. 12.00 (ISBN 0-685-08817-0). Destiny.

Study in Tolerance As Practiced by Muhammed & His Immediate Successors. Adolph L. Wismar. LC 27-24455. (Columbia University. Contributions to Oriental History & Philology: No. 13). Repr. of 1927 ed. 14.00 (ISBN 0-404-50543-0). AMS Pr.

Study of a Sixteenth-Century Tagalog Manuscript on the Ten Commandments: Its Significance & Implications. Antonio Rosales. (Illus.). 166p. 1985. text ed. 16.00x (ISBN 0-8248-0971-8). UH Pr.

Study of American Indian Religions. Ake Hultkrantz. Ed. by Christopher Vecsey. LC 82-10533. (American Academy of Religion - Studies in Religion). 142p. 1983. 12.95 (ISBN 0-89130-587-4, 01 00 29). Scholars Pr GA.

Study of Ancient Judaism, 2 vols. Jacob Neusner. 1982. Vol. I. 37.50x ea. (ISBN 0-87068-892-8). Vol. II (ISBN 0-87068-893-6). Ktav.

Study of Anthroposophy As an Aspect of the Free Spiritual Life. Alan Howard. 1985. pap. 2.00 (ISBN 0-916786-80-3). St George Bk Serv.

Study of Bible Leaders. J. J. Turner. pap. 2.50 (ISBN 0-89315-290-0). Lambert Bk.

Study of Bossuet. William J. Simpson. (Church Historical Society London N. S. Ser.: No. 22). pap. 23.00 (ISBN 0-8115-3146-5). Kraus Repr.

Study of Daniel. John A. Copeland. 1973. pap. 4.50 (ISBN 0-89137-703-4). Quality Pubns.

Study of Death: Works of Henry Mills Alden. Henry M. Alden. (Works of Henry Mills Alden Ser.). vii, 335p. 1985. Repr. of 1895 ed. 39.00 (Pub. by Am Repr Serv). Am Biog Serv.

Study of Delaware Indian Medicine Practice & Folk Beliefs. Gladys Tantaquidgeon. LC 76-43864. (Pennsylvania Historical Commission). Repr. of 1942 ed. 18.00 (ISBN 0-404-15724-6). AMS Pr.

Study of Donne's Imagery: A Revelation of His Outlook on the World & His Vision of a Christian Monarchy. Kaichi Matsuura. LC 72-7223. Repr. of 1953 ed. lib. bdg. 25.00 (ISBN 0-8414-0270-1). Folcroft.

Study of Early Christianity. Joseph B. Tyson. Ed. by Kenneth J. Scott. (Illus.). 448p. 1973. text ed. write for info. (ISBN 0-02-421900-2). Macmillan.

Study of German Hymns in Current English Hymnals. J. S. Andrews. (German Language & Literature-European University Studies: No. 1, Vol. 614). 398p. 1982. pap. 36.30 (ISBN 3-261-05068-3). P Lang Pubs.

Study of Gregory Palamas. John Meyendorff. LC 65-56528. 245p. 1964. 12.95 (ISBN 0-913836-14-1). St Vladimirs.

Study of Heliocentric Science. Swami Abhedananda. 5.95 (ISBN 0-87481-619-X). Vedanta Pr.

Study of Judaism: Bibliographical Essays, Vol. 1. 229p. 12.50 (ISBN 0-686-95147-6). ADL.

Study of Judaism: Vol. 2. Ed. by Lawrence V. Berman et al. 25.00x (ISBN 0-87068-486-8). Ktav.

Study of Liturgy. Ed. by Cheslyn Jones et al. 1978. 27.00x (ISBN 0-19-520075-6); pap. 13.95x (ISBN 0-19-520076-4). Oxford U Pr.

Study of Milton's Paradise Lost. John A. Himes. LC 76-17888. 1976. lib. bdg. 42.00 (ISBN 0-8414-4841-8). Folcroft.

Study of Minor Prophets. Brodie Crouch. pap. 2.50 (ISBN 0-89315-291-9). Lambert Bk.

Study of Religion. Morris Jastrow, Jr. Ed. by William A. Clebsch. LC 81-9184. (Classics & Reprints Series of the American Academy of Religion & Scholars Press). 1981. text ed. 10.95 (ISBN 0-89130-519-X, 01-05-01). Scholars Pr GA.

Study of Religion & Its Meaning. J. Barnhart. 1977. 25.50x (ISBN 90-279-7762-3). Mouton.

Study of Religion in Colleges & Universities. Paul Ramsey. Ed. by John F. Wilson. LC 70-90957. 336p. 1970. 37.00x (ISBN 0-691-07161-6). Princeton U Pr.

Study of Religion in Two-Year Colleges. C. Freeman Sleeper & Robert A. Spivey. LC 75-28158. (American Academy of Religion, Individual Volumes). 1975. pap. 8.95 (ISBN 0-89130-031-7, 010801). Scholars Pr GA.

Study of St. Paul: His Character & Opinions. S. Baring-Gould. 1977. lib. bdg. 59.95 (ISBN 0-8490-2712-8). Gordon Pr.

Study of Spinoza. 3rd facsimile ed. James Martineau. LC 78-152994. (Select Bibliographies Reprint Ser). Repr. of 1895 ed. 23.50 (ISBN 0-8369-5746-6). Ayer Co Pubs.

Study of Spinoza's Ethics. Jonathan Bennett. LC 83-18568. 416p. 1984. lib. bdg. 25.00 (ISBN 0-915145-82-0); pap. text ed. 13.75 (ISBN 0-915145-83-9). Hackett Pub.

Study of Svatantrika. Donald S Lopez, Jr. 490p. (Orig.). 1987. lib. bdg. 35.00 (ISBN 0-937938-20-3); pap. 19.95 (ISBN 0-937938-19-X). Snow Lion.

Study of the Bible. rev. ed. Ernest C. Colwell. LC 64-23411. (Midway Reprint Ser.). pap. 54.50 (2026769). Bks Demand UMI.

Study of the Bible in the Middle Ages. Beryl Smalley. 1964. pap. 9.95x (ISBN 0-268-00267-3). U of Notre Dame Pr.

Study of the Book of Genesis. Gordon Talbot. LC 81-65578. 288p. (Orig.). 1981. pap. 6.95 (ISBN 0-87509-253-5); leader's guide 2.95 (ISBN 0-87509-311-6). Chr Pubns.

Study of the Delaware Indian Big House Ceremony: In Native Text Dictated by Witapanoxwe. Frank G. Speck. LC 76-43846. (Publications of the Pennsylvania Historical Commission: Vol. 2). Repr. of 1931 ed. 24.00 (ISBN 0-404-15698-3). AMS Pr.

Study of the Five Zarathustrian (Zorastrian) Gathas, 4 pts. in 1 vol, Pts. I-IV. Ed. by Lawrence H. Mills. LC 74-21252. Repr. of 1894 ed. 74.50 (ISBN 0-404-12803-3). AMS Pr.

Study of the Holy Ghost. James A. Cross. 1973. pap. 4.25 (ISBN 0-87148-006-9). Pathway Pr.

Study of the Holy Spirit. William E. Biederwolf. LC 84-25099. 128p. 1985. pap. 5.95 (ISBN 0-8254-2244-2). Kregel.

Study of the Impact of Buddhism Upon Japanese Life As Revealed in the Order of Kokin-Shu. Toyozo W. Nakarai. 59.95 (ISBN 0-8490-1156-6). Gordon Pr.

Study of the Language of Love in the Song of Songs & Ancient Egyptian Poetry. John B. White. LC 77-13399. (Society of Biblical Literature. Dissertation Ser.: Vol. 38). 1978. pap. 10.25 (ISBN 0-89130-192-5, 060138). Scholars Pr GA.

Study of the Mahavastu. Ed. by Bimala C. Law. LC 78-72469. Repr. of 1930 ed. 26.50 (ISBN 0-404-17339-X). AMS Pr.

Study of the Master Universe. Williams S. Sadler, Jr. LC 68-58958. (Illus.). 150p. 1968. 13.00 (ISBN 0-686-05760-0); pap. write for info. (ISBN 0-686-05761-9). Second Soc Foun.

Study of the Miracles. Ada R. Habershon. LC 62-19174. 336p. 1967. 12.95 (ISBN 0-8254-2801-7); pap. 9.95 (ISBN 0-8254-2851-3). Kregel.

Study of the Parables. Ada R. Habershon. LC 62-19175. 392p. 1967. 12.95 (ISBN 0-8254-2802-5); pap. 9.95 (ISBN 0-8254-2852-1). Kregel.

Study of the Psalms of Ascents: A Critical & Exegetical Commentary Upon Psalms 120-134. Cuthbert C. Keet. (Illus.). 200p. 1969. 9.50 (ISBN 0-7051-0041-3). Attic Pr.

Study of the Revelation. John A. Copeland. 1971. pap. 4.50 (ISBN 0-89137-702-6). Quality Pubns.

Study of the Sources of Bunyan's Allegories(with Special Reference to Deguileville's Pilgrimage of Man. James B. Wharey. LC 68-59038. 136p. 1968. Repr. of 1904 ed. 15.00x (ISBN 0-87752-120-4). Gordian.

Study of the Supernatural in Three Plays of Shakespeare. Edwin Wiley. LC 74-32191. 1913. lib. bdg. 15.00 (ISBN 0-8414-9382-0). Folcroft.

Study of the Types. Ada R. Habershon. LC 67-24340. 240p. 1975. pap. 7.95 (ISBN 0-8254-2850-5). Kregel.

Study of the "Villancico" up to Lope De Vega. Sr. M. Paulina St. Amour. LC 78-94170. (Catholic University of America Studies in Romance Languages & Literatures Ser: No. 21). Repr. of 1940 ed. 22.00 (ISBN 0-404-50321-7). AMS Pr.

Study of Theology. Gerhard Ebeling. Tr. by Priebe A. Duane. LC 78-5393. pap. 76.50 (2026983). Bks Demand UMI.

Study of War As a Contribution to Peace. Wolf Mendl. (Orig.). 1983. pap. 2.50x (ISBN 0-87574-247-5, 247). Pendle Hill.

Study of Yoga. 2nd rev. ed. Jajneshwar Ghosh. 1977. 16.95 (ISBN 0-89684-014-X, Pub. by Motilal Banarsidass India); pap. 12.50 (ISBN 0-89684-015-8). Orient Bk Dist.

Study on the Synoptic Gospels. Eduardo Martinez Dalmau. 1964. 5.95 (ISBN 0-8315-0013-1). Speller.

Study War No More. Ed. by David S. Young. (Orig.). 1981. pap. 3.95 (ISBN 0-87178-822-5). Brethren.

Studying the New Testament. Morna D. Hooker. LC 82-70959. 224p. (Orig.). 1982. pap. 10.95 (ISBN 0-8066-1934-1, 10-6140). Augsburg.

Studying the Old Testament. Henry McKeating. LC 82-70960. 224p. (Orig.). 1982. pap. 10.95 (ISBN 0-8066-1935-X, 10-6141). Augsburg.

Studying the Old Testament. Annemarie Ohler. 400p. 33.95 (ISBN 0-567-09335-2, Pub. by T & T Clard Ltd UK). Fortress.

Stuff of Survival. George Vandeman. (Stories That Win Ser.). 1978. pap. 1.25 (ISBN 0-8163-0209-X, 19689-9). Pacific Pr Pub Assn.

Stumbling Toward Maturity. Arnold T. Olson. LC 81-66943. (Heritage Ser.: Vol. 3). 208p. 1981. 8.95 (ISBN 0-911802-50-9). Free Church Pubns.

Style, Vol. 4. James H. Moulton. (Moulton's Grammar of New Testament Greek Ser.). 184p. 1976. 14.95 (ISBN 0-567-01018-X, Pub. by T & T Clark Ltd Uk). Fortress.

Style & Content in Christian Art. Jane Dillenberger. 320p. 1986. pap. 17.95 (ISBN 0-8245-0782-7). Crossroad NY.

Style & Content in Christian Art: From the Catacombs to the Chapel Designed by Matisse at Vence, France. Jane Dillenberger. LC 65-22293. pap. 80.50 (ISBN 0-317-10399-7, 2001274). Bks Demand UMI.

Style & Literary Method of Luke, 2 Vols. in 1. H. J. Cadbury. (Harvard Theo. Studies: No. 6). 1919-1920. 22.00 (ISBN 0-527-01006-5). Kraus Repr.

Style of Bana: An Introduction to Sanskrit Prose Poetry. Robert A. Hueckstedt. 228p. (Orig.). 1986. lib. bdg. 27.50 (ISBN 0-8191-4998-5); pap. text ed. 12.75 (ISBN 0-8191-4999-3). U Pr of Amer.

Style of John Wyclif's English Sermons. P. Knapp. 1977. 16.00x (ISBN 90-279-3156-9). Mouton.

Style of Pope St. Leo the Great, No. 59. William J. Halliwell. (Patristic Studies). 114p. 1984. 26.00x (ISBN 0-939738-25-2). Zubal Inc.

Stylistic Relationship Between Poetry & Prose in the Cantico Espiritual of San Juan De la Cruz. Sr. Rosa M. Icaza. LC 76-94191. (Catholic University of America Studies in Romance Languages & Literatures Ser: No. 54). 1969. Repr. of 1957 ed. 21.00 (ISBN 0-404-50354-3). AMS Pr.

Stylometric Study of the New Testament. Anthony Kenny. 160p. 1986. text ed. 38.00 (ISBN 0-19-826178-0). Oxford U Pr.

Su Poder Espiritual Y Emocional. Richard D. Dobbins. Tr. by Eliezer Oyola from Eng. Orig. Title: Your Spiritual & Emotional Power. (Span.). 171p. 1985. pap. 2.95 (ISBN 0-8297-0705-0). Life Pubs Intl.

Subdue Sins. large print ed. Ellen White. 41p. 1985. pap. 5.50 (ISBN 0-914009-44-3). VHI Library.

Subhasita Samgraha, Vol. III & IV. Vol. III - 142 p. pap. 2.00 (ISBN 0-686-95449-1); Vol. IV - 128 p. pap. 2.00 (ISBN 0-686-99508-2). Ananda Marga.

Subject Headings for Church or Synagogue Libraries. rev. ed. Dorothy B. Kersten. LC 78-818. (Guide Ser.: No. 8). 1984. pap. 4.95 (ISBN 0-915324-14-8); pap. 3.95 members. CSLA.

Subject Index of Holy Quran. A. Rahman. 29.00 (ISBN 0-317-14644-0). Kazi Pubns.

Subject Index of Hymns in the English Hymnal & Songs of Praise. Percy Dearmer. 59.95 (ISBN 0-8490-1159-0). Gordon Pr.

Subjectivity & Religious Belief. Stephens Evans. LC 82-40062. 238p. 1982. pap. text ed. 12.50 (ISBN 0-8191-2665-9). U Pr of Amer.

Sublime Puritan: Milton & the Victorians. James G. Nelson. LC 74-8794. (Illus.). 209p. 1974. Repr. of 1963 ed. lib. bdg. 24.75x (ISBN 0-8371-7586-0, NESP). Greenwood.

Sublimity of Faith. Frank S. Murray. LC 81-81770. (Illus.). 952p. 1982. 25.00 (ISBN 0-910840-20-2). Kingdom.

Submission Sayings of the Prophet Muhammad. Ed. by Ira Friedlander. 1977. pap. 5.95 (ISBN 0-06-090592-1, CN592, PL). Har-Row.

Submissive Wife & other Legends. Marsha Drake. 176p. (Orig.). 1987. pap. 5.95 (ISBN 0-87123-926-4). Bethany Hse.

Submitting. Churches Alive, Inc. Staff. LC 79-52131. (Love One Another Bible Study Ser.). (Illus.). 1979. wkbk. 3.00 (ISBN 0-934396-04-3). Churches Alive.

Submitting To A Sinning Husband. Wanda Burkhart. 64p. 1984. pap. 2.95 (ISBN 0-88144-042-6). Christian Pub.

Subordination & Equivalence: The Nature & Role of Women in Augustine & Thomas Aquinas. Kari E. Borresen. Tr. by Charles H. Talbot from Fr. & Ital. LC 80-67199. 390p. 1981. lib. bdg. 29.25 (ISBN 0-8191-1681-5). U Pr of Amer.

Substance & Shadow: Or, Morality & Religion in Their Relation to Life, an Essay upon the Physics of Creation. Henry James, Sr. LC 72-915. (Selected Works of Henry James, Sr.: Vol. 8). 552p. 1983. Repr. of 1863 ed. 49.50 (ISBN 0-404-10088-0). AMS Pr.

Substance, Body & Soul: Aristotelian Investigations. Edwin Hartman. LC 77-71984. 1977. text ed. 34.50x (ISBN 0-691-07223-X). Princeton U Pr.

Substance of Muhammahan Law. A. R. Chaudhri. 1970. 4.25x (ISBN 0-87902-157-8). Orientalia.

Substitute for Holiness, Or Antinomianism Revived. Daniel Steele. (Higher Christian Life Ser.). 370p. 1985. lib. bdg. 45.00 (ISBN 0-8240-6445-3). Garland Pub.

Substitution in the Hebrew Cultus, Vol. 3. Angel M. Rodriguez. (Andrews University Seminary Doctoral Dissertation Ser.). xiv, 339p. (Orig.). 1982. pap. 10.95 (ISBN 0-943872-35-9). Andrews Univ Pr.

Subtle Knot: Creative Scepticism in Seventeenth-Century England. Margaret L. Wiley. LC 68-54994. (Illus.). 1968. Repr. of 1952 ed. lib. bdg. 22.50x (ISBN 0-8371-0753-9, WISK). Greenwood.

Suburban Religion: Churches & Synagogues in the American Experience. W. Widick Schroeder et al. LC 74-82113. (Studies in Religion & Society). 1974. 19.95x (ISBN 0-913348-05-8); pap. 10.95x (ISBN 0-913348-11-2). Ctr Sci Study.

Subversion of Christianity. Jacques Ellul. Tr. by Geoffrey W. Bromiley from Fr. 224p. (Orig.). 1986. pap. 9.95 (ISBN 0-8028-0049-1). Eerdmans.

Succeeding as a Woman in Music Leadership. Judie Jones. LC 83-7249. 202p. (Orig.). 1983. pap. text ed. 8.95 perfect binding (ISBN 0-912801-00-X). Creat Arts Dev.

Success - It's Yours to Have. John J. Belmar. 1984. 5.75 (ISBN 0-8062-2305-7). Carlton.

Success Factor. Archibald D. Hart. 160p. 1984. pap. 5.95 (ISBN 0-8007-5138-8, Power Bks). Revell.

Success Fantasy. Anthony Campolo. LC 79-67852. 144p. 1980. pap. 5.95 (ISBN 0-88207-796-1). Victor Bks.

Success in God's Word: Bible Scriptures for a Fulfilling Life. Ed. by Charles R. Adams & William J. Seno. 112p. 1986. pap. 2.95 (ISBN 0-933437-01-3). Round River Pub.

Success in Marriage. David R. Mace. (Festival Ser.). 160p. 1980. pap. 3.95 (ISBN 0-687-40555-6). Abingdon.

Success, Motivation, & the Scriptures. new ed. William H. Cook. LC 74-82582. 192p. 1975. kivar 6.95 (ISBN 0-8054-5226-5). Broadman.

Success Motivation Through the Word. Charles Capps. 272p. 1982. pap. 3.95 (ISBN 0-89274-183-X, HH-183). Harrison Hse.

Success: The Glenn Bland Method. Glenn Bland. 1983. pap. 3.50 (ISBN 0-8423-6689-X). Tyndale.

Success: The Glenn Bland Method. 1975. pap. 4.95 (ISBN 0-8423-6690-3). Tyndale.

Success with Scientology. Church of Scientology Information Service Staff & L. Ron Hubbard. 112p. 1976. pap. 8.00 (ISBN 0-915598-01-9). Church of Scient Info.

Successful Children's Choir. Ruth K. Jacobs. 64p. 1984. pap. 5.00 (ISBN 0-912222-12-3). FitzSimons.

Successful Home Cell Groups. Paul Y. Cho & Harold Hostetler. LC 81-80025. 1981. pap. 5.95 (ISBN 0-88270-513-X, Pub. by Logos). Bridge Pub.

Successful Life. George Wood. Ed. by Jo Anne Sekowsky. 64p. 1984. pap. text ed. 3.25 (ISBN 0-930756-82-7, 531017). Aglow Pubns.

Successful Parishes: How They Meet the Challenge of Change. Thomas P. Sweetser. 204p. 1983. pap. 9.95 (ISBN 0-86683-694-2, HarpR). Har-Row.

Successful Single Adult Ministry. Linda Cahill et al. 144p. 1987. pap. price not set (ISBN 0-87403-229-6, 3219). Standard Pub.

Successful Soul Winning. Paul Sherrod. (Illus.). 1978. 6.95 (ISBN 0-686-14476-7, 1730394523). P Sherrod.

Successful Sunday School & Teachers Guidebook. revised ed. Elmer Towns. LC 75-23009. (Illus.). 430p. 1986. pap. 10.95 (ISBN 0-88419-118-4). Creation Hse.

Successful Sunday School Teaching. Myer Pearlman. 112p. 1935. pap. 1.35 (ISBN 0-88243-606-6, 02-0606). Gospel Pub.

Successful Writers & Editors Guidebook. Christian Writers Institute Staff. LC 76-62692. 1977. 10.95 (ISBN 0-88419-014-5). Creation Hse.

Succession in the Muslim Family. N. J. Coulson. 1971. 54.50 (ISBN 0-521-07852-0). Cambridge U Pr.

Succession to the Rule in Islam. A. Chejne. 1960. 5.30x (ISBN 0-87902-158-6). Orientalia.

Succession to the Rule in Muslim. Anwar Chejne. 154p. (Orig.). 1981. pap. 4.75 (ISBN 0-88004-001-7). Sunwise Turn.

Succession to the Throne of David. Leonhard Rost. (Historic Texts & Interpreters Ser: No. 1). Orig. Title: Uberlieferung von der Thronnachfolge Davids. 160p. 1982. text ed. 25.95x (ISBN 0-907459-12-9, Pub. by Almond Pr England); pap. text ed. 12.95x (ISBN 0-907459-13-7, Pub. by Almond Pr England). Eisenbrauns.

Successor: My Life. Kosho K. Otani. LC 84-23016. (Illus.). 114p. 1985. 16.95x (ISBN 0-914910-50-7). Buddhist Bks.

Such a Life. Edith La Zebnik. 1979. pap. 2.50 (ISBN 0-671-82282-9). PB.

Such a Vision of the Street: Mother Teresa; The Spirit & The Work. Eileen Egan. LC 81-43570. (Illus.). 456p. 1985. 16.95 (ISBN 0-385-17490-X). Doubleday.

Such a Vision of the Street: Mother Teresa-The Spirit & the Work. Eileen Egan. LC 81-43570. (Illus.). 528p. 1986. pap. 9.95 (ISBN 0-385-17491-8, Im). Doubleday.

Such Bright Hopes. Walter R. Scragg. Ed. by Raymond Woolsey. 377p. 1987. price not set (ISBN 0-8280-0389-0). Review & Herald.

Sudden Apprehension: Aspects of Knowledge in Paradise Lost. Lee A. Jacobus. (Studies in English Literature: No. 94). 225p. 1976. text ed. 27.20x (ISBN 90-2793-253-0). Mouton.

Sudden Clash of Thunder. Bhagwan Shree Rajneesh. Ed. by Ma Yoga Anurag. LC 78-901998. (Zen Ser.). (Illus.). 284p. (Orig.). 1977. 16.50 (ISBN 0-88050-135-9). Chidvilas Found.

Sudden Family. Steven Standiford & Deborah Standiford. 160p. 1986. 9.95 (ISBN 0-8499-0567-2). Word Bks.

Sudden Music. Roger White. 200p. 12.95 (ISBN 0-85398-162-0); pap. 7.95 (ISBN 0-85398-163-9). G Ronald Pub.

Suddenly It's Springtime. Vessa Harper. 1967. pap. 3.50 (ISBN 0-88027-050-0). Firm Foun Pub.

Suddenly Single. Jim Smoke. 120p. 1984. pap. 5.95 (ISBN 0-8007-5152-3, Power Bks). Revell.

Suffering. Norman B. Harrison. 1965. pap. 0.75 (ISBN 0-911802-34-7). Free Church Pubns.

Suffering. Dorothee Soelle. Tr. by Everett R. Kalin from Ger. LC 75-13036. 192p. 1975. 10.95 (ISBN 0-8006-1813-0, 1-813); pap. 5.95. Fortress.

Suffering: A Test of Theological Method. Arthur C. McGill. LC 82-6934. 130p. 1982. pap. 7.95 (ISBN 0-664-24448-3). Westminster.

Suffering & Evil. John Heagle. (Guidelines for Contemporary Catholics Ser.). (Orig.). 1987. pap. 7.95 (ISBN 0-88347-212-0). Thomas More.

Suffering & Martyrdom in the New Testament. Ed. by W. Horbury & B. McNeil. LC 80-40706. 240p. 1981. 49.50 (ISBN 0-521-23482-4). Cambridge U Pr.

Suffering & the Saints. John D. Clark. Ed. by James Goodman. 272p. (Orig.). 1987. pap. 9.95 (ISBN 0-89896-129-7, Linolean). Larksdale.

Suffering Is Optional! The Myth of the Innocent Bystander. Morris L. Haimowitz & Natalie R. Haimowitz. LC 77-72839. (Illus.). 1977. pap. 6.00 (ISBN 0-917790-01-4). Haimowoods.

Suffering: Issues of Emotional Living in an Age of Stress for Clergy & Religious. John A. Struzzo et al. Ed. by Richard J. Gilmartin. LC 84-9334. 144p. 1984. pap. 8.00 (ISBN 0-89571-020-X). Affirmation.

Suffering: Its Meaning & Ministry. James G. Emerson. 176p. (Orig.). 1986. pap. 8.95 (ISBN 0-687-40573-4). Abingdon.

Suffering of God: An Old Testament Perspective. Terence E. Fretheim. Ed. by Walter Brueggemann. LC 84-47921. (Overtures to Biblical Theology Ser.). 224p. 1984. pap. 10.95 (ISBN 0-8006-1538-7). Fortress.

Suffering Presence: Theological Reflections on Medicine, the Mentally Handicapped & the Church. Stanley Hauerwas. LC 85-40603. 224p. (Orig.). 1986. text ed. 19.95x (ISBN 0-268-01721-2, 85-17211, Dist. by Har-Row); pap. text ed. 9.95 (ISBN 0-268-01722-0, 85-17229). U of Notre Dame Pr.

Suffering: Psychological & Social Aspects in Loss, Grief, & Care. Ed. by Robert DeBellis et al. LC 85-31744. (Loss, Grief & Care Ser.: Vol. 1(1-2)). 196p. 1986. text ed. 32.95 (ISBN 0-86656-558-2). Haworth Pr.

Suffering, Sex & Other Paradoxes. Richard Hollway. 150p. 1985. 10.95 (ISBN 0-8192-1358-6). Morehouse.

Suffering.... Why Me? Paul Yonggi Cho. LC 86-70741. 1986. pap. 3.50 (ISBN 0-88270-601-2). Bridge Pub.

Sufferings & the Glories of the Messiah. John Brown. (Giant Summit Bks.). 352p. 1981. pap. 5.95 (ISBN 0-8010-0792-5). Baker Bk.

Sufficiency of Hope: Conceptual Foundations of Religion. James L. Muyskens. (Philosophical Monographs: 3rd Annual Ser.). 186p. 1979. 27.95 (ISBN 0-87722-162-6). Temple U Pr.

Sufficiently Radical: Catholicism, Progressivism, & the Bishops Program of 1919. Joseph M. McShane. 1986. 38.95 (ISBN 0-8132-0631-6). Cath U Pr.

Suffolk & the Tudors: Politics & Religion in an English County 1500-1600. Diarmaid MacCulloch. (Illus.). 360p. 1987. text ed. 66.00 (ISBN 0-19-822914-3). Oxford U Pr.

Sufi Doctrine of the Perfect Man. R. A. Nicholson. 1984. pap. 3.95 (ISBN 0-916411-48-6, Near Eastern). Holmes Pub.

Sufi Essays. Sayyed H. Nasr. 1973. 34.50x (ISBN 0-87395-233-2); pap. 10.95 (ISBN 0-87395-389-4). State U NY Pr.

Sufi Message of Hazrat Inayat Khan. (Sufi Message Ser.). 14.95 (ISBN 90-6325-101-7, Pub. by Servire BV Netherlands). Hunter Hse.

Sufi Music of India & Pakistan: Sound, Context & Meaning in Qawwali. Regula B. Qureshi. (Cambridge Studies in Ethnomusicology). (Illus.). 300p. 1987. 69.50 (ISBN 0-521-26767-6); cassette 18.96 (ISBN 0-521-32598-6). Cambridge U Pr.

Sufi Path of Love: The Spiritual Teachings of Rumi. William C. Chittick. LC 82-19511. (SUNY Series in Islam). 400p. 1983. 44.50x (ISBN 0-87395-723-7); pap. 12.95x (ISBN 0-87395-724-5). State U NY Pr.

Sufi Principles Action, Learning Methods, Imitators, Meeting-Places. H. Abbas & Emir A. Khan. (Sufi Research Ser.). 64p. 1982. pap. 4.95 (ISBN 0-86304-001-2, Pub. by Octagon Pr England). Ins Study Human.

Sufi Rule for Novices. Tr. by Menahem Milson from Arabic. LC 74-27750. (Middle Eastern Studies: No. 17). 112p. 1975. text ed. 8.95x (ISBN 0-674-85400-4); pap. 3.50 (ISBN 0-674-85403-9). Harvard U Pr.

Sufi Saint of the Twentieth Century: Shaikh Ahmad al-'Alawi, His Spiritual Heritage & Legacy. Martin Lings. (Near Eastern Center, UCLA Ser.). (Illus.). 242p. 1972. 30.00x (ISBN 0-520-02174-6); pap. 4.95 (ISBN 0-520-02486-9). U of Cal Pr.

Sufi Symbolism, Vol. 1. Dr. Javad Nurbakhsh. Tr. by Leonard Lewisohn & Terry Graham. 260p. 1986. 20.00 (ISBN 0-933546-12-2). Khaniqahi-Nimatullahi-Sufi.

Sufis. Idries Shah. LC 64-11299. 1971. pap. 6.95 (ISBN 0-385-07966-4, Anch). Doubleday.

Sufis. Idries Shah. 1983. 19.95 (ISBN 0-86304-020-9, Pub. by Octagon Pr England). Ins Study Human.

Sufis of Andalusia: The Ruh Al-Quds & Al-Durrat Al-Fakhirah of Ibn 'Arabi. R. W. Austin. Tr. by R. W. Austin. LC 77-165230. (California Library Reprint: Vol. 91). 1978. Repr. of 1971 ed. 33.00x (ISBN 0-520-03553-4). U of Cal Pr.

Sufis of Bijapur, 1300-1700 Social Roles of Sufis in Medieval India. Richard M. Eaton. LC 77-71978. (Illus.). 1978. 42.00x (ISBN 0-691-03110-X). Princeton U Pr.

Sufis of Today. Seyyed F. Hossain. (Sufi Research Ser.). 1981. pap. 4.95 (ISBN 0-86304-007-1, Pub. by Octagon Pr England). Ins Study Human.

Sufis: The People of the Path, 2 vols. Bhagwan Shree Rajneesh. Ed. by Ma Prema Veena. (Sufi Ser.). (Illus., Orig.). 1979. Vol. I, 552 pgs. 18.50 (ISBN 0-88050-136-7); Vol. II, 552 pgs. 1980. 19.50 (ISBN 0-88050-137-5). Chidvilas Found.

Sufism. R. Grisell. 120p. 1983. pap. 4.95 (ISBN 0-89496-038-5). Ross Bks.

Sufism & Taoism: A Comparative Study of Key Philosophical Concepts. Toshihiko Izutsu. LC 84-78. 493p. 1984. text ed. 40.00x (ISBN 0-520-05264-1). U of Cal Pr.

Sufism: Fear & Hope, Contraction & Expansion, Gathering & Dispersion, Intoxication, & Sobriety, Annihilation & Subsistence. Javad Nurbakhsh. Tr. by William Chittick from Persian. (Orig.). 1982. pap. 6.00x (ISBN 0-933546-07-6). KhaniQahi-Nimatullahi-Sufi.

Sufism-III: Submission, Contentment, Absence, Presence, Intimacy. Javad Nurbakhsh. Tr. by Terry Graham & Leonard Lewisohn. 133p. 1985. pap. 6.00x (ISBN 0-933546-19-X). KhaniQahi-Nimatullahi-Sufi.

Sufism: Meaning, Knowledge, & Unity. Javad Nurbakhsh. Tr. by Peter Wilson from Persian. 128p. (Orig.). 1981. pap. 6.00x (ISBN 0-933546-05-X). Khaniqahi-Nimatullahi-Sufi.

Sufism: Veil & Quintessence. Frithjof Schuon. LC 81-69573. (Library of Traditional Wisdom). 163p. pap. 7.00 (ISBN 0-941532-00-3). Wrld Wisdom Bks.

Suggested Curriculum for the Day School. N. W. Dessler. 7.00 (ISBN 0-914131-63-X, C01). Torah Umesorah.

Suggestions & Autosuggestions. Charles Baudouin. 1978. Repr. of 1920 ed. lib. bdg. 49.00 (ISBN 0-8495-0350-7). Arden Lib.

Suicidal Adolescents. Patricia A. Davis. 108p. 1983. 20.50x (ISBN 0-398-04866-5). C C Thomas.

Suicide. John Donne. Ed. by William A. Clebsch. LC 83-4466. (SP Studies in the Humanities). 134p. 1983. pap. 8.95 (ISBN 0-89130-624-2). Scholars Pr GA.

Suicide. Karen O. Savalan. 248p. 1982. 10.00 (ISBN 0-86690-210-4, 2363-01). Am Fed Astrologers.

Suicide: An Essay on Comparative Moral Statistics. Henry Morselli. LC 74-25770. (European Sociology Ser.). 402p. 1975. Repr. 27.00x (ISBN 0-405-06524-8). Ayer Co Pubs.

Suicide & Bereavement. Bruce L. Danto et al. 17.50 (ISBN 0-405-12505-4). Ayer Co Pubs.

Suicide & Ethics. Ed. by Margaret P. Battin & Ronald Maris. (Special Issue S Ser.: Vol. 13, No. 3). 112p. 1984. pap. 9.95. Guilford Pr.

Suicide & Morality: The Theories of Plato, Aquinas & Kant & Their Relevance for Suicidology. David Novak. LC 75-37543. x, 136p. 1976. lib. bdg. 7.50 (ISBN 0-685-69079-2). Scholars Studies.

Suicide & the Soul. James Hillman. LC 85-11901. (Dunquin Ser.: No. 8). 191p. 1964. pap. 12.00 (ISBN 0-88214-208-9). Spring Pubns.

Sukkah, 1 vol. 15.00 (ISBN 0-910218-58-7). Bennet Pub.

Sukkah & the Big Wind. Lily Edelman. (Holiday Series of Picture Story Books). (Illus.). 1956. 5.95 (ISBN 0-8381-0716-8). United Syn Bk.

Sukkot. Ed. by Hayyim H. Donin. 128p. pap. 4.50 (ISBN 0-686-95148-4). ADL.

Sukkot: A Time to Rejoice. Malka Drucker. LC 82-80814. (Jewish Holidays Bk.). (Illus.). 96p. 1982. Reinforced bdg. 10.95 (ISBN 0-8234-0466-8). Holiday.

Sulpicii Severi Libri Qui Supersunt. Sulpicius Severus. Ed. by Carolus Halm. (Corpus Scriptorum Ecclesiasticorum Latinorum Ser: Vol. 1). (Lat). unbound 50.00 (ISBN 0-384-54955-1). Johnson Repr.

Sumangala-Vilasini, 3 vols. Buddhaghosa. LC 78-72390. Repr. of 1886 ed. Set. 110.00 (ISBN 0-404-17580-5). Vol. 1 (ISBN 0-404-17581-3). Vol. 2 (ISBN 0-404-17582-1). Vol. 3 (ISBN 0-404-17583-X). AMS Pr.

Sumario de Doctrina Cristiana. 5th ed. Louis Berkhof. Tr. by David Vila from Eng. Tr. of Summary of Christian Doctrine. (Span.). 240p. 1986. pap. 3.00 (ISBN 0-939125-31-5). Evangelical Lit.

Sumerian Hymnology: The Ersemma. Mark E. Cohen. 1981. 18.75x (ISBN 0-87820-601-9). Ktav.

Sumerian Hymns from Cuneiform Texts in the British Museum. Ed. by Frederick A. Vanderburgh. LC 68-23118. (Columbia University. Contributions to Oriental History & Philology: No. 1). Repr. of 1908 ed. 14.00 (ISBN 0-404-50531-7). AMS Pr.

Sumerian Mythology. Samuel N. Kramer. (Illus.). 1972. pap. 10.95x (ISBN 0-8122-1047-6, Pa Paperbks). U of Pa Pr.

Sumerisch-Babylonische Hymnen und Gebete an Samas. Ed. by Anastasius Schollmeyer. Repr. of 1912 ed. 12.00 (ISBN 0-384-54240-9). Johnson Repr.

Summa Contra Gentiles, 4 bks. St. Thomas Aquinas. Incl. Bk. 1. God. Tr. by Anton C. Pegis. 317p. pap. 7.45x (ISBN 0-268-01678-X); Bk. 2. Creation. Tr. by James F. Anderson. 351p. text ed. 16.95 (ISBN 0-268-01679-8); pap. 7.45 (ISBN 0-268-01680-1); Bk. 3. Providence, 2 bks. in 1. Tr. by Vernon J. Bourke. 560p. text ed. 35.00x (ISBN 0-268-01681-X); pap. 15.00x (ISBN 0-268-01682-8); Bk. 4. Salvation. Tr. by Charles J. O'Neil. 360p. text ed. 16.95 (ISBN 0-268-01683-6); pap. 8.95x (ISBN 0-268-01684-4). LC 75-19883. 1975. Set. pap. 35.00. U of Notre Dame Pr.

Summa Contra Haereticos. Ed. by James A. Corbett & Joseph N. Garvin. (Mediaeval Studies Ser.: No. 15). (Lat). 1968. 23.95 (ISBN 0-268-00268-1). U of Notre Dame Pr.

Summa of the Christian Life, 3 vols. Louis Of Granada. Tr. by Jordan Aumann from Sp. LC 79-65716. 1979. Set. pap. 24.00 (ISBN 0-89555-121-7). Vol. 1 (ISBN 0-89555-118-7). Vol. 2 (ISBN 0-89555-119-5). Vol. 3 (ISBN 0-89555-120-9). TAN Bks Pubs.

Summa Theologiae, 61 vols. 1981. Set. 2000.00x (ISBN 0-686-75401-8, Pub. by Eyre & Spottiswoode England). State Mutual Bk.

Summa Theologica, 5 vols. St. Thomas Aquinas. 3057p. 1982. 225.00 (ISBN 0-87061-063-5); pap. 150.00 (ISBN 0-87061-069-4). Chr Classics.

Summary of Christian Doctrine. Louis Berkhof. 1939. pap. 5.95 (ISBN 0-8028-1513-8). Eerdmans.

Summary of Christian History. Robert A. Baker. (Illus.). 1959. 16.95 (ISBN 0-8054-6502-2). Broadman.

Summary of Scholastic Principles. Bernard Wuellner. LC 56-10903. 1956. 1.50 (ISBN 0-8294-0084-2). Loyola.

Summary of the Seven Sacraments. 2.75 (ISBN 0-8198-6858-2). Dghtrs St Paul.

Summary View of the Millennial Church, or United Society of Believers, Commonly Called Shakers. Shakers. LC 72-2993. Repr. of 1848 ed. 26.00 (ISBN 0-404-10755-9). AMS Pr.

Summerisch-Akkadische Parallelen Zum Aufbau Alttestamentlicher Psalmen. Friedrich Stummer. Repr. of 1922 ed. 15.00 (ISBN 0-384-58710-0). Johnson Repr.

Summit Living. Norman P. Grubb. 368p. 1985. 9.95 (ISBN 0-317-43397-0); pap. 7.95 (ISBN 0-87508-267-X). Chr Lit.

Summits of God Life: Samadhi & Siddhi. Sri Chinmoy. LC 80-65397. 145p. 1984. pap. 3.95 (ISBN 0-88497-145-7). Aum Pubns.

Summoned by Love. Carlo Carretto. Tr. by Alan Neame from Italian. LC 78-962. Orig. Title: Padre Mio me abbandono a Te. 1978. pap. 5.95 (ISBN 0-88344-472-0). Orbis Bks.

Sun. George Blattman. Tr. of Die Sonne. 240p. (Orig.). 1985. pap. text ed. 16.95 (ISBN 0-88010-148-2). Anthroposophic.

Sun & the Clouds. Menahem Stern. 1972. 6.95x (ISBN 0-87068-389-6). Ktav.

Sun Behind the Sun Behind the Sun. Bhagwan Shree Rajneesh. Ed. by Ma Prem Maneesha. LC 83-181209. (Initiation Talks Ser.). (Illus.). 648p. (Orig.). 1980. 21.95 (ISBN 0-88050-138-3). Chidvilas Found.

Sun Came Down: The History of the World as My Blackfeet Elders Told It. Percy Bullchild. LC 85-42771. (Illus.). 384p. 1985. 22.45 (ISBN 0-06-250107-0, HarpR). Har-Row.

Sun Clothed Woman. Date not set. pap. 0.95 (ISBN 0-937408-08-5). GMI Pubns Inc.

Sun-Clothed Woman & the Manchild. Gordon Lindsay. (Revelation Ser.). 1.25 (ISBN 0-89985-040-5). Christ Nations.

Sun Dance & Other Ceremonies of the Oglala Division of the Teton Dakota. J. R. Walker. LC 76-43886. (AMNH Anthropological Papers: Vol. 16, Pt. 2). Repr. of 1917 ed. 21.50 (ISBN 0-404-15745-9). AMS Pr.

Sun Dance Religion: Power for the Powerless. Joseph G. Jorgensen. LC 70-182089. 1972. pap. 12.50x (ISBN 0-226-41085-4). U of Chicago Pr.

Sun Dance Religion: Power for the Powerless. Joseph G. Jorgensen. LC 70-182089. (Illus.). xii, 360p. 1986. pap. 14.95 (ISBN 0-226-41086-2). U of Chicago Pr.

Sun Danced at Fatima. rev. ed. Joseph A. Pelletier. LC 83-45046. (Illus.). 240p. 1983. pap. 6.95 (ISBN 0-385-18965-6, Im). Doubleday.

Sun Dials & Roses of Yesterday. Alice M. Earle. LC 79-75790. 1969. Repr. of 1902 ed. 37.00x (ISBN 0-8103-3830-0). Gale.

Sun Flight. Gerald McDermott. LC 79-5067. (Illus.). 40p. 1980. 10.95 (ISBN 0-02-765610-1, Four Winds). Macmillan.

Sun Lore of All Ages. William T. Olcott. 1976. lib. bdg. 59.95 (ISBN 0-8490-2718-7). Gordon Pr.

Sun Lore of All Ages. William Tyler Olcott. 346p. 1984. Repr. of 1914 ed. lib. bdg. 25.00 (ISBN 0-89341-148-5). Longwood Pub Group.

Sun Men of the Americas. Grace Cooke. pap. 5.95 (ISBN 0-85487-057-1). De Vorss.

Sun, Moon, & Standing Stones. John E. Wood. (Illus.). 1978. 22.50x (ISBN 0-19-211443-3). Oxford U Pr.

Sun Myung Moon & the Unification Church. James Bjornstad. 160p. 1984. pap. 2.95 (ISBN 0-87123-301-0, 210301). Bethany Hse.

Sun Rises in the Evening. Bhagwan Shree Rajneesh. Ed. by Ma Prem Asha. LC 83-181196. (Zen Ser.). (Illus.). 372p. (Orig.). 1980. 17.95 (ISBN 0-88050-139-1). Chidvilas Found.

Sun Songs: Creation Myths from Around the World. Raymond Van Over. (Orig.). 1980. pap. 2.95 (ISBN 0-452-00730-5, Mer). NAL.

Sunbursts for the Spirit. C. W. Vandenbergh. LC 79-90313. (Sunbursts for the Spirit Ser.: Vol. 1). (Illus.). 56p. (Orig.). 1979. pap. 3.25 (ISBN 0-935238-02-6). Pine Row.

Sundara Kandam of Srimad Valmiki Ramayana. Valmiki. Tr. by Swami Tapasyananda. 286p. 1984. 15.00 (ISBN 0-87481-527-4, Pub. by Ramakrishna Math Madras India). Vedanta Pr.

Sunday after Sunday: Preaching the Homily as a Story. Robert Waznak. LC 82-62922. 128p. (Orig.). 1983. pap. 4.95 (ISBN 0-8091-2540-4). Paulist Pr.

Sunday Church School Teacher. Richard S. Hanson. 1986. 5.95 (ISBN 0-89536-796-3, 6814); leader's guide 1.75 (ISBN 0-89536-806-4, 6824). CSS of Ohio.

Sunday Dinner. William H. Willimon. LC 81-52215. 1981. pap. 4.50x (ISBN 0-8358-0429-1). Upper Room.

Sunday Laws of the United States & Leading Judicial Decisions Having Special Reference to the Jews. Albert M. Friedenberg. LC 12-23685. 42p. 1986. pap. 12.50 (ISBN 0-89941-475-3). W S Hein.

Sunday Mass: What Part Do You Play? Robert Rietcheck & Daniel Korn. 32p. 1985. pap. 1.50 (ISBN 0-89243-235-7). Liguori Pubns.

Sunday Morning: A Time for Worship. Ed. by Mark Searle. LC 82-15306. 200p. (Orig.). 1982. pap. 5.95 (ISBN 0-8146-1259-8). Liturgical Pr.

Sunday Morning: Aspects of Urban Ritual. Michael H. Ducey. LC 76-25342. 1977. 17.00 (ISBN 0-02-907640-4). Free Pr.

Sunday Morning Insights. Eugene F. Lauer. 252p. 1984. pap. 8.95 (ISBN 0-8146-1361-6). Liturgical Pr.

Sunday Night Sermons. Edward Fudge. pap. 2.00 (ISBN 0-686-12685-8). E Fudge.

Sunday No Sabbath: A Sermon. John Pocklington. LC 74-28881. (English Experience Ser.: No. 759). 1975. Repr. of 1636 ed. 6.00 (ISBN 90-221-0759-0). Walter J Johnson.

Sunday Readings. Kevin O'Sullivan. Incl. Cycle A. 428p. 1971. (ISBN 0-8199-0481-3); Cycle B. 487p. 1972. (ISBN 0-8199-0482-1); Cycle C. 444p. 1970. (ISBN 0-8199-0483-X). LC 74-141766. 9.00 ea. Franciscan Herald.

Sunday School Basics. Ed. by Floyd D. Carey. 1976. 5.25 (ISBN 0-87148-778-0); pap. 4.25 (ISBN 0-87148-777-2). Pathway Pr.

Sunday School Evangelism. Earl P. Paulk. 1958. 4.95 (ISBN 0-87148-759-4). Pathway Pr.

Sunday School Growth. J. Martin Baldree. 1971. 5.25 (ISBN 0-87148-761-6); pap. 4.25 (ISBN 0-87148-762-4). Pathway Pr.

Sunday School Growth & Renewal: How to Reach, Teach, Care, Share. Millie S. Goodson. LC 84-71642. 76p. (Orig.). DR014B. pap. 3.75 (ISBN 0-88177-014-0). Discipleship Res.

Sunday-School Movement, 1780-1917, & the American Sunday-School Union, 1817-1917. Edwin W. Rice. LC 70-165728. (American Education Ser, No. 2). (Illus.). 1971. Repr. of 1917 ed. 36.00 (ISBN 0-405-03717-1). Ayer Co Pubs.

Sunday School Outreach. W. W. Thomas. 112p. 1979. 5.25 (ISBN 0-87148-787-X); pap. 4.25 (ISBN 0-87148-788-8). Pathway Pr.

Sunday School Spirit. Stephen V. Rexroat. LC 79-51833. (Workers Training Book of the Year Ser.). 128p. (Orig.). 1979. pap. 1.50 (ISBN 0-88243-594-9, 02-0594). Gospel Pub.

Sunday School Teacher. O. W. Polen. 1956. pap. 5.25 (ISBN 0-87148-765-9). Pathway Pr.

Sunday School Teacher's Guide, 1984. William S. Deal. 1984. pap. 3.95 (ISBN 0-318-18717-5). Crusade Pubs.

Sunday Scriptures. Daniel Sullivan & Judy Andrews. 4.95 (ISBN 0-8091-9336-1). Paulist Pr.

Sunday Services of the Methodists in North America. John Wesley. 144p. (Orig.). 1984. pap. 4.95 (ISBN 0-687-40632-3). Abingdon.

Sunday Sister. large print ed. Charline Brians. 24p. 1985. pap. 4.00 (ISBN 0-914009-53-2). VHI Library.

Sunday Throughout the Week. Gaynell Cronin. LC 81-68992. (Illus.). 176p. (Orig.). 1981. pap. 5.95 (ISBN 0-87793-241-7). Ave Maria.

Sunday Word: A Commentary on the Sunday Readings. Dom H. Wansbrough. 400p. 1984. pap. 14.95 (ISBN 0-225-66254-X, HarpR). Har-Row.

Sunday Words for a Monday World. Gaylord L. Lehman. 75p. (Orig.). Date not set. pap. price not set (ISBN 0-938828-03-7). Falls Tar.

Sunday Work, 1794-1856. LC 72-2547. (British Labour Struggles Before 1850 Ser). (7 pamphlets). 1972. 12.00 (ISBN 0-405-04438-0). Ayer Co Pubs.

Sunday Worship. Kevin W. Irwin. 1983. pap. 14.95 (ISBN 0-916134-52-0). Pueblo Pub Co.

Sunlight & Shadows: Portraits of Priorities for Living & Dying. Louis R. Batzler. (Illus.). 60p. (Orig.). 1986. pap. 4.95 (ISBN 0-935710-09-4). Hid Valley MD.

Sunlit Path. Mother. 194p. 1984. pap. 4.95 (ISBN 0-89071-318-9, Pub. by Sri Aurobindo Ashram India). Matagiri.

Sunnier Side of Doubt. Fred M. Wood. LC 83-24020. 1984. pap. 4.95 (ISBN 0-8054-2253-6). Broadman.

Sunny-Side Up. Alma Barkman. (Quiet Time Bks.). 1984. pap. 3.50 (ISBN 0-8024-8431-X). Moody.

Sunrise. White Eagle. 1958. 3.95 (ISBN 0-85487-016-4). De Vorss.

Sunshine Basket. Lula Guthrie. (Illus.). 1986. pap. 1.95 (ISBN 0-89265-112-1). Randall Hse.

Sunshine Country. Cristina Roy. 160p. (YA) 6.50 (ISBN 0-686-05594-2); pap. 4.35 (ISBN 0-686-05595-0). Rod & Staff.

Sunshine in the Shadows. Peter Lappin. LC 79-57184. 218p. 1980. pap. 6.95 (ISBN 0-89944-042-8). Don Bosco Multimedia.

Sunshine on the Soapsuds. Beneth P. Jones. 86p. (Orig.). 1977. pap. 2.95 (ISBN 0-89084-054-7). Bob Jones Univ Pr.

Sunshine Through the Shadows. Hulen Jackson. 4.95 (ISBN 0-89315-283-8). Lambert Bk.

Sunshine Tree. JoAnn Parrott. 1979. pap. 2.50 (ISBN 0-911739-14-9). Abbott Loop.

Super & Superman. Philip Guedalla. 1924. Repr. 20.00 (ISBN 0-8274-3554-1). R West.

Super-Chords Made Super-Simple. Duane Shinn. 1976. pap. 6.95 (ISBN 0-912732-20-2). Duane Shinn.

Super Ideas for Youth Groups. Wayne Rice & Mike Yaconelli. (Orig.). 1979. pap. 6.95 (ISBN 0-310-34981-8, 10773P). Zondervan.

Super Natural Living. Betty Malz. 1983. pap. 2.50 (ISBN 0-451-12517-7, Sig). NAL.

Super Stitches: A Book of Superstitions. Ann Nevins. LC 82-15875. (Illus.). 64p. 1983. reinforced bdg. 9.95 (ISBN 0-8234-0476-5). Holiday.

Super Superintendent: A Layman's Guide to Sunday School Management. Harold J. Westing. LC 80-66721. (Accent Teacher Training Ser.). 160p. (Orig.). 1980. pap. 4.95 (ISBN 0-89636-057-1). Accent Bks.

Superconcious Meditation. Pandit U. Arya. 150p. 1978. pap. 6.95 (ISBN 0-89389-035-9). Himalayan Pubs.

Supererogation: Its Status in Ethical Theory. David Heyd. LC 81-15476. (Cambridge Studies in Philosophy). 180p. 1982. 37.50 (ISBN 0-521-23935-4). Cambridge U Pr.

Superimposition in Advaita Vedanta. T. M. Mahadevan. 80p. 1985. text ed. 20.00x (ISBN 0-86590-570-3, Pub. by Sterling Pubs India). Apt Bks.

Superintend with Success. rev. ed. Guy P. Leavitt. Ed. by A. Leon Langston. LC 79-66658. (Illus.). 144p. 1980. pap. 7.95 (ISBN 0-87239-377-1, 3203). Standard Pub.

Superintendent Plans His Work. Idris W. Jones. 1956. pap. 4.95 (ISBN 0-8170-0172-7). Judson.

Superior Follows the Master. James Alberione. (Orig.). 1965. pap. 2.00 (ISBN 0-8198-0153-4). Dghtrs St Paul.

Superiority of Christ. John MacArthur, Jr. (John MacArthur's Bible Studies). (Orig.). 1986. pap. 3.95 (ISBN 0-8024-5344-9). Moody.

Superman in Modern Literature: Flaubert, Carlyle, Emerson, Nietzsche. Leo Berg. Repr. 20.00 (ISBN 0-8274-3555-X). R West.

Supernatural. new ed. John P. Kenny. LC 72-3575. 165p. 1972. 4.95 (ISBN 0-8189-0251-5). Alba.

Supernatural in Relation to the Natural. James McCosh. LC 75-3267. Repr. of 1862 ed. 38.00 (ISBN 0-404-59255-4). AMS Pr.

Supernatural in Shakespeare. Helen H. Stewart. LC 72-13282. 1972. Repr. of 1908 ed. lib. bdg. 22.50 (ISBN 0-8414-1168-9). Folcroft.

Supernatural Omnibus. Montague Summers. 624p. 1982. 22.50 (ISBN 0-575-03120-4, Pub. by Gollancz England). David & Charles.

Supernatural Power of Jesus. John MacArthur, Jr. (John MacArthur's Bible Studies). 1985. pap. 3.50 (ISBN 0-8024-5113-6). Moody.

Superstition, Are You Superstitious? Maple. pap. 2.00 (ISBN 0-87980-245-6). Wilshire.

Superstition in All Ages. Paul H. D'Holbach & Jean Meslier. 69.95 (ISBN 0-87968-108-X). Gordon Pr.

Superstition in All Ages. Jean Meslier. Tr. by Anna Knoop from Fr. LC 77-161337. (Atheist Viewpoint Ser). (Illus.). 346p. 1972. Repr. of 1890 ed. 23.50 (ISBN 0-405-03795-3). Ayer Co Pubs.

Superstition in All Ages. Jean Meslier. Tr. by Anna Knopp. 346p. 1974. pap. 13.95 (ISBN 0-88697-008-3). Life Science.

Superstitions of Sailors. Angelo S. Rappoport. LC 71-158207. 1971. Repr. of 1928 ed. 43.00x (ISBN 0-8103-3739-8). Gale.

Superstitions of the Irish Country People. rev. ed. Padraic O'Farrell. 92p. 1982. pap. 5.95 (ISBN 0-85342-530-2, Pub. by Mercier Pr Ireland). Irish Bks Media.

Superstitions of the Irreligious. George P. Hedley. LC 78-10274. 1979. Repr. of 1951 ed. lib. bdg. 22.50x (ISBN 0-313-20755-0, HESU). Greenwood.

Supervision of Student-Teachers in Religious Education. F. H. Klyver. LC 79-176952. (Columbia University. Teachers College. Contributions to Education: No. 198). Repr. of 1925 ed. 22.50 (ISBN 0-404-55198-X). AMS Pr.

Supper of the Lamb: A Culinary Reflection. Robert F. Capon. LC 78-14937. 271p. 1979. pap. 3.95 (ISBN 0-15-686893-8, Harv). HarBracej.

Supper of the Lord: The New Testament, Ecumenical Dialogues & Faith & Order on "Eucharist". John Reumann. LC 84-47932. 224p. 1984. pap. 13.95 (ISBN 0-8006-1816-5). Fortress.

Supplement au Dictionnaire de la Bible, 7 vols. H. Cazelles et al. (Fr.). 128p. 1967. Set. 595.50 (ISBN 0-686-56943-1, M-6065). French & Eur.

Supplement for the Days of Remembrance & Thanksgiving. Norman Lamm. 1973. 0.85x (ISBN 0-87306-079-2). Feldheim.

Supplement to the Book of Hymns. Ed. by Carlton R. Young. 160p. (Orig.). 1981. pap. 4.75 (ISBN 0-687-03757-3); pap. 6.75 accompanist ed. (ISBN 0-687-03758-1). Abingdon.

Supplementary Prayers & Readings for the High Holidays. 216p. 1960. pap. 6.00 (ISBN 0-935457-34-8). Reconstructionist Pr.

Supplementary Prayers for the Pilgrimage Festivals: Sukkot & Simhat Torah, Vol. 2. 1956. pap. 3.50 (ISBN 0-935457-36-4). Reconstructionist Pr.

Supplementary Prayers for the Pilgrimage Festivals: Pesah & Shavuot, Vol. 1. 95p. 1956. pap. 3.00 (ISBN 0-935457-35-6). Reconstructionist Pr.

Supplicacyon for the Beggers. Simon Fish. LC 72-5989. (English Experience Ser.: No. 515). 16p. 1973. Repr. of 1529 ed. 6.00 (ISBN 90-221-0515-6). Walter J Johnson.

Supplication Made to the Privy Counsel. Walter Travers. LC 76-57419. (English Experience Ser.: No. 833). 1977. Repr. of 1591 ed. lib. bdg. 5.00 (ISBN 90-221-0833-3). Walter J Johnson.

Supplication: Makarim al-Akhlaq. Zayn Al-Abidin. Tr. by William C. Chittick. 30p. 1984. pap. 3.95 (ISBN 0-940368-45-5). Tahrike Tarsile Quran.

Supplications. Ali I. Talib. Tr. by William C. Chittick. LC 84-52746. 63p. 1985. pap. 4.95 (ISBN 0-940368-46-3). Tahrike Tarsile Quran.

Supplications (Du'a) Amir Al-Muminin. Tr. by William C. Chittick from Arabic & Eng. 63p. 1986. text ed. 24.95 (ISBN 0-7103-0156-1). Methuen Inc.

Supplicatyon... Unto Henry the Eighth. Robert Barnes. LC 73-6098. (English Experience Ser.: No. 567). 1973. Repr. of 1534 ed. 18.50 (ISBN 90-221-0567-9). Walter J Johnson.

Supplycacyon of Soulys: Agaynst the Supplycacyon of Beggars. Thomas More. LC 72-220. (English Experience Ser.: No. 353). 88p. 1971. Repr. of 1529 ed. 14.00 (ISBN 90-221-0353-6). Walter J Johnson.

Support for the Poor in the Mishnaic Law of Agriculture: Tractate Peah. Roger Brooks. LC 83-8719. (Brown Judaic Studies: No. 43). 220p. 1983. pap. 21.00 (ISBN 0-89130-632-3, 14 00 43). Scholars Pr GA.

Support of Schools in Colonial New York by the Society for the Propagation of the Gospel in Foreign Parts. William W. Kemp. LC 78-176933. (Columbia University. Teachers College. Contributions to Education: No. 56). Repr. of 1913 ed. 22.50 (ISBN 0-404-55056-8). AMS Pr.

Support of Schools in Colonial New York by the Society for the Propagation of the Gospel in Foreign Parts. William W. Kemp. LC 72-89192. (American Education: Its Men, Institutions, & Ideas, Ser. 1). 1969. Repr. of 1913 ed. 12.00 (ISBN 0-405-01430-9). Ayer Co Pubs.

Support of the Shaken Sangat: Meetings with Three Masters. A. S. Oberoi. Ed. by Russell Perkins. LC 84-50911. (Illus.). 256p. (Orig.). 1984. pap. 15.00 (ISBN 0-89142-043-6). Sant Bani Ash.

Support-Raising Handbook: A Guide for Christian Workers. Brian Rust & Barry McLeish. LC 84-22448. 156p. (Orig.). 1984. pap. 9.95 (ISBN 0-87784-326-0). Inter-Varsity.

Supportive Ministries. Michael Landsman. 1981. pap. 1.95 (ISBN 0-89274-181-3). Harrison Hse.

Supramental Manifestation on Earth. Sri Aurobindo. 108p. 1980. pap. 2.25 (ISBN 0-89071-307-3, Pub. by Sri Aurobindo Ashram India). Matagiri.

Supremacy of God. Ilon. LC 80-66408. 1980. pap. 4.50 (ISBN 0-9600958-6-1). Birth Day.

Supremacy of Jesus. Stephen Neill. LC 84-47740. (Jesus Library Ser.). 216p. 1984. pap. 6.95 (ISBN 0-87784-928-5). Inter-Varsity.

Supreme Court & Religion. Richard E. Morgan. LC 72-80077. 1972. 14.95 (ISBN 0-02-921970-1). Free Pr.

Supreme Court Decisions on Church & State. Ed. by William L. Miller & Charles T. Cureton. 570p. 1986. pap. 11.95x (ISBN 0-935005-08-0). Ibis Pub VA.

Supreme Doctrine: Discourses on the Kenopanishad. Bhagwan S. Rajneesh. 356p. (Orig.). 1980. pap. 12.95 (ISBN 0-7100-0572-5). Methuen Inc.

Supreme Doctrine: Psychological Studies in Zen Thought. Hubert Benoit. 248p. 1984. pap. 8.95 (ISBN 0-89281-058-0). Inner Tradit.

Supreme Godhead. Kenneth V. Reeves. Ed. by Mary H. Wallace. (Illus.). 100p. (Orig.). 1984. pap. 5.50 (ISBN 0-912315-74-1). Word Aflame.

Supreme, I Sing Only for You. Sri Chinmoy. 105p. (Orig.). 1974. pap. 2.00 (ISBN 0-88497-079-5). Aum Pubns.

Supreme Identity. Alan W. Watts. 1972. pap. 4.95 (ISBN 0-394-71835-6, Vin). Random.

Supreme Koan: An Artist's Spiritual Journey. Frederick Franck. LC 81-22037. (Illus.). 1982. pap. 12.95 (ISBN 0-8245-0430-5). Crossroad NY.

Supreme Mastery of Fear. Joseph Murphy. pap. 0.75 (ISBN 0-87516-340-8). De Vorss.

Supreme, Teach Me How to Cry. Sri Chinmoy. 100p. (Orig.). 1974. pap. 2.00 (ISBN 0-88497-120-1). Aum Pubns.

Supreme, Teach Me How to Surrender. Sri Chinmoy. 100p. (Orig.). 1975. pap. 2.00 (ISBN 0-88497-237-2). Aum Pubns.

Sur L'amour. Pierre Teilhard De Chardin. pap. 6.25 (ISBN 0-685-36602-2). French & Eur.

Sur le Bonheur. Pierre Teilhard De Chardin. pap. 6.25 (ISBN 0-685-36603-0). French & Eur.

Sure Foundation. T. David Sustar. LC 80-84008. 124p. (Orig.). 1980. pap. text ed. 3.00 (ISBN 0-87148-795-0); 2.00 (ISBN 0-87148-436-6). Pathway Pr.

Sure Thing. Cornelius Plantinga, Jr. LC 86-8280. (Illus.). 300p. 1986. lib. bdg. 11.95 (ISBN 0-930265-27-0); incl. tchr's. manual 7.95 (ISBN 0-930265-28-9). CRC Pubns.

Sure to Endure. Danny Lynchard. 43p. 1983. pap. 1.95 (ISBN 0-88144-043-4). Christian Pub.

Surest Path: The Political Treatise of a Nineteenth-Century Muslim Statesman. Khayr Al Tunisi. Tr. by Leon C. Brown. LC 67-25399. (Middle Eastern Monographs Ser: No. 16). pap. 5.00x (ISBN 0-674-85695-3). Harvard U Pr.

Surgeon on Safari. Paul J. Jorden & James R. Adair. (Living Bks.). 192p. (Orig.). 1985. pap. 3.95 (ISBN 0-8423-6686-5). Tyndale.

Surprise Me, Jesus. Herbert F. Brokering. LC 73-83785. 96p. (YA) 1973. pap. 6.95 (ISBN 0-8066-1338-6, 10-6150). Augsburg.

Surprise Paper Tearing Talks, No. 9. Arnold C. Westphal. 1976. pap. 4.95 (ISBN 0-915398-08-7). Visual Evangels.

Surprised by Joy: The Shape of My Early Life. C. S. Lewis. LC 56-5329. 248p. 1956. 12.95 (ISBN 0-15-187011-X). HarBraceJ.

Surprised by Joy: The Shape of My Early Life. C. S. Lewis. LC 56-5329. 1966. pap. 4.95 (ISBN 0-15-687011-8, Harv). HarBraceJ.

Surprised by Sin: The Reader in Paradise Lost. Stanley E. Fish. 1971. pap. 9.95 (ISBN 0-520-01897-4, CAL228). U of Cal Pr.

Surprised by the Spirit. Edward Farrell. 4.95 (ISBN 0-87193-030-7). Dimension Bks.

Surprises. Dick Hilliard & Beverly Valenti-Hilliard. (Center Celebration Ser.). (Illus.). 60p. (Orig.). 1981. pap. text ed. 3.95 (ISBN 0-89390-031-1). Resource Pubns.

Surprising Gospel: Intriguing Psychological Insights from the New Testament. Wilhelm H. Wuellner & Robert C. Leslie. 176p. (Orig.). 1983. pap. 11.95 (ISBN 0-687-40724-9). Abingdon.

Surrealist's Bible. Dierdre Luzwick. LC 75-44001. (Illus.). 128p. 1976. 10.00 (ISBN 0-8246-0206-4). Jonathan David.

Surrender: A Guide to Prayer. Nancy Schreck & Maureen Leach. (Take & Receive Ser.). 165p. (Orig.). 1986. pap. 6.95t (ISBN 0-88489-171-2). St Mary's.

Surrender & the Singing: Happiness Through Letting Go. Ray Ashford. 168p. (Orig.). 1985. pap. 7.95 (ISBN 0-86683-964-X, AY8546, HarpR). Har-Row.

Survey Course in Christian Doctrine, Vols. III & IV. C. C. Crawford. LC 71-1388. (Bible Study Textbook Ser.). 1964. 13.80 (ISBN 0-89900-054-1). College Pr Pub.

Survey in Basic Christianity. Jean Gibson. (Believer's Bible Lessons Ser.). 1979. pap. 5.50 (ISBN 0-937396-41-9). Walterick Pubs.

Survey of Bible Doctrine. Charles C. Ryrie. LC 72-77958. 192p. 1972. pap. 5.95 (ISBN 0-8024-8435-2). Moody.

Survey of Bible Prophecy. Raymond Ludwigson. (Contemporary Evangelical Perspective Ser.). Orig. Title: Outlines to Bible Eschatology. 192p. 1973. Repr. 6.95 (ISBN 0-310-28421-X, 10100P). Zondervan.

Survey of Christian Epistemology. Cornelius Van Til. 1967. pap. 6.95 (ISBN 0-87552-495-8). Presby & Reformed.

Survey of Christian Ethics. Edward L. Long, Jr. 1967. pap. 12.95x (ISBN 0-19-503242-X). Oxford U Pr.

Survey of Church History. J. D. O'Donnell. 1973. pap. 4.95 (ISBN 0-89265-009-5). Randall Hse.

Survey of Israel's History. rev. ed. Leon Wood & David O'Brien. 416p. 1986. 19.95 (ISBN 0-310-34770-X, 6505). Zondervan.

Survey of Jewish Affairs 1983. Ed. by William Frankel. 320p. 1985. 25.00 (ISBN 0-8386-3244-0). Fairleigh Dickinson.

Survey of Jewish Affairs, 1985. Ed. by William Frankel. 280p. 1985. 25.00x (ISBN 0-8386-3269-6). Fairleigh Dickinson.

Survey of London: The Parish of St. Mary Lambeth. Pt. 2, Southern Area. London County Council. LC 74-6546. Repr. of 1956 ed. 74.50 (ISBN 0-404-51676-9). AMS Pr.

Survey of Metaphysics & Esoterism. Frithjof Schuon. Tr. by Gustavo Polit from Fr. LC 86-13261. (Library of Traditional Wisdom). Orig. Title: Resume de Metaphysique Integral Sur les Traces de la Religion Perenne. 224p. (Orig.). 1986. pap. 12.00 (ISBN 0-941532-06-2). Wrld Wisdom Bks.

Survey of Old Testament Introduction. Gleason L. Archer. LC 64-20988. 582p. 1973. 16.95 (ISBN 0-8024-8447-6). Moody.

Survey of Recent Christian Ethics. Edward L. Long, Jr. 1982. pap. 8.95x (ISBN 0-19-503160-1). Oxford U Pr.

Survey of Rook-Cut Chamber-Tombs in Caria, Pt. I: Southeastern Caria & the Lyco-Carian Borderland. Paavo Roos. (Studies in Mediterranean Archaeology). (Illus.). 132p. (Orig.). 1985. pap. text ed. 82.50X (Pub. by Almqvist & Wiksell). Coronet Bks.

Survey of Taiwanese Religions in 1919, 2 vols. Marui Keijiro. (Asian Folklore & Social Life Monograph: Nos. 56-57). (Japanese.). 428p. 1974. 25.00 (ISBN 0-89986-053-2). Oriental Bk Store.

Survey of the Bible. rev. ed. William Hendriksen. LC 76-507. 515p. 1976. 17.95 (ISBN 0-8010-4288-7). Baker Bk.

Survey of the Books of History. J. D. O'Donnell & Ralph Hampton, Jr. 1976. pap. 3.25 (ISBN 0-89265-032-X). Randall Hse.

Survey of the Books of Poetry. J. D. O'Donnell & Ralph Hampton, Jr. 1976. pap. 2.25 (ISBN 0-89265-033-8). Randall Hse.

Survey of the Epistles. Charles W. Conn. 112p. 1969. 5.25 (ISBN 0-87148-007-7); pap. 4.25 (ISBN 0-87148-008-5). Pathway Pr.

Survey of the General Epistles & Revelation. Stanley Outlaw et al. 1976. pap. 2.95 (ISBN 0-89265-036-2). Randall Hse.

Survey of the Gospels. Stanley Outlaw & Charles Thigpen. 1976. pap. 1.95 (ISBN 0-89265-031-1). Randall Hse.

Survey of the Life of Christ, 2 vols. Melvin J. Wise. 2.50 ea.; Vol. 1. (ISBN 0-89315-288-9); Vol. 2. (ISBN 0-89315-289-7). Lambert Bk.

Survey of the Major Prophets. Robert Picirilli & Ralph Hampton, Jr. 1976. pap. 1.50 (ISBN 0-89265-034-6). Randall Hse.

Survey of the New Testament. Robert H. Gundry. (Illus.). 432p. 1982. 17.95 (ISBN 0-310-25410-8, 18280). Zondervan.

Survey of the New Testament. Outlaw et al. Ed. by Harrold D. Harrison. (Orig.). 1984. pap. 4.95 (ISBN 0-89265-090-7). Randall Hse.

Survey of the Old Testament. Outlaw et al. Ed. by Harrold D. Harrison. (Orig.). 1984. pap. 5.95 (ISBN 0-89265-089-3). Randall Hse.

Survey of the Old Testament. Stanley Outlaw. 1977. pap. 2.75 (ISBN 0-89265-048-6). Randall Hse.

Survey of the Pauline Epistles. Leroy Forlines & Robert Picirilli. 1976. pap. 3.75 (ISBN 0-89265-035-4). Randall Hse.

Survey of the Pentateuch. Stanley Outlaw & J. D. O'Donnell. 93p. 1975. pap. 2.95 (ISBN 0-89265-027-3). Randall Hse.

Survey of the Pretended Holy Dicipline. Richard Bancroft. LC 78-38148. (English Experience Ser.: No. 428). 472p. 1972. Repr. of 1593 ed. 67.00 (ISBN 90-221-0428-1). Walter J Johnson.

Survey of the Summe of Church-Discipline Wherein the Way of the Congregational Churches of Christ in New England Is Warranted & Cleared, by Scripture & Argument. Thomas Hooker. LC 78-141113. (Research Library of Colonial Americana). 1971. Repr. of 1648 ed. 40.00 (ISBN 0-405-03326-5). Ayer Co Pubs.

Survey of Western Palestine, 3 vols. Claude R. Conder. Ed. by E. H. Palmer & Walter Besant. LC 78-63331. (Crusades & Military Orders: Second Ser.). (Illus.). Repr. of 1883 ed. Set. 110.00 (ISBN 0-404-17010-2). AMS Pr.

Survey of Western Palestine. Charles Warren & Claude R. Conder. LC 78-63371. (Crusades & Military Orders: Second Ser.). Repr. of 1884 ed. 41.50 (ISBN 0-404-17047-1). AMS Pr.

Surveying the Historical Books. Joseph M. Gettys. 164p. 1963. pap. 4.00x (ISBN 0-8042-3664-X). Attic Pr.

Surveying the Pentateuch. Joseph M. Gettys. 147p. 1962. pap. 4.50x (ISBN 0-8042-3676-3). Attic Pr.

Surveying the Scriptures. Robert Hoggard. 1981. pap. 2.95 (ISBN 0-86544-013-1). Salv Army Suppl South.

Survival: A New Approach from the Life Sciences to the Major Problem of Our Time. Richard Van Praagh. LC 85-80038. 208p. (Orig.). 1985. pap. 7.95 (ISBN 0-941404-35-8). Falcon Pr Az.

Survival: Body, Mind & Death in the Light of Psychic Experience. David Lorimer. 288p. (Orig.). 1984. pap. 12.95 (ISBN 0-7102-0003-X). Methuen Inc.

Survival for What. Zvi Kolitz. LC 70-75761. 234p. 1969. 10.00 (ISBN 0-8022-2272-2). Philos Lib.

Survival Guide for Tough Times. Mike Phillips. LC 79-4261. 176p. 1979. pap. 3.95 (ISBN 0-87123-498-X, 210498). Bethany Hse.

Survival Guide to the Last Times. James A. Aderman. Ed. by William E. Fischer. (Bible Class Course for Young Adults Ser.). (Illus.). 64p. (Orig.). 1987. pap. text ed. 2.95 (ISBN 0-938272-30-6); tchr's ed. 2.95 (ISBN 0-938272-29-2). Wels Board.

Survival Kit for Marriage. Carolyn S. Self & William L. Self. LC 81-66091. 1981. pap. 5.95 (ISBN 0-8054-5643-0). Broadman.

Survival of American Innocence: Catholicism in An Era of Disillusionment, 1920-1940. William M. Halsey. LC 79-63360. (Studies in American Catholicism: No. 2). 1979. 19.95x (ISBN 0-268-01699-2, 85-16999). U of Notre Dame Pr.

Survival of Dogma: Faith, Authority & Dogma in a Changing World. Avery Dulles. (Crossroad Paperback Ser.). 240p. 1982. pap. 7.95 (ISBN 0-8245-0427-5). Crossroad NY.

Survival of the Chinese Jews: The Jewish Community of Kaifeng. Donald D. Leslie. (Illus.). 270p. 1973. text ed. 59.95 (ISBN 90-040-3413-7). Humanities.

Survival of the Gods: Classical Mythology in Medieval Art. Brown University Dept. of Art Staff. LC 86-72762. (Illus., Orig.). 1986. pap. text ed. 14.00 (ISBN 0-933519-10-9). D W Bell Gallery.

Survival of the Historic Vestments in the Lutheran Church after Fifteen Fifty-Five. Arthur Carl Piepkorn. 120p. 1956. write for info. Concordia Schl Grad Studies.

Survival of the Pagan Gods: The Mythological Tradition & Its Place in Renaissance Humanism & Art. Jean Seznec. Tr. by Barbara Sessions. (Bollingen Ser.: Vol. 38). (Illus.). 108p. 1972. pap. 9.50x (ISBN 0-691-01783-2). Princeton U Pr.

Survival Prayers for Young Mothers. Deborah A. Holmes. 6.95 (ISBN 0-8042-2195-2). John Knox.

Survival Tactics in the Parish. Lyle E. Schaller. LC 76-54751. (Orig.). 1977. pap. 8.75 (ISBN 0-687-40757-5). Abingdon.

Survival-Unite to Live. Jim Bakker. LC 80-84504. 1980. 7.95 (ISBN 0-89221-081-8). New Leaf.

Survivals of Roman Religion. Gordon Laing. LC 63-10280. (Our Debt to Greece & Rome Ser). 257p. 1963. Repr. of 1930 ed. 25.00x (ISBN 0-8154-0130-2). Cooper Sq.

Surviving Difficult Church Members. Robert D. Dale. 128p. (Orig.). 1984. pap. 6.95 (ISBN 0-687-40763-X). Abingdon.

Surviving the Breakup: How Children & Parents Cope with Divorce. Judith S. Wallerstein & Joan B. Kelly. 1982. pap. 9.95x (ISBN 0-465-08339-0, TB-5094). Basic.

Surviving the Crisis of Motherhood: Strategies for Caring for Your Child & Yourself. Paula L. Kollstedt. (Illus.). 117p. 1981. pap. 3.50 (ISBN 0-912228-91-1). St Anthony Mess Pr.

Survivor in Us All: Four Young Sisters in the Holocaust. Erna F. Rubinstein. 185p. 1986. 19.50 (ISBN 0-208-02025-X, Archon); pap. 12.50x (ISBN 0-208-02128-0). Shoe String.

Survivor of a Tarnished Ministry. Betty E. De Blase. 176p. (Orig.). 1983. pap. text ed. 6.95 (ISBN 0-913621-00-5). Truth CA.

Survivors: A Personal Story of the Holocaust. Jacob Biber. LC 85-22415. (Studies in Judaica & the Holocaust: No. 2). 208p. 1986. lib. bdg. 18.95x (ISBN 0-89370-370-2); pap. text ed. 8.95x (ISBN 0-89370-470-9). Borgo Pr.

Survivors: Children of the Holocaust. Judith Hemmendinger. Tr. of Les Enfants De Buchenwald. 200p. (Orig.). 1986. Repr. of 1984 ed. 15.95 (ISBN 0-915765-24-1). Natl Pr Inc.

Survivors, Victims & Perpetrators: Essays on the Nazi Holocaust. Ed. by Joel E. Dimsdale. LC 79-24834. (Illus.). 474p. 1980. text ed. 42.50 (ISBN 0-89116-145-7); pap. text ed. 32.95 (ISBN 0-89116-351-4). Hemisphere Pub.

Susanna. Glen Williamsen & Isabel Anders. 240p. (Orig.). 1985. pap. 3.50 (ISBN 0-8423-6691-1). Tyndale.

Susanna: Mother of the Wesleys. rev. ed. Rebecca L. Harmon. 1968. 7.50 (ISBN 0-687-40766-4). Abingdon.

Susanna Wesley, a Study Guide. Joe Ponzani & Mrs. Joe Ponzan. 1983. 1.75 (ISBN 0-89536-607-X, 1930). CSS of Ohio.

Susanna Wesley: Servant of God. Sandy Dengler. (Preteen Biographies Ser.). (YA) 1987. pap. text ed. 3.95 (ISBN 0-8024-8414-X). Moody.

Sustaining. Connie Rector. 79p. 1985. 7.95 (ISBN 0-934126-59-3). Randall Bk Co.

Sustaining Power of Hope. Leslie B. Flynn. 132p. 1985. pap. 4.95 (ISBN 0-89693-600-7). Victor Bks.

Sutra in Forty-Two Sections. Commentary by Tripitaka Master Hua. Tr. by Buddhist Text Translation Society. (Illus.). 114p. (Orig.). 1977. pap. 5.00 (ISBN 0-917512-15-4). Buddhist Text.

Sutra of Golden Light: A Mahayana Text. R. E. Emmerick. 1980. write for info. Dharma Pub.

Sutra of the Past Vows of Earth Store Bodhisattva. Tr. by Buddhist Text Translation Society Staff. (Illus.). 120p. (Orig.). 1982. pap. 6.00 (ISBN 0-88139-502-1). Buddhist Text.

Sutra of the Past Vows of Earth Store Bodhisattva. Commentary by Tripitaka Master Hua. Tr. by Buddhist Text Translation Society Staff. (Illus.). 235p. (Orig.). 1976. 16.00 (ISBN 0-915078-00-7). Buddhist Text.

Sutra of the Past Vows of Earthstore Bodhisattva: The Collected Lectures of Tripitaka Master Hsuan Hua. Husan Hua. Tr. by Heng Ching from Chinese. (IASWR Ser.). 235p. 1974. 12.75 (ISBN 0-686-47598-4, S-10); pap. 6.75 (ISBN 0-915078-00-7, S-11). Inst Adv Stud Wld.

Sutra of Wei Lang. Hui-neng. Tr. by Wong Mou-lam from Chinese. LC 73-879. (China Studies: from Confucius to Mao Ser.). 128p. 1973. Repr. of 1944 ed. 15.75 (ISBN 0-88355-073-3). Hyperion Conn.

Sutra Spoken by Vimilakirti. Ed. by Kevin O'Neil. pap. 6.00 (ISBN 0-86627-009-4). Crises Res Pr.

Sutta-Nipata. Ed. by Dines Andersen & Helmer Smith. LC 78-70124. Repr. of 1913 ed. 27.00 (ISBN 0-404-17383-7). AMS Pr.

Sutta Nipata: Or Dialogues & Discourses of Gotama Buddha. Intro. by Swamy M. Coomara. LC 78-70125. 1980. Repr. of 1874 ed. 23.00 (ISBN 0-404-17384-5). AMS Pr.

Suttons Synagogue: Or the English Centurion (A Sermon) Percival Burrell. LC 74-28822. (English Experience Ser.: No. 647). 1974. Repr. of 1629 ed. 3.50 (ISBN 90-221-0647-0). Walter J Johnson.

Svetasvataropanisad. Tr. by Swami Tyagisananda. (Sanskrit & Eng.). pap. 2.00 (ISBN 0-87481-418-9). Vedanta Pr.

Svjatejshij Tikhon, Patrijarkh Moskovskij i Vseja Rossij. Tr. of His Holiness Tikhon, Patriarch of Moscow & all Russia. 80p. 1965. pap. 3.00 (ISBN 0-317-29216-1). Holy Trinity.

Svjatitel' Tikhon, Episkop Voronjezhskij i Zadonskij. N. Sergijevsky. Tr. of St. Tikhon, Bishop pf Voronezh & Zadonsk. 213p. pap. 8.00 (ISBN 0-317-29184-X). Holy Trinity.

Svjatoj Ioann (Pommer) Arkiepiskop Rihskij i Latvijskij. Lugmilla Koehler. Tr. of St. John (Pommer) Archbishop of Riga & Latvia. (Illus.). 72p. 1985. pap. 3.00 (ISBN 0-317-29224-2). Holy Trinity.
Svjatoj Mark Efesskij i Florentijskaja Unia. Archimandrite Amvrossy Pogodin. Tr. of St. Mark of Ephesus & the Unia of Florence. 436p. (Orig.). 1963. pap. 15.00x (ISBN 0-88465-026-X). Holy Trinity.
Svjelij Otrok; Sbornik Statej o Tsarevichje Mutchenikje Alekseje i drugikh Tsarstvennikh Mutchenikakh. Tr. of Bright Child; A Collection of Articles about the Prince-Martyr & Other Royal Martyrs. (Illus.). 105p. pap. 5.00 (ISBN 0-317-29229-3). Holy Trinity.
Swami & Friends. R. K. Narayan. LC 80-16119. 192p. 1980. lib. bdg. 13.00x (ISBN 0-226-56829-6); pap. 6.95 (ISBN 0-226-56831-8). U of Chicago Pr.
Swami & Sam: A Yoga Book. Brandt Dayton. (Illus.). 95p. (Orig.). pap. 0.95 (ISBN 0-89389-014-6). Himalayan Pubs.
Swami Krishnananda: In Conversation. 1983. 30.00x (ISBN 0-7069-2346-4, Pub. by Vikas India). Advent NY.
Swami Muktananda American Tour 1970. Swami Muktananda. LC 76-670007. 103p. 1974. 2.95 (ISBN 0-914602-25-X). SYDA Found.
Swami Ramakrishnananda: The Apostle of Sri Ramakrishna to the South. Swami Tapasyananda. 276p. 1973. 2.50 (ISBN 0-87481-453-7). Vedanta Pr.
Swami Turiyananda. Swami Ritajananda. (Illus.). pap. 1.95 (ISBN 0-87481-473-1). Vedanta Pr.
Swami Vijanada: A Short Life. Compiled by Apurvananda. 173p. 1987. pap. 4.50 (ISBN 0-87481-547-9, Pub. by Ramakrishna Math Madras India). Vedanta Pr.
Swami Vijnanananda: His Life & Sayings. Swami Vishwashrayananda. Tr. by Devavrata Basu Ray from Bengoli. 72p. 1981. pap. 1.95 (ISBN 0-87481-502-9). Vedanta Pr.
Swami Vivekananda: His Second Visit to the West (New Discoveries) Marie L. Burke. 20.00 (ISBN 0-87481-151-1). Vedanta Pr.
Swami Vivekananda in the West: New Discoveries: His Prophetic Mission, 2 Vols, Vol. 1. new ed. Marie L. Burke. (Illus.). 515p. text ed. 12.95x (ISBN 0-317-03702-1, Pub. by Advaita Ashrama India). Vedanta Pr.
Swami Vivekananda in the West: New Discoveries, Vol. II. Marie L. Burke. (Illus.). 457p. 1985. 12.95x (ISBN 0-87481-219-4, Pub. by Advaita Ashrama India). Vedanta Pr.
Swami Vivekananda's Contribution to the Present Age. Swami Satprakashananda. (Illus.). 249p. 1978. 9.50 (ISBN 0-916356-58-2, 77-91628). Vedanta Soc St Louis.
Swan's Wide Waters: Ramakrishna & Western Culture. new ed. Harold W. French. LC 74-77657. (National University Publications Ser.). 214p. 1974. 23.50x (ISBN 0-8046-9055-3, Pub by Kennikat). Assoc Faculty Pr.
Swayed Pines Song Book. Henry B. Hays. x, 88p. 1981. wirebound 7.95 (ISBN 0-8146-1238-5). Liturgical Pr.
Swedenborg: A Hermetic Philosopher. Ethan A. Hitchcock. 59.95 (ISBN 0-8490-1164-7). Gordon Pr.
Swedenborg & the New Age. Edmund A. Beaman. LC 77-134422. (Communal Societies in America Ser.). Repr. of 1881 ed. 18.00 (ISBN 0-404-08458-3). AMS Pr.
Swedenborg Epic. Cyriel O. Sigstedt. LC 78-137269. (Illus.). Repr. of 1952 ed. 34.50 (ISBN 0-404-05999-6). AMS Pr.
Swedenborg's System of Degrees. Hugo L. Odhner. 25p. 1970. pap. 1.00 (ISBN 0-915221-16-0). Swedenborg Sci Assn.
Swedish Church. Herbert M. Waddams. LC 81-7021. (Illus.). viii, 70p. 1981. Repr. of 1946 ed. lib. bdg. 22.50x (ISBN 0-313-22184-7, WASW). Greenwood.
Swedish Contributions to Modern Theology: With Special Reference to Lundensian Thought. Nels F. Ferre. 1967. lib. bdg. 17.50x (ISBN 0-88307-092-8). Gannon.
Sweeper to Saint: Stories of Holy India. Baba Hari Dass. Ed. by Ma Renu. LC 80-52021. (Illus.). 208p. (Orig.). 1980. pap. 6.95 (ISBN 0-918100-03-8). Sri Rama.
Sweet Comfort for Feeble Saints. C. H. Spurgeon. 1978. pap. 0.95 (ISBN 0-686-28282-5). Pilgrim Pubns.
Sweet Dreams for Little Ones. Michael G. Pappas. (Illus.). 64p. (Orig.). 1982. pap. 6.95 (ISBN 0-86683-641-1, AY8156, HarpR). Har-Row.
Sweeter Than Honey. Jesse B. Deloe. pap. 4.95 (ISBN 0-88469-105-5). BMH Bks.
Sweeter Than Honey. Paul Tassell. 1978. pap. 2.95 (ISBN 0-87227-068-8). Reg Baptist.
Swiss Migration to America: The Swiss Mennonites. Leo Schelbert. Ed. by Francesco Cordasco. LC 80-891. (American Ethnic Groups Ser.). 1981. lib. bdg. 38.50x (ISBN 0-405-13452-5). Ayer Co Pubs.
Sword & Mitre: Government & Episcopate in France & England in the Age of Aristocracy. Norman Ravitch. 1966. text ed. 18.40x (ISBN 0-686-22467-1). Mouton.
Sword & the Flute-Kali & Krsna: Dark Visions of the Terrible & the Sublime in Hindu Mythology. David R. Kinsley. LC 73-91669. (Hermeneutics: Studies in the History of Religions). 175p. 1975. pap. 10.95x (ISBN 0-520-03510-0). U of Cal Pr.
Sword & Trowel, 5 vols. C. H. Spurgeon. 1985. pap. 7.50 ea. Pilgrim Pubns.
Sword Drill Games Can Be Fun. Lola H. Houmes. 48p. pap. 2.95 (ISBN 0-87403-126-5, 2778). Standard Pub.
Sword, Miter, & Cloister: Nobility & the Church in Burgundy, 980-1198. Constance B. Bouchard. LC 86-29158. (Illus.). 416p. 1987. text ed. 41.50x (ISBN 0-8014-1974-3). Cornell U Pr.
Sword of Gnosis: Metaphysics, Cosmology, Tradition, Symbolism. Ed. by John Needleman. 448p. 1986. pap. 10.95 (ISBN 0-317-40557-8). Methuen Inc.
Sword of His Mouth. Robert C. Tannehill. Ed. by William A. Beardslee. LC 75-18948. (Semeia Studies). 236p. 1976. pap. 7.95 (ISBN 0-8006-1501-8, 1-1501). Fortress.
Sword of the Lord. Wim Malgo. pap. 2.95 (ISBN 0-937422-24-X). Midnight Call.
Sword of the Spirit. John E. Steinmueller. 108p. 1977. pap. 3.00 (ISBN 0-912103-00-0). Stella Maris Bks.
Sword of Truth: The Life & Times of the Shehu Usuman Dan Fodlo. Mervyn Hiskett. (Illus.). 1973. pap. 3.00x (ISBN 0-19-501647-5). Oxford U Pr.
Sydney Smith. George W. E. Russell. 1973. lib. bdg. 20.00 (ISBN 0-8414-7488-5). Folcroft.
Sydney Smith. George W. E. Russell. LC 79-156929. 1971. Repr. of 1905 ed. 35.00x (ISBN 0-8103-3720-7). Gale.
Sydney Smith: A Biography & a Selection. Gerald W. Bullett. LC 77-138578. (Illus.). 1971. Repr. of 1951 ed. lib. bdg. 22.50x (ISBN 0-8371-5777-3, BUSS). Greenwood.
Syllabus, University of Healing. 1982. 1.00. U of Healing.
Sylvester Judd's New England. Richard D. Hathaway. LC 81-17854. (Illus.). 362p. 1982. 24.95x (ISBN 0-271-00307-3). Pa St U Pr.
Symbol & Art in Worship. Ed. by Luis Maldonado & David Power. (Concilium Ser.: Vol. 132). 128p. (Orig.). 1980. pap. 5.95 (ISBN 0-8164-2274-5, HarpR). Har-Row.
Symbol & Empowerment: Paul Tillich's Post-Theistic System. Richard Grigg. xvi, 148p. 1985. text ed. 14.50 (ISBN 0-86554-163-9, MUP H153). Mercer Univ Pr.
Symbol & Myth in Ancient Poetry. Herbert A. Musurillo. LC 77-2395. 1977. Repr. of 1961 ed. lib. bdg. 24.75x (ISBN 0-8371-9554-3, MUSM). Greenwood.
Symbol Art: Thirteen Squares, Circles & Triangles from Around the World. Leonard E. Fisher. LC 85-42805. (Illus.). 64p. 1986. 12.95 (ISBN 0-02-735270-6, Four Winds). Macmillan.
Symbol Discrimination Series: Books 1, 2, 3, 4, 5, & 6. Reusable ed. Ann Arbor Publishers Editorial Staff. (Symbol Discrimination Series). (Illus.). 16p. 1974. 3.00 ea.; Book 1. 3.00 (ISBN 0-89039-078-9); Book 2. 3.00 (ISBN 0-89039-079-7); Book 3. 3.00 (ISBN 0-89039-080-0); Book 4. 3.00 (ISBN 0-89039-081-9); Book 5. 3.00 (ISBN 0-89039-082-7); Book 6. 3.00 (ISBN 0-89039-083-5). Ann Arbor FL.
Symbol Patterns: Ideas for Banners, Posters, Bulletin Boards. 40p. (Orig.). 1981. pap. 4.95 (ISBN 0-8066-1897-3, 10-6173). Augsburg.
Symbolic Directions: Modern Astrology. Carter. 7.95 (ISBN 0-7229-5145-0). Theos Pub Hse.
Symbolic Images: Studies in the Art of the Renaissance, No. II. E. H. Gombrich. LC 84-28111. (Illus.). xii, 356p. 1985. pap. 14.95 (ISBN 0-226-30217-2). U of Chicago Pr.
Symbolic Prophecy of the Great Pyramid. 16th ed. H. Spencer Lewis. LC 37-3808. 192p. 1982. 8.95 (ISBN 0-912057-13-0, G-514). AMORC.
Symbolic Uses of Politics: With a New Afterword. Murray Edelman. LC 84-16195. 232p. 1985. pap. 6.95 (ISBN 0-252-01202-X). U of Ill Pr.
Symbolic Vision in Biblical Tradition. Susan Niditch. LC 83-8643. (Harvard Semitic Monographs). 270p. 1983. 15.00 (ISBN 0-89130-627-7, 04 00 30). Scholars Pr GA.
Symbolically Speaking. D. Douglas Schneider. Ed. by Von Bruck Michael. (Illus.). 85p. 1987. pap. 5.95 (ISBN 0-939169-01-0). World Peace Univ.
Symbolik und Mythologie der Alten Volker Besonders der Griechen, 6 vols. Georg F. Creuzer. Ed. by Kees W. Bolle. LC 77-79119. (Mythology Ser.). (Ger., Illus.). 1978. Repr. of 1823 ed. lib. bdg. 325.00x (ISBN 0-405-10531-2). Ayer Co Pubs.
Symbolism: A Comprehensive Dictionary. Steven Olderr. LC 85-42833. 159p. 1986. lib. bdg. 25.95 (ISBN 0-89950-187-7). McFarland & Co.
Symbolism & Growth: The Religious Thought of Horace Bushnell. David L. Smith. Ed. by Wendell S. Dietrich. LC 80-14600. (AAR Dissertation Ser.). pap. 9.95 (ISBN 0-89130-410-X, 01 01 36). Scholars Pr GA.
Symbolism & Interpretation. Tzvetan Todorov. Tr. by Catherine Porter from Fr. LC 82-5078. 192p. 1982. text ed. 24.95x (ISBN 0-8014-1269-2). Cornell U Pr.
Symbolism & Reality: A Study in the Nature of Mind. Charles W. Morris. LC 86-17602. (Foundations of Semiotics Ser.: No. 15). v, 150p. 1987. 34.00x (ISBN 90-272-3287-3). Benjamins North Am.
Symbolism in Relation to Religion. James B. Hannay. LC 79-118523. (Illus.). 1971. Repr. of 1915 ed. 28.50x (Pub by Kennikat). Assoc Faculty Pr.
Symbolism in the Bible. Paul Diel. 1986. 17.95 (ISBN 0-317-52369-4, HarpR). Har-Row.
Symbolism in the Prehistoric Painted Ceramics of China. Johan G. Anderson. 1929. 13.00 (ISBN 0-317-43918-9, Pub. by Han-Shan Tang Ltd). State Mutual Bk.
Symbolism of Churches & Church Ornaments. Gulielmus Durantis. 1980. lib. bdg. 64.95 (ISBN 0-8490-3166-4). Gordon Pr.
Symbolism of Churches & Church Ornaments: A Translation of the First Book of the Rationale Divinorum Officiorum. Gulielmus Durantis. Ed. by John M. Neale & Benjamin Webb. Repr. of 1843 ed. 28.00 (ISBN 0-404-04653-3). AMS Pr.
Symbolism of Evil. Paul Ricoeur. Tr. by Emerson Buchanan. LC 67-11506. 1969. pap. 11.95x (ISBN 0-8070-1567-9, BPA18). Beacon Pr.
Symbolism of Freemansonry. A. G. Mackey. 12.00x (ISBN 0-685-22122-9). Wehman.
Symbolism of Freemasonry. Jirah D. Buck. 12.00 (ISBN 0-685-19503-1). Powner.
Symbolism of Freemasonry. Albert G. Mackey. 12.00 (ISBN 0-685-19504-X). Powner.
Symbolism of the Biblical World Ancient Near Eastern Iconography & the Book of Psalms. Othmar Keel. (Illus.). 1978. 39.50x (ISBN 0-8245-0376-7). Crossroad NY.
Symbolism of the Cross. Rene Guenon. 134p. 1975. 35.00x (ISBN 0-317-39165-8, Pub. by Luzac & Co Ltd); pap. 19.00x (ISBN 0-317-39166-6). State Mutual Bk.
Symbolism of the East & West. Harriet Murray-Aynsley. LC 74-118538. 1971. Repr. of 1900 ed. 25.50x (ISBN 0-8046-1162-9, Pub by Kennikat). Assoc Faculty Pr.
Symbolism: The Universal Language. J. C. Cooper. LC 86-18838. 176p. 1986. lib. bdg. 19.95x (ISBN 0-8095-7001-7). Borgo Pr.
Symbolisme de la Salette. Paul Claudel. 64p. 1952. 2.95 (ISBN 0-686-54437-4). French & Eur.
Symbolist Art of Fernand Khnoff. Jeffery W. Howe. Ed. by Stephen Foster. LC 82-4734. (Studies in the Fine Arts: The Avant Garde: No. 28). 274p. 1982. 44.95 (ISBN 0-8357-1317-2). UMI Res Pr.
Symbols & Society: Essays on Belief Systems in Action. Ed. by Carole E. Hill. LC 74-21905. (Southern Anthropological Society Proceedings Ser: No. 9). 150p. 1975. pap. 6.50x (ISBN 0-8203-0371-2). U of Ga Pr.
Symbols & Their Meaning. Rudolph F. Norden. 1985. pap. 3.50 (ISBN 0-570-03949-5, 12-2883). Concordia.
Symbols for Communication: An Introduction to the Anthropological Study of Religion. 2nd, rev. ed. T. Van Baal & W. E. Van Beek. (Studies of Developing Countries: No. 11). 272p. 1985. pap. 30.00 (ISBN 90-232-2074-9, Pub. by Van Gorcum Holland). Longwood Pub Group.
Symbols of Church & Kingdom. R. Murray. LC 74-80363. 430p. 1975. 59.50 (ISBN 0-521-20553-0). Cambridge U Pr.
Symbols of Church Seasons & Days. John Bradner. (Illus.). 1977. pap. 6.95 (ISBN 0-8192-1228-8). Morehouse.
Symbols of Community: The Cultural System of a Swedish Church. Peter G. Stromberg. LC 85-30229. (Anthropology of Form & Meaning Ser.). 127p. 1986. 17.95x (ISBN 0-8165-0967-0). U of Ariz Pr.
Symbols of God's Love: Codes & Passwords. Jeanne S. Fogle. Ed. by Mary Jean Ducket & W. Benson Lane. LC 86-12014. (Illus.). 32p. (Orig.). 1986. pap. 4.95 (ISBN 0-664-24050-X, A Geneva Press Publication). Westminster.
Symbols of Heraldry Explained. (Illus.). 112p. 1980. pap. 3.95 (ISBN 0-9502455-5-0, Pub. by Heraldic Art). Irish Bks Media.
Symbols of Judaism: The Challenge to Learn & Create. pap. 4.00 (ISBN 0-686-96080-7). United Syn Bk.
Symbols of Numerology. Julia M. Seton. 304p. 1984. pap. 9.95 (ISBN 0-87877-071-2). Newcastle Pub.
Symbols of Numerology. Julia M. Seton. LC 84-9183. 304p. 1984. Repr. of 1984 ed. lib. bdg. 19.95x (ISBN 0-89370-671-X). Borgo Pr.
Symbols of the Church. Ed. by Carroll E. Whittemore. 64p. 1983. pap. 2.25 (ISBN 0-687-40786-9). Abingdon.
Symbols of Transformation in Dreams. Jean Clift & Wallace Clift. 144p. 1986. pap. 9.95 (ISBN 0-8245-0727-4). Crossroad NY.
Symbols That Stand for Themselves. Roy Wagner. LC 85-16448. (Illus.). 1986. lib. bdg. 27.00x (ISBN 0-226-86928-8); pap. text ed. 9.95x (ISBN 0-226-86929-6). U of Chicago Pr.
Symeon Neos Theologos, Hymnen Einleitung und kritischer Text. Ed. by Athanasios Kambylis. (Supplementa Byzantina, Vol. 3). 1976. 234.00x (ISBN 3-11-004888-4). De Gruyter.
Symeon, the New Theologian: The Discourses. C. J. De Catanzaro. LC 80-82414. (Classics of Western Spirituality Ser.). 416p. 1980. 13.95 (ISBN 0-8091-0292-7); pap. 9.95 (ISBN 0-8091-2230-8). Paulist Pr.
Symposium on Creation, No. 4. Ed. by Donald W. Patten. pap. 3.95 (ISBN 0-8010-6925-4). Baker Bk.
Symposium on Oneness Pentecostalism 1986. Compiled by United Pentecostal Church Int. & J. L. Hall. LC 86-19024. (Orig.). pap. 7.95 (ISBN 0-932581-03-X). Word Aflame.
Symposium on the Magisterium: A Positive Statement. Ed. by John J. O'Rourke & S. Thomas Greenburg. 1978. 5.95 (ISBN 0-8198-0559-9); pap. 4.50 (ISBN 0-8198-0560-2). Dghtrs St Paul.
Synagogue. rev ed. C. H. Kraeling. 1979. 100.00x (ISBN 0-87068-331-4). Ktav.
Synagogue Havurot: A Comparative Study. Gerald B. Bubis & Harry Wasserman. LC 82-23912. 160p. (Orig.). 1983. lib. bdg. 25.50 (ISBN 0-8191-2969-0, Co-pub. by Ctr Jewish Comm Studies); pap. text ed. 10.50 (ISBN 0-8191-2970-4). U Pr of Amer.
Synagogue in Late Antiquity: A Centennial Publication of the Jewish Theological Seminary of America. Ed. by Lee I. Levine. xiv, 223p. 1986. 26.95 (ISBN 0-89757-510-5, Dist. by Eisenbrauns); pap. 15.95 (ISBN 0-89757-509-1). Am Sch Orient Res.
Synagogue in the Central City: Temple Israel of Greater Miami 1922-1972. Charlton W. Tebeau. LC 72-85107. 5.00 (ISBN 0-87024-239-3). Rostrum Bks.
Synagogue in the Central City: Temple Israel of Greater Miami, 1922-1972. Charlton W. Tebeau. LC 71-85107. (Illus.). 144p. 1972. 9.95 (ISBN 0-87024-239-3). U of Miami Pr.
Synagogue Life: A Study in Symbolic Interaction. Samuel C. Heilman. LC 75-36403. 1976. 12.95x (ISBN 0-226-32488-5); pap. 9.95x (ISBN 0-226-32490-7, P824, Phoen). U of Chicago Pr.
Synagogue: Studies in Origins, Archeology, & Architecture. Joseph Gutmann. 1974. 35.00x (ISBN 0-87068-265-2). Ktav.
Synagogue Through the Ages: An Illustrated History of Judaism's Houses of Worship. Azriel Eisenberg. LC 73-77284. (Illus.). 1973. 15.00 (ISBN 0-8197-0290-0). Bloch.
Synagogues of Europe: Architecture, History, Meaning. Carol H. Krinsky. (Architectural History Foundation Ser.). 470p. 1987. pap. 25.00 (ISBN 0-262-61048-5). MIT Pr.
Synagogues of New York City. Oscar Israelowitz. 1983. 14.00 (ISBN 0-8446-5954-1). Peter Smith.
Synagogues of New York City: A Pictorial Survey in 150 Photographs. Oscar Israelowitz. (Illus.). 155p. (Orig.). pap. 6.00 (ISBN 0-486-24231-5). Dover.
Synagogues of New York's Lower East Side. Jo Renee Fine & Gerard R. Wolfe. LC 75-15126. (Illus.). 1978. 27.50 (ISBN 0-8147-2559-7). NYU Pr.
Synagogues Through the Ages. Geoffrey Wigoder. LC 86-45032. (Illus.). 208p. 1986. 35.00 (ISBN 0-06-069401-7, HarpR). Har-Row.
Synaxis: The Journal of Orthodox Theology, Vol. 2. 1977. pap. 4.00x (ISBN 0-913026-88-3). St Nectarios.
Syncretic Religion of Lin Chao-En. Judith A. Berling. LC 79-25606. (Institute for Advanced Studies of World Religions; Neo-Confucian Studies). 1980. 31.00x (ISBN 0-231-04870-X). Columbia U Pr.
Synergists. Ed. by Dorothy Walters. (Illus.). 269p. 1984. 16.95 (ISBN 0-934344-14-0, Pub. by Royal CBS). Fell.
Synesius of Cyrene: Philosopher & Bishop. A. Gardner. 1977. lib. bdg. 59.95 (ISBN 0-8490-2697-0). Gordon Pr.
Synesius of Cyrene: Philosopher-Bishop. Jay Bregman. LC 81-10293. (Transformation of the Classical Heritage Ser.: Vol. II). 1982. 33.00x (ISBN 0-520-04192-5). U of Cal Pr.
Synod Extraordinary: An Evaluation of the Catholic Church on the 20th Anniversary of Vatican Council II. Peter Hebblethwaite. LC 85-27160. 144p. 1986. 15.95 (ISBN 0-385-23466-X). Doubleday.

Synod of Sixteen Seventy-Two: Acts & Decrees of the Jerusalem Synod Held Under Dositheus, Containing the Confession Published Name of Cyril Lukaris. Orthodox Eastern Church. Tr. by J. N. Robertson. LC 78-81769. 1969. Repr. of 1899 ed. 18.50 (ISBN 0-404-03567-1). AMS Pr.

Synodicon Vetus. Ed. by John Duffy. John Parker. LC 79-52935. (Dumbarton Oaks Texts: Vol. 5). 209p. 1979. 35.00x (ISBN 0-88402-088-6). Dumbarton Oaks.

Synonyms of the New Testament. Robert C. Trench. 1950. pap. 8.95 (ISBN 0-8028-1520-0). Eerdmans.

Synonyms of the Old Testament. Robert B. Girdlestone. 1948. pap. 6.95 (ISBN 0-8028-1548-0). Eerdmans.

Synonyms of the Old Testament: Numerically Coded to Strong's Exhaustive Concordance. Robert B. Girdlestone. Ed. by Donald R. White. 400p. 1983. deluxe ed. 22.95 (ISBN 0-8010-3798-0); pap. 17.95 kivar bdg. (ISBN 0-8010-3789-1). Baker Bk.

Synopsis of the Books of the Bible, 5 vols. J. N. Darby. Set. 27.50 (ISBN 0-88172-070-4). Believers Bkshelf.

Synopsis of the First Three Gospels With the Addition of the Johannine Parallels. Albert Huck. 1982. 22.50x (ISBN 0-8028-3568-6). Eerdmans.

Synopsis of the Four Gospels (English Only) Ed. by K. Aland. 1983. 5.95x (ISBN 0-8267-0500-6, 08564). Am Bible.

Synopsis of the Four Gospels in a New Translation: Arranged According to the Two Gospel Hypothesis. John B. Orchard. LC 81-18753. 319p. 1982. English 9.95 (ISBN 0-86554-024-1, MUP-H22); Greek 21.00 (ISBN 0-86554-061-6, MUP-H70). Mercer Univ Pr.

Synopsis: Past-Present-Future. Worth S. Rough. LC 84-90177. 84p. 1984. 17.95 (ISBN 0-533-06227-6). Vantage.

Synoptic Abstract. Joseph B. Tyson & Thomas R. W. Longstaff. Ed. by J. Arthur Baird & David Noel Freedman. (The Computer Bible Ser.: Vol. XV). 1978. pap. 15.00 (ISBN 0-935106-05-7). Biblical Res Assocs.

Synoptic Approach to the Riddle of Existence. Arthur W. Munk. LC 77-818. 264p. 1977. 15.00 (ISBN 0-87527-165-0). Fireside Bks.

Synoptic Gospels: An Introduction. Keith F. Nickle. LC 79-92069. (Orig.). 1980. pap. 9.95 (ISBN 0-8042-0422-5). John Knox.

Synoptic Harmony of Samuel, Kings, & Chronicles. James D. Newsome, Jr. 272p. 1986. text ed. 16.95 (ISBN 0-8010-6744-8). Baker Bk.

Synoptic Problem. Robert H. Stein. 280p. 1987. pap. 17.95 (ISBN 0-8010-8272-2). Baker Bk.

Synoptic Problem: A Critical Analysis. William R. Farmer. LC 76-13764. xi, 308p. 1981. 18.95 (ISBN 0-915948-02-8, MUP-H005). Mercer Univ Pr.

Synopticon. Ed. by William R. Farmer. 1969. 80.00 (ISBN 0-521-07464-9). Cambridge U Pr.

Syntactical & Critical Concordance to the Greek Text of Baruch & the Epistle of Jeremiah. R. A. Martin. (Computer Bible Ser.: Vol. XII). (Gr.). 1977. pap. 15.00 (ISBN 0-935106-09-X). Biblical Res Assocs.

Syntax, Vol. 3. Nigel Turner. (Moulton's Grammar of New Testament Greek Ser.). 438p. 1963. 21.95 (ISBN 0-567-01013-9, Pub. by T & T Clark Ltd UK). Fortress.

Syntax of Moods & Tenses of New Testament Greek. Ernest D. Burton. 240p. 1898. 11.95 (ISBN 0-567-01002-3, Pub. by T & T Clark Ltd UK). Fortress.

Syntax of New Testament Greek. James A. Brooks & Carlton L. Winbery. LC 78-51150. 1978. pap. text ed. 8.00 (ISBN 0-8191-0473-6). U Pr of Amer.

Syntax of the Moods & Tenses of New Testament Greek. Ernest D. Burton. LC 76-25360. 238p. 1976. 12.95 (ISBN 0-8254-2256-6). Kregel.

Synthesis of Yoga. Sri Aurobindo. 1976. pap. 8.00 (ISBN 0-89071-268-9). Matagiri.

Synthesis of Yoga. 6th ed. Sri Aurobindo. 1979p. 36.00 (ISBN 0-89744-931-2). Auromere.

Synthesis of Yoga. Sri Aurobindo. 1979p. 30.00 (ISBN 0-89744-932-0). Auromere.

Synthesis of Yoga. Sri Aurobindo. (Life Companion Bible Bks.). 1984p. 24.95 (ISBN 0-89744-017-X). Auromere.

Synthesis of Yoga. Sri Aurobindo. 899p. 1984. 16.75 (ISBN 0-89071-313-8, Pub. by Sri Aurobindo Ashram India); pap. 12.50 (ISBN 0-89071-312-X, Pub. by Sri Aurobindo Ashram India). Matagiri.

Synthetic View of Vedanta. P. N. Srinivasachari. 2.75 (ISBN 0-8356-7512-2). Theos Pub Hse.

Syriac Manuscripts in the Harvard College Library: A Catalogue. Moshe H. Goshen-Gottstein. LC 77-13132. (Harvard Semitic Studies: No. 23). 1979. 15.00 (ISBN 0-89130-189-5, 040423). Scholars Pr GA.

Syriac Version of the Ps. Nonnos Mythological Scholia. Sebastian Brock. LC 79-139712. (Oriental Publications: No. 20). 1971. 62.50 (ISBN 0-521-07990-X). Cambridge U Pr.

Syriac Version of the Psalms of Solomon. Joseph L. Trafton. (SBL Septuagint & Cognate Studies). 1985. 22.95 (ISBN 0-89130-910-1, 06-04-11); pap. 15.95 (ISBN 0-89130-911-X). Scholars Pr GA.

Syrian-African Rift & Other Poems. Avoth Yeshurun. Ed. by Yehuda Amichai & Allen Mandelbaum. Tr. by Harold Schimmel. LC 80-13630. (Jewish Poetry Ser.). 160p. 1980. 11.95 (ISBN 0-8276-0181-6, 464); pap. 7.95 (ISBN 0-8276-0182-4, 463). Jewish Pubns.

Syrian Christians in Muslim Society: An Interpretation. Robert M Haddad. LC 81-6202. (Princeton Studies on the Near East). viii, 118p. 1981. Repr. of 1970 ed. lib. bdg. 22.50x (ISBN 0-313-23054-4, HASYC). Greenwood.

Syrian Desert. Christian P. Grant. LC 78-63341. (Crusades & Military Orders: Second Ser.). (Illus.). Repr. of 1937 ed. 41.00 (ISBN 0-404-17017-X). AMS Pr.

Syrische Kirchenbau. Hermann W. Beyer. (Studien Zur Spaetantiken Kunstgeschichte Ser.: Vol. 1). (Illus.). viii, 183p. 1978. Repr. of 1925 ed. 60.00x (ISBN 3-11-005705-0). De Gruyter.

System of Ethics. Leonard Nelson. 1956. 49.50x (ISBN 0-685-69846-7). Elliots Bks.

Systematic Hebrew. Shahar Yonay & Rina Yonay. 1986. 12.95 (ISBN 0-9616783-0-5). S Yonay.

Systematic Philosophy: An Overview of Metaphysics Showing the Development from the Greeks to the Contemporaries with Specified Directions & Projections. John E. Van Hook. (Illus.). 1979. 8.50 (ISBN 0-682-49398-8, University). Exposition Pr FL.

Systematic Theology. Louis Berkhof. 1978. 24.95 (ISBN 0-8028-3020-X). Eerdmans.

Systematic Theology, 8 vols. Lewis S. Chafer. 2700p. 1981. Repr. 94.95 (ISBN 0-310-22378-4). Zondervan.

Systematic Theology. R. L. Dabney. 903p. 1985. 19.95 (ISBN 0-85151-453-7). Banner of Truth.

Systematic Theology, 3 Vols. Charles Hodge. 1960. Set. 49.95 (ISBN 0-8028-8135-1). Eerdmans.

Systematic Theology, 3 Vols in 1. Augustus H. Strong. 21.95 (ISBN 0-8170-0177-8). Judson.

Systematic Theology. Augustus H. Strong. Incl. Doctrine of God; Doctrine of Man; Doctrine of Salvation. 1168p. 24.95 (ISBN 0-8007-0302-2). Revell.

Systematic Theology, 3 vols. in 1. Paul Tillich. LC 51-2235. 950p. 1967. 49.95x (ISBN 0-226-80336-8). U of Chicago Pr.

Systematic Theology, 3 vols. Ernest S. Williams. Incl. Vol. 1. pap. 6.95 (ISBN 0-88243-643-0, 02-0643); Vol. 2. pap. 6.95 (ISBN 0-88243-644-9, 02-0644); Vol. 3. pap. 6.95 (ISBN 0-88243-645-7, 02-0645). 1953. pap. 18.00 Set 3 vol (ISBN 0-88243-650-3, 02-0650). Gospel Pub.

Systematic Theology, Vol. 1. Paul Tillich. LC 51-2235. 1973. pap. 11.00x (ISBN 0-226-80337-6, P556, Phoen). U of Chicago Pr.

Systematic Theology, Vol. 2. Paul Tillich. LC 51-2235. xii, 188p. 1975. pap. 7.50X (ISBN 0-226-80338-4, P633, Phoen). U of Chicago Pr.

Systematic Theology: A Modern Protestant Approach. Kenneth Cauthen. LC 86-23807. (Toronto Studies in Theology: Vol. 25). 480p. 1986. lib. bdg. 69.95x (ISBN 0-88946-769-2). E Mellen.

Systematic Theology: Life & the Spirit History & the Kingdom of God, Vol. 3. Paul Tillich. LC 51-2235. 1976. pap. 11.00x (ISBN 0-226-80339-2, P706, Phoen). U of Chicago Pr.

Systematic Theology of the Christian Religion. James O. Buswell, Jr. 27.95 (ISBN 0-310-22190-0, 9364P). Zondervan.

Systemic Religious Education. Timothy A. Lines. LC 86-20383. 264p. (Orig.). 1987. pap. 14.95 (ISBN 0-89135-057-8). Religious Educ.

Systems of Buddhist Thought. Yamakami Sogen. 385p. Repr. of 1912 ed. text ed. 28.50x (ISBN 0-89644-474-0, Pub. by Chinese Matl Ctr). Coronet Bks.

T

T-R-A-I-N up the Children. Linda J. Burba & Keith V. Burba. 111p. 1985. pap. 4.50 (ISBN 0-8341-1062-8). Beacon Hill.

Taamim Lakorim. 1982. pap. 7.50 (ISBN 0-686-76267-3); cassette 7.50 (ISBN 0-686-76268-1); book & cassette 12.00 (ISBN 0-686-76269-X). Feldheim.

Ta'anith, 1 vol. 15.00 (ISBN 0-910218-62-5). Bennet Pub.

Tabernacle. M. R. DeHaan. 1979. pap. 6.95 (ISBN 0-310-23491-3, 9502P). Zondervan.

Tabernacle. Dirk H. Dolman. 525p. 1982. Repr. lib. bdg. 19.75 smythe sewn (ISBN 0-86524-152-X, 0203). Klock & Klock.

Tabernacle. John Ritchie. LC 82-178. 122p. 1982. pap. 4.50 (ISBN 0-8254-3616-8). Kregel.

Tabernacle: Camping with God. Stephen F. Olford. LC 78-173686. 1971. 8.95 (ISBN 0-87213-675-2). Loizeaux.

Tabernacle, God's Dwelling Place. Dean Guest. 64p. (Orig.). 1979. pap. 1.95 (ISBN 0-89841-012-6). Zoe Pubns.

Tabernacle in the Wilderness. David Little. pap. 1.50 (ISBN 0-87213-520-9). Loizeaux.

Tabernacle Menorah: A Synthetic Study of a Symbol from the Biblical Cult. Carol L. Meyers. LC 76-17105. (Amerian Schools of Oriental Research, Dissertation Ser.: Vol. 2). 243p. 1976. (Am Sch Orient Res); pap. text ed. 6.00x (ISBN 0-89757-101-0). Eisenbrauns.

Tabernacle of God in the Wilderness of Sinai. Paul F. Kiene. 1977. 19.95 (ISBN 0-310-36200-8, 11066). Zondervan.

Tabernacle of Israel. James Strong. LC 85-8100. (Illus.). 208p. 1987. pap. 10.95 (ISBN 0-8254-3745-8). Kregel.

Tabernacle of Moses. Kevin Conner. 119p. 1974. 7.95 (ISBN 0-914936-08-5). Bible Temple.

Tabernacle, Priesthood & Offerings. I. M. Haldeman. 408p. 14.95 (ISBN 0-8007-0303-0). Revell.

Tabernacle, Priesthood & the Offerings. Henry W. Soltau. LC 72-88590. 486p. 1974. 14.95 (ISBN 0-8254-3703-2); Published 1986. pap. 12.95 (ISBN 0-8254-3750-4). Kregel.

Tabernacle Talks Today. R. P. Daniel. pap. 5.25 (ISBN 0-88172-020-8). Believers Bkshelf.

Tabernacle Types & Teaching. Edward Laity. 1980. pap. 2.95 (ISBN 0-86544-011-5). Salv Army Suppl South.

Tabernaculo en el Desierto. John Ritchie. Orig. Title: Tabernacle in the Desert. (Span.). 144p. Date not set. pap. 3.95 (ISBN 0-8254-1616-7). Kregel.

Table & Tradition. Alasdair I. Heron. LC 83-14762. 206p. (Orig.). 1984. pap. 11.95 (ISBN 0-664-24516-1). Westminster.

Table Graces. Ed. by Nick Beilenson. LC 86-61119. (Illus.). 63p. 1986. 5.95 (ISBN 0-88088-509-2). Peter Pauper.

Table Graces for the Family. rev. ed. 128p. 1984. 4.95 (ISBN 0-8407-5369-1). Nelson.

Table in the Wilderness. Angus Kinnear. 1978. pap. 4.95 (ISBN 0-8423-6900-7). Tyndale.

Table in the Wilderness. Watchman Nee. 1969. pap. 4.95 (ISBN 0-87508-422-2). Chr Lit.

Table of Inwardness. Calvin Miller. LC 84-9134. 132p. (Orig.). 1984. pap. 4.95 (ISBN 0-87784-832-7). Inter-Varsity.

Table of the Lord. Gaynell B. Cronin. LC 86-70131. (Illus., Orig.). 1986. Child's Bk, 104 pgs. pap. text ed. 4.50 (ISBN 0-87793-299-9); Director's Manual, 168 pgs. 9.75 (ISBN 0-87793-325-1); Parent's Bk, 96 pgs. 3.50 (ISBN 0-87793-326-X). Ave Maria.

Table Prayers for the Family Circle. Walter L. Cook. 96p. (Orig.). 1982. pap. 3.45 (ISBN 0-8010-2471-4). Baker Bk.

Table Prayers: New Prayers, Old Favorites, Songs, & Responses. Compiled by Mildred Tengbom. LC 77-72451. 1977. pap. 4.95 (ISBN 0-8066-1594-X, 10-6185). Augsburg.

Tableaux Du Temple Des Muses, Repr. Of 1655 Ed. Michel de Marolles. Bd. with Iconologia or Moral Problems. Cesare Ripa. Repr. of 1709 ed. LC 75-27876. (Renaissance & the Gods Ser.: Vol. 31). (Illus.). 1976. lib. bdg. 80.00 (ISBN 0-8240-2080-4). Garland Pub.

Tablets of Baha'u'llah Revealed after the Kitab-i-Aqdas. Baha'u'llah. Tr. by Shoghi Effendi & Habib Taherzadeh. LC 79-670079. 1978. 14.95 (ISBN 0-85398-077-2, 103-021, Pub. by Universal Hse. of Justice); pap. 7.95 (ISBN 0-85398-137-X). Baha'i.

Tablets of the Divine Plan. rev. ed. Abdu'l-Baha. LC 76-10624. 1977. o.s.i 10.95 (ISBN 0-87743-107-8, 106-010); pap. 5.95 (ISBN 0-87743-116-7, 106-011). Baha'i.

Taboo: A Sociological Study. Hutton Webster. LC 73-4250. xii, 393p. 1973. Repr. of 1942 ed. lib. bdg. 26.00x (ISBN 0-374-98324-0, Octagon). Hippocrene Bks.

Taboo, Magic, Spirits: A Study of Primitive Elements in Roman Religion. Eli E. Burriss. LC 72-114489. x, 250p. Repr. of 1931 ed. lib. bdg. 22.50x (ISBN 0-8371-4724-7, BUTA). Greenwood.

Tabula of Cebes. John Fitzgerald & Michael White. LC 82-19118. (SBL Texts & Translations). 236p. 1983. pap. 14.25 (ISBN 0-89130-601-3, 06 02 24). Scholars Pr GA.

Tactics of Christian Resistance. Ed. by Gary North. LC 83-81783. (Christianity & Civilization Ser.: No. 3). 528p. 1983. pap. 14.95 (ISBN 0-939404-07-9). Geneva Ministr.

Tafhimul - Quran: Urdu Translation & Commentary. A. A. Maudadi. 95.00 (ISBN 0-686-18523-4). Kazi Pubns.

Tagore-Gandhi Controversy. M. K. Gandhi & Rabindranath Tagore. Ed. by R. K. Prabhu. 155p. (Orig.). 1983. pap. 2.00 (ISBN 0-934676-52-6). Greenlf Bks.

Tah-Koo Wah-Kan; Or, the Gospel Among the Dakotas. Stephen R. Riggs. LC 78-38460. (Religion in America, Ser. 2). 534p. 1972. Repr. of 1869 ed. 33.00 (ISBN 0-405-04081-4). Ayer Co Pubs.

Tahafut Al-Falasifah. Al-Ghazzali. 8.25x (ISBN 0-87902-054-7). Orientalia.

Taharath Hamishpacha: Jewish Family Laws. Zev Schostak. 1982. 3.95 (ISBN 0-87306-100-4). Feldheim.

T'ai Chi Chih! Joy Thru Movement. rev. ed. Justin F. Stone. (Illus.). 136p. 1986. pap. 9.95 (ISBN 0-937277-02-9). Satori Resources.

T'ai Chi Ch'uan. Y. Ming-Shih. 6.95x (ISBN 0-685-63782-4). Wehman.

T'ai Chi Ch'uan. Yang Ming-shih. (Quick & Easy Ser.). (Illus.). 60p. (Orig.). 1974. pap. 3.95 (ISBN 4-07-973783-1, Pub. by Shufunmato Co Ltd Japan). C E Tuttle.

T'ai Chi Ch'uan & I Ching: A Choreography of Body & Mind. Liu Da. LC 79-183640. 1987. pap. 5.95 (ISBN 0-06-091309-6, PL-1309, PL). Har-Row.

T'ai Chi Ch'uan for Health & Self-Defense: Philosophy & Practice. T. T. Liang. 1977. pap. 5.95 (ISBN 0-394-72461-5, Vin). Random.

T'ai Chi Ch'uan: Its Effects & Practical Applications. Y. K. Chen. 1979. pap. 6.95 (ISBN 0-87877-043-7). Newcastle Pub.

T'ai Chi Ch'uan the Philosophy of Yin & Yang & Its Applications. Douglas Lee. Ed. by Charles Lucas. LC 76-6249. (Ser. 317). (Illus.). 1976. pap. text ed. 6.95 (ISBN 0-89750-044-X). Ohara Pubns.

T'ai Chi Ch'uan: The Technique of Power. Ed. by Susan Kimmelman & Tem Horwitz. LC 76-41613. (Illus.). 1980. pap. 9.95 (ISBN 0-914090-24-0). Chicago Review.

T'ai Chi Handbook: Exercise, Meditation, Self-Defense. Herman Kauz. LC 73-10552. (Illus.). 192p. 1974. pap. 9.95 (ISBN 0-385-09370-5, Dolp). Doubleday.

T'ai Chi: Ten Minutes to Health. Chia S. Pang & Goh E. Hock. LC 85-22388. (Illus.). 131p. (Orig.). 1986. pap. 12.95 (ISBN 0-916360-30-X). CRCS Pubns NV.

T'ai-Chi the Supreme Ultimate Exercise for Health, Sport, & Self-Defense. Man-Ch'ing Cheng & Robert W. Smith. LC 67-23009. (Illus.). 1967. 22.50 (ISBN 0-8048-0560-1). C E Tuttle.

T'ai Shan: An Account of the Sacred Eastern Peak of China. Dwight C. Baker. lib. bdg. 79.95 (ISBN 0-87968-474-7). Krishna Pr.

Tain of the Mirror. Rodolphe Gasche. LC 86-4673. 384p. 1986. text ed. 25.00x (ISBN 0-674-86700-9). Harvard U Pr.

Taiping Rebel: The Deposition of Li Hsiu-Ch'eng. C. A. Curwen. LC 76-8292. (Cambridge Studies in Chinese History, Literature & Institutions). (Illus.). 1977. 57.50 (ISBN 0-521-21082-8). Cambridge U Pr.

Taiping Rebellion: Documents & Comments. Franz Michael & Chung-Li Chang. Incl. Vol. 2. 756p (ISBN 0-295-73959-2); Vol. 3. 1107p (ISBN 0-295-73958-4). LC 66-13538. (Publications on Asia of the Institute for Foreign & Area Studies: No. 14, Pt. 2). 1971. 35.00x ea. U of Wash Pr.

Taiping Rebellion: History, Vol. 1. Franz Michael & Chung-Li Chang. (Publications on Asia of the Institute for Foreign & Area Studies: No. 14, Pt. 1). 256p. 1966. pap. 8.95x (ISBN 0-295-95244-X). U of Wash Pr.

Taiping Revolution: A Failure of Two Missions. Robert H. Lin. 1979. pap. text ed. 10.75 (ISBN 0-8191-0734-4). U Pr of Amer.

Taitiriya Upanishad. Tr. by Alladi M. Sastry. 93p. 1980. 36.00 (ISBN 0-89744-145-1, Pub. by Samata Bks India). Auromere.

Taize Picture Bible. Ed. by Eric De Suassure. LC 69-11860. (Illus.). 298p. 1968. 9.95 (ISBN 0-8006-0005-3, 1-5). Fortress.

Take a Bible Break. William McCumber. 115p. 1986. pap. 3.95 (ISBN 0-8341-1080-6). Beacon Hill.

Take a Trip to Israel. Jonathan Rutland. (Take a Trip to Ser.). (Illus.). 32p. 1981. lib. bdg. 9.90 (ISBN 0-531-04318-5). Watts.

Take a Walk with Jesus. Genevieve Parkhurst. pap. 0.40 ea. 3 for 1.00 (ISBN 0-910924-31-7). Macalester.

Take & Read: Gems from the Bible. Alvin Manni. 280p. (Orig.). 1981. pap. 7.50 (ISBN 0-89944-054-1). Don Bosco Multimedia.

Take Care. C. W. Brister. LC 76-51022. 1979. pap. 3.95 (ISBN 0-8054-5578-7). Broadman.

Take Care: A Guide for Responsible Living. L. David Brown. LC 78-52200. 1978. pap. 6.95 (ISBN 0-8066-1665-2, 10-6190). Augsburg.

Take Charge of Your Life. Robert L. Backman. LC 83-70332. 168p. 1983. 7.95 (ISBN 0-87747-970-4). Deseret Bk.

Take Command. Vera D. Tait. LC 80-53217. 144p. 1981. 5.95 (ISBN 0-87159-150-2). Unity School.

Take God's Word for It. John F. MacArthur, Jr. LC 79-91704. 160p. 1980. pap. 2.50 (ISBN 0-8307-0674-7, S341107). Regal.

Take Heart, Father: A Hope-Filled Vision for Today's Priest. William J. Bausch. 216p. (Orig.). 1986. pap. 9.95 (ISBN 0-89622-309-4). Twenty-Third.

Take Hold of the Treasure. Leonard Griffith. 128p. 1983. pap. 5.95 (ISBN 0-8170-0997-3). Judson.

Take It Easy, 2 vols. Bhagwan Shree Rajneesh. Ed. by Ma Yoga Anurag & Ma Ananda Vandana. LC 83-177521. (Zen Ser.). (Illus., Orig.). 1979. Vol. I, 584 pgs. 21.95 ea. (ISBN 0-88050-141-3). Vol. II, 584 pgs (ISBN 0-88050-142-1). Chidvilas Found.

Take It, It's Yours. Lester Sumrall. 140p. (Orig.). 1986. pap. text ed. 3.95 (ISBN 0-88368-174-9). Whitaker Hse.

Take Jesus for Example. Thomas Babaja. (Illus.). 66p. (Orig.). 1985. pap. text ed. 3.50 (ISBN 0-318-18797-3). Dovehaven Pr Ltd.

Take Joy: The Tasha Tudor Christmas Book. Tasha Tudor. LC 66-10645. (Illus.). 1980. 14.95 (ISBN 0-399-20766-X, Philomel); PLB 12.99 (ISBN 0-399-61169-X). Putnam Pub Group.

Take Judaism, for Example: Studies Toward the Comparison of Religion. Ed. by Jacob Neusner. LC 82-16039. 1983. 22.50x (ISBN 0-226-57618-3). U of Chicago Pr.

Take Nothing for the Journey: Solitude as the Foundation for Non-Possessive Life. Mary Fritz. 88p. (Orig.). 1985. pap. 3.95 (ISBN 0-8091-2722-9). Paulist Pr.

Take off Your Shoes. Stefan C. Nadzo. 120p. 1981. pap. 4.57 (ISBN 0-937226-01-7). Coleman Pub.

Take off Your Shoes: A Guide to the Nature of Reality. Stefan C. Nadzo. LC 81-66185. 140p. (Orig.). 1981. pap. 5.95 (ISBN 0-937226-01-7). Eden's Work.

Take up Your Cross: Invitation to Abundant Life. Wallace D. Drotts. LC 84-61032. 80p. (Orig.). 1985. pap. 3.95 (ISBN 0-8091-2655-9). Paulist Pr.

Takes from the Talmud, 1906. E. R. Montague. 1977. 22.50 (ISBN 0-686-19672-4). Mill Bks.

Taking a Stand: What God Can Do Through Ordinary You. Howard G. Hendricks. LC 83-8241. 1983. pap. 4.95 (ISBN 0-88070-025-4). Multnomah.

Taking Charge. Compiled by Dale Dieleman. (Good Things for Youth Leaders Ser.). pap. 3.45 (ISBN 0-8010-2911-2). Baker Bk.

Taking Charge of Your Life. rev. ed. Ernest Wood. LC 84-40512. 136p. 1985. pap. 4.75 (ISBN 0-8356-0594-9). Theos Pub Hse.

Taking Charge: The Dynamics of Personal Decision-Making & Self-Management. Gordon McMinn & Larry Libby. LC 80-65061. 192p. (Orig.). 1980. pap. 4.95 (ISBN 0-89636-043-1). Accent Bks.

Taking Discipleship Seriously. Tom Sine. 80p. 1985. pap. 4.95 (ISBN 0-8170-1085-8). Judson.

Taking Dreams Off Hold. Clark B. McCall. (Out Ser.). 1984. pap. 1.25 (ISBN 0-8163-0551-X). Pacific Pr Pub Assn.

Taking God Seriously. Stuart Briscoe. 192p. 1986. 10.95 (ISBN 0-8499-0523-0, 0523-0). Word Bks.

Taking Leave of God. Don Cupitt. 192p. 1981. 9.95 (ISBN 0-8245-0045-8). Crossroad NY.

Taking on the Heart of Christ. John H. Newman. 1985. Repr. 4.95 (ISBN 0-87193-114-1). Dimension Bks.

Taking the Fruit: Modern Women's Tales of the Bible. Woman's Institute for Continuing Jewish Education. Ed. by Jane Sprague. (Illus.). 61p. 1982. pap. 5.95 (ISBN 0-9608054-1-9). Womans Inst-Cont Jewish Ed.

Taking the Path of Zen. Robert Aitken. LC 82-81475. (Illus.). 176p. (Orig.). 1982. pap. 9.50 (ISBN 0-86547-080-4). N Point Pr.

Taking Time Seriously: James Luther Adams. John R. Wilcox. LC 78-61391. 1978. pap. text ed. 12.25 (ISBN 0-8191-0600-3). U Pr of Amer.

Taking Your Faith to Work. Alfred A. Glenn. (Orig.). 1980. pap. 4.95 (ISBN 0-8010-3748-4). Baker Bk.

Tal Hermon: Sermon Material for Yom Kippur & Eulogy in Hebrew. P. S. Pollak. (Heb). 9.50 (ISBN 0-87559-086-1); pap. 5.00 (ISBN 0-87559-085-3). Shalom.

Tale of a Litvak. Morris S. Schulzinger. LC 84-7693. (Illus.). 379p. 1985. 24.95 (ISBN 0-8022-2454-7). Philos Lib.

Tale of the Nisan Shamaness: A Manchu Folk Epic. Margaret Nowak & Stephen Durrant. LC 76-49171. (Publications on Asia of the School of International Studies: No. 31). 192p. 1977. 15.00x (ISBN 0-295-95548-1). U of Wash Pr.

Tale of the Tell: Archaeological Studies by Paul W. Lapp. Ed. by Nancy L. Lapp. LC 75-5861. (Pittsburgh Theological Monographs: No. 5). 1975. pap. text ed. 9.25 (ISBN 0-915138-05-0). Pickwick.

Tale of Thebes. R. L. Green. LC 76-22979. (Illus.). 1977. o. p. 14.95 (ISBN 0-521-21410-6); pap. 6.95 (ISBN 0-521-21411-4). Cambridge U Pr.

Tale of Three Kings. Gene Edward. 120p. 1980. pap. 5.95 (ISBN 0-940232-03-0). Christian Bks.

Tale of Two Churches: Can Protestants & Catholics Get Together? George Carey. LC 84-28858. 180p. (Orig.). 1985. pap. 5.95 (ISBN 0-87784-972-2). Inter-Varsity.

Tale of Two Cities: The Mormons-Catholics. Bill Taylor. 1981. pap. 5.50 (ISBN 0-933046-02-2). Little Red Hen.

Tale of Two Testaments. William Riley. 176p. 1985. pap. 5.95 (ISBN 0-89622-240-3). Twenty Third.

Tale That Wags the God. James Blish. 1986. 15.00 (ISBN 0-911682-29-5). Advent.

Taleem-Ul-Islam, 4. M. Qaderi. pap. 7.50 (ISBN 0-686-18387-8). Kazi Pubns.

Talented, Tired, Beautiful Feet: A Bible Study for Women. Phyllis N. Kersten & E. Louise Williams. 64p. (Orig.). 1985. pap. 2.95 (ISBN 0-570-03967-3, 12-3002). Concordia.

Tales & Parables of Sri Ramakrishna. Sri Ramakrishna. pap. 5.00 (ISBN 0-87481-493-6). Vedanta Pr.

Tales & Teaching of the Buddha. John Garret-Jones. 1979. 18.95 (ISBN 0-04-294104-0). Allen Unwin.

Tales from Galilee. Florence DeGroat. 96p. (Orig.). 1982. pap. 4.50 (ISBN 0-87516-485-4). De Vorss.

Tales from Ramakrishna. Swami Ramakrishna. (Illus.). 54p. (Orig.). 1975. pap. 2.75 (ISBN 0-87481-152-X). Vedanta Pr.

Tales of a Magic Monastery. Theophane The Monk. LC 81-9765. (Illus.). 96p. 1981. pap. 8.95 (ISBN 0-8245-0085-7). Crossroad NY.

Tales of Christian Unity: The Adventures of An Ecumenical Pilgrim. Thomas P. Ryan. LC 82-60748. 224p. 1983. pap. 9.95 (ISBN 0-8091-2502-1). Paulist Pr.

Tales of Greek Heroes. Roger L. Green. (Orig.). 1974. pap. 2.95 (ISBN 0-14-030119-4, Puffin). Penguin.

Tales of King Saul. Charles Wengrov. (Biblical Ser.). (Illus.). 1969. 4.00 (ISBN 0-914080-21-0). Shulsinger Sales.

Tales of Love. Julia Kristeva. Tr. by Leon S. Roudiez from Fr. LC 86-28311. 448p. 1987. text ed. 30.00 (ISBN 0-231-06024-6). Columbia U Pr.

Tales of Noah & the Ark. Charles Wengrov. (Biblical Ser.). (Illus.). 1969. 4.00 (ISBN 0-914080-23-7). Shulsinger Sales.

Tales of Power. Carlos Castaneda. 1982. pap. 4.95 (ISBN 0-671-55329-1). WSP.

Tales of Rabbi Nachman. Martin Buber. LC 56-12330. 214p. 1972. 5.95 (ISBN 0-8180-1325-7). Horizon.

Tales of the Gods & Heroes. George W. Cox. LC 77-94564. 1979. Repr. of 1895 ed. lib. bdg. 25.00 (ISBN 0-89341-309-7). Longwood Pub Group.

Tales of the Hasidim, 2 vols. Martin Buber. Incl. The Early Masters. pap. 6.95 (ISBN 0-8052-0001-0); The Later Masters. pap. 5.95 (ISBN 0-8052-0002-9). LC 47-2952. 1961. pap. Schocken.

Tales of the Kingdom. Karen B. Mains & David Mains. (Illus.). 96p. 1983. 12.95 (ISBN 0-89191-560-5). Cook.

Tales of the Prophet Samuel. Charles Wengrov. (Biblical Ser.). (Illus.). 1969. 4.00 (ISBN 0-914080-22-9). Shulsinger Sales.

Tales of the Prophets. A. H. Nadvi. pap. 2.50 (ISBN 0-686-18388-6). Kazi Pubns.

Tales of Torture. 84p. 1977. pap. 2.00 (ISBN 0-686-95469-6). Ananda Marga.

Talk Does Not Cook the Rice: The Teachings of Agni Yoga. R. H. Guru. LC 81-70390. (Vol. 2). 198p. (Orig.). 1985. pap. 8.95 (ISBN 0-87728-535-7). Weiser.

Talk Given on "A Course in Miracles". 2nd ed. Kenneth Wapnick. 55p. 1985. pap. 4.00 (ISBN 0-933291-00-0). Foun Miracles.

Talk Is Not Enough. Bill D. Wooten & Sonja Hunt. LC 83-61814. 112p. (Orig.). 1983. pap. text ed. 4.25 (ISBN 0-87148-849-3); 7.95 (ISBN 0-87148-850-7). Pathway Pr.

Talk Thru the Bible: A Survey of a Setting & Content of Scripture. Bruce Wilkinson & Kenneth Boa. LC 83-4130. (Illus.). 469p. 1983. Repr. of 1981 ed. 14.95 (ISBN 0-8407-5286-5). Nelson.

Talk to God about The Sabbath. large type ed. Calkins & White. 70p. 1984. pap. 8.50x (ISBN 0-914009-22-2). VHI Library.

Talk to God...I'll Get the Message: Catholic Version. Norman Geller. (Illus.). 23p. 1983. pap. 4.95 (ISBN 0-915753-03-0). N Geller Pub.

Talk to God...I'll Get the Message: Jewish Version. Norman Geller. (Illus.). 23p. 1983. pap. 4.95 (ISBN 0-915753-02-2). N Geller Pub.

Talk to God...I'll Get the Message: Protestant Version. Norman Geller. (Illus.). 23p. 1983. pap. 4.95 (ISBN 0-915753-04-9). N Geller Pub.

Talking about God: Doing Theology in the Context of Modern Pluralism. David Tracy & John B. Cobb, Jr. 144p. 1983. 6.95 (ISBN 0-8164-2458-6, HarpR). Har-Row.

Talking about God Is Dangerous: The Diary of a Russian Dissident. Tatiana Goricheva. 144p. 1987. 11.95 (ISBN 0-8245-0798-3). Crossroad NY.

Talking about Prayer. Richard Bewes. LC 80-7781. 128p. (Orig.). 1980. pap. 2.95 (ISBN 0-87784-465-8). Inter-Varsity.

Talking about Something Important. Stan Stewart & Pauline Hubner. 128p. (Orig.). 1981. pap. 7.95 (ISBN 0-85819-328-0, Pub. by JBCE). ANZ Religious Pubns.

Talking to My Father: What Jesus Teaches on Prayer. Ray C. Stedman. LC 84-20783. (Authentic Christianity Bks.). 184p. 1985. pap. 6.95 (ISBN 0-88070-075-0). Multnomah.

Talking to My Friend Jesus: Two - Four. Vera Groomer. (Come Unto Me Ser.: Year 2, Bk. 4). 32p. 1980. pap. 1.65 (ISBN 0-8127-0273-5). Review & Herald.

Talking Together about Love & Sexuality. Mildred Tengbom. 160p. 1985. pap. 4.95 (ISBN 0-87123-804-7, 210804). Bethany Hse.

Talking Trees & Singing Whales. Charles C. Case. Ed. by Raymond H. Woolsey. (Devotional Ser.). 365p. 1985. 7.95 (ISBN 0-8280-0285-1). Review & Herald.

Talking with God: A Woman's Workshop on Prayer. Glaphre. (Woman's Workshop Ser.). 160p. (Orig.). 1985. pap. 3.95 (ISBN 0-310-45301-1, 12240P). Zondervan.

Talks & Dialogues of J. Krishnamurti. J. Krishnamurti. 1976. pap. 4.95 (ISBN 0-380-01573-0, Discus). Avon.

Talks by Edmond Bordeaux Szekely. Edmond B. Szekely. 48p. 1972. pap. 2.95 (ISBN 0-89564-067-8). IBS Intl.

Talks for Tots. Joyce B. Maughan. LC 85-70993. 171p. 1985. 8.95 (ISBN 0-87747-804-X). Deseret Bk.

Talks of John Paul II. 1979. 7.95 (ISBN 0-8198-0599-8); pap. 6.95 (ISBN 0-8198-0600-5). Dghtrs St Paul.

Talks on Agni. Torkom Saraydarian. LC 86-722414. 1987. pap. price not set (ISBN 0-911794-56-5). Aqua Educ.

Talks on Beelzebub's Tales. John G. Bennett. 1977. 6.95 (ISBN 0-900306-36-X, Pub. by Coombe Springs Pr). Claymont Comm.

Talks on Mystic Christianity. Andrew Lohr. Ed. by Patricia Challgren & Mildred Crater. LC 84-90346. (Illus.). 152p. (Orig.). 1984. pap. 6.50 (ISBN 0-9613401-0-X). Fiery Water.

Talks on the Gita. Vinoba Bhave. 241p. 1983. 10.00 (ISBN 0-934676-37-2). Greenlf Bks.

Talks on the Path of Occultism, Vol. 1: At the Feet of the Master. Leadbeater & Besant. 9.50 (ISBN 0-8356-7047-3). Theos Pub Hse.

Talks on the Path of Occultism, Vol. 2: Voice of the Silence. Beasant & Leadbeater. 9.50 (ISBN 0-8356-7021-X). Theos Pub Hse.

Talks on the Path of Occultism, Vol. 3: Light on the Path. Leadbeater & Besant. 7.95 (ISBN 0-8356-7068-6). Theos Pub Hse.

Talks to Priests. Antonio Rosmini. Tr. by Mary F. Ingoldsby from Ital. LC 82-61099. Tr. of Confrerenze Sui Doveri Ecclesiastici. 368p. 1983. 18.00 (ISBN 0-911782-43-5). New City.

Talks with Swami Vivekananda. Sharat C. Chakravarty. 6.95 (ISBN 0-87481-156-2). Vedanta Pr.

Tall Book of Bible Stories. Katherine Gibson. LC 57-10952. (Tall Bks.). (Illus.). 128p. 1980. 5.70i (ISBN 0-06-021935-1); PLB 7.89 (ISBN 0-06-021936-X). HarpJ.

Tall Tales Told & Retold in Biblical Hebrew. Joseph Anderson & Devora Lipshitz. (Hebrew., Illus.). 96p. (Orig.). 1983. pap. text ed. 8.95 (ISBN 0-939144-07-7). EKS Pub Co.

Talleyrand. Duff Cooper. 1932. 25.00x (ISBN 0-8047-0616-6). Stanford U Pr.

Talmage on Palestine: Series of Sermons. Thomas Talmage. Ed. by Moshe Davis. LC 77-70747. (America & the Holy Land Ser.). 1977. Repr. of 1890 ed. lib. bdg. 17.00x (ISBN 0-405-10293-3). Ayer Co Pubs.

Talmud: An Analytical Guide. Isaac Unterman. LC 73-148291. 351p. 1985. text ed. 17.95 (ISBN 0-8197-0189-0); pap. text ed. 10.95 (ISBN 0-8197-0005-3). Bloch.

Talmud As Law Or Literature: An Analysis of David W. Halivni's Mekorot Umasorot. Irwin H. Haut. x, 83p. pap. 6.95 (ISBN 0-87203-107-1). Hermon.

Talmud of Babylonia: An American Translation, VII Tractate Besah. Tr. by Alan J. Avery-Peck from Hebrew-Aramaic. (Brown Judaic Studies). 358p. 1986. pap. 39.95 (ISBN 1-55540-054-X, 14-01-17). Scholars Pr GA.

Talmud of Babylonia: An American Translation XXXV: Meilah & Tamid. Tr. by Peter J. Haas from Hebrew-Aramaic. (Brown Judaic Studies). 180p. 1986. 29.95 (ISBN 1-55540-086-8, 14-01-09). Scholars Pr GA.

Talmud of Babylonia: An American Translation XXIII: Tractate Sanhedrin-Chap. 9-11. Tr. by Jacob Neusner. (Brown Judiac Studies). 1985. 29.95 (ISBN 0-89130-803-2, 14-0087); pap. 23.00 (ISBN 0-89130-804-0). Scholars Pr GA.

Talmud of the Land of Israel: A Preliminary Translation & Explanation- Vol. 25, Gittin. Ed. by Jacob Neusner. (Chicago Studies in the History of Judaism). 270p. 1985. 33.00 (ISBN 0-226-57684-1). U of Chicago Pr.

Talmud of the Land of Israel: A Preliminary Translation & Explanation- Vol. 24, Nazir. Ed. by Jacob Neusner. (Chicago Studies in the History of Judaism). 268p. 1985. 33.00 (ISBN 0-226-57683-3). U of Chicago Pr.

Talmud of the Land of Israel: A Preliminary Translation & Explanation- Vol. 23, Nedarim. Ed. & tr. by Jacob Neusner. (Chicago Studies in the History of Judaism). 248p. 1985. 31.00 (ISBN 0-226-57682-5). U of Chicago Pr.

Talmud of the Land of Israel: A Preliminary Translation & Explanation: Hagigah & Moed Qatan, Vol. 20. Ed. & tr. by Jacob Neusner. LC 85-29037. (Chicago Studies in the History of Judaism). 242p. 1986. 35.00x (ISBN 0-226-57679-5). U of Chicago Pr.

Talmud of the Land of Israel: A Preliminary Translation & Explanation, Vol. 22: Ketubot. Ed. by Jacob Neusner. (Chicago Studies in the History of Judaism). 384p. 1985. lib. bdg. 49.00x (ISBN 0-226-57681-7). U of Chicago Pr.

Talmud of the Land of Israel: A Prelimimnary Translation & Explanation-Vol. 26, Qiddushin. Ed. & tr. by Jacob Neusner. 1984. 25.00 (ISBN 0-226-57686-8). U of Chicago Pr.

Talmud of the Land of Israel: A Preliminary Translation & Explanation-Vol. 27, Sotah. Ed. & tr. by Jacob Neusner. 1984. 25.00 (ISBN 0-226-57687-6). U of Chicago Pr.

Talmud of the Land of Israel: A Preliminary Translation & Explanation-Vol. 28, Baba Qamma. Ed. & tr. by Jacob Neusner. 1984. 25.00 (ISBN 0-226-57688-4). U of Chicago Pr.

Talmud of the Land of Israel: A Preliminary Translation & Explanation-Vol. 29, Baba Mesia. Ed. & tr. by Jacob Neusner. 1984. 25.00 (ISBN 0-226-57689-2). U of Chicago Pr.

Talmud of the Land of Israel: A Preliminary Translation & Explanation-Vol. 30, Baba Batra. Ed. & tr. by Jacob Neusner. 1984. 25.00 (ISBN 0-226-57690-6). U of Chicago Pr.

Talmud of the Land of Israel: A Preliminary Translation & Explanation-Vol. 31, Sanhedrin & Makkot. Ed. & tr. by Jacob Neusner. 1984. 45.00 (ISBN 0-226-57691-4). U of Chicago Pr.

Talmud of the Land of Israel: A Preliminary Translation & Explanation-Vol. 33, Abodah Zarah. Ed. & tr. by Jacob Neusner. 1982. 27.00 (ISBN 0-226-57693-0). U of Chicago Pr.

Talmud of the Land of Israel: A Preliminary Translation & Explanation-Vol. 34, Horayot & Niddah. Ed. & tr. by Jacob Neusner. 1982. 29.00 (ISBN 0-226-57694-9). U of Chicago Pr.

Talmud of the Land of Israel: A Preliminary Translation & Explanation-Vol. 35, Introduction & Taxonomy. Ed. & tr. by Jacob Neusner. 1984. 19.00 (ISBN 0-226-57695-7). U of Chicago Pr.

Talmud of the Land of Israel: A Preliminary Translation & Explanation: Vol. 19, Megillah. Ed. by Jacob Neusner. LC 86-25284. (Chicago Studies in the History of Judaism). 200p. 1987. text ed. 27.50 (ISBN 0-226-57678-7). U of Chicago Pr.

Talmud of the Land of Israel: A Preliminary Translation & Explanation-Yebamot, Vol. 21. Ed. & tr. by Jacob Neusner. LC 86-11406. (Chicago Studies in the History of Judaism). 514p. 1987. text ed. 58.00x (ISBN 0-226-57680-9). U of Chicago Pr.

Talmud Today. Ed. by Alexander Feinsilver. 320p. 1980. 14.95 (ISBN 0-312-78479-1). St Martin.

Talmud Unmasked. Prainatis. 1979. lib. bdg. 59.95 (ISBN 0-8490-3010-2). Gordon Pr.

Talmudic & Rabbinical Chronology. Edgar Frank. 1978. 6.95 (ISBN 0-87306-050-4). Feldheim.

Talmudic Anthology. Ed. by Louis I. Newman. LC 45-9682. 1978. pap. text ed. 12.95x (ISBN 0-87441-303-6). Behrman.

Talmudic Argument: A Study in Talmudic Reasoning & Methodology. Louis Jacobs. LC 84-4351. 240p. 1984. 44.50 (ISBN 0-521-26370-0). Cambridge U Pr.

Talmudic Law & the Modern State. Moshe Silberg. 1973. 9.00x (ISBN 0-8381-3112-3). United Syn Bk.

Talmudische Archaologie, 3 vols. Samuel Krauss. Ed. by Moses Finley. LC 79-4988. (Ancient Economic History). (Ger., Illus.). 1980. Repr. of 1912 ed. Set. lib. bdg. 172.00x (ISBN 0-405-12373-6); lib. bdg. 57.50x ea. Vol. 1 (ISBN 0-405-12374-4). Vol. 2 (ISBN 0-405-12375-2). Vol. 3 (ISBN 0-405-12376-0). Ayer Co Pubs.

Tambourines! Tambourines to Glory! Prayers & Poems. Nancy Larrick. LC 81-23158. (Illus.). 122p. 1982. 8.95 (ISBN 0-664-32689-7). Westminster.

Tamil Temple Myths: Sacrifice & Divine Marriage in the South Indian Saiva Tradition. David D. Shulman. LC 79-17051. 1980. 45.00x (ISBN 0-691-06415-6). Princeton U Pr.

Taming the Tongue: Why Christians Should Care about What They Say. Mark Kinzer. (Living as a Christian Ser.). 1982. pap. 2.95 (ISBN 0-89283-165-0). Servant.

Taming the TV Habit. Kevin Perrotta. 162p. (Orig.). 1982. pap. 6.95 (ISBN 0-89283-155-3). Servant.

Taming Your TV & Other Media. Dave Schwantes. LC 79-16848. (Orion Ser.). 1979. pap. 3.95 (ISBN 0-8127-0246-8). Review & Herald.

Tammuz & Ishtar. Stephen H. Langdon. LC 78-72750. (Ancient Mesopotamian Texts & Studies). Repr. of 1914 ed. 34.50 (ISBN 0-404-18193-7). AMS Pr.

Tanglewood Tales. Nathaniel Hawthorne. (Classics Ser). (Illus.). 1968. pap. 1.25 (ISBN 0-8049-0175-9, CL-175). Airmont.

Tanna Debe Eliyyahu. Tr. by William G. Braude & Israel J. Kapstein. LC 80-10805. Tr. of Lore of the School of Elijah. 660p. 1980. 27.50 (ISBN 0-8276-0174-3, 455). Jewish Pubns.

Tanner Bibliography. H. Michael Marquardt. 32p. pap. 3.00 (ISBN 0-942284-08-9). Restoration Re.

Tanner Lectures on Human Values, Vol. IV: 1983. Ed. by Sterling M. McMurrin. 300p. 1983. 20.00x (ISBN 0-87480-216-4). U of Utah Pr.

Tanner Lectures on Human Values, Vol. VII: Nineteen Eighty-Six. Ed. by Sterling M. McMurrin. 288p. 1986. 20.00x (ISBN 0-87480-259-8). U of Utah Pr.

Tannisho: A Resource for Modern Living. Alfred Bloom. LC 80-39523. 112p. (Orig.). 1981. pap. 6.95 (ISBN 0-938474-00-6). Buddhist Study.

Tannisho: A Shin Buddhist Classic. Taitetsu Unno & Ruth Tabrah. 73p. (Orig.). 1985. 12.50 (ISBN 0-938474-05-7); pap. 6.95 (ISBN 0-938474-04-9). Buddhist Study.

Tantra for the West: A Guide to Personal Freedom. Marcus Allen. LC 80-316. 235p. 1981. pap. 7.95 (ISBN 0-931432-06-5). Whatever Pub.

Tantra Mantra Yantra: The Tantra Psychology. S. K. Rao. (Illus.). 1977. text ed. 12.50x (ISBN 0-391-01286-X). Humanities.

Tantra of the Great Liberation. Arthur Avalon. (Illus.). 512p. 1913. pap. 8.50 (ISBN 0-486-20150-3). Dover.

Tantra, Spirituality & Sex. 2nd ed. Bhagwan Shree Rajneesh. Ed. by Ma Yoga Anurag. LC 83-16036. (Tantra Ser.). 160p. 1983. pap. 3.95 (ISBN 0-88050-696-2). Chidvilas Found.

Tantra: The Indian Cult of Ecstasy. Philip Rawson. (Art & Imagination Ser.). (Illus.). 1984. pap. 10.95f (ISBN 0-500-81001-X). Thames Hudson.

Tantra: The Supreme Understanding. 2nd ed. Bhagwan Shree Rajneesh. Ed. by Ma Prem Apa & Ma Anand Vadan. LC 84-42797. (Tantra Ser.). 336p. 1984. pap. 4.95 (ISBN 0-88050-643-1). Chidvilas Found.

Tantra Vision, 2 vols. Bhagwan Shree Rajneesh. Ed. by Ma Yoga Anurag. (Tantra Ser.). (Illus., Orig.). 1978. Vol. I, 340 pgs. 16.50 ea. (ISBN 0-88050-144-8). Vol. II, 344 pgs (ISBN 0-88050-145-6). Chidvilas Found.

Tantraraja Tantra. Arthur Avalon & Lakshmana Shastri. (Sanskrit.). 740p. 1982. text ed. 52.00 (ISBN 0-89744-238-5). Auromere.

Tantras: Their Philosophy & Occult Secrets. rev. 3rd ed. D. N. Bose. 1981. Repr. of 1956 ed. 12.00x (ISBN 0-8364-0737-7, Pub. by Mukhopadhyay). South Asia Bks.

Tantric Distinction. Jeffrey Hopkins. Ed. by Anne C. Klein. (Wisdom Intermediate Book, White Ser.). 184p. (Orig.). 1984. pap. 8.95 (ISBN 0-86171-023-1, Wisdom Pubns). Great Traditions.

Tantric Poetry of Kukai. Tr. by Morgan Gibson & Hiroshi Murakami. 1985. 7.00 (ISBN 0-934834-67-9). White Pine.

Tantric Practice in Nying-ma. Khetsun S. Rinbochay. Ed. by Jeffery Hopkins & Anne Klein. LC 86-3762. 238p. (Orig.). 1983. lib. bdg. 16.00 cancelled (ISBN 0-937938-13-0); pap. text ed. 12.50 (ISBN 0-937938-14-9). Snow Lion.

Tantric Tradition. Agehananda Bharati. LC 77-7204. 1977. Repr. of 1965 ed. lib. bdg. 22.50x (ISBN 0-8371-9660-4, AGTT). Greenwood.

Tanzanian Doctor. Leader Stirling. LC 78-316167. pap. 38.50 (ISBN 0-317-26454-0, 2023860). Bks Demand UMI.

Tao. Lao Tse. Tr. by Charles H. Mackintosh. 1971. pap. 3.25 (ISBN 0-8356-0426-8, Quest). Theos Pub Hse.

Tao & Chinese Culture. Da Liu. LC 78-26767. 192p. (Orig.). 1982. pap. 7.95 (ISBN 0-8052-0702-3). Schocken.

Tao & Longevity: Mind Body Transformation. Wen Kuan Chu. LC 82-60164. 192p. (Orig.). 1984. pap. 7.95 (ISBN 0-87728-542-X). Weiser.

Tao & T'ai Chi Kung. (Illus.). 55p. 1978. pap. 7.95x (ISBN 0-933740-00-X). Mindbody Inc.

Tao & the Daimon: Segments of a Religious Inquiry. Robert C. Neville. 304p. 1982. 44.50x (ISBN 0-87395-661-3); pap. 14.95x (ISBN 0-87395-662-1). State U NY Pr.

Tao Is Silent. Raymond M. Smullyan. LC 76-62939. (Orig.). 1977. 8.95 (ISBN 0-685-75421-9, HarpR); pap. 4.95i (ISBN 0-06-067469-5, RD 206, HarpR). Har-Row.

Tao Magic: The Secret Language of Diagrams & Calligraphy. Laszlo Legeza. LC 86-51463. (Illus.). 167p. 1987. pap. 10.95 (ISBN 0-500-27062-7). Thames Hudson.

Tao: Mastery of Life. 1962. 4.95 (ISBN 0-88088-508-4). Peter Pauper.

Tao of Chinese Religion. Milton M. Chiu. (Illus.). 432p. (Orig.). 1985. lib. bdg. 29.50 (ISBN 0-8191-4263-8); pap. text ed. 17.50 (ISBN 0-8191-4264-6). U Pr of Amer.

Tao of E Wing Chun Do, 2 pts, Vol. 1, pt. 1. 4th ed. James W. DeMile. (Illus.). 1983. 6.95 ea. (ISBN 0-918642-01-9); Pt. 1. Pt. 2. Tao of Wing.

Tao of Health: The Way of Total Well-Being. Michael Blate. (Illus., Orig.). 1978. pap. 6.95 (ISBN 0-916878-05-8). Falkynor Bks.

Tao of Jeet Kune Do. Bruce Lee. LC 75-13803. (Series 401). (Illus.). 1975. pap. 12.50 (ISBN 0-89750-048-2). Ohara Pubns.

Tao of Leadership: Lao Tzu's Tao te Ching Adapted for a New Age. John Heider. LC 84-19750. 184p. (Orig.). 1984. pap. 9.95 (ISBN 0-89334-079-0). Humanics Ltd.

Tao of Long Life: The Chinese Art of Ch'ang Ming. Chee Soo. 176p. 1983. pap. 7.95 (ISBN 0-85030-320-6). Newcastle Pub.

Tao of Medicine: Ginseng, Oriental Remedies & the Pharmacology of Harmony. Stephen Fulder. LC 82-1066. (Illus.). 328p. 1982. text ed. 9.95 (ISBN 0-89281-027-0, Destiny Bks). Inner Tradit.

Tao of Meditation: Way to Enlightenment. Tsung H. Jou. (Illus.). 186p. 1983. 15.00 (ISBN 0-8048-1465-1, Pub. by Tai Chi Foun). C E Tuttle.

Tao of Physics. Fritjof Capra. 1977. pap. 4.95 (ISBN 0-553-26379-X). Bantam.

Tao of Physics. 2nd ed. Fritjof Capra. LC 82-42679. (New Science Library Ser.). (Illus.). 308p. 1975. pap. 10.95 (ISBN 0-87773-246-9, 71612-4). Shambhala Pubns.

Tao of Pooh. Benjamin Hoff. (Illus.). 162p. 1982. 8.95 (ISBN 0-525-24124-8, 0869-260). Dutton.

Tao of Power. R. L. Wing. LC 85-10210. (Illus.). 192p. 1986. pap. 12.50 (ISBN 0-385-19637-7, Dolp). Doubleday.

Tao of Sexology. Stephen T. Chang. (Illus.). 224p. 1985. 17.00 (ISBN 0-942196-03-1). Tao Pub.

Tao of Symbols. James N. Powell. 1982. 11.50 (ISBN 0-688-01351-1). Morrow.

Tao of the Loving Couple: True Liberation Through the Tao. Jolan Chang. (Illus.). 129p. 1983. pap. 8.95 (ISBN 0-525-48042-0, 0869-260). Dutton.

Tao Te Ching. Lao Tsu. Ed. by Gia-Fu Feng. Tr. by Jane English. 1972. pap. 10.95 (ISBN 0-394-71833-X, V-833, Vin). Random.

Tao Te Ching. Lao Tsu. Tr. by Richard Wilhelm. 224p. 1985. pap. 5.95 (ISBN 1-85063-011-9). Methuen Inc.

Tao Te Ching. Lao Tzu. (Sacred Texts Ser.). Orig. Title: Chinese. viii, 88p. 1983. pap. 8.75 (ISBN 0-88695-007-4). Concord Grove.

Tao Teh King. Tr. by Mears. 5.25 (ISBN 0-8356-5123-1). Theos Pub Hse.

Tao: The Chinese Philosophy of Time & Change. Philip Rawson & Laszlo Legeza. (Art & Imagination Ser.). (Illus.). 1984. pap. 10.95f (ISBN 0-500-81002-8). Thames Hudson.

Tao: The Golden Gate, Vol. 1. Bhagwan Shree Rajneesh. Ed. by Ma Prem Asha. LC 84-42615. (Tao Ser.). 336p. (Orig.). 1984. pap. 4.95 (ISBN 0-88050-646-6). Chidvilas Found.

Tao: The Golden Gate, Vol. 2. Bhagwan Shree Rajneesh. Ed. by Swami Krishna Prabhu. LC 84-42615. (Tao Ser.). 304p. (Orig.). 1985. pap. 4.95 (ISBN 0-88050-647-4). Chidvilas Found.

Tao, the Great Luminant: Essays from Huai-Nan-Tzu. Huai-nan Tzu. Tr. by Evan Morgan from Chinese. 301p. Repr. of 1935 ed. text ed. 24.00x (ISBN 0-89644-062-1, Pub. by Chinese Matl Ctr). Coronet Bks.

Tao: The Pathless Path, 2 vols. Bhagwan Shree Rajneesh. Ed. by Ma Prem Asha & Ma Prema Veena. LC 82-232884. (Tao Ser.). (Illus.). 1979. Vol. I, 432 pgs. 17.95 ea. (ISBN 0-88050-148-0). Vol. II, 540 pgs (ISBN 0-88050-149-9). Vol. I, 440p. pap. 15.95 (ISBN 0-88050-648-2); Vol. II, 1978, 542p. pap. write for info. (ISBN 0-88050-649-0). Chidvilas Found.

Tao: The Subtle Universal Law & the Integral Way of Life. Hua-Ching Ni. LC 79-91720. (Illus.). 166p. (Orig.). 1979. pap. text ed. 7.50 (ISBN 0-937064-01-7). SEBT.

Tao-The Subtle Universal Law & the Integral Way of Life. Master Ni Hua-Ching & Hua-Ching. LC 79-91720. 166p. 1980. pap. text ed. 7.50 (ISBN 0-937064-01-7). Wisdom Garden.

Tao: The Three Treasures, 4 vols. Bhagwan Shree Rajneesh. Ed. by Ma Prema Veena & Swami Anand Somendra. LC 76-905202. (Tao Ser.). (Illus., Orig.). 1977. Vol. II, 346 pgs., 1976. 15.95 ea. (ISBN 0-88050-151-0). Vol. III, 404 pgs. 1976 (ISBN 0-88050-152-9). Vol. IV, 422 pgs. 1977 (ISBN 0-88050-153-7). Chidvilas Found.

Tao: The Watercourse Way. Alan Watts & Al Chung-Liang Huang. LC 76-4762. 1977. pap. 5.95 (ISBN 0-394-73311-8). Pantheon.

Taoism & Chinese Religion. Henri Maspero. Tr. by Frank A. Kierman, Jr. from Fr. LC 80-13444. Orig. Title: Taoisme et les religions Chinoises. 656p. 1981. lib. bdg. 40.00x (ISBN 0-87023-308-4). U of Mass Pr.

Taoism & the Rite of Cosmic Renewal. Michael R. Saso. (Illus.). 1972. pap. 4.00x (ISBN 0-87422-011-4). Wash St U Pr.

Taoism: The Parting of the Way. Holmes Welch. Orig. Title: Parting of the Way. 1966. pap. 6.95 (ISBN 0-8070-5973-0, BP224). Beacon Pr.

Taoism: The Road to Immortality. John Blofeld. LC 77-90882. 195p. 1978. pap. 9.95 (ISBN 0-87773-116-0, 73582-X). Shambhala Pubns.

Taoism: The Way of the Mystic. J. C. Cooper. 1973. pap. 7.95 (ISBN 0-85030-096-7). Weiser.

Taoist Health Exercise Book. 3rd ed. Da Liu. (Illus.). 172p. 1983. pap. 5.95 (ISBN 0-399-50745-0, Perigee). Putnam Pub Group.

Taoist Inner View of the Universe & the Immortal Realm. Hua-Ching Ni. LC 79-92389. (Illus.). 218p. (Orig.). 1979. pap. text ed. 12.50 (ISBN 0-937064-02-5). SEBT.

Taoist Inner View of the Universe & the Immortal Realm. Master Ni Hua-Ching & Hua-Ching. LC 79-91720. 218p. 1980. pap. text ed. 12.50x (ISBN 0-937064-02-5). Wisdom Garden.

Taoist Secrets of Love: Cultivating Male Sexual Energy. Mantak Chia. 1984. pap. 14.00 (ISBN 0-943358-19-1). Aurora Press.

Taoist Texts. Frederic H. Balfour. lib. bdg. 79.95 (ISBN 0-87968-191-8). Krishna Pr.

Taoist Vision. Ed. by William McNaughton. LC 70-143183. (Illus.). 1971. 7.95 (ISBN 0-472-09174-3). U of Mich Pr.

Taoist Ways to Transform Stress into Vitality: The Inner Smile - Six Healing Sounds. Mantak Chia. LC 85-81656. (Illus.). 160p. (Orig.). 1986. pap. 9.95 (ISBN 0-935621-00-8). Heal Tao Bks.

Taoist Yoga. Charles Luk. 1970. pap. 6.95 (ISBN 0-87728-067-3). Weiser.

Taoist Yoga: The Chinese Art of K'ai Men. Chee Soo. 160p. 1983. pap. 7.95 (ISBN 0-85030-332-X). Newcastle Pub.

Tapestry. Ed. by Wilfred Bockelman. 128p. (Orig.). 1985. pap. 3.95 (ISBN 0-8066-2177-X, 10-6201). Augsburg.

Tapu Removal in Maori Religion. Jean Smith. 96p. 1974. text ed. 12.00x (ISBN 0-8248-0591-7). UH Pr.

Taranatha's History of Buddhism in India. Ed. by Debiprasad Chattopadhyaya. Tr. by Alaka Chattopadhyay. 1980. 28.00x (ISBN 0-8364-1484-5, Pub. by KP Bagchi India). South Asia Bks.

Taranatha's History of Buddhism in India. Taranath. Ed. by Debiprsdad Chattopadhyaya & A. Chattopadhyaya. 1980. Repr. of 1970 ed. 27.00x (ISBN 0-8364-1597-3, Pub. by KP Bagchi & Co.). South Asia Bks.

Targilon for Sefer Bamidbar, Vol. I. Israel Rosenfeld. text ed. 4.00 (ISBN 0-914131-64-8, A23). Torah Umesorah.

Targilon for Sefer Bemidbar, Vol. II. Israel Rosenfeld. text ed. 4.00 (ISBN 0-914131-65-6, A24). Torah Umesorah.

Targum & Testament: Aramaic Paraphrases of the Hebrew Bible: a Light on the New Testament. Martin McNamara. 226p. 1972. 17.50x (ISBN 0-7165-0619-X, BBA 02203, Pub. by Irish Academic Pr Ireland). Biblio Dist.

Targum Onkelos on Deuteronomy. Israel Drazin. 1981. 45.00x (ISBN 0-87068-755-7). Ktav.

Targum Onkelos to Genesis. M. Aberbach & B. Grossfeld. 45.00x (ISBN 0-87068-339-X). Ktav.

Targum Pseudo-Jonathan of the Pentateuch. E. G. Clarke. 1983. 150.00x (ISBN 0-88125-015-5). Ktav.

Targumic Approaches to the Gospels: Essays in the Mutual Definition of Judaism & Christianity. Bruce Chilton. 200p. (Orig.). 1987. lib. bdg. 24.75 (ISBN 0-8191-5731-7, Pub. by Studies in Judaism); pap. text ed. 12.25 (ISBN 0-8191-5732-5). U Pr of Amer.

Targumic Traditions. J. T. Forestell. LC 79-19293. (Society of Biblical Literature Aramaic Studies: No. 4). 151p. 1984. pap. 12.00 (ISBN 0-89130-352-9, 06-13-04). Scholars Pr GA.

Targums & Rabbinic Literature. John Bowker. LC 71-80817. 1969. 67.50 (ISBN 0-521-07415-0). Cambridge U Pr.

Targums of Onkelos & Jonathan Ben Uzziel on the Pentateuch with the Fragments of the Jerusalem Targum from the Chaldee. J. W. Etheridge. 1969. Repr. of 1865 ed. 59.50x (ISBN 0-87068-045-5). Ktav.

Targun Neophyti One: A Textual Study: Introduction, Genesis, Exodus. B. B. Levy. LC 86-11117. (Studies in Judaism). 470p. (Orig.). 1986. lib. bdg. 36.50 (ISBN 0-8191-5464-4, Pub. by Studies in Judaism); pap. text ed. 21.75 (ISBN 0-8191-5465-2). U Pr of Amer.

Tarjuma'n Al-Ashwa'q. Ibn Arabi. 14.25 (ISBN 0-8356-5505-9). Theos Pub Hse.

Tarjuman Al-Qura'n: A Critical Analysis of Maulana Abul Kalam Azad's Approach to the Understanding of the Qura'n. I. Azad Faruqi. 128p. 1983. text ed. 15.95x (ISBN 0-7069-1342-6, Pub. by Vikas India). Advent NY.

Tarot. Mouni Sadhu. pap. 8.00 (ISBN 0-87980-157-3). Wilshire.

Tarot: A Key to the Wisdom of the Ages. Paul Foster Case. (Illus.). 215p. 1981. Repr. of 1977 ed. softcover 6.95 (ISBN 0-88053-767-1). Macoy Pub.

Tarot Cards Painted by Bonifacio Bembo for the Visconti-Sforza Family. Gertrude Moakley. (Illus.). 124p. 1966. 15.00 (ISBN 0-87104-175-8). NY Pub Lib.

Taryag: The Six Hundred Thirteenth Mitzvos. Rabbi Alon I. Tolwin. 106p. 1983. pap. 5.95 (ISBN 0-87306-378-3). Feldheim.

Tashlich. Avrohom C. Feuer. (Art Scroll Mesorah Ser.). 64p. 1979. 6.95 (ISBN 0-89906-158-3); pap. 4.95 (ISBN 0-89906-159-1). Mesorah Pubns.

Taste & See: A Personal Guide to the Spiritual Life. William O. Paulsell. LC 76-5634. 1977. pap. 2.95 (ISBN 0-88489-093-7). St Mary's.

Taste of Grace, Vol. 1. Gerald Twombly & Timothy Kennedy. (Illus.). 182p. 1982. pap. 7.50 (ISBN 0-910219-04-4). Little People.

Taste of Heaven: Adventures in Food & Faith. new ed. Lionel Blue & June Rose. (Orig.). 1978. pap. 4.50 (ISBN 0-87243-077-4). Templegate.

Taste of Joy: Recovering the Lost Glow of Discipleship. Calvin Miller. LC 83-7839. Orig. Title: Illusive Thing Called Joy. 144p. 1983. pap. 4.95 (ISBN 0-87784-831-9). Inter-Varsity.

Taste of Shabbos, The Complete Cookbook. Compiled by Aish Hatorah Women's Organization Staff. 1987. 16.95. Feldheim.

Tattva-Sangraha of Santaraksita with Commentary of Kamalasila. Shantaraksita. Tr. by Ganganath Jha. 1593p. 1986. Repr. of 1937 ed. Set. 85.00 (ISBN 0-317-46526-0, Pub. by Motilal Banarsidass India); Vol. 1. 50.00 (ISBN 81-208-0059-1); Vol. 2. 50.00 (ISBN 81-208-0060-5). South Asia Bks.

Tattvarthadhigama Sutra (A Treatise on the Essential Principles of Jainism) Umasvati. Ed. & intro. by J. L. Jaini. LC 73-3836. (Sacred Books of the Jainas: No. 2). Repr. of 1920 ed. 21.50 (ISBN 0-404-57702-4). AMS Pr.

Tauferaktenband Osterreich III. Grete Mecenseffy. (TAK Ser.: Vol. XIV). (Ger.). 795p. 1982. 105.00 (ISBN 0-8361-1265-2). Herald Pr.

Taufertum Und Reformation Im Gesprach. John H. Yoder. 221p. 1969. 29.00x (ISBN 0-8361-1164-8). Herald Pr.

Taurus. Kathleen Paul. (Sun Signs Ser.). (Illus.). 1978. PLB 7.95 (ISBN 0-87191-642-8); pap. 3.95 (ISBN 0-89812-072-1). Creative Ed.

Tavistock Abbey. H. P. Finberg. LC 69-10850. (Illus.). 1969. Repr. of 1951 ed. 35.00x (ISBN 0-678-05597-1). Kelley.

Tax Exempt Charitable Organizations. 2nd ed. Paul E. Treusch & Norman A. Sugarman. LC 83-70067. 726p. 1983. text ed. 95.00 (ISBN 0-8318-0429-7, B429). Am Law Inst.

Taz Rabbi David Halevi. Elijah J. Schochet. 10.00x (ISBN 0-87068-687-9). Ktav.

Te Alabamos Senor: We Praise You O Lord. Patricia Fritz. Tr. by Alicia Sarre from Span. 112p. 1984. pap. 3.95 (ISBN 0-8091-2641-9). Paulist Pr.

Te Damos Gracias, Dios. Paulina G. De Patterson. (Illus.). 28p. 1981. pap. 0.60 (ISBN 0-311-38508-7). Casa Bautista.

Te Decet Laus: To Thee Belongeth Praise. Revised ed. Ed. by Oliver S. Beltz. (Illus.). viii, 223p. 1982. 9.95 (ISBN 0-943872-84-7). Andrews Univ Pr.

Teach As He Taught: How to Apply Jesus' Teaching Methods. Robert G. Delnay. (Orig.). 1987. pap. 5.95 (ISBN 0-8024-4340-0). Moody.

Teach Dynamic Truths. C. S. Lovett. 1973. pap. 5.95 tchr's. guide (ISBN 0-938148-14-1). Personal Christianity.

Teach Me How to Live. Kay Arthur. 384p. (Orig.). 1983. pap. 6.95 (ISBN 0-8007-5125-6, Power Bks). Revell.

Teach Me in My Way: A Collection for L.D.S. Children. Hope C. Gardner & Sally Gunnell. LC 80-84147. 1980. soft cover 5.95 (ISBN 0-913420-85-9). Olympus Pub Co.

Teach Me to Pray. W. E. Sangster. 1959. pap. 1.50x (ISBN 0-8358-0125-X). Upper Room.

Teach Me to Teach. Dorothy G. Swain. pap. 4.95 (ISBN 0-8170-0316-9). Judson.

Teach My People. Vincent M. Walsh. 104p. 1983. pap. 4.00 (ISBN 0-943374-04-9). Key of David.

Teach the Word. Paul F. Henson. 1972. 5.25 (ISBN 0-87148-826-4); pap. 4.25 (ISBN 0-87148-827-2). Pathway Pr.

Teach Them About Satan. C. S. Lovett. 1970. pap. 5.45 tchr's guide (ISBN 0-938148-26-5). Personal Christianity.

Teach Them Diligently. Arthur Nazigian. 1986. pap. 2.95 (ISBN 0-8010-6747-2). Baker Bk.

Teach Us to Pray. Elaine Dull & Jo Anne Sekowsky. (Aglow Bible Study Book Enrichment). 64p. 1980. pap. 2.95 (ISBN 0-930756-49-5, 522002). Aglow Pubns.

Teach Us to Pray. Charles Fillmore & Cora Fillmore. 1976. 5.95 (ISBN 0-87159-152-9). Unity School.

Teach Us to Pray. Dawn Tullis. 2.25 (ISBN 0-686-13717-5). Crusade Pubs.

Teach Us To Pray: The Disciples Request Cast Anew. Fred C. Lofton. 96p. 1983. pap. 4.00 (ISBN 0-89191-751-9). Prog Bapt Pub.

Teach What You Preach. Anderson. 1982. pap. 8.95 (ISBN 0-8298-0481-1). Pilgrim NY.

Teach Witnessing. C. S. Lovett. 1966. pap. 5.95 tchr's. guide (ISBN 0-938148-09-5). Personal Christianity.

Teach Yourself Biblical Hebrew. Roland K. Harrison. (Teach Yourself Ser.). pap. 6.95 (ISBN 0-679-10180-2). McKay.

Teachable Moments. Kay K. Berg & Donald B. Rogers. LC 85-71827. 52p. (Orig.). 1985. pap. 3.95 (ISBN 0-88177-019-1, DR019B). Discipleship Res.

Teachable Spirit. Paulette Woods. 72p. 1984. pap. 3.50 (ISBN 0-8341-0904-2). Beacon Hill.

Teacher! A Christlike Model in Students. Neal F. McBride. (Complete Teacher Training Meeting Ser.). 48p. 1986. 9.95 (ISBN 0-89191-313-0). Cook.

Teacher & Christian Belief. Ninian Smart. 208p. 1966. 6.95 (ISBN 0-227-67703-X). Attic Pr.

Teacher & Religion. F. H. Hilliard. 191p. 1963. 7.95 (ISBN 0-227-67675-0). Attic Pr.

Teacher & the World's Religions. D. W. Gundry. 160p. 1968. 6.50 (ISBN 0-227-67456-1). Attic Pr.

Teacher as Minister Weekly Plan Book. 208p. 1979. 4.80 (ISBN 0-686-39948-X). Natl Cath Educ.

Teacher in the Catholic School. Francis Raftery. 61p. 1986. 6.60 (ISBN 0-318-20567-X). Natl Cath Educ.

Teacher, The Free Choice of the Will, Grace & Free Will. St. Augustine. Bd. with Two Works on Free Will. LC 67-30350. (Fathers of the Church Ser.: Vol. 59). 232p. 1968. 17.95x (ISBN 0-8132-0059-8). Cath U Pr.

Teacher's Bible Commentary. Ed. by Hobbs & Paschall. LC 75-189505. 24.95 (ISBN 0-8054-1116-X). Broadman.

Teacher's Guide for Melachim I: A Teacher's Guide. C. D. Rabinowitz. 5.00 (ISBN 0-914131-66-4, B45). Torah Umesorah.

Teacher's Guide for Sefer Shoftim. (Hebrew.). 4.00 (ISBN 0-914131-67-2, B42). Torah Umesorah.

Teacher's Guide for Sefer Yehoshua. C. D. Rabinonwitz. (Hebrew.). 4.00 (ISBN 0-914131-68-0, B41). Torah Umesorah.

Teacher's Guide to Jewish Holidays. Robert Goodman. LC 83-70197. 224p. 1983. pap. text ed. 15.00 (ISBN 0-86705-036-5). AIRE.

Teacher's Guide to Jews & Their Religion. Ruth Seldin. 150p. 5.95 (ISBN 0-88464-041-8); pap. 2.95 (ISBN 0-686-99468-X). ADL.

Teachers of Gurdjieff. Rafael Lefort. LC 66-68145. 157p. (Orig.). 1975. pap. 6.95 (ISBN 0-87728-283-8). Weiser.

Teacher's Supplement to Genesis the Student's Guide Pt. 1. Louis Newman. pap. 2.95 (ISBN 0-8381-0403-7). United Syn Bk.

Teaching about Aging: Religious & Advocacy Perspectives. James B. Boskey & Susan C. Hughes. LC 82-17589. 184p. (Orig.). 1983. lib. bdg. 26.00 (ISBN 0-8191-2802-3); pap. text ed. 11.50 (ISBN 0-8191-2803-1). U Pr of Amer.

Teaching about Religion in the Public Schools. Charles R. Kniker. LC 84-62994. (Fastback Ser.: No. 224). 50p. (Orig.). 1985. pap. 0.90 (ISBN 0-87367-224-0). Phi Delta Kappa.

Teaching Adults Through Discussion. Ed. by Ed Stewart. 32p. 1978. pap. 1.50 (ISBN 0-8307-0508-2, 9970401). Regal.

Teaching Adults with Confidence. Paul E. Loth. 48p. 1984. pap. 3.95 (ISBN 0-910566-43-7); seminar planbook 3.95 (ISBN 0-910566-44-5). Evang Tchr.

Teaching & Celebrating Advent. rev. ed. Donald Griggs & Patricia Griggs. (Griggs Educational Resources Ser.). (Illus.). 1980. pap. 6.95 (ISBN 0-687-41080-0). Abingdon.

Teaching & Celebrating Lent-Easter. Patricia Griggs & Donald Griggs. (Griggs Educational Resources Ser.). 1980. pap. 6.95 (ISBN 0-687-41081-9). Abingdon.

Teaching & Learning America's Christian History. Rosalie J. Slater. LC 65-26334. 1965. lib. bdg. 10.00 (ISBN 0-912498-02-1). Found Am Christ.

Teaching & Morality. Francis C. Wade. LC 63-17962. 1963. 2.95 (ISBN 0-8294-0080-X). Loyola.

Teaching & Reaching: Junior Resources. Sally E. Stuart. 1983. pap. 7.95 (ISBN 0-87162-285-8, D5702). Warner Pr.

Teaching As a Moral Craft. Alan R. Tom. LC 83-17520. 256p. 1984. pap. text ed. 12.95 (ISBN 0-582-28307-8). Longman.

Teaching as Jesus Taught. Georgianna Summers. LC 83-70161. 96p. (Orig.). 1983. pap. 4.50 (ISBN 0-88177-000-0, DR000B). Discipleship Res.

Teaching Authority & Infallibility in the Church, No. 6. Ed. by Paul C. Empie et al. LC 79-54109. (Lutherans & Catholics in Dialogue). 352p. (Orig.). 1979. pap. 8.95 (ISBN 0-8066-1733-0, 10-6222). Augsburg.

Teaching Authority of the Believers. Ed. by Johannes-Baptist Metz & Edward Schillebeeckx. (Concilium Ser.). 128p. 1985. pap. 6.95 (Pub. by T & T Clark Ltd UK). Fortress.

Teaching Basics: Adult. Daryl Dale. (Illus.). 80p. (Orig.). 1985. pap. 2.00 (ISBN 0-87509-369-8). Chr Pubns.

Teaching Basics: Junior. Daryl Dale. (Illus.). 73p. (Orig.). 1985. pap. 2.00 (ISBN 0-87509-359-0). Chr Pubns.

Teaching Basics: Youth. Daryl Dale. (Illus.). 80p. (Orig.). 1985. pap. 2.00 (ISBN 0-87509-364-7). Chr Pubns.

Teaching Bible Stories More Effectively with Puppets. Roland Sylwester. (Illus.). 64p. 1976. pap. 3.95 (ISBN 0-570-03731-X, 12-2633). Concordia.

Teaching Bible Truths with Single Objects. Lindgren. 1979. 3.50 (ISBN 0-88207-036-3). Victor Bks.

Teaching Bioethics: Strategies, Problems & Resources. K. Danner Clouser. LC 80-10492. (Teaching of Ethics Ser.: Vol. IV). 77p. 1980. pap. 4.00 (ISBN 0-916558-07-X). Hastings Ctr.

Teaching Children. C. H. Spurgen. 1983. pap. 0.95 (ISBN 0-686-40816-0). Pilgrim Pubns.

Teaching Children Charity: A Program to Help Teens & Preteens Forget Themselves. Linda Eyre & Richard Eyre. LC 85-27468. (Illus.). 280p. 1986. 9.95 (ISBN 0-87579-024-0). Deseret Bk.

Teaching Children Joy. Linda Eyre & Richard Eyre. 203p. pap. 8.95 (ISBN 0-87747-888-0, Pub. by Shadow Mountain). Deseret Bk.

Teaching Children Joy. Linda Eyre & Richard Eyre. LC 84-201498. 240p. 1986. pap. 3.50 (ISBN 0-345-32704-7). Ballantine.

Teaching Children with Confidence. David Jenkins. 48p. 1983. pap. 3.95 (ISBN 0-910566-39-9); seminar planbook 3.95 (ISBN 0-910566-40-2). Evang Tchr.

Teaching Christian Values. Lucie W. Barber. LC 83-22981. 250p. (Orig.). 1984. pap. 12.95 (ISBN 0-89135-041-1). Religious Educ.

Teaching Christian Values in the Family. Jim Larson. (Illus.). 48p. 1982. pap. text ed. 29.95 (ISBN 0-89191-649-0). Cook.

Teaching Church. 2nd ed. L. T. Johnson & Edward A. Buchanan. (Enabling Ser.). (Illus.). 95p. (Orig.). 1984. pap. 5.95 (ISBN 0-935797-00-9). Harvest IL.

Teaching Church: Active in Mission. Paul Gehris & Kathy Gehris. 80p. 1987. pap. 5.95 (ISBN 0-8170-1080-7). Judson.

Teaching Church at Work. Ed. by Kenneth D. Blazier. 64p. 1980. pap. 3.50 (ISBN 0-8170-0879-9). Judson.

Teaching Church in Our Time. Ed. by George A. Kelly. 1978. 6.00 (ISBN 0-8198-0523-8); pap. 4.50 (ISBN 0-8198-0524-6). Dghtrs St Paul.

Teaching Early Adolescents Creatively: A Manual for Church School Teachers. Edward D. Seely. 222p. 1971. Westminster.

Teaching Faith & Morals. Suzanne M. De Benedittis. 200p. (Orig.). 1981. pap. 8.95 (ISBN 0-86683-621-7, HaprsR). Har-Row.

Teaching for Christian Maturity. George M. Flattery. 126p. 1968. 1.50 (ISBN 0-88243-618-X, 02-0618). Gospel Pub.

Teaching for Decision. Richard L. Dresselhaus. LC 73-75502. 124p. 1973. pap. 1.25 (ISBN 0-88243-616-3, 02-0616). Gospel Pub.

Teaching for Life-Changing Learning. Peggy Payne. (C. E. Ministries Ser.). 94p. (Orig.). 1984. pap. 3.50 (ISBN 0-89367-092-8). Light & Life.

Teaching for Life-Response. Dean Merril. (Complete Teacher Training Meeting Ser.). 48p. 1986. 9.95 (ISBN 0-89191-316-5). Cook.

Teaching for Results. Findley B. Edge. 1956. 10.95 (ISBN 0-8054-3401-1). Broadman.

Teaching from the Tabernacle. Roy L. De Witt. LC 86-60046. (Illus.). 168p. (Orig.). pap. 8.95 (ISBN 0-9616360-0-9). Revival Teach.

Teaching Gifts. Irene V. Grindall. LC 85-71784. 64p. (Orig.). 1985. pap. 3.50 (ISBN 0-88177-020-5, DR020B). Discipleship Res.

Teaching Human Beings: One Hundred One Subversive Activities for the Classroom. Jeffrey Schrank. LC 73-179154. 288p. (Orig.). 1972. 9.95x (ISBN 0-8070-3176-3); pap. 5.95x (ISBN 0-8070-3177-1, BP425). Beacon Pr.

Teaching in the Community of Faith. Charles R. Foster. 160p. (Orig.). 1982. pap. 8.75 (ISBN 0-687-41086-X). Abingdon.

Teaching in the Congregation. Paul M. Lederach. LC 79-83594. (Mennonite Faith Ser: No. 7). 1979. pap. 1.50 (ISBN 0-8361-1886-3). Herald Pr.

Teaching Kindergarteners. Ruth Beechick. LC 79-53295. (Accent Teacher Training Ser.). 192p. 1980. pap. 4.95 (ISBN 0-89636-038-5). Accent Bks.

Teaching Life Skills to Children: A Practical Guide for Teachers & Parents. Dale R. Olen. 1984. pap. 6.95 (ISBN 0-8091-2618-4). Paulist Pr.

Teaching Methods of Christ: Characteristics of Our Lord's Ministry. John Harris. 444p. 1984. lib. bdg. 16.75 (ISBN 0-86524-161-9, 9516). Klock & Klock.

Teaching Ministry of the Church: An Examination of Basic Principles of Christian Education. James D. Smart. LC 54-10569. 208p. 1971. pap. 6.95 (ISBN 0-664-24910-8). Westminster.

Teaching Ministry of the Pulpit: Its History, Theology, Psychology & Practice for Today. Craig Skinner. 1979. pap. 6.95 (ISBN 0-8010-8165-3). Baker Bk.

Teaching Morality & Religion. Alan Harris. 104p. 1975. 14.95x (ISBN 0-8464-1274-8). Beekman Pubs.

Teaching of Addai. George Howard. LC 81-5802. (SBL Texts & Translations Ser.). 1981. pap. 13.50 (ISBN 0-89130-490-8, 060216). Scholars Pr GA.

Teaching of Calvin: A Modern Interpretation. Adam M. Hunter. LC 83-45618. Date not set. Repr. of 1950 ed. 37.50 (ISBN 0-404-19836-8). AMS Pr.

Teaching of Christ. 2nd ed. Ronald Lawler et al. LC 75-34852. 640p. 1983. pap. 9.95 (ISBN 0-87973-850-2, 850). Our Sunday Visitor.

Teaching of Christ. G. Campbell Morgan. 352p. 1984. 16.95 (ISBN 0-8007-0395-2). Revell.

Teaching of Ethics & the Social Sciences. Donald P. Warwick. LC 80-10154. (Teaching of Ethics Ser.). 69p. 1980. pap. 4.00 (ISBN 0-916558-11-8). Hastings Ctr.

Teaching of Ethics in Higher Education: A Report by the Hastings Center. Ed. by Daniel Callahan. LC 80-10294. (Teaching of Ethics Ser.). 103p. 1980. pap. 5.00 xerox form only (ISBN 0-916558-09-6). Hastings Ctr.

Teaching of Ethics in the Military. Peter L. Stromberg et al. LC 81-86583. (Teaching of Ethics in Higher Education Ser.: Vol. XII). 85p. (Orig.). 1982. pap. 5.00 (ISBN 0-916558-16-9). Hastings Ctr.

Teaching of Judaica in American Universities: Proceedings. Leon A. Jick. 1970. 10.00x (ISBN 0-87068-127-3). Ktav.

Teaching of Prayer: A Teacher's Guide. C. D. Rabinowitz. 2.25 (ISBN 0-914131-71-0, B50). Torah Umesorah.

Teaching of Saint Gregory: An Early Armenian Catechism. Gregory. Tr. by Robert W. Thomson et al from Arm. LC 78-115482. (Armenian Texts & Studies: No. 3). 1971. 14.00x (ISBN 0-674-87038-7). Harvard U Pr.

Teaching of Sri Aurobindo. M. P. Pandit. (Illus., Orig.). 1978. pap. 3.50 (ISBN 0-89744-982-7, Pub. by Bharatiya Vidya Bhavan India). Auromere.

Teaching of Sri Satya Sai Baba. 144p. 1974. pap. 2.95 (ISBN 0-317-20878-0). CSA Pr.

Teaching of the Early Church on the Use of Wine & Strong Drink. Irving W. Raymond. LC 79-120207. (Columbia University. Studies in the Social Sciences: No. 286). Repr. of 1927 ed. 14.50 (ISBN 0-404-51286-0). AMS Pr.

Teaching of the Epistle to the Hebrews. Geerhardus Vos. pap. 4.95 (ISBN 0-87552-503-2). Presby & Reformed.

Teaching of the Master. Joseph V. Cesar. 120p. (Orig.). pap. text ed. 5.95 (ISBN 0-937816-01-9). Tech Data.

Teaching of the New Testament. Donald Guthrie. 1983. pap. 4.95 (ISBN 0-87508-179-7). Chr Lit.

Teaching of the Qur'An, with an Account of Its Growth & Subject Index. H. U. Stanton. LC 74-90040. 1969. Repr. 18.00 (ISBN 0-8196-0253-1). Biblo.

Teaching Preschoolers. Barbara Hanna & Janet Hoover. 3.95 (ISBN 0-89137-608-9). Quality Pubns.

Teaching Preschoolers: It's Not Exactly Easy but Here Is How to Do It. Ruth Beechick. LC 78-73252. (Accent Teacher Training Ser.). 1979. pap. 4.95 (ISBN 0-89636-019-9). Accent Bks.

Teaching Preschoolers with Confidence. Robert E. Clark. 48p. 1983. pap. 3.95 (ISBN 0-910566-37-2); seminar planbook 3.95 (ISBN 0-910566-38-0). Evang Tchr.

Teaching Primaries. Ruth Beechick. LC 80-66723. (Accent Teacher Training Ser.). 128p. (Orig.). 1980. pap. 4.95 (ISBN 0-89636-054-7). Accent Bks.

Teaching Primaries. Diane Mauck & Janet Jenkins. 4.50 (ISBN 0-89137-610-0); write for info. wkbk. (ISBN 0-89137-612-7). Quality Pubns.

Teaching Primaries Workbook. Mauck & Jenkins. pap. 2.95 (ISBN 0-89137-432-9). Quality Pubns.

Teaching Religion Effectively Program. Mary Cove & Jane Regan. 96p. 1982. pap. 3.50 (ISBN 0-697-01825-3); program manual 24.95 (ISBN 0-697-01826-1). Wm C Brown.

Teaching Religion: The Secularization of Religion Instruction in a West German School System. W. Clinton Terry, III. LC 80-5569. 208p. 1981. pap. text ed. 12.25 (ISBN 0-8191-1367-0). U Pr of Amer.

Teaching Teachers to Teach: A Basic Manual for Church Teachers. Donald L. Griggs. (Griggs Educational Resources Ser.). 1983. pap. 7.95 (ISBN 0-687-41120-3). Abingdon.

Teaching Techniques. rev. ed. Clarence H. Benson. 96p. 1983. pap. text ed. 4.95 (ISBN 0-910566-05-4); Perfect bdg. instr's. guide 5.95 (ISBN 0-910566-23-2). Evang Tchr.

Teaching Techniques of Jesus. Herman H. Horne. LC 64-16634. 224p. 1971. pap. 5.95 (ISBN 0-8254-2804-1). Kregel.

Teaching Teens the Truth. Kathryn Griffin. LC 78-58567. 1978. pap. 4.95 (ISBN 0-8054-3425-9, 4234-25). Broadman.

Teaching the Adult Bible Class. Chris Willerton. 2.95 (ISBN 0-89137-609-7). Quality Pubns.

Teaching the Baha'i Faith: Spirit in Action. Nathan Rutstein. 192p. 11.95 (ISBN 0-85398-175-2); pap. 6.95 (ISBN 0-85398-176-0). G Ronald Pub.

Teaching the Bible. John Conaway. (Complete Teacher Training Meeting ser.). 48p. 1986. tchr's ed 9.95 (ISBN 0-89191-319-X). Cook.

Teaching the Bible: Creative Techniques for Bringing Scripture to Life. Willard A. Scofield. 112p. 1986. pap. 6.95 (ISBN 0-8170-1094-7). Judson.

Teaching the Bible to Adults & Youth. Dick Murray. (Creative Leadership Ser.). 176p. 1987. pap. 8.95 (ISBN 0-687-41082-7). Abingdon.

Teaching the Bible to Change Lives. Kathy Hyde. LC 84-47801. 143p. (Orig.). 1984. pap. 6.95 (ISBN 0-89840-064-3). Heres Life.

Teaching the Catholic Faith Today. Ed. by Eugene Kevane. (Resources for Catechetical Teachers). 352p. 1982. 12.00 (ISBN 0-8198-7319-5, EP1048); pap. 10.00 (ISBN 0-8198-7320-9). Dghtrs St Paul.

Teaching the Holocaust to Children: A Review & Bibliography. Diane Roskies. pap. 7.50x (ISBN 0-87068-469-8). Ktav.

Teaching the Meaning of Church Ordinances to Children. Terri Breeden. (Orig.). 1986. pap. 5.95 (ISBN 0-89265-097-4). Randall Hse.

Teaching the Scriptures: A Syllabus for Bible Study. Russell D. Robinson. (Illus.). 156p. 1977. 11.95 (ISBN 0-9600154-3-4); pap. 9.95 (ISBN 0-9600154-4-2). Bible Study Pr.

Teaching the Ten Commandments. 20p. 1982. pap. 7.55 (ISBN 0-88479-035-5). Arena Lettres.

Teaching the Way: Jesus, the Early Church & Today. Joseph A. Grassi. LC 82-7054. 176p. 1982. lib. bdg. 26.75 (ISBN 0-8191-2501-6); pap. text ed. 11.50 (ISBN 0-8191-2502-4). U Pr of Amer.

Teaching the Word of Truth. Donald G. Barnhouse. 1958. Repr. 5.95 (ISBN 0-8028-1610-X). Eerdmans.

Teaching the Word, Reaching the World. Robert G. Flood & Jerry B. Jenkins. 1985. text ed. 14.95 (ISBN 0-8024-8567-7). Moody.

Teaching to Meet Crisis Needs. Billie Davis. LC 83-82815. 128p. (Orig.). 1984. pap. text ed. 2.95 (ISBN 0-88243-609-0, 02-0609). Gospel Pub.

Teaching Toddlers. Carol E. Miller. 1971. pap. 1.95 (ISBN 0-915374-22-6, 22-6). Rapids Christian.

Teaching Torah: A Treasury of Activities & Insights. Sorel G. Loeb & Barbara B. Kadden. LC 84-70318. 300p. 1984. pap. text ed. 15.00 (ISBN 0-86705-013-6). AIRE.

Teaching Visuals from Willmington's Guide to the Bible. 1981. pap. 14.95 (ISBN 0-8423-6939-2). Tyndale.

Teaching with Music Through the Church Year. Judy G. Smith. 1979. pap. 7.95 (ISBN 0-687-41133-5). Abingdon.

Teaching with Object Talks. Cara Roberts. (Illus.). 48p. (Orig.). 1982. pap. 2.95 (ISBN 0-87239-533-2, 2889). Standard Pub.

Teaching Your Child About God. Wes Haystead. LC 68-29315. 144p. 1981. text ed. 8.95 (ISBN 0-8307-0798-0, 5109406). Regal.

Teaching Your Child about Sex. Terrance Drake & Marvia Drake. LC 83-71726. 60p. 1983. 6.95 (ISBN 0-87747-951-8). Deseret Bk.

Teaching Youth. Larry Richards. 156p. 1982. pap. 4.95 (ISBN 0-8341-0776-7). Beacon Hill.

Teaching Youth with Confidence. Bill Bynum. 48p. 1983. pap. 3.95 (ISBN 0-910566-41-0); seminar planbook 3.95 (ISBN 0-910566-42-9). Evang Tchr.

Teachings & Miracles of Jesus. Daughters of St. Paul. 1981. 5.00 (ISBN 0-686-73821-7); pap. 4.00 (ISBN 0-8198-7302-0). Dghtrs St Paul.

Teachings from the American Earth: Indian Religion & Philosophy. Ed. by Dennis Tedlock & Barbara Tedlock. (Illus.). 304p. 1976. pap. 7.95 (ISBN 0-87140-097-9). Liveright.

Teachings of Christ Ungame Cards. 1.50 (ISBN 0-317-15786-8). Chr Marriage.

Teachings of Don Juan: A Yaqui Way of Knowledge. Carlos Castaneda. LC 68-17303. 1968. pap. 5.95 (ISBN 0-520-02258-0, CAL253). U of Cal Pr.

Teachings of Gurdjieff: The Journal of a Pupil. C. S. Nott. (Illus., Orig.). 1974. pap. 7.95 (ISBN 0-87728-395-8). Weiser.

Teachings of Hafiz. Gertrude Bell. 1979. 10.95 (ISBN 0-900860-63-4, Pub. by Octagon Pr England). Ins Study Human.

Teachings of Hasidism. Ed. by Joseph Dan. (Orig.). 1983. pap. text ed. 9.95x (ISBN 0-87441-346-X). Behrman.

Teachings of Islam: A Solution of Five Fundamental Religious Problems from the Muslim Point of View. M. G. Atemed. 208p. 1984. text ed. 23.00. Coronet Bks.

Teachings of Islam (Tablighi Nisab) M. Zakeriyya. Date not set. 25.00 (ISBN 0-933511-09-4). Kazi Pubns.

Teachings of Jehovah's Witnesses. John H. Gerstner. pap. 1.95 (ISBN 0-8010-3718-2). Baker Bk.

Teachings of Jesus. Norman Anderson. LC 83-4312. (Jesus Library). 216p. 1983. pap. 6.95 (ISBN 0-87784-926-9). Inter-Varsity.

Teachings of Kirpal Singh, 3 vols. Ed. by Ruth Seader. Vol. I, The Holy Path, 104 pp. 3.00 (ISBN 0-318-03046-2); Vol. III, The New Life, 200 pp. 3.50 (ISBN 0-318-03047-0); One-Volume Ed., 474 pp. 7.95 (ISBN 0-318-03048-9). Sant Bani Ash.

Teachings of Maimonides. Jacob Minkin. 450p. 1987. Repr. of 1957 ed. 35.00 (ISBN 0-87668-953-5). Aronson.

Teachings of Mormonism. John H. Gerstner. pap. 1.95 (ISBN 0-8010-3719-0). Baker Bk.

Teachings of Nature in the Kingdom of Grace. C. H. Spurgeon. 1976. pap. 3.95 (ISBN 0-686-18094-1). Pilgrim Pubns.

Teachings of Old Testament. John Tos. (Bible Study Commentaries Ser.). 128p. 1984. pap. 4.50 (ISBN 0-317-43392-X). Chr Lit.

Teachings of Paul. Mark E. Peterson. LC 84-70647. 120p. 1984. 6.95 (ISBN 0-87747-843-0). Deseret Bk.

Teachings of Rumi: The Masnavi. Tr. by E. H. Whinfield. 1979. 15.95 (ISBN 0-900860-64-2, Pub. by Octagon Pr England). Ins Study Human.

Teachings of St. John Cassian. St. John Cassian. pap. 4.95 (ISBN 0-686-05665-5). Eastern Orthodox.

Teachings of Seventh-Day Adventism. John H. Gerstner. pap. 1.75 (ISBN 0-8010-3720-4). Baker Bk.

Teachings of Sri Ramakrishna. Sri Ramakrishna. pap. 4.95 (ISBN 0-87481-133-3). Vedanta Pr.

Teachings of Sri Saranda Devi. (Holy Mother Ser.). 175p. 1983. 3.00 (ISBN 0-87481-520-7, Pub. by Ramakrishna Math Madras India). Vedanta Pr.

Teachings of Sri Satya Sai Baba. Ed. by Roy E. Davis. 2.95 (ISBN 0-317-46972-X). CSA Pr.

Teachings of Swami Vivekananda. Swami Vivekananda. 1971. pap. 3.95 (ISBN 0-87481-134-1). Vedanta Pr.

Teachings of the Compassionate Buddha. Ed. by Edwin A. Burtt. (Orig.). 1955. pap. 3.95 (ISBN 0-451-62450-5, ME2282, Ment). NAL.

Teachings of the Essenes from Enoch to the Dead Sea Scrolls. Edmond B. Szekely. (Illus.). 112p. 1981. pap. 4.80 (ISBN 0-89564-006-6). IBS Intl.

Teachings of the Great Mystics. Karl Pruter. LC 85-13306. 118p. 1985. Repr. lib. bdg. 19.95x (ISBN 0-89370-595-0). Borgo Pr.

Teachings of the Magi. Robert C. Zaehner. 1976. pap. 7.95 (ISBN 0-19-519857-3). Oxford U Pr.

Teachings of the Parables. Peter R. Jones. LC 78-654367. 1982. 13.95 (ISBN 0-8054-1371-5). Broadman.

Teachings of the Prophet Joseph Smith. Joseph F. Smith. LC 76-111624. 437p. 1977. pap. 2.50 (ISBN 0-87747-778-7). Deseret Bk.

Teachings of the Prophet Joseph Smith. Joseph F. Smith. 1976. 9.95 (ISBN 0-87747-626-8). Deseret Bk.

Teachings of the Temple, 3 vols. Ed. by The Temple of the People Publications Staff. 1985. Set. 25.00 (ISBN 0-933797-08-7); Vol. 1, 661p. 11.25 ea. (ISBN 0-933797-03-6). Vol. 2, 400p (ISBN 0-933797-04-4). Vol. 3, 400p (ISBN 0-933797-05-2) (ISBN 0-933797-05-2). Halcyon Bk.

Teachings of Tibetan Yoga. Garma C. Chang. 128p. 1974. pap. 3.45 (ISBN 0-8065-0460-9). Citadel Pr.

Teachings of Yogi Bhajan. Yogi Bhajan. 1985. pap. 8.95 (ISBN 0-317-38485-6). Arcline Pubns.

Teachings of Yogi Bhajan: The Power of the Spoken Word. Khalsa S. Harbhajan. LC 85-22347. 196p. 1985. Repr. of 1977 ed. lib. bdg. 19.95x (ISBN 0-89370-878-X). Borgo Pr.

Team. Dody Donnelly. LC 77-74584. 168p. (Orig.). 1977. pap. 5.95 (ISBN 0-8091-2013-5). Paulist Pr.

Team Ministry. Dick Iverson & Ray Grant. (Illus.). 143p. 1984. pap. 8.95 (ISBN 0-914936-61-1). Bible Temple.

Team Teaching Children in Bible Class. Ron Bailey & Betty Bailey. 1972. 4.95 (ISBN 0-931097-05-3). Sentinel Pub.

Tear Catchers. Harold I. Smith. 160p. (Orig.). 1984. pap. 9.50 (ISBN 0-687-41184-X). Abingdon.

Tearful Celebration: Courage in Crisis. James Means. LC 85-343. 1985. pap. 5.95 (ISBN 0-88070-078-5). Multnomah.

Tears of Joy. Ted Curtas. cancelled (ISBN 0-686-12741-2); pap. 3.95 (ISBN 0-686-12742-0). Grace Pub Co.

Tears of Lady Meng: A Parable of People's Political Theology. Choan-Seng Song. LC 82-2295. (Illus.). 80p. (Orig.). 1982. pap. 4.95 (ISBN 0-88344-505-0). Orbis Bks.

Tears of Silence. Jean Vanier. 3.95 (ISBN 0-87193-011-0). Dimension Bks.

Technique for Developing Enlightened Consciousness: A Traditional Buddhist Meditation on Avalokiteshvara. Tangtong Gyalpo. Tr. by Janet Gyatso from Tibetan. (Basic Buddhism Ser.). 26p. (Orig.). 1980. pap. 1.50 (ISBN 0-915078-02-3, P-01). Buddhist Assn US.

Technique of Canon. Hugo Norden. 1982. pap. 9.00 (ISBN 0-8283-1839-5). Branden Pub Co.

Technique of the Disciple. 4th ed. Raymond Andrea. 168p. 1981. pap. 7.95 (ISBN 0-912057-12-2, G-643). AMORC.

Technique of the Master. 12th ed. Raymond Andrea. 174p. 1981. 7.95 (ISBN 0-912057-10-6, G-513). AMORC.

Technique of the Spiritual Life. 2nd ed. Clara M. Codd. 1963. 6.95 (ISBN 0-8356-7090-2). Theos Pub Hse.

Technological Powers & the Person: Nuclear Energy & Reproductive Technology. Pope John Center Staff. Ed. by Larry D. Lossing & Edward J. Bayer. (Illus.). 370p. (Orig.). 1983. pap. 15.95 (ISBN 0-935372-12-1). Pope John Ctr.

Technometry. William Ames. Tr. by Lee W. Gibbs from Lat. LC 78-65117. (Haney Foundation Ser.). (Illus.). 1979. 31.50x (ISBN 0-8122-7756-2). U of Pa Pr.

Ted Engstrom: Man with a Vision. Bob Owen. 214p. 1984. pap. 5.95 (ISBN 0-8423-6942-2). Tyndale.

Ted Studebaker: A Man Who Loved Peace. Joy H. Moore. LC 86-19419. (Illus.). 40p. (Orig.). 1987. pap. 9.95 (ISBN 0-8361-3427-3). Herald Pr.

TEE in Japan: A Realistic Vision: the Feasibility of Theological Education by Extension for Churches in Japan. W. Frederic Sprunger. LC 81-7739. (Illus., Orig.). 1981. pap. 15.95x (ISBN 0-87808-434-7). William Carey Lib.

Teen-Agers' Treasure Chest. Floyd D. Carey, Jr. 100p. 1963. pap. 1.25 (ISBN 0-87148-830-2). Pathway Pr.

Teen Talks with God. Robert Boden. 1980. pap. 3.50 (ISBN 0-570-03812-X, 12-2921). Concordia.

Teen Teacher Survival Kit. Robert Klausmeier. 80p. 1986. tchr's ed 9.95 (ISBN 0-89191-364-5). Cook.

Teenage Survival Manual: How to Enjoy the Trip to Twenty. H. Samm Coombs. (Illus.). 1978. pap. 5.95 (ISBN 0-87516-277-0). De Vorss.

Teenager's (Absolutely Basic) Introduction to the New Testament. Jim Auer. 96p. 1986. pap. 2.95 (ISBN 0-89243-257-8). Liguori Pubns.

Teenagers & Purity, Teenagers & Going Steady, Teenagers & Looking Ahead to Marriage. Robert Fox. 1978. pap. 0.75 (ISBN 0-8198-0370-7). Dghtrs St Paul.

Teenagers Pocket Companion, No. 2. Floyd D. Carey. 1962. pap. 0.25 (ISBN 0-87148-828-0). Pathway Pr.

Teenagers Pocket Companion, No. 3. Floyd D. Carey. 1962. pap. 0.25 (ISBN 0-87148-829-9). Pathway Pr.

Teenagers Pray. William A. Kramer. LC 55-12193. 1956. 4.50 (ISBN 0-570-03018-8, 6-1054). Concordia.

Teenagers Today. Daughters of St. Paul. 1981. 4.00 (ISBN 0-8198-7303-9); pap. 3.00 (ISBN 0-8198-7304-7). Dghtrs St Paul.

Teens & Self Esteem: Helping Christian Youth Discover Their Worth. Jerry McCant. 152p. (Orig.). 1985. pap. 5.95 (ISBN 0-8341-1055-5). Beacon Hill.

Teens Encounter Christ. Andre Cirino & Francine Rogers. LC 77-88321. (Illus., Orig.). 1978. pap. 2.25 (ISBN 0-8189-1156-5, 156, Pub. by Alba Bks). Alba.

Teepee Neighbors. Grace Coolidge. LC 83-40487. 200p. 1984. pap. 7.95 (ISBN 0-8061-1889-X). U of Okla Pr.

Teetering on the Tightrope. Carol Amen. LC 79-18718. (Orion Ser.). 1979. pap. 2.95 (ISBN 0-8127-0250-6). Review & Herald.

Teetotalism, Eighteen Forty-Two. 25p. 1984. pap. text ed. 12.50 (ISBN 0-87556-380-5). Saifer.

Tefillin Handbook. David Rosoff. (Orig.). 1984. pap. 4.95 (ISBN 0-87306-373-2). Feldheim.

Tehillim: Psalms, 2 vols. A. C. Feuer. 1985. 39.95 (ISBN 0-317-38548-8); pap. 29.95 (ISBN 0-317-38549-6). Mesorah Pubns.

Tehillim (Psalms, 3 vols. Avrohom C. Fever. Incl. Vol. 1. Psalms 1-30. 368p. 1977. (ISBN 0-89906-050-1); pap. (ISBN 0-89906-051-X); Vol. 2. Psalms 31-55. 352p. 1978. (ISBN 0-89906-052-8); pap. (ISBN 0-89906-053-6); Vol. 3. Psalms 56-85. 384p. 1979. (ISBN 0-89906-054-4); pap. (ISBN 0-89906-055-2). (Art Scroll Tanach Ser.). 15.95 ea.; pap. 12.95 ea. Mesorah Pubns.

Teilhard & the Unity of Knowledge. Ed. by Thomas M. King & James F. Salmon. LC 82-60590. 1983. pap. 6.95 (ISBN 0-8091-2491-2). Paulist Pr.

Teilhard de Chardin: In Quest of the Perfection of Man. Ed. by Joseph L. Alioto et al. LC 72-9596. 290p. 1973. 24.50 (ISBN 0-8386-1258-X). Fairleigh Dickinson.

Teilhard de Chardin's Vision of the Future. Francis Neilson. 1979. lib. bdg. 39.50 (ISBN 0-685-96664-2). Revisionist Pr.

Teilhard in Chardin's Biological Ideas. Alexander Wolsky. (Teilhard Studies). 1981. 2.00 (ISBN 0-89012-024-2). Anima Pubns.

Teilhard in the Ecological Age. Thomas Berry. (Teilhard Studies). 1982. 2.00 (ISBN 0-89012-032-3). Anima Pubns.

Teilhard, Scripture, & Revelation: Teilhard de Chardin's Reinterpretation of Pauline Themes. Richard W. Kropf. LC 73-20907. 352p. 1980. 29.50 (ISBN 0-8386-1481-7). Fairleigh Dickinson.

Teilhard's Mysticism of Knowing. Thomas M. King. 192p. 1981. 14.95 (ISBN 0-8164-0491-7, HarpR). Har-Row.

Tela Ignea Satanae, 2 vols. Joh. Chr. Wagenseil. 1631p. Date not set. Repr. of 1681 ed. text ed. 207.00x (ISBN 0-576-80110-0, Pub by Gregg Intl Pubs England). Gregg Intl.

Telecare Ministry: Using the Telephone in a Care Ministry. Harald Grindal. 40p. 1984. pap. 3.95 (ISBN 0-8066-2099-4, 23-1899). Augsburg.

Telegraph in America: Its Founders, Promoters & Noted Men. James D. Reid. LC 74-7493. (Telecommunications Ser). (Illus.). 926p. 1974. Repr. of 1879 ed. 63.00 (ISBN 0-405-06056-4). Ayer Co Pubs.

Televangelism: The Marketing of Popular Religion. Razelle Frankl. (Illus.). 224p. 1987. 19.95 (ISBN 0-8093-1299-9). S Ill U Pr.

Television & Religion: The Shaping of Faith & Value. William F. Fore. 208p. (Orig.). 1987. pap. 11.95 (ISBN 0-8066-2268-7, 10-6229). Augsburg.

Tell All the Little Children. Kenneth L. Chafin. 1976. pap. 0.95 (ISBN 0-8054-6211-2). Broadman.

Tell El-Amarna & the Bible. Charles F. Pfeiffer. (Baker Studies in Biblical Archaeology). 1976. pap. 2.95 (ISBN 0-8010-7002-3). Baker Bk.

Tell It to the Church. Lynn R. Buzzard & Laurence Eck. 192p. (Orig.). 1985. pap. 6.95 (ISBN 0-8423-6986-4). Tyndale.

Tell It to the World. Mervyn Maxwell. LC 76-6619. 1976. 6.95 (ISBN 0-8163-0217-0, 20077-4). Pacific Pr Pub Assn.

Tell It Well. J. T. Seamands. 236p. (Orig.). 1981. pap. 6.95 (ISBN 0-8341-0684-1). Beacon Hill.

Tell Me a Story. Mary Branch. LC 78-53210. (Stories That Win Ser.). 1978. pap. 1.25 (ISBN 0-8163-0210-3, 20079-0). Pacific Pr Pub Assn.

Tell Me about God. Linda Humble. LC 81-86703. (Happy Day Bks.). (Illus.). 24p. (Orig.). 1982. pap. 1.59 (ISBN 0-87239-544-8, 3590). Standard Pub.

Tell Me about God: 12 Lessons, Vol. 1. Lois J. Haas. (Tiny Steps of Faith Ser.). 1966. complete kit 12.95 (ISBN 0-86508-011-9); text only 2.95 (ISBN 0-86508-012-7); color & action book 0.90 (ISBN 0-86508-013-5). BCM Intl Inc.

Tell Me about Jesus. Elizabeth E. Watson. 1980. pap. 3.95 (ISBN 0-570-03484-1, 56-1705). Concordia.

Tell Me about Jesus: 16 Lessons, Vol. 2. Lois J. Haas. (Tiny Steps of Faith Ser.). 1967. complete kit 12.95 (ISBN 0-86508-014-3); text only 2.95 (ISBN 0-86508-015-1); color & action book 0.90 (ISBN 0-86508-016-X). BCM Intl Inc.

Tell Me Again, Lord, I Forget. Ruth H. Calkin. (Living Bks.). 160p. (Orig.). 1986. 3.50 (ISBN 0-8423-6990-2). Tyndale.

Tell Me How to Please God: 16 Lessons, Vol. 4. Lois J. Haas. (Tiny Steps of Faith Ser.). 1974. complete kit 10.95 (ISBN 0-86508-020-8); text only 2.95 (ISBN 0-86508-021-6); color & action book 0.90 (ISBN 0-86508-022-4). BCM Intl Inc.

Tell Me How to Trust God: 16 Lessons, Vol. 3. Lois J. Haas. (Tiny Steps of Faith Ser.). 1970. complete kit 12.95 (ISBN 0-86508-017-8); text only 2.95 (ISBN 0-86508-018-6); color & action book 0.90 (ISBN 0-86508-019-4). BCM Intl Inc.

Tell Me Who I Am. Adrian Van Kaam & Susan Muto. 4.95 (ISBN 0-87193-145-1). Dimension Bks.

Tell Me Why: A Guide to Children's Questions about Faith & Life. Marilyn F. Holm. LC 85-7355. 144p. (Orig.). 1985. pap. 6.95 (ISBN 0-8066-2160-5, 10-6230). Augsburg.

Tell the Next Generation: Homilies & Near Homilies. Walter J. Burghardt. LC 79-91895. 240p. 1980. pap. 8.95 (ISBN 0-8091-2252-9). Paulist Pr.

Tell the Truth. 2nd ed. Will Metzger. LC 83-25304. 187p. (Orig.). 1981. pap. 6.95 (ISBN 0-87784-934-X). Inter Varsity.

Tell Them I Am Coming. Richard E. Eby. 1980. pap. 5.95 (ISBN 0-8007-5045-4, Power Bks). Revell.

Tell Them I Am Coming. Richard E. Eby. 160p. 1984. pap. 2.50 (ISBN 0-8007-8496-0, Spire Bks). Revell.

Tell Them to Me. P. Gwyn Filby. 200p. 1986. 40.00x (ISBN 0-947939-01-6, Pub. by Elmcrest Uk). State Mutual Bk.

Tell Us Our Names: Story Theology from an Asian Perspective. C. S. Song. LC 84-5139. (Illus.). 224p. (Orig.). 1984. pap. 10.95 (ISBN 0-88344-512-3). Orbis Bks.

Tell Your Secret. Fran Lance & Pat King. 128p. 1986. pap. 5.95 (ISBN 0-89221-142-3). New Leaf.

Telling: A Loving Hagadah for Passover (Non-Sexist, Yet Traditional) rev. ed. Dov ben Khayyim. (Illus.). 48p. 1984. pap. 4.00 (ISBN 0-9612500-0-3). Rakhamim Pubns.

Telling Lives: The Biographer's Art. Ed. by Marc Pachter. LC 81-10312. 151p. 1981. pap. 10.95 (ISBN 0-8122-1118-9). U of Pa Pr.

Telling Right from Wrong: What Is Moral, What Is Immoral & What Is Neither One Nor the Other. Timothy J. Cooney. 158p. 1985. 18.95 (ISBN 0-87975-297-1). Prometheus Bks.

Telling the Next Generation: The Educational Development in North American Calvinist Christian Schools. Harro W. Van Brummelen. (Illus.). 332p. (Orig.). 1986. lib. bdg. 27.50 (ISBN 0-8191-5307-9, Pub. by Inst Christ Stud); pap. text ed. 14.75 (ISBN 0-8191-5308-7). U Pr of Amer.

Telling the Story of the Local Church: The Who, What, When, Where & Why of Communication. Velma Sumrall & Lucille Germany. (Orig.). 1979. pap. 5.00 (ISBN 0-8164-2193-5, HarpR); wkbk. avail. (ISBN 0-685-59466-1). Har-Row.

Telling the Story: Variety & Imagination in Preaching. Richard A. Jensen. LC 79-54113. 190p. (Orig.). 1979. pap. 9.95 (ISBN 0-8066-1766-7, 10-6232). Augsburg.

Telling the Truth: The Gospel As Tragedy, Comedy, & Fairy Tale. Frederick Buechner. LC 77-7839. 1977. 12.45 (ISBN 0-06-061156-1, HarpR). Har-Row.

Telling the Truth to Troubled People. William Backus. 256p. (Orig.). 1985. pap. 6.95 (ISBN 0-87123-811-X, 210811). Bethany Hse.

Telling the Whole Story. George M. Bass. 1983. 6.95 (ISBN 0-89536-642-8, 2007). CSS of Ohio.
Telling Your Story, Exploring Your Faith. B. J. Hateley. Ed. by Herbert Lambert. LC 85-13307. 120p. (Orig.). 1985. pap. 8.95 (ISBN 0-8272-3626-3). CBP.
Telling Yourself the Truth. William Backus & Marie Chapian. LC 80-10136. 41p. (Orig.). 1980. pap. 5.95 (ISBN 0-87123-562-5, 210562); study guide 2.50 (ISBN 0-87123-567-6, 210567). Bethany Hse.
Temas de Isaias. Ronald Youngblood. Orig. Title: Themes from Isaiah. (Span.). 1986. write for info. (ISBN 0-8297-0896-0). Life Pubs Intl.
Tempel Von Jerusalem. Konrad Rupprecht. (Beihefte 144 Zur Zeitschrift Fuer die Alttestamentliche Wissenschaft). 1976. text ed. 22.80x (ISBN 3-11-006619-X). De Gruyter.
Tempel von Paestum, 2 pts. Friedrich Krauss. (Denkmaeler Antiker Architektur, Vol. 9, Pt. 1, Fascicule 1). (Ger., Illus.). 97p. 1978. Repr. of 1959 ed. 70.0000169042x (ISBN 3-110022-37-0). De Gruyter.
Temperament & the Christian Faith. O. Hallesby. LC 62-9093. 106p. 1978. pap. 3.95 (ISBN 0-8066-1660-1, 10-6237). Augsburg.
Templar Tradition in the Age of Aquarius. Gaetan Delaforge. (Illus.). 175p. (Orig.). 1987. pap. 10.00 (ISBN 0-939660-20-2). Threshold VT.
Templars: Knights of God. Edward Burman. (Crucible Ser.). 208p. 1987. pap. 9.95 (ISBN 0-85030-396-6). Thorsons Pubs.
Temple, & Other Poems. Tr. by Arthur Waley. LC 78-70137. Repr. of 1923 ed. 25.00 (ISBN 0-404-17407-8). AMS Pr.
Temple Arts of Kerala: A South Indian Tradition. Ronald M. Berner. 272p. 100.00 (ISBN 0-317-52158-6, Pub. by S Chand India). State Mutual Bk.
Temple Beyond Time: Mount Moriah - From Solomon's Temple to Christian & Islamic Shrines. rev. ed. Herbert A. Klein. Ed. by Joseph Simon. (Illus.). 192p. 1986. Repr. of 1970 ed. 27.50 (ISBN 0-934710-14-7). J Simon.
Temple Culture of South India. V. R. Pillai. (Illus.). xii, 201p. 1986. text ed. 45.00x (ISBN 81-210-0168-4, Pub. by Inter India Pubns N Delhi). Apt Bks.
Temple Documents of the Third Dynasty of Ur from Umma. Ed. by George G. Hackman. LC 78-63524. (Babylonian Inscriptions in the Collection of James B. Nies: No. 5). Repr. of 1937 ed. 28.50 (ISBN 0-404-60135-9). AMS Pr.
Temple Flowers. J. P. Vaswani & Jyoti Mirchandani. 182p. 1986. text ed. 25.00x (ISBN 0-317-43153-6, Pub. by Chopmen Pubs Singapore). Advent NY.
Temple Gateways of South India: The Architecture & Iconography of the Cidambaram Gopuras. J. C. Harle. (Illus.). 179p. 1963. 65.00x (ISBN 0-317-39167-4, Pub. by Luzac & Co Ltd). State Mutual Bk.
Temple in Man: Sacred Architecture & the Perfect Man. R. A. Schwaller De Lubicz. Tr. by Robert Lawlor & Deborah Lawlor. LC 81-13374. (Illus.). 132p. 1981. pap. 6.95 (ISBN 0-89281-021-1). Inner Tradit.
Temple, Its Ministry & Services. Alfred Edersheim. 1950. 5.95 (ISBN 0-8028-8133-5). Eerdmans.
Temple Legend. Rudolf Steiner. Tr. by John Wood from German. 1986. 28.00 (ISBN 0-85440-780-4, Pub by Steinerbooks). Anthroposophic.
Temple Messages. Ed. by Temple of the People Publications Staff. (Illus.). 183p. 1983. 10.50 (ISBN 0-933797-07-9). Halcyon Bk.
Temple of Divine Truth. Mark Lowry. 1986. 6.95 (ISBN 0-8062-2423-1). Carlton.
Temple of God. Annalee Skarin. pap. 5.95 (ISBN 0-87516-093-X). De Vorss.
Temple of Jerusalem. Andre Parrot. Tr. by Beatrice E. Hooke from Fr. LC 85-8037. (Studies in Biblical Archaeology: No. 5). Tr. of Temple de Jerusalem. (Illus.). 112p. 1985. Repr. of 1957 ed. lib. bdg. 35.00x (ISBN 0-313-24224-0, PATJ). Greenwood.
Temple of Khonsu: Vol. 2, Scenes & Inscriptions in the Court & the First Hypostyle Hall. The Epigraphic Survey. LC 80-82999. (Oriental Institute Publications Ser.: Vol. 103). 1981. pap. 95.00x incl. 96 plates in portfolio (ISBN 0-918986-29-X). Oriental Inst.
Temple of Mentuhotep at Dier El Bahari. Dieter Arnold. (Publications of the Metropolitan Museum of Art Egyptian Expedition: Vol. XXI). (Illus.). 1979. 60.00 (ISBN 0-87099-163-9). Metro Mus Art.
Temple of Solomon: Archaeological Fact & Medieval Tradition in Christian, Islamic & Jewish Art. Ed. by Joseph Gutmann. LC 75-19120. 1976. 9.00 (ISBN 0-89130-013-9, 090103). Scholars Pr GA.
Temple of the Holy Spirit. Matthew J. O'Connell. 345p. 1983. pap. 17.50 (ISBN 0-916134-64-4). Pueblo Pub Co.
Temple of Your Being. S. King. 1985. Book & Cassette Pack. 27.50x (ISBN 0-317-54328-8, Pub. by J Richardson UK). State Mutual Bk.
Temple of Zeus at Nemea. rev., suppl. ed. Bert H. Hill. Ed. by Charles Williams. LC 67-102135. (Illus.). 1966. portfolio 22.00x (ISBN 0-87661-921-9). Am Sch Athens.
Temple: Sacred Poems & Private Ejaculations. 6th ed. George Herbert. LC 72-5489. (Select Bibliographies Reprint Ser.). 1972. Repr. of 1882 ed. 18.00 (ISBN 0-8369-6915-4). Ayer Co Pubs.
Temple Scroll: An Introduction, Translation & Commentary. Johann Maier. (No. 34). xii, 147p. 1985. text ed. 28.50x (ISBN 1-85075-003-3, Pub. by JSOT Pr England); pap. text ed. 13.50x (ISBN 1-85075-004-1). Eisenbrauns.
Temple Talks: On Willingness to Be Wrong. 56p. 1978. pap. 2.95 (ISBN 0-933740-02-6). Mindbody Inc.
Temples & Idol Worship. Panduranga R. Malyala. Date not set. 4.99 (ISBN 0-938924-02-8). Sri Shirdi Sai.
Temples & Temple-Service in Ancient Israel. Menahem Haran. 416p. 1985. Repr. of 1978 ed. text ed. 20.00x (ISBN 0-931464-18-8). Eisenbrauns.
Temples & Tombs of Ancient Nubia. Ed. by Torgny Save-Soderbergh. LC 86-50517. (Illus.). 1987. 29.95 (ISBN 0-500-01392-6). Thames Hudson.
Temples, Churches & Mosques: A Guide to the Appreciation of Religious Architecture. J. G. Davies. LC 82-13130. (Illus.). 256p. 1982. 27.50 (ISBN 0-8298-0634-2). Pilgrim NY.
Temples of Anking & Their Cults, a Study of Modern Chinese Religion. John K. Shryock. LC 70-38083. Repr. of 1931 ed. 26.00 (ISBN 0-404-56947-1). AMS Pr.
Temples of Napal: An Introductory Survey. Ronald M. Bernier. (Illus.). 247p. 1970. text ed. 27.50x. Coronet Bks.
Temples of Nepal. Ronald M. Bernier. 204p. 25.00X (ISBN 0-317-52159-4, Pub. by S Chand India). State Mutual Bk.
Temporal Man: The Meaning & Uses of Social Time. Robert H. Lauer. LC 81-11917. 192p. 1981. 34.95 (ISBN 0-03-059719-6). Praeger.
Temptation. Jack Coombe. 1984. pap. 6.95 (ISBN 0-89896-127-0). Larksdale.
Temptation: Help for Struggling Christians. Charles Durham. LC 82-153. 164p. (Orig.). 1982. pap. 4.95 (ISBN 0-87784-382-1). Inter-Varsity.
Temptation: How Christians Can Deal with It. Frances L. Carroll. 192p. 1984. 13.95 (ISBN 0-13-903229-0); pap. 5.95 (ISBN 0-13-903211-8). P-H.
Temptation (Magazine Format, No. 3. John C. Souter. 64p. 1984. 4.95 (ISBN 0-8423-6957-0). Tyndale.
Temptation of Christ. John Bale. LC 74-133636. (Tudor Facsimile Texts. Old English Plays: No. 22). Repr. of 1909 ed. 49.50 (ISBN 0-404-53322-1). AMS Pr.
Temptation of Jesus. Mervin A. Marquardt. (Arch Bks.). (Illus.). 24p. 1986. pap. 0.99 saddlestitched (ISBN 0-570-06204-7, 59-1427). Concordia.
Temptation of Saint Anthony. Gustave Flaubert. Tr. by Kitty Mrosovsky. LC 80-70452. (Illus.). 288p. 1981. 29.95x (ISBN 0-8014-1239-0). Cornell U Pr.
Temptations for the Theology of Liberation. Bonaventure Kloppenberg. (Synthesis Ser.). 1974. 0.75 (ISBN 0-8199-0362-0). Franciscan Herald.
Temptations of Jesus. Howard Thurman. LC 78-74718. 1979. pap. 3.95 (ISBN 0-913408-47-6). Friends United.
Tempted by Happiness: Razantzakis Post-Christian Christ. Peter Bien. 1984. pap. 2.50x (ISBN 0-317-12307-6, 253). Pendle Hill.
Temurah, 1 vol. 15.00 (ISBN 0-910218-84-6). Bennet Pub.
Ten Basic Steps Teachers Manual. 2nd ed. Bill Bright. 512p. 1983. pap. 8.95 (ISBN 0-918956-97-8). Campus Crusade.
Ten Catholics: Lives to Remember. Kenneth Christopher. (Nazareth Bks). 120p. 1983. pap. 3.95 (ISBN 0-86683-715-9, HarpR). Har-Row.
Ten Christians: By Their Deeds You Shall Know Them. Boniface Hanley. LC 79-53836. (Illus.). 272p. (Orig.). 1979. pap. 6.95 (ISBN 0-87793-183-6). Ave Maria.
Ten Commandments. Maureen Curley. (Children of the Kingdom Activities Ser.). 1976. 9.95 (ISBN 0-89837-015-9, Pub. by Pflaum Pr). Peter Li.
Ten Commandments. Emmet Fox. LC 53-8369. 1953. 12.45 (ISBN 0-06-062990-8, HarpR). Har-Row.
Ten Commandments. Joseph Lewis. 644p. cancelled (ISBN 0-911826-36-X). Am Atheist.
Ten Commandments. Lawrence G. Lovasik. (Saint Joseph Picture Bks.). (Illus.). flexible bdg. 0.95 (ISBN 0-89942-287-X, 287). Catholic Bk Pub.
Ten Commandments. G. Campbell Morgan. (Morgan Library). 1974. pap. 3.95 (ISBN 0-8010-5954-2). Baker Bk.
Ten Commandments. J. I. Packer. 1982. pap. 3.95 (ISBN 0-8423-7004-8); leader's guide 2.95 (ISBN 0-8423-7005-6). Tyndale.
Ten Commandments. Arthur W. Pink. pap. 2.50 (ISBN 0-685-00740-5). Reiner.
Ten Commandments. Thomas Watson. 245p. pap. 8.45 (ISBN 0-85151-146-5). Banner of Truth.
Ten Commandments & Human Rights. Walter Harrelson. Ed. by Walter Brueggemann & John R. Donahue. LC 77-15234. (Overtures to Biblical Theology Ser.). 240p. 1980. pap. 10.95 (ISBN 0-8006-1527-1, 1-1527). Fortress.
Ten Commandments & the Sermon on the Mount. Rudolf Steiner. Tr. by Frieda Solomon from Ger. 44p. 1978. pap. 2.00 (ISBN 0-910142-79-3). Anthroposophic.
Ten Commandments & Today's Christian. Finbarr Connolly & Peter Burns. 48p. 1985. pap. 1.50 (ISBN 0-89243-233-0). Liguori Pubns.
Ten Commandments for Today. William Barclay. LC 83-6103. 208p. (Orig.). 1983. pap. 7.95 (ISBN 0-06-060417-4, RD 476, HarpR). Har-Row.
Ten Commandments for Wives. Benny Bristow. pap. 4.95 (ISBN 0-89137-430-2). Quality Pubns.
Ten Commandments in Today's World. George Drew. 48p. (Orig.). 1979. pap. 6.95 (ISBN 0-940754-00-2). Ed Ministries.
Ten Commandments: Learning about God's Law. G. A. Truitt. LC 56-1398. (Concept Bks.: Series 4). 1983. pap. 3.95 (ISBN 0-570-08527-6). Concordia.
Ten Commandments: Then & Now. Jim Lewis. LC 84-50912. 95p. (Orig.). 1984. pap. 5.95 (ISBN 0-942482-07-7). Unity Church Denver.
Ten Commandments Yesterday & Today. James B. Coffman. pap. 4.50 (ISBN 0-88027-094-2). Firm Foun Pub.
Ten Commandments: Youth & Adult Student. Carol E. Miller. 1971. pap. 0.85 (ISBN 0-915374-45-5). Rapids Christian.
Ten Dates for Mates. Dave Arp & Claudia Arp. LC 83-3954. 176p. 1983. pap. 7.95 (ISBN 0-8407-5845-6). Nelson.
Ten Days in the Light of 'Akka. rev. ed. Julia M. Grundy. LC 79-12177. 1979. pap. 6.95 (ISBN 0-87743-131-0, 332-040). Baha'i.
Ten Decisive Battles of Christianity. Frank S. Mead. LC 72-117823. (Essay Index Reprint Ser). 1937. 15.00 (ISBN 0-8369-1812-6). Ayer Co Pubs.
Ten Dharma Realms Are Not Beyond a Single Thought. Tripitaka Master Hua. Tr. by Buddhist Text Translation Society. (Eng., Illus.). 72p. (Orig.). 1976. pap. 4.00 (ISBN 0-917512-12-X). Buddhist Text.
Ten Essays on Zionism & Judaism. Achad Ha-am, pseud. LC 73-2202. (Jewish People; History, Religion, Literature Ser.). Repr. of 1922 ed. 26.50 (ISBN 0-405-05267-7). Ayer Co Pubs.
Ten Fingers for God: The Complete Biography of Dr. Paul Brand. Dorothy C. Wilson. LC 82-24600. 288p. 1982. pap. 5.95 (ISBN 0-8407-5834-0). Nelson.
Ten for Our Time. Lowell Erdahl. 1986. 5.50 (ISBN 0-89536-786-6, 6804). CSS of Ohio.
Ten Four-Part Motets for the Church's Year. Giovanni P. Palestrina. Tr. by Alec Harman. (Lat. & Eng.). 1964. 9.95 (ISBN 0-19-353332-4). Oxford U Pr.
Ten Grandmothers. Alice Marriott. LC 45-1584. (Civilization of the American Indians Ser.: Vol. 26). 306p. 1985. pap. 9.95 (ISBN 0-8061-1825-3). U of Okla Pr.
Ten Hands for God. J. Harry Haines. 80p. (Orig.). 1983. pap. 3.50 (ISBN 0-8358-0449-6). Upper Room.
Ten Ideas That Make a Difference. Ernest Holmes. Ed. by Willis H. Kinnear. 96p. 1966. pap. 4.50 (ISBN 0-911336-32-X). Sci of Mind.
Ten Lives of the Buddha: Siamese Temple Paintings & Jataka Tales. Elizabeth Wray et al. LC 73-179982. (Illus.). 156p. 1972. 20.00 (ISBN 0-8348-0067-5). Weatherhill.
Ten Luminous Emanations, Vol. 1. Yehuda Ashlag. 1970. 11.95 (ISBN 0-943688-08-6); pap. 9.95 (ISBN 0-943688-29-9). Res Ctr Kabbalah.
Ten Luminous Emanations, Vol. 2. Yehuda Ashlag. Ed. by Philip S. Berg. 1972. 11.95 (ISBN 0-943688-09-4); pap. 9.95 (ISBN 0-943688-25-6). Res Ctr Kabbalah.
Ten Miracles. J. H. Collins. 1975. pap. 0.50 (ISBN 0-8198-0479-7). Dghtrs St Paul.
Ten New England Leaders. Williston Walker. LC 76-83445. (Religion in America Ser). 1969. Repr. of 1901 ed. 28.00 (ISBN 0-405-00278-5). Ayer Co Pubs.
Ten Pennies for Jesus. Alton Ward. (Illus.). 24p. (Orig.). 1986. pap. 3.50 (ISBN 0-570-04132-5, 56-1560). Concordia.
Ten Personal Studies. Wilfrid P. Ward. LC 73-107742. (Essay Index Reprint Ser.). 1908. 21.00 (ISBN 0-8369-1584-4). Ayer Co Pubs.
Ten Plus One Bible Stories from Creation to Samson, Retold in Everyday Language for Today's Children. John Behnke. LC 83-82022. (Orig.). 1984. pap. 2.95 (ISBN 0-8091-6552-X). Paulist Pr.
Ten Principal Upanishads. Swami S. Patanjali. Tr. by W. B. Yeats. (Orig.). 1970. pap. 5.95 (ISBN 0-571-09363-9). Faber & Faber.
Ten Principal Upanishads. A. Wade. 75.00 (ISBN 0-8490-1183-3). Gordon Pr.
Ten Principal Upanishads. William B. Yeats & Swami Shree. 1975. pap. 6.95 (ISBN 0-02-071550-1, Collier). Macmillan.
Ten Questions on Prayer. Gerald Heard. LC 51-10133. (Orig.). 1951. pap. 2.50x (ISBN 0-87574-058-8, 058). Pendle Hill.
Ten Religions of the East. Edward Rice. LC 78-6186. (Illus.). 160p. 1978. 8.95 (ISBN 0-02-776210-6, Four Winds). Macmillan.
Ten Rungs: Hasidic Sayings. Martin Buber. LC 62-13135. 1962. pap. 3.95 (ISBN 0-8052-0018-5). Schocken.
Ten Sails in the Sunrise. Allan Campbell. 200p. 1986. 14.95 (ISBN 0-317-39595-5). C I L Inc.
Ten Series of Meditations on the Mysteries of the Rosary. John Ferraro. (Illus., Orig.). 1964. 5.00 (ISBN 0-8198-0157-7); pap. 4.00 (ISBN 0-8198-0158-5). Dghtrs St Paul.
Ten Signs of Faith. Hassan Kazemi. Ed. by Helen Graves. LC 85-51959. 154p. 1986. 8.95 (ISBN 1-55523-012-1). Winston-Derek.
Ten Steps for Church Growth. Donald A. McGavran & Winfield C. Arn. LC 76-62950. 1977. pap. 6.95 (ISBN 0-06-065352-3, RD 215, HarpR). Har-Row.
Ten Steps to the Good Life. Harold J. Brokke. LC 75-44926. 160p. 1976. pap. 1.95 (ISBN 0-87123-332-0, 200332). Bethany Hse.
Ten Steps to Victory over Depression. Tim LaHaye. 1974. pap. 1.50 (ISBN 0-310-27002-2, 18074P). Zondervan.
Ten Super Sunday Schools in the Black Community. Sidney Smith. LC 86-926. 1986. pap. 5.95 (ISBN 0-8054-6252-X). Broadman.
Ten Tests of Abraham. Shoshana Lepon. (Bible Series for Young Children). (Illus.). 32p. (Orig.). 1986. 7.95 (ISBN 0-317-52412-7); pap. 5.95 (ISBN 0-910818-67-3). Judaica Pr.
Ten Theologians Respond to the Unification Church. Herbert Richardson. LC 81-70679. 199p. 1981. pap. 10.95. Rose Sharon Pr.
Ten Theologians Respond to the Unification Church. Ed. by Herbert Richardson. LC 81-70679. (Conference Ser.: No. 10). xv, 199p. (Orig.). 1981. pap. text ed. 9.95 (ISBN 0-932894-10-0, Pub. by New Era Bks). Paragon Hse.
Ten Thousand Illustrations from the Bible. Charles Little. pap. 15.95 (ISBN 0-8010-5606-3). Baker Bk.
Ten Timely Truths. Don DeWelt. 1949. pap. 2.00 (ISBN 0-89900-135-1). College Pr Pub.
Ten True Tales of Reincarnation. Tilly H. Gandy. 1984. 6.00 (ISBN 0-8062-2292-1). Carlton.
Ten Ways to Meditate. Paul Reps. LC 70-83639. (Illus.). 64p. 1981. 9.95 (ISBN 0-8348-0163-9). Weatherhill.
Ten Words of Freedom: An Introduction to the Faith of Israel. LC 75-139344. pap. 60.00 (2026879). Bks Demand UMI.
Ten Words That Will Change Your Life. Ervin Seale. 192p. 1972. pap. 6.95 (ISBN 0-911336-38-9). Sci of Mind.
Ten Years in Oregon. Daniel Lee & Joseph H. Frost. LC 72-9457. (Far Western Frontier Ser.). (Illus.). 348p. 1973. Repr. of 1844 ed. 24.50 (ISBN 0-405-04985-4). Ayer Co Pubs.
Tenacity of Prejudice: Anti-Semitism in Contemporary America. Gertude J. Selznick & Stephen Steinberg. LC 78-31365. (Univ of California Five-Year Study of Anti-Semitism). (Illus.). 1979. Repr. of 1969 ed. lib. bdg. 24.75x (ISBN 0-313-20965-0, SETP). Greenwood.
Tender Shepherd. John Killinger. 208p. (Orig.). 1985. pap. 9.95 (ISBN 0-687-41242-0). Abingdon.
Tender Touch: Biogenic Fulfillment. Edmond B. Szekely. (Illus.). 120p. 1977. text ed. 5.50 (ISBN 0-89564-020-1). IBS Intl.
Tenderly I Care. Albert J. Nimeth. 1977. 5.00 (ISBN 0-685-85844-8). Franciscan Herald.
Tending & Teaching Babies. Lynda T. Boardman. 83p. (Orig.). 1985. pap. 3.50 (ISBN 0-8341-1063-6). Beacon Hill.
Tending the Family Tree: A Family-Centered, Bible-Based Experience for Church Groups. Mary Y. Nilsen. 80p. (Orig.). 1982. pap. 7.95 (ISBN 0-86683-169-X, HarpR). Har-Row.
Tending the Garden: Essays on the Gospel & the Earth. Ed. by Wes Granberg-Michaelson. 176p. (Orig.). 1987. pap. 8.95 (ISBN 0-8028-0230-3). Eerdmans.
Tending the Light. Mary E. Feagins. 1984. pap. 2.50x (ISBN 0-87574-255-6, 255). Pendle Hill.
Tenets of Islam. A. M. Muhajir. 1969. 7.25x (ISBN 0-87902-107-1). Orientalia.
Tenets of Islam. 12.50 (ISBN 0-686-18485-8). Kazi Pubns.

Tennyson an Occultist. A. P. Sinnett. LC 72-2102. (Studies in Tennyson, No. 27). 1972. Repr. of 1920 ed. lib. bdg. 46.95x (ISBN 0-8383-1485-6). Haskell.

Tennyson's Use of the Bible. Edna M. Robinson. 119p. 1968. Repr. of 1917 ed. 12.50x (ISBN 0-87752-093-3). Gordian.

Tension Getters. Wayne Rice & Mike Yaconelli. 128p. (Orig.). (YA) 1985. pap. 6.95 (ISBN 0-310-45241-4, 11371P). Zondervan.

Tension Getters II. rev. ed. Wayne Rice & Mike Yaconelli. (Orig.). 1985. pap. 6.95 (ISBN 0-310-34931-1, 10774P). Zondervan.

Tensions Between the Churches of the First World & the Third World, Vol. 144. Ed. by Virgil Elizondo & Norbert Greinacher. (Concilium 1981). 128p. (Orig.). 1981. pap. 6.95 (ISBN 0-8164-2311-3, HarpR). Har-Row.

Tensions in American Puritanism. R. Reinitz. LC 70-100325. (Problems in American History Ser.). pap. 52.00 (ISBN 0-8357-9991-3, 2019292). Bks Demand UMI.

Tensions in Contemporary Theology. 2nd ed. Ed. by Stanley N. Gundry & Alan F. Johnson. 478p. 1983. pap. 15.95 (ISBN 0-8010-3796-4). Baker Bk.

Tensions in the Connection. R. Sheldon Dueuker. 128p. 1983. pap. 4.95 (ISBN 0-687-41243-9). Abingdon.

Tent Life in the Holy Land. William C. Prime. Ed. by Moshe Davis. LC 77-70734. (America & the Holy Land Ser.). (Illus.). 1977. Repr. of 1857 ed. lib. bdg. 38.50x (ISBN 0-405-10278-X). Ayer Co Pubs.

Tent of Meeting Catalogue & Guide. Ed. by Anna Walton. 40p. (Orig.). 1985. 5.00 (ISBN 0-9615531-1-1). Tent Meeting.

Tent of Meeting Texts. Ed. by John Menken. (Illus.). 134p. (Orig.). 1985. pap. 8.00 (ISBN 0-9615531-0-3). Tent Meeting.

Tentatio et Consolatio: Studien zu Bugenhagens Interpretatio in Librum Psalmorum. Hans H. Holfelder. LC 73-80563. (Arbeiten Zur Kirchengeschichte, Vol. 46). (Ger.). 132p. 1974. 35.60 (ISBN 3-11-004327-0). De Gruyter.

Tenth Famine: Judaism Without God. Bat Yaakov. 96p. (Orig.). 1986. pap. 7.95 (ISBN 0-9617361-0-0). Bat Yaakov Pubns.

Tenth Generation: The Origins of the Biblical Tradition. George E. Mendenhall. 266p. 1973. 25.00x (ISBN 0-8018-1267-4); pap. 8.95x (ISBN 0-8018-1654-8). Johns Hopkins.

Teologia de la Liberaction: Una Introduccion. Robert Compton. (Span.). 112p. (Orig.). 1985. pap. 3.75 (ISBN 0-311-09106-7). Casa Bautista.

Teologia del Nuevo Testamento. Frank Stagg. Tr. by Arnoldo Canclini. 346p. 1985. pap. 9.95 (ISBN 0-311-09077-X). Casa Bautista.

Teresa: A Woman; A Biography of Teresa of Avila. Victoria Lincoln. Ed. by Elias Rivers & Antonio T. De Nicolas. LC 84-8561. (Series in Cultural Perspectives). 440p. 1984. 44.50x (ISBN 0-87395-936-1); pap. 16.95 (ISBN 0-87395-937-X). State U NY Pr.

Teresa of Avila: The Interior Castle. Tr. by Kieran Kavanaugh & Otilio Rodrigues. LC 79-66484. (Classics of Western Spirituality Ser.). 256p. 1979. 12.95 (ISBN 0-8091-0303-6); pap. 9.95 (ISBN 0-8091-2254-5). Paulist Pr.

Teresa of Calcutta. D. Jeanene Watson. LC 84-60313. (Sowers Ser.). 1984. 8.95 (ISBN 0-88062-013-7); pap. 4.95 (ISBN 0-88062-012-9). Mott Media.

Terra Christa. Ken Carey. (Illus.). 237p. 1986. pap. 9.95 (ISBN 0-913299-31-6, Dist. by NAL). Stillpoint.

Terra Christa: The Global Spiritual Awakening. Ken Carey. Ed. by Jim Gross. 256p. (Orig.). 1985. pap. 7.95t (ISBN 0-912949-02-3). Uni-Sun.

Terrace of the Great God at Abydos: The Offering Chapels of Dynasties 12 & 13, Vol. 5. William K. Simpson. LC 73-88231. 1974. 25.00 (ISBN 0-686-05519-5). Penn-Yale Expedit.

Terracotta Figurines from Kourion in Cyprus. J. H. Young & S. H. Young. (University Museum Monographs: No. 11). (Illus.). x, 260p. 1955. 16.50x (ISBN 0-934718-03-2). Univ Mus of U PA.

Terrifying Goal of the Ecumenical Movement. Dr. G. Wasserzug. 1.45 (ISBN 0-937422-77-0). Midnight Call.

Territorial Dimension of Judaism. W. D. Davies. LC 81-53. (Quantum Bk.). 160p. 1982. 15.95x (ISBN 0-520-04331-6). U of Cal Pr.

Terror That Comes in the Night: An Experience Centered Study of Supernatural Assault Traditions. David J. Hufford. LC 82-40350. 352p. 1982. 27.50x (ISBN 0-8122-7851-8). U of Pa Pr.

Terry Bradshaw. Sam Hasegawa. (Sports Superstars Ser.). (Illus.). 1977. pap. 3.95 (ISBN 0-89812-212-0). Creative Ed.

Tertullian, the Treatise Against Hermogenes. Ed. by W. J. Burghardt et al. LC 56-13257. (Ancient Christian Writers Ser.: No. 24). 179p. 1956. 10.95 (ISBN 0-8091-0148-3). Paulist Pr.

Tertullian, Treatise on Marriage & Remarriage: To His Wife, an Exhortation to Chastity Monogamy. Ed. by W. J. Burghardt et al. LC 78-62462. (Ancient Christian Writers Ser.: No. 13). 103p. 1951. 10.95 (ISBN 0-8091-0149-1). Paulist Pr.

Tertullian, Treatise on Penance: On Penitence & on Purity. Ed. by W. J. Burghardt et al. LC 58-10746. (Ancient Christian Writers Ser.: No. 28). 138p. 1959. 12.95 (ISBN 0-8091-0150-5). Paulist Pr.

Teshuvah: A Guide for the Newly Observant Jew. Adin Steinsaltz. 192p. 1987. 19.95 (ISBN 0-02-931150-0). Free Pr.

Test of Faith: Challenges of Modern Day Christians. C. Michael Botterweck. 304p. (Orig.). 1983. pap. 8.95 (ISBN 0-911541-01-2). Gregory Pub.

Test Your Bible Power: A Good Book Quiz. Ed. by Stanley Shank. (Epiphany Bks.). 1983. pap. 1.95 (ISBN 0-345-30663-5). Ballantine.

Test Your Salvation. Kent A. Field. 0.60 (ISBN 0-89137-531-7). Quality Pubns.

Testament of Abraham. Ed. by M. R. James. (Texts & Studies: No. 1, Vol. 2, Pt. 2). pap. 19.00 (ISBN 0-8115-1685-7). Kraus Repr.

Testament of Abraham. Michael E. Stone. LC 72-88770. (Society of Biblical Literature. Texts & Translation-Psuedepigrapha Ser.). 1972. pap. 8.95 (ISBN 0-89130-170-4, 060202). Scholars Pr GA.

Testament of Adam: An Examination of the Syriac & Greek Traditions. Stephen E. Robinson. LC 80-12209. (Society of Biblical Literature Dissertation Ser.: No. 52). pap. 13.50 (ISBN 0-89130-399-5, 06-01-52). Scholars Pr GA.

Testament of Cain. Tr. by Keith Bradfield from Swedish. Kieth Bradfield. cancelled (ISBN 0-86538-019-8); pap. cancelled (ISBN 0-686-32482-X). Ontario Rev NJ.

Testament of Devotion. Thomas R. Kelly. 1941. 12.45 (ISBN 0-06-064370-6, HarpR). Har-Row.

Testament of Jesus: A Study of the Gospel of John in the Light of Chapter 17. Ernst Kasemann. LC 78-104781. 96p. (Orig.). 1978. pap. 3.95 (ISBN 0-8006-1399-6, 1-1399). Fortress.

Testament of Jesus-Sophia: A Redaction-Critical Study of the Eschatological Discourse in Matthew. Fred W. Burnett. LC 80-67211. 491p. (Orig.). 1981. lib. bdg. 35.75 (ISBN 0-8191-1743-9); pap. text ed. 19.75 (ISBN 0-8191-1744-7). U Pr of Amer.

Testament of Job. Robert A. Kraft. LC 74-15201. (Society of Biblical Literature. Text & Translation-Psuedepigrapha Ser.: No. 5). pap. 17.70 (ISBN 0-8357-9580-2, 2017530). Bks Demand UMI.

Testaments of Love: A Study of Love in the Bible. Leon Morris. (Orig.). 1981. 12.95 (ISBN 0-8028-3502-3). Eerdmans.

Testaments of the Twelve Patriarchs: A Critical History of Research. H. Dixon Slingerland. LC 75-34233. (Society of Biblical Literature. Monograph). 1977. 13.50 (ISBN 0-89130-084-8, 060021); pap. 9.95 (ISBN 0-89130-062-7). Scholars Pr GA.

Tested by Temptation. W. Graham Scroggie. LC 79-2559. (W. Graham Scroggie Library). 76p. 1980. pap. 4.50 (ISBN 0-8254-3732-6). Kregel.

Testigos de Jehova. Walter Martin. 80p. 1982. 2.25 (ISBN 0-88113-285-3). Edit Betania.

Testigos de Jehova. M. W. Nelson. 130p. 1984. pap. 2.50 (ISBN 0-311-06352-7). Casa Bautista.

Testimonie of Antique. Abbot Aelfric. LC 73-36208. (English Experience Ser.: No. 214). Repr. of 1567 ed. 13.00 (ISBN 90-221-0214-9). Walter J Johnson.

Testimonies for the Church, 9 vols. Ellen G. White. 1948. 5.95 ea. (ISBN 0-8163-0152-2); Set. 79.95 (ISBN 0-8163-0153-0, 20140-0). Pacific Pr Pub Assn.

Testimonies in the Life, Character, Revelations, & Doctrines of Mother Ann Lee. 2nd ed. Shakers. LC 72-2994. Repr. of 1888 ed. 20.00 (ISBN 0-404-10756-7). AMS Pr.

Testimonies to Ministers. Ellen G. White. 10.95 (ISBN 0-317-28268-9). Pacific pr Pub Assn.

Testimony in Stone. J. Bernard Nicklin. 1961. 6.00 (ISBN 0-685-08818-9). Destiny.

Testimony of God. Watchman Nee. Tr. by Stephen Kaung. 1979. pap. 2.75 (ISBN 0-935008-44-6). Christian Fellow Pubs.

Testimony of God Against Slavery, or a Collection of Passages from the Bible, Which Show the Sin Holding Property in Man. La Roy Sunderland. LC 73-92444. 1970. Repr. of 1835 ed. 17.00x (ISBN 0-403-03707-7, 403-00183-8). Scholarly.

Testimony of Justin Martyr to Early Christianity. George T. Purves. 1977. lib. bdg. 59.95 (ISBN 0-8490-2735-7). Gordon Pr.

Testimony of the Evangelists. Simon Greenleaf. 640p. 1984. Repr. of 1874 ed. 19.95 (ISBN 0-8010-3803-0). Baker Bk.

Testimony of Two. Mary Youmans & Roger Youmans. pap. 7.95 (ISBN 0-910924-91-0). Macalester.

Testimony to Hilaire Belloc. Eleanor Jebb & Reginald Jebb. 1956. 25.00 (ISBN 0-8274-3587-8). R West.

Testing Myself As a Prophet. large print ed. Charline Brians. 1985. pap. 5.00 (ISBN 0-914009-10-9). VHI Library.

Testing Tongues by the Word. Milikin. pap. 3.50 (ISBN 0-8054-1918-7). Broadman.

Tests of Eternal Life: Studies in First John. Herbert W. Butt. pap. 0.50 (ISBN 0-685-00745-6). Reiner.

Tests of Life. 3rd ed. Robert Law. (Thornapple Commentary Ser.). 1978. pap. 11.95 (ISBN 0-8010-5501-6). Baker Bk.

Teufelbuecher in Auswahl, 3 vols. Ed. by Ria Stambaugh. (Ausgaben Deutscher Literatur des 15. bis 18. Jahrh). (Ger). Vol. 1, 1970. write for info (ISBN 3-11-006388-3); Vol. 2, 1972. 112.00x (ISBN 3-11-003924-9); Vol. 3, 1973. 141.00x (ISBN 3-11-004127-8). De Gruyter.

Teutonic Legends in the Nibelungen Lied & the Nibelungen Ring. W. C. Sawyer. 1976. lib. bdg. 59.95 (ISBN 0-8490-2736-5). Gordon Pr.

Teutonic Myth & Legend. Donald A. MacKenzie. LC 77-91530. 1978. Repr. of 1912 ed. lib. bdg. 50.00 (ISBN 0-89341-313-5). Longwood Pub Group.

Texas & Christmas: A Collection of Traditions, Memories & Folklore. Ed. by Judy Alter & Joyce G. Roach. LC 83-4717. (Illus.). 86p. 1983. pap. 6.50 (ISBN 0-912646-81-0). Tex Christian.

Texas Baptist Leadership & Social Christianity, 1900-1980. John W. Storey. LC 85-40747. (Texas A&M Southwestern Studies: No. 5). (Illus.). 237p. 1986. 22.50x (ISBN 0-89096-251-0). Tex A&M Univ Pr.

Texas Cannibals, or, Why Father Serra Came to California. Sibley S. Morrill. 28p. 1964. octavo wrappers 5.00 (ISBN 0-910740-04-6). Holmes.

Texas Christmas, Vol. II. Ed. by John E. Weems. 130p. 1986. 19.95 (ISBN 0-939722-30-5). Pressworks.

Text & Context: Old Testament & Semitic Studies for F.C. Fensham. W. Claassen. (JSOT Supplement Ser.: No. 48). 220p. 1987. text ed. 28.50x (ISBN 1-85075-040-8, Pub. by JSOT Pr England). Eisenbrauns.

Text & Iconography of Joinville's Credo. Lionel J. Friedman. LC 58-7918. 1958. 12.00x (ISBN 0-910956-42-1). Medieval Acad.

Text & Image in Fifteenth-Century Illustrated Dutch Bibles (1977) Sandra Hindman. (Corpus Sacrae Scripturae Neerlandicae Medii Aevi Ser.: Miscellanea: Vol. 1). (Illus.). 35.00 (ISBN 90-04-04901-0). Heinman.

Text & Interpretation: A Practical Commentary, Revelation. L. Van Hartingsveld. Ed. by A. S. Van Der Woude. (Text & Interpretation Ser.). (Dutch.). 128p. (Orig.). 1985. pap. 6.95 (ISBN 0-8028-0100-5). Eerdmans.

Text & Interpretation: Studies in the New Testament. Ed. by Ernest Best & R. McL. Wilson. LC 78-2962. pap. 71.50 (ISBN 0-317-26088-X, 2024416). Bks Demand UMI.

Text & Reality: Aspects of Reference in Biblical Texts. Bernard C. Lategan & Willem S. Vorster. LC 85-47735. 144p. 1985. pap. 9.95 (ISBN 0-8006-1514-X). Fortress.

Text & Reality: Aspects of Reference in Biblical Texts. Bernard C. Lategan & Willem S. Vorster. 14.95 (ISBN 0-89130-822-9, 06 06 14); pap. 9.95 (ISBN 0-89130-823-7). Scholars Pr GA.

Text & Texture: Close Readings of Selected Biblical Texts. Michael Fishbane. LC 79-14083. 154p. 1982. pap. 7.95 (ISBN 0-8052-0726-0). Schocken.

Text-Critical Methodology & the Pre-Caesarean Text. Larry Hurtado. 112p. (Orig.). 1981. pap. 15.00x (ISBN 0-8028-1872-2). Eerdmans.

Text of Piers Plowman. R. W. Chambers. LC 72-195253. lib. bdg. 10.00 (ISBN 0-8414-3015-2). Folcroft.

Text of the Epistles: A Disquisition upon the Corpus Paulinum. G. Zuntz. (Schweich Lectures on Biblical Archaeology). 306p. 1946. 8.25 (ISBN 0-85672-715-6, Pub. by British Acad). Longwood Pub Group.

Text of the Greek Bible. 3rd, rev. ed. F. G. Kenyon. 1975. 40.50 (ISBN 0-7156-0641-7, Pub. by Duckworth London); pap. 13.50 (ISBN 0-7156-0652-2). Longwood Pub Group.

Text of the Holocaust: A Documentation of the Nazis' Extermination Propaganda from 1919-45. C. C. Aronsfeld. 1985. 16.00 (ISBN 0-916288-17-X); pap. 10.00 (ISBN 0-916288-18-8). Micah Pubns.

Text of the New Testament. Kurt Aland & Barbara Aland. Tr. by Erroll F. Rhodes from Ger. (Illus.). 344p. 1987. 29.95x (ISBN 0-8028-3620-8). Eerdmans.

Text of the New Testament: Its Transmission, Corruption, & Restoration. 2nd ed. Bruce M. Metzger. 1968. 13.95x (ISBN 0-19-500391-8). Oxford U Pr.

Text of the Old Testament. E. Naville. (British Academy, London, Schweich Lectures in Biblical Archaeology Series, 1915). pap. 19.00 (ISBN 0-8115-1257-6). Kraus Repr.

Text of the Old Testament. Ernst Wurthwein. Tr. by Erroll F. Rhodes. LC 79-15492. Tr. of Text Des Alten Testaments. (Illus.). 1980. text ed. 16.95 (ISBN 0-8028-3530-9). Eerdmans.

Text of the Septuagint: Its Corruptions & Their Emendation. Peter Katz. Ed. by D. W. Gooding. LC 74-161292. pap. 110.00 (ISBN 0-317-28405-3, 2022451). Bks Demand UMI.

Textbook of Christian Ethics. Robin Gill. 571p. 1986. pap. 19.95 (ISBN 0-567-29127-8, Pub. by T & T Clark Ltd UK). Fortress.

Textbook of Theosophy. Leadbeater. 6.95 (ISBN 0-8356-7110-0). Theos Pub Hse.

Textbook of Yoga. Yogeswar. (Illus.). 574p. 1980. 24.95x (ISBN 0-940500-37-X). Asia Bk Corp.

Texte und Untersuchungen Zur Safatenisch - Arabischen Religion. Hubert Grimme. 1929. pap. 15.00 (ISBN 0-384-20070-2). Johnson Repr.

Textos Encogidoes de la Reforma Radical. Ed. by John H. Yoder. (Span.). 500p. (Orig.). 1984. pap. 25.00 (ISBN 0-8361-1237-7). Herald Pr.

Texts & Manuscripts: Litterae Textuales. Ed. by J. P. Gumbert & M. J. De Haan. (Illus.). 110p. 1972. 46.50 (ISBN 0-8390-0105-3). Abner Schram Ltd.

Texts & Studies. Saul Lieberman. 1973. 35.00x (ISBN 0-87068-210-5). Ktav.

Texts & Studies in Jewish History & Literature, 2 Vols. rev. ed. Jacob Mann. 1970. Set. 99.50x (ISBN 0-87068-085-4). Ktav.

Texts & Testaments: Critical Essays on the Bible & Early Church Fathers. Ed. by W. Eugene March. LC 79-92585. 321p. 1980. 15.00 (ISBN 0-911536-80-9). Trinity U Pr.

Texts from the Buddhist Canon. Dhammapada. Tr. by Samuel Beal from Chin. LC 78-72420. Repr. of 1878 ed. 22.50 (ISBN 0-404-17284-9). AMS Pr.

Texts in Transit. Graydon Snyder & Kenneth Shaffer. (Orig.). 1976. pap. 2.95 (ISBN 0-685-61334-8). Brethren.

Texts of Taoism, 2 vols. Tr. by James Legge. Ed. by F. Max Muller. 396p. 1891. Vol. 1. pap. 6.95 (ISBN 0-486-20990-3); Vol. 2. pap. 6.95 (ISBN 0-486-20991-1). Dover.

Texts of Taoism: The Sacred Books of China, 2 Vols. Tr. by J. Legge. (Sacred Books of the East Ser). 28.50 set (ISBN 0-8446-3059-4). Peter Smith.

Texts of Terror: Literary-Feminist Readings of Biblical Narratives. Phyllis Trible. LC 83-48906. (Overtures to Biblical Theology Ser.). 144p. 1984. pap. 8.95 (ISBN 0-8006-1537-9, 1-1537). Fortress.

Texts on Zulu Religion: Traditional Zulu Ideas about God. Ed. by Irving Hexham. (African Studies). 496p. 1987. text ed. 69.95 (ISBN 0-88946-181-3). E Mellen.

Textual & Subject Indexes of C. H. Spurgeon's Sermons. C. H. Spurgeon. (Key to the Metropolitan Tabernacle Pulpit set). 1971. 2.95 (ISBN 0-686-09095-0). Pilgrim Pubns.

Textual Commentary on the Greek New Testament. Ed. by Bruce M. Metzger. 776p. 1975. 5.45x (ISBN 3-438-06010-8, 08515, Pub. by United Bible). Am Bible.

Textual Concordance of the Holy Scriptures: (Bible Passages Taken from the Douay-Rheims Bible) Ed. by Thomas D. Williams. LC 85-52025. 848p. (Orig.). 1985. Repr. of 1908 ed. pap. 30.00 (ISBN 0-89555-286-8). Tan Bks Pubs.

Textual Criticism of the Old Testament: The Septuagint After Qumran. Ralph W. Klein. Ed. by Gene M. Tucker. LC 74-80420. (Guides to Biblical Scholarship: Old Testament Ser.). 96p. (Orig.). 1974. pap. 3.95 (ISBN 0-8006-1087-3, 1-1087). Fortress.

Textual Criticism: Recovering the Text of the Hebrew Bible. P. Kyle McCarter, Jr. LC 86-4388. (Guides to Biblical Scholarship, Old Testament Ser.). 96p. 1986. pap. 4.95 (ISBN 0-8006-0471-7, 1-471). Fortress.

Textual Studies in Hinduism. Arvind Sharma. 1980. lib. bdg. 14.95x (ISBN 0-914914-15-4). New Horizons.

Textual Studies in Hinduism. Arvind Sharma. 1985. 12.50x (ISBN 0-8364-1291-5, Pub. by Manohar India). South Asia Bks.

Textual Studies in the Book of Joshua. Leonard Greenspoon. LC 83-3434. (Harvard Semitic Monographs). 412p. 1983. 21.75 (ISBN 0-89130-622-6, 04 00 28). Scholars Pr GA.

Texture of Knowledge: An Essay on Religion & Science. James W. Jones. LC 80-69036. 112p. 1981. lib. bdg. 23.00 (ISBN 0-8191-1360-3); pap. text ed. 8.50 (ISBN 0-8191-1361-1). U Pr of Amer.

Teyku: The Unsolved Problem in the Babylonian Talmus. Louis Jacobs. LC 80-70887. 312p. 1981. 20.00 (ISBN 0-8453-4501-X, Cornwall Bks). Assoc Univ Prs.

Thai Buddhism: Its Rites & Activities. Kenneth E. Wells. LC 77-87081. (Illus.). viii, 320p. Repr. of 1960 ed. 34.50 (ISBN 0-404-16876-0). AMS Pr.

Thai Values & Behavior Patterns. Robert L. Mole. LC 71-130419. (Illus.). 1971. 4.75 (ISBN 0-8048-0947-X). C E Tuttle.

Thailand: Buddhist Kingdom As Modern Nation State. Charles F. Keyes. (Profiles-Nations of Contemporary Asia Ser.). 240p. 1987. 32.50 (ISBN 0-86531-138-2). Westview.

Thanatology Abstracts 1979. Otto S. Margolis & Daniel J. Cherico. 15.00 (ISBN 0-405-14222-6, 19702). Ayer Co Pubs.

Thank God Ahead of Time: The Life & Spirituality of Solanus Casey. Michael H. Crosby. 1985. 9.50 (ISBN 0-8199-0879-7). Franciscan Herald.

Thank God for Everything. Frederick K. Price. 31p. pap. 0.75 mini-bk. (ISBN 0-89274-056-6). Harrison Hse.

Thank God for My Breakdown. Walter Reiss. 1980. 4.95 (ISBN 0-8100-0114-4, 12N1717). Northwest Pub.

Thank God for New Churches! Church Planting: Source of New Life. James H. Lehman. 108p. (Orig.). 1984. pap. 6.95 (ISBN 0-87178-840-3). Brethren.

Thank God for Prayer. Russell W. Lake. LC 83-50397. 293p. 1983. 5.95 (ISBN 0-87159-159-6). Unity School.

Thank God for the Crumbs. Bonnie Kotter. Ed. by Gerald Wheeler. (Banner Bks.). 96p. (Orig.). 1986. pap. 6.50 (ISBN 0-8280-0315-7). Review & Herald.

Thank God I Have a Teenager. Charles S. Mueller. LC 84-24363. 128p. (Orig.). 1985. pap. 5.95 (ISBN 0-8066-2126-5, 10-6239). Augsburg.

Thank God I'm a Teenager. Charles S. Mueller & Donald R. Bardill. LC 76-3854. 1976. pap. 5.95 (ISBN 0-8066-1536-2, 10-6242). Augsburg.

Thank God It's Friday: Meditations For Hard-Working Catholics. Andrew Costello. 1987. 12.95 (ISBN 0-88347-213-9). Thomas More.

Thank God, It's Monday! William E. Diehl. LC 81-71390. 192p. 1982. pap. 6.95 (ISBN 0-8006-1656-1, 1-1656). Fortress.

Thank You, Dad. Richard Haffey. (Greeting Book Line Ser.). 24p. (Orig.). 1986. pap. 1.50 (ISBN 0-89622-305-1). Twenty-Third.

Thank You for Being a Friend. Jill Briscoe. 192p. (Orig.). 1981. pap. 5.95 (ISBN 0-310-21851-9, 9261P). Zondervan.

Thank You for My Grandchild. Betty Isler. 1983. pap. 4.95 (ISBN 0-570-03915-0, 12-2850). Concordia.

Thank You for My Spouse. Jeanette Groth. LC 12-2826. 1983. pap. 2.50 (ISBN 0-570-03885-5). Concordia.

Thank You for the World. (Illus.). 16p. 1982. pap. 0.99 (ISBN 0-86683-655-1, AY8234, HarpR). Har-Row.

Thank You, God. Debby Anderson. (Sparkler Bks.). (Illus.). 1986. plastic comb bdg. 2.95 (ISBN 0-89191-931-7, 59311, Chariot Bks). Cook.

Thank You, God. Marian Bennett. (My Surprise Book Ser.). (Illus.). 10p. 1985. 4.95 (ISBN 0-87239-906-0, 2730). Standard Pub.

Thank You, God. Lucille E. Hein. (Illus.). 32p. 1981. pap. 3.50 (ISBN 0-8170-0912-4). Judson.

Thank You God. Gordon Stowell. (Little Fish Books About You & Me Ser.: III). 14p. 1984. mini-bk 0.59 (ISBN 0-8307-0960-6, 5608436). Regal.

Thank You God. (First Prayer Ser.). 2.95 (ISBN 0-86112-196-1, Pub. by Brimax Bks). Borden.

Thank You, God, for Water. Dorothy Mock. (Happy Day Bks.). (Illus.). 24p. 1985. 1.59 (ISBN 0-87239-880-3, 3680). Standard Pub.

Thank You, God: Prayers for Young Children. Ron Klug & Lyn Klug. LC 80-67800. 32p. (Orig.). 1980. pap. 3.95 (ISBN 0-8066-1862-0, 10-6243). Augsburg.

Thank You Lord. Louise Reece. (Illus.). 164p. (Orig.). 1983. pap. 3.95x (ISBN 0-9614264-0-3). Lovejoy Pr.

Thank You, Lord, for Little Things. Annice H. Brown. 3.95 (ISBN 0-8042-2580-X). John Knox.

Thank You, Lord, for My Home. Gigi Tchividjian. 1980. Repr. of 1979 ed. 3.95 (ISBN 0-89066-023-9). World Wide Pubs.

Thank You, Mom. Richard Haffey. (Greeting Book Line Ser.). 24p. (Orig.). 1986. pap. 1.50 (ISBN 0-89622-306-X). Twenty-Third.

Thank You Prayers. (Illus.). 16p. 1982. pap. 0.99 (ISBN 0-86683-654-3, AY8233, HarpR). Har-Row.

Thankful Praise. Keith Watkins. LC 86-24514. 192p. (Orig.). 1987. pap. 9.95 (ISBN 0-8272-3650-6). CBP.

Thankful Praise: A Studyguide. Cy Rowell. 24p. (Orig.). 1987. pap. 2.50 (ISBN 0-8272-3651-4). CBP.

Thanks Giving: Stewardship Sermons out of the Ethnic Minority Experience. Ed. by J. LaVon Kincaid, Sr. LC 83-73266. 88p. 1984. pap. text ed. 6.95 (ISBN 0-88177-007-8, DR007B). Discipleship Res.

Thanks Lord, I Needed That. Charlene Potterbaum. 1979. Repr. of 1977 ed. pocket size 2.95 (ISBN 0-88270-411-7, Pub. by Logos). Bridge Pub.

Thanks Songbook. Gary L. Johnson. 32p. 1980. pap. 2.50 (ISBN 0-87123-776-8, 280776). Bethany Hse.

Thanksgiving. Lee Wyndham. LC 63-13890. (Holiday Bks.). (Illus.). 1963. PLB 7.56 (ISBN 0-8116-6551-8). Garrard.

Thanksgiving for a Liberated Prophet: An Interpretation of Isaiah Chapter Fifty-Three. R. N. Whybray. (Journal for the Study of the Old Testament Supplement Ser.: No. 4). 184p. 1978. (Pub. by JSOT Pr England); pap. text ed. 10.95 (ISBN 0-905774-04-3, Pub. by JSOT Pr England). Eisenbrauns.

That Better Country. John Barrett. 1966. 15.50x (ISBN 0-522-83525-2, Pub. by Melbourne U Pr). Intl Spec Bk.

That Christ May Live in Me. James Alberione. 1980. 3.50 (ISBN 0-8198-7300-4); pap. 2.25 (ISBN 0-8198-7301-2). Dghtrs St Paul.

That Door with the Lock. James Petty & Frances Petty. 1973. pap. 2.95 (ISBN 0-88428-023-3, 314). Parchment Pr.

That Everyone May Hear. 3rd ed. Ed. by Edward R. Dayton. 91p. 1983. pap. 4.60 (ISBN 0-912552-41-7). Missions Adv Res Com Ctr.

That Everyone May Hear: Workbook. Edward R. Dayton. pap. 5.75 (ISBN 0-912552-53-0). Missions Adv Res Com Ctr.

That Frenchman, John Calvin. Robert W. Miles. LC 83-45625. Date not set. Repr. of 1939 ed. 29.00 (ISBN 0-404-19843-0). AMS Pr.

That Friday in Eden. Alberta Mazat. (Redwood Ser.). 1981. pap. 4.95 (ISBN 0-8163-0401-7). Pacific Pr Pub Assn.

That I May Know. George Stob. 128p. 1982. pap. 3.95 (ISBN 0-933140-51-7); pap. 3.95 student wkbk (ISBN 0-933140-52-5). CRC Pubns.

That I May See: A Prayerful Discovery Through Imagination. Salvino Briffa. 140p. 1986. 6.95 (ISBN 0-87193-251-2). Dimension Bks.

That Incredible Christian. A. W. Tozer. 135p. 1964. pap. 4.45; 3.45 (ISBN 0-87509-304-3). Chr Pubns.

That Man Is You. Louis Evely. Tr. by Edmond Bonin. LC 63-23494. 297p. 1964. pap. 4.95 (ISBN 0-8091-1697-9). Paulist Pr.

That Motherly Mother of Guadalupe. L. M. Dooley. 2.25 (ISBN 0-8198-0634-X); pap. 1.25 (ISBN 0-8198-0635-8). Dghtrs St Paul.

That None Be Lost. Oliver V. Dalaba. LC 77-74553. (Workers' Training Ser.). 128p. 1977. 1.25 (ISBN 0-88243-621-X, 02-621). Gospel Pub.

That Old-Time Religion. Archibald T. Robertson. LC 78-24159. 1979. Repr. of 1950 ed. lib. bdg. 24.75x (ISBN 0-313-20823-9, ROOT). Greenwood.

That Reminds Me. Girault M. Jones. (Illus.). xiv, 211p. (Orig.). 1984. pap. write for info. (ISBN 0-918769-08-6). Univ South.

That Strange Divine Sea: Reflections on Being a Catholic. Christopher Derrick. LC 83-80190. 189p. (Orig.). 1983. pap. 8.95 (ISBN 0-89870-029-9). Ignatius Pr.

That the World May Believe: The Acts of the Apostles. Helen S. Thomsen. 1978. pap. 2.25x (ISBN 0-8192-4085-0); tchrs guide 2.25x (ISBN 0-8192-4084-2). Morehouse.

That They All May Be One. National Conference of Directors of Religious Education. 1977. 3.60 (ISBN 0-318-00800-9). Natl Cath Educ.

That They All May Be One. 26p. 1977. 3.60 (ISBN 0-318-20611-0). Natl Cath Educ.

That They May All Be One. Elbridge B. Linn. 1969. 4.50 (ISBN 0-88027-020-9). Firm Foun Pub.

That They May Know You. Andrew Thompson. 112p. 1982. 10.55 (ISBN 0-318-00801-7). Natl Cath Educ.

That They May Live: Theological Reflections on the Quality of Life. Ed. by George Devine. 314p. 1984. pap. text ed. 10.50 (ISBN 0-8191-3852-5, College Theo Soc). U Pr of Amer.

That Unforgettable Encounter. David S. McCarthy. 108p. (Orig.). 1983. pap. 2.95 (ISBN 0-8341-0834-8). Beacon Hill.

That Unknown Day. Carlos E. Portillo. LC 85-52117. (Illus.). 400p. (Orig.). 1986. 14.95 (ISBN 0-937365-00-9); pap. 9.95 (ISBN 0-937365-01-7). WCP Pubns.

That We May Be Willing to Receive. Elise N. Morgan. (Meditation Ser.). 1938. 3.50 (ISBN 0-87516-331-9). De Vorss.

That We May Have Fellowship: Studies in First John. John Lineberry. 112p. 1986. pap. 4.95 (ISBN 0-87227-115-3). Reg Baptist.

That We Might Have Life. Martha Popson. LC 80-2080. 128p. 1981. pap. 2.95 (ISBN 0-385-17438-1, Im). Doubleday.

That Ye May Abound. Mrs. Charles Walker. (Illus.). 80p. (Orig.). 1980. pap. 3.00 (ISBN 0-89114-096-4). Baptist Pub Hse.

That Ye May Heal: A Manual for Individual & Group Study of Meditation for Healing, from the Edgar Cayce Records. rev. ed. Compiled by Mary A. Woodward. 53p. 1970. pap. 3.50 (ISBN 0-87604-075-X). ARE Pr.

That Ye May Know. Guy H. Wilson. 2.50 (ISBN 0-910924-47-3). Macalester.

That You May Believe (John) Leader's Guide. (New Horizons Bible Study). 48p. 1983. pap. 1.95 (ISBN 0-89367-082-0). Light & Life.

That You May Believe: Miracles & Faith-Then & Now. Colin Brown. 224p. (Orig.). 1985. pap. 8.95 (ISBN 0-8028-0086-6). Eerdmans.

That You May Believe: Studies in the Gospel of John. Homer Hailey. (Illus.). 1982. 9.95 (ISBN 0-913814-51-2). Nevada Pubns.

That Your Joy May Be Full. 3.50 (ISBN 0-318-02211-7). Chrstphrs NY.

That Your Joy Might Be Full. Joseph L. Palotta. 247p. 1981. pap. 6.95 (ISBN 0-9604852-1-X). Revelation Hse.

That's a Good Question. 2nd ed. Roger Forster & Paul Marston. Tr. by Hugo S. Sun & Silas Chan. (Chinese.). 204p. 1982. pap. write for info (ISBN 0-941598-01-2). Living Spring Pubns.

That's Life. Ruthann Hall. 1974. pap. 2.25 (ISBN 0-89265-020-6). Randall Hse.

That's My Brother. Ruth O. Szittya. LC 82-70603. (Illus.). 32p. (Orig.). 1982. pap. 3.95 (ISBN 0-913408-74-3). Friends United.

That's Tough: Four Simulation Games on Christian Commitment for Junior High Youth Groups. Paul Boostrom. (Best of Young Teen Action Ser.). 32p. 1985. pap. 4.95 (ISBN 0-317-39454-1). Cook.

Thayer's Greek-English Lexicon of the New Testament. Ed. by Joseph Thayer. 1984. 22.95 (ISBN 0-8010-8872-0). Baker Bk.

Thayer's Greek-English Lexicon of the New Testament. Joseph H. Thayer. LC 78-67264. (Gr. & Eng.). 1978. pap. 16.95 (ISBN 0-8054-1376-6). Broadman.

Theater of God: Story in Christian Doctrine. Robert P. Roth. LC 84-48725. 208p. 1985. pap. 10.95 (ISBN 0-8006-1841-6, 1-1841). Fortress.

Theatre Francais Avant La Renaissance, 1430-1550. Ed. by Edouard Fournier. 1965. Repr. of 1872 ed. 32.00 (ISBN 0-8337-1225-X). B Franklin.

Theatre of Scottish Worthies, & the Lyf, Doings & Deathe of William Elphinston, Bishop of Aberdee. Alexander Gardyne. Repr. of 1878 ed. 40.00 (ISBN 0-384-17655-0). Johnson Repr.

Theatre of the Spirit: A Worship Handbook. Rey O'Day & Edward Powers. LC 80-14165. 190p. (Orig.). 1980. pap. 7.95 (ISBN 0-8298-0363-7). Pilgrim NY.

Theatric Aspects of Sanskrit Drama. G. K. Bhat. 1985. 12.50x (ISBN 0-8364-1365-2, Pub. by Bhanarkar Oriental Inst). South Asia Bks.

Theatrum Redivivum, 17 vols. Ed. by Peter Davison. Repr. 535.00 (ISBN 0-384-59985-0). Johnson Repr.

Theban Temples, Vol. 2. rev ed. Bertha Porter & Rosalind Moss. (Topographical Bibliography of Ancient Egyptian Hieroglyphic Texts, Reliefs & Paintings Ser.). 586p. 1972. text ed. 60.00 (ISBN 0-900416-18-1, Pub. by Aris & Phillips UK). Humanities.

Their Brothers' Keepers. Philip Friedman. LC 57-8773. 232p. 1978. pap. 12.95 (ISBN 0-89604-002-X). Holocaust Pubns.

Their Brother's Keepers: American Jewry & the Holocaust. Seymour M. Finger. 300p. 1988. text ed. 34.50x (ISBN 0-8419-1036-7). Holmes & Meier.

Their Brothers' Keepers: The Christian Heroes & Heroines Who Helped the Oppressed Escape the Nazi Terror. Philip Friedman. LC 57-8773. 1978. pap. 8.95 (ISBN 0-8052-5002-6, Pub. by Holocaust Library). Schocken.

Their Brothers' Keepers: The Christian Heroes & Heroines Who Helped the Oppressed Escaper the Nazi Terror. Philip Friedman. 232p. Repr. 4.95 (ISBN 0-686-95090-9). ADL.

Their Morals & Ours. new ed. Leon Trotsky et al. Ed. by House. LC 73-82168. 96p. 1974. 14.00 (ISBN 0-87348-318-9); pap. 4.95 (ISBN 0-87348-319-7). Path Pr NY.

Their Music Is Mary. Clifford J. Laube. 3.50 (ISBN 0-910984-11-5). Montfort Pubns.

Their Name Is Pius. Lillian Olf. LC 74-107729. (Essay Index Reprint Ser). 1941. 27.50 (ISBN 0-8369-1768-5). Ayer Co Pubs.

Their Religion. facs. ed. Arthur J. Russell. LC 78-128308. (Essay Index Reprint Ser). 1935. 20.00 (ISBN 0-8369-2131-3). Ayer Co Pubs.

Their Rights & Liberties. Thomas O. Hanley. 160p. 1984. 9.95 (ISBN 0-8294-0471-6). Loyola.

Their Solitary Way: The Puritan Social Ethic in the First Century of Settlement in New England. Stephen Foster. LC 76-151573. (Yale Historical Publications Miscellany Ser.: No. 94). pap. 59.50 (ISBN 0-317-29587-X, 2021997). Bks Demand UMI.

Their Story-Our Story. Forrest W. Jackson. LC 85-6623. 1985. pap. 4.95 (ISBN 0-8054-3618-9, 4236-18). Broadman.

Their Story: Twentieth Century Pentecostals. Fred J. Foster. Ed. by Mary H. Wallace. LC 86-26718. (Illus.). 192p. 1983. pap. 4.95 (ISBN 0-912315-05-9). Word Aflame.

Theirs Is the Kingdom. Lowell Hagan & Jack Westerhof. LC 86-11679. (Illus.). 336p. 1986. 16.95 (ISBN 0-8028-5013-8). Eerdmans.

Theism. Clement Dore. 1984. lib. bdg. 34.50 (ISBN 0-318-00886-6, Pub. by Reidel Holland). Kluwer Academic.

Theism & Cosmology. facs. ed. John Laird. LC 74-84317. (Essay Index Reprint Ser). 1942. 21.50 (ISBN 0-8369-1147-4). Ayer Co Pubs.

Theism & Humanism. A. J. Balfour. Repr. of 1915 ed. 32.00 (ISBN 0-527-04810-0). Kraus Repr.

Theism & the Christian Faith. Charles C. Everett. Ed. by Edward Hale. LC 75-3139. Repr. of 1909 ed. 34.00 (ISBN 0-404-59148-5). AMS Pr.

Theism & Thought: A Study in Familiar Beliefs. Arthur J. Balfour. LC 77-27208. (Gifford Lectures: 1922-23). Repr. of 1923 ed. 22.50 (ISBN 0-404-60469-2). AMS Pr.

Theism... Comprising the Deems Lectures for 1902. Borden P. Bowne. LC 75-3075. (Philosophy in America Ser.). Repr. of 1902 ed. 37.50 (ISBN 0-404-59076-4). AMS Pr.

Theism in Medieval India. J. Estlin Carpenter. 1977. Repr. of 1921 ed. 22.50x (ISBN 0-89684-457-9). Orient Bk Dist.

Theism in Medieval India. J. Estlin Carpenter. 564p. Repr. of 1921 ed. text ed. 37.50x. Coronet Bks.

Theism in Medieval India. Joseph E. Carpenter. LC 77-27152. (Hibbert Lectures: 1919). Repr. of 1921 ed. 48.00 (ISBN 0-404-60419-6). AMS Pr.

Theism in Medieval India. K. Carpenter. 1977. 22.50x (ISBN 0-8364-0100-X). South Asia Bks.

Theism in the Discourse of Jonathan Edwards. R. C. de Prospo. LC 84-40406. 296p. 1985. 37.50 (ISBN 0-87413-281-9). U Delaware Pr.

Theism of Edgar Sheffied Brightman. James J. McLarney. LC 75-3089. Repr. of 1936 ed. 11.50 (ISBN 0-404-59087-X). AMS Pr.

Theism: The Implication of Experience. William W. Fenn. 1969. 10.00 (ISBN 0-87233-005-2). Bauhan.

Theist & Atheist: A Typology of Non-Belief. Thomas Molnar. 1979. text ed. 30.00x (ISBN 90-279-7788-7). Mouton.

Theistic Evolution. Bert Thompson. pap. 5.50 (ISBN 0-89315-300-1). Lambert Bk.

Theistic Evolution. Bert Thompson. 235p. (Orig.). 1977. pap. 5.50 (ISBN 0-932859-08-9). Apologetic Pr.

Theme of Spenser's "Foure Hymnes". J. W. Bennett. LC 76-100731. 1970. pap. 39.95x (ISBN 0-8383-0003-0). Haskell.

Theme of the Pentateuch. David J. Clines. (Journal for the Study of the Old Testament Supplement Ser.: No. 10). 152p. 1978. text ed. 22.50 (ISBN 0-905774-14-0, Pub. by JSOT Pr England); pap. text ed. 10.95x (ISBN 0-905774-15-9, Pub. by JSOT Pr England). Eisenbrauns.

Themes & Theses of Six Recent Papal Documents: A Commentary. Robert F. Morneau. 160p. (Orig.). 1985. pap. 5.95 (ISBN 0-8189-0482-8). Alba.

Themes from Acts. Paul E. Pierson. LC 82-80153. (Bible Commentary for Laymen Ser.). (Orig.). 1982. pap. 3.50 (ISBN 0-8307-0819-7, S361107). Regal.

Themes from Isaiah. Ronald Youngblood. LC 83-19128. (Bible Commentary for Laymen Ser.). 1983. pap. text ed. 3.50 (ISBN 0-8307-0906-1, S373106). Regal.

Themes in Old Testament Theology. William A. Dyrness. LC 79-2380. 1979. pap. 8.95 (ISBN 0-87784-726-6). Inter-Varsity.

Themes in the Christian History of Central Africa. Ed. by T. O. Ranger & John Weller. 1974. 44.00x (ISBN 0-520-02536-9). U of Cal Pr.

Then & Now. facs. ed. Ed. by Anna Brinton. LC 72-128214. (Essay Index Reprint Ser). 1960. 21.50 (ISBN 0-8369-1905-X). Ayer Co Pubs.

Then the Sun Came Up. Helen Tucker. (Orig.). 1986. pap. 7.00 (ISBN 0-915541-10-6). Star Bks Inc.

Theo-History: The Parallel Covenants Theory. Loren Andersen. 120p. 1983. pap. 4.25 (ISBN 0-9611310-0-4). Day Bk Co.

Theodicies in Conflict: A Dilemma in Puritan Ethics & Nineteenth-Century American Literature. Richard Forrer. LC 85-27220. (Contributions to the Study of Religion: No. 17). 302p. 1986. lib. bdg. 37.95 (ISBN 0-313-25191-6, FTS/). Greenwood.

Theodicy in Islamic Thought. Eric Ormsby. LC 84-3396. 320p. 1984. text ed. 30.00x (ISBN 0-691-07278-7). Princeton U pr.

Theodicy in the Old Testament. Ed. by James L. Crenshaw. LC 83-8885. (Issues in Religion & Theology Ser.). 176p. 1983. pap. 7.95 (ISBN 0-8006-1764-9). Fortress.

Theodore Beza, The Counsellor of the French Reformation, 1519-1605. Henry M. Baird. LC 76-121596. 1970. Repr. of 1899 ed. 25.50 (ISBN 0-8337-0151-7). B Franklin.

Theodore of Studium, His Life & Times 759-826. Alice Gardner. 1905. 19.50 (ISBN 0-8337-1280-2). B Franklin.

Theodore Parker. Henry S. Commager. 1982. pap. 6.45 (ISBN 0-933840-15-2). Unitarian Univ.

Theodore Parker: A Descriptive Bibliography. Joel Myerson. LC 81-43354. 238p. 1981. lib. bdg. 33.00 (ISBN 0-8240-9279-1). Garland Pub.

Theodore Parker: American Transcendentalist: A Critical Essay & a Collection of His Writings. Robert E. Collins. LC 73-9593. 277p. 1973. 17.50 (ISBN 0-8108-0641-X). Scarecrow.

Theodore Parker: Preacher & Reformer. John W. Chadwick. LC 72-144939. 1971. Repr. of 1900 ed. 39.00x (ISBN 0-403-00925-1). Scholarly.

Theodore Parker: Yankee Crusader. H. S. Commager. 11.25 (ISBN 0-8446-1884-5). Peter Smith.

Theodore Roethke's Meditative Sequences: Contemplation & the Creative Process. Ann T. Foster. LC 85-3041. (Studies in Art & Religious Interpretation: Vol. 4). 210p. 1985. 49.95x (ISBN 0-88946-555-X). E Mellen.

Theodore Thornton Munger: New England Minister. 1913. 65.00x (ISBN 0-686-83814-9). Elliots Bks.

Theodotionic Revision of the Book of Exodus. Kevin G. O'Connell. LC 70-160026. (Semitic Monographs Ser: No. 3). 509p. 1972. 20.00x (ISBN 0-674-87785-3). Harvard U Pr.

Theogenesis. Ed. by Temple of the People Publications Staff. (Illus.). 548p. 1981. 21.00 (ISBN 0-933797-06-0). Halcyon Bk.

Theologia Gentili, 3 vols. Gerardus Vossius. LC 75-27872. (Renaissance & the Gods Ser.: Vol. 28). (Illus.). 1976. Repr. of 1641 ed. Set. lib. bdg. 265.00 (ISBN 0-8240-2077-4). Garland Pub.

Theologia Germanica of Martin Luther. Ed. by Bengt Hoffman. LC 80-50155. (Classics of Western Spirituality). 224p. 1980. 12.95 (ISBN 0-8091-0308-7); pap. 8.95 (ISBN 0-8091-2291-X). Paulist Pr.

Theologia Mystica. Bhagwan Shree Rajneesh. Ed. by Ma Prem Asha. LC 83-11086. (Western Mystics Ser.). 400p. (Orig.). 1983. pap. 4.95 (ISBN 0-88050-655-5). Chidvilas Found.

Theologia: The Fragmentation & Unity of Theological Education. Edward Farley. LC 82-48621. 224p. 1983. pap. 14.95 (ISBN 0-8006-1705-3). Fortress.

Theologia Twenty-One Encyclopedia, 2 vols. A. S. Otto. 1985. Set. vinyl 39.95 (ISBN 0-912132-16-7). Dominion Pr.

Theologian & His Universe: Theology & Cosmology from the Middle Ages to the Present. N. Max Wildiers. 320p. (Orig.). 1982. 21.95 (ISBN 0-8164-0533-6, HarpR). Har-Row.

Theologians & Authority Within the Living Church. James J. Mulligan. 131p. (Orig.). 1986. pap. 13.95 (ISBN 0-935372-18-0). Pope John Ctr.

Theologians in Transition. Ed. by James M. Wall. 288p. 1981. 14.95 (ISBN 0-8245-0101-2); pap. 7.95 (ISBN 0-8245-0103-9). Crossroad NY.

Theologians of Our Time. Ed. by A. W. Hastings & E. Hastings. LC 66-73626. 224p. pap. 7.95 (ISBN 0-567-22301-9, Pub. by T & T Clark Ltd UK). Fortress.

Theologians of Our Time. Ed. by Leonhard Reinisch. 1964. 17.95x (ISBN 0-268-00271-1); pap. 7.95x (ISBN 0-268-00378-5). U of Notre Dame Pr.

Theologians under Hitler. Robert P. Erickson. LC 84-40731. 256p. 1987. pap. 8.95 (ISBN 0-300-03889-5, Y-618). Yale U Pr.

Theologians under Hitler: Gerhard Kittel, Paul Althaus, & Emanuel Hirsch. Robert P. Ericksen. LC 84-40731. (Illus.). 256p. 1985. 20.00x (ISBN 0-300-02926-8). Yale U Pr.

Theologic Principle of Universalism: A Way of Life. Joe Jenkins. (Orig.). 1984. pap. 4.00 (ISBN 0-916801-00-4). Inst Univ.

Theological Aesthetics: Theology. Jeffrey A. Kay. (European University Studies: Ser. 23, Vol. 60). 115p. 1976. pap. 12.90 (ISBN 3-261-01893-3). P Lang Pubs.

Theological & Dogmatic Works. St. Ambrose. (Fathers of the Church Ser.: Vol. 44). 343p. 1963. 21.95x (ISBN 0-8132-0044-X). Cath U Pr.

Theological & Grammatical Phrasebook of the Bible. William White, Jr. 1984. 12.95 (ISBN 0-8024-0218-6). Moody.

Theological & Miscellaneous Works, 25 vols. in 26. Joseph Priestley. Repr. Set. 1352.00 (ISBN 0-527-72751-2). Kraus Repr.

Theological & Religious Reference Materials: Practical Theology. Compiled by G. E. Gorman et al. LC 86-380. (Bibliographies & Indexes in Religious Studies: No. 7). 402p. 1986. lib. bdg. 49.95 (ISBN 0-313-25397-8, GPA/). Greenwood.

Theological & Religious Reference Materials: Systematic Theology & Church History. G. E. Gorman & Lyn Gorman. LC 83-22759. (Bibliographies & Indexes in Religious Studies: No. 2). xiv, 401p. 1985. lib. bdg. 47.50 (ISBN 0-313-24779-X, GOS/). Greenwood.

Theological Anthropology. Ed. by J. Patout Burns. LC 81-43080. (Sources of Early Christian Thought Ser.). 1981. pap. 7.95 (ISBN 0-8006-1412-7). Fortress.

Theological Cautions. Paul Toinet. Tr. by Michael J. Wrenn. 1982. 12.00 (ISBN 0-8199-0835-5). Franciscan Herald.

Theological Department in Yale College, 1822-1858. John T. Wayland. Ed. by Bruce Kuklick. (American Religious Thought of the 18th & 19th Centuries Ser.). 500p. 1987. lib. bdg. 70.00 (ISBN 0-8240-6962-5). Garland Pub.

Theological Development of Edwards Amasa Park: Last of the "Consistent Calvinists". Anthony C. Cecil, Jr. LC 74-83338. (American Academy of Religion. Dissertation Ser.). 1974. pap. 9.95 (ISBN 0-88420-118-X, 010101). Scholars Pr GA.

Theological Dictionary of the New Testament, 10 vols. Ed. by Gerhard Kittel & Gerhard Friedrich. Incl. Vol. 1. 1964. 29.95 (ISBN 0-8028-2243-6); Vol. 2. 1965. 29.95 (ISBN 0-8028-2244-4); Vol. 3. 1966. 29.95 (ISBN 0-8028-2245-2); Vol. 4. 1967. 29.95 (ISBN 0-8028-2246-0); Vol. 5. 1968. 29.95 (ISBN 0-8028-2247-9); Vol. 6. 1969. 29.95 (ISBN 0-8028-2248-7); Vol. 7. 1970. 29.95 (ISBN 0-8028-2249-5); Vol. 8. 1972. 29.95 (ISBN 0-8028-2250-9); Vol. 9. 1973. 29.95 (ISBN 0-8028-2322-X); Vol; Vol. 10. 1976. 29.95 (ISBN 0-8028-2323-8); Vol. 10. 1976. 29.95 (ISBN 0-8028-2323-8). Set. 299.50 (ISBN 0-8028-2324-6). Eerdmans.

Theological Dictionary of the New Testament. abridged ed. Ed. by Gerhard Kittel & Gerhard Friedrich. Tr. by Geoffrey Bromiley from Ger. 1300p. 1985. pap. 49.95 cloth (ISBN 0-8028-2404-8). Eerdmans.

Theological Dictionary of the Old Testament, 5 vols. Ed. by G. Johannes Botterweck & Helmer Ringgren. 560p. 1978. Set. 137.50 (ISBN 0-8028-2338-6); Vol. I. 27.50 ea. (ISBN 0-8028-2325-4). Vol. II (ISBN 0-8028-2326-2). Vol. III (ISBN 0-8028-2327-0). Vol. IV (ISBN 0-8028-2328-9). Vol. V (ISBN 0-8028-2329-7). Eerdmans.

Theological Diversity & the Authority of the Old Testament. John Goldingay. 240p. (Orig.). 1987. pap. 14.95 (ISBN 0-8028-0229-X). Eerdmans.

Theological Essays. Frederick D. Maurice. 436p. (Orig.). Date not set. pap. write for info. (ISBN 0-87921-048-6). Attic Pr.

Theological Essays. W. G. Shedd. 1981. lib. bdg. 26.00 (ISBN 0-86524-079-5, 8602). Klock & Klock.

Theological Essays of the Later Benjamin Jowett. Benjamin Jowett. 1906. 20.00 (ISBN 0-932062-91-1). Sharon Hill.

Theological Ethics, 2 vols. Helmut Thielicke. Incl. Foundations; Politics; Vol. III. Sex. pap. 8.95 (ISBN 0-8028-1794-7). LC 78-31858. Eerdmans.

Theological Ethics. Helmut Thielicke. LC 78-31858. Repr. of 1979 ed. 160.00 (2027550). Bks Demand UMI.

Theological-Exegetical Approach to Glossolalia. Watson E. Mills. 192p. (Orig.). 1985. lib. bdg. 25.00 (ISBN 0-8191-4526-2); pap. text ed. 10.75 (ISBN 0-8191-4527-0). U Pr of Amer.

Theological Ferment: Personal Reflections. Paul Clasper. 226p. (Orig.). 1982. pap. 6.75 (ISBN 0-686-37687-0, Pub. by New Day Philippines). Cellar.

Theological Foundations for Ministry. Ray S. Anderson. LC 78-13613. 1978. pap. 8.95 (ISBN 0-8028-1776-9). Eerdmans.

Theological Foundations of the Mormon Religion. Sterling M. McMurrin. LC 65-26131. 1965. pap. 9.95 (ISBN 0-87480-051-X). U of Utah Pr.

Theological German. Helmut W. Ziefle. 256p. 1986. pap. 14.95 (ISBN 0-8010-9931-5). Baker Bk.

Theological Imagination: Constructing the Concept of God. Gordon D. Kaufman. LC 81-12960. 310p. 1981. pap. 13.95 (ISBN 0-664-24393-2). Westminster.

Theological Interpretation of American History. rev. ed. C Gregg Singer. 1981. pap. 7.95 (ISBN 0-87552-426-5). Presby & Reformed.

Theological Interpretation of American History. Gregg Singer. kivar 7.95 (ISBN 0-934532-23-0). Presby & Ref.

Theological Investigations, Vols. 1-17, 20. Karl Rahner. Incl. Vol. 1. 22.50x (ISBN 0-8245-0377-5); Vol. 2. Man & the Church. 22.50x (ISBN 0-8245-0378-3); Vol. 3. Theology of the Spiritual Life. 24.50x (ISBN 0-8245-0379-1); Vol. 4. More Recent Writings. 24.50x (ISBN 0-8245-0380-5); Vol. 5. Later Writings. 27.50x (ISBN 0-8245-0381-3); Vol. 6. Concerning Vatican Council II. 24.50x (ISBN 0-8245-0382-1); Vol. 7. Further Theology of the Spiritual Life I. 19.50x (ISBN 0-8245-0383-X); Vol. 8. Further Theology of the Spiritual Life II. 19.50x (ISBN 0-8245-0384-8); Vol. 9. Writings of 1965-1967, I. 19.50x (ISBN 0-8245-0385-6); Vol. 10. Writings of 1965-1967, II. 22.50x (ISBN 0-8245-0386-4); Vol. 11. Confrontation I. 22.50 (ISBN 0-8245-0387-2); Vol. 12. Confrontations II. 22.50x (ISBN 0-8245-0388-0); Vol. 13. Theology Anthropology, Christology. 22.50x (ISBN 0-8245-0389-9); Vol. 14. In Dialogue with the Future. 22.50 (ISBN 0-8245-0390-2); Penance in the Early Church. 590p. 29.50x (ISBN 0-8245-0025-3); Vol. 16. **Experience of the Spirit: Source of Theology. 1979. 19.50x (ISBN 0-8245-0392-9); Vol. 17. Jesus, Man & the Church. 19.50x (ISBN 0-8245-0026-1); Vol. 20. Concern for the Church. 14.50x (ISBN 0-8245-0027-X). Crossroad NY.**

Theological Investigations, Vol. 22: Humane Society & the Church of Tomorrow. Karl Rahner. 288p. 1987. 24.50 (ISBN 0-8245-0802-5). Crossroad NY.

Theological Libraries at Oxford. Thomas P. Slavens. 160p. 1984. pap. text ed. 32.50 (ISBN 3-598-10563-0). K G Saur.

Theological Method in Luther & Tillich: Law-Gospel & Correlation. Wayne G. Johnson. LC 80-5691. 204p. 1982. lib. bdg. 27.50 (ISBN 0-8191-1895-8); pap. text ed. 12.50 (ISBN 0-8191-1896-6). U Pr of Amer.

Theological Method of Karl Rahner. Anne Carr. LC 76-51639. (American Academy of Religion, Dissertation Ser.: No. 19). pap. 72.30 (ISBN 0-317-08410-0, 2017556). Bks Demand UMI.

Theological Methodology of Hans Kung. Catherine M. LaCugna. LC 81-16654. (American Academy of Religion Academy Ser.). 1982. 12.95 (ISBN 0-89130-546-7, 01 01 39). Scholars Pr GA.

Theological Models for the Parish. Sabbas Kilian. LC 76-42986. 1977. 5.95 (ISBN 0-8189-0337-6). Alba.

Theological Papers of John Henry Newman: On Biblical Inspiration & on Infallibility, Vol. 2. John H. Newman. Ed. by J. Derek Holmes. 1979. text ed. 22.50x (ISBN 0-19-920081-5). Oxford U Pr.

Theological Papers of John Henry Newman: On Faith & Certainty, Vol. 1. John H. Newman. Ed. by Derek Holmes. 1976. 22.50x (ISBN 0-19-920071-8). Oxford U Pr.

Theological Perspectives on Church Growth. Harvie M. Conn. 1976. pap. 4.95 (ISBN 0-87552-150-9). Presby & Reformed.

Theological Questions: Analysis & Argument. Owen C. Thomas. LC 83-60658. 134p. (Orig.). 1983. pap. 8.95 (ISBN 0-8192-1328-4). Morehouse.

Theological Reflections: Essays on Related Themes. Henry Stob. LC 81-1472. pap. 69.30 (ISBN 0-317-20015-1, 2023223). Bks Demand UMI.

Theological Retreat. Bertrand De Margerie. 280p. 1977. 8.95 (ISBN 0-8199-0584-4). Franciscan Herald.

Theological Science. Thomas F. Torrance. 1969. pap. 7.95 (ISBN 0-19-520083-7). Oxford U Pr.

Theological Tractates. Boethius. Bd. with Consolation of Philosophy. (Loeb Classical Library: No. 74). 13.95x (ISBN 0-674-99083-8). Harvard U Pr.

Theological Transition in American Methodism, 1790-1935. Robert E. Chiles. LC 83-16666. 238p. 1983. pap. text ed. 11.25 (ISBN 0-8191-3551-8). U Pr of Amer.

Theological Treatises on the Trinity. Marius Victorinus. (Fathers of the Church Ser.: Vol. 69). 357p. 1981. 29.95x (ISBN 0-8132-0069-5). Cath U Pr.

Theological Word Book of the Bible. Alan Richardson. 1962. 7.95 (ISBN 0-02-603060-8). Macmillan.

Theological Wordbook of the Bible. Alan Richardson. 1962. pap. 7.95 (ISBN 0-02-089090-7, Collier). Macmillan.

Theological Wordbook of the Old Testament, 2 Vols. Ed. by R. Laird Harris et al. LC 80-28047. 1800p. 1980. text ed. 39.95 (ISBN 0-8024-8631-2). Moody.

Theological Works of Isaac Barrow, 9 Vols. Isaac Barrow. Ed. by Alexander Napier. LC 72-161751. Repr. of 1859 ed. Set. lib. bdg. 215.00 (ISBN 0-404-00670-1); lib. bdg. 25.00 ea. AMS Pr.

Theologico-Political Treatise: Political Treatise. Benedict Spinoza. Tr. by R. H. Elwes. pap. text ed. 6.95 (ISBN 0-486-20249-6). Dover.

Theologies of the Body: Humanist & Christian. Benedict M. Ashley. (Illus.). 770p. (Orig.). 1985. pap. 20.95 (ISBN 0-935372-15-6). Pope John Ctr.

Theologies of the Eucharist in the Early Scholastic Period. Gary Macy. (Illus.). 1984. 32.00x (ISBN 0-19-826669-3). Oxford U Pr.

Theologische Grundstrukturen des Alten Testaments. Georg Fohrer. (Theologische Bibliothek Toepelmann, 24). 1972. pap. 23.20x (ISBN 3-11-003874-9). De Gruyter.

Theologische Lebenswerk Johannes Oekolampads. Ernst Staehelin. 61.00 (ISBN 0-384-57419-X); pap. 55.00 (ISBN 0-384-57418-1). Johnson Repr.

Theologische Realenzyklopaedie: Agende-Anselm Von Cantebury, Vol. 2. Ed. by Michael Wolter. (Illus.). 1978. 128.00x (ISBN 3-11-007379-X). De Gruyter.

Theologische Realeuzyklopaedic, 25 vols. Ed. by G. Krause & G. Mueller. (Ger.). write for info. De Gruyter.

Theology, 5 vols. Timothy Dwight. LC 75-3132. Repr. of 1819 ed. 200.00 set (ISBN 0-404-59136-1). AMS Pr.

Theology - The Quintessence of Science. William B. Turner. LC 80-82649. 306p. 1981. 17.50 (ISBN 0-8022-2375-3). Philos Lib.

Theology After Freud: An Interpretive Inquiry. Peter Homans. LC 76-84162. 1970. 29.50x (ISBN 0-672-51245-9); pap. text ed. 16.95x (ISBN 0-8290-1399-7). Irvington.

Theology after Wittgenstein. Fergus Kerr. 224p. 1986. text ed. 45.00 (ISBN 0-631-14688-1). Basil Blackwell.

Theology: An Assessment of Current Trends Report. Lutheran Church in America Task Group for Long-Range Planning. LC 68-557557. pap. 43.50 (2026880). Bks Demand UMI.

Theology: An Orthodox Standpoint. Apostolos Makrakis. Ed. by Orthodox Christian Educational Society. Tr. by Denver Cummings from Hellenic. (Logos & Holy Spirit in the Unity of Christian Thought Ser.: Vol. 4). 216p. 1977. pap. 5.00x (ISBN 0-938366-03-3). Orthodox Chr.

Theology & Bioethics: Exploring the Foundation & Frontiers. Earl E. Shelp. 1985. lib. bdg. 39.50 (ISBN 90-277-1857-1, Pub. by Reidel Holland). Kluwer Academic.

Theology & Ethics in Paul. Victor P. Furnish. LC 68-17445. 1978. pap. 12.95 (ISBN 0-687-41499-7). Abingdon.

Theology & Ethics of Sex. Sakae Kubo. (Horizon Ser.). 1980. pap. 5.95 (ISBN 0-8127-0288-3). Review & Herald.

Theology & Meaning: A Critique of Metatheological Scepticism. Raeburne S. Heimbeck. LC 68-13146. 1969. 22.50x (ISBN 0-8047-0704-9). Stanford U Pr.

Theology & Ministry in Context & Crisis: A South African Perspective. John W. DeGruchy. 182p. (Orig.). 1987. pap. 9.95 (ISBN 0-8028-0290-7). Eerdmans.

Theology & Modern Life. Ed. by Paul Schilpp. LC 70-117852. (Essay Index Reprint Ser). 1940. 19.00 (ISBN 0-8369-1727-8). Ayer Co Pubs.

Theology & Modern Life: Essays in Honor of Harris Franklin Rall. Ed. by Paul A. Schilpp. (Essay Index Reprint Ser.). 307p. 1982. Repr. of 1940 ed. lib. bdg. 18.00 (ISBN 0-686-79705-1). Irvington.

Theology & Modern Literature. Amos N. Wilder. LC 58-11556. pap. 39.30 (ISBN 0-317-10086-6, 2003002). Bks Demand UMI.

Theology & Narrative: A Critical Introduction. Michael Goldberg. 304p. (Orig.). 1982. pap. 11.95 (ISBN 0-687-41503-9). Abingdon.

Theology & Pastoral Care. John B. Cobb, Jr. Ed. by Howard J. Clinebell & Howard W. Stone. LC 76-7862. (Creative Pastoral Care & Counseling Ser.). 96p. 1977. pap. 4.50 (ISBN 0-8006-0557-8, 1-557). Fortress.

Theology & Philosophical Inquiry: An Introduction. Vincent Brummer. LC 81-11557. 320p. (Orig.). 1982. pap. 16.95 (ISBN 0-664-24398-3). Westminster.

Theology & Poetry Studies in the Medieval Piyyut. Ed. & tr. by Jacob J. Petuchowski. (Littman Library of Jewish Civilization). 1978. 18.50x (ISBN 0-19-710014-7). Oxford U Pr.

Theology & Political Society. Charles Davis. LC 80-40014. 180p. 1980. 27.95 (ISBN 0-521-22538-8). Cambridge U Pr.

Theology & Practice. Duncan B. Forrester. 1986. 32.00x (Pub. by Hesketh UK). State Mutual Bk.

Theology & Praxis: Epistemological Foundations. Clodovis Boff. Tr. by Robert R. Barr. LC 86-21671. Tr. of Teologia e Pratica: Teologia do Politico e Suas Mediacoes. (Port.). 416p. (Orig.). 1987. pap. 19.95 (ISBN 0-88344-416-X). Orbis Bks.
Theology & Religious Pluralism: The Challenge of Other Religions. Gavin D'Costa. (Signposts in Theology Ser.). 160p. 1986. text ed. 39.95 (ISBN 0-631-14517-6); pap. text ed. 14.95 (ISBN 0-631-14518-4). Basil Blackwell.
Theology & Sanity. rev. ed. F. J. Sheed. LC 78-62340. 1978. pap. 6.95 (ISBN 0-87973-854-5). Our Sunday Visitor.
Theology & Science in Mutual Modification. Harold Nebelsick. 1981. text ed. 19.95x (ISBN 0-19-520273-2). Oxford U Pr.
Theology & Setting of Discipleship in the Gospel of Mark. John R. Donahue. LC 83-60749. (Pere Marquette Lecture Ser.). 1983. 7.95 (ISBN 0-87462-538-6). Marquette.
Theology & Technology: Essays in Christian Analysis & Exegesis. Ed. by Carl Mitcham & Jim Grote. LC 84-2183. 534p. (Orig.). 1984. lib. bdg. 36.00 (ISBN 0-8191-3808-8); pap. text ed. 20.50 (ISBN 0-8191-3809-6). U Pr of Amer.
Theology & the Cain Complex. Richard Hughes. LC 81-43698. 148p. (Orig.). 1982. lib. bdg. 24.75 (ISBN 0-8191-2357-9); pap. text ed. 9.50 (ISBN 0-8191-2358-7). U Pr of Amer.
Theology & the Church. Dumitru Staniloae. Tr. by Robert Barringer from Romanian. LC 80-19313. 240p. 1980. pap. 7.95 (ISBN 0-913836-69-9). St Vladimirs.
Theology & the Church: A Response to Cardinal Ratzinger. Juan L. Segundo. LC 85-51459. 175p. 1985. 14.95 (ISBN 0-86683-491-5, HarpR). Har-Row.
Theology & the Kingdom of God. Wolfhart Pannenberg. LC 69-12668. 144p. 1969. pap. 5.95 (ISBN 0-664-24842-X). Westminster.
Theology & the Philosophy of Science. Wolfhart Pannenberg. Tr. by Francis McDonagh. LC 76-20763. 464p. 1976. 17.50 (ISBN 0-664-21337-5). Westminster.
Theology & the Problem of Evil. Kenneth Surin. (Signposts in Theology Ser.). 192p. 1986. text ed. 39.95 (ISBN 0-631-14664-4); pap. text ed. 14.95 (ISBN 0-631-14663-6). Basil Blackwell.
Theology & the Third World Church. J. Andrew Kirk. LC 83-8560. (Outreach & Identity: Evangelical Theological Monographs). 64p. (Orig.). 1983. pap. 2.95 (ISBN 0-87784-892-0). Inter-Varsity.
Theology As an Empirical Science. Douglas C. Macintosh. Ed. by Edwin S. Gaustad. LC 79-52601. (Baptist Tradition Ser.). 1980. Repr. of 1919 ed. lib. bdg. 23.00x (ISBN 0-405-12466-X). Ayer Co Pubs.
Theology As Hermeneutics: Rudolf Bultmann's Theology of the History of Jesus. John Painter. (Historic Texts & Interpreters Ser.: No. 4). 220p. 1986. text ed. 23.95x (ISBN 1-85075-050-5, Pub. by Almond Pr England); pap. text ed. 14.95x (ISBN 1-85075-051-3). Eisenbrauns.
Theology As Thanksgiving: From Israel's Psalms to the Church's Eucharist. Harvey H. Guthrie, Jr. 1981. 15.95 (ISBN 0-8164-0486-0, HarpR). Har-Row.
Theology Beyond Christendom. Essays on the Centenary of the Birth of Karl Barth, May 10, 1886. Ed. by John Thompson. (Princeton Theological Monograph Ser.: No. 6). (Orig.). 1986. pap. 36.00 (ISBN 0-915138-85-9). Pickwick.
Theology, Church & Ministry. John Macquarrie. 224p. 1986. 16.95 (ISBN 0-8245-0787-8). Crossroad NY.
Theology, Death & Dying. Ray S. Anderson. LC 85-30806. 192p. 1986. 34.95 (ISBN 0-631-14846-9); pap. 8.95 (ISBN 0-631-14847-7). Basil Blackwell.
Theology for a Nuclear Age. Gordon D. Kaufman. 78p. 1985. 12.95 (ISBN 0-664-21400-2); pap. 8.95 (ISBN 0-664-24628-1). Westminster.
Theology for Aging. William L. Hendricks. 1986. 10.95 (ISBN 0-8054-1712-5). Broadman.
Theology for Beginners. Rev. ed. F. J. Sheed. 200p. 1982. pap. 6.95 (ISBN 0-89283-124-3). Servant.
Theology for Children. William L. Hendricks. LC 80-65539. 1980. 10.95 (ISBN 0-8054-1711-7). Broadman.
Theology for Ministry. George Tavard. (Theology & Life Ser.: Vol. 6). pap. 7.95 (ISBN 0-89453-337-1). M Glazier.
Theology for Nonbelievers: Post-Christian & Post-Marxist Reflections. Franco Ferrarotti. LC 86-10782. (Studies in Social Thought: Polity & Civil Society). Tr. of Una Teologia per Atei. 208p. 1987. text ed. 21.50x (ISBN 0-8046-9401-X, 9401). Assoc Faculty Pr.
Theology from the Womb of Asia. C. S. Song. 256p. (Orig.). 1986. pap. 12.95 (ISBN 0-88344-518-2, 85-31008). Orbis Bks.
Theology in a New Key: Responding to Liberation Themes. Robert M. Brown. LC 78-6494. 212p. 1978. pap. 8.95 (ISBN 0-664-24204-9). Westminster.
Theology in Africa. Kwesi A. Dickson. LC 84-5154. 240p. (Orig.). 1984. pap. 9.95 (ISBN 0-88344-508-5). Orbis Bks.
Theology in Anglicanism. Arthur A. Vogel et al. LC 84-60624. (Anglican Studies). 160p. (Orig.). 1984. pap. 8.95 (ISBN 0-8192-1344-6). Morehouse.
Theology in the Americas. Sergio Torres. Ed. by John Eagleson. LC 76-22545. 466p. (Orig.). 1976. 12.95 (ISBN 0-88344-479-8); pap. 12.95 (ISBN 0-88344-476-3). Orbis Bks.
Theology in the English Poets. Stopford A. Brooke. 59.95 (ISBN 0-8490-1189-2). Gordon Pr.
Theology in the English Poets: Cowper, Coleridge, Wordsworth & Burns. 6th ed. Stopford A. Brooke. LC 79-129367. Repr. of 1880 ed. 10.00 (ISBN 0-404-01116-0). AMS Pr.
Theology in the Philippine Setting: A Case Study in the Contextualization of Theology. Rodrigo D. Tano. 184p. 1981. pap. 7.50x (ISBN 0-686-32582-6, Pub. by New Day Phillipines). Cellar.
Theology in the Responsa. Louis Jacobs. (Littman Library of Jewish Civilization). 1975. 35.50x (ISBN 0-19-710022-8). Oxford U Pr.
Theology in the Shape of Dance: Using Dance in Worship & Theological Process. Judith Rock. 1977. 2.50 (ISBN 0-941500-16-0). Sharing Co.
Theology in Turmoil: The Roots, Course & Significance of the Conservative-Liberal. Alan P. Sell. 144p. 1984. pap. 9.95 (ISBN 0-8010-8246-3). Baker Bk.
Theology Meets Progress: Human Implications of Development. Ed. by Philip Land. 1971. pap. 6.50 (ISBN 0-8294-0326-4, Pub. by Gregorian U Pr). Loyola.
Theology of a Classless Society. Geervarghese M. Osthathios. LC 79-27013. 160p. (Orig.). 1980. pap. 2.24 (ISBN 0-88344-500-X). Orbis Bks.
Theology of Abraham Bibago: A Defense of the Divine Will, Knowledge, & Providence in Fifteenth-Century Spanish-Jewish Philosophy. Allan Lazaroff. LC 77-10611. (Judaic Studies Ser.). 192p. 1981. text ed. 17.50 (ISBN 0-8173-6906-6). U of Ala Pr.
Theology of Administration: A Bibical Basis for Organizing the Congregation. Harris W. Lee. LC 81-147067. 40p. 1981. pap. 3.95 (ISBN 0-8066-1875-2, 10-6290). Augsburg.
Theology of Albert Schweitzer. E. N. Mozley. LC 73-16630. 108p. 1974. Repr. of 1950 ed. lib. bdg. 22.50x (ISBN 0-8371-7204-7, SCTH). Greenwood.
Theology of Albert Schweitzer for Christian Inquirers. Albert Schweitzer. Ed. by E. N. Mozley. 1977. lib. bdg. 59.95 (ISBN 0-8490-2740-3). Gordon Pr.
Theology of Anabaptism. Robert Friedmann. LC 73-7886. (Studies in Anabaptist & Mennonite History, No. 15). 176p. 1973. 12.95x (ISBN 0-8361-1194-X). Herald Pr.
Theology of Ancient Judaism, 2 vols. Abraham J. Heschel. (Hebrew.). 1973. Set. 14.95x (ISBN 0-685-32988-7). Bloch.
Theology of Artistic Sensibilities: The Visual Arts & the Church. John Dillenberger. 280p. 1986. 22.50 (ISBN 0-8245-0783-5). Crossroad NY.
Theology of Bernard Lonergan. Hugo A. Meynell. (Studies in Religion). 1986. text ed. 15.95 (ISBN 1-55540-015-9, 01-00-42); pap. 11.95 (ISBN 1-55540-016-7). Scholars Pr GA.
Theology of Change: A Christian Concept of God in an Eastern Perspective. Jung Y. Lee. LC 78-16745. 155p. (Orig.). 1979. pap. 5.95 (ISBN 0-88344-492-5). Orbis Bks.
Theology of Christian Counseling: More Than Redemption. (Jay Adams Library). 1986. pap. 11.95 (ISBN 0-310-51101-1, 12122P). Zondervan.
Theology of Christian Education. Lawrence O. Richards. 320p. 1975. 17.95 (ISBN 0-310-31940-4, 18135). Zondervan.
Theology of Christian Marriage. Walter Kasper. LC 81-5444. 112p. 1983. pap. 7.95 (ISBN 0-8245-0559-X). Crossroad NY.
Theology of Christian Solidarity. Jon Sobrino & Juan H. Pico. Tr. by Phillip Berryman from Span. LC 84-16533. Orig. Title: Teologia de la Solidaridad Chrisiana. 112p. (Orig.). 1985. pap. 7.95 (ISBN 0-88344-452-6). Orbis Bks.
Theology of Church & Ministry. Franklin M. Segler. LC 60-14146. 1960. bds. 11.95 (ISBN 0-8054-2506-3). Broadman.
Theology of Church Growth. George Peters. 368p. 1981. pap. 10.95 (ISBN 0-310-43101-8, 11285P). Zondervan.
Theology of Church Leadership. Lawrence O. Richards & Clyde Hoeldtke. (Illus.). 352p. 1980. 17.95 (ISBN 0-310-31960-9, 18136). Zondervan.
Theology of Congregationalism. Hugo R. Pruter. LC 85-12844. 100p. 1985. Repr. lib. bdg. 19.95x (ISBN 0-89370-597-7). Borgo Pr.
Theology of Culture. Paul Tillich. Ed. by Robert C. Kimball. 1959. pap. 8.95 (ISBN 0-19-500711-5). Oxford U Pr.
Theology of Culture. Paul Tillich. 1983. 14.50 (ISBN 0-8446-6021-3). Peter Smith.
Theology of Dietrich Bonhoeffer. Ernst Feil. Tr. by H. Martin Rumscheidt. LC 84-47919. 272p. 1985. 19.95 (ISBN 0-8006-0696-5, 1-696). Fortress.
Theology of Emil G. Hirsch. Ed. by David E. Hirsch. 1977. pap. text ed. 12.50x (ISBN 0-87655-539-3). Collage Inc.
Theology of Encounter: The Ontological Ground for a New Christology. Charles B. Ketcham. LC 77-21905. 1978. 22.50x (ISBN 0-271-00520-3). Pa St U Pr.
Theology of Existence. Fritz Buri. Tr. by Harold H Oliver. 128p. 1965. 3.95 (ISBN 0-87921-001-X). Attic Pr.
Theology of Freedom: The Legacy of Jacque Maritain & Reinhold Niebuhr. John W. Cooper. ix, 186p. 1985. text ed. 16.95 (ISBN 0-86554-172-8, MUP-H162). Mercer Univ Pr.
Theology of Generosity: Principles & Practice of Giving Based on Bible Teaching. W. W. Berrie. 32p. 1982. pap. 2.50 (ISBN 0-8192-1293-8). Morehouse.
Theology of Grace & the American Mind: A Representation of Catholic Doctrine. Daniel Liderbach. LC 83-22154. (Toronto Studies in Theology: Vol. 15). 170p. 1983. lib. bdg. 39.95x (ISBN 0-88946-761-7). E Mellen.
Theology of Grace of Theodore of Mopsuestia. Joanne Dewart. LC 65-18319. (Studies in Christian Antiquity: Vol. 16). 160p. 1971. 12.95x (ISBN 0-8132-0523-9). Cath U Pr.
Theology of H. Richard Niebuhr. Libertus Hoedemaker. LC 78-139271. 1979. pap. 6.95 (ISBN 0-8298-0186-3). Pilgrim NY.
Theology of Haham David Nieto. Jakob J. Petuchowski. 1970. 10.00x (ISBN 0-87068-015-3). Ktav.
Theology of History According to St. Bonaventure. J. Ratzinger. 12.50 (ISBN 0-8199-0415-5). Franciscan Herald.
Theology of Hope. Jurgen Moltmann. LC 67-21550. 1976. pap. 10.00x (ISBN 0-06-065900-9, RD127, HarpR). Har-Row.
Theology of Huldrych Zwingli. W. P. Stephens. 360p. 1985. 52.00x (ISBN 0-19-826677-4). Oxford U Pr.
Theology of John Wesley: With Special Reference to the Doctrine of Justification. William R. Cannon. 284p. 1984. pap. text ed. 12.75 (ISBN 0-8191-4001-5). U Pr of Amer.
Theology of Karl Barth: An Introduction. Herbert Hartwell. (Studies in Theology). 201p. 1964. pap. 13.50 (ISBN 0-7156-0356-6, Pub. by Duckworth London). Longwood Pub Group.
Theology of "La Lozana Andaluza". Pamela Brakhage. 27.50 (ISBN 0-916379-34-5). Scripta.
Theology of Limits & the Limits of Theology: Reflections on Language, Environment & Death. Hugh T. McElwain. LC 83-1331. 190p. (Orig.). 1983. lib. bdg. 26.00 (ISBN 0-8191-3093-1); pap. text ed. 11.50 (ISBN 0-8191-3094-X). U Pr of Amer.
Theology of Love. Mildred B. Wynkoop. 327p. 1972. 8.95 (ISBN 0-8341-0102-5). Beacon Hill.
Theology of Marriage & Celibacy. 9.00 (ISBN 0-8198-7333-0); 8.00 (ISBN 0-8198-7334-9). Dghtrs St Paul.
Theology of Martin Luther. Paul Althaus. Tr. by Robert C. Schultz from Ger. LC 66-17345. 480p. 1966. pap. 12.95 (ISBN 0-8006-1855-6, 1-855). Fortress.
Theology of Ministry. Thomas F. O'Meara. LC 82-60588. 1983. pap. 11.95 (ISBN 0-8091-2487-4). Paulist Pr.
Theology of Modern Literature. Samuel L. Wilson. LC 76-47565. 1976. Repr. of 1899 ed. lib. bdg. 40.00 (ISBN 0-8414-9484-3). Folcroft.
Theology of Nature. George S. Hendry. LC 79-27375. 258p. 1980. pap. 13.95 (ISBN 0-664-24305-3). Westminster.
Theology of Paul Tillich. rev. ed. Ed. by Charles W. Kegley. LC 82-301. 432p. 1982. pap. 10.95 (ISBN 0-8298-0499-4). Pilgrim NY.
Theology of Personal Ministry. Lawrence Richards & Gib Martin. 272p. 1981. 17.95 (ISBN 0-310-31970-6, 18137). Zondervan.
Theology of Politics. Nathaniel Micklem. 10.75 (ISBN 0-8369-7119-1, 7953). Ayer Co Pubs.
Theology of Post-Reformation Lutheranism: A Study of Theological Prolegomena. Robert D. Preus. LC 70-121877. 1970. 16.95 (ISBN 0-570-03211-3, 15-2110). Concordia.
Theology of Post-Reformation Lutheranism, Vol. 2. Robert D. Preus. 350p. 1972. 16.95 (ISBN 0-570-03226-1, 15-2123). Concordia.
Theology of Prayer. Reverend John Hardon. 1979. 3.75 (ISBN 0-8198-7311-X); pap. 2.50 (ISBN 0-8198-7312-8). Dghtrs St Paul.
Theology of Preaching: The Dynamics of the Gospel. Richard Lischer. LC 81-1470. (Abingdon Preacher's Library). (Orig.). 1981. pap. 6.95 (ISBN 0-687-41570-5). Abingdon.
Theology of Revelation. Rene Latourelle. LC 65-15734. 1966. pap. 12.95 (ISBN 0-8189-0143-8). Alba.
Theology of Revelation. Gabriel Moran. 1968. pap. 5.95 (ISBN 0-8164-2567-1, HarpR). Har-Row.
Theology of Ronald Gregor Smith. K. W. Clements. (Zeitschrift fur Religions- und Geistesgeschichte Ser.: No. 27). xii, 328p. 1986. pap. 49.00 (ISBN 90-04-07298-5, Pub. by E J Brill). Heinman.
Theology of St. Luke. Hans Conzelmann. LC 82-2372. 256p. 1982. pap. 9.95 (ISBN 0-8006-1650-2, 1-1650). Fortress.
Theology of St. Paul. 2nd ed. D. E. Whiteley. 312p. 1975. pap. 14.95x (ISBN 0-631-16430-8). Basil Blackwell.
Theology of St. Paul. D. E. Whiteley. 312p. 1967. 45.00x (ISBN 0-631-15710-7). Basil Blackwell.
Theology of Salomon Ludwig Steinheim. Aharon Shear-Yashuv. (Studies in Judaism in Modern Times: Vol. 7). (Illus.). x, 115p. 1986. 27.23 (ISBN 90-04-07670-0, Pub. by E J Brill). Heinman.
Theology of Schleiermacher. Karl Barth. Tr. by Geoffrey W. Bromiley. 287p. 1982. 13.95 (ISBN 0-8028-3565-1). Eerdmans.
Theology of the Book of Joel. Willem S. Prinsloo. (Beihefte zur Zeitschrift fur die Alttestamentliche Wissenschaft: Vol. 163). viii, 136p. 1985. 43.75x (ISBN 3-11-010301-X). De Gruyter.
Theology of the Church & Its Mission: A Pentecostal Perspective. Melvin L. Hodges. LC 76-20892. 1977. 6.95 (ISBN 0-88243-605-8, 02-0605); pap. 3.95 (ISBN 0-88243-607-4, 02-0607). Gospel Pub.
Theology of the Early Greek Philosophers: The Gifford Lectures, 1936. Werner W. Jaeger. Tr. by Edward S. Robinson. LC 79-9940. vi, 259p. 1980. Repr. of 1947 ed. lib. bdg. 55.00x (ISBN 0-313-21262-7, JATH). Greenwood.
Theology of the Epistles. Harry A. Kennedy. LC 20-15157. (Studies in Theology: No. 13). 1919. 6.00x (ISBN 0-8401-6013-5). A R Allenson.
Theology of the Holy Spirit. Frederick D. Bruner. LC 76-103445. 1970. pap. 9.95 (ISBN 0-8028-1547-2). Eerdmans.
Theology of the Icon. Leonid Ouspensky. Tr. by Elizabeth Meyendorff from Fr. LC 77-11882. (Illus.). 232p. 1978. pap. 12.95 (ISBN 0-913836-42-7). St Vladimirs.
Theology of the Lutheran Confessions. Friedrich Mildenberger. Tr. by Erwin Lueker. LC 85-47727. 272p. 1986. 19.95 (ISBN 0-8006-0749-X). Fortress.
Theology of the Major Sects. John H. Gerstner. (Twin Brooks Ser). 1960. pap. 6.95 (ISBN 0-8010-3656-9). Baker Bk.
Theology of the New Testament. Rudolf Bultmann. (Contemporary Theology Ser.). 278p. 1951. pap. text ed. write for info. (ISBN 0-02-305580-4, Pub. by Scribner). Macmillan.
Theology of the New Testament. George E. Ladd. 1974. 24.95 (ISBN 0-8028-3443-4). Eerdmans.
Theology of the New Testament. George B. Stevens. 636p. 1918. 19.95 (ISBN 0-567-07215-0, Pub. by T & T Clark Ltd UK). Fortress.
Theology of the New Testament: Jesus & the Gospels, Vol I. Leonard Goppelt. Tr. by John E. Alsup. LC 80-28947. 316p. 1981. 15.95 (ISBN 0-8028-2384-X). Eerdmans.
Theology of the New Testament: The Variety & Unity of the Apostolic Witness to Christ, Vol. II. Leonhard Goppelt. 248p. 1983. 17.95 (ISBN 0-8028-2385-8). Eerdmans.
Theology of the Old Testament. A. B. Davidson. Ed. by S. D. Salmond. 572p. 1904. 16.95 (ISBN 0-567-27206-0, Pub. by T & T Clark Ltd UK). Fortress.
Theology of the Old Testament, 2 Vols. Walther Eichrodt. Tr. by J. Baker. LC 61-11867. (Old Testament Library). 1967. 22.95 ea. Vol. 1, 542p (ISBN 0-664-20352-3). Vol. 2, 574p (ISBN 0-664-20769-3). Westminster.
Theology of the Old Testament. John L. McKenzie. LC 86-9230. 336p. 1986. pap. text ed. 12.00 (ISBN 0-8191-5354-0). U Pr of Amer.
Theology of the Old Testament. Gustave Oehler. 1978. 22.50 (ISBN 0-86524-125-2, 8702). Klock & Klock.
Theology of the Older Testament. J. Barton Payne. 1962. 12.95 (ISBN 0-310-30721-X, 10545P). Zondervan.
Theology of the Program of Restoration of Ezekiel Forty to Forty-Eight. Jon D. Levenson. LC 76-3769. (Harvard Semitic Museum, Monographs). 1976. 9.00 (ISBN 0-89130-105-4, 040010). Scholars Pr GA.
Theology of the Psalms. Hans J. Kraus. Tr. by Keith Crim from Ger. LC 86-17267. 240p. 1986. 24.95 (ISBN 0-8066-2225-3, 10-6292). Augsburg.
Theology of the World. Johannes B. Metz. 1969. pap. 3.95 (ISBN 0-8245-0396-1). Crossroad NY.

Theology of Things. Conrad Bonifazi. LC 76-7549. 1976. Repr. of 1967 ed. lib. bdg. 22.50x (ISBN 0-8371-8838-5, BOTT). Greenwood.

Theology of Uncreated Energies of God. George S. Maloney. (Pere Marquette Lecture Ser.). 1978. 7.95 (ISBN 0-87462-516-5). Marquette.

Theology of Vatican II. rev. ed. Christopher Butler. 238p. 1981. pap. 17.50 (ISBN 0-87061-062-7). Chr Classics.

Theology of William Newton Clarke: Doctoral Dissertation. Claude L. Howe, Jr. Ed. by Edwin S. Gaustad. LC 79-52571. (Baptist Tradition Ser.). 1980. lib. bdg. 14.00x (ISBN 0-405-12440-6). Ayer Co Pubs.

Theology Primer. John J. Davis. LC 81-67093. 128p. (Orig.). 1981. pap. 5.95 (ISBN 0-8010-2912-0). Baker Bk.

Theology, Sociology & Politics: The German Protestant Social Conscience 1890-1933. W. Reginald Ward. 250p. 1979. 29.90 (ISBN 3-261-04617-1). P Lang Pubs.

Theology to Live By. Herman A. Preus. 1977. pap. 7.95 (ISBN 0-570-03739-5, 12-2643). Concordia.

Theonas. facs. ed. Jacques Maritain. LC 74-84325. (Essay Index Reprint Ser). 1933. 17.25 (ISBN 0-8369-1095-8). Ayer Co Pubs.

Theonomy & Autonomy: Studies in Paul Tillich's Engagement with Modern Culture. Ed. by John J. Carey. LC 83-25847. xxii, 287p. 1984. Repr. of 1978 ed. 21.95 (ISBN 0-86554-105-1, MUP/H99). Mercer Univ Pr.

Theonomy in Christian Ethics. Greg Bahnsen. 1977. kivar 12.50 (ISBN 0-934532-00-1). Presby & Reformed.

Theophany. John Stahl. 24p. deluxe ed. 100.00 (ISBN 0-318-21735-X). Evanescent Pr.

Theophany. John Stahl. (Illus.). 24p. 100.00 (ISBN 0-318-21736-8); Proofs of main edition, 1979. 20.00; Early manuscript edition, 1978. 20.00. Evanescent Pr.

Theophoric Personal Names in Ancient Hebrew: A Comparative Study. Jeaneane D. Fowler. (JSOT Supplement Ser.: No. 49). 400p. 1987. text ed. 37.50x (ISBN 1-85075-038-6, Pub. by JSOT Pr England); pap. text ed. 18.95x (ISBN 1-85075-039-4, Pub. by JSOT Pr England). Eisenbrauns.

Theoretical Explorations in African Religion. Ed. by Wim M. J. Van Binsbergen & J. Matthew Schoffeleers. 330p. 1984. 49.95x (ISBN 0-7103-0049-2). Methuen Inc.

Theorie De la Connaissance et Philosophie De la Parole Dans le Brahmanisme Classique. Madeleine Biardeau. (Le Monde D'outre-Mer Passe et Present, Etudes: No. 23). 1963. pap. 34.80x (ISBN 90-2796-178-6). Mouton.

Theorie der Theologie: Enzyklopaedie als Methodenlehre. Friedrich Mildenberger. (Ger.). 164p. 1972. 12.95 (ISBN 3-7668-0384-0, M-7094). French & Eur.

Theories of Americanization: A Critical Study. Isaac B. Berkson. LC 77-87743. (American Education: Its Men, Institutions & Ideas, Ser. 1). 1969. Repr. of 1920 ed. 15.00 (ISBN 0-405-01387-6). Ayer Co Pubs.

Theories of Americanization: A Critical Study, with Special Reference to the Jewish Group. Isaac B. Berkson. LC 78-176558. (Columbia University. Teachers College. Contributions to Education: No. 109). Repr. of 1920 ed. 22.50 (ISBN 0-404-55109-2). AMS Pr.

Theories of Ethics. Ed. by Philippa Foot. (Oxford Readings in Philosophy Ser.). 1967. pap. 8.95x (ISBN 0-19-875005-6). Oxford U Pr.

Theories of Preaching: Selected Readings in the Homiletical Tradition. Ed. by Richard Lischer. 384p. 1987. pap. 30.00 (ISBN 0-939464-46-2); pap. 15.95 (ISBN 0-939464-45-4). Labyrinth Pr.

Theories of Primitive Religion. E. E. Evans-Pritchard. LC 85-22003. (Sir D. Owens Evan Lectures, 1962). 138p. 1985. Repr. of 1965 ed. lib. bdg. 29.75x (ISBN 0-313-24978-4, EPTP). Greenwood.

Theories of Primitive Religion. Edward E. Evans-Pritchard. 1965. pap. 9.95x (ISBN 0-19-823131-8). Oxford U Pr.

Theories of Revelation. H. D. McDonald. 1979. pap. 10.95 (ISBN 0-8010-6081-8). Baker Bk.

Theories of the Chakras. Hiroshi Motoyama. LC 81-51165. 350p. (Orig.). 1982. pap. 8.95 (ISBN 0-8356-0551-5, Quest). Theos Pub Hse.

Theories, Practices & Training Systems of a Sufi School. Canon W. H. T. Gairdner. (Sufi Research Ser.). 1980. pap. 5.95 (ISBN 0-86304-003-9, Pub. by Octagon Pr England). Ins Study Human.

Theory & Experiment in Psychical Research. new ed. William G. Roll. LC 75-7398. (Perspectives in Psychical Research Ser.). (Illus.). 1975. 38.50x (ISBN 0-405-07047-0). Ayer Co Pubs.

Theory & Practice. Jurgen Habermas. Tr. by John Viertel from Ger. LC 72-6227. 320p. 1973. pap. 10.95x (ISBN 0-8070-1527-X, BP489). Beacon Pr.

Theory & Practice of Meditation. 2nd ed. Himalayan Institute. 150p. (Orig.). 1986. pap. 5.95 (ISBN 0-89389-075-8). Himalayan Pubs.

Theory & Practice of Mysticism. Charles M. Addison. 1977. lib. bdg. 59.95 (ISBN 0-8490-2742-X). Gordon Pr.

Theory & Practice of Virtue. Gilbert C. Meilaender. LC 83-40598. 202p. 1985. pap. text ed. 8.95 (ISBN 0-268-01858-8, 85-18581). U of Notre Dame Pr.

Theory & Religious Understanding: A Critique of the Hermeneutics of Joachim Wach. Charles M. Wood. LC 75-26839. (American Academy of Religion. Dissertation Ser.). 1975. pap. 9.95 (ISBN 0-89130-026-0, 010112). Scholars Pr GA.

Theory of Celestial Influence: Man, The Universe, & Cosmic Mystery. Rodney Collin. LC 83-20286. (Illus.). 392p. (Orig.). 1984. pap. 10.95 (ISBN 0-87773-267-1, 72391-0). Shambhala Pubns.

Theory of Christian Education Practice: How Theology Affects Christian Education. Randolph C. Miller. LC 80-15886. 312p. (Orig.). 1980. pap. 12.95 (ISBN 0-89135-049-7). Religious Educ.

Theory of Conscious Harmony. Rodney Collin. LC 84-5494. 211p. 1984. pap. 8.95 (ISBN 0-87773-285-X, 72698-7). Shambhala Pubns.

Theory of Eternal Life. Rodney Collin. LC 83-20288. (Illus.). 132p. (Orig.). 1984. pap. 5.95 (ISBN 0-87773-273-6, 72399-6). Shambhala Pubns.

Theory of Free Will. St. Augustine. (Illus.). 117p. 1984. 66.55 (ISBN 0-89266-466-5). Am Classical Coll Pr.

Theory of History & Society, with Special Reference to the Chronographia of Michael Psellus: Eleventh Century Byzantium. 2nd ed. A. A. Gadolin. (Illus.). 244p. 1986. lib. bdg. 45.00x (ISBN 90-256-0906-6, Pub. by A M Hakkert). Coronet Bks.

Theory of Knowledge of Vital Du Four. John E. Lynch. (Philosophy Ser). 1972. 17.00 (ISBN 0-686-11546-5). Franciscan Inst.

Theory of Moral Sentiments. Adam Smith. (Glasgow Edition of the Works & Correspondence of Adam Smith Ser.). (Illus.). 1976. 54.00x (ISBN 0-19-828189-7). Oxford U Pr.

Theory of Morality. Alan Donagan. LC 76-25634. 1979. pap. 10.00x (ISBN 0-226-15567-6, P838, Phoen); 20.00x (ISBN 0-226-15566-8). U of Chicago Pr.

Theory of Morals. Edgar F. Carritt. LC 73-3021. 144p. 1974. Repr. of 1928 ed. lib. bdg. 22.50 (ISBN 0-8371-6827-9, CATM). Greenwood.

Theory of Morals: An Introduction to Ethical Philosophy. E. F. Carritt. 144p. 1982. Repr. of 1928 ed. lib. bdg. 30.00 (ISBN 0-89984-118-X). Century Bookbindery.

Theory of Sin & the Equilibrium Between the Emotional & the Rational in Man. Anthony L. Villafranca. (Illus.). 104p. 1986. 88.50 (ISBN 0-89266-568-8). Am Classical Coll Pr.

Theory of Sin & the Problem of the Damnation of Man. Lawrence Lovelace. (Illus.). 137p. 1987. 97.75 (ISBN 0-89920-145-8). Am Inst Psych.

Theory of the Good & the Right. Richard B. Brandt. 1979. 32.00x (ISBN 0-19-824550-5); pap. 15.95x (ISBN 0-19-824744-3). Oxford U Pr.

Theory of the Moral Emotions. Edward Westermarck. (Illus.). 161p. 1984. 89.75x (ISBN 0-89266-464-9). Am Classical Coll Pr.

Theory of the Physical Spirit & the Nature of God. John W. Montstuart. (Illus.). 129p. 1987. 98.85 (ISBN 0-89266-591-2). Am Classical Coll Pr.

Theory of the Soul, 2 vols. Emmanuel Swedenborg. (Illus.). 245p. 1986. Set. 187.45 (ISBN 0-89901-261-2). Found Class Reprints.

Theory of the World Soul. A. Fielding-Hall. (Illus.). 161p. 1985. Repr. of 1910 ed. 88.85 (ISBN 0-89901-235-3). Found Class Reprints.

Theory of Toleration under the Later Stuarts. Alexander A. Seaton. 1972. lib. bdg. 23.00x (ISBN 0-374-97233-8, Octagon). Hippocrene Bks.

Theosophia: An Introduction. Lydia Ross & Charles J. Ryan. 1974. pap. 1.75 (ISBN 0-913004-13-8). Point Loma Pub.

Theosophical Articles & Notes. H. P. Blavatsky et al. 300p. 1985. Repr. 10.50 (ISBN 0-938998-29-3). Theosophy.

Theosophical Articles: Articles by Wm. Q. Judge Reprinted from Nineteenth-Century Theosophical Periodicals, 2 vols. William Q. Judge. 1276p. 1980. Set. 25.00 (ISBN 0-938998-20-X). Theosophy.

Theosophical Articles: Reprinted from the Theosophist, Lucifer & other Nineteenth-Century Journals, 3 vols. H. P. Blavatsky. 1692p. 1982. Set. 37.50 (ISBN 0-938998-26-9). Theosophy.

Theosophical Glossary. Helene P. Blavatsky. LC 74-142546. 1971. Repr. of 1892 ed. 46.00x (ISBN 0-8103-3679-0). Gale.

Theosophical Glossary: A Photographic Reproduction of the Original Edition, As First Issued at London, England, 1892. Helena P. Blavatsky. Ed. & intro. by G. R. Mead. vi, 389p. 1930. Repr. of 1892 ed. 8.50 (ISBN 0-938998-04-8). Theosophy.

Theosophical Movement, 1875-1950. rev. ed. xiii, 351p. 1951. 6.00 (ISBN 0-938998-14-5). Cunningham Pr.

Theosophical Movement 1875-1950: Theosophy Company. xiii, 351p. 1951. 6.00 (ISBN 0-938998-14-5). Theosophy.

Theosophist: Oct. Eighteen Seventy-Nine to Sept. Eighteen Eighty. 2nd ed. Helena P. Blavatsky. (Secret Doctrine Reference Ser.). (Illus.). 320p. 1979. pap. 12.00 (ISBN 0-913510-31-9). Wizards.

Theosophy. Robert Ellwood. LC 85-40843. (Illus.). 236p. (Orig.). 1986. pap. 6.50 (ISBN 0-8356-0607-4, Quest). Theos Pub Hse.

Theosophy: An Introduction to Supersensible Knowledge. rev. ed. Rudolf Steiner. LC 78-135997. 195p. (Orig.). 1971. 14.00 (ISBN 0-910142-65-3); pap. 6.95 (ISBN 0-910142-39-4). Anthroposophic.

Theosophy: An Introduction to the Supersensible Knowledge of the World & the Destination of Man. Rudolf Steiner. Tr. by Henry B. Monges from Ger. Tr. of Theosophie: Einfuehrung in uebersinnliche Welterkenntnis und Menschenbestimmung. 200p. 1987. pap. 6.95 (ISBN 0-88010-179-2). Anthroposophic.

Theosophy & Christianity. rev. ed. Henry T. Edge. Ed. by W. Emmett Small & Helen Todd. (Theosophical Manual: No. 12). 80p. 1974. pap. 2.00 (ISBN 0-913004-17-0). Point Loma Pub.

Theosophy: Introduction to the Supersensible Knowledge of the World & the Destination of Man. Rudolf Steiner. Ed. by Gilbert Church. Tr. by Henry B. Monges. Tr. of Theosophie: Einfuehrung in uebersinnliche Welterkenntnis und Mmenschenbestimmung. (Ger.). 195p. 1986. pap. cancelled (ISBN 0-910142-39-4). Anthroposophic.

Theosophy of the Rosicrucian. Rudolf Steiner. Tr. by Mabel Cotterell & D. S. Osmond. (Ger.). 168p. 1981. 15.95 (ISBN 0-85440-113-X, Pub. by Steinerbooks); pap. 11.95 (ISBN 0-85440-401-5). Anthroposophic.

Theosophy: Or, Psychological Religion. Friedrich M. Mueller. LC 73-18830. (Gifford Lectures: 1892). Repr. of 1903 ed. 47.00 (ISBN 0-404-14460-8). AMS Pr.

Theosophy Simplified. Irving S. Cooper. 59.95 (ISBN 0-8490-1191-4). Gordon Pr.

Theosophy Simplified. new ed. Irving S. Cooper. LC 78-64905. 1979. pap. 3.25 (ISBN 0-8356-0519-1, Quest). Theos Pub Hse.

Theosophy: The Path of the Mystic. 3rd rev ed. Katherine Tingley. LC 77-82604. 1977. 8.50 (ISBN 0-911500-33-2); pap. 5.00 (ISBN 0-911500-34-0). Theos U Pr.

Theosophy under Fire: A Miniature Key to Theosophy As Recorded in a Legal Deposition. 2nd ed. Iverson L. Harris. 120p. (Orig.). 1970. pap. 3.00 (ISBN 0-913004-03-0). Point Loma Pub.

Theosophy: What's It All About. Geoffrey Farthing. 1967. 5.25 (ISBN 0-8356-5075-8). Theos Pub Hse.

Theotokos: A Theological Encyclopedia of the Blessed Virgin Mary. Michael O'Carroll. 1982. pap. 19.95 (ISBN 0-89453-268-5). M Glazier.

Therapeutic Value of Yoga. Himalayan International Institute. 108p. (Orig.). pap. 3.95 (ISBN 0-89389-054-5). Himalayan Pubs.

Therapist Responds. Clifton E. Kew & Clinton J. Kew. LC 79-171467. 1972. 6.95 (ISBN 0-8022-2070-3). Philos Lib.

Therapist's View of Personal Goals. Carl R. Rogers. LC 60-11607. (Orig.). 1960. pap. 2.50x (ISBN 0-87574-108-8). Pendle Hill.

Theravada Buddhism in Southeast Asia. Robert C. Lester. LC 71-185154. 1973. 7.95 (ISBN 0-472-06184-4). U of Mich Pr.

Theravada Meditation: The Buddhist Transformation of Yoga. Winston L. King. LC 79-25856. 192p. 1980. 22.75x (ISBN 0-271-00254-9). Pa St U Pr.

There & Back: Memories & Thoughts of a Jewish Actor - Moreuski. LC 67-27245. 256p. 1967. 6.95 (ISBN 0-87527-057-3). Green.

There Can Be a New You: A Positive Approach to Life. Don Polston. LC 77-84892. 160p. 1980. pap. 3.95 (ISBN 0-89081-099-0, 0990). Harvest Hse.

There Is a Place Where You Are Not Alone. Hugh Prather. LC 80-912. 224p. 1980. pap. 6.95 (ISBN 0-385-14778-3, Dolp). Doubleday.

There Is a Rainbow. Louis Gittner. (Illus.). 65p. (Orig.). 1981. pap. 5.95 (ISBN 0-9605492-1-8). Touch Heart.

There Is a Season. Search Institute Staff. Ed. by Dorothy Williams. 1985. program manual 24.95 (ISBN 0-697-02047-9); pap. 4.95 parent book (ISBN 0-697-02046-0); video cassettes avail. Wm C Brown.

There Is a Season: An Inspirational Journal. Robert F. Morneau. LC 84-11622. (Illus.). 175p. 1984. 18.95 (ISBN 0-13-914755-1, Busn); pap. 9.95 (ISBN 0-13-914706-3). P-H.

There Is a Singing Underneath: Meditations in Central Park. Thomas P. Coffey. 128p. 1985. pap. 4.95 (ISBN 0-87193-217-2). Dimension Bks.

There is a Solution. Alvin O. Smith. 1983. 5.95 (ISBN 0-8062-1951-3). Carlton.

There Is a Way. Stefan Nadzo. 129p. 1981. pap. 4.75 (ISBN 0-937226-00-9). Coleman Pub.

There Is a Way: Meditations for a Seeker. Stefan C. Nadzo. LC 80-66831. (Illus.). 129p. (Orig.). 1980. pap. 5.95 (ISBN 0-937226-00-9). Eden's Work.

There Is a Way Out. Vernon Howard. LC 75-11137. 173p. 1982. pap. 6.00 (ISBN 0-87516-472-2). De Vorss.

There Is an Answer. Leith Samuel. pap. 2.50 (ISBN 0-87508-469-9). Chr Lit.

There Is Help for Your Church. Howard Ball. LC 81-65669. 40p. (Orig.). 1981. pap. text ed. 1.50 (ISBN 0-934396-14-0). Churches Alive.

There Is Hope. Oswald C. Hoffman. 104p. 1985. 9.95 (ISBN 0-570-03979-7, 15-2184). Concordia.

There Is No Death. Florence Marryat. 69.95 (ISBN 0-8490-1192-2). Gordon Pr.

There Is No Happiness Without a Feeling. Edward J. Smith. 119p. 1984. 20.00 (ISBN 0-682-40130-7). Exposition Pr FL.

There Is No Male & Female: The Fate of a Dominical Saying in Paul & Gnosticism. Dennis R. MacDonald. LC 86-45200. (Harvard Dissertations in Religion Ser.). 160p. 1987. pap. 14.95 (ISBN 0-8006-7076-0, 1-7076). Fortress.

There Is Something Else. Chuck Patterson. Ed. by Mary H. Wallace. (Illus., Orig.). 1982. pap. 5.95 (ISBN 0-912315-23-7). Word Aflame.

There Is Still Love. Malachi Martin. 224p. 1984. 12.95 (ISBN 0-02-580440-5). Macmillan.

There Must Be Heresies. J. C. Metcalfe. 1963. pap. 2.25 (ISBN 0-87508-922-4). Chr Lit.

There Shall Be One Christ. Ed. by Michael Meilach. (Spirit and Life Ser). 1968. 2.50 (ISBN 0-686-11576-7). Franciscan Inst.

There Shall Be Signs from 1948 to 1982. Wim Malgo. 1980. 2.95 (ISBN 0-937422-00-2). Midnight Call.

There Shines Forth Christ. Julian Stead. 1983. pap. 8.95 (ISBN 0-932506-29-1). St Bedes Pubns.

There We Sat Down: Talmudic Judaism in the Making. Jacob Neusner. pap. 9.95x (ISBN 0-87068-676-3). Ktav.

Therefore. J. Glenn Harvey. (Orig.). 1984. pap. 3.95 (ISBN 0-915059-02-9). Ind Christ Pubns.

Therefore Stand. Wilbur Smith. LC 81-81096. (Shepherd Illustrated Classics Ser.). (Illus.). 660p. 1982. pap. 9.95 (ISBN 0-87983-260-6). Keats.

There's a New Day Coming. Henry Vander Lught. LC 83-81267. 160p. 1983. pap. 3.95 (ISBN 0-89081-389-2, Pub. by Radio B C). Harvest Hse.

There's a New World Coming. Hal Lindsey. 320p. 1975. pap. 3.95 (ISBN 0-553-24555-4). Bantam.

There's a New World Coming. Hal Lindsey. LC 73-87773. 308p. 1973. text ed. 2.95 (ISBN 0-88449-001-7, A324292). Vision Hse.

There's a New World Coming: An In-Depth Analysis of the Book of Revelation. updated ed. Hal Lindsey. 288p. 1984. pap. 6.95 (ISBN 0-89081-440-6). Harvest Hse.

There's a Snake in My Garden. Jill Briscoe. 1977. pap. 5.95 (ISBN 0-310-21821-7, 9256P). Zondervan.

There's a Way Back to God. William MacDonald. 1986. pap. 2.25 (ISBN 0-937396-42-7). Walterick Pubs.

There's an Angel in My Locker. Mary L. Carney. 112p. (Orig.). 1985. pap. 4.95 (ISBN 0-310-28471-6, 11341P). Zondervan.

There's Dynamite in Praise. rev. ed. Don Gossett. 1974. pap. 3.50 (ISBN 0-88368-048-3). Whitaker Hse.

There's More to Being Thin Than Being Thin. Neva Coyle & Marie Chapian. 170p. (Orig.). 1984. pap. 5.95 (ISBN 0-87123-443-2, 210443). Bethany Hse.

There's New Life in the Small Congregation: Why It Happens & How. Ronald Crandall & Ray Sells. LC 83-71697. 120p. (Orig.). 1983. pap. 7.50 (ISBN 0-88177-001-9, DR001B). Discipleship Res.

There's Sheep in My Mirror. Susie Shellenberger. 108p. 1985. pap. 4.50 (ISBN 0-8341-1054-7). Beacon Hill.

Therese. Dorothy Day. 1979. pap. 7.95 (ISBN 0-87243-090-1). Templegate.

Therese Neumann. Johannes Steiner. LC 66-27536. (Illus.). 1967. pap. 5.95 (ISBN 0-8189-0144-6). Alba.

Therese of Lisieux: A Biography. Patricia O'Connor. LC 83-63169. 168p. 1984. pap. 5.95 (ISBN 0-87973-607-0, 607). Our Sunday Visitor.

Therese of Lisieux: A Vocation of Love. Marie-Pascale Ducrocq. LC 81-20512. 77p. (Orig.). 1982. pap. 3.95 (ISBN 0-8189-0431-3). Alba.
Thesauri Hymnologica Hymnarium, 2 Vols. Ed. by Clemens Blume. Repr. of 1909 ed. 60.00 ea. Johnson Repr.
Thesauri Hymnologica Prosarium, 2 Vols in 3. Ed. by Clemens Blume. (Illus.). Repr. of 1922 ed. 60.00 ea. Johnson Repr.
Thesaurus of Medieval Hebrew Poetry, 4 Vols. rev. ed. Israel Davidson. (Library of Jewish Classics). 1970. Set. 150.00x (ISBN 0-87068-003-X). Ktav.
These & Those. Simon Schwab. 3.50 (ISBN 0-87306-076-8). Feldheim.
These Are Gifts: A Study Guide for Understanding Spiritual Gifts. Skip Bell. 72p. 1985. pap. write for info. (ISBN 0-910347-03-4). Chatham Comm Inc.
These Are My People. Mildred T. Howard. (Illus.). 152p. (Orig.). 1984. pap. 5.95 (ISBN 0-89084-242-6). Bob Jones Univ Pr.
These Are My People: The New Testament Church. Harold S. Bender. LC 62-12947. (Conrad Grebel Lecture Ser.). 136p. 1962. pap. 6.95 (ISBN 0-8361-1479-5). Herald Pr.
These Are My Rites: A Brief History of the Eastern Rites of Christianity. Edward E. Finn. LC 79-24937. (Illus.). 104p. 1980. pap. 4.95 (ISBN 0-8146-1058-7). Liturgical Pr.
These Are the Garments. Charles W. Slemming. 1963. pap. 2.95 (ISBN 0-87508-507-5). Chr Lit.
These Are the Sacraments. A. M. Coniaris. 1981. pap. 6.95 (ISBN 0-937032-22-0). Light&Life Pub Co MN.
These Cults. Annie R. Hale. 1981. 8.95 (ISBN 0-686-76751-9). B of A.
These Earthen Vessels. W. T. Purkiser. 118p. 1985. pap. 4.95 (ISBN 0-8341-0977-8). Beacon Hill.
These Live Tomorrow. Clinton L. Scott. 1964. pap. write for info. (ISBN 0-933840-06-3). Unitarian Univ.
These Splendid Priests. facs. ed. Compiled by James J. Walsh. LC 68-29252. (Essay Index Reprint Ser). 1968. Repr. of 1926 ed. 17.00 (ISBN 0-8369-0973-9). Ayer Co Pubs.
These Splendid Sisters. Compiled by James J. Walsh. LC 75-128326. (Essay Index Reprint Ser). 1927. 18.00 (ISBN 0-8369-1856-8). Ayer Co Pubs.
These Stones Will Shout: A New Voice for the Old Testament. Mark Link. LC 82-74383. (Illus.). 300p. 1983. pap. 7.95x (ISBN 0-89505-117-6). Argus Comm.
These Strange Ashes. Elisabeth Elliot. LC 74-25684. 132p. 1979. pap. 6.95 (ISBN 0-06-062234-2, RD 488, HarpR). Har-Row.
These Things Are Written: An Introduction to the Religious Ideas of the Bible. James M. Efird. LC 77-15749. (Biblical Foundations Ser.). 1978. pap. 8.95 (ISBN 0-8042-0073-4). John Knox.
These Things I've Loved. Perry Tanksley. 5.95 (ISBN 0-686-21184-7). Allgood Bks.
These Truths Can Change Your Life. Joseph Murphy. 280p. 1982. pap. 7.50 (ISBN 0-87516-476-5). De Vorss.
These Two Commandments. 2nd ed. Boyce Mouton. (Orig.). 1978. pap. 2.95 (ISBN 0-89900-138-6). College Pr Pub.
Theses on Islam, Middle East, & Northwest Africa, 1880-1978. Compiled by Peter Sluglett. 160p. 1983. 27.00x (ISBN 0-7201-1651-1). Mansell.
Theseus & the Minotaur. Adapted by C. J. Naden. LC 80-50067. (Illus.). 32p. 1980. PLB 9.79 (ISBN 0-89375-363-7); pap. 2.50 (ISBN 0-89375-367-X). Troll Assocs.
Theseus & the Road to Athens. Pamela Espeland. LC 80-27713. (Myths for Modern Children Ser.). (Illus.). 32p. 1981. PLB 6.95 (ISBN 0-87614-141-6). Carolrhoda Bks.
Thesis of Paradise Lost. Gerald A. Wilkes. LC 76-28374. 1976. Repr. of 1961 ed. lib. bdg. 20.00 (ISBN 0-8414-9514-9). Folcroft.
Thessalonian Correspondence: Pauline Rhetoric & Millenarian Piety. Robert Jewett. LC 86-45204. (Foundations & Facets Ser.). 256p. 1986. text ed. 17.95 (ISBN 0-8006-2111-5, 1-2111). Fortress.
Thessalonian Epistles. John F. Walvoord. 1958. pap. 4.95 (ISBN 0-310-34071-3, 6392P). Zondervan.
Thessalonians, Vol. X. Beacon Bible Commentary Staff. 6.95 (ISBN 0-8010-0743-7). Baker Bk.
Thessalonians. David P. Kuske. (People's Bible Ser.). 1984. pap. 4.95 (ISBN 0-8100-0193-4, 15N0406). Northwest Pub.
Thessalonians. William MacDonald. 5.00 (ISBN 0-686-27147-5); pap. 3.95 (ISBN 0-937396-43-5). Walterick Pubs.
Thessalonians. (Erdmans Commentaries Ser.). 2.95 (ISBN 0-8010-3408-6). Baker Bk.
Thessalonians. D. E. Whiteley. (New Clarendon Bible Ser). (Illus.). 1969. 8.95x (ISBN 0-19-836906-9). Oxford U Pr.
Thessalonians & Galations. Stephen Doyle. (Read & Pray Ser.). 1980. 1.75 (ISBN 0-8199-0635-2). Franciscan Herald.
Thessalonians, Philippians, & Philemon One & Two. Ernest W. Saunders. Ed. by John Hayes. (Knox Preaching Guides Ser.). 1983. pap. 4.95. John Knox.
Thessalonians, Timothy & Titus. William Hendriksen. 404p. 1979. 21.95 (ISBN 0-8010-4213-5). Baker Bk.
They Built on Rock: The Story of the Celtic Christian Church. Diana Leathem. 1977. lib. bdg. 59.95 (ISBN 0-8490-2743-8). Gordon Pr.
They Built with Faith: True Tales of God's Guidance in L.D.S. Chapel Building World-Wide. H. Dyke Walton. LC 79-89353. 125p. 1979. 5.95 (ISBN 0-88290-122-2). Horizon Utah.
They Came to Louisiana: Letters of a Catholic Mission, 1854-1882. Ed. by Sr. Dorothea O. McCants. LC 72-96258. (Illus.). Repr. of 1970 ed. 72.80 (ISBN 0-8357-9392-3, 2020997). Bks Demand UMI.
They Chose Life: Jewish Resistance in the Holocaust. Yehuda Bauer. LC 73-89085. (Illus.). 64p. (Orig.). 1973. pap. 2.00 (ISBN 0-87495-000-7). Am Jewish Comm.
They Chose to Live: The Racial Agony of an American Church. J. Herbert Gilmore. LC 72-75577. pap. 51.50 (ISBN 0-317-07872-0, 2012911). Bks Demand UMI.
They Cry, Too. Lucille Lavender. 176p. 1986. pap. 6.95 (ISBN 0-310-41651-5, 9970P). Zondervan.
They Dwell in Monasteries. Frank Monaco. (Illus.). 80p. (Orig.). 1982. pap. 7.95 (ISBN 0-8164-2409-8, HarpR). Har-Row.
They Followed His Call. Adrienne Von Speyr. Tr. by Erasmo Leiva-Merikakis from Ger. LC 86-80294. Tr. of Sie Folgten Seinem Ruf. 137p. (Orig.). 1986. pap. 6.95 (ISBN 0-89870-100-7). Ignatius Pr.
They Followed Jesus: Word Search Puzzles. John H. Tiner. 48p. pap. 2.50 (ISBN 0-87239-586-3, 2784). Standard Pub.
They Fought Back: The Story of Jewish Resistance in Nazi Europe. Yuri Suhl. 316p. Repr. 7.95 (ISBN 0-686-95093-3). ADL.
They Found the Secret: Twenty Lives that Reveal a Touch of Eternity. V. Raymond Edman. 176p. 1984. pap. 5.95 (ISBN 0-310-24051-4, 9564P, Clarion Class). Zondervan.
They Have Found a Faith. facsimile ed. Marcus L. Bach. LC 74-134049. (Essay Index Reprint Ser). Repr. of 1946 ed. 18.00 (ISBN 0-8369-2481-9). Ayer Co Pubs.
They Looked for a City. Lydia Buksbazen. 1977. pap. 3.95 (ISBN 0-87508-041-3). Chr Lit.
They Looked for a City. LC 58-17705. 1955. pap. 3.95 (ISBN 0-915540-15-0). Friends Israel-Spearhead Pr.
They Marched to Heaven's Drumbeat. Clarence B. Finsaas. 1985. pap. 5.95 (ISBN 0-88419-193-1). Creation Hse.
They Meet the Master. Robert E. Coleman. 160p. 1979. pap. 5.95 (ISBN 0-8007-1037-1). Revell.
They Met God: A Number of Conversion Accounts & Personal Testimonies of God's Presence & Leading in the Lives of Children. Ed. by J. C. Wenger. LC 64-15344. pap. 48.00 (ISBN 0-317-26611-X, 2025422). Bks Demand UMI.
They Met Jesus, Neighborhood Bible Study. Marilyn Kunz & Catherine Schell. 1971. pap. 2.95 (ISBN 0-8423-7080-3). Tyndale.
They Met the Master: Sermons on Contemporary Saints. Carroll R. Gunkel. 1980. 4.50 (ISBN 0-89536-388-7, 2035). CSS of Ohio.
They Never Stopped Teaching. Richard Spindle. 96p. 1982. pap. 2.50 (ISBN 0-8341-0735-X). Beacon Hill.
They of Rome. Lois Parker. 128p. 1980. pap. 5.95 (ISBN 0-8127-0308-1). Review & Herald.
They Overcame: An Exposition of the First Three Chapters of Revelation. Marcus L. Loane. (Canterbury Books). 144p. 1981. pap. 3.95 (ISBN 0-8010-5609-8). Baker Bk.
They Preached Liberty. Franklin P. Cole. LC 76-26327. 1976. 5.95 (ISBN 0-913966-16-9, Liberty Pr); pap. 1.25 (ISBN 0-913966-20-7). Liberty Fund.
They Sang with the Spirit. Frank Eifert & Evelyn Stenbock. 104p. 1983. pap. 3.95 (ISBN 0-8341-0824-0). Beacon Hill.
They Saw His Glory: Stories of Conversion & Service. Ed. by Byron Burkholder. 186p. (Orig.). 1984. pap. 5.95 (ISBN 0-919797-40-7). Kindred Pr.
They Saw It Happen. Gordon Lindsay. 1.50 (ISBN 0-89985-010-3). Christ Nations.
They Saw the Lord: The Resurrection Appearances. Bonnell Spencer. LC 83-61765. 235p. 1983. pap. 8.95 (ISBN 0-8192-1332-2). Morehouse.
They Shall Be Mine. John Tallach. 128p. 1981. pap. 5.45 (ISBN 0-85151-320-4). Banner of Truth.
They Shall Be My People. John Timmer. LC 83-15380. 200p. 1983. pap. 6.95 (ISBN 0-933140-82-7); pap. 5.95 leader's guide (ISBN 0-933140-83-5). CRC Pubns.
They Speak with Other Tongues. John Sherrill. 144p. 1966. pap. 3.50 (ISBN 0-8007-8041-8, Spire Bks). Revell.
They Were There. R. Andersen & R. Barlag. 1977. pap. 4.50 (ISBN 0-570-03769-7, 12-2704). Concordia.
They Were Women Like Me: Women of the New Testament in Devotions for Today. Joy Jacobs. 216p. 1985. 14.95 (ISBN 0-13-917048-0); pap. 7.95 (ISBN 0-13-917030-8). P-H.
They Were Women, Too. Joy Jacobs. LC 1-67319. 375p. 1981. pap. 8.95 (ISBN 0-87509-304-3). Chr Pubns.
Thiagaraja: A Great Musician Saint. M. S. Aiyar. 238p. 1986. Repr. 20.00X (ISBN 0-8364-1766-6, Pub. by Usha). South Asia Bks.
Thief in the Night. William Sears. 320p. 1961. 8.95 (ISBN 0-85398-096-9); pap. 3.95 (ISBN 0-85398-008-X). G Ronald Pub.
Thine Enemy. Ralph W. Neighbour, Sr. 1986. pap. 5.95 (ISBN 0-937931-06-3). Global TN.
Thine Is the Kingdom. Heini Arnold. 36p. 1985. pap. 1.50 (ISBN 0-87486-182-9). Plough.
Things. Sandy Larsen. 144p. 1984. pap. 3.95 (ISBN 0-88207-109-2). Victor Bks.
Things Divine & Supernatural Conceived by Analogy with Things Natural & Human. Peter Browne. Ed. by Rene Wellek. LC 75-11203. (British Philosophers & Theologians of the 17th & 18th Centuries: Vol. 9). 1976. Repr. of 1733 ed. lib. bdg. 51.00 (ISBN 0-8240-1758-7). Garland Pub.
Things for Kids to Do. Thelma Griffhorn. 132p. 1985. pap. 6.95 (ISBN 0-89693-525-6). Victor Bks.
Things I Have Learned: Chapel Talks. Bob Jones, Sr. 224p. 1944. pap. 3.95 (ISBN 0-89084-022-9). Bob Jones Univ Pr.
Things My Children Are Teaching Me. Charles B. Bugg. LC 81-70409. 1982. pap. 3.95 (ISBN 0-8054-5650-3). Broadman.
Things Surely to Be Believed. E. Schuyler English. 1970. Repr. of 1946 ed. 4.95 (ISBN 0-87213-146-7). Loizeaux.
Things That Accompany Salvation. R. K. Campbell. 40p. pap. 0.45 (ISBN 0-88172-013-5). Believers Bkshelf.
Things That Are Not Caesar's. Jacques Maritain. Tr. by J. F. Scanlan. 227p. 1983. Repr. of 1930 ed. lib. bdg. 40.00 (ISBN 0-89760-589-6). Telegraph Bks.
Things That Make for Peace: A Personal Search for a New Way of Life. John Schramm & Mary Schramm. LC 76-3861. 96p. (Orig.). 1976. pap. 5.95 (ISBN 0-8066-1537-0, 110-6400). Augsburg.
Things That Make for Peace: Biblical Meditations. Barbara Gerlach. (Illus.). 64p. (Orig.). 1983. pap. 4.95 (ISBN 0-8298-0664-4). Pilgrim NY.
Things the Baptism in the Holy Spirit Will Do for You. Alice Shevkenek. 1976. pap. 1.00 (ISBN 0-89350-005-4). Fountain Pr.
Things to Come. J. Dwight Pentecost. 1958. 18.95 (ISBN 0-310-30890-9, 6355, Pub by Dunhan). Zondervan.
Things to Come for Planet Earth. Aaron L. Plueger. 1977. pap. 3.95 (ISBN 0-570-03762-X, 12-2691). Concordia.
Things to Make & Do for Christmas. Ellen Weiss. (Things to Make & Do Bks.). 1980. PLB 8.90 (ISBN 0-531-02293-5, C02); pap. 3.95 (ISBN 0-531-02145-9). Watts.
Things to Make & Do for Thanksgiving. (Things to Make & Do Ser.). 1977. lib. bdg. 8.90 (ISBN 0-531-01324-3). Watts.
Things to Make & Do for Valentine's Day. Tomie De Paola. (Things to Make & Do Ser.). (Illus.). 48p. 1976. PLB 8.90 (ISBN 0-531-01187-9). Watts.
Things Unutterable: Paul's Ascent to Paradise in Its Greco-Roman, Judaic & Early Christian Contexts. James Tabor. LC 86-18924. (Studies in Judaism Ser.). 166p. (Orig.). 1986. lib. bdg. 23.50 (ISBN 0-8191-5643-4, Pub. by Studies in Judaism); pap. text ed. 11.50 (ISBN 0-8191-5644-2, Pub. by Studies in Judaism). U Pr of Amer.
Things Which Become Sound Doctrine. J. Dwight Pentecost. 1970. Repr. 5.95 (ISBN 0-310-30901-8, 6504P). Zondervan.
Things Which Soon Must Come to Pass: Commentary on Revelation. Philip Mauro. 1984. Repr. 14.95 (ISBN 0-317-11813-7). Reiner.
Think. 2nd ed. Gerard P. Weber et al. (Word Is Life Ser.). 1979. 3.60 (ISBN 0-02-658700-9); tchrs. ed. 8.00 (ISBN 0-02-658710-6); family handbook 0.64 (ISBN 0-02-658750-5). Benziger Pub Co.
Think It Through. George Howard. 48p. (Orig.). 1984. pap. 2.95 (ISBN 0-89109-163-7). NavPress.
Think Jewish: A Contemporary View of Judaism, a Jewish View of Today's World. Zalman I. Posner. LC 78-71323. 1979. 8.95 (ISBN 0-9602394-0-5); pap. 4.95 (ISBN 0-9602394-1-3). Kesher.
Think of Your Future. William MacDonald. pap. 1.95 (ISBN 0-937396-44-3). Walterick Pubs.
Think on These Things. Jiddu Krishnamurti. 1970. pap. 4.95 (ISBN 0-06-080192-1, P192, PL). Har-Row.
Think on These Things. John Maxwell. 128p. 1979. pap. 2.95 (ISBN 0-8341-0600-0). Beacon Hill.
Think Your Troubles Away. Ernest Holmes. Ed. by Willis H. Kinnear. 96p. 1963. pap. 4.50 (ISBN 0-911336-29-X). Sci of Mind.
Thinking about Ethics. Richard Purtill. 160p. 1976. pap. text ed. write for info. (ISBN 0-13-917716-7). P-H.
Thinking about Faith: An Introductory Guide to Philosophy & Religion. David Cook. 1986. pap. 8.95 (ISBN 0-310-44131-5). Zondervan.
Thinking about God. Brian Davies. 1986. pap. 16.95 (ISBN 0-317-52367-8, HarpR). Har-Row.
Thinking about God. Fisher Humphreys. LC 74-81556. 228p. (Orig.). 1974. pap. 9.00 (ISBN 0-914520-00-8). Insight Pr.
Thinking about Knowing. Alan Howard. 1985. pap. 5.95 (ISBN 0-916786-81-1). St George Bk Serv.
Thinking about Morality. William K. Frankena. (Michigan Faculty Ser.). 112p. 1980. pap. 4.95 (ISBN 0-472-06316-2). U of Mich Pr.
Thinking about Paul: His Life, Letters, & Theology. Marion J. Soards. 224p. (Orig.). 1987. pap. 8.95 (ISBN 0-8091-2864-0). Paulist Pr.
Thinking about Religion: A Philosophical Introduction to Religion. Richard Purtill. 1978. pap. text ed. write for info (ISBN 0-13-917724-8). P-H.
Thinking Through Confucius. David L. Hall & Roger T. Ames. (Systematic Philosophy Ser.). 320p. 1987. 39.50X (ISBN 0-88706-376-4); pap. 12.95x (ISBN 0-88706-377-2). State U NY Pr.
Thinking Through Thessalonians. Wilbur Fields. LC 77-1794. (Bible Study Textbook Ser.). (Illus.). 1963. 12.20 (ISBN 0-89900-042-8). College Pr Pub.
Third Adam. Frances C. Goodrich. LC 66-22003. 1967. 5.95 (ISBN 0-8022-0608-5). Philos Lib.
Third Collection: Papers by Bernard J. F. Longergan, S. J. Ed. by Frederick E. Crowe. LC 84-61028. 272p. 1985. pap. 12.95 (ISBN 0-8091-0363-X); pap. 9.95 (ISBN 0-8091-2650-8). Paulist Pr.
Third Eye. T. Lobsang Rampa. 1974. pap. 2.50 (ISBN 0-345-29023-2). Ballantine.
Third Eye, Book I. Wright Alton. (Third Eye Bks.). (Illus.). 160p. (Orig.). Date not set. pap. 10.95. Creat Gospel Prod A Wright.
Third-Eye Theology: Theology in Formation in Asian Settings. Choan-Seng Song. LC 79-4208. pap. 72.00 (ISBN 0-317-26666-7, 2025121). Bks Demand UMI.
Third Force in Missions. Paul Pomerville. 196p. 1986. pap. 9.95 (ISBN 0-913573-15-9). Hendrickson MA.
Third Generation Greek Americans: A Study of Religious Attitudes. Alice Scourby. Ed. by Francesco Cordasco. LC 80-893. (American Ethnic Groups Ser.). lib. bdg. 16.00x (ISBN 0-405-13454-1). Ayer Co Pubs.
Third Jewish Catalog: Creating Community. Ed. by Sharon Strassfeld & Michael Strassfeld. LC 80-19818. (Illus.). 416p. 1980. 9.95 (ISBN 0-8276-0183-2, 466). Jewish Pubns.
Third Music. Ann R. Colton. LC 82-71249. (Illus.). 432p. 1982. 15.95 (ISBN 0-917187-00-8). A R C Pub.
Third Peacock. Robert F. Capon. 108p. (Orig.). 1986. pap. 7.50 (ISBN 0-86683-497-4, HarpR). Har-Row.
Third Person. Lehman Strauss. 1954. 7.95 (ISBN 0-87213-827-5). Loizeaux.
Third Reformation: Charismatic Movements & the Lutheran Tradition. Carter Lindberg. LC 83-11371. x, 346p. 1983. 24.95 (ISBN 0-86554-075-6, MUP/H83). Mercer Univ Pr.
Third Reich & the Christian Churches. Ed. by Peter Matheson. 128p. Date not set. pap. 8.25 (ISBN 0-567-29105-7, Pub. by T & T Clark Ltd UK). Fortress.
Third Reich & the Palestine Question. Francis R. Nicosia. 335p. 1986. text ed. 35.00x (ISBN 0-292-72731-3). U of Tex Pr.
Third Sikh War? Towards or Away from Khalistan? D. H. Butani. 137p. 1986. 25.00x (ISBN 81-85002-02-9, Pub. by Promilla). South Asia Bks.
Third Testament of the Holy Bible. S. Joseph Iannarelli. 1985. 5.95 (ISBN 0-533-06645-X). Vantage.
Third Thousand Years. W. Cleon Skousen. 1964. 12.95 (ISBN 0-88494-122-1). Bookcraft Inc.
Third Wave & the Local Church. Dennis M. Davis & Steve Clapp. 175p. (Orig.). 1983. pap. 8.00 (ISBN 0-914527-54-1). C-Four Res.

Third Way. Paul M. Lederach. LC 80-26280. 152p. 1980. pap. 6.95 (ISBN 0-8361-1934-7). Herald Pr.
Third World Liberation Theologies: A Reader. Ed. by Deane W. Ferm. LC 85-15302. 400p. (Orig.). 1986. pap. 16.95 (ISBN 0-88344-516-6). Orbis Bks.
Third World Liberation Theologies: An Introductory Survey. Deane W. Ferm. LC 85-15534. pap. 10.95 (ISBN 0-88344-515-8). Orbis Bks.
Third World Tour of Kirpal Singh. Ed. by Russell Perkins. (Illus.). 1974. pap. 2.50 (ISBN 0-89142-008-8). Sant Bani Ash.
Thirsting for God: A Devotional Study of the Psalms in Light of Their Historical Background. C. Donald Cole. LC 85-72918. 350p. 1986. pap. 8.95 (ISBN 0-89107-376-0, Crossway Bks). Good News.
Thirsting for God in Scripture. James McCaffrey. 96p. 1984. pap. 2.95 (ISBN 0-914544-55-1). Living Flame Pr.
Thirteen Americans. Ed. by Louis Finkelstein. LC 68-26190. (Essay & General Literature Index Reprint Ser.). 1969. Repr. of 1953 ed. 23.50x (ISBN 0-8046-0219-0, Pub by Kennikat). Assoc Faculty Pr.
Thirteen Commandments. J. Sig Paulson. 154p. 1964. pap. 3.95 (ISBN 0-317-20872-1). CSA Pr.
Thirteen Going on Twenty. Penny V. Scwab. LC 83-12292. 144p. (Orig.). 1983. pap. 4.95 (ISBN 0-87123-587-0, 210587). Bethany Hse.
Thirteen Lessons in Christian Doctrine. 11th ed. Denver Sizemore. 1968. pap. 2.95 (ISBN 0-89900-136-X). College Pr Pub.
Thirteen Lessons in I & II Peter. Victor Knowles. (Bible Study Guide Ser.). 105p. (Orig.). pap. 2.95 (ISBN 0-89900-175-0). College Pr Pub.
Thirteen Lessons on Ephesians. Kenny Boles. (Bible Student Study Guides). 1978. pap. 2.95 (ISBN 0-89900-159-9). College Pr Pub.
Thirteen Lessons on Galatians. Kenny Boles. (Bible Student Study Guides). 1978. pap. 2.95 (ISBN 0-89900-158-0). College Pr Pub.
Thirteen Lessons on I & II Thessalonians. Tom Friskney. LC 82-71253. (Bible Student Study Guide Ser.). 122p. 1982. pap. 2.95 (ISBN 0-89900-172-6). College Pr Pub.
Thirteen Lessons on I, II, III John. Knofel Staton. LC 80-69722. (Bible Student Study Guide Ser.). 149p. 1980. pap. 2.95 (ISBN 0-89900-169-6). College Pr Pub.
Thirteen Lessons on James & Jude. Donald Fream. (Bible Student Study Guides). 1979. pap. 2.95 (ISBN 0-89900-161-0). College Pr Pub.
Thirteen Lessons on Philippians, Colossians & Philemon. Kenny Boles. LC 79-53714. (Bible Student Study Guides). (Orig.). 1979. pap. 2.95 (ISBN 0-89900-163-7). College Pr Pub.
Thirteen Lessons on Romans, Vol. II. Sherwood Smith. LC 81-65030. (Bible Student Study Guides Ser.). 114p. 1981. pap. 2.95 (ISBN 0-89900-170-X). College Pr Pub.
Thirteen Lessons on Romans, Vol. I. Sherwood Smith. LC 79-55509. (Bible Student Study Guides). 113p. (Orig.). 1980. pap. 2.95 (ISBN 0-89900-164-5). College Pr Pub.
Thirteen Lessons on the Gospel of Mark. Rhoderick Ice. (Bible Student Study Guides Ser). 1977. pap. 2.95 (ISBN 0-89900-151-3). College Pr Pub.
Thirteen Lessons on Timothy & Titus. John Pommert. (Bible Student Study Guides). 2.95 (ISBN 0-89900-162-9). College Pr Pub.
Thirteen Men Who Changed the World. Henk S. Vigeveno. LC 86-3209. (Illus.). 154p. 1986. pap. 5.95 (ISBN 0-8307-1150-3, 5418817) (ISBN 0-8307-1174-0, 6102292). Regal.
Thirteenth Apostle. Eugene Vale. 352p. 1983. pap. 7.95 (ISBN 0-9609674-0-0). Jubilee Pr.
Thirteenth-Century Church at St. Denis. Caroline A. Bruzelius. LC 85-3354. 256p. 1986. 30.00 (ISBN 0-300-03190-4). Yale U Pr.
Thirteenth-Century Tomb Near Fuzhou. Fujian Sheng Museum Staff. 145p. 1982. 100.00x (ISBN 0-317-43751-8, Pub. by Han-Shan Tang Ltd). State Mutual Bk.
Thirty Bible Reasons Why Christ Heals Today. Gordon Lindsay. (Divine Healing & Health Ser.). 1.25 (ISBN 0-89985-031-6). Christ Nations.
Thirty-Day Experiment in Prayer. Robert Wood. LC 78-65160. 1978. pap. 3.75 (ISBN 0-8358-0380-5). Upper Room.
Thirty Day Mental Diet. Willis Kinnear. 144p. 1965. pap. 7.95 (ISBN 0-911336-20-6). Sci of Mind.
Thirty Days Are Not Enough: More Images for Meditative Journaling. Robert Wood. 112p. (Orig.). 1983. pap. 3.75 (ISBN 0-8358-0445-3). Upper Room.
Thirty Days to Victorious Living: A Devotional Workbook. Joanna S. Seaman. 84p. (Orig.). 1986. pap. write for info. (ISBN 0-939113-00-7). Ansley Pubns.
Thirty-Eight Recipes for Bulletin Boards & Art Projects That Christian Kids Can Make. Jean Staffeld et al. (Illus.). 1978. pap. 4.95 (ISBN 0-570-03774-3, 12-2721). Concordia.
Thirty Favorite Bible Stories with Discussion Questions. John C. Reid. LC 81-21514. (Illus.). 192p. (Orig.). 1982. pap. 4.95 (ISBN 0-87239-498-0, 3373). Standard Pub.
Thirty Favorite Novenas. 31p. 1975. pap. 0.40 (ISBN 0-89555-105-5). TAN Bks Pubs.
Thirty Five Handicraft Projects for Children. LC 12-2957. 1982. pap. 4.95 (ISBN 0-570-03864-2). Concordia.
Thirty-Five Years of Luther Research. Johann M. Reu. LC 79-13505. (Illus.). Repr. of 1917 ed. 16.50 (ISBN 0-404-05284-3). AMS Pr.
Thirty-Four Two-Minute Talks for Youth & Adults. Stanley Cornils. 64p. 1985. pap. 2.95 (ISBN 0-87239-868-4, 2883). Standard Pub.
Thirty Hymns of the Wesleys. David Wright & Jill Wright. 65p. 1986. pap. 4.95 (ISBN 0-85364-414-4, Pub. by Paternoster UK). Attic Pr.
Thirty Minor Upanishads: Including the Yoga Upanishads. K. N. Aiyar. 300p. 1980. Repr. of 1914 ed. 16.95 (ISBN 0-935548-00-9). Santarasa Pubns.
Thirty Minute Panorama of the Bible. Robert G. Flood. (Orig.). 1984. pap. 1.95 (ISBN 0-8024-8747-5). Moody.
Thirty-One Day Experiment. Dick Purnell. LC 83-49023. 63p. (Orig.). 1984. pap. 2.95 (ISBN 0-89840-058-9). Heres Life.
Thirty Seconds with Your Bible: Learn How to Chart Your Horoscope, Predict Your Destiny, Luck, Fortune... Donatus O. Enyi. LC 86-70272. (Illus.). 80p. 1986. 9.95 (ISBN 0-937171-00-X); pap. 6.95 (ISBN 0-937171-01-8). D Enyi.
Thirty Six Creative Ideas for Children in the Church School. L. Brokering. LC 12-2958. 1982. pap. 4.95 (ISBN 0-570-03865-0). Concordia.
Thirty-Six Devotionals for Women's Groups. Idalee Vonk. LC 81-52993. 112p. (Orig.). 1982. pap. 3.95 (ISBN 0-87239-493-X, 3216). Standard Pub.
Thirty-Three Prayers. Gi-Gi Grant. 1986. 6.95 (ISBN 0-533-05468-0). Vantage.
Thirty Years a Watchtower Slave. William J. Schnell. (Direction Bks). pap. 3.95 (ISBN 0-8010-7933-0). Baker Bk.
Thirty Years of American Zionism, Vol.1. Louis Lipsky. Ed. by Moshe Davis. LC 77-70718. (America & the Holy Land Ser.). 1977. Repr. of 1927 ed. lib. bdg. 26.50x (ISBN 0-405-10263-1). Ayer Co Pubs.
Thirty Years of Buddhist Studies. Edward Conze. 274p. 1967. 40.00x (ISBN 0-317-39172-0, Pub. by Luzac & Co Ltd). State Mutual Bk.
This Call We Share. Martha Nelson. LC 76-29804. 1977. 8.50 (ISBN 0-8054-2701-5). Broadman.
This Child Shall Be Lent Unto the Lord. C. M. Ward. (Illus.). 32p. 1967. pap. 0.60 12 for 6.00 (ISBN 0-88243-822-0, 02-0822). Gospel Pub.
This Day Is Ours. Jacques Leclercq. Tr. by Dinah Livingstone from Fr. LC 80-50314. Orig. Title: Jour de L'Homme. 128p. (Orig.). 1980. pap. 1.74 (ISBN 0-88344-504-2). Orbis Bks.
This Day Is the Lord's. Corrie ten Boom. 1982. pap. 2.75 (ISBN 0-515-06734-2). Jove Pubns.
This Day is the Lord's Day. Boom. 2.75 (ISBN 0-318-18182-7). WCTU.
This Double Thread. Walter Starcke. 160p. 1969. 12.95 (ISBN 0-227-67738-2). Attic Pr.
This Drama Called Life: An Introduction to Advanced Christianity. Florence DeGroat. (Illus.). 49p. 1984. pap. 6.95 (ISBN 0-942494-89-X). Coleman Pub.
This Family Business. Mark Lee & James M. Grant. LC 82-73873. 150p. 1984. pap. 6.45 (ISBN 0-87509-328-0); pap. 2.95 (ISBN 0-87509-356-6). Chr Pubns.
This Far by Faith: American Black Worship & Its African Roots. Henry Mitchell et al. Ed. by Robert Hovda. LC 77-89744. 1977. pap. 7.95 (ISBN 0-918208-05-X). Liturgical Conf.
This Gift Is Mine. Ralph W. Neighbour. LC 73-93907. 1974. 5.50 (ISBN 0-8054-5223-0). Broadman.
This Gospel of the Kingdom: Dilemmas in Evangelism. George S. Gunn. 167p. 1964. 5.95 (ISBN 0-227-67660-2). Attic Pr.
This Gospel...Shall Be Preached: A History & Theology of Assemblies of God Foreign Missions to 1959. Gary B. McGee. LC 86-80015. 288p. (Orig.). 1986. pap. 8.95 (ISBN 0-88243-511-6, 02-0511). Gospel Pub.
This Grace Given. David H. Read. 144p. (Orig.). 1984. pap. 7.95 (ISBN 0-8028-0025-4). Eerdmans.
This Great Company: A Treasury of Sermons by Outstanding Preachers of the Christian Tradition. Ed. by David Poling. LC 74-75977. (Illus.). 1976. 8.95 (ISBN 0-87983-123-5); pap. 4.95 (ISBN 0-87983-124-3). Keats.
This Ground Is Holy: Church Sanctuary & Central American Refugees. Ignatius Bau. LC 84-60406. 304p. (Orig.). 1985. pap. 9.95 (ISBN 0-8091-2720-2). Paulist Pr.
This Hebrew Lord. John S. Spong. 1976. pap. 4.95 (ISBN 0-8164-2133-1, HarpR). Har-Row.
This I Believe. Charles T. Crabtree. LC 81-84913. 160p. (Orig.). 1982. pap. 2.95 (ISBN 0-88243-758-5, 02-0758). Gospel Pub.
This I Believe. Donald D. Day. 224p. 1972. pap. 1.95 (ISBN 0-9600500-1-9). Three D Pubs.
This I Can Believe. facs. ed. Alfred G. Walton. LC 79-142708. (Essay Index Reprint Ser). 1935. 18.00 (ISBN 0-8369-2207-7). Ayer Co Pubs.
This Immortal People: A Short History of the Jewish People. Emil B. Cohn. LC 84-62563. 180p. (Orig.). 1985. pap. 5.95 (ISBN 0-8091-2693-1). Paulist Pr.
This Is God Speaking: Twenty-Six Lessons for Children's Church. Jessie Sullivan. LC 81-18476. (Illus.). 112p. (Orig.). 1982. pap. 7.95 (ISBN 0-87239-496-4, 3371). Standard Pub.
This Is God's Home. Sri Chinmoy. 50p. (Orig.). pap. 2.00 (ISBN 0-88497-233-X). Aum Pubns.
This Is It. Bhagwan Shree Rajneesh. Ed. by ma Prem Maneesha. LC 82-230731. (Initiation Talks Ser.). (Illus.). 672p. (Orig.). 1979. 19.95 (ISBN 0-88050-156-1). Chidvilas Found.
This Is It. Alan W. Watts. 1972. pap. 3.95 (ISBN 0-394-71904-2, Vin). Random.
This Is It: It's How You Live It Now, the Endless Meditation. Bhagavan Jivananda. (Orig.). pap. cancelled (ISBN 0-941404-27-7). Falcon Pr AZ.
This Is Luther. Ewald Plass. 1984. pap. 8.95 (ISBN 0-570-03942-8, 12-2875). Concordia.
This Is My God. Herman Wouk. LC 79-78741. 1959. 14.95 (ISBN 0-385-02158-5). Doubleday.
This Is My God: The Jewish Way of Life. Herman Wouk. 1986. pap. 8.95 (ISBN 0-671-62258-7, Touchstone Bks). S&S.
This Is My Home, Lord. Helen Lee. 128p. 1983. pap. 4.95 (ISBN 0-86683-683-7, HarpR). Har-Row.
This Is My Song of Songs. Genevieve W. Syverud. (Orig.). 1966. pap. 2.95 (ISBN 0-8066-0613-4, 11-9495). Augsburg.
This Is My Story, This Is My Song. Mary Bramer. 1984. pap. 6.95 (ISBN 0-570-03923-1, 12-2857). Concordia.
This Is Our Hope. R. E. Orchard. 150p. 1966. 3.95 (ISBN 0-88243-617-1, 02-0617). Gospel Pub.
This Is Our Mass. Thomas Coyle. 144p. 1985. pap. 3.50 (ISBN 0-89622-233-0). Twenty-Third.
This Is Our St. Rose Church in Proctor Minnesota. Claire W. Schumacher. (Illus.). 100p. 1976. pap. 3.00 (ISBN 0-917378-02-4). Schumacher Pubns.
This Is Reality. Roy E. Davis. 160p. 1983. pap. 3.95 (ISBN 0-317-20863-2). CSA Pr.
This Is That: Personal Experiences, Sermons & Writings. Aimee S. McPherson. Ed. by Daonald W. Dayton. (Higher Christian Life Ser.). 685p. 1985. 85.00 (ISBN 0-8240-6428-3). Garland Pub.
This Is the Day. Nona Freeman. Ed. by Charles Clanton. 256p. (Orig.). 1978. pap. 4.95 (ISBN 0-912315-36-9). Word Aflame.
This Is the Day: Selected Sermons. 2nd ed. Theodore P. Ferris. LC 76-39640. 368p. 1980. pap. 10.00 (ISBN 0-911658-16-5). Yankee Bks.
This Is the Day: The Biblical Doctrine of the Christian Sunday in it's Jewish & Early Church Setting. Roger T. Beckwith & Wilfrid Scott. 192p. 1978. 9.50 (ISBN 0-551-05568-5). Attic Pr.
This Is the Faith. Francis J. Ripley. 317p. 1973. pap. 5.95 (ISBN 0-903348-02-0). Lumen Christi.
This Is the Prophet Jesus. Fred Howes. LC 82-72741. 276p. 1983. pap. 8.95 (ISBN 0-87516-497-8). De Vorss.
This Is the Way. Donald Gee. (Radiant Bks.). Orig. Title: Studies in Guidance. 64p. 1975. pap. 0.95 (ISBN 0-88243-630-9, 02-0630). Gospel Pub.
This Is the Word of the Lord. rev. ed. William Freburger. LC 83-72480. 176p. 1984. spiral bound 6.95 (ISBN 0-87793-309-X). Ave Maria.
This Is the Word of the Lord: Year A: The Year of Matthew. Ed. by Robin Duckworth. 1980. pap. 9.95 (ISBN 0-19-213248-2). Oxford U Pr.
This Is the Word of the Lord: Year B., the Year of the Mark. Robin Duckworth. 1981. pap. 9.95 (ISBN 0-19-826662-6). Oxford U Pr.
This Is the Word of the Lord: Year C. the Year of Luke. Robin Duckworth. (Orig.). 1982. pap. 9.95 (ISBN 0-19-826666-9). Oxford U Pr.
This Is Truth about the Self. 3rd ed. Ann Davies. 1984. 4.50 (ISBN 0-938002-03-1). Builders of Adytum.
This Is Wisdom. Satguru S. Keshavadas. (Illus.). 96p. (Orig.). 1975. pap. 3.50 (ISBN 0-942508-07-6). Vishwa.
This Lie Called Evil. Denise Breton. LC 82-80906. 130p. (Orig.). 1983. pap. 8.50 (ISBN 0-942958-02-0). Kappeler Inst Pub.
This Man from Lebanon. Barbara Young. (Illus.). (YA) 1950. 18.95 (ISBN 0-394-44848-0). Knopf.
This Messiah Fellow. Matt Bernstein. 1985. 6.75 (ISBN 0-8062-2344-8). Carlton.
This Morning with God. Ed. by Carol Adeney. LC 68-28080. 1978. pap. 9.95 (ISBN 0-87784-870-X). Inter-Varsity.
This Our Church: The People and Events That Shaped It. William A. Herr. (Basics of Christian Thought Ser.). 1986. 17.95 (ISBN 0-88347-193-0). Thomas More.
This People, This Parish. Robert K. Hudnut. 192p. 1986. pap. 7.95 (ISBN 0-310-38241-6, 12329P). Zondervan.
This Planted Vine: A Narrative History of the Episcopal Diocese of New York. James Elliott Lindsley. LC 84-47588. (Illus.). 320p. 1984. 24.50 (ISBN 0-06-015347-4, HarpT). Har-Row.
This Religion of Islam. Sayyid Qutb. Tr. of Hadha ad-Din. 104p. (Orig.). 1977. pap. 2.95x (ISBN 0-939830-08-6, Pub. by IIFSO Kuwait). New Era Pubns MI.
This Season's People: A Book of Spiritual Teachings. Stephen Gaskin. LC 86-159636. (Illus.). 1976. 3.00 (ISBN 0-913990-05-1). Book Pub Co.
This Thing Called Life. Ernest Holmes. 1947. 8.95 (ISBN 0-396-02851-9). Dodd.
This Time Count Me In. Phyllis A. Wood. LC 80-15068. (Hiway Book: A High Interest - Low Reading Level Book). 120p. 1980. 8.95 (ISBN 0-664-32665-X). Westminster.
This Train Is Bound for Glory. Irving Sussman & Cornelia Sussman. 1969. 4.95 (ISBN 0-8199-0154-7, L38874). Franciscan Herald.
This Treatise Concernynge the Fruytfull Saynges of Davyd..Was Made & Compyled by..John Fyssher..Bysshop of Rochester. John Fisher. LC 79-84106. (English Experience Ser.: No. 925). 296p. 1979. Repr. of 1509 ed. lib. bdg. 28.00 (ISBN 90-221-0925-9). Walter J Johnson.
This Tremendous Lover. M. Eugene Boylan. 396p. 1987. pap. 7.95 (ISBN 0-87061-138-0). Chr Classics.
This Very Body the Buddha. Bhagwan Shree Rajneesh. Ed. by Ma Ananda Vandana. LC 79-904227. (Zen Ser.). (Illus.). 360p. (Orig.). 1978. 16.95 (ISBN 0-88050-157-X). Chidvilas Found.
This Very Place the Lotus Paradise. Bhagwan Shree Rajneesh. Ed. by Swami Anand Madyapa. LC 84-42805. (Photobiography Ser.). 568p. (Orig.). 1984. 100.00x (ISBN 0-88050-705-5). Chidvilas Found.
This Was John Calvin. Thea B. Van Halsema. (Christian Biography Ser.). 184p. 1981. pap. 4.95 (ISBN 0-8010-9283-3). Baker Bk.
This Way Up. Charles Hunter & Frances Hunter. 1978. pap. 5.00 (ISBN 0-917726-23-5). Hunter Bks.
This We Believe. 2nd ed. Arnold T. Olson. LC 61-18801. 1965. Repr. of 1961 ed. 6.95 (ISBN 0-911802-01-0). Free Church Pubns.
This We Believe. James L. Slay. 1963. pap. 4.95 (ISBN 0-87148-832-9). Pathway Pr.
This We Believe. Mrs. Z. W. Swafford. (Illus.). 109p. (Orig.). 1983. pap. 2.50 (ISBN 0-89114-115-4). Baptist Pub Hse.
This We Believe. (Eng. & Ger.). pap. 0.60 (ISBN 0-8100-0004-0, 04-0622). Northwest Pub.
This We Believe. James Waltner. LC 68-20281. 1968. pap. 5.95 (ISBN 0-87303-845-2). Faith & Life.
This We Believe, Leader's Guide. Herman Enns. LC 78-130643. 1970. pap. 1.75 (ISBN 0-87303-846-0). Faith & Life.
This You Can Believe: Participant. John Brokhoff. (Orig.). 1987. pap. price not set (ISBN 0-89536-893-5, 7879). CSS of Ohio.
Thomas A'Kempis, 2 vols. S. Kettlewell. 1882. 85.00 set (ISBN 0-8274-3599-1). R West.
Thomas A'Kempis: His Age & Book. J. E. De Montmorency. LC 73-103183. 1970. Repr. of 1906 ed. 30.00x (ISBN 0-8046-0820-2, Pub by Kennikat). Assoc Faculty Pr.
Thomas & Bonaventure: A Septicentenary Commemoration. Ed. by George F. McLean. LC 75-319639. (Proceedings of the American Catholic Philosophical Association: Vol. 48). 1974. pap. 15.00 (ISBN 0-918090-08-3). Am Cath Philo.
Thomas & the Evangelists. Henry E. Turner & Hugh Montefiore. LC 63-59763. (Studies in Biblical Theology: No. 35). 1962. pap. 10.00x (ISBN 0-8401-3035-X). A R Allenson.
Thomas & the Physics of Nineteen Fifty-Eight: A Confrontation. Henry Margenau. (Aquinas Lecture). 1958. 7.95 (ISBN 0-87462-123-2). Marquette.
Thomas Aquinas & Radical Aristotelianism. Fernand Van Steenberghen. Tr. by Dominic J. O'Meara et al from Fr. 114p. 1980. pap. 6.95 (ISBN 0-8132-0552-2). Cath U Pr.

Thomas Aquinas: Selected Political Writings. Ed. by A. P. D'Entreves. Tr. by J. G. Dawson. 136p. 1981. 26.50x; pap. 9.95x (ISBN 0-389-20244-4). B&N Imports.
Thomas Becket. Frank Barlow. (Illus.). 360p. 1986. 25.00 (ISBN 0-520-05920-4). U of Cal Pr.
Thomas Becket. David Knowles. LC 77-143785. 1971. 15.00x (ISBN 0-8047-0766-9). Stanford U Pr.
Thomas Becket: A Textual History of His Letters. Anne Duggan. 1980. 56.00x (ISBN 0-19-822486-9). Oxford U Pr.
Thomas Bray. Henry P. Thompson. LC 54-32504. 1954. 12.50x (ISBN 0-8401-2335-3). A R Allenson.
Thomas Bray's Grand Design: Libraries of the Church of England in America, 1695-1785. Charles T. Laugher. LC 73-16332. (ACRL Publications in Librarianship Ser.: No. 35). pap. 31.30 (ISBN 0-317-29444-X, 2024224). Bks Demand UMI.
Thomas Chalmers & Godly Commonwealth in Scotland. Stewart J. Brown. (Illus.). 1982. 55.00x (ISBN 0-19-213114-1). Oxford U Pr.
Thomas Cranmer & the English Reformation, 1849-1556. Albert F. Pollard. LC 83-45587. Date not set. Repr. of 1927 ed. 42.50 (ISBN 0-404-19905-4). AMS Pr.
Thomas Cranner. Jasper Ridley. 450p. 1983. Repr. of 1962 ed. lib. bdg. 65.00 (ISBN 0-89987-737-0). Darby Bks.
Thomas Fuller, Selections: With Essays by Charles Lamb, Leslie Stephen & Co. E. K. Broadus. 1979. Repr. of 1928 ed. lib. bdg. 20.00 (ISBN 0-8492-3742-4). R West.
Thomas Hooker: Preacher, Founder, Democrat. George L. Walker. 1972. Repr. of 1891 ed. lib. bdg. 19.00 (ISBN 0-8422-8120-7). Irvington.
Thomas Hooker, 1586-1647. Frank Shuffelton. LC 76-45912. 1977. 38.00x (ISBN 0-691-05249-2). Princeton U Pr.
Thomas J. Comber, Missionary Pioneer to the Congo. John B. Myers. LC 74-98739. (Illus.). Repr. of 1888 ed. lib. bdg. cancelled (ISBN 0-8371-2769-6, MYC&, Pub. by Negro U Pr). Greenwood.
Thomas Jefferson's Life of Jesus. Thomas Jefferson. 1976. 2.95 (ISBN 0-87243-056-1). Templegate.
Thomas Ken & Izaak Walton: A Sketch of Their Lives & Family Connection. E. Marston. 1908. Repr. 35.00 (ISBN 0-8274-3613-0). R West.
Thomas Ken: Bishop & Non-Juror. Hugh A. L. Rice. LC 58-4172. 1958. 10.00x (ISBN 0-8401-2008-7). A R Allenson.
Thomas Mayhew, Patriarch to the Indians, 1593-1682. Lloyd C. Hare. LC 76-104347. (Illus.). Repr. of 1932 ed. 20.00 (ISBN 0-404-03108-0). AMS Pr.
Thomas Merton. Victor A. Kramer. (United States Authors Ser.: No. 462). 1984. lib. bdg. 17.95 (ISBN 0-8057-7402-5, Twayne). G K Hall.
Thomas Merton. Cornelia Sussman & Irving Sussman. LC 80-924. 176p. 1980. pap. 3.95 (ISBN 0-385-17172-2, Im). Doubleday.
Thomas Merton: A Bibliography. rev. ed. Frank Dell'Isola. LC 74-79148. (Serif Ser.: No. 31). 200p. 1975. 13.50x (ISBN 0-87338-156-4). Kent St U Pr.
Thomas Merton: A Pictorial Biography. James H. Forest. LC 80-82249. (Illus.). 112p. (Orig.). 1980. pap. 5.95 (ISBN 0-8091-2284-7). Paulist Pr.
Thomas Merton & Asia: His Quest for Utopia. Alexander Lipski. (Cistercian Studies: No. 74). 1983. 17.95 (ISBN 0-87907-874-X); pap. 7.95 (ISBN 0-87907-974-6). Cistercian Pubns.
Thomas Merton: Contemplative Critic. Henri J. Nouwen. LC 80-8898. 176p. 1981. pap. 6.95 (ISBN 0-06-066324-3, RD 357, HarpR). Har-Row.
Thomas Merton Monk & Poet: A Critical Study. George Woodcock. 200p. 1978. 7.95 (ISBN 0-374-27635-8); pap. 3.95 (ISBN 0-374-51487-9). FS&G.
Thomas Merton on Prayer. John J. Higgins. 200p. 1975. pap. 3.95 (ISBN 0-385-02813-X, Im). Doubleday.
Thomas Merton on St. Bernard. Intro. by Jean Leclercq. (Cistercian Studies: No. 9). 1980. 13.95 (ISBN 0-87907-809-X); pap. 4.95 (ISBN 0-87907-909-6). Cistercian Pubns.
Thomas Merton Reader. Ed. by Thomas P. McDonnell. LC 74-29. 600p. 1974. pap. 6.50 (ISBN 0-385-03292-7, Im). Doubleday.
Thomas Merton: Social Critic. James T. Baker. LC 76-132827. 184p. 1971. 17.00x (ISBN 0-8131-1238-9). U Pr of Ky.
Thomas Merton: The Development of a Spiritual Theologian. Donald Grayston. LC 84-27299. (Toronto Studies in Theology: Vol. 20). 225p. 1985. 49.95x (ISBN 0-88946-758-7). E Mellen.
Thomas Merton's Dark Path. rev. ed. William H. Shannon. 260p. 1987. pap. 8.95 (ISBN 0-374-52019-4). FS&G.
Thomas Merton's Shared Contemplation: A Protestant Perspective. Daniel J. Adams. Ed. by Teresa A. Doyle. (Cistercian Studies: No. 62). 1979. 8.00 (ISBN 0-87907-862-6). Cistercian Pubns.
Thomas Moore. Stephen Gwynn. LC 73-13838. 1905. Repr. lib. bdg. 15.00 (ISBN 0-8414-4448-X). Folcroft.
Thomas More. Christopher Hollis. 1934. Repr. 20.00 (ISBN 0-8274-3614-9). R West.
Thomas More. Anthony Kenny. (Past Master Ser.). 1983. text ed. 13.95x (ISBN 0-19-287574-4); pap. 4.95 (ISBN 0-19-287573-6). Oxford U Pr.
Thomas More. facs. ed. Daniel Sargent. LC 71-119963. (Select Bibliographies Reprint Ser). 1933. 19.00 (ISBN 0-8369-5406-8). Ayer Co Pubs.
Thomas More & Erasmus. Ernest E. Reynolds. LC 65-26739. x, 260p. 1966. 25.00 (ISBN 0-8232-0670-X). Fordham.
Thomas More: History & Providence. Alistair Fox. LC 82-11178. 288p. 1985. pap. text ed. 10.95x (ISBN 0-300-03415-6, Y-536). Yale U Pr.
Thomas More's Prayer Book: A Facsimile Reproduction of the Annotated Pages. St. Thomas More. Tr. by Louis L. Martz & Richard S. Sylvester. LC 69-15454. (Elizabethan Club Ser.: No. 4). (Lat. & Eng., Illus.). 1969. 26.00x (ISBN 0-300-00179-7). Yale U Pr.
Thomas Nast's Christmas Drawings. Thomas Nast. (Illus.). 1978. pap. 4.50 (ISBN 0-486-23660-9). Dover.
Thomas Percy's 'Life of Dr. Oliver Goldsmith' Richard L. Harp. Ed. by James Hogg. (Romantic Reassessment Ser.). 205p. (Orig.). 1976. pap. 15.00 (ISBN 3-7052-0507-2, Pub. by Salzburg Studies). Longwood Pub Group.
Thomas Saga Erkibyskups: A Life of Archbishop Thomas Becket, in Icelandic, with English Translation, Notes & Glossary, 2 vols. M. eirikr Magnusson. (Rolls Ser.: No. 65). Repr. of 1883 ed. Set. 120.00 (ISBN 0-8115-1133-2). Kraus Repr.
Thomas Stapleton & the Counter Reformation. M. R. O'Connell. 1964. 49.50x (ISBN 0-685-69850-5). Elliots Bks.
Thomas Tallis. Thomas Tallis et al. Ed. by P. C. Buck. (Tudor Church Music Ser.: Vol. 6). 1963. Repr. of 1928 ed. write for info. (ISBN 0-8450-1856-6). Broude.
Thomas Traherne. Gladys I. Wade. LC 73-96171. 1969. Repr. of 1944 ed. lib. bdg. 20.00x (ISBN 0-374-98113-2, Octagon). Hippocrene Bks.
Thomas Traherne's 'The Growth of a Mystic's Mind: A Study of the Evolution & the Phenomenology of Traherne's Mystical Consciousness. Franz K. Wohrer. Ed. by James Hogg. (Elizabethan & Renaissance Studies). 207p. (Orig.). 1982. pap. 15.00 (ISBN 3-7052-0747-4, Pub. by Salzburg Studies). Longwood Pub Group.
Thomas' Valedictory Sermons. Leslie G. Thomas. 1973. 6.95 (ISBN 0-88428-021-7). Parchment Pr.
Thomas Ware, a Spectator at the Christmas Conference: A Miscellany on Thomas Ware & the Christmas Conference. Ed. by William R. Phinney et al. LC 84-70457. (Illus.). 320p. (Orig.). 1984. pap. 8.95 smythsewn (ISBN 0-914960-48-2). Academy Bks.
Thomas Warton & the Early Poems of Milton. L. C. Martin. LC 77-9907. 1934. lib. bdg. 9.50 (ISBN 0-8414-6096-5). Folcroft.
Thomas Wolsey: Legate & Reformer. Ethelred L. Taunton. LC 72-112819. 1970. Repr. of 1902 ed. 23.50x (ISBN 0-8046-1086-X, Pub by Kennikat). Assoc Faculty Pr.
Thomism & Aristotelianism: A Study of the Commentary by Thomas Aquinas on the Nicomachean Ethics. Harry V. Jaffa. LC 78-21520. 1979. Repr. of 1952 ed. lib. bdg. 29.75x (ISBN 0-313-21149-3, JATA). Greenwood.
Thomism & Modern Thought. Ed. by Harry R. Klocker. LC 62-9414. 1962. 32.50x (ISBN 0-89197-451-2). Irvington.
Thomism in an Age of Renewal. Ed. by Ralph M. McInerny. 1968. pap. 5.95x (ISBN 0-268-00276-2). U of Notre Dame Pr.
Thomist Realism. Etienne Gilson. Tr. by Mark A. Wauck. LC 86-80104. 215p. 1986. pap. 12.95 (ISBN 0-89870-094-9). Ignatius Pr.
Thomistic Bibliography, 1940-1978. Compiled by Terry L. Miethe & Vernon J. Bourke. LC 80-1195. xxii, 318p. 1980. lib. bdg. 45.00 (ISBN 0-313-21991-5, MTH/). Greenwood.
Thomistic Papers, No. I. Ed. by Victor B. Brezik. LC 85-18508. 176p. 1983. text ed. 20.95 (ISBN 0-268-01850-2); pap. text ed. 10.95 (ISBN 0-268-01851-0). U of Notre Dame Pr.
Thompson Chain Reference Bible Survey. Howard Hanke. 1981. 19.95 (ISBN 0-8499-0272-X). Word Bks.
Thoreau: Mystic, Prophet, Ecologist. William J. Wolf. LC 73-22368. 224p. 1974. 6.95 (ISBN 0-8298-0269-X). Pilgrim NY.
Thoroughly Married. Dennis Guernsey. 145p. 1984. pap. text ed. 5.95 (ISBN 0-8499-3000-6, 3000-6). Word Bks.
Those Amazing Prophecies That Prove the Bible. Gordon Lindsay. (Prophecy Ser.). 1.25 (ISBN 0-89985-053-7). Christ Nations.
Those Controversial Gifts. George Mallone et al. LC 83-8. 168p. (Orig.). 1983. pap. 5.95 (ISBN 0-87784-823-8). Inter-Varsity.
Those Curious New Cults in the Eighties. rev. ed. Bill Petersen. LC 72-93700. 1982. pap. text ed. 3.95 (ISBN 0-87983-317-3). Keats.
Those Days. W. W. Weatherspool. 1981. 5.95 (ISBN 0-8062-1835-5). Carlton.
Those Happy Golden Years. Miriam Wood. 1980. 6.95 (ISBN 0-8280-0062-X, 20380-2). Review & Herald.
Those He Came to Save. Roy C. Putnam. LC 77-13764. Repr. of 1978 ed. 35.50 (ISBN 0-8357-9029-0, 2016414). Bks Demand UMI.
Those Mysterious Priests. Fulton J. Sheen. 1979. pap. 10.00 (ISBN 0-385-08102-2). Lumen Christi.
Those of the Street: The Catholic-Jews of Mallorca. Kenneth Moore. LC 76-636. 1979. pap. text ed. 7.95x (ISBN 0-268-01836-7). U of Notre Dame Pr.
Those Preachin' Women. Ed. by Ella P. Mitchell. 128p. 1985. pap. 7.95 (ISBN 0-8170-1073-4). Judson.
Those Superstitions. Charles Igglesden. LC 73-12798. 1974. Repr. of 1932 ed. 40.00x (ISBN 0-8103-3621-9). Gale.
Those Who Love Him. Basilea Schlink. LC 69-11639. 96p. 1981. pap. 2.95 (ISBN 0-87123-609-5, 200609). Bethany Hse.
Those Who Move with God. Elbert Willis. 1977. 1.25 (ISBN 0-89858-006-4). Fill the Gap.
Those Who Ponder Proverbs: Aphoristic Thinking & Biblical Literature. James G. Williams. (Bible & Literature Ser.: No. 2). 1981. text ed. 19.95x (ISBN 0-907459-02-1, Pub. by Almond Pr England); pap. text ed. 9.95x (ISBN 0-907459-03-X, Pub. by Almond Pr England). Eisenbrauns.
Those Who Remain. Charles R. Taylor. (Illus.). 104p. (Orig.). 1980. pap. 2.95 (ISBN 0-937682-02-0). Today Bible.
Those Who Saw Her: The Apparitions of Mary. Catherine M. Odell. 200p. (Orig.). 1986. pap. 6.95 (ISBN 0-87973-720-4, 720). Our Sunday Visitor.
Those Who Won't & Those Who Will. Darlene Loomis. (Illus.). 12p. (Orig.). 1977. pap. 1.00 (ISBN 0-686-36278-0). Drain Enterprise.
Those Who Would Be Catholic School Principals: Their Recruitment, Preparation, & Evaluation. 1985. 8.00 (ISBN 0-318-18577-6). Natl Cath Educ.
Thou Art Consecrated Unto Me. Stavsky. 1.50 (ISBN 0-87306-101-2). Feldheim.
Thou Art the Vine. Heini Arnold. 36p. 1985. pap. 1.50 (ISBN 0-87486-178-0). Plough.
Thou Dost Open up My Life. Rufus M. Jones. LC 63-11819. (Orig.). 1963. pap. 2.50x (ISBN 0-87574-127-4). Pendle Hill.
Thou Shalt Call His Name. (Illus.). 102p. 1975. pap. 2.50 (ISBN 0-915952-00-9). Lord's Line.
Thought & Style in the Works of Leon Bloy. Sr. M. Rosalie Brady. LC 70-94176. (Catholic Universtiy of America Studies in Romance Languages & Literatures Ser: No. 30). Repr. of 1945 ed. 19.00 (ISBN 0-404-50330-6). AMS Pr.
Thought Forms. Besant & Leadbeater. 8.75 (ISBN 0-8356-7187-9). Theos Pub Hse.
Thought Forms. abr. ed. Annie Besant & Charles W. Leadbeater. (Illus.). 1969. pap. 5.50 (ISBN 0-8356-0008-4, Quest). Theos Pub Hse.
Thought of Jacques Ellul: A Systematic Exposition. Darrell J. Fasching. LC 81-22529. (Toronto Studies in Theology: Vol. 7). 272p. 1982. 49.95x (ISBN 0-88946-961-X). E Mellen.
Thought of Paul Tillich. Ed. by James L. Adams et al. 1985. 24.45 (ISBN 0-06-060072-1). Har-Row.
Thought of the Evangelical Leaders: John Newton, Thomas Scott, Charles Simeon, Etc. Ed. by Josiah Pratt. 1978. 18.95 (ISBN 0-85151-270-4). Banner of Truth.
Thought Power. Besant. 4.50 (ISBN 0-8356-7460-6). Theos Pub Hse.
Thought Power: Its Control & Culture. Annie Besant. LC 73-7644. 1967. pap. 3.50 (ISBN 0-8356-0312-1, Quest). Theos Pub Hse.
Thought Structure of Romans with Special Reference to Chapter Six. Bruce N. Kaye. 203p. (Orig.). 1979. pap. 5.95 (ISBN 0-931016-03-7). Schola Pr TX.
Thoughtful Faith: Essays on Belief by Mormon Scholars. Ed. by Philip L. Barlow. LC 86-71882. 275p. 1986. 14.95 (ISBN 0-939651-00-9). Canon Pr.
Thoughts. James Alberione. 1973. 3.00 (ISBN 0-8198-0332-4). Dghtrs St Paul.
Thoughts & Aphorisms. Sri Aurobindo. 1979. pap. 6.00 (ISBN 0-89744-927-4). Auromere.
Thoughts & Glimpses. Sri Aurobindo. 30p. 1973. pap. 0.60 (ISBN 0-89071-308-1, Pub. by Sri Aurobindo Ashram India). Matagiri.
Thoughts Are Free: A Quaker Youth in Nazi Germany. Anna S. Halle. LC 85-61843. (Orig.). 1985. pap. 2.50 (ISBN 0-87574-265-3). Pendle Hill.
Thoughts Are Things. Ernest Holmes. Ed. by Willis H. Kinnear. 96p. 1967. pap. 4.50 (ISBN 0-911336-33-8). Sci of Mind.
Thoughts: Education for Peace & One World. Irene Taafaki. (Illus.). 336p. 1986. 19.95 (ISBN 0-85398-221-X); pap. text ed. 9.95 (ISBN 0-85398-222-8). G Ronald Pub.
Thoughts for Aspirants. Sri Ram. Series II. 3.95 (ISBN 0-8356-7449-5). Theos Pub Hse.
Thoughts for Aspirants. 7th ed. N. Sri Ram. (Series 2). 1969. 4.25 (ISBN 0-8356-7195-X). Theos Pub Hse.
Thoughts for Growing Christians. David R. Reid. LC 82-7913. 160p. 1982. pap. 3.95 (ISBN 0-8024-2200-4). Moody.
Thoughts for Men on the Move. Warren Wiersbe. 1970. pap. 3.50 (ISBN 0-8024-0132-5). Moody.
Thoughts for Our Times. Albert Schweitzer. Ed. by Erica Anderson. (Illus.). 64p. 1981. Repr. of 1975 ed. 3.95 (ISBN 0-8298-0448-X). Pilgrim NY.
Thoughts for the Quiet Hour. D. L. Moody. pap. 3.50 (ISBN 0-8024-8729-7). Moody.
Thoughts from Heaven. Lily Laney. 128p. 1986. 8.95 (ISBN 0-89962-542-8). Todd & Honeywell.
Thoughts from the Mount of Blessing. Ellen G. White. LC 56-7170. 172p. 1956. 6.95 (ISBN 0-8163-0047-X, 20401-6). Pacific Pr Pub Assn.
Thoughts in Solitude. Thomas Merton. 124p. 1976. pap. 4.25 (ISBN 0-374-51325-2). FS&G.
Thoughts in Solitude. Thomas Merton. 1983. 14.50 (ISBN 0-8446-5989-4). Peter Smith.
Thoughts, Letters, & Opuscules of Blaise Pascal. Blaise Pascal. 1978. Repr. of 1864 ed. lib. bdg. 35.00 (ISBN 0-8492-2094-7). R West.
Thoughts of a Modern Mystic. C. C. Massey. 59.95 (ISBN 0-8490-1209-0). Gordon Pr.
Thoughts of Blaise Pascal. Blaise Pascal. LC 78-12814. 1978. Repr. of 1961 ed. lib. bdg. 24.25 (ISBN 0-313-20530-2, PATH). Greenwood.
Thoughts of Blaise Pascal: Translated from the Text of M. Auguste Molinier. C. Kegan Paul. 1978. Repr. of 1888 ed. 30.00 (ISBN 0-8492-2095-5). R West.
Thoughts of Chairman Smyres: Chairman, under God, of His Own Life & Thought. Roy S. Smyres. vi, 146p. (Orig.). 1986. pap. 8.00 (ISBN 0-9616952-0-X). Smyres Pubns.
Thoughts of Gold: Wisdom for Living from the Book of Proverbs. Leroy Brownlow. 1974. gift ed. 6.95 (ISBN 0-915720-13-2). Brownlow Pub Co.
Thoughts of the Cure d'Ars. St. John Vianney. LC 84-50404. 79p. 1984. pap. 1.50 (ISBN 0-89555-240-X). TAN Bks Pubs.
Thoughts of the Servant of God, Mother Thecla Merlo. Daughters of St. Paul. LC 68-59045. 1974. flexible plastic 2.25 (ISBN 0-8198-0509-2). Dghtrs St Paul.
Thoughts on Death & Immortality: From the Pages of a Thinker, along with an Appendix of Theological Satirical Epigrams, Edited by One of His Friends. Ludwig Feuerbach. Tr. by James A. Massey from Ger. LC 80-25259. 263p. 1980. 33.00x (ISBN 0-520-04051-1); pap. 6.95 (ISBN 0-520-04062-7, CAL 486). U of Cal Pr.
Thoughts on Love & Peace: To Commemorate the Visit of Pope John Paul II, India, 1986. 104p. (YA) 1986. text ed. 12.95x (ISBN 0-7069-3059-2, Pub. by Vikas India). Advent NY.
Thoughts on Popery. William Nevins. Ed. by Gerald Grob. LC 76-46093. (Anti-Movements in America). 1977. Repr. of 1836 ed. lib. bdg. 17.00x (ISBN 0-405-09966-5). Ayer Co Pubs.
Thoughts on Religious Experience. Archibald Alexander. 1978. 11.95 (ISBN 0-85151-080-9). Banner of Truth.
Thoughts on the Run: Glimpses of Wholistic Spirituality. Thomas E. Legere. 144p. 1983. pap. 7.95 (ISBN 0-86683-698-5, HarpR). Har-Row.
Thoughts to Ponder. Robert Joyce. 1980. 6.00 (ISBN 0-8198-7305-5); pap. 5.00 (ISBN 0-8198-7306-3). Dghtrs St Paul.
Thousand & One Churches. W. M. Ramsay & Gertrude L. Bell. (Illus.). xvi, 580p. 1985. Repr. of 1905 ed. lib. bdg. 80.00x (ISBN 0-89241-121-X). Caratzas.
Thousand Buddhas. Aurel Stein. LC 77-94623. 1979. Repr. of 1921 ed. lib. bdg. 10.00 (ISBN 0-89341-249-X). Longwood Pub Group.
Thousand Months to Remember: An Autobiography. Joseph M. Dawson. 306p. 1964. 6.95 (ISBN 0-918954-03-7). Baylor Univ Pr.
Thousand Years & a Day. Claus Westermann. LC 62-8544. 292p. 1982. pap. 8.95 (ISBN 0-8006-1913-7, 1-1913). Fortress.

Thousand Years of Peace. Gordon Lindsay. (End of the Age Ser.: Vol. 8). 1.25 (ISBN 0-89985-074-X). Christ Nations.

Thousand Years of Stained Glass. Catherine Brisac. LC 85-4506. 200p. 1986. 40.00 (ISBN 0-385-23184-9). Doubleday.

Thousand Years of Yesterday. 22nd ed. H. Spencer Lewis. LC 20-9068. 156p. 1982. 8.95 (ISBN 0-912057-01-7, G-506). AMORC.

Threat of Falsehood: A Study in Jeremiah. Thomas Overholt. LC 71-131589. (Studies in Biblical Theology, 2nd Ser: No. 16). pap. 10.00x (ISBN 0-8401-3066-X). A R Allenson.

Threatened with Resurrection: Amenazado de Resurreccion. Julia Esquivel. (Eng. & Span.). 128p. 1982. pap. 4.95 (ISBN 0-87178-844-6). Brethren.

Three A. M. Meditations for the Middle of the Night. Richard A. Wing. LC 21-786068. 144p. (Orig.). 1985. pap. 9.95 (ISBN 0-934849-00-5). Arthur Pub.

Three Anglican Divines on Prayer: Jewel, Andrewes & Hooker. John E. Booty. vii, 48p. (Orig.). 1978. pap. 3.00 (ISBN 0-936384-00-X). Cowley Pubns.

Three Bears in the Ministry. Beverly Burgess. 32p. (Orig.). 1982. pap. 3.98 (ISBN 0-89274-252-6). Harrison Hse.

Three Big Words. Kenneth E. Hagin. 1983. pap. 0.50 mini bk. (ISBN 0-89276-258-6). Hagin Ministries.

Three Byzantine Saints. Tr. by Elizabeth Dawes & Norman H. Baynes. 275p. 1977. pap. 8.95 (ISBN 0-913836-44-3). St Vladimirs.

Three Catholic Afro-American Congresses. Congress of Colored Catholics of the United States. 14.00 (ISBN 0-405-10863-X, 11829). Ayer Co Pubs.

Three Catholic Reformers of the Fifteenth Century. facsimile ed. Mary H. Allies. LC 73-38755. (Essay Index Reprint Ser). Repr. of 1878 ed. 13.00 (ISBN 0-8369-2633-1). Ayer Co Pubs.

Three Catholic Writers of the Modern South. Robert H. Brinkmeyer, Jr. LC 84-19641. 1985. 20.00x (ISBN 0-87805-246-1). U Pr of Miss.

Three Centuries of English Church Music. W. H. Parry. 1977. lib. bdg. 59.95 (ISBN 0-8490-2745-4). Gordon Pr.

Three Centuries of Thumb Bibles. Ruth Adomeit. LC 78-68238. (Garland Reference Library of Humanities). (Illus.). 435p. 1980. 73.00 (ISBN 0-8240-9818-8). Garland Pub.

Three Chapters from the Samadhirajasutra. Tr. by Constantin Regamey from Sanskrit & Tibetan. 112p. 1984. Repr. of 1938 ed. lib. bdg. 17.50x (ISBN 0-88181-003-7). Canon Pubns.

Three Chapters of Letters Relating to the Suppression of Monasteries. Thomas Wright. 37.00 (ISBN 0-384-69545-0). Johnson Repr.

Three Chapters of Letters Relating to the Suppression of Monasteries. Ed. by Thomas Wright. LC 72-74268. (Camden Society, London. Publications First Ser.: No. 26). Repr. of 1843 ed. 37.00 (ISBN 0-404-50126-5). AMS Pr.

Three Christian Transcendentalists: James Marsh, Caleb Sprague Henry, Frederic Henry Hedge. Ronald V. Wells. LC 75-159256. xxxii, 290p. 1971. Repr. of 1943 ed. lib. bdg. 20.00x (ISBN 0-374-98345-3, Octagon). Hippocrene Bks.

Three Christmas Plays. Dorothy J. Goulding. 20p. Repr. of 1955 ed. 3.00 (ISBN 0-88020-103-7). Coach Hse.

Three Crosses. Leonard Peusch. 1978. 0.75 (ISBN 0-8199-0723-5). Franciscan Herald.

Three D Cookbook. LC 81-52188. 224p. 1982. 14.95 (ISBN 0-941478-01-7). Paraclete Pr.

Three Days Scene at the Temple in Jerusalem. 2nd ed. Jakob Lorber. Tr. by Dr. Nordewin & Hildegard Von Koerber. LC 82-83492. 128p. 1982. pap. 6.00 (ISBN 0-934616-10-8). Valkyrie Pub Hse.

Three Decades of Palestine: Speeches & Papers on the Upbuilding of the Jewish National Home. Arthur Ruppin. LC 70-97301. (Illus.). 342p. 1975. Repr. of 1936 ed. lib. bdg. 22.50x (ISBN 0-8371-2629-0, RUPA). Greenwood.

Three Devils: Luther's, Milton's & Goethe's. David Masson. LC 72-193946. 1874. lib. bdg. 20.00 (ISBN 0-8414-6495-2). Folcroft.

Three Dimensions of Hindu-Muslim Confrontation. AK Vakil. 1982. 6.00 (ISBN 0-8364-0844-6, Pub. By Minerva India). South Asia Bks.

Three Early Pentecostal Tracts. Ed. by Donald W. Dayton. (Higher Christian Life Ser.). 441p. 1985. 55.00 (ISBN 0-8240-6415-1). Garland Pub.

Three Eighteenth Century Figures: Sarah Churchill, John Wesley, Giacomo Casanova. Bonamy Dobree. LC 80-19398. xi, 248p. 1981. Repr. of 1962 ed. lib. bdg. 25.00x (ISBN 0-313-22682-2, DOTF). Greenwood.

Three Essays: On Reading the Gospel, on Reading the Holy Fathers, on Shunning Reading of Books Containing False Teachings. Ignatius Brianchaninov. pap. 0.25 (ISBN 0-686-16365-6). Eastern Orthodox.

Three Essays on Religion. John S. Mill. LC 76-130995. Repr. of 1874 ed. 23.45 (ISBN 0-404-04325-9). AMS Pr.

Three Essays on Religion. John S. Mill. Repr. of 1874 ed. lib. bdg. 37.50x (ISBN 0-8371-1986-3, MIER). Greenwood.

Three Essays, Seventeen Ninety-Three to Seventeen Ninety-Five: The Tubingen Essay, Berne Fragments, The Life of Jesus. G. W. Hegel. Ed. by Peter Fuss & John Dobbins. LC 83-40599. 192p. 1984. text ed. 18.95x (ISBN 0-268-01854-5, 85-18540). U of Notre Dame Pr.

Three Faces of God: Traces of the Trinity in Literature & Life. David L. Miller. LC 85-45493. 176p. 1986. pap. 11.95 (ISBN 0-8006-1895-5, 1-1895). Fortress.

Three Faces of Love. Paul A. Hauck. LC 83-10468. 174p. 1984. pap. 8.95 (ISBN 0-664-24486-6). Westminster.

Three Fighters for Freedom. Brian Peachment. 1974. pap. 1.60 (ISBN 0-08-017617-8). Pergamon.

Three from Galilee. Majorie Holmes. 240p. 1986. pap. 3.50 (ISBN 0-553-26166-5). Bantam.

Three Great Friday Sermons & Other Theological Discourses. Apostolos Makrakis. Ed. by Orthodox Christian Educational Society. Tr. by Denver Cummings from Hellenic. 107p. (Orig.). 1952. pap. 3.00x (ISBN 0-938366-48-3). Orthodox Chr.

Three Hundred Charts You Can Use in Preaching, Teaching & Studying on Divorce & Remarriage. Thomas B. Warren. 1978. pap. 11.00looseleaf (ISBN 0-934916-29-2). Natl Christian Pr.

Three Hundred Sermon Outlines From the New Testament. William H. Smitty. LC 81-86666. (Orig.). 1983. pap. 4.50 (ISBN 0-8054-2246-3). Broadman.

Three Hundred Sixty-Five Devotions, 1986-1987. Ed. by Leah A. Crussell. 1986. pocket ed. 3.95 (ISBN 0-87403-003-X, 3087); pap. 5.95 (ISBN 0-87403-004-8, 4087). Standard Pub.

Three Hundred Thirty-Five Crucial Questions on Christian Unity. Thomas B. Warren. 48p. 1984. pap. 1.50 (ISBN 0-934916-06-3). Natl Christian Pr.

Three Incredible Weeks with Meher Baba. Malcolm Schloss & Charles Purdom. Ed. by Filis Frederick. LC 80-109542. (Illus.). 165p. 1979. pap. 5.95 (ISBN 0-913078-36-0). Sheriar Pr.

Three Jewish Philosophers: Philo, Saadya, Gaon, Jehuda, Halevi. Ed. by Hans Lewy et al. LC 60-9081. 1969. pap. text ed. 7.95x (ISBN 0-689-70126-8, T6). Atheneum.

Three Keys to Spiritual Renewal. Clark Pinnock. 112p. 1986. pap. 4.95 (ISBN 0-87123-656-7). Bethany Hse.

Three Kinds of Love. M. Toyotome. pap. 0.75 (ISBN 0-87784-132-2). Inter-Varsity.

Three Kings of Israel. Mark E. Petersen. LC 80-36697. 179p. 1980. 6.95 (ISBN 0-87747-829-5). Deseret Bk.

Three Late Medieval Morality Plays: Mankind, Everyman & Mundis et Infans. Ed. by G. A. Lesker. (New Mermaids Ser.). 1984. pap. text ed. 6.95x (ISBN 0-393-90054-1). Norton.

Three Lectures on the Mystery Dramas. Rudolf Steiner. Tr. by Ruth Pusch from Ger. 101p. (Orig.). 1983. pap. 7.95 (ISBN 0-88010-060-5). Anthroposophic.

Three Letters from Africa. Edgar H. Brookes. LC 65-12948. (Orig.). 1965. pap. 2.50x (ISBN 0-87574-139-8, 139). Pendle Hill.

Three Little Africans. Alhaji Obaba Abdullahi Muhammad. (Illus.). 36p. (Orig.). 1978. pap. 2.50 (ISBN 0-916157-00-8). African Islam Miss Pubns.

Three Medieval Plays: The Coventry Nativity Play, Everyman, Master Pierre Pathelin. Ed. by John Allen. 1968. pap. 3.50x (ISBN 0-87830-529-7). Theatre Arts.

Three Men Came to Heidelberg. Thea Van Halsema. (Christian Biography Ser.). 96p. 1982. pap. 3.95 (ISBN 0-8010-9289-2). Baker Bk.

Three Men Who Walked in Fire. Joann Scheck. (Arch Bks: Set 4). 1967. laminated bdg. 0.99 (ISBN 0-570-06026-5, 59-1137). Concordia.

Three Middle English Religious Poems. Ed. by R. H. Bowers. LC 63-63267. (University of Florida Humanities Monographs: No. 12). 1963. pap. 3.50 (ISBN 0-8130-0025-4). U Presses Fla.

Three Mile an Hour God. Kosuke Koyama. LC 79-24785. 160p. (Orig.). 1980. pap. 3.48 (ISBN 0-88344-473-9). Orbis Bks.

Three Months' Residence at Nablus: And an Account of the Modern Samaritans. John Mills. LC 77-87610. Repr. of 1864 ed. 25.50 (ISBN 0-404-16434-X). AMS Pr.

Three Muslim Sages. Seyyed H. Nasr. LC 75-14430. 192p. 1976. pap. text ed. 10.00x (ISBN 0-88206-500-9). Caravan Bks.

Three Mysteries of Jesus. Glenn Clark. 1978. 0.95 (ISBN 0-910924-85-6). Macalester.

Three Mystic Poets: A Study of W. B. Yeats, A. E. & Rabindragth Tagore. Abinash C. Bose. LC 72-187263. 1945. lib. bdg. 12.50 (ISBN 0-8414-2534-5). Folcroft.

Three Nephites: Substance & Significance of the Legend in Folklore. Lee H. Hector. Ed. by Richard Dorson. LC 77-70608. (International Folklore Ser.). 1977. Repr. of 1949 ed. lib. bdg. 14.00x (ISBN 0-405-10105-8). Ayer Co Pubs.

Three of China's Mighty Men. Leslie Lyall. pap. 3.95 (ISBN 0-340-25561-7). OMF Bks.

Three-Personed God: The Trinity As a Mystery of Salvation. William J. Hill. LC 81-18012. 354p. 1982. 37.95x (ISBN 0-8132-0560-3). Cath U Pr.

Three Persons from the Bible: Or Babylon. Thomas H. Weisser. (Illus.). 44p. pap. 2.00 (ISBN 0-317-17477-0). Tom Weisser.

Three Physico-Theological Discourses: Primitive Chaos, & Creation of the World, the General Deluge, Its Causes & Effects. John Ray. Ed. by Claude C. Albritton, Jr. LC 77-6538. (History of Geology Ser.). 1978. Repr. of 1713 ed. lib. bdg. 34.50x (ISBN 0-405-10457-X). Ayer Co Pubs.

Three Pillars of Zen: Teaching, Practice, Enlightenment. Philip Kapleau. LC 78-22794. (Illus.). 1980. pap. 9.95 (ISBN 0-385-14786-4, Anch). Doubleday.

Three Poetical Prayer-Makers of the Island of Britain. Gwyn Jones. (Warton Lectures on English Peotry). 9p. 1981. pap. 3.00 (ISBN 0-85672-356-8, Pub. by British Acad). Longwood Pub Group.

Three Principles of the Divine Essence. Jacob Behem. 1978. Repr. of 1909 ed. 12.00 (ISBN 0-911662-65-0). Yoga.

Three Prophets of Religious Liberalism. Ed. by Conrad Wright. 1961. pap. 4.00 (ISBN 0-933840-20-9). Unitarian Univ.

Three Psalm Tunes by Thomas Tallis. Ed. by Hermione Abbey. 16p. (Orig.). 1982. pap. 2.50 (ISBN 0-939400-02-2). RWS Bks.

Three Reformation Catechisms: Catholic, Anabaptist, Lutheran. Ed. by Denis Janz. LC 82-20799. (Texts & Studies in Religion: Vol. 13). viii, 224p. 1982. 49.95x (ISBN 0-88946-800-1). E Mellen.

Three Reformers: Luther-Descartes-Rousseau. Jacques Maritain. Repr. of 1950 ed. lib. bdg. 22.50x (ISBN 0-8371-2825-0, MATR). Greenwood.

Three Religions of China. William E. Soothill. LC 73-899. (China Studies: from Confucius to Mao Ser.). (Illus.). 271p. 1973. Repr. of 1929 ed. 28.00 (ISBN 0-88355-093-8). Hyperion Conn.

Three Sermons: The Benefit of Contentation, the Affinitie of the Faithful, the Lost Sheep Is Found. Henry Smith. LC 76-57418. (English Experience Ser.: No. 832). 1977. Repr. of 1599 ed. lib. bdg. 7.00 (ISBN 90-221-0832-5). Walter J Johnson.

Three-Speed Dad in a Ten-Speed World. Kel Groseclose. LC 83-2765. 176p. (Orig.). 1983. pap. 4.95 (ISBN 0-87123-585-4, 210585). Bethany Hse.

Three Spiritual Directors for Our Time: Julian of Norwich, the Cloud of Unknowing Walter Hilton. Julia Gatta. LC 86-29169. 137p. (Orig.). 1987. pap. 8.95 (ISBN 0-936384-44-1). Cowley Pubns.

Three Steps Behind. Joyce Hardin. 320p. (Orig.). 1986. pap. 10.95 (ISBN 0-915547-91-0). Abilene Christ U.

Three Steps Forward, Two Steps Back. Charles R. Swindoll. 320p. 1985. pap. 11.95 (ISBN 0-8027-2506-6). Walker & Co.

Three Steps Forward, Two Steps Back: Persevering Through Pressure. Charles R. Swindoll. LC 80-11892. 176p. 1980. 9.95 (ISBN 0-8407-5187-7); pap. 5.95 (ISBN 0-8407-5723-9). Nelson.

Three Steps, One Bow. Bhikshu Hung Ju & Bhikshu Hung Yo. (Illus.). 160p. (Orig.). 1976. pap. 5.00 (ISBN 0-917512-18-9). Buddhist Text.

Three Steps to Answered Prayer. Peter Popoff. Ed. by Don Tanner. LC 81-70342. 92p. 1981. pap. 2.00 (ISBN 0-938544-10-1). Faith Messenger.

Three Steps to Heaven. Ruth Hall. 1981. 4.95 (ISBN 0-8062-1560-7). Carlton.

Three to Get Ready: A Christian Premarital Counselor's Manual. Howard A. Eyrich. 1978. pap. 4.95 (ISBN 0-87552-259-9). Presby & Refomed.

Three to Win. James E. Adams. LC 77-72255. (Radiant Life Ser.). 125p. pap. 2.50 (ISBN 0-88243-906-5, 02-0906); tchr's ed 3.95 (ISBN 0-88243-176-5, 32-0176). Gospel Pub.

Three Transcendentalists: Kant, Thoreau, & Contemporary. Richard S. Hoehler. LC 71-185781. (Illus.). 432p. 1972. 10.00 (ISBN 0-930590-00-7). R S Hoehler.

Three Treatises. rev. ed. Martin Luther. LC 73-114753. 320p. 1970. pap. 4.95 (ISBN 0-8006-1639-1, 1-1639). Fortress.

Three Treatises on Man: A Cistercian Anthropology. Ed. by Bernard McGinn. LC 77-184906. (Cistercian Fathers Ser.: No. 24). 1977. 13.95 (ISBN 0-87907-024-2). Cistercian Pubns.

Three Tudor Dialogues. LC 78-14887. 1979. 35.00x (ISBN 0-8201-1319-0). Schol Facsimiles.

Three Uses of Christian Discourse in John Henry Newman. Jouett L. Powell. LC 75-29423. (American Academy of Religion. Dissertation Ser.). 1975. pap. 9.95 (ISBN 0-89130-042-2, 010110). Scholars Pr GA.

Three Victorian Women Who Changed Their World: Josephine Butler, Octavia Hill, Florence Nightingale. Nancy Boyd. 1982. 22.95x (ISBN 0-19-520271-6). Oxford U Pr.

Three Ways of Asian Wisdom: Hinduism, Buddhism, Zen. Nancy W. Ross. (Illus.). 1978. pap. 12.95 (ISBN 0-671-24230-X, Touchstone Bks). S&S.

Three Ways of Love. Frances P. Keyes. 1975. 6.00 (ISBN 0-8198-0477-0); pap. 5.00 (ISBN 0-8198-0478-9). Dghtrs St Paul.

Three Ways of Modern Man. Harry Slochower. LC 37-17328. 1968. Repr. of 1937 ed. 20.00 (ISBN 0-527-83656-7). Kraus Repr.

Three Ways of the Spiritual Life. R. Garrigou-Lagrange. 1977. pap. 3.00 (ISBN 0-89555-017-2). TAN Bks Pubs.

Three Ways to One God. Abdoldjavad Falaturi & Petuchowski. 160p. 1987. 14.95 (ISBN 0-8245-0818-1). Crossroad NY.

Three Who Dared: Prudence Crandall, Margaret Douglass, Myrtilla Miner-Champions of Antebellum Black Education. Philip S. Foner & Josephine F. Pacheco. LC 83-12830. (Contributions in Women's Studies: No. 47). xviii, 234p. 1984. lib. bdg. 32.95 (ISBN 0-313-23584-8, FTH/). Greenwood.

Three Women & the Lord. Adrienne Von Speyr. Tr. by Graham Harrison. LC 86-80789. (Illus.). 115p. 1986. pap. 7.95 (ISBN 0-89870-059-0). Ignatius Pr.

Three Worlds of Christian Marxist Encounters. Ed. by Nicolas Piediscalzi & Robert G. Thobaben. LC 84-48724. 240p. 1985. pap. 14.95 (ISBN 0-8006-1840-8, 1-1840). Fortress.

Three Years in America: 1859-1862, 2 vols. in 1. facsimile ed. Israel B. Benjamin. Tr. by Charles Reznikoff from Ger. LC 74-27962. (Modern Jewish Experience Ser.). (Eng.). 1975. Repr. of 1956 ed. 52.00x (ISBN 0-405-06693-7). Ayer Co Pubs.

Threefold Garland: The World's Salvation in Mary's Prayer. Hans Urs Von Balthasar. Tr. by Erasmo Leiva-Merikakis from Ger. LC 81-83569. Tr. of Der Dreifache Kranz. 146p. (Orig.). 1982. pap. 7.95 (ISBN 0-89870-015-9). Ignatius Pr.

Threefold Lotus Sutra. Tr. by Bunno Kato et al. LC 74-23158. Orig. Title: Hokke Sambu-Kyo. 404p. 1975. 19.75 (ISBN 0-8348-0105-1); pap. 10.95 (ISBN 0-8348-0106-X). Weatherhill.

Threefold Refuge in the Theravada Buddhist Tradition. John R. Carter & George D. Bond. LC 82-26467. 1982. 4.95x (ISBN 0-89012-030-7). Anima Pubns.

Threescore & Ten-Wow. Agnes D. Pylant. LC 70-151621. 1971. pap. 2.75 (ISBN 0-8054-5213-3). Broadman.

Threshold Is High: The Brethren in Christ in Japan. Doyle C. Book. Ed. by Ray M. Zercher & Glen A. Pierce. (Illus.). xii, 210p. (Orig.). 1986. pap. 7.95 (ISBN 0-916035-15-8). Evangel Indiana.

Threshold of Religion. Robert R. Marett. LC 76-44755. Repr. of 1900 ed. 26.50 (ISBN 0-404-15950-8). AMS Pr.

Thresholds of Initiation. Joseph L. Henderson. LC 67-24110. 1967. pap. 10.95 (ISBN 0-8195-6061-8). Wesleyan U Pr.

Thrice Through the Valley. Valetta Steel & Ed Erny. (Living Books). 112p. 1986. 2.95 (ISBN 0-8423-7146-X). Tyndale.

Thrill of Faith. C. S. Lovett. 1960. pap. 2.95 (ISBN 0-938148-21-4). Personal Christianity.

Throat of the Peacock: Japanese Senryu on Filial Devotion. Tr. by Harold J. Isaacson. (Bhaisajaguru Ser.). 1977. pap. 1.85 (ISBN 0-87830-557-2). Theatre Arts.

Throbbing Drums: The Story of James H. Robinson. Amy Lee. (Orig.). 1968. pap. 0.95 (ISBN 0-377-84141-2). Friend Pr.

Throne & the Chariot: Studies in Milton's Hebraism. Kitty Cohen. (Studies in English Literature: No. 97). 1975. text ed. 23.20x (ISBN 0-686-22628-3). Mouton.

Throne of Wisdom: Wood Sculptures of the Madonna in Romanesque France. Ilene H. Forsyth. LC 72-166372. pap. 77.30 (ISBN 0-317-41726-6, 2052061). Bks Demand UMI.

Through African Skies. Ray Browneye. 136p. 1983. pap. 5.95 (ISBN 0-8010-0853-0). Baker Bk.
Through America: Nine Months in the United States. Walter G. Marshal. LC 73-13143. (Foreign Travelers in America, 1810-1935 Ser.). (Illus.). 490p. 1974. Repr. 32.00x (ISBN 0-405-05466-1). Ayer Co Pubs.
Through Bible Lands: Notes on Travel in Egypt, the Desert, & Palestine. Philip Schaff. Ed. by Moshe Davis. LC 77-70740. (America & the Holy Land Ser.). 1977. Repr. of 1878 ed. lib. bdg. 30.00x (ISBN 0-405-10286-0). Ayer Co Pubs.
Through Christ's Word: A Festschrift for Philip E. Hughes. Ed. by W. Robert Godfrey & Jesse L. Boyd, III. 272p. (Orig.). 1985. pap. 10.95 (ISBN 0-87552-274-2). Presby & Reformed.
Through Crisis to Freedom. Bill Cane. LC 79-89874. (Orig.). 1980. pap. 3.25 (ISBN 0-914070-14-2). ACTA Found.
Through Death to Life. Joseph M. Champlin. LC 78-74436. 88p. 1979. pap. 1.95 (ISBN 0-87793-175-5). Ave Maria.
Through Death to Rebirth. new ed. James S. Perkins. LC 61-13301. (Illus.). 124p. 1974. pap. 4.25 (ISBN 0-8356-0451-9, Quest). Theos Pub Hse.
Through Gates of Splendor. Elisabeth Elliot. 1981. 3.95 (ISBN 0-8423-7151-6). Tyndale.
Through Joy & Beyond: A Pictorial Biography of C. S. Lewis. Walter Hooper. LC 82-9884. 192p. 1982. 15.75 (ISBN 0-02-553670-2). Macmillan.
Through Lent to Resurrection. Flower A. Newhouse. Ed. by Melodie N. Bengtson. LC 77-77088. (Illus.). 1977. pap. 5.00 (ISBN 0-910378-13-4). Christward.
Through Many Windows. Arthur Gordon. 192p. 1985. pap. 6.95 (ISBN 0-8007-5207-4, Power Bks). Revell.
Through Other Eyes: Vivid Narratives of Some of the Bible's Most Notable Characters. Carl E. Price. 144p. (Orig.). 1987. pap. 6.95 (ISBN 0-8358-0555-7). Upper Room.
Through Prayer to Reality. Douglas A. Rhymes. LC 74-81813. 1976. pap. 3.95 (ISBN 0-88489-088-0). St Mary's.
Through Science & Philosophy to Religion. F. R. Ansari. pap. 1.25 (ISBN 0-686-18536-6). Kazi Pubns.
Through the Bible, Vol. I. Steve Clapp & Sue I. Mauck. (C-Four Youth Bible Materials Ser.). (Illus.). 138p. (Orig.). 1982. pap. 10.00 (ISBN 0-914527-15-0). C-Four Res.
Through the Bible Book by Book, 4 vols. Myer Pearlman. 1935. pap. 2.95 ea.; Vol. 1. (ISBN 0-88243-660-0, 02-0660); Vol. 2. (ISBN 0-88243-661-9, 02-0661); Vol. 3. (ISBN 0-88243-662-7, 02-0662); Vol. 4. (ISBN 0-88243-663-5, 02-0663). Gospel Pub.
Through the Bible in a Year: Pupil Workbook. Dana Eynon. 64p. 1975. wkbk. 1.95 (ISBN 0-87239-011-X, 3239). Standard Pub.
Through the Bible in a Year: Teacher. Dana Eynon. LC 74-27239. 176p. 1975. tchr's manual 7.95 (ISBN 0-87239-028-4, 3237). Standard Pub.
Through the Bible Quizzes for Children. Shirley Beegle. 64p. (Orig.). 1974. pap. 2.50 (ISBN 0-87239-324-0, 3249). Standard Pub.
Through the Bible Reading Program. McKinney et al. (Illus.). 112p. (Orig.). 1983. pap. 3.95 (ISBN 0-87239-647-9, 3076). Standard Pub.
Through the Bible Study Series, 7 vol. set. Ed. by A. L. Clanton. 2688p. 1982. text ed. 54.95 per set (ISBN 0-912315-51-2). Word Aflame.
Through the Bible Study Series, Vol. VII. Ed. by A. L. Clanton. 384p. 1982. text ed. 6.95 (ISBN 0-912315-58-X). Word Aflame.
Through the Bible Study Series, Vol. VI. Ed. by A. L. Clanton. 384p. 1981. text ed. 6.95 (ISBN 0-912315-57-1). Word Aflame.
Through the Bible Study Series, Vol. V. Ed. by A. L. Clanton. 384p. 1981. text ed. 6.95 (ISBN 0-912315-56-3). Word Aflame.
Through the Bible Study Series, Vol. IV. Ed. by A. L. Clanton. 384p. 1981. text ed. 6.95 (ISBN 0-912315-55-5). Word Aflame.
Through the Bible Study Series, Vol. III. Ed. by A. L. Clanton. 384p. 1981. text ed. 6.95 (ISBN 0-912315-54-7). Word Aflame.
Through the Bible Study Series, Vol. II. Ed. by J. L. Hall. 384p. 1981. text ed. 6.95 (ISBN 0-912315-53-9). Word Aflame.
Through the Bible Study Series, Vol. 1. Ed. by A. L. Clanton. 384p. 1981. text ed. 6.95 (ISBN 0-912315-52-0). Word Aflame.
Through the Bible with ABC's. Compiled by Patricia Mahany. (Story & Color Bks.). (Illus.). 64p. (Orig.). 1984. pap. 2.95 (ISBN 0-87239-798-X, 2374). Standard Pub.
Through the Bible with Preschoolers. Carole Matthews. 144p. 1985. 8.95 (ISBN 0-87239-945-1, 3330). Standard Pub.
Through the Eye of a Rose Window: A Perspective on the Environment for Worship. Richard S. Vosko. 1981. pap. text ed. 7.95 (ISBN 0-89390-028-1). Resource Pubns.
Through the Eye of the Dove: One Man's Journey into Reincarnation. Hal Wolfe. Date not set. pap. price not set. Dearen Pub.
Through the Eyes of the Masters. David Anrias. 1972. pap. 7.95 (ISBN 0-87728-116-5). Weiser.
Through the Fire. Joseph M. Stowell. 156p. 1985. pap. 5.95 (ISBN 0-89693-601-5). Victor Bks.
Through the Gateway of Death. Hodson. 2.95 (ISBN 0-8356-7202-6). Theos Pub Hse.
Through the Gospel with Dom Helder. Dom H. Camara. Tr. by Alan Neame from Fr. 160p. (Orig.). 1986. pap. 8.95 (ISBN 0-88344-266-3). Orbis Bks.
Through the Landscape of Faith. Lucy Bregman. LC 85-26381. 120p. (Orig.). 1986. pap. 9.95 (ISBN 0-664-24704-0). Westminster.
Through the Narrow Gate. Karen Armstrong. 288p. 1981. 12.95 (ISBN 0-312-80383-4). St Martin.
Through the Pentateuch Chapter by Chapter. W. H. Griffith Thomas. LC 85-10076. 192p. 1985. pap. 6.95 (ISBN 0-8254-3833-0). Kregel.
Through the Scriptures. A. P. Gibbs. pap. 5.95 (ISBN 0-937396-45-1). Walterick Pubs.
Through the Year with Francis of Assisi: Daily Meditations from His Words & Life. Murray Bodo. LC 87-4158. (Illus.). 240p. 1987. pap. 7.95 (ISBN 0-385-23823-1, Im). Doubleday.
Through the Year with Fulton Sheen: Inspiration Selections for Each Day of the Year. Fulton Sheen. 213p. 1985. pap. 6.95 (ISBN 0-89283-236-3). Servant.
Through the Year with the Church Fathers. Emily Harakas. 1985. pap. 8.95 (ISBN 0-937032-37-9). Light&Life Pub Co MN.
Through the Year with the DRE: A Seasonal Guide for Christian Educators. Gail T. McKenna. 128p. (Orig.). 1987. pap. 7.95 (ISBN 0-8091-2860-8). Paulist Pr.
Through the Year with Thomas Merton: Daily Meditations. Ed. by Thomas P. McDonnell. LC 85-11827. (Illus.). 240p. 1985. pap. 7.95 (ISBN 0-385-23234-9, Im). Doubleday.
Through Trials & Triumphs: A History of Augustana College. Donald Sneen. 192p. 1985. 17.00 (ISBN 0-931170-29-X). Ctr Western Studies.
Through Troubled Waters. Marinus Nijsse. (Children's Summit Bks.). pap. 1.95 (ISBN 0-8010-6728-6). Baker Bk.
Through Troubled Waters: A Young Father's Struggles with Grief. William H. Armstrong. 96p. (Orig.). 1983. pap. 3.35 (ISBN 0-687-41895-X, Festival). Abingdon.
Throw Away Society. Ted Haver. 140p. (Orig.). 1986. pap. write for info. (ISBN 0-914981-13-7). Paradigm ID.
Thunder & Trumpets: The Millerite Movement & Dissenting Religion in Upstate New York, 1800-1850. David Rowe. (American Academy of Religion Studies in Religion: No. 38). 1985. 24.95 (ISBN 0-89130-770-2, 01 00 38); pap. 16.95 (ISBN 0-89130-769-9). Scholars Pr GA.
Thunder in the Valley. Doug Knapp et al. (Orig.). 1986. pap. 6.95 (ISBN 0-8054-6342-9). Broadman.
Thunder in the Valley: The Massabielle Saga. James H. Klien. (Illus.). 92p. 4.00 (ISBN 0-8198-7316-0, MA0135); pap. 3.00 (ISBN 0-8198-7317-9). Dghtrs St Paul.
Thunder of Silence. Joel S. Goldsmith. LC 61-7340. 1961. 12.45 (ISBN 0-06-063270-4, HarpR). Har-Row.
Thunder on the Right: The Protestant Fundamentalists. Gary K. Clabaugh. LC 74-9551. 283p. 1974. 19.95x (ISBN 0-88229-108-4). Nelson-Hall.
Thunderweapon in Religion & Folklore. C. Blinkenberg. xii, 122p. 1985. Repr. of 1911 ed. lib. bdg. 25.00x (ISBN 0-89241-205-4). Caratzas.
Thunderweapon in Religion & Folklore. C. Blinkenberg. 1977. lib. bdg. 59.95 (ISBN 0-8490-2749-7). Gordon Pr.
Thurgarton Church. George Barker. 1969. write for info. (ISBN 0-685-01054-6, Pub. by Trigram Pr); signed ed. 100 copies 12.00 ea.; pap. 2.00 (ISBN 0-685-01056-2). Small Pr Dist.
Thus Saith the Lord: Giddyap: Metapsychiatric Commentaries on Human Experience & Spiritual Growth. Ann T. Linthorst. 106p. (Orig.). 1986. pap. 11.00 (ISBN 0-913105-18-X). PAGL Pr.
Thus Saith the Lord: The Autobiography of God. Charles C. Wise, Jr. LC 84-60414. 293p. (Orig.). 1984. pap. 7.95 (ISBN 0-917023-07-2). Magian Pr.
Thus Shalt Thou Serve. Charles W. Slemming. 1966. pap. 2.95 (ISBN 0-87508-508-3). Chr Lit.
Thus Spake Library: Teachings of Vivekananda, Ramakrishna, Sri Sarada Devi, Rama, Krishna, Buddha, Christ, Muhammad, Shankara & Guru Nanak. Swami Vivekananda et al. pap. 3.50 set 10 bklts (ISBN 0-87481-444-8). Vedanta Pr.
Thwaites' Jesuit Relations, Errata & Addenda. Joseph P. Donnelly. LC 66-27701. (American West Ser). 1967. 6.95 (ISBN 0-8294-0025-7). Loyola.
Thy Hidden Ones. Jessie Penn-Lewis. 1962. pap. 4.50 (ISBN 0-87508-998-4). Chr Lit.
Thy Kingdom Come. Johann C. Blumhardt & Christoph F. Blumhardt. Ed. by Vernard Eller. LC 80-19328. (Blumhardt Reader Ser.). 180p. 1980. text ed. 5.50 (ISBN 0-8028-3544-9, Pub. by Eerdmans). Plough.
Thy Kingdom Come. Mary E. Clark. 1.77 (ISBN 0-8091-9315-9). Paulist Pr.
Thy Kingdom Come. Huberto C. Medeiros. 1980. 3.00 (ISBN 0-8198-7307-1); pap. 1.95 (ISBN 0-8198-7308-X). Dghtrs St Paul.
Thy Kingdom Come: Studies in Daniel & Revelation. Rousas J. Rushdoony. pap. 7.95 (ISBN 0-87552-413-3). Presby & Reformed.
Thy Kingdom Come: The Basic Teachings of Jesus. Marilyn Norquist. 64p. 1986. pap. 1.50 (ISBN 0-89243-244-6). Liguori Pubns.
Thy Will Be Done: Praying the Our Father As Subversive Activity. Michael H. Crosby. LC 77-5118. 262p. (Orig.). 1977. pap. 6.95 (ISBN 0-88344-497-6). Orbis Bks.
Thy Word Is Truth. Edward J. Young. 1957. pap. 5.95 (ISBN 0-8028-1244-9). Eerdmans.
Tian Wen: A Chinese Book of Origins. Tr. by Stephen Field from Chinese. LC 86-12737. 128p. (Orig.). 1986. 22.95 (ISBN 0-8112-1010-3); pap. 8.95 (ISBN 0-8112-1011-1, NDP624). New Directions.
Tibetan & Buddhist Studies Commemorating the Two Hundreth Anniversary of the Birth of Alexander Csoma de Koros, 2 vols. Ed. by L. Ligeti. (Bibliotheca Orientalis Hungarica: No. 29). 827p. 1984. Set. text ed. 115.00x (ISBN 963-05-3573-4, Pub. by Akademiai Kiado Hungary). Vol. 1 (ISBN 963-05-3902-0). Vol. 2 (ISBN 963-05-3903-9). Humanities.
Tibetan & Buddhist Studies Commemorating the 200th Anniversary of the Birth of Alex-ander Csoma de Koros, 2 vols. Louis Ligeti. 388p. 1984. 350.00x (ISBN 0-569-08826-7, Pub. by Collets (UK)). State Mutual Bk.
Tibetan Book of the Dead: The Great Liberation Through Hearing in the Bardo. Tr. by Francesca Fremantle & Chogyam Trungpa. LC 74-29615. (Clear Light Ser.). (Illus.). 256p. 1975. pap. 7.95 (ISBN 0-87773-074-1). Shambhala Pubns.
Tibetan Book of the Great Liberation. Ed. by W. Y. Evans-Wentz. 1954. 24.95x (ISBN 0-19-501437-5). Oxford U Pr.
Tibetan Book of the Great Liberation. Ed. by W. Y. Evans-Wentz. (Illus.). 1968. pap. 9.95 (ISBN 0-19-500293-8). Oxford U Pr.
Tibetan Buddhism in Western Perspective. Herbert V. Guenther. LC 76-47758. (Illus.). 1977. pap. 8.95 (ISBN 0-913546-50-X). Dharma Pub.
Tibetan Buddhism with Its Mystic Cults Symbolism & Mythology, & in Its Relation to Indian Buddhism. Austine Waddell. (Illus.). 598p. 1972. pap. 8.95 (ISBN 0-486-20130-9). Dover.
Tibetan Buddhist Chant: Musical Notations & Interpretations of a Song Book by the Bkah Brgyud Pa & Sa Skya Pa Sects. Walter Kaufmann. Tr. by Thubten Jigme Norbu. LC 72-85606. (Humanities Ser.: No. 70). 578p. 1975. 25.00x (ISBN 0-253-36017-X). Ind U Pr.
Tibetan Mandalas: The Ngor Collection. Ngor Tharttse mKhanpo bSodnams rgyamtsho. Ed. by Musashi Tachikawa. (Tibetan, Sanskrit, Japanese & Eng., Illus.). 1985. Set. boxed ltd. ed. 1500.00x (ISBN 0-87773-800-9). Vol. 1, 300p. Vol. 2, 340p. Shambhala Pubns.
Tibetan Reflections. Peter Gold. (Illus.). 112p. (Orig.). 1984. pap. 11.95 (ISBN 0-86171-022-3, Wisdom Pubns). Great Traditions.
Tibetan Religious Dances. Rene De Nebesky-Wojkowitz. Ed. by Christoph Von Furer-Haimendorf. (Religion & Society: No. 2). 1976. text ed. 36.00x (ISBN 90-279-7621-X). Mouton.
Tibetan Symbolic World: Psychoanalytic Explorations. Robert A. Paul. LC 81-16505. (Chicago Originals Ser.). (Illus.). 360p. 1982. lib. bdg. 14.00x (ISBN 0-226-64987-3). U of Chicago Pr.
Tibetan Tantrik Tradition. S. K. Rao. (Illus.). 1977. text ed. 10.50x (ISBN 0-391-01105-7). Humanities.
Tibetan Yoga & Secret Doctrines. 2nd ed. Ed. by W. Y. Evans-Wentz. 1958. 24.95x (ISBN 0-19-501438-3). Oxford U Pr.
Tibetan Yoga & Secret Doctrines. Ed. by W. Y. Evans-Wentz. (Illus.). 1967. pap. 11.95 (ISBN 0-19-500278-4). Oxford U Pr.
Tibetan Yoga & Secret Doctrines: Or Seven Books of Wisdom of the Great Path. Ed. by Walter Y. Wentz. LC 78-70140. Repr. of 1935 ed. 49.50 (ISBN 0-404-17413-2). AMS Pr.
Tibet's Great Yogi, Milarepa. 2nd ed. Ed. by W. Y. Evans-Wentz. (Illus.). 1969. pap. 9.95 (ISBN 0-19-500301-2). Oxford U Pr.
Tibyan: Memoirs of Abd Allah b. Buluggin, Last Zirid Amir of Granada. Translated from the Emended Arabic Text & Provided with Introduction, Notes & Comments. Amin T. Tibi. (Medieval Iberian Peninsula Ser.: Vol. 5). xiii, 291p. 1986. 38.25 (ISBN 90-04-07669-7, Pub. by E J Brill). Heinman.
Tide of Islam. T. B. Irving. 7.95 (ISBN 0-686-83887-4). Kazi Pubns.
Tied to Masonic Apron Strings. Stewart M. Pollard. Ed. by Lewis C. Cook. 1979. pap. 4.50 (ISBN 0-88053-059-6, M-322). Macoy Pub.
Tiempo Pasada De La Palabra De Dios. Kenneth Hagin, Jr. (Span.). 1983. pap. 0.50 mini bk. (ISBN 0-89276-176-8). Hagin Ministries.
Ties That Bind: Moorings of a Life with God. Marvin Hein. LC 80-81705. 135p. (Orig.). 1980. pap. 5.95 (ISBN 0-937364-04-5). Kindred Pr.
Tigerlily. Mama S. Rampa. 1978. pap. 2.95 (ISBN 0-552-10735-2). Weiser.
Tiger's Fang. Paul Twitchell. 1979. 5.95 (ISBN 0-914766-51-1). IWP Pub.
Tikkun. S. Baer. 332p. 1900. Repr. text ed. 41.40x (ISBN 0-576-80143-7, Pub. by Gregg Intl Pubs England). Gregg Intl.
Tikoun Haklali. Rabbi Nachman. Tr. by Alon Dimermanas from Hebrew. (Fr.). 125p. 1986. pap. text ed. 3.00 (ISBN 0-930213-24-6). Breslov Res Inst.
Tikune Zohar: Hebrew Text, 2 vols. Yehuda Brandwein. 1973. Vol. 1. 25.00 (ISBN 0-943688-27-2); Vol. 2. 25.00 (ISBN 0-943688-28-0). Res Ctr Kabbalah.
Til Death Do Us Part: A Basic Education in Total Health: How to Keep Body & Soul Happily Together. Martin P. Cornelius, III. 256p. (Orig.). 1981. pap. 15.00 (ISBN 0-9607142-0-0). Health Ed & Life Exp Res.
Tilak & Sankara on Bhagvad Gita. G. V. Saroja. 200p. 1985. text ed. 20.00x (ISBN 0-86590-571-1, Pub. by Sterling Pubs India). Apt Bks.
Tilaka: Hindu Marks. Priyabala Shah. (Illus.). 108p. 1985. 29.95x (ISBN 0-318-20319-7, Pub. by New Order Bk Co India). Humanities.
Till Armageddon. Billy Graham. 224p. 1984. pap. 6.95 (ISBN 0-8499-2998-9, 2998-9). Word Bks.
Till He Come. C. H. Spurgeon. 1978. pap. 4.25 (ISBN 0-686-09089-6). Pilgrim Pubns.
Till the Heart Sings: A Biblical Theology of Manhood & Womanhood. Samuel Terrien. LC 85-47731. 272p. 1985. 24.95 (ISBN 0-8006-0752-X, 1-752). Fortress.
Tillich. David H. Freeman. (Modern Thinkers Ser.). 1960. pap. 2.00 (ISBN 0-87552-589-X). Presby & Reformed.
Tillich's System. Wayne W. Mahan. LC 73-91170. 1974. 10.00 (ISBN 0-911536-52-3). Trinity U Pr.
Tilling the Soul. Wingate. 1984. pap. 9.95 (ISBN 0-317-17441-X). Aurora Press.
Tilted Haloes. James Weekley. (Orig.). 1987. pap. price not set (ISBN 0-89536-871-4, 7857). CSS of Ohio.
Timaios of Locri, on the Nature of the World & the Soul. Thomas H. Tobin. (Society of Biblical Literature, Texts & Translations Ser.: No. 26). 1985. 14.95 (ISBN 0-89130-767-2, 06 02 26); pap. 9.95 (ISBN 0-89130-742-7). Scholars Pr GA.
Time & Eternity: An Essay in the Philosophy of Religion. Walter T. Stace. Repr. of 1952 ed. lib. bdg. 22.50x (ISBN 0-8371-1867-0, STTE). Greenwood.
Time & History. Siegfried Herrmann. Tr. by James L. Belvins. LC 80-25323. (Biblical Encounter Ser.). 208p. (Orig.). 1981. pap. 9.95 (ISBN 0-687-42100-4). Abingdon.
Time & Its End: A Comparative Existential Interpretation of Time & Eschatology. Howard A. Slaatte. LC 80-7814. 298p. 1980. pap. text ed. 13.25 (ISBN 0-8191-1070-1). U Pr of Amer.
Time & Myth. John S. Dunne. LC 74-32289. 128p. 1975. pap. 4.95 (ISBN 0-268-01828-6). U of Notre Dame Pr.
Time & Reality. John E. Boodin. LC 75-3064. (Philosophy in America Ser.). Repr. of 1904 ed. 20.00 (ISBN 0-404-59063-2). AMS Pr.
Time & Self. Paul Brockelman. 96p. 1985. pap. 10.95 (ISBN 0-8245-0703-7). Crossroad NY.
Time & Self: Phenomenological Explorations. Paul Brockelman. (AAR Studies in Religion). 1985. 17.95 (ISBN 0-89130-779-6, 01-00-39); pap. 10.95 (ISBN 0-89130-780-X). Scholars Pr GA.
Time & the Highland Maya. Barbara Tedlock. LC 80-54569. (Illus.). 245p. 1981. pap. 10.95x (ISBN 0-8263-0835-X). U of NM Pr.
Time for Anger. Franky Schaeffer. LC 82-71981. 192p. 1982. pap. 6.95 (ISBN 0-89107-263-2, Crossway Bks). Good News.
Time for Church. Donna Rathert & Lois Prahlow. 24p. 1985. pap. 2.95 (ISBN 0-570-04129-5, 56-1540). Concordia.

Time for Commitment. Ted Engstrom & Robert C. Larson. 112p. 1987. padded gift ed. 9.95 (ISBN 0-310-51010-4); pap. 4.95 (ISBN 0-310-51011-2). Zondervan.

Time for Compassion. Ron L. Davis & James D. Denney. (Crucial Questions Ser.). 224p. 1986. 13.95 (ISBN 0-8007-1492-X). Revell.

Time for Consideration: A Scholarly Appraisal of the Unification Church. 2nd ed. M. Darrol Bryant & Herbert W. Richardson. LC 78-61364. (Symposium Ser.: Vol. 3). xi, 332p. 1978. 19.95x (ISBN 0-88946-954-7). E Mellen.

Time for Every Purpose. Betty Isler. 80p. (Orig.). 1986. pap. 4.95 (ISBN 0-570-03986-X, 12-3013). Concordia.

Time for Everything Under the Sun. Ruth S. Whittenburg. LC 79-84856. 1980. 17.50 (ISBN 0-8022-2351-6). Philos Lib.

Time for Faith. James Alberione. 1978. 4.00 (ISBN 0-8198-0371-5); pap. 3.00 (ISBN 0-8198-0372-3). Dghtrs St Paul.

Time for God. Leslie D. Weatherhead. (Festival Ser.). 1981. pap. 1.75 (ISBN 0-687-42113-6). Abingdon.

Time for Intercession. Erwin C. Prange. LC 76-20085. 176p. 1979. pap. 3.95 (ISBN 0-87123-561-7, 210561). Bethany Hse.

Time for Me. Pat Farrell. (Everyday Ser.). (Illus.). 26p. (Orig.). 1983. pap. 3.00 (ISBN 0-915517-01-9). Everyday Ser.

Time for My Soul: A Treasury of Jewish Stories for Our Holy Days. Annette Labovitz & Eugene Labovitz. LC 86-32243. 400p. 1987. 30.00 (ISBN 0-87668-954-3). Aronson.

Time for Peace: Biblical Meditations for Advent. William F. Maestri. LC 83-22399. 94p. 1983. pap. 4.95 (ISBN 0-8189-0463-1). Alba.

Time for Reflection. J. Spencer Kinard. 1986. text ed. 9.95 (ISBN 0-87579-049-6). Deseret Bk.

Time for Remembering. Patricia D. Cornwell. 496p. 1985. pap. 16.95 (ISBN 0-8027-2501-5). Walker & Co.

Time for Remembering: The Ruth Bell Graham Story. Patricia D. Cornwell. LC 82-48922. (Illus.). 320p. 1983. 13.45 (ISBN 0-06-061685-7, HarpR). Har-Row.

Time in God's World. Beverly Beckmann. (In God's World Ser.). (Illus.). 24p. 1985. 5.95 (ISBN 0-570-04128-7, 56-1539). Concordia.

Time Is at Hand. Jay E. Adams. 1970. pap. 3.50 (ISBN 0-87552-060-X). Presby & Reformed.

Time Is Fulfilled. F. F. Bruce. LC 78-7373. 1978. pap. text ed. 3.95 (ISBN 0-8028-1756-4). Eerdmans.

Time Is Life. Avi Shulman. (Dynamics of Personal Achievement Ser.). 96p. (Orig.). 1985. pap. 4.95 (ISBN 0-87306-927-7). Feldheim.

Time Is Running Out: It's Much Later Than You Think. Leonard C. Hummel. 26p. (Orig.). 1986. pap. 1.95 (ISBN 0-940853-00-0). Power Word Pubns.

Time Line Display of Jewish History: Mural Edition. 1981. 18.00 (ISBN 0-686-46788-4). T Black.

Time Line Display of Jewish History: Poster Edition. 1982. 10.00 (ISBN 0-686-46792-2). T Black.

Time Management. Speed B. Leas. LC 78-8628. (Creative Leadership Ser.). 1978. pap. 5.95 (ISBN 0-687-42120-9). Abingdon.

Time of Favor: The Story of the Catholic Family of Southern Illinois. Betty Burnett. Ed. by Gregory M. Franzwa. xvi, 305p. 1987. 10.00 (ISBN 0-935284-48-6). Patrice Pr.

Time of Hope: Family Celebrations & Activities for Lent & Easter. Margaret Ehlen-Miller et al. (Illus., Orig.). 1979. pap. 4.95 (ISBN 0-8192-1247-4). Morehouse.

Time of Personal Regeneration. Richard J. Aschwanden & Maria Aschwanden. Ed. by Charles R. Aschwanden. 60p. 1984. pap. 3.40x (ISBN 0-913071-00-5, TX1-202-40). Rama Pub Co.

Time of the End. Henry J. Smith. (International Correspondence Program Ser.). 159p. (Orig.). pap. 6.95 (ISBN 0-87148-853-1). Pathway Pr.

Time of the Spirit. Ed. by George Every et al. LC 84-10696. 256p. (Orig.). 1984. pap. text ed. 9.95 (ISBN 0-88141-035-7). St Vladimirs.

Time Out. Al Bryant. pap. 2.95 (ISBN 0-310-22122-6). Zondervan.

Time Out for Coffee. Jeanette Lockerbie. (Quiet Time Bks.). 1978. pap. 3.50 (ISBN 0-8024-8759-9). Moody.

Time Out for God. Jane Sorenson. 64p. 1985. pap. 2.50 (ISBN 0-87239-895-1, 2825). Standard Pub.

Time Out for God, No. 2. Jane Sorenson. 64p. 1985. pap. 2.50 (ISBN 0-87239-896-X, 2826). Standard Pub.

Time Out for Grief: A Practical Guide to Passing Through Grief to Happiness. Jean G. Jones. LC 81-85051. 228p. 1982. pap. 4.50 (ISBN 0-87973-654-2, 654). Our Sunday Visitor.

Time Out: Prayers for Busy People. Basil Arbour. 96p. 1984. pap. 3.95 (ISBN 0-86683-828-7, HarpR). Har-Row.

Time Remembered: A Journal for Survivors. Earl A. Grollman. LC 86-47753. 98p. 1987. 10.00 (ISBN 0-8070-2704-9). Beacon Pr.

Time-Saving Sermon Outlines. Russell E. Spray. (Sermon Outline Ser.). (Orig.). 1981. pap. 2.50 (ISBN 0-8010-8193-9). Baker Bk.

Time, Space & Knowledge: A New Vision. Tarthang Tulku. LC 77-19224. (Illus.). 1977. 14.95 (ISBN 0-913546-08-9); pap. 10.95 (ISBN 0-913546-09-7). Dharma Pub.

Time, Talents, Things: A Woman's Workshop on Christian Stewardship. Latayne Scott. Ed. by J. Sloan. (Woman's Workshop Ser.). 96p. (Orig.). 1987. pap. 3.95 (ISBN 0-310-38771-X). Zondervan.

Time the Refreshing River: Science, Religion & Socialism & Other Essays. Joseph Needham. 292p. 1986. 39.95 (ISBN 0-85124-429-7, Pub. by Spokesman UK); pap. 12.50 (ISBN 0-85124-439-4, Pub. by Spokesman UK). Humanities.

Time to Be Born, A Time to Die. Robert L. Short. pap. 6.95i (ISBN 0-06-067677-9, RD 52, HarpR). Har-Row.

Time to Be Born, a Time to Die. pap. 3.50 (ISBN 0-686-96060-2); discussion Leader's guide 2.00 (ISBN 0-686-99692-5). United Syn Bk.

Time to Be Renewed. Warren W. Wiersbe. Ed. by James Adair. 400p. 1986. pap. 12.95 (ISBN 0-89693-391-1). Victor Bks.

Time to Build Joseph Breuer. 1982. Vol. 2. 8.95 (ISBN 0-686-76270-3). Feldheim.

Time to Dance: Symbolic Movement in Worship. Margaret F. Taylor. Ed. by Doug Adams. 192p. 1980. 5.95 (ISBN 0-941500-17-9). Sharing Co.

Time to Die. Glenn M. Vernon. 1977. 9.50 (ISBN 0-8191-0126-5). U Pr of Amer.

Time to Greez! Incantations from the Third World. Ed. by Janice Mirikitani et al. LC 75-355. (Illus.). 224p. (Orig.). 1975. pap. 4.95 (ISBN 0-912078-44-8). Volcano Pr.

Time to Grow. Joanne Putnam. Ed. by Mary Wallace. LC 85-20190. (Illus.). 112p. (Orig.). 1985. pap. 4.95 (ISBN 0-912315-92-X). Word Aflame.

Time to Keep: A History of the Christian Reformed Church. Herbert Brinks & A. James Heynen. text ed. cancelled (ISBN 0-933140-44-4); cancelled leader's guide (ISBN 0-933140-45-2). CRC Pubns.

Time to Laugh - or Grandpa Was a Preacher. Leroy Brownlow. 1973. gift ed. 6.95 (ISBN 0-915720-11-6). Brownlow Pub Co.

Time to Mourn. Jack Spiro. LC 67-30744. 160p. 1985. pap. text ed. 8.95 (ISBN 0-8197-0497-0). Bloch.

Time to Mourn: Expressions of Grief in Nineteenth Century America. Martha V. Pike & Janice G. Armstrong. LC 80-15105. (Illus.). 192p. 1980. pap. 14.95 (ISBN 0-295-96325-5, Pub. by Museums at Stony Brook). U of Wash Pr.

Time to Mourn: Judaism and the Psychology of Bereavement. Jack D. Spiro. 1968. 8.95 (ISBN 0-8197-0185-8). Bloch.

Time to Pray. Rose Goldstein. LC 72-91792. 10.00 (ISBN 0-87677-141-X). Hartmore.

Time to Stop & Think, Vol. 1. Michael Wharton. 1981. 12.00x (ISBN 0-7223-1422-1, Pub. by A H Stockwell England). State Mutual Bk.

Time to Stop Pretending. Luis Palau. 156p. 1985. pap. 5.95 (ISBN 0-89693-332-6). Victor Bks.

Time to Tell. David Hacohen. Tr. by Menachem Dagut. LC 84-45243. 256p. 1985. 18.50 (ISBN 0-8453-4789-6, Cornwall Bks). Assoc Univ Prs.

Time with God: Devotional Readings for Youth. Evelyn C. Foote. LC 72-97604. 1978. pap. 2.75 (ISBN 0-8054-5164-1, 4251-64). Broadman.

Timeless Christian. Erik Von Kuehnelt-Leddihn. LC 73-10604. 241p. 1976. 4.50 (ISBN 0-685-77519-4). Franciscan Herald.

Timeless Judaism for Our Time. Michael Kaniel. 1985. pap. 2.95 (ISBN 0-87306-944-7). Feldheim.

Timeless Spring: A Soto Zen Anthology. Tr. by Thomas Cleary. LC 79-26677. 176p. 1980. pap. 7.95 (ISBN 0-8348-0148-5). Weatherhill.

Timeless Trinity. Roy Lanier, Sr. pap. 9.95 (ISBN 0-89137-551-1). Quality Pubns.

Timeless Truth for Twentieth Century Times. Fred M. Barlow. 123p. 1970. 3.25 (ISBN 0-87398-838-8, Pub. by Bibl Evang Pr). Sword of Lord.

Timelessness of Jesus Christ. Richard C. Halverson. LC 82-80008. 1982. 8.95 (ISBN 0-8307-0838-3, 5109902). Regal.

Timely & the Timeless: Jews, Judaism & Society in a Storm-Tossed Decade. Immanuel Jakobovits. 432p. 1977. 25.00x (ISBN 0-85303-189-4, Pub. by Vallentine Mitchell England). Biblio Dist.

Time's Noblest Name: The Names & Titles of Jesus Christ, L-O. New rev. ed. Charles J. Rolls. pap. 5.95 (ISBN 0-87213-733-3). Loizeaux.

Times of Life: Prayers & Poems. Huub Oosterhuis. Tr. by N. D. Smith from Dutch. LC 79-89653. 128p. (Orig.). 1980. pap. 4.95 (ISBN 0-8091-2245-6). Paulist Pr.

Times Survey of the Foreign Ministries of the World. Ed. by Zara Steiner. (Illus.). 1982. 87.50x (ISBN 0-930466-37-3). Meckler Pub.

Timmerman's Lectures on Catholicism. S. F. Timmerman, Jr. 1952. 3.95 (ISBN 0-88027-085-3). Firm Foun Pub.

Timothy Flint: Pioneer, Missionary, Author, Editor, 1780-1840. John E. Kirkpatrick. LC 68-56780. (Research & Source Works Ser: No. 267). 1968. Repr. of 1911 ed. 21.50 (ISBN 0-8337-1930-0). B Franklin.

Timothy-James. Raymond Brown. 1983. pap. 4.95 (ISBN 0-87508-174-6). Chr Lit.

Timothy Principle. Roy Robertson. 120p. 1986. pap. 4.95 (ISBN 0-89109-550-0). NavPress.

Timothy, Titus & Philemon. H. A. Ironside. 9.95 (ISBN 0-87213-391-5). Loizeaux.

Timothy, Titus & You: A Workbook for Church Leaders. George C. Scipione. 96p. 1986. pap. 3.95 (ISBN 0-87552-439-7). Presby & Reformed.

Timothy: Young Pastor. Louise Caldwell. (BibLearn Ser..). (Illus.). 1978. 5.95 (ISBN 0-8054-4239-1, 4242-39). Broadman.

Tincraft for Christmas. Lucy Sargent. (Illus.). 1969. 7.95 (ISBN 0-688-02638-9); pap. 5.95 (ISBN 0-688-07638-6). Morrow.

Tinker of Bedford: A Historical Fiction on the Life & Times of John Bunyan. William S. Deal. 1977. pap. 2.95 (ISBN 0-686-19330-X). Crusade Pubs.

Tips for Ministers & Mates. Mary E. Bess. 1987. pap. 5.95 (ISBN 0-8054-6943-5). Broadman.

Tiptoeing Through the Minefield. Clark B. McCall. (Outreach Ser.). 32p. 1982. pap. 1.25 (ISBN 0-8163-0460-2). Pacific Pr Pub Assn.

Tirumalavadi Temple: History & Culture Through the Ages. C. Mookka Reddy. xii, 236p. 1986. text ed. 30.00x (ISBN 81-7018-329-4, Pub. by B. R. Pub Corp Delhi). Apt Bks.

Tishah B'av Service. Morris Silverman & Hillel. pap. 2.95x (ISBN 0-87677-068-5). Prayer Bk.

Tithe: Challenge or Legalism. Douglas W. Johnson. 128p. 1984. pap. 5.95 (ISBN 0-687-42127-6). Abingdon.

Tithing. Karen D. Merrell. 22p. pap. 4.95 (ISBN 0-87747-560-1). Deseret Bk.

Tithing. A. W. Pink. pap. 0.50 (ISBN 0-686-48166-6). Reiner.

Tithing: A Call to Serious, Biblical Giving. R. T. Kendall. 128p. 1983. pap. 4.95 (ISBN 0-310-38331-5, 9279P). Zondervan.

Tithing: God's Command Or Man's Demand - Which? Tony Badillo. (Illus.). 102p. (Orig.). 1984. pap. 9.50 (ISBN 0-912977-00-0). Xavier Pr.

Tito y Filemon: Comentario Biblico Portavoz. Edmond Hiebert. Orig. Title: Titus & Philemon (Everyman's Bible Commentary) (Span.). 136p. 1981. pap. 3.95 (ISBN 0-8254-1317-6). Kregel.

Tituba of Salem Village. Ann Petry. LC 64-20691. (YA) 1964. 14.70i (ISBN 0-690-82677-X, Crowell Jr Bks). HarpJ.

Titus. G. Michael Cocoris. 99p. (Orig.). 1985. pap. text ed. 2.00 (ISBN 0-935729-31-3). Church Open Door.

Titus & Philemon. D. Edmond Hiebert. (Everyman's Bible Commentary Ser.). 1957. pap. 5.95 (ISBN 0-8024-2056-7, MBP). Moody.

Titus & Philemon. W. Kelly. 6.50 (ISBN 0-88172-110-7). Believers Bkshelf.

TLC Prayer Network Training Manual. Iverna Tompkins. Ed. by Shirlee Green & Roberta Stultz. write for info. tchr's. manual (ISBN 0-9611260-3-5). I Tompkins.

Tlingit Myths & Texts. John R. Swanton. Repr. of 1909 ed. 34.00 (ISBN 0-384-59050-0). Johnson Repr.

Tlingit Myths & Texts. John R. Swanton. Repr. of 1909 ed. 49.00 (ISBN 0-403-03710-7). Scholarly.

Tlingit Tales: Potlach & Totem Pole. Lorie K. Harris. (Illus.). 64p. 11.95 (ISBN 0-87961-152-9); pap. 5.95 (ISBN 0-87961-153-7). Naturegraph.

TM: An Alphabetical Guide to the Transcendental Meditation Program. Nat Goldhaber & Denise Denniston. (Illus.). 1976. pap. 3.95 (ISBN 0-345-24096-0). Ballantine.

TM & Cult Mania. Michael A. Persinger et al. 208p. 1980. 10.95 (ISBN 0-8158-0392-3). Chris Mass.

TM Technique: A Skeptic's Guide to the TM Program. Peter Russell. 1977. pap. 7.95 (ISBN 0-7100-0337-4). Methuen Inc.

TM Technique & the Art of Learning. Stephen Truch. (Quality Paperback Ser: No. 329). 250p. 1977. pap. 4.95 (ISBN 0-8226-0329-2). Littlefield.

TM Wants You. David Haddon & Vail Hamilton. (Direction Bks). 160p. 1976. pap. 1.95 (ISBN 0-8010-4151-1). Baker Bk.

TNT: The Power Within You. C. Bristol & H. Sherman. 1954. pap. 4.95 (ISBN 0-13-922674-5). P-H.

To Act Justly, Love Tenderly, Walk Humbly: An Agenda for Ministers. Walter Brueggemann et al. 88p. 1986. pap. 3.95 (ISBN 0-8091-2760-1). Paulist Pr.

To Adam with Love. Douglas Roberts. pap. write for info (ISBN 0-515-09536-2). Jove Pubns.

To Advance the Gospel: New Testament Essays. J. A. Fitzmyer. 320p. 1981. 19.50x (ISBN 0-8245-0008-3). Crossroad NY.

To All Generations, a Study of Church History. Frank Roberts. 276p. (Orig.). 1981. pap. text ed. 10.95 (ISBN 0-933140-17-7); leader's guide 7.95 (ISBN 0-933140-18-5). CRC Pubns.

To Be a Catholic. Joseph V. Gallagher. LC 73-137884. 96p. 1970. pap. 1.95 (ISBN 0-8091-5143-X). Paulist Pr.

To Be a Christian. J. C. Metcalfe. 1966. pap. 2.25 (ISBN 0-87508-923-2). Chr Lit.

To Be a Girl, to Be a Woman. Ruth Vaughn. 160p. 1982. 8.95 (ISBN 0-8007-1328-1). Revell.

To Be a Jew. Hayim Donin. LC 72-89175. 1972. 17.95 (ISBN 0-465-08624-1). Basic.

To Be a Pilgrim: A Spiritual Notebook. Basil Hume. LC 84-47726. 240p. 1984. 13.45 (ISBN 0-06-064081-2, HarpR). Har-Row.

To Be a Pilgrim (John Bunyan) Joyce Reason. 1961. pap. 2.95 (ISBN 0-87508-625-X). Chr Lit.

To Be a Presbyterian. Louis Weeks. 96p. (Orig.). 1983. pap. 4.95 (ISBN 0-8042-1880-3). John Knox.

To Be a Priest: Perspectives on Vocation & Ordination. Robert E. Terwilliger & Urban T. Holmes. 192p. (Orig.). 1975. pap. 4.95 (ISBN 0-8164-2592-2, 8164-2592-2, HarpR). Har-Row.

To Be Fully Alive. Joseph Gelberman. 89p. pap. 5.95 (ISBN 0-942494-49-0). Coleman Pub.

To Be Human: An Introductory Experiment in Philosophy. Xavier O. Monasterio. 256p. (Orig.). 1985. pap. 7.95 (ISBN 0-8091-2704-0). Paulist Pr.

To Be in Christ. Hubert Van Zeller. LC 81-9793. (Illus.). 112p. 1981. 9.95x (ISBN 0-8245-0086-5). Crossroad NY.

To Be the Bridge: A Black Perspective on White Catholicism in America. Sandra Smithson. LC 84-50080. 200p. 1984. pap. 8.95 (ISBN 0-938232-48-7). Winston-Derek.

To Begin with Puzzles, Games & Mazes about the Book of Genesis. Zoe S. LeCours. (Illus.). 48p. (Orig.). 1985. pap. 4.49 (ISBN 0-934661-00-6, 7077). Lions Head Pr.

To Believe in Jesus. Ruth Burrows. 6.95 (ISBN 0-87193-154-0). Dimension Bks.

To Believe Is to Exist. John R. Sheets. 1986. pap. 14.95 (ISBN 0-87193-247-4). Dimension Bks.

To Belize with Love. Hannah B. Lapp. LC 86-70999. 380p. (Orig.). (YA) 1986. pap. 14.95 (ISBN 0-931494-94-X). Brunswick Pub.

To Bigotry, No Sanction: The Reverend Sun Myung Moon & the Unification Church. Mose Durst. LC 84-60571. (Illus.). 196p. 1984. pap. 6.95 (ISBN 0-89526-829-9). Regnery Bks.

To Boldly Go. Eric Delve. 132p. 1986. pap. 4.95 (ISBN 0-89693-275-3). Victor Bks.

To Brighten Each Day. J. Winston Pearce. LC 83-70001. 1983. 9.95 (ISBN 0-8054-5220-6). Broadman.

To Build & Be Church, Lay Ministry Resource Packet. 73p. 1979. pap. 6.50 (ISBN 1-55586-621-2). US Catholic.

To Change the World: Christology & Cultural Criticism. Rosemary R. Ruether. LC 81-9703. 96p. 1983. pap. 5.95 (ISBN 0-8245-0573-5). Crossroad NY.

To Cherish All Life: A Buddhist View of Animal Slaughter & Meat Eating. Roshi P. Kapleau. LC 81-51149. (Illus., Orig.). 1981. pap. text ed. 4.25 (ISBN 0-940306-00-X). Zen Ctr.

To China With Love: The Lives & Times of Protestant Missionaries in China, 1860-1900. Pat Barr. 1972. 16.95 (ISBN 0-436-03355-0, Pub. by Secker & Warburg UK). David & Charles.

To Come & See. 1985. 10.00 (ISBN 0-8199-0879-7). Franciscan Herald.

To Comfort All Who Mourn: A Parish Handbook for Ministry to the Grieving. Carol Luebering. (Illus.). 96p. 1985. pap. 4.95 (ISBN 0-86716-045-4). St Anthony Mess Pr.

To Comfort & Confront. Kenneth R. Overberg. 78p. (Orig.). 1983. pap. 2.95 (ISBN 0-914544-49-7). Living Flame Pr.

To Comfort You. Laurel Lee. Ed. by Cheryl M. Phillips & Bonnie C. Harvey. (Illus.). 32p. (Orig.). 1984. pap. 0.98 (ISBN 0-937420-11-5). Stirrup Assoc.

To Continue. Randy Blasing. 75p. (Orig.). 1983. cancelled 10.95 (ISBN 0-89255-070-8); pap. 5.95 (ISBN 0-89255-071-6). Persea Bks.

To Dad. Daniel R. Seagren. (Contempo Ser.). 1978. pap. 0.95 (ISBN 0-8010-8113-0). Baker Bk.

To Dance with God: Family Ritual & Community Celebration. Gertrud M. Nelson. 176p. 1986. pap. 9.95 (ISBN 0-8091-2812-8). Paulist Pr.

To Declare God's Forgiveness: Toward a Pastoral Theology of Reconciliation. Clark Hyde. LC 84-60626. 188p. (Orig.). 1984. pap. 8.95 (ISBN 0-8192-1348-9). Morehouse.

To Die in the Queen of Cities: A Story of the Christian Courage & Love in the Face of Roman Persecution. Sandy Dengler. 256p. 1986. pap. 6.95 (ISBN 0-8407-5996-7). Nelson.

To Die is Gain. Neal Carlson. (Solace Ser.). 1983. pap. 1.50 (ISBN 0-8010-2487-0). Baker Bk.

To Do the Work of Justice: A Plan of Action for the Catholic Community in the United States. pap. 1.95 (ISBN 1-55586-132-6, B-132). US Catholic.

To Dream Again. Robert D. Dale. LC 81-65386. 1981. pap. 5.95 (ISBN 0-8054-2541-1). Broadman.

To Drink of His Love. Mary F. Wuestefeld. Ed. by Gerald Wheeler. (Banner Ser.). 128p. (Orig.). 1986. pap. 6.50 (ISBN 0-8280-0312-2). Review & Herald.

To Drink or Not to Drink. J. Lawrence Burkholder. 24p. (Orig.). 1981. pap. text ed. 0.75 (ISBN 0-8361-1967-3). Herald Pr.

To Dwell in Unity: The Jewish Federation Movement in America, 1960-1980. Philip Bernstein. LC 83-9867. 394p. 1983. 19.95 (ISBN 0-8276-0228-6, 608). Jewish Pubns.

To Empower as Jesus Did: Acquiring Spiritual Power through Apprenticeship. Aaron Milavec. LC 82-6466. (Toronto Studies in Theology: Vol. 9). 358p. 1982. 59.95x (ISBN 0-88946-966-0). E Mellen.

To Follow His Way: A Parish Renewal Program. David Knight. 112p. (Orig.). 1980. pap. 3.95 (ISBN 0-912228-70-9). St Anthony Mess Pr.

To Free a People: American Jewish Leaders & the Jewish Problem in Eastern Europe, 1890 to 1914. Gary D. Best. LC 81-4265. (Contributions in American History Ser.: No. 98). xi, 240p. 1982. lib. bdg. 32.95 (ISBN 0-313-22532-X, BTO/). Greenwood.

To Give Life: The UJA in the Shaping of the American Jewish Community. Abraham J. Karp. LC 80-16487. 224p. 1980. 12.95 (ISBN 0-8052-3751-8). Schocken.

To Give the Love of Christ. James McGovern. LC 77-14832. (Emmaus Book). 128p. 1978. pap. 2.95 (ISBN 0-8091-2076-3). Paulist Pr.

To God Be the Glory. Lucile M. Campbell. (Orig.). 1981. pap. 1.95 (ISBN 0-9607114-0-6). L M Campbell.

To God Be the Glory. Billy Graham & Corrie Ten Boom. 62p. 1985. pap. text ed. 4.95 large print ed. (ISBN 0-8027-2473-6). Walker & Co.

To God the Glory. Annalee Skarin. pap. 5.95 (ISBN 0-87516-094-8). De Vorss.

To God Through Faith: From Christ to Sri Ramakrishna. Sri Surath. 1978. pap. 3.00 (ISBN 0-685-58452-6). Ranney Pubns.

To Grow in Spirit. Joe J. Christensen. 81p. 1983. 6.95 (ISBN 0-87747-968-2). Deseret Bk.

To Hallow This Life: An Anthology. Martin Buber. Ed. by Jacob Trapp. LC 73-11862. 174p. 1974. Repr. of 1958 ed. lib. bdg. 22.50x (ISBN 0-8371-7096-6, BUHL). Greenwood.

To Heal Again: Toward Serenity & the Resolution of Grief. Rusty Berkus. (Illus.). 32p. (Orig.). 1986. pap. 13.95 (ISBN 0-9609888-2-3). Red Rose Pr.

To Heal As Jesus Healed. Barbara L. Shlemon et al. LC 78-54126. 112p. 1978. pap. 2.95 (ISBN 0-87793-152-6). Ave Maria.

To Hear the Angels Sing. Dorothy Maclean. 217p. (Orig.). 1983. pap. text ed. 7.00 (ISBN 0-936878-01-0). Lorian Pr.

To Hear the Word: Invitation to Serious Study of the Bible. Milton P. Brown. 256p. 1987. 29.95 (ISBN 0-86554-251-1, MUP H-216); pap. 14.95 (ISBN 0-86554-252-X, MUP P-40). Mercer Univ Pr.

To Help You Through the Hurting. Marjorie Holmes. LC 81-43571. (Illus.). 160p. 1983. 9.95 (ISBN 0-385-17842-5). Doubleday.

To Help You Through the Hurting. Marjorie Holmes. 176p. 1985. pap. 8.95 (ISBN 0-8027-2508-2). Walker & Co.

To Him Who Conquers. Stephen Sanders. LC 73-111183. 210p. 1970. 25.00 (ISBN 0-385-06306-7). Fellowship Crown.

To Insure Peace Acknowledge God. Cardinal John Krol. 1978. 5.50 (ISBN 0-8198-0561-0); pap. 3.95 (ISBN 0-8198-0562-9). Dghtrs St Paul.

To Jerusalem. Folke G. Bernadotte Af Wisborg. LC 75-6424. (Rise of Jewish Nationalism & the Middle East Ser.). 280p. 1975. Repr. of 1951 ed. 23.65 (ISBN 0-88355-311-2). Hyperion Conn.

To Jerusalem & Back. Saul Bellow. 1977. pap. 1.95 (ISBN 0-380-01676-1, 33472-0). Avon.

To Kairwan the Holy. A. A. Boddy. 320p. 1985. 49.00x (ISBN 0-317-39199-2, Pub. by Luzac & Co Ltd). State Mutual Bk.

To Kiss the Joy. Robert A. Raines. 160p. 1983. pap. 4.35 (ISBN 0-687-42185-3). Abingdon.

To Know & Follow Jesus: Contemporary Christology. Thomas N. Hart. 160p. (Orig.). 1984. pap. 6.95 (ISBN 0-8091-2636-2). Paulist Pr.

To Know Christ Jesus. F. J. Sheed. 1980. pap. 4.95 (ISBN 0-89283-080-8). Servant.

To Know God: A Five-Day Plan. Morris Venden. Ed. by Raymond Woolsey. 125p. pap. 1.50 (ISBN 0-8280-0220-7). Review & Herald.

To Know the Knower. Swami Muktananda. 40p. 1.75 (ISBN 0-317-03900-8). SYDA Found.

To Know the Unknown. Florence Moore. 1984. 5.75 (ISBN 0-8062-2340-5). Carlton.

To Know Yourself: The Essential Teachings of Swami Satchidananda. Swami Satchidandananda. LC 77-80901. 1978. pap. 7.95 (ISBN 0-385-12613-1, Anch). Doubleday.

To Life! Yoga with Priscilla Patrick. Priscilla Patrick. LC 82-71187. (Illus.). 76p. (Orig.). 1982. pap. 9.95 (ISBN 0-943274-00-1). SC Ed Comm Inc.

To Listen Is to Heal. Albert J. Nimeth. 1984. 5.00 (ISBN 0-317-46887-1). Franciscan Herald.

To Live Again. Catherine Marshall. 1976. pap. 3.95 (ISBN 0-380-01586-2). Avon.

To Live As Jesus Did. new ed. Bernard Hayes. 128p. (Orig.). 1981. pap. 2.95 (ISBN 0-914544-35-7). Living Flame Pr.

To Live As We Worship. Lawrence E. Mick. 100p. (Orig.). 1984. pap. 4.95 (ISBN 0-8146-1327-6). Liturgical Pr.

To Live Each Day Is to Meditate. Evelyn Masset. (Illus.). 42p. 1982. pap. 5.00. Coleman Pub.

To Live Is Christ. T. A. Kantonen. 1978. pap. 4.50 (ISBN 0-89536-306-2, 2028). CSS of Ohio.

To Live or Die: Facing Decisions at the End of Life. C. E. Koop. (Christian Essentials Ser.). 48p. 1987. pap. 1.95 (ISBN 0-89283-322-X). Servant.

To Live the Word Inspired & Incarnate: An Integral Biblical Spirituality. Warren Dicharry. LC 85-7386. 464p. (Orig.). 1985. pap. 12.95 (ISBN 0-8189-0476-3). Alba.

To Live with Hope. G. Temp Sparkman. 112p. 1985. pap. 5.95 (ISBN 0-8170-1062-9). Judson.

To Look on Earth with More Than Mortal Eyes. Marjorie Spock. 1985. pap. 5.95 (ISBN 0-916786-79-X). St George Bk Serv.

To Love Again: Remarriage for the Christian. Helen K. Hoster. (Orig.). 1985. pap. 8.95 (ISBN 0-687-42187-X). Abingdon.

To Love & Be Loved. John Tormey. 1979. pap. 1.95 (ISBN 0-89243-093-1). Liguori Pubns.

To Love & to Cherish. Roy Gesch. 1985. 4.95 (ISBN 0-570-04214-3, 15-2174). Concordia.

To Love & to Cherish. Doreen Waggoner. 48p. 1986. 6.95 (ISBN 0-8378-5094-0). Gibson.

To Love Christ Jesus. Alphonsus Liguori. 96p. 1987. pap. 2.95 (ISBN 0-89243-262-4). Liguori Pubns.

To Love Each Other: A Woman's Workshop on First Corinthians. Latayne C. Scott. (Woman's Workshop Ser.). 112p. (Orig.). 1985. pap. 3.95 (ISBN 0-310-38921-6, 10454P). Zondervan.

To Love Is to Live. Spiros Zodhiates. (I Corinthians). 1967. 8.95 (ISBN 0-89957-503-X). AMG Pubs.

To Martin Luther King, with Love: A Southern Quaker's Tribute. David W. Pitre. 1984. pap. 2.50x (ISBN 0-87574-254-8, 254). Pendle Hill.

To Mend the World: Foundations of Future Jewish Thought. Emil L. Fackenhein. LC 81-16614. 352p. (Orig.). 1982. pap. 12.95 (ISBN 0-8052-0699-X). Schocken.

To My Son (II Timothy) Guy H. King. 1972. pap. 3.95 (ISBN 0-87508-287-4). Chr Lit.

To Parents, with Love: Practical Pointers for Family Success. Darla Hanks & Arlene Bascom. 341p. 1978. 10.95 (ISBN 0-88290-090-0). Horizon Utah.

To Pray As a Jew. Hayim H. Donin. LC 80-50554. 384p. 1980. 17.95 (ISBN 0-465-08628-4). Basic.

To Pray As Jesus. George Martin. 1978. pap. 2.50 (ISBN 0-89283-054-9). Servant.

To Pray or Not to Pray. John B. Cobb, Jr. 1974. pap. 1.25x (ISBN 0-8358-0310-4). Upper Room.

To Pray or Not to Pray: A Handbook for Study of Recent Supreme Court Decisions & American Church-State Doctrine. Charles W. Lowry. 1969. enlarged ed. 6.00 (ISBN 0-87419-013-4, U Pr of Wash). Larlin Corp.

To Pray or Not to Pray: A Handbook for Study of Recent Supreme Court Decisions & American Church-State Doctrine. Charles W. Lowry. (Special bicentennial facsimile of enlarged ed). 1978. 7.00 (ISBN 0-685-88420-1, U Pr of Wash). Larlin Corp.

To Proclaim the Faith. Alan K. Waltz. 144p. 1983. pap. 3.95 (ISBN 0-687-42252-3). Abingdon.

To Raise a Jewish Child: A Guide for Parents. Hayim H. Donin. LC 76-7679. 1977. 15.95 (ISBN 0-465-08626-8). Basic.

To Redeem the Soul of America: The Southern Christian Leadership Conference & Martin Luther King, Jr. Adam Fairclough. (Illus.). 456p. 1987. 35.00 (ISBN 0-8203-0898-6); pap. 17.95 (ISBN 0-8203-0938-9). U of Ga Pr.

To Reform the Nation: Theological Foundations of Wesley's Ethics. Leon O. Hynson. Ed. by Ben Chapman & Gerard Terpstra. 192p. (Orig.). 1984. pap. 7.95 (ISBN 0-310-75071-7, 17030P). Zondervan.

To Rome & Beyond (Acts B) Leader's Guide. (New Horizons Bible Study). 46p. (Orig.). 1982. pap. 1.95 (ISBN 0-89367-068-5). Light & Life.

To Rome & Beyond (Acts B) Student Guide. (New Horizons Bible Study). 68p. (Orig.). 1982. pap. 2.50 (ISBN 0-89367-069-3). Light & Life.

To Run & Not Be Weary. Stan Cottrell. (Illus.). 192p. 1985. 12.95 (ISBN 0-8007-1444-X). Revell.

To Save the Rest of Them: Gisi Fleischmann & the Rescue of Central European Jews. 2nd, rev. ed. Joan Campion. (Illus.). 196p. 1985. lib. bdg. 18.95 (ISBN 0-9614649-0-9); pap. text ed. 10.95 (ISBN 0-9614649-1-7). G Hein.

To Save Their Heathen Souls: Voyage to & Life in Foochow, China, Based on Wentworth Diaries & Letters, 1854-1858. Ed. by Polly Park. (Pittsburgh Theological Monographs: New Ser. 9). (Illus., Orig.). 1984. pap. 10.00 (ISBN 0-915138-66-2). Pickwick.

To Secure the Blessings of Liberty: American Constitutional Law & the New Religious Movements. William C. Shepherd. 128p. 1985. 12.95 (ISBN 0-8245-0664-2); pap. 8.95 (ISBN 0-8245-0670-7). Crossroad NY.

To See Ourselves As Others See Us: Christians Jews, "Others" in Late Antiquity. Ed. by Jacob Neusner & Ernest S. Frerichs. (Scholars Press Studies in the Humanities). (Orig.). 1985. 38.95 (ISBN 0-89130-819-9, 00-01-09); pap. 25.95 (ISBN 0-89130-820-2). Scholars Pr GA.

To See the Kingdom: The Theological Vision of H. Richard Niebuhr. James W. Fowler. LC 85-17878. 304p. 1985. pap. text ed. 13.75 (ISBN 0-8191-4938-1). U Pr of Amer.

To Set at Liberty: Christian Faith & Human Freedom. Delwin Brown. LC 80-21783. 144p. (Orig.). 1981. pap. 6.95 (ISBN 0-88344-501-8). Orbis Bks.

To Set One's Heart: Belief & Teaching in the Church. Sara Little. LC 82-49020. 160p. 1983. pap. 8.95 (ISBN 0-8042-1442-5). John Knox.

To Set Things Right: The Bible Speaks on Faith & Justice. Justin Vander Kolk. 48p. 1971. pap. 1.25 (ISBN 0-377-02001-X). Friend Pr.

To Share with God's Poor: Sister among the Outcasts. Emmanuelle Cinquin. LC 83-47735. (Illus.). 458p. 1983. pap. 5.95 (ISBN 0-06-061392-0, RD-485, HarpR). Har-Row.

To Simplify Our Life. NFCLC. 150p. 1982. wkbk. & cassette 10.00x (ISBN 0-913605-04-2). NFCLC.

To Spread the Power. George G. Hunter, III. 224p. 1987. pap. 9.95 (ISBN 0-687-42259-0). Abingdon.

To Stand & Speak for Christ. Joseph Fichtner. LC 81-10975. 166p. 1981. pap. 6.95 (ISBN 0-8189-0415-1). Alba.

To Teach as Jesus Did. 57p. 1972. pap. 2.95 (ISBN 1-55586-063-X). US Catholic.

To Teachers with Love. Ingeborg S. MacHaffie. Ed. by Margaret Nielsen. (Illus.). 90p. (Orig.). 1986. pap. 5.95 perfect bdg. (ISBN 0-9609374-2-0). Skribent.

To Tell of Gideon: The Art of Storytelling in the Church. John Harrell. 1975. 8.00x (ISBN 0-9615389-4-5); cassette 6.95x (ISBN 0-9615389-5-3). York Hse.

To the Church in America. 4.00 (ISBN 0-8198-7313-6); 3.00 (ISBN 0-8198-7314-4). Dghtrs St Paul.

To the Ends of the Earth. 2nd ed. Hugh Steven. 142p. 1986. pap. 3.10 (ISBN 0-938978-31-4). Wycliffe Bible.

To the Ends of the Earth: A General History of the Congregation of the Holy Ghost. Henry J. Koren. 656p. 1982. text ed. 18.50x (ISBN 0-8207-0157-2). Duquesne.

To the Ends of the Earth: A Pastoral Statement on the Missions. 1987. pap. 3.95 (ISBN 1-55586-112-1). US Catholic.

To the Ends of the Earth: A Pastoral Statement on World Mission. National Conference of Catholic Bishops Staff. 40p. (Orig.). pap. 3.95 (ISBN 1-55586-112-1). US Catholic.

To the Fountain of Christianity. Vila. pap. 3.95 (ISBN 0-935120-02-5). Christs Mission.

To the Hebrews. Tr. by George W. Buchanan. LC 72-76127. (Anchor Bible Ser.: Vol. 36). 1972. 14.00 (ISBN 0-385-02995-0, Anchor Pr). Doubleday.

To the Kid in the Pew-Series A. Eldon Weisheit. LC 74-4548. 128p. 1974. 6.75 (ISBN 0-570-03238-5, 15-2132). Concordia.

To the Kid in the Pew-Series B. Eldon Weisheit. LC 74-4548. 1975. 6.75 (ISBN 0-570-03252-0, 15-2160). Concordia.

To the Kid in the Pew-Series C. Eldon Weisheit. (To the Kid in the Pew Ser.). 128p. 1976. 6.75 (ISBN 0-570-03261-X, 15-2169). Concordia.

To the One I Love. Christopher Hills. Ed. by Ann Ray & Norah Hills. LC 84-11814. (Illus.). 256p. 1984. 14.95; pap. text ed. pns (ISBN 0-916438-51-1). Univ of Trees.

To the Orthodox Christians of the U. S. A. Chrysostemos Stratman. 6p. 1949. pap. 1.00 (ISBN 0-317-30430-5). Holy Trinity.

To the Refreshing of the Children of Light. Geoffrey F. Nuttall. 1983. pap. 2.50x (ISBN 0-87574-101-0, 101). Pendle Hill.

To the U. S. Bishops at Their Ad Ldmina Visita. Pope John Paul II. 108p. 1984. 3.50 (ISBN 0-8198-0723-0); pap. 2.50 (ISBN 0-8198-0724-9). Dghtrs St Paul.

To the Unknown God. Petru Dumitriu. Tr. by James Kirkup from Fr. LC 82-5722. 256p. 1982. pap. 11.95 (ISBN 0-8164-2424-1, HarpR). Har-Row.

To the Youth of the World. 64p. 1985. pap. 3.95 (ISBN 1-55586-962-9). US Catholic.

To Thessalonians with Love. John D. Hendrix. LC 81-70974. (Orig.). 1983. pap. 6.50 (ISBN 0-8054-1312-X). Broadman.

To Thine Own Self Be True: The Re-Birth of Values in the New Ethical Therapy. Lewis M. Andrews. 288p. 1987. 16.95 (ISBN 0-385-23736-7, Anch). Doubleday.

To Those Concerned Citizens. Gopi Krishna. (Illus.). 16p. 1978. pap. 3.95 (ISBN 0-88697-002-4). Life Science.

To Touch the Hem of His Garment. Mary Drahos. 224p. (Orig.). 1983. pap. 7.95 (ISBN 0-8091-2548-X). Paulist Pr.

To Understand Each Other. Paul Tournier. 6.95 (ISBN 0-8042-2235-5). John Knox.

To Walk & Not Grow Weary. Francis Sciacca. 84p. 1985. pap. 3.95 (ISBN 0-89109-034-7). NavPress.

To Walk As He Walked. T. B. Maston. LC 85-17173. 1985. pap. 5.95 (ISBN 0-8054-5024-6). Broadman.

To Walk in the Way. Urie A. Bender. LC 79-83511. 208p. 1979. pap. 5.95 (ISBN 0-8361-1884-7). Herald Pr.

To Walk Together Again: The Sacrament of Reconciliation. Richard M. Gula. LC 83-82021. (Orig.). 1984. pap. 8.95 (ISBN 0-8091-2603-6). Paulist Pr.

To Whom Is God Betrothed? Earl Paulk. 200p. (Orig.). 1985. pap. 4.95 (ISBN 0-917595-10-6). K-Dimension.

To Whom Shall We Go: Christ & the Mystery of Man. Zachary Hayes. (Synthesis Ser). 96p. 1975. 1.25 (ISBN 0-8199-0702-2). Franciscan Herald.

To Whom the Land of Palestine Belongs. Christopher C. Hong. 1979. 6.50 (ISBN 0-682-49161-6). Exposition Pr FL.

To Will & to Do. Jacques Ellul. Tr. by C. Edward Hopkin. LC 70-91166. 1969. 12.50 (ISBN 0-8298-0137-5). Pilgrim NY.

To Work & to Love: A Theology of Creation. Dorothee Soelle & Shirley A. Cloyes. LC 84-47936. 160p. 1984. pap. 7.95 (ISBN 0-8006-1782-7). Fortress.

To You Mom. Edith Sapone. (Illus.). 1961. 3.00 (ISBN 0-8198-0162-3); pap. 2.00 (ISBN 0-8198-0163-1). Dghtrs St Paul.

Tobias & the Angels. Phyllis Tickle. 96p. (Orig.). 1982. pap. text ed. 2.95 (ISBN 0-918518-23-7). St Luke TN.

Tobias Smollett. George S. Rousseau. 210p. 1982. 18.95 (ISBN 0-567-09330-1, Pub. by T&T Clark Ltd UK). Fortress.

Toby's Gift. Melvin Northrup. (Books I Can Read). 32p. (Orig.). 1980. pap. 1.95 (ISBN 0-8127-0291-3). Review & Herald.

Today & Tomorrow. 2nd ed. A. K. Mozumdar. 1979. pap. 2.50 (ISBN 0-87516-369-6). De Vorss.

Today & Tomorrow. Alvin N. Rogness. LC 77-84095. 1978. pap. 6.95 (ISBN 0-8066-1621-0, 10-6660). Augsburg.

Today I Feel Loved! William L. Coleman. LC 82-4184. 128p. (Orig.). 1982. pap. 4.95 (ISBN 0-87123-566-8, 210566). Bethany Hse.

Today Is Friday. Leila M. Ashton. (My Church Teaches Ser.). (Illus.). 1978. pap. 1.954 (ISBN 0-8127-0176-3). Review & Herald.

Today Is Mine. Leroy Brownlow. 1972. gift ed 7.95 (ISBN 0-915720-14-0); leather ed. 12.95 (ISBN 0-915720-57-4). Brownlow Pub Co.

Today with My Father. Noelene Johnsson. Ed. by Gerald Wheeler. (Illus.). 384p. 1984. 7.95 (ISBN 0-8280-0240-1). Review & Herald.

Today with the King. Bob Cook. 408p. 1985. 12.95 (ISBN 0-89693-364-4). Victor Bks.

Today's Dictionary of the Bible. Compiled by T. A. Bryant. LC 82-12980. 678p. (Orig.). 1982. 15.95 (ISBN 0-87123-569-2, 230569). Bethany Hse.

Today's Evangelism: It's Message & Methods. Ernest C. Reisinger. 1982. pap. 4.95 (ISBN 0-87552-417-6). Presby & Reformed.

Today's Father: A Guide to Understanding, Enjoying & Making Things for the Growing Family. Michael Goldsmith et al. (Winston Family Handbooks). 96p. (Orig.). 1984. pap. 9.95 (ISBN 0-86683-849-X, AY8494, HarpR). Har-Row.

Today's Gift. Illus. by David Spohn. (Meditation Ser.). 400p. (Orig.). 1985. pap. 5.95 (ISBN 0-89486-302-9). Hazelden.

Today's Gift. (Hazelden Mediation Ser.). 400p. (Orig.). 1985. pap. 5.95 (ISBN 0-86683-504-0, HarpR). Har-Row.

Today's Gift: Daily Meditations for Families. (Hazelden Bks.). 1984. scp 6.50t (ISBN 0-86683-504-0). Har-Row.

Today's Gospel. Walter Chantry. 1980. pap. 3.45 (ISBN 0-85151-027-2). Banner of Truth.

Today's Handbook of Bible Characters. E. M. Blaiklock. 848p. 1987. 17.95 (ISBN 0-87123-948-5). Bethany Hse.

Today's Handbook of Bible Times & Customs. William L. Coleman. (Illus.). 306p. 1984. 11.95 (ISBN 0-87123-594-3, 230594). Bethany Hse.

Today's Pastor in Tomorrow's World. Rev. ed. Carnegie S. Calian. LC 82-7114. 164p. 1982. pap. 8.95 (ISBN 0-664-24426-2). Westminster.

Today's Sects. M. C. Burrell & J. S. Wright. 4.50 (ISBN 0-8010-0855-7). Baker Bk.

Today's Tentmakers. J. Christy Wilson, Jr. 1979. pap. 5.95 (ISBN 0-8423-7279-2). Tyndale.

Today's Victorious Woman, Vol. 2. Mrs. J. B Livingston. pap. 4.00 (ISBN 0-89137-427-2). Quality Pubns.

Today's Woman in Search of Freedom. Ruthe White. 176p. (Orig.). 1985. pap. 4.95 (ISBN 0-89081-473-2). Harvest Hse.

Today's Woman, Tomorrow's Church. Kaye Ashe. 200p. 1984. pap. 8.95 (ISBN 0-88347-168-X). Thomas More.

Today's World Religions. M. Thomas Starkes. 1986. 10.95 (ISBN 0-937931-02-0); pap. 7.95. Global TN.

Todesverstaendnis bei Simone de Beauvoir: Eine Theologische Untersuchung. Erich Schmalenberg. LC 72-77421. (Theologische Bibliothek Toepelmann, No. 25). 1972. 20.80x (ISBN 3-11-004036-0). De Gruyter.

Togbukh Fun Vilner Geto. Herman Kruk. Ed. by Mordecai W. Bernstein. LC 62-56072. (Yivo Institute for Jewish Research, Memoirs Ser.: No. 1). (Yiddish., Illus.). 620p. 1961. 10.00 (ISBN 0-914512-29-3). Yivo Inst.

Together, a New People: Pastoral Statement on Migrants & Refugees. National Conference of Catholic Bishops Staff. 40p. (Orig.). 1987. pap. 3.95 (ISBN 1-55586-147-4). US Catholic.

Together: A Process for Parish Family Ministry. Joseph DiMauro & Sharon A. Tumulty. 1985. Envisioning. pap. 2.50 (ISBN 0-697-02024-X); Listening. pap. 3.50 (ISBN 0-697-02025-8); Responding. pap. 3.50 (ISBN 0-697-02026-6); Enabling. pap. 3.50 (ISBN 0-697-02027-4); Administering. pap. 3.50 (ISBN 0-697-02028-2); Administrator manual. 20.00 (ISBN 0-697-02023-1). Wm C Brown.

Together at Baptism. Joseph E. Payne et al. LC 73-144040. (Illus.). 80p. (Orig.). 1971. pap. 1.50 (ISBN 0-87793-031-7). Ave Maria.

Together at the Lord's Supper: Preparation for Holy Communion. Mary Montgomery & Herb Montgomery. (Illus.). 1977. pap. text ed. 3.25 (ISBN 0-03-021291-X, 141, HarpR); parent bk. 2.25 (ISBN 0-03-021286-3, 192); leader's guide 4.95 (ISBN 0-03-021296-0, 193). Har-Row.

Together by Your Side: A Book for Comforting the Sick & Dying. Joseph M. Champlin. LC 79-51016. 80p. 1979. pap. 1.95 (ISBN 0-87793-180-1). Ave Maria.

Together Each Day. Joan W. Brown & Bill Brown. 288p. 1980. pap. 7.95 (ISBN 0-8007-5226-0). Revell.

Together for Life: Regular Edition. rev. ed. Joseph M. Champlin. (Illus.). 96p. 1970. pap. 1.50 (ISBN 0-87793-018-X). Ave Maria.

Together for Life: Special Edition for Marriage Outside Mass. rev. ed. Joseph M. Champlin. (Illus.). 96p. 1972. pap. 1.50 (ISBN 0-87793-118-6). Ave Maria.

Together Forever. Anne Kristin Carroll. 256p. (Orig.). 1982. pap. 7.95 (ISBN 0-310-45021-7, 6885P). Zondervan.

Together in Mission. Ed. by Theodore Williams. 90p. (Orig.). 1983. pap. 2.00. World Evang Fellow.

Together in Peace for Children. Joseph M. Champlin & Brian A. Haggerty. LC 76-26348. (Illus.). 72p. 1976. 1.50 (ISBN 0-87793-119-4). Ave Maria.

Together in Peace: Penitents Edition. Joseph M. Champlin. 104p. (Orig.). 1975. pap. 1.50 (ISBN 0-87793-095-3). Ave Maria.

Together in Peace: Priests Edition. Joseph M. Champlin. (Illus.). 272p. 1975. pap. 3.95 (ISBN 0-87793-094-5). Ave Maria.

Together in Solitude. Douglas Steere. LC 82-14918. 160p. 1983. 12.95 (ISBN 0-8245-0531-X). Crossroad NY.

Together in Solitude. rev. ed. Douglas Steere. 208p. 1985. pap. 8.95 (ISBN 0-8245-0715-0). Crossroad NY.

Together: Jesus Helps Me Grow, Bk. 2. Linda Corbin & Pat Dys. (Orig.). Date not set. pap. 3.95 (ISBN 0-87509-374-4). Chr Pubns.

Together: Jesus Makes Us New, Bk. 1. Linda Corbin & Pat Dys. (Illus.). 24p. (Orig.). 1986. pap. 3.95 (ISBN 0-87509-373-6). Chr Pubns.

Together: Prayers & Promises for Newlyweds. John M. Robertson. 64p. 1982. pap. 2.50 (ISBN 0-8423-7282-2). Tyndale.

Together They Built a Mountain. Patricia T. Davis. LC 74-14727. (Illus.). 196p. 1974. 6.95 (ISBN 0-915010-00-3). Sutter House.

Together... Till Death Us Do Part. John Braaten. Ed. by Michael L. Sherer. (Orig.). 1987. pap. 5.95 (ISBN 0-89536-852-8, 7811). CSS of Ohio.

Together Toward Hope: A Journey to Moral Theology. Philip Rossi. LC 83-1279. 224p. 1983. 16.95x (ISBN 0-268-01844-8, 85-18441). U of Notre Dame Pr.

Together with God. George Douma. pap. 0.45 (ISBN 0-686-23478-2). Rose Pub MI.

Togetherness. Daniel R. Seagren. (Contempo Ser.). 32p. 1978. pap. 0.95 (ISBN 0-8010-8114-9). Baker Bk.

Tokugawa Religion. Robert N. Bellah. 272p. pap. 9.95 (ISBN 0-02-902460-9). Free Pr.

Tolerance & Movements of Religious Dissent in Eastern Europe. Ed. by Bela K. Kiraly. (East European Monographs: No. 13). 227p. 1976. 20.00x (ISBN 0-914710-06-0). East Eur Quarterly.

Tolerance Des Religions. Henry Basnage De Beauval. Repr. 20.00 (ISBN 0-384-03522-1). Johnson Repr.

Toleration, & Other Essays & Studies. facs. ed. John Bigelow. LC 78-84298. (Essay Index Reprint Ser). 1927. 14.25 (ISBN 0-8369-1075-3). Ayer Co Pubs.

Toleration & Parliament, Sixteen Sixty to Seventeen Nineteen. Raymond C. Mensing. LC 79-63260. 1979. pap. text ed. 10.75 (ISBN 0-8191-0723-9). U Pr of Amer.

Toleration & the Constitution. David A. Richards. LC 86-2358. 288p. 1986. 29.95x (ISBN 0-19-504018-X). Oxford U Pr.

Tomb of Ken-Amun at Thebes: Metropolitan Museum of Art Egyptian Expedition Publications, 2 vols. in 1, Vol. 5. Norman De Garis Davies. LC 78-168401. (Metropolitan Museum of Art Publications in Reprint). (Illus.). 208p. 1972. Repr. of 1930 ed. 39.00 (ISBN 0-405-02267-0). Ayer Co Pubs.

Tomb of Nefer-Hotep at Thebes: Metropolitan Museum of Art Egyptian Expedition Publications, 2 vols in 1, Vol. 9. Norman De Garis Davies. LC 71-168402. (Metropolitan Museum of Art Publications in Reprint). (Illus.). 192p. 1972. Repr. of 1933 ed. 39.00 (ISBN 0-405-02236-0). Ayer Co Pubs.

Tomb of Nyhetep-Ptah at Giza & the Tomb of 'Ankhm' Ahor at Saqqara. Alexander Badawy. (U. C. Publications: Occasional Papers Ser.: Vol. 11). 1978. pap. 29.00x (ISBN 0-520-09575-8). U of Cal Pr.

Tomb of Queen Meryet-Amun at Thebes: Metropolitan Museum of Art Egyptian Expedition Publication, Vol. 6. Herbert E. Winlock. LC 70-168415. (Metropolitan Museum of Art Publication in Reprint). (Illus.). 204p. 1972. Repr. of 1932 ed. 32.00 (ISBN 0-405-02253-0). Ayer Co Pubs.

Tomb of Ramesses VI, 2 vols. Ed. by A. Piankoff & N. Rambova. LC 54-5646. (Bollingen Ser.: No. 40). Vol. 1- Texts. pap. 145.80 (ISBN 0-317-28638-2, 2051348); Vol. 2- Plates. pap. 53.00 (ISBN 0-317-28639-0). Bks Demand UMI.

Tomb of Rekh-Mi-Re at Thebes: Metropolitan Museum of Art Egyptian Expedition Publications, 2 vols. in 1, Vol. 11. Norman Davies. LC 75-168403. (Metropolitan Museum of Art Publications in Reprint). (Illus.). 374p. 1972. Repr. of 1943 ed. 47.50 (ISBN 0-405-02267-0). Ayer Co Pubs.

Tomb of Senebtisi at Lisht: Metropolitan Museum of Art Egyptian Expedition Publications, Vol. 1. Arthur C. Mace & Herbert E. Winlock. LC 73-168408. (Metropolitan Museum of Art Publications in Reprint). (Illus.). 228p. 1972. Repr. of 1916 ed. 32.00 (ISBN 0-405-02241-7). Ayer Co Pubs.

Tomb of Tjanefer at Thebes. Keith C. Seele. LC 59-14285. (Oriental Institute Pubns. Ser: No. 86). (Illus.). 1959. 22.00x (ISBN 0-226-62187-1, OIP86). U of Chicago Pr.

Tomb of Tut-Ankh-Amen, 3 Vols. Howard Carter & A. C. Mace. LC 63-17462. (Illus.). Repr. of 1954 ed. Set. 85.00x (ISBN 0-8154-0048-9). Cooper Sq.

Tombs of Iteti, Sekhem ankh-Ptah, & Kaemnofert at Giza. Alexander Badawy. (University of California Publications, Occasional Papers, Archaeology: No. 9). pap. 26.30 (ISBN 0-317-29106-8, 2021386). Bks Demand UMI.

Tomorrow Is Today. Shelley Bruce. LC 83-3797. (Illus.). 224p. 1983. 15.95 (ISBN 0-672-52756-1). Bobbs.

Tomorrow Today. Larry Richards. 132p. 1986. pap. 4.95 (ISBN 0-89693-505-1). Victor Bks.

Tongan Myths & Tales. E. W. Gifford. (BMB). Repr. of 1924 ed. 25.00 (ISBN 0-527-02111-3, BMB, NO. 8). Kraus Repr.

Tongue in Check. Joseph Stowell. 132p. pap. 4.95 (ISBN 0-88207-293-5). Victor Bks.

Tongue of the Prophets. Robert St. John. pap. 7.00 (ISBN 0-87980-166-2). Wilshire.

Tongue of the Prophets: The Life Story of Eliezer Ben Yehuda. Robert St. John. LC 77-97303. 377p. 1972. Repr. of 1952 ed. lib. bdg. 22.50x (ISBN 0-8371-2631-2, STTP). Greenwood.

Tongue Speaking: The History & Meaning of the Charismatic Experience. Morton Kelsey. 256p. 1981. pap. 8.95 (ISBN 0-8245-0073-3). Crossroad NY.

Tongue-Tip Taste of Tao. Bhagwan Shree Rajneesh. Ed. by Ma Prem Maneesha. (Initiation Talks Ser.). (Illus.). 350p. 1981. 26.95 (ISBN 0-88050-158-8). Chidvilas Found.

Tongues!? Spiros Zodhiates. (I Corinthians Ser.). (Illus.). 1974. pap. 6.95 (ISBN 0-89957-512-9). AMG Pubs.

Tongues & Prophecy. Stanley M. Horton. (Charismatic Bks.). 32p. 1972. pap. 0.69 (ISBN 0-88243-917-0, 02-0917). Gospel Pub.

Tongues & the Holy Spirit. Frank Pack. (Way of Life Ser: No. 127). (Orig.). 1972. pap. text ed. 3.95 (ISBN 0-89112-127-7, Bibl Res Pr). Abilene Christ U.

Tongues in Biblical Perspective. Charles R. Smith. pap. 4.95 (ISBN 0-88469-005-9). BMH Bks.

Tongues Like As of Fire. Robert C. Dalton. 127p. 1945. pap. 1.25 (ISBN 0-88243-619-8, 02-0619). Gospel Pub.

Tongues Movement. Lewis Bauman. 1979. pap. 1.00 (ISBN 0-88469-047-4). BMH Bks.

Tongues of Fire: An Anthology of Religious & Poetic Experience. Ed. by Karen Armstrong. 444p. 1986. 19.95 (ISBN 0-670-80878-4). Viking.

Tongues of Men: Hegel & Hamann on Religious Language & History. Stephen N. Dunning. LC 79-10729. (American Academy of Religion, Dissertation Ser.: No. 27). 1979. 14.00 (ISBN 0-89130-283-2, 010127); pap. 9.95 (ISBN 0-89130-302-2). Scholars Pr GA.

Tongues Then & Now. George W. Marston. 1983. pap. 2.95 (ISBN 0-87552-288-2). Presby & Reformed.

Tony Valenti Story. Tony Valenti & Grazia P. Yonan. LC 80-83781. 160p. (Orig.). 1981. 2.50 (ISBN 0-88243-752-6, 02-0752). Gospel Pub.

Too Busy for God? Think Again! Louise D'Angelo. LC 81-52423. 120p. 1981. pap. 2.50 (ISBN 0-89555-166-7). TAN Bks Pubs.

Too Late. Leon Stewart. pap. 5.95 (ISBN 0-911866-66-3). Advocate.

Too Late to Hide. Winsome Speck. (Lifline Ser.). 140p. 1984. pap. 7.95 (ISBN 0-8163-0541-2). Pacific Pr Pub Assn.

Too Many Pastors? The State of the Clergy Job Market. Jackson Carroll & Robert Wilson. LC 80-16037. 1980. pap. 6.95 (ISBN 0-8298-0405-6). Pilgrim NY.

Too Many People? A Problem in Values. Christopher Derrick. LC 85-60469. 116p. (Orig.). 1986. pap. 6.95 (ISBN 0-89870-071-X, 85-60469). Ignatius Pr.

Too Many People? Answers & Hope for the Human Family. Laurie Tychsen. 46p. (Orig.). 1986. pap. 3.25 (ISBN 0-937779-03-2). Greenlawn Pr.

Too Proud to Die. Ezra Coppin. LC 82-50238. 168p. (Orig.). 1982. pap. 4.95 (ISBN 0-88449-082-3, A424615). Vision Hse.

Tools & the Man: Property & Industry under the Christian Law. Washington Gladden. LC 75-353. (Radical Tradition in America Ser). 308p. 1975. Repr. of 1893 ed. 23.65 (ISBN 0-88355-222-1). Hyperion Conn.

Tools for Active Christians. Herbert Miller. LC 79-14795. (P.A.C.E. Ser.). (Orig.). 1979. pap. 6.95 (ISBN 0-8272-3624-7). CBP.

Tools for Healing: Working Toward Harmony & Balance. Kathy Mengle. LC 84-72359. (Illus.). 172p. (Orig.). 1985. pap. 9.95 (ISBN 0-87516-548-6). De Vorss.

Tools for Preaching & Teaching the Bible. Stewart Custer. 240p. (Orig.). 1979. pap. 6.95 (ISBN 0-89084-064-4). Bob Jones Univ Pr.

Tools for Tantra. Harish Johari. (Illus.). 192p. 1986. pap. 14.95 (ISBN 0-89281-055-6, Inner Traditions). Inner Tradit.

Tools for Theological Research. rev. 7th ed. Ed. by John L. Sayre & Roberta Hamburger. LC 85-11979. 120p. (Orig.). 1985. pap. 5.00x (ISBN 0-912832-22-3). Seminary Pr.

Topical Dictionary of Bible Texts. James Inglis. (Paperback Reference Library). 528p. 1985. pap. 12.95 (ISBN 0-8010-5038-3). Baker Bk.

Topical Encyclopedia of Living Quotations. Sherwood Wirt & Kristen Beckstrom. LC 82-4503. 290p. 1982. pap. 7.95 (ISBN 0-87123-574-9, 210574). Bethany Hse.

Topical Guide to the Scriptures of the Church of Jesus Christ of Latter-Day Saints. 1977. pap. 2.95 (ISBN 0-87747-764-7). Deseret Bk.

Topical Index & Digest of the Bible. Harold E. Monser & A. T. Robertson. (Paperback Reference Library). 688p. 1983. pap. 14.95 (ISBN 0-8010-6160-1). Baker Bk.

Torah: A Modern Commentary. W. Gunther Plaut & Bernard J. Bamberger. (Illus.). 1824p. 1981. 30.00 (ISBN 0-8074-0055-6). UAHC.

Torah: A Modern Commentary: Numbers. W. Gunther Plaut. (Torah Commentary Ser.). 476p. 1980. 20.00 (ISBN 0-8074-0039-4, 381602). UAHC.

Torah & Canon. James A. Sanders. LC 72-171504. 144p. (Orig.). 1972. pap. 5.95 (ISBN 0-8006-0105-X, 1-105). Fortress.

Torah & Flora. Louis I. Rabinowitz. (Illus.). 1977. 11.95 (ISBN 0-88482-917-0, Sanhedrin Pr). Hebrew Pub.

Torah & the Haftarot. Philip Birnbaum. 933p. 1983. 19.50 (ISBN 0-88482-456-X). Hebrew Pub.

Torah Anthology: Mem Lo'ez, 9 vols. Yaakov Culi. Tr. by Aryeh Kaplan. Incl. Vol. 1. Beginnings: From Creation Until Abraham. 540p. 14.95 (ISBN 0-940118-01-7); Vol. 2. Patriarchs: From Abraham Until Jacob. 600p. 15.95 (ISBN 0-940118-02-5); Vol. 3. Twelve Tribes: From Jacob Until Joseph. 708p; Vol. 4. Israel in Egypt: Subjugation & Prelude to the Exodus. 280p. 12.95 (ISBN 0-940118-04-1); Vol. 5. Redemption: The Exodus from Egypt. 436p. 15.95 (ISBN 0-940118-05-X); Vol. 6. Ten Commandments: Revelation at Sinai. 534p. 16.95 (ISBN 0-940118-06-8); Vol. 7. Law: The First Codification. 363p. 13.95 (ISBN 0-940118-07-6); Vol. 8. Acceptance: Establishing the Covenant. 250p. 12.95 (ISBN 0-940118-08-4); Vol. 9. Tabernacle: Plans for the Sanctuary. 413p. 15.95 (ISBN 0-940118-09-2). (MeAm Lo'ez Ser.). (Illus.). 1977-1980. Maznaim.

Torah at Brandeis Institute: The Layman Expounds. Ed. by Robert M. Bleiweiss. LC 76-7776. (Illus.). 1976. 8.95 (ISBN 0-916952-00-2). Brandeis-Bardin Inst.

Torah Binders of the Judah L. Magnes Museum. Ruth Eis. LC 79-83877. 80p. 1979. pap. 18.00 (ISBN 0-943376-15-7). Magnes Mus.

Torah for Family Reading. Ed. by Joseph Gaer. LC 86-70620. 559p. 1986. Repr. 30.00 (ISBN 0-87668-915-2). Aronson.

Torah from Our Sages: Pirke Avot. Jacob Neusner. 214p. 1986. 18.95 (ISBN 0-940646-39-0); pap. 9.95. Rossel Bks.

Torah: From Scroll to Symbol in Formative Judaism. Jacob Neusner. LC 84-45190. (Foundations of Judaism Trilogy Ser.). 208p. 1985. 24.95 (1-734). Fortress.

Torah Is Written. Paul Cowan & Rachel Cowan. (Illus.). 32p. 1986. 12.95 (ISBN 0-8276-0270-7). Jewish Pubns.

Torah Lishmah: The Study of Torah for Its Own Sake in the Work of Rabbi Hayyim of Volozhin & His Contemporaries. Norman Lamm. 1987. 25.00 (ISBN 0-88125-117-8); pap. 16.95 (ISBN 0-88125-133-X). Ktav.

Torah Pointers in the Collection of the Judah L. Magnes Museum. Alice Perlman. (Illus.). 24p. (Orig.). 1987. pap. 4.95 (ISBN 0-943376-30-0). Magnes Mus.

Torah Readings for Festivals. 5.95 (ISBN 0-87677-069-3). Prayer Bk.

Torah Teddy Learns Colors. Shaindy Shulman. 1985. 3.95 (ISBN 0-87306-942-0). Feldheim.

Torah Teddy Learns to Count. Shaindy Shulman. 1985. 3.95 (ISBN 0-87306-943-9). Feldheim.

Torah Therapy: Reflections on the Weekly Sedra & Special Occasions. Reuven P. Bulka. LC 83-6155. 1983. 15.00x (ISBN 0-88125-033-3). Ktav.

Torah Toons I. Joel L. Grishaver. (Illus.). 115p. (Orig.). 1985. pap. text ed. 5.50 (ISBN 0-933873-01-8). Torah Aura.

Torah Toons II. Joel L. Grishaver. (Illus.). 114p. (Orig.). 1985. pap. text ed. 5.50 (ISBN 0-933873-02-6). Torah Aura.

Torah with Love: A Guide for Strengthening Jewish Values Within the Family. David Epstein & Suzanne Stutman. (Illus.). 208p. 1986. 16.95 (ISBN 0-13-925371-8). P-H.

Torch of Certainty. Jamgon Kongtrul. Tr. by Judith Hanson from Tibetan. LC 86-11835. 184p. 1986. pap. 12.95 (ISBN 0-87773-380-5). Shambhala Pubns.

Torch of the Testimony. John W. Kennedy. (Orig.). 1983. pap. 6.95 (ISBN 0-940232-12-X). Christian Bks.

Torchbearers. Torkom Saraydarian. 1981. pap. 2.50 (ISBN 0-911794-49-2). Aqua Educ.

Torches Together: The Beginning & Early Years of the Bruderhof Communities. Emmy Arnold. LC 63-23426. 1971. 8.95 (ISBN 0-87486-109-8). Plough.

Torches Together: The Beginning & Early Years of the Bruderhof Communities. Emmy Arnold. Tr. by Society of Brothers. LC 77-166341. (Illus.). 1976. pap. 6.00 (ISBN 0-87486-171-3). Plough.

Tormented? Christians Guide for Spiritual Warfare. rev. ed. Ken Curtis & Nancy Curtis. (Illus.). 1985. pap. 3.95 (ISBN 0-9615445-0-3, Dist. by Spring Arbor). Spiritual Warfare.

Tormented Master: A Life of Rabbi Nahman of Bratslav. Arthur Green. LC 78-16674. (Judaic Studies: No. 9). (Illus.). 400p. 1979. 30.00 (ISBN 0-8173-6907-4). U of Ala Pr.

Tortillas for the Gods: A Symbolic Analysis of Zinacanteco Rituals. Evon Z. Vogt. 256p. 1976. 18.00x (ISBN 0-674-89554-1). Harvard U Pr.

Tortured for Christ. Richard Wurmbrand. 1973. pap. 2.95 (ISBN 0-88264-001-1). Diane Bks.

Tortured for Christ. Richard Wurmbrand. LC 86-72054. 128p. 1987. pap. 4.95 (ISBN 0-89107-408-2, Crossway Bks). Good News.

Tortured for His Faith. Haralan Popov. pap. 3.95 (ISBN 0-310-31262-0, 18070P). Zondervan.

Tosefta, 5 Vols. Saul Lieberman. 25.00x ea. (ISBN 0-685-31430-8, Pub. by Jewish Theol Seminary). KTAV.

Tosefta: Structure & Sources. Jacob Neusner. (Brown University Ser.). 1986. 39.95 (ISBN 1-55540-049-3, 14-01-12). Scholars Pr GA.

Tosefta Translated from the Hebrew IV. Neziqin: The Order of Damages. Jacob Neusner. 1981. 45.00x (ISBN 0-87068-692-5). Ktav.

Tosefta Translated from the Hebrew I. Zeraim: The Order of Seeds. Jacob Neusner. 1986. 45.00x. Ktav.

Tosefta, Translated from the Hebrew: Pt. II. Moed. The Order of Appointed Times. Jacob Neusner. 45.00x (ISBN 0-87068-691-7). Ktav.

Tosefta, Translated from the Hebrew: Pt. III Nashim. The Order of Women. Jacob Neusner. 45.00x (ISBN 0-87068-684-4). Ktav.

Tosefta Translated from the Hebrew: The Order of Purities, Pt. 6. J. Neusner. 45.00x (ISBN 0-87068-430-2). Ktav.

Tosefta Translated from the Hebrew V. Qodoshim: The Order of Holy Things. Jacob Neusner. 1980. 45.00x (ISBN 0-87068-340-3). Ktav.

Total Church Life. Darrell W. Robinson. LC 85-7900. 1985. 7.95 (ISBN 0-8054-6250-3). Broadman.

Total Consecration to Mary, Spouse of the Holy Spirit. Anselm Romb. 64p. 1982. pap. 1.50 (ISBN 0-913382-13-2, 105-37). Prow Bks-Franciscan.

Total Evangelism. Ed. by Clayton Pepper. pap. 2.25 (ISBN 0-89137-203-2). Quality Pubns.

Total Man. Dan Benson. 1977. pap. 3.95 (ISBN 0-8423-7289-X). Tyndale.

Total Presence: The Language of Jesus & the Language of Today. Thomas J. Altizer. 128p. 1980. 9.95 (ISBN 0-8164-0461-5, HarpR). Har-Row.

Total Surrender to God. Arthur F. Hallam. 236p. (Orig.). 1985. pap. 19.95 (ISBN 0-938770-05-5). Capitalist Pr OH.

Total Teaching for Today's Church. rev. ed. Mary Wallace et al. Orig. Title: Centers of Interest. (Illus.). 200p. (Orig.). 1985. pap. 6.95 (ISBN 0-912315-85-7). Word Aflame.

Total Woman. Marabel Morgan. 192p. 1973. spire bks. 3.50 (ISBN 0-8007-8218-6). Revell.

Total Youth Ministry: A Handbook for Parishes. Maria Edwards. LC 76-29885. 1976. pap. 4.50 (ISBN 0-88489-085-6). St Mary's.

Totalitarian Claim of the Gospels. Dora Wilson. 1983. pap. 2.50x (ISBN 0-87574-004-9, 004A). Pendle Hill.

Totality in Essence. Vimala Thakar. 132p. 1986. pap. 7.00 (ISBN 81-208-0048-6, Pub. by Motilal Banarsidass India). Orient Bk Dist.

Totem & Taboo. Sigmund Freud. Tr. by James Strachey. 1962. pap. 3.95 (ISBN 0-393-00143-1, Norton Lib.). Norton.

Totem & Taboo. Sigmund Freud. Tr. by Abraham A. Brill. 1960. pap. 2.95 (ISBN 0-394-70124-0, Vin, V124). Random.

Totemism. Alexander Goldenweiser. 59.95 (ISBN 0-8490-1223-6). Gordon Pr.

Totemism. Claude Levi-Strauss. (Orig.). 1963. pap. 7.95x (ISBN 0-8070-4671-X, BP157). Beacon Pr.

Totemism, the T'AO-T'iEH & the Chinese Ritual Bronzes. enl. ed. Helen F. Snow. 100p. 1986. 35.00 (ISBN 0-686-64038-1). H F Snow.

Touch Me Again, Lord. Ruthe White. LC 82-84453. 136p. (Orig.). 1983. pap. 5.95 (ISBN 0-89840-038-4). Heres Life.

Touch of Friendship. Harold Dye. LC 79-51138. 1979. pap. 4.25 large type (ISBN 0-8054-5422-5). Broadman.

Touch of God: Eight Monastic Journeys. Ed. by Maria Boulding. LC 82-24055. 1983. pap. 7.95x (ISBN 0-932506-26-7). St Bedes Pubns.

Touch of Grace. Elizabeth Fuller. (Illus.). 256p. 1986. 14.95 (ISBN 0-396-08667-5). Dodd.

Touch of Heaven Here. Evan Welsh. 96p. 1985. pap. 3.95 (ISBN 0-8423-7294-6). Tyndale.

Touch of Infinity. Doris R. Deming. 1984. 6.75 (ISBN 0-8062-2224-7). Carlton.

Touch of Midas: Science, Values & the Environment in Islam & the West. Ed. by Ziauddin Sardar. LC 83-22262. 253p. 1984. 38.50 (ISBN 0-7190-0974-X, Pub. by Manchester Univ Pr). Longwood Pub Group.

Touch of the Earth. Jean Hersey. 396p. 1985. pap. 10.95 large print ed. (ISBN 0-8027-2481-7). Walker & Co.

Touch of the Master's Hand: Christ's Miracles for Today. Charles L. Allen. 160p. 1956. pap. 2.75 (ISBN 0-8007-8093-0, Spire Bks). Revell.

Touch of the Spirit. Ralph W. Neighbour, Jr. LC 72-84243. 1977. pap. 4.25 (ISBN 0-8054-5158-7). Broadman.

Touch of Wonder. Arthur Gordon. (Orig.). pap. 2.95 (ISBN 0-515-08987-7). Jove Pubns.

Touch the World Through Prayer. Wesley L. Duewel. 240p. 1986. pap. 3.95 (ISBN 0-310-36271-7, 17093P). Zondervan.

Touched by the Spirit: One Man's Struggle to Understand His Experience of the Holy Spirit. Richard A. Jensen. LC 75-2838. 160p. 1975. pap. 7.95 (ISBN 0-8066-1484-6, 10-6675). Augsburg.

Touching a Child's Heart: An Innovative Guide to Becoming a Good Storyteller. Mary T. Donze. LC 85-71557. 88p. (Orig.). 1985. pap. 3.95 (ISBN 0-87793-290-5). Ave Maria.

Touching Incidents & Remarkable Answers to Prayer. 135p. pap. 1.00 (ISBN 0-686-29172-7). Faith Pub Hse.

Touching the Heart of God. Ernest J. Gruen. (Orig.). 1986. pap. 3.95 (ISBN 0-88368-175-7). Whitaker Hse.

Touching the Untouchables. Laura B. Barnard & Georgia Hill. 224p. 1985. pap. 6.95 (ISBN 0-8423-7296-2). Tyndale.

Touchstone for This Time Present. Edward Hake. LC 74-80182. (English Experience Ser.: No. 663). 96p. 1974. Repr. of 1574 ed. 7.00 (ISBN 90-221-0663-2). Walter J Johnson.

Touchstones, 4 vols. Henry Baron. Incl. Vol. 1. Around Us (ISBN 0-8028-1532-4); Vol. 2. Within Us (ISBN 0-8028-1533-2); Vol. 3. Between Us (ISBN 0-8028-1534-0); Vol. 4. Above Us (ISBN 0-8028-1535-9). 1973. pap. 4.95 ea.; pap. 5.50 tchr's guide (ISBN 0-8028-1645-2). Eerdmans.

Touchstones for Prayer. William P. Roberts. 98p. 1983. pap. text ed. 2.95 (ISBN 0-86716-023-3). St Anthony Mess Pr.

Touchstones of Matthew Arnold. John S. Eells. LC 76-136388. Repr. of 1955 ed. 22.50 (ISBN 0-404-02263-4). AMS Pr.

Tough & Tender. rev. ed. Joyce Landorf. 160p. 1981. 9.95 (ISBN 0-8007-1283-8). Revell.

Tough Love: How Parents Can Deal with Drug Abuse. Pauline Neff. 160p. 1984. pap. 7.50 (ISBN 0-687-42407-0). Abingdon.

Tough Marriage. Paul Mickey & William Proctor. Ed. by Pat Golbitz. 256p. 1986. 14.95 (ISBN 0-688-05038-7). Morrow.

Tough-Minded Faith for Tender-Hearted People. Robert H. Schuller. LC 83-22144. 384p. 1984. 14.95 (ISBN 0-8407-5358-6). Nelson.

Tough Minded Faith for Tender Hearted People. Robert H. Schuller. Date not set. 16.95 (ISBN 0-8161-3806-0, Large Print Bks); pap. 9.95 (ISBN 0-8161-3815-X). G K Hall.

Tough Questions: Biblical Answers Part One. Jack Cottrell. 122p. (Orig.). pap. 3.95 (ISBN 0-89900-208-0). College Pr Pub.

Tough Questions: Biblical Answers Part Two. Jack Cottvell. Orig. Title: Bible Says. 128p. 1986. pap. 3.95 (ISBN 0-89900-213-7). College Pr Pub.

Tough Times Never Last but Tough People Do! Robert Schuller. 256p. 1984. pap. 3.95 (ISBN 0-553-24245-8). Bantam.

Tough Times Never Last, but Tough People Do! Robert H. Schuller. LC 83-4160. (Illus.). 240p. 1983. 12.95 (ISBN 0-8407-5287-3); pap. text ed. 5.95 (ISBN 0-8407-5936-3). Nelson.

Tough Times Never Last, but Tough People Do! Robert H. Schuller. (General Ser.). 1984. lib. bdg. 13.95 (ISBN 0-8161-3677-7, Large Print Bks). G K Hall.

Tough Truths for Today's Living. Stuart Briscoe. 178p. 1984. pap. text ed. 5.95 (ISBN 0-8499-2999-7, 2999-7). Word Bks.

Tough Turf. Bill Sanders. 168p. (Orig.). 1985. pap. 5.95 (ISBN 0-8007-5212-0). Revell.

Toulouse in the Renaissance: The Floral Games, University & Student Life: Etienne Dolet. John C. Dawson. (Columbia University. Studies in Romance Philology & Literature: No. 33). Repr. of 1923 ed. 18.50 (ISBN 0-404-50633-X). AMS Pr.

Tour of the Summa. Paul J. Glenn. LC 78-66307. 1978. pap. 12.50 (ISBN 0-89555-081-4). TAN Bks Pubs.

Tourist in His Footsteps. John V. Sheridan. LC 79-53024. (Presence Ser., Vol. 1). (Orig.). 1979. pap. 2.95 (ISBN 0-89003-034-0). Undena Pubns.

Tours of Hell: An Apocalyptic Form in Jewish & Christian Literature. Martha Himmelfarb. LC 83-23789. 256p. 1983. 23.00x (ISBN 0-8122-7882-8). U of Pa Pr.

Tours of Hell: An Apocalyptic Form in Jewish & Christian Literature. Martha Himmelfarb. LC 84-48729. 208p. 1985. pap. 12.95 (ISBN 0-8006-1845-9, 1-1845). Fortress.

Tova & Esty's Purim Surprise. 1982. pap. 1.95 (ISBN 0-87306-248-5). Feldheim.

Tova's Happy Purim: In Yerusholayim. Leah Dornblatt. (Illus.). cancelled (ISBN 0-87306-989-7). Feldheim.

Toward a Christian Economic Ethic: Stewardship & Social Power. Daniel R. Finn & Prentiss L. Pemberton. LC 83-25409. 266p. 1985. pap. 10.95 (ISBN 0-86683-876-7, 7919, HarpR). Har-Row.

Toward a Christian Moral Theology. Bernard Haring. 1966. 12.95x (ISBN 0-268-00281-9). U of Notre Dame Pr.

Toward a Christian Political Ethics. Jose M. Bonino. LC 82-48541. 144p. 1983. pap. 6.95 (ISBN 0-8006-1697-9, 1-1697). Fortress.

Toward a Contemporary Christianity. Brian Wicker. 1967. 21.95 (ISBN 0-268-00282-7). U of Notre Dame Pr.

Toward a Fuller Vision: Orthodoxy & the Anglican Experience. E. C. Miller, Jr. LC 84-61015. 188p. (Orig.). 1984. pap. 7.95 (ISBN 0-8192-1351-9). Morehouse.

Toward a General Theory of Healing. James E. Rush. LC 80-8264. (Illus.). 314p. (Orig.). 1982. lib. bdg. 25.75 (ISBN 0-8191-1880-X); pap. text ed. 13.50 (ISBN 0-8191-1881-8). U Pr of Amer.

Toward a Growing Marriage. Gary Chapman. LC 79-21376. 1979. pap. 5.95 (ISBN 0-8024-8787-4). Moody.

Toward a Healing Ministry: Exploring & Implementing a Congregational Ministry. Richard J. Backmen & Steven J. Nerheim. 72p. (Orig.). 1985. pap. 5.95 (ISBN 0-8066-2176-1, 12-2022). Augsburg.

Toward a Jewish Theology of Liberation. Marc H. Ellis. LC 86-23553. 160p. (Orig.). 1987. pap. 9.95 (ISBN 0-88344-358-9). Orbis Bks.

Toward a Metaphysics of the Sacred: Development of the Concept of the Holy. Stephen Beasley-Murray. LC 82-8288. viii, 110p. 1982. 7.95x (ISBN 0-86554-038-1, MUP-M08). Mercer Univ Pr.

Toward a New Age in Christian Theology. Richard H. Drummond. LC 85-5155. 272p. 1985. pap. 12.95 (ISBN 0-88344-514-X). Orbis Bks.

Toward a New Christendom. M. Therese Lawrence. LC 81-84244. (Illus.). 80p. 1982. pap. 5.95 write for info. (ISBN 0-938034-05-7). PAL Pr.

Toward a Perfect Love: The Spiritual Counsel of Walter Hilton. Walter Hilton. Ed. by David L. Jeffrey. LC 85-15470. (Classics of Faith & Devotion Ser.). 1986. 10.95 (ISBN 0-88070-103-X); pap. 7.95 (ISBN 0-88070-176-5). Multnomah.

Toward a Phenomenology of the Etheric World: Investigations into the Life of Nature & Man. Jochen Bockemuhl et al. Ed. by Malcolm Gardner et al. Tr. by John Meeks from Ger. (Illus.). 200p. (Orig.). 1985. pap. 16.95 (ISBN 0-88010-115-6). Anthroposophic.

Toward a Philosophy of Praxis. Pope John Paul II. Ed. by A. Bloch & G. T. Czuczka. LC 80-21239. 152p. 1981. 10.95 (ISBN 0-8245-0033-4). Crossroad NY.

Toward a Practical Theology of Aging. K. Brynolf Lyon. LC 85-47720. (Theology & Pastoral Care Ser.). 128p. 1986. pap. 7.95 (ISBN 0-8006-1735-5). Fortress.

Toward a Reformulation of Natural Law. Anthony Battaglia. 1981. 14.95 (ISBN 0-8164-0490-9, HarpR). Har-Row.

Toward a Renewal of Sacramental Theology. Raymond Vaillancourt. Tr. by Matthew O'Connell from Fr. LC 79-12621. 126p. 1979. pap. 4.50 (ISBN 0-8146-1050-1). Liturgical Pr.

Toward a Science of Translating: With Special Reference to Principles & Procedures Involved in Bible Translating. Eugene A. Nida. 1964. text ed. 39.95x (ISBN 0-391-02063-3). Humanities.

Toward a Solar Civilization. Omraam M. Aivanhov. (Izvor Collection Ser.: Vol. 201). (Illus.). 148p. 1982. pap. 4.95 (ISBN 0-911857-00-1). Prosveta USA.

Toward a Solution. facs. ed. Israel Goldstein. LC 79-128248. (Essay Index Reprint Ser). 1940. 21.00 (ISBN 0-8369-1877-0). Ayer Co Pubs.

Toward a Theology of Aging. Ed. by Seward Hiltner. LC 74-19593. (Special Issue of Pastoral Psychology). 83p. 1975. 16.95 (ISBN 0-87705-278-6); pap. 9.95 (ISBN 0-87705-287-5). Human Sci Pr.

Toward a Theology of Missions. M. Thomas Starkes. 1984. pap. 5.95 (ISBN 0-89957-055-0). AMG Pubs.

Toward a Whiteheadian Ethics. Lynne Belaief. LC 84-15248. 208p. (Orig.). 1985. lib. bdg. 26.00 (ISBN 0-8191-4229-8); pap. text ed. 12.75 (ISBN 0-8191-4230-1). U Pr of Amer.

Toward an American Catholic Moral Theology. Charles E. Curran. LC 86-40583. 256p. 1987. text ed. 18.95x (ISBN 0-268-01862-6, Dist. by Har-Row). U of Notre Dame Pr.

Toward an American Theology. Herbert W. Richardson. (Richard Ser.: No. 2). 1967. 29.95 (ISBN 0-88946-028-0). E Mellen.

Toward an Ecumenical Fundamental Theology. Randy L. Maddox. LC 84-13838. (American Academy of Religion Studies in Religion). 1984. 13.50 (ISBN 0-89130-771-0, 01 01 47). Scholars Pr GA.

Toward an Effective Pulpit Ministry. George Holmes. LC 72-152056. 1971. 4.00 (ISBN 0-88243-610-4, 02-0610). Gospel Pub.

Toward an Exegetical Theology. Walter C. Kaiser, Jr. LC 80-68986. 224p. 1981. 11.95 (ISBN 0-8010-5425-7). Baker Bk.

Toward an Expansive Christian Theology. Vergilius Ferm. LC 64-16359. 201p. 1964. 5.95 (ISBN 0-8022-0496-1). Philos Lib.

Toward an Old Testament Theology. Walter C. Kaiser, Jr. 1978. 16.95 (ISBN 0-310-37100-7, 12320). Zondervan.

Toward Awakening: An Approach to the Teaching of Gurdjieff. Jean Vaysse. LC 79-1779. 1979. pap. 5.95i (ISBN 0-06-068860-2, RD 304, HarpR). Har-Row.

Toward Benevolent Neutrality: Church, State, & the Supreme Court. rev. ed. Ed. by Robert T. Miller & Ronald B. Flowers. LC 82-81902. xi, 726p. 1982. 32.50x (ISBN 0-918954-28-2). Baylor Univ Pr.

Toward Benevolent Neutrality: Church, State, & the Supreme Court. 3rd ed. Ed. by Robert T. Miller & Ronald B. Flowers. LC 86-72072. 612p. 1987. 36.00x (ISBN 0-918954-44-4). Baylor Univ Pr.

Toward Continuous Misson: Strategizing for the Evangelization of Bolivia. W. Douglas Smith. LC 77-21490. 1978. pap. 4.95 (ISBN 0-87808-321-9). William Carey Lib.

Toward Effective Parish Religious Education for Children & Young People. 108p. 1986. 14.00. Natl Cath Educ.

Toward Freedom for All: North Carolina Quakers & Slavery. Hiram Hilty. 120p. 1984. pap. 9.95 (ISBN 0-913408-83-2). Friends United.

Toward Freedom in Singing. Dina S. Winter & Theodora Richards. 1986. pap. 4.50 (ISBN 0-916786-84-6). St George Bk Serv.

Toward Modernity: The European Jewish Model. Ed. by Jacob Katz. 246p. (Orig.). 1986. 24.95 (ISBN 0-88738-092-1). Transaction Bks.

Toward Old Testament Ethics. Walter C. Kaiser, Jr. 1986. 16.95 (ISBN 0-310-37110-4, 12321). Zondervan.

Toward Pacifism. Gunnar Sundberg. 1983. pap. 2.50x (ISBN 0-87574-056-1, 056). Pendle Hill.

Toward Pentecostal Unity. Donald Gee. Orig. Title: All with One Accord. 62p. 1961. pap. 0.60 (ISBN 0-88243-689-9, 02-0689). Gospel Pub.

Toward Recovery of the Primordial Tradition: Ancient Insights & Modern Discoveries, 2 bks, Vol. 1. John Rossner. Incl. Bk. 1. From Ancient Magic to Future Technology. LC 79-66892. 14.75 (ISBN 0-8191-0861-8); Bk. 2. Toward a Parapsychology of Religion: from Ancient Religion to Future Science. LC 79-66893. 14.25 (ISBN 0-8191-0862-6). 1979. U Pr of Amer.

Toward Responsible Discipleship. William B. Ward. LC 61-7078. (Orig.). 1961. pap. 2.50 (ISBN 0-8042-4049-3); leader's guide o.p. 1.00 (ISBN 0-8042-4050-7). John Knox.

Toward Samson Agonistes: The Growth of Milton's Mind. Mary Ann Radzinowicz. LC 77-85559. 1978. 50.00x (ISBN 0-691-06357-5). Princeton U Pr.

Toward the Conquest of the Inner Cosmos. Edmond B. Szekely. (Illus.). 64p. 1969. pap. 6.80 (ISBN 0-89564-053-8). IBS Intl.

Toward the Establishment of Liberal Catholicism in America. Joseph A. Varacalli. LC 82-23811. 326p. (Orig.). 1983. lib. bdg. 30.00 (ISBN 0-8191-2974-7); pap. text ed. 14.75 (ISBN 0-8191-2975-5). U Pr of Amer.

Toward the Extended Christian Family. Ed. by Paul F. Wilczak. LC 80-69137. (Marriage & Family Living in Depth Bk.). (Illus.). 80p. 1980. pap. 2.45 (ISBN 0-87029-170-X, 20247-3). Abbey.

Toward the Future: Catholic Social Thought & the U. S. Economy, a Lay Letter. Lay Commission on Catholic Social Teaching & the U. S. Economy. 120p. 1985. pap. text ed. 4.75 (ISBN 0-8191-4860-1). U Pr of Amer.

Toward the Goal Supreme. Swami Virajananda. LC 73-87782. 155p. 1973. pap. 3.50 (ISBN 0-87481-029-9). Vedanta Pr.

Toward the Heart of God. John Dalrymple. 108p. (Orig.). 1981. pap. 3.95 (ISBN 0-86683-602-0, HarpR). Har-Row.

Toward the New Jerusalem. Alma P. Burton. LC 85-10203. 172p. 1985. 7.95 (ISBN 0-87747-883-X). Deseret Bk.

Toward the Recovery of Unity. Frederick D. Maurice. Ed. by John F. Porter & William J. Wolf. LC 64-12942. 1964. text ed. 10.00x (ISBN 0-8401-1596-2). A R Allenson.

Toward the Understanding of St. Paul. Donald J. Selby. 1962. ref. ed. 26.67 (ISBN 0-13-925693-8). P-H.

Toward the Understanding of Shelley. Bennett Weaver. 1967. lib. bdg. 18.50x (ISBN 0-374-98284-8, Octagon). Hippocrene Bks.

Toward Theology. Jerry H. Gill. LC 82-45009. 130p. (Orig.). 1982. PLB 24.00 (ISBN 0-8191-2429-X); pap. text ed. 9.25 (ISBN 0-8191-2430-3). U Pr of Amer.

Toward Transfigured Life. S. Harakas. 1983. pap. 12.95 (ISBN 0-937032-28-X). Light&Life Pub Co MN.

Toward Understanding Islam: Contemporary Apologetic of Islam & Missionary Policy. Harry G. Dorman. LC 79-176727. (Columbia University. Teachers College. Contributions to Education: No. 940). Repr. of 1948 ed. 22.50 (ISBN 0-404-55940-9). AMS Pr.

Toward Undiscovered Ends. Anna Brinton. 1983. pap. 5.00x (ISBN 0-87574-062-6, 062). Pendle Hill.

Toward Wholeness: Rudolf Steiner Education in America. Mary C. Richards. LC 80-14905. 210p. 1980. 16.00 (ISBN 0-8195-5049-3); pap. 9.95 (ISBN 0-8195-6062-6). Wesleyan U Pr.

Toward World-Wide Christianity. Ed. by O. Frederick Nolde. LC 70-86049. (Essay & General Literature Index Reprint Ser). 1969. Repr. of 1946 ed. 23.50x (ISBN 0-8046-0581-5, Pub by Kennikat). Assoc Faculty Pr.

Towards a Christian Poetics. Michael Edwards. 260p. 13.95x (ISBN 0-8028-3596-1). Eerdmans.

Towards a Global Congress of the World's Religions. Ed. by Warren Lewis. LC 79-56121. 63p. 1979. pap. 2.95 (ISBN 0-932894-03-8). Rose Sharon Pr.

Towards a Global Congress of the Worlds's Religions. Ed. by Warren Lewis. LC 78-73771. 1978. write for info. (ISBN 0-932894-01-1). Rose Sharon Pr.

Towards a Global Congress of World's Religions. Ed. by Warren Lewis. LC 80-53764. 79p. 1980. pap. 3.25 (ISBN 0-932894-07-0). Rose Sharon Pr.

Towards a Metaphysics of the Sacred. Stephen Beasley-Murray. LC 82-8288. (Special Studies: No. 8). viii, 110p. 1982. pap. 7.95 (ISBN 0-86554-038-1). NABPR.

Towards a Modern Iran: Studies in Thought, Politics & Society. Ed. by Elie Kedourie & Sylvia G. Haim. 262p. 1980. 29.50x (ISBN 0-7146-3145-0, F Cass Co). Biblio Dist.

Towards a New Mysticism: Teilhard de Chardin & Eastern Religions. Ursula King. 320p. 1980. (HarpR); pap. 8.95 (ISBN 0-8164-2327-X). Har-Row.

Towards a New World Religion. Lola A. Davis. 256p. 1983. pap. 16.00 (ISBN 0-942494-77-6). Coleman Pub.

Towards a Theology for Inter-Faith Dialogue. Interfaith Consultative Group, Board for Mission & Unity, Church of England. (Lambeth Study Bks.). 56p. 1986. pap. 2.25 (ISBN 0-88028-058-1). Forward Movement.

Towards a Unified Faith. Arnulf K. Esterer. LC 62-20870. 1963. 5.95 (ISBN 0-8022-0459-7). Philos Lib.

Towards a World Theology: Faith & the Comparative History of Religion. Wilfred C. Smith. LC 80-50826. 212p. 1981. 20.00 (ISBN 0-664-21380-4). Westminster.

Towards Acceptance--the Ultimates: Aging, Pain, Fear & Death from an Integral Human View. Henry G. Fairbanks. 1986. pap. 8.95 (ISBN 0-8158-0433-4). Chris Mass.

Towards an Ontology of Number Mind & Sign. Charles B. Daniels et al. (Scots Philosophical Monographs: Vol. 10). 200p. 1986. 29.95x (ISBN 0-391-03397-2, Pub. by Aberdeen U Scotland); pap. 12.50 (ISBN 0-391-03398-0, Pub. by Aberdeen U Scotland). Humanities.

Towards Death with Dignity: Caring for Dying People. Sylvia Poss. 1981. 33.75x (ISBN 0-317-05777-4, Pub. by Natl Soc Work). State Mutual Bk.

Towards International Guarantees for Religious Liberty. Isaac Lewin. LC 81-52086. 128p. 7.95 (ISBN 0-88400-078-8). Shengold.

Towards Islamic Anthropology. Akbar S. Ahmad. 80p. (Orig.). 1986. pap. 7.50 (ISBN 0-317-52455-0). New Era Pubns MI.

Towards Islamic Arabic. I. R. Al Farugi. 64p. (Orig.). 1986. pap. 5.00 (ISBN 0-317-52453-4). New Era Pubns MI.

Towards Peace on Earth: The Church of Scientology. pap. 4.00 (ISBN 0-686-74643-0). Church of Scient Info.

Towards Quiescence & Immortality. Barenya K. Banerji. LC 80-81693. 149p. 1981. 10.95 (ISBN 0-8022-2366-4). Philos Lib.

Towards Recovery of the Primordial Tradition: Ancient Insights & Modern Discoveries, Vol. II. John Rossner. LC 83-14753. (Primordial Tradition in Contemporary Experience Ser.: Bk. 2). 152p. 1984. PLB 27.00 (ISBN 0-8191-3519-4); pap. 13.50 (ISBN 0-8191-3520-8). U Pr of Amer.

Towards the Life Divine: Sri Aurobindo's Vision. Thomas O'Neil. 1979. 10.50x (ISBN 0-8364-0546-3). South Asia Bks.

Towards the Twentieth Century. facs. ed. Harold V. Routh. LC 69-17587. (Essay Index Reprint Ser). 1937. 19.00 (ISBN 0-8369-0091-X). Ayer Co Pubs.

Towards the Unknown: The Journey into New-Dimensional Consciousness. Dada. LC 81-65123. (Illus.). 128p. (Orig.). 1981. pap. 8.00 (ISBN 0-930608-02-X). Dada Ctr.

Towards Understanding Islam. A. A. Maududi. pap. 5.50 (ISBN 0-686-18479-3). Kazi Pubns.

Towards Understanding Islam. Abul A. Maududi. Tr. by Khurshid Ahmad from Urdu. 116p. (Orig.). pap. 5.95x (ISBN 0-86037-053-4, Pub. by Islamic Found UK). New Era Pubns MI.

Towards Understanding Islam. S. A. Maududi. 5.50x (ISBN 0-87902-065-2). Orientalia.

Towards Understanding Islam. Sayyid A. Mawdudi. Tr. by Khurshid Ahmad from Urdu. Tr. of Risala-e-Diniyat. 179p. (Orig.). 1980. pap. 5.95 (ISBN 0-939830-22-1, Pub. by IIFSO Kuwait). New Era Pubns MI.

Towards Understanding Islam. Kausar Niazi. 232p. (Orig.). 1981. pap. 12.50 (ISBN 0-88004-009-2). Sunwise Turn.

Towards Understanding the Basics of Islam: Texts from Qur'an & Hadith. Kaukab Siddique. 52p. (Orig.). 1986. pap. 2.50 (ISBN 0-942978-01-3). Am Soc Ed & Rel.

Towards Understanding the Bible. Perry Yoder & Elizabeth Yoder. LC 78-53649. 1978. pap. 3.95 (ISBN 0-87303-006-0). Faith & Life.

Towards Union in Palestine: Essays on Zionism & Jewish-Arab Cooperation. Ed. by Martin Buber & J. L. Magnes. LC 76-97272. (Judaica Ser.). 124p. 1972. Repr. of 1947 ed. lib. bdg. 22.50x (ISBN 0-8371-2564-2, BUUP). Greenwood.

Towards Vatican III: The Work That Has to Be Done. Ed. by David Tracy et al. 1978. 14.95x (ISBN 0-8245-0397-X); pap. 5.95 (ISBN 0-8245-0398-8). Crossroad NY.

Towel & the Cross. John B. Nielson. 118p. (Orig.). 1983. pap. 3.95 (ISBN 0-8341-0847-X). Beacon Hill.

Tower of Babel. (Read, Show & Tell Ser.). (Eng. & Span., Illus.). 1977. Eng. Ed. 2.25 (ISBN 0-8326-2604-X, 3622). Span. Ed (5622). World Bible.

Tower Works: Devotional Writings. St. Thomas More. Ed. by Garry E. Haupt. Tr. by Clarence Miller from Lat. LC 78-16995. (Selected Works of St. Thomas More). (Illus.). 368p. 1980. text ed. 42.00x (ISBN 0-300-02265-4). Yale U Pr.

Towering Babble: God's People Without God's Word. Vernard Eller. LC 83-4621. (Illus.). 192p. (Orig.). 1983. pap. 7.95 (ISBN 0-87178-855-1). Brethren.

Towers with Three Bells or Less: Basingstoke. D. A. Holmes. 1985. 11.25x (ISBN 0-317-54325-3, Pub. by J Richardson UK). State Mutual Bk.

Tozer Pulpit, 8 vols. A. W. Tozer. Ed. by Gerald B. Smith. Incl. Vol. 1. Selected Quotations from the Sermons of A. W. Tozer. 158p. 1967. pap. 3.95 (ISBN 0-87509-199-7); Vol. 2. Ten Sermons on the Ministry of the Holy Spirit. 146p. 1968. pap. 3.95 (ISBN 0-87509-178-4); cloth 5.95 (ISBN 0-87509-177-6); Vol. 3. Ten Sermons from the Gospel of John. 167p. 1970. cloth 5.95 (ISBN 0-87509-201-2); Vol. 4. Twelve Sermons on Spiritual Perfection. 144p. 1972. 5.95 (ISBN 0-87509-204-7); Vol. 5. Twelve Sermons in Peter's First Epistle. 159p. 1974. 5.95 (ISBN 0-87509-207-1); Vol. 6. Twelve Messages on Well-Known & Favorite Bible Texts. 174p. 1975. 5.95 (ISBN 0-87509-210-1); Vol. 7. Twelve Sermons Relating to the Life & Ministry of the Christian Church. 1978. 5.95 (ISBN 0-87509-213-6); Vol. 8. Ten Sermons on the Voices of God Calling Man. 5.95 (ISBN 0-87509-225-X). pap. Chr Pubns.

Trabajo y Justicia. Joseph McLelland. 128p. 1983. Repr. of 1978 ed. 2.50 (ISBN 0-311-46060-7). Casa Bautista.

Trabelin' On: The Slave Journey to an Afro-Baptist Faith. Mechal Sobel. LC 77-84775. (Contributions in Afro-American & African Studies: No. 36). 1978. lib. bdg. 35.00 (ISBN 0-8371-9887-9, STO/). Greenwood.

Traces of God in a Frequently Hostile World. Diogenes Allen. LC 80-51570. 108p. (Orig.). 1981. pap. 6.00 (ISBN 0-936384-03-4). Cowley Pubns.

Traces on the Rhodian Shore: Nature & Culture in Western Thought from Ancient Times to the End of the Eighteenth Century. Clarence J. Glacken. LC 67-10970. 1973. pap. 15.50x (ISBN 0-520-03216-0, CAMPUS 170). U of Cal Pr.

Tracing the Rainbow Through the Rain. O. S. Hawkins. LC 85-6610. 1985. 7.95 (ISBN 0-8054-5020-3). Broadman.

Tracing the Spirit: Communities, Social Action & Theological Reflection. Ed. by James E. Hug. LC 82-62419. (Woodstock Studies: No. 7). 288p. 1983. pap. 9.95 (ISBN 0-8091-2529-3). Paulist Pr.

Tracings. Mara. LC 80-67934. (Earth Song Ser.). 84p. 1980. pap. 4.95 (ISBN 0-9605170-0-6). Earth-Song.

Tracking the Glorious Lord: Vital Scientific Proofs of the Existence of God. Vinson Brown. (Paperback Ser.). 96p. (Orig.). 1987. pap. 5.95 (ISBN 0-8022-2519-5). Philos Lib.

Tract: Questions on Divorce & Remarriage. Thomas B. Warren. 1984. 0.60 (ISBN 0-934916-04-7); dozen 6.00; hundred 40.00. Natl Christian Pr.

Tractate Baba Kamma. Ed. by I. Epstein. 1977. 22.95 (ISBN 0-900689-59-5). Soncino Pr.

Tractate Baba Kamma. Ed. by I. Epstein. 1964. student's ed. 15.00 (ISBN 0-900689-67-6). Soncino Pr.

Tractate Berakoth. Ed. by I. Epstein. 1960. 22.95 (ISBN 0-900689-56-0). Soncino Pr.

Tractate Erubin. Ed. by I. Epstein. 1983. 22.95 (ISBN 0-900689-80-3). Soncino Pr.

Tractate Gitten. Ed. by I. Epstein. 1973. 22.95 (ISBN 0-900689-58-7). Soncino Pr.

Tractate Hullin. Ed. by I. Epstein. 1980. 22.95 (ISBN 0-900689-17-X). Soncino Pr.

Tractate Kethuboth. Ed. by I. Epstein. 1971. 22.95 (ISBN 0-900689-06-4). Soncino Pr.

Tractate Nedarim. I. Epstein. 1985. 22.95 (ISBN 0-900689-90-0). Soncino Pr.

Tractate on the Jews: The Significance of Judaism for the Christian Faith. Franz Mussner. Tr. by Leonard Swidler from German. LC 83-5699. 352p. 1983. 29.95 (ISBN 0-8006-0707-4, 1-707). Fortress.

Tractate Pesachim. Ed. by I. Epstein. 1983. 22.95 (ISBN 0-900689-81-1). Soncino Pr.

Tractate Rosh Hashana, Bezah, Shekalim. 1983. 22.95 (ISBN 0-900689-82-X). Soncino Pr.

Tractate Sanhadrin. Ed. by I. Epstein. 1969. 22.95 (ISBN 0-900689-04-8). Soncino Pr.

Tractate Shabbath, 2 vols. Ed. by I. Epstein. 1972. Set. 45.95 (ISBN 0-900689-62-5). Soncino Pr.

Tractate Sukkah-Moedkattan. 1984. 22.95 (ISBN 0-900689-83-8). Soncino Pr.

Tractate Taanit, Megilla, Chagiga. 1984. write for info. (ISBN 0-900689-84-6). Soncino Pr.

Tractate Yevamoth. I. Epstein. 1984. 22.95 (ISBN 0-900689-92-7). Soncino Pr.

Tractate Yoma. Ed. by I. Epstein. 1974. 22.95 (ISBN 0-900689-63-3). Soncino Pr.

Tractates Baba Bathra, 2 Vols. Ed. by I. Epstein. 1976. Set. write for info. (ISBN 0-900689-64-1). Soncino Pr.

Tractatus de Mystica Theologia, Vol. 2. Nicolas Kempf. Ed. by James Hogg. (Analecta Cartusiana Ser.: No. 9). (Lat. & Fr.). 574p. (Orig.). 1973. pap. 50.00 (ISBN 3-7052-0010-0, Pub by Salzburg Studies). Longwood Pub Group.

Tractatus De Successivis Attributed to William Ockham. Ed. by Philotheus Boehner. (Philosophy Ser). 1944. 8.00 (ISBN 0-686-11531-7). Franciscan Inst.

Tracts for the New Times: No. 1 Letter to a Swedenborgian. Henry James, Sr. LC 72-916. (Selected Works of Henry James, Sr.: Vol. 9). 1983. Repr. of 1847 ed. 24.50 (ISBN 0-404-10089-9). AMS Pr.

Tracts for the Times, 6 Vols. Ed. by John H. Newman et al. 1833-1841. Set. lib. bdg. 295.00 (ISBN 0-404-19560-1). Vol. 1 (ISBN 0-404-04711-4). Vol. 2 (ISBN 0-404-04712-2). Vol. 3 (ISBN 0-404-04713-0). Vol. 4 (ISBN 0-404-04714-9). Vol. 5 (ISBN 0-404-04715-7). Vol. 6 (ISBN 0-404-04716-5). AMS Pr.

Tracts on Liberty of Conscience & Persecution. Ed. by Edwin B. Underhill. (Philosophy Monographs: No. 11). 1968. Repr. of 1846 ed. 29.50 (ISBN 0-8337-3594-2). B Franklin.

Tracy. John Benton. 192p. (Orig.). 1984. pap. 2.95 (ISBN 0-8007-8495-2, New Hope). Revell.

Trade for Freedom. Morris Brafman & David Schimel. LC 75-26371. 96p. 1975. 6.95 (ISBN 0-88400-043-5). Shengold.

Trade, Politics & Christianity in Africa & the East. Allan J. MacDonald. LC 77-89007. Repr. of 1916 ed. lib. bdg. cancelled (ISBN 0-8371-1755-0, MAT&, Pub. by Negro U Pr). Greenwood.

Trademark of God. George L. Murphy. 110p. (Orig.). 1986. pap. 6.95 (ISBN 0-8192-1382-9). Morehouse.

Tradition & Authority in Science & Theology. Alexander Thomson. (Theology & Science at the Frontiers of Knowledge Ser.: Vol. 4). 160p. 1986. 17.00 (ISBN 0-7073-0452-0, Pub. by Scot Acad Pr). Longwood Pub Group.

Tradition & Change in Jewish Experience: B.G. Rudolph Lectures in Judaic Studies. Ed. by A. Leland Jamison. 1978. pap. 5.95x (ISBN 0-8156-8097-X). Syracuse U Pr.

Tradition & Composition in the Parables of Enoch. David W. Suter. LC 79-17441. (Society of Biblical Literature. Dissertation Ser.: No. 47). 1979. pap. 9.95 (ISBN 0-89130-336-7, 060147). Scholars Pr GA.

Tradition & History of the Early Churches of Christ in Central Europe. Hans Grimm. pap. 1.00 (ISBN 0-88027-095-0). Firm Foun Pub.

Tradition & Interpretation. G. W. Anderson. 1979. 34.50x (ISBN 0-19-826315-5). Oxford U Pr.

Tradition & Interpretation in Matthew. Gunther Bornkamm et al. LC 63-10495. 308p. 1963. 13.95 (ISBN 0-664-20453-8). Westminster.

Tradition & Modernity: The Role of Traditionalism in the Modernization Process. Jesse G. Lutz & Salah S. El-Shakhs. LC 81-43464. 234p. 1982. lib. bdg. 29.00 (ISBN 0-8191-2326-9). U Pr of Amer.

Tradition & Politics: The Religious Parties of Israel. Gary S. Schiff. LC 77-5723. 267p. 1977. 25.00x (ISBN 0-8143-1580-1). Wayne St U Pr.

Tradition & Progress, & Other Historical Essays in Culture, Religion & Politics. Ross Hoffman. LC 68-26213. 1968. Repr. of 1938 ed. 23.50x (ISBN 0-8046-0211-5, Pub by Kennikat). Assoc Faculty Pr.

Tradition & Testament. John S. Feinberg & Paul D. Feinberg. LC 81-11223. 1982. 14.95 (ISBN 0-8024-2544-5). Moody.

Tradition & the Modern World: Reformed Theology in the Nineteenth Century. B. A. Gerrish. LC 78-4982. 1978. lib. bdg. 20.00x (ISBN 0-226-28866-8). U of Chicago Pr.

Tradition & Transformation in Religious Education. Ed. by Padraic O'Hare. LC 78-27506. 114p. (Orig.). 1979. pap. 6.95 (ISBN 0-89135-016-0). Religious Educ.

Tradition As Openness to the Future: Essays in Honor of Willis W. Fisher. Ed. by Fred O. Francis & Raymond P. Wallace. (Illus.). 236p. (Orig.). 1984. lib. bdg. 25.00 (ISBN 0-8191-3722-7); pap. text ed. 12.25 (ISBN 0-8191-3723-5). U Pr of Amer.

Tradition Becomes Innovation: Modern Religious Architecture in America. Bartlett Hayes. LC 82-18581. (Illus.). 176p. 1982. 27.50 (ISBN 0-8298-0635-0); pap. 12.95 (ISBN 0-8298-0624-5). Pilgrim NY.

Tradition History & the Old Testament. Walter E. Rast. Ed. by Gene M. Tucker. LC 70-171509. (Guides to Biblical Scholarship: Old Testament Ser.). 96p. (Orig.). 1972. pap. 4.50 (ISBN 0-8006-1460-7, 1-1460). Fortress.

Tradition in Greek Religion. Bernard C. Dietrich. xvi, 213p. 1986. 66.00x (ISBN 3-11-010695-7). De Gruyter.

Tradition in Science. Werner Heisenberg. 160p. (Orig.). 1983. pap. 10.95 (ISBN 0-8164-2488-8, HarpR). Har-Row.

Tradition in the Eastern Orthodox Church. pap. 0.35 (ISBN 0-686-16369-9). Eastern Orthodox.

Tradition of Teachers: Sankara & the Jagadgurus Today. William Cenker. 1983. 18.50 (ISBN 0-8364-0944-2); text ed. 13.00 (ISBN 0-8364-1058-0). South Asia Bks.

Tradition of the Goddess Fortuna in Medieval Philosophy & Literature. Howard R. Patch. Repr. of 1922 ed. lib. bdg. 15.00 (ISBN 0-8414-6751-X). Folcroft.

Tradition of the Goddess Fortuna in Roman Literature & in the Transitional Period. Howard R. Patch. LC 76-41188. 1976. Repr. of 1922 ed. lib. bdg. 15.50 (ISBN 0-8414-6753-6). Folcroft.

Tradition of the Goddess Fortuna in Roman Literature & in the Transitional Period. Howard R. Patch. 1980. Repr. of 1912 ed. 15.00 (ISBN 0-8482-5593-3). Norwood Edns.

Tradition Renewed: The Oxford Movement Conference Papers. Ed. by Geoffrey Rowell. (Princeton Theological Monograph Ser.: No. 3). (Orig.). 1986. pap. 30.00 (ISBN 0-915138-82-4). PickWick.

Tradition: The Catholic Story Today. Monika Hellwig. 96p. (Orig.). 1974. pap. 2.95 (ISBN 0-8278-9060-5, Pub. by Pflaum Pr). Peter Li.

Traditional Aspects of Hell. James Mew. LC 73-140321. 1971. Repr. of 1903 ed. 48.00x (ISBN 0-8103-3693-6). Gale.

Traditional Catholic Religious Orders. Edward A. Wynne. 224p. 1987. 24.95 (ISBN 0-88738-129-4). Transaction Bks.

Traditional Curing & Crop Fertility Rituals Among Otomi Indians of the Sierra de Puebla, Mexico: The Lopez Manuscripts. Alan R. Sandstrom. (Occasional Papers & Monographs: No. 3). (Illus.). vi, 104p. 1981. 4.00 (ISBN 0-9605982-0-0). W H Mathers Mus.

Traditional Education among Muslims: A Study of Some Aspects in Modern India. Mohammad A. Ahmad. viii, 216p. 1986. text ed. 30.00x (ISBN 81-7018-259-X, Pub. by B R Pub Corp Delhi). Apt Bks.

Traditional India: Structure & Change. Ed. by Milton Singer. (American Folklore Society Bibliographical & Special Ser.: No. 10). 356p. 1959. pap. 9.95x (ISBN 0-292-73504-9). U of Tex Pr.

Traditional Interpretation of the Apocalypse of St. John in the Ethiopian Orthodox Church. Roger W. Cowley. LC 82-19834. (University of Cambridge Oriental Publications Ser.: No. 33). 480p. 1983. 77.50 (ISBN 0-521-24561-3). Cambridge U Pr.

Traditional Islam in the Modern World. Seyyed H. Nasr. 320p. 1987. text ed. 39.95 (ISBN 0-7103-0177-4). Methuen Inc.

Traditional Islamic Craft in Moroccan Architecture, 2 vols. Andre Paccard. 1980. 495.00x (ISBN 0-686-69970-X, Pub. by Editions Atelier England). State Mutual Bk.

Traditional Jewish Family in Historical Perspective. Jacob Katz. 1983. pap. 1.00 (ISBN 0-87495-048-1). Am Jewish Comm.

Traditional Jewish Law of Sale. Stephen Passamaneck. 1983. 20.00x (ISBN 0-686-87788-8). Ktav.

Traditional Jewish Law of Sale: Shulhan Arukh Hoshen Mishpat, Chapters 189-240. Joseph Ben Ephraim Karo. Tr. by Stephen M. Passamaneck. LC 83-4287. (Hebrew Union College Monographs No. 9). 1983. 20.00x (ISBN 0-87820-408-3). Hebrew Union Coll Pr.

Traditional Ojibwa Religion & Its Historical Changes. Christopher Vecsey. LC 83-72209. (Mem. Ser.: Vol. 152). 1983. 12.00 (ISBN 0-87169-152-3). Am Philos.

Traditional Papermaking & Paper Cult Figures of Mexico. Alan R. Sandstrom & Pamela E. Sandstrom. LC 85-40947. (Illus.). 336p. 1986. 24.95 (ISBN 0-8061-1972-1). U of Okla Pr.

Traditional Sayings in the Old Testament: A Contextual Study. Carol R. Fontaine. (Bible & Literature Ser.: No. 5). 1982. text ed. 24.95x (ISBN 0-907459-08-0, Pub. by Almond Pr England); pap. text ed. 14.95x (ISBN 0-907459-09-9, Pub. by Almond Pr England). Eisenbrauns.

Traditionally Yours. Gail Kelley. LC 86-43230. 100p. (Orig.). 1987. pap. text ed. 7.95 (ISBN 0-89390-103-2). Resource Pubns.

Traditions & Superstitions of the New Zealanders. 2nd ed. Edward Shortland. LC 75-35270. Repr. of 1856 ed. 32.50 (ISBN 0-404-14439-X). AMS Pr.

Traditions in Transformation: Turning Points in Biblical Faith. Ed. by Baruch Halpern & Jon D. Levenson. 1981. 22.50 (ISBN 0-931464-06-4). Eisenbrauns.

Traditions of Eleazar Ben Azariah. Tzvee Zahavy. LC 76-46373. (Brown University. Brown Judaic Studies: No. 2). 1977. pap. 13.50 (ISBN 0-89130-095-3, 140002). Scholars Pr GA.

Traditions of Glastonbury. E. Raymond Capt. LC 82-72525. (Illus.). 128p. (Orig.). 1983. pap. 5.00 (ISBN 0-934666-10-5). Artisan Sales.

Traditions of Islam. Alfred Guillaume. LC 79-52552. (Islam Ser.). 1980. Repr. of 1924 ed. lib. bdg. 16.00x (ISBN 0-8369-9260-1). Ayer Co Pubs.

Traditions of Meditation in Chinese Buddhism. Ed. by Peter N. Gregory. LC 86-19243. (Studies in East Asian Buddhism: No. 4). 272p. 1987. pap. text ed. 16.00x (ISBN 0-8248-1088-0). UH Pr.

Traditions of Ministry. James H. Pragman. LC 12-2982. (Continued Applied Christianity Ser.). 1983. pap. 15.95 (ISBN 0-570-03900-2, 12-2982). Concordia.

Traditions of the Prophet, Vol. 2. Jawad Nurbakhsh. Tr. by Leonard Lewisohn & Terry Graham. 1984. pap. 6.00x (ISBN 0-933546-10-6). KhaniQahi-Nimatullahi-Sufi.

Traditions of the Prophet (Ahadith) Javad Nurbakhsh. Ed. by Jeffrey Rothschild et al. Tr. by Leonard Lewisehn & Ali-Reza Nurbakhsh. 104p. 1981. pap. 6.00x (ISBN 0-933546-06-8). KhaniQahi-Nimatullahi-Sufi.

Traditions of the Welsh Saints. Elissa R. Henken. 200p. 1986. 37.50 (ISBN 0-85991-221-3, Pub. by Boydell & Brewer). Longwood Pub Group.

Traduction: Theorie et Methode. Charles R. Taber & Eugene A. Nida. 1971. pap. 3.30x (ISBN 0-8267-0022-5, 51971, Pub. by United Bible). Am Bible.

Tragedies of Herod & Mariamne. Maurice J. Valency. LC 70-8450. Repr. of 1940 ed. 19.50 (ISBN 0-404-06750-6). AMS Pr.

Tragedy & Comedy in the Bible. Ed. by J. Cheryl Exum. (Semeia Ser.: No. 32). pap. 9.95 (06 20 32). Scholars Pr GA.

Tragedy in Eden: Original Sin in the Theology of Jonathan Edwards. C. Samuel Storms. LC 85-17866. 328p. 1986. lib. bdg. 27.25 (ISBN 0-8191-4936-5); pap. text ed. 12.75 (ISBN 0-8191-4937-3). U Pr of Amer.

Tragedy in the Church. W. Tozer. Ed. by Gerald Smith. 1978. pap. 3.45 (ISBN 0-87509-215-2). Chr Pubns.

Tragedy: Irony & Faith. John Tinsley. 75p. (Orig.). 1985. pap. 5.95x (ISBN 0-317-26992-5). Wyndham Hall.

Tragedy of Quebec. Robert Sellar. LC 72-1429. (Select Bibliographies Reprint Ser.). 1972. Repr. of 1907 ed. 17.25 (ISBN 0-8369-6836-0). Ayer Co Pubs.

Tragedy of Rejecting Salvation. John MacArthur, Jr. (John MacArthur's Bible Studies). (Orig.). 1986. pap. 3.50 (ISBN 0-8024-5346-5). Moody.

Tragedy of the Jews in Hungary: Essays & Documents. Ed. by Randolph L. Braham. (East European Monographs: No. 208). 288p. 1986. 30.00 (ISBN 0-88033-105-4). East Eur Quarterly.

Tragedy of the Reformation: Being the Authentic Narrative of the History & Burning of the "Christianismi Restitution", 1953, with a Succinct Account of the Theological Controversy Between Michael Servetus, Its Author, & the Reformer, John Calvin. David Cuthbertson. LC 83-45608. Date not set. Repr. of 1912 ed. 20.00 (ISBN 0-404-19826-0). AMS Pr.

Tragedy of Zionism. Bernard Avishai. LC 85-10235. 389p. 1985. 19.95 (ISBN 0-374-27863-6). FS&G.

Tragedy of Zionism. Bernard Avishai. 389p. 1986. pap. 8.95 (ISBN 0-374-52044-5). FS&G.

Tragic Cavalier: Governor Manuel Salcedo of Texas, 1808-1813. Felix D. Almaraz, Jr. 218p. 1971. pap. text ed. 6.95 (ISBN 0-292-78039-7). U of Tex Pr.

Tragic Psalms. Francis Sullivan. 1987. pap. 5.95. Pastoral Pr.

Tragic Sense of Life. Miguel De Unamuno. 14.00 (ISBN 0-8446-3100-0). Peter Smith.

Tragic Sense of Life. Miguel Unamuno. Tr. by J. Crawford Flitch. 1921. pap. 6.00 (ISBN 0-486-20257-7). Dover.

Tragic Vision & the Hebrew Tradition. W. Lee Humphreys. LC 85-47724. (Overtures to Biblical Theology Ser.). 176p. 1985. pap. 9.95 (ISBN 0-8006-1542-5). Fortress.

Tragic Week: A Study of Anticlericalism in Spain, 1875-1912. Joan C. Ullman. LC 67-27082. 1968. 27.50x (ISBN 0-674-90240-8). Harvard U Pr.

Trail Maker (David Livingstone) Robert O. Latham. 1973. pap. 2.95 (ISBN 0-87508-626-8). Chr Lit.

Trail of Peril. Yvonne Davy. Ed. by Gerald Wheeler. LC 83-17835. (A Banner Bk.). (Illus.). 94p. (Orig.). 1984. pap. 5.95 (ISBN 0-8280-0223-1). Review & Herald.

Trailblazers for Translators: The Influence of the "Chichicastenago Twelve". Anna M. Dahlquist. Date not set. pap. price not set (ISBN 0-87808-205-0). William Carey Lib.

Trailing Clouds of Glory: Spiritual Values in Children's Books. Madeleine L'Engle. 144p. 1985. 12.95 (ISBN 0-664-32721-4). Westminster.

Train up a Child. Clifton M. Kelly & Sherman P. Wantz. LC 82-84318. 110p. (Orig.). 1983. pap. 4.95. Highlands Pub.

Training Christians to Counsel. Norman Wright. 236p. 1983. Repr. 14.95 (ISBN 0-89081-422-8). Harvest Hse.

Training Church Members for Pastoral Care. Samuel Southard. 96p. 1982. pap. 4.95 (ISBN 0-8170-0944-2). Judson.

Training Evangelism Callers. Richard O. Hill. 64p. (Orig.). 1986. Leader Guide. pap. 4.95 (ISBN 0-8066-2227-X, 23-1960); Caller Manual. pap. 3.50 (ISBN 0-8066-2228-8, 23-1961). Augsburg.

Training for Evangelism. Richard Sisson. 1979. pap. 12.95 (ISBN 0-8024-8792-0). Moody.

Training for Hospital Visitation: A Three-Week Course for Laypersons. Richard W. Shockey. LC 86-42930. 40p. (Orig.). 1986. pap. 4.00 (ISBN 0-937021-01-6). Sagamore Bks MI.

Training for Leadership in the Church. Elmer Kettner. 1.95 (ISBN 0-933350-09-0). Morse Pr.

Training for Service: A Survey of the Bible. Orrin Root. Rev. by Eleanor Daniel. 128p. 1983. pap. 3.95 (ISBN 0-87239-704-1, 3212); tchr's. ed. 4.95 (ISBN 0-87239-703-3, 3211). Standard Pub.

Training in Christianity. Soren Kierkegaard. Tr. by Walter Lowrie. (American-Scandinavian Foundation Ser.). 1944. 31.00x (ISBN 0-691-07140-3); pap. 7.95x (ISBN 0-691-01959-2). Princeton U Pr.

Training of the Twelve. Alexander B. Bruce. LC 79-88121. (Shepherd Illustrated Classics). 1979. pap. 6.95 (ISBN 0-87983-206-1). Keats.

Training of the Twelve. Alexander B. Bruce. LC 73-129738. 566p. 1979. 13.95 (ISBN 0-8254-2212-4); pap. 9.95 (ISBN 0-8254-2236-1). Kregel.

Training When Meeting. Evangelical Teacher Training Association. 32p. 1981. pap. text ed. 2.95 (ISBN 0-910566-33-X); planbook 3.95 (ISBN 0-910566-34-8). Evang Tchr.

Traite De Droit Musulman Compare: Filiation - Incapacites - Liberalites Entre Vifs, Tome 3. Y. Linant De Bellefonds. (Recherches Mediterraneennes: No. 9). 1973. pap. 34.40x (ISBN 90-2797-199-4). Mouton.

Traite d'Iconographie Chretienne. X. Barbier De Montault. (Fr., Illus.). 972p. Repr. of 1890 ed. lib. bdg. 200.00x (ISBN 0-89241-137-6). Caratzas.

Traite Neo-Manicheen du XIIIe siecle. Liber de Duobus Principiis. LC 78-63185. (Heresies of the Early Christian & Medieval Era: Second Ser.). 1979. Repr. of 1939 ed. 32.00 (ISBN 0-404-16224-X). AMS Pr.

Traits of Divine Kingship in Africa. P. Hadfield. LC 78-32120. 1979. Repr. of 1949 ed. lib. bdg. 22.50x (ISBN 0-8371-5189-9, HDK&, Pub. by Negro U Pr). Greenwood.

Trajectories in the Study of Religion: Addresses at the Seventy-Fifth Anniversary of the American Academy of Religion. Ed. by Ray L. Hart. (Studies in Religion & Theological Scholarship (American Academy of Religion)). 333p. 25.95 (ISBN 1-55540-064-7, 00-08-03). Scholars Pr GA.

Trajectories through Early Christianity. James M. Robinson & Helmut Koester. LC 79-141254. 312p. 1971. pap. 9.95 (ISBN 0-8006-1362-7, 1-1362). Fortress.

Tramp for the Lord. Corrie ten Boom. 1976. pap. 2.95 (ISBN 0-515-08993-1). Jove Pubns.

Tramp for the Lord. Corrie Ten Boom & Jamie Buckingham. (Illus.). 192p. 1974. pap. 6.95 (ISBN 0-8007-0769-9). Revell.

Trance in Bali. Jane Belo. LC 77-6361. 1977. Repr. of 1960 ed. lib. bdg. 35.75x (ISBN 0-8371-9652-3, BETR). Greenwood.

Tranquillitas Ordinis: The Present Failure & Future Promise of American Catholic Thought on War & Peace. George Weigel, Jr. 416p. 1987. 27.50 (ISBN 0-19-504193-3). Oxford U Pr.

Tranquillity & Insight: An Introduction to the Oldest Form of Buddhist Meditation. Amadeo Sole-Leris. LC 86-11834. 176p. 1986. pap. 7.95 (ISBN 0-87773-385-6). Shambhala Pubns.

Trans-Atlantic Conservative Protestantism in the Evangelical Free & Mission Covenant Traditions. Frederick Hale. Ed. by Franklyn D. Scott. LC 78-15183. (Scandinavians in America Ser.). 1979. lib. bdg. 30.50x (ISBN 0-405-11638-1). Ayer Co Pubs.

Transactions of the Parisian Sanhedrim. Tr. by M. Diogene Tama. (Brown Classics in Judaica Ser.). 364p. 1985. pap. text ed. 15.25 (ISBN 0-8191-4488-6). U Pr of Amer.

Transatlantic Revivalism: Popular Evangelicalism in Britain & America, 1790-1865. Richard Carwardine. LC 77-94740. (Contributions in American History Ser.: No. 75). 1978. lib. bdg. 35.00 (ISBN 0-313-20308-3, CTR/). Greenwood.

Transcend: A Guide to the Spiritual Quest. Morton T. Kelsey. 240p. (Orig.). 1981. pap. 9.95 (ISBN 0-8245-0015-6). Crossroad NY.

Transcendence & Hermeneutics. Alan M. Olson. (Studies in Philosophy & Religion: No. 2). 1979. lib. bdg. 35.00 (ISBN 90-247-2092-3, Pub. by Martinus Nijhoff Netherlands). Kluwer Academic.

Transcendence & Immanence: A Study in Catholic Modernism & Integralism. Gabriel Daly. 1980. 37.50x (ISBN 0-19-826652-9). Oxford U Pr.

Transcendence & Providence: Reflections of a Physicist & Priest. W. G. Pollard. (Theology & Science at the Frontiers of Knowledge Ser.: Vol. 6). 146p. 1986. 17.00 (ISBN 0-7073-0486-5, Pub. by Scot Acad Pr). Longwood Pub Group.

Transcendence & the Sacred. Ed. by Alan M.. Olson & Leroy S. Rouner. LC 81-50456. 256p. 1981. 19.95 (ISBN 0-268-01841-3). U of Notre Dame Pr.

Transcendency. Gerald Stutsman. LC 81-69736. 96p. 1982. pap. 4.75 (ISBN 0-87516-466-8). De Vorss.

Transcendent Adventure: Studies of Religion in Science Fiction-Fantasy. Ed. by Robert Reilly. LC 84-542. (Contributions to the Study of Science Fiction & Fantasy Ser.: No. 12). x, 266p. 1985. lib. bdg. 35.00 (ISBN 0-313-23062-5, RET/). Greenwood.

Transcendent Justice: The Religious Dimensions of Constitutionalism. Carl J. Friedrich. LC 64-20097. ix, 116p. 1964. 13.75 (ISBN 0-8223-0061-3). Duke.

Transcendent Self. Adrian van Kaam. 5.95 (ISBN 0-87193-180-X). Dimension Bks.

Transcendent Selfhood: The Loss & Rediscovery of the Inner Life. Louis Dupre. 1976. 8.95 (ISBN 0-8164-0306-6, HarpR). Har-Row.

Transcendent Unity of Religions. Rev. ed. Frithjof Schuon. LC 84-239. 165p. 1984. pap. 7.95 (ISBN 0-8356-0587-6, Quest). Theos Pub Hse.

Transcendental Arguments & Science. Ed. by Rolf-Peter Horstmann et al. (Synthese Library: No. 133). 1979. lib. bdg. 34.00 (ISBN 90-277-0963-7, Pub. by Reidel Holland); pap. 16.00 (ISBN 90-277-0964-5). Kluwer Academic.

Transcendental Dancing. Margaret J. Phillippou. 1982. pap. 3.00 (ISBN 0-941500-29-2). Sharing Co.

Transcendental Meditation. Lit-Sen Chang. 1978. pap. 2.95 (ISBN 0-87552-133-9). Presby & Reformed.

Transcendental Meditation. new ed. David Haddon. 32p. (Orig.). 1975. pap. 0.75 (ISBN 0-87784-155-1). Inter-Varsity.

Transcendental Meditation. Marharishi Mahesh Yogi. 320p. 1973. pap. 4.95 (ISBN 0-451-14081-8, Sig). NAL.

Transcendental Self: A Comparative Study of Thoreau & the Psycho-Philosophy of Hinduism & Buddhism. A. K. Pillai. LC 85-686. 130p. (Orig.). 1985. lib. bdg. 21.75 (ISBN 0-8191-4572-6). U Pr of Amer.

Transcendental Temptation: A Critique of Religion & the Paranormal. Paul Kurtz. 450p. 1986. 18.95 (ISBN 0-87975-362-5). Prometheus Bks.

Transcendental Turn: The/Foundation of Kant's Idealism. Moltke S. Gram. LC 84-22047. xii, 260p. 1985. 30.00 (ISBN 0-8130-0787-9). U Presses Fla.

Transcendentalism As a Social Movement, 1830-1850. Anne C. Rose. LC 81-3340. 288p. 1986. pap. 11.95x (ISBN 0-300-03757-0). Yale U Pr.

Transcendentalism; bd. with Equality. William B. Greene. LC 81-8972. (Repr. of 1849 eds.). 1981. 35.00x (ISBN 0-8201-1366-2). Schol Facsimiles.

Transcendentalism in New England: A History. O. C. Frothingham. 11.25 (ISBN 0-8446-1191-3). Peter Smith.

Transcendentalism in New England: A History. Octavius B. Frothingham. LC 59-10346. 1972. pap. 14.95x (ISBN 0-8122-1038-7, Pa. Paperbacks). U of Pa Pr.

Transcendentalists: A Review of Research & Criticism. Ed. by Joel Myerson. (Reviews of Research Ser.). 450p. 1984. 30.00x (ISBN 0-87352-260-5); pap. 20.00x (ISBN 0-87352-261-3). Modern Lang.

Transcendentalists: An Anthology. Ed. by Perry G. Miller. LC 50-7360. 1950. pap. 9.95x (ISBN 0-674-90333-1). Harvard U Pr.

Transfiguracion. Catharose De Petri. (Span.). 1987. pap. 6.00. Rosycross Pr.

Transfiguration of Christ. Monks of New Skete. Tr. by Reverend Laurence Mancuso. (Liturgical Music Series I: Great Feasts: Vol. 1). 40p. (Orig.). 1986. pap. text ed. 12.00 (ISBN 0-935129-02-2). Monks of New Skete.

Transfiguration of Christ in Scripture & Tradition. John A. McGuckin. LC 86-23892. (Studies in Bible & Early Christianity: Vol. 9). 333p. 1987. 59.95 (ISBN 0-88946-609-2). E Mellen.

Transfiguration: Poetic Metaphor & the Languages of Religious Belief. Frank B. Brown. LC 82-24714. (Studies in Religion). x, 230p. 1983. 25.00x (ISBN 0-8078-1560-8). U of NC Pr.

Transfigurations: Studies in the Dynamics of Byzantine Iconography. Anthony Cutler. LC 75-1482. (Illus.). 226p. 1975. 32.50x (ISBN 0-271-01194-7). Pa St U Pr.

Transformation in Christ. George Devine. LC 70-39884. 125p. 1972. pap. 3.95 (ISBN 0-8189-0240-X). Alba.

Transformation-Night, Immortality-Dawn. 1975. 2.00 (ISBN 0-88497-111-2). Aum Pubns.

Transformation of Sikh Society. Ethne K. Marenco. 1974. pap. 16.95 (ISBN 0-913244-08-2). Hapi Pr.

Transformation of Sin: Studies in Donne, Herbert, Vaughan & Traherne. Patrick Grant. LC 73-93174. 308p. 1974. 20.00x (ISBN 0-87023-158-8). U of Mass Pr.

Transformation of Sin: Studies in Donne, Herbert, Vaughan & Traherne. Patrick Grant. LC 73-93174. pap. 63.50 (ISBN 0-317-26444-3, 2023850). Bks Demand UMI.

Transformation of the Inner Man. John Sandford & Paula Sandford. LC 82-72007. 432p. 1986. pap. 6.95 (ISBN 0-932081-13-4). Victory Hse.

Transformation of the New England Theology. Robert C. Whittemore. (American University Studies VII-Theology & Religion: Vol. 23). 441p. 1987. text ed. 42.00 (ISBN 0-8204-0374-1). P Lang Pubs.

Transformed by Thorns. Grant Martin. 156p. 1985. pap. 5.95 (ISBN 0-89693-397-0). Victor Bks.

Transformed Temperaments. Tim LaHaye. 1971. pap. 5.95 (ISBN 0-8423-7306-3). Tyndale.

Transformers-The Therapists of the Future. Jacquelyn Small. 272p. 1984. pap. 11.95 (ISBN 0-87516-529-X). De Vorss.

Transforming a People of God. Denham Grierson. 161p. (Orig.). 1984. pap. 11.95 (ISBN 0-85819-464-3, Pub. by JBCE). ANZ Religious Pubns.

Transforming Bible Study: A Leader's Guide. Walter Wink. LC 80-16019. 176p. 1980. pap. 7.95 (ISBN 0-687-42499-2). Abingdon.

Transforming Cross. Charles S. McCoy & Marjorie C. McCoy. LC 77-10884. Repr. of 1977 ed. 27.80 (ISBN 0-8357-9030-4, 2016417). Bks Demand UMI.

Transforming Discipleship in the Inclusive Church. Stephen D. Jones. 160p. 1984. pap. 6.95 (ISBN 0-8170-1049-1). Judson.

Transforming Friendship. Leslie D. Weatherhead. (Festival Books). 1977. pap. 1.25 (ISBN 0-687-42510-7). Abingdon.

Transforming Love. Robert Seyda. LC 82-91022. 162p. 1984. 12.50 (ISBN 0-533-05687-X). Vantage.

Transforming Mind. 2nd ed. Laurence Bendit & Phoebe Bendit. LC 74-103415. 161p. 1983. pap. 5.75 (ISBN 0-8356-0012-2, Quest). Theos Pub Hse.

Transforming Moment: Understanding Convictional Experiences. James E. Loder. LC 80-8354. 256p. 1981. 15.45 (ISBN 0-06-065276-4, HarpR). Har-Row.

Transforming Power of the Bible. Wayne B. Robinson. LC 83-23680. 240p. (Orig.). 1984. pap. 9.95 (ISBN 0-8298-0706-3). Pilgrim NY.

Transforming Problems. Bert Ghezzi. 140p. (Orig.). 1986. pap. 4.95 (ISBN 0-89283-294-0). Servant.

Transforming Vision: Shaping a Christian World View. Brian J. Walsh & J. Richard Middleton. LC 84-15646. 240p. (Orig.). 1984. pap. 6.95 (ISBN 0-87784-973-0). Inter-Varsity.

Transiency & Permanence: The Nature of Theology According to Saint Bonaventure. G. H. Tavard. 1974. Repr. of 1954 ed. 15.00 (ISBN 0-686-11588-0). Franciscan Inst.

Transition & Tradition in Moral Theology. Charles E. Curran. LC 78-20877. 272p. 1980. pap. text ed. 6.95 (ISBN 0-268-01838-3). U of Notre Dame Pr.

Transition & Tradition in Moral Theology. Charles E. Curran. LC 78-20877. 1979. text ed. 18.95x (ISBN 0-268-01837-5, Dist. by Har Row). U of Notre Dame Pr.

Transition in African Beliefs: Traditional Religion & Christian Change: A Study in Sukumaland, Tanzania, East Africa. Ralph E. Tanner. LC 67-21411. pap. 67.50 (ISBN 0-317-26638-1, 2025117). Bks Demand UMI.

Transition to an Ordinal Metaphysics. Stephen D. Ross. 162p. 1980. 44.50x (ISBN 0-87395-434-3); pap. 16.95x (ISBN 0-87395-435-1). State U NY Pr.

Transitions: Four Rituals in Eight Cultures. Martha N. Fried & Morton H. Fried. 1980. 14.95 (ISBN 0-393-01350-2). Norton.

Transitions in Biblical Scholarship. Ed. by J. Coert Rylaarsdam. LC 68-9135. (Essays in Divinity Ser: Vol. 6). 1968. 25.00x (ISBN 0-226-73287-8). U of Chicago Pr.

Translation. Julian J. Joyce. 1979. 9.95 (ISBN 0-89962-010-8). Todd & Honeywell.

Translation Debate. Eugene H. Glassman. LC 80-29286. 128p. (Orig.). 1981. pap. 4.25 (ISBN 0-87784-467-4). Inter Varsity.

Translation from the Quran. Altaf Gauhar. 16.95 (ISBN 0-686-18511-0). Kazi Pubns.

Translation of Lao Tzu's "Tao Te Ching" & Wang Pi's "Commentary.". Paul J. Lin. (Michigan Monographs in Chinese Studies: No. 30). 232p. (Orig.). 1977. pap. 8.50 (ISBN 0-89264-030-8). U of Mich Ctr Chinese.

Translation of the Greek Expressions in the Text of The Gospel of John, A Commentary by Rudolf Bultmann. Walter Eisenbeis. 160p. (Orig.). 1984. lib. bdg. 22.00 (ISBN 0-8191-3884-3); pap. text ed. 11.25 (ISBN 0-8191-3885-1). U Pr of Amer.

Translations of Eastern Poetry & Prose. Tr. by Reynold A. Nicholson. Repr. of 1922 ed. lib. bdg. 22.50 (ISBN 0-8371-2301-1, NIEP). Greenwood.

Translations of the Gospel Back into Tongues. C. D. Wright. LC 82-17047. (SUNY Poetry Ser.). 84p. 1982. 24.50x (ISBN 0-87395-652-4) (ISBN 0-87395-685-0). State U NY Pr.

Translator's Guide to Paul's First Letter to the Corinthians. R. G. Bratcher. LC 82-6951. (Helps for Translators Ser.). 1982. pap. 3.50x (ISBN 0-8267-0185-X, 08566). Am Bible.

Translator's Guide to Paul's Letters to Timothy & to Titus. Robert G. Bratcher. LC 83-4823. (Helps for Translators Ser.). viii, 138p. 1983. softcover 2.30x (ISBN 0-8267-0190-6, 08781, Pub. by United Bible). Am Bible.

Translator's Guide to Paul's Second Letter to the Corinthians. Robert G. Bratcher. LC 83-1383. (Helps for Translators Ser.). vii, 160p. 1983. pap. 3.00x (ISBN 0-8267-0186-8, 08571, Pub. by United Bible). Am Bible.

Translator's Guide to Selected Psalms. Heber F. Peacock. (Helps for Translators Ser.). 154p. 1981. pap. 3.30x (ISBN 0-8267-0299-6, 08737, Pub. by United Bible). Am Bible.

Translator's Guide to Selections from the First Five Books of the Old Testament. Heber F. Peacock. (Helps for Translators Ser.). 323p. 1982. pap. 4.30x (ISBN 0-8267-0298-8, 08765, Pub. by United Bible). Am Bible.

Translator's Guide to the Gospel of Luke. R. G. Bratcher. (Helps for Translators Ser.). 388p. 1982. pap. 4.50x (ISBN 0-8267-0181-7, 08712, Pub. by United Bible). Am Bible.

Translator's Guide to the Gospel of Mark. Robert G. Bratcher. (Helps for Translators Ser.). 236p. 1981. pap. 4.50x (ISBN 0-8267-0180-9, 08711, Pub. by United Bible). Am Bible.

Translator's Guide to the Gospel of Matthew. Robert G. Bratcher. LC 82-213977. (Helps for Translators Ser.). 388p. 1981. pap. 4.50x (ISBN 0-8267-0179-5, 08710, Pub. by United Bible). Am Bible.

Translator's Guide to the Letters from James, Peter, & Jude. Robert G. Bratcher. LC 83-18159. (Helps for Translators Ser.). viii, 200p. 1984. 2.30x (ISBN 0-8267-0192-2, 08572, Pub. by United Bible). Am Bible.

Translator's Guide to the Revelation to John. R. G. Bratcher. LC 84-8670. (Helps for Translators Ser.). viii, 204p. 1984. flexible bdg. 3.50x (ISBN 0-8267-0195-7, 08790, Pub. by United Bible). Am Bible.

Translator's Handbook on Paul's First Letter to the Corinthians. Paul Ellingworth & Howard Hatton. LC 85-1142. (Helps for Translators Ser.). viii, 352p. 1985. flexible 4.20x (ISBN 0-8267-0140-X, 08578, Dist. by American Bible Society). United Bible.

Translator's Handbook on Paul's Letters to the Colossians & to Philemon. Robert G. Bratcher & Eugene A. Nida. (Helps for Translators Ser.). 149p. soft cover 3.30x (ISBN 0-8267-0145-0, 08529, Pub. by United Bible). Am Bible.

Translator's Handbook on Paul's Letter to the Ephesians. Robert G. Bratcher & Eugene A. Nida. LC 81-19691. (Helps for Translators Ser.). viii, 199p. 1982. pap. 3.50x (ISBN 0-8267-0143-4, 08780, Pub. by United Bible). Am Bible.

Translator's Handbook on Paul's Letter to the Galatians. D. C. Arichea, Jr. & E. A. Nida. LC 79-115359. (Helps for Translators Ser.). 176p. Repr. of 1976 ed. soft cover 3.65x (ISBN 0-8267-0142-6, 08527, Pub. by United Bible). Am Bible.

Translator's Handbook on Paul's Letter to the Philippians. I. Loh & E. A. Nida. LC 82-17585. (Helps for Translators Ser.). 167p. 1977. 3.30x (ISBN 0-8267-0144-2, 08528, Pub. by United Bible). Am Bible.

Translator's Handbook on Paul's Letter to the Romans. B. M. Newman & E. A. Nida. LC 75-2229. (Helps for Translators Ser.). 325p. 1973. 5.00x (ISBN 0-8267-0139-6, 08517, Pub. by United Bible). Am Bible.

Translator's Handbook on Paul's Letter to the Thessalonians. P. Ellingworth & E. A. Nida. (Helps for Translators Ser.). 229p. 1975. 4.50x (ISBN 0-8267-0146-9, 08526, Pub. by United Bible). Am Bible.

Translator's Handbook on the Acts of the Apostles. B. M. Newman, Jr. & E. A. Nida. LC 73-162720. (Helps for Translators Ser.). 542p. 1972. 6.00x (ISBN 0-8267-0138-8, 08514, Pub. by United Bible). Am Bible.

Translator's Handbook on the Book of Amos. J. De Waard & W. A. Smalley. LC 80-490970. (Helps for Translators Ser.). 274p. 1979. 4.00x (ISBN 0-8267-0128-0, 08577, Pub. by United Bible). Am Bible.

Translator's Handbook on the Book of Jonah. Brynmor F. Price & Eugene A. Nida. (Helps for Translators Ser.). 95p. 1978. 3.30x (ISBN 0-8267-0199-X, 08552, Pub. by United Bible). Am Bible.

Translator's Handbook on the Book of Ruth. J. De Waard & E. A. Nida. (Helps for Translators Ser.). 111p. 1973. 3.30x (ISBN 0-8267-0107-8, 08518, Pub. by United Bible). Am Bible.

Translator's Handbook on the Books of Obadiah & Micah. D. J. Clark & N. Mundhenk. LC 82-8481. (Helps for Translators Ser.). viii, 208p. 1982. pap. 3.50x (ISBN 0-8267-0129-9, 08567, Pub. by United Bible). Am Bible.

Translator's Handbook on the Gospel of John. B. M. Newman & E. A. Nida. LC 81-452133. (Helps for Translators Ser.). 681p. 1980. 7.00x (ISBN 0-8267-0137-X, 08620, Pub. by United Bible). Am Bible.

Translator's Handbook on the Gospel of Luke. J. Reiling & J. L. Swellengrebel. LC 72-856530. (Helps for Translators Ser.). 798p. 1971. 8.40x (ISBN 0-8267-0198-1, 08512, Pub. by United Bible). Am Bible.

Translator's Handbook on the Gospel of Mark. R. G. Bratcher & E. A. Nida. LC 61-19352. (Helps for Translators Ser.). 534p. 1961. soft cover 5.90x (ISBN 0-8267-0135-3, 08501, Pub. by United Bible). Am Bible.

Translator's Handbook on the Letter to the Hebrews. Paul Ellingworth & Eugene A. Nida. LC 83-17947. (Helps for Translators Ser.). viii, 364p. 1983. 5.00x (ISBN 0-8267-0150-7, 08782, Pub. by United Bible). Am Bible.

Translator's Handbook on the Letters of John. C. Haas et al. LC 74-102407. (Helps for Translators Ser.). 171p. 1972. 3.30x (ISBN 0-8267-0154-X, 08516, Pub. by United Bible). Am Bible.

Transliterated Haggadah: Passover Haggadah. Ed. by Gabriel Pollak. (Heb, & Eng). deluxe ed. 18.50 leatherette bdg. (ISBN 0-87559-082-9). Shalom.

Transmigration of the Seven Brahmans. Arthur Christy. Tr. by Henry D. Thoreau. LC 72-3516. (American Literature Ser., No. 49). Orig. Title: Harivansa. 1972. Repr. of 1931 ed. lib. bdg. 29.95x (ISBN 0-8383-1563-1). Haskell.

Transmission: A Meditation for the New Age. rev. ed. Benjamin Creme. 100p. 1985. pap. 3.50 (ISBN 0-936604-06-9). Tara Ctr.

Transmission of Doubt. John Da Free. 475p. (Orig.). 1984. pap. 10.95 (ISBN 0-913922-77-3). Dawn Horse Pr.

Transmission of Faith to the Next Generation, Vol. 174. Ed. by Virgil Elizondo & Norbert Greinacher. (Concilium Ser.). 128p. pap. 6.95 (ISBN 0-567-30054-4, Pub. by T & T Clark Ltd UK). Fortress.

Transmission of the Mind Outside the Teaching. Charles Luk. LC 75-15055. 1976. pap. 2.95 (ISBN 0-394-17888-2, E666, Ever). Grove.

Transparenz der Wirklichkeit: Edzard Schaper und die innere Spannung in der christlichen Literatur des zwanzigstes Jahrhunderts. Irene Sonderegger-Kummer. (Quellen und Forschungen zur Sprach- und Kulturgeschichte der germanischen Voelker, No. 37). (Ger). 1971. 48.40x (ISBN 3-11-001845-4). De Gruyter.

Transpersonal Approaches to Counseling & Psychotherapy. Gay Hendricks & Barry Weinhold. 199p. 1982. pap. text ed. 12.95 (ISBN 0-89108-112-7). Love Pub Co.

Tratado Sobre la Predicacion. J. A. Broadus. Tr. by Ernesto Barocio. Orig. Title: On the Preparation & Delivery of Sermons. 336p. 1985. pap. 5.50 (ISBN 0-311-42034-6). Casa Bautista.

Trauma of Transparency: A Biblical Approach to Inter-Personal Communication. J. Grant Howard. LC 79-87716. (Critical Concern Bks). 1979. pap. 6.95 (ISBN 0-686-86369-0); study guide 2.95 (ISBN 0-930014-74-X). Multnomah.

Travail of Nature: The Ambiguous Ecological Promise of Christian Theology. H. Paul Santmire. LC 84-47934. 288p. 1985. 16.95 (ISBN 0-8006-1806-8, 1-1806). Fortress.

Travel with Inner Perceptiveness. Flower A. Newhouse. (Illus.). 112p. (Orig.). 1979. pap. text ed. 7.00 (ISBN 0-910378-16-9). Christward.

Travelers. Avy Stewart. (Orig.). 1982. pap. 2.95 (ISBN 0-937172-36-7). JLJ Pubs.

Traveler's Narrative: Written to Illustrate the Episode of the Bab. rev. ed. Abdu'l-Baha. Tr. by Edward G. Browne from Persian. LC 79-19025. 1980. 10.95 (ISBN 0-87743-134-5, 106-027); pap. 5.95 (ISBN 0-686-96668-6, 106-028). Baha'i.

Traveling Jewish in America: For Business & Pleasure. rev. ed. Brynna C. Bloomfield et al. 420p. (Orig.). 1987. pap. 9.95 (ISBN 0-9617104-1-1). Wandering You Pr.

Traveling Jewish in America: The Complete Guide for 1986 for Business & Pleasure. Brynna C. Bloomfield & Jane M. Moskowitz. 407p. (Orig.). 1986. pap. 9.95 (ISBN 0-9617104-0-3). Wandering You Pr.

Traveling Light. Eugene Peterson. LC 82-15314. 204p. (Orig.). 1982. pap. 5.25 (ISBN 0-87784-377-5). Inter-Varsity.

Traveller's Guide to Places of Worship. Charles Kightly. 1986. 14.95 (ISBN 0-918678-18-8). Historical Times.

Traveller's Guide to Spurgeon Country. Eric W. Hayden. 1974. pap. 1.95 (ISBN 0-686-10527-3). Pilgrim Pubns.

Traveller's Guide to the Astral Plane. Steve Richards. 112p. 1984. pap. 7.95 (ISBN 0-85030-337-0). Newcastle Pub.

Travelling in. Monica Furlong. LC 84-71182. 125p. 1984. pap. 6.00 (ISBN 0-936384-20-4). Cowley Pubns.

Travels in England: A Ramble with the City & Town Missionaries. John Shaw. LC 84-48282. (Rise of Urban Britain Ser.). 393p. 1985. 50.00 (ISBN 0-8240-6284-1). Garland Pub.

Travel's in Jewry. cancelled (ISBN 0-686-76271-1). Feldheim.

Travels in Syria & the Holy Land. John L. Burckhardt. LC 77-87614. (Illus.). 720p. 1983. Repr. of 1822 ed. 76.50 (ISBN 0-404-16437-4). AMS Pr.

Travels of an Alchemist: The Journey of the Taoist Ch'ang-Ch'un from China to the Hindukush. 1978. Repr. of 1931 ed. 12.00 (ISBN 0-89986-341-8). Oriental Bk Store.

Travels of Fa-hsien, 399 to 144 A.D. Or Record of the Buddhistic Kingdoms. Fl. Fa-hsien. Tr. by M. A. Giles & H. A. Giles. LC 81-13362. xx, 96p. 1982. Repr. of 1956 ed. lib. bdg. 22.50x (ISBN 0-313-23240-7, FATR). Greenwood.

Travels of Faith. Faith A. Sand. LC 85-17751. (Illus.). 152p. (Orig.). 1986. pap. 4.95 (ISBN 0-932727-03-4). Hope Pub Hse.

Travels of Macarius: Extracts from the Diary of the Travels of Macarius, Patriarch of Antioch. Ed. by Laura Ridding. LC 77-115577. (Russia Observed Ser). 1971. Repr. of 1936 ed. 12.00 (ISBN 0-405-03089-4). Ayer Co Pubs.

Traves del Ojo de la Mente. Ralph M. Lewis. Tr. by AMORC Staff. (Span.). 290p. (Orig.). 1983. pap. 8.00 (ISBN 0-912057-84-X, GS-646). AMORC.

Traza Bien la Palabra de Verdad. C. I. Scofield. Orig. Title: Rightly Dividing the Word of Truth. (Span.). 92p. 1971. pap. 3.25 (ISBN 0-8254-1660-4). Kregel.

Treacherous Journey: My Escape from Ethiopia. Samuel Auraham & Arlene Kushner. 1986. 14.95 (ISBN 0-933503-46-6). Shapolsky Pubs.

Treasure Hunt. Frederick Buechner. LC 84-47716. (Books of Bebb). 1984. pap. 3.95 (ISBN 0-06-061168-5, P-5010, HarpR). Har-Row.

Treasure in Clay: The Autobiography of Fulton J. Sheen. Fulton J. Sheen. LC 81-43271. (Illus.). 384p. 1980. 15.95 (ISBN 0-385-15985-4). Doubleday.

Treasure in Clay: The Autobiography of Fulton J. Sheen. Fulton J. Sheen. LC 81-43271. (Illus.). 384p. 1982. pap. 8.95 (ISBN 0-385-17709-7, Im). Doubleday.

Treasure of Hymns. facs. ed. Amos R. Wells. LC 70-128330. (Essay Index Reprint Ser). 1945. 19.50 (ISBN 0-8369-2096-1). Ayer Co Pubs.

Treasure of Montsegur. Walter Birks & R. A. Gilbert. (Crucible Ser.). 176p. 1987. pap. 9.95 (ISBN 0-85030-424-5). Inner Tradit.

Treasure of Sao Roque. William Tefler. (Church Historical Society London N. S. Ser.: No. 14). Repr. of 1932 ed. 40.00 (ISBN 0-8115-3137-6). Kraus Repr.

Treasure of the Magi: A Story of Modern Zoroastrianism. James H. Moulton. LC 73-173004. Repr. of 1917 ed. 21.75 (ISBN 0-404-04508-1). AMS Pr.

Treasure of the Magi: A Study of Modern Zoroastrianism. J. H. Moulton. lib. bdg. 59.95 (ISBN 0-8490-2759-4). Gordon Pr.

Treasure-Trove of American Jewish Humor. Henry D. Spalding. LC 75-40192. 429p. 1976. 16.95 (ISBN 0-8246-0204-8). Jonathan David.

Treasured Catholic Prayers & Devotions. David Konstant. 1987. pap. 4.95 (ISBN 0-89622-312-4). Twenty-Third.

Treasured Polish Christmas Customs & Traditions. 8.95 (ISBN 0-685-37594-3). Polanie.

Treasures from Paul's Letters, Vol. I. A. M. Coniaris. 1978. pap. 7.95 (ISBN 0-937032-05-0). Light&Life Pub Co MN.

Treasures from Paul's Letters, Vol. II. A. M. Coniaris. 1979. pap. 7.95 (ISBN 0-937032-06-9). Light&Life Pub Co MN.

Treasures from the Holy Scripture. T. B. Maston. (Orig.). 1987. pap. 3.25 (ISBN 0-8054-5043-2). Broadman.

Treasures from the Meher Baba Journals. Meher Baba et al. Ed. by Jane B. Haynes. LC 79-92169. (Illus.). 246p. 1980. pap. 6.95 (ISBN 0-913078-37-9). Sheriar Pr.

Treasures from the Original. Harold J. Berry. 1985. pap. 4.95 (ISBN 0-8024-2956-4). Moody.

Treasures in Earthen Vessels: The Vows, a Wholistic Approach. Joyce Ridick. LC 84-2817. 166p. 1984. pap. 9.95 (ISBN 0-8189-0467-4). Alba.

Treasures of Age. Peggy Scarborough. (International Correspondence Program Ser.). (Orig.). 1985. pap. text ed. 6.95 (ISBN 0-87148-856-6). Pathway Pr.

Treasures of Christmas: The Guideposts Family Christmas Book. 80p. pap. 7.95 (ISBN 0-687-42560-3). Abingdon.

Treasures of Darkness: A History of Mesoptamian Religon. Thorkild Jacobsen. LC 75-27576. (Illus.). 1976. pap. 9.95x (ISBN 0-300-02291-3). Yale U Pr.

Treasures of Half-Truths. Pat Bagley. 100p. 1986. pap. 4.95 (ISBN 0-941214-47-8). Signature Bks.

Treasures of Mount Athos: Illuminated Manuscripts, Vol. 1. S. M. Pelekanidis et al. (Patriarchal Institute for Patristic Studies). (Illus.). 500p. 1975. cancelled (ISBN 0-89241-003-5). Caratzas.

Treasures of Mount Athos, Volume 2: The Monasteries of Iveron, St. Panteleimon, Esphigmenou & Chilandari. Patriarchal Institute for Patristic Studies et al. (Illus.). 400p. 1976. cancelled (ISBN 0-89241-004-3). Caratzas.

Treasures of the Holy Land: A Visit to the Places of Christian Origins. Veselin Kesich & Lydia W. Kesich. LC 85-18403. (Illus., Orig.). 1985. pap. 6.95 (ISBN 0-88141-045-4). St Vladimirs.

Treasures of the Jewish Museum. Vivian B. Mann & Norman Kleeblatt. LC 85-28913. (Illus.). 216p. 1986. text ed. 35.00x (ISBN 0-87663-493-5); pap. 19.95 (ISBN 0-87663-890-6). Universe.

Treasures of the Orthodox Church Museum in Finland. (Illus.). 124p. (Orig.). 1985. pap. text ed. 57.50x (Pub. by Almqvist & Wiksell). Coronet Bks.

Treasures of the Vatican. M. Calvesi. 39.95 (ISBN 0-517-62643-8). Outlet Bk Co.

Treasures of Wisdom: Studies in Colossians & Philemon. Homer A. Kent, Jr. pap. 5.95 (ISBN 0-88469-062-8). BMH Bks.

Treasury of A. W. Tozer. A. W. Tozer. 1979. 9.95 (ISBN 0-87509-281-0); pap. 4.45 (ISBN 0-87509-176-8). Chr Pubns.

Treasury of American Sacred Song. facs. ed. W. G. Horder. LC 74-76944. (Granger Index Reprint Ser). 1896. 18.00 (ISBN 0-8369-6019-X). Ayer Co Pubs.

Treasury of Catholic Digest: Favorite Stories of Fifty Years, 1936-1986. Henry Lexau. LC 86-81597. 598p. 1986. 24.95 (ISBN 0-89870-115-5). Ignatius Pr.

Treasury of Catholic Wisdom. John A. Hardon. LC 86-19648. 768p. 1987. 27.50 (ISBN 0-385-23079-6). Doubleday.

Treasury of Chassidic Tales, Vol. 1. Shlomo Y. Zevin. Tr. by Uri Kaploun from Heb. (Art Scroll Judaica Classics Ser.). 320p. 1981. 13.95 (ISBN 0-89906-912-6); pap. 10.95 (ISBN 0-89906-913-4). Mesorah Pubns.

Treasury of Chassidic Tales: On the Torah, Vol. 2. Schlomo Y. Zevin. Tr. by Uri Kaploun. (Art Scroll Judaica Classics Ser.). 352p. 1980. 13.95 (ISBN 0-89906-902-9); pap. 10.95 (ISBN 0-89906-903-7); gift box ed. 29.95 (ISBN 0-89906-904-5). Mesorah Pubns.

Treasury of Christian Classics. Bd. with Greatest Thing in the World; As a Man Thinketh; Acres of Diamonds; Practice of the Presence of God. (Christian Library). 241p. 6.95 (ISBN 0-916441-47-4). Barbour & Co.

Treasury of Christian Poetry. Compiled by Lorraine Eitel. 192p. 1982. 12.95 (ISBN 0-8007-1291-9). Revell.

Treasury of Christmas Songs & Carols. 2nd ed. Henry A. Simon. 1973. 16.95 (ISBN 0-395-17786-3); pap. 9.95 (ISBN 0-395-17785-5). HM.

Treasury of Clean Church Jokes. Tal D. Bonham. LC 85-26837. 1986. pap. 3.50 (ISBN 0-8054-5719-4). Broadman.

Treasury of Comfort. Ed. by Sidney S. Greenberg. pap. 5.00 (ISBN 0-87980-167-0). Wilshire.

Treasury of David, 7 vols. C. H. Spurgen. 1983. Set. 75.00 (ISBN 0-686-40818-7). Pilgrim Pubns.

Treasury of David, 2 vols. Charles H. Spurgeon. 1983. Set. 45.00 (ISBN 0-8010-8256-0). Baker Bk.

Treasury of David, 2 vols. Charles H. Spurgeon. 1984. Repr. Psalms 1-78, Vol. I, 1440p. 39.95 set (ISBN 0-8407-5425-6). Psalms 79-150, Vol. II, 1464p. Nelson.

Treasury of David - A Commentary on the Psalms, 3 vols. Charles H. Spurgeon. 2912p. Date not set. 49.95 (ISBN 0-917006-25-9). Hendrickson MA.

Treasury of Devotion. A. J. Russell. 432p. 1986. 16.95 (ISBN 0-396-08885-6). Dodd.

Treasury of Easter Music & Music for Passiontide. Ed. by Will L. Reed. 1963. 12.95 (ISBN 0-87523-142-X). Emerson.

Treasury of Edith Hamilton. Ed. by Doris F. Reid. LC 70-90989. 1969. 5.00 (ISBN 0-393-04313-4). Norton.

Treasury of English Church Music 1545-1650. Ed. by Peter Le Huray. 250p. 1982. 47.50 (ISBN 0-521-24889-2); pap. 19.95 (ISBN 0-521-28405-8). Cambridge U Pr.

Treasury of Evangelical Writings. Ed. by David O. Fuller. LC 61-9768. 472p. 1974. pap. 11.95 (ISBN 0-8254-2613-8). Kregel.

Treasury of Great Hymns: And Their Stories. Guye Johnson. 382p. (Orig.). 1985. pap. 9.95 (ISBN 0-89084-249-3). Bob Jones Univ Pr.

Treasury of His Promises. Graham Miller. 386p. (Orig.). 1986. pap. 12.95 (ISBN 0-85151-472-3). Banner of Truth.

Treasury of Irish Religious Verse. Ed. by Patrick Murray. 1986. 17.95 (ISBN 0-8245-0776-2). Crossroad NY.

Treasury of Jewish Folklore. Ed. by Nathan Ausubel. 1948. 14.95 (ISBN 0-517-50293-3). Crown.

Treasury of Jewish Humor. Ed. by Nathan Ausubel. LC 51-10639. 1951. 17.95 (ISBN 0-385-04499-2). Doubleday.

Treasury of Jewish Literature: From Biblical Times to Today. Ed. by Gloria Goldreich. LC 81-6967. 256p. 1982. 13.45 (ISBN 0-03-053831-9). H Holt & Co.

Treasury of Joy & Enthusiasm. Norman V. Peale. 224p. 1982. pap. 2.50 (ISBN 0-449-24550-0, Crest). Fawcett.

Treasury of Mahayana Sutras: Selections from the Maharatnakuta Sutra. Ed. by Garma C. C. Chang. Tr. by Buddhist Association of the United States. LC 82-42776. (Institute for Advanced Study of World Religions (IASWR) Ser.). 512p. 1983. 26.75x (ISBN 0-271-00341-3). Pa St U Pr.

Treasury of Modern Biography: A Gallery of Literary Sketches of Eminent Men & Women of the 19th Century. Robert Cochrane. 1881. Repr. 50.00 (ISBN 0-8274-3645-9). R West.

Treasury of New Testament Synonyms. Stewart Custer. 161p. 1975. 7.95 (ISBN 0-89084-025-3). Bob Jones Univ Pr.

Treasury of Orthodox Hymnology: The Triodion. Savas J. Savas. 1983. pap. 4.95 (ISBN 0-937032-32-8). Light&Life Pub Co MN.

Treasury of Prayer. E. M. Bounds. LC 53-9865. 192p. 1981. pap. 5.95 (ISBN 0-87123-543-9, 210543). Bethany Hse.

Treasury of Quotations on Religious Subjects. F. B. Proctor. LC 76-15741. 832p. 1976. 21.95 (ISBN 0-8254-3500-5). Kregel.

Treasury of Scripture Knowledge. R. A. Torrey. 784p. 1973. 21.95 (ISBN 0-8007-0324-3). Revell.

Treasury of Scripture Knowledge. R. A. Torrey. 778p. Date not set. 17.95 (ISBN 0-917006-22-4). Hendrickson MA.

Treasury of Sephardic Laws & Customs. Hebert Dobrinsky. 500p. 1986. 29.50x (ISBN 0-88125-031-7); pap. text ed. 16.95. Ktav.

Treasury of Story Sermons for Children. Compiled by Charles L. Wallis. (Charles L. Wallis Library Pulpit Helps). 290p. 1974. pap. 6.95 (ISBN 0-8010-9556-5). Baker Bk.

Treasury of Tennessee Churches. Mayme H. Johnson. (Illus.). 160p. 1986. 29.95 (ISBN 0-939298-60-0, 600). J M Prods.

Treasury of the World's Great Sermons. Compiled by Warren W. Wiersbe. LC 77-72366. 1977. 24.95 (ISBN 0-8254-4011-4). Kregel.

Treasury of Tradition. Ed. by Norman Lamm. Walter S. Wurzburger. 462p. 1967. 9.95 (ISBN 0-88482-434-9). Hebrew Pub.

Treasury of Traditional Wisdom. Whitall N. Perry. 1986. pap. 19.95 (ISBN 0-317-52385-6, PL 4136, HarpR). Har-Row.

Treasury of Worship. Helena Dickinson. 59.95 (ISBN 0-8490-1230-9). Gordon Pr.

Treasury of Yiddish Stories. Ed. by Irving Howe & Eliezer Greenberg. LC 54-9599. (Illus.). 630p. 1973. pap. 11.95 (ISBN 0-8052-0400-8). Schocken.

Treatise Against Dicing, Dancing, Plays & Interludes. John Northbrooke. LC 77-149667. Repr. of 1843 ed. 19.00 (ISBN 0-404-04793-9). AMS Pr.

Treatise Against Iudicial Astrologie, 2 pts. John Chamber. LC 77-6872. (English Experience Ser.: No. 860). 1977. Repr. of 1601 ed. lib. bdg. 20.00 (ISBN 90-221-0860-0). Walter J Johnson.

Treatise Concerning Enthusiasme. Meric Casaubon. LC 77-119864. 1970. Repr. of 1656 ed. 45.00x (ISBN 0-8201-1077-9). Schol Facsimiles.

Treatise Concerning Eternal & Immutable Morality. Ralph Cudworth. Ed. by Rene Wellek. LC 75-11214. (British Philosophers & Theologians of the 17th & 18th Centuries Ser.: Vol. 17). 1976. Repr. of 1731 ed. lib. bdg. 51.00 (ISBN 0-8240-1768-4). Garland Pub.

Treatise Concernynge the Division Betwene the Spiritualitie & Temporalitie. Christopher Saint German. LC 72-6027. (English Experience Ser.: No. 453). 94p. 1972. Repr. of 1532 ed. 14.00 (ISBN 90-221-0453-2). Walter J Johnson.

Treatise of Ecclesiastical Discipline. Matthew Sutcliffe. LC 73-7082. (English Experience Ser.: No. 626). 1973. Repr. of 1590 ed. 21.00 (ISBN 90-221-0626-8). Walter J Johnson.

Treatise of Human Nature, 2 vols. David Hume. Ed. by T. H. Green & T. H. Grose. 1025p. 1981. Repr. of 1898 ed. lib. bdg. 200.00 (ISBN 0-89987-377-4). Darby Bks.

Treatise of Morall Philosophie. rev. ed. William Baldwin. LC 67-10126. 1967. Repr. of 1620 ed. 50.00x (ISBN 0-8201-1003-5). Schol Facsimiles.

Treatise of the Donation of Gyfts & Endowment of Possessyons Gyven & Graunted Unto Sylvester Pope of Rome by Constantyne Emperour of Rome. Constantine I. Tr. by William Marshall. LC 79-84096. (English Experience Ser.: No. 916). (Eng.). 152p. 1979. Repr. of 1534 ed. lib. bdg. 24.00 (ISBN 90-221-0916-X). Walter J Johnson.

Treatise of the Pool. Obadyah Maimonides. Tr. by Paul Fenton. 1981. 19.95 (ISBN 0-900860-87-1, Pub. by Octagon Pr England). Ins Study Human.

Treatise on Atonement. Hosea Ballou. Ed. by Ernest Cassara. 1986. pap. 7.95 (ISBN 0-933840-26-8, 0495000). Unitarian Univ.

Treatise on Byzantine Music. S. G. Hatherly. LC 77-75226. 1977. Repr. of 1892 ed. lib. bdg. 20.00 (ISBN 0-89341-071-3). Longwood Pub Group.

Treatise on Domestic Education. facs. ed. Daniel A. Payne. LC 75-157373. (Black Heritage Library Collection Ser). 1885. 16.00 (ISBN 0-8369-8811-6). Ayer Co Pubs.

Treatise on Grace & Other Posthumous Published Writings Including Observations on the Trinity. Jonathan Edwards. Ed. by Paul Helm. 141p. 1971. 13.95 (ISBN 0-227-67739-0). Attic Pr.

Treatise on Happiness. St. Thomas Aquinas. Tr. by John A. Oesterle. LC 83-17091. 224p. 1983. text ed. 15.95x (ISBN 0-268-01848-0, 85-18482); pap. text ed. 5.95x (ISBN 0-268-01849-9, 85-18490). U of Notre Dame Pr.

Treatise on Prayer: An Explanation of the Services of the Orthodox Church. Symeon of Thessalonike. Intro. by N. M. Vaporis. Tr. by H. L. Simmons from Gr. (Archbishop Iakovos Library of Ecclesiastical & Historical Sources: No. 9). Orig. Title: Peri Theias Kai Hieras Proseuches. (Orig.). 1984. 12.95; pap. text ed. 7.95 (ISBN 0-917653-05-X). Hellenic Coll Pr.

Treatise on Prayer & Meditation. Dominic Devas. Repr. of 1926 ed. lib. bdg. 25.00 (ISBN 0-8495-1026-0). Arden Lib.

Treatise on Response & Retribution. Lao Tze. Tr. by Paul Carus & D. T. Suzuki. LC 6-28775. (Illus.). 139p. 1973. pap. 2.95 (ISBN 0-87548-244-9). Open Court.

Treatise on Sunday Laws: The Sabbath-the Lord's Day, Its History & Observance, Civil & Criminal. George E. Harris. xxiii, 338p. 1980. Repr. of 1892 ed. lib. bdg. 32.50x (ISBN 0-8377-2232-2). Rothman.

Treatise on the Heathen Superstitions that Today Live among the Indians Native to this New Spain, 1629. Hernando Ruiz de Alarcon. Ed. by J. Richard Andrews & Ross Hassig. LC 83-47842. (Civilization of the American Indian Ser.: Vol. 164). (Illus.). 540p. 1984. text ed. 48.50x (ISBN 0-8061-1832-6). U of Okla Pr.

Treatise on the Love of God. Saint Francoise De Sales. Tr. by Henry B. Mackey. LC 71-156190. xiiv, 555p. Repr. of 1942 ed. lib. bdg. 31.75x (ISBN 0-8371-6139-8, FRLG). Greenwood.

Treatise on the Love of God, 2 vols. St. Francis de Sales. Tr. by John K. Ryan. 1975. Set. pap. 10.00 (ISBN 0-89555-064-4); Vol. 1. pap. (ISBN 0-89555-062-8, 166-I); Vol. 2. pap. (ISBN 0-89555-063-6). TAN Bks Pubs.

Treatise on the Millennium. Samuel Hopkins. LC 70-38450. (Religion in America, Series 2). 162p. 1972. Repr. of 1793 ed. 14.00 (ISBN 0-405-04070-9). Ayer Co Pubs.

Treatise on the Passions, So Far As They Regard the Stage. Samuel Foote. LC 72-144608. Repr. of 1747 ed. 11.50 (ISBN 0-404-02448-3). AMS Pr.

Treatise on the Pretended Divorce Between Henry Eighth & Catharine of Aragon. Nicholas Harpsfield. Ed. by N. Pocock. 1878. 27.00 (ISBN 0-384-21420-7). Johnson Repr.

Treatise on the Seven Rays, 5 vols. Alice A. Bailey. Incl. Vol. 1. Esoteric Psychology. 1984. 20.00 (ISBN 0-85330-018-6); pap. 9.00 (ISBN 0-85330-118-2); Vol. 2. Esoteric Psychology. 1982. 28.00 (ISBN 0-85330-019-4); pap. 17.00 (ISBN 0-85330-119-0); Vol. 3. Esoteric Astrology. 1983. 28.00 (ISBN 0-85330-020-8); pap. 17.00 (ISBN 0-85330-120-4); Vol. 4. Esoteric Healing. 1984. 28.00 (ISBN 0-85330-021-6); pap. 17.00 (ISBN 0-85330-121-2); Vol. 5. The Rays & the Initiations. 1982. 28.00 (ISBN 0-85330-022-4); pap. 17.00 (ISBN 0-85330-122-0). pap. Lucis.

Treatise on the Virtues. St. Thomas Aquinas. Tr. by John A. Oesterle. LC 84-10691. 171p. 1984. pap. text ed. 7.95 (ISBN 0-268-01855-3, 85-18557). U of Notre Dame Pr.

Treatise Ta'anit of the Babylonian Talmud. Tr. & Henry Malter. LC 78-1171. (JPS Library of Jewish Classics). 528p. 1978. 6.50 (ISBN 0-8276-0108-5, 422). Jewish Pubns.

Treatises & the Pastoral Prayer. Aelred of Rievaulx. pap. 5.00 (ISBN 0-87907-902-9). Cistercian Pubns.

Treatises I: Apologia, Precept & Dispensation. Bernard of Clairvaux. (Cistercian Fathers Ser.: No. 1). 190p. 7.95 (ISBN 0-87907-101-X). Cistercian Pubns.

Treatises on Marriage & Other Subjects. St. Augustine. LC 73-75002. (Fathers of the Church Ser.: Vol. 27). 456p. 1955. 34.95x (ISBN 0-8132-0027-X). Cath U Pr.

Treatises on Various Moral Subjects. St. Augustine. LC 65-18319. (Fathers of the Church Ser.: Vol. 16). 479p. 1952. 24.95x (ISBN 0-8132-0016-4). Cath U Pr.

Treatises Upon Several Subjects. John Norris. Ed. by Rene Wellek. LC 75-11244. (British Philosophers & Theologians of the 17th & 18th Centuries Ser.). 1978. Repr. of 1698 ed. lib. bdg. 51.00 (ISBN 0-8240-1796-X). Garland Pub.

Treatment of the Capital Sins. R. J. Ianucci. LC 70-140024. (Catholic University Studies in German: No. 17). Repr. of 1942 ed. 21.00 (ISBN 0-404-50237-7). AMS Pr.

Treatment of the Holocaust in Textbooks: The Federal Republic of Germany, Israel, the United States. Walter Renn et al. (Holocaust Studies). 288p. 1987. text ed. 30.00 (ISBN 0-88033-955-1). East Eur Quarterly.

Treatment of the Jews in the Christian Writers of the First Three Centuries, Vol. 81. Robert Wilde. (Patristic Studies). 255p. 1984. Repr. of 1949 ed. 38.00x (ISBN 0-939738-28-7). Zubal Inc.

Trece Lecciones de Doctrina Biblica. Denver Sizemore. Tr. by Raul Martinez from Eng. Tr. of Thirteen Lessons in Christian Doctrine. (Span.). 114p. pap. 1.95 (ISBN 0-89900-300-1). College Pr Pub.

Tree at the Center of the World: The Story of the California Missions. Bruce W. Barton. LC 79-26434. (Illus., Orig.). 1980. lib. bdg. 19.95 (ISBN 0-915520-30-3); pap. 12.95 (ISBN 0-915520-29-X). Ross-Erikson.

Tree Automata. F. Gecseq & M. Steinby. 1984. 99.00x (ISBN 0-569-08794-5, Pub. by Collets (UK)). State Mutual Bk.

Tree Is Lighted. Ellen Davies-Rogers. LC 84-90673. (Illus.). 1984. 5.00 (ISBN 0-317-19588-3). Plantation.

Tree Lore in the Bible. Lonsdale Ragg. Repr. of 1935 ed. lib. bdg. 30.00 (ISBN 0-8495-4528-5). Arden Lib.

Tree of Hope. Jessica Goronwy. 1985. 20.00x (ISBN 0-7223-1827-8, Pub. by A H Stockwell England). State Mutual Bk.

Tree of Knowledge: The Biological Roots of Human Understanding. Humberto R. Maurana & Francisco Varela. Ed. by Kendra Crossen. LC 86-29698. (Illus.). 215p. 1987. 19.95 (ISBN 0-87773-373-2); pap. 12.95 (ISBN 0-87773-403-8). Shambhala Pubns.

Tree of Life: An Anthology. De Solo Pinto et al. 1981. Repr. of 1929 ed. lib. bdg. 35.00 (ISBN 0-89984-390-5). Century Bookbindery.

Tree of Life: Diversity, Creativity, & Flexibility in Jewish Law. Louis Jacobs. (Littman Library of Jewish Civilization). 32.50x (ISBN 0-19-710039-2). Oxford U Pr.

Tree Tall to the Rescue. Shirlee Evans. (Tree Tall Ser.: No. 3). (Illus.). 144p. (Orig.). 1987. pap. 4.50 (ISBN 0-8361-3444-3). Herald Pr.

Tree That Always Said No. Leo Price. LC 73-90617. (Illus.). 1973. plastic bdg. 2.75 (ISBN 0-8198-0330-8); pap. 1.75 (ISBN 0-8198-0331-6). Dghtrs St Paul.

Tree: The Complete Book of Saxon Witchcraft. Raymond Buckland. LC 74-79397. (Illus.). 158p. 1974. pap. 5.95 (ISBN 0-87728-258-7). Weiser.

Trees of Christmas. Compiled by Edna Metcalfe. LC 79-12288. (Illus.). 1979. pap. 8.75 (ISBN 0-687-42591-3). Abingdon.

Trees of Restoration. Dean Guest. cancelled (ISBN 0-533-05752-3). Vantage.

Trends in Protestant Social Idealism. Neal Hughley. LC 74-167359. (Essay Index Reprint Ser.). Repr. of 1948 ed. 18.00 (ISBN 0-8369-2771-0). Ayer Co Pubs.

Tres Dramas De Navidad. Belia Perez. 24p. 1985. pap. 0.80 (ISBN 0-311-08221-1). Casa Bautista.

Trevor's Place: The Story of the Boy Who Brings Hope to the Homeless. Frank Ferrell et al. LC 84-48768. (Illus.). 138p. 1985. 12.45 (ISBN 0-06-062531-7, HarpR). Har-Row.

Triadic Mysticism. Paul E. Murphy. 1986. 23.00X (ISBN 81-208-0010-9, Pub. by Motilal Banarsidass). South Asia Bks.

Trial & Death of Jesus. H. Cohn. 14.95x (ISBN 0-87068-432-9). Ktav.

Trial & Error: The American Controversy over Creation & Evolution. Edward J. Larson. LC 85-7144. 232p. 1985. 17.95 (ISBN 0-19-503666-2). Oxford U Pr.

Trial & Error: The Autobiography of Chaim Weizmann. Chaim Weizmann. LC 70-156215. 498p. 1972. Repr. of 1949 ed. lib. bdg. 35.00x (ISBN 0-8371-6166-5, WETE). Greenwood.

Trial & Triumph Genesis B: Leader's Guide. (New Horizons Bible Study Ser.). 1981. pap. 1.95 (ISBN 0-89367-054-5). Light & Life.

Trial & Triumph Genesis B: Study Guide. (New Horizons Bible Study Ser.). 68p. 1981. pap. 2.50 (ISBN 0-89367-055-3). Light & Life.

Trial by Death & Fire. D. Carl Anderson. LC 80-14446. (Orion Ser.). 160p. 1980. pap. 3.95 (ISBN 0-8127-0292-1). Review & Herald.

Trial by Fire. Anne S. White. 108p. (Orig.). 1975. pap. 3.50 (ISBN 0-89228-045-X). Impact Bks MO.

Trial by Trial: Destiny of a Believer. Don Stephens. LC 85-80485. 176p. (Orig.). 1985. pap. 6.95 (ISBN 0-89081-498-8). Harvest Hse.

Trial of Beyers Naude: Christian Witness & the Rule of Law. International Commission of Jurists, Geneva. 1975. pap. 5.95 (ISBN 0-377-00057-4, Pub. by Search Pr England). Friend Pr.

Trial of C. B. Reynolds. Robert G. Ingersoll. 44p. (Orig.). 1986. pap. 3.00 (ISBN 0-910309-25-6). Am Atheist.

Trial of Christ. A. T. Innes & F. J. Powell. 287p. 1982. lib. bdg. 10.75 (ISBN 0-86524-138-4, 9513). Klock & Klock.

Trial of Christ: From a Legal & Scriptural Viewpoint. David K. Breed. (Pocket Pulpit Library). 96p. 1982. pap. 2.95 (ISBN 0-8010-0829-8). Baker Bk.

Trial of Faith. R. J. Owen. 1.60 (ISBN 0-08-017609-7). Pergamon.

Trial of Faith: Discussions Concerning Mormonism & Neo-Mormonism. William Call. 215p. (Orig.). Date not set. pap. write for info. (ISBN 0-916095-11-8). Pubs Pr UT.

Trial of Faith: Religion & Politics in Tocqueville's. Doris S. Goldstein. LC 75-4753. pap. 39.00 (2026263). Bks Demand UMI.

Trial of Faith: Religion & Politics in Tocqueville's Thought. Doris Goldstein. 144p. 1975. 21.00 (ISBN 0-444-99001-1). Elsevier.

Trial of Jesus. Chandler. (Illus.). 24.95 (ISBN 0-686-90784-1); deluxe ed. 44.95 (ISBN 0-686-90785-X); pap. 9.95 (ISBN 0-686-90786-8). Harrison Co GA.

Trial of Jesus. Giovanni Rosadi. 1977. lib. bdg. 59.95 (ISBN 0-8490-2767-5). Gordon Pr.

Trial of Jesus Christ. Aristarchus Vassilakos. Ed. by Orthodox Christian Educational Society. 64p. (Orig.). 1950. pap. 2.75x (ISBN 0-938366-47-5). Orthodox Chr.

Trial of Jesus from a Lawyer's Standpoint, 2 vols. Walter M. Chandler. LC 83-82312. 1983. Repr. of 1925 ed. 115.00 set (ISBN 0-89941-294-7). W S Hein.

Trial of Jesus of Nazareth. S. G. Brandon. LC 68-9206. (Illus.). 1979. pap. 4.95 (ISBN 0-8128-6018-7). Stein & Day.

Trial of Judaism in Contemporary Jewish Writing. Josephine Z. Knopp. LC 74-18319. 164p. 1975. 15.95 (ISBN 0-252-00386-1). U of Ill Pr.

Trial of Luther. Daniel Olivier. 1979. pap. 8.95 (ISBN 0-570-03785-9, 12-2743). Concordia.

Trial of the Templars. M. C. Barber. LC 77-85716. 320p. 1978. 54.50 (ISBN 0-521-21896-9); pap. 15.95 (ISBN 0-521-28018-4). Cambridge U Pr.

Trial of the Templars. Edward J. Martin. LC 76-29845. Repr. of 1928 ed. 24.50 (ISBN 0-404-15424-7). AMS Pr.

Triall of Witch-Craft Shewing the True Methode of the Discovery. John Cotta. LC 68-54629. (English Experience Ser.: No. 39). 128p. 1968. Repr. of 1616 ed. 21.00 (ISBN 90-221-0039-1). Walter J Johnson.

Trialogue Between Jew, Christian & Muslim. Ignay Maybaum. (Littman Library of Jewish Civilization). 192p. 1973. 18.50x (ISBN 0-19-710032-5). Oxford U Pr.

Trialogue of Abrahamic Faiths. I. R. Al Farugi. 88p. (Orig.). 1986. pap. 7.50 (ISBN 0-317-52454-2). New Era Pubns MI.

Trials & Triumphs of Eva Grant. Effie M. Williams. 94p. pap. 1.00 (ISBN 0-686-29173-5). Faith Pub Hse.

Trials of Daniel. As told by Catherine Storr. (People of the Bible Ser.). (Illus.). 32p. 1985. PLB 10.65 (ISBN 0-8172-2040-2). Raintree Pubs.

Trials of Discipleship: The Story of William Clayton, a Mormon. James B. Allen. 416p. 1987. 22.95 (ISBN 0-252-01369-7). U of Ill Pr.

Triangle Has Four Sides: True-to-Life Stories Show How Teens Deal with Feelings & Problems. Phyllis R. Naylor. LC 83-72123. 128p. (Orig.). (YA) 1984. pap. 3.95 (ISBN 0-8066-2067-6, 10-6700). Augsburg.

Triangles of Fire. Torkom Saraydarian. LC 77-82155. 1977. pap. 3.00 (ISBN 0-911794-35-2). Aqua Educ.

Triangular Clause Relationship in Aelfric's Lives of Saints & in Other Works. Ed. by Ruth Waterhouse. LC 83-5399. (American Universtiy Studies IV: English Language & Literature: Vol. 1). 119p. (Orig.). 1983. pap. text ed. 12.10 (ISBN 0-8204-0007-6). P Lang Pubs.

Triangular Pattern of Life. Donna Hitz. LC 79-84851. 94p. 1980. 7.95 (ISBN 0-8022-2249-8). Philos Lib.

Tribal Religion: Religious Beliefs & Practices Among the Santals. J. Troisi. 1979. 18.00x (ISBN 0-8364-0197-2). South Asia Bks.

Tribes of Yahweh: A Sociology of the Religion of Liberated Israel, 1250-1050 B.C. Norman K. Gottwald. LC 78-24333. 944p. (Orig.). 1979. pap. 19.95 (ISBN 0-88344-499-2). Orbis Bks.

Tribulation & the Church. Chuck Smith. 64p. (Orig.). 1980. pap. 1.50 (ISBN 0-936728-01-9). Word for Today.

Tribulation Temple. Dale A. Howard. (Illus.). 80p. 1987. pap. 5.00 (ISBN 0-940517-03-5). JCMC Louisiana.

Tribulation Temple. Gordon Lindsay. (Revelation Ser.). 1.25 (ISBN 0-89985-038-3). Christ Nations.

Tribute to Gleason Archer. Ed. by Ronald Youngblood & Walter C. Kaiser, Jr. 1986. text ed. 15.95 (ISBN 0-8024-8780-7). Moody.

Trick Paper Tears with Gospel Truth, No. 10. Arnold C. Westphal. 1977. pap. 4.95 (ISBN 0-915398-10-9). Visual Evangels.

Trickster: A Study in American Indian Mythology. Paul Radin. Repr. of 1956 ed. lib. bdg. 28.75x (ISBN 0-8371-2112-4, RATT). Greenwood.

Trickster: A Study in American Indian Mythology. Paul Radin. LC 74-88986. 223p. 1972. pap. 6.95 (ISBN 0-8052-0351-6). Schocken.

Trickster in West Africa: A Study of Mythic Irony & Sacred Delight. Robert D. Pelton. LC 77-75396. (Hermeneutics: Studies in the History of Religions). 1980. 42.00x (ISBN 0-520-03477-5). U of Cal Pr.

Tried & Transfigured. Leonard Ravenhill. LC 81-71752. 144p. 1982. pap. 4.95 (ISBN 0-87123-544-7, 210544). Bethany Hse.

Tried As by Fire: Southern Baptists & the Religious Controversies of the 1920's. James J. Jr Thompson. LC 82-8056. xvi, 224p. 1982. 13.95 (ISBN 0-86554-032-2, MUP-H62). Mercer Univ Pr.

Trilogy, 3 vols. Klass Schilder. 1978. Set. 48.00 (ISBN 0-86524-126-0, 9501). Klock & Klock.

Trilogy: More than Many Sparrows, Wisdom Shall Enter & Many Are One, 3 bks. in 1 vol. Leo J. Trese. 271p. 1984. pap. 6.95 (ISBN 971-117-023-X, Pub. by Sinag-Tala Pubs Philippines). Scepter Pubs.

Trilogy of Armageddon. David. LC 85-90253. 138p. 1986. 10.95 (ISBN 0-533-06739-1). Vantage.

Trilogy on Wisdom & Celibacy. J. Massingberd Ford. 1967. 16.95x (ISBN 0-268-00285-1). U of Notre Dame Pr.

Trinidad Del Hombre. Dennis Bennett & Rita Bennett. Ed. by Andy Carrodeguas. Tr. by Franscisco Lievano from Span. Orig. Title: Trinity of Man. 224p. 1982. pap. 3.50 (ISBN 0-8297-1298-4). Life Pubs Intl.

Trinitarian & Mystical Theology of St. Symeon the New Theologian. Constance N. Tsirpanlis. 42p. 1981. pap. 2.00 (ISBN 0-686-36331-0). EO Pr.

Trinitarian Concept of God. Wade H. Horton. 1964. pap. 1.95 (ISBN 0-87148-833-7). Pathway Pr.

Trinitarian Controversy. Ed. by William G. Rusch. LC 79-8889. (Sources of Early Christian Thought Ser.). 192p. 1980. pap. 7.95 (ISBN 0-8006-1410-0, 1-1410). Fortress.

Trinity. St. Augustine. LC 63-72482. (Fathers of the Church Ser.: Vol. 45). 539p. 1963. 27.95x (ISBN 0-8132-0045-8). Cath U Pr.

Trinity. Edward H. Bickersteth. LC 59-13770. 182p. 1976. pap. 5.95 (ISBN 0-8254-2226-4). Kregel.

Trinity. Gordon H. Clark. (Trinity Papers: No. 8). 139p. (Orig.). 1985. pap. 8.95 (ISBN 0-940931-08-7). Trinity Found.

Trinity. rev. ed. Robert Crossley. 32p. 1987. pap. 0.75 (ISBN 0-87784-077-6). Inter-Varsity.

Trinity. St. Hilary Of Poitiers. LC 67-28585. (Fathers of the Church Ser.: Vol. 25). 555p. 1954. 34.95 (ISBN 0-8132-0025-3). Cath U Pr.

Trinity & Temporality. John J. O'Donnell. (Oxford Theological Monographs). 1983. 32.50x (ISBN 0-19-826722-3). Oxford U Pr.

Trinity & the Kingdom. Jurgen Moltmann. LC 80-8352. 320p. 1981. 19.45 (ISBN 0-06-065906-8, HarpR). Har-Row.

Trinity & the Religious Experience of Man: Icon, Person, Mystery. Raimundo Panikkar. LC 73-77329. pap. 24.50 (ISBN 0-317-26668-3, 2025122). Bks Demand UMI.

Trinity College, Washington, DC: The First Eighty Years, 1897-1977. Columba Mullaly. 500p. 1987. 40.00 (ISBN 0-87061-140-2); pap. 35.00 (ISBN 0-87061-139-9). Chr Classics.

Trinity in the Gospel of John. Royce G. Gruenler. 1986. pap. 9.95 (ISBN 0-8010-3806-5). Baker Bk.

Trinity in the Universe. 2nd ed. Nathan R. Wood & G. Campbell Morgan. LC 78-5483. 220p. 1984. pap. 6.95 (ISBN 0-8254-4018-1). Kregel.

Trinity, Incarnation, & Redemption: Theological Treatises. Anselm of Canterbury. (Anselm Ser.: No. 6). 1974. 9.95 (ISBN 0-88946-008-6). E Mellen.

Trinity: Is the Doctrine Biblical-Is It Important? F. Donald Harris & Ronald A. Harris. LC 77-123613. 1971. pap. 1.50 (ISBN 0-87213-310-9). Loizeaux.

Trinity of Man. Dennis Bennett & Rita Bennett. LC 79-67378. (Illus.). 1979. pap. text ed. 6.95 (ISBN 0-88270-287-4). Bridge Pub.

Trinity, or the Tri-Personal Being of God. J. A. Synan. pap. 2.95 (ISBN 0-911866-00-0). Advocate.

Trinity Story. Calvin B. Hanson. LC 83-81575. 1983. 8.95 (ISBN 0-911802-58-4). Free Church Pubns.

Trinity Sunday Revisted. Robert F. Morneau. LC 79-25097. 96p. 1980. pap. 3.50 (ISBN 0-8146-1084-6). Liturgical Pr.

Trinity Teacher Training Workshop Booklet. Larry Christenson. (Trinity Bible Ser.). 80p. 1975. pap. 2.95 (ISBN 0-87123-552-8, 240552). Bethany Hse.

Trinity University: A Record of One Hundred Years. Donald E. Everett. LC 68-24632. (Illus.). 1968. 5.00 (ISBN 0-911536-21-3). Trinity U Pr.

Trio of Talks. Gerard Smith. 44p. pap. 4.95 (ISBN 0-87462-440-1). Marquette.

Tripartite Life of St. Patrick. pap. text ed. 3.95 (ISBN 0-686-25557-7). Eastern Orthodox.

Tripartite Life of St. Patrick, with Other Documents Related to the Saint with Translation & Indexes, 2 vols. Ed. by Whitley Stokes. (Rolls Ser.: No. 89). Repr. of 1888 ed. Set. 88.00 (ISBN 0-8115-1165-0). Kraus Repr.

Triple Goddess: An Exploration of the Archetypal Feminine. Adam McClean. 1987. pap. 10.00. Phanes Pr.

Triple Secreto Del Espiritu Santo. James H. McConkey. Tr. by Beatrice Agostini from Eng. Orig. Title: Three Fold Secret of the Holy Spirit. (Span.). 112p. 1980. pap. 1.95 (ISBN 0-311-09090-7). Casa Bautista.

Triple Way. George Peck. LC 77-79824. 321p. (Orig.). 1977. pap. 2.50x (ISBN 0-87574-213-0). Pendle Hill.

Trisulti: Art & Architecture. James Hogg. (Analecta Cartusiana Ser.: No. 74-2). (Orig.). 1984. pap. 25.00 (ISBN 3-7052-0110-7, Pub. by Salzburg Studies). Longwood Pub Group.

Triumph Born of Tragedy. Andre Thornton & Al Janssen. LC 82-82812. 160p. (Orig.). 1983. pap. 4.95 (ISBN 0-89081-367-1). Harvest Hse.

Triumph of Love. Margaret L. Hess. 96p. 1987. pap. 4.95 (ISBN 0-89693-247-8). Victor Bks.

Triumph of Moralism in New England Piety: A Study of Lyman Beecher, Harriet Beecher Stowe & Henry Ward Beecher. John Goodell. 50.00 (ISBN 0-405-14113-0). Ayer Co Pubs.

Triumph of Patience: Medieval & Renaissance Studies. Ed. by Gerald J. Schiffhorst. LC 77-12732. (Illus.). 1978. 10.00 (ISBN 0-8130-0590-6). U Presses Fla.

Triumph of Satan. Harry E. Wedeck. 160p. 1974. pap. 2.95 (ISBN 0-8065-0422-6). Citadel Pr.

Triumph of Subjectivity: An Introduction to Transcendental Phenomenology. 2nd ed. Quentin Lauer. LC 58-12363. xxiv, 182p. 1978. 20.00 (ISBN 0-8232-0336-0); pap. 9.00 (ISBN 0-8232-0337-9). Fordham.

Triumph of Surrender: Responding to the Greatness of God. William Fletcher. (Christian Character Library). 190p. Date not set. 8.95 (ISBN 0-89109-538-1). NavPress.

Triumph of the Holy See: A Short History of the Papacy in the Nineteenth Century. J. Derek Holmes. LC 78-18616. (Illus.). viii, 306p. 1978. 21.95x (ISBN 0-915762-06-4). Patmos Pr.

Triumph of the Lamb. Ted Grimsrud. LC 87-409. 192p. (Orig.). 1987. pap. 14.95 (ISBN 0-8361-3438-9). Herald Pr.

Triumph of the Meek: Why Early Christianity Succeeded. LC 86-45030. (Illus.). 256p. 1986. 17.95 (ISBN 0-06-069254-5, HarpR). Har-Row.

Triumph of Trust: Habakkuk. E. Harold Henderson. (Illus.). 96p. (Orig.). 1980. pap. 2.00 (ISBN 0-89114-092-1); study guide 0.75 (ISBN 0-89114-138-3). Baptist Pub Hse.

Triumph over Silence: Women in Protestant History. Ed. by Richard L. Greaves. LC 85-961. (Contributions to the Study of Religion Ser.: No. 15). xii, 295p. 1985. lib. bdg. 35.00 (ISBN 0-313-24799-4, GTS/). Greenwood.

Triumph Over Suffering. Cleo Pursell. 1982. pap. 1.50 (ISBN 0-89265-079-6). Randall Hse.

Triumph over Temptation. Ward Patterson. (Illus.). 96p. (Orig.). 1984. pap. 2.95 (ISBN 0-87239-730-0, 39976). Standard Pub.

Triumph over Temptation: Leader's Guide. Jon Underwood. 48p. (Orig.). 1984. pap. 2.95 (ISBN 0-87239-790-4, 39977). Standard Pub.

Triumph over Terror on Flight 847. John Testrake & Dave Wimbish. (Illus.). 1987. 14.95 (ISBN 0-8007-1527-6). Revell.

Triumph Through Temptation. Pat King & Myrna Botz. (Basic Bible Study). 64p. 1978. 2.95 (ISBN 0-932305-35-0, 521012). Aglow Pubns.

Triumphant Spirit. A. K. Mozumdar. 1978. pap. 6.50 (ISBN 0-87516-261-4). De Vorss.

Triumphant Strangers: A Contemporary Look at First Peter. Robert L. Hamblin. LC 81-67206. 1982. pap. 5.95 (ISBN 0-8054-1389-8). Broadman.

Triune God. rev. ed. Clarence H. Benson. 96p. 1970. pap. text ed. 4.95 (ISBN 0-910566-09-7); Perfect bdg. instr's. guide 5.95 (ISBN 0-910566-24-0). Evang Tchr.

Triune God: A Historical Study of the Doctrine of the Trinity. Edmund J. Fortman. (Twin Brooks Ser.). 408p. 1982. pap. 10.95 (ISBN 0-8010-3505-8). Baker Bk.

Triune God: An Ecumenical Study. E. L. Mascall. (Princeton Theological Monograph: No. 10). 1986. pap. 12.90 (ISBN 0-915138-96-4). Pickwick.

Triune Identity: God According to the Gospel. Robert W. Jenson. LC 81-43091. 1982. 16.95 (ISBN 0-8006-0672-8). Fortress.

Triune Identity: God According to the Gospel. Robert W. Jenson. LC 81-43091. pap. 51.80 (2029621). Bks Demand UMI.

Triune Symbol: Persons, Process & Community. Joseph A. Bracken. (Studies in Religion: No. 1). 216p. (Orig.). 1985. lib. bdg. 25.00 (ISBN 0-8191-4440-1, College Theo Soc); pap. text ed. 11.75 (ISBN 0-8191-4441-X). U Pr of Amer.

Triunfo del Crucificado. Erich Sauer. Orig. Title: Triumph of the Crucified. (Span.). 288p. 1980. pap. 6.50 (ISBN 0-8254-1655-8). Kregel.

Trodden Road. Hubert Van Zeller. 173p. 1982. 4.00 (ISBN 0-8198-7326-8, SP0773); pap. 3.00 (ISBN 0-8198-7327-6). Dghtrs St Paul.

Troisieme et Derniere Encyclopedie Theologique (Third Series, 66 vols. Ed. by J. P. Migne. (Fr.). 47232p. Repr. of 1873 ed. lib. bdg. 5716.75x (ISBN 0-89241-203-8). Caratzas.

Troisieme Sibylle. Valentin Nikiprowetzky. (Etudes Juives: No. 9). 1970. pap. 34.40x (ISBN 0-686-21819-1). Mouton.

Troparia & Kondakia. Tr. by The Monks of New Skete. 452p. 1984. 49.50x (ISBN 0-9607924-7-3). Monks of New Skete.

Trophies of Heaven. Ron Knott. Ed. by Mary Wallace. LC 86-26649. 160p. 1986. pap. 5.95 (ISBN 0-932581-06-4). Word Aflame.

Tropi Graduales, 2 Vols. Ed. by Clemens Blume. (Illus.). Repr. of 1906 ed. 60.00 ea. Johnson Repr.

Trorenija Svatago Efrema Sirina, Vol. 1. Saint John Moschus. Tr. of Works of St. Works of Ephraim. 475p. 21.00 (ISBN 0-317-28899-7); pap. 16.00 (ISBN 0-317-28900-4). Holy Trinity.

Troubadour for the Lord: The Story of John Michael Talbot. Daniel O'Neill. 192p. 1983. 9.95 (ISBN 0-8245-0567-0). Crossroad NY.

Trouble Enough: Joseph Smith & the Book of Mormon. Ernest H. Taves. LC 84-42790. (Illus.). 280p. 1984. 20.95 (ISBN 0-87975-261-0). Prometheus Bks.

Trouble on the Mountain! Barbara Brokhoff. Ed. by Michael L. Sherer. (Orig.). 1986. pap. 6.25 (ISBN 0-89536-825-0, 6834). CSS of Ohio.

Trouble Shooter for God in China. Arthur B. Coole. (Illus.). 1976. 20.00 (ISBN 0-912706-05-8). M Akers.

Trouble with Being Born. E. M. Cioran. Tr. by Richard Howard from Fr. LC 81-51526. Orig. Title: Inconvenient d'etre Ne. Tr. of Inconvenient d'Etre Ne. 208p. 1981. pap. 5.95 (ISBN 0-394-17847-5). Seaver Bks.

Troubled Waters of Evolution. 2nd ed. Henry M. Morris. LC 82-15254. (Illus.). 225p. 1975. pap. 6.95 (ISBN 0-89051-087-3). Master Bks.

Troubles Connected with the Prayer Book of 1549. Ed. by Nicholas Pocock. 1884. 27.00 (ISBN 0-384-47030-0). Johnson Repr.

Troubleshooting Guide to Christian Education. John Cionca. LC 85-73069. 176p. 1986. pap. 7.95 (ISBN 0-89636-191-8). Accent Bks.

Troubling Problems in Medical Ethics: The Third Volume in a Series on Ethics, Humanism & Medicine, Proceedings. Ethics, Humanisms & Medicine Conference, University of Michigan, Ann Arbor, MI. 1981 & Marc D. Basson. LC 81-20723. (Progress in Clinical & Biological Research: Vol. 76). 306p. 1981. 28.00 (ISBN 0-8451-0076-9). A R Liss.

Truce of God. Rowan Williams. 128p. (Orig.). 1983. pap. 3.95 (ISBN 0-8298-0660-1). Pilgrim NY.

True & False Paths in Spiritual Investigation. Rudolf Steiner. Tr. by A. H. Parker from Ger. Tr. of Initiaten-Bewusstsein. Die wahren und die falschen Wege der geistigen Forschung. 222p. 1986. pap. 10.95 (ISBN 0-88010-135-0). Anthroposophic.

True & False Repentance. Charles G. Finney. LC 66-10576. (Charles G. Finney Memorial Library). 122p. 1975. pap. 4.50 (ISBN 0-8254-2617-0). Kregel.

True & False Universality of Christianity. Ed. by Claude Geffre & Jean-pierre Jossua. (Concilium Ser.: Vol. 135). 128p. (Orig.). 1980. pap. 5.95 (ISBN 0-8164-2277-X, HarpR). Har-Row.

True & Invisible Rosicrucian Order. Paul F. Case. LC 85-3185. (Illus.). 352p. 1985. 22.50 (ISBN 0-87728-608-6). Weiser.

True & Strange Discourse of the Travailes of Two English Pilgrimes. Henry Timberlake. LC 74-80228. (English Experience Ser.: No. 699). 28p. 1974. Repr. of 1603 ed. 3.50 (ISBN 90-221-0699-3). Walter J Johnson.

True Authorship of the New Testament. Abelard Reuchlin. 1979. pap. 4.00 (ISBN 0-930808-02-9). Vector Assocs.

True Believer. Eric Hoffer. 1966. pap. 3.95 (ISBN 0-06-080071-2, P71, PL). Har-Row.

True Bounds of Christian Freedom. 1978. pap. 5.45 (ISBN 0-85151-083-3). Banner of Truth.

True Christian Science. Hani R. Abdu. 64p. 1981. 5.00 (ISBN 0-682-49632-4). Exposition Pr FL.

True Christianity. H. A Williams. 1975. 5.95 (ISBN 0-87243-059-6). Templegate.

True Church & the Poor. Jon Sobrino. Tr. by Mathew J. O'Connell from Span. LC 84-5661. Orig. Title: Resureccion de la Verdadera Iglesia, Los Pobres Lugar Teologica de la Eclesiologia. 384p. (Orig.). 1984. pap. 13.95 (ISBN 0-88344-513-1). Orbis Bks.
True Church of Christ. Sebastian Dabovich. pap. 0.25 (ISBN 0-686-11506-6). Eastern Orthodox.
True Confession of the Faith, Which Wee Falsley Called Brownists, Doo Hold. Henry Ainsworth. LC 78-26338. (English Experience Ser.: No. 158). 24p. 1969. Repr. of 1956 ed. 7.00 (ISBN 90-221-0158-4). Walter J Johnson.
True Confessions of a Sunday School Teacher. Hawley. 1983. 3.95 (ISBN 0-88207-285-4). Victor Bks.
True Confessions: Owning up to the Secret Everybody Knows. Philip Yancey. (Christian Essentials Ser.). 48p. (Orig.). 1987. pap. 1.95 (ISBN 0-89283-324-6). Servant.
True Devotion. Louis De Montfort. LC 63-12679. 1973. 3.50 (ISBN 0-8198-0517-3); pap. 2.50. Dghtrs St Paul.
True Devotion to Mary. Eddie Doherty. pap. 2.00 (ISBN 0-910984-02-6). Montfort Pubns.
True Devotion to Mary. De Montfort Louis. Ed. by The Fathers of the Company of Mary. LC 85-50571. 215p. 1985. pap. 5.00 (ISBN 0-89555-279-5). Tan Bks Pubs.
True Devotion to the Blessed Virgin. St. Louis Marie De Montfort. 4.95 (ISBN 0-910984-49-2); pap. 3.95 (ISBN 0-910984-50-6). Montfort Pubns.
True Difference Between Christian Subjection & Unchristian Rebellion. Thomas Bilson. LC 70-38154. (English Experience Ser.: No. 434). 854p. 1972. Repr. of 1585 ed. 143.00 (ISBN 90-221-0434-6). Walter J Johnson.
True Differences Between the Regal Power & the Ecclesiastical Power. Edward Fox. LC 73-6129. (English Experience Ser.: No. 595). 108p. 1973. Repr. of 1548 ed. 9.50 (ISBN 90-221-0595-4). Walter J Johnson.
True Discipleship. expanded ed. William MacDonald. pap. 3.25 (ISBN 0-937396-50-8). Walterick Pubs.
True Discipleship. William MacDonald. pap. 2.50 (ISBN 0-937396-49-4). Walterick Pubs.
True Evangelism. Lewis S. Chafer. pap. 5.95 (ISBN 0-310-22381-4, 6312P). Zondervan.
True Fellowship. Jerry Bridges. 150p. 1987. pap. 3.95 (ISBN 0-89109-175-0). NavPress.
True Gospel of Salvation Revealed Anew by Jesus, 3 Vols. James E. Padgett. Vol. I, III. pap. 7.50 ea. (ISBN 0-686-37147-X); Vols. II, III. pap. 9.00 ea. New Age Min Spiritualist.
True Gospel vs. Social Activism. Lit-Sen Chang. 1976. pap. 0.60 (ISBN 0-87552-134-7). Presby & Reformed.
True History of the Church of Scotland: From the Beginnings of the Reform to the End of the Reign of King James VI, 8 vols. David Calderwood. Ed. by Thomas Thomson. LC 83-45577. Date not set. Repr. of 1842 ed. Set. 525.00 (ISBN 0-404-19894-5). AMS Pr.
True Humanism. Jacques Maritain. Tr. by M. R. Adamson. LC 71-114888. (Select Bibliographies Reprint Ser). 1938. 22.00 (ISBN 0-8369-5292-8). Ayer Co Pubs.
True Humanism. 3rd ed. Jacques Maritain. Tr. by Margot Adamson. Repr. of 1941 ed. lib. bdg. 35.00x (ISBN 0-8371-2902-8, MAHU). Greenwood.
True Intellectual System of the Universe, 2 vols. Ralph Cudworth. Ed. by Rene Wellek. LC 75-11213. (British Philosophers & Theologians of the 17th & 18th Centuries Ser.: Vol. 16). 1978. Repr. of 1678 ed. Set. lib. bdg. 101.00 (ISBN 0-8240-1767-6). Garland Pub.
True Joy from Assisi. Raphael Brown. 276p. 1978. 8.95 (ISBN 0-8199-0688-3). Franciscan Herald.
True Joy of Positive Living. Norman Vincent Peale. 480p. 1985. pap. 16.95 (ISBN 0-8027-2503-1). Walker & Co.
True Life. Lewis Foster. LC 77-83656. 96p. (Orig.). 1978. pap. 2.25 (ISBN 0-87239-192-2, 40047). Standard Pub.
True Life of Jesus of Nazareth - the Confessions of St. Paul. Alexander Smyth. (Illus.). 1968. 7.95 (ISBN 0-932642-15-2); pap. write for info. (ISBN 0-932642-56-X). Unarius Pubns.
True Love Story. G. A. Holland. Date not set. 14.95 (ISBN 0-533-06799-5). Vantage.
True Meaning of Christ's Teaching, Vol. 215. Omraam M. Aivanhov. (Izvor Collection Ser.). (Illus.). 186p. (Orig.). 1984. pap. 4.95 (ISBN 2-85566-322-9). Prosveta USA.
True Meaning of the Lord of Heaven. Matteo Ricci. Tr. by Douglas Lancashire & Peter Hu Kuo-chen. Ed. by Edward J. Malatesta. LC 84-80944. (Jesuit Primary Sources in English Translations Series I: No. 6). (Eng. & Chinese., Illus.). 300p. 1985. 39.00 (ISBN 0-912422-78-5); smyth sewn 34.00 (ISBN 0-912422-77-7). Inst Jesuit.
True Organization of the New Church. Charles J. Hempel. LC 40-30032. Repr. of 1848 ed. 31.50 (ISBN 0-404-08464-8). AMS Pr.
True Path. Florence Widutis. (Illus.). 1979. pap. 5.95 (ISBN 0-87516-266-5). De Vorss.
True Prayer: An Invitation to Christian Spirituality. Kenneth Leech. LC 80-8358. 208p. 1981. 12.00 (ISBN 0-06-065227-6, HarpR). Har-Row.
True Prayer: An Invitation to Christian Spirituality. Kenneth Leech. LC 80-8358. 208p. 1986. pap. 7.95 (ISBN 0-06-065232-2, HarpR). Har-Row.
True Psychology. Swami Abhedanenda. 1987. 6.50 (ISBN 0-87481-613-0, Pub. by Ramakrishna Math Madras India). Vedanta Pr.
True Relation of the Life & Death of the Right Reverend Father in God William Bedell, Lord Bishop of Kilmore in Ireland. William Bedell. Ed. by Thomas W. Jones. Repr. of 1872 ed. 27.00 (ISBN 0-384-03740-2). Johnson Repr.
True Religion Explained & Defended. Hugo Grotius. Tr. by F. Coventry. LC 72-201. (English Experience Ser.: No. 318). 350p. 1971. Repr. of 1632 ed. 28.00 (ISBN 90-221-0318-8). Walter J Johnson.
True Resurrection. Harry A. Williams. 192p. 1983. pap. 7.95 (ISBN 0-87243-115-0). Templegate.
True Riches. Joseph L. Palotta. 319p. (Orig.). 1985. pap. 8.95 (ISBN 0-9604852-2-8). Revelation Hse.
True Sage. Bhagwan Shree Rajneesh. Ed. by Swami Christ Chaitanya. LC 83-183323. (Hasids Ser.). (Illus.). 410p. (Orig.). 1976. 16.50 (ISBN 0-88050-159-6). Chidvilas Found.
True Saints. Charles G. Finney. LC 66-24880. (Charles G. Finney Memorial Library). 120p. 1975. pap. 4.50 (ISBN 0-8254-2622-7). Kregel.
True Service. Harold Cooper. (Illus.). 111p. 1978. pap. text ed. 1.50 (ISBN 0-89114-081-6); P. 55. tchrs. ed. 1.25 (ISBN 0-89114-082-4). Baptist Pub Hse.
True Spirituality. Francis Schaeffer. 1972. pap. 6.95 (ISBN 0-8423-7351-9). Tyndale.
True Submission. Charles G. Finney. LC 66-24881. (Charles G. Finney Memorial Library). 128p. 1975. pap. 4.50 (ISBN 0-8254-2618-9). Kregel.
True Surrender & Christian Community of Goods, 1521-1578. Peter Walpot. 1957. pap. 4.00 (ISBN 0-87486-205-1). Plough.
True Vine. Andrew Murray. (Andrew Murray Ser.). pap. 3.50 (ISBN 0-8024-8798-X). Moody.
True Vine. Andrew Murray. 112p. 1983. pap. text ed. 3.50 (ISBN 0-88368-118-8). Whitaker Hse.
True Wilderness. H. A. Williams. (Crossroad Paperback Ser.). 160p. 1982. pap. 5.95 (ISBN 0-8245-0470-4). Crossroad NY.
True Worship. John MacArthur, Jr. (John MacArthur's Bible Studies). 1985. pap. 3.50 (ISBN 0-8024-5108-X). Moody.
True Yoga. Zom. 4.95 (ISBN 0-8065-0336-X). Citadel Pr.
Trujillo: A Jewish Community in Extremadura on the Eve of Expulsion from Spain. Haim Beinart. (Hispania Judaica Ser.: No. 2). 372p. 1980. text ed. 22.50x (ISBN 965-223-349-8, Pub. by Magnes Pr Israel). Humanities.
Truly Human-Truly Divine: Christological Language & the Gospel Form. W. Eugene Boring. Ed. by Herbert Lambert. LC 84-11382. 144p. 1984. pap. 11.95 (ISBN 0-8272-3625-5). CBP.
Truman, American Jewry, & Israel, 1945-1948. Zvi Ganin. 238p. 1979. text ed. 34.50x (ISBN 0-8419-0401-4); pap. 22.50 (ISBN 0-8419-0497-9). Holmes & Meier.
Trumpet in Darkness: Preaching to Mourners. Robert Hughes. LC 85-47719. (Fortress Resources for Preaching Ser.). 112p. 1985. pap. 5.95 (ISBN 0-8006-1141-1). Fortress.
Trumpet Judgments. Date not set. pap. 0.95 (ISBN 0-937408-10-7). GMI Pubns Inc.
Trumpet Shall Sound: A Study of Cargo Cults in Melanesia. Peter Worsley. LC 67-26995. (Illus.). 1968. pap. 8.95 (ISBN 0-8052-0156-4). Schocken.
Trumpeter of God: A Biography of John Knox. W. Stanford Reid. 372p. 1982. pap. 8.95 (ISBN 0-8010-7708-7). Baker Bk.
Trust. Robert Merchant. (Literacy Volunteers of America Readers Ser.). 32p. (Orig.). 1983. pap. 1.95 (ISBN 0-8428-9618-X). Cambridge Bk.
Trust Doctrines in Church Controversies. Dallin H. Oaks. LC 83-25058. xiv, 125p. 1984. 13.95x (ISBN 0-86554-104-3, MUP/H96). Mercer Univ Pr.
Trust Is the Key. Roxanne Sumners. (Illus.). 52p. (Orig.). 1983. pap. 4.95 (ISBN 0-913627-00-3). Agadir Pr.
Trust Yourself to Life. Clara M. Codd. LC 75-4245. 116p. 1975. pap. 1.75 (ISBN 0-8356-0464-0, Quest). Theos Pub Hse.
Trustful Surrender to Divine Providence: The Secret of Peace & Happiness. Jean B. Saint-Jure & Claude De La Colombiere. LC 83-50252. 139p. 1983. pap. 3.00 (ISBN 0-89555-216-7). TAN Bks Pubs.
Trusting: Theory & Practice. Carolyn Gratton. LC 82-9760. 240p. 1982. 17.50 (ISBN 0-8245-0496-8). Crossroad NY.
Trusting: Theory & Practice. Carolyn Gratton. LC 82-9760. 256p. 1983. pap. 9.95 (ISBN 0-8245-0548-4). Crossroad NY.
Trusting Together in God. Myron Chartier & Jan Chartier. LC 83-73132. (Illus.). 172p. (Orig.). 1984. pap. 6.95 (ISBN 0-87029-193-9, 20285-3). Abbey.
Trustworthiness of Religious Experience. D. E. Trueblood. LC 78-24656. 1979. pap. 2.45 (ISBN 0-913408-45-X). Friends United.
Truth. Joel S. Goldsmith. 1972. pap. 1.00 (ISBN 0-87516-141-3). De Vorss.
Truth: A Psychological Curse. Robert Firestone & Joyce Catlett. 234p. 1981. 13.95 (ISBN 0-02-538380-9). Macmillan.
Truth about Armageddon. William S. LaSor. 240p. 1987. pap. 6.95 (ISBN 0-8010-5637-3). Baker Bk.
Truth about Astral Projection. Llewellyn Staff. Ed. by Carl L. Weschcke. (Educational Guide Ser.). 32p. (Orig.). 1983. pap. 2.00 (ISBN 0-87542-350-7, L-350). Llewellyn Pubns.
Truth about Black Biblical Hebrew Israelites (Jews) Ella J. Hughley. (Orig.). 1982. pap. 5.00 (ISBN 0-9605150-1-1). Hughley Pubns.
Truth about Christmas. Ralph Becker. pap. 0.50 (ISBN 0-685-41826-X). Reiner.
Truth about Evolution & the Bible. Harriette Curtiss & F. Homer. 1928. 5.50 (ISBN 0-87516-308-4). De Vorss.
Truth about Hitler & the Roman Catholic Church. A. Ratcliffe. 1982. lib. bdg. 59.95 (ISBN 0-87700-362-9). Revisionist Pr.
Truth about Santa Claus. James C. Giblin. LC 85-47541. (Illus.). 96p. 1985. 11.70 (ISBN 0-690-04483-6, Crowell Jr Bks); PLB 11.89 (ISBN 0-690-04484-4). HarpJ.
Truth about Sin: What Does the Bible Say? William T. Bruner. 1977. 2.00 (ISBN 0-9606566-1-8). Bruner.
Truth about the Lie. David R. Mains. 128p. 1987. pap. 4.95 (ISBN 0-310-34831-5). Zondervan.
Truth about the Man Behind the Book That Sparked the War Between the States. Frances Cavanah. LC 75-11566. (Illus.). 188p. 1975. 7.95 (ISBN 0-664-32572-6). Westminster.
Truth about the Russian Church Abroad. M. Rodzianko. Tr. by Michael P. Hilko from Rus. LC 74-29321. (Illus.). 48p. (Orig.). 1975. pap. 1.50 (ISBN 0-88465-004-9). Holy Trinity.
Truth about Witchcraft. The Llewellyn Publications Staff. Ed. by Phyllis Galde. (Educational Guide Ser.). 32p. 1987. pap. 2.00 (ISBN 0-87542-357-4). Llewellyn Pubns.
Truth & Compassion: Essays on Judaism & Religion in Memory of Rabbi Dr. Solomon Frank, Vol. 12. Ed. by Howard Joseph et al. 217p. 1983. pap. text ed. 13.95x (ISBN 0-919812-17-1, Pub. by Wilfrid Laurier Canada). Humanities.
Truth & Health. Fannie B. James. 1970. 8.95 (ISBN 0-686-24356-0). Divine Sci Fed.
Truth & Knowledge: Introduction to "Philosophy of Spiritual Activity", Vol. 14. 2nd ed. Rudolf Steiner. Ed. by Paul M. Allen. Tr. by Rita Stebbing from Ger. LC 81-51762. (Major Writings of Rudolf Steiner in English Translation Ser.). 112p. 1981. Repr. of 1963 ed. lib. bdg. 10.00 (ISBN 0-89345-008-1, Spiritual Sci Lib). Garber Comm.
Truth & Light: Brief Explanations. M. R. Bawa Muhaiyaddeen. LC 74-76219. (Illus.). 144p. 1974. pap. 3.95 (ISBN 0-914390-04-X). Fellowship Pr PA.
Truth & Method. Hans-Georg Gadamer. 516p. 1982. pap. 16.95x (ISBN 0-8264-0431-6). Continuum.
Truth & the Disputed Questions on Truth. Saint Thomas Aquinas. (Illus.). 107p. 1987. 117.50 (ISBN 0-89266-582-3). Am Classical Coll Pr.
Truth & the Historicity of Man. Ed. by George F. McLean. (Proceedings of the American Catholic Philosophical Association: Vol. 43). 1969. pap. 15.00 (ISBN 0-918090-03-2). Am Cath Philo.
Truth & Tradition in Chinese Buddhism. Karl Reichelt. 59.95 (ISBN 0-8490-1234-1). Gordon Pr.
Truth-Antidote for Error. Anthony D. Palma. LC 76-52177. (Radiant Life Ser.). 128p. 1977. pap. 2.50 (ISBN 0-88243-904-9, 02-0904); teacher's ed 3.95 (ISBN 0-88243-174-9, 32-0174). Gospel Pub.
Truth, Beauty & Goodness. Rudolf Steiner. 1986. pap. 1.50 (ISBN 0-916786-86-2). St George Bk Serv.
Truth Beyond Words: Problems & Prospects for Anglican-Roman Catholic Unity. Paul Avis. 142p. (Orig.). 1985. pap. 7.95 (ISBN 0-936384-26-3). Cowley Pubns.
Truth for Life Bible Studies. Lela Birky. pap. write for info (ISBN 0-686-15481-9). Rod & Staff.
Truth in Crisis: The Controversy in the Southern Baptist Convention. James C. Hefley. LC 86-70962. 208p. 1986. pap. 7.95 (ISBN 0-937969-00-1). Criterion Pubns.
Truth Is Immortal: The Story of Baptists in Europe. Irwin Barnes. 127p. 1950. 2.95 (ISBN 0-87921-015-X); pap. 1.95 (ISBN 0-87921-019-2). Attic Pr.
Truth Is My Sword. Bo Hi Pak. LC 78-74661. 110p. (Orig.). 1978. pap. 2.00 (ISBN 0-318-03063-2). HSA Pubns.
Truth Is Symphonic: Aspects of Christian Pluralism. Hans U. Von Balthasar. Tr. by Graham Harrison from Ger. Tr. of Die Warheit Ist Symphonisch. 192p. 1987. pap. 9.95 (ISBN 0-89870-141-4). Ignatius Pr.
Truth Is Two-Eyed. John A. Robinson. LC 79-25774. 174p. 1980. pap. 6.95 (ISBN 0-664-24316-9). Westminster.
Truth, Knowledge & Modality: Philosophical Papers, Vol. III. G. H. Von Wright. 248p. 1985. 24.95x (ISBN 0-631-13367-4). Basil Blackwell.
Truth of Christmas Beyond the Myths: The Gospel of the Infancy of Christ. Rene Laurentin. (Studies in Scripture: Vol. III). 1986. pap. 29.95 (ISBN 0-932506-34-8). St Bedes Pubns.
Truth of Creation. T. W. Dow. LC 67-31148. (Illus.). 1968. 5.00 (ISBN 0-910340-04-8). Celestial Pr.
Truth of the Gospel: An Exposition of Galatians. Gerhard Ebeling. LC 84-47918. 288p. 1985. 19.95 (ISBN 0-8006-0728-7, 1-728). Fortress.
Truth of Value. Paul Ramsey. 139p. 1985. text ed. 15.00x (ISBN 0-391-03058-2). Humanities.
Truth or Tradition: What Is the Gospel? Maralene Wesner & Miles Wesner. LC 86-71139. 100p. 1986. pap. 4.95 (ISBN 0-936715-03-0). Diversity Okla.
Truth Seekers. Myrtle A. Pohle. (Daybreak Ser.). 144p. 1983. pap. 4.95 (ISBN 0-8163-0529-3). Pacific Pr Pub Assn.
Truth Shall Make You Free: An Inquiry into the Legend of God. Robert A. Steiner. LC 80-80646. (Illus.). 56p. (Orig.). 1980. pap. 3.95 (ISBN 0-9604044-0-6). Penseur Pr.
Truth Shall Triumph. 9th ed. Ralph V. Reynolds. 111p. 1983. pap. 2.95 (ISBN 0-912315-07-5). Word Aflame.
Truth, the Millennium, & the Battle of Armageddon. Leslie G. Thomas. 1979. pap. 2.50 (ISBN 0-89225-188-3). Gospel Advocate.
Truth the Poet Sings. Illus. by Alan W. Peterson. (Illus.). 220p. 1984. 5.95 (ISBN 0-87159-160-X). Unity School.
Truth to Tell. Glenn Clairmonte. LC 78-66006. 1979. 5.95 (ISBN 0-87159-155-3). Unity School.
Truth Will Make You Free. Mary L. Eaves. LC 83-90380. 59p. 1985. 7.95 (ISBN 0-533-05883-X). Vantage.
Truthfulness & Tragedy: Further Investigations in Christian Ethics. Stanley Hauerwas & Richard Bondi. LC 76-30425. 1977. 18.95x (ISBN 0-268-01831-6); pap. text ed. 9.95 (ISBN 0-268-01832-4). U of Notre Dame Pr.
Truths of Love. Javad Nurbakhsh. Tr. by Leonard Lewisohn. 1982. pap. 6.00x (ISBN 0-933546-08-4). KhaniQahi Nimatullahi-Sufi.
Truths That Transform. D. James Kennedy. 160p. 1974. power bks. 5.95 (ISBN 0-8007-5148-5). Revell.
Truths to Live by. facsimile ed. John E. Ross. LC 72-37834. (Essay Index Reprint Ser). Repr. of 1929 ed. 19.00 (ISBN 0-8369-2622-6). Ayer Co Pubs.
Try God, You'll Like Him. Katie Tonn. (Uplook Ser.). 1975. pap. 0.99 (ISBN 0-8163-0178-6, 20340-6). Pacific Pr Pub Assn.
Try This One... Too. Ed. by Lee Sparks. LC 82-81331. (Illus.). 80p. (Orig.). 1982. pap. 5.95 (ISBN 0-936664-05-3). Group Bks.
Tryal of the Witnesses of the Resurrection of Jesus. 2nd ed. Thomas Sherlock. Ed. by Rene Wellek. Bd. with Use & Extent of Prophecy. LC 75-25131. (British Philosophers & Theologians of the 17th & 18th Centuries Ser.). 348p. 1979. lib. bdg. 51.00 (ISBN 0-8240-1761-7). Garland Pub.
Tryall of Private Devotions. Henry Burton. LC 77-6863. (English Experience Ser.: No. 856). 1977. Repr. of 1628 ed. lib. bdg. 10.50 (ISBN 90-221-0856-2). Walter J Johnson.
Trying to Be a Christian. W. Norman Pittenger. LC 72-1567. 128p. 1972. 4.95 (ISBN 0-8298-0237-1). Pilgrim NY.
Tsa'ar Ba'ale Hayim. 1976. 6.95 (ISBN 0-87306-127-6). Feldheim.
Tsar Nicholas I & the Jews: The Transformation of Jewish Society in Russia, 1825-1855. Michael Stanislawski. (Illus.). 272p. 1983. 18.95 (ISBN 0-8276-0216-2, 497). Jewish Pubns.
Tserkov' Boga Ahivago, Stolp i Utverzhdjenije Istini. Archpriest Kyrill Zaits. Tr. of Church of the Living God, Piller & Affirmation of Truth. 92p. 1956. pap. 2.00 (ISBN 0-317-29113-0). Holy Trinity.
Tserkov', Rus' i Rim. N. N. Voieivkov. Tr. of Church, Russia & Rome. 512p. 1983. text ed. 25.00 (ISBN 0-88465-016-2); pap. text ed. 20.00 (ISBN 0-88465-015-4). Holy Trinity.

Tserkovnij Ustav. Alexander Svirelin. Tr. of Church Services. 143p. 1981. pap. text ed. 6.00 (ISBN 0-317-30282-5). Holy Trinity.

Tserkovno-Pjevcheskiji Sbornik, 5 Vols. Incl. Vol. 1. Vsjenoshchnoje Bdjenije. Tr. of All Night Vigil. 394p. 27.00 (ISBN 0-317-30454-2); Vol. 2. Bozhestvjennaja Liturgija (Nachjalo) Tr. of Divine Liturgy (Beginning) 381p. Pt. 1. 26.00 (ISBN 0-317-30455-0); Vol. 2. Bozhestvjennaja Liturgija (Konjets) Tr. of Divine Liturgy (End) 621p. Pt. 2. 33.00 (ISBN 0-317-30456-9); Vol. 3. Triod' Postnaja. Tr. of Lenten Triodion. 532p. Pt. 1. 31.00 (ISBN 0-317-30457-7); Vol. 3. Strastnaja Sedmitsa. Tr. of Passion Week. 1059p. Pt. 2. 40.00 (ISBN 0-317-30458-5); Vol. 4. Triod' Tsvjetnaja. Tr. of Pentacostarion. 680p. 33.00 (ISBN 0-317-30459-3); Vol. 5. Oktojikh. Tr. of Octoechos. 421p. 26.00 (ISBN 0-317-30460-7). Tr. of Collection of Sacred Hymns. 216.00 set (ISBN 0-317-30453-4). Holy Trinity.

Tsese-Ma'Heone-Nemeototse: Cheyenne Spiritual Songs. Ed. by David Graber. LC 82-83401. (Eng. & Cheyenne.). 227p. 1982. 29.95 (ISBN 0-87303-078-8). Faith & Life.

Tsewa'a Gift: Magic & Meaning in an Amazonian Society. Michael F. Brown. LC 85-40401. (Ethnographic Inquiry Ser.). (Illus.). 220p. 1986. 19.95x (ISBN 0-87474-294-3, BRTG). Smithsonian.

Tsimshian Mythology Based on Texts Recorded by Henry W. Tate. Franz Boas. (Landmarks in Anthropology Ser.). (Illus.). Repr. of 1916 ed. 60.00 (ISBN 0-384-04880-3). Johnson Repr.

TSOHAR. Rabbi Nachman of Breslov. Tr. by Avraham Greenbaum from Hebrew. 64p. (Orig.). 1986. pap. text ed. 1.50 (ISBN 0-930213-26-2). Breslov Res Inst.

Tu Bishvat. Norma Simon. (Festival Series of Picture Story Books). (Illus.). 1961. plastic cover 4.50 (ISBN 0-8381-0709-5). United Syn Bk.

Tu Fe. Ed. by John McPhee. Tr. by Olimpia Diaz. (Span.). (YA) 1980. pap. 1.95 (ISBN 0-89243-124-5, 48290). Liguori Pubns.

Tu Puedes! James D. Freeman. LC 82-70490. 256p. 1982. 5.95 (ISBN 0-87159-158-8). Unity School.

Tuamotuan Religion. J. F. Stimson. (BMB Ser.). Repr. of 1933 ed. 21.00 (ISBN 0-527-02209-8). Kraus Repr.

Tuamotuan Religious Structures & Ceremonies. K. P. Emory. (BMB Ser.). Repr. of 1947 ed. 14.00 (ISBN 0-527-02299-3). Kraus Repr.

Tubinger Predigten. Johann Von Staupitz. (Ger.). 34.00 (ISBN 0-384-57712-1); pap. 28.00 (ISBN 0-384-57711-3). Johnson Repr.

Tudor Books of Private Devotion. Helen C. White. LC 78-21661. (Illus.). 1979. Repr. of 1951 ed. lib. bdg. 24.75x (ISBN 0-313-21063-2, WHTB). Greenwood.

Tudor Books of Saints & Martyrs. Helen C. White. LC 63-13741. pap. 73.00 (ISBN 0-317-07866-6, 2004164). Bks Demand UMI.

Tudor Church Music. Ed. by P. C. Buck & E. H. Fellowes. Incl. Vol. 1. John Taverner - Part One (ISBN 0-8450-1851-5); Vol. 2. William Byrd - English Church Music, Part One (ISBN 0-8450-1852-3); Vol. 3. John Tavernen - Part Two (ISBN 0-8450-1853-1); Vol. 4. Orlando Gibbons (ISBN 0-8450-1854-X); Vol. 5. Robert White (ISBN 0-8450-1855-8); Vol. 6. Thomas Tallis (ISBN 0-8450-1856-6); Vol. 7. William Byrd (ISBN 0-8450-1857-4); Vol. 8. Thomas Tomkins (ISBN 0-8450-1858-2); Vol. 9 (ISBN 0-8450-1859-0); Vol. 10. Hugh Aston & John Marbeck (ISBN 0-8450-1860-4). 1963. Repr. of 1922 ed. 750.00x set (ISBN 0-8450-1850-7); 85.00x ea.; appendix 50.00x (ISBN 0-8450-1861-2). Broude.

Tudor Church Music. Denis Stevens. LC 73-4335. (Music Reprint Ser.). 144p. 1973. Repr. of 1955 ed. lib. bdg. 25.00 (ISBN 0-306-70579-6). Da Capo.

Tudor Puritanism: A Chapter in the History of Idealism. Marshall M. Knappen. LC 39-10082. 1965. pap. 3.45x (ISBN 0-226-44627-1, P194, Phoen). U of Chicago Pr.

Tughluq Dynasty. A. M. Husain. (Illus.). 1976. Repr. of 1935 ed. 30.00x (ISBN 0-89684-461-7). Orient Bk Dist.

Tukarama, His Person & His Religion: A Relio-Historical, Phenomenological & Typological Enquiry. Ajit Lokhande. (European University Studies: Series 20, Philosophy: Vol. 22). 210p. 1976. 23.50 (ISBN 3-261-02009-1). P Lang Pubs.

Tulip: Five Points of Calvinism. Duane E. Spencer. LC 78-73445. (Direction Bks). pap. 2.95 (ISBN 0-8010-8161-0). Baker Bk.

Tumbler of Our Lady & Other Miracles. Gautier De Coinci. Tr. by A. Kemp-Welch. (Medieval Library). (Illus.). Repr. of 1926 ed. 17.50x (ISBN 0-8154-0076-4). Cooper Sq.

Tumultuous Years - Schwenkfelder Chronicles Fifteen Eighty to Seventeen Fifty: The Reports of Martin John, Jr. & Balthazar Hoffmann. L. Allen Viehmeyer. 157p. (Orig.). 1980. pap. write for info. (ISBN 0-935980-00-8). Schwenkfelder Lib.

Tune In. Ed. by Herman C. Ahrens, Jr. LC 68-54031. (Illus.). 1968. pap. 3.95 (ISBN 0-8298-0138-3). Pilgrim NY.

T'ung Shu. Tr. by Martin Palmer from Chinese. LC 85-2520. (Illus.). 240p. 1986. pap. 7.95 (ISBN 0-87773-346-5, 74221-4, Dist. by Random). Shambhala Pubns.

Turbulence over the Middle East: Israel & the Nations in Confrontation & the Coming Kingdom of Peace on Earth. Louis Goldberg. (Illus.). 320p. 1982. pap. 7.95 (ISBN 0-87213-240-4). Loizeaux.

Turin Fragments of Tyconius' Commentary on Revelation. Ed. by F. Lo Bue. (Texts & Studies, N. S.: Vol. 7). Repr. of 1963 ed. 28.00 (ISBN 0-8115-1720-9). Kraus Repr.

Turkey: Ecumenical Pilgrimage. Pope John Paul II. 3.50 (ISBN 0-8198-0650-1); pap. 2.50 (ISBN 0-8198-0651-X). Dghtrs St Paul.

Turkeys, Pilgrims, & Indian Corn: The Story of the Thanksgiving Symbols. Edna Barth. LC 75-4703. (Illus.). 96p. 1975. 12.95 (ISBN 0-395-28846-0, Clarion). HM.

Turkish Transformation: A Study in Social & Religious Development. Henry E. Allen. LC 68-57588. (Illus.). 1968. Repr. of 1935 ed. lib. bdg. 22.50x (ISBN 0-8371-0284-7, ALTT). Greenwood.

Turn Again to Life. Abraham Schmitt. LC 86-33581. 136p. (Orig.). 1987. pap. 8.95 (ISBN 0-8361-3436-2). Herald Pr.

Turn Around One Hundred Times. Ian Hickingbotham. 1985. 21.00x (ISBN 0-7223-1917-7, Pub. by A H Stockwell England). State Mutual Bk.

Turn Back the Night: A Christian Response to Popular Culture. Stephen R. Lawhead. LC 84-72005. 192p. (Orig.). 1985. pap. 6.95 (ISBN 0-89107-340-X, Crossway Bks). Good News.

Turn Home Again. Herbert Harker. 245p. 1984. 6.95 (ISBN 0-934126-57-7). Randall Bk Co.

Turn off Your Age. Elsye Birkinshaw. LC 79-27693. 1980. pap. 7.95 (ISBN 0-912800-77-1). Woodbridge Pr.

Turn on, Tune in & Drop the Lot. Bhagwan Shree Rajneesh. Ed. by Ma Prem Maneesha. (Initiation Talks Ser.). (Illus.). 312p. (Orig.). 1980. pap. 18.95 (ISBN 0-88050-660-1). Chidvilas Found.

Turn to the South: Essays on Southern Jewry. Ed. by Nathan M. Kaganoff & Melvin I. Urofsky. LC 78-9306. 205p. 1979. 10.95x (ISBN 0-8139-0742-X). U Pr of Va.

Turn Toward Life: The Bible & Peacemaking. Jorg Zink. Tr. by Victoria Rhodin from Ger. LC 84-48709. 128p. 1985. pap. 7.95 (ISBN 0-8006-1829-7, 1-1829). Fortress.

Turn Us, Lord. Robert Campbell & Michael Sherer. 1985. 2.95 (ISBN 0-89536-728-9, 5812). CSS of Ohio.

Turnabout. Meir Malbim. Tr. by Mendel Weinbach. 1976. 5.95 (ISBN 0-87306-030-X). Feldheim.

Turned On: A Cassette Programmed Multi-Media Design for the Training of Religious Teachers, Based on an Exploration of Youth Culture. kit 49.95 (ISBN 0-02-640530-X, 64053); coordinator's handbk only 5.40 (ISBN 0-02-640540-7); student-teacher workbk. only 3.00 (ISBN 0-02-640520-2). Benziger Pub Co.

Turner & the Bible. Mordechai Omer. 48p. 1981. 5.50x (ISBN 0-900090-79-0, Pub. by Ashmolean Museum). State Mutual Bk.

Turner & the Bible. Mordechai Omer. (Illus.). 48p. (Orig.). 1981. pap. 7.75 (ISBN 0-900090-90-1, Pub. by Ashmolean Mus). Longwood Pub Group.

Turning East: The Promise & Peril of the New Orientalism. Harvey Cox. 1979. pap. 7.95 (ISBN 0-671-24405-1, Touchstone Bks). S&S.

Turning Fear to Hope: Help for Marrages Troubled by Abuse. Holly W. Green. 228p. (Orig.). 1984. pap. 5.95 (ISBN 0-8407-5937-1). Nelson.

Turning Hopeless Situations Around. Kenneth E. Hagin. 1981. pap. 1.00 (ISBN 0-89276-022-2). Hagin Ministries.

Turning Point II. (Outreach Literature Ser.). 32p. (Orig.). 1986. pap. 0.45 (ISBN 0-932305-42-3, 612002). Aglow Pubns.

Turning Point: Zionism & Reform Judaism. Howard Greenstein. LC 81-8996. (Brown BJS Ser.). 1981. pap. 12.00 (ISBN 0-89130-512-2, 140012). Scholars Pr GA.

Turning Points. Martha Smock. LC 75-41954. 1976. 5.95 (ISBN 0-87159-156-1). Unity School.

Turning Points. Jim Smoke. 192p. (Orig.). 1985. pap. 5.95 (ISBN 0-89081-484-8). Harvest Hse.

Turning Points in Religious Life. Ed. by Carol Quigley. LC 85-45565. 180p. (Orig.). 1987. pap. 8.95 (ISBN 0-89453-545-5). M Glazier.

Turning: Reflections on the Experience of Conversion. Emilie Griffin. LC 79-6652. 224p. 1982. 8.95 (ISBN 0-385-15823-8, Im); pap. 4.50 (ISBN 0-385-17892-1). Doubleday.

Turning Road. Ralph Kibildis. 112p. (Orig.). 1981. 2.95 (ISBN 0-914544-34-9). Living Flame Pr.

Turning Sorrow into Song. Jan Carpenter. 154p. 1986. 9.95 (ISBN 0-89066-081-6). World Wide Pubs.

Turning to Christ: A Theology of Renewal & Evangelization. Urban T. Holmes, III. 240p. (Orig.). 1981. pap. 8.95 (ISBN 0-8164-2289-3, HarpR). Har-Row.

Turning to God. William Barclay. 1978. pap. 3.25x (ISBN 0-7152-0388-6). Outlook.

Turning to God. Tuvya Zaretsky. 32p. (Orig.). 1984. pap. 0.75 (ISBN 0-87784-064-4). Inter-Varsity.

Turning Your Stress into Strength. Robert H. Schuller. LC 77-88865. 144p. 1978. pap. 4.95 (ISBN 0-89081-113-X). Harvest Hse.

Tut-Ankh-Amun-& His Friends. Cyril Aldred. pap. 2.95 (ISBN 0-88388-043-1). Bellerophon Bk.

Tutankhamen. Christiane Desroches-Noblecourt. LC 63-15145. 312p. 1976. pap. 8.95 (ISBN 0-8212-0695-8, 857017). NYGS.

Tutankhamen: Amenism, Atenism & Egyptain Monotheism. E. Wallis Budge. LC 79-160615. (Illus.). Repr. of 1923 ed. 12.75 (ISBN 0-405-08323-8, Blom Pubns). Ayer Co Pubs.

Tutankhamen & Other Essays. Arthur Weigall. LC 73-115210. 1971. Repr. of 1924 ed. 24.50x (ISBN 0-8046-1103-3, Pub by Kennikat). Assoc Faculty Pr.

TV, Movies & Morality: A Guide for Catholics. John Butler. LC 84-60753. 144p. 1984. pap. 6.95 (ISBN 0-87973-602-X, 602). Our Sunday Visitor.

TV News & the Dominant Culture. John Corry. Ed. by Media Institute Staff. LC 86-60785. (Media in Society Ser.). 54p. (Orig.). 1986. pap. 12.95 (ISBN 0-937790-34-6). Media Inst.

Twas Seeding Time. John L. Ruth. LC 76-41475. 220p. 1976. pap. 5.95 (ISBN 0-8361-1800-6). Herald Pr.

Twelve. Leslie Flynn. 156p. 1982. pap. 5.95 (ISBN 0-88207-310-9). Victor Bks.

Twelve Becoming, Biographies of Mennonite Disciples from the Sixteenth to the Twentieth Century. Cornelius J. Dyck. LC 73-75174. 1973. pap. 4.50 (ISBN 0-87303-865-7). Faith & Life.

Twelve Becoming: Leader's Guide for Juniors. new ed. Bertha F. Harder. (Illus.). 61p. 1973. pap. 2.00x (ISBN 0-87303-866-5). Faith & Life.

Twelve Days of Christmas. Illus. by Jan Brett. LC 85-46056. (Illus.). 32p. 1986. PLB 12.95 (ISBN 0-396-08821-X). Dodd.

Twelve Days of Christmas. 12p. 1985. paper wrapped limited ed. 10.00 (ISBN 0-317-38833-9). Walrus Pr.

Twelve Days of Christmas: The Twelve Stages of a Soul (The Creation of a Universe) John D. Rea & Alayna Rea. 40p. (Orig.). 1987. pap. 4.95 (ISBN 0-938183-04-4). Two Trees Pub.

Twelve Decisive Battles of the Mind: The Story of Propaganda During the Christian Era, with Abridged Versions of Texts That Have Shaped History. Gorham B. Munson. LC 72-167388. (Essay Index Reprint Ser.). Repr. of 1942 ed. 18.00 (ISBN 0-8369-2705-2). Ayer Co Pubs.

Twelve Dynamic Bible Study Methods. Richard Warren. 252p. 1981. pap. 7.95 (ISBN 0-88207-815-1). Victor Bks.

Twelve for Twelve. Edward F. Cox. 64p. 1982. pap. 3.50 (ISBN 0-8341-0787-2). Beacon Hill.

Twelve Hundred & Four-the Unholy Crusade. John Godfrey. (Illus.). 1980. 39.95x (ISBN 0-19-215834-1). Oxford U Pr.

Twelve Hundred Scripture Outlines. A. Naismith. (Source Book for Ministers). 1978. pap. 5.95 (ISBN 0-8010-6692-1). Baker Bk.

Twelve Keys to an Effective Church. Kennon L. Callahan. LC 83-47718. 1983. pap. 13.45 (ISBN 0-06-061297-5, HarpR). Har-Row.

Twelve Labors of Hercules. Corinne Heline. (In the Zodiacal School of Life Ser.). pap. 2.50 (ISBN 0-87613-029-5). New Age.

Twelve Minor Prophets. Hans C. von Orelli. 1977. 15.50 (ISBN 0-86524-114-7, 7001). Klock & Klock.

Twelve Minor Prophets. George L. Robinson. 5.95 (ISBN 0-8010-7669-2). Baker Bk.

Twelve Minor Prophets. George L. Robinson. 203p. 1981. Repr. of 1926 ed. lib. bdg. 35.00 (ISBN 0-89984-434-0). Century Bookbindery.

Twelve Minutes over Fatima. John McMillin & Jim Glenn. 1986. 10.95 (ISBN 0-533-06492-9). Vantage.

Twelve Modern Apostles & Their Creeds. facs. ed. G. K. Chesterton et al. LC 68-16982. (Essay Index Reprint Ser). 1926. 17.00 (ISBN 0-8369-0955-0). Ayer Co Pubs.

Twelve Months of Christmas. Annette M. Buchanan & Kay A. Martin. Ed. by John Bolt. (Illus.). 192p. 1980. pap. 7.95 (ISBN 0-939114-01-1). Partridge Pair.

Twelve Prophetic Voices. Mariano Di Gangi. 168p. 1985. pap. 5.95 (ISBN 0-89693-536-1). Victor Bks.

Twelve Prophets. A. Cohen. 368p. 1948. 10.95 (ISBN 0-900689-31-5). Soncino Pr.

Twelve Prophets. Ed. by K. Elliger. (Biblia Hebraica Stuttgartensia Ser.). x, 96p. 1970. pap. 2.50x (ISBN 3-438-05210-5, 61261, Pub. by German Bible Society). Am Bible.

Twelve Prophets, Vol. 1. Peter C. Craigie. LC 84-2372. (Daily Study Bible-Old Testament Ser.). 1984. 14.95 (ISBN 0-664-21810-5); pap. 7.95 (ISBN 0-664-24577-3). Westminster.

Twelve Prophets, Vol. 2. Peter C. Craigie. LC 84-2372. (Daily Study Bible-Old Testament). 260p. 1985. 15.95 (ISBN 0-664-21813-X); pap. 8.95 (ISBN 0-664-24582-X). Westminster.

Twelve Religions of the Bible. Rolland E. Wolfe. LC 82-20401. (Studies in the Bible & Early Christianity: Vol. 2). (Illus.). 440p. 1983. 69.95x (ISBN 0-88946-600-9). E Mellen.

Twelve Sermons on Holiness. C. H. Spurgeon. pap. 3.75 (ISBN 0-685-88395-7). Reiner.

Twelve: The Lives of the Apostles After Calvary. C. Bernard Ruffin. LC 83-63168. 194p. (Orig.). 1984. pap. 7.95 (ISBN 0-87973-609-7, 609). Our Sunday Visitor.

Twelve Tribes of Israel. Charles Wengrov. (Illus.). 1960. pap. 0.99 (ISBN 0-914080-64-4). Shulsinger Sales.

Twelve Ways to Develop a Positive Attitude. Galloway. 1975. pap. 1.95 (ISBN 0-8423-7550-3). Tyndale.

Twelve Who Followed: The Story of Jesus & His First Disciples. Harry N. Huold. 128p. (Orig.). (YA) 1986. pap. 6.95 (ISBN 0-8066-2242-3, 10-6722). Augsburg.

Twelve World Teachers. Manly P. Hall. pap. 6.50 (ISBN 0-89314-816-4). Philos Res.

Twelve Years in America Being Observations on the Country, the People, Institutions, & Religion. James Shaw. text ed. 25.50 (ISBN 0-8369-9234-2, 9088). Ayer Co Pubs.

Twelve Years with Sri Aurobindo. Nirodbaran. 306p. 1973. 5.00 (ISBN 0-89071-245-X); pap. 4.00 (ISBN 0-89071-244-1). Matagiri.

Twelve Years with the Sufi Herb Doctors. Najib Siddiqui. 1983. 4.95 (ISBN 0-86304-014-4, Pub. by Octagon Pr England). Ins Study Human.

Twentieth Century Handwriting on the Wall. Wim Malgo. 4.95 (ISBN 0-686-12823-0). Midnight Call.

Twentieth-Century Protestant Church Music in America. Talmage W. Dean. (Orig.). 1987. text ed. 14.95 (ISBN 0-8054-6813-7). Broadman.

Twentieth Century Pulpit, Vol. II. Ed. by James W. Cox & Patricia P. Cox. LC 77-21997. 1981. pap. 9.95 (ISBN 0-687-42716-9). Abingdon.

Twentieth Century Religion Thought: The Frontiers of Philosophy & Theology, 1900-1980. rev. ed. John Maquarrie. 429p. 1981. pap. text ed. write for info. (ISBN 0-02-374500-2, Pub. by Scribner). Macmillan.

Twentieth Century Religious Thought. John Macquarrie. LC 81-9349. 1981. pap. text ed. 18.95x (ISBN 0-684-17334-4). Scribner.

Twentieth Century Religious Thought. John Macquarrie. 1983. 19.95 (ISBN 0-684-17333-6). Scribner.

Twentieth-Century Schwenkfelders: A Narrative History. W. Kyrel Meschter. 1984. pap. write for info (ISBN 0-935980-03-2). Schwenkfelder Lib.

Twenty Centuries of Catholic Church Music. Erwin E. Nemmers. LC 78-17248. 1978. Repr. of 1949 ed. lib. bdg. 22.50x (ISBN 0-313-20542-6, NETW). Greenwood.

Twenty Centuries of Ecumenism. Jacques Desseaux. 1984. pap. 4.95 (ISBN 0-8091-2617-6). Paulist Pr.

Twenty-Fifth Anniversary: Voices from the Heart. Date not set. price not set (ISBN 0-934383-11-1). Pride Prods.

Twenty-First Century Pioneering: A Scrapbook of the Future. David P. Young. (Illus., Orig.). 1986. pap. 5.95 (ISBN 0-377-00160-0). Friend Pr.

Twenty-Five Days with Great Christian Mystics: A Journey into Practical Christianity. pap. 2.50 (ISBN 0-686-13933-X). Rorge Pub Co.

Twenty-Five Hour Woman. Sybil Stanton. 256p. 1986. 9.95 (ISBN 0-8007-1487-3). Revell.

Twenty-Five Keys to a Happy Marriage. William J. Krutza. (Contempo Ser). pap. 1.75 (ISBN 0-8010-5447-8). Baker Bk.

Twenty-Five Mornings & Evenings. Chadwick. pap. 3.95 (ISBN 0-686-12924-5). Schmul Pub Co.

Twenty-Five Objections to Divine Healing & the Bible Answers. Gordon Lindsay. (Divine Healing & Health Ser.). 1.25 (ISBN 0-89985-030-8). Christ Nations.

Twenty-Five Two-Minute Talks for Children. Stanley Cornils. 48p. 1985. pap. 2.95 (ISBN 0-87239-867-6, 2882). Standard Pub.

Twenty-Five Wonderful Years, Eighteen Eighty-Nine to Nineteen Fourteen: A Popular Sketch of the Christian & Missionary Alliance. G. P. Pardington. Ed. by Donald W. Dayton. (Higher Christian Life Ser.). 238p. 1985. 30.00 (ISBN 0-8240-6435-6). Garland Pub.

Twenty-Four Hours a Day. (Hazelden Bks.). scp 5.50t (ISBN 0-317-46478-7). Har-Row.

Twenty-Four Hours a Day for Everyone. Alan L. Roeck. LC 78-52007. 383p. (Orig.). 1977. pap. 5.95 (ISBN 0-89486-040-2). Hazelden.

Twenty-Four Negro Melodies. S. Coleridge-Taylor. (Music Reprint Ser.: 1980). 1980. Repr. of 1905 ed. lib. bdg. 35.00 (ISBN 0-306-76023-1). Da Capo.

Twenty-Four Women's Programs: Please Pass the Fruit. Jeanette Lockerbie. 96p. (Orig.). 1986. pap. 4.95 (ISBN 0-87403-226-1, 2979). Standard Pub.

Twenty Holy Hours. Mateo C. Boevey. 1978. pap. 5.00 (ISBN 0-8198-0563-7). Dghtrs St Paul.

Twenty New Ways of Teaching the Bible. Donald L. Griggs. (Griggs Educational Resources Ser.). 1979. pap. 7.25 (ISBN 0-687-42740-1). Abingdon.

Twenty New Ways to Get the Minister Out of Moneyraising. E. F. Brose. 1976. 2.50 (ISBN 0-941500-18-7). Sharing Co.

Twenty-One Scientists Who Believe in Creation. LC 77-81165. (Illus.). 1977. pap. 1.00 (ISBN 0-89051-038-5). Master Bks.

Twenty-One Things Shortly to Come to Pass in Israel. Gordon Lindsay. 1.25 (ISBN 0-89985-192-4). Christ Nations.

Twenty-Seven Books That Changed the World: A Guide to Readng the New Testament. William C. Tremmel. LC 80-27930. 1981. text ed. 21.95 (ISBN 0-03-052631-0, HoltC). H Holt & Co.

Twenty-Seven Things the Church Must Go Through Before the Great Tribulation. Peter Popoff. Ed. by Don Tanner. LC 81-68675. (Illus.). 50p. 1981. pap. 1.00 (ISBN 0-938544-08-X). Faith Messenger.

Twenty-Six Bible Programs for Preschoolers. Diana Brettschneider et al. 96p. 1987. tchr's wkbk. 8.95 (ISBN 0-87403-213-X, 3413). Standard Pub.

Twenty-Six Bible Programs for Preschoolers. D. Cachiaras et al. (Illus.). 96p. 1986. wkbk. 8.95 (ISBN 0-87403-063-3, 3408). Standard Pub.

Twenty-Six Bible Programs for Preschools. Bennett et al. (Illus.). 96p. 1987. 8.95 (ISBN 0-87403-147-8, 3417). Standard Pub.

Twenty-Six Children's Church Programs: Getting to Know Jesus. June Lang & Angela Carl. (Illus.). 112p. 1983. pap. 7.95 (ISBN 0-87239-608-8, 3378). Standard Pub.

Twenty-Six Complete Programs for Children's Church: Traveling with Bible People. Carolyn Lehman. (Children's Church Ser.). 144p. 1986. tchr's ed. 8.95 (ISBN 0-87403-060-9, 3324). Standard Pub.

Twenty-Six Lessons for Children's Worship: Listening When God Speaks. Louise B. Wyly. (Illus.). 144p. 1986. 8.95 (ISBN 0-87403-057-9, 3321). Standard Pub.

Twenty-Six Lessons on First Corinthians. Wallace Wartick. (Bible Study Guide Ser.). 176p. (Orig.). 1980. pap. 3.95 (ISBN 0-89900-168-8). College Pr Pub.

Twenty-Six Lessons on Hebrews. Wallace Wartick. LC 79-53713. (Bible Student Study Guides Ser.). 1979. pap. 3.95 (ISBN 0-89900-160-2). College Pr Pub.

Twenty-Six Lessons on Matthew, Vol. II. John Raymond. (Bible Student Study Guide Ser.). 130p. 1981. pap. 2.95 (ISBN 0-89900-171-8). College Pr Pub.

Twenty-Six Lessons on Matthew, Vol. 1. John Raymond. LC 80-67734. (Bible Student Study Guides). 130p. (Orig.). 1980. pap. 2.95 (ISBN 0-89900-167-X). College Pr Pub.

Twenty-Six Lessons on Revelation, Pt. 1. Paul T. Bulter. LC 82-71688. (Bible Student Study Guide Ser.). 133p. 1982. pap. 2.95 (ISBN 0-89900-173-4). College Pr Pub.

Twenty-Six Lessons on Revelation, Pt. 2. Paul T. Bulter. LC 82-71688. (Bible Student Study Guide Ser.). 284p. 1982. pap. 4.95 (ISBN 0-89900-176-9). College Pr Pub.

Twenty-Six Lessons on the Four Gospels. 2nd ed. Wallace Wartick. (Bible Student Study Guides Ser.). 1977. pap. 9.95 (ISBN 0-89900-157-2). College Pr Pub.

Twenty-Six Lessons on the Gospel of John. Stan Paregien. (Bible Student Study Guides Ser.). 1977. pap. 3.95 (ISBN 0-89900-152-1). College Pr Pub.

Twenty-Six New Testament Lessons. G. E. Jones. 111p. 1978. pap. 2.00 (ISBN 0-89114-080-8). Baptist Pub Hse.

Twenty-Six Programs for Preschoolers (Spring & Summer) Carmen Fellows et al. 96p. 1986. wkbk. 8.95 (ISBN 0-87403-011-0, 3404). Standard Pub.

Twenty-Six Vital Issues. LeRoy Koopman. (Contemporary Discussion Ser.). 1978. pap. 2.45 (ISBN 0-8010-5398-6). Baker Bk.

Twenty Stories of Bible Women. Dixie L. Harris. 1980. 12.50 (ISBN 0-682-49526-3). Exposition Pr FL.

Twenty-Third Psalm. Charles L. Allen. (Illus.). 64p. 1961. 7.95 (ISBN 0-8007-0330-8). Revell.

Twenty-Third Psalm. (The Inspirational Library Ser.). 24p. 3.95 (ISBN 0-8326-2005-X, 3252). World Bible.

Twenty Three Years: A Study of the Prophetic Career of Mohammad. Ali Dashti. Tr. by F. R. Bagley from Persian. 224p. 1985. 17.50 (ISBN 0-04-297048-2). Allen Unwin.

Twenty-Two Landmark Years: Christian Schools International, 1943-65. John A. Vander Ark. 160p. 1983. pap. 9.95 (ISBN 0-8010-9291-4). Baker Bk.

Twenty-Two More Object Talks for Children's Worship. John C. Reid. (Illus.). 80p. 1987. pap. 3.50 (ISBN 0-87403-239-3, 2879). Standard Pub.

Twenty-Two Object Talks for Children's Worship. Virginia A. Van Seters. (Illus.). 48p. 1986. pap. 2.95 (ISBN 0-87403-055-2, 2866). Standard Pub.

Twenty-Two Questions Most Frequently Asked by the Unsaved. Gordon Lindsay. 1.50 (ISBN 0-89985-118-5). Christ Nations.

Twenty Years Among Primitive Papuans. William E. Bromilow. LC 75-32800. Repr. of 1929 ed. 31.50 (ISBN 0-404-14103-X). AMS Pr.

Twenty Years of Jewish-Catholic Relations. James Rudin et al. 336p. (Orig.). 1986. pap. 11.95 (ISBN 0-8091-2762-8). Paulist Pr.

Twenty Years of Tidings. Friend Stuart. 180p. 1986. vinyl 29.95 (ISBN 0-912132-10-8). Dominion Pr.

Twice Freed: The Story of Onesimus, a Runaway Slave. Patricia St. John. (Orig.). 1985. pap. 3.95 (ISBN 0-8024-8848-X). Moody.

Twice Migrants: East African Sikh Settlers in Britain. Parminder Bhachu. 256p. 1986. text ed. 35.00 (ISBN 0-422-78910-0, 9773, Pub. by Tavistock England). Methuen Inc.

Twice the Challenge: Athlete & Christian. Leo Holland. LC 86-80387. 128p. (Orig.). 1986. pap. 4.95 (ISBN 0-89243-251-9). Liguori Pubns.

Twilight of Christianity. Harry E. Barnes. 75.00 (ISBN 0-87700-037-9). Revisionist Pr.

Twilight of Evolution. Henry M. Morris. LC 76-2265. 1963. pap. 4.95 (ISBN 0-8010-5862-7). Baker Bk.

Twillight Language: Explanations in Buddhist Meditation & Symbolism. R. S. Bucknell & Martin Stuart-Fox. 227p. 1986. 27.50 (ISBN 0-312-82540-4). St Martin.

Twins Visit Israel. Rita Maidat. (Shayna & Keppi Ser.). (Illus.). 1978. pap. 2.00 (ISBN 0-914080-72-5). Shulsinger Sales.

Twisted Road to Auschwitz: Nazi Policy Toward German Jews, 1933-1939. Karl A. Schleunes. LC 74-102024. pap. 72.00 (ISBN 0-317-11169-8, 2011134). Bks Demand UMI.

Twisting the Truth. Bruce Tucker. 192p. (Orig.). 1987. pap. 5.95 (ISBN 0-87123-931-0). Bethany Hse.

Two Ancient Christologies: A Study in the Christological Thought of the Schools of Alexandria & Antioch in the Early History of Christian Doctrine. Robert V. Sellers. (Church Historical Society London N. S. Ser.: No. 39). Repr. of 1940 ed. 50.00 (ISBN 0-8115-3162-7). Kraus Repr.

Two & the One. Mircea Eliade. Tr. by J. M. Cohen. LC 79-2268. 1979. pap. 7.00 (ISBN 0-226-20389-1, P811). U of Chicago Pr.

Two Aztec Wood Idols: Iconographic & Chronologic Analysis. H. B. Nicholson & Rainer Berger. LC 68-58701. (Studies in Pre-Columbian Art & Archaeology: No.5). (Illus.). 28p. 1968. pap. 3.00x (ISBN 0-88402-026-6). Dumbarton Oaks.

Two Babylons. Alexander Hislop. 9.95 (ISBN 0-87213-330-3). Loizeaux.

Two Babylons. Gordon Lindsay. (Revelation Ser.). 1.25 (ISBN 0-89985-046-4). Christ Nations.

Two Become One. J. Allan Petersen et al. 1973. pap. 3.95 (ISBN 0-8423-7620-8). Tyndale.

Two Blocks from Happiness. Lois Morse. 176p. 1985. pap. 6.95 (ISBN 0-87239-860-9, 3005). Standard Pub.

Two Books on Stanzas of Dzyan. Blavatsky. 4.95 (ISBN 0-8356-7223-9). Theos Pub Hse.

Two Brothers. 1982. pap. 1.95 (ISBN 0-87306-242-6). Feldheim.

Two-Career Marriage. G. Wade Rowatt, Jr. & Mary Jo Rowatt. LC 79-28408. (Christian Care Bks.: Vol. 5). 120p. 1980. pap. 7.95 (ISBN 0-664-24298-7). Westminster.

Two Centuries of Ecumenism. Georges H. Tavard. LC 78-6449. 1978. Repr. of 1960 ed. lib. bdg. 22.50x (ISBN 0-313-20490-X, TATC). Greenwood.

Two Choice & Useful Treatises: The One, One Lux Orientalis,...the Other, A Discourse of Truth by the Late Reverend Dr. Rust. Joseph Glanvill. Ed. by Rene Wellek. LC 75-11223. (British Philosophers & Theologians of the 17th & 18th Centuries Ser.). 532p. 1978. lib. bdg. 51.00 (ISBN 0-8240-1777-3). Garland Pub.

Two Christmas Plays. Nancy Funk. 1984. 4.50 (ISBN 0-89536-695-9, 4872). CSS of Ohio.

Two Christmas Plays. Pamela Urfer. 25p. (Orig.). pap. text ed. 3.95 (ISBN 0-912801-08-5). Creat Arts Dev.

Two Christs; Or, the Decline & Fall of Christianity. Stanley J. Marks. 1983. pap. 14.95 (ISBN 0-938780-03-4). Bur Intl Aff.

Two Cities. Norman St. Johh-Stevas. 352p. 1984. 27.50 (ISBN 0-571-13083-6). Faber & Faber.

Two-Clergy Marriages: A Special Case of Dual Careers. E. M. Rallings & David J. Pratto. 126p. (Orig.). 1985. 24.00 (ISBN 0-8191-4343-X); pap. text ed. 9.50 (ISBN 0-8191-4344-8). U Pr of Amer.

Two Contrariant Schools, Concerning the Establishment of a Christian University. Apostolos Makrakis. Ed. by Orthodox Christian Educational Society. Tr. by Denver Cummings from Hellenic. 87p. (Orig.). 1949. pap. 2.75x (ISBN 0-938366-27-0). Orthodox Chr.

Two, Corinthians. Handley Moule. 1976. pap. 4.95 (ISBN 0-87508-359-5). Chr Lit.

Two Covenants. Andrew Murray. 1974. pap. 3.50 (ISBN 0-87508-396-X). Chr Lit.

Two Disciples at the Tomb. Robert Mahoney. (Theologie und Wirklichkeit: Vol. 6). 344p. 1974. pap. 29.75 (ISBN 3-261-00943-8). P Lang Pubs.

Two Dissertations Concerning Sense, & the Immagination, with an Essay on Consciousness. Zachary Mayne. Ed. by Rene Wellek. LC 75-11234. (British Philosophers & Theologians of the 17th & 18th Centuries: Vol. 35). 1976. Repr. of 1728 ed. lib. bdg. 51.00 (ISBN 0-8240-1787-0). Garland Pub.

Two Early Political Associations: The Quakers & the Dissenting Deputies in the Age of Sir Robert Walpole. Norman Crowther-Hunt. LC 78-23805. 1979. Repr. of 1961 ed. lib. bdg. 24.75x (ISBN 0-313-21036-5, HUTW). Greenwood.

Two Early Tudor Lives. Ed. by Richard S. Sylvester & Davis P. Harding. Incl. Life & Death of Cardinal Wolsey. George Cavendish; Life of Sir Thomas More. William Roper. xxi, 260p. 1962. pap. 8.95x (ISBN 0-300-00239-4, Y81). Yale U Pr.

Two Elizabethan Puritan Diaries. Richard Rogers & Samuel Ward. Ed. by Marshall M. Knappen. 1933. 11.75 (ISBN 0-8446-1387-8). Peter Smith.

Two Faces of Reality. Robert Jastrow. Date not set. 14.95 (ISBN 0-393-02400-8). Norton.

Two Fish to You. Ken Schauer. 65p. 1985. pap. 4.95 (ISBN 0-933350-46-5). Morse Pr.

Two Generations of Zionism. Bernard A. Rosenblatt. LC 67-18134. 1967. 7.95 (ISBN 0-88400-017-6). Shengold.

Two Horizons. Anthony C. Thiselton. LC 79-14387. 1984. 12.95 (ISBN 0-8028-0006-8). Eerdmans.

Two Houses. Meryl Doney. (Illus.). 16p. 1982. pap. 0.99 (ISBN 0-86683-664-0, AY8246, HarpR). Har-Row.

Two Hundred & Thirty-Nine Days: Abdu'l-Baha's Journey in America. Allan L. Ward. LC 79-14713. (Illus.). 1979. 10.95 (ISBN 0-87743-129-9, 332-005). Baha'i.

Two Hundred One Sermon Outlines. Jabez Burns. LC 86-27758. 256p. 1987. pap. 8.95 (ISBN 0-8254-2269-8). Kregel.

Two Hundred (Religion) Class. Melvil Dewey. LC 79-55849. 1980. Repr. saddlewire pap. 4.95 (ISBN 0-8054-3107-1). Broadman.

Two Hundred Rooms in the Inn: The Story of Providence Mission Homes. Mercedes Gribble & Hope Friedmann. LC 83-15367. (Illus.). 112p. (Orig.). 1983. pap. 3.95 (ISBN 0-87808-195-X). William Carey Lib.

Two Hundred Sermon Outlines. Jabez Burns. LC 75-92502. 128p. 1987. pap. 6.95 (ISBN 0-8254-2264-7). Kregel.

Two Hundred Stewardship Meditations. Marshall Hayden. 112p. (Orig.). 1984. pap. 3.95 (ISBN 0-87239-780-7, 3034). Standard Pub.

Two Hundred Twenty Misconceptions about the Bible: A Handbook of Misinformation, Misquotation, & Misinterpretations of the Bible. Compiled by David C. Downing. 1987. pap. price not set (ISBN 0-8010-2975-9). Baker Bk.

Two Hundred Two Bulletin Boards for All Ages. Georgia Smelser & Eilene Enloe. LC 85-26522. (Illus.). 176p. (Orig.). 1986. pap. 5.50 (ISBN 0-912315-96-2). Word Aflame.

Two Hundred Years: The History of the Society for Promoting Christian Knowledge, 1698-1898. William O. Allen. LC 76-135171. (Research & Source Works Ser.: No. 622). 1971. Repr. of 1898 ed. 32.00 (ISBN 0-8337-0044-8). B Franklin.

Two Jerusalems in Prophecy. David Clifford. LC 78-14922. (Illus.). 1978. pap. 3.50 (ISBN 0-87213-081-9). Loizeaux.

Two Literary Riddles in the Exeter Book: Riddle 1 & the Easter Riddle. James E. Anderson. LC 85-40471. (Illus.). 288p. 1986. 27.50x (ISBN 0-8061-1947-0). U of Okla Pr.

Two Liturgies, A. D. Fifteen Forty-Nine, & A. D. Fifteen Fifty-Seven. 1844. 51.00 (ISBN 0-384-62140-6). Johnson Repr.

Two Lives of Saint Cuthbert. Ed. by Bertram Colgrave. 388p. 1985. 44.50 (ISBN 0-521-30925-5); pap. 16.95 (ISBN 0-521-31385-6). Cambridge U Pr.

Two Loves. Vincent A. McCrossen. LC 78-61110. 383p. 1979. 13.95 (ISBN 0-8022-2237-4). Philos Lib.

Two Maya Monuments in Yucatan: The Palace of the Stuccoes at Acanceh & the Temple of the Owls at Chicken Itza. Hasso Von Winning. (Frederick Webb Hodge Publications: No. XII). (Illus.). 104p. (Orig.). 1985. pap. write for info. (ISBN 0-916561-68-2). Southwest Mus.

Two Mexico City Choirbooks of 1717: An Anthology of Sacred Polyphony from the Cathedral of Mexico. Tr. by Steven Barwick. LC 82-3047. 213p. 1982. 16.95x (ISBN 0-8093-1065-1). S Ill U Pr.

Two Months with Mary: Short Reflections for Every Day of May & October. Ed. by Joseph A. Viano. (Illus.). 94p. (Orig.). 1984. pap. 4.95 (ISBN 0-8189-0466-6). Alba.

Two Moral Essays: Human Personality & on Human Obligations. Simone Weil. Repr. 2.50x (ISBN 0-686-79299-8). Pendle Hill.

Two Mystic Communities in America. John E. Jacoby. LC 75-326. (Radical Tradition in America Ser). 104p. 1975. Repr. of 1931 ed. 15.00 (ISBN 0-88355-230-2). Hyperion Conn.

Two Nativity Dramas. Edward S. Long. 1984. 4.75 (ISBN 0-89536-697-5, 4874). CSS of Ohio.

Two Natures in Christ. Martin Chemnitz. Tr. by J. A. Preus. LC 74-115465. Orig. Title: De Duabus Naturis in Christo. 1970. 24.95 (ISBN 0-570-03210-5, 15-2109). Concordia.

Two New Scriptures. pap. 1.00 (ISBN 0-89036-079-0). Hawkes Pub Inc.

Two Nichols: Spent for Missions. Jester Summers. LC 81-70910. (Meet the Missionary Ser.). 1982. 5.50 (ISBN 0-8054-4279-0, 4242-79). Broadman.

Two Rivers to Freedom. Stella Wuerffel. LC 80-66578. 385p. 1980. 11.95 (ISBN 0-915644-20-7). Clayton Pub Hse.

Two Saints: St. Bernard & St. Francis. G. G. Coulton. 1923. lib. bdg. 15.00 (ISBN 0-8414-3513-8). Folcroft.

Two Say Why. Hans Von Balthasar et al. 1973. pap. 1.75 (ISBN 0-8199-0434-1). Franciscan Herald.

Two Sermons. John Cotton. LC 79-141108. (Research Library of Colonial Americana). 1971. Repr. of 1642 ed. 22.00 (ISBN 0-405-03322-2). Ayer Co Pubs.

Two Sermons Upon S. Judes Epistle. Richard Hooker. LC 70-26033. (English Experience Ser.: No. 195). 56p. 1969. Repr. of 1614 ed. 8.00 (ISBN 90-221-0195-9). Walter J Johnson.

Two Shall Be One. C. M. Ward. (Orig.). 1986. pap. text ed. 3.95 (ISBN 0-88368-184-6). Whitaker Hse.

Two Sides of a Coin. Charles Hunter & Frances Hunter. 1973. pap. 3.95 (ISBN 0-917726-36-7). Hunter Bks.

Two Sides, the Best of Personal Opinion, 1964-1984. John H. Redekop. 306p. (Orig.). 1984. pap. 9.95 (ISBN 0-919797-13-X). Kindred Pr.

Two-Source Hypothesis: A Critical Appraisal. Ed. by Arthur J. Bellinzoni. x, 486p. 1985. 39.95 (ISBN 0-86554-096-9, MUP/H88). Mercer Univ Pr.

Two Sources of Morality & Religion. Henri Bergson. LC 74-10373. 308p. 1974. Repr. of 1935 ed. lib. bdg. 25.00x (ISBN 0-8371-7679-4, BETS). Greenwood.

Two Sources of Morality & Religion. Henri Bergson. Tr. by R. Ashley Audra from Fr. LC 77-89762. 1977. pap. text ed. 8.95 (ISBN 0-268-01835-9). U of Notre Dame Pr.

Two Stories Jesus Told. Lucy Diamond. (Ladybird Ser). (Illus.). 1959. bds. 2.50 (ISBN 0-87508-870-8). Chr Lit.

Two Studies on the Roman Pontifices. P. Preibisch. LC 75-10647. (Ancient Religion & Mythology Ser.). 1976. 12.00x (ISBN 0-405-07271-6). Ayer Co Pubs.

Two Tasks. Charles Malik. 37p. 1980. pap. 1.95 (ISBN 0-89107-212-8, Crossway Bks). Good News.

Two Thousand & One the Church in Crisis. Leonidas C. Contos. 60p. 1981. pap. 2.95 (ISBN 0-916586-46-4). Holy Cross Orthodox.

Two Thousand One Southern Superstitions. 2.00 (ISBN 0-936672-34-X). Aerial Photo.

Two Treatises: In the One of Which the Nature of Bodies; In the Other the Nature of Man's Soule is Look'd into the Way of Discovery of the Immortality of Reasonable Souls. Sir Kenelme Digby. Ed. by Rene Wellek. LC 75-11217. (British Philosophers & Theologians of the 17th & 18th Centuries Ser.). 514p. 1978. lib. bdg. 51.00 (ISBN 0-8240-1771-4). Garland Pub.

Two Treatises of Philo of Alexandria: A Commentary on De Gigantibus & Quod Deus Sit Immutabilis. David Winston & John Dillon. LC 82-786. (Brown Judaic Studies). 416p. 1983. pap. 15.00 (ISBN 0-89130-563-7, 14 00 25). Scholars Pr GA.

Two Treatises of Servetus on the Trinity. Michael Servetus. Tr. by Earl M. Wilbur. (Harvard Theological Studies). 1932. 24.00 (ISBN 0-527-01016-2). Kraus Repr.

Two Treatises on the Accentuation of the Old Testament. rev. ed. William Wickes. 1970. 35.00x (ISBN 0-87068-004-8). Ktav.

Two Treatises on the Christian Priesthood, 3 Vols. George Hickes. (Library of Anglo-Catholic Theology: No. 9). Repr. of 1848 ed. Set. 87.50 (ISBN 0-404-52100-2). AMS Pr.

Two Trends in Modern Quaker Thought. Albert Fowler. 1983. pap. 2.50x (ISBN 0-87574-112-6, 112). Pendle Hill.

Two Views of Freedom in Process & Thought. George R. Lucas. LC 79-12287. (American Academy of Religion, Dissertation Ser.: No. 28). 1979. 14.00 (ISBN 0-89130-285-9, 010128); pap. 9.95 (ISBN 0-89130-304-9). Scholars Pr GA.

Two Wesleys. C. H. Spurgeon. 1975. pap. 1.95 (ISBN 0-686-16834-8). Pilgrim Pubns.

Two Winchester Bibles. Walter Oakshott. (Illus.). 1981. 350.00x (ISBN 0-19-818235-X). Oxford U Pr.

Two Witnesses. Gordon Lindsay. (Revelation Ser.). 1.25 (ISBN 0-89985-039-1). Christ Nations.

Two Witnesses. Date not set. pap. 0.95 (ISBN 0-937408-12-3). GMI Pubns Inc.

Two Works of Grace. H. M. Riggle. 56p. pap. 0.40 (ISBN 0-686-29168-9); pap. 1.00 3 copies (ISBN 0-686-29169-7). Faith Pub Hse.

Two Worlds: Christianity & Communism. James Bales. pap. 2.25 (ISBN 0-686-80419-8). Lambert Bk.

Two-Year Mountain. Phil Deutschle. LC 86-4026. 256p. 1986. 15.95 (ISBN 0-87663-471-4). Universe.

Two Years Experience Among the Shakers. David R. Lamson. LC 71-134418. Repr. of 1848 ed. 19.00 (ISBN 0-404-08477-X). AMS Pr.

Two Zen Classics: Mumonkan & Hekiganroku. Ed. by A. V. Grimstone. Tr. by Katsuki Sekida from Chinese. LC 77-2398. 1977. 13.50 (ISBN 0-8348-0131-0); pap. 8.95 (ISBN 0-8348-0130-2). Weatherhill.

Tying Down the Sun. George Vandeman. LC 78-61749. (Stories That Win Ser.). 1978. pap. 1.25 (ISBN 0-8163-0211-1, 20990-8). Pacific Pr Pub Assn.

Tyndale Library of Great Biblical Novels, 6 vols. 23.95 (ISBN 0-8423-7643-7). Tyndale.

Types in Hebrews. Robert Anderson. LC 78-9545. (Sir Robert Anderson Library). 192p. 1978. pap. 4.95 (ISBN 0-8254-2129-2). Kregel.

Types of Jewish-Palestinian Piety from 70 BCE to 70 CE. Adolf Buchler. 264p. Repr. of 1922 ed. text ed. 62.10x (ISBN 0-576-80135-6, Pub by Gregg Intl Pubs England). Gregg Intl.

Types of Modern Theology. Young O. Kim. LC 83-80105. 296p. 1983. pap. 11.95 (ISBN 0-910621-32-2). Rose Sharon Pr.

Types of Religious Experience: Christian & Non-Christian. Joachim Wach. LC 51-9885. 275p. 1972. pap. 2.45x (ISBN 0-226-86710-2, P482, Phoen). U of Chicago Pr.

Types, Psalms & Prophecies. David Baron. 1981. lib. bdg. 14.00 (ISBN 0-86524-077-9, 9511). Klock & Klock.

Typology & Early American Literature. Ed. by Sacvan Bercovitch. LC 74-181362. (New England Writers Ser.). 352p. 1971. 20.00x (ISBN 0-87023-096-4). U of Mass Pr.

Typology in Scripture: A Study of Hermeneutical Tupos Structures. Richard M. Davidson. (Andrews University Seminary Doctoral Dissertation Ser.: Vol. 2). 496p. (Orig.). 1981. pap. 10.95 (ISBN 0-943872-34-0). Andrews Univ Pr.

Tyranny of the Urgent. Charles Hummel. pap. 0.75 (ISBN 0-87784-128-4). Inter-Varsity.

Tyranny of Time. Robert Banks. LC 84-28855. 265p. 1985. pap. 6.95 (ISBN 0-87784-338-4). Inter-Varsity.

Tyrant or Father? A Study of Calvin's Doctrine of God. Garret Wilterdink. 185p. (Orig.). 1985. pap. 9.95 (ISBN 0-932269-19-2). Wyndham Hall.

Tzaddik. Rabbi Nathan. Tr. by Avraham Greenbaum from Hebrew. Orig. Title: Chayey Moharan. Date not set. price not set (ISBN 0-930213-17-3). Breslov Res Inst.

Tzaddik in Our Time. Simcha Raz. Tr. by Charles Wengrow from Hebrew. (Illus.). 1976. 13.95 (ISBN 0-87306-130-6). Feldheim.

Tzaddik in Our Time: Life & Times of Rav Aryeh Levin of Jerusalem, Celebrated Tzaddik of Jerusalem. Simcha Raz. Tr. by Charles Wengrov from Hebrew. Tr. of Ish Tzaddik Hayah. (Illus.). 1978. pap. 10.95 (ISBN 0-87306-986-2). Feldheim.

Tzedakah. Amye Rosenberg. (Jewish Awareness Ser.). (Illus.). 1979. pap. text ed. 2.95x (ISBN 0-87441-279-X). Behrman.

Tzedakah: Can Jewish Philanthropy Buy Jewish Survival? Jacob Neusner. Ed. by David Altshuler. (Basic Jewish Ideas Ser.). 160p. 1982. pap. 7.95 (ISBN 0-940646-07-2). Rossel Bks.

Tzedakah Workbook. Jan Rabinowitz. (Illus.). 32p. (Orig.). 1986. pap. text ed. 3.95 (ISBN 0-933873-07-7). Torah Aura.

Tzorchei Tzibbur: Community & Responsibility in the Jewish Tradition. 6.00 (ISBN 0-686-96047-5); tchr's ed. 8.50 (ISBN 0-686-99687-9). United Syn Bk.

U

U. S. A. The Message of Justice, Peace & Love. Pope John Paul II. 1979. 5.95 (ISBN 0-8198-0630-7); pap. 4.95 (ISBN 0-8198-0631-5). Dghtrs St Paul.

U Thant: Divinity's Smile and Humanity's Cry. pap. 4.95 (ISBN 0-88497-341-7). Aum Pubns.

Uchenije o Pravoslavnom Bogosluzhenii. V. Mikhailovsky. Tr. of Teachings of the Orthodox Divine Services. 146p. pap. text ed. 6.00 (ISBN 0-317-30287-6). Holy Trinity.

Uchjebnik Tserkovnago Penija. A. Ryazhsky. Tr. of Textbook of Sacred Singing. 105p. 1966. pap. 5.00 (ISBN 0-317-30382-1). Holy Trinity.

Udalricus Wessofontanus. Ulrich V. Stocklin. Ed. by Guido M. Dreves. Repr. 60.00 (ISBN 0-384-58330-X). Johnson Repr.

Udana, or the Solemn Utterances of the Buddha. Tr. by D. M. Strong from Pali. LC 78-70131. Repr. of 1902 ed. 20.50 (ISBN 0-404-17399-3). AMS Pr.

Udanavarga: A Collection of Verses from the Buddhist Canon. Ed. by William H. Rockhill. Repr. of 1883 ed. text ed. 20.00 (ISBN 0-89644-342-6, Pub. by Chinese Matl Ctr). Coronet Bks.

Uddhava Gita or Last Message of Sri Krishna. Tr. by Madhavananda from Sanskrit. 425p. pap. 9.50 (ISBN 0-87481-211-9). Vedanta Pr.

Uganda Controversy: Minutes of the Zionist General Council, Vol. 1. Intro. by Michael Heymann. 136p. 1970. casebound 12.95x (ISBN 0-87855-185-9). Transaction Bks.

Ugarit. Adrian H. Curtis. (Cities of the Biblical World Ser.). 128p. (Orig.). 1985. pap 8.95 (ISBN 0-8028-0166-8). Eerdmans.

Ugarit & the Old Testament. Peter Craigie. 110p. (Orig.). 1983. pap. 5.95 (ISBN 0-8028-1928-1). Eerdmans.

Ukazanije Puti v Tsarstvije Nebsnoje. Metropolitan Innocent of Moscow Staff. Tr. of Indication of the Way Kingdom of Heaven. 59p. pap. 2.00 (ISBN 0-317-28978-0). Holy Trinity.

Ukrainian Catholic Church: 1945-1975. Ed. by Miroslav Labunka & Leonid Rudnytzky. LC 76-26753. 1976. 7.50 (ISBN 0-686-28475-5). St Sophia Religious.

Ukrainian Catholics in America: A History. Bohdan P. Procko. LC 81-43718. 184p. (Orig.). 1982. lib. bdg. 27.75 (ISBN 0-8191-2409-5); pap. text ed. 11.50 (ISBN 0-8191-2410-9). U Pr of Amer.

Ulrich Von Hutten & the German Reformation. Hajo Holborn. Tr. by Roland H. Bainton. LC 77-25067. (Yale Historical Publications Studies: No. XI). (Illus.). 1978. Repr. of 1937 ed. lib. bdg. 22.50x (ISBN 0-313-20125-0, HOUV). Greenwood.

Ulster's Uncertain Defenders: Protestant Political, Paramilitary & Community Groups & the Northern Ireland Conflict. Sarah Nelson. (Irish Studies). 206p. 1984. text ed. 32.00x (ISBN 0-8156-2316-X). Syracuse U Pr.

Ultima Llamada. Jack T. Chick. (Span., Illus.). 64p. (Orig.). 1972. pap. 1.95 (ISBN 0-937958-02-6). Chick Pubns.

Ultimate Alchemy, 2 vols. Bhagwan Shree Rajneesh. Ed. by Ma Ananda Prem. LC 75-905370. (Upanishad Ser.). (Illus.). 1976. Vol. I, 442 pgs. 18.95 ea. (ISBN 0-88050-161-8). Vol. II, 424 pgs (ISBN 0-88050-162-6). Chidvilas Found.

Ultimate Christmas Fake Book. (Fake Bk. Ser.). 84p. 1985. 9.95 (ISBN 0-88188-381-6, HL00240063). H Leonard Pub Corp.

Ultimate Deception. Sharon Hodder. 112p. 1982. pap. 4.95 (ISBN 0-89221-096-6). New Leaf.

Ultimate Defense: A Practical Plan to Prevent Man's Self-Destruction. Frederic F. Clair. LC 59-6490. 1959. 3.30 (ISBN 0-8048-0606-3). C E Tuttle.

Ultimate Destination. W. Norman Cooper. 95p. 1980. 7.50 (ISBN 0-87516-413-7); pap. 4.50 (ISBN 0-87516-381-5). De Vorss.

Ultimate Evil: An Investigation into America's Most Dangerous Satanic Cult. Maury Terry. LC 86-29203. (Illus.). 432p. 1987. 17.95 (ISBN 0-385-23452-X, Dolp). Doubleday.

Ultimate Game: The Rise & Fall of Bhagwan Shree. Kate Strelley. 1987. 18.95. Har-Row.

Ultimate Kingdom. 2nd ed. Earl Paulk. 264p. (Orig.). 1987. pap. 7.95 (ISBN 0-917595-13-0). K-Dimension.

Ultimate Official Jewish Joke Book. Larry Wilde. 192p. (Orig.). 1986. pap. 2.95 (ISBN 0-553-26227-0). Bantam.

Ultimate Priority. John MacArthur, Jr. 1983. pap. 5.50 (ISBN 0-8024-0186-4). Moody.

Ultimate Questions: An Anthology of Modern Russian Religious Thought. Ed. by Alexander Schmemann. 310p. 1977. pap. 8.95 (ISBN 0-913836-46-X). St Vladimirs.

Ultimate Reality. Hugh M. Woodman. LC 84-90244. 145p. 1985. 10.95 (ISBN 0-533-06292-6). Vantage.

Ultimate Reality & Spiritual Discipline. Ed. by James P. Duerlinger. (God Ser.). 240p. (Orig.). 1984. text ed. 21.95 (ISBN 0-913757-09-8, Pub. by New Era Bks); pap. text ed. 12.95 (ISBN 0-913757-08-X, Pub. by New Era Bks). Paragon Hse.

Ultimate Relationship. Dora Panorelli. 1985. 8.95 (ISBN 0-8062-2454-1). Carlton.

Ultimate Ripoff. Bill Stringfellow. LC 81-49329. 176p. 1981. pap. 3.95 (ISBN 0-939286-00-9). Concerned Pubns.

Umar the Great (Al-Farqu, 2 vols. M. Z. Khan & M. Saleem. 1970. Vol. 1. 12.50x (ISBN 0-87902-196-9); Vol. 2. 12.50x (ISBN 0-685-33011-7). Orientalia.

Umayyad Caliphate: A Political Study. Abd'al-Ameer'Abd Dixon. 222p. 1971. 95.00x (ISBN 0-317-39182-8, Pub. by Luzac & Co Ltd). State Mutual Bk.

Umayyads & Abbasids. Jirji Zaydan. Tr. by D. S. Margoliouth from Arabic. LC 79-2889. 325p. 1982. Repr. of 1907 ed. 29.00 (ISBN 0-8305-0056-1). Hyperion Conn.

Umbanda: Religion & Politics in Urban Brazil. Diana D. Brown. Ed. by Conrad Kottak. LC 85-20962. (Studies in Cultural Anthropology: No. 7). 270p. 1985. 44.95 (ISBN 0-8357-1556-6). UMI Res Pr.

Umstrittenes Taufertum 1525-1975. Ed. by Hans-Jurgen Goertz. 1975. 22.50x (ISBN 0-8361-1128-1). Herald Pr.

Una Interpretacion Del Apocalipsis. Domingo S. Fernandez. (Span.). 234p. 1985. pap. 3.50 (ISBN 0-311-04312-7). Casa Bautista.

Una Nueva Ilusion. Dale E. Galloway. Tr. by Rhode F. Ward. Tr. of Dream a New Dream. (Span.). 169p. 1982. pap. 3.95 (ISBN 0-89922-158-0). Edit Caribe.

Unabridged Bible Commentary, 3 vols. Jamieson et al. 1974. 75.00 (ISBN 0-8028-8033-9). Eerdmans.

Unabridged Woman. Bobbie McKay. LC 79-14297. (Orig.). 1979. pap. 5.95 (ISBN 0-8298-0369-6). Pilgrim NY.

Unacknowledged Harmony: Philo-Semitism & the Survival of European Jewry. Alan Edelstein. LC 81-1563. (Contributions in Ethnic Studies: No. 4). xii, 235p. 1982. lib. bdg. 29.95 (ISBN 0-313-22754-3, EDP/). Greenwood.

Unattended Moment: Excerpts from Autobiographies with Hints & Guesses. Michael Paffard. LC 76-368148. 1976. pap. text ed. 3.95x (ISBN 0-8401-1803-1). A R Allenson.

Unblessed. Berneice Lunday. LC 78-15244. (Orion Ser). 1979. pap. 3.50 (ISBN 0-8127-0200-X). Review & Herald.

Unborn Persons: Pope John Paul II & the Abortion Debate. James J. McCartney. (American University Studies VII-Theology & Religion: Vol. 21). 176p. 1987. text ed. 16.75 (ISBN 0-8204-0349-0). P Lang Pubs.

Unbound Spirit: God's Universal, Sanctifying Work. Charles DeCelles. LC 85-20047. 367p. (Orig.). 1985. pap. 9.95 (ISBN 0-8189-0486-0). Alba.

Uncertain Church: The New Catholic Problem. George A. Kelly. (Synthesis Ser.). 1977. pap. 1.25 (ISBN 0-8199-0705-7). Franciscan Herald.

Uncertain Saints. Alan Graebner. LC 75-1573. (Contributions in American History: No. 42). 320p. 1975. lib. bdg. 29.95 (ISBN 0-8371-7963-7, GUS/). Greenwood.

Unchurched: Who They Are & Why They Stay Away. J. Russell Hale. LC 79-2993. 192p. 1980. 12.00 (ISBN 0-06-063560-6, HarpR). Har-Row.

Uncivil Religion: Interreligious Hostility in America. Robert Bellah & Frederick Greenspahn. 256p. 1986. 16.95. Crossroad NY.

Uncivil Religions: Interreligious Hostility. Ed. by Robert N. Bellah & Frederick E. Greenspahn. 1987. 16.95. Crossroad NY.

Unclaimed Treasures. Baruch Silverstein. 1983. 15.00x (ISBN 0-88125-029-5). Ktav.

Uncle Ben's Instant Clip Quotes. Benjamin R. De Jong. 128p. 1985. pap. 5.95 (ISBN 0-8010-2954-6). Baker Bk.

Uncle Ben's Quotebook. Benjamin R. De Jong. 1976. 11.95 (ISBN 0-8010-2851-5). Baker Bk.

Uncle Bob Talks with My Digestive System. Bob DeVine. LC 85-4737. (Designed by God Ser.). (Illus.). 48p. 1985. pap. 4.95 (ISBN 0-89191-944-9, 59444, Chariot Bks). Cook.

Uncle Bob's Bible Stories. Bob Wolf. (Illus.). 108p. (Orig.). 1982. pap. 1.75 (ISBN 0-89323-028-6). Bible Memory.

Uncle Harry: An Autobiography. H. E. Wierwille. LC 78-73348. 55p. 1978. 5.95 (ISBN 0-910068-15-1). Am Christian.

Unclean Spirits: Possession & Exorcism in France & England in the Late 16th & Early 17th Centuries. D. P. Walker. LC 80-22649. 1981. 18.95x (ISBN 0-8122-7797-X). U of Pa Pr.

Uncomfortable Questions for Comfortable Jews. Meir Kahane. 288p. 1987. 18.00 (ISBN 0-8184-0438-8). Lyle Stuart.

Uncommon Prayers for Couples. Daniel R. Seagren. 1980. pap. 3.95 (ISBN 0-8010-8173-4). Baker Bk.

Uncommon Prayers: For Young Adults at Work. Daniel R. Seagren. 3.50 (ISBN 0-8010-8129-7). Baker Bk.

Uncommon Sense: The World's Fullest Compendium of Wisdom. Joseph Telushkin. 1986. 14.95 (ISBN 0-933503-48-2). Shapolsky Pubs.

Uncomplicated Christian. LeRoy Dugan. LC 78-66886. 128p. 1978. pap. 2.50 (ISBN 0-87123-572-2, 200572). Bethany Hse.

Unconditional Good News: Toward An Understanding of Biblical Universalism. Neal Punt. LC 80-10458. pap. 40.80 (ISBN 0-317-20014-3, 2023222). Bks Demand UMI.

Unconditional Good News: Toward an Understanding of Biblical Universalism. Neal Punt. LC 80-10458. pap. 44.80 (ISBN 0-317-39671-4, 2023222). Bks Demand UMI.

Unconditional Surrender: God's Program for Victory. 2nd ed. Gary North. LC 82-84385. 280p. 1983. pap. text ed. 9.95 (ISBN 0-939404-06-0). Geneva Ministr.

Unconquerable Spirit. Simon Zuker. Ed. by Gertrude Hirschler. (Illus.). 160p. 1980. pap. 8.95 (ISBN 0-89906-203-2). Mesorah Pubns.

Unconscious God. Victor Frankl. 1976. pap. 5.95 (ISBN 0-671-22426-3, Touchstone Bks). S&S.

Unconscious God. Viktor Frankl. 1985. pap. 3.50 (ISBN 0-671-54728-3). WSP.

Unconventional Women. Margaret Hess. 1981. pap. 5.95 (ISBN 0-88207-340-0). Victor Bks.

Under God's Arrest. Ida B. Bontrager. 1974. 11.50 (ISBN 0-87813-508-1). Christian Light.

Under His Wings. Ward Patterson. LC 86-70646. 160p. 1986. pap. 6.95 (ISBN 0-89636-216-7). Accent Bks.

Under the Broom Tree. Sean Caulfield. LC 82-60593. 80p. 1983. pap. 4.95 (ISBN 0-8091-2493-9). Paulist Pr.

Under the Cope of Heaven: Religion, Society & Politics in Colonial America. Patricia U. Bonomi. 292p. 1986. 24.95x (ISBN 0-19-504118-6). Oxford U Pr.

Under the Golden Cod: A Shared History of the Old North Church & the Town of Marblehead, Massachusetts. Three Hundred & Fiftieth Anniversary Book Committee of Old North Church. LC 84-7821. (Illus.). 160p. 1984. 17.95 (ISBN 0-914659-05-7). Phoenix Pub.

Under the Goldwood Tree. John Duffy. 64p. 1982. 5.00 (ISBN 0-682-49869-6). Exposition Pr FL.

Under the Guns in Beirut. Terry Raburn. LC 80-65308. 160p. 1980. pap. 2.50 (ISBN 0-88243-634-1, 02-0634). Gospel Pub.

Under the Nuptial Canopy. Rosenblatt. 1975. 6.00 (ISBN 0-87306-109-8). Feldheim.

Under the Sangre de Cristo. Paul Horgan. (Charlotte Ser.). 90p. 1985. 150.00x (ISBN 0-911292-00-4). Rydal.

Under the Shadow of Your Wings. Craig D. Erickson. Ed. by Michael L. Sherer. (Orig.). 1987. pap. 6.75 (ISBN 0-89536-844-7, 7803). CSS of Ohio.

Under the Shelter of His Wings. Glenn Clark. pap. 0.20 (ISBN 0-910924-50-3). Macalester.

Underground Literature, 2 vols. in 1. 80p. 1.95 (ISBN 0-686-74969-3). ADL.

Underground Manual for Spiritual Survival. Larry Neagle. (Orig.). 1986. pap. 4.95 (ISBN 0-8024-9052-2). Moody.

Understanding. Churches Alive, Inc. Staff. LC 79-52129. (Love One Another Bible Study Ser.). (Illus.). 1979. wkbk. 3.00 (ISBN 0-934396-02-7). Churches Alive.

Understanding Adolescence. Ronald L. Koteskey. 168p. 1987. pap. 5.95 (ISBN 0-89693-249-4). Victor Bks.

Understanding Aging Parents. Andrew D. Lester & Judith L. Lester. LC 80-17832. (Christian Care Bks.: Vol. 8). 120p. 1980. pap. 7.95 (ISBN 0-664-24329-0). Westminster.

Understanding American Jewish Philanthropy. Marc L. Raphael. 20.00x (ISBN 0-87068-689-5). Ktav.

Understanding American Jewry. Ed. by Marshall Sklare. LC 81-14795. 300p. 1982. text ed. 21.95x (ISBN 0-87855-454-8). Transaction Bks.

Understanding American Judaism: Toward the Description of a Modern Religion, 2 vols. Jacob Neusner. Incl. Vol. 1. The Synagogue & the Rabbi (ISBN 0-87068-279-2); Vol. 2. Reform, Orthodoxy, Conservatism, & Reconstructionism (ISBN 0-87068-280-6). pap. 11.95 ea. Ktav.

Understanding & Applying the Bible. Robertson McQuilkin. (Orig.). 1983. pap. 8.95 (ISBN 0-8024-0457-X). Moody.

Understanding & Being: An Introduction & Companion to Insight. Bernard J. F. Lonergan. Ed. by Elizabeth A. Morelli & Mark D. Morelli. (Toronto Studies in Theology: Vol. 5). xii, 368p. 1980. 59.95x (ISBN 0-88946-909-1). E Mellen.

Understanding & Believing: Essays. Joachim Wach. Ed. by Joseph M. Kitagawa. LC 75-31987. 204p. 1976. Repr. of 1968 ed. lib. bdg. 25.00x (ISBN 0-8371-8488-6, WAUB). Greenwood.

Understanding & Counseling the Alcoholic. rev. ed. Howard J. Clinebell, Jr. LC 56-10143. 1968. 13.95 (ISBN 0-687-42803-3). Abingdon.

Understanding & Implementing Development. Richard J. Burke. 1985. 4.80 (ISBN 0-318-18573-3). Natl Cath Educ.

Understanding & Teaching the Bible. Richard L. Jeske. Ed. by Harold W. Rast. LC 80-69756. (Lead Book). 128p. (Orig.). 1981. pap. 3.95 (ISBN 0-8006-1601-4, 1-1601). Fortress.

Understanding Authority for Effective Leadership. rev. ed. Doyle Harrison. 122p. (Orig.). 1985. pap. 3.50 (ISBN 0-89274-379-4). Harrison Hse.

Understanding Bible Doctrine. rev. ed. Charles C. Ryrie. (Elective Ser.). 1983. pap. 3.95 (ISBN 0-8024-0258-5). Moody.

Understanding Bible Doctrine: Leader's Guide. (Electives Ser.). 1983. pap. 2.50 (ISBN 0-8024-0308-5). Moody.

Understanding Biblical Symbols. Charles L. Edwards. 96p. 1981. 6.00 (ISBN 0-682-49704-5). Exposition Pr FL.

Understanding Buddhism. Nolan P. Jacobson. 224p. (Orig.). 1985. text ed. 19.95x (ISBN 0-8093-1224-7); pap. text ed. 10.95x (ISBN 0-8093-1225-5). S Ill U Pr.

Understanding Catholicism. Monika K. Hellwig. LC 81-80047. 200p. (Orig.). 1981. pap. 5.95 (ISBN 0-8091-2384-3). Paulist Pr.

Understanding Christian Missions. J. Herbert Kane. 16.95 (ISBN 0-8010-5344-7). Baker Bk.

Understanding Christian Morality. Ronald J. Wilkins. (To Live Is Christ Ser). 256p. 1982. pap. 5.75; tchr's. manual 5.00 (ISBN 0-697-01800-8); spirit masters 10.95 (ISBN 0-697-01801-6); kit 20.00 (ISBN 0-697-01675-7). Wm C Brown.

Understanding Christian Morality: Short Edition. Ronald J. Wilkins. (To Live Is Christ Ser.). 112p. 1977. pap. 4.20 (ISBN 0-697-01661-7); tchr's. manual 6.00 (ISBN 0-697-01667-6). Wm C Brown.

Understanding Christian Worship: School Edition. Ronald J. Wilkins. (To Live Is Christ Ser.). 216p. 1982. pap. 5.50 (ISBN 0-697-01802-4); tchr's. manual 5.00 (ISBN 0-697-01803-2); kit 32.00 (ISBN 0-697-01676-5); spirit masters 6.50 (ISBN 0-697-01902-0); poster 3.50 (ISBN 0-697-01903-9); activity cards 7.50 (ISBN 0-697-01904-7); progress in prayer 11.50 (ISBN 0-697-01905-5); prayer planning forms 3.00 (ISBN 0-697-01906-3). Wm C Brown.

Understanding Christian Worship: Short Edition. Ronald J. Wilkins. (To Live Is Christ Ser.). 80p. 1977. pap. 3.95 (ISBN 0-697-01663-3); tchr's. ed. 6.00 (ISBN 0-697-01669-2). Wm C Brown.

Understanding Chronicles One & Two. John Heading. pap. 7.95 (ISBN 0-937396-10-9). Walterick Pubs.

Understanding Church Finances: The Economics of the Local Church. Loyde H. Hartley. LC 83-23769. 192p. (Orig.). 1984. pap. 10.95 (ISBN 0-8298-0708-X). Pilgrim NY.

Understanding Church Growth. rev. ed. Donald McGavran. 488p. (Orig.). 1980. pap. 12.95 (ISBN 0-8028-1849-8). Eerdmans.

Understanding Church Growth & Decline, 1950-78. Ed. by Dean R. Hoge & David A. Roozen. LC 79-4166. (Illus.). 1979. pap. 9.95 (ISBN 0-8298-0358-0). Pilgrim NY.

Understanding Conservative Judaism. Robert Gordis. 15.00x (ISBN 0-87068-680-1). Ktav.

Understanding Cults & New Religions. Irving Hexham & Karla Poewe. 192p. (Orig.). 1986. pap. 8.95 (ISBN 0-8028-0170-6). Eerdmans.

Understanding Cultural Values. Ida R. Bellegarde. LC 79-51620. 1979. 4.45x (ISBN 0-918340-09-8). Bell Ent.

Understanding Divine Healing. Richard M. Sipley. 168p. 1986. pap. 5.95 (ISBN 0-89693-263-X). Victor Bks.

Understanding Exodus. Moshe Greenberg. 214p. 1969. pap. 9.95x (ISBN 0-87441-265-X). Behrman.

Understanding Genesis: The Heritage of Biblical Israel. Nahum M. Sarna. LC 66-23626. 1970. pap. 7.50 (ISBN 0-8052-0253-6). Schocken.

Understanding Hebrew Literature: A Guide to a Better Understanding of the Bible As a Source Book for the Humanities. John C. Kersten. 2.25 (ISBN 0-89942-145-8, 145/04). Catholic Bk Pub.

Understanding Human Values: Individual & Societal. Milton Rokeach. LC 78-24753. (Illus.). 1979. 14.95 (ISBN 0-02-926760-9). Free Pr.

Understanding Islam. Frithjof Schuon. Tr. by D. M. Matheson. (Unwin Paperback Ser.). 1976. pap. 5.95 (ISBN 0-04-297035-0). Allen Unwin.

Understanding Islam: An Introduction to the Moslem World. Thomas W. Lippman. LC 81-85142. 208p. 1982. pap. 3.50 (ISBN 0-451-62501-3, ME2079, Ment). NAL.

Understanding Islam Through Hadis: Religious Faith or Fanaticism? Ram Swarup. 1983. 13.95 (ISBN 0-682-49948-X). Exposition Pr FL.

Understanding Israel: A Social Studies Approach. Amos Elon. Ed. by Morris J. Sugarman. LC 76-18282. (Illus.). 256p. 1976. pap. text ed. 6.95x (ISBN 0-87441-234-X). Behrman.

Understanding Jesus: Who Jesus Christ Is & Why He Matters. Allister E. McGrath. Ed. by E. Van der Maas. (Orig.). 1987. Repr. write for info. (ISBN 0-310-29810-5). Zondervan.

Understanding Jewish Mysticism: A Source Reader, No. I. D. R. Blumenthal. (Library of Judaic Learning). Vol. II. 20.00x (ISBN 0-87068-334-9); pap. 9.95. Ktav.

Understanding Jewish Mysticism: The Philosophic-Mystical Tradition & the Hasidic Tradition, Vol.II. David Blumanthal. 20.00x (ISBN 0-87068-205-9); pap. 9.95 (ISBN 0-87068-225-3). Ktav.

Understanding Jewish Prayer. Ed. by Jakob J. Petuchowski. 1972. pap. 7.95x (ISBN 0-87068-186-9). Ktav.

Understanding Jewish Theology. Jacob Neusner. 1973. pap. 11.95x (ISBN 0-87068-215-6). Ktav.

Understanding Jewish Theology: Classsical Issues & Modern Perspective. Jacob Neusner. 280p. pap. 9.95 (ISBN 0-686-95185-9). ADL.

Understanding Judaism. Eugene Borowitz. 1979. 7.50 (ISBN 0-8074-0027-0, 341800). UAHC.

Understanding Karl Rahner, 2 vols. George Vass. (Orig.). 1985. Vol. 1, 153 pgs. pap. 12.50 (ISBN 0-87061-115-1); Vol. 2, 200 pgs. pap. 12.50 (ISBN 0-87061-116-X); Set. pap. 25.00 (ISBN 0-317-20726-1). Chr Classics.

Understanding Karl Rahner: An Introduction to His Life & Thought. Herbert Vorgrimler. 176p. 1986. 14.95 (ISBN 0-8245-0790-8). Crossroad NY.

Understanding Locke. J. J. Jenkins. 192p. 1983. 15.00x (ISBN 0-85224-449-5, Pub. by Edinburgh U Pr Scotland). Columbia U Pr.

Understanding Man. Ray C. Stedman. LC 86-16463. (Authentic Christianity Ser.). (Orig.). 1986. pap. 6.95 (ISBN 0-88070-156-0). Multnomah.

Understanding Modern Theology I: Cultural Revolutions & New World. Jeffery Hopper. LC 86-45210. 192p. 1986. 14.95 (ISBN 0-8006-1929-3). Fortress.

Understanding Mourning: A Guide for Those Who Grieve. Glen W. Davidson. LC 84-14527. 112p. (Orig.). 1984. pap. 5.95 (ISBN 0-8066-2080-3, 10-6805). Augsburg.

Understanding My Church. rev. ed. Samuel J. Stoesz. LC 82-73214. 216p. 1983. pap. 5.95 (ISBN 0-87509-325-6); leader's guide 2.95 (ISBN 0-87509-331-0). Chr Pubns.

Understanding Non-Christian Religions. Josh McDowell & Don Stewart. LC 81-86543. (Handbook of Today's Religion Ser.). 208p. 1982. pap. 6.95 (ISBN 0-86605-092-2, 402834). Heres Life.

Understanding of the Church: Sources of Early Christian Thought. Ed. & tr. by E. Glenn Hinson. pap. 6.95 (ISBN 0-317-52518-2). Fortress.

Understanding Paul. Richard L. Anderson. LC 83-72103. 448p. 1983. 10.95 (ISBN 0-87747-984-4). Deseret Bk.

Understanding People: Children, Youth, Adults. J. Omar Brubaker & Robert E. Clark. LC 75-172116. 96p. 1981. pap. text ed. 4.95 (ISBN 0-910566-15-1); Perfect bdg. instr's. guide 5.95 (ISBN 0-910566-25-9). Evang Tchr.

Understanding Popular Culture: Europe from the Middle Ages to the Nineteenth Century. Ed. by Steven L. Kaplan. LC 84-1001. (New Babylon, Studies in the Social Sciences: No. 40). viii, 311p. 1984. 64.75x (ISBN 3-11-009600-5). Mouton.

Understanding Rabbinic Judaism: From Talmudic to Modern Times. Jacob Neusner. 1974. pap. 11.95x (ISBN 0-685-56200-X). Ktav.

Understanding Rabbinic Midrash. Gary G. Porton. 1985. 14.95 (ISBN 0-88125-056-2). Ktav.

Understanding Religion. Eric J. Sharpe. LC 82-25055. 160p. 1984. 19.95 (ISBN 0-312-83208-7). St Martin.

Understanding Religious Convictions. James W. McClendon, Jr. LC 74-34519. 256p. 1975. text ed. 16.95x (ISBN 0-268-01903-7); pap. 7.95x (ISBN 0-268-01904-5). U of Notre Dame Pr.

Understanding Religious Life. 3rd ed. Streng. 1984. write for info. (ISBN 0-534-03699-6). Wadsworth Pub.

Understanding Scripture. 2nd ed. A. Berkeley Mickelsen & Alvera M. Mickelsen. LC 81-52231. (Better Bible Study Ser.). 1982. pap. 3.50 (ISBN 0-8307-0795-6, 5017302). Regal.

Understanding Scripture: Explorations of Jewish & Christian Traditions of Interpretation. Ed. by Clemens Thoma & Michael Wyschgrod. 1987. pap. 7.95 (ISBN 0-8091-2873-X). Paulist Pr.

Understanding Scripture: What Is the Bible & How Does It Speak? John F. Balchin. LC 81-8271. 98p. (Orig.). 1981. pap. 2.95 (ISBN 0-87784-875-0). Inter-Varsity.

Understanding Sectarian Groups in America. George W. Braswell, Jr. 1986. pap. 10.95 (ISBN 0-8054-6607-X). Broadman.

Understanding Secular Religions. Josh McDowell & Don Stewart. 140p. 1982. pap. 6.95 (ISBN 0-86605-093-0). Here's Life.

Understanding Seeking Faith: Essays on the Case of Judaism Vol. 1: Dabates on Method Reports of Results. Jacob Neusner. (Brown University Ser.). 158p. 1986. 25.95 (ISBN 1-55540-053-1, 14-01-16). Scholars Pr GA.

Understanding Self & Society. Dorothy B. Fardan. LC 80-81696. 232p. 1981. 14.95 (ISBN 0-8022-2370-2). Philos Lib.

Understanding Shmittah. David Marchant. 1987. 10.95. Feldheim.

Understanding Sunday School. 96p. 1980. pap. text ed. 4.95 (ISBN 0-910566-31-3); Perfect bdg. instr's guide by Robert E. Clark 5.95 (ISBN 0-910566-32-1). Evang Tchr.

Understanding Teaching. Kenneth O. Gangel. LC 68-24579. 96p. 1979. pap. text ed. 4.95 (ISBN 0-910566-14-3); Perfect bdg. instr's. guide 5.95 (ISBN 0-910566-26-7). Evang Tchr.

Understanding the Anointing. Kenneth Hagin. 1983. pap. 3.50 (ISBN 0-89276-507-0). Hagin Ministries.

Understanding the Atonement for the Mission of the Church. John Driver. LC 86-3133. 288p. (Orig.). 1986. pap. 19.95 (ISBN 0-8361-3403-6). Herald Pr.

Understanding the Bible. 2nd ed. Stephen L. Harris. 1985. pap. 19.95 (ISBN 0-87484-696-X). Mayfield Pub.

Understanding the Bible. rev. ed. John R. Stott. 256p. 1982. pap. 6.95 (ISBN 0-310-41451-2, 12610P). Zondervan.

Understanding the Bible. 2nd ed. John R. Stott. 192p. 1985. pap. 6.95 (ISBN 0-310-41431-8). Zondervan.

Understanding the Bible & Science. Paul L Walker. LC 75-25343. (Illus.). 1976. pap. 1.99 (ISBN 0-87148-878-7). Pathway Pr.

Understanding the Bible: School Edition. rev. ed. Ronald J. Wilkins. (To Live Is Christ Ser.). 212p. 1982. pap. 5.75 (ISBN 0-697-01786-9); tchr's. manual 5.00 (ISBN 0-697-01787-7); spirit masters 12.95. Wm C Brown.

Understanding the Bible: Short Edition. Ronald J. Wilkins. (To Live Is Christ Ser.). 1977. pap. 3.95 (ISBN 0-697-01659-5); tchr's. manual 6.00 (ISBN 0-697-01665-X); spirit masters 12.95. Wm C Brown.

Understanding the Bible Through History & Archaeology. Harry M. Orlinsky. 1969. 12.50x (ISBN 0-87068-096-X). Ktav.

Understanding the Christian Faith. Charles D. Barrett. (Illus.). 1980. text ed. write for info. (ISBN 0-13-935882-X). P-H.

Understanding the Christian Faith. Georgia Harkness. (Festival Ser.). 192p. 1981. pap. 1.95 (ISBN 0-687-42955-2). Abingdon.

Understanding the Cults. Josh McDowell & Don Stewart. LC 81-81850. (Handbook of Today's Religion Ser.). 199p. 1982. pap. 6.95 (ISBN 0-86605-090-6, 402826). Heres Life.

Understanding the Difficult Words of Jesus. David Bivin. LC 83-61850. (Illus.). 172p. (Orig.). 1983. pap. 8.95 (ISBN 0-918873-00-2). Ctr Judaic-Christ Studies.

Understanding the Faith of the Church. Richard A. Norris. (Church's Teaching Ser.: Vol. 4). 288p. 1979. 5.95 (ISBN 0-8164-0421-6, HarpR); pap. 3.95 (ISBN 0-8164-2217-6, Crossroad Bks); user guide .95 (ISBN 0-8164-2224-9). Har-Row.

Understanding the Fear of the Lord. Dennis Burke. 1982. pap. 2.25 (ISBN 0-89274-265-8, HH-265). Harrison Hse.

Understanding the Feasts of the Lord, God's Time Clock for the Ages. Roger V. Houtsma. 195p. (Orig.). 1986. pap. 6.95 (ISBN 0-9617623-0-6). World Outreach.

Understanding the Greek Orthodox Church: Its Faith, History & Practice. Demetrios J. Constantelos. 214p. 1982. (HarpR); pap. 9.95 (ISBN 0-8164-2367-9). Har-Row.

Understanding the Heart. rev. ed. Francis Larkin. LC 80-81066. 127p. 1980. pap. 5.95 (ISBN 0-89870-007-8). Ignatius Pr.

Understanding the High Holyday Service. Jeffrey M. Cohen. 218p. 1983. 12.50 (ISBN 0-317-26854-6). Hebrew Pub.

Understanding the Human Jesus: A Journey in Scripture & Imagination. Andrew Canale. LC 84-61027. 208p. 1985. pap. 7.95 (ISBN 0-8091-2654-0). Paulist Pr.

Understanding the Jewish Experience. 54p. 2.00 (ISBN 0-686-74981-2). ADL.

Understanding the Living Word. G. Hansel. 1980. pap. 8.95 (ISBN 0-8163-0372-X). Pacific Pr Pub Assn.

Understanding the Mass Today. Lawrence E. Mick. 20p. 1985. pap. 0.30 (ISBN 0-8146-1390-X). Liturgical Pr.

Understanding the Message of Paul. Norbert Brox. Tr. by Joseph Blenkinsopp. (Orig.). 1968. pap. 1.45x (ISBN 0-268-00286-X). U of Notre Dame Pr.

Understanding the New Religions. Ed. by Jacob Needleman & George Baker. 1978. (HarpR); pap. 8.95 (ISBN 0-8164-2188-9). Har-Row.

Understanding the New Testament. 4th ed. Howard C. Kee. (Illus.). 464p. 1983. text ed. 33.00 (ISBN 0-13-936591-5). P-H.

Understanding the New Testament. O. Jessie Lace. (Cambridge Bible Commentary on the New English Bible, New Testament Ser.). 16.95 (ISBN 0-521-04205-4); pap. 9.95 (ISBN 0-521-09281-7). Cambridge U Pr.

Understanding the New Testament. Francis B. Rhein. LC 65-23532. 1974. pap. text ed. 6.95 (ISBN 0-8120-0027-7). Barron.

Understanding the Old Testament. 4th ed. Bernhard W. Anderson. (Illus.). 672p. 1986. text ed. write for info (ISBN 0-13-935925-7). P-H.

Understanding the Old Testament. A. H. Gunneweg. Tr. by John Bowden. LC 78-6696. (Old Testament Library). 272p. 1978. Westminster.

Understanding the Old Testament. Ed. by O. Jessie Lace. LC 75-178282. (Cambridge Bible Commmentary on the New English Bible, Old Testament Ser.). (Illus.). 200p. 1972. 18.95 (ISBN 0-521-08415-6); pap. 9.95 (ISBN 0-521-09691-X). Cambridge U Pr.

Understanding the Old Testament. Jay G. Williams. LC 74-162825. 1972. pap. 6.95 (ISBN 0-8120-0424-8). Barron.

Understanding the Old Testament: The Way of Holiness. J. E. Fison. LC 78-21116. 1979. Repr. of 1952 ed. lib. bdg. 24.75x (ISBN 0-313-20839-5, FIUO). Greenwood.

Understanding the Prophets. Sheldon Blank. 144p. 1983. pap. text ed. 4.00 (ISBN 0-8074-0250-8, 382755). UAHC.

Understanding the Psalms. John H. Hayes. LC 75-22034. 128p. 1976. pap. 4.95 (ISBN 0-8170-0683-4). Judson.

Understanding the Pupil, 3 pts. Marjorie E. Soderholm. Incl. Pt. 1. Pre-School Child; Pt. 2. Primary & Junior Child; Pt. 3. Adolescent. pap. 2.50 (ISBN 0-8010-7922-5). pap. Baker Bk.

Understanding the Quran. Morteza Mutahhari. Tr. by Mohammad S. Tawheedi from Persian. LC 84-50586. 64p. 1985. pap. 3.95 (ISBN 0-940368-35-8). Tahrike Tarsile Quran.

Understanding the Scriptures. Lowell L. Bennion. LC 81-66422. 88p. 1981. 6.95 (ISBN 0-87747-863-5). Deseret Bk.

Understanding the Sermon on the Mount. Harvey K. McArthur. LC 78-16404. 1978. Repr. of 1960 ed. lib. bdg. 22.50 (ISBN 0-313-20569-8, MCUS). Greenwood.

Understanding the Signs of the Times. Ed. by Franz Bockle. LC 67-25694. (Concilium Ser.: Vol. 25). 176p. 1967. 7.95 (ISBN 0-8091-0152-1). Paulist Pr.

Understanding the Talmud. Allan Corre. 1971. pap. 8.95x (ISBN 0-685-22510-0). Ktav.

Understanding the Talmud. Ernest R. Trattner. LC 77-27887. 1978. Repr. of 1955 ed. lib. bdg. 22.50x (ISBN 0-313-20253-2, TRUT). Greenwood.

Understanding the Teaching of Jesus. David Abernathy & Norman Perrin. 288p. (Orig.). 1983. pap. 13.95 (ISBN 0-8164-2438-1, HarpR). Har-Row.

Understanding the Times. G. I. Williamson. 1979. pap. 2.95 (ISBN 0-87552-541-5). Presby & Reformed.

Understanding the Times of Christ. William W. Menzies. 128p. 1969. 1.50 (ISBN 0-88243-622-8, 02-0622). Gospel Pub.

Understanding the Word: Essays in Honor of Bernhard W. Anderson. James T. Butler et al. (JSOT Supplement Ser.: No. 37). 390p. 1986. text ed. 37.50x (ISBN 0-905774-88-4, Pub. by JSOT Pr England). Eisenbrauns.

Understanding Violence. Graeme R. Newman. 1979. pap. text ed. 15.50 scp (ISBN 0-397-47396-6, HarpC). Har-Row.

Understanding World Religions. George W. Braswell, Jr. LC 81-65828. (Orig.). 1983. pap. 7.95 (ISBN 0-8054-6605-3). Broadman.

Understanding Your Church's Curriculum. rev. ed. Howard P. Colson & Raymond M. Rigdon. LC 80-67351. 1981. pap. 5.95 (ISBN 0-8054-3201-9). Broadman.

Understanding Your Emotions. Joyce M. Smith. 1977. pap. 2.95 (ISBN 0-8423-7770-0). Tyndale.

Understanding Your Faith: An Introduction to Catholic Christianity for Freshmen. Thomas Zanzig. LC 80-50258. (Illus.). 192p. 1980. pap. text ed. 7.00x (ISBN 0-88489-115-1); tchr's guide 9.00x (ISBN 0-88489-122-4); spiritmasters 9.95 (ISBN 0-88489-131-3). St Mary's.

Understanding Your Temperament: A Self-Analysis with a Christian Viewpoint. Peter Blitchington & Robert J. Cruise. 38p. (Orig.). 1979. pap. 2.95 (ISBN 0-943872-67-7). Andrews Univ Pr.

Understanding Yourself, Society & Marriage. Nehemiah M. Palmer. 288p. 1984. pap. 7.95 (ISBN 0-912315-82-2). Word Aflame.

Understandings of Man. Perry LeFevre. LC 66-10432. 186p. 1966. pap. 6.95 (ISBN 0-664-24678-8). Westminster.

Understandings of Prayer. Perry LeFevre. LC 81-11622. 212p. 1981. pap. 10.95 (ISBN 0-664-24382-7). Westminster.

Understandings of the Church. Ed. by E. Glenn Hinson. LC 86-45227. (Sources of Early Christian Thought Ser.). 128p. 1986. pap. 7.95 (ISBN 0-8006-1415-1, 1-1415). Fortress.

Underworld Initiation: A Journey Towards Psychic Transformation. R. J. Stewart. 272p. 1985. pap. 11.95 (ISBN 0-85030-399-0). Newcastle Pub.

Undiscovered Country: In Search of Gurdjieff. Kathryn Hulme. 1972. pap. 4.95 (ISBN 0-316-38138-1, Pub. by Atlantic Monthly Pr). Little.

Undisturbed Soldier. Ed Irsch. 1983. 4.25 (ISBN 0-89536-602-9, 2105). CSS of Ohio.

Undivided Self: Bringing Your Whole Life in Line with God's Will. Earl D. Wilson. LC 83-6189. 191p. (Orig.). 1983. pap. 5.95 (ISBN 0-87784-842-4). Inter-Varsity.

Undoing Yourself with Energized Meditation & Other Devices. Christopher S. Hyatt. LC 82-83293. 114p. 1982. pap. 6.95 (ISBN 0-941404-06-4). Falcon Pr Az.

Undying Dedication. R. Vernon Boyd. 1985. pap. 5.95 (ISBN 0-89225-281-2). Gospel Advocate.

Uneasy at Home: Antisemitism & the American Jewish Experience. Leonard Dinnerstein. LC 87-521. 272p. 1987. 25.00 (ISBN 0-231-06252-4). Columbia U Pr.

Unequally Yoked. 2nd ed. William S. Deal. LC 80-67387. 112p. 1987. pap. 4.95 (Crossway Bks). Good News.

Unequally Yoked Wives. C. S. Lovett. 1968. pap. 5.45 (ISBN 0-938148-22-2). Personal Christianity.

Unexpected Meditations Late in the Twentieth Century. James V. Schall. 142p. 1986. 9.95 (ISBN 0-8199-0885-1). Franciscan Herald.

Unexpected News: Reading the Bible with Third World Eyes. Robert M. Brown. LC 84-2380. 166p. 1984. pap. 7.95 (ISBN 0-664-24552-8). Westminster.

Unfettered Mind: Writings of the Zen Master to the Sword Master. Takuan Soho. LC 86-45072. 92p. 1986. 12.95 (ISBN 0-87011-776-9). Kodansha.

Unfinished Agenda: An Autobiography. Lesslie Newbigin. (Illus.). 280p. (Orig.). 1985. pap. 11.95 (ISBN 0-8028-0091-2). Eerdmans.

Unfinished Animal. Theodore Roszak. 1977. pap. 5.95 (ISBN 0-06-090537-9, CN 537, PL). Har-Row.

Unfinished Church: A Brief History of the Union of the Evangelical United Brethern Church & the Methodist Church. Paul Washburn. 176p. 14.95 (ISBN 0-687-01378-X). Abingdon.

Unfinished Dialogue: Martin Buber & the Christian Way. John M. Oesterreicher. LC 85-12410. 128p. 1986. 14.95 (ISBN 0-8022-2495-4). Philos Lib.

Unfinished Dialogue: Martin Buber & the Christian Way. John M. Osterreicher. 136p. 1987. pap. 5.95 (ISBN 0-8065-1050-1). Citadel Pr.

Unfinished... Essays in Honor of Ray L. Hart. Ed. by Mark C. Taylor. (JAAR Thematic Studies). 1981. pap. 13.50 (ISBN 0-89130-680-3, 01-24-81). Scholars Pr GA.

Unfinished Image. George McCauley. 462p. (Orig.). 1983. pap. 10.95 (ISBN 0-8215-9903-8). Sadlier.

Unfinished Man & the Imagination: Toward an Ontology & a Rhetoric of Revelation. Ray Hart. (Reprints & Translations Ser.). 1985. pap. text ed. 12.95 (ISBN 0-89130-937-3, 00-07-15). Scholars Pr GA.

Unfinished Mystery. John Walchars. (Orig.). 1978. pap. 5.95 (ISBN 0-8164-2184-6, HarpR). Har-Row.

Unfinished Reformation. facs. ed. Charles C. Morrison. LC 68-20322. (Essay Index Reprint Ser). 1953. 17.50 (ISBN 0-8369-0723-X). Ayer Co Pubs.

Unfinished Task. Compiled by John E. Kyle. LC 84-11727. 1984. pap. 6.95 (ISBN 0-8307-0983-5, 5418342). Regal.

Unfolding Daniel. R. A. Anderson. LC 75-16526. (Dimension Ser.). 192p. 1975. pap. 6.95 (ISBN 0-8163-0180-8, 21390-0). Pacific Pr Pub Assn.

Unfolding Drama of the Bible. rev. ed. Bernhard W. Anderson. LC 78-14057. 1971. pap. 3.95 (ISBN 0-8329-1068-6, Assn Pr). New Century.

Unfolding of Neo-Confucianism. Ed. by W. Theodore De Bary. LC 74-10929. (Neo-Confucian Series & Studies in Oriental Culture: No. 10). 593p. 1975. 38.00x (ISBN 0-231-03828-3); pap. 18.50x (ISBN 0-231-03829-1). Columbia U Pr.

Unfolding Plan of Redemption. Leland M. Haines. 1982. 3.50 (ISBN 0-87813-517-0). Christian Light.

Unfolding the Revelation. Roy A. Anderson. LC 61-10884. (Dimension Ser.). 223p. 1961. pap. 6.95 (ISBN 0-8163-0027-5, 21400-7). Pacific Pr Pub Assn.

Unforgiveness. Kenneth Hagin, Jr. 1983. pap. 0.50 (ISBN 0-89276-716-2). Hagin Ministries.

Unforgotten Things. (Illus.). 6.95 (ISBN 0-686-46782-5). Inspiration Conn.

Unfortunate Fall: Theodicy & the Moral Imagination of Andrew Marvell. John Klause. LC 83-13521. x, 208p. 1984. 22.50 (ISBN 0-208-02026-8, Archon Bks). Shoe String.

Unfriendly Governor. Anthony A. Lee. (Stories About 'Abdu'l-Baha Ser.). (Illus.). 24p. 1980. pap. 2.50 (ISBN 0-933770-02-2). Kalimat.

Unger's Bible Dictionary. Merrill F. Unger. 1961. 22.95 (ISBN 0-8024-9035-2). Moody.

Unger's Bible Dictionary. Merrill F. Unger. (Affordables Ser.). (Illus.). 1200p. 13.95 (ISBN 0-8024-0418-9). Moody.

Unger's Bible Handbook. Merrill F. Unger. LC 66-16224. 1966. 9.95 (ISBN 0-8024-9039-5). Moody.

Unger's Commentary On The Old Testament: Genesis-Song of Solomon, Vol. 1. Merrill F. Unger. 360p. 1981. 25.95 (ISBN 0-8024-9028-X). Moody.

Unger's Commentary on the Old Testament: Vol. 2 (Isaiah-Malachi) Merrill F. Unger. LC 81-2542. 1000p. 1982. 25.95 (ISBN 0-8024-9029-8). Moody.

Unger's Concise Bible Dictionary: With Complete Pronunciation Guide to Bible Names by W. Murray Severance. Merrill F. Unger. 296p. 1985. pap. 7.95 (ISBN 0-8010-9208-6). Baker Bk.

Unger's Survey of the Bible. Merill F. Unger. LC 81-82675. 432p. 1981. pap. 12.95 (ISBN 0-89081-298-5). Harvest Hse.

Unheeded Teachings of Christ or Christ Rejected. Emanuel M. Josephson. 1979. write for info. (ISBN 0-685-96472-8). Revisionist Pr.

Unheeded Teachings of Jesus Christ or Christ Rejected: The Strangest Story Never Told. Emanuel Josephson. LC 59-15870. (Blacked-Out History Ser.). (Illus.). 96p. 1959. 3.50 (ISBN 0-686-32441-2); pap. 3.00 (ISBN 0-686-32442-0). A-albionic Res.

Unheeded Teachings of Jesus: Christ Rejected. Emanuel M. Josephson. (Illus.). 50.00 (ISBN 0-685-07976-7). Chedney.

Unholy Devotion: Why Cults Lure Christians. Harold L. Bussell. 160p. 1983. pap. 5.95 (ISBN 0-310-37251-8, 12388P). Zondervan.

Unholy Rollers: The Selling of Jesus. Arthur F. Ide. LC 85-19883. (Illus.). 120p. 1985. pap. 5.95 (ISBN 0-935175-01-6). Lib Arts Pr.

Unicorn. Sri Donato. Ed. by Morningland Publications, Inc. (Illus.). 207p. (Orig.). 1981. pap. 10.00 (ISBN 0-935146-16-4). Morningland.

Unicorn & the Garden. Ed. by Betty Parry. LC 78-64531. (Illus.). 1978. perfect bdg. 10.00 (ISBN 0-915380-04-8). Word Works.

Unification Church in America: Sects & Cults in America. Michael J. Mickler. LC 83-48225. (Bibliographical Guides Ser.). 130p. 1986. lib. bdg. 19.00 (ISBN 0-8240-9040-3). Garland Pub.

Unification Church Policy on South Africa. Dibinga wa Said. (Christian Churches Policies on South Africa Ser.). 14p. (Orig.). 1986. pap. write for info. (ISBN 0-943324-26-2). Omenana.

Unification Theology. Young O. Kim. LC 80-52872. 294p. 1980. pap. 8.95 (ISBN 0-318-11689-8). Rose Sharon Pr.

Unification Theology & Christian Thought. Young O. Kim. LC 74-32590. 302p. 1976. pap. 6.95 (ISBN 0-318-11688-X). Rose Sharon Pr.

Unification Theology & Christian Thought. Dr. Young Oon Kim. pap. 4.00 (ISBN 0-686-13407-9). Unification Church.

Unification Theology Seminar, Virgin Islands: Proceedings. Ed. by Darrol Bryant. LC 80-52594. 323p. 1980. pap. 9.95. Rose Sharon Pr.

Unification Thought. 1975. pap. 5.00 (ISBN 0-686-13405-2); Study Guide. pap. text ed. 1.50 (ISBN 0-686-13406-0). Unification Church.

Uniformity with God's Will. St. Alphonsus de Liguori. 1977. pap. 1.00 (ISBN 0-89555-019-9). TAN Bks Pubs.

Unio Mystica, 2 vols. 2nd ed. Bhagwan Shree Rajneesh. Ed. by Ma Ananda Vandana. LC 82-245842. (Sufi Ser.). (Illus.). 1980. Vol. I 384p. 17.95 ea. (ISBN 0-88050-163-4). Vol. II (ISBN 0-88050-164-2). Vol. I. pap. 13.95 ea. (ISBN 0-88050-663-6). Vol. II 368p 1981 (ISBN 0-88050-664-4). Chidvilas Found.

Union & Communion. Hudson Taylor. 96p. 1971. pap. 2.95 (ISBN 0-87123-571-4, 200571). Bethany Hse.

Union & Oneness. Sri Chinmoy. 50p. (Orig.). 1976. pap. 2.00 (ISBN 0-88497-266-6). Aum Pubns.

Union Haggadah. 1977. Repr. of 1923 ed. 4.75 (ISBN 0-916694-08-9). Central Conf.

Union Home Prayerbook. 1951. 7.95 ea. (ISBN 0-916694-19-4); leatherbound 7.00 ea. (ISBN 0-916694-60-7). Central Conf.

Union Prayerbook, 2 vols. 1977. Vol. 1. 10.00 (ISBN 0-916694-09-7); Vol. 2. 10.00 (ISBN 0-916694-10-0); pulpit ed. 15.00 (ISBN 0-686-67882-6). Central Conf.

Union with Christ. Norman Douty. 10.95 (ISBN 0-685-36792-4). Reiner.

Union with Christ: A Biblical View of the New Life in Jesus Christ. rev. ed. Lewis B. Smedes. Orig. Title: All Things Made New. 208p. 1983. pap. 4.95 (ISBN 0-8028-1963-X). Eerdmans.

Union with God. Jeanne Guyon. Ed. by Gene Edwards. 117p. 1981. pap. 5.95 (ISBN 0-940232-05-7). Christian Bks.

Union with the Lord in Prayer: Beyond Meditation to Affective Prayer, Aspiration & Contemplation. Venard Poslusney. (Illus., Orig.). 1973. pap. 1.50 (ISBN 0-914544-03-9). Living Flame Pr.

Unique Advantages of Being a Mormon. W. Lynn Fluckiger. pap. 3.95 (ISBN 0-89036-138-X). Hawkes Pub Inc.

Unique World of Women. Eugenia Price. 248p. 1982. pap. 7.95 (ISBN 0-310-31351-1, 16216P). Zondervan.

Unitarian Conscience. Daniel W. Howe. LC 75-116737. 15.00 (ISBN 0-674-92121-6). Harvard U Pr.

Unitarian Controversy, 1819-1823, 2 vols. Ed. by Bruce Kuklick. (American Religious Thought of the 18th & 19th Centuries Ser.). 857p. 1987. Set. lib. bdg. 120.00 (ISBN 0-8240-6958-7). Garland Pub.

Unitarianism in America. George W. Cooke. LC 72-155153. Repr. of 1902 ed. 12.50 (ISBN 0-404-01699-5). AMS Pr.

Unitarians & India. Spencer Lavan. 1984. pap. 5.95 (ISBN 0-933840-23-3). Unitarian Univ.

Unitarians & the Universalists. David Robinson. LC 84-9031. (Denominations in America Ser.: No. 1). xiii, 368p. 1985. lib. bdg. 37.50 (ISBN 0-313-20946-4, RUN/). Greenwood.

Unitas: Hispanic & Black Children in a Healing Community. Anne Farber & LLoyd H. Rogler. 128p. 1982. 18.95 (ISBN 0-87073-505-5); pap. 8.95 (ISBN 0-87073-506-3). Schenkman Bks Inc.

Unite. 1973. 2.94 (ISBN 0-02-649670-4, 64967); tchr's annotated ed. 6.00 (ISBN 0-02-649690-9, 64969); activity bk. 1.74 (ISBN 0-02-640630-6); activity bk. tchr's ed. 2.16 (ISBN 0-02-640750-7, 64075); parents' handbk. 0.75 (ISBN 0-02-649680-1); testing program 0.69 (ISBN 0-02-640840-6, 64084); testing program tchr's manual 0.33 (ISBN 0-02-641090-7, 64109). Benziger Pub Co.

Unite at the Lord's Table. Gerard P. Weber et al. (Word Is Life Ser.). 4p. 1977. 3.92 (ISBN 0-02-658400-X); tchrs. ed. 8.00 (ISBN 0-02-658410-7); family handbook 1.00 (ISBN 0-02-658450-6). Benziger Pub Co.

United Church of Christ Hymnal. Ed. by John Ferguson & William Nelson. LC 74-12571. 1974. Pew Edition. spiral bound 12.50x (ISBN 0-8298-0300-9); 9.95x. Pilgrim NY.

United Church of Christ: Studies in Identity & Polity. Ed. by Dorothy C. Bass & Kenneth B. Smith. LC 86-83022. (Studies in Ministry & Parish Life). 112p. 1987. text ed. 16.95x (ISBN 0-913552-37-2); pap. text ed. 6.95x (ISBN 0-913552-36-4). Exploration Pr.

United in Marriage: A Guide to Premarital Counseling. Richard T. Ulyat. 47p. 1984. pap. 3.50 (ISBN 0-86544-023-9). Salv Army Suppl South.

United Methodist Altars: A Guide for the Local Church. Hoyt L. Hickman. 96p. 1984. pap. 6.95 (ISBN 0-687-42985-4). Abingdon.

United Methodist Studies: Basic Bibliographies. Ed. by Kenneth E. Rowe. 40p. (Orig.). 1982. pap. 2.00 (ISBN 0-687-43109-3). Abingdon.

U. N. Declaration on the Elimination of Religious Intolerance & Discrimination. Sidney Liskofsky. 20p. 1982. pap. 2.00 (ISBN 0-87495-041-4). Am Jewish Comm.

United Order Among the Mormons (Missouri Phase) An Unfinished Experiment in Economic Organization. Joseph A. Geddes. LC 72-8247. Repr. of 1924 ed. 19.50 (ISBN 0-404-11001-0). AMS Pr.

United Reformed Church. Kenneth Slack. 1978. pap. 3.15 (ISBN 0-08-021414-2). Pergamon.

United States & Vatican Policies, 1914-1918. Dragan Zivojinovic. LC 78-52438. 1978. 22.50x (ISBN 0-87081-112-6). Colo Assoc.

United States Catholic Elementary & Secondary Schools, 1984-85. Frank H. Bredeweg. 1985. 6.60; member 4.95. Natl Cath Educ.

United States Catholic Elementary & Secondary Schools, 1985-86. Frank H. Bredeweg. 21p. 1986. 6.60. Natl Cath Educ.

United States Catholic Elementary & Secondary Schools, 1985-86. Frank H. Bredweg. 21p. 1986. 7.30 (ISBN 0-318-20578-5). Natl Cath Educ.

United States Catholic Elementary Schools & their Finances, 1986. Frank H. Bredweg. 1986. 6.00 (ISBN 0-318-20577-7). Natl Cath Educ.

United States Catholic Elementary Schools & Their Finances 1984. 6.00 (ISBN 0-318-03695-9). Natl Cath Educ.

U. S. Catholic Institutions & Labor Unions, 1960-1980. Patrick J. Sullivan. LC 85-20171. 550p. (Orig.). 1986. lib. bdg. 40.50 (ISBN 0-8191-4970-5); pap. text ed. 22.75 (ISBN 0-8191-4971-3). U Pr of Amer.

U. S. Catholic Schools: 1973 to 1974. 92p. 1974. 2.40. Natl Cath Educ.

United States Documents in the Propaganda Fide Archives, Vol. 9. Ed. by Debevec et al. 1982. 40.00 (ISBN 0-88382-210-5). AAFH.

United States Documents in the Propaganda Fide Archives, Vol. 10. Ed. by Mathias Kiemen et al. 1984. 40.00 (ISBN 0-88382-211-3). AAFH.

United States Foreign Policy & Human Rights: Principles, Priorities & Practice. 1979. pap. 3.00 (ISBN 0-934654-22-0). UNA-USA.

United States, the United Nations, & Human Rights: The Eleanor Roosevelt & Jimmy Carter Eras. A. Glenn Mower, Jr. LC 78-22134. (Studies in Human Rights Ser.: No. 4). xii, 215p. 1979. lib. bdg. 29.95 (ISBN 0-313-21090-X, MUH/). Greenwood.

United to Christ. Tony Floyd. (Illus.). 80p. (Orig.). 1983. pap. 5.95 (ISBN 0-85819-420-1, Pub. by JBCE). ANZ Religious Pubns.

United We Stand. Arthur L. Clanton. (Illus.). 207p. 1970. pap. 5.95 (ISBN 0-912315-42-3). Word Aflame.

Unities & Diversities in Chinese Religion. Robert P. Weller. LC 86-9085. 250p. 1986. 22.50x (ISBN 0-295-96397-2). U of Wash Pr.

Unitl the Mashiach: The Life of Rabbi Nachman. Rabbi Aryeh Kaplan. Ed. by Dovid Shapiro. 379p. 1986. text ed. 15.00 (ISBN 0-930213-08-4). Breslov Res Inst.

Unity: A Quest for Truth. Eric Butterworth. (Orig.). 1965. pap. 3.00 (ISBN 0-8315-0020-4). Speller.

Unity: A Quest for Truth. Eric Butterworth. 160p. 1985. 5.95 (ISBN 0-87159-165-0, X1965, ROBERT SPELLER & SONS PUB.). Unity School.

Unity & Development in Plato's Metaphysics. William J. Prior. LC 85-5073. 202p. 1985. 24.95 (ISBN 0-8126-9000-1). Open Court.

Unity & Diversity: Essays in the History, Literature, & Religion of the Ancient Near East. Ed. by Hans Goedicke & J. J. Roberts. LC 74-24376. (Johns Hopkins University Near Eastern Studies). pap. 60.00 (ISBN 0-317-11301-1, 2016572). Bks Demand UMI.

Unity & Diversity in the New Testament: An Inquiry into the Character of Earliest Christianity. James D. Dunn. LC 77-22598. 488p. 1984. pap. 14.95 (ISBN 0-664-24525-0). Westminster.

Unity & Jesus Forsaken. Chiara Lubich. LC 85-72397. 105p. 1985. pap. 4.95 (ISBN 0-911782-53-2). New City.

Unity & Variety in Muslim Civilization. Armand Abel et al. Ed. by Gustave E. Von Grunebaum. LC 55-11191. (Comparative Studies of Cultures & Civilizations: No. 7). pap. 99.30 (ISBN 0-317-11328-3, 2013614). Bks Demand UMI.

Unity in Action: Romans Fourteen vs One Through Fifteen-Thirteen. John MacArthur, Jr. (John MacArthur Bible Studies Ser.). 1987. pap. 3.95 (ISBN 0-8024-5307-4). Moody.

Unity in Christ. Leonard Mullens. 1958. 3.00 (ISBN 0-88027-053-5). Firm Foun Pub.

Unity in Creation. Russell Maatman. 143p. (Orig.). 1978. pap. 4.95 (ISBN 0-932914-00-4). Dordt Coll Pr.

Unity in Diversity. Ed. by O. P. Ghai. 132p. 1986. text ed. 15.95x (ISBN 0-86590-762-5, Pub. by Sterling Pubs India). Apt Bks.

Unity in Diversity. Ed. by Henry O. Thompson. LC 83-51715. 436p. (Orig.). 1984. pap. 12.95 (ISBN 0-932894-20-8). Rose Sharon Pr.

Unity of Anglicanism: Catholic & Reformed. Henry R. McAdoo. 48p. 1983. pap. 4.95 (ISBN 0-8192-1324-1). Morehouse.

Unity of Good. Mary B. Eddy. Indonesian ed. 12.50 (ISBN 0-87952-177-5); French Ed. 7.50 (ISBN 0-87952-123-6). First Church.

Unity of Good, Rudimental Divine Science. Mary B. Eddy. pap. 4.50 (ISBN 0-87952-043-4). First Church.

Unity of Good, Two Sermons. Mary B. Eddy. Danish 12.50 (ISBN 0-87952-106-6); Norwegian 12.50 (ISBN 0-87952-197-X); German o.p. 6.00 (ISBN 0-87952-159-7). First Church.

Unity of Isaiah. Oswald T. Allis. 1952. pap. 4.50 (ISBN 0-87552-105-3). Presby & Reformed.

Unity of Isaiah: A Study in Prophecy. Oswald T. Allis. 1974. pap. 4.50 (ISBN 0-8010-0111-0). Baker Bk.

Unity of Luke's Theology: An Analysis of Luke-Acts. Robert F. O'Toole. (Good News Studies Ser.: Vol. 9). 1984. pap. 8.95 (ISBN 0-89453-438-6). M Glazier.

Unity of One. George L. Pink. 160p. 1982. 8.00 (ISBN 0-682-49838-6). Exposition Pr FL.

Unity of Religious Ideals. Hazrat I. Khan. (Collected Works of Hazrat Inayat Khan Ser.). 264p. 1979. 9.95 (ISBN 0-930872-09-6); pap. 6.95 (ISBN 0-930872-10-X). Omega Pr NM.

Unity of Religious Ideals. Inayat Khan. (Sufi Message of Hazrat Inayat Khan Ser.: Vol. 9). 280p. 1979. 14.95 (ISBN 90-6325-097-5, Pub. by Servire BV Netherlands). Hunter Hse.

Unity of the Bible. Harold H. Rowley. LC 78-2684. 1978. Repr. of 1953 ed. lib. bdg. 22.50x (ISBN 0-313-20346-6, ROUB). Greenwood.

Unity of the Churches: An Actual Possibility. Heinrich Fries & Karl Rahner. Tr. by E. Gritsch & R. Gritsch. LC 84-8122. 160p. pap. 6.95 (ISBN 0-8006-1820-3). Fortress.

Unity of the Churches: An Actual Possibility. Heinrich Fries & Karl Rahner. 1985. pap. 6.95 (ISBN 0-8091-2671-0). Paulist Pr.

Unity of the Moral & Spiritual Life. William E. May. (Synthesis Ser). 1978. pap. 0.75 (ISBN 0-8199-0745-6). Franciscan Herald.

Unity of the Muslim World. 1.00 (ISBN 0-686-18622-2). Kazi Pubns.

Unity Way. Marcus Bach. LC 82-50085. 387p. 1982. 5.95 (ISBN 0-87159-164-2). Unity School.

Universal Bead. Joan M. Erikson. LC 68-20819. (Illus.). 1969. 13.95 (ISBN 0-393-04233-2). Norton.

Universal Heart: The Life & Vision of Brother Roger of Taize. Kathryn Spink. LC 86-45027. (Illus.). 192p. 1986. 14.95 (ISBN 0-06-067504-7, HarpR). Har-Row.

Universal Jewish History, 4 vols. Philip Biberfeld. Vol. 1. 8.95 (ISBN 0-87306-052-0, Spero Foundation); Vol. 2. 8.95 (ISBN 0-87306-053-9); Vol. 3. 10.95 (ISBN 0-87306-054-7); Set. cancelled (ISBN 0-87306-051-2). Feldheim.

Universal Jewish History: The Exodous, Vol. 4. 1982. 9.95 (ISBN 0-686-76273-8). Feldheim.

Universal Majesty. Milton L. Zeuner. (Illus.). 80p. 1984. 6.00 (ISBN 0-682-40159-5, Chart). Exposition Pr FL.

Universal Man. Florence DeGroat. LC 80-69413. 117p. 1981. pap. 6.50 (ISBN 0-87516-428-5). De Vorss.

Universal Meaning of the Kabbalah. Leo Schaya. 1972. 6.95 (ISBN 0-8216-0167-9). Univ Bks.

Universal Path. rev ed. Jan Van Rijckenborgh & Catharose De Petri. (Cornerstone Ser.: No. 2). Tr. of Het Universele Pad. 99p. 1986. pap. 11.00 (ISBN 90-6732-007-2). Rosycross Pr.

Universal Prayers. Tr. by Swami Yatiswarananda from Sanskrit. (Sanskrit & Eng.). 3.95 (ISBN 0-87481-443-X). Vedanta Pr.

Universal Primacy of Christ. Francesco S. Pancheri. Tr. by Juniper B. Carol from Italian. Orig. Title: Il Primato universale de Christo. 144p. (Orig.). 1984. pap. 6.95 (ISBN 0-931888-16-6). Christendom Pubns.

Universal Pronouncing Dictionary of Biography & Mythology, 2 Vols. 5th ed. Joseph Thomas. LC 76-137298. Repr. of 1930 ed. Set. 225.00 (ISBN 0-404-06386-1). AMS Pr.

Universal Register of the Baptist Denomination in North America for the Years 1790, 1791, 1792, 1793, & Part of 1794. John Asplund. Ed. by Edwin S. Gaustad. LC 79-52581. (Baptist Tradition Ser.). 1980. Repr. of 1794 ed. lib. bdg. 14.00x (ISBN 0-405-12448-1). Ayer Co Pubs.

Universal Sikhism. A. S. Sethi. 1972. 5.95 (ISBN 0-88253-767-9). Ind-US Inc.

Universalism in America. Ed. by Ernest Cassara. 1984. pap. 5.95 (ISBN 0-933840-21-7). Unitarian Univ.

Universe As Pictured in Milton's Paradise Lost. William F. Warren. LC 73-12894. 1915. lib. bdg. 15.00 (ISBN 0-8414-9418-5). Folcroft.

Universe As Pictured in Milton's Paradise Lost: An Illustrated Study for Personal & Class Use. William F. Warren. LC 68-59037. (Illus.). 80p. 1968. Repr. of 1915 ed. 10.00x (ISBN 0-87752-117-4). Gordian.

Universe Earth & Man. Rudolf Steiner. (Russian Language Ser.). 136p. 1985. pap. 8.00 (ISBN 0-89345-903-8, Steiner). Garber Comm.

Universe, God, & God-Realization: From the Viewpoint of Vedanta. Swami Satprakashananda. LC 77-79829. 310p. 1977. 12.50 (ISBN 0-916356-57-4). Vedanta Soc St Louis.

Universe Is a Green Dragon: A Cosmic Creation Story. Brian Swimme. LC 84-72255. (Illus.). 173p. (Orig.). 1984. pap. 8.95 (ISBN 0-939680-14-9). Bear & Co.

Universe Next Door: A Basic World View Catalog. James W. Sire. LC 75-32129. 240p. (Orig.). 1976. pap. 7.95 (ISBN 0-87784-772-X). Inter-Varsity.

Universe of Numbers. Ed. by Ralph M. Lewis. LC 83-51126. 209p. (Orig.). 1984. pap. 7.95 (ISBN 0-912057-11-4, G-649). AMORC.

Universidad de la Palabra. Dick Eastman. Tr. by Jose D. Silva from English. (Span.). 239p. 1986. pap. text ed. 3.50 (ISBN 0-8297-0443-4). Life Pubs Intl.

Universities, Academics & the Great Schism. R. N. Swanson. LC 78-56764. (Cambridge Studies in Medieval Life & Thought: 3rd Ser., No. 12). 1979. 49.50 (ISBN 0-521-22127-7). Cambridge U Pr.

University at Prayer. Alfred C. Payne. LC 86-14613. (Illus.). 1987. 13.95x (ISBN 0-9617635-0-7). VA Tech Educ Found.

University of Chicago Readings in Western Civilization: The Church in the Roman Empire, Vol. 3. Ed. by John W. Boyer & Julius Kirshner. LC 85-16328. 1986. lib. bdg. 20.00x (ISBN 0-226-06938-9); pap. text ed. 7.95x (ISBN 0-226-06939-7). U of Chicago Pr.

University of Hard Knocks. Ralph Parlette. 1966. gift ed. 6.95 (ISBN 0-915720-05-1). Brownlow Pub Co.

University of the Word. Dick Eastman. LC 83-17763. 1983. pap. 3.95 (ISBN 0-8307-0903-7, 5018301). Regal.

University Work of the United Lutheran Church in America: A Study of the Work Among Lutheran Students at Non-Lutheran Institutions. Howard M. Le Sourd. LC 70-176990. (Columbia University. Teachers College. Contributions to Education: No. 377). Repr. of 1929 ed. 17.50 (ISBN 0-404-55377-X). AMS Pr.

Unknowable: An Ontological Introduction to the Philosophy of Religion. S. L. Frank. Tr. by Boris Jakim from Russian. xxii, 313p. 1983. text ed. 26.95x (ISBN 0-8214-0676-0, 82-84440). Ohio U Pr.

Unknowable Gurdjieff. 1st 1973 ed. Margaret Anderson. (Illus.). 212p. (Orig.). 1969. pap. 7.50 (ISBN 0-87728-219-6). Weiser.

Unknown Christ of Hinduism. Raimundo Panikkar. LC 81-2886. 208p. (Orig.). 1981. pap. 7.95 (ISBN 0-88344-523-9). Orbis Bks.

Unknown History of the Jewish People, 2 vols. Charles K. Foster. (Illus.). 247p. 1986. Set. 187.45. Found Class Reprints.

Unknown Life of Jesus Christ. N. Notovich. 69.95 (ISBN 0-87968-073-3). Gordon Pr.

Unknown Paul: Essays on Luke-Acts & Early Christian History. Jacob Jervell. LC 84-24605. 192p. (Orig.). 1984. pap. 10.95 (ISBN 0-8066-2119-2, 10-6815). Augsburg.

Unknown Prophet Jakob Lorber. Kurt Eggenstein. LC 79-89530. 78p. (Orig.). 1979. pap. 3.50 (ISBN 0-912760-99-0). Valkyrie Pub Hse.

Unknown Samuel Johnson. Ed. by John J. Burke, Jr. & Donald Kay. LC 81-70159. (Illus.). 224p. 1983. 32.50x (ISBN 0-299-09150-3). U of Wis Pr.

Unknown Sanctuary. Aime Palliere. Tr. by Louise W. Wise. LC 79-150294. 243p. 1985. pap. 8.95x (ISBN 0-8197-0498-9). Bloch.

Unleashing the Church. Frank R. Tillapaugh. LC 82-9783. 1985. pap. 5.95 (ISBN 0-8307-1024-8, 5418433). Regal.

Unless One Is Born Anew. Dorothy Hutchinson. LC 65-26994. (Orig.). 1965. pap. 2.50x (ISBN 0-87574-143-6, 143). Pendle Hill.

Unless You Become Like a Little Child. Jean Gill. 88p. (Orig.). 1985. pap. 4.95 (ISBN 0-8091-2717-2). Paulist Pr.

Unlikely Cast: Dramatic Monologues for Advent. Alan E. Siewert. 1976. pap. 3.50 (ISBN 0-89536-245-7, 2107). CSS of Ohio.

Unlikely Catechism: Some Challenges for the Creedless Catholic. William Reiser. 184p. (Orig.). 1985. pap. 6.95 (ISBN 0-8091-2706-7). Paulist Pr.

Unlisted Legion. Jock Purves. 1978. pap. 4.45 (ISBN 0-85151-245-3). Banner of Truth.

Unlocking the Old Testament. Victor L. Ludlow. LC 81-68266. (Illus.). 239p. 1981. 8.95 (ISBN 0-87747-873-2). Deseret Bk.

Unlocking the Scriptures. Hans Finzel. 144p. 1986. 7.95 (ISBN 0-89693-276-1). Victor Bks.

Unlovelinesse of Love-Lockes. William Prynne. LC 76-57410. (English Experience Ser.: No. 825). 1977. Repr. of 1628 ed. lib. bdg. 10.50 (ISBN 90-221-0825-2). Walter J Johnson.

Unmasking. Jan Van Rijckenborgh. 70p. 1987. pap. 3.00. Rosycross Pr.

Unmasking the New Age. Douglas R. Groothuis. LC 85-23832. 200p. (Orig.). 1986. pap. 6.95 (ISBN 0-87784-568-9). Inter-Varsity.

Unmasking the Powers: The Invisible Forces That Determine Human Existence. Walter Wink. LC 85-45480. 224p. 1986. pap. 12.95 (ISBN 0-8006-1902-1, 1-1902). Fortress.

Unmentionable Vice: Homosexuality in the Later Medieval Period. Michael Goodich. LC 78-13276. 179p. 1980. pap. 7.95 (ISBN 0-87436-300-4). Ross-Erikson.

Unofficial Sunday School Teacher's Handbook. Joanne Owens. (Illus.). 240p. (Orig.). 1987. pap. 7.95 (ISBN 0-916260-42-9). Meriwether Pub.

Unopened Gift. Norvel Hayes. cancelled (ISBN 0-89841-002-9). Zoe Pubns.

Unorthodox Judaism. Norman B. Mirsky. LC 78-8683. 227p. 1978. 17.50 (ISBN 0-8142-0283-7). Ohio St U Pr.

Unpardonable Sin Explained. 6th ed. 1976. pap. 0.50 (ISBN 0-686-15424-X). Crusade Pubs.

Unpremeditated Verse Feeling & Perception in Milton's Paradise Lost. W. Shumaker. 1967. 26.00x (ISBN 0-691-06134-3). Princeton U Pr.

Unprofitable Servants: Conferences on Humility. Nivard Kinsella. 1981. 5.95 (ISBN 0-317-46888-X). Franciscan Herald.

Unquestionable Right to Be Free: Black Theology from South Africa. Ed. by Itumeleng J. Mosala & Buti Tlhagale. 224p. (Orig.). 1986. pap. 11.95 (ISBN 0-88344-251-5). Orbis Bks.

Unquiet Dead: A Psychologist Works with Spirit Possession. Edith Fiore. LC 86-29096. 192p. 1987. 15.95 (ISBN 0-385-23904-1, Dolp). Doubleday.

Unquiet Souls: Fourteenth-Century Saints & Their Religious Milieu. Richard Kieckhefer. LC 84-210. 248p. 1984. lib. bdg. 24.95x (ISBN 0-226-43509-1). U of Chicago Pr.

Unquiet Souls: Fourteenth Century Saints & Their Religious Milieu. Richard Kieckhefer. LC 84-210. (Illus.). viii, 238p. 1987. pap. 10.95 (ISBN 0-226-43510-5). U of Chicago Pr.

Unraveling Zen's Red Thread: Ikkyu's Controversial Way. Jon Carter Covell & Abbot S. Yamada. LC 80-81040. (Illus.). 341p. 1980. 21.50x (ISBN 0-930878-19-1). Hollym Intl.

Unreached Peoples, Eighty-One. C. Peter Wagner et al. (Orig.). 1981. pap. 8.95 (ISBN 0-89191-331-9). Cook.

Unreached Peoples '80. Edward Dayton & C. Peter Wagner. LC 79-57522. 1980. pap. 8.95 (ISBN 0-89191-837-X). Cook.

Unreached Peoples '80. LC 79-57522. 383p. 1980. 7.95 (ISBN 0-912552-50-6). Missions Adv Res Com Ctr.

Unreached Peoples '82. LC 81-69100. 435p. 7.95 (ISBN 0-912552-52-2). Missions Adv Res Com Ctr.

Unreached Peoples '86: Clarifying the Task. Ed. by Harley Schreck & David Barrett. pap. write for info. (ISBN 0-912552-58-1). Missions Adv Res Com Ctr.

Unresponsive: Resistant or Neglected? The Hakka Chinese in Taiwan Illustrate the Homogeneous Unit Principle. David Liao. LC 73-175494. 1979. pap. 5.95 (ISBN 0-87808-735-4). William Carey Lib.

Unsealed Book: An Amillennial View of Revelation. Wade Jernigan. 1975. pap. 3.50 (ISBN 0-89265-028-1). Randall Hse.

Unsearchable Riches. David N. Power. 160p. (Orig.). 1984. pap. 9.95 (ISBN 0-916134-62-8). Pueblo Pub Co.

Unsearchable Riches of Christ. D. Martyn Lloyd-Jones. 1980. 12.95 (ISBN 0-8010-5597-0). Baker Bk.

Unsearchable Wisdom of God: A Study of Providence in Richardson's Pamela. James L. Fortuna, Jr. LC 80-14919. (University of Florida Humanities Monographs: No. 49). vii, 130p. 1980. pap. 6.50 (ISBN 0-8130-0676-7). U Presses Fla.

Unsecular America. Paul Johnson et al. Ed. by Richard J. Neuhaus. (Encounter Ser.). 176p. (Orig.). 1986. pap. 8.95 (ISBN 0-8028-0202-8). Eerdmans.

Unsecular Man. Andrew M. Greeley. LC 85-2459. 297p. 1985. pap. 8.95 (ISBN 0-8052-0794-5). Schocken.

Unseen Warfare. Lorenzo Scupoli. 280p. 1978. pap. 8.95 (ISBN 0-913836-52-4). St Vladimirs.

Unseen World: Catholic Theology & Spiritualism. A. M. Lepicier. 69.95 (ISBN 0-8490-1251-1). Gordon Pr.

Unselfishness of God & How I Discovered It. Hannah W. Smith. (Higher Christian Life Ser.). 312p. 1985. lib. bdg. 40.00 (ISBN 0-8240-6443-7). Garland Pub.

Unspoken Worlds. Ed. by Nancy A. Falk & Rita M. Gross. LC 79-2989. (Women's Religious Lives Ser.). 304p. (Orig.). 1980. pap. text ed. 5.95x (ISBN 0-06-063492-8, RD 308, HarpR). Har-Row.

Unsung Heroes: How to Recruit & Train Volunteers. Les Christie. 176p. 1987. text ed. 12.95 (ISBN 0-310-35150-2). Zondervan.

Unsuspected Power of the Psalms. Thomas R. Hawkins. LC 84-51828. 128p. (Orig.). 1985. pap. 5.95 (ISBN 0-8358-0499-2). Upper Room.

Untangling Bible Doctrine. rev. ed. G. Michael Cocoris. 107p. 1985. pap. text ed. 2.00 (ISBN 0-935729-03-8). Church Open Door.

Untersuchungen zu den Passionbetrachtungen in der "Vita Christi" des Ludolfvon Sachsen: Ein Quellen-Kritischer Beitrag zu Leben und Werk Ludolfs und Zur Geschichte des Passionstheologie, 3 Vols. Walter Baier. Ed. by James Hogg. (Analecta Cartsiana Ser.: No. 44-1, 2, 3). (Ger.). 614p. (Orig.). 1977. pap. 32.00 (ISBN 3-7052-0060-7, Pub. by Salzburg Studies). Longwood Pub Group.

Untersuchungen zur Redaktionsgeschichte des Pentateuch. Peter Weimar. 1977. 34.40x (ISBN 3-11-006731-5). De Gruyter.

Untersuchungen Zur Reichskirchenpolitik Lothars III, 1125-1137: Zwischen Reichskirchlicher Tradition Und Reformkurie. Marie-Luise Crone. (European University Studies: No.3, Vol. 170). 398p. 1982. 40.55 (ISBN 3-8204-7019-0). P Lang Pubs.

Unthinking Faith & Enlightenment: Nature & Politics in a Post-Hegelian Era. Jane Bennett. 192p. 1987. 30.00 (ISBN 0-8147-1095-6). NYU Pr.

Until Justice & Peace Embrace. Nicholas Wolterstorff. 232p. (Orig.). 1983. 13.95 (ISBN 0-8028-3344-6). Eerdmans.

Until: The Coming of Messiah & His Kingdom. Robert Shank. LC 81-72098. 520p. 1982. pap. 11.95 (ISBN 0-911620-04-4). Westcott.

Until You Die. Bhagwan Shree Rajneesh. Ed. by Ma Yoga Anurag. LC 77-900984. (Sufi Ser.). (Illus.). 280p. (Orig.). 1976. 15.95 (ISBN 0-88050-165-0). Chidvilas Found.

Unto a Perfect Man. 4th ed. Carl Coffman. 209p. 1982. pap. 8.95 (ISBN 0-943872-83-9). Andrews Univ Pr.

Unto Christ. H. L. Heijkoop. 47p. pap. 0.60 (ISBN 0-88172-087-9). Believers Bkshelf.

Unto God & Caesar: Religious Issues in the Emerging Commonwealth 1891-1906. R. Ely. 1976. 22.00x (ISBN 0-522-84093-0, Pub. by Melbourne U Pr). Intl Spec Bk.

Unto Him Be Glory. Paul Byers. 220p. 1974. 4.95 (ISBN 0-89114-047-6); pap. 2.95 (ISBN 0-89114-046-8). Baptist Pub Hse.

Unto Him Shall We Return: Selections from the Baha'i Writings on the Reality & Immortality of the Human Soul. Compiled by Hushidar Motlagh. 144p. 1985. pap. 9.95 (ISBN 0-87743-201-5). Baha'i.

Unto the Churches: Jesus Christ, Christianity, & the Edgar Cayce Readings. Richard H. Drummond. 1978. pap. 7.95 (ISBN 0-87604-102-0). ARE Pr.

Unto the Hills. Sara Yoder. 1985. 2.95 (ISBN 0-87813-523-5). Christian Light.

Unto the Hills: A Devotional Treasury from Billy Graham. Billy Graham. 384p. 1986. 14.95 (ISBN 0-8499-0603-2). Word Bks.

Unto the Islands of the Sea: A History of the Latter-day Saints in the Pacific. R. Lanier Britsch. LC 85-27463. (Illus.). 599p. 1986. 16.95 (ISBN 0-87747-754-X). Deseret Bk.

Unto the Least of These: Special Education in the Church. Andrew Wood. LC 84-16077. 1984. pap. 4.95 (ISBN 0-87227-099-8). Reg Baptist.

Unto the Uttermost. Mrs. Bob White. (Illus.). 80p. 1977. pap. 1.00 (ISBN 0-89114-079-4). Baptist Pub Hse.

Unto Thee I Grant. 32nd ed. Rev. by Sri Ramatherio. LC 49-15007. 96p. 1979. 8.95 (ISBN 0-912057-02-5, G-505). AMORC.

Unto Us. Claracy L. Waldrop. (Orig.). 1957. pap. 1.95 (ISBN 0-8054-9704-8). Broadman.

Unto Us a Child is Born. Reuel Lemmons & John Bannister. Compiled by Rex Kyker. 126p. (Orig.). 1982. pap. 2.95 (ISBN 0-88027-109-4). Firm Foun Pub.

Unto You & to Your Children. Grace Wiens. (Illus.). 229p. (Orig.). 1976. pap. 5.95 (ISBN 0-912315-10-5). Word Aflame.

Unto You Is the Promise. Robert W. Cummings. pap. 0.79 (ISBN 0-88243-750-X, 02-0750). Gospel Pub.

Untold Story: Jesus Son of God. Clarice Albritton. LC 83-73188. 1983. pap. 5.95 (ISBN 0-318-00817-3). W P Brownell.

Untold Story of Jesus Christ. Kent Estevez. LC 86-81086. 100p. (Orig.). 1986. pap. 10.00 (ISBN 0-9616660-0-5). Holland Pub Hse.

Unused Cradle. Esther T. Barker. pap. 1.50x (ISBN 0-8358-0231-0). Upper Room.

Unusual Court. Torkom Saraydarian. LC 77-86720. 1979. pap. 4.00 (ISBN 0-911794-44-1). Aqua Educ.

Unvanquished Puritan: A Portrait of Lyman Beecher. Stuart C. Henry. LC 85-30520. 299p. 1986. Repr. of 1973 ed. lib. bdg. 45.00x (ISBN 0-313-25097-9, HEUN). Greenwood.

Unveiled Faces: Men & Women of the Bible. Sr. Mary C. Barron. LC 80-27728. 95p. 1981. softcover 4.50 (ISBN 0-8146-1212-1). Liturgical Pr.

Unwanted Generation. Paul D. Meier & Linda Burnett. 1981. 7.95 (ISBN 0-8010-6101-6). Baker Bk.

Unwrap Your Spiritual Gifts. Kenneth O. Gangel. 120p. 1983. pap. 4.95 (ISBN 0-88207-102-5). Victor Bks.

Unwrapping Your Spiritual Gifts. David A. Hubbard. 160p. 1985. 9.95 (ISBN 0-8499-0478-1, 0478-1). Word Bks.

Unwrinkling Plays. Paul Reps. LC 65-12270. (Illus., Orig.). 1965. pap. 4.75 (ISBN 0-8048-0607-1). C E Tuttle.

Unwritten Literature of Hawaii: The Sacred Songs of the Hula. Nathaniel B. Emerson. LC 65-12971. (Illus.). 1965. pap. 6.75 (ISBN 0-8048-1067-2). C E Tuttle.

Unwritten Literature of Hawaii; the Sacred Songs of the Hula. Nathaniel B. Emerson. Repr. of 1909 ed. 39.00x (ISBN 0-403-03720-4). Scholarly.

Up from Apathy: A Study of Moral Awareness & Social Involvement. Richard A. Hoehn. LC 83-7057. 179p. (Orig.). 1983. pap. 10.95 (ISBN 0-687-43114-X). Abingdon.

Up from Eden: A Transpersonal View of Human Evolution. Ken Wilber. LC 82-42678. (Illus.). 384p. 1983. pap. 8.95 (ISBN 0-87773-228-0). Shambhala Pubns.

Up from Grief. Bernardine Kreis & Alice Pattie. 292p. 1984. pap. 9.95 large print ed. (ISBN 0-8027-2486-8). Walker & Co.

Up from Grief: Patterns of Recovery. Bernadine Kreis & Alice Pattie. 160p. 1982. pap. 5.95 (ISBN 0-8164-2364-4, AY7442, HarpR). Har-Row.

Up the Ladder in Foreign Missions. Lewis G. Jordan. Ed. by Edwin S. Gausted. LC 79-52596. (Baptist Tradition Ser.). (Illus.). 1980. Repr. of 1901 ed. lib. bdg. 27.50x (ISBN 0-405-12463-5). Ayer Co Pubs.

Up with Creation! Acts, Facts, Impacts, Vol. 3. Duane T. Gish. LC 78-55612. (Illus.). 1978. pap. 6.95 (ISBN 0-89051-048-2). Master Bks.

Upadesa Sahasri: A Thousand Teachings. Shankara. Tr. by Swami Jagadananda. (Sanskrit & Eng). pap. 4.95 (ISBN 0-87481-423-5). Vedanta Pr.

Upanayanam (Thread Marriage) Panduranga R. Malyala. (Illus.). 20p. 1983. pap. text ed. 2.00 (ISBN 0-938924-15-X). Sri Shirdi Sai.

Upanayanam: (Twice Born) 1983. pap. 2.00 (ISBN 0-938924-15-X). Sri Shirdi Sai.

Upanisads. 2nd ed. Tr. by Srisa Chandra Vasu. LC 73-4980. (Sacred Books of the Hindus: No. 1). Repr. of 1911 ed. 27.50 (ISBN 0-404-57801-2). AMS Pr.

Upanisads: Gateways of Knowledge. 2nd ed. M. P. Pandit. 1968. 4.00 (ISBN 0-89744-111-7, Pub. by Ganesh & Co. India). Auromere.

Upanisads: The Selections from 108 Upanisads. T. M. Mahadevan. Tr. by T. M. Mahadevan from Sanskrit. 240p. (Orig.). 1975. pap. 3.20 (ISBN 0-88253-985-X). Ind-US Inc.

Upanishads. Sri Aurobindo. (Sanskrit & Eng.). 466p. 1981. 40.00 (ISBN 0-89744-026-9, Pub. by Sri Aurobindo Ashram Trust India); pap. 30.00 (ISBN 0-89744-025-0). Auromere.

Upanishads, 2 vols. F. Max Muller. 1974. lib. bdg. 250.00 (ISBN 0-8490-1252-X). Gordon Pr.

Upanishads. Ed. by F. Max Muller. (Sacred Bks. of the East: Vol 1 & 15). both vols. 30.00 (ISBN 0-686-97473-5); 15.00 ea. Asian Human Pr.

Upanishads: A Selection for the Modern Reader. 1987. 10.95 (ISBN 0-915132-40-0); pap. 5.95 (ISBN 0-915132-39-7). Nilgiri Pr.

Upanishads: Breath of the Eternal. Tr. by Swami Prabhavananda & Frederick Manchester. LC 48-5935. pap. 6.95 (ISBN 0-87481-040-X). Vedanta Pr.

Upanishads: Texts, Translations & Commentaries, Pt. 1. Sri Aurobindo. 466p. 1986. 14.95 (ISBN 0-89071-295-6, Pub. by Sri Aurobindo Ashram India); pap. 11.95 (ISBN 0-89071-294-8). Matagiri.

Upanishads: The Crown of India's Soul. 1972. pap. 2.00 (ISBN 0-87847-012-3). Aum Pubns.

Upanishas: The Thirteen Principal Upanishads. 2nd ed. Tr. by R. E. Hume from Sanskrit. 1931. pap. 16.95x (ISBN 0-19-561641-3). Oxford U Pr.

Upasaka Two & One. Buddhadharma. 1981. pap. 3.95 (ISBN 0-87881-078-1). Mojave Bks.

Update. Fred Hartley. 160p. 1982. pap. 2.95 (ISBN 0-8007-8431-6, Spire Bks). Revell.

Update on Christian Counseling, Vol. II. Jay E. Adams. 1981. pap. 2.75 (ISBN 0-87552-071-5). Presby & Reformed.

Update on Christian Counseling, 2 vols. Jay E. Adams. (Jay Adams Library). 288p. 1986. pap. 9.95 (ISBN 0-310-51051-1, 12117P). Zondervan.

Update on Christian Counseling, Vol. 1. Jay E. Adams. pap. 3.50 (ISBN 0-8010-0153-6). Baker Bk.

Update on Christian Counseling, Vol. 1. Jay E. Adams. 1979. pap. 3.50 (ISBN 0-87552-062-6). Presby & Reformed.

Update on Christian Counseling, Vol. 2. Jay E. Adams. 1981. pap. 2.75 (ISBN 0-8010-0180-3). Baker Bk.

Updated Devotion to the Sacred Heart. Walter Kern. LC 75-9277. (Illus.). 192p. 1975. pap. 2.95 (ISBN 0-8189-1124-7, Pub. by Alba Bks). Alba.

Updating of Religious Formation. Elio Gambari. LC 75-98171. 1969. pap. 2.00 (ISBN 0-8198-0168-2). Dghtrs St Paul.

Uplifting the Race: The Black Minister in the New South 1865-1902. Edward L. Wheeler. 198p. (Orig.). 1986. lib. bdg. 24.75 (ISBN 0-8191-5161-0); pap. text ed. 11.75 (ISBN 0-8191-5162-9). U Pr of Amer.

Upon the Potter's Wheel. Ralph V. Reynolds. Ed. by Mary H. Wallace. LC 85-31583. 144p. (Orig.). 1981. pap. 4.95 (ISBN 0-912315-22-9). Word Aflame.

Upon the Types of the Old Testament. Edward Taylor. Ed. by Charles W. Mignon. 1988. price not set (ISBN 0-8032-3075-3). U of Nebr Pr.

Upon This Rock, 3 vols. C. T. Davidson. 692p. 1973. Vol. 1. 11.95 (ISBN 0-934942-16-1); Vol. 2. 14.95 (ISBN 0-934942-17-X); Vol. 3. 13.95 (ISBN 0-934942-18-8). White Wing Pub.

Upper Egypt Chief Temples, Six. Bertha Porter & Rosalind Moss. (Topographical Bibliography of Ancient Egyptian Hieroglyphic Texts, Reliefs & Paintings Ser.: Vol. 6). 264p. 1939. text ed. 38.50 (ISBN 0-900416-30-0, Pub. by Aris & Phillips UK). Humanities.

Upper Room. J. C. Ryle. 1983. pap. 9.95 (ISBN 0-85151-017-5). Banner of Truth.

Upper Room Disciplines, 1986. Ed. by Tom Page. 382p. (Orig.). 1985. pap. 3.95 (ISBN 0-8358-0507-7). Upper Room.

Upper Room Disciplines 1987. 382p. (Orig.). 1986. pap. 4.50 (ISBN 0-8358-0531-X). Upper Room.

Upper Room: Retreat Readings for Priests. Thomas Plassmann. (Spirit & Life Ser). 1954. 4.50 (ISBN 0-686-11565-1). Franciscan Inst.

Upper Room to Garden Tomb: Messages for Lent & Easter on the Passion Narrative in Mark. Herbert E. Hohenstein. LC 84-21735. 80p. (Orig.). 1984. pap. 4.95 (ISBN 0-8066-2117-6, 10-6840). Augsburg.

Upper Room Worshipbook. Compiled by Elise S. Eslinger. 208p. (Orig.). 1985. pap. 7.50 (ISBN 0-8358-0515-8). Upper Room.

Upside Down & Inside Out: A Study Experience in Christian Clowning. Jack Krall & Jan Kalberer. 120p. 1987. cancelled (ISBN 0-317-46796-4). Resource Pubns.

Upside-Down Kingdom. Donald B. Kraybill. LC 78-9435. (Christian Peace Shelf Ser.). 328p. 1978. pap. 6.95 (ISBN 0-8361-1860-X). Herald Pr.

Upward Moving & Emergence Way: The Gishin Biye Version. Berard Haile. Ed. by Karl W. Luckert. LC 81-7441. (American Tribal Religions Ser.: Vol. 7). xvi, 239p. 1981. 19.95x (ISBN 0-8032-2320-X); pap. 11.95x (ISBN 0-8032-7212-X, BB 786, Bison). U of Nebr Pr.

Upward Path. Jim Lewis. LC 82-60277. 150p. (Orig.). 1982. pap. 7.95 (ISBN 0-942482-04-2). Unity Church Denver.

Urania: A Choice Collection of Psalm-Tunes, Anthems & Hymns. James Lyon. LC 69-11667. (Music Reprint Ser.). 198p. 1974. Repr. of 1761 ed. lib. bdg. 37.50 (ISBN 0-306-71198-2). Da Capo.

Urban Challenge. Ed. by Larry L. Rose & C. Kirk Hadaway. LC 82-71026. 1982. pap. 5.95 (ISBN 0-8054-6238-4). Broadman.

Urban Christian. Raymond Bakke. 160p. 1987. pap. 6.95 (ISBN 0-87784-523-9). Inter-Varsity.

Urban Impact on American Protestantism, 1865-1900. Aaron I. Abell. x, 275p. 1962. Repr. of 1943 ed. 22.50 (ISBN 0-208-00587-0, Archon). Shoe String.

Urban Ministry. David Claerbaut. 224p. 1984. pap. 7.95 (ISBN 0-310-45961-3, 12605P). Zondervan.

Urban Mission: Essays on the Building of a Comprehensive Model for Evangelical Urban Ministry. Craig Ellison. LC 82-23764. 230p. 1983. pap. text ed. 12.50 (ISBN 0-8191-2968-2). U Pr of Amer.

Urban Religion & the Second Great Awakening. Terry D. Bilhartz. LC 83-49455. 240p. 1986. 27.50x (ISBN 0-8386-3227-0). Fairleigh Dickinson.

Urban World. Larry L. Rose et al. LC 84-12649. 1984. pap. 8.95 (ISBN 0-8054-6339-9). Broadman.

Urdu Letters of Mirza Asadu'llah Khan Ghalib. Ed. & tr. by Daud Rahbar. 628p. 1987. 48.50 (ISBN 0-88706-412-4). State U NY Pr.

Urgency of Marxist - Christian Dialogue. Herbert Aptheker. LC 73-109081. 1976. Repr. of 1970 ed. 24.00 (ISBN 0-527-03002-3). Kraus Repr.

Urim & Thumim: The Secret of God. I. L. Cohen. Ed. by G. Murphy. LC 82-24578. (Illus.). 280p. 1983. 16.95 (ISBN 0-910891-00-1). New Research.

Urkunden Des Cistercienser-Stiftes Heiligenkreuz Im Wiener Walde, 2 vols. Heiligenkreuz. Austria (Cistercian Abbey) 1856-1859. Vol. 11. pap. 23.00 (ISBN 0-384-22083-5); Vol. 16. pap. 62.00 (ISBN 0-685-27596-5). Johnson Repr.

Urkundenbuch Des Stiftes Klosterneuburg Bis Zum Ende Des Vierzehnten Jahrhunderts. Ed. by Hartmann Zeibig. (Ger). Repr. of 1857 ed. 62.00 (ISBN 0-384-29875-3). Johnson Repr.

Urodivoi: Fools for God. Catherine De Hueck Doherty. LC 82-23530. 112p. 1983. 9.95 (ISBN 0-8245-0553-0). Crossroad NY.

Uroki po Pastirskomu Bogosloviju. Basil Boshtchanovsky. Tr. of Studies in Pastoral Theology. 100p. 1961. pap. text ed. 5.00 (ISBN 0-317-30267-1). Holy Trinity.

Use & Abuse of the Bible. Dennis Nineham. LC 76-15690. (Library of Philosophy & Religion Ser.). (Illus.). 295p. 1976. text ed. 28.50x (ISBN 0-06-495178-2). B&N Imports.

Use Even Me. George Barrington. 1983. pap. 10.00 (ISBN 0-8309-0375-5). Herald Hse.

Use It or Lose It: The Word of Faith. Roy H. Hicks. (Orig.). 1976. pap. 2.95 (ISBN 0-89274-002-7). Harrison Hse.

Use of Daniel in Jewish Apocalyptic Literature & in the Relevation of St. John. G. K. Beale. 364p. (Orig.). 1985. lib. bdg. 26.00 (ISBN 0-8191-4290-5); pap. text ed. 15.25 (ISBN 0-8191-4291-3). U Pr of Amer.

Use of Myth to Create Suspense. William W. Flint. (Studies in Comparative Literature, No. 35). 1970. pap. 24.95x (ISBN 0-8383-0030-8). Haskell.

Use of Praying. J. Neville Ward. 1977. 10.95x (ISBN 0-19-520106-X); pap. 5.95 (ISBN 0-19-519959-6). Oxford U Pr.

Use of Scripture in Counseling. Jay E. Adams. 1975. pap. 2.95 (ISBN 0-87552-063-4). Presby & Reformed.

Use of Silence. Geoffrey Hoyland. 1983. pap. 2.50x (ISBN 0-87574-083-9, 083). Pendle Hill.

Use of the Bible in Christian Ethics. Thomas W. Ogletree. LC 83-5489. 240p. 1983. 19.95 (ISBN 0-8006-0710-4, 1-710). Fortress.

Use of the Bible in Milton's Prose. H. Fletcher. LC 75-95425. (Studies in Milton, No. 22). 1970. Repr. of 1929 ed. lib. bdg. 39.95x (ISBN 0-8383-0974-7). Haskell.

Use of the Bible in Milton's Prose. Harris F. Fletcher. 1973. lib. bdg. 59.95 (ISBN 0-87968-014-8). Gordon Pr.

Use of the Bible in Milton's Prose. Harris F. Fletcher. Repr. of 1929 ed. 15.00. Johnson Repr.

Use of the Bible in Preaching. Reginald H. Fuller. LC 80-2377. 80p. (Orig.). 1981. pap. 3.95 (ISBN 0-8006-1447-X, 1-1447). Fortress.

Use of the Bible in Theology. Ed. by Robert K. Johnston. LC 84-48513. 1985. pap. 11.95 (ISBN 0-8042-0530-2). John Knox.

Use of Tora by Isaiah: His Debate with the Wisdom Tradition. Joseph Jensen. LC 73-83134. (Catholic Biblical Quarterly Monographs: No. 3). 3.00 (ISBN 0-915170-02-7). Catholic Biblical.

Use of Traditional Materials in Colossians: Their Significance for the Problem of Authenticity. George C. Cannon. LC 83-8181. viii, 253p. 1983. 17.95 (ISBN 0-86554-074-8, H51). Mercer Univ Pr.

Uses of Hebraisms in Recent Bible Translations. Fred S. Heuman. 154p. 1977. 9.95 (ISBN 0-8022-2190-4). Philos Lib.

Uses of Scripture in Recent Theology. David H. Kelsey. LC 74-26344. 240p. 1975. pap. 7.95 (ISBN 0-8006-1374-0, 1-1374). Fortress.

Uses of the Old Testament in the New. Walter C. Kaiser. 1985. 13.95 (ISBN 0-8024-9085-9). Moody.

Usher's Manual. Leslie Parrott. 1969. pap. 2.95 (ISBN 0-310-30651-5, 10513P). Zondervan.

Using a Computer in Church Ministry. James P. Emswiler. 1986. pap. 6.95 (ISBN 0-87193-248-2). Dimension Bks.

Using Behavioral Methods in Pastoral Counseling. Howard W. Stone. Ed. by Howard J. Clinebell & Howard E. Stone. LC 79-2287. (Creative Pastoral Care & Counseling Ser.). 96p. 1980. pap. 0.50 (ISBN 0-8006-0563-2, 1-563). Fortress.

Using Computers in Religious Education. E. V. Clemans. 80p. 1986. pap. 6.95 (ISBN 0-687-43120-4). Abingdon.

Using Media in Religious Education. Ronald A. Sarno. LC 86-33844. 230p. (Orig.). 1987. pap. 13.95 (ISBN 0-89135-058-6). Religious Educ.

Using Nonbroadcast Video in the Church. Daniel W. Holland et al. 128p. 1980. pap. 5.95 (ISBN 0-8170-0895-0). Judson.

Using Our Gifts. Hoyt E. Stone. 38p. (Orig.). 1981. pap. text ed. 1.00 (ISBN 0-87148-880-9). Pathway Pr.

Using Personal Computers in the Church. Kenneth Bedell. 112p. 1982. pap. 5.95 (ISBN 0-8170-0948-5). Judson.

Using Policy Simulation Analysis to Guide Correctional Reform - Utah. 7.00 (ISBN 0-318-20317-0). Natl Coun Crime.

Using Problem Solving in Teaching & Training. LeRoy Ford. LC 77-178060. (Multi-Media Teaching & Training Ser.). (Orig.). 1972. pap. 5.50 (ISBN 0-8054-3415-1). Broadman.

Using Puppetry in the Church. Ed. by Everett Robertson. LC 78-72842. 1979. pap. 6.95 (ISBN 0-8054-7517-6). Broadman.

Using Simulation Games. Pat Baker & Mary R. Marshall. (Youth Work Guide Ser.). (Illus.). 96p. (Orig.). 1973. pap. 7.95 (ISBN 0-85819-090-7, Pub. by JBCE). ANZ Religious Pubns.

Using Spiritual Gifts. R. Wayne Jones. LC 83-70642. 1985. pap. 4.95 (ISBN 0-8054-6940-0). Broadman.

Using Storytelling in Christian Education. Patricia R. Griggs. LC 80-26468. 64p. (Orig.). 1981. pap. 7.25 (ISBN 0-687-43117-4). Abingdon.

Using the Bible in Groups. Roberta Hestenes. LC 84-15291. 118p. (Orig.). 1985. pap. 6.95 (ISBN 0-664-24561-7). Westminster.

Using Your Emotions Creatively. Garnett M. Wilder. 80p. 1984. pap. 2.95 (ISBN 0-8170-1020-3). Judson.

Using Your Money Wisely: Guidelines from Scripture. Larry Burkett. 1986. pap. 7.95 (ISBN 0-8024-3425-8). Moody.

Usos y Costumbres de las Tierras Biblicas. Fred H. Wight. Orig. Title: Manners & Customs of Bible Lands. (Span.). 336p. 1981. pap. 7.95 (ISBN 0-8254-1873-9). Kregel.

Uspenije Presvjatija Bogorodits. M. Skaballanovitch. Tr. of Dormition of the Mother of God. 114p. pap. 4.00 (ISBN 0-317-29164-5). Holy Trinity.

Usted Puede Tener lo Que Diga. Kenneth E. Hagin. (Span.). 1983. pap. 0.50 mini bk. (ISBN 0-89276-154-7). Hagin Ministries.

USY Parshat HaShavuan Series. 10.00 (ISBN 0-686-96100-5). United Syn Bk.

Utah & the Mormons. B. G. Ferris. LC 77-134394. Repr. of 1856 ed. 27.00 (ISBN 0-404-08436-2). AMS Pr.

Utah & the Mormons. Donald W. Hemingway. (Illus.). 1979. pap. 2.50 (ISBN 0-686-30193-5). D W Hemingway.

Utah & the Mormons. Ed. by Donald W. Hemingway. (Travel Ser.). (Illus.). 32p. 1983. pap. write for info. (ISBN 0-938440-47-0). Colourpicture.

Utilice Su Casa para Evangelizar. Lee Baggett. 32p. 1984. Repr. of 1983 ed. 1.50 (ISBN 0-311-13832-2). Casa Bautista.

Utility of Prayers. A. Rahman. pap. 3.50 (ISBN 0-686-18590-0). Kazi Pubns.

Utopia II: An Investigation into the Kingdom of God. John Schmidt. (Orig.). 1986. pap. 3.50 (ISBN 0-89540-154-1). Sun Pub.

Utopia of Pope John XXIII. Giancarlo Zizola. Tr. by Helen Barolini from Ital. LC 79-4347. Orig. Title: Utopia de Papa Giovanni. 391p. (Orig.). 1979. pap. 2.49 (ISBN 0-88344-520-4). Orbis Bks.

Utopian Dilemma: American Judaism & Public Policy. Murray Friedman. LC 85-7068. 125p. (Orig.). 1985. 12.00 (ISBN 0-89633-092-3); pap. 7.95 (ISBN 0-89633-093-1). Ethics & Public Policy.

Uttaratantra, or Ratnagotravibhaga: Sublime Science of the Great Vehicle to Salvation. Aryasanga Maitreya. Tr. by E. Obermiller from Tibetan. 225p. 1984. Repr. of 1931 ed. lib. bdg. 22.50x (ISBN 0-88181-001-0). Canon Pubns.

V

V Mire Molitvi. Protopresbyer Michael Pomazansky. Tr. of Prayer in the World. 148p. 1957. pap. 5.00 (ISBN 0-317-29096-7). Holy Trinity.

V Zashchitu Pravoslavnoj Vjeri ot Sektantov. Michael Polsky. Tr. of In Defence of Orthodoxy Against Sectarians. 1950. pap. 1.00 (ISBN 0-317-30261-2). Holy Trinity.

Vacation Bible School. Doris Freese. LC 77-76179. 96p. 1977. pap. text ed. 4.95 (ISBN 0-910566-11-9); Perfect bdg. instr's. guide by Werner Graendorf 5.95 (ISBN 0-910566-27-5). Evang Tchr.

Vacation Moscow Washington Alliance. Avro Manhattan. 352p. (Orig.). pap. 7.95 (ISBN 0-937958-12-3). Chick Pubns.

Vacation with the Lord: A Personal, Directed Retreat. Thomas H. Green. LC 86-71143. 176p. (Orig.). 1986. pap. 4.95 (ISBN 0-87793-343-X). Ave Maria.
Vadiraja's Refutation of Sankara's Non-Dualism: Clearing the Way for Theism. L. Stafford Betty. 1978. 9.95 (ISBN 0-89684-001-8). Orient Bk Dist.
Vahweh vs. Baal. Norman C. Habel. 128p. 1964. write for info. Concordia Schl Grad Studies.
Vailala Madness & the Destruction of Native Ceremonies in the Gulf Division. Francis E. Williams. LC 75-35166. (Territory of Papua. Anthropological Report: No. 4). Repr. of 1923 ed. 20.00 (ISBN 0-404-14180-3). AMS Pr.
Vain Siecle Guerpir: A Literary Approach to Sainthood through Old French Hagiography of the Twelfth Century. Phyllis Johnson & Brigitte Cazelles. (Studies in the Romance Languages & Literatures: No.205). 320p. 1979. pap. 19.50x (ISBN 0-8078-9205-X). U of NC Pr.
Vairagya-Satakam: The Hundred Verses on Renunciation. Bhartrihari. (Sanskrit & Eng.). pap. 1.75 (ISBN 0-87481-070-1). Vedanta Pr.
Vaisesika Sutras of Kanada, with the Commentary of Sankara & Extracts from the Gloss of Jayanarayana. Kanada. Tr. & intro. by Nandalal Sinha. Incl. Notes from the Commentary of Chandrakanta. LC 73-3791. (Sacred Books of the Hindus: No. 6). Repr. of 1911 ed. 42.50 (ISBN 0-404-57806-3). AMS Pr.
Vaisnava Behavior: Twenty-Six Qualities of a Devotee. Satsvarupa Das Goswami. Ed. by Mandalesvara Dasa. 201p. 1984. text ed. 5.50 (ISBN 0-911233-18-0). Gita Nagari.
Vaisnavism & Society in Northern India. Urmila Bhagowalia. 1980. 22.00x (ISBN 0-8364-0664-8, Pub. by Intellectual India). South Asia Bks.
Vaisnavism Saivism & Minor Religious Systems. R. G. Bhandarkar. 238p. 1986. Repr. 14.00X (ISBN 0-8364-1704-6, Pub. by Minerva India). South Asia Bks.
Vakyavritti & Atmajnanopadeshavidhi. Shankara. (Sanskrit & Eng). pap. 1.95 (ISBN 0-87481-424-3). Vedanta Pr.
Valarie. John Benton. 192p. (Orig.). 1982. pap. 2.95 (ISBN 0-8007-8430-8, New Hope Bks.). Revell.
Valdika Mantras with Transliteration & Translation. Uma A. Saini. LC 85-52267. (Sanskrit.). 288p. 1986. text ed. 19.00 (ISBN 0-9616357-0-3). U & K Pub.
Valentine's Day. Elizabeth Guilfoile. LC 65-10086. (Holiday Bks.). (Illus.). 1965. PLB 7.56 (ISBN 0-8116-6556-9). Garrard.
Valerian Persecution: A Study of the Relations Between Church & State in the Third Century A. D. Patrick J. Healy. LC 76-185943. xv, 285p. 1972. Repr. of 1905 ed. 21.00 (ISBN 0-8337-4169-1). B Franklin.
Valiant for Truth: The Story of John Bunyan. Anne Arnott. 160p. (Orig.). 1986. pap. 5.95 (ISBN 0-8028-0192-7). Eerdmans.
Valiant Pilgrim: The Story of John Bunyan & Puritan England. Vera Brittain. 1950. 30.00 (ISBN 0-8274-3665-3). R West.
Valiant Woman: At the Heart of Reconciliation. Sr. Vivian Jennings. LC 74-6037. 128p. 1974. 3.95 (ISBN 0-8189-0291-4). Alba.
Valignano's Mission Principles for Japan: Vol. I (1573-1582), Pt. I - The Problem (1573-1580) Josef F. Schutte. Tr. by John J. Coyne from Ger. LC 78-69683. (Modern Scholarly Studies About the Jesuits, in English Translations, Ser. II: No. 3). (Illus.). xxiv, 428p. 1980. 14.00 (ISBN 0-912422-36-X); pap. 12.00 smyth sewn (ISBN 0-912422-35-1). Inst Jesuit.
Valignano's Mission Principles for Japan: Vol. I (1573-1582), Pts. I & II: The Problem 1573-1580 & The Solution 1580 to 1582. Josef F. Schutte. Ed. by G. E. Ganss & P. C. Fischer. LC 78-69683. (Modern Scholarly Studies about the Jesuits, in English Translations: No. 5). Orig. Title: Valignanos Missionsgrundsatze Fur Japan. Tr. of Ger. 398p. 1985. 16.00 (ISBN 0-912422-76-9); pap. 14.00 sewn (ISBN 0-912422-75-0). Inst Jesuit.
Valley of Discord: Church & Society along the Connecticut River, 1636-1725. Paul R. Lucas. LC 75-22520. (Illus.). 288p. 1976. 25.00x (ISBN 0-87451-121-6). U Pr of New Eng.
Valley of Mekong. Matt Menger. 1970. 4.95 (ISBN 0-685-79412-1); pap. 3.95 (ISBN 0-685-79413-X). Guild Bks.
Valley of Silence: Catholic Thought in Contemporary Poland. Ed. by James J. Zatko. 1967. 21.95x (ISBN 0-268-00290-8). U of Notre Dame Pr.
Valley of Silence: Catholic Thought in Contemporary Poland. Ed. by James J. Zatko. LC 67-12125. pap. 101.80 (2029313). Bks Demand UMI.
Valley of the Shadow. Carol R. Murphy. LC 72-80095. 24p. (Orig.). 1972. pap. 2.50x (ISBN 0-87574-184-3). Pendle Hill.
Valleys of the Assassins. rev. ed. Freya Stark. (Illus.). 1972. 28.50 (ISBN 0-7195-2429-6). Transatl Arts.
Valmiki Ramayanan. V. Sitaramiah. 1982. Repr. 7.00x (ISBN 0-317-47015-9, Pub. by National Sahitya Akademi). South Asia Bks.
Value Development: A Practical Guide. Bruce Kalven et al. 1982. pap. 10.00 (ISBN 0-8091-2445-9); learning summaries 2.50 (ISBN 0-8091-2520-X); time diary 3.00 (ISBN 0-8091-2519-6). Paulist Pr.
Value of Dedication: The Story of Albert Schweitzer. Spencer Johnson. LC 79-21805. (Value Tales Ser.). (Illus.). 1979. 7.95 (ISBN 0-916392-44-9, Dist. by Oak Tree Pubns.). Value Comm.
Value of Determination: The Story of Helen Keller. 2nd ed. Ann D. Johnson. LC 76-54762. (Valuetales Ser). (Illus.). 1976. 7.95 (ISBN 0-916392-07-4, Dist. by Oak Tree Pubns.). Value Comm.
Value of Honesty: The Story of Confucius. Spencer Johnson. LC 78-4351. (ValueTales Ser.). (Illus.). 1979. 7.95 (ISBN 0-916392-36-8, Dist. by Oak Tree Pubns). Value Comm.
Value of Prayer in Psychological Integration. Manly P. Hall. pap. 2.50 (ISBN 0-89314-366-9). Philos Res.
Value of Voluntary Simplicity. Richard B. Gregg. 1983. pap. 2.50x (ISBN 0-87574-003-0, 003). Pendle Hill.
Value Systems & Personality in a Western Civilization: Norwegians in Europe & America. Christen T. Jonassen. LC 83-11391. 400p. 1984. 25.00x (ISBN 0-8142-0347-7). Ohio St U Pr.
Values: A Symposium. Ed. by Brenda Almond & Bryan Wilson. 300p. 1987. text ed. 45.00 (ISBN 0-391-03368-9). Humanities.
Values Across the Curriculum. Ed. by Peter Tomlinson & Margaret Quinton. LC 85-10389. 225p. 1986. 27.00x (ISBN 0-905273-75-3, Falmer Pr); pap. 15.00x (ISBN 0-905273-76-1). Taylor & Francis.
Values & Faith: Value Clarifying Exercises for Family & Church Groups. Roland Larson & Doris Larson. (Illus.). 260p. 1976. pap. 6.95 (ISBN 0-86683-673-X, HarpR). Har-Row.
Values & Imperatives: Studies in Ethics. Clarence I. Lewis. Ed. by John Lange. LC 69-13181. 1969. 17.50x (ISBN 0-8047-0687-5). Stanford U Pr.
Values & Religion in China Today: A Teaching Workbook & Lesson Series. Mary L. Martin & Donald MacInnis. 141p. (Orig.). 1985. pap. 12.95 (ISBN 0-88344-527-1). Orbis Bks.
Values & Society: An Introduction to Ethics & Social Philosophy. Peter A. Facione et al. 1978. pap. text ed. write for info (ISBN 0-13-940338-8). P-H.
Values & the Search for Self. James A. Bellance. LC 75-12724. pap. 27.80 (ISBN 0-317-42175-1, 2025922). Bks Demand UMI.
Values & Voices. 3rd ed. Betty Renshaw et al. 334p. 1986. pap. text ed. 16.95 (ISBN 0-03-071039-1, HoltC). HR&W.
Values, Ethics & Aging, Vol. 4. Ed. by Gari Lesnoff-Caravaglia. (Frontiers in Aging Ser.). 196p. 1985. 29.95 (ISBN 0-89885-162-9). Human Sci Pr.
Values for Tomorrow's Children. Ed. by John H. Westerhoff, III. LC 72-125961. 1979. pap. 5.95 (ISBN 0-8298-0377-7). Pilgrim NY.
Values in an Age of Confrontation: A Symposium Sponsored by the Religion in Education Foundation. Ed. by Jeremiah W. Canning. LC 72-109054. (Studies of the Person). pap. 41.10 (ISBN 0-317-09226-X, 2055239). Bks Demand UMI.
Values in Conflict: Christianity, Marxism, Psychoanalysis & Existentialism. Ed. by Victor Comerchero. LC 74-111099. 986p. (Orig., Free booklet, "Suggestions for Instructors," available). 1970. pap. text ed. 19.95x (ISBN 0-89197-463-6). Irvington.
Values to Cherish. Helen R. Harrison. (Orig.). 1978. pap. 4.50 (ISBN 0-87881-071-4). Mojave Bks.
Valuing Suffering As a Christian: Some Psychological Perspectives. C. P. Simons. (Synthesis Ser.). 1976. pap. 0.75 (ISBN 0-8199-0708-1). Franciscan Herald.
Valuing the Self: What We Can Learn from Other Cultures. Dorothy Lee. (Illus.). 1986. pap. text ed. 6.95x (ISBN 0-88133-229-1). Waveland Pr.
Vampirism in Literature: Shadow of a Shade. Margaret L. Carter. 1974. lib. bdg. 69.95 (ISBN 0-87968-225-6). Gordon Pr.
Van Eyck Problem. Maurice W. Brockwell. LC 78-138101. (Illus.). 1971. Repr. of 1954 ed. lib. bdg. 22.50x (ISBN 0-8371-5677-7, BRVE). Greenwood.
Van Til & the Use of Evidence. Thom Notaro. 1980. pap. 4.50 (ISBN 0-87552-353-6). Presby & Reformed.
Vance Havner Devotional Treasury: Daily Meditations for a Year. Vance Havner. (Direction Books). 192p. 1981. pap. 4.50 (ISBN 0-8010-4257-7). Baker Bk.
Vance Havner Quotebook. Vance Havner. 208p. 1986. 9.95 (ISBN 0-8010-4299-2). Baker Bk.
Vance Havner Treasury. Vance Havner. Compiled by Dennis Hester. 264p. Date not set. 9.95 (ISBN 0-8010-4315-8). Baker Bk.
Vancouver Voices. Charles H. Long. 144p. (Orig.). 1983. pap. 1.40 (ISBN 0-88028-026-3). Forward Movement.
Vandalism. Dan Carr. (God I Need to Talk to You About...Ser.). (Illus.). 1984. pap. 0.75 (ISBN 0-570-08726-0, 56-1470). Concordia.
Vanished Arcadia: Being Some Account of the Jesuits in Paraguay. Robert B. Graham. LC 68-25238. (Studies in Spanish Literature, No. 36). 1969. Repr. of 1901 ed. lib. bdg. 50.95x (ISBN 0-8383-0949-6). Haskell.
Vanished World. Roman Vishniac. LC 83-16420. (Illus.). 192p. 1983. 65.00 (ISBN 0-374-28247-1). FS&G.
Vanished World. Roman Vishniac. (Illus.). 192p. 1986. pap. 19.95 (ISBN 0-374-52023-2). FS&G.
Vanitie & Downe-Fall of Superstitious Popish Ceremonies. Peter Smart. LC 77-7428. (English Experience Ser.: No. 894). 1977. Repr. of 1628 ed. lib. bdg. 6.00 (ISBN 90-221-0894-5). Walter J Johnson.
Vanquished Hope: The Church in Russia on the Eve of the Revolution. James Cunningham. 1981. pap. 40.00x (Pub. by Mowbrays Pub Div). State Mutual Bk.
Vanquished Hope: The Movement for Church Renewal in Russia, 1905-1906. James W. Cunningham. LC 81-9077. 384p. 1981. pap. text ed. 10.95 (ISBN 0-913836-70-2). St Vladimirs.
Vanquished Nation, Broken Spirit: The Virtues of the Heart in Formative Judaism. Jacob Neusner. 208p. Date not set. price not set (ISBN 0-521-32832-2); pap. price not set (ISBN 0-521-33801-8). Cambridge U Pr.
Vanya. Myrna Grant. 208p. 1976. 3.25 (ISBN 0-88113-310-8). Edit Betania.
Varia Codicologica: Litterae Textuales. Ed. by J. P. Gumbert & M. J. De Haan. (Illus.). 110p. 1972. 46.50 (ISBN 0-8390-0106-1). Abner Schram Ltd.
Variant Versions of Targumic Traditions Within Codex Neofiti 1. Shirley Lund & Julia A. Foster. LC 77-5389. (Society of Biblical Literature. Aramaic Studies). 1977. pap. 10.50 (ISBN 0-89130-137-2, 061302). Scholars Pr GA.
Variations on a Theme. Sr. Mary Francis. 1977. 5.00 (ISBN 0-8199-0664-6). Franciscan Herald.
Varieties of American Religion. facsimile ed. Ed. by Charles S. Braden. LC 76-156616. (Essay Index Reprint Ser). Repr. of 1936 ed. 15.50 (ISBN 0-8369-2307-3). Ayer Co Pubs.
Varieties of Christian Apologetics. Bernard Ramm. (Twin Brooks Ser.). pap. 5.95 (ISBN 0-8010-7610-2). Baker Bk.
Varieties of Jewish Belief. Louis Barish & Rebecca Barish. 1979. Repr. 9.95 (ISBN 0-8246-0242-0). Jonathan David.
Varieties of Religious Experience. William James. LC 37-27013. 1936. 6.95 (ISBN 0-394-60463-6). Modern Lib.
Varieties of Religious Experience. William James. pap. 4.50 (ISBN 0-451-62486-6, ME2069, Ment). NAL.
Varieties of Religious Experience. William James. (Works of William James). (Illus.). 728p. 1985. text ed. 45.00x (ISBN 0-674-93225-0). Harvard U Pr.
Varieties of Religious Experience: A Study in Human Nature. William James. Ed. by Martin Marty. (Penguin American Library). 1982. pap. 4.95 (ISBN 0-14-039034-0). Penguin.
Varieties of Religious Experiences. William James. 1961. pap. 3.95 (ISBN 0-02-085960-0, Collier). Macmillan.
Varieties of Religious Presence: Mission in Public Life. David A. Roozen & William McKinney. 400p. (Orig.). 1984. pap. 12.95 (ISBN 0-8298-0724-1). Pilgrim NY.
Varieties of Southern Evangelicalism. Ed. by David E. Harrell, Jr. LC 81-11312. xii, 114p. 1981. 9.95 (ISBN 0-86554-015-2, MUP-H18). Mercer Univ Pr.
Variety Book of Puppet Scripts. Sarah W. Miller. LC 78-57276. 1978. pap. 4.50 (ISBN 0-8054-7515-X). Broadman.
Variety for Worship: Resources for Festival Worship Liturgies. Frederick W. Kemper. 1984. pap. 7.95 (ISBN 0-570-03936-3, 12-2871). Concordia.
Variety in Biblical Preaching. Harold Freeman. 192p. 1986. 12.95 (ISBN 0-8499-0562-1). Word Bks.
Various Prospects of Mankind, Nature & Providence. Robert Wallace. LC 69-19550. 1969. Repr. of 1761 ed. 39.50x (ISBN 0-678-00491-9). Kelley.
Varon Llamado Job. Clyde T. Francisco. Tr. by Jack A. Glaze from Eng. (Reflexiones Teologicas Ser.). Orig. Title: Man Called Job. 64p. 1981. pap. 1.95 (ISBN 0-311-04659-2). Casa Bautista.
Varon y Su Temperamento. Tim LaHaye. 217p. 1978. 3.95 (ISBN 0-88113-340-X). Edit Betania.
Vastusutra Upanisad: The Essence of Form in Sacred Art. Alice Boner. xii, 192p. 1986. 32.00 (Pub. by Motilal Banarsidass). South Asia Bks.
Vaterunser Polyglott: The Lord's Prayer in 42 Languages (Sprachen Mit 75 Text Fassungen) Ed. by Gernot Buhring. (Ger.). 278p. 1984. 10.00x (ISBN 3-87118-666-X, Pub. by Helmut Buske Verlag Hamburg). Benjamins North AM.
Vatican. Peter Hebblethwaite et al. LC 80-50854. (Illus.). 226p. 1980. 50.00 (ISBN 0-86565-002-0). Vendome.
Vatican. Malachi Martin. LC 85-42645. 672p. 1986. 18.45 (ISBN 0-06-015478-0, HarpT). Har-Row.
Vatican & Christian Rome. Photos by Mario Carrieri. (Illus.). 522p. 1979. 100.00 (ISBN 0-89860-025-1). Eastview.
Vatican & Hungary 1846-1878: Reports & Correspondence on Hungary of the Apostolic Nuncios in Vienna. Lajos Lukacs. Tr. by Zsofia Kormos. 795p. 1981. text ed. 65.00x (ISBN 963-05-2446-5, Pub. by Akademiai Kiado UK). Humanities.
Vatican & Italian Fascism, Nineteen Twenty-Nine to Nineteen Thirty-Two: A Study in Conflict. John F. Pollard. 240p. 1985. 34.50 (ISBN 0-521-26870-2). Cambridge U Pr.
Vatican & the American Hierarchy from 1870 to 1965. Gerald P. Fogarty. 1985. pap. 16.95 (ISBN 0-317-42752-0). M Glazier.
Vatican & the Reagan Administration. Ana M. Ezcurra. Ed. by New York CIRCUS Publications, Inc. Staff. Tr. of Vaticano y la Administracion Reagan. 220p. (Orig.). 1986. pap. text ed. 6.95 (ISBN 0-318-20240-9). NY Circus Pubns.
Vatican & the Third World: Diplomacy & the Future. DH - TE Research Studies. LC 75-14400. 1975. pap. 3.50 (ISBN 0-686-11971-1). Bks Intl DH-TE.
Vatican Billions. Avro Manhattan. 304p. (Orig.). 1983. pap. 7.50 (ISBN 0-937958-16-6). Chick Pubns.
Vatican City-State. Michael J. Walsh. (World Bibliographical Ser.: No. 41). 105p. 1983. lib. bdg. 22.00 (ISBN 0-903450-72-0). ABC-Clio.
Vatican Council II. Ed. by Austin Flannery. 1976. pap. 7.95 (ISBN 0-685-77498-8). Franciscan Herald.
Vatican Council II: The Conciliar & Post Conciliar Documents, Vol. 2. Austin Flannery. 994p. 1983. pap. 9.95 (ISBN 0-8146-1299-7). Liturgical Pr.
Vatican Diplomacy: A Study of Church & State on the International Plane. Robert A. Graham. LC 59-13870. pap. 113.00 (ISBN 0-317-08423-2, 2015012). Bks Demand UMI.
Vatican Diplomacy & the Jews During the Holocaust, 1939-1943. John F. Morley. 1980. 25.00x (ISBN 0-87068-701-8). Ktav.
Vatican Diplomacy & the Jews During the Holocaust 1939-1943. John F. Morley. 320p. 25.00. ADL.
Vatican Frescoes of Michelangelo, 2 vols. Intro. by Andre Chastel. Tr. by Raymond Rosenthal from Fr. LC 80-66646. (Illus.). 528p. 1980. ltd. ed. 7500.00 (ISBN 0-89659-158-1). Abbeville Pr.
Vatican II & Phenomenology. John F. Kobler. 1986. lib. bdg. 37.50 (ISBN 90-247-3193-3, Pub. by Martinus Nijhoff Netherlands). Kluwer-Academic.
Vatican II: More Postconciliar Documents. Ed. by Austin P. Flannery. 944p. (Orig.). 1983. pap. 9.95 (ISBN 0-8028-1638-X). Eerdmans.
Vatican II: Open Questions & New Horizons. Ed. by Gerald M. Fagin. (Theology & Life Ser.: Vol. 8). pap. 6.95 (ISBN 0-89453-366-5). M Glazier.
Vatican in Politics. 4th ed. Daniel De Leon. 1962. pap. text ed. 0.50 (ISBN 0-935534-31-8). NY Labor News.
Vatican Plato & Its Relations. Levi A. Post. (APA Philological Monographs). 22.50 (ISBN 0-89130-704-4, 40-00-04). Scholars Pr GA.
Vatican: Spirit & Art of Christian Rome. 1983. 60.00 (ISBN 0-8109-1711-4). Abrams.
Vatican Stanze: Functions & Decoration. J. Shearman. (Italian Lectures). 1971. pap. 2.50 (ISBN 0-85672-062-3, Pub. by British Acad). Longwood Pub Group.
Vatican, the Bishops & Irish Politics: Church & State in Ireland, 1919-1939. Dermot F. Keogh. (Illus.). 318p. 1986. 39.50 (ISBN 0-521-30129-7). Cambridge U Pr.
Vatican Two Revisited: By Those Who Were There. Ed. by Dom A. Stacpoole. 448p. 1986. 24.50 (ISBN 0-86683-531-8, HarpR). Har-Row.
Vatican Two Sunday Missal. 1974. 8.75 (ISBN 0-8198-0513-0); pap. 5.95 (ISBN 0-8198-0514-9); gold edge bonded leather 14.95 (ISBN 0-8198-0515-7); genuine leather 18.95 (ISBN 0-8198-0516-5). Dghtrs St Paul.

Vatican Two Weekday Missal. 1975. red edge 18.50 (ISBN 0-8198-0497-5); bonded leather, gold edge 24.95 (ISBN 0-8198-0498-3); genuine leather 29.95 (ISBN 0-8198-0499-1). Dghtrs St Paul.

Vayu Purana. Tr. by G. V. Tagare. write for info. Asian Human Pr.

Veda of the Black Yajus School: Taittiriya Sanhita, 2 vols. A. B. Keith. 1967. Repr. Set. 42.00 (ISBN 0-89684-334-3). Orient Bk Dist.

Veda Recitation in Varanasi. Wayne Howard. 1986. 42.00x (ISBN 0-8364-0872-1). South Asia Bks.

Vedanta & Christian Faith. Bede Griffiths. LC 73-88179. 85p. 1973. pap. 3.95 (ISBN 0-913922-04-8). Dawn Horse Pr.

Vedanta & the Bengal Renaissance: Progress or Reaction. Niranjan Dhar. LC 76-52210. 1977. 11.00x (ISBN 0-88386-837-7). South Asia Bks.

Vedanta Doctrine of Sri Sankaracharya. A. Mahadeva Sastri. 245p. 1986. Repr. of 1899 ed. lib. bdg. 16.95 (ISBN 81-7030-029-0, Pub. by Sri Satguru Pubns India). Orient Bk Dist.

Vedanta for the Western World: A Symposium on Vedanta. Ed. by Christopher Isherwood. LC 46-25052. 1945. pap. 7.95 (ISBN 0-87481-000-0). Vedanta Pr.

Vedanta in Brief. Jyotir Maya Nanda. (Orig.). 1978. pap. 3.99 (ISBN 0-934664-37-4). Yoga Res Foun.

Vedanta in Practice. 3rd ed. Swami Paramananda. 1985. pap. 3.50 (ISBN 0-911564-04-7). Vedanta Ctr.

Vedanta-Paribhasa. Dharmaraja Adhvarindra. Tr. by Swami Madhavananda. (English & Sanskrit). pap. 8.95 (ISBN 0-87481-072-8). Vedanta Pr.

Vedanta Philosophy. F. M. Muller. 182p. 1984. text ed. 27.00x. Coronet Bks.

Vedanta-Sara-Sangraha. Anantendra-Yati. Tr. by T. M. Mahadevan. 1974. pap. 3.50 (ISBN 0-89744-124-9, Pub. by Ganesh & Co. India). Auromere.

Vedanta: Seven Steps to Samadhi. Bhagwan Shree Rajneesh. Ed. by Ma Yoga Pratima. LC 77-904425. (Upanishad Ser.). (Illus.). 518p. (Orig.). 1976. 16.50 (ISBN 0-88050-166-9). Chidvilas Found.

Vedanta Sutras. G. Thibaut. (Sacred Bks. of the East: Vols. 34, 38). both vols. 30.00 (ISBN 0-89581-530-3); 15.00 ea. Asian Human Pr.

Vedanta Sutras. Ed. by G. Thibaut. 1974. lib. bdg. 75.00 (ISBN 0-8490-1256-2). Gordon Pr.

Vedanta Sutras of Badarayana with the Commentary of Baladeva. Tr. by Srisa Chandra Vasu. LC 73-3790. (Sacred Books of the Hindus: Vol. 5). Repr. of 1912 ed. 57.50 (ISBN 0-404-57805-5). AMS Pr.

Vedantasara of Sadananda. Sadananda. pap. 3.00 (ISBN 0-87481-073-6). Vedanta Pr.

Vedantic Approaches to God. Eric Lott. LC 78-17886. (Library of Philosophy & Religion Ser.). 214p. 1980. text ed. 28.50x (ISBN 0-06-494365-8). B&N Imports.

Vedantic Buddhism of Buddha. J. G. Jennings. 1974. Repr. 28.00 (ISBN 0-8426-0683-1). Orient Bk Dist.

Vedas: Immortality's First Call. 1972. pap. 2.00 (ISBN 0-87847-018-2). Aum Pubns.

Vedas of Raja Rammohan Rai. rev. ed. J. L. Shastri. 1977. 7.95 (ISBN 0-89684-335-1). Orient Bk Dist.

Vedi. Ved Mehta. (Illus.). 1982. 18.95x (ISBN 0-19-503005-2). Oxford U Pr.

Vedic Experience. Raimundo Panniker. 937p. 1983. 28.50 (ISBN 0-89744-011-0). Auromere.

Vedic Hymns. F. Muller & H. Oldenberg. (Sacred Bks. of the East: Vols. 32, 46). both vols. 30.00 (ISBN 0-89581-529-X); 15.00 ea. Asian Human Pr.

Vedic India. G. S. Ghurye. 1979. 46.00 (ISBN 0-89684-061-1, Pub. by Motilal Banarsidass India). Orient Bk Dist.

Vedic Metaphysics. Bharata Krsna Tirthaji Maharaj. 1978. Repr. 16.95 (ISBN 0-89684-337-8). Orient Bk Dist.

Vedic Metre in Its Historical Development. E. V. Arnold. 1967. Repr. 25.00 (ISBN 0-89684-338-6). Orient Bk Dist.

Vedic Mythology, Vol. I. rev. 2nd ed. Alfred Hillebrandt. Tr. by Sreeramula R. Sarma from Ger. Tr. of Vedische Mythologie. 472p. 1980. text ed. 22.00 (ISBN 0-89684-098-0, Pub. by Motilal Banarsidass India). Orient Bk Dist.

Vedic Mythology. A. A. Macdonell. 1974. Repr. 15.50 (ISBN 0-8426-0674-2). Orient Bk Dist.

Vedic Mythology. Arthur A. MacDonell. 69.95 (ISBN 0-87968-153-5). Gordon Pr.

Vedic Religion. Abel Bergaigne. Tr. by V. G. Paranjpe. 1978. 25.00 (ISBN 0-89684-006-9, Pub. by Motilal Banarsidass India). Orient Bk Dist.

Vedic Religion & Philosophy. Swami Prabhavananda. 3.95 (ISBN 0-87481-411-1). Vedanta Pr.

Vedic Studies, Vol. 2. A. Venkatasubbiah. 5.25 (ISBN 0-8356-7447-9). Theos Pub Hse.

Vedic Vision. Ed. by John B. Alphonso-Karkala. 80p. 1980. pap. 4.50 (ISBN 0-86578-004-8). Ind-US Inc.

Vegetalismo: Shamanism among the Mestizo Population of the Peruvian Amazon. Luis E. Luna. (Stockholm Studies in Comparative Religion). (Illus.). 202p. (Orig.). 1986. pap. text ed. 20.00x. Coronet Bks.

Vegetarianism & the Jewish Tradition. Louis A. Berman. LC 81-11729. 120p. 1982. 10.00x (ISBN 0-87068-756-5); pap. 7.95. Ktav.

Veil. Robert Williams. 20p. 1976. pap. 3.95 (ISBN 0-89536-247-3, 2200). CSS of Ohio.

Veil Too Thin: Reincarnation Out of Control. Betty Riley. LC 84-50090. 96p. 1984. pap. 2.95 (ISBN 0-911842-37-3). Valley Sun.

Veiled Gazelle: Seeing How to See. Idries Shah. 103p. 1977. 9.95 (ISBN 0-900860-58-8, Pub. by Octagon Pr England). Ins Study Human.

Veintinueve Soldados de Plomo. George Verwer. 112p. 1981. 2.50 (ISBN 0-88113-331-0). Edit Betania.

Vena Aguillard: Woman of Faith. Marsha Barrett. LC 82-73664. (Meet the Missionary Ser.). 1983. 5.50 (ISBN 0-8054-4281-2, 4242-81). Broadman.

Vendanta Sutras, 3 vols. Tr. by G. Thibaut. lib. bdg. 300.00 (ISBN 0-87968-562-X). Krishna Pr.

Venerable Bede: Commentary on the Catholic Epistles. David Hurst. 1985. 24.95 (ISBN 0-317-18074-6); pap. 9.00 (ISBN 0-317-18075-4). Cistercian Pubns.

Venerable Bede: His Life & Writings. G. F. Browne. LC 76-52505. 1972. Repr. of 1919 ed. lib. bdg. 35.00 (ISBN 0-8414-1652-4). Folcroft.

Venerable One. Ann R. Colton. 166p. 1963. 5.95 (ISBN 0-917187-11-3). A R C Pub.

Veneration of Icons. St. John of Damascus. pap. 0.50 (ISBN 0-686-05666-3). Eastern Orthodox.

Vengeance of the Gods. Rex Warner. 192p. 1955. 3.50 (ISBN 0-87013-009-9). Mich St U Pr.

Vengeance: The Fight Against Injustice. Pietro Marongiu & Graeme Newman. 176p. 1987. 27.50. Rowman.

Venida del Senor. 2nd ed. Jorge Cutting. Ed. by Gordon H. Bennett. Tr. by Sara Bautista from Eng. (Serie Diamante). Tr. of Lord's Coming. (Span., Illus.). 48p. 1982. pap. 0.85 (ISBN 0-942504-10-0). Overcomer Pr.

Venom in My Veins: The Terry Jones Story. Terry L. Jones & David L. Nixon. 88p. (Orig.). 1985. pap. 3.95 (ISBN 0-8341-1078-4). Beacon Hill.

Venture Inward: Edgar Cayce's Story & the Mysteries of the Unconscious Mind. Hugh L. Cayce. LC 85-42772. 256p. 1985. pap. 4.95 (ISBN 0-06-250131-3, HarpR). Har-Row.

Venture of Islam: Conscience & History in World Civilization, 3 vols. Marshall G. Hodgson. LC 73-87243. 1975. 30.00x ea.; Vol. 2. (ISBN 0-226-34680-3); Vol. 3. (ISBN 0-226-34681-1). U of Chicago Pr.

Ventures in Discipleship. John R. Martin. LC 84-19140. 304p. (Orig.). 1984. pap. 12.95 (ISBN 0-8361-3378-1). Herald Pr.

Ventures in Leisure-Time Christian Education. Norma E. Koenig. (Orig.). 1979. pap. 4.15 (ISBN 0-687-43670-2). Abingdon.

Vercelli Book. Ed. by George P. Krapp. LC 32-10861. 152p. 1932. 27.50 (ISBN 0-231-08766-7). Columbia U Pr.

Verdades que Cambian Vidas. Marcelino Ortiz. (Span.). 96p. (Orig.). 1981. pap. 2.50 (ISBN 0-89922-173-4). Edit Caribe.

Verdict on the Shroud: Evidence for the Death & Resurrection of Jesus Christ. Kenneth Stevenson & Gary B. Habermas. (Illus.). 220p. 1981. pap. 6.95 (ISBN 0-89283-174-X). Servant.

Verhaeltnis von Amt und Gemeinde im Neueren Katholizismus. Ursula Schnell. (Theologische Bibliothek Toepolmann: Vol. 29). 1977. pap. 41.20x (ISBN 3-11-004929-5). De Gruyter.

Verifying the Vision: A Self-Evaluation Instrument for the Catholic Elementary School. Carleen Reck & Judith Coreil. 160p. 1984. 12.00 (ISBN 0-318-17778-1). Natl Cath Educ.

Vernon Manuscript: Bodleian Library MS. English Poet a.1. Intro. by I. A. Doyle. (Illus.). 704p. 1987. facsimile 695.00 (ISBN 0-85991-200-0, Pub. by Boydell & Brewer). Longwood Pub Group.

Verses & Meditations. Rudolf Steiner. Tr. by George Adams & Mary Adams. (Ger.). 253p. 1979. Repr. of 1961 ed. 9.95 (ISBN 0-85440-119-9, Pub. by Steinerbooks). Anthroposophic.

Verses in Sermons: "Fasciculus morum" & Its Middle English Poems. Siegfried Wenzel. LC 78-55887. 1978. 20.00x (ISBN 0-910956-66-9). Medieval Acad.

Versiculos "Llave". Guillermo Woggon. Tr. by Nola Granberry. (Libros Para Colorear). Tr. of Key Bible Verses. (Span., Illus.). 16p. 1985. pap. 1.25 (ISBN 0-311-38565-6). Casa Bautista.

Verus Israel. Marcal Simon. Tr. by H. McKeating. 592p. 1985. 57.00x (ISBN 0-19-710035-X). Oxford U Pr.

Very Godly Defense, Defending the Marriage of Priests. Philip Melanchthon. Tr. by L. Beuchame. LC 76-25643. (English Experience Ser.: No. 199). 1969. Repr. of 1541 ed. 8.00 (ISBN 90-221-0199-1). Walter J Johnson.

Very Practical Meditation. Serene West. LC 79-20249. 116p. (Orig.). 1981. pap. 4.95 (ISBN 0-89865-006-2, Unilaw). Donning Co.

Very Special Baby-Jesus. Lynn Groth. (Cradle Roll Program Ser.). 8p. (Orig.). 1985. pap. 1.25 (ISBN 0-938272-76-4). Wels Board.

Very Special Day. Lois Rau. (Redwood Ser.). 1982. pap. 2.95 (ISBN 0-8163-0447-5). Pacific Pr Pub Assn.

Very Special Night. Ruth Odor. (Happy Day Book). (Illus.). 24p. (Orig.). 1980. 1.59 (ISBN 0-87239-405-0, 3637). Standard Pub.

Very Special Person. Lois Rau. (Sunshine Ser.). 1982. pap. 2.95 (ISBN 0-8163-0445-9). Pacific Pr Pub Assn.

Very Special Planet. Lois Rau. (Sunshine Ser.). 1982. pap. 2.95 (ISBN 0-8163-0446-7). Pacific Pr Pub Assn.

Very Special Promise. Lois Rau. (Sunshine Ser.). 1982. pap. 2.95 (ISBN 0-8163-0448-3). Pacific Pr Pub Assn.

Very Special Yarmulka. 1982. pap. 2.50 (ISBN 0-87306-186-1). Feldheim.

Very Truly Yours. Jacob P. Rudin. 1971. 6.50x (ISBN 0-8197-0279-X). Bloch.

Vessels Unto Honor. Connie Broome. LC 76-22242. 1977. pap. 3.50 (ISBN 0-87148-879-5). Pathway Pr.

Vestibules of Heaven. Mid McKnight. 1982. pap. 3.95 (ISBN 0-89225-219-7). Gospel Advocate.

Vestry Book & Register of St. Peter's Parish, New Kent & James City Counties, Virginia, 1684-1786. C. G. Chamberlayne. xxvi, 840p. 1973. Repr. of 1937 ed. 12.50 (ISBN 0-88490-037-1). VA State Lib.

Vestry Book of Blisland (Blissland) Parish, New Kent & James City Counties, Virginia, 1721-1786. Ed. by C. G. Chamberlayne. LC 79-16401. ixii, 277p. 1979. Repr. of 1935 ed. 10.00 (ISBN 0-88490-030-4). VA State Lib.

Vestry Book of Petsworth Parish, Glouster County, Virginia, 1670-1793. Ed. by C. G. Chamberlane. LC 79-13640. xv, 429p. 1979. Repr. of 1933 ed. 10.00 (ISBN 0-88490-032-0). VA State Lib.

Vestry Book of St. Paul's Parish, Hanover County, Virginia, 1706-1786. Ed. by C. G. Chamberlayne. xx, 672p. 1973. Repr. of 1940 ed. 12.50 (ISBN 0-88490-038-X). VA State Lib.

Vestry Book of Stratton Major Parish, King & Queen County, Virginia, 1729-1783. Ed. by C. G. Chamberlyne. LC 80-14672. xxi, 257p. 1980. Repr. of 1933 ed. 10.00 (ISBN 0-88490-087-8). VA State Lib.

Vestry Book of the Upper Parish, Nansemond County, Virginia, 1793-1943. Ed. by Wilmer L. Hall. LC 50-9492. ixxiv, 328p. 1949. 10.00 (ISBN 0-88490-039-8). VA State Lib.

Vestry Member's Guide. rev. ed. Van S. Bowen. 80p. 1983. pap. 3.95 (ISBN 0-8164-2464-0, HarpR). Har-Row.

Vestry Minute Book of the Parish of Stratford-on-Avon from 1617 to 1699. Ed. by George Arbuthnot. LC 72-142244. Repr. of 1899 ed. 11.50 (ISBN 0-404-00366-4). AMS Pr.

Vetus Disciplina Canocorum Regularium & Saecularium ex Documentis Magna Parte Hucusque Ineditis a Temporibus Apostolicis ad Saeculum XVII. Eusebio Amort. 1112p. 1747. text ed. 248.40x (ISBN 0-576-99833-8, Pub. by Gregg Intl Pubs England). Gregg Intl.

Via, Veritas, Vita: Lectures on "Chrisitianity in Its Most Simple & Intelligible Form". 2nd ed. James Drummond. LC 77-27160. (Hibbert Lectures: 1894). Repr. of 1895 ed. 31.50 (ISBN 0-404-60412-9). AMS Pr.

Vial Judgments, or, The Seven Last Plagues. Gordon Lindsay. (Revelation Ser.). 1.25 (ISBN 0-89985-045-6). Christ Nations.

Vials of the Seven Last Plagues. Seven Archangels. LC 76-28083. 156p. (Orig.). 1977. pap. 5.95 (ISBN 0-916766-23-3). Summit Univ.

Vicarious Sacrifice. Ernest M. Ligon & Character Research Project Staff. Incl. Junior High Unit-Lesson Book. 2.00 (ISBN 0-915744-15-5); Junior High Unit-PLAN. 0.75 (ISBN 0-915744-17-1); Junior High Unit-Home Assignment Sheets. 0.75 (ISBN 0-915744-16-3). (Research Curriculum for Character Education Ser.). (Illus.). 1979. Character Res.

Vichy France & the Jews. Michael R. Marrus & Robert O. Paxton. LC 82-16869. 432p. (Orig.). 1983. pap. 12.95 (ISBN 0-8052-0741-4). Schocken.

Vicitrakarnika-Vadanoddhrta: A Collection of Buddhistic Legends. Ed. by Hans Jorgensen. LC 78-70134. Repr. of 1931 ed. 34.50 (ISBN 0-404-17404-3). AMS Pr.

Victims & Neighbors: A Small Town in Nazi Germany Remembered. Frances Henry. (Illus.). 216p. 1984. 27.95 (ISBN 0-89789-047-7); pap. 12.95 (ISBN 0-89789-048-5). Bergin & Garvey.

Victor el Victorioso. Robert Owen & David M. Howard. Tr. by Eugenio Orellana from Eng. Tr. of Victor. (Span.). 152p. 1981. pap. 3.25 (ISBN 0-89922-206-4). Edit Caribe.

Victor Family Story Bible. V. Gilbert Beers & Ronald Beers. 640p. 1985. 19.95 (ISBN 0-88207-822-4). Victor Bks.

Victor Handbook of Bible Knowledge. Popular ed. Gilbert Beers. LC 81-50695. 640p. 1981. 29.95 (ISBN 0-88207-811-9); pap. 21.95 (ISBN 0-88207-808-9). Victor Bks.

Victor Paul Wierwille & the Way International. J. L. Williams. LC 79-22007. 1979. pap. 3.95 (ISBN 0-8024-9233-9). Moody.

Victorian Cathedral Music in Theory & Practice. William J. Gatens. 300p. 1986. 39.50 (ISBN 0-521-26808-7). Cambridge U Pr.

Victorian Celebration of Death: The Architecture & Planning of the 19th-Century Necropolis. James S. Curl. LC 70-184048. 222p. 1972. 35.00x (ISBN 0-8103-2000-2). Gale.

Victorian Christian Socialists. Edward Norman. 210p. Date not set. price not set (ISBN 0-521-32515-3). Cambridge U Pr.

Victorian Christmas: 1876. Elspeth. 1974. pap. 1.50 (ISBN 0-87588-106-8). Hobby Hse.

Victorian Church Art. John Physick. (Illus.). 212p. (Orig.). 1984. pap. 12.95 (ISBN 0-901486-36-1, Pub. by Victoria & Albert Mus UK). Faber & Faber.

Victorian Clergy. Alan Haig. 380p. 1984. 33.00 (ISBN 0-7099-1230-7, Pub. by Croom Helm Ltd). Methuen Inc.

Victorian Country Parsons. Brenda Colloms. LC 77-82027. (Illus.). 284p. 1978. 21.50x (ISBN 0-8032-0981-9). U of Nebr Pr.

Victorian Devotional Poetry: The Tractarian Mode. G. B. Tennyson. LC 80-14416. 1980. text ed. 18.50x (ISBN 0-674-93586-1). Harvard U Pr.

Victorian "Lives" of Jesus. Daniel L. Pals. LC 82-81018. (Trinity University Monograph Series in Religion). 225p. 1982. 20.00 (ISBN 0-911536-95-7). Trinity U Pr.

Victorian Science & Religion: A Bibliography of Works on Ideas & Institutions with Emphasis on Evolution, Belief & Unbelief, Published from 1900 to 1975. Sydney Eisen & Bernard V. Lightman. LC 82-24497. xix, 696p. 1984. lib. bdg. 49.50 (ISBN 0-208-02010-1, Archon Bks). Shoe String.

Victorian Values: Secularism & the Smaller Family. J. A. Banks. 288p. 1981. 26.95x (ISBN 0-7100-0807-4). Methuen Inc.

Victorious Christ (Revelation) Leader's Guide. (New Horizons Bible Study Ser.). 48p. 1983. pap. 1.95 (ISBN 0-89367-089-8). Light & Life.

Victorious Christ (Revelation) Student Guide. 68p. 1983. pap. 2.50 (ISBN 0-89367-088-X). Light & Life.

Victorious Christian Faith. Alan Redpath. 192p. 9.95 (ISBN 0-8007-1208-0). Revell.

Victorious Christian Living: Studies in the Book of Joshua. Alan Redpath. 256p. 1955. 10.95 (ISBN 0-8007-0336-7). Revell.

Victorious Christian Service: Studies in the Book of Nehemiah. Alan Redpath. 192p. 9.95 (ISBN 0-8007-0337-5). Revell.

Victorious Christians You Should Know. Warren W. Wiersbe. 176p. 1984. pap. 4.95 (ISBN 0-8010-9667-7). Baker Bk.

Victorious Decision. Harold Weiser. 1983. 6.75 (ISBN 0-8062-2002-3). Carlton.

Victorious Faith. Richard Wurmbrand. 1979. pap. 3.95 (ISBN 0-88264-120-4). Diane Bks.

Victors. Leslie Hardinge. (Anchor Ser.). 112p. 1982. pap. 5.95 (ISBN 0-8163-0490-4). Pacific Pr Pub Assn.

Victors & Vanquished: The German Influences on Army & Church in France after 1870. Allan Mitchell. LC 83-25917. xiv, 169p. 1984. 32.00x (ISBN 0-8078-1603-5). U of NC Pr.

Victorverehrung Im Christlichen Altertum. Felix Rutten. Repr. of 1936 ed. 15.00 (ISBN 0-384-52655-1). Johnson Repr.

Victory & Dominion Over Fear. Lester Sumrall. 104p. 1982. pap. 2.75 (ISBN 0-89274-233-X, HH-233). Harrison Hse.

Victory Bible Reading Plan. James McKeever. 1984. 1.00 (ISBN 0-86694-102-9). Omega Pubns OR.

Victory Dances: The Story of Fred Berk, a Modern Day Jewish Dancing Master. Judith Inger. 225p. pap. 15.95 (ISBN 0-934682-11-9). Emmett.

Victory in Christ. Charles Trumbull. 1970. pap. 2.95 (ISBN 0-87508-533-4). Chr Lit.

Victory in Failure. Alexander MacLaren. LC 79-88309. (Shepherd Illustrated Classics Ser.). 208p. (Orig.). 1980. pap. 5.95 (ISBN 0-87983-212-6). Keats.

Victory in Faith: Experiences of NSA Members. Ed. by George M. Williams. 100p. (Orig.). 1985. pap. text ed. 5.00 (ISBN 0-915678-14-4). World Tribune Pr.

Victory in Prayer. James McKeever. 32p. (Orig.). 1985. pap. 1.00 (ISBN 0-86694-103-7). Omega Pubns OR.

Victory in the Valleys of Life. Charles L. Allen. 128p. 1984. pap. 2.95 (ISBN 0-8007-8488-X, Spire Bks). Revell.
Victory: Life Maps. Chuck Swindoll. 64p. 1984. 5.95 (ISBN 0-8499-0442-0, 0442-0). Word Bks.
Victory of the Lamb. Bonnie B O'Brien & Chester C. 182p. 1982. pap. 12.75 (ISBN 0-311-72280-6). Casa Bautista.
Victory on Praise Mountain. Merlin R. Carothers. 175p. (Orig.). 1979. pap. 4.95 (ISBN 0-943026-04-0). Carothers.
Victory over Death. Ronda Chervin. LC 85-8213. (Orig.). 1985. pap. 3.95 (ISBN 0-932506-43-7). St Bedes Pubns.
Victory over Sin & Self. David Wilkerson. 80p. 1982. pap. 2.95 (ISBN 0-8007-8434-0, Spire Bks). Revell.
Victory over the Devil. Jack R. Taylor. LC 72-96149. 128p. 1973. pap. 4.95 (ISBN 0-8054-5131-5). Broadman.
Victory over the Impossible. Elbert Willis. 1978. 1.25 (ISBN 0-89858-008-0). Fill the Gap.
Victory Over the World. Charles G. Finney. LC 66-24879. (Charles G. Finney Memorial Library). 124p. 1975. pap. 4.50 (ISBN 0-8254-2619-7). Kregel.
Victory: The Work of the Spirit. Pieter Potgieter. 42p. 1984. pap. 1.45 (ISBN 0-85151-430-8). Banner of Truth.
Victory Through Surrender: Self-Realization Through Self-Surrender. E. Stanley Jones. (Festival Ser.). 128p. 1980. pap. 1.50 (ISBN 0-687-43750-4). Abingdon.
Victory Through Word Confessions. Wadene C. Ward. 47p. 1985. pap. 1.95 (ISBN 0-88144-040-X). Christian Pub.
Vida Abundante. Ray Baughman. Orig. Title: Abundant Life. (Span.). 192p. 1959. pap. 3.95 (ISBN 0-8254-1056-8). Kregel.
Vida de Elias. A. W. Pink. (Span.). 360p. 1984. pap. 4.95 (ISBN 0-85151-424-3). Banner of Truth.
Vida de Jesucristo. James Stalker. (Span.). 177p. pap. 3.50. Edit Caribe.
Vida de San Pablo. James Stalker. (Span.). 160p. 1973. pap. 3.50 (ISBN 0-89922-025-8). Edit Caribe.
Vida Disciplinada. Richard S. Taylor. 144p. 1979. 2.75 (ISBN 0-88113-341-8). Edit Betania.
Vida en Cristo. James J. Killgallon et al. Tr. by Manuel Pascual from Eng. LC 76-26451. 1978. pap. 2.25 (ISBN 0-914070-12-6). ACTA Found.
Vida en el Redil. Phillip Keller. Tr. by Carlos A. Vargas from Eng. LC 76-14500. Tr. of Shepherd Looks at Psalm Twenty-Three. (Span.). 141p. 1976. pap. 3.50 (ISBN 0-89922-073-8). Edit Caribe.
Vida Mistica de Jesus. 14th ed. H. Spencer Lewis. Tr. by AMORC Staff. (Span., Illus.). 234p. (Orig.). 1981. pap. 8.00 (ISBN 0-912057-63-7, GS 503). AMORC.
Vida Que Nace de la Muerte. T. A. Hegre. 272p. 1977. 2.95 (ISBN 0-88113-311-6). Edit Betania.
Vida Responsable: Orientacion Biblica Sobre Nuestro Estilo De Vivir. C. A. Ray. Tr. by Albert C. Lopez. Orig. Title: Living the Responsible Life. 160p. 1982. Repr. of 1980 ed. 3.75 (ISBN 0-311-46079-8). Casa Bautista.
Vida y Ministerio de Cristo: Texto Programado. Weldon E. Viertel. Tr. by Ruben O. Zorzoli from Span. Tr. of Life & Ministry of Christ. 192p. 1985. pap. text ed. write for info. (ISBN 0-311-04356-9). Casa Bautista.
Video Pencil: Cable Communications for Church & Community. Gene Jaberg & Louis G. Wargo, Jr. LC 80-7951. 156p. 1980. lib. bdg. 24.00 (ISBN 0-8191-1085-X); pap. text ed. 9.75 (ISBN 0-8191-1086-8). U Pr of Amer.
Video Seminar Planbook for Dynamic Bible Teaching. Evangelical Teacher Training Association. 64p. 1983. pap. 5.95 (ISBN 0-910566-60-7). Evang Tchr.
Vie de Ramakrishna. Romain Rolland. 1978. 16.95 (ISBN 0-686-55279-2). French & Eur.
Vie de Rance. Rene de Chateaubriand & Marius Francois Guyard. 3.95 (ISBN 0-686-54375-0). French & Eur.
Vie De Saint Gilles. Guillaume De Berneville. Ed. by Gaston Paris & Alphonse Bos. 34.00 (ISBN 0-384-20300-0); pap. 28.00 (ISBN 0-384-20285-3). Johnson Repr.
Vie De Saint Louis, Roi De France, 6 Vols. Louis S. Le Nain De Tillemont. 255.00 (ISBN 0-384-32195-X); pap. 220.00 (ISBN 0-384-32196-8). Johnson Repr.
Vie de Vivekananda. Romain Rolland. 352p. 1978. 16.95 (ISBN 0-686-55280-6). French & Eur.
Vie Religieuse Dans l'Empire Byzantin Au Temps Des Comnenes et Des Anges. Lysimaque Oeconomos. LC 77-184705. (Research & Source Works Ser.). (Fr.). 252p. 1972. Repr. of 1918 ed. lib. bdg. 23.50 (ISBN 0-8337-2602-1). B Franklin.
Vietnam, Curse or Blessing. John L. Steer & Cliff Dudley. LC 82-82016. (Illus.). 192p. (Orig.). 1982. pap. 5.95 (ISBN 0-89221-091-5). New Leaf.
Vietnamese Pilgrimage. Max Ediger. LC 78-53650. (Illus.). 1978. pap. 5.25 (ISBN 0-87303-007-9). Faith & Life.
View from the Steeple. Joseph Manton. LC 85-60519. 180p. (Orig.). 1985. pap. 7.95 (ISBN 0-87973-591-0, 591). Our Sunday Visitor.
View of the Gita. Moraji Desai. 1974. text ed. 10.00x. Coronet Bks.
View of the Prinicpal Deistical Writers That Have Appeared in England in the Last & Present Century, 3 vols. Ed. by Rene Wellek. LC 75-11232. (British Philosophers & Theologians of the 17th & 18th Centuries Ser.). 1348p. 1978. lib. bdg. 153.00 (ISBN 0-8240-1785-4). Garland Pub.
View the Land. Anne Dexter. 1986. pap. 3.50 (ISBN 0-88270-609-8). Bridge Pub.
Viewpoints. Michael Baybak. 32p. 1976. pap. 6.00 (ISBN 0-915598-09-4). Church of Scient Info.
Views from the Pews: Christian Beliefs & Attitudes. Ed. by Roger A. Johnson. LC 82-18237. 272p. 1983. pap. 15.95 (ISBN 0-8006-1695-2, 1-1695). Fortress.
Views of Christian Nurture & Subjects Related Thereto. Horace Bushnell. LC 74-23297. 264p. 1975. Repr. of 1847 ed. lib. bdg. 40.00x (ISBN 0-8201-1147-3). Schol Facsimiles.
Vigil of Prayer. Nolan P. Howington. (Orig.). 1987. pap. 4.95 (ISBN 0-8054-1505-X). Broadman.
Vignettes from the Life of Abdu'l-Baha. Annamarie Honnold. (Illus.). 224p. pap. 8.95 (ISBN 0-85398-129-9). G Ronald Pub.
Vijnana Bhairava or Divine Consciousness. Jaideva Singh. 1979. text ed. 14.00 (ISBN 0-89684-100-6, Pub. by Motilal Banarsidas India); pap. 9.95 (ISBN 0-89684-099-9). Orient Bk Dist.
Viking Jews: The History of the Jews of Denmark. I. Nathan Bamberger. LC 83-50474. (Illus.). 160p. 1983. 10.95 (ISBN 0-88400-098-2). Shengold.
Vikram & the Vampire, or Tales of the Hindu Diety. Vetalapancavimsati. Ed. by Isadel Burton. Tr. by Richard F. Burton. (Illus.). 264p. Repr. of 1893 ed. text ed. 20.00x. Coronet Bks.
Village Communities of Cape Anne & Salem, from the Historical Collections of the Essex Institute. Herbert B. Adams. pap. 9.00 (ISBN 0-384-00334-6). Johnson Repr.
Village Gods of South India. Henry Whitehead. (Illus.). 175p. 1986. Repr. 15.00X (ISBN 0-8364-1709-7, Pub. by Usha). South Asia Bks.
Village of the Brothers. Rivka Guber. LC 78-54568. (Illus.). 1979. 10.00 (ISBN 0-88400-059-1). Shengold.
Villainage in England: Essays in English Medieval History. Paul Vinogradoff. 1968. Repr. of 1892 ed. 9.00x (ISBN 0-403-00048-3). Scholarly.
Vilna Goan Views Life. 1982. 4.00 (ISBN 0-686-76275-4). Feldheim.
Vinaya Texts, 3 vols. Rhys Davids. lib. bdg. 300.00 (ISBN 0-87968-513-1). Krishna Pr.
Vinaya Texts. T. W. Davids & H. Oldenberg. (Sacred Bks. of the East: Vols. 13, 17, 20). 3 vols. 45.00 (ISBN 0-89581-522-2); 15.00 ea. Asian Human Pr.
Vincent's Word Studies in th New Testament, 4 vols. M. R. Vincent. 2720p. 49.95 (ISBN 0-917006-30-5). Hendrickson MA.
Vindication of the Government of New-England Churches. John Wise. Ed. by Perry Miller. LC 58-5422. Repr. of 1717 ed. 30.00x (ISBN 0-8201-1246-1). Schol Facsimiles.
Vines Expository Dictionary of New Testament Words. W. E. Vine. (Barbour Bks). 351p. 1985. 14.95 (ISBN 0-916441-31-8); pap. 10.95 (ISBN 0-916441-34-2). Barbour & Co.
Vine's Expository Dictionary of New Testament Words. William E. Vine. 1376p. Date not set. 14.95 (ISBN 0-917006-03-8). Hendrickson MA.
Vine's Expository Dictionary of Old & New Testament Words. W. E. Vine. 1568p. 1981. 19.95 (ISBN 0-8007-1282-X). Revell.
Vine's Expository Dictionary of Old & New Testament Words. W. E. Vine & F. F. Bruce. (Reference Library Edition). 1568p. 1987. Repr. text ed. 14.95 (ISBN 0-529-06374-3). World Bible.
Vingt Annees De Missions Dans le Nord-Ouest De L'amerique. Alexandre A. Tache. (Canadiana Before 1867 Ser). (Fr). Repr. of 1866 ed. 18.00 (ISBN 0-384-59425-5). Johnson Repr.
Vingt Annees De Missions Dans le Nord-Ouest De L'amerique Par Mgr. Alex. Tache Eveque De Saint-Boniface (Montreal, 1866) Alexandre A. Tache. (Canadiana Avant 1867: NO. 21). 1970. 16.80x (ISBN 90-2796-343-6). Mouton.
Vintage Muggeridge: Religion & Society. Ed. by Geoffrey Barlow. 200p. (Orig.). 1986. pap. 7.95 (ISBN 0-8028-0181-1). Eerdmans.
Vintage Years: Growing Older with Meaning & Hope. William E. Hulme. LC 85-26399. 120p. (Orig.). 1986. pap. 8.95 (ISBN 0-664-24684-2). Westminster.
Violence & Religious Commitment: Implications of Jim Jones's People's Temple Movement. Ed. by Ken Levi. LC 81-83147. (Illus.). 224p. 1982. 24.50x (ISBN 0-271-00296-4). Pa St U Pr.
Violence & Responsibility. John Harris. 1980. 20.00x (ISBN 0-7100-0448-6). Methuen Inc.
Violence Within. 2nd ed. Paul Tournier. LC 78-3139. 208p. 1982. pap. 6.95 (ISBN 0-06-068295-7, RD376, HarpR). Har-Row.
Violent Grace. Gini Andrews. 112p. 1987. pap. 4.95 (ISBN 0-310-20131-4). Zondervan.
Violent Origins: Walter Burkert, Rene Girard, & Jonathan Z. Smith on Ritual Killing & Cultural Formation. Ed. by Robert G. Hamerton-Kelly. LC 86-23009. 296p. 1987. 32.50x (ISBN 0-8047-1370-7). Stanford U Pr.
Vipassana Dipani; or the Manual of Insight. U. Nyana. LC 78-70107. Repr. of 1930 ed. 22.00 (ISBN 0-404-17357-8). AMS Pr.
Viraha-Bhakti: The Early History of Krsna Devotion in South India. Friedhelm E. Hardy. (Illus.). 1983. 55.00x (ISBN 0-19-561251-5). Oxford U Pr.
Virgil's Prophecy on the Saviour's Birth. Ed. by Paul Carus. 97p. 1918. 2.95 (ISBN 0-317-40414-8). Open Court.
Virgin Birth & the Incarnation, Vol. 5. Arthur C. Custance. 1976. 12.95 (ISBN 0-310-22990-1). Zondervan.
Virgin Birth in the Theology of the Ancient Church. Hans Von Campenhausen. LC 64-55217. (Studies in Historical Theology: No. 2). 1964. pap. 10.00x (ISBN 0-8401-0322-0). A R Allenson.
Virgin Birth of Christ. Robert G. Gromacki. 200p. 1981. pap. 5.95 (ISBN 0-8010-3765-4). Baker Bk.
Virgin Birth of Christ. J. Gresham Machen. 427p. 1958. Repr. of 1930 ed. 13.95 (ISBN 0-227-67630-0). Attic Pr.
Virgin Birth of Christ. J. Gresham Machen. (Twin Brooks Ser). 1967. pap. 10.95 (ISBN 0-8010-5885-6). Baker Bk.
Virginal Conception & Bodily Resurrection of Jesus. Raymond E. Brown. LC 72-97399. 1973. pap. 5.95 (ISBN 0-8091-1768-1). Paulist Pr.
Virginia Wingo: Teacher & Friend. Barbara Massey. LC 82-73665. (Meet the Missionary Ser.). 1983. 5.50 (ISBN 0-8054-4282-0, 4242-82). Broadman.
Virgins. Caryl Rivers. 256p. 1984. 12.95 (ISBN 0-312-84951-6, Pub. by Marek). St Martin.
Virgo. James A. Lely. (Sun Signs Ser.). (Illus.). 1978. pap. 3.95 (ISBN 0-89812-076-4). Creative Ed.
Virtue of Faith & Other Essays in Philosophical Theology. Robert M. Adams. 256p. 1987. 29.95 (ISBN 0-19-504145-3); pap. 12.95 (ISBN 0-19-504146-1). Oxford U Pr.
Virtue: Public & Private. James Billington et al. Ed. by Richard J. Neuhaus. (Encounter Ser.). 96p. (Orig.). 1986. pap. 5.95 (ISBN 0-8028-0201-X). Eerdmans.
Virtues & Vices. James D. Wallace. LC 77-90912. (Contemporary Philosophy Ser.). 208p. 1986. pap. 7.95x (ISBN 0-8014-9372-2). Cornell U Pr.
Virtues & Vices, & Other Essays in Moral Philosophy. Philippa R. Foot. LC 78-54794. 1979. 32.50x (ISBN 0-520-03686-7); pap. 5.95 (ISBN 0-520-04396-0, CAL 494). U of Cal Pr.
Virtues: Contemporary Essay of Moral Character. Kruschwitz & Roberts. Ed. by Ken King. (Orig.). 1986. write for info. (ISBN 0-534-06720-4). Wadsworth Pub.
Virtues of Salat. M. Zakariya. 1970. 3.95x (ISBN 0-87902-193-4). Orientalia.
Virtues of the Holy Quran. M. Hafiz. pap. 7.50 (ISBN 0-686-18508-0). Kazi Pubns.
Visage of Muhammad. Ali Shariati. 28p. (Orig.). 1979. pap. 1.25 (ISBN 0-318-03828-5). Book-Dist-Ctr.
Vishishtadvaita: Philosophy & Religion. Ramanuja Research Society. 273p. 1975. 10.75 (ISBN 0-88253-683-4). Ind-US Inc.
Vishnu Purana. Ed. by Fitzedward Hall. Tr. by Horace M. Wilson from Sanskrit. LC 74-78004. (Secret Doctrine Reference Ser.). 2150p. Date not set. lib. bdg. 95.00 (ISBN 0-913510-14-9). Wizards.
Vishnu Sahasranamam. P Malyala. (Illus.). 18p. (Orig.). 1986. pap. text ed. 5.00 (ISBN 0-938924-28-1). Sri Shirdi Sai.
Visible Community of Love. (Divine Master Ser.). (First Semester). 5.00 (ISBN 0-8198-0003-1); pap. 4.00 (ISBN 0-8198-0004-X); discussion & project manual 0.50 (ISBN 0-8198-0005-8). Dghtrs St Paul.
Visible Saints: The History of a Puritan Idea. Edmund S. Morgan. LC 63-9999. 168p. 1965. pap. 6.95x (ISBN 0-8014-9041-3). Cornell U Pr.
Visible Signs of the Gospel. Pope John Paul II. 1980. 4.00 (ISBN 0-8198-8000-0); pap. 2.95 (ISBN 0-8198-8001-9). Dghtrs St Paul.
Visible Witness. Wilmer J. Young. 1983. pap. 2.50x (ISBN 0-87574-118-5, 118). Pendle Hill.
Visible Words of God: An Exposition of the Sacramental Theology of Peter Martry Vermigli A.D. 1500-1562. Joseph C. McLelland. LC 58-9551. 1957. text ed. 17.50x (ISBN 0-8401-1515-6). A R Allenson.
Vision. Ken Carey. 90p. 1986. pap. 6.95 (ISBN 0-913299-30-8, Dist. by NAL). Stillpoint.
Vision. Ronald D. Tucker. (Illus.). 24p. (Orig.). 1983. pap. 1.50 (ISBN 0-933643-12-8). Grace World Outreach.
Vision. David Wilkerson. (Orig.). 1984. pap. 2.95. Jove Pubns.
Vision. David Wilkerson. 144p. 1974. pap. 3.50 (ISBN 0-8007-8150-3, Spire Bks). Revell.
Vision & Character: A Christian Educator's Alternative to Kohlberg. Craig Dykstra. LC 81-82340. 160p. (Orig.). 1981. pap. 5.95 (ISBN 0-8091-2405-X). Paulist Pr.
Vision & Conflict in the Holy Land. Ed. by Richard I. Cohen. LC 85-1972. 350p. 1985. 29.95 (ISBN 0-312-84967-2). St Martin.
Vision & Discernment: An Orientation in Theological Study. Charles M. Wood. (Studies in Religious & Theological Scholarship). 1985. 15.95 (ISBN 0-89130-922-5, 00-08-02); pap. 11.95 (ISBN 0-89130-923-3). Scholars Pr GA.
Vision & Strategy for Church Growth. 2nd ed. Waldo J. Werning. 1983. pap. 4.50 (ISBN 0-8010-9658-8). Baker Bk.
Vision & Strategy: The Plan of Pastoral Action for Family Ministry. National Conference of Catholic Bishops, United States Catholic Conference. (Illus., Orig.). 1978. pap. 3.75 (ISBN 1-55586-961-0). US Catholic.
Vision & the Reality: The Story of Home Missions in the General Conference Mennonite Church. Lois Barrett. LC 83-80402. 339p. (Orig.). 1983. pap. 16.95 (ISBN 0-87303-079-6). Faith & Life.
Vision & Values in the Catholic School: Participant's Guide. 96p. 1981. 4.20 (ISBN 0-686-39942-0). Natl Cath Educ.
Vision & Virtue: Essays in Christian Ethical Reflection. Stanley Hauerwas. LC 80-54877. 264p. 1981. text ed. 7.95 (ISBN 0-268-01921-5). U of Notre Dame Pr.
Vision Clara de Dios. Ed. by Eva Quinones de Dailey. (Span.). pap. 4.95 (ISBN 0-87148-884-1). Pathway Pr.
Vision for the Catechetical Ministry: An Instrument for Diocesan & Parish Planning. 1985. 5.30 (ISBN 0-318-18576-8); 4.00. Natl Cath Educ.
Vision for the Church. Mike Phillips. 110p. 1981. pap. 3.95 (ISBN 0-940652-02-1). Sunrise Bks.
Vision for the Future. Ann R. Colton. 139p. 1960. 5.95 (ISBN 0-917187-12-1). A R C Pub.
Vision Glorious: Themes & Personalities of the Catholic Revival in Anglicanism. Geoffrey Rowell. 280p. 1983. text ed. 27.00x (ISBN 0-19-826443-7). Oxford U Pr.
Vision in Action: The Art of Taking & Shaping Initiatives. Christopher Schaefer & Tijno Voors. 199p. (Orig.). 1986. pap. text ed. 12.95 (ISBN 0-88010-150-4). Anthroposophic.
Vision Obscured: Perceptions of Some Twentieth-Century Catholic Novelists. Ed. by Melvin J. Friedman. LC 72-126130. 1970. 25.00 (ISBN 0-8232-0890-7). Fordham.
Vision of Cosmic Order in the Vedas. Jeanine Miller. 320p. 1985. 39.95x (ISBN 0-7102-0369-1). Methuen Inc.
Vision of Dhamma: The Buddhist Writings of Nyanaponika Thera. Nyanaponika Thera. Ed. by Bhikkhu Bodhi. 296p. (Orig.). 1986. pap. 12.50 (ISBN 0-87728-669-8). Weiser.
Vision of God. Vladimir Lossky. 139p. 1963. 7.95 (ISBN 0-913836-19-2). St Vladimirs.
Vision of God. Nicholas Of Cusa. Tr. by Emma G. Satter. LC 60-9104. pap. 3.95x (ISBN 0-8044-6594-0). Ungar.
Vision of God: The Christian Doctrine of the Summum Bonum. abr. ed. Kenneth E. Kirk. Ed. by G. R. Dunstan. 223p. 1977. Repr. of 1934 ed. 13.95 (ISBN 0-227-67830-3). Attic Pr.
Vision of God's Dawn. Sri Chinmoy. 67p. 1974. pap. 2.00 (ISBN 0-685-53062-0). Aum Pubns.
Vision of Hope: The Churches & Change in Latin America. Ed. by Trevor Beeson & Jenny Pearce. LC 83-48927. 288p. 1984. pap. 6.95 (ISBN 0-8006-1758-4, 1-1758). Fortress.
Vision of Matthew: Christ, Church & Morality in the First Gospel. John P. Meier. LC 78-70820. 1979. pap. 8.95 (ISBN 0-8091-2171-9). Paulist Pr.
Vision of Renewal. Wilfred Le Sage. (Orig.). 1967. 4.00 (ISBN 0-8198-0169-0); pap. 3.00 (ISBN 0-8198-0170-4). Dghtrs St Paul.
Vision of Self in Early Vedanta. W. Beidler. 1975. 12.50 (ISBN 0-8426-0990-3). Orient Bk Dist.

Vision of the Disinherited: The Making of American Pentecostalism. Robert M. Anderson. 1979. 24.95x (ISBN 0-19-502502-4). Oxford U Pr.

Vision of the Trinity. George H. Tavard. LC 80-5845. 166p. (Orig.). 1981. lib. bdg. 25.25 (ISBN 0-8191-1412-X); pap. text ed. 10.75 (ISBN 0-8191-1413-8). U Pr of Amer.

Vision of the Vedic Poets. J. Gonda. (Disputationes Rheno-Trajectinae Ser.: No. 8). (Orig.). 1963. pap. text ed. 28.80x (ISBN 90-2790-034-5). Mouton.

Vision of the Void: Theological Reflections on the Works of Elie Wiesel. Michael Berenbaum. LC 78-27321. 1978. 17.50x (ISBN 0-8195-5030-2). Wesleyan U Pr.

Vision of the Void: Theological Reflections on the Works of Elie Wiesel. Michael Berenbaum. xii, 240p. 1987. pap. 12.95 (ISBN 0-8195-6189-4). Wesleyan U Pr.

Vision of Youth Ministry: Bilingual Edition. (Eng. & Span.). 48p. 1986. pap. text ed. 2.95 (ISBN 1-55586-107-5). US Catholic.

Vision y Valores Manual del Participante. (Span.). 96p. 1982. 4.20 (ISBN 0-686-39943-9). Natl Cath Educ.

Visionaries & Their Apocalypses. Ed. by Paul D. Hanson. LC 83-5488. (Issues in Religion & Theology Ser.). 176p. 1983. pap. 7.95 (ISBN 0-8006-1765-7). Fortress.

Visionary Christian: One Hundred & Thirty-One Readings from C. S. Lewis. Ed. by Chad Walsh. 288p. 1984. 5.95 (ISBN 0-02-086730-1, Collier). Macmillan.

Visionary Christian: One Hundred Thirty-One Readings from C. S Lewis, Selected & Edited by Chad Walsh. C. S. Lewis. 256p. 1981. 10.95 (ISBN 0-02-570540-7). Macmillan.

Visionary Girls: Witchcraft in Salem Village. Marion Starkey. 1973. 15.45i (ISBN 0-316-81087-8). Little.

Visionary Poetics: Milton's Tradition & His Legacy. Joseph A. Wittreich, Jr. LC 78-52569. (Illus.). 324p. 1979. 29.95 (ISBN 0-87328-101-2). Huntington Lib.

Visionary Spires: The Most Beatiful Churches That Never Were. Patrick Sweeney & Sarah Crewe. LC 85-43038. (Illus.). 144p. 1985. 25.00 (ISBN 0-8478-0660-X). Rizzoli Intl.

Visiones Profecticas de Daniel. Abraao De Almeida. Tr. of Prophetic Visions of Daniel. (Span.). 224p. 1986. pap. 3.95 (ISBN 0-8297-0497-3). Life Pubs Intl.

Visioning. Strange De Jim. LC 79-66208. (Illus.). 112p. (Orig.). 1979. pap. 5.95 (ISBN 0-9605308-0-0). Ash-Kar Pr.

Visions & Metaphysical Experiences. Manly P. Hall. pap. 2.50 (ISBN 0-89314-378-2). Philos Res.

Visions & Prophecies for a New Age. Mark A. Thurston. (Illus.). 228p. 1981. pap. 6.95 (ISBN 0-87604-136-5). ARE Pr.

Visions Beyond the Veil. H. A. Baker. 1973. pap. 3.95 (ISBN 0-88368-019-X). Whitaker Hse.

Visions of Apocalypse: End or Rebirth? Ed. by Saul Friedlander et al. 272p. 1985. text ed. 28.50x (ISBN 0-8419-0673-4); pap. text ed. 15.50x (ISBN 0-8419-0755-2). Holmes & Meier.

Visions of Faith: An Anthology of Reflections. Reverend William G. Sykes. 544p. 1986. 19.95 (ISBN 0-920792-25-1). Eden Pr.

Visions of Glory. David J. Wieand. 144p. (Orig.). 1980. pap. 4.95 (ISBN 0-87178-905-1). Brethren.

Visions of Peace. Shirley J. Heckman. LC 83-16522. 75p. (Orig.). 1984. pap. 5.95 (ISBN 0-377-00140-6). Friend Pr.

Visions of Peace: The Story of the Messianic Expectation. Aaron H. Shovers. LC 81-86206. 237p. (Orig.). 1985. pap. 12.75 (ISBN 0-9613613-0-1); wkbk. 8.75 (ISBN 0-9613613-1-X). Three Dimensional.

Visions of Sri Ramakrishna. Compiled by Swami Yogeshananda. 150p. 1974. 2.75 (ISBN 0-87481-455-3). Vedanta Pr.

Visions of the End: A Study in Daniel & Revelation. Adam C. Welch. 260p. 1958. Repr. of 1922 ed. 10.95 (ISBN 0-227-67631-9). Attic Pr.

Visions of the End: Apocalyptic Traditions in the Middle Ages. Bernard McGinn. LC 79-4303. (Records of Civilization XCVI). 1979. 38.00 (ISBN 0-231-04594-8). Columbia U Pr.

Visions of the Fathers of Lascaux. Clayton Eshleman. 44p. (Orig.). 1983. pap. 5.00 (ISBN 0-915572-70-2). Panjandrum.

Visions of the New Life. DeWitt B. Lucas. 1963. pap. 2.50 (ISBN 0-910140-11-1). C & R Anthony.

Visions of Therese Newmann. Johannes Steiner. LC 75-34182. 245p. 1976. pap. 5.95 (ISBN 0-8189-0318-X). Alba.

Visions of Wonders: An Anthology of Christian Fantasy. Boyer & Zahorski. 1986. pap. 2.50 (ISBN 0-380-78824-1, 78824-1). Avon.

Visit of the Tomten. Barry L. Johnson. LC 81-70361. pap. 4.95x (ISBN 0-8358-0439-9). Upper Room.

Visit to Salt Lake. William Chandless. LC 76-134391. Repr. of 1857 ed. 24.50 (ISBN 0-404-08434-6). AMS Pr.

Visit to the Missions of Southern California in February & March 1874. Henry L. Oak. Ed. by Ruth F. Axe et al. LC 81-52830. (Illus.). 87p. 1981. 20.00 (ISBN 0-916561-66-6). Southwest Mus.

Visit to the Vatican for Young People. Donald Wuerl & Michael Wilson. (Illus.). 1980. 3.50 (ISBN 0-8198-8002-7). Dghtrs St Paul.

Visitation Evangelism Leader's Guide. rev. ed. Churches Alive, Inc. Staff. LC 84-73068. (Illus.). 112p. 1985. pap. text ed. 11.95 (ISBN 0-934396-40-X). Churches Alive.

Visitation Evangelism Member's Notebook. rev. ed. Churches Alive, Inc. Staff. (Illus.). 80p. 1985. pap. text ed. 9.95 (ISBN 0-934396-39-6). Churches Alive.

Visitation: Key to Church Growth. Gordon Lindsay. 1.25 (ISBN 0-89985-119-3). Christ Nations.

Visitation Made Easy. C. S. Lovett. 1959. pap. 2.95 (ISBN 0-938148-15-X). Personal Christianity.

Visitations & Memorials of Southwell Minister. Southwell Cathedral. Ed. by Arthur F. Leach. Repr. of 1891 ed. 27.00 (ISBN 0-384-56770-3). Johnson Repr.

Visitations of Churches Belonging to St. Paul's Cathedral in 1297 & 1458. London - St. Paul'S Cathedral. Repr. of 1895 ed. 27.00 (ISBN 0-384-33490-3). Johnson Repr.

Visitations of the Diocese of Norwich, A. D. 1492-1532. Norwich England Diocese. Ed. by A. Jessopp. Repr. of 1888 ed. 30.00 (ISBN 0-384-41985-2). Johnson Repr.

Visiting: A Pastoral Care Ministry. Pastoral Care Office, Reorganized Church of Jesus Christ of Latter Day Saints. 186p. (Orig.). 1985. pap. 10.25 (ISBN 0-8309-0429-8). Herald Hse.

Visiting Teaching: A Call to Serve. Johanna Flynn & Anita Canfield. 80p. (Orig.). 1984. pap. 3.95 (ISBN 0-934126-42-9). Randall Bk Co.

Visiting the Shakers in 1857: Harper's New Monthly Magazine. Facsimile ed. Benson T. Lossing. (Illus.). 14p. 1975. pap. 2.50 (ISBN 0-937942-14-6). Shaker Mus.

Visiting Two-by-Two: Visitor's Guide. George E. Koehler. LC 86-70579. 72p. (Orig.). 1986. 2.95 (ISBN 0-88177-034-5, DR034B). Discipleship Res.

Visitor. Jack Hayford. 128p. 1986. pap. 4.95 (ISBN 0-8423-7802-2). Tyndale.

Visits to Monasteries in the Levant. Robert Curzon. 400p. 1983. pap. 11.95 (ISBN 0-686-46958-5, 021260104X). Hippocrene Bks.

Visits to Monasteries in the Levant. Robert C. Zouche. LC 80-2200. Repr. of 1916 ed. 45.00 (ISBN 0-404-18989-X). AMS Pr.

Visnuism & Sivaism: A Comparison. J. Gonda. LC 71-545904. 1976. 12.50x (ISBN 0-89684-465-X). Orient Bk Dist.

Visoko-Dechanskaja Lavra na Kosovje Polje (v Serbii) P. N. Paganuzzi. Tr. of Visoko-Dechansky Monastery at Kosova Polija (in Serbia) 1976. pap. 1.00 (ISBN 0-317-30331-7). Holy Trinity.

Visokopreosvjashennij Theofan, Arkhiepiskop Poltavsky i Perejaslavsky. Archbishop Averky Taushev. Tr. of His Eminance Theophan, Archbishop of Poltava & Perejaslavl. 88p. 1974. pap. 5.00 (ISBN 0-317-29284-6). Holy Trinity.

Vistas from Mount Moriah. Levi. 6.95 (ISBN 0-87306-983-8). Feldheim.

Vistazo a la Doctrina Romana. Un Adolfo Robleto. 128p. 1984. pap. 2.95 (ISBN 0-311-05319-X). Casa Bautista.

Visual Art in the Life of the Church: Encouraging Creative Worship & Witness in the Congregation. Richard R. Caemmerer, Jr. LC 83-70504. 96p. (Orig.). 1983. pap. 10.95 (ISBN 0-8066-2010-2, 10-6855). Augsburg.

Visual Arts & Christianity in America: The Colonial Period Through the Nineteenth Century. John Dillenberger. LC 84-3897. (Scholars Press Studies in the Humanities). 1984. 29.25 (ISBN 0-89130-734-6, 00 01 05); pap. 19.50 (ISBN 0-89130-761-3). Scholars Pr GA.

Visual Dimension: Aspects of Jewish Art. Ed. by Clare Moore. (Publications of the Oxford Centre for Postgraduate Hebrew Study Ser.: Vol. 5). (Illus.). 320p. 1987. text ed. 40.00x (ISBN 0-86598-081-0, Rowman & Littlefield). Rowman.

Visual Evangels, 6 vols. Arnold C. Westphal. (Orig.). 1979. pap. text ed. 4.95 ea. No. 1 (ISBN 0-915398-12-5). No. 2 (ISBN 0-915398-13-3). No. 3 (ISBN 0-915398-14-1). No. 4 (ISBN 0-915398-15-X). No. 5 (ISBN 0-915398-16-8). No. 6 (ISBN 0-915398-17-6). Visual Evangels.

Viswambhara. C. Narayana Reddy. 66p. 1987. text ed. 12.50x (ISBN 81-207-0578-5, Pub. by Sterling Pubs India). Apt Bks.

Vita Christi of Ludolph of Saxony & Late Medieval Devotion Centered on the Incarnation: A Descriptive Analysis. Charles A. Conway, Jr. Ed. by James Hogg. (Analecta Cartusiana Ser.: No. 34). 153p. (Orig.). 1976. pap. 25.00 (ISBN 3-7052-0036-4, Pub. by Salzburg Studies). Longwood Pub Group.

Vita Sancti Columbae. Saint Adamnan. Ed. by William Reeves. LC 79-174801. (Bannatyne Club, Edinburgh. Publications: No. 103). Repr. of 1857 ed. 45.00 (ISBN 0-404-52858-9). AMS Pr.

Vital Christianity Study Guide. Lars Wilhelmsson & Nancy Wilhelmsson. (Religion Ser.). 64p. (Orig.). 1982. pap. 2.25 (ISBN 0-941018-08-3). Martin Pr CA.

Vital Signs: Emerging Social Trends & the Future of American Christianity. George Barna & William P. McKay. LC 84-70658. 160p. (Orig.). 1984. 12.95 (ISBN 0-89107-324-8, Crossway Bks). Good News.

Vital Signs of Family Life & the YMCA: Resource Notebook. YMCA of the USA. (Illus.). 26p. (Orig.). 1983. pap. 19.95 3 ring Notebook (ISBN 0-88035-014-8, YMCA USA). Human Kinetics.

Vital Tradition: The Catholic Novel in a Period of Convergence. Gene Kellogg. LC 74-108375. 1970. 8.35 (ISBN 0-8294-0192-X). Loyola.

Vitality & Aging: Implications of the Rectangular Curve. James F. Fries & Lawrence M. Crapo. LC 81-4566. (Illus.). 172p. 1981. text ed. 23.95 (ISBN 0-7167-1308-X); pap. text ed. 13.95 (ISBN 0-7167-1309-8). W H Freeman.

Vitality of the Christian Tradition. facsimile ed. Ed. by George F. Thomas. LC 70-134143. (Essay Index Reprint Ser). Repr. of 1944 ed. 22.00 (ISBN 0-8369-2378-2). Ayer Co Pubs.

Vitality Old Testament Traditions. 2nd ed. Walter Brueggemann & Hans W. Wolff. LC 82-7141. pap. 7.95 (ISBN 0-8042-0112-9). John Knox.

Vitam Alere, Franciscan Readings. Ed. by Marion A. Habig. (Tau Ser.). 1979. 5.95 (ISBN 0-8199-0769-3). Franciscan Herald.

Vitas Patrum: The Lyff of the Olde Auncyent Fathers Hermytes. Saint Jerome. Tr. by W. Caxton. LC 77-7409. (English Experience Ser.: No. 874). 1977. Repr. of 1495 ed. lib. bdg. 99.00 (ISBN 90-221-0874-0). Walter J Johnson.

Viva Cristo Rey: The Cristero Rebellion & the Church-State Conflict in Mexico. David C. Bailey. (Illus.). 360p. 1974. 22.50x (ISBN 0-292-78700-6). U of Tex Pr.

Vivamos En el Espiritu Cada Dia. Pat H. Carter. 160p. 1982. pap. 3.25 (ISBN 0-311-09089-3). Casa Bautista.

Viveka-Chudamani or the Crest Jewel of Wisdom. Mohini M. Chatterji. 5.75 (ISBN 0-8356-7091-0). Theos Pub Hse.

Vivekachudamani of Shri Shankaracharya. Shankara. Tr. by Swami Madhavananda. (Sanskrit & Eng.). pap. 3.50 (ISBN 0-87481-147-3). Vedanta Pr.

Vivekananda: A Biography. Swami Nikhilananda. LC 53-7851. 364p. 5.95 (ISBN 0-911206-08-6). Ramakrishna.

Vivekananda: A Biography in Pictures. 2nd ed. Swami Vivekananda. Ed. by Advaita Ashrama Staff. (Illus.). 1974. 30.00x (ISBN 0-87481-136-8). Vedanta Pr.

Vivekananda: The Yogas & Other Works. Compiled by Swami Nikhilananda. LC 53-7534. (Illus.). 1018p. includes biography 19.95 (ISBN 0-911206-04-3). Ramakrishna.

Vivendo Sob Pressao. Gene A. Getz. Orig. Title: When the Pressure Is on. (Port.). 1986. write for info. (ISBN 0-8297-0897-9). Life Pubs Intl.

Vivir la Misa. (Span.). pap. text ed. 2.75 (ISBN 0-8198-8007-8). Dghtrs St Paul.

Vivo en El Espiritu. (Span. & Eng.). pap. text ed. 2.75 (ISBN 0-8198-8006-X). Dghtrs St Paul.

Vizsoly Biblia, 1590, 2 vols. facs. ed. 1982. Set. 395.00x (ISBN 0-686-44667-4, Pub. by Collets (UK)). State Mutual Bk.

Vjetkhij Zavjet v Novozavjetnoi Tserkvi. Protopresbyter Michael Pomazansky. Tr. of Old Testament in the New Testament Church. 38p. 1961. pap. 2.00 (ISBN 0-317-29101-7). Holy Trinity.

Vladimir Soloviev: Russian Mystic, Vol. 9. Paul M. Allen. LC 72-81592. (Spiritual Science Library). (Illus.). 544p. 1978. lib. bdg. 22.00 (ISBN 0-89345-032-4, Spiritual Sci Lib); pap. 10.00 (ISBN 0-89345-213-0, Steinerbks). Garber Comm.

Vocabulaire Biblique. Ed. by Jean-Jacques Von Allmen. (Fr.). 320p. 1964. pap. 24.95 (ISBN 0-686-57248-3, M-6759). French & Eur.

Vocabulario Culto. 2nd ed. Gladys Neggers. (Span.). 168p. 1977. pap. 8.75 (ISBN 84-359-0034-7, S-50023). French & Eur.

Vocabulario de Teologila Biblica. 9th ed. Leon Dufour. (Span.). 976p. 1977. 35.95 (ISBN 84-254-0809-1, S-50205); pap. 29.95 (ISBN 84-254-0808-3, S-50204). French & Eur.

Vocabulario Practico De la Biblia. Anton Grabner Haider. (Span.). 892p. 1975. 41.95 (ISBN 84-254-0964-0, S-50206). French & Eur.

Vocabulario Teologico del Evangelio de Saint Juan. J. Mateos Alvarez. (Span.). 310p. 1980. pap. 13.95 (ISBN 84-7057-270-9, S-33107). French & Eur.

Vocabulary & Style of the Soliloquies & Dialogues of St. Augustine, Vol. 42. Mary Inez Bogan. (Patristic Studies). 238p. 1984. Repr. of 1935 ed. 28.00x (ISBN 0-939738-27-9). Zubal Inc.

Vocabulary of the Greek New Testament. James H. Moulton & George Milligan. (Gr.). 1949. 35.95 (ISBN 0-8028-2178-2). Eerdmans.

Vocabulary of the Greek Testament: Illustrated from the Papyri & Other Non-Literary Sources, 2 vols. J. H. Moulton & G. Milligan. 1977. lib. bdg. 250.00 (ISBN 0-8490-2800-0). Gordon Pr.

Vocabulary of the Language of San Antonio Mission, California. Buenaventura Sitjar. LC 10-26367. (Library of American Linguistics: No. 7). (Span.). Repr. of 1861 ed. 28.50 (ISBN 0-404-50987-8). AMS Pr.

Vocal & Literary Interpretation of the Bible. S. E. Curry. 1979. Repr. of 1903 ed. 30.00 (ISBN 0-8414-9988-8). Folcroft.

Vocal & Literary Interpretation of the Bible. S. S. Curry. 1909. 32.50 (ISBN 0-8274-3677-7). R West.

Vocal Solos for Christian Churches: A Descriptive Reference of Solo Music for the Church Year. 3rd ed. Noni Espina. LC 84-51398. 256p. 25.00 (ISBN 0-8108-1730-6). Scarecrow.

Vocalised Talmudic Manuscripts in the Cambridge Genizah Collections: Taylor-Schnechter Old Series, Vol. 1. Shelomo Morag. (Cambridge University Library Genizan Ser.: No. 4). 60p. Date not set. Vol. I: Taylor-Schechter Old Series. price not set (ISBN 0-521-26863-X). Cambridge U Pr.

Vocation & Spirituality of the Director of Religious Education. 25p. 1980. 4.20 (ISBN 0-686-29244-8). Natl Cath Educ.

Vocation & Spirituality of the DRE. 25p. 1980. 4.20 (ISBN 0-318-20610-2). Natl Cath Educ.

Vocation of Man. Johann G. Fichte. Tr. by William Smith. LC 56-44104. 1956. pap. 5.99 scp (ISBN 0-672-60220-2, LLA50). Bobbs.

Vocation of Man. Johann G. Fichte. Tr. by William Smith from Ger. 190p. 1965. 12.95 (ISBN 0-87548-074-8); pap. 5.95 (ISBN 0-87548-075-6). Open Court.

Vocation of the Theologian. Ed. by Theodore W. Jennings, Jr. LC 84-48722. 160p. 1985. pap. 7.95 (ISBN 0-8006-1838-6, 1-1838). Fortress.

Vocations & Church Leadership. Ed. by David Byers. 96p. (Orig.). 1986. pap. 5.95 (ISBN 1-55586-108-3). US Catholic.

Voces: Eine Bibliographie zu Woertern und Begriffen aus der Patristik (1918-1978) Hermann J. Sieben. (Bibliographia Patristica). 461p. 1979. text ed. 55.20x (ISBN 3-11-007966-6). De Gruyter.

Voegelin & the Theologian: Ten Studies in Interpretation. Ed. by John Kirby & William M. Thompson. LC 82-22914. (Toronto Studies in Theology: Vol. 10). 392p. 1983. 59.95x (ISBN 0-88946-751-X). E Mellen.

Voice from Heaven. Ralph W. Neighbour, Sr. 1986. pap. 5.95 (ISBN 0-937931-04-7). Global TN.

Voice from the Forest. Nahum Kohn & Howard Roiter. LC 80-81685. (Illus.). 256p. (Orig.). 1985. 16.95 (ISBN 0-89604-020-8); pap. 10.95 (ISBN 0-89604-021-6). Holocaust Pubns.

Voice from the Forest: Memoirs of a Jewish Partisan. Nahum Kohn & Howard Roiter. (Illus.). 288p. pap. 5.95 (ISBN 0-686-95099-2). ADL.

Voice in the Wilderness: A History of the Cumberland Presbyterian Church in Texas. R. Douglas Brackenridge. LC 68-20136. (Illus.). 192p. 1968. 4.00 (ISBN 0-911536-03-5). Trinity U Pr.

Voice of Black Theology in South Africa. Louise Kretzschmar. 136p. 1986. pap. 10.95 (ISBN 0-86975-269-3, Pub. by Ravan Pr). Ohio U Pr.

Voice of Christian & Jewish Dissenters in America: U. S. Internal Revenue Service Hearings, December 1978. Martin P. Claussen & Evelyn B. Claussen. xv, 591p. 1982. pap. 25.00. Piedmont.

Voice of Human Justice. George Jordac. Tr. by M. Fazal Haq. 508p. 1984. 25.00 (ISBN 0-941724-24-7). Islamic Seminary.

Voice of Illness. Aarne Siirala. 225p. 1981. Repr. of 1964 ed. 49.95 (ISBN 0-88946-995-4). E Mellen.

Voice of Jerusalem. Israel Zangwill. 1976. lib. bdg. 59.95 (ISBN 0-8490-2801-9). Gordon Pr.

Voice of Revelation. Lillian De Waters. 5.95 (ISBN 0-686-05714-7). L De Waters.

Voice of Silence. 5th ed. Starr Farish. (Illus.). 119p. 1983. pap. 6.95 (ISBN 0-9605492-2-6). Touch Heart.

Voice of the Blood. William J. O'Malley. LC 79-90055. (Five Christian Martyrs of Our Time Ser.: No. 633). 195p. (Orig.). 1980. pap. 1.99 (ISBN 0-88344-539-5). Orbis Bks.

Voice of the Buddha: The Beauty of Compassion, 2 vols. Buddhist Sutra. Tr. by Gwendolyn Bays from Fr. (Translation Ser.). (Illus.). 704p. 1983. Set. 60.00. Vol. I (ISBN 0-913546-84-4). Vol. II (ISBN 0-913546-85-2). Dharma Pub.

Voice of the Silence. Helena P. Blavatsky. LC 73-7619. 1970. pap. 2.50 (ISBN 0-8356-0380-6, Quest). Theos Pub Hse.

Voice of the Silence: Chosen Fragments from the Book of the Golden Precepts. Tr. & intro. by Helena P. Blavatsky. iv, 110p. 1928. Repr. of 1889 ed. 3.00 (ISBN 0-938998-06-4). Theosophy.

Voice of the Silence: Verbatim with 1889 ed. Helena P. Blavatsky. LC 76-25345. 1976. 5.00 (ISBN 0-911500-04-9); pap. 2.75 (ISBN 0-911500-05-7). Theos U Pr.

Voice over the Water. William Breault. LC 84-73051. 128p. (Orig.). 1985. pap. 4.95 (ISBN 0-87793-281-6). Ave Maria.

Voice Still Heard: The Sacred Songs of the Ashkenazic Jews. Eric Werner. LC 75-26522. 1976. 32.50 (ISBN 0-271-01167-X). Pa St U Pr.

Voice Still Speaks. Morris Adler. Ed. by Jacob Chinitz. LC 68-57433. 1969. pap. text ed. 20.00x (ISBN 0-8197-0052-5). Bloch.

Voice Within: Love & Virtue in the Age of the Spirit. Helen Luke. 128p. 1984. pap. 7.95 (ISBN 0-8245-0659-6). Crossroad NY.

Voices from the East: Documents of the Present State & Working of the Oriental Church. John M. Neale. LC 75-173069. Repr. of 1859 ed. 18.00 (ISBN 0-404-04659-2). AMS Pr.

Voices from the Heart: Four Centuries of American Piety. Ed. by Roger Lundin & Mark Noll. 416p. 1987. 19.95 (ISBN 0-8028-3633-X). Eerdmans.

Voices from the Holocaust. Ed. by Sylvia Rothchild. 464p. 1982. pap. 10.95 (ISBN 0-452-00860-3, Mer). NAL.

Voices from the Old Testament. James E. Hightower, Jr. LC 81-68611. (Orig.). 1983. pap. 3.95 (ISBN 0-8054-2245-5). Broadman.

Voices of a People: The Story of Yiddish Folksong. Ruth Rubin. LC 79-84679. 558p. 1979. pap. 8.95 (ISBN 0-8276-0121-2, 445). Jewish Pubns.

Voices of Authority. Nicholas Lash. LC 76-29603. viii, 119p. 1976. pap. 3.95x (ISBN 0-915762-03-X). Patmos Pr.

Voices of Christmas. Norma Leary. (Orig.). 1983. pap. 3.25 (ISBN 0-937172-55-3). JLJ Pubs.

Voices of Earth & Sky. Vinson Brown. LC 76-41761. (Illus.). 177p. 1976. pap. 6.95 (ISBN 0-87961-060-3). Naturegraph.

Voices of Inspiration. Renee Arrington et al. 34p. 1982. pap. 3.50 (ISBN 0-939296-04-7). Bond Pub Co.

Voices of Jacob, Hands of Esau: Jews in American Life & Thought. Stephen J. Whitfield. LC 83-25720. x, 322p. 1984. lib. bdg. 25.00 (ISBN 0-208-02024-1, Archon Bks). Shoe String.

Voices of Praise. Mary V. Reilly & Margaret K. Wetterer. (Illus., Orig.). 1980. pap. 4.95 (ISBN 0-8192-1276-8). Morehouse.

Voices of Resurgent Islam. Ed. by John L. Esposito. 1983. 27.00x (ISBN 0-19-503339-6); pap. 12.95x (ISBN 0-19-503340-X). Oxford U Pr.

Voices of the Spirit. George Matheson. (Direction Bks). 1979. pap. 3.45 (ISBN 0-8010-6078-8). Baker Bk.

Voices of Twelve Hebrew Prophets. G. Campbell Morgan. (Morgan Library). 128p. 1975. pap. 3.95 (ISBN 0-8010-5977-1). Baker Bk.

Voices on Fire: A Book of Meditations. John Walchars. LC 81-7767. 250p. 1981. pap. 7.95 (ISBN 0-8245-0094-6). Crossroad NY.

Voices Within the Ark. Ed. by Howard Schwartz & Anthony Rudolf. 1983. pap. 15.95 (ISBN 0-380-76109-2, 80119). Avon.

Void: A Psychodynamic Investigation of the Relationship Between Mind & Space. A. H. Almaas. LC 85-82559. 175p. (Orig.). 1986. pap. 8.00 (ISBN 0-936713-00-3). Almaas Pubns.

Voix sur Israel. Paul Claudel. 46p. 1950. 2.95 (ISBN 0-686-54445-5). French & Eur.

Vollstaendige Konkordanz zum griechischen Neuen Testament, 2 vols. Ed. by Institut fuer Neutestamentliche Textforschung, Muenster-Westf. & Kurt Aland. viii, 96p. Vol. 1, 2 pts., 1983. 908.00 (ISBN 3-11-009698-6); Vol. 2, 1978. 105.00 (ISBN 3-11-007349-8). De Gruyter.

Voltaire, Pascal & Human Destiny. Mina Waterman. LC 70-120676. 1970. Repr. lib. bdg. 14.50x (ISBN 0-374-98279-1, Octagon). Hippocrene Bks.

Voltaire's Old Testament Criticism. B. E. Schwartzbach. 275p. (Orig.). 1970. pap. text ed. 24.00x (Pub. by Droz Switzerland). Coronet Bks.

Voluntary Controls: Exercises for Creative Meditation & for Activating the Potential of the Chakras. Jack Schwarz. 1978. pap. 7.95 (ISBN 0-525-47494-3, 0772-230). Dutton.

Voluntary Religion, Vol. 23. Ed. by W. J. Sheils & Diana Wood. 544p. 1987. text ed. 49.95 (ISBN 0-631-15054-4). Basil Blackwell.

Volunteer Minister's Handbook. L. Ron Hubbard. 76.00 (ISBN 0-686-30805-0). Church Scient NY.

Volunteer Minister's Handbook. L. Ron Hubbard. 1976. 124.33 (ISBN 0-88404-039-9). Bridge Pubns Inc.

Volunteers. Robert J. Yeager. (How to Ser.). 28p. 1986. 5.65 (ISBN 0-318-20573-4). Natl Cath Educ.

Volunteers & Ministry: A Manual for Developing Parish Volunteers. Suzanne Donovan & William J. Bannon. LC 82-62963. 112p. 1983. pap. 6.95 (ISBN 0-8091-2545-5). Paulist Pr.

Von Balthasar Reader. Hans U. Von Balthasar. Ed. by Medard Kehl & Werner Loser. Tr. by Fred Lawrence & Robert J. Daly. 400p. 1982. 27.50 (ISBN 0-8245-0468-2). Crossroad NY.

Von Christlicher Religion und Christlicher Bildung. Martin Luther. (Classics in German Literature & Philosophy Ser). (Ger). 1968. Repr. of 1883 ed. 18.00 (ISBN 0-384-34280-9). Johnson Repr.

Voodoo Contra. Robert Gover. LC 84-52293. 128p. (Orig.). 1985. pap. 6.95 (ISBN 0-87728-619-1). Weiser.

Voodoo in Haiti. Alfred Metraux. LC 77-185327. (Illus.). 1972. pap. 8.95 (ISBN 0-8052-0341-9). Schocken.

Voodoo in New Orleans. Robert Tallant. 248p. 1983. pap. 3.50 (ISBN 0-88289-336-X). Pelican.

Voodoo Lost Arts & Sciences. abr. ed. Luanna C. Blagrove. 250p. 1987. 25.95 (ISBN 0-939776-22-7); text ed. 24.95. Blagrove Pubns.

Voodoo Queen. Robert Tallant. 314p. 1983. pap. 3.50 (ISBN 0-88289-332-7). Pelican.

Voodoo Tales As Told among the Negroes of the Southwest. facs. ed. Mary A. Owen. LC 70-149874. (Black Heritage Library Collection). (Illus.). 1893. 17.00 (ISBN 0-8369-8754-3). Ayer Co Pubs.

Voodoo Tales, As Told among the Negroes of the Southwest. Mary A. Owen. LC 78-78773. (Illus.). Repr. of 1893 ed. cancelled (ISBN 0-8371-1395-4). Greenwood.

Voodoos & Obeahs. Joseph J. Williams. LC 74-11170. 1970. Repr. of 1932 ed. 23.00 (ISBN 0-404-06986-X). AMS Pr.

Vor Dem Nichts. Peter Henke. (Theologischo Bibliothek Toepelmann: Vol. 34). (Illus.). 1978. 26.80 (ISBN 3-11-007254-8). De Gruyter.

Vorformen der Schriftexegese innerhalb des Alten Testaments. Ina Willi-Plein. 286p. 1971. 43.20x (ISBN 3-11-001897-7). De Gruyter.

Vorlesungen ueber die Juedischen Philosophen des Mittelalters, 3vols in 2 vols. Moritz Eisler. 1965. Repr. of 1884 ed. 39.50 (ISBN 0-8337-4086-5). B Franklin.

VOS Story Bible, 3 vols. Set. pap. 27.50 (ISBN 0-85151-442-1). Banner of Truth.

VOS Story Bible: New Testament. pap. 9.50 (ISBN 0-85151-237-2). Banner of Truth.

VOS Story Bible: Old Testament (Genesis-Ruth) pap. 9.50 (ISBN 0-85151-250-X). Banner of Truth.

VOS Story Bible: Old Testament (Samuel-Malachi) pap. 9.50 (ISBN 0-85151-251-8). Banner of Truth.

Votre Force Spirituelle et Emotionnelle. Richard D. Dobbins. Ed. by Annie L. Cosson. Tr. by Valerie Chardenal from Eng. Tr. of Your Spiritual & Emotional Power. (Fr.). 188p. 1985. pap. text ed. 2.25 (ISBN 0-8297-0703-4). Life Pubs Intl.

Voudoun Fire: The Living Reality of the Mystical Religions. Melita Denning & Osborne Phillips. LC 79-3375. (Mystery Religions Series: No. 1). (Illus.). 172p. (Orig.). 1979. pap. 9.95 (ISBN 0-87542-699-9). Llewellyn Pubns.

Vowed Life. Adrian Van Kaam. 19.95 (ISBN 0-87193-040-4). Dimension Bks.

Vox Populi: Essays in the History of an Idea. George Boas. LC 69-13538. (Seminars in the History of Ideas Ser.). (Illus.). pap. 77.00 (ISBN 0-317-41626-X, 2025833). Bks Demand UMI.

Vox Populi: Popular Opinion & Violence in the Religious Controversies of the Fifth Century A.D. Timothy E. Gregory. LC 79-16885. 257p. 1979. 25.00x (ISBN 0-8142-0291-8). Ohio St U Pr.

Voyage Au Purgatoire De Saint Patrice, Visions De Tindale & De Saint Paul. Ed. by A. Jeanroy & A. Vignaux. Repr. of 1903 ed. 21.00 (ISBN 0-384-64950-5). Johnson Repr.

Voyage into the Past: Continuous Life Through 35 Centuries. Carl T. Endemann. LC 81-81554. (Illus.). 1981. 9.95 (ISBN 0-931926-10-6). Alta Napa.

Voyage Litteraire de Deux Benedictins de la Congregation de Saint-Maur, 2 vols. Edmond Martene & Ursin Durand. 1042p. Repr. of 1717 ed. text ed. 207.00x (ISBN 0-576-99707-2, Pub. by Gregg Intl Pubs England). Gregg Intl.

Voyage of Life on a Paper Boat, No. 12. Arnold C. Westphal. pap. 4.95 (ISBN 0-915398-22-2). Visual Evangels.

Voyage of Re-Discovery: The Veneration of St. Vincent. Anne F. Francis. 1978. 15.00 (ISBN 0-682-48429-6, University). Exposition Pr FL.

Voyage of Saint Brendan: Journey to the Promised Land. John J. O'Meara. (Dolmen Texts: No. 1). (Illus.). 1978. pap. text ed. 9.95x (ISBN 0-85105-384-X). Humanities.

Voyage to America in Eighteen Forty-Seven: The Diary of a Bohemian Jew on His Voyage from Hamburg to New York in 1847. S. E. Rosenbaum. (Studies in Judaica & the Holocaust: No. 3). 60p. 1987. lib. bdg. 19.95x (ISBN 0-89370-371-0); pap. text ed. 9.95x (ISBN 0-89370-471-7). Borgo Pr.

Voyage to Freedom: Story of the Pilgrim Fathers. David Gay. pap. 5.45 (ISBN 0-85151-384-0). Banner of Truth.

Voyages & Cargoes. Carroll M. Sparrow. 1947. 3.00 (ISBN 0-685-09018-3). Dietz.

Voyages Liturgiques de France. Sieur de Moleon. 694p. Repr. of 1718 ed. text ed. 165.60x (ISBN 0-576-99713-7, Pub. by Gregg Intl Pubs England). Gregg Intl.

Vozdvizhenije Tchestnago Krjesta Gospodnja. M. Skaballanovitch. Tr. of Exaltation of the Life Giving Cross. 173p. pap. 6.00 (ISBN 0-317-29152-1). Holy Trinity.

Vuela del Triunfador. Ed. by Armida O. De Hernandez Carrera. (Span.). Date not set. pap. 3.95 (ISBN 0-87148-306-8). Pathway Pr.

Vulture & the Bull: Religious Responses to Death. Antonio R. Gualtieri. 194p. (Orig.). 1984. lib. bdg. 26.00 (ISBN 0-8191-3963-7); pap. text ed. 11.75 (ISBN 0-8191-3964-5). U Pr of Amer.

Vvedenie v Sviatootecheskoe Bogoslovia. rev. ed. John Meyendorff. Tr. by Larisa Volokhonsky from Eng. LC 85-61006. (Rus.). 359p. 1985. pap. 16.00 (ISBN 0-934927-00-6). RBR.

Vvedenije vo Khram Presvjatija Bogoroditsi. M. Skaballanovitch. Tr. of Entrance of the Mother of God into the Temple. 115p. pap. 4.00 (ISBN 0-317-29157-2). Holy Trinity.

W

W. A. P Martin: Pioneer of Progress in China. Ralph Covell. LC 77-13321. Repr. of 1978 ed. 59.10 (ISBN 0-8357-9133-5, 2012723). Bks Demand UMI.

W. Graham Scroggie Library Series, 7 vols. W. Graham Scroggie. 1981. pap. 28.00 (ISBN 0-8254-3740-7). Kregel.

W. Norman Cooper - a Prophet for Our Time. Filip Field. LC 79-52443. 1979. 7.50 (ISBN 0-87516-417-X); pap. 4.50 (ISBN 0-87516-372-6). De Vorss.

W. Norman Cooper: A View of a Holy Man. Roselyn Witt. LC 81-70657. 96p. 1982. 7.50 (ISBN 0-87516-492-7); pap. 4.50 (ISBN 0-87516-471-4). De Vorss.

W. Robertson Smith & the Sociological Study of Religion. T. O. Beidelman. LC 73-87311. 1974. pap. 1.95x (ISBN 0-226-04160-3, P618, Phoen). U of Chicago Pr.

W. W. True & Just Recorde of the Information, Examination & Confession of All the Witches, Taken at S. Oses in the Countie of Essex. LC 81-4330. 1981. Repr. of 1582 ed. 35.00x (ISBN 0-8201-1363-8). Schol Facsimiles.

Wages of Zen. James Melville. 224p. 1985. pap. 2.95 (ISBN 0-449-20838-9, Crest). Fawcett.

Wait for the Lord: Meditations on the Christian Life. Theodore Plantinga. 137p. (Orig.). 1981. pap. 5.75 (ISBN 0-932914-12-8). Dordt Coll Pr.

Wait Guys & Girls. D. L. Halbrook & Becky Halbrook. pap. 4.25 (ISBN 0-89137-805-7). Quality Pubns.

Wait in Joyful Hope! Mary V. Reilly et al. (Illus., Orig.). 1980. pap. 4.95 (ISBN 0-8192-1275-X). Morehouse.

Waiting & Loving: Thoughts Occasioned by the Illness & the Death of a Parent. Martha H. Hickman. LC 83-51399. 160p. (Orig.). 1984. pap. 5.95 (ISBN 0-8358-0483-6). Upper Room.

Waiting Father. Helmut Thielicke. Tr. by J. W. Doberstein from Ger. 192p. 1978. Repr. 13.95 (ISBN 0-227-67634-3). Attic Pr.

Waiting Father. Helmut Thielicke. LC 75-12284. 192p. 1981. 5.95 (ISBN 0-06-067991-3, RD-364, HarpR). Har-Row.

Waiting for God. Simone Weil. pap. 5.95 (ISBN 0-06-090295-7, CN295, PL). Har-Row.

Waiting for My Baby. Barbara O. Webb. 80p. 1985. 6.95 (ISBN 0-570-04219-4, 15-2180). Concordia.

Waiting for the Apocalypse: Doomsday Deferred. rev. ed. Daniel Cohen. LC 83-62189. (Illus.). 260p. 1983. pap. 10.95 (ISBN 0-87975-223-8). Prometheus Bks.

Waiting on God. Andrew Murray. (Andrew Murray Ser.). pap. 3.50 (ISBN 0-8024-0026-4). Moody.

Waiting on God. Andrew Murray. 160p. 1981. pap. 3.50 (ISBN 0-88368-101-3). Whitaker Hse.

Wake of the Gods: Melville's Mythology. H. Bruce Franklin. 1963. pap. 16.95x (ISBN 0-8047-0137-7). Stanford U Pr.

Wake up & Preach. James F. Finley. LC 85-26667. 111p. (Orig.). 1986. pap. 5.95 (ISBN 0-8189-0492-5). Alba.

Wake Up O' Sleeping World. 48p. 1983. 9.95 (ISBN 0-89962-315-8). Todd & Honeywell.

Wake up World! Jesus Is Coming Soon! George B. Eager. 40p. (Orig.). 1980. pap. 1.00 (ISBN 0-9603752-3-6). Mailbox.

Wakefield Mystery Plays. Ed. by Martial Rose. 1969. pap. 10.95x (ISBN 0-393-00483-X, Norton Lib). Norton.

Wakefield Pageants in the Towneley Cycle. Ed. by A. C. Cawley. (Old & Middle English Texts). 187p. 1975. pap. 10.95x (ISBN 0-06-491013-X, 06392). B&N Imports.

Waking of the Human Soul & the Forming of Destiny - The Need for Understanding Christ. Rudolf Steiner. Tr. by Olin D. Wannamaker. (Ger.). 25p. 1983. pap. 3.00 (ISBN 0-919924-19-0, Pub by Steiner Book Centre Canada). Anthroposophic.

Waking up. Charles T. Tart. LC 86-11844. 300p. 1986. 17.95 (ISBN 0-87773-374-0, Pub. by New Sci Lib-Shambhala). Shambhala Pubns.

Waldeck-Rousseau, Combes, & the Church: The Politics of Anticlericalism, 1899-1905. Malcolm O. Partin. LC 74-76167. pap. 77.80 (ISBN 0-317-20441-6, 2023432). Bks Demand UMI.

Waldeck-Rousseau, Combes, & the Church, 1899-1905: The Politics of Anticlericalism. Malcolm O. Partin. LC 74-76167. (Duke Historical Publication Ser). 299p. 1969. 23.25 (ISBN 0-8223-0130-X). Duke.

Waldo Emerson. Fay W. Allen. (Illus.). 782p. 1982. pap. 10.95 (ISBN 0-14-006278-5). Penguin.

Waldo Emerson: A Biography. Gay W. Allen. LC 81-65275. (Illus.). 696p. 1981. 25.00 (ISBN 0-670-74866-8). Viking.

Waldorf Parenting Handbook: Useful Information on Child Development & Education from Anthroposophical Sources. 2nd, rev. ed. Lois Cusick. 1985. pap. 9.95 (ISBN 0-916786-75-7). St George Bk Serv.

Walk According to the Spirit. 6.00 (ISBN 0-8198-8220-8); 5.00 (ISBN 0-8198-8221-6). Dghtrs St Paul.

Walk down the Road to Tomorrow. Edna I. Purdy. 1983. 6.95 (ISBN 0-8062-2172-0). Carlton.

Walk in Love. Carmeline Koller. 10.50 (ISBN 0-8199-0843-6). Franciscan Herald.

Walk on in Peace. Dorothy Edgerton. LC 82-73133. 64p. (Orig.). 1982. pap. 1.45 (ISBN 0-87029-187-4, 20278-8). Abbey.

Walk on Water, Pete! Luis Palau. LC 80-39955. 1974. pap. 2.95 (ISBN 0-930014-34-0). Multnomah.

Walk the Distant Hills: The Story of Longri Ao. Richard G. Beers. (Bold Believers Ser.). 1969. pap. 0.95 (ISBN 0-377-84171-4). Friend Pr.

Walk Together Children. Ashley Bryan. (Illus.). 1981. pap. 2.95 (ISBN 0-689-70485-2, Aladdin). Macmillan.

Walk Where Jesus Walked: A Pilgrim's Guide with Prayer & Song. Willard F. Jabusch. LC 86-71224. (Illus.). 200p. (Orig.). 1986. pap. 6.95 (ISBN 0-87793-339-1). Ave Maria.

Walk with Me in White. Elmer T. Church. LC 86-81184. 154p. 1986. perfect bdg. 9.95 (ISBN 0-318-21723-6). E T Church.

Walk with Praise. Janet Van Rys. (Devotional Ser.). (Illus.). 200p. (Orig.). 1986. pap. 4.95 (ISBN 0-9616989-0-X). Jan Van Pubns.

Walk Without Feet, Fly Without Wings, & Think Without Mind. Bhagwan Shree Rajneesh. Ed. by Ma Yoga Anurag. LC 83-181337. (Questions & Answers Ser.). (Illus.). 384p. (Orig.). 1979. 16.50 (ISBN 0-88050-167-7). Chidvilas Found.

Walker's Comprehensive Bible Concordance. J. B. Walker. LC 76-15841. 1976. kivar 14.95 (ISBN 0-8254-4012-2). Kregel.

Walking Among the Unseen. Hannah Hurnard. 1977. pap. 3.50 (ISBN 0-8423-7805-7). Tyndale.

Walking & Leaping. Merlin R. Carothers. 129p. (Orig.). 1974. pap. 4.95 (ISBN 0-943026-05-9). Carothers.

Walking in God's Light. Jim Larson. LC 84-9963. 1984. pap. 3.95 (ISBN 0-8307-0953-3, S181216). Regal.

Walking in Love. A. B. Simpson. 1975. Repr. 2.95 (ISBN 0-87509-040-0). Chr Pubns.

Walking in Missionary Shoes. Lima L. Williams. 1986. pap. 14.95 (ISBN 0-87162-417-6, D8750). Warner Pr.

Walking in the Garden: Inner Peace from the Flowers of God. Paula Connor. (Illus.). 170p. 1984. 14.95 (ISBN 0-13-944280-4); pap. 5.95 (ISBN 0-13-944264-2). P-H.

Walking in the Light. Joyce M. Smith. 1980. pap. 2.95 (ISBN 0-8423-7813-8). Tyndale.

Walking in the Light. R. Pearsall Smith. 128p. 1987. pap. 4.95 (ISBN 0-310-20921-8). Zondervan.

Walking in the Spirit. Zenas J. Bicket. LC 76-51000. 96p. 1977. pap. 1.25 (ISBN 0-88243-611-2, 02-0611, Radiant Bks). Gospel Pub.

Walking in the Spirit. Michael Harper. 112p. (Orig.). 1983. pap. 3.95 (ISBN 0-87123-614-1, 210614). Bethany Hse.

Walking in Wisdom: A Woman's Workshop on Ecclesiastes. Barbara Bush. (Woman's Workshop Ser.). 128p. (Orig.). 1982. pap. 3.50 (ISBN 0-310-43041-0, 12014P). Zondervan.

Walking in Zen, Sitting in Zen. Bhagwan Shree Rajneesh. Ed. by Rajneesh Foundation International. LC 82-24025. (Questions & Answers Ser.). 444p. (Orig.). 1982. pap. 10.95 (ISBN 0-88050-668-7). Chidvilas Found.

Walking into Light. David Winter. 160p. 1986. pap. 3.50 (ISBN 0-87788-916-3). Shaw Pubs.

Walking into the Morning. Margaret Walpole. 48p. 1986. 6.95 (ISBN 0-8378-5093-2). Gibson.

Walking on the Water: Women Talk about Spirituality. Ed. by Jo Garcia. Sara Maitland. (Illus.). 224p. 1984. pap. 5.95 (ISBN 0-86068-381-8, Pub by Virago Pr). Salem Hse Pubs.

Walking on Thorns: The Call to Christian Obedience. Allan Boesak. 80p. (Orig.). 1984. pap. 4.95 (ISBN 0-8028-0041-6). Eerdmans.

Walking on Water. Leo Booth. 180p. (Orig.). 1985. pap. 8.95 (ISBN 0-932194-28-1). Health Comm.

Walking on Water: Reflections on Faith & Art. Madeleine L'Engle. LC 80-21066. (Wheaton Literary Ser.). 198p. 1980. 10.95 (ISBN 0-87788-918-X); pap. 6.95 (ISBN 0-87788-919-8). Shaw Pubs.

Walking Straight in a Crooked World. Don M. Aycock. (Orig.). 1987. pap. 3.25 (ISBN 0-8054-5034-3). Broadman.

Walking Through the Bible with H. M. S. Richards. Ken Richards. 384p. 1983. 9.95 (ISBN 0-8163-0433-5). Pacific Pr Pub Assn.

Walking to Jesus: Scenes from My Journey. Mark Shutts. LC 84-91288. (Illus.). 80p. (Orig.). 1984. pap. 3.98 (ISBN 0-9614077-1-9). Shutts Minist.

Walking with a Hero: Children's Bible Studies for Children's Church. Ruth Powell. 96p. (Orig.). 1982. pap. 7.95 (ISBN 0-87239-593-6, 3375). Standard Pub.

Walking with Christ. rev. ed. The Navigators Staff. (Design for Discipleship Ser.: Bk. 3). 1980. pap. text ed. 1.95 (ISBN 0-934396-18-3). Churches Alive.

Walking with God. W. Phillip Keller. 160p. 1980. pap. 5.95 (ISBN 0-8007-5187-6). Revell.

Walking with God. 8.95 (ISBN 0-318-18183-5). WCTU.

Walking with Jesus. V. Gilbert Beers & Ronald A. Beers. (Illus.). 192p. 1984. 14.95 (ISBN 0-89840-069-4). Heres Life.

Walking with Loneliness. Paula Ripple. LC 82-73048. 176p. (Orig.). 1982. pap. 4.95 (ISBN 0-87793-259-X). Ave Maria.

Walking with Loneliness. Paula Ripple. 318p. 1985. pap. 9.95 large print ed. (ISBN 0-8027-2490-6). Walker & Co.

Walking with the Giants: A Minister's Guide to Good Reading & Great Preaching. Warren W. Wiersbe. LC 76-22989. 304p. 1976. 14.95 (ISBN 0-8010-9578-6). Baker Bk.

Walks of Usefulness: Or Reminiscenes of Mrs. Margaret Prior. Sarah R. Ingraham. Ed. by Carolyn Gifford & Donald Dayton. (Women in American Protestant Religion 1800-1930 Ser.). 324p. 1987. lib. bdg. 45.00 (ISBN 0-8240-0666-6). Garland Pub.

Wall Between Church & State. Ed. by Dallin H. Oaks. LC 63-20897. 1963. pap. 1.95X (ISBN 0-226-61429-8, P137, Phoen). U of Chicago Pr.

Wall of Controversy. Francis G. Lee. 1986. lib. bdg. 6.50 (ISBN 0-89874-828-3). Krieger.

Wall of Separation: The Constitutional Politics of Church & State. Frank J. Sorauf. LC 75-3476. 420p. 1976. 40.00x (ISBN 0-691-07574-3). Princeton U Pr.

Wall Scenes from the Tomb of Amenhotep (Huy) Governor of Bahria Oasis. Charles C. Van Siclen, III. (Illus.). ii, 46p. 1981. pap. text ed. 11.00x (ISBN 0-933175-00-0). Van Siclen Bks.

Walled in Light: St. Colette. Mother Mary Francis. 1985. 9.50 (ISBN 0-8199-0889-4). Franciscan Herald.

Wallington's World: A Puritan Artisan in Seventeenth-Century London. Paul S. Seaver. LC 84-40447. 272p. 1985. 29.50x (ISBN 0-8047-1267-0). Stanford U Pr.

Walloons & Their Church at Norwich: Their History & Registers, 1565-1832, 2 pts. in 1 vol. William J. Moens. (Hugenot Society of London Publications Ser.: Vol. 1). Repr. of 1887 ed. 30.00 (ISBN 0-8115-1642-3). Kraus Repr.

Walls Are Crumbling. John M. Oesterreicher. (Illus.). 10.00 (ISBN 0-8159-7201-6). Devin.

Walls Came Tumbling Down. Dave Hill. (Arch Bks.: Set 4). 1967. laminated bdg 0.99 (ISBN 0-570-06024-9, 59-1135). Concordia.

Walls: Physical & Psychological. Robert E. Reuman. LC 66-24444. (Orig.). pap. 2.50x (ISBN 0-87574-147-9). Pendle Hill.

Walter Benjamin: The Story of a Friendship. Gershom Scholem. Tr. by Harry Zohn from Ger. LC 81-11790. (Illus.). 240p. 1981. 13.95 (ISBN 0-8276-0197-2). Jewish Pubns.

Walter Burleigh De Puritate Artis Logicae Tractus Langios. Philotheus Boehner. Incl. Tractatus Brevior. (Text Ser). 1955. 6.00 (ISBN 0-686-17965-X). Franciscan Inst.

Walter Hilton's Mixed Life. Ogilvie Thomson. Ed. by James Hogg. (Elizabethan & Renaissance Studies). (Orig.). 1985. pap. 15.00 (ISBN 3-7052-0756-3, Pub. by Salzburg Studies). Longwood Pub Group.

Walter Martin's Cults Reference Bible. Walter R. Martin. LC 81-52881. 1248p. 1981. 19.99 (ISBN 0-88449-075-0, VH301). Vision Hse.

Walter Rauscenbusch: Selected Writings. Ed. by Winthrop S. Hudson. (Sources of American Spirituality Ser.). 252p. 1985. text ed. 14.95 (ISBN 0-8091-0356-7). Paulist Pr.

Walter Scott. Daniel D. Schantz. (Restoration Booklets Ser.). (Illus.). 16p. (Orig.). 1984. pap. 0.75 (ISBN 0-87239-777-7, 3297). Standard Pub.

Walther on the Church. C. F. Walther. Tr. by John M. Dreckamer. (Selected Writings of C. F. W. Walther Ser.). 1981. 12.95 (ISBN 0-570-08278-1, 15-2736). Concordia.

Walvoord: A Tribute. Ed. by Donald K. Campbell. LC 81-16888. 396p. 1982. 15.95 (ISBN 0-8024-9227-4). Moody.

Wandering Jew: Essays in the Interpretation of a Christian Legend. Ed. by Galit Hasan-Rokem & Alan Dundes. LC 84-48248. (Illus.). 288p. 1986. 27.50x (ISBN 0-253-36340-3). Ind U Pr.

Wandering People of God: An Investigation of the Letter to the Hebrews. Ernst Kasemann. Tr. by Roy A. Harrisville. LC 84-20523. 272p. (Orig.). 1984. 21.95 (ISBN 0-8066-2121-4, 10-6940). Augsburg.

Wandering Taoist. Deng Ming-Dao. LC 82-48925. (Illus.). 272p. 1986. pap. 6.95 (ISBN 0-06-250226-3, HarpR). Har-Row.

Wanderings: Chaim Potok's History of the Jews. Chaim Potok. LC 78-54915. 1978. 29.95 (ISBN 0-394-50110-1). Knopf.

Wanderings of Clare Skymer. George MacDonald. Ed. by Dan Hamilton. 168p. 1987. pap. 3.95 (ISBN 0-89693-757-7). Victor Bks.

Waning of the Middle Ages. J. Huizinga. LC 54-4529. pap. 5.95 (ISBN 0-385-09288-1, A42, Anch). Doubleday.

Wannsee Protocol & a 1944 Report on Auschwitz by the Office of Strategic Services. J. Mendelsohn. LC 81-80319. (Holocaust Ser.). 264p. 1982. lib. bdg. 61.00 (ISBN 0-8240-4885-7). Garland Pub.

Wanted: World Christians. J. Herbert Kane. 204p. 1986. pap. 9.95 (ISBN 0-8010-5474-5). Baker Bk.

Wanted Your Daily Life. M. B. Room. 1976. pap. 2.50 (ISBN 0-87508-011-1). Chr Lit.

War Against Proslavery Religion: Abolitionism & the Northern Churches, 1830-1865. John R. McKivigan. LC 83-45933. 328p. 1984. 32.50x (ISBN 0-8014-1589-6). Cornell U Pr.

War Against Sleep: The Philosophy of Gurdjieff. Colin Wilson. 96p. 1980. pap. 6.95 (ISBN 0-85030-198-X). Weiser.

War Against the Idols: The Reformation of Worship from Erasmus to Calvin. Carlos M. Eire. 320p. 1986. 37.50 (ISBN 0-521-30685-X). Cambridge U Pr.

War Against the Jews: 1933-1945. Lucy S. Dawidowicz. 640p. 1976. pap. 10.95 (ISBN 0-553-34302-5). Bantam.

War Against the Jews, 1933-1945. Lucy S. Dawidowicz. 496p. 1986. 22.95 (ISBN 0-02-908030-4). Free Pr.

War & Christian Ethics. Arthur F. Holmes. LC 75-14602. pap. 13.95 (ISBN 0-8010-4170-8). Baker Bk.

War & Christianity. Elliott Coues. 250.00 (ISBN 0-8490-1276-7). Gordon Pr.

War & Conscience in South Africa: Churches & Consicentious Objection. 112p. 1982. 5.00 (ISBN 0-317-36647-5). Africa Fund.

War & Moral Discourse. Ralph B. Potter. LC 69-18111. (Orig.). 1969. pap. 3.95 (ISBN 0-8042-0863-8). John Knox.

War & Peace: A Christian Foreign Policy. John W. Robbins. (Trinity Papers: No. 1). 250p. (Orig.). 1987. pap. 8.95 (ISBN 0-940931-21-4). Trinity Found.

War & Peace from Genesis to Revelation. Vernard Eller. LC 80-26280. (Christian Peace Shelf Ser.). 232p. 1981. pap. 9.95 (ISBN 0-8361-1947-9). Herald Pr.

War & Peace in the World's Religions. John Ferguson. 1978. pap. 5.95 (ISBN 0-19-520074-8). Oxford U Pr.

War & the Christian. Charles E. Raven. LC 75-147675. (Library of War & Peace; Relig. & Ethical Positions on War). 1972. lib. bdg. 46.00 (ISBN 0-8240-0432-9). Garland Pub.

War & the Christian Conscience: How Shall Modern War Be Conducted Justly? Paul Ramsey. LC 61-10666. xxiv, 331p. 1985. pap. 9.95 (ISBN 0-8223-0361-2). Duke.

War & the Christian Conscience: How Shall Modern War be Conducted Justly? Paul Ramsey. LC 61-10666. pap. 88.30 (ISBN 0-317-26099-5, 2023766). Bks Demand UMI.

War & the Gospel. Jean Lasserre. Tr. by O. Coburn. 248p. 1962. 9.95 (ISBN 0-227-67635-1). Attic Pr.

War & the Gospel. Jean Lasserre. (Christian Peace Shelf Ser.). 243p. 1962. 12.95 (ISBN 0-8361-1475-2). Herald Pr.

War & the Minds of Men. Frederick S. Dunn. LC 79-131371. xvi, 115p. 1971. Repr. of 1950 ed. 15.00 (ISBN 0-208-00945-0, Archon). Shoe String.

War Beyond the Stars. Joel French & Jane French. LC 79-90267. (Illus.). 128p. 1979. pap. 4.95 (ISBN 0-89221-067-2). New Leaf.

War: Four Christian Views. Herman A. Hoyt et al. Ed. by Robert G. Clouse. 216p. (Orig.). 1981. pap. 5.95 (ISBN 0-88469-097-0). BMH Bks.

War in Vietnam: The Religious Connection. Madalyn M. O'Hair. 83p. (Orig.). 1982. pap. 4.00 (ISBN 0-911826-28-9). Am Atheist.

War Inconsistent with the Religion of Jesus Christ. David L. Dodge. LC 75-137540. (Peace Movement in America Ser). xxiv, 168p. 1972. Repr. of 1905 ed. lib. bdg. 15.95x (ISBN 0-89198-067-9). Ozer.

War is the Enemy. A. J. Muste. 1983. pap. 2.50x (ISBN 0-87574-015-4, 015). Pendle Hill.

War of the Chariots. Clifford Wilson. LC 78-55211. 1978. pap. 3.95 (ISBN 0-89051-050-4). Master Bks.

War of the Doomed: Jewish Armed Resistance in Poland, 1942-1944. Shmuel Krakowski. LC 83-18537. 340p. 1984. text ed. 44.50x (ISBN 0-8419-0851-6). Holmes & Meier.

War of the Gods: The Social Code in Indo-European Mythology. Jarich G. Oosten. (International Library of Anthropology). 240p. 1985. 32.50x (ISBN 0-7102-0289-X). Methuen Inc.

War of the Star Lords. Hegstad & Munson. 34p. 1983. pap. 2.50 (ISBN 0-8163-0517-X). Pacific Pr Pub Assn.

War of Titans: Blake's Critique of Milton & the Politics of Religion. Jackie DiSalvo. LC 82-11136. 403p. 1983. 38.95x (ISBN 0-8229-3804-9). U of Pittsburgh Pr.

War on Christ in America: The Christian Fortress America under Siege Christophobes of the Media & of the Supreme Court in Action Demonic Maladies of the Western Culture, Freud, Marx Skinner & Other Ugly Pagans. 538p. 1985. 22.95 (ISBN 0-930711-01-7); pap. 15.95 (ISBN 0-317-19107-1). Ichthys Bks.

War on Light: The Destruction of the Image of God in Man Through Modern Art. Margaret E. Stucki. 1975. 15.00 (ISBN 0-686-23419-7). Birds' Meadow Pub.

War on Light: The Destruction of the Image of God in Man Through Modern Art. Margaret E. Stucki. 5.95 (ISBN 0-686-18059-3). Freedom Univ-FSP.

War on the Saints. 9th ed. Jessie Penn-Lewis & Evan Roberts. 1986. Repr. of 1912 ed. 10.50 (ISBN 0-913926-02-7). T E Lowe.

War, Peace & Nonresistance. rev. ed. Guy F. Hershberger. LC 53-7586. (Christian Peace Shelf Ser.). 375p. 1969. 15.95 (ISBN 0-8361-1449-3). Herald Pr.

War, Peace & the Bible. J. Carter Swaim. LC 81-16889. 144p. (Orig.). 1982. pap. 3.48 (ISBN 0-88344-752-5). Orbis Bks.

War, Poverty, Freedom: The Christian Response. Franz Bockle. (Concilium Ser.: Vol. 15). 7.95 (ISBN 0-8091-0154-8). Paulist Pr.

War Resistance in Historical Perspective. Larry Gara. 1983. pap. 2.50x (ISBN 0-87574-171-1, 171). Pendle Hill.

Warfare with Satan. Jessie Penn-Lewis. 1962. pap. 4.15 (ISBN 0-87508-999-2). Chr Lit.

Warm Hug Book. William Coleman. 128p. (Orig.). 1985. pap. 4.95 (ISBN 0-87123-794-6, 210794). Bethany Hse.

Warm Nest. (Color-a-Story Bks.). (Illus.). 1985. pap. 0.89 (ISBN 0-89191-997-X, 59972). Cook.

Warren Akin Candler: The Conservative As Idealist. Mark K. Bauman. LC 80-22230. 290p. 1981. 20.00 (ISBN 0-8108-1368-8). Scarecrow.

Warren-Ballard Debate. Thomas B. Warren & L. S. Ballard. 1979. 9.00 (ISBN 0-934916-39-X). Natl Christian Pr.

Warren-Barnhart Debate on Ethics. Thomas B. Warren & Joe Barnhart. 1981. pap. 13.00 (ISBN 0-934916-47-0). Natl Christian Pr.

Warren-Flew Debate on the Existence of God. Ed. by Thomas B. Warren & A. G. N. Flew. 1977. 14.00 (ISBN 0-934916-40-3). Natl Christian Pr.

Warren-Matson Debate on the Existence of God. Thomas B. Warren & Wallace I. Matson. LC 78-64546. 1979. 14.00 (ISBN 0-934916-41-1); pap. 11.00 (ISBN 0-934916-45-4). Natl Christian Pr.

Warrior Koans: Early Zen in Japan. Trevor Leggett. 256p. 1985. pap. 8.95 (Ark Paperbks). Methuen Inc.

Warrior Songs for the White Cavalry. 4th ed. Intro. by Frank W. Sandford. 1972. 7.50 (ISBN 0-910840-14-8). Kingdom.

Warriors, Gods & Spirits from Central & South American Mythology. Douglas Gifford. (World Mythologies Ser.). (Illus.). 132p. 1983. 15.95 (ISBN 0-8052-3857-3). Schocken.

Wars of America: Christian Views. Ronald A. Wells. 280p. (Orig.). 1981. pap. 9.95 (ISBN 0-8028-1899-4). Eerdmans.

Wars of the Lord, Vol. 2, bks. 2, 3, & 4. Gersonides, pseud. Tr. by Seymour Feldman from Hebrew. 288p. 1987. 23.95 (ISBN 0-8276-0275-8). Jewish Pubns.

Wars of the Lord: Immortality of the Soul, Vol. I: Book 1. Levi B. Gershom. Tr. by Seymour Feldman from Hebrew. 256p. 1984. 23.95 (ISBN 0-8276-0220-0, 605). Jewish Pubns.

Wars of Truth: Studies in the Decay of Christian Humanism in the Earlier 17th Century. Herschel Baker. 11.75 (ISBN 0-8446-0472-0). Peter Smith.

Warsaw Diary of Adam Czerniakow: Prelude to Doom. Ed. by Raul Hilberg & Stanislaw Staron. 480p. Repr. 14.00 (ISBN 0-686-95101-8). ADL.

Warsaw Ghetto. R. Conrad Stein. LC 84-23202. (World at War Ser.). (Illus.). 48p. 1985. lib. bdg. 10.60 (ISBN 0-516-04779-5). Childrens.

Warsaw Ghetto in Pictures: Illustrated Catalog. LC 79-26657. (Yivo Institute for Jewish Research Guide & Catalogs Ser.: No. 1). (Illus.). 1970. pap. 5.00 (ISBN 0-914512-08-0). Yivo Inst.

Warsaw Ghetto Revolt. Reuben Ainstein. (Illus.). 238p. 1979. pap. 10.95 (ISBN 0-89604-007-0). Holocaust Pubns.

Warsaw Ghetto Revolt. Reuben Ainsztein. LC 78-71295. (Illus.). 1979. pap. 10.95 (ISBN 0-8052-5007-7, Pub. by Holocaust Library). Schocken.

Wartime Correspondence: Between President Roosevelt & Pope Pius 12th. Ed. by Myron Taylor. (FDR & the Era of the New Deal Ser). 1975. Repr. of 1947 ed. lib. bdg. 22.50 (ISBN 0-306-70709-8). Da Capo.

Warwords: U. S. Militarism the Catholic Right & the Bulgarian Connection. David Eisenhower & John Murray. Ed. by Betty Smith. 138p. 1987. pap. 3.95 (ISBN 0-7178-0650-2). Intl Pubs Co.

Was Christ God? Spiros Zodhiates. 1966. 7.95 (ISBN 0-89957-504-8). AMG Pubs.

Was Jesus Crucified? A. Deedat. pap. 1.50 (ISBN 0-686-63916-2). Kazi Pubns.

Was Jesus Married? The Distortion of Sexuality in the Christian Tradition. William E. Phipps. LC 85-32319. 250p. 1986. pap. text ed. 11.75 (ISBN 0-8191-5191-2). U Pr of Amer.

Washing & Dressing Prayers with Jesus. Shirley Lamb. 1983. pap. 1.50 (ISBN 0-910709-41-6). PTL Repro.

Washington University Papyri I: Non-Literary Texts, Nos. 1-16. Verne B. Schuman. LC 79-14199. (American Society of Papyrologists Ser.: No. 310017). 15.00 (ISBN 0-89130-286-7, 310017). Scholars Pr GA.

Washo Shamans & Peyotists: Religious Conflict in an American Indian Tribe. Edgar E. Siskin. (Illus.). 300p. 1983. 25.00x (ISBN 0-87480-223-7). U of Utah Pr.

Wat Haripunjaya: A Study of the Royal Temple of the Buddha's Relic, Lamphun, Thailand. Donald K. Swearer. LC 75-33802. (American Academy of Religion. Studies in Religion). 1976. pap. 9.95 (ISBN 0-89130-052-X, 010010). Scholars Pr GA.

Watch Your Teaching: Home Study. Garver. pap. 4.95 (ISBN 0-935120-03-3). Christs Mission.

Watcher. Charlotte Eldridge. (Orig.). 1981. pap. write for info. Shamar Bk.

Watches, Prayers, Arguments. Ed. by Mary B. Eddy & Gilbert C. Carpenter. 100p. 1985. pap. 12.00 (ISBN 0-930227-01-8). Pasadena Pr.

Watchmaker's Daughter: The Life of Corrie Ten Boom for Young People. Jean Watson. (Illus.). 160p. 1983. pap. 4.95 (ISBN 0-8007-5116-7, Power Bks). Revell.

Watchman in Babylon: A Study Guide to Ezekiel. John Job. 112p. (Orig.). pap. 4.95 (ISBN 0-85364-339-3). Attic Pr.

Watchmen of Eternity: Blake's Debt to Jacob Boehme. Bryan Aubrey. (Illus.). 208p. (Orig.). 1986. PLB 27.00 (ISBN 0-8191-5220-X); pap. text ed. 13.25 (ISBN 0-8191-5221-8). U Pr of Amer.

Watchtower Files. Duane Magnani & Arthur Barrett. 340p. (Orig.). 1985. pap. 6.95 (ISBN 0-87123-816-0, 210816). Bethany Hse.

Water, 4 bks. Bessie Love & Paul Newey. Incl. Bk. 1. Source of Life; Bk. 2. Destroyer; Bk. 3. Sustainer; Bk. 4. Transformer. (Illus., Orig.). 1974. Set. pap. 3.50x (ISBN 0-8192-4041-9); leaders guide 2.50x (ISBN 0-8192-4042-7). Morehouse.

Water Baptism. Jack Hayford. 96p. (Orig.). cancelled (ISBN 0-8423-7814-6). Tyndale.

Water Baptism: Sealed by Christ, the Lord. Jack W. Hayford. LC 84-80750. (Orig.). 1984. pap. 2.95 (ISBN 0-916847-01-2). Living Way.

Water Bugs & Dragonflies: Explaining Death to Children. Doris Stickney. (Illus.). 24p. 1982. pap. 1.25 (ISBN 0-8298-0609-1). Pilgrim NY.

Water Carriers in Hades: A Study of Catharsis Through Toil in Classical Antiquity. E. Keuls. (Illus.). 179p. 1974. pap. text ed. 48.50 (Pub. by A. M. Hakkert). Coronet Bks.

Water in the Wilderness: Paths of Prayer. Francis W. Vanderwall. 1985. pap. 5.95 (ISBN 0-8091-2680-X). Paulist Pr.

Water into Wine: A Study of Ritual Idiom in the Middle East. Ethel S. Drower. LC 77-87663. Repr. of 1956 ed. 23.50 (ISBN 0-404-16401-3). AMS Pr.

Water Mirror Reflecting Heaven. Tripitaka Master Hua. Tr. by Buddhist Text Translation Society. (Illus.). 82p. (Orig.). 1982. pap. 4.00 (ISBN 0-88139-501-3). Buddhist Text.

Water of Life. John Bunyan. pap. 1.50 (ISBN 0-685-88397-3). Reiner.

Waterbuffalo Theology. Kosuke Koyama. LC 74-80980. (Illus.). 250p. (Orig.). 1974. pap. 7.95 (ISBN 0-88344-702-9). Orbis Bks.

Watering the Seed. Luke Ciampi. 1977. 5.95 (ISBN 0-685-71934-0). Franciscan Herald.

Waters of Darkness: Scenes from the Life of an American Jew, Vol. 2. John Sanford. 294p. (Orig.). 1986. 20.00 (ISBN 0-87685-672-5); signed cloth 30.00 (ISBN 0-87685-673-3); pap. 12.50 (ISBN 0-87685-671-7). Black Sparrow.

Waters of Mormon. Robert H. Moss. 176p. 1986. 9.95. Horizon Utah.

Waters of Siloe. Thomas Merton. LC 79-10372. 377p. 1979. pap. 6.95 (ISBN 0-15-694954-7, Harv). HarBraceJ.

Watervliet Shaker Cemetery, Albany, N. Y. Elizabeth D. Shaver. 1986. pap. 2.50. Shaker Her Soc.

Watervliet Shaker Meeting House. Elizabeth Shaver. 6p. 1986. pap. 2.50. Shaker Her Soc.

Waterway. Berard Haile. LC 79-66605. (American Tribal Religions Ser.: Vol. 5). (Illus.). vi, 153p. 1979. pap. 12.95x (ISBN 0-89734-030-2, Pub. by Mus Northern Ariz). U of Nebr Pr.

Watunna: An Orinoco Creation Cycle. Marc De Civrieux. Ed. by David Guss. LC 80-82440. (Illus.). 216p. 1980. 20.00 (ISBN 0-86547-002-2); pap. 12.50 (ISBN 0-86547-003-0). N Point Pr.

Way. A. L. Anderson. 1978. pap. 2.50 (ISBN 0-8100-0006-7, 12N1715). Northwest Pub.

Way. Josemaria Escriva de Balaguer. (Foreign language editions avail.). 1965. 9.95 (ISBN 0-933932-00-6). Scepter Pubs.

Way. Josemaria Escriva de Balaguer. Orig. Title: Camino. 1979. pap. 4.95 (ISBN 0-933932-01-4). Scepter Pubs.

Way. Elise N. Morgan. (Meditation Ser.). 1972. 3.50 (ISBN 0-87516-332-7). De Vorss.

Way Back in the Hills. James C. Hefley. (Living Bks.). 352p. (Orig.). 1985. 3.95 (ISBN 0-8423-7821-9). Tyndale.

Way: Catholic Edition. LC 72-84415. 1116p. 1973. pap. 11.95 (ISBN 0-87973-831-6). Our Sunday Visitor.

Way Down & Out: The Occult in Symbolist Literature. John Senior. LC 68-23326. (Illus.). 1968. Repr. of 1959 ed. lib. bdg. 22.50x (ISBN 0-8371-0218-9, SESL). Greenwood.

Way for All Seasons. William P. Tuck. 1987. 9.95 (ISBN 0-8054-1541-6). Broadman.

Way God Fights. Lois Barrett. (Peace & Justice Ser.: No. 1). 96p. (Orig.). 1987. pap. 4.95 (ISBN 0-8361-3445-1). Herald Pr.

Way Home. Raymond Rawson. LC 84-90242. 113p. 1985. 10.95 (ISBN 0-533-06294-2). Vantage.

Way Home Beyond Feminism, Back to Reality. Mary Pride. LC 84-73078. 240p. (Orig.). 1985. pap. 7.95 (ISBN 0-89107-345-0, Crossway Bks). Good News.

Way I See Him: A Writer's Look at Jesus. Joseph T. McGloin. LC 86-8030. 212p. (Orig.). 1986. pap. 6.95 (ISBN 0-8189-0498-4). Alba.

Way in the World: Family Life as Spiritual Discipline. Ernest Boyer, Jr. LC 83-48983. 192p. 1984. 13.45 (ISBN 0-06-061032-8, HarpR). Har-Row.

Way into the Holiest. F. B. Meyer. 1968. pap. 4.50 (ISBN 0-87508-353-6). Chr Lit.

Way It Was in Bible Times. Merrill T. Gilbertson. LC 59-10759. (Illus.). 1959. pap. 6.95 (ISBN 0-8066-1442-0, 10-7000). Augsburg.

Way Jesus Walked: Spontaneous Reflections on the Way of the Cross. Joseph L. Priestly. 224p. (Orig.). 1982. pap. 6.95 (ISBN 0-89962-252-6). Todd & Honeywell.

Way: Living in Love. Elena S. Whiteside. LC 72-89132. 284p. 1972. 5.95 (ISBN 0-910068-06-2). Am Christian.

Way: Living in Love. Elena S. Whiteside. LC 72-89132. Devin.

Way of a Pilgrim. Tr. by Reginald M. French from Rus. (Illus.). 242p. 1974. (HarpR); pap. 7.95 (ISBN 0-86683-898-8, SP18). Har-Row.

Way of All the Earth: Experiments in Truth & Religion. John S. Dunne. LC 78-1575. 1978. text ed. 19.95x (ISBN 0-268-01927-4); pap. 7.95 (ISBN 0-268-01928-2). U of Notre Dame Pr.

Way of Anthroposophy: Answers to Modern Questions. Stewart Easton. 102p. (Orig.). 1986. pap. 7.00 (ISBN 0-85440-464-3, Pub. by Steinerbooks). Anthroposophic.

Way of Attainment. Sydney T. Klein. 220p. 1981. pap. 13.00 (ISBN 0-89540-106-1, SB-106). Sun Pub.

Way of Biblical Justice. Jose Gallardo. LC 82-83386. (Mennonite Faith Ser.: Vol. 11). 80p. (Orig.). 1983. pap. 1.50 (ISBN 0-8361-3321-8). Herald Pr.

Way of Blessedness. Lord S. Blanch. 272p. 1987. pap. 3.50 (ISBN 0-345-34310-7, Pub. by Ballantine Epiphany). Ballantine.

Way of Chuang Tzu. Thomas Merton. LC 65-27556. (Illus.). 1969. pap. 4.95 (ISBN 0-8112-0103-1, NDP276). New Directions.

Way of Dharma. Paul Twitchell. 1970. pap. 3.95 (ISBN 0-914766-18-X). IWP Pub.

Way of Dialogue: Christians & People of Other Faiths. Wesley Ariarajah & T. K. Thomas. 40p. (Orig.). 1986. pap. 4.50 (ISBN 0-377-00164-3). Friend Pr.

Way of Discipleship to Christ. Stephen Isaac. LC 76-57021. 1976. pap. 4.50 (ISBN 0-910378-12-6). Christward.

Way of Discovery: An Introduction to the Thought of Michael Polanyi. Richard Gelwick. 1977. pap. 4.95 (ISBN 0-19-502193-2). Oxford U Pr.

Way of Divine Love. Josefa Menendez. LC 79-112493. 504p. 1972. pap. 12.00 (ISBN 0-89555-030-X). TAN Bks Pubs.

Way of Divine Love. Josefa Menendez. 506p. 1981. pap. 5.00 (ISBN 0-89555-276-0). TAN Bks Pubs.

Way of Everyday Life. Hakuyu T. Maezumi & John D. Loori. LC 78-8309. (Illus.). 1978. 17.50 (ISBN 0-916820-17-3); pap. 9.95 (ISBN 0-916820-06-8). Center Pubns.

Way of Faith. Ed. by James M. Pitts. 176p. (Orig.). 1985. pap. 8.95 (ISBN 0-913029-10-6). Stevens Bk Pr.

Way of God's Will. Sun M. Moon. 418p. (Orig.). Date not set. pap. 6.95 (ISBN 0-910621-31-4). HSA Pubns.

Way of Heaven: An Introduction to the Confucian Religious Lufe. R. L. Taylor. (Iconography of Religions XII Ser.: No. 3). (Illus.). xi, 37p. 1986. pap. 29.50 (ISBN 90-04-07423-6, Pub. by E J Brill). Heinman.

Way of Holiness. Samuel L. Brengle. 1966. Repr. of 1902 ed. 3.95 (ISBN 0-86544-008-5). Salv Army Suppl South.

Way of Holiness. John H. Noyes. LC 75-337. (Radical Tradition in America Ser.). 230p. 1975. Repr. of 1838 ed. 21.50 (ISBN 0-88355-240-X). Hyperion Conn.

Way of Korean Zen. Kusan Sunim. Tr. by Martine Fages. (Illus.). 182p. pap. 12.50 (ISBN 0-8348-0201-5). Weatherhill.

Way of Lao Tzu. Wing-Tsit Chan. 1963. pap. text ed. write for info. (ISBN 0-02-320700-0). Macmillan.

Way of Liberation: Essays & Lectures on the Transformation of the Self. Alan Watts. Ed. by Mark Watts & Rebecca Shropshire. LC 82-21917. 120p. 1983. pap. 8.95 (ISBN 0-8348-0181-7). Weatherhill.

Way of Life. Charles Hodge. 1978. pap. 4.95 (ISBN 0-85151-273-9). Banner of Truth.

Way of Life. Arthur J. Vincellette. 160p. 1983. 7.95 (ISBN 0-89962-312-3). Todd & Honeywell.

Way of Living Faith. Segundo Galilea. 12.45 (ISBN 0-317-52400-3, HarpR). Har-Row.

Way of Love. Ed. by E. Rozanne Elder. (Cistercian Fathers Ser.: No. 16). (Illus.). 1977. 7.95 (ISBN 0-87907-616-X); pap. 4.50 (ISBN 0-87907-966-5). Cistercian Pubns.

Way of Love: A Thought & a Prayer a Day at a Time. Denis Duncan. LC 81-15925. 96p. 1982. Westminster.

Way of Man. Martin Buber. 1966. pap. 2.95 (ISBN 0-87574-106-1, 106). Citadel Pr.

Way of Man. Martin Buber. 44p. 1985. pap. 3.50 (ISBN 0-8065-0024-7). Citadel Pr.

Way of My Cross: The Masses & Homilies of Father Jerzy Popieluszko. Jerzy Popieluszko. Tr. by Michael Wren from Polish & Fr. 200p. pap. 9.95 (ISBN 0-89526-806-X). Regnery Bks.

Way of Mysticism. Joseph James. 256p. 1981. pap. 14.50 (ISBN 0-89540-086-3, SB-086). Sun Pub.

Way of Mysticism: An Anthology. Joseph James. 1977. lib. bdg. 59.95 (ISBN 0-8490-2810-8). Gordon Pr.

Way of Non-Attachment: The Practice of Insight Meditation. Dhiravamsa. 160p. 1984. pap. 9.95 (ISBN 0-85500-210-7). Newcastle Pub.

Way of Peace. J. C. Wenger. LC 77-86349. (Mennonite Faith Ser.: No. 3, Christian Peace Shelf Ser). 72p. 1977. pap. text ed. 1.50 (ISBN 0-8361-1835-9). Herald Pr.

Way of Peace & Blessedness. 3rd ed. Swami Paramananda. 1961. 4.50 (ISBN 0-911564-06-3). Vedanta Ctr.

Way of Perfection. St. Teresa of Avila. pap. 4.95 (ISBN 0-385-06539-6, D176, Im). Doubleday.

Way of Response: Selections from His Writings. Martin Buber. Ed. by Nahum N. Glatzer. LC 66-26977. 1971. pap. 5.95 (ISBN 0-8052-0292-7). Schocken.

Way of St. Francis. Robert H. Garner. 1984. 6.95 (ISBN 0-8062-1605-0). Carlton.

Way of St. Francis: The Challenge of Franciscan Spirituality for Everyone. Murray Bodo. LC 83-14066. 192p. 1984. 12.95 (ISBN 0-385-19073-5). Doubleday.

Way of St. Francis: The Challenge of Franciscan Spirituality for Everyone. Murray Bodo. LC 83-14066. 1985. 6.95 (ISBN 0-385-19913-9, Im). Doubleday.

Way of St. James, 3 vols. Georgianna G. King. LC 78-63469. Repr. of 1920 ed. Set. 140.00 (ISBN 0-404-17160-5). AMS Pr.

Way of Salvation N. T. 1982. pap. 3.95 (ISBN 0-89225-220-0). Gospel Advocate.

Way of Seeing. Edith Schaeffer. 256p. 1977. pap. 6.95 (ISBN 0-8007-5036-5, Power Bks). Revell.

Way of Siddhartha: A Life of the Buddha. David J. Kalupahana & Indrani Kalupahana. 242p. 1987. pap. text ed. 11.75 (ISBN 0-8191-6066-0). U Pr of Amer.

Way of Spiritual Direction. Francis K. Nemeck & Marie T. Coombs. 1985. pap. 8.95 (ISBN 0-89453-447-5). M Glazier.

Way of Splendor: Jewish Mysticism & Modern Psychology. Edward Hoffman. LC 81-50967. (Illus.). 224p. 1981. pap. 10.95 (ISBN 0-87773-210-8). Shambhala Pubns.

Way of Tao: Part II. Bhagwan S. Rajneesh. Tr. by Dolli Didi. 1979. 24.00 (ISBN 0-89684-056-5, Pub. by Motilal Banarsidass India). Orient Bk Dist.

Way of Tenderness. Kevin O'Shea. LC 78-61728. (Orig.). 1978. pap. 2.95 (ISBN 0-8091-2166-2). Paulist Pr.

Way of the Ascetics. Tito Colliander. 130p. Repr. of 1960 ed. cancelled 5.95 (ISBN 0-913026-22-0). St Nectarios.

Way of the Buddha. C. A. Burland. (Way Ser.). pap. 5.95 (ISBN 0-7175-0590-1). Dufour.

Way of the Christian. J. Catling Allen. (Way Ser.). pap. 5.95 (ISBN 0-7175-0782-3). Dufour.

Way of the Cross. Ed Carley. 1985. 9.95 (ISBN 0-89837-101-5, Pub. by Pflaum Press). Peter Li.

Way of the Cross. Josemaria Escriva. (Illus.). 123p. 1983. 10.95 (ISBN 0-906138-05-1); pap. 6.95 (ISBN 0-906138-06-X); pocket size 3.95 (ISBN 0-906138-07-8). Scepter Pubs.

Way of the Cross. Tolbert McCarroll. LC 84-61025. 128p. (Orig.). 1985. pap. 4.95 (ISBN 0-8091-2653-2). Paulist Pr.

Way of the Cross. Mary C. Morrison. LC 85-60516. 32p. (Orig.). 1985. pap. 2.50x (ISBN 0-87574-260-2). Pendle Hill.

Way of the Cross for Congregational Use. Ed. by Jeremy Harrington. (Illus.). 28p. (Orig.). 1976. pap. text ed. 0.65 (ISBN 0-912228-24-5). St Anthony Mess Pr.

Way of the Cross for the Separated & Divorced. Anajean Hauber. (Illus.). 45p. (Orig.). 1985. pap. text ed. 2.95 (ISBN 0-86716-050-0). St Anthony Mess Pr.

Way of the Cross: Giant Print Edition. rev. ed. Fulton J. Sheen. (Illus.). 64p. 1982. pap. 2.50 (ISBN 0-87973-659-3, 659); roncote pocket-size 2.50 (ISBN 0-87973-660-7, 660). Our Sunday Visitor.

Way of the Cross: Way of Justice. Leonardo Boff. Tr. by John Drury from Port. LC 79-23776. Tr. of Via-Sacra Da Justica. 144p. (Orig.). 1980. pap. 4.95 (ISBN 0-88344-701-0). Orbis Bks.

Way of the Disciple. Codd. 5.00 (ISBN 0-8356-7049-X). Theos Pub Hse.

Way of the Greeks. Frank R. Earp. LC 75-136393. Repr. of 1929 ed. 21.50 (ISBN 0-404-02234-0). AMS Pr.

Way of the Heart. Henri J. Nouwen. (Epiphany Bks.). 1983. pap. 2.50 (ISBN 0-345-30530-2). Ballantine.

Way of the Heart: Desert Spirituality & Contemporary Ministry. Henri J. Nouwen. 96p. 1981. 8.95 (ISBN 0-86683-913-5, AY7443, HarpR). Har-Row.

Way of the Hindu. Swami Yogeshananda. (Way Ser.). pap. 5.95 (ISBN 0-7175-0626-6). Dufour.

Way of the Immortal Threefold Self: The Straight Path. Robert E. Birdsong. (Aquarian Academy Monograph: Ser. E, No. 4). 1980. pap. 1.45 (ISBN 0-917108-29-9). Sirius Bks.

Way of the Jews. Louis Jacobs. (Way Ser.). pap. 5.95 (ISBN 0-7175-0875-7). Dufour.

Way of the Kabbalah. Z'Ev Ben Shimon Halevi. 1976. pap. 6.50 (ISBN 0-87728-305-2). Weiser.

Way of the Muslim. Muhammad Iqbal. (Way Ser.). pap. 5.95 (ISBN 0-7175-0632-0). Dufour.

Way of the Mystics. H. C. Graef. 1977. lib. bdg. 59.95 (ISBN 0-8490-2811-6). Gordon Pr.

Way of the Mystics: The Early Christian Mystics & the Rise of the Sufis. Margaret Smith. 1978. pap. 6.95 (ISBN 0-19-519967-7). Oxford U Pr.

Way of the Pilgrim & the Pilgrim Continues His Way. Tr. by R. M. French. 256p. pap. 7.95 (ISBN 0-86683-898-8, AY7444, HarpR). Har-Row.

Way of the Preacher. Simon Tugwell. (Orig.). 1979. pap. 7.95 (ISBN 0-87243-093-6). Templegate.

Way of the Sacred Tree. Edna Hong. LC 82-72643. 192p. 1983. pap. 10.95 (ISBN 0-8066-1949-X, 10-6958). Augsburg.

Way of the Saints: The Collected Short Writings of Kirpal Singh. Kirpal Singh. Ed. by Russell Perkins. LC 76-21987. 402p. 1978. 8.00 (ISBN 0-89142-026-6). Sant Bani Ash.

Way of the Sikh. W. H. McLeod. (Way Ser.). pap. 5.95 (ISBN 0-7175-0731-9). Dufour.

Way of the Soul: The "Heart Path" to Human Perfection. Robert E. Birdsong. (Aquarian Academy Monograph: Ser. D, No. 2). 1980. pap. 1.45 (ISBN 0-917108-28-0). Sirius Bks.

Way of the Spirit: The "Head Path" to Human Perfection, Ser. C, No. 2. Robert E. Birdsong. (Aquarian Academy Monograph). 1980. pap. 1.45 (ISBN 0-917108-27-2). Sirius Bks.

Way of the Sufi. Idries Shah. 1970. pap. 8.95 (ISBN 0-525-47261-4, 0869-260). Dutton.

Way of the Sufi. Idries Shah. 1983. 16.95 (ISBN 0-900860-80-4, Pub. by Octagon Pr England). Ins Study Human.

Way of the Ways Tao. Lao Tzu. Tr. by Herrymon Maurer from Chinese. 108p. 1985. 10.95 (ISBN 0-8052-3985-5). Schocken.

Way of the White Clouds. Lama A. Govinda. (Illus.). 305p. 1970. pap. 10.95 (ISBN 0-87773-007-5). Shambhala Pubns.

Way of the Wilderness. G. I. Davies. LC 77-95442. (Society for Old Testament Monographs). (Illus.). 1979. 32.50 (ISBN 0-521-22057-2). Cambridge U Pr.

Way of the Wind. W. Mallis. (YA) 1971. pap. 1.50 (ISBN 0-87508-326-9). Chr Lit.

Way of the Wise. Compiled by T. O. Tollett. 64p. 1970. pap. 1.00 (ISBN 0-89114-061-1). Baptist Pub Hse.

Way of the Wolf. Martin Bell. (Epiphany Ser.). 144p. 1983. pap. 2.95 (ISBN 0-345-30522-1). Ballantine.

Way of the Wolf: The Gospel in New Images. Martin Bell. LC 77-120366. (Illus.). 128p. 1970. pap. 8.95 (ISBN 0-8164-0202-7, AY6445, HarpR); 2 records 8.95 ea. Har-Row.

Way of Theology in Karl Barth: Essays & Comments. Ed. by H. Martin Rumscheidt. (Princeton Theological Monograph Ser.: No. 8). 1986. pap. 9.90 (ISBN 0-915138-61-1). Pickwick.

Way of Torah: An Introduction to Judaism. 3rd ed. Jacob Neusner. 164p. 1979. pap. text ed. write for info. (ISBN 0-87872-217-3). Wadsworth Pub.

Way of Torah: An Introduction to Judaism. 4th ed. Jacob Neusner. Ed. by Sheryl Fullerton. 192p. (Orig.). 1987. price not set. Wadsworth Pub.

Way of Tradition I. Sun M. Moon. 326p. (Orig.). Date not set. pap. 6.95 (ISBN 0-910621-22-5). HSA Pubns.

Way of Tradition II. Sun M. Moon. 295p. Date not set. pap. 6.95 (ISBN 0-910621-23-3). HSA Pubns.

Way of Tradition III. Sun M. Moon. 541p. Date not set. pap. 6.95 (ISBN 0-910621-24-1). HSA Pubns.

Way of Tradition IV. Sun M. Moon. 462p. 1980. pap. 8.00 (ISBN 0-910621-35-7). HSA Pubns.

Way of True Riches. Milo Kaufman. LC 79-83505. (Mennonite Faith Ser: No. 6). 64p. 1979. pap. 1.50 (ISBN 0-8361-1885-5). Herald Pr.

Way of Vaisnava Sages: A Medieval Story of South Indian Sadhus. N. S. Narasimha & Ramananda Babaji. LC 86-28251. (Sanskrit Notes of Visnu-vijay Swami). 422p. (Orig.). 1987. lib. bdg. 33.50 (ISBN 0-8191-6060-1); pap. text ed. 18.75 (ISBN 0-8191-6061-X). U Pr of Amer.

Way of Victor Paul Wierwille. Joel A. MacCollam. 32p. 1978. pap. 0.75 (ISBN 0-87784-162-4). Inter-Varsity.

Way of Widsom. R. B. Scott. 1972. pap. 7.95 (ISBN 0-02-089280-2, Collier). Macmillan.

Way of Zen. Alan W. Watts. 1974. pap. 4.95 (ISBN 0-394-70298-0, Vin). Random.

Way Out. Jeanne Guyon. (Orig.). 1985. pap. 6.95 (ISBN 0-940232-20-0). Christian Bks.

Way Out. pap. 4.00 (ISBN 0-87516-302-5). De Vorss.

Way Out Ideas for Youth Groups. Wayne Rice & Mike Yaconelli. pap. 6.95 (ISBN 0-310-34961-3, 10795P). Zondervan.

Way Out Is the Way In. Sheldon Kopp. 224p. Date not set. 13.95 (ISBN 0-87477-413-6). J P Tarcher.

Way Out Is Up. J. O. Wilson. (Redwood Ser.). 1982. pap. 2.95 (ISBN 0-8163-0450-5). Pacific Pr Pub Assn.

Way Out of Agnosticism: Or the Philosophy of Free Religion. Francis E. Abbot. LC 75-3014. (Philosophy in America Ser.). Repr. of 1890 ed. 20.00 (ISBN 0-404-59008-X). AMS Pr.

Way That I Teach. Da Free John. LC 77-94503. 1978. 10.95 (ISBN 0-913922-38-2); pap. 6.95 (ISBN 0-913922-34-X). Dawn Horse Pr.

Way, the Truth, & the Life: An Introduction to Lutheran Christianity. Duane W. Arnold & C. George Fry. (Illus.). 204p. (Orig.). 1982. pap. 9.95 (ISBN 0-8010-0189-7). Baker Bk.

Way: Three Hundred Sixty-Four Adventures in Daily Living. E. Stanley Jones. 368p. (Orig.). 1984. pap. 4.35 (ISBN 0-687-44099-8). Abingdon.

Way to a New Life. J. C. Wenger. LC 77-86326. (Mennonite Faith Ser.: No. 2). 72p. 1977. pap. 1.50 (ISBN 0-8361-1834-0). Herald Pr.

Way to Christianity: The Pilgrim. Richard Chilson. 1980. pap. 8.95 (ISBN 0-03-053426-7, HarpR). Har-Row.

Way to Contemplation: Encountering God Today. Willigis Jager. Tr. by Matthew J. O'connell. 1987. pap. 7.95. Paulist Pr.

Way to Get What You Want. W. M. Davis. 1941. pap. 3.50 (ISBN 0-88027-022-5). Firm Foun Pub.

Way to God. D. L. Moody. pap. 3.95 (ISBN 0-8024-9231-2). Moody.

Way to God. D. L. Moody. 160p. 1983. pap. text ed. 3.50 (ISBN 0-88368-131-5). Whitaker Hse.

Way to God According to the Rule of Saint Benedict. Emmanuel Heufelder. Tr. by Luke Eberle from Ger. (Cistercian Studies: No. 49). 1983. 25.95 (ISBN 0-87907-849-9); pap. 8.00 (ISBN 0-87907-949-5). Cistercian Pubns.

Way to Happiness in Your Home: Bible Study on Family Living. Jack Terry. 36p. 1982. pap. 3.50 (ISBN 0-939298-06-6). J M Prods.

Way to Liberation: Moksha Dharma of Mahabharata, 2 vols. Swami Jyotir Maya Nanda. (Illus.). 1976. Ea. pap. 4.99 (ISBN 0-934664-11-0). Yoga Res Foun.

Way to Life. Helmut Gollwitzer. Tr. by David Cairns from Ger. Tr. of Wendung Zum Leben. 232p. 1981. 21.95 (ISBN 0-567-09322-0, Pub. by T&T Clark Ltd UK); pap. 11.95 (ISBN 0-567-29322-X). Fortress.

Way to Life & Immortality. R. Swinburne Clymer. 244p. 1948. 7.95 (ISBN 0-932785-48-4). Philos Pub.

Way to Nirvana: Six Lectures on Ancient Buddhism As a Discipline of Salvation. Louis de La Vallee Poussin. LC 77-27154. (Hibbert Lectures Ser.: 1916). Repr. of 1917 ed. 24.50 (ISBN 0-404-60417-X). AMS Pr.

Way to Oneness. 4th ed. Disciples of Morningland. 1979. pap. 3.95 (ISBN 0-935146-00-8). Morningland.

Way to Peace. 11.95 (ISBN 0-87418-037-6). Coleman Pub.

Way to Peace: Liberation Through the Bible. John Topel. LC 78-9148. 208p. (Orig.). 1979. pap. 7.95 (ISBN 0-88344-704-5). Orbis Bks.

Way to Pentecost. Samuel Chadwick. 1960. pap. 2.95 (ISBN 0-87508-096-0). Chr Lit.

Way to Perfection. Joseph F. Smith. 365p. 1972. 8.95 (ISBN 0-87747-300-5). Deseret Bk.

Way to Power & Poise. E. Stanley Jones. (Festival Bks). 1978. pap. 2.25 (ISBN 0-687-44190-0). Abingdon.

Way to Remember. Susan Davis. Ed. by Tom Davis. 32p. 1980. pap. 2.95 (ISBN 0-8280-0023-9). Review & Herald.

Way to the Kingdom. 2nd ed. 345p. 1972. pap. 6.00 (ISBN 0-87516-164-2). De Vorss.

Way to the Sun: A Guide to Celestial Living. David F. Barrus. 104p. 1972. 5.95 (ISBN 0-88290-008-0). Horizon Utah.

Way to Wealth, Wherein Is Plainly Taught a Remedy for Sedicion. Richard Crowley. LC 74-28843. (English Experience Ser.: No. 724). 1975. Repr. of 1550 ed. 3.50 (ISBN 90-221-0724-8). Walter J Johnson.

Way to Wholeness: A Guide to Christian Self-Counseling. Frans M. J. Brandt. LC 84-70657. 208p. 1984. pap. 6.95 (ISBN 0-89107-316-7, Crossway Bks). Good News.

Way We Pray. Leonel L. Mitchell. 96p. (Orig.). 1984. pap. 1.35 (ISBN 0-88028-039-5). Forward Movement.

Waybill to Lost Spanish Signs & Symbols. Gale R. Rhoades. (Illus., Orig.). 1982. pap. 6.00 (ISBN 0-942688-02-3). Dream Garden.

Wayfinders: For Believers & Non-Believers. Lucille J. Plewe. LC 77-78794. 1977. pap. 5.00 (ISBN 0-89555-028-8). TAN Bks Pubs.

Ways & Crossways. facs. ed. Paul Claudel. Tr. by Fr. J. O'Conner. LC 67-28732. (Essay Index Reprint Ser.). 1933. 20.00 (ISBN 0-8369-0313-7). Ayer Co Pubs.

Ways & Crossways. Paul Claudel. LC 68-15820. 1968. Repr. of 1933 ed. 21.50 (ISBN 0-8046-0079-1, Pub. by Kennikat). Assoc Faculty Pr.

Ways of Being Religious: Readings for a New Approach to Religion. Frederick J. Streng et al. (Illus.). 608p. 1973. 34.00 (ISBN 0-13-946277-5). P-H.

Ways of God: Paths into the New Testament. Harry C. Griffith. 149p. 1986. pap. 7.95 (ISBN 0-8192-1377-2). Morehouse.

Ways of Imperfection. Simon Tugwell. 252p. 1985. 12.95 (ISBN 0-87243-136-3). Templegate.

Ways of Indian Wisdom. Teresa VanEtten. LC 86-5924. 96p. (Orig.). 1987. pap. 8.95 (ISBN 0-86534-090-0). Sunstone Pr.

Ways of Medieval Life & Thought. Frederick M. Powicke. LC 64-13394. (Illus.). 1949. 12.00 (ISBN 0-8196-0137-3). Biblo.

Ways of Mental Prayer. Dom V. Lehodey. 408p. 1982. pap. 8.00 (ISBN 0-89555-178-0). TAN Bks Pubs.

Ways of Reading the Bible. Ed. by Michael Wadsworth. 232p. 1981. 28.50x (ISBN 0-389-20119-7). B&N Imports.

Ways of Religion. Ed. by Roger Eastman. 608p. 1975. pap. text ed. 21.95 scp (ISBN 0-06-382595-3, CP, HarpC). Har-Row.

Ways of Wisdom: Readings on the Good Life. Ed. by Steve Smith. (Illus.). 312p. (Orig.). 1983. lib. bdg. 29.75 (ISBN 0-8191-3387-6); pap. text ed. 14.25 (ISBN 0-8191-3388-4). U Pr of Amer.

Ways to Paradise: The Chinese Quest for Immortality. Michael Loewe. (Illus.). 1979. text ed. 34.00x (ISBN 0-04-181025-2). Allen Unwin.

Ways to Pray. Ed. by Thomas Shaw. LC 84-71180. (Sermon Ser.: No. 4). 92p. (Orig.). 1984. pap. 5.00 (ISBN 0-936384-19-0). Cowley Pubns.

Ways to Shiva: Life & Ritual in Hindu India. Joseph M. Dye. LC 80-25113. (Illus.). 94p. (Orig.). 1980. pap. 4.95 (ISBN 0-87633-038-3). Phila Mus Art.

Ways to the Center: An Introduction to World Religions. Dennis L. Carmody & John T. Carmody. 432p. 1981. text ed. write for info. (ISBN 0-534-00890-9). Wadsworth Pub.

Ways Women Can Witness. Muriel Larson. LC 84-5006. 1984. pap. 5.95 (ISBN 0-8054-5250-8). Broadman.

Wayward Puritans: A Study in the Sociology of Deviance. Kai T. Erikson. LC 66-16140. (Deviance & Criminology Ser.). 228p. 1968. pap. text ed. write for info. (ISBN 0-02-332200-4). Macmillan.

Wayward Shepards: Prejudice & the Protestant Clergy. Rodney Stark & Bruce D. Foster. 130p. pap. 6.95 (ISBN 0-686-95186-7). ADL.

We Are Accountable. Leonard Edelestein. pap. 2.50x (ISBN 0-87574-024-3, 024). Pendle Hill.

We Are Christians Because... Robert E. Wells. LC 84-28762. 119p. 1985. 7.95 (ISBN 0-87747-639-X). Deseret Bk.

We Are Here: Songs of the Holocaust in Yiddish & Singable English Translation. Eleanor G. Mlotek & Malke Gottlieb. 104p. 1983. 10.00 (ISBN 0-686-40805-5). Workmen's Circle.

We Are Like Dreamers. Walter Beyerlin. Tr. by Dinah Livingstone from Ger. Tr. of Wir Sind Wie Traumende. 76p. 1982. 13.95 (ISBN 0-567-09315-8, Pub. by T&T Clark Ltd). Fortress.

We Are Muslim Children. Saida Chaudhry. pap. 4.00 (ISBN 0-89259-050-5). Am Trust Pubns.

We Are One in the Lord: Developing Caring Groups in the Church. Dennis Denning. LC 81-14958. 96p. (Orig.). 1982. pap. 5.50 (ISBN 0-687-44281-8). Abingdon.

We Are the Church: The Book. John J. Weigand. 128p. (Orig.). 1986. pap. 12.95 (ISBN 0-941850-16-1). Sunday Pubns.

We Are the Church: The Manual. John Weigand. 80p. (Orig.). 1986. pap. 2.50 (ISBN 0-941850-17-X). Sunday Pubns.

We Are the Lord's. Jean A. Vis. 3.50 (ISBN 0-686-23479-0). Rose Pub MI.

We Are the Mainstream. Jenefer Ellingston. Ed. by Constance McKenna. (Illus.). 16p. 1981. pap. 1.00 (ISBN 0-915365-02-2). Cath Free Choice.

We Are the Shakers. A. F. Joy. Orig. Title: Queen of the Shakers. (Illus.). 130p. (Orig.). 1985. pap. 5.00 (ISBN 0-934703-00-0). Saturscent Pubns.

We Are the Shakers. rev., & abr. ed. A. F. Joy. (Illus.). 130p. 1985. pap. 5.50 (ISBN 0-318-18279-3). A F Joy.

We Are Thy Children. Heini Arnold. 36p. 1985. pap. 1.50 (ISBN 0-87486-193-4). Plough.

We Be Brethen. J. D. Thomas. 1958. 13.95 (ISBN 0-89112-001-7, Bibl Res Pr). Abilene Christ U.

We Beheld His Glory. Nicolai S. Arsen'ev. Tr. by Mary A. Ewer. LC 76-113545. Repr. of 1936 ed. 18.00 (ISBN 0-404-00407-5). AMS Pr.

We Believe. Sr. Mary D. Bothwell. (Christ Our Life Ser.). (Illus.). 1981. pap. text ed. 4.20 (ISBN 0-8294-0367-1); tchr's ed. 12.95 (ISBN 0-8294-0368-X). Loyola.

We Believe. Paul Erb. LC 69-15831. 112p. (Orig.). 1969. pap. 3.95 (ISBN 0-8361-1587-2). Herald Pr.

We Believe. Theodore Huggenvik. 1950. pap. 3.95 (ISBN 0-8066-0151-5, 15-7102). Augsburg.

We Believe. Douglas Leroy. (Illus.). 56p. 1975. pap. 3.95 (ISBN 0-87148-906-6). Pathway Pr.

We Believe. Ralph M. Riggs. 184p. 1954. 3.50 (ISBN 0-88243-780-1, 02-0780). Gospel Pub.

We Believe... A Guide to a Better Understanding of the Bible As a Source Book for the Humanities. school ed. School ed. 0.75 (ISBN 0-89942-247-0, 247.05-SD). Catholic Bk Pub.

We Believe: A Study of the Book of Confessions for Church Officers. Harry W. Eberts, Jr. LC 87-2097. 120p. (Orig.). 1987. pap. price not set (ISBN 0-664-24063-1, A Geneva Press Publication). Westminster.

We Believe & Teach. Martin J. Heinecken. Ed. by Harold W. Rast. LC 80-16363. (Lead Book). 128p. (Orig.). 1980. pap. 3.95 (ISBN 0-8006-1387-2, 1-1387). Fortress.

We Believe in Creation. Charles Ryrie. 62p. 1976. pap. 0.50 (ISBN 0-937396-54-0). Walterick Pubs.

We Believe in One God: Creed & Scripture. Frank E. Eakin, Jr. LC 85-51755. 165p. 1985. pap. text ed. 21.95 (ISBN 0-932269-64-8). Wyndham Hall.

We Belong Together. Bruce Milne. LC 78-13882. 1979. pap. 2.95 (ISBN 0-87784-455-0). Inter-Varsity.

We Break Bread in Loving Thanksgiving. 2.85 (ISBN 0-02-649450-7, 64945); tchr's manual 2.52 (ISBN 0-02-649460-4, 64946). Benziger Pub Co.

We Can Make It...Together. Joseph A. Jordan. (Illus.). 64p. 1984. 5.50 (ISBN 0-682-40157-9). Exposition Pr FL.

We Can Share God's Love. Jean Richards. 80p. 1984. pap. 2.95 (ISBN 0-8170-1010-6). Judson.

We Cannot Find Words. Tad Dunne. casebound 8.95 (ISBN 0-87193-138-9). Dimension Bks.

We Celebrate Our Marriage. John Van Bemmel & Dolores Van Bemmel. (Greeting Book Line Ser.). 32p. (Orig.). 1986. pap. 1.50 (ISBN 0-89622-304-3). Twenty-Third.

We Christians & Jews. Paul J. Kirsch. 160p. pap. 3.95 (ISBN 0-686-95187-5). ADL.

We Christians & Jews. Paul J. Kirsch. LC 74-26332. pap. 40.00 (2026838). Bks Demand UMI.

We Confess: The Sacraments. Herman Sasse. (We Confess Ser.: Vol. II). 160p. 1985. 11.95 (ISBN 0-570-03982-7, 12-2899). Concordia.

We Confess, Vol. 1: Jesus Christ. Herman Sasse. Tr. by Norman Nagel. 1984. pap. 10.95 (ISBN 0-570-03941-X, 12-2877). Concordia.

We Didn't Know They Were Angels. Doris W. Greig. Ed. by Mary Beckwith. 300p. (Orig.). 1987. pap. 7.95 (ISBN 0-8307-1145-7, 5418802). Regal.

We Die Before We Live: Talking with the Very Ill. Daniel Berrigan. 160p. 1980. 11.95 (ISBN 0-8164-0462-3, HarpR). Har-Row.

We Don't Have Any Here. Toby Gould et al. 52p. 1986. pap. 4.95 (ISBN 0-88177-030-2, DR030B). Discipleship Res.

We Drink from Our Own Wells: The Spiritual Journey of a People. Gustavo Gutierrez. Tr. by Matthew J. O'Connell from Span. LC 83-22008. Orig. Title: Beber en Supropio Pozo: En el Itinerario Espiritual de un Pueblo. 208p. (Orig.). 1984. pap. 7.95 (ISBN 0-88344-707-X). Orbis Bks.

We Endeavor. C. H. Spurgeon. 1975. pap. 2.25 (ISBN 0-686-16835-6). Pilgrim Pubns.

We Follow Jesus. 2.82 (ISBN 0-02-649490-6, 64949); tchr's manual 2.52 (ISBN 0-02-649500-7, 64950). Benziger Pub Co.

We Gather, Remember, & Eat. Joan Mitchell. 1986. tchr's. ed. 2.00 (ISBN 0-89837-110-4); wkbk. 5.25 (ISBN 0-89837-109-0). Peter Li.

We Give Thanks. Iris V. Cully. (Illus., Orig.). 1976. pap. text ed. 1.95x (ISBN 0-8192-4070-2); tchr's. ed. 4.50x (ISBN 0-8192-4069-9); guidebk. for parents 1.95x (ISBN 0-8192-4071-0). Morehouse.

We Go Forward: Stories of United Methodist Pathmakers. Carolyn Wolcott & Leonard Wolcott. LC 83-73225. 72p. pap. 5.25 (ISBN 0-88177-008-6, DR008B). Discipleship Res.

We Grow in God's Family: Preparation for Confirmation. Gerard P. Weber et al. (Illus., Orig.). 1968. pap. 2.32 (ISBN 0-02-649060-9, 64906); pap. 1.50 tchr's. manual (ISBN 0-02-649070-6, 64907). Benziger Pub Co.

We Have but Faith. Ed. by Tom E. Kakonis & John Scally. LC 74-20434. 152p. 1975. 6.95 (ISBN 0-88498-023-5). Brevet Pr.

We Have the Mind of Christ. Dennis F. Kinlaw. 128p. Date not set. pap. text ed. 5.95 (ISBN 0-310-75231-0). Zondervan.

We Have Tomorrow. Louis B. Reynolds. Ed. by Raymond H. Woolsey. 480p. 1984. 19.95 (ISBN 0-8280-0232-0). Review & Herald.

We Hold These Truths. Zenas J. Bicket. LC 78-56133. (Workers Training Book of the Year). (Illus.). 128p. 1978. pap. 1.50 (ISBN 0-88243-631-7, 02-0631). Gospel Pub.

We Imperialists: Notes on Ernest Seilliere's "Philosophy of Imperialism". Cargill Sprietsma. LC 70-176005. Repr. of 1931 ed. 16.50 (ISBN 0-404-06198-2). AMS Pr.

We Interrupt This Crisis. Kenneth D. Barney. 63p. 1970. pap. 1.25 (ISBN 0-88243-704-6, 02-0704). Gospel Pub.

We Jews & Jesus. Samuel Sandmel. LC 65-11529. 1965. pap. 7.95 (ISBN 0-19-501676-9). Oxford U Pr.

We Knew His Power: Nine Whose Lives Were Touched by Jesus. G. Curtis Jones. LC 75-44181. pap. 24.40 (ISBN 0-8357-9031-2, 2016419). Bks Demand UMI.

We Left Jehovah's Witnesses. Edmond C. Gruss. pap. 5.95 (ISBN 0-8010-3696-8). Baker Bk.

We Left Jehovah's Witnesses: A Non-Prophet Organization. Edmond C. Gruss. 1974. pap. 5.95 (ISBN 0-87552-307-2). Presby & Reformed.

We Live Forever. Lehman Strauss. 1947. pap. 5.95 (ISBN 0-87213-830-5). Loizeaux.

We Lived There Too: A Documentary History of Pioneer Jews & the Westward Movement of America, 1630-1930. Kenneth Libo & Irving Howe. LC 84-11787. (Illus.). 352p. 1984. 24.95 (ISBN 0-312-85866-3, Pub. by Marek). St Martin.

We Lived There Too: In Their Own Words & Pictures-Pioneer Jews & the Westward Movement of America 1630-1930. Kenneth Libo & Irving Howe. (Illus.). 352p. 1985. pap. 13.95 (ISBN 0-312-85867-1, Pub. by Marek). St Martin.

We Love God. Cathy Falk. (Bible Lessons for Little People Ser.: Bk. 2). 144p. (Orig.). 1983. pap. 7.95 (ISBN 0-87239-613-4, 3360). Standard Pub.

We Need Each Other. Guy Greenfield. 1984. 8.95 (ISBN 0-8010-3799-9); pap. 5.95 (ISBN 0-8010-3800-6). Baker Bk.

We Please God. Cathy Falk. (Bible Activities Ser.: Bk. 4). 24p. (Orig.). 1983. pap. 1.50 (ISBN 0-87239-679-7, 2454). Standard Pub.

We Praise You, O Lord! Patricia Fritz. 2.95 (ISBN 0-8091-2518-8). Paulist Pr.

We Pray to the Lord: General Intercessions Based on the Scriptural Readings for Sundays & Holy Days. Richard Mazziotta. LC 84-71135. 208p. (Orig.). 1984. pap. 9.95 (ISBN 0-87793-323-5). Ave Maria.

We Preach Jesus. Compiled by T. O. Tollett. 40p. 1971. pap. 1.00 (ISBN 0-89114-063-8). Baptist Pub Hse.

We Really Do Need Each Other. Reuben Welch. 112p. 1982. pap. 4.95 (ISBN 0-310-70221-6, 14012P). Zondervan.

We Receive the Spirit of Jesus (Confirmation Program) Brian A. Haggerty & Thomas P. Walters. wkbk. 3.50 (ISBN 0-8091-9532-1); parent's notes 2.45 (ISBN 0-8091-9533-X); celebration's bk. 9.95 (ISBN 0-8091-9531-3); director's manual 7.50 (ISBN 0-8091-9530-5). Paulist Pr.

We Receive the Spirit of Jesus Filmstrips. Brian A. Haggerty & Thomas P. Walters. with guidebook & cassette 49.95 (ISBN 0-8091-7664-5). Paulist Pr.

We Saw Brother Francis. Francis De Beer. 1983. 12.00 (ISBN 0-8199-0803-7). Franciscan Herald.

We Share New Life (Baptism Program) Brian A. Haggerty et al. Reflections & Activities for Families. 2.95 (ISBN 0-8091-9183-0); Activities for Children. 2.75 (ISBN 0-8091-9182-2); director's manual 7.95 (ISBN 0-8091-9181-4); celebrations bk. 4.95 (ISBN 0-8091-9184-9). Paulist Pr.

We Speak for Ourselves: Experiences in Homosexual Counseling. Jack Babuscio. LC 77-78623. pap. 40.00 (2026837). Bks Demand UMI.

We Still Love You, Bob. Dorothea Nyberg. 144p. 1984. pap. 6.95 (ISBN 0-87178-925-6). Brethren.

We Talk of Christ, We Rejoice in Christ. Neal A. Maxwell. LC 84-71873. 180p. 8.95 (ISBN 0-87747-762-0). Deseret Bk.

We Went to Gabon. Carol M. Klein. 1974. pap. 2.95 (ISBN 0-87509-151-2). Chr Pubns.

We Will Celebrate a Church Wedding. George R. Szews. 88p. 1983. pap. 1.50 (ISBN 0-8146-1288-1). Liturgical Pr.

We Will Prove Them Herewith. Neal A. Maxwell. LC 82-1532. 132p. 1982. 6.95 (ISBN 0-87747-912-7). Deseret Bk.

We Wish You a Merry Christmas. Derek Pearson. 1983. 30.00x (ISBN 0-86334-017-2, Pub. by macdonald Pub UK). State Mutual Bk.

We Worship. Sr. Mary D. Bothwell. (Christ Our Life Ser.). (Illus.). 1982. text ed. 4.20 (ISBN 0-8294-0391-4); tchrs. ed. 12.95 (ISBN 0-8294-0392-2). Loyola.

Wealth of Christians. Redmond Mullin. LC 84-7262. 256p. (Orig.). 1984. pap. 10.95 (ISBN 0-88344-709-6). Orbis Bks.

Wealth, Walk & Warfare of the Christian. Ruth Paxson. 224p. 1939. 11.95 (ISBN 0-8007-0340-5). Revell.

Weapon of Prayer. E. M. Bounds. (Direction Bks.). 57p. 1975. pap. 3.95 (ISBN 0-8010-0634-1). Baker Bk.

Weapon of Prayer. Basilea Schlink. 1974. Gift ed. 0.95 (ISBN 3-87209-658-3). Evang Sisterhood Mary.

Weapons of Our Warfare: Help for Troubled Minds. (Illus.). 144p. 1987. pap. 3.95 (ISBN 0-936369-06-X). Son-Rise Pubns.

Web of Belief. 2nd ed. W. V. Quine & J. S. Ullian. 1978. pap. text ed. 7.00 (ISBN 0-394-32179-0, RanC). Random.

Weber & Islam: A Critical Study. Bryan S. Turner. 1978. pap. 9.95x (ISBN 0-7100-8942-2). Methuen Inc.

Webster 'Reformed' A Study of Post-Restoration Versions of John Webster's Plays, 2 vols. James Hogg. (Jacobean Drama Studies). (Orig.). 1986. pap. 30.00 (ISBN 3-7052-0323-1, Pub. by Salzburg Studies). Longwood Pub Group.

Webster's Concise Dictionary of Modern English. 608p. 1987. pap. 5.95 (ISBN 0-8407-3110-8). Nelson.

Wedded Unmother. K. Halverson & Karen Hess. LC 79-54123. 128p. 1980. pap. 5.95 (ISBN 0-8066-1768-3, 10-7015). Augsburg.

Wedding Bells. Dunbar H. Ogden. (Orig.). 1945. pap. 3.25 (ISBN 0-8042-1884-6). John Knox.

Wedding Ceremony Idea Book. George W. Knight. 96p. 1982. pap. 7.95 (ISBN 0-939298-01-5). J M Prods.

Wedding: (Hindu) (Illus.). Date not set. pap. price not set (ISBN 0-938924-16-8). Sri Shirdi Sai.

Weddings: A Guide to All Religious & Interfaith Marriage Services. Abraham J. Klausner. LC 86-7892. (Life-Cycle Bookshelf Ser.). (Orig.). 1986. pap. 11.90 (ISBN 0-933771-00-2). Alpha Pub Co.

Weddings, Funerals, Special Events. Eugene Peterson et al. (Leadership Library). 175p. 1987. 9.95 (ISBN 0-917463-13-7). Chr Today.

Wedge of Gold. W. A. Scott. 1974. pap. 3.95 (ISBN 0-685-52824-3). Reiner.

Wedges & Wings: The Patterning of Paradise Regained. Burton J. Weber. LC 74-20703. (Literary Structure Ser.). 144p. 1975. 10.00x (ISBN 0-8093-0673-5). S Ill U Pr.

Wee Color Wee Sing for Christmas. Pamela C. Beall & Susan H. Nipp. (Wee Sing Ser.). (Illus.). 48p. 1986. pap. 1.95 (ISBN 0-8431-1781-8); book & cassette 6.95 (ISBN 0-8431-1782-6). Price Stern.

Wee Sing Bible Songs. Pamela C. Beall & Susan H. Nipp. (Illus.). 64p. 1986. pap. 2.25 (ISBN 0-8431-1566-1); book & cassette 8.95 (ISBN 0-8431-1780-X). Price Stern.

Wee Sing for Christmas. Pam Beall & Susan Nipp. (Illus.). 64p. (Orig.). 1984. pap. 2.25 (ISBN 0-8431-1197-6). Price Stern.

Weeds among the Wheat: Discernment: Where Prayer & Action Meet. Thomas Green. LC 84-70663. 208p. (Orig.). 1984. pap. 4.95 (ISBN 0-87793-318-9). Ave Maria.

Week That Changed the World. Ernest C. Wilson. 1968. 5.95 (ISBN 0-87159-170-7). Unity School.

Weekday Prayer Book. Morris Silverman & United Synagogue. 8.95 (ISBN 0-87677-071-5). Prayer Bk.

Weekday Prayerbook. 6.25 (ISBN 0-686-96031-9). United Syn Bk.

Weep Not for Me. John V. Taylor. 64p. 1987. pap. 3.95 (ISBN 0-89622-313-2). Twenty-Third.

Weep Not for Me: Meditations on the Cross & the Resurrection. John V. Taylor. (Risk Book Ser.). 56p. 1986. pap. 3.50 (ISBN 2-8254-0850-6). Wrld Coun Churches.

Weeping Church: Confronting the Crisis of Church Polity. Clayton Nuttall. LC 85-10760. 1985. pap. 5.95 (ISBN 0-87227-104-8). Reg Baptist.

Weeping in Ramah. J. R. Lucas. LC 85-70477. 250p. (Orig.). 1985. pap. 7.95 (ISBN 0-89107-357-4, Crossway Bks). Good News.

Wege ins Alte Testament - und Zurueck: Vom Sinn und den Moeglichkeiten einer "Theologie mit dem Alten Testament" in der Arbeit mit Erwachsenen, Vol 211. Heinrich Dickerhoff. (European University Studies: No. 23). (Ger.). 409p. 1983. 40.55 (ISBN 3-8204-7734-9). P Lang Pubs.

Weight. Joel Kauffmann. LC 79-27262. 176p. 1980. pap. 5.95 (ISBN 0-8361-3335-8). Herald Pr.

Weight Group Therapist: Spiritual Gifts. large type ed. Prophet Pearl. 32p. 1984. pap. 6.00 (ISBN 0-914009-16-8). VHI Library.

Weight Loss from the Inside Out: Help for the Compulsive Eater. Marion Bilich. LC 83-633. 192p. (Orig.). 1983. pap. 9.95 (ISBN 0-8164-2485-3, HarpR). Har-Row.

Weimar & the Vatican, 1919-1933. Stewart A. Stehlin. LC 83-42544. (Illus.). 512p. 1986. pap. 19.95x (ISBN 0-691-10195-7); text ed. 52.50x (ISBN 0-691-05399-5). Princeton U Pr.

Weird Eschatology: An Alternative View of the Second Coming. Alvin Miller. LC 86-80018. (Illus.). 52p. (Orig.). 1986. pap. 3.00 (ISBN 0-9616435-0-1). Last Things.

Welcome. Morris Greidanus et al. LC 82-12907. 71p. 1982. pap. 3.50 (ISBN 0-933140-48-7); pap. 3.50 leader's guide (ISBN 0-933140-49-5). CRC Pubns.

Welcome: An Adult Education Program Based on RCIA. Gary Timmons. LC 81-84388. 64p. (Orig.). 1982. pap. 4.95 (ISBN 0-8091-2429-7). Paulist Pr.

Welcome Back Jesus. Stanley M. Horton. 1975. pap. 1.25 (ISBN 0-88243-629-5, 02-0629). Gospel Pub.

Welcome Back to Jesus. Lyle Pointer. (Christian Living Ser.). 32p. (Orig.). 1987. pap. write for info. (ISBN 0-8341-1190-X). Beacon Hill.

Welcome, Blessed Morning! G. Franklin Gray & Charles A. Woods. Ed. by Michael L. Sherer. (Orig.). 1987. pap. 3.50 (ISBN 0-89536-849-8, 7808). CSS of Ohio.

Welcome Brothers: Poems of a Changing Man's Consciousness. David Steinberg. (Illus.). 1976. pap. 3.00 (ISBN 0-914906-04-6). Red Alder.

Welcome: Christian Parenting. Judith Tate-O'Brien. 68p. (Orig.). 1980. pap. 4.00 (ISBN 0-936098-37-6); instrs.' guide 3.00 (ISBN 0-936098-36-8). Intl Marriage.

Welcome, Holy Spirit: A Study of Charismatic Renewal in the Church. Ed. by Larry Christenson. 400p. (Orig.). 1987. pap. 16.95 (ISBN 0-8066-2273-3, 10-7021). Augsburg.

Welcome Home, Davey. Dave Rover & Harold Fickett. 208p. 1986. 12.95 (ISBN 0-8499-0553-2). Word Bks.

Welcome, New Church Member. D. O. Silvey. 20p. 1964. pap. 0.60 (ISBN 0-89114-112-X). Baptist Pub Hse.

Welcome the Stranger. Carol Greene. (Illus.). 1984. 7.95 (ISBN 0-570-04105-8, 561497). Concordia.

Welcome to the Church. Terry Powell. (Lay Action Ministry Program Ser.). 96p. 1987. pap. 4.95 (ISBN 0-89191-514-1). Cook.

Welcome to the Real World. Tim Floyd. LC 84-5876. 1984. pap. 5.95 (ISBN 0-8054-5001-7). Broadman.

Welcome to the World - A Jewish Baby's Record Book. Women's League for Conservative Judaism. (Illus.). 40p. 1985. 12.95 (ISBN 0-936293-00-4). WLCJ.

Welcome to Your Ministry. Terry Powell. (Lay Action Ministry Program Ser.). 96p. 1987. pap. 4.95 (ISBN 0-89191-515-X). Cook.

Welcomes & Ceremonies for the Year's Program. 34p. 1985. Repr. s.p. soft cover 1.25 (ISBN 0-88053-332-3). Macoy Pub.

Welcoming God's Forgiveness. Carol C. Castro. 120p. 1978. pap. text ed. 3.95 (ISBN 0-697-01681-1); leader's guide 4.50 (ISBN 0-697-01682-X); classroom tchr's guide .75 (ISBN 0-697-01907-1); adult resource book, pack/10,10.25 1.05 (ISBN 0-697-01685-4). Wm C Brown.

Welcoming Jesus. Carol C. Castro. 120p. 1979. pap. 3.95 (ISBN 0-697-01702-8); leader's guide 4.50 (ISBN 0-697-01703-6); classroom teacher's guide .75 (ISBN 0-697-01909-8); adult resource book, pack/10, 10.25 1.05 (ISBN 0-697-01704-4). Wm C Brown.

Well & the Cathedral. 5th ed. Ira Progoff. LC 76-20823. (Entrance Meditation Ser.). 166p. 1983. 4.95; pap. 11.50 incl. cassette (ISBN 0-87941-005-1). Dialogue Hse.

Well... Excuse Me. Dennis Roberts. LC 80-84233. 48p. (Orig.). 1980. pap. 1.50 (ISBN 0-89081-265-9). Harvest Hse.

Well Family Book. Charles T. Kuntzleman. 256p. 1985. 13.95 (ISBN 0-89840-092-9). Heres Life.

Wellness Spirituality. John J. Pilch. 112p. 1985. pap. 7.95 (ISBN 0-8245-0710-X). Crossroad NY.

Wellness, Spirituality & Sports. Thomas Ryan. LC 86-4923. 224p. 1986. pap. 8.95 (ISBN 0-8091-2801-2). Paulist Pr.

Wellness: Your Invitation to Full Life. John J. Pilch. Ed. by Miriam Frost. Orig. Title: Wellness. 128p. (Orig.). 1981. pap. text ed. 5.95 (ISBN 0-86683-758-2, HarpR). Har-Row.

Wells of Salvation. Edmund E. Wells. (Orig.). pap. 2.00 (ISBN 0-686-30400-4). WOS.

Wells of Salvation: Meditations of Isaiah. Charles Ellis & Norma Ellis. 224p. (Orig.). 1986. pap. 5.95 (ISBN 0-85151-457-X). Banner of Truth.

Wellspring of Guidance: Messages 1963-1968. rev. ed. The Universal House of Justice. LC 76-129996. 1976. 9.95 (ISBN 0-87743-032-2, 225-005); pap. 4.95 (ISBN 0-87743-033-0, 225-006). Baha'i.

Wellsprings: A Book of Spiritual Exercises. Anthony DeMello. LC 84-13655. 216p. 1985. 13.95 (ISBN 0-385-19616-4). Doubleday.

Wellsprings: A Book of Spiritual Exercises. Anthony DeMello. LC 86-4478. 240p. 1986. pap. 7.95 (ISBN 0-385-19617-2, Im). Doubleday.

Wellsprings of the Pentecostal Movement. David Womack. 96p. 1968. pap. 1.50 (ISBN 0-88243-628-7, 02-0628). Gospel Pub.

Wellsprings of Torah. Alexander Z. Friedman. Tr. by Gertrude Hirschler from Yiddish. 584p. 1980. slipcased 18.95 (ISBN 0-910818-20-7); pap. 16.95 (ISBN 0-910818-04-5). Judaica Pr.

Welsh Church from Conquest to Reformation. Glanmor Williams. 612p. 1976. text ed. 28.50x (ISBN 0-7083-0651-9, Pub. by U of Wales). Humanities.

Welsh Elizabethan Catholic Martyrs. D. Aneurin Thomas. 331p. 1971. text ed. 28.50 (ISBN 0-900768-97-5, Pub. by U of Wales). Humanities.

Welsh Proverbs with English Translations. Henry H. Vaughan. LC 68-17945. (Eng. & Welsh.). 1969. Repr. of 1889 ed. 43.00x (ISBN 0-8103-3205-1). Gale.

Weltwende. 1982. pap. 6.00 (ISBN 0-686-76278-9). Feldheim.

Wendy & the Whine. Carol Greene. (Illus.). 32p. 1987. pap. 3.95 (ISBN 0-570-04157-0, 56-1615). Concordia.

Werden und Wesen Des 107 Psalms. Walter Beyerlin. (Beiheft 153 Zur Zeitschrift Fur Die Alttestamentliche Wissenschaft). 1979. 29.20 (ISBN 3-11-007755-8). De Gruyter.

We're in This Thing Together. Perry Tanksley. 1974. 4.50 (ISBN 0-8007-0664-1). Allgood Bks.

Werewolf. Montague Summers. 308p. 1973. pap. 3.95 (ISBN 0-8065-0392-0). Citadel Pr.

Wesley & Methodism. F. J. Snell. 243p. 1983. Repr. of 1900 ed. lib. bdg. 43.50 (ISBN 0-8495-4977-9). Arden Lib.

Wesley & Sanctification. Harold Lindstrom. LC 83-17025. 256p. (Orig.). 1984. 8.95 (ISBN 0-310-75011-3, 17025P). Zondervan.

Wesley Speaks on Christian Vocation. Paul W. Chilcote. 104p. (Orig.). 1987. pap. 6.95 (ISBN 0-88177-041-8, DR041B). Discipleship Res.

Wesleyan & Tractarian Worship. Trevor Dearing. LC 66-72190. 1966. text ed. 15.00x (ISBN 0-8401-0531-2). A R Allenson.

Wesleyan Bible Commentary, 6 vols. Charles W. Carter. 4484p. 1986. 149.50 (ISBN 0-913573-33-7). Hendrickson MA.

Wesleyan Bible Commentary, 2 vols. Ed. by Charles W. Carter. 808p. 1986. 24.95 (ISBN 0-913573-36-1). Hendrickson MA.

Wesleyan Bible Commentary, Vol. 1. Charles W. Carter. 1060p. 1986. 27.95 (ISBN 0-913573-34-5). Hendrickson MA.

Wesleyan Bible Commentary, Vol. 2. Charles W. Carter. 660p. 1986. 27.95 (ISBN 0-913573-35-3). Hendrickson MA.

Wesleyan Bible Commentary, Vol. 4. Charles W. Carter. 752p. 1986. 27.95 (ISBN 0-913573-37-X). Hendrickson MA.

Wesleyan Bible Commentary, Vol. 5. Charles W. Carter. 676p. 1986. 27.95 (ISBN 0-913573-38-8). Hendrickson MA.

Wesleyan Bible Commentary, Vol. 6. Charles W. Carter. 528p. 1986. 27.95 (ISBN 0-913573-39-6). Hendrickson MA.

Wesleyan Movement in the Industrial Revolution. Wellman J. Warner. LC 66-24768. 1967. Repr. of 1930 ed. 8.00x (ISBN 0-8462-0960-8). Russell.

Wesleyan Theology: A Sourcebook. Thomas A. Langford. 326p. 1984. lib. bdg. 24.95 (ISBN 0-939464-40-3); pap. 14.95 (ISBN 0-939464-41-1). Labyrinth Pr.

Wesley's Christology: An Interpretation. John Deschner. LC 85-2274. 244p. pap. 12.95x (ISBN 0-87074-200-0). SMU Press.

Wesley's Fifty-Two Standard Sermons. 9.95 (ISBN 0-686-12929-6). Schmul Pub Co.

Wesley's New Testament Notes. 14.95 (ISBN 0-686-12927-X). Schmul Pub Co.

Wesley's Old & New Testament Notes. 200.00 (ISBN 0-686-12928-8). Schmul Pub Co.

Wesley's Veterans, 7 vols. pap. 5.95 ea. Schmul Pub Co.

Wesley's Works, 14 vols. 125.00 set (ISBN 0-686-23581-9). Schmul Pub Co.

Wesleys World Parish. 3.50 (ISBN 0-686-27780-5). Schmul Pub Co.

Wesner Conjectures. R. Wesner. LC 82-21421. 128p. 1985. pap. 4.95 (ISBN 0-88437-070-4). Psych Dimensions.

West Africa & Christianity. Peter B. Clarke. 280p. 1986. pap. text ed. 17.95 (ISBN 0-7131-8263-6). E Arnold.

West Africa & Islam. Peter Clarke. 280p. 1982. pap. text ed. 19.95 (ISBN 0-7131-8029-3). E Arnold.

West African Christianity: The Religious Impact. Lamin Sanneh. 304p. (Orig.). 1983. pap. 11.95 (ISBN 0-88344-703-7). Orbis Bks.

West African Sufi: The Religious Heritage & Spiritual Quest of Cerno Bokar Saalif Taal. Louis Brenner. LC 83-4803. 215p. 1984. lib. bdg. 24.95x (ISBN 0-520-05008-8). U of Cal Pr.

West German Reparations to Israel. Nicholas Balabkins. LC 70-152724. 1971. 32.00 (ISBN 0-8135-0691-3). Rutgers U Pr.

West Indies: Their Social & Religious Condition. Edward B. Underhill. LC 73-107525. Repr. of 1862 ed. 24.75x (ISBN 0-8371-3772-1, UWI&). Greenwood.

Western Apache Witchcraft. Keith H. Basso. LC 69-16329. (University of Arizona, Anthroplological Papers: No. 15). pap. 20.30 (ISBN 0-317-28645-5, 2055359). Bks Demand UMI.

Western Approach to the Law & the Prophets of the Ancient World. P. Ramanathan. (Illus.). 188p. 1984. 88.95 (ISBN 0-89920-113-X). Am Inst Psych.

Western Approach to Zen. Christmas Humphreys. LC 72-76428. 212p. 1981. pap. 5.50 (ISBN 0-8356-0550-7, Quest). Theos Pub Hse.

Western Asceticism. Ed. by Owen Chadwick. LC 58-8713. (Library of Christian Classics). 364p. 1979. softcover 8.95 (ISBN 0-664-24161-1). Westminster.

Western Attitudes Toward Death: From the Middle Ages to the Present. Philippe Aries. Tr. by Patricia Ranum from Fr. LC 73-19340. (Symposia in Comparative History Ser). (Illus.). 122p. 1974. pap. 4.95x (ISBN 0-8018-1762-5). Johns Hopkins.

Western Christian Thought in the Middle Ages. Sydney H. Mellone. 1977. lib. bdg. 59.95 (ISBN 0-8490-2816-7). Gordon Pr.

Western Church in the Later Middle Ages. Francis Oakley. LC 79-7621. 352p. 1985. 32.50x (ISBN 0-8014-1208-0); pap. text ed. 9.95x (ISBN 0-8014-9347-1). Cornell U Pr.

Western Civilization Through Muslim Eyes. Sayyed M. Musavi. Tr. by F. J. Goulding from Persian. 146p. 1977. 4.95 (ISBN 0-941722-20-1); pap. 3.95 (ISBN 0-941722-06-6). Book-Dist-Ctr.

Western Contribution to Buddhism. William Peiris. 372p. 1974. lib. bdg. 79.95 (ISBN 0-87968-550-6). Krishna Pr.

Western Contribution to Buddhism. William Peiris. 1973. 11.25 (ISBN 0-8426-0537-1). Orient Bk Dist.

Western Europe in the Middle Ages, 300-1475. 4th ed. Brian Tierney & Sidney Painter. 1982. text ed. 24.00 (ISBN 0-394-33060-9, RanC). Random.

Western Experiment: New England Transcendentalists in the Ohio Valley. Elizabeth R. McKinsey. LC 72-83467. (Essays in History & Literature Ser.). 80p. 1973. pap. 4.95x (ISBN 0-674-95040-2). Harvard U Pr.

Western Heritage & American Values: Law, Theology & History. Alberto R. Coll. Ed. by Kenneth W. Thompson. LC 81-43761. (American Values Projected Abroad Ser.: Vol. I). 126p. 1982. lib. bdg. 24.00 (ISBN 0-8191-2526-1); pap. text ed. 8.25 (ISBN 0-8191-2527-X). U Pr of Amer.

Western Inner Workings. William G. Gray. LC 82-62846. (Sangreal Sodality Ser.: Vol. 1). 188p. 1983. pap. 8.95 (ISBN 0-87728-560-8). Weiser.

Western Mandala: A Survey of the Mandala in the Western Esoteric Tradition. Adam McClean. (Illus.). 1987. pap. 10.00. Phanes Pr.

Western Medieval Civilization. Deno J. Geanakoplos. 1979. text ed. 23.95 (ISBN 0-669-00868-0). Heath.

Western Mystical Tradition: An Intellectual History of Western Civilization, Vol. 1. Thomas Katsaros & Nathaniel Kaplan. 1969. 15.95x (ISBN 0-8084-0316-8); pap. 11.95x (ISBN 0-8084-0317-6). New Coll U Pr.

Western Mysticism: A Guide to the Basic Works. Compiled by Mary Ann Bowman. LC 78-18311. vi, 114p. 1979. pap. 9.00 (ISBN 0-8389-0266-9). ALA.

Western Mysticism: Neglected Chapters in the History of Religion. C. Butler. 69.95 (ISBN 0-87968-244-2). Gordon Pr.

Western Portal of Saint-Loup-De-Naud. Clark Maines. LC 78-74373. (Fine Arts Dissertations, Fourth Ser.). (Illus.). 511p. 1979. lib. bdg. 53.00 (ISBN 0-8240-3960-2). Garland Pub.

Western Religion: A Country by Country Sociological Inquiry. Ed. & intro. by Hans Mol. (Religion & Reason Ser.: No. 2). (Illus.). 642p. 1972. text ed. 59.00x (ISBN 90-2797-004-1). Mouton.

Western Reports on the Taiping: A Selection of Documents. Ed. by Prescott Clarke & J. S. Gregory. LC 81-68942. 484p. 1982. text ed. 25.00x (ISBN 0-8248-0807-X); pap. text ed. 15.95x (ISBN 0-8248-0809-6). UH Pr.

Western Response to Zoroaster. J. Duchesne-Guillemin. LC 72-9593. 112p. 1973. Repr. of 1958 ed. lib. bdg. 27.50x (ISBN 0-8371-6590-3, DUWR). Greenwood.

Western Society after the Holocaust. Ed. by Lyman H. Letgers. (Replica Editon Ser.). 200p. 1984. 20.00x (ISBN 0-86531-985-5). Westview.

Western Society & the Church in the Middle Ages. R. W. Southerm. (History of the Church). (Orig.). 1970. pap. 5.95 (ISBN 0-14-020503-9, Pelican). Penguin.

Western Spirituality: Historical Roots, Ecumenical Routes. Matthew Fox. LC 81-67364. 440p. 1981. pap. 11.95 (ISBN 0-939680-01-7). Bear & Co.

Western Theology. Wes Seeliger. LC 72-96685. 103p. 1985. pap. 6.95 (ISBN 0-915321-00-9). Pioneer Vent.

Western Views of Islam in the Middle Ages. R. W. Southern. LC 62-13270. 1978. 12.50x (ISBN 0-674-95055-0); pap. 4.95x (ISBN 0-674-95065-8). Harvard U Pr.

Western Ways to the Center: An Introduction to Religions of the West. Denise L. Carmody & John T. Carmody. 272p. 1982. pap. text ed. write for info. (ISBN 0-534-01328-7). Wadsworth Pub.

Western Women in Colonial Africa. Caroline Oliver. LC 81-24194. (Contributions in Comparative Colonial Studies: No. 12). xv, 201p. 1982. lib. bdg. 29.95 (ISBN 0-313-23388-8, OWA/). Greenwood.

Western Women in Eastern Lands: An Outline Study of Fifty Years of Women's Work in Foreign Missions. Helen B. Montgomery. Ed. by Carolyn Gifford & Donald Dayton. (Women's American Protestant Religion 1800-1930 Ser.). 286p. 1987. lib. bdg. 40.00 (ISBN 0-8240-0670-4). Garland Pub.

Westminister Pulpits, 10 vols. Campbell G. Morgan. 1983. Set. deluxe ed. 99.95 (ISBN 0-8010-6155-5). Baker Bk.

Westminster Abbey & Its Estates in the Middle Ages. Barbara Harvey. (Illus.). 1977. text ed. 55.00x (ISBN 0-19-822455-9). Oxford U Pr.

Westminster Abbey Re-Examined. William R. Lethaby. LC 69-13244. (Illus.). Repr. of 1925 ed. 27.50 (ISBN 0-405-08744-6, Pub. by Blom). Ayer Co Pubs.

Westminster Abbey: The New Bell's Cathedral Guides. Christopher Wilson et al. (New Bell's Cathedral Guides). 1986. cancelled 24.95 (ISBN 0-918678-12-9). Historical Times.

Westminster Concise Bible Dictionary. Barbara Smith. LC 80-25771. (Illus.). 188p. 1981. pap. 5.95 (ISBN 0-664-24363-0). Westminster.

Westminster Concise Handbook for the Bible. C. Vincent Wilson. LC 79-15498. (Illus.). 112p. 1979. pap. 4.50 (ISBN 0-664-24272-3). Westminster.

Westminster Confession in the Church Today: Church of Scotland Panel on Doctrine. Ed. by Alasdair I. Heron. 1982. 9.95x (ISBN 0-7152-0497-1). Outlook.

Westminster Confession of Faith. John McPherson. (Handbooks for Bible Classes & Private Students). 182p. 1882. pap. 6.95 (ISBN 0-567-28143-4, Pub. by T & T Clark Ltd Uk). Fortress.

Westminster Confession of Faith. G. I. Williamson. pap. 6.95 (ISBN 0-8010-9591-3). Baker Bk.

Westminster Confession of Faith: A Study Manual. G. I. Williamson. 1964. pap. 5.50 (ISBN 0-87552-538-5). Presby & Reformed.

Westminster Confession of Faith: An Authentic Modern Version. rev., 2nd ed. Pref. by L. Edward Davis. x, 89p. (Orig.). 1985. pap. text ed. write for info. (ISBN 0-9614303-1-1). Summertown.

Westminster Dictionary of Christian Ethics. rev. ed. Ed. by James F. Childress & John Macquarrie. LC 85-22539. 704p. 1986. 34.95 (ISBN 0-664-20940-8). Westminster.

Westminster Dictionary of Christian Spirituality. Ed. by Gordon S. Wakefield. LC 83-14527. 416p. 1983. 20.95 (ISBN 0-664-21396-0). Westminster.

Westminster Dictionary of Christian Theology. Ed. by Alan Richardson & John Bowden. LC 83-14521. 632p. 1983. 24.95 (ISBN 0-664-21398-7). Westminster.

Westminster Dictionary of Church History. Ed. by Jerald C. Brauer. LC 69-11071. 900p. 1971. 27.50 (ISBN 0-664-21285-9). Westminster.

Westminster Dictionary of Worship. Ed. by J. G. Davies. LC 78-25582. (Illus.). 400p. 1979. 18.95 (ISBN 0-664-21373-1). Westminster.

Westminster Historical Atlas to the Bible. rev. ed. Ed. by G. Ernest Wright & Floyd V. Filson. LC 56-9123. 130p. 1956. 18.95 (ISBN 0-664-20535-6). Westminster.

Westminster Historical Maps of Bible Lands. Ed. by G. Ernest Wright & F. V. Filson. 24p. pap. 2.50 (ISBN 0-664-29077-9). Westminster.

Westminster, Whitehall, & the Vatican: The Role of Cardinal Hinsley, 1935-43. Thomas Moloney. LC 85-19381. (Illus.). 263p. 1985. text ed. 24.95x (ISBN 0-268-01938-X, Pub. by Burns & Oates London). U of Notre Dame Pr.

We've got the Power: Witches among Us. Lady Foxglove. LC 81-11098. (A Jem Book Ser.). (Illus.). 64p. (Teens reading on a 2-3rd grade level). 1981. lib. bdg. 9.29 (ISBN 0-671-43604-X). Messner.

Whakairo: Maori Tribal Art. David Simmons. (Illus.). 1985. 34.95x (ISBN 0-19-558119-9). Oxford U Pr.

What a Savior! W. A. Criswell. LC 77-82399. 1978. 7.50 (ISBN 0-8054-5155-2). Broadman.

What a Teenager Ought to Know About God. Carlo M. Flumiani. (Illus.). 1978. 42.50 (ISBN 0-89266-140-2). Am Classical Coll Pr.

What a Teenager Ought to Know About Sex & God. Jack D. Pierson. (Teenager's Essential Education Library). (Illus.). 147p. 1981. 48.75 (ISBN 0-89266-288-3). Am Classical Coll Pr.

What about Baptism? Larry Christenson. 24p. (Orig.). 1986. pap. 1.35 (ISBN 0-8066-2257-1, 23-3009). Augsburg.

What about Divorce. Spiros Zodhiates. 7.95 (ISBN 0-89957-574-9). AMG Pubs.

What About Jehovah's Witnesses? Gordon Lindsay. 1.25 (ISBN 0-89985-017-0). Christ Nations.

What about Me? Joann Klusmeyer. (Illus.). 1987. 3.95 (ISBN 0-570-03641-0). Concordia.

What about Nouthetic Counseling? J. Adams. 1976. pap. 2.50 (ISBN 0-87552-064-2). Presby & Reformed.

What about Nouthetic Counseling? The Question & Answer Book. Jay E. Adams. 1977. pap. 2.50 (ISBN 0-8010-0114-5). Baker Bk.

What about the Russians? A Christian Approach to US-Soviet Conflict. Mark Hatfield et al. Ed. by Dale W. Brown. 144p. 1984. pap. 6.95 (ISBN 0-87178-751-2). Brethren.

What after World War III. Aliene M. Haynes. 1987. 11.95 (ISBN 0-533-06842-8). Vantage.

What Agitates the Mind of the East. M. I. Siddiqui. 1981. 1.25 (ISBN 0-686-97862-5). Kazi Pubns.

What an Altar Guild Should Know. Paul H. Lang. 1964. ring bdg. 5.95 (ISBN 0-570-03501-5, 14-1528). Concordia.

What Anglicans Believe. David L. Edwards. 128p. 1975. pap. 1.90 (ISBN 0-88028-003-4, 503). Forward Movement.

What Are Norms? A Study of Beliefs & Action in a Maya Community. F. Cancian. LC 74-77833. 256p. 1975. 34.50 (ISBN 0-521-20536-0). Cambridge U Pr.

What Are Norms? A Study of Beliefs & Action in a Maya Community. Francesca M. Cancian. LC 74-77833. pap. 55.50 (2027284). Bks Demand UMI.

What Are Saints: Fifteen Chapters in Sanctity. facs. ed. Cyril C. Martindale. LC 68-16954. (Essay Index Reprint Ser). 1932. 13.75 (ISBN 0-8369-0681-0). Ayer Co Pubs.

What Are Saints? Fourteen Studies in Sanctity. C. C. Martindale. 1982. pap. 3.95 (ISBN 0-89453-270-7). M Glazier.

What Are the Theologians Saying. Monika Hellwig. (Orig.). 1970. pap. 2.95 (ISBN 0-8278-9051-6, Pub. by Pflaum Pr). Peter Li.

What Are They Saying about Biblical Archaeology? Leslie J. Hoppe. LC 83-63110. (WATSA Ser.). 1984. pap. 4.95 (ISBN 0-8091-2613-3). Paulist Pr.

What Are They Saying about Christ & World Religions? Lucien Richard. LC 81-80878. 96p. (Orig.). 1981. pap. 4.95 (ISBN 0-8091-2391-6). Paulist Pr.

What Are They Saying about Christian-Jewish Relations? John T. Pawlikowski. LC 79-56135. 144p. (Orig.). 1980. pap. 3.95 (ISBN 0-8091-2239-1). Paulist Pr.

What Are They Saying about Creation? Zachary Hayes. LC 80-80870. 128p. 1980. pap. 3.95 (ISBN 0-8091-2286-3). Paulist Pr.

What Are They Saying about Death & Christian Hope? Monika K. Hellwig. LC 78-61726. 1978. pap. 3.95 (ISBN 0-8091-2165-4). Paulist Pr.

What Are They Saying about Dogma? William E. Reiser. LC 78-58955. 1978. pap. 3.95 (ISBN 0-8091-2127-1). Paulist Pr.

What Are They Saying about Euthenasia? Richard S. Gula. (W. A. T. S. A. Ser.). 192p. (Orig.). 1986. pap. 5.95 (ISBN 0-8091-2766-0). Paulist Pr.

What Are They Saying about Jesus? Rev. ed. Gerald O'Collins. LC 77-70640. 1982. pap. 3.95 (ISBN 0-8091-2521-8). Paulist Pr.

What Are They Saying about Mark? Frank J. Matera. 1987. pap. 5.95. Paulist Pr.

What Are They Saying about Mary? Anthony J. Tambasco. (WATSA Ser.). (Orig.). 1984. pap. 4.95 (ISBN 0-8091-2626-5). Paulist Pr.

What Are They Saying about Matthew? Donald Senior. LC 82-62967. (WATSA Ser.). 96p. (Orig.). 1983. pap. 3.95 (ISBN 0-8091-2541-2). Paulist Pr.

What Are They Saying about Moral Norms? Richard M. Gula. LC 81-83188. 128p. (Orig.). 1982. pap. 4.95 (ISBN 0-8091-2412-2). Paulist Pr.

What Are They Saying about Mysticism? Harvey D. Egan. (WATSA Ser.). 128p. 1982. pap. 4.95 (ISBN 0-8091-2459-9). Paulist Pr.

What Are They Saying about Non-Christian Faith? Denise L. Carmody. (WATSA Ser.). 96p. (Orig.). 1982. pap. 4.95 (ISBN 0-8091-2432-7). Paulist Pr.

What Are They Saying about Papal Primacy? Michael Miller. (WATSA Ser.). 128p. 1983. pap. 4.95 (ISBN 0-8091-2501-3). Paulist Pr.

What Are They Saying about Peace & War? Thomas A. Shannon. (WATSA Ser.). 128p. 1983. pap. 4.95 (ISBN 0-8091-2499-8). Paulist Pr.

What Are They Saying about Salvation? Denis Edwards. 100p. 1986. pap. 4.95 (ISBN 0-8091-2793-8). Paulist Pr.

What Are They Saying about Scripture & Ethics? William C. Spohn. (WATSA Ser.). (Orig.). 1984. pap. 4.95 (ISBN 0-8091-2624-9). Paulist Pr.

What Are They Saying about Sexual Morality? James Hanigan. (WATSA Ser.). 128p. (Orig.). 1982. pap. 4.95 (ISBN 0-8091-2451-3). Paulist Pr.

What Are They Saying about the End of the World? Zachary Hayes. (WATSA Ser.). 80p. (Orig.). 1983. pap. 4.95 (ISBN 0-8091-2550-1). Paulist Pr.

What Are They Saying about the Grace of Christ? Brian O. McDermott. (WATSA Ser.). 1984. pap. 4.95 (ISBN 0-8091-2584-6). Paulist Pr.

What Are They Saying about the Prophets? David P. Reid. LC 80-80869. 112p. (Orig.). 1980. pap. 3.95 (ISBN 0-8091-2304-5). Paulist Pr.

What Are They Saying about the Social Setting of the New Testament? Carolyn Osiek. (WATSA Ser.). (Orig.). 1984. pap. 4.95 (ISBN 0-8091-2625-7). Paulist Pr.

What Are They Saying about Theological Method? J. J. Mueller. LC 84-61031. (WATSA Ser.). 88p. (Orig.). 1985. pap. 4.95 (ISBN 0-8091-2657-5). Paulist Pr.

What Are They Saying about Virtue. John W. Crossin. (WATSA Ser.). pap. 4.95 (ISBN 0-8091-2674-5). Paulist Pr.

What Are They Saying about Wisdom Literature? Dianne Bergant. LC 83-82027. (WATSA Ser.). (Orig.). 1984. pap. 4.95 (ISBN 0-8091-2605-2). Paulist Pr.

What Are We Doing Here? Associated Women's Organization, Mars Hill Bible School. 1972. pap. 4.95 (ISBN 0-89137-404-3). Quality Pubns.

What Are We Living for. John G. Bennett. 4.95 (ISBN 0-900306-07-6, Pub. by Coombe Springs Pr.). Claymont Comm.

What Augustine Says. Aurelius Augustine. Ed. by Norman L. Geisler. 204p. (Orig.). 1982. pap. 8.95 (ISBN 0-8010-0185-4). Baker Bk.

What Baptists Believe. Herschel H. Hobbs. LC 64-12411. 1963. bds. 4.25 (ISBN 0-8054-8101-X). Broadman.

What Belongs to Caeser? Donald D. Kaufman. LC 70-109939. 128p. 1969. pap. 5.95 (ISBN 0-8361-1621-6). Herald Pr.

What Can a Free Man Believe. E. Haldeman-Julius. 55p. pap. cancelled (ISBN 0-911826-99-8). Am Atheist.

What Can I Do for Christ? Clementine Lenta. 5.50 (ISBN 0-910984-17-4). Montfort Pubns.

What Can I Say? Roger F. Miller. Ed. by Herbert Lambert. 96p. (Orig.). 1987. pap. 4.95 (ISBN 0-8272-4220-4). CBP.

What Can I Say to You, God? Elspeth Murphy. (David & I Talk to God Ser.). (Illus.). 1980. pap. 2.95 (ISBN 0-89191-276-2). Cook.

What Can We Believe. Vergilius Ferm. 1952. 5.95 (ISBN 0-8022-0497-X). Philos Lib.

What Can We Share? A Lutheran-Episcopal Resource & Study Guide. Ed. by William Norgren et al. (Lutheran-Episcopal Dialogue Ser.). 88p. (Orig.). 1985. pap. 2.00 (ISBN 0-88028-047-6). Forward Movement.

What Can You Believe in the Bible. Robert Ingersoll. 106p. 1987. 4.00. Am Atheist.

What Catholics Believe. Lawrence G. Lovasik. (Illus.). 1977. pap. 2.50 (ISBN 0-89555-027-X). TAN Bks Pubs.

What Catholics Believe: A Primer of the Catholic Faith. Josef Pieper & Heinrich Raskop. Tr. by Jan Van Heurck. LC 82-1411. 116p. 1983. 8.50 (ISBN 0-8199-0796-0). Franciscan Herald.

What Catholics Should Know About Jews: And Other Christians. Edward Zerin. 1980. pap. 3.25 (ISBN 0-697-01739-7). Wm C Brown.

What Child Is This? Martha Marshall. 1982. text ed. 4.95 (Sonflower Bks). SP Pubns.

What Child Is This? Martha Marshall. LC 82-7239. (Illus.). 1982. lib. bdg. 6.95 (ISBN 0-89693-204-4). Dandelion Hse.

What Child Is This? Readings & Prayers for Advent-Christmas. Samuel H. Miller. LC 82-5084. (Illus.). 64p. (Orig.). 1982. pap. 3.50 (ISBN 0-8006-1638-3, 1-1638). Fortress.

What Christians Believe. Richard Harries. 176p. 1982. pap. 4.95 (ISBN 0-86683-677-2, HarpR). Har-Row.

What Christians Believe. Moody Press Editors. 1951. pap. 3.50 (ISBN 0-8024-9378-5). Moody.

What Christians Believe. Hans Schwarz. LC 86-45923. 112p. 1987. pap. 4.95 (ISBN 0-8006-1959-5). Fortress.

What Christians Believe about the Bible. Donald K. McKim. 183p. 1985. pap. 8.95 (ISBN 0-8407-5968-1). Nelson.

What Christians Believe about the Bible. Thomas Nelson. 183p. 1985. pap. 7.95 (ISBN 0-317-43242-7). Ideals.

What Color Is Your Balloon? Wesley Runk. (Orig.). 1987. pap. price not set (ISBN 0-89536-883-8, 7869). CSS of Ohio.

What Color Is Your God? Black Consciousness & the Christian Faith. Christopher Salley & Ronald Behm. LC 81-6758. 132p. (Orig.). 1981. pap. 4.50 (ISBN 0-87784-791-6). Inter-Varsity.

What Comes After Pentecost. Robert Thompson. 1982. pap. 6.95 (ISBN 0-686-95485-8). Omega Pubns Or.

What Constitutes Authentic Christianity? N. F. Grundtvig. Ed. & tr. by Ernest D. Nielsen. LC 84-48728. 128p. 1985. pap. 6.95 (ISBN 0-8006-1844-0, 1-1844). Fortress.

What Crucified Jesus? The Political Execution of a Charismatic. Ellis Rivkin. 128p. 1984. pap. 7.50 (ISBN 0-687-44637-6). Abingdon.

What Did God Make? Marilyn McAuley. (Peek & Find Bks.). (Illus.). 28p. 1984. board book 3.95 (ISBN 0-89191-878-7, 58784). Cook.

What Did Jesus Say about That? Stanley C. Baldwin. 224p. 1984. pap. 2.95 missal size (ISBN 0-89693-312-1). Victor Bks.

What Difference Did the Deed of Christ Make? Jocelyn Beredene. 1979. pap. 1.50 (ISBN 0-88010-103-2). Anthroposophic.

What Difference Does Jesus Make? Frank Sheed. LC 76-162382. 264p. 1982. pap. 6.95 (ISBN 0-87973-810-3, 810). Our Sunday Visitor.

What Do I Do Now Lord? Chris Jones. LC 76-3860. 96p. (Orig.). 1976. pap. 3.95 (ISBN 0-8066-1539-7, 10-7044). Augsburg.

What Do Presbyterians Believe? Gordon H. Clark. 1965. pap. 6.95 (ISBN 0-87552-140-1). Presby & Reformed.

What Do They Expect of Me? Robert G. Davidson. 80p. 1986. pap. 9.95 (ISBN 0-940754-32-0). Ed Ministries.

What Do We Mean Religion? Roger Kite. 1985. 19.00x (ISBN 0-7062-3906-7, Pub. by Ward Lock Educ Co Ltd). State Mutual Bk.

What Do We Really Know about God? Kenneth McNeely. LC 86-91364. 1987. 12.00 (ISBN 0-87212-201-8). Libra.

What Do You Ask for Your Child. Carol Luebering. 64p. (Orig.). 1980. pap. 1.35 (ISBN 0-912228-64-4). St Anthony Mess Pr.

What Do You Communicate. Bob Humphrey. 1985. pap. 4.50 (ISBN 0-89349-000-8). Gospel Advocate.

What Do You Fear? David W. Augsburger. (New Life Ser.). pap. 3.00 (ISBN 0-8361-1687-9). Herald Pr.

What Do You Seek? William F. Maestri. LC 85-60887. 170p. (Orig.). 1985. pap. 6.95 (ISBN 0-87973-803-0, 803). Our Sunday Visitor.

What Do You Think about God. Douglas A. Fox. 96p. 1985. pap. 4.95 (ISBN 0-8170-1077-7). Judson.

What Do You Want? David W. Augsburger. (New Life Ser.). pap. 3.00 (ISBN 0-8361-1688-7). Herald Pr.

What Does a Witch Need? Ida DeLage. LC 76-143305. (Old Witch Bks.). (Illus.). 48p. 1971. PLB 6.69 (ISBN 0-8116-4058-2). Garrard.

What Does God Do All Day? Joseph R. Swain. 1977. 7.00 (ISBN 0-682-48919-0, Testament). Exposition Pr FL.

What Does God Want Me to Do with My Life? How to Decide about School, Job, Friends, Sex, Marriage. Steve Swanson. LC 79-50086. 104p. 1979. pap. 3.95 (ISBN 0-8066-1722-5, 10-7046). Augsburg.

What Does He Mean by "A Little While?". Ralph J. Wallace. (Orig.). 1981. pap. 5.95 (ISBN 0-937172-30-8). JLJ Pubs.

What Does It Mean? Bill Loader. 64p. (Orig.). 1985. pap. 6.95 (ISBN 0-85819-472-4, Pub. by JBCE). ANZ Religious Pubns.

What Does It Mean to Believe in Jesus. Lois B. Sovenson. (Cornerstone Ser.). 32p. 1981. pap. 2.00 (ISBN 0-930756-64-9, 533004). Aglow Pubns.

What Does It Profit...? Christian Dialogue on the U. S. Economy. Shantilal P. Bhagat & T. Wayne Rieman. LC 83-3687. 144p. (Orig.). 1983. pap. 6.95 (ISBN 0-87178-927-2). Brethren.

What Does Revelation Mean for the Modern Jew? Michael Oppenheim. LC 85-18929. (Symposium Ser.: Vol. 17). 152p. 1985. lib. bdg. 39.95x (ISBN 0-88946-708-0). E Mellen.

What Does the Lord Require? The Old Testament Call to Social Witness. Bruce C. Birch. LC 85-610. 120p. 1985. pap. 8.95 (ISBN 0-664-24630-3). Westminster.

What Does the Old Testament Say About God? new ed. Claus Westerman. Ed. by F. W. Golka. LC 78-52448. 1979. 8.95 (ISBN 0-8042-0190-0). John Knox.

What Does This Mean? Luther's Catechisms Today. Ed. by Phillip E. Pederson. LC 79-50082. 1979. pap. 7.95 (ISBN 0-8066-1723-3, 10-7047). Augsburg.

What Doth the Lord Require of Thee? Mildred B. Young. 1983. pap. 2.50x (ISBN 0-87574-145-2, 145). Pendle Hill.

What Ever Happened to Commitment? Edward R. Dayton. 224p. 1983. pap. 6.95 (ISBN 0-310-23161-2, 10748P). Zondervan.

What Every American Should Know about Islam & the Muslims. Muhammad A. Nu'man. 74p. (Orig.). 1985. pap. 5.00 (ISBN 0-933821-04-2). New Mind Prod.

What Every Christian Should Know about Bible Prophecy. Rick Yohn. LC 81-85895. 80p. (Orig.). 1982. pap. 3.95 (ISBN 0-89081-311-6, 3116). Harvest Hse.

What Every Christian Should Know about God: A Study Manual. Rick Yohn. LC 76-20396. 80p. 1976. 3.95 (ISBN 0-89081-054-0). Harvest Hse.

What Every Christian Should Know about Growing. LeRoy Eims. LC 75-44842. 168p. 1976. pap. 5.95 (ISBN 0-88207-727-9). Victor Bks.

What Every Christian Should Know about the Bible. Adib K. Timbuktu. 1984. 6.95 (ISBN 0-8062-2308-1). Carlton.

What Every Church Member Should Know about Clergy. Robert G. Kemper. 180p. 1985. pap. 7.95 (ISBN 0-8298-0728-4). Pilgrim NY.

What Every Family Needs or Whatever Happened to Mom, Dad, & the Kids. Carl Brecheen & Paul Faulkner. LC 78-68726. (Journey Bks.). 1979. pap. 3.95 (ISBN 0-8344-0104-5). Sweet.

What Every Husband Should Know. Jack R. Taylor. LC 81-65389. 1981. 8.95 (ISBN 0-8054-5642-2). Broadman.

What Every Jehovah's Witness Should Know. Arthur M. Bowser. 1975. micro book 1.95 (ISBN 0-916406-35-0). Accent Bks.

What Every Mormon Should Know. Edmond C. Gruss. (Orig.). 1975. micro book 1.95 (ISBN 0-916406-34-2). Accent Bks.

What Every Pastor Needs to Know about Music, Youth, & Education. Garth Bolinder et al. (Leadership Library). 192p. 1986. 9.95 (ISBN 0-917463-09-9). Chr Today.

What Every Pastor's Wife Should Know. Ruthe White. 176p. (Orig.). 1986. pap. 5.95 (ISBN 0-8423-7932-0). Tyndale.

What Every Person Should Know About God: Bible Study for New Christians. John A. Ishee. 36p. 1982. pap. 3.50 (ISBN 0-939298-05-8). J M Prods.

What Every Woman Still Knows: A Celebration of the Christian Liberated Woman. Mildred Cooper & Martha Fanning. LC 78-17182. 182p. 1978. 7.95 (ISBN 0-87131-271-9). M Evans.

What Every Young Christian Should Know. William S. Deal. 1982. 1.95. Crusade Pubs.

What Everyone Should Know about Islam & Muslims. S. Haneef. pap. 9.95 (ISBN 0-686-63919-7). Kazi Pubns.

What Faith Is. 2nd ed. Kenneth E. Hagin. 1966. pap. 1.00 (ISBN 0-89276-002-8). Hagin Ministries.

What Faith Really Means. Henry G. Graham. LC 82-74243. 94p. 1982. pap. 2.00 (ISBN 0-89555-204-3). TAN Bks Pubs.

What God Can Do. Mabel N. McCaw. LC 81-70865. 1982. 5.95 (ISBN 0-8054-4290-1, 4242-90). Broadman.

What God Expects of Me. William T. George. LC 82-60828. 175p. (Orig.). 1982. pap. text ed. 6.95 (ISBN 0-87148-918-X). Pathway Pr.

What God Gave Me. Alice Greenspan. LC 84-50286. (Little Happy Day Bks.). (Illus.). 24p. (Orig.). 1984. pap. 0.49 (ISBN 0-87239-804-8, 2164). Standard Pub.

What God Has Joined. Elisabeth Elliot. 32p. 1983. Repr. 1.50 (ISBN 0-89107-276-4). Good News.

What God Has Wrought: A History of the Southern New Jersey Conference of the United Methodist Church. Robert B. Steelman. LC 86-70275. 368p. (Orig.). 1986. text ed. 12.50x (ISBN 0-914960-60-1); pap. text ed. 10.00x (ISBN 0-914960-56-3). Academy Bks.

What God Hath Wrought. Agnes N. LaBerge. Ed. by Donald W. Dayton. (Higher Christian Life Ser.). 127p. 1985. 20.00 (ISBN 0-8240-6425-9). Garland Pub.

What God Hath Wrought: The Complete Works of O. F. Fauss. O. F. Fauss. Ed. by Mary H. Wallace. (Illus.). 300p. (Orig.). 1985. pap. 6.95 (ISBN 0-912315-84-9). Word Aflame.

What God Wants. Thomas Hora. 35p. 1987. pap. 4.00 (ISBN 0-913105-11-2). PAGL Pr.

What Great Men Think of Religion. Ira D. Cardiff. LC 71-161322. (Atheist Viewpoint Ser). 504p. 1972. Repr. of 1945 ed. 29.00 (ISBN 0-405-03625-6). Ayer Co Pubs.

What Happened When Grandma Died. Peggy Barker. 4.95 (ISBN 0-570-04090-6, 56-1458). Concordia.

What Happens After Death? Some Musing on -- Is God Through with a Person After Death? John R. Richardson. LC 81-52115. 1981. 6.95 (ISBN 0-686-79843-0). St Thomas.

What Happens When God Answers. Evelyn Christenson. 160p. 1986. 9.95 (ISBN 0-8499-0569-9). Word Bks.

What Happens When We Die? Carolyn Nystrom. (Children's Bible Basics Ser.). 32p. 1981. 4.95 (ISBN 0-8024-5995-1). Moody.

What Happens When Women Pray. Evelyn Christenson & Viola Blake. 144p. 1975. pap. 5.95 (ISBN 0-88207-715-5). Victor Bks.

What Happy Families Are Doing. Eric Stephan & Judith S. Smith. LC 81-15151. 131p. 1981. 7.95 (ISBN 0-87747-877-5). Deseret Bk.

What Helped Me When My Loved One Died. Ed. by Earl A. Grollman. LC 80-68166. 168p. 1982. pap. 7.95 (ISBN 0-8070-3229-8, BP 626). Beacon Pr.

What High School Students Should Know about Creation. Kenneth N. Taylor. (YA) 1983. pap. 2.50 (ISBN 0-8423-7872-3). Tyndale.

What High School Students Should Know about Evolution. Kenneth N. Taylor. 70p. (YA) 1983. pap. 2.50 (ISBN 0-8423-7873-1). Tyndale.

What Husbands Wish Their Wives Knew about Money. Larry Burkett. 1977. pap. 3.95 (ISBN 0-88207-758-9). Victor Bks.

What I Believe. W. H. Auden et al. Ed. by Mark Booth. 182p. 1984. 16.95 (ISBN 0-8245-0676-6); pap. 8.95 (ISBN 0-8245-0677-4). Crossroad NY.

What I Believe About God. Joseph R. Narot. pap. 0.95 (ISBN 0-686-15803-2). Rostrum Bks.

What I Believe: Catholic College Students Discuss Their Faith. Ed. by David Murphy. 164p. 1985. 11.95 (ISBN 0-88347-181-7). Thomas More.

What I Can Give. 2.98 (ISBN 0-8010-5114-2). Baker Bk.

What I Wish My Parents Knew about Sexuality. Josh McDowell. 1987. pap. 6.95. Heres Life.

What If...? Joan P. Berry. 1985. 3.50 (ISBN 0-89536-729-7, 5813). CSS of Ohio.

What in the World Is a Christian? John Blanchard. 1987. pap. 6.95 (ISBN 0-310-20101-2). Zondervan.

What in the World Will Happen Next? Ivor C. Powell. LC 85-7579. 176p. (Orig.). 1985. pap. 5.95 (ISBN 0-8254-3524-2). Kregel.

What Is a Christian? Carolyn Nystrom. (Children's Bible Basics Ser.). 32p. 1981. 4.95 (ISBN 0-8024-5997-8). Moody.

What Is a Family? Edith Schaeffer. 256p. 1982. pap. 7.95 (ISBN 0-8007-5088-8, Power Bks). Revell.

What Is a Flood? Barbara King. 61p. 1981. pap. 3.00 (ISBN 0-317-20874-8). CSA Pr.

What Is a Freckle? Carol H. Schramm. 1975. pap. 1.25 (ISBN 0-8198-0484-3). Dghtrs St Paul.

What Is a Jew? Israel Ministry. 1975. 30.00 (ISBN 0-379-13904-9). Oceana.

What Is a Jew. rev. ed. Morris N. Kertzer. LC 73-77280. 217p. 1973. Repr. of 1953 ed. 8.95x (ISBN 0-8197-0299-4). Bloch.

What Is a Jew? 4th ed. Morris N. Kertzer. 1978. pap. 4.95 (ISBN 0-02-086350-0, Collier). Macmillan.

What Is a Miracle? Barbara King. 61p. 1981. pap. 3.00 (ISBN 0-317-20876-4). CSA Pr.

What Is a Spiritual Master? Omraam M. Aivanhov. (Izvor Collection Ser.: Vol. 207). 185p. pap. 4.95 (ISBN 2-85566-230-3, Pub. by Prosveta France). Prosveta USA.

What Is a Thing? Martin Heidegger. Tr. by W. B. Barton & Vera Deutsch. 320p. 1985. pap. text ed. 8.75 (ISBN 0-8191-4545-9). U Pr of Amer.

What Is & What Ought to Be Done: An Essay on Ethics & Epistemology. Morton White. 1981. 14.95x (ISBN 0-19-502916-X). Oxford U Pr.

What Is Anglicanism? Urban T. Holmes, 3rd. LC 81-84715. 112p. (Orig.). 1982. pap. 5.95 (ISBN 0-8192-1295-4). Morehouse.

What Is Anthroposophy? Otto Frankl-Lundborg. Tr. by Joseph Wetzl. 1977. pap. 2.95 (ISBN 0-916786-14-5). St George Bk Serv.

What is Chanukah? A Programmed Text. Louis Nulman. text ed. 2.25 (ISBN 0-914131-73-7, A30). Torah Umesorah.

What Is Christian Doctrine? John P. Newport. LC 83-71266. (Layman's Library of Christian Doctrine Ser.). 1984. 5.95 (ISBN 0-8054-1631-5). Broadman.

What Is Christianity. John W. Alexander. pap. 0.75 (ISBN 0-87784-133-0). Inter-Varsity.

What Is Christianity? Michael Green. 64p. 1982. 10.95 (ISBN 0-687-44650-3). Abingdon.

What Is Christianity? Adolf Harnack. LC 78-15359. 1978. Repr. lib. bdg. 32.50 (ISBN 0-8414-4869-8). Folcroft.

What Is Christianity? Adolf Von Harnack. 301p. 1980. Repr. of 1901 ed. lib. bdg. 35.50 (ISBN 0-8482-1228-2). Norwood Edns.

What Is Christianity? Adolf von Harnack. LC 86-45209. (Texts in Modern Theology Ser.). Tr. of Das Wesen des Christentums. 320p. 1986. pap. 12.95 (ISBN 0-8006-3201-X, 1-3201). Fortress.

What Is Christianity. Adolph Harnack. 1958. 17.50 (ISBN 0-8446-2208-7). Peter Smith.

What Is Christmas? Joy Dueland. (Illus.). 9p. 1978. pap. 1.50. Phunn Pubs.

What Is Contemplation? Thomas Merton. 80p. 1981. pap. 4.95 (ISBN 0-87243-103-7). Templegate.

What is Creation Science. Henry M. Morris. LC 82-70114. (Illus.). 1982. pap. 8.95 (ISBN 0-89051-081-4). Master Bks.

What Is Election? W. J. Ouweneel. pap. 2.25 (ISBN 0-88172-162-X). Believers Bkshelf.

What Is Faith? Kathy England. (Illus.). 27p. 1981. pap. 4.95 (ISBN 0-87747-876-7). Deseret Bk.

What Is Faith? Virginia Mueller. (Happy Day Book). (Illus.). 24p. (Orig.). 1980. 1.59 (ISBN 0-87239-411-5, 3643). Standard Pub.

What Is Form Criticism. Edgar V. McKnight. Ed. by Dan O. Via, Jr. LC 71-81526. (Guides to Biblical Scholarship: New Testament Ser.). 96p. (Orig.). 1969. pap. 4.50 (ISBN 0-8006-0180-7, 1-180). Fortress.

What Is God? How to Think about the Divine. John F. Haught. 160p. (Orig.). 1986. pap. 7.95 (ISBN 0-8091-2754-7). Paulist Pr.

What Is God Like? Eugenia Price. 192p. 1982. pap. 5.95 (ISBN 0-310-31441-0, 16242P). Zondervan.

What Is God Like? Lee O. Rohwer. (Illus.). 64p. (Orig.). 1986. pap. 5.95 (ISBN 0-9617788-0-6). Damon Pub.

What Is Is, What Ain't, Ain't. Bhagwan Shree Rajneesh. Ed. by Ma Prem Maneesha. LC 83-177697. (Initiation Talks Ser.). (Illus.). 624p. (Orig.). 1980. 18.95 (ISBN 0-88050-670-9). Chidvilas Found.

What Is Islam? Montgomery Watt. 1968. 25.00x (ISBN 0-685-77133-4). Intl Bk Ctr.

What Is Islam? 2nd ed. W. Montgomery Watt. (Arab Background Ser.). 1979. text ed. 29.95x (ISBN 0-582-78302-X). Longman.

What Is Karma & All about God. Harbhajan S. Bajaj. 1987. 6.95 (ISBN 0-533-06697-2). Vantage.

What is Kosher? A Programmed Text. Louis Nulman. text ed. 2.50 (ISBN 0-914131-74-5, A40). Torah Umesorah.

What Is Life All About. Percy E. Iverson. 1985. 10.95 (ISBN 0-533-06511-9). Vantage.

What Is Living & What Is Dead of the Philosophy of Hegel. Benedetto Croce. Tr. by Douglas Ainslie from Ital. 268p. 1985. pap. text ed. 10.50 (ISBN 0-8191-4279-4). U Pr of Amer.

What Is Living, What Is Dead in Christianity Today. Charles Davis. 200p. (Orig.). 1986. 16.95 (ISBN 0-86683-511-3, HarpR). Har-Row.

What Is Love. C. Wynanda. LC 83-12729. 96p. 1984. 7.95 (ISBN 0-310-37571-1). Zondervan.

What Is Man? Eric S. Dillett. 80p. 1985. 6.50 (ISBN 0-682-40254-0). Exposition Pr FL.

What Is Man. Leslie B. Flynn. Tr. by Lorna Y. Chao. (Chinese.). 1985. pap. write for info. (ISBN 0-941598-27-6). Living Spring Pubns.

What Is Man? & Other Philosophical Writings. Mark Twain. Ed. & intro. by Paul Baender. LC 78-104109. (Mark Twain Works: Vol. 19). 1973. 29.00x (ISBN 0-520-01621-1). U of Cal Pr.

What Is Man? Leader's Guide. James Long. Tr. by Lorna Y. Chao. (Basic Doctrine Ser.). 1986. pap. write for info. (ISBN 0-941598-36-5). Living Spring Pubns.

What is Marriage: Marriage in the Catholic Church. Theodore Mackin. LC 81-84386. (Marriage in the Catholic Church Ser.: Vol. 1). 384p. (Orig.). 1982. pap. 11.95 (ISBN 0-8091-2442-4). Paulist Pr.

What Is New Testament Theology? The Rise of Criticism & the Problem of a Theology of the New Testament. Hendrikus Boers. Ed. by Dan O. Via, Jr. LC 79-7372. (Guides to Biblical Scholarship: New Testament Ser.). 96p. 1979. pap. 4.50 (ISBN 0-8006-0466-0, 1-466). Fortress.

What Is Prayer? Carolyn Nystrom. (Children's Bible Basics Ser.). 32p. 1980. pap. 4.95 (ISBN 0-8024-5991-9). Moody.

What Is Redaction Criticism? Norman Perrin. Ed. by Dan O. Via, Jr. LC 72-81529. (Guides to Biblical Scholarship). 96p. (Orig.). 1969. pap. 4.50 (ISBN 0-8006-0181-5, 1-181). Fortress.

What Is Religion? Rubem Alves. Tr. by Don Vinzant from Portugese. LC 83-19398. Orig. Title: O Que E Religiao. 96p. (Orig.). 1984. pap. 4.95 (ISBN 0-88344-705-3). Orbis Bks.

What Is Religion? An Inquiry for Christian Theology, Concilium 136. Ed. by Mircea Eliade & David Tracy. (New Concilium 1980). 128p. 1980. pap. 5.95 (ISBN 0-8164-2278-8, HarpR). Har-Row.

What is Religious Life? Thomas Dubay. 5.95 (ISBN 0-87193-116-8). Dimension Bks.

What Is Religious Life? A Critical Reappraisal. Jerome Murphy-O'Connor. pap. 4.95 (ISBN 0-89453-074-7). M Glazier.

What Is Revelation? Frederick D. Maurice. LC 76-173061. Repr. of 1859 ed. 37.50 (ISBN 0-404-04276-7). AMS Pr.

What Is Scientology? L. Ron Hubbard. 50.00 (ISBN 0-686-30807-7). Church Scient NY.

What Is Scientology? Taken from the Works of L. Ron Hubbard. 1978. 47.16 (ISBN 0-88404-061-5). Bridge Pubns Inc.

What Is Secular Humanism? Why Humanism Became Secular & How It Is Changing Our World. James Hitchcock. (Illus.). 158p. 1982. pap. 6.95 (ISBN 0-89283-163-4). Servant.

What Is Structural Exegesis? Daniel Patte. Ed. by Dan O. Via, Jr. LC 75-36454. (Guides to Biblical Scholarship: New Testament Ser.). 96p. (Orig.). 1976. pap. 4.50 (ISBN 0-8006-0462-8, 1-462). Fortress.

What Is Taoism? And Other Studies in Chinese Cultural History. Herrlee G. Creel. LC 77-102905. (Midway Reprint Ser.). viii, 192p. 1982. pap. text ed. 11.00x (ISBN 0-226-12047-3). U of Chicago Pr.

What Is the Bible? Carolyn Nystrom. (Children's Bible Basics Ser.). 32p. 1982. 4.95 (ISBN 0-8024-0157-0). Moody.

What Is the Bible? A Nazareth Book. Robert R. Barr. 128p. 1984. pap. 4.95 (ISBN 0-86683-727-2, HarpR). Har-Row.

What Is the Christian's Hope? W. J. Ouweneel. 53p. pap. 2.95 (ISBN 0-88172-116-6). Believers Bkshelf.

What Is the Church? Charles P. Conn & Charles W. Conn. 1977. pap. 1.99 (ISBN 0-87148-907-4). Pathway Pr.

What Is the Church, Bk. 3. Bruce L. Shelly. Tr. by Lorna Y. Chao. (Basic Doctrine Ser.). (Chinese.). 1985. pap. write for info. (ISBN 0-941598-25-X). Living Spring Pubns.

What Is the Church? Leader's Guide. S. P. Publications Editors. Tr. by Lorna Y. Chao. (Basic Doctrine Ser.). 1986. pap. write for info. (ISBN 0-941598-35-7). Living Spring Pubns.

What Is the Reformed Faith? John R. DeWitt. (Orig.). 1981. pap. text ed. 1.45 (ISBN 0-85151-326-3). Banner of Truth.

What Is the Sonship of Christ? W. J. Ouweneel. pap. 2.25 (ISBN 0-88172-170-0). Believers Bkshelf.

What Is Theology? M. F. Wiles. 1977. pap. 5.95x (ISBN 0-19-289066-2). Oxford U Pr.

What Is Theosophy? A General View of Occult Doctrine. rev. ed. Charles J. Ryan. Ed. by W. Emmett Small & Helen Todd. (Theosophical Manual: No. 1). 92p. 1975. pap. 2.25 (913004-18-9). Point Loma Pub.

What Is This Thing Called Love. Nelson M. Smith. 1970. 8.75 (ISBN 0-89137-505-8); pap. 4.95 (ISBN 0-89137-504-X). Quality Pubns.

What Is Transfiguration? Jan Van Rijckenborgh. 40p. 1987. pap. 1.50. Rosycross Pr.

What Is Your Destination? Marvin J. Ashton. LC 78-14982. 1978. 8.95 (ISBN 0-87747-719-1). Deseret Bk.

What Islam Gave to Humanity? A. H. Siddiqui. pap. 2.50 (ISBN 0-686-63918-9). Kazi Pubns.

What Islam Is? M. Naumani. 10.50 (ISBN 0-686-18477-7). Kazi Pubns.

What It Means to Be a Christian. Stuart Briscoe & Jill Briscoe. 128p. 1987. pap. 4.95 (ISBN 1-55513-803-9). Cook.

What It Means to Be a Christian. William L. Ludlow. 1986. 7.95 (ISBN 0-8158-0434-2). Chris Mass.

What It Means to Be a Church Leader: A Biblical Point of View. Norman Shawchuck. (Illus.). 71p. (Orig.). 1984. pap. 7.95 (ISBN 0-938180-13-4). Org Resources Pr.

What It Means to Forgive. Ivan A. Beals. (Christian Living Ser.). 32p. (Orig.). 1987. pap. write for info. (ISBN 0-8341-1185-3). Beacon Hill.

What Jesus Asks: Meditations on Questions in the Gospels. Harry B. Adams. Ed. by Herbert Lambert. LC 85-18991. 160p. (Orig.). 1986. pap. 10.95 (ISBN 0-8272-4217-4). CBP.

What Jesus Means to Me. Herman W. Gockel. 1956. 4.95 (ISBN 0-570-03021-8, 6-1008). Concordia.

What Jesus Said About. Morris Venden. 1984. pap. 6.95 (ISBN 0-8163-0555-2). Pacific Pr Pub Assn.

What Jesus Taught in Secret. Max F. Long. (Illus.). 144p. 1983. pap. 5.95 (ISBN 0-87516-510-9). De Vorss.

What Kids Need Most in a Dad. Tim Hansel. LC 83-22902. 192p. 1984. 10.95 (ISBN 0-8007-1390-7). Revell.

What Kind of God Is God? George E. Drew. 65p. (Orig.). 1986. pap. 6.95 (ISBN 0-940754-33-9). Ed Ministries.

What Lack We Yet? Church of Christ Staff. Ed. by J. D. Thomas. LC 74-170920. 319p. 1974. 13.95 (ISBN 0-89112-027-0, Bibl Res Pr). Abilene Christ U.

What Made Them So Brave? Basilea Schlink. (Illus.). 1978. gift edition 2.25 (ISBN 3-87209-655-9). Evang Sisterhood Mary.

What Makes a Missionary. David M. Howard. (Orig.). 1987. pap. 5.95 (ISBN 0-8024-5204-3). Moody.

What Makes Us Episcopalians? John E. Booty. 48p. 1982. pap. 3.50 (ISBN 0-8192-1302-0, 82-80468). Morehouse.

What Manner of Man. St. Bonaventure. (Sermons on Christ Ser). 1974. 5.95 (ISBN 0-8199-0497-X). Franciscan Herald.

What Masonry Means. William E. Hammond. 1978. Repr. of 1939 ed. 5.50 (ISBN 0-88053-051-0, M-311). Macoy Pub.

What Meaneth This? a Pentecostal Answer to a Pentecostal Question. Carl Brumback. 352p. 1947. pap. 4.95 (ISBN 0-88243-626-0, 02-0624). Gospel Pub.

What Men Are Asking. facs. ed. Henry S. Coffin. LC 70-117770. (Essay Index Reprint Ser). 1933. 12.50 (ISBN 0-8369-1791-X). Ayer Co Pubs.

What Men Live By. Richard C. Cabot. 341p. 1985. Repr. of 1941 ed. lib. bdg. 35.00 (ISBN 0-89760-187-4). Telegraph Bks.

What Men or Gods Are These? A Genealogical Approach to Classical Mythology. Fred Boswell & Jeanetta Boswell. LC 80-13780. 324p. 1980. 27.50 (ISBN 0-8108-1314-9). Scarecrow.

What Mennonites Believe, Vol. 2. J. C. Wenger. LC 77-86338. 72p. 1977. pap. 1.50 (ISBN 0-8361-1833-2). Herald Pr.

What More Can God Say? 2nd ed. Ray C. Stedman. LC 74-176002. 256p. 1977. pap. 3.95 (ISBN 0-8307-0457-4, S283123). Regal.

What Must the Church Do? facsimile ed. Robert S. Bilheimer. LC 70-134053. (Essay Index Reprints - Interseminary Ser.: Vol. 5). Repr. of 1947 ed. 17.00 (ISBN 0-8369-2384-7). Ayer Co Pubs.

What Next in Mission? Paul A. Hopkins. LC 77-21776. 122p. 1977. pap. 3.95 (ISBN 0-664-24143-3). Westminster.

What of Tomorrow. Challoner. 5.95 (ISBN 0-8356-5300-5). Theos Pub Hse.

What on Earth Are You Doing? Michael Griffiths. 1983. pap. 4.95 (ISBN 0-8010-3792-1). Baker Bk.

What on Earth Is an Atheist? Madalyn M. O'Hair. LC 71-88701. (Fifty-Two Programs from the American Atheist Radio Ser.). 282p. 1969. pap. 6.00 (ISBN 0-911826-00-9). Am Atheist.

What on Earth Is an Atheist. Madalyn M. O'Hair. LC 74-161339. (Atheist Viewpoint Ser). 288p. 1972. Repr. of 1969 ed. 18.00 (ISBN 0-405-03802-X). Ayer Co Pubs.

What on Earth Is God Doing? Satan's Conflict with God. Renald E. Showers. LC 73-81551. 1973. pap. 3.95 (ISBN 0-87213-784-8). Loizeaux.

What on Earth Is God Doing? Satan's Conflict with God: Study Guide. Renald E. Showers. 48p. 1983. pap. 3.50 (ISBN 0-87213-785-6). Loizeaux.

What One Person Can Do to Help Prevent Nuclear War. 2nd ed. Ronald Freund. 144p. 1983. pap. 5.95 (ISBN 0-89622-192-X). Twenty-Third.

What Present-Day Theologians Are Thinking. rev. ed. Daniel D. Williams. LC 78-16410. 1978. Repr. of 1959 ed. lib. bdg. 22.50x (ISBN 0-313-20587-6, WIWP). Greenwood.

What Price Zion? Carol P. McIntosh & Carole O. Cole. LC 82-23567. 126p. 1983. 6.95 (ISBN 0-87747-927-5). Deseret Bk.

What Really Happened When Christ Died. M. H. Dinsmore. LC 79-52539. 1979. pap. 4.95 (ISBN 0-89636-025-3). Accent Bks.

What Really Matters. Eugenia Price. LC 82-25236. (Illus.). 120p. 1983. 7.95 (ISBN 0-385-27659-1, Dial). Doubleday.

What Really Matters. Eugenia Price. 160p. 1985. pap. 2.95 (ISBN 0-515-08989-3). Jove Pubns.

What Religion Is. Bernard Bosanquet. LC 78-12709. 1979. Repr. of 1920 ed. lib. bdg. 22.50x (ISBN 0-313-21202-3, BOWR). Greenwood.

What Religion Is in the Words of Vivekananda. Swami Vivekananda. Ed. by John Yale. pap. 5.95 (ISBN 0-87481-213-5). Vedanta Pr.

What Return Can I Make? The Dimensions of the Christian Experience. M. Scott Peck et al. LC 85-11945. 96p. 1985. 24.95 (ISBN 0-317-38030-3). S&S.

What Shall This Man Do. Watchman Nee. 1965. pap. 2.95 (ISBN 0-87508-427-3). Chr Lit.

What Shall This Man Do? Watchman Nee. 1978. pap. 4.50 (ISBN 0-8423-7910-X). Tyndale.

What Southern Catholics Need to Know about Evangelical Religion. Richard Tristano. 1984. pap. 3.00x (ISBN 0-914422-14-6). Glenmary Res Ctr.

What the Bible Does Not Say. John L. Stout. LC 80-84340. (Illus.). 208p. 1981. 10.95 (ISBN 0-8187-0042-4). Harlo Pr.

What the Bible is All About. Rev. ed. Henrietta C. Mears. 642p. 1987. pap. 9.95 (ISBN 0-8423-7902-9). Tyndale.

What the Bible Is All About. rev. ed. Henrietta C. Mears et al. Rev. by Ronald Youngblood & Merrill C. Tenney. LC 83-4333. 1982. 13.95 (ISBN 0-8307-0902-9, 5110704); pap. 9.95 (ISBN 0-8307-0862-6, 5417202). Regal.

What the Bible Is All about for Young Explorers. Frances Blankenbaker. (Illus.). 364p. 1987. pap. 12.95 (ISBN 0-8307-1179-1, 5111647). Regal.

What the Bible Really Says about Marriage, Divorce & Remarriage. Edward Dobson. 160p. 1986. 9.95 (ISBN 0-8007-1493-8). Revell.

What the Bible Really Says: Casting New Light on the Book of Books. Manfred Barthel. Tr. by Mark Howson. LC 81-18679. Orig. Title: Was Wirklich in der Bibel Steht. (Illus.). 416p. 1982. 15.50 (ISBN 0-688-00821-6). Morrow.

What the Bible Really Says: Casting New Light on the Book of Books. Manfred Barthel. Tr. by Mark Howson from Ger. LC 83-3001. Tr. of Was Wirklich in der Bibel Steht. (Illus.). 416p. 1983. pap. 10.95 (ISBN 0-688-01979-X, Quill). Morrow.

What the Bible Says About Angels. A. C. Gaebelein. (Direction Bks). 120p. 1975. pap. 4.95 (ISBN 0-8010-3810-3). Baker Bk.

What the Bible Says about Angels. A. C. Gaebelein. 116p. 1987. pap. 4.95 (ISBN 0-8010-3810-3). Baker Bk.

What the Bible Says about Angels & Demons. Victor Knowles. LC 86-71104. (What the Bible Says Ser.). 405p. 1986. 13.95 (ISBN 0-89900-252-8). College Pr Pub.

What the Bible Says About Child Training. J. Richard Fugate. (What the Bible Says about...Ser.). (Illus.). 287p. 1980. pap. 5.95 (ISBN 0-86717-000-X). Aletheia Pubs.

What the Bible Says about End Time. 3rd ed. Russel Boatman. LC 79-56542. (What the Bible Says Ser.). 1980. 13.95 (ISBN 0-89900-075-4). College Pr Pub.

What the Bible Says about Faith. C. C. Crawford. LC 82-72621. (What the Bible Says Ser.). 380p. 1982. cancelled (ISBN 0-89900-089-4). College Pr Pub.

What the Bible Says about Families. Ed. by Bill Norris & Judy Norris. (What the Bible Says Ser.). 425p. (Orig.). text ed. 13.95 (ISBN 0-89900-099-1). College Pr Pub.

What the Bible Says about Fasting. Don DeWelt & John Baird. LC 79-57087. (What the Bible Says Ser.). 1984. 13.95 (ISBN 0-89900-077-0). College Pr Pub.

What the Bible Says about God the Creator. Jack Cottrell. (What the Bible Says Ser.). 1983. 13.95 (ISBN 0-89900-094-0). College Pr Pub.

What the Bible Says about God the Ruler. Jack Cottvell. (What the Bible Says about Ser.). 465p. 13.95 (ISBN 0-89900-094-0). College Pr Pub.

What the Bible Says About Goodness. Georgaan Bennett. LC 80-69626. (What the Bible Says Ser.). 405p. 1981. 13.50 (ISBN 0-89900-080-0). College Pr Pub.

What the Bible Says about Leadership. Arthur Harrington. (What the Bible Says Ser.). 425p. text ed. 13.95 (ISBN 0-89900-250-1). College Pr Pub.

What the Bible Says about Muhammad? A. Deedat. 1.75 (ISBN 0-686-63917-0). Kazi Pubns.

What the Bible Says about Praise & Promise. James Van Buren & Don Dewett. LC 80-66127. (What the Bible Says Ser.). 450p. 1980. 13.95 (ISBN 0-89900-078-9). College Pr Pub.

What the Bible Says about Resurrection. Charles R. Gresham. LC 82-7411. (What the Bible Says Ser.). 351p. 1983. 13.95 (ISBN 0-89900-090-8). College Pr Pub.

What the Bible Says about Salvation. Virgil Warren. LC 82-73345. (What the Bible Says Ser.). 640p. 1982. 13.95 (ISBN 0-89900-088-6). College Pr Pub.

What the Bible Says about Self Esteem. Bruce Parmenter. LC 86-70211. (What the Bible Says Ser.). 405p. 13.95 (ISBN 0-89900-251-X). College Pr Pub.

What the Bible Says about Sex. Friend Stuart. 40p. 1985. pap. 4.95 (ISBN 0-912132-17-5). Dominion Pr.

What the Bible Says about Sexuality Identity. Eleanor Daniel. LC 81-71836. (What the Bible Says Ser.). 350p. 1982. 13.95 (ISBN 0-89900-085-1). College Pr Pub.

What the Bible Says about Stewardship. A. Q. Van Benschoten, Jr. 96p. 1983. pap. 4.95 (ISBN 0-8170-0993-0). Judson.

What the Bible Says about Suffering. Willie W. White. (What the Bible Says Ser.). 350p. 1984. 13.95 (ISBN 0-317-05126-1). College Pr Pub.

What the Bible Says about the Church. Russell Boatman. (What the Bible Says Ser.). text ed. 13.95 (ISBN 0-89900-098-3). College Pr Pub.

What the Bible Says about the Covenant. 2nd ed. Mont Smith. LC 81-65516. (What the Bible Says Ser.). 472p. 1981. 13.95 (ISBN 0-89900-083-5). College Pr Pub.

What the Bible Says about the Great Tribulation. William Kimball. LC 83-71918. (What the Bible Says Ser.). (Illus.). 291p. 1983. 13.95 (ISBN 0-89900-093-2). College Pr pub.

What the Bible Says about the Great Tribulation. William R. Kimball. 304p. 1985. pap. 7.95 (ISBN 0-8010-5466-4). Baker Bk.

What the Bible Says about the Lords's Supper. Andrew Paris. LC 86-71103. (What the Bible Says Ser.). text ed. 13.95 (ISBN 0-89900-253-6). College Pr Pub.

What the Bible Says about the Promised Messiah. James E. Smith. (What the Bible Says Ser.). 530p. 1984. 13.95 (ISBN 0-89900-095-9). College Pr Pub.

What the Bible Says about the Unfolded Plan of God. Don Hunt. LC 81-82988. (What the Bible Says Ser.). 500p. 1981. 13.95 (ISBN 0-89900-084-3). College Pr Pub.

What the Bible Says about Tongues. Robert Picirilli. 1981. pap. 0.95 (ISBN 0-89265-071-0). Randall Hse.

What the Bible Says about Women. Julia Staton. LC 80-66128. (What the Bible Says Ser.). 400p. 1980. 13.95 (ISBN 0-89900-079-7). College Pr Pub.

What the Bible Says about Worship. Lynn Hieronymus. (What the Bible Says Ser.). 300p. 1984. 13.95 (ISBN 0-89900-097-5). College Pr Pub.

What the Bible Teaches. F. G. Smith. 576p. Repr. of 1914 ed. 5.50 (ISBN 0-686-29174-3). Faith Pub Hse.

What the Bible Teaches. F. G. Smith. 1970. pap. 4.95 (ISBN 0-87162-104-5, D8850). Warner Pr.

What the Bible Teaches, 2 vols. Leslie G. Thomas. 1962. Vol. 1. 5.95 (ISBN 0-88027-023-3). Vol. II (ISBN 0-88027-024-1). Firm Foun Pub.

What the Bible Teaches. 20th ed. Reuben A. Torrey. 544p. 1984. 15.95 (ISBN 0-8007-0344-8). Revell.

What the Bible Teaches about Jesus. Geoffrey W. Grogan. 1979. pap. 3.95 (ISBN 0-8423-7884-7). Tyndale.

What the Bible Teaches about the Church. John F. Balchin. 1979. pap. 3.95 (ISBN 0-8423-7883-9). Tyndale.

What the Bible Teaches about the Holy Spirit. John Peck. 1979. pap. 3.95 (ISBN 0-8423-7882-0). Tyndale.

What the Bible Teaches about What Jesus Did. F. F. Bruce. 1979. pap. 3.95 (ISBN 0-8423-7885-5). Tyndale.

What the Bible Tells Me. John G. Churchill. 60p. 1976. pap. 1.50 (ISBN 0-8341-0412-1). Beacon Hill.

What the Bible Tells Us: A Series for Young Children. Illus. by Kees De Kort. Incl. Jesus Is Born (ISBN 0-8066-1576-1, 10-3520); Jesus at the Wedding (ISBN 0-8066-1577-X, 10-3490); The Good Samaritan (ISBN 0-8066-1578-8, 10-2815); Jesus Is Alive (ISBN 0-8066-1579-6, 10-3518). (Illus.). 1977. pap. 2.95 ea. Augsburg.

What the Bible Tells Us: A Series for Young Children. Incl. Jesus Heals a Blind Man (ISBN 0-8066-1684-9, 10-3514); Jesus Heals a Sick Man (ISBN 0-8066-1685-7, 10-3515); Jesus & the Storm (ISBN 0-8066-1683-0, 10-3485); Zacchaeus (ISBN 0-8066-1699-7, 10-7550). (Second Ser.). (Illus.). 1979. pap. 2.95 ea. Augsburg.

What the Bible Tells Us: Third Series, 4 bks. Illus. by Kees De Kort. Incl. Baby Called John. 28p (ISBN 0-8066-1770-5, 10-0538); Jesus & a Little Girl. 28p (ISBN 0-8066-1771-3, 10-3479); Son Who Left Home. 28p (ISBN 0-8066-1773-X, 10-5852); Jesus Goes Away. 28p (ISBN 0-8066-1774-8, 10-3510). 1980. pap. 2.95 ea. Augsburg.

What the Buddha Taught. rev. ed. Walpola Rahula. (Illus.). 168p. 1974. pap. 6.95 (ISBN 0-394-17827-0, E641, Ever). Grove.

What the Church of England Stands For. J. W. Wand. LC 76-106700. 131p. 1972. Repr. of 1951 ed. lib. bdg. 22.50x (ISBN 0-8371-3382-3, WACE). Greenwood.

What the Cults Believe. rev. ed. Irvine G. Robertson. 1966. pap. 5.95 (ISBN 0-8024-9411-0). Moody.

What the Faith Is All About. Elmer L. Towns. LC 83-70235. 480p. 1983. pap. 9.95 (ISBN 0-8423-7870-7); leader's guide 2.95 (ISBN 0-8423-7869-3). Tyndale.

What the Gospels Say about Jesus. LC 78-53636. (Journeys Ser). 1978. pap. text ed. 6.00x (ISBN 0-88489-103-8); tchrs' guide 6.00x (ISBN 0-88489-105-4). St Marys.

What the Great Religions Believe. Joseph Gaer. pap. 3.95 (ISBN 0-451-14320-5, AE1978, Sig). NAL.

What the Heart Already Knows. Phyllis A. Tickle. (Orig.). 1985. pap. 5.95 (ISBN 0-8358-0522-0). Upper Room.

What the Jews Believe. Philip S. Bernstein. LC 77-28446. (Illus.). 1978. Repr. of 1951 ed. lib. bdg. 22.50x (ISBN 0-313-20228-1, BEWJ). Greenwood.

What the Mormons Believe: An Introduction to the Doctrines of the Church of Jesus Christ of Latter-Day Saints. Ken Miller. LC 81-80958. 248p. 1981. 9.95 (ISBN 0-88290-177-X, 1040). Horizon Utah.

What the New Testament Is All About. Henrietta C. Mears. 288p. pap. 3.95 (ISBN 0-8307-0525-2, 5015618). Regal.

What the Old Testament Is All About. Henrietta C. Mears. LC 76-51196. (Illus.). 1977. pap. 3.50 (ISBN 0-8307-0466-3, S111128). Regal.

What the Stones Say. C. H. Spurgeon. 1975. pap. 2.50 (ISBN 0-686-18095-X). Pilgrim Pubns.

What the World Is Coming To. Chuck Smith. LC 77-3186. 224p. 1980. pap. 1.95 (ISBN 0-936728-00-0). Word for Today.

What the World Needs. Victor L. Dox. LC 67-31068. 3.50 (ISBN 0-8198-0328-6); pap. 2.50 (ISBN 0-8198-0329-4). Dghtrs St Paul.

What, Then, Is Man? A Symposium. 356p. 1971. 10.50 (12-2361). Concordia.

What Think You of Christ. Rosalie M. Levy. 1962. 1.50 (ISBN 0-8198-0172-0). Dghtrs St Paul.

What Time Is It? David Willoughby. Ed. by Arthur L. Clanton. 126p. 1974. 3.95 (ISBN 0-912315-49-0). Word Aflame.

What to Do about Worry. J. Adams. 1972. pap. 0.75 (ISBN 0-87552-065-0). Presby & Reformed.

What to Do about Worry. Jay E. Adams. 1976. pap. 1.50 (ISBN 0-8010-0048-3). Baker Bk.

What to Do on a Jewish Holiday? Sol Scharfstein. 1985. 6.95 (ISBN 0-88125-170-4). Ktav.

What to do on Thursday: A Layman's Guide to the Practical Use of the Scriptures. Jay E. Adams. 144p. 1982. pap. 3.95 (ISBN 0-8010-0188-9). Baker Bk.

What to Do till Jesus Comes. Knofel Staton. LC 81-14594. 112p. 1983. pap. 2.25 (ISBN 0-87239-481-6, 41016). Standard Pub.

What to Do When Faith Seems Weak & Victory Lost. Kenneth E. Hagin. 1979. pap. 3.50 (ISBN 0-89276-501-1). Hagin Ministries.

What to Do When You Pray. Lucille Walker. LC 78-60948. 181p. 1983. pap. text ed. 6.95 (ISBN 0-87148-920-1). Pathway Pr.

What to Do When Your Friends Reject Christ. C. S. Lovett. 1966. pap. 4.25 (ISBN 0-938148-06-0). Personal Christianity.

What to Do with Sunday Morning. Harold M. Daniels. LC 78-21040. 132p. 1979. softcover 4.95 (ISBN 0-664-24237-5). Westminster.

What to Tell Your Children about Cults. Kevin R. O'Neil. 52p. (Orig.). 1982. pap. 9.95 (ISBN 0-86627-001-9). Crises Res Pr.

What Was the Original Gospel in 'Buddhism'? C. Rhys Davids. LC 78-72416. Repr. of 1938 ed. 17.00 (ISBN 0-404-17277-6). AMS Pr.

What We Believe: A Biblical Catechism of the Apostles Creed. Pheme Perkins. 144p. (Orig.). 1986. pap. 3.95 (ISBN 0-8091-2764-4). Paulist Pr.

What We Believe about Children. Marvin K. Yoder. LC 83-82878. (Mennonite Faith Ser.: No. 13). 72p. 1984. pap. 1.50 (ISBN 0-8361-3357-9). Herald Pr.

What We Have Seen & Heard: A Pastoral Letter on Evangelization from the Black Bishops of the United States. James P. Lyke. 40p. (Orig.). 1984. pap. text ed. 1.95 (ISBN 0-86716-040-3). St Anthony Mess Pr.

What We Know about Heaven. James E. Nelson. 80p. 1987. 2.95, paper (ISBN 0-8423-7921-5). Tyndale.

What We May Be: Techniques for Psychological & Spiritual Growth. Piero Ferrucci. LC 81-51107. (Illus.). 256p. 1982. 6.95 (ISBN 0-87477-262-1). J P Tarcher.

What We Mean by Religion. Rev., 3rd ed. Ira Eisenstein. LC 57-14413. 173p. 1958. pap. 7.95 (ISBN 0-935457-06-2). Reconstructionist Pr.

What We Mean by Religion. facsimile ed. Willard L. Sperry. LC 78-128316. (Essay Index Reprint Ser.). Repr. of 1940 ed. 17.00 (ISBN 0-8369-2370-7). Ayer Co Pubs.

What We See & Hear in a Greek Eastern Orthodox Church. G. Polyzoides. 92p. 4.00 (ISBN 0-686-83965-X). Divry.

What Will You Do with King Jesus. James A. Harnish. 128p. (Orig.). 1986. pap. 5.95 (ISBN 0-8358-0530-1, ICN 613108, Dist. by Abingdon Pr). Upper Room.

What Wives Wish Their Husbands Knew about Women. James Dobson. 1975. 9.95 (ISBN 0-8423-7890-1). Tyndale.

What Wives Wish Their Husbands Knew about Women. James Dobson. 1977. pap. 5.95 (ISBN 0-8423-7889-8); pap. 3.50 (ISBN 0-8423-7896-0, Living Books). Tyndale.

What Works & What Doesn't in Youth Ministry. Nido Qubein. Ed. by Arthur L. Zapel & Kathy Pijanowski. (Illus.). 211p. 1986. pap. 7.95 (ISBN 0-916260-40-2). Meriwether Pub.

What Works When Life Doesn't. rev. ed. Stuart Briscoe. 176p. 1984. pap. 2.95 (ISBN 0-89693-709-7). Victor Bks.

What Would Jesus Do? Glenn Clark. pap. 7.95 (ISBN 0-910924-20-1). Macalester.

What Would You Do? A Child's Book about Divorce. (Youth Publications). 3.50. Borden.

What You Can Say When You Don't Know What to Say: Reaching out to Those Who Hurt. Lauren Littauer Briggs. 176p. (Orig.). 1985. pap. 4.95 (ISBN 0-89081-465-1). Harvest Hse.

What You Say Is What You Get. Don Gossett. 192p. 1976. pap. 3.95 (ISBN 0-88368-066-1). Whitaker Hse.

What You Should Know about Inerrancy. Charles C. Ryre. (Current Christian Issues Ser.). pap. 4.50 (ISBN 0-8024-8785-8). Moody.

What You Should Know about Jewish Religion, History, Ethics, & Culture. Sidney L. Markowitz. 226p. 1973. pap. 5.95 (ISBN 0-8065-0028-X). Citadel Pr.

What You Should Know about Social Responsibility. Charles C. Ryrie. LC 81-16804. (Current Christian Issues Ser.). 1982. pap. 4.50 (ISBN 0-8024-9417-X). Moody.

What You Should Know about the Bible: A Practical Guide to Bible Basics. Stanford Herlick. LC 85-82137. (Illus.). 255p. 1985. 12.50 (ISBN 0-9616026-0-0). FBF Pubns.

What You Should Know about the Holy Spirit. J. W. Jepson. LC 85-81719. 160p. 1986. pap. 3.95 (ISBN 0-88243-639-2, 02-0639). Gospel Pub.

What You Should Know about the Rapture. Charles C. Ryrie. LC 81-4019. (Current Christian Issues Ser.). 128p. 1981. pap. 4.50 (ISBN 0-8024-9416-1). Moody.

What You Think of Me Is None of My Business. Terry Cole-Whittaker. 194p. (Orig.). 1982. pap. 9.95 (ISBN 0-86679-002-0). Oak Tree Pubns.

What Your Wedding Can Be. William J. Peters. LC 80-65402. 136p. (Orig.). 1980. pap. 2.95 (ISBN 0-87029-163-7, 20350-5). Abbey.

Whatever Became of Sin? Karl Menninger. 1973. (Hawthorn); pap. 9.50 (ISBN 0-8015-8554-6, 0922-280, Hawthorn). Dutton.

Whatever God Wants. Humberto C. Medeires. 690p. 1984. 6.95 (ISBN 0-8198-8208-9); pap. 5.95 (ISBN 0-8198-8209-7). Dghtrs St Paul.

Whatever Happened to Friday? & Other Questions Catholics Ask. Joseph C. Gibbons. LC 79-91275. (Orig.). 1980. pap. 3.95 (ISBN 0-8091-2278-2). Paulist Pr.

Whatever Happened to Good Old Plastic Jesus? Earnest Larsen. 144p. 1978. pap. 3.95 (ISBN 0-697-01696-X). Wm C Brown.

Whatever Happened to Hope. Roy H. Hicks. 1978. mini book 0.75 (ISBN 0-89274-074-4). Harrison Hse.

Whatever Happened to the Human Race? C. Everett Koop & Francis A. Schaeffer. LC 83-70955. 168p. 1983. pap. 7.95 (ISBN 0-89107-291-8, Crossway Bks). Good News.

Whatever Happened to Worship? A. W. Tozer. Ed. by Gerald B. Smith. LC 85-71185. 128p. (Orig.). 1985. pap. 5.95 (ISBN 0-87509-367-1). Chr Pubns.

What's a Nice Person Like You Doing Sick? Paul E. Parker & David R. Enlow. LC 74-82838. (Illus.). 80p. 1974. pap. 1.50 (ISBN 0-88419-082-X). Creation Hse.

What's a Parent to Do? C. S. Lovett. 1971. pap. 6.45 (ISBN 0-938148-27-3). Personal Christianity.

What's a Woman to Do in Church? David R. Nicholas. 148p. 1979. 7.95 (ISBN 0-88469-123-3). BMH Bks.

What's Ahead? Charles Harris. LC 80-84173. (Radiant Life Ser.). 128p. (Orig.). 1982. pap. 2.50 (ISBN 0-88243-897-2, 02-0897); teacher's ed. 3.95 (ISBN 0-88243-195-1, 32-0195). Gospel Pub.

What's Baptism All about? Herbert Mjorud. LC 77-80413. 1978. pap. 2.95 (ISBN 0-88419-173-7). Creation Hse.

What's Eating You? Elizabeth Keyes & Paul K. Chivington. (Illus.). 1978. pap. 4.50 (ISBN 0-87516-263-0). De Vorss.

What's Gone Wrong with the Harvest? James F. Engel & Wilbert H. Norton. 192p. 1975. pap. 7.95 (ISBN 0-310-24161-8, 18417P). Zondervan.

What's in a Muslim Name? M. A. Qazi. pap. 3.50 (ISBN 0-686-18582-X). Kazi Pubns.

What's It Worth? Probing Our Values with Questions Jesus Asked. Margaret Ragland. 1977. pap. 4.95 (ISBN 0-89137-409-4). Quality Pubns.

What's Keeping You, Santa? A Christmas Musical Program Package. Margaret E. Pickett. (Illus.). 74p. (Program package incl. Production Guide with choir arranged songs, cassette tape of songs & thirty slides from book.). 1983. 44.95 (ISBN 0-913939-01-3). TP Assocs.

What's New in Religion? A Critical Study of New Theology, New Morality & Secular Christianity. Kenneth Hamilton. 176p. 1969. pap. 3.95 (ISBN 0-85364-092-0). Attic Pr.

What's Right? Eugene Baker. Ed. by Jane Buerger. LC 80-17552. (Illus.). 112p. 1980. 5.95 (ISBN 0-89565-175-0, 4932). Standard Pub.

What's Right? A Teenager's Guide to Christian Living. Jim Auer. 96p. 1987. pap. 3.25 (ISBN 0-89243-265-9). Liguori Pubns.

What's the Bible Like: New Testament. Vivian Gunderson. (Illus.). 1983. pap. 1.25 (ISBN 0-8323-0418-2). Binford-Metropolitan.

What's the Good Word? The All New Super Incredible Bible Study Book for Junior Highs. John Souter. 64p. 1983. pap. 3.50 (ISBN 0-310-45891-9, 12474P). Zondervan.

What's the Matter with Christy? Ruth Allen. LC 82-8036. 110p. (Orig.). 1982. pap. 3.95 (ISBN 0-87123-629-X, 210629). Bethany Hse.

What's the Point? Norman Warren. Ed. by A. Reynolds. 80p. 1987. pap. 2.50 (ISBN 0-7459-1224-9). Lion USA.

What's This World Coming To? Ray C. Stedman. LC 86-6439. 1986. pap. 5.95 (ISBN 0-8307-1154-6, 5418825). Regal.

What's Wrong with God. T. Steeman. Ed. by Fantan McNamee. (Synthesis Ser.). pap. 0.75 (ISBN 0-8199-0391-4). Franciscan Herald.

What's Wrong with Human Rights. T. Robert Ingram. LC 78-68732. (Orig.). 1979. pap. 3.50 (ISBN 0-686-24267-X). St Thomas.

What's Your S. Q.? (Spiritual Quotient) Maralene Wesner & Miles Wesner. LC 86-71133. 100p. 1986. pap. 4.95 (ISBN 0-936715-04-9). Diversity Okla.

Wheat: Humor & Wisdom of J. Golden Kimball. Mikal Lofgren. LC 80-81556. 95p. 1980. 6.50 (ISBN 0-936718-04-8). Moth Hse.

Whedon Commentary: Psalms. boards 13.95 (ISBN 0-686-27779-1). Schmul Pub Co.

Whedon's Commentary on First Corinthians, Vol. 4. 13.95 (ISBN 0-686-13331-5). Schmul Pub Co.

Whedon's Commentary on Luke, Vol. 2. 13.95 (ISBN 0-686-13330-7). Schmul Pub Co.

Whedon's Commentary on Matthew, Vol. 1. 13.95 (ISBN 0-686-13329-3). Schmul Pub Co.

Whedon's Commentary on Titus & Revelations, Vol. 5. 13.95 (ISBN 0-686-13332-3). Schmul Pub Co.

Whedon's Commentary Revised, 2 vols. D. D. Whedon. 1981. Vol. Matthew Mark. 7.65 (ISBN 0-87813-917-6); Vol. Luke John. 7.65 (ISBN 0-87813-918-4). Christian Light.

Whee! We, Wee All the Way Home: A Guide to a Sensual Prophetic Spirituality. Matthew Fox. LC 81-67365. 257p. 1981. pap. 8.95 (ISBN 0-939680-00-9). Bear & Co.

Wheel of the Law: Buddhism Illustrated from Siamese Sources. Henry Alabaster. 384p. Repr. of 1871 ed. text ed. 49.68x (ISBN 0-576-03126-7, Pub. by Gregg Intl Pubs England). Gregg Intl.

Wheels of a Soul. Philip S. Berg. (Hebrew.). 160p. 1986. 12.95 (ISBN 0-943688-41-8); pap. 9.95 (ISBN 0-943688-42-6). Res Ctr Kabbalah.

Wheels of a Soul. Philip S. Berg. (Span.). 256p. 1986. 12.95 (ISBN 0-943688-45-0); pap. 9.95 (ISBN 0-943688-46-9). Res Ctr Kabbalah.

When a Christian Sins. John R. Rice. 1954. pap. 3.50 (ISBN 0-8024-9434-X). Moody.

When a Congregation Cares. Abraham Schmitt & Dorothy Schmitt. LC 84-19294. 128p. (Orig.). 1984. pap. 6.95 (ISBN 0-8361-3410-9). Herald Pr.

When a Family Loses a Loved One. Paul F. Wilczak. LC 81-68846. (WHEN Bk. Ser.). 96p. (Orig.). 1981. pap. 2.45 (ISBN 0-87029-179-3, 20272-1). Abbey.

When a Father Is Hard to Honor. Elva McAllaster. 126p. (Orig.). 1984. pap. 6.95 (ISBN 0-87178-930-2). Brethren.

When a Good God Lets Bad Things Happen. Duane Kelderman. 1983. 3.25 (ISBN 0-89536-583-9, 2333). CSS of Ohio.

When a Good Man Falls. Erwin W. Luzer. 132p. 1985. pap. 4.95 (ISBN 0-89693-361-X). Victor Bks.

When a Jew Celebrates. Harry Gersh. LC 70-116678. (Jewish Values Ser.). (Illus.). 256p. 1971. pap. text ed. 6.95x (ISBN 0-87441-091-6). Behrman.

When a Jew Prays. Seymour Rossel. Ed. by Eugene B. Borowitz & Hyman Chanover. LC 73-1233. (Illus.). 192p. 1973. pap. text ed. 6.95x (ISBN 0-87441-093-2). Behrman.

When a Jew Seeks Wisdom: The Sayings of the Fathers. Seymour Rossel. LC 75-14119. (Jewish Values Ser.). pap. 6.95x (ISBN 0-87441-089-4). Behrman.

When a Loved One Dies. Philip W. Williams. LC 75-22713. 96p. 1976. pap. 5.95 (ISBN 0-8066-1520-6, 10-7056). Augsburg.

When a Member of the Family Needs Counseling. John A. Larsen. LC 79-51274. (When Bk). (Illus.). 1979. pap. 2.45 (ISBN 0-87029-147-5, 20234-1). Abbey.

When a Pastor Search Committee Comes... or Doesn't. J. William Harbin. LC 85-13541. 1985. pap. 4.95 (ISBN 0-8054-2545-4). Broadman.

When a Person Dies: Pastoral Theology in Death Experiences. Robert L. Kinast. LC 84-11431. 160p. (Orig.). 1984. pap. 9.95 (ISBN 0-8245-0657-X). Crossroad NY.

When Adam Clarke Preached, People Listened. Wesley Tracy. 238p. (Orig.). 1981. pap. 4.95 (ISBN 0-8341-0714-7). Beacon Hill.

When All Hell Breaks Loose. C. E. Douglas. 1974. pap. 4.95 (ISBN 0-9601124-0-5). Tusayan Gospel.

When Angels Appear. Hope MacDonald. 128p. (Orig.). 1982. pap. 4.95 (ISBN 0-310-28531-3, 10047P). Zondervan.

When Apples Are Ripe. Geraldine G. Harder. LC 73-160722. (Illus.). 224p. 1972. pap. 3.95 (ISBN 0-8361-1694-1). Herald Pr.

When Bad Happens to God's People. Richard Rice. 1984. pap. 4.95 (ISBN 0-8163-0570-6). Pacific Pr Pub Assn.

When Bad Things Happen, God Still Loves. Joe Blair. LC 85-13240. 1986. pap. 4.95 (ISBN 0-8054-5010-6). Broadman.

When Bad Things Happen to Good People. Harold S. Kushner. LC 81-40411. 160p. 1981. 11.95 (ISBN 0-8052-3773-9). Schocken.

When Bad Things Happen to Good People. Harold S. Kushner. (General Ser.). 1982. lib. bdg. 13.95 (ISBN 0-8161-3465-0, Large Print Bks). G K Hall.

When Burdens Become Bridges. Henry G. Bosch. (Solace Ser.). 1984. pap. 1.50 (ISBN 0-8010-0867-0). Baker Bk.

When Calls the Heart. Janette Oke. LC 82-24451. 221p. (Orig.). 1983. pap. 5.95 (ISBN 0-87123-611-7, 210611). Bethany Hse.

When Calls the Heart. Large type ed. Janette Oke. (Canadian West Ser.). 221p. (Orig.). 1986. pap. 7.95 (ISBN 0-87123-885-3). Bethany Hse.

When Can a Child Believe. Chamberlain. LC 73-80778. pap. 4.95 (ISBN 0-8054-6208-2). Broadman.

When Can I Say, "I Love You"? Max M. Rice & Vivian B. Rice. LC 76-54926. 1977. pap. 4.95 (ISBN 0-8024-9436-6). Moody.

When Caring Is Not Enough: Resolving Conflicts Through Fair Fighting. David W. Augsburger. LC 83-80999. (Caring Enough Ser.: No. 4). 196p. (Orig.). 1983. pap. 5.95 (ISBN 0-8361-3343-9). Herald Pr.

When Catholics Marry Again: A Guide for the Divorced, Their Families & Those Who Minister to Them. Gerald S. Twomey. 194p. (Orig.). 1982. pap. 7.95 (ISBN 0-86683-633-0, HarpR). Har-Row.

When Children Ask about God. Harold S. Kushner. LC 76-9140. 1976. pap. 4.95 (ISBN 0-8052-0549-7). Schocken.

When Children Ask about Sex. CSAA. 42p. 1974. pap. 1.50 (ISBN 0-87183-243-7). Jewish Bd Family.

When Christ Was Preached to Christ. Basil Overton. pap. 5.50 (ISBN 0-89137-545-7). Quality Pubns.

When Churches Mind the Children: A Study of Day Care in Local Parishes. Eileen W. Lindner et al. LC 83-22545. 192p. (Orig.). 1983. pap. 10.00 (ISBN 0-931114-23-3). High-Scope.

When Daylight Comes. Howard Murphet. LC 74-18958. (Illus.). 304p. (Orig.). 1975. cloth 8.95 (ISBN 0-8356-0461-6). Theos Pub Hse.

When Death has Touched Your Life. Biegert. 1981. pap. 1.25 (ISBN 0-8298-0455-2). Pilgrim NY.

When Death Means Life: Choosing the Way of the Cross. Stanley C. Baldwin. (Living Theology Ser.). 1986. pap. 6.95 (ISBN 0-88070-161-7). Multnomah.

When Death Touches Your Life: Practical Help in Preparing for Death. Mervin E. Thompson. 224p. 1986. 11.95 (ISBN 0-933173-02-4). Prince Peace Pub.

When Did We See You Lord? Chiara Lubich. Tr. by Hugh Moran from Ital. LC 79-88680. Tr. of Gesu Nel Fratello. 134p. 1979. pap. 3.50 (ISBN 0-911782-34-6). New City.

When Do You Talk To God? Prayers for Small Children. Patricia McKissack & Fredrick McKissack. LC 86-71903. (Illus.). 32p. (Orig.). 1986. pap. 4.95 (ISBN 0-8066-2239-3, 10-7078). Augsburg.

When Each Leaf Shines: Voices of Women's Ministry. Mary E. Giles. 1986. pap. 4.95 (ISBN 0-87193-246-6). Dimension Bks.

When Easy Answers Play Hard to Get: Decision Making for Young Teens. Stephen Sorenson & Amanda Sorenson. LC 84-11123. (Young Teens Ser.). 128p. (Orig.). 1984. pap. 3.95 (ISBN 0-8066-2084-6, 10-7080). Augsburg.

When Enough Is Enough. David Augsburger. LC 84-11644. 1984. pap. 5.95 (ISBN 0-8307-0979-7, 5418273). Regal.

When Enough Is Enough. Jim Larson. LC 84-11644. (Caring Enough Ser.). 64p. 1985. pap. 3.95 (ISBN 0-8307-0987-8, 6101872). Regal.

When Faith Meets Faith. rev. ed. David M. Stowe. 1972. pap. 2.95 (ISBN 0-377-37201-3). Friend Pr.

When Faith Meets the Impossible. Gerald R. Nash. (Outreach Ser.). pap. 1.25 (ISBN 0-686-78874-5). Pacific Pr Pub Assn.

When Families Hurt. W. Douglas Cole. LC 79-51133. 1979. 6.50 (ISBN 0-8054-5638-4). Broadman.

When Fathers Ruled: Family Life in Reformation Europe. Steven Ozment. LC 83-6098. (Illus.). 238p. 1983. text ed. 17.50x (ISBN 0-674-95120-4). Harvard U Pr.

When God & I Talk. Clyde L. Herring. LC 80-70917. 1981. pap. 4.95 (ISBN 0-8054-5334-2, 4253-34). Broadman.

When God & Man Failed: Non-Jewish Views of the Holocaust. Ed. by Henry J. Cargas. 320p. 1981. 16.95 (ISBN 0-02-521300-8). Macmillan.

When God Began in the Middle. Joseph J. Juknialis. (Illus.). 80p. (Orig.). 1981. pap. text ed. 7.95 (ISBN 0-89390-027-3). Resource Pubns.

When God Breaks Through: And Other Challenging Talks. Vance Havner. 96p. 1987. Repr. price not set. Baker Bk.

When God Calls a Woman: The Struggle of a Woman Pastor in France & Algeria. Elisabeth Schmidt. Tr. by Allen Hackett from Fr. LC 81-12009. 224p. (Orig.). 1981. pap. 7.95 (ISBN 0-8298-0430-7). Pilgrim NY.

When God Came Down. Andrew W. Blackwood, Jr. (Pocket Paperback Library Ser.). 1978. pap. 1.45 (ISBN 0-8010-0753-4). Baker Bk.

When God Can't Answer (Divine Limitations) Maralene Wesner & Miles E. Wesner. LC 86-70753. 100p. 1986. pap. 4.95 (ISBN 0-936715-26-X). Diversity Okla.

When God First Thought of You. Lloyd J. Ogilvie. 1980. pap. 9.95 (ISBN 0-8499-2945-8). Word Bks.

When God Guides. Denis Lane. 1984. pap. 3.95 (ISBN 9971-972-16-6). OMF Bks.

When God Has Put You on Hold. Bill Austin. 112p. 1986. pap. 4.95 (ISBN 0-8423-7989-4). Tyndale.

When God Is at Home with Your Family. David M. Thomas. LC 78-73019. (When Bk.). (Illus.). 1978. pap. 2.45 (ISBN 0-87029-146-7, 20231-7). Abbey.

When God Laid Down the Law. Evelyn Marxhausen. LC 59-1259. (Arch Bk.). 1981. pap. 0.99 (ISBN 0-570-06142-3). Concordia.

When God Lived in a Tent. Susan Davis. (My Church Teaches Ser.). (Illus.). 1978. 1.95 (ISBN 0-8127-0181-X). Review & Herald.

When God-Love Descends. Sri Chinmoy. 50p. 1975. pap. 2.00 (ISBN 0-88497-210-0). Aum Pubns.

When God Says You're OK: A Christian Approach to Transactional Analysis. new ed. Jon T. Murphree. LC 75-21452. 132p. 1975. pap. 2.95 (ISBN 0-87784-716-9). Inter-Varsity.

When God Was a Woman. Merlin Stone. LC 77-16262. (Illus.). 265p. 1978. pap. 6.95 (ISBN 0-15-696158-X, Harv). HarBraceJ.

When God Was at Calvary: Messages on the Seven Words. George Gritter. (Pocket Pulpit Library). 144p. 1982. pap. 3.50 (ISBN 0-8010-3785-9). Baker Bk.

When God's Children Suffer. Horatius Bonar. LC 80-84441. (Shepherd Illustrated Classics Ser.). (Illus.). 144p. 1981. pap. 5.95 (ISBN 0-87983-221-5). Keats.

When Going to Pieces Holds You Together. William A. Miller. LC 76-3853. 128p. (Orig.). 1976. pap. 6.95 (ISBN 0-8066-1543-5, 10-7063). Augsburg.

When Harley Heard from Heaven. Harley W. Vail. LC 82-72633. 84p. 1982. pap. 2.95 (ISBN 0-9609096-0-5). Bethel Pub Or.

When He Is Come. A. W. Tozer & G. B. Smith. Orig. Title: Tozer Pulpit, Vol. 2: Ten Sermons on the Ministry of the Holy Spirit. 146p. (Orig.). 1980. pap. 3.45 (ISBN 0-87509-221-7). Chr Pubns.

When I Am Sick. Christine Tangvald. (I Am Special Bks.). (Illus.). 20p. 1985. 3.95 (ISBN 0-89191-908-2, 59089). Cook.

When I Left God in Heaven. Sri Chinmoy. 50p. (Orig.). 1975. pap. 2.00 (ISBN 0-88497-223-2). Aum Pubns.

When I Relax I Feel Guilty. Tim Hansel. LC 78-73460. 1979. pap. 6.95 (ISBN 0-89191-137-5). Cook.

When I Saw Him. Roy Hession. 1975. pap. 2.95 (ISBN 0-87508-239-4). Chr Lit.

When I Talk to God. Linda S. Chandler. LC 84-4967. (Illus.). 1984. 5.95 (ISBN 0-8054-4291-X, 4242-91). Broadman.

When I'm a Daddy. Ginger A. Fulton. 1985. pap. 2.95 (ISBN 0-8024-0387-5). Moody.

When I'm a Mommy: A Little Girl's Paraphrase of Proverbs 31. Ginger A. Fulton. (Illus.). 1984. pap. 2.95 (ISBN 0-8024-0367-0). Moody.

When in Doubt, Hug 'em: How to Develop a Caring Church. Cecil B. Murphey. LC 77-15751. 1978. 5.95 (ISBN 0-8042-1890-0). John Knox.

When Is an Example Binding? Thomas B. Warren. (Biblical Hermeneutics Ser.). 1975. pap. 7.00 (ISBN 0-934916-43-8). Natl Christian Pr.

When Is It Right to Fight? Robert A. Morey. 160p. (Orig.). 1985. pap. 4.95 (ISBN 0-87123-810-1, 210810). Bethany Hse.

When It Hurts Too Much to Cry. Jerry Falwell. 160p. 1984. 9.95 (ISBN 0-8423-7993-2). Tyndale.

When It Hurts Too Much to Wait: Understanding God's Timing. Larry Richards. 160p. 1985. 9.95 (ISBN 0-8499-0489-7, 0489-7). Word Bks.

When It's Hard to Forgive. Goldie Bristol & Carol McGinnis. 168p. 1982. pap. 5.95 (ISBN 0-88207-311-7). Victor Bks.

When Jesus Comes. Nancee Berry. (Come Unto Me Library). 1979. pap. 1.65 (ISBN 0-8127-0210-7). Review & Herald.

When Jesus Comes. Charles R. Taylor. (Illus.). 76p. (Orig.). 1985. pap. 4.95 (ISBN 0-937682-08-X). Today Bible.

When Jesus Comes Again. Everett I. Carver. 1979. pap. 7.95 (ISBN 0-87552-159-2). Presby & Reformed.

When Jesus Confronts the World: An Exposition of Matthew 8-10. D. A. Carson. 240p. 1987. pap. price not set (ISBN 0-8010-2522-2). Baker Bk.

When Jesus Was a Baby. Dan Burrow. LC 84-70244. (Augsburg Open Window Bks.). (Illus.). 12p. (Orig.). 1984. pap. 4.95 (ISBN 0-8066-2078-1, 10-7082). Augsburg.

When Jesus Was a Lad. R. Oetting. LC 68-56816. (Illus.). 1968. PLB 9.26x (ISBN 0-87783-047-9). Oddo.

When Jesus Was a Lad. Rae Otting. (Illus.). 1978. pap. 1.25 (ISBN 0-89508-055-9). Rainbow Bks.

When Jesus Was a Little Boy. 32p. 1981. pap. 2.95 (ISBN 0-8249-8009-3). Ideals.

When Jesus Was Born. Daughters of St. Paul. (Illus.). 1973. plastic bdg. 2.00 (ISBN 0-8198-0326-X); pap. 1.25 (ISBN 0-8198-0327-8). Dghtrs St Paul.

When Jesus Was Born. Maryann J. Dotts. LC 79-3958. (Illus.). 1979. 9.95 (ISBN 0-687-45020-9). Abingdon.

When Jesus Was Born. Sharon Mullen. LC 86-17558. (Bible-&-Me Ser.). 1987. 5.95 (ISBN 0-8054-4177-8). Broadman.

When Jesus Was Four-or Maybe Five. Mary D. Bangham. (Illus., Orig.). 1968. pap. 3.95 (ISBN 0-8066-0824-2, 10-7058). Augsburg.

When Jew & Christian Meet. LaVonne Althouse. (Illus.). 1966. pap. 1.50 (ISBN 0-377-36221-2). Friend Pr.

When King Was Carpenter. Maria Von Trapp. LC 75-46021. 142p. 1976. pap. 2.95 (ISBN 0-89221-018-4). New Leaf.

When Kings Come Marching In: Isaiah & the New Jerusalem. Richard Mouw. 96p. (Orig.). 1983. pap. 3.95 (ISBN 0-8028-1935-4). Eerdmans.

When Light Pierced the Darkness: Christian Rescue of Jews in Nazi-Occupied Poland. Nechama Tec. (Illus.). 320p. 1986. 19.95 (ISBN 0-19-503643-3). Oxford U Pr.

When Living Hurts. Sol Gordon. 1985. pap. 8.95 (ISBN 0-8074-0310-5). UAHC.

When Love Isn't Easy. Phyllis L. Hobe. 192p. 1986. pap. 3.50 (ISBN 0-553-26055-3). Bantam.

When Love Unites the Church. Richard M. Lawless. LC 81-72000. (When Bks.). 88p. (Orig.). 1982. pap. 2.45 (ISBN 0-87029-181-5, 20273-9). Abbey.

When Loved Ones Are Called Home. Herbert Wernecke. (Ultra Bks Ser). pap. 1.95 (ISBN 0-8010-9513-1). Baker Bk.

When Loved Ones Are Taken in Death. Lehman Strauss. pap. 2.50 (ISBN 0-310-33102-1, 6340P). Zondervan.

When Man Becomes God: Humanism & Hybris in the Old Testament. Donald E. Gowan. LC 75-17582. (Pittsburgh Theological Monographs: No. 6). 1975. pap. 8.75 (ISBN 0-915138-06-9). Pickwick.

When Memory Comes. Saul Friedlander. Tr. by Helen Lane from Fr. 192p. 1979. 9.95 (ISBN 0-374-28898-4). FS&G.

When Messiah Comes. Paul Hegele. Ed. by Michael L. Sherer. (Orig.). 1986. pap. 6.25 (ISBN 0-89536-823-4, 6832). CSS of Ohio.

When Millions Saw the Shroud. Peter M. Rinaldi. LC 79-53065. (Illus.). 1979. 6.95 (ISBN 0-89944-023-1); pap. 2.95 (ISBN 0-89944-024-X). Don Bosco Multimedia.

When Night Becomes as Day. Compiled by Denise George. LC 86-6887. (Orig.). 1986. pap. 5.95 (ISBN 0-8054-5434-9). Broadman.

When Opposites Attract. John M. Drescher. LC 79-53272. (When Bks.). (Illus., Orig.). 1979. pap. 2.45 (ISBN 0-87029-153-X, 20239-0). Abbey.

When Our Church Building Burned Down. Martha W. Hickman. 48p. 1986. 9.95 (ISBN 0-687-45023-3). Abingdon.

When Our Love Is Charity. Chiara Lubich. LC 72-85632. 82p. 1972. pap. 2.95 (ISBN 0-911782-02-8). New City.

When Parents Die: A Guide for Adults. Edward Myers. 208p. 1986. 13.95 (ISBN 0-670-80771-0). Viking.

When Past & Present Meet. Douglas E. Brown. 112p. 1986. 4.95 (ISBN 0-913573-46-9). Hendrickson MA.

When Prayer Makes News. Ed. by Allan A. Boesak & Charles Villa-Vicencio. 192p. (Orig.). 1986. pap. 10.95 (ISBN 0-664-24035-6). Westminster.

When Pregnancy Is a Problem. Regis Walling. LC 79-51280. (When Book Ser.). (Illus.). 1980. pap. 2.45 (ISBN 0-87029-152-1, 20235-8). Abbey.

When Puppets Talk, Everybody Listens. Shelly Roden. LC 78-55265. 72p. 1978. pap. 4.95 (ISBN 0-88207-266-8). Victor Bks.

When Reason Fails. Myron S. Augsburger. 112p. 1985. pap. 4.95 (ISBN 0-8423-7999-1). Tyndale.

When Religion Doesn't Work. Marvin Moore. Ed. by Richard W. Coffen. (Better Living Ser.). 32p. (Orig.). 1986. pap. 1.25 (ISBN 0-8280-0314-9). Review & herald.

When Revival Comes. Jack R. Taylor & C. S. Hawkins. LC 80-66956. 1980. pap. 5.50 (ISBN 0-8054-6226-0). Broadman.

When Science Fails. John H. Tiner. (Direction Bks). 1974. pap. 2.95 (ISBN 0-8010-8823-2). Baker Bk.

When Shadows Fall. William A. Lauterbach. 1945. pap. 0.85 (ISBN 0-570-03537-6, 14-1573). Concordia.

When Silence Becomes Singing. Helen Kylin. LC 84-61827. 32p. (Orig.). 1985. pap. 2.50x (ISBN 0-87574-258-0). Pendle Hill.

When Someone Asks for Help: A Practical Guide to Counseling. Everett L. Worthington, Jr. LC 82-81. (Illus.). 239p. (Orig.). 1982. pap. 7.95 (ISBN 0-87784-375-9). Inter-Varsity.

When Someone Dies. Edgar N. Jackson. Ed. by William E. Hulme. LC 76-154488. (Pocket Counsel Bks). 58p. (Orig.). 1971. pap. 2.50 (ISBN 0-8006-1103-9, 1-1103). Fortress.

When Someone You Love Dies. Lawrence Ruegg. 1984. 0.95 (ISBN 0-89536-659-2, 2355). CSS of Ohio.

When Someone You Love Is Dying. Norma S. Upson. 192p. 1986. pap. 6.95 (ISBN 0-671-61079-1, Fireside). S&S.

When Someone You Love Is Dying: A Handbook for Counselors & Those Who Care. 2nd ed. Ruth Kopp & Stephen Sorenson. 240p. 1985. pap. 8.95 (ISBN 0-310-41601-9, 11165P). Zondervan.

When Stars Came Down to Earth: Cosmology of the Skidi Pawnee Indians of North America. Von Del Chamberlain. LC 82-16390. (Ballena Press Anthropological Papers: No. 26). (Illus.). 260p. (Orig.). 1982. pap. 17.95 (ISBN 0-87919-098-1). Ballena Pr.

When the Angels Go Away. Jon L. Joyce. (Orig.). 1980. pap. 3.95 (ISBN 0-937172-14-6). JLJ Pubs.

When the Answer Is No. Dandi D. Knorr. 1985. pap. 4.95 (ISBN 0-8054-5801-8). Broadman.

When the Brave Ones Cried. Lee Dalton. 176p. 1986. 8.95 (ISBN 0-88290-282-2). Horizon Utah.

When the Comforter Came. Albert B. Simpson. pap. 2.95 (ISBN 0-87509-042-7). Chr Pubns.

When the Doctor Says "It's Cancer". abr. ed. Mary B. Moster. (Pocket Guides Ser.). 96p. 1986. 1.95 (ISBN 0-8423-7981-9). Tyndale.

When the Going Gets Tough. D. Stuart Briscoe. LC 82-11205. 1982. 5.95 (ISBN 0-8307-0802-2, 5417507). Regal.

When the Handwriting on the Wall Is in Brown Crayon. Susan Lenzkes. 1986. pap. 4.95 (ISBN 0-310-43631-1, 6891P). Zondervan.

When the Holy Ghost Is Come. Samuel L. Brengle. 1980. pap. 3.95 (ISBN 0-86544-009-3). Salv Army Suppl South.

When the Hurt Won't Go Away. Paul Powell. 144p. 1986. pap. 4.95 (ISBN 0-89693-365-2). Victor Bks.

When the Latch Is Lifted. Frances J. Roberts. 1970. 3.95 (ISBN 0-932814-18-2). Kings Farspan.

When the Man You Love Is an Alcoholic. Jean Klewin & Thomas Klewin. LC 79-51276. (When Bks). (Illus.). 1979. pap. 2.45 (ISBN 0-87029-149-1, 20232-5). Abbey.

When the Mental Patient Comes Home. George Bennett. LC 79-23809. (Christian Care Bks.). 118p. 1980. pap. 7.95 (ISBN 0-664-24295-2). Westminster.

When the Pieces Don't Fit... God Makes the Difference. Glaphre. 176p. 1984. pap. 5.95 (ISBN 0-310-45341-0, 12239P). Zondervan.

When the Road Gets Tough. Edward Hindson & Walter Byrd. 160p. 1986. 9.95 (ISBN 0-8007-1495-4). Revell.

When the Saints Go Marching Out. Chuck Murphy & Anne Murphy. 1987. pap. 5.95 (Chosen Bks). Revell.

When the Shoe Fits. Bhagwan Shree Rajneesh. Ed. by Ma Prema Veena. LC 76-904914. (Zen Masters Ser.). (Illus.). 388p. (Orig.). 1976. 16.50 (ISBN 0-88050-171-5). Chidvilas Found.

When the Spirit Comes. Melvin L. Hodges. (Charismatic Bks.). 46p. 1972. pap. 0.69 (ISBN 0-88243-919-7, 02-0919). Gospel Pub.

When the Sun Moves Northward. Mabel Collins. LC 86-40402. 195p. (Orig.). 1987. pap. 4.75 (ISBN 0-8356-0614-7). Theos Pub Hse.

When the Time Had Fully Come: Christmas Service for Church Schools. Sharon Lee. 32p. (Orig.). 1984. pap. 0.90 ea. (ISBN 0-8066-2101-X, 23-3010). Augsburg.

When the Time Was Fulfilled: Talks & Writings on Advent & Christmas. Eberhard Arnold et al. LC 65-17599. 1965. 7.00 (ISBN 0-87486-104-7). Plough.

When the Well Runs Dry: Prayer Beyond the Beginnings. Thomas H. Green. LC 79-52404. 176p. (Orig.). 1979. pap. 4.95 (ISBN 0-87793-182-8). Ave Maria.

When the Woman You Love Is an Alcoholic. Joan Curlee-Salisbury. LC 78-73017. (When Bk). (Illus.). 1978. pap. 2.45 (ISBN 0-87029-143-2, 20229-1). Abbey.

When the Word Dwells Richly: Baptists in Perspective. Virgil Bopp. 192p. (Orig.). 1987. pap. 5.95 (ISBN 0-87227-119-6). Reg Baptist.

When the Word Is Given... A Report on Elijah Muhammad, Malcolm X, & the Black Muslim World. Louis E. Lomax. LC 78-14002. (Illus.). 1979. Repr. of 1964 ed. lib. bdg. 22.50x (ISBN 0-313-21002-0, LOWW). Greenwood.

When the Working Men Rise & Shine. Rostelle Sanders. 1984. 4.95 (ISBN 0-8062-2136-4). Carlton.

When There Is No Miracle. Robert L. Wise. LC 77-89394. 176p. 1978. pap. 4.95 (ISBN 0-8307-0582-1, 5408008); study guide o.p. 1.39 (ISBN 0-8307-0651-8, 6101518). Regal.

When They Ask for Bread: Pastoral Care & Counseling. G. F. Bennett. LC 77-15743. 1978. 8.95 (ISBN 0-8042-1159-0). John Knox.

When Things Go Wrong. 2.98 (ISBN 0-8010-5112-6). Baker Bk.

When to Take a Risk. Terry Muck. (Leadership Library). 175p. 1987. 9.95 (ISBN 0-917463-12-9). Chr Today.

When to Take a Risk, No. 9. Terry C. Muck. 192p. 1987. 9.95 (ISBN 0-8499-0615-6). Word Bks.

When Trouble Comes: How to Find God's Help in Difficult Times. Ed. by Roger Schoenhals. (Orig.). 1978. pap. 2.95 (ISBN 0-89367-027-8). Light & Life.

When Two Become One: Reflections for the Newly Married. William E. Hulme. LC 76-176481. 1974. pap. 5.95 (ISBN 0-8066-1438-2, 10-7061). Augsburg.

When War Is Unjust: Being Honest in Just-War Thinking. John H. Yoder. LC 84-2859. 96p. (Orig.). 1984. pap. 5.95 (ISBN 0-8066-2077-3, 10-7084). Augsburg.

When We Die. Farthing. 3.25 (ISBN 0-8356-5118-5). Theos Pub Hse.

When We Gather: A Book of Prayers for Worship, Year A. James G. Kirk. LC 83-14221. (Illus.). 142p. 1983. pap. 8.95 (ISBN 0-664-24505-6, A Geneva Press Publication). Westminster.

When We Gather: A Book of Prayers for Worship, Year B. James G. Kirk. LC 83-14221. (Illus.). 144p. 1984. pap. 8.95 (ISBN 0-664-24553-6). Geneva Pr.

When We Gather: A Book of Prayers for Worship, Year C. James G. Kirk. LC 83-14221. (Illus.). 142p. 1985. pap. 8.95 (ISBN 0-664-24652-4, A Geneva Press Publication). Westminster.

When We Grow up. Bahiyyih Nakhjavani. 120p. 1979. 9.95 (ISBN 0-85398-085-3); pap. 4.95 (ISBN 0-85398-086-1). G Ronald Pub.

When We Pray: Meditation on the Lord's Prayer. Eugene LaVerdiere. LC 82-73512. 176p. 1983. pap. 4.95 (ISBN 0-87793-263-8). Ave Maria.

When Will Ye Be Wise? Stephen Neill et al. Ed. by C. A. Kilmister. 208p. (Orig.). 1984. pap. 6.95. St Thomas.

When Work Goes Sour. James E. Dittes. 120p. (Orig.). 1987. pap. 6.95 (ISBN 0-664-24045-3). Westminster.

When You Are Angry with God. Pat McCloskey. 1987. pap. 4.95. Paulist Pr.

When You Are Feeling Lonely. Charles Durham. LC 84-10499. 180p. (Orig.). 1984. pap. 5.95 (ISBN 0-87784-915-3). Inter-Varsity.

When You Feel Like a Failure. Margaret Parker. (Study & Grow Electives). 64p. 1985. pap. 3.95 leader's guide (ISBN 0-8307-1036-1, 6102073). Regal.

When You Feel You Haven't Got It. rev. ed. Gene A. Getz. LC 86-540. (Biblical Renewal Ser.). 160p. 1986. pap. 5.95 (ISBN 0-8307-1123-6, 5418757). Regal.

When You Go to Tonga. Edward Tremblay. (Illus.). 1954. 3.25 (ISBN 0-8198-0173-9). Dghtrs St Paul.

When You Hear Hoofbeats, Think of a Zebra Talks on Sufism. Shems Friedlander. LC 86-45657. 128p. (Orig.). 1987. pap. 5.95 (ISBN 0-06-096128-7, PL 6128, PL). Har-Row.

When You Lose a Loved One. Charles L. Allen. 64p. 1959. 7.95 (ISBN 0-8007-0347-2). Revell.

When You Lose a Loved One-Life Is Forever. Charles L. Allen & Helen S. Rice. 128p. 1979. pap. 5.95 (ISBN 0-8007-5031-4, Power Bks). Revell.

When You Need a Special Sermon Series. 1981. pap. 5.95 (ISBN 0-570-03836-7, 12-2801). Concordia.

When You Pray - Things Happen. Bob Fitts. LC 82-82018. 144p. 1982. 2.95 (ISBN 0-89221-089-3). New Leaf.

When You Pray: Thinking Your Way Into God's World. Douglas J. Hall. 176p. 1987. pap. 9.95 (ISBN 0-8170-1105-6). Judson.

When You Walk Through the Fire. Warren McWilliams. (Orig.). 1986. pap. 7.95 (ISBN 0-8054-1621-8). Broadman.

When Your Child... John M. Drescher et al. LC 86-4831. 144p. (Orig.). 1986. pap. 7.95 (ISBN 0-8361-3416-8). Herald Pr.

When Your Child Hurts. Charlotte Adelsperger. LC 81-68639. 1985. pap. 5.95 (ISBN 0-8066-2161-3, 10-7088). Augsburg.

When Your Friend Needs You. abr. ed. Paul Welter. (Pocket Guides Ser.). 96p. 1986. mass 1.95 (ISBN 0-8423-7998-3). Tyndale.

When Your Marriage Goes Stale. James Kenny & Mary Kenny. LC 79-51277. (When Bks). (Illus.). 1979. pap. 2.45 (ISBN 0-87029-150-5, 20236-6). Abbey.

When Your Money Fails. Mary S. Relfe. 234p. (Orig.). 1981. pap. text ed. 5.95 (ISBN 0-9607986-0-9). Ministries.

When Your Mountain Won't Move. Craig Selness. 156p. 1984. pap. 5.95 (ISBN 0-88207-619-1). Victor Bks.

When Your Parents Divorce, Vol. 1. William V. Arnold. LC 79-20055. (Christian Care Bks.). 118p. 1980. pap. 7.95 (ISBN 0-664-24294-4). Westminster.

When Your Patient Dies. William G. Justice, Jr. LC 83-15064. 60p. 1983. pap. 7.50 (ISBN 0-87125-091-8). Cath Health.

When Your Teenager Stops Going to Church. James Di Giacomo. LC 80-65401. (When Books). (Illus.). 96p. (Orig.). 1980. pap. 2.45 (ISBN 0-87029-165-3, 20260-6). Abbey.

When Your Wife Wants to Work. Mary Shivanandan. LC 79-51278. (When Bks). (Illus.). 1980. pap. 2.45 (ISBN 0-87029-151-3, 20237-4). Abbey.

When You're Confused & Uncertain. rev. ed. Gene A. Getz. LC 86-477. (Biblical Renewal Ser.). 160p. 1986. pap. 5.95 (ISBN 0-8307-1122-8, 5418749). Regal.

When You're Divorced & Catholic. James J. Young. LC 80-69090. (When Bk). 96p. 1980. pap. 2.45 (ISBN 0-87029-172-6, 20265-5). Abbey.

When You're in You're Out. Mollie Thompson. LC 86-10977. (Illus.). 192p. (Orig.). 1986. pap. 5.95 (ISBN 0-932581-50-1). Word Aflame.

When You're the News. Rick Taylor. 112p. 1987. pap. 5.95 (ISBN 0-87403-225-3, 3185). Standard Pub.

Where Angels Fear to Tread. O. S. Hawkins. LC 83-24022. 1984. pap. 4.95 (ISBN 0-8054-5538-8). Broadman.

Where Are We Running? June Strong. LC 78-26271. (Orion Ser.). 1979. pap. 3.50 (ISBN 0-8127-0207-7). Review & Herald.

Where Are You, God? Elspeth Murphy. (David & I Talk to God Ser.). (Illus.). 1980. pap. 2.50 (ISBN 0-89191-274-6). Cook.

Where Are You, God? Elizabeth E. Watson. (Illus.). 1977. bds. 5.50 (ISBN 0-8054-4235-9, 4242-35). Broadman.

Where Are You Going? A Guide to the Spiritual Journey. Swami Durgananda. LC 81-52192. 176p. (Orig.). 1981. pap. 6.95 (ISBN 0-914602-75-6). SYDA Found.

Where Are You, Lord? Mary A. Kerl. LC 82-70949. (Young Readers Ser.). 112p. (Orig.). 1982. pap. 3.95 (ISBN 0-8066-1924-4, 10-7069). Augsburg.

Where Christ is Still Tortured. Richard Wurmbrand. 160p. 1982. pap. 3.95 (ISBN 0-88264-162-X). Diane Bks.

Where Christ Still Suffers. Richard Wurmbrand. Tr. of Where Christ Is Still Tortured. 1984. pap. 3.50 (ISBN 0-88270-578-4). Bridge Pub.

Where Do I Go from Here. Linda B. Elvey. 1983. 6.00 (ISBN 0-8062-2194-1). Carlton.

Where Do We Go from Here? Kenneth Hagin, Jr. 1982. pap. 0.50 mini bk (ISBN 0-89276-712-X). Hagin Ministries.

Where Do We Live? (Illus.). 1986. 2.95 (ISBN 1-55513-176-X, Chariot Bks). Cook.

Where Do You Draw the Line. R. Garry Shirts. 1977. 29.00 (ISBN 0-686-10238-X). Simile II.

Where Do You Grow from Here? LeRoy Lawson. 128p. 1985. pap. 2.95 (ISBN 0-87239-967-2, 41034). Standard Pub.

Where Does a Mother Go to Resign? Barbara Johnson. LC 79-12686. 160p. 1979. pap. 4.95 (ISBN 0-87123-606-0, 210606). Bethany Hse.

Where Does the Church Stand, Vol. 146. Ed. by Giuseppe Alberigo. (Concilium 1981). 128p. (Orig.). 1981. pap. 6.95 (ISBN 0-8164-2313-X, HarpR). Har-Row.

Where Faith Begins. C. Ellis Nelson. pap. 8.95 (ISBN 0-8042-1471-9). John Knox.

Where Flowers Grow. Belle B. Broadbent. 16p. 1982. pap. 1.95 (ISBN 0-939298-04-X). J M Prods.

Where God Meets Man: Luther's Down-to-Earth Approach to the Gospel. Gerhard O. Forde. LC 72-78569. 128p. 1972. pap. 6.95 (ISBN 0-8066-1235-5, 10-7060). Augsburg.

Where Gods May Dwell: Understanding the Human Condition. S. D. Gaede. 168p. (Orig.). 1985. pap. 7.95 (ISBN 0-310-42971-4, 12756P). Zondervan.

Where Grown Men Cry: An Endeavor to Free the Spirit. James N. Slaughter, Jr. & David J. Jackson. LC 86-32665. (Illus.). 176p. 1986. pap. 12.95 (ISBN 0-9617749-0-8). Cormac Inc.

Where Have All Our People Gone? New Choices for Old Churches. Carl S. Dudley. LC 79-525. (Illus.). 1979. pap. 6.95 (ISBN 0-8298-0359-9). Pilgrim NY.

Where Have All the Little Angels Gone? Thomas L. Hakes. (Illus.). 10p. 1985. pap. 2.00x (ISBN 0-915020-58-0). Bardic.

Where Heavens Hide. Dolores Dahl. LC 84-51375. (Illus.). 48p. (Orig.). 1984. pap. 3.95 (ISBN 0-9608960-2-3). Single Vision.

Where in the World Is God? God's Presence in Every Moment of Our Lives. Robert Brizee. 160p. 1987. pap. 6.95 (ISBN 0-8358-0556-5). Upper Room.

Where Is Bobby Now? Marvin Moore. (Flame Ser.). 1976. pap. 0.99 (ISBN 0-8127-0106-2). Review & Herald.

Where Is God In My Praying? Biblical Responses to Eight Searching Questions. Daniel J. Simundson. LC 86-22294. 96p. (Orig.). 1986. pap. 5.50 (ISBN 0-8066-2241-5, 10-7096). Augsburg.

Where Is God in My Suffering? Biblical Responses to Seven Searching Questions. Daniel J. Simundson. LC 83-72108. 80p. 1984. pap. 4.95 (ISBN 0-8066-2052-8, 10-7071). Augsburg.

Where Is God When It Hurts? Philip Yancey. 1977. pap. 5.95 (ISBN 0-310-35411-0, 9992P); 2.95 (ISBN 0-310-35431-5, 9992G). Zondervan.

Where Is God When It Hurts. Phillip Yancey. 7.95 (ISBN 0-310-35417-X). Zondervan.

Where Is History Going? John W. Montgomery. LC 69-11659. 256p. 1969. 7.95 (ISBN 0-87123-640-0, 210640). Bethany Hse.

Where Is It Written? An Introductory, Annotated Bibliography in Spirituality. John Weborg. 1978. 0.75 (ISBN 0-8199-0739-1). Franciscan Herald.

Where Is Jesus? Joyce Morse. (Books I Can Read). 32p. 1980. pap. 1.95 (ISBN 0-8127-0280-8). Review & Herald.

Where Is Joey? Lost among the Hare Krishnas. Morris Yanoff. LC 81-11280. x, 260p. 1982. 15.95 (ISBN 0-8040-0414-5, Pub by Swallow). Ohio U Pr.

Where Is the Lost Ark? Doug Wead. LC 82-71755. 122p. (Orig.). 1982. pap. 2.95 (ISBN 0-87123-628-1, 200628). Bethany Hse.

Where Is the Rainbow? Nancy R. Vaughn & Johnny W. Sloan. LC 84-52691. (Illus.). 144p. (Orig.). 1985. pap. 5.95 (ISBN 0-318-04447-1). Vaughn Pub KY.

Where Jesus Walked. William H. Stephens. LC 80-67422. 1981. soft cover 14.95 (ISBN 0-8054-1138-0). Broadman.

Where Jesus Walked: Through the Holy Land with the Master. Frank M. Field. Ed. by Moshe Davis. LC 77-70681. (America & the Holy Land Ser.). (Illus.). 1977. Repr. of 1951 ed. lib. bdg. 20.00x (ISBN 0-405-10244-5). Ayer Co Pubs.

Where Judaism Differed. Abba H. Silver. 1972. pap. 5.95 (ISBN 0-02-089360-4, Collier). Macmillan.

Where Judaism Differed. Abba H. Silver. 318p. 1987. Repr. of 1956 ed. 25.00 (ISBN 0-87668-957-8). Aronson.

Where Legends Live. Douglas A. Rossman. (Illus.). 48p. (Orig.). 1986. pap. 5.00x (ISBN 0-935741-10-0). Cherokee Pubns.

Where Life Begins. Barry Callen. 128p. 1973. pap. 2.50 (ISBN 0-87162-146-0, D9026). Warner Pr.

Where Love is Found. Marion K. Rich. 124p. (Orig.). 1984. pap. 5.95 (ISBN 0-8341-0922-0). Beacon Hill.

Where Moth & Rust Do Not Consume. A. M. Coniaris. 1983. pap. 5.95 (ISBN 0-937032-30-1). Light&Life Pub Co MN.

Where on Earth Is God? Richard Howard. 144p. 1983. pap. 3.95 (ISBN 0-8341-0823-2). Beacon Hill.

Where One Is Gathered in His Name. Dan R. Crawford. LC 85-19519. 1986. 6.95 (ISBN 0-8054-5025-4). Broadman.

Where Our Lives Touch. Mary H. Johnson. 35p. (Orig.). 1985. pap. 3.00 (ISBN 0-914631-00-4). Questpr.

Where the Eagles Gather: Vol. 24, Bks. I & II. Elizabeth C. Prophet. LC 81-86682. 636p. 1982. 35.90; Bk. I. 17.95 (ISBN 0-916766-49-7); Bk. II. 17.95 (ISBN 0-916766-57-8). Summit Univ.

Where the Gospel Meets the World. Daughters of St. Paul. 1977. 6.95 (ISBN 0-8198-0482-7); pap. 5.00 (ISBN 0-8198-0483-5). Dghtrs St Paul.

Where the Jews Fail. M. M. Feuerlight. 1984. lib. bdg. 79.95 (ISBN 0-87700-569-9). Revisionist Pr.

Where the Passion Is: A Reading of Kierkegaard's Philosophical Fragments. H. A. Nielsen. LC 83-6923. 209p. 1983. 20.00 (ISBN 0-8130-0742-9). U Presses Fla.

Where the Rivers Flow: Exploring the Sources of Faith Formation. Scott Walker. 160p. 1986. 10.95 (ISBN 0-8499-0538-9, 0538-9). Word Bks.

Where the Saints Meet, Nineteen Eight-Four. 1979. pap. text ed. 10.00 (ISBN 0-686-25231-4). Firm Foun Pub.

Where the Wind Begins: Stories of Hurting People Who Said Yes to Life. Paula D'Arcy. 144p. 1985. pap. 5.95 (ISBN 0-87788-925-2). Shaw Pubs.

Where There's a Wall, There's a Way. Donald H. Polston. (Living Books). 224p. 1985. pap. 2.95 (ISBN 0-8423-8204-6). Tyndale.

Where Time Becomes Space. Judith Antony. 1978. 8.95 (ISBN 0-8199-0699-9). Franciscan Herald.

Where to Go with Your Troubles. William F. Burton. 80p. 1969. pap. 1.00 (ISBN 0-88243-627-9, 02-0627). Gospel Pub.

Where Two or Three Are Gathered. Leonard Mann. 1986. 6.25 (ISBN 0-89536-791-2, 6809). CSS of Ohio.

Where We Are: American Catholics in the 1980's. Ed. by Michael Glazier. 1985. pap. 7.95 (ISBN 0-89453-471-8). M Glazier.

Where We Got the Bible... Our Debt to the Catholic Church. Henry G. Graham. 153p. 1977. pap. 3.00 (ISBN 0-89555-137-3). TAN Bks Pubs.

Wherever He Leads I'll Go: The Story of B. B. McKinney. Paul Powell. 50p. (Orig.). 1974. pap. 2.00 (ISBN 0-914520-04-0). Insight Pr.

Wherever I Go, I Go to Jerusalem. Hillel Goldberg. 240p. 1986. 12.95 (ISBN 0-940646-09-9); pap. 8.95 (ISBN 0-940646-10-2). Rossel Bks.

Wheston's Commentaries on Acts, Romans, Vol. 3. 13.95 (ISBN 0-686-13906-2). Schmul Pub Co.

Which Bible? 6th, rev. ed. Ed. by David O. Fuller. LC 70-129737. 360p. 1975. pap. 8.95 (ISBN 0-8254-2612-X). Kregel.

Which Church. Carl Ketcherside. pap. 0.50 (ISBN 0-686-70363-4). Reiner.

Which Translation Do You Prefer. Carol E. Mille. 1975. pap. 1.00 (ISBN 0-915374-52-8, 52-8). Rapids Christian.

Which Way Are You Leading Me, Lord? Bible Devotions for Boys. Nathan Aaseng. LC 84-21562. (Young Readers Ser.). 112p. (Orig.). 1984. pap. 3.95 (ISBN 0-8066-2113-3, 10-7099). Augsburg.

Which Way to Happiness? Dan Baumann. LC 81-50302. 144p. 1981. pap. 3.50 (ISBN 0-8307-0773-5, S351100). Regal.

Which Way to Lutheran Unity? A History of Efforts to Unite the Lutherans of America. John H. Tietjen. LC 66-25270. 176p. 1975. pap. text ed. 7.50 (ISBN 0-915644-01-0). Clayton Pub Hse.

While It Is Day. Elton Trueblood. 163p. 1983. pap. write for info. (ISBN 0-932970-36-2). Yokefellow Pr.

While It Was Still Dark. Adaline Bjorkman. (Illus.). 1978. pap. 3.95 (ISBN 0-910452-34-2). Covenant.

While the Gods Play. Alain Danielou. 352p. (Orig.). 1987. pap. 12.95 (ISBN 0-89281-115-3). Inner Tradit.

While You Can. Palmer Gedde. (Orig.). 1987. pap. price not set (ISBN 0-89536-891-9, 7877). CSS of Ohio.

Whirling Ecstasy. Aflaki. Tr. by C. Huart. (Illus.). 30p. (Orig.). 1973. pap. 1.95 (ISBN 0-915424-02-9, Prophecy Pressworks). Sufi Islamia-Prophecy.

Whirlpool of Torment: The Oppressive Presence of God in Ancient Israel. James L. Crenshaw. LC 83-18479. (Overtures to Biblical Theology Ser.). 144p. 1984. pap. 7.95 (ISBN 0-8006-1536-0, 1-1536). Fortress.

Whisper of Christmas: Reflections for Advent & Christmas. Joe E. Pennel, Jr. LC 84-50839. 128p. (Orig.). 1984. pap. 4.95 (ISBN 0-8358-0492-5). Upper Room.

Whisper of His Grace: A Fresh Look at Suffering Through the Eyes of Job & Jesus. David McKenna. 192p. 1987. 12.95 (ISBN 0-8499-0560-5). Word Bks.

Whisperings in the Silence. Zella Townsend. 1972. pap. 2.00 (ISBN 0-87516-121-9). De Vorss.

Whispers from Eternity. 9th ed. Paramahansa Yogananda. LC 86-60584. (Illus.). 239p. 1986. 7.95 (ISBN 0-87612-103-2); pap. 3.50x Span. ed. (ISBN 0-87612-101-6); German ed. 10.00x (ISBN 3-85399-034-7). Self Realization.

Whispers from Eternity. Paramhansa Yogananda. LC 85-71375. 1978. pap. 12.95 (ISBN 0-937134-03-1). Amrita Found.

Whispers from Eternity, First Vision. Paramahansa Yogananda. 1977. 6.95 (ISBN 0-87612-102-4). Self Realization.

Whispers from the Other Shore. Ravi Ravindra. LC 84-40164. 170p. (Orig.). 1984. pap. 6.50 (ISBN 0-8356-0589-2, Quest). Theos Pub Hse.

Whispers of His Power. Amy Carmichael. 256p. 1985. pap. 6.95 (ISBN 0-8007-5206-6, Power Bks). Revell.

Whistling in the Dark: The Story of Fred Lowery, the Blind Whistler. Fred Lowery. As told to John McDowell. LC 83-4085. (Illus.). 416p. 1983. 15.95 (ISBN 0-88289-298-3). Pelican.

White & Negro Spirituals, Their Life Span & Kinship. George P. Jackson. (Music Reprint Ser.). (Illus.). xii, 349p. 1975. Repr. of 1944 ed. lib. bdg. 42.50 (ISBN 0-306-70667-9). Da Capo.

White Bird of Tao. Manly P. Hall. pap. 4.00 (ISBN 0-89314-371-5). Philos Res.

White Eagle Lodge Book of Health & Healing. Joan Hodgson. 240p. 1983. text ed. 10.50 (ISBN 0-85487-063-6). De Vorss.

White Fox of Andhra. Donald S. Fox. 216p. 1978. 6.95 (ISBN 0-8059-2432-9). Dorrance.

White Goddess: A Historical Grammar of Poetic Myth. rev. & enl. ed. Robert Graves. 511p. 1966. pap. 9.95 (ISBN 0-374-50493-8). FS&G.

White Goddess (amended & enlarged edition) Robert Graves. 1983. 16.50 (ISBN 0-8446-5983-5). Peter Smith.

White Lotus. Bhagwan Shree Rajneesh. Ed. by Ma Prem Asha. LC 81-903266. (Zen Ser.). (Illus.). 430p. 1981. 17.95 (ISBN 0-88050-172-3); pap. 13.95 (ISBN 0-88050-672-5). Chidvilas Found.

White Lotus: At the Feet of the Mother. Ravindra. (Illus.). 1978. 8.50x (ISBN 0-89684-466-8). Orient Bk Dist.

White Planet. Frank E. Stranges. 24p. 1985. pap. text ed. 2.00 (ISBN 0-933470-04-5). Intl Evang.

White Robed Monk. 3rd, rev. & enl. ed. Ira Progoff. LC 79-1553. (Entrance Meditation Ser.). 111p. 1983. pap. 3.95 (ISBN 0-87941-007-8); pap. 11.50 incl. cassette. Dialogue Hse.

White Roots & the Mysteries of God: About the Dead Sea Scrolls. Lena E. Rudder. (Illus.). 144p. (Orig.). 1986. pap. write for info. (ISBN 0-937581-00-3). Zarathustrotemo Pr.

White Roots & the Mysteries of God: And the Dead Sea Scrolls. rev. ed. Lena E. Rudder. (Illus.). 144p. (Orig.). 1986. write for info. (ISBN 0-937581-01-1). Zarathustrotemo Pr.

White Thunder. Dane Rudhyar. 1976. pap. 3.50 (ISBN 0-916108-07-4). Seed Center.

Whitefield & Wesley on the New Birth. Timothy L. Smith. 544p. 1986. pap. 7.95 (ISBN 0-310-75151-9). Zondervan.

Whitehead & God: Prolegomena to Theological Reconstruction. Laurence Wilmot. 200p. 1979. text ed. 17.25x (ISBN 0-88920-070-X, Pub. by Wilfrid Laurier Canada). Humanities.

Whiteheadian Thought as a Basis for a Philosophy of Religion. Forrest Wood, Jr. LC 86-9282. 110p. (Orig.). 1986. lib. bdg. 19.50 (ISBN 0-8191-5422-9); pap. text ed. 8.75 (ISBN 0-8191-5423-7). U Pr of Amer.

Whitehead's Metaphysics: A Critical Examination of Process & Reality. Edward Pols. LC 67-10721. 217p. 1967. 8.95x (ISBN 0-8093-0280-2). S Ill U Pr.

Whitehead's Metaphysics: An Introductory Exposition. Ivor Leclerc. LC 86-4027. 248p. 1986. pap. text ed. 11.00 (ISBN 0-8191-4852-0). U Pr of Amer.

Whitehead's Metaphysics of Extension & Solidarity. Jorge L. Nobo. (Philosophy Ser.). 544p. (Orig.). 1986. 49.50x (ISBN 0-88706-261-X); pap. 24.50x (ISBN 0-88706-262-8). State U NY Pr.

Whitehead's Ontology. John Lango. LC 78-171184. 1972. 34.50x (ISBN 0-87395-093-3). State U NY Pr.

Whither Islam? A Survey of Modern Movements in the Moslem World. Ed. by Hamilton A. Gibb. LC 73-180338. Repr. of 1932 ed. 27.00 (ISBN 0-404-56263-9). AMS Pr.

Whither Thou Goest. Carolyn S. Hind. LC 85-51991. (Illus.). 192p. 1985. 12.50 (ISBN 0-936029-00-5). Western Bk Journ.

Whittier: Crusader & Prophet. Arthur Rowntree. LC 73-13660. 1946. Repr. 15.00 (ISBN 0-8414-7230-0). Folcroft.

Whittier's Use of the Bible. James S. Stevens. LC 74-13173. 1974. Repr. of 1930 ed. lib. bdg. 15.00 (ISBN 0-8414-7798-1). Folcroft.

Who Am I? Norman P. Grubb. 1975. pap. 2.95 (ISBN 0-87508-227-0). Chr Lit.

Who Am I? Paul L. Walker & Charles P. Conn. LC 74-82934. 1974. pap. 1.99 (ISBN 0-87148-905-8). Pathway Pr.

Who Am I? A Look in the Mirror. Carolyn Nystrom & Mathew Floding. (Young Fisherman Bible Studyguides). 64p. (Orig.). (YA) 1987. pap. 4.95 tchr's. ed. (ISBN 0-87788-933-3); pap. 2.95 student ed. (ISBN 0-87788-932-5). Shaw Pubs.

Who Am I & What Am I Doing Here. Mark W. Lee. 1986. pap. 5.95 (ISBN 0-8010-5643-8). Baker Bk.

Who Am I & What Difference Does It Make? David L. Hocking. LC 85-8810. (Living Theology Ser.). 1985. pap. 7.95 (ISBN 0-88070-102-1). Multnomah.

Who Am I, Lord? Betty S. Everett. LC 82-72645. (Young Readers Ser.). 112p. (Orig.). 1983. pap. 3.95 (ISBN 0-8066-1951-1, 10-7072). Augsburg.

Who Am I Lord... & Why Am I Here? William Hulme & Dale Hulme. LC 83-25175. 1984. pap. 4.95 (ISBN 0-570-03926-6, 12-2860). Concordia.

Who Are the Amish? Merle Good. LC 85-70283. (Illus.). 128p. (Orig.). 1985. 24.95 (ISBN 0-934672-28-8); pap. 15.95 (ISBN 0-934672-26-1). Good Bks PA.

Who Are "The Jews" Today? D. Lutzweiler. 1984. lib. bdg. 79.95 (ISBN 0-87700-568-0). Revisionist Pr.

Who Are the Mennonite Brethern? Katie F. Wiebe. LC 84-82049. 107p. (Orig.). 1984. pap. 5.95 (ISBN 0-919797-31-8). Kindred Pr.

Who Are the Peacemakers? The Christian Case for Nuclear Deterrence. Jerram Barrs. LC 83-62684. 60p. 1983. pap. 2.95 (ISBN 0-89107-307-8, Crossway Bks). Good News.

Who Are the Unchurched? An Exploratory Study. J. Russell Hale. LC 77-81922. 1977. pap. 2.00x (ISBN 0-914422-06-5). Glenmary Res Ctr.

Who Are They? (Contemporary Vedic Library Series Based on the Teachings of A. C. Bhaktivedanta Swami Prabhupada). 1.50 (ISBN 0-89213-111-X). Bhaktivedanta.

Who Are You? Jon L. Joyce. (Orig.). 1985. pap. 2.95 (ISBN 0-937172-61-8). JLJ Pubs.

Who Are You & Why Are You Here? Peter D. Francuch. LC 83-51781. 256p. (Orig.). 1984. pap. 4.95 (ISBN 0-939386-07-0). TMH Pub.

Who Are You Monsieur Gurdjieff? Rene Zuber. Tr. by Jenny Koralek. 80p. 1980. pap. 4.95 (ISBN 0-7100-0674-8). Methuen Inc.

Who Are You: The Life of St. Cecilia. Marie C. Buehrle. LC 70-158918. 1971. pap. 2.95 (ISBN 0-913382-07-8, 101-7). Prow Bks-Franciscan.

Who Becomes a Bishop? A Study of Priests Who Become Bishops in the Episcopal Church (1960 to 1980) John H. Morgan. 65p. (Orig.). 1985. pap. 6.95x (ISBN 0-932269-28-1). Wyndham Hall.

Who Can We Trust? Mary Bernard. LC 80-80531. 128p. 1980. 2.50 (ISBN 0-89221-075-3). New Leaf.

Who Cares? A Handbook of Christian Counselling. Evelyn H. Peterseon. 181p. 1982. pap. text ed. 6.95 (ISBN 0-85364-272-9). Attic Pr.

Who Cares? A Handbook of Christian Counselling. Evelyn Peterson. LC 82-60447. (Illus.). 192p. 1982. pap. 7.95 (ISBN 0-8192-1317-9). Morehouse.

Who Crucified Jesus? Solomon Zeitlin. 1976. pap. 6.95x (ISBN 0-8197-0013-4). Bloch.

Who Do Americans Say That I Am? George Gallup, Jr. & George O'Connell. LC 85-26383. 130p. (Orig.). 1986. pap. 10.95 (ISBN 0-664-24685-0). Westminster.

Who Do People Say I Am? The Interpretation of Jesus in the New Testament Gospels. Marvin W. Meyer. LC 82-24229. pap. 23.80 (ISBN 0-317-30155-1, 2025337). Bks Demand UMI.

Who Do You Say? Jesus Christ in Latin American Theology. Claus Bussmann. Tr. by Robert Barr from Ger. LC 84-16476. Tr. of Beifreung durch Jesus? 192p. (Orig.). 1985. pap. 9.95 (ISBN 0-88344-711-8). Orbis Bks.

Who Do You Say That I Am? Joseph E. Monti. LC 83-82023. (Orig.). 1984. pap. 4.95 (ISBN 0-8091-2598-6). Paulist Pr.

Who Do You Say That I Am? An Adult Inquiry into the First Three Gospels. Edward J. Ciuba. LC 74-10808. 155p. 1974. pap. 5.95 (ISBN 0-8189-0295-7). Alba.

Who Do You Say You Are? Christ's Love for Us. George A. Maloney. (Orig.). 1986. pap. 4.95 (ISBN 0-914544-64-0). Living Flame Pr.

Who Do you Think You Are. Sue Armstrong. 1983. 24.00x (ISBN 0-86334-046-6, Pub. by Macdonald Pub UK). State Mutual Bk.

Who Gets to the Top? Executive Suite Discrimination in the Eighties. Richard L. Zweigenhaft. LC 84-70044. 48p. 1984. pap. 3.00 (ISBN 0-87495-059-7). Am Jewish Comm.

Who Has the Say in the Church, Vol. 148. Ed. by Hans Kung & Jurgen Moltman. (Concilium 1981). 128p. (Orig.). 1981. pap. 6.95 (ISBN 0-8164-2348-2, HarpR). Har-Row.

Who I Am in Jesus. Sarah Hornsby. (Illus.). 160p. 1986. 8.95 (ISBN 0-8007-9087-1). Revell.

Who I Will Be: Is There Joy & Suffering in God? Robert Wild. 5.95 (ISBN 0-87193-089-7). Dimension Bks.

Who in the World in Christ Are You? Bill Kaiser. 231p. (Orig.). 1983. pap. text ed. 5.50 (ISBN 0-914307-12-6, Dist. by Harrison Hse). Word Faith.

Who Is a Christian? 24.95 (ISBN 0-87193-188-5). Dimension Bks.

Who Is Christ. Bill Kaiser. 152p. (Orig.). 1983. pap. text ed. 4.95 (ISBN 0-914307-01-0, Dist. by Harrison Hse). Word Faith.

Who Is Christ? A Theology of the Incarnation. Galot. Tr. by M. Angeline Bouchard. 423p. 1981. 10.00 (ISBN 0-8199-0813-4). Franciscan Herald.

Who Is Father Christmas? Shirley Harrison. (Illus.). 64p. 1983. 7.50 (ISBN 0-7153-8222-5). David & Charles.

Who Is God? Carolyn Nystrom. (Children's Bible Basics Ser.). 32p. 1980. pap. 4.95 (ISBN 0-8024-5992-7). Moody.

Who Is Jesus? Bruce A. Demarest. 132p. 1983. pap. 4.50 (ISBN 0-88207-103-3). SP Pubns.

Who Is Jesus. Bruce A. Demarest. Tr. by Ruth T. Chen. (Basic Doctrine Ser.: Bk. 1). 1985. pap. write for info. (ISBN 0-941598-26-8). Living Spring Pubns.

Who Is Jesus? Carolyn Nystrom. (Children's Bible Basics Ser.). 32p. 1980. pap. 4.95 (ISBN 0-8024-5993-5). Moody.

Who Is Jesus? Pope Paul The Sixth. LC 72-80446. pap. 2.25 (ISBN 0-8198-0325-1). Dghtrs St Paul.

Who Is Jesus? R. C. Sproul. 96p. 1983. pap. 2.95 (ISBN 0-8423-8216-X). Tyndale.

Who Is Jesus? A Woman's Workshop on Mark. Carolyn Nystrom. (Woman's Workshop Ser.). 144p. 1987. pap. 3.95 (ISBN 0-310-42001-6). Zondervan.

Who Is Jesus Christ? William L. Hendricks. LC 83-71265. (Layman's Library of Christian Doctrine Ser.). 1985. 5.95 (ISBN 0-8054-1632-3). Broadman.

Who Is Jesus? Leader's Guide. Robert Clark. Tr. by Lorna Y. Chao. (Basic Doctrine Ser.). 1986. pap. write for info. (ISBN 0-941598-33-0). Living Spring Pubns.

Who Is My Mother? Mary T. Malone. 144p. 1984. pap. 6.95 (ISBN 0-697-02019-3). Wm C Brown.

Who Is Padre Pio? Tr. by Laura C. White. (Illus.). 44p. 1974. pap. 1.00 (ISBN 0-89555-101-2). TAN Bks Pubs.

Who Is Responsible for Sickness. Elbert Willis. 1978. 1.25 (ISBN 0-89858-010-2). Fill the Gap.

Who Is Sun Myung Moon? Paul Duncan. 21p. (Orig.). 1981. pap. text ed. 1.25 (ISBN 0-87148-914-7). Pathway Pr.

Who Is Teresa Neumann? Charles M. Carty. 1974. pap. 1.25 (ISBN 0-89555-093-8). TAN Bks Pubs.

Who Is the Antichrist? John L. Benson. LC 78-2426. 1978. pap. 2.50 (ISBN 0-87227-058-0). Reg Baptist.

Who Is the Master Omraam Mikhael Aivanhov. (Testimonials Ser.). (Illus.). 156p. (Orig.). 1982. pap. 9.00 (ISBN 2-85566-190-0, Pub. by Prosveta France). Prosveta USA.

Who Is the Minister's Wife? A Search for Personal Fulfillment. Charlotte Ross. LC 79-24027. 132p. 1980. pap. 6.95 (ISBN 0-664-24302-9). Westminster.

Who is the True Guru. Roy E. Davis. 192p. 1981. pap. 4.95 (ISBN 0-317-20864-0). CSA Pr.

Who Is the Woman of the Apocalypse? John M. Haffert. 104p. 1982. pap. 1.95 (ISBN 0-911988-47-5). AMI Pr.

Who Is This Christ? Gospel Christology & Contemporary Faith. Reginald Fuller & Pheme Perkins. LC 82-48590. 176p. 1983. pap. 8.95 (ISBN 0-8006-1706-1, 1-1706). Fortress.

Who Is This God You Pray To. Bernard Hayes. 96p. (Orig.). 1981. pap. 2.95 (ISBN 0-914544-41-1). Living Flame Pr.

Who Is Worth Following. Spiros Zodhiates. 1982. pap. 4.95 (ISBN 0-89957-514-5). AMG Pubs.

Who Knows One? A Book of Jewish Numbers. Yaffa Ganz. 1981. 8.95 (ISBN 0-87306-285-X). Feldheim.

Who Knows Ten: Children's Tales of the Ten Commandments. Molly Cone. LC 65-24639. (Illus.). 1968. text ed. 6.00 (ISBN 0-8074-0080-7, 102551); record o.p. 5.95 (ISBN 0-8074-0081-5, 102552). UAHC.

Who Made God. Emmy L. Murphy. 1978. pap. 2.25 (ISBN 0-915374-07-2, 07-2). Rapids Christian.

Who Made These Things? Joyce W. Crapps. LC 86-18773. (Bible-&-Me Ser.). 1987. 5.95 (ISBN 0-8054-4178-6). Broadman.

Who Me? A Missionary? Daniel W. Bacon. 1985. pap. 1.25 (ISBN 9971-972-32-8). OMF Bks.

Who, Me, Give a Speech? Handbook for the Reluctant Christian Woman. Nancy I. Alford. 160p. (Orig.). 1987. pap. price not set (ISBN 0-8010-0211-7). Baker Bk.

Who, Me Teach My Child Religion? rev. ed. Dolores Curran. 156p. 1981. pap. 6.95 (HarpR). Har-Row.

Who Moved the Stone. Frank Morison. pap. 3.95 (ISBN 0-310-29562-9, 10371P). Zondervan.

Who Needs the Family? O. R. Johnston. LC 80-7780. 152p. (Orig.). 1980. pap. 5.95 (ISBN 0-87784-588-3). Inter-Varsity.

Who, or What, Is God? Parker L. Johnstone. 212p. 1984. 7.95 (ISBN 0-917802-12-8). Theoscience Found.

Who Owns the Family. Ray R. Sutton. (Biblical Blueprint ser.). 1986. pap. 6.95 (ISBN 0-8407-3097-7). Nelson.

Who Put All These Cucumbers in My Garden? Patricia F. Wilson. LC 83-51398. 144p. (Orig.). 1984. pap. 5.50 (ISBN 0-8358-0475-5). Upper Room.

Who Put Jesus on the Cross. A. W. Tozer. 1976. pap. 3.45 (ISBN 0-87509-212-8). Chr Pubns.

Who Rules Your Life? Prentice A. Meador, Jr. LC 79-64089. (Journey Bks.). 1979. pap. 3.50 (ISBN 0-8344-0107-X). Sweet.

Who Said Life Is Fair? Jerry Gladson. Ed. by Gerald Wheeler. 128p. 1985. pap. 6.95 (ISBN 0-8280-0242-8). Review & Herald.

Who Says? A Black Perspective on the Authority of New Testament Exegesis Highlighting the Foundation for Its Interpretations & Applications. Walter A. McCray. Ed. by William H. Bentley. 75p. (Orig.). pap. write for info. (ISBN 0-933176-35-X). Black Light Fellow.

Who Says Get Married? How to Be Happy & Single. Don Meredith. LC 81-16949. 176p. 1981. pap. 4.95 (ISBN 0-8407-5741-7). Nelson.

Who Should Care: The Development of Kilkenny Social Services. Stanislaus Kennedy. (Turoe Press Ser.). 228p. pap. 12.95 (ISBN 0-905223-26-8, Dist. by Scribner). M Boyars Pubs.

Who Switched Price Tags? How to Make Life Better in Your Work, Family & Church. Tony Campolo. 224p. 1986. 11.95 (ISBN 0-8499-0491-9). Word Bks.

Who Tarnished My Saints? Merle G. Franke. 1984. 5.95 (ISBN 0-89536-986-9, 7534). CSS of Ohio.

Who Then Is Paul? Hubert R. Johnson. Ed. by Chevy Chase Manuscripts Staff. LC 80-1406. 272p. 1981. lib. bdg. 28.25 (ISBN 0-8191-1364-6); pap. text ed. 10.00 (ISBN 0-8191-1365-4). U Pr of Amer.

Who Was Jesus? Roy A. Rosenberg. LC 85-29523. 132p. (Orig.). 1986. lib. bdg. 23.75 (ISBN 0-8191-5177-7); pap. 9.25 (ISBN 0-8191-5178-5). U Pr of Amer.

Who Was Jew: Rabbinic & Halakhic Perspectives on the Jewish-Christian Schism. Lawrence H. Schiffman. (Illus.). 140p. 1985. 14.95 (ISBN 0-88125-053-8); pap. 8.95 (ISBN 0-88125-054-6). Ktav.

Who Was Muhammad? S. Hosain. pap. 3.50 (ISBN 0-686-18418-1). Kazi Pubns.

Who Was St. Patrick? E. A. Thompson. LC 85-14624. (Illus.). 192p. 1986. 21.95 (ISBN 0-312-87084-1). St Martin.

Who We Are Is How We Pray: Matching Personality & Spirituality. Dr. Charles J. Keating. 144p. (Orig.). 1987. 13.95 (ISBN 0-89622-292-6); pap. 7.95 (ISBN 0-89622-321-3). Twenty-Third.

Who Were the Israelites? Gosta W. Ahlstrom. x, 134p. 1986. text ed. 12.50x (ISBN 0-931464-24-2). Eisenbrauns.

Who, What, When, Where Bible Busy Book. William Coleman. 32p. 1984. pap. 1.50 (ISBN 0-89191-853-1). Cook.

Who, What, When, Where Book about the Bible. William Coleman. (Illus.). 1980. 11.95 (ISBN 0-89191-291-6). Cook.

Who? What? Where? Bible Quizzes. Max Stilson. (Quiz & Puzzle Bks.). 96p. 1980. pap. 2.95 (ISBN 0-8010-8012-6). Baker Bk.

Who Will Be My Teacher? The Christian Way to Stronger Schools. Marti W. Garlett. 256p. 1985. 12.95 (ISBN 0-8499-0471-4, 0471-4). Word Bks.

Who Will Deliver Us? Paul Zahl. 170p. 1985. pap. 7.95 large print ed. (ISBN 0-8027-2487-6). Walker & Co.

Who Will Deliver Us? Paul F. Zahl. 96p. (Orig.). 1983. pap. 5.95 (ISBN 0-8164-2468-3, HarpR). Har-Row.

Who Will Listen to Me? Prayer Thoughts for High School Girls. Judith Mattison. LC 77-72450. (Illus.). 1977. pap. 3.95 (ISBN 0-8066-1596-6, 10-7085). Augsburg.

Who Will Teach Me? Joseph F. Girzone. 61p. 1982. 6.00 (ISBN 0-911519-00-9). Richelieu Court.

Who Wrote The Bible. Richard E. Friedman. 1987. 16.95. Summit Bks.

Who Wrote the Bible? A Book for the People. Washington Gladden. LC 72-5435. (Select Bibliographies Reprint Ser.). 1972. Repr. of 1891 ed. 22.00 (ISBN 0-8369-6909-X). Ayer Co Pubs.

Whobody There? Charles Morse & Ann Morse. 1977. pap. 4.95x (ISBN 0-8358-0350-3). Upper Room.

Who'd Be a Missionary. Helen Morgan. 1972. pap. 1.50 (ISBN 0-87508-365-X). Chr Lit.

Who'd Stay a Missionary. Helen Morgan. 1972. pap. 1.50 (ISBN 0-87508-366-8). Chr Lit.

Whole Christ. E. Mersch. 638p. 1981. 39.00x (ISBN 0-234-77051-1, Pub. by Dobson Bks England). State Mutual Bk.

Whole Counsel of God. Carl E. Braaten. LC 73-88345. pap. 44.00 (2026840). Bks Demand UMI.

Whole Lay Ministry Catalog. Barbara Kuhn. (Orig.). 1979. pap. 8.95 (ISBN 0-8164-2187-0, HarpR). Har-Row.

Whole Man: Body Mind is Sprit. Roscoe Van Nuys. LC 77-145467. 134p. 1971. 6.95 (ISBN 0-8022-2050-9). Philos Lib.

Whole Person. (Benziger Family Life Program Ser.). 7p. 1978. 2.45 (ISBN 0-02-651800-7); tchrs. ed. 4.00 (ISBN 0-02-651810-4); family handbook 1.00 (ISBN 0-02-651840-6). Benziger Pub Co.

Whole Person in a Broken World: A Biblical Remedy for Today's World. Paul Tournier. LC 81-6885. 192p. 1981. pap. 6.95 (ISBN 0-06-068312-0, HarpR, RD 360). Har-Row.

Whole Treatise of the Cases of Conscience. William Perkins. LC 74-38218. (English Experience Ser.: No. 482). 690p. 1972. Repr. of 1606 ed. 43.00 (ISBN 90-221-0482-6). Walter J Johnson.

Whole Truth About Man. Pope John Paul II. 1981. 7.95 (ISBN 0-686-73822-5); pap. 6.95 (ISBN 0-8198-8202-X). Dghtrs St Paul.

Whole Woman: Fashioned in His Image. Faye C. Stowe. 135p. 1984. pap. 4.95 (ISBN 0-8341-0913-1). Beacon Hill.

Whole Works of John Howe, 6 Vols. John Howe. Ed. by H. Rogers. LC 71-169450. Repr. of 1863 ed. Set. lib. bdg. 115.00 (ISBN 0-404-03360-1); lib. bdg. 20.00 ea. AMS Pr.

Whole World Singing. Edith L. Thomas. 1950. 6.95 (ISBN 0-377-30882-X); pap. 4.95 (ISBN 0-377-30881-1). Friend Pr.

Wholehearted Integration: Harmonizing Psychology & Christianity Through Word & Deed. Kirk E. Farnsworth. 160p. 1986. 6.95 (ISBN 0-8010-3513-9). Baker Bk.

Wholeness & Holiness: Readings in the Psychology, Theology of Mental Health. H. Newton Malony. 304p. (Orig.). 1983. pap. 12.95 (ISBN 0-8010-6147-4). Baker Bk.

Wholeness in Worship. Sharon Neufer & Tom N. Emswiler. LC 79-2982. 192p. (Orig.). 1980. pap. 6.95 (ISBN 0-06-062247-4, RD 314, HarpR). Har-Row.

Wholeness of Life. J. Krishnamurti. LC 78-19495. 256p. 1981. pap. 8.95 (ISBN 0-06-064868-6, RD362, HarpR). Har-Row.

Wholeness: The Legacy of Jesus. Adolfo Quezada. 89p. (Orig.). 1983. pap. 2.95 (ISBN 0-914544-48-9). Living Flame Pr.

Wholesight. Frederick Parker-Rhodes. LC 77-95406. 30p. (Orig.). 1978. pap. 2.50x (ISBN 0-87574-217-3). Pendle Hill.

Wholistic Christianity: An Appeal for a Dynamic, Balanced Faith. David O. Moberg. 228p. 1985. 11.95 (ISBN 0-87178-931-0). Brethren.

Wholistic Health & Living Yoga. Malcolm Strutt. LC 77-85790. (Illus.). 320p. (Orig.). 1978. pap. 9.95 (ISBN 0-916438-08-2). Univ of Trees.

Wholly for God. William Law. Ed. by Andrew Murray. LC 76-6622. 336p. 1976. pap. 4.95 (ISBN 0-87123-602-8, 200602). Bethany Hse.

Wholly Holy. Herb Brokering. 96p. (Orig.). 1981. pap. 3.95 (ISBN 0-942562-00-3). Brokering Pr.

Wholly Human: Essays on the Theory & Language of Morality. Bruno Schuller. Tr. by Peter Heinegg from Ger. Orig. Title: Der Menschliche Mensch. 256p. (Orig.). 1986. 17.95 (ISBN 0-87840-427-9); pap. 9.95 (ISBN 0-87840-422-8). Georgetown U Pr.

Wholly Sanctified: Legacy Edition. Rev. ed. A. B. Simpson. Intro. by L. L. King. 136p. 1982. pap. 4.95 (ISBN 0-87509-306-X). Chr Pubns.

Whom God Chooses: The Child in the Church. rev. ed. Ralph R. Sundquist, Jr. 94p. 1973. pap. 1.65 (ISBN 0-664-71004-2, Pub. by Geneva Pr). Westminster.

Whom God Hath Joined. rev. ed. David R. Mace. LC 73-8871. 96p. 1984. pap. 6.95 (ISBN 0-664-24510-2). Westminster.

Whom Shall I Marry? Dorothy Voshell. 1979. pap. 4.50 (ISBN 0-87552-509-1). Presby & Reformed.

Whom Shall I Send? Watchman Nee. Tr. by Stephen Kaung. 1979. pap. 2.25 (ISBN 0-935008-45-4). Christian Fellow Pubs.

Who...Me? A Study in Identification by Seeking the Will of God. Vincent M. O'Flaherty. 200p. 1974. 4.95 (ISBN 0-8199-0540-2). Franciscan Herald.

Who's a Friend of the Water-Spurting Whale? Sanna A. Baker. (Illus.). 1987. 7.95 (ISBN 0-89191-587-7). Cook.

Who's My Friend? Alan T. Dale. (Rainbow Books (Bible Story Books for Children)). 16p. 1978. pap. 1.00 (ISBN 0-8192-1236-9). Morehouse.

Who's Number One. Joe White. 144p. 1986. pap. 4.95 (ISBN 0-8423-8215-1). Tyndale.

Who's the Boss? Love, Authority & Parenting. Gerald E. Nelson & Richard W. Lewak. LC 85-8184. Orig. Title: One-Minute Scolding. (Illus.). 164p. 1985. pap. 6.95 (ISBN 0-87773-342-2, 74223-0). Shambhala Pubns.

Who's Who Among Bible Women. Peggy Musgrove. LC 81-81126. 128p. (Orig.). 1981. 2.50 (ISBN 0-88243-883-2, 02-0883); teacher's ed. 3.95 (ISBN 0-88243-193-5, 32-0193). Gospel Pub.

Who's Who among Free Will Baptists. Ed. by H. D. Harrison. 1978. 18.95 (ISBN 0-89265-052-4). Randall Hse.

Who's Who among the Colored Baptists of the United States. Samuel W. Bacote. Ed. by Edwin S. Gaustad. LC 79-52588. (Baptist Tradition Ser.). (Illus.). 1980. Repr. of 1913 ed. lib. bdg. 28.50x (ISBN 0-405-12455-4). Ayer Co Pubs.

Who's Who in Greek & Roman Mythology. David Kravitz. 256p. 1977. (C N Potter Bks); pap. 5.95 (ISBN 0-517-52747-2). Crown.

Who's Who in Israel & Jewish Personalities from All over the World, 1985-86. 20th ed. Ed. by I. Ben. (Who's Who in Israel Ser.). 1985. 100.00x (ISBN 0-318-18965-8). Heinman.

Who's Who in the Bible. Albert E. Sims & George Dent. 1979. pap. 2.95 (ISBN 0-8065-0705-5). Citadel Pr.

Who's Who in the Bible. Albert E. Sims & George Dent. 1982. pap. 4.95 (ISBN 0-8022-1577-7). Philos Lib.

Who's Who in the Talmud. rev. ed. Alfred J. Kolatch. LC 64-24891. 228p. 1981. Repr. 9.95 (ISBN 0-8246-0263-3). Jonathan David.

"Who's Who" of Heaven: Saints for All Seasons. John P. Kleinz. 220p. (Orig.). 1987. pap. 12.95 (ISBN 0-87061-136-4). Chr Classics.

Whose Body Is It? The Troubling Issue of Informed Consent. Carolyn Faulder. 168p. (Orig.). 1986. pap. 6.95 (ISBN 0-86068-645-0, Pub. by Virago Pr). Salem Hse Pubs.

Whose Church Is This Anyway? Robert Versteeg. 1985. 6.95 (ISBN 0-89536-767-X, 5874). CSS of Ohio.

Whose Experience Counts in Theological Reflection? Monika Hellwig. LC 82-80331. (Pere Marquette Lecture Ser.). 112p. 1982. 7.95 (ISBN 0-87462-537-8). Marquette.

Why a Friends School. Douglas Heath. LC 75-81158. (Orig.). 1969. pap. 2.50x (ISBN 0-87574-164-9). Pendle Hill.

Why a Gift on Sunday. 1979. 2.95 (ISBN 0-8198-0603-X); pap. 1.95 (ISBN 0-8198-0604-8). Dghtrs St Paul.

Why Am I Afraid to Love? rev. ed. John Powell. (Illus.). 120p. 1972. pap. 3.50 (ISBN 0-913592-03-X). Argus Comm.

Why Am I Afraid to Tell You I'm a Christian? Don Posterski. LC 83-12958. 112p. (Orig.). 1983. pap. 2.95 (ISBN 0-87784-847-5). Inter-Varsity.

Why Am I Afraid to Tell You Who I Am? John Powell. LC 70-113274. (Illus.). 168p. 1969. pap. 2.95 (ISBN 0-913592-02-1). Argus Comm.

Why Am I Crying? Martha Maughon. 1983. pap. 5.95 (ISBN 0-310-37671-8, 11221P). Zondervan.

Why Am I Shy? Turning Shyness into Confidence. Norman B. Rohrer & S. Philip Sutherland. LC 78-52182. 1978. pap. 6.95 (ISBN 0-8066-1656-3, 10-7130). Augsburg.

Why & How of Burial & Death of a Muslim. Abdullah. (Illus.). 22p. (Orig.). 1985. pap. 1.50 (ISBN 0-916157-04-0). African Islam Miss Pubns.

Why Another Sect? B. T. Roberts. (Higher Christian Life Ser.). 321p. 1985. lib. bdg. 40.00 (ISBN 0-8240-6441-0). Garland Pub.

Why Are You Afraid. Michael Buckley. pap. 5.95 (ISBN 0-87061-060-0). Chr Classics.

Why Are You Here Now? Joyce Sanderson. 83p. (Orig.). 1981. pap. 6.95 (ISBN 0-942494-10-5). Coleman Pub.

Why Are You Home, Dad? Mary H. Sayler. 1983. 4.95 (ISBN 0-8054-4276-6, 4242-76). Broadman.

Why Be a Catholic? Ed. by Brennan Hill & Mary R. Newland. 108p. (Orig.). 1979. pap. 2.00 (ISBN 0-697-01713-3). Wm C Brown.

Why Be a Christian. Ralph Martin. 48p. (Orig.). 1987. pap. 1.95 (ISBN 0-89283-336-X). Servant.

Why Be Jewish? Intermarriage, Assimilation, & Alienation. Meir Kahane. LC 77-8774. 264p. 1982. pap. 7.95 (ISBN 0-8128-6129-9). Stein & Day.

Why Be Without a Gripe? Helen L. Snyder. 1978. pap. 5.00 (ISBN 0-89536-310-0, 2344). CSS of Ohio.

Why Believe? Richard Koffarnus. LC 80-53673. 96p. (Orig.). 1981. pap. 2.25 (ISBN 0-87239-425-5, 40090). Standard Pub.

Why Believe the Bible. John F. MacArthur, Jr. LC 79-91704. 160p. 1980. 5.95 (ISBN 0-8307-0750-6, 5413818). Regal.

Why Belong to the Church? Jerry L. Schmalenberger. 1971. 3.50 (ISBN 0-89536-261-9). CSS of Ohio.

Why Children Misbehave. Bruce Narramore. 152p. 1984. pap. 5.95 (ISBN 0-310-30361-3). Zondervan.

Why Choose Judaism: New Dimensions of Jewish Outreach. David Belin. 32p. 1985. pap. text ed. 4.00 (ISBN 0-8074-0302-4, 381900). UAHC.

Why Choose the Episcopal Church? John M. Krumm. 160p. 1974. pap. 1.35 (ISBN 0-88028-030-1). Forward Movement.

Why Christians Burn Out. Charles E. Perry, Jr. LC 82-2098. 168p. 1982. pap. 4.95 (ISBN 0-8407-5800-6). Nelson.

Why Christians Should Be the Healthiest People in the World. Sandi Mitchell. 300p. (Orig.). 1987. pap. 9.95 (ISBN 0-9617419-1-0). But It Really Works Bks.

Why Churches Die. Hollis Green. 224p. (Orig.). 1972. pap. 5.95 (ISBN 0-87123-642-7, 210642). Bethany Hse.

Why Cow Protection? Panduranga R. Malyala. Date not set. 1.99 (ISBN 0-938924-01-X). Sri Shirdi Sai.

Why Cults Succeed Where the Church Fails. Ronald M. Enroth & Gordon J. Melton. 128p. 1985. 6.95 (ISBN 0-87178-932-9). Brethren.

Why Denominationalism? Murry M. Campbell. LC 84-90492. 140p. 1985. 10.00 (ISBN 0-533-06376-0). Vantage.

Why Did Christ Die? F. E. Marsh. LC 85-18093. Orig. Title: Greatest Theme in the World. 204p. 1985. pap. 6.95 (ISBN 0-8254-3249-9). Kregel.

Why Did God Let Grandpa Die? Phoebe Cranor. LC 76-17737. 128p. 1976. pap. 3.50 (ISBN 0-87123-603-6, 200603). Bethany Hse.

Why Did Jesus Fast? Herman Arndt. 87p. 1962. pap. 7.95 (ISBN 0-88697-039-3). Life Science.

Why Do Christians Break Down? William A. Miller. LC 73-78260. 1973. pap. 6.95 (ISBN 0-8066-1325-4, 10-7140). Augsburg.

Why Do Good People Suffer? Milton H. Allen. LC 82-82949. 1983. pap. 4.95 (ISBN 0-8054-5208-7). Broadman.

Why Do I Do Things Wrong? Carolyn Nystrom. (Children's Bible Basics Ser.). 32p. 1981. 4.95 (ISBN 0-8024-5996-X). Moody.

Why Do I Do What I Don't Want to Do? William Backus & Marie Chapian. LC 84-6336. 144p. 1984. pap. 4.95 (ISBN 0-87123-625-7, 210625). Bethany Hse.

Why Do Mullet Jump? And Other Puzzles & Possibilities of God's Creation. Gene Zimmerman. 128p. (Orig.). 1986. pap. 6.95 (ISBN 0-935311-01-7). Post Horn Pr.

Why Do People Fall under the Power? Kenneth E. Hagin. 1981. pap. 0.50 mini bk (ISBN 0-89276-254-3). Hagin Ministries.

Why Do the Jews Need a Land of Their Own? Ed. by Joseph Leftwich & Mordecai S. Chertoff. LC 83-45297. 242p. 1984. 19.95 (ISBN 0-8453-4774-8, Cornwall Bks). Assoc Univ Prs.

Why Do the Righteous Suffer? Gordon Lindsay. (Divine Healing & Health Ser.). 1.50 (ISBN 0-89985-032-4). Christ Nations.

Why Do They Do It? Gordon Lindsay. 1.00 (ISBN 0-89985-120-7). Christ Nations.

Why Do They Dress That Way? Stephen Scott. LC 86-81058. (People's Place Booklet Ser.: No. 7). (Illus.). 160p. (Orig.). 1986. pap. 5.50 (ISBN 0-934672-18-0). Good Bks PA.

Why Doctrines? Charles Hefling. LC 82-83553. 196p. (Orig.). 1984. pap. 8.00 (ISBN 0-936384-09-3). Cowley Pubns.

Why Does God Allow It? A. E. Wilder-Smith. LC 80-80283. 1980. pap. 2.95 (ISBN 0-89051-060-1). Master Bks.

Why Doesn't God Do Something? Phoebe Cranor. LC 78-118. 144p. (YA) 1978. pap. 3.50 (ISBN 0-87123-605-2, 200605). Bethany Hse.

Why Doesn't God Do What We Tell Him? Earle Megathlin. 192p. 1984. pap. 10.95 (ISBN 0-8059-2929-0). Dorrance.

Why Doesn't God Intervene? Basilea Schlink. Tr. by Evangelical Sisterhood of Mary. 32p. 1982. pap. 0.50 (ISBN 3-87209-629-X). Evang Sisterhood Mary.

Why Don't You Believe What We Tell You. 39p. 1983. pap. 1.00 (ISBN 0-939482-06-1). Noontide.

Why Friends Are Friends. Jack L. Willcuts. 90p. (Orig.). 1984. pap. 3.95 (ISBN 0-913342-45-9). Barclay Pr.

Why God Allows Trials & Disappointments. Gerald R. Nash. (Uplook Ser.). 31p. 1972. pap. 0.99 (ISBN 0-8163-0082-8, 23618-2). Pacific Pr Pub Assn.

Why God Became Man & the Virgin Conception & Original Sin. Anselm of Canterbury. Tr. & intro. by Joseph M. Colleran. LC 71-77166. 256p. (Orig.). 1982. pap. text ed. 4.95x (ISBN 0-87343-025-5). Magi Bks.

Why God Gave Me Pain. Shirley Holdren. 128p. 1984. pap. 3.95 (ISBN 0-8294-0469-4). Loyola.

Why God Permits Accidents. Spiros Zodhiates. LC 79-51340. 1982. pap. 2.25 (ISBN 0-89957-537-4). AMG Pubs.

Why Good People Suffer: A Practical Treatise on the Problem of Evil. Bartholomew Gottemoller. 1987. 9.95 (ISBN 0-533-07107-0). Vantage.

Why Have I Accepted Islam? A. Chattopadhya. pap. 1.75 (ISBN 0-686-18476-9). Kazi Pubns.

Why I Am a Jew. 2nd facsimile ed. Edmond Fleg. Tr. by Louise W. Wise from Fr. LC 74-27984. (Modern Jewish Experience Ser.). (Eng.). 1975. Repr. of 1945 ed. 13.00 (ISBN 0-405-06711-9). Ayer Co Pubs.

Why I Am a Jew. Edmond Fleg. Tr. by Louise W. Wise from Fr. LC 75-4124. 1985. pap. 4.95 (ISBN 0-8197-0009-6). Bloch.

Why I Am a Jew. Joseph R. Narot. pap. 0.95 (ISBN 0-686-15802-4). Rostrum Bks.

Why I Am a Preacher: A Plain Answer to an Oft-Repeated Question. Uldine Utley. Ed. by Carolyn D. Gifford & Donald Dayton. (Women in American Protestant Religion 1800-1930 Ser.). 152p. 1987. lib. bdg. 25.00 (ISBN 0-8240-0680-1). Garland Pub.

Why I Am An Atheist. rev. ed. Madalyn O'Hair. 39p. 1980. Repr. of 1966 ed. 3.25 (ISBN 0-911826-12-2). Am Atheist.

Why I Am an Atheist. Carl Shapiro. 14p. (Orig.). 1979. write for info. (ISBN 0-914937-02-2); incl. cassette 10.00 (ISBN 0-317-18464-4). Ind Pubns.

Why I Am Not a Christian & Other Essays on Religion & Related Subjects. Bertrand Russell. 1967. pap. 6.95 (ISBN 0-671-20323-1, Touchstone Bks). S&S.

Why I Became a Buddhist. William Constandse. 130p. (Orig.). 1985. pap. 6.95 (ISBN 0-911527-02-8). Utama Pubns Inc.

Why I Believe. D. James Kennedy. 1980. 6.95 (ISBN 0-8499-2943-1). Word Bks.

Why I Believe in God. Cornelius Van Til. 1948. pap. 0.75 (ISBN 0-87552-496-6). Presby & Reformed.

Why I Believe in the Baptism with the Holy Spirit. Stanford E. Linzey. 1962. pap. 0.75 (ISBN 0-88243-764-X, 02-0764). Gospel Pub.

Why I Can Say I Am God. Herbert L. Beierle. 1978. 1.00 (ISBN 0-940480-04-2). U of Healing.

Why I Left Jehovah's Witnesses. Ted Dencher. 1966. pap. 5.95 (ISBN 0-87508-183-5). Chr Lit.

Why I Left Scofieldism. William E. Cox. 1975. pap. 0.50 (ISBN 0-87552-154-1). Presby & Reformed.

Why I Left the Roman Catholic Church. Charles Davis. 27p. 1976. 3.00 (ISBN 0-911826-11-4). Am Atheist.

Why I Preach That the Bible Is Literally True. W. A. Criswell. LC 73-93142. 1969. pap. 3.95 (ISBN 0-8054-5536-1). Broadman.

Why I Trust the Bible. John Macarthur, Jr. 120p. 1983. pap. 4.95 (ISBN 0-88207-389-3). Victor Bks.

Why I'm a Seventh-Day Adventist. William G. Johnsson. Ed. by Richard W. Coffen. (Better Living Ser.). 32p. (Orig.). 1986. pap. 1.25 (ISBN 0-8280-0352-1). Review & Herald.

Why Is Hanukkah. Ben Vered. (Illus.). 1961. pap. 2.50 (ISBN 0-914080-59-8). Shulsinger Sales.

Why Is Life Worth Living? 2.25 (ISBN 0-8198-8211-9). Dghtrs St Paul.

Why Islam Forbids Free Mixing of Men & Women. M. I. Siddiqui. 19.95. Kazi Pubns.

Why Islam Forbids Intoxicants & Gambling. M. I. Siddiqui. 1981. 15.75 (ISBN 0-686-97852-8). Kazi Pubns.

Why Isn't God Giving Cash Prizes? Lorraine Peterson. (Devotionals for Teens Ser.: No. 3). (Illus.). 160p. 1982. pap. 4.95 (ISBN 0-87123-626-5, 210626). Bethany Hse.

Why J. R.? A Psychiatrist Discusses the Villain of Dallas. Lew Ryder. LC 82-82836. 153p. (Orig.). 1983. pap. 4.95 (ISBN 0-910311-02-1). Huntington Hse Inc.

Why Jesus Never Had Ulcers. Robert M. Holmes. 96p. (Orig.). 1986. pap. 6.95 (ISBN 0-687-45359-3). Abingdon.

Why Judaism? A Search for Meaning in Jewish Identity. Henry Cohen. 192p. 1973. pap. 5.00 (ISBN 0-8074-0077-7, 161901). UAHC.

Why Knock Rock? Dan Peters et al. 272p. (Orig.). 1984. pap. 6.95 (ISBN 0-87123-440-8, 210440). Bethany Hse.

Why Live the Christian Life? T. B. Maston. LC 79-55292. 1980. pap. 5.95 (ISBN 0-8054-6121-3). Broadman.

Why Me? How to Heal What's Hurting You. Arleen Lorrance. LC 77-88151. 186p. 1982. 6.95 (ISBN 0-916192-19-9). L P Pubns.

Why Me, Lord? Paul W. Powell. 120p. 1981. pap. 4.95 (ISBN 0-89693-007-6). Victor Bks.

Why Me, Lord? Meaning & Comfort in Times of Trouble. Carl W. Berner. LC 73-78267. 112p. (Orig.). 1973. pap. 5.95 (ISBN 0-8066-1331-9, 10-7172). Augsburg.

Why Me? Why Anyone? Hirshel Jaffe et al. 256p. 1986. 15.95 (ISBN 0-312-87803-6, Pub. by Marek). St Martin.

Why Meditation. Vimala Thakar. 82p. 1986. pap. 6.00 (ISBN 81-208-0047-8, Pub. by Motilal Banarsidass India). Orient Bk Dist.

Why Men Confess. O. John Rogge. LC 74-22067. (Quality Paperbacks Ser.). iv, 298p. 1975. pap. 5.95 (ISBN 0-306-80006-3). Da Capo.

Why Men Go Back. Charles W. Conn. 1983. 6.95 (ISBN 0-87148-902-3); pap. 5.95 (ISBN 0-87148-917-1). Pathway Pr.

Why Monks? Francis Vandenbroucke. LC 75-182090. (Cistercian Studies: Vol. 17). 1972. 4.00 (ISBN 0-87907-817-0). Cistercian Pub.

Why Not? Accept Christ's Healing & Wholeness. Lloyd J. Ogilvie. 192p. 1984. 9.95 (ISBN 0-8007-1223-4). Revell.

Why Not Creation? Walter E. Lammerts. (Illus.). 388p. (Orig.). 1970. pap. 6.95 (ISBN 0-8010-5528-8). Creation Research.

Why Not? Daring to Live the Challenge of Christ. William J. O'Malley. LC 86-14059. 169p. (Orig.). 1986. pap. 6.95 (ISBN 0-8189-0504-2). Alba.

Why Not I, 2 vols. write for info. Dghtrs St Paul.

Why, O Lord? Psalms & Sermons from Namibia. Zephania Kameeta. LC 86-45211. 80p. 1987. pap. 3.95 (ISBN 0-8006-1923-4, 1-1923). Fortress.

Why O Lord? The Inner Meaning of Suffering. Carlo Carretto. Tr. by Robert R. Barr from Ital. LC 85-29874. Tr. of Perche Signore? Il Dolore: Segreto Nascosto Nei Secoli. 128p. (Orig.). 1986. 10.95 (ISBN 0-88344-224-8); pap. 6.95 (ISBN 0-88344-222-1). Orbis Bks.

Why Pray? Spiros Zodhiates. LC 82-71266. (Luke Trio Ser.). 1982. pap. 5.95 (ISBN 0-89957-554-4). AMG Pubs.

Why Preach? Why Listen? William Muehl. LC 86-45216. 96p. 1986. pap. 4.95 (ISBN 0-8006-1928-5, 1-1928). Fortress.

Why? Psychic Development & How! Ed. by Mystic Jhamom Staff. (Conversations with a Mystic Ser.: No. 2). (Illus.). 176p. 1985. pap. 11.75 (ISBN 0-933961-05-7). Mystic Jhamom.

Why Revival Tarries. Leonard Ravenhill. 176p. 1979. pap. 4.95 (ISBN 0-87123-607-9, 210607). Bethany Hse.

Why Sermon Outlines. Russell E. Spray. (Sermon Outline Ser.). 48p. (Orig.). 1980. pap. 2.50 (ISBN 0-8010-8188-2). Baker Bk.

Why Should "I" Speak in Tongues. Charles Hunter & Frances Hunter. 1976. pap. 4.95 (ISBN 0-917726-02-2). Hunter Bks.

Why Should I Speak in Tongues? 1984. pap. 0.95 (ISBN 0-930756-85-1, 541012). Aglow Pubns.

Why Sing? Toward a Theology of Catholic Church Music. Miriam T. Winter. 346p. (Orig.). 1984. pap. 11.95 (ISBN 0-912405-07-4). Pastoral Pr.

Why So Many Churches. Victor H. Prange. 1985. pap. 2.95 (ISBN 0-8100-0188-8, 15N0413). Northwest Pub.

Why Some Are Not Healed. Gordon Lindsay. (Divine Healing & Health Ser.). 1.25 (ISBN 0-89985-033-2). Christ Nations.

Why Squander Illness? Charles M. Carty. 1974. pap. 1.50 (ISBN 0-89555-051-2). TAN Bks Pubs.

Why Stay Married? Jane Sawyer. (Outreach Ser.). 1982. pap. 1.25 (ISBN 0-8163-0443-2). Pacific Pr Pub Assn.

Why Study Christian Science as a Science? Max Kappeler. 30p. 1973. pap. 3.50 (ISBN 0-85241-040-9). Kappeler Inst Pub.

Why Teenagers Act the Way They Do. G. Keith Olson. (Orig.). 1987. pap. 15.95 (ISBN 0-931529-17-4). Group Bks.

Why the Church Must Teach. Lucien E. Coleman, Jr. LC 84-4966. 1984. pap. 6.95 (ISBN 0-8054-3234-5). Broadman.

Why the Cookie Crumbles. Marjorie L. Lloyd. (Outreach Ser.). pap. 1.25 (ISBN 0-8163-0400-9). Pacific Pr Pub Assn.

Why the Green Nigger? Re-Mything Genesis. Elizabeth Dodson Gray. LC 79-89193. x, 166p. 1979. 12.95 (ISBN 0-934512-01-9). Roundtable Pr.

Why the Jews? The Reason for Anti-Semitism. Dennis Prager & Joseph Telushkin. 224p. 1983. 14.95 (ISBN 0-671-45270-3). S&S.

Why the King James Version. J. Reuben Clark, Jr. LC 79-15008. (Classics in Mormon Literature Ser.). 535p. 1979. 7.95 (ISBN 0-87747-773-6). Deseret Bk.

Why Tongues? Kenneth E. Hagin. 1975. pap. 0.50 mini bk (ISBN 0-89276-051-6). Hagin Ministries.

Why Tragedy Happens to Christians. Charles Capps. 187p. (Orig.). 1980. pap. 3.75 (ISBN 0-89274-175-9, HH-175). Harrison Hse.

Why Two Worlds: Relation of Physical to Spiritual Realities. Fred S. Mayer. LC 78-134425. Repr. of 1934 ed. 21.00 (ISBN 0-404-08465-6). AMS Pr.

Why Us? When Bad Things Happen to God's People. Warren Wiersbe. 160p. 1985. pap. 5.95 (ISBN 0-8007-5208-2, Power Bks). Revell.

Why Violence? A Philosophical Interpretation. Sergio Cotta. Tr. by Giovanni Gullace from Ital. LC 84-25779. Orig. Title: Perche la violenza? Una Interpretazione Filosofica. xiv, 150p. 1985. pap. 12.00 (ISBN 0-8130-0824-7). U Presses Fla.

Why Waste Your Illness: Let God Use It for Growth. Mildred Tengbom. LC 83-72113. 144p. (Orig.). 1984. pap. 6.95 (ISBN 0-8066-2057-9, 10-7182). Augsburg.

Why We Are Baptized. Kathleen England. LC 78-19180. (Illus.). 1978. 5.95 (ISBN 0-87747-893-7). Deseret Bk.

Why We Do Not Speak in Tongues. Don R. Pegram. 1982. pap. 1.25 (ISBN 0-89265-086-9). Randall Hse.

Why We Live in Community. Eberhard Arnold. 1976. pap. 1.50 (ISBN 0-87486-168-3). Plough.

Why We Need Confession. Russell Shaw. LC 85-63153. 125p. (Orig.). 1986. pap. 4.95 (ISBN 0-87973-537-6, 537). Our Sunday Visitor.

Why We Serve: Personal Stories of Catholic Lay Ministers. Ed. by Doug Fisher. 176p. (Orig.). 1984. pap. 6.95 (ISBN 0-8091-2640-0). Paulist Pr.

Why We're Here. Robert G. Krebs. 1987. 7.95 (ISBN 0-533-07098-8). Vantage.

Why Were You Created. Jim McKeever. 1980. 1.00 (ISBN 0-86694-083-9). Omega Pubns OR.

Why World Evangelism. David Howard. pap. 0.75 (ISBN 0-87784-141-1). Inter-Varsity.

Whyte's Bible Characters: From the Old Testament & the New Testament. Alexander Whyte. (Illus.). 1968. 24.95 (ISBN 0-310-34410-7, 11008). Zondervan.

Wickedness. Mary Midgley. 232p. 1986. pap. 8.95 (ISBN 0-7448-0053-6, 0053W). Methuen Inc.

Wiclif & Hus. Johann Loserth. Tr. by M. J. Evans. LC 78-63198. (Heresies of the Early Christian & Medieval Era: Second Ser.). 1979. Repr. of 1884 ed. 48.00 (ISBN 0-404-16236-3). AMS Pr.

Wide Horizon. Anna Brinton. 1983. pap. 2.50x (ISBN 0-87574-038-3, 038). Pendle Hill.

Wide Was His Parish. Edward Elson. 320p. 1986. 12.95 (ISBN 0-8423-8205-4). Tyndale.

Wideness of God's Mercy: Litanies to Enlarge Our Prayer, 2 vols. Jeffrey W. Rowthorn. Set. pap. 29.95 (ISBN 0-86683-789-2, HarpR). Har-Row.

Widening Circle: Sermons in Acts. W. E. McCumber. 80p. (Orig.). 1983. pap. 2.95 (ISBN 0-8341-0838-0). Beacon Hill.

Widening the Horizons: Pastoral Responses to a Fragmented Society. Charles V. Gerkin. LC 86-7832. 154p. (Orig.). 1986. pap. 11.95 (ISBN 0-664-24037-2). Westminster.

Wider Horizons in Christian Adult Education. Lawrence C. Little. LC 62-14381. pap. 87.00 (ISBN 0-8357-9763-5, 2017871). Bks Demand UMI.

Wider Horizons of American History. Herbert E. Bolton. 1967. pap. 5.95x (ISBN 0-268-00301-7). U of Notre Dame Pr.

Widow-to-Widow. Phyllis R. Silverman. 240p. 1986. text ed. 19.95 (ISBN 0-8261-5030-6). Springer Pub.

Widowed. Philip Jebb. LC 83-11160. 1984. pap. 3.95 (ISBN 0-932506-30-5). St Bedes Pubns.

Wie Kam und Wie Kommt Es Zum Osterglauben? Hans-Willi Winden. (Disputationes Theologicae: Vol. 12). (Ger.). 352p. 1982. 39.45 (ISBN 3-8204-5820-4). P Lang Pubs.

Wife, Mother & Mystic: Blessed Anna Maria Taigi. Albert Bessieres. Ed. by Douglas Newton. Tr. by Stephen Rigby from Fr. (Eng.). 1977. pap. 5.50 (ISBN 0-89555-058-X). TAN Bks Pubs.

Wife Number Nineteen: The Story of a Life in Bondage, Being a Complete Expose of Mormonism, & Revealing the Sorrows, Sacrifices & Sufferings of Women in Polygamy. Ann E. Young. LC 72-2634. (American Women Ser: Images & Realities). (Illus.). 632p. 1972. Repr. of 1875 ed. 36.50 (ISBN 0-405-04488-7). Ayer Co Pubs.

Wife's Role in Initiating Divorce in Jewish Law & the Agunah Problem: A Halakhic Solution. Shlomo Riskin. 1987. 17.95 (ISBN 0-88125-122-4); pap. 11.95 (ISBN 0-88125-132-1). Ktav.

Wilberforce. John Pollock. LC 77-86525. (Illus.). 1978. 26.00x (ISBN 0-312-87942-3). St Martin.

Wilberforces & Henry Manning: The Parting of Friends. David H. Newsome. LC 67-2. (Illus.). 1966. 30.00x (ISBN 0-674-95280-4, Belknap Pr). Harvard U Pr.

Wild Beasts & Angels. Arthur W. Anderson. 1979. pap. 4.50 (ISBN 0-910452-43-1). Covenant.

Wild Bill. Bill Montieth. 164p. (Orig.). 1984. pap. 5.95 (ISBN 0-89274-324-7). Harrison Hse.

Wild Geese & the Water. Bhagwan Shree Rajneesh. Ed. by Swami Krishna Prabhu. LC 85-43053. (Responses to Questions Ser.). 416p. (Orig.). 1985. pap. 4.95 (ISBN 0-88050-673-3). Chidvilas Found.

Wild Knight of Battersea: G. K. Chesterton. F. A. Lea. 1973. Repr. of 1945 ed. 25.00 (ISBN 0-8274-0321-6). R West.

Wilderness & the City: American Classical Philosophy As a Moral Quest. Michael A. Weinstein. LC 82-4769. 176p. 1982. lib. bdg. 17.50x (ISBN 0-87023-375-0). U of Mass Pr.

Wilderness Christians: The Moravian Mission to the Delaware Indians. Elma E. Gray & Leslie R. Gray. LC 72-84988. (Illus.). xiv, 354p. 1973. Repr. of 1956 ed. 22.00x (ISBN 0-8462-1701-5). Russell.

Wilderness Lost: The Religious Origins of the American Mind. David R. Williams. LC 85-43475. 296p. 1987. 38.50x (ISBN 0-941664-21-X). Susquehanna U Pr.

Wildlife's Christmas Treasury. Joseph W. Krutch et al. Ed. by Natalie S. Rifkin. LC 76-12388. (Illus.). 160p. 1976. 11.95 (ISBN 0-912186-22-4). Natl Wildlife.

Wilfred Grenfell, His Life & Work. James L. Kerr. LC 73-21177. 1977. lib. bdg. 22.50x (ISBN 0-8371-6068-5, KEWG). Greenwood.

Wilhelm Marr: The Patriarch of Anti-Semitism. Moshe Zimmerman. (Studies in Jewish History). 192p. 1986. 19.95x (ISBN 0-19-504005-8). Oxford U Pr.

Wilhelm Schmidt & the Origin of the Idea of God. Ernest Brandewie. 352p. (Orig.). 1983. lib. bdg. 30.00 (ISBN 0-8191-3363-9); pap. text ed. 15.50 (ISBN 0-8191-3364-7). U Pr of Amer.

Will a Man Rob God? C. Phillip Johnson. 1981. pap. 3.00 (ISBN 0-933184-29-8). Flame Intl.

Will & Spirit: A Comtemplative Psychology. Gerald G. May. LC 82-47751. 384p. 1982. 24.45 (ISBN 0-686-98141-3, HarpR). Har-Row.

Will Christians Go Through the Great Tribulation? Gordon Lindsay. (Prophecy Ser.). 1.50 (ISBN 0-89985-065-0). Christ Nations.

Will for Peace: Peace Action in the United Methodist Church: A History. Herman Will, Jr. 300p. 9.95 (CS1007). General Board.

Will God Run. Charles B. Hodge. LC 70-187827. (Illus.). 1965. 6.95 (ISBN 0-89112-053-X, Bibl Res Pr). Abilene Christ U.

Will Herberg: From Right to Right. Harry J. Ausmus. LC 86-19357. (Studies in Religion). xx, 276p. 1987. 29.95x (ISBN 0-8078-1724-4). U of NC Pr.

Will I Cry Tomorrow? Susan Stanford. 1987. 9.95 (ISBN 0-8007-1512-8). Revell.

Will of God. Morris Ashcraft. LC 80-65714. 1980. pap. 4.95 (ISBN 0-8054-1620-X). Broadman.

Will of God. Leslie D. Weatherhead. (Festival Books). 1976. pap. 2.95 (ISBN 0-687-45600-2). Abingdon.

Will Our Children Have Faith? John H. Westerhoff, III. 144p. 1983. pap. 6.95 (ISBN 0-8164-2435-7, AY7452, HarpR). Har-Row.

Will the Antichrist Come Out of Russia? Gordon Lindsay. (Prophecy Ser.). 1.25 (ISBN 0-89985-066-9). Christ Nations.

Will the Real Israel Please Stand Up? 2nd ed. Leon Fine. (Illus.). 278p. (Orig.). 1984. pap. 10.95 (ISBN 965-10-0003-1, Pub. by Massada Israel). Hermon.

Will the Real Jesus Christ & Christians Please Stand? (Orig.). 1983. pap. 2.75 (ISBN 0-914335-00-6). Highland.

Will the Real Phony Please Stand up? rev. ed. Ethel Barrett & Peggy Parker. LC 84-17777. 224p. 1984. pap. 4.95 (ISBN 0-8307-1001-9, 5418383); Leader's Guide 3.95 (ISBN 0-8307-1009-4, 6101966). Regal.

Will the Real Winner Please Stand Up. Dallas Groten. 160p. 1985. pap. 4.95 (ISBN 0-87123-819-5, 210819). Bethany Hse.

Will the Real You Please Remain Standing! John A. Lynn. 191p. 1981. pap. 2.95 (ISBN 0-910068-38-0). Am Christian.

Will the Real You Please Stand Up! John A. Lynn. 113p. 1980. pap. 2.95 (ISBN 0-910068-28-3). Am Christian.

Will to Believe. Marcus Bach. 186p. 1973. pap. 7.50 (ISBN 0-911336-46-X). Sci of Mind.

Will to Believe & Human Immortality. William James. pap. 5.95 (ISBN 0-486-20291-7). Dover.

Will to Believe & Other Essays in Popular Philosophy & Human Immortality. William James. 15.75 (ISBN 0-8446-2313-X). Peter Smith.

Will You Hear My Confession? How to Make a Good Examination of Conscience & a Good Confession. Hector Munoz. Tr. by Robert Bair from Span. LC 82-20597. 162p. 1983. pap. 6.95 (ISBN 0-8189-0439-9). Alba.

Willging Years: Seventeen Years with the First Catholic Bishop of Pueblo. Patrick C. Stauter & Howard L. Delaney. (Illus., Orig.). 1987. pap. text ed. 24.95 (ISBN 0-9617847-0-9). P C Stauter.

William Barclay: A Spiritual Autobiography. William Barclay. LC 73-76528. 1977. pap. 1.50 (ISBN 0-8028-1667-3). Eerdmans.

William Billings: Data & Documents. Hans Nathan. LC 75-33593. (Bibliographies in American Music: No. 2). 1976. 10.00 (ISBN 0-911772-67-7). Info Coord.

William Billings of Boston: Eighteenth-Century Composer. David McKay & Richard Crawford. LC 74-2971. (Illus.). 320p. 1975. 37.00x (ISBN 0-691-09118-8). Princeton U Pr.

William Blake & the Moderns. Ed. by Robert J. Bertholf & Annette S. Levitt. 352p. 1982. 44.50x (ISBN 0-87395-615-X); pap. 18.95x (ISBN 0-87395-616-8). State U NY Pr.

William Blake: His Mysticism. Maung Ba Han. 1978. Repr. of 1924 ed. lib. bdg. 35.00 (ISBN 0-8495-0377-9). Arden Lib.

William Blake: His Mysticism. Maung Ba Han. LC 72-13650. 1974. Repr. of 1924 ed. lib. bdg. 30.00 (ISBN 0-8414-1234-0). Folcroft.

William Blake: Mystic. Adeline M. Butterworth. LC 74-8017. 1911. lib. bdg. 15.00 (ISBN 0-8414-3186-8). Folcroft.

William Blake on the Lord's Prayer: 1757-1827. John H. Clarke. LC 70-95421. (Studies in Blake, No. 3). 1971. Repr. of 1927 ed. lib. bdg. 48.95x (ISBN 0-8383-0967-4). Haskell.

William Blake: Poet & Mystic. P. Berger. LC 67-31287. (Studies in Blake, No. 3). 1969. Repr. of 1914 ed. lib. bdg. 75.00x (ISBN 0-8383-0778-7). Haskell.

William Blake's Circle of Destiny. Milton O. Percival. 1964. lib. bdg. 27.50x (ISBN 0-374-96384-3, Octagon). Hippocrene Bks.

William Blake's Jerusalem. Minna Doskow. LC 81-65463. (Illus.). 388p. 1982. 37.50 (ISBN 0-8386-3090-1). Fairleigh Dickinson.

William Carey. Basil Miller. 154p. 1985. pap. 3.50 (ISBN 0-87123-850-0, 200850). Bethany Hse.

William Clayton's Journal: A Daily Record of the Journey of the Original Company of Mormon Pioneers from Nauveo, Illinois, to the Valley of the Great Salt Lake. William Clayton. LC 72-9435. (Far Western Frontier Ser.). 380p. 1973. Repr. of 1921 ed. 26.50 (ISBN 0-405-04965-X). Ayer Co Pubs.

William Courtenay: Archbishop of Canterbury, 1381-1396. Joseph Dahmus. LC 66-18194. 1966. 28.75x (ISBN 0-271-73121-4). Pa St U Pr.

William Ellery Channing: Selected Writings. Ed. by David Robinson. LC 84-62567. (Source of American Spirituality Ser.: Vol. 2). 320p. 1985. 12.95 (ISBN 0-8091-0359-1). Paulist Pr.

William Farel & the Story of the Swiss Reform. William M. Blackburn. Date not set. Repr. of 1865 ed. 40.00 (ISBN 0-404-19870-8). AMS Pr.

William G. Brownlow: Fighting Parson of the Southern Highlands. E. Merton Coulter. LC 71-136309. (Tennesseana Editions Ser.). (Illus.). pap. 114.50 (ISBN 0-8357-9767-8, 2016173). Bks Demand UMI.

William George Ward & the Catholic Revival. Wilfrid P. Ward. LC 75-29626. Repr. of 1893 ed. 41.75 (ISBN 0-404-14042-4). AMS Pr.

William George Ward & the Oxford Movement. Wilfrid P. Ward. LC 75-29625. Repr. of 1889 ed. 41.75 (ISBN 0-404-14043-2). AMS Pr.

William Holman Hunt & Typological Symbolism. George Landow. LC 77-91017. 1979. 42.00x (ISBN 0-300-02196-8). Yale U Pr.

William Law: A Serious Call to a Devout & Holy Life & the Spirit of Love. Ed. by Paul Stanwood & Austin Warren. LC 78-61418. (Classics of Western Spirituality). 542p. 1978. 14.95 (ISBN 0-8091-0265-X); pap. 9.95 (ISBN 0-8091-2144-1). Paulist Pr.

William Law & Eighteenth-Century Quakerism. William Law. Ed. by Stephen Hobhouse. LC 77-175870. (Illus.). Repr. of 1927 ed. 24.50 (ISBN 0-405-08736-5). Ayer Co Pubs.

William Law: Christian Perfection. Rev. ed. William Law. 96p. 1986. pap. 4.95 (ISBN 0-8423-0259-X). Tyndale.

William Law on Christian Perfection. Ed. by Erwin Rudolph. 146p. 1981. pap. 3.95 (ISBN 0-87123-117-4, 210117). Bethany Hse.

William Law: Selections on the Interior Life. William Law. Ed. by Mary Morrison. LC 62-15272. (Orig.). 1962. pap. 2.50x (ISBN 0-87574-120-7). Pendle Hill.

William Lloyd Garrison on Nonresistance Together with a Personal Sketch by His Daughter and a Tribute by Leo Tolstoi. Ed. by Fanny G. Villard. LC 74-137556. (Peace Movement in America Ser). xii, 79p. 1972. Repr. of 1924 ed. lib. bdg. 11.95x (ISBN 0-89198-087-3). Ozer.

William Lloyd's Life of Pythagoras, with a New Thesis on the Origin of the New Testament. Arthur F. Hallam. 84p. (Orig.). 1982. pap. 8.50 (ISBN 0-938770-01-2). Capitalist Pr OH.

William of St. Thierry: Exposition on the Epistle to the Romans. William of St. Thierry. Ed. by John D. Anderson. (Cistercian Fathers Ser.: No. 27). 1980. 17.95 (ISBN 0-87907-327-6). Cistercian Pubns.

William of St. Thierry, Golden Epistle. LC 72-152482. (Cistercian Fathers Ser.: No. 12). 1971. pap. 4.00 (ISBN 0-87907-712-3). Cistercian Pubns.

William of St. Thierry: On Contemplating God, Prayer, Meditations. Tr. by Sr. Penelope. (Cistercian Fathers Ser.: No. 3). 1970. pap. 5.00 (ISBN 0-87907-903-7). Cistercian Pubns.

William of St. Thierry: The Enigma of Faith, Vol. 3. LC 74-4465. (Cistercian Fathers Ser.: No. 9). 1974. 7.95 (ISBN 0-87907-309-8). Cistercian Pubns.

William of St. Thierry: The Man & His Work. Jean M. Dechanet. Tr. by Richard Strachen from Fr. LC 73-152485. (Cistercian Studies: No. 10). Tr. of Guillaume de Saint-Thierry. 192p. 1972. 10.95 (ISBN 0-87907-810-3). Cistercian Pubns.

William Penn. facsimile ed. William I. Hull. LC 78-179525. (Select Bibliographies Reprint Ser). Repr. of 1937 ed. 32.00 (ISBN 0-8369-6654-6). Ayer Co Pubs.

William Penn & Our Liberties. William W. Comfort. (Illus.). 146p. 1976. pap. 3.00 (ISBN 0-941308-02-2). Religious Soc Friends.

William Penn & the Founding of Pennsylvania, 1680-1684: A Documentary History. Ed. by Jean R. Soderlund & Richard S. Dunn. (Illus.). 380p. 1983. 26.50x (ISBN 0-8122-7862-3); pap. 10.95x (ISBN 0-8122-1131-6). U of Pa Pr.

William Penn As Social Philosopher. Edward C. Beatty. 1972. lib. bdg. 24.50x (ISBN 0-374-90506-1, Octagon). Hippocrene Bks.

William Penn: Mystic. Elizabeth G. Vining. LC 74-95891. (Orig.). 1969. pap. 2.50x (ISBN 0-87574-167-3, 167). Pendle Hill.

William Penn, Quaker & Pioneer. Bonamy Dobree. LC 78-15258. 1978. Repr. of 1932 ed. lib. bdg. 35.00 (ISBN 0-8414-3790-4). Folcroft.

William Penn, Quaker & Pioneer. Bonamy Dobree. 346p. 1983. Repr. of 1932 ed. lib. bdg. 35.00 (ISBN 0-8492-4227-4). R West.

William Penn, Thomas Gray & an Account of the Historical Associations of Stoke Poges. F. McDermott. 1973. Repr. of 1930 ed. lib. bdg. 25.00 (ISBN 0-8414-6026-4). Folcroft.

William Penn: 17th Century Founding Father. Edwin B. Bronner. LC 75-32728. (Illus.). 36p. (Orig.). 1975. pap. 2.50x (ISBN 0-87574-204-1). Pendle Hill.

William Penn's Holy Experiment; the Founding of Pennsylvania Sixteen Eighty-One to Seventeen Hundred & One. Edwin B. Bronner. LC 78-5882. (Illus.). 306p. 1978. Repr. of 1963 ed. lib. bdg. 22.50x (ISBN 0-313-20432-2, BRWP). Greenwood.

William Temple: An Archbishop for All Seasons. Charles W. Lowry. LC 81-43869. 170p. (Orig.). 1982. lib. bdg. 22.25 (ISBN 0-8191-2355-2); pap. text ed. 7.75 (ISBN 0-8191-2356-0). U Pr of Amer.

William Temple, Archbishop of Canterbury: His Life & Letters. Frederick A. Iremonger. LC 83-45439. Repr. of 1948 ed. 62.50 (ISBN 0-404-20128-8). AMS Pr.

William Temple, Twentieth-Century Christian. Joseph F. Fletcher. LC 63-12587. 1963. text ed. 15.00x (ISBN 0-8401-0741-2). A R Allenson.

William Temple's Philosophy of Religion. Owen C. Thomas. LC 61-4400. 1961. 10.00x (ISBN 0-8401-2330-2). A R Allenson.

William Tyndale. James F. Mozley. LC 70-109801. (Illus.). 1971. Repr. of 1937 ed. lib. bdg. 22.50x (ISBN 0-8371-4292-X, MOWT). Greenwood.

William Tyndale & the Translation of the English Bible. G. Barnett Smith. 20.00 (ISBN 0-8274-3719-6). R West.

William Whewell, D.D., Master of Trinity College, Cambridge, 2 Vols. Isaac Todhunter. (Sources of Science Ser.: No. 92). Repr. of 1876 ed. 68.00 (ISBN 0-384-60880-9). Johnson Repr.

Williams Pantycelyn. Glyn T. Hughes. (Writer of Wales Ser.). 180p. 1983. pap. text ed. 8.50x (ISBN 0-7083-0840-6, Pub. by U of Wales). Humanities.

Williamsburg Christmas. Donna Sheppard. LC 80-7487. (Illus.). 84p. 1980. 11.95 (ISBN 0-03-057639-3). H Holt & Co.

Williamsburg Christmas. Donna C. Sheppard. LC 80-17179. (World of Williamsburg Ser.). (Illus.). 78p. (Orig.). 1980. pap. 6.95 (ISBN 0-87935-054-7). Williamsburg.

Willian Perkins 1558-1602, English Puritanist--His Pioneer Works on Casuistry: Discourse on Conscience & the Whole Treatise of Cases of Conscience. Thomas F. Merrill. xx, 242p. 1966. text ed. 28.50x (Pub. by B De Graaf Netherlands). Coronet Bks.

Willmington's Guide to the Bible. H. L. Willmington. 1981. 29.95 (ISBN 0-8423-8804-4). Tyndale.

Willmington's Survey of the Old Testament. Harold L. Willmington. 624p. 1987. 19.95. Victor Bks.

Wilson's Dictionary of Bible Types. Walter L. Wilson. 1957. pap. 10.95 (ISBN 0-8028-1453-0). Eerdmans.

Wilt Thou Be Made Whole? Raymond Bates. (Orig.). Date not set. pap. 5.00 (ISBN 0-915541-08-4). Star Bks Inc.

Wilton Way to Decorate for Christmas. LC 76-16083. 1976. 6.99 (ISBN 0-912696-07-9). Wilton.

Win the Battle for Your Mind. Richard Strauss. 132p. 1986. pap. 5.95 (ISBN 0-87213-835-6). Loizeaux.

Winchester Psalter: An Iconographic Study. Kristine E. Haney. (Illus.). 204p. 1986. text ed. 60.00x (ISBN 0-7185-1260-X, Pub. by Leicester U Pr). Humanities.

Wind & Shadows. Daughters Of St. Paul. (Encounter Ser.). 3.00 (ISBN 0-8198-0174-7); pap. 2.00 (ISBN 0-8198-0175-5). Dghtrs St Paul.

Wind in Both Ears. 2nd ed. Angus MacLean. 1987. pap. write for info. (ISBN 0-933840-30-6, Skinner Hse Bks). Unitarian Univ.

Wind in the Rigging. Randal E. Denny. 120p. 1985. pap. 4.50 (ISBN 0-8341-0937-9). Beacon Hill.

Wind of the Spirit. 2nd, rev. ed. G. De Purucker. LC 84-50118. 328p. 1984. 10.00 (ISBN 0-911500-67-7); pap. 5.00 (ISBN 0-911500-68-5). Theos U Pr.

Wind of the Spirit. James S. Stewart. 192p. 1984. pap. 6.95 (ISBN 0-8010-8250-1). Baker Bk.

Wind River Winter: How the World Dies. Virginia S. Owens. 288p. 1987. pap. 10.95 (ISBN 0-310-45861-7). Zondervan.

Wind Sweeps Away the Plum Blossoms: The Principles & Techniques of Yang Style T'ai Chi Spear & Staff. Stuart A. Olson. Tr. by Stuart A. Olson from Chinese. (Illus.). 150p. (Orig.). 1986. pap. 14.95 (ISBN 0-938045-00-8). Bubbling Well.

Wind Through the Valleys. Donald Zelle. (Orig.). 1987. pap. price not set (ISBN 0-89536-876-5, 7862). CSS of Ohio.

Winding Quest. Alan T. Dale. (Illus.). 432p. (Orig.). 1973. pap. 9.95 (ISBN 0-8192-1150-8). Morehouse.

Window into Chant. Richard Pugsley. 1987. pap. 5.95 (ISBN 0-941478-50-5). Paraclete Pr.

Window of Eternity. Edgar Biamonte. LC 83-9944. 145p. 1984. 14.95 (ISBN 0-87949-230-9). Ashley Bks.

Windows of Portsmouth Cathedral. E. K. Barnard. 1977. 42.00x (ISBN 0-317-43731-3, Pub. by City of Portsmouth). State Mutual Bk.

Windows of St. Justin Martyr. Louis P. Giorgi. LC 80-67119. (Illus.). 136p. 1982. 25.00 (ISBN 0-87982-034-9). Art Alliance.

Windows of Soul. Robert Kugelmann. LC 81-70032. 220p. 1983. 24.50 (ISBN 0-8387-5035-4). Bucknell U Pr.
Windows of the Soul. Dale Rumble. (Orig.). 1977. pap. 3.50 (ISBN 0-89350-017-8). Fountain Pr.
Windows on Life. facs. ed. Carl H. Kopf. LC 70-76908. (Essay Index Reprint Ser). 1941. 17.50 (ISBN 0-8369-1041-9). Ayer Co Pubs.
Windows on the Holy Land. J. C. Pedlow. (Illus.). 150p. 1980. pap. 8.95 (ISBN 0-227-67839-7). Attic Pr.
Windows on the Parables. rev. ed. Warren W. Wiersbe. 160p. 1984. pap. 2.95 (ISBN 0-89693-710-0). Victor Bks.
Windows on the World. Ed. by Dennis J. DeHaan. 1984. pap. 4.95 (ISBN 0-8010-2946-5). Baker Bk.
Winds of God. 2nd ed. Ethel E. Goss. (Illus.). 288p. 1958. pap. 5.95 (ISBN 0-912315-26-1). Word Aflame.
Winds of God. Norvel Hayes. 90p. (Orig.). 1985. pap. 4.95 (ISBN 0-89274-375-1). Harrison Hse.
Windsor Bible Dictionary. Ed. by Edward G. Finnegan. (Illus.). 1979. pap. 1.25 (ISBN 0-685-02398-2). World Bible.
Windthorst: A Political Biography. Margaret L. Anderson. 1981. 75.00x (ISBN 0-19-822578-4). Oxford U Pr.
Wine & the Will: Rabelais's Bacchic Christianity. Florence M. Weinberg. LC 78-181450. Repr. of 1972 ed. 47.30 (2027593). Bks Demand UMI.
Wine in the Chalice. Peter Lappin. (Orig.). 1972. pap. 3.25 (ISBN 0-89944-031-2). Don Bosco Multimedia.
Wine of Astonishment. William Sears. 192p. 1963. pap. 3.95 (ISBN 0-85398-009-8). G Ronald Pub.
Wine of Endless Life: Taoists Drinking Songs. Tr. by Jerome Seaton. 1985. 6.00 (ISBN 0-934834-59-8). White Pine.
Wing-Footed Wanderer: Conscience & Transcendence. Donald E. Miller. LC 77-1503. Repr. of 1977 ed. 45.60 (ISBN 0-8357-9032-0, 2016421). Bks Demand UMI.
Winged Bull. Dion Fortune. 328p. (Orig.). 1980. pap. 6.95 (ISBN 0-87728-501-2). Weiser.
Wings. Jill Briscoe. 384p. 1984. 11.95 (ISBN 0-8407-5328-4). Nelson.
Wings of Love & Random Thought. Bhagwan S. Rajneesh. 1979. pap. 4.50 (ISBN 0-89684-031-X, Pub. by Motilal Barnarsidass India). Orient Bk Dist.
Wings of Song. 544p. 1984. 6.95 (ISBN 0-87159-176-6). Unity School.
Wings Unfolding. Wesley LaViolette. LC 70-140225. 1971. 4.95 (ISBN 0-87516-040-9). De Vorss.
Wingspread. Aiden W. Tozer. pap. 3.95 (ISBN 0-87509-218-7). Chr Pubns.
Winners & Losers. Brian Blandford. LC 84-26709. 1985. pap. 3.95 (ISBN 0-8307-1012-4, S181422). Regal.
Winner's Circle: Triumph of Jesus Christ. Kenneth R. Jones. 1987. 16.95 (ISBN 0-533-07092-9). Vantage.
Winner's World. Mike Murdock. (Orig.). 1986. pap. 4.95 (ISBN 0-89274-398-0). Harrison Hse.
Winning. Daniel E. Caslow. 1981. pap. 5.95 (ISBN 0-8163-0462-9). Pacific Pr Pub Assn.
Winning by Losing: Eleven Biblical Paradoxes That Can Change Your Life. Richard A. Fowler. (Orig.). 1986. pap. 6.95 (ISBN 0-8024-9564-8). Moody.
Winning Church. Roland Griswold. 144p. 1986. pap. 4.95 (ISBN 0-89693-527-2). Victor Bks.
Winning the Battles of Life (Joshua) rev. ed. Paul E. Toms. LC 86-15417. 224p. 1986. pap. 4.95 (ISBN 0-8307-1161-9, S413129). Regal.
Winning the Battles of Life: This Land Is Your Land. Paul E. Toms. LC 75-23512. 1977. pap. 2.50 (ISBN 0-8307-1161-9, S413129). Regal.
Winning the Innovation Game. Robert Tucker & Denis Waitley. 256p. 1986. 15.95 (ISBN 0-8007-1494-6). Revell.
Winning the Invisible War. E. M. Bounds. 160p. 1984. pap. 3.50 (ISBN 0-88368-145-5). Whitaker Hse.
Winning Through Caring: The Handbook on Friendship Evangelism. Matthew Prince. 96p. (Orig.). 1981. pap. 3.95 (ISBN 0-8010-7065-1). Baker Bk.
Winning Through Enlightenment. 2nd ed. Ron Smothermon. 226p. 1982. pap. 9.95 (ISBN 0-932654-01-0). Context Pubns.
Winning Through Integrity. Cliff Jones. 160p. 1985. 9.95 (ISBN 0-687-45604-5). Abingdon.
Winning Through Positive Spiritual Attitudes. J. J. Turner. pap. 4.25 (ISBN 0-89137-318-7). Quality Pubns.
Winning Ways. LeRoy Eims. LC 74-77319. 160p. 1974. pap. 4.50 (ISBN 0-88207-707-4). Victor Bks.
Winning Ways for Minister's Wives. (Orig.). 1987. pap. 6.95 (ISBN 0-8054-2710-4). Broadman.
Winning with Christ. Rick Arndt. 1982. pap. 4.95 (ISBN 0-570-03627-5, 39-1073). Concordia.
Winning Words: Devotions for Athletes. Curtis French. LC 77-75467. 1983. pap. 5.95 (ISBN 0-8499-2805-2). Word Bks.
Winston Churchill on Jewish Problems. Oscar K. Rabinowicz. LC 74-43. 231p. 1974. Repr. of 1960 ed. lib. bdg. 22.50x (ISBN 0-8371-7357-4, RAWC). Greenwood.
Winston Commentary on the Gospels. Michael Fallon. 470p. 1982. pap. 12.95 (ISBN 0-86683-680-2, JHarpR). Har-Row.
Winter Grace, Spirituality for the Later Years. Kathleen R. Fischer. LC 84-61975. 1985. pap. 7.95 (ISBN 0-8091-2675-3). Paulist Pr.
Winter Pascha. Thomas Hopko. LC 84-27622. 1983. pap. text ed. 6.95 (ISBN 0-88141-025-X). St Vladimirs.
Winter Quarters. Conrey Bryson. LC 86-2146. (Illus.). 191p. 1986. 9.95 (ISBN 0-87579-011-9). Deseret Bk.
Winterthur Portfolio No. 8: Thematic Issue on Religion in America. Ed. by Ian M. Quimby. (Winterthur Bk.). (Illus.). 1973. 15.00X (ISBN 0-226-92134-4). U of Chicago Pr.
Wisconsin Chippewa Myths & Tales & Their Relation to Chippewa Life. Victor Barnouw. LC 76-53647. 304p. 1977. 25.00x (ISBN 0-299-07310-6). U of Wis Pr.
Wisdom. Eugene H. Maly. (Bible Ser.). pap. 1.00 (ISBN 0-8091-5156-1). Paulist Pr.
Wisdom. John E. Rybolt. (Collegeville Bible Commentary: Old Testament Ser.: Vol. 20). 112p. 1986. pap. 2.95 (ISBN 0-8146-1477-9). Liturgical Pr.
Wisdom: A Manifesto. Jacques Maritain et al. 1965. pap. 1.00x (ISBN 0-87343-015-8). Magi Bks.
Wisdom & Guidance. Charles Nieman. 206p. (Orig.). 1984. pap. text ed. 5.00 (ISBN 0-914307-19-3, Dist. by Harrison Hse). Word Faith.
Wisdom & Law in the Old Testament: The Ordering of Life in Israel & Early Judaism. Joseph Blenkinsopp. (Oxford Bible Ser.). (Orig.). 1983. pap. 9.95 (ISBN 0-19-213253-9). Oxford U Pr.
Wisdom & Love in Saint Thomas Aquinas. Etienne Gilson. (Aquinas Lecture). 1951. 7.95 (ISBN 0-87462-116-X). Marquette.
Wisdom & Spirit: An Investigation of 1 Corinthians 1.18-3.20 Against the Background of Jewish Sapiential. James A. Davis. (Traditions in the Greco-Roman Period Ser.). 270p. (Orig.). 1984. lib. bdg. 27.25 (ISBN 0-8191-4210-7); pap. text ed. 13.75 (ISBN 0-8191-4211-5). U Pr of Amer.
Wisdom & the Book of Proverbs. Bernhard Lang. 192p. 1985. pap. 10.95 (ISBN 0-8298-0568-0). Pilgrim NY.
Wisdom & the Faminine in the Book of Proverbs. Claudia Camp. (Bible & Literature Ser.: No. II). 360p. 1985. text ed. 29.95x (ISBN 0-907459-42-0, Pub. by Almond Pr England); pap. text ed. 15.95x (ISBN 0-907459-43-9). Eisenbrauns.
Wisdom & the Hebrew Epic: Ben Sira's Hymn in Praise of the Fathers. Burton L. Mack. LC 85-8564. (Chicago Studies in the History of Judiasm). xiv, 264p. 1986. lib. bdg. 25.00x (ISBN 0-226-50049-7). U of Chicago Pr.
Wisdom as a Hermeneutical Construct: A Study in the Sapientalizing of the Old Testament. Gerald T. Sheppard. (Beihefte Zur Zeitschrift Fuer Die Alttestamentliche Wissenschaft: No. 151). 1979. 41.00x (ISBN 3-1100-7504-0). De Gruyter.
Wisdom As a Lifestyle: Building Biblical Life-Codes. David Wright. 1987. pap. 6.95 (ISBN 0-310-44311-3). Zondervan.
Wisdom Beyond the Mind. Manly P. Hall. pap. 2.50 (ISBN 0-89314-372-3). Philos Res.
Wisdom, Christology, & Law in Matthew's Gospel. M. Jack Suggs. LC 75-95930. Repr. of 1970 ed. 36.00 (ISBN 0-8357-9185-8, 2017749). Bks Demand UMI.
Wisdom Energy: Basic Buddhist Teachings. Lama Yeshe & Zopa Rinpoche. Ed. by Jonathan Landaw & Alexander Berzin. (Wisdom Basic Book: Orange Ser.). (Illus.). 151p. 1982. pap. 7.95 (ISBN 0-86171-008-8, Pub. by Wisdom Pubns). Great Traditions.
Wisdom for Living. Jerry Falwell. 156p. 1984. pap. 5.95 (ISBN 0-89693-370-9). Victor Bks.
Wisdom for the New Age. Azrael. LC 81-85815. 208p. (Orig.). 1982. pap. 6.95 (ISBN 0-87516-477-3). De Vorss.
Wisdom for Today's Family. John W. Drakeford. LC 77-94449. 1978. pap. 5.50 (ISBN 0-8054-5592-2). Broadman.
Wisdom from Atlantis. Ruth B. Drown. 153p. 1981. pap. 9.00 (ISBN 0-686-78074-4, SB-098). Sun Pub.
Wisdom from Mount Athos: The Writings of Staretz Silouan, 1866-1938. Archimandrite Sophrony. 124p. 1974. pap. 5.95 (ISBN 0-913836-17-6). St Vladimirs.
Wisdom from the East: Meditations, Reflections, Proverbs & Chants. Ellen K. Hua. LC 73-21886. (Illus.). 128p. (Orig.). 1974. pap. 3.00 (ISBN 0-87407-202-6, FP2). Thor.
Wisdom Goddess: Feminine Motifs in Eight Nag Hammadi Documents. Rose H. Arthur. Tr. by Richard L. Arthur. (Illus.). 256p. (Orig.). 1984. lib. bdg. 26.25 (ISBN 0-8191-4171-2); pap. text ed. 13.50 (ISBN 0-8191-4172-0). U Pr of Amer.
Wisdom in Israel. rev. ed. Gerhard Von Rad. Tr. by James D. Martin from Ger. Orig. Title: Weisheit in Israel. 336p. 1973. 15.95 (ISBN 0-687-45757-2). Abingdon.
Wisdom in the Old Testament Traditions. Donn F. Morgan. LC 80-84653. 180p. 1982. 17.50 (ISBN 0-8042-0188-9); pap. 9.50 (ISBN 0-8042-0189-7). John Knox.
Wisdom Instructs Her Children: The Power of the Spirit & the Word. John Randall. 128p. (Orig.). 1981. pap. 3.95 (ISBN 0-914544-36-5). Living Flame Pr.
Wisdom Literature: An Introduction. James D. Wood. LC 67-108276. (Studies in Theology: No. 64). 1967. text ed. 8.50x (ISBN 0-8401-6064-X). A R Allenson.
Wisdom Literature & Psalms: Interpreting Biblical Texts. Roland E. Murphy. Ed. by Lloyd R. Bailey & Victor P. Furnish. 160p. (Orig.). 1983. pap. 8.95 (ISBN 0-687-45759-9). Abingdon.
Wisdom Literature: Job, Proverbs, Ecclesiastes. John T. Willis. LC 81-69494. (Way of Life Ser.: No. 145). 1982. pap. 3.95 (ISBN 0-89112-145-5, Biblo Res Pr). Abilene Christ U.
Wisdom Literature: Ruth, Esther, Job, Proverbs, Ecclesiastes, Canticles. Roland E. Murphy. (The Forms of the Old Testament Literature Ser.). (Orig.). 1981. pap. 12.95 (ISBN 0-8028-1877-3). Eerdmans.
Wisdom of Accepted Tenderness. Brennan Manning. casebound 5.95 (ISBN 0-87193-110-9); pap. 4.95. Dimension Bks.
Wisdom of Buddhism. 2nd, rev. ed. Ed. by Christmas Humphreys. 280p. 1987. pap. text ed. 9.95 (ISBN 0-391-03464-2, Pub. by Humanities Press & Curzon Pr England). Humanities.
Wisdom of Christendom. Marvin L. Brown, Jr. 131p. 1982. pap. 5.95. Edenwood Hse.
Wisdom of Confucius. Confucius. (Illus.). 131p. 1982. 63.45 (ISBN 0-89266-359-6). Am Classical Coll Pr.
Wisdom of Confucius. Confucius. 1965. 5.95 (ISBN 0-88088-100-3). Peter Pauper.
Wisdom of Confucius. Confucius. Ed. & tr. by Lin Yutang. LC 38-27366. 290p. 1938. 5.95 (ISBN 0-394-60426-1). Modern Lib.
Wisdom of Confucius. Ed. by Epiphanius Wilson. 15.95 (ISBN 0-89190-545-6, Pub. by Am Repr). Amereon Ltd.
Wisdom of Confucius. LC 68-56192. 1968. 5.00 (ISBN 0-8022-0853-3). Philos Lib.
Wisdom of God. David Jeremiah. 1986. pap. 5.95 (ISBN 0-8010-5220-3). Baker Bk.
Wisdom of God Manifested in the Works of the Creation. John Ray. LC 75-11250. (British Philosophers & Theologians in the 17th & 18th Century Ser.). 247p. 1979. lib. bdg. 51.00 (ISBN 0-8240-1801-X). Garland Pub.
Wisdom of God Manifested in the Works of the Creation: Heavenly Bodies, Elements, Meteors, Fossils, Vegetables, Animals. John Ray. Ed. by Frank N. Egerton, 3rd. LC 77-74250. (History of Ecology Ser.). 1978. Repr. of 1717 ed. lib. bdg. 40.00x (ISBN 0-405-10419-7). Ayer Co Pubs.
Wisdom of Islamic Civilization. M. A. Baig. 9.95 (ISBN 0-317-01595-8). Kazi Pubns.
Wisdom of John Woolman: With a Selection from His Writings As a Guide to the Seekers of Today. Reginald Reynolds. LC 79-8724. xii, 178p. 1981. Repr. of 1948 ed. lib. bdg. 22.50x (ISBN 0-313-22190-1, REJW). Greenwood.
Wisdom of Laotse. Iverson L. Harris. 36p. 1972. pap. 0.75 (ISBN 0-913004-05-7). Point Loma Pub.
Wisdom of Man: Selected Discourses. M. R. Bawa Muhaiyaddeen. LC 80-20541. (Illus.). 168p. 1980. 7.95 (ISBN 0-914390-16-3). Fellowship Pr PA.
Wisdom of Proverbs, Job & Ecclesiastes. Derek Kidner. LC 85-11826. 176p. 1985. pap. 5.95 (ISBN 0-87784-405-4). Inter-Varsity.
Wisdom of Saankhya. K. P. Bahadur. LC 78-901698. (Wisdom of India Ser.: Vol. 2). 222p. 1977. 9.25 (ISBN 0-89684-469-2). Orient Bk Dist.
Wisdom of St. Francis & His Companions. Compiled by Stephen Clissold. LC 78-27504. (Wisdom Books). 1979. pap. 4.95 (ISBN 0-8112-0721-8, NDP477). New Directions.
Wisdom of St. John. Bo Yin Ra. Tr. by Bodo A. Reichenbach from Ger. LC 74-15272. 112p. 1975. 8.00 (ISBN 0-915034-01-8). Kober Pr.
Wisdom of Solomon. E. G. Clarke. (Cambridge Bible Commentary on the New English Bible, Old Testament Ser.). 148p. 1973. 18.95 (ISBN 0-521-08635-3); pap. 8.95 (ISBN 0-521-09756-8). Cambridge U Pr.
Wisdom of Solomon. David Winston. LC 78-18150. (Anchor Bible Ser.: Vol. 43). 1979. 16.00 (ISBN 0-385-01644-1, Anchor Pr). Doubleday.
Wisdom of Solomon Schechter. Bernard Mandelbaum. 1963. pap. 2.50 (ISBN 0-8381-3103-4). United Syn Bk.
Wisdom of the Body. Yogi A. Desai. Ed. by Lisa Sarasohn. (Illus.). 40p. (Orig.). 1984. pap. 2.00 (ISBN 0-940258-13-7). Kripalu Pubns.
Wisdom of the Desert. Thomas Merton. LC 59-15021. 1970. 6.50 (ISBN 0-8112-0313-1); pap. 3.95 (ISBN 0-8112-0102-3, NDP295). New Directions.
Wisdom of the Desert Fathers. 1979. pap. 3.95 (ISBN 0-686-25228-4). Eastern Orthodox.
Wisdom of the Early Buddhists. Geoffrey Parrinder. LC 77-7945. (New Directions Wisdon Ser.). 1977. pap. 4.95 (ISBN 0-8112-0667-X, NDP444). New Directions.
Wisdom of the English Mystics. Ed. by Robert Way. LC 78-6435. 1978. pap. 3.75 (ISBN 0-8112-0700-5, NDP466). New Directions.
Wisdom of the Forest: Selections from the Hindu Upanishads. Tr. & intro. by Geoffrey Parrinder. LC 75-42114. (Wisdom Bks). 96p. 1976. pap. 1.95 (ISBN 0-8112-0607-6, NDP414). New Directions.
Wisdom of the Heart: Katherine Tingley Speaks. Katherine Tingley. Ed. by W. Emmett Small. LC 78-65338. 1978. pap. 5.75 (ISBN 0-913004-33-2). Point Loma Pub.
Wisdom of the Hindus. Brian Brown. 320p. 1981. pap. 18.00 (ISBN 0-89540-093-6, SB-093). Sun Pub.
Wisdom of the Lord: Homilies for Weekdays & Feast Days. Rev. Gene Ulses. LC 86-60910. 254p. (Orig.). 1986. 12.95 (ISBN 0-87973-512-0, 512). Our Sunday Visitor.
Wisdom of the Mystic Masters. John K. Weed. 1968. 10.95 (ISBN 0-13-961516-4, Reward); pap. 4.95 (ISBN 0-13-961532-6). P-H.
Wisdom of the Prophets. Ibn'Arabi. Tr. by Titus Burckardt. 1976. pap. write for info. (ISBN 0-685-67327-8). Weiser.
Wisdom of the Saints: An Anthology of Voices. Jill H. Adels. 288p. 1987. 16.95 (ISBN 0-19-504152-6). Oxford U Pr.
Wisdom of the Sands, 2 vols. Bhagwan Shree Rajneesh. Ed. by Ma Yoga Sudha. LC 80-903299. (Sufi Ser.). (Illus., Orig.). 1980. Vol. I, 380 pgs. 19.95 ea. (ISBN 0-88050-174-X). Vol. II, 404 pgs. 1980 (ISBN 0-88050-175-8). Vol.1 386p 1980. pap. 15.95 ea. (ISBN 0-88050-674-1). Chidvilas Found.
Wisdom of the Sands. Bhagwan Shree Rajneesh & Ma Yoga Sudha. LC 80-903299. (Sufi Ser.: Vol. II). 412p. (Orig.). 1980. pap. 15.95 (ISBN 0-88050-675-X). Chidvilas Found.
Wisdom of the Sands. Saint Antoine De Saint-Exupery. Tr. by Stuart Gilbert from Fr. LC 79-15938. 1979. pap. 10.95 (ISBN 0-226-73372-6, P826). U of Chicago Pr.
Wisdom of the Spanish Mystics. Stephen Clissold. (Wisdom Bks.). 3.95 (ISBN 0-8112-0663-7). New Directions.
Wisdom of the Sufis. Kenneth Cragg. LC 76-7032. (Wisdom Books). 1976. pap. 2.75 (ISBN 0-8112-0627-0, NDP424). New Directions.
Wisdom of the Throne: An Introduction to the Philosophy of Mulla Sadra. Mulla Sadra. Tr. by James W. Morris from Arabic. LC 81-47153. (Princeton Library of Asian Translations). 300p. 1981. 34.50x (ISBN 0-691-06493-8). Princeton U Pr.
Wisdom of the Upanishads. Besant. 3.50 (ISBN 0-8356-7092-9). Theos Pub Hse.
Wisdom of the Vedas. J. C. Chatterji. LC 80-51550. 100p. 1980. pap. 3.95 (ISBN 0-8356-0538-8, Quest). Theos Pub Hse.
Wisdom of the Zen Masters. Ed. by Irmgard Schloegl. LC 75-42115. (Wisdom Bks.). 96p. 1976. pap. 5.95 (ISBN 0-8112-0610-6, NDP415). New Directions.
Wisdom of the Zohar, 3 vols. Ed. by Isaiah Tishby. Tr. by David Goldstein. (Litman Library of Jewish Civilization). 2000p. 1986. Set. 198.00x (ISBN 0-19-710043-0). Oxford U Pr.
Wisdom of Vaisheshika. K. P. Bahadur. (Wisdom of India Ser.: Vol. 4). 207p. 1979. 10.50 (ISBN 0-89684-470-6). Orient Bk Dist.
Wisdom of Words: Language, Theology & Literature in the New England Renaissance. Philip F. Gura. x, 203p. 1985. pap. 12.95 (ISBN 0-8195-6120-7). Wesleyan U Pr.
Wisdom of Yoga. K. P. Bahadur. LC 77-985594. (Wisdom of India Ser.: Vol. 1). 116p. 1977. 9.25 (ISBN 0-89684-471-4). Orient Bk Dist.
Wisdom, or Mind, Will, & Understanding. LC 70-133770. (Tudor Facsimile Texts. Old English Plays Ser.: No. 2). Repr. of 1907 ed. 49.50 (ISBN 0-404-53302-7). AMS Pr.
Wisdom Tree. Gary D. Guthrie. 56p. (Orig.). Date not set. pap. price not set (ISBN 0-9612980-0-6). Gary Guthrie.
Wisdom Tree. Emma Hawkridge. LC 72-128257. (Essay Index Reprint Ser.). 1945. 33.00 (ISBN 0-8369-1881-9). Ayer Co Pubs.
Wisdom-Waves in New York, 2 pts. Sri Chinmoy. (Orig.). 1979. pap. 2.00 ea. Pt. 1, 53p (ISBN 0-88497-487-1). Pt. 2, 50p (ISBN 0-88497-488-X). Aum Pubns.

Wisdom's Fool. Eddie Doherty. 4.95 (ISBN 0-910984-08-5); pap. 2.95 (ISBN 0-910984-09-3). Montfort Pubns.

Wise Men. (Read, Show & Tell Ser.). (Eng. & Span., Illus.). 1977. Eng. Ed. 2.25 (ISBN 0-8326-2606-6, 3624). Span. Ed (5624). World Bible.

Wise Men of Helm. Solomon Simon. 1942. pap. 4.95 (ISBN 0-87441-125-4). Behrman.

Wise up & Live. 2nd ed. Paul E. Larsen. LC 73-86222. 256p. pap. 3.50 (ISBN 0-8307-0453-1, S274124). Regal.

Wise Woman. Joyce Rogers. LC 80-68538. 1981. 8.95 (ISBN 0-8054-5289-3). Broadman.

Wise Woman Knows. Bessie Patterson. 4.95 (ISBN 0-89137-422-1). Quality Pubns.

Wise Words & Quaint Counsels of Thomas Fuller: Selected & Arranged with a Short Sketch of the Author's Life. Augustus Jessop. 1979. Repr. of 1892 ed. lib. bdg. 45.00 (ISBN 0-8492-5602-X). R West.

Wise Words in a Wicked World: Studies in Proverbs. Charles W. Turner. pap. 4.95 (ISBN 0-88469-028-8). BMH Bks.

Wise Words to the Graduate. Robert J. Martin. (Contempo Ser.). 1978. pap. 1.50 (ISBN 0-8010-6043-5). Baker Bk.

Wisedome of the Ancients. Francis Bacon. Tr. by A. Gorges. LC 68-54614. (English Experince Ser.: No. 1). 176p. 1968. Repr. of 1619 ed. 13.00 (ISBN 90-221-0001-4). Walter J Johnson.

Wisely Train the Younger Women. Mrs. Elmer Patterson. 1973. pap. 4.95 (ISBN 0-89137-406-X). Quality Pubns.

Wishful Thinking: A Theological ABC. Frederick Buechner. LC 72-9872. 128p. 1973. 12.45 (ISBN 0-06-061155-3, HarpR). Har-Row.

Wit & Wisdom from West Africa: A Book of Proverbial Philosophy, Idioms, Enigmas, & Laconisms. Richard F. Burton. LC 77-79952. 1969. Repr. of 1865 ed. 16.00 (ISBN 0-8196-0243-4). Biblo.

Wit & Wisdom of D. L. Moody. Compiled by Stanley Gundry & Patricia Gundry. (Direction Bks.). 78p. 1982. pap. 2.95 (ISBN 0-8010-3780-8). Baker Bk.

Wit & Wisdom of the Christian Fathers of Egypt: The Syrian Version of the Apophthegmata Patrum. Compiled by Anan Isho. Tr. by Ernest A. Wallis Budge. LC 80-2354. Repr. of 1934 ed. 53.50 (ISBN 0-404-18900-8). AMS Pr.

Wit & Wisdom of the Rev. Sydney Smith. Sydney Smith. 1880. Repr. 25.00 (ISBN 0-8274-3728-5). R West.

Wit & Wisdom of the Talmud. 2nd ed. Reuven P. Bulka. (PPP Gift Editions). (Illus.). 1983. 5.95 (ISBN 0-88088-507-6). Peter Pauper.

Wit & Wisdom of the Talmud. Madison C. Peters. 169p. 1980. Repr. of 1900 ed. lib. bdg. 20.00 (ISBN 0-8414-6852-4). Folcroft.

Wit & Wisdom of William Bacon Evans. Anna C. Brinton. 1966. pap. 2.50x (ISBN 0-87574-146-0, 146). Pendle Hill.

Witch Amongst Us. Lois Bourne. 208p. 1986. 13.95 (ISBN 0-312-88425-7). St Martin.

Witch Doctor: Memoirs of a Partisan. Michael Temchin. (Illus.). 192p. (Orig.). 1983. 16.95 (ISBN 0-8052-5046-8); pap. 10.95 (ISBN 0-8052-5047-6). Holocaust Pubns.

Witch Hunting in Southwestern Germany, 1562-1684: The Social & Intellectual Foundations. H. Erik Midelfort. LC 75-183891. 320p. 1972. 26.50x (ISBN 0-8047-0805-3). Stanford U Pr.

Witchcraft. Charles A. Hoyt. LC 80-24731. 160p. 1981. pap. 12.95 (ISBN 0-8093-1015-5). S Ill U Pr.

Witchcraft. Bernard Sleigh. 69.95 (ISBN 0-8490-1311-9). Gordon Pr.

Witchcraft & Religion: The Politics of Popular Belief. Christina Larner. 256p. 1984. 29.95x (ISBN 0-631-13447-6). Basil Blackwell.

Witchcraft & Religion: The Politics of Popular Belief. Christina Larner. Ed. by Alan Macfarlane. 184p. 1986. pap. text ed. 12.95x (ISBN 0-631-14779-9). Basil Blackwell.

Witchcraft & Second Sight in the Highlands & Islands of Scotland. John G. Campbell. 1976. Repr. 20.00x (ISBN 0-85409-978-6). Charles River Bks.

Witchcraft & Sorcery. Ed. by Max Marwick. 494p. 1987. pap. 6.95 (ISBN 0-14-022678-8, Pelican). Penguin.

Witchcraft & Superstitious Record in the Southwestern District of Scotland. J. Maxwell Wood. (Illus.). 1976. 25.00x (ISBN 0-7158-1139-8). Charles River Bks.

Witchcraft & Superstitious Record in the Southwestern District of Scotland. John M. Wood. LC 76-25108. 1976. 40.00 (ISBN 0-8414-9530-0). Folcroft.

Witchcraft & the Black Art: A Book Dealing with the Psychology & Folklore of the Witches. J. W. Wickwar. LC 71-151817. 1971. Repr. of 1925 ed. 48.00x (ISBN 0-8103-3692-8). Gale.

Witchcraft at Salem. Chadwick Hansen. LC 69-15825. (Illus.). 1969. 11.95 (ISBN 0-8076-0492-5). Braziller.

Witchcraft at Salem. Chadwick Hansen. LC 99-943950. 252p. (YA) pap. 3.95 (ISBN 0-451-62214-6, ME2214, Ment). NAL.

Witchcraft at Salem. Chadwick Hansen. (Illus.). 252p. 1985. pap. 7.95 (ISBN 0-8076-1137-9). Braziller.

Witchcraft Delusion in Colonial Connecticut, 1647-1747. John Taylor. 172p. 1974. 16.95 (ISBN 0-87928-053-0). Corner Hse.

Witchcraft Delusion in Colonial Connecticut, 1647-97. John M. Taylor. LC 73-165414. (American Classics in History & Social Science Ser.: No. 196). 1971. Repr. of 1908 ed. lib. bdg. 21.00 (ISBN 0-8337-4445-3). B Franklin.

Witchcraft Delusion in New England, 3 vols. Samuel G. Drake. LC 79-120720. (Research & Source Works Ser.: No. 471). 1970. Repr. of 1866 ed. lib. bdg. 62.00 (ISBN 0-8337-0908-9). B Franklin.

Witchcraft from the Inside. 2nd ed. Raymond Buckland. (Illus.). 145p. 1975. pap. 3.95 (ISBN 0-87542-085-0). Llewellyn Pubns.

Witchcraft in Europe, 1100-1700: A Documentary History. Ed. by Alan C. Kors & Edward Peters. LC 71-170267. (Illus.). 1972. pap. 13.95x (ISBN 0-8122-1063-8, Pa Paperbks). U of Pa pr.

Witchcraft in History. Ronald Holmes. 1977. pap. 5.95 (ISBN 0-8065-0575-3). Citadel Pr.

Witchcraft in Ireland. Patrick Byrne. 80p. 1967. pap. 6.95 (ISBN 0-85342-038-6, Pub. by Mercier Pr Ireland). Irish Bk Ctr.

Witchcraft in the Middle Ages. Jeffrey B. Russel. (Illus.). 1976. pap. 5.95 (ISBN 0-8065-0504-4). Citadel Pr.

Witchcraft in the Southwest: Spanish & Indian Supernaturalism on the Rio Grande. Marc Simmons. LC 79-18928. (Illus.). xiv, 184p. 1980. pap. 5.50 (ISBN 0-8032-9116-7, BB 729, Bison). U of Nebr Pr.

Witchcraft, Magic & Religion in Seventeenth Century Massachusetts. Richard Weisman. LC 83-15542. 288p. 1985. pap. text ed. 9.95x (ISBN 0-87023-494-3). U of MAss Pr.

Witchcraft of Salem Village. Shirley Jackson. (Landmark Ser.: No. 69). (Illus.). 1956. PLB 6.99 (ISBN 0-394-90369-2, BYR). Random.

Witchcraft Papers. Peter Haining. 1974. 7.95 (ISBN 0-8216-0223-3). Univ Bks.

Witchcraft: The Gay Counterculture. Arthur Evans. 1977. pap. 5.95 (ISBN 0-915480-01-8). Fag Rag.

Witchcraft: The Heritage of a Heresy. H. Sebald. 262p. 1978. pap. 15.50 (ISBN 0-444-99059-3). Elsevier.

Witchcraft: The Old Religion. Leo L. Martello. 1987. pap. 6.95 (ISBN 0-8065-1028-5). Citadel Pr.

Witchcraft-the Sixth Sense. Justine Glass. pap. 7.00 (ISBN 0-87980-174-3). Wilshire.

Witchcraft Today. Gerald B. Gardner. 1970. pap. 2.45 (ISBN 0-8065-0002-6). Citadel Pr.

Witchcraft Today. Gerard B. Gardner. (Illus.). 184p. pap. 9.95 (ISBN 0-939708-03-5). Magickal Childe.

Witches. Colin Hawkins. LC 85-40425. (Illus.). 32p. 1985. 7.45 (ISBN 0-382-09132-9). Silver.

Witches. Olga Hoyt. LC 68-13233. (Illus.). 1969. 11.70i (ISBN 0-200-71593-3, B91350, AbS-J). HarpJ.

Witches. Erica Jong. (Illus.). 1982. pap. 12.50 (ISBN 0-452-25357-8, Z5357, Plume). NAL.

Witches. Rawson & Carlwright. (Story Book). 1979. 6.95 (ISBN 0-86020-341-7, Usborne-Hayes); PLB 11.96 (ISBN 0-88110-057-9); pap. 2.95 (ISBN 0-86020-340-9). EDC.

Witches. Therese R. Revesz. LC 77-10626. (Myth, Magic, & Superstition Ser.). (Illus.). 1977. PLB 14.65 (ISBN 0-8172-1034-2). Raintree Pubs.

Witches' Advocate: Basque Witchcraft & the Spanish Inquisition, 1609-1614. Gustav Henningsen. LC 79-20340. (Basque Book Ser.). (Illus.). xxxii, 607p. 1980. 24.00 (ISBN 0-87417-056-7). U of Nev Pr.

Witches & Demons in History & Folklore. F. Roy Johnson. (Illus.). 1978. Repr. 9.50 (ISBN 0-930230-31-0). Johnson NC.

Witches & Historians: Interpretations of Salem. Marc Mappen. LC 78-2579. (American Problem Studies). 126p. 1980. pap. 6.50 (ISBN 0-88275-653-2). Krieger.

Witches & Sorcerers. Dauraul. pap. 2.95 (ISBN 0-8065-0286-X). Citadel Pr.

Witches & Warlocks. Phillip W. Sargeant. 1976. 20.00x (ISBN 0-7158-1028-6). Charles River Bks.

Witches & Warlocks. Philip W. Sergeant. LC 72-82208. (Illus.). Repr. of 1936 ed. 24.50 (ISBN 0-405-08898-1). Ayer Co Pubs.

Witches & Warlocks. Philip W. Sergeant. LC 72-164055. (Illus.). 290p. 1975. Repr. of 1936 ed. 34.00x (ISBN 0-8103-3979-X). Gale.

Witches & Warlocks. Philip W. Sergeant. 1972. 24.50 (ISBN 0-405-08950-3, 1457). Ayer Co Pubs.

Witches & Witch-Hunters. Roberts. 1978. Repr. of 1973 ed. lib. bdg. 27.50 (ISBN 0-8414-2928-6). Folcroft.

Witches Bible, 2 vols. Janet Farrar & Stuart Farrar. (Illus., Orig.). 1984. Vol. I - The Sabbats. pap. 10.95 (ISBN 0-939708-06-X); Vol. II - The Rituals. pap. 10.95 (ISBN 0-939708-07-8); pap. 21.90 boxed set (ISBN 0-939708-08-6). Magickal Childe.

Witches, Demons & Fertility Magic. Anne Runeberg. 273p. 1980. Repr. of 1947 ed. lib. bdg. 30.00 (ISBN 0-8414-7399-4). Folcroft.

Witches, Demons & Fertility Magic. Arne Runeberg. LC 74-3091. (Folklore Ser). 39.50 (ISBN 0-88305-560-0). Norwood Edns.

Witches, Ghosts & Signs, Folklore of the Southern Appalachians. Patrick W. Gainer. LC 75-29893. 192p. 1975. 7.95 (ISBN 0-89092-006-0). Seneca Bks.

Witch's Handbook. Malcolm Bird. (Illus.). 96p. 1985. 10.95 (ISBN 0-312-88458-3). St Martin.

With a Merry Heart. Paul J. Phelan. 353p. 1981. Repr. of 1943 ed. lib. bdg. 25.00 (ISBN 0-89760-710-4). Telegraph Bks.

With All Due Respect. Paul A. Corcoran. 1983. 4.50 (ISBN 0-89536-609-6, 2354). CSS of Ohio.

With All My Heart. Jennifer K. Adams. Ed. by Mary Wallace. (Illus.). 104p. 1984. pap. 4.95 (ISBN 0-912315-78-4). Word Aflame.

With All Your Heart: Bechol Levavcha, 2 vols. Harvey J. Fields. (Illus.). 1977. Set. 10.00 (ISBN 0-8074-0197-8, 142611). UAHC.

With Bible & Spade. Walter E. Sabins. (Orig.). 1987. pap. price not set (ISBN 0-89536-897-8, 7883). CSS of Ohio.

With Christ after the Lost. rev. ed. Lee R. Scarborough. Ed. by E. D. Head. 1953. 12.95 (ISBN 0-8054-6203-1). Broadman.

With Christ in Heavenly Realms: A Study of Ephesians. Phyllis Mitchell. (Enrichment Bible Studies). 60p. 1986. pap. 2.95 (ISBN 0-932305-22-9, 522007). Aglow Pubns.

With Christ in the School of Obedience. Andrew Murray. 108p. 1986. pap. 4.95 (ISBN 0-89693-281-8). Victor Bks.

With Christ in the School of Prayer. Andrew Murray. 288p. 1981. pap. 3.50 (ISBN 0-88368-106-4). Whitaker Hse.

With Christ in the School of Prayer. Andrew Murray. 288p. 1983. pap. 5.95 (ISBN 0-310-29771-0, 10527P, Clarion Class). Zondervan.

With Clumsy Grace: The American Catholic Left, 1961-1975. Charles Meconis. 1979. 9.95 (ISBN 0-8264-0175-9). Continuum.

With Concerts of Prayer. David Bryant. LC 84-17916. 1985. pap. 6.95 (ISBN 0-8307-0975-4, 5418295). Regal.

With Courage to Spare. John B. Toews. 185p. (Orig.). 1978. pap. 4.95 (ISBN 0-919797-26-1); 7.95 (ISBN 0-919797-25-3). Kindred Pr.

With Death at My Back. Donna Huyck. (Uplook Ser.). pap. 0.99 (ISBN 0-8163-0427-0). Pacific Pr Pub Assn.

With Each Passing Moment. Mary Higginbotham. pap. 1.25 (ISBN 0-686-12748-X). Grace Pub Co.

With Faith All Things Are Possible. Compiled by Karen Kauffman. (Illus.). 1983. 8.00 (ISBN 0-8378-1802-8). Gibson.

With Firmness in the Right: American Diplomatic Action Affecting Jews, 1840-1945. Cyrus Adler & Aaron M. Margalith. Ed. by Moshe Davis. LC 77-70651. (America & the Holy Land Ser.). 1977. Repr. of 1946 ed. lib. bdg. 40.00x (ISBN 0-405-10222-4). Ayer Co Pubs.

With Freedom Fired: The Story of Robert Robinson, Cambridge Nonconformist. G. W. Hughes. 123p. 1955. Repr. 2.95 (ISBN 0-87921-018-4). Attic Pr.

With Fury Poured Out: A Torah Perspective on the Holocaust. 300p. 1987. 16.95 (ISBN 0-88125-107-0). KTAV.

With Glad & Generous Hearts. William H. Willimon. 176p. 1986. pap. 7.95 (ISBN 0-8358-0536-0, ICN 613183, Dist. by Abingdon Press). Upper Room.

With God in Hell: Judaism in the Ghettos & Deathcamps. Eliezer Berkovits. 1979. 9.95 (ISBN 0-88482-937-5, Sanhedrin Pr). Hebrew Pub.

With God in Solitary Confinement. Richard Wurmbrand. 1979. pap. 4.95 (ISBN 0-88264-002-X). Diane Bks.

With God on Our Side. Anthony Tuttle. 1978. pap. 2.25 (ISBN 0-89083-324-9). Zebra.

With God's Help Flowers Bloom. Elaine Anderson. 1978. pap. 4.95 (ISBN 0-89137-411-6); study guide 2.85 (ISBN 0-89137-412-4). Quality Pubns.

With Good Heart: Yaqui Beliefs & Ceremonies in Pascua, Village. Muriel T. Painter. Ed. by Edward H. Spicer & Wilma Kaemlein. LC 86-893. (Illus.). 533p. 1986. 35.00x (ISBN 0-8165-0875-5). U of Ariz Pr.

With Good Intentions: Quaker Work among the Pawnees, Otos, & Omahas in the 1870's. Clyde A. Milner, II. LC 81-16238. (Illus.). xvi, 246p. 1982. 21.50x (ISBN 0-8032-3066-4). U of Nebr Pr.

With Gurdjieff in St. Petersburg. Anna Butkovsky-Hewitt. 1978. 9.95 (ISBN 0-7100-8527-3). Weiser.

With Him in the Struggle: A Woman's Workshop on II Samuel. Myrna Alexander. (Woman's Workshop Ser.). 128p. 1986. pap. 3.95 (ISBN 0-310-37211-9, 10918P). Zondervan.

With Jesus on the Scout Trail. Walter D. Cavert. (Orig.). 1970. pap. 3.75 (ISBN 0-687-45849-8). Abingdon.

With Justice for All. John Perkins. LC 80-50262. 216p. 1982. text ed. 10.95 (ISBN 0-8307-0754-9, 5108802); pap. 5.95 (ISBN 0-8307-0934-7, 5418181). Regal.

With Love from Dad. Judson Edwards. 208p. 1986. pap. 5.95 (ISBN 0-89081-501-1). Harvest Hse.

With Malice Toward Some: A Documented Sampling of U. S. Government Conspiracy-Infiltration-Manipulation 1950-1979. pap. 7.00 (ISBN 0-686-74642-2). Church of Scient Info.

With One Accord in One Place. Armin R. Gesswein. 93p. (Orig.). 1978. pap. 1.75 (ISBN 0-87509-161-X). Chr Pubns.

With One Heart Bowing to the City of Ten Thousand Buddhas, Vol. IV. Heng Sure & Heng Chau. (Illus.). 136p. (Orig.). 1980. pap. 4.00 (ISBN 0-917512-90-1). Buddhist Text.

With One Heart Bowing to the City of Ten Thousand Buddhas, Vol. VI. Heng Sure & Heng Chau. (Illus.). 200p. (Orig.). 1981. pap. 6.00 (ISBN 0-917512-92-8). Buddhist Text.

With One Heart Bowing to the City of Ten Thousand Buddhas, Vol. I. Heng Sure & Heng Chau. (Illus.). 180p. (Orig.). 1977. pap. 6.00 (ISBN 0-917512-21-9). Buddhist Text.

With One Heart Bowing to the City of Ten Thousand Buddhas, Vol. II. Heng Sure & Heng Chau. (Illus.). 322p. (Orig.). 1979. pap. 7.00 (ISBN 0-917512-23-5). Buddhist Text.

With One Heart Bowing to the City of Ten Thousand Buddhas, Vol. IX. Heng Sure & Heng Chau. 220p. (Orig.). 1983. pap. 7.50 (ISBN 0-88139-016-X). Buddhist Text.

With One Heart Bowing to the City of Ten Thousand Buddhas, Vol. III. Heng Sure & Heng Chau. (Illus.). 154p. (Orig.). 1980. pap. 5.00 (ISBN 0-917512-89-8). Buddhist Text.

With One Heart Bowing to the City of Ten Thousand Buddhas, Vol. VII. Heng Sure & Heng Chau. (Illus.). 160p. (Orig.). 1982. pap. 5.00 (ISBN 0-917512-99-5). Buddhist Text.

With One Heart Bowing to the City of Ten Thousand Buddhas, Vol. VIII. Heng Sure & Heng Chau. (Illus.). 232p. (Orig.). 1982. pap. 7.50 (ISBN 0-917512-53-7). Buddhist Text.

With One Heart Bowing to the City of Ten Thousand Buddhas, Vol. V. Heng Sure & Heng Chau. (Illus.). 127p. (Orig.). 1981. pap. 4.00 (ISBN 0-917512-91-X). Buddhist Text.

With Open Hands. Henri Nouwen. 96p. 1985. pap. 4.95 large print ed. (ISBN 0-8027-2475-2). Walker & Co.

With Open Hands. Henri J. Nouwen. LC 71-177600. (Illus.). 160p. 1972. pap. 3.95 (ISBN 0-87793-040-6). Ave Maria.

With Open Heart. Michel Quoist. 264p. (Orig.). 1983. pap. 8.95 (ISBN 0-8245-0569-7). Crossroad NY.

With Perfect Faith. David Bleich. 1982. 25.00x (ISBN 0-87068-891-X); pap. 14.95. Ktav.

With Prayer & Psalm: The History of Wilmot, New Hampshire Churches. Florence Langley. LC 81-5116. 80p. 1981. 7.95x (ISBN 0-914016-77-6). Phoenix Pub.

With Signs Following. Stanley H. Frodsham. 188p. 1946. pap. 5.95 (ISBN 0-88243-635-X, 02-0635). Gospel Pub.

With the Church. Ed. by Mathias Goossens. 6.95 (ISBN 0-8199-0148-2, L39000). Franciscan Herald.

With the Good Shepherd. Leroy Brownlow. 1969. gift ed. 6.95 (ISBN 0-915720-12-4). Brownlow Pub Co.

With the Huckleberry Christ: A Spiritual Journey. Kristen J. Ingram. 96p. (Orig.). 1985. pap. 5.95 (ISBN 0-86683-798-1, HarpR). Har-Row.

With the Lord Today, 4 vols. Hal M. Helms. (Orig.). 1985. Set. 14.95 set (ISBN 0-941478-39-4). Paraclete Pr.

With the Pilgrims to Canterbury: And the History of the Hospital of St. Thomas. Stanley G. Wilson. LC 70-178306. Repr. of 1934 ed. 14.50 (ISBN 0-404-06997-5). AMS Pr.

With the Pilgrims to Mecca: The Great Pilgrimage of A.H. 1319, A.D. 1902. Gazanfar A. Khan & Wilfred Sparroy. LC 77-876447. Repr. of 1905 ed. 24.50 (ISBN 0-404-16417-X). AMS Pr.

With the Ups Comes the Downs. Florence K. Biros. (Illus.). 104p. (Orig.). 1986. pap. 2.95 (ISBN 0-936369-01-9). Son-Rise Pubns.

With Thine Adversary in the Way: A Quaker Witness for Reconciliation. Margarethe Lachmund. Tr. by Florence Kite. LC 79-91957. (Orig.). pap. 2.50x (ISBN 0-87574-228-9). Pendle Hill.

With This Ring. Marian Wells. LC 84-9301. 200p. (Orig.). 1984. pap. 4.95 (ISBN 0-87123-615-X, 210615). Bethany Hse.
With Wandering Steps & Slow. Joy Hoffman. LC 81-18566. 140p. (Orig.). 1982. pap. 4.95 (ISBN 0-87784-804-1). Inter-Varsity.
With Wings As Eagles. William S. Pinkston, Jr. (Illus.). 127p. 1983. pap. 5.95 (ISBN 0-89084-231-0). Bob Jones Univ Pr.
With Wings of Eagles. Richard C. Hoefler. 1983. 5.35 (ISBN 0-89536-624-X, 2352). CSS of Ohio.
With You, Dear Child, in Mind. Lynn Groth. (Cradle Roll Program Ser.). 16p. (Orig.). 1985. pap. 1.25 (ISBN 0-938272-77-2). Wels Board.
Withhold Not Correction. Bruce Ray. pap. 3.45 (ISBN 0-8010-7687-0). Baker Bk.
Withhold Not Correction. Bruce Ray. 1978. pap. 3.45 (ISBN 0-87552-400-1). Presby & Reformed.
Within Heaven's Gates. Rebecca Springer. 128p. 1984. pap. 3.50 (ISBN 0-88368-125-0). Whitaker Hse.
Within Human Experience: The Philosophy of William Ernest Hocking. Leroy S. Rouner. LC 71-75433. (Illus.). 1969. text ed. 20.00x (ISBN 0-674-95380-0). Harvard U Pr.
Within My Heart. Shirley Sealy. 168p. 1983. 7.95 (ISBN 0-934126-37-2). Randall Bk Co.
Within Our Reach. David M. Call. LC 83-26162. 68p. 1984. 5.95 (ISBN 0-87747-975-5). Deseret Bk.
Within the Castle. Madeline, Sr. 1983. 9.50 (ISBN 0-8199-0820-7). Franciscan Herald.
Within the Gates. Gordon Lindsay. (Sorcery & Spirit World Ser.). 1.75 (ISBN 0-89985-095-2). Christ Nations.
Within the Halls of Pilate. David T. Lusk. 4.50 (ISBN 0-89137-538-4). Quality Pubns.
Within the Pale: The True Story of Anti-Semitic Persecutions in Russia. facsimile ed. Michael Davitt. LC 74-27976. (Modern Jewish Experience Ser.). 1975. Repr. of 1903 ed. 25.50x (ISBN 0-405-06705-4). Ayer Co Pubs.
Within the Rock of Ages: Life & Work of Augustus Moretague Toplady. George Lawton. 249p. 1983. 25.00 (ISBN 0-227-67836-2). Attic Pr.
Within You Is the Power. Joseph Murphy. LC 77-86026. 1978. pap. 6.00 (ISBN 0-87516-247-9). De Vorss.
Without a Man in the House. Wilma Burton. LC 78-68403. pap. 5.95 (ISBN 0-89107-158-X). Good News.
Without Controversy Great Is the Mystery of Godliness. rev. ed. Clarence Harris. Ed. by Althea Haris. (Illus.). 185p. 1982. pap. 4.95 (ISBN 0-686-39817-3). Gospel Place.
Without God, Without Creed: The Origins of Unbelief in America. James Turner. LC 84-15397. (New Studies in American Intellectual & Cultural History). 336p. 1986. pap. text ed. 12.95x (ISBN 0-8018-3407-4). Johns Hopkins.
Witness. Beau Beausoleil. LC 76-39971. (Illus.). 60p. 1976. pap. 6.00 (ISBN 0-915572-23-0). Panjandrum.
Witness. John G. Bennett. 1983. 8.95 (ISBN 0-934254-05-2). Claymont Comm.
Witness & Service in North America. Cornelius J. Dyck. LC 80-10975. (MCC Story Ser.: Vol. 3). 1980. pap. 3.95x (ISBN 0-8361-1231-8). Herald Pr.
Witness & the Revelation in the Gospel of John. James M. Boice. 192p. 1970. pap. 4.95 (ISBN 0-85364-099-8). Attic Pr.
Witness Extraordinary: A Bibliography of Elder Heinrich Voth, 1851-1918. J. A. Froese. (Trailblazer Ser.). 60p. (Orig.). 1975. pap. 1.00 (ISBN 0-919797-20-2). Kindred Pr.
Witness for Life. Elie Wiesel. 12.95 (ISBN 0-87068-766-2); pap. 7.95x (ISBN 0-87068-767-0). Ktav.
Witness of Little Things. Dorothy Donnelly. (Orig.). Date not set. pap. price not set (ISBN 0-913382-37-X, 101-37). Prow Bks-Franciscan.
Witness of the Stars. Ethelbert W. Bullinger. LC 68-16762. 212p. 1984. pap. 10.95 (ISBN 0-8254-2245-0). Kregel.
Witness of the Synoptic Gospels to Christ. Ned B. Stonehouse. (Twin Brooks Ser.). 1979. pap. 8.95 (ISBN 0-8010-8181-5). Baker Bk.
Witness of "The Vulgate," "Peshitta" & "Septuagint" to the Text of "Zephaniah". Sidney Zandstra. LC 72-948. (Columbia University. Contributions to Oriental History & Philology Ser.: No. 4). Repr. of 1909 ed. 12.50 (ISBN 0-404-50534-1). AMS Pr.
Witness of William Penn. Ed. by Frederick Tolles & Gordon E. Alderfer. 1980. Repr. of 1957 ed. lib. bdg. 18.50x (ISBN 0-374-97950-2, Octagon). Hippocrene Bks.
Witness: One Response to Vatican II. Margaret M. Baney. 1987. 12.50 (ISBN 0-533-07210-7). Vantage.
Witness Primer. Erwin J. Kolb. 128p. (Orig.). 1986. pap. 4.95 (ISBN 0-570-04441-3). Concordia.
Witness the Witness of Arithmetic to Christ. F. W. Grant. 64p. 1980. pap. 2.25 (ISBN 0-87213-272-2). Loizeaux.
Witness to Pentecost: The Life of Frank Bartleman. Ed. by Donald W. Dayton & Cecil M. Robeck. (Higher Christian Life Ser.). 439p. 1985. 55.00 (ISBN 0-8240-6405-4). Garland Pub.
Witness to Permanence. Paul Hallett. LC 86-82637. 279p. (Orig.). 1986. pap. 11.95 (ISBN 0-89870-134-1). Ignatius Pr.
Witness to the Sacred: Mystical Tales of Primitive Hasidism. Alan A. Berger. (Illus.). 1977. pap. text ed. 4.00x (ISBN 0-914914-10-3). New Horizons.
Witness to the Word: A Commentary on John 1. Karl Barth. Ed. by Walther Furst. Tr. by Geoffrey W. Bromiley from Ger. 160p. (Orig.). 1986. pap. 10.95 (ISBN 0-8028-0186-2). Eerdmans.
Witnesses Before Dawn. William D. Apel. 1984. pap. 6.95 (ISBN 0-8170-1031-9). Judson.
Witnesses of Christ. Pope John Paul II. 398p. 1983. 5.50 (ISBN 0-8198-8206-2); pap. 4.25 (ISBN 0-8198-8207-0). Dghtrs St Paul.
Witnesses of Hope: The Persecution of Christians in Latin America. Ed. by Martin Lange & Reinhold Iblacker. Tr. by William E. Jerman from Ger. LC 81-38378. Orig. Title: Christenverfolgung in SudAmerica: Zeugen du Hoffnung. Tr. of Christenverfalgung in Sudamerica: Zeugen der Hoffreung. 176p. (Orig.). 1981. pap. 6.95 (ISBN 0-88344-759-2). Orbis Bks.
Witnesses of Jehovah. Leonard Chretien & Marjorie Chretien. 208p. (Orig.). 1987. pap. 6.95 (ISBN 0-89081-587-9). Harvest Hse.
Witnesses of the Light. facs. ed. Washington Gladden. LC 77-84307. (Essay Index Reprint Ser). 1903. 17.75 (ISBN 0-8369-1081-8). Ayer Co Pubs.
Witnesses of the Way. George A. Turner. 176p. (Orig.). 1981. pap. 3.95 (ISBN 0-8341-0692-2). Beacon Hill.
Witnesses Through Trial. Marvin L. Moore. LC 78-24294. (Orion Ser). 1979. pap. 3.50 (ISBN 0-8127-0216-6). Review & Herald.
Witnesses to a Third Way. Ed. by Henry J. Schmidt. 160p. (Orig.). 1986. pap. 5.95 (ISBN 0-87178-940-X). Brethren.
Witnesses to the Historicity of Jesus. Arthur Drews. Tr. by Joseph McCabe. LC 70-161327. (Atheist Viewpoint Ser.). 332p. 1972. Repr. of 1912 ed. 23.50 (ISBN 0-405-03811-9). Ayer Co Pubs.
Witnesses to the Historicity of Jesus. Arthur Drews. 69.95 (ISBN 0-8490-1313-5). Gordon Pr.
Witnessing Community: The Biblical Record of God's Purpose. Suzanne De Dietrich. LC 58-5020. 180p. 1978. pap. 3.95 (ISBN 0-664-24199-9). Westminster.
Witnessing Made Easy. C. S. Lovett. 1964. pap. 5.95 (ISBN 0-938148-01-X). Personal Christianity.
Witnessing, Telling Others about Jesus. (Teaching Bks.). (Illus.). 15p. 1972. pap. text ed. 2.95 (ISBN 0-86508-155-7). BCM Intl Inc.
Witnessing to Jehovah's Witnessess. T. David Sustar. (Truthway Ser.). 31p. (Orig.). 1981. pap. text ed. 1.25 (ISBN 0-87148-915-5). Pathway Pr.
Witnessing to the Kingdom: Melbourne & Beyond. Ed. by Gerald H. Anderson. LC 82-3530. 176p. (Orig.). 1982. pap. 7.95 (ISBN 0-88344-708-8). Orbis Bks.
Wittenberg, Revisited: A Polymorphous Critique of Religion & Theology. Howard P. Kainz. LC 81-40729. 236p. (Orig.). 1982. lib. bdg. 27.50 (ISBN 0-8191-1949-0); pap. text ed. 12.50 (ISBN 0-8191-1950-4). U Pr of Amer.
Wittgenstein: From Mysticism to Ordinary Language: A Study of Viennese Positivism & the Thought of Ludwig Wittgenstein. Russell Nieli. (SUNY Series in Philosophy). 224p. 1987. 39.50x (ISBN 0-88706-397-7); pap. 12.95x (ISBN 0-88706-398-5). State U NY Pr.
Wittgenstein: Lectures & Conversations on Aesthetics, Psychology, & Religious Belief. Ludwig Wittgenstein. Ed. by Cyril Barrett. 1967. pap. 3.50 (ISBN 0-520-01354-9, CAL83). U of Cal Pr.
Wittgenstein's Relevance for Theology. Ignace D'hert. (European University Studies: Ser. 23, Vol. 44). 237p. 1978. pap. 27.15 (ISBN 3-261-03092-5). P Lang Pubs.
Wives of the God-King: The Rituals of the Devadasis of Puri. Frederique A. Marglin. (Illus.). 1985. 29.95x (ISBN 0-19-561731-2). Oxford U Pr.
Wives of the Prophet. F. Hussain. 9.50 (ISBN 0-686-18463-7). Kazi Pubns.
Wives of the Prophet. Fida H. Malik. 185p. (Orig.). 1981. pap. 5.75 (ISBN 0-686-31657-6) (ISBN 0-88004-005-X). Sunwise Turn.
Wizard of the Four Winds: A Shaman's Story. Douglas Sharon. LC 78-3204. (Illus.). 1978. 19.95 (ISBN 0-02-928580-1). Free Pr.
Wizards. Cartwright & Rawson. (Story Books). 1980. 6.95 (ISBN 0-86020-381-6, Usborne-Hayes); PLB 11.96 (ISBN 0-88110-052-8); pap. 2.95 (ISBN 0-86020-380-8). EDC.
Woerterbuch Biblischer Bilder und Symbole. Manfred Lurker. (Ger.). 1973. 25.00 (ISBN 3-466-20158-6, M-7046). French & Eur.
Woerterbuch der Mythologie, Vol. 2. Hans V. Haussig. (Ger.). 1973. 175.00 (ISBN 3-12-909820-8, M-6979). French & Eur.
Woerterbuch zum Religionsunterricht. (Ger.). 1976. 10.95 (ISBN 0-686-56606-8, M-6906). French & Eur.
Wolf & the Raven: Totem Poles of Southeastern Alaska. 2nd ed. Viola E. Garfield & Linn A. Forrest. LC 49-8492. (Illus.). 161p. 1961. pap. 8.95 (ISBN 0-295-73998-3). U of Wash Pr.
Wolf in Winter: A Story of Francis Assisi. John Sack. LC 85-60296. 128p. (Orig.). 1985. pap. 4.95 (ISBN 0-8091-6556-2). Paulist Pr.
Wolfhart Pannenberg. Don Olive. 120p. 1984. pap. text ed. 8.95 (ISBN 0-8499-3003-0, 3003-0). Word Bks.
Wolfhart Pannenberg & Religious Philosophy. David McKenzie. LC 80-8171. 169p. 1980. lib. bdg. 25.00 (ISBN 0-8191-1314-X); pap. text ed. 11.25 (ISBN 0-8191-1315-8). U Pr of Amer.
Wolsey. Hilaire Belloc. 1978. Repr. of 1933 ed. lib. bdg. 20.00 (ISBN 0-8495-0382-5). Arden Lib.
Woman. Leo Jung. 239p. 1970. 9.50 (ISBN 0-900689-07-2). Soncino Pr.
Woman. Spencer W. Kimball et al. LC 79-64908. 1979. 8.95 (ISBN 0-87747-758-2). Deseret Bk.
Woman. 1977. pap. 3.00 (ISBN 0-933574-19-3). Agni Yoga Soc.
Woman - Torch of the Future. Torkom Saraydarian. LC 80-67680. 1980. pap. 8.00 (ISBN 0-911794-00-X). Aqua Educ.
Woman & Man: Biblical Encounter Ser. Erhard S. Gerstenberger & Wolfgang Schrage. Tr. by Douglas W. Stott from Ger. LC 81-10898. 256p. (Orig.). 1982. pap. 10.95 (ISBN 0-687-45920-6). Abingdon.
Woman & Temperance; or, the Work & Workers of the Woman's Christian Temperance Union. Frances E. Willard. LC 74-38443. (Religion in America, Ser. 2). 654p. 1972. Repr. of 1883 ed. 38.00 (ISBN 0-405-04093-8). Ayer Co Pubs.
Woman as Priest, Bishop & Laity in the Early Catholic Church to 440 A.D. 2nd ed. Arthur F. Ide. LC 81-13464. (Woman in History Ser.: Vol. 9B). (Illus.). viii, 125p. 1983. 20.95 (ISBN 0-86663-037-6); pap. 5.95 (ISBN 0-86663-038-4). Ide Hse.
Woman at the Well. Adrian Van Kaam. 6.95 (ISBN 0-87193-092-7). Dimension Bks.
Woman: Aware & Choosing. new ed. Betty J. Coble. LC 75-7943. 156p. 1975. 8.95 (ISBN 0-8054-5613-9). Broadman.
Woman, Church, & State: A Historical Account of the Status of Woman Through the Christian Ages, with Reminiscenses of the Matriarchate. 2nd ed. Matilda J. Gage. LC 72-2602. (American Women Ser.: Images & Realities). 558p. 1972. Repr. of 1900 ed. 32.00 (ISBN 0-405-04458-5). Ayer Co Pubs.
Woman Clothed with the Sun. Ed. by John J. Delaney. LC 60-5922. 1961. pap. 4.50 (ISBN 0-385-08019-0, Im). Doubleday.
Woman, Earth & Spirit: The Feminine in Symbol & Myth. Helen Luke. 144p. 1981. 9.95 (ISBN 0-8245-0018-0). Crossroad NY.
Woman Evangelist: The Life & Times of Charismatic Evangelist Maria B. Woodworth-Etter. Wayne E. Warner & Wayne E. Warner. LC 86-11854. (Studies in Evangelicalism: No. 8). (Illus.). 354p. 1986. 32.50 (ISBN 0-8108-1912-0). Scarecrow.
Woman: First among the Faithful. Francis J. Moloney. LC 85-73197. 128p. 1986. pap. 4.95 (ISBN 0-87793-333-2). Ave Maria.
Woman God Can Use. Pamela Heim. LC 85-73070. 176p. 1986. pap. 6.95 (ISBN 0-89636-190-X). Accent Bks.
Woman: Her Influence & Zeal. James Alberione. (Orig.). 1964. 3.50 (ISBN 0-8198-0176-3); pap. 1.25 (ISBN 0-8198-0177-1). Dghtrs St Paul.
Woman in Christian Tradition. George H. Tavard. LC 72-12637. pap. 67.30 (ISBN 0-317-26144-4, 2024373). Bks Demand UMI.
Woman in Islam. Wiebke Walther. (Image of Women Ser.). (Illus.). 192p. 1982. 35.00 (ISBN 0-8390-0256-4, Allanheld & Schram). Abner Schram Ltd.
Woman in Islam: A Manual with Special Reference to Conditions in India. Violet R. Jones. LC 79-2942. (Illus.). 455p. 1980. Repr of 1941 ed. 31.50 (ISBN 0-8305-0107-X). Hyperion Conn.
Woman in Judaism. Denese B. Mann. 1979. pap. 5.50 (ISBN 0-9603348-0-7). Jonathan Pubns.
Woman in Modern Life. Ed. by William C. Bier. LC 68-20626. (Pastoral Psychology Ser.: No. 5). x, 278p. 1968. 20.00 (ISBN 0-8232-0800-1). Fordham.
Woman in the Bible. Mary J. Evans. LC 84-4641. 160p. 1984. pap. 6.95 (ISBN 0-87784-978-1). Inter-Varsity.
Woman in the Church. Louis Bouyer. Tr. by Marilyn Teichert from Fr. LC 79-84878. Orig. Title: Mystere et Ministeres de la femme dans l'Eglise. 132p. (Orig.). 1979. pap. 7.95 (ISBN 0-89870-002-7). Ignatius Pr.
Woman in the Modern World: Six Hundred & Thirty-Seven Pronouncements from Leo Thirteenth to Pius Twelfth. Ed. by Monks Of Solesmes. 4.00 (ISBN 0-8198-0178-X). Dghtrs St Paul.
Woman in the Muslim Unconscious. Fatna A. Sabbah. LC 84-11343. (Athene Ser.). 188p. 1984. 27.00 (ISBN 0-08-031626-3); pap. 11.00 (ISBN 0-08-031625-5). Pergamon.
Woman in the Pulpit. Frances E. Willard. LC 75-34240. 1976. Repr. of 1889 ed. 15.95 (ISBN 0-89201-014-2). Zenger Pub.
Woman in the Sacred Scriptures of Hinduism. Mildred W. Pinkham. LC 41-7015. Repr. of 1941 ed. 16.50 (ISBN 0-404-05055-7). AMS Pr.
Woman in the Word. Mina R. Brawner. 1.25 (ISBN 0-89985-105-3). Christ Nations.
Woman in the World of Jesus. Evelyn Stagg & Frank Stagg. LC 77-28974. 292p. 1978. pap. 9.95 (ISBN 0-664-24195-6). Westminster.
Woman: New Dimensions. Ed. by Walter J. Burghardt. LC 76-50965. 1977. pap. 5.95 (ISBN 0-8091-2011-9). Paulist Pr.
Woman of Faith. Daughters Of St. Paul. (Illus.). 1965. 3.00 (ISBN 0-8198-0179-8). Dghtrs St Paul.
Woman of God. Hallie A. Kellogg. 1962. pap. 3.95 (ISBN 0-88027-051-9). Firm Foun Pub.
Woman of Tekoah & Other Sermons on Bible Characters. Clarence E. Macartney. (Macartney Bible Characters Library). 1977. pap. 2.95 (ISBN 0-8010-6020-6). Baker Bk.
Woman Question. 2nd ed. Kenneth E. Hagin. 1983. pap. 2.50 (ISBN 0-89276-405-8). Hagin Ministries.
Woman Sealed in the Tower: A Psychological Approach to Feminine Spirituality. Betsy Caprio. 1983. pap. 5.95 (ISBN 0-8091-2486-6). Paulist Pr.
Woman Shall Conquer. rev. ed. Don Sharkey. 258p. 1976. pap. 4.95 (ISBN 0-913382-01-9, 101-1). Prow Bks-Franciscan.
Woman: Survivor in the Church. Joan Ohanneson. (Orig.). 1980. pap. 6.95 (ISBN 0-86683-607-1, HarpR). Har-Row.
Woman to Woman. Eugenia Price. pap. 3.95 (ISBN 0-310-31392-9, 10589P). Zondervan.
Woman to Woman: Selected Talks from the BYU Women's Conferences. LC 86-2048. 223p. 1986. 9.95 (ISBN 0-87579-035-6). Deseret Bk.
Woman Under Monasticism. Lina Eckenstein. 59.95 (ISBN 0-8490-1318-6). Gordon Pr.
Woman Under Monasticism: Chapters on Saint-Lore & Convent Life Between A. D. 500 & A. D. 1500. Lina Eckenstein. LC 63-11028. 1963. Repr. of 1896 ed. 10.00x (ISBN 0-8462-0363-4). Russell.
Woman Who Couldn't Be Stopped. S. Delphine Wedmore. LC 86-61680. (Illus.). 515p. (Orig.). 1986. pap. 10.50 (ISBN 0-9616887-0-X). Sisters Christ Charity.
Woman Who Lost Her Names: Selected Writings by American Jewish Women. Ed. by Julia W. Mazow. LC 79-2986. 240p. 1981. pap. text ed. 10.00 (ISBN 0-06-250567-X, CN 4017, HarpR). Har-Row.
Woman Wrapped in Silence. John W. Lynch. 288p. 1976. pap. 4.95 (ISBN 0-8091-1905-6). Paulist Pr.
Womanguides: Readings Toward a Feminist Theology. Rosemary R. Ruether. LC 84-14508. 286p. 1986. 21.95 (ISBN 0-8070-1202-5); pap. 10.95 (ISBN 0-8070-1203-3, BP 726). Beacon Pr.
Womanhood in Radical Protestantism: 1525-1675. Joyce L. Irwin. LC 79-66370. (Studies in Women & Religion: Vol. 1). xxx, 296p. 1979. 49.95x (ISBN 0-88946-547-9). E Mellen.
Womanhood: The Feminine in Ancient Hellenism Gnosticism, Christianity & Islam. Raoul Morley. 119p. 1985. 16.95 (ISBN 0-9594165-0-1, Pub. by Delacroix Pr); pap. 8.95 (ISBN 0-317-41343-0). Intl Spec Bk.
Womanpriest: A Personal Odyssey. Alla Bozarth-Campbell. 229p. 1978. 9.95 (ISBN 0-8091-0243-9). Wisdom House.
Woman's Bible, 2 vols. in 1. Elizabeth C. Stanton. LC 72-2626. (American Women Ser: Images & Realities). 380p. 1972. Repr. of 1895 ed. 25.50 (ISBN 0-405-04481-X). Ayer Co Pubs.
Woman's Bible. Elizabeth C. Stanton. 1974. Repr. 12.95 (ISBN 0-9603042-1-5). Coalition Women-Relig.
Woman's Body, Woman's Right: Birth Control in America. Linda Gordon. 1977. pap. 8.95 (ISBN 0-14-004683-6). Penguin.
Woman's Choice: Living Through Your Problems. Eugenia Price. 192p. 1983. pap. 5.95 (ISBN 0-310-31381-3, 16217P). Zondervan.
Woman's Choices: The Relief Society Legacy Lectures. LC 83-25517. 196p. 1984. 7.95 (ISBN 0-87747-999-2). Deseret Bk.

Woman's Encyclopedia of Myths & Secrets. Barbara G. Walker. LC 83-47736. 1124p. (Orig.). 1983. 34.45 (ISBN 0-06-250926-8, HarpR); pap. 20.95 (ISBN 0-06-250925-X, CN 4066). Har-Row.

Woman's Holistic Headache Relief Book. June Biermann & Barbara Toohey. 212p. Repr. of 1979 ed. 8.95 (ISBN 0-686-35967-4). Sugarfree.

Woman's Ministry: Mary Collson's Search for Reform as a Unitarian Minister, Hull House Social Worker, & a Christian Science Practioner. Cynthia G. Tucker. (American Civilization Ser.). 222p. 1984. 27.95 (ISBN 0-87722-338-6). Temple U Pr.

Woman's Mysteries. M. Esther Harding. 1976. pap. 6.95 (ISBN 0-06-090525-5, CN525, PL). Har-Row.

Woman's Path to Godliness. Martha Reapsome. 176p. 1986. 10.95 (ISBN 0-8407-9067-8). Oliver-Nelson.

Woman's Place. R. K. Campbell. 32p. pap. 0.60 (ISBN 0-88172-014-3). Believers Bkshelf.

Woman's Place: Equal Partnership in Daily Ministry. Judith R. Diehl. LC 84-47915. 128p. 1985. pap. 5.95 (ISBN 0-8006-1791-6, 1-1791). Fortress.

Woman's Priorities. Joyce M. Smith. 1976. pap. 2.95 (ISBN 0-8423-8380-8). Tyndale.

Woman's Role in the Church. John M. Jicks & Bruce L. Morton. pap. 2.95 (ISBN 0-89315-362-1). Lambert Bk.

Woman's Song. Joy M. Davis. LC 83-70376. (Orig.). 1984. pap. 5.95 (ISBN 0-8054-5243-5). Broadman.

Woman's Transformation: A Psychological Theology. Jenny Hammett. LC 82-14287. (Symposium Ser.: Vol. 8). 112p. 1982. pap. 19.95x (ISBN 0-88946-918-0). E Mellen.

Woman's Work for Jesus. Annie T. Wittenmyer. Ed. by Carolyn D. Gifford & Donald Dayton. (Women in American Protestant Religion 1800-1930 Ser.). 240p. 1987. lib. bdg. 35.00 (ISBN 0-8240-0685-2). Garland Pub.

Woman's Work in the Church. John M. Ludlow. LC 75-33300. 1976. Repr. of 1866 ed. 14.95 (ISBN 0-89201-007-X). Zenger Pub.

Woman's Workshop on David & His Psalms. Carolyn Nystrom. (Woman's Workshop Ser.). 144p. 1982. pap. 3.95 (ISBN 0-310-41931-X, 11276P). Zondervan.

Woman's Workshop on Faith. Martha Hook. (A Woman's Workshop Ser.). 1977. leaders 3.95 (ISBN 0-310-26231-3, 11681P); students 2.95 (ISBN 0-310-26241-0, 11682P). Zondervan.

Woman's Workshop on Forgiveness. Kirkie Morrissey. (Woman's Workshop Ser.). 160p. 1982. pap. 3.95 (ISBN 0-310-44931-6, 16245P). Zondervan.

Woman's Workshop on James. Carolyn Nystrom & Margaret Fromer. (Woman's Workshop Ser.). 144p. (Orig.). 1980. pap. 2.95 (ISBN 0-310-41901-8, 11273P). Zondervan.

Woman's Workshop on Philippians. Margaret Fromer & Paul Fromer. (Woman's Workshop Ser.). 128p. 1982. pap. 2.95 (ISBN 0-310-44771-2, 11312P). Zondervan.

Womans Workshop on Proverbs. Diane Bloem. 1978. leader's manual 5.95 (ISBN 0-310-21371-1, 10684); student manual 2.95 (ISBN 0-310-21361-4, 10683). Zondervan.

Woman's Workshop on Romans-Leader's Manual. Carolyn Nystrom. 112p. (Orig.). 1981. pap. 3.95 (ISBN 0-310-41911-5, 11274P). Zondervan.

Woman's Workshop on Romans-Student's Manual. Carolyn Nystrom. 144p. (Orig.). 1981. pap. 3.95 (ISBN 0-310-41921-2, 11275P). Zondervan.

Woman's Workshop on the Beautitudes. Diane Bloem. (Orig.). 1981. Leader's Manual, 160 Pages. pap. 3.95 (ISBN 0-310-42641-3, 112160); Student's Manual, 96 Pages. pap. 2.95 (ISBN 0-310-42651-0, 11217). Zondervan.

Womanspirit Rising: A Feminist Reader in Religion. Carol P. Christ & Judith Plaskow. LC 78-3363. (Orig.). 1979. pap. 8.95 (ISBN 0-06-061385-8, RD 275, HarpR). Har-Row.

Women among the Brethren: Stories of Fifteen Mennonite Brethren & Krimmer Mennonite Brethren Women. Katie F. Wiebe. LC 79-54802. 197p. (Orig.). 1979. pap. 6.95 (ISBN 0-935196-00-5). Kindred Pr.

Women & Atheism: The Ultimate Liberation. Madalyn M. O'Hair. 23p. 1979. 2.50 (ISBN 0-911826-17-3). Am Atheist.

Women & Folklore: A Bibliographic Survey. Compiled by Francis A. De Caro. LC 83-12837. xiv, 170p. 1983. lib. bdg. 35.00 (ISBN 0-313-23821-9, DWF/). Greenwood.

Women & Folklore: Images & Genres. Ed. by Claire R. Farrer. (Illus.). 100p. 1986. pap. text ed. 6.95x (ISBN 0-88133-227-5). Waveland Pr.

Women & Her Rights. Murtaza Nutanhhery. Tr. by M. A. Ansari from Arabic. 286p. 1984. pap. 9.00 (ISBN 0-941724-30-1). Islamic Seminary.

Women & Human Wholeness. Canadian Christian Movement for Peace Staff. Ed. by Alyson Huntly et al. (People Living for Justice Ser.). 160p. 1983. pap. text ed. 29.95 (ISBN 0-697-01920-9). Wm C Brown.

Women & Islamic Law in a Non-Muslim State. Ahron Layish. 369p. 1975. 19.95. Transaction Bks.

Women & Jesus. Alicia C. Faxon. LC 72-11868. 1973. 4.95 (ISBN 0-8298-0244-4). Pilgrim NY.

Women & Jewish Law: An Exploration of Women's Issues in Halakhic Sources. Rachel Biale. LC 83-40457. 256p. 1984. 18.95 (ISBN 0-8052-3887-5). Schocken.

Women & Jewish Law: An Exploration of Women's Issues in Halakhic Sources. Rachel Biale. 304p. 1986. pap. 8.95 (ISBN 0-8052-0810-0). Schocken.

Women & Ministry in the New Testament: Called to Serve. Elisabeth M. Tetlow. 170p. 1985. pap. text ed. 10.75 (ISBN 0-8191-4461-4, College Theo Soc). U Pr of Amer.

Women & Quakerism. Hope E. Luder. LC 74-82914. 36p. (Orig.). 1974. pap. 2.50x (ISBN 0-87574-196-7). Pendle Hill.

Women & Religion. Judith Plaskow. Ed. by Joan Arnold & Joan A. Romero. LC 74-83126. (American Academy of Religion. Aids for the Study of Religion). Repr. of 1974 ed. 54.00 (ISBN 0-8357-9581-0, 2017557). Bks Demand UMI.

Women & Religion: A Reader for the Clergy. Regina Coll. 128p. 1982. pap. 5.95 (ISBN 0-8091-2461-0). Paulist Pr.

Women & Religion in America: Nineteen Hundred to Nineteen Sixty-Eight, Vol. 3. Ed. by Rosemary R. Ruether & Rosemary S. Keller. (Illus.). 452p. 1986. 26.45 (ISBN 0-06-066833-4, HarpT). Har-Row.

Women & Religion in America: The Colonial & Revolutionary Period, Vol. II. Ed. by Rosemary R. Ruether & Rosemary S. Keller. LC 80-8346. (Illus.). 448p. 1983. 24.45 (ISBN 0-06-066832-6, HarpR). Har-Row.

Women & Religion: Readings in the Western Tradition from Aeschylus to Mary Daly. Ed. by Elizabeth Clark & Herbert W. Richardson. LC 76-9975. 1976. pap. 9.95 (ISBN 0-06-061398-X, RD-178, HarpR). Har-Row.

Women & Spirituality. Carol Ochs. LC 83-3397. (New Feminist Perspectives Ser.). 166p. 1983. 18.95x (ISBN 0-8476-7232-8, Rowman & Allanheld); pap. 9.95x (ISBN 0-8476-7233-6). Rowman.

Women & the Authority of Inspiration: A Reexamination of Two Prophetic Movements from a Contemporary Feminist Perspective. Elaine C. Huber. LC 85-15823. 262p. (Orig.). 1985. lib. bdg. 27.75 (ISBN 0-8191-4903-9); pap. text ed. 13.75 (ISBN 0-8191-4904-7). U Pr of Amer.

Women & the Church. Ed. by Christopher Nichol. 102p. (Orig.). 1984. pap. 8.95 (ISBN 0-318-20037-6, Pub. by Tertiary Christian Studies). ANZ Religious Pubns.

Women & the Enlightenment. Ed. by Margaret Hunt & Margaret Jacob. LC 84-590. (Women & History: No. 9). 93p. 1984. text ed. 24.95 (ISBN 0-86656-190-0). Haworth Pr.

Women & the Ministries of Christ. Ed. by Roberta Hestenes & Lois Curley. pap. 6.95x (ISBN 0-9602638-2-9). Fuller Theol Soc.

Women & the Priesthood: Essays from the Orthodox Tradition. Kallistos Ware & Georges Barrois. Ed. by Thomas Hopko. 190p. 1982. pap. 8.95 (ISBN 0-88141-005-5). St Vladimirs.

Women & the Word of God. Susan Foh. pap. 6.95 (ISBN 0-87552-268-8). Presby & Reformed.

Women & Worship. rev., expanded ed. Sharon Emswiler & Thomas Neufer. LC 83-48459. 144p. 1984. pap. 5.95 (ISBN 0-06-066101-1, RD 507, HarpR). Har-Row.

Women Around Jesus. Elisabeth Moltmann-Wendel. LC 82-72478. 160p. 1982. pap. 7.95 (ISBN 0-8245-0535-2). Crossroad NY.

Women As Pastors. Ed. by Lyle E. Schaller. LC 81-20667. (Creative Leadership Ser.). (Orig.). 1982. pap. 5.95 (ISBN 0-687-45957-5). Abingdon.

Women at the Well: Expressions of Faith, Life & Worship Drawn from Our Own Wisdom. Ed. by Betty Jo Buckingham. Tr. by Maria E. Carachei. LC 87-6224. (Orig.). (YA) 1987. pap. 7.95 (ISBN 0-9618243-0-1). Womens Caucus Church.

Women, Authority & the Bible. Alvera Mickelsen. LC 86-7158. 252p. (Orig.). 1986. pap. 9.95 (ISBN 0-87784-608-1). Inter-Varsity.

Women, Branch Stories, & Religious Rhetoric in a Tamil Buddhist Text. Paula Richman. (Foreign & Comparative Studies-South Asian Ser.: No. 12). (Orig.). 1987. pap. write for info. (ISBN 0-915984-90-3). Syracuse U Foreign Comp.

Women Called to Witness: Evangelical Feminism in the Nineteenth Century. Nancy A. Hardesty. LC 83-45959. 176p. (Orig.). 1984. pap. 8.95 (ISBN 0-687-45959-1). Abingdon.

Women, Change, & the Church. Nancy Van Scoyoc. LC 80-15739. (Into Our Third Century Ser.). 96p. (Orig.). 1980. pap. 3.95 (ISBN 0-687-45958-3). Abingdon.

Women Christian: New Vision. Mary T. Malone. 176p. 1985. pap. 6.95 (ISBN 0-697-02064-9). Wm C Brown.

Women-Church. Rosemary R. Ruether. 1986. 16.45 (ISBN 0-06-066834-2). Har-Row.

Women Clergy: Breaking Through Gender Barriers. Edward C. Lehman, Jr. 300p. 1985. 24.95 (ISBN 0-88738-071-9). Transaction Bks.

Women Composers & Hymnists: A Concise Biographical Dictionary. Gene Claghorn. LC 83-20429. 288p. 1984. 22.50 (ISBN 0-8108-1680-6). Scarecrow.

Women Exploited: The Other Victims of Abortion. Paula Ervin. 200p. (Orig.). 1985. pap. 6.95 (ISBN 0-87973-847-2, 847). Our Sunday Visitor.

Women, Faith, & Economic Justice. Jackie M. Smith. (Illus.). 80p. (Orig.). 1985. pap. 5.95 (ISBN 0-664-24600-1). Westminster.

Women, Freedom, & Calvin. Jane D. Douglass. LC 85-8778. 156p. 1985. pap. 11.95 (ISBN 0-664-24663-X). Westminster.

Women in a Man's Church, Concilium 134. Ed. by Virgil Elizondo & Norbert Greinacher. (New Concilium 1980: Vol. 134). 128p. 1980. pap. 5.95 (ISBN 0-8164-2276-1, HarpR). Har-Row.

Women in American Religion. Ed. by Janet W. James. LC 79-5261. 288p. 1980. 32.00x (ISBN 0-8122-7780-5); pap. 13.50x (ISBN 0-8122-1104-9). U of Pa Pr.

Women in American Religious History: An Annotated Bibliography. Dorothy C. Bass & Sandra H. Boyd. (Reference Bks). 205p. 1986. lib. bdg. 30.00x (ISBN 0-8161-8151-9). G K Hall.

Women in Antiquity. Charles T. Seltman. LC 78-20490. 1981. Repr. of 1956 ed. 25.85 (ISBN 0-88355-867-X). Hyperion Conn.

Women in Baptist Life. Leon McBeth. LC 78-54245. 1979. 7.95 (ISBN 0-8054-6925-7). Broadman.

Women in Buddhism: Images of the Feminine in the Mahayana Tradition. Diana Paul. 1985. 35.00x (ISBN 0-520-05445-8); pap. 10.95 (ISBN 0-520-05428-8, CAL 740). U of Cal Pr.

Women in English Religion, Seventeen Hundred thru Nineteen Twenty-Five. Ed. by Dale A. Johnson. LC 83-12124. (Studies in Women & Religion: Vol. 10). 368p. 1984. 49.95x (ISBN 0-88946-539-8). E Mellen.

Women in Frankish Society: Marriage & the Cloister, 500-900. Suzanne F. Wemple. LC 80-54051. (Illus.). 352p. 1985. pap. text ed. 18.95 (ISBN 0-8122-1209-6). U of Pa Pr.

Women in Greek Myth. Mary R. Lefkowitz. LC 86-7146. 164p. 1986. text ed. 22.50x (ISBN 0-8018-3367-1). Johns Hopkins.

Women in Islam. Aisha Lemu & Fatima Heeren. 51p. (Orig.). 1978. pap. 3.50 (ISBN 0-86037-004-6, Pub. by Islamic Found UK). New Era Pubns MI.

Women in Islam. M. M. Siddiqui. 10.50 (ISBN 0-686-18462-9). Kazi Pubns.

Women in Islam. M. M. Siddiqui. 1969. 10.50 (ISBN 0-87902-069-5). Orientalia.

Women in Islam: Social Attitudes & Historical Perspectives. Ed. by V. Boutas. 224p. 1983. 30.00x (ISBN 0-7007-0154-0, Pub. by Curzon England). State Mutual Bk.

Women in Ministry. Anne A. Jackson & Cleola I. Spears. (Illus.). 350p. (Orig.). pap. write for info. (ISBN 0-9605892-3-6). Dawn Ministries.

Women in Ministry. L. E. Maxwell. 156p. 1987. pap. 6.95 (ISBN 0-89693-337-7). Victor Bks.

Women in Muslim Family Law. John L. Esposito. LC 81-18273. (Contemporary Issues in the Middle East Ser.). 172p. 1982. pap. text ed. 10.95X (ISBN 0-8156-2278-3). Syracuse U Pr.

Women in Muslim History. Charis Waddy. LC 80-40161. (Illus.). 224p. 1980. text ed. 27.95x (ISBN 0-582-78084-5). Longman.

Women in Muslim Rural Society. Joseph Ginat. LC 79-66432. 259p. 1981. 29.95 (ISBN 0-87855-342-8). Transaction Bk.

Women in Neighborhood Evangelism. Marjorie Stewart. LC 77-93410. 128p. 1978. pap. 1.50 (ISBN 0-88243-723-2, 02-0723, Radiant Books). Gospel Pub.

Women in New Worlds: Vol. 1. Ed. by Hilah F. Thomas & Rosemary S. Keller. LC 81-7984. (Historical Perspectives on the Wesleyan Tradition Ser.). 448p. (Orig.). 1981. pap. 13.95 (ISBN 0-687-45968-0). Abingdon.

Women in Search of Mission. Gladys V. Goering. LC 80-66787. (Illus.). 136p. 1980. pap. 3.95 (ISBN 0-87303-062-1). Faith & Life.

Women in the Bible: Helpful Friends. Judy Latham. (BibLearn Ser.). (Illus.). 1979. 5.95 (ISBN 0-8054-4248-0, 4242-48). Broadman.

Women in the Changing Islamic System. Ruth F. Woodsmall. (Illus.). 432p. 1983. text ed. 60.00x (ISBN 0-86590-154-6). Apt Bks.

Women in the Church. Dennis R. Kuhns. LC 78-53968. 80p. (Orig.). 1978. pap. 2.95 (ISBN 0-8361-1852-9). Herald Pr.

Women in the Early Church. Elizabeth A. Clark. (Message of the Fathers of the Church Ser.: Vol. 13). 17.95 (ISBN 0-89453-353-3); pap. 12.95 (ISBN 0-89453-332-0). M Glazier.

Women in the Life of Jesus. Jill Briscoe. 96p. 1986. pap. 4.95 (ISBN 0-89693-254-0). Victor Bks.

Women in the Middle Ages: Religion, Marriage & Letters. Angela Lucas. LC 82-42578. 215p. 1984. 11.95 (ISBN 0-312-88744-2). St Martin.

Women in the Ministry of Jesus: A Study of Jesus' Attitude to Women & Their Roles As Reflected in His Earthly Life. Ben Witherington. LC 83-18957. (Society for the New Testament Studies Monograph: No. 51). 210p. 1984. 29.95 (ISBN 0-521-25658-5). Cambridge U Pr.

Women in the Muslim World. Ed. by Lois Beck & Nikki Keddie. LC 78-3633. 712p. 1978. 40.00x (ISBN 0-674-95480-7); pap. 12.50 (ISBN 0-674-95481-5). Harvard U Pr.

Women in the Resistance & in the Holocaust: The Voices of Eyewitnesses. Ed. by Vera Laska. LC 82-12018. (Contributions in Women Studies: No. 37). xv, 330p. 1983. lib. bdg. 29.95 (ISBN 0-313-23457-4, LWH/). Greenwood.

Women in the World Religions, Past & Present. Ed. by Ursula King. (God Ser.). 256p. (Orig.). 1987. 22.95 (ISBN 0-913757-32-2, Pub. by New Era Bks.); pap. 12.95 (ISBN 0-913757-33-0, Pub. by New Era Bks). Paragon Hse.

Women in Today's Church. George Watkins. 56p. 1984. pap. 2.25 (ISBN 0-88144-025-6). Christian Pub.

Women in World Religions. Ed. by Arvind Sharma. (McGill Studies in the History of Religions). 256p. (Orig.). 1986. 34.50x (ISBN 0-88706-374-8); pap. 10.95x (ISBN 0-88706-375-6). State U NY Pr.

Women: Invisible In Church & Theology. Ed. by Elisabeth S. Fiorenza & Mary Collins. (Concilium Ser.: Vol. 182). 128p. 1985. pap. 6.95 (Pub. by T & T Clark Ltd UK). Fortress.

Women, Law, & the Genesis Tradition. C. Carmichael. 112p. 1979. 16.50x (ISBN 0-85224-364-2, Pub. by Edinburgh U Pr Scotland). Columbia U Pr.

Women Leaders in the Ancient Synagogue: Inscriptional Evidence & Background Issues. Bernadette J. Brooten. LC 82-10658. (Brown Judaic Studies). 292p. 1982. pap. 20.00 (ISBN 0-89130-587-4, 14 00 36). Scholars Pr GA.

Women, Men, & the Bible. Virginia R. Mollenkott. LC 76-40446. 1977. pap. 8.95 (ISBN 0-687-45970-2) (ISBN 0-687-81914-8). Abingdon.

Women Ministers: A Quaker Contribution. Robert J. Leach. Ed. by Ruth Blattenberger. LC 79-84922. 1979. pap. 2.50x (ISBN 0-87574-227-0). Pendle Hill.

Women Ministers: How Women Are Re-defining Traditional Roles. Ed. by Judith L. Weidman. LC 80-8345. 192p. (Orig.). 1981. pap. 7.95 (ISBN 0-06-069291-X, RD 528, HarpR). Har-Row.

Women Ministers?! Women in Paul & Adventchristendom. Craig R. Dunham. 98p. (Orig.). 1986. pap. 4.95 (ISBN 0-913439-04-5). Henceforth.

Women, Ministry, & the Church. Joan Chittister. LC 82-62418. 1983. pap. 5.95 (ISBN 0-8091-2528-5). Paulist Pr.

Women of Calvary. Marguerite D. Brown. 1982. pap. 5.25 ea. (ISBN 0-89536-526-X, 2331). CSS of Ohio.

Women of Early Christianity. Alexander Carroll. 75.00 (ISBN 0-87968-268-X). Gordon Pr.

Women of Faith. Gladys Seashore. 1983. pap. 2.25 (ISBN 0-911802-55-X). Free Church Pubns.

Women of Faith & Spirit: Profiles of Fifteen Biblical Witnesses. Margaret Wold. LC 86-28770. 128p. (Orig.). 1987. pap. 6.95 (ISBN 0-8066-2251-2, 10-7236). Augsburg.

Women of Faith in Dialogue. Virginia R. Mollencott. 144p. (Orig.). 1987. pap. 9.95 (ISBN 0-8245-0823-8). Crossroad NY.

Women of Grace. Betty J. Grams. LC 77-93409. 128p. 1978. pap. 3.95 (ISBN 0-88243-751-8, 02-0751, Radiant Books); tchr's. ed 3.95 (ISBN 0-88243-336-9, 02-0336). Gospel Pub.

Women of Grace: A Biographical Dictionary of British Women Saints, Martyrs & Reformers. Kathleen Parbury. 224p. 1985. 25.00x (ISBN 0-85362-213-2, Oriel). Methuen Inc.

Women of Methodism: Its Three Foundresses, Susanna Wesley, the Countess of Huntingdon, & Barbara Heck. Abel Stevens. Ed. by Carolyn D. Gifford & Donald Dayton. (Women in American Protestant Religion 1800-1930 Ser.). 304p. 1987. lib. bdg. 45.00 (ISBN 0-8240-0676-3). Garland Pub.

Women of Mr. Wesley's Methodism. Earl K. Brown. LC 83-22010. (Studies in Women & Religion: Vol. 11). 273p. 1984. 49.95x (ISBN 0-88946-538-X). E Mellen.

Women of Omdurman: Life, Love & the Cult of Virginity. Anne Cloudsley. LC 83-40625. 181p. 1985. 22.50 (ISBN 0-312-88755-8). St Martin.

Women of Spirit. Rosemary Ruether & Eleanor McLaughlin. 1979. pap. 10.95 (ISBN 0-671-24805-7, Touchstone Bks). S&S.

Women of the Bible. Daughters of St. Paul. LC 71-145574. (Illus.). 5.95 (ISBN 0-8198-0322-7); pap. 4.95 (ISBN 0-8198-0323-5). Dghtrs St Paul.

Women of the Bible. rev. ed. Frances VanderVelde. LC 83-19894. (Illus.). 260p. 1973. pap. 6.95 (ISBN 0-8254-3951-5). Kregel.

Women of the Bible: Sculpture. Edwina Sandys & James P. Morton. Ed. by Thomas Piche, Jr. LC 86-83188. (Illus.). 24p. (Orig.). 1986. pap. text ed. write for info. (ISBN 0-914407-07-4). Everson Mus.

Women of the Bible Speak to Women of Today. Dorothy Elder. LC 86-70873. (Illus.). 288p. (Orig.). 1986. pap. 12.00 (ISBN 0-87516-574-5). De Vorss.

Women of the Bible Tell Their Stories. Mary E. Jensen. LC 78-52193. 1978. pap. 6.95 (ISBN 0-8066-1663-6, 10-7235). Augsburg.

Women of the Cloth: New Opportunity for the Churches. Jackson W. Carroll & Barbara J. Hargrove. LC 82-47740. 288p. 1983. 14.45 (ISBN 0-06-061321-1, HarpR). Har-Row.

Women of the Gospel. Daughters of St. Paul. LC 74-32122. 1975. 5.95 (ISBN 0-8198-0495-9); pap. 4.95 (ISBN 0-8198-0496-7). Dghtrs St Paul.

Women of the New Testament. Abraham Kuyper. pap. 4.95 (ISBN 0-310-36751-4, 9996P). Zondervan.

Women of the Old Testament. Rebecca Daniel. (Our Greatest Heritage Ser.). (Illus.). 32p. 1983. wkbk. 3.95 (ISBN 0-86653-142-4, SS 811). Good Apple.

Women of the Old Testament. Abraham Kuyper. pap. 5.95 (ISBN 0-310-36761-1, 9997P). Zondervan.

Women of the Roman Aristocracy As Christian Monastics. Anne E. Hickey. Ed. by Margaret R. Miles. LC 86-19242. (Studies in Religion: No. 1). 159p. 1986. 39.95 (ISBN 0-8357-1757-7). UMI Res Pr.

Women of the Shtetl: Through the Eye of Y. L. Peretz. Ruth Adler. LC 78-69895. (Illus.). 152p. 1979. 17.50 (ISBN 0-8386-2336-0). Fairleigh Dickinson.

Women of the Word: Contemporary Sermons by Women Clergy. Bracken et al. Ed. by Charles Hackett. LC 84-52656. (Illus.). 144p. (Orig.). 1985. pap. 7.95 (ISBN 0-932419-00-3). Susan Hunter.

Women of Valor: The Trials & Triumphs of Seven Saints. Alicia Von Stamwitz. 64p. 1986. pap. 1.95 (ISBN 0-89243-258-6). Liguori Pubns.

Women of Wisdom. Tsultrim Allione. (Illus.). 224p. (Orig.). 1985. pap. 12.95 (ISBN 0-7102-0240-7). Methuen Inc.

Women Pray. Ed. by Karen L. Roller. 96p. (Orig.). 1986. pap. 3.95 (ISBN 0-8298-0737-3). Pilgrim NY.

Women Priests: An Emerging Ministry in the Episcopal Church (1960 to 1980) John H. Morgan. 185p. (Orig.). 1985. pap. 12.95x (ISBN 0-932269-48-6). Wyndham Hall.

Women Priests & Other Fantasies. Vincent P. Miceli. LC 80-66294. 1985. 19.95 (ISBN 0-8158-0423-7). Chris Mass.

Women Priests in the Catholic Church? A Theological-Historical Investigation. Haye S. Van Der Meer. Tr. by Leonard Swidler & Arlene Swidler. LC 73-79480. Orig. Title: Priestertum der Frau? 230p. 1973. 12.95 (ISBN 0-87722-059-X). Temple U Pr.

Women Recounted: Narrative Thinking & the God of Israel. James G. Williams. (Bible & Literature Ser.: No. 6). 128p. 1982. text ed. 21.95x (ISBN 0-907459-18-8, Pub. by Almond Pr England); pap. 10.95x (ISBN 0-907459-19-6). Eisenbrauns.

Women, Religion, & Development in the Third World. Theodora C. Foster. LC 83-13670. 288p. 1984. 30.95 (ISBN 0-03-064108-X). Praeger.

Women, Religion, & Social Change. Ed. by Yvonne Y. Haddad & Ellison B. Findly. (Illus.). 564p. 1985. 49.00x (ISBN 0-88706-068-4); pap. 19.50x (ISBN 0-88706-069-2). State U NY Pr.

Women Saints of East & West. Ed. by Swami Ghanananda & John Steward-Wallace. LC 79-65731. 1979. pap. 7.95 (ISBN 0-87481-036-1). Vedanta Pr.

Women Speak To God: The Prayers & Poems of Jewish Women. Ed. by Marcia C. Spiegel & Deborah L. Kremsdorf. LC 86-51498. 100p. (Orig.). 1987. pap. 9.98 (ISBN 0-9608054-6-X). Womans Inst-Cont Jewish Ed.

Women Surviving: The Holocaust-Proceedings of the Conference. Esther Katz & Joan M. Ringelheim. (Occasional Papers: No. 1). 100p. (Orig.). 1983. pap. write for info. (ISBN 0-913865-00-1). Inst Res Hist.

Women, the Challenge & the Call: An Agenda for Christian Women in Today's World. Dee Jepsen. (Christian Essentials Ser.). 48p. (Orig.). 1987. pap. 1.95 (ISBN 0-89283-323-8). Servant.

Women Through the Bible: Devotions for Women's Groups. Marlys Taege. 160p. 1987. pap. 5.95 (ISBN 0-570-04460-X, 12-3064). Concordia.

Women under Primitive Buddhism. I. B. Horner. 1975. Repr. 12.50 (ISBN 0-8426-0955-5). Orient Bk Dist.

Women versus Men: A Conflict of Navajo Emergence. Berard Haile. Ed. by Karl W. Luckert. LC 81-7433. (American Tribal Religions Ser.: Vol. 6). viii, 119p. 1981. 14.95x (ISBN 0-8032-2319-6); pap. 9.95x (ISBN 0-8032-7211-1, BB 785, Bison). U of Nebr Pr.

Women Who Achieved for God. Winnie Christensen. (Fisherman Bible Studyguide). 80p. 1984. pap. 2.95 (ISBN 0-87788-937-6). Shaw Pubs.

Women Who Believed God. Winnie Christensen. (Fisherman Bible Studyguide Ser.). 77p. 1983. saddle-stiched 2.95 (ISBN 0-87788-936-8). Shaw Pubs.

Women Who Encountered Jesus. Faye Field. LC 81-65798. 1982. 4.50 (ISBN 0-8054-5182-X). Broadman.

Women's Adornment: What Does the Bible Really Say? Ralph Woodrow. LC 76-17711. (Illus.). 1976. pap. 3.00 (ISBN 0-916938-01-8). R Woodrow.

Women's Bible Studies--Colossians. Ruth Spradley. (Women's Bible Studies Ser.). (Illus.). 144p. 1987. pap. 4.95 (ISBN 0-87403-232-6, 39932). Standard Pub.

Women's Bible Studies--Philippians. Ruth Spradley. (Women's Bible Studies Ser.). (Illus.). 144p. 1987. pap. 4.95 (ISBN 0-87403-231-8, 39931). Standard Pub.

Women's Bible: Study Guide. Coalition on Women & Religion Staff. 1975. 5.95 (ISBN 0-9603042-2-3). Coalition Women-Relig.

Women's Challenge: Ministry in the Flesh. M. Timothy Prokes. 2.95 (ISBN 0-87193-006-4). Dimension Bks.

Women's Devotional Talks for Special Occasions. Carol Wolf. 64p. (Orig.). 1984. pap. 3.95 (ISBN 0-87239-745-9, 2976). Standard Pub.

Women's Issues in Religious Education. Ed. by Fern M. Giltner. 190p. 1985. pap. 12.95 (ISBN 0-89135-051-9). Religious Educ.

Women's Ministries in the New Testament Church. Dick Benjamin. 1983. pap. 1.75 (ISBN 0-911739-16-5). Abbott Loop.

Women's Prayer Groups: A Halakhic Analysis. Avraham Weiss. 1987. pap. 8.95 (ISBN 0-88125-126-7). Ktav.

Women's Psyche, Women's Spirit: The Reality of Relationships. Mary L. Randour. LC 86-17180. 240p. 1987. 25.00x (ISBN 0-231-06250-8). Columbia U Pr.

Women's Religious Experience. Ed. by Pat Holden. LC 82-24314. 218p. 1983. text ed. 28.50x (ISBN 0-389-20363-7, 07226). B&N Imports.

Women's Religious History Sources. Ed. by Sr. Evangeline Thomas. 264p. 1983. 65.00 (ISBN 0-8352-1681-0). Bowker.

Women's Spirit Bonding. Ed. by Janet Klaven & Mary I. Buckley. 320p. (Orig.). 1984. pap. 12.95 (ISBN 0-8298-0707-1). Pilgrim NY.

Women's Spirituality: Resources for Christian Development. Ed. by Joan W. Conn. 336p. (Orig.). 1986. pap. 11.95 (ISBN 0-8091-2752-0). Paulist Pr.

Women's Workshop on Bible Marriages. Diane B. Bloem & Robert C. Bloem. (Woman's Workshop Series of Study Books). 128p. (Orig.). 1980. pap. 2.95 student's manual (ISBN 0-310-21391-6, 10687); pap. 3.95 leader's manual (ISBN 0-310-21401-7, 10688). Zondervan.

Wonder. Edythe Draper. 448p. 1984. 5.95 (ISBN 0-8423-8385-9). Tyndale.

Wonder & Worship. James Carroll. LC 70-133469. 168p. 1970. pap. 2.95 (ISBN 0-8091-1871-8). Paulist Pr.

Wonder Book. Nathaniel Hawthorne. (Classics Ser.). pap. 1.25 (ISBN 0-8049-0118-X, CL-118). Airmont.

Wonder Book & Tanglewood Tales. Nathaniel Hawthorne. Ed. by William Charvat et al. LC 77-150221. (Centenary Edition of the Works of Nathaniel Hawthorne Ser.: Vol. 7). (Illus.). 476p. 1972. 25.00 (ISBN 0-8142-0158-X). Ohio St U Pr.

Wonder-Filled. Mary Fearon & Mary J. Tully. 1983. pap. 4.00 (ISBN 0-697-01853-9); tchr's. manual 6.00 (ISBN 0-697-01854-7); parent book 3.50 (ISBN 0-697-01855-5). Wm C Brown.

Wonder O' the Wind. Phillip Keller. 1986. 7.95 (ISBN 0-8499-3061-8). Word Bks.

Wonder O' the Wind. W. Phillip Keller. 1982. 9.95 (ISBN 0-8499-0337-8). Word Bks.

Wonder of Comfort. Ed. by Phyllis Hobe. LC 82-8322. (Small Wonders Ser.). (Illus.). 108p. (Orig.). 1982. pap. 4.95 (ISBN 0-664-26003-9, A Bridgebooks Publication). Westminster.

Wonder of Guadalupe. Francis Johnston. LC 81-53041. 143p. 1981. pap. 4.50 (ISBN 0-89555-168-3). TAN Bks Pubs.

Wonder of Love. Ed. by Phyllis Hobe. LC 82-8376. (Small Wonders Ser.). (Illus.). 112p. 1982. pap. 4.95 (ISBN 0-664-26001-2, A Bridgebooks Publication). Westminster.

Wonder of Prayer. Ed. by Phyllis Hobe. LC 82-8317. (Small Wonders Ser.). (Illus.). 112p. (Orig.). 1982. pap. 4.95 (ISBN 0-664-26002-0, A Bridgebooks Publication). Westminster.

Wonder of the Real: A Sketch in Basic Philosophy. rev., enlarged ed. Francis J. Klauder. LC 72-94706. (Illus.). 116p. 1973. 9.95 (ISBN 0-8158-0300-1). Chris Mass.

Wonder of Words, Bk. II. Edward Chinn. Ed. by Michael L. Sherer. (Orig.). 1987. pap. 7.50 (ISBN 0-89536-867-6, 7826, Co. Pub. by Forward Movement). CSS of Ohio.

Wonder of Words, Bk. 2. Edward Chinn. (Orig.). 1987. pap. 7.50 (ISBN 0-88028-059-X, Co-Pub. by CSS of OH). Forward Movement.

Wonder of Words: One Hundred Words & Phrases Shaping How Christians Think & Live. Edward Chinn. (Orig.). 1985. pap. 5.75 (ISBN 0-89536-737-8, 5822). CSS of Ohio.

Wonder: The Book of We. (Infinity Ser.: No. 9). 1972. text ed. 2.50 (ISBN 0-03-004011-6, 243, HarpR); tchr's. guide 1.15 (ISBN 0-03-004016-7, 244). Har-Row.

Wonderful Discoveries of the Witchcrafts of M. & P. Flower. Margaret Flower. LC 72-5992. (English Experience Ser.: No. 517). 50p. 1972. Repr. of 1619 ed. 6.00 (ISBN 90-221-0517-2). Walter J Johnson.

Wonderful Names of Our Wonderful Lord. LC 79-50205. 1979. Repr. deluxe ed. 8.95 (ISBN 0-88270-365-X). Bridge Pub.

Wonderful Story of God's Creation. Terrie K. Tomoko. 1978. plastic bdg. 2.50 (ISBN 0-8198-0375-8); pap. 1.75 (ISBN 0-8198-0376-6). Dghtrs St Paul.

Wonderful Way That Babies Are Made. Larry Christenson. LC 82-12813. 48p. (Orig.). 1982. 8.95 (ISBN 0-87123-627-3, 230627). Bethany Hse.

Wonderful World of Magic & Witchcraft. Leonard R. Ashley. LC 85-25310. (Illus.). 1986. 17.50 (ISBN 0-934878-71-4); pap. 10.95 (ISBN 0-934878-72-2). Dembner Bks.

Wonderful World of Superstition, Prophecy & Luck. Leonard R. Ashley. LC 83-23182. (Illus.). 192p. (Orig.). 1984. pap. 8.95 (ISBN 0-934878-33-1). Dembner Bks.

Wonderfully Made for This Life & the Next. Russell Shull. 1980. pap. 0.50 (ISBN 0-910924-70-8). Macalester.

Wonderous Power, Wonderous Love. 250p. 1983. 8.95 (ISBN 0-89066-048-4); pap. 5.95 (ISBN 0-89066-052-2). World Wide Pubs.

Wonders. Dick Hilliard & Beverly Valenti-Hilliard. (Center Celebration Ser.). (Illus.). 60p. (Orig.). 1981. pap. text ed. 3.95 (ISBN 0-89390-032-X). Resource Pubns.

Wonders in the Midst. Ward Patterson. LC 78-62709. 96p. (Orig.). 1979. pap. 2.25 (ISBN 0-87239-237-6, 40076). Standard Pub.

Wonders of Creation. Alfred M. Rehwinkel. LC 74-8416. 288p. 1973. pap. 7.95 (ISBN 0-87123-649-4, 210649). Bethany Hse.

Wonders of Man. Gary Webster. LC 57-6055. 1957. 3.50 (ISBN 0-685-42655-6, Pub. by Sheed). Guild Bks.

Wonders of Prophecy. John Urquhart. pap. 3.95 (ISBN 0-87509-155-5). Chr Pubns.

Wonders of Salvation. John L. Shuler. 1985. pap. 5.95 (ISBN 0-8163-0591-9). Pacific Pr Pub Assn.

Wonders of the Holy Name. 1976. pap. 1.50x (ISBN 0-932104-01-0). St George Pr.

Wonders of the Invisible World. large type ed. Cotton Mather. pap. 6.95 (ISBN 0-910122-46-6). Amherst Pr.

Wonders of the World, Ordeals of the Soul, Revelations of the Spirit. Rudolf Steiner. Tr. by Dorothy Lenn et al from Ger. 190p. 1983. pap. 11.00 (ISBN 0-85440-363-9, Pub by Steinerbooks). Anthroposophic.

Wondrous Is God in His Saints. Ed. by Father Benedict. LC 85-63506. (Illus.). 190p. (Orig.). 1985. pap. 6.95 (ISBN 0-936649-00-3). St Anthony Orthodox.

Won't You Join the Dance. Bhagwan Shree Rajneesh. Ed. by Ma Prem Maneesha. LC 83-43217. (Initiation Talks Ser.). 320p. (Orig.). 1983. pap. 4.95 (ISBN 0-88050-676-8). Chidvilas Found.

Wooden Churches of Eastern Europe: An Introductory Survey. David Buxton. (Illus.). 384p. 1982. 90.00 (ISBN 0-521-23786-6). Cambridge U Pr.

Woods. Shrikrishna Alanahally. Tr. by Rajeeve Taranath from Kannada. Orig. Title: Kaadu. 112p. 1979. pap. 2.95 (ISBN 0-86578-091-9). Ind-US Inc.

Woods: The Human Self & the Realism of Jesus. R. M. Davis. 79p. 1971. pap. 4.00 (ISBN 0-9600434-0-3, 03). Camda.

Woolman & Blake: Prophets of Today. Mildred B. Young. LC 72-170018. (Orig.). 1971. pap. 2.50x (ISBN 0-87574-177-0). Pendle Hill.

Word. John C. Souter. 96p. 1985. 4.95 (ISBN 0-8423-8394-8). Tyndale.

Word Alive: Reflections & Commentaries on the Sunday Readings Cycles A, B, & C. Eugene H. Maly. LC 81-20571. (Illus.). 322p. 1982. pap. 12.95 (ISBN 0-8189-0416-X). Alba.

Word & Eucharist Handbook. Lawrence Johnson. LC 86-60896. 150p. (Orig.). 1985. pap. text ed. 9.95 (ISBN 0-89390-067-2). Resource Pubns.

Word & History. E. C. Osborn. 1967. pap. 2.60x (ISBN 0-85564-020-0, Pub. by U of W Austral Pr). Intl Spec Bk.

Word & Spirit: Calvin's Doctrine of Biblical Authority. H. Jackson Forstman. 1962. 20.00x (ISBN 0-8047-0070-2). Stanford U Pr.

Word & Spirit VIII. Ed. by Santiago Sia. (Studies in Process Theology). 1986. pap. 7.00 (ISBN 0-932506-46-1). St Bedes Pubns.

Word & Table. Hoyt Hickman. 1983. pap. 3.95 (ISBN 0-687-46127-8). Abingdon.

Word & the Spirit. Yves Congar. 192p. 1986. 15.95 (ISBN 0-86683-538-5, HarpR). Har-Row.

Word & the World: God's Priorities for Today. James A. Brown. 64p. 1984. 7.95 (ISBN 0-89962-419-7). Todd & Honeywell.

Word & Words: Towards a Theology of Preaching. Eric C. Rust. LC 82-8032. xii, 131p. 1982. 10.95 (ISBN 0-86554-055-1, MUP-H36). Mercer Univ Pr.

Word & Worship: CCD Ed. Ed. by G. P. Weber et al. Incl. Our Brother Jesus. pap. 2.56 (ISBN 0-02-649370-5, 64937); Jesus with Us. pap. 2.88 (ISBN 0-02-649330-6, 64933); We Follow Jesus. pap. 3.76 (ISBN 0-02-649470-1, 64947); Father, Son & Spirit Show Their Love. pap. 3.80 (ISBN 0-02-649150-8, 64915); We Break Bread in Loving Thanksgiving. 2nd ed. pap. 3.80 (ISBN 0-02-649110-9, 64941); God's Saving Word. pap. 4.36 (ISBN 0-02-649290-3, 64929); God's Saving Mystery. 2nd ed. pap. 4.36 (ISBN 0-02-649190-7, 64919); God's Saving Presence. pap. 4.36 (ISBN 0-02-649250-4, 64925). 1966-70. tchr's manual 3.36 ea.; parent's guide 2.00 (ISBN 0-02-649140-0, 64914). Benziger Pub Co.

Word As Truth: A Critical Examination of the Christian Doctrine of Revelation in the Writings of Thomas Aquinas & Karl Barth. Alan M. Fairweather. LC 78-26040. 1979. Repr. of 1944 ed. lib. bdg. cancelled (ISBN 0-313-20808-5, FAWT). Greenwood.

Word at World's End. Francis Brabazon. 88p. 1971. 5.95 (ISBN 0-940700-04-2); pap. 3.45 (ISBN 0-940700-03-4). Meher Baba Info.

Word Became Flesh. E. Stanley Jones. (Festival Bks). 1979. pap. 3.25 (ISBN 0-687-46128-6). Abingdon.

Word Becoming Flesh. Horace Hummel. 1979. 22.95 (ISBN 0-570-03273-3, 15-2718). Concordia.

Word Bible Handbook. Lawrence O. Richards. 1982. 10.95 (ISBN 0-8499-0279-7). Word Bks.

Word for Every Day: Three Hundred & Sixty-Five Devotional Reading. Alvin N. Rogness. LC 81-65650. 376p. 1981. kivar 12.95 (ISBN 0-8066-1886-8, 10-7284). Augsburg.

Word for Us, Gospels of John & Mark, Epistles to the Romans, & the Galations. Joann Haugerud. LC 77-83418. 1977. 7.95 (ISBN 0-9603042-3-1). Coalition Women-Relig.

Word Gifts: Keys to Charismatic Power. Fred Lilly. 100p. (Orig.). 1984. pap. 2.95 (ISBN 0-89283-182-0). Servant.

Word: God's Manual for Maturity. Agnes Lawless & Eadie Goodboy. (Bible Study Enrichment Ser.). 64p. (Orig.). 1980. pap. 2.95 (ISBN 0-930756-59-2, 522004). Aglow Pubns.

Word in Season. William F. Maestri. LC 84-11026. 153p. (Orig.). 1983. pap. 6.95 (ISBN 0-8189-0459-3). Alba.

Word in Season, Vol. 1. Dick Mills. (Orig.). 1986. pap. 6.95 (ISBN 0-89274-418-9). Harrison Hse.

Word in Season: Essays in Honour of William McKane. James D. Martin & Phillip R. Davies. (JSOT Supplement Ser.: No. 42). 225p. 1986. text ed. 30.00x (ISBN 1-85075-016-5, Pub. by JSOT Pr England); pap. text ed. 15.95x (ISBN 1-85075-047-5). Eisenbrauns.

Word in Time. Arthur J. Dewey. 204p. (Orig.). 1986. pap. 14.95 (ISBN 0-941850-18-8). Sunday Pubns.

Word in Worship. William Skudlarek. LC 80-25525. (Abingdon Preacher's Library). 128p. (Orig.). 1981. pap. 6.95 (ISBN 0-687-46131-6). Abingdon.

Word into Silence. John Main. LC 80-84660. 96p. 1981. pap. 4.95 (ISBN 0-8091-2369-X). Paulist Pr.

Word Is True. Helen W. Barr. 1986. 5.75 (ISBN 0-8062-2355-3). Carlton.

Word Made Flesh. Lillian De Waters. (Practical Demonstration Ser.). pap. 0.95 (ISBN 0-686-05718-X). L De Waters.
Word Made Flesh: Homilies for the Sundays of the Three Cycles. Charles E. Miller et al. LC 83-8819. 353p. 1983. pap. 14.95 (ISBN 0-8189-0436-4). Alba.
Word Meanings in the New Testament. Ralph Earle. 374p. 1987. text ed. 24.95 (ISBN 0-8010-3434-5). Baker Bk.
Word Meanings in the New Testament: Hebrews-Revelation, Vol. 6. Ralph Earle. 174p. 1984. 9.95 (ISBN 0-8341-0943-3). Beacon Hill.
Word Meanings in the New Testament: I & II Corinthians, Galatians & Ephesians, Vol. 4. Ralph Earle. 1979. 9.95 (ISBN 0-8010-3349-7). Baker Bk.
Word Meanings in the New Testament: Romans, Vol. 3. Ralph Earle. 9.95 (ISBN 0-8010-3322-5). Baker Bk.
Word Meanings in the New Testament, Vol. 3: Romans. Ralph Earle. 264p. 1974. 9.95 (ISBN 0-8341-0512-8). Beacon Hill.
Word Meanings in the New Testament, Vol. 1: Matthew, Mark, Luke. Ralph Earle. 285p. 1980. 9.95 (ISBN 0-8341-0683-3). Beacon Hill.
Word Meanings in the New Testament, Vol. 5: Philemon-Philippians. Ralph Earle. 1977. 9.95 (ISBN 0-8341-0493-8). Beacon Hill.
Word Meanings in the New Testament: 1 & 2 Corinthians, Ephesians, Vol. 4. Ralph Earle. 350p. 1979. 9.95 (ISBN 0-8341-0567-5). Beacon Hill.
Word Meanings: Matthew-Luke, Vol. 1. Ralph Earle. 9.95 (ISBN 0-8010-3362-4). Baker Bk.
Word Meanings: Philippians-Philemon, Vol. 5. Ralph Earle. 9.95 (ISBN 0-8010-3330-6). Baker Bk.
Word of a Gentleman: Meditations for Modern Man. Richard C. Halverson. 208p. 1983. pap. 5.95 (ISBN 0-310-25811-1, 6878P). Zondervan.
Word of Encouragement. Ernest S. Williams. 25p. pap. 0.40 (ISBN 0-88243-840-9, 02-0840). Gospel Pub.
Word of Faith. Anthony L. Ash. Ed. by J. D. Thomas. LC 73-89757. (Twentieth Century Sermons Ser.). 1973. 11.95 (ISBN 0-89112-308-3, Bibl Res Pr). Abilene Christ U.
Word of God. Kenneth E. Jones. 1980. pap. 3.95 (ISBN 0-87162-224-6, D9205). Warner Pr.
Word of God. Ronald D. Tucker. 43p. (Orig.). 1985. pap. 2.50 (ISBN 0-933643-26-8). Grace World Outreach.
Word of God & Mankind. Augustin Bea. 1968. 6.50 (ISBN 0-8199-0149-0, L39003). Franciscan Herald.
Word of God & the Mind of Man: The Crisis of Revealed Truth in Contemporary Theology. Ronald H. Nash. 176p. (Orig.). 1982. pap. 6.95 (ISBN 0-310-45131-0, 12380P). Zondervan.
Word of God & the Word of Man. Karl Barth. Tr. by Douglas Horton. 1958. 13.50 (ISBN 0-8446-1599-4). Peter Smith.
Word of God in the Ethics of Jacques Ellul. David W. Gill. LC 83-20165. (ATLA Monograph Ser.: No. 20). 231p. 1984. 19.00 (ISBN 0-8108-1667-9). Scarecrow.
Word of God in Words: Reading & Preaching the Gospels. Bernard B. Scott. LC 85-5227. (Fortress Resources for Preaching). 96p. 1985. pap. 4.95 (ISBN 0-8006-1142-X). Fortress.
Word of God, Word of Earth. Davie Napier. LC 75-45312. 120p. 1976. 5.95 (ISBN 0-8298-0304-1); pap. 3.25 (ISBN 0-8298-0307-6). Pilgrim NY.
Word of Joy. (Words of... Ser.). (Illus.). 48p. 1983. 3.95 (ISBN 0-8407-5336-5). Nelson.
Word of Love. (Words of... Ser.). (Illus.). 48p. 1983. 3.95 (ISBN 0-8407-5338-1). Nelson.
Word of the Lord Shall Go Forth: Essays in Honor of David Noel Freedman in Celebration of His Sixtieth Birthday. Ed. by Carol L. Meyers & M. O'Connor. (American Schools of Oriental Research, Special Volume Ser.: No. 1). 1983. text ed. 35.00x (ISBN 0-931464-19-6). Eisenbrauns.
Word of Truth. Dale Moody. 624p. 1981. 24.95 (ISBN 0-8028-3533-3). Eerdmans.
Word on Families: A Bibical Guide to Family Well-Being. G. William Sheek. Ed. by Lyle E. Schaller. 160p. (Orig.). 1985. pap. 7.50 (ISBN 0-687-46135-9). Abingdon.
Word Parents Handbook. Lawrence O. Richards. 1983. 9.95 (ISBN 0-8499-0328-9). Word Bks.
Word: People Participating in Preaching. Martin E. Marty. LC 83-16611. 112p. 1984. pap. 3.95 (ISBN 0-8006-1778-9, 1-1778). Fortress.
Word Pictures in the New Testament, 6 vols. A. T. Robertson. 1982. 75.00 (ISBN 0-8010-7710-9). Baker Bk.
Word Pictures in the New Testament, 6 vols. Archibald Robertson. Incl. Vol. 1. Matthew & Mark (ISBN 0-8054-1301-4); Vol. 2. Luke (ISBN 0-8054-1302-2); Vol. 3. Acts (ISBN 0-8054-1303-0); Vol. 4. Epistles of Paul (ISBN 0-8054-1304-9); Vol. 5. John & Hebrews (ISBN 0-8054-1305-7); Vol. 6. Genesis, Epistles, Revelation & John (ISBN 0-8054-1306-5). 1943. 11.95 ea.; Set. 67.50 (ISBN 0-8054-1307-3). Broadman.
Word Search: Favorite Bible Stories from Genesis. John H. Tiner. pap. 2.70 (ISBN 0-89137-615-1). Quality Pubns.
Word Studies in the Greek New Testament, for the English Reader, 16 bks. Kenneth S. Wuest. Incl. Bk. 1. Golden Nuggets. pap. 4.95 (ISBN 0-8028-1242-2); Bk. 2. Bypaths. pap. 3.95 (ISBN 0-8028-1318-6); Bk. 3. Treasures. pap. 3.95 (ISBN 0-8028-1243-0); Bk. 4. Untranslatable Riches. pap. 4.95 (ISBN 0-8028-1241-4); Bk. 5. Studies in Vocabulary. pap. 3.95 (ISBN 0-8028-1240-6); Bk. 6. Great Truths to Live by. pap. 4.95 (ISBN 0-8028-1246-5); Bk. 7. Mark. pap. 5.95 (ISBN 0-8028-1230-9); Bk. 8. Romans. pap. 4.95 (ISBN 0-8028-1231-7); Bk. 9. Galatians. pap. 4.95 (ISBN 0-8028-1232-5); Bk. 10. Ephesians & Colossians. pap. 5.95 (ISBN 0-8028-1233-3); Bk. 11. Philippians. pap. 4.95 (ISBN 0-8028-1234-1); Bk. 12. Pastoral Epistles. pap. 6.95 (ISBN 0-8028-1236-8); Bk. 13. Hebrews. pap. 6.95 (ISBN 0-8028-1235-X); Bk. 14. First Peter. pap. 4.95 (ISBN 0-8028-1237-6); Bk. 15. In These Last Days. pap. 4.95 (ISBN 0-8028-1238-4); Bk. 16. Prophetic Light in the Present Darkness. pap. 2.95 (ISBN 0-8028-1239-2). Set. pap. 80.20 (ISBN 0-8028-1248-1); Current 4 vols. **69.95 (ISBN 0-8028-2280-0). Eerdmans.**
Word Studies in the New Testament, 4 Vols. Marvin Vincent. 1957. 49.95 (ISBN 0-8028-8083-5). Eerdmans.
Word Studies on the Holy Spirit. Ethelbert W. Bullinger. LC 85-7631. 232p. 1985. pap. 7.95 (ISBN 0-8254-2246-9). Kregel.
Word Study New Testament & Concordance. Ralph Winter. 1978. text ed. 39.95 (ISBN 0-8423-8390-5). Tyndale.
Word System. Happy Caldwell. 60p. 1981. pap. 1.50 (ISBN 0-89274-176-7). Harrison Hse.
Word: The English from Hebrew Dictionary. Isaac E. Mozeson. 1986. 16.95 (ISBN 0-933503-44-X). Shapolsky Pubs.
Word, The New Century Version: New Testament. LC 84-51094. (Illus.). 556p. 1984. 13.95 (ISBN 0-8344-0123-1, BB400C). Sweet.
Word to the Wise. Hudson T. Armerding. 1980. pap. 3.95 (ISBN 0-8423-0099-6). Tyndale.
Word to the Wise. Donald Gee. (Radiant Bks.). Orig. Title: Proverbs for Pentecost. 80p. 1975. pap. 0.95 (ISBN 0-88243-632-5, 02-0632). Gospel Pub.
Word Today. Alton Wedel. 1984. 5.25 (ISBN 0-89536-684-3, 4860). CSS of Ohio.
Word, Water, Wine, & Bread. William H. Willimon. 1980. pap. 5.95 (ISBN 0-8170-0858-6). Judson.
Wordly Saints: The Puritans As They Really Were. Leland Ryken. 272p. 1986. 18.95 (ISBN 0-310-32500-5). Zondervan.
Wordly Spirituality: The Call to Take Care of the Earth. Wesley Granberg-Michaelson. LC 83-48997. 224p. 1984. 13.45 (ISBN 0-06-063380-8, HarpR). Har-Row.
Words. Kenneth E. Hagin. 1979. pap. 0.50 mini bk. (ISBN 0-89276-057-5). Hagin Ministries.
Words about the Word: A Guide to Choosing & Using Your Bible. John R. Kohlenberger, III. 176p. 1986. pap. 9.95 (ISBN 0-310-39361-2, 6287P). Zondervan.
Words & Objects: Towards a Dialogue Between Archaeology & History of Religion. (Institute for Comparative Research in Human Culture, Oslo, Series LXX A Norwegian University Press Publication). 304p. 64.00 (ISBN 82-00-07751-9). Oxford U Pr.
Words & Silence: On the Poetry of Thomas Merton. Sr. Therese Lentfoehr. LC 78-21475. 1979. 12.50 (ISBN 0-8112-0712-9); pap. 4.95 (ISBN 0-8112-0713-7, NDP472). New Directions.
Words & Testimonies. Thomas H. Silcock. LC 72-80097. (Orig.). 1972. pap. 2.50x (ISBN 0-87574-186-X). Pendle Hill.
Words & the Word. Christopher Derrick. 134p. 1987. pap. 6.95 (ISBN 0-89870-130-9). Ignatius Pr.
Words & the Word: Language Poetics, & Biblical Interpretation. Stephen Prickett. 288p. 1986. 39.50 (ISBN 0-521-32248-0). Cambridge U Pr.
Words & the Word: Notes on Our Catholic Vocabulary. Christopher Derrick. 1987. pap. 6.95. Ignatius Pr.
Words & Works of Jesus Christ. J. Dwight Pentecost. 576p. 1981. 19.95 (ISBN 0-310-30940-9, 17015). Zondervan.
Words Fitly Spoken: Reflections & Prayers. Robert H. Klenck. LC 79-13449. 1979. 10.95 (ISBN 0-934878-35-8, 07764-1, Dist. by W.W. Norton). Dembner Bks.
Words for All Seasons. Arthur Lerner. (Illus.). 104p. (Orig.). 1983. pap. 6.95 (ISBN 0-938292-06-4). Being Bks.
Words for the Quiet Moments. Reva Mendes. 35p. 1973. pap. 1.00 (ISBN 0-87516-185-5). De Vorss.
Words for the Weary. Allen Puffenberger. (Orig.). 1987. pap. price not set (ISBN 0-89536-875-7, 7861). CSS of Ohio.
Words from the Myths. Isaac Asimov. (Illus.). 224p. 1961. 12.95 (ISBN 0-395-06568-2). HM.
Words from the Myths. Isaac Asimov. (Illus.). 144p. 1969. pap. 2.50 (ISBN 0-451-14097-4, Sig). NAL.
Words in Swedenborg & Their Meanings in Modern English. 54p. 1985. pap. 2.75 (ISBN 0-910557-13-6). Acad New Church.
Words Made Flesh: God Speaks to Us in the Ordinary Things of Life. Harry Blamires. 173p. (Orig.). 1985. pap. 6.95 (ISBN 0-89283-235-5). Servant.
Words Made Flesh: Scripture, Psychology & Human Communication. Fran Ferder. LC 85-73255. 184p. (Orig.). 1986. pap. 5.95 (ISBN 0-87793-331-6). Ave Maria.
Words of Certitude. Pope John Paul II. 266p. 1985. pap. 7.95 large print ed. (ISBN 0-8027-2477-9). Walker & Co.
Words of Certitude: Excerpts from His Talks & Writings As Bishop & Pope. Pope John Paul II. Tr. by Anthon Buono from It. LC 80-81440. 136p. 1980. pap. 3.95 (ISBN 0-8091-2302-9). Paulist Pr.
Words of Cheer for Daily Life. C. H. Spurgeon. 1978. pap. 2.50 (ISBN 0-686-09101-9). Pilgrim Pubns.
Words of Christ. Gustaf H. Dalman. 1981. lib. bdg. 13.50 (ISBN 0-86524-080-9, 9509). Klock & Klock.
Words of Christ. Illus. by Judy Pelikan. Ed. by Pat Golbitz. LC 86-60824. (Illus.). 64p. 1986. 14.95 (ISBN 0-688-06240-7). Morrow.
Words of Comfort. Amy Bolding. (Bolding Library). 132p. 1984. pap. 3.95 (ISBN 0-8010-0860-3). Baker Bk.
Words of Comfort. J. R. Miller. (Illus.). 1976. 5.95 (ISBN 0-89957-518-8); pap. 2.95 (ISBN 0-89957-517-X). AMG Pubs.
Words of Comfort. (Words of... Ser.). (Illus.). 48p. 1983. 3.95 (ISBN 0-8407-5331-4). Nelson.
Words of Counsel for Christian Workers. C. H. Spurgeon. 160p. 1985. pap. 2.95. Pilgrim Pubns.
Words of Ecstasy in Sufism. Carl W. Ernst. (SUNY Series in Islam). 230p. 1985. 44.50x (ISBN 0-87395-917-5); pap. 16.95x (ISBN 0-87395-918-3). State U NY Pr.
Words of Encouragement. (Words of... Ser.). (Illus.). 48p. 1983. 3.95 (ISBN 0-8407-5332-2). Nelson.
Words of Faith. Karl Rahner. 96p. 1986. pap. 5.95 (ISBN 0-8245-0788-6). Crossroad NY.
Words of Faith. (Words of... Ser.). (Illus.). 48p. 1983. 3.95 (ISBN 0-8407-5333-0). Nelson.
Words of Faith: A Devotional Dictionary. Charles S. Mueller. 160p. (Orig.). 1985. pap. 5.95 (ISBN 0-570-03968-1, 12-3003). Concordia.
Words of Friendship. (Words of... Ser.). (Illus.). 48p. 1983. 3.95 (ISBN 0-8407-5334-9). Nelson.
Words of Hope. (Words of... Ser.). (Illus.). 48p. 1983. 3.95 (ISBN 0-8407-5335-7). Nelson.
Words of Inspiration. Clinton Gripper. 32p. 1987. 5.95 (ISBN 0-89962-569-X). Todd & Honeywell.
Words of Jesus: Arranged for Meditation. Louis Michaels. 1977. 6.95 (ISBN 0-87243-071-5). Templegate.
Words of Jesus Christ from the Cross. C. H. Spurgeon. 1978. pap. 2.75 (ISBN 0-686-23028-0). Pilgrim Pubns.
Words of Jesus in Our Gospel. Stanley B. Marrow. LC 79-52105. 160p. 1979. pap. 5.95 (ISBN 0-8091-2215-4). Paulist Pr.
Words of Jesus on Peace. Ed. by Larry Langdon. LC 84-28866. (Illus.). 72p. 1985. pap. 3.95 (ISBN 0-943726-02-6). Langdon Pubns.
Words of Jesus, with Key Readings from New & Old Testaments. Jose D. Vinck. 320p. 1977. deluxe ed. 30.00 boxed, slipcover, hand-made full morocco (ISBN 0-911726-26-8). Alleluia Pr.
Words of Life. 5th ed. Ed. by Charles L. Wallis. LC 81-47850. (Illus.). 256p. 1982. 12.50 (ISBN 0-06-069239-1, HarpR). Har-Row.
Words of Life. (Words of... Ser.). (Illus.). 48p. 1983. 3.95 (ISBN 0-8407-5337-3). Nelson.
Words of Love. Josefa Menedez et al. LC 84-51596. 95p. (Orig.). 1985. pap. 3.00 (ISBN 0-89555-244-2). Tan Bks Pubs.
Words of Patience. (Words of... Ser.). (Illus.). 48p. 1983. 3.95 (ISBN 0-8407-5339-X). Nelson.
Words of Peace. (Words of... Ser.). (Illus.). 48p. 1983. 3.95 (ISBN 0-8407-5340-3). Nelson.
Words of Power. James F. McNulty. LC 83-2514. 226p. (Orig.). 1983. pap. 8.95 (ISBN 0-8189-0442-9). Alba.
Words of Promise. (Words of... Ser.). (Illus.). 48p. 1983. 3.95 (ISBN 0-8407-5341-1). Nelson.
Words of Revolution: A Call Involvement in the Real Revolution. Tom Skinner. 44p. 1971. pap. 4.25 (ISBN 0-85364-113-7). Attic Pr.
Words of St. Francis. Rev. ed. James Meyer. 1982. 6.00 (ISBN 0-8199-0833-9). Franciscan Herald.
Words of Thanks. (Words of... Ser.). (Illus.). 48p. 1983. 3.95 (ISBN 0-8407-5342-X). Nelson.
Words of the Apostle Paul. John Eadie. 462p. 1985. smythe sewn 18.50 (ISBN 0-86524-191-0, 4405). Klock & Klock.
Words of the Apostles. Rudolf E. Stier. 1982. lib. bdg. 18.75 (ISBN 0-86524-087-6, 4403). Klock & Klock.
Words of the Father. J. L. Moreno. 8.00 (ISBN 0-685-06817-X); pap. 6.00 (ISBN 0-685-06818-8). Beacon Hse.
Words of the Master. Sri Ramakrishna. Ed. by Swami Brahmananda. pap. 1.50 (ISBN 0-87481-135-X). Vedanta Pr.
Words of the Risen Christ. Rudolf E. Stier. 1982. lib. bdg. 8.25 (ISBN 0-86524-088-4, 9512). Klock & Klock.
Words of the World's Religion. Robert S. Ellwood, Jr. 1977. pap. text ed. 24.33x (ISBN 0-13-965004-0). P-H.
Words of Warning for Daily Life. C. H. Spurgeon. 1980. pap. 2.50 (ISBN 0-686-09100-0). Pilgrim Pubns.
Words of Welcome. Amy Bolding. (Preaching Helps Ser.). (Orig.). 1965. pap. 4.50 (ISBN 0-8010-0550-7). Baker Bk.
Words of Wisdom. 1979. 9.50 (ISBN 0-8198-0605-6). Dghtrs St Paul.
Words of Wisdom for Daily Life. C. H. Spurgeon. pap. 2.50 (ISBN 0-686-09099-3). Pilgrim Pubns.
Words of Wisdom from the Masters. 2nd ed. Cylvia Archer Lowe. 120p. 1981. pap. 6.95 (ISBN 0-9606080-0-1). Book Dept.
Words on Target: For Better Christian Communication. Sue Nichols. LC 63-16410. (Illus., Orig.). 1963. pap. 5.50 (ISBN 0-8042-1476-X). John Knox.
Words Our Saviour Gave Us. Daniel Berrigan. 1978. pap. 4.95 (ISBN 0-87243-081-2). Templegate.
Words That Heal Today. Ernest Holmes. 1948. 10.95 (ISBN 0-396-03093-9). Dodd.
Words That Hurt, Words That Heal. Carole Mayhall. 112p. 1986. hdbk. 8.95 (ISBN 0-89109-543-8). NavPress.
Words That Hurt, Words That Heal. Carole Mayhall. 112p. Date not set. pap. 3.95 (ISBN 0-89109-178-5). NavPress.
Words to Live by: Chiara Lubich & Christians from All over the World. Ed. by Hugh Moran. Tr. by Raymond Dauphinais & Hugh Moran. LC 80-82419. 157p. 1980. pap. 4.50 (ISBN 0-911782-08-7). New City.
Words to Love By. Mother Teresa. LC 82-73373. (Illus.). 80p. (Orig.). 1983. pap. 4.95 (ISBN 0-87793-261-1). Ave Maria.
Words to Love By. Mother Teresa. 160p. 1985. pap. 6.95 large print ed. (ISBN 0-8027-2478-7). Walker & Co.
Words to Winners of Souls. Horatius Bonar. (Summit Bks.). 1979. pap. 2.50 (ISBN 0-8010-0773-9). Baker Bk.
Word's Way. Victor P. Wierwille. LC 70-176281. (Studies in Abundant Living: Vol. 3). 276p. 1971. 4.95 (ISBN 0-910068-04-6). Am Christian.
Work. Cardinal Wyszynski. 184p. 1960. 5.95 (ISBN 0-933932-18-9). Scepter Pubs.
Work & Career. Nancy Van Vuuren. LC 83-12338. (Choices: Guides for Today's Woman: Vol. 2). 116p. (Orig.). 1983. pap. 6.95 (ISBN 0-664-24539-0). Westminster.
Work & Co-Creation. Canadian Christian Movement for Peace Staff. Ed. by Alyson Huntly et al. (People Living for Justice Ser.). 160p. 1983. pap. text ed. 29.95 (ISBN 0-697-01921-7). Wm C Brown.
Work & Faith in Society. Ed. by Maurice M. Omi. 96p. (Orig.). 1986. pap. 6.95 (ISBN 1-55586-988-2). US Catholic.
Work & Islam. Mehdi Bazargan. Tr. by Mohammack Yousefi from Persian. 62p. 1979. 4.00 (ISBN 0-941722-04-X). Book-Dist-Ctr.
Work & Words of Jesus. rev. ed. Archibald M. Hunter. LC 73-7559. 230p. 1973. pap. 8.95 (ISBN 0-664-24976-0). Westminster.
Work & Workship among the Shakers. Edward D. Andrews & Faith Andrews. (Illus.). 224p. 1982. pap. 6.00 (ISBN 0-486-24382-6). Dover.
Work & Worship among the Shakers. Edward D. Andrews & Faith Andrews. 1983. 14.00 (ISBN 0-8446-5942-8). Peter Smith.
Work Concerning the Trewnesse of the Christian Religion. Philippe de Mornay. Tr. by Philip Sidney from Fr. LC 75-45384. 680p. 1976. Repr. of 1587 ed. lib. bdg. 90.00x (ISBN 0-8201-1166-X). Schol Facsimiles.
Work of an Evangelist. 888p. 1984. 19.95 (ISBN 0-89066-049-2). World Wide Pubs.

Work of Craft. Carla Needleman. 160p. 1987. pap. 8.95 (ISBN 1-85063-061-5, 30615, Ark Paperbks). Methuen Inc.

Work of Faith. Spiros Zodhiates. (Trilogy Ser.: Vol. 2). (Illus.). pap. 6.95 (ISBN 0-89957-545-5). AMG Pubs.

Work of God Goes On. Gerhard Lohfink. LC 86-45202. (Bible for Christian Life Ser.). 80p. 1987. pap. 4.95 (ISBN 0-8006-2026-7). Fortress.

Work of Holy Spirit. Elmer L. Roy. pap. 2.50 (ISBN 0-89315-108-4). Lambert Bk.

Work of Jesus Christ As an Advocate. John Bunyan. pap. 3.95 (ISBN 0-685-19844-8). Reiner.

Work of Richard Sibbes, 7 Vols. Set. 108.95 (ISBN 0-85151-398-0). Banner of Truth.

Work of T. B. Barratt. Ed. by Donald W. Dayton. (Higher Christian Life Ser.). 435p. 1985. 55.00 (ISBN 0-8240-6404-6). Garland Pub.

Work of the Church: Getting the Job Done in Boards & Committees. David. R. Sawyer. 128p. 1987. pap. 6.95 (ISBN 0-8170-1116-1). Judson.

Work of the Church Treasurer. Thomas E. McLeod. 80p. 1981. pap. 6.95 (ISBN 0-8170-0908-6). Judson.

Work of the Church Trustee. Orlando L. Tibbetts. 1979. pap. 4.95 (ISBN 0-8170-0825-X). Judson.

Work of the Clerk. Zelotes Grenell & Agnes G. Goss. 1967. pap. 3.95 (ISBN 0-8170-0383-5). Judson.

Work of the Deacon & Deaconess. Harold Nichols. (Orig.). pap. 4.95 (ISBN 0-8170-0328-2). Judson.

Work of the Holy Spirit. Octavius Winslow. 223p. 1984. pap. 5.45 (ISBN 0-85151-152-X). Banner of Truth.

Work of the Kabbalist. Z'ev B. Halevi. (Illus.). 223p. (Orig.). 1985. pap. 9.95 (ISBN 0-87728-637-X). Weiser.

Work of the Pastoral Relations Committee. Emmett V. Johnson. 128p. 1983. pap. 4.95 (ISBN 0-8170-0984-1). Judson.

Work of the Usher. Alvin D. Johnson. (Orig.). pap. 3.95 (ISBN 0-8170-0356-8). Judson.

Work on Myth. Hans Blumenberg. Tr. by Robert M. Wallace from Ger. (German Social Thought Ser.). 770p. 1985. text ed. 40.00x (ISBN 0-262-02215-X). MIT Pr.

Work Trap. Martin C. Helldorfer. LC 80-52059. 96p. 1983. pap. 5.95 (ISBN 0-89571-017-X). Affirmation.

Work You Give Us to Do: A Mission Study. The Episcopal Church Center. 179p. (Orig.). 1982. pap. 4.95 (ISBN 0-8164-7116-9, HarpR); study guide 1.25 (ISBN 0-8164-7117-7). Har-Row.

Workable Faith. June S. Wood. 1975. 6.95 (ISBN 0-8022-2152-1). Philos Lib.

Workbook for Planning Christian Education. Kenneth D. Blazier. 48p. 1983. pap. 3.95 (ISBN 0-8170-0996-5). Judson.

Workbook for Spiritual Development of All People. Ni Hua Ching. LC 83-51083. 240p. 1983. text ed. 12.50 (ISBN 0-937064-06-8). SEBT.

Workbook for the Restoration Ideal. Marshall Leggett. 96p. 1986. pap. 2.95 wkbk. (ISBN 0-87403-068-4, 3176). Standard Pub.

Workbook of Intercessory Prayer. Maxie D. Dunnam. LC 78-65617. 1979. pap. 4.50x (ISBN 0-8358-0382-1). Upper Room.

Workbook of Living Prayer. Maxie D. Dunnam. 1975. 4.50x (ISBN 0-8358-0323-6). Upper Room.

Workbook on Becoming Alive in Christ. Maxie Dunnam. 160p. (Orig.). 1986. pap. 5.50 (ISBN 0-8358-0542-5). Upper Room.

Workbook on Christian Doctrine. Joseph H. Dampier. 64p. (Orig.). 1943. pap. 1.95 (ISBN 0-87239-072-1, 3343). Standard Pub.

Workbook on Christian Doctrine- NIV. rev. ed. Joseph H. Dampier. 64p. 1986. wkbk. 2.50 (ISBN 0-87403-177-X, 3344). Standard Pub.

Workbook on Morality: A Biblical View of Sexuality. Dennis Eeningenburg. 74p. (Orig.). 1981. pap. 4.95 (ISBN 0-8341-0717-1). Beacon Hill.

Workbook on Spiritual Disciplines. Maxie Dunnam. LC 83-51402. 160p. 1984. wkbk. 4.50 (ISBN 0-8358-0479-8). Upper Room.

Workbook on the Book of Acts. J. Vernon Jacobs & John W. Wade. 112p. 1986. pap. 3.95 (ISBN 0-87403-095-1, 3346). Standard Pub.

Workbook on the Four Gospels. Richard C. Mills. (Illus.). 128p. (Orig.). 1948. pap. 3.95 (ISBN 0-87239-327-5, 3347). Standard Pub.

Working It Through. Elisabeth Kubler-Ross. (Illus.). 176p. 1987. pap. 5.95 (ISBN 0-02-022000-6, Collier). Macmillan.

Working Manual for Altar Guilds. rev. ed. Dorothy C. Diggs. (Orig.). 1957. pap. 3.95 (ISBN 0-8192-1028-5). Morehouse.

Working Miracles of Love: A Collection of Teachings. Yogi A. Desai. LC 85-50126. (Illus.). 184p. 1985. pap. text ed. 5.95 (ISBN 0-940258-15-3). Kripalu Pubns.

Working Out Together: Keeping Your Group in Shape. Sharrel Keyes. (Fisherman Bible Studyguides). 64p. (Orig.). 1985. pap. 1.00 (ISBN 0-87788-263-0). Shaw Pubs.

Working Out What God Works in. Samuel Young. (Harvest Ser.). 1981. pap. 4.95 (ISBN 0-8163-0440-8). Pacific Pr Pub Assn.

Working Out Your Own Beliefs: A Guide for Doing Your Own Theology. Douglas E. Wingeier. LC 79-21097. (Orig.). 1980. pap. 4.95 (ISBN 0-687-46190-1). Abingdon.

Working Partners Working Parents. William Blackwell & Muriel Blackwell. LC 79-51134. 1979. 5.95 (ISBN 0-8054-5637-6). Broadman.

Working People & Their Employers. Washington T. Gladden. LC 75-89734. (American Labor: From Conspiracy to Collective Bargaining Ser., No. 1). 1969. Repr. of 1876 ed. 15.00 (ISBN 0-405-02123-2). Ayer Co Pubs.

Working the Angles: A Trigonometry for Pastoral Work. Eugene H. Peterson. 266p. (Orig.). 1987. pap. 7.95 (ISBN 0-8028-0265-6). Eerdmans.

Working Together on Rudolf Steiner's Mystery Dramas. Hans Pusch. LC 80-67024. (Steiner's Mystery Dramas Ser.). (Illus.). 144p. (Orig.). 1980. 15.95 (ISBN 0-910142-90-4); pap. 9.95 (ISBN 0-910142-91-2). Anthroposophic.

Working with Children & the Liturgy. Paul Larose. LC 81-14984. (Illus.). 95p. 1982. pap. 2.95 (ISBN 0-8189-0428-3). Alba.

Working with God. Gardner Hunting. 1934. 5.95 (ISBN 0-87159-174-X). Unity School.

Working with Older Adults. J. Stanley Rendahl. LC 84-80708. (Equipping Ser.). (Illus., Orig.). 1984. pap. 5.95 (ISBN 0-935797-08-4). Harvest IL.

Working with People. Doran C. McCarty. (Orig.). 1987. pap. 5.95 (ISBN 0-8054-3241-8). Broadman.

Working with Religious Issues in Therapy. Robert J. Lovinger. LC 84-6198. 328p. 1984. 30.00x (ISBN 0-87668-727-3). Aronson.

Working with the Intermarried: A Practical Guide for Workshop Leaders. Andrew Baker & Lori Goodman. LC 85-71160. 36p. (Orig.). 1985. pap. 4.00 (ISBN 0-87495-071-6). Am Jewish Comm.

Working with Volunteer Leaders in the Church. Reginald M. McDonough. LC 75-16579. 140p. 1976. pap. 6.50 (ISBN 0-8054-3214-0). Broadman.

Workings of Old Testament Narrative. Peter D. Miscall. LC 82-48570. (Semeia Studies). 160p. 1983. pap. 8.95 (ISBN 0-8006-1512-3). Fortress.

Workings of Old Testament Narrative. Peter D. Miscall. LC 82-5993. (SBL Semeia Studies). 158p. 1983. pap. 8.95 (ISBN 0-89130-584-X, 06-06-12). Scholars Pr GA.

Workmen of God. Oswald Chambers. 1965. pap. 2.95 (ISBN 0-87508-131-2). Chr Lit.

Workmen of God. William S. Deal. 1975. pap. 0.95 (ISBN 0-686-11025-0). Crusade Pubs.

Works, 4 vols. Samuel Clarke. LC 75-11207. (British Philosophers & Theologians of the 17th & 18th Century Ser.: Vol. 12). 3274p. 1976. Repr. of 1742 ed. Set. lib. bdg. 204.00 (ISBN 0-8240-1762-5). Garland Pub.

Works. Roger Hutchinson. 1842. 31.00 (ISBN 0-384-25120-X). Johnson Repr.

Works, 4 Vols. John Jewel. 1845-1850. Set. 204.00 (ISBN 0-384-27217-7). Johnson Repr.

Works, 3 vols. Thomas Shepard. Ed. by John A. Albro. LC 49-1393. Repr. of 1853 ed. Set. 85.00 (ISBN 0-404-05990-2). Vol. 1 (ISBN 0-404-05991-0). Vol. 2 (ISBN 0-404-05992-9). Vol. 3 (ISBN 0-404-05993-7). AMS Pr.

Works. C. H. Spurgeon. 1976. pap. 1.50 (ISBN 0-686-16845-3). Pilgrim Pubns.

Works - Centenary Edition, 15 vols. Theodore Parker. LC 75-3307. Repr. of 1911 ed. 595.00 set (ISBN 0-404-59300-3). AMS Pr.

Works & Wonders. Ed. by Unity School of Christianity. LC 78-68931. 1979. 5.95 (ISBN 0-87159-175-8). Unity School.

Works, Examined, Corrected & Published: By H. Holland. Richard Greenham. LC 72-5999. (English Experience Ser.: No. 524). 496p. 1973. Repr. of 1599 ed. 70.00 (ISBN 90-221-0524-5). Walter J Johnson.

Works of Anne Frank. Anne Frank. LC 73-16643. (Illus.). 332p. 1974. Repr. of 1959 ed. lib. bdg. 32.50x (ISBN 0-8371-7206-3, FRWO). Greenwood.

Works of Apostolic Fathers, 2 vols. Apostolic Fathers. Incl. Vol. 1. Clement, Ignatius, Polycarp, Didache, Barnabas (ISBN 0-674-99027-7); Vol. 2. Shepherd of Hermas, Martyrdom of Polycarp, Epistle to Diognetus (ISBN 0-674-99028-5). (Loeb Classical Library: No. 24-25). 13.95x ea. Harvard U Pr.

Works of Benjamin B. Warfield, 10 vols. B. B. Warfield. 1981. Repr. of 1932 ed. 149.50 (ISBN 0-8010-9645-6). Baker Bk.

Works of Bishop Joseph Hall, 10 Vols. Joseph Hall. Ed. by P. Wynter. LC 76-86830. Repr. of 1863 ed. Set. 375.00 (ISBN 0-404-03070-X); 37.50 ea. AMS Pr.

Works of Brooks, 6 vols. Thomas Brooks. 1980. Set. 108.95 (ISBN 0-85151-302-6). Banner of Truth.

Works of George Fox, Vols. 1-8. George Fox. Incl. Vols. 1 & 2. Journal or Historical Account of the Life, Travels, Sufferings, Christian Experiences & Labour of Love in the Work of the Ministry, of That Ancient, Eminent, & Faithful Servant of Jesus Christ, George Fox. LC 75-16194. Vol. 1 (ISBN 0-404-09351-5). Vol. 2 (ISBN 0-404-09352-3); Vol. 3. Great Mystery of the Great Whore Unfolded. LC 75-16195. 616p (ISBN 0-404-09353-1); Vols. 4-6. Gospel Truth Demonstrated, in a Collection of Doctrinal Books, Given Forth by That Faithful Minister of Jesus Christ, George Fox. LC 75-16199. Vol. 4 (ISBN 0-404-09354-X). Vol. 5 (ISBN 0-404-09355-8). Vol. 6 (ISBN 0-404-09356-6); Vols. 7 & 8. Collection of Many Select & Christian Epistles, Letters & Testimonies. LC 75-16207. Vol. 7 (ISBN 0-404-09357-4). Vol. 8 (ISBN 0-404-09358-2). Repr. of 1831 ed. Set. 320.00 (ISBN 0-404-09350-7); 40.00 ea. AMS Pr.

Works of Hugh Latimer, Sometime Bishop of Worcester, Martyr, 1555, 2 Vols. Hugh Latimer. Repr. of 1845 ed. Set. 80.00 (ISBN 0-384-31480-5). Johnson Repr.

Works of Jakob Boehme, 4 vols. Jakob Boehme. 1974. lib. bdg. 1500.00 (ISBN 0-87968-465-8). Gordon Pr.

Works of James Pilkington, Lord Bishop of Durham. James Pilkington. 1842. Repr. of 1842 ed. 55.00 (ISBN 0-384-46530-7). Johnson Repr.

Works of John & Charles Wesley. 2nd rev. ed. Richard Green. LC 74-26049. Repr. of 1906 ed. 23.00 (ISBN 0-404-12924-2). AMS Pr.

Works of John Flavel, 6 vols. Set. 108.95 (ISBN 0-85151-060-4). Banner of Truth.

Works of John Knox, 6 Vols. John Knox. Ed. by David Laing. LC 67-35016. Repr. of 1864 ed. Set. 345.00 (ISBN 0-404-52880-5). AMS Pr.

Works of John Newton, 6 vols. John Newton. 1985. Repr. of 1820 ed. Set. 125.00 (ISBN 0-85151-460-X). Banner of Truth.

Works of John Owen, Vol. I. John Owen. 1980. 16.95 (ISBN 0-85151-123-6). Banner of Truth.

Works of John Owen, Vol. II. John Owen. 1980. 16.95 (ISBN 0-85151-124-4). Banner of Truth.

Works of John Owen, Vol. III. John Owen. 1980. 16.95 (ISBN 0-85151-125-2). Banner of Truth.

Works of John Owen, Vol. IV. John Owen. 1980. 16.95 (ISBN 0-85151-068-X). Banner of Truth.

Works of John Owen, Vol. V. John Owen. 1980. 16.95 (ISBN 0-85151-067-1). Banner of Truth.

Works of John Owen, Vol. VI. John Owen. 1980. 16.95 (ISBN 0-85151-126-0). Banner of Truth.

Works of John Owen, Vol. VII. John Owen. 1980. 16.95 (ISBN 0-85151-127-9). Banner of Truth.

Works of John Owen, Vol. VIII. John Owen. 1980. 16.95 (ISBN 0-85151-066-3). Banner of Truth.

Works of John Owen, Vol. IX. John Owen. 1980. 16.95 (ISBN 0-85151-065-5). Banner of Truth.

Works of John Owen, Vol. X. John Owen. 1980. 16.95 (ISBN 0-85151-064-7). Banner of Truth.

Works of John Owen, Vol. XI. John Owen. 1980. 16.95 (ISBN 0-85151-128-7). Banner of Truth.

Works of John Owen, Vol. XII. John Owen. 1980. 16.95 (ISBN 0-85151-129-5). Banner of Truth.

Works of John Owen, Vol. XIII. John Owen. 1980. 16.95 (ISBN 0-85151-063-9). Banner of Truth.

Works of John Owen, Vol. XIV. John Owen. 1980. 16.95 (ISBN 0-85151-062-0). Banner of Truth.

Works of John Owen, Vol. XV. John Owen. 1980. 16.95 (ISBN 0-85151-130-9). Banner of Truth.

Works of John Owen, Vol. XVI. John Owen. 1980. 16.95 (ISBN 0-85151-061-2). Banner of Truth.

Works of John Owen, 16 vols. John Owen. 1980. Set. 244.95 (ISBN 0-85151-392-1). Banner of Truth.

Works of John Wesley, 14 vols. John Wesley. Set. 249.50 (ISBN 0-8010-9616-2). Baker Bk.

Works of John Wesley: A Collection of Hymns for the Use of the People Called Methodists, Vol. 7. John Wesley. Ed. by Franz Hilderbrandt & Oliver A. Beckerlegge. (Oxford Edition of the Works of John Wesley Ser.). (Illus.). 1984. 86.00x (ISBN 0-19-812529-1). Oxford U Pr.

Works of John Wesley: Letters I, 1721-1739, Vol. 25. John Wesley. Ed. by Frank Baker. (Oxford Edition of the Works of John Wesley Ser.). 1980. 45.00x (ISBN 0-19-812545-3). Oxford U Pr.

Works of John Wesley: (Letters II), 1740-1755, Vol. 26. John Wesley. Ed. by Frank Baker. (Oxford Edition of the Works of John Wesley Ser.). (Illus.). 1982. 45.00x (ISBN 0-19-812546-1). Oxford U Pr.

Works of John Wesley: Sermons 1-33, Vol. 1. 1008p. 1984. 49.95 (ISBN 0-687-46210-X). Abingdon.

Works of John Wesley, Volume 2: Sermons II, 34-70. Albert C. Outler. 600p. 1985. 49.95 (ISBN 0-687-46211-8). Abingdon.

Works of Jonathan Edwards, 2 vols. Jonathan Edwards. 1979. Set. 66.95 (ISBN 0-85151-397-2); Vol. 1. 36.95 (ISBN 0-85151-216-X); Vol. 2. 36.95 (ISBN 0-85151-217-8). Banner of Truth.

Works of Josephus, 9 vols. Josephus. Ed. by E. H. Warmington. Incl. Vol. 1. Life; Against Apion (ISBN 0-674-99205-9); Vols 2-3. Jewish War. Vol. 2, Bks 1-3. (ISBN 0-674-99223-7); Vol. 3, Bks. 4-7, Index To Vols. 2 & 3. (ISBN 0-674-99232-6); Vols 4-9. Antiquities. Vol. 4, Bks 1-4. (ISBN 0-674-99267-9); Vol. 5, Bks 5-8. (ISBN 0-674-99310-1); Vol. 6, Bks 9-11. (ISBN 0-674-99360-8); Vol. 7, Bks 12-14. (ISBN 0-674-99402-7); Vol. 8, Bks 15-17. (ISBN 0-674-99451-5); Vol. 9, Bks 18-20, General Index. (ISBN 0-674-99477-9). (Loeb Classical Library: No. 186, 203, 210, 242, 281, 326, 365, 410, 433). 13.95x ea. Harvard U Pr.

Works of Love: Some Christian Reflections in the Form of Discourse. Soren Kierkegaard. pap. 7.95x (ISBN 0-06-130122-1, TB122, Torch). Har-Row.

Works of Love: Some Christian Reflections in the Form of Discourses. Soren Kierkegaard. Tr. by Long. LC 64-7445. 1962. 17.75 (ISBN 0-8446-2373-3). Peter Smith.

Works of Matthew Arnold, 15 Vols. Matthew Arnold. LC 70-107157. 1970. Repr. of 1903 ed. Set. 395.00x (ISBN 0-403-00201-X); 40.00 ea. Scholarly.

Works of Mencius. Mencius. Tr. by James Legge. 15.75 (ISBN 0-8446-0331-7). Peter Smith.

Works of Mercy. John B. Martin & Catherine Martin. 1.17 (ISBN 0-8091-9337-X). Paulist Pr.

Works of Nicholas Ridley, D.D., Sometime Lord Bishop of London, Martyr, 1555. Nicholas Ridley. Repr. of 1841 ed. 41.00 (ISBN 0-384-50840-5). Johnson Repr.

Works of President Edwards, 10 Vols. Jonathan Edwards. Ed. by Edward Williams & Edward Parsons. LC 68-56782. (Research & Source Works Ser.: No. 271). 1968. Repr. of 1847 ed. 245.00 (ISBN 0-8337-1019-2). B Franklin.

Works of Reverend G. W, 6 vols. George Whitefield. LC 75-31107. Repr. of 1772 ed. 230.00 set (ISBN 0-404-13530-7). AMS Pr.

Works of Richard Sibbes, Vol. VI. Richard Sibbes. 560p. 1983. Repr. 16.95 (ISBN 0-85151-372-7). Banner of Truth.

Works of Richard Sibbes, Vol. IV. Richard Sibbes. 527p. 1983. Repr. 16.95 (ISBN 0-85151-371-9). Banner of Truth.

Works of Richard Sibbes, Vol. 1. Richard Sibbes. 1979. 16.95 (ISBN 0-85151-169-4). Banner of Truth.

Works of Richard Sibbes, Vol. 3. Richard Sibbes. 543p. 1981. 16.95 (ISBN 0-85151-329-8). Banner of Truth.

Works of Robert Traill, 2 vols. Robert Traill. 1975. Set. 28.95 (ISBN 0-85151-393-X). Vol. 1 (ISBN 0-85151-229-1). Vol. 2 (ISBN 0-85151-230-5). Banner of Truth.

Works of Saint Patrick: Saint Secundius Hymn on St. Patrick. (Ancient Christian Writers Ser.: No. 17). 10.95. Paulist Pr.

Works of Spinoza, 2 Vols. Benedict D. Spinoza. Tr. by Elwes. Set. 29.50 (ISBN 0-8446-2986-3). Peter Smith.

Works of That Learned & Judicious Divine Mr. Richard Hooker with an Account of His Life & Death by Isaac Walton, 3 vols. 7th ed. Richard Hooker. LC 76-125020. (Research & Source Works Ser.: No. 546). 1970. Repr. of 1888 ed. 103.00 (ISBN 0-8337-1731-6). B Franklin.

Works of the Ever Memorable Mr. John Hales of Eaton, 3 vols. in 2. John Hales. Ed. by D. Dalrymple. LC 77-131037. Repr. of 1765 ed. 82.50 (ISBN 0-404-03050-5). AMS Pr.

Works of the Most Reverend Father in God, William Laud, D. D, 3 vols. William Laud. LC 74-5373. (Library of Anglo-Catholic Theology: No. 11). Repr. of 1860 ed. Set. 350.00 (ISBN 0-404-52120-7). AMS Pr.

Works of the Reverend Sydney Smith, 3 Vols. 1984. Repr. of 1845 ed. Set. lib. bdg. 200.00 (ISBN 0-8492-8121-0). Vol. 1, 474 pp. Vol. 2, 495 pp. Vol. 3, 479 pp. R West.

Works of the Seraphic Father St. Francis of Assisi: Translated by a Religious of the Order. 269p. 1982. Repr. of 1890 ed. lib. bdg. 40.00 (ISBN 0-89984-015-9). Century Bookbindery.

Works of Wesley, Vol. 3 & 4: The Journal of John Wesley. John Wesley. 1986. Vol. 3, 496p. 24.95 (ISBN 0-310-51290-5); Vol. 4, 544p. 24.95 (ISBN 0-310-51300-6). Zondervan.

Works of Wesley: Wesley's Standard Sermons, 2 vols. John Wesley. Ed. by E. H. Sugden & Joseph Allison. 544p. 1986. Vol. 1. 24.95 (ISBN 0-310-51270-0, 17170); Vol. 2. 24.95 (ISBN 0-310-51280-8, 17171). Zondervan.

Works of William Chillingworth, 3 Vols. William Chillingworth. Repr. of 1838 ed. Set. lib. bdg. 95.00 (ISBN 0-404-01570-0). Vol. 1 (ISBN 0-404-01571-9). Vol. 3 (ISBN 0-404-01572-7). Vol. 4 (ISBN 0-404-01573-5). AMS Pr.

Works of William E. Channing, D.D. 1060p. 1982. Repr. of 1889 ed. lib. bdg. 100.00 (ISBN 0-8495-0959-9). Arden Lib.

Works of William Ellery Channing, 2 vols. in 1. William E. Channing. LC 70-114815. (Research & Source Works Ser.: No. 626). 1971. Repr. of 1882 ed. lib. bdg. 46.50 (ISBN 0-8337-0530-X). B Franklin.

Works on Subud, 3 vols. J. G. Bennett. 300.00 (ISBN 0-8490-1332-1). Gordon Pr.

Workshoes for Christ. A. D. Wright. 1979. pap. 3.75 (ISBN 0-89225-185-9). Gospel Advocate.

World According to the Heart of God. Tr. by Bertha Gonzalez from Span. LC 85-73186. 176p. (Orig.). 1986. pap. 5.00 (ISBN 0-9607590-1-8). Action Life Pubns.

World & Its God. Philip Mauro. 95p. 1981. pap. 2.95 (ISBN 0-89084-151-9). Bob Jones Univ Pr.

World & Literature of the Old Testament. Ed. by John T. Willis. (Bible Study Textbook Ser.). 1979. Repr. of 1978 ed. 11.60 (ISBN 0-89900-058-4). College Pr Pub.

World & the Profits: Mormanism & Earlt Christianity. Hugh Nibley. 1987. 10.95 (ISBN 0-87579-078-X). Deseret Bk.

World & the Word: Between Science & Religion. Michael Heller. Tr. by Adam C. Kisiel from Polish. LC 86-61668. (Philosophy in Science Library: Vol. 1). 184p. 1987. pap. 14.95 (ISBN 0-88126-724-4). Pachart Pub Hse.

World As I See It. Albert Einstein. 1979. pap. 2.95 (ISBN 0-8065-0711-X). Citadel Pr.

World As Power. new ed. John Woodroffe. Bd. with Mahamaya: Power As Consciousness. John Woodroffe & Pramatha N. Mukhyopadhyaya. 1981. 24.00 (ISBN 0-89744-119-2, Pub. by Ganesh & Co. India). Auromere.

World at Prayer. Robert J. Fox. LC 78-74623. 1979. pap. 3.95 (ISBN 0-87973-633-X). Our Sunday Visitor.

World Bibliography of Translations of the Meanings of the Holy Qur'an: Printed Translations 1515-1980. Ismet Binark & Halit Eren. 600p. 1987. text ed. 125.00 (ISBN 0-7103-0229-0, Kegan Paul). Methuen Inc.

World Christian Encyclopedia: A Comparative Survey of Churches & Religions in the Modern World, A. D. 1900 to 2000. Ed. by David Barrett. (Illus.). 1982. text ed. 165.00x (ISBN 0-19-572435-6). Oxford U Pr.

World Christianity: Central America & the Caribbean. Ed. by Clifton L. Holland. LC 79-89819. 1981. pap. 15.00 (ISBN 0-912552-36-0). Missions Adv Res Comm Ctr.

World Christianity: Middle East. Ed. by Don M. McCurry. LC 79-87790. 156p. 1979. pap. text ed. 12.00 (ISBN 0-912552-27-1). Missions Adv Res Com Ctr.

World Christianity: Oceania. Ed. by Leonora M. Douglas. pap. 15.00 (ISBN 0-912552-48-4). Missions Adv Res Com Ctr.

World Citizen: Action for Global Justice. Adam Corson-Finnerty. LC 81-16918. 178p. (Orig.). 1982. pap. 6.95 (ISBN 0-88344-715-0). Orbis Bks.

World Conqueror & World Renouncer. S. J. Tambiah. LC 76-8290. (Cambridge Studies in Social Anthropology: No. 15). 1976. 65.00 (ISBN 0-521-21140-9); pap. 19.95 (ISBN 0-521-29290-5). Cambridge U Pr.

World Council of Churches. David P. Gaines. 1966. 18.50 (ISBN 0-87233-816-9). Bauhan.

World Council of Churches & Race Relations. Neville Richardson. (IC-Studies in the Intercultural History of Christianity: Vol. 9). 78p. 1977. pap. 15.65 (ISBN 3-261-01718-X). P Lang Pubs.

World Council of Churches & the Catholic Church. John J. McDonnell. (Toronto Studies in Theology: Vol. 21). 479p. 1985. lib. bdg. 49.95x (ISBN 0-88946-765-X). E Mellen.

World Economy & World Hunger: The Response of the Churches. Robert L. McCan. 119p. 1982. 16.00 (ISBN 0-89093-497-5); pap. 5.00. U Pubns Amer.

World Ephemeris for the Twentieth Century. Para Research. 1983. Midnight calculations. pap. 12.95 (ISBN 0-914918-60-5); Noon calculations. pap. 12.95 (ISBN 0-914918-61-3). Para Res.

World Faith. facs. ed. Ruth Cranston. LC 68-58782. (Essay Index Reprint Ser). 1949. 15.00 (ISBN 0-8369-0108-8). Ayer Co Pubs.

World Has a Familiar Face. Tom Galt. 85p. 1981. pap. 5.00 (ISBN 0-938050-03-6). Shearwater.

World History in the Light of Anthroposophy: And As a Foundation for Knowledge of the Human Spirit. new ed. Rudolf Steiner. Tr. by George Adams & Mary Adams. 159p. 1977. 12.50 (ISBN 0-85440-315-9); pap. 9.00 (ISBN 0-85440-316-7). Anthroposophic.

World Hunger: The Responsibility of Christian Education. Suzanne C. Toton. LC 81-16906. 224p. (Orig.). 1982. pap. 7.95 (ISBN 0-88344-716-9). Orbis Bks.

World in Between: Christian Healing & the Struggle for Spiritual Survival. Emmanuel Milingo. Ed. by Mona Macmillan. 144p. (Orig.). 1985. pap. 5.95 (ISBN 0-88344-354-6). Orbis Bks.

World in My Mirror. Margaret J. Jones. LC 79-17730. 1979. 8.75 (ISBN 0-687-46270-3). Abingdon.

World in Reading. 14.00 (ISBN 0-8198-8213-5). Dghtrs St Paul.

World into Which Jesus Came. Sylvia R. Tester. LC 82-9430. (Illus.). 96p. 1982. PLB 12.95 (ISBN 0-89565-232-3, 4951, Pub. by Childs World). Standard Pub.

World Is a Wedding: Explorations in Christian Spirituality. A. M. Allchin. (Crossroad Paperback Ser.). 512p. 1982. pap. 6.95 (ISBN 0-8245-0411-9). Crossroad NY.

World Is New. Joel S. Goldsmith. LC 62-7953. 1978. 8.95 (ISBN 0-06-063291-7, HarpR). Har-Row.

World Is Not Enough. Tom Finley. Ed. by Annette Parrish. LC 86-22049. 252p. (Orig.). (YA) 1986. pap. 4.25 (ISBN 0-8307-1151-1, S183329). Regal.

World Jewry & the State of Israel. Ed. by Moshe Davis. LC 77-72730. (Indivual Publications Ser.). 1977. lib. bdg. 14.00x (ISBN 0-405-10305-0). Ayer Co Pubs.

World Literature I. Center for Learning Staff. 1985. pap. text ed. 34.95 (ISBN 0-697-02073-8). Wm C Brown.

World Literature II. Center for Learning Staff. 1985. pap. text ed. 34.95 (ISBN 0-697-02074-6). Wm C Brown.

World Love It or Leave It. Roger L. Dudley. (Anchor Ser.). 80p. (Orig.). 1987. pap. 5.95 (ISBN 0-8163-0665-6). Pacific Pr Pub Assn.

World Mission & World Survival. E. Luther Copeland. LC 84-14963. 1985. pap. 5.95 (ISBN 0-8054-6335-6). Broadman.

World Missions: Building Bridges or Barriers. Ed. by Theodore Williams. 101p. (Orig.). 1979. pap. 2.00 (ISBN 0-936444-02-9). World Evang Fellow.

World Missions Today. Terry C. Hulbert. LC 78-68233. 96p. 1979. pap. text ed. 4.95 (ISBN 0-910566-16-X); Perfect bdg. instr's. guide 5.95 (ISBN 0-910566-28-3). Evang Tchr.

World More Human: A Church More Christian. Ed. by George Devine. 204p. 1984. pap. text ed. 9.50 (ISBN 0-8191-3851-7, College Theo Soc). U Pr of Amer.

World-Mystery: Four Comparative Studies in General Theosophy. G. R. Mead. 201p. 1987. pap. text ed. 15.95 (ISBN 0-915032-73-2). Natl Poet Foun.

World of Allah. David D. Duncan. 1982. 40.00 (ISBN 0-395-32504-8). HM.

World of Buddhism: Buddhist Monks & Nuns in Society & Culture. Ed. by Heinz Bechert & Richard Gombrich. LC 84-8125. 1984. 49.95 (ISBN 0-87196-982-3). Facts on File.

World of Buddhist Awakening. Takamaro Shigaraki. 96p. 1983. pap. 6.95 (ISBN 0-938474-03-0). Buddhist Study.

World of Difference: Following Christ Beyond Your Cultural Walls. Thom Hopler. LC 81-57818. 192p. (Orig.). 1981. pap. 7.95 (ISBN 0-87784-747-9); pap. 1.95 study guide (ISBN 0-87784-802-5). Inter-Varsity.

World of Friendship. Compiled by Jayne Bowman. (Illus.). 1983. 8.00 (ISBN 0-8378-1801-X). Gibson.

World of Grace. L. J. O'Donovan. 1980. pap. 14.95x (ISBN 0-8245-0406-2). Crossroad NY.

World of Islam. Thomas B. Irving. Orig. Title: Tide of Islam. (Illus.). 200p. 1985. 17.50 (ISBN 0-915597-20-9); pap. 9.95 (ISBN 0-915597-18-7). Amana Bks.

World of Islam. Xavier de Planhol. 153p. 1959. pap. 8.95x (ISBN 0-8014-9830-9). Cornell U Pr.

World of Islam. John B. Taylor. (Orig.). 1979. pap. 3.95 (ISBN 0-377-00086-8). Friend Pr.

World of John of Salisbury. Ed. by Michael J. Wilks. (Studies in Church History: Subsidia 3). 400p. 1985. text ed. 45.00x (ISBN 0-631-13122-1). Basil Blackwell.

World of Moses. Paul F. Bork. LC 78-5022. (Horizon Ser.). 1978. pap. 5.95 (ISBN 0-8127-0166-6). Review & Herald.

World of Myths: A Dictionary of Universal Mythology. F. C. Bray. 75.00 (ISBN 0-8490-1335-6). Gordon Pr.

World of Our Fathers. Irving Howe. LC 75-16342. (Illus.). 714p. 1976. 14.95 (ISBN 0-15-146353-0). HarBraceJ.

World of Our Fathers. Irving Howe. 560p. 1983. pap. 12.95 (ISBN 0-671-49252-7, Touchstone). S&S.

World of Our Fathers: The Jews of Eastern Europe. Milton Meltzer. LC 74-14755. (Illus.). 256p. 1974. 11.95 (ISBN 0-374-38530-0). FS&G.

World of Philip Potter. William H. Gentz. 1974. pap. 2.95 (ISBN 0-377-00006-X). Friend Pr.

World of Prayer, 2 vols. Elie Munk. 19.95 set (ISBN 0-87306-080-6); Vol. 1. 9.50 (ISBN 0-87306-081-4); Vol. 2. 11.50 (ISBN 0-87306-082-2). Feldheim.

World of Prayer. Elie Munk. Tr. by Henry Biberfeld & Leonard Oschry. Orig. Title: Welt der Gebete. 1978. pap. 10.95 (ISBN 0-87306-170-5). Feldheim.

World of Prayer. Adrienne Von Speyr. Tr. by Graham Harrison from Ger. LC 84-80904. Tr. of Welt des Gebetes. 311p. (Orig.). 1985. pap. 10.95 (ISBN 0-89870-033-7). Ignatius Pr.

World of Rosaphrenia: The Sexual Psychology of the Female. Major J. Baisden, Jr. LC 72-178852. 224p. 1971. 6.95 (ISBN 0-912984-01-5). Allied Res Soc.

World of St. John: The Gospels & the Epistles. E. Earle Ellis. 96p. (Orig.). 1984. pap. 4.95 (ISBN 0-8028-0013-0). Eerdmans.

World of Sholom Aleichem. Maurice Samuel. LC 86-47697. 344p. 1986. pap. 9.95 (ISBN 0-689-70709-6, 343). Atheneum.

World of the Bible. Ed. by A. S. van der Woude. Tr. by Sierd Woudstra from Dutch. (Illus.). 496p. 1986. 34.95 (ISBN 0-8028-2405-6). Eerdmans.

World of the Buddha: An Introduction to Buddhist Literature. Lucien Stryk. 1982. pap. 9.95 (ISBN 0-394-17974-9, E803, Ever). Grove.

World of the New Testament. E. M. Blaiklock. (Bible Study Commentary Ser.). 127p. 1983. pap. 4.95 (ISBN 0-87508-176-2). Chr Lit.

World of the New Testament. Sean Freyne. (New Testament Message Ser.: Vol. 2). 12.95 (ISBN 0-89453-190-5); pap. 8.95 (ISBN 0-89453-125-5). M Glazier.

World of the New Testament. Ed. by J. I. Packer & Merrill C. Tenney. LC 82-12548. 1982. pap. 6.95 (ISBN 0-8407-5821-9). Nelson.

World of the Old Testament. Ed. by J. I. Packer et al. LC 82-12563. 1982. pap. 6.95 (ISBN 0-8407-5820-0). Nelson.

World of the Polynesians Seen Through Their Myths & Legends, Poetry, & Art. Antony Alpers. (New Zealand Classics Ser.). (Illus.). 432p. 1986. 10.95 (ISBN 0-19-558142-3). Oxford U Pr.

World of the Ranters: Religious Radicalism in the English Revolution. A. L. Morton. 232p. 1970. 14.95x (ISBN 0-8464-0980-1). Beekman Pubs.

World of the Reformation. Hans J. Hillerbrand. (Twin Brooks Ser.). 229p. 1981. pap. 6.95 (ISBN 0-8010-4248-8). Baker Bk.

World of the Senses & the World of the Spirit. Rudolf Steiner. (Ger.). 88p. 1979. pap. 4.95 (ISBN 0-919924-10-7, Pub. by Steiner Book Centre Canada). Anthroposophic.

World of the Sufi. Idries Shah. 1979. 18.95 (ISBN 0-900860-66-9). Ins Study Human.

World of the Talmud. 2nd ed. Morris Adler. LC 63-18390. 1963. pap. 4.95 (ISBN 0-8052-0058-4). Schocken.

World of the Yeshiva: An Intimate Portrait of Orthodox Jewry. William B. Helmreich. 405p. 1982. 19.95 (ISBN 0-02-914640-2). Free Pr.

World of the Yeshiva: An Intimate Portrait of Orthodox Jewry. William N. Helmreich. LC 81-67440. 424p. 1986. pap. 14.95x (ISBN 0-300-03715-5). Yale U Pr.

World of Thought in Ancient China. Benjamin I. Schwartz. (Illus.). 456p. 1985. text ed. 27.50x (ISBN 0-674-96190-0, Belknap Pr). Harvard U Pr.

World of Treasure. Ben Kendrick. LC 82-332. 1981. pap. 4.95 (ISBN 0-87227-081-5). Reg Baptist.

World of Unseen Spirits. Bernard N. Schneider. pap. 5.95 (ISBN 0-88469-024-5). BMH Bks.

World of Witches. Julio C. Baroja. Tr. by O. N. Glendinning. LC 64-15829. (Nature of Human Society Ser.). xiv, 314p. 1973. pap. 12.00x (ISBN 0-226-03763-0, P497, Phoen). U of Chicago Pr.

World of Words. Israel Rosenberg. 224p. 1973. 8.95 (ISBN 0-8022-2101-7). Philos Lib.

World of Zen. Ed. by Nancy W. Ross. (Illus.). 1960. pap. 8.95 (ISBN 0-394-70301-4, Vin). Random.

World Order of Baha'u'llah. 2nd rev. ed. Shoghi Effendi. LC 56-17685. 1974. 16.95 (ISBN 0-87743-031-4, 108-020); pap. 8.95 (ISBN 0-87743-004-7, 108-021). Baha'i.

World Outreach Intercessory Prayer Warriors. Dee Deason & Velma Deason. 1983. pap. 2.50 (ISBN 0-910709-40-8). PTL Repro.

World Peace Gathering. Dharma Realm Buddhist Association Staff. (Illus.). 128p. (Orig.). pap. 5.00 (ISBN 0-917512-05-7). Buddhist Text.

World Poverty, Can It Be Solved. Barbara Ward. pap. 0.75 (ISBN 0-8199-0394-9, L39010). Franciscan Herald.

World Register of University Studies in Jewish Civilization. 14.50 (ISBN 0-8160-1475-2). Facts on File.

World Register of University Teaching of Jewish Civilization. Ed. by International Center for University Teaching of Jewish Civilization Staff & Mervin Verbit. LC 85-40514. (Selected Syllabi in University Teaching of Jewish Civilization Ser.). 250p. 1985. pap. text ed. 14.50x (ISBN 0-910129-30-4). Wiener Pub Inc.

World Religions. Young Oon Young. 1976. pap. 10.00 (ISBN 0-686-13408-7). Unification Church.

World Religions, Vol. 1. Young O. Kim. LC 76-23739. 275p. 1982. pap. 8.95 (ISBN 0-318-11690-1). Rose Sharon Pr.

World Religions, Vol. 2. Young O. Kim. LC 76-23739. 413p. 1982. pap. 10.95 (ISBN 0-318-11691-X). Rose Sharon Pr.

World Religions & Global Ethics. Ed. by S. Cromwell Crawford. (Contemporary Discussion Ser.). 168p. 21.95 (ISBN 0-913757-57-8); pap. 12.95 (ISBN 0-913757-58-6). Paragon Hse.

World Religions & World Community. Robert H. Slater. LC 63-9805. (Lectures on the History of Religions Ser.: No. 6). 1963. 28.00x (ISBN 0-231-02615-3). Columbia U Pr.

World Religions: Beliefs Behind Today's Headlines. rev. ed. John Catoir. xxiii, 148p. pap. 5.00 (ISBN 0-317-46551-1). Chrstphrs NY.

World Religions: Beliefs Behind Today's Headlines. rev. ed. John T. Catoir. 160p. 1985. pap. 4.95 (ISBN 0-940518-04-X). Guildhall Pubs.

World Religions: From Ancient History to the Present. Geoffrey Parrinder. (Illus.). 224p. 1984. 29.95 (ISBN 0-87196-129-6). Facts on File.

World Religions: From Ancient History to the Present. Ed. by Geoffrey Parrinder. (Illus.). 528p. 1985. pap. 14.95 (ISBN 0-8160-1289-X). Facts on File.

World Religions I: Near & Middle Eastern Religions. 2nd, rev. ed. Young O. Kim. 275p. 1982. pap. 5.75 (ISBN 0-910621-36-5). HSA Pubns.

World Religions II: India's Religious Quest & the Faiths of the Far East. 2nd rev. ed. Young O. Kim. 415p. 1982. pap. 7.75 (ISBN 0-910621-37-3). HSA Pubns.

World Religions Series. S. A. Nigosian. (Comparative Religions Ser.). 1976. pap. text ed. 6.45 (ISBN 0-88343-688-4). McDougal-Littell.

World Scriptures: An Introduction to Comparative Religion. Kenneth Kramer. LC 85-62933. 304p. 1986. pap. 12.95 (ISBN 0-8091-2781-4). Paulist Pr.

World Seen. Herbert H. Skoglund. LC 85-80101. 120p. (Orig.). 1985. pap. 3.95 (ISBN 0-935797-18-1). Harvest IL.

World Shakers. Kathy R. Judd & Joanne Kalnitz. 224p. 1986. pap. text ed. 13.95 (ISBN 0-03-006503-8, HoltC). HR&W.

World Task of Pacifism. A. J. Muste. 1983. pap. 2.50x (ISBN 0-87574-013-8, 013). Pendle Hill.

World That Perished. John C. Whitcomb. pap. 5.95 (ISBN 0-8010-9537-9). Baker Bk.

World That Perished. John C. Whitcomb. pap. 4.95 (ISBN 0-88469-059-8). BMH Bks.

World That Shaped the New Testament. Calvin J. Roetzel. LC 85-12492. 180p. 1985. pap. 11.95 (ISBN 0-8042-0455-1). John Knox.

World Their Household: The American Women's Foreign Mission Movement & Cultural Transformation, 1870-1920. Patricia R. Hill. (Women & Culture Ser.). 300p. 1985. text ed. 19.50x (ISBN 0-472-10055-6). U of Mich Pr.

World Two Thousand A.D. Gordon Lindsay. (Prophecy Ser.). 2.50 (ISBN 0-89985-064-2). Christ Nations.

World under God's Law. 5th ed. T. Robert Ingram. LC 62-16216. 1970. pap. text ed. 3.50 (ISBN 0-686-05040-1). St Thomas.

World Union Company. John Stahl. 60p. 1980. pap. 5.00 (ISBN 0-318-21734-1). Evanescent Pr.

World Was Flooded with Light: A Mystical Experience Remembered. Genevieve Foster & David J. Hufford. LC 84-22013. 216p. 1985. 14.95 (ISBN 0-8229-3512-0). U of Pittsburgh Pr.

World Without Chance. Kurt E. Koch. LC 72-85598. 96p. 1974. pap. 2.95 (ISBN 0-8254-3012-7). Kregel.

World Youth & the Family. Joseph A. Cussen. 1984. pap. 6.95 (ISBN 0-941850-14-5). Sunday Pubns.

Worldly Theologians: The Persistence of Religion in Nineteenth Century American Thought. Michael D. Clark. LC 80-5840. 328p. (Orig.). 1982. lib. bdg. 29.25 (ISBN 0-8191-1778-1); pap. text ed. 14.50 (ISBN 0-8191-1779-X). U Pr of Amer.

World's Best Christmas Carols. rev. ed. 64p. 1987. pap. 2.95 (ISBN 0-87403-212-1, 9848). Standard Pub.

World's Best Hymns. Louis K. Harlow. Ed. by J. W. Churchill. 1978. Repr. of 1893 ed. lib. bdg. 25.00 (ISBN 0-8495-2323-0). Arden Lib.

World's Best Religious Quotations. James G. Lawson. 1979. Repr. lib. bdg. 35.00 (ISBN 0-8492-1610-9). R West.

World's Congress Addresses. Charles C. Bonney. 88p. 1900. pap. 6.95 (ISBN 0-912050-48-9). Open Court.

World's First Love. Fulton J. Sheen. 240p. 1976. 4.50 (ISBN 0-385-11559-8, Im). Doubleday.

World's Great Love: The Prayer of the Rosary. Fulton J. Sheen. (Illus.). 1978. pap. 4.95 (ISBN 0-8164-2182-X, HarpR). Har-Row.

World's Great Religious Poetry. Ed. by Caroline M. Hill. LC 70-137058. 836p. 1973. Repr. of 1938 ed. lib. bdg. 47.50x (ISBN 0-8371-5521-5, HIRP). Greenwood.

World's Greatest Collection of Heavenly Humor. Bob Phillips. LC 81-82676. 192p. (Orig.). 1982. pap. text ed. 2.95 (ISBN 0-89081-297-7). Harvest Hse.

World's Greatest Name, Names & Titles of Jesus Christ Beginning with H-K. rev. ed. Charles J. Rolls. 183p. 1985. pap. 5.95 (ISBN 0-87213-732-5). Loizeaux.

World's Handy Dictionary of the Bible. Ed. by James L. Dow. 640p. 1986. pap. 4.95 (ISBN 0-529-06320-4). World Bible.

World's Living Religions. Archie J. Bahm. (Arcturus Books Paperbacks). 384p. 1971. pap. 12.95x (ISBN 0-8093-0529-1). S Ill U Pr.

World's Living Religions. rev. ed. Robert E. Hume. LC 58-12515. 335p. 1978. pap. text ed. write for info. (ISBN 0-02-358450-5, Pub. by). Macmillan.

Worlds of Delight: A Literary Introduction to the Bible. Leland Ryken. 372p. 1987. pap. 17.95 (ISBN 0-8010-7743-5). Baker Bk.

World's Religions. rev. ed. J. N. Anderson. LC 75-26654. 1976. pap. 5.95 (ISBN 0-8028-1636-3). Eerdmans.

World's Religious Traditions. Frank Whaling. 320p. (Orig.). 1986. pap. 14.95 (ISBN 0-8245-0747-9). Crossroad NY.

World's Religious Traditions. Ed. by Frank Whaling. 320p. 1984. 22.95 (ISBN 0-567-09353-0, Pub. by T&T Clark Ltd UK). Fortress.

World's Rim: Great Mysteries of the North American Indians. Hartley B. Alexander. LC 53-7703. (Illus.). xx, 259p. 1967. pap. 7.95 (ISBN 0-8032-5003-7, BB 160, Bison). U of Nebr Pr.

World's Sixteen Crucified Saviors. Kersey Graves. 436p. spiral bdg. 8.50. Truth Seeker.

Worlds That Passed. facsimile ed. Abraham S. Sachs. Tr. by Harold Berman & Judah Joffe. LC 74-29521. (Modern Jewish Experience Ser.). (Eng.). 1975. Repr. of 1928 ed. 24.50x (ISBN 0-405-06746-1). Ayer Co Pubs.

Worlds Torn Asunder. Dov B. Edelstein. 1985. 12.95 (ISBN 0-88125-040-6). Ktav.

World's Twenty Largest Churches. John N. Vaughan. 1984. pap. 12.95 (ISBN 0-8010-9297-3). Baker Bk.

Worldview & Communication of the Gospel. Marguerite G. Kraft. LC 78-10196. (Illus.). 1978. pap. 7.95 (ISBN 0-87808-324-3). William Carey Lib.

Worldviews. Ninian Smart. LC 82-16877. 190p. 1983. pap. 7.95x (ISBN 0-684-17812-5). Scribner.

Worldviews: Crosscultural Explorations in Human Beliefs. Ninian Smart. (Illus.). 224p. 1983. 13.95 (ISBN 0-684-17811-7, ScribT). Scribner.

Worldwide Church of God. Bryce Pettitt. (Truthway Ser.). 26p. (Orig.). 1981. pap. text ed. 1.25 (ISBN 0-87148-916-3). Pathway Pr.

Worldwide Impact of Religion on Comtemporary Politics. Ed. by Richard L. Rubenstein. 224p. 1987. 21.95 (ISBN 0-88702-203-0, Pub. by Wash Inst DC); pap. 12.95 (ISBN 0-88702-211-1, Pub.by Wash Inst DC). Paragon Hse.

Worrell New Testament. A. S. Worrell. 1980. Repr. of 1904 ed. 11.95 (ISBN 0-88243-392-X, 01-0392). Gospel Pub.

Worry: A Maieutic Analysis. M. G. Campion. 350p. 1986. text ed. 47.50x (ISBN 0-566-05118-4). Gower Pub Co.

Worry Free Worry. Ben Leach. (Uplook Ser.). 32p. 1982. pap. 0.99 (ISBN 0-8163-0516-1). Pacific Pr Pub Assn.

Worry Pill & Other Stories Based on Proverbs. 4.95 (2850001). CEF Press.

Worship. John E. Burkhardt. LC 81-23116. 162p. 1982. pap. 8.95 (ISBN 0-664-24409-2). Westminster.

Worship. Siudy. 1980. 5.50 (ISBN 0-8298-0393-9). Pilgrim NY.

Worship. Evelyn Underhill. LC 78-20499. 1983. Repr. of 1937 ed. 31.35 (ISBN 0-88355-874-2). Hyperion Conn.

Worship. Evelyn Underhill. (Crossroad Paperback Ser.). (Illus.). 1982. pap. 12.95 (ISBN 0-8245-0466-6). Crossroad NY.

Worship. John Woolman. 1983. pap. 2.50x (ISBN 0-87574-051-0, 051). Pendle Hill.

Worship & Ethics: A Study in Rabbinic Judaism. Max Kadushin. LC 63-10586. 350p. 1975. pap. 8.95x (ISBN 0-8197-0011-8). Bloch.

Worship & Ethics: A Study in Rabbinic Judaism. Max Kadushin. LC 77-18849. 1978. Repr. of 1964 ed. lib. bdg. cancelled (ISBN 0-313-20217-6, KAWE). Greenwood.

Worship & Freedom: A Black American Church in Zambia. Walton J. Johnson. LC 77-22388. 190p. 1978. text ed. 34.50x (ISBN 0-8419-0315-8, Africana). Holmes & Meier.

Worship & Hymnody. Gary R. Shiplett. (Illus.). 122p. (Orig.). 1980. pap. text ed. 8.95 (ISBN 0-916260-08-9). Meriwether Pub.

Worship & Politics. Rafael Avila. Tr. by Alan Neely. LC 81-38356. 144p. (Orig.). 1981. pap. 6.95 (ISBN 0-88344-714-2). Orbis Bks.

Worship & Reformed Theology: The Liturgical Lessons of Mercersburg. Jack M. Maxwell. LC 75-45492. (Pittsburgh Theological Monographs: No. 10). 1976. pap. 12.00 (ISBN 0-915138-12-3). Pickwick.

Worship & Secular Man: An Essay on the Liturgical Nature of Man. Raimundo Panikkar. LC 72-93339. pap. 29.80 (ISBN 0-317-26670-5, 2025123). Bks Demand UMI.

Worship & Spirituality. Don E. Saliers. LC 84-7211. (Spirituality & the Christian Life Ser.: Vol. 5). 114p. 1984. pap. 7.95 (ISBN 0-664-24634-6). Westminster.

Worship & Witness. (Faith & Life Ser.). 2.10 (ISBN 0-02-805110-6, 80511). Benziger Pub Co.

Worship & Work. Colman J. Barry. LC 80-10753. (Illus.). 526p. 1980. pap. text ed. 12.50 (ISBN 0-8146-1123-0). Liturgical Pr.

Worship As Celebration of Covenant & Incarnation. Alvin J. Beachy. LC 68-57497. 1968. pap. 2.00 (ISBN 0-87303-940-8). Faith & Life.

Worship As Pastoral Care. rev. ed. William H. Willimon. LC 79-894. 1979. 11.95 (ISBN 0-687-46388-2). Abingdon.

Worship Celebrations for Youth. John Brown. 1980. pap. 4.95 (ISBN 0-8170-0866-7). Judson.

Worship: Exploring the Sacred. James Empereur. 1987. pap. 11.95. Pastoral Pr.

Worship Handbook: A Practical Guide to Reform & Renewal. Thomas A. Langford, III & Bonnie S. Jones. LC 84-70648. 88p. (Orig.). 1984. pap. 5.95 (ISBN 0-88177-011-6, DRO11B). Discipleship Res.

Worship His Majesty. Ed. by Larry Reftery. 32p. 1981. pap. 0.75 (ISBN 0-88144-056-6). Christian Pub.

Worship Hymnal. 671p. 1971. 6.95 (ISBN 0-318-18907-0); piano ed. 16.00 (ISBN 0-919797-30-X). Kindred Pr.

Worship in Islam. Al-Ghazzali. Ed. by Edwin E. Calverley. LC 79-2860. 242p. 1981. Repr. of 1925 ed. 23.00 (ISBN 0-8305-0032-4). Hyperion Conn.

Worship in Our Family. Paul Henshaw & Harold Weemhoff. LC 81-52045. 84p. 1981. pap. 4.95x (ISBN 0-8358-0421-6). Upper Room.

Worship in the Early Church. rev. ed. Ralph P. Martin. 144p. 1975. pap. 7.95 (ISBN 0-8028-1613-4). Eerdmans.

Worship in the Round: Patterns of Informative & Participative Worship. Ed. by Keith Pearson. (Illus.). 88p. (Orig.). 1983. pap. 5.95 (ISBN 0-85819-343-4, Pub. by JBCE). ANZ Religious Pubns.

Worship in the World's Religions. 2nd ed. Geoffrey Parrinder. (Quality Paperback: No. 316). 239p. 1976. pap. 4.95 (ISBN 0-8226-0316-0). Littlefield.

Worship Is a Verb. Robert E. Webber. 224p. 1985. 12.95 (ISBN 0-8499-0371-8, 0371-8). Word Bks.

Worship Is All of Life. Robert A. Morey. LC 83-73375. (Illus.). 115p. (Orig.). 1984. pap. 5.45 (ISBN 0-87509-336-1). Chr Pubns.

Worship Leader's Guide. Shari Iverson. (Illus.). 40p. 1986. pap. 4.50 (ISBN 0-914936-97-2). Bible Temple.

Worship of God: Some Theological, Pastoral & Practical Reflections. Ralph P. Martin. 237p. (Orig.). 1982. pap. 10.95 (ISBN 0-8028-1934-6). Eerdmans.

Worship of Nature. James G. Frazer. LC 73-21271. (Gifford Lectures: 1924-25). Repr. of 1926 ed. 41.50 (ISBN 0-404-11427-X). AMS Pr.

Worship of Priapus. Richard P. Knight. LC 73-76829. (Illus.). 300p. 1974. Repr. of 1786 ed. 25.00 (ISBN 0-8216-0207-1). Univ Bks.

Worship of the Dead: The Origin & Nature of Pagan Idolatry & Its Bearing Upon the Early History of Egypt & Babylonia. J. Garnier. LC 77-85617. 1977. Repr. of 1904 ed. lib. bdg. 50.00 (ISBN 0-89341-300-3). Longwood Pub Group.

Worship of the Early Church. Ferdinand Hahn. Ed. by John Reumann. Tr. by David E. Green from Ger. LC 72-87063. 144p. 1973. pap. 4.95 (ISBN 0-8006-0127-0, 1-127). Fortress.

Worship of the Scottish Reformed Church, 1550-1638: The Hastie Lectures in the University of Glasgow, 1930. William McMillan. LC 83-45585. Date not set. Repr. of 1931 ed. 35.00 (ISBN 0-404-19903-8). AMS Pr.

Worship Old & New. Robert E. Webber. 256p. 1982. 11.95 (ISBN 0-310-36650-X, 12207); pap. 9.95 (ISBN 0-310-36651-8, 12207P). Zondervan.

Worship: Our Gift to God. Cathi Trzeciak. (Concept Ser.). (Illus.). 24p. 1986. pap. 3.95 saddlestitched (ISBN 0-570-08531-4, 56-1558). Concordia.

Worship Planbook. Paul E. Engle. (Orig.). 1981. pap. 3.95 (ISBN 0-934688-03-6). Great Comm Pubns.

Worship: Rediscovering the Missing Jewel. Ronald B. Allen & Gordon Borror. (Critical Concern Bks.). 1987. pap. 7.95 (ISBN 0-88070-140-4). Multnomah.

Worship Resources for Youth. Jerry O. Cok. 133p. (Orig.). 1983. pap. 12.00 (ISBN 0-914527-25-8). C-Four Res.

Worship: The Christian's Highest Occupation. A. P. Gibbs. pap. 5.95 (ISBN 0-937396-57-5). Walterick Pubs.

Worship the Lord. Louis Pratt. 1983. 4.35 (ISBN 0-89536-580-4, 2332). CSS of Ohio.

Worship: The Missing Jewel of the Evangelical Church. A. W. Tozer. 30p. 1979. bklet 0.95 (ISBN 0-87509-219-5). Chr Pubns.

Worshipable Deity & Other Poems. Satvarupa Das Goswami. Ed. by Bimala dasi. 140p. 1985. pap. text ed. 4.00 (ISBN 0-911233-30-X). Gita Nagari.

Worshipbook: Services. deluxe ed. 10.00 (ISBN 0-664-21287-5). Westminster.

Worshipbook: Services & Hymns. Pew ed. 688p. 1972. 7.95 (ISBN 0-664-10108-9). Westminster.

Worshipful Master's Assistant. rev/ ed. Robert Macoy. 302p. 1980. Repr. s.p. hardcover 11.95 (ISBN 0-88053-008-1). Macoy Pub.

Worshipful Master's Assistant. 10.00 (ISBN 0-685-19506-6). Powner.

Worshipful Preaching. Gerard S. Sloyan. LC 83-48911. (Fortress Resources for Preaching Ser.). 80p. 1984. pap. 3.95 (ISBN 0-8006-1781-9, 1-1781). Fortress.

Worshiping Community. Peter A. Judd. 177p. 1984. pap. text ed. 9.00 (ISBN 0-8309-0403-4). Herald Hse.

Worshiping God. Mrs. Z. W. Swafford. (God & Us Ser.). 32p. 1983. pap. 2.00 (ISBN 0-89114-103-0); coloring book 0.69 (ISBN 0-89114-104-9). Baptist Pub Hse.

Worshipping the Father in Spirit & in Truth. David Ingles. 40p. (Orig.). 1986. wkbk. 4.95 (ISBN 0-914307-63-0). Word Faith.

Worshipping the Unknown God. Rod Parsley. 31p. 1986. pap. 2.75 (ISBN 0-88144-070-1). Christian Pub.

Worth of a Soul. Steven A. Cramer. 127p. 1983. 7.95 (ISBN 0-934126-29-1). Randall Bk Co.

Worth of Religious Truth-Claims: A Case for Religious Education. Tan Tai Wei. LC 81-43864. 128p. (Orig.). 1982. pap. text ed. 9.50 (ISBN 0-8191-2369-2). U Pr of Amer.

Worthingtom Miner: A Directors Guild of America Oral History. Franklin J. Schaffner. LC 84-22184. 323p. 1985. 22.50 (ISBN 0-8108-1757-8). Scarecrow.

Worthy Is the Lamb. Ray Summers. 1951. 11.95 (ISBN 0-8054-1314-6). Broadman.

Worthy Matron's Year Book. 1985. Repr. s.p. hardcover, looseleaf 10.00 (ISBN 0-88053-333-1). Macoy Pub.

Worthy Tract of Paulus Iovius. Paolo Giovio. Tr. by Samuel Daniel. LC 76-13497. 300p. 1976. Repr. of 1585 ed. lib. bdg. 50.00x (ISBN 0-8201-1272-0). Schol Facsimiles.

Worthy Vessels: Clay in the Hands of the Master. Nell Kennedy. 160p. (Orig.). 1984. 8.95 (ISBN 0-310-47100-1, 11287). Zondervan.

Wortsinn und Wortschoepfung Bei Meister Eckehart. R. Fahrner. pap. 9.00 (ISBN 0-384-15090-X). Johnson Repr.

Wounded Body of Christ. 2nd ed. Earl Paulk. 160p. 1985. pap. 4.95 (ISBN 0-917595-06-8). K-Dimension.

Wounded Healer: Ministry in Contemporary Society. Henri J. Nouwen. LC 72-186312. 1979. pap. 3.50 (ISBN 0-385-14803-8, Im). Doubleday.

Wounded Parent. Guy Greenfield. LC 82-70463. 128p. 1982. pap. 4.95 (ISBN 0-8010-3779-4). Baker Bk.

Wow God. Frances Clare. 189p. pap. 4.95 (ISBN 0-89221-131-8). New Leaf.

Wow! God Made Me. Ruth A. Noble. 1981. 5.75 (ISBN 0-89536-479-4, 2330). CSS of Ohio.

Wrath of Allah: Islamic Revolution & Reaction in Iran. Ramy Nima. 170p. (Orig.). 1983. pap. 9.50 (ISBN 0-86104-733-8, Pub by Pluto Pr). Longwood Pub Group.

Wrath of Athena. Jenny S. Clay. LC 83-2996. 240p. 1983. 29.00x (ISBN 0-691-06574-8). Princeton U Pr.

Wrath of God. David S. Cole. 1986. 11.95 (ISBN 0-533-06517-8). Vantage.

Wrath of God. John MacArthur, Jr. (John MacArthur's Bible Studies). (Orig.). 1986. pap. 3.50 (ISBN 0-8024-5096-2). Moody.

Wreath of Christmas Poems. Ed. by Albert Hayes & J. Laughlin. LC 72-80975. 32p. 1972. pap. 1.95 (ISBN 0-8112-0459-6, NDP347). New Directions.

Wrestlin Jacob: A Portrait of Religion in the Old South. Erskine Clark. LC 78-52453. 1979. pap. 3.95 (ISBN 0-8042-1089-6). John Knox.

Wrestling with Romans. John A. Robinson. LC 79-11645. 160p. 1979. pap. 5.95 (ISBN 0-664-24275-8). Westminster.

Write for the Religion Market. John A. Moore. LC 80-25607. 128p. 1981. 9.95 (ISBN 0-88280-084-1). ETC Pubns.

Write Your Own Wedding: A Personal Guide for Couples of All Faiths. rev. ed. Mordecai Brill et al. LC 85-7156. 120p. 1985. pap. 5.95 (ISBN 0-8329-0398-1). New Century.

Writers & Their Background: Matthew Arnold. Ed. by Kenneth Allott. LC 75-15339. (Writers & Their Background Ser.). xxvi, 353p. 1976. 20.00x (ISBN 0-8214-0197-1); pap. 10.00x (ISBN 0-8214-0198-X). Ohio U Pr.

Writing for Religious & Other Specialty Markets. Dennis E. Hensley & Rose A. Adkins. (Orig.). 1987. pap. 8.95 (ISBN 0-8054-7911-2). Broadman.

Writing for the Religious Market. Marvin Ceynar. 1986. 2.25 (ISBN 0-89536-804-8, 6822). CSS of Ohio.

Writing for Theological Education by Extension. Lois McKinney. 64p. (Prog. Bk.). 1975. 1.95x (ISBN 0-87808-905-5). William Carey Lib.

Writing on Christianity & History. Herbert Butterfield. 1979. 19.95x (ISBN 0-19-502454-0). Oxford U Pr.

Writing Religiously. Don M. Aycock & Leonard G. Goss. 1986. 13.95 (ISBN 0-8010-0210-9). Baker Bk.

Writing Verse As a Hobby. Una G. Reeves. 1962. 6.95 (ISBN 0-8158-0172-6). Chris Mass.

Writing Your Own Worship Materials. G. Temp Sparkman. 1980. pap. 2.95 (ISBN 0-8170-0857-8). Judson.

Writings Ascribed to Richard Rolle Hermit of Hampole & Materials for His Biography. Hope E. Allen. 568p. 1981. Repr. of 1927 ed. lib. bdg. 125.00 (ISBN 0-89987-023-6). Darby Bks.

Writings Ascribed to Richard Rolle, Hermit of Hampole & Materials for His Biography. Hope E. Allen. (MLA. MS Ser.). 1927. 44.00 (ISBN 0-527-01280-7). Kraus Repr.

Writings from the Philokalia. E. Kadloubowsky. Tr. by G. E. Palmer. (Illus.). 420p. 1951. 18.95 (ISBN 0-571-07062-0). Faber & Faber.

Writings from the "Western Standard". George Q. Cannon. Repr. of 1864 ed. 25.00 (ISBN 0-404-01379-1). AMS Pr.

Writings in the Dust. Carl E. Price. 112p. (Orig.). 1984. pap. 4.75 (ISBN 0-8358-0474-7). Upper Room.

Writings-Kethubim: A New Translation of the Holy Scriptures According to the Traditional Hebrew Text. 624p. blue cloth 10.95 (ISBN 0-8276-0202-2); black leatherette, boxed, gold edges 19.95 (ISBN 0-8276-0203-0). Jewish Pubns.

Writings of Bradford. John Bradford. 1979. Set. 34.95 (ISBN 0-85151-359-X). Vol. 1 (ISBN 0-85151-283-6). Vol. 2 (ISBN 0-85151-284-4). Banner of Truth.

Writings of Catherine Booth, 6 Vols. Catherine Booth. 1986. Repr. of 1880 ed. Set. deluxe ed. 19.95 (ISBN 0-86544-038-7). Salvation Army.

Writings of Catherine Booth. Catherine Booth. 1101p. 1986. 19.95 (ISBN 0-86544-031-X). Salv Army Suppl South.

Writings of John Bradford...Martyr, 1555, 2 Vols. John Bradford. Repr. of 1853 ed. Set. 92.00 (ISBN 0-384-05440-4). Johnson Repr.

Writings of Jonathan Edwards: Theme, Motif, & Style. William J. Scheick. LC 75-18689. 192p. 1975. 14.50x (ISBN 0-89096-004-6). Tex A&M Univ Pr.

Writings of Junipero Serra, 4 vols. Ed. by Antonine Tibesar. (Documentary Ser.). (Illus.). 1966. 60.00 (ISBN 0-88382-003-X). AAFH.

Writings of Martin Buber. Martin Buber. Ed. by Will Herberg. (Orig.). pap. 8.95 (ISBN 0-452-00616-3, F616, Mer). NAL.

Writings of Pilgrim Marpeck. Ed. by William Klassen & Walter Klaassen. LC 77-87419. (Classics of the Radical Reformation Ser.: No. 2). (Illus.). 608p. 1978. 24.95x (ISBN 0-8361-1205-9). Herald Pr.

Writings of President Frederick M. Smith, Vol. 1. Ed. by Norman D. Ruoff. LC 78-6428. 1978. pap. 10.00 (ISBN 0-8309-0215-5). Herald Hse.

Writings of President Frederick M. Smith, Vol. 2. Ed. by Norman D. Ruoff. LC 78-6428. 1979. pap. 10.00 (ISBN 0-8309-0239-2). Herald Hse.

Writings of President Frederick M. Smith, Vol. III: The Zionic Enterprise. Ed. by Norman D. Ruoff. 1981. pap. 10.00 (ISBN 0-8309-0300-3). Herald Hse.

Writings of Robert Grosseteste, Bishop of Lincoln: 1235-1253. S. H. Thomson. Repr. of 1940 ed. 29.00 (ISBN 0-527-89820-1). Kraus Repr.

Writings of Saint Francis of Assisi. Saint Frances D'Assisi. Tr. by Paschal Robinson. 1977. lib. bdg. 59.95 (ISBN 0-8490-2822-1). Gordon Pr.

Writings of St. Patrick, with the Metrical Life of St. Patrick. Saint Patrick & Saint Fiacc. pap. 2.95 (ISBN 0-686-25558-5). Eastern Orthodox.

Writings of St. Paul. St. Paul. Ed. by Wayne Meeks. (Critical Edition Ser). 1972. 12.95 (ISBN 0-393-04338-X); pap. 9.95x (ISBN 0-393-09979-2). Norton.

Writings of the Ante-Nicene Fathers, 10 vols. Ante-Nicene Fathers. Ed. by A. Roberts & J. Donaldson. 1951. Set. 179.50 (ISBN 0-8028-8097-5); 17.95 ea. Eerdmans.

Writings of the New Testament: An Interpretation. Luke T. Johnson. LC 85-16202. 640p. 1986. 34.95 (ISBN 0-8006-0886-0, 1-886); pap. 18.95 (ISBN 0-8006-1886-6, 1-1886). Fortress.

Writings of the Nicene & Post-Nicene Fathers, 28 vols. Nicene & Post-Nicene Fathers. Incl. First Series, 14 Vols. 251.30 set (ISBN 0-8028-8114-9); St. Augustine only, 8 Vols. 143.60 set (ISBN 0-8028-8106-8); St. Chrysostom only, 6 Vols. 107.70 set (ISBN 0-8028-8113-0); Second Series, 14 Vols. 251.30 set (ISBN 0-8028-8129-7). 1952-56. Repr. 17.95 ea. Eerdmans.

Writings of Thomas Hooker: Spiritual Adventure in Two Worlds. Sargent Bush, Jr. LC 79-5404. 400p. 1980. 29.50x (ISBN 0-299-08070-6). U of Wis Pr.

Writings on Spiritual Direction by Great Christian Masters. Ed. by Jerome N. Neufelder & Mary C. Coelho. 224p. (Orig.). 1982. pap. 11.95 (ISBN 0-8164-2420-9, HarpR). Har-Row.

Written History As an Act of Faith. Charles A. Beard. 1960. pap. 3.00 (ISBN 0-87404-084-1). Tex Western.

Wrong Kind of Dragon. Annis Shepard. LC 83-6023. (Illus.). 48p. (Orig.). 1983. pap. 4.50 (ISBN 0-687-46569-9). Abingdon.

Wrong Road. Vivian D. Gunderson. 1964. pap. 1.75 (ISBN 0-915374-15-3, 15-3). Rapids Christian.

Wrongly Dividing the Word of Truth. H. A. Ironside. pap. 1.25 (ISBN 0-87213-392-3). Loizeaux.

Wyclif. Anthony Kenny. (Past Masters Ser.). 1985. 13.95x (ISBN 0-19-287647-3); pap. 4.95 (ISBN 0-19-287646-5). Oxford U Pr.

Wycliffe & Movements for Reform. Reginald L. Poole. LC 77-84729. Repr. of 1889 ed. 28.00 (ISBN 0-404-16129-4). AMS Pr.

Wycliffe & the Lollards. J. C. Carrick. 1977. lib. bdg. 59.95 (ISBN 0-8490-2824-8). Gordon Pr.

Wycliffe Bible, 2 vols. Sven L. Fristedt. LC 78-63195. (Heresies of the Early Christian & Medieval Era: Second Ser.). Repr. of 1953 ed. 45.00 set (ISBN 0-404-16370-X). AMS Pr.

Wycliffe Bible Commentary. Everett Harrison & Charles F. Pfeiffer. (Affordables Ser.). 1525p. 16.95 (ISBN 0-8024-0420-0). Moody.

Wycliffe Bible Commentary. Ed. by Everett Harrison & Charles F. Pfeiffer. 29.95 (ISBN 0-8024-9695-4). Moody.

Wycliffe Bible Encyclopedia, 2 vols. Ed. by Charles F. Pfeiffer et al. (Illus.). 1875p. 1975. 54.95 (ISBN 0-8024-9697-0). Moody.

Wycliffe Biographical Dictionary of the Church. Elgin Moyer. 1982. 19.95 (ISBN 0-8024-9693-8). Moody.

Wycliffe Handbook of Preaching & Preachers. Warren Wiersbe & Lloyd M. Perry. 1984. 18.95 (ISBN 0-8024-0328-X). Moody.

Wycliffe Historical Geography of Bible Lands. Charles F. Pfeiffer & Howard F. Vos. 1967. 25.95 (ISBN 0-8024-9699-7). Moody.

Wycliffe, Select English Writings. John D. Wycliffe. Ed. by Herbert E. Winn. LC 75-41303. Repr. of 1929 ed. 18.50 (ISBN 0-404-14635-X). AMS Pr.

Wycliffite Sermons, Vol. 1. John Wycliffe. Ed. by Anne Hudson. (Oxford English Texts). (Illus.). 1983. 105.00x (ISBN 0-19-812704-9). Oxford U Pr.

Wyclyf Tradition. Vaclav Mudroch. Ed. by A. Compton Reeves. LC 77-92253. xvii, 91p. 1979. 15.00x (ISBN 0-8214-0403-2). Ohio U Pr.

Wyeth's Repository of Sacred Music, 1 & 2 pts. John Wyeth. LC 64-18989. (Music Reprint Ser.). 148p. 1964. Repr. of 1820 ed. Pt. 1. 25.00 (ISBN 0-306-70903-1); Pt. 2. 25.00 (ISBN 0-686-85854-9). Da Capo.

X

X-Rated Bible. Ben E. Akerley. pap. 8.00. Am Atheist.

X-Rated Bible: An Irreverent Survey of Sex in the Scriptures. Ben E. Akerley. (Illus.). 428p. (Orig.). 1985. pap. 8.00 (ISBN 0-910309-19-1). Am Atheist.

Xultun Tarot: A Maya Tarot Deck. 2nd ed. Peter Balin. (Illus.). 78p. 1982. pap. 12.95 (ISBN 0-910261-00-8). Arcana Pub.

Y

Y Ahora, Que Hago, Senor? Chris Jones. Tr. by Susana Cabeza from Eng. Tr. of What Do I Do Now, Lord? (Span.). 107p. 1978. pap. 2.75 (ISBN 0-89922-123-8). Edit Caribe.

Y Basics: Yesterday, Today, & Tomorrow in the YMCA. YMCA of the U. S. A. Staff. LC 84-23443. 93p. 1984. pap. text ed. 5.00x (ISBN 0-931250-77-3). Human Kinetics.

Y Despues de la Muerte, Que? Edgar Contreras. Orig. Title: After Death, What. (Span.). 1988. pap. 4.95 (ISBN 0-8254-1130-0). Kregel.

Yachas Harav V'hatalmid. (Hebrew.). 0.50 (ISBN 0-914131-75-3, E05). Torah Umesorah.

Yagna (The Eternal Energy) Panduranga Malyala. (Illus.). 36p. (Orig.). 1984. pap. text ed. 4.00x (ISBN 0-938924-23-0). Sri Shirdi Sai.

Yagua Mythology: Epic Tendencies in a New World Mythology. Paul S. Powlison. Ed. by William R. Merrifield. LC 84-63152. (International Museum of Cultures Publications: No. 16). (Illus.). 132p. (Orig.). 1985. pap. 14.00 (ISBN 0-88312-172-7); microfiche (2) 4.00 (ISBN 0-88312-254-5). Summer Inst Ling.

Yahweh & Son: A Teenager's Guide to the Bible. Anthony J. Marinelli. 160p. (Orig.). 1986. pap. 7.95 (ISBN 0-8091-9568-2). Paulist Pr.

Yahweh & the Gods of Canaan: An Historical Analysis of Two Contrasting Faiths. William F. Albright. 1978. Repr. of 1968 ed. 12.00x (ISBN 0-931464-01-3). Eisenbrauns.

Yahweh Is a Warrior. Millard C. Lind. LC 80-16038. (Christian Peace Shelf Ser.). 240p. 1980. pap. 11.95x (ISBN 0-8361-1233-4). Herald Pr.

Yahweh: The Divine Name in the Bible. G. H. Parke-Taylor. 134p. 1975. text ed. 14.95x (ISBN 0-88920-014-9, Pub. by Wilfrid Laurier Canada). Humanities.

Yajurveda (Summary) Date not set. 5.00 (ISBN 0-938924-30-3). Sri Shirdi Sai.

Yako s Nami Bog. S. Lavroff. Tr. of For God is with Us. 73p. 1980. pap. 3.00 (ISBN 0-317-29142-4). Holy Trinity.

Yale Lectures on Preaching. Henry W. Beecher. 1976. Repr. of 1872 ed. 39.00x (ISBN 0-403-06546-1, Regency). Scholarly.

Yale Lectures on Preaching. Henry W. Beecher. (Works of Henry Ward Beecher Ser.). vii, 359p. Repr. of 1873 ed. lib. bdg. 29.00 (ISBN 0-932051-02-2, Pub. by Am Repr Serv). Am Biog Serv.

Yamamoto Returns: A True Story of Reincarnation. Dennis Dallison. (Illus.). 200p. 1985. pap. 5.95 (ISBN 0-932642-98-5). Unarius Pubns.

Yamin Nora'im-Laws of the Synagogue. write for info. United Syn Bk.

Yankee Saint: John Humphrey Noyes & the Oneida Community. Robert A. Parker. LC 75-187456. (American Utopian Adventure Ser.). 322p. 1973. Repr. of 1935 ed. lib. bdg. 27.50x (ISBN 0-87991-009-7). Porcupine Pr.

Yankee Saint: John Humphrey Noyes & the Oneida Community. Robert A. Parker. LC 73-2570. (Illus.). 332p. 1973. Repr. of 1935 ed. 29.50 (ISBN 0-208-01319-9, Archon). Shoe String.

Yaqui Easter. Muriel T. Painter. LC 74-153706. 40p. 1971. pap. 3.95 (ISBN 0-8165-0168-8). U of Ariz Pr.

Yasmin Meets a Yak. Olive Groom. 1973. pap. 1.95 (ISBN 0-87508-806-6). Chr Lit.

Yatindramatadipika. Srinivasadasa. Tr. by Swami Adidevananda. (Sanskrit & Eng.). 2.75 (ISBN 0-87481-428-6). Vedanta Pr.

Yavanajataka of Sphujidhvaja, 2 vols. Tr. by David Pingree. (Harvard Oriental Ser: No. 48). 1978. Set. 80.00x (ISBN 0-674-96373-3). Harvard U Pr.

Ye Are Gods. Annalee Skarin. 343p. 1973. pap. 5.95 (ISBN 0-87516-344-0). De Vorss.

Ye Are My Friends. Marvin J. Ashton. 151p. 1982. 7.95 (ISBN 0-87747-934-8). Deseret Bk.

Ye Gods! Anne S. Baumgartner. 192p. 1984. 14.95 (ISBN 0-8184-0349-7). Lyle Stuart.

Ye Olden Blue Laws. Gustavus Myers. 274p. 1980. Repr. of 1921 ed. lib. bdg. 25.00 (ISBN 0-8495-3795-9). Arden Lib.

Ye Search the Scriptures. Watchman Nee. Tr. by Stephen Kaung. 1974. 4.75 (ISBN 0-935008-46-2); pap. 3.75 (ISBN 0-935008-47-0). Christian Fellow Pubs.

Ye Shall Receive Power: The Amazing Miracle of Holy Spirit Baptism. Peter Popoff. Ed. by Don Tanner. LC 82-71629. (Illus.). 96p. 1982. pap. 2.00 (ISBN 0-938544-14-4). Faith Messenger.

Ye Solace of Pilgrimes. John Capgrave. Ed. by C. A. Mills. LC 78-63453. (Crusades & Military Orders: Second Ser.). Repr. of 1911 ed. 25.00 (ISBN 0-404-16375-0). AMS Pr.

Year of Children's Sermons. Leon W. Castle. LC 76-6717. (Illus.). 144p. 1976. pap. 4.95 (ISBN 0-8054-4918-3). Broadman.

Year of Crisis, Year of Hope: Russian Jewry & the Pogroms of 1881-1882. Stephen M. Berk. LC 84-25216. (Contributions in Ethnic Studies Ser.: No. 11). xvi, 231p. 1985. lib. bdg. 39.95 (ISBN 0-313-24609-2, BPG/). Greenwood.

Year of Grace. Victor Gollancz. 1950. 15.95 (ISBN 0-575-00982-9, Pub. by Gollancz England). David & Charles.

Year of Grace of the Lord. Ed. by Deborah Cowen. 254p. (Orig.). 1980. pap. 8.95 (ISBN 0-913836-68-0). St Vladimirs.

Year of Luke. Ed. by Hugh McGinlay. 96p. (Orig.). 1982. pap. 8.95 (Pub. by JBCE). ANZ Religious Pubns.

Year of Mark. Ed. by Hugh McGinlay. 86p. (Orig.). 1984. text ed. 8.95 (ISBN 0-85819-477-5, Pub. by JBCE). ANZ Religious Pubns.

Year of Matthew. Ed. by Hugh McGinlay. 94p. (Orig.). 1983. pap. 8.95 (ISBN 0-85819-454-6, Pub. by JBCE). ANZ Religious Pubns.

Year of Programs for Today's Women. Irene Brand. 96p. (Orig.). 1984. pap. 3.95 (ISBN 0-87239-744-0, 2975). Standard Pub.

Year of the Catholic Worker. Marc Ellis. LC 78-61722. 144p. 1978. pap. 3.50 (ISBN 0-8091-2140-9). Paulist Pr.

Year of the Locust. David Nixon. 138p. (Orig.). 1980. pap. 3.95 (ISBN 0-8341-0675-2). Beacon Hill.

Year of the Lord: A. D. 1844. Charles W. Meister. LC 82-23976. 264p. 1983. lib. bdg. 18.95x (ISBN 0-89950-037-4). McFarland & Co.

Year of the Lord: Reflections on the Sunday Readings. Alfred McBride. 240p. cycle A 6.95 (ISBN 0-697-01847-4); cycle B 6.95 (ISBN 0-697-01848-2); cycle C 6.95 (ISBN 0-697-01849-0). Wm C Brown.

Year of the Lord's Favor: Preaching the Three-Year Lectionary. Sherman E. Johnson. 300p. 1983. pap. 13.95 (ISBN 0-8164-2359-8, HarpR). Har-Row.

Year of the Oath. George R. Stewart. LC 77-150422. (Civil Liberties in American History Ser). 1971. Repr. of 1950 ed. lib. bdg. 22.50 (ISBN 0-306-70103-0). Da Capo.

Year Participated. Rudolf Steiner. Tr. by Owen Barfield from Ger. Tr. of Anthroposophischer Seelenkalender. 52p. 1986. pap. 7.95 (ISBN 0-85440-790-1, Pub. by Steinerbooks). Anthroposophic.

Year 'Round Sermon Outlines. C. W. Keiningham. (Pulpit Library). 96p. 1987. pap. price not set (ISBN 0-8010-5483-4). Baker Bk.

Year Two Thousand. Ed. by John R. Stott. LC 83-12871. 179p. 1983. pap. 7.95 (ISBN 0-87784-845-9). Inter-Varsity.

Year with Mary. John Paul, II. Tr. by Anthony M. Buono from Italian. 320p. (Orig.). 1986. pap. 6.00 (ISBN 0-89942-370-1, 370/22). Catholic Bk Pub.

Year with the Baha'is of India & Burma. Sidney Sprague. (Historical Reprint Ser.). (Illus.). 1986. 8.95 (ISBN 0-933770-57-X). Kalimat.

Yearbook of American & Canadian Church 1986. Ed. by Constant H. Jacquet, Jr. 304p. (Orig.). 1986. pap. 17.95 (ISBN 0-687-46641-5). Abingdon.

Yearbook of American & Canadian Churches, 1987. Ed. by H. Constant Jacquet. 304p. 1987. pap. 18.95 (ISBN 0-687-46642-3). Abingdon.

Yearly Planning Guide for the Church Usher. Thomas L. Clark. 1986. pap. 3.95 (ISBN 0-8054-9407-3). Broadman.

Yearning of a Soul. Flavian Bonifazi. 1979. 4.95 (ISBN 0-8198-0614-5); pap. 3.50 (ISBN 0-8198-0615-3). Dghtrs St Paul.

Years after Fifty. Wingate M. Johnson. 14.00 (ISBN 0-405-18502-2). Ayer Co Pubs.

Years of Darkness, Days of Glory. Larry Richards. LC 76-6582. (Bible Alive Ser). (Illus.). 1977. pap. text ed. 2.95 (ISBN 0-912692-97-9); tchr's. ed. o.p. 3.95 (ISBN 0-912692-96-0). Cook.

Years of No Decision. Muhammad El Farra. 350p. 1987. 37.50 (ISBN 0-7103-0215-0, Kegan Paul). Methuen Inc.

Years of Wrath, Days of Glory. 2nd ed. Yitshaq Ben-Ami. LC 83-60834. (Illus.). 620p. 1983. Repr. of 1982 ed. 17.50 (ISBN 0-88400-096-6). Shengold.

Yeast, Salt & Secret Agents. Kenneth L. Gibble. 1979. pap. 4.95 (ISBN 0-87178-968-X). Brethren.

Yebamoth, 3 vols. 45.00 (ISBN 0-910218-64-1). Bennet Pub.

Yechezkel-Ezekiel, 3 vols. Moshe Eisemann. (Art Scroll Tanach Ser.). (Illus.). 832p. 1980. Set. 55.95 (ISBN 0-89906-085-4); Set. pap. 45.95 (ISBN 0-89906-086-2). Mesorah Pubns.

Yechezkel-Ezekiel, Vol. 1. Moshe Eisermann. (Art Scroll Tanach Ser.). 352p. 1977. 17.95 (ISBN 0-89906-075-7); pap. 14.95 (ISBN 0-89906-076-5). Mesorah Pubns.

Yechezkel-Ezekiel, Vol. 2. Moshe Eisemann. (Art Scroll Tanach Ser.). 272p. 1980. 17.95 (ISBN 0-89906-077-3); pap. 14.95 (ISBN 0-89906-078-1). Mesorah Pubns.

Yechezkel-Ezekiel, Vol. 3. Moshe Eisemann. (Art Scroll Tanach Ser.). (Illus.). 208p. 1980. 17.95 (ISBN 0-89906-083-8); pap. 14.95 (ISBN 0-89906-084-6). Mesorah Pubns.

Yehudis Prepares for Shabbos. 1982. pap. 0.99 (ISBN 0-686-76280-0). Feldheim.

Yemenite Jewry: Origins, Culture, & Literature. Reuben Ahroni. LC 84-48649. (Jewish Literature and Culture Ser.). (Illus.). 288p. 1986. 27.50x (ISBN 0-253-36807-3). Ind U Pr.

Yemenite Jews: A Photographic Essay. Zion M. Ozeri. (Illus.). 96p. 1985. 19.95 (ISBN 0-8052-3980-4). Schocken.

Yenan: Colonel Peterkin's Dixie Mission to China. William Head. 1986. write for info. (ISBN 0-89712-175-9). Documentary Pubns.

Yenching University & Sino-Western Relations, 1916-1952. Philip West. (East Asian Ser.: No. 85). 1976. 18.50x (ISBN 0-674-96569-8). Harvard U Pr.

Yes. Kim Kulp. 144p. (Orig.). 1987. pap. 5.95 (ISBN 0-937947-03-2). Publius Pub.

Yes Book. Jose D. Vinck. 1976. pap. 3.75 (ISBN 0-685-77499-6). Franciscan Herald.

Yes Book: An Answer to Life (a Manual of Christian Existentialism) Jose D. Vinck. LC 77-190621. 200p. 1972. 12.75 (ISBN 0-911726-12-8); pap. 8.75 (ISBN 0-911726-11-X). Alleluia Pr.

Yes, God Can. Jerry Hayner. LC 84-4153. 1985. 6.95 (ISBN 0-8054-2258-7). Broadman.

Yes, God...I Am a Creative Woman. Anne Ortlund et al. LC 83-80610. 225p. (Orig.). 1983. pap. 4.50 (ISBN 0-935797-02-5). Harvest IL.

Yes, I Am. Norman P. Grubb. 1982. pap. text ed. 4.95 (ISBN 0-87508-206-8). Chr Lit.

Yes Is Forever. Daughters of St. Paul. (Encounter Ser.). (Illus.). 109p. 1982. 3.00 (ISBN 0-8198-8700-5, EN0260); pap. 2.00 (ISBN 0-8198-8702-1). Dghtrs St Paul.

Yes!, Jesus Loves Me. Ed. by Judy Sparks. (Happy Day Bks.). (Illus.). 24p. 1985. 1.59 (ISBN 0-87239-882-X, 3682). Standard Pub.

Yes, Lord. rev. ed. Harald Bredesen. LC 72-91776. 199p. 1982. pap. 4.95 (ISBN 0-910311-00-5). Huntington Hse Inc.

Yes or No? Straight Answers to Tough Questions about Christianity. Peter Kreeft. 168p. (Orig.). 1984. 5.95 (ISBN 0-89283-217-7). Servant.

Yes to Life. Tr. by Daughters of St. Paul. 1977. 6.95 (ISBN 0-8198-0485-1); pap. 5.95 (ISBN 0-8198-0486-X). Dghtrs St Paul.

Yes to Mission. Douglas Webster. LC 66-72166. 1966. text ed. 6.00x (ISBN 0-8401-2703-0). A R Allenson.

Yes, Virginia, There Is Right & Wrong. Kathleen M. Gow. 255p. 1985. 12.95 (ISBN 0-8423-8558-4); pap. 6.95 (ISBN 0-8423-8561-4). Tyndale.

Yes, We Sang! Songs of the Ghettos & Concentration Camps. Shoshana Kalisch & Barbara Meister. LC 84-48172. (Illus.). 160p. 1985. 22.45 (ISBN 0-06-015448-9, HarpT). Har-Row.

Yeshiva Children Write Poetry: From the Heart We Sing. Ed. by Manfred Gans. 6.95 (ISBN 0-914131-76-1, D43). Torah Umesorah.

Yeshiva in America. William B. Helmreich. 384p. 1981. text ed. 19.95 (ISBN 0-02-914640-2, 914640). Free Pr.

Yesterday: A Study of Hebrews in the Light of Chapter 13. Floyd V. Filson. LC 67-7015. (Studies in Biblical Theology: 2nd Ser., No. 4). 1967. pap. text ed. 10.00x (ISBN 0-8401-3054-6). A R Allenson.

Yesterday & Today: Continuites in Christology. Colin Gunton. 240p. (Orig.). 1983. pap. 7.95 (ISBN 0-8028-1974-5). Eerdmans.

Yesterday's Radicals: A Study of the Affinity Between Unitarianism & Broad Church Anglicanism in the Nineteenth Century. Dennis G. Wigmore-Beddoes. 182p. 1971. 19.95 (ISBN 0-227-67751-X). Attic Pr.

Yesterday's Word Today. John F. Craghan. LC 82-12648. 496p. 1982. pap. 14.95 (ISBN 0-8146-1273-3). Liturgical Pr.

Yet Not I. David Campbell. 88p. (Orig.). 1978. pap. 1.95 (ISBN 0-912315-39-3). Word Aflame.

Yet Will I Serve Him. Hoyt E. Stone. 1976. pap. 3.95 (ISBN 0-87148-931-7). Pathway Pr.

Yet Will I Trust Him. Rob Burkhart. LC 79-91705. (Study & Grow Electives). 64p. 1985. pap. 3.95 (ISBN 0-8307-1016-7, 6102002). Regal.

Yet Will I Trust Him. Peg Rankin. LC 79-91705. 160p. 1980. 5.95 (ISBN 0-8307-0741-7, 5412005). Regal.

YHWH: Tetragrammaton. Henry Little. LC 84-90091. 177p. 1985. 12.95 (ISBN 0-533-06173-3). Vantage.

Yhwh's Combat with the Sea: A Canaanite Tradition in the Religion of Ancient Israel. Carola Kloos. 243p. 1986. pap. 35.75 (ISBN 90-04-08096-1, Pub. by E J Brill). Heinman.

Yiddish-English-Hebrew Dictionary. Ed. by Alexander Harkavy. LC 86-31414. 624p. 1987. Repr. 29.95 (ISBN 0-8052-4027-6). Schocken.

Yiddish in America: Socio-Linguistic Description & Analysis. Joshua A. Fishman. LC 65-63395. (General Publications Ser: Vol. 36). (Orig.). 1965. pap. text ed. 9.95x (ISBN 0-87750-110-6). Res Ctr Lang Semiotic.

Yiddish Literature, 10 Vols, No. IV. Ed. by R. Gordon 1986. lib. bdg. 975.00 (ISBN 0-8490-3859-6). Gordon Pr.

Yiddish Literature, 10 Vols, No. III. Ed. by R. Gordon. 1986. lib. bdg. 950.95 (ISBN 0-8490-3858-8). Gordon Pr.

Yiddish Literature, 10 Vols, No. II. Ed. by R. Gordon. 1986. lib. bdg. 975.00 (ISBN 0-8490-3857-X). Gordon Pr.

Yiddish Literature, 10 Vols, Series I. Ed. by R. Grodon. 1986. lib. bdg. 975.95 (ISBN 0-8490-3856-1). Gordon Pr.

Yiddish Proverbs. Ed. by Hanan J. Ayalti. LC 49-11135. (Illus., Bilingual). 1963. pap. 4.75 (ISBN 0-8052-0050-9). Schocken.

Yiddish Proverbs: A Collection. Malachi McCormick. (Proverbs of the World Ser.). (Illus.). 60p. (Orig.). 1982. pap. text ed. 12.50 (ISBN 0-943984-02-5). Stone St Pr.

Yidish Launiversitah: Hebrew Edition of "College Yiddish". Uriel Weinreich. Tr. by S. Bahat & M. Goldwasser. (Illus.). 1977. pap. text ed. write for info. (ISBN 0-914512-35-8). Yivo Inst.

Yielding to the Power of God: The Importance of Surrender, Abandonment, & Obedience to God's Will. Ann Shields. 48p. (Orig.). 1987. pap. 1.95 (ISBN 0-89283-348-3). Servant.

Yin & Yang: Two Hands Clapping. John W. Garvy, Jr. Ed. by Jeremiah Liebermann. (Five Phase Energetics Ser.: No. 2). (Illus.). 1985. pap. 3.00 (ISBN 0-943450-01-2). Wellbeing Bks.

Yin Chih Wen: The Tract of the Quiet Way. Ed. by Paul Carus. Tr. by Teitaro Suzuki & Paul Carus. 52p. 1950. pap. 0.95 (ISBN 0-87548-245-7). Open Court.

Yitzchak, Son of Abraham. Zev Paamoni. (Biblical Ser.). (Illus.). 1970. 4.00 (ISBN 0-914080-25-3). Shulsinger Sales.

Yivo Biblyografye 1942-1950: Bibliography of the Publications of the Yiddish Scientific Institute, Vol. 2. LC 47-36672. (Yivo Institute for Jewish Research, Organizatsye Fun der Yidisher Visnshaft: No. 38). (Yiddish.). 158p. 1955. 5.00 (ISBN 0-914512-30-7). Yivo Inst.

Yo? Obedecer a Mi Marido? Elisabeth R. Handford. Orig. Title: Me? Obey Him? Tr. of Me? Obey Him. (Span.). 128p. 1984. pap. 3.25 (ISBN 0-8254-1302-8). Kregel.

Yoga. J. F. C. Fuller. 180p. 1975. 7.00 (ISBN 0-911662-55-3). Yoga.

Yoga: A Bibliography. Mark Weiman. 135p. 1979. lib. bdg. 22.50 (ISBN 0-8482-7051-7). Norwood Edns.

Yoga & Depth Psychology. I. P. Sachdeva. 269p. 1978. 16.95x (ISBN 0-317-12334-3, Pub. by Motilal Banarsi). Asia Bk Corp.

Yoga & Health. Selvarajan Yesudian & Elisabeth Haich. (Unwin Paperbacks). (Illus.). 1978. pap. 5.95 (ISBN 0-04-149033-9). Allen Unwin.

Yoga & Indian Philosophy. Karel Werner. 1977. 11.00 (ISBN 0-8426-0900-8, Pub. by Motilal Banarsidass India). Orient Bk Dist.

Yoga & Indian Philosophy. Karel Werner. 1979. 12.50x (ISBN 0-8364-0479-3). South Asia Bks.

Yoga & Its Objects. Sri Aurobindo. 33p. 1984. pap. 0.75 (ISBN 0-89071-314-6, Pub. by Sri Aurobindo Ashram India). Matagiri.

Yoga & Mysticism: An Introduction to Vedanta. Swami Prabhavananda. 53p. 1984. pap. 3.95 (ISBN 0-87481-020-5). Vedanta Pr.

Yoga & Prayer. Michaelle. Tr. by Diane Cumming. pap. 6.50 (ISBN 0-87061-059-7). Chr Classics.

Yoga & Psychotherapy: The Evolution of Consciousness. Swami Rama et al. 332p. 13.95 (ISBN 0-89389-000-6); pap. 9.95 (ISBN 0-89389-036-7). Himalayan Pubs.

Yoga & Spiritual Life. rev. ed. Sri Chinmoy. LC 74-81309. 160p. 1974. pap. 4.95 (ISBN 0-88497-040-X). Aum Pubns.

Yoga & the Bhagavad-Gita. Tom McArthur. 128p. 1986. pap. 11.95 (ISBN 0-85030-479-2). Newcastle Pub.

Yoga & the Bhagavad-Gita. Tom McArthur. 1986. Repr. lib. bdg. 19.95x (ISBN 0-8095-7037-8). Borgo Pr.

Yoga & the Hindu Tradition. Jean Varenne. Tr. by Derek Coltman from Fr. LC 75-19506. 1976. pap. 5.45X (ISBN 0-226-85116-8, P744, Phoen). U of Chicago Pr.

Yoga & the Jesus Prayer Tradition: An Experiment in Faith. Thomas Matus. 200p. (Orig.). 1984. pap. 8.95 (ISBN 0-8091-2638-9). Paulist Pr.

Yoga & Yogic Powers. Yogi Gupta. LC 63-14948. (Illus.). 1963. 20.00 (ISBN 0-911664-02-5). Yogi Gupta.

Yoga Aphorisms. W. Q. Judge. 59.95 (ISBN 0-8490-1343-7). Gordon Pr.

Yoga Aphorisms of Patanjali. Tr. & pref. by William Q. Judge. xxi, 74p. 1930. Repr. of 1889 ed. 3.00 (ISBN 0-938998-11-0). Theosophy.

Yoga As Philosophy & Religion. S. Dasgupta. lib. bdg. 79.95 (ISBN 0-87968-104-7). Krishna Pr.

Yoga As Philosophy & Religion. S. Dasgupta. 1978. Repr. 13.95 (ISBN 0-8426-0488-X). Orient Bk Dist.

Yoga Can Change Your Life. Swami Jyotir Maya Nanda. (Illus.). 1975. pap. 4.99 (ISBN 0-934664-14-5). Yoga Res Foun.

Yoga During Pregnancy. Vibeke Berg. 1983. 6.95 (ISBN 0-686-44925-8, Fireside). S&S.

Yoga Essays for Self-Improvement. Jyotir Swami & Maya Nanda. LC 81-65248. 248p. 1981. pap. 4.99 (ISBN 0-934664-39-0, 030). Yoga Res Foun.

Yoga, Facts & Fancies. K. Raghavan. 1983. 7.50x (ISBN 0-8364-0950-7, Pub. by Mukhopadhyay India). South Asia Bks.

Yoga for All Ages. Cheryl Isaacson. (Illus., Orig.). 1986. pap. 10.95 (ISBN 0-7225-1210-4). Thorsons Pubs.

Yoga for Americans. Indra Devi. 1971. pap. 2.25 (ISBN 0-451-09869-2, E9869, Sig). NAL.

Yoga for Beginners. Swami Gnaneswarananda. Ed. by Mallika C. Gupta. LC 74-29557. 200p. 1975. pap. 4.95 (ISBN 0-9600826-1-1). Vivekananda.

Yoga for Handicapped People. Barbara Brosnan. (Human Horizon Ser.). (Illus.). 208p. 1982. pap. 15.95 (ISBN 0-285-64952-3, Pub. by Souvenir Pr England). Brookline Bks.

Yoga for Health. Richard Hittleman. LC 82-90825. 256p. (Orig.). 1983. pap. 7.95 (ISBN 0-345-30852-2). Ballantine.

Yoga for Musicians & Other Special People. Eleanor Winding. (Illus.). 68p. (Orig.). 1982. pap. 7.95 (ISBN 0-88284-193-9). Alfred Pub.

Yoga for Physical & Mental Fitness. Sachindra K. Majumdar. LC 68-31613. (Illus.). 1968. 7.95 (ISBN 0-87396-013-0); pap. 3.95 (ISBN 0-87396-014-9). Stravon.

Yoga for Rejuvenation. Nergis Dalal. 128p. (Orig.). 1984. pap. 6.95 (ISBN 0-7225-0948-0). Thorsons Pubs.

Yoga for the Disabled: A Practical Self-Help Guide to a Happier Healthier Life. Howard Kent. (Illus.). 160p. 1985. pap. 7.95 (ISBN 0-7225-0902-2). Thorsons Pubs.

Yoga for the Eighties. (Illus.). 36p. 6.95 (ISBN 0-89509-055-4). Arcline Pubns.

Yoga for the Eighties: Kundalini Yoga. Harbhajan S. Khalsa. LC 85-11680. 1985. Repr. lib. bdg. 19.95x (ISBN 0-89370-879-8). Borgo Pr.

Yoga for the Fun of It! Hatha Yoga for Preschool Children. 2nd ed. Suzanne L. Schreiber. (Illus.). 54p. (Orig.). 1981. pap. 6.00 (ISBN 0-9608320-0-9). Sugar Marbel Pr.

Yoga for the Modern Man. M. P. Pandit. 115p. 1979. 4.00 (ISBN 0-941524-13-2). Lotus Light.

Yoga for the West: A Manual for Designing Your Own Practice. Ian Rawlinson. Ed. by Alastair McNeilage. (Illus.). 200p. (Orig.). 1987. lib. bdg. 12.95 (ISBN 0-916360-26-1). CRCS Pubns NV.

Yoga Guide. Swami Jyotir Maya Nanda. (Illus.). 1972. pap. 2.99 (ISBN 0-934664-16-1). Yoga Res Foun.

Yoga Illustrated Dictionary. Harvey Day. (Illus.). 1970. 10.95 (ISBN 0-87523-177-2). Emerson.

Yoga: Immortality & Freedom. 2nd ed. Mircea Eliade. Tr. by Willard R. Trask. LC 58-8986. (Bollingen Ser.: Vol. 56). 1970. 45.00x (ISBN 0-691-09848-4); pap. 11.50x (ISBN 0-691-01764-6). Princeton U Pr.

Yoga in Daily Life. K. S. Joshi. 163p. 1971. pap. 2.00 (ISBN 0-88253-044-5). Ind-US Inc.

Yoga in Life. Swami Lalitananda. (Illus.). 1972. pap. 2.99 - (ISBN 0-934664-17-X). Yoga Res Foun.

Yoga in Practice. Swami Jyotir Maya Nanda. (Illus.). 1974. pap. 0.99 (ISBN 0-934664-18-8). Yoga Res Foun.

Yoga in Pregnancy. Vibeke Berg. 135p. 1977. 11.95 (ISBN 0-940500-24-8, Pub. by D B Taraporwala India). Asia Bk Corp.

Yoga in Sri Aurobindo's Epic Savitri. Sri M. Pandit. 236p. 1979. 7.95 (ISBN 0-941524-15-9). Lotus Light.

Yoga Integral. Swami Jyotir Maya Nanda. (Span., Illus.). 112p. 1984. pap. 2.85 (ISBN 0-934664-51-X). Yoga Res Foun.

Yoga Lessons for Developing Spiritual Consciousness. A. P. Mukerji. 7.00 (ISBN 0-911662-24-3). Yoga.

Yoga: Meaning, Values & Practice. Phulgenda Sinha. 1973. pap. 2.50 (ISBN 0-88253-259-6). Ind-US Inc.

Yoga Moves with Alan Finger. Alan Finger & Lynda Guber. (Illus.). 160p. (Orig.). 1984. pap. 9.95 (ISBN 0-671-50064-3, Wallaby). S&S.

Yoga Mystic Songs for Meditation, 6 Vols. Swami Lalitananda. 1975. pap. 2.99 ea. (ISBN 0-934664-19-6). Yoga Res Foun.

Yoga Mystic Stories & Parables. Swami Jyotir Maya Nanda. (Illus.). 1974. pap. 3.99 (ISBN 0-934664-24-2). Yoga Res Foun.

Yoga of Consideration & the Way That I Teach. Da Free John. (Orig.). 1982. pap. 3.95 (ISBN 0-913922-63-3). Dawn Horse Pr.

Yoga of Divine Love: A Commentary on Narada Bhakti Sutras. Swami Jyotir Maya Nanda. 1982. pap. 4.99 (ISBN 0-934664-42-0). Yoga Res Foun.

Yoga of Divine Works. 2nd ed. Sri Aurobindo. (Life Companion Library). (Illus.). 270p. Date not set. pap. 8.95 (ISBN 0-89744-015-3). Auromere.

Yoga of Knowledge. M. P. Pandit. LC 79-88735. (Talks at Centre Ser.: Vol. II). 1979. pap. 5.95 (ISBN 0-89744-003-X). Auromere.

Yoga of Knowledge: Talks at Centre, Vol. II. M. P. Pandit. LC 86-80692. 282p. (Orig.). 1986. pap. 7.95 (ISBN 0-941524-23-X). Lotus Light.

Yoga of Light: The Classic Esoteric Handbook of Kundalini Yoga. Rieker Hans-Ulrich. Tr. by Elsy Becherer. LC 79-167868. (Illus.). 1974. pap. 7.95 (ISBN 0-913922-07-2). Dawn Horse Pr.

Yoga of Love. Madhav P. Pandit. LC 81-86373. (Talks at Center Ser.: Vol. III). 112p. (Orig.). 1982. pap. 3.95 (ISBN 0-941524-16-7). Lotus Light.

Yoga of Nutrition. Omraam M. Aivanhov. (Izvor Collection Ser.: Vol. 204). 130p. pap. 4.95 (ISBN 0-911857-03-6). Prosveta USA.

Yoga of Perfect Sight. 3rd ed. R. S. Agarwal. 1979. pap. 14.00 (ISBN 0-89744-948-7). Auromere.

Yoga of Perfect Sight: With Letters of Sri Aurobindo. R. S. Agarwal. (Illus.). 1974. pap. 5.45 (ISBN 0-89071-261-1). Matagiri.

Yoga of Perfection (Srimad Bhagavad Gita) Swami Jyotir Maya Nanda. (Illus.). 1973. pap. 3.99 (ISBN 0-934664-25-0). Yoga Res Foun.

Yoga of Self-Perfection. Madhav P. Pandit. LC 83-81299. (Talks at Centre Ser.: Vol. IV). 312p. (Orig.). 1983. pap. 7.95 (ISBN 0-941524-20-5). Lotus Light.

Yoga of Sex-Sublimation, Truth & Non-Violence. Swami Jyotir Maya Nanda. (Illus.). 1974. pap. 3.99 (ISBN 0-934664-26-9). Yoga Res Foun.

Yoga of the Bhagavat Gita. Prem Krishna Sri. 1982. Repr. 15.00x (ISBN 0-318-20320-0, Pub. by New Order Bk Co India). Humanities.

Yoga of the Guhyasamajatantra. Alex Wayman. 1977. 28.00 (ISBN 0-89684-003-4, Pub. by Motilal Banarsidass India). Orient Bk Dist.

Yoga of the Guhyasamjatantra. Alex Wayman. 386p. 1980. pap. 7.95 (ISBN 0-87728-451-2). Weiser.

Yoga of the Inward Path. Ronald P. Beesley. 1978. pap. 4.95 (ISBN 0-87516-269-X). De Vorss.

Yoga of the Kathopanishad. Sri Krishna Prem. 1983. Repr. 15.00x (ISBN 0-318-20321-9, Pub. by New Order Bk Co India). Humanities.

Yoga of Works: Talks at Centre I. M. P. Pandit. LC 85-50695. 192p. 1985. pap. 7.95 (ISBN 0-941524-21-3). Lotus Light.

Yoga of Yama. W. Cornold. 64p. 1970. pap. 4.95 (ISBN 0-88697-041-5). Life Science.

Yoga Philosophy of Patanjali: Containing His Yoga Aphorisms with Vyasa's Commentary in Sanskrit & a Translation with Annotations Containing Many Suggestions for the Practice of Yoga. S. Hariharananda Aranya. Tr. by P. N. Mukerji from Sanskrit. 510p. 1983. 39.50x (ISBN 0-87395-728-8); pap. 10.95x (ISBN 0-87395-729-6). State U NY Pr.

Yoga Postures for Higher Awareness. 2nd, enl. ed. Swami Kriyananda. (Illus.). 140p. 1971. pap. 8.95 (ISBN 0-916124-25-8). Dawn Pubns CA.

Yoga Psychology. Swami Abhedananda. 10.95 (ISBN 0-87481-614-9). Vedanta Pr.

Yoga Psychology: A Practical Guide to Meditation. rev. ed. Swami Ajaya. LC 76-374539. 115p. 1976. pap. 5.95 (ISBN 0-89389-052-9). Himalayan Pubs.

Yoga Quotations from the Wisdom of Swami Jyotir Maya Nanda. Ed. by Swami Lalitananda. (Illus.). 1974. pap. 3.99 (ISBN 0-934664-27-7). Yoga Res Foun.

Yoga, Science of the Self. rev. ed. Marcia Moore & Mark Douglas. LC 67-19602. (Illus.). 1979. 10.00 (ISBN 0-912240-01-6). Arcane Pubns.

Yoga Secrets of Psychic Powers. Swami Jyotir Maya Nanda. (Illus.). 1974. pap. 4.99 (ISBN 0-934664-28-5). Yoga Res Foun.

Yoga Self-Taught. Andre Van Lysebeth. Tr. by Carola Congreve from Fr. Orig. Title: J'Apprends le Yoga. (Illus.). 264p. 1973. pap. 5.95 (ISBN 0-06-463360-8, EH 360, B&N Bks). Har-Row.

Yoga Stories & Parables. Swami Jyotir Manda. (Illus.). 1976. pap. 3.99 (ISBN 0-934664-41-2). Yoga Res Foun.

Yoga Sutra of Patanjali on Concentration of Mind. Fernanda Tola & D. Carmen. 1986. 21.00 (ISBN 81-208-0258-6, Pub. by Motilal Banarsidass). South Asia Bks.

Yoga-Sutras of Patanjali. Ballantyne & Shastri. Ed. by S. B. Tailang. Repr. of 1983 ed. 8.50 (ISBN 0-89684-474-9). Orient Bk Dist.

Yoga Sutras of Patanjali. 7th ed. Patanjali. Tr. by Charles Johnston from Sanskrit. 1984. pap. 6.00 (ISBN 0-914732-08-0). Bro Life Inc.

Yoga-Sutras of Patanjali with the Exposition of Vyasa: A Translation & Commentary Volume I. Pandit U. Arya. xxi, 493p. 1986. pap. 16.95 (ISBN 0-89389-092-8). Himalayan Pubs.

Yoga System. rev. ed. Mithrapuram K. Alexander. LC 77-140373. (Illus.). 1971. 8.95 (ISBN 0-8158-0257-9); pap. 6.95 (ISBN 0-686-66311-X). Chris Mass.

Yoga System of Health. Yogi Vithaldas. 1981. pap. 3.95 (ISBN 0-686-82888-7). Cornerstone.

Yoga System of Health & Relief from Tension. Vithaldes. 1961. pap. 4.95 (ISBN 0-346-12500-6). Cornerstone.

Yoga-System of Patanjali. James H. Woods. 1977. Repr. 19.50 (ISBN 0-89684-272-X, Pub. by Motilal Banarsidass India). Orient Bk Dist.

Yoga-Systems of Patanjali: The Doctrine of the Concentration of the Mind. James Woods. lib. bdg. 90.00 (ISBN 0-87968-083-0). Krishna Pr.

Yoga: The Alpha & the Omega, 10 vols, Vols. 1-5. Bhagwan Shree Rajneesh. Ed. by Ma Ananda Prem & Ma Yoga Sudha. LC 76-902396. (Yoga Ser.). (Illus., Orig.). 1976. Vol I, 272 pgs. 16.95 ea. (ISBN 0-88050-177-4). Vol II, 266 pgs. 1976 (ISBN 0-88050-178-2). Vol. III, 298 pgs. 1976 (ISBN 0-88050-179-0). Vol. IV, 280 pgs. 1976 (ISBN 0-88050-180-4). Vol. V, 266 pgs. 1976 (ISBN 0-88050-181-2). Chidvilas Found.

Yoga: The Alpha & the Omega, 10 vols, Vols. 6-10. Bhagwan Shree Rajneesh. Ed. by Swami Prem Chinmaya & Ma Yoga Sudha. LC 76-902396. (Yoga Ser.). (Illus., Orig.). 1977. Vol. VI, 270 pgs. 16.95 ea. (ISBN 0-88050-182-0). Vol. VII250p 1977 (ISBN 0-88050-183-9). Vol. VIII, 298 pgs. 1977 (ISBN 0-88050-184-7). Vol. IX, 346 pgs. 1978 (ISBN 0-88050-185-5). Vol. X, 270 pgs. 1978 (ISBN 0-88050-186-3). Chidvilas Found.

Yoga: The Art of Integration. Mehta. 15.95 (ISBN 0-8356-7513-0). Theos Pub Hse.

Yoga... The Art of Living: The Hunza-Yoga Way to Better Living. Renee Taylor. LC 78-75329. (Illus.). 224p. 1975. pap. 4.50 (ISBN 0-87983-112-X). Keats.

Yoga: The Hatha Yoga & Raja Yoga of India. Annie Besant. 73p. 1974. pap. 7.95 (ISBN 0-88697-035-0). Life Science.

Yoga: The Science of the Soul, Vol. 1. 2nd ed. Bhagwan Shree Rajneesh. Ed. by Swami Krishna Mahasattva. LC 84-42812. (Yoga Ser.). 304p. 1984. pap. 4.95 (ISBN 0-88050-677-6). Chidvilas Found.

Yoga: The Spirit of Union. Lar Caughlan. 96p. 1981. pap. text ed. 13.00 (ISBN 0-8403-2487-1). Kendall-Hunt.

Yoga: The Technique of Liberation. Virenda Shekhawat. 90p. 1979. text ed. 7.50 (ISBN 0-89684-264-9, Pub. by Sterling India). Orient Bk Dist.

Yoga Unveiled, Part 1. 1977. 16.50 (ISBN 0-8426-1031-6, Pub. by Motilal Banarsidass India). Orient Bk Dist.

Yoga Vasistha, Vol. III. Swami Jyotirmayananda. 304p. (Orig.). 1986. pap. 4.99 (ISBN 0-934664-33-1). Yoga Res Foun.

Yoga Vasistha Ramayana. rev. ed. D. N. Bose. 1984. Repr. of 1954 ed. 12.50x (ISBN 0-8364-1181-1, Pub. by Mukhopadhyaya India). South Asia Bks.

Yoga Way Cookbook: Natural Vegetarian Recipes. rev. ed. Himalayan International Institute. LC 80-81994. (Illus.). 249p. 1980. spiral bdg. 9.95 (ISBN 0-89389-067-7). Himalayan Pubs.

Yoga Wisdom of the Upanishads: Kena..Mundaka..Prashna..Ishavasya. Jyotir M. Nanda. (Illus.). 1974. pap. 4.99 (ISBN 0-934664-36-6). Yoga Res Foun.

Yoga: Yogic Suksma Vyayama. Dhirenda Brahmachari. (Illus.). 232p. 1975. 8.95 (ISBN 0-88253-802-0). Ind-US Inc.

Yoga, You, Your New Life. K. Japananda. (Illus.). 208p. pap. 5.95 spiral bdg. (ISBN 0-9613099-0-3). Temple Kriya Yoga.

Yoga, Youth & Reincarnation. Jess Stearn. (Illus.). 352p. 1986. pap. 3.95 (ISBN 0-553-26057-X). Bantam.

Yogananda Returns. Robert R. Leichtman. (From Heaven to Earth Ser.). 104p. (Orig.). 1981. pap. 3.50 (ISBN 0-89804-066-3). Ariel OH.

Yogasutra of Patanjali: With Commentary of Vyasa. Bangali Baba. 115p. 1982. 12.95 (ISBN 81-208-0154-7, Pub. by Motilal Banarsidass India); pap. 9.95 (ISBN 81-208-0155-5, Pub. by Motilal Banarsidass India). Orient Bk Dist.

Yogi, the Commissar & the Third World Church. Paul D. Clasper. 92p. (Orig.). 1982. pap. 5.00 (ISBN 0-686-37580-7, Pub. by New Day Philippines). Cellar.

Yogic Pranayama: Breathing for Long, Long Life. K. S. Joshi. 180p. 1983. pap. 9.00 (ISBN 0-86578-222-9). Ind-US Inc.

Yoke of the Thorah, by Sidney Luska. Henry Harland. Repr. of 1887 ed. 23.00 (ISBN 0-384-21370-7). Johnson Repr.

Yom Kippur. Norma Simon. (Festival Series of Picture Story Books). (Illus.). 1959. plastic cover 4.50 (ISBN 0-8381-0702-8). United Syn Bk.

Yom Kippur Anthology. Ed. by Philip Goodman. LC 72-151312. (Illus.). 399p. 1971. 9.95 (ISBN 0-8276-0026-7, 245). Jewish Pubns.

Yoma: Or, Yom Kippur, 2 vols. 30.00 (ISBN 0-910218-57-9). Bennet Pub.

Yon Mountain: A Doctor of Faith Walks with God. Alta W. Eitel. LC 85-90286. 101p. 1986. 10.95 (ISBN 0-533-06783-9). Vantage.

Yonah-Jonah. Meir Zlotowitz. (Art Scroll Tanach Ser.). 160p. 1978. 11.95 (ISBN 0-89906-081-1); pap. 8.95 (ISBN 0-89906-082-X). Mesorah Pubns.

Yoni. Howard Bogot. 1982. pap. 4.00 (ISBN 0-686-82564-0). UAHC.

Yonitantra. Ed. by J. A. Schoterman. 1985. 11.00x (ISBN 0-8364-1326-1, Pub. by Manohar India). South Asia Bks.

Yontefdike Teg. Compiled by Chane Mlotek & Malke Gottlieb. (Songbook for the Holidays Ser.). (Illus.). 105p. pap. 6.00 (ISBN 0-318-20363-4). Workmen's Circle.

York Minister. John Hutchinson & David O'Connor. (New Bell's Cathedral Guides Ser.). 1986. cancelled 24.95 (ISBN 0-918678-14-5). Historical Times.

York Plays: The Plays Performed on the Day of Corpus Christi in the 14th, 15th, & 16th Centuries. Ed. by Lucy T. Smith. LC 63-15180. (Illus.). 1963. Repr. of 1885 ed. 21.00x (ISBN 0-8462-0313-8). Russell.

Yorkshire Cistercian Heritage: Introduction. James Hogg. (Orig.). 1985. pap. 16.00 (ISBN 3-7052-0260-X, Pub. by Salzburg Studies). Longwood Pub Group.

Yorkshire Cistercian Heritage, Vol. 2: Rievaulx, Jervaulx, Byland. James Hogg. (Orig.). 1978. pap. 16.00 (ISBN 3-7052-0261-8, Pub. by Salzburg Studies). Longwood Pub Group.

Yorkshire Cistercian Heritage, Vol. 3: Fountains, Kirstall, Meaux. James Hogg. (Orig.). 1978. pap. 16.00 (ISBN 3-7052-0262-6, Pub. by Salzburg Studies). Longwood Pub Group.

Yorkshire Writers, Richard Rolle of Hampole, 2 vols. C. Horstman. 1979. Repr. of 1895 ed. Set. lib. bdg. 400.00 (ISBN 0-8492-5264-4). R West.

Yoruba of Southwestern Nigeria. William Bascom. (Illus.). 118p. 1984. pap. text ed. 7.95x (ISBN 0-88133-038-8). Waveland Pr.

Yossef Mokir Shabbos: Hebrew-English. 1982. pap. 4.95 (ISBN 0-87306-189-6). Feldheim.

Yossef Mokir Shabbos: Hebrew-French. 1982. pap. 4.95 (ISBN 0-686-76282-7). Feldheim.

Yossef Mokir Shabbos: Hebrew-Yiddish. 1982. pap. 4.95 (ISBN 0-686-76283-5). Feldheim.

Yossel Zissel & the Wisdom of Chelm. Amy Schwartz. (Illus.). 32p. 9.95 (ISBN 0-8276-0258-8). Jewish Pubns.

You. Frances Wilshire. pap. 3.00 (ISBN 0-87516-319-X). De Vorss.

You Ain't Seen Nothing Yet. Bhagwan Shree Rajneesh. Ed. by Ma Prem Maneesha. LC 84-42614. (Initiation Talks Ser.). 304p. (Orig.). 1984. pap. 4.95 (ISBN 0-88050-687-3). Chidvilas Found.

You & Me. Tessa Colina. Ed. by Jane Buerger. (Illus.). 112p. 1980. 5.95 (ISBN 0-89565-179-3, 4936). Standard Pub.

You & Public Opinion: I Corinthians. Spiros Zodhiates. (Illus.). 1977. pap. 2.95 (ISBN 0-89957-522-6). AMG Pubs.

You & the Alcoholic in Your Home. Duane Mehl. LC 78-66947. 1979. pap. 6.95 (ISBN 0-8066-1697-0, 10-7408). Augsburg.

You & The Bibles: Tough Questions & Straight Answers. Patrick Kaler. 64p. (Orig.). 1985. pap. 1.95 (ISBN 0-89243-240-3). Liguori Pubns.

You & Your Bible-You & Your Life. Clarence Y. Fretz. (Christian Day School Ser). pap. 4.10x (ISBN 0-87813-902-8); teachrs guide 13.75x (ISBN 0-87813-903-6). Christian Light.

You & Your Child. 2nd ed. Charles R. Swindoll. 1982. pap. 4.95 (ISBN 0-8407-5616-X). Nelson.

You & Your Church. 3rd ed. Free Church. 1978. pap. 1.95. Free Church Pubns.

You & Your Conscience. Gerald R. Nash. (Outreach Ser.). 1981. pap. 1.25 (ISBN 0-8163-0428-9). Pacific Pr Pub Assn.

You & Your Parents: Strategies for Building an Adult Relationship. Harold I. Smith. 176p. (Orig.). 1987. pap. 8.95 (ISBN 0-8066-2267-9, 10-7407). Augsburg.

You & Your Teen. Charles Bradshaw. (Family Ministry Ser.). (Illus.). 54p. 1985. pap. text ed. 19.95 (ISBN 0-89191-950-3). Cook.

You Are a Rainbow. Ed. by Norah Hills. LC 79-13393. (Illus.). 128p. (Orig.). 1979. pap. 4.95 (ISBN 0-916438-25-2). Univ of Trees.

You Are a Special Person. Bob Bird. 16p. (Orig.). 1974. pap. 1.50 (ISBN 0-934804-06-0). Inspiration MI.

You Are an Acolyte: A Manual for Acolytes. (Illus.). 1977. pap. 2.95 (ISBN 0-8066-1552-4, 10-7409). Augsburg.

You Are Gifted. R. B. Thomas. (International Correspondence Program Ser.). (Orig.). 1985. pap. text ed. 6.95 (ISBN 0-87148-935-X). Pathway Pr.

You Are God. Mary. 1955. pap. 4.95 (ISBN 0-87516-057-3). De Vorss.

You Are Greater Than You Know. Lou Austin. 7.50 (ISBN 0-934538-16-6); pap. 4.50 (ISBN 0-934538-11-5). Partnership Foundation.

You Are Loved. (Four Very Special Gift Bks.). 48p. 1985. 2.25 (ISBN 0-8407-6680-7). Nelson.

You Are Loved & Forgiven. rev. ed. Lloyd John Ogilvie. LC 86-10186. 192p. 1986. text ed. 12.95 (ISBN 0-8307-1168-6, 5111616); pap. text ed. 4.95 (ISBN 0-8307-1110-4, S412117). Regal.

You Are My Beloved Sermon Book. Frederick Kemper & George M. Bass. 1980. pap. 6.95 (ISBN 0-570-03821-9, 12-2761). Concordia.

You Are My Favorites. Pope John Paul II. 1980. 6.95 (ISBN 0-8198-8701-3). Dghtrs St Paul.

You Are My God: A Pioneer of Renewal Recounts His Pilgrimage in Faith. David Watson. 196p. 1984. pap. 5.95 (ISBN 0-87788-972-4). Shaw Pubs.

You Are Never Alone. Charles L. Allen. 160p. 1984. pap. 5.95 (ISBN 0-8007-5145-0, Power Bks). Revell.

You Are Not Alone. (Four Very Special Gift Bks.). 48p. 1985. 2.25 (ISBN 0-8407-6679-3). Nelson.

You Are Special. Alma Kern. (Illus.). 144p. (Orig.). 1985. pap. 5.00 (ISBN 0-9614955-0-2, 2050). Lutheran Womens.

You Are Special to Jesus. Annetta Dellinger. 1984. pap. 4.95 (ISBN 0-570-04089-2, 56-1457). Concordia.

You Are the Future You Are My Hope. Pope John Paul II. 1979. pap. 3.95 (ISBN 0-8198-0633-1). Dghtrs St Paul.

You Are the World. Jiddu Krishnamurti. 160p. 1973. pap. 4.95 (ISBN 0-06-080303-7, P303, PL). Har-Row.

You Are Very Special: A Biblical Guide to Self-Worth. Verna Birkey. 160p. 1977. pap. 5.95 (ISBN 0-8007-5032-2, Power Bks). Revell.

You Are Welcome. 2nd rev. ed. Keith H. Parks. 32p. 1981. pap. 2.49 (ISBN 0-88151-013-0). Lay Leadership.

You Are What You Breathe: The Negative Ion Story. Robert Massy. 32p. 1980. 1.50 (ISBN 0-916438-41-4, Dist. by New Era Pr). Univ of Trees.

You Are What You Choose. Maralene Wesner & E. Miles. LC 84-3110. (Orig.). 1984. pap. 4.95 (ISBN 0-8054-5247-8). Broadman.

You Are What You Swallow. Elaine Rossignol. LC 86-83406. 220p. (Orig.). 1987. pap. 9.95 (ISBN 0-89896-240-4). Larksdale.

You Are What You Think: Basic Issues in Pastoral Counseling. Robert C. Brien. 182p. (Orig.). 1986. pap. 5.95 (ISBN 0-87227-102-1). Reg Baptist.

You Be the Judge. Don Stewart. 96p. (Orig.). 1983. 2.95 (ISBN 0-89840-055-4). Heres Life.

You Believe. James Bales. pap. 2.95 (ISBN 0-89315-425-3). Lambert Bk.

You Belong. Allen H. Marheine. LC 79-21954. (Orig.). 1980. pap. 2.95 (ISBN 0-8298-0380-7). Pilgrim NY.

You Better Believe It. Kenneth J. Roberts. LC 77-84944. (Illus.). 1977. pap. 5.95 (ISBN 0-87973-750-6). Our Sunday Visitor.

You Bring the Confetti. Luci Swindoll. 160p. 1986. 9.95 (ISBN 0-8499-0527-3). Word Bks.

You Can Avoid Divorce. Paul D. Meier. (Christian Counseling Aids Ser.). 1978. pap. 1.50 (ISBN 0-8010-6052-4). Baker Bk.

You Can Be a Better Parent. Joseph F. Nielson. (Christian Counseling Aids Ser.). 1977. pap. 0.95 (ISBN 0-8010-6691-3). Baker Bk.

You Can Be a Great Parent. Charlie W. Shedd. LC 76-128353. 1982. pap. 2.25 (ISBN 0-8499-4166-0, 98070). Word Bks.

You Can Be a Soul Winner, Here's How! Nate Krupp. LC 78-64961. 176p. 1978. pap. 3.95 (ISBN 0-89221-050-8). New Leaf.

You Can Be a Soulwinner. Norvel Hayes. 150p. (Orig.). 1983. pap. 4.95 (ISBN 0-89274-269-0). Harrison Hse.

You Can Be Absolutely Irrefutably Supernaturally Healed by God Today. Walter E. Adams. 100p. (Orig.). 1987. pap. 4.95 (ISBN 0-937408-39-5). GMI Pubns Inc.

You Can Be an Effective Sunday School Superintendent. Kenneth Gangel. 64p. 1981. pap. 3.50 (ISBN 0-88207-141-6). Victor Bks.

You Can Be Creative. William Coleman. LC 83-80474. 160p. (Orig.). 1984. pap. 3.95 (ISBN 0-89081-387-6, 3876). Harvest Hse.

You Can Be Full of Joy. (Four Very Special Gift Bks.). 48p. 1985. 2.25 (ISBN 0-8407-6681-5). Nelson.

You Can Be the Wife of a Happy Husband. Darien B. Cooper. LC 74-77450. 156p. 1974. pap. 5.95 (ISBN 0-88207-711-2). Victor Bks.

You Can Become the Person You Want to Be. Robert H. Schuller. 160p. 1976. pap. 2.95 (ISBN 0-8007-8235-6, Spire Bks). Revell.

You Can Become Whole Again: A Guide to Healing for Christians in Grief. Jolonda Miller. LC 80-84652. 1981. pap. 6.50 (ISBN 0-8042-1156-6). John Knox.

You Can Bet the Ranch. Pat Wellman. 88p. (Orig.). 1986. pap. 4.50 (ISBN 0-8341-1155-1). Beacon Hill.

You Can Climb Higher: The Christian Persuit of Excellence. George W. Sweeting. 192p. 1985. 10.95 (ISBN 0-8407-5424-8). Nelson.

You Can Develop a Positive Self-Image. Louis O. Caldwell. (Christian Counseling Aids Ser.). pap. 1.25 (ISBN 0-8010-2503-6). Baker Bk.

You Can Find Help Through Counseling: Christain Counseling Aids. Louis O. Caldwell. 1983. pap. 0.95 (ISBN 0-8010-2484-6). Baker Bk.

You Can Give a Chalk Talk. W. R. Rogers. LC 80-65775. 1981. saddlewire 5.25 (ISBN 0-8054-6931-1). Broadman.

You Can Grow in a Small Group. Ronald J. Lavin. 144p. 1976. pap. 5.75 (ISBN 0-89536-273-2, 2500). CSS of Ohio.

You Can Have a Family Where Everybody Wins. Earl H. Gaulke. LC 75-23574. 104p. 1975. pap. 3.50 (ISBN 0-570-03723-9, 12-2625). Concordia.

You Can Have Joy. Lois S. Bigart. 1984. 5.00 (ISBN 0-8062-2414-2). Carlton.

You Can Have What You Say. Kenneth E. Hagin. 1978. mini bk. 0.50 (ISBN 0-89276-054-0). Hagin Ministries.

You Can Heal Your Life. Louise L. Hay. 224p. (Orig.). 1984. lib. bdg. 10.00 (ISBN 0-317-52419-4); pap. 10.00 (ISBN 0-937611-01-8). Hay House.

You Can Help the Alcoholic: A Christian Plan for Intervention. Jack Marsh. LC 82-74499. 88p. (Orig.). 1983. pap. 2.95 (ISBN 0-87793-270-0). Ave Maria.

You Can Help with Your Healing: A Guide for Recovering Wholeness in Body, Mind, & Spirit. Vernon J. Bittner. LC 78-66946. 1979. pap. 6.95 (ISBN 0-8066-1698-9, 10-7411). Augsburg.

You Can Live with a Heartache: Hope for Long-Term Heartaches. James E. De Vries. (Christian Counseling Aids Ser.). 1977. pap. 0.95 (ISBN 0-8010-2876-0). Baker Bk.

You Can Make Your Marriage Stronger. Anthony Florio. (Christian Counseling Aids Ser). 1978. pap. 1.25 (ISBN 0-8010-3484-1). Baker Bk.

You Can Overcome Your Fears, Phobias, & Worries. Louis O. Caldwell. 1985. pap. 1.25 (ISBN 0-8010-2506-0). Baker Bk.

You Can Prevent or Overcome a Nervous Breakdown. Louis O. Caldwell. (Christian Counseling Aids Ser.). 1978. pap. 1.25 (ISBN 0-8010-2415-3). Baker Bk.

You Can Reach Families Through Their Babies. Elizabeth Gangel & Elsiebeth McDaniel. 64p. 1976. pap. 3.50 (ISBN 0-88207-140-8). Victor Bks.

You Can Receive the Holy Ghost Today. Bob Buess. 1967. pap. 2.50 (ISBN 0-934244-14-6). Sweeter Than Honey.

You Can Say That Again: Cultivating New Life in Time-Worn Christian Sayings. Richard A. Lundy. LC 80-67556. 72p. 1980. pap. 2.95 (ISBN 0-89505-051-X). Argus Comm.

You Can Start a Bible Study Group: Making Friends, Changing Lives. rev. ed. Gladys Hunt. (Resource for Fisherman Bible Studyguides). 96p. 1984. Repr. of 1971 ed. lib. bdg. 2.95 (ISBN 0-87788-974-0). Shaw Pubs.

You Can Still Change the World. 3.50 (ISBN 0-318-02218-4). Chrstphrs NY.

You Can Stop Feeling Guilty. Louis O. Caldwell. (Christian Counseling Aids Ser.). 1978. pap. 1.25 (ISBN 0-8010-2414-5). Baker Bk.

You Can Teach Adults Successfully. Ron Davis et al. (Training Successful Teachers Ser.). 48p. (Orig.). 1984. pap. 2.95 (ISBN 0-87239-808-0, 3208). Standard Pub.

You Can Teach Children Successfully. Twila Sias. (Training Successful Teachers Ser.). 48p. (Orig.). 1984. pap. 2.95 (ISBN 0-87239-806-4, 3206). Standard Pub.

You Can Teach Preschoolers Successfully. Betty Aldridge. (Training Successful Teachers Ser.). 48p. (Orig.). 1984. pap. 2.95 (ISBN 0-87239-805-6, 3205). Standard Pub.

You Can Teach Two's & Three's. Mary E. Barbour. 64p. 1981. pap. 3.50 (ISBN 0-88207-149-1). Victor Bks.

You Can Too. Mary C. Crowley. 176p. 1980. pap. 5.95 (ISBN 0-8007-5028-4, Power Bks). Revell.

You Can Trust Your Bible. Neale Pryor. 3.95 (ISBN 0-89137-524-4). Quality Pubns.

You Can Understand the Bible. Fernon Retzer. 1984. pap. 1.95 (ISBN 0-317-28295-6). Pacific Pr Pub Assn.

You Can Win. Roger Campbell. 132p. 1985. pap. 4.95 (ISBN 0-89693-317-2). Victor Bks.

You Can Win with Love. Dale Galloway. LC 76-15129. 176p. 1980. pap. 2.95 (ISBN 0-89081-233-0). Harvest Hse.

You Can Witness with Confidence. Rosalind Rinker. pap. 2.95 (ISBN 0-310-32152-2). Zondervan.

You Can Witness with Confidence. Rosalind Rinker. 112p. 1984. pap. 5.95 (ISBN 0-310-32151-4, 10714P). Zondervan.

You Cannot Hold Back the Dawn. John C. Dowd. LC 74-75619. 1974. 4.95 (ISBN 0-8198-0320-0); pap. 3.95 (ISBN 0-8198-0321-9). Dghtrs St Paul.

You Can't Beat the Beatitudes. George O. Wood & William J. Krutza. LC 78-58721. 1978. pap. 1.25 (ISBN 0-88243-719-4, 02-0719, Radiant Bks). Gospel Pub.

You Can't Lose. James A. Aderman. Ed. by William E. Fischer. (Bible Class for Young Adults Ser.). (Illus.). 64p. (Orig.). 1987. pap. 2.95 (ISBN 0-938272-28-4). Wels Board.

You Can't Manage Alone. John S. Morgan & J. R. Philp. 256p. (Orig.). 1985. pap. 4.95 (ISBN 0-310-33602-3, 12766P). Zondervan.

You Can't Manage Alone: Practical Prayers for Conscientious Managers. John Morgan. 272p. 1986. gift ed. 12.95 (ISBN 0-310-33608-2). Zondervan.

You Can't Start a Car with a Cross. Ron Lavin. 1984. 5.95 (ISBN 0-89536-648-7, 2507). CSS of Ohio.

You Can't Steal First Base. Charles G. Hamilton. LC 74-164909. 1972. 6.95 (ISBN 0-8022-2057-6). Philos Lib.

You Count-You Really Do! William A. Miller. LC 76-27078. 1976. pap. 5.95 (ISBN 0-8066-1569-9, 10-7420). Augsburg.

You Don't Have to Go It Alone. Leslie B. Flynn. LC 80-66722. 160p. (Orig.). 1981. pap. 4.95 (ISBN 0-89636-058-X). Accent Bks.

You Don't Know My God. Peter A. Duro & Carol J. Duro. LC 85-81388. 238p. (Orig.). 1985. pap. 5.95 (ISBN 0-9615955-0-7). Emmanuel Christian.

You Gentiles. Maurice Samuels. pap. 3.00x (ISBN 0-911038-08-6). Noontide.

You Gotta Keep Dancin' Tim Hansel. LC 85-11298. 150p. 1985. pap. 6.95 (ISBN 0-89191-722-5, 57224). Cook.

You Know You're a Mother When... Melodie M. Davis. 112p. 1987. pap. 4.95 (ISBN 0-310-44811-5). Zondervan.

You Learn by Living. Eleanor Roosevelt. LC 83-6838. 224p. 1983. pap. 9.95 (ISBN 0-664-24494-7). Westminster.

You Live after Death. Harold Sherman. 176p. 1987. pap. 2.95 (GM). Fawcett.

You Me He. Sammy Tippit & Jerry Jenkins. LC 77-95030. 119p. 1978. pap. 3.95 (ISBN 0-88207-766-X). Victor Bks.

You Mean the Bible Teaches That. Charles C. Ryrie. 1974. pap. 5.95 (ISBN 0-8024-9828-0). Moody.

You: Prayer for Beginners & Those Who Have Forgotten How. Mark Link. LC 76-41584. 1976. pap. 2.95 (ISBN 0-913592-78-1). Argus Comm.

You Promised, Lord: Prayers for Boys. Ron Klug. LC 83-70502. (Young Readers Ser.). 80p. (Orig.). 1983. pap. 3.95 (ISBN 0-8066-2008-0, 10-7417). Augsburg.

You Promised Me God. Donald Deffner. LC 12-2792. (Illus.). 1981. pap. 4.95 (ISBN 0-570-03827-8). Concordia.

You Shall Be As Gods: A Radical Interpretation of the Old Testament & Its Tradition. Erich Fromm. 1977. pap. 2.50 (ISBN 0-449-30763-8, Prem). Fawcett.

You Shall Be My Witnesses: How to Reach Your City for Christ. Larry Rosenbaum. LC 86-90426. 144p. (Orig.). 1986. pap. 5.00 (ISBN 0-938573-00-4). SOS Minist Pr.

You Shall Have No Other Gods: Israelite Religion in the Light of Hebrew Inscriptions. Jeffrey H. Tigay. (Harvard Semitic Studies). 130p. 1987. 16.95 (ISBN 1-55540-063-9, 04-04-31). Scholars Pr GA.

You Shall Not Steal: Community & Property in the Biblical Tradition. Robert Gnuse. LC 85-4810. 176p. (Orig.). 1985. pap. 9.95 (ISBN 0-88344-799-1). Orbis Bks.

You Take Jesus, I'll Take God. Samuel Levine. LC 80-82731. 134p. (Orig.). 1980. pap. 4.95 (ISBN 0-9604754-1-9); pap. 4.95 (ISBN 0-9604754-1-9). Hamoroh Pr.

You Too Can Be Prosperous. Robert A. Russell. 162p. 1975. pap. 3.95 (ISBN 0-87516-205-3). De Vorss.

You, Too, Can Find Peace. Madge Haines. Ed. by Raymond H. Woolsey. (Banner Ser.). 128p. (Orig.). 1987. pap. 6.50 (ISBN 0-8280-0366-1). Review & Herald.

You Try It. Robert A. Russell. 1953. pap. 5.50 (ISBN 0-87516-326-2). De Vorss.

You Unlimited. Norman Lunde. LC 65-23608. 1985. pap. 5.95 (ISBN 0-87516-249-5). De Vorss.

You Want Me to Know What? 2nd ed. Terry Powell. (Foundation Ser.). (Illus.). 142p. (Orig.). 1986. pap. 2.95 (ISBN 0-935797-04-1). Harvest IL.

You Will Never Be the Same. Basilea Schlink. 192p. 1972. pap. 3.50 (ISBN 0-87123-661-3, 200661). Bethany Hse.

You Will Take It with You. Fay M. Clark. 135p. 1976. pap. 5.00 (ISBN 0-686-12934-2). Hiawatha Bondurant.

You Write the Ticket, Lord. Dorothy Galde. 144p. 1983. pap. 5.95 (ISBN 0-89840-047-3). Heres Life.

You, Your Child & Drugs. CSAA. 1971. pap. 1.75 (ISBN 0-87183-238-0). Jewish Bd Family.

You...& Being a Teenager. Feryl J. Bergin. (Illus.). 112p. 4.95 (ISBN 0-936955-00-7). Eminent Pubns.

You'll Be Old Someday, Too. Richard Worth. LC 85-29419. 128p. 1986. lib. bdg. 11.90 (ISBN 0-531-10158-4). Watts.

Young Adult Living Handbook. Ed. by Jean M. Hiesberger. LC 79-92005. (Paths of Life Ser.). 126p. 1980. 2.95 (ISBN 0-8091-2259-6). Paulist Pr.

Young Adult Ministry. Terry Hershey. LC 86-3103. 276p. (Orig.). 1986. pap. 12.95 (ISBN 0-931529-08-5). Group Bks.

Young Augustine: An Introduction to the Confessions of St. Augustine. John J. O'Meara. 224p. 1980. pap. text ed. 10.95x (ISBN 0-582-49110-X). Longman.

Young Calvin in Paris: Or, the Scholar & the Cripple. William W. Blackburn. LC 83-45602. Date not set. Repr. of 1868 ed. 30.00 (ISBN 0-404-19869-4). AMS Pr.

Young Child: Creative Living with Two to Four Year Olds. Daniel Udo de Haes. Tr. by Simon Blaxland de Lange & Paulamaria Blaxland de Lange. 90p. (Orig.). 1986. pap. 10.95 (ISBN 0-88010-169-5). Anthroposophic.

Young Children & the Eucharist. rev. ed. Urban T. Holmes, III. 128p. 1982. pap. 6.95 (ISBN 0-8164-2425-X, HarpR). Har-Row.

Young Christian's Life. Richard Grunze. 1979. 9.95 (ISBN 0-8100-0104-7, 06N0557). Northwest Pub.

Young Disciples. Joyce M. Smith. 50p. 1983. pap. 2.95 (ISBN 0-8423-8599-1). Tyndale.

Young Elder: From Ambrose of Milkova. Anthony Medvedev. 70p. 1974. pap. 3.00 (ISBN 0-317-30442-9). Holy Trinity.

Young Ideas. 3.50 (ISBN 0-318-02217-6). Chrstphrs NY.

Young Jesus in the Temple. Alyce Bergey. (Arch Bks.). (Illus.). 24p. 1986. pap. 0.99 saddlestitched (ISBN 0-570-06203-9, 59-1426). Concordia.

Young Krishna. Francis G. Hutchins. LC 80-66834. (Illus.). 132p. 1980. 29.50 (ISBN 0-935100-01-6); pap. 14.00 (ISBN 0-935100-05-9). Amarta Pr.

Young Luther. Robert H. Fife. LC 79-131040. 1970. Repr. of 1928 ed. 19.50 (ISBN 0-404-02385-1). AMS Pr.

Young Man in a Hurry (William Carey) Iris Clinton. 1961. pap. 2.95 (ISBN 0-87508-630-6). Chr Lit.

Young Man Luther. Erik H. Erikson. 1962. pap. 5.95 (ISBN 0-393-00170-9). Norton.

Young Man Shinran. Takamichi Takahatake. (SR Supplements Ser.: Vol. 18). 180p. 1987. pap. 15.00 (ISBN 0-88920-169-2, Pub. by Wilfrid Laurier Canada). Humanities.

Young Moses. Diana Craig. LC 84-50449. (Bible Stories Ser.). (Illus.). 24p. 1984. PLB 6.96 (ISBN 0-382-06797-5); 5.45 (ISBN 0-382-06946-3). Silver.

Young People Learning to Care: Making a Difference through Youth Participation. Mary C. Kohler. 160p. 1983. pap. 7.95 (ISBN 0-8164-2429-2, HarpR). Har-Row.

Young People's Medicine. Euteline Johnson. 32p. 1986. 5.95 (ISBN 0-89962-522-3). Todd & Honeywell.

Young Person's Book of Catholic Signs & Symbols. Francis Tiso & Catholic Heritage Press. LC 81-43459. 128p. 1982. pap. 3.50 (ISBN 0-385-17951-0, Im). Doubleday.

Young Person's History of Israel. David Bamberger. Ed. by Nicholas Mandelkern. (Illus.). 150p. (Orig.). 1985. pap. 6.95 (ISBN 0-87441-393-1). Behrman.

Young Reader's Book of Church History. Frederick A. Norwood & Jo Carr. LC 81-20505. (Illus.). 176p. 1982. 11.95 (ISBN 0-687-46827-2). Abingdon.

Young Reinhold Niebuhr: The Early Writings - 1911 to 1931. rev. ed. Ed. by William G. Chrystal. 256p. 1982. pap. 8.95 (ISBN 0-8298-0607-5). Pilgrim NY.

Young Richelieu: A Psychoanalytic Approach to Leadership. Elizabeth W. Marvick. LC 82-24754. (Orig.). 1983. 32.00x (ISBN 0-226-50904-4); pap. 14.00x (ISBN 0-226-50905-2). U of Chicago Pr.

Young Server's Book of the Mass. Kenneth Guentert. LC 86-60894. 1987. pap. 4.95 (ISBN 0-89390-078-8). Resource Pubns.

Young Witness: Evangelism to & by Children & Youth. Jane Hagstrom. LC 23-3036. 56p. (Orig.). 1986. pap. 4.95 (ISBN 0-8066-2233-4). Augsburg.

Younger Church in Search of Maturity: Presbyterianism in Brazil from 1910-1959. Paul E. Pierson. LC 73-89596. 306p. 1974. 8.00 (ISBN 0-911536-49-3). Trinity U Pr.

Younger Churchmen Look at the Church. facsimile ed. Ed. by Ralph H. Read. LC 74-156708. (Essay Index Reprint Ser). Repr. of 1935 ed. 21.50 (ISBN 0-8369-2330-8). Ayer Co Pubs.

Youngest Day: Nature & Grace on Shelter Island. Robert F. Capon. LC 82-48414. (Illus.). 160p. 1983. 11.49 (ISBN 0-06-061309-2, HarpR). Har-Row.

Youngest Prophet: The Life of Jacinta Marto, Fatima Visionary. Christopher Rengers. LC 85-30789. 144p. (Orig.). 1986. pap. 5.95 (ISBN 0-8189-0496-8). Alba.

Young's Analytical Concordance to the Bible. rev. ed. Robert Young. 1220p. 1986. 22.95 (ISBN 0-8407-4945-7). Nelson.

Young's Analytical Concordance to the Bible. Robert Young. 1216p. Date not set. 18.95 (ISBN 0-917006-29-1). Hendrickson MA.

Young's Bible Dictionary. G. Douglas Young. 608p. 1984. 9.95 (ISBN 0-8423-8598-3). Tyndale.

Young's Literal Translation of the Bible. Robert Young. pap. 24.95 (ISBN 0-8010-9921-8). Baker Bk.

Youniverse: Gestalt Therapy, Non-Western Religions & the Present Age. Jesse J. Thomas. LC 77-89164. (Illus.). 1978. 8.95 (ISBN 0-930626-00-1); pap. 4.95 (ISBN 0-930626-01-X). Psych & Consul Assocs.

Your Adversary the Devil. J. Dwight Pentecost. 192p. 1976. pap. 6.95 (ISBN 0-310-30911-5, 17010P). Zondervan.

Your Aladdin's Lamp. William H. Hornaday & Harlan Ware. 288p. 1979. pap. 8.50 (ISBN 0-911336-75-3). Sci of Mind.

Your Attitude: Key to Success. John Maxwell. 156p. 1985. pap. 5.95 (ISBN 0-89840-102-X). Heres Life.

Your Baby... Gift of God. Elizabeth A. Hambrick-Stowe. (Looking Up Ser.). (Orig.). 1985. pap. 1.25 (ISBN 0-8298-0549-4). Pilgrim NY.

Your Beginning with God. Ed. by Dwayne Norman. 31p. 1982. pap. 1.95 (ISBN 0-88144-063-9). Christian Pub.

Your Better Self: Christianity, Psychology, & Self-Esteem. Ed. by Craig W. Ellison. LC 82-47742. 224p. (Orig.). 1982. pap. 8.95 (ISBN 0-686-97230-9, RD/408, HarpR). Har-Row.

Your Bible: An Introduction to the Word. rev. ed. R. Laird Harris. 96p. 1976. pap. text ed. 4.95 (ISBN 0-910566-12-7); instr's. guide 5.95 (ISBN 0-910566-29-1). Evang Tchr.

Your Body, His Temple: Reaching a Balanced Christian View of Diet & Physical Fitness. Alfred L. Heller. LC 81-1897. 192p. 1981. pap. 4.95 (ISBN 0-8407-5769-7). Nelson.

Your Brain & the Mind of Christ. William G. Rorick. LC 84-50081. 140p. 1984. 4.95 (ISBN 0-938232-43-6). Winston-Derek.

Your Catholic Wedding: A Complete Plan-Book. Christopher Aridas. LC 81-43250. (Illus.). 192p. 1982. pap. 2.95 (ISBN 0-385-17731-3, Im). Doubleday.

Your Children Should Know: Teach Your Children the Strategies That Will Keep Them Safe from Assault & Crime. Flora Colao & Tamar Hosansky. LC 83-5981. (Illus.). 192p. 1983. 16.95 (ISBN 0-672-52777-4). Bobbs.

Your Child's Confirmation: Reflections for Parents on the Sacrament of Christian Identity. Carol Luebering. 1987. pap. 1.95. St Anthony Mess Pr.

Your Child's First Communion: A Look at Your Dreams. 32p. (Orig.). 1984. pap. 1.35 (ISBN 0-86716-035-7). St Anthony Mess Pr.

Your Child's Mind: Making the Most of Public Schools. Helen P. Barnette. LC 83-26109. (Potentials: Guides for Productive Living Ser.: Vol. 2). 112p. (Orig.). 1984. pap. 7.95 (ISBN 0-664-24519-6). Westminster.

Your Christian Wedding. Elizabeth Swadley. LC 66-15149. 1966. 8.95 (ISBN 0-8054-7902-3). Broadman.

Your Church & You. Michael Pennock. LC 83-70053. (Illus.). 288p. (Orig.). 1983. pap. 5.50 student text (ISBN 0-87793-268-9); tchr's. ed. 3.50 (ISBN 0-87793-269-7). Ave Maria.

Your Church Can Be Healthy. C. Peter Wagner. LC 79-974. (Creative Leadership Ser.). 1979. pap. 7.50 (ISBN 0-687-46870-1). Abingdon.

Your Church Can Grow. rev. ed. C. Peter Wagner. LC 84-8314. 1984. pap. 6.95 (ISBN 0-8307-0978-9, 5418284). Regal.

Your Church Has a Fantastic Future. Robert H. Schuller. LC 86-11906. 364p. (Orig.). 1986. pap. 7.95 (ISBN 0-8307-1126-0, 5418785). Regal.

Your Church Has a Fantastic Future! A Possibility Thinker's Guide to a Successful Church. rev. ed. Robert H. Schuller. LC 86-11906. (Illus.). 336p. 1986. pap. 14.95 (ISBN 0-8307-1180-5, 5111659). Regal.

Your Church Has Personality. Kent R. Hunter. Ed. by Lyle E. Schaller. (Creative Leadership Ser.). 129p. (Orig.). 1985. pap. 6.95 (ISBN 0-687-46875-2). Abingdon.

Your Church's Ministry of Prayer. Robert V. Dodd. 1981. 3.00 (ISBN 0-89536-476-X, 2501). CSS of Ohio.

Your Completeness in Christ. John MacArthur, Jr. (John MacArthur's Bible Studies). 1985. pap. 3.50 (ISBN 0-8024-5114-4). Moody.

Your Conscience As Your Guide. Peter Toon. LC 83-62870. 102p. (Orig.). 1984. pap. 5.95 (ISBN 0-8192-1339-X). Morehouse.

Your Creative Workshop. Rose Oster. 1977. pap. 0.75 (ISBN 0-87516-236-3). De Vorss.

Your Crocodile Is Ready. Wayne Haas. 1984. 6.25 (ISBN 0-89536-620-7, 4888). CSS of Ohio.

Your Daughters Shall Prophesy: Feminist Alternatives in Theological Education. Cornwall Collective Staff. LC 80-14891. 155p. 1980. pap. 6.95 (ISBN 0-8298-0404-8). Pilgrim NY.

Your Emotional Life & What You Can Do about It. James Drane. 204p. 1984. 9.95 (ISBN 0-88347-157-4). Thomas More.

Your Encounter with Life, Death & Immortality. Ruth E. Norman. (Illus.). 1978. pap. 2.00 (ISBN 0-932642-43-8). Unarius Pubns.

Your Faith: A Popular Presentation of Catholic Belief. LC 81-85557. (Redemptorist Pastoral Publication Ser.). 64p. 1982. pap. 2.95 (ISBN 0-89243-154-7). Liguori Pubns.

Your Faith Account. Dana Holmes. 48p. (Orig.). 1983. pap. 0.95 (ISBN 0-88144-019-1, CPS/019). Christian Pub.

Your Faith & You. rev. ed. Michael Pennock. LC 86-70575. (Ave Maria Press' High School Religion Text Programs Ser.). (Illus.). 320p. 1986. pap. text ed. 6.95 (ISBN 0-87793-334-0). Ave Maria.

Your Faith Can Heal You. Norvel Hayes. 80p. 1983. pap. 2.50 (ISBN 0-89274-273-9). Harrison Hse.

Your Faith Is Growing! N. R. Day. 51p. (Orig.). 1981. pap. 5.45 (ISBN 0-940754-10-X). Ed Ministries.

Your Faith Is Your Fortune. Neville. pap. 5.50 (ISBN 0-87516-078-6). De Vorss.

Your Faith: Leader's Guide. Louis J. Bamonte. 1978. tchr's ed 2.95 (ISBN 0-89243-085-0). Liguori Pubns.

Your Faith on Trial. Wallis C. Metts. 180p. (Orig.). 1979. pap. 3.95 (ISBN 0-89084-112-8). Bob Jones Univ Pr.

Your Family. rev. & expanded ed. John MacArthur, Jr. (Moody Press Electives Ser.). 1983. pap. 3.95 (ISBN 0-8024-0257-7). Moody.

Your Family & You. (Benziger Family Life Program Ser.). 1978. 2.00 (ISBN 0-02-651550-4); tchrs. ed. 4.00 (ISBN 0-02-651560-1); family handbook 1.00 (ISBN 0-02-651590-3). Benziger Pub Co.

Your Family: Leader's Guide. (Electives Ser.). 1983. pap. 2.50 (ISBN 0-8024-0307-7). Moody.

Your Family Worship Guidebook. Reuben Herring. LC 78-19976. 1978. 4.50 (ISBN 0-8054-5627-9). Broadman.

Your Father Loves You: Daily Insights for Knowing God. James I. Packer. Ed. & compiled by Jean Watson. 392p. 1986. pap. 9.95 (ISBN 0-87788-975-9). Shaw Pubs.

Your Fortune in Your Name; or Kabalistic Astrology. Sepharial. LC 81-21658. 200p. 1981. Repr. of 1981 ed. lib. bdg. 15.95x (ISBN 0-89370-656-6). Borgo Pr.

Your Freedom to Be Whole. Henlee Barnette. LC 84-2381. (Potentials: Guides to Productive Living Ser.: Vol. 7). 118p. 1984. pap. 7.95 (ISBN 0-664-24526-9). Westminster.

Your Friend the Holy Spirit. Morris Venden. (Anchor Ser.). 80p. (Orig.). 1987. pap. 6.95 (ISBN 0-8163-0682-6). Pacific Pr Pub Assn.

Your Future & You. James Finley. LC 81-65228. (Illus.). 176p. (Orig.). 1981. pap. 4.50 (ISBN 0-87793-223-9); tchrs. ed. 2.25 (ISBN 0-87793-224-7). Ave Maria.

Your Future: George Sweeting on Bible Prophecy. George Sweeting. 1984. 6.95 (ISBN 0-8024-0404-9). Moody.

Your Future Mate. Nancy Van Pelt. (Outreach Ser.). 32p. 1983. pap. 0.95 (ISBN 0-8163-0531-5). Pacific Pr Pub Assn.

Your Gift of Administration: How to Discover & Use It. Ted Engstrom. LC 83-8327. 192p. 1983. 9.95 (ISBN 0-8407-5297-0). Nelson.

Your God-Given Potential. Winifred W. Hausmann. LC 77-80458. 1978. 5.95 (ISBN 0-87159-182-0). Unity School.

Your God Is Alive & Well & Appearing in Popular Culture. John W. Nelson. LC 76-26092. 216p. 1976. softcover 5.95 (ISBN 0-664-24866-7). Westminster.

Your God Is Too Small. John B. Phillips. pap. 3.95 (ISBN 0-02-088540-7, Collier). Macmillan.

Your God, My God. Mike Creswell. Ed. by Celeste Pennington. (Human Touch-Photo Text Ser.). 172p. 1980. 7.95 (ISBN 0-937170-22-4). Home Mission.

Your God, My God: A Woman's Workshop on Ruth. Anne Wilcox. (Woman's Workshop Ser.). 1985. tchr's. manual 2.95 (ISBN 0-310-44691-0, 12026P); student's manual 2.95 (ISBN 0-310-44711-9, 12027P). Zondervan.

Your Healing Is Today. 5th ed. Tom Johnson. 64p. 1986. pap. 4.95 (ISBN 0-941992-07-1). Los Arboles Pub.

Your Healing Is Within You. Canon J. Glennon. LC 80-82616. 1980. pap. 4.95 (ISBN 0-88270-457-5). Bridge Pub.

Your Health & You: How Awareness, Attitudes, & Faith Contribute to a Healthy Life. Edgar N. Jackson. LC 86-22226. (Augsburg Religion & Medicine). 112p. (Orig.). 1986. pap. 5.95 (ISBN 0-8066-2221-0, 10-7426). Augsburg.

Your Home, a Lighthouse. Bob Jacks et al. LC 85-73824. 142p. (Orig.). 1986. pap. text ed. 4.95 (ISBN 0-934396-41-8). Churches Alive.

Your Home: A Lighthouse. rev ed. Bob Jacks et al. LC 87-60179. 150p. 1987. pap. 5.95 (ISBN 0-89109-127-0). NavPress.

Your Husband & Your Emotional Needs. Margaret Hardisty. LC 80-81471. 176p. 1982. pap. text ed. 2.95 (ISBN 0-89081-312-4). Harvest Hse.

Your Inner Therapist. Eileen Walkenstein. LC 83-19842. 128p. 1983. pap. 8.95 (ISBN 0-664-26005-5, A Bridgebooks Publication). Westminster.

Your Invisible Power. Genevieve Behrend. 1921. pap. 2.75 (ISBN 0-87516-004-2). De Vorss.

Your Jewish Child. Morrison D. Bial. Ed. by Daniel B. Syme. 1978. pap. 5.00 (ISBN 0-8074-0012-2, 101200). UAHC.

Your Jewish Lexicon. Edith Samuel. (Hebrew.). 192p. (Orig.). 1982. 10.00 (ISBN 0-8074-0054-8); pap. 5.95 (ISBN 0-8074-0061-0). UAHC.

Your Jewish Wedding. Helen Latner. LC 83-45567. (Illus.). 224p. 1985. pap. 4.95 (ISBN 0-385-18873-0). Doubleday.

Your Kingdom Come: Bible Studies for the Church Year Based on the Wcc Mission & Evangelism Theme, Melbourne 1980. (Orig.). 1980. pap. 2.25 (ISBN 0-377-00093-0). Friend Pr.

Your Last Goodbye. Salem Kirban. LC 70-87000. (Illus.). 1969. pap. 5.95 (ISBN 0-912582-06-5). Kirban.

Your Life Can Be Changed. Alan Walker. LC 85-71706. 56p. (Orig.). 1985. pap. 2.95 (ISBN 0-88177-022-1, DR022B). Discipleship Res.

Your Life in Christ. Brooks. 1.95 (ISBN 0-8054-2520-9). Broadman.

Your Life in Christ. rev. ed. Navigators Staff. (Design for Discipleship Ser.: Bk. 1). 1980. pap. text ed. 1.95 (ISBN 0-934396-16-7). Churches Alive.

Your Little One Is in Heaven. John B. Marchbanks. pap. 1.95 (ISBN 0-87213-642-6). Loizeaux.

Your Lone Journey. M. B. Goffstein. LC 86-45107. (Illus.). 32p. 12.45 (ISBN 0-06-015659-7, HarpT). Har-Row.

Your Manners Are Showing. Eugene Baker. Ed. by Jane Buerger. (Illus.). 112p. 1980. 5.95 (ISBN 0-89565-178-5, 4935). Standard Pub.

Your Marriage Can Be Great. Ed. by Thomas B. Warren. 1978. pap. 14.00 (ISBN 0-934916-44-6). Natl Christian Pr.

Your Marriage Has Real Possibilities. Cyril J. Barber & Aldyth A. Barber. LC 83-25537. 168p. (Orig.). 1984. pap. text ed. 6.95 (ISBN 0-8254-2249-3). Kregel.

Your Marriage Is God's Affair. Dwight H. Small. 352p. 1979. pap. 7.95 (ISBN 0-8007-5024-1, Power Bks). Revell.

Your Mass. B. Vasconcelos. 137p. 1961. 4.95 (ISBN 0-933932-13-8); pap. 2.50 (ISBN 0-933932-14-6). Scepter Pubs.

Your Mind Matters. John R. Stott. LC 72-94672. 64p. 1973. pap. 3.50 (ISBN 0-87784-441-0). Inter-Varsity.

Your Money & Your Life: Practical Guidance for Earning, Managing & Giving Money. Ken Wilson. (Living as a Christian Ser.). 96p. (Orig.). 1983. pap. 2.95 (ISBN 0-89283-171-5). Servant.

Your Money: Frustration or Freedom? Howard Dayton. 1979. pap. 5.95 (ISBN 0-8423-8725-0). Tyndale.

Your Money Matters. Malcolm MacGregor & Stanley C. Baldwin. LC 75-56123. 176p. 1977. pap. 4.95 (ISBN 0-87123-662-1, 210662). Bethany Hse.

Your Money or Your Life: A New Look at Jesus' View of Wealth & Power. John Alexander. LC 86-45010. 256p. 1986. 13.95 (ISBN 0-06-060151-5, HarpR). Har-Row.

Your Move, God. Francis Clare. LC 82-81212. 144p. 1982. pap. 4.95 (ISBN 0-89221-102-4). New Leaf.

Your Needs Met. Jack Addington & Cornelia Addington. 156p. 1982. pap. 3.95 (ISBN 0-87516-490-0). De Vorss.
Your Neighbor Celebrates. Arthur Gilbert & Oscar Tarcov. 38p. 0.75 (ISBN 0-686-74967-7). ADL.
Your Neighbor Celebrates. Arthur Gilbert & Oscar Tarcov. 6.00x (ISBN 0-87068-364-0, Pub. by Friendly Hse). Ktav.
Your Neighbor Worships. Arthur Gilbert. 31p. 1.50 (ISBN 0-686-74968-5). ADL.
Your New Beginning: Step Two. Willie Malone. 64p. (Orig.). 1983. pap. 2.50 (ISBN 0-88144-008-6). Christian Pub.
Your New Birth. Robert Halverstadt. 1982. pap. 0.75 (ISBN 0-88144-001-9, CPS-001). Christian Pub.
Your Next Big Step. G. Kearnie Keegan. LC 60-9533. 1960. gift ed. 8.95 (ISBN 0-8054-5317-2, 4253-17). Broadman.
Your Own Path. Elise N. Morgan. (Meditation Ser.). 1928. 4.50 (ISBN 0-87516-333-5). De Vorss.
Your Own Pigs You May Not Eat. Paula G. Rubel & Abraham Rosman. LC 78-7544. (Illus.). 1978. lib. bdg. 30.00x (ISBN 0-226-73082-4). U of Chicago Pr.
Your Parish - Where the Action Is. Robert C. Broderick. 1974. pap. 2.25 (ISBN 0-8199-0486-4). Franciscan Herald.
Your Particular Grief. Wayne E. Oates. LC 81-3328. 114p. 1981. pap. 6.95 (ISBN 0-664-24376-2). Westminster.
Your Past Lives & the Healing Process. Adrian Finkelstein. 233p. (Orig.). 1985. pap. 9.95x (ISBN 0-87418-001-5). Coleman Pub.
Your Past Lives & the Healing Process. Adrian Finkelstein. 233p. (Orig.). 1985. pap. 9.95x. A Finkelstein.
Your Pastor, Your Shepherd. James L. Beall & Marjorie Barber. LC 77-77579. 1977. pap. 4.95 (ISBN 0-88270-216-5). Bridge Pub.
Your People, My People: The Meeting of Jews & Christians. Ed. by A. R. Eckardt. 212p. 7.95 (ISBN 0-686-95188-3). ADL.
Your Personal Handbook of Prayer. Phyllis Hobe. LC 83-3475. 256p. 1983. 11.95 (ISBN 0-664-27007-7, A Bridgebooks Publication). Westminster.
Your Personal Handbook of Prayer. Phyllis Hobe. LC 83-3475. 256p. 1987. 11.95 (A Bridgebooks Publication). Westminster.
Your Phone's Ringing! J. David Lang. (Illus.). 64p. 1985. pap. 2.50 (ISBN 0-87239-897-8, 2827). Standard Pub.
Your Phone's Ringing, No. 2. J. David Lang. (Illus.). 64p. 1985. pap. 2.50 (ISBN 0-87239-898-6, 2828). Standard Pub.
Your Power of Encouragement. Jeanne Doering. (Moody Press Electives Ser.). (Orig.). 1985. pap. text ed. 3.95 (ISBN 0-8024-0687-4); leader's guide 2.50 (ISBN 0-8024-0688-2). Moody.
Your Power Tube. J. Sig Paulson. 166p. 1969. pap. 3.95 (ISBN 0-317-20870-5). CSA Pr.
Your Real Beauty. Cindy Christovale. 80p. (Orig.). 1983. pap. 2.95 (ISBN 0-88144-018-3, CPS-018). Christian Pub.
Your Rewards in Heaven. Max M. Rice. LC 80-68885. 160p. 1981. pap. 4.95 (ISBN 0-89636-063-6). Accent Bks.
Your Right to Be Different. Roberta L. Bonnici. (Discovery Bks.). (Illus.). 48p. (YA) 1982. pap. text ed. 1.50 (ISBN 0-88243-842-5, 02-0842); tchr's ed 3.95 (ISBN 0-88243-333-4, 02-0333). Gospel Pub.
Your Right to Be Informed. Daughters of St Paul. LC 68-59042. (Divine Master Ser.: Vol. 1). 1969. 7.95 (ISBN 0-8198-0518-1); pap. 6.50 (ISBN 0-8198-0519-X); teacher manual 8.50 (ISBN 0-8198-0520-3). Dghtrs St Paul.
Your Right to Rest. Wayne E. Oates. LC 83-26045. (Potentials: Guides for Productive Living Ser.: Vol. 1). 104p. (Orig.). 1984. pap. 7.95 (ISBN 0-664-24517-X). Westminster.
Your Road to Recovery. Oral Roberts. 224p. 1986. 12.95 (ISBN 0-8407-9058-9). Oliver-Nelson.
Your Self, My Self & the Self of the Universe. Alfred B Starratt. LC 79-9971. (Illus.). 192p. 1979. 12.95 (ISBN 0-916144-38-0); pap. 4.95 (ISBN 0-916144-39-9). Stemmer Hse.
Your Spiritual & Emotional Power. Richard D. Dobbins. 160p. (Orig.). 1984. pap. 4.95Bks (ISBN 0-8007-5136-1, Power Bks). Revell.
Your Spiritual Deposit. Ed. by Earl H. Burton. 68p. 1982. pap. 2.00 (ISBN 0-910068-66-6). Am Christian.
Your Spiritual Gifts Can Help Your Church Grow. Jim Larson & Joanne Feldmeth. 64p. 1985. pap. 3.95 (ISBN 0-8307-1008-6, 6101951). Regal.
Your Spiritual Gifts Can Help Your Church Grow. C. Peter Wagner. LC 78-53353. 272p. 1979. pap. 7.95 (ISBN 0-8307-0644-5, 5410606). Regal.
Your Spiritual Growth Handbook. Barbara Lugenbeel. LC 84-61016. 164p. (Orig.). 1984. pap. 5.95 (ISBN 0-8192-1352-7). Morehouse.
Your Spiritual Weapons. Terry Law. (Illus.). 48p. 1985. pap. 1.95 (ISBN 0-932081-00-2). Victory Hse.
Your Spiritual Weapons & How to Use Them. Terry Law. (Orig.). 1983. pap. write for info. (ISBN 0-88144-028-0, CPS028). Christian Pub.
Your Sunday School at Work. Richard Dresselhaus. 78p. 1980. pap. 2.95 (ISBN 0-88243-793-3, 02-0793). Gospel Pub.
Your Temperament: Discover Its Potential. Tim LaHaye. 400p. 1984. 12.95 (ISBN 0-8423-8752-8). Tyndale.
Your Temperament: Discover Its Potential. Tim LaHaye. (Living Bk). 400p. 1987. pap. cancelled (ISBN 0-8423-8757-9). Tyndale.
Your Thoughts Can Change Your Life. Donald Curtis. pap. 7.00 (ISBN 0-87980-179-4). Wilshire.
Your Wealth in God's World. John J. Davis. 144p. 1984. pap. 4.95 (ISBN 0-87552-219-X). Presby & Reformed.
Your Word Is Near. Huub Oosterhuis. Tr. by N. D. Smith from Dutch. LC 68-20848. 192p. 1968. pap. 4.95 (ISBN 0-8091-1775-4, Deus). Paulist Pr.
Your Word Is Your Wand. Florence S. Shinn. 1978. pap. 2.50 (ISBN 0-87516-259-2). De Vorss.
Your Words in Prayer in Time of Illness. Arnaldo Pangrazzi. 72p. (Orig.). 1982. pap. 1.25 (ISBN 0-8189-0417-8). Alba.
Your Work on the Pulpit Committee. Leonard E. Hill. LC 70-93916. 1970. pap. 3.25 (ISBN 0-8054-3502-6). Broadman.
You're a Mormon Now: A Handbook for New Members of the Church of Jesus Christ of Latter-day Saints. Dennis Lythgoe et al. 75p. (Orig.). 1983. pap. 6.95 (ISBN 0-913420-37-9). Olympus Pub Co.
You're God's Masterpiece. Wesley Runk. 1985. 4.50 (ISBN 0-89536-757-2, 5863). CSS of Ohio.
You're Hired! Insights for Christian Women Who Work Outside the Home. Millie Van Wyke. 120p. 1983. pap. 5.95 (ISBN 0-8010-9292-2). Baker Bk.
You're in Charge. Cecil G. Osborne. pap. write for info (ISBN 0-515-09688-1). Jove Pubns.
You're in Control: A Guide for Latter-Day Saint Youth. Ron Woods. (YA) 1986. 8.95 (ISBN 0-87579-046-1). Deseret Bk.
You're My Best Friend, Lord. Lois W. Johnson. LC 76-3866. 96p. (Orig.). 1976. pap. 3.95 (ISBN 0-8066-1541-9, 10-7490). Augsburg.
You're Nearly There: Christian Sex Education for Ten-to-Teens. Mary Kehle. LC 73-85963. (Illus.). 80p. 1973. pap. 2.50 (ISBN 0-87788-969-4). Shaw Pubs.
You're Only Old Once: Devotions in Large Print. large type ed. Catharine Brandt. LC 76-27085. 1977. pap. 6.95 (ISBN 0-8066-1570-2, 10-7495). Augsburg.
You're Worth It! But Do You Believe It? Brent D. Earles. 112p. 1985. pap. 5.95 (ISBN 0-8010-3427-2). Baker Bk.
Yours Is a Share: The Call of Liturgical Ministry. Austin Fleming. 1985. pap. 4.95 (ISBN 0-317-38558-5). Pastoral Pr.
Yours Is the Power. Florence Widutis. LC 57-9315. 1978. pap. 4.95 (ISBN 0-87516-245-2). De Vorss.
Youth Aflame. Winkey Pratney. 448p. (Orig.). 1983. pap. 7.95 (ISBN 0-87123-659-1, 210659). Bethany Hse.
Youth & the Future of the Church: Ministry with Youth & Young Adults. Michael Warren. 160p. 1982. 10.95 (ISBN 0-8164-0513-1, HarpR). Har-Row.
Youth & the Future of the Church: Ministry with Youth & Young Adults. Michael Warren. 156p. 1985. pap. 8.95 (ISBN 0-86683-917-8, 7915, Winston-Seabury). Har-Row.
Youth & Values: Getting Self Together. Carl A. Elder. LC 76-58063. 1978. 6.75 (ISBN 0-8054-5326-1, 4253-26). Broadman.
Youth as Learners. Leroy Kettinger. (C. E. Ministries Ser.). 96p. 1983. pap. 3.50 (ISBN 0-89367-086-3). Light & Life.
Youth Bible Study Notebook. John Souter & Susan Souter. 1977. pap. 5.95 (ISBN 0-8423-8790-0). Tyndale.
Youth Education in the Church. Ed. by Roy B. Zuck & Warren S. Benson. 1978. 13.95 (ISBN 0-8024-9844-2). Moody.
Youth Empowerment in the Church. Pyatt. 1983. pap. 5.95 (ISBN 0-8298-0605-9). Pilgrim NY.
Youth Experiential Annual Resource 1. Steve Clapp et al. 122p. (Orig.). 1981. pap. 10.00 (ISBN 0-914527-42-8). C-Four Res.
Youth Face Today's Issues 2. William J. Krutza & Philip P. Dicicco. (Contemporary Discussion Ser.). pap. 3.50 (ISBN 0-8010-5311-0). Baker Bk.
Youth for Peace: A Handbook for Young Christian Peacemakers. Vincent J. Giese. LC 84-60751. 120p. 1984. pap. 5.95 (ISBN 0-87973-596-1, 596). Our Sunday Visitor.
Youth Group How-To Book. Ed. by Lee Sparks. LC 81-81966. (Illus.). 224p. (Orig.). 1981. pap. 14.95 (ISBN 0-936664-03-7). Group Bks.
Youth Group Meeting Guide. Richard W. Bimler. LC 83-82574. 256p. (Orig.). 1984. pap. 11.95 (ISBN 0-936664-17-7). Group Bks.
Youth in Revolt. facsimile ed. Shmarya Levin. Tr. by Maurice Samuel. LC 74-27998. (Modern Jewish Experience Ser.). (Eng.). 1975. Repr. of 1930 ed. 24.50x (ISBN 0-405-06725-9). Ayer Co Pubs.
Youth in the Community of Disciples. David Ng. 80p. 1984. pap. 3.95 (ISBN 0-8170-1015-7). Judson.
Youth in the Vanguard: Memoirs & Letters Collected by the First Baha'i Student at Berkeley & at Stanford University. Marion C. Yazdi. LC 82-6793. (Illus.). xx, 211p. 1982. 14.95 (ISBN 0-87743-173-6, 332-089). Baha'i.
Youth Leader's Sourcebook. Gary Dausey. 320p. 1983. 15.95 (ISBN 0-310-29310-3, 11633). Zondervan.
Youth Leadership Resource Manual. Ed. by Sonjia Hunt. 32p. (Orig.). 1981. pap. text ed. 1.75 (ISBN 0-87148-933-3, 817206). Pathway Pr.
Youth Leadership Resource Manual, Vol. 2. Ed. by Sonjia Hunt. 54p. (Orig.). 1982. pap. text ed. 2.00 (ISBN 0-87148-934-1). Pathway Pr.
Youth Ministries Handbook. Barrie Smith & Ruth Smith. 120p. 1984. pap. text ed. 12.50 (ISBN 0-8309-0402-6). Herald Hse.
Youth Ministries Ideas III. Dale Jones. 1986. pap. 6.00 (ISBN 0-8309-0470-0). Herald Hse.
Youth Ministries Ideas Two. Lauren E. Say et al. (Orig.). 1985. pap. 6.00 (ISBN 0-8309-0427-1). Herald Hse.
Youth Ministries: Thinking Big With Small Groups. Carolyn C. Brown. 96p. 1984. pap. 7.95 (ISBN 0-687-47203-2). Abingdon.
Youth Ministry & Wilderness Camping. Erik C. Madsen. 160p. 1982. pap. 7.95 (ISBN 0-8170-0962-0). Judson.
Youth Ministry Cargo. Joani Schultz et al. LC 86-14836. (Illus.). 410p. (Orig.). 1986. 18.95 (ISBN 0-931529-14-X). Group Bks.
Youth Ministry from Start to Finish. Janet Litherland. Ed. by Arthur L. Zapel. LC 85-62467. (Illus.). 115p. (Orig.). 1985. pap. 7.95 (ISBN 0-916260-35-6, B-193). Meriwether Pub.
Youth Ministry Ideabook. 1986. 5.95 (ISBN 0-89536-797-1, 6815). CSS of Ohio.
Youth Ministry in the Church. Stanley J. Watson. LC 78-73597. 1978. pap. 2.50 (ISBN 0-8054-3228-0, 4232-28). Broadman.
Youth Ministry: Its Renewal In the Local Church. rev. ed. Lawrence O. Richards. 1972. 15.95 (ISBN 0-310-32010-0). Zondervan.
Youth Ministry: Making & Shaping Disciples. Jeffrey D. Jones. 96p. 1986. pap. 5.95 (ISBN 0-8170-1091-2). Judson.
Youth Ministry: The New Team Approach. Ginny W. Holderness. LC 80-82186. (Illus.). 160p. (Orig.). 1981. pap. 11.95 (ISBN 0-8042-1410-7). John Knox.
Youth Outreach & Evangelism: Youth Work Guides Ser. Ed. by John Mallison. (Illus.). 104p. (Orig.). 1975. pap. 5.95 (ISBN 0-85819-108-3, Pub. by JBCE). ANZ Religious Pubns.
Youth Program Hour Idea Book. Compiled by Larry Leonard & Jack McCormick. 156p. 1985. pap. 6.95 (ISBN 0-8341-0949-2). Beacon Hill.
Youth Retreats: Creating Sacred Space for Young People. Aileen A. Doyle. (Illus.). 107p. 1986. spiral bdg. 12.95 (ISBN 0-88489-177-1). St Mary's.
Youth Specialties Clip Art Book. Wayne Rice. 240p. (Orig.). 1985. pap. 14.95 (ISBN 0-310-34911-7, 10824P). Zondervan.
Youth Specialties Clip Art Book, Vol. II. Compiled by Wayne Rice. 112p. 1987. pap. 14.95 (ISBN 0-310-39791-X). Zondervan.
Youth Without a Future, Vol. 181. Ed. by John Coleman & Gregory Baum. (Conciliun Ser.). 128p. 1985. pap. 6.95 (ISBN 0-567-30061-7, Pub. by T&T Clark Ltd UK). Fortress.
Youth Worker's Manual. Daryl Dale. 95p. 1985. pap. write for info. (ISBN 0-87509-350-7). Chr Pubns.
Youth Worker's Personal Management Handbook. Ed. by Lee Sparks. LC 84-73152. 264p. 1985. 16.95 (ISBN 0-931529-03-4). Group Bks.
Youth's Search for Self. Thomas L. Reynolds, Jr. LC 82-70866. (Orig.). 1983. pap. 4.50 (ISBN 0-8054-5338-5, 4253-38). Broadman.
You've Got Charisma. Lloyd J. Ogilvie. 177p. 1983. pap. 4.35 (ISBN 0-687-47268-7). Abingdon.
You've Gotta Hand It to God! Timothy M. Powell. LC 84-73557. 128p. 1985. 2.95 (ISBN 0-88243-859-X, 02-0859); tchr's. ed. 3.95 (ISBN 0-88243-199-4, 32-0199). Gospel Pub.
You've Really Got Me, God! Alan Porter. (Direction Bks.). pap. 1.45 (ISBN 0-8010-7019-8). Baker Bk.
Y'shua. Moishe Rosen. 128p. (Orig.). 1983. pap. 3.50 (ISBN 0-8024-9842-6). Moody.
Ystoire de la Passion. E. A. Wright. Repr. of 1944 ed. 14.00 (ISBN 0-384-70484-0). Johnson Repr.
Yuan Thought: Chinese Thought & Religion Under the Mongols. Ed. by Hok-Lam Chan & W. Theodore DeBary. LC 82-1259. 512p. 1982. 39.00x (ISBN 0-231-05324-X). Columbia U Pr.
Yuganta: The End of an Epoch. Iravati Karve. 1974. lib. bdg. 4.50x (ISBN 0-8364-0482-3). South Asia Bks.
Yuki, Temple Dog: How a California Pound Dog Became Guardian of a Japanese Buddhist Temple. Yuki. (Illus.). 1986. 16.95 (ISBN 0-914910-37-X). Buddhist Bks.
Yule & Christmas. Alexander Tille. 1977. lib. bdg. 59.95 (ISBN 0-8490-2855-8). Gordon Pr.
Yuletide Lost. Mark Day. 1981. 4.95 (ISBN 0-89536-484-0, 2506). CSS of Ohio.
Yurok Myths. Alfred L. Kroeber. LC 75-3772. 460p. 1976. 31.00x (ISBN 0-520-02977-1); pap. 6.95 (ISBN 0-520-03639-5, CAL 386). U of Cal Pr.

Z

Zaccheus Meets Jesus. Diane Stortz. (Happy Day Bible Stories Bks.). (Illus.). 24p. 1984. 1.59 (ISBN 0-87239-766-1, 3726). Standard Pub.
Zacharias Ursinus: The Reluctant Reformer-His Life & Times. Derk Visser. 192p. 1983. pap. 7.95 (ISBN 0-8298-0691-1). Pilgrim NY.
Zaddick Christ: A Suite of Wood Engravings. Bernard A. Solomon. (Illus.). 84p. 1974. 16.95 (ISBN 0-87921-022-2). Attic Pr.
Zaddik: The Doctrine of the Zaddik According to the Writings of Rabbi Yaakov Yosef of Polnoy. Samuel H. Dresner. LC 60-7228. 312p. 1974. pap. 4.95 (ISBN 0-8052-0437-7). Schocken.
Zakhor: Jewish History & Jewish Memory. Yosef H. Yerushalmi. LC 82-15989. (Samuel & Althea Stroum Lectures in Jewish Studies). 162p. 1982. 17.50x (ISBN 0-295-95939-8). U of Wash Pr.
Zalem, or the Madness of God. Elie Wiesel. 171p. 1985. pap. 7.95 (ISBN 0-8052-0777-5). Schocken.
Zalmoxis: The Vanishing God. Mircea Eliade. LC 72-76487. (Comparative Studies in the Religions & Folklore of Dacia & Eastern Europe). x, 260p. 1986. pap. text ed. 16.00x (ISBN 0-226-20385-9, Midway Reprint). U of Chicago Pr.
Zanoni: A Rosicrucian Tale. 3rd ed. Edward Bulwer-Lytton. LC 78-157505. (Spiritual Fiction Publications: Vol. 1). 416p. 1985. cancelled (ISBN 0-8334-0000-2, Spiritual Fiction). Garber Comm.
Zanoni: A Rosicrucian Tale, Vol. 4. Edward Bulwer-Lytton. LC 78-157505. (Spiritual Science Library). 412p. 1971. lib. bdg. 18.00 (ISBN 0-89345-014-6, Spiritual Sci Lib); pap. 11.50 (ISBN 0-89345-015-4, Steinerbks). Garber Comm.
Zapiski Palomnitsi. Alexandra Gavriilova. Tr. of Diary of a Pilgrim. 175p. (Orig.). 1968. pap. 6.00 (ISBN 0-317-30250-7). Holy Trinity.
Zarandeo del Adventismo. Geoffrey J. Paxton. Orig. Title: Shaking of Adventism. (Span.). 172p. 1982. pap. 5.75 (ISBN 0-311-05604-0, Edit Mundo). Casa Bautista.
Zarathushtra in the Gathas & in the Greek & Roman Classics. 2nd ed. Ed. by Wilhelm Geiger & Friedrich Windischmann. LC 74-21260. Repr. of 1899 ed. 24.50 (ISBN 0-404-12810-6). AMS Pr.
Zarathushtra, Philo, the Achaemenids & Israel. Lawrence H. Mills. LC 74-21261. Repr. of 1906 ed. 34.50 (ISBN 0-404-12815-7). AMS Pr.
Zarza Sique Ardiendo. Lloyd J. Ogilvie. Orig. Title: Bush Is Still Burning. (Span.). 1986. write for info. (ISBN 0-8297-1094-9). Life Pubs Intl.
Zeal of His House. Eldon Weisheit. LC 73-76988. 1973. 3.50 (ISBN 0-570-03516-3, 14-2020). Concordia.
Zebahim, 2 vols. 36.00 (ISBN 0-910218-79-X). Bennet Pub.
Zechariah. J. Carl Laney. (Everyman's Bible Commentary Ser.). (Orig.). 1984. pap. 5.95 (ISBN 0-8024-0445-6). Moody.
Zechariah & His Prophecies. Charles H. Wright. 1980. 24.95 (ISBN 0-86524-020-5, 3801). Klock & Klock.
Zehariah-Malachi: Prisoners of Hope. John B. Nielson. 80p. (Orig.). 1986. pap. 2.50 (ISBN 0-8341-1100-4). Beacon Hill.
Zehn Bucher Frankischer Geschichte, 3 vols. 4th ed. Saint Gregorius. Ed. by S. Hellmann. Tr. by Wilhel M Von Geisebrecht. 1911-1913. 34.00 ea. (ISBN 0-384-19908-9). Johnson Repr.

Zeit und Ewigkeit: Studien zum Wortschatz der Geistlichen Texte des Alt-und Fruehmittelhochdeutschen. Harald Burger. LC 74-174177. (Studia Linguistica Germanica: Vol. 6). 1972. 34.00x (ISBN 3-11-003995-8). De Gruyter.

Zemiros Shabbos. 1982. pap. 1.50 large (ISBN 0-686-76284-3); pap. 1.25 medium; pap. 0.50 small. Feldheim.

Zemiroth - Sabbath Songs. Nosson Scherman. Ed. by Meir Zlotowitz. (Artscroll Mesorah Ser.). 1979. 13.95 (ISBN 0-89906-156-7); pap. 10.95 (ISBN 0-89906-157-5). Mesorah Pubns.

Zemlja Imjeninnitsa. V. Nikiforoff-Volgin. Tr. of Feast of the Land. 182p. 1960. pap. 6.00 (ISBN 0-317-30418-6). Holy Trinity.

Zen: A Way of Life. Christmas Humphreys. LC 65-17332. 1971. pap. 7.70i (ISBN 0-316-38160-8). Little.

Zen Action-Zen Person. T. P. Kasulis. LC 80-27858. 192p. 1985. pap. text ed. 7.95x (ISBN 0-8248-1023-6). UH Pr.

Zen & American Thought. Van Meter Ames. 1978. Repr. of 1962 ed. lib. bdg. 26.50 (ISBN 0-313-20066-1, AMZA). Greenwood.

Zen & Christian: The Journey Between. John Eusden. 224p. 1981. 10.95 (ISBN 0-8245-0099-7). Crossroad NY.

Zen & Creative Management. Albert Low. 272p. 1982. pap. 3.50 (ISBN 0-86721-083-4). Jove Pubns.

Zen & Hasidism. Ed. by Harold Heifetz. LC 78-9073. 1978. 10.95 (ISBN 0-8356-0514-0). Theos Pub Hse.

Zen & Japanese Culture. D. T. Suzuki. (Bollingen Ser.: Vol. 64). (Illus.). 1959. 52.00x (ISBN 0-691-09849-2); pap. 10.95x (ISBN 0-691-01770-0). Princeton U Pr.

Zen & Modern Japanese Religions. Michael Pye. 1985. 13.00 (ISBN 0-7062-3148-1, Pub. by Ward Lock Educ Co Ltd). State Mutual Bk.

Zen & Shinto: The Story of Japanese Philosophy. Chikao Fujisawa. LC 78-139133. 92p. Repr. of 1959 ed. lib. bdg. 22.50x (ISBN 0-8371-5749-8, FUZS). Greenwood.

Zen & the Art of Calligraphy. Omori Sogen & Terayama Katsujo. Tr. by John Stevens from Japanese. (Illus.). 128p. (Orig.). 1983. pap. 13.95 (ISBN 0-7100-9284-9). Methuen Inc.

Zen & the Art of Writing. Manjushri J Vitale. 90p. (Orig.). 1984. pap. 10.95 (ISBN 0-932896-07-3). Westcliff Pubns.

Zen & the Bible: A Priest's Experience. J. K. Kadowaki. (Orig.). 1980. pap. 8.95 (ISBN 0-7100-0402-8). Methuen Inc.

Zen & the Birds of Appetite. Thomas Merton. LC 68-25546. 1968. 6.50 (ISBN 0-8112-0314-X); pap. 4.95 (ISBN 0-8112-0104-X, NDP261). New Directions.

Zen & the Fine Arts. Shinichi Hisamatsu. Tr. by Gishin Tokiwa. LC 76-136562. (Illus.). 400p. 1982. pap. 24.95 (ISBN 0-87011-519-7). Kodansha.

Zen & the Mind: A Scientific Approach to Zen Practice. Tomio Hirai. (Illus., Orig.). 1978. 10.50 (ISBN 0-87040-391-5). Japan Pubns USA.

Zen & the Taming of the Bull: Towards the Definition of Buddhist Thought. Walpola Rahula. 1978. text ed. 17.50x (ISBN 0-900406-69-0). Humanities.

Zen & the Ways. Trevor Leggett. Ed. by Florence Sakade. (Illus.). 258p. (Orig.). 1987. pap. 9.95 (ISBN 0-8048-1524-0). C E Tuttle.

Zen & Zen Classics: Selections from R. H. Blyth. Ed. by Frederick Franck. (Illus.). 1978. pap. 7.95 (ISBN 0-394-72489-5, Vin). Random.

Zen Approach to Bodytherapy: From Rolf to Feldenfrais to Tanouye Roshi. Dub Leigh. 1987. pap. 10.95x (ISBN 0-8248-1099-6, Pub. by Inst Zen Studies). UH Pr.

Zen Art for Meditation. Stewart W. Holmes & Chimyo Horioka. LC 73-78279. (Illus.). 1978. pap. 4.75 (ISBN 0-8048-1255-1). C E Tuttle.

Zen Buddhism & Psychoanalysis. Erich Fromm et al. LC 60-5293. 1970. pap. 6.95 (ISBN 0-06-090175-6, CN175, PL). Har-Row.

Zen Buddhism: Selected Writings of D. T. Suzuki. D. T. Suzuki. 1956. pap. 5.50 (ISBN 0-385-09300-4, A90, Anch). Doubleday.

Zen Comics. Ioanna Salajan. LC 74-35679. 88p. 1974. pap. 4.95 (ISBN 0-8048-1120-2). C E Tuttle.

Zen Comments on the Mumonkan. Zenkei Shibayama. LC 73-18692. (Illus.). 384p. 1984. pap. 10.95 (ISBN 0-06-067278-1, CN 4091, HarpR). Har-Row.

Zen Concrete & Etc. D. A. Levy et al. (Illus.). 100p. 1987. pap. 10.00 (ISBN 0-941160-04-1). Ghost Pony Pr.

Zen: Dawn in the West. Philip Kapleau. LC 78-22794. (Illus.). 1980. pap. 5.95 (ISBN 0-385-14274-9, Anch). Doubleday.

Zen Dictionary. Ernest Wood. LC 72-77518. 1972. pap. 5.25 (ISBN 0-8048-1060-5). C E Tuttle.

Zen: Direct Pointing to Reality. Anne Bancroft. Ed. by Jill Purce. LC 81-67702. (Illustrated Library of Sacred Imagination). (Illus.). 96p. 1982. pap. 9.95 (ISBN 0-8245-0068-7). Crossroad NY.

Zen: Direct Pointing to Reality. Anne Bancroft. (Art & Imagination Ser.). (Illus.). 1987. pap. 10.95. Thames Hudson.

Zen Doctrine of No Mind. D. T. Suzuki. 1981. pap. 8.50 (ISBN 0-87728-182-3). Weiser.

Zen Edge. Alexander Eliot. 1979. 3.95 (ISBN 0-8264-0177-5). Continuum.

Zen Effects: The Life of Alan Watts. Monica Furlong. 1986. 17.95 (ISBN 0-395-35344-0). HM.

Zen Enlightenment: Origins & Meaning. Heinrich Dumoulin. LC 78-27310. 188p. 1979. pap. 7.95 (ISBN 0-8348-0141-8). Weatherhill.

Zen Experience. Thomas Hoover. (Illus., Orig.). 1980. pap. 5.95 (ISBN 0-452-25315-2, Z5315, Plume). NAL.

Zen Eye. Sokei-an Sasaki. Ed. by Mary Farkas. LC 84-48129. 136p. (Orig.). Date not set. pap. 10.95 (ISBN 0-87011-696-7). Kodansha.

Zen Flesh, Zen Bones. Paul Reps. LC 57-10199. (Illus.). 1957. 11.50 (ISBN 0-8048-0644-6). C E Tuttle.

Zen Flesh, Zen Bones: A Collection of Zen & Pre-Zen Writings. Ed. by Paul Reps. pap. 3.95 (ISBN 0-385-08130-8, A233, Anch). Doubleday.

Zen for Americans: Including the Sutra of Forty-Two Chapters. Soyen Shaku. Tr. by D. T. Suzuki. 220p. 1974. pap. 6.95 (ISBN 0-87548-273-2). Open Court.

Zen for Beginners. Judith Blackstone & Zoran Josipovic. (Writers & Readers Documentary Comic Bks.). (Illus.). 176p. (Orig.). 1986. pap. 6.95 (ISBN 0-86316-116-2). Writers & Readers.

Zen Forest: Sayings of the Masters. Soiku Shigematsu. LC 81-31. (Illus.). 200p. 1981. 19.95 (ISBN 0-8348-0159-0). Weatherhill.

Zen Guide: Where to Meditate in Japan. Martin Roth & John Stevens. (Illus.). 152p. pap. 7.50 (ISBN 0-8348-0202-3). Weatherhill.

Zen Imagery Exercises: Meridian Exercises for Wholesome Living. Shizuto Masunaga & Stephen Brown. LC 86-80220. (Illus.). 192p. (Orig.). 1986. pap. 13.95 (ISBN 0-87040-669-8). Japan Pubns USA.

Zen in the Art of Archery. Eugen Herrigel. 1971. pap. 3.95 (ISBN 0-394-71663-9, V663, Vin). Random.

Zen in the Art of Flower Arrangement: An Introduction to the Spirit of the Japanese Art of Flower Arrangement. Gustie L. Herrigel. 1974. pap. 6.95 (ISBN 0-7100-7942-7). Methuen Inc.

Zen in the Art of J. D. Salinger. Gerald Rosen. LC 77-72494. (Modern Authors Monograph Ser.: No. 3). 40p. 1977. pap. 3.50 (ISBN 0-916870-06-5). Creative Arts Bk.

Zen in the Martial Arts. Joe Hyams. 144p. 1982. pap. 3.50 (ISBN 0-553-26078-2). Bantam.

Zen Ink Paintings. Sylvan Barnet & William Burto. LC 82-80648. (Great Japanese Art Ser.). (Illus.). 96p. 1982. 22.95 (ISBN 0-87011-521-9). Kodansha.

Zen Inklings: Some Stories, Fables, Parables, Sermons & Prints with Notes & Commentaries. Donald Richie. LC 82-2561. (Illus.). 162p. 1982. 17.95 (ISBN 0-8348-0170-1). Weatherhill.

Zen Koan. Isshu Miura & Ruth F. Sasaki. LC 65-19104. (Illus.). 156p. 1966. pap. 7.95 (ISBN 0-15-699981-1, Harv). HarBraceJ.

Zen Life: D. T. Suzuki Remembered. Ed. by Masao Abe. (Illus.). 288p. (Orig.). 1986. pap. 19.95 (ISBN 0-8348-0213-9). Weatherhill.

Zen Life: Daily Life in a Zen Monastery. Koji Sato. Tr. by Ryojun Victoria. LC 79-185602. (Illus.). 194p. 1983. pap. 7.50 (ISBN 0-8348-1517-6). Weatherhill.

Zen-Man Ikkyu. James H. Sanford. LC 81-5724. (Harvard Studies in World Religions). 1981. 18.00 (ISBN 0-89130-499-1, 030002); pap. 13.50 (ISBN 0-89130-500-9). Scholars Pr GA.

Zen Master Dogen: An Introduction with Selected Writings. Yuho Yokoi & Daizen Victoria. LC 75-33200. (Illus.). 220p. 1976. 12.50 (ISBN 0-8348-0112-4); pap. 9.75 (ISBN 0-8348-0116-7). Weatherhill.

Zen Master Hakuin: Selected Writings. Hakuin. Tr. by Philip B. Yampolsky from Japanese. 253p. 1985. 29.00 (ISBN 0-231-03463-6); pap. 14.00x (ISBN 0-231-06041-6). Columbia U Pr.

Zen Meditation & Psychotherapy. Tomio Hirai. LC 85-81591. (Illus.). 160p. (Orig.). 1986. pap. 11.95 (ISBN 0-87040-666-3). Japan Pubns USA.

Zen Mind, Beginner's Mind. Shunryu Suzuki. Ed. by Trudy Dixon. LC 70-123326. 132p. 1970. 9.95 (ISBN 0-8348-0052-7); pap. 5.95 (ISBN 0-8348-0079-9). Weatherhill.

Zen of Running. Fred Rohe. 1975. pap. 5.95 (ISBN 0-394-73038-0). Random.

Zen of Seeing. Frederick Franck. 1973. pap. 8.95 (ISBN 0-394-71968-9, V968, Vin). Random.

Zen of the Bright Virtue. Manly P. Hall. pap. 4.00 (ISBN 0-89314-374-X). Philos Res.

Zen Philosophy, Zen Practice. Thich Thien-An. LC 75-20003. (Illus.). 192p. 1975. pap. 7.95 (ISBN 0-913546-33-X). Dharma Pub.

Zen Poems of Ryokan. Tr. by Nobuyuki Yuasa from Jap. LC 80-8585. (Princeton Library of Asian Translations). (Illus.). 196p. 1981. 25.00x (ISBN 0-691-06466-0). Princeton U Pr.

Zen Poems of the Five Mountains. David Pollack. LC 84-13910. (American Academy of Religion Studies in Religion). 1984. 22.50 (ISBN 0-89130-776-1, 01 00 37); pap. 14.95 (ISBN 0-89130-775-3). Scholars Pr GA.

Zen: Poems, Prayers, Sermons, Anecdotes, Interviews. Tr. by Lucien Stryk & Takashi Ikemoto. LC 81-50909. 210p. 1982. 18.95x (ISBN 0-8040-0377-7, 82-75232, Pub by Swallow); pap. 8.95 (ISBN 0-8040-0378-5, 82-75240, Pub by Swallow). Ohio U Pr.

Zen Sensualism: The Union of Spirituality & Sexuality. Dale Watts. LC 86-82338. 56p. (Orig.). 1986. pap. 9.25 (ISBN 0-937497-39-8). Hart Eden Pr.

Zen Song: Twenty Meditations for the Black Martial Artist. Patrique Hunttmiller. 52p. 1986. pap. 5.95 (ISBN 0-9615560-3-X). Scojtia Renee.

Zen Teaching of Huang Po: On the Transmission of the Mind. Huang Po. Tr. by John Blofeld. 1959. pap. 9.95 (ISBN 0-394-17217-5, E171, Ever). Grove.

Zen Telegrams: Seventy-Nine Picture Poems. Paul Reps. LC 59-8189. (Illus.). 1959. pap. 7.95 (ISBN 0-8048-0645-4). C E Tuttle.

Zen: The Path of Paradox, 3 vols. Bhagwan Shree Rajneesh. Ed. by Ma Prema Veena & Ma Ananda Vandana. LC 82-246214. (Zen Ser.). (Illus.). 1978. Vol. I, 376 pgs. 16.95 ea. (ISBN 0-88050-188-X). Vol. II, 372pgs 1979 (ISBN 0-88050-189-8). Vol. III, 392 pgs. 1979 (ISBN 0-88050-190-1). Chidvilas Found.

Zen: The Special Transmission. Bhagwan Shree Rajneesh. Ed. by Ma Prem Rajo & Ma Deva Sarito. LC 84-43010. (Zen Ser.). 368p. (Orig.). 1984. pap. 4.95 (ISBN 0-88050-691-1). Chidvilas Found.

Zen Training: Methods & Philosophy. Katsuki Sekida. Ed. by A. V. Grimstone. LC 75-17573. (Illus.). 264p. 1975. 12.50 (ISBN 0-8348-0111-6); pap. 9.95 (ISBN 0-8348-0114-0). Weatherhill.

Zen Wave: Basho's Haiku & Zen. Robert Aitken. LC 78-13243. (Illus.). 192p. 1979. pap. 9.95 (ISBN 0-8348-0137-X). Weatherhill.

Zen Way - Jesus Way. Tucker N. Callaway. LC 76-6032. 1976. 11.00 (ISBN 0-8048-1190-3). C E Tuttle.

Zen Without Zen Masters. 2nd ed. Camden Benares. (Illus.). 128p. 1985. pap. 6.95 (ISBN 0-941404-34-X). Falcon Pr AZ.

Zen Yoga. P. J. Saher. 1976. 15.00 (ISBN 0-8426-0822-2). Orient Bk Dist.

Zen Yoga Therapy. Masahiro Oki. LC 79-1060. (Illus.). 1979. pap. 12.50 (ISBN 0-87040-459-8). Japan Pubns USA.

Zen: Zest, Zip Zap & Zing. Bhagwan Shree Rajneesh. Ed. by Ma Prem Asha. LC 83-183222. (Question & Answer Ser.). (Illus.). 472p. (Orig.). 1981. pap. 19.95 468p 1981 (ISBN 0-88050-692-X). Chidvilas Found.

Zend-Avesta, 3 vols. Tr. by J. Darmesteter & L. H. Mills. Repr. 125.00 (ISBN 0-87902-154-3). Orientalia.

Zend-Avesta, 3 vols. James Darmesteter & L. H. Mills. 1974. lib. bdg. 300.00 (ISBN 0-87968-509-3). Krishna Pr.

Zend-Avesta. (Sacred Bks. of the East: Vols. 4, 23, 31). 3 vols. 45.00 (ISBN 0-686-97477-8); 15.00 ea. Asian Human Pr.

Zend-Avesta of Zarathustra. Edmond B. Szekely. (Illus.). 100p. 1973. pap. 4.80 (ISBN 0-89564-058-9). IBS Intl.

Zend-Avesta, Ouvrage de Zoroastre. A. H. Anquetil-Duperron. Ed. by Burton Feldman & Robert Richardson. LC 78-60878. (Myth & Romanticism Ser.). 1984. lib. bdg. 240.00 (ISBN 0-8240-3550-X). Garland Pub.

Zend-Avesta: Selections. Tr. by James Darmesteter. 1984. pap. 6.95 (ISBN 0-916411-41-9, Near Eastern). Holmes Pub.

Zenzen: A Book of Illustrated Koans. Glen Lovelace. (Illus.). 1978. pap. 4.00 (ISBN 0-87516-279-7). De Vorss.

Zero Experience. Bhagwan Shree Rajneesh. Ed. by Ma Prem Maneesha. (Initiation Talks Ser.). (Illus.). 632p. (Orig.). 1979. 21.50 (ISBN 0-88050-193-6). Chidvilas Found.

Zero People. Ed. by Jeffrey Hensley. 310p. 1983. pap. 7.95 (ISBN 0-89283-126-X). Servant.

Zeus: A Study of Ancient Religion, 2 vols. Arthur B. Cook. Incl. Vol. 1. Zeus, God of the Bright Sky. LC 64-25839. (Illus.). 885p. Repr. of 1914 ed. 50.00x (ISBN 0-8196-0148-9); Vol. 2. Zeus, God of the Dark Sky: Thunder & Lightning, 2 pts. LC 64-25839. Repr. of 1925 ed. 100.00xset (ISBN 0-8196-0156-X); Vol. 2, Pt. 1. Text & Notes. xliii, 858p; Vol. 2, Pt. 2. Appendixes & Index. (Illus.). 539p. Biblo.

Zhitie Prepodobnago Antonija Velikago. Saint Athanasius. Tr. of Life of St. Anthony the Great. 47p. pap. 2.00 (ISBN 0-317-29181-5). Holy Trinity.

Zhitija Russkikh Svatikh, v 2 tom, 2 vols. Mother Thais. LC 82-81204. Tr. of Lives of the Russian Saints. Vol. 1. pap. 10.00 (ISBN 0-88465-012-X); Vol. 2. pap. 13.00 (ISBN 0-88465-020-0). Holy Trinity.

Zhitija Svjatikh v 12 tomov, 12 vols. Saint Dimitri Rostov. Tr. of Lives of the Saints. 10000p. Repr. of 1968 ed. 360.00 (ISBN 0-317-29175-0). Holy Trinity.

Zhitije Prepodobnago Vasilia Novago i Videnije Grirorije, utchenika Ego. Tr. of Life of St. Basil the New & the Vision of Gregory His Disciple. 125p. pap. 5.00 (ISBN 0-317-29188-2). Holy Trinity.

Zhitije Svjatago Pravednago Ioanna Kronshtatdskago Tchudotvortsa. Tr. of Life of St. John the Miracle-worker of Kronstadt. 23p. 1964. pap. 1.00 (ISBN 0-317-29199-8). Holy Trinity.

Zhizn' dlja vsjekh i smert' za vsjekh. V. V. Kniazev. Tr. of Life is for All & Death is for All. 1971. pap. 1.00 (ISBN 0-317-30338-4). Holy Trinity.

Zhizn' Valaamskago Monakha Germana (Aljaskinskago)-Amerikanskago Missionjera. Tr. of Life of the Valaam Monk Herman (of Alaska)-Missionary to America. 24p. pap. 1.00 (ISBN 0-317-29192-0). Holy Trinity.

Zhizneopisanie i Tvorenije Blazhennejshago Antonia, Mitropolita Kievskago i Galitzkago, v 17 tomakh, 17 vols. Ed. by Archbishop Nikon Rklitsky. Tr. of Life & Works of His Beatitude Anthony, Metropolitan of Kiev & Galitch. 6000p. 1971. pap. 200.00 (ISBN 0-317-29015-0). Holy Trinity.

Zikr, the Remembrance of God. M. R. Bawa Muhaiyaddeen. LC 75-27816. 52p. 1975. pap. 2.95 (ISBN 0-914390-05-8). Fellowship Pr PA.

Zinzendorf: Nine Public Lectures on Important Subjects in Religion. Ed. & tr. by George W. Forell. LC 74-93784. 170p. 1973. text ed. 15.00 (ISBN 0-87745-036-6). U of Iowa Pr.

Zion & State: Nation, Class & the Shaping of Modern Israel. Mitchell Cohen. 288p. 1987. 24.95 (ISBN 0-631-15243-1). Basil Blackwell.

Zion in America. rev. ed. Henry L. Feingold. (American Immigrant Ser.). 1981. pap. 10.95 (ISBN 0-88254-592-2). Hippocrene Bks.

Zion, the City of the Great King: A Theological Symbol of the Jerusalem Cult. Ben C. Ollenburger. (JSOT Supplement Ser.: No. 41). 240p. 1986. text ed. 28.50x (ISBN 1-85075-015-7, Pub. by JSOT Pr England); pap. text ed. 13.50x (ISBN 1-85075-014-9). Eisenbrauns.

Zion, the Growing Symbol. Ed. by David Premoe. 1980. pap. 6.00 (ISBN 0-8309-0301-1). Herald Hse.

Zionism: A Basic Reader. Ed. by Mordechai Chertoff. 1976. 1.00 (ISBN 0-685-82601-5). Herzl Pr.

Zionism & Arabism in Palestine & Israel. Ed. by Elie Kedourie & Sylvia G. Haim. 266p. 1982. text ed. 37.50x (ISBN 0-7146-3169-8, F Cass Co). Biblio Dist.

Zionism & Faith-Healing in Rhodesia: Aspects of African Independent Churches. M. L. Daneel. Tr. by V. A. February Communications. (Illus.). 1970. pap. 6.00x (ISBN 90-2796-278-2). Mouton.

Zionism & History: Zionist Attitudes to the Jewish Historical Past, 1896-1906. Shmuel Almog. Tr. by Ina Friedman from Hebrew. 350p. 1986. 29.95 (ISBN 0-312-89885-1). St Martin.

Zionism & Territory: The Socio-Territorial Dimensions of Zionist Politics. Baruch Kimmerling. LC 83-102. (Illus.). xii, 288p. 1983. pap. 12.50x (ISBN 0-87725-151-7). U of Cal Intl St.

Zionism & the Arabs, Nineteen Thirty-Six to Nineteen Thirty-Nine. Ian Black. (Outstanding Theses from the London School of Economics & Political Science Ser.). 500p. 1987. lib. bdg. 75.00 (ISBN 0-8240-1911-3). Garland Pub.

Zionism & the Economy. Barach Kimmering. 170p. 1983. 18.95 (ISBN 0-87073-775-9); pap. 11.25 (ISBN 0-87073-784-8). Schenkman Bks Inc.

Zionism & the Future of Palestine. Morris Jastrow. (Rise of Jewish Nationalism & the Middle East Ser.). 159p. 1975. Repr. of 1919 ed. 18.15 (ISBN 0-88355-326-0). Hyperion Conn.

Zionism & the Jewish Future. Ed. by Harry Sacher. LC 75-6452. (Rise of Jewish Nationalism & the Middle East Ser.). viii, 252p. 1975. Repr. of 1916 ed. 25.85 (ISBN 0-88355-338-4). Hyperion Conn.

Zionism-Conceptual Bases in the Prayerbook-Kit. pap. 2.00 (ISBN 0-686-96092-0). United Syn Bk.

Zionism: Enemy of Peace & Social Progress. (Miscellany of Papers under the General Editorship of Lionel Dadiani). 160p. 1981. 7.50x (ISBN 0-317-53802-0, Pub. by Collets (UK)). State Mutual Bk.

Zionism: Enemy of Peace & Social Progress Issue, No. 3. Tr. by Barry Jones from Rus. 220p. 1984. 13.75x (ISBN 0-317-53829-2, Pub. by Collets (UK)). State Mutual Bk.

Zionism in Germany 1897-1933: The Shaping of a Jewish Identity. Stephen M. Poppel. LC 76-14284. 229p. 1977. 7.95 (ISBN 0-8276-0085-2, 395). Jewish Pubns.

Zionism in Poland: The Formative Years, 1915-1926. Ezra Mendelsohn. LC 81-10301. 416p. 1982. text ed. 42.00x (ISBN 0-300-02448-7). Yale U Pr.

Zionism in the Age of the Dictators. Lenni Brenner. LC 82-23369. 300p. 1983. pap. 8.95 osi (ISBN 0-88208-164-0). Lawrence Hill.

Zionism in Transition. Ed. by Moshe Davis. LC 80-67905. 1980. lib. bdg. 24.00x (ISBN 0-405-13825-3). Ayer Co Pubs.

Zionism in Transition. Ed. by Moshe Davis. 1980. pap. 8.00 (ISBN 0-930832-61-2). Herzl Pr.

Zionism Is Racism in the Service of Imperialism. Marxist-Leninist Party, USA. Ed. by National Executive Committee of the MLP, USA. (Illus.). 112p. (Orig.). 1983. pap. 1.00 (ISBN 0-86714-025-9). Marxist-Leninist.

Zionism, Israel & Asian Nationalism. G. H. Jansen. 347p. 1971. 6.00 (ISBN 0-88728-112-5); pap. 3.00 (ISBN 0-88728-113-3). Inst Palestine.

Zionism Stands Accused. I. Yaroslavtsev. 157p. 1985. pap. 3.95 (ISBN 0-8285-3095-5, Pub. by Progress Pubs USSR). Imported Pubns.

Zionism: The Formative Years. David Vital. 1982. 34.50x (ISBN 0-19-827443-2). Oxford U Pr.

Zionism: The Myth & the Reality. Ismail Zayed. Date not set. pap. 2.75 (ISBN 0-89259-013-0). Am Trust Pubns.

Zionism: The Saga of a National Liberation Movement. Jacob Tsur. LC 76-24801. Tr. of L'epopee Du Siosnisme. 112p. 1977. pap. text ed. 9.95x (ISBN 0-87855-631-1). Transaction Bks.

Zionism, the Superpowers, & the P.L.O. Henry Paolucci. LC 82-15728. 80p. 1982. pap. 7.95 (ISBN 0-918680-18-2, GHGP 708). Griffon Hse.

Zionism Today: A Symposium. LC 86-70642. 72p. (Orig.). 1986. pap. 5.00 (ISBN 0-87495-079-1). Am Jewish Comm.

Zionism Within Early American Fundamentalism, 1878-1918: A Convergence of Two Traditions. David A. Rausch. LC 79-66371. (Texts & Studies in Religion: Vol. 4). viii, 386p. 1980. 59.95x (ISBN 0-88946-875-3). E Mellen.

Zionist Career of Louis Lipsky, 1900-1921. Deborah E. Lipstadt. 35.00 (ISBN 0-405-14086-X). Ayer Co Pubs.

Zionist Character in the English Novel. Hani Al-Raheb. 220p. 1985. pap. 9.95 (ISBN 0-86232-364-9, Pub. by Zed Pr England). Humanities.

Zionist Congress Resolutions, 1897-1972. Ed. by Walid Khalidi. Date not set. text ed. price not set (ISBN 0-88728-164-8). Inst Palestine.

Zionist Connection II. Alfred M. Lilienthal. 1983. pap. 10.95 (ISBN 0-949667-33-1). Concord Bks.

Zionist Connection II: What Price Peace? Rev. ed. Alfred M. Lilienthal. LC 82-61135. 904p. 1982. 11.95 (ISBN 0-686-43256-8); pap. 9.95. North American Inc.

Zionist Dream Revisited: From Herzl to Gush Emunim & Back. Amnon Rubinstein. LC 83-40471. 224p. 1984. 14.95 (ISBN 0-8052-3886-7). Schocken.

Zionist Dream Revisited: From Herzl to Gush Emunim & Back. Amnon Rubinstein. LC 83-40470. 224p. 1987. pap. 8.95 (ISBN 0-8052-0835-6). Schocken.

Zionist Evidence Before the Peel Commission, 1933-1937. Aaron Klieman. Ed. by Howard M. Sachar. (Rise of Israel Ser.). 320p. 1987. lib. bdg. 65.00 (ISBN 0-8240-4921-7). Garland Pub.

Zionist Idea: A Historical Analysis & Reader. Ed. by Arthur Hertzberg. LC 77-90073. (Temple Books). 1969. pap. text ed. 7.95x (ISBN 0-689-70093-8, T4). Atheneum.

Zionist Idea: A Historical Analysis & Reader. Ed. by Arthur Hertzberg. Repr. of 1959 ed. 23.50x (ISBN 0-8371-2565-0, HEZI). Greenwood.

Zionist Mind, No. 39. Alan R. Taylor. 1974. 6.00 (ISBN 0-88728-118-4); pap. 4.00 (ISBN 0-88728-119-2). Inst Palestine.

Zionist Plan for the Middle East. Tr. by Oded Yinon & Israel Shahak. (Special Document: No. 1). 26p. (Orig.). 1983. pap. text ed. 2.50 (ISBN 0-937694-56-8). Assn Arab-Amer U Grads.

Zionist Relations with Nazi Germany. Faris Glubb. LC 79-90569. 6.00 (ISBN 0-911026-11-8). New World Press NY.

Zionist Revolution. H. Fisch. LC 78-424. 1978. 19.95x (ISBN 0-312-89886-X). St Martin.

Zionist Work in Palestine. Ed. by Israel Cohen. LC 75-6428. (Rise of Jewish Nationalism & the Middle East Ser.). (Illus.). 208p. 1975. Repr. of 1911 ed. 24.75 (ISBN 0-88355-315-5). Hyperion Conn.

Zionists. George Armstrong. 1982. lib. bdg. 69.95 (ISBN 0-87700-341-6). Revisionist Pr.

Zion's Call: Christian Contributions to the Origins & Development of Israel. Lawrence J. Epstein. LC 84-15184. 176p. (Orig.). 1984. lib. bdg. 23.00 (ISBN 0-8191-4185-2); pap. text ed. 11.25 (ISBN 0-8191-4186-0). U Pr of Amer.

Zion's Camp: Expedition to Missouri, 1834. Roger D. Launius. 1984. pap. 14.00 (ISBN 0-8309-0385-2). Herald Hse.

ZOE: The God-Kind of Life. Kenneth E. Hagin. 1981. pap. 2.50 (ISBN 0-89276-402-3). Hagin Ministries.

Zoe's Book. Gail Pass. 224p. 1987. pap. 7.95 (ISBN 0-930044-95-9). Naiad Pr.

Zohar. Tr. by Maurice Simon & Paul Levertoff. 1934. 75.00 (ISBN 0-900689-39-0); pap. 55.00. Soncino Pr.

Zohar: Bereshith. rev.,3rd ed. Nurho De Manhar. (Secret Doctrine Reference Ser.). 432p. 1985. 21.00 (ISBN 0-913510-53-X). Wizards.

Zohar: Hebrew Text, 21 vols. Shimon Bar Yohai. 378.00 set (ISBN 0-943688-67-1); 18.00 ea. Res Ctr Kabbalah.

Zohar: Hebrew Text, 10 vols. condensed ed. Shimon Bar Yohai. 1981. 15.00 ea. (ISBN 0-943688-68-X); 150.00 set. Res Ctr Kabbalah.

Zohar: Parashat Pinhas, Vol. II. Phillip S. Berg. 288p. 1987. 14.95 (ISBN 0-943688-52-3); pap. 9.95 (ISBN 0-943688-53-1). Res Ctr Kabbalah.

Zohar: Parashat Pinhas, Vol. III. Phillip S. Berg. 288p. 1987. 14.95 (ISBN 0-943688-54-X); pap. 9.95 (ISBN 0-943688-55-8). Res Ctr Kabbalah.

Zohar, The Book of Enlightment. Daniel C. Matt. (Classics of Western Spirituality). 320p. 1982. 12.95 (ISBN 0-8091-0320-6); pap. 9.95 (ISBN 0-8091-2387-8). Paulist pr.

Zohar-The Book of Splendor: Basic Readings from the Kabbalah. Ed. by Gershom Scholem. LC 63-11040. 1963. pap. 3.95 (ISBN 0-8052-0045-2). Schocken.

Zondervan Nineteen Eighty-Seven Pastor's Annual: A Planned Preaching Program for the Year. T. T. Crabtree. (Pastor's Annual Ser.). 384p. 1986. 12.95 (ISBN 0-310-22701-1, 11384P). Zondervan.

Zondervan Pastor's Annual, 1986. T. T. Crabtree. 384p. 1985. pap. 11.95 (ISBN 0-310-22691-0, 11383P). Zondervan.

Zondervan Pastor's Annual 1988: A Planned Preaching Program. rev. ed. T. T. Crabtree. Ed. by M. Smith. (Zondervan Pastor's Annuals). 384p. 1987. Repr. of 1968 ed. price not set (ISBN 0-310-22711-9). Zondervan.

Zondervan Pictorial Bible Atlas. E. M. Blaiklock. (Illus.). 1969. 24.95 (ISBN 0-310-21240-5). Zondervan.

Zondervan Pictorial Bible Dictionary. Ed. by Merrill C. Tenney. (Illus.). 1969. 21.95 (ISBN 0-310-33160-9, 6750); indexed o.p. 23.95 (ISBN 0-310-33170-6). Zondervan.

Zondervan Pictorial Encyclopedia of the Bible, 5 vols. new ed. Ed. by Merrill C. Tenney. (Illus.). 1974. Set. text ed. 149.95 (ISBN 0-310-33188-9, 6700). Zondervan.

Zoological Mythology, 2 Vols. Angelo De Gubernatis. LC 68-58904. 1968. Repr. of 1872 ed. Set. 56.00x (ISBN 0-8103-3527-1). Gale.

Zorba the Buddha. Bhagwan S. Rajneesh. Ed. by Ma Prem Maneesha. LC 82-50463. (Initiation Talks Ser.). (Illus.). 344p. 1982. pap. 21.95 (ISBN 0-88050-694-6). Chidvilas Found.

Zorba the Buddha Rajneesh Cookbook. Zorba the Buddha Rajneesh Restaurants & Staff. Ed. by Swami Premdharma & Ma Dhyan Yogini. LC 84-61260. 240p. (Orig.). 1984. pap. 4.95 (ISBN 0-918963-00-1). Rajneesh Neo-Sannyas Intl.

Zoroaster: Prophet of Ancient Iran. Abraham V. Jackson. LC 98-2277. (Columbia University. Indo-Iranian Ser.: No. 14). Repr. of 1928 ed. 26.00 (ISBN 0-404-50484-1). AMS Pr.

Zoroaster's Influence on Anaxagoras, the Greek Tragedians & Socrates. Ruhi Afnan. LC 68-18733. 161p. 1969. 6.95 (ISBN 0-8022-2250-1). Philos Lib.

Zoroaster's Influence on Greek Thought. Ruhi Afnan. LC 64-20423. 1965. 8.95 (ISBN 0-8022-0011-7). Philos Lib.

Zoroastrian Civilization from the Earlist Times to the Downfall of the Last Zoroastrian Empire, 651 A. D. M. N. Dhalla. 1976. lib. bdg. 59.95 (ISBN 0-8490-2857-4). Gordon Pr.

Zoroastrian Civilization: From the Earliest Times to the Downfall of the Last Zoroastrian Empire, 651 A.D. Maneckji N. Dhalla. LC 74-21258. Repr. of 1922 ed. 30.00 (ISBN 0-404-12808-4). AMS Pr.

Zoroastrian Doctrine of a Future Life from Death to the Individual Judgment. 2nd. ed. Jal D. Pavry. LC 79-10518. Repr. of 1929 ed. 16.50 (ISBN 0-404-50481-7). AMS Pr.

Zoroastrian Theology. M. N. Dhalla. lib. bdg. 79.95 (ISBN 0-87968-516-6). Krishna Pr.

Zoroastrian Theology from the Earliest Times to the Present Day. Maneckji N. Dhalla. LC 70-131038. Repr. of 1914 ed. 30.00 (ISBN 0-404-02123-9). AMS Pr.

Zoroastrianism. Mary Boyce. Tr. by Mary Boyce. (Textual Sources for the Study of Religion). 224p. 1987. pap. 11.75 (ISBN 0-389-20717-9). B&N Imports.

Zoroastrianism. Ed. by Mary Boyce. LC 84-383. (Textual Sources for the Study of Religion Ser.). 176p. 1984. 23.50x (ISBN 0-389-20478-1, 08040); pap. 11.75x (ISBN 0-389-20717-9). B&N Imports.

Zoroastrianism. Cyrus R. Pangborn. 178p. 1982. text ed. 15.95x (ISBN 0-89891-006-4). Advent NY.

Zoroastrianism & Judaism. George W. Carter. LC 70-112489. 1970. Repr. of 1918 ed. 14.00 (ISBN 0-404-01396-1). AMS Pr.

Zoroastrianism & the Parsis. John Hinnells. 1985. 13.00x (ISBN 0-7062-3973-3, Pub. by Ward Lock Educ Co Ltd). State Mutual Bk.

Zoroastrians. Mary Boyce. Ed. by John Hinnells. (Library of Religious Beliefs & Practices). 260p. 1986. pap. text ed. 9.95 (ISBN 0-7102-0156-7). Methuen Inc.

Zorostrian Studies: Iranian Religion & Various Monographs. Abraham V. Jackson. LC 28-29344. (Columbia University. Indo-Iranian Ser.: No. 12). Repr. of 1928 ed. 27.50 (ISBN 0-404-50482-5). AMS Pr.

Zumarraga & the Mexican Inquisition: 1536-1543. Richard E. Greenleaf. (Monograph Ser.). (Illus.). 1962. 20.00 (ISBN 0-88382-053-6). AAFH.

Zuni Fetishes. Frank H. Cushing. LC 66-23329. (Illus.). 43p. 1966. pap. 3.00 (ISBN 0-916122-03-4). KC Pubns.

Zuni Mythology, 2 Vols. Ruth Benedict. LC 75-82366. (Columbia Univ. Contributions to Anthropology Ser.: No. 21). 1969. Repr. of 1935 ed. Set. 70.00 (ISBN 0-404-50571-6); 35.00 ea. AMS Pr.

Zur Gesellschaft & Religion der Nueer. J. P. Crazzolara. 1953. 46.00 (ISBN 0-384-10150-X). Johnson Repr.

Zur Grundlegung Christlicher Ethik Theologische Konzeptionen der Gegenwart im Lichte des Analogie-Problems. Kotaro Okayama. (Theologische Bibliothek Toepelmann: Vol. 30). 1977. 24.40x (ISBN 3-11-005812-X). De Gruyter.

Zur Sprache und Literatur der Mandaer: Mit Beitraegen von Kurt Rudolph & Eric Segelberg. Rudolf Macuch. 1976. 76.00x (ISBN 3-11-004838-8). De Gruyter.

Zurich Letters, 2 Vols. 1842-1845. 51.00 ea. (ISBN 0-384-71255-X). Johnson Repr.

Zvi. LC 78-56149. 1978. pap. 3.95 (ISBN 0-915540-23-1). Friends Israel-Spearhead Pr.

Zwickau in Transition, Fifteen-Hundred to Fifteen Forty-Seven: The Reformation as an Agent of Change. Susan C. Karant-Nunn. 1987. 29.50x (ISBN 0-8142-0421-X). Ohio St U Pr.

Zwingli. John Milton & G. R. Potter. LC 75-46136. (Illus.). 1977. 59.50 (ISBN 0-521-20939-0). Cambridge U Pr.

Zwingli & Bullinger. Ed. by G. W. Bromiley. LC 53-1533. (Library of Christian Classics). 360p. 1979. softcover 8.95 (ISBN 0-664-24159-X). Westminster.

Zwingli Bibliography. Compiled by H. Wayne Pipkin. LC 73-153549. (Bibliographia Tripotamopolitana: No.7). 1972. 7.00x (ISBN 0-931222-06-0). Pitts Theolog.

Zwingli or the Rise of the Reformation in Switzerland. R. Christoffel. 1977. lib. bdg. 59.95 (ISBN 0-8490-2859-0). Gordon Pr.

Zwingli und Luther, Ihr Streit uber das Abendmahl nach Seinen Politischen und Religiosen Beziehung En. Walther Kohler. (Ger.). 61.00 (ISBN 0-384-30019-7); pap. 55.00 (ISBN 0-384-30018-9). Johnson Repr.

Zwischen Hadit und Theologie: Studien Zum Entstehen Praedestinatianischer Ueberlieferung. Josef Von Ess. LC 73-91809. (Studien Zur Sprache, Geschichte und Kultur Des Islamischen Orients, N.F. Vol. 7). (Ger.). 1974. 53.20x (ISBN 3-11-004290-8). De Gruyter.

Zwischen Krieg und Frieden. William F. Sollmann. 1983. pap. 2.50x (ISBN 0-87574-045-6, 045). Pendle Hill.

Zyklon B: Nazi Mass Murder by Poison Gas. Ed. by Eugen Kogon et al. 1987. 19.95 (ISBN 0-89604-110-7); pap. 13.95 (ISBN 0-89604-111-5). Holocaust Pubns.

Serials Subject Index

ABSTRACTING AND INDEXING SERVICES
see also Bibliographies

ABSTRACTS OF RESEARCH IN PASTORAL CARE AND COUNSELING. see *RELIGIONS AND THEOLOGY — Abstracting, Bibliographies, Statistics*

BULLETIN SIGNALETIQUE. PART 519: PHILOSOPHIE. see *PHILOSOPHY — Abstracting, Bibliographies, Statistics*

BULLETIN SIGNALETIQUE. PART 527: HISTOIRE ET SCIENCES DES RELIGIONS. see *RELIGIONS AND THEOLOGY — Abstracting, Bibliographies, Statistics*

CANON LAW ABSTRACTS; half-yearly review of periodical literature in Canon Law. see *RELIGIONS AND THEOLOGY — Abstracting, Bibliographies, Statistics*

CATHOLIC PERIODICAL AND LITERATURE INDEX. see *RELIGIONS AND THEOLOGY — Abstracting, Bibliographies, Statistics*

CHRISTIAN PERIODICAL INDEX; an index to subjects, authors and book reviews. see *RELIGIONS AND THEOLOGY — Abstracting, Bibliographies, Statistics*

INDEX OF ARTICLES ON JEWISH STUDIES/ RESHIMAT MA'AMARIM BE-MADA'E HA-YAHADUT. see *RELIGIONS AND THEOLOGY — Abstracting, Bibliographies, Statistics*

NEW TESTAMENT ABSTRACTS; a record of current literature. see *RELIGIONS AND THEOLOGY — Abstracting, Bibliographies, Statistics*

OLD TESTAMENT ABSTRACTS. see *RELIGIONS AND THEOLOGY — Abstracting, Bibliographies, Statistics*

RELIGION INDEX ONE: PERIODICALS. see *RELIGIONS AND THEOLOGY — Abstracting, Bibliographies, Statistics*

RELIGIOUS & THEOLOGICAL ABSTRACTS. see *RELIGIONS AND THEOLOGY — Abstracting, Bibliographies, Statistics*

THEOLOGICAL AND RELIGIOUS BIBLIOGRAPHIES. see *RELIGIONS AND THEOLOGY — Abstracting, Bibliographies, Statistics*

ADULT EDUCATION
see Education–Adult Education

ADVERTISING AND PUBLIC RELATIONS
see also Business and Economics–Marketing and Purchasing

659.1 200 US
CHRISTIAN ADVERTISING FORUM. 1981. bi-m. $18. Wike Associates, Inc., 5007 Carriage Dr., S.W., Roanoke, VA 24018. TEL 703-989-1330 Ed. Stephen M. Wike. adv. circ. 2,460.

COMMUNICATIO SOCIALIS; Zeitschrift fuer Publizistik in Kirche und Welt. see *RELIGIONS AND THEOLOGY*

AGRICULTURE
see also Food and Food Industries

INFORMATION BULLETIN FOR CATHOLIC RURAL ORGANIZATIONS. see *RELIGIONS AND THEOLOGY — Roman Catholic*

LAND AKTUELL. see *POLITICAL SCIENCE*

NEUES DORF; Jugend und Familie auf dem Land. see *RELIGIONS AND THEOLOGY — Protestant*

ANTHROPOLOGY
see also Folklore

CENTRE PROTESTANT D'ETUDES DE GENEVE. BULLETIN. see *RELIGIONS AND THEOLOGY — Protestant*

FLAMBEAU; revue trimestrielle de theologie pour l'engagement de l'eglise dans le monde africain. see *RELIGIONS AND THEOLOGY*

572 200 US ISSN 0091-8296
MISSIOLOGY; an international review. 1953. q. $15 to individuals; institutions $20. c/o American Society of Missiology, Box 10000, Denver, CO 80210. TEL 303-761-2482 Ed. Ralph R. Covell. adv. bk. rev. index. circ. 3,200. (also avail. in microform from UMI; reprint service avail. from UMI) Indexed: Hist.Abstr. Rel.Per. Amer.Hist.& Life. CERDIC. Chr.Per.Ind. Rel.Ind.One. Rel.& Theol.Abstr.
Formerly: Practical Anthropology (ISSN 0032-633X)

PIEMME; Piccolo Pissionario. see *RELIGIONS AND THEOLOGY*

STUDIES ON RELIGION IN AFRICA. see *RELIGIONS AND THEOLOGY*

ARCHAEOLOGY

220 913 US
ARCHAEOLOGY AND BIBLICAL RESEARCH. 1972-1983; resumed 1987. q. $12. Associates for Biblical Research, Box 31, Willow Grove, PA 19090. TEL 215-445-5864 Ed. David Livingston. bk. rev. film rev. charts. illus. index. circ. 1,500. (tabloid format; also avail. in microfilm) Indexed: Chr.Per.Ind.
Formerly (until 1983): Bible and Spade (ISSN 0162-9301)

BIBBIA E ORIENTE; rivista per la conoscenza della Bibbia. see *RELIGIONS AND THEOLOGY*

913 200 US ISSN 0006-0895
BIBLICAL ARCHAEOLOGIST. 1938. q. $18 to individuals; institutions $25. (American Schools of Oriental Research) A S O R Publications Office, Box HM, Duke Sta., Durham, NC 27706. Ed. Eric M. Meyers. adv. bk. rev. bibl. charts. illus. index. circ. 7,500. (also avail. in microform from UMI; reprint service avail. from UMI) Indexed: Cath.Ind. Hum.Ind. M.L.A. Old Test.Abstr. Rel.Per. Art Ind. Abstr.Anthropol. Art & Archaeol.Tech.Abstr. Chr.Per.Ind. New Test.Abstr. Numis.Lit. Rel.Ind.One. Rel.& Theol.Abstr.

913 200 AT ISSN 0007-6260
BURIED HISTORY. 1964. q. Aus.$10($11) Australian Institute of Archaeology, 174 Collins St., Melbourne 3000, Victoria, Australia. Ed. P.T. Crocker. bk. rev. illus. circ. 1,000. (also avail. in microform from MIM) Indexed: Old Test.Abstr. Chr.Per.Ind.

913 709 IT ISSN 0577-2168
CENTRO CAMUNO DI STUDI PREISTORICI. BOLLETTINO. (Text in various languages) 1967. a. $40. Centro Camuno di Studi Preistorici, 25044 Capo di Ponte, Brescia, Italy. Ed. Emmanuel Anati. bk. rev. bibl. charts. illus. Indexed: Br.Archaeol.Abstr.

913 200 FR
MONDE DE LA BIBLE. 1957. 5/yr. 298 F. Bayard Presse, 5 rue Bayard, 75380 Paris Cedex 08, France. adv. bk. rev. circ. 9,500. Indexed: Old Test.Abstr.
Supersedes: Bible et Terre Sainte (ISSN 0006-0712)

913 US ISSN 0036-1275
S E H A NEWSLETTER AND PROCEEDINGS. 1951. 6/yr. membership. ‡ Society for Early Historic Archaeology, Box 7482, University Sta., Provo, UT 84602. Ed. Ross T. Christensen. bk. rev. illus. cum.index. circ. 500.
Formerly: U A S Newsletter.

TERRA SANTA. see *RELIGIONS AND THEOLOGY*

ARCHITECTURE
see also Building and Construction

YOUR CHURCH. see *RELIGIONS AND THEOLOGY*

ART
see also Advertising and Public Relations

700 800 301 200 IT
L'ALTRA EUROPA. 1960. bi-m. L.20000. Centro Studi Russia Cristiana, Via Ponzio, 44, I-20133 Milan, Italy. Ed. Lia Tommasi. adv. bk. rev. index. circ. 6,500. Indexed: CERDIC.
Former titles: Centro Studi Russia Cristiana. Rivista; Russia Cristiana (ISSN 0036-018X)

704.948 IT ISSN 0003-1747
AMICO DELL'ARTE CRISTIANA. 1930. q. Scuola Beato Angelico, 19 Viale S. Gimignano, 20146 Milan, Italy.

704.948 JA ISSN 0004-2889
ARS BUDDHICA/BUKKYO GEIJUTSU. (Text in Japanese; title, contents page and summaries in English) 1948. bi-m. $71.75. Japan Publications Trading Co. Ltd., Box 5030, Tokyo International, Tokyo 100-31, Japan (Or 1255 Howard St., San Francisco, CA 94103) adv. illus. circ. 1,000. (also avail. in microform from MIM)

704.948 IT ISSN 0004-3400
ARTE CRISTIANA; rivista internazionale di storia dell'arte e di arti liturgiche. 1913; N.S. 1983. bi-m. L.27000. Scuola Beato Angelico, Viale S. Gimignano 19, 20146 Milan, Italy. Ed. Dr. Arch. Don Valerio Vigorelli. adv. bk. rev. bibl. charts. index. cum.index. Indexed: RILA.
Ecclesiastical

BAMPTON LECTURES IN AMERICA. see *RELIGIONS AND THEOLOGY*

BOOKS AND ARTICLES ON ORIENTAL SUBJECTS PUBLISHED IN JAPAN. see *HISTORY — History Of Asia*

CENTRO CAMUNO DI STUDI PREISTORICI. BOLLETTINO. see *ARCHAEOLOGY*

DIE CHRISTENGEMEINSCHAFT; Monatsschrift zur religioesen Erneuerung. see *RELIGIONS AND THEOLOGY*

CITTA DI VITA; bimestrale di religione arte e scienza. see *RELIGIONS AND THEOLOGY*

704.948 SW ISSN 0106-1348
ICO-ICONOGRAPHISK POST; Nordisk tidskrift foer bildtolkning/Nordic iconographic review. (Text in Danish, Norwegian and Swedish; summaries and captions in English) 1970. q. Kr.60. Riksantikvarieambetet - Central Board of National Antiquities, Box 5405, S-114 84 Stockholm, Sweden. Ed.Bd. bk. rev. bibl. illus. cum.index:1970-1974, 1975-1985. circ. 1,500.
Formerly (1970-77): Iconographiske Post.

ISLAM AND THE MODERN AGE. see *RELIGIONS AND THEOLOGY — Islamic*

700 NE ISSN 0160-208X
JOURNAL OF JEWISH ART. (Text in English, French) 1974. a. $25. (Hebrew University of Jerusalem) E.J. Brill, P.O. Box 9000, 2300 PA Leiden, Netherlands. Ed. Bezalel Narkiss. bk. rev. bibl. illus. circ. 2,000. (also avail. in microform from UMI; back issues avail.; reprint service avail. from UMI) Indexed: Curr.Cont. Ind.Jew.Per. RILA.

704.943 AU ISSN 0034-3935
RELIGIOESE GRAPHIK; Blaetter fuer Freunde Christlicher Gebrauchsgraphik. 1946. irreg. (2-3/yr.) S.10($0.50) per no. Stephanus-Verlag, Box 303, A-1071 Vienna, Austria. Ed. Josef Franz Aumann. bk. rev. illus. circ. 2,500.

REVISTA CULTULUI MOZAIC. see *LITERATURE*

700 282 IT ISSN 0391-7819
SANTO; rivista antoniana di storia dottrina arte. (Text in English, French, Italian and Latin) 1961. 3/yr. L.20000($20) Centro Studi Antoniani, Basilica del Santo, Piazza del Santo 11, 35123 Padua, Italy. Eds. Vergilio Gamboso, Luciano Bertazzo. bk. rev. circ. 450. (back issues avail.)

SHAKER MESSENGER. see *RELIGIONS AND THEOLOGY — Other Denominations And Sects*

BANKING AND FINANCE
see Business and Economics–Banking and Finance

BEVERAGES
see also Food and Food Industries

BIBLIOGRAPHIES

200 016 AG ISSN 0326-6680
BIBLIOGRAFIA TEOLOGICA COMENTADA DEL AREA IBEROAMERICANA. (Summaries in English) 1973. a. $60. Instituto Superior Evangelico de Estudios Teologicos, Camacua 282, 1406 Buenos Aires, Argentina. Ed. Eduardo Bierzychudek. bk. rev. bibl. index. circ. 1,000. (back issues avail.)

011 200 GW
BIBLIOTHECA DISSIDENTIUM. (Subseries of: Bibliotheca Bibliographica Aureliana) (Text in English, French, German and Italian) 1980. irreg. price varies. Verlag Valentin Koerner, Postfach 304, D-7570 Baden-Baden 1, W. Germany (B.R.D.) Ed.Bd. circ. 1,000.

296 011 IS ISSN 0023-1851
KIRYAT SEFER; bibliographical quarterly. (Text in various languages) 1924. q. $50. ‡ Jewish National and University Library, Box 503, Jerusalem, Israel. Ed. Dr. Avigdor Shinan. bk. rev. bibl. index. circ. 1,000.

200 016 US ISSN 0000-0868
RELIGIOUS AND INSPIRATIONAL BOOKS AND SERIALS IN PRINT. 1978. biennial. $79.95. R.R. Bowker Company, Database Publishing Group, 245 W. 17th St., New York, NY 10011. TEL 800-521-8110
•Also available online.
Formerly: Religious Books and Serials in Print (ISSN 0000-0612)

BIOGRAPHY

920 US
CENTRUM JANA PAWLA II BIULETYN. English edition: Pope John Paul II Center Newsletter. (Text in Polish.) 1979. 5/yr. $5. Pope John Paul II Center, Orchard Lake Schools, Orchard Lake Schools, Orchard Lake, MI 48033. TEL 313-683-0408 Ed. Rev. Roman Nir. bk. rev. circ. 328. (back issues avail.)

KATERI; Lily of the Mohawks. see *RELIGIONS AND THEOLOGY*

BIOGRAPHY — Abstracting, Bibliographies, Statistics

BIBLIOGRAPHIA FRANCISCANA. see *RELIGIONS AND THEOLOGY — Abstracting, Bibliographies, Statistics*

BIOLOGY
see also Medical Sciences

BIOLOGY — Physiology
see also Medical Sciences

BIRTH CONTROL
see also Population Studies

613.9 200 312 US
A L L NEWS. 1984. w. $29.95. American Life League, Box 1350, Stafford, VA 22554. TEL 703-659-4171 Ed. J. Vincent Fitzpatrick. circ. 2,500.

CHURCH WORLD SERVICE. FAMILY LIFE AND POPULATION PROGRAM BRIEFS. see *RELIGIONS AND THEOLOGY*

301.4 US
HUMAN LIFE ISSUES. 1975. q. $6. Human Life Center, University of Steubenville, Steubenville, OH 43952. Eds. Mike Marker, Rita Marker. circ. 6,000. (tabloid format; back issues avail.) Indexed: CERDIC.
Formerly: Love/Life/Death/Issues.

BLIND
see also Social Services and Welfare

028.5 200 US
BRAILLE PILOT. q. Gospel Association for the Blind, Inc., Box 62, Delray Beach, FL 33447. TEL 305-499-8900

212.5 US ISSN 0006-8918
BRAILLE STAR THEOSOPHIST. 1926. bi-m. free. (Theosophical Society) Theosophical Book Association for the Blind, Inc., Krotona 54, Ojai, CA 93023. TEL 805-646-2121 Ed. Dennis Gottschalk. circ. 1,600. (also avail. in audio cassette)

282 US ISSN 0008-8323
CATHOLIC REVIEW (NEW YORK) 1943. 11/yr. free. Xavier Society for the Blind, 154 E. 23rd St., New York, NY 10010. TEL 212-473-7800 Ed. Ann Hynes. circ. 1,780.
Braille

362 UK ISSN 0009-1529
CHANNELS OF BLESSING. 1893. bi-m. £0.70. Royal National Institute for the Blind, Braille House, 338-346 Goswell Rd., London EC1V 7JE, England. Ed. R.W. Heath. circ. 187.
Braille

260 US ISSN 0009-5583
CHRISTIAN RECORD TALKING MAGAZINE. 1955. bi-m. free. Christian Record Braille Foundation, Inc., 4444 S. 52nd St., Lincoln, NE 68506. TEL 402-488-0981 Ed. R.J. Kaiser. circ. 22,300.
Talking book

289.5 252 US ISSN 0146-7166
CHRISTIAN SCIENCE BIBLE LESSONS (BRAILLE EDITION) m. $2.50. (First Church of Christ, Scientist) Christian Science Publishing Society, One Norway St., Boston, MA 02115. TEL 617-450-2000

CHRISTOFFEL-BLINDENMISSION. BERICHT. see *RELIGIONS AND THEOLOGY*

200 UK
CHURCH OF SCOTLAND BRAILLE MAGAZINE. 1934. m. £0.3. Church of Scotland, Publications Department, 121 George St., Edinburgh EH2 4YN, Scotland. Ed. Sheila Wilkie. circ. 150.

240 US ISSN 0017-2359
GOSPEL MESSENGER. vol. 19, 1966. m. free to the blind. ‡ Gospel Association for the Blind, Inc., Box 62, Del Ray Beach, FL 33447. TEL 305-499-8900 Ed. Dr. Ralph Montanus. circ. 1,600.
Braille

296 US ISSN 0021-6321
JEWISH BRAILLE REVIEW. 1931. m. free to the blind. Jewish Braille Institute of America, Inc., 110 E. 30th St., New York, NY 10016. TEL 212-889-2525 Ed. Dr. Jacob Freid. bk. rev. bibl. circ. 2,300.

200 US
JOHN MILTON MAGAZINE. 1935. m. membership. John Milton Society for the Blind, Rm.2492, 475 Riverside Dr., New York, NY 10115. TEL 212-870-3335 Ed. Pam Toplisky. (avail. in braille and large type)
For adults, digest of printed religious journals

JOHN MILTON SUNDAY SCHOOL QUARTERLY. see *CHILDREN AND YOUTH — For*

015 US ISSN 0021-7220
JOHN MILTON TALKING BOOK. 1952. bi-m. free. John Milton Society for the Blind, Rm.249, 475 Riverside Dr., New York, NY 10115. TEL 212-870-3335 Ed. Chenoweth J. Watson. circ. 6,500.

371.911 US
JOTTINGS. 1950. m. free. Gospel Association for the Blind, Inc., Box 62, Delray Beach, FL 33447. TEL 305-449-8900 Ed. Ralph Montanus. circ. 15,000.

284 US ISSN 0024-7480
LUTHERAN MESSENGER FOR THE BLIND. 1927. m. free. Lutheran Church-Missouri Synod, Board for Mission Services, 1333 S. Kirkwood Rd., St. Louis, MO 63122. TEL 314-965-9000 Ed. Rev. Edward Heinicke. bk. rev. circ. 900.
Braille

289.3 US
NEW MESSENGER (TALKING BOOK) 1953. bi-m. Church of Jesus Christ of Latter-Day Saints, 50 E. North Temple St., Salt Lake City, UT 84150. TEL 801-531-2531 circ. 2,200.

362 647.965 US
ST. JOSEPH'S MESSENGER AND ADVOCATE OF THE BLIND. 1898. q. $4. St. Joseph Home, Sisters of St. Joseph of Peace, Box 288, Jersey City, NJ 07303. TEL 201-798-4141 Ed. Sr. Ursula Maphet. illus. circ. 35,000.
Formerly: Orphan's Messenger and Advocate of the Blind (ISSN 0030-5774)
Inkprint

SCOPE (MINNEAPOLIS) see *RELIGIONS AND THEOLOGY — Protestant*

200 UK ISSN 0049-3651
THEOLOGICAL TIMES. (Text in Braille) 1950. q. £1.10. Royal National Institute for the Blind, Braille House, 338-346 Goswell Rd., London EC1V 7JE, England. Ed. Rev. Colin Wood. circ. 76.

284 US ISSN 0041-0357
TRACT MESSENGER. (Text in Braille) 1953. m. free. Lutheran Braille Evangelism Association, 660 E. Montana Ave., St. Paul, MN 55106. TEL 612-776-8430 Ed. Rev. Carl C. Sunwall. circ. 700.

280 US ISSN 0041-8188
UNITY DAILY WORD. 1935. m. free. (Unity School of Christianity) Clovernook Printing House for Blind, 7000 Hamilton Ave., Cincinnati, OH 45231. TEL 513-522-3860 Ed. Colleen Zuck.
Braille

UPPER ROOM; daily devotional guide, interdenominational, international. see *RELIGIONS AND THEOLOGY — Protestant*

BUILDING AND CONSTRUCTION
see also Architecture

690 UK ISSN 0045-687X
CHURCH AND SCHOOL EQUIPMENT NEWS. 1962. bi-m. Trade & Technical Press Ltd., Crown House, Morden, Surrey SM4 5EW, England. Ed. C. Dickenson. adv. bk. rev. illus. cum.index. circ. 8,562.

BUSINESS AND ECONOMICS
see also Advertising and Public Relations; Business and Economics–Banking and Finance; Business and Economics–International Development and Assistance; Business and Economics–Labor and Industrial Relations; Business and Economics–Management; Business and Economics–Marketing and Purchasing; Business and Economics–Public Finance, Taxation; Insurance; Labor Unions also specific industries

BUSINESS AND ECONOMICS — Banking And Finance
see also Insurance

CHURCH AND CLERGY FINANCE. see *RELIGIONS AND THEOLOGY*

BUSINESS AND ECONOMICS — International Development And Assistance

BIJEEN; maandblad over internationale samenleving, bijzonder op het terrein van godsdienst en ontwikkeling. see *RELIGIONS AND THEOLOGY*

VOICE FROM JERUSALEM. see *RELIGIONS AND THEOLOGY — Judaic*

BUSINESS AND ECONOMICS — Labor And Industrial Relations
see also Labor Unions

331 282 ZA
WORKERS' CHALLENGE; from the workers to the workers. 1982. bi-m. Workers' Pastoral Centre, Box 25035, Kitwe, Zambia. Eds. Fr. Jean Marc, Joseph Komakoma. circ. 6,000.

331 SA
YOUNG WORKER. 1976. irreg. R.1. Y.C.W. Publications, Box 47160, Greyville 4023, South Africa. Ed. M.G. Cloete. circ. 10,000.

BUSINESS AND ECONOMICS — Management

CHURCH ADMINISTRATION. see *RELIGIONS AND THEOLOGY — Protestant*

BUSINESS AND ECONOMICS — Marketing And Purchasing
see also Advertising and Public Relations

658 284 282 US
TRIADS. 1984. q. free. Thomas Nelson Publishers, Box 14100, Nashville, TN 37214-1000. TEL 615-226-1890 Ed. Robert Schwalb. adv. bk. rev. charts. illus. circ. 30,000. (back issues avail.)

BUSINESS AND ECONOMICS — Public Finance, Taxation

336 US ISSN 0163-1241
ABINGDON CLERGY INCOME TAX GUIDE. 1972. a. $5.95. Abingdon, 201 Eighth Ave. S., Box 801, Nashville, TN 37202. TEL 615-749-6347
Formerly (until 1978): Clergy's Federal Income Tax Guide (ISSN 0090-9866)

CERAMICS, GLASS AND POTTERY
see also Art

CHILDREN AND YOUTH — About
see also Education

367 UY
ASOCIACION. 1959, suspended in 1978, resumed in 1979. q. free. Confederacion Latinoamericana de Asociaciones Cristianas de Jovenes - Latin American Confederation of YMCAs, Colonia 1884, P.3, Montevideo, Uruguay. Ed. Edgardo G. Crovetto.
Formerly: Confederacion Sudamericana de Asociaciones Cristianas de Jovenes. Noticias (ISSN 0010-5503)

200 369.4 UK ISSN 0045-2831
BRIGADE. 1891. s-a. £0.25. Church Lads' and Church Girls' Brigade, Claude Hardy House, 15 Etchingham Park Rd., Finchley, London N3 2DU, England. Ed. Rev. Charles Grice. bk. rev. circ. 1,200.

267 US ISSN 0009-1723
CHARITY AND CHILDREN; the voice of child care. 1887. 20/yr. Baptist Children's Homes of North Carolina, Inc., 515 Watson Ave., Box 338, Thomasville, NC 27360. TEL 919-476-6183 Ed. J.R. Stegall. adv. bk. rev. circ. 70,000.

267 258 US
CHILDWORLD. 1976. bi-m. free. Christian Children's Fund, Inc., Development Office, Box 26511, Richmond, VA 23261. TEL 804-644-4654 Ed. Charles Gregg. illus. abstr. circ. 900,000.
Formerly (until Aug. 1978): C C F World News.

CRUSADER. see *RELIGIONS AND THEOLOGY — Protestant*

EQUIPPING YOUTH; the training magazine for youth leaders. see *RELIGIONS AND THEOLOGY — Protestant*

369.4 200 US
EVANGELIZING TODAY'S CHILD. 1942. bi-m. $12. Child Evangelism Fellowship, Box 348, Warrenton, MO 63383. Ed. Elsie Lippy. adv. bk. rev. index. circ. 28,000. Indexed: Chr.Per.Ind.

GATEWAY. see *SOCIAL SERVICES AND WELFARE*

HOME LIFE; a Christian family magazine. see *RELIGIONS AND THEOLOGY — Protestant*

KEEPING POSTED WITH N C S Y. (National Conference of Synagogue Youth) see *RELIGIONS AND THEOLOGY — Judaic*

NEUES DORF; Jugend und Familie auf dem Land. see *RELIGIONS AND THEOLOGY — Protestant*

649 268 GW ISSN 0342-7145
THEORIE UND PRAXIS DER SOZIALPAEDAGOGIK. 1949. bi-m. DM.34.50. (Evangelische Bundesarbeitsgemeinschaft fuer Sozialpaedagogik im Kindersalter e.V. (EBASKA)) Luther-Verlag, Cansteinstr. 1, 4800 Bielefeld 14, W. Germany (B.R.D.) Ed. Egbert Haug-Zamp. adv. bk. rev. circ. 6,100.
Formerly: Evangelische Kinderpflege fuer Kindergarten, Hort, Heim und Familie (ISSN 0014-3421)

YOUNG IDEAS. see *RELIGIONS AND THEOLOGY — Other Denominations And Sects*

CHILDREN AND YOUTH — For

ACTION (WINONA LAKE) see *RELIGIONS AND THEOLOGY — Protestant*

AKTIE; maandblad voor jongeren. see *RELIGIONS AND THEOLOGY*

AKTION; Zeitung junger Arbeiter. see *RELIGIONS AND THEOLOGY*

268 US ISSN 0002-5461
ALIVE (ST. LOUIS); for young teens. 1950. m. $15. (Christian Church-Disciples of Christ) Christian Board of Publication, 1316 Convention Plaza, Box 179, St. Louis, MO 63166. TEL 314-231-8500 Ed. Michael E. Dixon. bk. rev. film rev. illus. circ. 13,750. (also avail. in microform from UMI)
Grades 7-9

200 DK
ALLE BOERNS JUL. 1982. a. Kr.13. Danmarks Folkekirkelige Soendagsskoler og Boernegudstjenester, Boernebladet, Korskaervej 25, 7000 Fredericia, Denmark. illus.
Formerly: Boernebladets Jul (ISSN 0105-709X)

ANNALS MAGAZINE. see *RELIGIONS AND THEOLOGY*

ARMONIA DI VOCI. see *MUSIC*

028.5 US ISSN 0745-1172
BETWEEN TIMES. 1919. q. $10. Warner Press, Inc., Box 2499, Anderson, IN 46018. TEL 317-644-7721 Ed. Caroline S. Smith. illus. circ. 7,000.
Formerly: Reach (ISSN 0034-0308)

268 US ISSN 0006-0828
BIBLE-TIME. 1938. q. $5.50. Scripture Press Publications, Inc., 1825 College Ave., Wheaton, IL 60187. TEL 312-668-6000 Ed. Linda S. Winder. illus. circ. 120,000.
Ages 4-5

BIJBELLESSEN VOOR DE KINDEREN. see *RELIGIONS AND THEOLOGY*

028.5 649.7 PO
BOA SEMENTE. m. Casa Publicadora das Assembleias de Deus, Av. Alm. Gago Coutinho 158, 1700 Lisbon, Portugal. Ed. Fernando Martinez da Silva. circ. 7,500.

BRAILLE PILOT. see *BLIND*

BREMER MISSIONSSCHIFF; Kinderbrief aus der Weltmission. see *RELIGIONS AND THEOLOGY*

268 GW ISSN 0007-5833
BUND DER DEUTSCHEN KATHOLISCHEN JUGEND. INFORMATIONSDIENST. 1952. s-m. DM.12 priced half yearly. Jugendhaus Duesseldorf E.V., Carl-Mosterts-Platz 1, 4000 Duesseldorf, W. Germany (B.R.D.) Ed. Andreas Plaeshen. bk. rev. stat. circ. 4,000. (back issues avail.)

BUZZ. see *RELIGIONS AND THEOLOGY*

028.5 649.7 PO
CAMINHO. bi-m. Esc.70. Casa Publicadora das Assembleias de Deus, Av. Alm. Gago Coutinho 158, 1700 Lisbon, Portugal. Ed. Fernando Martinez da Silva. circ. 3,500.
Youth

CHEERING WORDS. see *RELIGIONS AND THEOLOGY*

CHRISTLICH-PAEDAGOGISCHE BLAETTER; Zeitschrift fuer den katechetischen Dienst. see *RELIGIONS AND THEOLOGY*

028.5 284 US
CLUBHOUSE. 1951. 10/yr. $3. Your Story Hour, Inc., Box 15, Berrien Springs, MI 49103. TEL 616-471-9009 Ed. Elaine Meseraull. circ. 17,000.

COMINO. see *RELIGIONS AND THEOLOGY*

028.5 284 GW ISSN 0343-3935
CONTRAPUNKT; christliche Zweimonatszeitschrift fuer junge Leute. 1925. bi-m. DM.16 per no. M B K-Verlag, Hermann-Loens-Str. 14, Postfach 560, D-4902 Bad Salzuflen 1, W. Germany (B.R.D.) Ed. Hans-Hermann Boehm. circ. 20,000. (back issues avail.)

248.82 US ISSN 0011-0019
COUNSELOR. 1943. q. $5.50. Scripture Press Publications, Inc., 1825 College Ave., Wheaton, IL 60187. TEL 312-668-6000 Eds. Joyce Gibson, Grace Fox Anderson. adv. bk. rev. illus. circ. 170,000.
Ages 8-11

CRUSADER. see *RELIGIONS AND THEOLOGY — Protestant*

268 UK
CRUSADER. 1928. m. (Oct.-Jul.) £1. Crusade of the Blessed Sacrament, 7 Edge Hill, London SW19 4LR, England. Ed. Joseph Raybould. adv. illus. circ. 25,000.
Formerly: Crusade Messenger (ISSN 0011-2143)
For ages 8-15

028.5 284 US
CRUSADER MAGAZINE. 1958. 7/yr. $5.50. Calvinist Cadet Corps, 1333 Alger St., Box 7259, Grand Rapids, MI 49510. TEL 616-241-5616 Ed. G. Richard Broene. adv. circ. 12,000.

268 PO ISSN 0011-2194
CRUZADA EUCARISTICA. 1930. m. Esc.90($3) L. das Teresinhas 5, Braga, Portugal. Ed. Fernando Leite. circ. 60,000.

284 US
DISCOVERIES. 1920. w. $6.25. (Children's Ministries) Nazarene Publishing House, Box 527, Kansas City, MO 64141. TEL 816-931-1900 Ed. Janet Sawyer. illus. circ. 60,000.

DISCOVERY (NEW YORK) see *RELIGIONS AND THEOLOGY*

EMMAUS LETTER. see *RELIGIONS AND THEOLOGY — Roman Catholic*

028.5 US ISSN 0015-9077
FOUR AND FIVE. 1918. w. $6.50 per set of 5 for 3 months. ‡ Standard Publishing, 8121 Hamilton Ave., Cincinnati, OH 45231. TEL 513-931-4050 Ed. Heather Smith Turner. illus. circ. 140,000.

248.83 US
FREEWAY; a power/line paper. 1966. q. $5.50. Scripture Press Publications, Inc., 1825 College Ave., Wheaton, IL 60187. Eds. Ardith Hooten, Cindy Atoji. circ. 65,000.
Formerly: Power Life (ISSN 0032-6046)
For ages 16-19

FRIEND. see *RELIGIONS AND THEOLOGY — Other Denominations And Sects*

FRIENDLY COMPANION. see *RELIGIONS AND THEOLOGY*

GOSPEL STANDARD. see *RELIGIONS AND THEOLOGY*

GROUP (LOVELAND); the youth ministry magazine. see *RELIGIONS AND THEOLOGY*

GROUP'S JR. HIGH MINISTRY MAGAZINE. see *RELIGIONS AND THEOLOGY*

GUIDE (HAGERSTOWN) see *RELIGIONS AND THEOLOGY — Other Denominations And Sects*

HICALL. see *RELIGIONS AND THEOLOGY — Other Denominations And Sects*

IN-TOUCH. see *RELIGIONS AND THEOLOGY — Protestant*

266 028.5 IT ISSN 0021-2806
ITALIA MISSIONARIA. Cover title: I M. 1919. m. L.10000($7) Pontificio Istituto Missioni Estere, Via Mose Bianchi 94, 20149 Milan, Italy. Ed. P. Piero Gheddo. adv. bk. rev. bibl. illus. circ. 15,000.
Missions

268 US
IT'S OUR WORLD; mission news from the Holy Childhood Association. (In 3 Editions: Grades K-2, 3-5, 6-8) vol.74, 1974. q. $0.10. ‡ (Pontifical Association of the Holy Childhood) Holy Childhood Association, National Office-U.S., 1720 Massachusetts Ave., N.W., Washington, DC 20036. TEL 202-775-8637 circ. 350,000.
Formerly: Annals of the Holy Childhood (ISSN 0003-4940)

028.5 200 UK
J A M. (Jesus and Me) 1985. m. £15. Herlad House Ltd., 27 Chapel Rd., Worthing, Sussex BN11 1EG, England. Ed. Christina Lacey. circ. 23,000.

790 FI ISSN 0781-7177
J P. (Joka Poika); paper for boys and girls. 1938. m.(10/yr.) Fmk.90. Poikien Keskus r.y., Box 345, 00101 Helsinki 10, Finland. Ed. Seppo Koivistoinen. adv. bk. rev. circ. 29,200.
Former titles: J P Joka Poika (ISSN 0355-4201); Joka Poika (ISSN 0047-2050)

J'AIME LIRE. see *RELIGIONS AND THEOLOGY*

268 SP
JESUS MAESTRO. 1872. m. 800 ptas.($17) Compania de Santa Teresa de Jesus, Ganduxer 85, Barcelona-22, Spain. Ed. Maria Victoria Molins. bk. rev. index every 5 yrs. circ. 14,000.

JEWISH CURRENT EVENTS. see *ETHNIC INTERESTS*

200 US
JOHN MILTON SUNDAY SCHOOL QUARTERLY. 1935. 4/yr. free. John Milton Society for the Blind, Rm. 249, 475 Riverside Dr., New York, NY 10115. TEL 212-870-3335 Ed. Pam Toplisky. (Braille; also avail. in talking book)

JONGE KERK. see *RELIGIONS AND THEOLOGY*

JUNGE GEMEINDE. see *RELIGIONS AND THEOLOGY*

JUNGSCHARHELFER; Mitarbeiterhilfe fuer Jungen- und Maedchenarbeit. see *RELIGIONS AND THEOLOGY*

JUNIOR LIFE. see *RELIGIONS AND THEOLOGY*

JUNIOR TRAILS. see *RELIGIONS AND THEOLOGY — Other Denominations And Sects*

028.5 UG ISSN 0023-1975
KIZITO; children's own magazine. (Text in Luganda) 9/yr. 4s. Kampala Archdiocese, Box 14125 Mengo, Kampala, Uganda. Ed. Sister Anna Maria.

KOLEINU. see *RELIGIONS AND THEOLOGY — Judaic*

028.5 284 US ISSN 0737-8173
LIGHTED PATHWAY. 1929. m. $6.50. (Church of God) Pathway Press, 922-1080 Montgomery Ave., Cleveland, TN 37311. TEL 615-476-4512 Ed. Marcus V. Hand. circ. 25,000.

MY DEVOTIONS. see *RELIGIONS AND THEOLOGY*

NEW BEGINNINGS (PISGAH FOREST) see *RELIGIONS AND THEOLOGY — Protestant*

NEW DISCIPLES. see *RELIGIONS AND THEOLOGY — Protestant*

369.4 200 NO
NY DAG. s-m. Norges Kristelige Ungdomsforbund - Norwegian Christian Youth Organization, St. Olavsplass, Box 6905, Oslo 1, Norway. adv. circ. 6,300.

NYT FRA D U K. (Danmarks Unge Katolikker) see *RELIGIONS AND THEOLOGY — Roman Catholic*

OLOMEINU/OUR WORLD. see *RELIGIONS AND THEOLOGY — Judaic*

ONS JEUG. see *RELIGIONS AND THEOLOGY — Protestant*

268 US ISSN 0030-6894
OUR LITTLE FRIEND. French edition: Notre Petit Ami. 1890. w. $14.95. (Seventh-Day Adventists) Pacific Press Publishing Association, 1350 Kings Rd., Nampa, ID 83651. TEL 208-467-6600 Ed. Louis Schutter. illus. circ. 65,785.
Ages 3-6

268 UK ISSN 0030-7327
OUTWARD BOUND. m. £1.20. Presbyterian Church in Ireland, Church House, Fisherwick Place, Belfast BT1 6DW, N. Ireland. Ed. Brian Murphy. circ. 6,500.
Ages 8 to 10

PAA VEJ; en bibelnoegle for juniorer. see *RELIGIONS AND THEOLOGY*

POCKETS. see *RELIGIONS AND THEOLOGY — Protestant*

028.5 US ISSN 0032-8286
PRIMARY FRIEND. 1953. w. $7. (Aldersgate Publications Association) Light & Life Press, Winona Lake, IN 46590. TEL 219-267-7161 Ed. Marie E. Beck. circ. 37,000.

PRIMERA LUZ. see *RELIGIONS AND THEOLOGY*

PROBE (MEMPHIS) see *RELIGIONS AND THEOLOGY — Protestant*

028.5 US ISSN 0162-5217
R-A-D-A-R. 1886. w. $6.50 per set of 5 for 3 months. ‡ Standard Publishing, 8121 Hamilton Ave., Cincinnati, OH 45231. TEL 513-931-4050 Ed. Margaret Williams. illus. circ. 111,000.
Former titles: Jet Cadet (ISSN 0022-6645); Junior Life.
Ages 8-12

RAYONS; revue des jeunesses mariales. see *RELIGIONS AND THEOLOGY — Roman Catholic*

REGENBOGEN; Zeitung fuer Maedchen und Buben. see *RELIGIONS AND THEOLOGY*

268 US ISSN 0034-5660
RESOURCES FOR YOUTH MINISTRY. 1969. q. $14.95. ‡ Lutheran Church-Missouri Synod, Board for Youth Services, 1333 S. Kirkwood Rd., St. Louis, MO 63122. TEL 314-965-9000 Ed. LeRoy Wilke. bk. rev. illus. circ. 3,000.

ROEDDERNE. see *RELIGIONS AND THEOLOGY — Protestant*

SLINGERVEL; publication for the youth. see *RELIGIONS AND THEOLOGY — Protestant*

268 US ISSN 0039-2006
STORY FRIENDS. 1905. w. $9. Mennonite Publishing House, 616 Walnut Ave., Scottdale, PA 15683. TEL 412-887-8500 Ed. Marjorie Waybill. bk. rev. illus. circ. 11,800.
Ages 4-9

200 US ISSN 0044-071X
T Q. (Teen Quest) 1946. 11/yr. (except Jul.-Aug. combined) $10. Good News Broadcasting Association, Inc., Back to the Bible Broadcast, Box 82808, Lincoln, NE 68501. TEL 402-474-4567 Ed. Nancy Brumbaugh Bayne. illus. circ. 80,000.
Formerly: Young Ambassador.

TALKS AND TALES. see *RELIGIONS AND THEOLOGY*

200 US
TEEN POWER (1979); a power/line paper. 1966. q. $5.50. ‡ Scripture Press Publications, Inc., 1825 College Ave., Wheaton, IL 60187. TEL 312-668-6000 Eds. Norma Felske, Pam Campbell. circ. 110,000. (looseleaf format)
Former titles: Connect; Teen Power; Young Teen Power (ISSN 0044-0922)
For ages 12-16

200 US
TEENS TODAY. 1969. w. $6.25. (Church of the Nazarene) Nazarene Publishing House, Box 527, Kansas City, MO 64141. TEL 816-931-1900 Ed. Gary Silverwright. illus. circ. 60,000.

TZIVOS HASHEM CHILDREN'S NEWSLETTER. see *RELIGIONS AND THEOLOGY — Judaic*

267 UK ISSN 0049-6901
WARRIOR. 1940. m., (except Aug.) £2.20. ‡ W E C International, Bulstrode, Gerrards Cross, Bucks SL9 8SZ, England. Ed. C.D. Scott. illus. circ. 17,000.
Formerly: Young Warrior.

WEEKLY BIBLE READER. see *RELIGIONS AND THEOLOGY*

DIE WENDE; Oesterreichs groesste Wolhenzeitung fuer junge Erwachsene. see *RELIGIONS AND THEOLOGY — Roman Catholic*

WINDOW. see *RELIGIONS AND THEOLOGY — Protestant*

268 US ISSN 0043-6984
WITH; a magazine for the middle teens. 1968. m. $13.15. Mennonite Publishing House, 616 Walnut Ave., Scottdale, PA 15683. TEL 412-887-8500 (Co-publisher: Faith and Life Press) Ed. Susan E. Janzen. illus. circ. 6,250.

266 CN ISSN 0707-2279
WORLDWIND. vol.2, 1979. 2/yr. Can.$1.00 per no. United Church of Canada, 85 St. Clair Ave. E., Toronto, Ont. M4T 1M8, Canada. TEL 416-925-5931 Ed. Rebekah Chevalier. illus.

WYZER. see *RELIGIONS AND THEOLOGY — Other Denominations And Sects*

YOUNG SOLDIER. see *RELIGIONS AND THEOLOGY — Other Denominations And Sects*

267 MF ISSN 0049-8459
YOUTH MIRROR. (Text in English and French) 1968. m. $1. Young Men's Muslim Associaion, 53 Magon St., P.O. Box 292, Port Louis, Mauritius. Ed. Azad Dhomun. adv. bk. rev. play rev. illus. circ. 20,000.

CIVIL DEFENSE
see also Military

CIVIL RIGHTS
see Political Science–Civil Rights

CLASSICAL STUDIES
see also Archaeology; History; Linguistics; Literature

870 200 BE
INSTRUMENTA LEXICOLOGIA LATINA. SERIES A & B. 1979. irreg., approx. 10 vols. per yr. (Cetedoc) N.V. Brepols I.G.P., Rue Baron Francois du Four 8, B-2300 Turnhout, Belgium.

ROEMISCHE HISTORISCHE MITTEILUNGEN. see *HISTORY — History Of Europe*

VERBA SENIORUM. see *RELIGIONS AND THEOLOGY*

CLUBS
see also College and Alumni

CALVINIST CONTACT. see *RELIGIONS AND THEOLOGY — Protestant*

367 US
TODAY'S SINGLE; serving the singles of America. 1980. q. $10. National Association of Christian Singles, 1933 W. Wisconsin Ave., Milwaukee, WI 53233. TEL 414-344-7300 Ed. John M. Fisco, Jr. adv. bk. rev. circ. 12,000.

367 US
TORCHLIGHT. 1941. q. $2. ‡ Federation of Jewish Men's Clubs Inc., 475 Riverside Dr., Ste. 244, New York, NY 10027. TEL 212-749-8100 adv. bk. rev. illus. circ. 40,000.
Formerly (until 1977): Torch (Chicago) (ISSN 0049-416X)

COLLEGE AND ALUMNI
see also Literary and Political Reviews; Literature

AKADEMISCHE MONATSBLAETTER. see *RELIGIONS AND THEOLOGY — Roman Catholic*

378.1 UK ISSN 0012-5695
DOUAI MAGAZINE. 1894. a. £2.50. Douai Abbey, Woolhampton, Near Reading, Berkshire, England. Ed. D.E. Power. adv. bk. rev. illus. circ. 1,300.

378.1 US ISSN 0017-7040
HAMEVASER. 1962. m. $7.50. Yeshiva University, Jewish Studies Division, 500 W. 185 St, New York, NY 10033. TEL 212-960-5277 Ed. Adam Karp. adv. bk. rev. index. circ. 5,000. (tabloid format)

378.1 US ISSN 0017-8047
HARVARD DIVINITY BULLETIN. 1935. bi-m. (5/yr.) free. ‡ Harvard Divinity School, 45 Francis Ave., Cambridge, MA 02138. TEL 617-495-5085 Ed. J. Michael West. bk. rev. illus. circ. 25,000. Indexed: Rel.Per.

378.1 SA ISSN 0019-2716
IMBONGI. (Text in English) 1964. s-a. free. ‡ Amanzimtoti Zulu Training School, P.O. Adams Mission, Durban 4100, Natal, South Africa. illus. circ. 1,000. (newspaper)

378 266 US
MEMORANDUM (ST. PAUL) 1969. 3/yr. free. College of St. Thomas, 2115 Summit Ave., St. Paul, MN 55105. TEL 612-647-5000 Ed. Bill Kirchgessnerski. circ. 32,500.

NAROPA MAGAZINE. see *RELIGIONS AND THEOLOGY — Oriental*

378.1 AU ISSN 0013-2489
RUNDBRIEF EHEMALIGER SCHUELER UND FREUNDE DER SCHULBRUEDER. 1948. s-a. S.80. Provinzialat der Brueder der Christlichen Schulen, Anton Boeckgasse 20, A-1215 Vienna, Austria. adv. bk. rev. abstr. bibl. charts. illus. stat. circ. 3,000.

COMMUNICATIONS
see also Communications–Radio and Television; Journalism

CATHOLIC MEDIA COUNCIL. INFORMATION BULLETIN. see *RELIGIONS AND THEOLOGY — Roman Catholic*

CHRISTIAN COMMUNICATIONS. see *RELIGIONS AND THEOLOGY*

CULTURAL INFORMATION SERVICE; the magazine for lifelong learners. see *EDUCATION*

301.16 200 US ISSN 0149-6980
MEDIA & VALUES; a quarterly magazine/educational resource analyzing the social impact of mass media and new technologies on the family, youth and children. 1977. q. $12. Media Action Research Center, Inc., 1962 S. Shenandoah, Los Angeles, CA 90034. TEL 213-559-2944 Ed. Sr. Elizabeth Thoman. bk. rev. circ. 2,500.

COMMUNICATIONS — Postal Affairs
see also Hobbies–Philately

COMMUNICATIONS — Radio And Television

384.54 286 US
BEAM. bi-m. free. Southern Baptist Radio and Television Commission, 6350 W. Freeway, Fort Worth, TX 76150. TEL 817-737-4011 Ed. Gregory D. Warner. circ. controlled.

384.54 286 US
BEAM INTERNATIONAL; newsletter serving broadcasters around the world. (Text in English & Spanish) 1950; N.S. 1968. bi-m. free. Southern Baptist Radio and Television Commission, 6350 W. Freeway, Fort Worth, TX 76150. TEL 817-737-4011 Ed. Gregory D. Warner. circ. controlled.

INTERLIT. see *RELIGIONS AND THEOLOGY*

260 GW
MEDIA DEVELOPMENT. (Text in English, French, German and Spanish) 1970. q. DM.20($7) Eckart-Verlag, Richard-Wagner-Strasse 1, 4812 Brackwede, W. Germany (B.R.D.) Ed. Hans-Wolfgang Hessler. bk. rev. illus. circ. 3,000. Indexed: CERDIC. Commun.Abstr.
Formerly: World Association for Christian Communication. Journal (ISSN 0092-7821)

384 200 US ISSN 0034-4079
RELIGIOUS BROADCASTING. 1969. m.(11/yr.) $18. National Religious Broadcasters, Inc, CN 1926, Morristown, NJ 07960. TEL 201-428-5400 Ed. Dr. Ben Armstrong. adv. bk. rev. charts. illus. circ. 9,500. (back issues avail.) Indexed: Chr.Per.Ind.

384 200 US
UNDA-U S A NEWSLETTER. 1963. bi-m. membership. Unda-U S A, National Catholic Association for Broadcasters and Allied Communicators, 3015 Fourth St., N.E., Washington, DC 20017. Ed. Rosemary Jeffries. bk. rev. stat. circ. 500.
Formerly: Catholic Broadcasters Association. Newsletter (ISSN 0016-3686)
Religious

COMPUTER APPLICATIONS
see Humanities: Comprehensive Works–Computer Applications

COMPUTERS — Computer Industry, Vocational Guidance
see also Education

COMPUTERS — Computer Sales
see also Business and Economics–Marketing and Purchasing

DANCE
see also Music

793.31 200 US
SACRED DANCE GUILD JOURNAL. 1958. q. membership. Sacred Dance Guild, c/o Toni Intravaia, Ed., 201 Hewitt, Carbondale, IL 62901. bk. rev. circ. 600.

DEAF
see also Social Services and Welfare

EDUCATION
see also Education–Adult Education; Education–Guides to Schools and Colleges; Education–Higher Education; Education–International Education Programs; Education–School Organization and Administration; Education–Teaching Methods and Curriculum

377.9 US ISSN 0002-6093
ALLIANCE REVIEW. vol.25, 1973. irreg. membership. American Friends of the Alliance Israelite Universelle Inc., 135 William St., New York, NY 10038. TEL 212-349-0537 Ed. Saadiah Cherniak. illus.
Religious

CARMELUS; Commentarii ab Instituto Carmelitano Editi. see *RELIGIONS AND THEOLOGY — Roman Catholic*

CATHOLIC EDUCATION. see *RELIGIONS AND THEOLOGY — Roman Catholic*

CHILDREN'S LEADER. see *RELIGIONS AND THEOLOGY — Protestant*

CHRISTOPHORUS. see *RELIGIONS AND THEOLOGY — Roman Catholic*

370 301.16 US ISSN 0097-952X
CULTURAL INFORMATION SERVICE; the magazine for lifelong learners. 1972. 18/yr. $25. CIStems, Inc., Box 786, New York, NY 10159. TEL 212-691-5240 Ed. Frederic A. Brussat. bk. rev. index.
Education and media

377.9 US
CURRENT ISSUES IN CATHOLIC HIGHER EDUCATION. 1975. s-a. price varies. Association of Catholic Colleges and Universities, One Dupont Circle, Ste. 650, Washington, DC 20036. TEL 202-457-0650 Ed. David M. Johnson. circ. 2,000. (also avail. in microform from EDR; reprint service avail. from UMI) Indexed: ERIC.
Supersedes (1975-1980): National Catholic Educational Association. Occasional Papers.

377.9 IT ISSN 0012-9518
ECO DELL'EDUCAZIONE EBRAICA. 1946. q. L.1500. ‡ (Histadruth Ha-Morim) Associazione Insegnanti Ebrei d'Italia, Via Canova 7A, Milan, Italy. Eds. G.L. Luzzatto, Lydia Bedarida. adv. bk. rev. illus. circ. 500.
Religious

EDUCATION NEWSLINE. see *RELIGIONS AND THEOLOGY — Protestant*

377.8 268 GW ISSN 0014-3413
DER EVANGELISCHE ERZIEHER; Zeitschrift fuer Paedagogik und Theologie. 1945. bi-m. DM.36. Verlag Moritz Diesterweg, Hochstr. 29-31, D-6000 Frankfurt/Main 1, W. Germany (B.R.D.) Ed.Bd. adv. bk. rev. abstr. index. circ. 3,500.
Religious

370 US ISSN 0020-5117
INTERACTION (ST. LOUIS); a magazine church school workers grow by. 1960. m. $8.75. (Lutheran Church-Missouri Synod, Board for Parish Services) Concordia Publishing House, 1333 S. Kirkwood Rd., St. Louis, MO 63122. TEL 314-664-7000 Ed. Martha Jander. bk. rev. illus. index. circ. 20,000. (also avail. in microform from UMI) Indexed: Curr.Cont.

JEWISH CURRENT EVENTS. see *ETHNIC INTERESTS*

377.9 US ISSN 0021-6429
JEWISH EDUCATION. 1929. q. $12.50. (Council for Jewish Education) J.E.S.N.A., 730 Broadway, 2nd Fl., New York, NY 10003-9502. Ed. Dr. Alvin Schiff. adv. bk. rev. index. cum.index: 5 years and 25 years (vols.1-43) circ. 1,500. (also avail. in microform from UMI; reprint service avail. from UMI) Indexed: Educ.Ind. Psychol.Abstr. Ind.Jew.Per. Rel.& Theol.Abstr.
Religious

JOURNAL OF CHRISTIAN EDUCATION OF THE AFRICAN METHODIST EPISCOPAL CHURCH. see *RELIGIONS AND THEOLOGY — Protestant*

377.8 NE ISSN 0022-8354
KANDELAAR. 1947. m. fl.47.50. Nederlandse Vereniging van Vrijzinnige Zondagsscholen, c/o Mevr M. Spyker v.d. Laan, Maskweg 28, 6871 kx Renkuu, Netherlands. Ed. C. van Santen-Teeling. bk. rev. circ. 1,200.
Religious

KATOLICKI UNIWERSYTET LUBELSKI. ZESZYTY NAUKOWE. see *RELIGIONS AND THEOLOGY — Roman Catholic*

377.8 US ISSN 0023-0839
KEY TO CHRISTIAN EDUCATION. 1962. q. $4. ‡ Standard Publishing, 8121 Hamilton Ave., Cincinnati, OH 45231. TEL 513-931-4050 Ed. Virginia Beddow. index. circ. 68,000. Indexed: CERDIC. Chr.Per.Ind.
Religious

LUMEN VITAE; international review of religious education. see *RELIGIONS AND THEOLOGY — Roman Catholic*

370 377.8 US ISSN 0024-7448
LUTHERAN EDUCATION. 1864. 5/yr. $8. Concordia College, 7400 Augusta St., River Forest, IL 60305. TEL 312-771-8300 Ed. Merle L. Radke. adv. bk. rev. illus. index. circ. 4,200. (also avail. in microfilm from UMI) Indexed: Educ.Ind. CERDIC.

MAESTRO. see *RELIGIONS AND THEOLOGY — Roman Catholic*

MAISON-DIEU; revue de Pastorale Liturgique. see *RELIGIONS AND THEOLOGY*

MISCELANEA COMILLAS; revista de teologia y ciencias humanas. see *RELIGIONS AND THEOLOGY*

377.9 US ISSN 0550-5682
N C E A NOTES. 5/yr. membership. National Catholic Educational Association, 1077 30 St., N.W., Washington, DC 20007. TEL 202-293-5954

377.8 CN
O E C T A REPORTER. vol.3, 1974. 8/yr. Can.$5 membership. Ontario English Catholic Teachers Association, 1260 Bay St., Toronto 5, Ont. M5R 2B4, Canada. TEL 416-925-2493 Ed. Aleda O'Connor. adv. bk. rev. abstr. illus. circ. 20,000.
Formerly: O E C T A Review (ISSN 0029-7070)

O I E C BULLETIN. (Catholic International Education Office) see *RELIGIONS AND THEOLOGY — Roman Catholic*

P R R C: EMERGING TRENDS. (Princeton Religion Research Center, Inc.) see *RELIGIONS AND THEOLOGY*

377.9 US
PARISH COORDINATOR OF RELIGIOUS EDUCATION. q. membership. (National Forum of Religious Educators) National Catholic Educational Association, 1077 30 St. N.W., Ste. 100, Washington, DC 20007. TEL 202-293-5954 (reprint service avail. from UMI)

PLANBOOK FOR LEADERS OF CHILDREN. see *RELIGIONS AND THEOLOGY — Protestant*

PRISMET; pedagogisk tidsskrift. see *RELIGIONS AND THEOLOGY*

377.8 GW
RELIGION HEUTE. (Supplement to "Religion Heute") 1982. q. DM.40 to individuals; students, DM. 26.75. Arbeitsgemeinschaft Religionspaedagogik Verlags-GmbH, Alter Boesperder Weg 21, D-5750 Menden 1, W. Germany (B.R.D.), W. Germany (B.R.D.) Ed.Bd. adv. bk. rev.
Formerly: Zeitschrift fuer Religionspaedagogik (ISSN 0722-9151)

RELIGION IN AMERICA. see *RELIGIONS AND THEOLOGY*

RELIGIONE E SCUOLA; mensile per l'animazione culturale e la ricerca religiosa. see *RELIGIONS AND THEOLOGY — Roman Catholic*

377.8 GW ISSN 0341-8960
RELIGIONSUNTERRICHT AN HOEHEREN SCHULEN. 1958. bi-m. DM.38. (Bundesverband der Katholischen Religionslehrer an Gymnasien e.V.) Patmos Verlag, Am Wehrhahn 100, Postfach 6213, 4000 Duesseldorf 1, W. Germany (B.R.D.) Ed. Roman Mensing. adv. bk. rev. index. circ. 2,000. Indexed: CERDIC.
Religions

RELIGIOUS EDUCATION; a platform for the free discussion of issues in the field of religion and their bearing on education. see *RELIGIONS AND THEOLOGY*

ROSICRUCIAN DIGEST. see *PHILOSOPHY*

RUIMZICHT. see *RELIGIONS AND THEOLOGY*

SANTUARIO DE APARECIDA. see *RELIGIONS AND THEOLOGY*

371.4 377.8 US ISSN 0887-1167
SINGLE ADULT MINISTRY INFORMATION. 1973. m. $15. Institute for Singles Dynamics, Box 11394, Kansas City, MO 64112. TEL 816-763-9401 Ed. Donald W. Davidson.
Formerly: Single.

268 370 GW ISSN 0012-2580
SONNTAGSCHULMITARBEITER; religionspaedagogisches Monatsblatt. 1971. q. DM.20. Verlag J. G. Oncken Nachf. GmbH, Langenbeckstr. 28/30, 3500 Kassel 1, W. Germany (B.R.D.) Ed. Hartmut Priebe. bk. rev. stat. index. circ. 7,500.
Formed by the merger of: Dienst am Kinde & Sonntags Schulhelfer.
Religious

TEACHING 7-10'S. see *RELIGIONS AND THEOLOGY*

THEOLOGICAL EDUCATION. see *RELIGIONS AND THEOLOGY*

377.8 US ISSN 0040-8441
TODAY'S CATHOLIC TEACHER. 1967. m. (Sep.-May) $14.95. ‡ Peter Li, Inc., 2451 E. River Rd., Dayton, OH 45439. TEL 513-294-5785 Ed. Ruth A. Matheny. adv. bk. rev. film rev. charts. illus. stat. circ. 51,719. (also avail. in microfilm from UMI; reprint service avail. from UMI) Indexed: Cath.Ind. Biol.Dig. CERDIC.

377.8 CN ISSN 0009-5680
VANGUARD (TORONTO) 1970. 6/yr. Can.$8($8) Wedge Publishing Foundation, P.O. Box 489 Stn. J, Toronto, Ont., Canada. Ed. Bert Witvoet. adv. bk. rev. film rev. illus. circ. 3,000. Indexed: CERDIC. RILA.

VITA GIUSEPPINA. see *RELIGIONS AND THEOLOGY — Roman Catholic*

377.9 US ISSN 0044-1007
YOUR CHILD. 1967. 4/yr. $3. (Family Education Committee) United Synagogue of America, Commission on Jewish Education, 155 5th Ave., New York, NY 10010. TEL 212-260-8450 Ed. Morton K. Sicgel. bk. rev. circ. 10,000.

YOUTH PLANBOOK. see *RELIGIONS AND THEOLOGY — Protestant*

EDUCATION — Abstracting, Bibliographies, Statistics

MEDIA-INFORMATIEDIENST. see *RELIGIONS AND THEOLOGY — Abstracting, Bibliographies, Statistics*

EDUCATION — Adult Education

EXPOSITOR BIBLICO (TEACHER EDITION) see *RELIGIONS AND THEOLOGY — Protestant*

INFORMATORE DI URIO. see *RELIGIONS AND THEOLOGY — Roman Catholic*

JOVENES BIBLICO (STUDENT EDITION) see *RELIGIONS AND THEOLOGY — Protestant*

SYNTHESIS (MYSTIC) see *RELIGIONS AND THEOLOGY — Roman Catholic*

EDUCATION — Guides To Schools And Colleges

ASSOCIATION OF THEOLOGICAL SCHOOLS IN THE UNITED STATES AND CANADA. DIRECTORY. see *RELIGIONS AND THEOLOGY*

378.002 US
GRADUATE SCHOOL GUIDE. a. $5. Catholic News Publishing Co., Inc., 210 N. Ave., New Rochelle, NY 10801. TEL 914-632-7771 Ed. Victor L. Ridder, Jr. adv. stat. circ. 35,000.

378.002 US
NATIONAL DIRECTORY OF CATHOLIC HIGHER EDUCATION. a. $10. Catholic News Publishing Co., Inc., 210 N. Ave., New Rochelle, NY 10801. TEL 914-632-1220 Ed. Victor L. Ridder. adv.

EDUCATION — Higher Education
see also College and Alumni

378 268 US ISSN 0094-260X
A A B C NEWSLETTER. 1958. 3/yr. $4. American Association of Bible Colleges, Box 1523, Fayetteville, AR 72701. TEL 501-521-8164 Ed. Randall Bell. circ. 1,850.

ASSOCIATION FOR PROFESSIONAL EDUCATION FOR MINISTRY. REPORT OF THE BIENNIAL MEETING. see *RELIGIONS AND THEOLOGY*

M I E C SERVICO DE DOCUMENTACION. (Movimiento Internacional de Estudiantes Catolicos) see *RELIGIONS AND THEOLOGY — Roman Catholic*

378 297 UA
MAJALLAT AL-AZHAR. (Text in Arabic & English) 1931. m. P.T.20. Council of Islamic Research, Al-Azhar University, Cairo, Egypt. (Co-sponsor: Al-Azhar University) Ed. Ali Al-Khatib. bk. rev.

N I C M JOURNAL FOR JEWS AND CHRISTIANS IN HIGHER EDUCATION. (National Institute for Campus Ministries) see *RELIGIONS AND THEOLOGY*

NAROPA MAGAZINE. see *RELIGIONS AND THEOLOGY — Oriental*

377.8 US ISSN 0028-5374
NEW HORIZONS. vol.38, 1970. 3/yr. free. United Board for Christian Higher Education in Asia, 475 Riverside Drive, New York, NY 10115. TEL 212-870-2608 Ed. Merle L. Bender. bk. rev. illus. circ. 7,000.

EDUCATION — International Education Programs

RELIGION FOR PEACE. see *RELIGIONS AND THEOLOGY*

EDUCATION — School Organization And Administration

CHURCH AND SCHOOL EQUIPMENT NEWS. see *BUILDING AND CONSTRUCTION*

371 DK ISSN 0109-3886
K S BULLETIN. 1979. q. free. (Foreningen af Katolske Skoler i Danmark) Joergen Frost-Jensen, Skt. Ibs Skole, Kildegade 18, 8700 Horsens, Denmark. illus.

EDUCATION — Special Education And Rehabilitation
see also Blind; Social Services and Welfare

EDUCATION — Teaching Methods And Curriculum
see also specific subjects

371.3 200 GW
INFORMATIONEN ZUM RELIGIONSUNTERRICHT. (Teacher's aid for series "Religion Heute") 1968. q. DM.18. Arbeitsgemeinschaft Religiouspaedagogik GmbH, Dalihaus Str. 8, D-5750 Merden 1, W. Germany (B.R.D.) Ed.Bd.

377.8 NE ISSN 0036-6544
SCHOOL EN GODSDIENST; catechetical periodical for elementary school teachers. 1947. 8/yr. fl.38.50 to individuals; students fl.30.00. (Centraal Bureau voor het Katholiek Onderwijs - Higher Catechetical Institute) Hoger Katechetisch Instituut, Nijmegen, Postbus 38089, 6503 AB Nijmegen, Netherlands. adv. bk. rev. bibl. illus. index. circ. 2,400. Indexed: CERDIC.

370 NE ISSN 0049-3805
THOMAS; maandblad voor lichamelijke opvoeding. 1960. m. fl.45 to individuals; students fl.40. Katholieke Vereniging van Leerkrachten in de Lichamelijke Opvoeding "Thomas van Aquino", Willem van Oranjelaan 33, 5211 CP den Bosch, Netherlands. Ed. H.M.P.G. van der Loo. adv. bk. rev. film rev. illus. circ. 6,000.

377.8 NE ISSN 0166-6002
VERBUM; tijdschrift voor katechese. 1930. 8/yr. fl.38.50 to individuals; students fl.30.00. (Centraal Bureau voor het Katholiek Onderwijs) Hoger Katechetisch Instituut, Nijmegen, Postbus 38089, 6503 AB Nijmegen, Netherlands. illus. circ. 1,000. Indexed: CERDIC.

ELECTRICITY AND ELECTRICAL ENGINEERING
see also Communications–Radio and Television

ENCYCLOPEDIAS AND GENERAL ALMANACS

CARITAS-KALENDER. see *RELIGIONS AND THEOLOGY*

ENGINEERING — Civil Engineering
see also Building and Construction

ETHNIC INTERESTS

A J L NEWSLETTER. (Association of Jewish Libraries) see *LIBRARY AND INFORMATION SCIENCES*

296 US ISSN 0364-0094
A J S REVIEW. 1975. s-a. $15. (Association for Jewish Studies) Ktav Publishing House, 900 Jefferson St., No.6249, Hoboken, NJ 07030-7205. TEL 201-903-9524 Ed. Robert Chazan. bk. rev. bibl. circ. 1,500. Indexed: Hist.Abstr. Amer.Bibl.Slavic & E.Eur.Stud. Amer.Hist.& Life.
Jewish interests

AGADA; Jewish literary bi-annual; stories, poetry, midrash. see *RELIGIONS AND THEOLOGY — Judaic*

AMERICAN COUNCIL FOR JUDAISM. SPECIAL INTEREST REPORT; a digest of news items and articles in the area of the council's interest. see *RELIGIONS AND THEOLOGY — Judaic*

296 900 US ISSN 0002-905X
AMERICAN JEWISH ARCHIVES; devoted to the preservation and study of the American Jewish experience. 1948. s-a. free to qualified personnel. American Jewish Archives, 3101 Clifton Ave., Cincinnati, OH 45220. TEL 513-221-1875 Eds. Jacob R. Marcus, Abraham J. Peck. bk. rev. bibl. illus. index. circ. 5,000. (also avail. in microfiche) Indexed: Curr.Cont. Hist.Abstr. Amer.Bibl.Slavic & E.Eur.Stud. Arts & Hum.Cit.Ind. Amer.Hist.& Life. Ind.Jew.Per. Rel.Ind.One.
Jewish interests

296 US ISSN 0163-1365
AMERICAN JEWISH CONGRESS. CONGRESS MONTHLY; a journal of opinion and Jewish affairs. 1935. 7/yr. $7.50. American Jewish Congress, 15 E. 84th St., New York, NY 10028. TEL 212-879-4500 Ed. Maier Deshell. adv. bk. rev. film rev. play rev. circ. 31,000. Indexed: Ind.Jew.Per. Key Title: Congress Monthly.
Formerly: American Jewish Congress. Congress Bi-Weekly (ISSN 0010-5872)
Jewish interests

296 US
AMERICAN JEWISH CONGRESS. NEWS. m. American Jewish Congress, Stephen Wise Congress House, 15 E. 84th St., New York, NY 10028. TEL 212-879-4500
Jewish interests

296 US ISSN 0002-9084
AMERICAN JEWISH WORLD. 1912. w. $16. A J W Publishing, Inc., 4509 Minnetonka Blvd., Minneapolis, MN 55416-4027. Ed. Stacey R. Bush. adv. bk. rev. charts. illus. circ. 7,000. (tabloid format)
Jewish interests

296 US ISSN 0003-102X
AMERICAN SEPHARDI. 1966. s-a. $15. Yeshiva University, Sephardic Studies Program, 500 W. 185 St., New York, NY 10033. TEL 212-960-5277 Ed. H.P. Salomon. bk. rev. bibl. illus. circ. 7,000. Indexed: M.L.A.
Jewish interests

296 AT ISSN 0004-9379
AUSTRALIAN JEWISH NEWS. (Editions in English and Yiddish) 1933. w. Aus.$12 for English edition; Aus.$10 for Yiddish edition. York Press Ltd., 1-19 Hoddle St., Abbotsford, Vic. 3067, Australia. Eds. H. Licht (English edt.), I.H. Rubinstein (Yiddish edt.) adv. bk. rev. film rev. play rev. bibl. illus. circ. 8,360. (tabloid format)
Jewish interests

296 IS
BATFUTZOT. 1974. m. free. World Jewish Congress, P.O. Box 4293, Jerusalem 91042, Israel. Ed. Dinah Goren.
Jewish interests

BITZARON: A QUARTERLY OF HEBREW LETTERS. see *LITERARY AND POLITICAL REVIEWS*

910.03 286 US
BLACK MINISTRIES. a. Episcopal Commission for Black Ministries, Executive Council, 815 Second Ave., New York, NY 10017. TEL 212-867-8400

296 301 US ISSN 0887-1639
C M J S CENTERPIECES. 1985. s-a. free. Center for Modern Jewish Studies, Brandeis University, Waltham, MA 02254. TEL 617-736-2063 Ed. Sylvia Barack Fishman. charts. stat. circ. 8,500.

296 CN ISSN 0576-5528
CANADIAN JEWISH ARCHIVES (NEW SERIES) 1955; N.S. 1974. irreg. price varies. Canadian Jewish Congress, 1590 Dr. Penfield Ave., Montreal, Que. H3G 1C5, Canada. TEL 514-931-7531 Ed. David Rome. circ. 500. (back issues avail.)

296 CN ISSN 0008-3941
CANADIAN JEWISH NEWS. 1961. w. Can.$15($10) 562 Eglinton Ave. E., Ste. 401, Toronto, Ont. M4P 1P1, Canada. TEL 416-483-9331 Ed. Maurice Lucow. adv. bk. rev. illus. music rev. theatre rev. circ. 52,000. (tabloid format)
Supersedes: Canadian Jewish Chronicle Review (ISSN 0008-3925)
Jewish interests

CANADIAN MUSLIM. see *RELIGIONS AND THEOLOGY — Islamic*

296 US
CENTRAL CALIFORNIA JEWISH HERITAGE. w. $8.50. Heritage Publishing Co., 2130 S. Vermont Ave., Los Angeles, CA 90007 (Subscr. to: 333 W. Shaw, Ste. 8, Fresno, CA 93704) Ed. Dan Brin. adv. (tabloid format)
Jewish interests

CHRONICLE OF THE CATHOLIC CHURCH IN LITHUANIA. see *RELIGIONS AND THEOLOGY — Roman Catholic*

296 FR
COLLECTION FRANCO-JUDAICA. a. price varies. (Commission Francaise des Archives Juives) Editions Edouart Privat, 14, rue des Arts, 31000 Toulouse, France. Ed. Bernhard Blumenkranz. Indexed: Bull.Signal.

296 US ISSN 0160-7057
CONFERENCE OF PRESIDENTS OF MAJOR AMERICAN JEWISH ORGANIZATIONS. ANNUAL REPORT. 1965. a. free. Conference of Presidents of Major American Jewish Organizations, 515 Park Ave., New York, NY 10022. TEL 212-752-1616 Ed. Richard Cohen. illus.
Former titles: Conference of Presidents of Major American Jewish Organizations. Report; Conference of Presidents of Major American Jewish Organizations. Annual Report (ISSN 0160-7049)

296 US ISSN 0147-1694
CONTEMPORARY JEWRY; a journal of sociological inquiry. 1974. a. $19.95. (Association for the Sociological Study of Jewry) Transaction Periodicals Consortium, Rutgers University, New Brunswick, NJ 08903. TEL 201-932-2280 Ed. Arnold Dashefsky. circ. 1,500. (also avail. in microform from UMI; reprint service avail. from UMI)
Jewish interests

CROSS OF LANGUEDOC. see *RELIGIONS AND THEOLOGY — Protestant*

DANICA; hrvatski tjednik. see *RELIGIONS AND THEOLOGY — Other Denominations And Sects*

296 AG
DAVKE; revista Israelita. (Text in Spanish and Yiddish) 1949. q. Brandsen 1634, Buenos Aires, Argentina. Ed. Salomon Suskovich. bk. rev. bibl.
Jewish interests

296 US
DETROIT JEWISH NEWS LTD. PARTNERSHIP. 1942. w. $21. 20300 Civic Center Dr., Rm. 240, Southfield, MI 48086-4138. TEL 313-354-6060 adv. bk. rev. film rev. illus. play rev. (tabloid format)
Formerly: Detroit Jewish News (ISSN 0011-9644)
Jewish interests

282 CN ISSN 0381-8950
DEUTSCHE KATHOLIK IN KANADA. (Text in German) 1964. m. Can.$15. 131 McCaul St., Toronto, Ont. M5T 1W3, Canada. Ed. Rev. Karl J. Schindler. circ. 2,500.

DRAUGAS. see *RELIGIONS AND THEOLOGY — Roman Catholic*

ESKIMO. see *RELIGIONS AND THEOLOGY — Roman Catholic*

914.606 200 SP
FOC NOU; revista al servei dels cristians. (Text in Catalan) 1974. m. 900 ptas. Publicaciones de el Ciervo, S.A., Calvet 56, 0802 Barcelona, Spain. Ed. Roser Bofill Portabella. adv. bk. rev. illus. circ. 3,000.

297 914.406 FR
FRANCE-ISLAM. m. Amicale des Musulmans en Europe, 59 rue Claude Bernard, 75005 Paris, France. (Co-sponsor: Centre Culturel Islamique)

296 AU ISSN 0021-2334
DIE GEMEINDE. 1958. m. S.250. Israelitische Kultusgemeinde Wien, Bauernfeldgasse 4, A-1190 Vienna, Austria. Ed. Karl Pfeifer. adv. bk. rev. illus. circ. 6,000.
Jewish interests

296 IS ISSN 0435-8406
GESHER; quarterly review of Jewish affairs. (Text in Hebrew) vol.24, 1978. q. IS.12. World Jewish Congress, 4 Rotenberg St., Jerusalem, Israel. Ed. Shlomo Shafir. circ. 1,100. Indexed: Ind.Heb.Per.

059.8 281.9 UK ISSN 0265-6922
GREEK ORTHODOX CALENDAR. 1983. a. £5. Kyriakos H. Metaxas, Ed. & Pub., 55 Westbourne Grove, London W2 4UA, England. adv. circ. 12,000.

GREEK SUNDAY NEWS/KYRIAKATIKA NEA. see *RELIGIONS AND THEOLOGY — Other Denominations And Sects*

296 NE ISSN 0017-6346
HABINJAN; de opbouw. 1947. m. Portugees-Israelietische Gemeente, Gerrit van der Veenstr. 141, 1077 DX Amsterdam, Netherlands. Eds. Dr. J.Z. Baruch, Rabbi B. Drukarch. bk. rev. circ. 13,000.
Jewish interests

296 US
HARVARD JUDAIC MONOGRAPHS. 1975. irreg., no.5, 1985. price varies. Center for Jewish Studies, Cambridge, MA 02138 (Distr. by: Harvard University Press, 79 Garden St., Cambridge, MA 02138)

296 956.94 US ISSN 0360-9049
HEBREW UNION COLLEGE ANNUAL. (Text in English, French, German and Hebrew) 1924. a. $20. Hebrew Union College-Jewish Institute of Religion, 3101 Clifton Ave., Cincinnati, OH 45220. TEL 513-221-1875 Eds. Sheldon H. Blank, Herbert H. Paper. cum.index 1924-1982 in 1982 vol. circ. 2,500. (also avail. in microfilm; back issues avail.) Indexed: Hist.Abstr. Old Test.Abstr. Amer.Hist.& Life. CERDIC. New Test.Abstr. Rel.Ind.One. Rel.& Theol.Abstr.
Supersedes: Journal of Jewish Lore and Philosophy (ISSN 0190-4361)

296 US ISSN 0275-9993
HEBREW UNION COLLEGE ANNUAL SUPPLEMENTS. 1976. irreg. Hebrew Union College-Jewish Institute of Religion, 3101 Clifton Ave., Cincinnati, OH 45220 TEL 513-221-1875 (Dist. by: Ktav Publishing House, Inc., 900 Jefferson St., Hoboken, NJ 07030) Eds. Sheldon H. Blank, Herbert H. Paper. Indexed: Old Test.Abstr.

296 US ISSN 0018-1862
HILLEL GATE. 1969. m. (during school year) free. B'nai B'rith Hillel Foundation at Brooklyn College, 2901 Campus Rd., Brooklyn, NY 11210. TEL 718-859-1151 Eds. Paul Appelbaum, Barbara Robinson. adv. bk. rev. film rev. play rev. illus. circ. 4,000. (tabloid format)
Jewish interests

IEVANHEL'S'KYI HOLOS. see *RELIGIONS AND THEOLOGY — Other Denominations And Sects*

296 US
IGERET. m. B'nai B'rith Hillel Foundations, 1640 Rhode Island Ave., N.W., Washington, DC 20036. TEL 202-857-6560 Ed. Ruth Gruber Fredman, Ph.D.

970.1 CN ISSN 0226-9317
INDIAN LIFE. 1967. bi-m. $5. Intertribal Christian Communications, Box 3765, Sta. B, Winnipeg, Man. R2W 3R6, Canada. TEL 204-661-9333 Ed. George McPeek. adv. bk. rev. circ. 24,000.
Formerly: American Indian Life.
American Indian interests

296 FR ISSN 0020-0107
INFORMATION JUIVE; le journal des communautes. 1948. m. 140 F. Consistoire Israelite de Paris, 17 rue Saint-Georges, 75009 Paris, France. Ed. Jacques Lazarus. adv. bk. rev. bibl. circ. 12,000. (also avail. in microform from UMI; reprint service avail. from UMI)
Incorporating: Journal des Communautes (ISSN 0021-8022)

296 US ISSN 0047-0511
INTERMOUNTAIN JEWISH NEWS. 1913. w. $32. 1275 Sherman St., Denver, CO 80203. Ed. Miriam Goldberg. adv. bk. rev. film rev. charts. illus. circ. 9,742. (tabloid format; also avail. in microfilm)
Jewish interests

ISRAEL BOOK NEWS. see *PUBLISHING AND BOOK TRADE*

296 IS
ISRAEL REPORT. (Text in English) 1973. m. free. World Jewish Council, P.O. Box 4293, Jerusalem 91042, Israel. Ed. Nathan Lerner.
Jewish interests

296 US ISSN 0021-3772
J T A DAILY NEWS BULLETIN. 1922. d. except Sat. & Sun. $150. Jewish Telegraphic Agency, 165 W. 46 St., Rm. 511, New York, NY 10036. TEL 212-575-9370 Ed. Murray Zuckoff. circ. 2,500.
Jewish interests

296 YU ISSN 0021-6240
JEVREJSKI PREGLED. (Text in Serbo-Croatian; summaries in English) 1950. m. 1200 din.($14) Savez Jevrejskih Opstina Jugoslavije, 7. Jula 71a, Belgrade, Yugoslavia. Ed. Luci Petrovic. illus. circ. 2,700.
Jewish interests

296 US ISSN 0021-6348
JEWISH CIVIC PRESS. 1965. m. $3. Box 15500, New Orleans, LA 70115. TEL 504-895-8784 Ed. Abner L. Tritt. adv. bk. rev. film rev. play rev. illus. circ. 3,285(controlled) (tabloid format)
Jewish interests

296 US ISSN 0021-6380
JEWISH CURRENT EVENTS. 1959. bi-w. $5.95. Current Publishing Co., 430 Keller Ave., Elmont, NY 11003. Ed. Samuel Deutsch. bk. rev. film rev. play rev. illus. stat. (tabloid format)
Jewish interests

JEWISH GUARDIAN. see *RELIGIONS AND THEOLOGY — Judaic*

JEWISH LANGUAGE REVIEW. see *LINGUISTICS*

296 US ISSN 0021-6674
JEWISH PRESS (BROOKLYN) 1950. w. $30. Jewish Press, Inc., c/o Sholom Klass, Ed. & Pub., 338 Third Ave., Brooklyn, NY 11215. TEL 718-330-1100 adv. bk. rev. film rev. play rev. bibl. illus. circ. 200,000. (tabloid format)

JEWISH PRESS FEATURES. see *JOURNALISM*

JEWISH PROCLAIMER. see *RELIGIONS AND THEOLOGY — Judaic*

JEWISH SOCIAL STUDIES. see *SOCIAL SCIENCES: COMPREHENSIVE WORKS*

296 CN ISSN 0021-6739
JEWISH STANDARD. 1929. s-m. Can.$6. Julius Hayman Ltd., Suite 139, 67 Mowat Ave., Toronto, Ont. M6K 3E3, Canada. adv. illus. circ. 8,200.
Jewish interests

296 UK ISSN 0021-6755
JEWISH TELEGRAPH. 1950. w. £26. Jewish Telegraph Ltd., Telegraph House, 11 Park Hill, Bury Old Rd., Prestwich, Manchester M25 8HH, England. Ed. Paul Harris. adv. bk. rev. film rev. play rev. illus. circ. 11,500. (tabloid format)
Jewish interests

JEWISH TRADITION. see *RELIGIONS AND THEOLOGY — Judaic*

296 US ISSN 0021-678X
JEWISH TRANSCRIPT. 1924. s-m. $12. ‡ Jewish Federation of Greater Seattle, Ste. 510, Securities Bldg., Seattle, WA 98101. TEL 206-624-0136 Ed. Richard I. Gordon. adv. bk. rev. charts. illus. circ. 3,453. (tabloid format)
Formerly: Transcript.
Jewish interests

296 US ISSN 0021-6860
JEWISH WEEKLY NEWS. 1945. w. $12. Bennett-Scott Publications Corp., Box 1569, Springfield, MA 01101. Ed. Leslie B. Kahn. adv. bk. rev. illus. circ. 8,235. (tabloid format)
Jewish interests

296 DK ISSN 0021-7131
JOEDISK ORIENTERING. 1929. m. Kr.120. Mosaisk Troessamfund i Koebenhavn - Jewish Congregation in Copenhagen, Ny Kongensgade 6, 1472 Copenhagen K, Denmark. Ed. Arne Notkin. adv. bk. rev. illus. circ. 3,000.
Formerly: Joedisk Samfund.
Jewish interests

296 CS ISSN 0022-5738
JUDAICA BOHEMIAE. (Text in English, French, German, Russian) 1965. s-a. 40 Kcs.($15.40) (Statni Zidovske Museum) Panorama, Halkova 1, 120 72 Praha 2, Czechoslovakia. Ed. Erik Klima. bk. rev. bibl. stat. Indexed: Hist.Abstr. Amer.Hist.& Life.
Jewish interests

JUDAICA BOOK NEWS. see *PUBLISHING AND BOOK TRADE*

KASHRUS; magazine for the kosher consumer. see *RELIGIONS AND THEOLOGY — Judaic*

KASHRUT GUIDE. see *RELIGIONS AND THEOLOGY — Judaic*

282 US
KATOLICKY SOKOL. 1911. w. $15. Slovak Catholic Sokol, 205 Madison St, Passaic, NJ 07055. TEL 201-777-4010 Ed. Daniel F. Tanzone. bk. rev. illus. circ. 10,000.

KATOLIKUS MAGYAROK VASARNAPJA; Catholic Hungarians' Sunday. see *RELIGIONS AND THEOLOGY — Roman Catholic*

296 US
KOL HA-T'NUAH/VOICE OF THE MOVEMENT. vol.32, 1975. m. $1.25. National Young Judaea, 50 W. 58th St., New York, NY 10019. Ed. Jonathan Levine. illus. (tabloid format)
Jewish interests

KOLENU. see *RELIGIONS AND THEOLOGY — Judaic*

296 US
KOSHER DIRECTORY. a. Union of Orthodox Jewish Congregations of America, Kashruth Division, 45 W. 36 St., New York, NY 10018. TEL 212-564-8330 Ed. Goldie Feinberg. adv.

296 301 US
LEADERS' DIGEST. 1981. 5/yr. American Jewish Committee, Institute of Human Relations, 165 E. 56 St., New York, NY 10022. circ. 4,000.

296 US ISSN 0199-2899
LONG ISLAND JEWISH WORLD. 1971. w. $15. Empire Publishing Corp., 115 Middle Neck Rd., Great Neck, NY 11021. TEL 516-829-4000 Ed. Naomi Lippman. adv. bk. rev. circ. 45,000.
Jewish interests

LUZ; la revista israelita para toda sudamerica. see *LITERARY AND POLITICAL REVIEWS*

296 US
MABUEY HANCHAL. 1983. q. 35 Lee Ave., Brooklyn, NY 11211. Ed. Rabbi Mordechai Turetz.

296 CK ISSN 0025-939X
MENORAH. 1950. m. $30. Editorial Menorah, Carrera 5A no.14-80 403, Apdo. Aereo 9081, Bogota, Colombia. Ed. Eliecer Celnik. adv. bk. rev. circ. 10,000.
Jewish interests

MESSAGGERO. see *RELIGIONS AND THEOLOGY — Roman Catholic*

MUNDO ISRAELITA; actualidad de la semana en Israel y en el mundo judio. see *RELIGIONS AND THEOLOGY — Judaic*

296 US ISSN 0161-2115
N C J W JOURNAL. 1978. q. $2. National Council of Jewish Women, 15 E. 26th St., New York, NY 10010. TEL 212-532-1740 Ed. Michele Spirn. adv. bk. rev. circ. 100,000.
Formerly: Council Woman.
Jewish interests

NOTRE VOIX. see *POLITICAL SCIENCE*

ORITA; Ibadan journal of religious studies. see *RELIGIONS AND THEOLOGY*

296 CN ISSN 0834-0242
OUTLOOK. 1963. 10/yr. Can.$12.50 to individuals; institutions Can$20. Canadian Jewish Outlook Society, 6184 Ash St., Ste. 3, Vancouver, B.C. V5Z 3G9, Canada. TEL 604-324-5101 Ed. Henry Rosenthal. adv. bk. rev. circ. 3,000. (also avail. in microfilm)
Continues: Canadian Jewish Outlook (ISSN 0045-5059)
Jewish interests

947 US
OUTREACH (NEW YORK) 1977. m. free. Armenian Apostolic Church of America, 138 E. 39th St., New York, NY 10016. TEL 212-389-7810 Ed. Mesrob Ashjian. adv. bk. rev. circ. 10,500.

POLKA; Polish women's quarterly magazine. see *WOMEN'S INTERESTS*

POSOL/MESSENGER; religious monthly for Slovak Catholics. see *RELIGIONS AND THEOLOGY — Roman Catholic*

PROVIDENT BOOK FINDER. see *RELIGIONS AND THEOLOGY — Protestant*

296 BE ISSN 0035-2055
REVUE DES ETUDES JUIVES. (Text in French) 1880. q. 2500 Fr. (Societe des Etudes Juives, FR) Editions Peeters s.p.r.l., Bondgenotenlaan 153, B-3000 Louvein, Belgium. Dir. Georges Vajda. bk. rev. charts. illus. circ. 1,800. Indexed: Bull.Signal. Lang.& Lang.Behav.Abstr. New Test.Abstr.
Jewish interests

296 US
ROCKY MOUNTAIN JEWISH HISTORICAL NOTES. vol. 2, 1979. q. $15. (Rocky Mountain Jewish Historical Society) University of Denver, Department of Graphics, Center for Judaic Studies, Denver, CO 80208. TEL 303-871-2959 Ed. John Livingston. circ. 500.
Jewish interests

RUNESTONE (BRECKENRIDGE) see *RELIGIONS AND THEOLOGY — Other Denominations And Sects*

296 US
S C A REPORT. m. Synagogue Council of America, 327 Lexington Ave., New York, NY 10016. TEL 212-686-8670
Jewish interests

296 US
SAN DIEGO JEWISH PRESS HERITAGE. 1914. w. $15. Heritage Publishing Co., 2130 S. Vermont Ave., Los Angeles, CA 90007. Ed. Dan Brin. adv.
Jewish interests

296 IT ISSN 0037-3265
SHALOM. 1967. m. L.25000 to non-members. Comunita Israelitica di Roma, Lungotevere Cenci, 00186 Rome, Italy. Ed. Lia Levi. adv. bk. rev. film rev. illus. circ. 10,000. (tabloid format)
Formerly: Voce della Comunita.
Jewish interests

SHUPIHUI. see *RELIGIONS AND THEOLOGY*

296 IS
SHVUT; Jewish problems in the USSR and Eastern Europe. (Text in Hebrew; summaries in English) 1973. a. $6. ‡ Tel-Aviv University, Diaspora Research Institute, Sales Division, Tel Aviv, Israel. Ed. M. Minc. bk. rev. circ. 1,500. Indexed: Ind.Heb.Per.

SIONISTE. see *POLITICAL SCIENCE*

296 US ISSN 0038-4674
SOUTHWEST JEWISH CHRONICLE. 1929. q. $6. ‡ 314-B N. Robinson St., Oklahoma City, OK 73102. TEL 405-236-4226 Ed. E.F. Friedman. adv. bk. rev. illus.
Jewish interests

SV. PRANCISKAUS VARPELIS/BELL OF ST. FRANCIS. see *RELIGIONS AND THEOLOGY — Roman Catholic*

296 US
SYRACUSE JEWISH OBSERVER. 1979. fortn. free. Syracuse Jewish Federation Inc., Box 510, Syracuse, NY 13214-0510. TEL 315-422-4104 Ed. Judith A. Rubenstein. adv. bk. rev. charts. film rev. illus. play rev. circ. 5,800. (tabloid format; back issues avail.)

WAY-UKRAINIAN CATHOLIC BI-WEEKLY/ WAY. see *RELIGIONS AND THEOLOGY — Roman Catholic*

296 900 US
WESTERN STATES JEWISH HISTORY. 1968. q. $15. Western States Jewish History Association, 2429 23rd St., Santa Monica, CA 90405. TEL 213-450-9246 Ed. Dr. Norton B. Stern. bk. rev. charts. illus. index. circ. 1,000. Indexed: Hist.Abstr. Amer.Hist.& Life. Ind.Jew.Per.
Formerly (until 1983): Western States Jewish Historical Quarterly (ISSN 0043-4221)
Jewish interests

WIND RIVER RENDEZVOUS. see *RELIGIONS AND THEOLOGY — Roman Catholic*

WOMEN'S ZIONIST ORGANIZATION OF SOUTH AFRICA. NEWS AND VIEWS. see *RELIGIONS AND THEOLOGY — Judaic*

296 US
WORKING PAPERS IN YIDDISH AND EAST EUROPEAN JEWISH STUDIES/IN GANG FUN ARBET: YIDISH UN MIZRAKH EYROPEISHE YIDISHE SHTUDIES. (Text in various languages) 1974. irreg. $12 to institutions. YIVO Institute for Jewish Research, Max Weinreich Center for Advanced Jewish Studies, 1048 Fifth Ave., New York, NY 10028. TEL 212-535-6700 Ed. Joan Bratkowsky. circ. 125. Indexed: M.L.A.

296 US
YESHIVA UNIVERSITY SEPHARDIC BULLETIN. 1973. a. free. Yeshiva University, Sephardic Studies Program, 500 W. 185th St., New York, NY 10033. TEL 212-960-5277 Ed. Rabbi M. Mitchell Serels. circ. 24,000.

YIDDISH LITERARY AND LINGUISTIC PERIODICALS AND MISCELLANIES; a selective annotated bibliography. see *LINGUISTICS*

296 IS ISSN 0044-4758
ZION; a quarterly for research in Jewish history. (Text in Hebrew; summaries in English) 1935. q. $25. Historical Society of Israel, Box 4179, Jerusalem, Israel. Ed. Bd. bk. rev. bibl. circ. 1,000. (reprint service avail. from ISP) Indexed: Curr.Cont. Hist.Abstr. Ind.Heb.Per. Arts & Hum.Cit.Ind. Int.Z.Bibelwiss. Rel.& Theol.Abstr.
Jewish interests

FOLKLORE

BAYERISCHES SONNTAGSBLATT FUER DIE KATHOLISCHE FAMILIE. see *RELIGIONS AND THEOLOGY — Roman Catholic*

200 900 US ISSN 0528-1458
CARL NEWELL JACKSON LECTURES. irreg. price varies. Harvard University Press, 79 Garden St., Cambridge, MA 02138. TEL 617-495-2600

RUNESTONE (BRECKENRIDGE) see *RELIGIONS AND THEOLOGY — Other Denominations And Sects*

VOICE FROM JERUSALEM. see *RELIGIONS AND THEOLOGY — Judaic*

FOOD AND FOOD INDUSTRIES
see also Agriculture

664.6 SZ
D J I N; Delta journal suisse d'informations macrobiotiques. (Text in French; summaries occasionally in English or French) 1978. 5/yr. 10 Fr.($5) Centre Macrobiotique de Lausanne, Raelle de Bourg 7, 1003 Lausanne, Switzerland. circ. 1,200. (back issues avail.)
Formerly: Delta.

FUNERALS

614.6 US
CATHOLIC CEMETERY. 1949. m. $15 to non-members. National Catholic Cemetery Conference, 710 N. River Rd., Des Plaines, IL 60016. TEL 312-824-8131 Ed. James R. Mulvaney. adv. circ. 1,951.

GENEALOGY AND HERALDRY

HUGUENOT TRAILS. see *HISTORY — History Of North And South America*

929 200 US ISSN 0737-8246
QUAKER YEOMEN. 1974. q. $15. Brookside Business Consultants, Inc., 2330 S.E. Brookwood Ave., Ste. 108, Hillsboro, OR 97123. Ed. James E. Bellarts. adv. bk. rev. bibl. charts. index. circ. 300. (also avail. in microform; back issues avail.) Indexed: Geneal.Per.Ind.

GENERAL INTEREST PERIODICALS — Australasia
see also General Interest Periodicals–New Zealand

GENERAL INTEREST PERIODICALS — Brazil

FAMILIA CRISTA; revista da paz e do amor - revista mensal para a familia. see *RELIGIONS AND THEOLOGY*

GENERAL INTEREST PERIODICALS — Canada

JEWISH STANDARD. see *ETHNIC INTERESTS*

054.1 CN ISSN 0034-3781
RELATIONS. 1941. m. Can.$16. (Peres de la Compagnie de Jesus) Editions Bellarmin, 8100 Bd. St.-Laurent, Montreal, Que. H2P 2L9, Canada. TEL 514-387-2541 Ed. Albert Beaudry. adv. bk. rev. bibl. index. circ. 8,108. (also avail. in microform from UMI; reprint service avail. from UMI) Indexed: Cath.Ind. Can.Ind. CERDIC. Pt.de Rep.

GENERAL INTEREST PERIODICALS — Germany, West

BAYERISCHES SONNTAGSBLATT FUER DIE KATHOLISCHE FAMILIE. see *RELIGIONS AND THEOLOGY — Roman Catholic*

GENERAL INTEREST PERIODICALS — Italy

055.1 200 IT ISSN 0014-7095
FAMIGLIA CRISTIANA. 1931. w. L.15000. ‡ Pia Societa San Paolo, Piazza San Paolo 14, 12051 Alba (Cuneo), Italy. Ed. Giuseppe Zilli. adv. bk. rev. charts. film rev. illus. play rev. stat. index. cum.index every 5 years. circ. 1,670,000. (tabloid format)

GENERAL INTEREST PERIODICALS — New Zealand

WAR CRY. see *RELIGIONS AND THEOLOGY — Other Denominations And Sects*

GENERAL INTEREST PERIODICALS — Philippines

052 PH ISSN 0115-2971
HOMELIFE; the Philippines' family magazine. 1954. m. P.60. Society of St. Paul, Inc., MCPO 525, Makati, Metro Manila, Philippines. Ed. Nick Reforeal. adv. bk. rev. illus. circ. 49,628.

GENERAL INTEREST PERIODICALS — South America
see also General Interest Periodicals–Brazil

GENERAL INTEREST PERIODICALS — U S S R

ISKRA. see *RELIGIONS AND THEOLOGY*

GENERAL INTEREST PERIODICALS — United States

AMERICA; national Catholic weekly review. see *RELIGIONS AND THEOLOGY — Roman Catholic*

CATHOLIC DIGEST. see *RELIGIONS AND THEOLOGY — Roman Catholic*

CHRISTIAN LIFE; the guide to better living. see *RELIGIONS AND THEOLOGY*

GEOGRAPHY
see also History; Travel and Tourism

OCCASIONAL PAPERS ON RELIGION IN EASTERN EUROPE. see *RELIGIONS AND THEOLOGY*

WORLD LITHUANIAN ROMAN CATHOLIC DIRECTORY. see *RELIGIONS AND THEOLOGY — Roman Catholic*

GERONTOLOGY AND GERIATRICS

258 362.615 US
HORIZON (NEPTUNE) 1977. q. free. United Methodist Homes of New Jersey, Box 1166, Neptune, NJ 07753. TEL 201-922-9800 Ed. Gordon L. Hesse. illus. circ. 18,000. Indexed: R.G. Mag.Ind.
Supersedes, in 1977: Methodist Homes Quarterly (ISSN 0026-1246)

MATURE YEARS. see *RELIGIONS AND THEOLOGY — Protestant*

GIFTWARE AND TOYS

679 US
CHRISTIAN FAMILY CATALOG. Variant title: Abbey Press Christian Family Catalog. 1963. 7/yr. $1. Abbey Press, 52 Hill Dr., St. Meinrad, IN 47577. circ. 23,000.

GUIDES TO SCHOOLS AND COLLEGES
see Education–Guides to Schools and Colleges

HIGHER EDUCATION
see Education–Higher Education

HISTORY
see also History–History of Africa; History–History of Asia; History–History of Europe; History–History of North and South America; History–History of the Near East; Anthropology; Archaeology; Folklore
also specific subjects

AD FONTES. see *RELIGIONS AND THEOLOGY*

ALABAMA BAPTIST HISTORIAN. see *RELIGIONS AND THEOLOGY — Protestant*

AMERICAN BAPTIST QUARTERLY; a Baptist journal of history, theology and ministry. see *RELIGIONS AND THEOLOGY — Protestant*

AMERICAN BENEDICTINE REVIEW. see *RELIGIONS AND THEOLOGY — Roman Catholic*

AMERICAN CATHOLIC HISTORICAL SOCIETY OF PHILADELPHIA. RECORDS. see *RELIGIONS AND THEOLOGY — Roman Catholic*

AMERICAN JEWISH ARCHIVES; devoted to the preservation and study of the American Jewish experience. see *ETHNIC INTERESTS*

AMERICAN PRESBYTERIANS: JOURNAL OF PRESBYTERIAN HISTORY. see *RELIGIONS AND THEOLOGY — Protestant*

AMERICAN UNIVERSITY STUDIES. SERIES 7. THEOLOGY AND RELIGION. see *RELIGIONS AND THEOLOGY*

ANALECTA BOLLANDIANA; revue critique d'hagiographie. see *RELIGIONS AND THEOLOGY*

ARCHIV FUER SCHLESISCHE KIRCHENGESCHICHTE. see *RELIGIONS AND THEOLOGY*

ARCHIVUM FRANCISCANUM HISTORICUM. see *RELIGIONS AND THEOLOGY — Roman Catholic*

ASPRENAS; Rivista di Scienze Teologiche. see *RELIGIONS AND THEOLOGY — Roman Catholic*

BAPTIST HISTORY AND HERITAGE. see *RELIGIONS AND THEOLOGY — Protestant*

BAPTIST QUARTERLY. see *RELIGIONS AND THEOLOGY — Protestant*

BELARUSKAJA CARKVA. see *RELIGIONS AND THEOLOGY*

BIBBIA E ORIENTE; rivista per la conoscenza della Bibbia. see *RELIGIONS AND THEOLOGY*

CANADIAN CHURCH HISTORICAL SOCIETY JOURNAL. see *RELIGIONS AND THEOLOGY*

CATHOLIC HISTORICAL REVIEW. see *RELIGIONS AND THEOLOGY — Roman Catholic*

CERCLE ERNEST RENAN. CAHIERS. see *RELIGIONS AND THEOLOGY*

CHRISTIAN HISTORY MAGAZINE. see *RELIGIONS AND THEOLOGY*

CHURCH OF ENGLAND HISTORICAL SOCIETY (DIOCESE OF SYDNEY). JOURNAL. see *RELIGIONS AND THEOLOGY — Protestant*

CLAIRLIEU: TIJDSCHRIFT GEWIJD AAN DE GESCHIEDENIS DER KRUISHEREN. see *RELIGIONS AND THEOLOGY*

CONCORDIA HISTORICAL INSTITUTE QUARTERLY. see *RELIGIONS AND THEOLOGY — Protestant*

EPOCHE; journal of the history of religions at U.C.L.A. see *RELIGIONS AND THEOLOGY*

900 200 US
FIDES ET HISTORIA. 1968. 3/yr. $15. Conference on Faith and History, c/o Richard V. Pierard, Dept. of History, Indiana State University, Terre Haute, IN 47809. TEL 812-232-2707 Ed. James E. Johnson. adv. bk. rev. circ. 850. (back issues avail.) Indexed: Hist.Abstr. Old Test.Abstr. Amer.Hist.& Life. CERDIC. Chr.Per.Ind. Rel.Ind.One. Rel.& Theol.Abstr.

GREEK ORTHODOX THEOLOGICAL REVIEW. see *RELIGIONS AND THEOLOGY — Other Denominations And Sects*

HISPANIA SACRA; revista de historia eclesiastica. see *RELIGIONS AND THEOLOGY*

900 284 US ISSN 0270-4919
HISTORICAL INTELLIGENCER. 1980. a. $4. United Church of Christ, Historical Council, 105 Madison Ave., New York, NY 10016. Ed. Harold F. Worthley. circ. 1,000.

HISTORICAL MESSENGER. see *RELIGIONS AND THEOLOGY — Protestant*

HISTORIOGRAPHER. see *RELIGIONS AND THEOLOGY — Protestant*

HISTORY OF RELIGIONS; an international journal for comparative historical studies. see *RELIGIONS AND THEOLOGY*

INNES REVIEW. see *RELIGIONS AND THEOLOGY — Roman Catholic*

DER ISLAM; Zeitschrift fuer Geschichte und Kultur des islamischen Orients. see *ORIENTAL STUDIES*

ITINERARIUM; revista quadrimestral de cultura. see *RELIGIONS AND THEOLOGY — Roman Catholic*

JOURNAL OF ECCLESIASTICAL HISTORY. see *RELIGIONS AND THEOLOGY*

JOURNAL OF RELIGIOUS HISTORY. see *RELIGIONS AND THEOLOGY*

MEMORIE DOMENICANE. see *RELIGIONS AND THEOLOGY*

MISCELLANEA FRANCESCANA; rivista trimestrale di scienze teologiche e di studi francescani. see *RELIGIONS AND THEOLOGY — Roman Catholic*

A I U LES NOUVEAUX CAHIERS. (Alliance Israelite Universelle en France) see *RELIGIONS AND THEOLOGY — Judaic*

NUMEN; international review for the history of religions. see *RELIGIONS AND THEOLOGY*

PARDES. see *RELIGIONS AND THEOLOGY — Judaic*

PENNSYLVANIA MENNONITE HERITAGE. see *RELIGIONS AND THEOLOGY — Other Denominations And Sects*

REVUE D'HISTOIRE ET DE PHILOSOPHIE RELIGIEUSES. see *RELIGIONS AND THEOLOGY*

REVUE DE L'HISTOIRE DES RELIGIONS. see *RELIGIONS AND THEOLOGY*

REVUE DES ETUDES JUIVES. see *ETHNIC INTERESTS*

REVUE DES SCIENCES RELIGIEUSES. see *RELIGIONS AND THEOLOGY — Roman Catholic*

RIVISTA DI STORIA E LETTERATURA RELIGIOSA. see *RELIGIONS AND THEOLOGY*

RIVISTA DI STORIA E LETTERATURA RELIGIOSA. BIBLIOTECA; studi e testi. see *RELIGIONS AND THEOLOGY*

STUDIA MONASTICA; commentarium ad rem monasticam historice investigandam. see *RELIGIONS AND THEOLOGY*

STUDIES IN JUDAICA & THE HOLOCAUST. see *RELIGIONS AND THEOLOGY — Judaic*

TERRA SANTA. see *RELIGIONS AND THEOLOGY*

WESLEY HISTORICAL SOCIETY. PROCEEDINGS. see *RELIGIONS AND THEOLOGY — Protestant*

ZION; a quarterly for research in Jewish history. see *ETHNIC INTERESTS*

HISTORY — History Of Africa

AU COEUR DE L'AFRIQUE. see *RELIGIONS AND THEOLOGY*

HISTORY — History Of Asia
see also Oriental Studies

952 890 299.56
709 JA ISSN 0524-0654
BOOKS AND ARTICLES ON ORIENTAL SUBJECTS PUBLISHED IN JAPAN. (Text in English, Japanese) 1956. a. 4500 Yen($25) Toho Gakkai, 2-4-1 Nishi-Kanda, Chiyoda-ku, Tokyo 101, Japan. Ed.Bd. (back issues avail.)

INDIAN CHURCH HISTORY REVIEW. see *RELIGIONS AND THEOLOGY*

HISTORY — History Of Europe
see also Classical Studies

940 PL
ACTA MEDIAEVALIA. (Text in Latin or Polish; summaries in French) 1973. irreg. price varies. Katolicki Uniwersytet Lubelski, Towarzystwo Naukowe, Chopina 29, 20-023 Lublin, Poland.

ANALECTA CARTUSIANA; review for Carthusian history and spirituality. see *RELIGIONS AND THEOLOGY*

943 296 GW ISSN 0341-8340
ARBEITSINFORMATIONEN UEBER STUDIENPROJEKTE AUF DEM GEBIET DER GESCHICHTE DES DEUTSCHEN JUDENTUMS UND DES ANTISEMITISMUS. 1963. irreg. DM.5. Germania Judaica, Koelner Bibliothek zur Geschichte des Deutschen Judentums, Josef-Haubrich-Hof 1, 5000 Cologne, W. Germany (B.R.D.) circ. 1,500.

ARCHIEF VOOR DE GESCHIEDENIS VAN DE KATHOLIEKE KERK IN NEDERLAND. see *RELIGIONS AND THEOLOGY — Roman Catholic*

980 SP ISSN 0004-0452
ARCHIVO IBERO-AMERICANO; revista de estudios historicos. (Text in Portuguese and Spanish) 1914. q. 1.400 ptas.($30) Franciscanos Espanoles, Joaquin Costa 36, 28002 Madrid, Spain. Dir. Juan Mesequer Fernandez. bk. rev. bibl. index. circ. 550. Indexed: Hist.Abstr. Amer.Hist.& Life. Hisp.Amer.Per.Ind.

ARCHIVUM HISTORICUM SOCIETATIS IESU. see *RELIGIONS AND THEOLOGY — Roman Catholic*

027.83 PL
ARCHIWA, BIBLIOTEKI I MUZEA KOSCIELNE. (Text in Polish; summaries in Latin) 1956. s-a. 100 Zl. Katolicki Uniwersytet Lubelski, Towarzystwo Naukowe, Chopina 29, 20-023 Lublin, Poland. Ed. Stanislaw Librowski. index. circ. 10,025.

ARISTOTELION PANEPISTEMION THESSALONIKES. THEOLOGIKE SCHOLE. EPISTEMONIKE EPETERIS. see *RELIGIONS AND THEOLOGY*

940 BE
ARMARIUM CODICUM INSIGNIUM. 1980. irreg. N.V. Brepols I.G.P., Rue Baron Francois du Four 8, B-2300 Turnhout, Belgium. Ed.Bd.

DIE BEIDEN TUERME; Niederaltaicher Rundbrief. see *RELIGIONS AND THEOLOGY*

940 IT
BENEDICTINA. (Text in Italian; ocasionally in English, French) 1947. s-a. L.40400. Abbazia San Paolo, Via Ostiense, 186, 00146 Rome, Italy. Ed. Lorenzo de Lorenzi. bk. rev. index; cum.index. circ. 1,000. (back issues avail.)

BIBLE RESEARCHER; Revisionist history. see *RELIGIONS AND THEOLOGY*

BLAETTER FUER WUERTTEMBERGISCHE KIRCHENGESCHICHTE. see *RELIGIONS AND THEOLOGY*

909.07 FR ISSN 0007-9731
CAHIERS DE CIVILISATION MEDIEVALE. 1958. q. 370 F. Universite de Poitiers, Centre d'Etudes Superieures de Civilisation Medievale, Hotel Berthelot, 24 rue de la Chaine, 86022 Poitiers, France. adv. bk. rev. bibl. illus. index. Indexed: Curr.Cont. M.L.A. Arts & Hum.Cit.Ind. Br.Archaeol.Abstr. CERDIC. Numis.Lit. RILA.

CIRPLAN. see *RELIGIONS AND THEOLOGY — Protestant*

270 940 UK ISSN 0070-1394
COURTENAY LIBRARY OF REFORMATION CLASSICS. 1963. irreg., no.15, 1984. price varies. Sutton Courtenay Press, c/o Appleford, Abingdon, Oxford OX14 4PB, England. Ed. G.E. Duffield.

230 940 UK
COURTENAY REFORMATION FACSIMILES. 1973. irreg. price varies. Sutton Courtenay Press, c/o Appleford, Abingdon, Oxford OX14 4PB, England. Ed. G.E. Duffield.
Formerly: Courtenay Facsimiles.

230 940 UK ISSN 0070-1408
COURTENAY STUDIES IN REFORMATION THEOLOGY. 1966. irreg., no.5, 1984. price varies. Sutton Courtenay Press, c/o Appleford, Abingdon, Oxford OX 14 4PB, England. Ed. G.E. Duffield.

DER DEUTSCHE HUGENOTT. see *RELIGIONS AND THEOLOGY — Protestant*

940 270 GW ISSN 0344-2934
DEUTSCHER HUGENOTTEN-VEREIN E.V. GESCHICHTSBLAETTER. 1890. irreg. price varies. Deutscher Hugenotten-Verein E.V., Postfach 35, D 3305 Sickte, W. Germany (B.R.D.), W. Germany (B.R.D.) Ed. Helmut Kimmel. circ. 1,000.

949.2 286 NE
DOOPSGEZINDE BIJDRAGEN. 1975. a. Doopsgezinde Historische Kring, Singel 425, 1000 Amsterdam, Netherlands. bk. rev. bibl. Indexed: CERDIC.

DUKHOVNA AKADEMIYA SV. KLIMENT OKHRIDSKI. GODISHNIK. see *RELIGIONS AND THEOLOGY*

943 200 GW
FRANKFURTER KIRCHLICHES JAHRBUCH. 1967. a. Evangelischer Gemeindeverband Frankfurt am Main, 6000 Frankfurt, W. Germany (B.R.D.) illus.

943.6 284 AU
GESELLSCHAFT FUER DIE GESCHICHTE DES PROTESTANTISMUS IN OESTERREICH. JAHRBUCH. 1880. a. DM.30. Gesellschaft fuer die Geschichte des Protestantismus in Oesterreich, Severin-Schreiber-G. 3, A-1180 Vienna, Austria. Ed. Peter F. Barton. bk. rev. circ. 30. Indexed: Hist.Abstr. Amer.Hist.& Life.

943 284 GW ISSN 0072-4238
GESELLSCHAFT FUER NIEDERSAECHSISCHE KIRCHENGESCHICHTE. JAHRBUCH. 1896. a. DM.15 to individuals; institutions DM.20. (Gesellschaft fuer Niedersaechsische Kirchengeschichte) Buchdruckerei Willi Rihn, 4733 Blomberg, W. Germany (B.R.D.) Ed. Hans-Walter Krumwiede. bk. rev. circ. 250.

949.5 281.9 GR
GREGORIOS HO PALAMAS. 1917. 5/yr. $20. Mitropolis Thessalonikes, P.O. Box 335, Salonika, Greece. Ed. Ioannis E. Anastasiou. bk. rev. bibl. circ. 1,000. Indexed: M.L.A. CERDIC.

940 US ISSN 0883-3559
HISTORIANS OF EARLY MODERN EUROPE. 1966. a. $10. Sixteenth Century Journal Publishers, Inc., Northeast Missouri State University, LB 115, Kirksville, MO 63501. TEL 816-785-4665 (Co-sponsors: Society for Reformation Research; Sixteenth Century Studies Conference) Ed. R.V. Schnucker. adv. circ. 1,800. (back issues avail.)
Incorporating: American Society for Reformation Research. Newsletter.

HISTORICAL SOCIETY OF THE CHURCH IN WALES. JOURNAL. see *RELIGIONS AND THEOLOGY — Protestant*

HISTORICAL SOCIETY OF THE PRESBYTERIAN CHURCH OF WALES. JOURNAL. see *RELIGIONS AND THEOLOGY — Protestant*

LEO BAECK INSTITUTE. YEAR BOOK. see *RELIGIONS AND THEOLOGY — Judaic*

LUTHERISCHE BEITRAEGE. see *RELIGIONS AND THEOLOGY — Protestant*

207 FR ISSN 0047-8105
MOREANA; time trieth truth. (Text in English and French) 1963. q. 195 F.($34) to individuals; institutions 250 F.($50) (Amici Thomae Mori) Moreana Publications, B.P. 808, 49005 Angers, France. Ed. Germain Marc'hadour. adv. bk. rev. film rev. play rev. abstr. illus. cum.index vols. 1-20 (1963-1983) circ. 1,000 (controlled) Indexed: Abstr.Engl.Stud. Curr.Cont. Hist.Abstr. M.L.A. Arts & Hum.Cit.Ind. Amer.Hist.& Life.

943.8 282 PL ISSN 0137-3218
NASZA PRZESZLOSC. 1946. 2/yr. 390 Zl. Institut Wydawniczy Nasza Przeszlosc, Ul. Strzelnicza 6, 30-215 Cracow, Poland. Ed. Jan Jukata. bk. rev. cum.index 1946-1971. circ. 1,500. Indexed: Hist.Abstr. Amer.Hist.& Life. CERDIC.

940 282 GW ISSN 0340-7993
PAEPSTE UND PAPSTTUM. (Text in German and English) 1971. irreg., vol.24, 1987. Anton Hiersemann Verlag, Rosenbergstr. 113, Postfach 723, 7000 Stuttgart 1, W. Germany (B.R.D.) Ed. G. Denzler.

940 282 UK ISSN 0034-1932
RECUSANT HISTORY. 1957. 2/yr. £12-13. Catholic Record Society, Secretary, c/o 114 Mount St., London W1, England. Ed.Bd. adv. index; cum.index covering 2 years. circ. 800. (back issues avail.) Indexed: Br.Hum.Ind. CERDIC.

RIVISTA DI STORIA DELLA CHIESA IN ITALIA. see *RELIGIONS AND THEOLOGY*

940 AU ISSN 0080-3790
ROEMISCHE HISTORISCHE MITTEILUNGEN. 1958. a. price varies. (Oesterreichisches Kulturinstitut, Rome, IT) Verlag der Oesterreichischen Akademie der Wissenschaften, Dr. Ignaz Seipel-Platz 2, A-1010 Vienna, Austria. circ. 500.

RUSSKOE VOZROZHDENIE; nezavisimyi russkii pravoslavnyi natsional'nyi zhurnal. see *RELIGIONS AND THEOLOGY — Other Denominations And Sects*

STILLE SCHAR. see *RELIGIONS AND THEOLOGY — Roman Catholic*

UNITARIAN HISTORICAL SOCIETY, LONDON. TRANSACTIONS. see *RELIGIONS AND THEOLOGY — Protestant*

WESTFALIA SACRA; Quellen und Forschungen zur Kirchengeschichte Westfalens. see *RELIGIONS AND THEOLOGY*

WORCESTERSHIRE RECUSANT. see *RELIGIONS AND THEOLOGY — Roman Catholic*

HISTORY — History Of North And South America

BAMPTON LECTURES IN AMERICA. see *RELIGIONS AND THEOLOGY*

970 929 CN ISSN 0441-6910
HUGUENOT TRAILS. 1968. q. Can.$20($20) Huguenot Society of Canada, P.O. Box 1003, Sta. A, Toronto, Ont. M5W 1G5, Canada. Ed. Michael Harrison. bk. rev. circ. 300.

MENNONITE HISTORICAL BULLETIN. see *RELIGIONS AND THEOLOGY — Other Denominations And Sects*

974 255 US ISSN 0738-7237
MIRROR. 1969. bi-m. membership. Lancaster Mennonite Historical Society, 2215 Mill Stream Rd., Lancaster, PA 17602. TEL 717-393-9745 Ed. Carolyn C. Wenger. illus. circ. 8,000.

OKLAHOMA BAPTIST CHRONICLE. see *RELIGIONS AND THEOLOGY — Protestant*

REVUE D'HISTOIRE ECCLESIASTIQUE. see *RELIGIONS AND THEOLOGY — Roman Catholic*

HISTORY — History Of The Near East

956 SP ISSN 0212-159X
ANDALUCIA ISLAMICA. TEXTOS Y ESTUDIOS. 1980. a. 2500 ptas. Universidad de Granada, Facultad de Filosofia y Letras, Departamento de Historia del Islam, Campus Universitario de Cartuja, Granada, Spain. Ed. J. Bosch-Vila. adv. bk. rev. circ. 1,000.

BEER-SHEVA. see *RELIGIONS AND THEOLOGY — Judaic*

956 SP
CUADERNOS DE HISTORIA DEL ISLAM. 1967. irreg. 2500 ptas. Universidad de Granada, Facultad de Filosofia y Letras, Departamento de Historia del Islam, Campus Universitario de Cartuja, Granada, Spain. Ed. J. Bosch-Vila. adv. bk. rev. index. circ. 1,000. Indexed: Hist.Abstr. Amer.Hist.& Life.
Formerly: Cuadernos de Historia del Islam. Serie Monografica Islamica Occidentalia (ISSN 0070-1696)

956.94 IS ISSN 0334-8903
DISPERSION Y UNIDAD. (Text in Spanish) 1978. a. IS.27($35) Semana Publishing Co., P.O. Box 2427, Jerusalem 91023, Israel. Ed. Julio Adin. circ. 2,000.

HOLY LAND; illustrated quarterly of the Franciscan custody of the holy land. see *RELIGIONS AND THEOLOGY — Roman Catholic*

HOLY PLACES OF PALESTINE. see *RELIGIONS AND THEOLOGY*

956 297 US ISSN 0888-9007
JUSUR; the U C L A journal of Middle Eastern studies. 1985. a. $6 to individuals; students $4.50. University of California, Los Angeles, Von Grunebaum Center for Near Eastern Studies, 10286 Bunche Hall, Los Angeles, CA 90024. TEL 213-825-1181 Ed. William C. Young. bk. rev. film rev. circ. 200. (back issues avail.) Indexed: Amer.Hist.& Life. Hist.Abstr.

QUADERNI DE "LA TERRA SANTA". see *RELIGIONS AND THEOLOGY*

HOBBIES
see also Hobbies–Philately

HOBBIES — Antiques
see also Art

HOBBIES — Philately

769.56 IT ISSN 0016-3694
GABRIEL; informatore filatelico. 1962. q. L.10000($8) Gabriel Italiana, Casella Postale 7090, 00100 Rome, Italy. Ed. Nicolo Musumeci. adv. circ. 600.

HOMOSEXUALITY

301 US ISSN 0741-9872
CONCORD. 1976. q. $10. Lutherans Concerned North America, Box 10461, Fort Dearborn Sta., Chicago, IL 60610. circ. 1,200.

301 US ISSN 0147-1139
DIGNITY. 1969. m. $20. Dignity, Inc., 1500 Massachusetts Ave. N.W., Ste. 11, Washington, DC 20005. TEL 202-861-0017 Ed. Michael J. Bushek. bk. rev. tr.lit. circ. 5,000.

392 US
METROLINE. 1972. m. $8. Metropolitan Community Church, Box 325, Hartford, CT 06103. TEL 203-522-5575 Ed. John D. Crowley. adv. bk. rev. circ. 6,500.
Formerly: Gay Christian.

285 322.4 US ISSN 0889-3985
MORE LIGHT UPDATE. 1980. m. (combined June/July) $10. Presbyterians for Lesbian - Gay Concerns, Inc., Box 38, New Brunswick, NJ 08903-0038. TEL 201-846-1510 Ed. James D. Anderson. adv. bk. rev. circ. 2,500. (back issues avail.)

HOSPITALS
see also Medical Sciences

362 CN ISSN 0226-5923
C H A C REVIEW. French edtition: Revue A C C S (ISSN 0226-5931) (Text in English) 1958. 4/yr. Can.$25($30) Catholic Health Association of Canada, 1247 Kilborn Ave., Ottawa, Ont. K1H 6K7, Canada. TEL 613-238-8471 Ed. E. MacNeil. adv. bk. rev. circ. 1,523.
Former titles: Catholic Hospital (ISSN 0008-8099); C H A C Bulletin.

362 200 US
CATHOLIC HEALTH ASSOCIATION OF THE UNITED STATES. GUIDEBOOK. a. Catholic Health Association of the United States, 4455 Woodson Rd., St. Louis, MO 63134. TEL 314-427-2500
Formerly: Guidebook of Catholic Hospitals (ISSN 0090-2535)

362 200 US
CATHOLIC HEALTH WORLD. 1985. 24/yr. $24. Catholic Health Association of the U S, 4455 Woodson Rd., St. Louis, MO 63134. TEL 314-427-2500 adv. circ. 6,600.

613 271.979 US
MEDICAL MISSION SISTERS NEWS. 1927. q. free. ‡ Society of Catholic Medical Missionaries, Inc., 8400 Pine Rd., Philadelphia, PA 19111. Ed. Monica M. McGinley. illus. index. cum.index. circ. 35,000.
Supersedes: Medical Missionary (ISSN 0025-7389)

NACHRICHTEN AUS DER AERZTLICHEN MISSION. see *RELIGIONS AND THEOLOGY*

HOTELS AND RESTAURANTS
see also Travel and Tourism

HOUSING AND URBAN PLANNING
see also Building and Construction

HUMANITIES: COMPREHENSIVE WORKS

ANSTOESSE; aus der Arbeit der Evangelischen Akademie Hofgeismar. see *RELIGIONS AND THEOLOGY*

378 200 FR ISSN 0008-9605
CENTRE CATHOLIQUE DES INTELLECTUELS FRANCAIS. RECHERCHES ET DEBATS. 4/yr. 110 F. Centre Catholique des Intellectuels Francais, 61 rue Madame, 75006-Paris, France. Ed. Desdee De Brouwer.

200 US ISSN 0009-7527
CITHARA; essays in Judaeo-Christian tradition. 1961. s-a. $4. Franciscan Institute, St. Bonaventure University, Box BC, St. Bonaventure, NY 14778. TEL 716-375-2000 Ed. John Mulryan. bk. rev. cum.ind. every 2 vols. circ. 700. (also avail. in microfilm from UMI) Indexed: Cath.Ind. Curr.Cont. Hist.Abstr. M.L.A. Arts & Hum.Cit.Ind. Hist.Abstr.& Life. Abstr.Engl.Stud.

IMPACTS. see *RELIGIONS AND THEOLOGY — Roman Catholic*

PONTIFICIA UNIVERSIDADE CATOLICA DE SAO PAULO. REVISTA. see *RELIGIONS AND THEOLOGY — Roman Catholic*

STUDIES IN FORMATIVE SPIRITUALITY. see *RELIGIONS AND THEOLOGY*

VITA SOCIALE. see *RELIGIONS AND THEOLOGY — Roman Catholic*

HUMANITIES: COMPREHENSIVE WORKS — Computer Applications

200 001.6 BE
CENTRE; Bible data bank. (Text in English, French, German) 1981. biennial. 250 Fr. (Association Internationale "Bible et Informatique") N.V. Brepols I.G.P., Rue Baron du Four 8, B-2300 Turnhout, Belgium. Ed. R.F. Poswick. bibl. stat. circ. 1,200. (also avail. in magnetic tape)

INDUSTRIAL HEALTH AND SAFETY
see also Business and Economics–Labor and Industrial Relations

INSURANCE

UNITED CHURCH OF CHRIST. PENSION BOARDS (ANNUAL REPORT) see *RELIGIONS AND THEOLOGY — Other Denominations And Sects*

INTERNATIONAL DEVELOPMENT AND ASSISTANCE
see Business and Economics–International Development and Assistance

INTERNATIONAL EDUCATION PROGRAMS
see Education–International Education Programs

INTERNATIONAL RELATIONS
see Political Science–International Relations

ISLAM
see Religions and Theology–Islamic

JOURNALISM

070 282 US ISSN 0008-8129
CATHOLIC JOURNALIST. 1945. m. $12. Catholic Press Association, 119 North Park Ave., Rockville Centre, NY 11570. TEL 516-766-3400 Ed. James A. Doyle. adv. bk. rev. illus. stat. tr.lit. circ. 2,500. (tabloid format) Indexed: Cath.Ind.

070 US
FREEDOM. 1968. m. $12 for 12 nos. North Star Publishing, Inc., 1301 N. Catalina, Los Angeles, CA 90027. TEL 213-663-2058 Ed. Thomas G. Whittle. adv. bk. rev. illus. circ. 50,000.
Formerly: Freedom Magazine.

070.4 282 US
HEIGHTS (NEW YORK) s-a. Cathedral Church of St. John the Divine, 1047 Amsterdam Ave. at 112 St., New York, NY 10025. TEL 212-678-6888

070.48 296 US
JEWISH PRESS FEATURES. 1971. m. $50. Jewish Student Press Service, 15 E. 26th St., New York, NY 10010. TEL 212-679-1411 Ed. Larry Ydelson. bk. rev. circ. 150.

PARISH COMMUNICATION. see *RELIGIONS AND THEOLOGY — Roman Catholic*

070 200 US ISSN 0034-4109
R N A NEWSLETTER. 1953. bi-m. $5. Religion Newswriters Association, c/o Ben Kaufman, Cincinnati Enquirer, 617 Vine St., Cincinnati, OH 45202. circ. 125. (processed)
Religious journalism

JUDAISM
see Religions and Theology–Judaic

LABOR AND INDUSTRIAL RELATIONS
see Business and Economics–Labor and Industrial Relations

LABOR UNIONS
see also Business and Economics–Labor and Industrial Relations

EVANGELIE EN MAATSCHAPPIJ. see *RELIGIONS AND THEOLOGY*

331.88 282 BE
GIDS OP MAATSCHAPPELIJK GEBIED; tijdschrift voor sociale cultur. 1902. m. 1200 Fr. (Algemeen Christelijk Werkersverbond - Catholic Workers Movement) V.Z.W. Vormingscentrum Ter Munk, Wetstraat 121, 1040 Brussels, Belgium. Ed. A. Vanempten. bk. rev. Indexed: Key to Econ.Sci.

LAW

340 200 US ISSN 0736-0142
C L S QUARTERLY. 1980. 3/yr. $15. Christian Legal Society, Box 2069, Oak Park, IL 60303. TEL 312-848-7735 Ed. Lynn Robert Buzzard. adv. bk. rev. circ. 10,000. Indexed: Leg.Per. C.L.I. L.R.I.

340 US ISSN 0008-8137
CATHOLIC LAWYER. 1955. q. $5. St. John's University, School of Law, Grand Central and Utopia Parkways, Jamaica, NY 11439. TEL 718-990-6600 Ed. Edward Fagan. bk. rev. illus. index. cum.index every 2 years. circ. 2,500. (also avail. in microfilm from RRI) Indexed: Cath.Ind. Leg.Per. C.L.I. CERDIC. Canon Law Abstr. L.R.I.

340 296 US ISSN 0094-9701
HA-MESIVTA. (Text in Hebrew) 1940. a. $4. Yeshivath Torah Vodaath, Inc., 452 E. 9th St., Brooklyn, NY 11218. TEL 718-462-6087 Ed. Elie Goldberg. adv. circ. 1,000.

349 IT ISSN 0021-3268
IUSTITIA. 1948. q. L.40000. (Unione Giuristi Cattolici Italiani) Casa Editrice Dott. A. Giuffre, Via B. Arsizio 40, 20151 Milan, Italy. Ed. Pietro Gismondi. adv. bk. rev. index. circ. 1,300. Indexed: CERDIC.

JEWISH LAW ANNUAL. see *RELIGIONS AND THEOLOGY — Judaic*

JOURNAL OF CHURCH AND STATE. see *RELIGIONS AND THEOLOGY*

340 200 US
JOURNAL OF LAW AND RELIGION. 1983. s-a. $12. Hamline University School of Law, Journal of Law and Religion, 1536 Hewitt Ave., St. Paul, MN 55104. Eds. Michael Scherschligt, Wilson Yates. (also avail. in microfilm from WSH) Indexed: Rel.Per.

340 AU ISSN 0259-0735
KIRCHE UND RECHT. irreg., no.17, 1985. price varies. Verband der Wissenschaftliche Gesellschaften Oesterreichs, Lindengasse 37, A-1070 Vienna, Austria.

340 UK
LAW & JUSTICE. (Text in English) 1962. q. £12.50. ‡ Edmund Plowden Trust, 51 High St., Hampton, Middlesex TW12 2SX, England. Ed. Rev. Richard Regan. adv. bk. rev. abstr. bibl. circ. 250. Indexed: C.L.I. CERDIC. Canon Law Abstr. L.R.I.
Formerly: Quis Custodiet (ISSN 0033-6610)

MOREANA; time trieth truth. see *HISTORY — History Of Europe*

340 AU ISSN 0029-9820
OESTERREICHISCHES ARCHIV FUER KIRCHENRECHT. 1896. 4/yr. S.588. Verband der Wissenschaftlichen Gesellschaften Oesterreichs, Lindengasse 37, A-1070 Vienna, Austria. (Co-sponsor: Universitaet Wien, Rechts- und Staatswissenschaftliche Fakultaet, Institut fuer Kirchenrecht) Eds. I. Gampl, R. Potz, B. Primetshofer. Indexed: Hist.Abstr. CERDIC.
Canon law

340 200 FR ISSN 0758-802X
PRAXIS JURIDIQUE ET RELIGION. (Text in French; summaries in English and Spanish) 1984. s-a. 250 F. (Universite de Strasbourg II, C E R D I C Publications) C E R D I C Publications, 9 place de l'Universite, 67084 Strasbourg Cedex, France. Ed. Marie Zimmerman. adv. circ. 1,000. Indexed: Cath.Ind. Rel.Ind.One.

ZEITSCHRIFT FUER EVANGELISCHES KIRCHENRECHT. see *RELIGIONS AND THEOLOGY — Protestant*

LIBRARY AND INFORMATION SCIENCES
see also Bibliographies

A D R I S NEWSLETTER. (Association for the Development of Religious Information Services) see *RELIGIONS AND THEOLOGY*

020 296 US
A J L NEWSLETTER. 4/yr. $25 includes Judaica Librarianship. Association of Jewish Libraries, c/o National Foundation for Jewish Culture, 122 E. 42nd St., Rm. 1512, New York, NY 10168. TEL 212-490-2280 Ed. Irene Levin. (back issues avail.)

ARCHIEF VAN DE KERKEN. see *RELIGIONS AND THEOLOGY*

020 200 100 UK ISSN 0305-781X
ASSOCIATION OF BRITISH THEOLOGICAL AND PHILOSOPHICAL LIBRARIES. BULLETIN. N.S. 1974. 3/yr. £8($15) Association of British Theological and Philosophical Libraries, New College Library, Mound Place, Edinburgh EH1 2LU, Scotland (Subscr. address: M.J. Walsh, Heythrop College Library, 11-13 Cavendish Square, London W1M 0AN, England) Ed. John V. Howard. adv. bk. rev. abstr. bibl. circ. 250. (back issues avail.) Indexed: LISA.

020 282 US ISSN 0008-8161
CATHOLIC LIBRARY ASSOCIATION. NORTHERN ILLINOIS CHAPTER. NEWSLETTER. 1957. 3/yr. $6. Catholic Library Association, Northern Illinois Chapter, c/o Thomas J. Neihengen, Gordontech, 3633 N. California, Chicago, IL 60618. Ed. Kathleen O'Leary. bk. rev. circ. 450. (processed)

026 280 US ISSN 0412-3131
CHRISTIAN LIBRARIAN. vol.23, 1979. q. $12 to non-members; institutions $15. Association of Christian Librarians Inc., Cedarville College Library, Cedarville, OH 45314. Ed. Ron Jordahl. adv. bk. rev. illus. circ. 325. (reprint service avail. from UMI) Indexed: Sci.Abstr. Chr.Per.Ind.

020 266 200 UK ISSN 0309-4170
CHRISTIAN LIBRARIAN. 1976. a. £1.40. Librarians' Christian Fellowship, c/o Graham Hedges, Ed., 34 Thurlestone Ave., Seven Kings, Ilford, Essex IG3 9DU, England. adv. bk. rev. abstr. circ. 450. (back issues avail.) Indexed: Chr.Per.Ind.

026 US ISSN 0009-6342
CHURCH AND SYNAGOGUE LIBRARIES. 1967. bi-m. $15. Church and Synagogue Library Association, Box 1130, Bryn Mawr, PA 19010. TEL 215-853-2870 Ed. William H. Gentz. adv. bk. rev. charts. illus. index. circ. 3,400. (back issues avail.; reprint service avail. from UMI) Indexed: CERDIC. Chr.Per.Ind.
Formerly: Church and Synagogue Library Association. News Bulletin.

020 286 US
CHURCH MEDIA LIBRARY MAGAZINE. 1970. q. $11. ‡ Southern Baptist Convention, Sunday School Board, 127 Ninth Ave., N., Nashville, TN 37203. TEL 615-251-2000 bk. rev. record rev. bibl. charts. illus. index. cum.index. circ. 20,000. Indexed: South.Bap.Per.Ind.
Formerly: Media: Library Services Journal (ISSN 0009-6423); Which supersedes: Church Library Magazine.
Church libraries

020 US ISSN 0010-5821
CONGREGATIONAL LIBRARY. BULLETIN. 1949. 3/yr. $5. (American Congregational Association) Congregational Library, 14 Beacon St., Boston, MA 02108. TEL 617-523-0470 Ed. Dr. Harold F. Worthley. bk. rev. bibl. illus. circ. 1,500.

026 266 US ISSN 0272-6122
INTERNATIONAL BULLETIN OF MISSIONARY RESEARCH. 1950. N.S. 1977. q. $14. Overseas Ministries Study Center, Box 2057, Ventnor, NJ 08406 TEL 609-823-6671 (Subscr. to: Box 1308E, Fort Lee, NJ 07024) Ed. Gerald H. Anderson. adv. bk. rev. bibl. index. cum.index: 1977-80; 1981-84. circ. 8,000. (also avail. in microform from UMI; reprint service avail. from UMI) Indexed: CERDIC. Chr.Per.Ind. G.Soc.Sci.& Rel.Per.Lit. Rel.& Theol.Abstr. Rel.Ind.One.
Formed by the merger of: Gospel in Context (ISSN 0193-8320) & Occasional Bulletin of Missionary Research (ISSN 0364-2178); Until 1977: Missionary Research Library. Occasional Bulletin (ISSN 0026-606X)

020 266 200 UK ISSN 0308-5473
LIBRARIANS' CHRISTIAN FELLOWSHIP NEWSLETTER. 1974. 3/yr. £5. Librarians' Christian Fellowship, c/o Graham Hedges, Ed., 34 Thurlestone Ave., Seven Kings, Ilford, Essex IG3 9DU, England. adv. bk. rev. abstr. circ. 450. (back issues avail.)

020 284 US ISSN 0024-7472
LUTHERAN LIBRARIES. 1958. q. $15 (bulk rates avail.) Lutheran Church Library Association, 122 W. Franklin Ave., Minneapolis, MN 55404. TEL 612-870-3623 Ed. Ron Klug. adv. bk. rev. illus. tr.lit. circ. 9,000. (back issues avail.) Indexed: CERDIC.

MARIAN LIBRARY STUDIES. NEW SERIES. see *RELIGIONS AND THEOLOGY*

SOURCES FOR THE STUDY OF RELIGION IN MALAWI. see *RELIGIONS AND THEOLOGY*

020.6 026 BE
V.R.B. - INFORMATIE. (Text in Flemish, French) 1971. q. 250 Fr. Vereniging van Religieus-Wetenschappelijke Bibliothecarissen - Association of Scientific-Religious Librarians, Minderbroedersstraat 5, 3800 Sint-Truiden, Belgium. Ed. K. van de Casteele. bk. rev. bibl. circ. 100.

LINGUISTICS
see also Classical Studies; Oriental Studies

BELMONDA LETERO. see *RELIGIONS AND THEOLOGY — Other Denominations And Sects*

CAHIERS DE CIVILISATION MEDIEVALE. see *HISTORY — History Of Europe*

492 220 US ISSN 0073-0637
HARVARD SEMITIC MONOGRAPHS. 1968. irreg., no.6, 1973. price varies. Scholars Press, 101 Salem St., Box 1608, GA 30031-1608.

410 296 US ISSN 0146-4094
HEBREW STUDIES; a journal devoted to the Hebrew language, the Bible and related areas of scholarship. vol. 16, 1975. a. $20. National Association of Professors of Hebrew, 1346 Van Hise Hall, 1220 Linden Dr., University of Wisconsin-Madison, Madison, WI 53706. TEL 608-262-3204 Ed. Michael V. Fox. adv. bk. rev circ. 400. Indexed: Old Test.Abstr. Rel.Ind.One.
Formerly, until vol. 17, 1976: Hebrew Abstracts (ISSN 0438-895X)

IN OTHER WORDS. see *RELIGIONS AND THEOLOGY*

410 296 800 IS ISSN 0333-8347
JEWISH LANGUAGE REVIEW. (Text mainly in English, occasionally in French and Hebrew) 1981. a. $18 to individuals; institutions $24. Association for the Study of Jewish Languages, 1610 Eshkol Tower, University of Haifa, Mount Carmel, Haifa 31 999, Israel. Eds. David L. Gold, Leonard Prager. adv. bk. rev. bibl. (back issues avail) Indexed: Bull.Signal. Curr.Cont. M.L.A. Sociol.Abstr. Arts & Hum.Cit.Ind. Lang.& Lang.Behav.Abstr.

JOURNAL OF SEMITIC STUDIES. see *RELIGIONS AND THEOLOGY — Judaic*

296.68 US
LAMISHPAHA. 1963. m. $10. Histadruth Ivrith of America, Inc., 1841 Broadway, New York, NY 10023. TEL 212-581-5151 Eds. Yuval Shem-Ur, Hanita Brand. adv. bk. rev. circ. 6,500. (back issues avail.)

200 400 GW ISSN 0342-0884
LINGUISTICA BIBLICA; Interdisziplinaere Zeitschrift fuer Theologie und Linguistik. (Text in German, English, French; summaries in English) 1970. 2/yr. DM.35. Verlag Linguistica Biblica, Postfach 130154, 5300 Bonn 1, W. Germany (B.R.D.) Ed. Erhardt Guettgemanns. adv. bk. rev. abstr. bibl. illus. index. circ. 675. Indexed: Curr.Cont. M.L.A. Old Test.Abstr. Arts & Hum.Cit.Ind. CERDIC. Lang.& Lang.Behav.Abstr. New Test.Abstr. Rel.& Theol.Abstr.

410 808 US
N A O S; notes and materials for the linguistic study of the sacred. (Editions in English and Spanish) 1985. 3/yr. $9. University of Pittsburg, Department of Hispanic Languages and Literatures, Names of the Sacred Project, 1309 Cathedral of Learning, Pittsburgh, PA 15260. Ed. Juan Adolfo Vasquez.

PATRISTICS. see *RELIGIONS AND THEOLOGY*

220 400 UK ISSN 0260-0943
PRACTICAL PAPERS FOR THE BIBLE TRANSLATOR. 1950. s-a. $6 ($12 including Technical Papers for the Bible Translator) United Bible Societies, c/o University of Aberdeen, Dept. of Religious Studies, Aberdeen AB9 2UB, Scotland. Ed. E. McG. Fry. bk. rev. index. cum.index. circ. 3,000. (also avail. in microform from UMI; microfiche; reprint service avail. from UMI) Indexed: Old Test.Abstr. Chr.Per.Ind. New Test.Abstr. Rel.Ind.One. Rel.& Theol.Abstr.
Supersedes in part (from 1972): Bible Translator (ISSN 0006-0844)

SEMEIA; an experimental journal for biblical criticism. see *RELIGIONS AND THEOLOGY*

SEMIOTIQUE ET BIBLE. see *RELIGIONS AND THEOLOGY*

220 400 UK ISSN 0260-0935
TECHNICAL PAPERS FOR THE BIBLE TRANSLATOR. 1950. s-a. $6 ($12 including Practical Papers for the Bible Translator) United Bible Societies, c/o University of Aberdeen, Dept. of Religious Studies, Aberdeen AB9 2UB, Scotland. Ed. Paul Ellingworth. bk. rev. index. cum.index every 10 yrs. circ. 3,000. (also avail. in microfilm; microfiche; reprint service avail. from UMI) Indexed: Old Test.Abstr. Chr.Per.Ind. New Test.Abstr. Rel.Ind.One. Rel.& Theol.Abstr.
Supersedes in part (from 1972): Bible Translator (ISSN 0006-0844)

UNIVERSITE SAINT-JOSEPH. FACULTE DES LETTRES ET DES SCIENCES HUMAINES. RECHERCHE. SERIE A: LANGUE ARABE ET PENSEE ISLAMIQUE. see *RELIGIONS AND THEOLOGY — Islamic*

410 296 800 IS
YIDDISH LITERARY AND LINGUISTIC PERIODICALS AND MISCELLANIES; a selective annotated bibliography. 1982. irreg. Association for the Study of Jewish Languages, 1610 Eshkol Tower, University of Haifa, Mount Carmel, Haifa 31 999, Israel (Subscr. to: Norwood Editions, Box 38, Norwood, PA 19074, U.S.A.) Ed. Leonard Prager.

LITERARY AND POLITICAL REVIEWS

053.1 AU
ACADEMIA; Zeitschrift fuer Politik und Kultur. 1949. bi-m. S.150. Oesterreichischer Cartell-Verband, Lerchenfelderstr. 14, A-1080 Vienna, Austria. Ed. Clemens Martin. bk. rev. film rev. charts. illus. stat. circ. 20,000.

059.92 US
BITZARON: A QUARTERLY OF HEBREW LETTERS. (Text in Hebrew; summaries in English) 1939. q. $15 domestic; foreign $17. (Hebrew Literary Foundation) Bitzaron, Inc., Box 623, Cooper Sta., New York, NY 10003. (Co-sponsor: Institute of Hebrew Culture and Education) Ed. Hayim Leaf. adv. bk. rev. play rev. illus. stat. index. circ. 18,800. (back issues avail.) Indexed: Hist.Abstr. Ind.Heb.Per. M.L.A. Amer.Hist.& Life.
Supersedes (1939-1978): Bitzaron: the Hebrew Monthly of America (ISSN 0006-3932)

800 200 US ISSN 0148-3331
CHRISTIANITY AND LITERATURE. 1950. q. $10 to individuals; institutions $15. Conference on Christianity and Literature, Baylor University, Waco, TX 76798. Ed. James Barcus. adv. bk. rev. bibl. circ. 1,400. (back issues avail.) Indexed: Curr.Cont. M.L.A. Arts & Hum.Cit.Ind. Amer.Bibl.Slavic & E.Eur.Stud. Abstr.Engl.Stud. CERDIC. Chr.Per.Ind. LCR. Rel.Ind.One.
Formerly: Conference on Christianity and Literature. Newsletter.

CIVILTA CATTOLICA. see *RELIGIONS AND THEOLOGY — Roman Catholic*

051 300 US ISSN 0010-3330
COMMONWEAL. 1924. bi-w. $28. Commonweal Foundation, 15 Dutch St., New York, NY 10038. TEL 212-683-2042 Ed. Peter Steinfels. adv. bk. rev. film rev. play rev. index. circ. 19,000. (also avail. in microform from BLH,MIM,UMI) Indexed: Bk.Rev.Dig. Cath.Ind. Hist.Abstr. M.L.A. Old Test.Abstr. R.G. Amer.Bibl.Slavic & E.Eur.Stud. Abstrax. A.I.P.P. Bk.Rev.Ind. Amer.Hist.& Life. CERDIC. Child.Bk.Rev.Ind. Curr.Lit.Fam.Plan. Film Lit.Ind. G.Soc.Sci.& Rel.Per.Lit. Media Rev.Dig. Mag.Ind. PMR.

054.1 FR ISSN 0014-1941
ETUDES. 1856. m. 355 F. Assas Editions, 14 rue d'Assas, 75006 Paris, France. Ed. Paul Valadier. adv. bk. rev. abstr. bibl. index. cum.index: 1961-1978. circ. 10,000. Indexed: Cath.Ind. Hist.Abstr. M.L.A. Amer.Hist.& Life. CERDIC. New Test.Abstr. Phil.Ind. Pt.de Rep.

296 IS ISSN 0334-2506
FORUM; a quarterly on the Jewish people, Zionism and Israel. (Text in English) 1963/64. q. IS.4000($15) World Zionist Organization, Information Department, Box 92, Jerusalem, Israel. Ed. Amnon Hadary. bk. rev. cum.index. circ. 6,000. (also avail. in microform from UMI; reprint service avail. from UMI)
Formerly: Dispersion and Unity (ISSN 0070-6701)

GESHER. see *RELIGIONS AND THEOLOGY — Judaic*

808.8 282 US
IDEA INK; the national Catholic opinion quarterly. 1982. q. I.D.E.A., Inc., Box 4010, Madison, WI 53711-0010. TEL 608-273-0330 Ed. Fr. Charles Fiore, O.P. adv. circ. 70,000.

296 PL ISSN 0019-1507
IDISZE SZRIFTN/JEWISH CULTURAL AFFAIRS. m. $2.70. Wydawnictwo Idisz Buch, Nowogrodzka 5, Warsaw, Poland.

296 US
JEWISH CHRONICLE (NEW YORK) 1968. w. $10. Jewish Chronicle, 122 S. Broadway, Yonkers, NY 10701. TEL 914-423-5009 Ed. Carolyn Weiner. adv. bk. rev. film rev. circ. 50,000. (back issues avail.)

JUDAISM; a quarterly journal of Jewish life and thought. see *RELIGIONS AND THEOLOGY — Judaic*

296 YU ISSN 0022-748X
KADIMA. (Text in Serbo-Croatian) 1959. m. 200 din.($5) Savez Jevrejskih Opstina Jugoslavije, 7. Jula 71a, Belgrade, Yugoslavia. Ed. David Albahari. circ. 2,500.
Literary and informative magazine for Jewish youth

KIRKE OG KULTUR. see *RELIGIONS AND THEOLOGY*

296 AG ISSN 0024-7693
LUZ; la revista israelita para toda sudamerica. 1931. fortn. Pasteur 359, Buenos Aires, Argentina. Ed. Nissim Elnecave. bk. rev. bibl. illus. circ. 25,000.

281.62 LE ISSN 0025-4975
MASSIS. 1947. w. £L20($12) Armenian Catholic Patriarchate, Place Debbas, Beirut, Lebanon. Ed. Fr. Vartan Tekeyan. charts. illus. (tabloid format)

028 AU ISSN 0026-0126
MERLEG; folyoiratok es konyvek szemleje. (Text in Hungarian; summaries in English and German) 1965. q. S.252. Verlag Herder, Wollzeile 33, A-1010 Vienna, Austria. Eds. Janos Boor, Ladislaus Balint. adv. bk. rev. abstr. bibl. index. circ. 3,000. Indexed: Old Test.Abstr.

MUSLIM WORLD; a journal devoted to the study of Islam and of Christian-Muslim relationship in past and present. see *RELIGIONS AND THEOLOGY — Islamic*

ST. LOUIS REVIEW. see *RELIGIONS AND THEOLOGY — Roman Catholic*

296.67 IS ISSN 0082-4585
SOURCES OF CONTEMPORARY JEWISH THOUGHT/MEKEVOT. Title varies: To the Source/El Ha'ayin. (Text in English, French, Spanish, Hebrew) 1968. irreg., no.6, 1975. price varies. World Zionist Organization, Department for Torah Education and Culture in the Diaspora, Box 92, Jerusalem, Israel (Subscr. to: Jewish Agency, Publication Service, 515 Park Ave., New York, NY 10022) Ed.Bd.

290 US
SYNAPSE (BOSTON) 1983. 3/yr. free. Young Religious Unitarian Universalists, 25 Beacon St., Boston, MA 02108. Ed. Eric Kaminetzky. adv. bk. rev. circ. 7,000. (tabloid format; back issues avail.)
Formerly: People Soup (ISSN 0360-8247)

TABLET. see *RELIGIONS AND THEOLOGY*

200 FR ISSN 0040-2923
TEMOIGNAGE CHRETIEN. 1941. w. 525 F. Editions du Temoignage Chretien, 49 Faubourg Poissonniere, 75009 Paris, France. Ed. Georges Montaron. adv. bk. rev. film rev. play rev. tele.rev. circ. 80,000. (tabloid format; also avail. in microform) Indexed: CERDIC.

055.1 IT ISSN 0040-3989
TESTIMONIANZE; quaderni mensili. 1957. 10/yr. £30000. Via dei Roccettini 11, 50016 S. Domenico, Florence, Italy. Ed. Lodovico Grassi. adv. bk. rev. illus. index. circ. 7,000. Indexed: Old Test.Abstr. CERDIC.

378.1 US ISSN 0041-9524
UNIVERSITY OF DAYTON REVIEW. 1964. irreg., approx. 3/yr. free on request. (University of Dayton) University of Dayton Press, 300 College Park Ave., Dayton, OH 45469. TEL 513-229-0123 Ed. Robert C. Conard. charts. illus. index. circ. 1,000. Indexed: M.L.A. Amer.Hum.Ind. Amer.Bibl.Slavic & E.Eur.Stud. Abstr.Engl.Stud.

WAY (SAN FRANCISCO) see *RELIGIONS AND THEOLOGY — Roman Catholic*

LITERATURE
see also Literature–Poetry; Publishing and Book Trade

L'ALTRA EUROPA. see *ART*

AMERICAN BENEDICTINE REVIEW. see *RELIGIONS AND THEOLOGY — Roman Catholic*

ANALECTA CARTUSIANA; review for Carthusian history and spirituality. see *RELIGIONS AND THEOLOGY*

BOOKS AND ARTICLES ON ORIENTAL SUBJECTS PUBLISHED IN JAPAN. see *HISTORY — History Of Asia*

CAHIERS DE CIVILISATION MEDIEVALE. see *HISTORY — History Of Europe*

FELLOWSHIP IN PRAYER. see *RELIGIONS AND THEOLOGY — Other Denominations And Sects*

ISLAM AND THE MODERN AGE. see *RELIGIONS AND THEOLOGY — Islamic*

JEWISH LANGUAGE REVIEW. see *LINGUISTICS*

LITERATURE AND BELIEF. see *RELIGIONS AND THEOLOGY*

289.7 800 CN ISSN 0315-8101
MENNONITE MIRROR. (Text in English and German) 1971. 10/yr. Can.$10. Mennonite Literary Society, 207-1317A Portage Ave., Winnipeg, Man. R3G 0V3, Canada. TEL 204-786-2289 Ed. Al Reimer. adv. bk. rev. illus. circ. 7,000. (also avail. in microfilm)

METHODIST HISTORY. see *RELIGIONS AND THEOLOGY — Protestant*

PROOFTEXTS; a journal of Jewish literary history. see *RELIGIONS AND THEOLOGY — Judaic*

QUESTION DE RACINES, PENSEES, SCIENCES ECLAIREES. see *PARAPSYCHOLOGY AND OCCULTISM*

RASSEGNA MENSILE DI ISRAEL. see *RELIGIONS AND THEOLOGY — Judaic*

810 US
RELIGION AND LITERATURE. 1957; N.S. vol.8, 1972/73. 3/yr. $12 to individuals; $15 to libraries. University of Notre Dame, Department of English, Notre Dame, IN 46556. TEL 219-239-5725 Ed. Tracy Burke Carrier. adv. bk. rev. bibl. circ. 500. (processed; also avail. in microform from UMI; back issues avail.) Indexed: Cath.Ind. Curr.Cont. M.L.A. Amer.Hum.Ind. Arts & Hum.Cit.Ind. Abstr.Engl.Stud. CERDIC. Rel.& Theol.Abstr. Rel.Ind.One.
Formerly: Notre Dame English Journal (ISSN 0029-4500)

700 RM ISSN 0034-754X
REVISTA CULTULUI MOZAIC. (Text in English, Hebrew, Rumanian and Yiddish) 1956. bi-m. Federatia Comunitatilor Evreiesti din Republica Socialista Romania, Str. Sf. Vineri nr.9, Bucharest, Rumania. adv. bk. rev. illus. circ. 10,000.

REVUE DES ETUDES AUGUSTINIENNES. see *RELIGIONS AND THEOLOGY*

STUDIES IN ISLAM. see *RELIGIONS AND THEOLOGY — Islamic*

VIGILIA. see *RELIGIONS AND THEOLOGY — Roman Catholic*

YIDDISH LITERARY AND LINGUISTIC PERIODICALS AND MISCELLANIES; a selective annotated bibliography. see *LINGUISTICS*

LITERATURE — Poetry

800 282 UK ISSN 0262-8937
DOWRY; a quarterly of Catholic poetry. 1982. q. £2($4) Gild of St. George, 19 Grosvenor Driveadassah Grove, New Brighton, Merseyside, England. Ed. Alex Anderson. adv. bk. rev. circ. 100.

808.81 US
JACKSONVILLE POETRY QUARTERLY. 1960. q. $25. Arcane Order Press, 2904 Rosemary Ln., Falls Church, VA 22042. Eds. Dell Lebo, L.J. Mather. index. cum.index. circ. 1,000. (looseleaf format; also avail. in microfiche; back issues avail.)

811 US
SHIRIM; a Jewish poetry journal. 1982. s-a. $5. c/o Hillel Macor, 900 Hilgard Ave., Los Angeles, CA 90024. Ed. Marc Steven Dworkin. circ. 700.

808.81 284 US ISSN 0889-9118
SILVER WINGS; poems. 1983. q. $6. Box 1000, Pearblossom, CA 93553-1000. TEL 805-264-3726 Ed. Jackson Wilcox. bk. rev. circ. 500. (back issues avail.)

MANAGEMENT
see Business and Economics–Management

MARKETING AND PURCHASING
see Business and Economics–Marketing and Purchasing

MEDICAL SCIENCES
see also Medical Sciences–Nurses and Nursing; Medical Sciences–Psychiatry and Neurology; Gerontology and Geriatrics; Hospitals; Physical Fitness and Hygiene

ARUT PERUM JOTHI. see *RELIGIONS AND THEOLOGY — Oriental*

C H A C REVIEW. see *HOSPITALS*

362.1 CN ISSN 0828-5748
CATHOLIC HEALTH ASSOCIATION OF CANADA. DIRECTORY. (Text in English and French) 1968. biennial. Can.$17 to non-members. Catholic Health Association of Canada, 1247 Kilborn Ave., Ottawa, Ont. K1H 6K7, Canada. TEL 613-238-8471 Ed. Freda Fraser. circ. 975.
Formerly: Catholic Hospital Association of Canada. Directory (ISSN 0380-8475)

610 200 UK ISSN 0008-8226
CATHOLIC MEDICAL QUARTERLY. 1923. q. $15. Guild of Catholic Doctors, Ed. Dr. W.H. Reynolds, Broad Towers, Caerleon, Newport, Mon., Wales. adv. bk. rev. bibl. index. circ. 2,500.

610 II ISSN 0009-5443
CHRISTIAN MEDICAL ASSOCIATION OF INDIA. JOURNAL. (Text in English) 1925. m. Rs.20($7) ‡ E.L. Press, Bangalore, Karnataka, India. Ed. Dr. Samuel Joseph. adv. bk. rev. abstr. charts. illus. index. circ. 1,500. Indexed: Biol.Abstr.

610 US ISSN 0009-546X
CHRISTIAN MEDICAL SOCIETY JOURNAL. vol. 20, 1969. q. $16. Christian Medical Society, Box 830689, 1616 Gateway Blvd., Richardson, TX 75083-0689. TEL 214-783-8384 Eds. Edwin A. Blum, D. Theol. adv. bk. rev. circ. 8,275. Indexed: Chr.Per.Ind.

CONTACT. see *RELIGIONS AND THEOLOGY*

ETHICS AND MEDICS. see *PHILOSOPHY*

610 JA ISSN 0019-1582
MEDICINE AND GOSPEL/IGAKU TO FUKUIN. (Text in Japanese) vol.25, 1973. m. 100 Yen($50) Japan Christian Medical Association - Nihon Kirisutosha Ika Renmai, 1- 551-23 Totsuka, Shinjuku-ku, Tokyo 160, Japan. Ed. Dr. Tadao Makino. circ. 1,200.

610 NE ISSN 0022-9350
METAMEDICA; blad voor metamedische vraagstukken. 1919. bi-m. fl.49 to individuals; institutions fl. 98.50. Uitgeversmaatschappij De Tijdstroom, Postbus 14, 7240 BA Lochem, Netherlands. Ed.Bd. adv. bk. rev. abstr. bibl. illus. index. circ. 1,500. Indexed: Excerp.Med.
Formerly: Katholiek Artsenblad.

174.2 US
NATIONAL FEDERATION OF CATHOLIC PHYSICIANS' GUILDS. NEWSLETTER. q. National Federation of Catholic Physicians Guilds, 850 Elm Grove Rd., Elm Grove, WI 53122. TEL 414-784-3435

610 IT ISSN 0014-8784
RES MEDICAE. 1935. bi-m. L.6000. (Ordine Ospedaliero di S. Giovanni di Dio) Fatebenefratelli, Via S. Vittore 12, 20123 Milan, Italy. adv. bk. rev. bibl. charts. illus. stat. index. circ. 6,000.

MEDICAL SCIENCES — Nurses And Nursing
see also Gerontology and Geriatrics; Hospitals

610.73 US ISSN 0743-2550
JOURNAL OF CHRISTIAN NURSING. 1951. q. $16. Inter-Varsity Christian Fellowship, Nurses Christian Fellowship, 233 Langdon St., Madison, WI 53703 TEL 608-257-1103 (Subscr. to: Box 1650, Downers Grove, IL 60515) Ed. Ramona Cass. adv. bk. rev. abstr. cum.index. circ. 11,000. (also avail. in microform from UMI) Indexed: Int.Nurs.Ind. CINAHL.
Formerly (until 1984): Nurses Lamp.

MEDICAL SCIENCES — Psychiatry And Neurology

616 301 US ISSN 0547-7115
NATIONAL GUILD OF CATHOLIC PSYCHIATRISTS. BULLETIN. 1948. a. $12. National Guild of Catholic Psychiatrists, c/o J. Sullivan, 9 Spring St., Whitinsville, MA 01588. TEL 617-234-6266 Ed. Anna Polcino, M.D. bk. rev. circ. 300. (back issues avail.) Indexed: Cath.Ind.

MILITARY

355 NE ISSN 0005-6146
BASIS. vol.17, 1975. s-m. fl.25. Stichting Geestelijke Weerbaarheid, Zomerstraat 1, Heerlen, Netherlands. Ed. M.G. Haringman. adv. bk. rev. illus. circ. 4,000.

355.347 UK
GREAT BRITAIN. ROYAL ARMY CHAPLAINS' DEPARTMENT. JOURNAL. 1922. s-a. £2. Ministry of Defense (Army), Royal Army Chaplains' Department Centre, Bagshot Park, Bagshot, Surrey, England. adv. bk. rev. circ. 1,000.
Formerly: Royal Army Chaplains Department. Quarterly Journal (ISSN 0035-8657)

LUTHERANS IN STEP. see *RELIGIONS AND THEOLOGY — Protestant*

355.347 GW ISSN 0047-7362
MILITAERSEELSORGE. 1958. q. free. ‡ Katholisches Militaerbischofsamt, Adenauerallee 115, 5300 Bonn, W. Germany (B.R.D.) Ed. Werner Koester. bk. rev. circ. 3,000.
Chaplains

262 355 US ISSN 0026-3958
MILITARY CHAPLAIN. 1931. bi-m. $10 for non-members. Military Chaplains Association of the United States of America, Box 645, Riverdale, MD 20737. Ed. William F. Emery. illus. circ. 2,350. Indexed: Air Un.Lib.Ind.
Chaplains

355.347 US ISSN 0360-9693
MILITARY CHAPLAINS' REVIEW. 1972. q. free. U.S. Army Chaplain Board, Fort Monmouth, NJ 07703. TEL 201-532-1366 Ed. Chaplain (Maj.) William Noble. bk. rev. circ. 6,000. (also avail. in microfiche) Indexed: Ind.U.S.Gov.Per.
Chaplains

355.347 US ISSN 0028-1654
NAVY CHAPLAINS BULLETIN. 1955. q. free to qualified personnel. ‡ U.S. Navy, Bureau of Naval Personnel, Office of the Navy Chief of Chaplains, Washington, DC 20370. TEL 202-545-6700 circ. 2,400. Indexed: CERDIC.

MUSIC
see also Dance; Sound Recording and Reproduction

783 282 GW
ALLGEMEINER CAECILIEN-VERBAND. SCHRIFTENREIHE. irreg., latest no.15. price varies. Allgemeiner Caecilien-Verband, Andreasstr. 9, D-8400 Regensburg, W. Germany (B.R.D.)

783 028.5 IT ISSN 0391-5425
ARMONIA DI VOCI. 1946. bi-m. L.23000. (Centro Catechistico Salesiano) Editrice Elle Di Ci, Corso Francia 214, 10096 Leumann (Turin), Italy. Ed. Antonio Fant. adv. circ. 1,500.
Sacred

783 FR ISSN 0335-5012
ASSEMBLEE NOUVELLE. 1969. q. 20 F. Editions du Levain, 1 rue de l'Abbe-Gregoire, 75006 Paris, France. Ed. Claude Truchot. adv. bk. rev. rec.rev.

780 US ISSN 0746-0066
CONTEMPORARY CHRISTIAN; music and more. 1978. m. $15. C C M Publications, Inc., Box 6300, Laguna Hills, CA 92654. TEL 714-951-9106 Ed. John W. Styll. adv. bk. rev. rec. rev. circ. 35,000. (back issues avail.)
Formerly (until 1983): Contemporary Christian Music.

783 FR ISSN 0071-2086
ETUDES GREGORIENNES; revue de musicologie religieuse. (Text in English, French and Italian) 1954. irreg, latest vol.20, 1981. price varies. ‡ Editions Abbaye Saint-Pierre de Solesmes, 72300 Sable sur Sarthe, France. Dir. D. Jean Claire. bk. rev. circ. 500. Indexed: RILM.

GOSPEL CHOIR. see *RELIGIONS AND THEOLOGY — Protestant*

783.9 US ISSN 0018-8271
HYMN. 1949. q. membership. Hymn Society of America, National Headquarters, Texas Christian University, Fort Worth, TX 76129. TEL 817-921-7608 Ed. Paul Westermeyer. adv. bk. rev. index. circ. 3,500. (back issues avail.) Indexed: Chr.Per.Ind. Music Ind. Rel.Ind.One. Rel.& Theol.Abstr.
Hymnology

JAHRBUCH FUER LITURGIK UND HYMNOLOGIE. see *RELIGIONS AND THEOLOGY*

783.02 US ISSN 0197-0100
JOURNAL OF JEWISH MUSIC AND LITURGY. (Text in English and Hebrew) 1976. a. $6. Cantorial Council of America, c/o Yeshiva University, 500 W. 185th St., New York, NY 10033. TEL 212-960-5353 Ed. Macy Nulman. circ. 300.

780 200 GW
KIRCHENMUSIKALISCHE NACHRICHTEN. 1950. q. DM.9. Evangelische Kirche in Hessen und Nassau in Frankfurt, Amt fuer Kirchenmusik, Miquelallee 7, 6000 Frankfurt 90, W. Germany (B.R.D.) bk. rev. circ. 1,800.

783 GW ISSN 0023-1819
DER KIRCHENMUSIKER. 1950. bi-m. DM.18. (Verband Evangelischer Kirchenmusiker Deutschlands) Verlag Merseburger Berlin GmbH, Motz Str. 13, 3500 Kassel, W. Germany (B.R.D.) Ed. D. Schuberth. adv. bk. rev. illus. record rev. index. circ. 5,600. Indexed: RILM.
Sacred music

783 SZ ISSN 0023-2068
KLEINE CHORZEITUNG; Mitteilungsblatt fuer die katholischen Kirchenchoere. (Supplement to: Katholische Kirchenmusik) 1950. irreg. (2-3/yr.) 0.50 Fr. per no. Paulus-Verlag GmbH, Murbacherstr. 29, 6003 Lucerne, Switzerland.
Formerly: Kirchensaenger.

783 SW ISSN 0281-286X
KYRKOMUSIKERNAS TIDNING. 1935-1982; resumed 1984. 18/yr. Kr.160. Kyrkomusikernas Riksfoerbund, Sveriges Laerarfoerbund, Box 12229, S-102 26 Stockholm, Sweden. Ed. Stellan Sagvik. adv. bk. rev. illus. circ. 4,300.
Formerly: Svensk Kyrkomusik (Edition AB for Church Musicians); Incorporating: Kyrkomusikernas Tidning; Kyrkosaangsfoerbundet (ISSN 0347-416X)
Sacred music

780 US ISSN 0027-4372
MUSIC LEADER. 1966. q. $7.25. Southern Baptist Convention, Sunday School Board, Church Music Department, 127 Ninth Ave., Nashville, TN 37243. TEL 615-251-2000 adv. bk. rev. circ. 30,000.
Formerly: Children's Music Leader.

781.7 US
MUSICA JUDAICA. (Text in English and Hebrew) 1976. a. $20. American Society for Jewish Music, 155 Fifth Ave., New York, NY 10010. TEL 212-533-2601 Ed. Israel J. Katz. adv. bk. rev. circ. 1,500. Indexed: Ind.Jew.Per. Music Ind. RILM.

783 GW ISSN 0027-4771
MUSIK UND KIRCHE. 1930. bi-m. DM.32. Baerenreiter-Verlag, Heinrich-Schuetz-Allee 31-37, 3500 Kassel-Wilhelmshoehe, W. Germany (B.R.D.) Ed.Bd. adv. bk. rev. bibl. illus. circ. 4,000. Indexed: Curr.Cont. Arts & Hum.Cit.Ind. RILM. Music Ind.

783 NE
MUZIEKBODE. 1932. m. fl.16. Nederlandse Federatie van Christelijke Muziekbonden, c/o W. Dragstra, Hillehagersweg 110, 6201 AH Mechelen-Wittem, Netherlands (Subscr. addr.: Postbus 204, 7100 AE Winterswijk, Netherlands) Ed. Wim Dragstra. adv. bk. rev. abstr. bibl. illus. play rev. stat. tr.lit. circ. 4,500.
Formerly: Christelijke Muziekbode (ISSN 0009-5176)

780 621.389 200 US
RECORDING LOCATOR. 1974. q. $160. Resource Publications, Inc., 160 E. Virginia St., No. 290, San Jose, CA 95112. TEL 408-286-8505 circ. 1,000.
Formerly: Musicatalog.

783 IT ISSN 0008-8706
SELEBRIAMO; rivista mensile di musica per la liturgia. 1970. bi-m. L.35000. Casa Musicale Edizioni Carrara, Casella Postale 158, Via Calepio 4, 24100 Bergamo, Italy. Dir. Vinicio Carrara. adv.
Supersedes: Musica Sacra; Schola e Assemblea; Lodiamo Il Signore; Fiori dell'Organo; Maestri dell'Organo.

783 AU ISSN 0037-5721
SINGENDE KIRCHE; Zeitschrift fuer katholische Kirchenmusik. 1953. q. S.35. Oesterreichische Bischofskonferenz, Arbeitsgemeinschaft der Oesterr Dioezesankommission fuer Kirchenmusik, Stock-im-Eisen Platz 3/V, A-1010 Vienna, Austria. Ed. Walter Sengstschmid. adv. bk. rev. abstr. bibl. illus. circ. 3,500. Indexed: Music Ind. RILM.
Sacred music

780 GW ISSN 0344-1407
TASCHENBUCH FUER LITURGIE KIRCHENMUSIK UND MUSIKERZIEHUNG. (Did not appear in 1978; resumed with 1979 volume) 1958. a. DM.19.80. Verlag Friedrich Pustet, Gutenbergstr. 8, 8400 Regensburg 1, W. Germany (B.R.D.) Ed. Franz Johann Loeffler. adv. bk. rev. circ. 2,500.
Former titles: Taschenbuch fuer Liturgie und Kirchenmusik (ISSN 0082-187X); Taschenbuch fuer den Kirchenmusiker.

UNISON. see *RELIGIONS AND THEOLOGY*

790 US
UP WITH PEOPLE NEWS. 1971. q. free. Up with People, Inc., 3103 N. Campbell Ave., Tucson, AZ 85719. TEL 602-327-7351 Ed. Bruce L. Erley. illus. circ. 100,000(controlled)

NURSES AND NURSING
see Medical Sciences–Nurses and Nursing

OCCUPATIONS AND CAREERS
see also Business and Economics–Labor and Industrial Relations

ORIENTAL RELIGIONS
see Religions and Theology–Oriental

ORIENTAL STUDIES
see also History–History of Asia; Linguistics

BANGALORE THEOLOGICAL FORUM. see *RELIGIONS AND THEOLOGY*

954 II
BHARATYA VIDYA. (Text in English and Sanskrit) 1939. Rps.30. Bharatiya Vidya Bhavan, Kulapnati K.M. Munshi Marg, Bombay 400 007, India. Eds. J.H. Dave, S.A. Upadhyaya. (back issues avail.) Indexed: M.L.A.

BIBLICA ET ORIENTALIA. see *RELIGIONS AND THEOLOGY — Roman Catholic*

BIBLICAL ARCHAEOLOGIST. see *ARCHAEOLOGY*

BIBLIOTHECA ISLAMICA. see *RELIGIONS AND THEOLOGY — Islamic*

954 II ISSN 0001-902X
BRAHMAVIDYA. Variant title: Adyar Library Bulletin. (Text in English and Sanskrit; occasionally French and German) 1937. a. Rs.50($10) Adyar Library and Research Centre, Theosophical Society, Adyar, Madras 600 020, India. Ed.Bd. adv. bk. rev. cum.index: vols.1-46. circ. 300. (back issues avail.) Indexed: M.L.A.

BULLETIN CRITIQUE DES ANNALES ISLAMOLOGIQUES. see *RELIGIONS AND THEOLOGY — Islamic*

950 FR ISSN 0007-4349
BULLETIN DE L'OEUVRE D'ORIENT. 1856. bi-m. 10 F.($1) Association de l'Oeuvre d'Orient, 20 rue du Regard, 75006 Paris, France. Ed. Georges Vernade. circ. 190,000.

CHING FENG; quarterly notes on Christianity and Chinese religion and culture. see *RELIGIONS AND THEOLOGY*

CHRISTELIJK OOSTEN. see *RELIGIONS AND THEOLOGY*

CHRISTIAN INSTITUTE FOR ETHNIC STUDIES IN ASIA. BULLETIN. see *RELIGIONS AND THEOLOGY*

CHRISTIAN INSTITUTES OF ISLAMIC STUDIES BULLETIN. see *RELIGIONS AND THEOLOGY — Islamic*

ETUDES PRELIMINAIRES AUX RELIGIONS ORIENTALES DANS L'EMPIRE ROMAIN. see *RELIGIONS AND THEOLOGY*

956 297 GW ISSN 0170-3285
FREIBURGER ISLAMSTUDIEN. irreg., vol.11, 1987. price varies. Franz Steiner Verlag Wiesbaden GmbH, Birkenwaldstr. 44, Postfach 347, D-7000 Stuttgart 1, W. Germany (B.R.D.) Ed. Hans Robert Roemer.

ISLAM. see *RELIGIONS AND THEOLOGY — Islamic*

297 GW ISSN 0021-1818
DER ISLAM; Zeitschrift fuer Geschichte und Kultur des islamischen Orients. (Text in English, French and German) 1910. 2/yr. $58. Walter de Gruyter und Co., Genthiner Str. 13, 1000 Berlin 30, W. Germany (B.R.D.) (U.S. adress: Walter de Gruyter, Inc., 200 Saw Mill Rd., Hawthorne, N.Y. 10532) Eds. Albercht Noth, Bertold Spuler. adv. bk. rev. bibl. illus. circ. 300. Indexed: Curr.Cont. M.L.A. Numis.Lit. Rel.Ind.One.

JAPANESE JOURNAL OF RELIGIOUS STUDIES. see *RELIGIONS AND THEOLOGY*

JOURNAL OF CHINESE RELIGIONS. see *RELIGIONS AND THEOLOGY — Oriental*

294.6 II
JOURNAL OF SIKH STUDIES. (Text in English) 1974. s-a. Rs.8. Guru Nanak Dev University, Department of Guru Nanak Studies, Amritsar, India. Ed. Madanjit Kaur. adv. bk. rev. circ. 1,000.

LEVANT MORGENLAND. see *RELIGIONS AND THEOLOGY*

NANZAN INSTITUTE FOR RELIGION AND CULTURE. BULLETIN. see *RELIGIONS AND THEOLOGY*

950 200 VC
ORIENTALIA CHRISTIANA ANALECTA. 1923. irreg. price varies. Pontificio Istituto Orientale, Piazza S. Maria Maggiore 7, 00185 Rome, Italy. Ed. Stanislas Swierkosz-Lenart. circ. 1,000.
Continues (since 1935): Orientalia Christiana.

221 FR ISSN 0035-1725
REVUE DE QUMRAN. (Text in English, French, German, Italian, Latin, Spanish) 1958. s-a. 352 F. J. Gabalda et Cie, 90 rue Bonaparte, 75006 Paris, France. Ed. Jean Carmignac. bk. rev. circ. 1,000. Indexed: Old Test.Abstr. Rel.Per. New Test.Abstr. Rel.Ind.One. Rel.& Theol.Abstr.
Dead Sea scrolls

297 FR
REVUE DES ETUDES ISLAMIQUES. (Includes supplement - Abstracta Islamica) 1927. 2/yr. Librairie Orientaliste Paul Geuthner, 12 rue Vavin, 75006 Paris, France. Ed. D. Sourdel. abstr. charts. (back issues avail.) Indexed: M.L.A.
Continues: Revue du Monde Musulman.
Cultural, sociological and historical studies of Islamic world

950 296 NE
SEMITIC STUDY SERIES. (Text in English) 1902; N.S. 1952. irreg., vol.5, 1981. E.J. Brill, P.O. Box 9000, 2300 PA Leiden, Netherlands.
Jewish interests

955 200 LE
UNIVERSITE SAINT-JOSEPH. FACULTE DES LETTRES ET DES SCIENCES HUMAINES. RECHERCHE. SERIE B: ORIENT CHRETIEN. (Previously published by its Institut des Lettres Orientales in 4 series) 1956; NS. 1971. irreg. price varies. Dar el-Mashreq S.A.R.L., 2 rue Huvelin, Box 946, Beirut, Lebanon (Subscr. to: Librairie Orientale, Box 946, Beirut, Lebanon)

YAQEEN INTERNATIONAL. see *RELIGIONS AND THEOLOGY — Islamic*

294.3 JA ISSN 0386-4251
YOUNG EAST; a quarterly on Buddhism and Japanese culture. (Text in English) 1925-1966; N.S. 1975. q. 2000 Yen($10) (Young East Association) Tohokai, Inc., 6-2-17 Nishitenma, Kita-ku, Osaka 530, Japan. Ed. Nara Yasuaki. circ. 20,000.

PARAPSYCHOLOGY AND OCCULTISM

BEACON (NEW YORK) see *PHILOSOPHY*

133 284 282 UK ISSN 0308-6194
CHRISTIAN PARAPSYCHOLOGIST. 1975. q. £4($8) Churches' Fellowship for Psychical & Spiritual Studies, St. Mary Abchurch, Abchurch Lane, London EC4N 7BA, England. bk. rev. abstr. circ. 1,500.

THE HERMETIC JOURNAL. see *RELIGIONS AND THEOLOGY — Other Denominations And Sects*

133 200 800 FR
QUESTION DE RACINES, PENSEES, SCIENCES ECLAIREES. 1973. q. 250 F. (Centre d'Etudes Litteraires Traditionnelles) Edition Question de, 10 rue de la Vacquerie, 75011 Paris, France. Dir. Marc de Smedt. adv. bk. rev. bibl. charts. illus. circ. 12,000.
Formerly: Question de Spiritualite, Tradition, Litteratures.

133.9 294 II
REVIEW OF INDIAN SPIRITUALISM. (Text in English) vol. 6, 1974. m. Rs.6($3) Sinha Publishing House, 39 S. R. Das Rd., Calcutta 700026, India. Ed. Amiya Kumar Sinha. adv. bk. rev. circ. 1,000.

133 US
SPIRALS. 1977. bi-m. $4.50. Box 13157, Oakland, CA 94661. TEL 415-654-6312 Ed. Vivienne Verdon-Roe. bk. rev. circ. 1,000.

VENTURE INWARD. see *RELIGIONS AND THEOLOGY*

221 US
WORLDWIDE NEWS. q. Pocket Testament League, Box 368, 117 Main St., Lincoln Park, NJ 07035. TEL 201-696-1900

PHILATELY
see Hobbies–Philately

PHILOSOPHY
see also Religions and Theology

170 US ISSN 0001-1118
A E U REPORTS. 1965. q. free. American Ethical Union, 2 W. 64 St., New York, NY 10023. TEL 212-873-6500 Ed. Jean Somerville Kotkin. bk. rev. illus.
Formerly: Ethical Culture Today.

100 200 IT ISSN 0065-1540
ACTA PHILOSOPHICA ET THEOLOGICA. (Text in English, French, German, Italian, Rumanian, Spanish) 1958. irreg. price varies. Societa Accademica Romena, Foro Traiano 1a, 00187 Rome, Italy.

ALMAS. see *RELIGIONS AND THEOLOGY*

282 206 US
AMERICAN CATHOLIC PHILOSOPHICAL ASSOCIATION. PROCEEDINGS. 1926. a. $12. American Catholic Philosophical Association, The Catholic University of America, 403 Administration Bldg., Washington, DC 20064. TEL 202-635-5518 adv. cum.index: vols.1-32, 1926-58. (also avail. in microfilm from UMI; reprint service avail. from UMI) Indexed: Cath.Ind. Curr.Cont. Arts & Hum.Cit.Ind. Phil.Ind.

AMERICAN JOURNAL OF THEOLOGY & PHILOSOPHY. see *RELIGIONS AND THEOLOGY*

100 282 IT ISSN 0003-3081
ANGELICUM; periodicum trimestre pontificae studiorum. (Text in English, French, German, Italian and Spanish) 1924. q. $25. Pontificia Universita S. Tommaso d'Aquino, Largo Angelicum 1, 00184 Rome, Italy. Eds. Jordan Aumann, Raimondo Spiazzi. bk. rev. circ. 800. Indexed: M.L.A. CERDIC. New Test.Abstr. Old Test.Abstr. Rel.& Theol.Abstr.

100 282 VC ISSN 0003-7362
AQUINAS; rivista internazionale di filosofia. (Text in English, French, Italian, Latin and Spanish) 1958. 3/yr. $24. Pontificia Universita Lateranense, Piazza S. Giovanni in Laterano 4, 00120 Vatican City, Vatican. Ed. Aniceto Molinaro. bk. rev. Indexed: M.L.A. Phil.Ind.

ASSOCIATION OF BRITISH THEOLOGICAL AND PHILOSOPHICAL LIBRARIES. BULLETIN. see *LIBRARY AND INFORMATION SCIENCES*

100 IT
ATHEISM AND DIALOGUE/ATHEISME ET DIALOGUE/ATEISMO Y DIALOGO. (Text in English, French, and Spanish) 1966. q. $25. Segretariato Per i Non Credenti, S.C. Vaticano, Italy. circ. 1,000.

149 US ISSN 0304-1409
ATHEIST. (Issued as a supplement to the Truth Seeker) 1946. irreg. $9. (Atheist Association) Truth Seeker Co., Inc., Box 2832, San Diego, CA 92112. TEL 619-574-7600 Ed. James Hervey Johnson. circ. 500.

BACK TO GODHEAD; magazine of the Hare Krisna movement. see *RELIGIONS AND THEOLOGY — Oriental*

100 US ISSN 0005-7339
BEACON (NEW YORK) 1922. bi-m. $11. Lucis Publishing Co., 113 University Pl., 11th Fl., New York, NY 10003 TEL 212-982-8770 (European and British Commonwealth countries, except Canada, subscr. to: Lucis Press Ltd., 3 Whitehall Court, Suite 54, London, SW1A 2EF, England) Ed.Bd. bk. rev. circ. 5,000. (back issues avail.)

THEOLOGIA 21. see *RELIGIONS AND THEOLOGY*

THEOLOGIE UND PHILOSOPHIE. see *RELIGIONS AND THEOLOGY*

212.5 NE ISSN 0040-5868
THEOSOFIA. 1897. bi-m. fl.25. Theosofische Vereniging in Nederland, Kruisstraat 7, Utrecht, Netherlands. Ed. A. Heybroek. adv. bk. rev. index. circ. 1,200.

212.5 UK ISSN 0040-5876
THEOSOPHICAL JOURNAL. 1960. bi-m. £2. Theosophical Society in England, 50 Gloucester Place, London W1H 3HJ, England. adv. bk. rev. circ. 2,500.

200 US
THIS WORLD. 1982. q. $16. Institute for Educational Affairs, 1112 16th St., N.W., Apt. 1500, Washington, DC 20036. Ed. Michael A. Scully. bk. rev. circ. 3,000. (also avail. in microfiche from UMI) Indexed: Rel.Ind.One.

THOMIST; a speculative quarterly review of theology and philosophy. see *RELIGIONS AND THEOLOGY — Roman Catholic*

TRADITION (NEW YORK); a journal of orthodox Jewish thought. see *RELIGIONS AND THEOLOGY — Judaic*

100 200 CN ISSN 0709-549X
ULTIMATE REALITY AND MEANING; interdisciplinary studies in the philosophy of understanding. 1978. q. Can.$25 to individuals; Can.$43 to institutions. University of Toronto Press, Front Campus, Toronto, Ont. M5S 1A6, Canada. TEL 613-667-7781 Ed. Tibor Horvath. bibl. circ. 424. Indexed: Arts & Hum.Cit.Ind. Amer.Bibl.Slavic & E.Eur. G.Soc.Sci.& Rel.Per.Lit. Lang.& Lang.Behav.Abstr. Phil.Ind. Rel.Ind.One. Rel.& Theol.Abstr.
Supersedes: Institute for Encyclopedia of Human Ideas on Ultimate Reality and Meaning. Newsletter.

UNIVERSITY OF NOTRE DAME. STUDIES IN THE PHILOSOPHY OF RELIGION. see *RELIGIONS AND THEOLOGY*

VAJRA BODHI SEA. see *RELIGIONS AND THEOLOGY — Oriental*

VANGUARD (TORONTO) see *EDUCATION*

181 II ISSN 0042-2983
VEDANTA KESARI. (Text in English) 1914. m. Rs.24($10) Sri Ramakrishna Math, 16 Ramakrishna Math Rd., Mylapore, Madras 600004, India. Ed. Swami Tapasyananda. adv. bk. rev. charts. illus. stat. index. cum.index. circ. 3,000.
Exposition of Vedanta philosophy

100 200 II
VEDIC LIGHT. (Text in English) vol. 8, 1974. m. Rs.11. International Aryan League - Sarvadishik Arya Pratinidhi Sabha, Dayanand Bhavan 3/5, Asaf Sli Road, New Delhi 110002, India. Ed. S.C. Pathak. adv. bk. rev. circ. 1,000.

100 II ISSN 0042-7187
VISVA-BHARATI JOURNAL OF PHILOSOPHY. 1964. s-a. Rs.5.($1.50) Centre of Advanced Study in Philosophy, Visva-Bharati, Santiniketan, West Bengal, India. Ed. Prof. Kalidas Bhattacharyya. bk. rev. circ. 250. Indexed: Ind.Per.Lit.

WANDERER. see *RELIGIONS AND THEOLOGY*

WORLD ORDER; a Baha'i magazine. see *RELIGIONS AND THEOLOGY — Other Denominations And Sects*

100 II
WORLD'S WISDOM SERIES. (Text in English) 1976. irreg. Oriental Publishers and Distributors, 1488, Pataudi House, Darya Ganj, New Delhi 110002, India.

181.45 294.54 DK ISSN 0044-0485
YOGA; tidsskrift for universel religion. English edition: Yoga; magazine for the universal religion (ISSN 0107-7414) 1958. 4/yr. Kr.60($8.80) Narayanananda Universal Yoga Trust & Ashrama, c/o Joergen Fog, Gyllin, DK-8300 Odder, Denmark. Ed. Swami Sanatanananda. adv. bk. rev. index. circ. 1,000.

ZEITSCHRIFT FUER KATHOLISCHE THEOLOGIE. see *RELIGIONS AND THEOLOGY — Roman Catholic*

ZNAK. see *RELIGIONS AND THEOLOGY*

PHILOSOPHY — Abstracting, Bibliographies, Statistics

300 100 016 FR ISSN 0007-554X
BULLETIN SIGNALETIQUE. PART 519: PHILOSOPHIE. 1947. q. 340 F. Centre National de la Recherche Scientifique, Centre de Documentation Sciences Humaines, 54 bd. Raspail, 75260 Paris Cedex, France. cum.index. •Also available online. Vendors: European Space Agency.

PHYSICAL FITNESS AND HYGIENE
see also Medical Sciences

CATALOGUE OF CONFERENCES, SEMINARS, WORKSHOP. see *RELIGIONS AND THEOLOGY*

613.7 200 US ISSN 0885-4726
JOURNAL OF HEALTH CARE CHAPLAINCY. 1987. s-a. $20 to individuals; institutions $32; libraries $42. Haworth Press, Inc., 28 E. 22nd St., New York, NY 10010-6194. Ed. Laurel Arthur Burton. (also avail. in microfiche)

NACHRICHTEN AUS DER AERZTLICHEN MISSION. see *RELIGIONS AND THEOLOGY*

PHYSICS — Sound
see also Sound Recording and Reproduction

POETRY
see Literature–Poetry

POLITICAL SCIENCE
see also Political Science–Civil Rights; Political Science–International Relations

320.531 MF
ALTERNATIVE. (Text in French) m. Mouvement Chretien pour le Socialisme, 1A, Colonel Draper, Beau Bassin, Mauritius.
Socialism

AMERICAN COUNCIL FOR JUDAISM. SPECIAL INTEREST REPORT; a digest of news items and articles in the area of the council's interest. see *RELIGIONS AND THEOLOGY — Judaic*

AUFBAU; Schweizerische Zeitschrift fuer Recht, Freiheit und Frieden. see *RELIGIONS AND THEOLOGY*

BEGEGNUNG; zeitschrift fuer Katholiken in Kirche und Gesellschaft. see *RELIGIONS AND THEOLOGY — Roman Catholic*

BULLETIN ON THE T F P'S. (American Society for the Defense of Tradition, Family and Property, Inc.) see *RELIGIONS AND THEOLOGY — Roman Catholic*

C C I A BACKGROUND INFORMATION. (World Council of Churches, Commission on International Affairs) see *RELIGIONS AND THEOLOGY*

341.1 200 NZ
C P S BULLETIN. 1936. q. NZ.$5. New Zealand Christian Pacifist Society, 396 Port Hills Rd., Christchurch 2, New Zealand. Ed. Bruce H. Barnitt. bk. rev. circ. 600. (tabloid format) Indexed: CERDIC.
Former titles: Peace Bulletin; New Zealand Christian Pacifist (ISSN 0028-7997)

CATHOLIC ACTIVIST. see *RELIGIONS AND THEOLOGY — Roman Catholic*

CHRISTIAN JEWISH RELATIONS. see *RELIGIONS AND THEOLOGY*

CHRISTIAN STATESMAN. see *RELIGIONS AND THEOLOGY*

CHURCH & STATE; a monthly review. see *RELIGIONS AND THEOLOGY*

320.531 284 FR
CITE NOUVELLE. 1945. m. 50 F. 46 rue de Vaugirard, 75006 Paris, France.

GOSPEL TRUTH. see *RELIGIONS AND THEOLOGY — Other Denominations And Sects*

IN DE WAAGSCHAAL. see *RELIGIONS AND THEOLOGY*

320 297 US ISSN 8755-8912
ISLAM INTERNATIONAL. 1986. $20. Siveast Consultants, Inc., Box 271, 410 S. State St., Dover, DE 19901. Ed. C.V. Ramasastry. adv. bk. rev. circ. 100.

296 US
J T A COMMUNITY NEWS REPORTER. w. $25. Jewish Telegraphic Agency, 165 W. 46th St., Rm. 511, New York, NY 10036. TEL 212-575-9370 (processed)

320.532 296 US ISSN 0021-6305
JEWISH AFFAIRS. 1970. bi-m. $5. Communist Party, U.S.A, Central Committee, 235 W. 23rd St., 7th Fl., New York, NY 10011. TEL 212-989-4994 Ed. Dr. Herbert Aptheker. adv. bk. rev. bibl. circ. 2,000.

JOURNAL OF CHURCH AND STATE. see *RELIGIONS AND THEOLOGY*

943 GW ISSN 0340-7837
LAND AKTUELL. s-m. DM.7.80. Katholische Bundesarbeitsgemeinschaft Land, Lothstr. 29, 8000 Munich 40, W. Germany (B.R.D.) Ed. H. Schruefer. bk. rev.
Formerly: Dorf Aktuell (ISSN 0012-5547)

325 IT ISSN 0391-5492
MIGRANTI-PRESS. (Supplement to: Servizio Migranti) 1979. w. L.30000($50) Ufficio Centrale per l'Emigrazione Italiana (U.C.E.I.), Circonvallazione Aurelia 50, 00165 Rome, Italy. Ed. S. Ridolfi.

MUNDO ISRAELITA; actualidad de la semana en Israel y en el mundo judio. see *RELIGIONS AND THEOLOGY — Judaic*

320 296 FR
NOTRE VOIX. (Text in Yiddish) vol. 37, 1974. bi-m. 50 F. B. Goutmann, Ed. & Pub., 52 rue Rene Boulanger, 75010 Paris, France.

RADIUS. see *RELIGIONS AND THEOLOGY*

REPORT FROM THE CAPITAL. see *RELIGIONS AND THEOLOGY — Protestant*

320 297 II
SANT SIPAHI. (Text in Punjabi) vol.27, 1972. m. Rs.10. Lal Haveli, Gate Mahan Singh, Amritsar 24, India. adv.
Sikh politics and religion

325 IT ISSN 0037-2803
SERVIZIO MIGRANTI. 1965. m. L.30000($50) Ufficio Centrale per l'Emigrazione Italiana (U.C.E.I.), Circonvallazione Aurelia, 50, 00165 Rome, Italy. Ed. S. Ridolfi. adv. bk. rev. stat. index. circ. 2,700.
Formerly: Ufficio Centrale per l'Emigrazione Italiana, Bollettino.
Emigration and immigration

SHVUT; Jewish problems in the USSR and Eastern Europe. see *ETHNIC INTERESTS*

956.940 296 FR ISSN 0049-061X
SIONISTE. 1971. m. 20 F. Organisation Sioniste de France, 47 rue de Chabrol, Paris, France. Ed. Joseph Weinberg. illus.
Zionism

323.1 947 296 UK ISSN 0038-545X
SOVIET JEWISH AFFAIRS; a journal on Jewish problems in the USSR and Eastern Europe. 1971. 3/yr. £12($20) to individuals; institutions £16($25) ‡ Institute of Jewish Affairs, 11 Hertford St., London W1Y 7DX, England. (Co-sponsor: World Jewish Congress) Ed. Dr. L. Hirszowicz. adv. bk. rev. bibl. index. circ. 1,500. (also avail. in microform from UMI; reprint service avail. from UMI) Indexed: Hist.Abstr.

WOMEN'S ZIONIST ORGANIZATION OF SOUTH AFRICA. NEWS AND VIEWS. see *RELIGIONS AND THEOLOGY — Judaic*

POLITICAL SCIENCE — Abstracting, Bibliographies, Statistics

ZIONIST LITERATURE. see *PUBLISHING AND BOOK TRADE — Abstracting, Bibliographies, Statistics*

POLITICAL SCIENCE — Civil Rights

323.4 AT
ASIAN BUREAU AUSTRALIA. NEWSLETTER. 1971. 4/yr. Aus.$10. Asian Bureau Australia, 173 Royal Pde., Parkville, Vic. 3052, Australia. adv. bk. rev. circ. 3,500.

CATACOMBES; messager supraconfessionel de l'Eglise du silence. see *RELIGIONS AND THEOLOGY*

261 SZ
CONSCIENCE ET LIBERTE. 1948/1950; N.S. 1971. 2/yr. 18 Fr.($8) International Association for the Defense of Religious Liberty - Association Internationale pour la Defense de la Liberte Religieuse, Schosshaldenstr. 17, CH-3006 Berne, Switzerland. Ed. G. Rossi. bk. rev. bibl. circ. 10,750. Indexed: CERDIC.

GLAUBE IN DER 2. WELT; Zeitschrift fuer Religionsfreiheit und Menschenrechte. see *RELIGIONS AND THEOLOGY*

KATALLAGETE. see *RELIGIONS AND THEOLOGY*

NETWORK (WASHINGTON, 1971); Catholic social justice lobby. see *RELIGIONS AND THEOLOGY — Roman Catholic*

OTHER SIDE (PHILADELPHIA); justice rooted in discipleship. see *RELIGIONS AND THEOLOGY*

323.4 289.6 CN ISSN 0229-1916
QUAKER CONCERN. 1977. q. donations. Canadian Friends Service Committee, 60 Lowther Ave., Toronto, Ont. M5R 1C7, Canada. TEL 416-920-5213 Ed. Carl Stieren. bk. rev. illus. circ. 3,100. (tabloid format; back issues avail.)

355.224 US ISSN 0034-4796
REPORTER FOR CONSCIENCE' SAKE. 1942. m. $10. National Interreligious Service Board for Conscientious Objectors, 800 Eighteenth St., N.W., Ste. 600, Washington, DC 20006. TEL 202-293-5962 Ed. Shawn Perry. bk. rev. bibl. illus. index. circ. 4,000. (also avail. in microform from UMI; back issues avail.; reprint service avail. from UMI) Indexed: CERDIC.
Counseling service for those who object to military service for reasons of conscience

POLITICAL SCIENCE — International Relations

AMITIES CATHOLIQUES FRANCAISES. see *RELIGIONS AND THEOLOGY — Roman Catholic*

327 US
C A L C REPORT. 1975. m. (except May/Jun. and Nov./Dec.) $20. Clergy and Laity Concerned, 198 Broadway, Rm.302, New York, NY 10038. TEL 212-964-6730 Ed. Shermane Austin. bk. rev. illus. circ. 5,000. (back issues avail.)
Incorporating: T W C Bulletin (Third World Caucus); Formerly: American Report.

CHALLENGE (LONDON, 1961) see *RELIGIONS AND THEOLOGY — Protestant*

327 200 CS ISSN 0009-5567
CHRISTIAN PEACE CONFERENCE. German edition: Christliche Friedenskonferenz. 1962. q. $9.70. Christian Peace Conference, International Secretariat, Jungmannova 9, 110 00 Prague 1, Czechoslovakia (Subscr. to: Artia, Ve Smeckach 30, 111 27 Prague 1) Ed. Jiri Svoboda. bk. rev. circ. 4,000.

327 296 US
FOCUS: NORTH AMERICAN STUDENT ZIONIST FORUM. (Text in English and Hebrew) q. $15. Brandeis University, B'nai B'rith Hillel, Box 2466, Waltham, MA 02254. TEL 617-647-2177 Eds. Thomas A. Rose, Wendy Senor. film rev. play rev. stat. circ. 20,000.

JUSTPEACE. see *RELIGIONS AND THEOLOGY*

KERK EN VREDE. see *RELIGIONS AND THEOLOGY*

KOLEINU. see *RELIGIONS AND THEOLOGY — Judaic*

LUCHA/STRUGGLE. see *RELIGIONS AND THEOLOGY — Roman Catholic*

PURA VERDAD; noticiario de comprension. see *RELIGIONS AND THEOLOGY — Other Denominations And Sects*

PURE VERITE. see *RELIGIONS AND THEOLOGY — Other Denominations And Sects*

100 230 GW ISSN 0067-5024
BEITRAEGE ZUR GESCHICHTE DER PHILOSOPHIE UND THEOLOGIE DES MITTELALTERS NEUE FOLGE. 1894; N.S. 1970. irreg. price varies. Aschendorffsche Verlagsbuchhandlung, Soester Str. 13, 4400 Muenster, W. Germany (B.R.D.) Eds. Ludwig Hoedl, Wolfgang Kluxen.

BHARATYA VIDYA. see *ORIENTAL STUDIES*

BIJDRAGEN; tijdschrift voor filosofie en theologie. see *RELIGIONS AND THEOLOGY*

BOODSCHAP. see *RELIGIONS AND THEOLOGY — Other Denominations And Sects*

BOSTON UNIVERSITY STUDIES IN PHILOSOPHY AND RELIGION. see *RELIGIONS AND THEOLOGY*

BRAHMANA-GAURAVA. see *RELIGIONS AND THEOLOGY — Oriental*

BRAHMAVADIN. see *RELIGIONS AND THEOLOGY — Oriental*

BUDDHIST TEXT INFORMATION. see *RELIGIONS AND THEOLOGY — Oriental*

149 US ISSN 0360-618X
CENTER FOR PROCESS STUDIES. NEWSLETTER. 1975. q. $5. School of Theology at Claremont, Center for Process Studies, 1325 N. College Ave., Claremont, CA 91711. Ed. Laurie Huff. circ. 850. (looseleaf format; back issues avail.)

CENTRE PROTESTANT D'ETUDES DE GENEVE. BULLETIN. see *RELIGIONS AND THEOLOGY — Protestant*

CHICAGO CATHOLIC. see *RELIGIONS AND THEOLOGY — Roman Catholic*

CROSS CURRENTS. see *RELIGIONS AND THEOLOGY — Roman Catholic*

100 II ISSN 0011-6734
DARSHANA INTERNATIONAL; an international quarterly of philosophy, psychology, sociology, psychical research, religion and mysticism. (Text in English) 1961. q. Rs.20($10) Moradabad 244001, India. Ed. Prof. J.P. Atreya. adv. bk. rev. charts. illus. index. circ. 1,100. Indexed: Curr.Cont. Phil.Ind.

181 MY ISSN 0012-1746
DHARMA; a quarterly devoted to universal religion, righteousness & culture. (Not issued in 1976) 1949. q. M.$6. Pure Life Society, Batu 6, Jalan Puchong, Jalan Kelang Lama P.O., Kuala Lumpur, Malaysia. Ed. Sister A. Mangalam. bk. rev. circ. 3,000.

DIVUS THOMAS; commentarium de philosophia et theologia. see *RELIGIONS AND THEOLOGY*

EAST AND WEST SERIES; an interpreter of the life of the spirit. see *RELIGIONS AND THEOLOGY*

100 SP ISSN 0014-0716
ESPIRITU. 1952. s-a. 1200 ptas. (Fundacion Balmesiana) Editorial Balmes, S.A., Apdo. 1382, Duran y Bas 9, 08002 Barcelona, Spain. Ed. Juan Pegueroles. bk. rev. cum.index: 1952-1977. circ. 525. Indexed: Bull.Signal. Hist.Abstr. Amer.Hist.& Life. Phil.Ind.

215 US
ETHICS AND MEDICS. 1976. m. $12. Pope John XXIII Medical-Moral Research and Education Center, 186 Forbes Rd., Braintree, MA 02184. TEL 617-848-6965 cum.index: 1976-1984. circ. 25,000. (back issues avail.)

100 200 US
FAITH AND PHILOSOPHY. 1984. q. $15 individuals; institutions $25. Society of Christian Philosophers, Department of Philosophy, Asbury College, Wilmore, KY 40390. Ed. William P. Alston. adv. bk. rev. index. circ. 1,100. (back issues avail.) Indexed: Phil.Ind. Rel.Ind.One.
Formerly: Faith and Reason.

FAITH AND THOUGHT; a journal devoted to the study of the inter-relation of the Christian revelation and modern research. see *RELIGIONS AND THEOLOGY*

FRANCISCAN STUDIES. see *RELIGIONS AND THEOLOGY — Roman Catholic*

100 UK ISSN 0016-0687
FREETHINKER. 1881. m. £3.60($9.20) G.W. Foote & Co., 702 Holloway Rd., London N19 3NL, England. Ed. William McIlroy. bk. rev. circ. 1,500. (also avail. in microform)

100 200 SZ ISSN 0016-0725
FREIBURGER ZEITSCHRIFT FUER PHILOSOPHIE UND THEOLOGIE. (Text in French and German) 1954. 2/yr. 50 Fr. (Universite de Fribourg, Dominikaner-Professoren der Theologischen Fakultaet) Editions Saint Paul, Perolles 42, CH-1700 Fribourg, Switzerland. bk. rev. bibl. index. circ. 600. Indexed: M.L.A. CERDIC. New Test.Abstr. Phil.Ind.

GESHER. see *RELIGIONS AND THEOLOGY — Judaic*

100 GW ISSN 0017-3088
GRALSWELT; Zeitschrift fuer wahren Aufbau durch neues Wissen. 1950. bi-m. DM.25.80. Stiftung Gralsbotschaft, Lenzhalde 15, 7000 Stuttgart 1, W. Germany (B.R.D.) Ed. Edith Jansen-Runge. bk. rev.

GREEK ORTHODOX THEOLOGICAL REVIEW. see *RELIGIONS AND THEOLOGY — Other Denominations And Sects*

GREGORIANUM. see *RELIGIONS AND THEOLOGY — Roman Catholic*

THE HERMETIC JOURNAL. see *RELIGIONS AND THEOLOGY — Other Denominations And Sects*

HEYTHROP JOURNAL; a review of philosophy and theology. see *RELIGIONS AND THEOLOGY*

144 CN ISSN 0018-7402
HUMANIST IN CANADA. 1967. q. Can.$10. ‡ Canadian Humanist Publications, Box 2007, Sta. D, Ottawa, Ont. K1P 5W3, Canada. TEL 613-283-7210 Ed. Don Page. adv. bk. rev. abstr. bibl. charts. illus. stat. index; cum.index. circ. 2,000. (also avail. in microfilm from UMI; reprint service avail. from UMI)
Formed by the merger of: Montreal Humanist & Victoria Humanist.

181.45 US ISSN 0149-6026
INNER PATHS. 1977. 12/yr. $15. Inner Paths Publications, Inc., 26 Reichert Circle, Westport, CT 06880. Ed. Louis Rogers. adv. bk. rev. circ. 33,500.

INTERNATIONAL JOURNAL FOR PHILOSOPHY OF RELIGION. see *RELIGIONS AND THEOLOGY*

ISKRA. see *RELIGIONS AND THEOLOGY*

ITINERARIUM; revista quadrimestral de cultura. see *RELIGIONS AND THEOLOGY — Roman Catholic*

100 200 DK ISSN 0075-6032
KIERKEGAARDIANA. (Text in Danish, English, French and German; summaries in English) 1955. biennial. Kr.200($25) (Soren Kierkegaard Selskabet, Filosofisk Institut) C.A. Reitzels Forlag, Kobmagergade 50, 1150 Copenhagen K, Denmark. Ed.Bd. bk. rev. circ. 500.

100 200 US ISSN 0363-1664
LAUGHING MAN; the alternative to scientific materialism and religious provincialism. 1976. q. $23.95. (Laughing Man Institute) Dawn Horse Press, 750 Adrian Way, San Rafael, CA 94903. TEL 415-492-9382 Ed. Richard Schorske. adv. bk. rev. illus. circ. 6,000. (back issues avail.)

LAVAL THEOLOGIQUE ET PHILOSOPHIQUE. see *RELIGIONS AND THEOLOGY*

LAW & JUSTICE. see *LAW*

100 200 UK
LIBRARY OF PHILOSOPHY AND RELIGION. irreg. price varies. Macmillan Press Ltd., 4 Little Essex St., London WC2R 3LF, England. Ed. Prof. John Hick.

LIVING PRAYER. see *RELIGIONS AND THEOLOGY*

LOGOS (NEW YORK); the Swedenborg Foundation newsletter. see *RELIGIONS AND THEOLOGY — Other Denominations And Sects*

MAHA BODHI; international Buddhist monthly. see *RELIGIONS AND THEOLOGY — Oriental*

018 200 US ISSN 0736-7392
METHOD: JOURNAL OF LONERGAN STUDIES. 1983. s-a. $12 to individuals; institutions $20. Loyola Marymount University, Department of Philosophy, 7101 W. 80 St., Los Angeles, CA 90045. TEL 213-642-3379 (Co-sponsor: Institute for Integrative Studies, Inc.) Ed. Mark D. Morelli. bk. rev. circ. 200. (back issues avail.) Indexed: Phil.Ind. Phil.Ind.

MILLTOWN STUDIES. see *RELIGIONS AND THEOLOGY*

MISCELANEA COMILLAS; revista de teologia y ciencias humanas. see *RELIGIONS AND THEOLOGY*

MISCELLANEA FRANCESCANA; rivista trimestrale di scienze teologiche e di studi francescani. see *RELIGIONS AND THEOLOGY — Roman Catholic*

MITZION TETZEH TORAH. M.T.T. see *RELIGIONS AND THEOLOGY — Judaic*

180 II ISSN 0027-2574
MOUNTAIN PATH. 1964. q. Rs.20($10) Sri Ramanasramam, Tiruvannamalai 606603, India. Ed. K. Swaminathan. adv. bk. rev. charts. illus. index. circ. 5,000.

294.54 II
NANDAN KANAN. 1975. m. Rs.50. Adarsha Prakashani, Mandir Kharagpur, 721305 West Bengal, India. circ. 2,000.

NEWS AND VIEWS. see *RELIGIONS AND THEOLOGY*

OOMOTO. see *RELIGIONS AND THEOLOGY — Other Denominations And Sects*

100 200 US
OPINION; the way I see it. 1957-19??; resumed 19?? q. $5. (Gospel Truth Association) Opinion Publications, c/o James E. Kurtz, Ed., Box 2803, Joliet, IL 60434. adv. bk. rev. illus. tr.lit. index. circ. 3,700. (back issues avail.)

ORIENTIERUNG; katholische Blaetter fuer weltanschauliche Information. see *RELIGIONS AND THEOLOGY*

100 200 II
PATHWAY TO GOD. (Text in English) 1966. q. Rs.10. Academy of Comparative Philosophy and Religion, Belgaum, Hindwadi, Belgaum 590011, India. Ed. P.K. Bhagoji. adv. bk. rev. circ. 1,000.

100 206 US ISSN 0739-1218
PHILOSOPHY AND THE ARTS; a literary and philosophical review. 1975. a. $2.98. Philosophy and the Arts, Box 431, Jerome Ave. Sta., Bronx, NY 10468. TEL 212-654-3955 Ed. Daniel Manesse. bk. rev.
Incorporating: Bertrand Russell Today.

181 II ISSN 0032-6178
PRABUDDHA BHARATA/AWAKENED INDIA. (Text in English) 1896. m. Rs.20($14) (Ramakrishna Order) Advaita Ashrama, 5 Dehi Entally Rd., Calcutta 700 014, India. adv. bk. rev. charts. illus. index. circ. 5,000.

PURE LIFE SOCIETY. ANNUAL REPORT. see *RELIGIONS AND THEOLOGY*

RECONSTRUCTIONIST. see *RELIGIONS AND THEOLOGY — Judaic*

REFORMED REVIEW. see *RELIGIONS AND THEOLOGY — Protestant*

RELIGION AND SOCIETY. see *RELIGIONS AND THEOLOGY*

RELIGIOUS HUMANISM; a quarterly journal of religious and ethical humanism. see *RELIGIONS AND THEOLOGY — Other Denominations And Sects*

REVUE DE THEOLOGIE ET DE PHILOSOPHIE. see *RELIGIONS AND THEOLOGY*

REVUE THOMISTE; revue doctrinale de theologie et de philosophie. see *RELIGIONS AND THEOLOGY*

RICERCHE STORICHE SALESIANE; rivista semestrale di storia religiosa e civile. see *RELIGIONS AND THEOLOGY — Roman Catholic*

366.4 135.43 US ISSN 0035-8339
ROSICRUCIAN DIGEST. 1916. bi-m. $9. ‡ Rosicrucian Order, AMORC, Rosicrucian Park, San Jose, CA 95191. TEL 408-287-9171 Ed. Robin M. Thompson. circ. 70,000.

SALESIANUM. see *RELIGIONS AND THEOLOGY — Roman Catholic*

100 200 IT ISSN 0036-4711
SAPIENZA; rivista internazionale di filosofia e di teologia. (Text in English, French, Italian) 1948. q. L.28000($20.50) Dominican Fathers, Vicoletto S. Pietro a Maiella 4, 80134 Napoli, Italy. Ed. Michele Miele. adv. bk. rev. abstr. bibl. index. circ. 2,500. Indexed: M.L.A. CERDIC. Old Test.Abstr. New Test.Abstr. Phil.Ind.

200 CN ISSN 0316-5345
SCIENCE ET ESPRIT. 1948. 3/yr. Can.$14. Editions Bellarmin, c/o Helene Desmarais, 8100, Saint-Laurent, Montreal, Que. H2P 2L9, Canada. TEL 514-387-2541 bk. rev. index. circ. 375. Indexed: M.L.A. Old Test.Abstr. Rel.Per. CERDIC. New Test.Abstr. Pt.de Rep. Rel.Ind.One.

SCIENCE OF MIND. see *RELIGIONS AND THEOLOGY — Other Denominations And Sects*

SEIKYO TIMES. see *RELIGIONS AND THEOLOGY — Other Denominations And Sects*

131.3 200 US ISSN 0037-1564
SELF-REALIZATION. 1925. q. $2.40. Self-Realization Fellowship, Inc., 3880 San Rafael Ave., Los Angeles, CA 90065. TEL 213-225-2471 Ed. Jane Brush. bk. rev. illus. index. circ. 24,000. (back issues avail.)

SERENITY SENTINEL. see *RELIGIONS AND THEOLOGY*

100 UK ISSN 0262-9356
SHARE IT; a magazine to celebrate & promote awareness of our true identity. 1979. irreg. £1 per no. c/o Anne Seward, Ed., Roots Church Ln., Playford, Ipswich IP6 9DS, England. bk. rev. illus.
Formerly: Nacton Newsletter.

200 100 II ISSN 0251-1746
SHREE HARI KATHA. (Text in English and Hindi) 1974. m. Rs.31. Shiksha Sansthan, B-12/223, Lodi Rd., New Delhi 110003, India. Ed. Surendra Agrawal. circ. 1,000.

SINTESE. see *SOCIAL SCIENCES: COMPREHENSIVE WORKS*

SOKA GAKKAI NEWS. see *RELIGIONS AND THEOLOGY — Oriental*

SOPHIA; a journal for discussion in philosophical theology. see *RELIGIONS AND THEOLOGY*

SOUTHWESTERN JOURNAL OF THEOLOGY. see *RELIGIONS AND THEOLOGY*

SPELING. see *RELIGIONS AND THEOLOGY*

131 UK ISSN 0038-7622
SPIRITUAL HEALER; journal of spiritual healing and philosophy. 1953. bi-m. free. Harry Edwards Spiritual Healing Sanctuary Trust, Burrows Lea, Shere, Guildford, Surrey GU5 9QG, England. Eds. Ramus Branch & Joan Branch. adv. bk. rev. illus. index. circ. 7,000.

215 AG ISSN 0049-2353
STROMATA; antigua ciencia y fe. 1944. q. $20. (Universidad del Salvador, Facultades de Filosofia y Teologia) Asociacion Civil Facultades Loyola, Avda. Mitre 3226, C.C. 10-1663 San Miguel, Argentina. Ed. Jorge R. Seibold. adv. bk. rev. abstr. bibl. circ. 1,000. Indexed: Bull.Signal. Old Test.Abstr. Hisp.Amer.Per.Ind. New Test.Abstr. Phil.Ind.

STUDIA PATAVINA; rivista di scienze religiose. see *RELIGIONS AND THEOLOGY*

100 200 SW
STUDIA PHILOSOPHIAE RELIGIONIS. (Text in English) 1975. irreg., no.12, 1984. price varies. Liber Forlag, S-205 10, Malmo, Sweden. Eds. Hans Hof, Hampus Lyttkens.

294.54 II
SUDHI SAHITYA. 1977. m. Rs.50. Adarsha Prakashani, Mandir Kharagpur, 721305 West Bengal, India. circ. 5,000.

TEILHARD REVIEW AND JOURNAL OF CREATIVE EVOLUTION. see *RELIGIONS AND THEOLOGY*

R C D A-RELIGION IN COMMUNIST DOMINATED AREAS. see *RELIGIONS AND THEOLOGY*

THIS WORLD. see *PHILOSOPHY*

ULTIMATE ISSUES. see *RELIGIONS AND THEOLOGY — Judaic*

POPULATION STUDIES
see also Birth Control

A L L NEWS. (American Life League) see *BIRTH CONTROL*

C M J S CENTERPIECES. (Center for Modern Jewish Studies) see *ETHNIC INTERESTS*

PROTESTANTISM
see Religions and Theology-Protestant

PSYCHIATRY AND NEUROLOGY
see Medical Sciences-Psychiatry and Neurology

PSYCHOLOGY
see also Medical Sciences-Psychiatry and Neurology

ARCHIV FUER RELIGIONSPSYCHOLOGIE. see *RELIGIONS AND THEOLOGY*

CATALOGUE OF CONFERENCES, SEMINARS, WORKSHOP. see *RELIGIONS AND THEOLOGY*

DARSHANA INTERNATIONAL; an international quarterly of philosophy, psychology, sociology, psychical research, religion and mysticism. see *PHILOSOPHY*

ENVOY (PITTSBURG) see *RELIGIONS AND THEOLOGY*

150 284 US ISSN 0197-3096
HUMAN DEVELOPMENT. 1980. q. $18. (Jesuit Educational Center for Human Development) Le Jacq Publishing, Inc., 53 Park Pl., New York, NY 10007. TEL 212-766-4300 Ed. James J. Gill, M.D. bk. rev. circ. 13,000. (back issues avail.) Indexed: Cath.Ind. Educ.Ind. C.I.J.E. Lang.& Lang.Behav.Abstr.

INWARD LIGHT. see *RELIGIONS AND THEOLOGY — Other Denominations And Sects*

JOURNAL OF PASTORAL CARE. see *RELIGIONS AND THEOLOGY*

616.89 200 US ISSN 0886-5477
JOURNAL OF PASTORAL PSYCHOTHERAPY. 1986. a. $24 to individuals; institutions $32; libraries $42. Haworth Press, Inc., 28 E. 22nd St., New York, NY 10010-6194. Ed. Harold T. Kriesel. (also avail. in microfiche)

150 US ISSN 0147-7978
JOURNAL OF PSYCHOLOGY AND CHRISTIANITY. 1982. q. $50. Christian Association for Psychological Studies International, 26705 Farmington Rd., Farmington Hills, MI 48018. Ed. J. Harold Ellens. adv. bk. rev. circ. 2,000. (also avail. in microfilm from UMI; reprint service avail. from UMI) Indexed: A.S.& T.Ind. Psychol.Abstr. Educ.Ind. R.G. Soc.Sci.Ind. Rel.Ind.One.
Supersedes (1974-1981): Christian Association for Psychological Studies. Bulletin; Incorporates: Christian Association for Psychological Studies. Proceedings (ISSN 0092-072X)

156 296 US ISSN 0700-9801
JOURNAL OF PSYCHOLOGY AND JUDAISM. 1976. q. $34 to individuals; institutions $88. Human Sciences Press, Inc., 72 Fifth Ave., New York, NY 10011. TEL 212-243-6000 Ed. Dr. Reuven P. Bulka. adv. bk. rev. circ. 1,000. (also avail. in microform from UMI; reprint service avail. from ISI,UMI) Indexed: Curr.Cont. Excerp.Med. MLA. Psychol.Abstr. SSCI. G.Soc.Sci.& Rel.Per.Lit. Ind.Jew.Per. Past.Care & Couns.Abstr. Rel.& Theol.Abstr. Rel.Ind.One.

JOURNAL OF PSYCHOLOGY AND THEOLOGY; an evangelical forum for the integration of psychology and theology. see *RELIGIONS AND THEOLOGY*

150 200 US
JOURNAL OF RELIGION AND THE APPLIED BEHAVIORAL SCIENCES. 1979. 3/yr. $12.50. Association for Creative Change Within Religious and Other Social Systems, Box 219, Frederick, MD 21701-0219. bk. rev. charts. stat. circ. 600.

MISCELANEA COMILLAS; revista de teologia y ciencias humanas. see *RELIGIONS AND THEOLOGY*

NATIONAL GUILD OF CATHOLIC PSYCHIATRISTS. BULLETIN. see *MEDICAL SCIENCES — Psychiatry And Neurology*

VEDANTA KESARI. see *PHILOSOPHY*

PUBLIC ADMINISTRATION
see also Social Services and Welfare

PUBLIC FINANCE, TAXATION
see Business and Economics-Public Finance, Taxation

PUBLIC HEALTH AND SAFETY
see also Birth Control; Funerals

PUBLISHING AND BOOK TRADE
see also Bibliographies; Journalism

028.1 200 US ISSN 0890-0841
BOOKS AND RELIGION; a monthly review. 1971. m. (except Jul. & Aug.) $16. Duke University, Divinity School, Durham, NC 27706. Ed. Christopher Walters-Bugbee. adv. bk. rev. bibl. index. circ. 15,000. (also avail. in microform from UMI; reprint service avail. from UMI) Indexed: Rel.Per. Rel.Ind.One.
Former titles: Review of Books and Religion (ISSN 0732-5800); (1976-1980): New Review of Books and Religion (ISSN 0146-0609); Review of Books and Religion (ISSN 0048-7465)

658.8 282 US ISSN 0006-7563
BOOKSTORE JOURNAL. 1968. m. $25. (Christian Booksellers Association) C B A Service Corp., 2620 Venetucci Blvd., Box 200, Colorado Springs, CO 80901. TEL 303-576-7880 Ed. Cherie Rayburn. adv. bk. rev. illus. circ. 7,220.
Religious

CATHOLIC TRUTH. see *RELIGIONS AND THEOLOGY — Roman Catholic*

CHRISTIAN LIBRARIAN. see *LIBRARY AND INFORMATION SCIENCES*

658.8 200 US ISSN 0749-2510
CHRISTIAN RETAILING; the trade magazine of religious retailing. 1955. m. $18. Strang Communications Co., 190 N. Westmonte Dr., Altamonte Springs, FL 32714. TEL 305-869-5005 Ed. Nancy Sabbag. adv. bk. rev. circ. 9,800. (reprint service avail. from UMI)
Formerly: Christian Bookseller (ISSN 0009-5273)
Religious

028 296 IS ISSN 0333-953X
ISRAEL BOOK NEWS. 1970. q. ‡ Israel Export Institute, Book and Printing Center, 29 Hamered St., P.O. Box 50084, Tel Aviv 61500, Israel. adv. bk. rev. circ. 2,500.
Former titles: Jerusalem Post Literary Supplement & Israel Book World (ISSN 0021-1974)

028 296 016 US ISSN 0022-5754
JUDAICA BOOK NEWS. 1969. s-a. $8. ‡ Book News, Inc., 303 W. 10th St., New York, NY 10014. TEL 212-691-3817 Ed. Ernest L. Weiss. adv. bk. rev. bibl. circ. 18,000. (also avail. in microform from UMI; reprint service avail. from UMI)

LIBRARIANS' CHRISTIAN FELLOWSHIP NEWSLETTER. see *LIBRARY AND INFORMATION SCIENCES*

NEW BOOKS QUARTERLY ON ISLAM & THE MUSLIM WORLD. see *RELIGIONS AND THEOLOGY — Islamic*

PROVIDENT BOOK FINDER. see *RELIGIONS AND THEOLOGY — Protestant*

028 GW ISSN 0043-2490
DIE WELT DER BUECHER. 1954. 2/yr. DM.11 per no. Verlag Herder GmbH und Co. KG, Hermann-Herder-Str. 4, D-7800 Freiburg im Breisgau, W. Germany (B.R.D.) adv. bk. rev. bibl.

PUBLISHING AND BOOK TRADE — Abstracting, Bibliographies, Statistics

100 200 016 SP ISSN 0211-4143
ACTUALIDAD BIBLIOGRAFICA DE FILOSOFIA Y TEOLOGIA; selecciones de libros. 1964. s-a. 1800 ptas.($12) Instituto de Teologia Fundamental, Facultad de Teologia de Barcelona, Llaseres 30, Sant Cugat del Valles, Barcelona, Spain (Subscr. to: Selecciones de Teologia, Roger de Lluria 13, 08010 Barcelona, Spain) Ed. Josep Boada. adv. bk. rev. abstr. bibl. index. circ. 700. Indexed: Hist.Abstr. Amer.Hist.& Life. CERDIC.
Formerly: Selecciones de Libros (ISSN 0037-1181)

DAS NEUE BUCH; Buchprofile fuer die Katholische Buechereiarbeit. see *RELIGIONS AND THEOLOGY — Abstracting, Bibliographies, Statistics*

020 296 016 US ISSN 0039-3568
STUDIES IN BIBLIOGRAPHY AND BOOKLORE; devoted to research in the field of Jewish bibliography. (Text in English, Hebrew and other languages) 1953. irreg. price varies. Hebrew Union College - Jewish Institutional of Religion, Library, 3101 Clifton Ave., Cincinnati, OH 45220. TEL 513-221-1875 Ed.Bd. bk. rev. bibl. cum.index: vols. 1-16. circ. 1,100. Indexed: Hist.Abstr. Amer.Hist. & Life. Ind.Jew.Per.

296 016 IS ISSN 0044-4774
ZIONIST LITERATURE. (Text in English and Hebrew) 1936. bi-m. free. ‡ World Zionist Organization, Central Zionist Archives, Box 92, Jerusalem 91000, Israel. Ed. Ms. H.A. Abrahami. circ. 1,250.

RADIO AND TELEVISION
see Communications-Radio and Television

REAL ESTATE
see also Architecture; Building and Construction

RELIGIONS AND THEOLOGY
see also Religions and Theology-Islamic; Religions and Theology-Judaic; Religions and Theology-Oriental; Religions and Theology-Protestant; Religions and Theology-Roman Catholic; Religions and Theology-Other Denominations and Sects

200 KE
A A C C BULLETIN. (Text in English and French) 1983. q. EAs.36($2.10) All Africa Conference of Churches, Box 14205, Nairobi, Kenya. Ed. Maxime V. Rafransoa. adv. bk. rev. circ. 1,000.
Formed by the 1983 merger of: A A C C Quarterly Bulletin & A A C C Newsletter.

200 KE
A A C C MAGAZINE. (Text in English and French) q. All Africa Conference of Churches, Communication Unit, P.O. Box 14205, Nairobi, Kenya.

268 US ISSN 0277-1071
A A R ACADEMY SERIES. 1974. irreg. (American Academy of Religion) Scholars Press, Box 1608, Decatur, GA 30031-1608. Ed. Carl Raschke.
Formerly: A A R Dissertation Series.

200 US ISSN 0084-6287
A A R STUDIES IN RELIGION. 1970. irreg., no.34, 1984. (American Academy of Religion) Scholars Press, Box 1608, Decatur, GA 30031-1608. Eds. Charley Hardwick, James Duke.

200 621.38 US ISSN 0300-7022
A D R I S NEWSLETTER. 1971. q. $7. (Association for the Development of Religious Information Services) Fordham University, Department of Theology, Fordham University, Bronx, NY 10458-5165. TEL 212-579-2400 Ed. Richard F. Smith. bk. rev. abstr. bibl. index. circ. 514. Indexed: CERDIC.

283 276 KE ISSN 0001-1134
A F E R. (African Ecclesial Review) 1959. bi-m. EAs.121($17.60) (Amecea Pastoral Institute) Gaba Publications, P.O. Box 4002, Eldoret, Kenya. Ed. Felician Rwehikiza. bk. rev. index. circ. 2,500. (back issues avail.) Indexed: Cath.Ind. Canon Law Abstr. New Test.Abstr. Rel.Ind.One.

200 SA
A F M KOINONIA; bulletin of Christian fellowship. (Text in English) 1983. q. free. Apostolic Faith Mission of South Africa, P.O. Box 89735, Lyndhurst 2106, South Africa. Ed. Edgar J. Gschwend. abstr. circ. 2,000. (back issues avail.)

266 276 US
A I M INTERNATIONAL. 1917. q. free. Africa Inland Mission International, P.O. Box 178, Pearl River, NY 10965. TEL 914-735-4014 Ed. Rev. Peter Stam. bk. rev. illus. circ. 25,000. (also avail. in microfilm)
Former titles: Inland Africa (ISSN 0020-1464); Hearing and Doing (1896-1916)
Missions

200 FR
A I M MONASTIC BULLETIN; aide inter-monasteres pour les jeunes eglises. (Text in English; French and Spanish editions avail.) 1965. s-a. 50 F.($8) Aide Inter-Monasteres Secretariat, Benedictine Sisters, 7 rue d'Issy, 92170 Vanves, France (U. S. center: Aide a l'Implantation Monastique, Benedictine Convent of Perpetual Adoration, 8300 Morganford Rd., St. Louis, MO 63123) Ed. Dom Marie-Bernard de Sous. bk. rev. illus. circ. 1,000. (also avail. in microform)
Formerly: A I M Bulletin (ISSN 0007-4314)

A L L NEWS. (American Life League) see *BIRTH CONTROL*

200 KE
A P S BULLETIN. (All Africa Press Service) (Text in English) 1979. w. $150. Africa Church Information Service, Box 14205, Nairobi, Kenya. Ed. Richard L. Sakala. bk. rev. circ. 350.

200 US
A T L A BIBLIOGRAPHY SERIES. irreg., no.17, 19837. price varies. (American Theological Library Association) Scarecrow Press, Inc., 52 Liberty St., Box 4167, Metuchen, NJ 08840. TEL 201-548-8600 Ed. Kenneth E. Rowe.

200 US
A T L A MONOGRAPH SERIES. irreg., no.22, 1985. (American Theological Library Association) Scarecrow Press, Inc., 52 Liberty St., Box 4167, Metuchen, NJ 08840. TEL 201-548-8600 Ed. Dr. Kenneth E. Rowe.

255 NO ISSN 0400-227X
AARBOK FOR DEN NORSKE KIRKE. 1951. a. Kr.55. Verbum Kirkeraadet, Underhaugsveien 15, Oslo 3, Norway. Ed. Gunnar Roedahl. stat. index. circ. 3,500.

ABINGDON CLERGY INCOME TAX GUIDE. see *BUSINESS AND ECONOMICS — Public Finance, Taxation*

ACADEMIA; Zeitschrift fuer Politik und Kultur. see *LITERARY AND POLITICAL REVIEWS*

264 US ISSN 0276-2358
ACCENT ON WORSHIP. 1981. 4/yr. membership. Liturgical Conference, 806 Rhode Island Ave. N.E., Washington, DC 20018. Ed. Rachel Reeder.
Former titles (until 1981): Accent on Liturgy (ISSN 0272-7951); Until 1980: Living Worship (ISSN 0360-6244)

ACCION; revista paraguaya de reflexion y dialogo. see *SOCIAL SCIENCES: COMPREHENSIVE WORKS*

249 US ISSN 0001-5083
ACT. 1947. m. (bi-m. Jan.-Feb.; Jul.-Aug.) $5. Christian Family Movement, Sixth & Kellogg, Rm. 202, Box 272, Ames, IA 50010. TEL 515-232-7432 Eds. LaVerne and Robert Sober. bk. rev. circ. 2,500.

200 DK ISSN 0065-1354
ACTA JUTLANDICA. 1985. irreg. Bibliotekscentralen, Telegrafvej 5, DK-2750 Ballerup, Denmark.

ACTA PHILOSOPHICA ET THEOLOGICA. see *PHILOSOPHY*

200 NE ISSN 0065-1672
ACTA THEOLOGICA DANICA. (Text in English and German) 1958. irreg., vol.19, 1986. price varies. E. J. Brill, P.O. Box 9000, 2300 PA Leiden, Netherlands.

200 UK ISSN 0143-3253
ACTION NEWSLETTER. 1969. 10/yr. $10. World Association for Christian Communication, 122 King's Rd., London SW3 4TR, England. Ed. Ann Shakespeare. bk. rev. circ. 2,200.

258 SZ ISSN 0001-7507
ACTION SOCIALE. s-m. 12 Fr. Organisations Chretiennes-Sociales, Rue de l'Abbe Bovet 6, 1700 Fribourg, Switzerland.

200 NE ISSN 0001-7930
AD FONTES. 10/yr. fl.15.75 (fl. 12.75 to students) J. Terpstra, Sarphatipark 7 III, Amsterdam, Netherlands. adv.

220 US ISSN 0149-8347
ADULT BIBLE STUDIES. q. $6. (United Methodist Church, Board of Discipleship) Graded Press, 201 Eighth Ave. S., Box 801, Nashville, TN 37202. TEL 615-749-6421 Ed. Victor J. Jacobs.

200 AT ISSN 0001-8619
ADVANCE AUSTRALIA. 1965. m. Aus.$0.25 per no. Knights of the Southern Cross, Box 184C. G.P.O., Melbourne, Victoria 3001, Australia. Ed. H. Ocloga n. adv. bk. rev. illus. circ. 2,500.

200 IT ISSN 0001-8740
ADVENIAT. 1929. m. L.8000. Opera della Regalita' di N.S.G.C., Via L. Necchi 2, 20123 Milan, Italy. Ed.Bd. circ. 18,000.

200 TZ ISSN 0856-0048
AFRICA THEOLOGICAL JOURNAL. 1968. 3/yr. EAs.100($27) All Africa Lutheran Churches Information and Coordination Centre, P.O. Box 314, Arusha, Tanzania. Ed. Mutembe Gaetan. adv. bk. rev. circ. 1,500. Indexed: CERDIC. New Test.Abstr. Rel.Ind.One.

200 282 NR
AFRICAN JOURNAL OF BIBLICAL STUDIES. s-a. $20. Nigerian Association for Biblical Studies, c/o Department of Religious Studies, University of Ibadan, Oyo State, Nigeria.

268 KE
AFRIKA YA KESHO. (Text in Swahili) 1961. bi-m. EAs.25($10) (Africa Inland Church) Kesho Publications, Box 60, Kijabe, Kenya. Ed. John Ndeti Somba. adv. circ. 4,000. Indexed: CERDIC.
Formerly: Kesho (ISSN 0023-0723)

200 UK ISSN 0261-5630
AGAPE. 1982. m. £7.75. Emmaus Family of Prayer, 11 York Rd., Birkdale, Southport, Merseyside PR8 2AD, England. illus.
Formerly: Maranatha.

200 US
AGLOW. 1969. bi-m. $9. (Women's Aglow Fellowship, International) Aglow Publications, Box I, Lynnwood, WA 98046-1557. Ed. Gwen Weising. adv. bk. rev. circ. 27,000.

267 NE ISSN 0002-3744
AKTIE; maandblad voor jongeren. 1951. 11/yr. fl.30. Stichting Youth for Christ Nederland, Postbus 8, 7640 AA Wierden, Netherlands. Ed. Johan Ten Brinke. adv. bk. rev. circ. 10,500.
Formerly: Jeugd in Aktie.

200 GW
AKTION; Zeitung junger Arbeiter. 1949. m. DM.11.40. Christliche Arbeiter-Jugend, Huettmannstr. 52, 4300 Essen 1, W. Germany (B.R.D.) adv. bk. rev.
Former titles: C A J Christliche Arbeiter-Jugend; Junge Christliche Arbeitnehmer. Befreing (ISSN 0022-622X)

200 US ISSN 0272-7250
ALBANIAN CATHOLIC BULLETIN/ BULETINI KATOLIK SHQIPTAR. (Text in Albanian and English) 1980. a. donations. Albanian Catholic Information Center, Box 1217 University, Santa Clara, CA 95053. Ed. Gjon Sinishta. bk. rev. circ. 1,500. (back issues avail.)

200 UK
ALCUIN. 1897. a. $18. Alcuin Club, 5 St. Andrew St., London EC4A 3AB, England. bk. rev.

248.05 CN ISSN 0319-6984
ALERTE AU QUEBEC. 1975. m. Can.$5. Publications Alerte, 25 av. Royale, Ste-Petronille I.O., Quebec G0A 4C0, Canada.

200 NE ISSN 0002-5267
ALGEMEEN MACONNIEK TIJDSCHRIFT. 1946. m. membership. Grand East of the Netherlands, Fluwelenburgwal 22, The Hague, Netherlands. Ed. Bote de Boer Lzn. adv. bk. rev. illus. circ. 6,800.

ALIVE (ST. LOUIS); for young teens. see *CHILDREN AND YOUTH — For*

220 UK
ALIVE TO GOD; bible guidelines for living by the spirit. 1984. q. £4. Scripture Union, 130 City Rd., London EC1V 2NJ, England (Subscr. addr.: P.O. Box 38, Bristol BS99 7NA, England) Ed. Elizabeth Hume. adv. circ. 55,000.

266 KE
ALL AFRICA CONFERENCE OF CHURCHES. REFUGEE DEPARTMENT. PROGRESS REPORT. a., latest 1974. All Africa Conference of Churches, Refugee Department, Pioneer House, Government Rd., Box 20301, Nairobi, Kenya.

266 KE
ALL AFRICA CONFERENCE OF CHURCHES. REFUGEE DEPARTMENT. PROJECT LIST. a., latest 1977. All Africa Conference of Churches, Refugee Department, Pioneer House, Government Rd., Box 20301, Nairobi, Kenya.

ALLE BOERNS JUL. see *CHILDREN AND YOUTH — For*

ALLIANCE REVIEW. see *EDUCATION*

240 SP
ALMANAQUE MISAL. a. 424 ptas.($3.50) Editorial Sal Terrae, Guevara 20, Santander, Spain.

266 MX ISSN 0002-628X
ALMAS. 1950. m. Mex.$200($3) (Misioneros de Guadalupe) Editora Escalante, Cordoba 17, Apdo. 24-550, Mexico 7, D. F., Mexico. Ed. Carlos M. Jimenez. illus. circ. 200,000.

ALTERNATIVE. see *POLITICAL SCIENCE*

L'ALTRA EUROPA. see *ART*

213 US ISSN 0882-2123
AMBASSADOR REPORT. 1977. q. $20. Box 60068, Pasadena, CA 91106. TEL 818-798-6112 Ed. John Trechak. bk. rev. circ. 2,500. (back issues avail.)

200 US
AMERICAN ACADEMY OF RELIGION. ANNUAL MEETING. a. Scholars Press, Box 1608, Decatur, GA 30031-1608. (Co-sponsor: Society of Biblical Literature)

200 US ISSN 0002-7189
AMERICAN ACADEMY OF RELIGION. JOURNAL. 1933. q. $50. (American Academy of Religion) Scholars Press, Box 1608, Decatur, GA 30031-1608. Ed. William Scott Green. adv. bk. rev. bibl. index; cum.index: 1933-1979. circ. 6,000. (also avail. in microform from UMI) Indexed: Curr.Cont. Hist.Abstr. Hum.Ind. Rel.Per. SSCI. Arts & Hum.Cit.Ind. Amer.Hist.& Life. Bibl.Ind. Old Test.Abstr. CERDIC. New Test.Abstr. Rel.Ind.One. Rel.& Theol.Abstr.
Formerly: Journal of Bible and Religion.

220 US ISSN 0006-0801
AMERICAN BIBLE SOCIETY RECORD. 1818. m. $3. American Bible Society, 1865 Broadway, New York, NY 10023. TEL 212-581-7400 Ed. Clifford P. Macdonald. illus. index. circ. 400,000.
Formerly: Bible Society Record.

200 100 US ISSN 0194-3448
AMERICAN JOURNAL OF THEOLOGY & PHILOSOPHY. 1980. 3/yr. $15. c/o Dr. Larry Axel, Ed., Department of Philosophy, Purdue University, West Lafayette, IN 47907 TEL 404-737-1710 (Subscr. to: Dr. Creighton Peden, Ed. Dept. of Philosophy, Augusta College, Augusta, GA 30910) index. circ. 350. (back issues avail.) Indexed: Phil.Ind. Rel.Ind.One.

291.2 US ISSN 0740-0446
AMERICAN UNIVERSITY STUDIES. SERIES 7. THEOLOGY AND RELIGION. 1984. irreg. Peter Lang Publishing, Inc., 62 W. 45th St., New York, NY 10036. TEL 212-302-6740 Ed. Jay Wilson.

200 US
AMERICAN WALDENSIAN AID SOCIETY. NEWSLETTER. 1923. s-a. membership. American Waldensian Aid Society, 475 Riverside Dr., Rm. 1850, New York, NY 10115. TEL 212-870-2671 Ed. Rev. Frank G. Gibson, Jr. bk. rev. circ. 5,000.

200 IT ISSN 0003-1739
AMICIZIA EBRAICO-CRISTIANA DI FIRENZE. BOLLETTINO. 1951. q. free. Amicizia Ebraico-Cristiana di Firenze, Casella Postale 282, 50100 Florence, Italy. Ed. Ines Zilli Gay. bk. rev. bibl. circ. 500.

AMICO DELL'ARTE CRISTIANA. see *ART*

200 FR ISSN 0003-1909
AMITIES SPIRITUELLES. BULLETIN. 1919. q. 45 F. Association de Amities Spirituelles, 5 rue de Savoie, 75006 Paris, France. Ed. Jacques Sardin. bk. rev. circ. 1,200.

200 UK ISSN 0003-2018
AMPLEFORTH JOURNAL. 1895. 2/yr. £5.50. Ampleforth Abbey, York YO6 4EN, England. Ed. J. Felix Stephens. adv. bk. rev. charts. illus. circ. 3,400. (also avail. in microfiche; back issues avail.)

200 NE ISSN 0169-0272
AMSTERDAM STUDIES IN THEOLOGY. 1979. irreg. Editions Rodopi B.V., Keizersgracht 302-304, 1016 EX Amsterdam, Netherlands.

200 US
ANAHATA NADA/SOUNDLESS SOUND. 1974. q. $1. (Sri Chinmoy Centre) AUM Publications, 85-42 160th St., Jamaica, NY 11432. TEL 718-523-1166 Ed. David Burke. bk. rev. illus.

209 BE ISSN 0003-2468
ANALECTA BOLLANDIANA; revue critique d'hagiographie. (Text in English, French, Latin and other international languages) 1882. s-a. 2.500 Fr.($60) Societe des Bollandistes, 24 bd. Saint-Michel, 1040 Brussels, Belgium. bk. rev. index; cum. index every 20 yrs. (vols. 1-80 in 4 vols.) circ. 1,250. Indexed: M.L.A. CERDIC.
History

809 AU
ANALECTA CARTUSIANA; review for Carthusian history and spirituality. (Text in various languages) 1970. irreg., no. 113, 1986. DM.65 per no. Universitaet Salzburg, Institut fuer Englische Sprache, Akademiestr. 24, A-5020 Salzburg, Austria. Ed. James Hogg. circ. 300. (back issues avail) Indexed: M.L.A.

207.11 US ISSN 0003-2980
ANDREWS UNIVERSITY SEMINARY STUDIES. (Text in English, French & German) 1963. 3/yr. $12 to individuals; libraries $15. Andrews University Press, Berrien Springs, MI 49104. TEL 616-471-6023 Ed. Kenneth A. Strand. bk. rev. charts. illus. index. circ. 750. (tabloid format) Indexed: Rel.Per. CERDIC. New Test.Abstr. Old Test.Abstr. Rel.& Theol.Abstr. Rel.Ind.One.

200 FR ISSN 0003-3030
ANGE GARDIEN. 1891. 6/yr. 65 F.($15) Association de l'Ange Gardien, 28 rue du Bon Pasteur, B.P. 4384, 69242 Lyon Cedex 04, France. Ed. Louis Chauffour. circ. 5,100.

248.83 AT
ANNALS MAGAZINE. 1889. m. (10/yr) Aus.$15. (Missionaries of the Sacred Heart) Chevalier Press, Box 13, Kensington, N.S.W. 2033, Australia. Ed. Paul Stenhouse. adv. bk. rev. bibl. illus. stat. circ. 21,000. Indexed: Gdlns.
Formerly: Our Lady of the Sacred Heart (ISSN 0030-6878)
Youth magazine with emphasis on current topical issues

200 FR ISSN 0066-2860
ANNUAIRE DES INSTITUTS DE RELIGIEUSES EN FRANCE. 1959. irreg., latest 1980. 50 F. Service National des Vocations Francais, 106 rue du Bac, 75341 Paris, France.

200 GW ISSN 0003-519X
DIE ANREGUNG; Seelsorglicher Dienst in der Welt von heute. 1948. m. DM.3 per no. Verlag Wort und Werk GmbH, Arnold-Janssen-Str. 20, 5205 St. Augustin 1, W. Germany (B.R.D.) Ed.Bd. bk. rev.

260 GW
ANRUF. 1902. m. DM.21. (Deutscher Verband der Jugenbuende fuer Entschiedenes Christentum e.V.) Verlag Born, Frankfurter Str. 180, Postfach 420220, 3500 Kassel, W. Germany (B.R.D.) Ed. Christoffer Pfeiffer. adv. bk. rev. illus.

200 US ISSN 0735-0864
ANSELM STUDIES; an occasional journal. 1983. irreg. $35. Kraus International Publications (Subsidiary of: Kraus-Thomson Organization Ltd.) One Water St., White Plains, NY 10601. TEL 914-761-9600

207.11 GW ISSN 0003-5270
ANSTOESSE; aus der Arbeit der Evangelischen Akademie Hofgeismar. 1954. 4/yr. DM.20. Evangelische Akademie von Kurhessen-Waldeck, Schloesschen Schoenburg, 3520 Hofgeismar, W. Germany (B.R.D.) Eds. H. Schmidt, K. Haendler. bk. rev. index. circ. 2,000. (tabloid format)

268 377.8 UK ISSN 0003-6161
ANTUR. 1966. m. 8p. (Cyngor Ysgolion Ac Addysg Grefyddol Cymru - Welsh Council for Sunday Schools and Religious Education) Welsh Calvinistic Methodist Book Agency, Caernarfon, N. Wales. Ed. Rev. Dafydd H. Edwards. bk. rev. circ. 8,500.

200 GW ISSN 0003-6285
ANZEIGER DES REICHES DER GERECHTIGKEIT; Menschenfreundliche Zeitung fuer Jedermann. (Summaries in Dutch, English, French, Italian, Portuguese and Spanish) 1938. m. DM.16. (Menschenfreundliche Gesellschaft) Verlag der Engel des Herrn, Baeckerweg 12, Postfach 3608, 6000 Frankfurt 1, W. Germany (B.R.D.) Ed. Miss Roulin. circ. 120,000.

266 FR
APPEL DE L'AFRIQUE. 1967. 3/yr. (plus special annual no.) 20 F. Societe des Missions Africaines, 36 rue Miguel Hidalgo, 75019 Paris, France. circ. 40,000.
Formerly: Almanach Noir.
Missions

200 GW
ARBEITEN ZUR GESCHICHTE DES PIETISMUS. 1979. irreg. Vandenhoeck & Ruprecht, Robert-Bosch-Breite 6, Postfach 3753, D-3400 Goettingen, W. Germany (B.R.D.) Ed.Bd.

200 GW
ARBEITEN ZUR KIRCHLICHEN ZEITGESCHICHTE. REIHE B; Darstellung. 1975. irreg. Vandenhoeck & Ruprecht, Robert-Bosch-Breite 6, Postfach 3753, D-3400 Goettingen, W. Germany (B.R.D.) Ed.Bd.

200 GW
ARBEITEN ZUR PASTORALTHEOLOGIE. 1962. irreg. (Verlagsbuchhandlung) Vandenhoeck & Ruprecht, Robert-Bosch-Breite 6, Postfach 3753, D-3400 Goettingen, W. Germany (B.R.D.) Ed.Bd.

200 GW ISSN 0066-5711
ARBEITEN ZUR THEOLOGIE. REIHE 1. 1960. irreg., vol.69, 1984. price varies. Calwer Verlag, Scharnhauser Str.44, 7000 Stuttgart 70, W. Germany (B.R.D.)

ARCHAEOLOGY AND BIBLICAL RESEARCH. see *ARCHAEOLOGY*

282 209 NE ISSN 0022-9342
ARCHIEF VAN DE KERKEN. m. fl.99.50. Ark, Hamersveldseweg 91, 3833 GM Leusden, Netherlands. Ed. H. J. van Santvoort. bibl. index. circ. 2,000. (looseleaf format) Indexed: CERDIC.
Formerly: Katholiek Archief.

243 GW ISSN 0066-6386
ARCHIV FUER LITURGIEWISSENSCHAFT. 1950. a. DM.208. (Abt-Herwegen-Institut fuer Liturgische und Monastische Forschung) Verlag Friedrich Pustet, Gutenbergstr. 8, 8400 Regensburg 1, W. Germany (B.R.D.) Ed. Emmanuel v. Severus. bk. rev. circ. 800. Indexed: CERDIC. New Test.Abstr. Rel.Ind.One.

209 GW ISSN 0066-6432
ARCHIV FUER MITTELRHEINISCHE KIRCHENGESCHICHTE. 1949. a. DM.48. Gesellschaft fuer Mittelrheinische Kirchengeschichte, Jesuitenstr. 13, 5500 Trier, W. Germany (B.R.D.) Indexed: Bibl.Cart.

270 GW ISSN 0003-9381
ARCHIV FUER REFORMATIONSGESCHICHTE/ARCHIVE FOR REFORMATION HISTORY; Internatonale Zeitschrift zur Erforschung der Reformation und ihrer Weltwirkungen. (Text in English and German) 1904. s-a. (Verein fuer Reformations Geschichte) Guetersloher Verlagshaus Gerd Mohn, Koenigstr. 23-25, Postfach 1343, 4830 Guetersloh, W. Germany (B.R.D.) (Co-sponsor: American Society for Reformation Research) Ed.Bd. bk. rev. circ. 800. Indexed: M.L.A. Rel.Per. Rel.& Theol.Abstr. Arts & Hum.Cit.Ind. Amer.Hist.& Life. Rel.Ind.One.

200 150 GW ISSN 0084-6724
ARCHIV FUER RELIGIONSPSYCHOLOGIE. vol. 4, 1929. irreg., vol. 15, 1982. price varies. (Internationale Gesellschaft fuer Religionspsychologie) Vandenhoeck und Ruprecht, Theaterstr. 13, Postfach 37 53, 3400 Goettingen, W. Germany (B.R.D.) Eds. K. Krenn, Wilhelm Keilbach.

209 GW ISSN 0066-6491
ARCHIV FUER SCHLESISCHE KIRCHENGESCHICHTE. 1949. a. DM.25. (Institut fuer Ostdeutsche Kirchen- und Kulturgeschichte) Verlag August Lax, Postfach 10 08 65, 3200 Hildesheim, W. Germany (B.R.D.) circ. 900. (reprint service avail. from CIP) Indexed: Numis.Lit.

260 IT ISSN 0066-6688
ARCHIVIO ITALIANO PER LA STORIA DELLA PIETA. (Text in language of contributor) 1951. irreg., vol. 7, 1980. price varies. Edizioni di Storia e Letteratura, Via Lancellotti 18, 00186 Rome, Italy. Ed. Romana Guarnieri.

200 949.5 GR
ARISTOTELION PANEPISTEMION THESSALONIKES. THEOLOGIKE SCHOLE. EPISTEMONIKE EPETERIS. 1953. a. Theologike Schole Panepistemiou Thessalonikes, Serron 39, Triandria, Salonika, Greece. Indexed: Chem.Abstr.

200 DK ISSN 0107-363X
ARKEN. 1979. bi-m. Kr.5 per no. (Teologiske Fakultet) Forlaget Arken, Koebmagergade 44-46, 1150 Copenhagen K, Denmark. illus.
Formerly: Teologiske Fakultet. Bladet.

200 DK ISSN 0107-4520
ARKEN-TRYK. no. 15, 1982. irreg. price varies. (Teologiske Fakultet) Forlaget Arken, Koebmagegade 44-46, 1150 Copenhagen K, Denmark.

ARMARIUM CODICUM INSIGNIUM. see *HISTORY — History Of Europe*

ARMONIA DI VOCI. see *MUSIC*

ARTE CRISTIANA; rivista internazionale di storia dell'arte e di arti liturgiche. see *ART*

207.11 US
ASBURY THEOLOGICAL JOURNAL. 1946. s-a. $5. Asbury Theological Seminary, 204 N. Lexington Ave., Wilmore, KY 40390. Ed. Laurence Wood. bk. rev. cum.index: 1946-66 in vol. 21. circ. 1,200. (also avail. in microform from UMI; reprint service avail. from UMI) Indexed: CERDIC. Chr.Per.Ind. Rel.& Theol.Abstr.
Formerly: Asbury Seminarian (ISSN 0004-4253)

200 UK
ASCENT. 1975. q. £2. Christian Endeavor Union of G.B. & Ireland, 18 Leam Terrace, Royal Leamington Spa CV31 1BB, England. Ed. Mrs. Sandra O'Nions. adv. bk. rev. circ. 2,000.

240 MY ISSN 0044-9180
ASIAN BEACON. 1969. m. M.$8($4) Asian Beacon Fellowship, Box 269, Jalan Sultan, Petaling Jaya, Selangor, Malaysia. Ed. Goh Poh Gaik. adv. bk. rev. film rev. illus. circ. 4,500. (back issues avail.)

ASOCIACION. see *CHILDREN AND YOUTH — About*

ASSEMBLEE NOUVELLE. see *MUSIC*

200 060 FR ISSN 0066-8907
ASSOCIATION DES AMIS DE PIERRE TEILHARD DE CHARDIN. BULLETIN. 1966. a. Association des Amis de Pierre Teilhard de Chardin, 38 rue Geoffroy-Saint-Hilaire, 75005 Paris, France. bibl.

378 US
ASSOCIATION FOR PROFESSIONAL EDUCATION FOR MINISTRY. REPORT OF THE BIENNIAL MEETING. 1950. biennial. $10. Association for Professional Education for Ministry, c/o Oliver Williams, Pres., University of Notre Dame, Notre Dame, IN 46556 TEL 219-239-5000 (Orders to: Joseph Kelly, Treas., St. Bernard's Seminary, 2260 Lake Ave., Rochester, NY 14612) Ed. Gaylord Noyce. circ. 400.
Missions

230 IT
ASSOCIATION INTERNATIONALE D'ETUDES PATRISTIQUES. BULLETIN D'INFORMATION ET DE LIAISON. (Text in English, French) 1968. irreg., 1-2/yr. 30 F. per no. for libraries only. (International Association for Patristic Studies - Association Internationale d'Etudes Patristiques) Brepols Publisher, c/o A. Di Berardino, Sec. Gen., Institutum Patristicum Augustinianum, Via S. Uffizio, 25, 00193 Rome, Italy (Subscr. to: B. Gain, 7, av. Aumont, 60500 Chantilly, France) Ed. A. di Berardino. bk. rev. bibl. circ. 800.

ASSOCIATION OF BRITISH THEOLOGICAL AND PHILOSOPHICAL LIBRARIES. BULLETIN. see *LIBRARY AND INFORMATION SCIENCES*

268 UK ISSN 0305-9286
ASSOCIATION OF CHRISTIAN TEACHERS. DIGEST. 1976. 3/yr. £2.25. Association of Christian Teachers, 130 City Rd., London EC1V 2NJ, England. Ed. W. Kay. bk. rev. circ. 1,200.

268 US ISSN 0362-1472
ASSOCIATION OF THEOLOGICAL SCHOOLS IN THE UNITED STATES AND CANADA. BULLETIN. 1937. biennial. $5. Association of Theological Schools, Box 130, Vandalia, OH 45377. TEL 513-898-4654 Ed. David Schuler. circ. 2,000.
Formerly: American Association of Theological Schools in the United States and Canada. Bulletin (ISSN 0065-7360)

268 US
ASSOCIATION OF THEOLOGICAL SCHOOLS IN THE UNITED STATES AND CANADA. DIRECTORY. 1918. a. $3.50. Association of Theological Schools, Box 130, Vandalia, OH 45377. TEL 513-898-4654 Ed. Jill Scott Norton.
Formerly: American Association of Theological Schools in the United States and Canada. Directory (ISSN 0065-7379)

ATHEIST. see *PHILOSOPHY*

967.5 200 BD ISSN 0563-4245
AU COEUR DE L'AFRIQUE. 1961. bi-m. 900 Fr.CFA (300Fr.CFA to students and teachers of religion) Association des Conference des Ordinaires du Rwanda et Burundi, B.P. 1390, Bujumbura, Burundi. Ed. Adrien Ntabona. adv. bk. rev. circ. 1,000. Indexed: CERDIC.

200 UK ISSN 0004-7481
AUDENSHAW PAPERS. 1967. 6/yr. £5. Audenshaw Foundation, 2 Eaton Gate, London SW1W 9BL, England. Ed. Mark Gibbs. bk. rev. circ. 3,000. Indexed: CERDIC.
Supersedes: Christian Comment.

261 SZ ISSN 0004-7821
AUFBAU; Schweizerische Zeitschrift fuer Recht, Freiheit und Frieden. 1919. fortn. 40 Fr. Verein der Freunde des "Aufbau", Postfach 1008, 8036 Zurich, Switzerland. (Co-sponsor: Neue Religioes-Soziale Vereingung) Ed. Otto Huerlimann. adv. bk. rev. circ. 600.

207.11 AU ISSN 0004-7872
DER AUFTRAG/MANDATE. 1958. s-a. free. (Theologen des Innsbrucker Priesterseminars) Rauchdruck GmbH & Co. KG, Kugelfangweg 15, A-6040 Innsbruck, Austria. Ed. Dr. Klaus Egger.

200 GW
AUFWAERTS (GIESSEN); die Zietschrift mit den guten Nachrichten. m. DM.5. Brunnen Verlag GmbH, Postfach 5205, 6300 Giessen 1, W. Germany(B.R.D.)

200 GW
DIE AUSLESE; Zeitschrift fuer Offerten auserlesener Firmen des kirchlichen Bedarfs. 1958. 4/yr. DM.4.80. Dr. Krueger Verlag, Am Schiessberg 19, 6348 Herborn, W. Germany (B.R.D.) Ed. Hans-Joachim Krueger. adv. bk. rev. circ. 21,000(controlled)

200 283 AT ISSN 0812-0811
AUSTRALIAN LECTIONARY (YEAR) 1978. a. Aus.$2. Anglican Information Office, 1st Floor, St. Andrews House, Sydney Square, N.S.W. 2000, Australia. Ed. Gilbert Sinden. circ. 13,000. (back issues avail.)

255 IT ISSN 0005-3783
BADIA GRECA DI GROTTAFERRATA. BOLLETTINO. 1947. s-a. L.15000. (Monastero Esarchico di Grottaferrata) Badia Greca di Grottaferrata, 00046 Grottaferrata (Rome), Italy. bk. rev. illus. cum.index (10 yr.) circ. 350. Indexed: CERDIC.

297.89 CN ISSN 0708-5052
BAHA'I STUDIES. 1976. irreg. Can.$4 per no. Association for Baha'i Studies, 34 Copernicus St., Ottawa, Ont. K1N 7K4, Canada. TEL 613-233-1903 Ed.Bd. circ. 2,000.

297.89 IS ISSN 0045-1320
BAHA'I WORLD. (Text primarily in English; occasional articles in French, German and Persian) 1925. irreg., vol.17, 1982. price varies. Baha'i World Centre, Box 155, Haifa 31-001, Israel (U.S. dist.: Baha'i Publishing Trust, 415 Linden Ave., Wilmette, Illinois 60091) Ed. Roger White. circ. 15,000.

970 001 US ISSN 0067-3129
BAMPTON LECTURES IN AMERICA. 1949. irreg., no.20, 1978. price varies. Columbia University Press, 562 W. 113th St., New York, NY 10025. TEL 212-678-6777

200 UK
BAND OF HOPE CHRONICLE. 1877. bi-m. United Kingdom Band of Hope Union, Hope House, 45 Great Peter St., London SW1P 3LT, England.

200 950 II ISSN 0253-9365
BANGALORE THEOLOGICAL FORUM. (Text in English) 1968. q. Rs.25($10) United Theological College, 17 Miller's Rd., Bangalore, S. India 560 046, India. Eric J. Lott. adv. bk. rev. abstr. circ. 550. (also avail. in microform from UMI; back issues avail.) Indexed: New Test.Abstr. Rel.Ind.One.

BASIS. see *MILITARY*

200 SZ ISSN 0005-6189
BASLER PREDIGTEN; eine monatliche Predigtfolge. 1936. m. 22 Fr. Friedrich Reinhardt Verlag, Missionsstr. 36, CH-4012 Basel, Switzerland. Ed.Bd. circ. 3,500.

200 GW ISSN 0005-6618
DAS BAUGERUEST; Mitarbeiterzeitschrift fuer ausserschul. Jugendbildung. 1949. 4/yr. DM.22. Verein zur Foerderung Evangelischer Jugendarbeit e.V., Hummelsteiner Weg 100, 8500 Nuernberg, W. Germany (B.R.D.) Ed. Gernard Bucke. bk. rev. bibl. tr.lit. index. circ. 2,600. (avail. on records)

200 NE ISSN 0005-7312
BAZUIN. 1917. w. fl.150. Stichting De Bazuin, Box 2456, 3500 GL Utrecht, Netherlands. Ed. K. Derksen. adv. bk. rev. illus. circ. 7,500(controlled) Indexed: CERDIC.

BEACON (NEW YORK) see *PHILOSOPHY*

280 GW
DIE BEIDEN TUERME; Niederaltaicher Rundbrief. 1965. s-a. free. Benediktinerabtei Niederaltaich, 8351 Niederaltaich, W. Germany (B.R.D.) Ed. P. Bonifaz Pfister. circ. 4,500.

BEITRAEGE ZUR GESCHICHTE DER PHILOSOPHIE UND THEOLOGIE DES MITTELALTERS NEUE FOLGE. see *PHILOSOPHY*

266 GW ISSN 0342-1341
BEITRAEGE ZUR GESCHICHTE DES ALTEN MOENCHTUMS UND DES BENEDIKTINERORDENS. 1912. irreg. price varies. Aschendorffsche Verlagsbuchhandlung, Soester Str. 13, 4400 Muenster, W. Germany (B.R.D.) Ed. Emmanuel v. Severus.

230 GW ISSN 0067-5172
BEITRAEGE ZUR OEKUMENISCHEN THEOLOGIE. 1967. irreg., vol.18, 1981. price varies. Ferdinand Schoeningh, Juehenplatz 1, 4790 Paderborn, W. Germany (B.R.D.) Ed. Heinrich Fries. circ. 500.

200 US ISSN 0005-8327
BELARUSKAJA CARKVA. 1956. s-a. $4. Belaruskaja Vydaveckaja Siabrynia, 3006 Logan Blvd., Chicago, IL 60647. Ed. Vaclau Panucevic. bk. rev. charts. illus. index. circ. 500.

BELTANE PAPERS; a new-journal of women's spirituality and thealogy. see *WOMEN'S INTERESTS*

200 NE ISSN 0005-8734
BENEDICTIJNS TIJDSCHRIFT; voor Evangelische bezinning. 1937. q. fl.17.50. Sint-Adelbertabdij, Egmond-Binnen, Netherlands. Ed. P.J. Berkhout. adv. bk. rev. bibl. circ. 2,800. Indexed: CERDIC.

260 GW
BERCKERS KATOLISCHER TASCHENKALENDER. 1955. a. DM.8.50. Verlag Butzon und Bercker, Hoogeweg 71, Postfach 215, 4178 Kevelaer, W. Germany (B.R.D.) circ. 20,000.
Former titles: Berckers Taschenkalender; Berckers Katholischer Taschenkalender.

200 US ISSN 0005-8890
BEREAN SEARCHLIGHT. 1940. m. (except Jul.) free. Berean Bible Society, 7609 W. Belmont Ave., Chicago, IL 60635. TEL 312-456-7889 Ed. Cornelius R. Stam. charts. illus. circ. 16,500. (also avail. in microfilm from UMI; reprint service avail. from UMI)

200 GW ISSN 0174-2477
BERLINER ISLAMSTUDIEN. 1981. irreg., vol.4, 1986. price varies. (Institut fuer Islamwissenschaft der Freien Universitaet Berlin) Franz Steiner Verlag Wiesbaden GmbH, Birkenwaldstr. 44, Postfach 347, D-7000 Stuttgart 1, W. Germany (B.R.D.) Ed.Bd.

268 BE
BESTUURSBLAD. 1946. m. 50 Fr. (Katholiek Vormingswerk voor Landelijke Vrouwen) Belgische Boerenbond, Economaat, Minderbroedersstr. 8, B-3000 Louvain, Belgium. bk. rev. illus. circ. 16,000.

220 296 IS ISSN 0005-979X
BET MIKRA. (Text in Hebrew) 1956. q. $15. World Jewish Bible Society, Box 7024, Jerusalem, Israel. Ed. Ben-Zion Luria. bk. rev. circ. 1,700. Indexed: Ind.Heb.Per. Rel.& Theol.Abstr.

BETWEEN TIMES. see *CHILDREN AND YOUTH — For*

220 IT ISSN 0006-0585
BIBBIA E ORIENTE; rivista per la conoscenza della Bibbia. (Supplements avail.) 1959. q. L.13000($25) Centro Studi Arti Grafiche, 25040 Bornato (Brescia), Italy. Ed. Prof. Giovanni Rinaldi. bk. rev. illus. index. Indexed: Old Test.Abstr. Rel. & Theol.Abstr. New Test.Abstr.

220 GW
BIBEL IM JAHR(YEAR) 1964. a. DM.6.80. Katholisches Bibelwerk e.V., Silberburgstr. 121, 7000 Stuttgart 1, W. Germany (B.R.D.) Ed. P.G. Mueller. adv. bk. rev. illus. index.

220 SW ISSN 0006-0607
BIBEL-JOURNALEN. bi-m. Kr.10. Ryska Bibelsaellskapet - Russian Bible Society, Box 1712, Oerebro, Sweden. Ed. Ingemar Hallzon. illus. circ. 15,000.

220 GW ISSN 0006-0615
BIBEL UND GEMEINDE. 1954. q. DM.28($12) Bibelbund, Wiesenstr 27, D-7517 Waldbronn 2, W. Germany (B.R.D.) Dir. Hans Passarge. bk. rev. circ. 3,500.

220 282 GW ISSN 0006-0623
BIBEL UND KIRCHE. 1946. q. DM.20. Katholisches Bibelwerk E.V., Silberburgstr. 121, 7000 Stuttgart 1, W. Germany (B.R.D.) Ed. P.G. Mueller. adv. bk. rev. abstr. index. circ. 25,000. Indexed: Old Test.Abstr. CERDIC. New Test.Abstr.

220 AU ISSN 0006-064X
BIBEL UND LITURGIE. 1926. q. S.272. Pius-Parsch-Institut, Stiftsplatz 8, A-3400 Klosterneuburg, Austria. (Co-sponsor: Oesterreichisches Katholisches Bibelwerk) Ed. Norbert W. Hoeslinger. adv. bk. rev. abstr. bibl. tr.lit. index. circ. 3,000. Indexed: Old Test.Abstr. CERDIC. New Test.Abstr.

200 GW
BIBELREPORT. 1968. q. free. Deutsche Bibelgesellschaft, Balinger Str. 31, 7000 Stuttgart 80, W. Germany (B.R.D.) Eds. Helmut Haug, Roland Velten. bk. rev. illus. circ. 88,000. (back issues avail.)

266 SW ISSN 0006-0658
BIBELTROGNA VAENNERS MISSIONSTIDNING. 1912. m. Kr.60. Missionssaellskapet Bibeltrogna Vaenner, Upplandsgatan 43, S-113 28 Stockholm, Sweden. Ed. Rune Karlsson. bk. rev. index. circ. 3,500.
Missions

220 US ISSN 0006-0739
BIBLE FRIEND; of biblical faith and Christ's teaching. 1903. m. $3. Osterhus Publishing House, Inc., 4500 W. Broadway, Minneapolis, MN 55422. TEL 612-537-8335 Ed. Mrs. Cyrus Osterhus. illus. circ. 40,000.

220 US
BIBLE-IN-LIFE FRIENDS. w. David C. Cook Publishing Co., 850 N. Grove Ave., Elgin, IL 60120. Ed. Ramona Warren.
Grades 1-2

220 SW ISSN 0347-2787
BIBLE RESEARCHER; Revisionist history. (Text in English, French, German, Polish and Swedish; summaries in English) 1975. m. Kr.120($20) Bible Researcher, Marknadsvagen 289 2tr, S-183 34 Taby, Sweden. Ed. Ditlieb Felderer. bk. rev. circ. 1,000. (back issues avail.)

220 US
BIBLE SCIENCE NEWSLETTER. 1963. m. $12. Bible Science Association, 2911 E. 42nd St., Minneapolis, MN 55406. TEL 612-724-1883 Ed. Paul A. Bartz. bk. rev. illus. circ. 15,000.

200 US ISSN 0006-081X
BIBLE STANDARD AND HERALD OF CHRIST'S KINGDOM. French edition: Etendard de la Bible et Heraut du Royaume de Christ. (Editions also in Danish and Polish) 1920. m. $1. Laymen's Home Missionary Movement, Chester Springs, PA 19425. TEL 215-827-7665 Ed. Bernard W. Hedman. circ. 7,500. Indexed: CERDIC.
Missions

200 UK
BIBLE STUDY MONTHLY. 1924. bi-m. membership. Bible Fellowship Union, 11 Lyncroft Gardens, Hounslow, Middlesex, England.

BIBLE-TIME. see *CHILDREN AND YOUTH — For*

220 US ISSN 0006-0836
BIBLE TODAY; a periodical promoting scripture for life 7 ministry. 1962. bi-m. $14. Liturgical Press, St. John's Abbey, Collegeville, MN 56321. TEL 612-363-2213 Ed. Diane Bergantmueller. adv. bk. rev. illus. index. circ. 12,500. (also avail. in microform from UMI; back issues avail.; reprint service avail. from UMI) Indexed: Cath.Ind. Old Test.Abstr. New Test.Abstr.

266 US
BIBLES FOR THE WORLD NEWS. 1966. bi-m. free to donors. Bibles for the World, Box 805, Wheaton, IL 60189. TEL 312-668-7733 Ed.Bd. bk. rev. circ. 50,000.
Missions

220 US
BIBLEWORLD. 1908. bi-m. free. International Bible Society, 144 Tices Lane, East Brunswick, NJ 08816. TEL 201-238-5454 Ed. Rev. Richard K. Barnard. illus. circ. 125,000.
Formerly: Bible in New York (ISSN 0006-0747)

220 IT ISSN 0006-0879
BIBLIA REVUO. (Text in Esperanto) 1964. q. $6. Internacia Asocio de Bibliistoj Kaj Orientalistoj, Piazza Duomo 4, 48100 Ravenna, Italy. Dir. Angelo Duranti. adv. bk. rev. charts. illus. circ. 3,000. Indexed: Old Test.Abstr. New Test.Abstr.

BIBLICAL ARCHAEOLOGIST. see *ARCHAEOLOGY*

200 US ISSN 0740-7998
BIBLICAL EVANGELIST; America's most conservative Christian voice. 1966. m. free. (Biblical Evangelism, An Independent Baptist Evangelistic Association) Biblical Evangelism Press, Box 1513, Murfreesboro, TN 37133-1513. TEL 615-890-3495 Ed. Dr. Robert L. Sumner. adv. bk. rev. illus. circ. 21,500. (tabloid format)

220 US ISSN 0067-6535
BIBLICAL RESEARCH. 1956. a. $5. (Chicago Society of Biblical Research) Franciscan Publishers, Franciscan Center, Pulaski, WI 54162. TEL 312-241-7800 Ed. Robert Boling. index. circ. 700. (also avail. in microform from UMI; back issues avail.) Indexed: Old Test.Abstr. CERDIC. New Test.Abstr. Rel.Ind.One.

200 US ISSN 0277-0474
BIBLICAL SCHOLARSHIP IN NORTH AMERICA. irreg. (Society of Biblical Literature) Scholars Press, Box 1608, Decatur, GA 30031-1608. Ed. Kent Harold Richards.

230 IE ISSN 0006-0917
BIBLICAL THEOLOGY. 1950. s-a. $3. Donegal Democrat, Ballyshannon, Co. Donegal, Ireland. Eds. Rev. Dr. J. Thompson, Rev. R. D. Drysdale. bk. rev. circ. 250.

220 US ISSN 0146-1079
BIBLICAL THEOLOGY BULLETIN. 1971. 4/yr. $12. Biblical Theology Bulletin, Inc., c/o Theology Department, St. John's University, Jamaica, NY 11439. Eds. David M. Bossman, Leland J. White. adv. bk. rev. bibl. index. cum.index. circ. 1,800. (also avail. in microform from UMI; reprint service avail. UMI) Indexed: Old Test.Abstr. Rel.Per. Bk.Rev.Ind. CERDIC. New Test.Abstr. Rel.Ind.One. Rel.& Theol.Abstr.

230 US ISSN 0006-0925
BIBLICAL VIEWPOINT. 1967. s-a. $3.50. Bob Jones University, Greenville, SC 29614. TEL 803-242-5100 Ed. Stewart Custer. bibl. Indexed: Chr.Per.Ind. Rel.& Theol.Abstr.

220 SW ISSN 0345-1453
BIBLICUM; tidskrift foer biblisk tro och forskning. 1972. q. (plus 3 supplements) Kr.60($7) Stiftelsen Biblicum, S. Rudbecksgatan 6, 752 36 Uppsala, Sweden. Ed. Seth Erlandsson. bk. rev. circ. 1,500.
Supersedes: Foer Biblisk Tro (ISSN 0015-5217)

BIBLIOGRAFIA TEOLOGICA COMENTADA DEL AREA IBEROAMERICANA. see *BIBLIOGRAPHIES*

200 SP ISSN 0067-740X
BIBLIOTECA DE TEOLOGIA. 1964. irreg., no.16, 1983. price varies. (Universidad de Navarra, Facultad de Teologia) Ediciones Universidad de Navarra, S.A., Apdo. 396, 31080 Pamplona, Spain.

200 SW
BIBLIOTECA THEOLOGIAE PRACTICAE. (Text in Swedish; summaries in English or German) 1957. irreg., no. 40, 1983. price varies. Liber Forlag, S-205 10, Malmo, Sweden. Eds. Carl-Gustaf Andren, Aake Andren.

209 PL ISSN 0519-8658
BIBLIOTEKA PISARZY REFORMACYJNYCH. (Text in Latin and Polish) 1958. irreg., vol.15, 1982. price varies. (Polska Akademia Nauk, Instytut Filozofii i Socjologii) Panstwowe Wydawnictwo Naukowe, Ul. Miodowa 10, 00-251 Warsaw, Poland (Dist. by: Ars Polona, Krakowskie Przedmiescie 7 ,00-068 Warsaw, Poland) Ed. L. Szczucki. circ. 350.

BIBLIOTHECA DISSIDENTIUM. see *BIBLIOGRAPHIES*

200 BE
BIBLIOTHECA EPHEMERIDUM THEOLOGICARUM LOVANIENSIUM. vol. 31, 1972. irreg, vol. 77, 1987. Leuven University Press, Krakenstraat 3, B-3000 Louvain, Belgium. Indexed: Rel.Ind.Two.

200 NE
BIBLIOTHECA HUMANISTICA & REFORMATORICA. (Text in English, French or German) 1971. irreg., vol. 37, 1986. price varies. De Graaf Publishers, Box 6, 2420 AA Nieuwkoop, Netherlands.

220 SZ ISSN 0582-1673
BIBLISCHE BEITRAEGE. 1961. irreg., no. 13, 1977. price varies. (Schweizerisches Katholische Bibelwerk) Verlag S K B, c/o Pierre Casetti, Ed., Pfisternweg 5, CH-6015 Reussbuehl, Switzerland. adv. illus. circ. 1,750.

220 GW ISSN 0523-5154
BIBLISCHE UNTERSUCHUNGEN. 1967. irreg., vol.17, 1986. price varies. Verlag Friedrich Pustet, Gutenbergstr. 8, 8400 Regensburg 1, W. Germany (B.R.D.) Eds. Jost Eckert, Josef Hainz. circ. 800.

220 GW ISSN 0006-2014
BIBLISCHE ZEITSCHRIFT. N.S. 1957. s-a. DM.55. Ferdinand Schoeningh, Juehenplatz 1, Postfach 2540, 4790 Paderborn, W. Germany (B.R.D.) Eds. J. Schreiner, R. Schnackenburg. adv. bibl. index. (also avail. in microform from UMI; reprint service avail. from UMI) Indexed: Curr.Cont. Old Test.Abstr. Rel.Per. Arts & Hum.Cit.Ind. CERDIC. New Test.Abstr. Rel.Ind.One. Rel.& Theol.Abstr.
Bible

220 GW
BIBLISCHES SEMINAR. 1967. irreg. price varies. Calwer Verlag, Scharnhauser Str. 44, 7000 Stuttgart 70, W. Germany (B.R.D.)

268.1 NE ISSN 0006-2235
BIJBELLESSEN VOOR DE KINDEREN. 1912. q. fl.0.75. (Zevende-Dags Adventisten - Seventh-Day Adventists) Stichting Uitgeverij "Veritas", Biltseweg 14, 3735 ME Boschen Duin, Netherlands.

230 201 NE ISSN 0006-2278
BIJDRAGEN; tijdschrift voor filosofie en theologie. (Text in Dutch, English, French and German) 1938. 4/yr. fl.95 students fl.25. (Nederlandse Organisatie voor Zuiver-Wetenschappelijk Onderzoek) Stichting Bijdragen, Keizersgracht 105, 1015 CH Amsterdam, Netherlands. Ed.Bd. bk. rev. index. circ. 500. Indexed: CERDIC. Old.Test.Abstr. Int.Z.Bibelwiss. New Test.Abstr. Rel.& Theol.Abstr. Rel.Ind.One.

266 338.91 NE ISSN 0006-2308
BIJEEN; maandblad over internationale samenleving, bijzonder op het terrein van godsdienst en ontwikkeling. 1968. m. (11/yr.) fl.63. Stichting Gezamenlijke Missiepubliciteit, Postbus 750, 5201 AT 's-Hertogenbosch, Netherlands. Ed.Bd. adv. bk. rev. film rev. play rev. charts. illus. circ. 50,000. (processed; also avail. in microfiche) Indexed: CERDIC.
Missions

270 940 GW
BLAETTER FUER WUERTTEMBERGISCHE KIRCHENGESCHICHTE. 1895. a. DM.60. Verein fuer Wuerttembergische Kirchengeschichte, Gaensheidestr. 4, Postfach 92, 7000 Stuttgart 1, W. Germany (B.R.D.) Eds. Gerhard Schaefer, Martin Brecht. bk. rev. index. Indexed: Hist.Abstr. Amer.Hist.& Life.

200 GW
BLAUES KREUZ. 1897. m. DM.24.00. Blaues Kreuz in Deutschland e. V., Freiligrathstr. 27, Postfach 201610, 5600 Wuppertal 2, W. Germany (B.R.D.) (Subscr. to: Blaukreuz-Verlag, Postfach 20 16 10, 5600 Wuppertal 2, W. Germany (B.R.D.)) Ed. Alexander Schubert. circ. 4,700.

261 US ISSN 0006-4696
BLESSINGS OF LIBERTY. 1956. q. $3. Foundation for Religious Action in the Social and Civil Order, Box 1829, Pinehurst, NC 28374. Ed. Charles W. Lowry. bk. rev. circ. 1,100.

200 NE ISSN 0006-4777
BLIJDE BOODSCHAP. 1878. 2/m. fl.11. Uitgeverij H. Medema, Postbus 113, 8170 AC Vaassen, Netherlands. circ. 8,500.

BOA SEMENTE. see *CHILDREN AND YOUTH — For*

200 NE ISSN 0006-5439
BODE VAN HET HEIL IN CHRISTUS. 1858. m. fl.35. Uitgeverij H. Medema, Box 113, 8170 AC Vaassen, Netherlands. bk. rev. circ. 2,500.
Formerly: Bode des Heils.

200 YU ISSN 0006-5714
BOGOSLOVLJE. (Text in Serbocroatian) 1926. s-a. 20 din.($3) Pravoslavni Bogoslovski Fakultet u Beogradu, 7 Jula 2, Belgrade, Yugoslavia. Ed. Cedomir S. Draskovic. bk. rev. circ. 1,200.

200 YU ISSN 0006-5722
BOGOSLOVNI VESTNIK. (Text in Slovenian) 1920-1940; resumed 1948. q. 800 din. Teoloska Fakulteta v Ljubljani, Poljanska 4, 61000 Ljubljana, Yugoslavia. Ed. Anton Stres. bk. rev. circ. 1,200.

200 SP
BOLETIN OFICIAL ECLESIASTICO DEL ARZOBISPADO CASTRENSE DE ESPANA. (Text and summaries in Latin and Spanish) 1950. m. 1250 ptas.($10) Vicariato General Castrense, Nuncio 13, Madrid-5, Spain. bk. rev. bibl. index. circ. controlled.
Formerly (until Jan. 1986): Boletin Oficial de la Jurisdiccion Eclesiastica Castrense.

268 IT ISSN 0300-4589
BOLLETTINO DI COLLEGAMENTO; fra comunita cristiane in Italia. 1969. m. c/o Tony Sansone, Via delle Cascine 22, 50144 Florence, Italy. Eds. Maurizio Matteuzzi, Tony Sansone. bk. rev. film rev. bibl. index. circ. 3,000.

BOOKS AND RELIGION; a monthly review. see *PUBLISHING AND BOOK TRADE*

BOOKSTORE JOURNAL. see *PUBLISHING AND BOOK TRADE*

200 100 US
BOSTON UNIVERSITY STUDIES IN PHILOSOPHY AND RELIGION. 1980. irreg. University of Notre Dame Press, Notre Dame, IN 46556. TEL 219-239-6346 Ed. Leroy S. Rouner. Indexed: Rel.Ind.Two.

200 GW ISSN 0068-0443
BOTSCHAFT DES ALTEN TESTAMENTS; Erlauterungen Alttestamentlicher Schriften. 1958. irreg., vol.7/8, 1980. price varies. Calwer Verlag, Scharnhauser Str. 44, 7000 Stuttgart 70, W. Germany (B.R.D.)

200 GW
BOTSCHAFT HEUTE. m. Bergmoser & Hoeller Verlag GmbH, Karl-Friedrich-Str. 76, 5100 Aachen, W. Germany (B.R.D.)

200 NE ISSN 0006-8349
BOUWEN AAN DE NIEUWE AARDE. 1953. bi-m. fl.15. Stichting Bouwen aan de Nieuwe Aarde, Laagstraat 372-374, 5654 PR Eindhoven, Netherlands. bk. rev. circ. 5,000.

200 IT
BOZZE. 1978. bi-m. L.30000. Edizioni Dedalo S.p.A., Casella Postale 362, 70100 Bari, Italy. Dir. Raniero La Valle. circ. 9,000.

BRAILLE PILOT. see *BLIND*

266 GW ISSN 0006-9574
BREMER MISSIONSSCHIFF; Kinderbrief aus der Weltmission. 1904. m. free. Norddeutsche Mission, Vahrer Str. 243, 2800 Bremen 44, W. Germany (B.R.D.) Ed. Ingrid Michel. abstr. illus. circ. 15,000.
Incorporating: Kinderbrief aus der Weltmission.
Missions

200 GW
BRENNPUNKT SEELSORGE; Beitraege zur biblischen Lebensberatung. q. DM.8. Brunnen Verlag GmbH, Postfach 5205, 6300 Giessen 1, W. Germany (B.R.D.)

BRIGADE. see *CHILDREN AND YOUTH — About*

377 200 UK ISSN 0141-6200
BRITISH JOURNAL OF RELIGIOUS EDUCATION. 1934. 3/yr. £13.50. Christian Education Movement, Lancaster House, Borough Rd., Isleworth, Middlesex TW7 5DU, England. Ed. Dr. J.M. Hull. adv. bk. rev. charts. illus. index. circ. 4,000. (also avail. in microform from UMI; back issues avail., reprint service avail. from UMI) Indexed: Br.Educ.Ind. Rel. & Theol.Abstr. Abstr.Musl.Rel. CERDIC.
Supersedes (in 1978): Learning for Living (ISSN 0023-9704) & Religion in Education.

207 268.8 US ISSN 0068-2721
BROADMAN COMMENTS; INTERNATIONAL SUNDAY SCHOOL LESSONS. 1945. a. or q. $5.95. Broadman Press, 127 Ninth Ave. N., Nashville, TN 37234. TEL 615-251-2000 Ed. Donald F. Ackland. circ. 14,500.

266 US ISSN 0007-2494
BROWN GOLD. 1943. m. $6. (New Tribes Mission) Brown Gold Publications, 1000 E. First St., Sanford, FL 32771. Ed. Macon G. Hare. illus. circ. 40,000.
Missions

266 FR ISSN 0007-4330
BULLETIN DE L'OEUVRE APOSTOLIQUE. 1913. q. 15 F. Oeuvre Apostolique pour les Missions de Fondation Francaise a l'Etranger, 8 Av. Daniel Lesueur, 75007 Paris, France. Ed. P. Rebstock. circ. 1,500.
Missions

230 BE ISSN 0007-442X
BULLETIN DE THEOLOGIE ANCIENNE ET MEDIEVALE. s-a. 700 Fr. Abbaye du Mont-Cesar, 202 Mechelse Straat, B-3000 Louvain, Belgium. Ed. H. Bascour. bk. rev. bibl. index.

220 GR
BULLETIN OF BIBLICAL STUDIES. (Text in English, French, German and Greek) 1971; N.S. 1980. s-a. Dr.300($10) Editions Artos Zoes, Efranoros 12, 116 35 Athens, Greece. Ed. S. Agouridis. bk. rev. circ. 1,000.

230 SP ISSN 0521-8195
BURGENSE; collectanea scientifica. (Text in French, Latin and Spanish) 1960. s-a. 2000 ptas.($28) (Facultad de Teologie) Ediciones Aldecoa, Martinez del Compo, 10, Apartado 50, 09003 Burgos, Spain. Ed. Nicolas Lopez Martinez. bk. rev. bibl. circ. 600. Indexed: Old Test.Abstr. CERDIC. New Test.Abstr.

BURIED HISTORY. see *ARCHAEOLOGY*

200 US ISSN 0007-6309
BURNING BUSH. 1902. bi-m. $2. Metropolitan Church Association, 323 Broad St., Lake Geneva, WI 53147. TEL 414-248-6786 Ed. E.L. Adams. circ. 600.

200 028.5 UK ISSN 0045-3692
BUZZ. 1965. m. £9.95. Elm House Christian Communications Ltd., 37 Elm Rd., New Malden, Surrey KT3 3HB, England. Ed. Steve Goddard. adv. bk. rev. film rev. circ. 23,731.

C A L C REPORT. (Clergy and Laity Concerned) see *POLITICAL SCIENCE — International Relations*

200 SZ
C C I A BACKGROUND INFORMATION. 1975. irreg.(approx. 2/yr.) $20. World Council of Churches, Commission on International Affairs, 150 Route de Ferney, Box 66, 1211 Geneva 20, Switzerland. Ed. Erich Weingaertner. circ. 2,000.

C L S QUARTERLY. (Christian Legal Society) see *LAW*

200 IT
C O M-NUOVI TEMPI. 1973. w. $10. N T C News, Via Firenze, 38, 00184 Rome, Italy. Ed. Giorgio Girardet. circ. 11,000. Indexed: CERDIC.
Formed by the merger of: C O M & Nuovi Tempi.

255 AT ISSN 0007-9073
C S C NEWSLETTER. 1966. 3/yr. £1.50. Community of the Sisters of the Church, c/o Sister Audrey C.S.C., P.O. Box 539, Mordialloc, Victoria 3145, Australia. bk. rev. circ. 2,000. Indexed: CERDIC.
Supersedes: Our Work.

266 UK ISSN 0308-5252
C W I HERALD; a quarterly record of Christian Witness to Israel. 1976. q. $3.50. Christian Witness to Israel, Seven Trees, 44 Lubbock Rd., Chislehurst, Kent BR7 5JX, England. Ed. M.A. MacLeod. bk. rev. circ. 12,000. (also avail. in microform from UMI; reprint service avail. from UMI)
Former titles: Herald; Immanuel's Witness (ISSN 0019-2759)

200 FR ISSN 0008-0063
CAHIERS D'ETUDES CATHARES. 1948. q. 200 F. Societe du Souvenir et des Etudes Cathares, Chateau de Ferrieres, 81260 Brassac, Tarn, France, France. bk. rev. index. circ. 650. Indexed: CERDIC.

CAHIERS DE CIVILISATION MEDIEVALE. see *HISTORY — History Of Europe*

261 FR ISSN 0007-9669
CAHIERS DE L'ACTUALITE RELIGIEUSE ET SOCIALE. 1933. s-m. 250 F. Assas Editions, 14 rue d'Assas, 75006 Paris, France. Ed. Pierre de Charentenay. index. circ. 11,000. Indexed: CERDIC.
Formerly: Cahiers d'Action Religieuse et Sociale.

200 CN
CAHIERS DE RECHERCHE ETHIQUE. (Text in French) 1977. irreg. price varies. Editions Fides, 5710 Ave. Decelles, Montreal, Que. H3S 2C5, Canada. TEL 514-735-6406 Indexed: CERDIC.

243 FR ISSN 0222-9714
CAHIERS EVANGILE. (Supplements avail.) 1951. q. 114 F. (Service Biblique Evangile et Vie) Editions du Cerf, 29 bd. Latour Maubourg, 75007 Paris, France. Ed. H.M. Sevin. bk. rev. abstr. circ. 25,000. Indexed: Old Test.Abstr. Pt.de Rep.
Formerly: Cahiers Bibliques Trimestriels (ISSN 0007-960X)

266 US
CALL TO PRAYER. 1919. m. (10/yr.) $10 donation. World Gospel Mission, 3783 State Road 18 East, Box WGM, Marion, IN 46952. TEL 317-664-7331 Ed. Dr. Thomas H. Hermiz. circ. 40,000. (tabloid format)

220 GW
CALWER THEOLOGISCHE MONOGRAPHIEN. REIHE A: BIBELWISSENSCHAFT. 1972. irreg., no.14, 1984. price varies. Calwer Verlag, Scharnhauser Str. 44, 7000 Stuttgart 70, W. Germany (B.R.D.) Eds. Peter Stuhlmacher, Claus Westermann.

200 GW
CALWER THEOLOGISCHE MONOGRAPHIEN. REIHE C: PRAKTISCHE THEOLOGIE UND MISSIONSWISSENSCHAFT. 1973. irreg., vol.12, 1985. price varies. Calwer Verlag, Scharnhauser Str. 44, 7000 Stuttgart 70, W. Germany (B.R.D.) Ed. S.H. Buekle, M. Seitz.

230 GW
CALWER THEOLOGISCHE MONOGRAPHIEN. REIHE B: SYSTEMATISCHE THEOLOGIE UND KIRCHENGESCHICHTE. 1973. irreg., no.9, 1985. price varies. Calwer Verlag, Scharnhauser Str. 44, 7000 Stuttgart 70, W. Germany (B.R.D.) Ed.Bd.

200 361 US
CAMILLIAN. 1968. bi-m. $15. National Association of Catholic Chaplains, 3257 S. Lake Dr., Milwaukee, WI 53207. TEL 414-483-4898 Ed. Rev. Edward J. Dietrich. bk. rev. circ. 3,400. Indexed: CERDIC.

CAMINHO. see *CHILDREN AND YOUTH — For*

200 CN
CANADIAN BIBLE SOCIETY QUARTERLY NEWSLETTER. (Editions in English and French) 1960. q. free. Canadian Bible Society, 10 Carnforth Rd., Toronto, Ont. M4A 2S4, Canada. TEL 416-757-4171 Ed. William R. Russell. circ. 175,000.

270 CN ISSN 0008-3208
CANADIAN CHURCH HISTORICAL SOCIETY JOURNAL. 1950. s-a. Can.$12($12) Canadian Church Historical Society, c/o Archives, Anglican Church of Canada, 600 Jarvis St., Toronto, Ont. M4Y 1J6, Canada. Ed. Elwood Jones. bk. rev. cum.index. circ. 450. (also avail. in microform from UMI) Indexed: Amer.Hist.& Life. Hist.Abstr. CERDIC. Rel.Per. Rel.Ind.One.
Church history

250 CN ISSN 0045-4605
CANADIAN COUNCIL OF CHURCHES. COUNCIL COMMUNICATOR. 1970. 4/yr. free. ‡ Canadian Council of Churches, 40 St. Clair Ave. E., Toronto, Ont. M4T 1M9, Canada. TEL 416-921-4152 bk. rev. circ. 3,000.

277.1 CN ISSN 0701-4309
CANADIAN COUNCIL OF CHURCHES. RECORD OF PROCEEDINGS. 1944. triennial. Canadian Council of Churches - Conseil Canadien des Eglises, 40 St. Clair Ave., East, Toronto. Ont. M4T 1M9, Canada. TEL 416-921-4152

200 CN
CANADIAN ECUMENICAL NEWS. 1976. 7/yr. $5. Canadian Ecumenical Action, 1410 W. 12th Ave., Vancouver, B.C. V6H 1M8, Canada. TEL 604-736-1613 Ed. Val J. Anderson. adv. circ. 40,000.
Formerly: B.C. Ecumenical News.

200 CN ISSN 0316-8743
CANADIAN RELIGIOUS CONFERENCE. BULLETIN. French edition (ISSN 0316-8751) (Editions in English and French) 1955. 4/yr. Canadian Religious Conference, 324 Laurier Ave. E., Ottawa, Ont. K1N 6P6, Canada. TEL 613-236-0824

220 CN ISSN 0068-970X
CANADIAN SOCIETY OF BIBLICAL STUDIES. BULLETIN/SOCIETE CANADIENNE DES ETUDES BIBLIQUES. BULLETIN. (Not issued 1960-1963) 1935. a. included in membership fee. Canadian Society of Biblical Studies, c/o Memorial University of Newfoundland, Dept. of Religious Studies, St. John's, Nfld. A1C 5S7, Canada. TEL 709-737-8166 Ed. Dr. D.J. Hawkin. circ. 220.

266 JM ISSN 0008-6436
CARIBBEAN CHALLENGE. 1957. m. $6. Christian Literature Crusade Inc., Box 186, 55 Church St., Kingston, Jamaica, W. Indies. Ed.Bd. adv. circ. 23,000. (tabloid format)

268 JM
CARIBBEAN JOURNAL OF RELIGIOUS STUDIES; a forum for discussion of religious issues. 1975. s-a. 6($10) United Theological College of the West Indies, Golding Ave., P.O. Box 136, Mona, Kingston 7, Jamaica, W.I. Ed. Ashley M. Smith. bk. rev. bibl. circ. 400. Indexed: Rel.Ind.One.

260 GW
CARITAS-KALENDER. 1924. a. DM.5.80. (Deutscher Caritasverband) Lambertus-Verlag GmbH, Woelflinstr. 4, Postfach 1026, 7800 Freiburg, W. Germany (B.R.D.) Ed. Peter Gralla. adv. circ. 70,000.

CARL NEWELL JACKSON LECTURES. see *FOLKLORE*

200 US ISSN 0008-672X
CAROLINA CHRISTIAN. 1959. m. $6.50. Carolina Christian, Inc., Box 5423, Sta. B, Greenville, SC 29606. Ed. Howard Winters. adv. bk. rev. circ. 2,450.

200 323.4 FR
CATACOMBES; messager supraconfessionel de l'Eglise du silence. 1971. m. 90 F. Sergiu Grossu, Ed. & Pub., B.P. 98, 92405 Courbevoie, France. bk. rev. circ. 10,000. (tabloid format)

259 150.19 US
CATALOGUE OF CONFERENCES, SEMINARS, WORKSHOP. 1958. 3/yr. membership; non-members $5. (Wainwright House,Inc.) Center for the Development of Human Potential, Wainwright House, 260 Stuyvesant Ave., Rye, NY 10580. TEL 914-967-6080 Ed. Stacy C. Orphanos. bk. rev. circ. 18,000.
Former titles: Trends (Rye) & Laymen's Movement Review (ISSN 0023-9518)

377.8 US ISSN 0008-7726
CATECHIST. 1967. m. (Aug.-Apr.) $15.95. Peter Li, Inc., 2451 E. River Rd., Dayton, OH 45439. TEL 513-294-5785 Ed. Patricia Fischer. bk. rev. film rev. illus. circ. 42,674. (also avail. in microform from UMI; reprint service avail. from UMI) Indexed: Cath.Ind. CERDIC.

240 SP
CATEQUETICA. 3/yr. 790 ptas.($7) Editorial Sal Terrae, Calle Guevara 20, Santander, Spain.

222 US
CATHOLIC BIBLE QUARTERLY MONOGRAPH SERIES. 1971. irreg. price varies. Catholic Biblical Association of America, Catholic University of America, Washington, DC 20064. TEL 202-635-5519 Ed.Bd. circ. 1,000. Indexed: Cath.Ind. Old Test.Abstr. Rel.Per. New Test.Abstr.

CATHOLIC HEALTH ASSOCIATION OF THE UNITED STATES. GUIDEBOOK. see *HOSPITALS*

CATHOLIC HEALTH WORLD. see *HOSPITALS*

CENTRE; Bible data bank. see *HUMANITIES: COMPREHENSIVE WORKS — Computer Applications*

CENTRO CAMUNO DI STUDI PREISTORICI. BOLLETTINO. see *ARCHAEOLOGY*

200 FR ISSN 0411-5562
CERCLE ERNEST RENAN. CAHIERS. 1954. bi-m. 70 F. membership. Cercle Ernest Renan, 3 rue Recamier, 75341 Paris Cedex 07, France. Ed. J. Coryne. bk. rev. bibl. circ. 1,000. Indexed: CERDIC. Int.Z.Bibelwiss. New Test.Abstr.
Incorporating: Cercle Ernest Renan. Bulletin.

200 IT
CERTEZZE; rivista dei gruppi biblici universitari. 1953. 9/yr. L.18000($18) Gruppi Biblici Universitari, Via Michelangelo Poggioli 9/17, 00161 Rome, Italy. Ed. Jean Elliott. bk. rev. circ. 500. (back issues avail.)

266 US
CHALLENGE (WHEATON) 1954. bi-m. free. Conservative Baptist Home Mission Society, Box 828, Wheaton, IL 60189. TEL 312-653-4900 Ed. Dr. Jack Estep. circ. 92,000. (back issues avail.)

200 MW
CHANCELLOR COLLEGE. DEPARTMENT OF RELIGIOUS STUDIES. STAFF SEMINAR PAPER. irreg., no. 4, 1979. Chancellor College, Department of Religious Studies, Box 280, Zomba, Malawi.

CHANNELS OF BLESSING. see *BLIND*

200 FR ISSN 0009-160X
LES CHANTIERS DU CARDINAL. 1963. q. 10 F. 106 rue du Bac, 75341 Paris Cedex 07, France. Ed. M. Poisson. adv. illus. circ. 75,000.

200 DK ISSN 0108-4453
CHAOS; Dansk-Norsk tidsskrift for religionshistoriske studier. 1982. s-a. Kr.61 per no. Koebenhavns Universitet, Institut for Religionshistorie, Copenhagen, Denmark (Orders to: Museum Tusculanums Forlag, Njalsgade 94, DK-2300 Copenhagen S, Denmark) (Co-sponsor: Religionshistorisk Forening) illus.

200 US ISSN 0279-0424
CHARISMA. 1975. m. $16.97. Strang Communications Co., 190 N. Westmonte Dr., Altamonte Springs, FL 32714. TEL 305-869-5005 Ed. Stephen Strang. adv. bk. rev. circ. 150,000. (also avail. in microform from UMI; reprint service avail. from UMI) Indexed: Chr.Per.Ind. G.Soc.Sci.& Rel.Per.Lit.

CHART AND COMPASS INTERNATIONAL. see *SOCIAL SERVICES AND WELFARE*

200 UK ISSN 0009-2126
CHEERING WORDS. 1851. m. £3.75. D. Oldham, Ed. & Pub., 22 Victoria Rd., Stamford, Lincs. PE9 1HB, England. bk. rev. illus. index. circ. 4,500.

200 US
CHICAGO HISTORY OF AMERICAN RELIGION. 1973. irreg., latest 1981. price varies. University of Chicago Press, 5801 S. Ellis Ave., Chicago, IL 60637. TEL 312-962-7600 Ed. Martin E. Marty. adv. bk. rev. (reprint service avail. from UMI,ISI)

200 US
CHICAGO THEOLOGICAL SEMINARY REGISTER. 3/yr. $5. Chicago Theological Seminary, 5757 University Ave., Chicago, IL 60637. TEL 312-752-5757 Ed. Perry LeFevre. bk. rev. circ. 4,000. Indexed: Rel.Ind.One.

CHILDWORLD. see *CHILDREN AND YOUTH — About*

291 HK ISSN 0009-4668
CHING FENG; quarterly notes on Christianity and Chinese religion and culture. (Editions in Chinese and English) 1957. q. $10. Tao Fong Shan Ecumenical Centre, P.O. Box 33, Shatin N.T., Hong Kong. Ed. Peter K.H. Lee. adv. bk. rev. circ. 1,200. (also avail. in microform from NBI,UMI) Indexed: Rel.Ind.One.

266 US ISSN 0199-6487
CHINMAYA MISSION WEST NEWSLETTER. m. membership. Chinmaya Mission, Box 397, Los Altos, CA 94023. Eds. Renu Prasad, Lolita Lodhia.

200 SZ ISSN 0009-4994
CHOISIR; revue de reflexion chretienne. 1960. m. 45 Fr. Society of Jesus, 18 Rue Jacques-Dalphin, CH-1227 Carouge-Geneve, Switzerland. Ed.Bd. adv. bk. rev. index. circ. 3,000.

200 GW ISSN 0009-5060
DER CHRIST IM ZWANZIGSTEN JAHRHUNDERT. 1955. q. DM.6($3) Verlagsverein der Christ im Zwanzigsten Jahrhundert, Wasmannstr 15, 2000 Hamburg 60, W. Germany (B.R.D.) Ed.Dieter Alten. bk. rev. circ. 5,000(approx.)

200 GW ISSN 0009-5087
CHRIST UND BUCH; eine Hilfe fuer die Auswertung und Andwendung des gedruckten Wortes. 1960. q. membership. Evangelische Buchhilfe e.V., Alte Hauptstr. 14, Postfach 3180, 3502 Vellmar 3, W. Germany (B.R.D.) Ed. Oskar Schnetter. bk. rev. circ. 10,000.

200 NE ISSN 0009-5141
CHRISTELIJK OOSTEN. (Text in Dutch; summaries in English, French, German) 1948. q. fl.60. Instituut voor Byzantijnse en Oecumenische Studies te Nijmegen, Louiseweg 12, 6523 NB Nijmegen, Netherlands. Ed. A. Burg. adv. bk. rev. bibl. illus. index. cum.index. circ. 450. Indexed: CERDIC.

200 GW ISSN 0009-5184
DIE CHRISTENGEMEINSCHAFT; Monatsschrift zur religioesen Erneuerung. 1924. m. DM.48. Verlag Urachhaus Johannes M. Mayer GmbH, Urachstr. 41, 7000 Stuttgart 1, W. Germany (B.R.D.) Ed. Dr. Rudolf Frieling. adv. bk. rev. index. circ. 10,000. (processed) Indexed: CERDIC.

200 US ISSN 0009-5214
CHRISTIAN ADVENTURER. 1955. w. $0.80 per quarter. Messenger Publishing House, Box 850, Joplin, MO 64802. TEL 417-624-7050 Ed. Rosmarie Foreman. circ. 3,500. (tabloid format)

CHRISTIAN ADVERTISING FORUM. see *ADVERTISING AND PUBLIC RELATIONS*

240 UK ISSN 0264-598X
CHRISTIAN ARENA. 1948. q. £4. ‡ Universities and Colleges Christian Fellowship, 38 de Montfort St., Leicester LE1 7GP, England. Ed. N. Ladbury. bk. rev. circ. 10,000.
Formerly: Christian Graduate (ISSN 0045-6802)

262 US ISSN 0009-5281
CHRISTIAN CENTURY; an Ecumenical weekly. 1908. w. $28. Christian Century Foundation, 407 S. Dearborn St., Chicago, IL 60605. TEL 312-427-5380 Ed. James M. Wall. adv. bk. rev. s-a. index. circ. 38,000. (also avail. in microform from BLH,UMI) Indexed: Hist.Abstr. R.G. Rel.Per. Bk.Rev.Dig. Abstrax. Amer.Hist.& Life. Child.Bk.Rev.Ind. Film Lit.Ind. G.Soc.Sci.& Rel.Per.Lit. Media Rev.Dig. Mag.Ind. PMR. Rel.Ind.One. Rel.& Theol.Abstr.

200 US
CHRISTIAN CHRONICLE; an international newspaper for members of Churches of Christ. 1943. m. membership. Oklahoma Christian College, Rt. 1, Box 141, Oklahoma City, OK 73111. TEL 405-478-1661 Ed. Howard W. Norton. adv. bk. rev. illus. circ. 95,000. (tabloid format)

261 CN ISSN 0009-5303
CHRISTIAN COMMUNICATIONS. 1962. q. Can.$2. Saint Paul Society, 223 Main St., Ottawa K1S 1C4, Canada. Ed. John W. Mole. bk. rev. cum.index: 1962-73. circ. 2,000. (also avail. in microform from UMI) Indexed: CERDIC.

200 US ISSN 0195-265X
CHRISTIAN CRUSADE; international Christian newspaper. 1969. m. $2. Church of Christian Crusade, Box 977, Tulsa, OK 74102. TEL 918-836-2206 Ed. Bill Sampson. bk. rev. circ. 90,000. (also avail. in microfilm from UMI)
Formerly: Christian Crusade Weekly; Supersedes: Weekly Crusader (ISSN 0509-9498)

266 US
CHRISTIAN EDUCATION JOURNAL. 1980. s-a. $7. Scripture Press Ministries, Inc., Box 513, Glen Ellyn, IL 60138. Ed. Wesley R. Willis. bk. rev. circ. 1,200. Indexed: CERDIC. Chr.Per.Ind. Rel.Ind.One. Rel.& Theol.Abstr.
Formerly: Journal of Christian Education (ISSN 0277-9935)

268 US
CHRISTIAN EDUCATORS JOURNAL. 1961. q. $4.50 to non-members; members $3.50. Christian Educators Journal Association, c/o Donald Hunderman, Bus.Mgr., 1500 Cornell S.E., Grand Rapids, MI 49506. Ed. Lorna Van Gilst. adv. bk. rev. illus. circ. 5,000. (back issues avail.) Indexed: Chr.Per.Ind. G.Soc.Sci.& Rel.Per.Lit.

200 US ISSN 0009-5338
CHRISTIAN ENDEAVOR WORLD; the voice of Christian Endeavor. 1886. 4/yr. membership. International Society of Christian Endeavor, 1221 E. Broad St., Box 1110, Columbus, OH 43216. TEL 614-258-9545 Ed. David G. Jackson. bk. rev. illus. circ. 4,200. (also avail. in microfilm)

CHRISTIAN FAMILY CATALOG. see *GIFTWARE AND TOYS*

200 MW
CHRISTIAN FORUM. (Text in Chichewa or English) q. Christian Council of Malawi, Lilongwe, Malawi (Dist. by: Christian Literature Association in Malawi, Box 503, Blantyre, Malawi)

200 UK
CHRISTIAN HERALD. 1866. w. £17.50. Herald House Ltd., 27 Chapel Rd., Worthing, Sussex BN11 1EG, England. Ed. C.M. Reeves. adv. bk. rev. circ. 33,000. Indexed: Access. G.Soc.Sci.& Rel.Per.Lit. Mag.Ind.

200 US ISSN 0009-5354
CHRISTIAN HERALD (CHAPPAQUA) 1878. m. $15.97. Christian Herald Association, 40 Overlook Dr., Chappaqua, NY 10514. Ed. Dean Merrill. adv. bk. rev. charts. film rev. illus. record rev. circ. 200,000. (also avail. in microform from BLH,UMI; reprint service avail. from UMI) Indexed: Access Index. Chr.Per.Ind. G.Soc.Sci.& Rel.Per.Lit. Mag.Ind.

200 900 US
CHRISTIAN HISTORY MAGAZINE. 1983. q. $12. Christian History Institute, Box 540, 2030 Wentz Church Rd., Worcester, PA 19490 (Subscr. to: Box 3000, Department C, Denville, NJ 07834) Ed. A.K. Curtis. adv. illus. circ. 5,000. (back issues avail.)

377.8 US ISSN 0009-5389
CHRISTIAN HOME & SCHOOL. 8/yr. $8. ‡ Christian Schools International, Box 8709, Grand Rapids, MI 49508. TEL 616-957-1070 Ed. Gordon L. Bordewyk. adv. bk. rev. circ. 13,000.

266 CN
CHRISTIAN INFO. 1982. bi-w. Can.$9.75. Christian Info (B.C.) Society, 195 W. 2nd Ave., Ste. 250, Vancouver, B.C. V5Y 1B8, Canada. adv. bk. rev. film rev. play rev. circ. 15,000. (tabloid format; back issues avail.)

275 PH ISSN 0045-6810
CHRISTIAN INSTITUTE FOR ETHNIC STUDIES IN ASIA. BULLETIN. vol. 4, 1970. 2-3/yr. Christian Institute for Ethnic Studies in Asia, Box 3167, Manila, Philippines. Eds. Alex J. Grant, Rufino Tima. bk. rev. bibl. charts.

291 UK ISSN 0144-2902
CHRISTIAN JEWISH RELATIONS. 1968. q. £12($20) to individuals; institutions £16($25) Institute of Jewish Affairs, 11 Hertford St., London W1Y 7DX, England. (Co-sponsor: World Jewish Congress) Ed. Rabbi N. Solomon. adv. bk. rev. bibl. circ. 1,500. Indexed: Hist.Abstr. CERDIC. Rel.Ind.One.
Formerly: Christian Attitudes on Jews and Judaism (ISSN 0009-5249)

260 US
CHRISTIAN LEADERSHIP LETTER. 1973. m. free. ‡ World Vision International, 919 West Huntington Dr., Monrovia, CA 91016. TEL 818-357-7979 Eds. Ted Engstrom, Edward Dayton. circ. 48,000. (reprints service avail.)

200 US ISSN 0009-5427
CHRISTIAN LIFE; the guide to better living. 1939. m. $15.95. Strang Communications Co., 190 N. Westmonte Dr., Altamonte Springs, FL 32714. TEL 305-869-5005 Ed. Robert Walker. adv. bk. rev. charts. film rev. illus. record rev. tr.lit. circ. 95,000. (reprint service avail. from UMI) Indexed: Chr.Per.Ind. G.Soc.Sci.& Rel.Per.Lit.

CHRISTIAN MEDICAL ASSOCIATION OF INDIA. JOURNAL. see *MEDICAL SCIENCES*

CHRISTIAN MEDICAL SOCIETY JOURNAL. see *MEDICAL SCIENCES*

250 US ISSN 0033-4138
CHRISTIAN MINISTRY; a professional journal for clergy. vol. 40, 1969. bi-m. $10. Christian Century Foundation, 407 S. Dearborn St., Chicago, IL 60605. TEL 312-427-5380 Ed. James M. Wall. adv. bk. rev. index. circ. 12,000. (also avail. in microform from UMI) Indexed: G.Soc.Sci.& Rel.Per.Lit. Rel.Ind.One.
Formerly: Pulpit.

200 US ISSN 0744-4052
CHRISTIAN MISSIONS IN MANY LANDS. vol.33, 1970. m. (11/yr.) free. Christian Missions in Many Lands, Inc., Box 13, Spring Lake, NJ 07762. TEL 201-449-8880 Ed.Bd. bk. rev. illus. circ. 14,000.
Formerly: Fields (ISSN 0015-0762)
Missions

248 US
CHRISTIAN MOTHER (PITTSBURGH) 1942? q. $1. ‡ Archconfraternity of Christian Mothers, 220 37th St., Pittsburgh, PA 15201. TEL 412-683-2400 Ed. Rev. Bertin Roll. circ. 30,000.

200 IS ISSN 0009-5532
CHRISTIAN NEWS FROM ISRAEL. (Editions in English, French and Spanish) 1949. s-a. $5. Ministry of Religious Affairs, Box 1167, 30 Jaffa St., Jerusalem, Israel. Ed. Shalom Ben-Zakkai. adv. bk. rev. bibl. illus. index. circ. 10,000. (also avail. in microfilm from UMI; reprint service avail. from UMI) Indexed: Old Test.Abstr. New Test.Abstr.

CHRISTIAN PEACE CONFERENCE. see *POLITICAL SCIENCE — International Relations*

CHRISTIAN RECORD TALKING MAGAZINE. see *BLIND*

207 US
CHRISTIAN RESEARCH JOURNAL. 1975. triennial. $7.50. Christian Research Institute, Box 500, San Juan Capistrano, CA 92693-0500. TEL 714-855-9926 Ed. Elliot Miller. adv. bk. rev. bibl. circ. 10,000.
Former titles: Forward (San Juan Capistrano) & Christian Research Institute. Newsletter (ISSN 0045-6845)

CHRISTIAN RETAILING; the trade magazine of religious retailing. see *PUBLISHING AND BOOK TRADE*

200 US ISSN 0017-2251
CHRISTIAN SCHOLAR'S REVIEW; a Christian quarterly of the arts and sciences. 1970. q. $12 to individuals; libraries $15. R.F.D. No. 2, Box 622, Union, ME 04862 (Subscr. address: Circulation Department, Calvin College, Grand Rapids, MI 49506) Ed. Clifton J. Orlebeke. adv. bk. rev. abstr. bibl. index. cum.index. circ. 3,500. (also avail. in microform from UMI; microfiche; back issues avail.) Indexed: Hist.Abstr. M.L.A. Abstr.Engl.Stud. Bibl.Engl.Lang.& Lit. Amer.Hist.& Life. CERDIC. Chr.Per.Ind. G.Soc.Sci.& Rel.Per.Lit. New Test.Abstr. Rel.& Theol.Abstr. Rel.Ind.One.

200 MW
CHRISTIAN SERVICE COMMITTEE OF THE CHURCHES IN MALAWI. ANNUAL REPORT. (Text in English) a. free. Christian Service Committee of the Churches in Malawi, Box 51294, Limbe, Malawi.

200 US ISSN 0009-5656
CHRISTIAN STANDARD. 1866. w. $14. ‡ Standard Publishing, 8121 Hamilton Ave., Cincinnati, OH 45231. TEL 513-931-4050 Ed. Sam E. Stone. bk. rev. illus. index: cum.index: 1866-1966. circ. 66,000. (also avail. in microfilm) Indexed: G.Soc.Sci.& Rel.Per.Lit.

261 300 US ISSN 0009-5664
CHRISTIAN STATESMAN. 1867. bi-m. $5. National Reform Association, 422 Seventh Ave., Patterson Heights, Beaver Falls, PA 15010. Ed. D. Howard Elliott. bk. rev. circ. 2,000. (also avail. in microform)
Christian citizenship

200 US ISSN 0009-5702
CHRISTIAN WOMAN. 1932. 6/yr. $12. Gospel Advocate Company, 1006 Elm Hill Pike, Nashville, TN 37210. TEL 615-254-8781 Ed. Sandra Humphrey. adv. bk. rev. illus. index. circ. 33,000.

267 AT
CHRISTIAN WOMAN. 1953. 11/yr. Aus.$2. Christian Women's Conventions International, Box 285, Strathfield, N.S.W. 2135, Australia. Ed. Robyn Collins. adv. bk. rev. circ. 11,000.

200 UK
CHRISTIAN WOMAN. 1982. m. £18. Herald House Ltd., 27 Chapel Rd., Worthing, Sussex BN11 1EG, England. Ed. Gail Lawther. circ. 17,500.

200 US ISSN 0009-5745
CHRISTIANITY AND CRISIS; a Christian journal of opinion. 1941. fortn. $21 to individuals; institutions $24. Christianity and Crisis Inc., 537 W. 121st St., New York, NY 10027. TEL 212-662-5907 Ed. Leon Howell. adv. bk. rev. film rev. illus. play rev. index. circ. 20,000. (also avail. in microform from BLH,UMI; reprint service avail. from UMI) Indexed: P.A.I.S. Rel.Per. Hist.Abstr. Hum.Ind. Amer.Hist.& Life. CERDIC. G.Soc.Sci.& Rel.Per.Lit. Rel.Ind.One.

CHRISTIANITY AND LITERATURE. see *LITERARY AND POLITICAL REVIEWS*

200 US ISSN 0009-5753
CHRISTIANITY TODAY. 1956. s-m. $21. Christianity Today, Inc., 465 Gunderson Dr., Carol Stream, IL 60188 TEL 312-260-6200 (Subscr. to: Box 1915, Marion., OH 43305) Ed. Terry Muck. adv. bk. rev. bibl. index. circ. 185,000. (also avail. in microform from UMI,BLH; reprint service avail. from UMI) Indexed: Old Test.Abstr. Rel.Per. R.G. Biog.Ind. Chr.Per.Ind. G.Soc.Sci.& Rel.Per.Lit. New Test.Abstr. Mag.Ind. PMR. Peace Res.Abstr. Rel.& Theol.Abstr. Rel.Ind.One.

268 AU ISSN 0009-5761
CHRISTLICH-PAEDAGOGISCHE BLAETTER; Zeitschrift fuer den katechetischen Dienst. 1887. bi-m. S.288. (Katechetisches Institut) Verlag Herder, Wollzeile 33, A-1010 Vienna, Austria. Ed. Edgar Josef Korherr. adv. bk. rev. abstr. index. circ. 3,800. Indexed: Canon Law Abstr.

200 AU ISSN 0009-5796
CHRISTLICHE INNERLICHKEIT; Schrift fuer Gebet und gelebtes Christentum. 1965. bi-m. S.70($5) Werk Christliche Innerlichkeit, Karmelweg 1, A-8630 Mariazell, Austria. (Affiliate: Order of Discalced Carmelite Fathers in Austria) Ed. P. Suitbert Siedl O.C.D. bk. rev. circ. 5,000.

266 GW ISSN 0009-580X
CHRISTOFFEL-BLINDENMISSION. BERICHT. 1908. bi-m. free. ‡ Christoffel Blindenmission e. V., Nibelungenstr. 124, 6140 Bensheim-Schoenberg, W. Germany (B.R.D.) Ed. S. Wiesinger. illus. circ. 500,000.
Missions

266 US ISSN 8755-6901
CHRISTOPHER NEWS NOTES. 1946. 7/yr. free. ‡ Christophers, Inc., 12 E. 48th St., New York, NY 10017. TEL 212-759-4050 Ed. Joseph R. Thomas. circ. 800,000.

200 GW ISSN 0009-5869
DIE CHRISTUS-POST. bi-m. DM.5. Christliche Postvereinigung in Deutschland, Kamerunweg 14, 3000 Hannover-Linden, W. Germany (B.R.D.) bk. rev. abstr. bibl. circ. 1,200.

266 UK
CHRYSOSTOM. 1960. 2/yr. £2. Society of St. John Chrysostom, Marian House, Holden Ave., London N12 8HY, England. Ed. H. E. Georgiadis. bk. rev. index every 3 yrs. circ. 700. (tabloid format; also avail. in microform from UMI; reprint service avail. from UMI) Indexed: CERDIC.

220 US
CHURCH ADVOCATE. 1835. m. $8.35. Churches of God, General Conference, Box 926, Findlay, OH 45839. charts. illus. circ. 7,900. Indexed: CERDIC.
Former titles: Bible Advocate & Bible Advocate and Herald of the Coming Kingdom (ISSN 0006-0674)

200 US ISSN 0045-6861
CHURCH AND CLERGY FINANCE. 1970. s-m. $18. Ministers Life Resources, 3100 W. Lake St., Minneapolis, MN 55416. TEL 612-927-7131 Ed. Manfred Holck, Jr. index. circ. 2,000. (processed)

CHURCH AND SCHOOL EQUIPMENT NEWS. see *BUILDING AND CONSTRUCTION*

200 SZ
CHURCH AND SOCIETY NEWSLETTER; Christian social thought in a future perspective. 1970. 3/yr. World Council of Churches, Department on Church and Society, 150 Route de Ferney, Box 66, 1211 Geneva 20, Switzerland. Ed. David Gosling. circ. 5,000. Indexed: CERDIC.
Formerly: Anticipation; Which superseded: Background Information for Church and Society.

261 323 US ISSN 0009-6334
CHURCH & STATE; a monthly review. 1948. m. (Sep.-Jul.) $10. Americans United for Separation of Church and State, 8120 Fenton St., Silver Spring, MD 20910. TEL 301-589-3707 Ed. Joseph L. Conn. bk. rev. illus. index. circ. 55,000. (also avail. in microform from UMI; reprint service avail. from UMI) Indexed: P.A.I.S. CERDIC.

CHURCH AND SYNAGOGUE LIBRARIES. see *LIBRARY AND INFORMATION SCIENCES*

200 UK
CHURCH ARMY. REVIEW. 1906. q. £1. Church Army, Independents Rd., Blackheath, London SE3 9LG, England. Ed. Donald Woodhouse. bk. rev. circ. 30,000. (tabloid format)
Former titles: New Review; (until 1983): Church Army Review (ISSN 0009-6350)

270 US ISSN 0009-6407
CHURCH HISTORY. 1932. q. $25. American Society of Church History, 305 E. Country Club Ln., Wallingford, PA 19086. Ed.Bd. adv. bk. rev. bibl. index. cum.index. circ. 3,400. (also avail. in microform) Indexed: Curr.Cont. Hist.Abstr. Hum.Ind. Old Test.Abstr. Rel.Per. Amer.Bibl.Slavic & E.Eur.Stud. Arts & Hum.Cit.Ind. Bk.Rev.Ind. Amer.Hist.& Life. CERDIC. Chr.Per.Ind. Hist.Abstr. Lang.& Lang.Behav.Abstr. Rel.& Theol.Abstr. Rel.Ind.One. RILA.
Church history

200 US
CHURCH MESSENGER/CERKOVNYJ VISTNIK. 1944. bi-w. $10. ‡ American Carpatho-Russian Orthodox Greek Catholic Diocese, 312 Garfield St., Johnstown, PA 15906. Ed. Rev. James S. Dutko. adv. bk. rev. film rev. illus. circ. 7,200.

200 UK ISSN 0009-6474
CHURCH NEWS. 1946. m. £3.25. Home Words Printing & Publishing Co. Ltd., Box 44, Guildford, Surrey GU1 1XL, England. Ed. Rev. Canon C. Rhodes. adv. bk. rev. illus. circ. 105,000.

200 UK ISSN 0009-6482
CHURCH OBSERVER. 1948. 3/yr. £5. (Church Union) Church Literature Association, Faith House, 7 Tufton St., London SW1P 3QN, England. Ed. Peter Geldard. adv. bk. rev. illus. circ. 8,000. (also avail. in microfilm from UMI) Indexed: CERDIC.

CHURCH OF SCOTLAND BRAILLE MAGAZINE. see *BLIND*

268 UK
CHURCH POCKET BOOK AND DIARY. a. price varies. Society for Promoting Christian Knowledge, c/o Mrs. Cazz Colmer, Holy Trinity Church, Marylebone Rd., London NW1 4DU, England. circ. 6,000.
Formerly: Churchman's Pocket Book and Diary (ISSN 0069-4029)

252 UK ISSN 0069-4002
CHURCH PULPIT YEAR BOOK; sermon outlines. 1903. a. £1.75. ‡ Chansitor Publications, 46 Bedford Row, London WC1R 4LR, England. adv. index. circ. 3,000.

267.4 US ISSN 0009-6598
CHURCH WOMAN. 1934. bi-m. $6. Church Women United, 475 Riverside Dr., Rm. 812, New York, NY 10115 TEL 212-870-2347 (Subscr. to: Church Women United, Box 37815, Cincinnati, OH 45237) Ed. Virginia Baron. bk. rev. illus. circ. 10,000.

200 US ISSN 0009-6601
CHURCH WORLD. 1930. w. $15. Diocese of Portland, Maine, Box 698, Brunswick, ME 04011. TEL 207-729-8753 Ed. Henry Gosselin. adv. bk. rev. film rev. play rev. illus. circ. 9,647. (tabloid format)

301.426 US
CHURCH WORLD SERVICE. FAMILY LIFE AND POPULATION PROGRAM BRIEFS. 1970. q. free. (National Council of the Churches of Christ) Church World Service, Office of C W S Communications, 475 Riverside Dr., Rm. 620, New York, NY 10115. TEL 212-870-2427 Eds. Iluminada Rodriguez, Sherie Hawley. circ. 4,000.
Former titles: F L P P Newsletter; Until 1977: Church World Service. Planned Parenthood Program. Newsletter.
Planned parenthood

200 301 US ISSN 0009-6628
CHURCHMAN'S HUMAN QUEST. 1804. m.; bi-m. in summer. $10. ‡ (Churchman Associates, Inc.) Churchman Company, Inc., 1074 23rd Ave., N., St. Petersburg, FL 33704. TEL 813-894-0097 Ed. Edna Ruth Johnson. adv. bk. rev. bibl. circ. 10,000. (also avail. in microform from UMI; back issues avail.) Indexed: Hist.Abstr. Amer.Hist.& Life. CERDIC. Chr.Per.Ind. Rel.Ind.One.
Formerly: Churchman.

200 297 GW ISSN 0721-0035
CIBEDO - DOKUMENTATIONEN UND TEXTE. 1978. bi-m. DM.25. Cibedo, Guiollettstr. 35, Postfach 170427, D-Frankfurt 17, W. Germany (B.R.D.) Ed. Weisse Vaeter. bk. rev. circ. 1,000. (back issues avail.)

200 US
CINCINNATI CHRISTIAN SEMINARY. SEMINARY REVIEW. 1954. s-a. $3. Cincinnati Christian Seminary, 2700 Glenway Ave., Cincinnati, OH 45204. TEL 513-244-8100 Ed. James B. North. bk. rev. circ. 1,200. (back issues avail.)

CITHARA; essays in Judaeo-Christian tradition. see *HUMANITIES: COMPREHENSIVE WORKS*

200 700 IT ISSN 0009-7632
CITTA DI VITA; bimestrale di religione arte e scienza. 1946. bi-m. L.35000. Piazza S. Croce 16, 50122 Florence, Italy. Ed. Massimiliano G. Rosito. adv. bk. rev. bibl. illus. index. circ. 2,000. Indexed: M.L.A.

200 900 BE
CLAIRLIEU: TIJDSCHRIFT GEWIJD AAN DE GESCHIEDENIS DER KRUISHEREN. (Editions in Dutch, English, French and German) 1943. a. 350 Fr. Geschiedkundige Kring "Clairlieu", Catharinadal 3, 3590 Achel, Belgium. Ed. A. Ramaekers. bk. rev. Indexed: Hist.Abstr. Amer.Hist.& Life.

250 US ISSN 0009-6431
CLERGY JOURNAL. Cover title: Church Management: The Clergy Journal. 1924. 10/yr. $21. Church Management Inc., Box 162527, Austin, TX 78716. Ed. Manfred Holck, Jr. adv. bk. rev. circ. 20,000. (also avail. in microfilm from UMI)

200 AG
COLECCION AMANECE. no. 4, 1976. irreg. Editora Patria Grande, Casilla de Correo 5, Buenos Aires 1408, Argentina.

200 SP ISSN 0069-505X
COLECCION CANONICA. 1959. irreg., no.89, 1986. price varies. (Universidad de Navarra, Facultad de Derecho Canonico) Ediciones Universidad de Navarra, S.A., Apdo. 396, 31080 Pamplona, Spain.
Canon law

200 CK
COLECCION COMUNICACION. 1977. irreg. Ediciones Paulinas, Apdo. 100282, Bogota, Colombia.

262.9 SP ISSN 0210-0711
COLECTANEA DE JURISPRUDENCIA CANONICA. 1974. a. 850 ptas.($22) Universidad Pontificia de Salamanca, Calle Compania 1, Salamanca, Spain. Ed. Juan Luis Acebal.
Canon law

261 US
COLORADO KAIROS. 1965. 11/yr. free. Colorado Council of Churches, 1370 Pennsylvania, Ste. 100, Denver, CO 80203. TEL 303-861-1884 Ed. Barbara McIntyre. abstr. bibl. illus. circ. 4,500.
Formerly (until 1982): Colorado Councillor (ISSN 0010-1540); Supersedes: Rocky Mountain Churchman.
Organization news

220 CN ISSN 0316-3040
COME AND SEE. 1974. bi-m. free. Nathanael Literature Distributors, 64 Hills Rd., Ajax, Ont. L1S 2W4, Canada. Ed. John van Dijk. circ. 6,500.

268 MX ISSN 0010-2385
COMINO. 1944. bi-m. $5. Iglesia Metodista de Mexico, Secretaria de Educacion Cristiana, Balderas 47, Mexico City, Mexico. Ed. Maria C. De Flores. illus. circ. 900.

200 UK ISSN 0010-325X
COMMON GROUND; to combat all forms of religious and racial intolerance. 1946. 3/yr. £5. Council of Christians and Jews, 1 Dennington Park Rd., London NW6 1AX, England. Ed. Rev. Marcus Braybrooke. adv. bk. rev. illus. circ. 3,300. (also avail. in microform from UMI) Indexed: CERDIC.

200 CN ISSN 0010-3454
COMMUNAUTE CHRETIENNE. 1962. bi-m. Can.$18. Institut de Pastorale, 2715 Chemin de la Cote Sainte-Catherine, Montreal, P.Q. H3T 1B6, Canada. Ed. Laurent Dupont. adv. bk. rev. bibl. circ. 2,500. Indexed: CERDIC. Pt.de Rep.

250 BE
COMMUNAUTES ET LITURGIES; revue d'action liturgique et pastorale. 1919. 6/yr. 850 Fr. Monastere de Saint Andre, Allee de Clerlande 1, B-1340 Ottignies, Belgium. Ed. Dieudonne Dufrasne. adv. bk. rev. bibl. index. cum.index. Indexed: Old Test.Abstr. CERDIC.
Formerly (until 1975): Paroisse et Liturgie (ISSN 0031-2347)

254.4 659.2 GW ISSN 0010-3497
COMMUNICATIO SOCIALIS; Zeitschrift fuer Publizistik in Kirche und Welt. (Text in German; summaries in English, French and Spanish) 1968. q. DM.38. Ferdinand Schoeningh, Juehenplatz 1, 4790 Paderborn, W. Germany (B.R.D.) Ed. Dr. Franz-Josef Eilers. adv. bk. rev. film rev. Indexed: CERDIC. Lang.& Lang.Behav.Abstr.

230 SP ISSN 0010-3705
COMMUNIO; commentarii Internationales de Ecclesia et Theologia. 1968. 3/yr. 2000 ptas.($30) Estudio General Dominicano, Provincia Betica (Espana), Apdo. 820, 41080 Seville, Spain. Ed. Miguel de Burgos. bk. rev. cum.index. circ. 300. Indexed: Old Test.Abstr. CERDIC. New Test.Abstr. Rel.& Theol.Abstr.

200 CS ISSN 0010-3713
COMMUNIO VIATORUM; a theological quarterly. (Text in English, French and German) 1958. q. 19 Fr. Comenius Faculty of Protestant Theology (Ecumenical Institut), Jungmannova 9, 110 00 Prague 1, Czechoslovakia (Subscr. to: Artia, Ve Smeckach 30, 111 27 Prague 1, Czechoslovakia) Ed.Bd. bk. rev. index. circ. 1,000. Indexed: New Test.Abstr. Rel.Per. Rel.Ind.One.

261 UK ISSN 0045-7809
COMPASS. 1961. m. 36p. Christian News Ltd., Centre One, Devonshire House, High St., Birmingham, B12 0LP, England. Ed. Rev. M.W. Blood.
Formerly: Christian News.

200 FR
CONCILIUM; revue international de theologie. 1965. 6/yr. 280 F. Editions Beauchesne, 72 rue des Saints Peres, 75007 Paris, France. Indexed: CERDIC.

200 UK ISSN 0010-5236
CONCILIUM. 1965. bi-m. £24.95($45) T. & T. Clark Ltd., 59 George St., Edinburgh EH2 2LQ, Scotland. Ed. Fr. Marcus Lefebure. adv. circ. 3,000. Indexed: CERDIC. Canon Law Abstr.

200 NE ISSN 0167-1200
CONCILIUM. 6/yr. fl.89. Gooi en Sticht B.V., Postbus 17, 1200 AA Hilversum, Netherlands. circ. 2,250.

200 US ISSN 0145-7233
CONCORDIA JOURNAL. 1975. q. $10. Concordia Seminary, 801 DeMun Ave., St. Louis, MO 63105. TEL 314-721-5934 Ed. Quentin Wesselschmidt. bk. rev. circ. 9,000. Indexed: Old Test.Abstr. CERDIC. Chr.Per.Ind. Int.Z.Biblewiss. New Test.Abstr. Rel.Ind.One. Rel.& Theol.Abstr.

207.11 US
CONCORDIA THEOLOGICAL QUARTERLY. N.S. 1959. q. $5. Concordia Theological Seminary, 6600 N. Clinton St., Fort Wayne, IN 46825. TEL 219-482-9611 Ed. Dr. David P. Scaer. adv. bk. rev. cum.index: 1959-1964. circ. 9,000. (also avail. in microfilm from UMI; reprint service avail. from UMI) Indexed: Old Test.Abstr. Rel.Per. CERDIC. New Test.Abstr. Rel.Ind.One. Rel.& Theol.Abstr.
Formerly (until vol.40, no.2, 1976): Springfielder (ISSN 0038-8610)

200 UY
CONFEDERACION LATINOAMERICANA DE ASOCIACIONES CRISTIANAS DE JOVENES. CONFEDERACION. 1982. q. free. Confederacion Latinoamericana de Asociaciones Cristianas de Jovenes - Latin American Confederation of YMCAs, Colonia 1884, p.1, Montevideo, Uruguay. Ed. Edgardo G. Crovetto.

200 UY
CONFEDERACION LATINOAMERICANA DE ASOCIACIONES CRISTIANAS DE JOVENES. CONTACTO. 1982. m. free. Confederacion Latinoamericana de Asociaciones Cristianas de Jovenes - Latin American Confederation of YMCAs, Colonia 1884, p.1, Montevideo, Uruguay. Ed. Edgardo G. Crovetto.

369.4 UY
CONFEDERACION LATINOAMERICANA DE ASOCIACIONES CRISTIANAS DE JOVENES. CARTA. (Editions in English and Spanish) irreg. free. Confederacion Latinoamericana de Asociaciones Cristianas de Jovenes, Casilla 172, Montevideo, Uruguay.
Formerly: Federacion Sudamericana de Asociaciones Cristianas de Jovenes. Noticias (ISSN 0428-1039)

200 SW ISSN 0069-8946
CONIECTANEA BIBLICA. NEW TESTAMENT SERIES. (Text in English and French) 1966. irreg., no.14, 1985. price varies. Liber Forlag, S-205 10, Malmo, Sweden. Eds. Birger Gerhardson, Lars Hartman.
Continues: Acta Seminarii Neotestamentici Upsaliensis & Coniectanea Neotestamentica.

200 SW ISSN 0069-8954
CONIECTANEA BIBLICA. OLD TESTAMENT SERIES. 1967. irreg., no.23, 1984. price varies. Liber Forlag, S-205 10, Malmo, Sweden. Eds. Tryggve Mettinger, Helmer Ringgren.

200 IT ISSN 0035-600X
CONSACRAZIONE E SERVIZIO; rivista delle religiose. 1952. m. L.5000. Unione Superiore Maggiori d'Italia, Via Zanardelli 32, Rome 00186, Italy. Dir. A. Ravazzi. bk. rev. index. circ. 12,000.
Formerly: Rivista delle Religiose.

CONSCIENCE ET LIBERTE. see *POLITICAL SCIENCE — Civil Rights*

200 US
CONSULTATION ON CHURCH UNION. DIGEST. 1962. irreg., approx. every 18 mos., latest issue 1984. price varies. Consultation on Church Union, Research Park, 151 Wall St., Princeton, NJ 08540-1514. Ed. Gerald F. Moede.
Former titles: Consultation on Church Union. Official Record (ISSN 0272-8958); Consultation on Church. Digest (ISSN 0589-4867)

200 610 SZ
CONTACT. (Text in English, French, Portuguese and Spanish) bi-m. 15 F. World Council of Churches, Christian Medical Commission, 150 Route de Ferney, 1211 Geneva 20, Switzerland. Ed. Eric Ram. circ. 26,000.

200 UK
CONTACT (ALDERSHOT) 1920. q. £3. Officers' Christian Union, Havelock House, Barrack Rd., Aldershot GU11 3NP, England. Ed. Sqn. Ldr. Mike Warwood. bk. rev. circ. 4,500. Indexed: CERDIC.
Formerly: Practical Christianity (ISSN 0032-6364)

200 FR ISSN 0045-8325
CONTACTS; revue francaise de l'Orthodoxie. 1949. q. 200 F.($34) Centre Ecumenique Enotikon, c/o John J. Balzon & Germaine Revault d'Allones, 43 rue du Fer-a-Moulin, 75005 Paris, France. Ed. John J. Balzon. bk. rev. bibl. index. circ. 3,000. Indexed: CERDIC.

CONTEMPORARY CHRISTIAN; music and more. see *MUSIC*

200 US ISSN 0361-8854
CONTEXT; a commentary on the interaction of religion and culture. 1972. fortn. $24.95. Claretian Publications, 205 W. Monroe St., Chicago, IL 60606. TEL 312-236-7782 Ed. Rev. Mark J. Brummel. circ. 5,726. (reprint service avail. from UMI) Indexed: Numis.Lit.

268 US
CONTINUING EDUCATOR. 1969. 4/yr. membership. Society for Advancement of Continuing Education for Ministry, 855 Locust St., Collegeville, PA 19426. TEL 215-489-6358 Ed. Patricia Cremins. bk. rev. circ. 450.
Former titles: Continuing Education; S A C E M Newsletter.

200 US ISSN 0196-7053
CONTRIBUTIONS TO THE STUDY OF RELIGION. 1981. irreg. price varies. Greenwood Press, 88 Post Rd. W., Box 5007, Westport, CT 06881. TEL 203-226-3571 Ed. Henry W. Bowden.

200 US
CONVENTION HERALD. 1955. m. $5. ‡ (Inter-Church Holiness Convention) Old Paths Tract Society, 3589 New Garden Rd., Salem, OH 44460. Ed. H. E. Schmul. adv. bk. rev. circ. 10,000.

200 NE
COPTIC STUDIES. 1978. irreg. price varies. E.J. Brill, P.O. Box 9000, 2300 PA Leiden, Netherlands. Ed. M. Krause.

200 US ISSN 0275-2743
CORNERSTONE (CHICAGO) 1972. bi-m. $6.95. Jesus People U S A, 4707 N. Malden, Chicago, IL 60640. TEL 312-989-2080 Ed. Dawn Herrin. adv. bk. rev. circ. 90,000.

COUNSELOR. see *CHILDREN AND YOUTH — For*

226 PK ISSN 0254-7856
COUNSELOR/AL-MUSHIR. (Text in English or Urdu) 1959. q. Rs.50($12) Christian Study Centre, 126-B Murree Rd., Rawalpindi, Pakistan. Ed. Yusuf Jalil. bk. rev. circ. 650.

200 UK ISSN 0011-0124
COUNTRY CHURCHMAN. 1953. m. 24p. Country Churchman Ltd., Abbey Press, Abingdon, Berkshire, England. Ed. John Hooke. adv. illus. circ. 25,000.

COURTENAY LIBRARY OF REFORMATION CLASSICS. see *HISTORY — History Of Europe*

COURTENAY REFORMATION FACSIMILES. see *HISTORY — History Of Europe*

COURTENAY STUDIES IN REFORMATION THEOLOGY. see *HISTORY — History Of Europe*

200 US ISSN 0738-6001
CREATION/EVOLUTION. irreg. $9 for 4 issues. American Humanist Association, 7 Harwood Dr., Box 146, Amherst, NY 14226-0146. TEL 716-839-5080 Ed. Frederick Edwords. bk. rev. bibl. circ. 1,500. (back issues avail.)

280 IT
CRISTIANESIMO NELLA STORIA; ricerche storiche esegetiche teologiche. (Text in English, French, German, Italian and Spanish; summaries in English) 1980. 3/yr. L.30000($25) (Istituto per le Scienze Religiose) Centro Editoriale Dehoniano, Via Nosadella 6, 40123 Bologna, Italy. Ed. Prof. Giuseppe Alberigo. bk. rev. bibl. index. circ. 1,000. (back issues avail.) Indexed: Old Test.Abstr. CERDIC. Canon Law Abstr. New Test.Abstr. Rel.& Theol.Abstr.

CRUSADER. see *CHILDREN AND YOUTH — For*

200 CN ISSN 0011-2186
CRUX; a quarterly journal of Christian thought and opinion. 1966. q. Can.$10. Regent College, 2130 Wesbrook Mall, Vancouver, B.C. V6T 1W6, Canada. TEL 604-224-3245 Ed. Dr. James Houston. bk. rev. bibl. charts. illus. stat. index. cum.index. circ. 825. (microform) Indexed: Old Test.Abstr. New Test.Abstr. Rel.Ind.One. Rel.& Theol.Abstr.

282 US ISSN 0591-2296
CRUX OF THE NEWS. 1966. w. $39.50. Gabriel Publishing Co., Inc., 75 Champlain St., Albany, NY 12204. TEL 518-465-4591 Ed. Richard A. Dowd. adv. bk. rev. circ. 5,800.

282 SP ISSN 0574-5101
CRUZADA ESPANOL. vol.18, 1975. s-m. 500 ptas.($9) c/o Jose Oriol Cuffi Canadell, Ed., Via Layetana 103, 3, 1, Barcelona 9, Spain. bk. rev. (tabloid format)

CRUZADA EUCARISTICA. see *CHILDREN AND YOUTH — For*

200 CR
CUADERNOS D E I. 1980. irreg., no. 5, 1981. Departamento Ecumenico de Investigaciones, Apdo. 339, S. Pedro Montes de Oca, San Jose, Costa Rica.

230 SP ISSN 0011-2453
CUADERNOS DE ORIENTACION FAMILIAR. vol.97, 1985. q. 1000 ptas. Instituto Catolico de Estudios Sociales de Barcelona, Enrique Granados, 2, 08007 Barcelona, Apartado de Correos 5217, Spain. Ed. Maria Martinell. bk. rev. abstr. circ. 2,700.
Formerly (1961-1969): Delta (Barcelona) (ISSN 0210-3869)
Spanish theological studies

200 UK ISSN 0260-2202
CUBIT; Christian magazine for students. 1980. 3/yr. £3.40. Universities and Colleges Christian Fellowship, 38 De Montfort St., Leicester LE1 7GP, England. Ed. R.C. Nixson. bk. rev. illus. circ. 6,000.
Formerly: C.U. News.

200 BL
CULTURA E FE. 1978. q. Institutio de Desenvolvimento Cultural, Av. Alberto Bins 467, Caixa Postal 702, 90000 Porto Alegre, Brazil.

200 SZ
CURRENT DIALOGUE. (Text in English) q. World Council of Churches, Sub-unit on Dialogue with People of Living Faiths, 150 Route de Ferney, Box 66, 1211 Geneva 20, Switzerland. Indexed: Abstr.Musl.Rel.
Formerly: Church and the Jewish People.

200 US ISSN 0098-2113
CURRENTS IN THEOLOGY AND MISSION. 1974. bi-m. $13.50. Christ Seminary-Seminex, 1100 E. 55th St., Chicago, IL 60615. TEL 312-288-0800 Ed. Ralph W. Klein. adv. bk. rev. circ. 3,700. (also avail. in microform from UMI; reprint service avail. from UMI) Indexed: Old Test.Abstr. Rel.Per. CERDIC. Int.Z.Bibelwiss. New Test.Abstr. Rel.Ind.One. Rel.& Theol.Abstr.

200 AU ISSN 0011-4057
CURSILLO; fuer eine Kirche in Bewegung. 1964. m. S.125. Arbeitsgemeinschaft der Dioezesansekretariate der Cursillo-Bewegung, Bennogasse 21, A-1080 Vienna, Austria. Ed. Josef G. Cascales. bk. rev. bibl.
Formerly: Karat.

270 GW ISSN 0070-2234
CUSANUS-GESELLSCHAFT. BUCHREIHE. 1964. irreg. price varies. Aschendorffsche Verlagsbuchhandlung, Soester Str. 13, 4400 Muenster, W. Germany (B.R.D.) Eds. Rudolf Haubst, Erich Meuthen, Josef Stallmach.

200 IT
DALLO SCOGLIO DI SANTA RITA. 1940. w. free to qualified personnel. Santuario di Santa Rita di Roccaporena di Cascia, c/o Luigi di Giannicola, Ed., Via Stazione di S. Pietro 6, 00165 Rome, Italy. bk. rev.

200 DK
DANSK KIRKEHILSEN. 1927. bi-m. Kr.55. Dansk Kirke i Udlandet, Noerrevaenget 43B, 5100 Odense C, Denmark. Ed. Egon Christiansen. adv. circ. 6,500.

266 DK ISSN 0011-6378
DANSK MISSIONSBLAD. 1834. m. Kr.112. Danske Missionsselskab - Danish Missionary Society, Strandagervej 24, DK-2900 Hellerup, Denmark. Ed. Jakob Roennow. adv. bk. rev. abstr. illus. index. circ. 11,000. Indexed: CERDIC.
Missions

DAUGHTERS OF SARAH. see *WOMEN'S INTERESTS*

266 UK ISSN 0070-2994
DAWN IN CENTRAL ASIA. 1903. 3/yr. 50p. Central Asian Mission, 166 Tonbridge Rd., Maidstone, Kent ME16 85R, England. Ed. P.F. Cook. adv. circ. 2,800.
Missions

266 GW ISSN 0011-7692
DEIN REICH KOMME. English edition: Light in the East News. 1920. bi-m. free. Licht im Osten, Missionsbund, Zuffenhauser Str. 37, Postfach 1340, D-7015 Korntal-Muenchingen 1, W. Germany (B.R.D.) Ed. E. Damson. bk. rev. bibl. illus. circ. 27,000.

200 FR
DEMAIN D'AVANTAGE QU'HIER. 15/yr. 200 F. Nouvelles Editions Latines, 1 rue Palatine, 75006 Paris, France. bk. rev. bibl.

200 US ISSN 0193-6883
DENOMINATIONS IN AMERICA. 1985. irreg. price varies. Greenwood Press, 88 Post Rd. W., Box 5007, Westport, CT 06881. TEL 203-226-3571 Ed. Harry Bowden.

240 GW ISSN 0012-1967
DIAKONIA; internationale Zeitschrift fuer praktische Theologie. 1966. bi-m. DM.78. Matthias Gruenewald Verlag GmbH, Max-Hufschmidt-Str. 4a, 6500 Mainz-Weisenau, W. Germany (B.R.D.) Ed. Helmut Erharter. adv. bk. rev. bibl. stat. index. circ. 4,000. Indexed: Cath.Ind.

200 AU
DIAKONIE; Zeitschrift fuer Freunde und Mitarbeider des Evangelischen Diakoniewerkes Gallneukirchen. 1875. q. S.90. ‡ Evangelisches Diakoniewerk Gallneukirchen, Martin Boos-Strasse 4, A-4210 Gallneukirchen, Austria. Ed. Gerhard Gaebler. bk. rev. circ. 4,000.
Formerly: Gallneukirchner Bote (ISSN 0016-4143)

200 GW ISSN 0341-826X
DIAKONIE. 1975. bi-m. DM.40. (Diakonisches Werk der Evang. Kirche in Deutschland und des Internationalen Verbandes fuer Innere Mission und Diakonie) Verlagswerk der Diakonie, Kniebisstr. 29, Postfach 476, 7000 Stuttgart 1, W. Germany (B.R.D) circ. 2,500. Indexed: CERDIC.

230 US ISSN 0012-2033
DIALOG; a journal of theology. 1962. q. $16. Dialog, Inc., 2481 Como Ave., St. Paul, MN 55108. Ed. Carl E. Braaten. adv. bk. rev. circ. 2,000. (also avail. in microform from UMI; reprint service avail. from UMI) Indexed: Old Test.Abstr. Rel.Per. CERDIC. New Test.Abstr. Rel.Ind.One. Rel.& Theol.Abstr.

200 SP ISSN 0210-2870
DIALOGO ECUMENICO. 1966. 3/yr. $20. Universidad Pontificia Salamanca, Centro Estudios Orientales y Ecumenicos, Compania , 5, 37008 Salamanca, Spain. Ed. Adolfo Gonzalez-Montes. adv. bk. rev. circ. 400. Indexed: CERDIC.

378 268 US ISSN 0012-2289
DIALOGUE ON CAMPUS. 1950. 4/yr. $10. Association for the Coordination of University Religious Affairs, Executive Committee, c/o George W. Jones, Ed., Office of Religious Programs, Ball State University, Muncie, IN 47306. TEL 317-285-1092 bk. rev. bibl. circ. 300. (looseleaf format; back issues avail.) Indexed: ERIC. High.Educ.Abstr.

200 PO
DICIONARIO DE HISTORIA DA IGREJA EM PORTUGAL. 1979. m. Esc.900 for 6 mos. Editorial Resistencia S.A.R.L., Rua Nova de Sao Mamede 27, 2 Esq., 1200 Lisbon, Portugal. Ed. Antonio Alberto Banha da Andrade.

221 GW
DIELHEIMER BLAETTER ZUM ALTEN TESTAMENT UND SEINER REZEPTION IN DER ALTEN KIRCHE. 1972. s-a. DM.7. Wissenschaftlich-Theologisches Seminar der Universitaet Heidelberg, Kisselgasse 1, D-6900 Heidelberg, W. Germany (B.R.D.) Eds. Bernd Jorg Diebner, Claudia Nauerth. bk. rev. circ. 250.
Formerly: Dielheimer Blaetter zum Alten Testament.

200 GW ISSN 0012-2572
DIENENDER GLAUBE; Zeitschrift fuer Ordensfrauen. 1924. m. DM.49.50. Verlag Butzon und Bercker, Hoogeweg 71, Postfach 215, 4178 Kevelaer, W. Germany (B.R.D.) Ed. Dr. Justin Lang. adv. bk. rev. circ. 4,900.
Formerly: An Heiligen Quellen.

250 GW ISSN 0720-9916
DIENST AM WORT - GEDANKEN ZUR SONNTAGSPREDIGT. 1950. 8/yr. DM.77. Religioese Bildungsarbeit Stuttgart GmbH-Verlag, Boeheimstr. 44, 7000 Stuttgart 1, W. Germany (B.R.D.) Eds. A. Bauer, H. Feifel. adv. bk. rev. index. circ. 7,000.

200 IT ISSN 0046-0303
DIO E POPOLO; periodico mazziniano aderente al partito naziona "la Giovine Italia". vol. 25, 1971. w. Piazzale Prenestino 53, Rome, Italy. bk. rev.

200 US
DIRECTORY OF CHURCHES AND SYNAGOGUES. 1934. a. $10. Council of Churches of the City of New York, 475 Riverside Dr., New York, NY 10115. TEL 212-749-1214 Ed. Rev. Leland Gartrell. adv. circ. 2,500.

200 US
DIRECTORY OF DEPARTMENTS AND PROGRAMS OF RELIGIOUS STUDIES IN NORTH AMERICA. 1978. a. price varies. Council on the Study of Religion, Mercer University, Macon, GA 31207. TEL 912-741-2376 Ed. Watson E. Mills.

200 GW
DIREKTORIUM FUER DAS BISTUM MUENSTER. a. DM.8.50. Verlag Regensberg, Daimlerweg 58, Postfach 6748, 4400 Muenster, W. Germany (B.R.D.)

262.9 IT
DIRITTO ECCLESIASTICO E RASSEGNA DI DIRITTO MATRIMONIALE. (Text in Italian and Latin) 1889. q. L.100000. Casa Editrice Dott. A. Giuffre, Via B. Arsizio 40, 20151 Milan, Italy. Ed. S. Biancolli. bk. rev. bibl. index. circ. 700. Indexed: CERDIC.
Formerly: Diritto Ecclesiastico (ISSN 0012-3455)
Religious law

200 US ISSN 0092-8372
DISCIPLE (ST. LOUIS) 1974. m. $10. Christian Board of Publication, 1316 Convention Plaza, Box 179, St. Louis, MO 63166. TEL 314-231-8500 Ed. James L. Merrell. adv. bk. rev. charts. illus. index. circ. 58,200. (reprint service avail. from UMI) Indexed: CERDIC.
Supersedes: World Call (ISSN 0043-8308); Formerly (1862-1974): Christian (ISSN 0009-5206)

200 US
DISCOVERY (NEW YORK) 1935. m. free. John Milton Society for the Blind, Rm. 249, 475 Riverside Dr., New York, NY 10115. TEL 212-870-3335 Ed. Pam Toplisky. circ. 10,000. (Braille) Indexed: Biol.Dig. PMR. South.Bap.Per.Ind.
For children ages 8-18

230 100 IT ISSN 0012-4257
DIVUS THOMAS; commentarium de philosophia et theologia. (Text in English, French, Italian, Latin, German and Spanish) 1880. q. L.25000($14) Collegio Alberoni, 29100 Piacenza, Italy. Ed. Perini Giuseppe, C.M. bk. rev. index. circ. 600. Indexed: M.L.A. Old Test.Abstr. CERDIC. New Test.Abstr.

200 SP
DOCUMENTS D'ESGLESIA. (Text in Catalan) fortn. 2800 ptas.($33) Publicaciones de l' Abadia de Montserrat, Ausias March 92-98, Ap. 244, Barcelona 13, Spain.

200 CN ISSN 0318-0123
DONUM DEI. French edition (ISSN 0318-0131) (Editions in English and French) 1958. a. price varies. ‡ Canadian Religious Conference, 324 Laurier E, Ottawa, Ont. K1N 6P6, Canada. TEL 613-236-0824 Ed. Albert Landry. circ. 8,000(both edts.)

266 US
DOOR OF HOPE. 1972. m. $3 min. donation. (Door of Hope International) Door of Hope Press, Box 10460, Glendale, CA 91209. Ed. Paul Popov. adv. bk. rev. film rev. play rev. bibl. tr.lit. circ. 35,000.

220 IS ISSN 0334-2166
DOR LE-DOR. (Text in English) 1972. q. $12. World Jewish Bible Society, Box 7024, Jerusalem, Israel. Ed. Louis Katzoff. bk. rev. circ. 1,800. Indexed: Old Test.Abstr. Rel.& Theol.Abstr.
Formerly: Bible Readers' Union Bulletin (ISSN 0006-0771)

220 FR ISSN 0761-7267
DOSSIERS DE LA BIBLE. 1984. 5/yr. 99 F. Editions du Cerf, 29 bd. Latour-Maubourg, 75007 Paris, France. bk. rev. rec.rev. charts. illus. cum.index. circ. 15,000. (tabloid format)
Formerly (until 1984): Bible et Son Message (ISSN 0006-0704)

DOUAI MAGAZINE. see *COLLEGE AND ALUMNI*

200 AU ISSN 0012-6764
DRUZINA IN DOM. (Text in Slovene) m. S.2($8) Druzba Sv. Mohorja, Viktringer Ring 26, A-9020 Klagenfurt, Austria.

200 947 BU ISSN 0323-9578
DUKHOVNA AKADEMIYA SV. KLIMENT OKHRIDSKI. GODISHNIK. 1923. a. Sinodalno Izdatelstvo, Ul. Sveta Sofia 2, Sofia, Bulgaria (Subscr. to: Hemus Foreign Trade Co., 6 Ruski Blvd., 1000 Sofia, Bulgaria)
Formerly: Sofia. Universitet. Bogoslovski Fakultet. Godishnik.

200 AT
E.C.M. NEWS. 1965. bi-m. free. European Christian Mission (Australian Section) Inc., P.O. Box 15, Croydon, N.S.W. 2132, Australia. Ed. Rev. Jim Bosma. bk. rev. circ. 2,100.
Formerly: Prayer Union.

200 US
E P F NEWSLETTER. 1939. q. $20. Episcopal Peace Fellowship, 620 G St., S.E., Washington, DC 20003. TEL 202-543-7168 Ed. Dana Grubb. bk. rev. circ. 2,500.

248.83 GW ISSN 0012-7981
E S G - NACHRICHTEN. 1953. irreg., 7-8/yr. DM.25. (Evangelische Studentengemeinde in der Bundesrepublik Deutschland und Berlin (West)) Alektor-Verlag, Kniebisstr. 29, 7000 Stuttgart 1, W. Germany (B.R.D.) Ed. Ekkehard Pohlmann. adv. bk. rev. circ. 800. (processed)

291 II ISSN 0012-8384
EAST AND WEST SERIES; an interpreter of the life of the spirit. (Text in English) 1954. m. Rs.3.($2) Gita Publishing House, 10 Sadhu Vaswani Rd., Mira Nagar, Poona 1, India. Ed. J.P. Vaswani. bk. rev. bibl. (back issues avail.)

284 FR ISSN 0397-0736
ECHANGES; journal de l'eglise reformee...Provence, Cote d'Azur, Corse. 1955. m. 80 F. Association l'Eglise Reformee Vous Parle, 15 rue Grignan, 13006 Marseille, France. Ed. Maurice Pont. adv. bk. rev. film rev. illus. circ. 7,000. Indexed: Geo.Abstr. Pt.de Rep.
Formerly: Eglise Reformee Vous Parle.

266 276 NE
ECHO UIT AFRIKA EN ANDERE WERELDDELEN. 1933. bi-m. fl.15. Missionary Sisters of St. Peter Claver, Bouillonstraat 4, 6211 LH Maastricht, Netherlands. Ed.Bd. charts. illus. circ. 15,000.
Formerly: Echo uit Afrika (ISSN 0012-9305)
Missions

ECO DELL'EDUCAZIONE EBRAICA. see *EDUCATION*

200 IT
L'ECO DELLE VALLI VALDESI. 1848. w. L.31000. A.I.P., Via Pio V 15, 10125 Turin, Italy. circ. 5,000.

200 FR ISSN 0070-8860
ECRITS LIBRES. 1955. irreg., no. 16, 1973. 63 F. Librairie Fischbacher, 33 rue de Seine, 75006 Paris, France.

200 US ISSN 0013-0761
ECUMENICAL COURIER. 1941. q. $10 contributions. ‡ (Friends of the World Council of Churches, Inc.) United States Conference for the World Council of Churches, 475 Riverside Dr., New York, NY 10027. TEL 212-749-1214 Ed. Bruno Kroker. bk. rev. circ. 10,000. (also avail. in microform)

200 IO
ECUMENICAL NEWS. 1973. m. Council of Churches in Indonesia, Jalan Selemba Raya 10, Jakarta, Indonesia. (processed)

200 SZ
ECUMENICAL PRESS SERVICE. Short title: E P S. (Text in English and French) 1934. w. (approx. 45/yr.) 69.50 Fr.($37.50) World Council of Churches, 150 Route de Ferney, 1211 Geneva 20, Switzerland. Ed. Thomas Dorris. circ. 2,500. (back issues avail.) Indexed: CERDIC.

200 SZ ISSN 0013-0796
ECUMENICAL REVIEW. 1948. q. 37.50 Fr.($19.95) World Council of Churches, 150 Route de Ferney, 1211 Geneva 20, Switzerland. Ed. Emilio E. Castro. adv. bk. rev. index. circ. 4,000. (also avail. in microfilm from UMI; reprint service avail. from UMI) Indexed: Curr.Cont. Hum.Ind. Rel.Per. Arts & Hum.Cit.Ind. Bk.Rev.Ind. CERDIC. New Test.Abstr. Old Test.Abstr. Rel.Ind.One.

200 CN
ECUMENISM. (Editions in English and French) 1966. q. Can.$8. Canadian Centre for Ecumenism, 2065 Sherbrooke St. W., Montreal, Que. H3H 1G6, Canada. bk. rev. circ. 1,000. Indexed: Rel.Ind.One.

270 US ISSN 0013-080X
ECUMENTIST; a journal for promoting Christian unity. 1962. bi-m. free. Paulist Press, 997 Macarthur Blvd., Mahwah, NJ 07430. TEL 201-825-7300 Eds. Gregory Baum, Rev. Kevin A. Lynch. bk. rev. circ. 8,000. (also avail. in microform from BLH,UMI; reprint service avail. from UMI) Indexed: Cath.Ind. Old Test.Abstr. CERDIC. New Test.Abstr.

268 FR ISSN 0223-5854
EGLISE AUJOURD'HUI; en monde rural. 1944. m. 120 F. Chretiens dans le Monde Rural, 21 rue du Faubourg-Saint-Antoine, 75550 Paris Cedex 11, France. Ed. Bernard Cointre. adv. bk. rev. Indexed: CERDIC.

200 CN ISSN 0013-2322
L'EGLISE CANADIENNE; documents et informations. (Text in French) 1968. 21/yr. Can.$25. Revue L'Eglise Canadienne Inc., 1073 Blvd. St. Cyrille, W., Quebec, P.Q. G1S 4R5, Canada. TEL 418-681-8109 Ed. Jacques Barnard. adv. bk. rev. index. circ. 7,200. Indexed: CERDIC. Pt.de Rep.

260 CN ISSN 0013-2349
EGLISE ET THEOLOGIE. (Text in English and French) 1970. 3/yr. Can.$30. Saint Paul University, Faculty of Theology, 223 Main St., Ottawa K1S 1C4, Ont., Canada. TEL 613-236-1393 Ed. Leo Laberge. bk. rev. index. (also avail. in microform from UMI; reprint service avail. from UMI) Indexed: Bull.Signal. Old Test.Abstr. Rel.Per. Canon Law Abstr. CERDIC. Int.Z.Bibelwiss. New Test.Abstr. Rel.Ind.One. Rel.& Theol.Abstr.

200 US
ELISABETH ELLIOT NEWSLETTER. 1982. 6/yr. Servant Publications, Box 7711, Ann Arbor, MI 48107. TEL 313-761-8505

200 NE ISSN 0013-6212
ELISABETHBODE. 1929. w. fl.22.50($22.50) Stichting Elisabethbode, Postbus 100, 7240 AC Lochem, Netherlands. circ. 220,000.

266 UK ISSN 0305-005X
EMERGENCY POST. 1939. m. £3.36($5.04) Paternoster Press Ltd., Paternoster House, 3 Mount Radford Crescent, Exeter EX1 4JW, England. Ed. John Allan. circ. 60,000.

266 IT ISSN 0013-6697
EMIGRATO ITALIANO. 1903. m. L.1000($4.) Congregazione dei Missionari di S. Carlo, Via Scalabrini 3, 36061 Bassano del Grappa (Vicenza), Italy. Ed. P.G.B. Saraggi. adv. charts. stat. index. circ. 5,000.

200 US ISSN 0194-5246
EMPHASIS ON FAITH AND LIVING. 1969. m. donations. (Missionary Church, Inc.) Bethel Publishing Co., 3901 S. Wayne Ave., Ft. Wayne, IN 46807. TEL 219-456-4502 Ed. Michael B. Reynolds. adv. bk. rev. circ. 22,800. Indexed: G.Soc.Sci.& Rel.Per.Lit.

200 FR ISSN 0013-6921
EN AVANT. 1882. w. 175 F. ‡ Armee du Salut, 76 rue de Rome, 75008 Paris, France. Ed. J.P. Thoeni. bk. rev. circ. 10,000.

200 US ISSN 0013-7081
ENCOUNTER (INDIANAPOLIS) 1956. q. $12. Christian Theological Seminary, 1000 W. 42nd St., Indianapolis, IN 46208. TEL 317-924-1331 Ed. Clark M. Williamson. adv. bk. rev. index. circ. 650. (also avail. in microfilm from UMI; reprint service avail. from UMI) Indexed: Hum.Ind. Int.Z.Bibelwiss. New Test.Abstr. Old Test.Abstr. Rel.& Theol.Abstr. Hist.Abstr. Arts & Hum.Cit.Ind. Amer.Hist.& Life. G.Soc.Sci.& Rel.Per.Lit. Rel.Ind.One.

200 SP
ENSENANZA DE LA RELIGION. 1982. irreg., no.2, 1986. price varies. (Universidad de Navarra, Facultad de Teologia) Ediciones Universidad de Navarra, S.A., Apdo. 396, 31080 Pamplona, Spain.

200 AU ISSN 0017-4602
ENTSCHLUSS; Zeitschrift fuer plants Praxis und Theologie. 1946. m. S.300. Styria Verlag, Schoenaugasse 64, A-8011 Graz, Austria. Ed. Werner Reiss. adv. bk. rev. record rev. bibl. charts. index. circ. 8,000. Indexed: CERDIC.
Formerly: Grosse Entschluss.

200 150 US ISSN 0013-9408
ENVOY (PITTSBURG) 1963. 6/yr. $6. Duquesne University, Institute of Formative Spirituality, 600 Forbes Ave., Pittsburgh, PA 15282. TEL 412-434-6028 Ed. Adrian van Kaam. circ. 8,000. (also avail. in microform from UMI; reprint service avail. from UMI) Indexed: Cath.Ind.

262 IT ISSN 0013-9505
EPHEMERIDES LITURGICAE; commentarium bimestre de re liturgica. (Text in various languages) 1887. 5/yr. L.40000($30) Centro Liturgico Vincenziano, Via Pompeo Magno. 21, 00192 Rome, Italy. (Co-sponsor: Vincentian Fathers) adv. bk. rev. circ. 1,500. Indexed: CERDIC. Canon Law Abstr. New Test.Abstr.

200 US
EPIPHANY JOURNAL; a journal of faith and insight. 1980. q. $18.50. Epiphany Press, Box 14727, San Francisco, CA 94114. Ed. Stephen Muratore. bk. rev. circ. 1,000. (back issues avail.) Indexed: Rel.Ind.One.
Formerly: Epiphany.

200 DK ISSN 0105-6867
EPISKOPET; religionspaedagogisk samvirke. q. Bibliotekscentralen, Telegrafvej 5, DK-2750 Ballerup, Denmark.

200 901 US
EPOCHE; journal of the history of religions at U.C.L.A. 1972. a. $6. University of California, Los Angeles, Graduate Student Association, 301 Kerchoff Hall, 308 Westwood Plaza, Los Angeles, CA 90024 (Subscr. to: Dept. of History, Los Angeles, CA 90024) Ed. Rick Talbott. cum.index: 1972-82. circ. 850. (back issues avail.)

200 AU ISSN 0013-9912
ER RUFT. 1962. q. free. Vereinigung der Ehemaligen Don Boscos, Hagenmuellergasse 31, A-1030 Vienna 3, Austria. Ed. Friedrich Jerney. circ. 1,200.

200 GW ISSN 0014-0201
ERMLANDBRIEFE. 1946. q. DM.10. Apostolischer Visitator fuer Klerus und Glaeubige des Ermlandes, Ermlandweg 22, 4400 Muenster, W. Germany (B.R.D.) Ed. Johannes Schwalke. bk. rev. illus. circ. 33,000.

ESPIRITU. see *PHILOSOPHY*

200 FR ISSN 0014-0775
ESPRIT ET VIE. (In 2 Parts: Doctrine & Predication) 1879. w. 320 F. (for both parts) B.P. 4, 52200 Langres, France. bk. rev. bibl. index. Indexed: CERDIC. New Test.Abstr.
Formerly: Ami du Clerge.

240 FR ISSN 0396-969X
ESPRIT SAINT; revue de spiritualite. 1952. q. 35 F. Congregation du Saint-Esprit, Fraternites du Saint-Esprit, 30 rue Lhomond, 75005 Paris, France. Ed. Michel Picard. bk. rev. bibl. cum.index. circ. 6,000.
Formerly: Devotion au Saint-Esprit (ISSN 0012-1711)

220 SP ISSN 0014-1437
ESTUDIOS BIBLICOS. 1941. q. 1500 ptas.($5.05) Consejo Superior de Investigaciones Cientificas, Instituto de Teologia "Francisco Suarez", Duque de Medinaceli 4, Madrid 14, Spain. bk. rev. bibl. Indexed: Old Test.Abstr. New Test.Abstr. Rel.Ind.One.

200 SP ISSN 0210-1610
ESTUDIOS ECLESIASTICOS; revista de teologia. 1922. q. 5148 ptas.($39) (Compania de Jesus, Facultades de Teologia) Casa de Escritores, S.J., Pablo Aranda 3, E-28006 Madrid, Spain. Ed.Bd. bk. rev. bibl. Indexed: Hist.Abstr. Old Test.Abstr. Amer.Hist.& Life. CERDIC. Canon Law Abstr. New Test.Abstr.

200 SP ISSN 0210-0363
ESTUDIOS TRINITARIOS. 1967. 3/yr. 1900 ptas.($25) Ediciones Secretariado Trinitario, Filiberto Villalobos, 82, 37007 Salmanca, Spain. Ed. P. Nerea Silanes. bk. rev. Indexed: CERDIC.

200 IT
ETA DELL'ACQUARIO; the magazine of the new plane of consciousness. 1971. bi-m. L.25000($30) Via Lamarmore, 37, 10128 Turin, Italy. Ed. Edoardo Bresci. bk. rev. circ. 2,000. (back issues avail.)

200 FR
ETENDARD DE LA BIBLE ET HERAUT DU ROYAUME DE CHRIST. English edition: Bible Standard and Herald of Christ's Kingdom (ISSN 0006-081X) 1957. bi-m. 5 F. Mouvement Missionnaire Interieur Laique, c/o Gilbert Hermetz, 2 rue du Dr. Capiaux, 62620 Barlin, France. Ed. Bernard Hedman. circ. 500.
Missions

ETUDES GREGORIENNES; revue de musicologie religieuse. see *MUSIC*

200 950 NE ISSN 0531-1950
ETUDES PRELIMINAIRES AUX RELIGIONS ORIENTALES DANS L'EMPIRE ROMAIN. 1961. irreg., vol. 105, 1985. price varies. E. J. Brill, P.O. Box 9000, 2300 PA Leiden, Netherlands. Indexed: Rel.Ind.Two.

200 060 FR ISSN 0082-2612
ETUDES TEILHARDIENNES/TEILHARDIAN STUDIES. 1969. irreg. price varies. Editions du Seuil, 27 rue Jacob, 75261 Paris Cedex 06, France. Ed. J.P. DeMoulin. Indexed: Rel.Ind.One.

200 PL ISSN 0014-2298
EUHEMER; przeglad religioznawczy. (Text in Polish; table of contents and summaries in English and French) 1957. q. $25. (Polskie Towarzystwo Religioznawcze) Panstwowe Wydawnictwo Naukowe, Ul. Miodowa 10, 00-251 Warsaw, Poland (Dist. by: Ars Polona, Krakowskie Przedmiescie 7, 00-068 Warsaw, Poland) Ed. W. Tyloch. bk. rev. bibl. illus. index. circ. 860.

266 US
EURO VISION ADVANCE. 1927. bi-m. $1. (Eastern European Mission) Euro Vision, 232 N. Lake Ave., Rm. 206, Pasadena, CA 91101. TEL 818-796-5425 Ed. Rev. Charles Rogers. circ. 4,000. (also avail. in microfiche; back issues avail.)
Formerly (until 1985): Gospel Call.
Missions

266 US ISSN 0014-3359
EVANGELICAL MISSIONS QUARTERLY. 1964. q. $14.95. Evangelical Missions Information Service, Box 794, Wheaton, IL 60189. TEL 312-653-2158 Ed. James W. Reapsome. adv. bk. rev. index. circ. 8,000. Indexed: CERDIC. Chr.Per.Ind. Rel.& Theol.Abstr. Rel.Ind.One.
Missions

200 UK ISSN 0014-3367
EVANGELICAL QUARTERLY. 1929. q. £9($24.75) Paternoster Press Ltd., Paternoster House, 3 Mount Radford Crescent, Exeter EX1 4JW, England. Ed. I. Howard Marshall. bk. rev. index. circ. 1,500. (also avail. in microfilm from UMI; reprint service avail. from UMI) Indexed: CERDIC. Chr.Per.Ind. Old Test.Abstr. Rel.Per. New Test.Abstr. Rel.Ind.One. Rel.& Theol.Abstr.

200 US
EVANGELICAL REVIEW MAGAZINE; reviewing God's work through people today. 1979. q. $3. Hillwood Ministries, Inc., Rutland Rd., No. 6, Mt. Juliet, TN 37122. Ed. Robert C. Hill. adv. bk. rev. film rev. circ. 100,000. (back issues avail.)

200 UK ISSN 0144-8153
EVANGELICAL REVIEW OF THEOLOGY. 1977. q. £8.40($23.10) Paternoster Press Ltd., Paternoster House, 3 Mount Radford Cresc., Exeter EX1 4JW, England. Ed. Sunand Sumithra. bk. rev. circ. 1,800. (also avail. in microform from UMI; reprint service avail. from UMI) Indexed: CERDIC. Rel.Ind.One.

200 331.8 NE ISSN 0014-3383
EVANGELIE EN MAATSCHAPPIJ. 1947. bi-m. fl.12.50. Christelijk Nationaal Vakverbond in Nederland, Postbus 2475, Utrecht, Netherlands. Ed. J. van der Neyden. bk. rev. charts. stat. circ. 8,300. Indexed: Key to Econ.Sci.

266 SP
EVANGELIO Y MISIONCOMPANIA. 1964. m. donation. Compania de Jesus, Plaza de San Marcos 1, Leon 1, Spain. Ed. J. Pedraz. illus. circ. 5,000.
Formerly: Boletin Intimo de Compania.
Missions

DER EVANGELISCHE ERZIEHER; Zeitschrift fuer Paedagogik und Theologie. see *EDUCATION*

200 GW ISSN 0300-4236
EVANGELISCHE KOMMENTARE; Monatsschrift zum Zeitgeschehen in Kirche und Gesellschaft. 1968. m. DM.86. Kreuz-Verlag Zeitschriften GmbH, Breitwiesenstr. 30, Postfach 800669, 7000 Stuttgart 80, W. Germany (B.R.D.) Ed.Bd. adv. bk. rev. circ. 10,500.

240 GW ISSN 0014-3502
EVANGELISCHE THEOLOGIE. 1934. bi-m. DM.62.45 (DM.52.45 to students) Christian Kaiser Verlag, Postfach 509, 8000 Munich 43, W. Germany (B.R.D.) adv. circ. 3,500. (also avail. in microform from UMI; reprint service avail. from UMI) Indexed: Old Test.Abstr. Rel.Per. CERDIC. New Test.Abstr. Rel.& Theol.Abstr. Rel.Ind.One.

266 SW
EVANGELISKA OESTASIENMISSIONEN. 1919. m. (10/yr.) Kr.50. Evangeliska Oestasienmissionen, Duvkullavaegen 10, 172 37 Sundbyberg, Sweden. Ed. Arne Wisktroem. bk. rev. illus. circ. 5,500.
Formed by the merger of: Sinims Land & Ljusglimtar (ISSN 0024-5410)
Missions

243 UK
EVANGELISM TODAY. 1972. m. £4.50. 320 Ashley Down Rd., Bristol, England. Ed. Bill Spencer. adv. bk. rev. circ. 7,000.

EVANGELIZING TODAY'S CHILD. see *CHILDREN AND YOUTH — About*

200 IT
EVANGELIZZARE; mensile per animatori di catechesi. 1974. bi-m. L.18000. Edizioni Dehoniane Bologna, V. Nosadella 6, 40123 Bologna, Italy.

262.9 SP
EXCERPTA E DISSERTATIONIBUS IN IURE CANONICO. 1983. irreg., no.3, 1984. 3,000 ptas. (Universidad de Navarra, Facultad de Derecho Canonico) Ediciones Universidad de Navarra, S.A., Apdo. 396, 31080 Pamplona, Spain.
Canon Law

255 US ISSN 0362-0867
EXPLOR. 1975. a. free. Garrett-Evangelical Theological Seminary, c/o T. Thomas Nustad, 2121 Sheridan Rd., Evanston, IL 60201. Ed. S. Dean McBride. illus. circ. 6,500. Indexed: Old Test.Abstr. Rel.Ind.One.

200 UK ISSN 0014-5246
EXPOSITORY TIMES. 1889. m. £12.95($24) T. & T. Clark Ltd., 59 George St., Edinburgh EH2 2LQ, Scotland. Ed. Rev. Dr. C.S. Rodd. adv. bk. rev. index. circ. 8,250. Indexed: Br.Hum.Ind. Curr.Cont. Old Test.Abstr. Arts & Hum.Cit.Ind. New Test.Abstr. Rel.& Theol.Abstr. Rel.Ind.One.

200 IT ISSN 0014-5912
F.I.R.O. QUADERNI. 1954. q. L.5000. Unione Superiore Maggiori d'Italia, Via Zanardelli 32, 00186 Rome, Italy. Ed. F. Molinari. bk. rev. index. circ. 2,000.

F T I NEWSLETTER. (Feminist Theological Institute, Inc.) see *WOMEN'S INTERESTS*

200 US ISSN 0361-6061
FACE-TO-FACE (NEW YORK); an interreligious bulletin. vol.2, 1976. 3/yr. $12. Anti-Defamation League of B'nai B'rith, 823 United Nations Plaza, New York, NY 10017. TEL 212-490-2525 Ed.Bd. bk. rev. circ. 7,000. (reprint service avail. from UMI)

200 US
FACT BOOK ON THEOLOGICAL EDUCATION. 1971. a. $15. Association of Theological Schools, Box 130, Vandalia, OH 45377. TEL 513-898-4654 Ed. Marvin J. Taylor. circ. 700.

200 UK
FAITH. 1968. bi-m. £2.50. Faith-Keyway Publications, The Presbytery, 42 Arbrook Ln., Esher, Surrey KT10 9EE, England. Ed. Rev. Edward Holloway. adv. bk. rev. circ. 3,000.

200 UK ISSN 0014-701X
FAITH AND FREEDOM; a journal of progressive religion. 1947. 3/yr. £5($10) Manchester College, Oxford, England (Subscr. address: c/o Rev. Peter B. Godfrey, Ed., 62 Hastings Rd., Sheffield S7 2GU, England) adv. bk. rev. circ. 1,200.(controlled) (also avail. in microform from UMI) Indexed: CERDIC.

200 SZ ISSN 0512-2589
FAITH AND ORDER PAPERS. 1949; N.S. irreg., no.134, 1984. price varies. World Council of Churches, 150 Route de Ferney, CH-1211 Geneva 20, Switzerland (Dist. in the U.S. by: World Council of Churches Distribution Center, Rt 111 & Sharadin Road, P.O. Box 346, Kutztown, PA 19530-0346) cum.index: 1910-70. Indexed: Rel.Ind.Two.

FAITH AND PHILOSOPHY. see *PHILOSOPHY*

230.05 US ISSN 0098-5449
FAITH & REASON. 1975. q. $18. (Christendom College) Christendom College Press, Rt. 3, Box 87, Front Royal, VA 22630. Ed. Timothy T. O'Donnell. bk. rev. circ. 1,000. Indexed: Cath.Ind. CERDIC.

215 UK ISSN 0014-7028
FAITH AND THOUGHT; a journal devoted to the study of the inter-relation of the Christian revelation and modern research. 1866. 2/yr. £10($20) ‡ Victoria Institute, Philosophical Society of Great Britain, 29 Queen St., London EC4R 1BH, England (Subscr. to: Paternoster Press, Box 11127, Birmingham, AL 35202, U.S.A.) Ed. A.B. Robins. bk. rev. bibl. index. cum.index every 5 years. circ. 600. Indexed: CERDIC.

FAMIGLIA CRISTIANA. see *GENERAL INTEREST PERIODICALS — Italy*

249 BL ISSN 0014-7125
FAMILIA CRISTA; revista da paz e do amor - revista mensal para a familia. 1934. m. Cr.$160. Pia Sociedade Filhas de Sao Paulo, Rua Domingos de Morais 678, Sao Paulo 04010, Brazil. Ed. Joana Terezinha Puntel. adv. bk. rev. charts. illus. circ. 160,000.

200 FR ISSN 0014-7184
FAMILLE NOUVELLE. 1969. q. 36 F. Editions du Levain, 1 rue de l'Abbe Gregoire, 75006 Paris, France. bk. rev. circ. 100. (processed)
Formerly: Orphee Contact.

200 UK
FAMILY. 1979. m. £9.50. Elm House Christian Communications Ltd., 37 Elm Rd., New Malden, Surrey KT3 3HB, England. Ed. Mary Reid. adv. bk. rev. illus. circ. 18,175.
Former titles (until Aug. 1980): Life of Faith Monthly; (until Feb. 1979): Life of Faith (ISSN 0024-3175)

200 NO ISSN 0014-8733
FAST GRUNN. 1948. bi-m. Kr.180. Lunde Forlag og Bokhandel A-S, Grensen 19, 0159 Oslo 1, Norway. Eds. Steinar Hunnestad, Jon Kvalbein. bk. rev. illus. index. circ. 3,800.

260 FR ISSN 0015-0371
FETES ET SAISONS. 1945. 10/yr. 163 F. Editions du Cerf, 29 bd. Latour Maubourg, 75007 Paris, France. circ. 70,000. Indexed: Pt.de Rep.

FIDES ET HISTORIA. see *HISTORY*

200 IT
FILOSOFIA DELLA RELIGIONE. TESTI E STUDI. 1977. irreg., latest no. 3. price varies. Paideia Editrice, Via Corsica 130, 25125 Brescia, Italy.

207.11 IT ISSN 0015-2528
FIORI DI S. ANTONIO. 1951. s-m. free. ‡ Convento di Giaccherino, 51030 Pontelungo, Italy. Ed. P. Lorenzo Lazzeri. illus. circ. 17,000.

261 CM ISSN 0015-3435
FLAMBEAU; revue trimestrielle de theologie pour l'engagement de l'eglise dans le monde africain. q. (Centre de Litterature Evangelique) Editions C L E, B. P. 1501, Yaounde, Cameroon. Ed. Gerard Markhoff. bk. rev. circ. 1,000. Indexed: Rel.Ind.One.

200 US
FLOODTIDE; literature evangelism. 1948. bi-m. free. Christian Literature Crusade, Inc., Box 1449, Fort Washington, PA 19034. TEL 215-542-1242 Ed. Leona Hepburn. bk. rev. circ. 6,500.

FOC NOU; revista al servei dels cristians. see *ETHNIC INTERESTS*

200 FR
FOI AUJOURD'HUI. 1977. m. 270 F. Bayard Presse, 5 rue Bayard, 75380 Paris Cedex 08, France. circ. 40,000.

250 IT ISSN 0015-5802
FOLIUM DIOCESANUM BAUZANENSE-BRIXINENSE. (Text in German, Italian and Latin) 1964. m. L.5000. Curia Episcopalis Bauzanensis-Brixinensis, 39100 Bolzano, Italy. index. circ. 800. (tabloid format)

200 GW
FORSCHUNGEN ZUR KIRCHEN- UND DOGMENGESCHICHTE. 1954. irreg. Vandenhoeck & Ruprecht, Robert-Bosch-Breite 6, Postfach 3753, D-3400 Goettingen, W. Germany (B.R.D.)

200 GW
FORSCHUNGEN ZUR RELIGION UND LITERATUR DES ALTEN UND NEUEN TESTAMENTS. 1930. irreg. Vandenhoeck & Ruprecht, Robert-Bosch-Breite 6, Postfach 3753, D-3400 Goettingen, W. Germany (B.R.D.) Eds. Wolfgang Schrage, Rudolf Smend.

200 GW
FORUM. BERICHTE AUS DER ARBEIT. 1955. q. DM.20. Evangelische Akademie Iserlohn, Haus Ortlohn, Berliner Platz 12, 5860 Iserlohn, W. Germany (B.R.D.) Eds. G. Ebbrecht, R. Sareika. bk. rev. illus. circ. 850. (avail. on records)
Former Titles: Forum Haus Ortlohn. Freundsbrief (ISSN 0015-8534); Freundsbrief.

200 US
FORUM NEWSLETTER. q. membership. National Catholic Educational Association, Department of Religious Education, 1077 30th St., N.W., Washington, DC 20007. TEL 202-293-5954 (reprint service avail. from UMI)

200 GW ISSN 0343-7744
FORUM RELIGION. 1975. q. DM.24. Kreuz-Verlag Zeitschriften GmbH, Breitwiesenstr. 30, 7000 Stuttgart 80, W. Germany (B.R.D.) Ed.Bd. bk. rev. circ. 2,500.

220 US
FOUNDATION COMMENTATOR. 1974. m. Foundation for Biblical Research, Box 499, Pasadena, CA 91102. TEL 818-794-7439 Ed. Kenneth E. Fischer. adv. bk. rev. circ. 2,500. (looseleaf format; back issues avail.)

FOUR AND FIVE. see *CHILDREN AND YOUTH — For*

200 FR ISSN 0015-9239
FOYERS MIXTES; informations et reflexions pour un oecumenisme vecu. 1968. q. 96 F.($15) combined subscr. including Unite des Chretiens 132 F. Centre Saint Irenee, 2 place Gailleton, 69002 Lyon, France. Ed. Rene Beaupere. adv. bk. rev. index. circ. 1,800.

FRANKFURTER KIRCHLICHES JAHRBUCH. see *HISTORY — History Of Europe*

200 GW ISSN 0722-8120
FRAU UND MUTTER. 1918. every 4 weeks. DM.11. (Arbeitsgemeinschaft Frau und Mutter) Kreuz-Verlag Zeitschriften GmbH, Breitwiesenstr. 30, 7000 Stuttgart 80, W. Germany (B.R.D.) circ. 70,000. (looseleaf format)

FREETHINKER. see *PHILOSOPHY*

FREEWAY; a power/line paper. see *CHILDREN AND YOUTH — For*

261 GW ISSN 0016-0776
FREIE RELIGION; Monatsschrift fuer religioese Selbstbestimmung. 1962. m. DM.18. (Freireligioese Landesgemeinde Baden) Freireligioese Verlagsbuchhandlung, L 10, 4-6, 6800 Mannheim 1, W. Germany (B.R.D.) Ed. Dr. Eckhart Pilick. bk. rev. abstr. illus. circ. 5,000. (processed) Indexed: CERDIC.

200 UK ISSN 0016-1292
FRIENDLY COMPANION. 1857. m. £3.36. Gospel Standard Publications, 69, Langham Gardens, Grange Park, London N21 1DL, England. Ed. B.A. Ramsbottom. circ. 1,600.

200 GW ISSN 0340-6091
FROHE BOTSCHAFT; Predigten fuer jeden Sonntag des Jahres. bi-m. DM.17.60. Vandenhoeck und Ruprecht, Theaterstr. 14, Postfach 37 53, 3400 Goettingen, W. Germany (B.R.D.) Ed. Rudolf Hofmann. circ. 4,700.

200 US ISSN 0276-4679
FULNESS; a magazine dedicated to encouragement in knowing the fulness of Christ. 1978. bi-m. $19.95. Fulness House, Inc., Box 79350, Fort Worth, TX 76179. TEL 817-232-9171 Ed. Ras Robinson. adv. bk. rev. circ. 25,000.

267 AT
G.B. DIGEST. 1962. q. Aus.$0.75. Girls Brigade, 9 Albion Place, Sydney, N.S.W. 2000, Australia. Ed. J. A. Christie.

266 US
G E M'S EUROPE REPORT. 1971. bi-m. free. Greater Europe Mission, P.O. Box 668, Wheaton, IL 60189. TEL 312-462-8050 Ed. Don Brugman. adv. bk. rev. circ. 40,000. (tabloid format; back issues avail.)
Formerly: Greater Europe Report.
Missions

200 KE
GABA REPRINTS. (Text in English) 1970. 20/yr. EAs.60.50($8.80) (Amecea Pastoral Institute) Gaba Publications, P.O. Box 4002, Eldoret, Kenya. Ed. Felician N. Rwehikiza. circ. 1,200. (looseleaf format; back issues avail.)

GABRIEL; informatore filatelico. see *HOBBIES — Philately*

200 SA ISSN 0016-5204
GATEWAY. 1950. m. R.12 free. Cathedral Church of St. George the Martyr, Wale St., Cape Town 8001, South Africa. Ed. Rev. Edward L. King. adv. bk. rev. circ. 750.

200 GW ISSN 0016-5735
GEBETSAPOSTOLAT UND SEELSORGE. 1949. 6/yr. DM.6.20. Gebetsapostolat, c/o Peter Leinekugel, Melibocusstr. 41, 6000 Frankfurt 71, W. Germany (B.R.D.) Ed. Otto Syre. circ. 11,000.

200 149.3 200 GW ISSN 0016-5921
GEIST UND LEBEN. 1927. bi-m. DM.51.60 (students DM. 45) Echter-Verlag, Juliuspromenade 64, Postfach 5560, 8700 Wuerzburg 1, W. Germany (B.R.D.) Ed. P. Paul Imhof. adv. bk. rev. circ. 5,000. Indexed: CERDIC. New Test.Abstr.

200 NE ISSN 0016-6065
GEMEENTELEVEN. 1956. m. fl.25. Remonstrantse Gemeente Groningen, Coehoornsingel 14, 9711 BS Groningen, Netherlands. adv. bk. rev. circ. 500.

200 NE ISSN 0016-6324
GENADEKLANKEN; nieuws voor nu. 1947. s-m. fl.5. ‡ Stichting Ga Uit, Postbus 61, 7090 AB Dinxperlo, Netherlands. circ. 80,000.

200 US
GENERAL CONVENTION OF THE NEW JERUSALEM. JOURNAL. 1817. a. $10. General Convention of the New Jerusalem, 48 Sargent St., Newton, MA 02158. Ed. Ethelwyn Worden. circ. 500.

266 IT ISSN 0016-6960
GENTES. 1927. m. L.4000. ‡ Lega Missionaria Studenti, Via degli Astalli, 16, 00186 Rome, Italy. Dir. Cristoforo Sironi. bk. rev. bibl. illus. stat. index. circ. 10,000.
Missions

200 SZ ISSN 0016-9021
GESCHAEFTSMANN UND CHRIST. 1960/61. m. (11/yr.) 32 Fr. Internationale Vereinigung Christlicher Geschaeftsleute, Gruppe Zurich, Box 29, 8034 Zurich, Switzerland. Ed.Bd. bk. rev. illus. circ. 14,000.

248.83 IT ISSN 0017-0542
GIOVENTU EVANGELICA. 1947. bi-m. L.25000. Consiglio della Federazione della Gioventu Evangelica Italiana, Via Grotte Bianche, 7, 95219 Catania, Italy. Ed. Samuele Bernardini. illus. circ. 3,000.

271 IT ISSN 0072-4548
GIOVENTU PASSIONISTA/PASSIONIST YOUTH; rivista di formazione e d'informazione passionista. (Text in various languages; summaries in English) 1955. irreg., no. 3, 1960. $3. Edizioni E C O, 64048 S. Gabriele (Teramo), Italy. Ed. P. Natale Cavatassi.

200 US ISSN 0732-7781
GIST. 1975. m. $12. University of Healing Press, 1101 Far Valley Rd., Campo, CA 92006. TEL 619-478-5111 Ed. Dr. Herbert L. Beierle. circ. 3,000.

200 YU ISSN 0017-0925
GLASNIK. 1920. m. $20. Sveti Arhijerejski Sinod Srpske Pravoslavne Crkve, 7 Jula 5, Belgrade, Yugoslavia. Ed. Bishop Danilo Krstic. adv. bk. rev. circ. 2,600.

200 323.4 GW ISSN 0254-4377
GLAUBE IN DER 2. WELT; Zeitschrift fuer Religionsfreiheit und Menschenrechte. 1973. m. 45 Fr. Institut Glaube in der 2. Welt, Postfach 9, Bergstr. 6, CH-8702 Zollikon-Zurich, Switzerland. Ed. Eugen Voss. (back issues avail.)

200 GW ISSN 0179-3551
GLAUBE UND LERNEN; Zeitschrift fuer theologische Urteilsbildung. a. DM.29.80. Vandenhoeck & Ruprecht, Postfach 3753, Theaterstr. 13, D-3400 Goettingen, W. Germany (B.R.D.) Ed.Bd.

266 US
GLENMARY CHALLENGE. 1937. q. ‡ Glenmary Home Missioners, Box 465618, Cincinnati, OH 45246-5618. TEL 513-874-8900 Ed. Rev. Robert R. Bond. charts. illus. stat. circ. 102,000.
Formerly: Glenmary's Challenge.
Missions

200 UK ISSN 0017-1301
GLOUCESTER DIOCESAN GAZETTE. 1880. m. The Rectory, Swindon, Cheltenham, Glos. GL51 9RD, England. Ed. Rev. M.E. Bennett. bk. rev. circ. 42,000.

200 US
GLOW INTERNATIONAL. 1966. q. $18. Glow International, 599 Edison Dr., East Windsor, NJ 08520-5207. TEL 609-426-4345 Ed. Naosherwan Anzar. adv. bk. rev. circ. 1,000. (back issues avail.)

200 GW ISSN 0017-1409
GNADE UND HERRLICHKEIT. vol.28, 1976. bi-m. DM.30. Paulus-Verlag Karl Geyer, Goethestr. 38, 7100 Heilbronn, W. Germany (B.R.D.) Ed. Heinz Schumacher. Indexed: CERDIC.

251 GW ISSN 0340-6083
GOETTINGER PREDIGTMEDITATIONEN. 1946. q. DM.59. Vandenhoeck und Ruprecht, Theaterstr. 13, Postfach 37 53, 3400 Goettingen, W. Germany (B.R.D.) Ed. W. Fuerst. adv. index. circ. 4,900.

266 SA ISSN 0017-2146
GOOD NEWS/GOEIE NUUS; the magazine with a message. (Editions in Afrikaans and English) 1951. q. R.3($4) ‡ Good News Missionary Society, Box 7848, Johannesburg, South Africa. Ed. Sean O'Sullivan. circ. 5,000(Eng. edt.); 2,500(Afrikaans edt.)
Missions

266 UK ISSN 0262-2874
GOOD NEWS (BIRMINGHAM) 1837. s-a. £0.20 per no. Additional Curates Society for England and Wales, 246a Washwood Heath Rd., Birmingham B8 2XS, England. Ed. A.J. Prescott. illus. circ. 20,000. (also avail. in microform)
Formerly (until vol.48, 1981): Home Mission News.
Missions

200 US ISSN 0017-2332
GOSPEL CARRIER. 1954. w. $0.80 per quarter. Messenger Publishing House, Box 850, Joplin, MO 64802. TEL 417-624-7050 Ed. Rosemarie Foreman. circ. 3,400. (tabloid format)

200 CN ISSN 0829-4666
GOSPEL HERALD. 1936. m. Can.$7.50($8.50) Gospel Herald Foundation, Box 94, Beamsville, Ont. L0R 1B0, Canada. TEL 416-563-7503 Eds. Roy D. Merritt, Eugene C. Perry. adv. bk. rev. circ. 1,525.

GOSPEL MESSENGER. see *BLIND*

200 UK ISSN 0017-2367
GOSPEL STANDARD. 1835. m. £5.16. Gospel Standard Publications, 69, Langham Gardens, Grange Park, London N21 1DL, England. Ed. B.A. Ramsbottom. circ. 2,600. Indexed: CERDIC.

200 GW ISSN 0017-2480
GOTTES WORT. 3/yr. DM.58. Echter-Verlag, Juliuspromenade 64, Postfach 5560, 8700 Wuerzburg 1, W. Germany (B.R.D.) Ed. Rainer Rack.

200 GW ISSN 0343-8732
GOTTESDIENST; Information u. Handreichung der Liturgischen Institute Deutschlands, Oesterreichs u. der Schweiz. 1966. s-m. DM.39.60. Verlag Herder GmbH & Co. KG, Hermann-Herder-Str. 4, D-7800 Freiburg im Breisgau, W. Germany (B.R.D.) (back issues avail.)

200 GW
GOTTESDIENSTE MIT KINDERN UND JUGENDLICHEN. m. Bergmoser & Hoeller Verlag GmbH, Karl-Friedrich-Str. 76, 5100 Aachen, W. Germany (B.R.D.) circ. 4,800.

200 PO ISSN 0017-2758
GRACAS DO SERVO DE DEUS: PADRE CRUZ. 1949. bi-m. Cr.$150. Causa Beatificaciao do Padre Cruz, Rua da Madalena 179, Apdo. 2661, 1117 Lisbon Codex, Portugal. Dir. P. Manuel Baptista. adv. bk. rev. circ. 27,000.

200 UK ISSN 0046-6239
GRACE. 1833. m. £6. Grace Magazine Trust, 33 St. John's Wood Rd., London NW8 9PU, England (Distr. addr.: 4-6 Beechwood Rd., Caterham, Surrey CR3 6NA, England) Ed. Dr. J.K. Davies. adv. bk. rev. circ. 1,900.

200 US ISSN 0198-666X
GRACE THEOLOGICAL JOURNAL. 1980. s-a. $11.50. Grace Theological Seminary, 200 Seminary Dr., Winona Lake, IN 46590. TEL 219-267-8191 Eds. John C. Whitcomb, John J. Davis. bk. rev. circ. 2,000. (also avail. in microfilm from UMI; microfiche from UMI; reprint service avail. from UMI) Indexed: Old Test.Abstr. Rel.& Theol.Abstr. CERDIC. Chr.Per.Ind. New Test.Abstr. Rel.Ind.One.

GRALSWELT; Zeitschrift fuer wahren Aufbau durch neues Wissen. see *PHILOSOPHY*

230 BL ISSN 0046-6271
GRANDE SINAL. 1947. 6/yr. $50. Editora Vozes Ltda., Rua Frei Luis 100, Caixa Postal 90023, 25689 Petropolis, Rio de Janeiro, Brazil. Ed. Neylor Jose Tonin. bk. rev. abstr. bibl. illus. stat. index. circ. 2,900. (tabloid format)

GREAT BRITAIN. ROYAL ARMY CHAPLAINS' DEPARTMENT. JOURNAL. see *MILITARY*

200 UK ISSN 0046-6352
GREATER WORLD. 1928. bi-w. £9. Greater World Association Trust, 3 Lansdowne Rd., Holland Park, London W11 3AL, England. Ed. A.S. Clifton. adv. bk. rev. circ. 3,000.

200 US ISSN 0163-8971
GROUP (LOVELAND); the youth ministry magazine. 1974. 8/yr. $19.50. Thom Schultz Publications, Inc., 2890 N. Monroe, Box 481, Loveland, CO 80539 TEL 303-669-3836 (Subscr. to Box 202, Mt. Morris, IL 61054) Ed. Joani Schultz. adv. bk. rev. film rev. index. circ. 70,000. (back issues avail.) Indexed: Biol.Abstr.

200 028.5 US ISSN 0884-0504
GROUP'S JR. HIGH MINISTRY MAGAZINE. 1985. 5/yr. $19.50. Thom Schultz Publications, Inc., Box 481, Loveland, CO 80539 TEL 303-669-3836 (Subscr. to: Box 407, Mt. Morris, IL 61054) Ed. Joani Schultz. adv. circ. 20,000.

268 260 US
GUIDE TO CHRISTIAN CAMPS & CONFERENCE CENTERS. 1981. a. $9.95. Christian Camping International, Box 646, Wheaton, IL 60189. TEL 312-462-0300 Ed. Charlyene Wall. adv. circ. 9,000.
Former titles: Guide to Christian Camps; Christian Camping International Directory (ISSN 0069-3855); Before 1969: Christian Camp and Conference Association. International Directory.

200 US ISSN 0017-5331
GUIDEPOSTS. 1945. m. $5.95. ‡ Guideposts Associates, Inc., 747 Third Ave., New York, NY 10017. TEL 212-754-2200 Eds. Ruth Stafford Peale, Norman Vincent Peale. circ. 3,290,000.

200 GW ISSN 0017-5730
GUSTAV-ADOLF-BLATT. 1955. irreg. (1-4/yr.) DM.5. (Evangelische Kirche in Deutschland) Gustav-Adolf-Werk, Olgastr. 8, 3500 Kassel 1, W. Germany (B.R.D.) Ed. Dr. Fritz Heinrich Ryssel. bk. rev. circ. 25,000.

200 GW
GUTE BESSERUNG. 1977. m. Bergmoser and Holler Verlag, Karl-Friedrich-Str. 76, 5100 Aachen, W. Germany (B.R.D.) Ed. Paul Ostermann. circ. 42,000.

268 US ISSN 0072-9787
HANDBOOK OF DENOMINATIONS IN THE U.S. quinquennial. $10.95. Abingdon, 201 8th Ave. S, Box 801, Nashville, TN 37202. TEL 615-749-6347

266 UK
HAPPY DAY DIARY. 1928. a. 50p. ‡ Lord's Day Observance Society, 5 Victory Ave., Morden, Surrey SM4 6DL, England. Ed. J.G. Roberts. circ. 45,000.

HARVARD DIVINITY BULLETIN. see *COLLEGE AND ALUMNI*

HARVARD SEMITIC MONOGRAPHS. see *LINGUISTICS*

230 US ISSN 0017-8160
HARVARD THEOLOGICAL REVIEW. 1908. q. $40. Harvard Divinity School, 45 Francis Ave., Cambridge, MA 02138. Ed. Helmut Koester. adv. charts. circ. 1,900. (also avail. in microfiche) Indexed: Curr.Cont. Hist.Abstr. Hum.Ind. M.L.A. Old Test.Abstr. Rel.Per. Arts & Hum.Cit.Ind. Amer.Hist.& Life. CERDIC. New Test.Abstr. Rel.Ind.One. Rel.& Theol.Abstr.

201 US ISSN 0073-0726
HARVARD THEOLOGICAL STUDIES. 1916. irreg., no. 34, 1982. price varies. Harvard Divinity School, 45 Francis Ave., Cambridge, MA 02138.

200 UK ISSN 0017-8217
HARVESTER. 1900. m. £10.20($28.05) Paternoster Press Ltd., Paternoster House, 3 Mount Radford Crescent, Exeter EX1 4JW, England. Ed. J. Lamb. adv. bk. rev. illus. circ. 3,000. (tabloid format)
Incorporating: Witness.

266 UK ISSN 0017-8829
HEALING HAND. 1850. 3/yr. free. Edinburgh Medical Missionary Society, 14 Mayfield Terrace, Edinburgh EH9 1SA, Scotland. Ed. John R. Barclay. adv. bk. rev. circ. 2,000.
Missions

200 UK ISSN 0017-9477
HEBREW CHRISTIAN. 1928. q. $2. International Hebrew Christian Alliance, Shalom, Brockenhurst Rd., Ramsgate, England. Ed. Rev. Ronald H. Lewis. bk. rev. circ. 6,000. Indexed: CERDIC.

200 AU ISSN 0017-9620
HEILIGER DIENST. 1947. q. S.132. (Institutum Liturgicum) Verlag St. Peter, Postfach 113, A-5010 Salzburg, Austria. Ed. P. Rupert Schindlauer. adv. bk. rev. circ. 1,200. Indexed: CERDIC.

200 SW ISSN 0018-0335
HEMMETS VAEN; kristlig veckotidning. 1897. w. Kr.259($40) Evangeliipress, Box 1712, S-70117 Oerebro, Sweden. Ed. Stig Hallzon. adv. bk. rev. illus. circ. 45,000. (tabloid format)

200 US
HERALD OF HIS COMING. 1941. m. free. Gospel Revivals, Inc., Box 3457, Terminal Annex, Los Angeles, CA 90051. TEL 818-790-2128 Ed. Lois J. Stucky. circ. 90,000.

200 NE
HERKENNING; tijdschrift voor Joden en Christenen. q. fl.39.80. Boekencentrum B.V., Scheveningseweg 72, Box 84176, The Hague, Netherlands.

200 US
HERMENEUTICS: STUDIES IN THE HISTORY OF RELIGION. irreg. price varies. University of California Press, 2120 Berkeley Way, Berkeley, CA 94720. TEL 415-642-4247

200 GW ISSN 0440-7180
HERMENEUTISCHE UNTERSUCHUNGEN ZUR THEOLOGIE. (Text in English, German) irreg., latest vol.23, 1985. J.C.B. Mohr (Paul Siebeck), Wilhelmstr. 18, Postfach 20 40, D-7400 Tuebingen, W. Germany (B.R.D.) Ed.Bd.

266 NE
HERNHUTTER SURINAME ZENDING. 1834. q. free. Zendingsgenootschap der Evangelische Broedergemeente, Box 19, 3700 AA Zeist, Netherlands. Ed.Bd. bk. rev. illus. circ. 150,000.
Formerly: Suriname Zending (ISSN 0039-6141)

200 AU ISSN 0018-0815
HEROLD DES KOSTBAREN BLUTES. 1924. m. DM.10.50. P. Adalbert Stummbillig, Ed. & Pub., Kleinholz-Postfach 7, A-6330 Kufstein, Austria. bk. rev. circ. 6,000. Indexed: Curr.Cont.Africa.
Incorporating: Kontinente.

100 200 UK ISSN 0018-1196
HEYTHROP JOURNAL; a review of philosophy and theology. 1960. q. $30. Heythrop College (University of London), 11 Cavendish Square, London W1M 0AN, England. Ed. Joseph Munitiz. adv. bk. rev. bibl. charts. illus. index. circ. 950. Indexed: Cath.Ind. Curr.Cont. Old Test.Abstr. Arts & Hum.Cit.Ind. CERDIC. Canon Law Abstr. Int.Z.Bibelwiss. New Test.Abstr. Phil.Ind. Rel.& Theol.Abstr.

200 NE
HIER EN GINDER. m. fl.16. Missiethuisfront, Akkerstraat 12, 6617 BA Bergharen, Netherlands. Ed. J. van Gelder. bk. rev. circ. 1,250.
Missions

248.83 US
HIS MAGAZINE; monthly magazine for college students. 1941. m. (Oct.-April) $12.95. Inter-Varsity Christian Fellowship, 233 Langdon St., Madison, WI 53703 TEL 312-964-5700 (Subscr. address: 5206 Main St., Box 1450, Downers Grove, IL 60515) Ed. Verne Becker. adv. bk. rev. illus. index. circ. 25,000. (also avail. in microfilm from UMI; reprint service avail. from UMI) Indexed: A.I.P.P. CERDIC. Chr.Per.Ind. G.Soc.Sci.& Rel.Per.Lit.
Formerly (until Oct.1985): His (ISSN 0018-2095)

209 SP ISSN 0018-215X
HISPANIA SACRA; revista de historia eclesiastica. 1948. s-a. 800 ptas. Instituto Enrique Florez, Serrano 123, Madrid 6, Spain (Distr. by: Consejo Superior de Investigaciones Cientificas, Apdo. 14458, Vitruvio 8, Madrid 6, Spain) bk. rev. illus. (also avail. in microfilm) Indexed: Hist.Abstr. Amer.Hist.& Life.
History

HISTORIANS OF EARLY MODERN EUROPE. see *HISTORY — History Of Europe*

291 209 US ISSN 0018-2710
HISTORY OF RELIGIONS; an international journal for comparative historical studies. 1961. q. $27.50 to individuals; institutions $45. University of Chicago Press, 5801 S. Ellis Ave., Chicago, IL 60637 TEL 312-962-7600 (Orders to: Box 37005, Chicago, IL 60637) Ed.Bd. adv. bk. rev. index. circ. 1,750. (also avail. in microform from MIM; reprint service avail. from UMI,ISI) Indexed: Curr.Cont. Hist.Abstr. Hum.Ind. Old Test.Abstr. Rel.Per. Amer.Hist.& Life. Arts & Hum.Cit.Ind. CERDIC. G.Soc.Sci.& Rel.Per.Lit. Int.Z.Bibelwiss. New Test.Abstr. Rel.Ind.One. Rel.& Theol.Abstr.
History

258 SP
HOJA PARROQUIAL. 1972. m. free. Parroquia Immaculada Concepcion, c/o Sebastian Oliver Balaguer, Espartero, 9, Palma de Mallorca, Baleares, Spain.

200 933 IS
HOLY PLACES OF PALESTINE. (Text in various languages) 1970. irreg. Franciscan Printing Press, Box 14064, Jerusalem 91140, Israel.

249 UK ISSN 0018-3946
HOME AND FAMILY. 1886. q. £1. ‡ Mothers' Union, Mary Sumner House, 24 Tufton St., Westminster, London SW1P 3RB, England. Ed.Bd. adv. bk. rev. illus. circ. 140,000.

251 SP ISSN 0439-4208
HOMILETICA. 3/yr. 795 ptas.($7.50) Editorial Sal Terrae, Apartado 77, Santander, Spain.

251 GW ISSN 0018-4276
HOMILETISCHE MONATSHEFTE. 1925. m. DM.79.20. Vandenhoeck und Ruprecht, Theaterstr. 13, Postfach 37 53, 3400 Goettingen, W. Germany (B.R.D.) Ed. Ludwig Schmidt. adv. bk. rev. index. circ. 4,200.

200 US
HOMILY HELPS. 62/yr. $20. St. Anthony Messenger Press, 1615 Republic St., Cincinnati, OH 45210. TEL 513-241-5615 Ed. Rev. Hilarion Kistner, O.F.M. circ. 8,400. (looseleaf format)

264 US ISSN 0732-1872
HOMILY SERVICE. 1968. m. $36. Liturgical Conference, 806 Rhode Island Ave. N.E., Washington, DC 20018. TEL 202-529-7400

200 FR ISSN 0018-4322
HOMME NOUVEAU. 1946. bi-m. 85 F.($15) place Saint-Sulpice, 75006 Paris, France. Ed. M. Marcel Clement. circ. 75,000.

220 US ISSN 0195-9085
HORIZONS IN BIBLICAL THEOLOGY. 1979. a. $12 to individuals; institutions $15; students $8. Pittsburgh Theological Seminary, 616 N. Highland Ave., Pittsburgh, PA 15206. TEL 412-362-5610 Eds. G. Coates,, D. Gowan. adv. bk. rev. circ. 300. (back issues avail.) Indexed: Old Test.Abstr. New Test.Abstr. Rel.Ind.One. Rel.& Theol.Abstr.

200 JA ISSN 0073-3938
HUMANITIES, CHRISTIANITY AND CULTURE. (Text in Japanese, English, French, and German; summaries in English and Japanese) 1964. approx. a. 400 Yen per no. International Christian University, Institute for the Study of Christianity and Culture - Kokusai Kirisutokyo Daigaku Kirisutokyo to Bunka Kenkyujo, 3-10-2 Osawa, Mitaka, Tokyo 181, Japan. Ed. Koichi Namiki. circ. 560.
Formerly: International Christian University. Publications IV-B. Christianity and Culture.

HYMN. see *MUSIC*

266 US ISSN 0018-9723
I F M A NEWS. vol.24, 1973. q. free. ‡ Interdenomination Foreign Mission Association of North America, Inc., P.O. Box 395, Wheaton, IL 60189. Ed. Grace Frizen. stat. circ. 6,500.
Missions

266 ZA
ICENGELO; Christian magazine in Bemba. (Text in Bemba) 1970. m. K.12($1) Mission Press, Box 71581, Ndola, Zambia. Eds. Rev. U. Davoli, L. Muleba. circ. 40,000.
Missions

ICO-ICONOGRAPHISK POST; Nordisk tidskrift foer bildtolkning/Nordic iconographic review. see *ART*

220 US
ICONOCLAST. 1979. m. $36. Foundation of Human Understanding, 8780 Venice Blvd., Los Angeles, CA 90034. Ed. Roy Masters.

200 NE
ICONOGRAPHY OF RELIGIONS. irreg. price varies. (Rijksuniversiteit te Groningen, Institute of Religious Iconography) E. J. Brill, P.O. Box 9000, 2300 PA Leiden, Netherlands. Ed.Bd.

207.11 US ISSN 0019-1795
ILIFF REVIEW. 1944. 3/yr. $4. Iliff School of Theology, 2201 S. University Blvd., Denver, CO 80210. Ed. Charles S. Milligan. bk. rev. cum.index every 10 yrs. circ. 500. Indexed: M.L.A. Old Test.Abstr. CERDIC. Rel.Ind.One.

200 GW ISSN 0019-2597
IM LANDE DER BIBEL; neue Folge der neuesten Nachrichten aus dem Morgenland. 1955. 3/yr. DM.12. (Jerusalemsverein) Berliner Missionswerk, Handjery Str. 19, 1000 Berlin 41, W. Germany (B.R.D.) Ed. Rev. Paul E. Hoffman. bk. rev. bibl. illus. circ. 8,000.

IMBONGI. see *COLLEGE AND ALUMNI*

266 IS ISSN 0302-8127
IMMANUEL; religious thought and research in Israel. (Text in English) 1972. 2/yr. $6. ‡ Ecumenical Theological Research Fraternity in Israel, Box 249, Jerusalem, Israel. Ed. Coos Schoneveld. adv. bk. rev. bibl. circ. 1,000. Indexed: Curr.Cont. Old Test.Abstr. CERDIC. Ind.Artic.Jew.Stud. New Test.Abstr. Rel.Ind.One.

200 US ISSN 0363-5058
IN COMMON. 1971. irreg. $2. ‡ Consultation on Church Union, Research Park, 151 Wall St., Princeton, NJ 08540-1514. Ed. David W. Taylor. circ. 10,000.

200 NE ISSN 0019-3151
IN DE RECHTE STRAAT/EN LA CALLE RECTA. (Editions in Dutch and Spanish) 1958. m. (Dutch edt.); q. (Spanish edt.) fl.22.75. Stichting In de Rechte Straat, Boulevard 11, 6881 HN Velp, Netherlands. Ed. Rev. H. J. Hegger. bk. rev. illus. circ. 13,000. Indexed: CERDIC.

200 NE ISSN 0019-316X
IN DE WAAGSCHAAL. 1945. fortn. fl.17. Amaco, Eglantiersgracht 75-79, Amsterdam, Netherlands. Ed. Prof. Dr. K. H. Miskotte. circ. 2,000. Indexed: CERDIC.

220 US
IN OTHER WORDS. 1943. every 6 wks. free to U.S. subscribers only. ‡ Wycliffe Bible Translators, Inc., 19891 Beach Blvd., Huntington Beach, CA 92648. TEL 714-536-9346 Ed. Hyatt Moore. illus. circ. 180,000.
Supersedes: Translation (ISSN 0041-1221)
Bible translation

200 UK ISSN 0019-3283
IN TOUCH (PINNER) 1969. q. £3. Grail, 125 Waxwell Lane, Pinner, Middlesex, England. Ed. Mary Grasar. bk. rev. play rev. illus. circ. 1,300. (tabloid format)
Formerly: Mosaic.

322.1 200 US
INDEPENDENT VOICE. 1940. m. $3. ‡ Christian Citizens Crusade Inc., Box 1866, Greenville, SC 29602. TEL 803-233-3060 Ed. Sherman A. Patterson. illus. circ. 20,000. (tabloid format)
Formerly: Militant Truth (ISSN 0026-3893)

200 II
INDIA CULTURES. (Text in English) vol.22, 1965. q. Rs.10($5) Leonard Theological College, School of Research, Jabalpur 482001, Madhya Pradesh, India. Ed. Rev. Jacob Paul. bk. rev. illus. circ. 500.
Formerly: India Cultures Quarterly (ISSN 0019-4166)

209 II ISSN 0019-4530
INDIAN CHURCH HISTORY REVIEW. (Text in English) 1967. s-a. $5. Church History Association of India, Mackin-Chan Hall, Wilson College, Bombay 7, India. Ed. Dr. H. Grafe. bk. rev. index. circ. 500. (back issues avail.) Indexed: Rel.Per. Rel.Ind.One.
History

230 II ISSN 0019-5685
INDIAN JOURNAL OF THEOLOGY. (Text in English) 1952. q. $7. Indian Journal of Theology, c/o Bishops's College, 224 Lower Circular Rd., Calcutta 700017, India. Ed.Bd. adv. bk. rev. bibl. index. circ. 500. Indexed: Old Test.Abstr. New Test.Abstr. Rel.Per. Rel.Ind.One. Rel.& Theol.Abstr.

INFORMATIONEN ZUM RELIGIONSUNTERRICHT. see *EDUCATION — Teaching Methods And Curriculum*

INNER PATHS. see *PHILOSOPHY*

200 UK ISSN 0020-1723
INQUIRER. 1842. fortn. £7.50($18) Inquirer Publishing Co. Ltd., 1-6 Essex St., London W.C.2, England. Ed. Fred M. Ryde. adv. bk. rev. illus. circ. 2,500.

200 US ISSN 0164-7709
INSIGHTS (SPRINGFIELD); the publication for parish pastors--sermon resources on Unified Lectionary texts. 1973. 7/yr. $19. J L J Publishers, 824 Shrine Rd., Springfield, OH 45504-3999. TEL 513-322-4454 Ed. Jon L. Joyce. circ. 1,000.

220 DK ISSN 0107-959X
INSPIRATION; tidsskrift for bibelsk teologi. 1972. q. Kr.30. Paul Birch, Daadyrvaenget 404, 2980 Kokkedal, Denmark. illus.

200 200 GW
INSTITUT FUER EUROPAEISCHE GESCHICHTE, MAINZ. VEROEFFENTLICHUNGEN. ABTEILUNG UNIVERSALGESCHICHTE UND ABTEILUNG FUER ABENDLAENDISCHE RELIGIONSGESCHICHTE. (Text in English, French, and German) irreg., vol.124, 1987. price varies. Franz Steiner Verlag Wiesbaden GmbH, Birkenwaldstr. 44, Postfach 347, D-7000 Stuttgart 1, W. Germany (B.R.D.) Eds. K.O. von Aretin, P. Manns.
Formerly: Institut fuer Europaeische Geschichte, Mainz. Veroeffentlichungen. Abteilung Universitaetsgeschichte und Abteilung fuer Abendlaendische Religionsphilosophie (ISSN 0537-7919)

200 200 GW
INSTITUT FUER EUROPAEISCHE GESCHICHTE, MAINZ. VORTRAEGE. ABTEILUNG UNIVERSALGESCHICHTE UND ABTEILUNG FUER ABENDLAENDISCHE RELIGIONSGESCHICHTE. (Text in English, French, and German) irreg., vol.79, 1984. price varies. Franz Steiner Verlag Wiesbaden GmbH, Birkenwaldstr. 44, Postfach 347, D-7000 Stuttgart 1, W. Germany (B.R.D.) Eds. K. O. von Aretin, P. Manns.
Formerly: Institut fuer Europaeische Geschichte, Mainz. Vortraege. Abteilung Universalgeschichte und Abteilung fuer Abendlaendische Religionsphilosophie (ISSN 0537-7927)

200 MX
INSTITUTO SUPERIOR DE ESTUDIOS ECLESIASTICOS. LIBRO ANUAL. vol. 9, 1980. a. Instituto Superior de Estudios Eclesiasticos, Victoria 21, Mexico 22, D.F., Mexico. bk. rev. Indexed: New Test.Abstr.

200 UY
INSTITUTO TEOLOGICO DEL URUGUAY. CUADERNOS. no. 4, 1978. irreg. Instituto Teologico del Uruguay, Av. de Octubre 3060, Montevideo, Uruguay.

INSTRUMENTA LEXICOLOGIA LATINA. SERIES A & B. see *CLASSICAL STUDIES*

200 AT ISSN 0047-0430
INTERCHANGE; papers on biblical and current questions. 1967. s-a. Aus.$15. Australian Fellowship of Evangelical Students, Graduate Fellowship of Australia, The Business Manager, 120 Chalmers St., Surry Hills, N.S.W. 2010, Australia. Ed. Allan Friend. bk. rev. circ. 1,300. Indexed: Phil.Ind.

266 UK ISSN 0020-5265
INTERCON. 1962. 3/yr. membership. Intercontinental Church Society, 175 Tower Bridge Rd., London SE1 2AQ, England. Ed. Lance Bidewell. bk. rev. circ. 5,000(controlled) (tabloid format)

230.05 US ISSN 0092-6558
INTERDENOMINATIONAL THEOLOGICAL CENTER, ATLANTA. JOURNAL. 1973. s-a. $6 to individuals; institutions $8. Interdenominational Theological Center, 671 Beckwith St., Atlanta, GA 30314. TEL 404-522-1772 Ed. John C. Diamond Jr. bk. rev. circ. 2,500. Indexed: Rel.Per. CERDIC. New Test.Abstr. Rel.& Theol.Abstr. Rel.Ind.One.
Key Title: Journal of the Interdenominational Theological Center.

200 US ISSN 0362-4668
INTERDEPENDENCE. 1972. s-a. $10. ‡ International Association for Religious Freedom, North American Chapter, c/o Unitarian Universalist Assn., 25 Beacon St., Boston, MA 02108. TEL 617-742-2100 Ed. Rev. Charles Eddis. circ. 400.

200 US ISSN 0020-5575
INTERLIT. 1964. q. free to qualified personnel; $2.50 to others. ‡ (David C. Cook Foundation) David C. Cook Publishing Co., Cook Square, Elgin, IL 60120. TEL 312-741-2400 Ed. Gladys J. Peterson. bk. rev. circ. 7,000. Indexed: CERDIC.

367 US
INTERNATIONAL ASSOCIATION OF LIBERAL RELIGIOUS WOMEN. NEWSLETTER. 1949. a. membership. International Association of Liberal Religious Women, c/o Tina Jas, Sec., 43 Coolidge Ave., Lexington, MA 02173 (Edit. address: Havikhorst 17hs, Amsterdam 1083 TM, Netherlands) Ed. Gusta Greve.
Former titles: International Union of Liberal Christian Women. Newsletter; International League of Liberal Christian Women. Newsletter (ISSN 0074-6746)

200 CH ISSN 0074-297X
INTERNATIONAL CONFERENCE FOR THE SOCIOLOGY OF RELIGION. 1948. biennial, 18th, 1985, Leuven-louvain-la-Neuve. 35 Fr. International Conference for the Sociology of Religion, 10 Terreaux, 1003 Lausanne, Switzerland. bk. rev.

201 NE ISSN 0020-7047
INTERNATIONAL JOURNAL FOR PHILOSOPHY OF RELIGION. 1970. s-a. fl.212($75) Martinus Nijhoff Publishers, Spuiboulevard 50, 3311 GR Dordrecht, Netherlands (Orders to: Kluwer Academic Publishers Group, Distribution Center, Box 322, 3300 AH Dordrecht, Netherlands) Eds. Bowman L. Clarke, Frank R. Harrison III. bk. rev. bibl. (back issues avail.) Indexed: Curr.Cont. Hum.Ind. Arts & Hum.Cit.Ind. Phil.Ind. Rel.Ind.One. Rel.& Theol.Abstr.

268 US
INTERNATIONAL LESSON ANNUAL; commentary and teaching suggestions on the International Sunday School lessons. a. $7.50. Abingdon, 201 Eighth Ave. S., Box 801, Nashville, TN 37202. TEL 615-749-6347 Ed. Horace R. Weaver.

266 SZ ISSN 0020-8582
INTERNATIONAL REVIEW OF MISSION. 1911. q. 32.50 Fr.($17.50) World Council of Churches, Commission on World Mission and Evangelism, 150 Route de Ferney, 1211 Geneva 20, Switzerland. Ed. Eugene Stockwell. adv. bk. rev. bibl. index. circ. 4,000. (also avail. in microform from UMI; reprint service avail. from UMI) Indexed: Br.Hum.Ind. Hist.Abstr. Abstr.Musl.Rel. Amer.Hist.& Life. Chr.Per.Ind. CERDIC. Rel.& Theol.Abstr. Rel.Per. Rel.Ind.One.
Missions

220 US
INTERNATIONALE BIBELLEKTIONEN. (Text in German) 1919. q. $3.40. ‡ (German Church of God in U. S. A.) Christian Unity Press, 2211 Lincoln Ave., Box 527, York, NE 68467. TEL 402-362-5133 Ed. Rev. Fritz Friedrich. circ. 2,300. (processed)

200 SZ ISSN 0020-9252
INTERNATIONALE KIRCHLICHE ZEITSCHRIFT. 1911. q. 52 Fr.($26) Staempfli und Cie AG, Postfach 2728, 3001 Berne, Switzerland. Ed. Hans Frei. bk. rev. bibl. index. circ. 600. (tabloid format) Indexed: Old Test.Abstr. CERDIC. New Test.Abstr.

220 230 US ISSN 0020-9643
INTERPRETATION (RICHMOND); a journal of Bible and theology. 1947. q. $12. Union Theological Seminary in Virginia, 3401 Brook Rd., Richmond, VA 23227. TEL 804-355-0671 Ed. Paul J. Achtemeier. adv. bk. rev. bibl. index. cum.index: 1947-1956; 1957-1971; 1972-1981. circ. 12,000. (also avail. in microform from UMI; back issues avail; reprint service avail. from UMI) Indexed: Bk.Rev.Ind. Int.Z.Bibelwiss. New Test.Abstr. Hum.Ind. Chr.Per.Ind. Old Test.Abstr. Soc.Sci.Ind. G.Soc.Sci.& Rel.Per.Lit. Ind.Artic.Jew.Stud. Rel.Per. Rel.Ind.One. Rel.& Theol.Abstr.

267 JM ISSN 0020-5087
INTER-SCHOOL & INTER-VARSITY CHRISTIAN FELLOWSHIP; for prayer and praise. m. free. Students Christian Fellowship and Scripture Union, 22 Hagley Park Plaza, Box 281, Kingston 10, Jamaica. Ed. Sam McCook. bk. rev. circ. 800. (processed)
Formerly: Inter-School & Inter-Varsity Christian Fellowship of the West Indies.

255 BE ISSN 0021-0978
IRENIKON. 1926. q. 950 Fr.($30) Monastere de Chevetogne, 5395 Chevetogne, Belgium. Ed. Emmanuel Lanne. adv. bk. rev. bibl. index. circ. 1,500. Indexed: Ind.Med. Rel.Per. CERDIC. New Test.Abstr. Rel.Ind.One.

200 IE ISSN 0332-4427
IRISH BIBLICAL ASSOCIATION. PROCEEDINGS. 1976. a. £16. Irish Biblical Association, Trinity College, Dublin 2, Ireland. Ed.Bd. adv. circ. 250. (back issues avail.) Indexed: Old Test.Abstr. New Test.Abstr.

200 IE ISSN 0021-1400
IRISH THEOLOGICAL QUARTERLY. 1906. q. £14. St. Patrick's College, Faculty of Theology, Maynooth, Co. Kildare, Ireland. Ed.Bd. index. circ. 1,000. (also avail. in microform from UMI; reprint service avail. from UMI) Indexed: Cath.Ind. Old Test.Abstr. Canon Law Abstr. New Test.Abstr. Rel.& Theol.Abstr.

200 057.1 CN ISSN 0021-1761
ISKRA. (Text in English and Russian) 1943. fortn. Can.$30. Soyuz Dukhovnykh Obshchin Krista - Union of Spiritual Communities of Christ, Box 760, Grand Forks, B.C., Canada V0H 1H0. TEL 604-442-8252 Ed. D.E. Popoff. adv. bk. rev. circ. 1,000. (processed)

281 FR ISSN 0021-2423
ISTINA. 1954. q. 255 F. Centre d'Etudes Istina, 45 rue de la Glaciere, 75013 Paris, France. (Affiliate: Centre National de la Recherche Scientifique, Paris) Dir. B.D. Dupuy. bk. rev. index. circ. 1,000. (also avail. in microform from UMI; back issues avail.; reprint service avail. from UMI) Indexed: Bull.Signal. Rel.Per. CERDIC. New Test.Abstr. Rel.Ind.One.

262.9 SP ISSN 0021-325X
IUS CANONICUM. (Summaries in English and Latin) 1961. 2/yr. 3500 ptas.($35) (Universidad de Navarra, Instituto Martin de Azpilcueta) Ediciones Universidad de Navarra, S.A., Apdo. 396, 31080 Pamplona, Spain. Ed. Tomas Rincon. bk. rev. circ. 1,000. Indexed: CERDIC. Canon Law Abstr.
Canon law

J A M. (Jesus and Me) see *CHILDREN AND YOUTH — For*

J P; paper for boys and girls. see *CHILDREN AND YOUTH — For*

J S A C GRAPEVINE. (Joint Strategy and Action Committee) see *SOCIAL SERVICES AND WELFARE*

200 GW ISSN 0342-6513
JA, DAS WORT FUER ALLE. 1982. m. DM.11. (Berliner Stadtmission) Kreuz Verlag Zeitschriften GmbH, Breitwiesenstr. 30, 7000 Stuttgart 80, W. Germany (B.R.D.) circ. 40,000. (looseleaf format)

JACKSONVILLE POETRY QUARTERLY. see *LITERATURE — Poetry*

270 GW ISSN 0075-2541
JAHRBUCH FUER ANTIKE UND CHRISTENTUM. 1958. a. price varies. (Universitaet Bonn, Franz Joseph Doelger-Institut) Aschendorffsche Verlagsbuchhandlung, Soester Str. 13, Postfach 1124, 4400 Muenster, W. Germany (B. R. D.) bk. rev. Indexed: Br.Archaeol.Abstr. New Test.Abstr. RILA.

270 GW ISSN 0075-2568
JAHRBUCH FUER BERLIN-BRANDENBURGISCHE KIRCHENGESCHICHTE. vol. 55, 1985. a. DM.28. (Arbeitsgemeinschaft fuer Berlin-Brandenburgische Kirchengeschichte) Wichern-Verlag GmbH, Abt. CZV-Verlag, Bachstr. 1-2, 1000 Berlin 21, W. Germany (B.R.D.) circ. 850.
Supersedes: Jahrbuch fuer Brandenburgische Kirchengeschichte.

JAHRBUCH FUER CHRISTLICHE SOZIALWISSENSCHAFTEN. see *SOCIOLOGY*

264 245 GW ISSN 0075-2681
JAHRBUCH FUER LITURGIK UND HYMNOLOGIE. 1955. a. price varies. (International Fellowship of Research in Hymnology - Internationale Arbeitsgemeinschaft fuer Hymnologie) Johannes Stauda Verlag GmbH, Heinrich-Schuetz-Allee 33, 3500 Kassel-Wilhelmshoehe, W. Germany (B.R.D.) Ed.Bd. bk. rev. circ. 1,000. Indexed: CERDIC. RILM.

270 GW ISSN 0075-2762
JAHRBUCH FUER SCHLESISCHE KIRCHENGESCHICHTE. 1882. a. DM.34. (Verein fuer Schlesische Kirchengeschichte e.V.) Verlag Unser Weg, Meesenring 15, 2400 Luebeck 1, W. Germany (B.R.D.) Ed. Dietrich Meyer. bk. rev.

260 GW
JAHRBUCH MISSION. 1969. a. DM.6.80. (Verband Evangelischer Missionskonferenzen) Missionshilfe Verlag, Mittelweg 143, 2000 Hamburg 13, W. Germany (B.R.D.) Ed. Joachim Wietzke. bk. rev. circ. 10,000.
Formerly: Evangelische Mission Jahrbuch (ISSN 0531-4798)
Missions

268 FR
J'AIME LIRE. 1977. m. 309 F. Bayard Presse, 5, rue Bayard, 75380 Paris Cedex 08, France. circ. 180,000.
For children 7 to 9 years

200 JA ISSN 0021-4353
JAPAN CHRISTIAN ACTIVITY NEWS. (Text in English) 1952. m. 3000 Yen($15) ‡ National Christian Council in Japan, Japan Christian Center, Rm. 24, 2-13-18 Nishi Waseda, Shinju-ku, Tokyo 160, Japan. Ed.Bd. bk. rev. circ. 600. (processed) Indexed: I.C.U.I.S.Abstr.Ser.

266 JA ISSN 0021-4361
JAPAN CHRISTIAN QUARTERLY. (Text in English) 1925. q. $32. (Fellowship of Christian Missionaries) Japan Publications Trading Co., Ltd., Box 5030, Tokyo International, Tokyo 100-31, Japan. circ. 5,000. Indexed: M.L.A. Rel.Per. Rel.Ind.One.
Missions

266 JA ISSN 0021-440X
JAPAN HARVEST. (Text in English) 1951. q. $15. Japan Evangelical Missionary Association, 2-1 Kanda Surugadai, Chiyoda-ku, Tokyo 101, Japan. Ed. Siegfried Buss. adv. bk. rev. charts. illus. circ. 1,200.
Missions

266 JA ISSN 0021-4531
JAPAN MISSIONARY BULLETIN. (Text in English) 1947. q. 4000 Yen. Oriens Institute for Religious Research, 2-28-5 Matsubara, Setagaya-ku, Tokyo 156, Japan. Ed. Raymond P. Renson. adv. bk. rev. charts. illus. index. circ. 1,500.
Missions

291 952 JA ISSN 0304-1042
JAPANESE JOURNAL OF RELIGIOUS STUDIES. (Text in English) 1960. q. 3500 Yen individuals ($20); 5000 Yen institutions ($25) Nanzan Institute for Religion and Culture, 18 Yamazato-cho, Showa-ku, Nagoya 466, Japan. Ed. Jan Swyngedouw. adv. bk. rev. illus. stat. index. cum.index. circ. 600. Indexed: Curr.Cont. Arts & Hum.Cit.Ind. Rel.Ind.One.
Formerly: Contemporary Religions in Japan (ISSN 0010-7557)

290 JA ISSN 0448-8954
JAPANESE RELIGIONS. (Text in English) 1959. s-a. 3600 Yen($16) for 2 yrs. National Christian Council of Japan, N C C Center for the Study of Japanese Religions, c/o Kyoto Diocese of Japan Episcopal Church, Karasuma-Shimotachiuri, Kamikyo-ku, Kyoto 602, Japan. Ed. Doi Masatoshi. bk. rev. circ. 500. Indexed: Rel.& Theol.Abstr. Rel.Ind.One.

200 CK ISSN 0021-5562
JAVERIANA. no.438, 1977. m. (Feb.-Nov.) Col.2000($45) Compania de Jesus de Colombia, Carrera 23 no. 39-69, Apdo. Aereo 24773, Bogota, Colombia. Ed. Alberto Gutierrez. adv. bk. rev. bibl. index. circ. 8,000.

JESUS MAESTRO. see *CHILDREN AND YOUTH — For*

JOHN MILTON MAGAZINE. see *BLIND*

JOHN MILTON SUNDAY SCHOOL QUARTERLY. see *CHILDREN AND YOUTH — For*

JOHN MILTON TALKING BOOK. see *BLIND*

200 NE ISSN 0021-7395
JONGE KERK. 1917. m. fl.12. Apostolaat van het Gebed, Postbus 418, 6500 AK Nijmegen, Netherlands. Ed. Chr. Swueste. adv. bk. rev. index. circ. 15,000.

255 US ISSN 0021-7603
JOSEPHITE HARVEST. 1888. q. $2. Society of St. Joseph of the Sacred Heart, 1130 N. Calvert St., Baltimore, MD 21202. TEL 301-727-3386 Ed. Earle A. Newman. adv. circ. 40,000.

200 US ISSN 0021-8294
JOURNAL FOR THE SCIENTIFIC STUDY OF RELIGION. 1961. q. $35 to non-members. Society for the Scientific Study of Religion, Marist Hall, Rm. 108, Catholic University of America, Washington, DC 20064. TEL 202-635-5447 Ed. Don Capps. adv. bk. rev. charts. stat. index. cum.index: 1961-1981. circ. 3,500. (also avail. in microform from UMI; reprint service avail. from UMI) Indexed: Curr.Cont. Hist.Abstr. Hum.Ind. Old Test.Abstr. Psychol.Abstr. Rel.Per. SSCI. Sociol.Abstr. Amer.Bibl.Slavic & E.Eur.Stud. Abstr.Anthropol. Arts & Hum.Cit.Ind.x. Amer.Hist.& Life. CERDIC. G.Soc.Sci.& Rel.Per.Lit. Lang.& Lang.Behav.Abstr. Rel.Ind.One. Rel.& Theol.Abstr.

200 UK ISSN 0142-064X
JOURNAL FOR THE STUDY OF THE NEW TESTAMENT. 1978. 3/yr. $19.50 to individuals; institutions $50. J S O T Press, 343 Fulwood Rd., Univ. of Sheffield, Sheffield S10 3BP, England. Indexed: New.Test.Abstr. Rel.Ind.One. Rel.& Theol.Abstr.

200 UK ISSN 0143-5108
JOURNAL FOR THE STUDY OF THE NEW TESTAMENT. SUPPLEMENT SERIES. irreg. price varies. J S O T Press, 343 Fulwood Rd., University of Sheffield, Sheffield S10 3BP, England. Indexed: New Test.Abstr.

221 UK ISSN 0309-0892
JOURNAL FOR THE STUDY OF THE OLD TESTAMENT. 1976. 3/yr. $19.50 to individuals; institutions $50. J S O T Press, 343 Fulwood Rd., University of Sheffield, Sheffield S10 3BP, England. Ed.Bd. Indexed: Bull.Signal. Old Test.Abstr. Rel.Per. Int.Z.Bibelwiss. New Test.Abstr. Rel.Ind.One. Rel.Ind.Two. Rel.& Theol.Abstr.

221 UK ISSN 0309-0787
JOURNAL FOR THE STUDY OF THE OLD TESTAMENT. SUPPLEMENT SERIES. irreg. price varies. J S O T Press, 343 Fulwood Rd., University of Sheffield, Sheffield S10 3BP, England. Ed.Bd. Indexed: Old Test.Abstr.

220 US ISSN 0021-9231
JOURNAL OF BIBLICAL LITERATURE. 1882. q. $50 to non-members. (Society of Biblical Literature) Scholars Press, Box 1608, Decatur, GA 30031-1608. Ed. Victor Paul Furnish. adv. bk. rev. index. circ. 6,000. (also avail. in microfilm from UMI; reprint service avail. from UMI) Indexed: Curr.Cont. Hum.Ind. Old Test.Abstr. Rel.Per. Arts & Hum.Cit.Ind. Bk.Rev.Ind. CERDIC. G.Soc.Sci.& Rel.Per.Lit. Ind.Jew.Per. New Test.Abstr. Rel.& Theol.Abstr. Rel.Ind.One.

JOURNAL OF CHRISTIAN NURSING. see *MEDICAL SCIENCES — Nurses And Nursing*

230.05 US ISSN 0360-1420
JOURNAL OF CHRISTIAN RECONSTRUCTION. 1974. s-a. $14 to individuals; $12 to libraries. Chalcedon, Inc., Box 158, Vallecito, CA 95251. TEL 209-736-4365 Ed. R.J. Rushdoony. bk. rev. circ. 1,500. Indexed: Chr.Per.Ind.

322 261 US ISSN 0021-969X
JOURNAL OF CHURCH AND STATE. 1959. 3/yr. $15. Baylor University, J.M. Dawson Institute of Church-State Studies, Box 380, Waco, TX 76798. TEL 817-755-1510 Ed. James E. Wood, Jr. adv. bk. rev. index. circ. 1,400. (also avail. in microfilm from WSH) Indexed: Amer.Hist.& Life. Hist.Abstr. P.A.I.S. Rel.Per. Abstr.Bk.Rev.Curr.Leg.Per. Amer.Bibl.Slavic & E.Eur.Stud. Arts & Hum.Cit. Bk.Rev.Ind. CERDIC. C.L.I. Chr.Per.Ind. Educ.Admin.Abstr. L.R.I. Rel.& Theol.Abstr. Rel.Ind.One.

JOURNAL OF COMPARATIVE SOCIOLOGY & RELIGION. see *SOCIOLOGY*

200 II
JOURNAL OF DHARMA; an international quarterly of world religions. 1975. q. Rs.36($18) (Dharma Research Association) Dharmaram College, Centre for the Study of World Religions, Bangalore 560029, India. Ed. Thomas Kadankavil. adv. bk. rev. circ. 1,800. (also avail. in microform; reprint service avail. from ISI,UMI) Indexed: Curr.Cont. Phil.Ind. Arts & Hum.Cit.Ind. Rel.Ind.One.

209 UK ISSN 0022-0469
JOURNAL OF ECCLESIASTICAL HISTORY. 1953. q. $57 to individuals; $110 to institutions. Cambridge University Press, Edinburgh Bldg., Shaftesbury Rd., Cambridge CB2 2RU, England (And 32 E. 57th St., New York NY 10022) Eds. Brendan Bradshaw, Peter Linehan. adv. bk. rev. bibl. index. circ. 1,100. (also avail. in microform from UMI; reprint service avail. from UMI) Indexed: Br.Hum.Ind. Curr.Cont. Hist.Abstr. Hum.Ind. Rel.Per. Arts & Hum.Cit.Ind. Amer.Hist.& Life. Br.Archaeol.Abstr. CERDIC. G.Soc.Sci.& Rel.Per.Lit. New Test.Abstr. Rel.& Theol.Abstr. Rel.Ind.One.
History

260 US ISSN 0022-0558
JOURNAL OF ECUMENICAL STUDIES. 1964. 4/yr. $17.50. Temple University, Philadelphia, PA 19122. TEL 215-787-7714 Ed. Leonard Swidler. adv. bk. rev. abstr. index. circ. 2,200. (also avail. in microfilm from WSH) Indexed: Cath.Ind. Curr.Cont. Hist.Abstr. Hum.Ind. Leg.Per. Old Test.Abstr. Rel.Per. Amer.Bibl.Slavic & E.Eur.Stud. Arts & Hum.Cit.Ind. Amer.Hist.& Life. CERDIC. C.L.I. G.Soc.Sci.& Rel.Per.Lit. Int.Z.Bibelwiss. New Test.Abstr. Rel.& Theol.Abstr. Rel.Ind.One.

JOURNAL OF HEALTH CARE CHAPLAINCY. see *PHYSICAL FITNESS AND HYGIENE*

JOURNAL OF LAW AND RELIGION. see *LAW*

250 US ISSN 0022-3409
JOURNAL OF PASTORAL CARE. 1948. q. $15. Journal of Pastoral Care Publications, Inc., 1549 Clairmont Rd., Ste. 103, Decatur, GA 30030. Ed. Orlo Strunk. adv. bk. rev. index. circ. 10,000. (also avail. in microfilm from UMI; reprint service avail. from UMI) Indexed: Psychol.Abstr. Rel.Per. CERDIC. Rel.& Theol.Abstr. Rel.Ind.One.

200 US
JOURNAL OF PASTORAL PRACTICE; a professional periodical for church leaders. 1978. q. $16. Christian Counseling & Educational Foundation, 1790 E. Willow Grove Ave., Laverock, PA 19118. Ed. Dr. Jay E. Adams. bk. rev. circ. 525. (back issues avail.) Indexed: Chr.Per.Ind.

JOURNAL OF PASTORAL PSYCHOTHERAPY. see *PSYCHOLOGY*

JOURNAL OF PSYCHOLOGY AND CHRISTIANITY. see *PSYCHOLOGY*

200 150 US ISSN 0091-6471
JOURNAL OF PSYCHOLOGY AND THEOLOGY; an evangelical forum for the integration of psychology and theology. 1973. q. $20. Biola University, Rosemead School of Psychology, 13800 Biola Ave., La Mirada, CA 90639. TEL 213-944-0351 Ed. William F. Hunter. adv. bk. rev. circ. 1,700. (also avail. in microform from UMI; back issues avail.; reprint service avail. from UMI) Indexed: Curr.Cont. Old Test.Abstr. Psychol.Abstr. SSCI. Arts & Hum.Cit.Ind. CERDIC. Chr.Per.Ind. G.Soc.Sci.& Rel.Per.Lit. Psychol.R.G. Rel.& Theol.Abstr. Rel.Ind.One.

200 US ISSN 0022-4189
JOURNAL OF RELIGION. 1882. q. $22 to individuals; institutions $35. University of Chicago Press, 5801 S. Ellis Ave., Chicago, IL 60637 TEL 312-962-7600 (Orders to: Box 37005, Chicago, IL 60637) Ed.Bd. adv. bk. rev. index. circ. 2,200. (also avail. in microform from MIM,UMI; reprint service avail. from UMI,ISI) Indexed: Curr.Cont. Hist.Abstr. Hum.Ind. Old Test.Abstr. Rel.Per. SSCI. Arts & Hum.Cit.Ind. Bk.Rev.Ind. Bk.Rev.Dig. Amer.Hist.& Life. G.Soc.Sci.& Rel.Per.Lit. Int.Z.Bibelwiss. New Test.Abstr. Rel.Ind.One. Rel.& Theol.Abstr.

200 150 US ISSN 0022-4197
JOURNAL OF RELIGION AND HEALTH. 1961. q. $37 to individuals; institutions $95. ‡ (Institute of Religion) Human Sciences Press, Inc., 72 Fifth Ave., New York, NY 10011. TEL 212-243-6000 (Co-Sponsor: Institute of Health) Ed. Harry C. Meserve. adv. bk. rev. charts. index. circ. 2,000. (also avail. in microform from UMI; reprint service avail. from ISI,UMI) Indexed: Curr.Cont. Excerp.Med. Psychol.Abstr. SSCI. Arts & Hum.Cit.Ind. G.Soc.Sci.& Rel.Per.Lit. Past.Care & Couns.Abstr. Rel.& Theol.Abstr. Rel.Ind.One.

JOURNAL OF RELIGION AND THE APPLIED BEHAVIORAL SCIENCES. see *PSYCHOLOGY*

200 NE ISSN 0022-4200
JOURNAL OF RELIGION IN AFRICA/ RELIGION EN AFRIQUE. (Text in English and French) 1967. 3/yr. fl.86. E. J. Brill, P.O. Box 9000, 2300 PA Leiden, Netherlands. bk. rev. bibl. charts. illus. Indexed: Curr.Cont. Hist.Abstr. Rel.Per. Arts & Hum.Cit.Ind. Amer.Hist.& Life. CERDIC. Curr.Cont.Africa. Rel.Ind.One.

200 US ISSN 0384-9694
JOURNAL OF RELIGIOUS ETHICS. 1973. s-a. $12 to individuals; institutions $15. (Religious Ethics, Inc.) University of Notre Dame Press, Notre Dame, IN 46556. TEL 219-239-6346 Ed. James Johnson. circ. 1,200. (also avail. in microform from UMI; reprint service avail. from UMI) Indexed: Curr.Cont. Hum.Ind. Old Test.Abstr. Rel.Per. Arts & Hum.Cit.Ind. CERDIC. Phil.Ind. Rel.Ind.One. Rel.& Theol.Abstr.

209 AT ISSN 0022-4227
JOURNAL OF RELIGIOUS HISTORY. 1960. s-a. Aus.$16 to individuals; Aus. $29. to institutions. (Association for the Journal of Religious History) Sydney University Press, University of Sydney, North Ryde, N.S.W. 2006, Australia. Eds. B.E. Mansfield, A.E. Cahill. bk. rev. bibl. index. cum.index every 2 yrs. circ. 700. (also avail. in microform from MIM) Indexed: Curr.Cont. Hist.& Abstr. Rel.Per. Aus.P.A.I.S. Arts & Hum.Cit.Ind. Amer.Hist.& Life. CERDIC. Rel.Ind.One. Rel.& Theol.Abstr.
History

200 II ISSN 0047-2735
JOURNAL OF RELIGIOUS STUDIES. (Text and summaries in English) 1969. s-a. Rs.30($13) Punjabi University, Department of Religious Studies, Patiala 147002, Punjab, India. Ed. Wazir Singh. bk. rev. circ. 800. Indexed: New Test.Abstr. Rel.Ind.One.

200 US ISSN 0193-3604
JOURNAL OF RELIGIOUS STUDIES. 1972. s-a. $4. Cleveland State University, Department of Religion, Cleveland, OH 44115. Ed. Dr. Frederick Holck. adv. bk. rev. illus. circ. 1,200. (back issues avail.) Indexed: Rel.Per. CERDIC. New Test.Abstr. Rel.Ind.One.
Formerly: Ohio Journal of Religious Studies (ISSN 0094-5668)

700 US ISSN 0022-4235
JOURNAL OF RELIGIOUS THOUGHT. 1943. s-a. $12 to individuals; institutions $14. (Howard University, Divinity School) Howard University Publishing Company, 2900 Van Ness St., N.W., Washington, DC 20008. TEL 202-636-7766 Ed. Cain H. Felder. adv. bk. rev. bibl. cum.index. circ. 750. (also avail. in microform from UMI; reprint service avail. from UMI) Indexed: Ind.Sel.Per. Hist.Abstr. Rel.Per. Amer.Hist.& Life. New Test.Abstr. Rel.Ind.One. Rel.& Theol.Abstr.

377.8 US ISSN 0160-7774
JOURNAL OF SUPERVISION AND TRAINING IN MINISTRY. 1978. irreg., vol.8, 1986. $10. Association for Clinical Pastoral Education, North Central Region, Box 6777, Chicago, IL 60680. TEL 312-942-5572 (Co-sponsor: American Association of Pastoral Counselors. Central Region) Ed. George Fitchett. adv. bk. rev. circ. 1,000. Indexed: Rel.Per. Rel.Ind.One.

230 UK ISSN 0022-5185
JOURNAL OF THEOLOGICAL STUDIES. 1899. s-a. £36($80) Oxford University Press, Walton St., Oxford OX2 6DP, England. Eds. Prof. G.B. Caird, Dr. H. Chadwick. adv. bk. rev. abstr. bibl. charts. illus. index. circ. 1,500. (also avail. in microform from UMI) Indexed: Br.Hum.Ind. Curr.Cont. M.L.A. Old Test.Abstr. Rel.Per. Arts & Hum.Cit.Ind. CERDIC. New Test.Abstr. Rel.Ind.One. Rel.& Theol.Abstr.

200 SA ISSN 0047-2867
JOURNAL OF THEOLOGY FOR SOUTHERN AFRICA. 1972. q. R.10($15) for individuals; R.15 for Libraries. University of Cape Town, Department of Religious Studies, c/o University of Cape Town, Dept. of Religious Studies, 7700 Rodenbosch, Cape Town, South Africa. Ed. J.W. de Gruchy. adv. bk. rev. abstr. index. circ. 1,000. Indexed: Old Test.Abstr. CERDIC. Ind.S.A.Per. New Test.Abstr. Rel.Ind.One.

JOURNAL OF WOMEN AND RELIGION. see *WOMEN'S INTERESTS*

JUDAICA BOHEMIAE. see *ETHNIC INTERESTS*

268 AU ISSN 0022-6289
JUNGE GEMEINDE. 1948. q. S.20. Evangelisches Jugendwerk in Oesterreich, Liechtensteinstr. 20, A-1090 Vienna, Austria. Ed. F. SChlacheren. adv. bk. rev. abstr. circ. 2,000. (tabloid format)
Articles of interest to youth leaders

200 GW ISSN 0022-6319
JUNGE KIRCHE; eine Zeitschrift Europaeischer Christen. 1933. m. DM.56($27.50) Verlag Junge Kirche, Mathildenstr. 86, 2800 Bremen 1, W. Germany (B.R.D.) Ed.Bd. adv. bk. rev. index. circ. 6,800. Indexed: CERDIC.

268 GW ISSN 0022-6467
JUNGSCHARHELFER; Mitarbeiterhilfe fuer Jungen- und Maedchenarbeit. 1954. q. DM.20. (Gemeindejugendwerk) Verlag J. G. Oncken Nachf. GmbH, Langenbeckstr. 28/30, 3500 Kassel 1, W. Germany (B.R.D.) Ed. Hartmut Schwarz. bk. rev. circ. 2,100. (tabloid format)

268 248.82 US
JUNIOR LIFE. 1955. w. $0.80 per quarter. Messenger Publishing House, Box 850, Joplin, MO 64802. TEL 417-624-7050 Ed. Rosmarie Foreman. illus. circ. 3,200. (tabloid format)
Formerly: Commandos (ISSN 0010-2512)
Ages 9-11

200 UK ISSN 0306-7645
JUSTPEACE. 1936. 8/yr. £2.50. Pax Christi, St. Francis of Assisi Centre, Pottery Lane, London W11 4NQ, England. adv. bk. rev. circ. 3,500.
Formerly: Pax Bulletin (ISSN 0031-3319)

200 AU ISSN 0022-7757
KAIROS; Zeitschrift fuer Religionswissenschaft und Theologie. 1959. q. S.300. Otto Mueller Verlag, Ernest-Thun-Str. 11, Postfach 167, A-5021 Salzburg, Austria. Ed.Bd. adv. bk. rev. bibl. index. circ. 700. Indexed: Rel.Per. CERDIC. New Test.Abstr. Rel.Ind.One.

200 GW ISSN 0022-779X
KAISERSWERTHER MITTEILUNGEN. 1836. m. free. Diakoniewerk Kaiserswerth, Alte Landstr. 121, 4000 Duesseldorf 31-Kaiserswerth, W. Germany (B.R.D.) Eds. F. Schlingensiepen, M. Klaemmt. bk. rev. illus. circ. 33,000.

200 II ISSN 0022-8028
KALYAN. (Text in Hindi) 1927. m. Rs.30. Gita Press, Sagdesh Psesad Jalan, Gorakhpur, India. Ed.Bd.

KANDELAAR. see *EDUCATION*

200 GW ISSN 0022-9245
KASSELER SONNTAGSBLATT; christliches Volksblatt fuer Deutschland. 1879. w. DM.56.40. Verlag Thiele und Schwarz, Wilhelmshoeher Allee 254, Postfach 160, 3500 Kassel-Wilhelmshoehe, W. Germany (B.R.D.) Ed. Heinrich Schwarz. adv. bk. rev. illus. mkt. circ. 95,000. (tabloid format)

261 US ISSN 0022-9288
KATALLAGETE. 1965. irreg. $10 for 4 issues. Katallagete, Inc., Box 2307, College Sta., Berea, KY 40404. TEL 606-986-8218 Ed. James Y. Holloway. bk. rev. illus. circ. 4,500. (also avail. in microform from UMI) Indexed: Rel.Per. CERDIC. Rel.Ind.One.

200 920 CN ISSN 0315-8020
KATERI; Lily of the Mohawks. (Editions in French and English) 1949. q. Can.$2. Cause for the Canonization of Bl. Kateri Tekakwitha, Box 70, Kahnawake, Que. J0L 1B0, Canada. TEL 514-525-3611 Ed. Rev. Henri Bechard, S.J. circ. 16,800.

KATOLIKUS MAGYAROK VASARNAPJA; Catholic Hungarians' Sunday. see *RELIGIONS AND THEOLOGY — Roman Catholic*

200 327 NE
KERK EN VREDE. 1925. m. fl.25. Kerk en Vrede, Utrechtseweg 159, Amersfoort, Netherlands. Ed. R. Langman. bk. rev. abstr. circ. 3,000. Indexed: CERDIC.
Formerly: Militia Christi (ISSN 0026-4156)

200 NE
KERKBODE VAN NEDERLANDS GEREFORMEERDE KERKEN. 1945. 17/yr. fl.37.50. Buijten en Schipperheijn, B. V., Valkenburgerstraat 106, Amsterdam C, Netherlands. Ed.Bd. adv. bk. rev. circ. 1,800. (tabloid format)
Formerly: Kerkbode van Gereformeerde Kerken in Noord en Zuid-Holland (ISSN 0023-0618)

200 NE ISSN 0023-0685
KERUGMA. 1957. 6/yr. fl.45. Gooi en Sticht B.V., Postbox 17, 1200 AA Hilversum, Netherlands. Eds. B. Robben, A. Willems. Indexed: CERDIC.

266 CN ISSN 0023-0693
KERYGMA. (Text in English and French) 1967. s-a. $12. Saint Paul University, Institute of Mission Studies, 223 Main St., Ottawa K1S 1C4, Ont., Canada. TEL 613-235-1421 Ed. Achiel Peelman. bk. rev. circ. 250. Indexed: New Test.Abstr.
Missions

200 US
KERYGMA. 1981. 4/yr. $12. J L J Publishers, 824 Shrine Rd., Springfield, OH 45504-3999. TEL 513-322-4454 Ed. Jon L. Joyce. circ. 500.

KEY TO CHRISTIAN EDUCATION. see *EDUCATION*

KIERKEGAARDIANA. see *PHILOSOPHY*

268 NE ISSN 0023-1444
KIND EN ZONDAG. 1930. m. fl.45. Nederlandsche Zondagsschool Vereeniging, Bloemgracht 65, 1016 KG Amsterdam, Netherlands. Eds. J.J. Sinnema, C.M. de Vries. adv. bk. rev. circ. 20,000.

200 GW ISSN 0341-7190
KINDERGOTTESDIENST/LASS MICH HOEREN. 1890. q. DM.17.80. Guetersloher Verlagshaus Gerd Mohn, Koenigstr. 23-25, Postfach 1343, D-4830 Guetersloh 1, W. Germany (B.R.D.) (Subscr. to: Bechauf Verlag, Friedrichstr. 48, D-4800 Bielefeld 1, W. Germany (B.R.D.))

200 US ISSN 0023-1614
KINGDOM DIGEST. vol.29, 1968. m. $10. 806 W. Kiest Blvd., Box 24600, Dallas, TX 75224. TEL 214-374-8802 Ed. J. A. Lovell. bk. rev. bibl. Indexed: CERDIC.

KINSHIP. see *SOCIAL SERVICES AND WELFARE*

250 AU
KIRCHE BUNT. 1946. w. S.208. Dioecesis St. Poelten, Gutenbergstr. 12, 3100 St. Poelten, Austria. Ed. Franz Willinger. bk. rev. circ. 75,000.
Formerly: St. Poeltner Kirchenzeitung (ISSN 0036-3170)

KIRCHE IN MARBURG; Mitteilungen der evangelischen und katholischen Gemeinden. see *RELIGIONS AND THEOLOGY — Roman Catholic*

200 GW
KIRCHE UND KONFESSION. 1962. irreg. (Konfessionskundliche Institut des Ev. Bundes) Vandenhoeck & Ruprecht, Robert-Bosch-Breite 6, Postfach 3753, D-3400 Goettingen, W. Germany (B.R.D.)

KIRCHE UND RECHT. see *LAW*

KIRCHENMUSIKALISCHE NACHRICHTEN. see *MUSIC*

DER KIRCHENMUSIKER. see *MUSIC*

200 GW ISSN 0023-1827
KIRCHLICHES AMTSBLATT FUER DAS BISTUM ESSEN. 1958. s-m. DM.34. Bishchoefliches Generalvikariat Essen, Zwoelfling 16, Postfach 100464, 4300 Essen 1, W. Germany (B.R.D.) index. circ. 2,200. (looseleaf format)

058.82 NO ISSN 0023-186X
KIRKE OG KULTUR. 1894. m. (10/yr.) Kr.135. Gyldendal Norsk Forlag, Sehestedsgt. 4, 0164 Oslo 1, Norway (Subscr. to: Forlagsentralen Tidsskriftavd, Postboks 6079, Etterstad, Oslo 6, Norway) Ed. Inge Loenning. adv. bk. rev. index. circ. 3,000. Indexed: M.L.A.

200 DK ISSN 0107-9824
KIRKEFONDETS AARBOG. 1929. a. Kr.50. Kirkefondet, Valby Tingsted 7, 2500 Valby, Denmark. adv. illus. circ. 6,000.
Formerly: Koebenhavnske Kirkefondets Aarbog.

209 DK ISSN 0450-3171
KIRKEHISTORISKE SAMLINGER. (Text in Danish, English, German and Swedish) 1849. a. Kr.105. (Selskabet for Danmarks Kirkehistorie) Akademisk Forlag, Store Kannikestraede 8, P.O. Box 54, 1002 Copenhagen K, Denmark (Orders to: Danske Boghandleres Kommissionsanstalt, Siljangade 6, 2300 Copenhagen S, Denmark)

KIZITO; children's own magazine. see *CHILDREN AND YOUTH — For*

200 DK ISSN 0105-4821
KOEBENHAVNS UNIVERSITET. INSTITUT FOR RELIGIONSHISTORIE. SKRIFTER. 1976. irreg. Koebenhavns Universitet, Institut for Religionshistorie, Copenhagen, Denmark.

200 NE ISSN 0023-4389
KRACHT VAN OMHOOG. 1937. every 3 weeks. fl.12. Postbus 84, 4200 AB Gorinchem, Netherlands. Ed. J. E. van den Brink and P. Bronsveld. bk. rev. illus. tr.lit. circ. 4,000.

200 GW
KRAFT FUER DEN TAG; evangelisches Sonntagsblatt. w. DM.22. Brunnen Verlag GmbH, Postfach 5205, 6300 Giessen 1, W. Germany (B.R.D.)

200 CS ISSN 0023-4613
KRESTANSKA REVUE. vol.37, 1970. 10/yr. 30 Kcs.($14.50) (Kostnicka Jednota) Ustredni Cirkevni Nakladatelstvi, Jecna 2, 120 00 Prague 2, Czechoslovakia (Subscr. to: Artia, Ve Smeckach 30, 111 27 Prague 1, Czechoslovakia) Ed. Josef Smolik. bk. rev. circ. 1,800. Indexed: CERDIC.

200 NE
KRUISTOCHT. m. Stichting Nationaal Kruisleger, Hoge Nieuwstraat 9, 3311 AH Dordrecht, Netherlands. bk. rev. circ. 10,000.

200 II
KUNDALINI; a quarterly magazine of international spiritual & scientific progress. (Text in English) 1977. q. Rs.16($8) Kundalini Research and Publication Trust, D-291 Sarvodaya Enclave, New Delhi 110017, India. Ed. Anil Vidyalankar. adv. bk. rev. circ. 4,000. (back issues avail.) Indexed: Ind.India.
Formerly (until 1979): Spiritual India.

266 KO
KUSEGONGBO. (Text in Korean) 1909. m. $1. Salvation Army, C.P.O. Box 1192, Seoul 100, S. Korea. Ed. Captain Han, Kwang-Soo. circ. 15,000. (newspaper)

200 UK ISSN 0023-5814
KVAKERA ESPERANTISTO. (Text in Esperanto) 1950. 3/yr. £4. Kvakera Esperantista Societo, c/o Brian F. Bone, 5 Lane End Close, Shinfield, Reading RG2 9AS, England. adv. bk. rev. circ. 400.

262.9 SW ISSN 0023-6136
KYRKOFOERFATTNINGAR. 1957. 5/yr. Kr.135. Verbum Forlag AB, Box 152 69, S-104 65 Stockholm, Sweden. Ed. Karin Andren. charts. index. circ. 3,300(controlled)
Canon law

200 SW ISSN 0085-2619
KYRKOHISTORISK AARSSKRIFT. (Text in Swedish and English; summaries in English, German and French) 1900. a. Kr.75. Svenska Kyrkohistoriska Foereningen, Box 1604, S-751 46, Sweden. Ed. Harry Lenhammar. adv. bk. rev. circ. 1,000. Indexed: Hist.Abstr. Amer.Hist.& Life.

KYRKOMUSIKERNAS TIDNING. see *MUSIC*

266 SW ISSN 0345-7842
LAERARNAS MISSIONSFOERENING. MEDDELANDE TILL L M F. (Text in Danish, Norwegian, and Swedish) 1902. bi-m. Kr.20. Laerarnas Missionsfoerening, Vasaplatsen 4, 411 34 Goeteborg, Sweden. Ed. Florence Waestvind. bk. rev. illus. circ. 4,000.
Formerly: Laerarinnornas Missionsfoerening. Meddelande till L M F. (ISSN 0023-6322)
Missions

200 US ISSN 0023-8635
LAST DAY MESSENGER. 1963. q. free on request. (Interstate Bible Chapel, Inc.) Gospel Tract Distributors, Box 17406, Portland, OR 97217. Ed. Dee L. McCroskey. illus. circ. 11,000.

200 VC
LATERANUM. 1976. s-a. $24. Pontificia Universita Lateranense, Piazza S. Giovanni in Laterano 4, 00120 Vatican City. Ed. Alessandro Galuzzi. bk. rev. Indexed: CERDIC. Old Test.Abstr.

200 301 PE
LATINAMERICA PRESS. Spanish edition: Noticias Aliadas. (Text in English) 1969. w. $40 to individuals; institutions $60. Noticias Aliadas, Apdo. 5594, Lima 100, Peru. Ed.Bd. bk. rev. index. cum.index. circ. 1,200. Indexed: I.C.U.I.S.Abstr.Serv.

LAUGHING MAN; the alternative to scientific materialism and religious provincialism. see *PHILOSOPHY*

200 100 CN ISSN 0023-9054
LAVAL THEOLOGIQUE ET PHILOSOPHIQUE. (Text in English and French) 1945. 3/yr. Can.$12. Presses de l'Universite Laval, C.P. 2447, Quebec G1K 7R4, Canada. TEL 418-656-3809 Eds. Pierre Gaudette, L. Ponton. bk. rev. bibl. index. cum.index. circ. 1,000. Indexed: Cath.Ind. Curr.Cont. Old Test.Abstr. Arts & Hum.Cit.Ind. CERDIC. New Test.Abstr. Pt.de Rep. Phil.Ind.

LAW & JUSTICE. see *LAW*

266 UG ISSN 0047-424X
LEADERSHIP; a magazine for Christian leaders in Africa. 1956. m. EAs.50($17) (Comboni Missionaries) Leadership Publications, Box 2522, Kampala, Uganda. Ed. John Troy. adv. bk. rev. illus. stat. circ. 38,000. Indexed: Rel.& Theol.Abstr.

200 SZ
LEBEN; monatszeitschrift der Fokolar-Bewegung in der Schweiz. (Text in German) 1974. m. 10 Fr.($7.50) (Fokolar-Bewegung) Verlag Neue Stadt, Seestrasse 426, Postfach 435, Ch-8038 Zurich, Switzerland. circ. 2,600. (back issues avail.)

200 US ISSN 0075-8531
LECTURES ON THE HISTORY OF RELIGIONS. NEW SERIES. no. 9, 1971. irreg., no. 11, 1977. Columbia University Press, 562 W. 113th St., New York, NY 10025. TEL 212-678-6777

200 NE ISSN 0024-0427
LEGIOEN VAN MARIA. 1945. q. fl.6. Senaat van Het Legioen van Maria in Nederland, Pb. 77, 5000 AB Tilburg, Netherlands. illus.

200 UK
LENGO. (Text in Swahili) fortn. EAs.35. Middle East Economic Digest Ltd., Meed House, 21 John St., London WC1N 2BP, England. adv.

266.025 UK ISSN 0075-8809
LEPROSY MISSION, LONDON. ANNUAL REPORT. 1874. a. free. ‡ Leprosy Mission, 50 Portland Place, London W1N 3DG, England. Ed. U. Sadie. circ. 9,000.
Formerly: Mission to Lepers, London. Annual Report.
Missions

255 FR
LERINS. 1930. q. 50 Fr. Abbaye de Lerins, Ile St. Honorat, B.P. 157, 06406 Cannes, France. circ. 1,200.
Supersedes: Congregation Cistercienne de Senaque et de la Pieuse Ligue Universelle pour les Ames de l'Abbaye de Lerins. (Publication) (ISSN 0010-5813)

266 FR ISSN 0024-1490
LEVANT MORGENLAND. (Text in French and German) 1923. bi-m. 5 F. Action Chretienne en Orient, 7 rue du General-Offenstein, Strasbourg, France. Ed. Pasteur R. Brecheisen. illus. circ. 12,500.

200 NE
LEVENSWOORDEN. 1947. m. fl.7.50. Gereformeerd Traktaatgenootschap Filippus, Postbus 695, 6800 AR Arnhem, Netherlands. Ed. H. Schriemer. circ. 1,200.

207.11 US ISSN 0160-8770
LEXINGTON THEOLOGICAL QUARTERLY. 1954. q. free to qualified personnel or on exchange basis. Lexington Theological Seminary, 631 S. Limestone St., Lexington, KY 40508. TEL 312-434-0706 Ed. William R. Barr. bk. rev. circ. 2,300. Indexed: Old Test.Abstr. CERDIC. New Test.Abstr. Rel.Ind.One. Rel.& Theol.Abstr.
Formerly: College of the Bible Quarterly (ISSN 0024-1628)

261 US ISSN 0024-2055
LIBERTY (WASHINGTON, 1906); a magazine of religious freedom. 1888. bi-m. $6.75. (International Religious Liberty Association) Review and Herald Publishing Association, 55 West Oak Ridge Dr., Hagerstown, MD 21740. TEL 301-791-7000 Ed. Roland R. Hegstad. adv. bk. rev. illus. index. cum.index. circ. 268,000. (also avail. in microform from UMI; reprint service avail. from UMI)

LIBRARY OF PHILOSOPHY AND RELIGION. see *PHILOSOPHY*

200 GW ISSN 0047-4584
LICHT UND LEBEN. 1889. m. DM.16.80. (Evangelische Gesellschaft fuer Deutschland e.V.) Licht und Leben Verlag, Kaiserstr. 78, D-5600 Wuppetal 11, W. Germany (B.R.D.) Ed. H. Becker. adv. bk. rev. circ. 10,000.

268 NE
LICHTHOEVE. 1932. q. fl.7.50. Lichthoeve, Oude Barnevelderweg 7, 3886 PT Garderen, Netherlands. Ed. M. Maring. circ. 10,000.
Formerly: Lichthoeve-Kinderwerk (ISSN 0024-2853)

200 UK ISSN 0047-4657
LIGHT (LONDON, 1969); on a new world. 1969. bi-m. 70p.($1.20) ‡ (Bexley Christadelphians Ecclesia) Light Bible Publications, 3 Dickens Close, Hartley, Dartford, Kent DA3 8DP, England. Ed. D.J. Evans. circ. 3,500. (also avail. in microform)

268 II
LIGHT OF LIFE; all India magazine of Christian growth. (Text in English) 1957. m. $15. Christian Digest Society of India, 21 YMCA Rd., Bombay 400008, India. Ed. Benny Joseph. adv. bk. rev. illus. circ. 3,000.

266 UK ISSN 0024-3396
LIGHTBEARER. 1904. bi-m. £3. S.U.M. Fellowship, 75 Granville Rd., Sidcup, Kent DA14 4BU, England. Ed. David Calcott. maps. stat. circ. 5,200. Indexed: CERDIC.
Missions

LINGUISTICA BIBLICA; Interdisziplinaere Zeitschrift fuer Theologie und Linguistik. see *LINGUISTICS*

200 800 US ISSN 0732-1929
LITERATURE AND BELIEF. 1981. a. $4. Brigham Young University, College of Humanities, Center for the Study of Christian Values in Literature, Jesse Knight Bldg., Provo, UT 84602. TEL 801-378-2304 Ed. Jay Fox. bk. rev. circ. 1,000. Indexed: M.L.A. Abstr.Engl.Stud. LCR.

200 IT
LITTERAE COMMUNIONIS. 1975. m. L.40000. (Gruppi di Comunione e Liberazione) Cooperativa Editoriale Nuovo Mondo, Via Mose Bianchi 94, 20149 Milan, Italy. Ed. Maurizio Vitali. adv. bk. rev.
Formerly: Comunione e Liberazione.

200 US ISSN 0460-1297
LITTLE LAMP; a journal for leading the spiritual life through the practice of meditation. 1967. q. $8. (Blue Mountain Center of Meditation) Nilgiri Press, Box 477, Petaluma, CA 94953. Ed. Christine Easwaran. circ. 2,000. (back issues avail.)

200 GW ISSN 0344-9092
LITURGIE KONKRET. 1978. m. DM.42.80. Friedrich Pustet, Gutenbergstr. 8, 8400 Regensburg 11, W. Germany (B.R.D.) Ed.Bd.

200 GW ISSN 0076-0048
LITURGIEWISSENSCHAFTLICHE QUELLEN UND FORSCHUNGEN. 1919. irreg. price varies. Aschendorffsche Verlagsbuchhandlung, Soester Str. 13, 4400 Muenster, W. Germany (B.R.D.) Ed. W. Heckenbach.

264 GW ISSN 0024-5100
LITURGISCHES JAHRBUCH. 1951. 4/yr. DM.48. (Liturgisches Institut Trier) Aschendorffsche Verlagsbuchhandlung, Soester Str. 13, 4400 Muenster, W. Germany (B.R.D.) Ed. Andreas Heinz. adv. bk. rev. index. Indexed: Rel.Ind.One.

200 US ISSN 0458-063X
LITURGY; teaching prayer. 1955; N.S. 1980. q. $20. Liturgical Conference, 806 Rhode Island Ave. N.E., Washington, DC 20018. TEL 202-529-7400 adv. bk. rev. bibl. (back issues avail.) Indexed: Cath.Ind. CERDIC. Rel.& Theol.Abstr.

200 US ISSN 0890-5568
LIVING PRAYER. 1967. bi-m. $12. Contemplative Review Inc., Beckley Hill, Barre, VT 05641. Ed. Sr. Mary Roman. bk. rev. circ. 7,000. (also avail. in microform from UMI) Indexed: Cath.Ind.
Formerly (until Sep.1986): Contemplative Review (ISSN 0193-8452)

200 UK ISSN 0261-3514
LIVING SUNDAY. 6/yr. £6.50. Diocese of Northampton, Religious Education Service, St. Mary's R.E. Centre, 118 Bromham Rd., Bedford MK40 2QR, England. Eds. Rev. John P. Glen, Kevin McGinnell. circ. 150.

200 UK ISSN 0024-5445
LLAN. (Text in Welsh) w. Church in Wales Publications, Woodland Place, Penarth; Glam CF6 2EX, Wales. Ed. Hadyn Rowlands. adv. bk. rev. circ. 1,000.

200 060 PH ISSN 0076-0471
LOGOS; a series of monographs in scripture, theology, philosophy. (Text in English) 1966. irreg., no.14, 1985. price varies. Loyola School of Theology, Ateneo de Manila University, Box 4082, Manila, Philippines. Ed. Joseph L. Roche. circ. 500. Indexed: Chr.Per.Ind.

200 US ISSN 0148-2009
LONERGAN WORKSHOP. s-a. $18. Scholars Press, Box 1608, Decatur, GA 30031-1608. Ed. Fred Lawrence.

LOOKOUT. see *TRANSPORTATION — Ships And Shipping*

200 040 BE ISSN 0024-6964
LOUVAIN STUDIES. 1966. q. 800 Fr.($18) Katholieke Universiteit Leuven, Faculty of Theology, St.Michielstraat 2-6, B-3000 Leuven, Belgium. Ed. Raymond F. Collins. adv. bk. rev. index. circ. 1,500. (also avail. in microform from UMI; back issues avail) Indexed: Cath.Ind. Old Test.Abstr. CERDIC. Canon Law Abstr. New Test.Abstr. Rel.& Theol.Abstr.

200 FR ISSN 0024-7332
LUMIERE. 1953. q. 100 F.($12) Agence Mondiale d'Information, 3 rue Geoffrey St. Hilaire, 75005 Paris, France. bk. rev. Indexed: Old Test.Abstr.

266 FR ISSN 0024-7340
LUMIERE DU MONDE. 1920. q. 30 F. (Societe Presse et Publications Missionnaires) Oeuvre de Saint Pierre Apotre, 12 rue Sala, 69287 Lyon Cedex 1, France. abstr. charts. illus. stat. circ. 70,000.
Missions

220 264 FR ISSN 0024-7359
LUMIERE ET VIE; revue de formation et de reflexion theologiques. 1951. 5/yr. 180 F. Association Lumiere et Vie, 2 place Gailleton, 69002 Lyon, France. Ed. Michel Demaison. adv. bk. rev. index. circ. 5,000. Indexed: Cath.Ind. CERDIC. New Test.Abstr.

274 PO ISSN 0076-1508
LUSITANIA SACRA. 1956. a. 140 esc. Centro de Estudos de Historia Eclesiastica, Campo dos Martires da Patria, 45, Lisbon-1, Portugal. Ed. Isaias da Rosa Pereira. Indexed: Hist.Abstr. Amer.Hist.& Life.

200 UR ISSN 0024-7871
LYUDYNA I SVIT. 1965. m. $4.20. Izdatel'stvo Radyanska Ukraina, Brest-Litovskii Prospekt, 94, Kiev, Ukrainian S.S.R., U.S.S.R. index.
Formerly: Voiovnychyi Ateyist.

266 US
M A R C NEWSLETTER. bi-m. free. Missions Advanced Research & Communication Center, (Subsidiary of: World Vision International) 919 W. Huntington Dr., Monrovia, CA 91016. TEL 818-303-8811 Indexed: CERDIC.
Missions

200 US ISSN 0362-0808
M S S. (Master Sermon Series) 1970. m. $25. Cathedral Publishers, 324 E. Fourth St., Royal Oak, MI 48068. Ed. Carl G. Howie. (looseleaf format)

200 IT ISSN 0024-9599
MADONNA DI CASTELMONTE. 1913. m. L.10000. Frati Minori Cappuccini Veneti, 33040 Castelmonte (UD), Italy. Ed.Bd. illus. circ. 60,000.

200 FR
MAGNIFICAT - LA VERITE. (Editions in Dutch, English, French, German and Italian) 1961. m. 25 F. Association du Magnificat, Clemery 54610 Nomeny, Nancy, France. Ed. Pere Bernardin. illus. circ. 5,000.
Formerly: Verite (ISSN 0042-3971)

200 FR ISSN 0025-0937
MAISON-DIEU; revue de Pastorale Liturgique. 1945. 4/yr. 218 F. Editions du Cerf, 29 bd. Latour-Maubourg, 75007 Paris, France. adv. bk. rev. index. Indexed: CERDIC. New Test.Abstr.

266 CN ISSN 0225-7068
MANDATE. 1969. 7/yr. Can.$5. United Church of Canada, 85 St. Clair Ave. E., Toronto, Ont. M4T 1M8, Canada. TEL 416-925-5931 Ed. Dean Salter. circ. 36,000.
Missions

266 CN
MANDATE "SPECIAL". 1977. s-a. Can.$1.50. United Church of Canada, 85 St. Clair Ave. E., Toronto, Ont. M4T 1M8, Canada. TEL 416-925-5931 Ed. Rebekah Chevalier. charts. illus. circ. 39,000. (back issues)
Formerly: Mission Magazine (ISSN 0706-5590)
Missions

200 JM
MANNA. q. Jam.$70. University and Colleges Christian Fellowship, 22 Hagley Park Plaza, Box 281, Kingston 10, Jamaica. circ. 2,000.

200 SP
MANRESA; revista de investigacion e informacion ascetica y mistica. 1925. q. 1800 ptas.($22) (Loyola, Centro de Espiritualidad) Casa de Escritores S.J. (C E S I), Pablo Aranda 3, 28006 Madrid, Spain. adv. bk. rev. circ. 1,000. Indexed: Hist.Abstr. Amer.Hist.& Life. CERDIC. New Test.Abstr.

200 AU ISSN 0025-2999
MARIAHILFER PFARRBOTE. 1924. q. contribution. Pfarramt Mariahilf, Barnabitengasse 14, 1060 Vienna, Austria. Ed. Waldemar Posch. bk. rev. abstr. charts. illus. stat. index. circ. 3,000.

200 020 US ISSN 0076-4434
MARIAN LIBRARY STUDIES. NEW SERIES. (Text in language of author) 1951; 1969 N.S. a. $10. University of Dayton, Marian Library, Dayton, OH 45469-0001. TEL 513-229-4214 Ed. Theodore Koehler. circ. 200. Indexed: Cath.Ind. CERDIC. New Test.Abstr.

266 232 AU ISSN 0025-3022
MARIANNHILL. bi-m. S.30. Missionare von Mariannhill, Riedegg 1, A-4210 Gallneukirchen, Austria. Eds. Br. Franziskus Puehringer, P.A. Balling. bk. rev. circ. 45,000. (tabloid format)
Missions

282 US
MARKINGS. 1971. m. $29.95. Thomas More Association, 223 W. Erie St., Chicago, IL 60610. TEL 312-951-2100

260 II
MASIHI AVAZA. (Text in Hindi) vol. 45, 1972. m. Rs.5. 277 Angrahpuri, Gaya, Bihar, India. bibl. illus.
Christianity

266 UK
MASTER AND THE MULTITUDE. 1853. q. £1. Open-Air Mission, 19 John St., London WC1N 2DL, England. Ed. Alan J. Greenbank. illus. circ. 5,000.
Missions

200 GW
MATERIALDIENST; der evangelische Zentralstelle fuer Weltanschauungsfragen. 1937. m. DM.36. Quell Verlag, Furtbachstr. 12A, D-7000 Stuttgart 1, W. Germany (B.R.D.) circ. 5,000.

200 GW
MATHILDE-ZIMMER-STIFTUNG. BLAETTER. 1906. bi-m. DM.11. (Mathilde-Zimmer-Stiftung e.V.) Christlicher Zeitschriftenverlag, Bachstr. 1-2, 1000 Berlin 21, W. Germany (B.R.D.) Ed. E. Zimmer. adv. bk. rev. circ. 2,000.

MEDIA & VALUES; a quarterly magazine/educational resource analyzing the social impact of mass media and new technologies on the family, youth and children. see *COMMUNICATIONS*

MEDIA DEVELOPMENT. see *COMMUNICATIONS — Radio And Television*

266 610 UK ISSN 0025-7370
MEDICAL MISSIONARY NEWS. 1946. q. Medical Mission Sisters, 3 Blakesley Ave., Ealing, London WC5 2DN, England. illus. circ. 1,000.
Missions

MEDICINE AND GOSPEL/IGAKU TO FUKUIN. see *MEDICAL SCIENCES*

200 US
MEGIDDO MESSAGE. 1914. m. $2. Megiddo Church, 481 Thurston Rd., Rochester, NY 14619-1697. TEL 716-436-1614 Ed. Newton H. Payne. index. cum.index: 1915-1944, 1960-1980. circ. 7,900. (also avail. in looseleaf format)

200 PP ISSN 0256-856X
MELANESIAN JOURNAL OF THEOLOGY. (Text in English) 1985. s-a. $6. Melanesian Association of Theological Schools, Summer Institute of Linguistic, c/o Martin Luther Seminary, Box 80, Lae, Papua New Guinea. Ed. John D.A. May. (back issues avail.)

200 MM
MELITA THEOLOGICA. (Text in English and Italian) 1946. a. $8. Mater Admirabilis College, Faculty of Theology, Tal-Virtu', Rabat, Malta. (Co-sponsor: Theological Students' Association) adv. bk. rev. index. circ. 1,000. Indexed: Old Test. Abstr. New Test.Abstr. Rel.& Theol.Abstr.

MEMORANDUM (ST. PAUL) see *COLLEGE AND ALUMNI*

200 IT
MEMORIE DOMENICANE. 1884; N.S. 1970. a. price varies. Centro Riviste della Provincia Romana dei Frati Predicatori, Piazza S. Domenico 1, 51100 Pistoia, Italy. Ed. Eugenio Marino. bk. rev. bibl. circ. 400. (tabloid format) Indexed: CERDIC. RILA.

200 DK
MENIGHEDSRAADENES BLAD. m. (11/yr.) (Foreningen af Menighedsraadsmedlemmer) Harlang og Toksvig Bladforlag A-S, Dr. Tvaergade 30, 1302 Copenhagen K, Denmark. Ed. Joergen Ginnerup. adv. circ. 22,000.

200 SP ISSN 0211-6561
MENSAJERO; del corazon de Jesus. 1866. m. 1050 ptas. Ediciones Mensajero S.A., Sancho de Azpeitia, 2, Apdo. 73, 48080 Bilbao, Spain. Ed. Luis Manuel de la Encina. adv. bk. rev. illus. circ. 35,000.

200 EC
MENSAJERO. 1884. m. (10/yr.) S/400($13) Ediciones Mensajero, Apdo. 4100, Quito, Ecuador. Ed.Bd. circ. 5,000.

MERLEG; folyoiratok es konyvek szemleje. see *LITERARY AND POLITICAL REVIEWS*

200 US ISSN 0026-0231
MESSAGE (HAGERSTOWN) 1934. bi-m. $11.95. ‡ Review and Herald Publishing Association, 55 West Oak Ridge Dr., Hagerstown, MD 21740. TEL 301-791-7000 Ed. Delbert W. Baker. bk. rev. illus. record rev. index. circ. 68,000.
Formerly: Message Magazine (ISSN 0162-6019)

220 US
MESSAGE OF THE OPEN BIBLE. 1920. m. $6. Open Bible Standard Churches, Open Bible Publishers, 2020 Bell Ave., Des Moines, IA 50315. TEL 515-288-6761 Ed. Betty C. Bowlin. bk. rev. circ. 4,550.

200 IT
MESSAGGERO CAPPUCCINO. 1957. bi-m. L.8000($20) Messaggero Cappuccino, Via Villa Clelia 10, 40026 Imola, Italy. Ed. Dino Dozzi. (back issues avail.)

200 US ISSN 0026-0363
MESSENGER/MESSAGGERO. (Text in English & Italian) 1921. m. $1. Messenger Publishing Co. (Kansas City), 544 Wabash, Kansas City, MO 64124. Ed. Dr. J. B. Bisceglia. adv. bk. rev. bibl. illus. circ. 1,000. (tabloid format; also avail. in microform)

METHOD: JOURNAL OF LONERGAN STUDIES. see *PHILOSOPHY*

200 301.3 US
METRO - MINISTRY NEWS. 1985. q. $8. Institute on Church in Urban-Industrial Society, 5700 S. Woodlawn, Chicago, IL 60637. TEL 312-643-7111 Ed. L. Dale Richesin. bk. rev. circ. 3,000.

MIGRANTI-PRESS. see *POLITICAL SCIENCE*

MILITARY CHAPLAIN. see *MILITARY*

MILITARY CHAPLAINS' REVIEW. see *MILITARY*

200 100 IE ISSN 0332-1428
MILLTOWN STUDIES. 1977. s-a. £7. Milltown Institute of Theology & Philosophy, Milltown Park, Dublin 6, Ireland. Ed. Wilfrid Harrington. adv. bk. rev. circ. 200. Indexed: Old Test.Abstr. New Test.Abstr.

297 297 UA
MINBAR AL ISLAM. (Editions in Arabic and English) m. (Arabic ed.); q. (English ed.) $6 (English ed. or Arabic ed.) Supreme Council for Islamic Affairs, 3 Kadadar St., Tahrier Sq., Cairo, Egypt. Ed. Muhammad Tawfick Oweida. bibl. illus.

267 270 ZA ISSN 0076-8901
MINDOLO NEWS LETTER. 1961. irreg., no. 33, 1970. K.2($3) donation. (Mindolo Ecumenical Foundation) Mission Press, Ndola, P.O. Box 1493, Kitwe, Zambia. Ed. Jonathan C. Phiri. adv. circ. 4,000 (approx.)

200 SZ
MINISTERIAL FORMATION. (Text in English) q. World Council of Churches, Programme in Theological Education, 150 Route de Ferney, Box 66, 1211 Geneva 20, Switzerland. Indexed: Rel.Ind.One.

200 US
MINISTRIES; the magazine for Christian leaders. 1983. q. $24. Strang Communications Co., 190 N. Westmonte Dr., Altamonte Springs, FL 32714. TEL 305-869-5005 Ed. Stephen Strang. circ. 30,000.

200 100 370.1
150 SP ISSN 0210-9522
MISCELANEA COMILLAS; revista de teologia y ciencias humanas. 1943. s-a. 1,200 ptas. Universidad Pontificia Comillas de Madrid, Facultades de Filosofia y Letras y Teologia, E-28049 Madrid, Spain. Ed. Jose Joaquin Alemany. adv. bk. rev. Indexed: Hist.Abstr. Amer.Hist.& Life. CERDIC. New Test.Abstr.

266 SP
MISIONEROS JAVERIANOS. 1963. m. free. Misioneros Javerianos, Monserrat. 9, Madrid-8, Spain. illus. circ. 48,000. (tabloid format)
Missions

200 FR ISSN 0026-5977
MISSI; magazine d'information spirituelle et de solidarite internationale. 1935. m. 120 F. 6 rue d'Auvergne, 69287 Lyon Cedex 1, France. Ed. Georges Naidenoff. bk. rev. index. circ. 50,000. Indexed: CERDIC.

MISSIOLOGY; an international review. see *ANTHROPOLOGY*

266 DK
MISSION; Nordisk missions tidsskrift. 1889. q. Kr.75. Dansk Missionraad - Danish Missionary Council, Norrebrogade 56, 2200 Copenhagen N, Denmark. Ed. J. Aagaard. bk. rev. charts. stat. index. circ. 1,000.
Formerly: Nordisk Missions Tidsskrift (ISSN 0029-1447)
Missions

266 FR ISSN 0026-6124
MISSION. MESSAGES. 1920. bi-m. 25 F. ‡ Procure des Missions du Levant, 32 rue Boissonade, 75014 Paris, France. Ed. Jean Delcroix. bk. rev. illus. stat. circ. 4,500.

266 US ISSN 0161-7133
MISSIONARY MONTHLY. 1896. m. (9/yr.) $9. (Reformed Bible College) Missionary Monthly, Inc., Box 6181, Grand Rapids, MI 49506. TEL 616-458-0404 Ed. Dr. Dick L. Van Halsema. adv. bk. rev. circ. 4,000.
Missions

266 US ISSN 0026-6051
MISSIONARY NEWS SERVICE. 1953. s-m. $17.95. Evangelical Missions Information Service, Box 794, Wheaton, IL 60189. TEL 312-653-2158 Ed. James W. Reapsome. circ. 1,800.

266 CN ISSN 0026-6116
MISSIONS-ETRANGERES. (Text in French) 1941. bi-m. Can.$3. ‡ Societe des Missions-Etrangeres, 160 Place Juge-Desnoyers, Pont-Viau, Ville de Laval H7G 1A4, Que., Canada. TEL 514-384-0026 Ed. Frank Belec. charts. illus. stat. circ. 50,000.
Missions

266 UK
MISSIONS TO SEAMEN ANNUAL REPORT. 1856. a. free. Missions to Seamen, St. Michael Paternoster Royal, College Hill, London EC4R 2RL, England. Ed. Gillian Ennis. index.
Formerly: Missions to Seamen Handbook (ISSN 0076-9401)
Missions

266 SW ISSN 0026-6132
MISSIONSBANERET. 1921. w. Kr.78($10) Oerebromissionens Foerlag, Box 1623, S-701 16 Oerebro, Sweden. Ed. Ingemar Ringsvaag. adv. bk. rev. illus. circ. 13,000. (tabloid format)
Missions

266 GW ISSN 0076-941X
MISSIONSWISSENSCHAFTLICHE ABHANDLUNGEN UND TEXTE/ETUDES ET DOCUMENTS MISSIONNAIRES/ MISSION STUDIES AND DOCUMENTS. 1917. irreg. price varies. (Internationales Institut fuer Missionswissenschaftliche Forschungen) Aschendorffsche Verlagsbuchhandlung, Soester Str. 13, 4400 Muenster, W. Germany (B.R.D.)
Missions

266 GW ISSN 0076-9428
MISSIONSWISSENSCHAFTLICHE FORSCHUNGEN. 1962. irreg. price varies. Guetersloher Verlagshaus Gerd Mohn, Koenigstr. 23-25, Postfach 1343, 4830 Guetersloh, W. Germany (B.R.D.)
Missions

268 TZ ISSN 0047-7583
MLEZI; a journal for preaching and teaching religion. (Text in Swahili) 1970. bi-m. EAs.30($6) ‡ (Benedictine Abbey Peramiho) Peramiho Publications, Box 41, Peramiho, Tanzania. Ed. Gerold Rupper. adv. bk. rev. illus. circ. 19,200.

200 GW
MODELLE FUER DEN RELIGIONSUNTERRICHT. Short title: M.R.U. 1975. irreg., no.8, 1979. price varies. (Religionspaedagogische Projektentwicklung in Baden und Wuerttemberg) Calwer Verlag, Scharnhauser Str. 44, 7000 Stuttgart 70, W. Germany (B.R.D.) (Co-publisher: Koesel-Verlag) Eds. Klaus Dessecker, Gerhard Martin.

200 UK ISSN 0026-7597
MODERN CHURCHMAN. 1911. q. £5($8) to non-members. Modern Churchmen's Union, School House, Leysters, Leominster, Herefordshire HR6 0HB, England. Ed. Prof. A.O. Dyson. adv. bk. rev. index. circ. 1,200. (also avail. in microfilm from UMI) Indexed: Rel.Per. CERDIC. New Test.Abstr. Rel.Ind.One.

260 US ISSN 0363-504X
MODERN LITURGY. 1973. 9/yr. $36. Resource Publications, Inc., 160 E. Virginia St., San Jose, CA 95112. TEL 408-286-8505 Ed. Kenneth E. Guentert. adv. bk. rev. circ. 15,000. (also avail. in microform from UMI; reprint service avail. from UMI) Indexed: Cath.Ind. Music Artic. Guide. CERDIC. Music Ind.
Formerly: Folk Mass and Modern Liturgy (ISSN 0094-775X); Incorporating (as of Sep. 1979): Worship Times.

200 UK ISSN 0266-7177
MODERN THEOLOGY. 1984. q. £15($25) to individuals; institutions £30($60) Basil Blackwell Ltd., 108 Cowley Rd., Oxford OX4 1JF, England. Ed. Kenneth Surin. adv. bk. rev. circ. 500. (also avail. in microform)

MONDE DE LA BIBLE. see *ARCHAEOLOGY*

200 DK ISSN 0901-2982
MONTHLY JOURNAL OF SCIENTOLOGY. m. (Church of Scientology, Bibliotekscentralen) Bibliotekscentralen, Telegrafvej 5, DK-2750 Ballerup, Denmark.

200 SZ
MONTHLY LETTER ON EVANGELISM. (Editions in English, French, German, Spanish) 1956. 10/yr. 12 Fr. donation. World Council of Churches, Commission on World Mission and Evangelism, 150 Route de Ferney, Box 66, 1211 Geneva 20, Switzerland. Ed. Raymond Fung. circ. 4,000 (all edts.) Indexed: CERDIC.

200 US ISSN 0027-0806
MOODY MONTHLY; the Christian magazine for all the family. 1900. m. (11/yr.) $16.95. Moody Bible Institute of Chicago, 820 N. La Salle St., Chicago, IL 60610. TEL 312-508-6820 Ed. Michael Umlandt. adv. bk. rev. illus. index. circ. 190,000. (also avail. in microform from UMI) Indexed: R.G. Chr.Per.Ind. G.Soc.Sci.& Rel.Per.Lit.

200 US
MOODY STUDENT. 1935. fortn. $9. Moody Bible Institute, 820 N. LaSalle, Chicago, IL 60610. TEL 312-895-3720 Ed. Richard Van Dyke. adv. circ. 2,100. (tabloid format)

MOREANA; time trieth truth. see *HISTORY — History Of Europe*

MOUNTAIN PATH. see *PHILOSOPHY*

266 SP
MUNDO NEGRO; revista misional africana. 1960. m. 700 ptas.($5) Misioneros Combonianos, Congregacion Misionera, Arturo Soria, 101, Madrid-33, Spain. Ed. Antonio Villarino Rodriquez. adv. bk. rev. illus. stat. index. circ. 90,000(controlled) (back issues avail.)
Missions

MUSIK UND KIRCHE. see *MUSIC*

200 UG ISSN 0541-4385
MUSIZI. (Text in Luganda) 1955. m. EAs.1200. Munno Publications, Box 4027, Kampala, Uganda. Ed. Rev. Francis Tebukozza. adv. circ. 25,000.

MUZIEKBODE. see *MUSIC*

242 US ISSN 0027-5387
MY DEVOTIONS. 1958. m. $5.10. Concordia Publishing House, 1333 S. Kirkwood Rd., St. Louis, MO 63122. TEL 314-664-7000 Ed. Don Hoeferkamp. illus. circ. 80,000. (also avail. in microfilm)

200 CK ISSN 0027-5638
MYSTERIUM. 1946. q. Col.$50. Provincia Occidental Claretianos de Colombia, Apdo Aereo 51-841, Medellin, Colombia. bk. rev. bibl. index. (tabloid format) Indexed: Hist.Abstr. Amer.Hist.& Life.

N A O S; notes and materials for the linguistic study of the sacred. see *LINGUISTICS*

260 378 US ISSN 0362-0794
N I C M JOURNAL FOR JEWS AND CHRISTIANS IN HIGHER EDUCATION. Variant title: N I C M Journal. 1976. q. $20. National Institute for Campus Ministries, Anabel Taylor Hall, Cornell University, Ithaca, NY 14853. TEL 607-256-8266 Indexed: Rel.Ind.One.

200 IT
N T C NEWS. (Text in English) 1973. s-m. $10. N T C News, Via Firenze 38, 00184 Rome, Italy. Ed. Ed Grace. circ. 625.

266 610 GW ISSN 0027-7398
NACHRICHTEN AUS DER AERZTLICHEN MISSION. 1950. q. free. ‡ Deutsches Institut fuer Aerztliche Mission - German Institute for Medical Missions, Paul-Lechler-Str. 24, 740 Tuebingen, W. Germany (B.R.D.) Ed. Dr. R. Bastian. bk. rev. illus. circ. 15,000.
Missions

200 GW
NADEZHDA; khristianskoye chtenie. (Text and summaries in Russian) 1978. a. DM.20. Possev-Verlag, Flurscheideweg 15, D-6230 Frankfurt am Main 80, W. Germany (B.R.D.) circ. 2,000. (back issues avail.)

200 NE
NAG HAMMADI STUDIES. 1971. irreg., vol.29, 1985. price varies. E.J. Brill, P.O. Box 9000, 2300 PA Leiden, Netherlands. Ed.Bd.

200 II ISSN 0027-7770
NANAK PRAKASH PATRIKA. (Text in English, Hindi, or Panjabi) 1969. m. Rs.3. ‡ Punjabi University, Patiala 4, Punjab, India. Ed. Dr. Taran Singh. bk. rev. circ. 600. (processed)

200 952 JA ISSN 0386-720X
NANZAN INSTITUTE FOR RELIGION AND CULTURE. BULLETIN. (Text In English) 1977. a. free. Nanzan Institute for Religion and Culture, 18 Yamazato-cho, Showa-ku, 466 Nagoya, Japan. Ed. Jan Van Bragt. circ. 1,200. (back issues avail.)

200 UK
NATIONAL MESSAGE. 1922. m. £9($15) (British Israel World Federation) National Message Ltd., 6 Buckingham Gate, London SW1E 6JP, England. Ed. G.L.S. Currie. adv. bk. rev. charts. illus. index. circ. 5,000.
Formerly: Message to the Anglo-Saxon and Celtic Peoples (ISSN 0261-7404); Formed by the merger of: British Israel World Federation. National Message (ISSN 0047-8962); Wake Up.

200 AT
NATIONAL OUTLOOK; Australian Christian monthly. 1979. m. Aus.$20($35) Outlook Media Ltd., GPO Box 2134, Sydney, N.S.W. 2001, Australia. Ed. David Thomas. adv. bk. rev. circ. 4,000. (back issues avail.)

200 UR ISSN 0028-1239
NAUKA I RELIGIYA. 1959. m. 10.20 Rub. Vsesoyuznoe Obshchestvo "Znanie", Proezd Serova, 4, Moscow, Russian S.F.S.R., U.S.S.R. Ed. A.S. Ivanov. bk. rev. bibl. illus. stat. circ. 285,000. Indexed: CERDIC. Curr.Dig.Sov.Press.

200 US
NAVLOG. 1940. bi-m. free. ‡ Navigators, Box 6000, Colorado Springs, CO 80934. TEL 303-598-1212 Ed. Richard Greene. bk. rev. circ. 72,000.
Formerly: Navigators Log.

NAVY CHAPLAINS BULLETIN. see *MILITARY*

200 IT ISSN 0028-1700
NAZARETH. vol.90, 1970. bi-m. contributions. Via Filitteria 10, 06049 Spoleto, Italy. circ. 2,000(controlled) (processed)

270 NE ISSN 0028-2030
NEDERLANDS ARCHIEF VOOR KERKGESCHIEDENIS. 1900. 2/yr. fl.86. E. J. Brill, P.O. Box 9000, 2300 PA Leiden, Netherlands. Ed.Bd. bk. rev. bibl. Indexed: Hist.Abstr. Amer.Hist.& Life. CERDIC. Rel.Ind.One.
Church history

230 NE ISSN 0028-212X
NEDERLANDS THEOLOGISCH TIJDSCHRIFT. vol.30, 1975. q. fl.78. Boekencentrum B.V., Box 84176, The Hague, Netherlands. Ed. A. van den Beld. adv. bk. rev. bibl. index. circ. 800. Indexed: Old Test.Abstr. Rel.Per. CERDIC. New Test.Abstr. Rel.Ind.One. Rel.& Theol.Abstr.

220 DK ISSN 0108-3023
NEMALAH. 1982. q. Kr.15 per no. Dansk Bibel Institut, Frederiksborggade 1A/2, 1360 Copenhagen K, Denmark. Ed. Finn Ronn Pedersen. bk. rev. circ. 400.

276 UK ISSN 0028-2820
NET. 1866. s-a. £5. Zululand Swaziland Association, c/o W. A. Sanders, Nine Chimney House, Balsham, Cambridge CB1 6ES, England. Ed. Rev. P. Burtwell. charts. illus. circ. 1,000.

266 SZ ISSN 0028-3495
NEUE ZEITSCHRIFT FUER MISSIONSWISSENSCHAFT/NOUVELLE REVUE DE SCIENCE MISSIONAIRE. (Text in English, French, German and Italian) 1945. q. 34.40 Fr. Verein zur Foerderung der Missionswissenschaft - Association for Promoting Mission Studies, CH-6405 Immensee, Switzerland. Ed. J. Specker. adv. bk. rev. bibl. illus. index. circ. 800. Indexed: CERDIC. Curr.Cont.Africa.
Missions

200 GW ISSN 0028-3665
NEUES LEBEN; Christliches Monatsmagazin. 1956. m. DM.48. ‡ (Missionwerk Neues Leben e.V.) Brendow Verlag, Gutenbergstr. 1, 4130 Moers 1, W. Germany (B.R.D.) Ed. Anton Schulte. adv. bk. rev. illus. circ. 40,000.

266 US
NEW AGE CHRISTIAN NEWSLETTER. m. Church of the New Birth, Box 87051, San Diego, CA 92138.

200 US ISSN 0028-4254
NEW AURORA. (Text in English and Italian) 1903. m. (except July & Aug.) $3. Association of Evangelicals for Italian Missions, 314 Richfield Rd., Upper Darby, PA 19082. TEL 215-352-2396 Ed. Rev. Dr. Anthony F. Vasquez. adv. circ. 1,500.

200 PH
NEW CITY. 1966. bi-m. P.20($3) Focolare Movement for Men, Box 332, Manila, Philippines. Ed. Guido Mirti. circ. 16,000.

200 US ISSN 0360-0181
NEW CONVERSATIONS. 1975. 3/yr. $10. United Church Board for Homeland Ministries, c/o William McKinney, Ed., 132 W. 31st St., New York, NY 10001. bk. rev. circ. 1,500.

200 US ISSN 0149-4244
NEW OXFORD REVIEW. 1940. m.(10/yr.) $19. New Oxford Review, Inc., 1069 Kains Ave., Berkeley, CA 94706. TEL 415-526-5374 Ed. Dale Vree. adv. bk. rev. illus. circ. 8,000. (also avail. in microform from UMI; reprint service avail. from UMI)
Formerly (until Feb. 1977): American Church News (ISSN 0002-791X)

200 CN
NEW RELIGIONS NEWSLETTER. 1978. m. $10. c/o Prof. Herbert Richardson, 81 St. Mary's St., Toronto, Ont. M5S 1J4, Canada.

225 UK ISSN 0028-6885
NEW TESTAMENT STUDIES. (Text in English, French and German) 1954. q. $50 to individuals; $75 to institutions. (Studiorum Novi Testamenti Societas) Cambridge University Press, Edinburgh Bldg., Shaftesbury Rd., Cambridge CB2 2RU, England (And 32 E. 57th St., New York NY 10022) Ed. G.N. Stanton. adv. bk. rev. circ. 2,600. (also avail. in microform from UMI; reprint service avail. from UMI) Indexed: Curr.Cont. Hum.Ind. Rel.Per. Arts & Hum.Cit.Ind. CERDIC. New Test.Abstr. Rel.Ind.One. Rel.& Theol.Abstr.

220 NE ISSN 0077-8842
NEW TESTAMENT TOOLS AND STUDIES. 1960. irreg., vol. 10, 1980. price varies. E. J. Brill, P.O. Box 9000, 2300 PA Leiden, Netherlands. Ed. Bruce M. Metzger.

200 US ISSN 0194-438X
NEW WINE. 1969. m. $10 institutional contribution. Christian Growth Ministries, c/o Don Basham, Ed., Box 1720, Elyria, OH 44036. illus. circ. 92,000.

200 100 AT
NEWS AND VIEWS. 1986. bi-m. Aus.$20($15) Rationalist Society of Australia, 4th Fl., Commerce House, 328 Flinders St., Melbourne, Vic. 3000, Australia. Ed. James Gerrand. circ. 500. (back issues avail.)

200 NR ISSN 0029-005X
NIGERIAN CHRISTIAN. (Text in English) 1967-1982; N.S. 1984. m. $10. (Christian Council of Nigeria) Daystar Press, Box 1261, Ibadan, Nigeria. Ed. Rachel Alao. adv. bk. rev. illus. circ. 4,000. Indexed: CERDIC.

266 IT ISSN 0029-0173
NIGRIZIA; fatti e problemi del mondo nero. 1883. m. L.12000($18) Missionari Comboniani, Vicolo Pozzo 1, 37129 Verona, Italy. Ed. Alessandro Zanotelli. adv. bk. rev. illus. stat. index. circ. 50,000. Indexed: CERDIC. Curr.Cont.Africa.

200 NE
NISABA. 1973. irreg., vol. 15, 1986. price varies. E. J. Brill, P.O. Box 9000, 2300 PA Leiden, Netherlands.

260 GW
NORDELBISCHE MISSION; Breklumer Sonntagsblat fuers Haus. 1974. m. DM.10. Nordelbisches Zentrum fuer Weltmission und Kirchlichen Weltdienst, Agathe-Lasch Weg 16, 2000 Hamburg 52, W. Germany (B.R.D.) Ed. Jens Waubke. bk. rev. circ. 10,000.
Missions

200 SW ISSN 0085-4212
NORDISK EKUMENISK AARSBOK. (Text in Danish, Norwegian and Swedish) 1972. biennial, latest 84-85. Kr.70. Nordiska Ekumeniska Institutet - Nordic Ecumenical Institute, Box 438, S-751 06 Uppsala, Sweden. Ed. Kjell Ove Nilsson. adv. bk. rev. illus. index. circ. 1,000. Indexed: CERDIC.

230 NO ISSN 0029-2176
NORSK TEOLOGISK TIDSSKRIFT/ NORWEGIAN THEOLOGICAL JOURNAL. 1900. q. $35. Norwegian University Press, Kolstadgt. 1, Box 2959-Toeyen, 0608 Oslo 6, Norway (U.S. address: Publications Expediting Inc., 200 Meacham Ave., Elmont, NY 11003) Ed. Ludvig Munthe. adv. bk. rev. abstr. index. index. circ. 600. Indexed: Hist.Abstr. Amer.Hist.& Life. CERDIC. Old Test.Abstr. New Test.Abstr. Rel.Per. Rel.Ind.One.

266 NO ISSN 0029-2214
NORSK TIDSSKRIFT FOR MISJON. q. $25. (Egede Institute) Universitetsforlaget, Kolstadgt. 1, Box 2959-Toeyen, 0608 Oslo 6, Norway. Eds. Nils Bloch-Hoell, Aage Holter. adv. bk. rev. index. circ. 950. Indexed: CERDIC.
Missions

250 II
NORTH INDIA CHURCHMAN. (Text in English) 1971. m. Rs.10($4) Indian Society for Promoting Christian Knowledge, I.S.P.C.K., Box 1585, Kashmere Gate, Delhi 110006, India. Ed. V. H. Devdas. adv. bk. rev. circ. 1,200.

200 301 PE
NOTICIAS ALIADAS. English edition: Latinamerica Press. w. $40 to individuals; institutions $60. Noticias Aliadas, Apdo. 5594, Lima 100, Peru. Dir. David Molineaux.

266 NQ
NOTICIAS EVANGELICAS. bi-m. Comite Evangelico pro Ayudo al Desarrollo, Apdo. Postal 3091, Managua, Nicaragua.

230 BE ISSN 0029-4845
NOUVELLE REVUE THEOLOGIQUE. 1868. 6/yr. 960 Fr.($37) (Centre de Documentation et de Recherche Religieuses) Casterman, S.A., 28 rue des Soeurs Noires, 7500 Tournai, Belgium (Subscr. to: Aquinas Agency, 561 Fort Road, St Paul, MN 55102) bk. rev. bibl. index. circ. 4,600. Indexed: Cath.Ind. Old Test.Abstr. CERDIC. Canon Law Abstr. New Test.Abstr. Rel.& Theol.Abstr.

200 FR ISSN 0029-487X
NOUVELLES DE CHRETIENTE; notes, documents. 1953. w. 40 F. Civitec, 1134 rue de Rivoli, 75001 Paris, France. Eds. Charles Pierre Doazan, Lucien Garrido.

225 NE ISSN 0048-1009
NOVUM TESTAMENTUM. (Text in English, French and German) 1956. 4/yr. fl.115. E. J. Brill, P.O. Box 9000, 2300 PA Leiden, Netherlands. Indexed: Curr.Cont. Rel.Per. Arts & Hum.Cit.Ind. CERDIC. New Test.Abstr. Rel.& Theol.Abstr. Rel.Ind.One.

225 NE
NOVUM TESTAMENTUM. SUPPLEMENTS. 1958. irreg., vol.55, 1985. price varies. E.J. Brill, P.O. Box 9000, 2300 PA Leiden, Netherlands. Eds. C.K. Barrett, A.F.J. Klijn, J. Smit Sibinga. Indexed: Rel.Ind.One.

200 DR ISSN 0029-5752
NUESTRO AMIGO. 1931. m. free. Iglesia Evangelica Dominicana, Apartado 727, Santo Domingo, Dominican Republic. Ed. Herman Gonzalez Roca. circ. 2,500. (tabloid format; also avail. in cards)

200 AG
NUEVO MUNDO. 1971. s-a. $10. Ediciones Castaneda, Centenario 1399, 1718 San Antonio de Padua, Buenos Aires, Argentina.

209 NE ISSN 0029-5973
NUMEN; international review for the history of religions. (Supplement avail.: Numen Supplements) (Text in English, French, German and Italian) 1954. s-a. fl.84. (International Association for the History of Religions) E. J. Brill, P.O. Box 9000, 2300 PA Leiden, Netherlands. Ed. Dr. Heerma van Voss. bk. rev. bibl. (back issues avail.) Indexed: Curr.Cont. Rel.Per. CERDIC. New Test.Abstr. Rel.Ind.One.
History

200 NE
NUMEN SUPPLEMENTS. 1954. irreg., vol.48, 1986. price varies. E. J. Brill, P.O. Box 9000, 2300 PA Leiden, Netherlands. Indexed: Rel.Ind.Two.
Formerly: Studies in the History of Religions (ISSN 0585-7260)

NY DAG. see *CHILDREN AND YOUTH — For*

266 DK ISSN 0108-8297
NYE AAR; kirkelig forening for den indre mission i Danmark. 1906. a. Kr.50. (Kirkelig Forening) Lohse, Fredericia, Denmark. Ed. Verner Andersen. adv. illus.

200 DK ISSN 0109-3169
NYHEDSBREV. 1983. s-a. free. Aarhus Universitet, Teologiske Fakultet, Universitetsparken, 8000 Aarhus C, Denmark. Ed. Povl Lind-Petersen. bk. rev. circ. 2,000.
Formerly: T F-Nyhedsbrev (ISSN 0108-8939)

220 DK ISSN 0108-898X
NYT FRA BIBELSELSKABET. 1982. q. membership. Danske Bibelselskab, Frederiksborggade 50, 1360 Copenhagen K, Denmark. illus.
Formerly: Danske Bibelselskab. Medlemsbrev.
Bible

282 YU ISSN 0351-3947
OBNOVLJENI ZIVOT/LIFE RENEWED; dvomjesecnik za religioznu kulturu. (First published 1919-1944; suspended 1945-1970; resumed 1971) (Text in Croatian; summaries in German, French, English and Latin) 1919. bi-m. 2000 din.($20) Filozofsko-Teoloski Insitut Druzbe Isusove, Jordanovac 110, Zagreb, Yugoslavia. Ed. Franjo Psenicnjak. bk. rev. abstr. bibl. stat. index. circ. 2,000. (back issues avail.)

200 947 US ISSN 0731-5465
OCCASIONAL PAPERS ON RELIGION IN EASTERN EUROPE. 1981. irreg. (approx. 6-8/yr) $35. (Christian Associated for Relationships with Eastern Europe) Princeton Theological Seminary, c/o Rosemont College, Rosemont, PA 19010. TEL 215-527-0200 Ed. Paul Mojzes. bk. rev. circ. 700. (looseleaf format; back issues avail.)

280 GW ISSN 0029-8654
OEKUMENISCHE RUNDSCHAU. 1952. q. DM.38($9) (Deutscher Oekumenischer Studienausschuss) Verlag Otto Lembeck, Leerbachstr. 42, 6000 Frankfurt 1, W. Germany (B.R.D.) Ed.Bd. adv. bk. rev. index. circ. 2,000. Indexed: CERDIC.

OESTERREICHISCHES ARCHIV FUER KIRCHENRECHT. see *LAW*

266 GW ISSN 0030-011X
OFFENE TUEREN. 1907. bi-m. DM.10. ‡ Missionshaus Bibelschule Wiedenest, Olper Strasse 10, 5275 Bergneustadt, W. Germany (B.R.D.) Ed. Daniel Herm. bk. rev. illus. circ. 10,500.
Missions

200 SA
OLD TESTAMENT ESSAYS. (Text in English and German; summaries in English) 1983. a. R.8. Old Testament Essays, Department of Old Testament, P.O. Box 392, 0001 Pretoria, South Africa. Ed. J.J. Burden. circ. 300. (back issues avail.) Indexed: Old Test.Abstr.

200 AT ISSN 0310-9348
ON THE MOVE. 1973. q. Aus.$13.60. Joint Board of Christian Education, 10 Queen St., 2nd Fl., Melbourne, Victoria 3000, Australia. Ed. Pat Baker. bk. rev. circ. 2,000. (back issues avail.)

200 SZ ISSN 0303-125X
ONE WORLD. (Text in English) 1975. 10/yr. 35 Fr.($18.95) World Council of Churches, Publications Office, 150 Route de Ferney, CH-1211 Geneva 20, Switzerland. Ed. Marlin van Elderen. illus. circ. 10,000. (also avail. in microform from UMI; reprint service avail. from UMI) Indexed: CERDIC. Rel.Ind.One.

200 NE ISSN 0030-2678
ONS GEESTELIJK LEVEN; tijdschrift voor informatie, bezinning en gesprek. 1923. bi-m. fl.32.50. Missionarissen van het H. Hart, St. Goedelestraat 2, 5643 MK Eindhoven, Netherlands. bk. rev. bibl. index. circ. 1,000. Indexed: CERDIC.

200 NE ISSN 0030-3267
OORSPRONKELIJK CHRISTENDOM. 1950. bi-m. free. ‡ Internationale Gemeenschap van Christenen, Drakenstein 39, 1083 XS Amsterdam, Netherlands. Ed. J. M. Burgers-Zijp. bk. rev. illus. circ. 1,450.

OPINION; the way I see it. see *PHILOSOPHY*

200 CN ISSN 0030-4344
ORATOIRE. (Editions in English and French) 1912. bi-m. Can.$5. Oratoire Saint-Joseph du Mont-Royal, 3800 Chemin Reine-Marie, Montreal, Que. H3V 1H6, Canada. TEL 514-733-8211 illus. circ. 80,000.

200 FR ISSN 0030-4352
ORATORIANA. 1960. s-a. 10 F. Oratoire de France, 75 rue de Vaugirard, 75006 Paris, France. bk. rev. bibl. illus.

200 GW ISSN 0340-6407
ORIENS CHRISTIANUS; Hefte fuer die Kunde des christlichen Orients. 1911. a. DM.80 (approx.) Verlag Otto Harrassowitz, Taunusstr. 14, Postfach 2929, 6200 Wiesbaden 1, W. Germany (B.R.D.) Ed. Julius Assfalg, Hubert Kanfholt. adv. bk. rev. circ. 400. (back issues avail.) Indexed: Rel.Ind.One.

200 VC ISSN 0030-5375
ORIENTALIA CHRISTIANA PERIODICA; commentarii de re orientali aetatis christianae sacra et profana. (Text in English, French, German, Italian, Latin and Spanish) 1935. s-a. $27. Pontificio Istituto Orientale, Piazza S. Maria Maggiore 7, 00185 Rome, Italy. Ed. V. Poggi. bk. rev. charts. index. circ. 1,000. (back issues avail.) Indexed: Bull.Signal. Rel.& Theol.Abstr. Amer.Bibl.Slavic & E.Eur.Stud. CERDIC. New Test.Abstr. Rel.Ind.One.

200 IT ISSN 0472-0784
ORIENTAMENTI PASTORALI. 1953. m. L.15000. Centro di Orientamento Pastorale, c/o Franco Gualtieri, Collegio Internazionale, Via Casale S. Pio V, 20, 00165 Rome, Italy. Ed. G. Bonicelli. adv. circ. 4,500. Indexed: CERDIC.

200 SZ ISSN 0030-5502
ORIENTIERUNG; katholische Blaetter fuer weltanschauliche Information. 1937. s-m. 38 Fr. Institut fuer Weltanschauliche Fragen, Scheideggstr. 45, CH-8002 Zurich, Switzerland. Ed. L. Kaufmann. adv. bk. rev. abstr. bibl. stat. index. cum.index. circ. 15,000. (looseleaf format) Indexed: Old Test.Abstr. CERDIC.

200 NR ISSN 0030-5596
ORITA; Ibadan journal of religious studies. (Text in English) 1967. s-a. $16. University of Ibadan, Department of Religious Studies, Ibadan, Nigeria. Ed. J. Kenny. adv. bk. rev. illus. cum.index. circ. 500(controlled) (tabloid format) Indexed: Afr.Abstr.
African interests

248 US
ORTHODOX AMERICA. 1979. 10/yr. $8. Nikodemus Orthodox Publication Society, Box 2132, Redding, CA 96099. Ed. Father Alexey Young. adv. bk. rev. circ. 2,300. (tabloid format)

323.4 200 US ISSN 0145-7675
OTHER SIDE (PHILADELPHIA); justice rooted in discipleship. 1965. 10/yr. $19.75. Other Side, Inc., 300 W. Apsley St., Philadelphia, PA 19144. TEL 215-849-2178 Ed. Mark Olson. adv. bk. rev. film rev. illus. circ. 14,500. (also avail. in microfiche from UMI; back issues avail.) Indexed: Chr.Per.Ind. Rel.Ind.One.

221 NE
OUDTESTAMENTISCHE STUDIEN. (Text in English and German) 1942. irreg., vol.23, 1984. price varies. E.J. Brill, P.O. Box 9000, 2300 PA Leiden, Netherlands. Ed. A.S. van der Woude. Indexed: Old Test.Abstr.

200 II
OUR LINK. (Text in English) 1954. q. Rs.1 per no. Union of Evangelical Students of India, 10 Millers Rd, Madras 600010, India. Ed. P. Selvin Samuel Raj. adv. bk. rev. circ. 1,500 (controlled)
Formerly (until Jan. 1977): Evangelical Student.

OUR LITTLE FRIEND. see *CHILDREN AND YOUTH — For*

200 US ISSN 0030-6967
OUR SUNDAY VISITOR. 1912. w. $20. Vincent Giese, Pub., 200 Noll Plaza, Huntington, IN 46750. TEL 219-356-8400 Ed. Robert Lockwood. adv. bk. rev. film rev. play rev. illus. circ. 265,000. Indexed: Cath.Ind.

OUTWARD BOUND. see *CHILDREN AND YOUTH — For*

266 UK ISSN 0048-2579
OXFORD MISSION. 1894. q. £0.25. Bocardo Press, Robin Hill, The Straight Mile, Romsey, Hampshire SO5 9BA, England. Ed. J. Wilson. circ. 3,200. (processed)
Missions

201 US ISSN 0078-7272
OXFORD THEOLOGICAL MONOGRAPHS. irreg. Oxford University Press, 200 Madison Ave., New York, NY 10016 TEL 212-679-7300 (and Ely House, 37 Dover St., London W1X 4AH, England) Ed.Bd.

200 US
P A C E. (Professional Approaches for Christian Educators) 1970. 8/yr. $56. St. Mary's Press, Terrace Heights, Winona, MN 55987. TEL 507-452-9090 Ed. Mary Perkins Ryan. index. cum.index: vols.10-16. circ. 1,750. (looseleaf format; back issues avail.)

200 SZ
P C R INFORMATION; reports and background papers. 1979. 4/yr. free. World Council of Churches, Programme to Combat Racism, 150 Route de Ferney, Box 66, 1211 Geneva 20, Switzerland. Ed. Anwar Barkat. bk. rev. circ. 5,000.

200 US
P R R C: EMERGING TRENDS. 1979. 10/yr. $30. (Princeton Religion Research Center, Inc.) Gallup Organization, Inc., Box 628, Princeton, NJ 08542. TEL 609-924-9600 Ed. George Gallup Jr. circ. 1,900. (looseleaf format; back issues avail.)

268 SP
P S. 1899. m. 200 ptas.($4) Editorial Perpetuo Socorro, Covarrubias, 19, Madrid-10, Spain. Ed. Basilio Caballero. adv. bk. rev. illus. circ. 12,000(controlled)

220 028.5 DK ISSN 0900-3355
PAA VEJ; en bibelnoegle for juniorer. 1985. q. Kr.15. Bibellaeser-Ringen, Korskaervej 25, 7000 Fredericia, Denmark. illus.

PACIFIC THEOLOGICAL REVIEW. see *RELIGIONS AND THEOLOGY — Protestant*

255 248 IT ISSN 0030-9214
PADRE SANTO; periodico dei Cappuccini liguri. 1912. m. ‡ Frati Minori Cappuccini, Provincia di Genova, Piazza Cappuccini 1, 16122 Genoa, Italy. Ed. Toso Domenico.

266 GW ISSN 0031-0395
PALLOTTIS WERK. 1949. q. free. (Provinzialat der Pallottiner) Pallottiner Druck und Lahn-Verlag, Wiesbadener Str. 1, Postfach 1162, 6250 Limburg, W. Germany (B.R.D.) Ed. P.W. Schuetzeichel. bk. rev. circ. 60,000.
Missions

200 FR ISSN 0048-2838
PANORAMA AUJOURD'HUI; revue de reflexion chretienne. 1968. m. 264 F. Bayard Presse, 5 rue Bayard, 75380 Paris Cedex 08, France. adv. bk. rev. film rev. illus. circ. 96,000.

200 LE
PAROLE DE L'ORIENT. (Text in English and French) 1970. s-a. £L100($30) Universite Saint Esprit Kaslik, B.P. 446, Jounieh, Lebanon. bk. rev. circ. 1,000.

250 UK ISSN 0031-2436
PARSON AND PARISH; National Church News. 1938. s-a. 50p. Parochial Clergy Association, Mildenhall, Marlborough, England. Ed. Rev. David Scott. adv. bk. rev. circ. 2,000.

200 US ISSN 0747-9190
PARTNERSHIP; the magazine for wives in ministry. bi-m. $14.95. Christianity Today, Inc., 465 Gundersen Dr., Carol Stream, IL 60188. TEL 312-260-6200 Ed. Ruth Senter.

250 US ISSN 0031-2762
PASTORAL LIFE; the magazine for today's ministry. 1952. m. $15. Society of St. Paul (Canfield), Canfield, OH 44406. TEL 216-533-5503 Ed. Jeffrey Mickler. adv. bk. rev. illus. index. circ. 9,700. (also avail. in microfilm from UMI; reprint service avail. from UMI) Indexed: Cath.Ind. CERDIC.

266 SP ISSN 0210-3559
PASTORAL MISIONERA. 1965. 8/yr. 1200 ptas.($17) Editorial Popular, S.A., Bola 3, Madrid 13, Spain. Ed. Fernando Urbina de la Quintana. bk. rev.
Missions

200 US ISSN 0031-2789
PASTORAL PSYCHOLOGY. 1952. q. $29 to individuals; institutions $76. (Princeton Theological Seminary) Human Sciences Press, Inc., 72 Fifth Ave., New York, NY 10011. Ed. Lewis R. Rambo. adv. bk. rev. (also avail. in microform from UMI; reprint service avail. from ISI,UMI) Indexed: Curr.Cont. Psychol.Abstr. SSCI. CERDIC. G.Soc.Sci.& Rel.Per.Lit. Rel.Per. Past.Care & Couns.Abstr. Rel.& Theol.Abstr. Rel.Ind.One.

266 US ISSN 0744-8279
PASTORAL RENEWAL. 1976. 11/yr. $15 suggested contribution. Servant Ministries, Inc., Center for Pastoral Renewal, Box 8617, Ann Arbor, MI 48107. TEL 313-761-8505 Ed. John Blattner. bk. rev. index. circ. 15,000. (back issues avail.)

250 GW ISSN 0031-2800
PASTORALBLAETTER. 1860. m. DM.40. Kreuz-Verlag Zeitschriften GmbH, Breitwiesenstr. 30, 7000 Stuttgart 80, W. Germany (B.R.D.) Ed. Hans-Georg Lubkoll. adv. circ. 3,500.

200 CR
PASTORALIA. 1974. s-a. $4.50 (or exchange) Centro Evangelico Latinoamericano de Estudios Pastorales, Apartado 1307, 1000 San Jose, Costa Rica. Dir. Plutarco Bonilla A. bk. rev. circ. 1,600.
Supersedes (since vol.4, nos.1/2, 1977): C E L E P Ensayos Ocasionales.

250 GW ISSN 0720-6259
PASTORALTHEOLOGIE - MONATSSCHRIFT FUER WISSENSCHAFT UND PRAXIS IN KIRCHE UND GESELLSCHAFT. 1904. m. DM.95. Vandenhoeck und Ruprecht, Theaterstr. 13, Postfach 37 53, 3400 Goettingen, W. Germany (B.R.D.) Eds. Guenter Brakelmann, Peter Stolt. adv. bk. rev. index. circ. 3,000. Indexed: CERDIC.
Former titles: Wissenschaft und Praxis in Kirche und Gesellschaft (ISSN 0031-2827); Pastoraltheologie.

200 SA ISSN 0031-2932
PATH OF TRUTH. Afrikaans edition: Huis van Geluk. 1937. m. free. School of Truth Ltd., South Africa Centre, 5th Fl., 253 Bree St., Johannesburg, South Africa. Ed. Colin Campbell.

PATHWAY TO GOD. see *PHILOSOPHY*

200 US ISSN 0360-652X
PATRISTICS. 1972. s-a. $15 to individuals; institutions $10; students $6. ‡ North American Patristics Society, Emmanuel School of Religion, Johnson City, TN 37601. TEL 615-926-1186 Ed. Frederick W. Norris. bk. rev. circ. 350.

266 CN ISSN 0031-3335
PAX REGIS. 1942. s-a. $2. ‡ Westminster Abbey Ltd., Mission, British Columbia V2V 4J2, Canada. TEL 604-826-8975 Ed. Augustine Kalberer. illus. circ. 1,500.

200 FR ISSN 0031-4145
PELERIN DU VINGTIEME SIECLE. 1873. w. 704 F. Bayard Presse, 5 rue Bayard, 75380 Paris Cedex 08, France. Ed. Jean Gelamur. adv. bk. rev. bibl. film rev. illus. mkt. play rev. circ. 560,000.
Formerly: Pelerin.

200 SA
PENDULUM. (Text in Afrikaans and English) 1974. q. R.10. (Bet-El Evangelistic Action) Bet-El Publishers, P.O. Box 23227, Innesdale, Pretoria 0031, South Africa. Ed. Robbie Engelbrecht. adv. bk. rev. circ. 30,000. (back issues avail.)
Formerly: Evangelist.

200 AU ISSN 0031-5141
PERCHTOLDSDORFER PFARRBOTE. 1950. m. contributions. Pfarramt Perchtoldsdorf, Marktplatz 14, A-2380 Perchtoldsdorf, Austria. Ed. Msgr. Karl Seemann. circ. 4,700.

200 US
PERE MARQUETTE THEOLOGY LECTURE SERIES. 1969. a. $7.95. Marquette University Press, 1324 W. Wisconsin Ave., Milwaukee, WI 53233. TEL 414-224-1564

268 US
PERSPECTIVE (WHEATON) 1967. q. $4. Pioneer Ministries, Inc., 27 W. 130 St. Charles Rd., Box 788, Wheaton, IL 60189. TEL 312-293-1600 Ed. Lorraine Mulligan Davis. bk. rev. circ. 25,000.

215 US
PERSPECTIVES ON SCIENCE AND CHRISTIAN FAITH. 1949. q. $30. American Scientific Affiliation, Box 668, Ipswich, MA 01938. TEL 617-356-5656 Ed. Wilbur L. Bullock. adv. bk. rev. abstr. circ. 3,500. (also avail. in microform from UMI; reprint service avail. from UMI) Indexed: CERDIC. Chr.Per.Ind. G.Soc.Sci.& Rel.Per.Lit. Rel.& Theol.Abstr.
Formerly: American Scientific Affiliation. Journal: Evangelical Perspectives on Science and Christian Faith (ISSN 0003-0988)

200 NE
PFARRAGO. q. fl.20. Vrije Universiteit, Theologische Fakulteit, De Boelelaan 1105, Amsterdam, Netherlands.

200 AU ISSN 0031-6709
PFARRBRIEF; fuer die evangelischen Gemeinden Purkersdorf und Pressbaum. 1955. 6/yr. S.50. Evangelische Pfarrgemeinde Purkersdorf, Wintergasse 13-15, A-3002 Purkersdorf, Austria. Ed. Pfarrer Ludwig Drexler. circ. 1,000.

PHILOSOPHY AND THE ARTS; a literary and philosophical review. see *PHILOSOPHY*

200 GR ISSN 0031-8396
PHONI TOU EVANGELIOU/VOICE OF THE GOSPEL. 1944. m. Dr.50($5) A. M. G. International, 28 Emm. Benaki St., Athens 142, Greece. Ed. George Z. Constantinidis. bk. rev. abstr. bibl. illus. index. circ. 6,500.

266 301.2 IT
PIEMME; Piccolo Pissionario. 1927. s-m. L.8000. Missionari Comboniani, Vicolo Pozzo 1, 37129 Verona, Italy. Ed. Giuseppe Roncari. adv. bk. rev. circ. 120,000.
Formerly: Piccolo Missionario (ISSN 0031-9600)
Missions

250 US
PILGRIMAGE: THE JOURNAL OF PSYCHOTHERAPY AND PERSONAL EXPLORATION. 1972. 3/yr. $8. Pilgrimage Press, Inc., 427 Lakeshore Dr., Atlanta, GA 30307. Ed. David Barstow. bk. rev. circ. 1,000.
Formerly: Pilgrimage: The Journal of Pastoral Psychotherapy (ISSN 0361-0802)

266 UK ISSN 0048-4202
PIONEER. 1888. q. £2. ‡ Africa Evangelical Fellowship (SAGM), 30 Lingfield Rd., London SW19 4PU, England. Ed. Michael Chesterman. circ. 4,000. (tabloid format)

200 NE ISSN 0032-0056
PIONIER. 1939. m. free. Stichting Alliance Zendings, Centrum Parousia, Julianaweg 354, 3523 XL Utrecht, Netherlands. Ed. A. Stringer. illus. circ. 4,000.

200 300 US ISSN 0740-9125
PLOUGH. 1938-1958; resumed 1983. bi-m. (Hutterian Brethren) Plough Publishing House (Subsidiary of: Woodcrest Service Comittee, Inc.) Hutterian Brethren, Route 213, Rifton, NY 12471. TEL 914-658-3141 Ed. J. Christoph Arnold. bk. rev. illus. tr.lit. index. circ. 13,000. (also avail. in Braille; back issues avail.)

268 FR
POINTS DE REPERE. 1955. 7/yr. 131 F. (Centre National de l'Enseignement Religieux (C.N.E.R.)) Bayard Presse, 5, rue Bayard, 75380 Paris Cedex 08, France. circ. 60,000.
Formerly: Catechistes d'Aujourd'hui (ISSN 0008-7742)

207 268.8 US ISSN 0079-2543
POINTS FOR EMPHASIS; INTERNATIONAL SUNDAY SCHOOL LESSONS IN POCKET SIZE. (Large type edition also avail.) 1917. a. $2.95 (large type edt. $3.95) Broadman Press, 127 Ninth Ave. N., Nashville, TN 37234. TEL 615-251-2000 Ed. William J. Fallis. circ. 46,000.

200 NE ISSN 0032-2415
POKROF; bi-monthly review about eastern Christianity. 1954. 5/yr. fl.17.50. Pokrof Monastery, Raamweg 42, 2596 HN The Hague, Netherlands. Ed. P. Gabriel Muenninghoff. bk. rev. illus. index every 4 yrs. circ. 1,500. Indexed: CERDIC.

POLKA; Polish women's quarterly magazine. see *WOMEN'S INTERESTS*

200 GE ISSN 0032-4132
POMHAJ BOH. 1950. m. M.3.60. VEB Domowina Verlag, Tuchmacherstr. 27, 86 Bautzen, E. Germany (D.D.R.) Ed. Konvent Sorbischer Evangelischer Geistlicher. illus.

200 VC
PONTE D'ORO. 1966. m. L.4500. Pontificia Opera della Santa Infanzia, Via di Propaganda 1, 00187 Rome, Italy. Ed. Giuliani Sandro. circ. 30,000.

200 360 IT
POPOLO. 1922. w. L.5000. Giunta Diocesana di A.C., Via Trento, 33170 Pordenone, Italy (Subscriptions to: Il Popolo, Casella Postale 103, Pordenone, Italy)

242 US ISSN 0032-4884
PORTALS OF PRAYER; daily devotions for adults. German edition: Taegliche Andachten. (Braille and Large Print editions also available) 1937. q. $3. Concordia Publishing House, 3558 S. Jefferson, St. Louis, MO 63118. TEL 314-664-7000 Ed. Rudolph F. Norden. circ. 900,000. (also avail. in microfilm)

200 US ISSN 0032-6003
POWER FOR LIVING. 1942. q. $5.50. Scripture Press Publications Inc., 1825 College Ave., Wheaton, IL 60187. TEL 312-668-6000 Ed. Roy Irving. bk. rev. illus. circ. 360,000.

200 US ISSN 0032-6011
POWER FOR TODAY. 1955. q. $6.95. 20th Century Christian Foundation, 2809 Granny White Pike, Nashville, TN 37204. TEL 615-383-3842 Eds. Steven S. & Emily Y. Lemley. adv. circ. 50,000. (processed; also avail. in microfilm from UMI; reprint service avail. from UMI)

PRACTICAL PAPERS FOR THE BIBLE TRANSLATOR. see *LINGUISTICS*

200 DK ISSN 0106-6218
PRAESTEFORENINGENS BLAD. 1899. w. (50/yr.) Kr.360. Danske Praesteforening, Rosenvaengets Hovedvej 19, 2100 Copenhagen, Denmark. Ed. Jacob Grosboell. adv. bk. rev. circ. 3,500.

200 CN
PRAIRIE OVERCOMER. 1928. 11/yr. Can.$11($9) (Prairie Bible Institute) Prairie Press, Three Hills, Alberta, Canada T0M 2A0. Ed. T.S. Rendall. circ. 8,000. Indexed: Chr.Per.Ind.

200 US ISSN 0032-7018
PRAVOSLAVNAYA RUS; tzerkovno-obshchestvennyi organ. (Monthly supplement Pravoslavnaya Zhyzn) (Text in Russian) 1928. fortn. $24 (including supplement) Holy Trinity Monastery, Box 36, Jordanville, NY 13361. TEL 315-858-0940 bk. rev. circ. 2,500. (tabloid format) Indexed: CERDIC.

255 248 US ISSN 0032-6992
PRAVOSLAVNAYA ZHYZN/ORTHODOX LIFE. (Text in Russian) 1950. m. $10. Holy Trinity Monastery, Box 36, Jordanville, NY 13361. TEL 315-858-0940 circ. 2,625. (tabloid format) Indexed: Amer.Bibl.Slavic & E.Eur.Stud. CERDIC.

200 YU ISSN 0032-700X
PRAVOSLAVNO MISAO. (Text in Serbo-Croatian) 1959. a. 100 din.($5) Udruzenje Pravoslavnog Svestenstva SFR Jugoslavije, Glavni Savez, Francuska 31-1, Belgrade, Yugoslavia. Ed. Dusan Strbac. bk. rev. circ. 1,600.
Cyrillic alphabet

281 CS ISSN 0079-4937
PRAVOSLAVNY THEOLOGICKY SBORNIK. (Text in Czech or Slovak) 1967. irreg., no. 4, 1974. 52 Kcs.($7) Pravoslavna Cirkev Ceskoslovenska, V jame 6, 110 00 Prague 1, Czechoslovakia. adv. circ. 3,000.

PRAXIS JURIDIQUE ET RELIGION. see *LAW*

200 US ISSN 0882-7036
PREACHING. 1985. bi-m. $15. Preaching Resources, Inc., 1529 Cesery Blvd., Jacksonville, FL 32211. TEL 904-743-5994 Ed. Michael Duduit. adv. bk. rev. circ. 5,000. (back issues avail.)

200 GW ISSN 0079-4961
PREDIGTSTUDIEN. 1968. s-a. DM.29 per vol. Kreuz-Verlag, Breitwiesenstr. 30, 7000 Stuttgart 80, W. Germany (B.R.D.) circ. 7,000.

200 AT ISSN 0729-3542
PRESBYTERIAN BANNER. 1913. m. Aus.$10. Presbyterian Church of Eastern Australia, 360 Mountain Highway, Wantirna, Vict. 3152, Australia. Ed. Rowland Ward. adv. bk. rev. index. circ. 475. (back issues avail.)

200 CN ISSN 0079-4996
PRESBYTERIAN CHURCH IN CANADA. GENERAL ASSEMBLY. ACTS AND PROCEEDINGS. a. Can.$7. Presbyterian Church in Canada, General Assembly, 50 Wynford Dr., Don Mills M3C IJ7, Ont., Canada. TEL 416-441-1111

200 CK
PRESENCIA. 1950. m. $14. Editorial Presencia Ltda., Calle 23 no. 24-20, Bogota D.E., Colombia. Ed. Maria Carrizosa de Umana. adv. abstr. bibl. circ. 15,000.

250 FR ISSN 0032-7956
PRETRES DIOCESAINS. 1862. m. 170 F.($29) Pretres Diocesains, 179 rue de Tolbiac, 75013 Paris, France. bk. rev. abstr. bibl. index. (tabloid format)

250 282 US ISSN 0032-8200
PRIEST. 1945. m. (11/yr.) $16.50. Our Sunday Visitor, Inc., 200 Noll Plaza, Huntington, IN 46750. TEL 219-356-8400 Ed. Vincent J. Giese. adv. bk. rev. tr.lit. circ. 12,000. (also avail. in microform from UMI; reprint service avail. from UMI) Indexed: Cath.Ind. CERDIC.

268 US ISSN 0032-8278
PRIMARY DAYS; makes Bible truths live. vol.5, 1939. q. $5.50. Scripture Press Publications Inc., 1825 College Ave., Wheaton, IL 60187. TEL 312-668-6000 Ed. Joanne Willanger. charts. illus. circ. 170,000.

268 028.5 SP
PRIMERA LUZ. 1972. m. 1200 ptas.($10) Juan A. Monroy, Apdo. 2029, Madrid 2, Spain. bk. rev. circ. 3,000.

200 AT
PRISM. 1968. q. Aus.$5.50. Lutheran Publishing House, 205 Halifax St., Adelaide, SA 5000, Australia. Ed. J.E. Prenzler. circ. 2,000.

200 US
PRISM; a theological forum for the United Church of Christ. 1985. s-a. $7. (United Theological Seminary of the Twin Cities) Prism Publishers, Box 12092, St. Paul, MN 55112. Eds. Louis H. Gunnemann, John Von Rohr. circ. 1,500.

377.8 NO ISSN 0032-8847
PRISMET; pedagogisk tidsskrift. 1950. 8/yr. Kr.90. (Institutt for Kristen Oppseding - Institute for Christian Education) Universitetsforlaget A-S, Box 2959 Toeyen, 0608 Oslo 6, Norway. Ed.Bd. adv. bk. rev. circ. 3,000.

200 NE
PROBLEME DER AEGYPTOLOGIE. 1953. irreg. price varies. E.J. Brill, P.O. Box 9000, 2300 PA Leiden, Netherlands. Ed. W. Helck.

200 US ISSN 0360-6503
PROCESS STUDIES. 1971. q. $12 to individuals; institutions $16. School of Theology at Claremont, Center for Process Studies, 1325 N. College Ave., Claremont, CA 91711. TEL 714-626-3521 Ed. Lewis S. Ford. adv. bk. rev. abstr. circ. 1,000. (also avail. in microform from UMI; back issues avail.; reprint service avail. from ISI,UMI) Indexed: Curr.Cont. Old Test.Abstr. Rel.Per. Arts & Hum.Cit.Ind. CERDIC. Phil.Ind. Rel.Ind.One. Rel.& Theol.Abstr.

209 956 IS ISSN 0032-9622
PROCHE-ORIENT CHRETIEN. (Text in English and French) 1951. q. $14. Peres Blancs de Sainte-Anne de Jerusalem, B.P. 19079, Jerusalem, Israel. Ed. Frans Bouwen. bk. rev. index. cum.index: 1951-1970. circ. 1,000. (also avail. in microform from IDC) Indexed: Bull.Signal. CERDIC. Rel.Ind.One.
History

220 CN ISSN 0048-5578
PROPHETIC EXPOSITOR. 1964. m. membership. British Israel World Federation (Canada) Inc., 313 Sherbourne St., Toronto, Ont., Canada. TEL 416-921-5996 Ed. D.C. Nesbit, K.E. Eason. adv. bk. rev. abstr. bibl. charts. illus. stat. index. circ. 1,600. (processed)

200 SP ISSN 0478-6378
PROYECCION; teologia y mundo actual. 1954. q. 1200 ptas.($22) Facultad de Teologia, Granada, Apartado 2002, 18080 Granada, Spain. Ed. Ildefonso Camacho. adv. bk. rev. circ. 2,100. (tabloid format; back issues avail.) Indexed: Old Test.Abstr.

220 NE ISSN 0079-7197
PSEUDEPIGRAPHA VETERIS TESTAMENTI GRAECE. 1964. irreg., vol.4, 1977. price varies. (Rijksuniversiteit te Leiden) E. J. Brill, P.O. Box 9000, 2300 PA Leiden, Netherlands.

250 US ISSN 0160-838X
PULPIT DIGEST (1978) N.S. 1972. bi-m. $10. Pulpit Publishing Co., Inc., Box 5199, Jackson, MS 39216. TEL 601-366-6469 Ed. Chas. L. Wallis. adv. bk. rev. index. circ. 12,000.
Formerly: New Pulpit Digest (ISSN 0145-7969); Which was formed by the merger of: Pulpit Digest (ISSN 0033-4146); Pulpit Preaching (ISSN 0160-3515)

200 US ISSN 0193-3914
PULPIT HELPS. 1975. m. $15. Advancing the Ministries of the Gospel International, 6815 Shallowford Rd., Chattanooga, TN 37422. Eds. Spiros Zodhiates, Joe Walker. adv. bk. rev. illus. circ. 210,000. (also avail. in microfiche; back issues avail.)

200 US ISSN 0195-1548
PULPIT RESOURCE. 1973. q. $28. Pulpit Resource, Inc., 121 Maono Pl., Honolulu, HI 96821. TEL 808-373-4410 Ed. Glendon E. Harris. circ. 7,000. (back issues avail.)

266 US
PULSE. Logo title: World Pulse. 1967. s-m. $24.95. Evangelical Missions Information Service, Box 794, Wheaton, IL 60189. TEL 312-653-2158 Ed. James W. Reapsome. circ. 4,500. Indexed: Int.Nurs.Ind.
Formerly: Europe Pulse.
Missions

297 MY ISSN 0552-6426
PURE LIFE SOCIETY. ANNUAL REPORT. 1953. a. membership. Pure Life Society, Batu 6, Jalan Puchong, Jalan Kelang Lama P.O., Kuala Lumpur, Malaysia.

200 933 IS
QUADERNI DE "LA TERRA SANTA". (Text in various languages) 1963. irreg. Franciscan Printing Press, Box 14064, Jerusalem 91140, Israel.

200 IT
QUADERNI DEL GALLO. 1946. m. $18. Associazione Culturale il Gallo, Casella Postale 1242, 16100 Genoa, Italy. Ed. Germano Beringheli. bk. rev. index. circ. 2,000. (also avail. in microform from UMI; reprint service avail. from UMI) Indexed: CERDIC.
Formerly: Gallo (ISSN 0016-416X)

289.6 US ISSN 0033-5096
QUAKER SERVICE BULLETIN. 1947. 3/yr. contribution $10. American Friends Service Committee, Inc., 1501 Cherry St., Philadelphia, PA 19102. TEL 215-241-7051 Ed. Diane Shandor. illus. circ. 85,000. (also avail. in microform from UMI; reprint service avail. from UMI)
Formerly (until 1960): Bulletin (Philadelphia)

266 US ISSN 0033-6017
QUEEN. 1950. bi-m. $8. (Montfort Missionaries) Queen of All Hearts, 40 So. Saxon Ave., Bay Shore, NY 11706. TEL 516-665-0726 Ed. Rev. James McMillan, S.M.M. bk. rev. illus. circ. 7,341.

260 GW ISSN 0079-9084
QUELLEN UND FORSCHUNGEN ZUR WUERTTEMBERGISCHEN KIRCHENGESCHICHTE. 1967. irreg., vol.7, 1981. Calwer Verlag, Scharnhauser Str. 44, 7000 Stuttgart 70, W. Germany (B.R.D.) Eds. Martin Brecht, Gerhard Schaefer.

QUESTION DE RACINES, PENSEES, SCIENCES ECLAIREES. see *PARAPSYCHOLOGY AND OCCULTISM*

R-A-D-A-R. see *CHILDREN AND YOUTH — For*

261 322 US ISSN 0034-3978
R C D A-RELIGION IN COMMUNIST DOMINATED AREAS. 1962. q. $20. Research Center for Religion & Human Rights in Closed Societies, Ltd., 475 Riverside Dr., Ste. 448, New York, NY 10115. TEL 212-870-2481 Ed. Rev. Blahoslav S. Hruby. bk. rev. illus. index. circ. 3,000. (also avail. in microform from UMI; back issues avail.)

240 CN ISSN 0079-9351
R.M. BUCKE MEMORIAL SOCIETY FOR THE STUDY OF RELIGIOUS EXPERIENCE. PROCEEDINGS OF THE CONFERENCE. 1965. irreg., vol.7, 1974. price varies. R.M. Bucke Memorial Society, 1033 Pine Ave. W., Montreal, Que. H3A 1A1, Canada. Ed. Raymond H. Prince. circ. 300. (back issues avail.)

R N A NEWSLETTER. (Religion Newswriters Association) see *JOURNALISM*

200 US
RADICAL OPTION. 1985. bi-m. $15. Growth Associates, Box 215, Weston, VT 05161. TEL 802-824-3440 Eds. Bill and Patty Coleman. abstr. stat. (looseleaf format)

200 371.8 GW ISSN 0033-8532
RADIUS. 1955. q. DM.42.90. (Evangelische Akademikerschaft in Deutschland) Radius-Verlag GmbH, Kniebisstr. 29, 7000 Stuttgart 1, W. Germany (B.R.D.) Ed.Bd. adv. bk. rev. illus. index. cum.index: 1955-1970. circ. 9,000.

201 301 US ISSN 0275-0147
RADIX (BERKELEY) 1969. 4/yr. $10. Radix Magazine, Inc., Box 4307, Berkeley, CA 94704. TEL 415-548-5329 Ed. Sharon Gallagher. adv. bk. rev. film rev. illus. circ. 7,000.
Formerly (until 1976): Right On.

200 UK ISSN 0033-9245
RANSOMER. 1893. 3/yr. £2. ‡ Guild of Our Lady of Ransom, 31 Southdown Rd., London SW20 8QJ, England. Ed. Mgr. Anthony George Stark. adv. bk. rev. circ. 3,000.

200 IT ISSN 0033-9644
RASSEGNA DI TEOLOGIA; rivista bimestrale per un aggiornamento cristiano teorico e pratico. 1960. bi-m. L.30000 to individuals; members and students L. 15000. Editrice A.V.E, Via Aurelia 481, 00165 Rome, Italy. Ed. Antonio Barruffo. adv. bk. rev. bibl. index. circ. 2,000. Indexed: CERDIC. New Test.Abstr.
Formerly: Digest Cattolico.

200 US ISSN 0034-0987
REALITY; a national monthly of Christian belief and opinion. 1965. m. free. Reality Inc., 1 Canyon Dr., Alexandria, VA 22305 TEL 703-836-0565 (Subscr. to: Box 50, Washington, DC 20044) Ed. Dr. Paul Rader. adv. bk. rev. charts. illus. circ. 9,831. (tabloid format; also avail. in microform from UMI; reprint service avail. from UMI)
Formerly: Magazine of Reality.

200 FR ISSN 0034-1258
RECHERCHES DE SCIENCE RELIGIEUSE. 1910. q. 190 F. Association Recherches de Science Religieuse, 15 rue Monsieur, 75007 Paris, France. Ed. Joseph Moingt. bk. rev. index. cum.index: 1910-1960. circ. 1,310. Indexed: Bull.Signal. M.L.A. Old Test.Abstr. Rel.Per. CERDIC. New Test.Abstr. Rel.Ind.One.

230 BE ISSN 0034-1266
RECHERCHES DE THEOLOGIE ANCIENNE ET MEDIEVALE. (Text in English, French and German) 1929. s-a. 750 Fr. Abbaye du Mont Cesar, 202 Mechelse Straat, B-3000 Louvain, Belgium. Ed. D.H. Bascour. adv. bk. rev. bibl. index. Indexed: M.L.A. CERDIC. New Test.Abstr. Rel.& Theol.Abstr.

262.9 200 FR
RECHERCHES INSTITUTIONNELLES. (In 4 Series: Droit et Eglises; Institutions et Histoire; Culture et Religion; Recherche Documentaire) irreg. Universite de Strasbourg II, Centre de Recherche et de Documentation des Institutions Chretiennes, 9 Place de l'Universite, 67084 Strasbourg Cedex, France. Eds. J. Schlick, M. Zimmerman. circ. 2,000.

255 NE
RECONCILIATION INTERNATIONAL. 1919. 5/yr. DM.30($15) International Fellowship of Reconciliation, Hof van Sonoy 15-17, 1811 LD Alkmaar, Netherlands. Ed. James H. Forest. bk. rev. circ. 2,500. (back issues avail.) Indexed: Alt.Press Ind.
Formerly(until 1985): I F O R Report (ISSN 0167-174X)

RECORDING LOCATOR. see *MUSIC*

200 CN ISSN 0034-2122
REDEEMER'S VOICE/HOLOS SPASYTELYA. (Text and title in English and Ukrainian) 1922. m. Can.$7.50. Redeemer's Voice Press, 165 Catherine St., Yorkton, Sask. S3N 2V7, Canada. TEL 306-783-4487 Eds. Rev. L. Ratushniak, Rev. Michael Schudlo. bk. rev. bibl. illus. circ. 1,775.

200 US
REFLECTION (NEW HAVEN) 1965. q. free. Yale University, Divinity School, 409 Prospect St., New Haven, CT 06510. (Co-sponsor: Berkeley Divinity School) Ed. Harry B. Adams. bk. rev. circ. 7,000.

200 261 SZ ISSN 0034-3021
REFORMATIO; Evangelische Zeitschrift fuer Kultur und Politik. m. 50 Fr. (Evangelisch-Kirchliche Vereinigung in der Schweiz) Benteli-Verlag, 3018 Berne, Switzerland. Ed. Hans-Rudolph Schar. adv. bk. rev. circ. 1,600. Indexed: Rel.Per. Rel.Ind.One.

280 US ISSN 0034-303X
REFORMATION REVIEW. (Vol. 22 not published) 1953. q. $10. (International Council of Christian Churches) Christian Beacon Press, Collingswood, NJ 08108. TEL 609-858-0700 Ed. J.C. Maris. bk. rev. index. circ. 850. Indexed: CERDIC.

200 US ISSN 0486-252X
REFORMED JOURNAL; a periodical of reformed comment and opinion. 1951. 12/yr. $15. Wm. B. Eerdmans Publishing Co., 255 Jefferson Ave. S.E., Grand Rapids, MI 49503. TEL 616-459-4591 adv. bk. rev. index. circ. 2,500. Indexed: CERDIC. Rel.Ind.One.

200 US
REFORMED SCOPE. 1971. m. free. Orthodox Reformed Publishing Society, 3268 Chestnut, S.W., Grandville, MI 49418. TEL 616-534-4093 Ed. Peter G. Elzinga. bk. rev. circ. 750. (processed)

230 AT ISSN 0034-3072
REFORMED THEOLOGICAL REVIEW. 1942. 3/yr. Aus.$6.90($6.90) Box 2587W, Elizabeth St. P.O., Melbourne, Victoria 3001, Australia. Eds. R. Swanton, D.G. Peterson. bk. rev. index. Indexed: Rel.Per. New Test.Abstr. CERDIC. Int.Z.Bibelwiss. Rel.& Theol.Abstr. Rel.Ind.One.

266 US
REFUGEES AMONG US- UNREACHED PEOPLES. 1979. a. $9.95. Missions Advanced Research and Communications Center, 919 W. Huntington Dr., Monrovia, CA 91016. TEL 818-303-8811 Eds. Edward R. Dayton, Samuel Wilson. circ. 600.
Formerly: Unreached Peoples.

248.82 AU
REGENBOGEN; Zeitung fuer Maedchen und Buben. 1946. w. S.120. Bischoefliches Seelsorgeamt Klagenfurt, Waaggasse 18, A-9010 Klagenfurt, Austria. Ed. Martin Bliem. bk. rev. illus. circ. 40,000. (looseleaf format)
Formerly (1946-1977, Mar.): Gotteskinder (ISSN 0017-2510)
For ages 8-12

250 GW ISSN 0034-3250
REGENSBURGER BISTUMSBLATT. 1926. w. DM.25. (Bischoeflicher Stuhl Regensburg) Verlag Regensburger Bistumsblatt, Koenigsstr. 2, 8400 Regensburg 2, W. Germany (B.R.D.) Ed. Anton Reiter.

200 IT ISSN 0009-000X
REGNO-DOCUMENTI. 1966. m. L.20500($14) Centro Editoriale Dehoniano, Via Nosadella 6, 40123 Bologna, Italy. adv. circ. 11,000. (looseleaf format)

200 GW
REGULAE BENEDICTI STUDIA. ANNUARIUM INTERNATIONALE. (Text in English, French and German) 1972. a. price varies. Eos Verlag, Erzabtei St. Ottilien, D-8917 St. Ottilien, W. Germany (B.R.D) Eds. B. Jaspert, E. Manning.

200 BL ISSN 0034-3633
REINO; de deus no mundo dos homens. 1943. m. Cr.$35. ‡ Promocao-Da-Familia Editora, Caixa Postal-1133, Belo Horizonte-MG., Brazil. Ed. Osvaldo Goncalves. illus. circ. 12,000.
Formerly: Reino dos Sagrados Coracoes.

RELIGIOESE GRAPHIK; Blaetter fuer Freunde Christlicher Gebrauchsgraphik. see *ART*

200 UK ISSN 0048-721X
RELIGION; the established journal of the history, structure and theory of religion and religions. vol.12, 1982. q. £37($85) Academic Press Inc. (London) Ltd., 24-28 Oval Rd., London NW1 7DX, England (Dist. in U.S. by: Academic Press Inc., 111 Fifth Ave., New York, NY 10003) Eds. Stuart Mews, Ivan Strenski. Indexed: Curr.Cont. Old Test.Abstr. Arts & Hum.Cit.Ind. CERDIC. New Test.Abstr. Rel.Ind.One.

200 US ISSN 0730-2363
RELIGION AND LIFE LETTERS. 1981. fortn. $25. Spiritual Studies Center, Box 1104, Rockville, MD 20850. TEL 301-963-9243 Ed. Elisabeth Nachtwey.

RELIGION AND LITERATURE. see *LITERATURE*

290 200 GW ISSN 0080-0848
RELIGION AND REASON; METHOD AND THEORY IN THE STUDY AND INTERPRETATION OF RELIGION. 1972. irreg. price varies. Walter de Gruyter & Co., Mouton Publishers, Postfach 110240, D-1000 Berlin 11, W. Germany (B.R.D.) (U.S. addr.: Mouton Publishers, division of Walter de Gruyter, Inc., 200 Saw Mill River Road, Hawthorne, NY 10532) Ed. J.D.J. Waardenburg.

261 301 II ISSN 0034-3951
RELIGION AND SOCIETY. vol. 20, 1973. q. Rs.20($15) Christian Institute for the Study of Religion and Society, Publications Trust, Box 4600, 17 Miller's Rd., Bangalore 560046, India. Ed.Bd. adv. bk. rev. circ. 1,250. (also avail. in microfilm; reprint service avail. from UMI) Indexed: Rel.Per. G. Indian Per.Lit. CERDIC. Rel.Ind.One. Rel.Ind.Two.

200 100 GW
RELIGION AND SOCIETY. 1976. irreg. price varies. Walter de Gruyter & Co., Mouton Publishers, Postfach 110240, D-1000 Berlin 11, W. Germany (B.R.D.) (U.S. addr.: Mouton Publishers, division of Walter de Gruyter, Inc., 200 Saw Mill River Road, Hawthorne, NY 10532) Eds. J.D.J. Waardenburg, L. Laeyendecker.

200 FR ISSN 0080-0864
RELIGION ET SCIENCES DE L'HOMME. 1971. irreg. price varies. Editions du Centurion, 17 rue du Babylone, Paris 75007, France.

200 370.196 US
RELIGION FOR PEACE. 1970. q. $5. World Conference on Religion and Peace, 777 United Nations Plaza, New York, NY 10017. TEL 212-687-2163 Ed. John B. Taylor. circ. 2,500.

RELIGION HEUTE. see *EDUCATION*

200 US
RELIGION IN AMERICA. 1967. s-a. $25. (Princeton Religion Research Center, Inc.) Gallup Organization, Inc., Box 310, Princeton, NJ 08541. TEL 609-924-9600 Ed. George Gallup, Jr. (back issues avail.)

200 335 UK ISSN 0307-5974
RELIGION IN COMMUNIST LANDS. 1973. 3/yr. £16. Keston College, Heathfield Rd., Keston, Kent BR2 6BA, England. Ed. Paul Booth. adv. bk. rev. bibl. index. circ. 2,000. (also avail. in microform from UMI; reprint service avail. from UMI) Indexed: Abstr.Musl.Rel. CERDIC. Rel.Ind.One.

200.968 SA
RELIGION IN SOUTHERN AFRICA. 1980. s-a. R.8($12) to individuals; R.8. to institutions. Association for the Study of Religion (Southern Africa), Box 375, Pietermaritzburg 3200, South Africa. Ed. M. H. Prozesky. adv. bk. rev. circ. 170. (back issues avail.) Indexed: Ind.S.A.Per. Rel.Ind.One.

268 US ISSN 0034-401X
RELIGION TEACHER'S JOURNAL. 1967. 7/yr. $14. Twenty-Third Publications, Box 180, Mystic, CT 06355. TEL 203-536-2611 Ed. Gwen Costello. adv. abstr. illus. index. circ. 39,500. (also avail. in microform from UMI; reprint service avail. from UMI) Indexed: Cath.Ind. CERDIC.

200 UK ISSN 0267-1700
RELIGION TODAY. 1984. 3/yr. £5($10) to individuals. Ethnographica, 19 Westbourne Rd., London N7, England. Ed. Peter B. Clarke. adv. bk. rev. circ. 1,000.

200 060 AU
RELIGION, WISSENSCHAFT, KULTUR. SCHRIFTENREIHE. 1950. a. Verlag Herold, Freyung 6, A-1010 Vienna, Austria.
Formerly: Religion, Wissenschaft, Kultur. Jahrbuch (ISSN 0080-0872)

200 301 IT ISSN 0391-853X
RELIGIONE E SOCIETA. 1977. irreg. price varies. Edizioni Studium, Via Cassiodoro 14, 00193 Rome, Italy.

200 DK
RELIGIONSLAEREREN. bi-m. Religionslaererforeningen, Birkevej 13, Nr. Nissum, 7620 Lemvig, Denmark. Ed. Henning Fogde. adv. circ. 3,500. Indexed: Abstr.Musl.Rel.
Study and Teaching

200 GW
RELIGIONSPAEDAGOGISCHE PRAXIS. Short title: R P P. 1971. irreg., vol.20, 1977. price varies. Calwer Verlag, Scharnhauser Str. 44, 7000 Stuttgart 70, W. Germany (B.R.D.) (Co-publisher: Koesel-Verlag) Eds. Horst Klaus Berg, Wolfgang Langer. (back issues avail.)

RELIGIONSUNTERRICHT AN HOEHEREN SCHULEN. see *EDUCATION*

200 DK ISSN 0108-1993
RELIGIONSVIDENSKABELIGT TIDSSKRIFT. (Text in Danish; summaries in English) 1982. s-a. Kr.75. Jysk Selskab for Religionsvidenskab, c/o Kirsten Nielsen, Institut for Kristendomskundskab, Hovedbygningen, Ndr. Ringgade 1, 8000 Aarhus C, Denmark. Ed.Bd. adv. bk. rev. circ. 350.

200 IT ISSN 0034-4036
RELIGIOSE NELL'APOSTOLATO DIRETTO. 1963. q. L.3500. Unione Superiore Maggiori d'Italia, Via Zanardelli 32, 00186 Rome, Italy. Ed. A. Ravazzi. bk. rev. film rev. bibl. circ. 2,500.

RELIGIOUS AND INSPIRATIONAL BOOKS AND SERIALS IN PRINT. see *BIBLIOGRAPHIES*

RELIGIOUS BROADCASTING. see *COMMUNICATIONS — Radio And Television*

200 II
RELIGIOUS CONSULTANCY. 1978. 4/yr. Rs.135($27) K.K. Roy (Private) Ltd., 55 Gariahat Rd., Box 10210, Calcutta 700019, India. Ed. Dr. K.K. Roy. adv. abstr. bibl. index. circ. 980.

200 370 US ISSN 0034-4087
RELIGIOUS EDUCATION; a platform for the free discussion of issues in the field of religion and their bearing on education. 1906. q. membership. Religious Education Association, 409 Prospect St., New Haven, CT 06511. TEL 203-865-6141 Eds. John Westerhoff, Randolph Crump Miller. adv. bk. rev. index. circ. 4,000. (also avail. in microform from UMI; reprint service avail. from UMI) Indexed: Curr.Cont. Educ.Ind. CERDIC. Ind.Jew.Per. Rel.Ind.One. Rel.& Theol.Abstr.

200 UK ISSN 0034-4125
RELIGIOUS STUDIES. 1965. q. $52 to individuals; $109 to institutions. Cambridge University Press, Edinburgh Bldg., Shaftesbury Rd., Cambridge CB2 2RU, England (And 32 E. 57th St., New York NY 10022) Ed. Prof. S. Sutherland. adv. bk. rev. index. circ. 1,200. (also avail. in microform from UMI) Indexed: Br.Hum.Ind. Curr.Cont. Hum.Ind. Rel.Per. Arts & Hum.Cit.Ind. Bk.Rev.Ind. CERDIC. New Test.Abstr. Phil.Ind. Rel.Ind.One. Rel.& Theol.Abstr.

200 US ISSN 0319-485X
RELIGIOUS STUDIES REVIEW; a quarterly review of publications in the field of religion and related disciplines. 1975. q. $30. Council on the Study of Religion, Mercer University, Macon, GA 31207. TEL 912-741-2376 Eds. Glenn Yocum, Watson Mills. adv. bk. rev. bibl. circ. 2,672. Indexed: Old Test.Abstr. Rel.Per. New Test.Abstr. Bk.Rev.Ind. CERDIC. Child.Bk.Rev.Ind. Rel.Ind.One.

200 IT ISSN 0034-4486
RENOVATIO. 1966. q. L.4000. Gianni Baget Bozzo, Ed. & Pub., Via 12 Ottobre 14, Genoa, Italy. bk. rev. index. circ. 1,200(controlled) Indexed: CERDIC.

REPORTER FOR CONSCIENCE' SAKE. see *POLITICAL SCIENCE — Civil Rights*

RES MEDICAE. see *MEDICAL SCIENCES*

200 CN ISSN 0708-2177
RESTORATION. 1947. 10/yr. Can.$2. ‡ Madonna House, Inc., Combermere, Ont. K0J 1L0, Canada. TEL 613-756-3713 Ed. Rev. David May. bk. rev. circ. 13,000. (also avail. in microform from UMI; reprint service avail. from UMI)

200 US ISSN 0034-5830
RESTORATION HERALD. 1925. m. (except Aug.) $6. Christian Restoration Association, 5664 Cheviot Rd., Cincinnati, OH 45247. TEL 513-385-0461 Ed. Thomas D. Thurman. adv. bk. rev. illus. circ. 7,000.

222 US ISSN 0486-5642
RESTORATION QUARTERLY. 1958. q. $11. Restoration Quarterly Corporation, Box 8227, Abilene, TX 79699. Ed. Everett Ferguson. adv. bk. rev. circ. 1,400. Indexed: Old Test.Abstr. CERDIC. New Test.Abstr. Rel.& Theol.Abstr. Rel.Ind.One.

266 CN ISSN 0034-6284
REVEIL MISSIONNAIRE. 1966. bi-m. Can.$3. ‡ Missionnaires de la Consolata, 2505 W. Bd. Gouin, Montreal, Que. H3M 1B5, Canada. TEL 514-334-1910 Ed. Jean Pare. adv. illus. circ. 25,000.
Missions

200 US ISSN 0034-639X
REVIEW FOR RELIGIOUS. 1942. bi-m. $11. Missouri Province Educational Institute, Box 6070, Duluth, MN 55806. Ed. Daniel F.X. Meenan, S.J. bk. rev. index. circ. 18,000. (also avail. in microform from UMI; reprint service avail. from UMI) Indexed: Cath.Ind. Bk.Rev.Ind. CERDIC. New Test.Abstr.

200 US ISSN 0034-673X
REVIEW OF RELIGIOUS RESEARCH. 1959/60. 4/yr. $30. Religious Research Association, Marist Hall, Rm. 108, Catholic University of America, Washington, DC 20064 (Editorial address: c/o Edward Lehman, State University of New York at Brockport, Sociology Dept., Brockport, NY 14420) Ed. Edward Lehman. adv. bk. rev. abstr. bibl. stat. index; cum.index: vols. 1-10. circ. 1,200. (also avail. in microform from UMI; reprint service avail. from UMI) Indexed: Curr.Cont. Leg.Per. Rel.Per. SSCI. Sociol.Abstr. Arts & Hum.Cit.Ind. CERDIC. C.L.I. G.Soc.Sci.& Rel.Per.Lit. Lang.& Lang.Behav.Abstr. Rel.Ind.One. Rel.& Theol.Abstr.

220 AG ISSN 0034-7078
REVISTA BIBLICA. 1939. q. $16. Sociedad Argentina de Profesores de Sagrada Escritura, Casilla Postal 33, 1425 Buenos Aires, Argentina. Dir. Armando Levoratti. adv. bk. rev. bibl. index. cum.index. circ. 700. Indexed: New Test.Abstr. Int.Z.Bibelwiss. Rel.Ind.One.
Bible

200 SP ISSN 0034-8147
REVISTA DE ESPIRITUALIDAD. 1941. q. 1.450 ptas. Padres Carmelitas Descalzados, Triana 9, 28016 Madrid, Spain. Ed. Secundino Castro Sanchez. adv. bk. rev. bibl. index. circ. 1,200. Indexed: New Test.Abstr.

200 BL
REVISTA ECLESIASTICA BRASILEIRA. 1941. q. $60. Editora Vozes Ltda., Rua Frei Luis 100, Caixa Postal 90023, 25689 Petropolis, Rio de Janeiro, Brazil. Ed. Leonardo Boff. adv. bk. rev. bibl. circ. 3,000. Indexed: Cath.Ind. Old Test.Abstr. New Test.Abstr.

262.9 SP ISSN 0034-9372
REVISTA ESPANOLA DE DERECHO CANONICO. (Text in French, Italian, Latin, Spanish; summaries in English, Latin, Spanish) 1946. 3/yr. 2000 ptas.($29) Consejo Superior de Investigaciones Cientificas, Instituto de Derecho Canonico "San Raimundo de Penafort", Compania 1, Salamanca, Spain. Ed. Lamberto de Echeverria. bk. rev. bibl. index. cum.index every 20 years. circ. 1,000. (tabloid format) Indexed: CERDIC. Canon Law Abstr.
Canon law

220 FR ISSN 0035-0907
REVUE BIBLIQUE. 1892. q. 668 F. (Ecole Biblique et Archeologique de Jerusalem) J. Gabalda et Cie, 90 rue Bonaparte, 75006 Paris, France. Ed. R.P. Tournay. bk. rev. bibl. charts. illus. index. cum.index: 1892-1972. Indexed: Curr.Cont. Old Test.Abstr. Rel.Per. Arts & Hum.Cit.Ind. CERDIC. New Test.Abstr. Rel.Ind.One. Rel.& Theol.Abstr.
Bible

274 FR ISSN 0048-7988
REVUE D'HISTOIRE DE L'EGLISE DE FRANCE. 1910. s-a. 240 F. Societe d'Histoire Religieuse de la France, 28 rue d'Assas, 75006 Paris, France. Ed. M. Venard. bk. rev. circ. 40. Indexed: CERDIC.

200 FR ISSN 0035-2403
REVUE D'HISTOIRE ET DE PHILOSOPHIE RELIGIEUSES. 1921. q. 140 F. (Universite de Strasbourg II) Presses Universitaires de France, 108 bd. Saint Germain, 75279 Paris Cedex 6, France. Ed. M.A. Chevallier. adv. bk. rev. charts. illus. index. cum.index: vol.1, 1920-1945; vol.2, 1946-1974. circ. 1,800. (reprint service avail. from KTO) Indexed: Curr.Cont. Rel.Per. Arts & Hum.Cit.Ind. CERDIC. New Test.Abstr. Rel.Ind.One. Rel.& Theol.Abstr.

209 FR ISSN 0035-1423
REVUE DE L'HISTOIRE DES RELIGIONS. 1880. q. 275 F. Presses Universitaires de France, 108 bd. Saint Germain, 75279 Paris Cedex 6, France (Subscr. to: Service des Periodiques, 12 rue Jean de Beauvais, 75005 Paris) Dir. Henri-Charles Puech. bk. rev. index every 4 mos. (reprint service avail. from KTO) Indexed: Curr.Cont. Rel.Per. Arts & Hum.Cit.Ind. New Test.Abstr. Rel.Ind.One.
History

REVUE DE QUMRAN. see *ORIENTAL STUDIES*

230 100 SZ ISSN 0035-1784
REVUE DE THEOLOGIE ET DE PHILOSOPHIE. 1868. q. 58 Fr. Revue de Theologie et de Philosophie, Chemin des Cedres, 7, CH-1004 Lausanne, Switzerland. bk. rev. index. Indexed: Bull.Signal. Old Test.Abstr. CERDIC. New Test.Abstr. Phil.Ind. Rel.Ind.One.

230 809 FR ISSN 0035-2012
REVUE DES ETUDES AUGUSTINIENNES. (Text in various languages) 1955. q. 300 F.($44) Institut des Etudes Augustiniennes, 3 rue de l'Abbaye, 75006 Paris, France. Dir. Georges Folliet. bk. rev. bibl. illus. index. circ. 1,000. Indexed: Bull.Signal. M.L.A. CERDIC. New Test.Abstr. Phil.Ind.

REVUE MABILLON. see *RELIGIONS AND THEOLOGY — Roman Catholic*

230 FR ISSN 0035-4295
REVUE THOMISTE; revue doctrinale de theologie et de philosophie. 1893. q. 350 F. Association Culturelle de Publications, Dominicains de la Province de Toulouse, 1 av. Lacordaire, 31078 Toulouse, France (Subscr. to: Kraus Reprint and Periodicals, Route 100, Milwood, NY 10546) Ed. Pere Marie-Vincent Leroy. adv. bk. rev. index. circ. 1,100. Indexed: Bull.Signal. M.L.A. CERDIC. New Test.Abstr. Phil.Ind.

RICERCHE DI STORIA SOCIALE E RELIGIOSA. see *SOCIOLOGY*

264 IT ISSN 0035-6395
RIVISTA DI PASTORALE LITURGICA. 1962. bi-m. L.27000. Editrice Queriniana, Via Piamarta 6, 25100 Brescia, Italy. Ed.Bd.

274 900 IT ISSN 0035-6557
RIVISTA DI STORIA DELLA CHIESA IN ITALIA. (Text in English, French, German, Italian, Latin, Spanish) 1947. s-a. $50. Herder Editrice e Libreria s.r.l., Piazza di Montecitorio 120, 00186 Rome, Italy. Ed. Michele Maccarrone. bk. rev. bibl. charts. stat. tr.lit. index. (tabloid format)
History

209 IT ISSN 0035-6573
RIVISTA DI STORIA E LETTERATURA RELIGIOSA. (Text in English, French, German, Italian) 1965. 3/yr. L.55000. Casa Editrice Leo S. Olschki, Casella Postale 66, 50100 Florence, Italy. Ed. Franco Bolgiani. adv. bk. rev. circ. 1,000. Indexed: M.L.A. CERDIC. New Test.Abstr.

209 IT
RIVISTA DI STORIA E LETTERATURA RELIGIOSA. BIBLIOTECA; studi e testi. 1967. irreg., no.7, 1984. price varies. Casa Editrice Leo S. Olschki, Casella Postale 66, 50100 Florence, Italy. Indexed: Arts & Hum.Cit.Ind.

205 IT ISSN 0391-108X
ROCCA. 1940. fortn. L.65000. Pro Civitate Christiana, Via Ancaiani 3, 06081 Assisi, Italy. Ed. Gesuino Bulla. adv. bk. rev. circ. 39,638.

ROEMISCHE HISTORISCHE MITTEILUNGEN. see *HISTORY — History Of Europe*

200 GW ISSN 0035-7812
ROEMISCHE QUARTALSCHRIFT FUER CHRISTLICHE ALTERTUMSKUNDE UND KIRCHENGESCHICHTE. 1905. s-a. DM.142. Verlag Herder GmbH und Co. KG, Hermann-Herder-Str. 4, D-7800 Freiburg im Breisgau, W. Germany (B.R.D.) adv. bk. rev. charts. illus. Indexed: Numis.Lit. RILA. RILA.

200 NE ISSN 0035-8169
ROND DE TAFEL; leerkrant liturgie. 1892; N.S. 1946. bi-m. fl.10. ‡ Abdij van Berne, Abdijstraat 53, 5473 AC Heeswijk-Dinther, Netherlands. bk. rev. illus. index. circ. 2,400. Indexed: CERDIC.
Formerly: Offer.

280 NE
RUIMZICHT. 1875. q. fl.15($7) Vereniging Hervormd Opleidingscentrum, Hoofdstraat 88, Box 28, Driebergen, Netherlands. Ed. Rev. G.H. Wolfensberger. bk. rev. illus. circ. 1,100.
Formerly: Nieuw Ruimzicht (ISSN 0028-9841)

RUNDBRIEF EHEMALIGER SCHUELER UND FREUNDE DER SCHULBRUEDER. see *COLLEGE AND ALUMNI*

200 UR ISSN 0044-4553
RUSSKAYA PRAVOSLAVNAYA TSERKOV'. MOSKOVSKAYA PATRIARKHIYA. ZHURNAL/JOURNAL OF THE MOSCOW PATRIARCHATE. (Editions in English and Russian) 1931. m. 12 Rub. Moskovskaya Patriarkhiya, Novodevichii pr., 1, Moscow G-435, Russian S.F.S.R., U.S.S.R. Ed. Archbishop Pitirim. bibl. illus. Indexed: CERDIC. Curr.Dig.Sov.Press. Rel.Ind.One.

280 100 US ISSN 0883-1300
S C P JOURNAL. 1977. q. donation. Spiritual Counterfeits Project, Inc., Box 4308, Berkeley, CA 94704. TEL 415-540-0300 Ed. Robert J.L. Burrows. bk. rev. circ. 17,500. (back issues avail.) Indexed: Chr.Per.Ind.

200 BL ISSN 0036-1267
S E D O C. (Servicio de Documentacao) 1968. m. $50. Editora Vozes Ltda., Rua Frei Luis 100, Caixa Postal 90023, 25689 Petropolis, Rio de Janeiro, Brazil. Ed. Antonio Moser. circ. 2,400.

S E H A NEWSLETTER AND PROCEEDINGS. (Society for Early Historic Archaeology) see *ARCHAEOLOGY*

266 UK
S G M NEWS. 1943. q. free. ‡ Scripture Gift Mission, Radstock House, 3 Eccleston St., London SW1W 9LZ, England. illus. circ. 20,000.
Formerly: S G M News Digest (ISSN 0048-9859)
Missions

200 IT
S I D I C. (Text in English and French) 1968. 3/yr. $20. Service International de Documentation Judeo-Chretienne, Via del Plebiscito 112, 00186 Rome, Italy (Subscr. to: Dr. Eugene Fisher, Secretariat for Catholic-Jewish Relations, 1312 Massachusetts Ave., N.W., Washington, D.C. 20005) Ed.Bd. bk. rev. bibl. circ. 1,500. (back issues avail.) Indexed: Cath.Ind.

266 CN ISSN 0711-6683
S I M NOW. (Sudan Interior Mission) 1958. bi-m. free in Canada and U.S. S I M International, 10 Huntingdale Blvd., Scarborough, Ont. M1W 2S5, Canada TEL 416-497-2424 (U.S. address: Box 7900, Charlotte, N.C., 28217) Ed. Rev. K.E. Lovering. bk. rev. circ. 125,000. (reprint service avail. from UMI) Indexed: Curr.Cont.Africa.
Formerly (until Jan. 1982): Africa Now (ISSN 0044-6513)

266 US
S.O.W. 1962. q. free. (Church of God World Missions) Pathway Press, 822-1080 Montgomery Ave., Cleveland, TN 37311. TEL 615-476-5197 Ed. Christopher Moree. charts. illus. stat. circ. 87,000.

200 US ISSN 0036-214X
SABBATH RECORDER. 1844. m. free. ‡ (American Sabbath Tract Society) Seventh Day Baptist Center, Box 1678, Janesville, WI 53547. TEL 608-752-5055 Ed. D. Scott Smith. bk. rev. illus. circ. 4,200.

200 100 IT ISSN 0036-2190
SACRA DOCTRINA. 1956. 5/yr. $30. Edizioni Studio Domenicano, Piazza S. Domenico 13, 40124 Bologna, Italy. Ed. Ottorino Benetollo. adv. bk. rev. bibl. index. circ. 1,500. (tabloid format) Indexed: CERDIC. New Test.Abstr.

SACRED DANCE GUILD JOURNAL. see *DANCE*

220 SP
SAGRADA BIBLIA. 1976. irreg., no.8, 1986. price varies. (Universidad de Navarra, Facultad de Teologia) Ediciones Universidad de Navarra, S.A., Apdo. 396, 31080 Pamplona, Spain.
Bible

266 US
ST. GEORGE ASSOCIATION NEWSLETTER. q. St. George Association of the U.S.A., 83 Christopher St., New York, NY 10014. TEL 212-242-5737 Ed. Fred P. Eckhardt. circ. controlled. (processed)

ST. JOSEPH'S MESSENGER AND ADVOCATE OF THE BLIND. see *BLIND*

207.11 US
ST. LUKE'S JOURNAL OF THEOLOGY. 1957. q. $10 to individuals; libraries $15. University of the South, School of Theology, Sewanee, TN 37375. TEL 615-598-5931 Ed. John M. Gessell. adv. bk. rev. index. cum.index: 1956-1967,1967-1977. circ. 2,750. (also avail. in microfilm from UMI; reprint service avail. from UMI) Indexed: Old Test.Abstr. Rel.Per. CERDIC. Rel.Ind.One.
Formerly: St. Luke's Journal (ISSN 0036-309X)

207.11 AT ISSN 0036-3103
ST. MARK'S REVIEW. 1955. q. Aus.$12.50. St. Mark's Institute of Theology, Library, P.O. Box 67, Canberra, A.C.T. 2600, Australia. Ed. Rev. B.M. Porter. adv. bk. rev. cum.index. circ. 1,300. (also avail. in microform from UMI; reprint service avail. from UMI) Indexed: Aus.P.A.I.S. CERDIC. Rel.Ind.One.

200 US ISSN 0038-8815
ST. PAUL'S PRINTER. 1958. q. $5. Society of St. Paul, 17430 Scenic St., Box 100, Sandy, OR 97055. TEL 503-668-4108 Ed. Rev. Andrew Rank. bk. rev. illus. stat. circ. 12,000.

250 AU ISSN 0036-3162
ST. POELTNER DIOEZESANBLATT. 1785. irreg. (at least 12/yr.) S.400. Bischoefliches Ordinariat Sanct Poelten, Domplatz 1, A-3100 St. Poelten, Austria. Ed. Dr. Heinrich Fasching. bk. rev. bibl. charts. circ. 800.

200 US ISSN 0082-4208
ST. THOMAS MORE LECTURES. 1964. irreg., no.3, 1969. price varies. Yale University Press, 92A Yale Station, New Haven, CT 06520. TEL 203-432-0940

200 SP ISSN 0211-4569
SAL TERRAE. m. 2120 ptas.($23) Editorial Sal Terrae, Calle Guevara 20, Santander, Spain. Indexed: CERDIC. Canon Law Abstr.

266 US ISSN 0036-3480
SALESIAN. 1947. bi-m. $2. Salesian Society, Inc., Box 30-148 Main St., New Rochelle, NY 10802. TEL 914-633-8344 Ed. Rev. E.J. Cappelletti. illus. circ. 3,000,000.
Missions

282 US
SALT; for grassroots Christians seeking social justice. 1981. 10/yr. $10. Claretian Publications, 205 W. Monroe St., Chicago, IL 60606. TEL 312-236-7782 Ed. Rev. Mark J. Brummel. adv. bk. rev. illus. circ. 10,915.

200 CN ISSN 0709-616X
SALT. 1979. a. Can.$15. Alberta Teachers' Association, Religious Studies and Moral Education Council, 11010 142nd St., Edmonton, Alta. T5N 2R1, Canada. Ed. Rose Marie Hague. bk. rev. circ. 242.

200 AT ISSN 0816-0031
SALT. 1985. q. Aus.$7.50($7) Australian Fellowship of Evangelical Students, 120 Chalmers St., Surry Hills, N.S.W. 2010, Australia. Ed. Andrew Reid. bk. rev. film rev. illus. tr.lit. circ. 1,500. (back issues avail.)

200 IT ISSN 0036-3723
SAMARITANO. 1856. m. L.2500. Societa di San Vincenzo de Paoli, Consiglio Superiore Italiano, Piazza Duomo 16, 20122 Milan, Italy. bk. rev.

200 US
SAMIZDAT REVIEW. 1982. q. (Door of Hope International) Door of Hope Press, Box 10460, Glendale, CA 91209.

200 IT ISSN 0036-424X
SAN SALVATORE DA HORTA. 1927. fortn. L.4000. Chiesa Santa Rosalia, Cagliari 09100, Italy.

200 BL ISSN 0036-4614
SANTUARIO DE APARECIDA. 1900. w. Cr.$200. (Congregacao do Santissimo Redentor) Editora Santuario, Rua Padre Claro Monteiro 342, 12570 Aparecida SP, Brazil. Ed. Jose Geraldo Rodrigues. adv. bk. rev. illus. circ. 45,000.

200 IT ISSN 0036-4630
SANTUARIO DI N.S.D. GRAZIE E DI S. MARIA GORETTI. 1908. m. L.6000($6) Santuario di Nettuno, 00048 Nettuno (Rome), Italy. circ. 4,000.

266 610 UK ISSN 0036-5106
SAVING HEALTH. 1962. q. £2.50. ‡ Medical Missionary Association, 6 Canonbury Place, London N1 2NJ, England. Ed. Dr. P.F. Green. bk. rev. illus. circ. 900. Indexed: CERDIC.
Medical missions

266 CN ISSN 0700-6802
SCARBORO MISSIONS. 1919. m. Can.$5. Scarboro Foreign Mission Society, 2685 Kingston Rd., Scarborough, Ont. M1M 1M4, Canada. TEL 416-261-7135 Ed. Rev. Joseph M. Young. adv. bk. rev. circ. 45,000. (back issues avail.)
Missions

200 UK ISSN 0261-5703
SCHOOLS OF PRAYER. 1980. 3/yr. £2. Diocese of Northampton, Religious Education Service, St. Mary's R.E. Centre, 118 Bromham Rd., Bedford MK40 2QR, England. Ed. J. Glen, K. McGinnell. bk. rev. illus. circ. 200.

200 NE
SCHRIFT; populair bijbeltijdschrift. 1953. bi-m. fl.31.50. (Paters Montfortanen) Janssen-Print, Heilige Land Stichting 14, Nijmegen, Netherlands. Ed. H. Manie. bk. rev. circ. 3,000. Indexed: CERDIC.
Formerly: Boek der Boeken (ISSN 0006-5544)

SCIENCE ET ESPRIT. see *PHILOSOPHY*

SCIENCE OF RELIGION; abstracts and index of recent articles. see *RELIGIONS AND THEOLOGY — Abstracting, Bibliographies, Statistics*

200 UK ISSN 0264-5572
SCOTTISH CHURCH HISTORY SOCIETY. RECORDS. 1923. a. £5($10) Scottish Church History Society, Grange Manse, 51 Portland Rd., Kilmarnock, Ayrshire KA1 2EQ, Scotland. Ed. James Kirk. bibl. index. circ. 260. (back issues avail.)

266 UK ISSN 0048-9778
SCOTTISH INSTITUTE OF MISSIONARY STUDIES BULLETIN. 1967. s-a. £2($5) Scottish Institute of Missionary Studies, Department of Religious Studies, University of Aberdeen, King's College, Aberdeen AB9 2UB, Scotland. Ed. A. F. Walls. bk. rev. circ. 500. (processed; also avail. in microform from UMI; reprint service avail. from UMI) Indexed: CERDIC.

230 UK ISSN 0036-9306
SCOTTISH JOURNAL OF THEOLOGY. 1948. 4/yr. £30($65) to institutions; individuals £12($27.50) Scottish Academic Press Ltd., 33 Montgomery St., Edinburgh EH7 5JX, Scotland. Eds. A.I.C. Heron, J. Houston. adv. bk. rev. index. circ. 1,200. Indexed: Curr.Cont. Old Test.Abstr. Rel.Per. Arts & Hum.Cit.Ind. CERDIC. New Test.Abstr. Rel.Ind.One. Rel.& Theol.Abstr.

200 FI ISSN 0582-3226
SCRIPTA INSTITUTI DONNERIANI ABOENSIS. (Text in English, French, German) 1967. triennial. Fmk.100. Donner Institute for Research in Religious and Cultural History, Gezeliusgatan 2, P.O. Box 70, SF-20501 Aabo/Turku, Finland (Subscr. to: Almqvist & Wiksell International, Box 62, S-10120 Stockholm, Sweden) Tore Ahlbaeck. circ. 250. Indexed: Arts & Hum.Cit.Ind.

200 SP ISSN 0036-9764
SCRIPTA THEOLOGICA. 1969. 3/yr. 2500 ptas.($35) (Universidad de Navarra, Facultad de Teologia) Ediciones Universidad de Navarra, S.A., Apdo. 396, 31080 Pamplona, Spain. Ed. Pedro Rodriguez. bk. rev. Indexed: Old Test.Abstr. New Test.Abstr.

220 UK
SCRIPTURE EXAMINATION MATERIAL AND ANNUAL SCRIPTURE PROJECT. a. £1. National Christian Education Council, Robert Denholm House, Nutfield, Redhill, Surrey RH1 4HW, England. Ed. H. Snashall. circ. 16,800.

200 IT ISSN 0036-9950
SE VUOI. 1960. bi-m. L.8000. Society of St. Paul, Via A. Severo 58, 00145 Rome, Italy. (Co-sponsor: Istituto Regian Apostolorum) Ed. Maria De Luca. bk. rev. circ. 6,500.

200 US
SEEK. 1970. q. (in weekly parts) $6.50 for sets of five. Standard Publishing, 8121 Hamilton Ave., Cincinnati, OH 45231. TEL 513-931-4050 Ed. Eileen H. Wilmoth. circ. 53,000.

201 IT
SEGNI DEI TEMPI; mensile per un cristianesimo attuale. 1921. m. L.12000. Edizioni A.D.V., l'Araldo della Verita, 1 Via Chiantigiana 30, Falciani, 1-50023 Impruneta, Florence, Italy. Ed. Giuseppe De Meo. adv. index. circ. 12,000.

230 SP ISSN 0037-119X
SELECCIONES DE TEOLOGIA. 1962. q. 1500 ptas.($10) Instituto de Teologia Fundamental, Facultad de Teologia de Barcelona, Llaseres 30, Sant Cugat del Valles, Barcelona, Spain (Subscr. to: Selecciones de Teologia, Roger De Lluria 13, 08010 Barcelona, Spain) Ed. Rafael de Sivatte. adv. index. circ. 6,000. Indexed: CERDIC.

SELF-REALIZATION. see *PHILOSOPHY*

200 US ISSN 0095-571X
SEMEIA; an experimental journal for biblical criticism. (Text in English, Greek and Hebrew) 1974. q. $25 for individuals; $35 for institutions. (Society of Biblical Literature) Scholars Press, Box 1608, Decatur, GA 30031-1608. Ed. John Dominic Crossan. adv. bk. rev. bibl. charts. illus. cum.index. circ. 1,300. (also avail. in microfiche) Indexed: Old Test.Abstr. Arts & Hum.Cit.Ind. CERDIC. New Test.Abstr. Rel.& Theol.Abstr. Rel.Ind.One.
Bible

220 410 FR ISSN 0154-6902
SEMIOTIQUE ET BIBLE. 1975. q. 100 F. Centre pour l'Analyse du Discours Religieux, 25 rue du Plat, 69002 Lyon Cedex, France. Ed. Jean Delorme. bk. rev. circ. 800. Indexed: CERDIC. New Test.Abstr.

200 AU ISSN 0037-2129
SENDBOTE DES HERZENS JESU. 1865. m. S.168. Jesuitenkolleg, Sillgasse 6, A-6021 Innsbruck, Austria. Ed. Josef Fiedler. bk. rev. bibl. illus. index. circ. 8,000.

294.54 US
SERENITY SENTINEL. 1968. m. $11. Serenity Spiritualist Association, 322 Upper Rd., San Rafael, CA 94903. TEL 415-472-3633 Ed. Richard P. Goodwin. circ. 300.

252 US ISSN 0037-248X
SERMON BUILDER; preacher's professional periodical. 1953. m. $6. Church Extension Service, Inc., Box 988, Golden, CO 80401. TEL 303-279-1011 Ed. Glen Williamson. adv. bk. rev. circ. 5,000.

200 IT ISSN 0037-2773
SERVIZIO DELLA PAROLA. 1968. m. L.40000. Editrice Queriniana, Via Piamarta 6, 25100 Brescia, Italy. Ed. Luigi Della Torre.

SERVIZIO MIGRANTI. see *POLITICAL SCIENCE*

SHALOM. see *RELIGIONS AND THEOLOGY — Judaic*

266 UK
SHARE. (Includes: Partners' News) 1867. 4/yr. £1. ‡ South American Missionary Society, Allen Gardiner House, Pembury Rd., Tunbridge Wells, Kent TN2 3QU, England. Ed. Jone P. Collins. bk. rev. circ. 12,000. Indexed: CERDIC.
Formerly: Sent (ISSN 0037-2269)
Missions

200 US ISSN 0193-8274
SHARING THE PRACTICE. 1978. q. $20. Academy of Parish Clergy, Inc., Box 427, Marshville, NC 28103-0427 (Subscr. to: Rev. Roger I. Perks, Bus.Mgr., 12604 Britton Dr., Cleveland, OH 44120) Ed. Dr. Robert E. Lair, Jr. adv. bk. rev. circ. 700. (tabloid format; also avail. in microform from UMI)
Formerly: Academy of Parish Clergy. News and Views.

200 KO
SHINANGGYE/WORLD OF FAITH. (Text in Korean) 1967. m. 3500 Won($7) Full Gospel Central Church in Korea, 1-20 Yeouidodong, Youngdungpoku, Seoul, S. Korea. Ed. Wan-Ki Choi. adv. bk. rev. circ. 33,000.

200 919.306 PE
SHUPIHUI. 1976. 4/yr. $18. Centro de Estudios Teologicos de la Amazonia, Putmayo 355, Iquitos, Peru. Ed. Joaquin Garcia Sanchez. bk. rev.

SINGLE ADULT MINISTRY INFORMATION. see *EDUCATION*

SINTESE. see *SOCIAL SCIENCES: COMPREHENSIVE WORKS*

200 FR ISSN 0075-4544
SIR MOSES MONTEFIORE COLLECTIONS DES JUIFS CELEBRES. Title varies: Juifs Celebres. 1969. irreg. 35 F. Librairie du Centre Communautaire, 19 bd. Poissonniere, 75002 Paris, France. circ. 10,000.

260 YU ISSN 0037-7074
SLUZBA BOZJA; liturgijsko-pastoralna revija. 1961. q. 800 din.($17) Franjevacka Visoka Bogoslovija, Makarska - Franciscan High School for Theology at Makarska, Zrtava Fasizma 1, 58300 Makarska, Yugoslavia. Ed. Vicko Kapitanovic. adv. bk. rev. index. circ. 1,400.

200 IT ISSN 0037-7562
SOCCORSO PERPETUO DI MARIA. 1946. m. L.2000. Santuario della Madonna del Perpetuo Soccorso, 37012 Bussolengo, Verona, Italy. illus. circ. 8,000.

SOCIAL COMPASS; international review of sociology of religion. see *SOCIOLOGY*

SOCIAL STUDIES; Irish journal of sociology. see *SOCIOLOGY*

200 CN ISSN 0537-6211
SOCIETE SAINT-JEAN-BAPTISTE DE MONTREAL. INFORMATION NATIONALE. 1962. m. Can.$5. Societe de Publication l'Information Nationale Inc., 82 rue Sherbrooke, W., Montreal, Que. H2x 1X3, Canada. TEL 514-843-8851 Ed. Gerard Turcotte. adv. bk. rev. illus. circ. 15,000.
Formerly: Societe Saint-Jean-Baptiste de Montreal Bulletin.

200 500 US
SOCIETY FOR COMMON INSIGHTS. JOURNAL. 1976. s-a. $5 to individuals; institutions $6. Society for Common Insights, c/o Kurt Johnson, Dept. of Biology, City University of New York, Convent Ave. and 138th St., New York, NY 10031. (Affiliate: National Council for the Church and Social Action) Eds. Kurt Johnson, Eric L. Quinter. bk. rev. charts. illus. (back issues avail.) Indexed: CERDIC.

225 UK ISSN 0081-1432
SOCIETY FOR NEW TESTAMENT STUDIES. MONOGRAPH SERIES. 1965. irreg., no.51, 1984. $29.50 for latest vol. Cambridge University Press, Edinburgh Bldg., Shaftesbury Rd., Cambridge CB2 2RU, England (and 32 E. 57 St., New York NY 10022) Ed. R. Wilson. index.

221 UK
SOCIETY FOR OLD TESTAMENT STUDIES. MONOGRAPHS. 1972. irreg., no.6, 1979. $21.95 for latest vol. Cambridge University Press, Edinburgh Bldg., Shaftesbury Rd., Cambridge CB2 2RU, England (And 32 E. 57th St., New York, NY 10022)

200 US
SOCIETY FOR THE SCIENTIFIC STUDY OF RELIGION. MONOGRAPH SERIES. irreg., no.4, 1984. Society for the Scientific Study of Religion, Marist Hall, Rm. 108, Catholic University of America, Washington, DC 20064.

220 US ISSN 0145-2711
SOCIETY OF BIBLICAL LITERATURE. SEMINAR PAPERS (YEAR) a. $15. (Society of Biblical Literature) Scholars Press, Box 1608, Decatur, GA 30031-1608. Ed. Kent H. Richards. (back issues avail.) Indexed: Rel.Ind.One.

200 US ISSN 0732-4928
SOCIETY OF CHRISTIAN ETHICS. ANNUAL. 1975. a. $12. Georgetown University Press, Intercultural Center, Georgetown University, Washington, Canada, DC 20057. TEL 912-744-2880 Ed. Diane Yeager. adv. circ. 850. (also avail. in microfilm)

200 FR ISSN 0336-335X
SOLIDAIRES. 1822. m. 30 F. Propagation de la Foi, 5 rue Monsieur, 75007 Paris, France. charts. illus. stat. circ. 120,000.
Formerly: Annales de la Propagation de la Foi (ISSN 0003-4045)

SONNTAGSCHULMITARBEITER; religionspaedagogisches Monatsblatt. see *EDUCATION*

201 AT ISSN 0038-1527
SOPHIA; a journal for discussion in philosophical theology. 1962. 3/yr. Aus.$6($7.50) Philosophical Theology Society, c/o School of Humanities, Deakin University, Victoria 3217, Australia. Ed. M. J. Charlesworth. tr.lit. circ. 750. Indexed: M.L.A. Aus.P.A.I.S. CERDIC. Phil.Ind.

260 301 US
SOURCE (SEATTLE) 1960. m. $10. Church Council of Greater Seattle, 4759 15 Ave. N.E. (3rd. Fl.), Seattle, WA 98105. TEL 206-525-1213 Ed. Margaret Lueders. adv. bk. rev. circ. 10,500. (tabloid format)
Supersedes (as of 1976): Church Council of Greater Seattle. Occasional News (ISSN 0010-9924); Formerly: Council in Action.

200 027.7 MW
SOURCES FOR THE STUDY OF RELIGION IN MALAWI. (Text in English) 1979. irreg., latest no.11, 1984. $2.50 per no. University of Malawi, Chancellor College, Department of Religion, P.O. Box 280, Zomba, Malawi. Ed. J.C. Chakanza. circ. 200.

266 SA ISSN 0038-2523
SOUTH AFRICAN OUTLOOK; a journal dealing with ecumenical and racial affairs. 1870. m. R.16. Outlook Publications (Pty) Ltd., Box 245, Rondebosch 7700, South Africa. Ed. Francis Wilson. adv. bk. rev. index. circ. 1,400. Indexed: CERDIC. Ind.S.A.Per.

200 US
SOUTH FLORIDA FOCUS. 4/yr. $10. Spiritual Hierarchy Information Center, 2220 N. 47 Ave., Hollywood, FL 33021. TEL 305-966-7272 Ed. Dorothy Chinn. illus.

200 286 US ISSN 0038-4828
SOUTHWESTERN JOURNAL OF THEOLOGY. 1958. 3/yr. $13. Southwestern Baptist Theological Seminary, Faculty, School of Theology, Box 22000 2E, Fort Worth, TX 76122. TEL 817-923-1921 Ed. Dan Kent. adv. bk. rev. circ. 3,500. (also avail. in microform from UMI; reprint service avail. from UMI) Indexed: Old Test.Abstr. Rel.Per. CERDIC. Chr.Per.Ind. New Test.Abstr. Rel.Ind.One. Rel.& Theol.Abstr. South.Bap.Per.Ind.

200 SA ISSN 0038-5980
SOWER/SAAIER. (Text in Afrikaans, English) 1957. q. free. ‡ Bible Society of South Africa, Box 6215, Roggebaai, Cape Town 8012, South Africa. Ed. N. Turley. illus. circ. 59,000. (also avail. in microfiche)

200 360 AT ISSN 0158-1090
SOWER. 1956. q. Aus.$15. Bible Society in Australia, G.P.O. Box 507, Canberra, A.C.T. 2601, Australia. Ed. Paul Ainsworth. illus. circ. 75,000. (back issues avail.)

268 UK
SOWER (1979) 1919. q. £5. Huddleston Press, Our Lady of Peace, Lower Britwell Rd., Slough, Berks SL2 2NL, England. Ed.Bd. adv. bk. rev. circ. 2,000.
Formerly: New Sower; Which was formed by the merger of: Sower (ISSN 0049-1772); Christian Celebration.

266 UK
SPAN (LONDON) 1835. bi-m. contributions. London City Mission, 175 Tower Bridge Rd., London SE1 2AH, England. Ed. S. Seymour. bk. rev. circ. 41,000. Indexed: Apic.Abstr. Fuel & Energy Abstr.
Formerly: London City Mission Magazine (ISSN 0047-5025)

200 KE
SPEARHEAD. (Text in English) 1969. 5/yr. EAs.121($17.60) (Amecea Pastoral Institute) Gaba Publications, P.O. Box 4002, Eldoret, Kenya. Ed. Felician N. Rwehikiza. circ. 2,000. (back issues avail.) Indexed: CERDIC.
Formerly (until 1977): Gaba Pastoral Papers.

268 UK ISSN 0305-7917
SPECTRUM; a magazine for Christians in education. 1968. 3/yr. £4.50($3) Association of Christian Teachers, 130 City Rd., London EC1V 2NJ, England. Ed. Richard Wilkins. adv. bk. rev. illus. cum.index: vols. 1-6. circ. 2,000. Indexed: Excerp.Med. Br.Educ.Ind. Abstr.Engl.Stud. CERDIC.

200 255 NE ISSN 0038-7320
SPELING. 1948. q. fl.42. H. Gianotten B.V., Bredaseweg 61, 5038 NA Tilburg, Netherlands. Ed. Jo Tigcheler. bk. rev. illus. play rev. circ. 2,500. Indexed: CERDIC.
Formerly: Carmel.

SPIRALS. see *PARAPSYCHOLOGY AND OCCULTISM*

266 FR ISSN 0038-7665
SPIRITUS; experience et recherche missionnaires. 1959. q. 85 F. Association de la Revue Spiritus, 40 rue La Fontaine, 75781 Paris Cedex 16, France. Ed. Francois Nicolas. bk. rev. abstr. bibl. index. circ. 3,500. Indexed: CERDIC.

266 IT ISSN 0038-8750
SQUILLA. 1925. bi-m. L.5000. Fratini Missionari di Recco, Collegio Serafico, Via S. Francesco 4, 16036 Recco, Genoa, Italy. Ed. Amelia Capurro. adv. illus. circ. 4,000(controlled) (tabloid format)
Missions

200 IT ISSN 0038-8769
SQUILLA DI S. GERARDO. 1923. bi-m. free. Parrocchia S. Gerardo, Piedimonte Etneo 95017, Sicily, Italy.

268.8 US ISSN 0081-4245
STANDARD LESSON COMMENTARY; International Sunday School lessons. 1954. a. $9.50 casebound; $7.95 kivar. ‡ Standard Publishing, 8121 Hamilton Ave., Cincinnati, OH 45231. TEL 513-931-4050 Ed. James Fehl. circ. 180,000.

266 GW
STEYLER MISSIONSCHRONIK. 1959. s-a. DM.14.90. (Steyler Missionswissenschafliches Institut) Steyler Verlag, D-4054 Nettetal 2, W. Germany (B.R.D.) circ. 20,000.
Missions

200 GW
STIMME DER MAERTYRER; Nachrichten der Hilfsaktion Maertyrerkirche. 1969. m. DM.12. Hilfsaktion Martyrerkirche e.V., Tuefingerstr. 3-5, Postfach 1160, D-7772 Uhldingen 1, W. Germany (B.R.D.) Ed. Hans Martin Braun. circ. 38,000. (back issues avail.)

200 GW ISSN 0039-1492
STIMMEN DER ZEIT; Monatsschrift fuer das Geistesleben der Gegenwart. 1865. m. DM.106.80. Verlag Herder GmbH und Co. KG, Hermann-Herder-Str. 4, D-7800 Freiburg im Breisgau, W. Germany (B.R.D.) Ed. Dr. Wolfgang Seibel, S.J. adv. bk. rev. circ. 5,400. Indexed: Cath.Ind. M.L.A. CERDIC. New Test.Abstr.

200 DK ISSN 0108-2884
STORE GLAEDE. 1973. a. Kr.10. Nyt Liv Folkekirkeligt Forbund for Evangelisation i Danmark, Rosenvej 1, 4340 Toelloese, Denmark. illus.

248.83 US
STRAIGHT (1981) 1977. w. $6.50 per set of 5 for 3 months. ‡ Standard Publishing, 8121 Hamilton Ave., Cincinnati, OH 45231. TEL 513-931-4050 Ed. Dawn B. Korth. illus. circ. 85,000.
Former titles: Now; Straight (ISSN 0039-2081)
Ages 12-19

STROMATA; antigua ciencia y fe. see *PHILOSOPHY*

266 US
STUDENT AND WORLD CONNECTION; helping students mobilize for missions. 2/yr. free. InterVarsity Christian Fellows, 6400 Scroeder Rd., Ed. Greg.

220 IT ISSN 0039-2898
STUDI BIBLICI; collezione di argomento biblico. 1968. q. L.40000. Paideia Editrice, Via Corsica 130, 25125 Brescia, Italy. Ed. Giuseppe Scarpat. bk. rev.

200 IT ISSN 0393-3687
STUDI ECUMENICI. 1983. q. L.23000. Istituto di Studi Ecumenici, Stradone A. Provolo, 28, 37123 Verona, Italy. Ed.Bd. index. (back issues avail.)

220 NE
STUDIA AD CORPUS HELLENISTICUM NOVI TESTAMENTI. (Text in English, French and German) 1970. irreg., vol. 6, 1980. price varies. E. J. Brill, P.O. Box 9000, 2300 PA Leiden, Netherlands. Eds. H.D. Betz, G. Delling, W.C. van Unnik.

262.9 CN ISSN 0039-310X
STUDIA CANONICA; a Canadian canon law review. (Text in English, French, Latin) 1967. s-a. Can.$25($25) Saint Paul University, Faculty of Canon Law, 223 Main St, Ottawa, Ont. K1S 1C4, Canada. TEL 613-236-1393 Ed. Francis G. Morrisey. bk. rev. circ. 1,400. Indexed: Cath.Ind. Leg.Per. Canon Law Abstr. CERDIC. C.L.I.
Canon law

268 IT
STUDIA EPHEMERIDIS AUGUSTINIANUM. 1967. irreg. Institutum Patristicum Augustinianum, Via S. Uffizio, 25, 00193 Rome, Italy. (back issues avail.)

220 NE
STUDIA IN VETERIS TESTAMENTI PSEUDEPIGRAPHA. 1970. irreg., vol.8, 1985. price varies. E.J. Brill, P.O. Box 9000, 2300 PA Leiden, Netherlands. Eds. A.M. Denis, M. de Jonge.

100 GW ISSN 0081-6663
STUDIA IRENICA. (Text in English and German) 1968. irreg., no. 19, 1971. Gertenberg Verlag, Rathausstr. 18, Postfach 390, 3200 Hildesheim, W. Germany (B.R.D.) Ed. Axel Hilmar Swinne.
Before 1971: Frankfurt am Main. Universitaet. Institut fuer Wissenschaftliche Irenik. Schriften.

240 NE ISSN 0039-3207
STUDIA LITURGICA; an international review quarterly for liturgical research and renewal. (Text and summaries in English) 1962. q. fl.40. Liturgical Ecumenical Center Trust, P.B. 25088, 3001 HB Rotterdam, Netherlands. Pastor W. Vos. circ. 2,000. (back issues avail.) Indexed: Rel.Per. CERDIC. New Test.Abstr. Rel.Ind.One. Rel.& Theol.Abstr.

271 900 SP ISSN 0039-3258
STUDIA MONASTICA; commentarium ad rem monasticam historice investigandam. (Text in Catalan, English, French, German, Italian, Latin, Portuguese, Spanish) 1959. s-a. 4600 ptas.($50) Publicacions de l' Abadia de Montserrat, Ausias March 92-98, Apdo. 244, Barcelona 13, Spain. Ed. Rev. Josep Massot Muntaner. adv. bk. rev. abstr. bibl. charts. illus. index. circ. 800. Indexed: M.L.A. Arts & Hum.Cit.Ind. CERDIC.
History

240 VC ISSN 0081-6736
STUDIA MORALIA. (Text in English, French, German, Italian, Spanish; summaries in English, French) 1963. s-a. L.15000($20) Editiones Academiae Alfonsianae, Via Merulana 31, C.P. 2458, 00100 Rome, Italy. Ed.Bd. bk. rev. index. circ. 1,200. Indexed: CERDIC.

230 100 IT ISSN 0039-3304
STUDIA PATAVINA; rivista di scienze religiose. 1954. 3/yr. L.35000($22) Seminario Vescovile, Facolta Teologica, Via del Seminario 29, 35122 Padua, Italy. Ed.Bd. adv. bk. rev. index. circ. 600. Indexed: Old Test.Abstr. CERDIC. New Test.Abstr.

STUDIA PHILOSOPHIAE RELIGIONIS. see *PHILOSOPHY*

200 NE ISSN 0585-5500
STUDIA POST-BIBLICA. 1959. irreg., vol. 36, 1986. price varies. E. J. Brill, P.O. Box 9000, 2300 PA Leiden, Netherlands.

266 SP
STUDIA SILENSIA. (Text in English, French, German, Portuguese and Spanish) 1975. a. price varies. Abadia de Santo Domingo de Silos, E-09610, Libreria de la Abadia, Burgos, Spain. Ed. Clemente de la Serna. illus. stat. tr.lit. index. cum.index. circ. 1,500. (back issues avail.)

230 NO ISSN 0039-338X
STUDIA THEOLOGICA; Scandinavian journal of theology. (Text in English and German) 1948. s-a. $30. Norwegian University Press, Kolstadgt. 1, Box 2959-Toeyen, 0608 Oslo 6, Norway (U.S. address: Publications Expediting Inc., 200 Meacham Ave., Elmont, NY 11003) Eds. Arvid S. Kapelrud, Jacob Jervell. adv. bk. rev. bibl. index. cum.index every 10 yrs. circ. 550. (also avail. in microform from UMI) Indexed: Curr.Cont. M.L.A. Rel.Per. Arts & Hum.Cit.Ind. CERDIC. New Test.Abstr. Rel.Ind.One. Rel.& Theol.Abstr.

200 GW
STUDIEN ZUR KIRCHENGESCHICHTE NIEDERSACHSENS. 1919. irreg. Vandenhoeck & Ruprecht, Robert-Bosch-Breite 6, Postfach 3753, D-3400 Goettingen, W. Germany (B.R.D.) Ed. Hans W. Krummede.

200 GW
STUDIEN ZUR THEOLOGIE UND GEISTESGESCHICHTE DES 19. JAHRHUNDERTS. 1972. irreg. Vandenhoeck & Ruprecht, Robert-Bosch-Breite 6, Postfach 3753, D-3400 Goettingen, W. Germany (B.R.D.) Ed.Bd.

200 GW
STUDIEN ZUR UMWELT DES NEUEN TESTAMENTS. 1968. irreg Vandenhoeck & Ruprecht, Robert-Bosch-Breite 6, Postfach 3753, D-3400 Goettingen, W. Germany (B.R.D.) Ed.Bd.

200 US
STUDIES IN AMERICAN RELIGION. 1980. irreg., vol.22, 1986. $39.95 per no. Edwin Mellen Press, Box 450, Lewiston, NY 14092. Ed. Herbert Richardson. bibl. index.

291 UK ISSN 0039-3622
STUDIES IN COMPARATIVE RELIGION. 1941. q. £8.80($20) Perennial Books Ltd., Pates Manor, Bedfont, Middlesex, TW14, 8JP, England. Ed.Bd. adv. bk. rev. index. circ. controlled. (also avail. in microform from UMI; reprint service avail. from UMI) Indexed: Curr.Cont. Hum.Ind. Arts & Hum.Cit.Ind. CERDIC. Rel.Ind.One.
Formerly: Tomorrow.

150 US ISSN 0193-2748
STUDIES IN FORMATIVE SPIRITUALITY. 1980. 3/yr. $16. Duquesne University, Institute of Formative Spirituality, 600 Forbes Ave., Pittsburgh, PA 15282. TEL 412-434-6028 Ed. Dr. Adrian Van Kaam. abstr. bibl. index. circ. 3,000. (also avail. in microform from UMI; reprint service avail. from UMI) Indexed: Cath.Ind. Curr.Cont. Hum.Ind. Arts & Hum.Cit.Ind. CERDIC. Rel.& Theol.Abstr.
Supersedes (1965-1979): Humanitas (ISSN 0018-7496)

200 NE
STUDIES IN GREEK AND ROMAN RELIGION. 1980. irreg., vol.3, 1986. price varies. E.J. Brill, P.O. Box 9000, 2300 PA Leiden, Netherlands. Ed. H.S. Versnel.

200 NE ISSN 0585-6914
STUDIES IN MEDIEVAL AND REFORMATION THOUGHT. 1966. irreg., vol. 37, 1986. price varies. E. J. Brill, P.O. Box 9000, 2300 PA Leiden, Netherlands. Ed. H.A. Oberman. (back issues avail.)

200 US
STUDIES IN RELIGION AND SOCIETY. 1981. irreg., vol.17,, 1987. $39.95 per no. Edwin Mellen Press, Box 450, Lewiston, NY 14092. Indexed: Rel.Ind.Two.

230 NE ISSN 0081-8607
STUDIES IN THE HISTORY OF CHRISTIAN THOUGHT. 1966. irreg., vol. 36, 1986. price varies. E. J. Brill, P.O. Box 9000, 2300 PA Leiden, Netherlands. Ed. Heiko A. Oberman.

200 301.412 US
STUDIES IN WOMEN AND RELIGION. 1979. irreg., vol.21, 1986. $39.95 per no. Edwin Mellen Press, Box 450, Lewiston, NY 14092.

200 NE
STUDIES ON RELIGION IN AFRICA. 1970. irreg., vol. 5, 1984. price varies. E. J. Brill, P.O. Box 9000, 2300 PA Leiden, Netherlands. bibl.

220 IS ISSN 0081-8909
STUDIUM BIBLICUM FRANCISCANUM. ANALECTA. (Language of text varies) 1962. irreg. price varies. Franciscan Printing Press, Box 14064, 91140 Jerusalem, Israel. circ. 1,000.

220 IS ISSN 0081-8917
STUDIUM BIBLICUM FRANCISCANUM. COLLECTIO MAIOR. (Text in various languages) 1941. irreg. price varies. Franciscan Printing Press, P.O.B. 14064, 91140 Jerusalem, Israel. circ. 1,000.

220 IS ISSN 0081-8925
STUDIUM BIBLICUM FRANCISCANUM. COLLECTIO MINOR. (Text in various languages) 1961. irreg., no. 33, 1984. price varies. Franciscan Printing Press, P.O.B. 14064, 91140 Jerusalem, Israel. circ. 1,000.

220 IS ISSN 0081-8933
STUDIUM BIBLICUM FRANCISCANUM. LIBER ANNUUS. (Text in various languages) 1951. a. price varies. Franciscan Printing Press, Box 14064, 91140 Jerusalem, Israel. circ. 1,200. Indexed: RILA.

209 BE
SUBSIDA HAGIOGRAPHICA. irreg., no.71, 1986. Societe des Bollandistes, 24 bd. Saint-Michel, 1040 Brussels, Belgium.

260 US
SUCCESSFUL WRITERS AND EDITORS GUIDEBOOK. 1977. irreg. $10.95. ‡ (Christian Writers Institute) Creation House, 396 E. St. Charles Rd., Carol Stream, IL 60188. TEL 312-653-1472 Ed. Robert Walker.
Formerly: Handbook for Christian Writers (ISSN 0069-391X)

200 US ISSN 0039-5188
SUNDAY DIGEST; selected reading for Christian adults. 1886. w. $3.50. David C. Cook Publishing Co., 850 N. Grove Ave., Elgin, IL 60120. TEL 312-741-2400 Ed. Judy Couchman. bk. rev. illus. circ. 125,000(approx.) (tabloid format) Indexed: A.I.P.P.

200 FR ISSN 0750-1455
LE SUPPLEMENT. 4/yr. 207 F. Editions du Cerf, 29 bd. Latour Maubourg, 75007 Paris, France. Indexed: Cath.Ind. CERDIC.

220 SW
SVENSK EXEGETISK AARSBOK. (Text in English or Swedish) 1936. a. (Uppsala Exegetiska Saellskap) Liber Forlag, S-205 10, Malmo, Sweden. bk. rev. illus. Indexed: Old Test.Abstr. New Test.Abstr.

200 SW ISSN 0039-6699
SVENSK PASTORAL TIDSKRIFT. 1959. w. Kr.225($40) Stiftelsen Kyrkligt Forum, Box 12041, S-750 12 Uppsala 12, Sweden. Ed. Carl Strandberg. adv. bk. rev. circ. 3,200.

230 SW ISSN 0039-6761
SVENSK TEOLOGISK KVARTALSKRIFT. 1925. q. Kr.85. Liber Forlag, S-205 10, Malmoe, Sweden. Eds. Bengt Hagglund, P.E. Persson. adv. bk. rev. abstr. index. cum.index every 10 yrs. circ. 1,000. Indexed: Old Test.Abstr. Rel.Per. CERDIC. New Test.Abstr. Rel.Ind.One.

266 SW ISSN 0039-6826
SVENSK VECKOTIDNING. 1882. w. Kr.224. Svensk Veckotidning, Box 6302, 113 81 Stockholm, Sweden. Ed. Per-Magnus Selinder. adv. bk. rev. play rev. circ. 28,000. (tabloid format)

254 SW
SVENSKA KYRKANS. 1946. 10/yr. Kr.20. Svenska Kyrkans Foersamlings- och Pastoratsfoerbund, Box 1737, S-111 87 Stockholm, Sweden. Ed. Per Olof Nilsson. adv. illus. stat. circ. 17,000.
Supersedes in part: Foersamlings- och Pastoratsfoervaltning (ISSN 0015-5284)
Church administration

200 US ISSN 0039-7547
SWORD OF THE LORD. 1934. w. $9. Sword of the Lord Foundation, Box 1099, 224 Bridge Ave., Murfreesboro, TN 37130. TEL 615-893-6700 Ed. Dr. John R. Rice. adv. bk. rev. index. circ. 200,000. (tabloid format)

SYDNEY TOWN EXPRESS. see *SOCIOLOGY*

SYNAPSE (BOSTON) see *LITERARY AND POLITICAL REVIEWS*

T Q. see *CHILDREN AND YOUTH — For*

290 US ISSN 0272-3913
T S F BULLETIN. 1977. 5/yr. $20. Theological Students Fellowship, 6400 Schroeder Rd., Box 7895, Madison, WI 53707-7895. TEL 608-274-9001 (Affiliate: Inter-Varsity Christian Fellowship) Ed. Vernon C. Grounds. adv. bk. rev. bibl. circ. 1,200. (also avail. in microfiche; back issues avail.) Indexed: Rel.Ind.One.

200 UK ISSN 0039-8837
TABLET. 1840. w. £45. Tablet Publishing Co., 48 Great Peter St., Westminster, London SW1P 2HB, England. Ed. John Wilkins. adv. bk. rev. film rev. index. circ. 12,500. (also avail. in microform from UMI; reprint service avail. from UMI) Indexed: Cath.Ind. CERDIC. Rural Recreat.Tour.Abstr. World Agri.Econ.& Rural Sociol.Abstr.

248.83 SA
TAGTIG. 1951. q. R.1.80. Afrikaanse Christen-Studentevereniging van Suid-Afrika, Box 25, Stellenbosch, South Africa. Ed. P.J.L. Brink. adv. bk. rev. circ. 34,000.
Formerly(until 1980): Ons Bou (ISSN 0030-2643)

296 US ISSN 0039-9213
TALKS AND TALES. (Editions in French, Hebrew, Italian, Spanish and Yiddish) 1942. m. $3. Merkos L'Inyonei Chinuch, Inc., 770 Eastern Parkway, Brooklyn, NY 11213. Ed. Nissan Mindel. index.

268.8 US ISSN 0082-1713
TARBELL'S TEACHER'S GUIDE; to the International Sunday School Lessons. 1905. a. $7.95. Fleming H. Revell Co., 184 Central Ave., Old Tappan, NJ 07675. TEL 201-768-8060 Ed. William P. Barker.

200 TZ ISSN 0039-9655
TARGET. 1968. fortn. EAs.150. East African Venture (Tanzania), Box 9290, Dar es Salaam, Tanzania. Ed. Donald Navetta. adv. bk. rev. charts. illus. circ. 60,000. (tabloid format)

205 UK
TARGET. (Text in English or Swahili) s-m. Middle East Economic Digest Ltd., Meed House, 21 john St., London WC1N 2BP, England.

TASCHENBUCH FUER LITURGIE KIRCHENMUSIK UND MUSIKERZIEHUNG. see *MUSIC*

220 US ISSN 8755-8769
TEACH; a newsletter for Christian teachers and church leaders. 1985. bi-m. $15.95. Sweet Publishing, 3934 Sandshell Dr., Fort Worth, TX 76137-2403. TEL 817-232-5661 Ed. Mary Hollingsworth. bk. rev. circ. 12,000.

377.8 UK
TEACHING UNDER 5'S. q. £1.10. Scripture Union, 130 City Rd., London EC1V 2NJ, England. Ed. Joan King. adv. illus. circ. 20,000.
Formerly: Teaching Beginners (ISSN 0040-0580)

377.8 UK
TEACHING 5-7'S. q. £1.10. Scripture Union, 130 City Rd., London EC1V 2NJ, England. Ed. Sally Ross. adv. illus. circ. 28,000.
Formerly: Teaching Primaries (ISSN 0040-0653)

377.8 UK
TEACHING 7-10'S. q. £1.10. Scripture Union, 130 City Rd., London EC1V 2NJ, England. Ed. Peter Graystone. adv. illus. circ. 34,000.
Formerly: Teaching Juniors (ISSN 0040-0629)

377.8 UK ISSN 0308-356X
TEACHING 10-13'S. q. £1.10. Scripture Union, 130 City Rd., London EC1V 2NJ, England. Ed. Archie Barker. adv. illus. circ. 18,000.
Formerly: Teaching Teenagers (ISSN 0040-067X)

TECHNICAL PAPERS FOR THE BIBLE TRANSLATOR. see *LINGUISTICS*

TEEN POWER (1979); a power/line paper. see *CHILDREN AND YOUTH — For*

TEENS TODAY. see *CHILDREN AND YOUTH — For*

200 NE ISSN 0040-2133
TEGENWOORDIG. 1946. bi-m. fl.5.25. Karmel, Bloemgracht 90, Amsterdam C, Netherlands (Subscr. address: Karmel, Rijksweg N. 35, Geleen, Netherlands) Ed.Bd. bk. rev. illus. circ. 17,000.
Formerly: Scapulier.

200 UK
TEILHARD REVIEW AND JOURNAL OF CREATIVE EVOLUTION. 1966. 3/yr. £7.50($20) Teilhard Centre for the Future of Man, 23 Kensington Square, London W83 F59, England. Ed. Michael Le Morvan. adv. bk. rev. bibl. charts. illus. cum.index: 1966-1971; 1972-1977. circ. 3,100. (tabloid format; also avail. in microform from UMI; reprint service avail. from UMI) Indexed: Cath.Ind. CERDIC.
Formerly (until 1981): Teilhard Review (ISSN 0040-2184)

200 ZR
TELEMA. (Text in French) 1975. q. $30. B.P. 3277, Kinshasha-Gombe, Zaire. Ed. Boka di Mpasi. adv. bk. rev. circ. 100. Indexed: Old Test.Abstr. CERDIC. Curr.Cont.Africa.

200 FI ISSN 0497-1817
TEMENOS (TURKU) (Text in English, French, German) 1965. a. Fmk.110. Finnish Society for the Study of Comparative Religion, Henrikinkatu 3, 20500 Turku, Finland. Ed. Lauri Honko. circ. 250. Indexed: Arts & Hum.Cit.Ind.

200 IT
TEMI DI PREDICAZIONE - OMELIE. 1957. m. L.27000($32) Edizioni Domenicane Italiane, Via L. Palmieri 19, 80133 Naples, Italy. Ed. P. Reginaldo Agostino Iannarone. adv. Indexed: CERDIC.

TEMOIGNAGE CHRETIEN. see *LITERARY AND POLITICAL REVIEWS*

266 JA ISSN 0040-3482
TENRIKYO. (Text in English) 1962-1970; resumed 1976. m. 600 Yen. Tenrikyo Overseas Mission Department, Tenrikyo Church Headquarters, Tenri, Nara, Japan. Ed. Y. Terada. illus. tr.lit. circ. 3,000. (tabloid format)

200 US ISSN 0272-6939
TENTMAKER'S JOURNAL. 1980. bi-m. $8 contribution. Tentmaker's Publishing Group, Inc., c/o Monroe, 128 Marimac Ln., Vernon Hills, IL 60061-2328. Ed. Ray E. Cooper. adv. bk. rev. circ. 42,000. (tabloid format)

230 FI ISSN 0040-3555
TEOLOGINEN AIKAKAUSKIRJA/ TEOLOGISK TIDSKRIFT. (Text in Finnish and Swedish) 1896. bi-m. Fmk.140. Teologinen Julkaisuseura r.y., Neitsytpolku 1 B, SF-00140 Helsinki 14, Finland. Ed. Eero Huovinen. adv. bk. rev. charts. illus. index. cum.index. circ. 2,900.

200 YU
TEOLOSKI POGLEDI; versko naucni casopis. (Text in Serbian; summaries in English) 1968. q. $10. Srpska Patrijarsija, 7 Jula 5, Belgrade, Yugoslavia. Ed. Danilo Krstic. bk. rev. bibl. circ. 1,200.

200 IS ISSN 0040-3784
TERRA SANTA. English edition: Holy Land. French edition: Terre Sainte (ISSN 0040-3873); Spanish edition: Tierra Santa (ISSN 0333-6212) (Editions in English, French, Italian, Spanish) m. price varies. Franciscan Printing Press, P.O.B. 14064, 91140 Jerusalem, Israel. Ed.Bd. Indexed: Numis.Lit.

TESTIMONIANZE; quaderni mensili. see *LITERARY AND POLITICAL REVIEWS*

200 IT
TESTIMONIO. 1884. m. L.20000($30) Unione Cristiana Evangelica Battista d'Italia, Piazza S. Lorenzo in Lucina, 35, 00186 Rome, Italy. Ed. Andrea Mannucci. adv. bk. rev. circ. 1,200. (back issues avail.)

200 465 GE ISSN 0082-3589
TEXTE UND UNTERSUCHUNGEN ZUR GESCHICHTE DER ALTCHRISTLICHEN LITERATUR. 1952. irreg., vol. 132, 1984. price varies. (Akademie der Wissenschaften der DDR, Zentralinstitut fuer Alte Geschichte und Archaeologie) Akademie-Verlag, Leipziger Str. 3-4, 1086 Berlin, E. Germany (D.D.R.)

220 IS ISSN 0082-3767
TEXTUS. (Text in English; summaries in Hebrew) 1960. approx. a. $6. (Hebrew University of Jerusalem, Bible Project) Magnes Press, The Hebrew University, Jerusalem, Israel. cum.index 1960-1966.

200 GW ISSN 0082-3775
TEXTUS PATRISTICI ET LITURGICI. 1964. irreg. price varies. (Institutum Liturgicum Ratisbonense) Verlag Friedrich Pustet, Gutenbergstr. 8, 8400 Regensburg 1, W. Germany (B. R. D.) Ed. Klaus Gamber. circ. 1,000.

268 UK ISSN 0307-8388
THEMELIOS. 1964. 3/yr. £3.20($6) Universities and Colleges Christian Fellowship, 38 De Montfort St., Leicester LE1 7GP, England (Subscr. in U.S. to: Box 5000-GG, Ridgefield, NJ 07657) (Co-sponsor: International Fellowship of Evangelical Students) Ed. David Wenham. bk. rev. bibl. circ. 5,500. (back issues avail.) Indexed: Old Test.Abstr. Rel.Ind.One.

230 CN ISSN 0225-7270
THEODOLITE. 1979. 2/yr. Can.$3. McMaster Divinity College, Hamilton, Ont. L8S 4K1, Canada. TEL 416-525-9140 Ed. Dr. T.R. Hobbs. bk. rev. circ. 1,000. Indexed: CERDIC.
Formerly: McMaster Theological Bulletin.

200 SA ISSN 0255-8858
THEOLOGIA EVANGELICA. (Text in Afrikaans and English) 1968. 3/yr. R.10.20. University of South Africa, Faculty of Theology, Box 392, Pretoria 0001, South Africa. Ed. J.A. Loader. adv. bk. rev. circ. 3,300. Indexed: Ind.S.A.Per. New Test.Abstr. Rel.Ind.One.

130 US ISSN 0362-0085
THEOLOGIA 21. 1970. s-a. $15 to non-members. (Affiliated Christian Emortalists) Dominion Press, Box 37, San Marcos, CA 92069. TEL 619-746-9430 Ed. A. Stuart Otto. bk. rev. bibl. charts. illus. stat. circ. 100. (looseleaf format; also avail. in microform from UMI; back issues avail.; reprint service avail. from UMI)
Formerly (until 1976): Immortality Newsletter (ISSN 0019-2783)

200 HU ISSN 0133-7599
THEOLOGIAI SZEMLE. 1958. 6/yr. $41. Magyarorszagi Egyhazak Okumenikus Tanacsa, Szabadsag Ter 2-1, 1054 Budapest, Hungary. Ed. Ottlyk Erno. bk. rev. circ. 1,000. Indexed: Hist.Abstr.

207 US ISSN 0040-5620
THEOLOGICAL EDUCATION. 1964. 2/yr. $5. Association of Theological Schools, Box 130, Vandalia, OH 45377. TEL 513-898-4654 Ed. David S. Schuller. stat. index. circ. 4,500. (also avail. in microform from UMI) Indexed: Curr.Cont. Rel.Per. CERDIC. Rel.Ind.One.
Study and teaching

200 US ISSN 0362-0603
THEOLOGICAL MARKINGS. 1971. a. free to qualified personnel. United Theological Seminary of the Twin Cities, 3000 Fifth St. N.W., New Brighton, MN 55112. TEL 612-633-4311 Ed. Eugene C. Jaberg. bk. rev. circ. 1,550. Indexed: Rel.Ind.One.

230 US ISSN 0040-5639
THEOLOGICAL STUDIES. 1940. q. $14. (Theological Faculties of the Society of Jesus in the U S) Theological Studies, Inc., Georgetown University, 37th and "O" Sts., N.W., Washington, DC 20057. TEL 202-338-0754 Ed. Walter J. Burghardt. adv. bk. rev. index. cum.index: vols. 1-40. circ. 6,464. (also avail. in microform from UMI) Indexed: Cath.Ind. Curr.Cont. Hum.Ind. Old Test.Abstr. Rel.Per. Arts & Hum.Cit.Ind. Bk.Rev.Ind. CERDIC. Canon Law Abstr. New Test.Abstr. Ref.Sour. Rel.Ind.One. Rel.& Theol.Abstr.

THEOLOGICAL TIMES. see *BLIND*

230 GW
THEOLOGIE UND DIENST. 1973. irreg., latest no. 30. price varies. (Prediger- und Missionsseminar St. Chrischona) Brunnen-Verlag GmbH, Gottlieb-Daimler-str. 22, Postfach 5205, 6300 Giessen 1, W. Germany (B.R.D.) Ed.Bd. circ. 3,000.

230 GW ISSN 0049-366X
THEOLOGIE UND GLAUBE. 1908. q. DM.48. Ferdinand Schoeningh, Juehenplatz 1, 4790 Paderborn, W. Germany (B.R.D.) Eds. Johannes Gamberoni, Winifred Schulz. adv. bk. rev. Indexed: Old Test.Abstr. Rel.Per. Rel.& Theol.Abstr. CERDIC. Canon Law Abstr. New Test.Abstr.

230 100 GW ISSN 0040-5655
THEOLOGIE UND PHILOSOPHIE. 1926. q. DM.142. Verlag Herder GmbH und Co. KG, Hermann-Herder-Str. 4, D-7800 Freiburg im Breisgau, W. Germany (B.R.D.) Ed. Hermann Josef Sieben. adv. bk. rev. bibl. index. circ. 700. Indexed: Rel.& Theol.Abstr. CERDIC. Canon Law Abstr. New Test.Abstr. Phil.Ind.
Formerly: Scholastik.

207 AU ISSN 0040-5663
THEOLOGISCH-PRAKTISCHE QUARTALSCHRIFT. 1848. q. S.288. (Theologische Hochschule der Dioezese Linz) Landesverlag, Landstr. 41, A-4010 Linz, Austria. Ed.Bd. adv. bk. rev. circ. 2,800. Indexed: CERDIC. Canon Law Abstr. New Test.Abstr.

266 GW ISSN 0342-2372
THEOLOGISCHE BEITRAEGE. 1970. bi-m. DM.34. R. Brockhaus Verlag, Champagne 7, Postfach 110152, 5600 Wuppertal 11, W. Germany (B.R.D.) Ed.Bd. adv. bk. rev. circ. 4,000. Indexed: Old Test.Abstr. CERDIC. New Test.Abstr.

230 SZ ISSN 0082-3902
THEOLOGISCHE DISSERTATIONEN. (Editions in English and German; summaries in English or German) 1969. irreg., no. 17, 1986. price varies. (Universitaet Basel, Theologische Fakultaet) Friedrich Reinhardt Verlag, Missionsstr. 36, CH-4012 Basel, Switzerland (Dist. by Albert J. Phiebig Books, Box 352, White Plains, NY 10602) Ed. Bo Reicke.

200 GE ISSN 0040-5671
THEOLOGISCHE LITERATURZEITUNG; Monatsschrift fuer das gesamte Gebiet der Theologie und Religionswissenschaft. 1876. m. DM.69.60. Evangelische Verlagsanstalt GmbH, Krautstr. 52, 1017 Berlin, E. Germany (D.D.R.) Ed. Dr. Ernst-Heinz Amberg. bk. rev. index. Indexed: Old Test.Abstr. Rel.Per. CERDIC. New Test.Abstr. Rel.& Theol.Abstr. Rel.Ind.One.

230 GW ISSN 0040-5698
THEOLOGISCHE RUNDSCHAU. 1929. q. DM.98 to individuals, students DM.58. Verlag J.C.B. Mohr (Paul Siebeck), Wilhelmstr. 18, Postfach 2040, 7400 Tuebingen, W. Germany (B.R.D.) Eds. J. Baur, L. Perlitt. adv. bk. rev. index. Indexed: Old Test.Abstr. Rel.Per. CERDIC. New Test.Abstr. Rel.Ind.One. Rel.& Theol.Abstr.

230 SZ ISSN 0040-5701
THEOLOGISCHE ZEITSCHRIFT. 1945. bi-m. 103 Fr. (Universitaet Basel, Theologische Fakultaet) Friedrich Reinhardt Verlag, Missionsstr. 36, CH-4012 Basel, Switzerland. Ed. K. Seybold. adv. bk. rev. abstr. bibl. cum.index. circ. 750. Indexed: Old Test.Abstr. CERDIC. New Test.Abstr. Rel.Ind.One. Rel.& Theol.Abstr.

200 UK ISSN 0040-571X
THEOLOGY. 1920. bi-m. £11.40($20) Society for Promoting Christian Knowledge, Holy Trinity Church, Marylebone Road, London NW1 4DU, England. Ed.Bd. adv. bk. rev. index. circ. 5,000. (also avail. in microform) Indexed: Br.Hum.Ind. New Test.Abstr. Rel.Ind.One. Rel.& Theol.Abstr.

THEOLOGY AND SCIENTIFIC CULTURE. see *SCIENCES: COMPREHENSIVE WORKS*

230 US ISSN 0040-5728
THEOLOGY DIGEST. 1953. q. $12. (St. Louis University, Department of Theological Studies) Theology Digest,Inc., 3634 Lindell Blvd., St. Louis, MO 63108-3395 TEL 314-658-2859 (Subscr. to: Box 6036, Duluth, MN 55806) Ed. Bernhard Asen. adv. bk. rev. restricted bibl. cum.index: 1953-1973. circ. 9,000. (also avail. in microfilm from UMI; back issues avail.) Indexed: Cath.Ind. Old Test.Abstr. CERDIC. Int.Z.Biblewiss. Rel.& Theol.Abstr.

230 US ISSN 0040-5736
THEOLOGY TODAY. 1944. q. $14. Princeton Theological Seminary, Box 29, Princeton, NJ 08542. TEL 609-921-8300 Ed. Hugh T. Kerr. adv. bk. rev. index. cum.index every 10 years. circ. 12,000. (also avail. in microform from MIM,UMI; back issues avail.) Indexed: Curr.Cont. Hum.Ind. Old Test.Abstr. Bk.Rev.Ind. Arts & Hum.Cit.Ind. Bk.Rev.Mo. CERDIC. New Test.Abstr. G.Soc.Sci.& Rel.Per.Lit. Rel.Ind.One. Rel.& Theol.Abstr.

THEORIE UND PRAXIS DER SOZIALPAEDAGOGIK. see *CHILDREN AND YOUTH — About*

THEOSOFIA. see *PHILOSOPHY*

THEOSOPHICAL JOURNAL. see *PHILOSOPHY*

131.35 US ISSN 0040-6074
THETA; Greek: thought, life, the spirit. m. membership. Church of Scientology of New York, 227 W. 46th St., New York, NY 10036. TEL 212-921-1210 Ed. Tom Wells. adv. charts. illus.

THIS WORLD. see *PHILOSOPHY*

200 US
THREE MINUTES A DAY; reflections for each day of the year. 1949. irreg. $5 per no. Christophers, Inc., 12 E. 48th St., New York, NY 10017. TEL 212-759-4050 Ed. Joseph R. Thomas.

200 UK ISSN 0260-4892
THRESHING FLOOR; a paper for religious renewal. 1980. 6/yr. £10. (Christian Community in Great Britain) Floris Books, 21 Napier Rd., Edinburgh EH10 5AZ, Scotland. Ed. Michael Tapp. adv. bk. rev. circ. 1,000.
Formerly: Christian Community.

200 IT ISSN 0040-6686
TI SALUTO FRATELLO. 1946. m. free. Segretariato Diocesano Malati, Via Longhin, 7, Treviso 31100 (Veneto), Italy. Ed. Luisa Maggio. circ. 7,500. (processed)

250 NO ISSN 0040-7194
TIDSSKRIFT FOR TEOLOGI OG KIRKE. q. $35. Norwegian University Press, Kolstadgt. 1, Box 2959-Toeyen, 0608 Oslo 6, Norway (U.S. address: Publications Expediting Inc., 200 Meacham Ave., Elmont, NY 11003) Ed.Bd. adv. bk. rev. bibl. index. circ. 1,100. Indexed: Old Test.Abstr. New Test.Abstr.

TIERRA NUEVA. see *SOCIOLOGY*

266 KE
TODAY IN AFRICA. (Text in English) 1967. bi-m. EAs.25($10) (Africa Inland Church) Kesho Publications, Box 60, Kijabe, Kenya. Ed. Sheldon Arensen. adv. bk. rev. circ. 8,000. Indexed: CERDIC.
Formerly: Today (ISSN 0040-8387)

TODAY'S CHRISTIAN WOMAN. see *WOMEN'S INTERESTS*

250 US ISSN 0040-8549
TODAY'S PARISH. 1969. 7/yr. $15. Twenty-Third Publications, Box 180, Mystic, CT 06355. TEL 203-536-2611 Ed. Mary Carol Kendzia. adv. bk. rev. abstr. illus. circ. 22,000. Indexed: Cath.Ind. CERDIC.

266 UK ISSN 0040-8824
TOILERS OF THE DEEP. 1886. 3/yr. contributions. Royal National Mission to Deep Sea Fishermen, 43 Nottingham Place, London W1M 4BX, England. Ed. R.B. Harvey. charts. illus. circ. 40,000.
Missions

200 IT ISSN 0040-960X
TORRE DAVIDICA. 1957. s-a. free. Chiesa Universale Giuris-Davidica, Via Tevere 21/5, 00198 Rome, Italy. Ed. Elvira Giro. illus. circ. 2,000.

200 BE
TRADUCTIONS HEBRAIQUES DES EVANGILES. 1982. irreg. N.V. Brepols I.G.P., Rue Baron du Four 8, B-2300 Turnhout, Belgium.

230 GW ISSN 0041-2945
TRIERER THEOLOGISCHE ZEITSCHRIFT. 1947. q. DM.64.80. (Theologische Fakultaet Trier) Paulinus-Verlag, Fleischstr. 61-65, 5500 Trier, W. Germany (B.R.D.) Ed. Theologische Fakultaet, Trier. bk. rev. index. Indexed: Old Test.Abstr. Canon Law Abstr. New Test.Abstr.

220 UK ISSN 0049-4712
TRINITARIAN BIBLE SOCIETY QUARTERLY RECORD. 1859. q. L.1($3) ‡ Trinitarian Bible Society, 217 Kingston Rd., London SW19 3NN, England. bk. rev.

280 US ISSN 0360-3032
TRINITY JOURNAL. 1971-1978; N.S. 1980. s-a. $7.50 to non-students; students $6.50. Trinity Evangelical Divinity School, 2065 Half Day Road, Deerfield, IL 60015. TEL 312-945-8800 Ed. D.A. Carson. bk. rev. circ. 1,000. Indexed: Bull.Signal. Old Test.Abstr. New Test.Abstr. Bk.Rev.Ind. Bk.Rev.Mo. Chr.Per.Ind. Curr.Bk.Rev.Cit. G.Soc.Sci.& Rel.Per.Lit. Int.Z.Bibelwissen. Rel.& Theol.Abstr. Rel.Ind.One.
Formerly: Trinity Studies (ISSN 0360-2915)

200 US ISSN 0742-2393
TRINITY UNIVERSITY MONOGRAPH SERIES IN RELIGION. 1972. irreg., (approx. every 18 mos.) Trinity University Press, 715 Stadium Dr., San Antonio, TX 78284. TEL 512-736-7619 Ed. William O. Walker, Jr.

266 SW ISSN 0041-3178
TRONS SEGRAR. 1890. w. Kr.140. Helgelsefoerbundet, Box 67, 692 01 Kumla, Sweden. Ed. Sven Kaarbrant. adv. bk. rev. illus. circ. 5,000.

200 AT ISSN 0813-796X
TROWEL AND SWORD. 1954. m. Aus.$15($20) Reformed Churches Publishing House, 55 Maud Street, Geelong 3220, Australia (Subscr. to: Trowel and Sword, POB 47, Geelong 3220, Australia) Ed. K.V. Warren. adv. bk. rev. circ. 2,500.

200 GW
TUDUV-STUDIE. REIHE RELIGIONSWISSENSCHAFTEN. 1975. irreg. price varies. Tuduv Verlagsgesellschaft mbH, Gabelsbergerstr. 15, 8000 Munich 2, W. Germany (B.R.D.)

207 UK ISSN 0082-7118
TYNDALE BULLETIN. 1956. a. £5.95. Inter-Varsity Press, Norton St., Nottingham NG7 3HR, England. Ed. M.J. Harris. bk. rev. circ. 600. (back issues avail.) Indexed: Old Test.Abstr. New Test.Abstr. Rel.& Theol.Abstr. Rel.Ind.One.

250 US
U M E CONNEXION. 1973. 2/yr. $3.50 (free to qualified personnel) United Ministries in Education, 14214 Edgecrest Dr., Dallas, TX 75240. Ed. Betsy A. Turecky. adv. bk. rev. illus. circ. 4,000.
Former titles: Connexion & U M H E Connexion.

200 DK ISSN 0107-7295
UD MED KIRKEN. 1980. 3/yr. free. (Danske Missionsselskab) Ole Raakjaer, H. Trollesgade 37/4, 2300 Aarhus N, Denmark. illus.

200 YU ISSN 0042-4552
UDRUZENJE PRAVOSLAVNOG SVESTENSTVA S.F.R. JUGOSLAVIJE. GLAVNI SAVEZ. VESNIK. 1949. m. 500 din. Udruzenje Pravoslavnog Svestenstva S.F.R. Jugoslavije, Glavni Savez, Francuska 31-1, Belgrade, Yugoslavia. Ed. Stanislav Mirovic. adv. bk. rev. circ. 3,000.
Cyrillic alphabet

ULTIMATE REALITY AND MEANING; interdisciplinary studies in the philosophy of understanding. see *PHILOSOPHY*

266 SA ISSN 0041-6274
UMAFRIKA. (Text in English, Zulu) 1911. w. R.12. Mariannhill Mission Society, Monastery Mariannhill, Mariannhill, Natal, South Africa. Ed. Anthony Ndlovu. adv. bk. rev. charts. illus. circ. 18,000.
Missions

200 GW ISSN 0041-6444
UNAUSFORSCHLICHER REICHTUM; Zweimonatsschrift fuer Gott und sein Wort. 1932. bi-m. DM.12.50($4.75) (Freunde Konkordanter Wortvekuendigung e.V. Pforzheim) Konkordanter-Verlag, Buechenbronner Str. 16, 7530 Pforzheim, W. Germany (B.R.D.) Eds. Herman H. Rocke, Heinz Hoffmann. adv. bk. rev. index. cum.index: 1932-1967. circ. 1,800.

200 FR ISSN 0396-2393
UNION DES SUPERIEURES MAJEURS DE FRANCE. ANNUAIRE. 1975. a. Union des Superieures Majeures des Instituts Religieux de France, 10 rue Jean-Bart, 75006 Paris, France.

207.11 371.8 US ISSN 0041-7025
UNION SEMINARY QUARTERLY REVIEW. 1939. 4/yr. $10 to individuals; institutions $12. Union Theological Seminary, 3041 Broadway, New York, NY 10027. TEL 212-662-7100 Ed.Bd. adv. bk. rev. bibl. index. circ. 1,500. (also avail. in microfilm from UMI) Indexed: Old Test.Abstr. Rel.Per. CERDIC. New Test.Abstr. Rel.Ind.One. Rel.& Theol.Abstr.

200 780 AT
UNISON. 1975. q. Aus.$2.80. Lutheran Publishing House, 205 Halifax St., Adelaide, S.A. 5000, Australia. Ed. V. Kleinig. circ. 550.

200 AT
UNITARIAN PIONEER. 1950. bi-m. Aus.$4. Sydney Unitarian Church, 15 Francis St., East Sydney, N.S.W. 2010, Australia. Ed. Geoffrey R. Usher. circ. 270. (back issues avail)

200 AT
UNITARIAN QUEST. 1961. s-a. Aus.$4. Australian and New Zealand Unitarian Association, P.O. Box 355, Darlinghurst, N.S.W. 2010, Australia. Ed. Geoffrey R. Usher. bk. rev. circ. 200. (back issues avail)

268 FR
UNITE DES CHRETIENS; revue de formation et d'information oecumenique. 1971. q. 85 (subscr. includes: Foyer Mixtes) Secretariat National pour l'Unite des Chretiens, 17 rue de l'Assomption, 75016 Paris, France. Ed. Jerome Cornelis. Indexed: CERDIC.

220 GW ISSN 0041-719X
UNITED BIBLE SOCIETIES. BULLETIN. 1950. q. $1.50 per no. United Bible Societies, Bible House, Postfach 810340, 7000 Stuttgart 80, W. Germany (B.R.D.) Ed. Ulrich Fick. circ. 4,700.

200 US ISSN 0270-9287
UNITED METHODIST BOARD OF HIGHER EDUCATION AND MINISTRY. QUARTERLY REVIEW; a scholarly journal for reflection on ministry. 1932. q. $20 to individuals; libraries $15. (United Methodist Board of Higher Education and Ministry) United Methodist Publishing House, Box 871, Nashville, TN 37203. TEL 615-749-6000 Ed. Charles E. Cole. adv. bk. rev. index. (also avail. in microform from UMI; reprint service avail. from UMI) Indexed: Hum.Ind. Old Test.Abstr. Rel.Per. Rel.& Theol.Abstr. CERDIC. G.Soc.Sci.& Rel.Per.Lit. Rel.Ind.One.
Supersedes (1980): Religion in Life (ISSN 0034-3986)

266 UK
UNITED SOCIETY FOR THE PROPAGATION OF THE GOSPEL. YEARBOOK. 1704. a. United Society for the Propagation of the Gospel, 15 Tufton St., London SW1P 3QQ, England.
Formerly: United Society for the Propagation of the Gospel. Annual Report/Review (ISSN 0144-9508)
Missions

UNITY DAILY WORD. see *BLIND*

200 US
UNIVERSAL LIFE-THE INNER RELIGION. 1985. irreg. Box 3549, Woodbridge, CT 06525. Ed. Kathleen Scott.
Formerly: Homebringing Mission of Jesus Christ.

200 SP ISSN 0078-8759
UNIVERSIDAD DE NAVARRA. FACULTAD DE DERECHO CANONICO. MANUALES: DERECHO CANONICO. 1973. irreg., no.6, 1984. price varies. Ediciones Universidad de Navarra, S.A., Apdo. 396, 31080 Pamplona, Spain.
Canon law

200 CK
UNIVERSIDAD JAVERIANA. FACULTAD DE TEOLOGIA. COLECCION PROFESORES. irreg. Col.400 price varies. Pontificia Universidad Javeriana, Facultad de Teologia, Apdo. Aereo 54-953, Bogota, D.E. 2, Colombia.

230 AU ISSN 0579-7780
UNIVERSITAET INNSBRUCK. THEOLOGISCHE FAKULTAET. STUDIEN UND ARBEITEN. (Subseries of: Universitaet Innsbruck. Veroeffentlichungen) 1968. irreg., vol. 10, 1974. price varies. Oesterreichische Kommissionsbuchhandlung, Maximilianstrasse 17, A-6020 Innsbruck, Austria. Ed. Hans Bernhard Meyer.

266 GW ISSN 0077-197X
UNIVERSITAET MUENSTER. INSTITUT FUER MISSIONSWISSENSCHAFT. VEROEFFENTLICHUNGEN. 1949. irreg. price varies. Aschendorffsche Verlagsbuchhandlung, Soester Str. 13, 4400 Muenster, W. Germany (B.R.D.) Ed. Josef Glazik.
Missions

UNIVERSITE SAINT-JOSEPH. FACULTE DES LETTRES ET DES SCIENCES HUMAINES. RECHERCHE. SERIE B: ORIENT CHRETIEN. see *ORIENTAL STUDIES*

UNIVERSITY OF DAYTON REVIEW. see *LITERARY AND POLITICAL REVIEWS*

200 100 US
UNIVERSITY OF NOTRE DAME. STUDIES IN THE PHILOSOPHY OF RELIGION. 1979. irreg. University of Notre Dame Press, Notre Dame, IN 46556. TEL 219-239-6346 Ed. Frederick Crosson.

220 US ISSN 0042-0476
UNSEARCHABLE RICHES. (Editions in English and German) 1909. bi-m. $1. ‡ Concordant Publishing Concern, 15570 Knochaven Rd., Canyon Country, CA 91351. TEL 805-252-2112 Ed. Dean H. Hough. index. cum.index every 10 yrs. circ. 2,000.
For students of the Scriptures

UP WITH PEOPLE NEWS. see *MUSIC*

290 DK ISSN 0108-7029
UPDATE (AARHUS); a quarterly journal on new religious movements. 1977. q. Kr.80($15) Dialog Center, Katrinebjergvej 46, DK-8200 Aarhus N, Denmark. Ed. Johannes Aagaard. adv. bk. rev. circ. 1,000. Indexed: Rel.Ind.One.
Formerly: New Religious Movements Up-Date (ISSN 0105-9998)

266 284 NE ISSN 0042-1650
UW KONINKRIJK KOME; zendingsblad. 1906. 8/yr. fl.9. Christelijke Gereformeerde Kerken in Nederland, Zendingshuis, Simon Stevinweg 144, 1222 SV Hilversum, Netherlands. Eds. M. Drayer, K. J. Velema. adv. bk. rev. illus. circ. 24,500.

V.R.B. - INFORMATIE. (Vereniging van Religieus-Wetenschappelijke Bibliothecarissen) see *LIBRARY AND INFORMATION SCIENCES*

200 SW ISSN 0042-2010
VAAR FANA. 1905. s-m. Kr.90. Svenska Fraelsningsarmen, Kungsgatan 17, S-502 31 Boraas, Sweden. illus.

200 SW ISSN 0042-2673
VAAR KYRKA. 1861. w. Kr.82. Svenska Kyrkans Centralraad, Fack, 104 32 Stockholm 19, Sweden. Ed. Kjell O. Nilsson. adv. bk. rev. illus. circ. 40,000.

VANGUARD (TORONTO) see *EDUCATION*

200 NE ISSN 0042-3262
VELUWS KERKBLAD. 1942. w. fl.33. (Gereformeerde Kerken in Classis Harderwijk en Nijkerk) Drukkerij Bolhuis B.V., Postbus 3, Ermelo, Netherlands. Ed. Dr. R. Van Den Berg. adv. bk. rev. circ. 6,500.

200 133 US ISSN 0748-3406
VENTURE INWARD. 1984. bi-m. membership. Association for Research and Enlightenment, Inc., Box 595, Virginia Beach, VA 23451. TEL 804-428-3588 Ed. A. Robert Smith. bk. rev. index. circ. 53,000.
Supercedes: A.R.E. Journal.

200 930 IT ISSN 0391-8564
VERBA SENIORUM. irreg. price varies. Edizioni Studium, Via Cassiodoro 14, 00193 Rome, Italy.

266 DK ISSN 0109-0062
VERDEN RUNDT. 1982. bi-m. Kr.60. Laegmandsbevaegelsen for Ydre Mission, c/o Anders Grave, Safirej 18, 8700 Horsens, Denmark. Ed. Simon Thorup. illus.
Formerly: Maend og Mission.

266 GW ISSN 0342-2410
VERKUENDIGUNG UND FORSCHUNG. Supplement to: Evangelische Theologie. 2/yr. DM.31. Christian Kaiser Verlag, Postfach 509, 8000 Munich 43, W. Germany (B.R.D.) (reprint service avail. from UMI) Indexed: CERDIC. New Test.Abstr.

200 CN ISSN 0042-434X
VERS DEMAIN. 1939. m. Can.$10($14) for 2 yrs. Institut d'Action Politique Pelerins de Saint Michel, Rougemont (Rouville), Que., Canada. Ed. Gilberte Cote-Mercier. charts. illus.

220 NE ISSN 0042-4935
VETUS TESTAMENTUM. (Text in English, French or German) 1951. 4/yr. fl.126. (International Organization for the Study of the Old Testament) E.J. Brill, P.O. Box 9000, 2300 PA Leiden, Netherlands. Ed. J.A. Emerton. bk. rev. bibl. Indexed: Curr.Cont. Old Test.Abstr. Rel.Per. Arts & Hum.Cit.Ind. New Test.Abstr. Rel.Ind.One. Rel.& Theol.Abstr.

221 NE ISSN 0083-5889
VETUS TESTAMENTUM. SUPPLEMENTS. 1953. irreg., vol.38, 1986. price varies. (International Organization for the Study of the Old Testament) E. J. Brill, P.O. Box 9000, 2300 PA Leiden, Netherlands.

200 BL ISSN 0507-7184
VIDA PASTORAL. 1960. bi-m. free. (Pia Sociedade de Sao Paulo) Edicoes Paulinas, R. Dr. Pinto Ferraz, 183, 04117 Sao Paulo, SP, Brazil. Ed. Angelo Songego. adv. bk. rev. bibl. illus. circ. 25,000.
Former titles: Pastoral Popular; Vida Pastoral (ISSN 0042-5265)

230 BE ISSN 0771-6842
VIE CONSACREE. 1925. bi-m. 400 Fr. Centre de Documentation et de Recherche Religieuses, Rue de Bruxelles 61, 5000 Namur, Belgium. bk. rev. bibl. index. circ. 6,000. Indexed: CERDIC. Canon Law Abstr.
Formerly (until 1965): Revue des Communautes Religieuses.

200 SZ
LA VIE OECUMENIQUE; reflets des activites du Conseil Oecumenique des Eglises. (Text in French) 1973. s-a. World Council of Churches, 150 Route de Ferney, Box 66, 1211 Geneva 20, Switzerland. Ed. Theo Buss. circ. 150,000.
Formerly: Justice et Service.

209 NE ISSN 0042-6032
VIGILIAE CHRISTIANAE; a review of early Christian life and language. (Text in several languages) vol.37, 1983. 4/yr. fl.108. Elsevier Science Publishers B.V., Box 211, 1000 AE Amsterdam, Netherlands (And: E.J. Brill, Oude Rijn 33a, 2312 HB Leiden, Netherlands) Ed.Bd. adv. bk. rev. index. Indexed: Curr.Cont. M.L.A. Rel.Per. Arts & Hum.Cit.Ind. New Test.Abstr. Rel.Ind.One. Rel.& Theol.Abstr.

VIRTUE. see *WOMEN'S INTERESTS*

200 NE ISSN 0169-5606
VISIBLE RELIGION; annual for religious iconography. (Text in English, French and German) 1982. a. price varies. (State University Groningen, Institute for Religious Iconography) E.J. Brill, P.O. Box 9000, 2300 PA Leiden, Netherlands. Ed. H.G. Kippenberg. circ. 200.

240 IT ISSN 0042-7330
VITA CONSACRATA; rivista mensile di studio e informazione per Istituti Religiosi e Secolari. 1964. m. L.25000. Editrice Ancora, Via G.B. Niccolini 8, 20154 Milan, Italy. Dir. Severino Medici. adv. bk. rev. bibl. index. circ. 1,200. Indexed: Canon Law Abstr.
Formerly: Vita Religiosa.

200 CN ISSN 0507-1690
VITA EVANGELICA. French edition (ISSN 0315-5048) (Editions in English and French) 1965. irreg., no.12, 1984. price varies. ‡ Canadian Religious Conference, 324 Laurier E., Ottawa, Ont. K1N 6P6, Canada. TEL 613-236-0824 Ed. Albert Landry. circ. 3,500 (French edt.); 3,500 (English edt.)

200 IT ISSN 0042-7284
LA VITA IN CRISTO E NELLA CHIESA; mensile di liturgia. 1951. m. L.15000. Congregazione Suore Pie Discepole del Divin Maestro, Via Portuense 739, 00148 Rome, Italy. Dir. J. Ricci. adv. bk. rev. illus. index. circ. 17,000.

200 IT
VITA PASTORALE. 1912. m. (10/yr.) L.500. Pia Societa San Paolo, Piazzo S. Paolo 14, 12051 Alba (Cuneo), Italy (And Via Alessandro Severo 56, 00145 Rome, Italy) Ed. Stefano Lamera. adv. circ. 33,000.

200 YU ISSN 0042-7659
VJESNIK NADBISKUPIJE SPLITSKO-MAKARSKE. (Text in Croatian) 1948. bi-m. Nadbiskupija Splitsko-Makarska, Zrinjsko-Francopanska 14, 58001 Split, Yugoslavia. Ed. Marijan Ivan Caglj. bk. rev. circ. 400.
Supersedes: Vjesnik Biskupije Splitske i Makarske.

200 261 IT ISSN 0042-7780
VOCE; settimanale religioso sociale. w. L.10000. 06012 Citta di Castello, Italy.

255 IT ISSN 0042-7888
VOCI FRATERNE. 1917. m. Via G. Amendola 5, 00185 Rome, Italy. Ed. Vacalebre Arcadio. adv. bk. rev. film rev. bibl. charts. illus. cum.index.

200 US ISSN 0042-8159
VOICE OF LIBERTY. 1960. s-a. donations. Voice of Liberty Association, 692 Sunnybrook Dr., Decatur, GA 30033. TEL 404-633-3634 Ed. Martha O. Andrews. charts. illus. circ. 3,500. (processed) Indexed: CERDIC.

200 US
VOICE OF THE MARTYRS. (Editions in several languages) 1967. m. free. Communist World, Inc., Box 938, Middlebury, IN 46540. TEL 219-825-2117 Ed. Rev. Richard D. Wurmbrand. bk. rev. circ. 1,000,000.

266 FR ISSN 0293-9932
VOIX D'AFRIQUE; d'Alsace et de Lorraine. (Text in French and German) 1923. 6/yr. 20. Peres Blancs Missionnaires d'Afrique, 60 allee de la Robertsau, 67000 Strasbourg, France. Ed. Pierre Federle. circ. 5,000.
Missions

200 GW ISSN 0083-6923
VORREFORMATIONSGESCHICHTLICHE FORSCHUNGEN. 1902. irreg. price varies. Aschendorffsche Verlagsbuchhandlung, Soester Str. 13, 4400 Muenster, W. Germany (B.R.D.) Ed. Erwin Iserloh.

200 CN ISSN 0715-8726
VOX BENEDICTINA; women and monastic spirituality. 1984. q. Can.$15 for individuals; institutions Can.$25. 409 Garrison Crescent, Saskatoon, Sask. S7H 2Z9, Canada. Ed. Margot H. King.

200 UK ISSN 0263-6786
VOX EVANGELICA. 1959. a. £3.95($10.85) (London Bible College) Paternoster Press Ltd., Paternoster House, 3 Mount Radford Crescent, Exeter, Devon EX2 4JW, England. Ed. Harold H. Rowdon. circ. 600. (tabloid format; back issues avail.) Indexed: Old Test.Abstr. CERDIC.

200 AT ISSN 0728-0912
VOX REFORMATA. 1962. s-a. Aus.$5.50($6) Reformed Theological College, Association for Christian Tertiary Education, 55 Maud Street, Geelong 3220, Australia. Ed. R.O. Zorn. adv. bk. rev. circ. 275. (also avail. in microfiche; back issues avail.) Indexed: CERDIC.

200 NE ISSN 0042-9155
VRIEND VAN OUD EN JONG; Christelijk weekblad. 1880. w. fl.25. ‡ B.V. Drukkerij J.J. Groen en Zoon, Pieterskerk Choorsteeg 18, Postbus 31, Leiden, Netherlands. adv.

266 NQ
WABUL. m? Comite Evangelico por Ayuda al Desarrollo, Centro de Historio y Cultura, Apdo. 3091, Puerto Cabezas, Nicaragua. Ed.Bd. circ. 1,500.

200 100 US
WANDERER. 1867. w. $25. Wanderer Printing Co., 201 Ohio St., St. Paul, MN 55107. TEL 612-224-5733 Ed. A.J. Matt Jr. adv. bk. rev. circ. 36,000. (also avail. in microfilm from BLH)

200 AT
WAR CRY. 1883. w. Aus.$25.70. Donald Campbell, 1-9, Drill St., Hawthorn, Melbourne 3122, Australia. Ed. Kenneth Peeke. bk. rev. illus. circ. 69,226.

WARRIOR. see *CHILDREN AND YOUTH — For*

200 US
WEEKDAY HOMILY HELPS. 1981. m. $45. St. Anthony Messenger Press, 1615 Republic St., Cincinnati, OH 45210. TEL 513-241-5615 Ed. Carol Luebering. circ. 3,800. (looseleaf format)

268 US
WEEKLY BIBLE READER. 1965. w. $6.50 for sets of five per quarter. Standard Publishing, 8121 Hamilton Avenue, Cincinnati, OH 45321. TEL 513-931-4050 Ed. Heather Smith Turner. circ. 104,000.

200 GW ISSN 0043-2040
WEGE ZUM MENSCHEN; Monatsschrift fuer Arzt und Seelsorger, Erzieher, Psychologen und Soziale Berufe. 1949. 8/yr. DM.82. Vandenhoeck und Ruprecht, Theaterstr. 13, Postfach 37 53, 3400 Goettingen, W. Germany (B.R.D.) Ed. Joachim Scharfenberg. adv. index. circ. 3,100. Indexed: CERDIC.

200 SZ
WEGE ZUM STUDIUM DER GEISTESWISSENSCHAFT UND ZUR BEWUSSTMACHUNG ANTHROPOSOPHISCHER VERANTWORTUNG. 1976. bi-m. DM.61.20. (Rudolf Steiner-Studienzentrum) Verlag die Kommenden AG, Gartenstr. 16, 8212 Neuhausen a/Rhf, Switzerland. Ed.Bd. circ. 700.
Formerly: Wege zur Pflege eines Meditativen Lebens und zu Einem Vertieften Christusverstaendniss.

DIE WELT DER BUECHER. see *PUBLISHING AND BOOK TRADE*

266 NE ISSN 0165-988X
WERELD EN ZENDING; tijdschrift voor missionaire informatie en bezinning. 1948. q. fl.35. Nederlandse Zendingsraad - Netherlands Missionary Council, Prins Hendriklaan 37, 1075 BA Amsterdam, Netherlands. (Co-sponsor: Nederlandse Missieraad) Ed. G. Verstraelen-Gilhuis. adv. bk. rev. index. circ. 2,000. Indexed: CERDIC.
Formerly: Heerbaan (ISSN 0017-9531)

266 BE
WERELDWIJD; tijdschrift over evangelizatie en ontwikkeling. 1970. m. (10/yr.) 600 Fr. V.Z.W. Wereldwijd, Arthur Goemaerelei 69, B-2000 Antwerp, Belgium. Ed. Mark Fillet. adv. circ. 60,000. Indexed: CERDIC.

270 NR ISSN 0083-8187
WEST AFRICAN RELIGION. 1963. s-a. £N3($8) per no. University of Nigeria, Department of Religion, Nsukka, Nigeria. Ed. O.U. Kalu. adv. bk. rev. circ. 1,000. Indexed: Rel.Per. CERDIC. Rel.Ind.One.

230 GW
WESTFALIA SACRA; Quellen und Forschungen zur Kirchengeschichte Westfalens. 1948. irreg. price varies. Aschendorffsche Verlagsbuchhandlung, Soester Str. 13, 4400 Muenster, W. Germany (B.R.D.) Ed. Alois Schroeer.

230 US ISSN 0043-4388
WESTMINSTER THEOLOGICAL JOURNAL. 1938. 2/yr. $15 to individuals; institutions $20. Westminster Theological Seminary, Chestnut Hill, Philadelphia, PA 19118. TEL 215-887-5511 Ed. Moises Silva. adv. bk. rev. index. circ. 1,200. (also avail. in microform from UMI) Indexed: Rel.Per. Chr.Per.Ind. CERDIC. Int.Z.Bibelwiss. New Test.Abstr. Old Test.Abstr. Rel.Ind.One. Rel.& Theol.Abstr.

222 GW
WISSENSCHAFTLICHE UNTERSUCHUNGEN ZUM NEUEN TESTAMENT. (Text in English and German) 1950. irreg. price varies. Verlag J.C.B. Mohr (Paul Siebeck), Wilhelmstr. 18, Postfach 2040, 7400 Tuebingen, W. Germany (B.R.D.) Ed. Martin Hengel, Otfried Hofius.

200 301.4 SZ
WOMEN IN A CHANGING WORLD. (Text in English) 1974. s-a. World Council of Churches, 150 Route de Ferney, Box 66, 1211 Geneva 20, Switzerland.

200 NE
WOORD EN DIENST. fortn. fl.51.50. Boekencentrum B.V., Box 84176, The Hague, Netherlands. Ed. Ds. W.R. van der Zee. adv. bk. rev. illus.

200 UK
WORD IN ACTION: THE BIBLE IN THE WORLD. 1973. 3/yr. free. ‡ British and Foreign Bible Society, Stonehill Green, Westlea, Swindon SN5 7DG, England. Ed. Jim Monck. charts. illus. circ. 200,000. (tabloid format)
Formerly: Bible Society News (ISSN 0006-0755)

200 AT ISSN 0813-7951
WORD OF SALVATION. 1955. m. Aus.$65($65) Reformed Churches Publishing House, 55 Maud St., Geelong 3220, Australia (Subscr. to: Word of Salvation, P.O. Box 47, Geelong 3220, Australia) Ed. W. Weirsma. circ. 100.

200 SZ ISSN 0084-1684
WORLD COUNCIL OF CHURCHES. MINUTES AND REPORTS OF THE CENTRAL COMMITTEE MEETING. (Text in English, German, French and Spanish) 1948. approx. a., 37th, 1985. price varies. World Council of Churches, 150 Route de Ferney, CH-1211 Geneva 20, Switzerland (Dist. in the U.S. by: World Council of Churches Distribution Center, Rt 222 & Sharadin Road, P.O. Box 346, Kutztown, PA 19530-0346)

268 SZ
WORLD COUNCIL OF CHURCHES. OFFICE OF EDUCATION. EDUCATION NEWSLETTER. (Editions in English, Korean, Spanish) 1972. 3/yr. donations. World Council of Churches, 150 Route de Ferney, 1211 Geneva 20, Switzerland. Ed. C. Payne. bk. rev. film rev. illus. circ. 5,000.

204 US ISSN 0273-1266
WORLD FAITHS INSIGHT. 3/yr. $10. (World Congress of Faiths) Anima Publications, 1053 Wilson Ave., Chambersburg, PA 17201. TEL 717-263-3803 (Co-sponsor: Temple of Understanding) Eds. K.L.S. Rao, Marcus Braybrooke. (back issues avail.) Indexed: Chr.Per.Ind.

200 US
WORLD MISSIONARY PRESS NEWS. 1961. 6/yr. free. World Missionary Press, Inc., Box 120, New Paris, IN 46553. TEL 219-831-2111 Ed. Gloria Byrnes. circ. 26,000.

WORLD'S WISDOM SERIES. see *PHILOSOPHY*

248 US
WORLDWIDE CHALLENGE. 1974. bi-m. $9.95. Campus Crusade for Christ, Arrowhead Springs, San Bernardino, CA 92414. TEL 714-886-5224 Ed. David Boehi. adv. illus. circ. 110,000.
Formerly (until Oct. 1974): World-Wide Impact.

WORLDWIND. see *CHILDREN AND YOUTH — For*

200 US ISSN 0084-3407
YALE PUBLICATIONS IN RELIGION. a. price varies. Yale University Press, 92A Yale Sta., New Haven, CT 06520. TEL 203-432-0940

200 US ISSN 0084-3644
YEARBOOK OF AMERICAN AND CANADIAN CHURCHES. 1916. a. $15.95. Abingdon, 201 Eighth Ave., So., Box 801, Nashville, TN 37202. TEL 615-749-6347 Ed. Constant H. Jacquet, Jr.
Formerly: Yearbook of American Churches.

260 US ISSN 0084-4128
YEARBOOKS IN CHRISTIAN EDUCATION. 1969. a. price varies. (Lutheran Church in America, Board of Publication) Fortress Press, 2900 Queen Lane, Philadelphia, PA 19129. TEL 215-848-6800

266 UK
YES. 1972. q. £1 to non-members. Church Missionary Society, 157 Waterloo Rd., London SE1 8UU, England. Ed. Robin E. Gurney. bk. rev. illus. circ. 38,000.
Missions

200 UK ISSN 0085-8374
YORK JOURNAL OF CONVOCATION. 1856. irreg. £2.50. (Convocation of York) Church Information Office, Church House, Westminster, London SW1, England. Ed. Canon R.J. Graham. circ. 400 (controlled)

267.2 US ISSN 0020-2673
YOUNG MEN'S INSTITUTE. INSTITUTE JOURNAL. 1890. bi-m. $3. Young Men's Institute, 50 Oak St., San Francisco, CA 94102. TEL 415-621-4948 Ed. Franklin J. Nelson. adv. bk. rev. illus. circ. 4,500(controlled)

267.5 US ISSN 0084-4306
YOUNG WOMEN'S CHRISTIAN ASSOCIATION OF THE UNITED STATES OF AMERICA. THE PRINTOUT. a. membership. Young Women's Christian Association of the United States of America, National Board, 726 Broadway, New York, NY 10003. TEL 212-614-2700 Ed.Bd.
Formerly: Tallies and Trends: Annual Statistical Report.

254 US ISSN 0049-8394
YOUR CHURCH. 1955. bi-m. $10. Religious Publishing Company, 198 Allendale Rd., King of Prussia, PA 19406. TEL 215-265-9400 Ed. Phyllis Mather Rice. adv. bk. rev. circ. 186,000. (also avail. in microform from UMI; reprint service avail. from UMI)
Church administration and design

266 US ISSN 0044-1015
YOUR EDMUNDITE MISSIONS NEWS LETTER. 1943. bi-m. $2. (Society of Saint Edmund) Southern Missions, Inc., 1428 Broad St., Selma, AL 36701. Ed.Bd. illus. circ. 72,044.
Missions

200 SZ
YOUTH NEWSLETTER. 1977. 4/yr. World Council of Churches, Youth Desk, 150 Route de Ferney, Box 66, 1211 Geneva 20, Switzerland. Ed. Heikki Huttunen.

267.3 II ISSN 0044-1414
YUVAK. (Text in English) bi-m. Rs.10($2) National Council of YMCA's of India, Box No. 14, New Delhi 110001, India. Ed. D.S. Chinnadorai. adv. circ. 2,500.
Formerly: Association Men.

221 GW ISSN 0044-2526
ZEITSCHRIFT FUER DIE ALTTESTAMENTLICHE WISSENSCHAFT. (Text in several languages) 1881. 3/yr. $75. Walter de Gruyter und Co., Genthiner Str. 13, 1000 Berlin 30, W. Germany (B.R.D.) (U.S. adress: Walter de Gruyter, Inc., 200 Saw Mill Rd., Hawthorne, N.Y. 10532) Ed. Otto Kaiser. bk. rev. abstr. index. (also avail. in microform) Indexed: Curr.Cont. Old Test.Abstr. Rel.Per. Rel.& Theol.Abstr. Arts & Hum.Cit.Ind. New Test.Abstr. Rel.Ind.One.

200 GW
ZEITSCHRIFT FUER DIE ALTTESTAMENTLICHE WISSENSCHAFT. BEIHEFTE. (Text in English and German) irreg., no.166, 1986. price varies. Walter de Gruyter und Co., Genthiner Str. 13, 1000 Berlin 30, W. Germany (B.R.D.) (U.S. adress: Walter de Gruyter, Inc., 200 Saw Mill Rd., Hawthorne, N.Y. 10532) Ed. Otto Kaiser. bibl. Indexed: Rel.& Theol.Abstr.

225 GW ISSN 0044-2615
ZEITSCHRIFT FUER DIE NEUTESTAMENTLICHE WISSENSCHAFT UND DIE KUNDE DER AELTEREN KIRCHE. 1900. 2/yr. $55.50. Walter de Gruyter und Co., Genthiner Str. 13, 1000 Berlin 30, W. Germany (B.R.D.) (U.S. adress: Walter de Gruyter, Inc., 200 Saw Mill Rd., Hawthorne, N.Y. 10532) Ed. Erich Graesser. adv. bk. rev. bibl. index. cum.index: vols. 1-37, 1900-1938. (also avail. in microform) Indexed: Rel.Per. CERDIC. New Test.Abstr. Rel.Ind.One. Rel.& Theol.Abstr.

241 261 GW ISSN 0044-2674
ZEITSCHRIFT FUER EVANGELISCHE ETHIK. 1957. bi-m. DM.64. Guetersloher Verlagshaus Gerd Mohn, Koenigstr. 23-25, Postfach 1343, 4830 Guetersloh, W. Germany (B.R.D.) Ed. Chr. Frey. bk. rev. bibl. Indexed: Curr.Cont. Rel.Per. Rel.& Theol.Abstr. Arts & Hum.Cit.Ind. CERDIC. Rel.Ind.One.

200 GW
ZEITSCHRIFT FUER GOTTESDIENST UND PREDIGT. 1983. bi-m. DM.8.80. Gutersloher Verlagshaus Mohn, Koenigstr. 23, 4830 Gutersloh, W. Germany (B.R.D.) Ed. Horst Nitschke. adv. bk. rev. circ. 3,400.

209 GW ISSN 0044-2925
ZEITSCHRIFT FUER KIRCHENGESCHICHTE. 1889. 3/yr. DM.172. W. Kohlhammer GmbH (Stuttgart), Hessbruehlstr. 69, Postfach 800430, 7000 Stuttgart 80, W. Germany (B.R.D.) Ed. Georg Schwaiger. adv. bk. rev. abstr. bibl. index. circ. 950. Indexed: Rel.Per. CERDIC. Rel.Ind.One. Rel.& Theol.Abstr.
History

266 GW ISSN 0342-9423
ZEITSCHRIFT FUER MISSION. 1975. q. DM.24. Evangelischer Missionsverlag GmbH, Postfach 31 11 41, 7000 Stuttgart 31, W. Germany (B.R.D.) adv. bk. rev. index. circ. 850. Indexed: CERDIC.
Until 1974: Evangelische Missionszeitschrift (ISSN 0014-3472)

266 GW ISSN 0044-3123
ZEITSCHRIFT FUER MISSIONSWISSENSCHAFT UND RELIGIONSWISSENSCHAFT. (Text in English, French, German) 1911. 4/yr. DM.44. (Internationales Institut fuer Missionswissenschaftliche Forschungen) Aschendorffsche Verlagsbuchhandlung, Soester Str. 13, Postfach 1124, 4400 Muenster, W. Germany (B.R..D.) Ed. Thomas Kramm. adv. bk. rev. index. Indexed: Rel.Per. CERDIC. Canon Law Abstr. Rel.Ind.One. Rel.& Theol.Abstr.
Missions

200 GW ISSN 0044-3441
ZEITSCHRIFT FUER RELIGIONS- UND GEISTESGESCHICHTE. 1948. q. DM.96. E. J. Brill GmbH, Antwerpener Str. 6, 5000 Cologne 1, W. Germany (B.R.D.) Ed.Bd. bk. rev. bibl. index. circ. 650. Indexed: Rel.Per. Rel.& Theol.Abstr. Arts & Hum.Cit.Ind. CERDIC. New Test.Abstr. Phil.Ind. Rel.Ind.One.

200 NE
ZEITSCHRIFT FUER RELIGIONS- UND GEISTESGESCHICHTE. BEIHEFTE. 1955. irreg., vol.30, 1986. price varies. E.J. Brill, P.O. Box 9000, 2300 PA Leiden, Netherlands. Indexed: Rel.& Theol.Abstr. Rel.Ind.One.

209 SZ ISSN 0044-3484
ZEITSCHRIFT FUER SCHWEIZERISCHE KIRCHENGESCHICHTE/REVUE D'HISTOIRE ECCLESIASTIQUE SUISSE. (Text and title in French and German) 1907. 2/yr. 35 Fr. (Vereinigung fuer Schweizerische Kirchengeschichte) Editions Saint-Paul, Perolles 42, CH-1700 Fribourg, Switzerland. bk. rev. bibl. Indexed: CERDIC.
History

220 SA ISSN 0028-3568
ZIONS FREUND. vol.9, 1969. q. R.10. ‡ Good News Missionary Society, P.O. Box 7848, Johannesburg, South Africa. Ed. Sean O'Sullivan. circ. 1,500.
Formerly: Neuer Zions Freund.

277 YU
ZNACI VREMENA; porodicni casopis za hriscansku renesansu. 1969. q. 24 din. Centar za Istrazivanje Biblije Dokumentaciju i Informacije, Klaiceva 40, Zagreb, Yugoslavia. Eds. Tomislav Stefanovic, Karlo Lenart. circ. 20,000.

200 PL ISSN 0044-488X
ZNAK. (Summaries in French) 1946. m. 252 Zl. Instytut Wydawniczy Znak, Wislna 12, Krakow, Poland. Ed. Hanna Malewska. bk. rev. index. circ. 7,500. Indexed: M.L.A. CERDIC.

200 NE ISSN 0044-5002
ZONDAGSMIS. 1951. 60/yr. fl.19. ‡ Abdij van Berne, Abdijstraat 53, 5473 AC Heeswijk-Dinther, Netherlands. circ. 120,000.

250 US ISSN 0084-5558
ZONDERVAN PASTOR'S ANNUAL. 1966. a. Zondervan Publishing House, 1415 Lake Dr. S.E., Grand Rapids, MI 49506. TEL 616-698-6900 Ed. T.T. Crabtree. circ. 14,000. (reprint service avail. from UMI)

200 GW
ZUM THEMA; Materialien zur Orientierung. 10/yr. DM.4.50. Kreuz Verlag Zeitschriften GmbH, Breitwiesenstr. 30, 7000 Stuttgart 80, W. Germany (B.R.D.) Ed. Peter H. Blaschke.

215 US ISSN 0591-2385
ZYGON; journal of religion and science. 1966. q. $25 to individuals; institutions $32; students $20. (Institute on Religion in an Age of Science) Joint Publication Board of Zygon, Rollins College, Winter Park, FL 32789. TEL 305-646-2134 (Co-sponsor: Center for Advanced Study in Religion and Science; Rollins College) Ed. Karl E. Peters. adv. bk. rev. index. cum.index: vols.1-10. circ. 2,000. (also avail. in microfilm from MIM,UMI; back issues avail; reprint service avail. UMI) Indexed: Curr.Cont. Hist.Abstr. Hum.Ind. Old Test.Abstr. Psychol.Abstr. Rel.Per. SSCI. Arts & Hum.Cit.Ind. Amer.Hist.& Life. Bk.Rev.Ind. CERDIC. G.Soc.Sci.& Rel.Per.Lit. New Test.Abstr. Phil.Ind. Rel.& Theol.Abstr. Rel.Ind.One.

200 US
7TH ANGEL. 1984. 10/yr. $15. J-S Arts & Features, Inc., 14 South Keim St., Box 334, Pottstown, PA 19464. TEL 215-327-1966 Ed. James A. Gittings. adv. bk. rev. circ. 12,000.

240 US ISSN 0162-6418
20TH CENTURY CHRISTIAN. 1938. m. $9.95. 20th Century Christian Foundation, 2809 Granny White Pike, Nashville, TN 37204. TEL 615-383-3842 Ed. Mike Cope. circ. 22,000.

RELIGIONS AND THEOLOGY — Abstracting, Bibliographies, Statistics

282 US ISSN 0737-3457
ABRIDGED CATHOLIC PERIODICAL AND LITERATURE INDEX. 1983. bi-m. Catholic Library Association, 461 W. Lancaster Ave., Haverford, PA 19041. TEL 215-649-5250 Ed. Natalie A. Logan. bk. rev. abstr. bibl. circ. 320.

250 016 US ISSN 0733-2599
ABSTRACTS OF RESEARCH IN PASTORAL CARE AND COUNSELING. 1972. a. $25. Joint Council on Research in Pastoral Care and Counseling, c/o Mary Fran Hughes-McIntyre, Box 5184, Richmond, VA 23220. TEL 804-353-3439 adv. bk. rev. circ. 400. (back issues avail.)
Formerly: Pastoral Care and Counseling Abstracts.

ACTUALIDAD BIBLIOGRAFICA DE FILOSOFIA Y TEOLOGIA; selecciones de libros. see *PUBLISHING AND BOOK TRADE — Abstracting, Bibliographies, Statistics*

271 VC ISSN 0570-7242
ARCHIVUM BIBLIOGRAPHICUM CARMELITANUM. (Text in Latin and modern languages) 1956. a. L.26000($12) Edizioni del Teresianum, Piazza S. Pancrazio 5-A, 00152 Rome, Italy. Ed. Father Simeon de la Sagrada Familia, O.C.D. circ. 400.

294.3 US ISSN 0888-5869
ASIAN RELIGIOUS STUDIES INFORMATION. 1987. s-a. $15 to individuals; institutions $35. Institute for Advanced Studies of World Religions, Melville Memorial Library, State University of New York at Stony Brook, Stony Brook, NY 11794-3383. TEL 516-632-6580 Eds. Richard A. Gard, Janet B. Gyatso. cum.index. circ. 1,500. (back issues avail.)
Incorporating: Buddhist Research Information (ISSN 0192-396X) & Sikh Religious Studies Information (ISSN 0193-1466) & Hindu Text Information (ISSN 0277-1349)

280.4 016 US ISSN 0066-8710
ASSOCIATED CHURCH PRESS. DIRECTORY. 1947. a. $20 ($6 to libraries) (Associated Church Press) Associated Church Press, Box 306, Geneva, IL 60134. TEL 312-232-1055 Ed. Donald F. Hetzler. adv. circ. 600.
Listing of Protestant and other religious publications in the United States and Canada

282 IT
BIBLIOGRAFIA MISSIONARIA. 1935. a. $20. Pontificia Universita Urbaniana, Pontificia Biblioteca Missionaria della S.C. per l'Evangelizzazione dei Popoli, Via Urbano VIII, 16, 000165 Rome, Italy. Ed. Willi Henkel. bk. rev. circ. 1,000.

255 011 920 IT
BIBLIOGRAPHIA FRANCISCANA. (Annual supplement to Collectanea Franciscana) (Text in Latin) 1931. a. price varies. Frati Minori Cappuccini, Istituto Storico, Casella Postale 9091, Circonv. Occidentale 6850 (GRA km 65) , 00163 Rome, Italy. circ. 800.

296 016 US ISSN 0067-6853
BIBLIOGRAPHICA JUDAICA. 1969. irreg., no.9, 1985. Library of Hebrew Union College-Jewish Institute of Religion, 3101 Clifton Ave., Cincinnati, OH 45220. TEL 513-221-1875 Ed. Herbert C. Zafren.

200 US ISSN 0742-6836
BIBLIOGRAPHIES AND INDEXES IN RELIGIOUS STUDIES. 1984. irreg. price varies. Greenwood Press (Subsidiary of: Congressional Information Service, Inc.) 88 Post Rd. W., Box 5007, Westport, CT 06881. TEL 203-226-3571 Ed. Gary E. Gorman.

BULLETIN SIGNALETIQUE. PART 519: PHILOSOPHIE. see *PHILOSOPHY — Abstracting, Bibliographies, Statistics*

200 016 FR ISSN 0180-9296
BULLETIN SIGNALETIQUE. PART 527: HISTOIRE ET SCIENCES DES RELIGIONS. 1947. q. 325 F. Centre National de la Recherche Scientifique, Centre de Documentation Sciences Humaines, 54 bd. Raspail, 75260 Paris Cedex, France. cum.index. •Also available online. Vendors: European Space Agency.
Formerly: Bulletin Signaletique. Part 527: Sciences Religieuse (ISSN 0007-5620)

262.9 016 IE ISSN 0008-5650
CANON LAW ABSTRACTS; half-yearly review of periodical literature in Canon Law. 1959. s-a. £5. Canon Law Society of Great Britain and Ireland, Archbishop's House, Westminster, London SW1P 1QJ, England. Ed. Rev. Ivan Payne. bk. rev. abstr. bibl. circ. 1,000. Indexed: Old Test.Abstr. CERDIC.
Canon law

282 011 US ISSN 0008-8285
CATHOLIC PERIODICAL AND LITERATURE INDEX. 1930. bi-m. with biennial cum. (service basis) Catholic Library Association, 461 W. Lancaster Ave., Haverford, PA 19041. TEL 215-649-5250 Ed. Natalie A. Logan. bk. rev. abstr. bibl. circ. 1,500. (also avail. in microfilm from UMI)
Former titles: Catholic Periodical Index (ISSN 0363-6895); Guide to Catholic Literature (ISSN 0145-191X)

200 011 FR ISSN 0181-7671
CENTRE PROTESTANT D'ETUDES ET DE DOCUMENTATION. BULLETIN. 1944. 10/yr. 200 F. Centre Protestant d'Etudes et de Documentation, 46 rue de Vaugirard, 75006 Paris, France. (Co-sponsor: Federation Protestante de France) Ed. Mrs. M.L. Fabre. adv. bk. rev. abstr. bibl. index. circ. 1,350. Indexed: CERDIC. New Test.Abstr.
Formerly: Federation Protestante de France. Centre d'Etudes et de Documentation. Bulletin (ISSN 0008-9842)

280 016 US ISSN 0069-3871
CHRISTIAN PERIODICAL INDEX; an index to subjects, authors and book reviews. 1959. q. plus annual. $60 (including annual) Association of Christian Librarians Inc., Cedarville College Library, Cedarville, OH 45314. Ed. Douglas J. Butler. circ. 450. (reprint service avail. from UMI)

200 US ISSN 0883-1440
CURRENT CHRISTIAN ABSTRACTS. 1985. m. $36. Current Christian Abstracts, Box 7596, Columbia, MO 65205. Eds. Betty Gibb, Sue Job. circ. 500.

220 016 VC
ELENCHUS BIBLIOGRAPHICUS BIBLICUS. a. $65. (Pontificio Istituto Biblico) Biblical Institute Press, Piazza della Pilotta 35, 00187 Rome, Italy. Ed. Robert North S.J.
Bible

016 200 NE
GODSDIENST EN MAATSCHAPPIJ. 1981. bi-m. fl.30.50. Nederlands Bibliotheek en Lektuur Centrum, Scheltemastr. 5, 2597 CP Amersfoort, Netherlands. Eds. Magda van der Grijn, L.M.D. de Viet. bk. rev. circ. 1,000.

296 016 IS ISSN 0073-5817
INDEX OF ARTICLES ON JEWISH STUDIES/RESHIMAT MA'AMARIM BE-MADA'E HA-YAHADUT. (Text in various languages) 1969. biennial. $20 single issue; $25 double issue. ‡ Jewish National and University Library, Box 503, Jerusalem, Israel. circ. 1,200.

289 016 US ISSN 0073-5981
INDEX TO PERIODICALS OF THE CHURCH OF JESUS CHRIST OF LATTER-DAY SAINTS. CUMULATIVE EDITION. 1961. a. $5 yearly; $10.00 cum. 1961-1970. Church of Jesus Christ of Latter-day Saints, 50 E. North Temple St., Salt Lake City, UT 84150 TEL 801-531-2531 (Subscr. to: Salt Lake Distribution Center, 1999 West 1700 South, Salt Lake City, UT 84104) index. circ. 5,000.

016 200 NE
INTERNATIONAL BIBLIOGRAPHY OF THE HISTORY OF RELIGIONS/ BIBLIOGRAPHIE INTERNATIONAL DE L'HISTOIRE DES RELIGIONS. 1954. a. price varies. E. J. Brill, P.O. Box 9000, 2300 PA Leiden, Netherlands.

297 GW ISSN 0724-2263
ISLAMIC BOOK REVIEW INDEX. (Text in English) 1982. a. DM.60($29) Wolfgang H. Behn Ed. & Pub., Rosenheimer Str. 5, D-1000 Berlin 30, W. Germany (B.R.D.) Ed. Wolfgang H. Behn. bk. rev. circ. 500. (back issues avail.)

016 282 NE
KATHOLIEK DOCUMENTATIE CENTRUM. BIBLIOGRAFIEEN. irreg. price varies. Katholiek Documentatie Centrum, Erasmuslaan 36, 6525 GG Nijmegen, Netherlands.

284 ZA
LUTHERAN CHURCH OF CENTRAL AFRICA. STATISTICAL REPORT. (Text in English) a. Lutheran Church of Central Africa, Box CH 195, Lusaka, Zambia.

370 200 016 NE ISSN 0025-6919
MEDIA-INFORMATIEDIENST. 1963. bi-m. fl.12($8.) Protestantse Stichting tot Bevordering van het Bibliotheekwezen en de Lektuurvoorlichting in Nederland, Parkweg 20a, Voorburg, Netherlands. circ. 3,000.

655 028.1 011 GW ISSN 0028-3118
DAS NEUE BUCH; Buchprofile fuer die Katholische Buechereiarbeit. 1925. bi-m. DM.26. Borromaeusverein, Wittelsbacherring 9, 5300 Bonn, W. Germany (B.R.D.) (And St. Michaelsbund, Herzog Wilhelmstr. 5, 8000 Munich 2, W. Germany (B.R.D.)) Eds. Hans Bemmann, Alois Auer. bk. rev. cum.index. circ. 10,000.

220 016 US ISSN 0028-6877
NEW TESTAMENT ABSTRACTS; a record of current literature. 1956. 3/yr. $24. Weston School of Theology, 3 Phillips Place, Cambridge, MA 02138 TEL 617-492-1960 (Subscr. to: Catholic Biblical Association of America, Catholic University of America, Washington, DC 20064) Ed. D. J. Harrington. adv. bk. rev. abstr. index; cum.index: vols. 1-15 (1956-1970) circ. 2,150. (back issues avail) Indexed: Int.Z.Bibelwiiss.

200 011 UR ISSN 0134-2932
NOVAYA SOVETSKAYA I INOSTRANNAYA LITERATURA PO OBSHCHESTVENNYM NAUKAM. PROBLEMY ATEIZMA I RELIGII. bi-m. 10.40 Rub. Akademiya Nauk S.S.S.R., Institut Nauchnoi Informatsii po Obshchestvennym Naukam, Ul. Krasikova 28/21, Moscow 117418, Russian S.F.S.R., U.S.S.R. Ed. I.I. Kravchenko.

016 260 FR
OECUMENE; international bibliography indexed by computer. (Text and summaries in English, French, German, Italian and Spanish) 1977. biennial. 260 F.($20) Universite de Strasbourg II, Centre de Recherche et de Documentation des Institutions Chretiennes, 9 Place de l'Universite, 67084 Strasbourg Cedex, France. bk. rev. circ. 1,000. (back issues avail.)

220 US ISSN 0364-8591
OLD TESTAMENT ABSTRACTS. 1978. 3/yr. $14. Catholic Biblical Association of America, Catholic University of America, Washington, DC 20064. TEL 202-635-5519 Ed. Bruce Vawter, C.M. circ. 20,000.

016 260 FR ISSN 0079-9300
R I C. (Repertoire Bibliographique des Institutions Chretiennes.) (Supplement avail: Thematic Bibliographies) 1966-67. s-a. 460 F. Universite de Strasbourg II, Centre de Recherche et de Documentation des Institutions Chretiennes, 9 Place de l'Universite, 67084 Strasbourg Cedex, France. Eds. Jean Schlick, Marie Zimmermann. bk. rev. circ. 1,500.

200 016 US ISSN 0149-8428
RELIGION INDEX ONE: PERIODICALS. 1949. s-a. plus a. cum. $285. American Theological Library Association, Religion Indexes, 5600 S. Woodlawn Ave., Chicago, IL 60637. TEL 312-947-9417 circ. 1,200. •Also available online. Vendors: BRS, DIALOG.
Formerly: Index to Religious Periodical Literature (ISSN 0019-4107)

200 US ISSN 0149-8436
RELIGION INDEX TWO: MULTI-AUTHOR WORKS. 1976. a. $177. American Theological Library Association, Religion Indexes, 5600 S. Woodlawn Ave., Chicago, IL 60637. TEL 312-947-9417 Ed. Erica Treesh. circ. 1,000. •Also available online. Vendors: BRS, DIALOG.

200 016 US ISSN 0034-4044
RELIGIOUS & THEOLOGICAL ABSTRACTS. 1958. q. $23.25 to individuals; institutions $46.50. Religious & Theological Abstracts Inc., Box 215, Myerstown, PA 17067. TEL 717-866-6734 Ed. J.C. Christman. abstr. index. circ. 1,100. (also avail. in microfiche; back issues avail.)

200 016 II ISSN 0034-4060
RELIGIOUS BOOK REVIEW INDEX. 1970. bi-m. Rs.150.($63.) K.K. Roy (Private) Ltd., 55 Gariahat Rd., Box 10210, Calcutta 700019, India. Ed. John A. Gillard. adv. bk. rev. bibl. circ. 1,000. (looseleaf format)

200 US ISSN 0730-2371
S S C BOOKNEWS. 1973. m. free. Spiritual Studies Center, Box 1104, Rockville, MD 20850. TEL 301-963-9243 Ed. Elisabeth Nachtwey. bk. rev. circ. 3,000.

200 016 US ISSN 0036-6358
SCHOLARS' CHOICE; significant current theological literature from abroad. 1960. s-a. $4. Union Theological Seminary in Virginia, Library, 3401 Brook Rd., Richmond, VA 23227. TEL 804-355-0671 Ed. Dr. John B. Trotti. bibl. circ. 650.

200 NE ISSN 0165-8794
SCIENCE OF RELIGION; abstracts and index of recent articles. 1976. q. fl.50. Vrije Universiteit, Institute for the Study of Religion, Box 7161, Amsterdam, Netherlands. Eds. Remmelt Bakker, Michael Pye. circ. 350.
Formerly: Science of Religion Bulletin.

200 UK ISSN 0081-1440
SOCIETY FOR OLD TESTAMENT STUDY. BOOK LIST. 1946. a. £12($12) ‡ Society for Old Testament Study, c/o M. E. J. Richardson, Middle Eastern Studies, University of Manchester, Manchester M13 9PL, England. Ed. G. Auld. adv. bk. rev. index. circ. 1,500.

STUDIES IN BIBLIOGRAPHY AND BOOKLORE; devoted to research in the field of Jewish bibliography. see *PUBLISHING AND BOOK TRADE — Abstracting, Bibliographies, Statistics*

200 016 UK
THEOLOGICAL AND RELIGIOUS BIBLIOGRAPHIES. 1972. irreg. £2. Theological Abstracting and Bibliographical Services, 33 Mayfield Grove, Harrogate, North Yorkshire HG1 5HD, England. Ed. G.P. Cornish. bk. rev. circ. 150. (also avail. in microfilm)
Formerly (until vol.3, 1981): Theological and Religious Index (ISSN 0306-087X)

200 US
TOPICS IN RELIGION: A BIBLIOGRAPHIC SERIES. irreg. price varies. Greenwood Press, 88 Post Rd. W., Box 5007, Westport, CT 06881. TEL 203-226-3571 Ed. Gary E. Gorman.

ZIONIST LITERATURE. see *PUBLISHING AND BOOK TRADE — Abstracting, Bibliographies, Statistics*

RELIGIONS AND THEOLOGY — Islamic

297 US
A M S S NEWSBULLETIN. vol.13, 1985. m. Association of Muslim Social Scientists (Plainfield), Box 38, Plainfield, IN 46168. TEL 317-839-8157 Ed. Mushtag Rahman.

297 SL ISSN 0044-653X
AFRICAN CRESCENT. 1955. m. Le.4. Ahmadiyya Muslim Mission, P.O. Box 353, Freetown, Sierra Leone. Ed. Maulana Khalil Mobashir. adv. bk. rev. circ. 1,000.

297 PK
AHL-I HADIS. (Text in Urdu) w. Rs.15. Hadis Manzil, 7 Aibak Rd., Anarkali, Lahore, Pakistan.

268 NR ISSN 0065-468X
AHMADU BELLO UNIVERSITY. CENTRE OF ISLAMIC LEGAL STUDIES. JOURNAL. 1966. irreg., vol. 5, 1974. Ahmadu Bello University, Centre of Islamic Legal Studies, P.M.B. 1013, Zaria, Nigeria (Overseas orders to: Wiley & Sons Ltd., Lincoln's Inn Archway, Carey St., London W.C. 2, England)

297 DK ISSN 0108-7290
AKTIV ISLAM. (Text in Danish) 1983. bi-m. Kr.30 free to libraries. Nusrat Djahan Moske, Eriksminde Alle 2, 2650 Hvidovre, Denmark. Ed. Nuh S. Hansen. bk. rev. circ. 750.

297 NE
ASFAR. 1977. irreg. price varies. Rijksuniversiteit te Leiden, Documentatiebureau Islam-Christendom, Theologisch Instituut, Rapenburg 59, Leiden, Netherlands.

956 297 GW ISSN 0170-3102
BIBLIOTHECA ISLAMICA. (Text in English and German) irreg., vol.32, 1987. price varies. (Deutsche Morgenlaendische Gesellschaft) Franz Steiner Verlag Wiesbaden GmbH, Birkenwaldstr. 44, Postfach 347, D-7000 Stuttgart 1, W. Germany (B.R.D.) Ed.Bd.

297 956 UA ISSN 0259-7373
BULLETIN CRITIQUE DES ANNALES ISLAMOLOGIQUES. 1986. a. Institut Francais d'Archeologie Orientale du Caire, 37 rue El Sheikh Aly Youssef, Mounira, Cairo, Egypt. circ. 800.

300 UK ISSN 0264-1356
BULLETIN ON ISLAM AND CHRISTIAN-MUSLIM RELATIONS IN AFRICA. 1983. q. £9($14) Selly Oak Colleges, Centre for the Study of Islam and Christian-Muslim Relations, Birmingham B29 6LE, England.

297.7 UK ISSN 0267-4890
BULLETIN SUR L'ISLAM ET LES RELATIONS ISLAMO-CHRETIENNES EN AFRIQUE. 1985. q. £9($14) Selly Oak Colleges, Centre for the Study of Islam and Christian-Muslim Relations, Birmingham B29 6LE, England.

297.65 CN ISSN 0707-2945
CANADIAN MUSLIM. (Text in Arabic and English) 1977. q. free contr. circ. Ottawa Muslim Association, Box 2952, Sta. D, Ottawa, Ont. 51P 5W9, Canada. TEL 613-725-0004 Ed. Mohammed Azhar Alikhan. adv. bk. rev. circ. 2,000.

297 UK ISSN 0143-8921
CENTRE FOR THE STUDY OF ISLAM AND CHRISTIAN MUSLIM RELATIONS. NEWSLETTER. 1979. 2/yr. £6($10) including News of Muslims in Europe. Selly Oak Colleges, Centre for the Study of Islam and Christian-Muslim Relations, Birmingham B29 6LE, England. Indexed: Abstr.Musl.Rel.

291 297 II
CHRISTIAN INSTITUTES OF ISLAMIC STUDIES BULLETIN. 1930. q. Rs.15($4.50) Henry Martyn Institute of Islamic Studies, Box 153, Hyderabad 500001, Andhra Pradesh, India. Ed. Rev. David. T. Lindell. bk. rev. circ. 400. Indexed: Abstr.Musl.Rel. Rel.Ind.One.
Supersedes: Al-Basheer; Formerly: Christian Institutes of Islamic Studies Bulletin (ISSN 0009-5397)

CIBEDO - DOKUMENTATIONEN UND TEXTE. see *RELIGIONS AND THEOLOGY*

297 CN ISSN 0705-3754
CRESCENT INTERNATIONAL. 1972. s-m. $30. Crescent Pak Inc., 338 Hollyberry Trail, Willowdale, Ont. M2H 2P6, Canada. Ed. Zafar Bangash. adv. bk. rev. circ. 12,000. (tabloid format; also avail. in microfilm; back issues avail.)

297 PK ISSN 0002-399X
DIRASAT AL-ISLAMIYAH. (Text in Arabic) 1965. bi-m. $20. Islamic Research Institute, Box 1035, Islamabad, Pakistan. Ed. Mahmood Ahmad Ghazi. bk. rev. circ. 1,000. (back issues avail.)
Islamic studies

297 PK ISSN 0430-4055
FIKR-O-NAZAR. (Text in Urdu) 1964. m. $15. Islamic Research Institute, Box 1035, Islamabad, Pakistan. Ed. Sahibzada Sajidur Rehman. (back issues avail.)

FRANCE-ISLAM. see *ETHNIC INTERESTS*

FREIBURGER ISLAMSTUDIEN. see *ORIENTAL STUDIES*

297 II
AL FURQAN. (Text in Urdu) 1933. m. Rs.25. 31 Naya Gaon West, Lucknow 226018, India.

297 PK
HAMDARD FOUNDATION. REPORT. 1980. biennial. free. Hamdard Foundation, Nazimabad, Karachi 8, Pakistan. circ. 2,000.

297 PK ISSN 0250-7196
HAMDARD ISLAMICUS. (Text in English) 1978. q. Rs.75($15) Hamdard Foundation, Nazimabad, Karachi 8, Pakistan. Ed. Hakim Mohammed Said. bk. rev. circ. 2,000. Indexed: Hist.Abstr. Abstr.Musl.Rel. Amer.Hist.& Life. Rel.Ind.One.

HOLY LAND; illustrated quarterly of the Franciscan custody of the holy land. see *RELIGIONS AND THEOLOGY — Roman Catholic*

297 US
INVITATION. q. Islamic Information Center of America, Box 4052, Des Plaines, IL 60016. TEL 312-541-8184 Ed. Musa Qutub.
Islam

DER ISLAM; Zeitschrift fuer Geschichte und Kultur des islamischen Orients. see *ORIENTAL STUDIES*

297 NE ISSN 0021-180X
ISLAM. 1947. m. fl.30. Ahmadiyya Muslim Mission Holland, Mobarak Moskee, Oostduinlaan 79, 2596 JJ The Hague, Netherlands. Eds. S.M. Frouws, H.N. Verhagen. adv. bk. rev. circ. 300.

297 RE ISSN 0151-7163
AL ISLAM. (Text in French) 1975. m. 150 F. Centre Islamique de la Reunion, B.P. 437, 97459 Saint-Pierre Cedex, Reunion. Ed. A. Saeed Ingar. circ. 1,000.

297 IT
ISLAM; storia e civilta. 1981. q. L.15000. Accademia dell Cultura Islamica, Unione Islamica in Occidente, Corso Trieste, 90, 00198 Rome, Italy. Ed. Salvatore Bono.

297 TU
ISLAM AKASTIRMALARI MERKEZI DERGISI. (Text in Arabic, English, Turkish; summaries in English) 1953. q. Istanbul University, Center of Islamic Studies, Istanbul, Turkey. Ed. Bekir Kutukoglu. bk. rev. illus. circ. 1,000. Indexed: Hist.Abstr. Amer.Hist.& Life.
Formerly: Islam Tetkikleri Enstitusu Dergisi.

297 II ISSN 0021-1826
ISLAM AND THE MODERN AGE. (Text in English) 1970. q. $20. Zakir Husain Institute of Islamic Studies, Jamia Nagar, New Delhi 110025, India. Ed. Z.H. Faruqi. adv. bk. rev. circ. 1,000. Indexed: Abstr.Musl.Rel. Ind.Islam.

297 BG ISSN 0379-4032
ISLAM AND THE MODERN WORLD. (Text in English) 1977. q. Tk.40($8) Council for Islamic and Christian Studies and Research, G.P.O. Box 242, 16-A Larmini St., Wari, Dacca 3, Bangladesh. Ed. A.B.M. Shamsuddoulah. bk. rev. bibl. circ. 1,250.

ISLAM INTERNATIONAL. see *POLITICAL SCIENCE*

297 MR
ISLAM TODAY/ISLAM AUJOURD'HUI. (Text in Arabic, English and French) 1983. 2/yr. $2.70. P.O. Box 755, Rabat, Morocco. Ed. M. Fassi Fihri. circ. 15,000.

297 US ISSN 8756-2367
ISLAMIC HORIZONS; I S N A News and Perspectives. 1963. m. $7 to students; individuals $12; institutions $16. Islamic Society of North America, Box 38, Plainfield, IN 46168. TEL 317-839-8157 Ed. Steve A. Johnson. adv. bk. rev. stat. circ. 30,000.

297 PK
ISLAMIC ORDER. (Text in English) 1979. q. Rs.100($20) Ismail Ahmad Minai, 0218 Bahadurabad, Karachi, Pakistan.

297 PK
ISLAMIC STUDIES. 1962. q. Rs.150($15) Islamic Research Institute, Box 1035, Islamabad, Pakistan. Ed. F.A. Shamsi. bk. rev. index. circ. 1,000. (back issues avail.) Indexed: Abstr.Musl.Rel.

297 IT
JIHAD; periodico Islamico. (Text in French, German, Italian) bi-m. L.5000($10) Edizioni Arktos, Via Gardezzana 57, Carmagnola, Italy. Ed. Giovanni Oggero.

JOURNAL OF SEMITIC STUDIES. see *RELIGIONS AND THEOLOGY — Judaic*

JUSUR; the U C L A journal of Middle Eastern studies. see *HISTORY — History Of The Near East*

297 PK ISSN 0541-5462
M.I.I. SERIES. 1966. irreg. Muslim Intellectuals' International, Box 5294, Karachi, Pakistan.

MAJALLAT AL-AZHAR. see *EDUCATION — Higher Education*

297 KE
MAPENZI YA MUNGU. (Text in Swahili) 1943. m. K.15. East African Ahmadiyya Muslim Mission, Box 40554, Nairobi, Kenya. Ed. Jamil R. Rafiq. adv. bk. rev. circ. 4,000.

297.7 MF
MESSAGE DE L'AHMADIYYA. 1965. m. $24. Ahmadiyya Muslim Association, Edward VII St., Rose Hill, Mauritius. Ed. Zafrullah Domun. bk. rev. circ. 2,000.
Formerly: Message.

266 PK
MINARET MONTHLY INTERNATIONAL. (Text in English) 1964. m. Rs.150. World Federation of Islamic Missions, Islamic Centre, B-Block, N. Nazimabad, Karachi 33, Pakistan. Ed. Muhammed Ja'Fer. adv. bk. rev. circ. 1,200. Indexed: Abstr.Musl.Rel.
Formerly (until Sept. 1976): Minaret (ISSN 0026-4415)
Missions

297 SA ISSN 0027-4887
MUSLIM DIGEST; international monthly of Muslim affairs. 1950. m. $8. Makki Publications, 100 Brickfield Rd., Durban, South Africa. adv. illus.

297 II ISSN 0027-4895
MUSLIM REVIEW. (Text in English) 1923. q. Rs.5($0.75) Madrasat-Ul-Waizeen, 16 Canning St., Lucknow, India. Ed. Shaheed Safipuri. bk. rev. circ. 500.

297 SU
MUSLIM SOLIDARITY/MAJALLAT AL-TADAMUM AL-ISLAMI. (Text in Arabic and English) m. free. Ministry of Pilgrimage and Endowments - Idarat al-Hajj al-Ammah, Mecca, Saudi Arabia. Ed. Mustafa Abdul Wahed. bk. rev. bibl. circ. 5,000.
Formerly: Majallat al-Hajj.

297 US
MUSLIM STAR. m. $10. Federation of Islamic Associations in the United States and Canada, 25341 Five Mile Rd., Redford Township, MI 48239. TEL 313-535-0014 adv. illus.

297 US ISSN 0027-4909
MUSLIM WORLD; a journal devoted to the study of Islam and of Christian-Muslim relationship in past and present. 1911. q. $15 individuals; institutions $20. (Duncan Black Macdonald Center) Hartford Seminary, 77 Sherman St., Hartford, CT 06105. TEL 203-232-4451 Ed. Willem A. Bijlefeld. adv. bk. rev. index. cum.index: vols.1-25 (1911-1935), vols.26-50 (1936-1960) circ. 1,200. (also avail. in microform from UMI; back issues avail.) Indexed: Curr.Cont. Hist.Abstr. Hum.Ind. Rel.Per. M.L.A. Amer.Bibl.Slavic & E.Eur.Stud. Amer.Hist.& Life. Rel.Ind.One. Rel.& Theol.Abstr.
Formerly (until 1948): Moslem World (ISSN 0362-4641)

297.7 UK ISSN 0260-3063
MUSLIM WORLD BOOK REVIEW. 1980. q. £6($22) to individuals; £10 to institutions. Islamic Foundation, 223 London Rd., Leicester, England. Eds. Khurram Murad, Manazir Ahsan. adv. bk. rev. circ. 1,000.

297 SU
MUSLIM WORLD LEAGUE. JOURNAL/RABETAT AL-ALAM AL-ISLAMI. JOURNAL. 1973. m. £2. ‡ Muslim World League, Press and Publications Department - Rebetat al-Alam al-Islami, Mecca, Saudi Arabia. Ed.Bd. index. circ. 5,000.

297 070.5 UK
NEW BOOKS QUARTERLY ON ISLAM & THE MUSLIM WORLD. 1982. q. £4. Islamic Council of Europe, 16 Grosvenor Crescent, London S.W.1., England. bk. rev.

297.7 UK ISSN 0143-9774
NEWS OF MUSLIMS IN EUROPE. 1980. 4/yr. £6($10) including Newsletter. Selly Oak Colleges, Centre for the Study of Islam and Christian-Muslim Relations, Birmingham B29 6LE, England. Ed. J.S. Nielsen. circ. 300.

297 UA
NIDA AL-ISLAM. m. £E60 per no. Dar al-Fikr Lil-Nashr Wa-al-Ilam, 58 Shari 26 Yuliyu, Cairo, Egypt.

297 KE
NUR-UL ISLAM. (Text in English or Swahili) 1980. q. Supreme Council of Kenya Muslims, Box 45163, Nairobi, Kenya.

297 US
OUR ISLAM. 1980. q. $6 for 12 issues. (African Islamic Mission Inc.) A.I.M. Publications, 1390 Bedford Ave., Brooklyn, NY 11216. Ed. Alhaji Obaba Muhammad. adv. bk. rev. circ. 4,000. (tabloid format; back issues avail.)

297 PK
QURANULHUDA. (Text in English) 1976. m. Rs.96. S.M.S.A. Hayat, Box 8677, 28 Qasr-e-Batool, Shahrah-e-Iraq, Karachi 3, Pakistan. Ed. M.R. Husain. adv. bk. rev. circ. 31,000.
Islamic teachings

297 UK
RESEARCH PAPERS: MUSLIMS IN EUROPE. 4/yr. £12($19) including Newsletter, News of Muslims in Europe. Selly Oak Colleges, Centre for the Study of Islam and Christian-Muslim Relations, Birmingham B29 6LE, England. Indexed: Abstr.Musl.Rel.
Formerly: Centre for the Study of Islam and Christian-Muslim Relations. Research Papers (ISSN 0260-3772)

291 PK ISSN 0034-6721
REVIEW OF RELIGIONS. (Text in English) 1902. m. £20. Tehrik-i-Jadid, Rabwah, Pakistan. Ed. B.A. Rafiq. adv. bk. rev. index; cum.index. circ. 7,300. (also avail. in microform from UMI; reprint service avail. from UMI)

REVUE DES ETUDES ISLAMIQUES. see *ORIENTAL STUDIES*

297 LE
RISALEH AL-ISLAMIYAH. irreg. £L1.50 per no. Box 155063, Beirut, Lebanon.

297 SI ISSN 0559-2674
SEDAR; journal of Islamic studies. 1968. biennial. S.$2. ‡ University of Singapore, Muslim Society, Yusof Ishak House, Clementi Rd., Kent Ridge, Singapore 5, Singapore. Ed. M. Dzulfighar Mohd. adv. bibl.

297 UK
SHIA WORLD. 1976. q. free. World Federation of Khoja Shia Ithnaasheri Muslim Communities, P.O. Box 60, Warren House, Wood Lane, Stanmore, Middlesex, England. circ. 3,000. (back issues avail.)

297.7 PK
SHIAH. (Text in Urdu) vol.56, 1977. w. Rs.12. Insaf Press, Railway Rd, Lahore, Pakistan.

297 II ISSN 0039-3711
STUDIES IN ISLAM. (Text in English) 1964. q. $12. Indian Institute of Islamic Studies, Panchkuin Rd., New Delhi 1, India. Ed. Hakim A. Hameed. adv. bk. rev. circ. 1,000. Indexed: Old Test.Abstr. Ind.Islam.

STUDIES IN ZIONISM; an international journal of social, political and intellectual history. see *RELIGIONS AND THEOLOGY — Judaic*

297 PK
TARJUMAN AL-HADITH. (Text in Urdu) 1974. m. Rs.151. Idara Tarjuman-us-Sunnah, Hadis Manzil, 7 Albak Road, Anarkali, Lahore, Pakistan (Subscr. to: Mu'tsini Villa, 21-6 Pak Block, Ispal Town, Lahore, Pakistan) Ed. Maulawa Ehran Ilahi Zaheer. circ. 2,000. (back issues avail.)

297 JO
THEOLOGY/SHARIA. (Text in Arabic) 1959. m. League of Islamic Sciences, Box 1829, Amman, Jordan. Ed. Tayseer Dhabian.

297 NR
TRUTH; the first Muslim weekly newspaper in Nigeria. (Text in English) 1951. w. £N15. Ahmadiyya Muslim Mission, 45, Idumagbo Ave., Box 418, Lagos, Nigeria. Ed. Maj. M.A. Giwa. adv. bk. rev. circ. 5,000. (newspaper; back issues avail.)

297 PK
UNIVERSAL MESSAGE. (Text in English) 1979. m. Rs.50($25) Islamic Research Academy, 10-C/163, Mansura, Federal B Area, Karachi 3805, Pakistan. Ed. Syed Wajahat Ali. adv. bk. rev. bibl. circ. 1,000. (back issues avail.)

297 400 LE
UNIVERSITE SAINT-JOSEPH. FACULTE DES LETTRES ET DES SCIENCES HUMAINES. RECHERCHE. SERIE A: LANGUE ARABE ET PENSEE ISLAMIQUE. (Previously published by its Institut des Lettres Orientales in 4 series) 1956; N.S. 1971. irreg. price varies. Dar el-Mashreq S.A.R.L., 2 rue Huvelin, Box 946, Beirut, Lebanon (Subscr. to: Librairie Orientale, Box 946, Beirut, Lebanon)

297 IR
UNIVERSITY OF FERDOWSI. FACULTY OF THEOLOGY AND ISLAMIC STUDIES. PUBLICATION/DANESHGAH-E FERDOWSI. DANESHKADE-YE ELAHIYAT VA MA'AREF-E ESLAMI. NASHRIYEH. (Text in Persian) 1972. q. Rs.120. University of Ferdowsi, Faculty of Theology and Islamic Studies, Mashhad, Iran. Ed. Gholamreza Nafeli. bk. rev.

297 PK ISSN 0042-8132
VOICE OF ISLAM. vol.16, 1968. m. Rs.10. Jamiyat-ul-Falah Karachi, Box 7141, Karachi 3, Pakistan. Ed. A.A. Alam. adv. bk. rev. circ. 5,000.

297 UG
VOICE OF ISLAM. m. Ahmaddiya Muslim Association, Box 16085, Kampala, Uganda.

297 MF
VOIX DE L'ISLAM. (Text in English and French) 1951. m. Rs.5. Abdool Azize Peeroo, Ed. & Pub., Parisot Rd., Mesnil, Phoenix, Mauritius. (back issues avail.)

200 PK ISSN 0084-2052
WORLD MUSLIM CONFERENCE. PROCEEDINGS. (Published in: Muslim World) (Text in English) biennial. World Muslim Congress - Motamar al-Alam al-Islami, 224, Sharafabad, Karachi 0511, Pakistan.

297 PK ISSN 0084-2060
WORLD MUSLIM GAZETTEER. (Text in English) 1964. quinquennial. $35. World Muslim Congress - Motamar Al-Alam al-Islami, 224, Sharafabad, Karachi 0511, Pakistan. Ed. Inamullah Khan.

297 GW ISSN 0040-8646
WUDD; dedicated to the cause of Islam. 1970. a. DM.2. Hadayatullah Huebsch, Wickerer Str. 12, 6000 Frankfurt 1, W. Germany (B.R.D.) adv. bk. rev. charts.
Formerly: Toern.

297 PK ISSN 0044-0213
YAQEEN INTERNATIONAL. (Text in Arabic and English) 1952. fortn. Rs.70. Darut-Tasnif Ltd., P.O. Darut Tasnif, Mujahidabad, Hub River Rd., Karachi 1, Pakistan. Ed. M.M. Ansari. bk. rev. bibl. circ. 5,000. Indexed: Abstr.Musl.Rel.

297 II
YOGASANA ALAYA VIJAYAM. (Text in English, Tamil) 1948. m. Rs.4. Yogazana Alayn, 462, T.H. Rd., Choolai Medu, Old Washermepet, Madras 600021, India. Ed. Pulavar B. Alwar. adv. bk. rev. circ. 800.

YOUTH MIRROR. see *CHILDREN AND YOUTH — For*

RELIGIONS AND THEOLOGY — Judaic
see also Ethnic Interests

A J L NEWSLETTER. (Association of Jewish Libraries) see *LIBRARY AND INFORMATION SCIENCES*

A J S REVIEW. (Association for Jewish Studies) see *ETHNIC INTERESTS*

296 US ISSN 0740-2392
AGADA; Jewish literary bi-annual; stories, poetry, midrash. 1981. s-a. $10. 2020 Essex St., Berkeley, CA 94703. TEL 415-848-0965 Ed. Reuven Goldfarb. bk. rev. circ. 500.

296 200 FR ISSN 0002-6050
ALLIANCE ISRAELITE UNIVERSELLE EN FRANCE. CAHIERS; paix et droit. 1947. 2/yr. free to qualified personnel. Alliance Israelite Universelle, c/o Professeur R. Bordet, 7 av. du General de Gaulle, 94704 Maisons Alfort, France. Eds. Jacques Levy, Colette Barr. bibl. circ. 5,000.

296 US ISSN 0065-6798
AMERICAN ACADEMY FOR JEWISH RESEARCH. PROCEEDINGS OF THE A A J R. 1929. a. $20. American Academy for Jewish Research, 3080 Broadway, New York, NY 10027. TEL 212-678-8864 Ed. Isaac E. Barzilay. circ. 400.

296 US ISSN 0741-465X
AMERICAN COUNCIL FOR JUDAISM. ISSUES. 1958. q. free. American Council for Judaism, 298 Fifth Ave., New York, NY 10001. TEL 212-947-8878 Ed. Marcia Friedman. bk. rev. circ. 8,000.
Formerly (until 1979): Brief (ISSN 0006-9922)

296 US ISSN 0740-8528
AMERICAN COUNCIL FOR JUDAISM. SPECIAL INTEREST REPORT; a digest of news items and articles in the area of the council's interest. 1968. m. American Council for Judaism, 298 Fifth Ave., New York, NY 10001. TEL 212-947-8878 Ed. Marcia Friedman. circ. 8,000. (back issues avail.)

AMERICAN JEWISH ARCHIVES; devoted to the preservation and study of the American Jewish experience. see *ETHNIC INTERESTS*

AMERICAN JEWISH CONGRESS. CONGRESS MONTHLY; a journal of opinion and Jewish affairs. see *ETHNIC INTERESTS*

AMERICAN JEWISH CONGRESS. NEWS. see *ETHNIC INTERESTS*

AMERICAN JEWISH WORLD. see *ETHNIC INTERESTS*

296 US ISSN 0065-8987
AMERICAN JEWISH YEAR BOOK. 1899. a. $25.95. (American Jewish Committee) Jewish Publication Society, 1930 Chestnut, Philadelphia, PA 19103 TEL 215-564-5925 Eds. David Singer, Milton Himmelfarb. index. circ. 5,000. Indexed: Amer.Bibl.Slavic & E.Eur.Stud.

267 US
AMERICAN MESSIANIC JEW. 1915. q. $5. Messianic Jewish Alliance of America, Box 1055, Havertown, PA 19083. Ed. Ruth Fleischer Snow. adv. bk. rev. bibl.
Former titles: American Messianic Jewish Quarterly & American Hebrew Christian.

AMERICAN SEPHARDI. see *ETHNIC INTERESTS*

296 NE ISSN 0066-5681
ARBEITEN ZUR GESCHICHTE DES ANTIKEN JUDENTUMS UND DES URCHRISTENTUMS. 1961. irreg., no.15, 1978. price varies. (Institutum Iudaicum, Tuebingen, GW) E. J. Brill, P.O. Box 9000, 2300 PA Leiden, Netherlands.

296 NE
ARBEITEN ZUR LITERATUR UND GESCHICHTE DES HELLENISTISCHEN JUDENTUMS. (Text in German) irreg., vol.19, 1986. price varies. E. J. Brill, P.O. Box 9000, 2300 PA Leiden, Netherlands.

ARBEITSINFORMATIONEN UEBER STUDIENPROJEKTE AUF DEM GEBIET DER GESCHICHTE DES DEUTSCHEN JUDENTUMS UND DES ANTISEMITISMUS. see *HISTORY — History Of Europe*

296 FR ISSN 0518-2840
ARCHE. 1957. m. 80 F. 14 rue Georges Berger, 75017 Paris, France. adv.

296 FR ISSN 0003-9837
ARCHIVES JUIVES. 1965. q. 65 F. Commission Francaise des Archives Juives, 87 rue Vieille du Temple, 75003 Paris, France. Ed. Bernhard Blumenkranz. bibl. index; cum.index (1965-1974; 1975-1979) circ. 650. Indexed: Bull.Signal. Numis.Lit.
History

296 IS
ASPAKLARIA/PERSPECTIVE. (Text in English and Hebrew) 1982. q. $3 per no. Institute for Science and Halacha, 1 Hapisga St., Jerusalem, Israel. Ed.Bd. adv. bk. rev. Indexed: Ind.Heb.Per.

AUSTRALIAN JEWISH NEWS. see *ETHNIC INTERESTS*

296 US ISSN 0067-2742
B.G. RUDOLPH LECTURES IN JUDAIC STUDIES. 1963. a. free. Syracuse University, Department of Religion, Jewish Studies Program, Syracuse, NY 13244-1170. TEL 315-423-3861 Ed. Alan L. Berger. circ. 7,500.

296 300 IS ISSN 0067-4109
BAR-ILAN: ANNUAL OF BAR-ILAN UNIVERSITY. (Text in Hebrew; summaries in English) 1963. a. $20. Bar-Ilan University, Ramat-Gan, Israel. Ed.Bd. Indexed: Ind.Heb.Per.

BATFUTZOT. see *ETHNIC INTERESTS*

296 IS
BEER-SHEVA. (Text in Hebrew; summaries in English) 1973. a. Ben-Gurion University of the Negev, Box 2053, Beersheva, Israel. Ed.Bd. illus.

BITZARON: A QUARTERLY OF HEBREW LETTERS. see *LITERARY AND POLITICAL REVIEWS*

296.68 US
B'KITZUR/BRIEFS. vol.3, 1973. irreg., 2-3/yr. free. (Solomon Schechter Day School Association) United Synagogue of America, Commission on Jewish Education, 155 5th Ave., New York, NY 10010. TEL 212-260-8450 Ed. Meir Efrati. bk. rev. stat. circ. 2,000.

296 US ISSN 0007-2435
BROTHERHOOD. 1967. q. $1. National Federation of Temple Brotherhoods, 838 Fifth Ave., New York, NY 10021. TEL 212-570-0707 Ed. Av Bondarin. adv. bk. rev. charts. illus. circ. 75,000 (controlled)

C M J S CENTERPIECES. (Center for Modern Jewish Studies) see *ETHNIC INTERESTS*

CANADIAN JEWISH ARCHIVES (NEW SERIES) see *ETHNIC INTERESTS*

CANADIAN JEWISH NEWS. see *ETHNIC INTERESTS*

CENTRAL CALIFORNIA JEWISH HERITAGE. see *ETHNIC INTERESTS*

296 US ISSN 0069-1607
CENTRAL CONFERENCE OF AMERICAN RABBIS. YEARBOOK. 1890. a. $17.50. ‡ (Central Conference of American Rabbis) C C A R Press, 21 E. 40th St., 14th Fl., New York, NY 10016. TEL 212-684-4990 Ed. Elliot L. Stevens. cum.index: 1951-1970. circ. 1,500. Indexed: Rel.Ind.Two.

296 FR ISSN 0763-062X
CLUB DES HEBRAISANTS. (Text in French and Hebrew) 1984. q. 50 F.($7) Association pour la Lecture de la Bible Hebraique, 39 Grande rue, 94130 Nogent sur Marne, France. bk. rev. (back issues avail.)

296 US
COALITION--THE TORAH ACTION JOURNAL. (Text in English, Yiddish) 1985. 5/yr. free. Agudath Israel of America, 5 Beckman St., Rm. 910, New York, NY 10039. TEL 212-791-1800 Ed. Y. Brandriss. circ. 50,000. (tabloid format; back issues avail)

296 SP
COLECCION SENDA ABIERTA. SERIE 2 (AZUL): JUDAISMO. 1974. irreg. 150 ptas. (Centro de Estudios Judeo-Cristianos) Studium Ediciones, Bailen 19, Madrid 13, Spain.

COLLECTION FRANCO-JUDAICA. see *ETHNIC INTERESTS*

296 NE
COMPENDIA RERUM IUDAICARUM AD NOVUM TESTAMENTUM. sect.1, no.2, 1976. irreg. price varies. Van Gorcum, Box 43, 9400 AA Assen, Netherlands.

CONFERENCE OF PRESIDENTS OF MAJOR AMERICAN JEWISH ORGANIZATIONS. ANNUAL REPORT. see *ETHNIC INTERESTS*

296 AG
CONGRESO JUDIO LATINOAMERICANO. BOLETIN INFORMATIVO OJI. 1970. fortn. free. ‡ Congreso Judio Latinoamericano - World Jewish Congress, Larrea 744, 1030 Buenos Aires, Argentina. Ed. Pedro J. Olschansky. adv. bk. rev. circ. 5,000.

296 US ISSN 0010-6542
CONSERVATIVE JUDAISM. 1945. q. $20. Rabbinical Assembly, 3080 Broadway, New York, NY 10027. TEL 212-678-8863 (Co-sponsor: Jewish Theological Seminary of America) Ed. David Wolf Silverman. adv. bk. rev. cum.index: 1955-1963, 1963-1976. circ. 2,000. Indexed: Amer.Bibl.Slavic & E.Eur.Stud. Ind.Jew.Per. Rel.& Theol.Abstr.

CONTEMPORARY JEWRY; a journal of sociological inquiry. see *ETHNIC INTERESTS*

DAVKE; revista Israelita. see *ETHNIC INTERESTS*

DETROIT JEWISH NEWS LTD. PARTNERSHIP. see *ETHNIC INTERESTS*

DISPERSION Y UNIDAD. see *HISTORY — History Of The Near East*

296 IS ISSN 0303-7819
ENCYCLOPAEDIA JUDAICA YEAR BOOK. (Text in English) 1973. a. Keter Publishing House Ltd., Givat Shaul Industrial Area, Box 7145, Jerusalem, Israel (U.S. orders to: Keter Inc., 440 Park Ave. South, New York, NY 10016)

296 NE
ETUDES SUR LE JUDAISME MEDIEVAL. 1968. irreg., vol.12, 1985. price varies. E. J. Brill, P.O. Box 9000, 2300 PA Leiden, Netherlands. Ed. G. Vajda.

296 UK ISSN 0014-3006
EUROPEAN JUDAISM. 1966. s-a. $9. Foundation for European Judaism, Kent House, Rutland Gardens, London S.W.7, England. Ed. Albert Friedlander. bk. rev. cum.index. circ. 1,000. Indexed: Ind.Jew.Per.

FOCUS: NORTH AMERICAN STUDENT ZIONIST FORUM. see *POLITICAL SCIENCE — International Relations*

FORUM; a quarterly on the Jewish people, Zionism and Israel. see *LITERARY AND POLITICAL REVIEWS*

296 US
FOUR WORLDS JOURNAL. 1983. q. $18. (Four Worlds Institute) Four Worlds Press, Box 540, East Meadow, NY 11554. TEL 212-496-4275 Ed. Edward Hoffman. bk. rev. circ. 500.

DIE GEMEINDE. see *ETHNIC INTERESTS*

GESHER; quarterly review of Jewish affairs. see *ETHNIC INTERESTS*

296 US ISSN 0016-9145
GESHER. (Text in English and Hebrew) a. $5. (Yeshiva University, Student Organization of Yeshiva) Rabbi Isaac Elchanan Theological Seminary, 500 W. 185th St., New York, NY 10033. TEL 212-960-5277 Ed.Bd.

HABINJAN; de opbouw. see *ETHNIC INTERESTS*

296 IS ISSN 0017-6508
HADASHOT ME HA-CHAIM HA-DATIYIM BE ISRAEL. 1961. bi-m. $2. Hechal Shlomo, Box 7440, Jerusalem, Israel. Ed. Rabbi Aaron Pechenick. bk. rev. circ. 3,000. (looseleaf format)

296 US ISSN 0017-6532
HADOROM. (Text in Hebrew; contents page in English) 1957. a. $10. Rabbinical Council of America, 275 Seventh Ave., New York, NY 10001. Ed. Rabbi Gdalia Schwartz. bk. rev. circ. 1,300.

HA-MESIVTA. see *LAW*

HAMEVASER. see *COLLEGE AND ALUMNI*

HARVARD JUDAIC MONOGRAPHS. see *ETHNIC INTERESTS*

HEBREW STUDIES; a journal devoted to the Hebrew language, the Bible and related areas of scholarship. see *LINGUISTICS*

296 US
HEBREW UNION COLLEGE. JEWISH INSTITUTE OF RELIGION. CHRONICLE. 1972. q. free. Hebrew Union College, Jewish Institute of Religion, 1 W. 4th St., New York, NY 10012. TEL 212-674-5300 Ed. Barbara Wachtel. bk. rev. bibl. illus. circ. 30,000.
Formerly (until 1977): Hebrew Union College. Jewish Institute of Religion. Reporter.

HEBREW UNION COLLEGE ANNUAL. see *ETHNIC INTERESTS*

HEBREW UNION COLLEGE ANNUAL SUPPLEMENTS. see *ETHNIC INTERESTS*

HILLEL GATE. see *ETHNIC INTERESTS*

HOLY LAND; illustrated quarterly of the Franciscan custody of the holy land. see *RELIGIONS AND THEOLOGY — Roman Catholic*

296 US ISSN 0441-4195
HUMANISTIC JUDAISM. 1967. q. $15. Society for Humanistic Judaism, 28611 W. 12 Mile Rd., Farmington Hills, MI 48018. TEL 313-478-7610 Eds. M. Bonnie Cousens, Ruth Duskin Feldman. bk. rev. circ. 2,500. Indexed: Ind.Jew.Per.

IDISZE SZRIFTN/JEWISH CULTURAL AFFAIRS. see *LITERARY AND POLITICAL REVIEWS*

IGERET. see *ETHNIC INTERESTS*

INFORMATION JUIVE; le journal des communautes. see *ETHNIC INTERESTS*

296 US
INTERCOM (NEW YORK, 1960?) (Text mainly in English; occasionally in Hebrew) vol.14, 1973. s-a. avail. to members and libraries/educational institutions. Association of Orthodox Jewish Scientists, 1373 Coney Island Ave., New York, NY 11230. Ed. Dr. Reuben Rudman. bk. rev. circ. 1,400. (also avail. in microform from MIM)

INTERMOUNTAIN JEWISH NEWS. see *ETHNIC INTERESTS*

ISRAEL BOOK NEWS. see *PUBLISHING AND BOOK TRADE*

ISRAEL REPORT. see *ETHNIC INTERESTS*

J T A COMMUNITY NEWS REPORTER. (Jewish Telegraphic Agency) see *POLITICAL SCIENCE*

J T A DAILY NEWS BULLETIN. see *ETHNIC INTERESTS*

296 US ISSN 0021-3780
J W B CIRCLE. 1946. 7/yr. $3. National Jewish Welfare Board, 15 E. 26th St., New York, NY 10010. TEL 212-532-4949 Ed. Lionel Koppman. bk. rev. circ. 15,000. (tabloid format)

JEVREJSKI PREGLED. see *ETHNIC INTERESTS*

JEWISH AFFAIRS. see *POLITICAL SCIENCE*

296 US ISSN 0075-3726
JEWISH BOOK ANNUAL. (Text in English, Hebrew and Yiddish) 1942. a. $25. J W B Jewish Book Coucil of America, 15 E. 26th St., New York, NY 10010. TEL 212-532-4949 Ed. Jacob Kabakoff. bk. rev. circ. 1,200. Indexed: Ind.Heb.Per. Amer.Bibl.Slavic & E.Eur.Stud.

JEWISH BRAILLE REVIEW. see *BLIND*

JEWISH CHRONICLE (NEW YORK) see *LITERARY AND POLITICAL REVIEWS*

JEWISH CIVIC PRESS. see *ETHNIC INTERESTS*

JEWISH CURRENT EVENTS. see *ETHNIC INTERESTS*

JEWISH EDUCATION. see *EDUCATION*

296 US
JEWISH GUARDIAN. 1974. bi-m. $4.50. Neturei Karta of U.S.A.-Guardians of the Holy City, P.O. 2143, Brooklyn, New York, NY 11202. Ed. Mordecai Weberman. adv. bk. rev. illus. circ. 10,000.

909 UK ISSN 0306-7998
JEWISH HISTORICAL SOCIETY OF ENGLAND. ANNUAL REPORT AND ACCOUNTS FOR THE SESSION. 1890. a. membership. Jewish Historical Society of England, Mocatta Library & Museum, University College, 33 Seymour Place, London W1H 5AP, England.
Continues: Jewish Historical Society of England. Report and Balance Sheet.

296 UK
JEWISH HISTORICAL SOCIETY OF ENGLAND. TRANSACTIONS. biennial. membership. Jewish Historical Society of England, Mocatta Library & Museum, University College, 33 Seymour Place, London W1H 5AP, England.

JEWISH JOURNAL OF SOCIOLOGY. see *SOCIOLOGY*

JEWISH LANGUAGE REVIEW. see *LINGUISTICS*

296 NE
JEWISH LAW ANNUAL. 1978. a. price varies. E.J. Brill, P.O. Box 9000, 2300 PA Leiden, Netherlands. Ed. Bernard S. Jackson. Indexed: Old Test.Abstr.

JEWISH PRESS (BROOKLYN) see *ETHNIC INTERESTS*

JEWISH PRESS FEATURES. see *JOURNALISM*

296 US
JEWISH PROCLAIMER. 1981. irreg. $15 donation. National Center for Understanding Judaism, Box 651, Woodmoor Station, Silver Spring, MD 20901. Ed. Ash Gerecht. circ. 6,000.

296 US ISSN 0021-6682
JEWISH QUARTERLY REVIEW. 1909. q. $25 to individuals; institutions $35. Annenberg Research Institute, 250 N. Highland Ave., Merion Sta, PA 19066. Ed.Bd. adv. bk. rev. bibl. illus. index. circ. 1,000. (also avail. in microfilm from UMI; reprint service avail. from UMI) Indexed: Curr.Cont. Hist.Abstr. M.L.A. Old Test.Abstr. Rel.Per. Arts & Hum.Cit.Ind. Amer.Hist.& Life. Ind.Jew.Per. New Test.Abstr. Rel.& Theol.Abstr. Rel.Ind.One.

296 UK
JEWISH REVIEW (1983) 1946. 10/yr. £2.50($6) Mizrachi Federation of Great Britain and Ireland, 2B Golders Green Rd., London NW11 8LH, England. Ed. Arieh L. Handler. adv. bk. rev. abstr. film rev. illus. play rev. record rev. stat. circ. 5,000. (tabloid format)
Former titles (until 1983): Religious Zionist Movement Newsletter; (until 1976): Jewish Review (ISSN 0021-6690)

296 US
JEWISH SCIENCE INTERPRETER. 1922. 8/yr. $5. (Society of Jewish Science) Jewish Science Publishing Co., 88 Sunnyside Blvd., Ste. 206, Plainview, NY 11803-1507. TEL 516-349-0022 Ed. David Goldstein.

JEWISH SOCIAL STUDIES. see *SOCIAL SCIENCES: COMPREHENSIVE WORKS*

JEWISH STANDARD. see *ETHNIC INTERESTS*

JEWISH TELEGRAPH. see *ETHNIC INTERESTS*

296 SA
JEWISH TRADITION. (Text in English) 1954. m. R.10. Union of Horthodox Synagogues of South Africa, 24 Raleigh St., Yeoville, Johannesburg 2198, South Africa. Ed. Leslie Winnett. adv. bk. rev. charts. illus. circ. 14,000. (tabloid format)
Formerly: Federation of Synagogues of South Africa. Federation Chronicle (ISSN 0014-9314)

JEWISH TRANSCRIPT. see *ETHNIC INTERESTS*

296 US ISSN 0021-6828
JEWISH VOICE. 1931. fortn. $7.50. Jewish Federation of Delaware, 101 Garden of Eden Rd., Wilmington, DE 19803. TEL 302-478-6200 Ed. Karen Moss. adv. bk. rev. circ. 3,000. (tabloid format; also avail. in microfiche)

JEWISH WEEKLY NEWS. see *ETHNIC INTERESTS*

296 UK ISSN 0075-3769
JEWISH YEAR BOOK. 1896. a. £2($16.50) Jewish Chronicle Publications, 25 Furnival St, London EC4A 1JT, England. Ed. Roger Japhet. adv. bk. rev. circ. 5,000. (also avail. in microform)

296 US ISSN 0740-5901
JEWS FOR JESUS NEWSLETTER. 1973. m. Jews for Jesus, 60 Haight St., San Francisco, CA 94102-5895. TEL 415-864-2600 Ed. Ceil Rosen. bk. rev. illus. circ. 230,00.

JOEDISK ORIENTERING. see *ETHNIC INTERESTS*

296 NE
JOURNAL FOR THE STUDY OF JUDAISM IN THE PERSIAN, HELLENISTIC AND ROMAN PERIOD. 1970. 2/yr. fl.88. E. J. Brill, P.O. Box 9000, 2300 PA Leiden, Netherlands. Indexed: Old Test.Abstr. Rel.Per. New Test.Abstr. Rel.Ind.One. Rel.& Theol.Abstr.
Formerly: Journal for the Study of Judaism (ISSN 0047-2212)

JOURNAL OF JEWISH ART. see *ART*

JOURNAL OF JEWISH MUSIC AND LITURGY. see *MUSIC*

296 UK ISSN 0022-2097
JOURNAL OF JEWISH STUDIES. (Text in English; occasionally in French) 1948. s-a. £13($27.50) Oxford Centre for Postgraduate Hebrew Studies, Oriental Institute, Pusey Lane, Oxford 0X1 2LE, England. Ed. Dr. G. Vermes. adv. bk. rev. bibl. index. circ. 1,000. (also avail. in microform from UMI) Indexed: Br.Hum.Ind. Curr.Cont. Hist.Abstr. Old Test.Abstr. Rel.Per. Adol.Ment.Hlth.Abstr. Arts & Hum.Cit.Ind. Amer.Hist.& Life. Ind.Jew.Per. New Test.Abstr. Rel.Ind.One. Rel.& Theol.Abstr.

JOURNAL OF PSYCHOLOGY AND JUDAISM. see *PSYCHOLOGY*

296 US ISSN 0149-712X
JOURNAL OF REFORM JUDAISM. 1953. q. $12. ‡ (Central Conference of American Rabbis) C C A R Press, 21 E. 40th St., 14th Fl., New York, NY 10016. TEL 212-684-4990 Ed. Samuel M. Stahl. adv. bk. rev. cum.index (25 yrs.) circ. 2,200. (also avail. in microform from UMI; reprint service avail. from UMI) Indexed: Ind.Jew.Per. Ind.Artic.Jew.Stud. Rel.& Theol.Abstr.
Formerly: C C A R Journal (ISSN 0007-7976)

296 297 410 UK ISSN 0022-4480
JOURNAL OF SEMITIC STUDIES. 1956. s-a. £30($45) (University of Manchester, Department of Near Eastern Studies) Oxford University Press, Walton St., Oxford OX2 6DP, England. Eds. C.E. Bosworth, M.G.J. Richardson. adv. bk. rev. bibl. index. circ. 750. (also avail. in microform from UMI; reprint service avail. from UMI) Indexed: Br.Hum.Ind. Curr.Cont. Hist.Abstr. M.L.A. Arts & Hum.Cit.Ind. Amer.Hist.& Life. Old Test.Abstr. Rel. Per. New Test.Abstr. Rel.Ind.One. Rel.& Theol.Abstr.

296 SZ ISSN 0022-572X
JUDAICA; Beitraege zum Verstaendnis des juedischen Schicksals in Vergangenheit und Gegenwart. 1945. q. 27 Fr.($13) (Stiftung fuer Kirche und Judentum) Judaica Verlag, Etzelstr. 19, CH-8038 Zurich, Switzerland. Eds. Kurt Hruby, Martin Cunz. adv. bk. rev. circ. 600. Indexed: Hist.Abstr. Old Test.Abstr. Amer.Hist.& Life. CERDIC.

JUDAICA BOOK NEWS. see *PUBLISHING AND BOOK TRADE*

296 US ISSN 0022-5762
JUDAISM; a quarterly journal of Jewish life and thought. 1952. q. $12. American Jewish Congress, 15 E. 84th St., New York, NY 10028. TEL 212-879-4500 Ed. Robert Gordis. adv. bk. rev. index. cum.index (20 yr.) circ. 5,000. (also avail. in microform from UMI; reprint service avail. from UMI) Indexed: Curr.Cont. Rel.Per. SSCI. Arts & Hum.Cit.Ind. Amer.Bibl.Slavic & E.Eur.Stud. CERDIC. G.Soc.Sci.& Rel.Per.Lit. New Test.Abstr. Rel.Ind.One. Rel.& Theol.Abstr.

KADIMA. see *LITERARY AND POLITICAL REVIEWS*

296.68 US
KASHRUS; magazine for the kosher consumer. 1980. bi-m. $10. Yeshiva Birkas Reuven, Box 96, Brooklyn, NY 11204. Ed. Rabbi Yosef Wikler. circ. 7,000.
Formerly: Kashrus Newsletter.

296 SA
KASHRUT GUIDE. 1977. free. Union of Horthodox Synagogues of South Africa, 24 Raleigh St., Yeoville, Johannesburg 2198, South Africa. circ. controlled.

296 US ISSN 0022-9636
KEEPING POSTED. 1955. m. (Oct.-Apr.) $6.25 (teachers edition $15.25) ‡ Union of American Hebrew Congregations, 838 Fifth Ave., New York, NY 10021. TEL 212-249-0100 Ed. Aron Hirt-Manheimer. illus. circ. 10,000. Indexed: Ind.Jew.Per.

296 US ISSN 0022-9644
KEEPING POSTED WITH N C S Y. (Reporter and Leadership Editions) 1959. q. $6. (Union of Orthodox Jewish Congregations of America) National Conference of Synagogue Youth, 70 W. 36th St., 9th Fl., New York, NY 10018-8002. Ed. Renee Straussad. adv. bk. rev. circ. 20,000.

296 US
KEREM SHLOMO. (Text in Hebrew) 1977. irreg., 10-12/yr. $15. Bobover Congregation, 1577 48th St., Brooklyn, NY 11219. TEL 718-438-2018 Ed. Shmerel Zitronenbaum. bibl. index. circ. 2,500. (back issues avail.)

KIRYAT SEFER; bibliographical quarterly. see *BIBLIOGRAPHIES*

296 AT
KIVUN. 1973. q. Aus.$5. Australasian Union of Jewish Students, 1584 St. Kilda Rd, Melbourne, Vic. 3004, Australia. Eds. Ilana Nayman, Leon Bach. adv. bk. rev. circ. 1,500.
Formerly: Massada Quarterly (ISSN 0310-0138)

KOL HA-T'NUAH/VOICE OF THE MOVEMENT. see *ETHNIC INTERESTS*

296 US
KOL YAVNEH. 1960. q. membership. ‡ Yavneh, 66-05 108 St., Forest Hills, NY 11375. Ed. Mory Korenblit. adv. bk. rev. circ. 20,000. (tabloid format)
Former titles: Authentic Voice & Jewish Collegiate Observer (ISSN 0021-6356)

296 327 028.5 UK
KOLEINU. (Text mainly in English; occasionally in Hebrew) 1980. bi-m. membership. Habonim-Dror Organization, 523 Finchley Rd., London NW3 7BD, England. (Co-sponsor: World Zionist Organisation. Youth and Hechalutz Department) Ed. Kevin Feddy. adv. film rev. circ. 300. (back issues avail.)

296 US
KOLENU. 1972. 2/yr. free. Cornell University, Student Finance Commission, G34 Anabel Taylor Hall, Ithaca, NY 14853. TEL 607-255-4227 Ed. June D. Bell. film rev. play rev. circ. 1,500. (back issues avail.)
Jewish commentary, Jewish campus news, Jewish art and poetry

KOSHER DIRECTORY. see *ETHNIC INTERESTS*

LAMISHPAHA. see *LINGUISTICS*

296 UK ISSN 0075-8744
LEO BAECK INSTITUTE. YEAR BOOK. 1956. a. £12. Secker & Warburg, 54 Poland St., London W1V 3DF, England (Dist. in U.S. by: Leo Baeck Institute, 129 E. 73rd St., New York, NY 10021) Ed. Arnold Paucker. bk. rev. index, cum.index: vols.1-20, pub. in 1982. circ. 2,500. Indexed: Hist.Abstr. Amer.Hist.& Life. Amer.Bibl.Slavic & E.Eur.Stud.

296 US
LIBRARY OF JEWISH LAW AND ETHICS. irreg., vol.4, 1977. price varies. Ktav Publishing House, 900 Jefferson St., No. 6249, Hoboken, NJ 07030-7205. TEL 201-963-9524

LONG ISLAND JEWISH WORLD. see *ETHNIC INTERESTS*

LUZ; la revista israelita para toda sudamerica. see *LITERARY AND POLITICAL REVIEWS*

MABUEY HANCHAL. see *ETHNIC INTERESTS*

296.68 US
MACHBERET HAMENAHEL. 1975. m. $6. National Conference of Yeshiva Principals, 160 Broadway, New York, NY 10038. TEL 212-406-4190 Ed. Rabbi Chaim Feuerman. bk. rev. circ. 900. (looseleaf format; back issues avail.)

MENORAH. see *ETHNIC INTERESTS*

296 UY
MENSAJE. vol. 4, 1978. bi-m. Comite Central Israelita del Uruguay, Rio Negro 1308, Montevideo, Uruguay. Ed. Jorge Sztarcevsky. Indexed: Biol.Abstr.

296 282 IS
MISHKAN; a theological forum on Jewish evangelism. 1984. s-a. $10. United Christian Council in Israel, P.O. Box 116, Jerusalem 91000, Israel. Ed. Ole Chr. M. Kvarme. adv. bk. rev. circ. 800.

296 IS ISSN 0541-5632
MITZION TETZEH TORAH. M.T.T. 1968. irreg., (approx. 2/yr.) price varies. Mitzion Tetzeh Torah, Ltd., Box 29435, 9 Derech Haifa Rd., Tel-Aviv, Israel. Ed. G. Rachaman. adv. bk. rev. circ. 1,000.

200 320 AG
MUNDO ISRAELITA; actualidad de la semana en Israel y en el mundo judio. 1923. w. Arg.$15($25) Editorial Mundo Israelita, Lavalle 2615, Buenos Aires, Argentina. Ed. Iftach Treguermansch. adv. bk. rev. illus.

MUSICA JUDAICA. see *MUSIC*

296 US
N A T A. JOURNAL. s-a. National Association of Temple Administrators, 838 Fifth Ave., New York, NY 10021. TEL 212-249-0100 Ed. Robert Mills. bk. rev. circ. 2,500.

296 US ISSN 0300-6689
N A T E NEWS. vol.20, 1977. 3/yr. membership. National Association of Temple Educators, 838 Fifth Ave., New York, NY 10021. Ed. Rabbi Jeffrey B. Lazar. adv. bk. rev. circ. 2,100.

N C J W JOURNAL. (National Council of Jewish Women) see *ETHNIC INTERESTS*

296 US
NEW TRADITIONS. 1984. 4/yr. $18. National Havurah Committee, 270 W. 89th St., New York, NY 10024. Ed. William Novak. circ. 1,000.

296 NE ISSN 0028-9833
NIEUW GELUID. 1952. m. fl.25($10) Bond Nederlands Israel, Box 45, 3640 AA Mijdrecht, Netherlands. Ed. G. van der Laan. bk. rev. index. circ. 1,200.

296 IS ISSN 0048-0460
NIV HAMIDRASHIA. (Text in English and Hebrew) 1963. irreg. $7 per no. Friends of the Midrashia, Israel, 3, Achuzath Bayeth St., Tel Aviv, Israel. Eds. Israel Sadan, Alexander Carlebach. adv. bk. rev. circ. 5,000. Indexed: Ind.Heb.Per.

NOTRE VOIX. see *POLITICAL SCIENCE*

296 FR ISSN 0029-4705
A I U LES NOUVEAUX CAHIERS. 1965. q. 140 F. Alliance Israelite Universelle en France, 45 rue la Bruyere, 75009 Paris, France. Ed. Colette Baer. adv. bk. rev. bibl. circ. 2,500.
Jewish history, philosophy, sociology and literature

296 US ISSN 0030-2139
OLOMEINU/OUR WORLD. (Text in English, Hebrew) 1945. m. (8/yr.) $7. National Society for Hebrew Day Schools, 160 Broadway, New York, NY 10038. TEL 212-227-1000 Eds. Rabbi Yaakov Fruchter, Rabbi Nosson Scherman. illus. circ. 16,000.
Ages 8-14

296 US ISSN 0362-2770
OPTIONS; the Jewish resources newsletter. 1974. m. $15. Options Publishing Co., Box 311, Wayne, NJ 07470. TEL 201-694-2327 Ed. Betty J. Singer. bk. rev. index. (back issues avail.)

296 IS ISSN 0333-9270
ORAITA; torah publication for Jewish thought and Halacha. (Text in Hebrew) 1977. s-a. IS.180($6) Kollel Tifereth Netanya "Yad Moshe", Box 245, Netanya 42102, Israel. Ed. Rabbi Amihud Levine. adv. bk. rev. circ. 2,000. (back issues avail.)

OUTLOOK. see *ETHNIC INTERESTS*

296 900 FR
PARDES. (Text in French; summaries in English) 1985. s-a. 160 Fr. Editions Lattes, 17 rue Jacob, 75006 Paris, France. Eds. Shmuel Trigano, Annie Kriegel. adv. bk. rev. circ. 2,000. (back issues avail.)

296 809 US ISSN 0272-9601
PROOFTEXTS; a journal of Jewish literary history. 1981. 3/yr. $32 to individuals; institutions $29.50. Johns Hopkins University Press, Journals Publishing Division, 701 W. 40th St., Ste. 275, Baltimore, MD 21211 TEL 301-338-6987 (Order to: Allen Press, Inc., 1041 New Hampshire St., Box 368, Lawrence, KS 66044) Eds. Alan Mintz, David G. Roskies. adv. circ. 1,500. (also avail. in microform from UMI; back issues avail.; reprint service avail. from UMI) Indexed: Curr.Cont. M.L.A. Old Test.Abstr. Arts & Hum.Cit.Ind. Amer.Bibl.Slavic & E.Eur.Stud. Ind.Jew.Per. Rel.& Theol.Abstr. Rel.Ind.One.

296 UK
R S G B INFORM NEWSLETTER. 1973. q. £1.50. Reform Synagogues of Great Britain, Manor House, 80 East End Rd., Finchley, London N3 2SY, England. Ed.Bd. illus. circ. 16,000.

296 US ISSN 0079-936X
RABBINICAL ASSEMBLY, NEW YORK. PROCEEDINGS. (Text in English with some Hebrew and Yiddish) 1927. a. (suspended 1970-1973) $7.50. Rabbinical Assembly, 3080 Broadway, New York, NY 10027. TEL 212-678-8060 Ed. Jules Harlow. cum.index: 1927-1968. circ. 1,400.

296 IT ISSN 0033-9792
RASSEGNA MENSILE DI ISRAEL. (Text in English, French, Italian) 1924. m. L.30000($65) Unione delle Comunita Israelitiche Italiane, Lungotevere Sanzio 9, Rome, Italy. Dir. Guido Fubini. bk. rev. charts. illus. index. circ. 1,000.

200 NE ISSN 0034-1487
RECONSTRUCTION. 1947. m. fl.20. Portugees-Israelietische Gemeente - Spanish and Portuguese Jewish Community at Amsterdam, c/o Dr. J. Z. Baruch, Ed., Gerrit van der Veenstr. 141, 1077 DX Amsterdam, Netherlands. bk. rev. circ. 13,000.

296 US ISSN 0034-1495
RECONSTRUCTIONIST. 1935. 8/yr. $20. Federation of Reconstructionist Congregations and Havurot, 270 W. 89th St., New York, NY 10024. Ed. Dr. Jacob J. Staub. adv. bk. rev. index. circ. 8,500. (also avail. in microform from UMI; reprint service avail. from UMI) Indexed: Ind.Jew.Per.

296 US ISSN 0482-0819
REFORM JUDAISM. 1972. 4/yr. $10 to individuals; students $5. Union of American Hebrew Congregations, 838 Fifth Ave., New York, NY 10021. TEL 212-249-0100 Ed. Aron Hirt-Manheimer. bk. rev. charts. illus. circ. 280,000.

REVISTA CULTULUI MOZAIC. see *LITERATURE*

REVUE DES ETUDES JUIVES. see *ETHNIC INTERESTS*

ROCKY MOUNTAIN JEWISH HISTORICAL NOTES. see *ETHNIC INTERESTS*

S C A REPORT. (Synagogue Council of America) see *ETHNIC INTERESTS*

266 US
SABBATH SENTINEL. 1945. m. $10. Bible Sabbath Association, R.R. 1, Box 222, Fairview, OK 73737. TEL 405-227-3200 Ed. Richard Wiedenheft. adv. bk. rev. bibl. illus. circ. 2,000. (back issues avail.)

SAN DIEGO JEWISH PRESS HERITAGE. see *ETHNIC INTERESTS*

SEMITIC STUDY SERIES. see *ORIENTAL STUDIES*

SHALOM. see *ETHNIC INTERESTS*

200 UK
SHALOM. 1962. 3/yr. £2.50. Church's Ministry Among the Jews, 30C Clarence Rd., St. Albans, Herts AL1 4JJ, England. Ed. B.F. Adeney. bk. rev. illus. circ. 5,300.
Former titles: C.M.J. Quarterly (ISSN 0007-8646); C.M.J. News.

377.9 US ISSN 0037-3656
SHEVILEY HAHINUCH. (Text in Hebrew) 1940. q. $10. (Council for Jewish Education) J.E.S.N.A., 730 Broadway, 2nd Fl., New York, NY 10003-9502. Ed. Mathew Musenkis. adv. bk. rev. circ. 1,200.

SHIRIM; a Jewish poetry journal. see *LITERATURE — Poetry*

370 200 US ISSN 0300-7960
SHMUESSEN MIT KINDER UN YUGENT. (Text in Yiddish) 1942. m. $3. Merkos L'Inyonei Chinuch, Inc., 770 Eastern Parkway, Brooklyn, NY 11213. Ed. Nissan Mindel. illus. index.

SHVUT; Jewish problems in the USSR and Eastern Europe. see *ETHNIC INTERESTS*

296 IS
SINAI. (Text in Hebrew) 1937. bi-m. $15. Rabbi Kook Foundation, P.O. Box 642, Jerusalem, Israel. Ed. Yitzchak Raphael. bk. rev. circ. 1,500. (back issues avail.) Indexed: Ind.Heb.Per.

SIONISTE. see *POLITICAL SCIENCE*

296 US ISSN 0196-2183
SOLOMON GOLDMAN LECTURES; perspectives in Jewish learning. 1977. irreg. $5 paperback; $7 hardback. Spertus College of Judaica Press, 618 S. Michigan Avenue, Chicago, IL 60605. TEL 312-922-9012 Ed. N. Stampfer. circ. 500.
Supersedes: Perspectives in Jewish Learning (ISSN 0079-1016)

SOURCES OF CONTEMPORARY JEWISH THOUGHT/MEKEVOT. see *LITERARY AND POLITICAL REVIEWS*

SOUTHWEST JEWISH CHRONICLE. see *ETHNIC INTERESTS*

SOVIET JEWISH AFFAIRS; a journal on Jewish problems in the USSR and Eastern Europe. see *POLITICAL SCIENCE*

296 IT
STORIA DELL'EBRAISMO IN ITALIA. 1980. irreg., vol.6, 1985. price varies. Casa Editrice Leo S. Olschki, Casella Postale 66, 50100 Florence, Italy.

296 NE ISSN 0081-6914
STUDIA SEMITICA NEERLANDICA. 1956. irreg., no. 17, 1975. price varies. Van Gorcum, Box 43, 9400 AA Assen, Netherlands.

296 US ISSN 0081-7511
STUDIES IN AMERICAN JEWISH HISTORY. 1951. irreg., 1968, no.5. price varies. ‡ American Jewish Historical Society, 2 Thornton Rd., Waltham, MA 02154. TEL 617-891-8110 index. circ. 1,000.

296.68 IS ISSN 0333-9661
STUDIES IN JEWISH EDUCATION. 1983. a. Hebrew University, Samuel Mendel Melton Centre for Jewish Education in Jerusalem, Mount Scopus, Jerusalem 91 905, Israel. circ. 1,000.

296 US ISSN 0884-6952
STUDIES IN JUDAICA & THE HOLOCAUST. 1985. irreg., latest no. 3. $19.95 cloth; 9.95 paper. Borgo Press, Box 2845, San Bernardino, CA 92406. TEL 714-884-5813

296 NE
STUDIES IN JUDAISM IN LATE ANTIQUITY. 1973. irreg., vol.37, 1984. price varies. E. J. Brill, P.O. Box 9000, 2300 PA Leiden, Netherlands.

296 NE
STUDIES IN JUDAISM IN MODERN TIMES. 1978. irreg., vol.7, 1986. price varies. E. J. Brill, P.O. Box 9000, 2300 PA Leiden, Netherlands. Ed. J. Neusner.

296 US ISSN 0334-1771
STUDIES IN ZIONISM; an international journal of social, political and intellectual history. (Text in English) 1980. s-a. $30. (Tel Aviv University, Institute for Zionist Research) Johns Hopkins University Press, Journals Publishing Division, 701 W. 40th St., Ste. 275, Baltimore, MD 21211 (Order from: Allen Press, Inc., 1041 New Hampshire St., Box 368, Lawrence, KS 66044) Ed. Anita Shapiro. adv. circ. 300. (also avail. in microfiche; back issues avail.) Indexed: Ind.Jew.Per.
Supersedes (in 1982): Zionism; Studies in the History of the Zionist Movement and of the Jews in Palestine/Ha-Tsiyonut (ISSN 0084-5523)

296 NE
STUDIES ON THE TEXTS OF THE DESERT OF JUDAH. 1957. irreg., vol.8, 1975. price varies. E.J. Brill, P.O. Box 9000, 2300 PA Leiden, Netherlands. Ed. J. van der Ploeg.

SYRACUSE JEWISH OBSERVER. see *ETHNIC INTERESTS*

296 CN ISSN 0704-5905
TARGUMIC AND COGNATE STUDIES. NEWSLETTER. 1974. s-a. $5. University of Toronto, Department of Near Eastern Studies, Toronto, Ontario, M5S 1A1, Canada. Ed. E.G. Clark. circ. 200. (back issues avail.)

296 SA ISSN 0040-2966
TEMPLE DAVID BULLETIN. 1969. s-m. free. ‡ Durban Progressive Jewish Congregation, 369 Ridge Rd., Durban, South Africa. adv. bk. rev. circ. 535. (tabloid format)
Formerly: Temple David Review.

296 GW
TEXTE UND STUDIEN ZUM ANTIKEN JUDENTUM. English Edition: Texts and Studies in Medieval and Early Modern Judaism. (Text in English, French and German) 1981. irreg. price varies. Verlag J.C.B. Mohr (Paul Siebeck), Wilhelmstr. 18, Postfach 2040, 7400 Tuebingen, W. Germany (B.R.D.) Eds. Martin Hengel, Peter Schaefer.

296 NE ISSN 0082-3899
THEOKRATIA; JAHRBUCH DES INSTITUTUM JUDAICUM DELITZSCHIANUM. 1967-69. a. price varies. (Institutum Judaicum Delitzschianum) E. J. Brill, P.O. Box 9000, 2300 PA Leiden, Netherlands.

296 IS
TORAH EDUCATION. (Text in English) 1971. q. World Zionist Organization, Department for Torah Education and Culture in the Diaspora, Box 92, Jerusalem, Israel. Ed. Avner Tomaschoff. bk. rev. charts. illus. circ. 8,000.

TORCHLIGHT. see *CLUBS*

296 US ISSN 0041-0608
TRADITION (NEW YORK); a journal of orthodox Jewish thought. 1958. q. $23 to individuals; institutions $66. Rabbinical Council of America, 275 Seventh Ave., New York, NY 10001. TEL 212-243-6000 Ed. Rabbi Walter S. Wurzburger. bk. rev. abstr. circ. 4,000(approx.) (also avail. in microform from UMI) Indexed: Old Test.Abstr. Arts & Hum.Cit.Ind. Ind.Jew.Per. Rel.& Theol.Abstr. Rel.Ind.One.

296 GW ISSN 0041-2716
TRIBUENE; Zeitschrift zum Verstaendnis d. Judentums. 1962. q. DM.28($7.55) Tribuene-Verlag, Habsburger Allee 72, 6000 Frankfurt, W. Germany (B.R.D.) Ed. Axel Silenius. adv. bk. rev. stat. circ. 5,000. Indexed: Phil.Ind.

296 028.5 US
TZIVOS HASHEM CHILDREN'S NEWSLETTER. 1981. 5/yr. $3 to non-members. Tzivos Hashem, 770 Eastern Pkwy., Brooklyn, NY 11213. TEL 718-467-6630 Eds. Rabbi A. Kass, David S. Pare. circ. 130,000.

296 327 US ISSN 0888-3440
ULTIMATE ISSUES. 1985. q. $15. Dennis Prager, Ed. & Pub., 2265 Westwood Blvd., Ste. 312, Los Angeles, CA 90064. TEL 213-558-3958 bibl. tr.lit. circ. 3,000. (looseleaf format; back issues avail.)

296 US ISSN 0041-8153
UNITED SYNAGOGUE REVIEW. 1943. biennial. $3. United Synagogue of America, 155 Fifth Ave., New York, NY 10010. TEL 212-533-7800 Ed. Ruth M. Perry. adv. bk. rev. illus. circ. 250,000. (also avail. in microform from UMI)

296 338.91 391 IS
VOICE FROM JERUSALEM. 1981. q. membership. B'nai B'rith World Centre, B'nai B'rith International Israel Lodge, P.O.B. 7522, 91074 Jerusalem, Israel. Ed. Wolf S. Matsdorf. adv. bk. rev. circ. 7,000.

296 US
VOICE OF JUDAISM. 1960. irreg. free. National Jewish Information Service, 5174 W. 8th St., Los Angeles, CA 90036. TEL 213-936-6033 Ed. Rabbi Moshe M. Maggal.

296 CN
VOICE OF THE VAAD. 1961. q. Jewish Community Council of Montreal, Suite 117, 5491 Victoria Ave., Montreal, Que. H3W 2P9, Canada. TEL 514-739-6363 Ed. Rabbi I.L. Hechtman. adv. bk. rev. (tabloid format)

296 US ISSN 0887-011X
WELLSPRINGS. 1984. 6/yr. free. Lubavitch Youth Organization, Student Affairs Office, 770 Eastern Pkwy., Brooklyn, NY 11213. TEL 718-953-1000 Ed. Rabbi Yehuda David Pearson. bk. rev. tr.lit. circ. 13,000. (back issues avail.)

WESTERN STATES JEWISH HISTORY. see *ETHNIC INTERESTS*

WOMEN'S AMERICAN O R T REPORTER. see *SOCIAL SERVICES AND WELFARE*

296 US ISSN 0043-7557
WOMEN'S LEAGUE OUTLOOK. 1930. q. $8. Women's League for Conservative Judaism, 48 E. 74 St., New York, NY 10021. TEL 212-628-1600 Ed. Yvette Rosenberg. adv. bk. rev. circ. 142,500.

296 956.940 SA
WOMEN'S ZIONIST ORGANIZATION OF SOUTH AFRICA. NEWS AND VIEWS. 1949. 3/yr. membership. Women's Zionist Organization of South Africa, Zionist Centre, Box 18, Johannesburg 2000, South Africa. Ed. Hetty Schwartz. adv. bk. rev. charts. illus. play rev. circ. 12,500.
Formerly: Women's Zionist Council of South Africa. News and Views (ISSN 0043-7603)
Zionism

956.940 IS
WORD AND DEED. (Text in English) irreg. World Zionist Organization, Youth and Hechalutz Department, Box 92, Jerusalem, Israel.

WORKING PAPERS IN YIDDISH AND EAST EUROPEAN JEWISH STUDIES/IN GANG FUN ARBET: YIDISH UN MIZRAKH EYROPEISHE YIDISHE SHTUDIES. see *ETHNIC INTERESTS*

296 IS ISSN 0084-2516
WORLD ZIONIST ORGANIZATION. GENERAL COUNCIL. ADDRESSES, DEBATES, RESOLUTIONS. (Text in English) a. World Zionist Organization, Box 92, Jerusalem, Israel.

296 IS
YAD L'ACHIM WALL CALENDAR. (Text in English) 1970. bi-m. $15. Peylim-Yad l'Achim, 4 Yona St., P.O.B. 5195, Jerusalem, Israel. Ed.Bd. circ. 3,000. (back issues avail.)

296 IS
YAD VASHEM STUDIES. (Text in English and Hebrew) 1957. irreg., vol.14, 1981. price varies. Yad Vashem Martyr's and Heroes Remembrance Authority, Box 3477, Jerusalem, Israel. Ed. Livia Rothkirchen. bk. rev. index. cum.index: 1957-67. circ. 1,500.
Formerly (until 1976): Yad Vashem Studies on the European Jewish Catastrophe and Resistance (ISSN 0084-3296)

296 US ISSN 0084-3369
YALE JUDAICA SERIES. 1948. irreg., no.23, 1982. price varies. Yale University Press, 92A Yale Sta., New Haven, CT 06520. TEL 203-432-0940

296 US ISSN 0044-0256
YAVNEH STUDIES. 1967. irreg. membership. Yavneh, 66-05 108 St., Forest Hills, NY 11375. Ed.Bd. circ. 4,000. (processed)
Topics in Jewish philosophy intended for a college audience

YESHIVA UNIVERSITY SEPHARDIC BULLETIN. see *ETHNIC INTERESTS*

296 US ISSN 0044-040X
YID; voice of American Orthodox Jewry. (Text in Yiddish) 1951. w. $32. (National Committee of Orthodox Jewish Communities) Yid Publishing, 543 Bedford Ave., Brooklyn, NY 11211. Ed. Sender Deutsch. adv. bk. rev. circ. 30,000. (tabloid format)

YIDDISH LITERARY AND LINGUISTIC PERIODICALS AND MISCELLANIES; a selective annotated bibliography. see *LINGUISTICS*

296 US ISSN 0044-0418
YIDDISHE HEIM/JEWISH HOME. (Text in English & Yiddish) 1958. q. $4. (Agudas Neshei Ubnos Chabad) Kehot Publication Society, 770 Eastern Parkway, Brooklyn, NY 11213. TEL 718-493-9571 Eds. Rachel Altein, Tema Gurary. illus. circ. 2,500.

296 US ISSN 0044-0809
YOUNG ISRAEL VIEWPOINT. 1937. m. (except Jul. & Aug.) $5 to non-members. National Council of Young Israel, 3 West 16th St, New York, NY 10011. TEL 212-929-1525 Ed. Yaakov Kornreich. adv. bk. rev. circ. 40,000(controlled) (tabloid format)

YOUR CHILD. see *EDUCATION*

ZION; a quarterly for research in Jewish history. see *ETHNIC INTERESTS*

RELIGIONS AND THEOLOGY — Oriental

297 II
ADVENT. (Text in English) 1944. q. Rs.10($7) Sri Aurobindo Ashram Trust, Pondicherry 605002, India. Ed. M.P. Pandit. adv. bk. rev. illus. Indexed: CERDIC.

294.3 US ISSN 0747-900X
AMERICAN BUDDHIST. 1981? m. $15. American Buddhist Movement, 301 W. 45th St., New York, NY 10036. TEL 212-489-1075 Ed. Kevin O'Neal. adv. bk. rev. circ. 5,000.
Former titles: American Buddhist Newsletter; (until 1984): American Buddhist News.

ARS BUDDHICA/BUKKYO GEIJUTSU. see *ART*

181.41 610 II
ARUT PERUM JOTHI. (Hindu philosophy and Siddha medicine) (Text in English and Tamil) vol.11, 1970. m. Rs.6. Arumbakkam, Madras 29, India. Ed.Bd. adv.

299 301.15 IO
ATMA JAYA RESEARCH CENTRE. SOCIO-RELIGIOUS RESEARCH REPORT/PUSAT PENELITIAN ATMA JAYA. LAPORAN PENELITIAN KEAGAMAAN. 1977. irreg. Atma Jaya Research Centre - Pusat Penelitian Atma Jaya, Jalan Jenderal Sudirman 49a, Box 2639, Jakarta 10001, Indonesia.

294 US ISSN 0005-3643
BACK TO GODHEAD; magazine of the Hare Krisna movement. 1944. 11/yr. $14. Back to Godhead, Inc., 41-51 W. Allens Ln., Philadelphia, PA 19119. TEL 215-247-4040 Ed. Satsvarupa Dasa Goswami. bk. rev. illus. circ. 750,000. (also avail. in microform from UMI)

294.3 KO
BEOP RYUN. (Text in Korean) 1968. m. 3000 Won($6) Beop Ryun Sa, 131-1 Pyoungchangdong, Jongro-Ku, Seoul, S. Korea. Ed. Park Wan Ill. adv. bk. rev. illus. circ. 20,000.

BHARATYA VIDYA. see *ORIENTAL STUDIES*

294 IT
BISERICA ROMANEASCA. 1976. q. free. Comunita Ortodossa Romena in Italia, Centro Stampa BG, Via Larga 11, 20122 Milan, Italy. (Co-sponsor: Fondazione Europea Dragan) circ. 1,700.

294.3 US
BLIND DONKEY. 1975. irreg. $10 for 4 issues. Diamond Sangha, Inc., 2119 Kaloa Way, Honolulu, HI 96822. bk. rev. circ. 400.

299 AU
BODHI BAUM; zeitschrift fuer buddhismus. 1976. 6/yr. S.270. (Buddhistisches Kultur- und Meditationszentrum Scheibbs) Octopus Verlag, Fleischmarkt 16, A-1010 Vienna, Austria. Ed. Franz Ritter. adv. bk. rev. bibl. index. circ. 1,500.

294 CE ISSN 0520-3325
BODHI LEAVES. (Includes: Wheel) (Text in English) q. Rs.100($8) Buddhist Publication Society, Inc., Box 61, Kandy, Sri Lanka. (back issues avail.)

BOOKS AND ARTICLES ON ORIENTAL SUBJECTS PUBLISHED IN JAPAN. see *HISTORY — History Of Asia*

294.5 181 II ISSN 0304-9272
BRAHMANA-GAURAVA. (Text in Hindi) 1965. m. Rs.3. Moti Katra, Agra 3, India.

100 200 II ISSN 0006-8721
BRAHMAVADIN. (Text in English) 1895. q. Rs.12.50($5) Vivekananda Rock Memorial Committee, 36 Singarachari St., Triplicane, Madras 600005, India. (Co-sponsor: Swami Vivekananda Centenary Celebration) Ed. Prof. A. Narasimhamurti. Indexed: Phil.Ind.
Religion and philosophy

BRAHMAVIDYA. see *ORIENTAL STUDIES*

294.3 II
BUDDHIST STUDIES. (Text in English, Hindi and Sanskrit) 1974. a. Rs.10. University of Delhi, Department of Buddhist Studies, Delhi 110007, India. Ed. Kewal Krishan Mittal. bk. rev.

294.37 UK ISSN 0265-2897
BUDDHIST STUDIES REVIEW. 1976. 2/yr. £6($9) to individuals; institutions £8($12) (Institut de Recherche Bouddhique Linh-Son, FR) Russell Webb, Ed. & Pub., 31 Russell Chambers, Bury Place, London WC1A 2JX, England. (Co-sponsor: Institut de Recherche Bouddhique Linh-Son (Paris)) adv. bk. rev. circ. 500.
Formerly (until 1983): Pali Buddhist Review (ISSN 0308-3756)

200 100 US ISSN 0360-6112
BUDDHIST TEXT INFORMATION. 1974. q. $10. Institute for Advanced Studies of World Religions, Melville Memorial Library, State University of New York at Stony Brook, Stony Brook, NY 11794-3383. TEL 516-632-6580 Ed. Richard A. Gard. index. circ. 350. (back issues avail.)

200 CH
CONFUCIUS & MENCIUS SOCIETY OF THE REPUBLIC OF CHINA JOURNAL. 1961. s-a. NT.$100($4) Confucius-Mencius Society of the Republic of China, 45, Nan Hai Rd., Taipei, Taiwan, Republic of China. Ed. Tung King-yu. bibl. cum.index.

294.3 US ISSN 0097-7209
CRYSTAL MIRROR; annual of Tibetan Buddhism. 1971. irreg., latest vol.7. (Tibetan Nyingma Meditation Center) Dharma Publishing, 2425 Hillside Ave., Berkeley, CA 94704. TEL 415-548-5407 illus.

D J I N; Delta journal suisse d'informations macrobiotiques. see *FOOD AND FOOD INDUSTRIES*

DARSHANA INTERNATIONAL; an international quarterly of philosophy, psychology, sociology, psychical research, religion and mysticism. see *PHILOSOPHY*

DHARMA; a quarterly devoted to universal religion, righteousness & culture. see *PHILOSOPHY*

294 II ISSN 0012-4265
DIVYA VANI/DIVINE VOICE. (Text in English) 1961. m. $6. Avatar Meher Baba Mission, 1-8-7 Sriramanagar, Kakinada 3, Andhra Pradesh, India. Ed. Swami Satya Prakash Meheranada. bk. rev. bibl. circ. 1,000.

294.3 II
DRELOMA. 1978. 2/yr. $10. Drepung Loseling Library Society, Lama Camp 2, Tibetan Col., Uttar Kannadia 581411, India. Ed. Pema Tsering. adv. bk. rev. circ. 1,000.

294.5 II
ECSTASY; inter-disciplinary journal of cultural renaissance. 1984. q. Rs.150. (Nityanand Institute of Culture) Brahmavidyapeeth, 23/354 Azadnagar, Jaiprakash Rd., Andheri, Bombay 400 058, India. Ed. M.R. Sinha. adv. bk. rev. charts. illus. index. circ. 3,500.

294 UK
F O L K NEWSLETTER. (Friends of Lord Krishna) 1981. 6/yr. £6. (International Society for Krishna Consciousness) Bhaktivedanta Books Ltd., Croome House, Sandown Rd., Watford, Herts WD2 4XA, England. Ed. Kripamoga Das. bk. rev. illus. circ. 10,000.
Formerly: F O L K Magazine (ISSN 0260-938X)

294.3 US
GATEWAYS. 1979. 12/yr. $8. Hanuman Fellowship, Mount Madonna Center, 445 Summit Rd., Watsonville, CA 95076-0759. TEL 408-847-7175 Ed. Baruna Lefterys. adv. bk. rev. circ. 500.

294.3 US ISSN 0738-2294
GESAR; the magazine of Buddhism in the West. 1973. q. $10. (Tibetan Nyingma Meditation Center) Dharma Publishing, 2425 Hillside Ave., Berkeley, CA 94704. TEL 415-548-5407 Ed. Sylvia Gretchen. bk. rev. film rev. circ. 3,000. (back issues avail)

294.6 II
GURA SANDESHA/GUR-SANDESH. (Text in Punjabi) m. Rs.12. Yamuna Nagar, Santpura, India.
Sikhism

294 II
GURMAT SAGAR. (Text in Punjabi) 1964. m. Rs.12. Giani Balwaut Singh Saut Sipahi, Ed. & Pub., M-90 Raghuvir Nagar, Najaf Garh Rd., New Delhi 110027, India.

294.6 II
GURU NANAK COMMEMORATIVE LECTURES. (Text in English) 1970. a. Punjabi University, Publication Bureau, Patiala 1470002, India. Ed. Taran Singh. circ. 1,100.

294.5 MF
HINDU. (Text in English and French) 1981. w. Hindi Publications House, 26, Av. Drapers, Quatre Bornes, Mauritius. Ed. Krishnaduth Bhorra.

200 II
HINDU REGENERATION. (Text in English) 1971. q. Rs.10. Bharat Sevashram Sangha, Hyderabad Branch, Lower Tank Bund Rd., Hyderabad 500029, India. Ed. Swami Shantananda. adv. circ. 1,000.

294.5 US
HINDUISM TODAY. 1979. bi-m. $19.95. (Hinduism's International Newspaper) Himalayan Academy, Box 157, Hanamaulu, HI 96715 TEL 808-822-7032 (Subscr. address: 3575 Sacramento St., San Francisco, CA 94118; 415-931-9175) Ed. Rev. Swami Sivasiva Palani. adv. bk. rev. circ. 16,000.

294.5 US ISSN 0748-2280
I S K C O N WORLD REVIEW; newspaper of the Hare Krishna Movement. 1980. m. $8. International Society for Krishna Consciousness, Office of Public Affairs, Box 7030, Laguna Niguel, CA 92677. TEL 714-494-0300 Ed. Mukunda Goswami. adv. circ. 60,000. (tabloid format; back issues avail.)

294.3 JA
INSTITUTE FOR THE COMPREHENSIVE STUDY OF LOTUS SUTRA. JOURNAL/HOKKE BUNKA KENKYU. (Text in English or Japanese) 1975. a. 3000 Yen. Rissho University, Institute for the Comprehensive Study of Lotus Sutra - Rissho Daigaku Hokekyo Bunka Kenkyujo, 4-2-16 Osaki, Shinagawa-ku, Tokyo 141, Japan. Ed. Zuiryu Nakamura. bk. rev. illus.

294.3 US ISSN 0193-600X
INTERNATIONAL ASSOCIATION OF BUDDHIST STUDIES. JOURNAL. 1978. s-a. $25 to individuals; institutions $50; students $15. International Association of Buddhist Studies, c/o University of Wisconsin, Department of South Asian Studies, 1258 Van Hise Hall, Madison, WI 53706. TEL 608-262-5881 Ed. A.K. Narain. adv. bk. rev. circ. 500. (also avail. in microform from UMI; back issues avail.; reprint service avail. from UMI)

294.3 US
INTERNATIONAL BUDDHIST CENTER. MONTHLY GUIDE. 12/yr. International Buddhist Center, 928 S. New Hampshire Ave., Los Angeles, CA 90006. TEL 213-384-0850

294.44 II ISSN 0021-4043
JAIN JOURNAL. (Text in English) 1966. q. Rs.60. Jain Bhawan, P-25 Kalakar St., Calcutta 700007, India. Ed. Ganesh Lalwani. adv. bk. rev. bibl. illus. index. circ. 1,000.

299.51 US
JOURNAL OF CHINESE RELIGIONS. 1975. a. $10 to individuals; institutions $10. Society for the Study of Chinese Religions, c/o Rodney L. Taylor, Ed., Department of Religious Studies, University of Colorado, Boulder, CO 80309. TEL 303-492-0111 bk. rev. circ. 125.
Formerly (until 1982): Society for the Study of Chinese Religions. Bulletin.

291 JA ISSN 0019-4344
JOURNAL OF INDIAN AND BUDDHIST STUDIES/INDOGAKU BUNKKYOGAKU KENKYU. (Text in Japanese; title in English) 1952. s-a. 9000 Yen($14) Japanese Association of Indian and Buddhist Studies - Nihon Indogaku-Bukkyogakukai, c/o Dept. of Indian Philosophy and Sanskrit Philology, Faculty of Letters, University of Tokyo, 7-3-1 Hongo, Bunkyo-ku, Tokyo 113, Japan. Ed.Bd. bibl. illus. index. circ. 3,000.

294.3 US
JOURNAL OF NICHIREN BUDDHISM. 1979. q. membership. Institute of Nichiren Buddhism, 301 W. 45 St., New York, NY 10036. Ed. Kevin R. O'Neil. adv. bk. rev. circ. 500.

JOURNAL OF SIKH STUDIES. see *ORIENTAL STUDIES*

294.592 AT ISSN 0706-6449
JOURNAL OF STUDIES IN THE BHAGAVADGITA. 1981. irreg. Aus.$10 to individuals; Aus.$15 to institutions. University of Sydney, Department of Religious Studies, Sydney, N.S.W. 2006, Australia. Ed.Bd. bk. rev. circ. 100. (back issues avail.) Indexed: Rel.Per. Rel.Ind.One.

268 II ISSN 0047-3693
KRISHNAMURTI FOUNDATION. BULLETIN. (Text in English) 1970. 3/yr. Rs.15($10) Krishnamurti Foundation (India), c/o Dr. Sunanda Patwardhan, 64/65 Greenways Rd., Madras 600028, India. Ed. Sunanda Patwardhan. bk. rev. circ. 1,300.
Philosophy

297.7 II
LIGHT OF PANDRIMALAI. (Text in English) 1974. q. Rs.12. T. D. Meenakchisundaram, Ed. & Pub., c/o Sakuntala, C-28 Eleventh Cross, Thillainagar, Trichy 18, India. adv. illus.
Hindu religion, philosophy, and culture

294.344 II ISSN 0025-0406
MAHA BODHI; international Buddhist monthly. (Text in English) 1892. m. Rs.12($4) Maha Bodhi Society of India, 4A Bankim Chatterjee St., Calcutta 73, India. Ed.Bd. adv. bk. rev. illus. index. circ. 2,500.

294.3 CE
MAHINDA. (Text in English) 1976. q. Rs.8($2) (Maha Mahinda International Dhammaduta Society) Buddhist English Speaking Society, 58 Sri Vipulasena Mawatha, Colombo 10, Sri Lanka.

294.1 US ISSN 0276-0444
MANANAM; Vedanta today. (Text in English and Sanskrit) 1978. q. $18. Chinmaya Mission, Box 397, Los Altos, CA 94023. Ed. Rudite Emir. adv. bk. rev. charts. illus. circ. 1,300. (back issues avail.)

294.344 UK ISSN 0026-3214
MIDDLE WAY. 1926. q. £6. Buddhist Society, 58 Eccleston Square, London S.W.1, England. Ed. John Snelling. adv. bk. rev. illus. index. circ. 2,500.

294.6 US
MORNINGLAND SPIRITUAL JOURNAL. 12/yr. $7. Morningland Publications, 2600 E. Seventh St., Long Beach, CA 90804. TEL 213-433-9906 Ed. Gopi Morningstar. adv.

NANDAN KANAN. see *PHILOSOPHY*

294.3 US
NAROPA MAGAZINE. 1984. s-a? Naropa Institute, (Subsidiary of: Nalanda Foundation) 2130 Arapahoe Ave., Boulder, CO 80302. Ed. Susan Fielding.

294.3 US ISSN 0891-1177
ORDER OF BUDDHIST CONTEMPLATIVES. JOURNAL. 1970. q. $15. (Order of Buddhist Contemplatives) Shasta Abbey, Box 199, Mt. Shasta, CA 96067. TEL 916-926-4208 Ed. Rev. L.B.H. Kinzan Learman. circ. 700. (back issues avail.)
Former titles: Shasta Abbey. Journal (ISSN 0732-8508) & Zen Mission Society. Journal.

295 II ISSN 0048-3036
PARSIANA. 1965. m. Rs.50. J. R. Patel, Ed. & Pub., c/o H. L. Rochat, Navsari Chambers, 39 A.K. Nayak Marg, Fort, Bombay 4000001, India. adv. bk. rev. illus. circ. 4,000. Indexed: Ind.India.

PATROLOGIA SYRIACA ET ORIENTALIS. see *RELIGIONS AND THEOLOGY — Roman Catholic*

200 II ISSN 0031-3467
PEACE. (Text in English) 1928. m. Rs.10. Shanti Ashram, P.O. Totapalli Hills Pin 533458, Via Shankavaram, E. Godavari Dist., Andhra Pradesh, India.
Hinduism

PRABUDDHA BHARATA/AWAKENED INDIA. see *PHILOSOPHY*

294 II ISSN 0554-9906
PRAKIT JAIN INSTITUTE RESEARCH PUBLICATION SERIES. (Text in English and Hindi) 1964. irreg. price varies. Bihar Research Institute of Prakit, Jainology, and Ahimsa, Vaishali, India. Ed. G.C. Choudhary.

REVIEW OF INDIAN SPIRITUALISM. see *PARAPSYCHOLOGY AND OCCULTISM*

294.5 II
SAI SUDDHA. (Text in English, Tamil or Telugu) m. All India Sai Samaj, Madras 4, Tamil Nadu, India. illus.

SANT SIPAHI. see *POLITICAL SCIENCE*

294.5 II
SANTI. (Text in Telegu) 1924. m. Rs.10. Shanti Ashram, P.O. Totapalli Hills Pin 533458, Via Shankavaram, E. Godavari Dist., Andhra Pradesh, India.

299 JA ISSN 0037-1084
SEISHIN STUDIES. (Text in English and Japanese) 1952. s-a. 900. Yen($3.) University of the Sacred Heart, Hiroo, 4-3-1 Shibuya-ku, Tokyo, Japan. Ed.Bd. bk. rev. illus. index; cum. index every 2 yrs. circ. 1,000. Indexed: Jap.Per.Ind.

297 II
SHREE GURUDEV ASHRAM NEWSLETTER. (Text in English) vol.7, 1978. m. Rs.10($6) (Shree Gurudev Ashram) Gurudev Siddhapeeth, P.O. Ganeshpuri District, Thana 401206, India. Ed. R. Pratap. illus.

SHREE HARI KATHA. see *PHILOSOPHY*

294.5 II
SIDDHA VANI. (Text in English or Hindi) 1972. a. Rs.6($1.50) Siddha Yoga Dham, S-174 Panch Shila Park, New Delhi 110017, India. Ed. Janak Nanda. adv. illus. circ. 2,000.

294 UK ISSN 0037-511X
SIKH COURIER. 1960. q. £4. Sikh Cultural Society of Great Britain, 88 Mollison Way, Edgware, Middlesex HA8 5QW, England. Ed. A.S. Chhatwal. adv. bk. rev. circ. 3,000. Indexed: CERDIC.

294 II ISSN 0037-5128
SIKH REVIEW. (Text in English) 1953. m. $25. Sikh Cultural Centre, 116 Karnani Mansion, Park St., Calcutta 16, India. Ed. Captain Bhag Singh. adv. bk. rev. circ. 4,000.

294.5 II ISSN 0037-5950
SIVAM. (Text in Bengali) 1963. m. Rs.15. Swami Bholananda Seva Mandal, 1 Mahesh Choudhury Lane, Calcutta 25, India. Eds. Sachindra Kumar Bhattacharyya, Amulya Kishore Lodh. adv. bk. rev. circ. 2,000. Indexed: Rel.& Theol.Abstr.

294.37 JA ISSN 0385-6321
SOKA GAKKAI NEWS. (Text in English) 1975. m. free. Soka Gakkai, International Office, 32 Shinano-machi, Shinjuku-ku, Tokyo 160, Japan. bk. rev. illus. circ. 12,300.

297 II
SRI AUROBINDO. ARCHIVES AND RESEARCH. 1977. biennial. Rs.40($7.50) Sri Aurobindo Ashram Trust, Pondicherry 605002, India. Ed. H. Patel.

290 GW ISSN 0340-6792
STUDIES IN ORIENTAL RELIGIONS. (Text in English and German) 1976. irreg., vol.14, 1986. price varies. Verlag Otto Harrassowitz, Taunusstr. 14, Postfach 2929, 6200 Wiesbaden 1, W. Germany (B.R.D.) Eds. W. Heissig, H.J. Klimkeit.

SUDHI SAHITYA. see *PHILOSOPHY*

200 II
TAPOVAN PRASAD. (Text in English) 1968. m. $15. (Tara Cultural Trust) Chinmaya Mission, 17 Harrington Rd., Madras 600031, Tamil Nadu, India (U.S. addr.: c/o Chinmaya Mission West, Box 397, Los Altos, CA 94023) Ed. Leela Nambiar. adv. bk. rev. circ. 7,000.
Hindu religion and philosophy

299.51 II
TIBETAN BULLETIN. 1969. bi-m. free. Central Tibetan Secretariat, Information Office, Gangchen Kyishong, Dharamsala 176215, Himachal Pradesh, India. Ed. Bhuchung K. Tsering. bk. rev. illus. circ. 2,000.

294 JA ISSN 0386-426X
TOHOKAI. 1973. m. 1200 Yen($6) Tohokai, Inc., 6-2-17 Nishitenma, Kita-ku, Osaka 530, Japan. Ed. Seigo Arashiba.

294.3 US
UDUMBARA. 1974. 2/yr. $5. Minnesota Zen Meditation Center, 3343 E. Calhoun Pkwy., Minneapolis, MN 55408. TEL 612-822-5313 Eds. Mike Port and Curt Dornberg. bk. rev. circ. 3,400.

294.3 US ISSN 0507-6986
VAJRA BODHI SEA. (Text in Chinese and English) 1970. m. $30. (Dharma Realm Buddhist Association) Vajra Bodhi Sea Publication Society, City of 10,000 Buddhas, Box 217, Talmage, CA 95481. Ed.Bd. bk. rev. illus. index. circ. 4,500.

VEDANTA KESARI. see *PHILOSOPHY*

VEDIC LIGHT. see *PHILOSOPHY*

VISVA-BHARATI JOURNAL OF PHILOSOPHY. see *PHILOSOPHY*

294.5 US
VIVEKANANDA VEDANTA SOCIETY OF CHICAGO. BULLETINS. 1930. m. free. Vivekananda Vedanta Society, 5423 S. Hyde Park Blvd., Chicago, IL 60615. TEL 312-363-0027 Ed. Swami Bhashyananda. circ. 750. (looseleaf format; back issues avail.)

294.44 II ISSN 0042-8086
VOICE OF AHINSA; magazine of the non-violence Ahinsa cult. (Text in English) 1951. m. Rs.25. World Jain Mission - Virendra Prasad Jain, Jain Bhawan, Aliganj, Etah, Uttar Pradesh 207247, India. Eds. D.J.P. Jain, V.P. Jain. adv. bk. rev. illus. circ. 750.
Jainism

294.344 MY ISSN 0042-8094
VOICE OF BUDDHISM. (Text in Chinese and English; summaries in English) 1963. s-a. M.$6($3) Buddhist Missionary Society, Buddhist Temple, Jalan Berhala, Brickfields, Kuala Lumpur 50470, Malaysia. Ed. Teh Thean Choo. adv. bk. rev. circ. 6,500. (back issues avail)

200 US
WASHINGTON BUDDHIST. 1969. q. $3 membership. Buddhist Vihara Society, 5017 16th St. N.W., Washington, DC 20011. TEL 202-723-0773 Ed. H. Gunaratana. bk. rev. circ. 700.

299.5 UK ISSN 0144-9818
WESTERN BUDDHIST. 1979. s-a. £1.90. Scientific Buddhist Association, 30 Hollingbourne Gdns., Ealing, London W13 8EN, England. Ed. Paul Ingram. adv. bk. rev. circ. 550.

294.3 CE ISSN 0049-7541
WHEEL; a series of Buddhist publications. (Includes: Bodhi Leaves) (Text in English) 1958. q. Rs.150($8) Buddhist Publication Society, Inc., Box 61, Kandy, Sri Lanka. Eds. Ven. Nyanaponika Maha Thera, Bhikkhu Bodhi. circ. 4,000. (back issues avail.)

294.392 US ISSN 0043-5708
WIND BELL. 1962. 2/yr. $6. ‡ Zen Center (San Francisco), 300 Page St., San Francisco, CA 94102. TEL 415-863-3136 Ed.Bd. circ. 3,000. (processed)

294 TH ISSN 0084-1781
WORLD FELLOWSHIP OF BUDDHISTS. BOOK SERIES. 1965. irreg., latest issue 1977. price varies. World Fellowship of Buddhists, 33 Sukhumvit Rd., Bangkok 10-100, Thailand.

294.344 TH ISSN 0043-8464
WORLD FELLOWSHIP OF BUDDHISTS REVIEW. q. B.160($8) World Fellowship of Buddhists, 33 Sukhumvit Rd., Between Soi 1-3, Bangkok 10-100, Thailand. Ed. Siri Buddhasukh. adv. bk. rev. charts. illus. circ. 2,000.

294.3 SI
YOUNG BUDDHIST. (Text in English and Chinese) a. Singapore Buddhist Youth Organisations Joint Celebrations Committee, 83 Silat Road, Singapore 3, Singapore. illus.

YOUNG EAST; a quarterly on Buddhism and Japanese culture. see *ORIENTAL STUDIES*

299.56 NE
ZEN EXTRA. 1981. a. price varies. Stichting Theresiahoeve, Dominicanenstr. 24, 5453 JN Langenboom, Netherlands. Ed. Judith Bossert. adv.

RELIGIONS AND THEOLOGY — Protestant

A A B C NEWSLETTER. (American Association of Bible Colleges) see *EDUCATION — Higher Education*

268 US
A L C-L C A AUGSBURG ADULT BIBLE STUDIES. ADULT QUARTERLY. 1968. q. $1.25 per no. (American Lutheran Church and Lutheran Church in America) Augsburg Publishing House, 426 S. Fifth St., Minneapolis, MN 55440. TEL 612-330-3300 Ed. Terence Y. Mullins. circ. 75,000.
Formerly: A L C-L C A Augsburg Adult Bible Studies.

268 US
A L C-L C A AUGSBURG ADULT BIBLE STUDIES. HOME BIBLE STUDIES. 1968. q. $2.75 per no. (American Lutheran Church and Lutheran Church in America) Augsburg Publishing House, 426 S. Fifth St., Minneapolis, MN 55440. TEL 612-330-3300 Ed. Terence Y. Mullins. circ. 750. (back issues avail.)
Former titles: A L C-L C A Augsburg Home Bible Studies; A L C-L C A Augsburg Adult Bible Studies. Home Bible Studies.

268 US
A L C-L C A AUGSBURG ADULT BIBLE STUDIES. TEACHER'S GUIDE. 1968. q. $3.10 per no. (American Lutheran Church and Lutheran Church in America) Augsburg Publishing House, 426 S. Fifth St., Minneapolis, MN 55440. TEL 612-330-3300 Ed. Terence Y. Mullins. circ. 8,000.

A M A A NEWS. (Armenian Missionary Association of America, Inc.) see *RELIGIONS AND THEOLOGY — Other Denominations And Sects*

200 US ISSN 0360-3725
A.M.E. CHURCH REVIEW. 1884. q. $6.50. African Methodist Episcopal Church, 468 Lincoln Drive, N. W., Atlanta, GA 30318. TEL 404-794-4991 Ed. Rev. William D. Johnson. bk. rev. bibl, charts, illus, stat. circ. 6,000. (also avail. in microform from UMI; back issues avail.)

268 US ISSN 0001-4516
ACCENT ON YOUTH. 1968. q. $5.75. (United Methodist Church) United Methodist Publishing House, Graded Press, 201 Eighth Ave. S., Nashville, TN 37203. TEL 615-749-6417 Ed. Sidney Fowler. bk. rev. illus.
Formerly: Twelve/Fifteen.

200 US ISSN 0273-3145
ACTION (WINONA LAKE) 1981. w. $8.95. (Aldersgate Publications Association) Light and Life Press, Winona Lake, IN 46590. TEL 219-267-7161 Ed. Vera Bethel. circ. 29,900.
Formerly (1970-1981): Discovery (Winona Lake) (ISSN 0039-2022); Which incorporated: Guide (ISSN 0017-5242) & Climb.

283 AT ISSN 0001-8147
ADELAIDE CHURCH GUARDIAN. 1906. m. Aus.$6.50. Anglican Church of Australia, Diocese of Adelaide, Anglican Church Office, 44 Currie St., Adelaide 5000, Australia. Ed. K. Williams. adv. bk. rev. circ. 4,500.

268 US ISSN 0162-4156
ADULT BIBLE STUDY. q. $4. Southern Baptist Convention, Sunday School Board, 127 Ninth Ave., North, Nashville, TN 37234. TEL 615-251-2000

268 US ISSN 0162-4164
ADULT BIBLE TEACHER. q. $9.25. Southern Baptist Convention, Sunday School Board, 127 Ninth Ave., North, Nashville, TN 37234. TEL 615-251-2000

268 US ISSN 0162-4172
ADULT LEADERSHIP. m. $11. Southern Baptist Convention, Sunday School Board, 127 Ninth Ave., North, Nashville, TN 37234. TEL 615-251-2000 Indexed: Sci.Abstr. South.Bap.Per.Ind.

268 US ISSN 0149-998X
ADULT PLANBOOK; resources for adult Christian education in United Methodist Churches. 1959. a. free. (United Methodist Church) United Methodist Publishing House, Graded Press, 201 Eighth Ave. S., Nashville, TN 37203. TEL 615-749-6417 Ed. John P. Gilbert. bk. rev. circ. 200,000.
Formerly: United Methodist Church (United States) Division of Education. Adult Planbook (ISSN 0082-7983)

268 US ISSN 0400-5880
ADULT TEACHER. q. $9.25. Southern Baptist Convention, Sunday School Board, 127 Ninth Ave., North, Nashville, TN 37234. TEL 615-251-2000

283 US ISSN 0001-8562
ADVANCE (CHICAGO) 1975. m. (except Aug.) $3. Episcopal Diocese of Chicago, 65 E. Huron St., Chicago, IL 60611. TEL 312-787-6410 Ed. James R. Rosenthal, II. adv. bk. rev. film rev. play rev. illus. circ. 10,500. Indexed: CERDIC.
Organization news

268 US ISSN 0162-4148
ADVANCED BIBLE STUDY. q. $5.50. Southern Baptist Convention, Sunday School Board, 127 Ninth Ave., North, Nashville, TN 37234. TEL 615-251-2000

286 NE
ADVENT. 1899. m. fl.1.50. (Zevende-Dags Adventisten - Seventh-Day Adventists) Stichting Uitgeverij "Veritas", Biltseweg 14, 3735 ME Boschen Duin, Netherlands. Ed. R. Bruinsma. illus. Indexed: CERDIC.
Formerly: Adventbode (ISSN 0001-8767)

286 JA
ADVENTIST LIFE. (Text in Japanese) m. 4400 Yen($15) Japan Publishing House, 1966 Kamikawai-cho, Asahi-ku, Yokohama 241, Japan.

286 US ISSN 0161-1119
ADVENTIST REVIEW. (Editions in English and Spanish) 1850. w. $36.20. Review and Herald Publishing Association, 55 West Oak Ridge Dr., Hagerstown, MD 21740. TEL 301-791-7000 Ed. William G. Johnsson. bk. rev. index. circ. 105,000. (tabloid format; reprint service avail. from UMI)
Former titles: Advent Review and Sabbath Herald (ISSN 0095-2397) & Review and Herald (ISSN 0034-6381)

268 US ISSN 0001-8783
ADVENTURE (NASHVILLE) m. in w. parts. $8.50. Southern Baptist Convention, Sunday School Board, 127 Ninth Ave., North, Nashville, TN 37234. TEL 615-251-2000

284 US ISSN 0044-6467
AFFIRM; our eternal Christ and his word for our changing and urgent needs. 1971. m. contributions. (Lutheran Church-Missouri Synod) Balance, Inc., c/o Walther Memorial Lutheran Church, 4040 West Fond du Lac Ave., Milwaukee, WI 53216. TEL 414-444-4133 Ed. Rev. Ewald J. Otto. bk. rev. circ. 104,000.

286 209 US ISSN 0002-4147
ALABAMA BAPTIST HISTORIAN. vol.5, 1969. s-a. $5. Alabama Baptist Historical Society, Sanford University Library, Birmingham, AL 35229. Ed. Irma R. Cruse. bk. rev. bibl. circ. 250. Indexed: Hist.Abstr. Amer.Hist.& Life.
History

200 US
ALIVE NOW; devotional reading. 1971. bi-m. $6. (United Methodist Church, General Board of Discipleship) Upper Room, 1908 Grand Ave., Box 189, Nashville, TN 37202. TEL 615-327-2700 Ed. Mary Ruth Coffman. bk. rev. illus. circ. 75,000. (back issues avail)

266 NE ISSN 0002-5666
ALLE DEN VOLCKE. 1907. m. fl.10. Gereformeerde Zendingsbond in de Nederlandse Hervormde Kerk - Board of the Reformed Mission League in the Netherlands Reformed Church, Faunalaan 89, 3972 PP Driebergen, Netherlands. Ed. T. Eikelboom. bk. rev. illus. circ. 48,500.

200 US ISSN 0745-3256
ALLIANCE WITNESS. 1882. fortn. $8.50. Christian and Missionary Alliance, 350 N. Highland Ave., Nyack, NY 10960-0992. TEL 914-353-0750 Ed. Maurice R. Irvin. adv. bk. rev. illus. index. circ. 60,000. (also avail. in microform from UMI; back issues avail.; reprint service avail. from UMI) Indexed: Chr.Per.Ind. G.Soc.Sci.& Rel.Per.Lit.

286 US ISSN 0002-757X
AMERICAN BAPTIST. 1803. 6/yr. $8.95. American Baptist Churches in the U.S.A., Box 851, Valley Forge, PA 19482-0851. TEL 215-768-2000 Ed. Philip E. Jenks. adv. bk. rev. charts. illus. circ. 97,000.
Formerly: Crusader and Mission.

286 US ISSN 0092-3478
AMERICAN BAPTIST CHURCHES IN THE U.S.A. YEARBOOK. Continues: American Baptist Convention. Yearbook. 1907. a. $5. American Baptist Churches in the U.S.A., Box 851, Valley Forge, PA 19482-0851. TEL 215-768-2000 Ed. Robert C. Campbell. illus. circ. 3,500. Key Title: Yearbook of the American Baptist Churches in the U.S.A.

286 US ISSN 0091-9381
AMERICAN BAPTIST CHURCHES IN THE U.S.A. DIRECTORY. 1971. a. $5. American Baptist Churches in the U.S.A., Box 851, Valley Forge, PA 19482-0851. TEL 215-768-2000 Ed. Robert C. Campbell. circ. 6,000.
Supersedes in part: American Baptist Convention. Directory (ISSN 0096-3380); American Baptist Convention. Yearbook.

286 209 US
AMERICAN BAPTIST QUARTERLY; a Baptist journal of history, theology and ministry. 1958. q. $15. American Baptist Historical Society, Linfield College, McMinnville, OR 97128 (Subscr. to: Dr. William H. Brackney, Box 857, Valley Forge, PA 19482) Ed. Dr. William R. Millar. bk. rev. circ. 1,200. (also avail. in microform from UMI; reprint service avail. from UMI) Indexed: Hist.Abstr. Rel.Per. Amer.Hist. & Life. Rel.Ind.One. Rel.& Theol.Abstr.
Former titles (until vol.25, 1982): Foundations (ISSN 0015-8992); Chronicle (Greensburg) (ISSN 0360-5779)
History

286 US ISSN 0886-5159
AMERICAN PRESBYTERIANS: JOURNAL OF PRESBYTERIAN HISTORY. 1901. q. $15. (United Presbyterian Church in the U.S.A., Presbyterian Historical Society and Historical Foundation) Presbyterian Church USA, 425 Lombard St., Philadelphia, PA 19147. TEL 215-627-1852 Ed. James H. Smylie. bk. rev. abstr. illus. index. cum.index: 1901-1962. circ. 1,400. (also avail. in microfilm) Indexed: Curr.Cont. Hist.Abstr. Rel.Per. Amer.Hist.& Life. Arts & Hum.Cit.Ind. Rel.Ind.One. Rel.& Theol.Abstr.
Former titles (until 1985): Journal of Presbyterian History (ISSN 0022-3883); Presbyterian Historical Society Journal.
History

286 US ISSN 0066-1708
ANDREWS UNIVERSITY. MONOGRAPHS. 1966. irreg., 1983, vol.13. price varies. Andrews University Press, Berrien Springs, MI 49104. TEL 616-471-3392 Ed. Robert E. Firth. adv. bk. rev.

283 CN ISSN 0517-7731
ANGLICAN. 1958. m. Can.$8. Anglican Church of Canada, Diocese of Toronto, 145 Adelaide St. E., Toronto, Ont. M5C 1L8, Canada. TEL 416-363-6021 Ed. Debbie Dimmick. adv. bk. rev. circ. 44,600. Indexed: CERDIC.

283 CN
ANGLICAN CHURCH OF CANADA. GENERAL SYNOD. JOURNAL. 1894. triennial. Anglican Church of Canada, General Synod, 600 Jarvis Street, Toronto, Ont. M4Y 2J6, Canada. TEL 416-924-9192 circ. 450.
Formerly (until 1980): Anglican Chiurch of Canada. General Synod. Journal of Proceedings (ISSN 0380-2469)

283 US ISSN 0003-3278
ANGLICAN DIGEST. 1958. bi-m. $5 or donation. (Society for Promoting and Encouraging Arts and Knowledge, Inc.) S P E A K, Inc., Hillspeak, Eureka Springs, AR 72632. TEL 501-253-9701 Ed. Rev. C. Frederick Barbee. adv. bk. rev. circ. 100,000. Indexed: CERDIC.

283 AT
ANGLICAN MESSENGER. 1969. m. Aus.$9. (Anglican Church in Western Australia) Wescolour Press, G.P.O. Box W2067, Perth 6001, Australia. Ed. D. Britton. adv. bk. rev. circ. 10,000. (tabloid format)

283 209 US ISSN 0003-3286
ANGLICAN THEOLOGICAL REVIEW. 1919. q. $15 to individuals; $18 institutions. Anglican Theological Review, Inc., 600 Haven St., Evanston, IL 60201. TEL 312-328-9300 Ed. James Dunkly. adv. bk. rev. abstr. index. cum.index (every 10 yrs.) circ. 1,800. (also avail. in microform from UMI; reprint service avail. from UMI) Indexed: Bull.Signal. Hist.Abstr. Amer.Hist.& Life. CERDIC. New Test.Abstr. Old Test.Abstr. Rel.& Theol.Abstr. Rel.Ind.One.
History

266 CN ISSN 0317-8765
ANGLICAN YEAR BOOK. 1900. a. Can.$17.95. (Anglican Church of Canada) Anglican Book Centre, 600 Jarvis St., Toronto, Ont. M4Y 2J6, Canada. TEL 416-924-9192 Ed. B. Lloyd. adv. stat. circ. 1,000.

284 FR ISSN 0066-362X
ANNUAIRE PROTESTANT; LA FRANCE PROTESTANTE ET LES EGLISES DE LANGUE FRANCAISE. 1922, 40th ed. a. 84 F. (Centrale du Livre Protestant) Librairie Fischbacher, 33 rue de Seine, 75006 Paris, France.

266 UK
ANVIL; an anglican evangelical journal for theology and mission. 1984. 3/yr. £9($15.75) c/o Revd. Peter Williams, Ed., Trinity College, 14-26 Stoke Hill, Bristol BS9 1JP, England. adv. circ. 1,100.

287 US ISSN 0003-6552
APOSENTO ALTO. Spanish edition of: Upper Room. (Large type edition avail.) 1938. bi-m. $4. (United Methodist Church, General Board of Discipleship) Upper Room, 1908 Grand Ave., Nashville, TN 37212. TEL 615-327-2700 Ed. Horacio M. Rios. illus. circ. 75,000. (back issues avail.)

260 US
ARKANSAS EPISCOPALIAN. vol.49, 1975. m. $3. Episcopal Diocese of Arkansas, Box 6120, Little Rock, AR 72216. TEL 501-372-2168 Ed. Cary Swanson. bk. rev. circ. 8,000 (controlled) (tabloid format)
Formerly: Arkansas Churchman.

287 US
ARKANSAS UNITED METHODIST. 1882. bi-m. $10. (United Methodist Church, Arkansas Area) Arkansas Methodist, Inc., Box 3547, Little Rock, AR 72203. TEL 501-374-4831 Ed. Georgia M. Daily. adv. bk. rev. circ. 11,000.
Formerly (until 1983): Arkansas Methodist.

285 US ISSN 0362-0816
ASSOCIATE REFORMED PRESBYTERIAN. 1976. m. $12. Associate Reformed Presbyterian, Inc., General Synod of the Associate Reformed Presbyterian Church, One Cleveland St., Greenville, SC 29601. TEL 803-232-8297 Ed. Ben Johnston. adv. bk. rev. circ. 6,400. (also avail. in microform from UMI; back issues avail.)

286 CN ISSN 0004-6752
ATLANTIC BAPTIST. 1827. m. Can.$7.50. United Baptist Convention of the Atlantic Provinces, Board of Publication, Box 756, Kentville, N.S. B4N 3X9, Canada. TEL 902-678-6868 Ed. Rev. Michael A. Lipe. adv. bk. rev. illus. index. circ. 8,500.

284 GW ISSN 0004-7848
AUFBRUCH; evangelische Kirchenzeitung fuer Baden. 1965. w. DM.30. Evangelischer Presseverband fuer Baden e.V., Blumenstr. 7, 7500 Karlsruhe, W. Germany (B.R.D.) adv. bk. rev. film rev. illus. circ. 69,000.

200 SZ ISSN 0004-7880
AUFTRAG. 1967. 6/yr. 12 Fr.($2) Kooperation Evangelischer Kirchen und Missionen, Missionstr. 21, 4003 Basel, Switzerland. Eds. Eduard Abel, Hanspeter Ruesch. illus. circ. 45,000.
Missions

286 AT ISSN 0004-8739
AUSTRALIAN BAPTIST. 1913. fortn. Aus.$13.75. Australian Baptist Publishing House Ltd., 68 Arundel St., Glebe, N.S.W. 2037, Australia. Ed. T.J. Cardwell. adv. bk. rev. illus. circ. 5,000.

280 AT ISSN 0004-8852
AUSTRALIAN CHRISTIAN; national journal of Churches of Christ. 1898. fortn. Aus.$15. (Federal Conference of Churches of Christ) Australian Christian Board of Management, Box 101, Essendon North, Victoria, 3041, Australia. Ed. G.R. Stirling. adv. bk. rev. index. circ. 5,000. Indexed: CERDIC.

AUSTRALIAN LECTIONARY (YEAR) see *RELIGIONS AND THEOLOGY*

285 AT ISSN 0005-0059
AUSTRALIAN PRESBYTERIAN LIFE. 1966. m. Aus.$15. Presbyterian Church of Australia, National Journal Committee, 44 Margaret St., Box 5023, Sydney, N.S.W. 2001, Australia. Ed. Rev. C. R. Thomas. adv. bk. rev. film rev. illus. circ. 6,700.

286 US ISSN 0162-6833
AWARE CONTENTS; the magazine for GA leaders. 1970. q. $6. Southern Baptist Convention, Women's Missionary Union, Highway 280 E., 100 Missionary Ridge, Birmingham, AL 35243-2798. TEL 205-991-8100 Ed. Barbara Massey. circ. 40,000.

286 CN
B.C. FELLOWSHIP BAPTIST. 1927. m. Can.$4.50. Fellowship of Regular Baptist Churches of British Columbia, 1420 E. 2nd Ave., Vancouver, BC V5N 5L9, Canada. TEL 604-255-5471 Ed. Donald W. Reed. bk. rev. circ. 3,000.
Formerly: B.C. Regular Baptist (ISSN 0702-1003)

285 US ISSN 0005-5557
BANNER (GRAND RAPIDS) 1866. 46/yr. $20.50. (Christian Reformed Church) C R C Publications, 2850 Kalamazoo Ave. S.E., Grand Rapids, MI 49560. TEL 616-246-0725 Ed. Rev. Andrew Kuyvenhoven. adv. bk. rev. illus. index. circ. 49,000. (also avail. in microform from UMI; reprint service avail. from UMI) Indexed: CERDIC. G.Soc.Sci.& Rel.Per.Lit.
Formerly: Banner of Truth.

286 NO ISSN 0005-5565
BANNERET. 1879. 30/yr. Kr.235($35) Norske Baptistsamfunn - Baptist Union of Norway, Micheletsvei 62, 1320 Stabekk, Norway. Ed. Peder M.I. Liland. adv. bk. rev. illus. circ. 3,000. (tabloid format)

268 US ISSN 0162-4180
BAPTIST ADULTS. q. $4.75. Southern Baptist Convention, Sunday School Board, 127 Ninth Ave., North, Nashville, TN 37234. TEL 615-251-2000

286 US ISSN 0005-5689
BAPTIST BULLETIN. 1933. m. (11/yr.) $6.50. General Association of Regular Baptist Churches, Council of Eighteen, 1300 North Meacham Rd., Schaumburg, IL 60173-4888. TEL 312-843-1600 Ed. Dr. Merle R. Hull. adv. bk. rev. circ. 45,000. (tabloid format) Indexed: G.Soc.Sci.& Rel.Per.Lit.

286 US ISSN 0005-5697
BAPTIST CHALLENGE; voice of independent Baptists. 1961. m. free. Central Baptist Church, Box 5567, Little Rock, AR 72215. TEL 501-664-3225 Ed. M.L. Moser Jr. adv. bk. rev. illus. circ. 5,300.

286 US ISSN 0005-5700
BAPTIST HERALD. 1923. m. (combined in Jan./Feb. July/Aug.) $8. North American Baptist Conference, 1 S. 210 Summit Ave., Oakbrook Terrace, IL 60181. TEL 312-495-2000 Ed. Barbara J. Binder. adv. illus. circ. 8,000. (also avail. in microfilm from UMI) Indexed: CERDIC.

286 209 US ISSN 0005-5719
BAPTIST HISTORY AND HERITAGE. 1965. q. $8.50. Southern Baptist Convention, Historical Commission, 901 Commerce St., Ste. 400, Nashville, TN 37203-3620. TEL 615-244-0344 Ed. Lynn E. May, Jr. bk. rev. charts. illus. index. circ. 2,250. Indexed: Hist.Abstr. Amer. Hist. & Life. CERDIC. Rel.Ind.One. South.Bap.Per.Ind.
History

286 US ISSN 0005-5727
BAPTIST LEADER. 1938. m. $15.75. American Baptist Churches in the U.S.A., Educational Ministries, Box 851, Valley Forge, PA 19482-0851. TEL 215-768-2000 Ed. Linda Isham. illus. index. circ. 13,000.

266 US ISSN 0091-2743
BAPTIST MISSIONARY ASSOCIATION OF AMERICA. DIRECTORY AND HANDBOOK. 1961. a. free. Baptist News Service, Box 97, Jacksonville, TX 75766. TEL 214-586-8617 Eds. Leon Gaylor, James C. Blaylock. circ. 5,000. Key Title: Directory and Handbook - Baptist Missionary Association of America.
Missions

266 UK ISSN 0067-4060
BAPTIST MISSIONARY SOCIETY, LONDON. ANNUAL REPORT. 1792. a. free. Baptist Missionary Society, 93 Gloucester Place, London, W1H 4AA, England. circ. 7,000.
Missions

266.6 UK ISSN 0067-4079
BAPTIST MISSIONARY SOCIETY, LONDON. OFFICIAL REPORT AND DIRECTORY OF MISSIONARIES. 1793. a. free. Baptist Missionary Society, 93 Gloucester Place, London W1H 4AA, England. circ. 6,000.
Missions

286 US ISSN 0005-5743
BAPTIST PROGRAM. 1927. m. $10. Southern Baptist Convention, Executive Committee, 901 Commerce, Nashville, TN 37219. TEL 615-244-2355 Ed. Ernest Mosley. adv. bk. rev. illus. index. circ. 63,000. Indexed: South.Bap.Per.Ind.

286 US ISSN 0005-5751
BAPTIST PROGRESS. 1912. w. $10.50. Baptist Missionary Association of Texas, Box 2085, Waxahachie, TX 75165. TEL 214-923-0756 Ed. Danny Pope. adv. bk. rev. circ. 15,000(controlled) (also avail. in microfilm)
Missions

286 US
BAPTIST PUBLIC RELATIONS ASSOCIATION NEWSLETTER. 1953. m. membership. Baptist Public Relations Association, 901 Commerce, Ste. 500, Nashville, TN 37203-3697. bk. rev. tr.lit. circ. controlled. (looseleaf format)

286 209 UK ISSN 0005-576X
BAPTIST QUARTERLY. N.S. 1922. q. £4 to non-members; libraries £16. Baptist Historical Society, 148 Greenvale Rd., London SE9 1PQ, England. Ed. J.H.Y. Briggs. adv. bk. rev. illus. index every 2 yrs.; cum.index in 3 vols.: 1908-1921; 1922-1941; 1942-1964. circ. 700. (also avail. in microfilm from UMI; reprint service avail. from UMI) Indexed: Br.Hum.Ind. Hist.Abstr. Hist.Abstr. Rel.Per. Amer.Hist.& Life. CERDIC. Rel.Ind.One. Rel.& Theol.Abstr.

286 US ISSN 0005-5778
BAPTIST RECORD. 1877. w. $7.35. Mississippi Baptist Convention Board, Box 530, Jackson, MS 39205. TEL 601-968-3800 Ed. Donald T. McGregor. adv. bk. rev. charts. illus. record rev. circ. 124,000. (newspaper; also avail. in microform) Indexed: CERDIC.

286 UK ISSN 0005-5786
BAPTIST TIMES. 1855. w. £14.16. Baptist Times Ltd., 4 Southampton Row, London WC1B 4AB, England. Ed. Geoffrey Locks. adv. bk. rev. illus. music rev. record rev. circ. 15,800.

286 US ISSN 0025-4169
BAPTIST TRUE UNION; newsjournal for Maryland and Delaware Southern Baptists. 1849. w. $4.75. Baptist Convention of Maryland - Delaware, Box 1003, Lutherville, MD 21093. TEL 301-321-7900 Ed. W. Fletcher Allen. adv. illus. stat. circ. 18,000. (tabloid format; also avail. in microfilm)
Former titles (until 1985): Maryland Baptist; Incorporating: True Union.

286.1 UK ISSN 0302-3184
BAPTIST UNION DIRECTORY. 1861. a. £4.20. Baptist Union of Great Britain and Ireland, 4, Southampton Row, London WC1B 4AB, England. Ed. B. Green. adv. circ. 2,500.

286 CN ISSN 0067-4087
BAPTIST UNION OF WESTERN CANADA. YEARBOOK. 1907. a. Can.$9. Baptist Union of Western Canada, 838 11th Ave. S.W., Suite 202, Calgary, Alberta T2R 0E5, Canada. TEL 403-243-6880 Ed. D.N. Moffat. circ. 700 (controlled) (also avail. in microfilm)

286 US ISSN 0005-5808
BAPTIST WORLD. (Includes q. supplements of B W A divisions of World Aid, Evangelism and Education) 1954. q. $6. Baptist World Alliance, Division of Communications, 6733 Curran St., McLean, VA 22101-3804. TEL 703-790-8980 Ed. John Mannen Wilkes. bk. rev. illus. circ. 8,000. (also avail. in microform from UMI; reprint service avail. from UMI)

286 US ISSN 0067-4095
BAPTIST WORLD ALLIANCE. CONGRESS REPORTS. 1905. quinquennial; 15th, Los Angeles, 1985 (published in 1986) $11.50. Baptist World Alliance, 6733 Curran St., McLean, VA 22101-3804. TEL 703-790-8980 Ed. John Mannen Wilkes. circ. 15,000.

268 US ISSN 0162-4806
BAPTIST YOUNG ADULTS. q. $4.50. Southern Baptist Convention, Sunday School Board, 127 Ninth Ave. N., Nashville, TN 37234. TEL 615-251-2000
Formerly (until Oct. 1979): Young Adults in Training.

268 US ISSN 0162-4199
BAPTIST YOUTH. q. $4.75. Southern Baptist Convention, Sunday School Board, 127 Ninth Ave., North, Nashville, TN 37234. TEL 615-251-2000

284 GW ISSN 0005-7282
BAYREUTHER GEMEINDEBLATT. 1922. m. DM.8. Evangelische-Lutheranische Kirchengemeinde Bayreuth, Kirchplatz 2, 8580 Bayreuth, W. Germany (B.R.D.) Ed. Helmut Beyer. adv. bk. rev. abstr. circ. 5,500. (looseleaf format)

BEAM. see *COMMUNICATIONS — Radio And Television*

BEAM INTERNATIONAL; newsletter serving broadcasters around the world. see *COMMUNICATIONS — Radio And Television*

268 US ISSN 0198-6201
BEGINNING (NASHVILLE) q. $3.50. Southern Baptist Convention, Sunday School Board, 127 Ninth Ave., North, Nashville, TN 37234. TEL 615-251-2000

268 US ISSN 0162-4202
BIBLE BOOK STUDY FOR ADULT TEACHERS. q. $9.75. Southern Baptist Convention, Sunday School Board, 127 Ninth Ave., North, Nashville, TN 37234. TEL 615-251-2000

268 US ISSN 0162-4849
BIBLE BOOK STUDY FOR ADULTS. q. $5.25. Southern Baptist Convention, Sunday School Board, 127 Ninth Ave., North, Nashville, TN 37234. TEL 615-251-2000

268 US ISSN 0162-4822
BIBLE BOOK STUDY FOR YOUTH. q. $5.25. Southern Baptist Convention, Sunday School Board, 127 Ninth Ave., North, Nashville, TN 37234. TEL 615-251-2000
Ages 12-17

268 US ISSN 0162-4830
BIBLE BOOK STUDY FOR YOUTH TEACHERS. q. $9.75. Southern Baptist Convention, Sunday School Board, 127 Ninth Ave., North, Nashville, TN 37234. TEL 615-251-2000

268 US ISSN 0162-4695
BIBLE DISCOVERERS. q. $3.75. Southern Baptist Convention, Sunday School Board, 127 Ninth Ave., North, Nashville, TN 37234. TEL 615-251-2000
Ages 8-9

268 US ISSN 0162-4687
BIBLE DISCOVERERS: TEACHER. q. $8.50. Southern Baptist Convention, Sunday School Board, 127 Ninth Avenue, North, Nashville, TN 37234. TEL 615-251-2000

283 UK ISSN 0006-0763
BIBLE LANDS. 1899. q. free to donors. Jerusalem and the Middle East Church Association, The Old Gatehouse, Castle Hill, Farnham, Surrey GU9 0AE, England. Ed. R.H. Roberts. adv. bk. rev. illus. index. circ. 5,000.

268 US ISSN 0162-4679
BIBLE LEARNERS. q. $4. Southern Baptist Convention, Sunday School Board, 127 Ninth Ave., North, Nashville, TN 37234. TEL 615-251-2000
Ages 6-8

268 US ISSN 0162-4857
BIBLE LESSON DIGEST. q. in w. parts. $2.75. Southern Baptist Convention, Sunday School Board, 127 Ninth Ave., North, Nashville, TN 37234. TEL 615-251-2000

268 US ISSN 0162-4717
BIBLE READER'S GUIDE. q. $1.75. Southern Baptist Convention, Sunday School Board, 127 Ninth Ave., North, Nashville, TN 37234. TEL 615-251-2000

268 US ISSN 0006-078X
BIBLE SEARCHERS. 1970. q. $4. Southern Baptist Convention, Sunday School Board, 127 Ninth Ave. N., Nashville, TN 37203. TEL 615-251-2000
Supersedes: Sunday School Junior Pupil.

268 US ISSN 0006-0798
BIBLE SEARCHERS: TEACHER. q. $8.50. Southern Baptist Convention, Sunday School Board, 127 Ninth Ave. N., Nashville, TN 37203. TEL 615-251-2000 Ed. W. Mark Moore. circ. 112,172.
Formerly: Junior Teacher.

268 US ISSN 0162-475X
BIBLE STUDY LEAFLET (LIFE AND WORK SERIES) q. in w. parts. $2.75. Southern Baptist Convention, Sunday School Board, 127 Ninth Ave., North, Nashville, TN 37234. TEL 615-251-2000

268 US ISSN 0162-4741
BIBLE STUDY POCKET COMMENTARY. q. $3.75. Southern Baptist Convention, Sunday School Board, 127 Ninth Ave., North, Nashville, TN 37234. TEL 615-251-2000

268 US
BIBLE STUDY-SPECIAL MINISTRIES. q. $4. Southern Baptist Convention, Sunday School Board, 127 Ninth Ave., N., Nashville, TN 37234. TEL 615-251-2000
Formerly: Simplified Bible Study (ISSN 0162-4644)

268 US ISSN 0195-4407
BIBLICAL ILLUSTRATOR. q. $11. Southern Baptist Convention, Sunday School Board, 127 Ninth Ave., North, Nashville, TN 37234. TEL 615-251-2000 Indexed: South.Bap.Per.Ind.
Formerly: Sunday School Lesson Illustrator (ISSN 0162-4407)

266 285 US ISSN 0006-0909
BIBLICAL MISSIONS. 1935. 6/yr. $6. Independent Board for Presbyterian Foreign Missions, 246 W. Walnut Lane, Philadelphia, PA 19144. TEL 215-438-0511 Ed. Rev. Earle R. White. adv. bk. rev. illus. circ. 3,000. Indexed: CERDIC.
Missions

230 US ISSN 0006-1921
BIBLIOTHECA SACRA; a theological quarterly. 1843. q. $8. Dallas Theological Seminary, 3909 Swiss Ave., Dallas, TX 75204. TEL 214-824-3094 Ed. Roy B. Zuck. bk. rev. abstr. bibl. index. circ. 8,000. (also avail. in microform from UMI; reprint service avail. from UMI) Indexed: Old Test.Abstr. Rel.Per. Int.Z.Bibelwiss. CERDIC. Chr.Per.Ind. New Test.Abstr. Rel.Ind.One. Rel.& Theol.Abstr.

BLACK MINISTRIES. see *ETHNIC INTERESTS*

284.2 SA ISSN 0006-4947
BLOEMHEUWEL-NUUS. (Text in Afrikaans) 1953. q. free. Nederduitse Gereformeerde Kerk, Bloemfontein - Dutch Reformed Church, Bloemfontein, Bloemheuwel, 15 General Hertzog Str., Bloemfontein, South Africa. Ed. Rev. H. C. J. Flemming. adv. bk. rev. bibl. circ. 1,000.

284.2 GW ISSN 0006-8276
BOTSCHAFTER DES KOMMENDEN KOENIGS. 1902. m. DM.13. Verlagsbuchhandlung Bethel - Dirk Dolman und Co. KG Nachfolger, Gluckstr. 53, 2000 Hamburg 76, W. Germany (B.R.D.) Ed. George Dolman.

260 GW
BREMER KIRCHENZEITUNG. 1928. bi-w. DM.10. (Bremische Evangelische Kirche) Carl Schuenemann Verlag, Zweite Schlachtpforte 7, Postfach 106067, 2800 Bremen 1, W. Germany (B.R.D.) Ed. H. Nemetschek. circ. 20,000.

250 UK
BRISTOL DIOCESAN NEWS. m. £1 for 100 copies. Diocese of Bristol, 23 Great George St., Bristol BS1 5QZ, England. Ed. Hugh Bunting. bk. rev. circ. 15,000.
Formerly: Bristol Diocesan Gazette (ISSN 0045-2858)

286 UK
BRITISH WEEKLY AND CHRISTIAN RECORD. 1886. w. £26. Christian Weekly Newspapers Ltd., Livingstone House, 11 Carteret St., London SW1H 9DJ, England. adv. bk. rev. film rev. record rev. illus.
Formed by the merger of: British Weekly and Christian World (ISSN 0007-1951) & Christian Record.

200 FR
BULLETIN D'INFORMATION PROTESTANT. 1961. w. 365 F. Federation Protestante de France, Service d'Information, 47 rue de Clichy, 75009 Paris, France. Ed. Claudette Marquet. abstr. circ. 800. (processed)
Formerly: Service Protestant Francais de Presse et d'Information (ISSN 0037-2625)

280 UK ISSN 0045-3536
BULWARK. 1851. 6/yr. $4. Scottish Reformation Society, 17 George Fourth Bridge, Edinburgh EH1 1EE, Scotland. Ed. A. Sinclair Horne. bk. rev. circ. 6,200.

266 282 SX
C C N INFORMATION. 1980. 11/yr. R.5. Council of Churches in Namibia, P.O. Box 41, Windhoek 9000, Namibia. Ed. D.J.K. Tjongarero. adv. bk. rev. circ. 2,000. (back issues avail.)

283 UK ISSN 0007-8255
C E N. (Church of England Newspaper) 1828. w. £26. Christian Weekly Newspapers Ltd., Livingstone House, 11 Carteret St., London SW1H 9DJ, England. adv. bk. rev. film rev. record rev. illus. circ. 11,000. (tabloid format)

267 UK
C W M REPORT. 1795. biennial. £1. Council for World Mission, 11 Carteret St., London SW1H 9DL, England. circ. 15,000.
Formerly: Congregational Council for World Mission. Annual Report (ISSN 0069-8857)
Missions

283 CN ISSN 0383-6509
CALEDONIA DIOCESAN TIMES. 1960. m. Anglican Church of Canada, Diocese of Caledonia, Dawson Creek, B.C., Canada. TEL 604-782-2939 illus.

286 US ISSN 0008-1558
CALIFORNIA SOUTHERN BAPTIST. 1941. w. $7.95. Southern Baptist General Convention of California, 678 E. Shaw Ave., Fresno, CA 93710. TEL 209-229-9533 Ed. Herb Hollinger. adv. bk. rev. illus. index. circ. 28,000.

207.11 US ISSN 0008-1779
CALVARY REVIEW. 1962. q. free. Calvary Bible College, 15800 Calvary Rd., Kansas City, MO 64147. TEL 816-322-0110 bk. rev. circ. 17,000.

284.2 NE ISSN 0008-1787
CALVIJN. 1919. m. fl.5($3) Nederlandse Hervormde Vereniging Calvijn - Dutch Reformed Society, A. Paulownastraat 38, Dordrecht, Netherlands. Ed. G.J. Edelman. circ. 500.

230 US ISSN 0008-1795
CALVIN THEOLOGICAL JOURNAL. 1966. s-a. $8. (Christian Reformed Board of Publications) Calvin Theological Seminary, 3233 Burton St. S.E., Grand Rapids, MI 49506. TEL 616-857-6000 Ed.Bd. bk. rev. index. circ. 2,000. (also avail. in microform from UMI; reprint service avail. from UMI) Indexed: Old Test.Abstr. Rel.Per. CERDIC. Chr.Per.Ind. Int.Z.Bibelwiss. New Test.Abstr. Rel.& Theol.Abstr. Rel.Ind.One.

284 366 CN ISSN 0410-3882
CALVINIST CONTACT. (Text in Dutch and English) vol.3, 1951. w. Can.$25. Calvinist Contact Publishing Limited, 99 Niagara St., St. Catharines, Ont. L2R 4L3, Canada. TEL 416-682-8311 Ed.Bd. adv. bk. rev. illus. circ. 7,500.
Continues: Contact (ISSN 0382-5949)

286 CN ISSN 0008-2988
CANADIAN BAPTIST. 1854. m. Can.$9($13) Baptist Convention of Ontario and Quebec, 217 St. George St., Toronto M5R 2M2, Ont., Canada. (Co-sponsor: Baptist Union of Western Canada) Ed. Dr. William H. Jones. adv. bk. rev. index. circ. 18,105. (also avail. in microform)

283 CN ISSN 0008-3216
CANADIAN CHURCHMAN. 1874. m. $4. Anglican Church of Canada, 600 Jarvis St., Toronto, Ont. M4Y 2J6, Canada. TEL 416-924-9192 Ed. Jerrold F. Hames. adv. bk. rev. film rev. illus. circ. 280,000. (tabloid format; also avail. in microfilm from MIM,UMI)

704.948 US ISSN 0008-7874
CATHEDRAL AGE; an international magazine devoted to cathedral interests throughout the world. 1925. q. $15 to non-members. Protestant Episcopal Cathedral Foundation in the District of Columbia, Mt. St. Alban, Washington, DC 20016. Ed. Linda R. Freeman. adv. bk. rev. film rev. illus. play rev. circ. 24,000. (also avail. in microform from UMI; reprint service avail. from UMI)
Ecclesiastical

200 US
CENTINELA. French edition: Sentinelle. (Text in Spanish) 1896. m. $6. (Seventh-Day Adventists) Pacific Press Publishing Association, 1350 Kings Rd., Nampa, ID 83651. TEL 208-467-6600 Ed. Tulio Peverini. circ. 113,000. (also avail. in microform from UMI)

284 572 100 SZ
CENTRE PROTESTANT D'ETUDES DE GENEVE. BULLETIN. (Text in French) 1948. bi-m. 30 F. Centre Protestant d'Etudes de Geneve, 7 rue Tabazan, CH-1204 Geneva, Switzerland. adv. circ. 1,300.

284 CS ISSN 0009-0778
CESKY BRATR. (Supplement to: Sbirka Kazani pro Ctene Sluzby Bozi) vol.47, 1971. 10/yr. 32 Kcs.($8.80) Evangelicka Cirkev Ceskobratrska, Rada, Jungmannova 9, 110 00 Prague 1, Czechoslovakia (Subscr. to: Artia, Ve Smeckach 30, 111 27 Prague 1) Ed. Josef Svaton.

200 CE
CEYLON CHURCHMAN. (Text in English) m. Rs.40($8) Dioceses of Colombo & Kurunagala, Diocesan Office, Bauddhaloka Mawatha, Colombo 7, Sri Lanka. Ed. C.N.V. Fernando. adv. bk. rev. circ. 1,500.

283 UK ISSN 0009-0999
CHALLENGE (LONDON, 1961) 1961. bi-m. 5p. per no. Anglican Pacifist Fellowship, St. Mary's Vicarage, Bayswater Rd., Headington, Oxford OX3 9EY, England. Ed. Rev. Robin Eastoe. bk. rev. circ. 1,900.
Formerly: Anglican Pacifist.

285 CN
CHANNELS. 1960. bi-m. Can.$8. Renewal Fellowship within the Presbyterian Church in Canada, c/o Rev. J.H. Hans Kouwenberg, Ed., 4553 Cascade Ave., Prince George, B.C. V2M 6J5, Canada. bk. rev. circ. 2,000.
Supersedes: Presbyterian Comment (ISSN 0383-7645)

284 US
CHAPLAIR. 1977? q. membership. Assembly of Episcopal Hospitals and Chaplains, 920 Cayots Corner Rd., Chesapeake City, MD 21915. circ. 800.

CHARITY AND CHILDREN; the voice of child care. see *CHILDREN AND YOUTH — About*

266 AT ISSN 0311-0737
CHECKPOINT. 1972. bi-m. Aus.$5. ‡ Church Missionary Society of Australia, 93 Bathurst St., Sydney, N.S.W. 2000, Australia. bk. rev. illus. circ. 8,400.
Supersedes: C M S News (ISSN 0007-8689)
Missions

280 370 US ISSN 0276-3427
CHILDREN'S LEADER. q. $7.50. (United Methodist Church, Board of Discipleship) Graded Press, 201 Eighth Ave. S., Box 801, Nashville, TN 37202. TEL 615-749-6421 Ed. Annella Creech.

266 US ISSN 0009-4412
CHINA NOTES. 1962. q. $12. National Council of the Churches of Christ in the U.S.A., Division of Overseas Ministries, East Asia and the Pacific Committee, China Program, Rm. 616, 475 Riverside Dr., New York, NY 10115. TEL 212-870-2175 Ed. Franklin J. Woo. bk. rev. film rev. bibl. index. circ. 2,000. (also avail. in microfilm)
Supersedes: China Bulletin.

268 US ISSN 0362-0409
CHORAL PRAISE. q. $6.25. Southern Baptist Convention, Sunday School Board, 127 Ninth Ave., North, Nashville, TN 37234. TEL 615-251-2000

200 US ISSN 0412-2968
CHRIST IN OUR HOME; daily devotions. 1954. q. $3.25. (American Lutheran Church, Commission on Evangelism) Augsburg Publishing House, 426 S. Fifth St., Minneapolis, MN 55440. TEL 612-330-3300 Ed. Omar Stuenkel. circ. 410,000. (back issues avail.; large print edt. avail.)

268 282 GE ISSN 0009-5192
CHRISTENLEHRE; Zeitschrift fuer den Katechetischen Dienst. 1948. m. M.28.80. Evangelische Verlagsanstalt GmbH, Krautstr. 52, 1017 Berlin, E. Germany (D.D.R.) Ed. Dieter Reiher. bk. rev.

286 UK ISSN 0143-7518
CHRISTIAN FELLOWSHIP. 1980. m. £0.25 per no. Churches of Christ in Great Britain and Ireland, 147 Northfield Rd., Kings Norton, Birmingham B30 1EA, England. Ed. Richard Stitt. adv. bk. rev. illus. charts. circ. 500.
Continues in part: Christian Advocate.

CHRISTIAN LIBRARIAN. see *LIBRARY AND INFORMATION SCIENCES*

CHRISTIAN LIBRARIAN. see *LIBRARY AND INFORMATION SCIENCES*

285 GH ISSN 0009-5478
CHRISTIAN MESSENGER. (Text in English, Ga, Twi) 1883. m. $20. Presbyterian Book Depot, Box 3075, Accra, Ghana. Ed. G.B.K. Owusu. adv. bk. rev. bibl. illus. stat. circ. 58,000. (tabloid format) Indexed: CERDIC.

284 US ISSN 0009-5494
CHRISTIAN MONTHLY. 1950. m. $10. Apostolic Lutheran Church of America, Rt. 2, Box 356, New York Mills, MN 56567. TEL 218-385-2970 Ed. Alvar Helmes. circ. 1,100.

284 US ISSN 0009-5516
CHRISTIAN NEWS. 1968. w. (except Aug.) $15. Lutheran News, Inc., Box 168, New Haven, MO 63068. Ed. Herman Otten. bk. rev. stat. index. circ. 13,000. (tabloid format)
Formerly (1962-1967): Lutheran News.

CHRISTIAN PARAPSYCHOLOGIST. see *PARAPSYCHOLOGY AND OCCULTISM*

268 US ISSN 0191-4294
CHRISTIAN SINGLE. m. $14.50. Southern Baptist Convention, Sunday School Board, 127 Ninth Ave., North, Nashville, TN 37234. TEL 615-251-2000

283 UK ISSN 0144-073X
CHRISTIAN STATESMAN. 1978. 4/yr. £2. c/o The Vicarage Flat, Carr St., Leigh, Lancs. WN7 4SY, England. Ed.Bd. adv. bk. rev. circ. 500.

200 UK
CHRISTIAN WORDS. 1849. m. 72p. Wesleyan Reform Union, Wesleyan Reform Church House, 123 Queen St., Sheffield S1 2DU, England. adv.

250 UK
CHRISTIAN YEAR. 1987. a. £4.95. Methodist Publishing House, Wellington Rd., Wimbledon, London SW19 8EU, England. circ. 25,000.

268 US ISSN 0412-4553
CHURCH ADMINISTRATION. m. $17.75. Southern Baptist Convention, Sunday School Board, 127 Ninth Ave., North, Nashville, TN 37234. TEL 615-251-2000 Indexed: South.Bap.Per.Ind.

200 AT ISSN 0314-6200
CHURCH & NATION. 1977. s-m. Aus.$20($28) ‡ Uniting Church in Australia, Synod of Victoria, Board of Communication, 130 Little Collins St., Melbourne, Victoria 3000, Australia. Ed. Warren Clarnette. adv. bk. rev. illus. circ. 6,200. (back issues avail.)
Former titles: New Spectator (ISSN 0300-3736); Spectator.
Emphasis on Uniting Church in Victoria and Tasmania

261 285 US ISSN 0037-7805
CHURCH AND SOCIETY. 1908. bi-m. $5. United Presbyterian Church in the U.S.A., Room 1244, 475 Riverside Dr., New York, NY 10027. TEL 212-870-2515 Ed. Earl Larson. bk. rev. bibl. charts. illus. circ. 5,000. (also avail. in microfilm from UMI; reprint service avail. from UMI) Indexed: Rel.Per. CERDIC. Rel.Ind.One.
Formerly: Social Progress.

200 UK
CHURCH ARMY. FRONT LINE. 1981. a. Church Army, Independents Rd., Blackheath, London SE3 9LG, England. illus.
Formerly: Church Army. Centenary News.

209 AT
CHURCH HERITAGE. 1978. s-a. Aus.$4. Church Records and Historical Society (NSW), P.O. Box 2395, North Parramatta, NSW 2151, Australia. Ed. E.G. Clancy. bk. rev. index. circ. 200.
Supersedes: Australasian Methodist Historical Society. Journal and Proceedings (ISSN 0084-6988)

CHURCH MEDIA LIBRARY MAGAZINE. see *LIBRARY AND INFORMATION SCIENCES*

283 UK ISSN 0307-7225
CHURCH OF ENGLAND. GENERAL SYNOD. REPORT OF PROCEEDINGS. 1970. 3/yr. £7 per no. C I O Publishing, Church House, Deans Yard, London SW1P 3NZ, England. index.

283 270 AT ISSN 0009-6490
CHURCH OF ENGLAND HISTORICAL SOCIETY (DIOCESE OF SYDNEY). JOURNAL. 1956. q. Aus.$10. Church of England Historical Society, Box 2902, G.P.O. Sydney, N.S.W. 2001, Australia. Ed. J.G. Thurling. bk. rev. circ. 250. (back issues avail.)

283 UK ISSN 0069-3987
CHURCH OF ENGLAND YEARBOOK. 1882. a. £12.50. C I O Publishing, Church House, Dean's Yard, London SW1P 3NZ, England. Ed. Mrs. Jo Linzey. adv. bk. rev. circ. 3,000.

280 US
CHURCH OF GOD EVANGEL. 1911. bi-w. (20/yr.) $8.50. Church of God, Keith and 25th St., N.W., Cleveland, TN 37311 TEL 615-472-3361 (Subscr. to: Pathway Press, 1080 Montgomery Ave., Cleveland, TN 37311 (615-476-4152)) Ed. O.W. Palen. circ. 42,000. (back issues avail.)

200 UK ISSN 0009-6512
CHURCH OF IRELAND GAZETTE. 1850. w. 15p. Church of Ireland Press, 48 Bachelor's Walk, Lisburn BT28 1XN, Northern Ireland. Ed. Rev. C.W.M. Cooper. adv. bk. rev. circ. 6,000.

285.241 UK ISSN 0069-3995
CHURCH OF SCOTLAND. YEARBOOK. 1885. a. £7.50. Saint Andrew Press, 121 George St., Edinburgh EH2 4YN, Scotland. Ed. Rev. Andrew Herron. adv. index. circ. 2,500.

268 US
CHURCH RECREATION MAGAZINE. q. $8.25. Southern Baptist Convention, Sunday School Board, 127 Ninth Ave., North, Nashville, TN 37234. TEL 615-251-2000 Indexed: Sportsearch.
Formerly: Church Recreation (ISSN 0529-7028)

283 AT ISSN 0009-6563
CHURCH SCENE; Australian National Anglican newspaper. 1971. w. Aus.$33. Church Press Ltd., Box 2035, St. Kilda West 3182, Australia. Ed. Gerald Charles Davis. adv. bk. rev. illus. circ. 9,250. (tabloid format)

283 UK ISSN 0009-658X
CHURCH TIMES. 1863. w. £22. G.J. Palmer & Sons Ltd., 7 Portugal St., London WC2A 2HP, England. Ed. Bernard H.M. Palmer. adv. bk. rev. illus. index. circ. 44,987. (tabloid format; also avail. in microfilm from UMI; reprint service avail. from UMI) Indexed: Chr.Per.Ind.

268 US ISSN 0162-4601
CHURCH TRAINING. m. $11. Southern Baptist Convention, Sunday School Board, 127 Ninth Ave., North, Nashville, TN 37234. TEL 615-251-2000 Indexed: South.Bap.Per.Ind.

283 UK ISSN 0009-661X
CHURCHMAN; a journal of Anglican theology. 1879. 4/yr. $19. Church Society, 186 Kennington Park Rd., London SE11 4BT, England. Ed. Rev. Gerald Bray. adv. bk. rev. index. circ. 1,200. (also avail. in microfilm from MIM) Indexed: CERDIC. Old Test.Abstr. Rel.Per. New Test.Abstr. Rel.Ind.One.

200 UK ISSN 0009-6636
CHURCHMAN'S MAGAZINE. 1846. bi-m. £2.20. Protestant Truth Society Inc, 184 Fleet St., London E.C.4, England. Ed. Alfred Latimer Kensit. adv. bk. rev. illus. circ. 3,200.

287 US ISSN 0146-9924
CIRCUIT RIDER (NASHVILLE) 1976. m. $6 (free to United Methodist clergy) United Methodist Publishing House, 201 Eighth Ave. So., Nashville, TN 37202. TEL 615-749-6000 Ed. Richard Peck. circ. 40,000.

287 940 UK ISSN 0950-8732
CIRPLAN. 1955. 2/yr. 75p. Society of Cirplanologists, 34 Fernhill Crescent, Stacksteads, Bacup, Lancs. 0L13 8JU, England. Ed. Ken F. Bowden. bk. rev. circ. 110. (processed; back issues avail.)

CITE NOUVELLE. see *POLITICAL SCIENCE*

CLUBHOUSE. see *CHILDREN AND YOUTH — For*

284 US
COMING CHANGES NEWSLETTER. Variant title: Changes Newsletter. 1979. 6/yr. $18. Changes Publishing Co., 937 St. Mary's St., DePere, WI 54115. Richard C. Green. bk. rev. illus. circ. 1,500. (back issues avail.)

266 US ISSN 0279-1196
COMMUNICARE. 1926. m. free. Christian Communications, Inc., Box 1601, Wichita, KS 67201. TEL 316-744-1208 Ed. Dr. Hart R. Armstrong. circ. 30,000.
Formerly (until 1981): Defender.

285 US
COMMUNIQUE (COLUMBUS); the newspaper of the Synod of the Covenant. 1974. bi-m. $3. United Presbyterian Church, Synod of the Covenant, 6172 Busch Blvd., Columbus, OH 43229. TEL 614-451-4836 Ed. Dennis E. Shoemaker. adv. circ. 11,000. (tabloid format; back issues avail.)

209 900 US ISSN 0010-5260
CONCORDIA HISTORICAL INSTITUTE QUARTERLY. 1928. q. $15. (Lutheran Church-Missouri Synod) Concordia Historical Institute, 801 DeMun Ave., St. Louis, MO 63105. TEL 314-721-5934 Ed. Hilton C. Oswald. adv. bk. rev. charts. illus, tr.lit. cum. index every 4 yrs. circ. 1,700. Indexed: Hist.Abstr. Hist.Abstr. Rel.Per. Amer.Hist.& Life. Geneal.Per.Ind. Rel.Ind.One.
History

284 US ISSN 0017-2154
CONFIDENT LIVING. 1941. 11/yr. (except Jul.-Aug. combined) $10. Good News Broadcasting Association, Inc., Back to the Bible Broadcast, Box 82808, Lincoln, NE 68501. TEL 402-474-4567 Ed. Norman A. Olson. illus. circ. 150,000. Indexed: G.Soc.Sci.& Rel.Per.Lit.
Formerly: Good News Broadcaster.

284 US ISSN 0361-8862
CONGREGATION. 1972. bi-m. $2. Lutheran Church in America, 2900 Queen Lane, Philadelphia, PA 19129. TEL 215-438-5600 Ed. W.G. Volker. circ. 150,000. (tabloid format)

285 US ISSN 0361-2376
CONGREGATIONAL JOURNAL. 1975. 3/yr. $6. American Congregational Center, 298 Fairfax Ave., Ventura, CA 93003 TEL 805-644-3397 (Or: 1515 Garfield Ave., South Pasadena, CA 91030) Ed. Henry David Gray. bk. rev. circ. 1,400.

CONGREGATIONAL LIBRARY. BULLETIN. see *LIBRARY AND INFORMATION SCIENCES*

285 US ISSN 0010-5856
CONGREGATIONALIST. 1816. s-m. $8. ‡ National Association of Congregational Christian Churches, 6134 Kerry Ave., Cheyenne, WY 82009. TEL 313-393-9433 Ed. Mary K. Woolsey. adv. bk. rev. illus. circ. 6,500.

266 AT ISSN 0159-1096
CONTACT (SYDNEY) 1976. 4/yr. free. Church Missionary Society of Australia, 93 Bathurst St., Sydney, N.S.W. 2000, Australia. circ. 63,000.
Missions

200 NE ISSN 0010-731X
CONTACTBLAD; voor cursisten en oud-cursisten van de stem der profetie. 1948. q. free. (Zevende Dags Adventisten) E S D A Institute, Pr. Alexanderweg 1C, 3712 AD Huis Ter Heide, Netherlands. Ed. A.F. Steens. adv. bk. rev. circ. 4,000. (microfilm)

286 US
CONTEMPO; a magazine for Baptist young women. 1970. m. $8.50. Southern Baptist Convention, Women's Missionary Union, Highway 280 E., 100 Missionary Ridge, Birmingham, AL 35243-2978. TEL 205-991-8100 Ed. Mary Ann Ward. circ. 65,000.

CONTRAPUNKT; christliche Zweimonatszeitschrift fuer junge Leute. see *CHILDREN AND YOUTH — For*

266 IT
CRISTIANO. 1888. m. L.7000. Associazione Stampe Pubblicazioni Evangeliche (A.S.P.E.), Via Magellano 21, 47037 Rimini FO, Italy. Ed. Samuele Negri. circ. 3,700.

286 FR
CROIRE ET SERVIR. 1946. m. 32 Fr. Federation des Eglises Evangeliques Baptistes, 123 Av du Maine, 75014 Paris, France. Ed. Andre Thobois. bk. rev. circ. 20,000.

270 US ISSN 0011-1961
CROSS OF LANGUEDOC. 1960. s-a. membership. National Huguenot Society, c/o Mrs. Luther Swanstrom, 9027 S. Damen Ave., Chicago, IL 60620. TEL 312-238-0423 Ed. Adam French. bk. rev. circ. 4,000. (processed)
Supersedes: National Huguenot Society Proceedings.

285 NZ
CROSSLINK. 1987. m. NZ.$15 free to members. Presbyterian Church of New Zealand, P.O. Box 10-000, The Terrace, Wellington, New Zealand. Ed. J.J. Kuiper. adv. bk. rev. illus. circ. 75,000.

283.713 CN ISSN 0706-8069
CROSSTALK. 1978. 10/yr. Can.$5. Anglican Church of Canada, Diocese of Ottawa, 71 Bronson Ave., Ottawa, Ont. K1R 6G6, Canada. TEL 613-232-7124 Ed. William A. Gilbert. adv. bk. rev. circ. 17,000.
Formerly: Canadian Churchman and Crosstalk (ISSN 0706-8069)

261 UK ISSN 0011-2100
CRUCIBLE. 1962. q. £5.60. (Board for Social Responsibility of the General Synod) C I O Publishing, Church House, Dean's Yard, London SW1P 3NZ, England. Ed. Michael Atkinson. adv. bk. rev. index. circ. 2,000. Indexed: CERDIC.

286 US ISSN 0011-2151
CRUSADER. 1970. m. $2.28 for 3 mos. Southern Baptist Convention, Brotherhood Commission, 1548 Poplar Ave., Memphis, TN 38104. Ed. James Warren. bk. rev. illus. circ. 100,000. Indexed: South.Bap.Per.Ind.
For boys ages 6-11

283 CN ISSN 0382-4314
CRUSADER (TORONTO) vol. 1, 1929. 2/yr. free. Church Army in Canada, 397 Brunswick Ave., Toronto, Ont. M5R 2Z2, Canada. TEL 416-924-9279 Ed. R. Taylor. illus. circ. 12,000.
Continues: Anglican Crusader (ISSN 0382-4306)

CRUSADER MAGAZINE. see *CHILDREN AND YOUTH — For*

285 US ISSN 0011-2976
CUMBERLAND PRESBYTERIAN. 1829. fortn. $9. Cumberland Presbyterian Church, Office of the General Assembly, 1978 Union Ave., Memphis, TN 38104. TEL 901-276-4572 Ed. J. Richard Magrill, Jr. adv. bk. rev. illus. circ. 7,225.

284 UK ISSN 0143-0076
Y CYLCHGRAWN EFENGYLAIDD. English edition: Evangelical Magazine of Wales (ISSN 0421-8094) 1948. bi-m. £4.14($6) Evangelical Press of Wales, Bryntirion, Bridgend, Mid Glamorgan CF31 4DX, Wales. Ed. Rev. Noel Gibbard. adv. circ. 2,000.

284 CS
CZECHOSLOVAK ECUMENICAL NEWS/ TSCHECHOSLOWAKISCHE OEKUMENISCHE NACHRICHTEN. (Text in English and German) 1954. bi-m. free. Ecumenical Council of Churches in C S S R, Vitkova 13, 186 00 Prague- Karlin, Czechoslovakia. Ed. Rev. Anna Lukesova. circ. 2,200.
Former titles (until no.2, 1984): Czech Ecumenical News (ISSN 0013-077X); (until 1964): Protestant Churches in Czechoslovakia.

284.2 SA
D R C NEWS. (Dutch Reformed Church) 1958. q. R.5. Nederduitse Gereformeerde Kerk in Suid-Afrika, Ecumenical Department - Dutch Reformed Church, Box 4445, Pretoria 0001, South Africa. Ed. P. Rossouw. bk. rev. circ. 2,000.
Former titles: D R C Africa News; D R C Newsletter (ISSN 0011-5118)

268 UK
DAILY WATCHWORDS; the Moravian textbook with almanack. 1722. a. £1.30. Moravian Union Inc., Moravian Book Room, 5 Muswell Hill, London N.10 3TJ, England. Ed. J.M. Cooper. circ. 5,000.

285 248.82 UK ISSN 0011-7102
DAYBREAK. m. £1.20. Presbyterian Church in Ireland, Church House, Fisherwick Place, Belfast BT1 6DW, N. Ireland. Ed. Zena McAllister. circ. 6,500.
Formerly: Primary Daybreak.
Ages 8 and under

254 US ISSN 0045-9771
DEACON. 1970. q. $9. Southern Baptist Convention, Sunday School Board, 127 Ninth Ave., N., Nashville, TN 37234. TEL 615-251-2000 cum.index (every 3 years) circ. 63,000. (tabloid format) Indexed: South.Bap.Per.Ind.

284 US ISSN 0011-7307
DECISION (MINNEAPOLIS) (Editions in Chinese, English, French, German, Japanese, Spanish) 1960. m., (except Aug.) $5. Billy Graham Evangelistic Association, 1300 Harmon Place, Minneapolis, MN 55403 TEL 612-338-0500 (Or Box 779, Minneapolis, MN 55440) Ed. Roger C. Palms. adv. illus. index. cum.index. circ. 2,000,000. Indexed: Chr.Per.Ind.

270 GW ISSN 0012-0294
DER DEUTSCHE HUGENOTT. 1929. q. DM.12. ‡ Deutscher Hugenotten-Verein e.V., Postfach 35, D-3305 Sickte, W. Germany (B.R.D.) Ed. Jochen Desel. bk. rev. abstr. bibl. illus. circ. 1,500. Indexed: Hist.Abstr. Amer.Hist.& Life.

DEUTSCHER HUGENOTTEN-VEREIN E.V. GESCHICHTSBLAETTER. see *HISTORY — History Of Europe*

284 US
DEVOTIONS (CINCINNATI) 1957. q. $3.75 (large print $5.50) Standard Publishing, 8121 Hamilton Ave., Cincinnati, OH 45231. TEL 513-931-4050 Ed. Eileen H. Wilmoth. circ. 97,000.

284.2 GW ISSN 0012-1975
DIAKONIE IM RHEINLAND. 1963. 6/yr. DM.20. Diakonisches Werk der Evangelischen Kirche im Rheinland, Lenaustr. 41, 4000 Duesseldorf 30, W. Germany (B.R.D.) Ed. Heinz Rossig. adv. illus.

287 SA ISSN 0046-0265
DIMENSION. (Supplement avail.: Profile) 1970. m. R.25. Methodist Church of Southern Africa, P.O. Box 34632, Jeppestown 2043, Transvaal, South Africa. Ed. Theo Coggin. adv. bk. rev. circ. 26,992. (tabloid format) Indexed: Cath.Ind.

286 US ISSN 0162-6825
DIMENSION (BIRMINGHAM) 1970. q. $6. Southern Baptist Convention, Women's Missionary Union, Highway 280 E., 100 Missionary Ridge, Birmingham, AL 35243-2798. TEL 205-991-8100 Ed. Oneta Gentry. circ. 45,000.

200 CN ISSN 0382-9391
DIOCESAN TIMES. 1946. m. (exc. July & Aug.) (Anglican Diocese of Nova Scotia) Diocesan Times Publishing Co., 5732 College St., Halifax, N.S. B3H 1X3, Canada. TEL 902-423-8301 Ed. Avard L. Bishop. adv. circ. 17,500.

284 US ISSN 0273-5865
DISCIPLESHIP JOURNAL. 1981. bi-m. $12. Navigators, Box 6000, Colorado Springs, CO 80934 TEL 303-598-1212 (Subscr. addr.: Box 1113, Dover, NJ 07801) Ed. E. Calvin Beisner. index. circ. 70,000. Indexed: Chr.Per.Ind.

286 US ISSN 0732-9881
DISCIPLIANA. 1941. q. $10 membership. Disciples of Christ Historical Society, 1101 Nineteenth Ave., S., Nashville, TN 37212. TEL 615-327-1444 Ed. James M. Seale. bk. rev. bibl. circ. 5,500. (also avail. in microfilm)

DISCOVERIES. see *CHILDREN AND YOUTH — For*

266 AT ISSN 0726-6286
DISCOVERY. 1973. bi-m. free. Church Missionary Society of Australia, 93 Bathurst St., Sydney, N.S.W. 2000, Australia. circ. 2,560.

DOOPSGEZINDE BIJDRAGEN. see *HISTORY — History Of Europe*

284 CN ISSN 0701-0214
DRAUDZES VESTIS. (Text in Latvian) 1953. m. Can.$5. Peace Latvian Lutheran Church, c/o Rev. E.A. Lange, Ed., 364 Pleasent Park Rd., Ottawa, Ont. K1H 5M8, Canada. adv. bk. rev. circ. 170.

284 GW ISSN 0012-608X
DREIKOENIGSBOTE. 1951. m. free. Evangelisch-Lutherische Dreikoenigsgemeinde, Oppenheimer Str. 5, 6000 Frankfurt 70, W. Germany (B.R.D.) bibl. circ. 800.

200 US ISSN 0012-6152
DREW GATEWAY; a journal of comment and criticism. 1930. 3/yr. 9. Drew University Theological School, Madison, NJ 07940. TEL 201-377-3000 Eds. Lala Kalyan Dey, Nelson S.T. Thayer. bk. rev. index. circ. 1,000. (also avail. in microfilm from UMI) Indexed: Rel.Per. CERDIC. Rel.Ind.One.

261 287 US ISSN 0164-5528
E/S A. 1973. m. $10. ‡ United Methodist Church, General Board of Church and Society, 100 Maryland Ave. N.E., Washington, DC 20002. TEL 202-488-5632 Ed. Lee Ranck. adv. bk. rev. illus. index. circ. 4,500. (also avail. in microfilm from UMI; reprint service avail. from UMI) Indexed: Rel.Per. CERDIC. Method.Per.Ind. Rel.Ind.One.
Formerly (until 1975): Engage/Social Action (ISSN 0090-3485); Which was formed by the merger of: Engage (ISSN 0013-7618); Social Action (ISSN 0037-7635)

284 CN ISSN 0831-4446
EASTERN SYNOD LUTHERAN. 1911. 10/yr. $4. Evangelical Lutheran Church in Canada, Eastern Synod, 50 Queen St. N., Kitchener, Ont. N2H 6P4, Canada. Ed. Jane Wahl. adv. bk. rev. circ. 22,500.
Formerly: Canada Lutheran (ISSN 0008-2716)

280 377.8 US
EDUCATION NEWSLINE. 1983. bi-m. $32. National Association of Christian Educators, Box 3200, Costa Mesa, CA 92628. Ed. Eric Buehrer. bk. rev. bibl. illus. circ. 5,500.
Formerly: Christians in Education.

284 UK ISSN 0013-6182
ELIM EVANGEL. 1919. w. £15.50($30) Elim Pentecostal Church, Elim Publications Board, Box 38, Cheltenham, Gloucestershire, England. Ed. Peter Smith. adv. bk. rev. circ. 6,400.

269.2 CN ISSN 0315-0097
ENCOUNTER. 1972. q. Ken Campbell Evangelistic Association, Box 100, Milton, Ont. L9T 2Y3, Canada. TEL 416-878-8461 illus. Indexed: Arts & Hum.Cit.Ind. G.Soc.Sci.& Rel.Per.Lit.

268 US ISSN 0162-4547
ENCOUNTER! q. $3.75. Southern Baptist Convention, Sunday School Board, 127 Ninth Ave., North, Nashville, TN 37234. TEL 615-251-2000 Indexed: Arts & Hum.Cit.Ind. Bk.Rev.Ind. CERDIC. G.Soc.Sci.& Rel.Per.Lit. New Test.Abstr. Rel.& Theol.Abstr. Rel.Ind.One.

200 UK
ENGLISH CHURCHMAN & ST. JAMES'S CHRONICLE. 1843. fortn. £8.58. English Churchman Trust Ltd., c/o Dr. D.A. Scales, Hon. Secy., 65 Bishops Court, Trumpington, Cambridge CB2 2NN, England. Ed. Rev. H.G.H. Hill. adv. bk. rev. (newspaper; back issues avail.)
Formerly: English Churchman (ISSN 0013-8223)

200 GW ISSN 0013-9092
ENTSCHEIDUNG. 1963. bi-m. DM.18. (Billy Graham Evangelistic Association Deutschland e.V.) Friedrich Hannssler KG, Bismarkstr. 4, Postfach 1220, 7303 Neuhausen/Stuttgart, W. Germany (B.R.D.) Ed. Irmhild Baerend. adv. bk. rev. bibl. circ. 50,000.

284 US
EPISCOPAL CLERICAL DIRECTORY. biennial. Church Hymnal Corporation, 800 Second Ave., New York, NY 10017.

283 US ISSN 0013-9610
EPISCOPAL RECORDER. 1823. m. (exc. Jul. & Aug.) $2. Episcopal Recorder, Inc., 4225 Chestnut St., Philadelphia, PA 19104-3014. Ed. Rev. Walter G. Truesdell. bk. rev. circ. 970. (also avail. in microform from UMI) Indexed: G.Soc.Sci.& Rel.Per.Lit.

283 US ISSN 0013-9629
EPISCOPALIAN. vol.125, 1960. m. $5. (Episcopal Church) Episcopalian, Inc., 1201 Chestnut St., Ste. 1200, Philadelphia, PA 19107-4101. TEL 215-564-2010 Ed. Henry L. McCorkle. adv. bk. rev. illus. circ. 260,000. (tabloid format)

250 UK
EPWORTH REVIEW. 1973. 3/yr. £3. Methodist Publishing House, Wellington Rd., Wimbledon, London SW19 8EU, England. Ed. Rev. John Stacey. circ. 2,750.

286 267 US ISSN 0196-0911
EQUIPPING YOUTH; the training magazine for youth leaders. 1981. q. $7.25. Southern Baptist Convention, Sunday School Board, 127 Ninth Ave. North, Nashville, TN 37234. TEL 615-251-2000 Ed. Martha Jo Glazer. circ. 8,000. (back issues avail.)

284 GW
ERNEUERUNG UND ABWEHR. 1966. m. Vorstand der Evangelischen Notgemeinschaft in Deutschland, Waldstr. 14, 8802 Sachsen, W. Germany (B.R.D.) circ. 6,500.

280 FR ISSN 0071-1330
ESPRIT ET LIBERTE; Protestantisme liberal. 1956. irreg., 1973, no. 24. 45 F. Librairie Fischbacher, 33 rue de Seine, 75006 Paris, France. Indexed: Canon Law Abstr.

230 FR ISSN 0014-2239
ETUDES THEOLOGIQUES ET RELIGIEUSES. 1926. q. 130 F.($20) Institut Protestant de Theologie, 13 rue Louis-Perrier, 34000 Montpellier, France. Eds. A. Gounelle, D. Lys. adv. bk. rev. bibl. index. circ. 2,200. (also avail. in microfilm from UMI; reprint service avail. from UMI) Indexed: Bull.Signal. Curr.Cont. Old Test.Abstr. Rel.Per. Arts & Hum.Cit.Ind. CERDIC. New Test.Abstr. Rel.Ind.One.

287 US ISSN 0162-1890
EVANGEL. 1896. w. $4.75. (Free Methodist Church of North America) Light & Life Press, 999 College Ave., Winona Lake, IN 46590. TEL 219-267-7161 Ed. Vera Bethel. circ. 34,000. Indexed: G.Soc.Sci.& Rel.Per.Lit.
Formerly: Light and Life (ISSN 0024-3299)

286 CN ISSN 0014-3324
EVANGELICAL BAPTIST. 1953. m. Can.$6. ‡ Fellowship of Evangelical Baptist Churches in Canada, 3034 Bayview Ave., Willowdale M2N 6J5, Ont., Canada. TEL 416-223-8696 Ed. R.W. Lawson. adv. bk. rev. illus. circ. 7,000.

286.1 CN ISSN 0317-266X
EVANGELICAL BAPTIST CHURCHES IN CANADA. FELLOWSHIP YEARBOOK. 1959. a. Fellowship of Evangelical Baptist Churches in Canada, 3034 Bayview Ave., Willowdale, Ont. M2N 6J5, Canada. TEL 416-223-8696 illus. Key Title: Fellowship Yearbook.
Formerly: Missions Digest and Year Book (ISSN 0544-439X)

285.73 US ISSN 0014-3332
EVANGELICAL BEACON. 1931. 17/yr. $12. ‡ Evangelical Free Church of America, 1515 E. 66th St., Minneapolis, MN 55423. TEL 612-866-3343 Ed. George Keck. adv. bk. rev. illus. circ. 40,000. (tabloid format)

285 US ISSN 0360-8808
EVANGELICAL THEOLOGICAL SOCIETY. JOURNAL. 1958. q. $15. Evangelical Theological Society, c/o Dr. Simon J. Kistemaker, Sec. Treas., 5422 Clinton Blvd., Jackson, MS 39209. Ed. Dr. Ronald Youngblood. bk. rev. circ. 2,100. (also avail. in microform from UMI; reprint service avail. from UMI) Indexed: Old Test.Abstr. CERDIC. Chr.Per.Ind. New Test.Abstr. Rel.Ind.One. Rel.& Theol.Abstr.
Formerly: E T S Bulletin (ISSN 0071-3171)

266 GW
EVANGELISCH-LUTHERISCH MISSIONSWERK IN NIEDERSACHSEN. JAHRBUCH (YEAR) 1954. a. DM.4. (Evangelisch-Lutherisch Missionswerk in Niedersachsen) Missionshandlung Hermannsburg, Harmsstr. 2-6, D-3102 Hermannsburg, W. Germany (B.R.D.) Ed. Reinhart Mueller. circ. 4,500. (back issues avail.)
Formerly(until 1979): Die Hermannsburger Mission im Jahre (Year)

284 GE ISSN 0423-8346
EVANGELISCH-LUTHERISCHE LANDESKIRCHE SACHSENS. AMTSBLATT. 1949. s-m. M.10.80. (Evangelisch-Lutherisches Landeskirchenamt Sachsens) Union-Verlag, Strasse der Befreiung 21, 8060 Dresden, E. Germany (D.D.R.) Ed.Bd. bk. rev. play rev. abstr. index. circ. 2,500.

284.2 GW ISSN 0014-343X
EVANGELISCHE KIRCHE IN DEUTSCHLAND. AMTSBLATT. 1946. m. DM.40. ‡ Kirchenamt der Evangelische Kirche in Deutschland, Herrenhaeuser Str. 12, 3000 Hannover- Herrenhausen, W. Germany (B.R.D.) Ed. Dr. D. Dahrmann. index. circ. 1,400. (tabloid format)

284 GW ISSN 0014-3529
EVANGELISCHE LANDESKIRCHE IN WUERTTEMBERG. AMTSBLATT. 1855. s-m. DM.24. Evangelical-Lutheran Church of Wuerttemberg, P.O. Box 92, D-7000 Stuttgart, W. Germany (B.R.D.) Ed. Dr. Daur. index. circ. 4,500.

284 GE ISSN 0014-326X
EVANGELISCHE-LUTHERISCHE KIRCHE IN THUERINGEN. AMTSBLATT. 1948. s-m. M.0.50. (Evangelische-Lutherische Kirche in Thueringen, Landeskirchenrat) Wartburg Verlag Max Kessler, Inselplatz 11, Jena, E. Germany (D.D.R.) Ed. Dr. Gottfried Mueller. bk. rev.

285 AU ISSN 0016-6154
EVANGELISCHE PFARRGEMEINDE A.B. WIEN-FAVORITEN-CHRISTUSKIRCHE. GEMEINDEBRIEF. 1963. q. contributions. ‡ Presbyterium der Evangelischen Gemeinde Wien-Favoriten-Christuskirche, Triester Str. 1, A-1100 Vienna, Austria. Ed. Alfred Jahn. bk. rev. abstr. bibl. illus. stat. circ. 3,000.

284 AU ISSN 0036-6943
EVANGELISCHER BUND IN OESTERREICH. SCHRIFTENREIHE. 1956. q. Evangelischer Bund in Oesterreich, Ungargasse 9, A 1030 Vienna, Austria. Ed. Paul Weiland. circ. 8,000.

284 GE ISSN 0014-3553
EVANGELISCHER NACHRICHTENDIENST IN DER DDR. 1947. w. M.72. Evangelische Verlagsanstalt GmbH, Krautstr. 52, 1017 Berlin, E. Germany (D.D.R.) Ed. Guenter Lorenz.

284 GW ISSN 0014-360X
EVANGELISCHES GEMEINDEBLATT FUER WUERTTEMBERG. 1905. w. DM.57.60. ‡ Evangelische Gemeindepresse GmbH, Furtbachstr. 12a, 7000 Stuttgart 1, W. Germany (B.R.D.) adv. bk. rev. illus. circ. 170,000.

284 FR
EVANGILE ET LIBERTE. 1885. m. 180 F. Association Evangile et Liberte, 17 bd. des Freses Voisin, Appart. 251, 75015 Paris, France. Ed. Jean Marc Charensol. adv. bk. rev. bibl.

284 YU ISSN 0014-3642
EVANJELICKY HLASNIK. 1965. m. 2 din. per issue. Slovenska Evanjelicka A.V. Cirkva v SFR Juhoslavii, Karadziceva 2, Novi Sad, Yugoslavia. Ed. Dr. Juro Struharik.

286 US ISSN 0014-374X
EVENT. 1970. m. $8.50. Southern Baptist Convention, Sunday School Board, 127 Ninth Ave. N., Nashville, TN 37203. TEL 615-251-2000 circ. 160,000. Indexed: Arts & Hum.Cit.Ind.
Supersedes: Upward.

268 US
EXPLORING 1. q. $3.75. Southern Baptist Convention, Sunday School Board, 127 Ninth Ave., North, Nashville, TN 37234. TEL 615-251-2000
Formerly, until 1982: Exploring A (ISSN 0162-4415)
Ages 6-8

268 US
EXPLORING 1 FOR LEADERS. q. $7.25. Southern Baptist Convention, Sunday School Board, 127 Ninth Ave., North, Nashville, TN 37234. TEL 615-251-2000
Formerly, until 1982: Exploring A for Leaders (ISSN 0162-4423)

268 US
EXPLORING 2. q. $3.75. Southern Baptist Convention, Sunday School Board, 127 Ninth Ave., North, Nashville, TN 37234. TEL 615-251-2000
Formerly, until 1982: Exploring C (ISSN 0162-4458)
Grades 4-6

268 US
EXPLORING 2 FOR LEADERS. q. $7.25. Southern Baptist Convention, Sunday School Board, 127 Ninth Ave., North, Nashville, TN 37234. TEL 615-251-2000
Formerly, until 1982: Exploring C for Leaders (ISSN 0162-4466)

286 AG ISSN 0014-522X
EXPOSITOR BAUTISTA. vol.59, 1966. bi-m. Arg.$3.50($10) Convencion Evangelica Bautista Argentina, Rivadavia 3474, 1203 Buenos Aires, Argentina. Ed. Horacio V. Franco. adv. charts. illus.

268 US ISSN 0014-5238
EXPOSITOR BIBLICO (TEACHER EDITION) (Text in Spanish) 1893. q. $4.80. Casa Bautista de Publicaciones, Box 4255, El Paso, TX 79914. TEL 915-566-9656 Ed. J.E. Diaz. adv. charts. illus. circ. 15,000.

266 US
FAITH AND FELLOWSHIP. 1933. s-m. $8. (Church of the Lutheran Brethren) Lutheran Brethren Publishing Co., Box 655, Fergus Falls, MN 56537. TEL 218-736-7357 Ed. Rev. David Rinden. circ. 5,000.

286 US ISSN 0740-0659
FAITH AND MISSION. 1983. s-a. $6. Southeastern Baptist Theological Seminary, Inc., Wake Forest, NC 27587. TEL 919-556-3101 Ed. Thomas H. Graves. adv. bk. rev. circ. 1,000(controlled) (back issues avail.) Indexed: Rel.Ind.One.

286 UK ISSN 0143-7917
FAMILY LIFE. 1979. 6/yr. £0.50. (Seventh-day Adventist Church) Stanborough Press Ltd., Alma Park, Grantham, Lincs. NG31 9SL, England. Ed. D.N. Marshall. illus. circ. 25,000.

284 IT
FEDELTA APOSTOLICA. 1976. m. free. Fedelta Apostolica, Via Vespucci 3/19, 50047 Prato, Firenze, Italy. Ed. Affuso Mario. circ. 400. (back issues avail.)

284 FR
FEDERATION PROTESTANTE DE FRANCE. ANNUAIRE. 1952. a. 180 F. Federation Protestante de France, c/o J. R. Graff, Ed., 47 rue de Clichy, 75009 Paris, France.
Formerly: France Prostestante (ISSN 0071-9064)

284 GW ISSN 0015-0320
DER FESTE GRUND. 1850. m. DM.16.80. Evangelische Gesellschaft fuer Deutschland e.V., Kaiser Str. 78, 5600 Wuppertal 11, W. Germany (B.R.D.) Ed. Pastor Heinrich Jochums. adv. bk. rev. circ. 10,000.
Merged with: Saemann.

286 UK ISSN 0143-7925
FOCUS (GRANTHAM) 1979. q. £0.15. (Seventh-day Adventist Church) Stanborough Press Ltd., Alma Park, Grantham, Lincs. NG31 9SL, England. Ed. D.N. Marshall. illus. circ. 50,000.

200 US
FORWARD; moving the Episcopal diocese of Erie. 1948. m. (Sep.-Jun.) $4. ‡ Episcopal Diocese of Erie, 145 W. Sixth St., Erie, PA 16501. TEL 814-456-4203 Ed. Rev. John A. Andrews. bk. rev. charts. film rev. illus. record rev. circ. 6,200.
Formerly: Forward in Erie (ISSN 0015-8623)

269 266 GE
FRIEDENSGLOCKE. 1893. s-m. M.6. Evangelisch-Methodistische Kirche in der DDR, Haydnstr. 18, 8019 Dresden, E. Germany (D.D.R.) Ed. G. Roegner.

266 285 AT ISSN 0016-2108
FRONTIER NEWS. 1930. a. free. Uniting Church, Frontier Services, 123 Clarence St., Sydney, N.S.W. 2000, Australia. Ed. Gray Birch. bk. rev. charts. illus. stat. circ. 17,500. (tabloid format)
Missions

284 GW ISSN 0016-2434
FUER ARBEIT UND BESINNUNG. 1947. s-m. DM.60. (Evangelischer Oberkirchenrat) Quell Verlag, Furtbachstr. 12A, Postfach 897, 7000 Stuttgart, W. Germany (B.R.D.) adv. bk. rev. index. circ. 3,800.

287 GW ISSN 0016-2442
FUER HEUTE. 1968. w. DM.12. (Evangelisch-methodistische Kirche) Christliches Verlagshaus GmbH, Motorstr. 36, 7000 Stuttgart 31, W. Germany (B.R.D.) circ. 23,300.
Formed by the 1968 merger of: Gute Botschaft & Friedensglocke.

286 US ISSN 0016-2744
FUNDAMENTALIST. 1927. m. $3. Baptist Fellowship, 4161 N. Powers Dr., Orlando, FL 32808. TEL 305-841-3428 Ed. Dr. Lloyd E. Meyer. circ. 9,500. Indexed: CERDIC.

GATEWAY. see *SOCIAL SERVICES AND WELFARE*

284 GW ISSN 0016-6073
DIE GEMEINDE. 1946. w. DM.72. (Bund Evangelisch-Freikirchlicher Gemeinden) Verlag J.G. Oncken Nachf. GmbH, Langenbeckstr. 28/30, 3500 Kassel 1, W. Germany (B.R.D.) Ed. Joachim Zieger. adv. bk. rev. abstr. illus. index. circ. 14,000. (tabloid format)

200 NE
GEREFORMEERD KERKHISTORISCH TIJDSCHRIFT. 1973. q. fl.12.50. ‡ Gereformeerd Historisch Instituut - Reformed Historical Institute, Zestienhovensekade 409, Rotterdam 3008, Netherlands. Ed. J. Lussenburg. adv. bk. rev.

284 230 NE ISSN 0016-8610
GEREFORMEERD THEOLOGISCH TIJDSCHRIFT. 1900. q. fl.36.80. J. H. Kok B. V., Box 130, 8260 AC Kampen, Netherlands. Ed. W. Bakker. bk. rev. index. Indexed: Old Test.Abstr. CERDIC. New Test.Abstr. Rel.& Theol.Abstr.

284.2 SA ISSN 0378-407X
GEREFORMEERDE VROUEBLAD. (Text in Afrikaans) 1947. m. R.8.20. Reformed Churches in South Africa - Gereformeerde Kerke in Suid-Afrika, Box 20008, Noordbrug 2522, Potchefstroom, South Africa. Ed. Mrs. A. de Bruyn. circ. 9,000.

GESELLSCHAFT FUER DIE GESCHICHTE DES PROTESTANTISMUS IN OESTERREICH. JAHRBUCH. see *HISTORY — History Of Europe*

GESELLSCHAFT FUER NIEDERSAECHSISCHE KIRCHENGESCHICHTE. JAHRBUCH. see *HISTORY — History Of Europe*

053.1 GW ISSN 0016-934X
GETROSTER TAG/HOPEFUL DAY. 1955. 3/yr. DM.9.90. Burckhardthaus-Laetare Verlag GmbH, Herzbachweg 2, 6460 Gelnhausen, W. Germany (B.R.D.) circ. 35,000.

285 266 CN ISSN 0017-0720
GLAD TIDINGS. 1925. m. Can.$5. Women's Missionary Society (WD), Presbyterian Church in Canada, Rm. 100, 50 Wynford Drive, Don Mills, Ont. M3C 1J7, Canada. TEL 416-441-2840 Ed. L. June Stevenson. bk. rev. illus. index. circ. 12,000.
Missions

288 GW ISSN 0017-1123
GLAUBE UND TAT; deutsch-unitarische Blaetter. 1950. m. DM.8 quarterly. Religionsgemeinschaft Deutsche Unitarier e.V., Goethestr. 27, 2300 Kiel 1, W. Germany (B.R.D.) Ed. Fritz Castagne. adv. bk. rev. illus. index. circ. 2,000.

266 AT ISSN 0705-2316
GOING ON. 1976. bi-m. free. Church Missionary Society of Australia, 93 Bathurst St., Sydney, N.S.W. 2000, Australia. circ. 1,750.

287 UK ISSN 0017-1700
GOLEUAD/LIGHT. 1871. w. 10p. per no. (Presbyterian Church of Wales) Y Llyfrfa, St. David's Rd., Caernarvon, Gwynedd LL55 1ER, Wales. Ed. Rev. Harri Parri. adv. bk. rev. circ. 5,000.

GOOD NEWS. see *RELIGIONS AND THEOLOGY — Roman Catholic*

268 US ISSN 0362-0417
GOSPEL CHOIR. q. $6.25. Southern Baptist Convention, Sunday School Board, 127 Ninth Ave., North, Nashville, TN 37234. TEL 615-251-2000

268 US ISSN 0162-4512
GROWING (NASHVILLE) q. $4. Southern Baptist Convention, Sunday School Board, 127 Ninth Ave., North, Nashville, TN 37234. TEL 615-251-2000

284 US
GUIDE FOR BIBLICAL STUDIES. 1885. q. $5. Church of the Brethren, General Board, 1451 Dundee Ave., Elgin, IL 60120. TEL 312-742-5100 Ed. Richard Gardner. adv. circ. 20,000.

268 US
HAPPY TIMES. 1964. m. $5.90. (Lutheran Church-Missouri Synod, Board for Parish Services) Concordia Publishing House, 1333 S. Kirkwood Rd., St. Louis, MO 63122. TEL 314-664-7000 Ed. Earl H. Gaulke. circ. 55,000. (also avail. in microfilm)
Supplementary stories and activities for Christian education on the preprimary level

283 US ISSN 0274-7154
HAWAIIAN CHURCH CHRONICLE. 1910. m. (8/yr.) $4. Episcopal Church in Hawaii, 229 Queen Emma Square, Honolulu, HI 96813. TEL 808-536-7776 Ed. Rev. John Paul Engelcke. bk. rev. circ. 7,650. (tabloid format)

287 US
HAWKEYE. 1957. 10/yr. $4 (free to all Iowa local officers) ‡ (Iowa United Methodist Church) Iowa United Methodist Communications, 1019 Chestnut St., Des Moines, IA 50309. TEL 515-283-1991 Ed. Mearle L. Criffith. adv. illus. circ. 26,000. (newspaper)
Former titles: Hawkeye United Methodist (ISSN 0017-8632); Hawkeye Methodist.

286 US
HEARTBEAT. 1961. m. free. Free Will Baptist Foreign Missions, 1134 Murfreesboro Rd., Nashville, TN 37217. TEL 615-361-1010 Ed. Don Robirds. circ. 31,500.

284 NE ISSN 0018-0920
HERVORMD ARNHEM. 1905. w. fl.15. (Hervormde Gemeente Arnhem) Drukkerij J.C. Willemsen, Postbus 79, Amersfoort, Netherlands (Subscr. address: Breyers Boekhandel, Looierstraat 1, Arnhem, Netherlands) Ed. P. M. Gerritse. adv. bk. rev. film rev. (looseleaf format)

284 NE ISSN 0018-0947
HERVORMD WAGENINGEN. 1945. fortn. fl.6.75($2.) Hervormde Gemeente Kerkelijk Bureau, Markt 17, Wageningen, Netherlands. adv. bk. rev. bl. circ. 4,000.

284 NE ISSN 0018-0955
HERVORMDE GEMEENTE MUSSELKANAAL. KERKBLAD. 1950. m. fl.3. Kerkeraad Hervormde Gemeente, Marktstraat 13, Musselkanaal, Netherlands. Eds. H. Hengeveld, H.S. de Vries.

284 SA
HERVORMER. (Text in Afrikaans) 1909. m. R.15. Ned. Hervormde Kerk van Afrika, 480 Paul Krugerstraat, P.O. Box 5777, Pretoria 0001, South Africa. Ed. D.J.C. van Wyk. adv. bk. rev. circ. 36,000.

200 SA ISSN 0018-1684
HIGHWAY. (Text in Afrikaans & English) 1940. m. R.5. ‡ Anglican Diocese of Kimberley and Kuruman, Box 45, Kimberley, South Africa. Ed.Bd. adv. bk. rev. circ. 1,950. (tabloid format)

284 US ISSN 0360-9030
HISTORICAL FOOTNOTES (ST. LOUIS) 1955. q. $15. Concordia Historical Institute, 801 De Mun Ave., St. Louis, MO 63105. TEL 314-721-5934 Ed. A.R. Suelflow. bk. rev. bibl. circ. 1,700.

287 US
HISTORICAL HIGHLIGHTS. 1971. s-a. $5. ‡ South Georgia Conference Commission on Archives and History of the United Methodist Church, Box 407, Epworth-by-the-Sea, St. Simons Island, GA 31522. TEL 912-638-3317 Ed. W. A. Harrell. bk. rev. circ. 275.
History

HISTORICAL INTELLIGENCER. see *HISTORY*

283 US ISSN 0018-2486
HISTORICAL MAGAZINE OF THE PROTESTANT EPISCOPAL CHURCH. 1932. q. $15. Episcopal Church, Historical Society, Box 2247, Austin, TX 78768. TEL 512-472-6816 Ed. Rev. John F. Woolverton. adv. bk. rev. bibl. index. circ. 1,500. (also avail. in microfilm from UMI; reprint service avail. from UMI) Indexed: Hist.Abstr. Rel.Per. Amer.Hist.& Life. CERDIC. Rel.Ind.One.
History

287 270 US
HISTORICAL MESSENGER. 1969. q. $2. ‡ United Methodist Church, Central Illinois Conference, Historical Society, Box 515, Bloomington, IL 61702-0515. TEL 309-828-5092 Ed. Vera Swantner. illus. stat. circ. 1,200.
Formerly: Central Illinois Historical Messenger (ISSN 0008-9419)
History

200 UK
HISTORICAL SOCIETY OF THE CHURCH IN WALES. JOURNAL. 1946. a. £2. Historical Society of the Church in Wales, c/o Owen W. Jones, The Vicarage, Builth Wells, Brec, Wales. Ed. Canon David Walker. charts. stat. Indexed: Br.Archaeol.Abstr.

940 200 UK
HISTORICAL SOCIETY OF THE PRESBYTERIAN CHURCH OF WALES. JOURNAL. (Text in English and Welsh) 1916. a. 50p. Historical Society of the Presbyterian Church of Wales, The Manse, Caradog Rd., Aberystwyth, Dyfed, Wales. Ed. Rev. Gomer M. Roberts. bk. rev. circ. 600.

283 209 US ISSN 0018-2591
HISTORIOGRAPHER. 1952. q. $10. Episcopal Diocese of Connecticut, 1335 Asylum Ave., Hartford, CT 06105. TEL 203-233-4481 Ed. Kenneth W. Cameron. bk. rev. charts. illus.stat. circ. 30.
History

286 US ISSN 0018-3229
HOGAR CRISTIANO. (Text in Spanish) 1957. q. $5.52. Casa Bautista de Publicaciones, Box 4255, El Paso, TX 79914. TEL 915-566-9656 Ed. Adolfo Robleto. illus. circ. 30,000.
For the family

249 286 US ISSN 0018-4071
HOME LIFE; a Christian family magazine. m. $9.75. Southern Baptist Convention, Sunday School Board, 127 Ninth Ave. N., Nashville, TN 37234. TEL 615-251-2000 circ. 800,000. Indexed: South.Bap.Per.Ind.

HORIZON (NEPTUNE) see *GERONTOLOGY AND GERIATRICS*

286 NE
HOUVAST. 1970. m. (10/yr.) fl.9.50. (Zevende-Dags Adventisten - Seventh-Day Adventists) Stichting Uitgeverij "Veritas", Box 630, The Hague, Netherlands. Ed. R. Bruinsma.

HUGUENOT TRAILS. see *HISTORY — History Of North And South America*

HUMAN DEVELOPMENT. see *PSYCHOLOGY*

283 CN ISSN 0018-7917
HURON CHURCH NEWS. 1950. m. Can.$4. Anglican Church of Canada, Diocese of Huron, 4-220 Dundas St., London, Ont., Canada. TEL 519-434-6893 Ed. Rev. Canon Geoffrey Dibbs. adv. bk. rev. illus. circ. 26,000. (tabloid format)

284 IT
I D E A. 1975. bi-m. L.8000. Alleanza Evangelica Italiana, Casella Postale 680, I-50100 Florence, Italy. Ed. Elio Milazzo. adv. bk. rev. circ. 1,100. (looseleaf format; back issues avail.)

280 US
I R F NEWSLETTER. bi-m. free. International Religious Foundation, Inc., 10 Dock Rd., Barrytown, NY 12507. TEL 914-758-8838 adv. bk. rev. circ. 2,000.
Supersedes (1981-1986, May/June): New E R A Newsletter (ISSN 0277-3082)

286 UK ISSN 0261-1325
I S ANNUAL. 1980. a. £1. Inter-School Christian Fellowship, 130 City Rd., London EC1V 2NJ, England. Ed. Tricia Williams. adv. bk. rev. illus. circ. 2,000.

284 AG ISSN 0019-1671
IGLESIA EVANGELICA DEL RIO DE LA PLATA. REVISTA PARROQUIAL. (Text in German, Spanish) 1895. m. Arg.$300($10) Convencion Evangelica Bautista Argentina, Rivadavia 3476, 1203 Buenos Aires, Argentina. Ed. Federico H. Schafer. adv. bk. rev. circ. 5,100.

284 TZ ISSN 0019-171X
IJA WEBONERE. (Text in Haya and Swahili) vol.14, 1968. m. Evangelical Lutheran Church of Tanzania, North Western Diocese, Box 98, Bukoba, Tanzania. Ed. Philip B. Tibaijuka. adv. stat. (looseleaf format)

286 US ISSN 0019-1868
ILLINOIS BAPTIST. 1905. w. $6. Illinois Baptist State Association, Box 3486, Springfield, IL 62708. TEL 217-786-2638 Ed. Robert J. Hastings. bk. rev. charts, illus, stat. circ. 46,000. (tabloid format; also avail. in microform)

284.2 SA ISSN 0378-4088
IMBONGI YENKOSI. (Text in Zulu) 1952. m. (11/yr.) R.1.50. Reformed Churches in South Africa - Gereformeerde Kerke in Suid-Afrika, Box 20008, Noordbrug 2522, Potchefstroom, South Africa. Ed. Rev. W.L. Kurpershoek. circ. 2,300.

286 US ISSN 0019-2821
IMPACT (WHEATON) 1943. 4/yr. $3. Conservative Baptist Foreign Mission Society, Box 5, Wheaton, IL 60189-0005. TEL 312-665-1200 Ed. Arthur Heerwagen. bk. rev. film rev. charts. illus. stat. tr. lit. circ. 40,375.
Formerly: Conservative Baptist Impact.
Missions

284 US
IN SEASON. 1974. w. $25. Cathedral Publishers, 324 E. 4th St., Royal Oak, MI 48068. Ed. H. Dean Lueking. circ. 2,000.

287 US
IN-TOUCH. 1971. w. $7.25. (Wesleyan Church) Wesley Press, c/o James Watkins, Ed., Box 2000, Marion, IN 46952. TEL 317-674-3301 illus. circ. 31,000. Indexed: Arts & Hum.Cit.Ind.
Former titles: Encounter; Venture; Vista (ISSN 0042-7098)

284 II
INDIAN LUTHERAN. (Text in English) vol.62, 1967. q. Rs.12. United Evangelical Lutheran Churches in India, No. 1 First St., Haddows Rd., Nungambakkam, Madras 600006, India. Ed. Dr. K. Rajaratnam. adv. bk. rev. circ. 1,000.
Formerly (until 1980): Gospel Witness (ISSN 0017-2391)

287 II ISSN 0019-6487
INDIAN WITNESS. 1871. s-m. Rs.10($6) to individuals; Rs. 15 to institutions. Methodist Church in India, 25 Lodi Rd., New Delhi 110003, India (U.S. subscr. address: c/o 1st United Methodist Church, 1589 W. Maple, Birmingham, MI 48010) Richard Renwick Smyth. adv. bk. rev. circ. 2,500.
Church news and views

284 IO
INDONESIA. DIRECTORATE GENERAL OF PROTESTANT AFFAIRS. ANNUAL REPORT/INDONESIA. DIREKTORAT JENDERAL BIMBINGAN MASYARAKAT KRISTEN/PROTESTAN LAPORAN TAHUNAN. (Text in Indonesian) a. Directorate General of Protestant Affairs, Jalan Moh. Husni Thamrin, Jakarta, Indonesia.

286 248.83 US ISSN 0020-1944
INSIGHT (HAGERSTOWN); a magazine of Christian understanding for young Adventists. 1970. w. $27.95. ‡ (General Conference of Seventh-day Adventists) Review and Herald Publishing Association, 55 West Oak Dr., Hagerstown, MD 21740. TEL 301-791-7000 Ed. Chris Blake. adv. bk. rev. illus. circ. 24,000. (reprint service avail. from UMI) Indexed: Chr.Per.Ind.
Supersedes: Youth's Instructor.

INTERACTION (ST. LOUIS); a magazine church school workers grow by. see *EDUCATION*

266 US
INTERCHANGE (NEW YORK) 1967. 4/yr. free. Lutheran Council in the U.S.A., Office of Communication and Interpretation, 360 Park Ave. So., New York, NY 10010. TEL 212-532-6350 Ed. Benjamin A. Bankson. circ. 24,000. (tabloid format)

286 CN ISSN 0383-6061
INTERCOM. 1968. irreg. Fellowship of Evangelical Baptist Churches in Canada, 3034 Bayview Ave., Willowdale, Ont. M2N 6J5, Canada. TEL 416-223-8696

INTERNATIONAL BULLETIN OF MISSIONARY RESEARCH. see *LIBRARY AND INFORMATION SCIENCES*

286 US ISSN 0162-4342
INTERPRETE; adultos en la Escuela Dominical. (Text in English and Spanish) q. $3.75. Southern Baptist Convention, Sunday School Board, 127 Ninth Ave. North, Nashville, TN 37234. Indexed: M.L.A.

287 US ISSN 0020-9678
INTERPRETER. 1957. m. $3. ‡ United Methodist Communications Council, 601 Riverview Ave., Dayton, OH 45406. TEL 513-222-7068 Ed. Darrell R. Shamblin. bk. rev. charts. illus. circ. 300,000. (also avail. in microfilm from UMI; reprint service avail. from UMI) Indexed: Comput.Lit.Ind. Met.Per.Ind.
Formed by the merger of: Spotlight & Methodist Story.

286.0415 UK ISSN 0075-0727
IRISH BAPTIST HISTORICAL SOCIETY. JOURNAL. 1969. a. £3($5.50) Baptist Union of Ireland, 3 Fitzwilliam St., Belfast BT9 6AW, Northern Ireland. Ed. Joshua Thompson. bk. rev. cum.index: vols.1-15 in prep. circ. 250.

283 JM ISSN 0047-1720
JAMAICA CHURCHMAN. 1970. m. 75p.($1.10) Diocese of Jamaica, Anglican Church Office, Kingston 5, Jamaica, W. Indies. Ed. Rev. Laurence Small. adv. illus. circ. 6,000.

268 US
JOURNAL OF CHRISTIAN EDUCATION OF THE AFRICAN METHODIST EPISCOPAL CHURCH. 1936. q. $3. African Methodist Episcopal Church, Christian Education Department, 500 8th Ave. S., Nashville, TN 37203. Ed. Rev. Edgar L. Mack. adv. bk. rev. charts. film rev. illus. record rev. circ. 6,000. (also avail. in microform from UMI; reprint service avail. from UMI)
Former titles (1980-1982): Journal of Religious Education of the African Methodist Episcopal Church (ISSN 0276-0770); (1936-1980): Journal of Religious Education (ISSN 0022-4219)

200 US ISSN 0361-1906
JOURNAL OF THEOLOGY. 1961. 4/yr. $5. Church of the Lutheran Confession (Eau Claire), 501 Grover Rd., Immanuel Lutheran College, Eau Claire, WI 54701 (Subscr. address: 2750 Oxford St., N., Roseville, MN 55113) Ed. John Lau. bk. rev. circ. 280.

286 US
JOVENES BIBLICO (STUDENT EDITION) 1890. q. $1.40. Casa Bautista de Publicaciones, Box 4255, El Paso, TX 79914. TEL 915-566-9656 Ed. J.E. Diaz. adv. charts. illus. circ. 40,000.
Formerly: Expositor Biblico (Student Edition)
Bible teaching for adults

284 301.412 US ISSN 0164-4882
JOYFUL WOMAN. 1978. bi-m. $11.95. Joyful Woman Ministries, Box 90028, Chattanooga, TN 37412. TEL 615-698-7318 Ed. Mrs. Walter Handford. adv. bk. rev. circ. 16,000.

285.834 US ISSN 0361-8668
KEEPING YOU POSTED. 1966. m. free. United Church of Christ, Office of Communication, 105 Madison Ave., New York, NY 10016. TEL 212-683-5656 Ed. Beverly J. Chain. bk. rev. illus. stat. circ. 16,000.

284.2 SA ISSN 0023-0596
KERKBLAD. (Text in Afrikaans) 1873. fortn. R.16.70. Reformed Churches in South Africa - Gereformeerde Kerke in Suid-Afrika, Box 20008, Noordbrug 2522, Potchefstroom, South Africa. Ed. J.J. Venter. adv. bk. rev. circ. 11,600.

284 SA
KERKBODE; amptelike blad van die Nederduitse Gereformeerde Kerk. (Text in Afrikaans) 1849. fortn. R.20($13.64) Tydskriftemaatskappy van die Nederduitse Gereformeerde Kerk in S.A., Nederduitse Gereformeerde Church Centre, Greys Pass, Box 1444, Cape Town, South Africa. Ed. G.S.J. Moller. adv. bk. rev. circ. 19,000. (back issues avail.)

280 AU ISSN 0023-1789
KIRCHE; Dioezesanblatt fuer die Kirchenprovinz Mitteleuropa. 1954. q. S.40. Verein zur Foerderung der Liberalkatholischen Kirche, Erdenweg 21, A-1140 Vienna, Austria. Ed. Rev. Rudolf Hammer. bk. rev. circ. 600.

284.2 SZ ISSN 0023-1797
KIRCHENBLATT FUER DIE REFORMIERTE SCHWEIZ: 1844. fortn. 91 Fr. Friedrich Reinhardt Verlag, Missionsstr. 36, CH-4012 Basel, Switzerland. Ed. Hans Riniker. adv. bk. rev. abstr. cum.index. circ. 1,720. (processed) Indexed: CERDIC.

289 GW
DER KRIEGSRUF. 1887. w. (Heilsarmee - Salvation Army) Heilsarmee Verlag GmbH, Salierring 27, 5000 Cologne 1, W. Germany (B.R.D.) Ed. Evelin Binsch. bk. rev. circ. 17,000.

266 MW
KUUNIKA. (Text in Chichewa) 1960. m. 72 T. (Christian Literature Fund) Presbyterian Church of Central Africa, Nkhoma Synod, P.O. Nkhoma, Malawi. Ed. M. J. Nkhalambayhusi Chirwa. bk. rev. circ. 6,000.

284 GW ISSN 0174-1764
L F B DOCUMENTATION. REPORT. 1978. irreg. DM.22($10) (Lutheran World Federation-Geneva) Kreuz Verlag Zeitschriften GmbH, Breitwiesenstr. 30, 7000 Stuttgart 80, W. Germany (B.R.D.) circ. 3,500.

266 US
L I R S BULLETIN. 1964. 2/yr. free to refugee sponsors. Lutheran Council in the U.S.A., Department of Information and Refugee Services, 360 Park Ave. So., New York, NY 10010. Ed. Lily R. Wu. circ. 11,000.
Formerly: L I R S Information Bulletin.

266.6 LB
LIBERIA BAPTIST MISSIONARY AND EDUCATIONAL CONVENTION. YEARBOOK. (Text in English) a. Liberia Baptist Missionary and Educational Convention, Bentol City, Liberia. illus.

LIBRARIANS' CHRISTIAN FELLOWSHIP NEWSLETTER. see *LIBRARY AND INFORMATION SCIENCES*

274 UK ISSN 0024-306X
LIFE AND WORK; the record of the Church of Scotland. 1879. m. £5.20. Church of Scotland, 121 George St., Edinburgh EH2 4YN, Scotland. Ed. R.D. Kernohan. adv. bk. rev. illus. circ. 124,856. Indexed: CERDIC.

266 SA ISSN 0024-3272
DIE LIGDRAER. 1940. fortn. R.12. Nederduitse Gereformeerde Sendingkerk - Dutch Reformed Mission Church, Private Bag X1, Belhar 7507, Cape Province, South Africa. Ed. Rev. D.P. Botha. adv. bk. rev. bibl. illus. stat. index. circ. 22,000.
Missions

LIGHTED PATHWAY. see *CHILDREN AND YOUTH — For*

284.2 SA ISSN 0024-0575
LIGSTRAAL/LEHLASEDI. (Text in Sotho and Tswana) 1944. m. R.3. Nederduitse Gereformeerde Kerk in Afrika, Box 19, Bloemfontein, South Africa. Ed. J. Xulu. adv. illus.

284.2 SA ISSN 0024-3442
LIGSTRAAL/UMSEBE/UMTHA. (Text in Xhosa and Zulu) 1943. m. R.3. Nederduitse Gereformeerde Kerk in Afrika, Box 19, Bloemfontein, South Africa. Ed. J. Xulu. adv. bk. rev. illus. circ. 23,000.

268 US ISSN 0162-4253
LIVING (NASHVILLE) q. $3.75. Southern Baptist Convention, Sunday School Board, 127 Ninth Ave., North, Nashville, TN 37234. TEL 615-251-2000

283 US ISSN 0024-5240
LIVING CHURCH; an independent weekly record of the news of the Church and the views of Episcopalians. 1878. w. $29.95. Living Church Foundation, Inc., 816 E. Juneau Ave., Milwaukee, WI 53202. TEL 414-276-5420 Ed. H. Boone Porter. adv. bk. rev. illus. circ. 10,897.

268 US ISSN 0162-4350
LIVING WITH PRESCHOOLERS. q. $9. Southern Baptist Convention, Sunday School Board, 127 Ninth Ave., North, Nashville, TN 37234. TEL 615-251-2000

268 US ISSN 0162-4261
LIVING WITH TEENAGERS. q. $9. Southern Baptist Convention, Sunday School Board, 127 Ninth Ave., North, Nashville, TN 37234. TEL 615-251-2000

287 UK ISSN 0024-5607
LOCAL PREACHERS MAGAZINE. 1850. q. membership. Methodist Local Preachers Aid Association, Head Office, Chorleywood Close, Rickmansworth, Herts WD3 4EG, England. Ed. G.J.H. Buss. bk. rev. circ. 15,000.

268 LB
LOMA WEEKLY PAPER. (Text in English, Loca) 1951. w. $1. Lutheran Church in Liberia, Loma Literacy Center, Box 1046, Wozi, Monrovia, Liberia.

268 US ISSN 0162-4369
LOOK AND LISTEN. q. in w. parts. $3.75. Southern Baptist Convention, Sunday School Board, 127 Ninth Ave., North, Nashville, TN 37234. TEL 615-251-2000

284 US
LOOKOUT (CINCINNATI) 1894. w. $16. Standard Publishing, 8121 Hamilton Ave., Cincinnati, OH 45231. TEL 513-931-4050 Ed. Mark A. Taylor. circ. 140,000.

286 US ISSN 0024-6743
LOUISIANA BAPTIST BUILDER. 1953. m. $5. Baptist Missionary Association of Louisiana, Box 1297, Denham Springs, LA 70727-1297. Ed. Leroy Mayfield. adv. bk. rev. illus. circ. 2,500. (tabloid format)
Missions

284 IT
LUCE (TURIN); settimanale delle chiese valdesi e metodiste. w. L.31000. A.I.P., Via S. Piov, no.15, 10125 Turin, Italy. Dir. Giorgio Gardiol. circ. 5,000.

284 GW ISSN 0340-6210
LUTHER. 1919. 3/yr. DM.26. (Luther-Gesellschaft) Vandenhoeck und Ruprecht, Theaterstr. 13, Postfach 3753, 3400 Goettingen, W. Germany (B.R.D.) Ed. Hans-Ludwig Szupina. adv. bk. rev. index. circ. 1,750. Indexed: CERDIC.

284.1 US ISSN 0024-743X
LUTHERAN; news magazine of the Lutheran Church in America. 1860. s-m. $6.50. Lutheran Church in America, 2900 Queen Lane, Philadelphia, PA 19129. TEL 215-438-6580 Ed. Edgar R. Trexler. adv. bk. rev. film rev. illus. circ. 539,000. (also avail. in microform from UMI) Indexed: CERDIC. G.Soc.Sci.& Rel.Per.Lit.

284 US
LUTHERAN ANNUAL. 1910. a. $4.95 paper, $6.95 spiral. ‡ (Lutheran Church-Missouri Synod) Concordia Publishing House, 1333 S. Kirkwood Rd., St. Louis, MO 63122. TEL 314-664-7000 Ed. Dr. Ralph R. Reinke. adv. circ. 30,000.

284 US
LUTHERAN CHURCH IN AMERICA. YEARBOOK. 1961. a. $4.50. Board of Publication on Lutheran Church in America, 2900 Queen Lane, Philadelphia, PA 19129. TEL 215-846-6800 Ed. R.T. Swanson. adv. circ. 15,000.
Formerly: American Lutheran Church. Yearbook (ISSN 0569-6348)

284 AT ISSN 0726-4305
LUTHERAN CHURCH OF AUSTRALIA. YEARBOOK. 1967. a. Aus.$6. Lutheran Publishing House, 205 Halifax St., Adelaide, S.A. 5000, Australia. Ed. K.J. Schmidt.
Formed by the merger of: Australian Lutheran Almanac & Lutheran Almanac.

284 CN ISSN 0316-800X
LUTHERAN CHURCHES IN CANADA. DIRECTORY. 1954-1985. a. Can.$3.50. ‡ Lutheran Council in Canada, 25 Old York Mills Rd., Willowdale, Ont. M2P 1B5, Canada. Ed. Lawrence Likness. adv. circ. 1,500.

280 US ISSN 0458-497X
LUTHERAN DIGEST. 1953. q. $6 for 2 yrs. Lutheran Digest, Inc., 10905 W 162nd St., Lakeville, MN 55044. TEL 612-435-5945 Ed. John W. Allen.

LUTHERAN EDUCATION. see *EDUCATION*

284.1 US ISSN 0024-7456
LUTHERAN FORUM; an independent journal. (Supplement: Una Sancta) 1967. q. $17 (includes subscr. to its Forum Letter) American Lutheran Publicity Bureau, 308 W. 46th St., New York, NY 10036-3894. TEL 212-757-1292 Ed. Rev. Glenn C. Stone. adv. bk. rev. illus. stat. circ. 4,000. (also avail. in microform from UMI; back issues avail.; reprint service avail. from UMI) Indexed: CERDIC. Rel.Ind.One.
Supersedes: American Lutheran Magazine.

284 US ISSN 0046-4732
LUTHERAN FORUM. FORUM LETTER. 1972. m. $17 (includes subscr. to Lutheran Forum) American Lutheran Publicity Bureau, 308 W. 46th St., New York, NY 10036-3894. TEL 212-757-1292 Ed. Richard J. Neuhaus. bk. rev. circ. 4,000. (also avail. in microfilm from UMI; back issues avail.; reprint service avail. from UMI) Indexed: CERDIC.

284 US ISSN 0460-0274
LUTHERAN HISTORICAL CONFERENCE NEWSLETTER. 1962. 3/yr. $7.50. Lutheran Historical Conference, Valparaiso University, Valparaiso, IN 46383. Ed. James L. Schaaf. bk. rev. circ. 225. Indexed: Rel.Ind.One.

284.1 US ISSN 0360-6945
LUTHERAN JOURNAL. 1937. q. $4. Outlook Publications, Inc., 7317 Cahill Rd., Edina, MN 55435. TEL 612-941-6830 Ed. Armin U. Deye. adv. bk. rev. illus. circ. 136,000. Indexed: A.I.P.P.
Former titles, 1943-47: Northwest Lutheran Journal; Lutheran Home Journal.

284 US ISSN 0024-7464
LUTHERAN LAYMAN. 1929. 8/yr. $3. ‡ International Lutheran Laymen's League, 2185 Hampton, St. Louis, MO 63139. Ed. Gerald Pershbacher. adv. bk. rev. illus. circ. 100,000. (tabloid format)

LUTHERAN LIBRARIES. see *LIBRARY AND INFORMATION SCIENCES*

LUTHERAN MESSENGER FOR THE BLIND. see *BLIND*

266 US ISSN 0279-4462
LUTHERAN PERSPECTIVE. 1973. bi-w. (m. in Jul., Aug., Dec.) free. Evangelical Lutherans in Mission, Box 578555, Chicago, IL 60657-8555. TEL 312-753-0784 Ed. Randall R. Lee. circ. 26,000. (tabloid format; also avail. in microform)
Formerly: Missouri in Perspective.

284.1 US ISSN 0024-7510
LUTHERAN SENTINEL. 1917. m. $4.50. ‡ (Evangelical Lutheran Synod) Graphic Publishing Co., Inc., 206 N. Second Ave. W, Lake Mills, IA 50450. TEL 515-592-2000 Ed. Paul G. Madson. bk. rev. circ. 5,100.

284.1 US ISSN 0024-7537
LUTHERAN SPOKESMAN. 1958. m. $5. Church of the Lutheran Confession (Minneapolis), 460 75th Ave. N.E., Minneapolis, MN 55432 TEL 414-425-6665 (Subscr. address: 2750 Oxford St. N., Roseville, MN 55113) Ed. Rev. Paul Fleisher. bk. rev. circ. 2,700.

284.1 US ISSN 0024-7545
LUTHERAN STANDARD. 1961. s-m. $8. (American Lutheran Church) Augsburg Publishing House, 426 S. Fifth St., Minneapolis, MN 55440. TEL 612-330-3300 Ed. Lowell G. Almen. adv. bk. rev. index. circ. 577,000. Indexed: G.Soc.Sci.& Rel.Per.Lit.

284.1 AT ISSN 0024-7553
LUTHERAN THEOLOGICAL JOURNAL. 1966. 3/yr. Aus.$11. ‡ (Lutheran Church of Australia) Lutheran Publishing House, 205 Halifax St., Adelaide, S.A. 5000, Australia. Ed. Dr. J.G. Strelan. bk. rev. circ. 600. Indexed: Old Test.Abstr. CERDIC. New Test.Abstr. Rel.Ind.One.

207.11 284 US
LUTHERAN THEOLOGICAL SEMINARY BULLETIN. 1921. q. free. ‡ Lutheran Theological Seminary, Gettysburg, PA 17325. TEL 717-334-6286 Ed. William O. Avery. circ. 3,500.
Formerly: Gettysburg Seminary Bulletin (ISSN 0362-0581)

284.1 US ISSN 0024-757X
LUTHERAN WITNESS. 1882. m. $6.50. (Lutheran Church-Missouri Synod) Concordia Publishing House, 1333 S. Kirkwood Rd., St. Louis, MO 63122. TEL 314-664-7000 Ed. Robin Mueller. adv. bk. rev. illus. circ. 450,000. (also avail. in microfilm from UMI) Indexed: G.Soc.Sci.& Rel.Per.Lit.

284.1 US ISSN 0024-7596
LUTHERAN WOMEN. 1908. 10/yr. $4.50. ‡ Lutheran Church Women, 2900 Queen Ln., Philadelphia, PA 19129. TEL 215-438-2200 Ed. Terry Schutz. bk. rev. illus. index. circ. 40,000. Indexed: A.I.P.P.

284.1 US ISSN 0076-1540
LUTHERAN WORLD FEDERATION. PROCEEDINGS OF THE ASSEMBLY. irreg., 1970, 5th, Evian-Les-Bains, France. Augsburg Publishing House, 426 South 5th St., Minneapolis, MN 55415. TEL 612-330-3300 Indexed: Rel.Ind.One.

284 US
LUTHERANS IN STEP. 1951. 5/yr. free to qualified personnel. Lutheran Council in the U.S.A., Division of Service to Military Personnel, Suite 300, 122 C St., N.W., Washington, DC 20001. TEL 202-783-7501 Ed. Bertram Gilbert. circ. 40,000.
Former titles: In Step (ISSN 0019-3267); Mighty Fortress.

284 948 SZ
LUTHERISCHE BEITRAEGE. 1970. 4/yr. Bund Evangelischer Lutherische Kirchen in der Schweiz, Hirschwiesenstr. 9, 8057 Zurich, Switzerland.

284.1 GW ISSN 0024-7618
LUTHERISCHE MONATSHEFTE. 1962. m. DM.66. Lutherisches Verlagshaus GmbH, Knochenhauerstr. 38/40, 3000 Hannover 1, W. Germany (B.R.D.) (Editorial address: Knochenhauer Str. 42, 3000 Hannover, W. Germany (B.R.D.)) adv. bk. rev. bibl. charts. index. circ. 9,500. Indexed: CERDIC.

284.1 AU ISSN 0024-7626
DIE LUTHERKIRCHE; Pfarrblatt. 1948. q. free. Evangelische Gemeinde A.B. Wien-Waehring, Martinstr. 25, A-1180 Vienna, Austria. Ed. Werner Puelz. circ. 4,500.

268 SW ISSN 0345-7389
LUTHERSK BARNTIDNING. 1952. w. Kr.60. Missionssaellskapet Bibeltrogna Vaenner, Upplandsgatan 43, 113 28 Stockholm, Sweden. Ed. Ingemar Andersson. circ. 4,000.

288 US
M S U U NEWSLETTER: GLEANINGS. 1974. q. membership. Ministerial Sisterhood Unitarian Universalist, c/o Unitarian Universalist Church of Atlanta, 1911 Cliff Valley Way, N.E., Atlanta, GA 30329. TEL 404-634-5134 Ed. Rev. Patricia L. Clarke. adv. bk. rev. circ. 300.
Formerly: M S U U Newsletter (ISSN 0360-7046)

270 AU
MARTIN LUTHER. 1972. s-a. Evangelischer Bund in Oesterreich, Ungargasse 9, A-1030 Vienna, Austria. (Co-sponsor: Martin Luther-Bund) circ. 800.

200 US ISSN 0162-427X
MATURE LIVING. 1977. m. $11.75. Southern Baptist Convention, Sunday School Board, 127 Ninth Avenue, North, Nashville, TN 37234. TEL 615-251-2000 circ. 100,000.

287 US ISSN 0025-6021
MATURE YEARS. 1954. q. $3.50. United Methodist Publishing House, 201 Eighth Ave., S., Nashville, TN 37203. TEL 615-749-6000 Ed. Daisy Dozier Warren. adv. bk. rev. illus. circ. 117,964. (also avail. in microform from UMI) Indexed: Meth.Per.Ind.

287 MX ISSN 0026-0185
MESIAS; boletin semanal de la iglesia Metodista. vol. 8, 1971. w. Iglesia Metodista el Mesias, Balderas 47, Mexico D. F., Mexico.

284.2 FR ISSN 0026-0274
MESSAGER EVANGELIQUE. (Text in French and German) 1945. w. 160 F. (Eglise de la Confession d'Ausburg) Librairie Oberlin, 18 rue Sainte Barbe, 67000 Strasbourg, France. (Co-sponsor: Eglise Reforme d'Alsace et de Lorraine) Ed. Michel Hoeffel. adv. bk. rev. illus. circ. 20,000.

286 IT
MESSAGGERO AVVENTISTA. 1926. m. L.16000. (Unione Italiana delle Chiese Cristiane Avventiste) Edizioni A.D.V. l'Araldo della Verita, Via Chiantigiana, 30-Falciani, 50023 Impruneta-Firenze, Italy. Ed. Paolo Tramuto. circ. 1,500.

286 UK ISSN 0309-3654
MESSENGER. 1895. fortn. £2. (British Union Conference of Seventh-day Adventists) Stanborough Press Ltd., Alma Park, Grantham, Lincs NG31 9SL, England. Ed. D. N. Marshall. adv. bk. rev. circ. 10,000.
Formerly: British Advent Messenger (ISSN 0045-2874)

286 US
MESSENGER (OMAHA) 1911. m. (10/yr.) $1. American Baptist Churches of Nebraska, 6404 Maple St., Omaha, NE 68104. TEL 402-556-4730 Ed. Kay Grabia. bk. rev. illus. circ. 5,455.
Formerly: Nebraska Baptist Messenger.

289 UK
METHODIST CONFERENCE. MINUTES AND YEARBOOK. 1932. a. £7. Methodist Publishing House, Wellington Rd., Wimbledon, London SW19 8EU, England. circ. 6,000.

691 UK
METHODIST DIARIES. 1850. a. Methodist Publishing House, Wellington Rd., Wimbledon, London SW19 8EU, England. circ. 8,000.

287 209 US ISSN 0026-1238
METHODIST HISTORY. 1962. q. $10. ‡ United Methodist Church, Commission on Archives and History, Box 127, Madison, NJ 07940. TEL 201-822-2787 Ed. Charles Yrigoyen, Jr. adv. bk. rev. charts. index. circ. 800. (also avail. in microfilm from UMI) Indexed: Meth Per.Ind. Hist.Abstr. Rel.Per. Amer.Hist.& Life. CERDIC. Rel.Ind.One. Rel.& Theol.Abstr.

287 UK ISSN 0026-1262
METHODIST RECORDER. 1861. w. $34. Methodist Newspaper Co., Ltd., 122 Golden Lane, London E.C.1., England. Ed. Michael Taylor. adv. bk. rev. charts. illus. play rev. record rev. circ. 29,539. (tabloid format; also avail. in microfilm from WMP)

287 SW ISSN 0543-6206
METODISTKYRKANS I SVERIGE. AARSBOK. 1896. a. Kr.35. (Metodistkyrkans i Sverige - United Methodist Church in Sweden) Foerlaget Sanctus, Box 5020, 102 41 Stockholm, Sweden. Rev. Lars Collin. stat. circ. 400.

200 US ISSN 0026-2072
MICHIGAN CHRISTIAN ADVOCATE. 1873. 32,00. $9. (United Methodist Church, West Michigan and Detroit Annual Conferences) Michigan Christian Advocate Publishing Co., 316 Springbrook Ave., Adrian, MI 49221. TEL 517-265-2075 Ed. Edward L. Duncan. adv. bk. rev. illus. circ. 21,000.

264 US
MICHIGAN LUTHERAN. 1882. m. Lutheran Church-Missouri Synod, Michigan District, 3773 Geddes Rd., Ann Arbor, MI 48105. TEL 313-665-3791 Ed. Holger G. Cattau. bk. rev. film rev. circ. 80,000(controlled)

284 US
MINNESOTA SYNOD LUTHERAN. 1963. 8/yr. membership. ‡ Lutheran Church in America, Minnesota Synod, 122 W. Franklin, Minneapolis, MN 55404. TEL 612-870-3610 Ed. David G. Jones. circ. 74,000.

266 284 US ISSN 0093-8130
MISSION HANDBOOK: NORTH AMERICAN PROTESTANT MINISTRIES OVERSEAS. 1951. triennial. $19.75. Missions Advanced Research and Communication Center, (Subsidiary of: World Vision International) 919 W. Huntington Dr., Monrovia, CA 91016. TEL 818-303-8811 Ed. Samuel Wilson. index.
Formerly: North American Protestant Ministries Overseas (ISSN 0078-1339)
Missions

266 US ISSN 0279-5345
MISSIONS U S A. 1930. m. $3.50. Southern Baptist Convention, Home Mission Board, 1350 Spring St., N.W., Atlanta, GA 30309. TEL 404-873-4041 Ed. Walker L. Knight. adv. bk. rev. illus. index. circ. 95,000. Indexed: South.Bap.Per.Ind.
Formerly: Home Missions (ISSN 0018-408X)

287 US
MISSISSIPPI UNITED METHODIST ADVOCATE. 1947. fortn. $3. ‡ United Methodist Church, North Mississippi and Mississippi Conference, Box 1093, Jackson, MS 39205. TEL 601-354-0515 Ed. Rev. J.R. Woodrick. adv. bk. rev. circ. 18,000. (tabloid format)
Formerly: Mississippi Methodist Advocate (ISSN 0026-6329)

284 GW
MITTEILUNGEN DER NORDDEUTSCHEN MISSION. BREMEN. 1949. bi-m. free. Norddeutsche Mission, Vahrer Str. 243, 2800 Bremen 44, W. Germany (B.R.D) Ed Rev. Dieter Lenz, Hilmar Froelich.
Missions

284.2 SA ISSN 0378-410X
MOLAETSA-MOLAETSA. (Text in South Suthu, Swana) 1957. 8/yr. R.1.50. Reformed Churches in South Africa - Gereformeerde Kerke in Suid-Afrika, Box 20008, Noordbrug 2522, Potchefstroom, South Africa. Ed. H.A. Louw.
Formerly: Rugama.

268 US ISSN 0162-4288
MORE (NASHVILLE) m. in w. parts. $6.50. Southern Baptist Convention, Sunday School Board, 127 Ninth Ave., North, Nashville, TN 37234. TEL 615-251-2000
For younger children, beginning readers

MORE LIGHT UPDATE. see *HOMOSEXUALITY*

200 SA ISSN 0027-1454
MOSUPA - TSELA. (Text in Setswana) 1900. m. R.1($1) ‡ (Evangelical Lutheran Church in South Africa, Western Diocese) Lutheran Book Depot, Box 536, 0300 Rustenburg, Transvaal, South Africa. Ed. Rev. M. Dillhale. bk. rev. illus. circ. 12,000.

284 GW
MUENCHNER GEMEINDEBLATT. 1892. w. DM.35.40. Evangelischer Presseverband fuer Bayern e.V., Birkerstr. 22, 8000 Munich 19, W. Germany (B.R.D.) adv. bk. rev. charts. illus. circ. 11,716.
Formerly: Evangelisches Gemeindeblatt fuer Muenchen (ISSN 0014-3588)

284.2 SA ISSN 0378-4126
MURUMIWA. (Editions in Tsonga and Venda) 1950. bi-m. R.1. Reformed Churches in South Africa - Gereformeerde Kerke in Suid-Afrika, Box 20008, Noordbrug 2522, Potchefstroom, South Africa. Ed. G.D. Affourtit.

MUSIC LEADER. see *MUSIC*

268 US ISSN 0162-4377
MUSIC MAKERS. q. $4. Southern Baptist Convention, Sunday School Board, 127 Ninth Ave., North, Nashville, TN 37234. TEL 615-251-2000 Indexed: Perf.Arts Biog.Master Ind.

266 UK ISSN 0077-3557
NATIONAL BIBLE SOCIETY OF SCOTLAND. ANNUAL REPORT. (Supplement to: Word at Work) 1860. a. free. National Bible Society of Scotland, 7 Hampton Terrace, Edinburgh EH12 5XU, Scotland. Ed. Colin S. Hay. circ. 1,000.

260 US
NATIONAL COUNCIL OF THE CHURCHES OF CHRIST IN THE U.S.A. TRIENNIAL REPORT. 1946. triennial. (National Council of the Churches of Christ in the U.S.A.) News and Information Office, 475 Riverside Dr., Rm. 850, New York, NY 10115. TEL 212-870-2141 Ed. Larry D. Hollon. circ. 12,500.

280 US
NAVIGATORS DAILY WALK. 1978. m. contributions. Walk Thru The Bible Ministries, Inc., 61 Perimeter Park, N.E., Box 80587, Atlanta, GA 30366. Ed. Peter M. Wallace. circ. 100,000.

284.2 SA ISSN 0024-8665
NEDERDUITSE GEREFORMEERDE KERK VAN NATAL GEMEENTE VRYHEID. MAANDBRIEF. 1965. m. free. Nederduitse Gereformeerde Kerk van Natal Gemeentevryheid, Smalstraat 82, Vryheid, Natal, South Africa. Ed. E. Oberholster. adv. circ. 600(controlled) (looseleaf format)

284.2 230 SA ISSN 0028-2006
NEDERDUITSE GEREFORMEERDE TEOLOGIESE TYDSKRIF. 1959. q. R.22. (Nederduitse Gereformeerde Kerk in Suid-Afrika, Faculties of Theology - Dutch Reformed Church in South Africa) Nederduitse Gereformeerde Kerk Uitgewers en -Boekhandel, Box 4539, Cape Town, South Africa. Ed. H.M. Venter. bk. rev. bibl. index. circ. 1,800. Indexed: Old Test.Abstr. CERDIC.

284.2 NE ISSN 0031-5567
NEDERLANDSE HERVORMDE KERK. PERSBUREAU. WEEKBULLETIN. 1945. w. fl.150. ‡ Nederlandse Hervormde Kerk, Persbureau - Netherlands Reformed Church, Overgoo 11, Postbus 405, 2260 AK Leidschendam, Netherlands. Ed. J.A. Bijsterveld. bk. rev. abstr. circ. 1,000.

284 GW ISSN 0028-3614
NEUES DORF; Jugend und Familie auf dem Land. 1965. bi-m. DM.9. (Evangelische Landjugend Bayern) Evangelischer Presseverband fuer Bayern e.V., Birkerstr. 22, 8000 Munich 19, W. Germany (B.R.D.) Ed. Paul Geissendoerfer.

284 028.5 US
NEW BEGINNINGS (PISGAH FOREST) 1982. bi-m. free. 1211 Williamson Creek Rd., Pisgah Forest, NC 28768. TEL 704-883-2222 Eds. Randall Blythe, Lisa Pickelsimer. adv. illus. circ. 400.

283 CN ISSN 0703-9409
NEW BRUNSWICK ANGLICAN. 1977. m. Can.$4. Anglican Church of Canada, Diocese of Fredericton, Tracy, N.B. N0G 3C0, Canada. Ed. Rev. E.F. Eaton. adv. bk. rev. circ. 4,000(controlled)

287 028.5 US
NEW DISCIPLES. 1982. q. $8.75. (United Methodist Board of Discipleship) United Methodist Publishing House, Graded Press, Box 801, Nashville, TN 37202. Ed. Betty Ann Driver. charts. illus. circ. 38,000.

NEW HORIZONS. see *EDUCATION — Higher Education*

287 AT
NEW TIMES. 1971. m. Aus.$25. ‡ (Uniting Church in Australia) News Times Incorporated, Epworth Building, 33 Pirie St., Adelaide 5000, Australia. Ed. David Busch. adv. bk. rev. illus. circ. 5,000. Indexed: CERDIC.
Former titles: Central Times (ISSN 0038-2949); South Australian Methodist.

266 284.1 US ISSN 0043-8812
NEW WORLD OUTLOOK; missions and ecumenical relationships. 1911; N.S. 1941. m. (combined Jul.-Aug. and Nov.-Dec.) $7. (United Methodist Church, General Board of Global Ministries) Parthenon Press (Subsidiary of: United Methodist Publishing House) 475 Riverside Dr., Rm. 1351, New York, NY 10115. TEL 212-870-3758 Eds. Arthur J. Moore, George M. Daniels. adv. bk. rev. illus. index. circ. 38,000. (also avail. in microfilm) Indexed: CERDIC.
Formerly: World Outlook.

286 NZ ISSN 0027-7177
NEW ZEALAND BAPTIST. 1881. m. free. Baptist Union of New Zealand, P.O. Box 27-390, Wellington, New Zealand. Ed. Rev. R.E. Bullen. adv. circ. 11,500. (tabloid format)

283 CN
NEWFOUNDLAND CHURCHMAN. 1888. m. Can.$5($7.50) Anglican Church of Newfoundland, 19 Kingsbridge Rd., St. John's, Nfld. A1C 3K4, Canada. TEL 709-726-6697 Ed. Hollis Hiscock. adv. bk. rev. circ. 33,000.

285 US ISSN 0362-1510
NEWS FROM THE CONGREGATIONAL CHRISTIAN HISTORICAL SOCIETY. 1969. s-a. membership. Congregational Christian Historical Society, Inc., 14 Beacon St., Boston, MA 02108. TEL 617-523-0470 Ed. Harold F. Worthley. circ. 1,200.

283 UK
NEWSCAN. 1965. m. 20p. Scottish Episcopal Church, 21 Grosvenor Crescent, Edinburgh EH12 5EE, Scotland. adv. bk. rev. circ. 8,000. (tabloid format)
Former titles: Outlook (ISSN 0306-2295); Scan (ISSN 0036-5475)

200 UK ISSN 0048-0304
NEWSPEACE. 1971. m. (11/yr.) £4. Fellowship of Reconciliation, 40-46 Harleyford Rd., Vauxhall, London SE11 5AY, England. Ed. Gordon Slater. bk. rev. bibl. illus. circ. 1,100. (also avail. in microform from UMI)

200 US ISSN 0029-2435
NORTH CAROLINA CHRISTIAN ADVOCATE. 1855. w. $10. (United Methodist Church, North Carolina Conference and Western North Carolina Conference) Methodist Board of Publication, Box 508, Greensboro, NC 27402. TEL 919-272-1196 Ed. Rev. C. A. Simonton, Jr. adv. bk. rev. circ. 20,000. (also avail. in microfiche)

284 US ISSN 0029-3512
NORTHWESTERN LUTHERAN. 1914. s-m. $6. ‡ (Wisconsin Evangelical Lutheran Synod) Northwestern Publishing House, 1250 N. 113th St., Box 26975, Milwaukee, WI 53226-0975. Ed. Rev. James P. Schaefer. bk. rev. index. circ. 58,000. Indexed: CERDIC.

284 AG ISSN 0029-425X
NOTICIERO DE LA FE. 1935. m. $1.50. Revista Luterana, Simbron 4667, Buenos Aires, Argentina. Ed. Ernesto Weigandt. adv. bk. rev. illus. circ. 3,100.

287 UK
NOW (LONDON, 1970) 1970. 10/yr. £1.80. Methodist Church Overseas Division, 25 Marylebone Rd., London NW1 5JR, England. Ed. J. Pickard. bk. rev. circ. 63,000. (also avail. in microform from UMI; reprint service avail. from UMI)
Formerly: Kingdom Overseas.

286 US
NUESTRA TAREA. (Text in Spanish) 1955. m. $8.50. Southern Baptist Convention, Women's Missionary Union, Highway 280 E., 100 Missionary Ridge, Birmingham, AL 35283-0010. TEL 205-991-8100 Ed. Elina Cabarcas. circ. 4,500.

200 SA ISSN 0029-6708
NUWE PROTESTANT. (Text in Afrikaans) 1947. m. R.3. Nuwe Protestantse Kerk in Afrika, Box 18348, Hercules 0030, Pretoria, Transvaal, South Africa. Ed. Rev. L.P. van Sittert. bk. rev. abstr. illus. circ. 1,200. Indexed: CERDIC.

286 976 US
OKLAHOMA BAPTIST CHRONICLE. 1958. s-a. $2. (Baptist General Convention of Oklahoma, Historical Commission) Messenger Press, 1141 N. Robinson, Oklahoma City, OK 73103. TEL 405-236-4341 Ed. J.M. Gaskin. circ. 400.

268 US ISSN 0162-4385
ON THE WING. q. $3.75. Southern Baptist Convention, Sunday School Board, 127 9th Ave.N., Nashville, TN 37234. TEL 615-251-2000

284.2 SA ISSN 0030-2694
ONS JEUG. 1951. m. R.10.80. ‡ Nederduitse Gereformeerde Kerk, Kerkjeugaksie - Dutch Reformed Church, Youth Commission, Box 396, Bloemfontein 9300, South Africa. Ed. L.C. Dressel. adv. bk. rev. illus. stat. index. circ. 13,000.

283 CN ISSN 0030-2848
ONTARIO CHURCHMAN. 1960. m. contributions. Synod of the Diocese of Ontario, Board of Parish Services, 90 Johnson St., Kingston, Ont., Canada. TEL 613-544-4774 Ed. Gordon Hendra. adv. bk. rev. circ. 8,500.

284.2 NE ISSN 0030-3356
OPBOUW; weekblad tot opbouw van het Gereformeerde leven. 1957. w. fl.40. Reformeerde Persverenigung Opbouwterdam, Anne Franklaan 14, 3417 GE Montfoort, Netherlands. Ed.Bd. adv. bk. rev. circ. 2,800.

200 NE ISSN 0030-3402
OPEN DEUR. 1936. m. fl.17.65. Boekencentrum B.V., Box 84176, The Hague, Netherlands. (Co-sponsors: Dutch Reformed Church; Lutheran Church; Roman Catholic Church; Geref. Foundation) Ed. Eimert Pruim. bk. rev. illus. circ. controlled.

268 US ISSN 0162-4296
OPEN WINDOWS. q. $3.75. Southern Baptist Convention, Sunday School Board, 127 Ninth Ave., North, Nashville, TN 37234. TEL 615-251-2000

268 US ISSN 0162-430X
OPUS ONE. q. $6.25. Southern Baptist Convention, Sunday School Board, 127 Ninth Ave., North, Nashville, TN 37234. TEL 615-251-2000

268 US ISSN 0147-1597
OPUS TWO. q. $6.25. Southern Baptist Convention, Sunday School Board, 127 Ninth Ave., North, Nashville, TN 37234. TEL 615-251-2000

283 US
OREGON EPISCOPAL CHURCHMAN. 1861. 9/yr. $2. Episcopal Diocese of Oregon, Box 467, Lake Oswego, OR 97034. TEL 503-636-5613 Ed. Annette L. Ross. adv. bk. rev. illus. stat. circ. 12,000. (tabloid format)
Formerly: Oregon Churchman (ISSN 0030-4646)

285 US ISSN 0030-7238
OUTLOOK (WAKE FOREST) 1951. bi-m. free. ‡ Southern Baptist Convention, Southeastern Baptist Theological Seminary, Wake Forest, NC 27587. TEL 919-556-3101 Ed. Rodney V. Byard. bk. rev. index. circ. 15,000(controlled)

200 US
P F N A NEWS. 1960. q. free. ‡ (Pentecostal Fellowship of North America) Gospel Publishing House, 1445 Boonville Ave., Springfield, MO 65802. TEL 417-862-2781 Ed. Juleen H. Turnage. circ. 12,500. (tabloid format)

200 US ISSN 0360-1897
PACIFIC THEOLOGICAL REVIEW. 1967. 3/yr. free to qualified personnel. San Francisco Theological Seminary, 2 Kensington Rd., San Anselmo, CA 94960. TEL 415-453-2280 Ed. Robert B. Coote. bk. rev. circ. 7,500. Indexed: CERDIC.
Formerly: Action-Reaction (ISSN 0001-7485) *Presbyterian*

284 US
PARACLETE. 1967. 4/yr. $4.25. (General Council of the Assemblies of God, Inc.) Gospel Publishing House, 1445 Boonville Ave., Springfield, MO 65802. Ed. H.W. Steinberg. bk. rev. index. cum.index every 5 yrs. circ. 7,500. Indexed: CERDIC.

284 US ISSN 0738-7962
PARISH TEACHER. 1977. m. $4.95. (American Lutheran Church, Division for Life and Mission) Augsburg Publishing House, 426 S. Fifth St., Minneapolis, MN 55440. TEL 612-330-3300 Ed. William Korte. circ. 33,000.

282 283 SA ISSN 0031-2088
PARISHIONER. 1902. 12/yr. contributions. Cathedral of St. Mary the Virgin, Box 2029, Johannesburg 2000, South Africa. Ed. Deirdre Beckett. adv. bk. rev. circ. 1,500.

268 UK ISSN 0079-0117
PARTNERS IN LEARNING. 1968. a. £5. Methodist Church, Division of Education and Youth, 2 Chester House, Pages Lane, London N10 1PR, England (and National Christian Education Council, Robert Denholm House, Nutfield, Redhill RH1 4HW Surrey, England) (Co-sponsor: Joint Publications Board) Ed. Wilfred Tooley. circ. 24,000.

284 282 US
PATHWAYS (GARDEN GROVE) 4/yr. New Order of Glastonbury, 12332 Loraleen St., Garden Grove, CA 92641. Ed. Charlotte Schick.

287 MY
PELITA METHODIST. 1977. m. M.$6($2) Methodist Church in Malaysia - Gereja Methodist Malaysia, 2 Jalan Wesley, Kuala Lumpur 50150, Malaysia (Or Methodist Headquarters, 65 Jalan 5/31, Petaling Jaya, Selangor, Malaysia) Ed. Rev. Denis C. Dutton. adv. bk. rev. circ. 2,000.
Former titles: Methodist Message (ISSN 0026-1254); Malaysia Methodist.

289.9 US ISSN 0031-4897
PENTECOSTAL EVANGEL. 1913. w. $11.95. (General Council of the Assemblies of God) Gospel Publishing House, 1445 Boonville Ave., Springfield, MO 65802. TEL 417-862-2781 Ed. Richard G. Champion. bk. rev. charts. illus. index. circ. 290,000. (also avail. in microfilm) Indexed: A.I.P.P. G.Soc.Sci.& Rel.Per.Lit.

289.9 US ISSN 0031-4919
PENTECOSTAL MESSENGER. 1919. m. $6. Messenger Publishing House, Box 850, Joplin, MO 64802. TEL 417-624-7050 Ed. Don Allen. adv. circ. 10,000. Indexed: CERDIC.

289.9 CN ISSN 0031-4927
PENTECOSTAL TESTIMONY. 1920. m. $15. Pentecostal Assemblies of Canada, 10 Overlea Blvd., Toronto, Ont. M4H 1A5, Canada. TEL 416-425-1010 Ed. Robert J. Skinner. adv. bk. rev. circ. 27,000. Indexed: CERDIC.

200 US ISSN 0093-531X
PERSPECTIVES IN RELIGIOUS STUDIES. 1974. q. $12. (National Association of Baptist Professors of Religion) Mercer University Press, c/o Dr. Watson E. Mills, Ed., Mercer University, Macon, GA 31207. TEL 912-744-2880 adv. bk. rev. abstr. bibl. charts. illus. stat. cum.index: 1974-1983. circ. 650. (back issues avail.) Indexed: Bk.Rev.Mo. CERDIC. Old Test.Abstr. Rel.Per. New Test.Abstr. Rel.Ind.One. Rel.& Theol.Abstr.

285.834 US
PILGRIM STATE NEWS. 1951. bi-m. free. (United Church of Christ, Massachusetts Conference) Beacon Communications Corporation, 20 Main St., Acton, MA 01720. TEL 617-875-5233 Ed. Rosemary K. Agnew. bk. rev. illus. circ. 4,500.
Former titles: Pilgrim State Newsletter (ISSN 0362-0557); Until 1974: Pilgrim States News.

289.9 SA ISSN 0031-9902
PINKSTER PROTESTANT. (Text in Afrikaans and English; summaries in Afrikaans) 1958. 4/yr. R.30. Pentecostal Protestant Church - Pinkster Protestante Kerk, Box 180, Isando, Transvaal, South Africa. Ed. Pastor P.J.J. Synman. adv. bk. rev. circ. 5,000.

266 CN
PIONEER; Christian Monthly. 1951. m. Can.$7.50. Council of the Reformed Church in Canada, 201 Paradise Rd. N., Hamilton, Ont. L8S 3T3, Canada. TEL 416-637-3434 Ed. Rev. Peter Yff. adv. bk. rev. circ. 2,500. (also avail. in microfilm)

280 370 US ISSN 0162-5381
PLANBOOK FOR LEADERS OF CHILDREN. a. (United Methodist Church, Board of Discipleship) Graded Press, 201 Eighth Ave. S., Box 801, Nashville, TN 37202. TEL 615-749-6421 Ed. Mary Frances Pope.

286 US ISSN 0162-1955
PLANNING HELPS. 1970. m. (except Jul./Aug.) $8. Southern Baptist Convention, Women's Missionary Union, Highway 280 E., 100 Missionary Ridge, Birmingham, AL 35243-2798. TEL 205-991-8100 Ed. Jan Turrentine. circ. 125,000. (also avail. in microfiche)

287 028.5 US ISSN 0278-565X
POCKETS. 1981. m. (exc. Jan.) $10.95. (United Methodist Church, General Board of Discipleship) Upper Room, 1908 Grand Ave., Box 189, Nashville, TN 37202. TEL 615-327-2700 Ed. Willie S. Teague.
For children ages 6 to 12

287 PO ISSN 0032-5066
PORTUGAL EVANGELICO. 1920. m. Esc.200($5) Igreja Evangelica Metodista Portuguesa, Igreja do Mirante, Praca Coronel Pacheco, Porto, Portugal. (Co-sponsor: Presbyterian Church in Portugal) Ed. Rev. Ireneu Da Silva Cunha. bk. rev. illus. circ. 2,000.

284 FR ISSN 0032-5228
POSITIONS LUTHERIENNES. 1953. q. 150 F. Association "Positions Lutheriennes", 16 rue Chauchat, 75009 Paris, France. Ed. J.N. Peres. bk. rev. bibl. circ. 550. Indexed: Bull.Signal. CERDIC.

289 US
POSSIBILITIES: THE MAGAZINE OF HOPE. 1983. bi-m. free. (Robert Schuller Ministries) Publishing Directions, 1223 Potomac St., N.W., Washington, DC 20007. Ed. Robert H. Schuller. adv. circ. 800,000.

266 FR ISSN 0751-5987
POUR LA VERITE. 1935. m. 80 F. Union Eglises Evangeliques Libres de France, c/o Jean Pongy, 12, Impasse Viala-rue Montaury, 30000 Nimes, France. Ed. S. Lauzet. bk. rev. circ. 1,500.

PRAYERS FOR WORSHIP. see *RELIGIONS AND THEOLOGY — Roman Catholic*

285 US
PRESBYTERIAN (DENTON) 1954. m. (except Jan., May, Augl., & Nov.) Synod of the Sun, 920 Stemmons Frwy., Denton, TX 76205. Ed. Hal Bray. adv. bk. rev. illus. circ. 117,000 (controlled) (tabloid format; also avail. in microfilm from UMI; reprint service avail. from UMI) Indexed: Old Test.Abstr. Chr.Per.Ind.
Formerly: Texas Presbyterian (ISSN 0040-4616)

285 US ISSN 0032-7522
PRESBYTERIAN GUARDIAN. 1935. 11/yr. $4.75. Presbyterian Guardian Publishing Corp., 7401 Old York Rd., Philadelphia, PA 19126. Ed. J. Cameron Fraser. adv. bk. rev. illus. circ. 4,000. Indexed: CERDIC.

285 UK ISSN 0032-7530
PRESBYTERIAN HERALD. m. £4.80. Presbyterian Church in Ireland, Church House, Fisherwick Place, Belfast, BT1 6DW, N. Ireland. Ed. Robert Cobain. adv. bk. rev. circ. 19,000. Indexed: CERDIC.

285 US ISSN 0555-0572
PRESBYTERIAN LAYMAN. 1968. s-m. free. Presbyterian Lay Committee, 1245 N. Providence Rd., Media, PA 19063. TEL 215-565-4764 Ed. James J. Cochran. circ. 455,000.

285 US ISSN 0032-7565
PRESBYTERIAN OUTLOOK. 1819. w. $12. Outlook Publishers, Inc., 512 E. Main St., Richmond, VA 23219. TEL 804-649-1371 Ed. George Laird Hunt. adv. bk. rev. illus. circ. 9,500. (also avail. in microform from UMI; reprint service avail. from UMI)

285 CN ISSN 0032-7573
PRESBYTERIAN RECORD. 1876. m. Can.$7. Presbyterian Church in Canada, 50 Wynford Dr., Don Mills, Ont. M3C 1J7, Canada. TEL 416-441-1111 Ed. James Ross Dickey. adv. bk. rev. film rev. index. circ. 82,694.

285 266 US ISSN 0032-759X
PRESBYTERIAN SURVEY. 1879. m. $11. (Presbyterian Church) Presbyterian Publishing House, 341 Ponce de Leon Ave., N. E., Atlanta, GA 30365. TEL 404-873-1549 Ed. Vic Jameson. adv. bk. rev. charts. film rev. illus. index. circ. 194,000. (also avail. in microform from UMI; reprint service avail. from UMI)
Incorporating: Today in World Missions. Successor to: Missionary (founded in 1861); Home Missionary (founded in 1890); Missionary Survey (founded in 1977)

285 US
PRESBYTERION. 1975. s-a. $6. Covenant Theological Seminary, 12330 Conway Rd., St. Louis, MO 63141. Ed.Bd. bk. rev. circ. 400. (also avail. in microform) Indexed: CERDIC. Chr.Per.Ind. New Test.Abstr. Old Test.Abstr. Rel.& Theol.Abstr. Rel.Ind.One.

268 US
PRESCHOOL BIBLE TEACHER A. q. $7.25. Southern Baptist Convention, Sunday School Board, 127 Ninth Ave., North, Nashville, TN 37234. TEL 615-251-2000
Formerly, until 1982: Guide A for Preschool Teachers (ISSN 0162-4474)

268 US
PRESCHOOL BIBLE TEACHER B. q. $8.50. Southern Baptist Convention, Sunday School Board, 127 Ninth Ave., North, Nashville, TN 37234. TEL 615-251-2000
Formerly, until 1982: Guide B for Preschool Teachers (ISSN 0162-4482)

268 US
PRESCHOOL BIBLE TEACHER C. q. $8.50. Southern Baptist Convention, Sunday School Board, 127 Ninth Ave., North, Nashville, TN 37234. TEL 615-251-2000
Formerly, until 1982: Guide C for Preschool Teachers (ISSN 0162-4490)

268 US ISSN 0162-4393
PRESCHOOL LEADERSHIP. q. $7.25. Southern Baptist Convention, Sunday School Board, 127 Ninth Ave., North, Nashville, TN 37234. TEL 615-251-2000 Indexed: South.Bap.Per.Ind.

PRIMARY FRIEND. see *CHILDREN AND YOUTH — For*

286 US ISSN 0032-9215
PROBE (MEMPHIS) 1970. m. $2.28 for 3 mos. ‡ Southern Baptist Convention, Brotherhood Commission, 1548 Poplar Ave., Memphis, TN 38104. Ed. Mike Day. illus. circ. 45,000. (also avail. in microform from UMI; reprint service avail. from UMI)
For boys ages 12-17

266 US ISSN 0162-4326
PROCLAIM; the pastor's journal for biblical preaching. 1970. q. $9.75. Southern Baptist Convention, Sunday School Board, 127 9th Ave. N., Nashville, TN 37234. TEL 615-251-2000 illus. circ. 14,200. Indexed: South.Bap.Per.Ind.

286 US ISSN 0033-1139
PROMOTOR DE EDUCACION CRISTIANA. (Text in Spanish) 1949. q. $4.20. Casa Bautista de Publicaciones, Box 4255, El Paso, TX 79914. TEL 915-566-9656 Ed. Jorge Enrique Diaz. bk. rev. charts. illus. index. circ. 6,000.
For leaders in church program

200 230 IT ISSN 0033-1767
PROTESTANTESIMO. 1946. q. L.22000. Facolta Valdese di Teologia, Via Pietro Cossa 42, 00193 Rome, Italy. Ed. Vittorio Subilia. bk. rev. bibl. index. Indexed: Bull.Signal. Int.Z.Bibelwiss. CERDIC. Rel.Ind.One.

284 917.306 US
PROVIDENT BOOK FINDER. 1970. bi-m. free. (Provident Bookstores) Mennonite Publishing House, 616 Walnut Ave., Scottdale, PA 15683. TEL 412-887-8500 Ed. Dorothy Cutrell. bk. rev. circ. 21,500. (back issues avail.)

284.2 SA ISSN 0033-6637
QUO VADIS. (Text in Afrikaans) 1950. 10/yr. R.3.50. ‡ Reformed Churches in South Africa - Gereformeerde Kerke in Suid-Afrika, Box 20008, Noordbrug 2522, Potchefstroom, South Africa. circ. 11,600.

205 US
R E S MISSION BULLETIN. 1981. irreg., approx. q. $5. Reformed Ecumenical Synod, 1677 Gentian Dr. S.E., Grand Rapids, MI 49508. TEL 616-455-1126 Paul G. Schrotenboer. circ. 700.
Formerly: R E S World Diaconal Bulletin.

285 US ISSN 0033-6904
R E S NEWS EXCHANGE. 1964. m. $6. Reformed Ecumenical Synod, 1677 Gentian Dr. S.E., Grand Rapids, MI 49508. TEL 616-455-1126 Ed. Dr. Paul G. Schrotenboer. bk. rev. circ. 1,200.

200 US
R E S THEOLOGICAL FORUM. 1973. q. $7. Reformed Ecumenical Synod, 1677 Gentian Dr. S.E., Grand Rapids, MI 49508. TEL 616-455-1126 Ed. Dr. Paul G. Schrotenboer. circ. 400.

260 UK ISSN 0300-3469
READER. 1904. q. £2. Church of England, Central Readers' Conference, Church House, Gt. Smith St., London SW1P 3NZ, England. Ed. M. Canny. adv. bk. rev. circ. 7,500.

289.9 CN ISSN 0034-0847
REAL LIVING. 1964. q. Can.$2.50. ‡ Pentecostal Assemblies of Canada, Men's Fellowship Department, 10 Overlea Blvd., Toronto, Ont. M4H 1A5, Canada. TEL 416-425-1010 Ed. Rev. Gordon R. Upton. circ. 15,000.

284 NZ ISSN 0034-107X
REAPER; New Zealand's Evangelical monthly. 1923. bi-m. NZ.$18. Bible College of New Zealand, Inc., 221 Lincoln Rd., Henderson, Auckland 8, New Zealand. Eds. D.G. Stewart, S.J. Sands. adv. bk. rev. circ. 6,000. (tabloid format)

200 UK ISSN 0034-1479
RECONCILIATION QUARTERLY. 1924. q. £5. Fellowship of Reconciliation, 40-46 Harleyford Rd., Vauxhall, London SE11 5AY, England. Eds. Elnora & John Ferguson. adv. bk. rev. illus. circ. 1,750. (also avail. in microform from UMI; reprint service avail. from UMI) Indexed: CERDIC.

285 UK ISSN 0306-7262
REFORM. 1972. 11/yr. £4.40. United Reformed Church in the United Kingdom, 86 Tavistock Place, London WC1H 9RT, England. Ed. Norman Hart. adv. bk. rev. film rev. illus. circ. 19,000.
Formed by the merger of: Congregational Monthly (ISSN 0010-583X) & Outlook (ISSN 0030-7203)

286 UK ISSN 0034-3048
REFORMATION TODAY. 1970. 6/yr. $12. Belvidere Road Church, 361 Aigburth Rd., Liverpool L17 0BP, England. Ed. Erroll Hulse. bk. rev. charts. circ. 3,000. Indexed: CERDIC.
Supersedes: Christians Pathway.

284 GW ISSN 0171-3469
REFORMATIONSGESCHICHTLICHE STUDIEN UND TEXTE. 1906. irreg., vol.123, 1985. price varies. Aschendorffsche Verlagsbuchhandlung, Soester Str. 13, 4400 Muenster, W. Germany (B.R.D.) Ed. Erwin Iserloh.

284 FR ISSN 0223-5749
REFORME. 1945. w. 395. 53-55 Avenue du Maine, 75014 Paris, France. Ed. Paul Viallaneix. illus. (tabloid format)

280 US ISSN 0080-0481
REFORMED CHURCH OF AMERICA. HISTORICAL SERIES. irreg., 1970, no.2. Wm. B. Eerdmans Publishing Co., 255 Jefferson Ave., S.E., Grand Rapids, MI 49503. TEL 616-459-4591

200 US ISSN 0034-3064
REFORMED REVIEW. 1947. 3/yr. $10. Western Theological Seminary, Holland, MI 49423. TEL 616-392-8555 Ed. James I. Cook. adv. bk. rev. bibl. cum.index. circ. 2,400. (also avail. in microform from UMI; reprint service avail. from UMI) Indexed: Int.Z.Bibelwiss. Rel.Per. CERDIC. New Test.Abstr. Rel.Ind.One. Rel.& Theol.Abstr.

284 SZ ISSN 0034-3056
REFORMED WORLD. 1971. q. $4. World Alliance of Reformed Churches, 150 Route de Ferney, 1211 Geneva 20, Switzerland. Ed. Edmond Perret. adv. bk. rev. index. circ. 11,500. (also avail. in microfilm from UMI; reprint service avail. from UMI) Indexed: Rel.Per. CERDIC. Rel.Ind.One. Rel.& Theol.Abstr.
Formerly: Reformed and Presbyterian World.

286 US
REPORT FROM THE CAPITAL. 1954. 10/yr. $6. Baptist Joint Committee on Public Affairs, 200 Maryland Ave., N.E., Washington, DC 20002. TEL 202-544-4226 Ed. Victor Tupitza. bk. rev. film rev. index. circ. 6,000. (back issues avail.) Indexed: South.Bap.Per.Ind.

284.1 US ISSN 0360-7119
REPORTER (ST. LOUIS. 1975) 1954. w. $9.75. (Lutheran Church-Missouri Synod.) Concordia Publishing House, 1333 S. Kirkwood Rd., St. Louis, MO 63122. TEL 314-664-7000 Ed. Roland Lovstad. (also avail. in microform from UMI)
Formerly (until 1975): Advance (St. Louis) (ISSN 0001-8570)

268.8 CN ISSN 0832-9354
RESOURCE. 1981. m. Can.$6. Pentecostal Assemblies of Canada, Church Ministries Department, 10 Overlea Blvd., Toronto, Ont. M4H 1A5, Canada. TEL 416-425-1010 Ed. Rick Hiebert. adv. bk. rev. circ. 18,000.
Former titles(until 1986): Source (ISSN 0229-4931); (until 1981): Pentecostal Assemblies of Canada. Cell Pak (ISSN 0707-1868)

RESOURCES FOR YOUTH MINISTRY. see *CHILDREN AND YOUTH — For*

287 US ISSN 0034-5725
RESPONSE (NEW YORK) 1969. m. (except Jul.-Aug.) $7. United Methodist Church, Department of Education and Cultivation, 475 Riverside Dr., Rm. 1344, New York, NY 10115. TEL 212-870-3755 Ed. Carol M. Herb. bk. rev. illus. index. circ. 85,000.
Supersedes (1940-1969): Methodist Womam.

286 US
RESPUESTA. (Text in Spanish) 1965. q. $3.92. Casa Bautista de Publicaciones, Box 4255, El Paso, TX 79914. TEL 915-566-9656 Ed. Esteban Ditmore. circ. 8,000.
For evangelism

286 US ISSN 0034-6373
REVIEW AND EXPOSITOR. 1904. q. $9. Southern Baptist Theological Seminary, 2825 Lexington Rd., Louisville, KY 40280. TEL 502-897-4407 Ed. R. Alan Culpepper. adv. bk. rev. index. circ. 6,000. (also avail. in microform from UMI; reprint service avail. from UMI) Indexed: Old Test.Abstr. Rel.Per. New Test.Abstr. CERDIC. Rel.Ind.One. Rel.& Theol.Abstr. South.Bap.Per.Ind.
Formerly: Baptist Review and Expositor (ISSN 0190-5856)

286 DK ISSN 0109-2952
ROEDDERNE. 1982. 9/yr. Kr.1 per no. (Baptisternes Soendagsskoler) Danske Baptisters Ungdomsforbund, Toelloese, Denmark (Orders to: Hanne Rasmussen, Danmarksgade 5, 9000 Aalborg, Denmark)

266 US ISSN 0035-9084
ROYAL SERVICE. 1906. m. $8.50. Southern Baptist Convention, Woman's Missionary Union, Hwy. 280 E., 100 Missionary Ridge, Birmingham, AL 35283-0010. TEL 205-991-8100 Ed. Carolyn Weatherford. bk. rev. illus. circ. 335,000.
Formerly: Our Mission Fields.
Missions

286.73 US ISSN 0098-9517
SABBATH WATCHMAN. 1926. bi-m. $8. Religious Liberty Publishing Association, 9999 E. Mississippi Ave., Denver, CO 80231-1927. TEL 303-363-9853 (Co-sponsor: Seventh-Day Adventist Church Reform Movement, American Union) Ed. L.D. Watts. bk. rev. illus. circ. 500.

200 UK ISSN 0036-3111
ST. MARTIN'S REVIEW; the journal with the international outlook. 1893. m. £7.50. St. Martin-In-The-Fields Church, 5 St. Martins Place, London W.C.2, England. Ed. Philip Chester. adv. bk. rev. play rev. illus. circ. 1,500.

SCHRIFTENREIHE FUER DIE EVANGELISCHE FRAU. see *WOMEN'S INTERESTS*

284 US ISSN 0036-8997
SCOPE (MINNEAPOLIS) 1961. m. $7.50. (American Lutheran Church Women) Augsburg Publishing House, 426 S. Fifth St., Minneapolis, MN 55440. TEL 612-330-3300 Ed. Constance W. Lovaas. bk. rev. illus. index. circ. 250,000. (large print edt. avail.)

286 UK ISSN 0036-9136
SCOTTISH BAPTIST MAGAZINE. 1860. m. £3.25. Baptist Union of Scotland, c/o Rev. Robert Armstrong, Ed., Baptist Church House, 14 Aytoun Rd., Glasgow G41 5RT, Scotland. adv. bk. rev. circ. 4,000.

284 UK
SCOTTISH BULLETIN OF EVANGELICAL THEOLOGY. s-a. £4. Rutherford House, 17 Claremont Park, Edinburgh EH6 7PJ, Scotland. (Co-sponsor: Scottish Evangelical Theology Society) Ed. Nigel M. de S. Cameron. adv. bk. rev. circ. 600.
Former titles (until 1983): Scottish Evangelical Theology Society Bulletin; Scottish Tynedale Bulletin (ISSN 0262-1053)

267 UK ISSN 0260-0617
SCOTTISH EPISCOPAL CHURCH YEARBOOK. 1879. a. £2.50. ‡ Scottish Episcopal Church, 21 Grosvenor Crescent, Edinburgh EH12 5EE, Scotland. index. circ. 800.

284 SA
SCRIPTURA; Tydskrif vir Bybelkunde /Journal of Biblical Studies. (Text and summaries in Afrikaans and English) 1980. q. R.12.50. University of Stellenbosh, Department of Biblical Studies, Stellenbosh 7600, South Africa. Ed. B.C. Lategan. bk. rev. illus. circ. 400. (back issues avail.) Indexed: New Test.Abstr. Rel.Ind.One.

268 US ISSN 0048-9913
SEARCH (NASHVILLE) q. $12. Southern Baptist Convention, Sunday School Board, 127 Ninth Ave. N., Nashville, TN 37234. TEL 615-251-2000 adv. bk. rev. index. circ. 10,000. Indexed: South.Bap.Per.Ind.

286 US ISSN 0739-2281
SEARCHING TOGETHER. 1972. q. $6. Word of Life Church, Box 548, St. Croix Falls, WI 54024. TEL 715-755-3560 Ed. Jon Zens. adv. bk. rev. circ. 3,000. (back issues avail.) Indexed: Rel.Per. CERDIC. Rel.Ind.One. Rel.& Theol.Abstr.
Formerly (until 1981): Baptist Reformation Review (ISSN 0276-7945)

286 US ISSN 0037-0606
SECRET PLACE. 1938. q. $2.95 large-print ed. $4.95. American Baptist Churches in the U.S.A., Educational Ministries, Box 851, Valley Forge, PA 19482-0851. TEL 215-768-2000 Eds. Vincie Alessi, Herschell H. Richmond.

283 AT ISSN 0037-0754
SEE. 1966. m. Aus.$8. Anglican Media, Diocese of Melbourne, Anglican Information Office, S. Paul's Cathedral Buildings, Flinders Lane, Melbourne, Vic. 3000, Australia. Ed. Barry Huggett. adv. bk. rev. film rev. play rev. illus. circ. 36,000. (tabloid format)

283 SA ISSN 0037-0827
SEEK. 1961. m. R.4.50. Church of the Province of Southern Africa, Seek Board, Box 45, Kimberley 8300, South Africa. Ed. I. Shapiro. adv. bk. rev. circ. 13,000. Indexed: CERDIC.

286 PO ISSN 0037-1874
SEMEADOR BAPTISTA. 1926. m. Esc.330($48) Convencao Baptista Portuguesa - Portuguese Baptist Convention, Rua Forno do Tijolo, 9-2 Dto., 1100 Lisbon, Portugal. Ed. Herlander Mario M.C. Felizardo. bk. rev. illus. circ. 2,000. (tabloid format)

261 SZ ISSN 0559-4065
SEMINAR OF AFRICAN CHRISTIAN STUDENTS IN EUROPE. REPORT. (Each vol. also has a distinctive title) a. Seminar of African Christian Students in Europe, John Knox House, Chemins des Crets, Grand Saconnex, Geneva, Switzerland.

268 US ISSN 0162-4733
SENIOR ADULT BIBLE STUDY. q. $4. Southern Baptist Convention, Sunday School Board, 127 Ninth Ave., North, Nashville, TN 37234. TEL 615-251-2000

220 US ISSN 0745-8304
SENIOR HIGH CLASS. 1969. q. $2.95. ‡ American Baptist Churches in the U.S.A., Educational Ministries, Box 851, Valley Forge, PA 19482-0851. adv. illus. circ. 4,900.

SILVER WINGS; poems. see *LITERATURE — Poetry*

266 CN ISSN 0700-5202
SLAVNA NADELE/GLORIOUS HOPE. (Text in Czech) 1974. q. Czechoslovak Baptist Convention in the United States and Canada, Box 1271, Windsor, Ont. N9A 6R3, Canada.

284.2 SA ISSN 0037-685X
SLINGERVEL; publication for the youth. (Text in Afrikaans) 1959. m. R.6.30. ‡ Reformed Churches in South Africa - Gereformeerde Kerke in Suid-Afrika, Box 20008, Noordbrug 2522, Potchefstroom, South Africa. Ed. P.W. Buys. bk. rev. circ. 10,000.

283 UK ISSN 0144-8722
SOBORNOST. 1928. s-a. £5($10.50) Fellowship of St. Alban & St. Sergius, 52 Ladbroke Grove, London W11 2PB, England. Ed.Bd. adv. bk. rev. illus. circ. 3,500. (also avail. in microform from UMI; reprint service avail. from UMI) Indexed: Br.Hum.Ind. Cath.Ind. Curr.Cont. Rel.Per. Arts & Hum.Cit.Ind. CERDIC. New Test.Abstr. Rel.& Theol.Abstr. Rel.Ind.One.
Incorporating (from 1979): Eastern Churches Review (ISSN 0012-8740)

301 US ISSN 0731-0234
SOCIAL QUESTIONS BULLETIN. 1911. bi-m. $10. Methodist Federation for Social Action, 76 Clinton Ave., Staten Island, NY 10301. TEL 718-273-4941 Ed. Rev. George D. McClain. bk. rev. circ. 2,000. (also avail. in microform from UMI; back issues avail.; reprint service avail. from UMI) Indexed: CERDIC.

284 FR ISSN 0035-3884
SOCIETE CALVINISTE DE FRANCE. REVUE REFORMEE. 1950. q. 150 F. Faculte de Theologie Reformee, 33 av. Jules Ferry, 13100 Aix en Province, France. Ed. Paul Wells. bk. rev. index. cum.index every 10 years. circ. 1,300. Indexed: Old Test.Abstr. New Test.Abstr.

384 FR ISSN 0037-9050
SOCIETE DE L'HISTOIRE DU PROTESTANTISME FRANCAIS. BULLETIN. (Summaries in English or German) 1852. q. 210 F. Societe de l'Histoire du Protestantisme Francais, 54 rue des Saints-Peres, 75007 Paris, France. Ed. Jacques Poujol. bk. rev. bibl. charts. illus. stat. index. cum.index. circ. 2,200. Indexed: Hist.Abstr. Amer.Hist.& Life. CERDIC.
French reformation

284 GW ISSN 0014-3391
SONNTAGSBLATT FUER DIE EVANGELISCH-LUTHERISCHE KIRCHE IN BAYERN. AUSGABE OBERFRANKEN. 1929. w. DM.35.40. (Evangelisch-Lutherischer Landeskirchenrat) Evangelischer Presseverband fuer Bayern e.V., Birkerstr. 22, 8000 Munich 19, W. Germany (B.R.D.) adv. bk. rev. illus. stat. circ. 13,130.
Formerly: Evangelisches Gemeindeblatt fuer Hof und Umgebung.

286 SA
SOUTH AFRICAN BAPTIST HANDBOOK. 1985. a. R.8.50($6.50) Baptist Union of Southern Africa, P.O. Box 1085, Roodepoort 1725, South Africa (Subscr.to: Baptist Publishing House, P.O. Box 50, Roodepoort 1725. South Africa) Ed. E.A. Hermanson. circ. 1,200. (back issues avail.)

286 US ISSN 0146-0196
SOUTH CAROLINA BAPTIST HISTORICAL SOCIETY JOURNAL. 1975. a. $3. South Carolina Baptist Historical Society, Furman University Library, Greenville, SC 29613. TEL 803-294-2194 Ed. J. Glenwood Clayton. circ. 200. (back issues avail.)

287 US
SOUTH CAROLINA UNITED METHODIST ADVOCATE. 1837. w. $10. (United Methodist Church, South Carolina Conference) Southern Christian Advocate, 4908 Colonial Dr., Columbia, SC 29203. TEL 803-786-9483 Ed. Maryneal Jones. adv. bk. rev. illus. circ. 16,000.
Former titles: South Carolina Methodist Advocate (ISSN 0038-3147) & Southern Christian Advocate.

286 016 US ISSN 0081-3001
SOUTHERN BAPTIST CONVENTION. ANNUAL. 1845. a. $7.50. Southern Baptist Convention, 901 Commerce, Nashville, TN 37203. TEL 615-244-2355 Ed. Martin Bradley. subject index cumulated irregularly, 1953 (1845-1953), 1965 (1954-1965) circ. 35,000. (also avail. in microfilm)

286 016 US ISSN 0081-301X
SOUTHERN BAPTIST CONVENTION. HISTORICAL COMMISSION. MICROFILM CATALOGUE. 1954. a. $8. Southern Baptist Convention, Historical Commission, 901 Commerce St., Ste. 400, Nashville, TN 37203-3620. TEL 615-244-0344 Ed. Lynn E. May, Jr. adv. circ. 1,500.

266 US ISSN 0162-4334
SOUTHERN BAPTIST CONVENTION. SUNDAY SCHOOL BOARD. QUARTERLY REVIEW; a survey of Southern Baptist progress. 1941. q. $9.75. Southern Baptist Convention, Sunday School Board, 127 Ninth Ave., N., Nashville, TN 37234. TEL 615-251-2000 bk. rev. charts. stat. cum.index. circ. 134,000.

377.8 US ISSN 0038-3848
SOUTHERN BAPTIST EDUCATOR. vol.12, 1947. 12/yr. $6. Southern Baptist Convention, Education Commission, 901 Commerce St., No. 600, Nashville, TN 37203-3620. Ed. Arthur L. Walker, Jr. bk. rev. bibl. stat. index. circ. 9,000.

286 US ISSN 0038-4917
SOUTHWESTERN NEWS. 1943. m. (Sep.-Jul.) free. Southwestern Baptist Theological Seminary, Box 22000 3e, Fort Worth, TX 76122. TEL 817-923-1921 Ed. John E. Seelig. circ. 38,000. (reprint service avail. from UMI) Indexed: South.Bap.Per.Ind.

274 301.412 UK
SPOTLIGHT (EDINBURGH) 1968. s-a. 30p. Church of Scotland, Woman's Guild, 121 George St., Edinburgh EH2 4YN, Scotland. Ed. Alison Twaddle. adv. bk. rev. circ. 25,000.

284 GE ISSN 0323-4304
STANDPUNKT; evangelische Monatsschrift. m. M.16.80. Buchexport, Leninstr. 16, DDR-7010 Leipzig, E. Germany (D.D.R.) (Orders to: Buchexport, Postfach 160, DDR-7010 Leipzig, E. Germany (D.D.R.))

287 US ISSN 0038-9870
STAR OF ZION. 1876. w. $11. African Methodist Episcopal Zion Church, Box 31005, Charlotte, NC 28231. Ed. Rev. Morgan W. Tann. adv. bk. rev. illus. circ. 8,000. (tabloid format; also avail. in microfilm from UMI; reprint service avail. from UMI)

286 US ISSN 0162-6841
START (BIRMINGHAM); the WMU magazine for mission friends leaders. 1970. q. $8. Southern Baptist Convention, Women's Missionary Union, Highway 280 E., 100 Missionary Ridge, Birmingham, AL 35243-2798. TEL 205-991-8100 Ed. Kathryn Kizer. circ. 30,500. (also avail. in microfiche)

284.2 SA
STROOIDAK. (Text in Afrikaans) 1949. q. free. ‡ Nederduitse Gereformeerde Gemeente die Paarl - Dutch Reformed Church, Paarl, Hoofstraat 144, Paarl, South Africa. Eds. S. Marais, J.J. Swart. circ. 1,000. (looseleaf format)
Formerly: Paarlse Padwyser (ISSN 0030-8455)

286 268 US ISSN 0039-2685
STUDENT (NASHVILLE) 1922. m. $16.75. Southern Baptist Convention, Sunday School Board, 127 Ninth Ave., N., Nashville, TN 37203. TEL 615-251-2000 bk. rev. film rev. illus. index. cum.index. circ. 25,000. (also avail. in microform from UMI; reprint service avail. from UMI)
Formerly: Baptist Student.

284 AU
STUDIEN UND TEXTE ZUR KIRCHENGESCHICHTE UND GESCHICHTE. (Consists of two series) 1975. irreg., vol. 4 (series 1), vol. 3 (series 2), 1979. price varies. Hermann Boehlaus Nachf., c/o Dr. Karl Lueger, Ring 12, A-1010 Vienna, Austria. Ed. Peter Barton. circ. 800. (back issues avail.) Indexed: Rel.Ind.Two.

268 US ISSN 0191-4219
STUDYING ADULT LIFE AND WORK LESSONS. q. $16.25. Southern Baptist Convention, Sunday School Board, 127 Ninth Ave., N., Nashville, TN 37234. TEL 615-251-2000

285.834 US
SUMMER SERVICE OPPORTUNITIES. 1970. a. free. United Church of Christ, Board for Homeland Ministries, Voluntary Service Office, 132 W. 31st St., New York, NY 10001. TEL 212-239-8700 Ed. Carl A. Bade. circ. 6,000.

268 US ISSN 0162-4911
SUNDAY SCHOOL ADULTS. q. $3.75. Southern Baptist Convention, Sunday School Board, 127 9th Ave., N., Nashville, TN 37234. TEL 615-251-2000 circ. 1,000,000.

268 US ISSN 0162-4318
SUNDAY SCHOOL LEADERSHIP; a monthly magazine for building a growing Sunday school. 1980. m. $11. Southern Baptist Convention, Sunday School Board, 127 Ninth Ave., N., Nashville, TN 37234. TEL 615-251-2000 Ed. David Seay. bk. rev. charts. illus. index. circ. 80,000. (also avail. in microform from UMI; reprint service avail. from UMI) Indexed: South.Bap.Per.Ind.
Formerly: Outreach (Nashville)

268 US
SUNDAY SCHOOL LESSONS SPECIAL MINISTRIES. q. $4. Southern Baptist Convention, Sunday School Board, 127 Ninth Ave., N., Nashville, TN 37234. TEL 615-251-2000
Formerly: Sunday School Lessons Simplified (ISSN 0162-4873)

268 US ISSN 0585-9328
SUNDAY SCHOOL SENIOR ADULTS. q. $4.75. Southern Baptist Convention, Sunday School Board, 127 9th Ave., N., Nashville, TN 37234. TEL 615-251-2000 circ. 220,000.

268 US ISSN 0162-4903
SUNDAY SCHOOL YOUNG ADULTS. q. $3.75. Southern Baptist Convention, Sunday School Board, 127 Ninth Ave., N., Nashville, TN 37234. TEL 615-251-2000

268 US
SUNDAY SCHOOL YOUTH. q. $4.50. Southern Baptist Convention, Sunday School Board, 127 Ninth Ave., N., Nashville, TN 37234. TEL 615-251-2000
Formerly: Sunday School Youth A (ISSN 0162-4881)

268 US
SUNDAY SCHOOL YOUTH-TEACHER. q. $7.75. Southern Baptist Convention, Sunday School Board, 127 Ninth Ave., N., Nashville, TN 37234. TEL 615-251-2000
Formerly: Youth Teacher (ISSN 0162-4865)

284 US ISSN 0273-8562
TAEGLICHE ANDACHTEN. English edition: Portals of Prayer (ISSN 0032-4884) (Text and summaries in German) 1937. q. $3. (Lutheran Church-Missouri Synod) Concordia Publishing House, 3558 S. Jefferson Ave., St. Louis, MO 63118. TEL 314-664-7000 Ed. Rudolph F. Norden. circ. 20,000. (also avail. in microfilm)

268 US ISSN 0040-0645
TEACHING PICTURES FOR BIBLE SEARCHERS. q. $19.50. Southern Baptist Convention, Sunday School Board, 127 Ninth Ave, N., Nashville, TN 37203. TEL 615-251-2000 circ. 23,750.
Formerly: Junior Teaching Pictures.

284.2 NE ISSN 0040-5612
THEOLOGIA REFORMATA. 1958. 4/yr. fl.50 (students fl.40) (Gereformeerde Bond in de Hervormde Kerk) Drukkerij Oosterbaan & Le Cointre, Postbus 25, 4460 AA Goes, Netherlands. Ed.Bd. bk. rev. index. circ. 750(controlled) Indexed: CERDIC.

284 UK ISSN 0309-3492
THIRD WAY. 1977. m. £12. Elm House Christian Communications Ltd., 37 Elm Rd., New Malden, Surrey KT3 3HB, England. Ed. Tim Dean. adv. bk. rev. charts. illus. circ. 3,500.

286 US ISSN 0040-7232
TIE. 1932. bi-m. free. Southern Baptist Theological Seminary, 2825 Lexington Rd., Louisville, KY 40280. TEL 502-897-4011 Ed. Michael Duduit. circ. 65,000. Indexed: South.Bap.Per.Ind.

TIJDSCHRIFT VOOR THEOLOGIE. see *RELIGIONS AND THEOLOGY — Roman Catholic*

284 UK ISSN 0262-8023
TODAY (LONDON) 1982. m. £12. Elm House Christian Communications Ltd., 37 Elm Rd., New Malden, Surrey KT3 3HB, England. Ed. Ian Cory. adv. bk. rev. charts. illus. circ. 16,500. (back issues avail.)
Formerly (until 1982): Crusade (ISSN 0011-2127)

266 NR
TODAY'S CHALLENGE. (Text in English) 1951. bi-m. £N6($12.50) ‡ (Evangelical Churches of West Africa) E C W A Productions Ltd., P.M. Bag 2010, Jos, Nigeria. Ed. Gabriel Abikoye. adv. bk. rev. charts. illus. circ. 15,000.
Formerly: African Challenge (ISSN 0001-9968)

268 UK ISSN 0307-5982
TOGETHER. 1956. 9/yr. £3.50. (Board of Education of the General Synod) C I O Publishing, Church House, Dean's Yard, London SW1P 3NZ, England. Ed. Pamela Egan. adv. bk. rev. illus. circ. 4,000. Indexed: Curr.Cont. CERDIC.
Formerly: Church Teacher (ISSN 0009-6571)

TRACT MESSENGER. see *BLIND*

284 US
TRI-COUNTY LUTHERAN. 1941. m. $6. Lutheran Center Association of Southeastern Michigan, 15637 Harper Ave., Detroit, MI 48224. Ed. Betty J. Mueller. adv. bk. rev. circ. 7,500.
Former titles: Detroit and Suburban Lutheran (ISSN 0011-9660); Detroit Lutheran.

TRIADS. see *BUSINESS AND ECONOMICS — Marketing And Purchasing*

284 UK ISSN 0082-6588
TRINITARIAN BIBLE SOCIETY. ANNUAL REPORT. 1831. a. 50p. ‡ Trinitarian Bible Society, 217 Kingston Rd., London SW19 3NN, England.

285 UK
TYST. (Text in Welsh) 1867. w. £10.40. Union of Welsh Independents, 11 St. Helen's Rd., Swansea, Wales. Ed. Rev. Gwyndaf Jones. adv. bk. rev. circ. 3,000.

U U W F FEDERATION NEWSLETTER. (Unitarian Universalist Women's Federation) see *WOMEN'S INTERESTS*

U U W F JOURNAL. see *WOMEN'S INTERESTS*

284 NE ISSN 0041-5944
UITZICHT. 1964. m. free. ‡ (Reformed Presbyterian Fellowship in the Great Congregation (Ps.40,10)) Evangelisatie-Boekhandel en Uitgeverij Horizont, Box 77, 7900 AB Hoogeveen (Dr.), Netherlands. Ed. Rev. G. Taverne. bk. rev. charts. circ. 400.

284.2 SA ISSN 0378-4134
UMTHOMBO WAMANDLA. (Text in Xhosa) 1972. bi-m. R.1. Reformed Churches in South Africa - Gereformeerde Kerke in Suid-Afrika, Box 20008, Noordbrug 2522, Potchefstroom, South Africa. Ed. W.D. Graham. circ. 1,200.

288 UK ISSN 0049-531X
UNITARIAN. 1905. m. £1.44. Manchester and District Association of Unitarian & Free Christian Churches Inc., c/o Keith M. Noble, Elbon House, 69 Downs Drive, Tinperley, Altrincham, Cheshire, England. Ed. Rev. John Rowland. adv. bk. rev. circ. 4,000.

267 UK
UNITARIAN AND FREE CHRISTIAN CHURCHES. HANDBOOK AND DIRECTORY OF THE GENERAL ASSEMBLY. 1890. a (directory); quinquennial (handbook) £5. General Assembly of Unitarian Free Christian Churches, Essex Hall, 1-6 Essex St., Strand, London, WC2R 3HY, England. Ed. Christine Hayhurst. circ. 850.
Formerly: Unitarian and Free Christian Churches. Yearbook of the General Assembly (ISSN 0082-7797)

288 UK ISSN 0082-7800
UNITARIAN HISTORICAL SOCIETY, LONDON. TRANSACTIONS. 1917. a. £4 to institutions. Unitarian Historical Society, c/o Hon. Treasurer, 58 Stoneygate Court, London Rd., Leicester LE2 2AJ, England. Ed. Rev. H.J. McLachlan. adv. bk. rev. index every 4 years. circ. 325. Indexed: Br.Hum.Ind.

266 US ISSN 0082-7827
UNITARIAN UNIVERSALIST DIRECTORY. 1961. a. $15. Unitarian Universalist Association, 25 Beacon St., Boston, MA 02108. TEL 617-742-2100 Ed. Rev. Mark W. Harris. adv. circ. 2,500. (also avail. in microform from UMI)

288 900 US
UNITARIAN UNIVERSALIST HISTORICAL SOCIETY. PROCEEDINGS. 1925. a. or biennal; latest vol.20, 1984/86. $8 per part (2 parts per vol.) Unitarian Universalist Historical Society, c/o Conrad Wright, Harvard Divinity School, Andover Hall, Cambridge, MA 02138. TEL 617-495-5750 Ed. Richard Myers. bk. rev. circ. 400.
Formerly: Unitarian Historical Society. Proceedings (ISSN 0082-7819)

288 US ISSN 0041-7122
UNITARIAN UNIVERSALIST WORLD. 1970. 12/yr. $5. ‡ Unitarian Universalist Association, 25 Beacon St., Boston, MA 02108. TEL 617-742-2100 Ed. David B. Parke. adv. bk. rev. charts. illus. circ. 107,000.

286 CN ISSN 0082-7843
UNITED BAPTIST CONVENTION OF THE ATLANTIC PROVINCES. YEARBOOK. 1963. a. price varies. United Baptist Convention of the Atlantic Provinces, 1655 Manawagonish Rd., Saint John, N.B. E2M 3Y2, Canada. TEL 506-674-2006 Ed. Eugene M. Thompson. index. circ. 2,200.

268 US
UNITED BRETHREN. 1885. m. $10. United Brethren in Christ Church, Department of Church Services, 302 Lake St., Huntington, IN 46750. TEL 219-356-2312 Ed. Steve Dennie. circ. 5,000.

286 US ISSN 0882-7214
UNITED CHURCH NEWS. 1985. m. $8. United Church of Christ, Office of Communication, 105 Madison Ave., New York, NY 10016. Ed. Rev. W. Evan Golder. adv. illus. circ. 115,000. (tabloid format)

287.92 CN ISSN 0041-7238
UNITED CHURCH OBSERVER. 1939. m. Can.$10. (United Church of Canada) R. Gordon Nodwell, 85 St. Clair Ave. E., Toronto, Ont. M4T 1M8, Canada. TEL 416-492-7330 Ed. Hugh McCullum. adv. bk. rev. film rev. circ. 301,000. (also avail. in microfilm from UMI)

200 CN ISSN 0082-786X
UNITED CHURCH OF CANADA. COMMITTEE ON ARCHIVES. BULLETIN. RECORDS AND PROCEEDINGS. 1948. a. United Church of Canada, Committee on Archives, Victoria University, 73 Queen's Park Cres., Toronto, Ont. M5S 1K7, Canada. TEL 416-585-4563 bk. rev. circ. 800. Indexed: Hist.Abstr. Amer.Hist.& Life.

200 CN ISSN 0082-7878
UNITED CHURCH OF CANADA. GENERAL COUNCIL. RECORD OF PROCEEDINGS. 1925. biennial. United Church of Canada, General Council, 85 St. Clair Ave. E., Toronto, Ont. M4T 1M8, Canada. TEL 416-925-5931 circ. 4,000.

200 CN ISSN 0082-7886
UNITED CHURCH OF CANADA. YEAR BOOK. 1925. a. United Church of Canada, 85 St. Clair Ave. E., Toronto, Ont. M4T 1M8, Canada. TEL 416-925-5931 circ. 4,000.

200 US ISSN 0041-7262
UNITED EVANGELICAL. 1923. 11/yr. $7. (Evangelical Congregational Church) Church Center Press, Box 186, Myerstown, PA 17067. Ed. David H. Reed. adv. bk. rev. illus. circ. 2,257.

200 US ISSN 0041-7270
UNITED EVANGELICAL ACTION. 1942. bi-m. $10. National Association of Evangelicals, Box 28, Wheaton, IL 60189. TEL 312-665-0500 Ed. Christoper M. Lutes. adv. bk. rev. illus. circ. 17,700. Indexed: Chr.Per.Ind. G.Soc.Sci.& Rel.Per.Lit.

285.241 UK ISSN 0082-7908
UNITED FREE CHURCH OF SCOTLAND. HANDBOOK. 1930. biennial. £1.25. United Free Church of Scotland, 11 Newton Place, Glasgow G3 7PR, Scotland. Ed. E.S. Nicoll. bk. rev. circ. 600.

284 US ISSN 0041-7300
UNITED LUTHERAN. (Text mainly in English; occasionally in Slovak) 1894. bi-m. free. United Lutheran Society, Ross Mt. Park Rd., Box 947, Ligonier, PA 15658. TEL 412-238-9505 Ed. Paul M. Payerchin, Jr. adv. circ. 5,000. (tabloid format)

287 US ISSN 0160-0885
UNITED METHODIST CHURCH. CURRICULUM PLANS. 1941. a. $6. United Methodist Church, General Board of Discipleship, Curriculum Resources Committee, Box 801, Nashville, TN 37202. TEL 615-749-6000 Ed. Dal Joon Won. circ. 500. Key Title: Curriculum Plans.

287 US ISSN 0503-3551
UNITED METHODIST CHURCH. GENERAL MINUTES OF THE ANNUAL CONFERENCES. 1968. a. $9 paperbound; $13 clothbound. (United Methodist Church, General Council on Finance and Administration) Parthenon Press, 1200 Davis St., Evanston, IL 60201. TEL 312-869-3345 Ed. Daniel A. Nielsen. illus. circ. 2,500. Key Title: General Minutes of the Annual Conferences of the United Methodist Church.

287.6 US ISSN 0503-356X
UNITED METHODIST DIRECTORY. irreg. $4.95. United Methodist Publishing House, 201 8th Ave. S., Nashville, TN 37203. TEL 615-749-6000

287 US
UNITED METHODIST REPORTER. (Text in English and Spanish) 1847. w. $15. United Methodist Communications Council, Newspaper Division, Box 660275, Dallas, TX 75266. TEL 214-630-6495 Ed. Spurgeon M. Dunnam, 3rd. adv. bk. rev. charts. illus. circ. 504,000. (newspaper; also avail. in microfilm)
Former titles: Texas Methodist/United Methodist Reporter; Texas Methodist (ISSN 0040-4489)

285 US ISSN 0082-8548
UNITED PRESBYTERIAN CHURCH IN THE UNITED STATES OF AMERICA. MINUTES OF THE GENERAL ASSEMBLY. a. $4. United Presbyterian Church in the U.S.A., 475 Riverside Drive, Room 1201, New York, NY 10027. TEL 212-870-2515 circ. 16,000.

285 UK ISSN 0049-5433
UNITED REFORMED CHURCH HISTORY SOCIETY. JOURNAL. 1973. s-a. $7. United Reformed Church History Society, Church House, 86 Tavistock Pl., London WC1H 9RT, England. Ed. Clyde Binfield. bk. rev. index. circ. 700. (back issues avail.) Indexed: Br.Hum.Ind. Hist.Abstr. Amer.Hist.& Life. CERDIC.
Former titles: Congregational Historical Society. Transactions; Presbyterian Historical Society. Journal.

285 UK
UNITED REFORMED CHURCH IN THE UNITED KINGDOM. UNITED REFORMED CHURCH YEAR BOOK. 1973. a. £6.50. ‡ United Reformed Church in the United Kingdom, 86 Tavistock Pl., London WC1H 9RT, England. Ed. Sheila Lowden, Cyril Lowden. adv. circ. 2,000.
Formerly: Congregational Church in England and Wales. Congregational Year book (ISSN 0069-8849)

285 UK
UNITED REFORMED CHURCH POCKET DIARY. a. £1.30. United Reformed Church, 86 Tavistock Pl., London WC1H 9RT, England.

285 UK
UNITED REFORMED CHURCH, YORKSHIRE PROVINCE, PROVINCIAL HANDBOOK. 1973. a. £0.90. United Reformed Church (Yorkshire Province), 43 Hunslet Ln., Leeds LS10 1JW, England. Ed. J.E.M. Gilbey. circ. 450.

242 US ISSN 0042-0735
UPPER ROOM; daily devotional guide, interdenominational, international. (Large type edition avail.) 1935. d? $4. (United Methodist Church, General Board of Discipleship) Upper Room, 1908 Grand Ave., Box 189, Nashville, TN 37202. TEL 615-327-2700 Ed. Janice T. Grana. circ. 2,750,000. (also avail. in Braille; audio cassette)

266 284 NO
UT I ALL VERDEN. q. Norsk Luthersk Misjonssamband, Grensen 19, Oslo 1, Norway. adv.
Missions

UW KONINKRIJK KOME; zendingsblad. see *RELIGIONS AND THEOLOGY*

284.2 NE
VANDAAR. 1902. 10/yr. fl.9. Zendingscentrum van de Gereformeerde Kerken in Nederland - Mission of the Reformed Churches in the Netherlands, Box 202, 3830 AE Leusden, Netherlands. Ed.Bd. adv. bk. rev. illus. index. circ. 210,000.
Formerly (until 1975): Zending (ISSN 0044-3972)
Missions

284 US ISSN 0042-2568
VANGUARD (MILWAUKEE) 1954. 6/yr. membership. Lutheran Human Relations Association, 2703 N. Sherman Blvd., Milwaukee, WI 53210. TEL 414-871-7300 Ed. Susan & Charles Ruehle. bk. rev. illus. circ. 10,000. (also avail. in microform from UMI; reprint service avail. from UMI)
Human rights

268 US ISSN 0042-3459
VENTANA; missionary magazine for women. (Text in Spanish) 1931. q. $2.60. ‡ Casa Bautista de Publicaciones, Box 4255, El Paso, TX 79914. TEL 915-566-9656 Ed. Mary Jo Stewart. adv. illus. circ. 11,600.

286 AT ISSN 0726-4097
VICTORIAN BAPTIST WITNESS. 1921. m. Aus.$5. Baptist Union of Victoria, 227 Burwood Rd., Hawthorn, Vic. 3122, Australia. Ed. Geoff Holland. adv. bk. rev. circ. 4,200.
Formerly: Baptist Witness (ISSN 0005-5794)

286 US ISSN 0083-6311
VIRGINIA BAPTIST REGISTER. 1962. a. $4.50 to non-members. Virginia Baptist Historical Society, Box 34, Univ. of Richmond, VA 23173. TEL 804-289-8437 Ed. John S. Moore. bk. rev. cum.index every 5 yrs. circ. 750. (also avail. in microfilm)
Early Virginia Baptist history

200 US
VIRGINIA EPISCOPALIAN. 1922. m. (except Aug.) $3.75. Episcopal Diocese of Virginia, 110 West Franklin, Richmond, VA 23220. TEL 804-643-8451 Ed. Sarah Bartenstein. adv. bk. rev. circ. 26,500. (tabloid format)
Formerly (1922-1986): Virginia Churchman.

287 US
VIRGINIA UNITED METHODIST ADVOCATE. 1832. fortn. $7.50. ‡ (United Methodist Church, Virginia Conference) Virginia United Methodist Communications, Inc., Box 11367, Richmond, VA 23230. TEL 804-359-9451 Ed. James D. Righter. adv. bk. rev. circ. 18,000.
Former titles: Virginia Advocate (ISSN 0042-6458); Virginia Methodist Advocate.

284 AT
VISION. bi-m. Aus.$7($15) Australian Baptist Missionary Society, 597 Burwood Rd., Hawthorn, Vic. 3122, Australia. Ed. Rosalind M. Gooden. bk. rev. index. circ. 10,000. (back issues avail)

284 US
VISION (GRAND RAPIDS) 6/yr. $8. Young Calvinist Federation, Box 7259, Grand Rapids, MI 49510. TEL 616-241-5616
Formerly: Y A M.

282 US ISSN 0277-2272
VOICE (NEWARK) 1878. m. (except Jul. & Aug.) contributions. ‡ Episcopal Diocese of Newark, Cathedral House, 24 Rector St., Newark, NJ 07102. TEL 201-622-4306 Ed. Stephen Galleher. bk. rev. charts. illus. stat. cum.index. circ. 21,000. (newspaper)
Formerly: Newark Churchman (ISSN 0028-8853)

287 UK ISSN 0042-8167
VOICE OF METHODISM. 1964. 3/yr. $1 to non-members. Voice of Methodism Association, 23 Manor House Court, Kirkby in Ashfield, Nottingham NG17 8LH, England. Ed. Oliver A. Beckerlegge. adv. bk. rev. circ. 6,000. Indexed: CERDIC.

266 US ISSN 0042-8175
VOICE OF MISSIONS. 1898. m. (Sep.-Jun.) $6.50. (African Methodist Episcopal Church (New York)) National Religious Press, 517-523 Ottawa Ave., N.W., Grand Rapids, MI 49502. TEL 212-870-2195 Ed. Rev. John W.P. Collier, Jr. bk. rev. illus. circ. 3,900.

266 US
VOLUNTEER. 1961. 4/yr. free. Lutheran World Ministries, Volunteer Service Office, 360 Park Ave. S., New York, NY 10010. TEL 212-532-6350 Ed. Harold Hanson. circ. 26,000. Indexed: Rehabil.Lit.
Formerly: Challenger.

284.2 SA ISSN 0042-8728
DIE VOORLIGTER. (Text in Afrikaans) 1937. m. R.6.26. Tydskriftemaatskappy van die Nederduitse Gereformeerde Kerk, Box 2406, Pretoria 0001, South Africa. Ed. W.L. Maree. adv. bk. rev. illus. circ. 174,000. Indexed: CERDIC.

283 US ISSN 0043-0544
WASHINGTON DIOCESE. 1933. m. (Sep.-Jun.) $2. Episcopal Diocese of Washington, Episcopal Church House, Mount Saint Alban, N.W., Washington, DC 20016. TEL 202-537-6560 Ed. Frances Antonucci. adv. bk. rev. charts. illus. stat. circ. 20,000. (tabloid format; also avail. in microfilm) Indexed: CERDIC.

284 NE ISSN 0043-2105
WEGWIJZER; maandblad voor Hoenderloo. 1931. m. fl.4.($1.) Hervormde Gemeente, Hoenderloo - Dutch Reformed Church, Hoenderloo, Hervormde Pastorie, Heldringseweg 8, Hoenderloo, Netherlands. adv. bk. rev.

250 UK
WELSH CHURCHMAN. 1973. m. £1. Church in Wales Publications, Woodland Place, Penarth, Glam. CF6 2EX, Wales. Ed. Rev. M.M. Daviss. adv. bk. rev. circ. 35,000.

266 GW
DIE WELTMISSION; das Wort in der Welt. 1915. bi-m. DM.9. (Evangelisches Missionswerk) Missionshilfe Verlag, Mittelweg 143, 2000 Hamburg 13, W. Germany (B.R.D.) Ed.Bd. bk. rev. illus. index. circ. 30,000.
Former titles: Wort in der Welt (ISSN 0341-082X); Allgemeine Missionsnachrichten (ISSN 0002-5909)
Missions

287 270 UK ISSN 0043-2873
WESLEY HISTORICAL SOCIETY. PROCEEDINGS. 1897. 3/yr. £5($10) membership. Wesley Historical Society, 87 Marshall Ave., Bognor Regis, W. Sussex PO21 2TW, England. Ed. E.A. Rose. adv. bk. rev. charts. illus. index. cum.index: vols.1-30 (1897-1958) circ. 1,100. Indexed: Br.Hum.Ind. CERDIC.
History

287.1 US ISSN 0043-289X
WESLEYAN ADVOCATE. 1842. fortn. $7. (Wesleyan Church) Wesley Press, Box 2000, Marion, IN 46952. TEL 317-674-3301 Ed. George E. Failing. bk. rev. circ. 21,000. Indexed: G.Soc.Sci.& Rel.Per.Lit.
Formed by the merger of: Wesleyan Methodist (ISSN 0190-6100) & Pilgrim Holiness Advocate.

200 US
WESLEYAN CHRISTIAN ADVOCATE. 1836. w. $10. (United Methodist Church, North and South Georgia Conferences) Wesleyan Christian Advocate, Inc., 159 Ralph McGill Blvd., Atlanta, GA 30308. TEL 404-659-0002 Ed. William M. Holt. adv. bk. rev. circ. 31,500.

287.1 US ISSN 0092-4245
WESLEYAN THEOLOGICAL JOURNAL. 1966. s-a. $3. Wesleyan Theological Society, c/o Wayne E. Caldwell, Sec.-Treas., 215 E. 43rd St., Marion, IN 46952. TEL 317-674-7270 Ed. Alex R.G. Deasley. adv. bk. rev. circ. 1,200. (also avail. in microform from UMI; reprint service avail. from UMI) Indexed: CERDIC. Chr.Per.Ind. Rel.Ind.One.

286 US ISSN 0043-4132
WESTERN RECORDER. 1826. w. $6.83 to individuals; churches $5. ‡ (Kentucky Baptist Convention) Western Recorder, Inc., 10701 Shelbyville Rd., Box 43401, Middletown, KY 40243. TEL 502-245-4101 Ed. Dr. Jack D. Sanford. adv. circ. 63,000. (tabloid format)

266 UK ISSN 0306-9028
WINDOW. 1841. q. free. Methodist Church Overseas Division, 25 Marylebone Rd., London NW1 5JR, England. circ. 80,000.
Formerly: At Home and Abroad (ISSN 0044-9830)
Missions

280 US ISSN 0197-8896
WITNESS. 1974. m. $15. Episcopal Church Publishing Co., Box 359, Ambler, PA 19002. TEL 215-643-7067 Ed. Mary Lou Suhor. illus. circ. 6,000. (also avail. in microfiche; microfilm) Indexed: CERDIC. Rel.Ind.One.

284 US ISSN 0199-8285
WITTENBURG DOOR. 1971. bi-m. $12. Youth Specialties, 1224 Greenfield Dr., El Cajon, CA 92021. Ed. Mike Yaconelli. bk. rev. illus. circ. 18,000. Indexed: Chr.Per.Ind.

286 US ISSN 0049-7959
WORD AND WAY. 1895. w. $5.80 to individuals; institutions $4.08. Missouri Baptist Convention, 400 E. High St., Jefferson City, MO 65101. TEL 314-635-7931 Ed. Bobby S. Terry. adv. bk. rev. illus. circ. 60,000. (tabloid format)

284 US
WORD & WITNESS. 1976. 6/yr. $30. Sunday Publications, Inc., 1937 Tenth Ave., N., Lake Worth, FL 33466-9501. TEL 305-533-0990 Ed. Dr. Charles Rice. bk. rev. index. (looseleaf format)

284 US ISSN 0275-5270
WORD & WORLD; theology for Christian ministry. 1981. q. $15. Luther Northwestern Seminary, 2481 Como Ave. West, St. Paul, MN 55108. TEL 612-641-3482 Ed. Arland J. Hultgren. adv. bk. rev. index. circ. 4,000. (back issues avail.) Indexed: Old Test.Abstr. New Test.Abstr. Rel.Ind.One. Rel.& Theol.Abstr.

266 UK
WORD AT WORK. 2/yr. National Bible Society of Scotland, 7 Hampton Terrace, Edinburgh EH12 5XU, Scotland.

266 284 US ISSN 0043-8413
WORLD ENCOUNTER. 1963. 4/yr. $6. Lutheran Church in America, Division for World Mission and Ecumenism, 2900 Queen Lane, Philadelphia, PA 19129. TEL 215-483-6360 Ed. James Solheim. adv. bk. rev. illus. circ. 12,000. (also avail. in microfilm from UMI; microfiche from UMI; reprint service avail. from UMI)
Missions

287 US
WORLD METHODIST HISTORICAL SOCIETY. HISTORICAL BULLETIN. 1971. q. $5. ‡ World Methodist Historical Society, Box 460, Mont Alto, PA 17237. Ed. Theodore Agnew. illus. circ. 200. (back issues avail.)
Formerly: World Methodist Historical Society. News Bulletin.

266 US
WORLD MISSION JOURNAL. vol.45, 1974. m. $6.20. Southern Baptist Convention, Brotherhood Commission, 1548 Poplar Ave., Memphis, TN 38104. Ed.Bd. circ. 40,000. (tabloid format) Indexed: South.Bap.Per.Ind.
Formerly: Baptist Men's Journal.
Missions

287 US ISSN 0043-8839
WORLD PARISH. 1948. bi-m. free. World Methodist Council, Box 518, Lake Junaluska, NC 28745. TEL 704-456-9432 Ed. Joe Hale. bk. rev. charts. illus. circ. 18,300.

250 UK ISSN 0032-7107
WORSHIP AND PREACHING. 1970. bi-m. £5.75. Methodist Publishing House, Wellington Rd., Wimbledon, London SW19 8EU, England. Ed. Rev. John Lampard. adv. bk. rev. index. circ. 3,000.
Supersedes: Preacher's Quarterly.

287 GW ISSN 0043-9444
WORT UND WEG; Sonntagsblatt der Evangelisch-Methodistischen Kirche. 1968. w. DM.61.20. (Evangelisch-methodistische Kirche) Christliches Verlagshaus GmbH, Motorstr. 36, 7000 Stuttgart 31, W. Germany (B.R.D.) Ed. Herbert Seeger. adv. bk. rev. bibl. illus. stat.
Formed by the 1968 merger of: Evangelischer Botschaft & Evangelist.

200 US ISSN 0044-0388
YEVANHELSKYJ RANOK/EVANGELICAL MORNING. (Includes an English section: Ukrainian Christian Herald, Protestant monthly) 1905. q. $5. Ukrainian Evangelical Alliance of North America, 5610 Trowbridge Dr., Dunwoody, GA 30338. TEL 404-394-7795 Ed. Rev. W. Borowsky. adv. bk. rev. illus. circ. 500. (reprint service avail. from UMI, ISI)

268 US ISSN 0162-4814
YOUNG ADULT BIBLE STUDY. 1970. q. $4. Southern Baptist Convention, Sunday School Board, 127 Ninth Ave, N., Nashville, TN 37234. TEL 615-251-2000 adv. bk. rev. charts. illus. circ. 350,000.

268 US ISSN 0162-4784
YOUTH IN ACTION. q. $4.50. Southern Baptist Convention, Sunday School Board, 127 Ninth Ave., N., Nashville, TN 37234. TEL 615-251-2000

268 US ISSN 0162-4792
YOUTH IN ACTION. TEACHER. q. $7.75. Southern Baptist Convention, Sunday School Board, 127 Ninth Ave., N., Nashville, TN 37234. TEL 615-251-2000

268 US
YOUTH IN DISCOVERY. q. $4.50. Southern Baptist Convention, Sunday School Board, 127 Ninth Ave., N., Nashville, TN 37234. TEL 615-251-2000

268 US ISSN 0162-4768
YOUTH IN DISCOVERY. TEACHER. q. $7.75. Southern Baptist Convention, Sunday School Board, 127 Ninth Ave., N., Nashville, TN 37234. TEL 615-251-2000

268 US ISSN 0162-4709
YOUTH LEADERSHIP. q. $7.25. Southern Baptist Convention, Sunday School Board, 127 Ninth Ave., N., Nashville, TN 37234. TEL 615-251-2000 Indexed: South.Bap.Per.Ind.

280 370 US ISSN 0512-9575
YOUTH PLANBOOK. a. (United Methodist Church, Board of Discipleship) Graded Press, 201 Eighth Ave. S., Box 801, Nashville, TN 37202. TEL 615-749-6421 Ed. Sharilyn Adair.

286 NE ISSN 0044-1562
ZAAIER. 1912. m. fl.8.50. Unie van Baptisten Gemeenten, c/o "De Vinkenhof", Biltseweg 10, 3735 MC Bosch en Duin, Netherlands. Ed. R. Reiling. bk. rev. circ. 15,000.

282 GE ISSN 0044-2038
ZEICHEN DER ZEIT; Evangelische Monatsschrift fuer Mitarbeiter der Kirche. 1947. m. M.30.60. Evangelische Verlagsanstalt GmbH, Krautstr. 52, 1017 Berlin, E. Germany (D.D.R.) Ed. Heinz Blauert. adv. bk. rev. index. circ. 7,000. Indexed: CERDIC.

284 GW ISSN 0342-4316
ZEITSCHRIFT FUER BAYERISCHE KIRCHENGESCHICHTE. 1926. a. DM.15. Verein fuer Bayerische Kirchengeschichte, Veilhofstr. 28, D-8500 Nuremburg 20, W. Germany (B.R.D.) Ed. Horst Weigelt. bk. rev. circ. 800.

262.9 284 GW ISSN 0044-2690
ZEITSCHRIFT FUER EVANGELISCHES KIRCHENRECHT. 1951. q. DM.110. Verlag J.C.B. Mohr (Paul Siebeck), Wilhelmstr. 18, Postfach 2040, 7400 Tuebingen, W. Germany (B.R.D.) Ed.Bd. adv. bk. rev. index. Indexed: CERDIC.
Canon law

284 GW ISSN 0513-9147
ZEITSCHRIFT FUER THEOLOGIE UND KIRCHE. 1891. q. DM.66 to individuals, students DM.46. Verlag J.C.B. Mohr (Paul Siebeck), Wilhelmstr. 18, Postfach 2040, 7400 Tuebingen, W. Germany (B.R.D.) Ed. Eberhard Juengel. adv. index. Indexed: Curr.Cont. Old Test.Abstr. Rel.Per. Arts & Hum.Cit.Ind. CERDIC. Rel.Ind.One. Rel.& Theol.Abstr.

284 GW ISSN 0722-3234
ZUVERSICHT UND STAERKE. 1982. bi-m. DM.28.80. (Ludwig-Hofacker-Vereinigung) Haenssler-Verlag, Bismarckstr. 4, Postfach 12 20, 7303 Neuhausen, W. Germany (B.R.D.) Ed.Bd. circ. 2,500. (back issues avail.)

288 NE ISSN 0044-5576
ZWINGLI. 1946. 11/yr. fl.20. Stichting Blad Zwingli, Giro 1968769, Assen, Netherlands. Ed. P.D. van Roijen. adv. bk. rev. bibl. illus. circ. 600. (looseleaf format)

RELIGIONS AND THEOLOGY — Roman Catholic

282 BL ISSN 0005-1934
A M. (Ave Maria) 1898. s-m. Cr.$15($6) Editora Ave Maria Ltda, Rua Martins Francisco 646, Caixa Postal, 615, 01000 Sao Paulo, Brazil. adv. bk. rev. illus. circ. 50,000 (controlled)

271 US ISSN 0567-6630
ACADEMY OF AMERICAN FRANCISCAN HISTORY. BIBLIOGRAPHICAL SERIES. 1953. irreg., no.4, vol.1, 1978. $17.50. Academy of American Franciscan History, Box 34440, West Bethesda, MD 20817. TEL 301-365-1763

271 US ISSN 0065-0633
ACADEMY OF AMERICAN FRANCISCAN HISTORY. DOCUMENTARY SERIES. 1951. irreg., vol.11, 1979. price varies. Academy of American Franciscan History, Box 34440, West Bethesda, MD 20817. TEL 301-365-1763
History

271 US ISSN 0065-0641
ACADEMY OF AMERICAN FRANCISCAN HISTORY. MONOGRAPH SERIES. 1953. irreg., vol.13, 1981. price varies. Academy of American Franciscan History, Box 34440, West Bethesda, MD 20817. TEL 301-365-1763

271 US ISSN 0065-065X
ACADEMY OF AMERICAN FRANCISCAN HISTORY. PROPAGANDA FIDE SERIES. 1966. irreg., vol.8, 1980. $40. Academy of American Franciscan History, Box 34440, West Bethesda, MD 20817. TEL 301-365-1763 Eds. Mathias Kiemen, Alexander Wyse. index.
History

282 VC ISSN 0001-5199
ACTA APOSTOLICAE SEDIS. COMMENTARIUM OFFICIALE. (Text in Latin and European Languages) 1909. m. L.65000($40) Libreria Editrice Vaticana, Citta del Vaticano, Rome, Italy. index. Indexed: Cath.Ind. CERDIC.

ACTA MEDIAEVALIA. see *HISTORY — History Of Europe*

270 VC ISSN 0065-1443
ACTA NUNTIATURAE GALLICAE. 1961. irreg. price varies. (Pontificia Universita Gregoriana, Facolta di Storia Ecclesiastica) Gregorian University Press, Piazza della Pilotta, 35, 00187 Rome, Italy. (Co-sponsor Ecole Francaise de Rome) Ed. Pierre Blet, S.J. circ. 1,000.

282 IT ISSN 0001-6411
ACTA ORDINIS FRATRUM MINORUM. (Text in Latin) 1882. bi-m. Ordinis Fratrum Minorum, Curia Generalis, Via S. Maria Mediatrice 25, I-00165 Rome, Italy. Ed. Desiderius Kalverkamp. index. cum.index. circ. controlled.

282 IT ISSN 0001-642X
ACTA ORDINIS SANCTI AUGUSTINI; commentarium officiale. (Text in Latin and various languages) 1956. a. L.5500. Order of Saint Augustine, Economato Generale, Via S. Uffizio 25, 00193 Rome, Italy. circ. 500. (back issues avail.)

282 AG ISSN 0587-4300
ACTUALIDAD PASTORAL. 1968. m. Arg.$30($40) Rams 261, 1708 Moron, Argentina. Ed. Vicente Oscar Vetrano. adv. bk. rev. charts. illus. index. circ. 5,000. (looseleaf format)

232 CN
ACTUALITE DIOCESAINE. (Text in English and French) 1970. bi-m. Can.$7. Eglise Catholique, Diocese de Saint-Jean-Longueuil, c/o Lucie Remillard, 740 Boul. Ste-Foy, C.P.40, Longueuil, Que. J4K 4X8, Canada. TEL 514-679-1100 adv. bk. rev. circ. 7,800.
Formerly (until 1983): Rythme de Notre Eglise (ISSN 0383-0152)

282 FR
ACTUALITE RELIGIEUSE DAN LE MONDE. 1955. m. 260 F. Malesherbes Publications, 163 bd. Malesherbes, 75017 Paris, France. adv. bk. rev. film rev. bibl. illus. index. circ. 30,000. (tabloid format)
Formerly (until 1983): Informations Catholiques Internationales (ISSN 0020-0441)

AFRICAN JOURNAL OF BIBLICAL STUDIES. see *RELIGIONS AND THEOLOGY*

282 IT
AGENDA. 1959. m. L.10000. Azione Cattolica, Via del Monte 5, 40126 Bologna, Italy. circ. 3,000. (tabloid format)

282 255 IT ISSN 0002-4066
AI NOSTRI AMICI. 1930. m. L.1000. Gesuiti di Sicilia, Missioni Rettoria Casa Professa, 90134 Palermo, Italy. Ed. Carmelo Salv. Bentivegna, S.J. adv. bk. rev. bibl. illus. stat. index. circ. 10,000.

282 267 GW ISSN 0002-3000
AKADEMISCHE MONATSBLAETTER. 1887. m. DM.46. Kartellverband Katholischer Deutscher Studentenvereine, Postfach 1505, 4720 Beckum, W. Germany (B.R.D.) bk. rev. index. circ. 20,000. (tabloid format)

282 CN ISSN 0316-473X
ALBERTA CATHOLIC DIRECTORY. 1920. a. Can.$6. Western Catholic Reporter, 10562 - 109th St., Edmonton, Alta, T5H 3B2, Canada. Ed. E. Abele. adv. circ. 1,500.
Missions

282 US
ALIVE AND WELL AND LIVING IN NEW YORK CITY SAINT PATRICK'S CATHEDRAL. vol.56, 1976. m. $6. (St. Patrick's Parish House) Cathedral Publications, 14 E. 51st St., New York, NY 10022. TEL 212-355-0823 Ed. P. Ryan. adv. bk. rev. illus. circ. 5,000.
Formerly: St. Patrick's Cathedral Bulletin.

ALLGEMEINER CAECILIEN-VERBAND. SCHRIFTENREIHE. see *MUSIC*

282 AU ISSN 0002-6514
ALT-KATHOLISCHE KIRCHENZEITUNG. 1966. m. S.60($6) Alt-Katholische Kirche Oesterreichs, Schottenring 17 1 3 12, A-1010 Vienna, Austria. Ed. Dr. Wilhelmine Zankl. adv. bk. rev. illus. circ. 2,900. (looseleaf format)
Formerly: Alt-Katholik.

282 NQ
AMANECER. 1981. 6/yr. C.$300($25) Centro Ecumenico Antonio Valdivieso, Apdo. 3205, Managua, Nicaragua. Ed. Jose Arguello. bk. rev. circ. 2,500.

200 FR
AME POPULAIRE. 1920. m. 120 F. Sillon Catholique, 4 Passage Olivier de Serres, 75015 Paris, France. Ed.Bd. adv. bk. rev. circ. 10,000.

282 US ISSN 0002-7049
AMERICA; national Catholic weekly review. 1909. w. $25. America Press Inc., 106 W. 56th St., New York, NY 10019. TEL 212-581-4640 Ed. George W. Hunt. adv. bk. rev. film rev. play rev. s-a index. circ. 35,000. (also avail. in microform (ISSN 0364-989X) from BLH,MIM,UMI) Indexed: Cath.Ind. Old Test.Abstr. R.G. A.I.P.P. Abstrax. Biog.Ind. Bk.Rev.Ind. Bk.Rev.Dig. CERDIC. Film Lit.Ind. G.Soc.Sci.& Rel.Per.Lit. Mag.Ind. Media Rev.Dig. PMR.

200 PE
AMERICA LATINA. BOLETIN. no. 15, Feb., 1978. irreg. Movimiento Internacional de Estudiantes Catolicos, Centro de Documentacion, Apartado 3564, Lima 100, Peru. illus.

282 207.11 US ISSN 0002-7650
AMERICAN BENEDICTINE REVIEW. 1950. 4/yr. $10. American Benedictine Review, Inc., Assumption Abbey, Box A, Richardton, ND 58652. Ed. Rev. Terrence Kardong. adv. bk. rev. index. circ. 1,200. (also avail. in microform from UMI; reprint service avail. from UMI) Indexed: Cath.Ind. Hist.Abstr. M.L.A. Rel.Per. Amer.Hist.& Life. New Test.Abstr.

282 209 US ISSN 0002-7790
AMERICAN CATHOLIC HISTORICAL SOCIETY OF PHILADELPHIA. RECORDS. 1886. q. $15. American Catholic Historical Society of Philadelphia, Box 84, Philadelphia, PA 19105. TEL 215-925-5752 Ed. Thomas R. Greene. bk. rev. index. cum.index. circ. 950. Indexed: Cath.Ind.
History

AMERICAN CATHOLIC PHILOSOPHICAL ASSOCIATION. PROCEEDINGS. see *PHILOSOPHY*

282 DR
AMIGO DEL HOGAR. no.442, 1983. m. $12. Apdo. Postal 1104, Santo Domingo, Dominican Republic. Ed. Juan Rodriquez. circ. 23,000.

282 FR ISSN 0003-1895
AMITIES CATHOLIQUES FRANCAISES. N.S. 1915. q. 35 F. Comite Catholique des Amities Francaises dans le Monde, 99 rue de Rennes, 75006 Paris, France. Ed. Pere Pierre Yves Pecqueux. adv. bk. rev. bibl. stat. index. circ. 3,300. (tabloid format)

282 GW ISSN 0003-2328
AMTSBLATT FUER DIE ERZDIOEZESE BAMBERG. (Text in German & Latin) 1878. s-m. DM.12. (Archdiocese Bamberg, Erzbischoefliches Ordinariat Bamberg) Sankt-Otto-Verlag, Laubanger 23, D-8600 Bamberg, W. Germany (B.R.D.) Ed. Dr. Heinrich Straub. bk. rev. stat. index. circ. 900.

255 IT
ANALECTA AUGUSTINIANA. (Text in Latin & various languages) 1905. fortn. L.14000($18) Order of Saint Augustine, Economato Generale, Via S. Uffizio 25, 00193 Rome, Italy. (back issues avail.)

282 IT ISSN 0066-135X
ANALECTA BIBLICA. (Texts in various languages) 1952. irreg., no.109. price varies. (Pontificio Istituto Biblico) Biblical Institute Press, Piazza della Pilotta 35, I-00187 Rome, Italy. Ed. P. Karl Ploetz, SJ. circ. 300.

270 282 VC ISSN 0066-1376
ANALECTA GREGORIANA. (Text in various languages) 1930. irreg., latest vol.212. price varies. (Pontificia Universita Gregoriana) Gregorian University Press, Piazza della Pilotta, 35, 00187 Rome, Italy. Ed. Gilles Pelland, S.J.

ANGELICUM; periodicum trimestre pontificae studiorum. see *PHILOSOPHY*

282 255 GR
ANICHTI ORIZONTES-ANGHELIAFOROS. 1900. m. Dr.1500($10) Jesuit Fathers, 27 Smyrnis Str., Athens 10439, Greece. Ed. Father Gabriel Marangos. adv. bk. rev. bibl. circ. 4,300.
Former titles (until 1977): Angheliaforos-Anichti Orizontes & Angheliaforos (ISSN 0003-3073)

282 CN ISSN 0318-434X
ANNALS OF GOOD ST. ANNE. (Editions in English and French) 1876. m. Can.$6.50. Redemptorist Fathers, Ste-Anne de Beaupre Province, Basilica of Ste. Anne, Quebec G0A 3C0, Canada. Ed. Bernard Mercier. bk. rev. film rev. circ. 185,000; 54,000 (English edt.); 130,000 (French edt.)

282 FR ISSN 0066-2488
ANNUAIRE CATHOLIQUE DE FRANCE. 1950. biennial. 340 F. Publicat, 17 bd. Poissonniere, 75002 Paris, France. adv.

282.675 ZR
ANNUAIRE DE L'EGLISE CATHOLIQUE AU ZAIRE. a. Edition du Secretariat-General, Kinshasa-Combe, Zaire. illus.

282 FR
ANNUAIRE DU DIOCESE DE LYON. 1826. a. 90 F. Archeveche de Lyon, 1 Place de Fourviere, 69321 Lyon Cedex 05, France.
Formerly (until 1972): Ordo et Annuaire de l'Archdiocese de Lyon.

266 IT ISSN 0066-4464
ANNUARIO CATTOLICO D'ITALIA. 1956. biennial. L.130000. Editoriale Italiana, Via Vigliena 10, Rome, Italy. index. circ. 8,000.

282 VC ISSN 0003-6064
ANTONIANUM. (Text in English, French, German, Italian, Latin, Spanish) 1926. q. L.40000($35) Pontificio Ateneo Antonianum, Via Merulana 124, 00185 Rome, Italy. Ed. Isaac Vazquez Janeiro. adv. bk. rev. abstr. bibl. index. cum.index. circ. 850. Indexed: Hist.Abstr. Hist.Abstr. M.L.A. Amer.Hist.& Life. CERDIC. Old Test.Abstr. New Test.Abstr. Rel.& Theol.Abstr.

282 GW ISSN 0721-1937
ANZEIGER FUER DIE SEELSORGE; aeltestes Organ fuer die Kath. Pfarraemter und Krankenhaeuser Kloester. 1891. m. DM.21.60. Verlag Herder, Hermann-Herder-Str. 4, D-7800 Freiburg, W. Germany (B.R.D.) Ed.Bd. (back issues avail.)

282 VC
APOLLINARIS. (Text in Italian and Latin) 1928. q. $30. Pontificia Universita Lateranense, Pontificio Istituto Utriusque Iuris, Piazza S. Giovanni in Laterno 4, 00120 Vatican City. Ed. Tarcisio Bertone. Indexed: CERDIC. Canon Law Abstr.

AQUINAS; rivista internazionale di filosofia. see *PHILOSOPHY*

282 IT ISSN 0003-7559
ARALDO DI S. ANTONIO; incontri con Papa Giovanni. 1949. w. free. Orfanotrofio Antoniano dei PP. Rogazionisti, 25015 Desenzano del Garda (Bs), Brescia, Italy. bk. rev. illus. circ. 125,000.

282 US
ARCHDIOCESE OF CINCINNATI DIRECTORY AND BUYER'S GUIDE. 1959. a. $12. Catholic Telegraph, 100 E. Eighth St., Cincinnati, OH 45202. TEL 513-421-3131 Ed. James Stackpoole. adv. stat. circ. 3,000.

282 IT ISSN 0003-8296
ARCHIDIOCESI DI MONREALE. BOLLETTINO ECCLESIASTICO. 1908. m. L.12000. Curia Arcivescovile di Monreale, Palermo, Italy. Ed. Msgr. Stefano Giordano. bk. rev.

200 SP
ARCHIDIOCESIS DE MADRID-ALCALA. BOLETIN OFICIAL. 1878. s-m. 1,500 ptas.($13) Arzobispado de Madrid, Bailen 8, 28013 Madrid, Spain. Ed. J. Gonzalez Prado. adv. bibl. index. circ. 1,500. (back issues avail.)

282 949.2 NE ISSN 0003-8326
ARCHIEF VOOR DE GESCHIEDENIS VAN DE KATHOLIEKE KERK IN NEDERLAND. 1959. s-a. fl.56. Dekker & Van de Vegt, P.O. Box 526, 6500 AM Nijmegen, Netherlands (Subscr. to: van Gorcum & Comp. B.V., Postbus 43, 9400 AA Assen, Netherlands) Ed. Th. Clemens. adv. bk. rev. bibl. index. circ. 800. Indexed: Hist.Abstr. Amer.Hist.& Life.

282 209 GW ISSN 0003-9160
ARCHIV FUER KATHOLISCHES KIRCHENRECHT. (Text in German and Latin) 1857. s-a. DM.80 per no. Verlag Kirchheim und Co. GmbH, Kaiserstr. 41, Postfach 2524, 6500 Mainz, W. Germany (B.R.D.) Ed. Klaus Moersdorf. adv. bibl. index. circ. 550. Indexed: CERDIC. Canon Law Abstr.

ARCHIVO IBERO-AMERICANO; revista de estudios historicos. see *HISTORY — History Of Europe*

271 IT ISSN 0004-0665
ARCHIVUM FRANCISCANUM HISTORICUM. (Text in English, French, German, Italian, Latin and Spanish) 1908. s-a. L.35000. Collegio San Bonaventura, Commissione Storica, Via Vecchia di Marino 28-30, Colle S. Antonio, 00046 Grottaferrata (Roma), Italy. Ed. R.P. Clement Schmitt. bk. rev. bibl. charts. illus. cum.index: 1908-1957. circ. 600. Indexed: Hist.Abstr. M.L.A. Amer.Hist.& Life. CERDIC.
History

282 VC ISSN 0066-6785
ARCHIVUM HISTORIAE PONTIFICAE. (Text in English, French,German, Italian, Latin or Spanish; summaries in Latin) 1963. a. $50. (Pontificia Universita Gregoriana, Facolta di Storia Ecclesiastica) Gregorian University Press, Piazza della Pilotta, 35, 00187 Rome, Italy. Ed. Paulius Rabikauskas, S.J. adv. bk. rev. bibl. circ. 750. (back issues avail.)

271 IT ISSN 0037-8887
ARCHIVUM HISTORICUM SOCIETATIS IESU. (Text and summaries in English, French, German, Italian, Latin, Portuguese, and Spanish) 1932. s-a. $30. Institutum Historicum Societatis Iesu - Jesuit Historical Institute, Via dei Penitenzieri 20, 00193 Rome, Italy. Ed. Laszlo Szilas. bk. rev. bibl. illus. cum.index: 1932-1951, 1952-1961; 1962-1981. circ. 900. (reprint service avail. from UMI) Indexed: Hist.Abstr. Amer.Hist.& Life.
History

ARCHIWA, BIBLIOTEKI I MUZEA KOSCIELNE. see *HISTORY — History Of Europe*

228 IT
ARCIDIOCESI DI REGGIO CALABRIA. RIVISTA PASTORALE. 1910. q. L.10000. Curia Metropolitan di Reggio Calabria, Via T. Campanella 63, 89100 Reggio Calabria, Italy. Ed. Sac. Antonino Denisi. adv. illus.
Formerly: Bollettino Ecclesiastico (ISSN 0006-6788)

282 US ISSN 0361-3712
ARLINGTON CATHOLIC HERALD. 1976. w. $10. (Arlington Catholic Herald, Inc.) Charles W. Carruth, Ed. & Pub., 200 North Glebe Rd., Ste. 614, Arlington, VA 22203. TEL 703-841-2590 adv. bk. rev. illus. circ. 27,500. (also avail. in microfilm)

282 CL
ARZOBISPADO DE SANTIAGO. VICARIA DE LA SOLIDARIDAD. ESTUDIOS. 1978. irreg. Arzobispado de Santiago, Vicaria de la Solidaridad, Plaza de Armas 444, Casilla 30D, Santiago, Chile.

250 SP
ARZOBISPADO DE SEVILLA. BOLETIN OFICIAL ECLESIASTICO. 1854. m. 2400 ptas. Arzobispado de Sevilla, Oficina Diocesana de Informacion, Apdo. Postal 6, Sevilla, Spain. Ed. Carlos Ros Carballar. adv. bk. rev.

282 209 IT ISSN 0004-4970
ASPRENAS; Rivista di Scienze Teologiche. 1953. q. $15. Pontificia Facolta Teologica dell'Italia Meridionale-Sezione di Capodimonte, Viale Colli Aminei 2, I-80131 Naples, Italy. Ed. Prof. Settimio Cipriani. adv. bk. rev. charts. illus. index. circ. 1,000. Indexed: CERDIC.

282 US ISSN 0094-5323
AUGUSTINIAN STUDIES. (Text in various languages) 1970. a. $15. (Villanova University, Augustinian Institute) Villanova University Press, c/o B.A. Paparella, Villanova, PA 19085. TEL 215-645-7500 Ed. Russell D. DeSimone. bk. rev. circ. 300. Indexed: Cath.Ind. Phil.Ind.

271 BE ISSN 0004-8003
AUGUSTINIANA; revue pour l'etude de Saint Augustin et de l'Ordre des Augustins. (Text in English, French, German and Latin) 1951. s-a. 1000 Fr. Augustijns Historisch Instituut - Institut Historique Augustinien, Pere August Pakenstraat 109, 3030 Heverlee-Louvain, Belgium. Ed. Dr. T. van Bavel. bk. rev. bibl. index. Indexed: M.L.A. CERDIC.

271 IT ISSN 0004-8011
AUGUSTINIANUM. 1961. 3/yr. L.40000. Institutum Patristicum Augustinianum, Via del S. Uffizio 25, 00193 Rome, Italy. Ed. V. Grossi. bk. rev. index. circ. 800. Indexed: M.L.A. Old Test.Abstr. New Test.Abstr.

271 SP ISSN 0004-802X
AUGUSTINUS. (Text in Spanish) 1956. q. 2500 ptas.($35) Padres Agustinos Recoletos, General Davila 5, Bajo D, 28003 Madrid, Spain. bk. rev. index. circ. 700. (processed) Indexed: M.L.A. CERDIC. Phil.Ind.

282 AT ISSN 0004-8321
AUSTRALASIAN CATHOLIC RECORD. 1924. q. Aus.$15. St. Patrick's College, Manly, N.S.W., Australia. Ed.Bd. adv. bk. rev. index. circ. 3,000. Indexed: Cath.Ind. Rel.& Theol.Abstr. Aus.P.A.I.S. Canon Law Abstr. New Test.Abstr.

282 LE ISSN 0005-1950
AVEDIK. 1932. m. £L10($4) Armenian Catholic Patriarchate, Place Debbas, Beirut, Lebanon. Ed. Fr. Vartan Tekeyan. illus.

282 249 GW ISSN 0005-7177
BAYERISCHES SONNTAGSBLATT FUER DIE KATHOLISCHE FAMILIE. 1879. w. DM.70.80. Bayerisches Sonntagsblatt Verlags GmbH, Nymphenbuerger Str. 156, 8000 Munich 19, W. Germany (B.R.D.) Eds. Guenther Beaugrand, Ursula Goldmann-Posch. adv. bk. rev. film rev. abstr. illus. circ. 44,000. (looseleaf format)

282 IT ISSN 0005-7436
BEATO ANGELO. 1924. m. L.7000($15) Frati Minori Cappuccini della Provincia Consentina, Covento del SS. Crocifisso, 87100 Cosenza, Italy. Dir. P. Elio Vittorino Vivacqua. adv. bk. rev. illus. circ. 3,000.

282 GE ISSN 0005-7800
BEGEGNUNG; zeitschrift fuer Katholiken in Kirche und Gesellschaft. 1961. m. M.24. Verlag Begegnung, Friedrichstr. 169-170, 108 Berlin, E. Germany (D.D.R.) (Subscr. to: Buchexport, Leninstr. 16, 701 Leipzig, E. Germany (D.D.R.)) Ed. Otto Hartmut Fuchs. adv. bk. rev. abstr. bibl. film rev. illus. index. Indexed: CERDIC.

BENEDICTINA. see *HISTORY — History Of Europe*

271 UK ISSN 0522-8883
BENEDICTINE YEARBOOK. 1863. a. $2. English Congregation of the Order of Saint Benedict, Ampleforth Abbey, York Y06 4EN, England. Ed. Rev. J. Gordon Beattie. adv. circ. 4,000.
Supersedes: Benedictine Almanac.

282 US ISSN 0005-8726
BENEDICTINES. 1946. s-a. $8. (Mount St. Scholastica Convent) Mount St. Scholastica, Inc., Atchison, KS 66002. TEL 913-367-6110 E. Sister Mary Alice Guilfoil. bk. rev. illus. cum.index: vols.1-9, 10-20, 21-30. circ. 800. (also avail. in microform from UMI; back issues avail.; reprint service avail. from UMI) Indexed: Bull.Signal. CERDIC.

282 AU ISSN 0005-8742
BENEDIKTUSBOTE. 1927. m. S.72. Verlag Franz Reisinger, A-4601 Wels, Austria. Ed. P. Berthold Egelseder OSB. bk. rev. abstr. bibl. illus.

282 IT
LA BIBBIA NELLA STORIA. 1984. irreg. Centro Editoriale Dehoniano, Via Nosadella 6, I-40123 Bologna, Italy. Ed.Bd.

220 282 GW ISSN 0006-0593
BIBEL HEUTE. 1965. q. DM.20($2) Katholisches Bibelwerk e.V., Silberburgstr. 121, 7000 Stuttgart 1, W. Germany (B.R.D.) Ed. P.G. Mueller. adv. bk. rev. illus. index. cum.index. circ. 24,000. Indexed: CERDIC.

220 II
BIBLEBHASHYAM; Indian Biblical quarterly. (Text in English) 1975. q. Rs.15($8) St. Thomas Apostolic Seminary, Post Box No. 1, Vadavathoor, Kottayam 686010, India. Ed. Matthew Vellanickal. adv. bk. rev. circ. 4,000. Indexed: Old Test.Abstr. New Test.Abstr.

282 BL
BIBLIA - GENTE. 1978. w. Cr.$100. (Pia Sociedade de Sao Paulo) Edicoes Paulinas, Via Raposo Tavares Km 18.5, C.P. 8107, 01051 Sao Paulo, Brazil. Ed. A.C. D'Elboux. illus. circ. 120,000.

220 VC ISSN 0006-0887
BIBLICA. (Text in English, French, German, Italian, Latin and Spanish) 1920. q. $35. (Pontificio Istituto Biblico) Biblical Institute Press, Piazza della Pilotta 35, 00187 Rome, Italy. Ed. S. Pisano S.J. bk. rev. index. cum.index: vols.1-25, 26-50. circ. 1,900. Indexed: Curr.Cont. Old Test.Abstr. Rel.Per. Arts & Hum.Cit.Ind. CERDIC. New Test.Abstr. Rel.Ind.One. Rel.& Theol.Abstr.

282 VC
BIBLICA ET ORIENTALIA. 1928. irreg., no.41, 1986. price varies. (Pontificio Istituto Biblico) Biblical Institute Press, Piazza della Pilotta 35, 00187 Rome, Italy.

282 VC
BIBLIOTECA APOSTOLICA VATICANA. CATALOGHI DI MANOSCRITTI. 1902. irreg., no.42, 1978. price varies. Biblioteca Apostolica Vaticana, 00120 Vatican City.

282 VC
BIBLIOTECA APOSTOLICA VATICANA. CATALOGHI DI MOSTRE. 1904. irreg., no.18, 1977. price varies. Biblioteca Apostolica Vaticana, 00120 Vatican City.

282 VC
BIBLIOTECA APOSTOLICA VATICANA. ILLUSTRAZIONI DI CODICI. CODICI VATICANI. SERIES MAJOR. 1902. irreg., no. 37, 1975. price varies. Biblioteca Apostolica Vaticana, 00120 Vatican City.

282 VC
BIBLIOTECA APOSTOLICA VATICANA. ILLUSTRAZIONI DI CODICI. CODICI VATICANI. SERIES MINOR. 1910. irreg., no. 4, 1978. price varies. Biblioteca Apostolica Vaticana, 00120 Vatican City.

282 VC
BIBLIOTECA APOSTOLICA VATICANA. STUDI E TESTI. 1900. irreg., no. 283, 1979. price varies. Biblioteca Apostolica Vaticana, 00120 Vatican City.

282 IT
BIBLIOTHECA INSTITUTI HISTORICI SOCIETATIS IESU. 1941. irreg., latest no.45, 1986. Institutum Historicum Societatis Iesu - Jesuit Historical Institute, Via dei Penitenzieri 20, 00193 Rome, Italy. (back issues avail.)

200 IT ISSN 0067-8163
BIBLIOTHECA SERAPHICO-CAPUCCINA. (Multilingual text) 1932. irreg., no.33, 1986. price varies. Frati Minori Cappuccini, Istituto Storico, Cas. Post. 9091, Circonv. Occidentale 6850 (GRA km 65), 00163 Rome, Italy. index. circ. 500.

200 BE ISSN 0067-8279
BIBLIOTHEQUE DE LA REVUE D'HISTOIRE ECCLESIASTIQUE. (Text in Dutch, English, French and Italian) 1928. irreg. Universite Catholique de Louvain, Bureau de la Revue d'Histoire Ecclesiastique, Bibliotheque, 1348 Louvain-la-Neuve, Louvain, Belgium.

282 301.4 CK
BOLETIN C E N P A F A L. 1976. q. Centro de Pastoral Familiar para America Latina, Carrera 7 no. 94-80, Bogota, Colombia.

282 PH
BOLETIN ECLESIASTICO DE FILLIPINAS; official organ of the Catholic hierarchy of the Philippines. (Text in English) 1923. m. $25. University of Santo Tomas, Espana St., Manila, Philippines. Ed. Vicente Cajilie. adv. bk. rev. bibl. index. circ. 1,800.

282 IT ISSN 0404-9462
BOLLETTINO DI S. NICOLA. (Text mainly in Italian; occasionally in other languages) 1906. m. L.5000($8) Padri Domenicani della Basilica di S. Nicola di Bari, Basilica di S. Nicola, 70122 Bari, Italy. Ed. P. Gerardo Cioffari. bk. rev. bibl. index. circ. 2,000. (back issues avail.)

282 IT
BOLLETTINO PER LE RELIGIOSE DOMENICANE IN ITALIA. bi-m. Gerardo Cappelluti, Ed. & Pub., Piazza della Minerva 42, 00186 Rome, Italy.

282 IT
BOLLETTINO SALESIANO; rivista fondata da San Giovanni Bosco. 1877. s-a. Direzione Generale Opere Salesiane, Via della Pisana 1111, 00163 Rome, Italy. Ed. Giuseppe Costa. (back issues avail.)

266 IT ISSN 0006-6907
BOLLETTINO VINCENZIANO. 1966. bi-m. L.3000. (Preti della Missione della Provincia di Roma) Centro Liturgico Vincenziano, Via Pompeo Magno 21, 00192 Rome, Italy. Ed. Dir. E. Fei. bk. rev. charts. illus. circ. 2,000.
Missions

254.4 GW ISSN 0006-7113
BONIFATIUSBLATT. 1849. q. free. Bonifatiuswerk der Deutschen Katholiken e.V., Kamp 22, 4790 Paderborn, W. Germany (B.R.D.) Ed. H.D. Huber. illus. stat. circ. 494,000. (avail. in talking book edt.)

282 CN ISSN 0225-0233
BONNE NOUVELLE. (Text in French) 1911. 10/yr. Can.$5. Secular Franciscan Order, 5730 Bd. Pie 9, Montreal, Que. H1X 2B9, Canada. TEL 514-727-8483 Ed.Bd. adv. bk. rev. bibl. charts. illus. stat. circ. 4,000. (back issues avail.) Indexed: CERDIC.

282 US
BRINGING RELIGION HOME; the newsletter that helps teach religion in the home. 1976. m. $12. Claretian Publications, 205 W. Monroe St., Chicago, IL 60606. TEL 312-236-7782 Ed. Rev. Mark J. Brummel. circ. 68,189. (reprint service avail. from UMI)

282 CN ISSN 0007-0483
BRITISH COLUMBIA CATHOLIC. 1931. w. Can.$12($20) Vancouver Archdiocese, Archibishop James Carney, 150 Robson St., Vancouver, B.C. V6B 2A7, Canada. TEL 604-683-0281 Ed. F.V. Hawkswell. adv. bk. rev. film rev. play rev. illus. circ. 16,200. (tabloid format)

240 FR ISSN 0007-4322
BULLETIN DE LITTERATURE ECCLESIASTIQUE. 1899. q. 217 F.($30) Institut Catholique de Toulouse, 31 rue de la Fonderie, 31068 Toulouse Cedex, France. Ed. Henri Crouzel. bk. rev. bibl. index. circ. 850. (back issues avail.) Indexed: Bull.Signal. M.L.A. Old Test.Abstr. CERDIC. New Test.Abstr.

282 320 301 US
BULLETIN ON THE T F P'S. (Editions in English, French, German, Italian, Portuguese, Spanish) 1982. 2/yr. free. American Society for the Defense of Tradition, Family and Property, Inc., Box 121, Pleasantville, NY 10570. Ed. John W. Horvat II. circ. 25,000.

BUND DER DEUTSCHEN KATHOLISCHEN JUGEND. INFORMATIONSDIENST. see *CHILDREN AND YOUTH — For*

266 UK
C A F O D JOURNAL. 1966. s-a. free. Catholic Fund for Overseas Development, 2 Garden Close, Stockwell Rd., London SW9 9TY, England. Ed. Martina Hutton. circ. 250,000.

282 UK ISSN 0262-6896
C A S NEWSLETTER. 1980. a. Catholic Archives Society, c/o M.A. Kuhn-Regnier, St. Peter's Grange, Prinknash Abbey, Cranham, Gloucester GL4 8EX, England.

C C N INFORMATION. (Council of Churches in Namibia) see *RELIGIONS AND THEOLOGY — Protestant*

C H A C REVIEW. see *HOSPITALS*

C W L NEWS. (Catholic Women's League) see *WOMEN'S INTERESTS*

282 CN ISSN 0007-9774
CAHIERS DE JOSEPHOLOGIE. (Text in English and French) 1953. s-a. Can.$20. Oratoire Saint-Joseph du Mont-Royal, 3800 Chemin Reine-Marie, Montreal H3V 1H6, Canada. TEL 514-733-8211 Ed. Roland Gauthier. bk. rev. bibl. illus. index. cum.index: 1953-1972. circ. 1,000. Indexed: Cath.Ind. Old Test.Abstr. New Test.Abstr. Rel.& Theol.Abstr.

282 255 NE ISSN 0008-221X
CAMILLUSBODE. 1950. s-a. free. Provincialaat van de Camillianen, Heinsbergerweg 174, 6045 CK Roermond, Netherlands. Ed. P. Schreur. illus. circ. 6,000. (tabloid format)
Formerly: St. Camillusbode.

282 255 IT ISSN 0008-2260
CAMMINO; annali Francescani. 1869. m. $2. Viale Piave 2, Milan 20129, Italy. Ed.Bd. bk. rev. film rev. play rev. illus. circ. 15,000.

282 CN
CANADIAN CATHOLIC HISTORICAL ASSOCIATION. ANNUAL REPORT. 1975. a. Can.$20. Canadian Catholic Historical Association, c/o Rev. Edward Jackman, P.O. Box 398, Kleinburg, Ont. L0J 1C0, Canada. TEL 902-892-4121 Ed. Alphonse de Valk. circ. 600.

282 CN ISSN 0714-7724
CANADIAN CATHOLIC REVIEW. 1983. 11/yr. Can.$25($25) Canadian Catholic Review Corporation, 1437 College Dr., Saskatoon, Sask, S7N OW6, Canada. Ed. Daniel Callam. adv. bk. rev. film rev. index. circ. 2,000. (back issues avail.) Indexed: Cath.Ind.

200 CN
CANADIAN CONFERENCE OF CATHOLIC BISHOPS. NATIONAL BULLETIN ON LITURGY. 1965. bi-m. $10. ‡ Canadian Conference of Catholic Bishops, Publications Service, 90 Parent Ave, Ottawa, Ontario K1N 7BI, Canada. TEL 613-236-9461 Ed. Patrick J. Byrne. bk. rev. index. circ. 6,000. (also avail. in microfilm from UMI)
Formerly: Canadian Catholic Conference. National Bulletin on Liturgy (ISSN 0084-8425)

285 PH
CARDINAL BEA STUDIES. Short title: C B S. 1970. irreg., no.7, 1977. Cardinal Bea Institute for Ecumenical Studies, Box 4082, Manila, Philippines. Ed. Pedro S. de Achutegui, S.J. circ. 750.

282 PO ISSN 0008-655X
CARIDADE. 1958. m. free. Centro de Caridade Nossa Senhora do Perpetuo Socorro, Rua D. Joao 4, 390, Porto, Portugal. Ed. Silva Ferraz. illus. (tabloid format)

282 US
CARING COMMUNITY. 1985. m. $9 (bulk rates avail.) National Catholic Reporter Publishing Company, Inc., 115 E. Armour Blvd., Box 281, Kansas City, MO 64141. TEL 816-531-0538 Ed. William Freburger. illus. circ. 20,895.

255 IE ISSN 0008-6665
CARMEL. 1930. bi-m. £3.75. Discalced Carmelite Fathers, Avila, Morehampton Rd., Dublin 4, Ireland. Ed. Vincent O'Hara. adv. circ. 8,000.

255 IT ISSN 0008-6673
CARMELUS; Commentarii ab Instituto Carmelitano Editi. (Text in English, French, German, Italian, Latin and Spanish) 1954. s-a. L.30000($25) Institutum Carmelitanum, Via Sforza Pallavicini 10, 00193 Rome, Italy. Ed. Joachim Smet. adv. bk. rev. illus. index. circ. 600. Indexed: Cath.Ind. CERDIC.

282 XK
CASTRIES CATHOLIC CHRONICLE. 1957. m. eC$0.50. Archdiocese of Castries, Cathedral Presbytery, Box 97, Castries, St. Lucia, W. Indies. Ed. Rev. Patrick Anthony. adv. circ. 2,500.

282 IT ISSN 0391-5433
CATECHESI. 1932. m. L.24000. (Centro Catechistico Salesiano) Editrice Elle Di Ci, Corso Francia 214, 10096 Leumann (Turin), Italy. Ed. Pietro Damu. circ. 8,000. Indexed: CERDIC.

240 US
CATECHIST'S CONNECTION. 1984. 10/yr. National Catholic Reporter Publishing Company, Inc., 115 E. Armour Blvd., Box 281, Kansas City, MO 64141. TEL 816-531-0538 Ed. Jean Marie Hiesburger. adv. bk. rev. circ. 31,830. (tabloid format)

282 US
CATHOLIC ACTIVIST. 1978. m. $38. American Classical College, Box 4526, Albuquerque, NM 87196. TEL 505-893-7749 Ed. C.M. Flumiani.

282 US ISSN 0008-7904
CATHOLIC ADVANCE. 1901. w. $5 in Kansas; $6 outside Kansas. Catholic Diocese of Wichita, c/o Bishop David M. Maloney, 424 N. Broadway, Wichita, KS 67202. TEL 316-263-6262 Ed. Father Arthur A. Busch. adv. bk. rev. circ. 13,000.
Formerly: Advance.

282 US ISSN 0045-5970
CATHOLIC AGITATOR. 1971. 10/yr. $1. (Ammon Hennacy House of Hospitality) Los Angeles Catholic Worker, 632 N. Brittania St., Los Angeles, CA 90033. TEL 213-267-8789 Ed. Jeff Dietrich. adv. bk. rev. circ. 7,000.

282 US ISSN 0069-1208
CATHOLIC ALMANAC. 1904. a. $13.95. Our Sunday Visitor, Inc., 200 Noll Plaza, Huntington, IN 46750. TEL 219-356-8400 Eds. Rev. Felician A. Fox, Rose A. Avalon. index.
Formerly: National Catholic Almanac.

282 UK ISSN 0261-4316
CATHOLIC ARCHIVES. 1981. a. £2. Catholic Archives Society, c/o R.M. Gard, Ed., 21 Larchwood Ave., North Gosforth, Newcastle-upon-Tyne NE13 6PY, England. circ. 350. Indexed: CERDIC.

220 282 US ISSN 0008-7912
CATHOLIC BIBLICAL QUARTERLY. 1939. q. $15. Catholic Biblical Association of America, Catholic University of America, Washington, DC 20064. TEL 202-635-5519 Ed. John P. Meier. adv. bk. rev. index. cum.index. circ. 4,100. (also avail. in microfilm) Indexed: Cath.Ind. Curr.Cont. Hum.Ind. Rel.Per. Arts & Hum.Cit.Ind. CERDIC. Old Test.Abstr. New Test.Abstr. Rel.Ind.One. Rel.& Theol.Abstr.

CATHOLIC CEMETERY. see *FUNERALS*

282 US ISSN 0069-1216
CATHOLIC CENTRAL UNION OF AMERICA. PROCEEDINGS. 1855. a. $3. Catholic Central Union of America, 3835 Westminster Place, St. Louis, MO 63108. TEL 314-371-0889 Ed. Harvey J. Johnson. circ. 1,250. (also avail. in microfilm)

282 US ISSN 8756-7482
CATHOLIC CHALLENGE. 1985. q. $15. Sanderleaf Publishing, Inc., 182 109th Ave., Elmont, NY 11003. TEL 516-488-7439 Ed. Rev. James P. Lisante.

282 US ISSN 0008-7971
CATHOLIC CHRONICLE. 1934. bi-w. $13. (Catholic Diocese of Toledo) Catholic Press Union Inc., 2130 Madison Ave., Box 1866, Toledo, OH 43603. TEL 419-243-4178 Ed. Daniel J. McCarthy. adv. film rev. circ. 41,000. (also avail. in microfilm)

280 FR
CATHOLIC COUNTER-REFORMATION IN THE XXTH CENTURY. (Text in English) 1970. m. $8. Contre Reforme Catholique, Maison Saint-Joseph, 10260-Saint-Parres-les-Vaudes, France. Ed. Frere Gerard Cousin. bk. rev. circ. 4,500.

282 US ISSN 0008-7998
CATHOLIC DIGEST. 1936. m. $10.97. College of St. Thomas, Box 64090, St. Paul, MN 55164. TEL 612-647-5000 Ed. Henry Lexau. adv. illus. circ. 620,000. (also avail. in microform from UMI; reprint service avail. from UMI) Indexed: Cath.Ind. CERDIC.

267 UK ISSN 0069-1224
CATHOLIC DIRECTORY. 1837. a. £8.95. Associated Catholic Publications (1912) Ltd., 33-39 Bowling Green Lane, London EC1R 0AB, England. Ed. Rev. David Morris. adv.

282 US
CATHOLIC DIRECTORY (SAN DIEGO) 1936. a. $8. Roman Catholic Diocese of San Diego, Box 81869, San Diego, CA 92138. TEL 619-574-6393 Ed. Bill Finley. adv. circ. 30,000.

267 UK ISSN 0306-5677
CATHOLIC DIRECTORY FOR SCOTLAND. 1828. a. £10. John S. Burns and Sons, 25 Finlas St., Possilpark, Glasgow, G22 5DS, Scotland.
Formerly: Catholic Directory for the Clergy and Laity in Scotland (ISSN 0069-1232)

282 UK
CATHOLIC DIRECTORY OF ENGLAND AND WALES. 1839. a. £12.50. Associated Catholic Newspapers Ltd., 33-39 Bowling Green Lane, London, EC1R 0AB, England. Ed. D. Norris. adv.

282 SA
CATHOLIC DIRECTORY OF SOUTHERN AFRICA. 1906. biennial. R.20. Southern African Catholic Bishops' Conference, 140 Visagie St., Pretoria 0001, South Africa. adv. stat. index. circ. 1,500.

282 US
CATHOLIC DIRECTORY OF THE ARCHDIOCESE OF BALTIMORE. 1921. a. $9. Cathedral Foundation, 320 Cathedral St., Baltimore, MD 21201. TEL 301-547-5314 adv. circ. 1,700.
Formerly: Archdiocese of Baltimore. Directory.

282 377.8 UK
CATHOLIC EDUCATION. 1978. biennial. £4. Catholic Education Council for England and Wales, 41 Cromwell Rd., London SW7 2DJ, England. Ed. R.F. Cunningham.

282 UK ISSN 0008-8064
CATHOLIC GAZETTE. 1910. m. £7. Catholic Missionary Society, 114 W. Heath Rd., London NW3 7TX, England. Ed. Kevin O'Connell. adv. bk. rev. index. circ. 6,000. Indexed: CERDIC.

CATHOLIC HEALTH ASSOCIATION OF CANADA. DIRECTORY. see *MEDICAL SCIENCES*

282 UK ISSN 0008-8072
CATHOLIC HERALD. 1884. w. $40. Catholic Herald Ltd., Herald House, Lambs Passage, Bunhill Row, London E.C.1., England. Ed. Terence J. Sheehy. adv. bk. rev. film rev. music rev. index. circ. 30,819. (also avail. in microform from MIM,WMP)

282 270 US ISSN 0008-8080
CATHOLIC HISTORICAL REVIEW. 1915. q. $22. (American Catholic Historical Association) Catholic University of America Press, 620 Michigan Ave., N.E., Washington, DC 20064. TEL 202-635-5052 Ed. Rev. Robert Trisco. adv. bk. rev. bibl. index. cum.index: vols.1-20, 21-50. circ. 2,138. (also avail. in microfilm from UMI; reprint service avail. from UMI) Indexed: Cath.Ind. Curr.Cont. Hist.Abstr. Hum.Ind. Old Test.Abstr. Amer.Bibl.SLavic & E.Eur.Stud. Arts & Hum.Cit.Ind. Amer.Hist.& Life. Bk.Rev.Ind. Rel.& Theol.Abstr. RILA. *History*

CATHOLIC JOURNALIST. see *JOURNALISM*

CATHOLIC LAWYER. see *LAW*

282 AT ISSN 0008-8145
CATHOLIC LEADER. 1928. w. Aus.$26. Box 228, Brisbane, Qld. 4001, Australia. Ed. G.C. Coleman. adv. bk. rev. film rev. play rev. illus. circ. 20,000. (tabloid format)

CATHOLIC LIBRARY ASSOCIATION. NORTHERN ILLINOIS CHAPTER. NEWSLETTER. see *LIBRARY AND INFORMATION SCIENCES*

266 US ISSN 0008-8218
CATHOLIC LIFE. 1954. m. (except Jul. & Aug.) $2. Pontifical Institute for Foreign Missionaries (PIME), 35750 Moravian Dr., Fraser, MI 48026. Ed. Robert C. Bayer. circ. 14,800. (also avail. in microfilm from UMI; reprint service avail. from UMI) Indexed: CERDIC.

282 GW ISSN 0930-8679
CATHOLIC MEDIA COUNCIL. INFORMATION BULLETIN. 1972. s-a. free. Catholic Media Council (Publizistiche Medienplanung fuer Entwicklungslaender, e.V.), Bendelstrasse 7, 5100 Aachen, W. Germany (B.R.D.) Ed. Marcel Vanhengel. bk. rev. charts. illus. circ. 500.

CATHOLIC MEDICAL QUARTERLY. see *MEDICAL SCIENCES*

282 US ISSN 0008-8234
CATHOLIC MESSENGER. 1882. w. $14. Roman Catholic Diocese of Davenport, 103 East Second St., Box 460, Davenport, IA 52805. TEL 319-323-9959 Ed. Rev. Francis C. Henricksen. adv. bk. rev. circ. 24,996. (newspaper; also avail. in microform)

282 US ISSN 0164-0674
CATHOLIC NEAR EAST MAGAZINE. 1974. q. $5. Catholic Near East Welfare Association, Inc., 1011 First Ave., New York, NY 10022. TEL 212-826-1480 Ed. Michael Healy. bk. rev. illus. circ. 130,000.

200 CN
CATHOLIC NEW TIMES. 1977. 23/yr. Can.$15($22) New Catholic Times Inc., 80 Sackville St., Toronto, Ont. M5A 3E5, Canada. TEL 416-361-0761 Ed. Frances Ryan. adv. bk. rev. circ. 12,000. (also avail. in microfiche)

282 US ISSN 0278-1174
CATHOLIC NEW YORK. 1981. w. $15. (Roman Catholic Diocese of New York) Ecclesiastical Communications Corp., 1011 First Ave., New York, NY 10022. TEL 212-688-2399 Ed. Gerald M. Costello. adv. bk. rev. circ. 130,000. (also avail. in microfiche)

282 US ISSN 0008-8277
CATHOLIC PEACE FELLOWSHIP BULLETIN. 1965. 3/yr. donation. Catholic Peace Fellowship, 339 Lafayette St., New York, NY 10012. TEL 212-673-8990 Ed. Bill Ofenloch. bk. rev. illus. circ. 5,500.

282 UK ISSN 0008-8293
CATHOLIC PICTORIAL. 1960. w. 30p. Catholic Pictorial Ltd., Media House, 34 Stafford St., Liverpool L3 8LX, England. Ed. Norman Cresswell. adv. bk. rev. illus. circ. 13,000. (tabloid format)

282 US ISSN 0701-0788
CATHOLIC QUOTE; instant inspiration. vol.37, 1974. m. $5. Rev. Jerome Pokorny, Ed. & Pub., Valparaiso, NE 68065. index. circ. 7,000. (back issues avail.)

282 CN ISSN 0383-1620
CATHOLIC REGISTER. 1893. w. Can.$16.95. Canadian Register Ltd., 67 Bond St., Toronto, Ont. M5B 1X6, Canada. TEL 416-362-6822 Ed. Peter Howell. adv. bk. rev. film rev. abstr. circ. 43,575. (tabloid format)
Formerly: Canadian Register (ISSN 0008-4913)

282 US ISSN 0008-8315
CATHOLIC REVIEW (BALTIMORE) 1913. w. $5. (Archdiocese of Baltimore) Cathedral Foundation, Inc., 320 Cathedral St., Box 777, Baltimore, MD 21203. TEL 301-547-5333 Ed. Daniel Medinger. adv. bk. rev. circ. 55,834. (also avail. in microfilm)

CATHOLIC REVIEW (NEW YORK) see *BLIND*

282 US ISSN 0008-8331
CATHOLIC RURAL LIFE. 1958. 5/yr. $20. National Catholic Rural Life Conference, 4625 N.W. Beaver Dr., Des Moines, IA 50310. TEL 515-270-2634 Ed. Sandra La Blanc. bk. rev. illus. circ. 3,000.

200 AT
CATHOLIC SCHOOL STUDIES. 1928. 2/yr. Aus.$15. Christian Brothers of the Australian and New Zealand Provinces, Mount St. Mary College, Strathfield, N.S.W. 2135, Australia. Ed. G.M. Rossiter. bk. rev. circ. 2,300. Indexed: Aus.Educ.Ind.
Former titles: Christian Brothers of the Australian and New Zealand Provinces. Our Studies (ISSN 0045-6780); Christian Brothers Studies; Catholic School Studies.

282 US ISSN 0162-2102
CATHOLIC SENTINEL (ARCHDIOCESE OF PORTLAND, OREGON) w. Oregon Catholic Press, 5536 NE Hassalo St., Portland, OR 97213. TEL 503-281-1191

282 US ISSN 0162-0363
CATHOLIC SENTINEL (DIOCESE OF BAKER) w. $20. Oregon Catholic Press, 5536 NE Hassalo St., Portland, OR 97213. TEL 503-281-1191 Ed. Robert Pfohman. adv. bk. rev. film rev. abstr. illus. circ. 23,142. (tabloid format; also avail. in microform)

200 US
CATHOLIC SPIRIT. 1934. w. $10. Catholic Diocese of Wheeling-Charleston, Box 230, Wheeling, WV 26003. TEL 304-233-0880 Ed. Deacon Hugh E. Walker. adv. bk. rev. film rev. circ. 9,900. (tabloid format; also avail. in microfiche; back issues avail.)

282 IE ISSN 0008-8366
CATHOLIC STANDARD. 1938. w. £25. Irish Catholic Ltd., 55 Lower Gardiner St., Dublin 1, Ireland. Ed. Terry Sheehy. adv. bk. rev. illus. circ. 5,000. Indexed: CERDIC.

282 US
CATHOLIC TELEGRAPH. 1831. w. $12. Archdiocese of Cincinnati, 100 E. 8th St., Cincinnati, OH 45202. TEL 513-421-3131 Ed. Jim Stackpoole. adv. bk. rev. film rev. circ. 45,000.

282 US
CATHOLIC TELEPHONE GUIDE. a. $22. Catholic News Publishing Co.,Inc., 210 N. Ave., New Rochelle, NY 10801. TEL 914-632-1220

282 US ISSN 0069-1267
CATHOLIC THEOLOGICAL SOCIETY OF AMERICA. PROCEEDINGS. 1946. a. $7.50. ‡ Catholic Theological Society of America, Bellarmine College, 2001 Newburg Rd., Louisville, KY 40205. Ed. George Kilcourse. index. cum.index. circ. 1,600. (also avail. in microform from UMI; reprint service avail. from UMI) Indexed: Cath.Ind. CERDIC. New Test.Abstr.

282 UK ISSN 0411-275X
CATHOLIC TRUTH. 1896. a. £1($2.40) ‡ Incorporated Catholic Truth Society, 38/40 Eccleston Square, London SW1V 1PD, England. Ed. David Murphy. adv. bk. rev. bibl. circ. 35,000(controlled)
Incorporating: Catholic Book Notes.

282 US
CATHOLIC TWIN CIRCLE WEEKLY MAGAZINE. 1965. w. $23. Twin Circle Publishing Co., 6404 Wilshire Blvd., No. 900, Los Angeles, CA 90048. Ed. Mary Louise Frawley. adv. bk. rev. film rev. play rev. illus. circ. 60,000. (tabloid format)
Former titles: Twin Circle Weekly Catholic Magazine & Twin Circle (ISSN 0041-4654)

282 US
CATHOLIC UPDATE. m. $6. (Franciscan Friars of St. John the Baptist Province) St. Anthony Messenger Press, 1615 Republic St., Cincinnati, OH 45210. TEL 513-241-5615 Ed. Rev. Jack Wintz. circ. 324,000.

282 US ISSN 0008-8404
CATHOLIC VIRGINIAN. 1946. w. $10. Diocese of Richmond, c/o Most. Rev. Walter F. Sullivan, Bishop of Richmond, 800 Cathedral Pl., Box 26843, Richmond, VA 23261. TEL 804-359-5654 Ed. Charles E. Mahon. adv. bk. rev. film rev. charts. illus. circ. 38,827. (tabloid format)

266 GH ISSN 0008-8412
CATHOLIC VOICE. 1926. m. NC.6.60($11) (Archdiocese of Cape Coast) Catholic Mission Press, Box 60, Cape Coast, Ghana. Ed. Sister Mary Ann SSND. illus. circ. 6,000. Indexed: CERDIC.

282 US ISSN 0008-8439
CATHOLIC WEEKLY. 1942. w. $15. Catholic Dioceses of Saginaw & Gaylord, 1520 Court St., Box 1405, Saginaw, MI 48605. TEL 517-799-7910 Ed. Rev. Neil O'Connor. adv. bk. rev. circ. 16,344. (back issues avail.)

282 US ISSN 0008-8447
CATHOLIC WITNESS. 1966. fortn. $6.25. (Diocese of Harrisburg) Harrisburg Catholic Publishing Associates, Box 2555, 4800 Union Deposit Rd., Harrisburg, PA 17105. TEL 717-657-4804 Ed. Rev. T.R. Haney. bk. rev. illus. circ. 55,141. (newspaper; also avail. in microfilm)

282 US ISSN 0008-8471
CATHOLIC WORKMAN. (Text in Czech and English) vol.63, 1970. m. $1.50. Box 56, Dodge, NE 68533. TEL 612-758-2229 Ed. Rev. F.J. Oborny. stat. circ. 8,300(controlled) (tabloid format)

282 GW ISSN 0008-8501
CATHOLICA; vierteljahresschrift fuer Oekumenische Theologie. 4/yr. DM.68. (Johann Adam Moehler-Institut Paderborn) Aschendorffsche Verlagsbuchhandlung, Soester Str. 13, 4400 Muenster, W. Germany (B.R.D.) Eds. Hans Joerg Urban, Peter Blaeser. adv. bk. rev. bibl. index. Indexed: Rel.Per. New Test.Abstr. Rel.Ind.One.

282 US
CATHOLICISM IN CRISIS; a journal of lay catholic opinion. 1982. m. $20. Jacques Maritain Center, Box 495, Notre Dame, IN 46556. TEL 219-239-6603 Ed. Ralph McInerny. bk. rev.

282 FR
CATHOLICISME HIER, AUJOURD'HUI, DEMAIN. 1935. irreg., (approx. 3/yr.) 131 F.($22) per vol. Letouzey et Ane Editeurs, 87 bd. Raspail, 75006 Paris, France. Ed.Bd.

200 US ISSN 0094-2421
CELEBRATION: A CREATIVE WORSHIP SERVICE. 1970. m. $54.50. National Catholic Reporter Publishing Company, Inc., 115 E. Armour Blvd., Box 281, Kansas City, MO 64141. TEL 816-531-0538 Ed. William Freburger. adv. bk. rev. circ. 10,500. (looseleaf format) Key Title: Celebration (Kansas City)

282 FR ISSN 0240-4656
CELEBRER. (Supplements avail.) 6/yr. 166 F. Editions du Cerf, 29 bd. Latour Maubourg, 75340 Paris Cedex 7, France.

CENTRE CATHOLIQUE DES INTELLECTUELS FRANCAIS. RECHERCHES ET DEBATS. see *HUMANITIES: COMPREHENSIVE WORKS*

CENTRUM JANA PAWLA II BIULETYN. see *BIOGRAPHY*

282 YU ISSN 0009-0387
CERKEV V SEDANJEM SVETU. 1967. bi-m. 120 din.($7) Slovenske Rimskokatoliske Skofije, Cankarjevo Nabrezje 3, 6100 Ljubljana, Yugoslavia. Ed. Ivan Merlak. bk. rev. bibl. circ. 2,500.

250 UK ISSN 0009-1014
CHALLENGE (SANDBACH); the magazine of St. Mary's Church, Sandbach. 1964. m. £1.80. Sandbach Parochial Church Council, Buttersfield, 66 Manor Rd., Sandbach, Cheshire CW11 0NB, England. Ed. John Minshull. adv. bk. rev. charts. illus. circ. 600.

200 US ISSN 0149-970X
CHICAGO CATHOLIC. 1892. w. $15. (Catholic Archdiocese of Chicago) Chicago Catholic Publishing Co., Inc., 155 E. Superior St., Chicago, IL 60611. TEL 312-751-8311 Ed. Robert L. Johnston. adv. bk. rev. circ. 76,900. (also avail. in microform) Indexed: CERDIC.
Formerly: New World (ISSN 0028-7016)

282 US ISSN 0009-3718
CHICAGO STUDIES. 1962. 3/yr. $12.50. (Faculty St. Mary of the Lake Seminary) Civitas Dei Foundation, Box 665, Mundelein, IL 60060. TEL 312-566-1462 Ed. Rev. George J. Dyer. adv. bk. rev. index. circ. 10,000. (also avail. in microform from UMI; reprint service avail. from UMI) Indexed: Cath.Ind. Old Test.Abstr. CERDIC. Canon Law Abstr. New Test.Abstr. Rel.& Theol.Abstr.

282 266 IT ISSN 0011-1465
CHRIST TO THE WORLD/CRISTO AL MUNDO; international review of Apostolic experiences. (Editions in English, French, and Spanish) 1955. bi-m. L.30000($16) Via di Propaganda 1-C, 00187 Rome, Italy. Ed. Fr. Basil M. Arthadeva. bk. rev. charts. film rev. illus. stat. index. circ. 12,000. Indexed: Cath.Ind. CERDIC.

282 US ISSN 0739-6422
CHRISTIAN LIFE COMMUNITIES HARVEST. 1967. bi-m. $7.50. National Federation of Christian Life Communities Inc., 3721 Westminster Pl., St. Louis, MO 63108. Ed. Michael Splaine. adv. bk. rev. index. circ. 1,600. (back issues avail.)
Formerly: Christian Life Communicator.

261 UK ISSN 0009-5559
CHRISTIAN ORDER. 1960. m. £1($3) 65 Belgrave Rd., London S.W. 1, England. Ed. Rev. Paul Crane, S.J. adv. Indexed: Cath.Ind. CERDIC.

CHRISTIAN PARAPSYCHOLOGIST. see *PARAPSYCHOLOGY AND OCCULTISM*

DIE CHRISTLICHE FRAU. see *WOMEN'S INTERESTS*

268 282 GW ISSN 0009-5818
CHRISTOPHORUS. 1955. q. DM.40. Dr. Klaus Goebel, Egenhoferstr. 16, 8000 Munich 60, W. Germany (B.R.D.) adv. bk. rev. charts.

200 FR ISSN 0009-5834
CHRISTUS; revue de pratique evangelique. 1954. q. 100 F. Assas Editions, 14 rue d'Assas, 75006 Paris, France. Ed. B. Mendiboure. adv. circ. 6,000. (also avail. in microfilm) Indexed: CERDIC.

282 US ISSN 0197-0348
CHRONICLE OF THE CATHOLIC CHURCH IN LITHUANIA. 1972. irreg. $12. Lithuanian Catholic Religious Aid, 351 Highland Blvd., Brooklyn, NY 11207. TEL 718-647-2434 Eds. Marian Skabeikis, Rev. Casimir Pugevicus. illus. circ. 6,500. (back issues avail.)

282 PL
CHRZESCIJANSKIE STOWARZYSZENIE SPOLECZNE. BIULETYN INFORMACYJNY "NOVUM". 1968. m. free. Chrzescijanskie Stowarzyszenie Spoleczne - Christian Social Association, Marszalkowska 4, 00-590 Warsaw, Poland. Ed. Wojciech Ketrzynski. circ. 1,500.

282 PL ISSN 0578-0594
CHRZESCIJANSKIE STOWARZYSZENIE SPOLECZNE. INFORMATION BULLETIN. (Text in English, French and German) 1957. m. $12 or on exchange basis. Chrzescijanskie Stowarzyszenie Spoleczne - Christian Social Association, Marszalkowska 4, 00-590 Warsaw, Poland (Dist. by: RSW "Prasa-Ksiazka-Ruch" Centrala Kolportazu Prasy i Wydawnictw, Towarowa 28, 00-958 Warsaw) Ed.Bd. adv. circ. 950.

282 PL
CHRZESCIJANSKIE STOWARZYSZENIE SPOLECZNE. MATERIALY PROBLEMOWE. 1965. m. $10. Chrzescijanskie Stowarzyszenie Spoleczne - Christian Social Association, Marszalkowska 4, 00-590 Warsaw, Poland. Ed. Jan Pawel Henne. adv. circ. 5,000.

200 SP ISSN 0210-0398
CIENCIA TOMISTA. 1910. q. 700 ptas.($15) Estudio Teologico de San Esteban, Convento de San Estaban., Apdo. 17, Salamanca, Spain. Ed. Antonio Osuna. Indexed: Cath.Ind. M.L.A. CERDIC.

200 AU
CISTERCIENSER CHRONIK. 1889. q. S.32. Cistercienser in Mehrerau, 6901 Bregenz, Austria. Ed. Hermann J. Roth. bk. rev. bibl.

271 BE ISSN 0009-7497
CITEAUX; commentarii Cistercienses. (Text in English, French and German) 1950. q. 750 Fr.($22) Citeaux V.Z.W., Cisterian Abbey Nazareth, B-2160 Brecht, Belgium. Ed. J.F. Holthof. bk. rev. bibl. illus. index. cum.index: 1950-74. (also avail. in microfiche) Indexed: Hist.Abstr. M.L.A. Amer.Hist.& Life.

282 255 SP ISSN 0009-7756
CIUDAD DE DIOS; revista Agustiniana. 1881. 3/yr. 2000 ptas.($25) Ediciones Escurialenses, Real Monasterio del Escorial, San Lorenzo del Escorial, Madrid, Spain. bk. rev. index. circ. 700. (also avail. in microfilm from UMI) Indexed: Hist.Abstr. M.L.A. Amer.Hist.& Life. CERDIC. New Test.Abstr.

282 IT ISSN 0009-8167
CIVILTA CATTOLICA. 1850. s-m. L.40000($55) Compagnia di Gesu, Via di Porta Pinciana 1, 00187 Rome, Italy. Ed. Gism Paolo Selvini. adv. bk. rev. film rev. play rev. bibl. index. cum.index: 1940-1960; 1960-1970; 1970-1980. circ. 20,000. Indexed: Cath.Ind. Hist.Abstr. Amer.Hist.& Life. CERDIC. New Test.Abstr.

282 VC ISSN 0578-4182
CLARETIANUM; commentaria theologica. (Text in various European languages) 1961. a. L.25000($20) Institutum Theologiae Vitae Religiosae, Largo Lorenzo Mossa 4, 00165 Rome, Italy. Ed. Bruno Proietti. bk. rev. bibl. circ. 300. Indexed: CERDIC. Canon Law Abstr.
Formerly: Theologica.

250 UK ISSN 0009-8736
CLERGY REVIEW. 1930. m. £22.50. (Catholic Church) Tablet Publishing Co., 48 Great Peter St., Westminster, London SW1P 2HB, England. Ed. Bernard Bickers. adv. bk. rev. index. circ. 2,200. (also avail. in microfilm from UMI) Indexed: Cath.Ind. Old Test.Abstr. CERDIC. Canon Law Abstr. New Test.Abstr. Rel.& Theol.Abstr.

CLUBHOUSE. see *CHILDREN AND YOUTH — For*

282 IT
CODICE DEL VATICANO II. 1984. irreg. Centro Editoriale Dehoniano, Via Nosadella 6, I-40123 Bologna, Italy.

282 BL
COLECAO FE E REALIDADE. no. 3, 1977. irreg. S Leopoldo, Rua Euclides da Cunha 241, 11165 Santos, SP, Brazil.

282 SP
COLECCION HISTORIA DE LA IGLESIA. 1971. irreg., no.15, 1986. price varies. (Universidad de Navarra, Departamento de Historia de la Iglesia) Ediciones Universidad de Navarra, S.A., Apdo. 396, 31080 Pamplona, Spain.

282 SP
COLECCION TEOLOGICA. 1970. irreg., no.49, 1986. price varies. (Universidad de Navarra, Facultad de Teologia) Ediciones Universidad de Navarra, S.A., Apdo. 396, 31080 Pamplona, Spain.

282 SP
COLEGIO MAYOR P. FELIPE SCIO. PUBLICACIONES. 1975. irreg. price varies. Ediciones Calasancias, Paseo de Canalejas 75, Apdo. 206, Salamanca, Spain.

282 IT ISSN 0069-5254
COLLANA RICCIANA. FONTI. 1963. irreg., no. 12, 1975. price varies. Casa Editrice Leo S. Olschki, Casella Postale 66, 50100 Florence, Italy. Ed. P. di Agresti. circ. 1,000.

271 BE
COLLECTANEA CISTERCIENSIA; revue de spiritualite monastique. English edition: Cistercian Studies (ISSN 0578-3224) (Text in French) 1966. q. 450 Fr.($15) or £7. Abbaye N.-D. de la Paix, B-6460 Chimay, Belgium (U.S. subscr. to Br.Kevin White, St. Joseph's Abbey, Spencer, MA 01562; U.K. subscr. to Fr. Aelred Williams, Caldey Island, Tenby, Dyfed SA70 7UH, Wales) (also avail. in microform from UMI) Indexed: Cath.Ind. CERDIC.

271 IT ISSN 0010-0749
COLLECTANEA FRANCISCANA. (Annual supplement: Bibliographia Franciscana) (Text in English, French, German, Italian, Latin, Portuguese and Spanish) 1931. s-a. $25. ‡ Frati Minori Cappuccini, Istituto Storico, G.R.A. Km 68,800, Rome, Italy. Ed. Oktavian Schmucki. bk. rev. bibl. index. cum.index: 1931-1970. circ. 800. Indexed: CERDIC.

282 249 US ISSN 0010-1869
COLUMBIA (NEW HAVEN); America's largest Catholic family magazine. 1921. m. $6. Knights of Columbus, Drawer 1670, New Haven, CT 06507. TEL 203-772-2130 Ed. Elmer Von Feldt. adv. bk. rev. index. circ. 1,399,623. Indexed: Cath.Ind.

266 US
COMBONI MISSIONS. 1948. q. $6. Comboni Missionaries of the Heart of Jesus, 8108 Beechmont Ave., Cincinnati, OH 45230. TEL 513-474-4997 Ed. Rev. Joseph Bragotti. illus. circ. 20,000(controlled)
Former titles: Verona Missions (ISSN 0164-4211); Verona Fathers Missions (ISSN 0042-4234)

262.9 IT ISSN 0010-2598
COMMENTARIUM PRO RELIGIOSIS ET MISSIONARIIS. (Text in Latin) 1920. q. L.30000($18) Claretian Juridical Institute in Rome, Via Giacomo Medici 5, 00153 Rome, Italy. Ed. Giuseppe Metteocci. bk. rev. bibl. index. circ. 5,000. (back issues avail.) Indexed: Canon Law Abstr. CERDIC.
Canon law

282 US
COMMON GOOD. 1978. q. $5. Pro Ecclesia Foundation, 663 Fifth Ave., New York, NY 10022. Ed. Timothy A. Mitchell.

COMMONWEAL. see *LITERARY AND POLITICAL REVIEWS*

282 US ISSN 0094-2065
COMMUNIO; international Catholic review. 1974. q. $18 to individuals; institutions $23. University of Notre Dame, Communio, Box 1046, Notre Dame, IN 46556. TEL 219-239-5723 Ed. Dr. David L. Schindler. adv. index. cum.index. circ. 2,000. (also avail. in microform from UMI; back issues avail.; reprint service avail. from UMI) Indexed: Cath.Ind. Old Test.Abstr. Rel.Ind.One. Rel.& Theol.Abstr.

282 AT ISSN 0004-9662
COMMUNION. 1962. q. Aus.$8. Liberal Catholic Church in Australia, 300 Blaxland Rd., Ryde, N.S.W. 2112, Australia. Ed. Rt. Rev. F.C. Bannister. bk. rev. illus. circ. 850. Indexed: CERDIC.
Formerly: Australian Liberal Catholic.

282 CN ISSN 0010-3985
COMPANION OF ST. FRANCIS AND ST. ANTHONY. 1937. m. (Sep.-Jun.); bi-m. (Jul.-Aug.) $6. ‡ Conventual Franciscan Friars, 15 Chestnut Park Rd., Toronto, Ont. M4W 1W5, Canada. TEL 416-924-6349 Ed. Friar Philip Kelly. adv. bk. rev. illus. circ. 9,000.

248.83 AT
COMPASS MAGAZINE. 1967. q. Aus.$10. (Missionaries of the Sacred Heart) Chevalier Press, Box 13, Kensington, N.S.W. 2033, Australia. Ed. Fr. Peter Malone. bk. rev. circ. 2,000.

282 SP
COMUNIDAD; semanario de la Iglesia Diocesana, Salamanca. 1971. w. 6 ptas.($3) per no. Semanario de la Iglesia Diocesana, Iscar Peyra, 26 Obispado, 37002 Salamanca, Spain. Ed. Moises S. Ramos. circ. 6,000 (controlled)

282 IT
COMUNITA E STORIA. 1974. bi-m. L.15000($10) Comunita e Storia, Via Mazzini 6a, 52100 Arezzo, Italy. Ed. Maria Grotti. circ. 500.

282 CN
CONFERENCE DES EVEQUES CATHOLIQUES DU CANADA. BULLETIN NATIONAL DE LITURGIE. (Text in French) 1965. 5/yr. $10. Conference Eveques Catholiques du Canada, Office National de Liturgie, 1225 Boul St. Joseph est, Montreal, Que. H2J 1L7, Canada. Ed. M. Jean-Bernard Allard. bk. rev. illus. circ. 2,000.
Formerly: Conference Catholique Canadienne. Bulletin National de Liturgie (ISSN 0384-5087)

282 IT
CONFERENZA ITALIANA SUPERIORI MAGGIORI. NOTIZIARIO. 1960. bi-m. free. Conferenza Italiana Superiori Maggiori, Via degli Scipioni, 256B, I-00192 Rome, Italy.

282 SZ ISSN 0010-8154
CONVERGENCE. (Editions in English and French) 1935. s-a. 26 Fr.($10) International Catholic Movement for Intellectual and Cultural Affairs - Pax Romana, General Secretariat, B.P. 85, 37-39 Rue de Vermont, CH-1211 Geneva 20-CIC, Switzerland. adv. bk. rev. bibl. charts. circ. 4,000. Indexed: Educ.Ind. CERDIC.

248 US ISSN 0010-8685
CORD. 1951. m. $11. Franciscan Institute, St. Bonaventure University, St. Bonaventure, NY 14778. TEL 716-375-2105 Ed. Michael Meilach, O.F.M. adv. bk. rev. bibl. illus. circ. 1,700. Indexed: CERDIC.

282 GW ISSN 0070-0320
CORPUS CATHOLICORUM. 1919. irreg. price varies. Aschendorffsche Verlagsbuchhandlung, Soester Str. 13, 4400 Muenster, W. Germany (B.R.D.) Ed. Erwin Iserloh.

282 BE
CORPUS CHRISTIANORUM. CONTINUATIO MEDIAEVALIS. 1966. irreg., (2-3/yr.) (Abbey of Steenbrugge) N.V. Brepols I.G.P., Rue Baron Francois du Four 8, B-2300 Turnhout, Belgium. Ed.Bd.

282 BE
CORPUS CHRISTIANORUM. SERIES APOCRYPHORUM. 1983. irreg. (Association pour l'Etude de la Litterature Apocrypha Chretienne) N.V. Brepols I.G.P., Rue Baron Frans du Four 8, B-2300 Turnhout, Belgium.

200 BE
CORPUS CHRISTIANORUM. SERIES GRAECA. 1977. irreg., (2-3/yr.) (Centrum voor Hellenisme en Kristendom, Leuven) N.V. Brepols I.G.P., Rue Baron Francois du Four 8, B-2300 Turnhout, Belgium. (Co-publisher: Leuven University Press)

282 BE
CORPUS CHRISTIANORUM. SERIES LATINA. 1952. irreg., (6-7/yr.) (Abbey of Steenbrugge) N.V. Brepols I.G.P., Rue Baron Francois du Four 8, B-2300 Turnhout, Belgium. Ed.Bd.

282 IT
COSCIENZA. 1946. m. L.20000. Movimento Ecclesiale di Impegno Culturale, Via della Conciliazione 1, 00193 Rome, Italy. Ed. Romolo Pietrobelli. bk. rev. illus. index. circ. 4,500. Indexed: CERDIC.

282 IT
CRISTIANESIMO OGGI. 1969. m. (10/yr.) L.5000. Editrice Lanterna, Via Robino 71/A.R., 16142 Genova, Italy. adv. circ. 5,000.

282 IT ISSN 0011-1651
CROCE. 1952. w. Curia Vescovile, 40022 Comacchio (Ferrara), Italy.

200 FR ISSN 0223-4734
CROIRE AUJOURD'HUI; revue pour la formation permanente de la foi. 1971. m. 145 F. Assas Editions, 14 rue d'Assas, 75006 Paris, France. Ed. Pere Marcel Domergue. bk. rev. Indexed: CERDIC.

282 FR
CROIX; l'evenement. 1880. d. 1640 F. Bayard Presse, 5, rue Bayard, 75380 Paris Cedex 08, France. circ. 120,000. (tabloid format)

282 US ISSN 0011-1953
CROSS CURRENTS. 1950. q. $10. (Convergence, Inc.) Mercy College, Dobbs Ferry, NY 10522. TEL 914-693-4500 Ed. Joseph E. Cunneen. adv. bk. rev. film rev. play rev. index. circ. 7,000. (also avail. in microform from UMI; reprint service avail. from UMI) Indexed: Cath.Ind. Hum.Ind. M.L.A. G.Soc.Sci.& Rel.Per.Lit. Old Test.Abstr. Rel.& Theol.Abstr.

282 PE
CUADERNOS DE ESTUDIO. 1979. irreg. $40 (includes subscr. to: Testimonios (en Historieta), Cuadernos de Capacitacion and Cuadernos Populares) Comision Evangelica Latinoamericana de Educacion Cristiana, Av. General Garzon 2267, Lima 11, Peru.

282 CK
CUADERNOS DE TEOLOGIA Y PASTORAL. irreg. Ediciones Paulinas, Apdo. 100282, Bogota, Colombia.

CURRENT ISSUES IN CATHOLIC HIGHER EDUCATION. see *EDUCATION*

D K K F-NYT. (Dansk Katolsk Kvinde-Forbund) see *WOMEN'S INTERESTS*

282 US ISSN 0011-6637
DARBININKAS. (Text in Lithuanian) 1915. w. $15. Franciscan Fathers, 341 Highland Blvd., Brooklyn, NY 11207. Ed. Rev. Cornelius Bucmys. adv. bk. rev.

DEUTSCHE KATHOLIK IN KANADA. see *ETHNIC INTERESTS*

282 GW
DIACONIA CHRISTI. 1966. q. DM.28. Internationales Diakonatszentrum, Postfach 420, D-7800 Freiburg, W. Germany (B.R.D.) bk. rev. bibl. circ. 900. (back issues avail.)
Formerly (until 1987): Diaconia XP (ISSN 0343-3218)

282 NQ
DIAKONIA; servicio de la fe y promocion de la justicia. 1977. q. C.$80($10) Centro Ignaciano de Centro America, Apartado 69, Managua, Nicaragua. Ed. Juan R. Moreno, S.J. circ. 600. Indexed: CERDIC.

282 PO
DIDASKALIA. (Text in various European languages; summaries in English and French) 1971. s-a. $6. Universidade Catolica Portuguesa, Faculdade de Teologia, Palma de Cima, Lisbon 4, Portugal. bk. rev. Indexed: Old Test.Abstr. CERDIC. New Test.Abstr.

DIGNITY. see *HOMOSEXUALITY*

200 BE ISSN 0012-2866
DIMANCHE. (Text in French) 1935. w. 750 Fr.($20) Dimanche, 20 Place de Vannes, 7000 Mons, Belgium. Ed. Eugene A. Collard. adv. bk. rev. film rev. circ. 580,000.

282 US
DIMENSIONS OF MINISTRY. 1979. m. $9. United States Catholic Conference, Department of Education, 1312 Massachusetts Ave., N.W., Washington, DC 20005. TEL 202-659-6718 Ed. Rev. Joseph J. Kenna, Jr. adv. bk. rev. circ. 2,000.

220 CN ISSN 0018-912X
DISCOVER THE BIBLE. French edition: Feuillet Biblique. 1964. w. (except Jul. & Aug.) Can.$14. Archdiocese of Montreal, Bible Centre, 2065 Sherbrooke West, Montreal, Que. H3H 1G6, Canada. TEL 514-931-7311 Ed. Rev. Walter Bedard. bk. rev. bibl. index. circ. 4,500.
Formerly: I Discover the Bible.

282 VC ISSN 0012-4222
DIVINITAS. 1957. 3/yr. $20. Pontificia Accademia Teologica Romana, Palazzo Canonici, 00120 Vatican City, Italy. adv. bk. rev. cum.index every 10 years. Indexed: New Test.Abstr. Rel.& Theol.Abstr.

282 IE ISSN 0012-446X
DOCTRINE AND LIFE. 1951. 10/yr. £6($18) Dominican Publications, St. Saviour's, Dublin 1, Ireland. Ed. Rev. Austin Flannery, O.P. adv. bk. rev. index. circ. 5,000. (also avail. in microfilm from UMI; reprint service avail. from UMI) Indexed: Cath.Ind. Old Test.Abstr. CERDIC. New Test.Abstr.

282 FR ISSN 0012-4613
DOCUMENTATION CATHOLIQUE. 1919. s-m. 436 F. Bayard Presse, 5 rue Bayard, 75380 Paris Cedex 08, France. Ed. P. Claude Musnier. adv. index. circ. 31,000. Indexed: Cath.Ind. CERDIC.

282 IT ISSN 0012-5288
DOMENICA. 1921. w. Viale Tunisi 43-C, 96100 Siracuse, Italy. Ed. Pino Filippelli.

282 BL
DOMINGO. (Supplements avail.) 1932. w. $100. (Pia Sociedade de Sao Paulo) Edicoes Paulinas, Via Raposo Tavares Km 18.5, C.P. 8107, 01051 Sao Paulo, Brazil. Ed. Virgilio Ciaccio. circ. 253,000.

282 US
DON BELL REPORTS. w. $40. Don Bell Reports, Box 2223, Palm Beach, FL 33480.

282 255 NE ISSN 0012-5504
DOORTOCHT; Franciscaans Evangelisch opinieblad. 1963. 8/yr. fl.10.50($4.50) Vereniging van Franciscaanse Tertiarissen, Malakkastraat 55, The Hague, Netherlands. bk. rev. illus. circ. 5,500.

282 UK ISSN 0012-5806
DOWNSIDE REVIEW; a quarterly of Catholic thought. 1880. q. £9($24) Downside Abbey, Stratton on the Fosse, Bath BA3 4RH, England. Ed. Dom Daniel Rees. adv. bk. rev. index. circ. 600. (also avail. in microform) Indexed: Cath.Ind. M.L.A. Rel.Per. CERDIC. New Test.Abstr. Old Test.Abstr. Rel.Per. Rel.Ind.One. Rel.& Theol.Abstr.

DOWRY; a quarterly of Catholic poetry. see *LITERATURE — Poetry*

282 US
DRAUGAS. 1909. 5/w. $60. Lithuanian Catholic Press Society, 4545 W. 63rd St., Chicago, IL 60629. TEL 312-585-9500 Ed. Rev. F. Garsva. circ. 7,000.

266 PH
EAST ASIAN PASTORAL REVIEW; a quarterly with focus on Asia for all church ministers and theology in context, interested laity and theological students. 1979. q. $12. East Asian Pastoral Institute, Box 1815, Manila, Philippines. Ed. Rev. Felipe Gomez. bk. rev. circ. 2,000. Indexed: Cath.Ind.
Formed by the merger of: Teaching All Nations (ISSN 0040-0564) & Good Tidings (ISSN 0436-1571) & Amen.

282 US ISSN 0012-883X
EASTERN KANSAS REGISTER. 1939. w. $4. Catholic Archdiocese of Kansas City, 2220 Central, Kansas City, KS 66110. TEL 913-221-4377 Ed. Rev. Harold Wickey. adv. bk. rev. film rev. circ. 31,622. (newspaper)

282 FR
EAUX - VIVES. 1941. m. 40 F. 21 Blvd. Voltaire, 75011 Paris, France. adv. illus.

282 SP ISSN 0012-9038
ECCLESIA. 1941. w. 3600 ptas.($29) Conferencia Episcopal Espanola, Alfonso 11, No. 4, 28014 Madrid, Spain. Ed. Jose Antonio Carro Celada. adv. bk. rev. bibl. charts. film rev. illus. index. circ. 30,000. Indexed: CERDIC.

282 IT
ECCLESIA MATER. 1963. 3/yr. L.12000. Editrice "Cor Unum" Figlie della Chiesa, Viale Vaticano 62, 00165 Rome, Italy. Dir. Giuseppe Macca. bk. rev. illus. circ. 1,200.
Incorporates: Mater Ecclesiae (ISSN 0025-522X)

282 IT
ECO DEL SANTUARIO DI N.S. DI LOURDES. 1926. m. L.8000. Santuario di N.S., Via Tortona 27, I-15100 Alessandria, Italy. circ. 5,500.

282 IT
L'ECO DI GIBILMANNA. 1919. bi-m. Arti Grafiche Siciliane, Frati Minori Cappuccini Santuario di Gibilmanna, Palermo, Italy.

282 248.8 US ISSN 0013-1016
EDMUNDITE. 1959. m. $1. ‡ Society of St. Edmund, St. Edmund's Novitiate, Enders Island, Mystic, CT 06355. TEL 203-572-9538 Ed. Rev. James F. Ryan. circ. 30,000.

282 MG
EGLISE CATHOLIQUE A MADAGASCAR. Cover title: Annuaire de l'Eglise Catholique a Madagascar. (Text in French or Malagasy) a. Impr. Catholique, 127, Arabe Lenine Vladimir, Antananarivo, Malagasy Republic.

200 CN ISSN 0381-0380
EGLISE DE MONTREAL. (Text in French) 1882. w. Can.$18. Archdiocese of Montreal, 2000 Sherbrooke St. West, Montreal, Que. H3H 1G4, Canada. TEL 514-931-7311 Ed. Rev. Yvan Desrochers. adv. bibl. index. circ. 2,500.

200 DR
EME EME; estudios Dominicanos. 1972. irreg. RD.$0.50 single issue. Universidad Catolica Madre y Maestra, Centro de Estudios Dominicanos, Santiago de los Caballeros, Dominican Republic. Ed. Frank Moya Pons. index. circ. 2,000. Indexed: Hist.Abstr. Amer.Hist.& Life.

253 US ISSN 0013-6719
EMMANUEL. 1895. m. (except Jan./Feb. & Jul./Aug.) $18. Congregation of Blessed Sacrament, 5384 Wilson Mill Rd., Cleveland, OH 44143. Ed. Rev. Eugene A. La Verdiere. adv. bk. rev. bibl. index. circ. 6,000. Indexed: New Test.Abstr. New Test.Abstr.

282 US
EMMAUS LETTER. 1978. q. $6. National Federation for Catholic Youth Ministry, 3900 A Harewood Rd. N.E., Washington, DC 20017. TEL 202-636-3825 Ed. Jean Sneeringer. bk. rev. illus. circ. 7,000.
Supersedes (with vol.14, 1977): Youth Program Service (ISSN 0044-1252)

282 CN ISSN 0317-851X
EN EGLISE. (Text in French) 1974. m. Can.$5. Eglise Catholique, Diocese de Chicoutimi, Office des Communications Sociales, 602, Racine Est., Chicoutimi, Que. G7H 6J6, Canada. TEL 418-543-0783 Ed. Jacques Bouchard. illus. circ. 1,125.

206 FR ISSN 0395-1766
EN EQUIPE AU SERVICE DE L'EVANGILE. 1976. q. 10 F. Action Catholique Generale Feminine, 98 rue de l'Universite, 75007 Paris, France. Ed. M. Genevieve de Diesbach.

282 UK
ENGLISH BENEDICTINE CONGREGATION. ORDO. 1885. a. £0.80. Ampleforth Abbey, York YO6 4EN, England. Ed. Rev. V. Wace. circ. 1,300.

262.9 IT ISSN 0013-9491
EPHEMERIDES IURIS CANONICI. (Text in various languages) 1945. q. L.4000($35) Officium Libri Catholici - Catholic Book Agency, Via dei Lucchesi 20, 00187 Rome, Italy. Ed. Pius Fedele. bk. rev. index. Indexed: CERDIC. Canon Law Abstr.
Canon law

266 SP ISSN 0425-1466
EPHEMERIDES MARIOLOGICAE; international revue of mariology. 1951. q. $22. (Ephemerides Mariologicae) Claretian Fathers, Calle Buen Suceso no. 22, 28008 Madrid, Spain. adv. bk. rev. index. circ. 550. (back issues avail.) Indexed: CERDIC. New Test.Abstr.

262.9 BE ISSN 0013-9513
EPHEMERIDES THEOLOGICAE LOVANIENSES; revue de theologie et de droit canon de Louvain/Leuvens tijdschrift voor theologie en kerkelijk recht/Louvain journal of theological and canonical studies. (Text in English, French and German) 1924. q. 1500 Fr. Editions Peeters s.p.r.l., Bondgenotenlaan, B-3000 Louvain, Belgium. bibl. index. Indexed: Old Test.Abstr. Rel.Per. CERDIC. New Test.Abstr. Rel.& Theol.Abstr. Rel.Ind.One.

EQUIPES ST VINCENT. see *SOCIAL SERVICES AND WELFARE*

282 255 GW ISSN 0013-9963
ERBE UND AUFTRAG; Benediktinische Monatsschrift. 1919. bi-m. DM.36. Beuroner Kunstverlag GmbH, 7792 Beuron, W. Germany (B.R.D.) Ed. B. Schwank. adv. bk. rev. abstr. bibl. illus. index. circ. 2,100. Indexed: Old Test.Abstr. New Test.Abstr.

266 CN ISSN 0318-7551
ESKIMO. French edition (ISSN 0318-756X) (Editions in English and French) 1944. s-a. $2. ‡ Diocese of Churchill Hudson Bay, P.O. Box 10, Churchill, Manitoba R0B 0E0, Canada. Ed. Rev. Guy Mary-Rousseliere. bk. rev. circ. 4,000. (also avail. in microfilm from MCA; back issues avail.)

200 SP ISSN 0425-340X
ESTUDIO AGUSTINIANO. (Text in Spanish, French, and English) 1914. 3/yr. $9. Estudio Teologico Agustiniano, Paseo de Filipinos, 7, Valladolid, Spain. Eds. Zacarias Herrero, Domingo Natal. bk. rev. index. circ. 500. (back issues avail.) Indexed: CERDIC. Canon Law Abstr.

282 SP ISSN 0210-7074
ESTUDIOS JOSEFINOS. 1947. s-a. 400 ptas.($15) Centro Josefino Espanol, c/o Fray Jose Antonio Carrasco, Pp. Carmelitas Descalzos, Valladolid, Spain. bk. rev. circ. 600.

ETUDES. see *LITERARY AND POLITICAL REVIEWS*

268 US ISSN 0743-524X
EUCHARISTIC MINISTER. 1984. m. $9 (bulk rates avail.) National Catholic Reporter Publishing Company, Inc., 115 E. Armour Blvd., Kansas City, MO 64141. TEL 816-531-0538 Ed. William Freburger. circ. 49,765. (tabloid format)

282 IT
EUNTES DOCETE. 1948. 3/yr. L.30000($30) (Pontificia Universita Urbaniana) Urbaniana University Press, Via Urbano VIII, 16, Vatican City, Italy. Ed. Jezernik Maksimilijan. bk. rev. circ. 1,000. (back issues avail.) Indexed: CERDIC. New Test.Abstr.

282 US ISSN 0738-8489
EVANGELIST. 1926. w. $10. (Roman Catholic Diocese of Albany) Albany Catholic Press Association, Inc., 39 Philip St., Albany, NY 12207. TEL 518-434-0107 Ed. James P. Breig. adv. bk. rev. film rev. bibl. stat. circ. 68,000. (also avail. in microfilm)

282 SP
EXCERPTA E DISSERTATIONIBUS IN SACRA THEOLOGICA. 1975. irreg., no.6, 1984. 3,000 ptas. (Universidad de Navarra, Facultad de Teologia) Ediciones Universidad de Navarra, S.A., Apdo. 396, 31080 Pamplona, Spain.

266 US
EXTENSION (ILLINOIS) 1906. 10/yr. free. Catholic Church Extension Society of the United States, 35 E. Wacker Dr., Chicago, IL 60601. TEL 312-236-7240 Ed. Bradley Collins. bk. rev. circ. 80,000. Indexed: Cath.Ind. CERDIC.
Missions

282 MX
FAMILIA CRISTIANA. 1953. m. Mex.$50 per no. Ediciones Paulinas, S.A., Taxquena 1792, Mexico 21 D.F., Mexico. Ed. Pedro Briseno Ch. adv. circ. 80,000.

282 US
THE FAMILY (BOSTON) 1958. m. $6. Daughters of St. Paul, 50 St. Paul's Ave., Boston, MA 02130. TEL 617-522-8911 Ed. Sr. M. Helen Wallace. circ. 48,000.

282 US ISSN 0014-8814
FATHERS OF THE CHURCH. 1947. irreg., vol.73, 1985. price varies. Catholic University of America Press, 620 Michigan Ave. N.E., Washington, DC 20064. TEL 202-635-5052

220 CN ISSN 0225-2112
FEUILLET BIBLIQUE. (Editions in French & English) 1958. w. (except Jul. & Aug.) Can.$14. Archdiocese of Montreal, Bible Centre, 2065 Sherbrooke West, Montreal, Que. H3H 1G6, Canada. TEL 514-931-7311 Ed. Rev. Paul A. Martin. bk. rev. bibl. index. circ. 11,800.
Formerly: Parole-Dimanche.

282 IT
FIACCOLA. 1926. m. L.6000. Seminario Arcivescovile, Segretariato pro Seminario, P.za Duomo 16, 20122 Milan, Italy (Subscr. to: Grafiche Alma, Via Brioschi 65, 20141 Milan, Italy) (back issues avail.)

282 US ISSN 0275-6145
FIRST CATHOLIC SLOVAK UNION OF AMERICA. MINUTES OF ANNUAL MEETING. a. First Catholic Slovak Union of America, 3289 E. 55th St., Cleveland, OH 44127. TEL 216-341-3355 Key Title: Minutes of the Annual Meeting of the First Catholic Slovak Union of the United States of America and Canada.

282 US ISSN 0015-394X
FLORIDA CATHOLIC NEWSPAPER. 1939. w. $6. Catholic Diocese of Orlando & St. Petersburg, Box 3551, Orlando, FL 32802. TEL 305-425-3556 Ed. Rev. David P. Page. adv. bk. rev. film rev. circ. 44,000. (newspaper)

282 FR ISSN 0015-5365
FOI ET VIE DE L'EGLISE AU DIOCESE DE TOULOUSE; semaine catholique de Toulouse. 1860. bi-m. 45 F. Archeveche de Toulouse, 1 Place Stes Scarbes, 31000 Toulouse, France. Ed. Chanoine Ducasse. adv. bk. rev. bibl. index. circ. 1,800.

282 IT
FONTI E STUDI PER LA STORIA DEL SANTO A PADOVA. (Text in English or Italian) 1976. irreg. L.40000. Neri Pozza Editore, Via Gazzolle 6, 36100 Vicenza, Italy. Ed. Antonino Poppi. bibl. illus.

282 FR
FRANCE CATHOLIQUE-ECCLESIA. 1925. w. 400 F. Soceval, 12 rue Edmond-Valentin, 75007 Paris, France. Ed. A. Chabadel. adv. bk. rev. circ. 70,000.
Formerly: France Catholique (ISSN 0015-9506)

271.3 US ISSN 0080-5459
FRANCISCAN STUDIES. 1941. a. $16. Franciscan Institute, St. Bonaventure University, Drawer F, St. Bonaventure, NY 14778. TEL 716-375-2105 Ed. Rev. Conrad L. Harkins, O.F.M. (also avail. in microform from UMI; reprint service avail. from UMI) Indexed: Cath.Ind. M.L.A. CERDIC. Phil.Ind. Rel.Ind.Two.

255 BE ISSN 0015-9840
FRANCISCANA; bijdragen tot de geschiedenis van de minderbroeders in de nederlanden. 1946. q. 300 Fr. Instituut voor Franciskaanse Geschiedenis, Minderbroedersstraat 5, 3800 Sint-Truiden, Belgium. Ed. J. Baetens. bk. rev. bibl. illus. index. cum.index. circ. 250. Indexed: Hist.Abstr. Amer.Hist.& Life.

255 CK ISSN 0120-1468
FRANCISCANUM; revista de las ciencias del espiritu. 1959. 3/yr. Col.1.500($15) ‡ Universidad de San Buenaventura, Calle 73 No. 10-45, Apdo. Aereo 52312, Bogota 2, Colombia. Ed. Jairo Munoz M. bk. rev. bibl. index. cum.index: 1959-1983. circ. 3,000.

282 255 NE ISSN 0015-9794
FRANCISKAANS LEVEN; tijdschrift tot verdieping en vernieuwing van de Franciskaanse beweging in Nederland en Vlaanderen. 1917. bi-m. fl.22.50. Franciskaanse Samenwerking in Nederland, Oude Gracht 23, 3511 AB Utrecht, Netherlands. Ed. J.M. van der Horst. bk. rev. bibl. index. cum.index. circ. 1,000.

271 GW ISSN 0016-0067
FRANZISKANISCHE STUDIEN. (Text in various languages) 1918. q. DM.34. Dietrich Coelde Verlag GmbH, Steinergraben 53, 4760 Werl, W. Germany (B.R.D.) Ed. P. Ildefons Vanderheyden. bk. rev. circ. 300. Indexed: M.L.A. CERDIC.

255 IT ISSN 0016-0091
FRATE FRANCESCO. vol.50, 1973. m. L.3000. Convento Cappuccini, Via Merulaana 124, 00185 Rome, Italy. Dir. P. Gherardo Losi. charts. illus.

FREIBURGER ZEITSCHRIFT FUER PHILOSOPHIE UND THEOLOGIE. see *PHILOSOPHY*

282 NE ISSN 0016-2175
FRONTLIJN; voor Katholieken in en buiten de kerk. 1953. m. fl.3.50. (Redemptorist Fathers) A.de Bot, Ed. & Pub., Sionsweg 2, 6525 EB Nijmegen, Netherlands. illus. circ. 8,000. (tabloid format)

282 IE ISSN 0016-3120
FURROW. 1950. m. £19($26) Furrow Trust, Maynooth, Co. Kildare, Ireland. Ed. Ronan Drury. adv. bk. rev. film rev. play rev. index every 6 months. circ. 8,000. (also avail. in microform from UMI; reprint service avail. from UMI) Indexed: Cath.Ind. Old Test.Abstr. CERDIC. Canon Law Abstr. New Test.Abstr.

282 NE
GEIST UND AUFTRAG. (Text in German) 1921. q. Charitable Cooperation of the Missionary Sisters e.V., Postfach 2308, 4054 Nettetal 2, Netherlands. Ed. Gabriele Hoelzer. bk. rev. circ. 48,000.

282 US
GENERATION; the spiritual enrichment newsletter for mature Catholics. 1980. m. $12. Claretian Publications, 205 W. Monroe St., Chicago, IL 60606. TEL 312-236-7782 Ed. Rev. Mark J. Brummel. circ. 24,270. (reprint service avail. from UMI)

282 US
GEORGIA BULLETIN. 1962. w. $12. Catholic Archdiocese of Atlanta, 680 W. Peachtree St. N.W., Atlanta, GA 30308. Ed. Gretchen R. Keiser. adv. bk. rev. circ. 29,693.

GIDS OP MAATSCHAPPELIJK GEBIED; tijdschrift voor sociale cultur. see *LABOR UNIONS*

282 IT ISSN 0017-1336
GIOVANI IN DIALOGO. 1903. s-m. L.1500($2.) Azione Cattolica Giovanile, Via S. Antonio 5, 20122 Milan, Italy. circ. 1,000. (tabloid format)

282 284 US
GOOD NEWS. 1973. m. $42. Sunday Publications, Inc., 1937 Tenth Ave., N., Lake Worth, FL 33466-9501. TEL 305-533-0990 Ed. Rev. Joseph T. Nolan. bk. rev. index. (looseleaf format) Indexed: Rehabil.Lit.
Incorporates (since 1983): Candle.

266 SA
GRACIOUS LIGHT. 1967. q. free. Saiva Sithantha Sungum of South Africa (Universal Mission), 37 Derby Street, Box 4677, Durban, Natal, South Africa. Ed. A.G. Ferguson.
Formerly: Saivite Light (ISSN 0036-3324)

GRADUATE SCHOOL GUIDE. see *EDUCATION — Guides To Schools And Colleges*

282 CN ISSN 0828-4083
GRAIL. 1985. q. Can.$12($12) to individuals; Can.$18($18) to institutions. University of St. Jerome's College Press, Waterloo, Ont. N2L 3G3, Canada. Ed. D.R. Letson. bk. rev. illus. circ. 2,500.

282 VC ISSN 0017-4114
GREGORIANUM. (Text in English, French, German, Italian and Spanish) 1920. q. $45. (Pontificia Universita Gregoriana) Gregorian University Press, Piazza della Pilotta, 35, 00187 Rome, Italy. Ed. R.P. Dupuis. bk. rev. bibl. index. cum.index: vols.1-31, 1920-1950. circ. 1,500. Indexed: Bull.Signal. Cath.Ind. Old Test.Abstr. Rel.Per. CERDIC. Canon Law Abstr. New Test.Abstr. Phil.Ind. Rel.Ind.One. Rel.& Theol.Abstr.

282 US
GUIDE TO RELIGIOUS MINISTRIES FOR CATHOLIC MEN AND WOMEN. 1979. a. $5. Catholic News Publishing Co., Inc., 210 N. Ave., New Rochelle, NY 10801. TEL 914-632-1220 Ed. Victor L. Ridder, Jr. adv. tr.lit. circ. 30,000.
Formerly: Guide to Religious Careers for Catholic Men and Women.

260 US
HAWAII CATHOLIC HERALD. 1936. w. $10. Roman Catholic Bishop of Honolulu, 1184 Bishop St., Honolulu, Honolulu, HI 96813. TEL 808-536-5494 Ed. Patrick Downes. adv. bk. rev. circ. 7,000.

HEIGHTS (NEW YORK) see *JOURNALISM*

282 PL ISSN 0017-9914
HEJNAL MARIACKI; miesiecznik o tematyce religijno-kulturalno-spolecznej. 1956. m. $6. Chrzescijanskie Stowarzyszenie Spoleczne - Christian Social Association, Marszalkowska 4, 00-590 Warsaw, Poland (Dist. by: RSW "Prasa-Ksiazka-Ruch" Centrala Kolportazu Prasy i Wyndawnictw, Ul. Towarowa 28, 00-958 Warsaw) Ed. Eugeniusz Zdanowicz. adv. illus. circ. 5,000.

282 GW ISSN 0018-0645
HERDER-KORRESPONDENZ; Monatshefte fuer Gesellschaft und Religion. 1946. m. DM.127.20. Verlag Herder GmbH und Co. KG, Hermann-Herder-Str. 4, D-7800 Freiburg im Breisgau, W. Germany (B.R.D.) Ed. Dr. David A. Seeber. adv. bk. rev. index. circ. 9,200. Indexed: Cath.Ind.

282 SP
HOJA TRINITARIA. m. 500 ptas. Ediciones Secretariado Trinitario, Filiberto Villalobos, 82, 37007 Salmanca, Spain.

282 296 297 956 IS
HOLY LAND; illustrated quarterly of the Franciscan custody of the holy land. 1975. q. $7. Franciscan Printing Press, P.O. Box 14064, Jerusalem, Israel. Ed. Raphael Bonanno. adv. bk. rev. cum.index: 1975-1984. circ. 5,000. (back issues avail.)

HOMELIFE; the Philippines' family magazine. see *GENERAL INTEREST PERIODICALS — Philippines*

250 US ISSN 0018-4268
HOMILETIC AND PASTORAL REVIEW. 1900. m. (bi-m. Aug.-Sep.) $20. Catholic Polls, Inc., 86 Riverside Dr., New York, NY 10024. TEL 212-799-2600 Ed. Rev. Kenneth Baker. adv. bk. rev. index. circ. 15,500. (also avail. in microform from UMI; reprint service avail. from UMI) Indexed: Cath.Ind. Rel.& Theol.Abstr. Old Test.Abstr. CERDIC. Canon Law Abstr. New Test.Abstr.

282 HK ISSN 0073-3210
HONG KONG CATHOLIC CHURCH DIRECTORY/HSIANG-KANG T'IEN CHU CHIAO SHOU T'SE. (Text in Chinese and English) 1954. a. $2.50. Catholic Truth Society, Catholic Diocese Centre, Box 2984, Hong Kong, Hong Kong. Ed. Louis Lee. adv. circ. 3,000.

282 US ISSN 0360-9669
HORIZONS (VILLANOVA) 1974. s-a. $12 to non-members; institutions $20. College Theology Society, c/o Villanova University, Villanova, PA 19085 TEL 215-645-7302 (Subscr. to: Wilfrid Laurier University Press, Waterloo, Ont. N2L 3C5, Canada) Ed. Walter E. Conn. adv. bk. rev. circ. 1,500. (also avail. in microfilm from UMI; reprint service avail. from UMI) Indexed: Cath.Ind. Old Test.Abstr. Rel.Per. SSCI. New Test.Abstr. Rel.Ind.One. Rel.& Theol.Abstr.

282 US ISSN 0018-6910
HRVATSKI KATOLICKI GLASNIK; mjesecnik za duhovnu izgradnju iseljenih Hrvata. 1942. m. $5. ‡ (Croatian Franciscan Fathers) Croatian Franciscan Press, 4851 Drexel Blvd., Chicago, IL 60615. TEL 312-268-2819 Ed. Fr. Gracijan Raspudic, O.F.M. adv. bk. rev. illus. circ. 3,000. Indexed: CERDIC.

IDEA INK; the national Catholic opinion quarterly. see *LITERARY AND POLITICAL REVIEWS*

282 SP
IGLESIA DE SEVILLA. s-a. 500 ptas. Arzobispado de Sevilla, Oficina Diocesana de Informacion, Apdo. Postal 6, Sevilla 41080, Sevilla, Spain. Ed. Carlos Ros Carballar.

200 SP
IMAGENES DE LA FE. 1963. m. 950 ptas.($16) (Pontificial University of Salamanca) Promocion Popular Cristiana, E. Jardiel Poncela 4, E-28016 Madrid, Spain. Ed. Lamberto de Echeverria. circ. 10,000.

282 FR
IMAGES DU MOIS. 1962. m. 163 Bd Malesherbes, 75849 Paris Cedex 17, France. Ed. Michel Houssin. circ. 600,000.

282 FR ISSN 0019-2899
IMPACTS. 1967. q. 153 F. (Universite Catholique de l'Ouest) Association Saint-Yves, 3 Place Andre-Leroy, 49005 Angers Cedex, France. Ed. Louis Collin. adv. bk. rev. abstr. bibl. circ. 850.

282 IT ISSN 0019-3186
IN FAMIGLIA; rassegna mensile delle attivita spirituali, culturali e artistiche dell'angelicum-chiesa di s.angelo. 1925. m. L.4000. Angelicum-Convento di S.Angelo, Piazza S. Angelo 2, 20121 Milan, Italy. Ed.Bd. adv. bk. rev. (tabloid format)

200 IT
INFORMATION BULLETIN FOR CATHOLIC RURAL ORGANIZATIONS. (Text in English and French) 1965. s-a. $10. International Catholic Rural Association, Piazza S. Calisto 16, 00153 Rome, Italy. Ed.Bd. adv. cum.index. (back issues avail.)

282 374 IT
INFORMATORE DI URIO. 1973. bi-m. (Associazione Ricerche e Studi) Edizioni A.R.E.S., Via Stradivari 7, 20131 Milan, Italy. Ed. Giorgio Carimati. circ. 4,760. (back issues avail.)

282 US ISSN 0020-1510
INLAND REGISTER. 1942. 17/yr. $12. Catholic Diocese of Spokane, W. 1023 Riverside Ave., Box 48, Spokane, WA 99210. TEL 509-456-7140 Ed. Eric Meisfjord. adv. bk. rev. circ. 20,000.

282 UK ISSN 0020-157X
INNES REVIEW. 1950. s-a. £10. (Scottish Catholic Historical Association) John S. Burns & Sons, 25 Finlas St., Glasgow N.2, Scotland. illus. cum.index: 1950-1959. circ. 500. Indexed: Br.Hum.Ind. Hist.Abstr. Amer.Hist.& Life. Br.Archaeol.Abstr.
Church and university in Scotland

200 230 FR
INSTITUT CATHOLIQUE DE PARIS. ANNUAIRE. a. Institut Catholique de Paris, 21, rue d'Assas, 75270 Paris Cedex 06, France.

282 BE ISSN 0770-4720
INTERFACE; lettre d'information trimestrielle. 1981. q. 1,500 Fr.($25) Centre Informatique et Bible, Promotion Biblique et Informatique, 13 rue de la Bruyere, B-5974 Opprebais, Belgium. Ed. Paul Maskens. adv. circ. 6,000. (back issues avail.)

282 CI ISSN 0074-5782
INTERNATIONAL EUCHARIST CONGRESS. PROCEEDINGS. irreg., 1968, 39th, Bogota. Luis Cardinal Goncha, c/o Cardinal James K. Knox, Via del Pozzeto 160, Rome, Italy.

282 BE
INTERNATIONALE KATHOLIEKE INFORMATIE. m. Orbis en Orion Uitgevers NV, Lieven Bauwenstraat 19, Brugge, Belgium. Ed. Ernest Milcent. bk. rev. film rev. bibl. illus. index. circ. 8,000. (tabloid format)

282 GW
INTERNATIONALE KATHOLISCHE ZEITSCHRIFT. 1972. s-m. DM.12 (single issue) Verlag fuer Christliche Literatur, Suerthestr. 107, 5000 Cologne 50, W. Germany (B.R.D.) Ed. Franz Greiner. adv. bk. rev. circ. 3,000. Indexed: Old Test.Abstr. CERDIC. New Test.Abstr. Rel.Ind.One.

282 IE
IRISH CATHOLIC. 1888. w. £0.25 per issue. Irish Catholic Ltd., 55 Lower Gardiner St., Dublin 1, Ireland. Ed. Nick Lundberg. adv. bk. rev. illus. circ. 39,000.

282 UK ISSN 0075-0735
IRISH CATHOLIC DIRECTORY. 1838. a. £7.95. (Roman Catholic Church in All Ireland) Associated Catholic Publications (1912) Ltd., 33-39 Bowling Green Lane, London EC1R 0AB, England. adv. index.

282 IT
ISTITUTO DI SCIENZE RELIGIOSE IN TRENTO. PUBBLICAZIONI. 1981. irreg. Centro Editoriale Dehoniano, Via Nosadella 6, I-40123 Bologna, Italy. Ed.Bd.

ITALIA MISSIONARIA. see *CHILDREN AND YOUTH — For*

946 PO ISSN 0021-3209
ITINERARIUM; revista quadrimestral de cultura. 1955. 3/yr. Esc.1000($10) (Portuguese Franciscans) Editorial Franciscana, Apdo. 17 Montariol, P 4701 Braga Codex, Portugal. Ed. Jose Antonio da Silva Soares. bk. rev. bibl. index. cum.index: 1955-1970. circ. 400. (back issues avail.) Indexed: Hist.Abstr. Amer.Hist.& Life. CERDIC.

IT'S OUR WORLD; mission news from the Holy Childhood Association. see *CHILDREN AND YOUTH — For*

IUSTITIA. see *LAW*

282 AU
JAHRBUCH DER ERZDIOESE VON WIEN. a. (Erzbischoefliches Pastoralamt Wien) Wiener Dom-Verlag GmbH, Strozzigasse 8, Postfach 321, 1081 Wien, Austria. Ed. Johannes Pesl. adv. illus.
Formerly: Jahrbuch fuer die Kirche von Wien.

282 CN ISSN 0021-5740
JE CROIS; magazine populaire Catholique. (Text in French) 1960. m. Can.$7. (Messagers Catholiques de la Bible Inc.) Editions le Renouveau Inc., C.P. 1557, Quebec, P.Q. G1K 7Y4, Canada. TEL 418-628-3362 Ed.Bd. bk. rev. bibl. illus. circ. 45,000.

282 II
JEEVADHARA. (Text in English or Malayalam) 1971. m. Rps.24($8) Jeevadhara Theological Society, Theology Centre, Kottayam 686 017, Kerala, India. Ed. Joseph Constantine Manalel. adv. bk. rev. index. circ. 1,000. (back issues avail.) Indexed: New Test.Abstr.

271 US
JESUIT BULLETIN. 1922. q. Society of Jesus, Missouri Province Educational Institute, 4511 W. Pine Blvd., St. Louis, MO 63108 TEL 314-361-3388 (Subscr. to: 2001 S. Hanley Rd., St. Louis, MO 63144) Ed. Rev. Michael Harter, S.J. circ. 33,000.

282 IT
JESUS CARITAS. 1961. q. L.18000($13) Fratel Carlo di Gesu, Via Limiti 57, 06038 Spello, Perugia, Italy. circ. 2,500.

282 US ISSN 0021-759X
JOSEPHINUM NEWSLETTER. 1976. 4/yr. Pontifical College Josephinum, Columbus, OH 43085. TEL 614-885-5585 circ. 8,300.
Supersedes: Josephinum Review.

266 282 GW
K M - DIE KATHOLISCHEN MISSIONEN; Zeitschrift des Internationalen Katholischen Missionwerkes (MISSIO) 1873. 6/yr. DM.14.40. Verlag Herder GmbH und Co. KG, Hermann-Herder-Str. 4, D-7800 Freiburg im Breisgau, W. Germany (B.R.D.) Ed. Jos. Alb. Otto. adv. bk. rev. abstr. bibl. charts. illus. index. circ. 75,000.
Formerly: Katholischen Missionen (ISSN 0022-9407)
Missions

K S BULLETIN. (Foreningen af Katolske Skoler i Danmark) see *EDUCATION — School Organization And Administration*

200 US
KALENDAR JEDNOTA. (Text in Slovak) 1897. a. First Catholic Slovak Union, 3289 E. 55th St., Cleveland, OH 44127 TEL 216-341-3355 (Subscr. addr.: Jednota Printery, Box 150, Middletown, PA 17057) Ed. Joseph C. Krajsa. Indexed: Hist.Abstr. Amer.Hist.& Life.
Formerly: Jednota Kalendar.

282 NE
KATHOLIEK DOCUMENTATIE CENTRUM. ARCHIEVEN. 1973. irreg. price varies. Katholiek Documentatie Centrum, Erasmuslaan 36, 6525 GG Nijmegen, Netherlands.

282 NE
KATHOLIEK DOCUMENTATIE CENTRUM. JAARBOEK. (Summaries in English and French) 1971. a. price varies. Katholiek Documentatie Centrum, Erasmuslaan 36, 6525 GG Nijmegen, Netherlands. (Co-sponsor: Archief voor de Geschiedenis van de Katholieke Kerk in Nederland) Indexed: CERDIC.

282 NE
KATHOLIEK DOCUMENTATIE CENTRUM. PUBLICATIES. 1971. irreg., vol. 11, 1983. price varies. Katholiek Documentatie Centrum, Erasmuslaan 36, 6525 GG Nijmegen, Netherlands. (back issues avail.)

282 267.4 AU ISSN 0022-9377
KATHOLISCHE FRAUENBEWEGUNG OESTERREICHS. FUEHRUNGSBLATT. 1951. q. S.80. Katholisches Frauenwerk in Oesterreich, Spiegelgasse 3/II, A-1010 Vienna, Austria. Ed. Christa Esterhazy. bk. rev. circ. 2,500.

282 GW ISSN 0047-3294
KATHOLISCHER DIGEST; Zeitschrift fuer die Familie. 1947. m. DM.30. Verlag Axel B. Trunkel, Werrastr. 24, 7000 Stuttgart 1, W. Germany (B.R.D.) Ed. Willy Schleunung. adv. bk. rev. film rev. illus. circ. 70,000.

200 GW ISSN 0170-7302
KATHOLISCHES LEBEN UND KIRCHENREFORM IM ZEITALTER DER GLAUBENSSPALTUNG. 1927. irreg. price varies. Aschendorffsche Verlagsbuchhandlung, Soester Str. 13, 4400 Muenster, W. Germany (B.R.D.) Ed. Erwin Iserloh.

201 PL
KATOLICKI UNIWERSYTET LUBELSKI. WYDZIAL TEOLOGICZNO-KANONICZNY. ROZPRAWY. (Text in Polish; summaries in English or French) 1947. irreg. price varies. Katolicki Uniwersytet Lubelski, Towarzystwo Naukowe, Chopina 29, 20-023 Lublin, Poland. index. circ. 3,150.

200 PL ISSN 0044-4405
KATOLICKI UNIWERSYTET LUBELSKI. ZESZYTY NAUKOWE. (In four parts) (Summaries in English & French) 1958. q. price varies. Katolicki Uniwersytet Lubelski, Towarzystwo Naukowe, Chopina 29, 20-023 Lublin, Poland. bk. rev. illus. index. circ. 1,125.

KATOLICKY SOKOL. see *ETHNIC INTERESTS*

282 US
KATOLIKUS MAGYAROK VASARNAPJA; Catholic Hungarians' Sunday. (Text in Hungarian) 1894. w. $20. (Commissariat of St. Stephen's Franciscan Province) Catholic Publishing Co., 1739 Mahoning Avenue, Youngstown, OH 44509 TEL 216-799-3335 (Subscr. to: Box 2464, Youngstown, Ohio 44509) Ed. Fr. Nicholas G. Dengl. adv. bk. rev. circ. 3,400. (back issues avail.)

282 IT ISSN 0022-9431
KATOLIKUS SZEMLE. (Text in Hungarian; summaries in English) 1949. q. L.25000($16) Actio Catholica Hungarorum in Exteris, Via Conciliazione 44, 00193 Rome, Italy. Ed. Gellert Bekes. bk. rev. index. circ. 1,500.

282 DK
KATOLSK ORIENTERING. 20/yr. Bredgade 69A, 1260 Copenhagen K, Denmark. adv. circ. 15,000.

282 GE ISSN 0138-2543
KATOLSKI POSOL. (Text in Upper Sorbian) 24/yr. M.13.20. Buchexport, Leninstr. 16, DDR-7010 Leipzig, E. Germany (D.D.R.) (Orders to: Buchexport, Postfach 160, DDR-7010 Leipzig, E. Germany (D.D.R.))

282 JA ISSN 0387-3005
KATORIKKU KENKYU. 1961. s-a. 1800 Yen. Sophia University, Theological Society - Katorikku Kenkyu, Kamishakujii 4-32-11, Nerima-ku, Tokyo 177, Japan. Ed. Peter Nemeshegyi. bk. rev. circ. 1,000. (back issues avail.)

282 283 SA ISSN 0022-9687
KEHILWENYANE; dikgang tsa bodumedi le morafe. (Text and summaries in English and Setswana) 1958. m. R.0.20 per no. (Roman Catholic Diocese of Kimberly) Kehilwenyane Publications, Box 309, Kimberley 8300, South Africa. Ed. Vincent Monyamane. bk. rev. abstr. illus. stat. circ. 4,500. Indexed: CERDIC.

283 UK
KEYS OF PETER. 1969. bi-m. £3. Christian Centre Party, 157 Vicarage Rd., London E10 5DU, England. Ed. Ronald King. bk. rev.

282 TZ
KIONGOZI/LEADER; gazeti la wananchi. (Text in Swahili) 1950. fortn. EAs.21.60. Catholic Publishers Ltd., Box 9400, Dar es Salaam, Tanzania. Ed. David Matipa. adv. bk. rev. circ. 130,000.
Incorporating: Ecclesia (ISSN 0012-9046)

284 GW
KIRCHE IN MARBURG; Mitteilungen der evangelischen und katholischen Gemeinden. 1936. m. DM.4.95. Gesamtverband der Evangelischen Kirchengemeinden in Marburg, Leipzigerstr. 20, 3550 Marburg 1, W. Germany (B.R.D.) (Co-sponsor: Katholische Pfarrgemeinde in Marburg-Stadt) Ed.Bd. adv. bk. rev. illus. circ. 5,000.
Formerly: Gemeindebote (ISSN 0016-6103)

KLEINE CHORZEITUNG; Mitteilungsblatt fuer die katholischen Kirchenchoere. see *MUSIC*

282 AU ISSN 0023-3676
KONTAKT DREI UND ZWANZIG. 1954. bi-m. contribution. Roemisches Katholisches Pfarramt Atzgersdorf, Peter Kirchenplatz 1, A-1230 Vienna, Austria. Ed. Pfarrer Otto Novotny. bk. rev. circ. 2,100.
Formerly: Liesinger Pfarrblatt.

028.5 GW ISSN 0023-3749
KONTRASTE IMPULS. 1960. q. DM.17.20. Verlag Herder GmbH und Co. KG, Hermann-Herder-Str. 4, D-7800 Freiburg im Breisgau, W. Germany (B.R.D.) Ed. Reinhold Lehmann. adv. bk. rev. illus. circ. 40,000.

282 US ISSN 0023-477X
KRISTAUS KARALIAUS LAIVAS/SHIP OF CHRIST THE KING. (Text in Lithuanian) 1922. s-m. $4. Congregation of Marian Fathers, 4545 W. 63rd St., Chicago, IL 60629. TEL 312-767-1687 Ed. Rev. J. Vaskas. bk. rev. illus. circ. 600.

LAND AKTUELL. see *POLITICAL SCIENCE*

270 IT ISSN 0023-902X
LAURENTIANUM. (Text in principal European languages) 1960. 3/yr. L.30000($20) (International College of the Capuchin Order) Collegio Internazionale S. Lorenzo da Brindisi, Circonvallazione Occidentale 6850, 00163 Rome, Italy. Ed. Davide Covi. bk. rev. index. circ. 500. (back issues avail.) Indexed: M.L.A. Old Test.Abstr. Canon Law Abstr. CERDIC. New Test.Abstr.

282 GW ISSN 0023-9941
LEBENDIGES ZEUGNIS. 1946. q. membership. ‡ Bonifatiuswerk der Deutschen Katholiken e.V., Kamp 22, 4790 Paderborn, W. Germany (B.R.D.) Ed. Bernhard Neumann. bk. rev. circ. 7,000. Indexed: CERDIC.

282 LO
LESOTHO CATHOLIC DIRECTORY. 1977. irreg. latest 1985. $5. (Lesotho Catholic Bishops Conference) Mazenod Printing Works Pty. Ltd., Box 39, Mazenod 160, Lesotho. Ed. F. Mairot. circ. 300.

282 UK ISSN 0024-1792
LIBERAL CATHOLIC. 1924. q. £5($11) (Liberal Catholic Church) St. Alban's Press, Drayton House, 30 Gordon St., London WC1H 0BE, England. Ed. Rt. Rev. E.J. Burton. adv. bk. rev. illus. circ. 700.

282 AU
LICHTENTALER PFARRNACHRICHTEN. 1978. 4/yr. free. Pfarre Lichtental, Marktgasse 40, A-1090 Vienna, Austria. adv. circ. 5,000.

282 IT
LIEB FRAUEN BOTE. (Text in German) 1950. bi-m. L.4000. Bertrand Vollmann, 39030 S. Lorenzo Sebato (BZ), Italy. circ. 4,000.

282 FR ISSN 0024-2926
LIEN ENTRE MERES ET PERES DE PRETRES. q. 3 F. (Diocese de Paris) Imprimerie Dalex a Montrouge, 5 et 7 rue Victor-Basch, Montrouge, France.

282 US ISSN 0024-3450
LIGUORIAN. 1913. m. $12. ‡ (Redemptorist Fathers, St. Louis Province) Liguori Publications, Liguori Dr., Liguori, MO 63057. TEL 314-464-2500 Ed. Rev. Norman J. Muckerman. bk. rev. illus. circ. 500,000. (also avail. in microform from UMI) Indexed: Cath.Ind. CERDIC.

282 US
LILY OF THE MOHAWKS. 1936. s-a. $2. Tekakwitha League, Auriesville, NY 12016. TEL 518-853-3153 Ed. Rev. Joseph S. McBride, S.J. bk. rev. circ. 10,000. (also avail. in microfilm; back issues avail.)

282 255 US ISSN 0024-4465
LISTY SV. FRANTISKA/LEAFLETS OF ST. FRANCIS. (Text in Slovak) 1924. q. $3. Franciscan Friars of the Custody of the Most Holy Savior, 232 S. Home Ave., Pittsburgh, PA 15202. Ed. Rev. Theodoric J. Zubek. illus. circ. 1,000.

282 UK
LIVERPOOL CATHOLIC DIRECTORY. 1928. a. £1. Catholic Pictorial Ltd., Media House, 34 Stafford St., Liverpool L3 8LX, England. Ed. Rev. Paul Thompson. adv. circ. 9,000.

377.8 US ISSN 0024-5275
LIVING LIGHT; an interdisciplinary review of Catholic religious education, catechesis and pastoral ministry. 1964. q. $15. (United States Catholic Conference, Department of Education) Mercer University Press, Macon, GA 31207. TEL 912-744-2880 Ed. Berard L. Marthaler. adv. bk. rev. index. circ. controlled. (also avail. in microform from BLH) Indexed: Cath.Ind. Old.Test.Abstr. CERDIC.

282 SP
LLUVIA DE ROSAS. 1923. bi-m. 350 ptas.($4) c/o P. Eugenio Alsina Valls, Apdo. 112, 25080 Lerida, Spain. circ. 20,000. (also avail. in microfilm)

282 CN ISSN 0024-5895
LOHOS; bohoslov'kyi kvartal'nyk. (Supplement: Homiletychnyi Dodatok) (Contents page in English and Ukrainian) 1950. bi-m. Can.$10. Redeemer's Voice Press, 165 Catherine St., Yorkton, Sask. S3N 2V7, Canada. TEL 306-783-4487 Ed. Stephen S. Shawel. bk. rev. bibl. index. circ. 400. Indexed: Amer.Bibl.Slavic & E.Eur.Stud.

282 US ISSN 0024-6255
LONG ISLAND CATHOLIC. 1962. w. $10. (Catholic Diocese of Rockville Centre) Catholic Press Association, 115 Greenwich St., Hempstead, NY 11551 TEL 516-538-8800 (Subscr. to: Long Island Catholic, Box 700, Hempstead, NY 11571) Ed. Msgr. Francis J. Maniscalco. adv. bibl. charts. illus. tr.lit. circ. 140,816.

282 GW
LOURDES-ROSEN. 1880. q. membership. Deutscher Lourdes-Verein, Schaalbengasse 10, 5000 Cologne 1, W. Germany (B.R.D.) circ. 25,000(controlled)

282 327 US
LUCHA/STRUGGLE. 1976. bi-m. $10 to individuals; institutions $20. New York Circus, Box 37, Times Square Station, New York, NY 10108. TEL 212-316-0040 adv. bk. rev. charts. illus. stat. (back issues avail.) Indexed: Alt.Press Ind.

268 BE ISSN 0770-2477
LUMEN VITAE; international review of religious education. French Edition (ISSN 0024-7324) (Editions in English and French) 1946. q. 800 Fr.($22) (International Centre for Religious Education) Lumen Vitae Press, 186 rue Washington, 1050 Brussels, Belgium. Ed. Pierre Mourlon Beernaert. bk. rev. bibl. index. circ. 3,200 (English edt. 1,400; French edt. 1,800) Indexed: Cath.Ind. Educ.Ind. CERDIC. New Test.Abstr. Rural Recreat.Tour.Abstr. Rel.& Theol.Abstr. World Agri.Econ.& Rural Sociol.Abstr.

200 IT
LUX. (Text in English, French) 1962. s-a. African Association of St. Augustine, Via Urbano VIII, 16, Rome, Italy. abstr. Indexed: C.I.S. Abstr.

200 378 PE
M I E C SERVICO DE DOCUMENTACION. 12/yr. $18 (includes subscr. to: SPES and America Latina Boletin) Movimiento Internacional de Estudiantes Catolicos, Centro de Documentacion, Apdo. 3564, Lima 100, Peru. bk. rev. bibl. illus.

282 IT
MADONNA. 1954. bi-m. L.20000. Opera Madonna del Divino Amore, Via Ardeatina, Km 12, 00134 Rome, Italy. Dir. Don Pasquale Silla. circ. 1,500.

282 IT
LA MADONNA DEL DIVINO AMORE; bollettino mensile del santuario. 1932. m. Opera Madonna del Divino Amore, Via Ardeatina, Km 12, 00134 Rome, Italy. Ed. Don Pasquale Silla. illus. circ. 100,000.

282 IT ISSN 0024-9580
MADONNA DI BARBANA; peridico mensile del santuario. 1910. m. L.5000. Santuario Madonna di Barbana, Isola di Barbana, 34073 Grado (Go), Italy. Ed.Bd.

266 SP
MADRE Y MAESTRA. 1871. m. (bi-m. Jul.-Aug.) 250 ptas.($5) Misioneros del Sagrado Corazon, Avenida Pio XII, 31, Madrid, 16, Spain. adv. bk. rev. illus. circ. 12,000.
Missions

282 IT ISSN 0024-9696
MAESTRO. 1944. m. L.7500. Associazione Italiana Maestri Cattolici, Clivio Monte del Gallo 50, 00165 Rome, Italy. Ed. Rita Ludovico. adv. bk. rev. illus. stat. circ. 60,000.

282 CN ISSN 0025-0007
MAGNIFICAT. English edition (ISSN 0381-0852) (Editions in English and French) 1965. m. contributions. Apostles of Infinite Love, Sanctuary of the Magnificat, Box 308, St.-Jovite, Que. J0T 2H0, Canada. Ed.Bd. bk. rev. illus. circ. 4,000(controlled) (processed) Indexed: Chem.Abstr. Eng.Ind.

232 SZ ISSN 0025-2972
MARIA; marianischer digest. 1950. 6/yr. 8.90 Fr. Bargezzi AG, Wasserwerkgasse 17, 3011 Berne, Switzerland. Ed. Josef Gruebel. adv. bk. rev. illus. circ. 28,000.

200 IT
MARIA NOSTRA LUCE. 1918. m. L.3000. Centro Nazionale Associazione Mariana, Via Francesco Albergotti 75, 00167 Rome, Italy. bk. rev. circ. 3,500.

282 US ISSN 0464-9680
MARIAN STUDIES. 1950. a. $10 domestic; foreign $12. Mariological Society of America, Marian Library, University of Dayton, Dayton, OH 45469-0001. TEL 513-229-4214 Ed. Theodore A. Loehler. adv. bibl. cum.index.

232 AU ISSN 0025-3014
MARIANIST. 1956. q. S.60. ‡ Gesellschaft Mariae in Oesterreich und Deutschland - Marianist Catholic Order, Salesianumweg 5, A-4020 Linz, Austria. Ed. Karl Kloybhofer. illus. circ. 3,000.

282 IT
MARIANUM. 1939. q. L.27000($24) Pontificia Facolta Teologica Marianum, Viale Trenta Aprile 6, 00153 Rome, Italy. Ed. Ignazio M. Calabuig. adv. bk. rev. circ. 800. Indexed: M.L.A. New Test.Abstr.

MARRIAGE AND FAMILY LIVING. see *SOCIOLOGY*

266 US ISSN 0025-4142
MARYKNOLL. 1907. m. $1. Maryknoll Society, Maryknoll, NY 10545. TEL 914-941-7590 (Co-sponsor: Catholic Foreign Mission Society of America) Ed. Moises Sandoval. illus. index. circ. 1,000,000. (also avail. in microform from UMI) Indexed: Cath.Ind. CERDIC.
Formerly: Field Afar; Supersedes: Channel (ISSN 0009-1456)
Missions

MASSIS. see *LITERARY AND POLITICAL REVIEWS*

282 PL ISSN 0076-5244
MATERIALY ZRODLOWE DO DZIEJOW KOSCIOLA W POLSCE. 1965. irreg. price varies. Towarzystwo Naukowe Katolickiego Uniwersytetu Lubelskiego, Al. Raclawickie 14, Lublin, Poland (Dist. by Ars Polona-Ruch, Krakowskie Przedmiescie 7, Warsaw, Poland) (Co-sponsor: Instytut Geografii Historycznej Kosciola w Polsce przy K.U.L.) Ed. Jerzy Kloczowski. circ. 1,000.

282 CK
MEDELLIN; teologia pastoral para America Latina. 1975. q. $15. Consejo Episcopal Latinoamericano, Instituto Teologico Pastoral, Apartado Aereo 1931, Medellin, Colombia. Ed. Boaventura Kloppenburg. bk. rev. circ. 1,500. (back issues avail.)

MEDICAL MISSION SISTERS NEWS. see *HOSPITALS*

200 FR ISSN 0025-8911
MELANGES DE SCIENCE RELIGIEUSE. 1944. q. 75 F. Institut Catholique de Lille, 60 bd. Vauban, 59046 Lille, France. Ed. Jacques Liebaert. bk. rev. cum.index: vols. 1-27, 1944-1970. circ. 500. (back issues avail.) Indexed: M.L.A. Bull.Signal. Int.Zeit.Bibelwiss. CERDIC. Old Test.Abstr. Rel.Per. New Test.Abstr. Rel.& Theol.Abstr. Rel.Ind.One.

282 CL ISSN 0716-0062
MENSAJE. 1951. 10/yr. $35. Compania de Jesus, Provincia Chilena, Residencia San Roberto Bellarmino, Almirante Barroso 24, Casilla 10445, Santiago, Chile. Ed. Renato Hevia. adv. bk. rev. film rev. play rev. bibl. illus. stat. cum.index. circ. 14,000. Indexed: Biol.Abstr.

282 FR ISSN 0026-0290
MESSAGES DU SECOURS CATHOLIQUE. 1945. m. 16 F. Editions S.O.S., 106 rue du Bac, 75341 Paris Cedex 07, France. Ed. Robert Prigent. adv. bk. rev. charts. illus. stat. circ. 975,000. (tabloid format)

267 325 AT
MESSAGGERO. (Text in Italian) 1961. m. Aus.$10. Scalabrinian Fathers, 378 Nicholson St., Fitzroy, Vic. 3068, Australia. Ed. Rev. Luciano Ferracin. adv. circ. 6,000.

282 255 IT ISSN 0026-0312
MESSAGGERO DI S. ANTONIO. (Editions in English, French, German, Italian, Portuguese and Spanish) 1897. s-m. L.11000. (Provincia Padovana dei Frati Minori Conventuali) Grafiche Messaggero, Via Orto Botanico, 11, 35123 Padua, Italy (Subscr. addr.: Basilica del Santo, 35123 Padua, Italy) Ed. Giacomo Panteghini. adv. bk. rev. film rev. circ. 1,200,000. (back issues avail.)

METAMEDICA; blad voor metamedische vraagstukken. see *MEDICAL SCIENCES*

268 US ISSN 0300-6158
MIESIECZNIK FRANCISZKANSKI. (Text in Polish) 1907? m. $6. (Catholic Order of the Franciscan Fathers) Franciscan Publishers, Franciscan Center, Pulaski, WI 54162. TEL 414-822-5833 Ed. Sebastian M. Kus. circ. 6,000.

MILITAERSEELSORGE. see *MILITARY*

200 SZ
MIRJAM; Monatszeitschrift der weltoffenen Frau. 1934. m. 34 Fr. (Arbeitsstelle Bildungsdienst) Verlag U. Cavelti AG, CH-9202 Gossau, Switzerland. Ed. Annelies Schuepp. adv. bk. rev. film rev. illus. play rev. index. circ. 16,000. (tabloid format)
Formerly: Ancilla (ISSN 0003-2867)

200 VC ISSN 0026-587X
MISCELLANEA FRANCESCANA; rivista trimestrale di scienze teologiche e di studi francescani. (Text in English, French, Italian, Latin) 1886. q. L.20000($30) (Pontificia Facolta Teologica S. Bonaventura) Casa Editrice Miscellanea Francescana, Via del Serafico 1, 00142 Rome, Italy. Ed. Orlando Todisco. bk. rev. illus. index. circ. 600. Indexed: Hist.Abstr. M.L.A. Amer.Hist.& Life. RILA.

MISHKAN; a theological forum on Jewish evangelism. see *RELIGIONS AND THEOLOGY — Judaic*

282 SP
MISIORAMA. (Supplement to Comunidad) m. free. Semanario de la Iglesia Diocesana, Iscar Peyra, 26 Obispado, 37002 Salamanca, Spain.

262 GW
MISSION AKTUELL. 1969. bi-m. DM.10. (Internationales Katholisches Missionswerk e.V.) Missio Aktuell Verlagsgesellschaft mbH, Bergdriesch 27, 5100 Aachen, W. Germany (B.D.R.) Ed. H.J. Theyssen. adv. bk. rev. circ. 1,150,000.
Former titles: Aktuell; Weltmission.
Missions

266 FR ISSN 0026-6035
MISSION DE L'EGLISE. 1925. q. 50 F. Union Pontificale Missionnaire, 5 rue Monsieur, 75007 Paris, France. Ed. Mgr. Orchampt. adv. bk. rev. bibl. index. circ. 23,000. Indexed: CERDIC.
Missions

266 282 US
MISSION HANDBOOK. 1950. a. $1.50. United States Catholic Mission Association, 1233 Lawrence St., N. E., Washington, DC 20017. TEL 202-832-3112 Ed. Sr. Mary Godfrey. circ. 1,500.
Former titles: United States Catholic Mission and Association. Handbook; United States Catholic Mission Council. Handbook; United States Catholic Missionary Personnel Overseas (ISSN 0082-9560)
Missions

266 US
MISSION INTERCOM. 1971. m. (10/yr.) $5 (foreign $7) United States Catholic Mission Association, 1233 Lawrence St., N. E., Washington, DC 20017. TEL 202-832-3112 Ed. Chuck Hackett. circ. 1,200.
Missions

055.1 IT
MISSIONARI DEL P.I.M.E. 1914. m. (11/yr.) L.50000. Pontificio Istituto Missioni Estere, Via Mose Biachi 94, 20149 Milan, Italy. Ed. Piero Gheddo. adv. bk. rev. circ. 20,000.

266 US ISSN 0026-6086
MISSIONHURST. 1948. 6/yr. (Congregation of the Immaculate Heart of Mary) Missionhurst, Inc., 4651 N. 25th St., Arlington, VA 22207. TEL 703-528-3800 Ed. Rev. Louis J. Tysmans. illus. circ. 150,000.
Missions

266 282 IT ISSN 0026-6108
MISSIONI DOMENICANE. 1926. m. (10/yr.) L.5000. Centro Missionario Domenicano, Piazza S. Domenico 1, 51100 Pistoia, Italy. Ed. P. Rossi Giuseppe. charts. illus. circ. 5,000.
Missions

282 CN ISSN 0700-4192
MISSIONS DES FRANCISCIANS. (Text in French) 1923. 4/yr. Can.$5($5) Imprimerie Nationale Joliette Ltee., 2080 Dorchester Ouest, Montreal, Que. H3H 1R6, Canada. TEL 514-932-6094 Ed.Bd. circ. 6,000. (back issues avail.)

059 LO
MOELETSI OA BASOTHO/COUNSELLOR OF BASOTHO. (Text in Sesotho) 1933. w. R.40. (Missionary Oblates of Mary Immaculate) Mazenod Printing Works (Pty) Ltd., P.O. Mazenod, Lesotho. Ed. William Lesenya. adv. circ. 13,000.
Missions

255 CN
MONASTIC STUDIES. 1963. a. $15. Benedictine Priory of Montreal, 1475 Pine Ave., Montreal, Que. H3G 1B3, Canada. TEL 514-849-2728 Ed. Laurence Freeman. bk. rev. circ. 2,500. (also avail. in microform from UMI) Indexed: Cath.Ind.
Supersedes: Cistercian Studies (ISSN 0026-9190)

282 IT
MONASTICA. 1960. q. contribution. Monastero di Santa Scolastica, I-00060 Civitella San Paolo (Rome), Italy. circ. 850. (back issues avail.)

282 266 IT ISSN 0026-6094
MONDO E MISSIONE. 1872. m. (10/yr.) L.20000. Pontificio Istituto Missioni Estere, Via Mose Bianchi 94, 20149-Milan, Italy. Ed. Piero Gheddo. adv. bk. rev. illus. index. circ. 50,000. Indexed: CERDIC.
Formerly: Missioni Cattoliche.
Missions

262.9 IT ISSN 0026-976X
MONITOR ECCLESIASTICUS; commentarius de re cannoica et pastorali post Vaticanum II. (Text in Latin & modern languages) 1876. q. L.5200.($8.50) Agnesotti S.a.S., Piazza M. Fani 2, 01100 Viterbo, Italy. bk. rev. circ. 1,000. Indexed: CERDIC. Canon Law Abstr.
Canon law

282 UK ISSN 0027-0172
MONTH. 1864. m. £10($24) Society of Jesus, British Province, 114 Mount St., London W1Y 6AH, England. Ed. John McDude, S.J. adv. bk. rev. index every 6 months. circ. 2,500. (also avail. in microform from UMI) Indexed: Br.Hum.Ind. Cath.Ind. CERDIC. New Test.Abstr.
Incorporating: Herder Correspondence.

200 IT ISSN 0077-1449
MONUMENTA HISTORICA ORDINIS MINORUM CAPUCCINORUM. (Text in Italian and Latin) 1937. irreg., no.17, 1985. price varies. Frati Minori Cappuccini, Istituto Storico, Cas. Post. 9091, Circonv. Occidentale 6850 (GRA km 65), 00163 Rome, Italy. Ed. Mariano d'Alatri. index. circ. 500.

282 IT
MONUMENTA HISTORICA SOCIETATIS IESU. irreg., latest vol.129. Institutum Historicum Societatis Iesu - Jesuit Historical Institute, Via dei Penitenzieri 20, 00193 Rome, Italy. (back issues avail.)

282 VC ISSN 0077-1457
MONUMENTA IURIS CANONICI. (Series A: Corpus Glossatorum; Series B: Corpus Collectionum; Series C: Subsidia) 1969. irreg. price varies. Biblioteca Apostolica Vaticana, c/o F. Werlen, Economo, 00120 Vatican City, Italy.

266 SP ISSN 0210-0851
MORALIA; revista de ciencias morales. 1963. q. $21. Instituto Superior de Ciencias Morales, Felix Boix, 13, 28036 Madrid, Spain. Ed. Rev. Miguel Rubio. adv. circ. 1,000. Indexed: CERDIC.
Formerly (until vol.16, Dec., 1978): Pentecostes (ISSN 0479-9828)

282 GW ISSN 0077-2011
MUENSTERSCHWARZACHER STUDIEN. 1965. irreg. price varies. (Benediktinerabtei Muensterschwarzach) Vier-Tuerme-Verlag, 8711 Muensterschwarzach, W. Germany (B.R.D.) Ed. Pirmin Hugger. adv. bk. rev.

266 CN ISSN 0316-8913
MY BROTHER AND I. 1968. q. Missionary Association of Mary Immaculate, Oblate Missionary Centre, Box 721, Winnipeg, Man. R3C 2K3, Canada. TEL 204-586-2906 illus. circ. 600.
Missions

282 US
MY DAILY VISITOR. 1955. bi-m. $6.75. Vincent Giese, Pub., 200 Noll Plaza, Huntington, IN 46750. TEL 219-356-8400 Ed. Jacquelyn Murphy. circ. 30,677.

N C E A NOTES. (National Catholic Educational Association) see *EDUCATION*

NASZA PRZESZLOSC. see *HISTORY — History Of Europe*

377.8 US ISSN 0026-914X
NATIONAL CATHOLIC EDUCATIONAL ASSOCIATION. MOMENTUM. 1970. 4/yr. $16. National Catholic Educational Association, 1077 30 St. N.W., Ste. 100, Washington, DC 20007. TEL 202-293-5954 Ed. Patricia Feistritzer. bk. rev. bibl. charts. illus. cum.index every 5 yrs. circ. 14,500. (also avail. in microfilm from UMI; reprint service avail. from UMI) Indexed: Cath.Ind. Curr.Cont. Educ.Ind.

282 US ISSN 0027-8920
NATIONAL CATHOLIC REGISTER. 1928. w. $15. ‡ Twin Circle Publishing Co., 6404 Wilshire Blvd., No. 900, Los Angeles, CA 90048. Ed. Francis X. Maier. adv. bk. rev. film rev. illus. circ. 74,280. Indexed: Cath.Ind.
Formerly: Denver Register.

282 US ISSN 0027-8939
NATIONAL CATHOLIC REPORTER. 1964. w. $27. National Catholic Reporter Publishing Company, Inc., 115 E. Armour Blvd., Box 281, Kansas City, MO 64141. TEL 816-531-0538 Ed. Thomas Fox. adv. bk. rev. illus. circ. 50,000. (tabloid format; also avail. in microform from BLH,UMI; reprint service avail. from UMI) Indexed: Cath.Ind. Access. CERDIC. Curr.Lit.Fam.Plan. Mag.Ind.

NATIONAL DIRECTORY OF CATHOLIC HIGHER EDUCATION. see *EDUCATION — Guides To Schools And Colleges*

NATIONAL FEDERATION OF CATHOLIC PHYSICIANS' GUILDS. NEWSLETTER. see *MEDICAL SCIENCES*

NATIONAL GUILD OF CATHOLIC PSYCHIATRISTS. BULLETIN. see *MEDICAL SCIENCES — Psychiatry And Neurology*

282 US ISSN 0199-5723
NETWORK (WASHINGTON, 1971); Catholic social justice lobby. 1971. bi-m. $20. 806 Rhode Island Ave., N.E., Washington, DC 20018. TEL 202-526-4070 Ed. Dorothy Vidulich. bk. rev. charts. illus. index. circ. 8,000. (tabloid format; back issues avail.)

282 GW
NEUE ORDNUNG. 1946. 6/yr. DM.39. (Institut fuer Gesellschaftswissenschaften Walberberg e.V.) I F G Verlagsgesellschaft mbH, Simrockstr. 19, D-5300 Bonn 1, W. Germany (B.R.D.) Ed. H. Basilius Streithofen. adv. circ. 2,400. (back issues avail.)

282 255 UK ISSN 0028-4289
NEW BLACKFRIARS. 1920; N.S. 1964. m. $23. (English Dominicans) Blackfriars, Oxford, England. Ed. Rev. John Orme Mills. adv. bk. rev. index. circ. 2,000. (also avail. in microfilm from UMI; reprint service avail. from UMI) Indexed: Cath.Ind. Br.Hum.Ind. CERDIC. Old Test.Abstr. New Test.Abstr.
Incorporating: Blackfriars; Life of the Spirit.

282 US
NEW CATHOLIC WORLD. 1865. bi-m. $10. (Missionary Society of St. Paul the Apostle in the State of New York) Paulist Press, 997 Macarthur Blvd., Mahwah, NJ 07430. TEL 201-825-7300 Ed. Laurie Felknor. bk. rev. index. circ. 12,000. (also avail. in microform from BLH,UMI; reprint service avail. from UMI) Indexed: Cath.Ind. Hist.Abstr. R.G. Access. Bk.Rev.Ind. Amer.Hist.& Life. CERDIC. G.Soc.Sci.& Rel.Per.Lit. Mag.Ind.
Formerly: Catholic World (ISSN 0008-848X)

200 US
NEW COVENANT. 1971. 11/yr. $4.95. Servant Publications, Box 8617, Ann Arbor, MI 48107. TEL 313-761-8505 bk. rev. illus. circ. 74,000. (back issues avail.) Indexed: Cath.Ind. CERDIC.
Formerly: Pastoral Newsletter.

282 US ISSN 0008-7890
NEW EARTH. 1938. 9/yr. $7. Catholic Diocese of Fargo, Media Office, c/o Bishop James S. Sullivan, 1310 Broadway, Box 1750, Fargo, ND 58107. TEL 701-235-6429 Ed. Sara McGarvey. adv. circ. 31,000. (tabloid format)
Formerly (until May 1980): Catholic Action News.

282 CN
NEW FREEMAN. 1900. w. Can.$14($24) New Freeman Ltd., One Bayard Drive, St. John, New Brunswick E2L 3L5, Canada. TEL 506-652-3667 Ed. Robert G. Merzetti. adv. bk. rev. (tabloid format; also avail. in microfilm)

282 NZ ISSN 0028-8748
NEW ZEALAND TABLET; New Zealand's national Catholic weekly. 1873. w. NZ.$30. (Roman Catholic Church) New Zealand Tablet Co. Ltd., 64 Vogel St., Dunedin, New Zealand. Ed. J.P. Kennedy. adv. bk. rev. film rev. play rev. bibl. illus. circ. 9,000.

282 281.9 IT
NICOLAUS. vol.6, 1978. s-a. L.10000($14) Istituto di Teologia Ecumenico-Patristica, Via Bisanzio e Rainaldo 15, 70122 Bari, Italy. Indexed: CERDIC.

282 UG ISSN 0048-041X
NILE GAZETTE. (Text in English; supplements in Alur, Logbara and Madi) 1958. m. EAs.6. Diocese of Arua, Box 3230, Kampala, Uganda. Ed. Rev. A. Dalfovo. illus. circ. 7,000. (tabloid format)

282 US
NORTH CAROLINA CATHOLIC. 1946. w. $12. (Roman Catholic Diocese of Raleigh) North Carolina Catholic, 300 Cardinal Gibbons Dr., Raleigh, NC 27606. TEL 919-821-9720 (Co-sponsor: Roman Catholic Diocese of Charlotte) adv. circ. 29,000. (tabloid format; also avail. in microfilm; back issues avail.)

200 028.5 IT ISSN 0029-3903
NOTE DI PASTORALE GIOVANILE. 1967. m. L.24000. (Centro Catechistico Salesiano) Editrice Elle Di Ci, Corso Francia 214, 10096 Leumann (Turin), Italy. Ed. Riccardo Tonelli. bk. rev. index. circ. 6,500. Indexed: CERDIC.

282 VC ISSN 0029-4306
NOTITIAE. (Text in English, French and Latin) 1965. m. L.40000($22) Libreria Editrice Vaticana, Vatican City. illus. index. Indexed: Cath.Ind. CERDIC. Canon Law Abstr.

282 US
NOTRE DAME STUDIES IN AMERICAN CATHOLICISM. 1979. irreg. University of Notre Dame Press, Notre Dame, IN 46556. TEL 219-239-6346 bibl.

266 CN ISSN 0029-4578
LES NOTRES. 1960. q. Can.$1. Procure des Missions Montfortaines, 665 Church St., Dorval, Que. H9S 1R4, Canada. TEL 514-631-1790 Ed. A. Williamson. circ. 15,000.

282 SZ ISSN 0029-5027
NOVA ET VETERA. (Text in French) 1926. q. 45 Fr. Editions Universitaires de Fribourg, 42 Bd. de Perolles, CH-1700 Fribourg, Switzerland. Ed. Georges Cottier. bk. rev. index. Indexed: CERDIC. New Test.Abstr.

282 US
NOVA ET VETERA. 1972. 6/yr. $39. Sunday Publications Inc., 1937 Tenth Ave., N., Lake Worth, FL 33466-9501. TEL 305-533-0990 Ed. Rev. Joseph P. LoCigno. bk. rev. index. (looseleaf format) Indexed: Old Test.Abstr. Rel.& Theol.Abstr.

282 IT ISSN 0078-253X
NOVARIEN. 1967. irreg. price varies. Associazione di Storia Ecclesiastica Novarese, Presso Archivio Storico Diocesano, Palazzo Vescovile, I-28100 Novara, Italy. Ed. Angelo L. Stoppa. bk. rev. circ. 1,000.

282 AG ISSN 0029-585X
NUEVA POMPEYA. 1924. m. Arg.$20000. (Santuario de la Virgen del Rosario) Orden de los Frailes Menores Capuchinos, Esquiu 974, C.C. 14-Suc.37, Buenos Aires, Argentina. Dir. R.P. Andres Guirao. index. circ. 18,000.

282 VC
NUNTIA. s-a. L.25000($16) Libreria Editrice Vaticana, Vatican City, Italy. Indexed: CERDIC. Canon Law Abstr.

282 IT
NUOVA UMANITA. 1979. 5/yr. L.16500. Citta Nuova Editrice, Via degli Scipioni 265, 00192 Rome, Italy. Ed. Giuseppe Zanghi.

282 DK ISSN 0109-0518
NYT FRA D U K. 1978. bi-m. free. Danmarks Unge Katolikker, Sct. Kjeldsgade 3, 2100 Copenhagen OE, Denmark. Ed.Bd. bk. rev. illus. circ. 800.

O E C T A REPORTER. (Ontario English Catholic Teachers Association) see *EDUCATION*

377 BE ISSN 0770-1683
O I E C BULLETIN. (Editions in Enlgish, French and Spanish) 1969. 6/yr. 500 Fr.($20) Catholic International Education Office - Office International de l'Enseignement Catholique, 60 rue des Eburons, 1040 Brussels, Belgium. Ed. L.M. Adams. adv. bk. rev. circ. 700.
Former titles: Catholic International Education Office. Bulletin Nouvelle Serie; Catholic International Education Office. Bulletin Trimestriel (ISSN 0084-8638)

282 UK ISSN 0144-9117
O R C NOTES. 1979. every 6 wks. free. Old Roman Catholic Church, Our Lady's Priory, 10 Barnmead Rd., Beckenham, Kent BR3 1JE, England. Ed. Archbishop-Primate F.G. Linale. bk. rev. circ. 2,000.

266 US
OBLATE WORLD AND VOICE OF HOPE; southern Province edition. 1915. 5/yr. membership. Society of Oblate Fathers for Missions Among the Poor, Inc., 350 Jamaica Way, Boston, MA 02130 TEL 617-266-5999 (And Box 96, San Antonio, TX 78291) Ed. Thomas J. Reddy. illus. circ. 154,400.
Formerly: O M I Mission Magazine.
Missions

282 US ISSN 0029-7739
OBSERVER (ROCKFORD) 1935. bi-w. $10. Catholic Diocese of Rockford, 921 W. State St., Rockford, IL 61102. TEL 815-963-3471 Ed. Owen Phelps, Jr. adv. bk. rev. film rev. circ. 28,500. (newspaper; also avail. in microfilm) Indexed: High.Educ.Curr.Aware.Bull.

282 MW ISSN 0300-4651
ODINI. (Text in Chichewa and English) 1950. fortn. K.5. (Diocese of Lilongwe) Likuni Press and Publishing House, Box 133, Lilongwe, Malawi. Ed. O. Makani. adv. bk. rev. illus. circ. 12,000. (tabloid format; also avail. in newspaper)
Formerly (until 1984): African.

270 239 AU
OESTERREICHISCHE AKADEMIE DER WISSENSCHAFTEN. KOMMISSION ZUR HERAUSGABE DES CORPUS DER LATEINISCHEN KIRCHENVAETER. VEROEFFENTLICHUNGEN. irreg. Verlag der Oesterreichischen Akademie der Wissenschaften, Ignaz Seipel-Platz 2, A-1010 Vienna, Austria.

282 US
OFFICIAL WISCONSIN PASTORAL HANDBOOK. 1962. a. $10 to qualified personnel. ‡ (Milwaukee Catholic Press Apostolate) Catholic Herald, 3501 S. Lake Dr., Box 1572, Milwaukee, WI 53201. adv. circ. 2,300(controlled)

282 UK ISSN 0030-252X
ONE IN CHRIST; a Roman Catholic ecumenical review. 1936. q. £15.35($25) Vita et Pax-Foundation for Unity, Regina Pacis, Turvey Abbey, Turvey, Beds. MK43 8DE, England. Ed. Paschal A. Hardiment. adv. bk. rev. bibl. index. circ. 1,000. (also avail. in microfilm from UMI; reprint service avail. from UMI) Indexed: Br.Hum.Ind. Cath.Ind. CERDIC. Old Test.Abstr. New Test.Abstr. Rel.Ind.One.
Incorporating: Ecumenical Notes.

282 IT ISSN 0030-4174
ORA ET LABORA; quaderni di interesse monastico. 1947. q. L.10000. Monastero S. Benedetto, Via Bellotti 10, 20129 Milan, Italy. Ed.Bd. bk. rev. bibl. circ. 600. Indexed: CERDIC.

282 255 BE ISSN 0030-4336
ORANTE. 1967. 10/yr. fl.17. Mariale Werken, Diestse Vest 25-29, Leuven, Belgium. Ed. Paters Monfortanen. illus. circ. 5,000.

266 CN ISSN 0472-0490
ORIENT. 1953. bi-m. Can.$2. Missions des Peres de Sainte-Croix, 4961 Coronet, Montreal, Que. H3V 1C9, Canada. Ed. Marcel Descheneaux. illus. circ. 15,000.
Missions

ORIENTALIA CHRISTIANA ANALECTA. see *ORIENTAL STUDIES*

282.73 US ISSN 0093-609X
ORIGINS, N C DOCUMENTARY SERVICE. 1971. 48/yr. $79. National Catholic News Service, 1312 Massachusetts Ave., N.W., Washington, DC 20005. TEL 202-659-6732 Ed. David Gibsonaw. circ. 8,500. Indexed: Cath.Ind. CERDIC. Canon Law Abstr. Key Title: Origins (Washington)

249 CN ISSN 0030-6843
OUR FAMILY; Canada's Catholic family monthly magazine. 1949. m. Can.$11($12) (Oblates of St. Mary's Province of Canada) Marian Press Ltd., Box 249, Battleford, Sask. S0M 0E0, Canada. Ed. Rev. Albert LaLonde. adv. illus. circ. 17,552.

282 US ISSN 0030-6886
OUR LADY'S DIGEST. 1946. 5/yr. $4 (bulk rates avail.) LaSalette Publications, 10-330 336th Ave., Box 1022, Twin Lakes, WI 53181. Ed. Rev. Stanley Matuszewski. bk. rev. circ. 50,000. (also avail. in microfilm from UMI; reprint service avail. from UMI) Indexed: CERDIC.

200 US ISSN 0030-6924
OUR NORTHLAND DIOCESE. 1946. 22/yr. $6.50. Northland Diocese Association, 1200 Memorial Dr., Crookston, MN 56716. TEL 218-281-1598 Ed. Ruth A. Ross. adv. bk. rev. circ. 14,500.

266 UK ISSN 0030-7211
OUTLOOK. 1950. q. £4($6) Pontifical Mission Aid Societies, 23 Eccleston Sq., London SW1V 1NU, England. Ed. Mark Swaby. circ. 4,000.

282 US ISSN 0030-7564
OVERVIEW (CHICAGO); a continuing survey of issues affecting Catholics. 1968. m. (11/yr.) $12.95. Thomas More Association, 223 W. Erie St., Chicago, IL 60610. TEL 312-951-2100 Ed. Matthew Schuck Scheiber. circ. 2,000.

266 US ISSN 0030-9222
PADRES' TRAIL. 1937. q. $2. Franciscan Friars, Our Lady of Guadalupe Province, Box 645, St. Michaels, AZ 86511-0645. Ed. Dave Speights. illus. circ. 8,827. (also avail. in microfilm from MCA)
Missions

PAEPSTE UND PAPSTTUM. see *HISTORY — History Of Europe*

200 CL
PANORAMA DE LA TEOLOGIA LATINOAMERICANA. 1974. a. $8. Universidad Catolica de Chile, Seminario Latinoamericano de Documentacon, Casilla 114 D, Santiago, Chile. circ. 3,000.

282 248.83 FR ISSN 0031-1561
PARABOLES. 1949. 4/yr. 16 F. Communautes Chretiennes Universitaires, 5 rue de l'Abbaye, 75006 Paris, France. Ed. Bernard Goudey. bk. rev. circ. 2,500.

282 US
PARISH COMMUNICATION. 1981. q. $17.50. Growth Associates, Box 215, Weston, VT 05161. TEL 802-824-3440 Ed. Patty R. Coleman. abstr. stat. circ. 950. (looseleaf format)

PARISH COORDINATOR OF RELIGIOUS EDUCATION. see *EDUCATION*

266 US
PARISH VISITOR. 1924. q. $2. Parish Visitors of Mary Immaculate, Box 658, Monroe, NY 10950. TEL 914-783-2251 Ed. Sr. Mary Josita Worlock. circ. 3,500.

220 IT ISSN 0031-2398
PAROLE DI VITA. 1956. bi-m. L.17000. (Centro Catechistico Salesiano) Editrice Elle Di Ci, Corso Francia 214, 10096 Leumann (Turin), Italy. Eds. Antonio Fanuli, Francesco Mosetto. bk. rev. index. circ. 3,500.

250 282 IT ISSN 0031-2428
PARROCCHIA. 1947. m. L.6000. Opera Madonna del Divino Amore, Via Ardeatina, Km 12, 00134 Rome, Italy. Dir. Pasquale Silla. bibl. illus. stat. index. cum.index. circ. 6,000.

PATHWAYS (GARDEN GROVE) see *RELIGIONS AND THEOLOGY — Protestant*

282 299 BE
PATROLOGIA SYRIACA ET ORIENTALIS. 1983. irreg. N.V. Brepols I.G.P., Rue Baron Frans du Four 8, B-2300 Turnhout, Belgium.

267 SZ ISSN 0079-0281
PAX ROMANA. Represents: International Catholic Movement for Intellectual Cultural Affairs. Proceedings of the Plenary Assembly. quadrennial, latest 1983. $10. International Catholic Movement for Intellectual and Cultural Affairs - Pax Romana, General Secretariat, B.P. 85, 37-39 Rue de Vermont, CH-1211 Geneva 20-CIC, Switzerland (Subscr. to: Mouvement International des Intellectuels CAtholiques, Pax Romana, 1701 Fribourg, Switzerland) circ. 600.

200 PO
PAZ E ALEGRIA. 1907. m. Esc.250($3) Familia Franciscana Portuguesa, R. Serpa Pinto, 7, P 1200 Lisboa, Portugal. bk. rev. circ. 3,000.
Supersedes: Alma (ISSN 0002-6239)

282 FR ISSN 0031-4781
PENSEE CATHOLIQUE; cahiers de synthese. 1946. bi-m. 500 F. Editions du Cedre, 13 rue Mazarine, 75006 Paris, France. Dir. Abbe Luc J. Lefevre. bk. rev. Indexed: CERDIC.

262.9 VC ISSN 0031-529X
PERIODICA DE RE MORALI CANONICA LITURGICA. (Text in Latin) 1905. q. $40. (Pontificia Universita Gregoriana) Gregorian University Press, Piazza della Pilotta, 35, 00187 Rome, Italy. Ed. Francisco J. Urrutia. index. circ. 1,500. Indexed: Canon Law Abstr.
Canon law

282 266 FR
PEUPLES DU MONDE. 1967. 10/yr. 50 F. S O C E N D I, 8 rue Francois Villon, 75015 Paris, France. illus. Indexed: CERDIC.

255 IT
PICENUM SERAPHICUM. (Text in Italian) irreg. L.3500. Biblioteca Francescana, Conto Corrente Postale 15/27009, Falconara M. 60015, Italy.

282 US ISSN 0032-0323
PITTSBURGH CATHOLIC. 1844. w. $9. ‡ (Catholic Diocese of Pittsburgh) Pittsburgh Catholic Publishing Associates, 100 Wood St., No. 500, Pittsburgh, PA 15222-1906. Ed. Robert Melder. adv. bk. rev. film rev. illus. play rev. circ. 121,500. (newspaper; also avail. in microform)

282 FR
POINT THEOLOGIQUE. irreg. 3141 Fr. Editions Beauchesne, 72 rue des Saints Peres, 75007 Paris, France. Ed. Charles Kannengiesser. Indexed: Rel.Ind.Two.

266 FR ISSN 0032-2504
POLE ET TROPIQUES; revue apostolique des missionnaires oblats. 1920. bi-m. 75 F. Missionnaires Oblats de Marie Immaculee, 145 Montee de Choulans, 69322 Lyon Cedex 05, France. Ed. Henri Mairot. abstr. illus. mkt. stat. index. circ. 23,000.
Missions

200 300 001.3 BL
PONTIFICIA UNIVERSIDADE CATOLICA DE SAO PAULO. REVISTA. q. Cr.$40($10) Pontificia Universidade Catolica de Sao Paulo, Rua Monte Alegre 984, Sao Paulo, Brazil. bk. rev. abstr. bibl.

270 VC
PONTIFICIA UNIVERSITA GREGORIANA. DOCUMENTA MISSIONALIA. (Multi-language text) 1964. irreg. price varies. Gregorian University Press, Piazza della Pilotta, 35, Italy. Ed. Mariasusai Dhavamony.

270 VC ISSN 0080-3979
PONTIFICIA UNIVERSITA GREGORIANA. MISCELLANEA HISTORIAE PONTIFICIAE. (Multi-language text) 1939. irreg., latest, vol.52. price varies. Gregorian University Press, Piazza della Pilotta, 35, 00187 Rome, Italy. Ed. Vincenzo Monachino.

266 VC ISSN 0080-3987
PONTIFICIA UNIVERSITA GREGORIANA. STUDIA MISSIONALIA. (Multi-language text) 1943. a. $40. Gregorian University Press, Piazza della Pilotta, 35, 00187 Rome, Italy. Ed. Mariasusai Dhavamony. Indexed: Cath.Ind. Rel.Ind.One.

282 262 US ISSN 0032-4353
POPE SPEAKS; the Church documents quarterly. 1954. q. $13. Vincent Giese, Pub., 200 Noll Plaza, Huntington, IN 46750. TEL 219-356-8400 Ed. Rev. Albert J. Nevins. adv. bk. rev. bibl. illus. index. circ. 10,500. (also avail. in microform from UMI; reprint service avail. from UMI) Indexed: Cath.Ind. CERDIC.
Papal letters and addresses and other major church documents

282 UK ISSN 0143-0149
POPE TEACHES; a monthly digest of the pastoral teaching of Pope John Paul II. 1978. m. £12($16.80) Incorporated Catholic Truth Society, 38-40 Eccleston Square, London SW1V 1PD, England. Ed. Brendan Walsh.

282 917.106 CN ISSN 0701-0192
POSOL/MESSENGER; religious monthly for Slovak Catholics. (Text in Slovak) 1974. m. Can.$10. Slovak Jesuit Fathers in Canada, P.O. Box 600, Cambridge, Ont. N1R 5W3, Canada. TEL 519-621-8491 Ed. Rajmund Ondrus. bk. rev. circ. 2,800. (back issues avail.)

282 CN ISSN 0032-664X
PRAIRIE MESSENGER. 1923. w. Can.$15.50($29) ‡ Order of St. Benedict, Inc., Muenster, Sask. SOK 2YO, Canada. TEL 306-682-5215 Ed. Andrew Britz. adv. bk. rev. film rev. illus. circ. 14,000. (tabloid format)

282 GW ISSN 0172-7478
PRAXIS IN DER GEMEINDE; materialien und erfahrungen. 1979. q. DM.15.50. Matthias-Gruenewald-Verlag, Postfach 3080, D-6500 Mainz-Weisenau, W. Germany (B.R.D.) Ed. Jakob Laubach. adv. bk. rev. cum.index. circ. 2,200. (back issues avail.)

282 284 US ISSN 0274-600X
PRAYERS FOR WORSHIP. 1978. q. $13.80. Sunday Publications, Inc., 1937 Tenth Ave., N., Lake Worth, FL 33466-9501. TEL 305-533-0990 Ed. Rev. L. Koopman. circ. 2,000. (looseleaf format)

282 US
PRAYING. 1983. bi-m. $7.50. National Catholic Reporter Publishing Company, Inc., 115 E. Armour Blvd., Box 281, Kansas City, MO 64141. TEL 816-531-0538 Ed. Art Winer. adv. bk. rev. illus. circ. 5,400.

282 GW ISSN 0032-7212
DER PREDIGER UND KATECHET. 1850. 6/yr. DM.51. Erich Wewel Verlag, Anzinger Str. 1, 8000 Munich 80, W. Germany (B.R.D.) adv. index. circ. 15,000.

282 250 IT ISSN 0032-7727
PRESENZA PASTORALE. 1931. 10/yr. L.20000. (Collegio Assistenti) Azione Cattolica Italiana, Via della Conciliazione 1, 00193 Rome, Italy. Ed. Fiorino Tagliaferri. bk. rev. bibl. Indexed: CERDIC.
Formerly: Assistente Ecclesiastico.

282 GW ISSN 0172-0929
PRIESTERJAHRHEFT. 1926. a. free. Bonifatiuswerk der Deutschen Katholiken e.V., Kamp 22, 4790 Paderborn, W. Germany (B.R.D.) Ed. Georg Walf. circ. 22,000 (controlled)

282 US
PRO ECCLESIA. 1970. m. $12. Pro Ecclesia Foundation, 663 Fifth Ave., New York, NY 10022. Ed. Timothy A. Mitchell. illus.

282 BE
PRO MUNDI VITA BULLETIN. (Text in English, French, Spanish, Dutch and German) 1963. q. Pro Mundi Vita, Rue de la Science 7, B-1040 Brussels, Belgium. circ. 10,000(controlled) (also avail. in microform from UMI; reprint service avail. from UMI) Indexed: CERDIC. Rel.Ind.One.

282 BE
PRO MUNDI VITA DOSSIERS. Spanish edition: Pro Mundi Vita. Informes. (Separate editions available for: Europe/North America; Asia/Australasia; Africa and Latin America) 1963. q. Pro Mundi Vita, Rue de la Science 7, B-1040 Brussels, Belgium. circ. 13,000(controlled) (also avail. in microform from UMI; reprint service avail. from UMI) Indexed: Rel.Per. CERDIC. Rel.Ind.One.
Formerly (until no.43, 1975): Pro Mundi Vita. Special Notes (ISSN 0079-5593)

282 US
PROBE (CHICAGO); the religious women. 1971. bi-m. $15. National Assembly of Religious Women (N.A.R.W.), 1307 S. Wabash, Rm. 206, Chicago, IL 60605. TEL 312-663-1980 Ed. S. Marjorie Tuite, OP. bk. rev. circ. 2,500. Indexed: CERDIC. South.Bap.Per.Ind.

282 BE
PROBLEMES D'HISTOIRE DU CHRISTIANISME. (Text in French) 1970/71. a. price varies. (Universite Libre de Bruxelles, Institut d'Histoire du Christianisme et de la Pensee Laique) Editions de l'Universite de Bruxelles, Avenue P. Heger, 26-C.P. 163, B-1050 Brussels, Belgium. Indexed: CERDIC.

282 CN ISSN 0033-054X
PROGRESS/POSTUP. (Editions in English and Ukrainian) 1959. w. Can.$20. (Ukrainian Catholic Archdiocese of Winnipeg) Progress Printing & Publishing Co. Ltd., 418 Aberdeen Ave., Winnipeg 4, Man., Canada. TEL 204-582-1940 Ed. Rev. S. Izyk. adv. bk. rev. film rev. play rev. illus. circ. 4,500.

266 CN ISSN 0035-3795
R N D. (Revue Notre Dame) (Text in French) 1903. m. Can.$8. (Revue Notre-Dame) Les Missionnaires du Sacre-Coeur, C.P. 400, Sillery, Quebec, P. Q. G1T 2R7, Canada. TEL 418-681-3581 Ed. Yvon Labbe. adv. illus. circ. 150,000. Indexed: Pt.de Rep.

282 II ISSN 0048-668X
RALLY. (Text in English) vol.50, 1973. bi-m. $6. All India Catholic University Federation, Sterling Rd., Madras 34, India. Ed. A. Tagore. bk. rev. circ. 3,000.

282 267 FR ISSN 0034-0197
RAYONS; revue des jeunesses mariales. 1900. 10/yr. 30 F. Marian Association for Young Girls, 67 rue de Sevres, 75006 Paris, France. bibl.

282 IE ISSN 0034-0960
REALITY. 1936. m. £1.80($5) Redemptorist Publications, 75 Orwell Rd., Dublin 6, Ireland. Ed. Brian Boyle. bk. rev. illus. circ. 34,000. Indexed: CERDIC.

RECUSANT HISTORY. see *HISTORY — History Of Europe*

200 CN ISSN 0025-3065
REGARD DE FOI; revue religieusse d'actualite. 1904. bi-m. Can.$6. Montfort Fathers, 5875 Est rue Sherbrooke, Montreal H1N 1B6, Canada. TEL 514-254-5376 Ed. Odilon Demers. illus. circ. controlled.
Formerly: Marie Reine des Coeurs.

282 IT
IL REGNO. (In 2 sections: Attualita and Documenti) 1956. s-m. L.38000($22) Centro Editoriale Dehoniano, Via Nosadella 6, 40125 Bologna, Italy. Ed. P. Alfio Filippi. circ. 11,000. Indexed: CERDIC.

282 IT ISSN 0034-3498
REGNO-ATTUALITA. 1956. m. L.20500($14) Centro Editoriale Dehoniano, Via Nosadella 6, 40123 Bologna, Italy. adv. bk. rev. bibl. index. cum.index. circ. 10,000.

266 US ISSN 0048-7155
REIGN OF THE SACRED HEART. 1934. m. Priests of the Sacred Heart, 6889 S. Lovers Ln., Hales Corners, WI 53130. TEL 414-425-5323 Ed. Father Brian. illus. circ. 170,000.

RELATIONS. see *GENERAL INTEREST PERIODICALS — Canada*

282 370 IT
RELIGIONE E SCUOLA; mensile per l'animazione culturale e la ricerca religiosa. m. (10/yr.) L.38000. Editrice Queriniana, Via Piamarta 6, 25187 Brescia, Italy. Ed. Flavio Pajer.

280 GW ISSN 0340-8280
RENOVATIO; Zeitschrift fuer das interdisziplinaere Gespraech. (Supplement: Albertus Magnus Blaetter) 1945. q. DM.20. J.P. Bachem Verlag GmbH, Ursulaplatz 1, 5000 Cologne 1, W. Germany (B.R.D.) (Co-sponsor: Katholische Aerztearbeit Deutschlands) Ed. Helmut-Josef Patt. bk. rev. circ. 6,500. Indexed: CERDIC. New Test.Abstr.
Formerly: Katholische Gedanke (ISSN 0022-9385)

282 CL
REVISTA CATOLICA. 1840. q. Esc.90. Imprenta San Jose, Av. El Bosque 822, Santiago 9, Chile. adv. bk. rev. circ. 600.

282 267 AG ISSN 0034-9070
REVISTA DEL HOGAR. s-m. Arg.$1.20. Jovenes de la Accion Catolica, Belgrand 239, Capillaudel Senor, Buenos Aires, Argentina. Ed. Reynaldo Dassat. (processed)

282 PE
REVISTA TEOLOGICA LIMENSE. 1966. 3/yr. $20. Facultad de Teologia Pontificia y Civil de Lima, Calle Carlos Bondy 700, Apdo. 1838, Lima 21, Peru. bk. rev. circ. 500.

282 ZR
REVUE AFRICAINE DE THEOLOGIE. (Text in English and French; summaries in French) 1977. s-a. 1200 Fr.CFA($30) Faculte de Theologie Catholique de Kinshasa, B.P. 1534, Kinshasa/Limetew, Zaire. (back issues avail.) Indexed: CERDIC. New Test.Abstr.

200 BE ISSN 0035-0893
REVUE BENEDICTINE; de critique, d'histoire et de litterature religieuses. (Text in English, French, German and Italian) 1884. 2/yr. $40. Abbaye de Maredsous, B-5198 Denee, Belgium. Dir. Pierre Patrick Verbraken. bk. rev. abstr. index. Indexed: Bull.Signal. M.L.A. Old Test.Abstr. New Test.Abstr.

209 BE ISSN 0035-2381
REVUE D'HISTOIRE ECCLESIASTIQUE. 1900. q. 2500 Fr.($54) fr.$24) Universite Catholique de Louvain, Bibliotheque, College Erasime, B-1348 Louvain-la-Neuve, Belgium. Ed. Roger Aubert. bk. rev. bibl. charts. index. cum.index every 15-20 yrs. circ. 250. Indexed: M.L.A. Rel.Per. Arts & Hum.Cit.Ind. New Test.Abstr. Rel.Ind.One. Rel.& Theol.Abstr.
History

209 FR ISSN 0035-2217
REVUE DES SCIENCES RELIGIEUSES. 1921. q. 59 F. Universite de Strasbourg II, Faculte de Theologie Catholique, 22 rue Rene Descartes, 67084 Strasbourg, France. Ed. Dr. Jacques E. Minard. bk. rev. index. circ. 700. Indexed: Old Test.Abstr. Rel.Per. CERDIC. New Test.Abstr. Rel.Ind.One.

248.894 FR ISSN 0035-3620
REVUE MABILLON. (Text in French and Latin) 1905. q. 180 F. Abbaye St. Martin, 86240 Liguge, France. Ed. Jean Becquet. adv. bibl. charts. illus. index. circ. 200. (also avail. in microform from JAI)
History of French monasteries

200 BE ISSN 0080-2654
REVUE THEOLOGIQUE DE LOUVAIN. 1970. 4/yr. 1000 Fr. Universite Catholique de Louvain, Faculte de Theologie et de Droit Canonique, Grand-Place 45, 1348 Louvain-la-Neuve, Belgium. Ed. J. Ponthot. bk. rev. circ. 1,300. Indexed: Cath.Ind. Arts & Hum.Cit.Ind. New Test.Abstr.

282 BE
REVUE THEOLOGIQUE DE LOUVAIN. CAHIERS. (Text in French) 1980. irreg., vol.2, 1980. (Universite Catholique de Louvain, Facultes de Theologie et de Droit Canonique) Editions Peeters s.p.r.l., Bondgenotenlaan 153, B-3000 Louvain, Belgium. Indexed: Old Test.Abstr. CERDIC.

282 100 IT ISSN 0393-3849
RICERCHE STORICHE SALESIANE; rivista semestrale di storia religiosa e civile. 1982. s-a. L.20000. (Istituto Storico Salesiano) Editrice L.A.S. (Libreria Ateneo Salesiano), Piazza dell'Ateneo Salesiano, 1, 00139 Rome, Italy. Ed. Pietro Braido. bk. rev. circ. 500.

282 IT ISSN 0042-7586
RIVISTA DEL CLERO ITALIANO. 1920. m. L.34000($20) (Universita Cattolica del Sacro Cuore) Vita e Pensiero, Largo Gemelli 1, 20123 Milan, Italy. Ed. Sandro Maggiolini. adv. bk. rev. bibl. index. Indexed: CERDIC.

282 IT
RIVISTA DI ASCETICA E MISTICA. s-a. Via Cavour, 56, Florence, Italy. Ed. A. Spinillo.

282 248 VC ISSN 0035-6638
RIVISTA DI VITA SPIRITUALE. 1947. bi-m. L.10000. (Pontificio Istituto di Spiritualita) Edizioni O.C.D., Via Gregorio VII, 133, 00165 Rome, Italy. Ed. R.P. Ermanno Ancilli. bk. rev. bibl. index. circ. 2,000.

282 IT ISSN 0035-6654
RIVISTA DIOCESANA DEL PATRIARCATO DI VENEZIA. 1925. 10/yr. L.5000. Curia Patriarcale di Venezia, S. Marco 320a, 30124 Venezia, Italy.

282 IT ISSN 0035-6956
RIVISTA LITURGICA. 1914. bi-m. L.26000. (Centro Catechistico Salesiano) Editrice Elle Di Ci, Corso Francia 214, 10096 Leumann (Turin), Italy. Ed. Ferdinando dell'Oro. bk. rev. cum.index: 1914-1974. circ. 2,200. Indexed: CERDIC.

262.9 PL ISSN 0035-7723
ROCZNIKI TEOLOGICZNO-KANONICZNE. (In six parts: 1. Holy Scripture; 2. Fundamental and Dogmatic Theology; 3. Moral Theology; 4. History of Church; 5. Canon Law; 6. Pastoral Theology) (Text in Polish; summaries in English, French, German, Italian and Latin) 1949. 6/yr. price varies. Katolicki Uniwersytet Lubelski, Towarzystwo Naukowe, Chopina 29, 20-023 Lublin, Poland. Ed.Bd. bk. rev. index. circ. 820. Indexed: Old Test.Abstr. CERDIC. New Test.Abstr.

282 PO ISSN 0035-8274
ROSARIO DE MARIA; publicacao mensal de espiritualidade rosario mariana. 1944. m. Esc.50($4) Dominican Convent Friars-Fatima, Secretariado Nacional do Rosario, Fatima, Portugal. Ed. L. Cerdeira. bk. rev. illus. index. circ. 7,000.

282 US ISSN 0745-3299
ROZE MARYI. (Text in Polish) 1944. m. $4. Association of Marian Helpers, Stockbridge, MA 01262. TEL 413-298-3691 Ed. Rev. Bernard Backiel. bk. rev. circ. 9,500.

S A; a journal in the sociology of religion. (Sociological Analysis) see *SOCIOLOGY*

266 IE
S M A-THE AFRICAN MISSIONARY. (Text in English & Gaelic) 1914. 5/yr. £2. ‡ S M A Fathers, Blackrock Road, Cork, Ireland. Ed. Rev. Tony Gill. adv. bk. rev. circ. 40,000.
Formerly: African Missionary (ISSN 0044-6580)
Missions

282 IE
SACRED HEART MESSENGER. 1888. m. £0.30. (Jesuit Fathers) Irish Messenger Publications, 37 Lower Leeson St., Dublin 2, Ireland. Ed. Rev. Father Paul Leonard, S.J. charts. illus. pat. tr.mk. circ. 205,000.
Formerly: Irish Messenger of the Sacred Heart (ISSN 0021-1303); Incorporating: Madonna (ISSN 0024-9572)

282 US ISSN 0036-276X
ST. ANTHONY MESSENGER. 1893. m. $12. (Franciscan Friars of St. John the Baptist Province) St. Anthony Messenger Press, 1615 Republic St., Cincinnati, OH 45210. TEL 513-241-5615 Ed. Rev. Norman Perry. adv. bk. rev. film rev. index. circ. 430,000. (also avail. in microform from UMI; reprint service avail. from UMI) Indexed: Cath.Ind. CERDIC.

200 US ISSN 0080-5432
SAINT BONAVENTURE UNIVERSITY. FRANCISCAN INSTITUTE. PHILOSOPHY SERIES. 1944. irreg., no.16, 1972. price varies. Franciscan Institute, St. Bonaventure University, St. Bonaventure, NY 14778. TEL 716-375-2105 Ed. Rev. George H. Marcil, O.F.M.

200 US ISSN 0080-5440
SAINT BONAVENTURE UNIVERSITY. FRANCISCAN INSTITUTE. TEXT SERIES. 1951. irreg., no.16, 1972. price varies. Franciscan Institute, St. Bonaventure University, St. Bonaventure, NY 14778. TEL 716-375-2105 Ed. Rev. George H. Marcil, O.F.M.

282 GE ISSN 0487-2088
ST. HEDWIGSBLATT; katholisches Kirchenblatt im Bistum Berlin. 1954. 52/yr. M.10.20. Bischofliches Ordinariat Berlin, Hinter der katholischen Kirche, 1080 Berlin, E. Germany (D.D.R.) bk. rev. circ. 25,000.

282 US ISSN 0036-3022
ST. LOUIS REVIEW. 1957. w. $10. ‡ Catholic Archdiocese of St. Louis, 462 N. Taylor Ave., St. Louis, MO 63108. Ed. Rev. Edward J. Sudekum. adv. bk. rev. film rev. illus. circ. 100,000. (also avail. in microfilm)

200 AT ISSN 0036-3219
SAINT VINCENT DE PAUL RECORD. 1935. q. Aus.$1. Saint Vincent de Paul Society, National Council of Australia, 7 Young St., Sydney N.S.W. 2000, Australia. Ed. John McFadden. bk. rev. illus. index. circ. 17,000.

200 FR ISSN 0036-3243
SAINTE THERESE DE LISIEUX. ANNALES. 1925. m. 60 F. Direction du Pelerinage de Lisieux, 33 rue du Carmel, B.P. 95, 14102 Lisieux Cedex, France. Ed. Pere Paul Gires. bk. rev. circ. 35,000.

200 VC ISSN 0036-3502
SALESIANUM. (Text in English, French, German, Italian, Latin, Spanish) 1939. q. L.45000($25) Universita Pontificia Salesiana, Piazza Ateneo Salesiano 1, 00139 Rome, Italy. adv. bk. rev. circ. 800. Indexed: M.L.A. CERDIC. Canon Law Abstr. New Test.Abstr. Rel.& Theol.Abstr.

200 260 SP ISSN 0036-3537
SALMANTICENSIS. 1954. 3/yr. 1200 ptas.($30) Universidad Pontificia de Salamanca, Calle Compania 1, Salamanca, Spain. bk. rev. bibl. index. circ. 2,000(controlled) (looseleaf format) Indexed: CERDIC. Rel.Ind.One.

282 US
SAN FRANCISCO CATHOLIC. 1985. m. $18. Archdiocese of San Francisco, Chancery Office, 441 Church St., San Francisco, CA 94114. TEL 415-565-3630 Ed. Maury L. Welsh. adv. bk. rev. film rev. play rev. circ. 48,000. (also avail. in microfilm)
Supersedes (1858-1985): Monitor (ISSN 0026-9743)

282 IT ISSN 0036-116X
SANTA CASA DI LORETO. MESSAGGIO. English edition: Shrine of the Holy House. Loreto. 1881 (Engl. edt. 1968) m. (Engl. edt. 3/yr.) L.3000($10) for Italian edt. Congregazione Universale della Santa Casa, 60025 Loreto (Ancona), Italy. Ed. Giuseppe Santorelli. bk. rev. illus. circ. 36,000.

SANTO; rivista antoniana di storia dottrina arte. see *ART*

282 255 IT ISSN 0036-4606
SANTO DEI VOLI. 1946. m. L.800($2) (Frati Minori Conventuali di Puglia, Provincia Religiosa) Santuario S. Giuseppe da Copertino, Via Piave 2, Copertino, Italy. Ed. Eugenio Galignano OFM. adv. bk. rev. film rev. cum.index. circ. 5,000. (cards)

266 IT ISSN 0036-4622
SANTUARIO DELLA MADONNA DELLE ROCCHE. 1920. bi-m. L.2000. Passionisti, 15074 Molare, Alessandria, Italy. bibl. charts. illus. stat. index. circ. 1,000. (tabloid format)

SAPIENZA; rivista internazionale di filosofia e di teologia. see *PHILOSOPHY*

SCHOOL EN GODSDIENST; catechetical periodical for elementary school teachers. see *EDUCATION — Teaching Methods And Curriculum*

266 US ISSN 0487-6830
SCHOOL SISTER OF NOTRE DAME. 1958. 3/yr. $3. School Sisters of Notre Dame, Milwaukee Province, 1233 N. Marshall St., Milwaukee, WI 53202. TEL 414-278-7300 Ed. Sr. Francele Sherburne. illus. circ. 14,000.

220 282 UK ISSN 0036-9780
SCRIPTURE BULLETIN. 1969. s-a. £3($10) Catholic Biblical Association of Great Britain, 1 Malcolm Rd., London SW19 4AS, England. (Co-sponsor: Bible Reading Fellowship) Ed. Michael Prior. adv. bk. rev. circ. 500. Indexed: Cath.Ind. Old Test.Abstr.

282 IE ISSN 0332-1150
SCRIPTURE IN CHURCH. 1970. q. £16.24($20) Dominican Publications, St. Saviour's, Upper Dorset St., Dublin 1, Ireland (U.S. distr. addr.: Costello Publishing, Nautilus Ave., Northport, NY 11768) Ed. Martin McNamara. circ. 6,200. (back issues avail.) Indexed: New Test.Abstr. Old Test.Abstr.

230 IT ISSN 0036-9810
SCUOLA CATTOLICA. 1873. bi-m. L.32000($32) Seminario Arcivescovile di Milano, Venegono Inferiore, Varese, Italy. Ed. T. Citeini. bk. rev. index. circ. 1,100. Indexed: CERDIC. New Test.Abstr. Rel.& Theol.Abstr.

SELEBRIAMO; rivista mensile di musica per la liturgia. see *MUSIC*

200 VC ISSN 0582-6314
SEMINARIUM; a review for seminaries, ecclesiastical vocations, universities. (Text in language of authors) 1950. N.S. 1961. q. L.30000($25) (Pontifical Society for Priestly Vocations) Libreria Editrice Vaticana, 00120 Vatican City, Italy. bk. rev. bibl. index. circ. 2,500. Indexed: Cath.Ind. CERDIC.

248.8 IT ISSN 0037-2439
SERAFICO VESSILLO; bollettino fer il Terz'Ordine e fer le Vocazioni. 1955. m. L.1000. (Terz'ordine e le Vocazioni Cappuccine Salernitane) Fratelli Jovane, Via Lungomare 162, Salerno, Italy. Ed. Dir. Aldo Catalano. circ. 2,000.

SINGENDE KIRCHE; Zeitschrift fuer katholische Kirchenmusik. see *MUSIC*

248 US ISSN 0037-590X
SISTERS TODAY. 1929. m. $14. Liturgical Press, Saint John's Abbey, Collegeville, MN 56321. TEL 612-363-2213 Ed. Sr. Mary Anthony Wagner. adv. bk. rev. index. circ. 8,460. (also avail. in microform from UMI; reprint service avail. from UMI) Indexed: Cath.Ind. A.I.P.P. CERDIC.
Formerly: Sponsa Regis.

200 CN ISSN 0085-6134
SLOVENSKI JEZUITI V KANADE. YEAR BOOK. (Text in Slovak; summaries in English) 1954. a. contr. free circ. Slovak Jesuit Fathers in Canada, Box 600, Cambridge, Ont. N1R 5W3, Canada. TEL 519-621-8491 Ed. Rev. Vincent Danco. adv. bk. rev. illus. stat. circ. 8,000.

SOCIAL JUSTICE REVIEW; pioneer American journal of Catholic social action. see *SOCIOLOGY*

SOCIAL WORK AND CHRISTIANITY; an international journal. see *SOCIAL SERVICES AND WELFARE*

282 US ISSN 0038-187X
SOUNDS OF TRUTH AND TRADITION. 1965. q. free to qualified personnel. Catholic Traditionalist Movement, Inc., 200 Park Ave., Ste. 303 E., Pan Am Bldg., New York, NY 10017. TEL 212-986-2515 Ed. Father Gommar A. De Pauw. bk. rev. Indexed: CERDIC.

282 SA ISSN 0038-4011
SOUTHERN CROSS. 1920. w. R.21. ‡ (Southern African Catholic Bishops' Conference) Catholic Newspaper and Publishing Co. Ltd., Box 2372, Cape Town 8000, South Africa. adv. bk. rev. film rev. illus. circ. 13,000. Indexed: CERDIC.

282 US ISSN 0745-0257
SOUTHERN CROSS. 1937. w. $15. Roman Catholic Diocese of San Diego, Box 81869, San Diego, CA 92138. TEL 619-574-6393 Ed. Bill Finley. adv. bk. rev. film rev. play rev. illus. tr.lit. circ. 22,000. (back issues avail.)

282 US ISSN 0038-4690
SOUTHWEST KANSAS REGISTER. 1966. w. $5 $4 outside Kansas. Catholic Diocese of Dodge City, Box 1317, Dodge City, KS 67801. Ed. Margaret Klenke. adv. bk. rev. illus. circ. 9,530. (tabloid format)

282 255 US ISSN 0038-7592
SPIRIT & LIFE. 1905. 6/yr. $5. Benedictine Convent of Perpetual Adoration, 8300 Morganford Rd., St. Louis, MO 63123 TEL 314-638-6427 (Subscr. addr.: Benedictine Convent of Perpetual Adoration, Clyde, MO 64432) Ed. Sr. M. Romanus Penrose. bk. rev. illus. circ. 6,000. (also avail. in microform from UMI; reprint service avail. from UMI) Indexed: CERDIC.

282 US ISSN 0038-7630
SPIRITUAL LIFE. 1955. q. $9. Discalced Carmelite Fathers, Washington Province, 2131 Lincoln Rd., N.E., Washington, DC 20002. TEL 202-832-6622 Eds. Rev. Christopher Latimer, Rev. Steven Payne. bk. rev. bibl. circ. 14,500. (also avail. in microform from UMI; reprint service avail. from UMI) Indexed: Cath.Ind. CERDIC.

230 282 US ISSN 0162-6760
SPIRITUALITY TODAY; a quarterly of spiritual theology. 1949. q. $9. (Dominicans, Province of St. Albert the Great) Spirituality Today Journal, Inc., 1909 S. Ashland Ave., Chicago, IL 60608. TEL 312-226-0075 Ed. Rev. Christopher Kiesling. bk. rev. index. circ. 4,500. (also avail. in microform from UMI; reprint service avail. from UMI) Indexed: Cath.Ind. CERDIC. Old Test.Abstr.
Formerly (until 1977): Cross and Crown (ISSN 0011-1910)

282 255 NE ISSN 0038-8904
STAD GODS. 1932. m. fl.9.20. Zusters Augustinessen van Sint Monica, Soestdijkerstraatweg 151, 1213 VZ Hilversum, Netherlands. bk. rev. illus. circ. 60,000.

282 GH ISSN 0038-9374
STANDARD; national Catholic weekly. 1938. w. NC.7. (Ghana Catholic Hierarchy) Catholic Mission Press, Royal Lane, Box 60, Cape Coast, Ghana. Ed. Rev. Martin T. Peters. circ. 11,000. (processed)

940 AU ISSN 0081-5594
STILLE SCHAR. 1953. a. S.35. Gebetsliga, Wickenburggasse 5/10, A-1080 Vienna, Austria. circ. 10,000.

250 IT ISSN 0039-2901
STUDI CATTOLICI; mensile di studi ed attualita. 1957. m. L.30000($40) (Associazione Ricerche e Studi) Edizioni A.R.E.S., Via A. Stradivari 7, 20131 Milan, Italy. Ed. Cesare Cavalleri. adv. bk. rev. bibl. charts. illus. index. Indexed: CERDIC.

282 IT
STUDI E RICERCHE FRANCESCANE. 1972. q. L.10000($11) Istituto Meridionale di Francescanesimo, Piazza S. Eframo Vecchio 21, 80137 Naples, Italy. Ed. Ferdinando Mastroianni. adv. bk. rev. index. circ. 400. Indexed: CERDIC.

271 IT ISSN 0039-3045
STUDI STORICI DELL'ORDINE DEI SERVI DI MARIA. (Text and summaries in English, French, German, Italian, Portuguese, Spanish) 1933. s-a. L.28000($18.60) Ordine dei Servi di Maria, Istituto Storico, Viale Trenta Aprile, 6, 00153 Rome, Italy. Ed. Davide M. Montagna. bk. rev. bibl. charts. illus. pat. stat. index. circ. 300.
History

282 GW
STUDIEN UND MITTEILUNGEN ZUR GESCHICHTE DES BENEDIKTINER. ORDENS UND SEINER ZWEIGE. 1880. 2/yr. Bayerische Benediktinerakademie, 8000 Munich, W. Germany (B.R.D.) illus. cum.index.

230 GW ISSN 0081-7295
STUDIEN ZUR GESCHICHTE DER KATHOLISCHEN MORALTHEOLOGIE. vol.3, 1955. irreg., vol.28, 1986. price varies. Verlag Friedrich Pustet, Gutenbergstr. 8, 8400 Regensburg 1, W. Germany (B.R.D.) Ed. Johannes Gruendel. circ. 500.

255 IT ISSN 0562-4649
SUBSIDIA SCIENTIFICA FRANCISCALIA. (Text in French, German, Italian and Latin) 1962. irreg., no.6, 1978. price varies. Frati Minori Cappuccini, Istituto Storico, Casella Postale 9091, Circonv. Occidentale 6850 (GRA km 65), 00163 Rome, Italy. index. circ. 500.

200 AT ISSN 0039-6184
SURSUM CORDA; lift up your hearts. 1955. bi-m. Aus.$6. Franciscan House of Formation of Australian - New Zealand Province, Box 79, Box Hill, Victoria 3128, Australia. Ed. Rev. Ralph Byrne. bk. rev. index every 2 yrs. circ. 5,100.

282 US
SV. PRANCISKAUS VARPELIS/BELL OF ST. FRANCIS. (Text in Lithuanian) 1942. 6/yr. $5. Franciscan Fathers of Maine, Franciscan Vicariate of St. Casimir, Kennebunkport, ME 04046. TEL 207-967-2011 Ed. Paulius Jurkus. bk. rev. circ. 2,000.

282 US
SYNTHESIS (MYSTIC) 1981. q. $17.50. Growth Associates, Box 215, Weston, VT 05161. TEL 802-824-3440 Ed. William V. Coleman. abstr. stat. circ. 600. (looseleaf format) Indexed: Chem.Abstr.

282 US ISSN 0039-8845
TABLET. 1908. w. $15. (Roman Catholic Diocese of Brooklyn) Tablet Publishing Co., Inc., 1 Hanson Pl., Brooklyn, NY 11243. TEL 718-789-1500 Ed. Edward Wilkinson. adv. bk. rev. illus. circ. 110,000. (also avail. in microform) Indexed: Cath.Ind.

282 GE ISSN 0492-1283
TAG DES HERRN; katholishes Kirchenblatt. 1951. bi-w. M.4.80. (Berliner Bischofskonferenz) St. Benno-Verlag, Thuringer Str. 1-3, 7033 Leipzig, E. Germany (D.D.R.) (Subscr. to: Tag des Herrn, Petersteinweg 17, 7010 Leipzig, D.D.R.) bk. rev. circ. 100,000.

282 US
TALKS OF POPE JOHN PAUL II. 1965. s-m. $10. Pro Ecclesia Foundation, 663 Fifth Ave., New York, NY 10022. Ed. Timothy A. Mitchell. illus.
Formerly: Talks of Pope Paul VI.

301.5 BL
TEOCOMUNICACAO. 1971. 4/yr. Cr.$80($25) (Pontificia Universidade Catolica do Rio Grande do Sul, Instituto de Teologia) Editorial da PUCRS, c/o Nilo Berto, Caixa Postal 1429, 90,000 Porto Alegre, Brazil. Ed. Urbano Zilles. bk. rev. circ. 1,500.

282 HU ISSN 0133-1779
TEOLOGIA. 1967. 4/yr. 40 Ft. Actio Catholica Orszagos Elnoksege, Karoly Mihaly U. 4-8, 1053 Budapest 5, Hungary. Ed. Szennay Andras. bk. rev. circ. 4,000. Indexed: CERDIC.

240 CL ISSN 0049-3449
TEOLOGIA Y VIDA. 1959. q. $22. Universidad Catolica de Chile, Facultad de Teologia, Jose Batile y Ordonez 3300, Casilla 114-D, Santiago, Chile. Ed. Marciano Barrios. adv. bk. rev. abstr. bibl. cum.index: 1960-1979. circ. 700. Indexed: Bull.Signal. Cath.Ind. Old Test.Abstr. Canon Law Abstr. New Test.Abstr.

282 VC
TERESIANUM. (Text in several languages) 1947. s-a. L.30000($26) (Pontificia Facolta Teresianum) Edizioni del Teresianum, Piazza S. Pancrazio 5-A, 00152 Rome, Italy. Ed. R.P. Virgilio Pasquetto. circ. 800. Indexed: Old Test.Abstr. CERDIC. New Test.Abstr.
Formerly (until vol.33, 1982): Ephemerides Carmeliticae.

282 IT ISSN 0040-3938
TESORO EUCARISTICO. 1917. bi-m. (except Jul.-Aug.) L.20000. Frati Minori Conventuali della Basilica di S. Francesco in Siena, Santuario delle Ss. Particole, 53100 Siena, Italy. Ed. P. Antonio Giannini. bk. rev. circ. 2,000.

282 IT
TESTIMONI; quindicinale di informazione e aggiornamento per istituti di vita consagrata. s-m. L.22000. Centro Editoriale Dehoniano, Via Nosadella, 6, 40123 Bologna, Italy. Ed.Bd. circ. 11,000.

200 CK
THEOLOGICA XAVERIANA. 1950. q. Col.$1500($20) Pontificia Universidad Javeriana, Facultad de Teologia, Carrera 10, No. 65-48, Bogota 2 D.E., Colombia. Dir. Alberto Parra. adv. bk. rev. index. circ. (controlled) (processed; back issues avail.) Indexed: Bull.Sign. Canon Law Abstr.
Formerly: Ecclesiastica Xaveriana (ISSN 0012-9054)

282 GW ISSN 0342-1430
THEOLOGISCHE QUARTALSCHRIFT. 1819. q. DM.56. Erich Wewel Verlag, Anzinger Str. 1, D-8000 Munich 80, W. Germany (B.R.D.) index. Indexed: Rel.Ind.One.

230 GW ISSN 0040-568X
THEOLOGISCHE REVUE. 6/yr. DM.90. (Universitaet Muenster, Katholisch-Theologische Fakultaet) Aschendorffsche Verlagsbuchhandlung, Soester Str. 13, Postfach 1124, 4400 Muenster, W. Germany (B.R.D.) Eds. Erwin Iserloh, Vinzenz Pfnuer. adv. bk. rev. bibl. index. Indexed: CERDIC. New Test.Abstr.

THOMAS; maandblad voor lichamelijke opvoeding. see *EDUCATION — Teaching Methods And Curriculum*

230 100 US ISSN 0040-6325
THOMIST; a speculative quarterly review of theology and philosophy. 1939. q. $15. (Dominican Fathers, Province of St. Joseph) Thomist Press, 487 Michigan Ave., N.E., Washington, DC 20017. TEL 202-529-5300 Ed. Rev. Joseph A. DiNoia. adv. bk. rev. bibl. index. cum.index: vol.1-15, 1939-1952. circ. 1,500. (also avail. in microfilm from UMI) Indexed: Cath.Ind. Curr.Cont. Arts & Hum.Cit.Ind. CERDIC. New Test.Abstr. Phil.Ind. Rel.& Theol.Abstr.

282 US ISSN 0040-6791
TIDINGS; official Catholic weekly newspaper of Los Angeles. (Text mainly in English; occasionally in Spanish) 1895. w. $12. (Roman Catholic Archdiocese of Los Angeles) Tidings Corp., 1530 W. Ninth St., Los Angeles, CA 90015. TEL 213-251-3360 Ed. Mr. Al Antczak. adv. bk. rev. film rev. play rev. illus. circ. 48,000. (also avail. in microform)

282 284 NE ISSN 0168-9959
TIJDSCHRIFT VOOR THEOLOGIE. (Text in Dutch; summaries in English) 1961. q. fl.62.50. Studia Catholica Foundation, Postbus 35, 6500 AA Nijmegen, Netherlands. Ed. T.M. Schoof. adv. bk. rev. index. circ. 2,500. (back issues avail.) Indexed: New Test.Abstr. Old Test.Abstr. CERDIC.

TODAY'S CATHOLIC TEACHER. see *EDUCATION*

282 AG
TRADICION, FAMILIA, PROPIEDAD. 1969. bi-m. $22. Sociedad Argentina de Defensa de la Tradicion, Familia y Propiedad, Avda. Figueroa Alcorta 3260, Buenos Aires, Argentina. illus. circ. 2,500.
Supersedes: Cruzada.

TRIADS. see *BUSINESS AND ECONOMICS — Marketing And Purchasing*

282 US ISSN 0041-7548
U S CATHOLIC. 1963. m. $15. Claretian Publications, 205 W. Monroe St., Chicago, IL 60606. TEL 312-236-7782 Ed. Rev. Mark J. Brummel. adv. bk. rev. illus. circ. 96,777. (also avail. in microform from BLH,UMI; reprint service avail. from UMI) Indexed: Cath.Ind. R.G. Abstrax. CERDIC. G.Soc.Sci.& Rel.Per.Lit. Mag.Ind. PMR.

UNDA-U S A NEWSLETTER. see *COMMUNICATIONS — Radio And Television*

282 US
U.S. PARISH; the newsletter that makes good parishes better. 1983. m. $24.95. Claretian Publications, 205 W. Monroe St., Chicago, IL 60606. TEL 312-236-7782 Ed. Rev. Mark J. Brummel. circ. 1,933.

282 UK ISSN 0041-8226
UNIVERSE. 1860. w. 15p. Associated Catholic Publications (1912) Ltd., 33-39 Bowling Green Lane, London EC1R 0AB, England. Ed. Christopher Monckton. adv. bk. rev. illus. circ. 160,900. (tabloid format)
Incorporating: Catholic Times.

200 CL ISSN 0069-3596
UNIVERSIDAD CATOLICA DE CHILE. FACULTAD DE TEOLOGIA. ANALES. 1940. irreg., vol.33, 1982. $25 per no. Universidad Catolica de Chile, Facultad de Teologia, Jose Batile y Ordonez 3300, Casilla 114-D, Santiago, Chile. cum.index: 1940-1969. circ. 500. Indexed: Bull.Sign. Cath.Ind.

282 BE
UNIVERSITE CATHOLIQUE DE LOUVAIN. FACULTES DE THEOLOGIE ET DE DROIT CANONIQUE. COLLECTION DES DISSERTATIONS PRESENTEES POUR L'OBTENTION DU GRADE DE MAITRE A LA FACULTE DE THEOLOGIE OU A LA FACULTE DE DROIT CANONIQUE. 1841. irreg. (series quarto, vol. 5, 1985) Universite Catholique de Louvain, Facultes de Theologie et de Droit Canonique, Grand-Place 45, 1348 Louvain-la-Neuve, Belgium.
Formerly: Universite Catholique de Louvain. Facultes de Theologie et de Droit Canonique. Dissertationes ad Gradum Magistri in Facultate Theologica Vel in Facultate Iuris Canonici Consequendum Conscriptae.

200 BE ISSN 0076-1230
UNIVERSITE CATHOLIQUE DE LOUVAIN. FACULTES DE THEOLOGIE ET DE DROIT CANONIQUE. TRAVAUX DE DOCTORAT EN THEOLOGIE ET EN DROIT CANONIQUE. NOUVELLE SERIE. 1969. irreg., vol. 11, 1985. exchange basis. Universite Catholique de Louvain, Facultes de Theologie et de Droit Canonique, Grand-Place 45, 1348 Louvain-la-Neuve, Belgium. circ. 120.

268 US ISSN 0070-3052
UNIVERSITY OF DAYTON. SCHOOL OF EDUCATION. WORKSHOP PROCEEDINGS. 1970. irreg., latest issue, 1971. $3.25. University of Dayton, School of Education, Dayton, OH 45469. TEL 513-229-3146 Ed. Louis J. Faerber.
Catholic education: elementary and secondary

264 US ISSN 0076-003X
UNIVERSITY OF NOTRE DAME. DEPARTMENT OF THEOLOGY. LITURGICAL STUDIES. 1955. irreg., no. 11, 1977. price varies. ‡ University of Notre Dame Press, Notre Dame, IN 46556. TEL 219-239-6346 Indexed: Cath.Ind.

282 IT ISSN 0042-2304
VALLE SANTA DI RIETI; periodico di cultura e propaganda Francescana. 1948. q. free. (Santuari Francescani Valle di Rieti) Convento S. Antonio al Monte, Rieti, Italy. Ed. Rev. Ettore Giustino Marini. adv. bk. rev. illus. circ. 5,000.

282 US
VATICAN VOICES AND NOTABLE PAPAL QUOTES. 1979. w. $18. Truth, Inc., 3400 W. Michigan St., Milwaukee, WI 53208. TEL 414-258-2665 Ed. Rev. Cletus Healy, S.J. index. circ. 200. (looseleaf format)

200 IT
VENGA IL TUO REGNO. 1945. m. (11/yr.) L.5000. Pontificio Istituto Missioni Estere (Naples), Viale Colli Aminei 36, 80131 Naples, Italy. Ed. Raffaele Trotta. adv. bk. rev. circ. 10,800.

VERBUM; tijdschrift voor katechese. see *EDUCATION — Teaching Methods And Curriculum*

282 US ISSN 0042-4145
VERMONT CATHOLIC TRIBUNE. 1957. bi-w. $8. Vermont Catholic Press Association, 351 North Ave., Bishop Brady Center, Burlington, VT 05401. TEL 802-658-6110 Ed. Mark D. Lombard. adv. bk. rev. film rev. illus. circ. 22,000. (also avail. in microfilm)

282 IT ISSN 0042-4242
VERONA FEDELE; settimanale cattolico della diocesi. 1946. w. L.33000. Editrice Verona Fedele, Via Pieta Vecchia 2, Verona 37100, Italy. Ed.Bd. adv. bk. rev. circ. 30,000.

255 IT ISSN 0042-4374
VERSO L'AZZURRO. 1963. m. free. Centro Nazionale Associazione Mariana, Via Francesco Albergotti 75, 00167 Rome, Italy. bk. rev. circ. 2,300.

266 SP ISSN 0211-9749
VIDA RELIGIOSA. 1944. s-m. (not issued Jul., Aug.) 2,300 ptas. Misioneros Hijos del Immaculado Corazon de Maria (Claretianos), Buen Suceso, 22, Madrid, 8, Spain. adv. bk. rev. bibl. charts. stat. tr.lit. index. circ. 10,000(controlled) (back issues avail.) Indexed: CERDIC. Canon Law Abstr.
Missions

282 II
VIDYAJYOTI; journal of theological reflection. 1938. m. Rs.24($7) Vidyajyoti Educational and Welfare Society, 23 Raj Nivas Marg, Delhi 110054, India. Ed. S. Arokiasamy. adv. bk. rev. circ. 2,500. Indexed: Old Test.Abstr. Canon Law Abstr. New Test.Abstr.
Formerly: Clergy Monthly.

282 FR ISSN 0042-5362
VIE CATHOLIQUE DU BERRY. 1865. bi-m. 120 F. Association Diocesaine de Bourges, Archeveche de Bourges, 4 Av. du 95e de Ligne, B.P. 95, 18002 Bourges (Cher), France. adv. bk. rev. circ. 1,400.

200 FR ISSN 0042-5613
VIE SPIRITUELLE. 1919. 5/yr. 218 F. Editions du Cerf, 29 bd. Latour-Maubourg, 75007 Paris, France. bk. rev. bibl. Indexed: Cath.Ind. Old Test.Abstr. CERDIC.

282 FR ISSN 0042-5621
VIE THERESIENNE. 1961. q. 60 F. Direction du Pelerinage de Lisieux, 33 rue du Carmel, B.P. 95, 14102 Lisieux Cedex, France. Ed. Pere Paul Gires. bk. rev. circ. 470.

282 800 HU ISSN 0042-6024
VIGILIA. (Text in Hungarian; summaries in English, French and German) 1935. m. 260 Ft.($25) Actio Catholica, Kossuth Lajos u. 1, 1053 Budapest 5, Hungary (Subscr. to: Kultura, Box 149, H-1389 Budapest, Hungary) Ed. Laszlo Lukacs. bk. rev. circ. 12,000. Indexed: CERDIC.

282 IT ISSN 0042-7233
VITA CATTOLICA. 1916. w. L.30000. Diocesi di Cremona, Piazza S.A.M. Zaccaria 3, 26100 Cremona, Italy. Ed. Erole Brocchieri. adv. illus. (tabloid format)

282 IT ISSN 0042-7276
VITA GIUSEPPINA. 1895. m. L.8000($5) Congregazione di S. Giuseppe (Giuseppini del Murialdo), Via degli Etruschi 7, 00185 Rome, Italy. Ed. Garuti Vittorio. adv. bk. rev. illus. index. cum.index. circ. 18,500. (back issues avail.)

282 IT ISSN 0042-7365
VITA SOCIALE. 1944. bi-m. L.25000. Centro Riviste della Provincia Romana dei Frati Predicatori, Piazza S. Domenico 1, 51100 Pistoia, Italy. Ed. Marino Eugenio. bk. rev. bibl. illus. stat. index. circ. 1,000. (tabloid format) Indexed: CERDIC.

200 IT ISSN 0042-7845
VOCE DELLA MADONNA DELLE GRAZIE. 1954. w. L.800($1.50) Opera Madonna delle Grazie, Via Andria, Corato, Bari 70033, Italy. Ed. Favia Ferrara Don Giuseppe. illus.

282 IT ISSN 0042-7853
VOCE DI FERRARA. 1954. w. L.10000. (Curia Arcivescovile di Ferrara) Casa Editrice Istituto Padano di Arti Grafiche, Via Montebello 8, Ferrara, Italy. adv. bk. rev. circ. 4,000. (tabloid format)
Formerly: Voce Cattolica.

282 JO
VOICE OF THE HOLY LAND/SAWT EL-ARD EL-MUKADDASH. (Text in Arabic) 1968. m. 5000 din. Catholic Bureau of Press and Publication, Box 1317, Amman, Jordan. Ed. Raouf Najjar. adv. bk. rev. circ. 2,000.

282 260 UK ISSN 0043-1575
WAY (LONDON, 1961); a quarterly review of Christian spirituality. (Supplement avail.) 1961. q. £12.20($25) (Society of Jesus) Way Publications, 39 Fitzjohn's Ave., London NW3 5JT, England. Eds. Rev. Philip Sheldrake, Rev. David Lonsdale. bk. rev. circ. 4,000. (also avail. in microform from UMI) Indexed: Cath.Ind. Old Test.Abstr. CERDIC. New Test.Abstr.

282 255 US
WAY (SAN FRANCISCO) 1948. 10/yr. $4. Franciscan Fathers of California, Inc., 109 Golden Gate Ave., San Francisco, CA 94102. TEL 212-235-5962 Ed. Fr. Simon Scanlon. adv. bk. rev. illus. circ. 9,972. Indexed: CERDIC.
Former titles: Way of St. Francis; Way-Catholic Viewpoints (ISSN 0043-1591)

282 US
WAY-UKRAINIAN CATHOLIC BI-WEEKLY/WAY. (Text in English and Ukrainian) 1939. bi-w. $10. (Ukrainian Catholic Archdiocese of Philadelphia) Apostolate, Inc., 827 N. Franklin St., Philadelphia, PA 19123. TEL 215-922-5231 Eds. Dr. Ronald Popivchak, Iwan Skoczylas. bk. rev. illus. circ. 9,900.
Formerly: Shlach (ISSN 0043-1583)

282 AU ISSN 0043-2679
DIE WENDE; Oesterreichs groesste Wolhenzeitung fuer junge Erwachsene. 1945. w. S.75 per quarter. (Katholisches Jugendwerk Oesterreichs) Styria Verlag, Schoenaugasse 64, A-8011 Graz, Austria. Ed. Hannes Labner. circ. 35,000.

282 US
WEST TEXAS ANGELUS. (Text in English, Spanish) 1964. s-m. $6. Catholic Diocese of San Angelo, Box 1829, San Angelo, TX 76902-1829. TEL 915-653-2466 Ed. Rev. Maurice J. Voity. adv. bk. rev. circ. 17,400. (tabloid format)
Formerly: Texas Concho Register (ISSN 0040-425X)

282 US
WEST TEXAS CATHOLIC. 1936. w. $8. ‡ Roman Catholic Diocese of Amarillo, c/o Bishop L.T. Matthiesen, Box 5644, Amarillo, TX 79117-5644. Ed. Deacon Leroy Behnke. adv. circ. 8,750.
Formerly: West Texas Register (ISSN 0043-3187)

282 CN ISSN 0512-5235
WESTERN CATHOLIC REPORTER. 1965. w. Can.$18($25) Great Western Press Ltd., 10562 109 St, Edmonton, Alta. T5H 3B2, Canada. TEL 403-420-1330 Ed. Shirley Pfister. adv. bk. rev. film rev. circ. 36,103. (tabloid format)

266 970.1 US
WIND RIVER RENDEZVOUS. 1971. q. $10. St. Stephens Indian Mission Foundation, St. Stephens, WY 82524. Ed. Ronald L. Mamot. illus. circ. 29,000.
Missions

942 UK
WORCESTERSHIRE RECUSANT. 1963. s-a. membership. Worcestershire Catholic History Society, c/o Thomas Rock, More House, Haywood Drive, Tettenhall, Wolverhampton WV6 8RF, England. Ed. J.D. McEvilly. bibl. circ. 150.

282 US ISSN 0193-9211
WORD & SPIRIT. 1979. a. price varies. (St. Scholastica Priory) St. Bede's Publications, Box 545, Rt. 32, Petersham, MA 01366. TEL 617-724-3407 Ed.Bd. circ. 300. (also avail. in microform from UMI; back issues avail.) Indexed: Cath.Ind. CERDIC. ERIC. Rel.& Theol.Abstr.

WORKERS' CHALLENGE; from the workers to the workers. see *BUSINESS AND ECONOMICS — Labor And Industrial Relations*

282 947 US
WORLD LITHUANIAN ROMAN CATHOLIC DIRECTORY. 1975. biennial. $10. Lithuanian R. C. Priests' League, 351 Highland Blvd., Brooklyn, NY 11207. TEL 718-827-1350 Ed. Victor Dabusis. adv. stat. circ. 1,000.

264 US ISSN 0043-941X
WORSHIP; concerned with the issues of liturgical renewal. 1926. bi-m. $18. Liturgical Press, St. John's Abbey, Collegeville, MN 56321. TEL 612-363-2213 Ed. Kevin Seasholtz. adv. bk. rev. index. cum.index every 25 yrs. circ. 6,210. (also avail. in microfilm from UMI; reprint service avail. from UMI) Indexed: Cath.Ind. Old Test.Abstr. Rel.Per. CERDIC. Canon Law Abstr. New Test.Abstr. Rel.Ind.One. Rel.& Theol.Abstr.

266 US
XAVERIAN MISSIONS NEWSLETTER. 1951. bi-m. $5. St. Francis Xavier Foreign Missionary Society, Inc., 101 Summer St., Holliston, MA 01746. Ed. Rev. Dominic Calarco. bk. rev. circ. 22,000. (looseleaf format)

282 US
YOUTH UPDATE. m. $6. (Franciscan Friars of St. John the Baptist Province) St. Anthony Messenger Press, 1615 Republic St., Cincinnati, OH 45210. TEL 513-241-5615 Ed. Carol Ann Morrow. circ. 48,000.

266 US ISSN 0514-2482
ZEAL. 1952. q. (St. Elizabeth Mission Society) Franciscan Sisters of Allegany, Allegany, NY 14706. TEL 716-373-0200 Ed. Sr. Eva Di Camillo. circ. 10,000.
Missions

282 NZ ISSN 0044-202X
ZEALANDIA; the Catholic newspaper. 1934. w. NZ.$820. Roman Catholic Bishop of Auckland, 2 St. Patricks Square, Auckland, New Zealand. Ed. Michael Fitzsimons. adv. bk. rev. film rev. play rev. bibl. circ. 14,000. (tabloid format)

282 AU ISSN 0044-2895
ZEITSCHRIFT FUER KATHOLISCHE THEOLOGIE. 1877. q. S.532. (Universitaet Innsbruck, Theologische Fakultaet) Verlag Herder, Wollzeile 33, A-1010 Vienna, Austria. Ed. P. Hans Bernh Meyer. adv. bk. rev. bibl. index. cum.index. circ. 900. Indexed: Old Test.Abstr. CERDIC. Canon Law Abstr.

280 GW
ZENTRALKOMITEE DER DEUTSCHEN KATHOLIKEN. MITTEILUNGEN. 1969. m. free. Zentralkomitee der Deutschen Katholiken, Hochkreuzallee 246, 5300 Bonn-Bad Godesberg, W. Germany (B.R.D.) Ed. Friedrich Kronenberg. circ. 1,500.

RELIGIONS AND THEOLOGY — Other Denominations And Sects

A E U REPORTS. (American Ethical Union) see *PHILOSOPHY*

281.62 266 US
A M A A NEWS. (Text in Armenian and English) 1967. bi-m. contributions. Armenian Missionary Association of America, Inc., 140 Forest Ave., Paramus, NJ 07652. TEL 201-265-2607 Eds. G.H. Chopourian, M.B. Janbazian. adv. bk. rev. illus. cum.index. circ. 10,000.
Formerly (until 1976): A.M.A.A. Newsletter; Incorporating: Armenian-American Outlook (ISSN 0004-2307)

289 US
ACTS & FACTS. 1972. m. free upon request; bulk rate avail. Institute for Creation Research, 2100 Greenfield Dr., El Cajon, CA 92021. Ed. Henry M. Morris. adv. circ. 60,000. Indexed: CERDIC.

289 DK ISSN 0109-1743
ADVANCE. German edition (ISSN 0109-1735) (Text in English) bi-m. Church of Scientology, Advanced Organisation Saint Hill Europe and Africa, Jernbanegade 6, 1608 Copenhagen V, Denmark. illus.

289.9 250 US ISSN 0001-8589
ADVANCE (SPRINGFIELD); a magazine for assemblies of God ministers and church leaders. 1965. m. $10. (General Council of the Assemblies of God) Gospel Publishing House, 1445 Boonville, Springfield, MO 65802. TEL 417-862-2781 Ed. Gwen Jones. adv. bk. rev. index. cum.index: 1965-1974; 1975-1979; 1980-1984. circ. 27,000.

286 US ISSN 0360-389X
ADVENTIST HERITAGE; a journal of Adventist history. 1974. s-a. $5. Loma Linda University, Department of Archives and Special Collections, Loma Linda, CA 92354. TEL 714-796-3741 Eds. Jonathan Butler, Gary Land. adv. bk. rev. illus. circ. 2,000. (also avail. in microfilm from UMI) Indexed: Hist.Abstr. Amer.Hist.& Life.

200 II
AIM. (Text in English) 1970. m. Rs.5($6) Evangelical Fellowship of India, M96 Greater Kailash I, New Delhi 110048, India. Ed. D. John Richard. adv. bk. rev. circ. 3,300.
Supersedes: Evangelical Fellowship Quarterly.

267.15 UK ISSN 0002-5623
ALL THE WORLD. 1884. q. £3.50. Salvation Army, 101 Queen Victoria St., London EC4P 4EP, England. Ed. Will Burrows. circ. 21,000.

200 GW
ALT-KATHOLISCHES JAHRBUCH. 1901. a. DM.6. Katholisches Bistum der Alt-Katholiken in Deutschland, Gregor-Mendel-Str. 28, 5300 Bonn 1, W. Germany (B.R.D.) circ. 6,000.

281.9 GR
ANALECTA VLATADON. irreg., latest no.49. price varies. Patriarchal Institute for Patristic Studies, Heptapyrgiou 64, 546 34 Thessaloniki, Greece.

200 FR ISSN 0083-6184
ASSEMBLEES DE DIEU DE FRANCE. ANNUAIRE. 1958. a. 8 F. Viens et Vois, 10 rue de Sentier, 75002 Paris, France.

ATHEISM AND DIALOGUE/ATHEISME ET DIALOGUE/ATEISMO Y DIALOGO. see *PHILOSOPHY*

281.9 GR
ATHENISIN ETHNIKON KAI KAPODISTRAKION PANEPISTEMION. THEOLOGIKE SCHOLE. EPISTEMONIKE EPETERIS. (Text in English, French and Greek) 1935. a. Athenisin Ethnikon kai Kapodistrakion, Theologike Schole, Odos Panepistimiou, Athens 143, Greece.

255 PO
AVIVAMENTO. q. Esc.70. Casa Publicadoradas Assembleias de Deus, Av. Alm. Gago Coutinho 158, 1700 Lisbon, Portugal. Ed. Fernanco Martinez da Silva. circ. 4,000.

282 US ISSN 0005-237X
AWAKE. (Editions in 53 Languages) 1919. s-m. $4. Watchtower Bible and Tract Society of New York, Inc., 25 Columbia Hts., Brooklyn, NY 11201. TEL 718-625-3600 circ. 10,480,000.

297.88 US ISSN 0005-2388
AWAKENER; a journal devoted to Meher Baba. 1953. a. $12. (Universal Spiritual League of America, Inc.) Awakener Press, 938 18th St., Hermosa Beach, CA 90254. TEL 213-379-2656 Ed. Filis Frederick. bk. rev. illus. circ. 1,000. (back issues avail.) Indexed: New Per.Ind.

281.9 US ISSN 0278-551X
AXIOS; the orthodox journal. 1980. m. $10. Axios Newsletter, Inc., 800 S. Euclid St., Fullerton, CA 92632. TEL 714-526-2131 Ed. Daniel John Gorham. adv. bk. rev. circ. 2,398.

281 CN ISSN 0382-6384
BEACON; Ukrainian rite bi-monthly. Ukrainian edition: Svitlo/Light (ISSN 0039-7164) (Text in English) 1966. bi-m. Can.$8($8) (Order of Saint Basil-The-Great in Canada) Basilian Press, 286 Lisgar St., Toronto, Ont. M6J 3G9, Canada. TEL 416-535-6483 Ed. Rev. Anthony Holowaychuk. adv. bk. rev. circ. 1,300.

268 US
BEADS OF TRUTH. 1972. s-a. $10. Three H O Foundation, 1620 Preuss Rd., Los Angeles, CA 90035. TEL 213-553-9935 Ed. S.S. Satsimran Kaur Khalsa. adv. bk. rev. illus. circ. 3,000.

297.89 499.9 US
BELMONDA LETERO. (Text in Esperanto) 1973. q. membership only. Bahaa Esperanto-Ligo, RR 1, Box 30, Wilber, NE 68465. TEL 301-270-8658 Ed. June Knudsen-Fritz. adv. bk. rev. circ. 250. (looseleaf format)

281.62 US ISSN 0199-8765
BEMA. 1980. m. free to members. Diocese of the Armenian Church of America, 630 Second Ave., New York, NY 10016. TEL 212-686-0710 Ed. Michael Zeytoonian. bk. rev. illus. circ. 8,500. Indexed: CERDIC.
Supersedes: Armenian Church (ISSN 0004-2315) & Hayastanyaitz Yegeghetzy (ISSN 0017-8667)

268.1 NE ISSN 0006-2243
BIJBELLESSEN VOOR DE SABBATSCHOOL. 1897. q. fl.1.75. (Zevende-Dags Adventisten - Seventh-Day Adventists) Stichting Uitgeverij "Veritas", Postbus 630, The Hague, Netherlands. illus.

377 CN ISSN 0006-4327
BLACKBOARD BULLETIN. 1957. m. (10/yr.) $2.00. Pathway Publishing Corporation, R.R.4, Aylmer, Ont., Canada. Ed. Elizabeth Miller. illus. circ. 15,500.
Amish interests

289 NE
BOODSCHAP. 1978. q. fl.20. Soefi-Orde Nederland, Hermelijnlaan 9, 1216 EB Hilversum, Netherlands. Ed. Akbar Helweg. adv. bk. rev. circ. 350.

289.7 US ISSN 0006-8209
BOTE; ein mennonitsches Familienblatt. (Text and summaries in German) 1924. w. $18. Mennonite Church, General Conference, 722 Main St., Box 347, Newton, KS 67114. TEL 316-283-5100 Ed. Gerhard Ens. adv. bk. rev. circ. 7,000. (tabloid format) Indexed: CERDIC.

BRAILLE STAR THEOSOPHIST. see *BLIND*

289.9 US ISSN 0006-9515
BREAD OF LIFE. 1951. m. (except Aug. & Sep.) $5. Ridgewood Pentecostal Church, 457 Harmon St., Brooklyn, NY 11237. Ed. Gordon P. Gardiner. bk. rev. charts. illus. biennial index. cum.index: 1951-1971. circ. 1,100. Indexed: CERDIC.

200 US
BREAKTHROUGH (WHEATON) 1971. bi-m. free. Slavic Gospel Association, Box 1122, Wheaton, IL 60189. TEL 312-690-8900 Ed. Wil Triggs. charts. illus. circ. 60,000.
Formerly: Slavic Gospel News (ISSN 0049-0709)

289.9 US ISSN 0006-9663
BRETHREN LIFE AND THOUGHT; a quarterly journal published in the interest of the Church of the Brethren. 1955. q. $12. (Brethren Journal Association) Brethren Press, Butterfield & Meyers Rds., Oak Brook, IL 60521. (Co-sponsor: Bethany Theological Seminary) Ed. Warren S. Kissinger. bk. rev. cum.index: vols.1-26. circ. 800. (also avail. in microfilm from UMI; reprint service avail. from UMI) Indexed: Rel.Per. Bk.Rev.Mo. CERDIC. Rel.Ind.One. Rel.& Theol.Abstr.

266 US ISSN 0161-5238
BRETHREN MISSIONARY HERALD. 1940. m. $8.25. (Fellowship of Grace Brethren Churches) Brethren Missionary Herald, Inc., Box 544, Winona Lake, IN 46590. TEL 219-267-7158 Ed. Charles W. Turner. adv. bk. rev. illus. circ. 9,000(controlled) (back issues avail.)
Missions

255 US ISSN 0007-2451
BROTHERS NEWSLETTER. vol.11, 1969. q. $3. National Assembly of Religious Brothers, 100 Monastery Ave, West Springfield, MA 01089. Ed. Brother Damian Carroll, C.P. adv. bk. rev. illus. circ. 3,500. Indexed: CERDIC.

266 GW
DER BRUEDERBOTE. 1949. m. DM.27. (Europaeisch-Festlaendische Brueder-Unitaet - Moravian Church of Europe) Quell Verlag, Postfach 897, 7000 Stuttgart 1, W. Germany (B.R.D.) adv. bk. rev. illus. circ. 1,500.

289 US
BUILDER (SCOTTDALE) 1950. m. $21.75. Mennonite Publishing House, 616 Walnut Ave., Scottdale, PA 15683. TEL 412-887-8500 (Co-publisher: Faith and Life Press) Ed. John Rogers. circ. 7,800.

289.9 US
C O G NEWSLETTER. 1975. 8/yr. donation. Covenant of the Goddess, Box 1226, Berkeley, CA 94704. Ed. M. Macha NightMare. adv. bk. rev. illus. circ. 200.

C P S BULLETIN. (New Zealand Christian Pacifist Society) see *POLITICAL SCIENCE*

299.6 ZR ISSN 0008-0047
CAHIERS DES RELIGIONS AFRICAINES. (Text in English and French) 1967. s-a. $20. Faculte de Theologie Catholique de Kinshasa, P.O. Box 712, Kinshasa/Limete, Zaire. (Co-sponsor: Centr D'Etudes de Religions Africaines) Ed. Prof. Vincent Mulago. adv. bk. rev. bibl. illus. circ. 1,000. Indexed: CERDIC. Curr.Cont.Africa.

281.62 CN
CANADA ARMENIAN PRESS. NEWSLETTER. (Text in Armenian and English) 1963. q. contributions. Armenian Evangelical Church, 34 Glenforest Rd., Toronto, Ont. M4N 1Z8, Canada. TEL 416-489-3188 Ed. Rev. Yesai Sarmazian. adv. bk. rev. illus. circ. 450.
Formerly: Canada Armenian Press (ISSN 0008-2562)

289 CN ISSN 0008-4425
CANADIAN MESSENGER OF THE SACRED HEART. 1891. m. Can.$5. Apostleship of Prayer, 661 Greenwood Ave., Toronto M4J 4B3, Ont., Canada. TEL 416-466-1195 Ed.Bd. adv. bk. rev. illus. circ. 15,500. (back issues avail.)

289.6 CN
CANADIAN QUAKER HISTORY NEWSLETTER. 1972. irreg., (2-3/yr.) Canadian Friends Historical Association, 60 Lowther Ave., Toronto, Ont. M5R 1C7, Canada. Eds. Kathleen Hertzberg, Jane Zavitz. circ. 150.

212.5 CN ISSN 0045-544X
CANADIAN THEOSOPHIST. 1920. bi-m. Can.$4.50. ‡ Theosophical Society in Canada, Box 5051, Postal Sta. A, Toronto, Ont. M5W 1N4, Canada. TEL 416-922-5571 Eds. Ted G. & Doris Davy. bk. rev. index. circ. 600.

CENTER FOR PROCESS STUDIES. NEWSLETTER. see *PHILOSOPHY*

289.9 US
CHILDREN OF THE EARTH; for Pagan families with kids. 4/yr. $5. Box 116, Berkeley Springs, WV 25411-0116. bk. rev. illus.

200 UK ISSN 0009-5117
CHRISTADELPHIAN; dedicated wholly to the hope of Israel. 1864. m. £12.50($19.35) Christadelphian Magazine and Publishing Association Ltd., 404 Shaftmoor Lane, Hall Green, Birmingham B28 8SZ, England. Ed. Michael Ashton. illus. index. circ. 6,700.

275.93 TH
CHRISTIAN DIRECTORY. (Text in English and Thai) a. B.75. Suthep Chaviwan, Box 1405, Bangkok, Thailand. illus.

267 UK
CHRISTIAN ENDEAVOUR PROGRAMME BOOK. 1896. a. £2.25 for each edt. ‡ Christian Endeavour Union of Great Britain and Ireland, 18 Leam Terrace, Royal Leamington Spa, Warwickshire CV31 1BB, England. Ed. Olive Woodham. adv. bk. rev. circ. 1,700.
Former titles: Christian Endeavour Topic Book; Christian Endeavour Year Book (ISSN 0069-3863)
Missions

289.7 US ISSN 0009-5419
CHRISTIAN LEADER. 1937. fortn. $12. ‡ (U S Conference of Mennonite Brethren Churches) Mennonite Brethren Publishing House, Box L, Hillsboro, KS 67063. Ed. Don Ratzlaff. adv. bk. rev. illus. index. circ. 9,500.

281.9 GR
CHRISTIAN LITERATURE. irreg., latest vol.2. price varies. Patriarchal Institute for Patristic Studies, Heptapyrgiou 64, 546 34 Thessaloniki, Greece.

CHRISTIAN SCIENCE BIBLE LESSONS (BRAILLE EDITION) see *BLIND*

289.5 US ISSN 0009-5613
CHRISTIAN SCIENCE JOURNAL. 1883. m. $24. Christian Science Publishing Society, One Norway St., Boston, MA 02115. TEL 617-450-2000 Ed. Allison W. Phinney. index. Indexed: CERDIC.

289.5 252 US ISSN 0145-7365
CHRISTIAN SCIENCE QUARTERLY (INKPRINT EDITION); Bible lessons. Danish edition (ISSN 0145-739X); Dutch edition (ISSN 0145-742X); French edition (ISSN 0145-7438); German edition (ISSN 0145-7411); Greek edition (ISSN 0145-9503); Italian edition (US ISSN 0145-7373) Japanese edition (US ISSN 0145-7527) Norwegian edition (US ISSN 0145-7381) Polish edition (US ISSN 0145-7446) Portuguese edition (US ISSN 0145-7454) (Editions in Braille; Also Spanish (ISSN 0145-7462), Swedish (ISSN 0145-7403)) 1890. q. $7. Christian Science Publishing Society, One Norway St., Boston, MA 02115. TEL 617-450-2000

289.5 US ISSN 0009-563X
CHRISTIAN SCIENCE SENTINEL. 1898. w. $36. Christian Science Publishing Society, One Norway St., Boston, MA 02115. TEL 617-450-2000 Ed. Allison W. Phinney. adv. index. Indexed: CERDIC.

282 GW
CHRISTIEN HEUTE; Zeitung der Alt-Katholiken fuer Christen heute. N.S. 1956. m. DM.18. Katholisches Bistum der Alt-Katholiken in Deutschland, Gregor-Mendel-Str. 28, D-5300 Bonn 1, W. Germany (B.R.D.)
Formerly: Alt-Katholische Kirchenzeitung (ISSN 0002-6522)

289.9 US ISSN 0009-630X
CHURCH ADVOCATE. 1835. m. $8.35. Churches of God, General Conference, Box 926, Findlay, OH 45839. TEL 419-424-1961 Ed. Linda Draper. bk. rev. illus. index. circ. 8,000.

285 US ISSN 0009-6393
CHURCH HERALD. 1826. fortn. $11. (Reformed Church in America) Church Herald, Inc., 1324 Lake Dr. S.E., Grand Rapids, MI 49506. TEL 616-458-5156 Ed. John Stapert. adv. bk. rev. illus. index. circ. 53,000. (also avail. in microfilm; reprint service avail. from UMI) Indexed: G.Soc.Sci.& Rel.Per.Lit.

266 289.9 US ISSN 0009-6504
CHURCH OF GOD MISSIONS. 1951. m. (except Aug.) $5. Church of God, Missions Education Committee, Box 2337, Anderson, IN 46018. TEL 317-649-7597 Ed. Dondeena Caldwell. adv. bk. rev. illus. circ. 11,500.

289.9 US
CIRCLE NETWORK NEWS; international neo-Pagan networking newspaper. 1980. 4/yr. $9. Circle Santuary, Box 9013, Mt. Horeb, WI 53572. Ed. Dennis Carpenter. adv. bk. rev. illus. (tabloid format)

266 US
COLUMBIA UNION VISITOR. 1895. s-m. $6. (Columbia Union Conference of Seventh-Day Adventists) Review and Herald Publishing Association, 5427 Twin Knolls Rd., Columbia, MD 21045. TEL 301-596-0800 Ed. Kermit Netteberg. adv. bk. rev. circ. 35,000.

289.9 US ISSN 0735-9780
COMING REVOLUTION. 1980. 4/yr. $10. Summit University Press, Box A, Malibu, CA 90265. adv. circ. 100,000.
Former titles (until 1986): Heart; Coming Revolution.

204 US
COMPANY; a magazine of the American Jesuits. 1983. q. Jesuit Conference, 3441 N. Ashland Ave., Chicago, IL 60657. TEL 312-281-1818 Ed. E.J. Mattimoe. circ. 230,000.

CONCORD. see *HOMOSEXUALITY*

281.9 BE ISSN 0070-0398
CORPUS SCRIPTORUM CHRISTIANORUM ORIENTALIUM: AETHIOPICA. (Text in Ethiopian) 1904. irreg., latest no.78, 1985. price varies. (Universitatis Catholicae Lovaniensis) Editions Peeters s.p.r.l., Bondgenotenlaan 153, B-3000 Louvain, Belgium. (Co-sponsor: Catholic University of America) bk. rev.

281.9 BE ISSN 0070-0401
CORPUS SCRIPTORUM CHRISTIANORUM ORIENTALIUM: ARABICA. (Text in Arabic) 1903. irreg., latest no.45, 1985. price varies. (Universitatis Catholicae Lovaniensis) Editions Peeters s.p.r.l., Bondgenotenlaan 153, B-3000 Louvain, Belgium. (Co-sponsor: Catholic University of America) bk. rev.

281.9 BE ISSN 0070-041X
CORPUS SCRIPTORUM CHRISTIANORUM ORIENTALIUM: ARMENIACA. (Text in Armenian) 1953. irreg., no.14, 1984. price varies. (Universitatis Catholicae Lovaniensis) Editions Peeters s.p.r.l., Bondgenotenlaan 153, B-3000 Louvain, Belgium. (Co-sponsor: Catholic University of America) bk. rev.

281.9 BE ISSN 0070-0428
CORPUS SCRIPTORUM CHRISTIANORUM ORIENTALIUM: COPTICA. (Text in Coptic) 1906. irreg., no. 42, 1980. price varies. (Universitatis Catholicae Lovaniensis) Editions Peeters s.p.r.l., Bondgenotenlaan 153, B-3000 Louvain, Belgium. (Co-sponsor: Catholic University of America) bk. rev.

281.9 BE ISSN 0070-0436
CORPUS SCRIPTORUM CHRISTIANORUM ORIENTALIUM: IBERICA. (Text in Georgian) 1950. irreg., latest no.20, 1984. price varies. (Universitatis Catholicae Lovaniensis) Editions Peeters s.p.r.l., Bondgenotenlaan 153, B-3000 Louvain, Belgium. (Co-sponsor: Catholic University of America) bk. rev.

281.9 BE ISSN 0070-0444
CORPUS SCRIPTORUM CHRISTIANORUM ORIENTALIUM: SUBSIDIA. (Text in English, French and German) 1950. irreg., no.73, 1985. price varies. (Universitatis Catholicae Lovaniensis) Editions Peeters s.p.r.l., Bondgenotenlaan, B-3000 Louvain, Belgium. (Co-sponsor: Catholic University of America) bk. rev.

281.9 BE ISSN 0070-0452
CORPUS SCRIPTORUM CHRISTIANORUM ORIENTALIUM: SYRIACA. 1903. irreg., no.202, 1985. price varies. (Universitatis Catholicae Lovaniensis) Editions Peeters s.p.r.l., Bondgenotenlaan, B-3000 Louvain, Belgium. (Co-sponsor: Catholic University of America) bk. rev.

289.9 US
COUNCIL OF THE MYSTIC ARTS. NEWSLETTER. 12/yr. $24. Council of the Mystic Arts, Spectrum of the Seven Keys, 538 Hammond Ave., San Antonio, TX 78210. illus.

285.734 US ISSN 0011-0671
COVENANT COMPANION. 1926. m. $18. (Evangelical Covenant Church) Covenant Publications, 5101 N. Francisco Ave., Chicago, IL 60625. TEL 312-784-3000 Ed. James R. Hawkinson. adv. bk. rev. index. circ. 27,000.

289 UK
COVENANT VOICE. 1945. m. £0.35 per issue to non-members. Covenant Peoples Fellowship, 87 St. Barnabas Rd., Woodford Green, Essex IG8 7BT, England. Ed. Rev. Francis Thomas. charts. illus. index. circ. 4,000.
Formerly (until Jun. 1982): Brith (ISSN 0007-0211)

207 YU ISSN 0352-4000
CRKVA U SVIJETU. (Text in Croatian; summaries in English and French) 1966. q. 2000 din.($16) Nadbiskupija Splitsko-Makarska, Zrinjsko-Frankopanska 14, 58001 Split, Yugoslavia. Ed. Drago Simundza. bk. rev. circ. 2,000.

266 UK ISSN 0045-9119
CROSSROADS. 1972. bi-m. £2. Middle East Christian Outreach Ltd., 22 Culverden Park Rd., Tunbridge Wells, Kent TN4 9RA, England. Ed. Peter D.L. Thomson. circ. 5,000.
Missions

289 US ISSN 0011-538X
DAILY BLESSING. 1959. q. $2. ‡ Oral Roberts Evangelistic Association Inc., Box 2187, Tulsa, OK 74102. TEL 918-495-6161 Eds. Oral Roberts, Betty Howard. circ. 425,000.

242.2 US ISSN 0092-7147
DAILY BREAD; a devotional guide for every day of the year. 1969. a. $7.50. (Reorganized Church of Jesus Christ of Latter Day Saints) Herald Publishing House, 3225 S. Noland Rd., Box HH, Independence, MO 64055. TEL 816-252-5010 Ed. Richard Brown. circ. 12,000.

289.9 US ISSN 0011-5525
DAILY WORD. (Editions in inkprint, large type, and Braille) 1924. m. $3 for inkprint edt.; large type $5; Braille edt. free. Unity School of Christianity, Unity Village, MO 64065. TEL 816-524-3550 Ed. Colleen Zuck. circ. 2,600,000. (also avail. in microform from UMI)

200 US
DANICA; hrvatski tjednik. (Text in Croatian; summaries in Croatian and English) 1921. w. $10. (Croatian Center Association) Croatian Franciscan Press, 4851 Drexel Blvd., Chicago, IL 60615. TEL 312-268-2819 Ed.Bd. adv. bk. rev. circ. 5,000. (tabloid format)

289.3 US ISSN 0093-786X
DESERET NEWS CHURCH ALMANAC. 1974. a. $4.75. Deseret News Publishing Co., Box 1257, Salt Lake City, UT 84110. TEL 801-237-2141 Ed. Dell Van Orden. illus. circ. 10,000.

261 CE ISSN 0012-2181
DIALOGUE. 1963. 3/yr. $3. Ecumenical Institute for Study and Dialogue, 490-5 Havelock Rd., Colombo 6, Sri Lanka. Ed. Fr. Aloysius Pieris. adv. bk. rev. circ. 1,000. Indexed: Rel.Ind.One.

289.3 US ISSN 0012-2157
DIALOGUE: A JOURNAL OF MORMON THOUGHT. 1966. q. $25 to individuals; students $15. Dialogue Foundation, 202 W. 300 N., Salt Lake City, UT 84103. TEL 801-355-9492 Eds. Linda King Newell, Leonard Jackson Newell. bk. rev. charts. illus. index. cum.index 1966-1976. circ. 4,000. (also avail. in microform from UMI; back issues avail.) Indexed: Hist.Abstr. Amer.Hist.& Life. Rel.Ind.One.

299 II ISSN 0253-519X
DISCOURSE. (Text in English) 1972. m. Rs.10($10) Society of Servants of God, Yashwant Place, Satya Marg, Chanakyapuri, New Delhi 110021, India. Ed. Sundri P. Vaswani. bibl. index. circ. 650.

264.01 UK ISSN 0012-8732
EASTERN CHURCHES NEWS LETTER. 1955. s-a. £1. Anglican & Eastern Churches Association, St. Dustan-in-the-West, 184 Fleet St., London EC4A 2EA, England. Ed. Columba Graham Flegg. bk. rev. circ. 600.

284.2 266 NE ISSN 0012-9119
ECHO; hervormd blad. 1952. 12/yr. fl.10. Hervormde Bond voor Inwendige Zending - Reformed Alliance for Home Mission, Johan van Oldenbarneveltlaan 10, Amersfoort, Netherlands. Ed. L. Westland. illus. circ. 20,000.
Missions

289.9 US
ECK MATA JOURNAL. 1976. a. $3.95. Eckankar Publications, Box 27300, Minneapolis, MN 55427-0300. Ed. Suzanne Vlcek. circ. 20,000.
Formerly: Eck News.

289.3 US ISSN 0013-8606
ENSIGN. 1971. m. $8. Church of Jesus Christ of Latter-day Saints, 50 E. North Temple St., Salt Lake City, UT 84150. TEL 801-531-2531 Ed.Bd. charts. illus. circ. 460,000.

261 US ISSN 0014-1682
ETERNITY; the magazine of Christian truth. 1950. m. $18.90. Evangelical Ministries, Inc., 1716 Spruce St., Philadelphia, PA 19103. TEL 215-546-3696 Ed. Donald J. McCrory. adv. bk. rev. illus. index. circ. 40,000. (also avail. in microform from UMI; reprint service avail. from UMI) Indexed: Chr.Per.Ind. G.Soc.Sci.& Rel.Per.Lit.

284 US ISSN 0014-3340
EVANGELICAL FRIEND. 1967. m. (except Aug. & Dec.) $7. (Evangelical Friends Alliance) Barclay Press, 600 E. Third St, Box 232, Newberg, OR 97132. TEL 503-538-7345 Eds. Lon Fendall, Harlow Ankeny. adv. bk. rev. illus. circ. 12,000.
Missions

289 UK ISSN 0046-2853
EVANGELICAL MAGAZINE. 1959. bi-m. £1($2.50) Providence House, 118 Falcon Rd., London S.W.11., England. Ed. Elizabeth Braund. bk. rev. circ. 2,000.

200 CN ISSN 0014-3375
EVANGELICAL TRUTH. (Text in English and Ukrainian) 1940. bi-m. $3.50. Rev. M. Fesenko, Ed. & Pub., 26 Robina Ave., Toronto, Ont. M6C 3Y6, Canada. TEL 416-654-4870 bk. rev. illus. circ. 1,000.

289.9 SW
EVANGELII HAEROLD. w. Pingstroerelsen, Dagen-huset, 105 36 Stockholm, Sweden. adv. circ. 32,275.
Pentecostal

200 NE ISSN 0014-3626
EVANGELIST. (Editions in Arabic, Armenian, Dutch, English, German) 1960. q. £L5($2) Bible Land Mission, Box 58, Woudenberg, Netherlands. Ed. Samuel Doctorian. illus. circ. 20,000.
Missions

248.4 SA ISSN 0014-7044
FAITH FOR DAILY LIVING; a guide to confident Christian living. (Text in English) 1960. m. free. Faith for Daily Living Foundation, Box 3737, Durban, Natal, South Africa. Ed. Arnold J. Walker. circ. 110,000.

289.73 CN ISSN 0014-7303
FAMILY LIFE. 1968. m. (11/yr.) $5. (Amish Church) Pathway Publishing Corporation, R.4, Aylmer, Ont., Canada. Ed. Elmo Stoll. bk. rev. illus. circ. 17,600. (also avail. in microform from UMI; reprint service avail. from UMI; back issues avail.)

266 US
FAR EAST REPORTER (HOUSTON) vol.22, 1976. m. $2. Release the World for Christ Foundation, Box 4275, 600 Jefferson, Houston, TX 77210. TEL 713-473-9500 Ed. Deanza Brock. illus. circ. 200,000.

200 US ISSN 0014-8830
FATIMA FINDINGS; the smallest newspaper on earth for the greatest cause in heaven. 1946. m. $4. Reparation Society of the Immaculate Heart of Mary, Inc., Fatima House, 100 E. 20th St., Baltimore, MD 21218-6091. TEL 301-685-7403 Ed. Rev. John Ryan. circ. 4,000(controlled)

200 US ISSN 0014-9837
FELLOWSHIP IN PRAYER. 1950. bi-m. free. Fellowship in Prayer, Inc., Franklin Office Park, 134 Franklin Corner Rd., Lawrenceville, NJ 08648. TEL 609-896-3636 Ed. Mary Ford-Grabowsky. bk. rev. circ. 2,500. (back issues avail.)

289.9 US
FIERY SYNTHESIS. 1965. 12/yr. $10. Aquarian Educational Group, Box 267, Sedona, AZ 86336. Ed. Torkum Saraydarian. bk. rev. circ. 300.
Formerly: Blue Aquarius.

266 UK ISSN 0015-4822
FLYING ANGEL. 1958. q. £0.80. Missions to Seamen, St. Michael Paternoster Royal, College Hill, London EC4R 2RL, England. Ed. Gillian Ennis. illus. circ. 12,000.
Missions

200 UK ISSN 0016-0326
FREE CHURCH CHRONICLE. 1946. q. £3.50. ‡ Free Church Federal Council Inc., 27 Tavistock Square, London WC1H 9HH, England. Ed. Rev. David Staple. adv. bk. rev. circ. 2,500.

200 UK ISSN 0016-0334
FREE CHURCH OF SCOTLAND. MONTHLY RECORD. (Text in English and Gaelic) 1843. m. £5. Free Church of Scotland Publications Committee, 15 N. Bank St., Edinburgh EH1 2LS, Scotland. Ed. Donald Macleod. bk. rev. circ. 7,500. (tabloid format; reprint service avail. from UMI)

289.6 UK ISSN 0016-1268
FRIEND; a Quaker weekly journal. 1843. w. £27.56($40) Friend Publications Ltd., Drayton House, Gordon St., London W.C.1, England. Ed. David Firth. adv. bk. rev. illus. index. circ. 6,350. (also avail. in microform from WMP)

289.6 248.82 US ISSN 0009-4102
FRIEND. 1971. m. (12/yr.) $8. Church of Jesus Christ of Latter-day Saints, Corporation of the President, 50 E. North Temple, Salt Lake City, UT 84150 (Braille ed.: Christian Record Braille Foundation, 4444 S. 52nd St., Lincoln, NE 68506) Ed. Vivian Paulsen. bk. rev. illus. index. circ. 210,000.
Supersedes: Children's Friend.
Ages 3-11

FRIENDLY WOMAN. see *WOMEN'S INTERESTS*

267 UK ISSN 0071-9587
FRIENDS HISTORICAL SOCIETY. JOURNAL. 1903. a. £4($6) to individuals; £6($9) to institutions. Friends Historical Society, Friends House, Euston Rd., London NW1 2BJ, England. Ed. Gerald A.J. Hodgett. adv. bk. rev. circ. 500. Indexed: Br.Hum.Ind. Hist.Abstr. Amer.Hist.& Life.

289.6 US ISSN 0016-1322
FRIENDS JOURNAL. 1955. s-m. $15. (Religious Society of Friends) Friends Publishing Corp., 1501 Cherry St., Philadelphia, PA 19102. TEL 215-241-7277 Ed. Vinton Deming. adv. bk. rev. illus. index. circ. 9,700. (also avail. in microform from UMI; reprint service avail. from UMI)

200 UK ISSN 0016-1357
FRIENDS' QUARTERLY. N.S. 1946. q. £4.72($10) Headley Bros. Ltd., Ashford, Kent, England. Ed. Melanie Barber. cum.index every 3 years. circ. 1,175. Indexed: Br.Hum.Ind.

242 US ISSN 0016-2264
FRUIT OF THE VINE; Friends daily devotional readings. 1961. q. $6. (Friends Church, Northwest Yearly Meeting) Barclay Press, 600 E. Third St., Box 232, Newberg, OR 97132. TEL 503-538-7345 Ed. Harlow Ankeny. illus. circ. 5,000.

200 US ISSN 0042-8264
FULL GOSPEL BUSINESS MEN'S VOICE. 1953. m. $4.95. Full Gospel Business Men's Fellowship International, Box 5050, Costa Mesa, CA 92626. TEL 714-754-1400 Ed. Dr. Jerry Jensen. bk. rev. circ. 750,000. (back issues avail.)

289 SA ISSN 0016-3988
GALAMUKANI! (Text in Chichewa) 1957. m. R.3.25. Watch Tower Bible & Tract Society, P.O. Box 2067, Krugersdorp 1740, South Africa. charts, illus. index. circ. 6,300.

200 UK ISSN 0072-0666
GENERAL CONFERENCE OF THE NEW CHURCH. YEARBOOK. 1789. a. ‡ General Conference of the New Church, c/o G.S. Kuphal, Ed., 20 Red Barn Rd., Brightlingsea, Golchester, Essex CO7 0SH, England. circ. 500.

289.9 US
GEORGIAN NEWSLETTER. 1974. 12/yr. $8. Georgian Church, 1908 Verde St., Bakersfield, CA 93304. TEL 805-323-3309 Eds. Dean & Lady Fauna. adv. bk. rev. illus.

289 US ISSN 0017-0739
GLAD TIDINGS OF GOOD THINGS. 1953. q. free to the blind; others $2.50. Sixteen & Vine Church of Christ, 1610 Vine St., Abilene, TX 79602. TEL 915-677-2892 Ed. Tim Conatser. circ. 350.

266 US ISSN 0731-1125
GLOBAL CHURCH GROWTH. 1964. q. $11. Overseas Crusades, 25 Corning Ave., Milpitas, CA 95035-5335. TEL 408-263-1101 Ed. James H. Montgomery. bk. rev. stat. index every 5 yrs. circ. 3,500. Indexed: CERDIC. Chr.Per.Ind.
Former titles: Global Church Growth Bulletin (ISSN 0273-7183) & Church Growth Bulletin (ISSN 0009-6385)
Missionaries

289.7 US ISSN 0017-2340
GOSPEL HERALD. 1908. w. $20.75. Mennonite Publishing House, 616 Walnut Ave., Scottdale, PA 15683. TEL 412-887-8500 Ed. Daniel Hertzler. bk. rev. illus. circ. 22,500.

200 US ISSN 0017-2383
GOSPEL TRUTH. 1938. m. contributions. ‡ Southwest Radio Church, Box 1144, Oklahoma City, OK 73101. TEL 405-235-5396 Ed. N.W. Hutchings. circ. 100,000. (also avail. in microform from UMI; reprint service avail. from UMI)

GREEK ORTHODOX CALENDAR. see *ETHNIC INTERESTS*

281.9 230 US ISSN 0017-3894
GREEK ORTHODOX THEOLOGICAL REVIEW. 1954. q. $16. (Holy Cross Greek Orthodox School of Theology, Hellenic College) Holy Cross Orthodox Press, 50 Goddard Ave., Brookline, MA 02146. TEL 617-731-3500 Ed. Rev. Dr. N.M. Vaporis. adv. bk. rev. cum.index every 5 years. circ. 1,075. (also avail. in microform from UMI; reprint service avail. from UMI) Indexed: Hist.Abstr. Old Test.Abstr. Rel.Per. Amer.Bibl.Slavic & E.Eur.Stud. Amer.Hist.& Life. CERDIC. New Test.Abstr. Rel.Ind.One. Rel.& Theol.Abstr.

200 US
GREEK SUNDAY NEWS/KYRIAKATIKA NEA. (Text in English and Greek) 1953. fortn. $12. c/o William A. Harris, 231 Harrison Ave., Boston, MA 02111. TEL 617-426-1948 adv. bk. rev. circ. 20,000. (tabloid format)

GREGORIOS HO PALAMAS. see *HISTORY — History Of Europe*

248.83 US ISSN 0017-5226
GUIDE (HAGERSTOWN) 1953. w. $27.95. (Seventh-day Adventist Church) Review and Herald Publishing Association, 55 West Oak Ridge Dr., Hagerstown, MD 21740. TEL 301-791-7000 Ed. Jeannette Johnson. adv. illus. index. circ. 45,000. (also avail. in microfilm from UMI; reprint service avail. from UMI)
Ages 10-16

281 AG ISSN 0017-8640
HAY GUETRON. (Text in Armenian and Spanish) 1932. m. $3. Institucion Administrativa de la Iglesia Armenia, Acevedo 1353, Buenos Aires, Argentina. adv. abstr. bibl. illus. circ. 1,200.

299 UK
HEATHEN. 1971. irreg. membership. Pagan Movement, Can y Lloer, Ffarmers, Llanwrda, Dyfed, Wales. adv. circ. 300.

289.5 US ISSN 0018-0475
HERALD OF CHRISTIAN SCIENCE. Swedish edition: Kristen Vetenskaps Herold (ISSN 0145-7543) Spanish edition: Heraldo de la Ciencia Cristiana (ISSN 0439-0148); Dutch edition: Heraut van de Christelijke Wetenschap (ISSN 0145-756X); German edition: Herold der Christlichen Wissenschaft (ISSN 0145-7578); Italian edition: Araldo della Scienza Cristiana (ISSN 0145-7519); Portuguese edition: Arauto da Ciencia Crista (ISSN 0145-7489); Danish edition: Kristen Videnskabs Herold (US ISSN 0145-7551) Greek edition (US ISSN 0145-9511) Indonesian edition: Bentara Ilmuipengetahuan Kristen (US ISSN 0409-0810) Japanese edition (US ISSN 0145-8019) Norwegian edition: Kristen Vitenskaps Herold (US ISSN 0145-7535) (Monthly editions in French, German, Spanish and Portuguese; quarterly editions in 8 different languages, and in English-Braille) 1903. monthly edts. $18; quarterly edts. $4; English-Braille edt. $1. Christian Science Publishing Society, One Norway St., Boston,TEL 617-450-2000 Ed. Allison W. Phinney.

208.9 US
HERMES. 12/yr. $10. Unni Theos Fellowship, Box 959, Santa Barbara, CA 93101.

289.9 133 100 UK ISSN 0141-6391
THE HERMETIC JOURNAL. 1978. q. £4.80($12) Hermetic Research Trust, 1 Banbury Rd., Tysoe, Warwickshire CV35 0TD, England. Ed. Adam McLean. bk. rev. circ. 600.

289.73 US ISSN 0300-8851
HEROLD DER WAHRHEIT. (Text in English and German) 1912. m. $5. Amish Mennonite Publishing Association, c/o Roy Beachy, Sec.-Treas., Route 2, Box 339, Kalona, IA 52247. TEL 319-656-2596 Eds. Lester B. Miller, Jonas J. Beachy. index. circ. 975.

289.9 US ISSN 0018-120X
HICALL. 1936. w. $3.85. General Council of the Assemblies of God, 1445 Boonville, Springfield, MO 65802. TEL 417-862-2781 Ed. Wm. P. Campbell. circ. 146,750.
For ages 12-17

HOME LEAGUER; a Christian magazine for women. see *WOMEN'S INTERESTS*

HUMANIST IN CANADA. see *PHILOSOPHY*

200 UK ISSN 0018-8913
I C F QUARTERLY. 1963. q. £2.50. Industrial Christian Fellowship, 4 Streche Rd., Swanage, Dorset BH19 1NF, England. Ed. John Davis. bk. rev. circ. 1,600.

286 917.309 CN ISSN 0383-2538
IEVANHEL'S'KYI HOLOS. (Text in Ukrainian) 1968. q. Can.$4. (Pentecostal Assemblies of Canada) Evangelical Voice, Box 39, Sta. A, Toronto, Ont. M6P 3J5, Canada. TEL 416-525-1010 Ed. P. Shelestowsky. illus. circ. 1,200(controlled) Key Title: Evangel's'kyj Golos.

220 289.9 SA ISSN 0019-008X
IMBONISELO. (Text in Xhosa) 1955. s-m. R.6.50. Watch Tower Bible & Tract Society, P.O. Box 2067, Krugersdrop 1740, South Africa. charts. illus. index. circ. 13,500.

INDIAN LIFE. see *ETHNIC INTERESTS*

220 289.9 SA ISSN 0019-0241
INQABAYOKULINDA. (Text in Zulu) 1950. s-m. R.6.50. Watch Tower Bible & Tract Society, P.O. Box 2067, Krugersdrop 1740, South Africa. charts. illus. index. circ. 31,500.

261 US ISSN 0073-9456
INSTITUTE OF MENNONITE STUDIES SERIES. 1961. irreg. price varies. ‡ (Associated Mennonite Biblical Seminaries) Faith and Life Press, 724 Main St., Box 347, Newton, KS 67114. TEL 316-283-5100 Ed. Maynard Shelly.

289.9 US ISSN 0161-1380
INTEGRAL YOGA. 1969. bi-m. $12. Integral Yoga Publications, Satchidananda Ashram-Yogaville, Rt. 1, Box 172, Buckingham, VA 23921. TEL 804-969-4801 Ed. Swami Prakashananda Ma. adv. bk. rev. circ. 1,600.

289.9 US ISSN 0031-4900
INTERNATIONAL PENTECOSTAL HOLINESS ADVOCATE. 1917. m. $4. International Pentecostal Holiness Church, Box 12609, Oklahoma City, OK 73157 TEL 404-245-7272 (Subscr. to: Advocate Press, Box 98, Franklin Springs, GA 30639) Ed. Leon O. Stewart. bk. rev. bibl. charts. illus. circ. 40,000. (also avail. in microform; back issues avail.) Indexed: CERDIC.

200 150 US ISSN 0021-0250
INWARD LIGHT. 1937. s-a. $6. (Friends Conference on Religion and Psychology) Inward Light, 749 Polo Rd., Bryn Mawr, PA 19010. Eds. Charles Perry, Eleanor Perry. bk. rev. circ. 1,400. Indexed: CERDIC.

299 US ISSN 0886-6910
ISKCON REVIEW; academic perspectives on the Hare Krishna movement. 1985. a. $6. Institute for Vaishnaya Studies, c/o Steven J. Gelberg, 41 West Allens Lane, Philadelphia, PA 19119. TEL 215-242-6578 bk. rev. circ. 1,200. (back issues avail.)

200 CN
ISSUE. 1974? irreg. free. United Church of Canada, 85 St. Clair Ave. E., Toronto, Ont. M4T 1M8, Canada. TEL 416-925-5931 Ed.Bd. illus. Indexed: Curr.Cont.Africa.

289 NE
JAARBOEK VAN DE CHRISTELIJKE GEREFORMEERDE KERKEN IN NEDERLAND. 1909. a. (Christelijke Gereformeerde Kerk) D.J. van Brummen, Buyten 2 Schipperheyn, Amsterdam, Netherlands. adv.

289.9 US ISSN 0075-3602
JEHOVAH'S WITNESSES YEARBOOK. Variant title: Yearbook of Jehovah's Witnesses. (Text in various European languages) 1927. a. $1. (Jehovah's Witnesses, Governing Body) Watchtower Bible and Tract Society of New York, Inc., 25 Columbia Hts., Brooklyn, NY 11201. TEL 718-625-3600 index. circ. 1,000,000.
Report of international preaching

JOTTINGS. see *BLIND*

377.8 US ISSN 0021-8480
JOURNAL OF ADVENTIST EDUCATION. 1939. bi-m. (except Jul.-Sep.) $10.95. General Conference of Seventh-day Adventists, Association of Seventh-day Adventist Educators, 6840 Eastern Ave., N.W., Washington, DC 20012. TEL 202-722-6410 Ed. Victor S. Griffiths. adv. bk. rev. illus. index. circ. 8,000. (reprint service avail. from UMI)
Formerly: Journal of True Education.

289.3 US ISSN 0094-7342
JOURNAL OF MORMON HISTORY. 1974. a. $7.50. Mormon History Association, Box 7010, University Sta., Provo, UT 84602. Ed. Dean May. circ. 1,000. Indexed: CERDIC.

200 UK ISSN 0022-5703
JOY & LIGHT; the Lord's Day magazine. 1843. 3/yr. £1. ‡ Lord's Day Observance Society, 5 Victory Ave., Morden, Surrey SM4 6DL, England. Ed. J.G. Roberts. bk. rev. circ. 20,000.

289.9 US ISSN 0022-6718
JUNIOR TRAILS. 1926. w. $3.85. General Council of the Assemblies of God, 1445 Boonville Ave., Springfield, MO 65802. TEL 417-862-2781 Ed. John Maempa. circ. 77,000.

291 II ISSN 0047-3367
KERALA SABHA. (Text in Malayalam) 1970. m. Rs.3($1.) Better Life Movement, Better Life Center, Aloor, Kollettumkara, Kerala, India. Ed. Fr. Jose Akkarakkaran. adv. bk. rev. film rev. play rev. abstr. bibl. charts. illus. pat. stat. tr.lit. cum.index. circ. 2,000(controlled)

281.9 GR
KLERONOMIA. (Text in English, German and Greek) 1969. 2/yr. $32. Patriarchal Institute for Patristic Studies, Heptapyrgiou 64, 546 34 Thessaloniki, Greece. Ed. Panagiotis C. Christou. bk. rev. bibl. circ. 2,000. Indexed: CERDIC.

299 UK
KOSMON UNITY. 1946. s-a. £1($1.25) (Confraternity of Faithists) Kosmon Press, BM-KCKP, London WC1V 6XX, England (Dist. in U.S. by: Kosmon Service Center, Box 664, Salt Lake City, UT 84110) Eds. Cyril Ward, Greta James. bk. rev.

289.6 SW ISSN 0345-6005
KVAEKARTIDSKRIFT. (Text in Danish, Norwegian & Swedish) 1949. q. Kr.40. Vaennernas Samfund i Sverige - Society of Friends of Sweden (Quakers), Box 9166, S-102 72 Stockholm, Sweden. Ed. Ingmar Hollsing. bk. rev. circ. 900.
Formerly: Nordisk Kvaekartidskrift (ISSN 0029-1404)

299 US
LATTER - DAY SENTINEL. (3 separate editions: 1 for Arizona; 1 for Southern California, 1 for Southern Neveda) 1979. bi-w. $14.88. Latter - Day Sentintel Newspapers, Inc., 721 W. Portland, Phoenix, AZ 85007 TEL 602-257-0220 (Subscr. to: Box 2440, Phoenix, AZ 85002) Ed. Crismon Lewis. film rev. illus. (tabloid format; back issues avail.)

289.9 SA
LEBONE LA KGALALELO. (Text in English, Pedi, Sotho, Tswana) 1954. q. R.0.75. ‡ (Church of the Nazarene) Africa Nazarene Publications, P.O. Box 44, Florida, Transvaal 1710, South Africa. illus. stat. circ. 700.
Formerly: Lebone la Kgalalelo Isibani Sobu Ngcwele (ISSN 0024-0060)

255 FR ISSN 0750-3695
LETTER FROM TAIZE. 1970. bi-m. $8. Communaute de Taize, 71250 Cluny, France.

289.9 NE ISSN 0024-1547
LEVEND WOORD/LIVING WORD; devoted to the restoration of New Testament Christianity. (Text in Dutch; summaries in English, French & German) 1960. m. fl.3.25($1.25) Churches of Christ, Meloenstraat 86, 2564 TK The Hague, Netherlands. Ed. Wil C. Goodheer. bk. rev. circ. 2,000.

200 100 US
LOGOS (NEW YORK); the Swedenborg Foundation newsletter. 1968. s-a. Swedenborg Foundation, Inc., 139 E. 23 St., New York, NY 10010. TEL 212-673-7310 Ed. Darrell Ruhl. bk. rev. circ. 30,000. Indexed: Met.Abstr. World Alum.Abstr.
Formerly: Swedenborg Foundation Newsletter.

281.62 US ISSN 0024-6476
LOOYS. (Text in Armenian and English) 1953. m. (10/yr.) contributions. St. James Armenian Apostolic Church, 465 Mt. Auburn St, Watertown, MA 02172. TEL 617-923-8860 circ. 1,275. (looseleaf format)

266 US
LOST & FOUND. 1979. q. free. ‡ Overseas Crusades, 25 Corning Ave., Milpitas, CA 95035-5336. TEL 408-263-1101 Ed. Jim Stephenson. circ. 40,000.
Formerly: World Spotlight; Supersedes (1962-1979): Cable (ISSN 0007-9286)
Missions

389.1 US ISSN 0885-9922
LUTHERAN PARTNERS. 1985. bi-m. $10. Augsburg Publishing House, 426 S. 5th St., Box 1209, Minneapolis, MN 55440. TEL 612-330-3300 (Co-Sponsors: Lutheran Church in America, American Lutheran Church, Association of Evangelical Lutheran Churches) Ed. Carl E. Linder. adv. bk. rev. circ. 21,500.

291 MY
MALAYSIA INTER-RELIGIOUS ORGANISATION. SUARA. 1970. q. M.$3 (single issue) Malaysia Inter-Religious Organisation, 16 Road 49E, Petaling Jaya, Selangor, Malaysia. illus.

266 US
MARIAN HELPERS BULLETIN. 1946. q. $1 for members only. (Association of Marian Helpers) Congregation of Marians, Stockbridge, MA 01262. TEL 413-298-3691 Ed. Rev. Walter F. Pelczynski, M.I.C. circ. 950,000.

200 US ISSN 0047-6064
MARTURION. no.244, 1984. m. $1. People of the Living God, 2101 Prytania St., New Orleans, LA 70130. TEL 504-522-4821 Ed. H. Reigart Miller. bk. rev. illus.

289.3 US ISSN 0094-5633
MEASURING MORMONISM. 1974. a. $3. Association for the Study of Sociology, Inc., 3646 East 3580 South, Salt Lake City, UT 84109 TEL 801-581-6153 (Or Glenn M. Vernon, Ed., University of Utah, Department of Sociology, Salt Lake City, UT 84112)

289.7 US ISSN 0025-9330
MENNONITE. 1885. s-m. $16.00. Mennonite Church, General Conference, 722 Main St., Box 347, Newton, KS 67114. TEL 316-283-5100 Ed. Muriel Stackley. adv. bk. rev. illus. index. circ. 13,000. Indexed: Rel.Per. G.Soc.Sci.& Rel.Per.Lit.

289.7 CN ISSN 0025-9349
MENNONITE BRETHREN HERALD. 1962. fortn. Can.$18. (Conference of Mennonite Brethren Churches of Canada) Christian Press Ltd., 159 Henderson Hwy., Winnipeg, Man. R2L 1L4, Canada. Ed. Herb Kopp. adv. bk. rev. illus. index. circ. 13,500.

289.7 390 US ISSN 0025-9357
MENNONITE HISTORICAL BULLETIN. 1940. q. $5. Mennonite Church, Historical Committee, 1700 South Main St., Goshen, IN 46526. TEL 219-533-3161 Ed. Leonard Gross. bk. rev. illus. cum.index every 10 yrs. circ. 400. (also avail. in microfilm from UMI) Indexed: Hist.Abstr. Amer.Hist.& Life. CERDIC.

290 US ISSN 0076-6429
MENNONITE HISTORY SERIES. vol.2, 1966. irreg. ‡ (Mennonite Church, General Conference, Commission on Education) Faith and Life Press, 724 Main St., Newton, KS 67114. TEL 316-283-5100 Ed. Maynard Shelly.

289.7 209 US ISSN 0025-9365
MENNONITE LIFE. 1946. q. $10. Bethel College, North Newton, KS 67117. bk. rev. bibl. charts. illus. cum.index every 5 yrs. circ. 900. (back issues avail.) Indexed: Hist.Abstr. Amer.Bibl.Slavic & E.Eur.Stud. Amer.Hist.& Life. Rel.Ind.One.
History

MENNONITE MIRROR. see *LITERATURE*

289.7 US ISSN 0025-9373
MENNONITE QUARTERLY REVIEW. (Text in English, occasional articles in Dutch, German, and other languages) 1927. q. $17. (Mennonite Historical Society) Goshen College, Goshen, IN 46526. TEL 219-533-3161 (Co-sponsor: Associated Mennonite Biblical Seminaries) Ed. John S. Oyer. adv. bk. rev. bibl. charts. illus. index. cum.index every 10 yrs. circ. 1,000. (also avail. in microfilm from AMS; reprint service avail. from AMS) Indexed: Amer.Hist.& Life. Rel.Per. Hist.Abstr. Amer.Bibl.Slavic & E.Eur.Stud. CERDIC. Rel.Ind.One. Rel.& Theol.Abstr.

289.7 CN ISSN 0380-0121
MENNONITE REPORTER. 1971. fortn. Can.$17. Mennonite Publishing Service, 3-312 Marsland Drive, Waterloo, Ontario N2J 3Z1, Canada. TEL 519-884-3810 Ed. Ron Rempel. adv. bk. rev. index. circ. 9,500. (also avail. in microfilm)
Continues: Canadian Mennonite Reporter (ISSN 0380-013X)

289.7 US
MENNONITE YEARBOOK AND DIRECTORY. 1905. biennial. $7.95. Mennonite Publishing House, 616 Walnut Ave., Scottdale, PA 15683. TEL 412-887-8500 Ed. James E. Horsch.

289.7 CN ISSN 0025-9314
MENNONITISCHE RUNDSCHAU/ MENNONITE REVIEW. (Text in German) 1877. fortn. Can.$14. (Mennonite Brethren Conference of Canada) Christian Press Ltd., 159 Henderson Highway, Winnipeg R2L 1L4, Manitoba, Canada. TEL 204-667-3560 Ed. Abraham W. Schellenberg. adv. bk. rev. illus. circ. 3,800.

281.9 FR ISSN 0026-0266
MESSAGER DE L'EXARCHAT DU PATRIARCHE RUSSE EN EUROPE OCCIDENTALE. (Text in French and Russian) 1950. a. 90 F. (Union des Associations Culturelles de l'Eglise Orthodoxe) Exarchat du Patriarche de Moscou, 26 rue Preclet, 75015 Paris, France. Ed.Bd. bk. rev. bibl. illus. cum.index. circ. 700. Indexed: CERDIC.

286 SI ISSN 0026-0371
MESSENGER. vol.18, 1968. bi-m. S.$3.50. Southeast Asia Union Mission of Seventh-Day Adventists, 251 Upper Serangoon Rd, Singapore, Singapore. Ed. Loralyn Horning. illus. circ. 2,000 (controlled)

282 US ISSN 0026-0355
MESSENGER (ELGIN) 1851. m. $10. ‡ Church of the Brethren, General Services Commission, 1451 Dundee Ave., Elgin, IL 60120. TEL 312-742-5100 Ed. Kermon Thomasson. adv. bk. rev. film rev. index. circ. 30,000.

200 US
MESSENGER (SAN FRANCISCO) 1852. m. $8. Swedenborgian Church, Department of Communications, 2107 Lyon St., San Francisco, CA 94115. Ed. Rev. Jim Lawrence. bk. rev. charts. illus. index. circ. 2,400.
Formerly: New Church Messenger (ISSN 0028-4424)

286.5 US
MESSENGER OF TRUTH. (Text in Ukrainian) vol.48, 1974. bi-m. $10. Ukrainian Evangelical Baptist Convention, 1042 North Damen Avenue, Chicago, IL 60622. TEL 312-278-0232 Ed. O.R. Harbuziuk. bk. rev. illus. circ. 5,000.

200 FR ISSN 0026-0401
MESSIDOR; la tribune de Dieu-revue de la vie totale. 1951. q. 120 F.($25) Alliance Universelle, La Prefete, B.P. 27, 84140 Montfavet, France.

METROLINE. see *HOMOSEXUALITY*

286 209 US ISSN 0026-5314
MINISTRY; a magazine for clergymen. 1928. m. $19.95. (General Conference of Seventh-day Adventists) Review and Herald Publishing Association, 55 West Oak Ridge Dr., Hagerstown, MD 21740. TEL 301-791-7000 Ed. J.R. Spangler. adv. bk. rev. charts. illus. index. circ. 15,000. (reprint service avail. from UMI) Indexed: CERDIC.
Church history

255 US ISSN 0026-5802
MIRACULOUS MEDAL. 1928. q. $1. Central Association of the Miraculous Medal, 475 E. Chelten Ave., Philadelphia, PA 19144. TEL 215-848-1010 Ed. Rev. Robert P. Cawley, C.M. illus. circ. 85,000.

MIRROR. see *HISTORY — History Of North And South America*

281 US
MODERN ORTHODOX SAINTS. 1971. irreg., vol.8, 1985. price varies. Institute for Byzantine and Modern Greek Studies, 115 Gilbert Rd., Belmont, MA 02178. TEL 617-484-6595 Ed. Constantine Cavarnos. bibl. illus. index. circ. 1,000.

200 289.9 SA ISSN 0026-9093
MOLULA-QHOOA. (Text in Sesotho) 1954. s-m. R.6.50. Watch Tower Bible & Tract Society, P.O. Box 2067, Krugersdrop 1740, South Africa. charts. illus. index. circ. 14,000.

200 289.9 SA ISSN 0027-1179
MOROKAMI. (Text in Sepedi) 1966. s-m. R.6.50. Watch Tower Bible & Tract Society, P.O. Box 2067, Krugersdrop 1740, South Africa. charts. illus. index. circ. 7,500.

289.9 US ISSN 0164-7253
MOUNTAIN MOVERS. 1959. m. $5 or contributions. Assemblies of God, Division of Foreign Missions, 1445 Boonville Ave., Springfield, MO 65802. TEL 417-862-2781 Ed. Nick Henry. circ. 166,000.
Former titles: Good News Crusades (ISSN 0017-2162); Global Conquest.

289.9 SA
MUKAI! (Text in Shona) 1982. q. Watch Tower Bible & Tract Society, P.O. Box 2067, Krugersdrop 1740, South Africa. charts. illus. circ. 7,000.

200 AT
MUSICIAN. 1947. fortn. Aus.$16.90. (Salvation Army) Donald Campbell, 1-9 Drill St., Hawthorn, Melbourne, Vic. 3122, Australia. Ed. Rowland Hill. bk. rev. circ. 4,016.

289.9 SA
MUTWALISI. (Text in Shangaan) q. R.0.75. (Church of the Nazarene) Africa Nazarene Publications, P.O. Box 44, Florida, Transvaal 1710, South Africa. circ. 700.

200 BG
NATIONAL COUNCIL OF CHURCHES, BANGLADESH. ANNUAL REPORT. (Text in English and Bengali) a. National Council of Churches, Bangladesh, 395, New Eskaton Rd., Dacca 2, Bangladesh. stat.

133 200 US
NATIONAL SPIRITUALIST. 1919. m. $7. (National Spiritualist Association of Churches) Summit Publishing by Stow, 668 E. 62nd St., Indianapolis, IN 46220. TEL 317-253-4796 Ed. William F. Melick. bibl. illus. circ. 3,500.

200 UK ISSN 0261-1708
NETWORK (LONDON, 1965) 1965. q. £1.90. United Society for the Propagation of the Gospel, 15 Tufton St., London SW1 3QQ, England. Ed. Anthony Richmond. bk. rev. charts. illus. circ. 16,000.

299 US
NEW AGE TEACHINGS. 1967. m. contributions. New Age Teaching Center of Learning, 37 Maple St., Brookfield, MA 01506. TEL 617-867-3754 Ed. Anita Afton. bk. rev. circ. 3,500.

200 UG
NEW CENTURY. 1959. m. $25. Church of Uganda, Box 6246, Kampala, Uganda. Ed. Canon Tom T. Nabeta. adv. bk. rev. play rev. circ. 10,000. (tabloid format)
Formerly: New Day (ISSN 0028-4556)

200 UK
NEW CHURCH MAGAZINE. 1881. 3/yr. £2. General Conference of the New Church, c/o G.S. Kuphal, 20 Red Barn Rd., Brightlingsea, Golchester, Essex CO7 0SH, England. Ed. J.D. Allsopp.

289.33 US
NEW ERA (SALT LAKE CITY) 1971. m. $6. Church of Jesus Christ of Latter-day Saints, 50 E. North Temple, Salt Lake City, UT 84150. TEL 801-531-2531 circ. 170,000. (also avail. in microform from UMI; back issues avail.; reprint service avail. from UMI) Indexed: A.I.P.P.

NEW MESSENGER (TALKING BOOK) see *BLIND*

150 US ISSN 0146-7832
NEW THOUGHT (SCOTTSDALE); a quarterly magazine dedicated to the spiritual enlightenment of the individual and of the world. 1916. q. $8. International New Thought Alliance, 7314 E. Stetson Dr., Scottsdale, AZ 85251. TEL 602-945-0744 Ed. Blaine C. Mays. adv. bk. rev. illus. circ. 5,000.
Formerly (until 1950): New Thought Bulletin (ISSN 0146-8170)

947 US
NEWSWIRE (WHEATON) 1984. bi-m. free. Slavic Gospel Association, Box 1122, Wheaton, IL 60189. TEL 312-690-8900 Ed. Kurt Luchs. bk. rev. circ. 60,000. (processed)
Supersedes (1976?-1983?): Sparks (Wheaton)

220 289.9 SA ISSN 0028-9639
NHARIREYOMURINDI. (Text in Shona) 1949. s-m. R.6.50. Watch Tower Bible & Tract Society, P.O. Box 2067, Krugersdrop 1740, South Africa. charts. illus. index. circ. 16,000.

NICOLAUS. see *RELIGIONS AND THEOLOGY — Roman Catholic*

284.6 US ISSN 0027-1012
NORTH AMERICAN MORAVIAN. 1856. m. (combined Jun.-Jul., Aug.-Sep.) $5.50 to non-members. ‡ Moravian Church in America-North and South, Publications Commission, Box 1245, Bethlehem, PA 18016. TEL 215-867-0594 Ed. Bernard E. Michel. adv. bk. rev. charts. illus. maps. stat. index. circ. 26,100.
Formerly: Moravian and Wachovia Moravian.

289.9 PO ISSN 0029-5116
NOVAS DE ALEGRIA. Abbreviated title: N A. 1943. m. Esc.150($6) Casa Publicadora das Assembleias de Deus, Av. Alm. Gago Coutinho 158, 1700 Lisbon, Portugal. Ed. Fernando Martinez da Silva. adv. bk. rev. abstr. illus. circ. 20,000 (controlled)

220 289.9 SA ISSN 0029-5442
NSANJA YA OLONDA. (Text in Chichewa) 1948. s-m. R.6.50. Watch Tower Bible & Tract Society, P.O. Box 2067, Krugersdrop 1740, South Africa. illus. circ. 21,000.

200 US ISSN 0029-7143
O L O G O S. 1949. bi-m. $4. ‡ Orthodox Lore Of the Gospel of Our Savior Mission, Box 5333, St. Louis, MO 63115. TEL 314-721-4342 Ed. Rev. George Mastrantonis. circ. 86,700.
Missions

289.4 SZ ISSN 0030-0101
OFFENE TORE; Beitraege zum neuen christlichen Zeitalter. 1957. 6/yr. 22 Fr.($12) Swedenborg Verlag, Postfach 247, CH-8032 Zurich, Switzerland. Ed. Dr. Friedemann Horn. bk. rev. circ. 1,000.

281.9 US ISSN 0030-2503
ONE CHURCH/YEDINAYA TSERKOV. 1947. bi-m. $6. Patriarchal Parishes of the Russian Orthodox Church in the U.S.A., c/o Rt. Rev. Feodor Kovalchuk, Ed., 727 Miller Ave., Youngstown, OH 44502. TEL 216-788-0151 bk. rev. illus. index. circ. 1,600. (also avail. in microform from UMI; reprint service avail. from UMI) Indexed: CERDIC.

220 289.9 SA ISSN 0030-316X
ONTWAAK! (Text in Afrikaans) 1939. s-m. R.6.50. Watch Tower Bible & Tract Society, P.O. Box 2067, Krugersdrop 1740, South Africa. charts. illus. index. circ. 25,000.

200 JA ISSN 0030-3259
OOMOTO. (Text in English) 1956. bi-m. 1200 Yen($5) ‡ Oomoto and Universal Love and Brotherhood Association, Kameoka, Kyoto-fu 621, Japan. Ed. Iwao P. Hino. bk. rev. illus. circ. 5,000.

266 MM
ORDER OF ST. JOHN OF JERUSALEM. BULLETIN. (Text in English) 1964. q. donation. Order of St. John of Jerusalem, Russian Grand Priory of Malta, 5-3 Scerberras Sq., Floriana, Malta. Ed. G. Tonna-Barthet. adv. charts. illus. circ. 1,300.

280 US ISSN 0048-2269
ORTHODOX CHURCH. 1965. m. $8. Orthodox Church in America, Metropolitan Council, Route 25 a, Box 675, Syosset, NY 11791. TEL 516-922-0550 Ed. Rev. Leonid Kishkovsky. bk. rev. charts. illus. circ. 30,000. (tabloid format) Indexed: CERDIC.

200 US ISSN 0145-7950
ORTHODOX CHURCH IN AMERICA. YEARBOOK AND CHURCH DIRECTORY. a. $9.50. Orthodox Church in America, Box 675, Syosset, NY 11791. TEL 516-922-0550 charts. illus. stat. circ. 3,000. Key Title: Yearbook and Church Directory of the Orthodox Church in America.
Supersedes: Russian Orthodox Greek-Catholic Church of America. Yearbook (ISSN 0095-2257); Russian Orthodox Greek Catholic Church of America. Yearbook and Church Directory (ISSN 0557-532X)

281.9 UK ISSN 0267-8470
ORTHODOX NEWS. 1979. m. £4. (St. George Orthodox Information Service) Stylite Publishing Ltd., 37 Salop Rd., Welsh Pool, Powys SY21 7EA, Wales. Ed. Andrew Bond. adv. bk. rev. circ. 2,500.

200 US ISSN 0731-2547
ORTHODOX OBSERVER. (Text and summaries in English and Greek) 1935. fortn. $12. (Greek Archdiocese of North and South America) Greek Archdiocese Press, 8 E. 79th St., New York, NY 10021. TEL 212-628-2590 Ed. Panagiotis J. Gazouleas. adv. bk. rev. circ. 130,000. (tabloid format; also avail. in microfilm)

281 US ISSN 0030-5839
ORTHODOX WORD. 1965. bi-m. $10. St. Herman of Alaska Brotherhood, Platina, CA 96076. Ed. Fr. Herman Podmoshensky. adv. bk. rev. illus. index. circ. 3,500. (also avail. in microfilm from UMI; reprint service avail. from UMI) Indexed: Rel.Per. CERDIC.

289.9 GW
OUR FAMILY; the new apostolic magazine. (Text in English) 1955. m. DM.27.60. Verlag Friedrich Bischoff GmbH, Postfach 110242, 6000 Frankfurt 1, W. Germany (B.R.D.) Ed. Hellmut Wernher. circ. 6,500.

OUTREACH (NEW YORK) see *ETHNIC INTERESTS*

289.9 US
PAGANA. 1980. 6/yr. $12. Pagan-Occult-Witchcraft Special Interest Group, Box 9336, San Jose, CA 95157. TEL 415-856-6911 Ed. Valerie Voigt. adv. bk. rev. illus. circ. 400.

200 FR ISSN 0031-0972
PANPERE. (Text in Armenian) 1925. m. 60 F.($12) Union of the Armenian Evangelical Churches in France, 13 rue des Allies, 69100 Villeurbanne, France. Ed. Ari Topouzkhanian. bk. rev. circ. 2,400.

281.9 GR
PATRIARCHAL INSTITUTE FOR PATRISTIC STUDIES. THEOLOGICAL STUDIES. irreg., latest no.5. price varies. Patriarchal Institute for Patristic Studies, Heptapyrgiou 64, 546 34 Thessaloniki, Greece. Ed. P.C. Christou.

PATTERNS (PORTLAND) see *SOCIAL SCIENCES: COMPREHENSIVE WORKS*

200 US ISSN 0031-4250
PENDLE HILL PAMPHLETS. 1934. 6/yr. $10. (Pendle Hill, a Quaker Center for Study and Contemplation) Pendle Hill Publications, 338 Plush Mill Road, Wallingford, PA 19086. TEL 215-566-4507 Ed. Rebecca Kratz Mays. circ. 3,000. (also avail. in microfilm from UMI) Indexed: Vert.File Ind.

289.7 209 US ISSN 0148-4036
PENNSYLVANIA MENNONITE HERITAGE. 1978. q. $20 includes membership. Lancaster Mennonite Historical Society, 2215 Millstream Rd., Lancaster, PA 17602. TEL 717-393-9745 Ed. Carolyn C. Wenger. bk. rev. illus. stat. cum.index: 1978-1982. circ. 2,200. Indexed: Hist.Abstr. Amer.Hist.& Life. Geneal.Per.Ind.
Supersedes (1960-1977): Mennonite Research Journal (ISSN 0025-9381)
History

220 289.9 SA ISSN 0031-6806
PHAPHAMA! (Text in Zulu) 1958. m. R.3.25. Watch Tower Bible & Tract Society, P.O. Box 2067, Krugersdrop 1740, South Africa. charts. illus. index. circ. 25,000.

051 US ISSN 0032-0420
PLAIN TRUTH (PASADENA); a magazine of understanding. Dutch edition: Echte Waarheid. French edition: Pure Verite (ISSN 0033-4588); German edition: Klar und Wahr. Spanish edition: Pura Verdad. Italian edition: Pura Verita. Norwegian edition: Dan Enkla Sannhet. 1934. m. free. (Worldwide Church of God) Ambassador Publishing Services, 300 W. Green St., Pasadena, CA 91129. circ. 5,600,000. (also avail. in audio cassette)
Incorporating: Good News of Tomorrow's World (ISSN 0093-5026)

200 UK
PLOUGH. 1931. 3/yr. £1.95. General Conference of the New Church, c/o G.S. Kuphal, 20 Red Barn Rd., Brightlingsea, Golchester, Essex CO7 0SH, England. (Co-sponsor: British New Church Federation) Eds. J. Lomax, B. Lomax.

268 US
PLUS: MAGAZINE OF POSITIVE THINKING. 1945. 10/yr. $7 contribution. Foundation for Christian Living, Box F C L, Pawling, NY 12564. TEL 914-855-5000 Ed. Eric Fellman. illus. circ. 900,000.
Former titles: Magazine of Positive Thinking (ISSN 0747-217X); Creative Help for Daily Living.

200 FR ISSN 0032-4922
PRESENCE ORTHODOXE. 1968. q. 70 F. Editions Friant, 96 bd. Auguste-Blanqui, 75013 Paris, France. abstr. bibl. Indexed: CERDIC.
Formerly: Portique Saint-Denis.

200 IT ISSN 0033-0728
PROGRESSIO. (Text in English, French and Spanish) 1924. 6/yr. (with s-a supplements) $12. World Federation of Christian Life Communities, Central Secretariat, Borgo Santo Spirito 8, Casella Postale 6139, 00195 Rome, Italy. Ed. Jose Gsell. illus. index. cum.index every 10 yrs. circ. 2,800.
Lay-apostolate

220 US ISSN 0033-1341
PROPHETIC NEWSLETTER; the news in the light of the Bible. m. contributions. World Prophetic Ministry, Inc., P.O. Drawer 907, Colton, CA 92324. TEL 714-825-2767 Ed. Howard C. Estep. illus.

200 UK ISSN 0033-135X
PROPHETIC WITNESS. 1918. m. £6($12) Prophetic Witness Movement International, Upperton House, The Avenue, Eastbourne, Sussex BN21 3YB, England. Ed. Rev. Ian Macpherson. adv. bk. rev. illus. circ. 8,000. Indexed: CERDIC.
Incorporating: Prophetic News and Israel's Watchman (ISSN 0033-1333)

261 US
PURA VERDAD; noticiario de comprension. Dutch edition: Echte Waarheid. English edition: Plain Truth (ISSN 0032-0420); French edition: Pure Verite (ISSN 0033-4588); German edition: Klar und Wahr. Norwegian edition: Dan Enkle Sannhet. Italian edition: Pura Verita. (Text in Spanish) 1968. m. free. Ambassador Publishing Services, 300 W. Green St., Pasadena, CA 91129. circ. 225,000.

289 US ISSN 0033-4588
PURE VERITE. Dutch edition: Echte Waarheid. English edition: Plain Truth (ISSN 0032-0420); German edition: Klar und Wahr. Spanish edition: Pura Verdad. Norwegian edition: Den Enkle Sannhet. Italian edition: Pura Verita. (Text in French) 1963. m. free. (Worldwide Church of God) Ambassador Publishing Services, 300 W. Green St., Pasadena, CA 91129. illus. circ. 250,000.

289.7 US ISSN 0163-7274
PURPOSE. 1978. w. $9.65. Mennonite Publishing House, 616 Walnut Ave., Scottdale, PA 15683. TEL 412-887-8500 Ed. James Horsch. bk. rev. illus. circ. 18,800.

Q P S REPORTER. (Quaker Peace and Service) see *SOCIAL SERVICES AND WELFARE*

QUAKER CONCERN. see *POLITICAL SCIENCE — Civil Rights*

289.6 US ISSN 0033-5053
QUAKER HISTORY. 1902. s-a. $10 membership. Friends Historical Association, Haverford College Library, Haverford, PA 19041. Ed. Arthur J. Mekeel. bk. rev. bibl. illus. cum.index every 5 yrs; vol.1-55 (in 10 vols.) circ. 825 (members); 200(libraries) (also avail. in microform from UMI) Indexed: Rel.Per. CERDIC. Rel.Ind.One.
Formerly: Friends' Historical Association. Bulletin.
History

289.6 UK
QUAKER INFORMATION NETWORK. 1986. 6/yr. £9($14) Friends World Committee for Consultation, Drayton House, 30 Gordon St., London WC1H 0AX, England (Subscr. addr.: 47 Ballyhooley Rd., Cork, Ireland)

289.6 US ISSN 0033-5061
QUAKER LIFE. 1960. 10/yr. $12. (Friends United Meeting (Quakers)) Friends United Press, 101 Quaker Hill Dr., Richmond, IN 47374. TEL 317-962-7573 Ed. Jack Kirk. adv. bk. rev. illus. index. circ. 8,700. Indexed: CERDIC.
Formed by the merger of: American Friend & Quaker Action.

200 UK ISSN 0033-507X
QUAKER MONTHLY. 1922. m. £6.75($12) Quaker Home Service, Friends House, Euston Rd, London NW1 2BJ, England. Ed. Meg Chignell. bk. rev. illus. circ. 4,000. Indexed: CERDIC.
Formerly: Wayfarer.

QUAKER PEACE & SERVICE. ANNUAL REPORT. see *SOCIAL SERVICES AND WELFARE*

289.6 US ISSN 0033-5088
QUAKER RELIGIOUS THOUGHT. 1959. irreg., (approx. 2/yr.) $12 for 4 nos. Quaker Theological Discussion Group, Rte. 4, Box 471-A, Easton, PA 18042. Ed. Dean Freiday. bk. rev. circ. 500. Indexed: CERDIC.

QUAKER YEOMEN. see *GENEALOGY AND HERALDRY*

289.9 US
RAILROAD EVANGELIST. 1931. bi-m. $6. (Railroad Evangelistic Association, Inc.) Light and Life Press, 999 College Ave., Winona Lake, IN 47460 TEL 219-267-7161 (Subscr. to: Box 97, Rte. 4, Spencer, IN 47460) Ed. Herman R. Rose. circ. 2,500.

211.6 US ISSN 0034-4095
RELIGIOUS HUMANISM; a quarterly journal of religious and ethical humanism. 1967. q. $12. Fellowship of Religious Humanists, Box 278, Yellow Springs, OH 45387. TEL 513-767-1324 Eds. Paul and Lucinda Beattie. adv. bk. rev. index. cum.index: vols.1-10. circ. 1,500. (also avail. in microform from UMI; reprints avail. from UMI) Indexed: Curr.Cont. Arts & Hum.Cit.Ind. Phil.Ind. CERDIC. G.Soc.Sci.& Rel.Per.Lit. Phil.Ind. Rel.& Theol.Abstr. Rel.Ind.One.

289.2 US ISSN 0730-2185
RESTORATION; the journal of Latter Day Saint history. 1982. q. $10. Restoration Research, Box 547, Bountiful, UT 84010. Ed. Steven L. Shields. bk. rev. charts, illus. index. circ. 450.

289.2 US
RESTORATION WITNESS; evangelistic magazine of the Reorganized Church of Jesus Christ of Latter Day Saints. 1963. bi-m. $8 to individuals; groups $7. (Reorganized Church of Jesus Christ of Latter Day Saints) Herald Publishing House, 3225 S. Noland Rd., Box HH, Independence, MO 64055. TEL 816-252-5010 Ed. Barbara Howard. adv. bk. rev. illus. tr.lit. circ. 13,000.

ROSICRUCIAN DIGEST. see *PHILOSOPHY*

289.9 917.306 398 US
RUNESTONE (BRECKENRIDGE) 1972. 6/yr. $9. Asatru Free Assembly, Box 1754, Breckenridge, TX 76024. Ed. Stephen McNallen. adv. circ. 500.

281.9 US ISSN 0036-0317
RUSSIAN ORTHODOX JOURNAL. 1927. m. (combined Jul.-Aug. & Jan.-Feb.) $10. Federated Russian Orthodox Clubs of America, 10 Downs Dr. (Plains), Wilkes-Barre, PA 18705 TEL 717-825-3158 Ed. Mark Soroka. adv. bk. rev. illus. index. circ. 3,800.

281.9 US ISSN 0222-1543
RUSSKOE VOZROZHDENIE; nezavisimyi russkii pravoslavnyi natsional'nyi zhurnal. (Text in Russian) 1978. q. $24. 1000 Anniversary Committee, 322 W. 108th St., New York, NY 10025. Ed.Bd. adv. bk. rev. circ. 800. (back issues avail.) Indexed: Amer.Bibl.Slavic & E.Eur.Stud.

200 US
SACRED NAME BROADCASTER. 1968. m. free. Assemblies of Yahweh, Drawer C, Bethel, PA 19507. TEL 717-933-4518 Ed. Jacob O. Meyer. illus. circ. 14,000.

230 US ISSN 0036-3227
ST. VLADIMIR'S THEOLOGICAL QUARTERLY. 1953. N.S. 1957. q. $15. St. Vladimir's Orthodox Theological Seminary, 575 Scarsdale Rd., Crestwood, Tuckahoe, NY 10707. TEL 914-961-8313 Ed. Very Rev. John Breck. adv. bk. rev. bibl. illus. index. circ. 1,800. (also avail. in microform from UMI; reprint service avail. from UMI) Indexed: Old Test.Abstr. Rel.Per. CERDIC. New Test.Abstr. Rel.& Theol.Abstr. Rel.Ind.One. Theol.& Rel.Ind.
Formerly: St. Vladimir's Seminary Quarterly.

289.3 US ISSN 0036-3251
SAINTS' HERALD; family magazine of the Reorganized Church of Jesus Christ of Latter Day Saints. 1860. m. $16.50 to individuals; groups $13.80. (Reorganized Church of Jesus Christ of Latter Day Saints) Herald Publishing House, 3225 S. Noland Rd., Box HH, Independence, MO 64055. TEL 816-252-5010 Ed. Roger Yarrington. adv. bk. rev. illus. tr.lit. circ. 42,000. (also avail. in microfilm)

284 GR ISSN 0036-357X
SALPISMA. 1945. m. Dr.40($3) Free Evangelical Churches of Greece, 3 Alkiviadou, Athens, Greece. bk. rev. cum. index every 4 yrs. circ. 1,500. Indexed: CERDIC.

289 US ISSN 0586-7282
SALT LAKE CITY MESSENGER. 1964. irreg., no.62, 1985. free. Utah Lighthouse Ministry, 1350 South West Temple St., Box 1884, Salt Lake City, UT 84110. TEL 801-485-8894 Ed. Jerald Tanner. adv. circ. 13,500. (looseleaf format)

267.15 UK ISSN 0080-567X
SALVATION ARMY YEAR BOOK. 1906. a. £2.95 paperback; £5.95 hardback. ‡ (Salvation Army) Salvationist Publishing and Supplies, Ltd., Judd St., Kings Cross, London WC1H 9NN, England. index. circ. 11,000.

289.9 301.412 US
SAPPHO'S UNDERSTUDIES. 4/yr. $5. Cabalistic Wicca Church, Box 28633, Sacramento, CA 95828. TEL 916-422-8532 Ed. Mary Bell. adv. illus.

362.8 KE
SAUTI YA VITA. (Text in English and Swahili) 1928. m. EAs.1. (Salvation Army) Kijabe Press, Box 40, Kijabe, Kenya. Ed. S. Ireri. circ. 12,000.

280 US ISSN 0036-8032
SCHWENKFELDIAN. 1903. 3/yr. $4 to non-members. (Schwenkfelder Church) Board of Publication of the Schwenkfelder General Conference, 1 Seminary St., Pennsburg, PA 18073. TEL 215-679-3103 Ed. Nancy MacQueen Byron. bk. rev. illus. circ. 1,700.

200 US ISSN 0036-8458
SCIENCE OF MIND. 1927. m. $15. United Church of Religious Science, 3251 W. Sixth St., Los Angeles, CA 90020. TEL 213-388-2181 Ed. John S. Niendorff. adv. illus. circ. 100,000. Indexed: CERDIC.

289.9 US ISSN 0276-7899
SECOND CENTURY; a journal of early Christian studies. 1981. q. $10. Second Century Journal, Inc., ACU Station, Box 8227, Abilene, TX 79699. Ed. Everett Ferguson. adv. circ. 650. Indexed: Rel.& Theol.Abstr. Rel.Ind.One.

299 US
SEIKYO TIMES. (Text in English) 1981. m. $3. (Nichiren Shoshu International Center) World Tribune Press, 525 Wilshire Blvd., Santa Monica, CA 90406. Ed. George M. Williams. circ. 80,000.

SELF-REALIZATION. see *PHILOSOPHY*

200 CN ISSN 0049-0202
SENTINEL (WILLOWDALE) 1875. 6/yr. Can.$6. (Grand Orange Lodge of Canada) British America Publishing Co. Ltd., Canadian Orange Hdqs., 94 Sheppard Ave. W., Willowdale, Ont. M2N 1M5, Canada. Ed. Norman R. Ritchie. adv. circ. 9,400. (also avail. in microfilm)

200 745.5 US ISSN 0270-9368
SHAKER MESSENGER. 1978. q. $10. World of Shaker, Box 45, Holland, MI 49423. TEL 616-396-3461 Ed. Diana Van Kolken. adv. bk. rev. charts. illus. circ. 2,000. (back issues avail.)
Supersedes: World of Shaker.

SHARE IT; a magazine to celebrate & promote awareness of our true identity. see *PHILOSOPHY*

299 UK ISSN 0260-0382
SHEPHERD; an Orthodox Christian pastoral magazine. 1980. m. contributions. St. Edward Brotherhood, St. Cyprian's Ave., Brookwood, Woking, Surrey, England. Ed. Fr. Alexis (Pobjoy) adv. bk. rev. circ. 330.

200 JA ISSN 0037-5055
SIGNS OF THE TIMES. (Text in Japanese) m. 3490 Yen($19.40) Japan Publishing House, 1966 Kamikawai-cho, Asahi-ku, Yokohama 241, Japan. Ed. Minoru Hirota. circ. 46,000.

286 SA ISSN 0037-5071
SIGNS OF THE TIMES/TEKENS VAN DIE TYE. (Editions in Afrikaans, English) 1923. q. R.2.50. (Seventh-Day Adventist Church) Southern Publishing Association, Rosmead Ave., Kenilworth, Cape Town, South Africa. Ed. Julian Hibbert. bk. rev. index. circ. 23,750 (13,250 English edt.; 11,500 Afrikaans edt.)

281.62 IS ISSN 0037-5810
SION. (Text in Armenian) 1866. bi-m. $5. Armenian Patriarchate, Old City, Jerusalem, Israel. Ed. Ara Kalaydjian. bk. rev. bl. illus. index. cum.index. circ. 1,500.

281.9 US ISSN 0038-1039
SOLIA; the Herald. (Text in English and Romanian) 1936. m. $12. Romanian Orthodox Episcopate of America, 2522 Grey Tower Rd., Jackson, MI 49201. TEL 517-522-4800 Ed. Rt. Rev. Bishop Nathaniel Popp. bk. rev. circ. 4,751. Indexed: CERDIC.

280 US ISSN 0194-7958
SOPHIA; the review of the Melkite Church in America. 1971. bi-m. $10. ‡ (Melkite Diocese of Newton) Sophia Press, Sophia Editorial Office, Box 265, Newton Centre, MA 02159. Ed. Ronald Golini. bk. rev. illus. circ. 9,500. Indexed: Cath.Ind.

200 US ISSN 0038-1756
SOUL. 1950. bi-m. $2. (World Apostolate of Fatima, Blue Army of Our Lady of Fatima in U.S. and Canada) Ave Maria Institute Press, Washington, NJ 07882. TEL 201-689-1700 Ed. John M. Haffert. charts. illus. circ. 360,000.

286 SA ISSN 0038-2795
SOUTH AFRICAN UNION LANTERN/SUID-AFRIKAANSE UNIE-LANTERN. (Editions in Afrikaans and English) 1940. bi-m. (South African Union Conference of Seventh-Day Adventists) Southern Publishing Association, Rosmead Ave., Kenilworth, Cape Town, South Africa. Ed. C.D. Verwey. circ. 8,325 (4,575 English edt.; 3,750 Afrikaans edt.)

250 II ISSN 0038-3465
SOUTH INDIA CHURCHMAN. 1947. m. Rs.12. Church of South India, c/o Christian Literature Society, Box 501, Park Town, Madras 600003, India. Ed. Rev. Dass Babu. adv. bk. rev. circ. 2,000.

289.6 US ISSN 0024-0591
SPARK. 1970. 5/yr. membership. New York Yearly Meeting of the Religious Society of Friends, 15 Rutherford Place, New York, NY 10003. TEL 212-673-5750 Ed. Joseph A. Vlaskamp. bk. rev. bibl. charts. illus. circ. 6,000. Indexed: Alt.Press Ind.

289.9 US
SPECTRUM (TAKOMA PARK) 1969. 5/yr. $20. Association of Adventist Forums, Box 5330, Takoma Park, MD 20912. Ed. Roy Branson. bk. rev. circ. 6,000.

200 US ISSN 0160-0354
SPIRITUAL COMMUNITY GUIDE; the new consciousness wource book. 1972. irreg;. no.6, 1985. $8.95. Arcline Publications, Box 1550, Pomona, CA 91769. TEL 714-623-1738 Ed. Parmatma Singh Khalsa. circ. 20,000.

SPIRITUAL HEALER; journal of spiritual healing and philosophy. see *PHILOSOPHY*

286 US ISSN 0038-9447
STANDARD BEARER (SACRAMENTO) vol. 11, 1973. q. $3. (Seventh-Day Adventist Reform Movement) Northwestern Publishing Association, Box 20234, Sacramento, CA 95820. TEL 916-428-2563 Ed. Alfon Sas Balbachas. adv. illus. circ. 1,300. Indexed: Rehabil.Lit.

289.9 UK ISSN 0308-4531
STELLA POLARIS. 1950. bi-m. £5($10) White Eagle Publishing Trust, White Eagle Lodge, New Lands, Brewells Lane, Liss, Hants GU33 7HY, England. Ed. Ylana Hayward. bk. rev. index. circ. 3,600. (back issues avail.)

STORY FRIENDS. see *CHILDREN AND YOUTH — For*

280 US ISSN 0081-7538
STUDIES IN ANABAPTIST AND MENNONITE HISTORY. 1929. irreg., no.27, 1984. price varies. (Mennonite Historical Society) Mennonite Publishing House, Herald Press, 616 Walnut Ave., Scottdale, PA 15683. TEL 412-887-8500

289 US
STUDIES IN EVANGELICALISM. 1980. irreg., no.8, 1986. Scarecrow Press, Inc., 52 Liberty St., Box 4167, Metuchen, NJ 08840. Eds. Kenneth E. Rowe, Donald W. Dayton.

200 US ISSN 0039-5161
SUNDAY; the magazine for the Lord's day. 1913. q. $5 membership. Lord's Day Alliance of the U.S., 2930 Flowers Rd. S., Ste. 107, Atlanta, GA 30341. TEL 404-451-7315 Ed. James P. Wesberry. bk. rev. charts. illus. circ. 13,500. Indexed: CERDIC.

268 289.1 US ISSN 0039-5285
SUNDAY SCHOOL COUNSELOR. 1940. m. $8. Assemblies of God, Sunday School Department, 1445 Boonville, Springfield, MO 65802. TEL 417-862-2781 Ed. Sylvia Lee. bk. rev. cum.index 1955-1986. circ. 35,000.

289.2 US ISSN 0363-1370
SUNSTONE. 1975. 12/yr. $27. Sunstone Foundation, 59 W. First S., Salt Lake City, UT 84101-1507. TEL 801-355-5926 Ed. Daniel Rector. adv. bk. rev. illus. index. circ. 6,000.

284.2 FR
SUR LE ROC. 1885. m. 106 F. Eglises Reformees Evangeliques Independantes de France, Comite Directeur du Roc, 55 Ave. Jean Moulin, 30380 St. Christol Les Ales, France. Ed. Andre Chante. adv. bk. rev. abstr. bibl. illus. play rev. circ. 5,000.
Former titles: Roc-Christ et France; Christ et France-sur le Roc (ISSN 0009-5052)

200 US ISSN 0039-7156
SVIT/LIGHT. (Text in English) 1910. bi-m. $3. Russian Orthodox Catholic Mutual Aid Society of U.S.A., 100 Hazle St., Wilkes-Barre, PA 18701. TEL 717-822-8591 adv. circ. 1,500. (tabloid format) Indexed: CERDIC.

281.62 LE ISSN 0040-0297
TCHAHERT/TORCH. (Text in Armenian) 1966. s-a. $4. Armenian Evangelical Brotherhood Church, Box 4944, Beirut, Lebanon. Ed.Bd. bk. rev. illus. circ. 1,500.

230.19 GR ISSN 0049-3635
THEOLOGIA. (Text in English, French, German, Greek or Italian) 1923. q. Dr.3900($30) Holy Synod of the Church of Greece, 14 Ioannou Gennadiou St., Athens 140, Greece. Ed. Evangelos Theodorou. bk. rev. bibl. illus. index. circ. 1,200. Indexed: CERDIC.

212.5 AT ISSN 0049-3694
THEOSOPHY IN AUSTRALIA. 1895. q. Aus.$6. Theosophical Society in Australia, 484 Kent St., Sydney, N.S.W. 2000, Australia. Ed. Dianne K. Kynaston. bk. rev. index every 2 yrs. circ. 1,300.

289 NZ ISSN 0049-3708
THEOSOPHY IN NEW ZEALAND. vol. 1,1900. q. NZ.$5. Theosophical Society, New Zealand Section, 18 Belvedere St., Epsom, Auckland 3, New Zealand. Ed. Elizabeth Sell. bk. rev. circ. 2,400.

289.9 301.412 US
THESMOPHORIA; voice of the new women's religion. 1979. 8/yr. $10. Susan B. Anthony Coven No. 1, Box 11363, Oakland, CA 94611. TEL 415-444-7724 Ed. J. Roslond. adv. bk. rev. illus. circ. 2,000. (back issues avail.)
Formerly: Themis.

289.9 NE
THETA. 1972. m. membership. Scientology Kerk, N.Z. Voorburgwal 271, 1012 RS Amsterdam, Netherlands. Ed. R. Meijns. bk. rev. circ. 5,000.
Formerly: Nieuwe Theta.

289.2 US
THIS PEOPLE. 1979. bi-m. $12. This People Publishing, Inc., Oakwood Plaza, 5 Triad Center, No. 500, Salt Lake City, UT 84180-1150. circ. 30,000.

289.9 US
THUNDERBOW. 1977. 12/yr. $8. Church of Seven Arrows, 4385 Hoyt St., No. 201, Wheatridge, CO 80033. TEL 303-424-3304 Eds. Rev. George Dew, Rev. Linda Hillshafer. adv. bk. rev. circ. 200.

281.9 ET
TINSAE. (Text in English) 1979. 3/yr. Eth.$6.25($3) Ethiopian Orthodox Mission, P.O. Box 3137, Addis Ababa, Ethiopia. Ed. Haddis Terrefe. charts. illus.

220 289.9 SA ISSN 0040-9391
TORA YA TEBELO. (Text in Tswana) 1961. s-m. R.6.50. Watch Tower Bible & Tract Society, P.O. Box 2067, Krugersdrop 1740, South Africa. charts. illus. index. circ. 9,000.

299 II
TRIBAL RELIGIONS. 1982. q. Rs.310($63) (International Institute of Tribal Religions) K.K. Roy (Private) Ltd., 55 Gariahat Rd., P.O. Box 10210, Calcutta 700019, India. Ed. Dr. K. K. Roy. adv. bk. rev. abstr. bibl. index. circ. 980.

266 CN ISSN 0821-6371
TRUTH ON FIRE. 1949. bi-m. Can.$5. Bible Holiness Movement, Box 223, Sta. A, Vancouver, B.C. V6C 2M3, Canada. TEL 604-683-1833 Ed. Wesley H. Wakefield. bk. rev. illus. circ. 5,000. (back issues avail.)

200 SA ISSN 0258-9052
TSHIINGAMO. (Text in Venda) 1983. m. R.3.25. Watch Tower Bible and Tract Society, P.O. Box 2067, Krugersdrop 1740, South Africa. charts. illus. index. circ. 2,000.

220 289.9 SA
TSOHA! (Text in Sesotho) 1973. m. R.3.25. Watch Tower Bible & Tract Society, P.O. Box 2067, Krugersdrop 1740, South Africa. charts. illus. index. circ. 11,000.

289.9 US
U L C NEWS. vol.15, 1981. bi-m. $5. Universal Life Church, Inc., 601 Third St., Modesto, CA 95351. TEL 209-527-8111 Ed. Kirby J. Hensley. adv. bk. rev. illus. circ. 100,000.
Formerly (until 1984): Universal Life.

281.9 US
U R O B A MESSENGER. (Text mainly in English; occasionally in Russian) 1925. bi-m. $5. ‡ United Russian Orthodox Brotherhood of America, 333 Blvd. of Allies, Pittsburgh, PA 15222. TEL 412-261-4277 circ. 2,000. (tabloid format)
Formerly: Russian Messenger/Russkij Vistnik (ISSN 0036-0287)

268 US ISSN 0147-1015
UKRAINIAN ORTHODOX WORD. ENGLISH EDITION. vol. 8, 1974. m. $6.50. Ukrainian Orthodox Church of the U.S.A., P. O. Box 495, So. Bound Brook, NJ 08880. TEL 201-356-0090 Ed. Rev. Joseph Kreta. bk. rev. film rev. play rev. bibl. stat. circ. 2,000. (tabloid format; back issues avail.)

200 US ISSN 0041-6258
ULTREYA. 1959. m. $6. U S Cusillo Movement, National Secretariat, Box 210226, 4500 W. Davis, Dallas, TX 75211. Ed. Gerald P. Hughes. bk. rev. illus. circ. 7,000.

289.9 SA
UMPHAKO WABASHUMAYELI. (Text in English and Zulu) q. free to Nazarene pastors and Bible college students. (Church of the Nazarene) Africa Nazarene Publications, P.O. Box 44, Florida, Transvaal 1710, South Africa.

289.9 SA
UMPHAPHAMISI. (Text in English and Zulu) 1920. q. R.0.75. (Church of the Nazarene) Africa Nazarene Publications, P.O. Box 44, Florida, Transvaal 1710, South Africa. stat. circ. 1,000.

658.32 US ISSN 0360-9782
UNITED CHURCH OF CHRIST. PENSION BOARDS (ANNUAL REPORT) 1967. a. free. United Church of Christ, Pension Boards, 132 W. 31st St., New York, NY 10001. TEL 212-239-8700 Ed. Edmund Tortora. circ. 15,000.
Key Title: Pension Boards.

289.9 US ISSN 0162-3567
UNITY. 1889. m. $5 for inkprint edt. Braille edt. is free. Unity School of Christianity, Unity Village, MO 64065. TEL 816-524-3550 Ed. Pamela Yearsley. circ. 500,000.

200 GW ISSN 0042-3696
VERBUM. (Text in English, French, German and Spanish) 1970. q. DM.34. (Missionswissenschaftliches Institut) Steyler Verlag, Bahnhofstr. 9, D-4054 Nettetal 2, W. Germany (B.R.D.) Ed. Rev. Horst Rzepkowski. bk. rev. abstr. charts. pat. tr.mk. index every 5 years. circ. 1,800.

286 AG
VIDA FELIZ. 1899. m. $15.50. (Iglesia Adventista del Septimo Dia) Asociacion Casa Editora Sudamericana, Avda. San Martin 4555, 1602 Florida, Buenos Aires, Argentina. Ed. Nestor Alberro. illus. circ. 45,000.

289.9 US ISSN 0042-7381
VITAL CHRISTIANITY. 1881. 20/yr. $16.50. (Church of God) Warner Press, Inc., Box 2499, Anderson, IN 46018. TEL 317-644-7721 Ed. Arlo F. Newell. bk. rev. charts. illus. circ. 28,000. Indexed: G.Soc.Sci.& Rel.Per.Lit.

289 US ISSN 0049-6669
VOICE (WESTCHESTER) 1930. 6/yr. $6. Independent Fundamental Churches of America, Box 7250, 1860 Mannheim Rd., Westchester, IL 60153. TEL 312-562-0234 Ed. Paul J. Dollaske. adv. bk. rev. illus. circ. 11,500.

294.6 II
VOICE OF SAMANVAYA. (Text in English) 1976. s-a. Rs.15. C.P. Ramaswami Aiyar Foundation, Centre for Studies in Tradition, Thought and Culture of India, The Grove, Eldams Rd, Madras 18, India. Ed. K. Seshadri.

289.9 US ISSN 0042-8213
VOICE OF THE NAZARENE-A UNIVERSAL CHALLENGER. vol. 19, 1970. m. free. God's Acres, Inc., Box 5175, Sun City, FL 33571-5175. Ed. W. L. King. bk. rev. illus. circ. 5,000. (processed)

281.9 US
VOICES (SALEM); in the wilderness. 6/yr. $12. Box 4486, Salem, MA 01970-6486.

200 289.9 SA
VUKANI! (Text in Xhosa) 1973. m. R.3.25. Watch Tower Bible & Tract Society, P.O. Box 2067, Krugersdrop 1740, South Africa. charts. illus. index. circ. 8,500.

220 289.9 SA
DIE WAGTORING. (Text in Afrikaans) 1943. s-m. R.6.50($4) Watch Tower Bible & Tract Society, P.O. Box 2067, Krugersdrop 1740, South Africa. charts. illus. index. circ. 29,500.

WAR CRY. see *RELIGIONS AND THEOLOGY*

267.15 CN ISSN 0043-0218
WAR CRY. 1884. w. Can.$12($1550) (Salvation Army, Canada Territorial Headquarters) Triumph Press, 455 North Service Road East, Oakville, Ont. L6H 1A5, Canada. TEL 416-844-2561 Ed. Major M. Ryan. bk. rev. illus. circ. 75,000. (tabloid format)

267.15 NR ISSN 0049-688X
WAR CRY. 1921. m. £N2.50. Salvation Army in Nigeria and Ghana, Territorial Headquarters, Box 125, Lagos, Nigeria. Ed. C.B. Ezekwere. bk. rev. circ. 5,600.

267.15 NZ ISSN 0043-0242
WAR CRY. 1883. w. NZ.$0.30 per no. Salvation Army, 204 Cuba St., Wellington 1, New Zealand. Ed. Kenneth J. Manson. bk. rev. circ. 15,000.

267.15 SA ISSN 0043-0250
WAR CRY/STRYDKREET. (Text in Afrikaans and English) 1884. w. R.17. ‡ Salvation Army, Box 153, Lansdowne 7780, Cape Town, South Africa (Subscr. addr.: P.O. Box 1018, Johannesburg 2000, South Africa) Ed. Martin McCarter. bk. rev. illus. circ. 10,000.

267.15 SI ISSN 0049-6898
WAR CRY. 1971. m. S.$5. Salvation Army in Malaysia and Singapore, 207 Clemenceau Ave., Singapore-9, Singapore. Ed. James R. Sloan. charts. illus.

267.15 UK ISSN 0043-0226
WAR CRY. 1879. w. £21. Salvation Army, 101 Queen Victoria St., London EC4P 4EP, England. Ed. Robert Street. bk. rev. illus. circ. 140,000.

067.15 US ISSN 0043-0234
WAR CRY. 1880. bi-w. $7.50. Salvation Army, 799 Bloomfield Ave., Verona, NJ 07044. TEL 201-239-0606 Ed. Lt. Col. Henry Gariepy. circ. 371,000. (also avail. in microfilm; back issues avail.)

289.9 US ISSN 0043-1087
WATCHTOWER; announcing Jehovah's kingdom. (Editions in 103 languages; also avail. in Braille) 1879. s-m. $4. ‡ (Jehovah's Witnesses, Governing Body) Watch Tower Bible and Tract Society of Pennsylvania, 25 Columbia Hts., Brooklyn, NY 11201. TEL 718-625-3600 circ. 11,630,000.

200 UK ISSN 0043-1605
WAY OF LIFE; the church's ministry of healing. 1911. q. £4. Guild of Health, 26 Queen Anne St., London W1M 9LB, England. Ed.Bd. bk. rev. index. circ. 1,900. Indexed: CERDIC.
Former titles: For Health; Healing.

294.37 US
WHEEL SERIES. 1973. irreg., no.3, 1982. Four Seasons Foundation, Box 31190, San Francisco, CA 94131 (Dist. by: Subco, Box 10233, Eugene, OR 97440) Ed. Donald Allen. circ. 3,000.

289.9 US
WHEREVER. 1976. 3/yr. $3. T.E.A.M. (The Evangelical Alliance Mission), Box 969, Wheaton, IL 60189. TEL 312-653-5300 Ed. Douglas B. Wicks. bk. rev. charts. illus. circ. 14,000.

133 US ISSN 0742-8820
WHITE LIGHT. 1974. q. $5. Light of Truth Church, Inc., Box 93124, Pasadena, CA 91109. Ed. Rev. Nelson H. White. adv. bk. rev. bibl. charts. illus. index. circ. 200.
Formerly: Ceremonial Magick.

289 US ISSN 0043-5007
WHITE WING MESSENGER. 1923. fortn. $8.50. (Church of God of Prophecy) White Wing Publishing House, Box 3000, Cleveland, TN 37311. TEL 615-476-8536 Ed. M. A. Tomlinson. illus. circ. 16,000.

WITH; a magazine for the middle teens. see *CHILDREN AND YOUTH — For*

289 AT ISSN 0158-6262
WORLD MISSIONS UPDATE. 1971. m. Aus.$1. Assemblies of God in Australia, Division of World Missions, P.O. Box 229, Nunawading, Vic. 3131, Australia. Ed. W.G. Forbes. circ. 10,500.
Formerly: Garamut (ISSN 0311-0362)

200 US ISSN 0043-8804
WORLD ORDER; a Baha'i magazine. 1966. q. $10. National Spiritual Assembly of the Baha'is of the United States, 415 Linden Ave., Wilmette, IL 60091 TEL 312-869-9039 (Subscr. to: World Order Subscr. Service, 415 Linden Ave., Wilmette, IL 60091) Ed. Betty J. Fisher. bk. rev. cum.index vols.1-12. circ. 5,000. (also avail. in microform from UMI; reprint service avail. from UMI) Indexed: Ind.Amer.Per.Verse. Rel.Ind.One.

266 US ISSN 0043-9215
WORLD VISION. 1958. m. free. ‡ World Vision International, 919 West Huntington Dr., Monrovia, CA 91016. TEL 818-357-7979 Ed. David Olson. charts. illus. stat. circ. 1,000,000. Indexed: Chr.Per.Ind.

267.15 NE
WYZER. 1898. bi-m. fl.5. Leger des Heils - Salvation Army in the Netherlands, Damstr. 15, Amsterdam, Netherlands. Ed. Major K. Kerkhoven. bk. rev. abstr. circ. 3,500.
Formerly: Jonge Kampvechter (ISSN 0021-7387)
Ages 6-14

200 289.9 SA ISSN 0258-9079
XIHONDZO XO RINDZA. (Text in Tsonga) 1974. s-m. R.6.50. Watch Tower Bible & Tract Society, P.O. Box 2067, Krugersdrop 1740, South Africa. charts. illus. index. circ. 5,000.

YOGA; tidsskrift for universel religion. see *PHILOSOPHY*

289 341.1 CN
YOUNG COMPANION. 1966. m. $3. (Amish Church) Pathway Publishing Corporation, R. 4, Aylmer, Ont., Canada. Ed. Joseph Stoll. bk. rev. bibl. illus. circ. 17,400.
Formerly: Ambassador of Peace (ISSN 0002-6921)

200 SA ISSN 0044-0787
YOUNG IDEAS. Afrikaans edition: Jong Dae. (Supplement to: The Path of Truth) 1937. m. free. School of Truth Ltd., South Africa Centre, 5th Fl., 253 Bree St., Johannesburg, South Africa. Ed. Gerita Gerryts-Elferink.

200 AT ISSN 0300-3264
YOUNG SOLDIER. 1890. w. Aus.$27.58. (Salvation Army) Donald Campbell, 1-9 Drill St, Hawthorn, Melbourne, Vic. 3122, Australia. Ed. Rowland Hill. illus. circ. 18,014.

289.9 NE
ZEN. 1980. q. fl.20. Stichting Theresiahoeve, Dominicanenstraat 24, 5453 JN Langenboom, Netherlands. Ed. Judith Bossert. adv. bk. rev. circ. 1,100.

ROMAN CATHOLICISM
see Religions and Theology–Roman Catholic

SCHOOL ORGANIZATION AND ADMINISTRATION
see Education–School Organization and Administration

SCIENCES: COMPREHENSIVE WORKS

INTERCOM (NEW YORK, 1960?) see *RELIGIONS AND THEOLOGY — Judaic*

NAUKA I RELIGIYA. see *RELIGIONS AND THEOLOGY*

PERSPECTIVES ON SCIENCE AND CHRISTIAN FAITH. see *RELIGIONS AND THEOLOGY*

SOCIETY FOR COMMON INSIGHTS. JOURNAL. see *RELIGIONS AND THEOLOGY*

500 200 US
THEOLOGY AND SCIENTIFIC CULTURE. irreg., no.3, 1982. Oxford University Press, Inc., 200 Madison Ave., New York, NY 10016. bibl. index.

V.R.B. - INFORMATIE. (Vereniging van Religieus-Wetenschappelijke Bibliothecarissen) see *LIBRARY AND INFORMATION SCIENCES*

SHIPS AND SHIPPING
see Transportation–Ships and Shipping

SOCIAL SCIENCES: COMPREHENSIVE WORKS

056.1 PY ISSN 0001-4605
ACCION; revista paraguaya de reflexion y dialogo. N.S. 1969. 6/yr. 2000 g.($10) Centro de Estudios Paraguayos Antonio Guasch, Calle Colon 1301, Casilla 1072, Asuncion, Paraguay. (Co-sponsor: Society of Jesus) Ed. Angel Camina. adv. bk. rev. illus. circ. 2,000.
Incorporating: Dimension.

AMERICAN BENEDICTINE REVIEW. see *RELIGIONS AND THEOLOGY — Roman Catholic*

BAR-ILAN: ANNUAL OF BAR-ILAN UNIVERSITY. see *RELIGIONS AND THEOLOGY — Judaic*

CHRISTIAN STATESMAN. see *RELIGIONS AND THEOLOGY*

CONFUCIUS & MENCIUS SOCIETY OF THE REPUBLIC OF CHINA JOURNAL. see *RELIGIONS AND THEOLOGY — Oriental*

296 US ISSN 0021-6704
JEWISH SOCIAL STUDIES. 1939. q. $30. Conference on Jewish Social Studies, Inc., 2112 Broadway, Rm. 206, New York, NY 10023. TEL 212-724-5336 Ed. Toby B. Gitelle. bk. rev. index. cum.index every 25 yrs. circ. 1,300. (also avail. in microform from MIM) Indexed: Curr.Cont. Hist.Abstr. P.A.I.S. SSCI. Soc.Sci.Ind. Amer.Bibl.Slavic & E.Eur.Stud. Adol.Ment.Hlth.Abstr. Arts & Hum.Cit.Ind. Abstr.Anthropol. Bk.Rev.Ind. Amer.Hist.& Life. Ind.Jew.Per. Lang.& Lang.Behav.Abstr.

230 US
PATTERNS (PORTLAND) 1973. bi-m. $10. Center for the Study of the Future, 4110 N.E. Alameda, Portland, OR 97212. Ed. Carl Townsend. bk. rev. circ. 100. Indexed: CERDIC.

PLOUGH. see *RELIGIONS AND THEOLOGY*

PONTIFICIA UNIVERSIDADE CATOLICA DE SAO PAULO. REVISTA. see *RELIGIONS AND THEOLOGY — Roman Catholic*

RELIGION AND SOCIETY. see *RELIGIONS AND THEOLOGY*

300 BL
SINTESE. 1959. q. $25. (Centro Joao XXIII (Rio de Janeiro)) Editora Fundacao Mariana Resende Costa (FUMARC), R. Rio Comprido 4,580, 32000 Contagem MG, Brazil. Ed. Henrique C. De Lima Vaz. bk. rev. circ. 1,000. Indexed: CERDIC.
Formerly: Sintese Politica, Economica e Social (ISSN 0037-5772)

VITA SOCIALE. see *RELIGIONS AND THEOLOGY — Roman Catholic*

SOCIAL SERVICES AND WELFARE
see also Blind

ALL THE WORLD. see *RELIGIONS AND THEOLOGY — Other Denominations And Sects*

BUND DER DEUTSCHEN KATHOLISCHEN JUGEND. INFORMATIONSDIENST. see *CHILDREN AND YOUTH — For*

CAMILLIAN. see *RELIGIONS AND THEOLOGY*

361 UK
CHART AND COMPASS INTERNATIONAL. 1818. bi-m. free. British Sailors' Society, P.O. Box 11, Ilford, Essex IG2 6NG, England. Ed. Rev. David A. Harries. adv. bk. rev. illus. circ. 35,000.
Formerly: Chart and Compass.

267 FR ISSN 0763-5184
EQUIPES ST VINCENT. 3/yr. 50 F. Federation Francaise des Equipes Saint-Vincent, 67 rue de Sevres, 75006 Paris, France. Ed. Mauricette Borldo. bk. rev. circ. 4,000.
Formerly: Echos des Charites de St. Vincent de Paul (ISSN 0070-8305)

362.7 UK
GATEWAY. 1881. q. free. Church of England Children's Society, Old Town Hall, Kennington, London SE11 4QD, England. Ed. Mary Thompson. bk. rev. circ. 400,000.
Child welfare

INFORMATION JUIVE; le journal des communautes. see *ETHNIC INTERESTS*

361.75 US
J S A C GRAPEVINE. 1969. m. $6. ‡ Joint Strategy and Action Committee, 475 Riverside Dr., Rm. 450, New York, NY 10115. TEL 212-870-3105 Ed. James Solheim. bk. rev. film rev. abstr. bibl. charts. stat. circ. 3,500. (tabloid format)

J W B CIRCLE. (National Jewish Welfare Board) see *RELIGIONS AND THEOLOGY — Judaic*

360 266 US ISSN 0023-1703
KINSHIP. 1961. q. free. Glenmary Home Mission Sisters of America, 3636 Semloh, Box 39188, Cincinnati, OH 45239. TEL 513-741-8846 Ed. Sr. Christine Beckett. illus. circ. 11,000.

LICHTHOEVE. see *RELIGIONS AND THEOLOGY*

POPOLO. see *RELIGIONS AND THEOLOGY*

362 UK ISSN 0265-7848
Q P S REPORTER. 1968. q. free. Quaker Peace and Service, Friends House, Euston Rd., London NW1 2BJ, England. Ed. Grace Crookall-Greening. illus.
Former titles: Quaker Peace & Service (ISSN 0141-5352); Peace Action Newsletter; Quaker Service (ISSN 0306-283X)

362 UK ISSN 0260-9584
QUAKER PEACE & SERVICE. ANNUAL REPORT. 1927. a. free. Quaker Peace and Service, Friends House, Euston Road, London NW1 2BJ, England. Ed. Grace Crookall-Greening. illus.
Formerly: Friends Service Council. Annual Report (ISSN 0071-9609)

360 282 US
SOCIAL WORK AND CHRISTIANITY; an international journal. 1974. s-a. $10. North American Association of Christians in Social Work, Box 90, St. Davids, PA 19087-0913. TEL 215-687-5777 Ed. David A. Sherwood. adv. bk. rev. circ. 1,000. (back issues avail.) Indexed: Chr.Per.Ind.

SOWER. see *RELIGIONS AND THEOLOGY*

SUMMER SERVICE OPPORTUNITIES. see *RELIGIONS AND THEOLOGY — Protestant*

360 371.4 US ISSN 0043-7514
WOMEN'S AMERICAN O R T REPORTER. 1966. q. $1 to members; non-members $5. ‡ Women's America ORT, Inc., 315 Park Ave. S., New York, NY 10010. TEL 212-505-7700 Ed. Elie Faust-Levy. adv. bk. rev. film rev. play rev. illus. circ. 150,000. (tabloid format)

SOCIOLOGY
see also Folklore; Social Sciences: Comprehensive Works; Social Services and Welfare

ACADEMIA; Zeitschrift fuer Politik und Kultur. see *LITERARY AND POLITICAL REVIEWS*

L'ALTRA EUROPA. see *ART*

ATMA JAYA RESEARCH CENTRE. SOCIO-RELIGIOUS RESEARCH REPORT/PUSAT PENELITIAN ATMA JAYA. LAPORAN PENELITIAN KEAGAMAAN. see *RELIGIONS AND THEOLOGY — Oriental*

BELARUSKAJA CARKVA. see *RELIGIONS AND THEOLOGY*

BOLETIN C E N P A F A L. see *RELIGIONS AND THEOLOGY — Roman Catholic*

BULLETIN ON THE T F P'S. (American Society for the Defense of Tradition, Family and Property, Inc.) see *RELIGIONS AND THEOLOGY — Roman Catholic*

C M J S CENTERPIECES. (Center for Modern Jewish Studies) see *ETHNIC INTERESTS*

CAHIERS DE L'ACTUALITE RELIGIEUSE ET SOCIALE. see *RELIGIONS AND THEOLOGY*

CAHIERS DES RELIGIONS AFRICAINES. see *RELIGIONS AND THEOLOGY — Other Denominations And Sects*

CATHOLIC RURAL LIFE. see *RELIGIONS AND THEOLOGY — Roman Catholic*

CHRISTIAN JEWISH RELATIONS. see *RELIGIONS AND THEOLOGY*

CHURCH AND SOCIETY. see *RELIGIONS AND THEOLOGY — Protestant*

CHURCHMAN'S HUMAN QUEST. see *RELIGIONS AND THEOLOGY*

COLORADO KAIROS. see *RELIGIONS AND THEOLOGY*

COMMON GROUND; to combat all forms of religious and racial intolerance. see *RELIGIONS AND THEOLOGY*

CONVERGENCE. see *RELIGIONS AND THEOLOGY — Roman Catholic*

E/S A. see *RELIGIONS AND THEOLOGY — Protestant*

FORUM. BERICHTE AUS DER ARBEIT. see *RELIGIONS AND THEOLOGY*

FRIENDS JOURNAL. see *RELIGIONS AND THEOLOGY — Other Denominations And Sects*

HUMAN LIFE ISSUES. see *BIRTH CONTROL*

INTERNATIONAL CONFERENCE FOR THE SOCIOLOGY OF RELIGION. see *RELIGIONS AND THEOLOGY*

261 GW ISSN 0075-2584
JAHRBUCH FUER CHRISTLICHE SOZIALWISSENSCHAFTEN. Title varies: Jahrbuch des Instituts fuer Christliche Sozialwissenschaften. 1960. a. DM.48. (Universitaet Muenster, Institut fuer Christliche Sozialwissenschaften) Verlag Regensberg, Daimlerweg 58, Postfach 6748/6749, 4400 Muenster, W. Germany (B.R.D.) Indexed: CERDIC.

301 UK ISSN 0021-6534
JEWISH JOURNAL OF SOCIOLOGY. 1959. s-a. £8($18) 187 Gloucester Place, London NW1 6BU, England. Ed. Judith Freedman. adv. bk. rev. bibl. index. Indexed: Curr.Cont. P.A.I.S. Psychol.Abstr. SSCI. Ind.Jew.Per. Lang.& Lang.Behav.Abstr.

301 200 CN ISSN 0709-3519
JOURNAL OF COMPARATIVE SOCIOLOGY & RELIGION. 1973. a. $50. Canada Sociological Research Centre, P.O. Box 7305, Ottawa K1N 6N5, Canada. Ed. Amarjit S. Sethi. adv. bk. rev. circ. 1,000. (back issues avail.)

JUNGE KIRCHE; eine Zeitschrift Europaeischer Christen. see *RELIGIONS AND THEOLOGY*

LATINAMERICA PRESS. see *RELIGIONS AND THEOLOGY*

LEADERS' DIGEST. see *ETHNIC INTERESTS*

301.42 US
MARRIAGE AND FAMILY LIVING. 1959. m. $11.95. (St. Meinrad Archabbey) Abbey Press, 52 Hill Dr., St. Meinrad, IN 47577. TEL 812-357-8011 Ed. Keith McClellan. adv. bk. rev. charts. illus. index. circ. 38,000. (reprint service avail. from UMI) Indexed: Cath.Ind. CERDIC. Curr.Lit.Fam.Plan. Sage Fam.Stud.Abstr.
Formerly (until 1974): Marriage (ISSN 0025-4010)

METRO - MINISTRY NEWS. see *RELIGIONS AND THEOLOGY*

MIGRANTI-PRESS. see *POLITICAL SCIENCE*

NOTICIAS ALIADAS. see *RELIGIONS AND THEOLOGY*

OPINION; the way I see it. see *PHILOSOPHY*

RADIX (BERKELEY) see *RELIGIONS AND THEOLOGY*

REINO; de deus no mundo dos homens. see *RELIGIONS AND THEOLOGY*

RELIGIONE E SOCIETA. see *RELIGIONS AND THEOLOGY*

REVIEW OF RELIGIOUS RESEARCH. see *RELIGIONS AND THEOLOGY*

291.17 IT
RICERCHE DI STORIA SOCIALE E RELIGIOSA. 1972. s-a. L.9000. (Centro Studi per le Fonti della Storia della Chiesa nel Veneto) Casa Editrice Ferraro, Via S. Sebastiano 54, 80134 Naples, Italy. (Co-publisher: Edizioni di Storia e Letteratura) (Co-Sponsor: Centro Studi di Storia Sociale e Religiosa nel Mezzogiorno) Ed. Gabriele De Rosa. illus. Indexed: CERDIC.

301 US ISSN 0038-0210
S A. (Sociological Analysis); a journal in the sociology of religion. 1940. q. $40. Association for the Sociology of Religion, Marist Hall, Rm. 108, Catholic University of America, Washington, DC 20064. TEL 202-635-5447 Ed. Barbara Hargrove. adv. bk. rev. charts. stat. index. cum.index: vols.1-24. circ. 1,325. (also avail. in microform from JAI,MIM,UMI; reprint service avail. from UMI) Indexed: Cath.Ind. Curr.Cont. Rel.Per. SSCI. Sociol.Abstr. Curr.Lit.Fam.Plan. Lang.& Lang.Behav.Abstr. Rel.Ind.One.
Formerly: American Catholic Sociological Review.

SAMARITANO. see *RELIGIONS AND THEOLOGY*

SERVIZIO MIGRANTI. see *POLITICAL SCIENCE*

300 261 BE ISSN 0037-7686
SOCIAL COMPASS; international review of sociology of religion. (Text in English and French) 1953. 4/yr. 1650 Fr. International Federation of Institutes for Social and Socio-Religious Research - Federation Internationale des Instituts de Recherches Socio-Religieuses, Batiment S.H. 2, Place Montesquieu 1, Boite 21, 1348 Louvain-la-Neuve, Belgium. Ed. A. Bastenier. adv. bk. rev. bibl. charts. stats. index. cum.index: 1953-1973. circ. 1,500. Indexed: Curr.Cont. Rel.Per. SSCI. ASCA. Arts & Hum.Cit.Ind. CERDIC. Lang.& Lang.Behav.Abstr. Rel.Ind.One. Rel.& Theol.Abstr.

361 US ISSN 0037-7767
SOCIAL JUSTICE REVIEW; pioneer American journal of Catholic social action. 1908. bi-m. $15. Catholic Central Union of America, 3835 Westminster Pl., St. Louis, MO 63108. TEL 314-371-0889 Ed. Rev. John H. Miller. adv. bk. rev. index. circ. 1,250. (also avail. in microfilm) Indexed: Cath.Ind. CERDIC.

SOCIAL QUESTIONS BULLETIN. see *RELIGIONS AND THEOLOGY — Protestant*

301 IE
SOCIAL STUDIES; Irish journal of sociology. 1947. q. £2.50($8) Christus Rex Society, c/o Department of Sociology, St. Patrick's College, Maynooth, County Kildare, Ireland. Ed. Liam Ryan. adv. bk. rev. charts. illus. stat. index. circ. 2,450. Indexed: Cath.Ind. Educ.Ind. P.A.I.S. SSCI. CERDIC. Child.Bk.Rev.Ind.
Formerly: Christus Rex (ISSN 0009-5877)

SOURCE (SEATTLE) see *RELIGIONS AND THEOLOGY*

SOUTH AFRICAN OUTLOOK; a journal dealing with ecumenical and racial affairs. see *RELIGIONS AND THEOLOGY*

301 AT ISSN 0310-5466
SYDNEY TOWN EXPRESS. 1972. m. Aus.$2. Voice Media, Box 682, Chatswood, N.S.W. 2067, Australia. Ed. Ken Woodhouse. bk. rev. circ. 1,500.

301 CK
TIERRA NUEVA. 1972. q. $27. ‡ Centro de Estudios para el Desarrollo e Integracion de America Latina, Carrera 90, No. 47-54, Apdo. Aereo 100572, Bogota, D.E. 10, Colombia. Ed. Maria B. Cabezas de Gonzalez. cum.index. circ. 1,000. Indexed: CERDIC.

SOUND RECORDING AND REPRODUCTION

see also Music

RECORDING LOCATOR. see *MUSIC*

STATISTICS

see also specific subjects

TAXATION

see Business and Economics–Public Finance, Taxation

TEACHING METHODS AND CURRICULUM

see Education–Teaching Methods and Curriculum

TECHNOLOGY: COMPREHENSIVE WORKS

CHURCH AND SOCIETY NEWSLETTER; Christian social thought in a future perspective. see *RELIGIONS AND THEOLOGY*

THEATER

see also Dance

TRANSPORTATION

see also Transportation–Ships and Shipping

TRANSPORTATION — Ships And Shipping

387 US ISSN 0024-6425
LOOKOUT. 1909. 3/yr. $5. ‡ Seamen's Church Institute of New York and New Jersey, 50 Broadway, New York, NY 10004. TEL 212-269-2710 Ed. Carlyle Windley. bk. rev. illus. circ. 6,000.

TRAVEL AND TOURISM

HOLY PLACES OF PALESTINE. see *RELIGIONS AND THEOLOGY*

QUADERNI DE "LA TERRA SANTA". see *RELIGIONS AND THEOLOGY*

VOICE FROM JERUSALEM. see *RELIGIONS AND THEOLOGY — Judaic*

WOMEN'S INTERESTS

208 US
BELTANE PAPERS; a new-journal of women's spirituality and thealogy. 1984. 12/yr. New Moon Collective, Box 8, Clear Lake, WA 98235. Ed. Helen G. Farias. adv. bk. rev. play rev. bibl. illus. circ. 500.

301.412 UK
C W L NEWS. 1911. q. £2. Catholic Women's League, 48 Great Peter St., London SW1P 2HP, England.

CHRISTIAN MOTHER (PITTSBURGH) see *RELIGIONS AND THEOLOGY*

053.1 GW ISSN 0009-5788
DIE CHRISTLICHE FRAU. 1903. 6/yr. membership. Katholischer Deutscher Frauenbund, Kaesenstr. 18, 5000 Cologne 1, W. Germany (B.R.D.) bk. rev. circ. 30,000.

301.412 DK ISSN 0109-1476
D K K F-NYT. 1981. bi-m. Kr.30. Dansk Katolsk Kvinde-Forbund, c/o Simone Pedersen, Elbaekvej 16, 8240 Risskov, Denmark. illus.

301.412 US ISSN 0739-1749
DAUGHTERS OF SARAH. 1974. bi-m. $14. 2716 W. Cortland, Chicago, IL 60647. TEL 312-252-3344 Ed. Reta Finger. adv. bk. rev. index. circ. 5,100. (also avail. in microform; back issues avail.)

301.412 US
F T I NEWSLETTER. 1982. q. membership. Feminist Theological Institute, Inc., Department of Women's Studies, Stephens College, Columbia, MD 65215. Ed. Rita N. Brock. adv. bk. rev. circ. 250.

301.412 289.6 US
FRIENDLY WOMAN. 4/yr. $4. Women in Santa Cruz-A F S Committee, 131 Dake Ave., Santa Cruz, CA 95062. Ed. Arlyn Goder.

051 CN
HOME LEAGUER; a Christian magazine for women. 1953. m. Can.$5. (Salvation Army, Canada Territorial Headquarters) Triumph Press, 455 North Service Road East, Oakville, Ont. L6H 1A5, Canada. TEL 416-844-2561 bk. rev. illus. circ. 11,250.
Formerly: Canadian Home Leaguer (ISSN 0008-3771)

301.412 200 320 US
JOURNAL OF WOMEN AND RELIGION. 1981. s-w. price varies. Center for Women and Religion, 2465 Le Conte Ave., Berkeley, CA 94709. TEL 415-841-9811 circ. 800. (back issues avail.)

JOYFUL WOMAN. see *RELIGIONS AND THEOLOGY — Protestant*

LUTHERAN WOMEN. see *RELIGIONS AND THEOLOGY — Protestant*

M S U U NEWSLETTER: GLEANINGS. (Ministerial Sisterhood Unitarian Universalist) see *RELIGIONS AND THEOLOGY — Protestant*

MIRJAM; Monatszeitschrift der weltoffenen Frau. see *RELIGIONS AND THEOLOGY — Roman Catholic*

917.309 US ISSN 0032-3594
POLKA; Polish women's quarterly magazine. 1935. q. $2. United Women's Societies of the Adoration of the Most Blessed Sacrament, Polish National Catholic Church of U.S. and Canada, 1004 Pittston Ave., Scranton, PA 18505. TEL 717-344-1513 Ed. Mary Ann Pyzowski. adv. circ. 1,200. Indexed: CERDIC.
Polish interests

SAPPHO'S UNDERSTUDIES. see *RELIGIONS AND THEOLOGY — Other Denominations And Sects*

053.1 200 GW ISSN 0036-696X
SCHRIFTENREIHE FUER DIE EVANGELISCHE FRAU. 1938. 6/yr. DM.19.80. Burckhardthaus-Laetare Verlag GmbH, Herzbachweg 2, 6460 Gelnhausen, W. Germany (B.R.D.) illus. circ. 8,000.

SPOTLIGHT (EDINBURGH) see *RELIGIONS AND THEOLOGY — Protestant*

STUDIES IN WOMEN AND RELIGION. see *RELIGIONS AND THEOLOGY*

THESMOPHORIA; voice of the new women's religion. see *RELIGIONS AND THEOLOGY — Other Denominations And Sects*

301.412 200 US ISSN 0163-1799
TODAY'S CHRISTIAN WOMAN. 1978. bi-m. $13.95. Christianity Today, Inc., 465 Gunderson Dr., Carol Stream, IL 60188. TEL 312-260-6200 Ed. Dale H. Bourke. adv. circ. 175,000.

288 US
U U W F FEDERATION NEWSLETTER. 1976. 5/yr. price varies. Unitarian Universalist Women's Federation, 25 Beacon St., Boston, MA 02108. TEL 617-742-2100 Ed. Ellen Spencer. circ. 9,000. (back issues avail.)

288 US
U U W F JOURNAL. 1976. 3/yr. membership. Unitarian Universalist Women's Federation, 25 Beacon St., Boston, MA 02108. TEL 617-742-2100 Ed. Ellen Spenser. circ. 150,000. (tabloid format; back issues avail.)
Formerly (until 1983): Kyriokos.

301.413 200 US
VIRTUE. 1978. 9/yr. $19.95. (Virtue Ministries, Inc.) Virtue Magazine, Inc., Box 850, Sisters, OR 97759. TEL 503-549-8261 Ed. Becky Durost Fish. adv. bk. rev. circ. 125,000.

WOMEN IN A CHANGING WORLD. see *RELIGIONS AND THEOLOGY*

Serials Title Index

A A B C Newsletter (American Association of Bible Colleges) (US ISSN 0094-260X) *1685,* 1727
A A C C Bulletin (All Africa Conference of Churches) (KE) *1695*
A A C C Magazine (All Africa Conference of Churches) (KE) *1695*
A A C C Newsletter *see* A A C C Bulletin *1695*
A A C C Quarterly Bulletin *see* A A C C Bulletin *1695*
A A R Academy Series (American Academy of Religion) (US ISSN 0277-1071) *1695*
A A R Dissertation Series *see* A A R Academy Series *1695*
A A R Studies in Religion (American Academy of Religion) (US ISSN 0084-6287) *1695*
A D R I S Newsletter (Association for the Development of Religious Information Services) (US ISSN 0300-7022) 1690, *1695*
A E U Reports (American Ethical Union) (US ISSN 0001-1118) *1692,* 1751
A F E R (African Ecclesial Review) (KE ISSN 0001-1134) *1695*
A F M Koinonia (Apostolic Faith Mission of South Africa) (SA) *1695*
A I M Bulletin *see* A I M Monastic Bulletin *1695*
A I M International (Africa Inland Mission International) (US) *1695*
A I M Monastic Bulletin (Aide Inter-Monasteres Secretariat) (FR) *1695*
A J L Newsletter (Association of Jewish Libraries) (US) 1685, *1690,* 1722
A J S Review (Association for Jewish Studies) (US ISSN 0364-0094) *1685,* 1722
A L C-L C A Augsburg Adult Bible Studies *see* A L C-L C A Augsburg Adult Bible Studies. Adult Quarterly *1727*
A L C-L C A Augsburg Adult Bible Studies. Adult Quarterly (American Lutheran Church and Lutheran Church in America) (US) *1727*
A L C-L C A Augsburg Adult Bible Studies. Home Bible Studies (American Lutheran Church and Lutheran Church in America) (US) *1727*
A L C-L C A Augsburg Adult Bible Studies. Teacher's Guide (American Lutheran Church and Lutheran Church in America) (US) *1727*
A L C-L C A Augsburg Home Bible Studies *see* A L C-L C A Augsburg Adult Bible Studies. Home Bible Studies *1727*
A L L News (American Life League) (US) *1682,* 1695, 1695
A M (Ave Maria) (BL ISSN 0005-1934) *1739*
A M A A News (Armenian Missionary Association of America, Inc.) (US) 1727, *1751*
A.M.A.A. Newsletter *see* A M A A News *1751*
A.M.E. Church Review (African Methodist Episcopal Church) (US ISSN 0360-3725) *1727*
A M S S Newsbulletin (Association of Muslim Social Scientists (Plainfield)) (US) *1721*
A P S Bulletin (KE) *1695*
A.R.E. Journal *see* Venture Inward *1719*
A T L A Bibliography Series (American Theological Library Association) (US) *1695*
A T L A Monograph Series (American Theological Library Association) (US) *1695*
Aarbok for den Norske Kirke (NO ISSN 0400-227X) *1695*
Abbey Press Christian Family Catalog *see* Christian Family Catalog *1687*
Abingdon Clergy Income Tax Guide (US ISSN 0163-1241) *1682,* 1695
Abridged Catholic Periodical and Literature Index(US ISSN 0737-3457) *1720*
Abstracts of Research in Pastoral Care and Counseling (US ISSN 0733-2599) 1681, *1720*
Academia (AU) *1690,* 1695, 1757
Academy of American Franciscan History. Bibliographical Series (US ISSN 0567-6630) *1739*
Academy of American Franciscan History. Documentary Series (US ISSN 0065-0633) *1739*
Academy of American Franciscan History. Monograph Series (US ISSN 0065-0641) *1739*
Academy of American Franciscan History. Propaganda Fide Series (US ISSN 0065-065X) *1739*
Academy of Parish Clergy. News and Views *see* Sharing the Practice *1715*
Accent on Liturgy *see* Accent on Worship *1695*
Accent on Worship (US ISSN 0276-2358) *1695*
Accent on Youth (US ISSN 0001-4516) *1727*
Accion (PY ISSN 0001-4605) 1695, *1757*
Act (US ISSN 0001-5083) *1695*
Acta Apostolicae Sedis. Commentarium Officiale (VC ISSN 0001-5199) *1739*
Acta Jutlandica (DK ISSN 0065-1354) *1695*
Acta Mediaevalia (PL) *1688,* 1739
Acta Nuntiaturae Gallicae (VC ISSN 0065-1443) *1739*
Acta Ordinis Fratrum Minorum (IT ISSN 0001-6411) *1739*
Acta Ordinis Sancti Augustini (IT ISSN 0001-642X) *1739*
Acta Philosophica et Theologica (IT ISSN 0065-1540) *1692,* 1695
Acta Seminarii Neotestamentici Upsaliensis *see* Coniectanea Biblica. New Testament Series *1701*
Acta Theologica Danica (NE ISSN 0065-1672) *1696*
Action (Winona Lake) (US ISSN 0273-3145) 1683, *1727*
Action Newsletter (UK ISSN 0143-3253) *1696*
Action-Reaction *see* Pacific Theological Review *1735*
Action Sociale (SZ ISSN 0001-7507) *1696*
Acts & Facts (US) *1751*
Actualidad Bibliografica de Filosofia y Teologia (SP ISSN 0211-4143) *1695,* 1720
Actualidad Pastoral (AG ISSN 0587-4300) *1739*
Actualite Diocesaine (CN) *1739*
Actualite Religieuse dan le Monde (FR) *1739*
Ad Fontes (NE ISSN 0001-7930) 1687, *1696*
Adelaide Church Guardian (AT ISSN 0001-8147) *1727*
Adult Bible Studies (US ISSN 0149-8347) *1696*
Adult Bible Study (US ISSN 0162-4156) *1727*
Adult Bible Teacher (US ISSN 0162-4164) *1727*
Adult Leadership (US ISSN 0162-4172) *1727*
Adult Planbook (US ISSN 0149-998X) *1727*
Adult Teacher (US ISSN 0400-5880) *1727*
Advance *see* Catholic Advance *1741*
Advance (DK ISSN 0109-1743) *1751*
Advance (Chicago) (US ISSN 0001-8562) *1727*
Advance (St. Louis) *see* Reporter (St. Louis. 1975) *1736*
Advance (Springfield) (US ISSN 0001-8589) *1751*
Advance Australia (AT ISSN 0001-8619) *1696*
Advanced Bible Study (US ISSN 0162-4148) *1727*
Adveniat (IT ISSN 0001-8740) *1696*
Advent (II) *1725*
Advent (NE) *1727*
Advent Review and Sabbath Herald *see* Adventist Review *1727*
Adventbode *see* Advent *1727*
Adventist Heritage (US ISSN 0360-389X) *1751*
Adventist Life (JA) *1727*
Adventist Review (US ISSN 0161-1119) *1727*
Adventure (Nashville) (US ISSN 0001-8783) *1727*
Adyar Library Bulletin *see* Brahmavidya *1692*
Affirm (US ISSN 0044-6467) *1727*
Africa Inland Mission International International *see* A I M International *1695*
Africa Theological Journal (TZ ISSN 0856-0048) *1696*
African *see* Odini *1747*
African Challenge *see* Today's Challenge *1737*
African Crescent (SL ISSN 0044-653X) *1721*
African Ecclesial Review *see* A F E R *1695*
African Journal of Biblical Studies (NR) *1696,* 1739
African Methodist Episcopal Church Church Review *see* A.M.E. Church Review *1727*
African Missionary *see* S M A-the African Missionary *1749*
Afrika Ya Kesho (KE) *1696*
Agada (US ISSN 0740-2392) 1685, *1722*
Agape (UK ISSN 0261-5630) *1696*
Agenda (IT) *1739*
Aglow (US) *1696*
Ahl-i Hadis (PK) *1721*
Ahmadu Bello University. Centre of Islamic Legal Studies. Journal (NR ISSN 0065-468X) *1721*
Ai Nostri Amici (IT ISSN 0002-4066) *1739*
Aide Inter-Monasteres Secretariat Monastic Bulletin *see* A I M Monastic Bulletin *1695*
Aim (II) *1751*
Akademische Monatsblaetter (GW ISSN 0002-3000) 1684, *1739*
Aktie (NE ISSN 0002-3744) 1683, *1696*
Aktion (GW) 1683, *1696*
Aktiv Islam (DK ISSN 0108-7290) *1721*
Aktuell *see* Mission Aktuell *1746*
Alabama Baptist Historian (US ISSN 0002-4147) 1687, *1727*
Albanian Catholic Bulletin/Buletini Katolik Shqiptar (US ISSN 0272-7250) *1696*
Alberta Catholic Directory (CN ISSN 0316-473X) *1739*
Alcuin (UK) *1696*
Alerte au Quebec (CN ISSN 0319-6984) *1696*
Algemeen Maconniek Tijdschrift (NE ISSN 0002-5267) *1696*
Alive (St. Louis) (US ISSN 0002-5461) *1683,* 1696
Alive and Well and Living in New York City Saint Patrick's Cathedral (US) *1739*
Alive Now (US) *1727*
Alive to God (UK) *1696*
All Africa Conference of Churches. Refugee Department. Progress Report (KE) *1696*
All Africa Conference of Churches. Refugee Department. Project List (KE) *1696*
All Africa Conference of Churches Bulletin *see* A A C C Bulletin *1695*
All Africa Conference of Churches Magazine *see* A A C C Magazine *1695*
All the World (UK ISSN 0002-5623) *1751,* 1757
Alle Boerns Jul (DK) *1683,* 1696
Alle den Volcke (NE ISSN 0002-5666) *1727*
Allgemeiner Caecilien-Verband. Schriftenreihe (GW) *1691,* 1739
Alliance Israelite Universelle en France. Cahiers (FR ISSN 0002-6050) *1722*
Alliance Israelite Universelle en France Nouveaux Cahiers *see* A I U Les Nouveaux Cahiers *1724*
Alliance Review (US ISSN 0002-6093) *1684,* 1696
Alliance Witness (US ISSN 0745-3256) *1727*
Alma *see* Paz e Alegria *1748*
Almanach Noir *see* Appel de l'Afrique *1696*
Almanaque Misal (SP) *1696*
Almas (MX ISSN 0002-628X) 1692, *1696*
Alt-Katholik *see* Alt-Katholische Kirchenzeitung *1739*
Alt-Katholische Kirchenzeitung (AU ISSN 0002-6514) *1739*
Alt-Katholische Kirchenzeitung *see* Christien Heute *1751*
Alt-Katholisches Jahrbuch (GW) *1751*
Alternative (MF) *1694,* 1696
L'Altra Europa (IT) *1681,* 1691, 1696, 1757
Amanecer (NQ) *1739*
Ambassador of Peace *see* Young Companion *1756*
Ambassador Report (US ISSN 0882-2123) *1696*
Ame Populaire (FR) *1739*
Amen *see* East Asian Pastoral Review *1743*
America (US ISSN 0002-7049) 1687, *1739*
America Latina. Boletin (PE) *1739*
American Academy for Jewish Research. Proceedings of the A A J R (US ISSN 0065-6798) *1723*
American Academy of Religion. Annual Meeting (US) *1696*

American Academy of Religion. Journal (US ISSN 0002-7189) *1696*
American Academy of Religion Academy Series *see* A A R Academy Series *1695*
American Academy of Religion Studies in Religion *see* A A R Studies in Religion *1695*
American Association of Bible Colleges Newsletter *see* A A B C Newsletter *1685*
American Association of Theological Schools in the United States and Canada. Bulletin *see* Association of Theological Schools in the United States and Canada. Bulletin *1697*
American Association of Theological Schools in the United States and Canada. Directory *see* Association of Theological Schools in the United States and Canada. Directory *1697*
American Baptist (US ISSN 0002-757X) *1727*
American Baptist Churches in the U.S.A. Directory (US ISSN 0091-9381) *1727*
American Baptist Churches in the U.S.A. Yearbook (US ISSN 0092-3478) *1727*
American Baptist Quarterly (US) 1687, *1728*
American Benedictine Review (US ISSN 0002-7650) 1687, 1691, *1739*, 1757
American Bible Society Record (US ISSN 0006-0801) *1696*
American Buddhist (US ISSN 0747-900X) *1726*
American Buddhist Newsletter *see* American Buddhist *1726*
American Catholic Historical Society of Philadelphia. Records (US ISSN 0002-7790) 1687, *1739*
American Catholic Philosophical Association. Proceedings (US) *1692*, 1739
American Catholic Sociological Review *see* S A *1757*
American Church News *see* New Oxford Review *1711*
American Council for Judaism. Issues (US ISSN 0741-465X) *1723*
American Council for Judaism. Special Interest Report (US ISSN 0740-8528) 1685, 1694, *1723*
American Ethical Union Reports *see* A E U Reports *1692*
American Friend *see* Quaker Life *1755*
American Hebrew Christian *see* American Messianic Jew *1723*
American Indian Life *see* Indian Life *1686*
American Jewish Archives (US ISSN 0002-905X) *1685*, 1687, 1723
American Jewish Congress. Congress Bi-Weekly *see* American Jewish Congress. Congress Monthly *1685*
American Jewish Congress. Congress Monthly (US ISSN 0163-1365) *1685*, 1723
American Jewish Congress. News (US) *1685*, 1723
American Jewish World (US ISSN 0002-9084) *1685*, 1723
American Jewish Year Book (US ISSN 0065-8987) *1723*
American Journal of Theology & Philosophy (US ISSN 0194-3448) 1692, *1696*
American Life League News *see* A L L News *1682*
American Lutheran Church. Yearbook *see* Lutheran Church in America. Yearbook *1733*
American Lutheran Church and Lutheran Church in America Augsburg Adult Bible Studies. Adult Quarterly *see* A L C-L C A Augsburg Adult Bible Studies. Adult Quarterly *1727*
American Lutheran Church and Lutheran Church in America Augsburg Adult Bible Studies. Home Bible Studies *see* A L C-L C A Augsburg Adult Bible Studies. Home Bible Studies *1727*
American Lutheran Church and Lutheran Church in America Augsburg Adult Bible Studies. Teacher's Guide *see* A L C-L C A Augsburg Adult Bible Studies. Teacher's Guide *1727*
American Lutheran Magazine *see* Lutheran Forum *1733*
American Messianic Jew (US) *1723*
American Messianic Jewish Quarterly *see* American Messianic Jew *1723*
American Presbyterians: Journal of Presbyterian History (US ISSN 0886-5159) 1687, *1728*
American Report *see* C A L C Report *1694*
American Scientific Affiliation. Journal: Evangelical Perspectives on Science and Christian Faith *see* Perspectives on Science and Christian Faith *1712*
American Sephardi (US ISSN 0003-102X) *1685*, 1723
American Society for Reformation Research. Newsletter *see* Historians of Early Modern Europe *1688*
American Society for the Defense of Tradition, Family and Property, Inc. Bulletin on the T F P's *see* Bulletin on the T F P's *1741*
American Theological Library Association Bibliography Series *see* A T L A Bibliography Series *1695*
American Theological Library Association Monograph Series *see* A T L A Monograph Series *1695*
American University Studies. Series 7. Theology and Religion (US ISSN 0740-0446) 1687, *1696*
American Waldensian Aid Society. Newsletter (US) *1696*
Ami du Clerge *see* Esprit et Vie *1703*
Amicizia Ebraico-Cristiana di Firenze. Bollettino (IT ISSN 0003-1739) *1696*
Amico dell'Arte Cristiana (IT ISSN 0003-1747) *1681*, 1696
Amigo del Hogar (DR) *1739*
Amities Catholiques Francaises (FR ISSN 0003-1895) 1694, *1739*
Amities Spirituelles. Bulletin (FR ISSN 0003-1909) *1696*
Ampleforth Journal (UK ISSN 0003-2018) *1696*
Amsterdam Studies in Theology (NE ISSN 0169-0272) *1696*
Amtsblatt fuer die Erzdioezese Bamberg (GW ISSN 0003-2328) *1739*
An Heiligen Quellen *see* Dienender Glaube *1702*
Anahata Nada/Soundless Sound (US) *1696*
Analecta Augustiniana (IT) *1739*
Analecta Biblica (IT ISSN 0066-135X) *1739*
Analecta Bollandiana (BE ISSN 0003-2468) 1687, *1696*
Analecta Cartusiana (AU) 1688, 1691, *1696*
Analecta Gregoriana (VC ISSN 0066-1376) *1739*
Analecta Vlatadon (GR) *1751*
Ancilla *see* Mirjam *1746*
Andalucia Islamica. Textos y Estudios (SP ISSN 0212-159X) *1689*
Andrews University. Monographs (US ISSN 0066-1708) *1728*
Andrews University Seminary Studies (US ISSN 0003-2980) *1696*
Ange Gardien (FR ISSN 0003-3030) *1696*
Angelicum (IT ISSN 0003-3081) *1692*, 1739
Angheliaforos *see* Anichti Orizontes-Angheliaforos *1739*
Angheliaforos-Anichti Orizontes *see* Anichti Orizontes-Angheliaforos *1739*
Anglican (CN ISSN 0517-7731) *1728*
Anglican Chiurch of Canada. General Synod. Journal of Proceedings *see* Anglican Church of Canada. General Synod. Journal *1728*
Anglican Church of Canada. General Synod. Journal (CN) *1728*
Anglican Crusader *see* Crusader (Toronto) *1730*
Anglican Digest (US ISSN 0003-3278) *1728*
Anglican Messenger (AT) *1728*
Anglican Pacifist *see* Challenge (London, 1961) *1729*
Anglican Theological Review (US ISSN 0003-3286) *1728*
Anglican Year Book (CN ISSN 0317-8765) *1728*
Anichti Orizontes-Angheliaforos (GR) *1739*
Annales de la Propagation de la Foi *see* Solidaires *1716*
Annals Magazine (AT) 1683, *1696*
Annals of Good St. Anne (CN ISSN 0318-434X) *1739*
Annals of the Holy Childhood *see* It's Our World *1683*
Annuaire Catholique de France (FR ISSN 0066-2488) *1739*
Annuaire de l'Eglise Catholique a Madagascar *see* Eglise Catholique a Madagascar *1743*
Annuaire de l'Eglise Catholique au Zaire (ZR) *1739*
Annuaire des Instituts de Religieuses en France (FR ISSN 0066-2860) *1696*
Annuaire du Diocese de Lyon (FR) *1739*
Annuaire Protestant; la France Protestante et les Eglises de Langue Francaise (FR ISSN 0066-362X) *1728*
Annuario Cattolico d'Italia (IT ISSN 0066-4464) *1739*
Die Anregung (GW ISSN 0003-519X) *1696*
Anruf (GW) *1696*
Anselm Studies (US ISSN 0735-0864) *1696*
Anstoesse (GW ISSN 0003-5270) 1689, *1696*
Anticipation *see* Church and Society Newsletter *1700*
Antonianum (VC ISSN 0003-6064) *1740*
Antur (UK ISSN 0003-6161) *1696*
Anvil (UK) *1728*
Anzeiger des Reiches der Gerechtigkeit (GW ISSN 0003-6285) *1696*
Anzeiger fuer die Seelsorge (GW ISSN 0721-1937) *1740*
Apollinaris (VC) *1740*
Aposento Alto (US ISSN 0003-6552) *1728*
Apostolic Faith Mission of South Africa Koinonia *see* A F M Koinonia *1695*
Appel de l'Afrique (FR) *1696*
Aquinas (VC ISSN 0003-7362) *1692*, 1740
Araldo della Scienza Cristiana *see* Herald of Christian Science *1753*
Araldo di S. Antonio (IT ISSN 0003-7559) *1740*
Arauto da Ciencia Crista *see* Herald of Christian Science *1753*
Arbeiten zur Geschichte des Antiken Judentums und des Urchristentums (NE ISSN 0066-5681) *1723*
Arbeiten zur Geschichte des Pietismus (GW) *1696*
Arbeiten zur Kirchlichen Zeitgeschichte. Reihe B (GW) *1696*
Arbeiten zur Literatur und Geschichte des Hellenistischen Judentums (NE) *1723*
Arbeiten zur Pastoraltheologie (GW) *1696*
Arbeiten zur Theologie. Reihe 1 (GW ISSN 0066-5711) *1696*
Arbeitsinformationen ueber Studienprojekte auf dem Gebiet der Geschichte des Deutschen Judentums und des Antisemitismus (GW ISSN 0341-8340) *1688*, 1723
Archaeology and Biblical Research (US) *1681*, 1696
Archdiocese of Baltimore. Directory *see* Catholic Directory of the Archdiocese of Baltimore *1741*
Archdiocese of Cincinnati Directory and Buyer's Guide (US) *1740*
Arche (FR ISSN 0518-2840) *1723*
Archidiocesi di Monreale. Bollettino Ecclesiastico (IT ISSN 0003-8296) *1740*
Archidiocesis de Madrid-Alcala. Boletin Oficial (SP) *1740*
Archief van de Kerken (NE ISSN 0022-9342) 1690, *1696*
Archief voor de Geschiedenis van de Katholieke Kerk in Nederland (NE ISSN 0003-8326) 1688, *1740*
Archiv fuer Katholisches Kirchenrecht (GW ISSN 0003-9160) *1740*
Archiv fuer Liturgiewissenschaft (GW ISSN 0066-6386) *1696*
Archiv fuer Mittelrheinische Kirchengeschichte (GW ISSN 0066-6432) *1696*
Archiv fuer Reformationsgeschichte/Archive for Reformation History (GW ISSN 0003-9381) *1697*
Archiv fuer Religionspsychologie (GW ISSN 0084-6724) 1695, *1697*
Archiv fuer Schlesische Kirchengeschichte (GW ISSN 0066-6491) 1687, *1697*
Archive for Reformation History *see* Archiv fuer Reformationsgeschichte *1697*
Archives Juives (FR ISSN 0003-9837) *1723*
Archivio Italiano per la Storia della Pieta (IT ISSN 0066-6688) *1697*
Archivo Ibero-Americano (SP ISSN 0004-0452) *1688*, 1740
Archivum Bibliographicum Carmelitanum (VC ISSN 0570-7242) *1720*
Archivum Franciscanum Historicum (IT ISSN 0004-0665) 1687, *1740*
Archivum Historiae Pontificae (VC ISSN 0066-6785) *1740*
Archivum Historicum Societatis Iesu (IT ISSN 0037-8887) 1688, *1740*
Archiwa, Biblioteki i Muzea Koscielne (PL) *1688*, 1740
Arcidiocesi di Reggio Calabria. Rivista Pastorale (IT) *1740*
Aristotelion Panepistemion Thessalonikes. Theologike Schole. Epistemonike Epeteris (GR) 1688, *1697*
Arkansas Churchman *see* Arkansas Episcopalian *1728*
Arkansas Episcopalian (US) *1728*
Arkansas Methodist *see* Arkansas United Methodist *1728*
Arkansas United Methodist (US) *1728*
Arken (DK ISSN 0107-363X) *1697*
Arken-Tryk (DK ISSN 0107-4520) *1697*
Arlington Catholic Herald (US ISSN 0361-3712) *1740*
Armarium Codicum Insignium (BE) *1688*, 1697
Armenian-American Outlook *see* A M A A News *1751*
Armenian Church *see* Bema *1751*
Armenian Missionary Association of America, Inc. News *see* A M A A News *1751*
Armonia di Voci (IT ISSN 0391-5425) 1683, *1691*, 1697
Ars Buddhica/Bukkyo Geijutsu (JA ISSN 0004-2889) *1681*, 1726
Arte Cristiana (IT ISSN 0004-3400) *1681*, 1697
Arut Perum Jothi (II) 1691, *1726*
Arzobispado de Santiago. Vicaria de la Solidaridad. Estudios (CL) *1740*
Arzobispado de Sevilla. Boletin Oficial Eclesiastico (SP) *1740*
Asbury Seminarian *see* Asbury Theological Journal *1697*
Asbury Theological Journal (US) *1697*
Ascent (UK) *1697*
Asfar (NE) *1721*
Asian Beacon (MY ISSN 0044-9180) *1697*
Asian Bureau Australia. Newsletter (AT) *1694*
Asian Religious Studies Information (US ISSN 0888-5869) *1720*
Asociacion (UY) *1682*, 1697
Aspaklaria/Perspective (IS) *1723*
Asprenas (IT ISSN 0004-4970) 1687, *1740*
Assemblee Nouvelle (FR ISSN 0335-5012) *1691*, 1697
Assemblees de Dieu de France. Annuaire (FR ISSN 0083-6184) *1751*
Assistente Ecclesiastico *see* Presenza Pastorale *1748*
Associate Reformed Presbyterian (US ISSN 0362-0816) *1728*
Associated Church Press. Directory (US ISSN 0066-8710) *1720*
Association des Amis de Pierre Teilhard de Chardin. Bulletin (FR ISSN 0066-8907) *1697*
Association for Jewish Studies Review *see* A J S Review *1685*
Association for Professional Education for Ministry. Report of the Biennial Meeting (US) 1685, *1697*
Association for the Development of Religious Information Services Newsletter *see* A D R I S Newsletter *1695*
Association Internationale d'Etudes Patristiques. Bulletin d'Information et de Liaison (IT) *1697*
Association Men *see* Yuvak *1720*
Association of British Theological and Philosophical Libraries. Bulletin (UK ISSN 0305-781X) *1690*, 1692, 1697
Association of Christian Teachers. Digest. (UK ISSN 0305-9286) *1697*
Association of Jewish Libraries Newsletter *see* A J L Newsletter *1690*
Association of Muslim Social Scientists (Plainfield) Newsbulletin *see* A M S S Newsbulletin *1721*
Association of Theological Schools in the United States and Canada. Bulletin (US ISSN 0362-1472) *1697*
Association of Theological Schools in the United States and Canada. Directory (US) 1685, *1697*
At Home and Abroad *see* Window *1738*
Ateismo y Dialogo *see* Atheism and Dialogue *1692*
Atheism and Dialogue/Atheisme et Dialogue/Ateismo y Dialogo (IT) *1692*, 1751
Atheisme et Dialogue *see* Atheism and Dialogue *1692*
Atheist (US ISSN 0304-1409) *1692*, 1697
Athenisin Ethnikon kai Kapodistrakion Panepistemion. Theologike Schole. Epistemonike Epeteris (GR) *1751*
Atlantic Baptist (CN ISSN 0004-6752) *1728*
Atma Jaya Research Centre. Socio-Religious Research Report/Pusat Penelitian Atma Jaya. Laporan Penelitian Keagamaan (IO) *1726*, 1757
Au Coeur de l'Afrique (BD ISSN 0563-4245) 1688, *1697*
Audenshaw Papers (UK ISSN 0004-7481) *1697*
Aufbau (SZ ISSN 0004-7821) 1694, *1697*
Aufbruch (GW ISSN 0004-7848) *1728*
Der Auftrag/Mandate (AU ISSN 0004-7872) *1697*
Auftrag (SZ ISSN 0004-7880) *1728*
Aufwaerts (Giessen) (GW) *1697*
Augustinian Studies (US ISSN 0094-5323) *1740*
Augustiniana (BE ISSN 0004-8003) *1740*
Augustinianum (IT ISSN 0004-8011) *1740*
Augustinus (SP ISSN 0004-802X) *1740*
Die Auslese (GW) *1697*
Australasian Catholic Record (AT ISSN 0004-8321) *1740*
Australasian Methodist Historical Society. Journal and Proceedings *see* Church Heritage *1730*
Australian Baptist (AT ISSN 0004-8739) *1728*
Australian Christian (AT ISSN 0004-8852) *1728*
Australian Jewish News (AT ISSN 0004-9379) *1685*, 1723
Australian Lectionary (Year) (AT ISSN 0812-0811) *1697*, 1728
Australian Liberal Catholic *see* Communion *1743*
Australian Lutheran Almanac *see* Lutheran Church of Australia. Yearbook *1733*
Australian Presbyterian Life (AT ISSN 0005-0059) *1728*
Authentic Voice *see* Kol Yavneh *1724*
Ave Maria *see* A M *1739*
Avedik (LE ISSN 0005-1950) *1740*
Avivamento (PO) *1751*
Awake (US ISSN 0005-237X) *1751*
Awakened India *see* Prabuddha Bharata *1693*
Awakener (US ISSN 0005-2388) *1751*
Aware Contents (US ISSN 0162-6833) *1728*
Axios (US ISSN 0278-551X) *1751*
B.C. Ecumenical News *see* Canadian Ecumenical News *1699*
B.C. Fellowship Baptist (CN) *1728*
B.C. Regular Baptist *see* B.C. Fellowship Baptist *1728*
B.G. Rudolph Lectures in Judaic Studies (US ISSN 0067-2742) *1723*
Back to Godhead (US ISSN 0005-3643) 1692, *1726*
Background Information for Church and Society *see* Church and Society Newsletter *1700*
Badia Greca di Grottaferrata. Bollettino (IT ISSN 0005-3783) *1697*
Baha'i Studies (CN ISSN 0708-5052) *1697*
Baha'i World (IS ISSN 0045-1320) *1697*
Bampton Lectures in America (US ISSN 0067-3129) 1681, 1689, *1697*
Band of Hope Chronicle (UK) *1697*
Bangalore Theological Forum (II ISSN 0253-9365) 1692, *1697*
Banner (Grand Rapids) (US ISSN 0005-5557) *1728*
Banneret (NO ISSN 0005-5565) *1728*
Baptist Adults (US ISSN 0162-4180) *1728*
Baptist Bulletin (US ISSN 0005-5689) *1728*
Baptist Challenge (US ISSN 0005-5697) *1728*
Baptist Herald (US ISSN 0005-5700) *1728*
Baptist History and Heritage (US ISSN 0005-5719) 1687, *1728*

Baptist Leader (US ISSN 0005-5727) 1728
Baptist Men's Journal see World Mission Journal 1739
Baptist Missionary Association of America. Directory and Handbook (US ISSN 0091-2743) 1728
Baptist Missionary Society, London. Annual Report (UK ISSN 0067-4060) 1728
Baptist Missionary Society, London. Official Report and Directory of Missionaries (UK ISSN 0067-4079) 1728
Baptist Program (US ISSN 0005-5743) 1728
Baptist Progress (US ISSN 0005-5751) 1728
Baptist Public Relations Association Newsletter (US) 1728
Baptist Quarterly (UK ISSN 0005-576X) 1687, 1728
Baptist Record (US ISSN 0005-5778) 1728
Baptist Reformation Review see Searching Together 1736
Baptist Student see Student (Nashville) 1737
Baptist Times (UK ISSN 0005-5786) 1728
Baptist True Union (US ISSN 0025-4169) 1728
Baptist Union Directory (UK ISSN 0302-3184) 1728
Baptist Union of Western Canada. Yearbook (CN ISSN 0067-4087) 1728
Baptist Witness see Victorian Baptist Witness 1738
Baptist World (US ISSN 0005-5808) 1728
Baptist World Alliance. Congress Reports (US ISSN 0067-4095) 1728
Baptist Young Adults (US ISSN 0162-4806) 1728
Baptist Youth (US ISSN 0162-4199) 1728
Bar-Ilan: Annual of Bar-Ilan University (IS ISSN 0067-4109) 1723, 1757
Bar-Ilan University. Studies in Judaica and the Humanities see Bar-Ilan: Annual of Bar-Ilan University 1723
Basis (NE ISSN 0005-6146) 1691, 1697
Basler Predigten (SZ ISSN 0005-6189) 1697
Batfutzot (IS) 1685, 1723
Das Baugeruest (GW ISSN 0005-6618) 1697
Bayerisches Sonntagsblatt fuer die Katholische Familie (GW ISSN 0005-7177) 1687, 1687, 1740
Bayreuther Gemeindeblatt (GW ISSN 0005-7282) 1728
Bazuin (NE ISSN 0005-7312) 1697
Beacon (CN ISSN 0382-6384) 1751
Beacon (New York) (US ISSN 0005-7339) 1692, 1692, 1697
Beads of Truth (US) 1751
Beam (US) 1684, 1728
Beam International (US) 1684, 1728
Beato Angelo (IT ISSN 0005-7436) 1740
Beer-Sheva. (IS) 1689, 1723
Begegnung (GE ISSN 0005-7800) 1694, 1740
Beginning (Nashville) (US ISSN 0198-6201) 1729
Die Beiden Tuerme (GW) 1688, 1697
Beitraege zur Geschichte der Philosophie und Theologie des Mittelalters Neue Folge (GW ISSN 0067-5024) 1693, 1697
Beitraege zur Geschichte des Alten Moenchtums und des Benediktinerordens (GW ISSN 0342-1341) 1697
Beitraege zur Oekumenischen Theologie (GW ISSN 0067-5172) 1697
Belaruskaja Carkva (US ISSN 0005-8327) 1688, 1697, 1757
Bell of St. Francis see Sv. Pranciskaus Varpelis 1749
Belmonda Letero (US) 1690, 1751
Beltane Papers (US) 1697, 1758
Bema (US ISSN 0199-8765) 1751
Benedictijns Tijdschrift (NE ISSN 0005-8734) 1697
Benedictina (IT) 1688, 1740
Benedictine Almanac see Benedictine Yearbook 1740
Benedictine Yearbook (UK ISSN 0522-8883) 1740
Benedictines (US ISSN 0005-8726) 1740
Benediktusbote (AU ISSN 0005-8742) 1740
Beop Ryun (KO) 1726
Berckers Katolischer Taschenkalender (GW) 1697
Berckers Taschenkalender see Berckers Katolischer Taschenkalender 1697
Berean Searchlight (US ISSN 0005-8890) 1697
Berliner Islamstudien (GW ISSN 0174-2477) 1697
Bertrand Russell Today see Philosophy and the Arts 1693
Bestuursblad (BE) 1697
Bet Mikra (IS ISSN 0005-979X) 1697
Between Times (US ISSN 0745-1172) 1683, 1697
Bharatya Vidya (II) 1692, 1693, 1726
Bibbia e Oriente (IT ISSN 0006-0585) 1681, 1688, 1697
La Bibbia nella Storia (IT) 1740
Bibel Heute (GW ISSN 0006-0593) 1740
Bibel im Jahr(Year) (GW) 1697
Bibel-Journalen (SW ISSN 0006-0607) 1697
Bibel und Gemeinde (GW ISSN 0006-0615) 1697
Bibel und Kirche (GW ISSN 0006-0623) 1697
Bibel und Liturgie (AU ISSN 0006-064X) 1697
Bibelreport (GW) 1697
Bibeltrogna Vaenners Missionstidning (SW ISSN 0006-0658) 1698
Bible Advocate see Church Advocate 1700
Bible Advocate and Herald of the Coming Kingdom see Church Advocate 1700
Bible and Spade see Archaeology and Biblical Research 1681
Bible Book Study for Adult Teachers (US ISSN 0162-4202) 1729
Bible Book Study for Adults (US ISSN 0162-4849) 1729
Bible Book Study for Youth (US ISSN 0162-4822) 1729
Bible Book Study for Youth Teachers (US ISSN 0162-4830) 1729
Bible Discoverers (US ISSN 0162-4695) 1729
Bible Discoverers: Teacher (US ISSN 0162-4687) 1729
Bible et Son Message see Dossiers de la Bible 1702
Bible et Terre Sainte see Monde de la Bible 1681
Bible Friend (US ISSN 0006-0739) 1698
Bible-in-Life Friends (US) 1698
Bible in New York see BibleWorld 1698
Bible Lands (UK ISSN 0006-0763) 1729
Bible Learners (US ISSN 0162-4679) 1729
Bible Lesson Digest (US ISSN 0162-4857) 1729
Bible Reader's Guide (US ISSN 0162-4717) 1729
Bible Readers' Union Bulletin see Dor le-Dor 1702
Bible Researcher (SW ISSN 0347-2787) 1688, 1698
Bible Science Newsletter (US) 1698
Bible Searchers (US ISSN 0006-078X) 1729
Bible Searchers: Teacher (US ISSN 0006-0798) 1729
Bible Society News see Word in Action: the Bible in the World 1720
Bible Society Record see American Bible Society Record 1696
Bible Standard and Herald of Christ's Kingdom (US ISSN 0006-081X) 1698
Bible Study Leaflet (Life and Work Series) (US ISSN 0162-475X) 1729
Bible Study Monthly (UK) 1698
Bible Study Pocket Commentary (US ISSN 0162-4741) 1729
Bible Study-Special Ministries (US) 1729
Bible-Time (US ISSN 0006-0828) 1683, 1698
Bible Today (US ISSN 0006-0836) 1698
Bible Translator see Practical Papers for the Bible Translator 1690
Bible Translator see Technical Papers for the Bible Translator 1690
Biblebhashyam (II) 1740
Bibles for the World News (US) 1698
BibleWorld (US) 1698
Biblia - Gente (BL) 1740
Biblia Revuo (IT ISSN 0006-0879) 1698
Biblica (VC ISSN 0006-0887) 1740
Biblica et Orientalia (VC) 1692, 1740
Biblical Archaeologist (US ISSN 0006-0895) 1681, 1692, 1698
Biblical Evangelist (US ISSN 0740-7998) 1698
Biblical Illustrator (US ISSN 0195-4407) 1729
Biblical Missions (US ISSN 0006-0909) 1729
Biblical Research (US ISSN 0067-6535) 1698
Biblical Scholarship in North America (US ISSN 0277-0474) 1698
Biblical Theology (IE ISSN 0006-0917) 1698
Biblical Theology Bulletin (US ISSN 0146-1079) 1698
Biblical Viewpoint (US ISSN 0006-0925) 1698
Biblicum (SW ISSN 0345-1453) 1698
Bibliografia Missionaria (IT) 1720
Bibliografia Teologica Comentada del Area Iberoamericana (AG ISSN 0326-6680) 1682, 1698
Bibliographia Franciscana (IT) 1682, 1720
Bibliographica Judaica (US ISSN 0067-6853) 1721
Bibliographie International de l'Histoire des Religions see International Bibliography of the History of Religions 1721
Bibliographies and Indexes in Religious Studies (US ISSN 0742-6836) 1721
Biblioteca Apostolica Vaticana. Cataloghi di Manoscritti (VC) 1740
Biblioteca Apostolica Vaticana. Cataloghi di Mostre (VC) 1740
Biblioteca Apostolica Vaticana. Illustrazioni di Codici. Codici Vaticani. Series Major (VC) 1740
Biblioteca Apostolica Vaticana. Illustrazioni di Codici. Codici Vaticani. Series Minor (VC) 1740
Biblioteca Apostolica Vaticana. Studi e Testi (VC) 1740
Biblioteca de Teologia (SP ISSN 0067-740X) 1698
Biblioteca Theologiae Practicae (SW) 1698
Biblioteka Pisarzy Reformacyjnych (PL ISSN 0519-8658) 1698
Bibliotheca Dissidentium (GW) 1682, 1698
Bibliotheca Ephemeridum Theologicarum Lovaniensium (BE) 1698
Bibliotheca Humanistica & Reformatorica (NE) 1698
Bibliotheca Instituti Historici Societatis Iesu (IT) 1740
Bibliotheca Islamica (GW ISSN 0170-3102) 1692, 1721
Bibliotheca Sacra (US ISSN 0006-1921) 1729
Bibliotheca Seraphico-Capuccina (IT ISSN 0067-8163) 1740
Bibliotheque de la Revue d'Histoire Ecclesiastique(BE ISSN 0067-8279) 1740
Biblische Beitraege (SZ ISSN 0582-1673) 1698
Biblische Untersuchungen (GW ISSN 0523-5154) 1698
Biblische Zeitschrift (GW ISSN 0006-2014) 1698
Biblisches Seminar (GW) 1698
Bijbellessen voor de Kinderen (NE ISSN 0006-2235) 1683, 1698
Bijbellessen voor de Sabbatschool (NE ISSN 0006-2243) 1751
Bijdragen (NE ISSN 0006-2278) 1693, 1698
Bijeen (NE ISSN 0006-2308) 1682, 1698
Biserica Romaneasca (IT) 1726
Bitzaron: a Quarterly of Hebrew Letters (US) 1685, 1690, 1723
Bitzaron: the Hebrew Monthly of America see Bitzaron: a Quarterly of Hebrew Letters 1690
B'kitzur/Briefs (US) 1723
Black Ministries (US) 1685, 1729
Blackboard Bulletin (CN ISSN 0006-4327) 1751
Blackfriars see New Blackfriars 1747
Blaetter fuer Wuerttembergische Kirchengeschichte (GW) 1688, 1698
Blaues Kreuz (GW) 1698
Blessings of Liberty (US ISSN 0006-4696) 1698
Blijde Boodschap (NE ISSN 0006-4777) 1698
Blind Donkey (US) 1726
Bloemheuwel-Nuus (SA ISSN 0006-4947) 1729
Blue Aquarius see Fiery Synthesis 1752
Boa Semente (PO) 1683, 1698
Bode des Heils see Bode van het Heil in Christus 1698
Bode van het Heil in Christus (NE ISSN 0006-5439) 1698
Bodhi Baum (AU) 1726
Bodhi Leaves (CE ISSN 0520-3325) 1726
Boek der Boeken see Schrift 1715
Boernebladets Jul see Alle Boerns Jul 1683
Bogoslovlje (YU ISSN 0006-5714) 1698
Bogoslovni Vestnik (YU ISSN 0006-5722) 1698
Boletin C E N P A F A L (CK) 1740, 1757
Boletin Eclesiastico de Fillipinas (PH) 1740
Boletin Intimo de Compania see Evangelio y MisionCompania 1703
Boletin Oficial de la Jurisdiccion Eclesiastica Castrense see Boletin Oficial Eclesiastico del Arzobispado Castrense de Espana 1698
Boletin Oficial Eclesiastico del Arzobispado Castrense de Espana (SP) 1698
Bollettino di Collegamento (IT ISSN 0300-4589) 1698
Bollettino di S. Nicola (IT ISSN 0404-9462) 1740
Bollettino Ecclesiastico see Arcidiocesi di Reggio Calabria. Rivista Pastorale 1740
Bollettino per le Religiose Domenicane in Italia (IT) 1740
Bollettino Salesiano (IT) 1740
Bollettino Vincenziano (IT ISSN 0006-6907) 1740
Bonifatiusblatt (GW ISSN 0006-7113) 1740
Bonne Nouvelle (CN ISSN 0225-0233) 1740
Boodschap (NE) 1693, 1751
Books and Articles on Oriental Subjects Published in Japan (JA ISSN 0524-0654) 1681, 1688, 1691, 1726
Books and Religion (US ISSN 0890-0841) 1695, 1698
Bookstore Journal (US ISSN 0006-7563) 1695, 1698
Boston University Studies in Philosophy and Religion (US) 1693, 1698
Bote (US ISSN 0006-8209) 1751
Botschaft des Alten Testaments (GW ISSN 0068-0443) 1698
Botschaft Heute (GW) 1698
Botschafter des Kommenden Koenigs (GW ISSN 0006-8276) 1729
Bouwen aan de Nieuwe Aarde (NE ISSN 0006-8349) 1698
Bozze (IT) 1698
Brahmana-Gaurava (II ISSN 0304-9272) 1693, 1726
Brahmavadin (II ISSN 0006-8721) 1693, 1726
Brahmavidya (II ISSN 0001-902X) 1692, 1726
Braille Pilot (US) 1682, 1683, 1698
Braille Star Theosophist (US ISSN 0006-8918) 1682, 1751
Bread of Life (US ISSN 0006-9515) 1751
Breakthrough (Wheaton) (US) 1751
Bremer Kirchenzeitung (GW) 1729
Bremer Missionsschiff (GW ISSN 0006-9574) 1683, 1698
Brennpunkt Seelsorge (GW) 1698
Brethren Life and Thought (US ISSN 0006-9663) 1751
Brethren Missionary Herald (US ISSN 0161-5238) 1751
Brief see American Council for Judaism. Issues 1723
Briefs see B'kitzur 1723
Brigade (UK ISSN 0045-2831) 1682, 1698
Bringing Religion Home (US) 1740
Bristol Diocesan News (UK) 1729
British Advent Messenger see Messenger 1734
British Columbia Catholic (CN ISSN 0007-0483) 1740
British Journal of Religious Education (UK ISSN 0141-6200) 1698
British Weekly and Christian Record (UK) 1729
British Weekly and Christian World see British Weekly and Christian Record 1729
Broadman Comments; International Sunday School Lessons (US ISSN 0068-2721) 1698
Brotherhood (US ISSN 0007-2435) 1723
Brothers Newsletter (US ISSN 0007-2451) 1751
Brown Gold (US ISSN 0007-2494) 1698
Der Bruederbote (GW) 1751
Buddhist Research Information see Asian Religious Studies Information 1720
Buddhist Studies (II) 1726
Buddhist Studies Review (UK ISSN 0265-2897) 1726
Buddhist Text Information (US ISSN 0360-6112) 1693, 1726
Builder (Scottdale) (US) 1751
Bukkyo Geijutsu see Ars Buddhica 1681
Buletini Katolik Shqiptar see Albanian Catholic Bulletin 1696
Bulletin (Philadelphia) see Quaker Service Bulletin 1713
Bulletin Critique des Annales Islamologiques (UA ISSN 0259-7373) 1692, 1721
Bulletin d'Information Protestant (FR) 1729
Bulletin de l'Oeuvre Apostolique (FR ISSN 0007-4330) 1698
Bulletin de l'Oeuvre d'Orient (FR ISSN 0007-4349) 1692
Bulletin de Litterature Ecclesiastique (FR ISSN 0007-4322) 1741
Bulletin de Theologie Ancienne et Medievale (BE ISSN 0007-442X) 1698
Bulletin of Biblical Studies (GR) 1699
Bulletin on Islam and Christian-Muslim Relations in Africa (UK ISSN 0264-1356) 1721
Bulletin on the T F P's (American Society for the Defense of Tradition, Family and Property, Inc.) (US) 1694, 1741, 1757
Bulletin Signaletique. Part 519: Philosophie (FR ISSN 0007-554X) 1681, 1694, 1721
Bulletin Signaletique. Part 527: Histoire et Sciences des Religions (FR ISSN 0180-9296) 1681, 1721
Bulletin Signaletique. Part 527: Sciences Religieuse see Bulletin Signaletique. Part 527: Histoire et Sciences des Religions 1721
Bulletin sur l'Islam et les Relations Islamo-Chretiennes en Afrique (UK ISSN 0267-4890) 1721
Bulwark (UK ISSN 0045-3536) 1729
Bund der Deutschen Katholischen Jugend. Informationsdienst (GW ISSN 0007-5833) 1683, 1741, 1757
Burgense (SP ISSN 0521-8195) 1699
Buried History (AT ISSN 0007-6260) 1681, 1699
Burning Bush (US ISSN 0007-6309) 1699
Buzz (UK ISSN 0045-3692) 1683, 1699
C A F O D Journal (Catholic Fund for Overseas Development) (UK) 1741
C A J Christliche Arbeiter-Jugend see Aktion 1696
C A L C Report (Clergy and Laity Concerned) (US) 1694, 1699
C A S Newsletter (Catholic Archives Society) (UK ISSN 0262-6896) 1741
C B S see Cardinal Bea Studies 1741
C C A R Journal see Journal of Reform Judaism 1724
C C I A Background Information (World Council of Churches, Commission on International Affairs) (SZ) 1694, 1699
C C N Information (Council of Churches in Namibia) (SX) 1729, 1741
C E L E P Ensayos Ocasionales see Pastoralia 1712
C E N (Church of England Newspaper) (UK ISSN 0007-8255) 1729
C H A C Review (CN ISSN 0226-5923) 1689, 1691, 1741
C L S Quarterly (Christian Legal Society) (US ISSN 0736-0142) 1689, 1699
C.M.J. Quarterly see Shalom 1725
C M J S Centerpieces (Center for Modern Jewish Studies) (US ISSN 0887-1639) 1685, 1695, 1723, 1757
C M S News see Checkpoint 1729
C O G Newsletter (Covenant of the Goddess) (US) 1751
C O M see C O M-Nuovi Tempi 1699
C O M-Nuovi Tempi (IT) 1699
C P S Bulletin (New Zealand Christian Pacifist Society) (NZ) 1694, 1751
C S C Newsletter (Community of the Sisters of the Church) (AT ISSN 0007-9073) 1699
C.U. News see Cubit 1702
C W I Herald (Christian Witness to Israel) (UK ISSN 0308-5252) 1699

C W L News (Catholic Women's League) (UK) 1741, *1758*
C W M Report (Council for World Mission) (UK) *1729*
Cable *see* Lost & Found *1753*
Cahiers Bibliques Trimestriels *see* Cahiers Evangile *1699*
Cahiers d'Action Religieuse et Sociale *see* Cahiers de l'Actualite Religieuse et Sociale *1699*
Cahiers d'Etudes Cathares (FR ISSN 0008-0063) *1699*
Cahiers de Civilisation Medievale (FR ISSN 0007-9731) *1688,* 1690, 1691, 1699
Cahiers de Josephologie (CN ISSN 0007-9774) *1741*
Cahiers de l'Actualite Religieuse et Sociale (FR ISSN 0007-9669) *1699,* 1757
Cahiers de Recherche Ethique (CN) *1699*
Cahiers des Religions Africaines (ZR ISSN 0008-0047) *1751,* 1757
Cahiers Evangile (FR ISSN 0222-9714) *1699*
Caledonia Diocesan Times (CN ISSN 0383-6509) *1729*
California Southern Baptist (US ISSN 0008-1558) *1729*
Call to Prayer (US) *1699*
Calvary Review (US ISSN 0008-1779) *1729*
Calvijn (NE ISSN 0008-1787) *1729*
Calvin Theological Journal (US ISSN 0008-1795) *1729*
Calvinist Contact (CN ISSN 0410-3882) 1684, *1729*
Calwer Theologische Monographien. Reihe A: Bibelwissenschaft (GW) *1699*
Calwer Theologische Monographien. Reihe B: Systematische Theologie und Kirchengeschichte(GW) *1699*
Calwer Theologische Monographien. Reihe C: Praktische Theologie und Missionswissenschaft (GW) *1699*
Camillian (US) *1699,* 1757
Camillusbode (NE ISSN 0008-221X) *1741*
Caminho (PO) *1683,* 1699
Cammino (IT ISSN 0008-2260) *1741*
Canada Armenian Press *see* Canada Armenian Press. Newsletter *1751*
Canada Armenian Press. Newsletter (CN) *1751*
Canada Lutheran *see* Eastern Synod Lutheran *1731*
Canadian Baptist (CN ISSN 0008-2988) *1729*
Canadian Bible Society Quarterly Newsletter (CN) *1699*
Canadian Catholic Conference. National Bulletin on Liturgy *see* Canadian Conference of Catholic Bishops. National Bulletin on Liturgy *1741*
Canadian Catholic Historical Association. Annual Report (CN) *1741*
Canadian Catholic Review (CN ISSN 0714-7724) *1741*
Canadian Church Historical Society Journal (CN ISSN 0008-3208) 1688, *1699*
Canadian Churchman (CN ISSN 0008-3216) *1729*
Canadian Churchman and Crosstalk *see* Crosstalk *1730*
Canadian Conference of Catholic Bishops. National Bulletin on Liturgy (CN) *1741*
Canadian Council of Churches. Council Communicator (CN ISSN 0045-4605) *1699*
Canadian Council of Churches. Record of Proceedings (CN ISSN 0701-4309) *1699*
Canadian Ecumenical News (CN) *1699*
Canadian Home Leaguer *see* Home Leaguer *1758*
Canadian Jewish Archives (New Series) (CN ISSN 0576-5528) *1686,* 1723
Canadian Jewish Chronicle Review *see* Canadian Jewish News *1686*
Canadian Jewish News (CN ISSN 0008-3941) *1686,* 1723
Canadian Jewish Outlook *see* Outlook *1687*
Canadian Mennonite Reporter *see* Mennonite Reporter *1754*
Canadian Messenger of the Sacred Heart (CN ISSN 0008-4425) *1751*
Canadian Muslim (CN ISSN 0707-2945) 1686, *1721*
Canadian Quaker History Newsletter (CN) *1751*
Canadian Register *see* Catholic Register *1741*
Canadian Religious Conference. Bulletin (CN ISSN 0316-8743) *1699*
Canadian Society of Biblical Studies. Bulletin/Societe Canadienne des Etudes Bibliques. Bulletin (CN ISSN 0068-970X) *1699*
Canadian Theosophist (CN ISSN 0045-544X) *1751*
Candle *see* Good News *1744*
Canon Law Abstracts (IE ISSN 0008-5650) 1681, *1721*
Cardinal Bea Studies (PH) *1741*
Caribbean Challenge (JM ISSN 0008-6436) *1699*
Caribbean Journal of Religious Studies (JM) *1699*
Caridade (PO ISSN 0008-655X) *1741*
Caring Community (US) *1741*
Caritas-Kalender (GW) 1685, *1699*
Carl Newell Jackson Lectures (US ISSN 0528-1458) *1687,* 1699
Carmel *see* Speling *1716*
Carmel (IE ISSN 0008-6665) *1741*
Carmelus (IT ISSN 0008-6673) 1684, *1741*
Carolina Christian (US ISSN 0008-672X) *1699*
Castries Catholic Chronicle (XK) *1741*
Catacombes (FR) 1694, *1699*
Catalogue of Conferences, Seminars, Workshop (US) 1694, 1695, *1699*
Catechesi (IT ISSN 0391-5433) *1741*
Catechist (US ISSN 0008-7726) *1699*
Catechistes d'Aujourd'hui *see* Points de Repere *1712*
Catechist's Connection (US) *1741*
Catequetica (SP) *1699*
Cathedral Age (US ISSN 0008-7874) *1729*
Catholic Action News *see* New Earth *1747*
Catholic Activist (US) 1694, *1741*
Catholic Advance (US ISSN 0008-7904) *1741*
Catholic Agitator (US ISSN 0045-5970) *1741*
Catholic Almanac (US ISSN 0069-1208) *1741*
Catholic Archives (UK ISSN 0261-4316) *1741*
Catholic Archives Society Newsletter *see* C A S Newsletter *1741*
Catholic Bible Quarterly Monograph Series (US) *1699*
Catholic Biblical Quarterly (US ISSN 0008-7912) *1741*
Catholic Book Notes *see* Catholic Truth *1742*
Catholic Broadcasters Association. Newsletter *see* Unda-U S A Newsletter *1684*
Catholic Cemetery (US) *1687,* 1741
Catholic Central Union of America. Proceedings (US ISSN 0069-1216) *1741*
Catholic Challenge (US ISSN 8756-7482) *1741*
Catholic Chronicle (US ISSN 0008-7971) *1741*
Catholic Counter-Reformation in the XXth Century (FR) *1741*
Catholic Digest (US ISSN 0008-7998) 1687, *1741*
Catholic Directory (UK ISSN 0069-1224) *1741*
Catholic Directory (San Diego) (US) *1741*
Catholic Directory for Scotland (UK ISSN 0306-5677) *1741*
Catholic Directory for the Clergy and Laity in Scotland *see* Catholic Directory for Scotland *1741*
Catholic Directory of England and Wales (UK) *1741*
Catholic Directory of Southern Africa (SA) *1741*
Catholic Directory of the Archdiocese of Baltimore (US) *1741*
Catholic Education (UK) 1684, *1741*
Catholic Fund for Overseas Development Journal *see* C A F O D Journal *1741*
Catholic Gazette (UK ISSN 0008-8064) *1741*
Catholic Health Association of Canada. Directory (CN ISSN 0828-5748) *1691,* 1741
Catholic Health Association of the United States. Guidebook (US) *1689,* 1699
Catholic Health World (US) *1689,* 1699
Catholic Herald (UK ISSN 0008-8072) *1741*
Catholic Historical Review (US ISSN 0008-8080) 1688, *1741*
Catholic Hospital *see* C H A C Review *1689*
Catholic Hospital Association of Canada. Directory *see* Catholic Health Association of Canada. Directory *1691*
Catholic International Education Office. Bulletin Nouvelle Serie *see* O I E C Bulletin *1747*
Catholic International Education Office Bulletin *see* O I E C Bulletin *1747*
Catholic Journalist (US ISSN 0008-8129) *1689,* 1741
Catholic Lawyer (US ISSN 0008-8137) *1689,* 1741
Catholic Leader (AT ISSN 0008-8145) *1741*
Catholic Library Association. Northern Illinois Chapter. Newsletter (US ISSN 0008-8161) *1690,* 1741
Catholic Life (US ISSN 0008-8218) *1741*
Catholic Media Council. Information Bulletin (GW ISSN 0930-8679) 1684, *1741*
Catholic Medical Quarterly (UK ISSN 0008-8226) *1691,* 1741
Catholic Messenger (US ISSN 0008-8234) *1741*
Catholic Near East Magazine (US ISSN 0164-0674) *1741*
Catholic New Times (CN) *1741*
Catholic New York (US ISSN 0278-1174) *1741*
Catholic Peace Fellowship Bulletin (US ISSN 0008-8277) *1741*
Catholic Periodical and Literature Index (US ISSN 0008-8285) 1681, *1721*
Catholic Periodical Index *see* Catholic Periodical and Literature Index *1721*
Catholic Pictorial (UK ISSN 0008-8293) *1741*
Catholic Quote (US ISSN 0701-0788) *1741*
Catholic Register (CN ISSN 0383-1620) *1741*
Catholic Review (Baltimore) (US ISSN 0008-8315) *1741*
Catholic Review (New York) (US ISSN 0008-8323) *1682,* 1741
Catholic Rural Life (US ISSN 0008-8331) *1741,* 1757
Catholic School Studies (AT) *1742*
Catholic Sentinel (Archdiocese of Portland, Oregon) (US ISSN 0162-2102) *1742*
Catholic Sentinel (Diocese of Baker) (US ISSN 0162-0363) *1742*
Catholic Spirit (US) *1742*
Catholic Standard (IE ISSN 0008-8366) *1742*
Catholic Telegraph (US) *1742*
Catholic Telephone Guide (US) *1742*
Catholic Theological Society of America. Proceedings (US ISSN 0069-1267) *1742*
Catholic Times *see* Universe *1750*
Catholic Truth (UK ISSN 0411-275X) 1695, *1742*
Catholic Twin Circle Weekly Magazine (US) *1742*
Catholic Update (US) *1742*
Catholic Virginian (US ISSN 0008-8404) *1742*
Catholic Voice (GH ISSN 0008-8412) *1742*
Catholic Weekly (US ISSN 0008-8439) *1742*
Catholic Witness (US ISSN 0008-8447) *1742*
Catholic Women's League News *see* C W L News *1758*
Catholic Workman (US ISSN 0008-8471) *1742*
Catholic World *see* New Catholic World *1747*
Catholica (GW ISSN 0008-8501) *1742*
Catholicism in Crisis (US) *1742*
Catholicisme Hier, Aujourd'hui, Demain (FR) *1742*
Celebration (Kansas City) *see* Celebration: a Creative Worship Service *1742*
Celebration: a Creative Worship Service (US ISSN 0094-2421) *1742*
Celebrer (FR ISSN 0240-4656) *1742*
Center for Modern Jewish Studies Centerpieces *see* C M J S Centerpieces *1685*
Center for Process Studies. Newsletter (US ISSN 0360-618X) *1693,* 1751
Centinela (US) *1729*
Central California Jewish Heritage (US) *1686,* 1723
Central Conference of American Rabbis. Yearbook (US ISSN 0069-1607) *1723*
Central Illinois Historical Messenger *see* Historical Messenger *1732*
Central Times *see* New Times *1734*
Centre (BE) *1689,* 1699
Centre Catholique des Intellectuels Francais. Recherches et Debats (FR ISSN 0008-9605) *1689,* 1742
Centre for the Study of Islam and Christian Muslim Relations. Newsletter (UK ISSN 0143-8921) *1721*
Centre for the Study of Islam and Christian-Muslim Relations. Research Papers *see* Research Papers: Muslims in Europe *1722*
Centre Protestant d'Etudes de Geneve. Bulletin (SZ) 1681, 1693, *1729*
Centre Protestant d'Etudes et de Documentation. Bulletin (FR ISSN 0181-7671) *1721*
Centro Camuno di Studi Preistorici. Bollettino (IT ISSN 0577-2168) *1681,* 1681, 1699
Centro Evangelico Latinoamericano de Estudios Pastorales Pastoralia *see* Pastoralia *1712*
Centro Studi Russia Cristiana. Rivista *see* L'Altra Europa *1681*
Centrum Jana Pawla II Biuletyn (US) *1682,* 1742
Cercle Ernest Renan. Bulletin *see* Cercle Ernest Renan. Cahiers *1699*
Cercle Ernest Renan. Cahiers (FR ISSN 0411-5562) 1688, *1699*
Ceremonial Magick *see* White Light *1756*
Cerkev v Sedanjem Svetu (YU ISSN 0009-0387) *1742*
Cerkovnyj Vistnik *see* Church Messenger *1701*
Certezze (IT) *1699*
Cesky Bratr (CS ISSN 0009-0778) *1729*
Ceylon Churchman (CE) *1729*
Challenge (London, 1961) (UK ISSN 0009-0999) 1694, *1729*
Challenge (Sandbach) (UK ISSN 0009-1014) *1742*
Challenge (Wheaton) (US) *1699*
Challenger *see* Volunteer *1738*
Chancellor College. Department of Religious Studies. Staff Seminar Paper (MW) *1699*
Changes Newsletter *see* Coming Changes Newsletter *1730*
Channels (CN) *1729*
Channels of Blessing (UK ISSN 0009-1529) *1682,* 1699
Les Chantiers du Cardinal (FR ISSN 0009-160X) *1699*
Chaos (DK ISSN 0108-4453) *1699*
Chaplair (US) *1729*
Charisma (US ISSN 0279-0424) *1699*
Charity and Children (US ISSN 0009-1723) *1683,* 1729
Chart and Compass International (UK) 1699, *1757*
Checkpoint (Church Missionary Society of Australia) (AT ISSN 0311-0737) *1729*
Cheering Words (UK ISSN 0009-2126) 1683, *1699*
Chicago Catholic (US ISSN 0149-970X) 1693, *1742*
Chicago History of American Religion (US) *1699*
Chicago Studies (US ISSN 0009-3718) *1742*
Chicago Theological Seminary Register (US) *1699*
Children of the Earth (US) *1751*
Children's Friend *see* Friend *1752*
Children's Leader (US ISSN 0276-3427) 1684, *1729*
Children's Music Leader *see* Music Leader *1692*
Childworld (US) *1683,* 1699
China Bulletin *see* China Notes *1729*
China Notes (US ISSN 0009-4412) *1729*
Ching Feng (HK ISSN 0009-4668) 1692, *1699*
Chinmaya Mission West Newsletter (US ISSN 0199-6487) *1699*
Choisir (SZ ISSN 0009-4994) *1699*
Choral Praise (US ISSN 0362-0409) *1729*
Der Christ im Zwanzigsten Jahrhundert (GW ISSN 0009-5060) *1699*
Christ in Our Home (US ISSN 0412-2968) *1729*
Christ to the World/Cristo al Mundo (IT ISSN 0011-1465) *1742*
Christ und Buch (GW ISSN 0009-5087) *1699*
Christadelphian (UK ISSN 0009-5117) *1751*
Christelijk Oosten (NE ISSN 0009-5141) 1692, *1699*
Christelijke Muziekbode *see* Muziekbode *1692*
Die Christengemeinschaft (GW ISSN 0009-5184) 1681, *1700*
Christenlehre (GE ISSN 0009-5192) *1729*
Christian Adventurer (US ISSN 0009-5214) *1700*
Christian Advertising Forum (US) *1681,* 1700
Christian Advocate *see* Christian Fellowship *1729*
Christian Arena (UK ISSN 0264-598X) *1700*
Christian Association for Psychological Studies. Bulletin *see* Journal of Psychology and Christianity *1695*
Christian Association for Psychological Studies. Proceedings *see* Journal of Psychology and Christianity *1695*
Christian Attitudes on Jews and Judaism *see* Christian Jewish Relations *1700*
Christian Bookseller *see* Christian Retailing *1695*
Christian Brothers of the Australian and New Zealand Provinces. Our Studies *see* Catholic School Studies *1742*
Christian Century (US ISSN 0009-5281) *1700*
Christian Chronicle (US) *1700*
Christian Comment *see* Audenshaw Papers *1697*
Christian Communications (CN ISSN 0009-5303) 1684, *1700*
Christian Community *see* Threshing Floor *1718*
Christian Crusade (US ISSN 0195-265X) *1700*
Christian Crusade Weekly *see* Christian Crusade *1700*
Christian Directory (TH) *1751*
Christian Education Journal (US) *1700*
Christian Educators Journal (US) *1700*
Christian Endeavor World (US ISSN 0009-5338) *1700*
Christian Endeavour Programme Book (UK) *1751*
Christian Endeavour Topic Book *see* Christian Endeavour Programme Book *1751*
Christian Family Catalog (US) *1687,* 1700
Christian Fellowship (UK ISSN 0143-7518) *1729*
Christian Forum (MW) *1700*
Christian Graduate *see* Christian Arena *1700*
Christian Herald (UK) *1700*
Christian Herald (Chappaqua) (US ISSN 0009-5354) *1700*
Christian History Magazine (US) 1688, *1700*
Christian Home & School (US ISSN 0009-5389) *1700*
Christian Info (CN) *1700*
Christian Institute for Ethnic Studies in Asia. Bulletin (PH ISSN 0045-6810) 1692, *1700*
Christian Institutes of Islamic Studies Bulletin (II) 1692, *1721*
Christian Jewish Relations (UK ISSN 0144-2902) 1694, *1700,* 1757
Christian Leader (US ISSN 0009-5419) *1751*
Christian Leadership Letter (US) *1700*
Christian Legal Society Quarterly *see* C L S Quarterly *1689*
Christian Librarian (US ISSN 0412-3131) *1690,* 1729
Christian Librarian (UK ISSN 0309-4170) *1690,* 1695, 1729
Christian Life (US ISSN 0009-5427) 1687, *1700*
Christian Life Communicator *see* Christian Life Communities Harvest *1742*
Christian Life Communities Harvest (US ISSN 0739-6422) *1742*
Christian Literature (GR) *1751*
Christian Medical Association of India. Journal (II ISSN 0009-5443) *1691,* 1700
Christian Medical Society Journal (US ISSN 0009-546X) *1691,* 1700
Christian Messenger (GH ISSN 0009-5478) *1729*
Christian Ministry (US ISSN 0033-4138) *1700*
Christian Missions in Many Lands (US ISSN 0744-4052) *1700*
Christian Monthly (US ISSN 0009-5494) *1729*
Christian Mother (Pittsburgh) (US) *1700,* 1758
Christian News *see* Compass *1701*
Christian News (US ISSN 0009-5516) *1729*
Christian News from Israel (IS ISSN 0009-5532) *1700*
Christian Order (UK ISSN 0009-5559) *1742*
Christian Parapsychologist (UK ISSN 0308-6194) *1692,* 1730, 1742
Christian Peace Conference (CS ISSN 0009-5567) *1694,* 1700
Christian Periodical Index (US ISSN 0069-3871) 1681, *1721*

Christian Record see British Weekly and Christian Record 1729
Christian Record Talking Magazine (US ISSN 0009-5583) 1682, 1700
Christian Research Institute. Newsletter see Christian Research Journal 1700
Christian Research Journal (US) 1700
Christian Retailing (US ISSN 0749-2510) 1695, 1700
Christian Scholar's Review (US ISSN 0017-2251) 1700
Christian Science Bible Lessons (Braille Edition) (US ISSN 0146-7166) 1682, 1751
Christian Science Journal (US ISSN 0009-5613) 1751
Christian Science Quarterly (Inkprint Edition) (Italian edition) (US ISSN 0145-7365) 1751
Christian Science Sentinel (US ISSN 0009-563X) 1751
Christian Service Committee of the Churches in Malawi. Annual Report (MW) 1700
Christian Single (US ISSN 0191-4294) 1730
Christian Standard (US ISSN 0009-5656) 1700
Christian Statesman (US ISSN 0009-5664) 1694, 1700, 1757
Christian Statesman (UK ISSN 0144-073X) 1730
Christian Witness to Israel Herald see C W I Herald 1699
Christian Woman (US ISSN 0009-5702) 1700
Christian Woman (AT) 1700
Christian Woman (UK) 1700
Christian Words (UK) 1730
Christian Year (UK) 1730
Christianity and Crisis (US ISSN 0009-5745) 1700
Christianity and Literature (US ISSN 0148-3331) 1690, 1700
Christianity Today (US ISSN 0009-5753) 1700
Christians in Education see Education Newsline 1731
Christians Pathway see Reformation Today 1736
Christien Heute (GW) 1751
Christlich-Paedagogische Blaetter (AU ISSN 0009-5761) 1683, 1700
Die Christliche Frau (GW ISSN 0009-5788) 1742, 1758
Christliche Friedenskonferenz see Christian Peace Conference 1694
Christliche Innerlichkeit (AU ISSN 0009-5796) 1700
Christoffel-Blindenmission. Bericht (GW ISSN 0009-580X) 1682, 1700
Christopher News Notes (US ISSN 8755-6901) 1700
Christophorus (GW ISSN 0009-5818) 1684, 1742
Christus (FR ISSN 0009-5834) 1742
Die Christus-Post (GW ISSN 0009-5869) 1700
Christus Rex see Social Studies 1758
Chronicle of the Catholic Church in Lithuania (US ISSN 0197-0348) 1686, 1742
Chrysostom (UK) 1700
Chrzescijanskie Stowarzyszenie Spoleczne. Biuletyn Informacyjny "Novum" (PL) 1742
Chrzescijanskie Stowarzyszenie Spoleczne. Information Bulletin (PL ISSN 0578-0594) 1742
Chrzescijanskie Stowarzyszenie Spoleczne. Materialy Problemowe (PL) 1742
Church Administration (US ISSN 0412-4553) 1682, 1730
Church Advocate (US) 1700
Church Advocate (US ISSN 0009-630X) 1751
Church and Clergy Finance (US ISSN 0045-6861) 1682, 1700
Church & Nation (AT ISSN 0314-6200) 1730
Church and School Equipment News (UK ISSN 0045-687X) 1682, 1685, 1700
Church and Society (US ISSN 0037-7805) 1730, 1757
Church and Society Newsletter (SZ) 1700, 1758
Church & State (US ISSN 0009-6334) 1694, 1700
Church and Synagogue Libraries (US ISSN 0009-6342) 1690, 1700
Church and Synagogue Library Association. News Bulletin see Church and Synagogue Libraries 1690
Church and the Jewish People see Current Dialogue 1702
Church Army. Front Line (UK) 1730
Church Army. Review (UK) 1700
Church Council of Greater Seattle. Occasional News see Source (Seattle) 1716
Church Growth Bulletin see Global Church Growth 1753
Church Herald (US ISSN 0009-6393) 1752
Church Heritage (AT) 1730
Church History (US ISSN 0009-6407) 1701
Church Library Magazine see Church Media Library Magazine 1690
Church Management: The Clergy Journal see Clergy Journal 1701
Church Media Library Magazine (US) 1690, 1730
Church Messenger/Cerkovnyj Vistnik (US) 1701
Church Missionary Society of Australia Checkpoint see Checkpoint 1729
Church News (UK ISSN 0009-6474) 1701
Church Observer (UK ISSN 0009-6482) 1701
Church of England. General Synod. Report of Proceedings (UK ISSN 0307-7225) 1730
Church of England Historical Society (Diocese of Sydney). Journal (AT ISSN 0009-6490) 1688, 1730
Church of England Newspaper see C E N 1729
Church of England Yearbook (UK ISSN 0069-3987) 1730
Church of God Evangel (US) 1730
Church of God Missions (US ISSN 0009-6504) 1752
Church of Ireland Gazette (UK ISSN 0009-6512) 1730
Church of Scotland. Yearbook (UK ISSN 0069-3995) 1730
Church of Scotland Braille Magazine (UK) 1682, 1701
Church Pocket Book and Diary (UK) 1701
Church Pulpit Year Book (UK ISSN 0069-4002) 1701
Church Recreation see Church Recreation Magazine 1730
Church Recreation Magazine (US) 1730
Church Scene (AT ISSN 0009-6563) 1730
Church Teacher see Together 1737
Church Times (UK ISSN 0009-658X) 1730
Church Training (US ISSN 0162-4601) 1730
Church Woman (US ISSN 0009-6598) 1701
Church World (US ISSN 0009-6601) 1701
Church World Service. Family Life and Population Program Briefs (US) 1682, 1701
Churchman see Churchman's Human Quest 1701
Churchman (UK ISSN 0009-661X) 1730
Churchman's Human Quest (US ISSN 0009-6628) 1701, 1757
Churchman's Magazine (UK ISSN 0009-6636) 1730
Churchman's Pocket Book and Diary see Church Pocket Book and Diary 1701
Cibedo - Dokumentationen und Texte (GW ISSN 0721-0035) 1701, 1721
Ciencia Tomista (SP ISSN 0210-0398) 1742
Cincinnati Christian Seminary. Seminary Review (US) 1701
Circle Network News (US) 1752
Circuit Rider (Nashville) (US ISSN 0146-9924) 1730
Cirplan (UK ISSN 0950-8732) 1688, 1730
Cistercian Studies see Collectanea Cisterciensia 1742
Cistercian Studies see Monastic Studies 1746
Cistercienser Chronik (AU) 1742
Cite Nouvelle (FR) 1694, 1730
Citeaux (BE ISSN 0009-7497) 1742
Cithara (US ISSN 0009-7527) 1689, 1701
Citta di Vita (IT ISSN 0009-7632) 1681, 1701
Ciudad de Dios (SP ISSN 0009-7756) 1742
Civilta Cattolica (IT ISSN 0009-8167) 1690, 1742
Clairlieu: Tijdschrift gewijd aan de Geschiedenis der Kruisheren (BE) 1688, 1701
Claretianum (VC ISSN 0578-4182) 1742
Clergy and Laity Concerned Report see C A L C Report 1694
Clergy Journal (US ISSN 0009-6431) 1701
Clergy Review (UK ISSN 0009-8736) 1742
Clergy's Federal Income Tax Guide see Abingdon Clergy Income Tax Guide 1682
Climb see Action (Winona Lake) 1727
Club des Hebraisants (FR ISSN 0763-062X) 1723
Clubhouse (US) 1683, 1730, 1742
Coalition--the Torah Action Journal (US) 1723
Codice del Vaticano II (IT) 1742
Colecao Fe e Realidade (BL) 1742
Coleccion Amanece (AG) 1701
Coleccion Canonica (SP ISSN 0069-505X) 1701
Coleccion Comunicacion (CK) 1701
Coleccion Historia de la Iglesia (SP) 1742
Coleccion Senda Abierta. Serie 2 (Azul): Judaismo(SP) 1723
Coleccion Teologica (SP) 1742
Colectanea de Jurisprudencia Canonica (SP ISSN 0210-0711) 1701
Colegio Mayor P. Felipe Scio. Publicaciones (SP) 1742
Collana Ricciana. Fonti (IT ISSN 0069-5254) 1742
Collectanea Cisterciensia (BE) 1742
Collectanea Franciscana (IT ISSN 0010-0749) 1742
Collection Franco-Judaica (FR) 1686, 1723
College of the Bible Quarterly see Lexington Theological Quarterly 1708
Colorado Kairos (US) 1701, 1757
Columbia (New Haven) (US ISSN 0010-1869) 1742
Columbia Union Visitor (US) 1752
Comboni Missions (US) 1742
Come and See (CN ISSN 0316-3040) 1701
Coming Changes Newsletter (US) 1730
Coming Revolution (US ISSN 0735-9780) 1752
Comino (MX ISSN 0010-2385) 1683, 1701
Commandos see Junior Life 1708
Commentarium pro Religiosis et Missionariis (IT ISSN 0010-2598) 1743
Common Good (US) 1743
Common Ground (UK ISSN 0010-325X) 1701, 1757
Commonweal (US ISSN 0010-3330) 1690, 1743
Communaute Chretienne (CN ISSN 0010-3454) 1701
Communautes et Liturgies (BE) 1701
Communicare (US ISSN 0279-1196) 1730
Communicatio Socialis (GW ISSN 0010-3497) 1681, 1701
Communio (SP ISSN 0010-3705) 1701
Communio (US ISSN 0094-2065) 1743
Communio Viatorum (CS ISSN 0010-3713) 1701
Communion (AT ISSN 0004-9662) 1743
Communique (Columbus) (US) 1730
Community of the Sisters of the Church Newsletter see C S C Newsletter 1699
Companion of St. Francis and St. Anthony (CN ISSN 0010-3985) 1743
Company (US) 1752
Compass (UK ISSN 0045-7809) 1701
Compass Magazine (AT) 1743
Compendia Rerum Iudaicarum Ad Novum Testamentum (NE) 1723
Comunidad (SP) 1743
Comunione e Liberazione see Litterae Communionis 1709
Comunita e Storia (IT) 1743
Concilium (FR) 1701
Concilium (UK ISSN 0010-5236) 1701
Concilium (NE ISSN 0167-1200) 1701
Concord (US ISSN 0741-9872) 1689, 1752
Concordia Historical Institute Quarterly (US ISSN 0010-5260) 1688, 1730
Concordia Journal (US ISSN 0145-7233) 1701
Concordia Theological Quarterly (US) 1701
Confederacion Latinoamericana de Asociaciones Cristianas de Jovenes. Confederacion (UY) 1701
Confederacion Latinoamericana de Asociaciones Cristianas de Jovenes. Contacto (UY) 1701
Confederacion Latinoamericana de Asociaciones Cristianas de Jovenes. Carta (UY) 1701
Confederacion Sudamericana de Asociaciones Cristianas de Jovenes. Noticias see Asociacion 1682
Conference Catholique Canadienne. Bulletin National de Liturgie see Conference des Eveques Catholiques du Canada. Bulletin National de Liturgie 1743
Conference des Eveques Catholiques du Canada. Bulletin National de Liturgie (CN) 1743
Conference of Presidents of Major American Jewish Organizations. Annual Report (US ISSN 0160-7057) 1686, 1723
Conference of Presidents of Major American Jewish Organizations. Report see Conference of Presidents of Major American Jewish Organizations. Annual Report 1686
Conference on Christianity and Literature. Newsletter see Christianity and Literature 1690
Conferenza Italiana Superiori Maggiori. Notiziario(IT) 1743
Confident Living (US ISSN 0017-2154) 1730
Confucius & Mencius Society of the Republic of China Journal (CH) 1726, 1757
Congregation (US ISSN 0361-8862) 1730
Congregation Cistercienne de Senaque et de la Pieuse Ligue Universelle pour les Ames de l'Abbaye de Lerins. (Publication) see Lerins 1708
Congregational Church in England and Wales. Congregational Year book see United Reformed Church in the United Kingdom. United Reformed Church Year Book 1738
Congregational Council for World Mission. Annual Report see C W M Report 1729
Congregational Historical Society. Transactions see United Reformed Church History Society. Journal 1738
Congregational Journal (US ISSN 0361-2376) 1730
Congregational Library. Bulletin (US ISSN 0010-5821) 1690, 1730
Congregational Monthly see Reform 1736
Congregationalist (US ISSN 0010-5856) 1730
Congreso Judio Latinoamericano. Boletin Informativo OJI (AG) 1723
Congress Monthly see American Jewish Congress. Congress Monthly 1685
Coniectanea Biblica. New Testament Series (SW ISSN 0069-8946) 1701
Coniectanea Biblica. Old Testament Series (SW ISSN 0069-8954) 1701
Coniectanea Neotestamentica see Coniectanea Biblica. New Testament Series 1701
Connect see Teen Power (1979) 1684
Connexion see U M E Connexion 1718
Consacrazione e Servizio (IT ISSN 0035-600X) 1701
Conscience et Liberte (SZ) 1694, 1701
Conservative Baptist Impact see Impact (Wheaton) 1732
Conservative Judaism (US ISSN 0010-6542) 1723
Consultation on Church Union. Digest (US) 1701
Contact (SZ) 1691, 1701
Contact (Aldershot) (UK) 1701
Contact (Sydney) (AT ISSN 0159-1096) 1730
Contactblad (NE ISSN 0010-731X) 1730
Contacts (FR ISSN 0045-8325) 1701
Contemplative Review see Living Prayer 1709
Contempo (US) 1730
Contemporary Christian (US ISSN 0746-0066) 1691, 1701
Contemporary Christian Music see Contemporary Christian 1691
Contemporary Jewry (US ISSN 0147-1694) 1686, 1723
Contemporary Religions in Japan see Japanese Journal of Religious Studies 1707
Context (US ISSN 0361-8854) 1701
Continuing Education see Continuing Educator 1701
Continuing Educator (US) 1701
Contrapunkt (GW ISSN 0343-3935) 1683, 1730
Contributions to the Study of Religion (US ISSN 0196-7053) 1701
Convention Herald (US) 1701
Convergence (SZ ISSN 0010-8154) 1743, 1757
Coptic Studies (NE) 1701
Cord (US ISSN 0010-8685) 1743
Cornerstone (Chicago) (US ISSN 0275-2743) 1701
Corpus Catholicorum (GW ISSN 0070-0320) 1743
Corpus Christianorum. Continuatio Mediaevalis (BE) 1743
Corpus Christianorum. Series Apocryphorum (BE) 1743
Corpus Christianorum. Series Graeca (BE) 1743
Corpus Christianorum. Series Latina (BE) 1743
Corpus Scriptorum Christianorum Orientalium: Aethiopica (BE ISSN 0070-0398) 1752
Corpus Scriptorum Christianorum Orientalium: Arabica (BE ISSN 0070-0401) 1752
Corpus Scriptorum Christianorum Orientalium: Armeniaca (BE ISSN 0070-041X) 1752
Corpus Scriptorum Christianorum Orientalium: Coptica (BE ISSN 0070-0428) 1752
Corpus Scriptorum Christianorum Orientalium: Iberica (BE ISSN 0070-0436) 1752
Corpus Scriptorum Christianorum Orientalium: Subsidia (BE ISSN 0070-0444) 1752
Corpus Scriptorum Christianorum Orientalium: Syriaca (BE ISSN 0070-0452) 1752
Coscienza (IT) 1743
Council for World Mission Report see C W M Report 1729
Council of Churches in Namibia Information see C C N Information 1729
Council of the Mystic Arts. Newsletter (US) 1752
Council Woman see N C J W Journal 1686
Counsellor of Basotho see Moeletsi Oa Basotho 1746
Counselor (US ISSN 0011-0019) 1683, 1701
Counselor/Al-Mushir (PK ISSN 0254-7856) 1702
Country Churchman (UK ISSN 0011-0124) 1702
Courtenay Facsimiles see Courtenay Reformation Facsimiles 1688
Courtenay Library of Reformation Classics (UK ISSN 0070-1394) 1688, 1702
Courtenay Reformation Facsimiles (UK) 1688, 1702
Courtenay Studies in Reformation Theology (UK ISSN 0070-1408) 1688, 1702
Covenant Companion (US ISSN 0011-0671) 1752
Covenant of the Goddess Newsletter see C O G Newsletter 1751
Covenant Voice (UK) 1752
Creation/Evolution (US ISSN 0738-6001) 1702
Crescent International (CN ISSN 0705-3754) 1721
Cristianesimo nella Storia (IT) 1702
Cristianesimo Oggi (IT) 1743
Cristiano (IT) 1730
Cristo al Mundo see Christ to the World 1742
Crkva u Svijetu (YU ISSN 0352-4000) 1752
Croce (IT ISSN 0011-1651) 1743
Croire Aujourd'hui (FR ISSN 0223-4734) 1743
Croire et Servir (FR) 1730
Croix (FR) 1743
Cross and Crown see Spirituality Today 1749
Cross Currents (US ISSN 0011-1953) 1693, 1743
Cross of Languedoc (US ISSN 0011-1961) 1686, 1730
Crosslink (NZ) 1730
Crossroads (UK ISSN 0045-9119) 1752
Crosstalk (CN ISSN 0706-8069) 1730
Crucible (UK ISSN 0011-2100) 1730
Crusade see Today (London) 1737
Crusade Messenger see Crusader 1683
Crusader (UK) 1683, 1702
Crusader (US ISSN 0011-2151) 1683, 1683, 1730
Crusader (Toronto) (CN ISSN 0382-4314) 1730
Crusader and Mission see American Baptist 1727
Crusader Magazine (US) 1683, 1730
Crux (CN ISSN 0011-2186) 1702
Crux of the News (US ISSN 0591-2296) 1702
Cruzada see Tradicion, Familia, Propiedad 1750
Cruzada Espanol (SP ISSN 0574-5101) 1702
Cruzada Eucaristica (PO ISSN 0011-2194) 1683, 1702
Crystal Mirror (US ISSN 0097-7209) 1726

Cuadernos D E I (Departamento Ecumenico de Investigaciones) (CR) *1702*
Cuadernos de Estudio (PE) *1743*
Cuadernos de Historia del Islam (SP) *1689*
Cuadernos de Historia del Islam. Serie Monografica Islamica Occidentalia *see* Cuadernos de Historia del Islam *1689*
Cuadernos de Orientacion Familiar (SP ISSN 0011-2453) *1702*
Cuadernos de Teologia y Pastoral (CK) *1743*
Cubit (UK ISSN 0260-2202) *1702*
Cultura e Fe (BL) *1702*
Cultural Information Service (US ISSN 0097-952X) 1684, *1684*
Cumberland Presbyterian (US ISSN 0011-2976) *1730*
Current Christian Abstracts (US ISSN 0883-1440) *1721*
Current Dialogue (SZ) *1702*
Current Issues in Catholic Higher Education (US) *1684,* 1743
Currents in Theology and Mission (US ISSN 0098-2113) *1702*
Curriculum Plans *see* United Methodist Church. Curriculum Plans *1738*
Cursillo (AU ISSN 0011-4057) *1702*
Cusanus-Gesellschaft. Buchreihe (GW ISSN 0070-2234) *1702*
Y Cylchgrawn Efengylaidd (UK ISSN 0143-0076) *1730*
Czech Ecumenical News *see* Czechoslovak Ecumenical News *1730*
Czechoslovak Ecumenical News/ Tschechoslowakische Oekumenische Nachrichten (CS) *1730*
D J I N (SZ) *1687,* 1726
D K K F-Nyt (Dansk Katolsk Kvinde-Forbund) (DK ISSN 0109-1476) 1743, *1758*
D R C Africa News *see* D R C News *1730*
D R C News (Dutch Reformed Church) (SA) *1730*
Daily Blessing (US ISSN 0011-538X) *1752*
Daily Bread (US ISSN 0092-7147) *1752*
Daily Watchwords (UK) *1730*
Daily Word (US ISSN 0011-5525) *1752*
Dallo Scoglio di Santa Rita (IT) *1702*
Dan Enkle Sannhet *see* Pura Verdad *1755*
Daneshgah-e Ferdowsi. Daneshkade-Ye Elahiyat Va Ma'aref-e Eslami. Nashriyeh *see* University of Ferdowsi. Faculty of Theology and Islamic Studies. Publication *1722*
Danica (US) 1686, *1752*
Danmarks Unge Katolikker Nyt fra D U K *see* Nyt fra D U K *1747*
Dansk Katolsk Kvinde-Forbund Nyt *see* D K K F-Nyt *1758*
Dansk Kirkehilsen (DK) *1702*
Dansk Missionsblad (DK ISSN 0011-6378) *1702*
Danske Bibelselskab. Medlemsbrev *see* Nyt fra Bibelselskabet *1711*
Darbininkas (US ISSN 0011-6637) *1743*
Darshana International (II ISSN 0011-6734) *1693,* 1695, 1726
Daughters of Sarah (US ISSN 0739-1749) 1702, *1758*
Davke (AG) *1686,* 1723
Dawn in Central Asia (UK ISSN 0070-2994) *1702*
Daybreak (UK ISSN 0011-7102) *1730*
Deacon (US ISSN 0045-9771) *1730*
Decision (Minneapolis) (US ISSN 0011-7307) *1730*
Defender *see* Communicare *1730*
Dein Reich Komme (GW ISSN 0011-7692) *1702*
Delta *see* D J I N *1687*
Demain d'Avantage qu'Hier (FR) *1702*
Den Enkle Sannhet *see* Pure Verite *1755*
Denominations in America (US ISSN 0193-6883) *1702*
Denver Register *see* National Catholic Register *1747*
Departamento Ecumenico de Investigaciones Cuadernos D E I *see* Cuadernos D E I *1702*
Deseret News Church Almanac (US ISSN 0093-786X) *1752*
Detroit and Suburban Lutheran *see* Tri-County Lutheran *1737*
Detroit Jewish News *see* Detroit Jewish News Ltd. Partnership *1686*
Detroit Jewish News Ltd. Partnership (US) *1686,* 1723
Der Deutsche Hugenott (GW ISSN 0012-0294) 1688, *1730*
Deutsche Katholik in Kanada (CN ISSN 0381-8950) *1686,* 1743
Deutscher Hugenotten-Verein E.V. Geschichtsblaetter (GW ISSN 0344-2934) *1688,* 1730
Devotion au Saint-Esprit *see* Esprit Saint *1703*
Devotions (Cincinnati) (US) *1731*
Dharma (MY ISSN 0012-1746) *1693,* 1726
Diaconia Christi (GW) *1743*
Diaconia XP *see* Diaconia Christi *1743*
Diakonia (GW ISSN 0012-1967) *1702*
Diakonia (NQ) *1743*
Diakonie (AU) *1702*
Diakonie (GW ISSN 0341-826X) *1702*
Diakonie im Rheinland (GW ISSN 0012-1975) *1731*
Dialog (US ISSN 0012-2033) *1702*
Dialogo Ecumenico (SP ISSN 0210-2870) *1702*
Dialogue (CE ISSN 0012-2181) *1752*
Dialogue: A Journal of Mormon Thought (US ISSN 0012-2157) *1752*
Dialogue on Campus (US ISSN 0012-2289) *1702*
Dicionario de Historia da Igreja em Portugal (PO) *1702*
Didaskalia (PO) *1743*
Dielheimer Blaetter zum Alten Testament *see* Dielheimer Blaetter zum Alten Testament und seiner Rezeption in der Alten Kirche *1702*
Dielheimer Blaetter zum Alten Testament und seiner Rezeption in der Alten Kirche (GW) *1702*
Dienender Glaube (GW ISSN 0012-2572) *1702*
Dienst am Kinde *see* Sonntagschulmitarbeiter *1685*
Dienst am Wort - Gedanken zur Sonntagspredigt (GW ISSN 0720-9916) *1702*
Dignity (US ISSN 0147-1139) *1689,* 1743
Dimanche (BE ISSN 0012-2866) *1743*
Dimension (SA ISSN 0046-0265) *1731*
Dimension *see* Accion *1757*
Dimension (Birmingham) (US ISSN 0162-6825) *1731*
Dimensions of Ministry (US) *1743*
Dio e Popolo (IT ISSN 0046-0303) *1702*
Diocesan Times (CN ISSN 0382-9391) *1731*
Dirasat al-Islamiyah (PK ISSN 0002-399X) *1721*
Directory and Handbook - Baptist Missionary Association of America *see* Baptist Missionary Association of America. Directory and Handbook *1728*
Directory of Churches and Synagogues (US) *1702*
Directory of Departments and Programs of Religious Studies in North America (US) *1702*
Direktorium fuer das Bistum Muenster (GW) *1702*
Diritto Ecclesiastico *see* Diritto Ecclesiastico e Rassegna di Diritto Matrimoniale *1702*
Diritto Ecclesiastico e Rassegna di Diritto Matrimoniale (IT) *1702*
Disciple (St. Louis) (US ISSN 0092-8372) *1702*
Discipleship Journal (US ISSN 0273-5865) *1731*
Discipliana (US ISSN 0732-9881) *1731*
Discourse (II ISSN 0253-519X) *1752*
Discover the Bible (CN ISSN 0018-912X) *1743*
Discoveries (US) *1683,* 1731
Discovery (AT ISSN 0726-6286) *1731*
Discovery (New York) (US) 1683, *1702*
Discovery (Winona Lake) *see* Action (Winona Lake) *1727*
Dispersion and Unity *see* Forum *1690*
Dispersion y Unidad (IS ISSN 0334-8903) *1689,* 1723
Divine Voice *see* Divya Vani *1726*
Divinitas (VC ISSN 0012-4222) *1743*
Divus Thomas (IT ISSN 0012-4257) 1693, *1702*
Divya Vani/Divine Voice (II ISSN 0012-4265) *1726*
Doctrine and Life (IE ISSN 0012-446X) *1743*
Documentation Catholique (FR ISSN 0012-4613) *1743*
Documents d'Esglesia (SP) *1702*
Domenica (IT ISSN 0012-5288) *1743*
Domingo (BL) *1743*
Don Bell Reports (US) *1743*
Donum Dei (CN ISSN 0318-0123) *1702*
Doopsgezinde Bijdragen (NE) *1688,* 1731
Door of Hope (US) *1702*
Doortocht (NE ISSN 0012-5504) *1743*
Dor le-Dor (IS ISSN 0334-2166) *1702*
Dorf Aktuell *see* Land Aktuell *1694*
Dossiers de la Bible (FR ISSN 0761-7267) *1702*
Douai Magazine (UK ISSN 0012-5695) *1684,* 1702
Downside Review (UK ISSN 0012-5806) *1743*
Dowry (UK ISSN 0262-8937) *1691,* 1743
Draudzes Vestis (CN ISSN 0701-0214) *1731*
Draugas (US) 1686, *1743*
Dreikoenigsbote (GW ISSN 0012-608X) *1731*
Dreloma (II) *1726*
Drew Gateway (US ISSN 0012-6152) *1731*
Druzina in Dom (AU ISSN 0012-6764) *1702*
Dukhovna Akademiya SV. Kliment Okhridski. Godishnik (BU ISSN 0323-9578) 1688, *1702*
Dutch Reformed Church News *see* D R C News *1730*
E.C.M. News (European Christian Mission (Australian Section) Inc.) (AT) *1702*
E P F Newsletter (US) *1702*
E P S *see* Ecumenical Press Service *1703*
E/S A (US ISSN 0164-5528) *1731,* 1757
E S G - Nachrichten (Evangelische Studentengemeinde in der Bundesrepublik Deutschland und Berlin (West)) (GW ISSN 0012-7981) *1702*
E T S Bulletin *see* Evangelical Theological Society. Journal *1731*
East and West Series (II ISSN 0012-8384) 1693, *1703*
East Asian Pastoral Review (PH) *1743*
Eastern Churches News Letter (UK ISSN 0012-8732) *1752*
Eastern Churches Review *see* Sobornost *1736*
Eastern Kansas Register (US ISSN 0012-883X) *1743*
Eastern Synod Lutheran (CN ISSN 0831-4446) *1731*
Eaux - Vives (FR) *1743*
Ecclesia (SP ISSN 0012-9038) *1743*
Ecclesia *see* Kiongozi *1745*
Ecclesia Mater (IT) *1743*
Ecclesiastica Xaveriana *see* Theologica Xaveriana *1750*
Echanges (FR ISSN 0397-0736) *1703*
Echo (NE ISSN 0012-9119) *1752*
Echo uit Afrika *see* Echo uit Afrika en Andere Werelddelen *1703*
Echo uit Afrika en Andere Werelddelen (NE) *1703*
Echos des Charites de St. Vincent de Paul *see* Equipes St Vincent *1757*
Eck Mata Journal (US) *1752*
Eck News *see* Eck Mata Journal *1752*
Eco del Santuario di N.S. di Lourdes (IT) *1743*
Eco dell'Educazione Ebraica (IT ISSN 0012-9518) *1684,* 1703
L'Eco Delle Valli Valdesi (IT) *1703*
L'Eco di Gibilmanna (IT) *1743*
Ecrits Libres (FR ISSN 0070-8860) *1703*
Ecstasy (II) *1726*
Ecumenical Courier (US ISSN 0013-0761) *1703*
Ecumenical News (IO) *1703*
Ecumenical Notes *see* One in Christ *1747*
Ecumenical Press Service (SZ) *1703*
Ecumenical Review (SZ ISSN 0013-0796) *1703*
Ecumenism (CN) *1703*
Ecumentist (US ISSN 0013-080X) *1703*
Editorial /Perpetuo Socorro *see* P S *1712*
Edmundite (US ISSN 0013-1016) *1743*
Education Newsline (US) 1684, *1731*
Eglise Aujourd'hui (FR ISSN 0223-5854) *1703*
L'Eglise Canadienne (CN ISSN 0013-2322) *1703*
Eglise Catholique a Madagascar (MG) *1743*
Eglise de Montreal (CN ISSN 0381-0380) *1743*
Eglise et Theologie (CN ISSN 0013-2349) *1703*
Eglise Reformee Vous Parle *see* Echanges *1703*
Elenchus Bibliographicus Biblicus (VC) *1721*
Elim Evangel (UK ISSN 0013-6182) *1731*
Elisabeth Elliot Newsletter (US) *1703*
Elisabethbode (NE ISSN 0013-6212) *1703*
Eme Eme (DR) *1743*
Emergency Post (UK ISSN 0305-005X) *1703*
Emigrato Italiano (IT ISSN 0013-6697) *1703*
Emmanuel (US ISSN 0013-6719) *1743*
Emmaus Letter (US) 1683, *1743*
Emphasis on Faith and Living (US ISSN 0194-5246) *1703*
En Avant (FR ISSN 0013-6921) *1703*
En Eglise (CN ISSN 0317-851X) *1743*
En Equipe au Service de l'Evangile (FR ISSN 0395-1766) *1743*
En la Calle Recta *see* In de Rechte Straat *1706*
Encounter (CN ISSN 0315-0097) *1731*
Encounter! (US ISSN 0162-4547) *1731*
Encounter *see* In-Touch *1732*
Encounter (Indianapolis) (US ISSN 0013-7081) *1703*
Encyclopaedia Judaica Year Book (IS ISSN 0303-7819) *1723*
Engage/Social Action *see* E/S A *1731*
English Benedictine Congregation. Ordo. (UK) *1743*
English Churchman *see* English Churchman & St. James's Chronicle *1731*
English Churchman & St. James's Chronicle (UK) *1731*
Ensenanza de la Religion (SP) *1703*
Ensign (US ISSN 0013-8606) *1752*
Entscheidung (GW ISSN 0013-9092) *1731*
Entschluss (AU ISSN 0017-4602) *1703*
Envoy (Pittsburg) (US ISSN 0013-9408) 1695, *1703*
Ephemerides Carmeliticae *see* Teresianum *1750*
Ephemerides Iuris Canonici (IT ISSN 0013-9491) *1744*
Ephemerides Liturgicae (IT ISSN 0013-9505) *1703*
Ephemerides Mariologicae (SP ISSN 0425-1466) *1744*
Ephemerides Theologicae Lovanienses (BE ISSN 0013-9513) *1744*
Epiphany *see* Epiphany Journal *1703*
Epiphany Journal (US) *1703*
Episcopal Clerical Directory (US) *1731*
Episcopal Diocese of Connecticut. Historiographer *see* Historiographer *1732*
Episcopal Recorder (US ISSN 0013-9610) *1731*
Episcopalian (US ISSN 0013-9629) *1731*
Episkopet (DK ISSN 0105-6867) *1703*
Epoche (US) 1688, *1703*
Epworth Review (UK) *1731*
Equipes St Vincent (FR ISSN 0763-5184) 1744, *1757*
Equipping Youth (US ISSN 0196-0911) 1683, *1731*
Er Ruft (AU ISSN 0013-9912) *1703*
Erbe und Auftrag (GW ISSN 0013-9963) *1744*
Ermlandbriefe (GW ISSN 0014-0201) *1703*
Erneuerung und Abwehr (GW) *1731*
Eskimo (CN ISSN 0318-7551) 1686, *1744*
Espiritu (SP ISSN 0014-0716) *1693,* 1703
Esprit et Liberte (FR ISSN 0071-1330) *1731*
Esprit et Vie (FR ISSN 0014-0775) *1703*
Esprit Saint (FR ISSN 0396-969X) *1703*
Estudio Agustiniano (SP ISSN 0425-340X) *1744*
Estudios Biblicos (SP ISSN 0014-1437) *1703*
Estudios Eclesiasticos (SP ISSN 0210-1610) *1703*
Estudios Josefinos (SP ISSN 0210-7074) *1744*
Estudios Trinitarios (SP ISSN 0210-0363) *1703*
Eta dell'Acquario (IT) *1703*
Etendard de la Bible et Heraut du Royaume de Christ *see* Bible Standard and Herald of Christ's Kingdom *1698*
Etendard de la Bible et Heraut du Royaume de Christ (FR) *1703*
Eternity (US ISSN 0014-1682) *1752*
Ethical Culture Today *see* A E U Reports *1692*
Ethics and Medics (US) 1691, *1693*
Etudes (FR ISSN 0014-1941) *1690,* 1744
Etudes et Documents Missionnaires *see* Missionswissenschaftliche Abhandlungen und Texte *1710*
Etudes Gregoriennes (FR ISSN 0071-2086) *1691,* 1703
Etudes Preliminaires aux Religions Orientales dans l'Empire Romain (NE ISSN 0531-1950) 1692, *1703*
Etudes sur le Judaisme Medieval (NE) *1723*
Etudes Teilhardiennes/Teilhardian Studies (FR ISSN 0082-2612) *1703*
Etudes Theologiques et Religieuses (FR ISSN 0014-2239) *1731*
Eucharistic Minister (US ISSN 0743-524X) *1744*
Euhemer (PL ISSN 0014-2298) *1703*
Euntes Docete (IT) *1744*
Euro Vision Advance (US) *1703*
Europe Pulse *see* Pulse *1713*
European Christian Mission (Australian Section) Inc. News *see* E.C.M. News *1702*
European Judaism (UK ISSN 0014-3006) *1723*
Evangel (US ISSN 0162-1890) *1731*
Evangelical Baptist (CN ISSN 0014-3324) *1731*
Evangelical Baptist Churches in Canada. Fellowship Yearbook (CN ISSN 0317-266X) *1731*
Evangelical Beacon (US ISSN 0014-3332) *1731*
Evangelical Fellowship Quarterly *see* Aim *1751*
Evangelical Friend (US ISSN 0014-3340) *1752*
Evangelical Magazine (UK ISSN 0046-2853) *1752*
Evangelical Magazine of Wales *see* Y Cylchgrawn Efengylaidd *1730*
Evangelical Missions Quarterly (US ISSN 0014-3359) *1703*
Evangelical Morning *see* Yevanhelskyj Ranok *1739*
Evangelical Quarterly (UK ISSN 0014-3367) *1703*
Evangelical Review Magazine (US) *1703*
Evangelical Review of Theology (UK ISSN 0144-8153) *1703*
Evangelical Student *see* Our Link *1711*
Evangelical Theological Society. Journal (US ISSN 0360-8808) *1731*
Evangelical Truth (CN ISSN 0014-3375) *1752*
Evangelie en Maatschappij (NE ISSN 0014-3383) 1689, *1703*
Evangelii Haerold (SW) *1752*
Evangelio y MisionCompania (SP) *1703*
Evangelisch-Lutherisches Missionswerk in Niedersachsen. Jahrbuch (Year) (GW) *1731*
Evangelisch-Lutherische Landeskirche Sachsens. Amtsblatt (GE ISSN 0423-8346) *1731*
Der Evangelische Erzieher (GW ISSN 0014-3413) *1684,* 1703
Evangelische Kinderpflege fuer Kindergarten, Hort, Heim und Familie *see* Theorie und Praxis der Sozialpaedagogik *1683*
Evangelische Kirche in Deutschland. Amtsblatt (GW ISSN 0014-343X) *1731*
Evangelische Kommentare (GW ISSN 0300-4236) *1703*
Evangelische Landeskirche in Wuerttemberg. Amtsblatt (GW ISSN 0014-3529) *1731*
Evangelisch-Lutherische Kirche in Thueringen. Amtsblatt (GE ISSN 0014-326X) *1731*
Evangelische Mission Jahrbuch *see* Jahrbuch Mission *1707*
Evangelische Missionszeitschrift *see* Zeitschrift fuer Mission *1720*
Evangelische Pfarrgemeinde A.B. Wien-Favoriten-Christuskirche. Gemeindebrief (AU ISSN 0016-6154) *1731*
Evangelische Studentengemeinde in der Bundesrepublik Deutschland und Berlin (West) Nachrichten *see* E S G - Nachrichten *1702*
Evangelische Theologie (GW ISSN 0014-3502) *1703*
Evangelischer Botschaft *see* Wort und Weg *1739*
Evangelischer Bund in Oesterreich. Schriftenreihe (AU ISSN 0036-6943) *1731*
Evangelischer Nachrichtendienst in der DDR (GE ISSN 0014-3553) *1731*
Evangelisches Gemeindeblatt fuer Hof und Umgebung *see* Sonntagsblatt fuer die Evangelisch-Lutherische Kirche in Bayern. Ausgabe Oberfranken *1737*
Evangelisches Gemeindeblatt fuer Muenchen *see* Muenchner Gemeindeblatt *1734*
Evangelisches Gemeindeblatt fuer Wuerttemberg (GW ISSN 0014-360X) *1731*
Evangeliska Oestasienmissionen (SW) *1703*
Evangelism Today (UK) *1703*

Evangelist see Pendulum 1712
Evangelist see Wort und Weg 1739
Evangelist (US ISSN 0738-8489) 1744
Evangelist (NE ISSN 0014-3626) 1752
Evangelizing Today's Child (US) 1683, 1703
Evangelizzare (IT) 1703
Evangel's'kyj Golos see Ievanhel's'kyi Holos 1753
Evangile et Liberte (FR) 1731
Evanjelicky Hlasnik (YU ISSN 0014-3642) 1731
Event (US ISSN 0014-374X) 1731
Excerpta e Dissertationibus in Iure Canonico (SP) 1704
Excerpta e Dissertationibus in Sacra Theologica (SP) 1744
Explor (US ISSN 0362-0867) 1704
Exploring A see Exploring 1 1731
Exploring A for Leaders see Exploring 1 for Leaders 1731
Exploring C see Exploring 2 1731
Exploring C for Leaders see Exploring 2 for Leaders 1731
Exploring 1 (US) 1731
Exploring 1 for Leaders (US) 1731
Exploring 2 (US) 1731
Exploring 2 for Leaders (US) 1731
Expositor Bautista (AG ISSN 0014-522X) 1731
Expositor Biblico (Student Edition) see Jovenes Biblico (Student Edition) 1733
Expositor Biblico (Teacher Edition) (US ISSN 0014-5238) 1685, 1731
Expository Times (UK ISSN 0014-5246) 1704
Extension (Illinois) (US) 1744
F.I.R.O. Quaderni (IT ISSN 0014-5912) 1704
F L P P Newsletter see Church World Service. Family Life and Population Program Briefs 1701
F O L K Magazine see F O L K Newsletter 1726
F O L K Newsletter (Friends of Lord Krishna) (UK) 1726
F T I Newsletter (Feminist Theological Institute, Inc.) (US) 1704, 1758
Face-to-Face (New York) (US ISSN 0361-6061) 1704
Fact Book on Theological Education (US) 1704
Faith (UK) 1704
Faith and Fellowship (US) 1731
Faith and Freedom (UK ISSN 0014-701X) 1704
Faith and Mission (US ISSN 0740-0659) 1731
Faith and Order Papers (SZ ISSN 0512-2589) 1704
Faith and Philosophy (US) 1693, 1704
Faith and Reason see Faith and Philosophy 1693
Faith & Reason (US ISSN 0098-5449) 1704
Faith and Thought (UK ISSN 0014-7028) 1693, 1704
Faith for Daily Living (SA ISSN 0014-7044) 1752
Famiglia Cristiana (IT ISSN 0014-7095) 1687, 1704
Familia Crista (BL ISSN 0014-7125) 1687, 1704
Familia Cristiana (MX) 1744
Famille Nouvelle (FR ISSN 0014-7184) 1704
Family (UK) 1704
The Family (Boston) (US) 1744
Family Life (UK ISSN 0143-7917) 1731
Family Life (CN ISSN 0014-7303) 1752
Far East Reporter (Houston) (US) 1752
Fast Grunn (NO ISSN 0014-8733) 1704
Fathers of the Church (US ISSN 0014-8814) 1744
Fatima Findings (US ISSN 0014-8830) 1752
Fedelta Apostolica (IT) 1731
Federacion Sudamericana de Asociaciones Cristianas de Jovenes. Noticias see Confederacion Latinoamericana de Asociaciones Cristianas de Jovenes. Carta 1701
Federation of Synagogues of South Africa. Federation Chronicle see Jewish Tradition 1724
Federation Protestante de France. Annuaire (FR) 1732
Federation Protestante de France. Centre d'Etudes et de Documentation. Bulletin see Centre Protestant d'Etudes et de Documentation. Bulletin 1721
Fellowship in Prayer (US ISSN 0014-9837) 1691, 1752
Fellowship Yearbook see Evangelical Baptist Churches in Canada. Fellowship Yearbook 1731
Feminist Theological Institute, Inc. Newsletter see F T I Newsletter 1758
Der feste Grund (GW ISSN 0015-0320) 1732
Fetes et Saisons (FR ISSN 0015-0371) 1704
Feuillet Biblique (CN ISSN 0225-2112) 1744
Fiaccola (IT) 1744
Fides et Historia (US) 1688, 1704
Field Afar see Maryknoll 1746
Fields see Christian Missions in Many Lands 1700
Fiery Synthesis (US) 1752
Fikr-o-Nazar (PK ISSN 0430-4055) 1721
Filosofia della Religione. Testi e Studi (IT) 1704
Fiori di S. Antonio (IT ISSN 0015-2528) 1704
First Catholic Slovak Union of America. Minutes of Annual Meeting (US ISSN 0275-6145) 1744
Flambeau (CM ISSN 0015-3435) 1681, 1704
Floodtide (US) 1704
Florida Catholic Newspaper (US ISSN 0015-394X) 1744
Flying Angel (UK ISSN 0015-4822) 1752
Foc Nou (SP) 1686, 1704
Focus (Grantham) (UK ISSN 0143-7925) 1732
Focus: North American Student Zionist Forum (US) 1694, 1723
Foer Biblisk Tro see Biblicum 1698
Foersamlings- och Pastoratsfoervaltning see Svenska Kyrkans 1717
Foi Aujourd'hui (FR) 1704
Foi et Vie de l'Eglise au Diocese de Toulouse (FR ISSN 0015-5365) 1744
Folium Diocesanum Bauzanense-Brixinense (IT ISSN 0015-5802) 1704
Folk Mass and Modern Liturgy see Modern Liturgy 1710
Fonti e Studi per la Storia del Santo a Padova (IT) 1744
Foreningen af Katolske Skoler i Danmark Bulletin see K S Bulletin 1685
Forschungen zur Kirchen- und Dogmengeschichte (GW) 1704
Forschungen zur Religion und Literatur des Alten und Neuen Testaments (GW) 1704
Forum (IS ISSN 0334-2506) 1690, 1723
Forum. Berichte aus der Arbeit (GW) 1704, 1757
Forum Haus Ortlohn. Freundsbrief see Forum. Berichte aus der Arbeit 1704
Forum Letter see Lutheran Forum. Forum Letter 1733
Forum Newsletter (US) 1704
Forum Religion (GW ISSN 0343-7744) 1704
Forward (US) 1732
Forward (San Juan Capistrano) see Christian Research Journal 1700
Forward in Erie see Forward 1732
Foundation Commentator (US) 1704
Four and Five (US ISSN 0015-9077) 1683, 1704
Four Worlds Journal (US) 1723
Foyers Mixtes (FR ISSN 0015-9239) 1704
France Catholique see France Catholique-Ecclesia 1744
France Catholique-Ecclesia (FR) 1744
France-Islam (FR) 1686, 1721
France Prostestante see Federation Protestante de France. Annuaire 1732
Franciscan Studies (US ISSN 0080-5459) 1693, 1744
Franciscana (BE ISSN 0015-9840) 1744
Franciscanum (CK ISSN 0120-1468) 1744
Franciskaans Leven (NE ISSN 0015-9794) 1744
Frankfurt am Main. Universitaet. Institut fuer Wissenschaftliche Irenik. Schriften see Studia Irenica 1716
Frankfurter Kirchliches Jahrbuch (GW) 1688, 1704
Franziskanische Studien (GW ISSN 0016-0067) 1744
Frate Francesco (IT ISSN 0016-0091) 1744
Frau und Mutter (GW ISSN 0722-8120) 1704
Free Church Chronicle (UK ISSN 0016-0326) 1752
Free Church of Scotland. Monthly Record (UK ISSN 0016-0334) 1752
Freedom (US) 1689
Freedom Magazine see Freedom 1689
Freethinker (UK ISSN 0016-0687) 1693, 1704
Freeway (US) 1683, 1704
Freiburger Islamstudien (GW ISSN 0170-3285) 1692, 1722
Freiburger Zeitschrift fuer Philosophie und Theologie (SZ ISSN 0016-0725) 1693, 1744
Freie Religion (GW ISSN 0016-0776) 1704
French Edition see Lumen Vitae 1746
Friedensglocke see Fuer Heute 1732
Friedensglocke (GE) 1732
Friend (US ISSN 0009-4102) 1683, 1752
Friend (UK ISSN 0016-1268) 1752
Friendly Companion (UK ISSN 0016-1292) 1683, 1704
Friendly Woman (US) 1752, 1758
Friends' Historical Association. Bulletin see Quaker History 1755
Friends Historical Society. Journal (UK ISSN 0071-9587) 1752
Friends Journal (US ISSN 0016-1322) 1752, 1757
Friends of Lord Krishna Newsletter see F O L K Newsletter 1726
Friends' Quarterly (UK ISSN 0016-1357) 1752
Friends Service Council. Annual Report see Quaker Peace & Service. Annual Report 1757
Frohe Botschaft (GW ISSN 0340-6091) 1704
Frontier News (AT ISSN 0016-2108) 1732
Frontlijn (NE ISSN 0016-2175) 1744
Fruit of the Vine (US ISSN 0016-2264) 1752
Fuer Arbeit und Besinnung (GW ISSN 0016-2434) 1732
Fuer Heute (GW ISSN 0016-2442) 1732
Full Gospel Business Men's Voice (US ISSN 0042-8264) 1752
Fulness (US ISSN 0276-4679) 1704
Fundamentalist (US ISSN 0016-2744) 1732
Al Furqan (II) 1722
Furrow (IE ISSN 0016-3120) 1744
G.B. Digest (Girls Brigade) (AT) 1704
G E M's Europe Report (Greater Europe Mission) (US) 1704
Gaba Pastoral Papers see Spearhead 1716
Gaba Reprints (KE) 1704
Gabriel (IT ISSN 0016-3694) 1689, 1704
Galamukani! (SA ISSN 0016-3988) 1752
Gallneukirchner Bote see Diakonie 1702
Gallo see Quaderni del Gallo 1713
Garamut see World Missions Update 1756
Gateway (UK) 1683, 1732, 1757
Gateway (SA ISSN 0016-5204) 1704
Gateways (US) 1726
Gay Christian see Metroline 1689
Gebetsapostolat und Seelsorge (GW ISSN 0016-5735) 1704
Geist und Auftrag (NE) 1744
Geist und Leben (GW ISSN 0016-5921) 1704
Gemeenteleven (NE ISSN 0016-6065) 1704
Die Gemeinde (AU ISSN 0021-2334) 1686, 1723
Die Gemeinde (GW ISSN 0016-6073) 1732
Gemeindebote see Kirche in Marburg 1745
Genadeklanken (NE ISSN 0016-6324) 1704
General Conference of the New Church. Yearbook (UK ISSN 0072-0666) 1752
General Convention of the New Jerusalem. Journal (US) 1704
General Minutes of the Annual Conferences of the United Methodist Church see United Methodist Church. General Minutes of the Annual Conferences 1738
Generation (US) 1744
Gentes (IT ISSN 0016-6960) 1704
Georgia Bulletin (US) 1744
Georgian Newsletter (US) 1752
Gereformeerd Kerkhistorisch Tijdschrift (NE) 1732
Gereformeerd Theologisch Tijdschrift (NE ISSN 0016-8610) 1732
Gereformeerde Vroueblad (SA ISSN 0378-407X) 1732
Gesar (US ISSN 0738-2294) 1726
Geschaeftsmann und Christ (SZ ISSN 0016-9021) 1704
Gesellschaft fuer die Geschichte des Protestantismus in Oesterreich. Jahrbuch (AU) 1688, 1732
Gesellschaft fuer Niedersaechsische Kirchengeschichte. Jahrbuch (GW ISSN 0072-4238) 1688, 1732
Gesher (IS ISSN 0435-8406) 1686, 1723
Gesher (US ISSN 0016-9145) 1690, 1693, 1723
Getroster Tag/Hopeful Day (GW ISSN 0016-934X) 1732
Gettysburg Seminary Bulletin see Lutheran Theological Seminary Bulletin 1734
Gids Op Maatschappelijk Gebied (BE) 1689, 1744
Giovani in Dialogo (IT ISSN 0017-1336) 1744
Gioventu Evangelica (IT ISSN 0017-0542) 1704
Gioventu Passionista/Passionist Youth (IT ISSN 0072-4548) 1704
Girls Brigade Digest see G.B. Digest 1704
Gist (US ISSN 0732-7781) 1704
Glad Tidings (CN ISSN 0017-0720) 1732
Glad Tidings of Good Things (US ISSN 0017-0739) 1753
Glasnik (YU ISSN 0017-0925) 1704
Glaube in der 2. Welt (GW ISSN 0254-4377) 1694, 1704
Glaube und Lernen (GW ISSN 0179-3551) 1704
Glaube und Tat (GW ISSN 0017-1123) 1732
Glenmary Challenge (US) 1704
Glenmary's Challenge see Glenmary Challenge 1704
Global Church Growth (US ISSN 0731-1125) 1753
Global Church Growth Bulletin see Global Church Growth 1753
Glorious Hope see Slavna Nadele 1736
Gloucester Diocesan Gazette (UK ISSN 0017-1301) 1704
Glow International (US) 1704
Gnade und Herrlichkeit (GW ISSN 0017-1409) 1704
Godsdienst en Maatschappij (NE) 1721
Goeie Nuus see Good News 1705
Goettinger Predigtmeditationen (GW ISSN 0340-6083) 1704
Going On (AT ISSN 0705-2316) 1732
Goleuad/Light (UK ISSN 0017-1700) 1732
Good News/Goeie Nuus (SA ISSN 0017-2146) 1705
Good News (US) 1732, 1744
Good News (Birmingham) (UK ISSN 0262-2874) 1705
Good News Broadcaster see Confident Living 1730
Good News Crusades see Mountain Movers 1754
Good News of Tomorrow's World see Plain Truth (Pasadena) 1755
Good Tidings see East Asian Pastoral Review 1743
Gospel Call see Euro Vision Advance 1703
Gospel Carrier (US ISSN 0017-2332) 1705
Gospel Choir (US ISSN 0362-0417) 1691, 1732
Gospel Herald (CN ISSN 0829-4666) 1705
Gospel Herald (US ISSN 0017-2340) 1753
Gospel in Context see International Bulletin of Missionary Research 1690
Gospel Messenger (US ISSN 0017-2359) 1682, 1705
Gospel Standard (UK ISSN 0017-2367) 1683, 1705
Gospel Truth (US ISSN 0017-2383) 1694, 1753
Gospel Witness see Indian Lutheran 1732
Gottes Wort (GW ISSN 0017-2480) 1705
Gottesdienst (GW ISSN 0343-8732) 1705
Gottesdienste mit Kindern und Jugendlichen (GW) 1705
Gotteskinder see Regenbogen 1713
Gracas do Servo de Deus: Padre Cruz (PO ISSN 0017-2758) 1705
Grace (UK ISSN 0046-6239) 1705
Grace Theological Journal (US ISSN 0198-666X) 1705
Gracious Light (SA) 1744
Graduate School Guide (US) 1685, 1744
Grail (CN ISSN 0828-4083) 1744
Gralswelt (GW ISSN 0017-3088) 1693, 1705
Grande Sinal (BL ISSN 0046-6271) 1705
Great Britain. Royal Army Chaplains' Department. Journal (UK) 1691, 1705
Greater Europe Mission Europe Report see G E M's Europe Report 1704
Greater Europe Report see G E M's Europe Report 1704
Greater World (UK ISSN 0046-6352) 1705
Greek Orthodox Calendar (UK ISSN 0265-6922) 1686, 1753
Greek Orthodox Theological Review (US ISSN 0017-3894) 1688, 1693, 1753
Greek Sunday News/Kyriakatika Nea (US) 1686, 1753
Gregorianum (VC ISSN 0017-4114) 1693, 1744
Gregorios ho Palamas (GR) 1688, 1753
Grosse Entschluss see Entschluss 1703
Group (Loveland) (US ISSN 0163-8971) 1683, 1705
Group's Jr. High Ministry Magazine (US ISSN 0884-0504) 1683, 1705
Growing (Nashville) (US ISSN 0162-4512) 1732
Guide see Action (Winona Lake) 1727
Guide (Hagerstown) (US ISSN 0017-5226) 1683, 1753
Guide A for Preschool Teachers see Preschool Bible Teacher A 1735
Guide B for Preschool Teachers see Preschool Bible Teacher B 1735
Guide C for Preschool Teachers see Preschool Bible Teacher C 1735
Guide for Biblical Studies (US) 1732
Guide to Christian Camps see Guide to Christian Camps & Conference Centers 1705
Guide to Christian Camps & Conference Centers (US) 1705
Guide to Religious Careers for Catholic Men and Women see Guide to Religious Ministries for Catholic Men and Women 1744
Guide to Religious Ministries for Catholic Men and Women (US) 1744
Guidebook of Catholic Hospitals see Catholic Health Association of the United States. Guidebook 1689
Guideposts (US ISSN 0017-5331) 1705
Gur-Sandesh see Gura Sandesha 1726
Gura Sandesha/Gur-Sandesh (II) 1726
Gurmat Sagar (II) 1726
Guru Nanak Commemorative Lectures (II) 1726
Gustav-Adolf-Blatt (GW ISSN 0017-5730) 1705
Gute Besserung (GW) 1705
Gute Botschaft see Fuer Heute 1732
Habinjan (NE ISSN 0017-6346) 1686, 1723
Hadashot Me ha-Chaim ha-Datiyim Be Israel (IS ISSN 0017-6508) 1723
Hadorom (US ISSN 0017-6532) 1723
Hamdard Foundation. Report (PK) 1722
Hamdard Islamicus (PK ISSN 0250-7196) 1722
Ha-Mesivta (US ISSN 0094-9701) 1689, 1723
Hamevaser (US ISSN 0017-7040) 1684, 1723
Handbook for Christian Writers see Successful Writers and Editors Guidebook 1717
Handbook of Denominations in the U.S. (US ISSN 0072-9787) 1705
Happy Day Diary (UK) 1705
Happy Times (US) 1732
Harvard Divinity Bulletin (US ISSN 0017-8047) 1684, 1705
Harvard Judaic Monographs (US) 1686, 1723
Harvard Semitic Monographs (US ISSN 0073-0637) 1690, 1705
Harvard Theological Review (US ISSN 0017-8160) 1705
Harvard Theological Studies (US ISSN 0073-0726) 1705
Harvester (UK ISSN 0017-8217) 1705
Hawaii Catholic Herald (US) 1744
Hawaiian Church Chronicle (US ISSN 0274-7154) 1732
Hawkeye (US) 1732
Hawkeye United Methodist see Hawkeye 1732
Hay Guetron (AG ISSN 0017-8640) 1753
Hayastanyaitz Yegeghetzy see Bema 1751
Healing Hand (UK ISSN 0017-8829) 1705
Heart see Coming Revolution 1752
Heartbeat (US) 1732
Heathen (UK) 1753
Hebrew Abstracts see Hebrew Studies 1690

Hebrew Christian (UK ISSN 0017-9477) *1705*
Hebrew Studies (US ISSN 0146-4094) *1690,* 1723
Hebrew Union College. Jewish Institute of Religion. Chronicle (US) *1723*
Hebrew Union College. Jewish Institute of Religion. Reporter *see* Hebrew Union College. Jewish Institute of Religion. Chronicle *1723*
Hebrew Union College Annual (US ISSN 0360-9049) *1686,* 1723
Hebrew Union College Annual Supplements (US ISSN 0275-9993) *1686,* 1723
Heerbaan *see* Wereld en Zending *1719*
Heights (New York) (US) *1689,* 1744
Heiliger Dienst (AU ISSN 0017-9620) *1705*
Hejnal Mariacki (PL ISSN 0017-9914) *1744*
Hemmets Vaen (SW ISSN 0018-0335) *1705*
Herald *see* C W I Herald *1699*
Herald of Christian Science (Danish edition: Kristen Videnskabs Herold) (US ISSN 0018-0475) *1753*
Herald of His Coming (US) *1705*
Heraldo de la Ciencia Cristiana *see* Herald of Christian Science *1753*
Heraut van de Christelijke Wetenschap *see* Herald of Christian Science *1753*
Herder Correspondence *see* Month *1746*
Herder-Korrespondenz (GW ISSN 0018-0645) *1744*
Herkenning (NE) *1705*
Hermeneutics: Studies in the History of Religion (US) *1705*
Hermeneutische Untersuchungen zur Theologie (GW ISSN 0440-7180) *1705*
Hermes (US) *1753*
The Hermetic Journal (UK ISSN 0141-6391) 1692, 1693, *1753*
Hernhutter Suriname Zending (NE) *1705*
Herold der Christlichen Wissenschaft *see* Herald of Christian Science *1753*
Herold der Wahrheit (US ISSN 0300-8851) *1753*
Herold des Kostbaren Blutes (AU ISSN 0018-0815) *1705*
Hervormd Arnhem (NE ISSN 0018-0920) *1732*
Hervormd Wageningen (NE ISSN 0018-0947) *1732*
Hervormde Gemeente Musselkanaal. Kerkblad (NE ISSN 0018-0955) *1732*
Hervormer (SA) *1732*
Heythrop Journal (UK ISSN 0018-1196) 1693, *1705*
HiCall (US ISSN 0018-120X) 1683, *1753*
Hier en Ginder (NE) *1705*
Highway (SA ISSN 0018-1684) *1732*
Hillel Gate (US ISSN 0018-1862) *1686,* 1723
Hindu (MF) *1726*
Hindu Regeneration (II) *1726*
Hindu Text Information *see* Asian Religious Studies Information *1720*
Hinduism Today (US) *1726*
His *see* His Magazine *1705*
His Magazine (US) *1705*
Hispania Sacra (SP ISSN 0018-215X) 1688, *1705*
Historians of Early Modern Europe (US ISSN 0883-3559) *1688,* 1705
Historical Footnotes (St. Louis) (US ISSN 0360-9030) *1732*
Historical Highlights (US) *1732*
Historical Intelligencer (US ISSN 0270-4919) *1688,* 1732
Historical Magazine of the Protestant Episcopal Church (US ISSN 0018-2486) *1732*
Historical Messenger (US) 1688, *1732*
Historical Society of the Church in Wales. Journal(UK) 1688, *1732*
Historical Society of the Presbyterian Church of Wales. Journal (UK) 1688, *1732*
Historiographer (US ISSN 0018-2591) 1688, *1732*
History of Religions (US ISSN 0018-2710) 1688, *1705*
Hogar Cristiano (US ISSN 0018-3229) *1732*
Hoja Parroquial (SP) *1705*
Hoja Trinitaria (SP) *1744*
Hokke Bunka Kenkyu *see* Institute for the Comprehensive Study of Lotus Sutra. Journal *1726*
Holos Spasytelya *see* Redeemer's Voice *1713*
Holy Land (IS) 1689, 1722, 1723, *1744*
Holy Land *see* Terra Santa *1717*
Holy Places of Palestine (IS) 1689, *1705,* 1758
Home and Family (UK ISSN 0018-3946) *1705*
Home Leaguer (CN) 1753, *1758*
Home Life (US ISSN 0018-4071) 1683, *1732*
Home Missions *see* Missions U S A *1734*
Homebringing Mission of Jesus Christ *see* Universal Life-The Inner Religion *1719*
Homelife (PH ISSN 0115-2971) *1687,* 1744
Homiletic and Pastoral Review (US ISSN 0018-4268) *1744*
Homiletica (SP ISSN 0439-4208) *1705*
Homiletische Monatshefte (GW ISSN 0018-4276) *1705*
Homily Helps (US) *1705*
Homily Service (US ISSN 0732-1872) *1705*
Homme Nouveau (FR ISSN 0018-4322) *1705*
Hong Kong Catholic Church Directory/Hsiang-Kang T'ien Chu Chiao Shou T'se (HK ISSN 0073-3210) *1744*
Hopeful Day *see* Getroster Tag *1732*
Horizon (Neptune) (US) *1687,* 1732
Horizons (Villanova) (US ISSN 0360-9669) *1744*
Horizons in Biblical Theology (US ISSN 0195-9085) *1705*
Houvast (NE) *1732*
Hrvatski Katolicki Glasnik (US ISSN 0018-6910) *1744*
Hsiang-Kang T'ien Chu Chiao Shou T'se *see* Hong Kong Catholic Church Directory *1744*
Huguenot Trails (CN ISSN 0441-6910) 1687, *1689,* 1732
Huis van Geluk *see* Path of Truth *1712*
Human Development (US ISSN 0197-3096) *1695,* 1732
Human Life Issues (US) *1682,* 1757
Humanist in Canada (CN ISSN 0018-7402) *1693,* 1753
Humanistic Judaism (US ISSN 0441-4195) *1723*
Humanitas *see* Studies in Formative Spirituality *1717*
Humanities, Christianity and Culture (JA ISSN 0073-3938) *1705*
Huron Church News (CN ISSN 0018-7917) *1732*
Hymn (US ISSN 0018-8271) *1691,* 1705
I C F Quarterly (Industrial Christian Fellowship) (UK ISSN 0018-8913) *1753*
I D E A (IT) *1732*
I Discover the Bible *see* Discover the Bible *1743*
I F M A News (Interdenomination Foreign Mission Association of North America, Inc.) (US ISSN 0018-9723) *1705*
I F O R Report *see* Reconciliation International *1713*
I M *see* Italia Missionaria *1683*
I R F Newsletter (International Religious Foundation, Inc.) (US) *1732*
I S Annual (Inter-School Christian Fellowship) (UK ISSN 0261-1325) *1732*
I S K C O N World Review (International Society for Krishna Consciousness) (US ISSN 0748-2280) *1726*
Icengelo (ZA) *1705*
ICO-Iconographisk Post (SW ISSN 0106-1348) *1682,* 1705
Iconoclast (US) *1706*
Iconographiske Post *see* ICO-Iconographisk Post *1682*
Iconography of Religions (NE) *1706*
Idea Ink (US) *1690,* 1744
Idisze Szriftn/Jewish Cultural Affairs (PL ISSN 0019-1507) *1690,* 1723
Ievanhel's'kyi Holos (CN ISSN 0383-2538) 1686, *1753*
Igaku to Fukuin *see* Medicine and Gospel *1691*
Igeret (US) *1686,* 1723
Iglesia de Sevilla (SP) *1744*
Iglesia Evangelica del Rio de la Plata. Revista Parroquial (AG ISSN 0019-1671) *1732*
Ija Webonere (TZ ISSN 0019-171X) *1732*
Iliff Review (US ISSN 0019-1795) *1706*
Illinois Baptist (US ISSN 0019-1868) *1732*
Im Lande der Bibel (GW ISSN 0019-2597) *1706*
Imagenes de la Fe (SP) *1745*
Images du Mois (FR) *1745*
Imbongi (SA ISSN 0019-2716) *1684,* 1706
Imbongi Yenkosi (SA ISSN 0378-4088) *1732*
Imboniselo (SA ISSN 0019-008X) *1753*
Immanuel (IS ISSN 0302-8127) *1706*
Immortality Newsletter *see* Theologia 21 *1717*
Impact (Wheaton) (US ISSN 0019-2821) *1732*
Impacts (FR ISSN 0019-2899) 1689, *1745*
In Common (US ISSN 0363-5058) *1706*
In de Rechte Straat/En la Calle Recta (NE ISSN 0019-3151) *1706*
In de Waagschaal (NE ISSN 0019-316X) 1694, *1706*
In Famiglia (IT ISSN 0019-3186) *1745*
In Gang Fun Arbet: Yidish Un Mizrakh Eyropeishe Yidishe Shtudies *see* Working Papers in Yiddish and East European Jewish Studies *1687*
In Other Words (US) 1690, *1706*
In Season (US) *1732*
In Step *see* Lutherans in Step *1734*
In-Touch (US) 1683, *1732*
In Touch (Pinner) (UK ISSN 0019-3283) *1706*
Independent Voice (US) *1706*
Index of Articles on Jewish Studies/Reshimat Ma'amarim Be-Mada'e Ha-Yahadut (IS ISSN 0073-5817) 1681, *1721*
Index to Periodicals of the Church of Jesus Christ of Latter-Day Saints. Cumulative Edition (US ISSN 0073-5981) *1721*
Index to Religious Periodical Literature *see* Religion Index One: Periodicals *1721*
India Cultures (II) *1706*
India Cultures Quarterly *see* India Cultures *1706*
Indian Church History Review (II ISSN 0019-4530) 1688, *1706*
Indian Journal of Theology (II ISSN 0019-5685) *1706*
Indian Life (CN ISSN 0226-9317) *1686,* 1753
Indian Lutheran (II) *1732*
Indian Witness (II ISSN 0019-6487) *1732*
Indogaku Bunkkyogaku Kenkyu *see* Journal of Indian and Buddhist Studies *1726*
Indonesia. Directorate General of Protestant Affairs. Annual Report/Indonesia. Direktorat Jenderal Bimbingan Masyarakat Kristen/Protestan Laporan Tahunan (IO) *1733*
Indonesia. Direktorat Jenderal Bimbingan Masyarakat Kristen/Protestan Laporan Tahunan *see* Indonesia. Directorate General of Protestant Affairs. Annual Report *1733*
Industrial Christian Fellowship Quarterly *see* I C F Quarterly *1753*
Information Bulletin for Catholic Rural Organizations (IT) 1681, *1745*
Information Juive (FR ISSN 0020-0107) *1686,* 1723, 1757
Informationen zum Religionsunterricht (GW) *1685,* 1706
Informations Catholiques Internationales *see* Actualite Religieuse dan le Monde *1739*
Informatore di Urio (IT) 1685, *1745*
Inland Africa *see* A I M International *1695*
Inland Register (US ISSN 0020-1510) *1745*
Inner Paths (US ISSN 0149-6026) *1693,* 1706
Innes Review (UK ISSN 0020-157X) 1688, *1745*
Inqabayokulinda (SA ISSN 0019-0241) *1753*
Inquirer (UK ISSN 0020-1723) *1706*
Insight (Hagerstown) (US ISSN 0020-1944) *1733*
Insights (Springfield) (US ISSN 0164-7709) *1706*
Inspiration (DK ISSN 0107-959X) *1706*
Institut Catholique de Paris. Annuaire (FR) *1745*
Institut fuer Europaeische Geschichte, Mainz. Veroeffentlichungen. Abteilung Universalgeschichte und Abteilung fuer Abendlaendische Religionsgeschichte (GW) *1706*
Institut fuer Europaeische Geschichte, Mainz. Veroeffentlichungen. Abteilung Universitaetsgeschichte und Abteilung fuer Abendlaendische Religionsphilosophie *see* Institut fuer Europaeische Geschichte, Mainz. Veroeffentlichungen. Abteilung Universalgeschichte und Abteilung fuer Abendlaendische Religionsgeschichte *1706*
Institut fuer Europaeische Geschichte, Mainz. Vortraege. Abteilung Universalgeschichte und Abteilung fuer Abendlaendische Religionsgeschichte (GW) *1706*
Institut fuer Europaeische Geschichte, Mainz. Vortraege. Abteilung Universalgeschichte und Abteilung fuer Abendlaendische Religionsphilosophie *see* Institut fuer Europaeische Geschichte, Mainz. Vortraege. Abteilung Universalgeschichte und Abteilung fuer Abendlaendische Religionsgeschichte *1706*
Institute for Encyclopedia of Human Ideas on Ultimate Reality and Meaning. Newsletter *see* Ultimate Reality and Meaning *1694*
Institute for the Comprehensive Study of Lotus Sutra. Journal/Hokke Bunka Kenkyu (JA) *1726*
Institute of Mennonite Studies Series (US ISSN 0073-9456) *1753*
Instituto Superior de Estudios Eclesiasticos. Libro Anual (MX) *1706*
Instituto Teologico del Uruguay. Cuadernos (UY) *1706*
Instrumenta Lexicologia Latina. Series A & B (BE) *1684,* 1706
Integral Yoga (US ISSN 0161-1380) *1753*
Interaction (St. Louis) (US ISSN 0020-5117) *1684,* 1733
Interchange (AT ISSN 0047-0430) *1706*
Interchange (New York) (US) *1733*
Intercom (CN ISSN 0383-6061) *1733*
Intercom (New York, 1960?) (US) *1723,* 1757
Intercon (UK ISSN 0020-5265) *1706*
Interdenomination Foreign Mission Association of North America, Inc. News *see* I F M A News *1705*
Interdenominational Theological Center, Atlanta. Journal (US ISSN 0092-6558) *1706*
Interdependence (US ISSN 0362-4668) *1706*
Interface (BE ISSN 0770-4720) *1745*
Interlit (US ISSN 0020-5575) 1684, *1706*
Intermountain Jewish News (US ISSN 0047-0511) *1686,* 1723
International Association of Buddhist Studies. Journal (US ISSN 0193-600X) *1726*
International Association of Liberal Religious Women. Newsletter (US) *1706*
International Bibliography of the History of Religions/Bibliographie International de l'Histoire des Religions (NE) *1721*
International Buddhist Center. Monthly Guide (US) *1726*
International Bulletin of Missionary Research (US ISSN 0272-6122) *1690,* 1733
International Catholic Movement for Intellectual Cultural Affairs. Proceedings of the Plenary Assembly *see* Pax Romana *1748*
International Christian University. Publications IV-B. Christianity and Culture *see* Humanities, Christianity and Culture *1705*
International Conference for the Sociology of Religion (CH ISSN 0074-297X) *1706,* 1757
International Eucharist Congress. Proceedings (CI ISSN 0074-5782) *1745*
International Fellowship of Reconciliation Reconciliation International *see* Reconciliation International *1713*
International Journal for Philosophy of Religion (NE ISSN 0020-7047) 1693, *1706*
International Lesson Annual (US) *1706*
International Pentecostal Holiness Advocate (US ISSN 0031-4900) *1753*
International Religious Foundation, Inc. Newsletter *see* I R F Newsletter *1732*
International Review of Mission (SZ ISSN 0020-8582) *1706*
International Society for Krishna Consciousness World Review *see* I S K C O N World Review *1726*
International Union of Liberal Christian Women. Newsletter *see* International Association of Liberal Religious Women. Newsletter *1706*
Internationale Bibellektionen (US) *1706*
Internationale Katholieke Informatie (BE) *1745*
Internationale Katholische Zeitschrift (GW) *1745*
Internationale Kirchliche Zeitschrift (SZ ISSN 0020-9252) *1706*
Interpretation (Richmond) (US ISSN 0020-9643) *1706*
Interprete (US ISSN 0162-4342) *1733*
Interpreter (US ISSN 0020-9678) *1733*
Inter-School & Inter-Varsity Christian Fellowship (JM ISSN 0020-5087) *1706*
Inter-School & Inter-Varsity Christian Fellowship of the West Indies *see* Inter-School & Inter-Varsity Christian Fellowship *1706*
Inter-School Christian Fellowship Annual *see* I S Annual *1732*
Invitation (US) *1722*
Inward Light (US ISSN 0021-0250) 1695, *1753*
Irenikon (BE ISSN 0021-0978) *1706*
Irish Baptist Historical Society. Journal (UK ISSN 0075-0727) *1733*
Irish Biblical Association. Proceedings (IE ISSN 0332-4427) *1706*
Irish Catholic (IE) *1745*
Irish Catholic Directory (UK ISSN 0075-0735) *1745*
Irish Messenger of the Sacred Heart *see* Sacred Heart Messenger *1749*
Irish Theological Quarterly (IE ISSN 0021-1400) *1706*
Iskcon Review (US ISSN 0886-6910) *1753*
Iskra (CN ISSN 0021-1761) 1687, 1693, *1706*
Der Islam (GW ISSN 0021-1818) 1688, *1692,* 1722
Islam (NE ISSN 0021-180X) 1692, *1722*
Al Islam (RE ISSN 0151-7163) *1722*
Islam (IT) *1722*
Islam Akastirmalari Merkezi Dergisi (TU) *1722*
Islam and the Modern Age (II ISSN 0021-1826) 1682, 1691, *1722*
Islam and the Modern World (BG ISSN 0379-4032) *1722*
Islam Aujourd'hui *see* Islam Today *1722*
Islam International (US ISSN 8755-8912) *1694,* 1722
Islam Tetkikleri Enstitusu Dergisi *see* Islam Akastirmalari Merkezi Dergisi *1722*
Islam Today/Islam Aujourd'hui (MR) *1722*
Islamic Book Review Index (GW ISSN 0724-2263) *1721*
Islamic Horizons (US ISSN 8756-2367) *1722*
Islamic Order (PK) *1722*
Islamic Studies (PK) *1722*
Israel Book News (IS ISSN 0333-953X) 1686, *1695,* 1723
Israel Book World *see* Israel Book News *1695*
Israel Report (IS) *1686,* 1723
Issue (CN) *1753*
Issues of the American Council for Judaism *see* American Council for Judaism. Issues *1723*
Istina (FR ISSN 0021-2423) *1706*
Istituto di Scienze Religiose in Trento. Pubblicazioni (IT) *1745*
Italia Missionaria (IT ISSN 0021-2806) *1683,* 1745
Itinerarium (PO ISSN 0021-3209) 1688, 1693, *1745*
It's Our World (US) *1683,* 1745
Ius Canonicum (SP ISSN 0021-325X) *1706*
Iustitia (IT ISSN 0021-3268) *1689,* 1745
J A M (Jesus and Me) (UK) *1683,* 1706
J P (FI ISSN 0781-7177) *1683,* 1706
J P Joka Poika *see* J P *1683*
J S A C Grapevine (Joint Strategy and Action Committee) (US) 1706, *1757*
J T A Community News Reporter (Jewish Telegraphic Agency) (US) *1694,* 1723
J T A Daily News Bulletin (US ISSN 0021-3772) *1686,* 1723
J W B Circle (National Jewish Welfare Board) (US ISSN 0021-3780) *1723,* 1757
Ja, Das Wort Fuer Alle (GW ISSN 0342-6513) *1706*
Jaarboek van de Christelijke Gereformeerde Kerken in Nederland (NE) *1753*
Jacksonville Poetry Quarterly (US) *1691,* 1706
Jahrbuch der Erzdioese von Wien (AU) *1745*
Jahrbuch des Instituts fuer Christliche Sozialwissenschaften *see* Jahrbuch fuer Christliche Sozialwissenschaften *1757*
Jahrbuch fuer Antike und Christentum (GW ISSN 0075-2541) *1706*

Jahrbuch fuer Berlin-Brandenburgische Kirchengeschichte (GW ISSN 0075-2568) *1706*
Jahrbuch fuer Brandenburgische Kirchengeschichte *see* Jahrbuch fuer Berlin-Brandenburgische Kirchengeschichte *1706*
Jahrbuch fuer Christliche Sozialwissenschaften (GW ISSN 0075-2584) 1706, *1757*
Jahrbuch fuer die Kirche von Wien *see* Jahrbuch der Erzdioese von Wien *1745*
Jahrbuch fuer Liturgik und Hymnologie (GW ISSN 0075-2681) 1691, *1707*
Jahrbuch fuer Schlesische Kirchengeschichte (GW ISSN 0075-2762) *1707*
Jahrbuch Mission (GW) *1707*
J'Aime Lire (FR) 1683, *1707*
Jain Journal (II ISSN 0021-4043) *1726*
Jamaica Churchman (JM ISSN 0047-1720) *1733*
Japan Christian Activity News (JA ISSN 0021-4353) *1707*
Japan Christian Quarterly (JA ISSN 0021-4361) *1707*
Japan Harvest (JA ISSN 0021-440X) *1707*
Japan Missionary Bulletin (JA ISSN 0021-4531) *1707*
Japanese Journal of Religious Studies (JA ISSN 0304-1042) 1692, *1707*
Japanese Religions (JA ISSN 0448-8954) *1707*
Javeriana (CK ISSN 0021-5562) *1707*
Je Crois (CN ISSN 0021-5740) *1745*
Jednota Kalendar *see* Kalendar Jednota *1745*
Jeevadhara (II) *1745*
Jehovah's Witnesses Yearbook (US ISSN 0075-3602) *1753*
Jerusalem Post Literary Supplement *see* Israel Book News *1695*
Jesuit Bulletin (US) *1745*
Jesus and Me *see* J A M *1683*
Jesus Caritas (IT) *1745*
Jesus Maestro (SP) *1683,* 1707
Jet Cadet *see* R-A-D-A-R *1683*
Jeugd in Aktie *see* Aktie *1696*
Jevrejski Pregled (YU ISSN 0021-6240) *1686,* 1723
Jewish Affairs (US ISSN 0021-6305) *1694,* 1723
Jewish Book Annual (US ISSN 0075-3726) *1723*
Jewish Braille Review (US ISSN 0021-6321) *1682,* 1723
Jewish Chronicle (New York) (US) *1690,* 1723
Jewish Civic Press (US ISSN 0021-6348) *1686,* 1723
Jewish Collegiate Observer *see* Kol Yavneh *1724*
Jewish Cultural Affairs *see* Idisze Szriftn *1690*
Jewish Current Events (US ISSN 0021-6380) 1683, 1684, *1686,* 1723
Jewish Education (US ISSN 0021-6429) *1684,* 1723
Jewish Guardian (US) 1686, *1723*
Jewish Historical Society of England. Annual Report and Accounts for the Session (UK ISSN 0306-7998) *1723*
Jewish Historical Society of England. Report and Balance Sheet *see* Jewish Historical Society of England. Annual Report and Accounts for the Session *1723*
Jewish Historical Society of England. Transactions(UK) *1723*
Jewish Home *see* Yiddishe Heim *1725*
Jewish Journal of Sociology (UK ISSN 0021-6534) 1724, *1757*
Jewish Language Review (IS ISSN 0333-8347) 1686, *1690,* 1691, 1724
Jewish Law Annual (NE) 1689, *1724*
Jewish Press (Brooklyn) (US ISSN 0021-6674) *1686,* 1724
Jewish Press Features (US) 1686, *1689,* 1724
Jewish Proclaimer (US) 1686, *1724*
Jewish Quarterly Review (US ISSN 0021-6682) *1724*
Jewish Review (1983) (UK) *1724*
Jewish Science Interpreter (US) *1724*
Jewish Social Studies (US ISSN 0021-6704) 1686, 1724, *1757*
Jewish Standard (CN ISSN 0021-6739) *1686,* 1687, 1724
Jewish Telegraph (UK ISSN 0021-6755) *1686,* 1724
Jewish Telegraphic Agency Community News Reporter *see* J T A Community News Reporter *1694*
Jewish Tradition (SA) 1686, *1724*
Jewish Transcript (US ISSN 0021-678X) *1686,* 1724
Jewish Voice (US ISSN 0021-6828) *1724*
Jewish Weekly News (US ISSN 0021-6860) *1686,* 1724
Jewish Year Book (UK ISSN 0075-3769) *1724*
Jews for Jesus Newsletter (US ISSN 0740-5901) *1724*
Jihad (IT) *1722*
Joedisk Orientering (DK ISSN 0021-7131) *1686,* 1724
Joedisk Samfund *see* Joedisk Orientering *1686*
John Milton Magazine (US) *1682,* 1707
John Milton Sunday School Quarterly (US) 1682, *1683,* 1707
John Milton Talking Book (US ISSN 0021-7220) *1682,* 1707
Joint Strategy and Action Committee Grapevine *see* J S A C Grapevine *1757*
Jong Dae *see* Young Ideas *1756*
Jonge Kampvechter *see* Wyzer *1756*
Jonge Kerk (NE ISSN 0021-7395) 1683, *1707*
Josephinum Newsletter (US ISSN 0021-759X) *1745*
Josephinum Review *see* Josephinum Newsletter *1745*
Josephite Harvest (US ISSN 0021-7603) *1707*
Jottings (US) *1682,* 1753
Journal des Communautes *see* Information Juive *1686*
Journal for the Scientific Study of Religion (US ISSN 0021-8294) *1707*
Journal for the Study of Judaism *see* Journal for the Study of Judaism in the Persian, Hellenistic and Roman Period *1724*
Journal for the Study of Judaism in the Persian, Hellenistic and Roman Period (NE) *1724*
Journal for the Study of the New Testament (UK ISSN 0142-064X) *1707*
Journal for the Study of the New Testament. Supplement Series (UK ISSN 0143-5108) *1707*
Journal for the Study of the Old Testament (UK ISSN 0309-0892) *1707*
Journal for the Study of the Old Testament. Supplement Series (UK ISSN 0309-0787) *1707*
Journal of Adventist Education (US ISSN 0021-8480) *1753*
Journal of Bible and Religion *see* American Academy of Religion. Journal *1696*
Journal of Biblical Literature (US ISSN 0021-9231) *1707*
Journal of Chinese Religions (US) 1692, *1726*
Journal of Christian Education *see* Christian Education Journal *1700*
Journal of Christian Education of the African Methodist Episcopal Church (US) 1684, *1733*
Journal of Christian Nursing (US ISSN 0743-2550) *1691,* 1707
Journal of Christian Reconstruction (US ISSN 0360-1420) *1707*
Journal of Church and State (US ISSN 0021-969X) 1689, 1694, *1707*
Journal of Comparative Sociology & Religion (CN ISSN 0709-3519) 1707, *1757*
Journal of Dharma (II) *1707*
Journal of Ecclesiastical History (UK ISSN 0022-0469) 1688, *1707*
Journal of Ecumenical Studies (US ISSN 0022-0558) *1707*
Journal of Health Care Chaplaincy (US ISSN 0885-4726) *1694,* 1707
Journal of Indian and Buddhist Studies/Indogaku Bunkkyogaku Kenkyu (JA ISSN 0019-4344) *1726*
Journal of Jewish Art (NE ISSN 0160-208X) *1682,* 1724
Journal of Jewish Lore and Philosophy *see* Hebrew Union College Annual *1686*
Journal of Jewish Music and Liturgy (US ISSN 0197-0100) *1691,* 1724
Journal of Jewish Studies (UK ISSN 0022-2097) *1724*
Journal of Law and Religion (US) *1689,* 1707
Journal of Mormon History (US ISSN 0094-7342) *1753*
Journal of Nichiren Buddhism (US) *1726*
Journal of Pastoral Care (US ISSN 0022-3409) 1695, *1707*
Journal of Pastoral Practice (US) *1707*
Journal of Pastoral Psychotherapy (US ISSN 0886-5477) *1695,* 1707
Journal of Presbyterian History *see* American Presbyterians: Journal of Presbyterian History *1728*
Journal of Psychology and Christianity (US ISSN 0147-7978) *1695,* 1707
Journal of Psychology and Judaism (US ISSN 0700-9801) *1695,* 1724
Journal of Psychology and Theology (US ISSN 0091-6471) 1695, *1707*
Journal of Reform Judaism (US ISSN 0149-712X) *1724*
Journal of Religion (US ISSN 0022-4189) *1707*
Journal of Religion and Health (US ISSN 0022-4197) *1707*
Journal of Religion and the Applied Behavioral Sciences (US) *1695,* 1707
Journal of Religion in Africa/Religion en Afrique (NE ISSN 0022-4200) *1707*
Journal of Religious Education *see* Journal of Christian Education of the African Methodist Episcopal Church *1733*
Journal of Religious Education of the African Methodist Episcopal Church *see* Journal of Christian Education of the African Methodist Episcopal Church *1733*
Journal of Religious Ethics (US ISSN 0384-9694) *1707*
Journal of Religious History (AT ISSN 0022-4227) 1688, *1707*
Journal of Religious Studies (II ISSN 0047-2735) *1707*
Journal of Religious Studies (US ISSN 0193-3604) *1707*
Journal of Religious Thought (US ISSN 0022-4235) *1707*
Journal of Semitic Studies (UK ISSN 0022-4480) 1690, 1722, *1724*
Journal of Sikh Studies (II) *1692,* 1726
Journal of Studies in the Bhagavadgita (AT ISSN 0706-6449) *1726*
Journal of Supervision and Training in Ministry (US ISSN 0160-7774) *1707*
Journal of the Interdenominational Theological Center *see* Interdenominational Theological Center, Atlanta. Journal *1706*
Journal of the Moscow Patriarchate *see* Russkaya Pravoslavnaya Tserkov'. Moskovskaya Patriarkhiya. Zhurnal *1715*
Journal of Theological Studies (UK ISSN 0022-5185) *1707*
Journal of Theology (US ISSN 0361-1906) *1733*
Journal of Theology for Southern Africa (SA ISSN 0047-2867) *1708*
Journal of True Education *see* Journal of Adventist Education *1753*
Journal of Women and Religion (US) 1708, *1758*
Jovenes Biblico (Student Edition) (US) 1685, *1733*
Joy & Light (UK ISSN 0022-5703) *1753*
Joyful Woman (US ISSN 0164-4882) *1733,* 1758
Judaica (SZ ISSN 0022-572X) *1724*
Judaica Bohemiae (CS ISSN 0022-5738) *1686,* 1708
Judaica Book News (US ISSN 0022-5754) 1686, *1695,* 1724
Judaism (US ISSN 0022-5762) 1690, *1724*
Juifs Celebres *see* Sir Moses Montefiore Collections des Juifs Celebres *1716*
Junge Gemeinde (AU ISSN 0022-6289) 1683, *1708*
Junge Kirche (GW ISSN 0022-6319) *1708,* 1757
Jungscharhelfer (GW ISSN 0022-6467) 1683, *1708*
Junior Life (US) 1683, *1708*
Junior Teacher *see* Bible Searchers: Teacher *1729*
Junior Teaching Pictures *see* Teaching Pictures for Bible Searchers *1737*
Junior Trails (US ISSN 0022-6718) 1683, *1753*
Justice et Service *see* La Vie Oecumenique *1719*
JustPeace (UK ISSN 0306-7645) 1694, *1708*
Jusur (US ISSN 0888-9007) *1689,* 1722
K M - Die Katholischen Missionen (GW) *1745*
K S Bulletin (Foreningen af Katolske Skoler i Danmark) (DK ISSN 0109-3886) *1685,* 1745
Kadima (YU ISSN 0022-748X) *1690,* 1724
Kairos (AU ISSN 0022-7757) *1708*
Kaiserswerther Mitteilungen (GW ISSN 0022-779X) *1708*
Kalendar Jednota (US) *1745*
Kalyan (II ISSN 0022-8028) *1708*
Kandelaar (NE ISSN 0022-8354) *1684,* 1708
Karat *see* Cursillo *1702*
Kashrus (US) 1686, *1724*
Kashrus Newsletter *see* Kashrus *1724*
Kashrut Guide (SA) 1686, *1724*
Kasseler Sonntagsblatt (GW ISSN 0022-9245) *1708*
Katallagete (US ISSN 0022-9288) 1694, *1708*
Kateri (CN ISSN 0315-8020) 1682, *1708*
Katholiek Archief *see* Archief van de Kerken *1696*
Katholiek Artsenblad *see* Metamedica *1691*
Katholiek Documentatie Centrum. Archieven (NE) *1745*
Katholiek Documentatie Centrum. Bibliografieen (NE) *1721*
Katholiek Documentatie Centrum. Jaarboek (NE) *1745*
Katholiek Documentatie Centrum. Publicaties (NE) *1745*
Katholische Frauenbewegung Oesterreichs. Fuehrungsblatt (AU ISSN 0022-9377) *1745*
Katholische Gedanke *see* Renovatio *1748*
Katholischen Missionen *see* K M - Die Katholischen Missionen *1745*
Katholischer Digest (GW ISSN 0047-3294) *1745*
Katholisches Leben und Kirchenreform im Zeitalter der Glaubensspaltung (GW ISSN 0170-7302) *1745*
Katolicki Uniwersytet Lubelski. Wydzial Teologiczno-Kanoniczny. Rozprawy (PL) *1745*
Katolicki Uniwersytet Lubelski. Zeszyty Naukowe(PL ISSN 0044-4405) 1684, *1745*
Katolicky Sokol (US) *1686,* 1745
Katolikus Magyarok Vasarnapja (US) 1686, 1708, *1745*
Katolikus Szemle (IT ISSN 0022-9431) *1745*
Katolsk Orientering (DK) *1745*
Katolski Posol (GE ISSN 0138-2543) *1745*
Katorikku Kenkyu (JA ISSN 0387-3005) *1745*
Keeping Posted (US ISSN 0022-9636) *1724*
Keeping Posted with N C S Y (National Conference of Synagogue Youth) (US ISSN 0022-9644) 1683, *1724*
Keeping You Posted (US ISSN 0361-8668) *1733*
Kehilwenyane (SA ISSN 0022-9687) *1745*
Kerala Sabha (II ISSN 0047-3367) *1753*
Kerem Shlomo (US) *1724*
Kerk en Vrede (NE) 1694, *1708*
Kerkblad (SA ISSN 0023-0596) *1733*
Kerkbode (SA) *1733*
Kerkbode van Gereformeerde Kerken in Noord en Zuid-Holland *see* Kerkbode van Nederlands Gereformeerde Kerken *1708*
Kerkbode van Nederlands Gereformeerde Kerken (NE) *1708*
Kerugma (NE ISSN 0023-0685) *1708*
Kerygma (CN ISSN 0023-0693) *1708*
Kerygma (US) *1708*
Kesho *see* Afrika Ya Kesho *1696*
Key to Christian Education (US ISSN 0023-0839) *1684,* 1708
Keys of Peter (UK) *1745*
Kierkegaardiana (DK ISSN 0075-6032) *1693,* 1708
Kind en Zondag (NE ISSN 0023-1444) *1708*
Kinderbrief aus der Weltmission *see* Bremer Missionsschiff *1698*
Kindergottesdienst/Lass mich Hoeren (GW ISSN 0341-7190) *1708*
Kingdom Digest (US ISSN 0023-1614) *1708*
Kingdom Overseas *see* Now (London, 1970) *1735*
Kinship (US ISSN 0023-1703) 1708, *1757*
Kiongozi/Leader (TZ) *1745*
Kirche (AU ISSN 0023-1789) *1733*
Kirche Bunt (AU) *1708*
Kirche in Marburg (GW) 1708, *1745*
Kirche und Konfession (GW) *1708*
Kirche und Recht (AU ISSN 0259-0735) *1689,* 1708
Kirchenblatt fuer die Reformierte Schweiz: (SZ ISSN 0023-1797) *1733*
Kirchenmusikalische Nachrichten (GW) *1691,* 1708
Der Kirchenmusiker (GW ISSN 0023-1819) *1692,* 1708
Kirchensaenger *see* Kleine Chorzeitung *1692*
Kirchliches Amtsblatt fuer das Bistum Essen (GW ISSN 0023-1827) *1708*
Kirke og Kultur (NO ISSN 0023-186X) 1690, *1708*
Kirkefondets Aarbog (DK ISSN 0107-9824) *1708*
Kirkehistoriske Samlinger (DK ISSN 0450-3171) *1708*
Kiryat Sefer (IS ISSN 0023-1851) *1682,* 1724
Kivun (AT) *1724*
Kizito (UG ISSN 0023-1975) *1683,* 1708
Klar und Wahr *see* Plain Truth (Pasadena) *1755*
Kleine Chorzeitung (SZ ISSN 0023-2068) *1692,* 1745
Kleronomia (GR) *1753*
Koebenhavns Universitet. Institut for Religionshistorie. Skrifter (DK ISSN 0105-4821) *1708*
Koebenhavnske Kirkefondets Aarbog *see* Kirkefondets Aarbog *1708*
Kol ha-T'nuah/Voice of the Movement (US) *1686,* 1724
Kol Yavneh (US) *1724*
Koleinu (UK) 1683, 1694, *1724*
Kolenu (US) 1686, *1724*
Kontakt Drei und Zwanzig (AU ISSN 0023-3676) *1745*
Kontinente *see* Herold des Kostbaren Blutes *1705*
Kontraste Impuls (GW ISSN 0023-3749) *1745*
Kosher Directory (US) *1686,* 1724
Kosmon Unity (UK) *1753*
Kracht van Omhoog (NE ISSN 0023-4389) *1708*
Kraft fuer den Tag (GW) *1708*
Krestanska Revue (CS ISSN 0023-4613) *1708*
Der Kriegsruf (GW) *1733*
Krishnamurti Foundation. Bulletin (II ISSN 0047-3693) *1726*
Kristaus Karaliaus Laivas/Ship of Christ the King (US ISSN 0023-477X) *1745*
Kristen Vetenskaps Herold (ISSN 0145-7543) *see* Herald of Christian Science *1753*
Kruistocht (NE) *1708*
Kundalini (II) *1708*
Kusegongbo (KO) *1708*
Kuunika (MW) *1733*
Kvaekartidskrift (SW ISSN 0345-6005) *1753*
Kvakera Esperantisto (UK ISSN 0023-5814) *1708*
Kyriakatika Nea *see* Greek Sunday News *1753*
Kyriokos *see* U U W F Journal *1758*
Kyrkofoerfattningar (SW ISSN 0023-6136) *1708*
Kyrkohistorisk Aarsskrift (SW ISSN 0085-2619) *1708*
Kyrkomusikernas Tidning (SW ISSN 0281-286X) *1692,* 1708
L F B Documentation. Report (GW ISSN 0174-1764) *1733*
L I R S Bulletin (Lutheran Council in the U.S.A., Department of Information and Refugee Services) (US) *1733*
L I R S Information Bulletin *see* L I R S Bulletin *1733*
Laerarinnornas Missionsfoerening. Meddelande till L M F. *see* Laerarnas Missionsfoerening. Meddelande till L M F *1708*
Laerarnas Missionsfoerening. Meddelande till L M F. (SW ISSN 0345-7842) *1708*
Lamishpaha (US) *1690,* 1724
Land Aktuell (GW ISSN 0340-7837) 1681, *1694,* 1745
Last Day Messenger (US ISSN 0023-8635) *1708*
Lateranum (VC) *1708*

Latinamerica Press (PE) *1708,* 1757
Latinamerica Press *see* Noticias Aliadas *1711*
Latter - Day Sentinel (US) *1753*
Laughing Man (US ISSN 0363-1664) *1693,* 1708
Laurentianum (IT ISSN 0023-902X) *1745*
Laval Theologique et Philosophique (CN ISSN 0023-9054) 1693, *1708*
Law & Justice (UK) *1689,* 1693, 1708
Laymen's Movement Review *see* Catalogue of Conferences, Seminars, Workshop *1699*
Leader *see* Kiongozi *1745*
Leaders' Digest (US) *1686,* 1757
Leadership (UG ISSN 0047-424X) *1708*
Leaflets of St. Francis *see* Listy Sv. Frantiska *1745*
Learning for Living *see* British Journal of Religious Education *1698*
Leben (SZ) *1708*
Lebendiges Zeugnis (GW ISSN 0023-9941) *1745*
Lebone la Kgalalelo (SA) *1753*
Lebone la Kgalalelo Isibani Sobu Ngcwele *see* Lebone la Kgalalelo *1753*
Lectures on the History of Religions. New Series (US ISSN 0075-8531) *1708*
Legioen van Maria (NE ISSN 0024-0427) *1708*
Lengo (UK) *1708*
Leo Baeck Institute. Year Book (UK ISSN 0075-8744) 1688, *1724*
Leprosy Mission, London. Annual Report (UK ISSN 0075-8809) *1708*
Lerins (FR) *1708*
Lesotho Catholic Directory (LO) *1745*
Letter from Taize (FR ISSN 0750-3695) *1753*
Levant Morgenland (FR ISSN 0024-1490) 1692, *1708*
Levend Woord/Living Word (NE ISSN 0024-1547) *1753*
Levenswoorden (NE) *1708*
Lexington Theological Quarterly (US ISSN 0160-8770) *1708*
Liberal Catholic (UK ISSN 0024-1792) *1745*
Liberia Baptist Missionary and Educational Convention. Yearbook (LB) *1733*
Liberty (Washington, 1906) (US ISSN 0024-2055) *1709*
Librarians' Christian Fellowship Newsletter (UK ISSN 0308-5473) *1690,* 1695, 1733
Library of Jewish Law and Ethics (US) *1724*
Library of Philosophy and Religion (UK) *1693,* 1709
Licht und Leben (GW ISSN 0047-4584) *1709*
Lichtentaler Pfarrnachrichten (AU) *1745*
Lichthoeve (NE) *1709,* 1757
Lichthoeve-Kinderwerk *see* Lichthoeve *1709*
Lieb Frauen Bote (IT) *1745*
Lien Entre Meres et Peres de Pretres (FR ISSN 0024-2926) *1745*
Liesinger Pfarrblatt *see* Kontakt Drei und Zwanzig *1745*
Life and Work (UK ISSN 0024-306X) *1733*
Life Renewed *see* Obnovljeni Zivot *1711*
Die Ligdraer (SA ISSN 0024-3272) *1733*
Light *see* Goleuad *1732*
Light (London, 1969) (UK ISSN 0047-4657) *1709*
Light and Life *see* Evangel *1731*
Light in the East News *see* Dein Reich Komme *1702*
Light of Life (II) *1709*
Light of Pandrimalai (II) *1726*
Lightbearer (UK ISSN 0024-3396) *1709*
Lighted Pathway (US ISSN 0737-8173) *1683,* 1733
Ligstraal/Lehlasedi (SA ISSN 0024-0575) *1733*
Ligstraal/Umsebe/Umtha (SA ISSN 0024-3442) *1733*
Liguorian (US ISSN 0024-3450) *1745*
Lily of the Mohawks (US) *1745*
Linguistica Biblica (GW ISSN 0342-0884) *1690,* 1709
Listy Sv. Frantiska/Leaflets of St. Francis (US ISSN 0024-4465) *1745*
Literature and Belief (US ISSN 0732-1929) 1691, *1709*
Litterae Communionis (IT) *1709*
Little Lamp (US ISSN 0460-1297) *1709*
Liturgie Konkret (GW ISSN 0344-9092) *1709*
Liturgiewissenschaftliche Quellen und Forschungen (GW ISSN 0076-0048) *1709*
Liturgisches Jahrbuch (GW ISSN 0024-5100) *1709*
Liturgy (US ISSN 0458-063X) *1709*
Liverpool Catholic Directory (UK) *1746*
Living (Nashville) (US ISSN 0162-4253) *1733*
Living Church (US ISSN 0024-5240) *1733*
Living Light (US ISSN 0024-5275) *1746*
Living Prayer (US ISSN 0890-5568) 1693, *1709*
Living Sunday (UK ISSN 0261-3514) *1709*
Living with Preschoolers (US ISSN 0162-4350) *1733*
Living with Teenagers (US ISSN 0162-4261) *1733*
Living Word *see* Levend Woord *1753*
Ljusglimtar *see* Evangeliska Oestasienmissionen *1703*
Llan (UK ISSN 0024-5445) *1709*
Lluvia de Rosas (SP) *1746*
Local Preachers Magazine (UK ISSN 0024-5607) *1733*
Logos (PH ISSN 0076-0471) *1709*
Logos (New York) (US) 1693, *1753*
Lohos (CN ISSN 0024-5895) *1746*
Loma Weekly Paper (LB) *1733*
London City Mission Magazine *see* Span (London) *1716*
Lonergan Workshop (US ISSN 0148-2009) *1709*
Long Island Catholic (US ISSN 0024-6255) *1746*
Long Island Jewish World (US ISSN 0199-2899) *1686,* 1724
Look and Listen (US ISSN 0162-4369) *1733*
Lookout (US ISSN 0024-6425) 1709, *1758*
Lookout (Cincinnati) (US) *1733*
Looys (US ISSN 0024-6476) *1753*
Lost & Found (US) *1753*
Louisiana Baptist Builder (US ISSN 0024-6743) *1733*
Lourdes-Rosen (GW) *1746*
Louvain Studies (BE ISSN 0024-6964) *1709*
Love/Life/Death/Issues *see* Human Life Issues *1682*
Luce (Turin) (IT) *1733*
Lucha/Struggle (US) 1694, *1746*
Lumen Vitae (BE ISSN 0770-2477) 1684, *1746*
Lumiere (FR ISSN 0024-7332) *1709*
Lumiere du Monde (FR ISSN 0024-7340) *1709*
Lumiere et Vie (FR ISSN 0024-7359) *1709*
Lusitania Sacra (PO ISSN 0076-1508) *1709*
Luther (GW ISSN 0340-6210) *1733*
Lutheran (US ISSN 0024-743X) *1733*
Lutheran Almanac *see* Lutheran Church of Australia. Yearbook *1733*
Lutheran Annual (US) *1733*
Lutheran Church in America. Yearbook (US) *1733*
Lutheran Church of Australia. Yearbook (AT ISSN 0726-4305) *1733*
Lutheran Church of Central Africa. Statistical Report (ZA) *1721*
Lutheran Churches in Canada. Directory (CN ISSN 0316-800X) *1733*
Lutheran Council in the U.S.A. Bulletin *see* L I R S Bulletin *1733*
Lutheran Digest (US ISSN 0458-497X) *1733*
Lutheran Education (US ISSN 0024-7448) *1684,* 1733
Lutheran Forum (US ISSN 0024-7456) *1733*
Lutheran Forum. Forum Letter (US ISSN 0046-4732) *1733*
Lutheran Historical Conference Newsletter (US ISSN 0460-0274) *1733*
Lutheran Journal (US ISSN 0360-6945) *1733*
Lutheran Layman (US ISSN 0024-7464) *1733*
Lutheran Libraries (US ISSN 0024-7472) *1690,* 1733
Lutheran Messenger for the Blind (US ISSN 0024-7480) *1682,* 1733
Lutheran News *see* Christian News *1729*
Lutheran Partners (US ISSN 0885-9922) *1753*
Lutheran Perspective (US ISSN 0279-4462) *1733*
Lutheran Sentinel (US ISSN 0024-7510) *1733*
Lutheran Spokesman (US ISSN 0024-7537) *1733*
Lutheran Standard (US ISSN 0024-7545) *1734*
Lutheran Theological Journal (AT ISSN 0024-7553) *1734*
Lutheran Theological Seminary Bulletin (US) *1734*
Lutheran Witness (US ISSN 0024-757X) *1734*
Lutheran Women (US ISSN 0024-7596) *1734,* 1758
Lutheran World Federation. Proceedings of the Assembly (US ISSN 0076-1540) *1734*
Lutherans in Step (US) 1691, *1734*
Lutherische Beitraege (SZ) 1688, *1734*
Lutherische Monatshefte (GW ISSN 0024-7618) *1734*
Die Lutherkirche (AU ISSN 0024-7626) *1734*
Luthersk Barntidning (SW ISSN 0345-7389) *1734*
Lux (IT) *1746*
Luz (AG ISSN 0024-7693) 1686, *1690,* 1724
Lyudyna i Svit (UR ISSN 0024-7871) *1709*
M A R C Newsletter (Missions Advanced Research & Communication Center) (US) *1709*
M I E C Servico de Documentacion (Movimiento Internacional de Estudiantes Catolicos) (PE) 1685, *1746*
M.I.I. Series (Muslim Intellectuals' International) (PK ISSN 0541-5462) *1722*
M.R.U. *see* Modelle fuer den Religionsunterricht *1710*
M S S (Master Sermon Series) (US ISSN 0362-0808) *1709*
M S U U Newsletter *see* M S U U Newsletter: Gleanings *1734*
M S U U Newsletter: Gleanings (Ministerial Sisterhood Unitarian Universalist) (US) *1734,* 1758
Mabuey Hanchal (US) *1686,* 1724
Machberet Hamenahel (US) *1724*
McMaster Theological Bulletin *see* Theodolite *1717*
Madonna (IT) *1746*
Madonna *see* Sacred Heart Messenger *1749*
La Madonna del Divino Amore (IT) *1746*
Madonna di Barbana (IT ISSN 0024-9580) *1746*
Madonna di Castelmonte (IT ISSN 0024-9599) *1709*
Madre y Maestra (SP) *1746*
Maend og Mission *see* Verden Rundt *1719*
Maestro (IT ISSN 0024-9696) 1684, *1746*
Magazine of Positive Thinking *see* Plus: Magazine of Positive Thinking *1755*
Magazine of Reality *see* Reality *1713*
Magnificat (CN ISSN 0025-0007) *1746*
Magnificat - la Verite (FR) *1709*
Maha Bodhi (II ISSN 0025-0406) 1693, *1726*
Mahinda (CE) *1726*
Maison-Dieu (FR ISSN 0025-0937) 1685, *1709*
Majallat al-Azhar (UA) *1685,* 1722
Majallat al-Hajj *see* Muslim Solidarity *1722*
Majallat al-Tadamum al-Islami *see* Muslim Solidarity *1722*
Malaysia Inter-Religious Organisation. Suara (MY) *1753*
Mananam (US ISSN 0276-0444) *1726*
Mandate *see* Der Auftrag *1697*
Mandate (CN ISSN 0225-7068) *1709*
Mandate "Special" (CN) *1709*
Manna (JM) *1709*
Manresa (SP) *1709*
Mapenzi ya Mungu (KE) *1722*
Maranatha *see* Agape *1696*
Maria (SZ ISSN 0025-2972) *1746*
Maria Nostra Luce (IT) *1746*
Mariahilfer Pfarrbote (AU ISSN 0025-2999) *1709*
Marian Helpers Bulletin (US) *1753*
Marian Library Studies. New Series (US ISSN 0076-4434) 1690, *1709*
Marian Studies (US ISSN 0464-9680) *1746*
Marianist (AU ISSN 0025-3014) *1746*
Mariannhill (AU ISSN 0025-3022) *1709*
Marianum (IT) *1746*
Marie Reine des Coeurs *see* Regard de Foi *1748*
Markings (US) *1709*
Marriage *see* Marriage and Family Living *1757*
Marriage and Family Living (US) 1746, *1757*
Martin Luther (AU) *1734*
Marturion (US ISSN 0047-6064) *1753*
Maryknoll (US ISSN 0025-4142) *1746*
Maryland Baptist *see* Baptist True Union *1728*
Masihi Avaza (II) *1709*
Massada Quarterly *see* Kivun *1724*
Massis (LE ISSN 0025-4975) *1690,* 1746
Master and the Multitude (UK) *1709*
Master Sermon Series *see* M S S *1709*
Mater Ecclesiae *see* Ecclesia Mater *1743*
Materialdienst (GW) *1709*
Materialy Zrodlowe do Dziejow Kosciola W Polsce (PL ISSN 0076-5244) *1746*
Mathilde-Zimmer-Stiftung. Blaetter (GW) *1709*
Mature Living (US ISSN 0162-427X) *1734*
Mature Years (US ISSN 0025-6021) 1687, *1734*
Measuring Mormonism (US ISSN 0094-5633) *1753*
Medellin (CK) *1746*
Media & Values (US ISSN 0149-6980) *1684,* 1709
Media Development (GW) *1684,* 1709
Media-Informatiedienst (NE ISSN 0025-6919) 1685, *1721*
Media: Library Services Journal *see* Church Media Library Magazine *1690*
Medical Mission Sisters News (US) *1689,* 1746
Medical Missionary *see* Medical Mission Sisters News *1689*
Medical Missionary News (UK ISSN 0025-7370) *1709*
Medicine and Gospel/Igaku to Fukuin (JA ISSN 0019-1582) *1691,* 1709
Megiddo Message (US) *1709*
Mekevot *see* Sources of Contemporary Jewish Thought *1691*
Melanesian Journal of Theology (PP ISSN 0256-856X) *1709*
Melanges de Science Religieuse (FR ISSN 0025-8911) *1746*
Melita Theologica (MM) *1709*
Memorandum (St. Paul) (US) *1684,* 1709
Memorie Domenicane (IT) 1688, *1709*
Menighedsraadenes Blad (DK) *1709*
Mennonite (US ISSN 0025-9330) *1753*
Mennonite Brethren Herald (CN ISSN 0025-9349) *1753*
Mennonite Historical Bulletin (US ISSN 0025-9357) 1689, *1753*
Mennonite History Series (US ISSN 0076-6429) *1753*
Mennonite Life (US ISSN 0025-9365) *1754*
Mennonite Mirror (CN ISSN 0315-8101) *1691,* 1754
Mennonite Quarterly Review (US ISSN 0025-9373) *1754*
Mennonite Reporter (CN ISSN 0380-0121) *1754*
Mennonite Research Journal *see* Pennsylvania Mennonite Heritage *1754*
Mennonite Review *see* Mennonitische Rundschau *1754*
Mennonite Yearbook and Directory (US) *1754*
Mennonitische Rundschau/Mennonite Review (CN ISSN 0025-9314) *1754*
Menorah (CK ISSN 0025-939X) *1686,* 1724
Mensaje (UY) *1724*
Mensaje (CL ISSN 0716-0062) *1746*
Mensajero (SP ISSN 0211-6561) *1709*
Mensajero (EC) *1709*
Merleg (AU ISSN 0026-0126) *1690,* 1709
Mesias (MX ISSN 0026-0185) *1734*
Message *see* Message de l'Ahmadiyya *1722*
Message (Hagerstown) (US ISSN 0026-0231) *1709*
Message de l'Ahmadiyya (MF) *1722*
Message of the Open Bible (US) *1709*
Message to the Anglo-Saxon and Celtic Peoples *see* National Message *1710*
Messager de l'Exarchat du Patriarche Russe en Europe Occidentale (FR ISSN 0026-0266) *1754*
Messager Evangelique (FR ISSN 0026-0274) *1734*
Messages du Secours Catholique (FR ISSN 0026-0290) *1746*
Messaggero (AT) 1686, *1746*
Messaggero *see* Messenger *1709*
Messaggero Avventista (IT) *1734*
Messaggero Cappuccino (IT) *1709*
Messaggero di S. Antonio (IT ISSN 0026-0312) *1746*
Messenger/Messaggero (US ISSN 0026-0363) *1709*
Messenger (UK ISSN 0309-3654) *1734*
Messenger *see* Posol *1748*
Messenger (SI ISSN 0026-0371) *1754*
Messenger (Elgin) (US ISSN 0026-0355) *1754*
Messenger (Omaha) (US) *1734*
Messenger (San Francisco) (US) *1754*
Messenger of Truth (US) *1754*
Messidor (FR ISSN 0026-0401) *1754*
Metamedica (NE ISSN 0022-9350) *1691,* 1746
Method: Journal of Lonergan Studies (US ISSN 0736-7392) *1693,* 1709
Methodist Conference. Minutes and Yearbook (UK) *1734*
Methodist Diaries (UK) *1734*
Methodist History (US ISSN 0026-1238) 1691, *1734*
Methodist Homes Quarterly *see* Horizon (Neptune) *1687*
Methodist Message *see* Pelita Methodist *1735*
Methodist Recorder (UK ISSN 0026-1262) *1734*
Methodist Story *see* Interpreter *1733*
Methodist Womam *see* Response (New York) *1736*
Metodistkyrkans i Sverige. Aarsbok (SW ISSN 0543-6206) *1734*
Metro - Ministry News (US) *1709,* 1757
Metroline (US) *1689,* 1754
Michigan Christian Advocate (US ISSN 0026-2072) *1734*
Michigan Lutheran (US) *1734*
Middle Way (UK ISSN 0026-3214) *1726*
Miesiecznik Franciszkanski (US ISSN 0300-6158) *1746*
Migranti-Press (IT ISSN 0391-5492) *1694,* 1709, 1757
Militaerseelsorge (GW ISSN 0047-7362) *1691,* 1746
Militant Truth *see* Independent Voice *1706*
Military Chaplain (US ISSN 0026-3958) *1691,* 1710
Military Chaplains' Review (US ISSN 0360-9693) *1691,* 1710
Militia Christi *see* Kerk en Vrede *1708*
Milltown Studies (IE ISSN 0332-1428) 1693, *1710*
Minaret *see* Minaret Monthly International *1722*
Minaret Monthly International (PK) *1722*
Minbar al Islam (UA) *1710*
Mindolo News Letter (ZA ISSN 0076-8901) *1710*
Ministerial Formation (SZ) *1710*
Ministerial Sisterhood Unitarian Universalist Newsletter: Gleanings *see* M S U U Newsletter: Gleanings *1734*
Ministries (US) *1710*
Ministry (US ISSN 0026-5314) *1754*
Minnesota Synod Lutheran (US) *1734*
Minutes of the Annual Meeting of the First Catholic Slovak Union of the United States of America and Canada *see* First Catholic Slovak Union of America. Minutes of Annual Meeting *1744*
Miraculous Medal (US ISSN 0026-5802) *1754*
Mirjam (SZ) *1746,* 1758
Mirror (US ISSN 0738-7237) *1689,* 1754
Miscelanea Comillas (SP ISSN 0210-9522) 1685, 1693, 1695, *1710*
Miscellanea Francescana (VC ISSN 0026-587X) 1688, 1693, *1746*
Mishkan (IS) *1724,* 1746
Misioneros Javerianos (SP) *1710*
Misiorama (SP) *1746*
Missi (FR ISSN 0026-5977) *1710*
Missiology (US ISSN 0091-8296) *1681,* 1710
Mission (DK) *1710*
Mission. Messages (FR ISSN 0026-6124) *1710*
Mission Aktuell (GW) *1746*
Mission de l'Eglise (FR ISSN 0026-6035) *1746*
Mission Handbook (US) *1746*
Mission Handbook: North American Protestant Ministries Overseas (US ISSN 0093-8130) *1734*
Mission Intercom (US) *1746*
Mission Magazine *see* Mandate "Special *1709*

Mission Studies and Documents see Missionswissenschaftliche Abhandlungen und Texte 1710
Mission to Lepers, London. Annual Report see Leprosy Mission, London. Annual Report 1708
Missionari del P.I.M.E. (Pontificio Istituto Missioni Estere) (IT) 1746
Missionary Monthly (US ISSN 0161-7133) 1710
Missionary News Service (US ISSN 0026-6051) 1710
Missionhurst (US ISSN 0026-6086) 1746
Missioni Cattoliche see Mondo e Missione 1746
Missioni Domenicane (IT ISSN 0026-6108) 1746
Missions Advanced Research & Communication Center Newsletter see M A R C Newsletter 1709
Missions des Franciscians (CN ISSN 0700-4192) 1746
Missions Digest and Year Book see Evangelical Baptist Churches in Canada. Fellowship Yearbook 1731
Missions-Etrangeres (CN ISSN 0026-6116) 1710
Missions to Seamen Annual Report (UK) 1710
Missions to Seamen Handbook see Missions to Seamen Annual Report 1710
Missions U S A (US ISSN 0279-5345) 1734
Missionsbaneret (SW ISSN 0026-6132) 1710
Missionswissenschaftliche Abhandlungen und Texte/Etudes et Documents Missionnaires/Mission Studies and Documents (GW ISSN 0076-941X) 1710
Missionswissenschaftliche Forschungen (GW ISSN 0076-9428) 1710
Mississippi Methodist Advocate see Mississippi United Methodist Advocate 1734
Mississippi United Methodist Advocate (US) 1734
Missouri in Perspective see Lutheran Perspective 1733
Mitteilungen der Norddeutschen Mission. Bremen(GW) 1734
Mitzion Tetzeh Torah. M.T.T. (IS ISSN 0541-5632) 1693, 1724
Mlezi (TZ ISSN 0047-7583) 1710
Modelle fuer den Religionsunterricht (GW) 1710
Modern Churchman (UK ISSN 0026-7597) 1710
Modern Liturgy (US ISSN 0363-504X) 1710
Modern Orthodox Saints (US) 1754
Modern Theology (UK ISSN 0266-7177) 1710
Moeletsi Oa Basotho/Counsellor of Basotho (LO) 1746
Molaetsa-Molaetsa (SA ISSN 0378-410X) 1734
Molula-Qhooa (SA ISSN 0026-9093) 1754
Monastic Studies (CN) 1746
Monastica (IT) 1746
Monde de la Bible (FR) 1681, 1710
Mondo e Missione (IT ISSN 0026-6094) 1746
Monitor see San Francisco Catholic 1749
Monitor Ecclesiasticus (IT ISSN 0026-976X) 1746
Month (UK ISSN 0027-0172) 1746
Monthly Journal of Scientology (DK ISSN 0901-2982) 1710
Monthly Letter on Evangelism (SZ) 1710
Montreal Humanist see Humanist in Canada 1693
Monumenta Historica Ordinis Minorum Capuccinorum (IT ISSN 0077-1449) 1746
Monumenta Historica Societatis Iesu (IT) 1746
Monumenta Iuris Canonici (VC ISSN 0077-1457) 1746
Moody Monthly (US ISSN 0027-0806) 1710
Moody Student (US) 1710
Moralia (SP ISSN 0210-0851) 1746
Moravian and Wachovia Moravian see North American Moravian 1754
More (Nashville) (US ISSN 0162-4288) 1734
More Light Update (US ISSN 0889-3985) 1689, 1734
Moreana (FR ISSN 0047-8105) 1688, 1689, 1710
Morningland Spiritual Journal (US) 1726
Morokami (SA ISSN 0027-1179) 1754
Mosaic see In Touch (Pinner) 1706
Mosupa - Tsela (SA ISSN 0027-1454) 1734
Mountain Movers (US ISSN 0164-7253) 1754
Mountain Path (II ISSN 0027-2574) 1693, 1710
Movimiento Internacional de Estudiantes Catolicos Servico de Documentacion see M I E C Servico de Documentacion 1746
Muenchner Gemeindeblatt (GW) 1734
Muensterschwarzacher Studien (GW ISSN 0077-2011) 1747
Mukai! (SA) 1754
Mundo Israelita (AG) 1686, 1694, 1724
Mundo Negro (SP) 1710
Murumiwa (SA ISSN 0378-4126) 1734
Al-Mushir see Counselor 1702
Music Leader (US ISSN 0027-4372) 1692, 1734
Music Makers (US ISSN 0162-4377) 1734
Musica Judaica (US) 1692, 1724
Musica Sacra see Selebriamo 1692
Musicatalog see Recording Locator 1692
Musician (AT) 1754
Musik und Kirche (GW ISSN 0027-4771) 1692, 1710
Musizi (UG ISSN 0541-4385) 1710
Muslim Digest (SA ISSN 0027-4887) 1722
Muslim Intellectuals' International Series see M.I.I. Series 1722
Muslim Review (II ISSN 0027-4895) 1722
Muslim Solidarity/Majallat al-Tadamum al-Islami (SU) 1722
Muslim Star (US) 1722
Muslim World (US ISSN 0027-4909) 1691, 1722
Muslim World Book Review (UK ISSN 0260-3063) 1722
Muslim World League. Journal/Rabetat al-Alam al-Islami. Journal (SU) 1722
Mutwalisi (SA) 1754
Muziekbode (NE) 1692, 1710
My Brother and I (CN ISSN 0316-8913) 1747
My Daily Visitor (US) 1747
My Devotions (US ISSN 0027-5387) 1683, 1710
Mysterium (CK ISSN 0027-5638) 1710
N A see Novas de Alegria 1754
N A O S (US) 1690, 1710
N A T A. Journal (National Association of Temple Administrators) (US) 1724
N A T E News (National Association of Temple Educators) (US ISSN 0300-6689) 1724
N C E A Notes (National Catholic Educational Association) (US ISSN 0550-5682) 1685, 1747
N C J W Journal (National Council of Jewish Women) (US ISSN 0161-2115) 1686, 1724
N I C M Journal for Jews and Christians in Higher Education (National Institute for Campus Ministries) (US ISSN 0362-0794) 1685, 1710
N T C News (IT) 1710
Nachrichten aus der Aerztlichen Mission (GW ISSN 0027-7398) 1689, 1694, 1710
Nacton Newsletter see Share It 1693
Nadezhda (GW) 1710
Nag Hammadi Studies (NE) 1710
Nanak Prakash Patrika (II ISSN 0027-7770) 1710
Nandan Kanan (II) 1693, 1726
Nanzan Institute for Religion and Culture. Bulletin (JA ISSN 0386-720X) 1692, 1710
Naropa Magazine (US) 1684, 1685, 1726
Nasza Przeszlosc (PL ISSN 0137-3218) 1688, 1747
National Association of Temple Administrators Journal see N A T A. Journal 1724
National Association of Temple Educators News see N A T E News 1724
National Bible Society of Scotland. Annual Report(UK ISSN 0077-3557) 1734
National Catholic Almanac see Catholic Almanac 1741
National Catholic Educational Association. Momentum (US ISSN 0026-914X) 1747
National Catholic Educational Association. Occasional Papers see Current Issues in Catholic Higher Education 1684
National Catholic Educational Association Notes see N C E A Notes 1685
National Catholic Register (US ISSN 0027-8920) 1747
National Catholic Reporter (US ISSN 0027-8939) 1747
National Conference of Synagogue Youth Keeping Posted with N C S Y see Keeping Posted with N C S Y 1724
National Council of Churches, Bangladesh. Annual Report (BG) 1754
National Council of Jewish Women Journal see N C J W Journal 1686
National Council of the Churches of Christ in the U.S.A. Triennial Report (US) 1734
National Directory of Catholic Higher Education (US) 1685, 1747
National Federation of Catholic Physicians' Guilds. Newsletter (US) 1691, 1747
National Guild of Catholic Psychiatrists. Bulletin (US ISSN 0547-7115) 1691, 1695, 1747
National Huguenot Society Proceedings see Cross of Languedoc 1730
National Institute for Campus Ministries Journal for Jews and Christians in Higher Education see N I C M Journal for Jews and Christians in Higher Education 1710
National Jewish Welfare Board Circle see J W B Circle 1723
National Message (UK) 1710
National Outlook (AT) 1710
National Spiritualist (US) 1754
Nauka i Religiya (UR ISSN 0028-1239) 1710, 1757
Navigators Daily Walk (US) 1734
Navigators Log see Navlog 1710
Navlog (US) 1710
Navy Chaplains Bulletin (US ISSN 0028-1654) 1691, 1710
Nazareth (IT ISSN 0028-1700) 1710
Nebraska Baptist Messenger see Messenger (Omaha) 1734
Nederduitse Gereformeerde Kerk van Natal Gemeente Vryheid. Maandbrief (SA ISSN 0024-8665) 1734
Nederduitse Gereformeerde Teologiese Tydskrif (SA ISSN 0028-2006) 1734
Nederlands Archief voor Kerkgeschiedenis (NE ISSN 0028-2030) 1710
Nederlands Theologisch Tijdschrift (NE ISSN 0028-212X) 1710
Nederlandse Hervormde Kerk. Persbureau. Weekbulletin (NE ISSN 0031-5567) 1734
Nemalah (DK ISSN 0108-3023) 1710
Net (UK ISSN 0028-2820) 1710
Network (London, 1965) (UK ISSN 0261-1708) 1754
Network (Washington, 1971) (US ISSN 0199-5723) 1694, 1747
Das Neue Buch (GW ISSN 0028-3118) 1695, 1721
Neue Ordnung (GW) 1747
Neue Zeitschrift fuer Missionswissenschaft/Nouvelle Revue de Science Missionaire (SZ ISSN 0028-3495) 1710
Neuer Zions Freund see Zions Freund 1720
Neues Dorf (GW ISSN 0028-3614) 1681, 1683, 1734
Neues Leben (GW ISSN 0028-3665) 1710
New Age Christian Newsletter (US) 1710
New Age Teachings (US) 1754
New Aurora (US ISSN 0028-4254) 1710
New Beginnings (Pisgah Forest) (US) 1683, 1734
New Blackfriars (UK ISSN 0028-4289) 1747
New Books Quarterly on Islam & the Muslim World (UK) 1695, 1722
New Brunswick Anglican (CN ISSN 0703-9409) 1734
New Catholic World (US) 1747
New Century (UG) 1754
New Church Magazine (UK) 1754
New Church Messenger see Messenger (San Francisco) 1754
New City (PH) 1710
New Conversations (US ISSN 0360-0181) 1710
New Covenant (US) 1747
New Day see New Century 1754
New Disciples (US) 1683, 1734
New E R A Newsletter see I R F Newsletter 1732
New Earth (US ISSN 0008-7890) 1747
New Era (Salt Lake City) (US) 1754
New Freeman (CN) 1747
New Horizons (US ISSN 0028-5374) 1685, 1734
New Messenger (Talking Book) (US) 1682, 1754
New Oxford Review (US ISSN 0149-4244) 1711
New Pulpit Digest see Pulpit Digest (1978) 1713
New Religions Newsletter (CN) 1711
New Religious Movements Up-Date see Update (Aarhus) 1719
New Review see Church Army. Review 1700
New Sower see Sower (1979) 1716
New Spectator see Church & Nation 1730
New Testament Abstracts (US ISSN 0028-6877) 1681, 1721
New Testament Studies (UK ISSN 0028-6885) 1711
New Testament Tools and Studies (NE ISSN 0077-8842) 1711
New Thought (Scottsdale) (US ISSN 0146-7832) 1754
New Times (AT) 1734
New Traditions (US) 1724
New Wine (US ISSN 0194-438X) 1711
New World see Chicago Catholic 1742
New World Outlook (US ISSN 0043-8812) 1734
New Zealand Baptist (NZ ISSN 0027-7177) 1734
New Zealand Christian Pacifist Society Bulletin see C P S Bulletin 1694
New Zealand Tablet (NZ ISSN 0028-8748) 1747
Newark Churchman see Voice (Newark) 1738
Newfoundland Churchman (CN) 1734
News and Views (AT) 1693, 1711
News from the Congregational Christian Historical Society (US ISSN 0362-1510) 1735
News of Muslims in Europe (UK ISSN 0143-9774) 1722
Newscan (UK) 1735
Newspeace (UK ISSN 0048-0304) 1735
Newswire (Wheaton) (US) 1754
Nharireyomurindi (SA ISSN 0028-9639) 1754
Nicolaus (IT) 1747, 1754
Nida al-Islam (UA) 1722
Nieuw Geluid (NE ISSN 0028-9833) 1724
Nieuw Ruimzicht see Ruimzicht 1715
Nieuwe Theta see Theta 1756
Nigerian Christian (NR ISSN 0029-005X) 1711
Nigrizia (IT ISSN 0029-0173) 1711
Nile Gazette (UG ISSN 0048-041X) 1747
Nisaba (NE) 1711
Niv Hamidrashia (IS ISSN 0048-0460) 1724
Nordelbische Mission (GW) 1711
Nordisk Ekumenisk Aarsbok (SW ISSN 0085-4212) 1711
Nordisk Kvaekartidskrift see Kvaekartidskrift 1753
Nordisk Missions Tidsskrift see Mission 1710
Norsk Teologisk Tidsskrift/Norwegian Theological Journal (NO ISSN 0029-2176) 1711
Norsk Tidsskrift for Misjon (NO ISSN 0029-2214) 1711
North American Moravian (US ISSN 0027-1012) 1754
North American Protestant Ministries Overseas see Mission Handbook: North American Protestant Ministries Overseas 1734
North Carolina Catholic (US) 1747
North Carolina Christian Advocate (US ISSN 0029-2435) 1735
North India Churchman (II) 1711
Northwest Lutheran Journal see Lutheran Journal 1733
Northwestern Lutheran (US ISSN 0029-3512) 1735
Norwegian Theological Journal see Norsk Teologisk Tidsskrift 1711
Note di Pastorale Giovanile (IT ISSN 0029-3903) 1747
Noticias Aliadas see Latinamerica Press 1708
Noticias Aliadas (PE) 1711, 1757
Noticias Evangelicas (NQ) 1711
Noticiero de la Fe (AG ISSN 0029-425X) 1735
Notitiae (VC ISSN 0029-4306) 1747
Notre Dame English Journal see Religion and Literature 1691
Notre Dame Studies in American Catholicism (US) 1747
Notre Petit Ami see Our Little Friend 1683
Notre Voix (FR) 1686, 1694, 1724
Les Notres (CN ISSN 0029-4578) 1747
A I U Les Nouveaux Cahiers (Alliance Israelite Universelle en France) (FR ISSN 0029-4705) 1688, 1724
Nouvelle Revue de Science Missionaire see Neue Zeitschrift fuer Missionswissenschaft 1710
Nouvelle Revue Theologique (BE ISSN 0029-4845) 1711
Nouvelles de Chretiente (FR ISSN 0029-487X) 1711
Nova et Vetera (SZ ISSN 0029-5027) 1747
Nova et Vetera (US) 1747
Novarien (IT ISSN 0078-253X) 1747
Novas de Alegria (PO ISSN 0029-5116) 1754
Novaya Sovetskaya i Inostrannaya Literatura po Obshchestvennym Naukam. Problemy Ateizma i Religii (UR ISSN 0134-2932) 1721
Novum Testamentum (NE ISSN 0048-1009) 1711
Novum Testamentum. Supplements (NE) 1711
Now see Straight (1981) 1716
Now (London, 1970) (UK) 1735
Nsanja Ya Olonda (SA ISSN 0029-5442) 1754
Nuestra Tarea (US) 1735
Nuestro Amigo (DR ISSN 0029-5752) 1711
Nueva Pompeya (AG ISSN 0029-585X) 1747
Nuevo Mundo (AG) 1711
Numen (NE ISSN 0029-5973) 1688, 1711
Numen Supplements (NE) 1711
Nuntia (VC) 1747
Nuova Umanita (IT) 1747
Nuovi Tempi see C O M-Nuovi Tempi 1699
Nur-ul Islam (KE) 1722
Nurses Lamp see Journal of Christian Nursing 1691
Nuwe Protestant (SA ISSN 0029-6708) 1735
Ny Dag (NO) 1683, 1711
Nye Aar (DK ISSN 0108-8297) 1711
Nyhedsbrev (Teologiske Fakultet) (DK ISSN 0109-3169) 1711
Nyt fra Bibelselskabet (DK ISSN 0108-898X) 1711
Nyt fra D U K (Danmarks Unge Katolikker) (DK ISSN 0109-0518) 1683, 1747
O E C T A Reporter (Ontario English Catholic Teachers Association) (CN) 1685, 1747
O E C T A Review see O E C T A Reporter 1685
O I E C Bulletin (Catholic International Education Office) (BE ISSN 0770-1683) 1685, 1747
O L O G O S (Orthodox Lore Of the Gospel of Our Savior Mission) (US ISSN 0029-7143) 1754
O M I Mission Magazine see Oblate World and Voice of Hope 1747
O R C Notes (Old Roman Catholic Church) (UK ISSN 0144-9117) 1747
Oblate World and Voice of Hope (US) 1747
Obnovljeni Zivot/Life Renewed (YU ISSN 0351-3947) 1711
Observer (Rockford) (US ISSN 0029-7739) 1747
Occasional Bulletin of Missionary Research see International Bulletin of Missionary Research 1690
Occasional Papers on Religion in Eastern Europe (US ISSN 0731-5465) 1687, 1711
Odini (MW ISSN 0300-4651) 1747
Oecumene (FR) 1721
Oekumenische Rundschau (GW ISSN 0029-8654) 1711
Oesterreichische Akademie der Wissenschaften. Kommission zur Herausgabe des Corpus der Lateinischen Kirchenvaeter. Veroeffentlichungen (AU) 1747
Oesterreichisches Archiv fuer Kirchenrecht (AU ISSN 0029-9820) 1689, 1711
Offene Tore (SZ ISSN 0030-0101) 1754
Offene Tueren (GW ISSN 0030-011X) 1711
Offer see Rond de Tafel 1714
Official Wisconsin Pastoral Handbook (US) 1747
Ohio Journal of Religious Studies see Journal of Religious Studies 1707
Oklahoma Baptist Chronicle (US) 1689, 1735
Old Roman Catholic Church Notes see O R C Notes 1747

Old Testament Abstracts (US ISSN 0364-8591) 1681, *1721*
Old Testament Essays (SA) *1711*
Olomeinu/Our World (US ISSN 0030-2139) 1683, *1724*
On the Move (AT ISSN 0310-9348) *1711*
On the Wing (US ISSN 0162-4385) *1735*
One Church/Yedinaya Tserkov (US ISSN 0030-2503) *1754*
One in Christ (UK ISSN 0030-252X) *1747*
One World (SZ ISSN 0303-125X) *1711*
Ons Bou *see* Tagtig *1717*
Ons Geestelijk Leven (NE ISSN 0030-2678) *1711*
Ons Jeug (SA ISSN 0030-2694) 1683, *1735*
Ontario Churchman (CN ISSN 0030-2848) *1735*
Ontario English Catholic Teachers Association Reporter *see* O E C T A Reporter *1685*
Ontwaak! (SA ISSN 0030-316X) *1754*
Oomoto (JA ISSN 0030-3259) 1693, *1754*
Oorspronkelijk Christendom (NE ISSN 0030-3267) *1711*
Opbouw (NE ISSN 0030-3356) *1735*
Open Deur (NE ISSN 0030-3402) *1735*
Open Windows (US ISSN 0162-4296) *1735*
Opinion (US) *1693*, 1711, 1757
Options (US ISSN 0362-2770) *1724*
Opus One (US ISSN 0162-430X) *1735*
Opus Two (US ISSN 0147-1597) *1735*
Ora et Labora (IT ISSN 0030-4174) *1747*
Oraita (IS ISSN 0333-9270) *1724*
Orante (BE ISSN 0030-4336) *1747*
Oratoire (CN ISSN 0030-4344) *1711*
Oratoriana (FR ISSN 0030-4352) *1711*
Order of Buddhist Contemplatives. Journal (US ISSN 0891-1177) *1726*
Order of St. John of Jerusalem. Bulletin (MM) *1754*
Ordo et Annuaire de l'Archdiocese de Lyon *see* Annuaire du Diocese de Lyon *1739*
Oregon Churchman *see* Oregon Episcopal Churchman *1735*
Oregon Episcopal Churchman (US) *1735*
Oriens Christianus (GW ISSN 0340-6407) *1711*
Orient (CN ISSN 0472-0490) *1747*
Orientalia Christiana Analecta (VC) *1692*, 1747
Orientalia Christiana Periodica (VC ISSN 0030-5375) *1711*
Orientamenti Pastorali (IT ISSN 0472-0784) *1711*
Orientierung (SZ ISSN 0030-5502) 1693, *1711*
Origins (Washington) *see* Origins, N C Documentary Service *1747*
Origins, N C Documentary Service (US ISSN 0093-609X) *1747*
Orita (NR ISSN 0030-5596) 1686, *1711*
Orphan's Messenger and Advocate of the Blind *see* St. Joseph's Messenger and Advocate of the Blind *1682*
Orphee Contact *see* Famille Nouvelle *1704*
Orthodox America (US) *1711*
Orthodox Church (US ISSN 0048-2269) *1754*
Orthodox Church in America. Yearbook and Church Directory (US ISSN 0145-7950) *1754*
Orthodox Life *see* Pravoslavnaya Zhyzn *1712*
Orthodox Lore Of the Gospel of Our Savior Mission *see* O L O G O S *1754*
Orthodox News (UK ISSN 0267-8470) *1754*
Orthodox Observer (US ISSN 0731-2547) *1754*
Orthodox Word (US ISSN 0030-5839) *1754*
Other Side (Philadelphia) (US ISSN 0145-7675) 1694, *1711*
Oudtestamentische Studien (NE) *1711*
Our Family (CN ISSN 0030-6843) *1747*
Our Family (GW) *1754*
Our Islam (US) *1722*
Our Lady of the Sacred Heart *see* Annals Magazine *1696*
Our Lady's Digest (US ISSN 0030-6886) *1747*
Our Link (II) *1711*
Our Little Friend (US ISSN 0030-6894) *1683*, 1711
Our Mission Fields *see* Royal Service *1736*
Our Northland Diocese (US ISSN 0030-6924) *1747*
Our Sunday Visitor (US ISSN 0030-6967) *1711*
Our Work *see* C S C Newsletter *1699*
Our World *see* Olomeinu *1724*
Outlook (CN ISSN 0834-0242) *1687*, 1724
Outlook *see* Newscan *1735*
Outlook *see* Reform *1736*
Outlook (UK ISSN 0030-7211) *1747*
Outlook (Wake Forest) (US ISSN 0030-7238) *1735*
Outreach (Nashville) *see* Sunday School Leadership *1737*
Outreach (New York) (US) *1687*, 1754
Outward Bound (UK ISSN 0030-7327) *1683*, 1711
Overview (Chicago) (US ISSN 0030-7564) *1747*
Oxford Mission (UK ISSN 0048-2579) *1711*
Oxford Mission Quarterly Paper *see* Oxford Mission *1711*
Oxford Theological Monographs (US ISSN 0078-7272) *1711*
P A C E (Professional Approaches for Christian Educators) (US) *1711*
P C R Information (World Council of Churches, Programme to Combat Racism) (SZ) *1712*
P F N A News (Pentecostal Fellowship of North America) (US) *1735*
P R R C: Emerging Trends (Princeton Religion Research Center, Inc.) (US) 1685, *1712*
P S (Editorial /Perpetuo Socorro) (SP) *1712*
Paa Vej (DK ISSN 0900-3355) 1683, *1712*
Paarlse Padwyser *see* Strooidak *1737*
Pacific Theological Review (US ISSN 0360-1897) 1712, *1735*
Padre Santo (IT ISSN 0030-9214) *1712*
Padres' Trail (US ISSN 0030-9222) *1747*
Paepste und Papsttum (GW ISSN 0340-7993) *1688*, 1747
Pagana (US) *1754*
Pallottis Werk (GW ISSN 0031-0395) *1712*
Panorama Aujourd'hui (FR ISSN 0048-2838) *1712*
Panorama de la Teologia Latinoamericana (CL) *1747*
Panpere (FR ISSN 0031-0972) *1754*
Paraboles (FR ISSN 0031-1561) *1747*
Paraclete (US) *1735*
Pardes (FR) 1688, *1724*
Parish Communication (US) 1689, *1747*
Parish Coordinator of Religious Education (US) *1685*, 1747
Parish Teacher (US ISSN 0738-7962) *1735*
Parish Visitor (US) *1747*
Parishioner (SA ISSN 0031-2088) *1735*
Paroisse et Liturgie *see* Communautes et Liturgies *1701*
Parole de l'Orient (LE) *1712*
Parole di Vita (IT ISSN 0031-2398) *1747*
Parole-Dimanche *see* Feuillet Biblique *1744*
Parrocchia (IT ISSN 0031-2428) *1747*
Parsiana (II ISSN 0048-3036) *1726*
Parson and Parish (UK ISSN 0031-2436) *1712*
Partners in Learning (UK ISSN 0079-0117) *1735*
Partnership (US ISSN 0747-9190) *1712*
Passionist Youth *see* Gioventu Passionista *1704*
Pastoral Care and Counseling Abstracts *see* Abstracts of Research in Pastoral Care and Counseling *1720*
Pastoral Life (US ISSN 0031-2762) *1712*
Pastoral Misionera (SP ISSN 0210-3559) *1712*
Pastoral Newsletter *see* New Covenant *1747*
Pastoral Popular *see* Vida Pastoral *1719*
Pastoral Psychology (US ISSN 0031-2789) *1712*
Pastoral Renewal (US ISSN 0744-8279) *1712*
Pastoralblaetter (GW ISSN 0031-2800) *1712*
Pastoralia (Centro Evangelico Latinoamericano de Estudios Pastorales) (CR) *1712*
Pastoraltheologie - Monatsschrift fuer Wissenschaft und Praxis in Kirche und Gesellschaft (GW ISSN 0720-6259) *1712*
Path of Truth (SA ISSN 0031-2932) *1712*
Pathway to God (II) *1693*, 1712
Pathways (Garden Grove) (US) *1735*, 1748
Patriarchal Institute for Patristic Studies. Theological Studies (GR) *1754*
Patristics (US ISSN 0360-652X) 1690, *1712*
Patrologia Syriaca et Orientalis (BE) 1726, *1748*
Patterns (Portland) (US) 1754, *1757*
Pax Bulletin *see* JustPeace *1708*
Pax Regis (CN ISSN 0031-3335) *1712*
Pax Romana (SZ ISSN 0079-0281) *1748*
Paz e Alegria (PO) *1748*
Peace (II ISSN 0031-3467) *1726*
Peace Bulletin *see* C P S Bulletin *1694*
Pelerin *see* Pelerin du Vingtieme Siecle *1712*
Pelerin du Vingtieme Siecle (FR ISSN 0031-4145) *1712*
Pelita Methodist (MY) *1735*
Pendle Hill Pamphlets (US ISSN 0031-4250) *1754*
Pendulum (SA) *1712*
Pennsylvania Mennonite Heritage (US ISSN 0148-4036) 1688, *1754*
Pensee Catholique (FR ISSN 0031-4781) *1748*
Pension Boards *see* United Church of Christ. Pension Boards (Annual Report) *1756*
Pentecostal Evangel (US ISSN 0031-4897) *1735*
Pentecostal Fellowship of North America News *see* P F N A News *1735*
Pentecostal Messenger (US ISSN 0031-4919) *1735*
Pentecostal Testimony (CN ISSN 0031-4927) *1735*
Pentecostes *see* Moralia *1746*
People Soup *see* Synapse (Boston) *1691*
Perchtoldsdorfer Pfarrbote (AU ISSN 0031-5141) *1712*
Pere Marquette Theology Lecture Series (US) *1712*
Periodica de Re Morali Canonica Liturgica (VC ISSN 0031-529X) *1748*
Perspective *see* Aspaklaria *1723*
Perspective (Wheaton) (US) *1712*
Perspectives in Jewish Learning *see* Solomon Goldman Lectures *1725*
Perspectives in Religious Studies (US ISSN 0093-531X) *1735*
Perspectives on Science and Christian Faith (US) *1712*, 1757
Peuples du Monde (FR) *1748*
Pfarrago (NE) *1712*
Pfarrbrief (AU ISSN 0031-6709) *1712*
Phaphama! (SA ISSN 0031-6806) *1754*
Philosophy and the Arts (US ISSN 0739-1218) *1693*, 1712
Phoni Tou Evangeliou/Voice of the Gospel (GR ISSN 0031-8396) *1712*
Piccolo Missionario *see* Piemme *1712*
Picenum Seraphicum (IT) *1748*
Piemme (IT) 1681, *1712*
Pilgrim Holiness Advocate *see* Wesleyan Advocate *1738*
Pilgrim State News (US) *1735*
Pilgrim State Newsletter *see* Pilgrim State News *1735*
Pilgrimage: The Journal of Pastoral Psychotherapy *see* Pilgrimage: The Journal of Psychotherapy and Personal Exploration *1712*
Pilgrimage: The Journal of Psychotherapy and Personal Exploration (US) *1712*
Pinkster Protestant (SA ISSN 0031-9902) *1735*
Pioneer (UK ISSN 0048-4202) *1712*
Pioneer (CN) *1735*
Pionier (NE ISSN 0032-0056) *1712*
Pittsburgh Catholic (US ISSN 0032-0323) *1748*
Plain Truth (Pasadena) (Norwegian edition: Dan Enkla Sannhet) (US ISSN 0032-0420) *1755*
Planbook for Leaders of Children (US ISSN 0162-5381) 1685, *1735*
Planning Helps (US ISSN 0162-1955) *1735*
Plough (US ISSN 0740-9125) *1712*, 1757
Plough (UK) *1755*
Plus: Magazine of Positive Thinking (US) *1755*
Pockets (US ISSN 0278-565X) 1683, *1735*
Point Theologique (FR) *1748*
Points de Repere (FR) *1712*
Points for Emphasis; International Sunday School Lessons in Pocket Size (US ISSN 0079-2543) *1712*
Pokrof (NE ISSN 0032-2415) *1712*
Pole et Tropiques (FR ISSN 0032-2504) *1748*
Polka (US ISSN 0032-3594) 1687, 1712, *1758*
Pomhaj Boh (GE ISSN 0032-4132) *1712*
Ponte d'Oro (VC) *1712*
Pontificia Universidade Catolica de Sao Paulo. Revista (BL) 1689, *1748*, 1757
Pontificia Universita Gregoriana. Documenta Missionalia (VC) *1748*
Pontificia Universita Gregoriana. Miscellanea Historiae Pontificiae (VC ISSN 0080-3979) *1748*
Pontificia Universita Gregoriana. Studia Missionalia (VC ISSN 0080-3987) *1748*
Pontificio Istituto Missioni Estere Missionari del P.I.M.E. *see* Missionari del P.I.M.E *1746*
Pope John Paul II Center Newsletter *see* Centrum Jana Pawla II Biuletyn *1682*
Pope Speaks (US ISSN 0032-4353) *1748*
Pope Teaches (UK ISSN 0143-0149) *1748*
Popolo (IT) *1712*, 1757
Portals of Prayer (US ISSN 0032-4884) *1712*
Portique Saint-Denis *see* Presence Orthodoxe *1755*
Portugal Evangelico (PO ISSN 0032-5066) *1735*
Positions Lutheriennes (FR ISSN 0032-5228) *1735*
Posol/Messenger (CN ISSN 0701-0192) 1687, *1748*
Possibilities: The Magazine of Hope (US) *1735*
Postup *see* Progress *1748*
Pour la Verite (FR ISSN 0751-5987) *1735*
Power for Living (US ISSN 0032-6003) *1712*
Power for Today (US ISSN 0032-6011) *1712*
Power Life *see* Freeway *1683*
Prabuddha Bharata/Awakened India (II ISSN 0032-6178) *1693*, 1726
Practical Anthropology *see* Missiology *1681*
Practical Christianity *see* Contact (Aldershot) *1701*
Practical Papers for the Bible Translator (UK ISSN 0260-0943) *1690*, 1712
Praesteforeningens Blad (DK ISSN 0106-6218) *1712*
Prairie Messenger (CN ISSN 0032-664X) *1748*
Prairie Overcomer (CN) *1712*
Prakit Jain Institute Research Publication Series (II ISSN 0554-9906) *1726*
Pravoslavnaya Rus' (US ISSN 0032-7018) *1712*
Pravoslavnaya Zhyzn/Orthodox Life (US ISSN 0032-6992) *1712*
Pravoslavno Misao (YU ISSN 0032-700X) *1712*
Pravoslavny Theologicky Sbornik (CS ISSN 0079-4937) *1712*
Praxis in der Gemeinde (GW ISSN 0172-7478) *1748*
Praxis Juridique et Religion (FR ISSN 0758-802X) *1689*, 1712
Prayer Union *see* E.C.M. News *1702*
Prayers for Worship (US ISSN 0274-600X) 1735, *1748*
Praying (US) *1748*
Preacher's Quarterly *see* Worship and Preaching *1739*
Preaching (US ISSN 0882-7036) *1712*
Der Prediger und Katechet (GW ISSN 0032-7212) *1748*
Predigtstudien (GW ISSN 0079-4961) *1712*
Presbyterian (Denton) (US) *1735*
Presbyterian Banner (AT ISSN 0729-3542) *1712*
Presbyterian Church in Canada. General Assembly. Acts and Proceedings (CN ISSN 0079-4996) *1712*
Presbyterian Guardian (US ISSN 0032-7522) *1735*
Presbyterian Herald (UK ISSN 0032-7530) *1735*
Presbyterian Layman (US ISSN 0555-0572) *1735*
Presbyterian Outlook (US ISSN 0032-7565) *1735*
Presbyterian Record (CN ISSN 0032-7573) *1735*
Presbyterian Survey (US ISSN 0032-759X) *1735*
Presbyterion (US) *1735*
Preschool Bible Teacher A (US) *1735*
Preschool Bible Teacher B (US) *1735*
Preschool Bible Teacher C (US) *1735*
Preschool Leadership (US ISSN 0162-4393) *1735*
Presence Orthodoxe (FR ISSN 0032-4922) *1755*
Presencia (CK) *1712*
Presenza Pastorale (IT ISSN 0032-7727) *1748*
Pretres Diocesains (FR ISSN 0032-7956) *1713*
Priest (US ISSN 0032-8200) *1713*
Priesterjahrheft (GW ISSN 0172-0929) *1748*
Primary Daybreak *see* Daybreak *1730*
Primary Days (US ISSN 0032-8278) *1713*
Primary Friend (US ISSN 0032-8286) *1683*, 1735
Primera Luz (SP) 1683, *1713*
Princeton Religion Research Center, Inc. Emerging Trends *see* P R R C: Emerging Trends *1712*
Printout *see* Young Women's Christian Association of the United States of America. The Printout *1720*
Prism (AT) *1713*
Prism (US) *1713*
Prismet (NO ISSN 0032-8847) 1685, *1713*
Pro Ecclesia (US) *1748*
Pro Mundi Vita. Informes *see* Pro Mundi Vita Dossiers *1748*
Pro Mundi Vita. Special Notes *see* Pro Mundi Vita Dossiers *1748*
Pro Mundi Vita Bulletin (BE) *1748*
Pro Mundi Vita Dossiers (BE) *1748*
Probe (Chicago) (US) *1748*
Probe (Memphis) (US ISSN 0032-9215) 1683, *1736*
Probleme der Aegyptologie (NE) *1713*
Problemes d'Histoire du Christianisme (BE) *1748*
Problemy Ateizma i Religii *see* Novaya Sovetskaya i Inostrannaya Literatura po Obshchestvennym Naukam. Problemy Ateizma i Religii *1721*
Process Studies (US ISSN 0360-6503) *1713*
Proche-Orient Chretien (IS ISSN 0032-9622) *1713*
Proclaim (US ISSN 0162-4326) *1736*
Professional Approaches for Christian Educators *see* P A C E *1711*
Progress/Postup (CN ISSN 0033-054X) *1748*
Progressio (IT ISSN 0033-0728) *1755*
Promotor de Educacion Cristiana (US ISSN 0033-1139) *1736*
Prooftexts (US ISSN 0272-9601) 1691, *1724*
Prophetic Expositor (CN ISSN 0048-5578) *1713*
Prophetic News and Israel's Watchman *see* Prophetic Witness *1755*
Prophetic Newsletter (US ISSN 0033-1341) *1755*
Prophetic Witness (UK ISSN 0033-135X) *1755*
Protestant Churches in Czechoslovakia *see* Czechoslovak Ecumenical News *1730*
Protestantesimo (IT ISSN 0033-1767) *1736*
Provident Book Finder (US) 1687, 1695, *1736*
Proyeccion (SP ISSN 0478-6378) *1713*
Pseudepigrapha Veteris Testamenti Graece (NE ISSN 0079-7197) *1713*
Pulpit *see* Christian Ministry *1700*
Pulpit Digest (1978) (US ISSN 0160-838X) *1713*
Pulpit Helps (US ISSN 0193-3914) *1713*
Pulpit Resource (US ISSN 0195-1548) *1713*
Pulse (US) *1713*
Pura Verdad (Italian edition: Pura Verita) (US) 1694, *1755*
Pure Life Society. Annual Report (MY ISSN 0552-6426) 1693, *1713*
Pure Verite (Italian edition: Pura Verita) (US ISSN 0033-4588) 1694, *1755*
Purpose (US ISSN 0163-7274) *1755*
Pusat Penelitian Atma Jaya. Laporan Penelitian Keagamaan *see* Atma Jaya Research Centre. Socio-Religious Research Report *1726*
Q P S Reporter (Quaker Peace and Service) (UK ISSN 0265-7848) 1755, *1757*
Quaderni de "la Terra Santa" (IS) 1689, *1713*, 1758
Quaderni del Gallo (IT) *1713*
Quaker Action *see* Quaker Life *1755*
Quaker Concern (CN ISSN 0229-1916) *1694*, 1755
Quaker History (US ISSN 0033-5053) *1755*
Quaker Information Network (UK) *1755*
Quaker Life (US ISSN 0033-5061) *1755*
Quaker Monthly (UK ISSN 0033-507X) *1755*
Quaker Peace & Service *see* Q P S Reporter *1757*
Quaker Peace & Service. Annual Report (UK ISSN 0260-9584) 1755, *1757*
Quaker Peace and Service Reporter *see* Q P S Reporter *1757*

Quaker Religious Thought (US ISSN 0033-5088) *1755*
Quaker Service Bulletin (US ISSN 0033-5096) *1713*
Quaker Yeomen (US ISSN 0737-8246) *1687,* 1755
Queen (US ISSN 0033-6017) *1713*
Quellen und Forschungen zur Wuerttembergischen Kirchengeschichte (GW ISSN 0079-9084) *1713*
Question de Racines, Pensees, Sciences Eclairees (FR) 1691, *1692,* 1713
Question de Spiritualite, Tradition, Litteratures *see* Question de Racines, Pensees, Sciences Eclairees *1692*
Quis Custodiet *see* Law & Justice *1689*
Quo Vadis (SA ISSN 0033-6637) *1736*
Quranulhuda (PK) *1722*
R-A-D-A-R (US ISSN 0162-5217) *1683,* 1713
R C D A-Religion in Communist Dominated Areas (US ISSN 0034-3978) 1695, *1713*
R E S Mission Bulletin (Reformed Ecumenical Synod) (US) *1736*
R E S News Exchange (Reformed Ecumenical Synod) (US ISSN 0033-6904) *1736*
R E S Theological Forum (Reformed Ecumenical Synod) (US) *1736*
R E S World Diaconal Bulletin *see* R E S Mission Bulletin *1736*
R I C (Repertoire Bibliographique des Institutions Chretiennes.) (FR ISSN 0079-9300) *1721*
R.M. Bucke Memorial Society for the Study of Religious Experience. Proceedings of the Conference (CN ISSN 0079-9351) *1713*
R N A Newsletter (Religion Newswriters Association) (US ISSN 0034-4109) *1689,* 1713
R N D (Revue Notre Dame) (CN ISSN 0035-3795) *1748*
R P P *see* Religionspaedagogische Praxis *1714*
R S G B Inform Newsletter (Reform Synagogues of Great Britain) (UK) *1725*
Rabbinical Assembly, New York. Proceedings (US ISSN 0079-936X) *1725*
Rabetat al-Alam al-Islami. Journal *see* Muslim World League. Journal *1722*
Radical Option (US) *1713*
Radius (GW ISSN 0033-8532) 1694, *1713*
Radix (Berkeley) (US ISSN 0275-0147) *1713,* 1757
Railroad Evangelist (US) *1755*
Rally (II ISSN 0048-668X) *1748*
Ransomer (UK ISSN 0033-9245) *1713*
Rassegna di Teologia (IT ISSN 0033-9644) *1713*
Rassegna Mensile di Israel (IT ISSN 0033-9792) 1691, *1725*
Rayons (FR ISSN 0034-0197) 1683, *1748*
Reach *see* Between Times *1683*
Reader (UK ISSN 0300-3469) *1736*
Real Living (CN ISSN 0034-0847) *1736*
Reality (US ISSN 0034-0987) *1713*
Reality (IE ISSN 0034-0960) *1748*
Reaper (NZ ISSN 0034-107X) *1736*
Recherches de Science Religieuse (FR ISSN 0034-1258) *1713*
Recherches de Theologie Ancienne et Medievale (BE ISSN 0034-1266) *1713*
Recherches Institutionnelles (FR) *1713*
Reconciliation International (International Fellowship of Reconciliation) (NE) *1713*
Reconciliation Quarterly (UK ISSN 0034-1479) *1736*
Reconstruction (NE ISSN 0034-1487) *1725*
Reconstructionist (US ISSN 0034-1495) 1693, *1725*
Recording Locator (US) *1692,* 1713, 1758
Recusant History (UK ISSN 0034-1932) *1688,* 1748
Redeemer's Voice/Holos Spasytelya (CN ISSN 0034-2122) *1713*
Reflection (New Haven) (US) *1713*
Reform (UK ISSN 0306-7262) *1736*
Reform Judaism (US ISSN 0482-0819) *1725*
Reform Synagogues of Great Britain Inform Newsletter *see* R S G B Inform Newsletter *1725*
Reformatio (SZ ISSN 0034-3021) *1713*
Reformation Review (US ISSN 0034-303X) *1713*
Reformation Today (UK ISSN 0034-3048) *1736*
Reformationsgeschichtliche Studien und Texte (GW ISSN 0171-3469) *1736*
Reforme (FR ISSN 0223-5749) *1736*
Reformed and Presbyterian World *see* Reformed World *1736*
Reformed Church of America. Historical Series (US ISSN 0080-0481) *1736*
Reformed Ecumenical Synod Mission Bulletin *see* R E S Mission Bulletin *1736*
Reformed Ecumenical Synod News Exchange *see* R E S News Exchange *1736*
Reformed Ecumenical Synod Theological Forum *see* R E S Theological Forum *1736*
Reformed Journal (US ISSN 0486-252X) *1713*
Reformed Review (US ISSN 0034-3064) 1693, *1736*
Reformed Scope (US) *1713*
Reformed Theological Review (AT ISSN 0034-3072) *1713*
Reformed World (SZ ISSN 0034-3056) *1736*
Refugees Among Us- Unreached Peoples (US) *1713*
Regard de Foi (CN ISSN 0025-3065) *1748*
Regenbogen (AU) 1683, *1713*
Regensburger Bistumsblatt (GW ISSN 0034-3250) *1713*
Il Regno (IT) *1748*
Regno-Attualita (IT ISSN 0034-3498) *1748*
Regno-Documenti (IT ISSN 0009-000X) *1713*
Regulae Benedicti Studia. Annuarium Internationale (GW) *1713*
Reign of the Sacred Heart (US ISSN 0048-7155) *1748*
Reino (BL ISSN 0034-3633) *1713,* 1757
Reino dos Sagrados Coracoes *see* Reino *1713*
Relations (CN ISSN 0034-3781) *1687,* 1748
Religioese Graphik (AU ISSN 0034-3935) *1682,* 1713
Religion (UK ISSN 0048-721X) *1713*
Religion and Life Letters (US ISSN 0730-2363) *1713*
Religion and Literature (US) *1691,* 1713
Religion and Reason; Method and Theory in the Study and Interpretation of Religion (GW ISSN 0080-0848) *1714*
Religion and Society (GW) 1693, *1714*
Religion and Society (II ISSN 0034-3951) *1714,* 1757
Religion en Afrique *see* Journal of Religion in Africa *1707*
Religion et Sciences de l'Homme (FR ISSN 0080-0864) *1714*
Religion for Peace (US) 1685, *1714*
Religion Heute (GW) *1685,* 1714
Religion in America (US) 1685, *1714*
Religion in Communist Lands (UK ISSN 0307-5974) *1714*
Religion in Education *see* British Journal of Religious Education *1698*
Religion in Life *see* United Methodist Board of Higher Education and Ministry. Quarterly Review *1718*
Religion in Southern Africa (SA) *1714*
Religion Index One: Periodicals (US ISSN 0149-8428) 1681, *1721*
Religion Index Two: Multi-Author Works (US ISSN 0149-8436) *1721*
Religion Newswriters Association Newsletter *see* R N A Newsletter *1689*
Religion Teacher's Journal (US ISSN 0034-401X) *1714*
Religion Today (UK ISSN 0267-1700) *1714*
Religion, Wissenschaft, Kultur. Jahrbuch *see* Religion, Wissenschaft, Kultur. Schriftenreihe *1714*
Religion, Wissenschaft, Kultur. Schriftenreihe (AU) *1714*
Religione e Scuola (IT) 1685, *1748*
Religione e Societa (IT ISSN 0391-853X) *1714,* 1757
Religionslaereren (DK) *1714*
Religionspaedagogische Praxis (GW) *1714*
Religionsunterricht an hoeheren Schulen (GW ISSN 0341-8960) *1685,* 1714
Religionsvidenskabeligt Tidsskrift (DK ISSN 0108-1993) *1714*
Religiose nell'Apostolato Diretto (IT ISSN 0034-4036) *1714*
Religious and Inspirational Books and Serials in Print (US ISSN 0000-0868) *1682,* 1714
Religious & Theological Abstracts (US ISSN 0034-4044) 1681, *1721*
Religious Book Review Index (II ISSN 0034-4060) *1721*
Religious Books and Serials in Print *see* Religious and Inspirational Books and Serials in Print *1682*
Religious Broadcasting (US ISSN 0034-4079) *1684,* 1714
Religious Consultancy (II) *1714*
Religious Education (US ISSN 0034-4087) 1685, *1714*
Religious Humanism (US ISSN 0034-4095) 1693, *1755*
Religious Studies (UK ISSN 0034-4125) *1714*
Religious Studies Review (US ISSN 0319-485X) *1714*
Renovatio (IT ISSN 0034-4486) *1714*
Renovatio (GW ISSN 0340-8280) *1748*
Repertoire Bibliographique des Institutions Chretiennes. *see* R I C *1721*
Report from the Capital (US) 1694, *1736*
Reporter (St. Louis. 1975) (US ISSN 0360-7119) *1736*
Reporter for Conscience' Sake (US ISSN 0034-4796) *1694,* 1714
Res Medicae (IT ISSN 0014-8784) *1691,* 1714
Research Papers: Muslims in Europe (UK) *1722*
Reshimat Ma'amarim Be-Mada'e Ha-Yahadut *see* Index of Articles on Jewish Studies *1721*
Resource (CN ISSN 0832-9354) *1736*
Resources for Youth Ministry (US ISSN 0034-5660) *1683,* 1736
Response (New York) (US ISSN 0034-5725) *1736*
Respuesta (US) *1736*
Restoration (CN ISSN 0708-2177) *1714*
Restoration (US ISSN 0730-2185) *1755*
Restoration Herald (US ISSN 0034-5830) *1714*
Restoration Quarterly (US ISSN 0486-5642) *1714*
Restoration Witness (US) *1755*
Reveil Missionnaire (CN ISSN 0034-6284) *1714*
Review and Expositor (US ISSN 0034-6373) *1736*
Review and Herald *see* Adventist Review *1727*
Review for Religious (US ISSN 0034-639X) *1714*
Review of Books and Religion *see* Books and Religion *1695*
Review of Indian Spiritualism (II) *1692,* 1726
Review of Religions (PK ISSN 0034-6721) *1722*
Review of Religious Research (US ISSN 0034-673X) *1714,* 1757
Revista Biblica (AG ISSN 0034-7078) *1714*
Revista Catolica (CL) *1748*
Revista Cultului Mozaic (RM ISSN 0034-754X) 1682, *1691,* 1725
Revista de Espiritualidad (SP ISSN 0034-8147) *1714*
Revista del Hogar (AG ISSN 0034-9070) *1748*
Revista Eclesiastica Brasileira (BL) *1714*
Revista Espanola de Derecho Canonico (SP ISSN 0034-9372) *1714*
Revista Presencia *see* Presencia *1712*
Revista Teologica Limense (PE) *1748*
Revue A C C S *see* C H A C Review *1689*
Revue Africaine de Theologie (ZR) *1748*
Revue Benedictine (BE ISSN 0035-0893) *1748*
Revue Biblique (FR ISSN 0035-0907) *1714*
Revue d'Histoire de l'Eglise de France (FR ISSN 0048-7988) *1714*
Revue d'Histoire Ecclesiastique (BE ISSN 0035-2381) 1689, *1748*
Revue d'Histoire Ecclesiastique Suisse *see* Zeitschrift fuer Schweizerische Kirchengeschichte *1720*
Revue d'Histoire et de Philosophie Religieuses (FR ISSN 0035-2403) 1688, *1714*
Revue de l'Histoire des Religions (FR ISSN 0035-1423) 1688, *1714*
Revue de Qumran (FR ISSN 0035-1725) *1692,* 1714
Revue de Theologie et de Philosophie (SZ ISSN 0035-1784) 1693, *1714*
Revue des Communautes Religieuses *see* Vie Consacree *1719*
Revue des Etudes Augustiniennes (FR ISSN 0035-2012) 1691, *1714*
Revue des Etudes Islamiques (FR) *1692,* 1722
Revue des Etudes Juives (BE ISSN 0035-2055) *1687,* 1688, 1725
Revue des Sciences Religieuses (FR ISSN 0035-2217) 1688, *1748*
Revue du Monde Musulman *see* Revue des Etudes Islamiques *1692*
Revue Mabillon (FR ISSN 0035-3620) 1714, *1748*
Revue Notre Dame *see* R N D *1748*
Revue Theologique de Louvain (BE ISSN 0080-2654) *1748*
Revue Theologique de Louvain. Cahiers (BE) *1748*
Revue Thomiste (FR ISSN 0035-4295) 1693, *1714*
Ricerche di Storia Sociale e Religiosa (IT) 1714, *1757*
Ricerche Storiche Salesiane (IT ISSN 0393-3849) 1693, *1748*
Right On *see* Radix (Berkeley) *1713*
Risaleh al-Islamiyah (LE) *1722*
Rivista del Clero Italiano (IT ISSN 0042-7586) *1748*
Rivista delle Religiose *see* Consacrazione e Servizio *1701*
Rivista di Ascetica e Mistica (IT) *1748*
Rivista di Pastorale Liturgica (IT ISSN 0035-6395) *1714*
Rivista di Storia della Chiesa in Italia (IT ISSN 0035-6557) 1688, *1714*
Rivista di Storia e Letteratura Religiosa (IT ISSN 0035-6573) 1688, *1714*
Rivista di Storia e Letteratura Religiosa. Biblioteca(IT) 1688, *1714*
Rivista di Vita Spirituale (VC ISSN 0035-6638) *1748*
Rivista Diocesana del Patriarcato di Venezia (IT ISSN 0035-6654) *1748*
Rivista Liturgica (IT ISSN 0035-6956) *1748*
Roc-Christ et France *see* Sur le Roc *1756*
Rocca (IT ISSN 0391-108X) *1714*
Rocky Mountain Jewish Historical Notes (US) *1687,* 1725
Roczniki Teologiczno-Kanoniczne (PL ISSN 0035-7723) *1749*
Roedderne (DK ISSN 0109-2952) 1683, *1736*
Roemische Historische Mitteilungen (AU ISSN 0080-3790) 1684, *1688,* 1714
Roemische Quartalschrift fuer Christliche Altertumskunde und Kirchengeschichte (GW ISSN 0035-7812) *1714*
Rond de Tafel (NE ISSN 0035-8169) *1714*
Rosario de Maria (PO ISSN 0035-8274) *1749*
Rosicrucian Digest (US ISSN 0035-8339) 1685, *1693,* 1755
Royal Army Chaplains Department. Quarterly Journal *see* Great Britain. Royal Army Chaplains' Department. Journal *1691*
Royal Service (US ISSN 0035-9084) *1736*
Roze Maryi (US ISSN 0745-3299) *1749*
Rugama *see* Molaetsa-Molaetsa *1734*
Ruimzicht (NE) 1685, *1715*
Rundbrief Ehemaliger Schueler und Freunde der Schulbrueder (AU ISSN 0013-2489) *1684,* 1715
Runestone (Breckenridge) (US) 1687, 1687, *1755*
Russian Messenger/Russkij Vistnik *see* U R O B A Messenger *1756*
Russian Orthodox Journal (US ISSN 0036-0317) *1755*
Russkaya Pravoslavnaya Tserkov'. Moskovskaya Patriarkhiya. Zhurnal/Journal of the Moscow Patriarchate (UR ISSN 0044-4553) *1715*
Russkoe Vozrozhdenie (US ISSN 0222-1543) 1688, *1755*
Rythme de Notre Eglise *see* Actualite Diocesaine *1739*
S A (Sociological Analysis) (US ISSN 0038-0210) 1749, *1757*
S C A Report (Synagogue Council of America) (US) *1687,* 1725
S C P Journal (Spiritual Counterfeits Project, Inc.) (US ISSN 0883-1300) *1715*
S E D O C (Servicio de Documentacao) (BL ISSN 0036-1267) *1715*
S E H A Newsletter and Proceedings (Society for Early Historic Archaeology) (US ISSN 0036-1275) *1681,* 1715
S G M News (Scripture Gift Mission) (UK) *1715*
S G M News Digest *see* S G M News *1715*
S I D I C (Service International de Documentation Judeo-Chretienne) (IT) *1715*
S I M Now (Sudan Interior Mission) (CN ISSN 0711-6683) *1715*
S M A-the African Missionary (IE) *1749*
S.O.W. (US) *1715*
S S C Booknews (Spiritual Studies Center) (US ISSN 0730-2371) *1721*
Saaier *see* Sower *1716*
Sabbath Recorder (US ISSN 0036-214X) *1715*
Sabbath Sentinel (US) *1725*
Sabbath Watchman (US ISSN 0098-9517) *1736*
Sacra Doctrina (IT ISSN 0036-2190) *1715*
Sacred Dance Guild Journal (US) *1684,* 1715
Sacred Heart Messenger (IE) *1749*
Sacred Name Broadcaster (US) *1755*
Saemann *see* Der feste Grund *1732*
Sagrada Biblia (SP) *1715*
Sai Suddha (II) *1726*
St. Anthony Messenger (US ISSN 0036-276X) *1749*
Saint Bonaventure University. Franciscan Institute. Philosophy Series (US ISSN 0080-5432) *1749*
Saint Bonaventure University. Franciscan Institute. Text Series (US ISSN 0080-5440) *1749*
St. Camillusbode *see* Camillusbode *1741*
St. George Association Newsletter (US) *1715*
St. Hedwigsblatt (GE ISSN 0487-2088) *1749*
St. Joseph's Messenger and Advocate of the Blind(US) *1682,* 1715
St. Louis Review (US ISSN 0036-3022) 1691, *1749*
St. Luke's Journal *see* St. Luke's Journal of Theology *1715*
St. Luke's Journal of Theology (US) *1715*
St. Mark's Review (AT ISSN 0036-3103) *1715*
St. Martin's Review (UK ISSN 0036-3111) *1736*
St. Patrick's Cathedral Bulletin *see* Alive and Well and Living in New York City Saint Patrick's Cathedral *1739*
St. Paul's Printer (US ISSN 0038-8815) *1715*
St. Poeltner Dioezesanblatt (AU ISSN 0036-3162) *1715*
St. Poeltner Kirchenzeitung *see* Kirche Bunt *1708*
St. Thomas More Lectures (US ISSN 0082-4208) *1715*
Saint Vincent de Paul Record (AT ISSN 0036-3219) *1749*
St. Vladimir's Seminary Quarterly *see* St. Vladimir's Theological Quarterly *1755*
St. Vladimir's Theological Quarterly (US ISSN 0036-3227) *1755*
Sainte Therese de Lisieux. Annales (FR ISSN 0036-3243) *1749*
Saints' Herald (US ISSN 0036-3251) *1755*
Saivite Light *see* Gracious Light *1744*
Sal Terrae (SP ISSN 0211-4569) *1715*
Salesian (US ISSN 0036-3480) *1715*
Salesianum (VC ISSN 0036-3502) 1693, *1749*
Salmanticensis (SP ISSN 0036-3537) *1749*
Salpisma (GR ISSN 0036-357X) *1755*
Salt (US) *1715*
Salt (CN ISSN 0709-616X) *1715*
Salt (AT ISSN 0816-0031) *1715*
Salt Lake City Messenger (US ISSN 0586-7282) *1755*
Salvation Army Year Book (UK ISSN 0080-567X) *1755*
Samaritano (IT ISSN 0036-3723) *1715,* 1757
Samizdat Review (US) *1715*
San Diego Jewish Press Heritage (US) *1687,* 1725
San Francisco Catholic (US) *1749*
San Salvatore da Horta (IT ISSN 0036-424X) *1715*
Sant Sipahi (II) *1694,* 1726

Santa Casa di Loreto. Messaggio (IT ISSN 0036-116X) 1749
Santi (II) 1726
Santo (IT ISSN 0391-7819) 1682, 1749
Santo dei Voli (IT ISSN 0036-4606) 1749
Santuario de Aparecida (BL ISSN 0036-4614) 1685, 1715
Santuario della Madonna delle Rocche (IT ISSN 0036-4622) 1749
Santuario di N.S.D. Grazie e di S. Maria Goretti (IT ISSN 0036-4630) 1715
Sapienza (IT ISSN 0036-4711) 1693, 1749
Sappho's Understudies (US) 1755, 1758
Sauti Ya Vita (KE) 1755
Saving Health (UK ISSN 0036-5106) 1715
Sawt el-Ard el-Mukaddash see Voice of the Holy Land 1750
Scapulier see Tegenwoordig 1717
Scarboro Missions (CN ISSN 0700-6802) 1715
Scholars' Choice (US ISSN 0036-6358) 1721
Scholastik see Theologie und Philosophie 1718
School en Godsdienst (NE ISSN 0036-6544) 1685, 1749
School Sister of Notre Dame (US ISSN 0487-6830) 1749
Schools of Prayer (UK ISSN 0261-5703) 1715
Schrift (NE) 1715
Schriftenreihe fuer die Evangelische Frau (GW ISSN 0036-696X) 1736, 1758
Schwenkfeldian (US ISSN 0036-8032) 1755
Science et Esprit (CN ISSN 0316-5345) 1693, 1715
Science of Mind (US ISSN 0036-8458) 1693, 1755
Science of Religion (NE ISSN 0165-8794) 1715, 1721
Science of Religion Bulletin see Science of Religion 1721
Scope (Minneapolis) (US ISSN 0036-8997) 1682, 1736
Scottish Baptist Magazine (UK ISSN 0036-9136) 1736
Scottish Bulletin of Evangelical Theology (UK) 1736
Scottish Church History Society. Records (UK ISSN 0264-5572) 1715
Scottish Episcopal Church Yearbook (UK ISSN 0260-0617) 1736
Scottish Evangelical Theology Society Bulletin see Scottish Bulletin of Evangelical Theology 1736
Scottish Institute of Missionary Studies Bulletin (UK ISSN 0048-9778) 1715
Scottish Journal of Theology (UK ISSN 0036-9306) 1715
Scripta Instituti Donneriani Aboensis (FI ISSN 0582-3226) 1715
Scripta Theologica (SP ISSN 0036-9764) 1715
Scriptura (SA) 1736
Scripture Bulletin (UK ISSN 0036-9780) 1749
Scripture Examination Material and Annual Scripture Project (UK) 1715
Scripture Gift Mission News see S G M News 1715
Scripture in Church (IE ISSN 0332-1150) 1749
Scuola Cattolica (IT ISSN 0036-9810) 1749
Se Vuoi (IT ISSN 0036-9950) 1715
Search (Nashville) (US ISSN 0048-9913) 1736
Searching Together (US ISSN 0739-2281) 1736
Second Century (US ISSN 0276-7899) 1755
Secret Place (US ISSN 0037-0606) 1736
Sedar (SI ISSN 0559-2674) 1722
See (AT ISSN 0037-0754) 1736
Seek (US) 1715
Seek (SA ISSN 0037-0827) 1736
Segni dei Tempi (IT) 1715
Seikyo Times (US) 1693, 1755
Seishin Studies (JA ISSN 0037-1084) 1726
Selebriamo (IT ISSN 0008-8706) 1692, 1749
Selecciones de Libros see Actualidad Bibliografica de Filosofia y Teologia 1695
Selecciones de Teologia (SP ISSN 0037-119X) 1715
Self-Realization (US ISSN 0037-1564) 1693, 1715, 1755
Semeador Baptista (PO ISSN 0037-1874) 1736
Semeia (US ISSN 0095-571X) 1690, 1715
Seminar of African Christian Students in Europe. Report (SZ ISSN 0559-4065) 1736
Seminarium (VC ISSN 0582-6314) 1749
Semiotique et Bible (FR ISSN 0154-6902) 1690, 1715
Semitic Study Series (NE) 1692, 1725
Sendbote des Herzens Jesu (AU ISSN 0037-2129) 1715
Senior Adult Bible Study (US ISSN 0162-4733) 1736
Senior High Class (US ISSN 0745-8304) 1736
Sent see Share 1715
Sentinel (Willowdale) (CN ISSN 0049-0202) 1755
Sentinelle see Centinela 1729
Serafico Vessillo (IT ISSN 0037-2439) 1749
Serenity Sentinel (US) 1693, 1715
Sermon Builder (US ISSN 0037-248X) 1715
Service International de Documentation Judeo-Chretienne see S I D I C 1715
Service Protestant Francais de Presse et d'Information see Bulletin d'Information Protestant 1729
Servicio de Documentacao see S E D O C 1715
Servizio della Parola (IT ISSN 0037-2773) 1715
Servizio Migranti (IT ISSN 0037-2803) 1694, 1715, 1757
Shaker Messenger (US ISSN 0270-9368) 1682, 1755
Shalom (IT ISSN 0037-3265) 1687, 1725
Shalom (UK) 1715, 1725
Share (UK) 1715
Share It (UK ISSN 0262-9356) 1693, 1755
Sharia see Theology 1722
Sharing the Practice (US ISSN 0193-8274) 1715
Shasta Abbey. Journal see Order of Buddhist Contemplatives. Journal 1726
Shepherd (UK ISSN 0260-0382) 1755
Sheviley Hahinuch (US ISSN 0037-3656) 1725
Shia World (UK) 1722
Shiah (PK) 1722
Shinanggye/World of Faith (KO) 1715
Ship of Christ the King see Kristaus Karaliaus Laivas 1745
Shirim (US) 1691, 1725
Shlach see Way-Ukrainian Catholic Bi-Weekly 1750
Shmuessen mit Kinder Un Yugent (US ISSN 0300-7960) 1725
Shree Gurudev Ashram Newsletter (II) 1727
Shree Hari Katha (II ISSN 0251-1746) 1693, 1727
Shrine of the Holy House. Loreto see Santa Casa di Loreto. Messaggio 1749
Shupihui (PE) 1687, 1715
Shvut (IS) 1687, 1694, 1725
Siddha Vani (II) 1727
Signs of the Times (JA ISSN 0037-5055) 1755
Signs of the Times/Tekens van Die Tye (SA ISSN 0037-5071) 1755
Sikh Courier (UK ISSN 0037-511X) 1727
Sikh Religious Studies Information see Asian Religious Studies Information 1720
Sikh Review (II ISSN 0037-5128) 1727
Silver Wings (US ISSN 0889-9118) 1691, 1736
Simplified Bible Study see Bible Study-Special Ministries 1729
Sinai (IS) 1725
Singende Kirche (AU ISSN 0037-5721) 1692, 1749
Single see Single Adult Ministry Information 1685
Single Adult Ministry Information (US ISSN 0887-1167) 1685, 1715
Sinims Land see Evangeliska Oestasienmissionen 1703
Sintese (BL) 1693, 1715, 1757
Sintese Politica, Economica e Social see Sintese 1757
Sion (IS ISSN 0037-5810) 1755
Sioniste (FR ISSN 0049-061X) 1687, 1694, 1725
Sir Moses Montefiore Collections des Juifs Celebres (FR ISSN 0075-4544) 1716
Sisters Today (US ISSN 0037-590X) 1749
Sivam (II ISSN 0037-5950) 1727
Slavic Gospel News see Breakthrough (Wheaton) 1751
Slavna Nadele/Glorious Hope (CN ISSN 0700-5202) 1736
Slingervel (SA ISSN 0037-685X) 1683, 1736
Slovenski Jezuiti V Kanade. Year Book (CN ISSN 0085-6134) 1749
Sluzba Bozja (YU ISSN 0037-7074) 1716
Sobornost (UK ISSN 0144-8722) 1736
Soccorso Perpetuo di Maria (IT ISSN 0037-7562) 1716
Social Compass (BE ISSN 0037-7686) 1716, 1757
Social Justice Review (US ISSN 0037-7767) 1749, 1757
Social Progress see Church and Society 1730
Social Questions Bulletin (US ISSN 0731-0234) 1736, 1758
Social Studies (IE) 1716, 1758
Social Work and Christianity (US) 1749, 1757
Societe Calviniste de France. Revue Reformee (FR ISSN 0035-3884) 1736
Societe Canadienne des Etudes Bibliques. Bulletin see Canadian Society of Biblical Studies. Bulletin 1699
Societe de l'Histoire du Protestantisme Francais. Bulletin (FR ISSN 0037-9050) 1736
Societe Saint-Jean-Baptiste de Montreal. Information Nationale (CN ISSN 0537-6211) 1716
Societe Saint-Jean-Baptiste de Montreal Bulletin see Societe Saint-Jean-Baptiste de Montreal. Information Nationale 1716
Society for Common Insights. Journal (US) 1716, 1757
Society for Early Historic Archaeology Newsletter and Proceedings see S E H A Newsletter and Proceedings 1681
Society for New Testament Studies. Monograph Series (UK ISSN 0081-1432) 1716
Society for Old Testament Studies. Monographs (UK) 1716
Society for Old Testament Study. Book List (UK ISSN 0081-1440) 1721
Society for the Scientific Study of Religion. Monograph Series (US) 1716
Society for the Study of Chinese Religions. Bulletin see Journal of Chinese Religions 1726
Society of Biblical Literature. Seminar Papers (Year) (US ISSN 0145-2711) 1716
Society of Christian Ethics. Annual (US ISSN 0732-4928) 1716
Sociological Analysis see S A 1757
Sofia. Universitet. Bogoslovski Fakultet. Godishnik see Dukhovna Akademiya SV. Kliment Okhridski. Godishnik 1702
Soka Gakkai News (JA ISSN 0385-6321) 1693, 1727
Solia (US ISSN 0038-1039) 1755
Solidaires (FR ISSN 0336-335X) 1716
Solomon Goldman Lectures (US ISSN 0196-2183) 1725
Sonntags Schulhelfer see Sonntagschulmitarbeiter 1685
Sonntagsblatt fuer die Evangelisch-Lutherische Kirche in Bayern. Ausgabe Oberfranken (GW ISSN 0014-3391) 1737
Sonntagschulmitarbeiter (GW ISSN 0012-2580) 1685, 1716
Sophia (AT ISSN 0038-1527) 1693, 1716
Sophia (US ISSN 0194-7958) 1755
Soul (US ISSN 0038-1756) 1755
Soundless Sound see Anahata Nada 1696
Sounds of Truth and Tradition (US ISSN 0038-187X) 1749
Source see Resource 1736
Source (Seattle) (US) 1716, 1758
Sources for the Study of Religion in Malawi (MW) 1690, 1716
Sources of Contemporary Jewish Thought/Mekevot (IS ISSN 0082-4585) 1691, 1725
South African Baptist Handbook (SA) 1737
South African Outlook (SA ISSN 0038-2523) 1716, 1758
South African Union Lantern/Suid-Afrikaanse Unie-Lantern (SA ISSN 0038-2795) 1755
South Carolina Baptist Historical Society Journal (US ISSN 0146-0196) 1737
South Carolina Methodist Advocate see South Carolina United Methodist Advocate 1737
South Carolina United Methodist Advocate (US) 1737
South Florida Focus (US) 1716
South India Churchman (II ISSN 0038-3465) 1755
Southern Baptist Convention. Annual (US ISSN 0081-3001) 1737
Southern Baptist Convention. Historical Commission. Microfilm Catalogue (US ISSN 0081-301X) 1737
Southern Baptist Convention. Sunday School Board. Quarterly Review (US ISSN 0162-4334) 1737
Southern Baptist Educator (US ISSN 0038-3848) 1737
Southern Christian Advocate see South Carolina United Methodist Advocate 1737
Southern Cross (SA ISSN 0038-4011) 1749
Southern Cross (US ISSN 0745-0257) 1749
Southwest Jewish Chronicle (US ISSN 0038-4674) 1687, 1725
Southwest Kansas Register (US ISSN 0038-4690) 1749
Southwestern Journal of Theology (US ISSN 0038-4828) 1693, 1716
Southwestern News (US ISSN 0038-4917) 1737
Soviet Jewish Affairs (UK ISSN 0038-545X) 1694, 1725
Sower/Saaier (SA ISSN 0038-5980) 1716
Sower (AT ISSN 0158-1090) 1716, 1757
Sower (1979) (UK) 1716
Span (London) (UK) 1716
Spark (US ISSN 0024-0591) 1755
Sparks (Wheaton) see Newswire (Wheaton) 1754
Spearhead (KE) 1716
Spectrum (UK ISSN 0305-7917) 1716
Spectrum (Takoma Park) (US) 1755
Speling (NE ISSN 0038-7320) 1693, 1716
Spirals (US) 1692, 1716
Spirit & Life (US ISSN 0038-7592) 1749
Spiritual Community Guide (US ISSN 0160-0354) 1755
Spiritual Counterfeits Project, Inc. Journal see S C P Journal 1715
Spiritual Healer (UK ISSN 0038-7622) 1693, 1755
Spiritual India see Kundalini 1708
Spiritual Life (US ISSN 0038-7630) 1749
Spiritual Studies Center Booknews see S S C Booknews 1721
Spirituality Today (US ISSN 0162-6760) 1749
Spiritus (FR ISSN 0038-7665) 1716
Sponsa Regis see Sisters Today 1749
Spotlight see Interpreter 1733
Spotlight (Edinburgh) (UK) 1737, 1758
Springfielder see Concordia Theological Quarterly 1701
Squilla (IT ISSN 0038-8750) 1716
Squilla di S. Gerardo (IT ISSN 0038-8769) 1716
Sri Aurobindo. Archives and Research (II) 1727
Stad Gods (NE ISSN 0038-8904) 1749
Standard (GH ISSN 0038-9374) 1749
Standard Bearer (Sacramento) (US ISSN 0038-9447) 1755
Standard Lesson Commentary (US ISSN 0081-4245) 1716
Standpunkt (GE ISSN 0323-4304) 1737
Star of Zion (US ISSN 0038-9870) 1737
Start (Birmingham) (US ISSN 0162-6841) 1737
Stella Polaris (UK ISSN 0308-4531) 1755
Steyler Missionschronik (GW) 1716
Stille Schar (AU ISSN 0081-5594) 1688, 1749
Stimme der Maertyrer (GW) 1716
Stimmen der Zeit (GW ISSN 0039-1492) 1716
Store Glaede (DK ISSN 0108-2884) 1716
Storia dell'Ebraismo in Italia (IT) 1725
Story Friends (US ISSN 0039-2006) 1684, 1755
Straight (1981) (US) 1716
Stromata (AG ISSN 0049-2353) 1693, 1716
Strooidak (SA) 1737
Strydkreet see War Cry 1756
Student (Nashville) (US ISSN 0039-2685) 1737
Student and World connection (US) 1716
Studi Biblici (IT ISSN 0039-2898) 1716
Studi Cattolici (IT ISSN 0039-2901) 1749
Studi e Ricerche Francescane (IT) 1749
Studi Ecumenici (IT ISSN 0393-3687) 1716
Studi Storici dell'Ordine dei Servi di Maria (IT ISSN 0039-3045) 1749
Studia Ad Corpus Hellenisticum Novi Testamenti (NE) 1716
Studia Canonica (CN ISSN 0039-310X) 1716
Studia Ephemeridis Augustinianum (IT) 1716
Studia in Veteris Testamenti Pseudepigrapha (NE) 1716
Studia Irenica (GW ISSN 0081-6663) 1716
Studia Liturgica (NE ISSN 0039-3207) 1716
Studia Monastica (SP ISSN 0039-3258) 1688, 1716
Studia Moralia (VC ISSN 0081-6736) 1716
Studia Patavina (IT ISSN 0039-3304) 1693, 1716
Studia Philosophiae Religionis (SW) 1693, 1716
Studia Post-Biblica (NE ISSN 0585-5500) 1716
Studia Semitica Neerlandica (NE ISSN 0081-6914) 1725
Studia Silensia (SP) 1716
Studia Theologica (NO ISSN 0039-338X) 1716
Studien und Mitteilungen zur Geschichte des Benediktiner. Ordens und Seiner Zweige (GW) 1749
Studien und Texte zur Kirchengeschichte und Geschichte (AU) 1737
Studien zur Geschichte der Katholischen Moraltheologie (GW ISSN 0081-7295) 1749
Studien zur Kirchengeschichte Niedersachsens (GW) 1716
Studien zur Theologie und Geistesgeschichte des 19. Jahrhunderts (GW) 1716
Studien zur Umwelt des Neuen Testaments (GW) 1716
Studies in American Jewish History (US ISSN 0081-7511) 1725
Studies in American Religion (US) 1717
Studies in Anabaptist and Mennonite History (US ISSN 0081-7538) 1756
Studies in Bibliography and Booklore (US ISSN 0039-3568) 1695, 1721
Studies in Comparative Religion (UK ISSN 0039-3622) 1717
Studies in Evangelicalism (US) 1756
Studies in Formative Spirituality (US ISSN 0193-2748) 1689, 1717
Studies in Greek and Roman Religion (NE) 1717
Studies in Islam (II ISSN 0039-3711) 1691, 1722
Studies in Jewish Education (IS ISSN 0333-9661) 1725
Studies in Judaica & the Holocaust (US ISSN 0884-6952) 1688, 1725
Studies in Judaism in Late Antiquity (NE) 1725
Studies in Judaism in Modern Times (NE) 1725
Studies in Medieval and Reformation Thought (NE ISSN 0585-6914) 1717
Studies in Oriental Religions (GW ISSN 0340-6792) 1727
Studies in Religion and Society (US) 1717
Studies in the History of Christian Thought (NE ISSN 0081-8607) 1717
Studies in the History of Religions see Numen Supplements 1711
Studies in Women and Religion (US) 1717, 1758
Studies in Zionism (US ISSN 0334-1771) 1722, 1725
Studies on Religion in Africa (NE) 1681, 1717
Studies on the Texts of the Desert of Judah (NE) 1725
Studium Biblicum Franciscanum. Analecta (IS ISSN 0081-8909) 1717
Studium Biblicum Franciscanum. Collectio Maior (IS ISSN 0081-8917) 1717
Studium Biblicum Franciscanum. Collectio Minor (IS ISSN 0081-8925) 1717
Studium Biblicum Franciscanum. Liber Annuus (IS ISSN 0081-8933) 1717
Studying Adult Life and Work Lessons (US ISSN 0191-4219) 1737
Subsida Hagiographica (BE) 1717
Subsidia Scientifica Franciscalia (IT ISSN 0562-4649) 1749
Successful Writers and Editors Guidebook (US) 1717
Sudan Interior Mission Now see S I M Now 1715
Sudhi Sahitya (II) 1693, 1727
Suid-Afrikaanse Unie-Lantern see South African Union Lantern 1755
Summer Service Opportunities (US) 1737, 1757

Sunday (US ISSN 0039-5161) 1756
Sunday Digest (US ISSN 0039-5188) 1717
Sunday School Adults (US ISSN 0162-4911) 1737
Sunday School Counselor (US ISSN 0039-5285) 1756
Sunday School Junior Pupil see Bible Searchers 1729
Sunday School Leadership (US ISSN 0162-4318) 1737
Sunday School Lesson Illustrator see Biblical Illustrator 1729
Sunday School Lessons Simplified see Sunday School Lessons Special Ministries 1737
Sunday School Lessons Special Ministries (US) 1737
Sunday School Senior Adults (US ISSN 0585-9328) 1737
Sunday School Young Adults (US ISSN 0162-4903) 1737
Sunday School Youth (US) 1737
Sunday School Youth A see Sunday School Youth 1737
Sunday School Youth-Teacher (US) 1737
Sunstone (US ISSN 0363-1370) 1756
Le Supplement (FR ISSN 0750-1455) 1717
Sur le Roc (FR) 1756
Suriname Zending see Hernhutter Suriname Zending 1705
Sursum Corda (AT ISSN 0039-6184) 1749
Sv. Pranciskaus Varpelis/Bell of St. Francis (US) 1687, 1749
Svensk Exegetisk Aarsbok (SW) 1717
Svensk Kyrkomusik (Edition AB for Church Musicians) see Kyrkomusikernas Tidning 1692
Svensk Pastoral Tidskrift (SW ISSN 0039-6699) 1717
Svensk Teologisk Kvartalskrift (SW ISSN 0039-6761) 1717
Svensk Veckotidning (SW ISSN 0039-6826) 1717
Svenska Kyrkans (SW) 1717
Svit/Light (US ISSN 0039-7156) 1756
Swedenborg Foundation Newsletter see Logos (New York) 1753
Sword of the Lord (US ISSN 0039-7547) 1717
Sydney Town Express (AT ISSN 0310-5466) 1717, 1758
Synagogue Council of America Report see S C A Report 1687
Synapse (Boston) (US) 1691, 1717
Synthesis (Mystic) (US) 1685, 1749
Syracuse Jewish Observer (US) 1687, 1725
T F-Nyhedsbrev see Nyhedsbrev 1711
T Q (US ISSN 0044-071X) 1684, 1717
T S F Bulletin (Theological Students Fellowship) (US ISSN 0272-3913) 1717
T W C Bulletin (Third World Caucus) see C A L C Report 1694
Tablet (UK ISSN 0039-8837) 1691, 1717
Tablet (US ISSN 0039-8845) 1749
Tadamun al-Islami see Muslim Solidarity 1722
Taegliche Andachten (US ISSN 0273-8562) 1737
Tag des Herrn (GE ISSN 0492-1283) 1749
Tagtig (SA) 1717
Talks and Tales (US ISSN 0039-9213) 1684, 1717
Talks of Pope John Paul II (US) 1749
Talks of Pope Paul VI see Talks of Pope John Paul II 1749
Tallies and Trends: Annual Statistical Report see Young Women's Christian Association of the United States of America. The Printout 1720
Tapovan Prasad (II) 1727
Tarbell's Teacher's Guide (US ISSN 0082-1713) 1717
Target (TZ ISSN 0039-9655) 1717
Target (UK) 1717
Targumic and Cognate Studies. Newsletter (CN ISSN 0704-5905) 1725
Tarjuman al-Hadith (PK) 1722
Taschenbuch fuer Liturgie Kirchenmusik und Musikerziehung (GW ISSN 0344-1407) 1692, 1717
Taschenbuch fuer Liturgie und Kirchenmusik see Taschenbuch fuer Liturgie Kirchenmusik und Musikerziehung 1692
Tchahert/Torch (LE ISSN 0040-0297) 1756
Teach (US ISSN 8755-8769) 1717
Teaching All Nations see East Asian Pastoral Review 1743
Teaching Beginners see Teaching Under 5's 1717
Teaching Juniors see Teaching 7-10's 1717
Teaching Pictures for Bible Searchers (US ISSN 0040-0645) 1737
Teaching Primaries see Teaching 5-7's 1717
Teaching Teenagers see Teaching 10-13's 1717
Teaching Under 5's (UK) 1717
Teaching 5-7's (UK) 1717
Teaching 7-10's (UK) 1685, 1717
Teaching 10-13's (UK ISSN 0308-356X) 1717
Technical Papers for the Bible Translator (UK ISSN 0260-0935) 1690, 1717
Teen Power (1979) (US) 1684, 1717
Teens Today (US) 1684, 1717
Tegenwoordig (NE ISSN 0040-2133) 1717
Teilhard Review and Journal of Creative Evolution (UK) 1693, 1717
Teilhardian Studies see Etudes Teilhardiennes 1703
Tekens van Die Tye see Signs of the Times 1755
Telema (ZR) 1717
Temenos (Turku) (FI ISSN 0497-1817) 1717
Temi di Predicazione - Omelie (IT) 1717
Temoignage Chretien (FR ISSN 0040-2923) 1691, 1717
Temple David Bulletin (SA ISSN 0040-2966) 1725
Temple David Review see Temple David Bulletin 1725
Tenrikyo (JA ISSN 0040-3482) 1717
Tentmaker's Journal (US ISSN 0272-6939) 1717
Teocomunicacao. (BL) 1749
Teologia (HU ISSN 0133-1779) 1749
Teologia y Vida (CL ISSN 0049-3449) 1750
Teologinen Aikakauskirja/Teologisk Tidskrift (FI ISSN 0040-3555) 1717
Teologisk Tidskrift see Teologinen Aikakauskirja 1717
Teologiske Fakultet. Bladet see Arken 1697
Teoloski Pogledi (YU) 1717
Teresianum (VC) 1750
Terra Santa (IS ISSN 0040-3784) 1681, 1688, 1717
Terre Sainte see Terra Santa 1717
Tesoro Eucaristico (IT ISSN 0040-3938) 1750
Testimoni (IT) 1750
Testimonianze (IT ISSN 0040-3989) 1691, 1717
Testimonio (IT) 1717
Texas Concho Register see West Texas Angelus 1750
Texas Methodist/United Methodist Reporter see United Methodist Reporter 1738
Texas Presbyterian see Presbyterian (Denton) 1735
Texte und Studien zum Antiken Judentum (GW) 1725
Texte und Untersuchungen zur Geschichte der Altchristlichen Literatur (GE ISSN 0082-3589) 1717
Texts and Studies in Medieval and Early Modern Judaism see Texte und Studien zum Antiken Judentum 1725
Textus (IS ISSN 0082-3767) 1717
Textus Patristici et Liturgici (GW ISSN 0082-3775) 1717
Themelios (UK ISSN 0307-8388) 1717
Themis see Thesmophoria 1756
Theodolite (CN ISSN 0225-7270) 1717
Theokratia; Jahrbuch des Institutum Judaicum Delitzschianum (NE ISSN 0082-3899) 1725
Theologia (GR ISSN 0049-3635) 1756
Theologia Evangelica (SA ISSN 0255-8858) 1717
Theologia Reformata (NE ISSN 0040-5612) 1737
Theologia 21 (US ISSN 0362-0085) 1694, 1717
Theologiai Szemle (HU ISSN 0133-7599) 1717
Theologica see Claretianum 1742
Theologica Xaveriana (CK) 1750
Theological and Religious Bibliographies (UK) 1681, 1721
Theological and Religious Index see Theological and Religious Bibliographies 1721
Theological Education (US ISSN 0040-5620) 1685, 1718
Theological Markings (US ISSN 0362-0603) 1718
Theological Students Fellowship Bulletin see T S F Bulletin 1717
Theological Studies (US ISSN 0040-5639) 1718
Theological Times (UK ISSN 0049-3651) 1682, 1718
Theologie und Dienst (GW) 1718
Theologie und Glaube (GW ISSN 0049-366X) 1718
Theologie und Philosophie (GW ISSN 0040-5655) 1694, 1718
Theologisch-Praktische Quartalschrift (AU ISSN 0040-5663) 1718
Theologische Beitraege (GW ISSN 0342-2372) 1718
Theologische Dissertationen (SZ ISSN 0082-3902) 1718
Theologische Literaturzeitung (GE ISSN 0040-5671) 1718
Theologische Quartalschrift (GW ISSN 0342-1430) 1750
Theologische Revue (GW ISSN 0040-568X) 1750
Theologische Rundschau (GW ISSN 0040-5698) 1718
Theologische Zeitschrift (SZ ISSN 0040-5701) 1718
Theology (UK ISSN 0040-571X) 1718
Theology/Sharia (JO) 1722
Theology and Scientific Culture (US) 1718, 1757
Theology Digest (US ISSN 0040-5728) 1718
Theology Today (US ISSN 0040-5736) 1718
Theorie und Praxis der Sozialpaedagogik (GW ISSN 0342-7145) 1683, 1718
Theosofia (NE ISSN 0040-5868) 1694, 1718
Theosophical Journal (UK ISSN 0040-5876) 1694, 1718
Theosophy in Australia (AT ISSN 0049-3694) 1756
Theosophy in New Zealand (NZ ISSN 0049-3708) 1756
Thesmophoria (US) 1756, 1758
Theta (US ISSN 0040-6074) 1718
Theta (NE) 1756
Third Way (UK ISSN 0309-3492) 1737
This People (US) 1756
This World (US) 1694, 1695, 1718
Thomas (NE ISSN 0049-3805) 1685, 1750
Thomist (US ISSN 0040-6325) 1694, 1750
Three Minutes a Day (US) 1718
Threshing Floor (UK ISSN 0260-4892) 1718
Thunderbow (US) 1756
Ti Saluto Fratello (IT ISSN 0040-6686) 1718
Tibetan Bulletin (II) 1727
Tidings (US ISSN 0040-6791) 1750
Tidsskrift for Teologi og Kirke (NO ISSN 0040-7194) 1718
Tie (US ISSN 0040-7232) 1737
Tierra Nueva (CK) 1718, 1758
Tierra Santa see Terra Santa 1717
Tijdschrift voor Theologie (NE ISSN 0168-9959) 1737, 1750
Tinsae (ET) 1756
To the Source/El Ha'ayin see Sources of Contemporary Jewish Thought 1691
Today see Today in Africa 1718
Today (London) (UK ISSN 0262-8023) 1737
Today in Africa (KE) 1718
Today in World Missions see Presbyterian Survey 1735
Today's Catholic Teacher (US ISSN 0040-8441) 1685, 1750
Today's Challenge (NR) 1737
Today's Christian Woman (US ISSN 0163-1799) 1718, 1758, 1758
Today's Parish (US ISSN 0040-8549) 1718
Today's Single (US) 1684
Toern see Wudd 1722
Together (UK ISSN 0307-5982) 1737
Tohokai (JA ISSN 0386-426X) 1727
Toilers of the Deep (UK ISSN 0040-8824) 1718
Tomorrow see Studies in Comparative Religion 1717
Topics in Religion: A Bibliographic Series (US) 1721
Tora Ya Tebelo (SA ISSN 0040-9391) 1756
Torah Education (IS) 1725
Torch see Tchahert 1756
Torch (Chicago) see Torchlight 1684
Torchlight (US) 1684, 1725
Torre Davidica (IT ISSN 0040-960X) 1718
Tract Messenger (US ISSN 0041-0357) 1682, 1737
Tradicion, Familia, Propiedad (AG) 1750
Tradition (New York) (US ISSN 0041-0608) 1694, 1725
Traductions Hebraiques des Evangiles (BE) 1718
Transcript see Jewish Transcript 1686
Translation see In Other Words 1706
Trends (Rye) see Catalogue of Conferences, Seminars, Workshop 1699
Tri-County Lutheran (US) 1737
Triads (US) 1682, 1737, 1750
Tribal Religions (II) 1756
Tribuene (GW ISSN 0041-2716) 1725
Trierer Theologische Zeitschrift (GW ISSN 0041-2945) 1718
Trinitarian Bible Society. Annual Report (UK ISSN 0082-6588) 1737
Trinitarian Bible Society Quarterly Record (UK ISSN 0049-4712) 1718
Trinity Journal (US ISSN 0360-3032) 1718
Trinity Studies see Trinity Journal 1718
Trinity University Monograph Series in Religion (US ISSN 0742-2393) 1718
Trons Segrar (SW ISSN 0041-3178) 1718
Trowel and Sword (AT ISSN 0813-796X) 1718
True Union see Baptist True Union 1728
Truth (NR) 1722
Truth on Fire (CN ISSN 0821-6371) 1756
Tschechoslowakische Oekumenische Nachrichten see Czechoslovak Ecumenical News 1730
Tshiingamo (SA ISSN 0258-9052) 1756
Tsoha! (SA) 1756
Tuduv-Studie. Reihe Religionswissenschaften (GW) 1718
Twelve/Fifteen see Accent on Youth 1727
Twin Circle see Catholic Twin Circle Weekly Magazine 1742
Twin Circle Weekly Catholic Magazine see Catholic Twin Circle Weekly Magazine 1742
Tyndale Bulletin (UK ISSN 0082-7118) 1718
Tyst (UK) 1737
Tzivos Hashem Children's Newsletter (US) 1684, 1725
U L C News (Universal Life Church, Inc.) (US) 1756
U M E Connexion (United Ministries in Education) (US) 1718
U M H E Connexion see U M E Connexion 1718
U R O B A Messenger (United Russian Orthodox Brotherhood of America) (US) 1756
U S Catholic (US ISSN 0041-7548) 1750
U U W F Federation Newsletter (Unitarian Universalist Women's Federation) (US) 1737, 1758
U U W F Journal (US) 1737, 1758
Ud med Kirken (DK ISSN 0107-7295) 1718
Udruzenje Pravoslavnog Svestenstva S.F.R. Jugoslavije. Glavni Savez. Vesnik (YU ISSN 0042-4552) 1718
Udumbara (US) 1727
Ufficio Centrale per l'Emigrazione Italiana, Bollettino see Servizio Migranti 1694
Uitzicht (NE ISSN 0041-5944) 1737
Ukrainian Orthodox Word. English Edition (US ISSN 0147-1015) 1756
Ultimate Issues (US ISSN 0888-3440) 1695, 1725
Ultimate Reality and Meaning (CN ISSN 0709-549X) 1694, 1718
Ultreya (US ISSN 0041-6258) 1756
Umafrika (SA ISSN 0041-6274) 1718
Umphako Wabashumayeli (SA) 1756
Umphaphamisi (SA) 1756
Umthombo Wamandla (SA ISSN 0378-4134) 1737
Unausforschlicher Reichtum (GW ISSN 0041-6444) 1718
Unda-U S A Newsletter (US) 1684, 1750
Union des Superieures Majeurs de France. Annuaire (FR ISSN 0396-2393) 1718
Union Seminary Quarterly Review (US ISSN 0041-7025) 1718
Unison (AT) 1692, 1718
Unitarian (UK ISSN 0049-531X) 1737
Unitarian and Free Christian Churches. Handbook and Directory of the General Assembly (UK) 1737
Unitarian and Free Christian Churches. Yearbook of the General Assembly see Unitarian and Free Christian Churches. Handbook and Directory of the General Assembly 1737
Unitarian Historical Society. Proceedings see Unitarian Universalist Historical Society. Proceedings 1737
Unitarian Historical Society, London. Transactions(UK ISSN 0082-7800) 1688, 1737
Unitarian Pioneer (AT) 1718
Unitarian Quest (AT) 1718
Unitarian Universalist Directory (US ISSN 0082-7827) 1737
Unitarian Universalist Historical Society. Proceedings (US) 1737
Unitarian Universalist Women's Federation Federation Newsletter see U U W F Federation Newsletter 1758
Unitarian Universalist World (US ISSN 0041-7122) 1737
Unite des Chretiens (FR) 1718
United Baptist Convention of the Atlantic Provinces. Yearbook (CN ISSN 0082-7843) 1737
United Bible Societies. Bulletin (GW ISSN 0041-719X) 1718
United Brethren (US) 1737
United Church News (US ISSN 0882-7214) 1737
United Church Observer (CN ISSN 0041-7238) 1737
United Church of Canada. Committee on Archives. Bulletin. Records and Proceedings (CN ISSN 0082-786X) 1738
United Church of Canada. General Council. Record of Proceedings (CN ISSN 0082-7878) 1738
United Church of Canada. Year Book (CN ISSN 0082-7886) 1738
United Church of Christ. Pension Boards (Annual Report) (US ISSN 0360-9782) 1689, 1756
United Evangelical (US ISSN 0041-7262) 1738
United Evangelical Action (US ISSN 0041-7270) 1738
United Free Church of Scotland. Handbook (UK ISSN 0082-7908) 1738
United Lutheran (US ISSN 0041-7300) 1738
United Methodist Board of Higher Education and Ministry. Quarterly Review (US ISSN 0270-9287) 1718
United Methodist Church. Curriculum Plans (US ISSN 0160-0885) 1738
United Methodist Church. General Minutes of the Annual Conferences (US ISSN 0503-3551) 1738
United Methodist Church (United States) Division of Education. Adult Planbook see Adult Planbook 1727
United Methodist Directory (US ISSN 0503-356X) 1738
United Methodist Reporter (US) 1738
United Ministries in Education Connexion see U M E Connexion 1718
United Presbyterian Church in the United States of America. Minutes of the General Assembly (US ISSN 0082-8548) 1738
United Reformed Church History Society. Journal(UK ISSN 0049-5433) 1738
United Reformed Church in the United Kingdom. United Reformed Church Year Book (UK) 1738
United Reformed Church Pocket Diary (UK) 1738
United Reformed Church, Yorkshire Province, Provincial Handbook (UK) 1738
United Russian Orthodox Brotherhood of America Messenger see U R O B A Messenger 1756

United Society for the Propagation of the Gospel. Annual Report/Review see United Society for the Propagation of the Gospel. Yearbook 1718
United Society for the Propagation of the Gospel. Yearbook (UK) 1718
U.S. Parish (US) 1750
United States Catholic Mission and Association. Handbook see Mission Handbook 1746
United Synagogue Review (US ISSN 0041-8153) 1725
Unity (US ISSN 0162-3567) 1756
Unity Daily Word (US ISSN 0041-8188) 1682, 1718
Universal Life see U L C News 1756
Universal Life Church, Inc. News see U L C News 1756
Universal Life-The Inner Religion (US) 1719
Universal Message (PK) 1722
Universe (UK ISSN 0041-8226) 1750
Universidad Catolica de Chile. Facultad de Teologia. Anales (CL ISSN 0069-3596) 1750
Universidad de Navarra. Facultad de Derecho Canonico. Manuales: Derecho Canonico (SP ISSN 0078-8759) 1719
Universidad Javeriana. Facultad de Teologia. Coleccion Profesores (CK) 1719
Universitaet Innsbruck. Theologische Fakultaet. Studien und Arbeiten (AU ISSN 0579-7780) 1719
Universitaet Muenster. Institut fuer Missionswissenschaft. Veroeffentlichungen (GW ISSN 0077-197X) 1719
Universite Catholique de Louvain. Facultes de Theologie et de Droit Canonique. Collection des Dissertations Presentees pour l'Obtention du Grade de Maitre a la Faculte de Theologie Ou a la Faculte de Droit Canonique (BE) 1750
Universite Catholique de Louvain. Facultes de Theologie et de Droit Canonique. Dissertationes ad Gradum Magistri in Facultate Theologica Vel in Facultate Iuris Canonici Consequendum Conscriptae see Universite Catholique de Louvain. Facultes de Theologie et de Droit Canonique. Collection des Dissertations Presentees pour l'Obtention du Grade de Maitre a la Faculte de Theologie Ou a la Faculte de Droit Canonique 1750
Universite Catholique de Louvain. Facultes de Theologie et de Droit Canonique. Travaux de Doctorat en Theologie et en Droit Canonique. Nouvelle Serie (BE ISSN 0076-1230) 1750
Universite Saint-Joseph. Faculte des Lettres et des Sciences Humaines. Recherche. Serie A: Langue Arabe et Pensee Islamique (LE) 1690, 1722
Universite Saint-Joseph. Faculte des Lettres et des Sciences Humaines. Recherche. Serie B: Orient Chretien (LE) 1692, 1719
University of Dayton. School of Education. Workshop Proceedings (US ISSN 0070-3052) 1750
University of Dayton Review (US ISSN 0041-9524) 1691, 1719
University of Ferdowsi. Faculty of Theology and Islamic Studies. Publication/Daneshgah-e Ferdowsi. Daneshkade-Ye Elahiyat Va Ma'aref-e Eslami. Nashriyeh (IR) 1722
University of Notre Dame. Department of Theology. Liturgical Studies (US ISSN 0076-003X) 1750
University of Notre Dame. Studies in the Philosophy of Religion (US) 1694, 1719
Unreached Peoples see Refugees Among Us-Unreached Peoples 1713
Unsearchable Riches (US ISSN 0042-0476) 1719
Up with People News (US) 1692, 1719
Update (Aarhus) (DK ISSN 0108-7029) 1719
Upper Room (US ISSN 0042-0735) 1682, 1738
Upper Room see Aposento Alto 1728
Upward see Event 1731
Ut i All Verden (NO) 1738
Uw Koninkrijk Kome (NE ISSN 0042-1650) 1719, 1738
V.R.B. - Informatie (Vereniging van Religieus-Wetenschappelijke Bibliothecarissen) (BE) 1690, 1719, 1757
Vaar Fana (SW ISSN 0042-2010) 1719
Vaar Kyrka (SW ISSN 0042-2673) 1719
Vajra Bodhi Sea (US ISSN 0507-6986) 1694, 1727
Valle Santa di Rieti (IT ISSN 0042-2304) 1750
Vandaar (NE) 1738
Vanguard (Milwaukee) (US ISSN 0042-2568) 1738
Vanguard (Toronto) (CN ISSN 0009-5680) 1685, 1694, 1719
Vatican Voices and Notable Papal Quotes (US) 1750
Vedanta Kesari (II ISSN 0042-2983) 1694, 1695, 1727
Vedic Light (II) 1694, 1727
Veluws Kerkblad (NE ISSN 0042-3262) 1719
Venga Il Tuo Regno (IT) 1750
Ventana (US ISSN 0042-3459) 1738
Venture Inward (US ISSN 0748-3406) 1692, 1719
Verba Seniorum (IT ISSN 0391-8564) 1684, 1719
Verbum (NE ISSN 0166-6002) 1685, 1750
Verbum (GW ISSN 0042-3696) 1756
Verden Rundt (DK ISSN 0109-0062) 1719
Vereniging van Religieus-Wetenschappelijke Bibliothecarissen Informatie see V.R.B. - Informatie 1690
Verite see Magnificat - la Verite 1709
Verkuendigung und Forschung (GW ISSN 0342-2410) 1719
Vermont Catholic Tribune (US ISSN 0042-4145) 1750
Verona Fedele (IT ISSN 0042-4242) 1750
Verona Missions see Comboni Missions 1742
Vers Demain (CN ISSN 0042-434X) 1719
Verso l'Azzurro (IT ISSN 0042-4374) 1750
Vetus Testamentum (NE ISSN 0042-4935) 1719
Vetus Testamentum. Supplements (NE ISSN 0083-5889) 1719
Victoria Humanist see Humanist in Canada 1693
Victorian Baptist Witness (AT ISSN 0726-4097) 1738
Vida Feliz (AG) 1756
Vida Pastoral (BL ISSN 0507-7184) 1719
Vida Religiosa (SP ISSN 0211-9749) 1750
Vidyajyoti (II) 1750
Vie Catholique du Berry (FR ISSN 0042-5362) 1750
Vie Consacree (BE ISSN 0771-6842) 1719
La Vie Oecumenique (SZ) 1719
Vie Spirituelle (FR ISSN 0042-5613) 1750
Vie Theresienne (FR ISSN 0042-5621) 1750
Vigilia (HU ISSN 0042-6024) 1691, 1750
Vigiliae Christianae (NE ISSN 0042-6032) 1719
Virginia Advocate see Virginia United Methodist Advocate 1738
Virginia Baptist Register (US ISSN 0083-6311) 1738
Virginia Churchman see Virginia Episcopalian 1738
Virginia Episcopalian (US) 1738
Virginia United Methodist Advocate (US) 1738
Virtue (US) 1719, 1758
Visible Religion (NE ISSN 0169-5606) 1719
Vision (AT) 1738
Vision (Grand Rapids) (US) 1738
Visva-Bharati Journal of Philosophy (II ISSN 0042-7187) 1694, 1727
Vita Cattolica (IT ISSN 0042-7233) 1750
Vita Consacrata (IT ISSN 0042-7330) 1719
Vita Evangelica (CN ISSN 0507-1690) 1719
Vita Giuseppina (IT ISSN 0042-7276) 1685, 1750
La Vita in Cristo e Nella Chiesa (IT ISSN 0042-7284) 1719
Vita Pastorale (IT) 1719
Vita Religiosa see Vita Consacrata 1719
Vita Sociale (IT ISSN 0042-7365) 1689, 1750, 1757
Vital Christianity (US ISSN 0042-7381) 1756
Vivekananda Vedanta Society of Chicago. Bulletins (US) 1727
Vjesnik Biskupije Splitske i Makarske see Vjesnik Nadbiskupije Splitsko-Makarske 1719
Vjesnik Nadbiskupije Splitsko-Makarske (YU ISSN 0042-7659) 1719
Voce (IT ISSN 0042-7780) 1719
Voce Cattolica see Voce di Ferrara 1750
Voce della Comunita see Shalom 1687
Voce della Madonna delle Grazie (IT ISSN 0042-7845) 1750
Voce di Ferrara (IT ISSN 0042-7853) 1750
Voci Fraterne (IT ISSN 0042-7888) 1719
Voice see Full Gospel Business Men's Voice 1752
Voice (Newark) (US ISSN 0277-2272) 1738
Voice (Westchester) (US ISSN 0049-6669) 1756
Voice from Jerusalem (IS) 1682, 1687, 1725, 1758
Voice of Ahinsa (II ISSN 0042-8086) 1727
Voice of Buddhism (MY ISSN 0042-8094) 1727
Voice of Islam (PK ISSN 0042-8132) 1722
Voice of Islam (UG) 1722
Voice of Judaism (US) 1725
Voice of Liberty (US ISSN 0042-8159) 1719
Voice of Methodism (UK ISSN 0042-8167) 1738
Voice of Missions (US ISSN 0042-8175) 1738
Voice of Samanvaya (II) 1756
Voice of the Gospel see Phoni Tou Evangeliou 1712
Voice of the Holy Land/Sawt el-Ard el-Mukaddash (JO) 1750
Voice of the Martyrs (US) 1719
Voice of the Movement see Kol ha-T'nuah 1686
Voice of the Nazarene-a Universal Challenger (US ISSN 0042-8213) 1756
Voice of the Vaad (CN) 1725
Voices (Salem) (US) 1756
Voiovnychyi Ateyist see Lyudyna i Svit 1709
Voix d'Afrique (FR ISSN 0293-9932) 1719
Voix de l'Islam (MF) 1722
Volunteer (US) 1738
Die Voorligter (SA ISSN 0042-8728) 1738
Vorreformationsgeschichtliche Forschungen (GW ISSN 0083-6923) 1719
Vox Benedictina (CN ISSN 0715-8726) 1719
Vox Evangelica (UK ISSN 0263-6786) 1719
Vox Reformata (AT ISSN 0728-0912) 1719
Vriend van Oud en Jong (NE ISSN 0042-9155) 1719
Vukani! (SA) 1756
Wabul (NQ) 1719
Die Wagtoring (SA) 1756
Wanderer (US) 1694, 1719
War Cry (NZ ISSN 0043-0242) 1687, 1756
War Cry (AT) 1719, 1756
War Cry (CN ISSN 0043-0218) 1756
War Cry (NR ISSN 0049-688X) 1756
War Cry/Strydkreet (SA ISSN 0043-0250) 1756
War Cry (SI ISSN 0049-6898) 1756
War Cry (UK ISSN 0043-0226) 1756
War Cry (US ISSN 0043-0234) 1756
Warrior (UK ISSN 0049-6901) 1684, 1719
Washington Buddhist (US) 1727
Washington Diocese (US ISSN 0043-0544) 1738
Watchtower (US ISSN 0043-1087) 1756
Way see Way-Ukrainian Catholic Bi-Weekly 1750
Way (London, 1961) (UK ISSN 0043-1575) 1750
Way (San Francisco) (US) 1691, 1750
Way of Life (UK ISSN 0043-1605) 1756
Way of St. Francis see Way (San Francisco) 1750
Way-Ukrainian Catholic Bi-Weekly/Way (US) 1687, 1750
Weekday Homily Helps (US) 1719
Weekly Bible Reader (US) 1684, 1719
Weekly Crusader see Christian Crusade 1700
Wege zum Menschen (GW ISSN 0043-2040) 1719
Wege Zum Studium der Geisteswissenschaft und zur Bewusstmachung Anthroposophischer Verantwortung (SZ) 1719
Wege zur Pflege eines Meditativen Lebens und zu Einem Vertieften Christusverstaendniss see Wege Zum Studium der Geisteswissenschaft und zur Bewusstmachung Anthroposophischer Verantwortung 1719
Wegwijzer (NE ISSN 0043-2105) 1738
Wellsprings (US ISSN 0887-011X) 1725
Welsh Churchman (UK) 1738
Die Welt der Buecher (GW ISSN 0043-2490) 1695, 1719
Die Weltmission (GW) 1738
Die Wende (AU ISSN 0043-2679) 1684, 1750
Wereld en Zending (NE ISSN 0165-988X) 1719
Wereldwijd (BE) 1719
Wesley Historical Society. Proceedings (UK ISSN 0043-2873) 1688, 1738
Wesleyan Advocate (US ISSN 0043-289X) 1738
Wesleyan Christian Advocate (US) 1738
Wesleyan Methodist see Wesleyan Advocate 1738
Wesleyan Theological Journal (US ISSN 0092-4245) 1738
West African Religion (NR ISSN 0083-8187) 1719
West Texas Angelus (US) 1750
West Texas Catholic (US) 1750
West Texas Register see West Texas Catholic 1750
Western Buddhist (UK ISSN 0144-9818) 1727
Western Catholic Reporter (CN ISSN 0512-5235) 1750
Western Recorder (US ISSN 0043-4132) 1738
Western States Jewish Historical Quarterly see Western States Jewish History 1687
Western States Jewish History (US) 1687, 1725
Westfalia Sacra (GW) 1688, 1719
Westminster Theological Journal (US ISSN 0043-4388) 1719
Wheel (CE ISSN 0049-7541) 1727
Wheel Series (US) 1756
Wherever (US) 1756
White Light (US ISSN 0742-8820) 1756
White Wing Messenger (US ISSN 0043-5007) 1756
Wind Bell (US ISSN 0043-5708) 1727
Wind River Rendezvous (US) 1687, 1750
Window (UK ISSN 0306-9028) 1684, 1738
Wissenschaft und Praxis in Kirche und Gesellschaft see Pastoraltheologie - Monatsschrift fuer Wissenschaft und Praxis in Kirche und Gesellschaft 1712
Wissenschaftliche Untersuchungen zum Neuen Testament (GW) 1720
With (US ISSN 0043-6984) 1684, 1756
Witness see Harvester 1705
Witness (US ISSN 0197-8896) 1738
Wittenburg Door (US ISSN 0199-8285) 1738
Women in a Changing World (SZ) 1720, 1758
Women's American O R T Reporter (US ISSN 0043-7514) 1725, 1757
Women's League Outlook (US ISSN 0043-7557) 1725
Women's Zionist Council of South Africa. News and Views see Women's Zionist Organization of South Africa. News and Views 1725
Women's Zionist Organization of South Africa. News and Views (SA) 1687, 1694, 1725
Woord en Dienst (NE) 1720
Worcestershire Recusant (UK) 1689, 1750
Word and Deed (IS) 1725
Word & Spirit (US ISSN 0193-9211) 1750
Word and Way (US ISSN 0049-7959) 1738
Word & Witness (US) 1738
Word & World (US ISSN 0275-5270) 1738
Word at Work (UK) 1738
Word in Action: the Bible in the World (UK) 1720
Word of Salvation (AT ISSN 0813-7951) 1720
Workers' Challenge (ZA) 1682, 1750
Working Papers in Yiddish and East European Jewish Studies/In Gang Fun Arbet: Yidish Un Mizrakh Eyropeishe Yidishe Shtudies (US) 1687, 1725
World Association for Christian Communication. Journal see Media Development 1684
World Call see Disciple (St. Louis) 1702
World Council of Churches. Faith and Order Papers see Faith and Order Papers 1704
World Council of Churches. Minutes and Reports of the Central Committee Meeting (SZ ISSN 0084-1684) 1720
World Council of Churches. Office of Education. Education Newsletter (SZ) 1720
World Council of Churches Background Information see C C I A Background Information 1699
World Council of Churches Information see P C R Information 1712
World Encounter (US ISSN 0043-8413) 1738
World Faiths Insight (US ISSN 0273-1266) 1720
World Fellowship of Buddhists. Book Series (TH ISSN 0084-1781) 1727
World Fellowship of Buddhists Review (TH ISSN 0043-8464) 1727
World Lithuanian Roman Catholic Directory (US) 1687, 1750
World Methodist Historical Society. Historical Bulletin (US) 1738
World Methodist Historical Society. News Bulletin see World Methodist Historical Society. Historical Bulletin 1738
World Mission Journal (US) 1739
World Missionary Press News (US) 1720
World Missions Update (AT ISSN 0158-6262) 1756
World Muslim Conference. Proceedings (PK ISSN 0084-2052) 1722
World Muslim Gazetteer (PK ISSN 0084-2060) 1722
World of Faith see Shinanggye 1715
World of Shaker see Shaker Messenger 1755
World Order (US ISSN 0043-8804) 1694, 1756
World Outlook see New World Outlook 1734
World Parish (US ISSN 0043-8839) 1739
World Pulse see Pulse 1713
World Spotlight see Lost & Found 1753
World Vision (US ISSN 0043-9215) 1756
World-Wide Impact see Worldwide Challenge 1720
World Zionist Organization. General Council. Addresses, Debates, Resolutions (IS ISSN 0084-2516) 1725
World's Wisdom Series (II) 1694, 1720
Worldwide Challenge (US) 1720
Worldwide News (US) 1692
Worldwind (CN ISSN 0707-2279) 1684, 1720
Worship (US ISSN 0043-941X) 1750
Worship and Preaching (UK ISSN 0032-7107) 1739
Worship Times see Modern Liturgy 1710
Wort in der Welt see Die Weltmission 1738
Wort und Weg (GW ISSN 0043-9444) 1739
Wudd (GW ISSN 0040-8646) 1722
Wyzer (NE) 1684, 1756
Xaverian Missions Newsletter (US) 1751
Xihondzo Xo Rindza (SA ISSN 0258-9079) 1756
Y A M see Vision (Grand Rapids) 1738
Yad l'Achim Wall Calendar (IS) 1725
Yad Vashem Studies (IS) 1725
Yad Vashem Studies on the European Jewish Catastrophe and Resistance see Yad Vashem Studies 1725
Yale Judaica Series (US ISSN 0084-3369) 1725
Yale Publications in Religion (US ISSN 0084-3407) 1720
Yaqeen International (PK ISSN 0044-0213) 1692, 1722
Yavneh Studies (US ISSN 0044-0256) 1725
Yearbook and Church Directory of the Orthodox Church in America see Orthodox Church in America. Yearbook and Church Directory 1754
Yearbook of American and Canadian Churches (US ISSN 0084-3644) 1720
Yearbook of American Churches see Yearbook of American and Canadian Churches 1720
Yearbook of Jehovah's Witnesses see Jehovah's Witnesses Yearbook 1753
Yearbook of the American Baptist Churches in the U.S.A see American Baptist Churches in the U.S.A. Yearbook 1727
Yearbooks in Christian Education (US ISSN 0084-4128) 1720
Yedinaya Tserkov see One Church 1754
Yes (UK) 1720
Yeshiva University Sephardic Bulletin (US) 1687, 1725
Yevanhelskyj Ranok/Evangelical Morning (US ISSN 0044-0388) 1739
Yid (US ISSN 0044-040X) 1725
Yiddish Literary and Linguistic Periodicals and Miscellanies (IS) 1687, 1690, 1691, 1725
Yiddishe Heim/Jewish Home (US ISSN 0044-0418) 1725
Yoga (DK ISSN 0044-0485) 1694, 1756
Yogasana Alaya Vijayam (II) 1722
York Journal of Convocation (UK ISSN 0085-8374) 1720

Young Adult Bible Study (US ISSN 0162-4814) *1739*
Young Adults in Training *see* Baptist Young Adults *1728*
Young Ambassador *see* T Q *1684*
Young Buddhist (SI) *1727*
Young Companion (CN) *1756*
Young East (JA ISSN 0386-4251) *1692,* 1727
Young Ideas (SA ISSN 0044-0787) 1683, *1756*
Young Israel Viewpoint (US ISSN 0044-0809) *1725*
Young Men's Institute. Institute Journal (US ISSN 0020-2673) *1720*
Young Soldier (AT ISSN 0300-3264) 1684, *1756*
Young Warrior *see* Warrior *1684*
Young Women's Christian Association of the United States of America. The Printout (US ISSN 0084-4306) *1720*
Young Worker (SA) *1682*
Your Child (US ISSN 0044-1007) *1685,* 1725
Your Church (US ISSN 0049-8394) 1681, *1720*
Your Edmundite Missions News Letter (US ISSN 0044-1015) *1720*
Youth in Action (US ISSN 0162-4784) *1739*
Youth in Action. Teacher (US ISSN 0162-4792) *1739*
Youth in Discovery (US) *1739*
Youth in Discovery. Teacher (US ISSN 0162-4768) *1739*
Youth Leadership (US ISSN 0162-4709) *1739*
Youth Mirror (MF ISSN 0049-8459) *1684,* 1722
Youth Newsletter (SZ) *1720*
Youth Planbook (US ISSN 0512-9575) 1685, *1739*
Youth Program Service *see* Emmaus Letter *1743*
Youth Teacher *see* Sunday School Youth-Teacher *1737*
Youth Update (US) *1751*
Youth's Instructor *see* Insight (Hagerstown) *1733*
Yuvak (II ISSN 0044-1414) *1720*
Zaaier (NE ISSN 0044-1562) *1739*
Zeal (US ISSN 0514-2482) *1751*
Zealandia (NZ ISSN 0044-202X) *1751*
Zeichen der Zeit (GE ISSN 0044-2038) *1739*
Zeitschrift fuer Bayerische Kirchengeschichte (GW ISSN 0342-4316) *1739*
Zeitschrift fuer die Alttestamentliche Wissenschaft(GW ISSN 0044-2526) *1720*
Zeitschrift fuer die Alttestamentliche Wissenschaft. Beihefte (GW) *1720*
Zeitschrift fuer die neutestamentliche Wissenschaft und die Kunde der Aelteren Kirche (GW ISSN 0044-2615) *1720*
Zeitschrift fuer Evangelische Ethik (GW ISSN 0044-2674) *1720*
Zeitschrift fuer Evangelisches Kirchenrecht (GW ISSN 0044-2690) 1690, *1739*
Zeitschrift fuer Gottesdienst und Predigt (GW) *1720*
Zeitschrift fuer katholische Theologie (AU ISSN 0044-2895) 1694, *1751*
Zeitschrift fuer Kirchengeschichte (GW ISSN 0044-2925) *1720*
Zeitschrift fuer Mission (GW ISSN 0342-9423) *1720*
Zeitschrift fuer Missionswissenschaft und Religionswissenschaft (GW ISSN 0044-3123) *1720*
Zeitschrift fuer Religions- und Geistesgeschichte (GW ISSN 0044-3441) *1720*
Zeitschrift fuer Religions- und Geistesgeschichte. Beihefte (NE) *1720*
Zeitschrift fuer Religionspaedagogik *see* Religion Heute *1685*
Zeitschrift fuer Schweizerische Kirchengeschichte/ Revue d'Histoire Ecclesiastique Suisse (SZ ISSN 0044-3484) *1720*
Zeitschrift fuer Theologie und Kirche (GW ISSN 0513-9147) *1739*
Zen (NE) *1756*
Zen Extra (NE) *1727*
Zen Mission Society. Journal *see* Order of Buddhist Contemplatives. Journal *1726*
Zending *see* Vandaar *1738*
Zentralkomitee der Deutschen Katholiken. Mitteilungen (GW) *1751*
Zion (IS ISSN 0044-4758) *1687,* 1688, 1725
Zionism; Studies in the History of the Zionist Movement and of the Jews in Palestine/Ha-Tsiyonut *see* Studies in Zionism *1725*
Zionist Literature (IS ISSN 0044-4774) 1694, *1695,* 1721
Zions Freund (SA ISSN 0028-3568) *1720*
Znaci Vremena (YU) *1720*
Znak (PL ISSN 0044-488X) 1694, *1720*
Zondagsmis (NE ISSN 0044-5002) *1720*
Zondervan Pastor's Annual (US ISSN 0084-5558) *1720*
Zum Thema (GW) *1720*
Zuversicht und Staerke (GW ISSN 0722-3234) *1739*
Zwingli (NE ISSN 0044-5576) *1739*
Zygon (US ISSN 0591-2385) *1720*
7th Angel (US) *1720*
20th Century Christian (US ISSN 0162-6418) *1720*

KEY TO PUBLISHERS' AND DISTRIBUTORS' ABBREVIATIONS

The entries in this list contain: Publisher's or distributor's abbreviation, followed by its full name, ISBN prefix, editorial address, telephone number, toll-free telephone number, and SAN (Standard Address Number). Ordering and/or distributor name and address are listed if they differ from the editorial address. Abbreviations used to identify publishers' imprints are followed by the full name of the imprint. See the example listed below:

Arbor Vitae, *(Arbor Vitae Productions; 0-933351),* 2461 Orange Thorpe, Suite 103, Fullerton, CA 92648 Tel 714-526-0119, Toll Free: 800-555-1212; (SAN 691-7607); Dist. by: Albaco Enterprises, 1284 Starlit Dr., Laguna Beach, CA 92651 (SAN 691-7615).

Book entries found in the main indexes of this work which include the term "Pub. by" should be ordered from the distributor, not the publisher. For example, the title listed below should be ordered from Kluwer Academic.

Reichardt, W. Acoustics Dictionary. Date not set. lib. bdg. 28.50 (ISBN 90-247-2707-3, Pub. by Martinus Nijhoff Netherlands). Kluwer Academic.

A A Coolidge
See Celestial Gems

A Adler Inst, *(Adler, Alfred, Institute of Chicago, Inc.; 0-918560),* 618 S. Michigan Ave., Chicago, IL 60605 (SAN 201-1956) Tel 312-294-7100.

A-albionic Res, *(A-albionic Research),* P.O. Box 20273, Ferndale, MI 48220 (SAN 210-6973) Tel 313-398-2896.

A & S Pr, *(A & S Pr.; 0-935930),* P.O. Box 3277, Chico, CA 95926 (SAN 214-4697) Tel 916-343-1493.

A C S Pubns Inc, *(ACS Pubns., Inc.; 0-917086; 0-935127),* P.O. Box 16430, San Diego, CA 92116-0430 (SAN 208-5380) Tel 619-297-9203; Toll free: 800-826-1085; Toll free: 800-525-1786 (in California). Do not confuse with ACS Publishing Co., also in San Diego.

A Cohen, *(Cohen, Alan; 0-910367),* P.O. Box 1036, New Brunswick, NJ 08903 (SAN 239-4227) Tel 201-699-1744; Dist. by: New Leaf Distributing, 1020 White St., SW, Atlanta, GA 30310 (SAN 169-1449) Tel 404-755-2665; Dist. by: DeVorss & Co., P.O. Box 550, 1046 Princeton Dr., Marina del Rey, CA 90294 (SAN 168-9886) Tel 213-870-7478.

A D Bragdon, *(Bragdon, Allen D., Pubs., Inc.; 0-916410),* Brownstone Library, Munchie Bks., 153 W. 82nd St., New York, NY 10024 (SAN 208-5623) Tel 212-787-6886; Dist. by: Kampmann & Co., 9 E. 40th St., New York, NY 10016 (SAN 202-5191) Tel 212-685-2928.

A E P, *(American Enterprise Pubns.; 0-9612198),* Box 6690, R.D. 6, Mercer, PA 16137 (SAN 202-4454) Tel 412-748-3726. Do not confuse with American Enterprise Institute for Public Policy Research, Washington, DC.

A Earle, *(Earle, Arthur; 0-9600788),* 10922 Nandina Ct., Philadelphia, PA 19116 (SAN 207-4648) Tel 215-676-9762.

A F Joy, *(Joy, A. F.),* 64 Gardenia Ct., Orange City, FL 32763 (SAN 695-4863) Tel 904-775-2067; Orders to: Saturscent Pubns., Box 358, South Wellfleet, MA 02663 (SAN 662-3484) Tel 617-349-2921.

A Finkelstein, *(Finkelstein, Adrian; 0-87418),* 855 E. Palatine Rd., Palatine, IL 60067 (SAN 693-4285); Dist. by: Coleman Publishing Co., 99 Milbar Blvd., Farmingdale, NY 11735 (SAN 238-1508) Tel 516-293-0383.

A Fishelis, *(Fishelis, Avraham, Pub.; 0-9605560),* 577 Grand St., New York, NY 10002 (SAN 240-0006) Tel 212-260-1760.

A H Clark, *(Clark, Arthur H., Co.; 0-87062),* P.O. Box 230, Glendale, CA 91209 (SAN 201-2006) Tel 213-254-1600.

A Khalid, *(Khalid, Anas; 0-9617422),* 30 Richmond Plaza, No. 26H, Bronx, NY 10453 (SAN 663-9488) Tel 212-731-4725.

A R Allenson, *(Allenson, Alec R., Inc.; 0-8401),* P.O. Box 447, Geneva, AL 36340 (SAN 162-4903).

A R C Pub, *(ARC Publishing Co.; 0-917187),* P.O. Box 1138, Glendale, CA 91209 (SAN 655-8704) Tel 818-244-0113; Dist. by: DeVorss & Co., P.O. Box 550, 1046 Princeton Dr., Marina del Rey, CA 90294 (SAN 168-9886).

A R Liss, *(Liss, Alan R., Inc.; 0-8451),* 41 E. 11th St., New York, NY 10003 (SAN 207-7558) Tel 212-475-7700.

A S Barnes, *(Barnes, A. S., & Co., Inc.; 0-498),* Subs. of Oak Tree Pubns., Inc., 9601 Aero Dr., San Diego, CA 92123 (SAN 201-2030) Tel 619-560-5163.

A Whitman, *(Whitman, Albert, & Co.; 0-8075),* 5747 W. Howard St., Niles, IL 60648 (SAN 201-2049) Tel 312-647-1355.

A Wofsy Fine Arts, *(Wofsy, Alan, Fine Arts; 0-915346; 1-55660),* P.O. Box 2210, San Francisco, CA 94126 (SAN 207-6438); 401 China Basin St., San Francisco, CA 94107 (SAN 662-7501) Tel 415-986-3030.

AAFH, *(Academy of American Franciscan History; 0-88382),* P.O. Box 34440, West Bethesda, MD 20817 (SAN 201-1964) Tel 301-365-1763.

AASLH Pr, *(American Assn. for State & Local History Pr.; 0-910050; 0-942063),* 172 Second Ave., N., Suite 102, Nashville, TN 37201 (SAN 201-1972) Tel 615-225-2971.

Abaris Bks, *(Abaris Bks., Inc.; 0-913870; 0-89835),* 24 W. 40th St., New York, NY 10018 (SAN 206-4588) Tel 212-354-1313.

ABBE Pubs Assn, *(ABBE Pubs. Assn. of Washington, D.C.; 0-941864; 0-88164),* 4111 Gallows Rd., Virginia Div., Annandale, VA 22003 (SAN 239-1430) Tel 703-750-0255; Georgetown 3724, 1215 31st St., NW, Washington, DC 20007 (SAN 668-9450).

Abbetira Pubns, *(Abbetira Pubns.; 0-913407),* P.O. Box 27297, Tucson, AZ 85726-7297 (SAN 697-709X) Tel 602-628-9949; Dist. by: Samuel Weiser, Inc., P.O. Box 612, York Beach, ME 03910 (SAN 202-9588); Dist. by: Starlite Distributors, P.O. Box 20729, Las Vegas, NV 89515 (SAN 662-7544).

Abbeville Pr, *(Abbeville Pr., Inc.; 0-89659),* 488 Madison Ave., New York, NY 10022 (SAN 211-4755) Tel 212-888-1969; Toll free: 800-227-7210.

Abbey, *(Abbey Pr. Printing & Publishing; 0-87029),* Hwy. 545, St. Meinrad, IN 47577 (SAN 201-2057) Tel 812-357-8011.

Abbott Loop, *(Abbott Loop Pubns.; 0-911739),* 2626 Abbott Rd., Anchorage, AK 99507-4299 (SAN 263-905X) Tel 907-349-9641.

ABC-Clio, *(ABC-Clio, Inc.; 0-87436; 1-85109; 0-903450),* 2040 Alameda Padre Serra, P.O. Box 4397, Santa Barbara, CA 93140-4397 (SAN 301-5467) Tel 805-963-4221; Toll free: 800-422-2546.

Abiding Word Pubns, *(Abiding Word Pubns.; 0-9617377),* 1483 Auburn Ct., Eagan, MN 55122 (SAN 663-8864) Tel 612-456-5682.

Abilene Christ U, *(Abilene Christian Univ. Pr.; 0-915547; 0-89112),* Div. of Abilene Christian Univ., 1634 Campus Ct., Abilene, TX 79601 (SAN 207-1681) Tel 915-674-2720; Toll free: 800-527-0575; Toll free: 800-592-1404 (TX).

Abingdon, *(Abingdon Pr.; 0-687),* Div. of United Methodist Publishing Hse., 201 Eighth Ave., S., Nashville, TN 37202 (SAN 201-0054) Tel 615-749-6290; Toll free: 800-251-3320; 1015 Visco Dr., Nashville, TN 37210 (SAN 699-9956). *Imprints:* Apex (Apex Books); Festival (Festival Books).

Ablex Pub, *(Ablex Publishing Corp.; 0-89391),* 355 Chestnut St., Norwood, NJ 07648 (SAN 209-3332) Tel 201-767-8450.

Abner Schram Ltd, *(Abner Schram Ltd.; 0-8390),* 36 Park St., Montclair, NJ 07042 (SAN 685-3129) Tel 201-744-7755; c/o Biblio Distribution Ctr., 81 Adams Dr., Totowa, NJ 07512 (SAN 680-0025) Tel 201-256-8600. *Imprints:* Allanheld & Schram (Allanheld & Schram).

Abrams, *(Abrams, Harry N., Inc.; 0-8109),* Subs. of Times Mirror Co., 100 Fifth Ave., New York, NY 10011 (SAN 200-2434) Tel 212-206-7715; Toll free: 800-345-1359; Orders to: Wayne Public Warehouse, 150 Parish Dr., Wayne, NJ 07470 (SAN 699-9964).

Abundant Life Pubns, *(Abundant Life Pubns.; 0-931867),* Subs. of Perry Gaspard Ministries, P.O. Box 336, Lake Charles, LA 70602 (SAN 686-0532) Tel 318-478-1112.

Acad Assoc, *(Academic Assocs.; 0-918260),* P.O. Box 628, Van Nuys, CA 91408 (SAN 210-1556) Tel 818-988-2479.

Acad Bks Pubs
See IBS Intl

Acad New Church, *(Academy of the New Church; 0-910557),* P.O. Box 278, Bryn Athyn, PA 19009 (SAN 266-0512) Tel 215-947-4200.

Acad Pr, *(Academic Pr., Inc.; 0-12),* Subs. of Harcourt Brace Jovanovich, Inc., Orlando, FL 32887 (SAN 206-8990) Tel 305-345-2700; Toll free: 800-321-5068.
Academic Intl, *(Academic International Pr.; 0-87569),* P.O. Box 1111, Gulf Breeze, FL 32561 (SAN 201-212X).
Academy Bks, *(Academy Bks.; 0-914960),* P.O. Box 757, Rutland, VT 05701-0757 (SAN 208-4325) Tel 802-773-9194; Dist. by: Charles E. Tuttle Co., Inc, P.O. Box 410, 28 S. Main St., Rutland, VT 05701-0410 (SAN 213-2621) Tel 802-773-8930.
Academy Chi Pubs, *(Academy Chicago Pubs.; 0-915864; 0-89733),* 425 N. Michigan Ave., Chicago, IL 60611 (SAN 213-2001) Tel 312-644-1723.
Accent Bks, *(Accent Bks.; 0-89636; 0-916406),* Div. of Accent Pubns., P.O. Box 15337, Lakewood Sta., Denver, CO 80215 (SAN 208-5097); Toll free: 800-525-5550; 12100 W. Sixth Ave., Denver, CO 80215 (SAN 208-5100) Tel 303-988-5300.
ACETO Bookmen, *(ACETO Bookmen; 0-9607906),* 5721 Antietam Dr., Sarasota, FL 33581 (SAN 237-9252) Tel 813-924-9170.
Acoma Bks, *(Acoma Bks.; 0-916552),* P.O. Box 4, Ramona, CA 92065 (SAN 207-7221) Tel 619-789-1288.
Acorn NC, *(Acorn Pr.; 0-89386),* 1318 Broad St., Box 4007, Duke Sta., Durham, NC 27706 (SAN 216-4833) Tel 919-286-9830.
Acropolis, *(Acropolis Bks.; 0-87491),* Subs. of Colortone Pr., Inc., 2400 17th St. NW, Washington, DC 20009 (SAN 201-2227) Tel 202-387-6805; Toll free: 800-621-5199.
ACTA Found, *(ACTA Foundation; 0-87946; 0-914070),* 4848 N. Clark St., Chicago, IL 60640 (SAN 204-7489) Tel 312-271-1030.
Action Life Pubns, *(Action & Life Pubns.; 0-9607590; 0-936707),* 504 E. Palace Ave., Santa Fe, NM 87501 (SAN 238-6607) Tel 505-983-1960.
Adama Pubs Inc, *(Adama Pubs., Inc.; 0-915361; 1-55774),* 306 W. 38th St., New York, NY 10018 (SAN 291-0640) Tel 212-594-5770; Toll free: 800-672-6672; Dist. by: Franklin Watts, Inc., 387 Park Ave., S., New York, NY 10016 (SAN 200-7002) Tel 212-686-7070.
Adams Bannister Cox, *(Adams, Bannister, Cox Pubs.; 0-937431),* 460 Riverside Dr., Suite 52, New York, NY 10027 (SAN 658-9707) Tel 212-749-6709.
Adar Pubns, *(Adar Pubns.; 0-916169),* 8434 Main St., Interlaken, NY 14847 (SAN 294-8842) Tel 607-532-4404.
Addison-Wesley, *(Addison-Wesley Publishing Co., Inc.; 0-201),* 1 Jacob Way, Reading, MA 01867 (SAN 200-2000) Tel 617-944-3700; Toll free: 800-447-2226.
ADL, *(Anti-Defamation League of B'nai B'rith; 0-88464),* 823 United Nations Plaza, New York, NY 10017 (SAN 204-7616) Tel 212-490-2525.
Adlen Bks, *(Adlen Bks.; 0-9615371),* 3303 Kerckhoff Ave., Fresno, CA 93702 (SAN 696-6322) Tel 209-264-5421.
Adler & Adler, *(Adler & Adler Pubs., Inc.; 0-917561),* 4550 Montgomery Ave., Suite 705, Bethesda, MD 20814 (SAN 656-5298) Tel 301-654-4271; Dist. by: Harper & Row Pubs., Inc., Keystone Industrial Pk., Scranton, PA 18512 (SAN 200-688X).
Adlers Foreign Bks, *(Adler's Foreign Bks., Inc.; 0-8417),* Affil. of Midwest European Publns., Inc. & Euopa Bookstores, 915 Foster St., Evanston, IL 60201 (SAN 201-2251) Tel 312-866-6329; Toll free: 800-235-3771. Do not confuse with Adler Publishing Co., Rochester, NY, nor with Adler & Adler Pubs., Bethesda, MD.
Adonis Pr, *(Adonis Pr.; 0-932776),* Hawthorne Valley, Ghentdale, NY 12075 (SAN 218-463X); Orders to: Christy Barnes, R.D., Hillsdale, NY 12529 (SAN 661-9320) Tel 518-325-7182.
Advent, *(Advent: Pubs., Inc.; 0-911682),* P.O. Box A3228, Chicago, IL 60690 (SAN 201-2286).
Advent NY, *(Advent Bks., Inc; 0-89891),* 141 E. 44th St., Suite 511, New York, NY 10017 (SAN 212-9973) Tel 212-697-0887.
Advocacy Pr, *(Advocacy Pr.; 0-911655),* Div. of Girls Club of Santa Barbara, P.O. Box 236, Santa Barbara, CA 93102 (SAN 263-9114) Tel 805-962-2728; Dist. by: Ingram Bk. Co., P.O. Box 17266, Nashville, TN 37217 (SAN 169-7978) Tel 615-361-5000; Dist. by: Publishers Group West, 5855 Beaudry St., Emeryville, CA 94608 (SAN 202-8522); Dist. by: Gordon's Bks. Inc., 2323 Delgany St., Denver, CO 80216 (SAN 169-0531) Tel 303-296-1830; Dist. by: Bookpeople, 2929 Fifth St., Berkeley, CA 94710 (SAN 168-9517) Tel 415-549-3030.
Advocate, *(Advocate Pr.; 0-911866),* 312 W. Main St., Franklin Springs, GA 30639 (SAN 201-2294) Tel 404-245-7272.
Advocate Pub Group, *(Advocate Publishing Group; 0-89894),* Subs. of Avatar Media Assocs., P.O. Box 351, Reynoldsburg, OH 43068-0351 (SAN 213-0238) Tel 614-861-7738.
Aegean Park Pr, *(Aegean Park Pr.; 0-89412),* P.O. Box 2837, Laguna Hills, CA 92654-0837 (SAN 210-0231) Tel 714-586-8811.
Aeonian Pr
See Amereon Ltd
Aerial Photo, *(Aerial Photography Services, Inc.; 0-936672),* 2511 S. Tryon St., Charlotte, NC 28203 (SAN 214-2791) Tel 704-333-5143.
Aero-Medical, *(Aero-Medical Consultants, Inc.; 0-912522),* 10912 Hamlin Blvd., Largo, FL 33544 (SAN 201-2316) Tel 813-596-2551.
Aero Pr, *(Aero Pr. Pubs.; 0-936450),* P.O. Box 2091, Fall River, MA 02722 (SAN 207-0650) Tel 617-644-2058.
AFC, *(Apostolate for Family Consecration, The; 0-932406),* Box 220, Kenosha, WI 53141 (SAN 223-6702) Tel 414-652-2600.
Affirmation, *(Affirmation Bks.; 0-89571),* 109 Woodland St., Natick, MA 01760 (SAN 209-5211) Tel 617-651-3893.
Africa Fund, *(Africa Fund; 0-943428),* 198 Broadway, New York, NY 10038 (SAN 224-0319) Tel 212-962-1210.
Africa World, *(Africa World Pr.; 0-86543),* P.O. Box 1892, Trenton, NJ 08607 (SAN 692-3925) Tel 609-695-3766. Do not confuse with Africa Research & Pubns. Project, Inc. at the same address.
African Islam Miss Pubns, *(African Islamic Mission Pubns., The; 0-916157),* Subs. of A.I.M. Graphics, 1390 Bedford Ave., Brooklyn, NY 11216 (SAN 294-6645) Tel 718-638-4607.
Africana *Imprint of* **Holmes & Meier**
Agadir Pr, *(Agadir Pr.; 0-913627),* P.O. Box 2015, Corvallis, OR 97339 (SAN 286-0309) Tel 503-929-5918; 424 S. 17th St., Philomath, OR 97370 (SAN 286-0317).
Agape IL, *(Agape; 0-916642),* Div. of Hope Publishing Co., 380 S. Main Pl., Carol Stream, IL 60188 (SAN 217-2224); Toll free: 800-323-1049.
Aglow Pubns, *(Aglow Pubns.; 0-930756; 0-932305),* Div. of Women's Aglow Fellowship International, P.O. Box I, Lynnwood, WA 98046-1557 (SAN 211-8297) Tel 206-775-7282.
Agni Review, *(Agni Review),* P.O. Box 660, Amherst, MA 01004 (SAN 219-4600) Tel 413-549-4912.
Agni Yoga Soc, *(Agni Yoga Society, Inc.; 0-933574),* 319 W. 107th St., New York, NY 10025-2799 (SAN 201-7121) Tel 212-864-7752.
Ahio Pub Co, *(Ahio Publishing Co.; 0-914347),* 4313 W. 43rd St., Tulsa, OK 74107 (SAN 289-582X) Tel 918-446-9278.
AIRE, *(Alternatives in Religious Education, Inc.; 0-86705),* 3945 S. Oneida St., Denver, CO 80237 (SAN 216-6534) Tel 303-363-7779.
Airmont, *(Airmont Publishing Co., Inc.; 0-8049),* 401 Lafayette St., New York, NY 10003 (SAN 206-8710) Tel 212-598-0222.
Al Rainey Pubns, *(Rainey, Al, Pubns.; 0-932971),* 1015 N. El Centro Ave., Los Angeles, CA 90038 (SAN 690-0488) Tel 213-463-7876.
ALA, *(American Library Assn.; 0-8389),* 50 E. Huron St., Chicago, IL 60611 (SAN 201-0062) Tel 312-944-6780; Toll free: 800-545-2433; Toll free: 800-545-2444 in Illinois; Toll free: 800-545-2455 in Canada.
Aladdin Bks *Imprint of* **Macmillan**
Alaska Hist, *(Alaska Historical Commission; 0-943712),* Div. of State of Alaska, P.O. Box 7001, Anchorage, AK 99510 (SAN 240-9933) Tel 907-762-4108; Dist. by: Alaska Pacific Univ., 4101 University Dr., Anchorage, AK 99508 (SAN 215-2908).
Alaska Northwest, *(Alaska Northwest Publishing Co.; 0-88240),* 130 Second Ave., S., Edmonds, WA 98020 (SAN 201-2383) Tel 206-774-4111.
Alba, *(Alba Hse.; 0-8189),* Div. of Society of St. Paul, 2187 Victory Blvd., Staten Island, NY 10314 (SAN 201-2405) Tel 718-761-0047.
Albanian Cath Info, *(Albanian Catholic Information Ctr.; 0-9614744),* P.O. Box 1217, Santa Clara, CA 95053 (SAN 692-7319) Tel 415-387-2020.
Albion NC, *(Albion; 0-932530),* Dept. of History, Appalachian State Univ., Boone, NC 28608 (SAN 212-2626) Tel 704-262-6004.
Alchemy Bks, *(Alchemy Bks.; 0-931290),* 717 Market, Suite 514, San Francisco, CA 94103 (SAN 211-304X) Tel 415-777-2197.
Aldine Pub
See De Gruyter Aldine
Alef Bet Comns, *(Alef Bet Communications; 0-9616488),* 14809 Bremer Rd., New Haven, IN 46774 (SAN 659-2740) Tel 219-749-0182.
Alert Pubs, *(Alert Pubs.; 0-938033),* P.O. Drawer 2459, Hemet, CA 92343 (SAN 659-6819) 261 W. Susan Ln., Hemet, CA 92343 (SAN 659-6827) Tel 714-929-2062.
Aletheia Pubs, *(Aletheia Pubs., Inc.; 0-86717),* Div. of Alpha Omega Pub., P.O. Box 1437, Tempe, AZ 85281 (SAN 216-7824) Tel 602-438-2702.
Alfred Pub, *(Alfred Publishing Co., Inc.; 0-88284),* 15335 Morrison St., Sherman Oaks, CA 91413 (SAN 201-243X) Tel 818-995-8811; Toll free: 800-821-6083.
Algonquin Bks, *(Algonquin Bks. of Chapel Hill; 0-912697),* P.O. Box 2225, Chapel Hill, NC 27515 (SAN 282-7506); 501 W. Franklin St., Suite 104, Chapel Hill, NC 27514 (SAN 662-2011) Tel 919-967-0108; Dist. by: Taylor Publishing Co., 1550 Mockingbird Ln., P.O. Box 597, Dallas, TX 75221 (SAN 202-7631) Tel 214-637-2800.
ALI-ABA
See Am Law Inst
Alivening Pubns, *(Alivening Pubns.; 0-9616707),* P.O. Box 1368, Land O Lakes, FL 33539 (SAN 659-6835) Tel 813-996-3659; 315 Geneva Rd., Land O Lakes, FL 33539 (SAN 659-6843).
Allanheld, *(Allanheld, Osmun & Co. Pubs., Inc.; 0-916672; 0-86598),* Div. of Littlefield, Adams & Co., 81 Adams Dr., Totowa, NJ 07512 (SAN 211-724X) Tel 201-256-8600.
Allanheld & Schram *Imprint of* **Abner Schram Ltd**
Alleluia Pr, *(Alleluia Pr.; 0-911726),* P.O. Box 103, Allendale, NJ 07401 (SAN 202-3601) Tel 201-327-3513; 672 Franklin Tpke., Allendale, NJ 07401 (SAN 202-361X).
Allen Unwin, *(Allen & Unwin, Inc.; 0-04; 0-86861),* Div. of Unwin Hyman, Ltd., 8 Winchester Pl., Winchester, MA 01890 (SAN 210-3362) Tel 617-729-0830; Toll free: 800-547-8889.
Allenson
See A R Allenson
Allenson-Breckinridge
See A R Allenson
Allgood Bks, *(Allgood Books),* P.O. Box 1329, Jackson, MS 39205 (SAN 208-1318) Tel 601-355-5419.
Allied Res Soc, *(Allied Research Society, Inc.; 0-912984),* 11057 New River Cir., Rancho Cordova, CA 95670 (SAN 201-2480) Tel 916-635-7728.
Almaas Pubns, *(Almaas Pubns.; 0-936713),* 5809 Ayala Ave., Oakland, CA 94609 (SAN 699-8771) Tel 415-652-1243; P.O. Box 10114, Berkeley, CA 94709 (SAN 699-878X); Dist. by: Bookpeople, 2929 Fifth St., Berkeley, CA 94710 (SAN 168-9517) Tel 415-549-3030.

Alpha Pub Co, *(Alpha Publishing Co.; 0-933771),* Div. of Special Edition, Inc., 3497 E. Livingston Ave., Columbus, OH 43227 (SAN 692-8048) Tel 614-231-4088; Dist. by: Quality Bks., 918 Sherwood Dr., Lake Bluff, IL 60044 (SAN 169-2127) Tel 312-295-2010; Dist. by: Talman Co. Inc., 150 Fifth Ave., Rm. 514, New York, NY 10011 (SAN 200-5204) Tel 212-620-3182.

Alpine Ent
See A-albionic Res

Alta Gaia Bks, *(Alta Gaia Books; 0-933432),* P.O. Box 541, Millerton, NY 12546 (SAN 222-6642).

Alta Napa, *(Alta Napa Pr.; 0-931926),* 1969 Mora Ave., Calistoga, CA 94515 (SAN 216-3276) Tel 707-942-4444.

Altai Pub, *(Altai Pubs.; 0-9609710),* P.O. Box 1972, Flagstaff, AZ 86002 (SAN 263-0281) Tel 602-779-0491.

Altair Pub UT, *(Altair Publishing Co.; 0-938117),* P.O. Box 20024, West Valley City, UT 84120 (SAN 659-6983); 3585 Cochise, West Valley City, UT 84120 (SAN 659-6991) Tel 801-967-3308.

Alternative Mus, *(Alternative Museum; 0-932075),* 17 White St., New York, NY 10013 (SAN 686-2616) Tel 212-226-2158.

Alyson Pubns, *(Alyson Pubns., Inc.; 0-932870; 1-55583),* 40 Plympton St., Boston, MA 02118 (SAN 213-6546) Tel 617-542-5679.

Am Acad Pol Soc Sci, *(American Academy of Political & Social Science; 0-87761),* 3937 Chestnut St., Philadelphia, PA 19104 (SAN 201-1239) Tel 215-386-4594; Dist. by: Sage Pubns., Inc., 2111 W. Hillcrest Dr., Newbury Park, CA 91320 (SAN 204-7217) Tel 805-499-0721.

Am Anthro Assn, *(American Anthropological Assn.; 0-913167),* Pubns. Dept., 1703 New Hampshire Ave., NW, Washington, DC 20009 (SAN 202-4284) Tel 202-232-8800.

Am Antiquarian, *(American Antiquarian Society; 0-912296),* 185 Salisbury St., Worcester, MA 01609 (SAN 206-474X) Tel 617-752-5813; Dist. by: Univ. Pr. of Virginia, P.O. Box 3608, University Sta., Charlottesville, VA 22903 (SAN 202-5361) Tel 804-924-3468.

Am Assn Law Libs, *(American Assn. of Law Libraries),* 53 W. Jackson Blvd., Chicago, IL 60604 (SAN 680-005X) Tel 312-939-4764.

Am Assn Sch Admin, *(American Assn. of School Administrators; 0-87652),* 1801 N. Moore St., Arlington, VA 22209 (SAN 202-3628) Tel 703-528-0700.

Am Atheist, *(American Atheist Pr.; 0-911826; 0-910309),* Subs. of Society of Separationists, Inc., P.O. Box 2117, Austin, TX 78768-2117 (SAN 206-7188); 2210 Hancock Dr., Austin, TX 78756 Tel 512-458-1244.

Am Baptist, *(American Baptist Historical Society; 0-910056),* 1106 S. Goodman St., Rochester, NY 14620 (SAN 201-257X) Tel 716-473-1740.

Am Bible, *(American Bible Society; 0-8267),* Member of United Bible Societies, 1865 Broadway, New York, NY 10023 (SAN 203-5189) Tel 212-581-7400; Orders to: American Bible Society, P.O. Box 5656, Grand Central Sta., New York, NY 10163 (SAN 662-7129) Tel 212-581-7400.

Am Biog Serv, *(American Biography Service, Inc.; 0-932051),* 14722 Newport, C184, Tustin, CA 92680 (SAN 686-2640) Tel 714-851-7733.

Am Buddhist Shim Do, *(American Buddhist Shim Gum Do Assn., Inc.; 0-9614427),* 203 Chestnut Hill Ave., Brighton, MA 02135 (SAN 690-050X) Tel 617-787-1506.

Am Bur Eco Res, *(American Bureau of Economic Research; 0-930462),* P.O. Box 7999, Tyler, TX 75711 (SAN 222-5069) Tel 214-593-7447.

Am Busn Comm Assn
See Assn Busn Comm

Am Canadian, *(American-Canadian Pubs., Inc.; 0-913844),* Box 4595, Santa Fe, NM 87502-4595 (SAN 201-260X) Tel 505-471-7863.

Am Cath Philo, *(American Catholic Philosophical Assn.; 0-918090),* Catholic Univ. of America, Administration Bldg., Rm. 403, Washington, DC 20064 (SAN 293-227X).

Am Cath Pr, *(American Catholic Pr.; 0-915866),* 1223 Rossell Ave., Oak Park, IL 60302 (SAN 202-4411) Tel 312-386-1366.

Am Christian, *(American Christian Pr., The Way International; 0-910068),* P.O. Box 328, New Knoxville, OH 45871 (SAN 206-9628) Tel 419-753-2523.

Am Classical Coll Pr, *(American Classical College Pr.; 0-913314; 0-89266),* P.O. Box 4526, Albuquerque, NM 87196 (SAN 201-2618) Tel 505-843-7749.

Am Developing, *(American Developing Industries; 0-8187),* 10520 First Way N., St. Petersburg, FL 33702 (SAN 217-2232) Tel 813-576-2027.

Am Enterprise, *(American Enterprise Institute for Public Policy Research; 0-8447),* 1150 17th St., NW, Washington, DC 20036 (SAN 202-4527) Tel 202-862-5800; Toll free: 800-223-2336. Do not confuse with American Enterprise Pubns., Mercer, PA.

Am Fed Astrologers, *(American Federation of Astrologers; 0-86690),* Box 22040, Tempe, AZ 85282 (SAN 225-1396) Tel 602-838-1751.

Am Fr Serv Comm, *(American Friends Service Committee; 0-910082),* 1501 Cherry St., Philadelphia, PA 19102 (SAN 201-2685) Tel 215-241-7000.

Am Hist Assn, *(American Historical Assn.; 0-87229),* 400 A St., SE, Washington, DC 20003 (SAN 201-159X) Tel 202-544-2422.

Am Ind Mus
See Mus Am Ind

Am Inst Conser Hist, *(American Institute for Conservation of Historic & Artistic Works),* 3545 Williamsburg Lane, NW, Washington, DC 20008 (SAN 225-4972) Tel 202-364-1036.

Am Inst Psych, *(American Institute for Psychological Research, The; 0-89920),* 607 McKnight St., NW, Albuquerque, NM 87102 (SAN 212-9302) Tel 505-843-7749.

Am Italian, *(American Italian Historical Assn., Inc.; 0-934675),* 209 Flagg Pl., Staten Island, NY 10304 (SAN 210-8828) Tel 718-454-9326.

Am Jewish Comm, *(American Jewish Committee; 0-87495),* 165 E. 56 St., New York, NY 10022 (SAN 675-0079) Tel 212-751-4000.

Am Jewish Hist Soc, *(American Jewish Historical Society; 0-911934),* Two Thornton Rd., Waltham, MA 02154 (SAN 202-4608) Tel 617-891-8110.

Am Jewish Holo, *(American Jewish Commission on the Holocaust; 0-9613537),* City Univ. of New York, Ralph Bunche Graduate Institute, New York, NY 10036 (SAN 669-7178) Tel 212-382-2114; Orders to: Holmes & Meier Pubs., Inc., 30 Irving Pl., New York, NY 10003 (SAN 665-8490) Tel 212-254-4100.

Am Law Inst, *(American Law Institute; 0-8318),* 4025 Chestnut St., Philadelphia, PA 19104 (SAN 204-756X) Tel 215-243-1600; Toll free: 800-253-6387.

Am Life Foun, *(American Life Foundation & Study Institute; 0-89257),* P.O. Box 349, Watkins Glen, NY 14891 (SAN 201-1646) Tel 607-535-4737.

Am Map, *(American Map Corp.; 0-8416),* Subs. of Langenscheidt Pubs., Inc., 46-35 54th Rd., Maspeth, NY 11378 (SAN 202-4624) Tel 718-784-0055.

Am New Church Sunday, *(American New Church Sunday School Assn.; 0-917426),* 48 Highland St., Sharon, MA 02067 (SAN 208-9432) Tel 617-784-5041; Dist. by: Swedenborg Library, 79 Newbury St., Boston, MA 02116 (SAN 208-9440).

Am Orient Soc, *(American Oriental Society; 0-940490),* 329 Sterling Memorial Library, Yale Sta., New Haven, CT 06520 (SAN 211-3082) Tel 203-432-1842; Dist. by: Eisenbrauns, P.O. Box 275, Winona Lake, IN 46590-0278 (SAN 200-7835) Tel 219-269-2011.

Am Philos, *(American Philosophical Society; 0-87169),* 104 S. Fifth St., Philadelphia, PA 19106 (SAN 206-9016) Tel 215-627-0706; Orders to: P.O. Box 40227-5227, Philadelphia, PA 19106 (SAN 661-9398).

Am Psychiatric, *(American Psychiatric Pr., Inc.; 0-89042; 0-88048),* Subs. of American Psychiatric Assn., 1400 K St., NW, Washington, DC 20005 (SAN 293-2288) Tel 202-682-6262; Toll free: 800-368-5777. Publishing arm of the American Psychiatric Assn.

Am Scandinavian, *(American-Scandinavian Foundation; 0-89067),* 127 E. 73rd St., New York, NY 10021 (SAN 201-7075) Tel 212-879-9779; Orders to: Heritage Resource Ctr., P.O. Box 26305, Minneapolis, MN 55426 (SAN 201-7083).

Am Sch Athens, *(American Schl. of Classical Studies at Athens; 0-87661),* c/o Institute for Advanced Study, Princeton, NJ 08543-0631 (SAN 201-1697) Tel 609-734-8387.

Am Sch Orient Res, *(American Schls. of Oriental Research; 0-89757),* P.O. Box HM, Duke Sta., Durham, NC 27706 (SAN 239-4057) Tel 919-684-3075; Dist. by: Eisenbrauns, P.O. Box 275, Winona Lake, IN 46590-0278 (SAN 213-4365) Tel 219-269-2011.

Am Soc Ed & Rel, *(American Society for Education & Religion, Inc.; 0-942978),* 29 Beaver Oak Ct., Baltimore, MD 21236 (SAN 240-334X) Tel 301-256-1349.

Am Trust Pubns, *(American Trust Pubns.; 0-89259),* 10900 W. Washington St., Indianapolis, IN 46231 (SAN 664-6158) Tel 317-839-8150.

Am U Field
See U Field Staff Intl

Amana Bks, *(Amana Bks.; 0-915597),* 58 Elliot St., Brattleboro, VT 05301 (SAN 292-4307) Tel 802-257-0872.

Amarta Pr, *(Amarta Pr.; 0-935100),* P.O. Box 723, Wellesley, MA 02181 (SAN 213-2761) Tel 617-237-6568.

Amber Co Pr, *(Amber Co. Pr.; 0-934965),* 2324 Prince St., Berkeley, CA 94705 (SAN 695-1112) Tel 415-549-2587; Dist. by: Publishers Group West, 5855 Beaudry St., Emeryville, CA 94608 (SAN 665-892X) Tel 415-658-3453.

Amer Bar Assn, *(American Bar Assn.; 0-89707),* 750 N. Lake Shore Dr., Chicago, IL 60611 (SAN 211-4798) Tel 312-988-5000; 1800 M St., NW, Washington, DC 20036 (SAN 668-968X) Tel 202-331-2200.

Amereon Ltd, *(Amereon, Ltd.; 0-88411; 0-89190; 0-8488),* P.O. Box 1200, Mattituck, NY 11952 (SAN 201-2413) Tel 516-298-5100.

American Ent Pubns
See A E P

AMG Pubs, *(AMG Pubs.; 0-89957),* 6815 Shallowford Rd., Chattanooga, TN 37421 (SAN 211-3074) Tel 615-894-6060.

Amherst Pr, *(Amherst Pr.; 0-942495),* Div. of Palmer Pubns., Inc., P.O. Box 296, Amherst, WI 54406 (SAN 213-9820); 318 N. Main St., Amherst, WI 54406 (SAN 666-6450) Tel 715-824-3214.

AMI Pr, *(AMI Pr.; 0-911988),* Div. of The Blue Army, Mountain View Rd., Washington, NJ 07882 (SAN 213-6791) Tel 201-689-1700.

Amity Hous Inc, *(Amity Hse., Inc.; 0-916349),* 106 Newport Bridge Rd., Warwick, NY 10990 (SAN 295-1037) Tel 914-258-4078.

Amon Carter, *(Amon Carter Museum of Western Art; 0-88360),* P.O. Box 2365, Fort Worth, TX 76113 (SAN 204-7608) Tel 817-738-1933; Dist. by: Univ. of Texas Pr., P.O. Box 7819, Austin, TX 78713 (SAN 212-9876) Tel 512-471-7233.

AMORC, *(AMORC; 0-912057),* Div. of Supreme Grand Lodge of AMORC, Inc., Rosicrucian Order, Park Naglee, San Jose, CA 95191 (SAN 211-3864) Tel 408-287-9171.

Amrita Found, *(Amrita Foundation, Inc.; 0-937134),* P.O. Box 8080, Dallas, TX 75205 (SAN 284-9666) Tel 214-521-1072.

AMS Pr, *(AMS Pr., Inc.; 0-404),* 56 E. 13th St., New York, NY 10003 (SAN 201-1743) Tel 212-777-4700.

AMSCO Sch, *(AMSCO School Pubns., Inc.; 0-87720),* 315 Hudson St., New York, NY 10013 (SAN 201-1751) Tel 212-675-7000.

Anacker Pub
See Ref Guide Bks

Ananda
See Dawn Pubns CA

Ananda Marga, *(Ananda Marga Pubns.; 0-88476),* 854 Pearl St., Denver, CO 80203 (SAN 206-3239) Tel 303-832-6465.

Anch *Imprint of* **Doubleday**
Anchor Pr *Imprint of* **Doubleday**
Anderson Publ, *(Anderson Publishing; 0-9602128),* P.O. Box 1751, Naples, FL 33939 (SAN 209-5238) Tel 813-262-5592.
Anderson World, *(Anderson World, Inc.; 0-89037),* 1400 Stierlin Rd., Mountain View, CA 94043 (SAN 281-2754) Tel 415-965-8777; Toll free: 800-257-5755; Orders to: P.O. Box 366, Mountain View, CA 94042 (SAN 281-2762).
Andersons Pubns, *(Anderson's Pubns.; 0-931353),* P.O. Box 11338, Santa Rosa, CA 95406 (SAN 693-7829) Tel 707-575-1280.
Andre Deutsch, *(Deutsch, Andre; 0-233),* c/o E. P. Dutton, 2 Park Ave., New York, NY 10016 (SAN 201-0070) Tel 212-725-1818; Orders to: New American Library, P.O. Box 120, Bergenfield, NJ 07261 (SAN 661-9444) Tel 201-387-0600.
Andrews McMeel Parker, *(Andrews, McMeel & Parker; 0-8362),* Affil. of Universal Press Syndicate, 4900 Main St., Kansas City, MO 64112 (SAN 202-540X) Tel 816-932-6700; Toll free: 800-826-4216.
Andrews Univ Pr, *(Andrews Univ. Pr.; 0-943872),* Berrien Springs, MI 49104 (SAN 241-0958) Tel 616-471-3392.
Angel Pr, *(Angel Pr. Pubs.; 0-912216),* 561 Tyler St., Monterey, CA 93940 (SAN 205-3330) Tel 408-372-1658.
Angriff Pr, *(Angriff Pr.; 0-913022),* P.O. Box 2726, Hollywood, CA 90078 (SAN 203-4743) Tel 213-233-9848.
Anima Pubns, *(Anima Pubns.; 0-89012),* Div. of Conococheague Assocs., Inc., 1053 Wilson Ave., Chambersburg, PA 17201 (SAN 281-2770) Tel 717-263-8303.
Anma Libri, *(Anma Libri; 0-915838),* P.O. Box 876, Saratoga, CA 95071 (SAN 212-5889) Tel 415-851-3375.
Ann Arbor FL, *(Ann Arbor Pubs., Inc.; 0-89039),* P.O. Box 7249, Naples, FL 33940 (SAN 213-8271) Tel 813-775-3528.
Anna Pub, *(Anna Publishing, Inc.; 0-89305),* P.O. Box 218, 8 S. Bluford Ave., Ocoee, FL 32761 (SAN 281-2789) Tel 305-656-6998.
Ansley Pubns, *(Ansley Pubns.; 0-939113),* Rte. 1, Box 248, Hoboken, GA 31542 (SAN 662-4707) Tel 912-458-2602.
Anthony
See C & R Anthony
Anthony Pub Co, *(Anthony Publishing Co.; 0-9603832),* 218 Gleasondale Rd., Stow, MA 01775 (SAN 213-9073) Tel 617-897-7191; Dist. by: Bookpeople, 2929 Fifth St., Berkeley, CA 94710 (SAN 168-9517) Tel 415-549-3030; Dist. by: DeVorss & Co., P.O. Box 550, Marina del Rey, CA 90294 (SAN 168-9886) Tel 213-870-7478; Dist. by: Inland Bk. Co., 22 Hemingway St., East Haven, CT 06512 (SAN 200-4151) Tel 203-467-4257; Dist. by: New Leaf Distributing Co., 1020 White St., SW, Atlanta, GA 30310 (SAN 169-1449) Tel 404-755-2665; Dist. by: The Distributors, 702 S. Michigan, South Bend, IN 46618 (SAN 169-2488) Tel 219-232-8500; Dist. by: Samuel Weiser, P.O. Box 612, York Beach, ME 03910 (SAN 202-9588) Tel 207-363-4393.
Anthroposophic, *(Anthroposophic Pr., Inc.; 0-910142; 0-88010),* Bell's Pond, Star Rte., Hudson, NY 12534 (SAN 201-1824) Tel 518-851-2054.
Antioch Pub Co, *(Antioch Publishing Co.; 0-89954),* 888 Dayton St., Yellow Springs, OH 45387 (SAN 654-7214) Tel 513-767-7379; Toll free: 800-543-2397.
ANZ Religious Pubns, *(ANZ Religious Pubns.),* Div. of KOI Trust, RFD 1, Box 171, Canterbury, NH 03224 (SAN 659-204X) Tel 603-753-4802; Orders to: Meyer Stone & Co., 1821 W. Third St., Bloomington, IN 47401 (SAN 665-9217) Tel 812-333-0313.
AOG, *(Arithmetic of God, The; 0-940532),* P.O. Box 573, Kings Mountain, NC 28086 (SAN 219-7642) Tel 704-739-7986.
Apex *Imprint of* **Abingdon**
Apollo, *(Apollo Bk.; 0-938290),* 5 Schoolhouse Ln, Poughkeepsie, NY 12603 (SAN 216-101X) Tel 914-462-0040; Toll free: 800-431-5003 Toll free: 800-942-8222 (NY)
Apollo Bks, *(Apollo Bks., Inc.; 0-916829),* 107 Lafayette, Winona, MN 55987 (SAN 654-1283); Toll free: 800-328-8963.
Apologetic Pr, *(Apologetics Press Inc.; 0-932859),* 230 Landmark Dr., Montgomery, AL 36117-2752 (SAN 688-9190) Tel 205-272-8558.
Appel, *(Appel, Paul P., Pub.; 0-911858),* 216 Washington St., Mt. Vernon, NY 10553 (SAN 202-3253) Tel 914-667-7365.
Apple Tree, *(Apple Tree Pr., Inc.; 0-913082),* P.O. Box 1012, Flint, MI 48501 (SAN 206-7366) Tel 313-234-5451.
Applied Arts, *(Applied Arts Pubs.; 0-911410),* Div. of Sowers Printing Co., Box 479, Lebanon, PA 17042 (SAN 204-4838) Tel 717-272-9442.
April Enterp, *(April Enterprises, Inc.; 0-9608772),* 14136 Janna Way, Sylmar, CA 91342 (SAN 238-2385) Tel 818-367-1666.
April Hill, *(April Hill Pubs.; 0-917780),* 79 Elm St., Springfield, VT 05156 (SAN 213-6554) Tel 802-885-3151.
Apt Bks, *(Apt Bks., Inc.; 0-86590),* 141 E. 44th St., Suite 511, New York, NY 10017 (SAN 215-7209) Tel 212-697-0887.
Aqua Educ, *(Aquarian Educational Group; 0-911794),* P.O. Box 267, Sedona, AZ 86336 (SAN 203-4816) Tel 602-282-2655.
Aquarian Bk Pubs, *(Aquarian Book Pubs.; 0-9605126),* 7011 Hammond Ave., Dallas, TX 75223 (SAN 216-096X) Tel 214-328-5144.
Aquarius, *(Aquarius Enterprises; 0-941200),* 53 Central Ave. 15, Wailuku, HI 96793 (SAN 203-4824) Tel 808-244-7347.
Aragorn Bks, *(Aragorn Bks., Inc.; 0-913862),* 14698 Nordhoff St., Panorama City, CA 91402 (SAN 203-4832) Tel 213-894-3104.
Arbit, *(Arbit Bks., Inc.; 0-930038),* 8050 N. Pt. Washington Rd., Milwaukee, WI 53217 (SAN 210-4695) Tel 414-352-4404; Toll free: 800-558-6908.
Arbor Hse, *(Arbor Hse. Pub. Co.; 0-87795),* Sub. of Hearst Corp., 105 Madison Ave., New York, NY 10016 (SAN 201-1522) Tel 212-481-0350.
Arcadia Corp, *(Arcadia Corp.; 0-9614745),* P.O. Box 534, Franklin, NH 03235 (SAN 692-9206) Tel 603-934-6186.
Arcana Pub, *(Arcana Publishing; 0-910261),* Div. of Lotus Light Pubns., P.O. Box 2, Wilmot, WI 53192 (SAN 241-3604) Tel 414-862-2395.
Arcane Pubns, *(Arcane Pubns.; 0-912240),* Box 36, York Harbor, ME 03911 (SAN 203-4840).
Archangel Pub, *(Archangel Publishing; 0-932661),* 310 W. Washington, Parisette, IL 61944 (SAN 687-7664) Tel 217-463-7895.
Archdiocesan, *(Archdiocesan Historical Commission; 0-9613644),* Div. of Archdiocese of Portland in Oregon, 5000 N. Williamette Blvd., Portland, OR 97203-5798 (SAN 670-7882) Tel 503-283-7111; 2838 E. Burnside, Portland, OR 97207-0351 (SAN 200-5417) Tel 503-234-5334; Dist. by: Pacific Northwest Bks., P.O. Box 314, Medford, OR 97501 (SAN 200-5263).
Archival Servs, *(Archival Services, Inc.; 0-910653),* P.O. Box 78191, Shreveport, LA 71137-8191 (SAN 270-1774) Tel 318-425-5646; P.O. Box 112, Blanchard, LA 71009 (SAN 662-0108) Tel 318-929-4707.
Archives Belmont, *(Archives of Belmont Abbey, The; 0-9614976),* Belmont Abbey, Belmont, NC 28012-2795 (SAN 693-6016) Tel 704-825-7031.
Archives Pr, *(Archives, The; 0-918501),* 1259 El Camino Real, No. 188, Menlo Park, CA 94025 (SAN 657-3207) Tel 415-326-6997.
Archon Bks *Imprint of* **Shoe String**
Archon Inst Leader Dev, *(Archon Institute for Leadership Development, Inc., The; 0-9616203),* 3700 Massachusetts Ave., No. 121, Washington, DC 20016 (SAN 658-3415) Tel 202-342-7710.
Archway, *(Archway Paperbacks; 0-671),* Div. of Simon & Schuster, Inc., 1230 Ave. of the Americas, New York, NY 10020 (SAN 665-651X) Tel 212-698-7200; Toll free: 800-223-2336; Orders to: Pocket Bks., 200 Old Tappan Rd., Old Tappan, NJ 07675 (SAN 202-5922).
Arcline Pubns, *(Arcline Pubns.; 0-913852),* P.O. Box 1550, Pomona, CA 91769 (SAN 203-2287) Tel 714-623-1738.
Arco, *(Arco Publishing, Inc.; 0-668),* Div. of Prentice-Hall, Inc., 1 Gulf & Western Bldg., New York, NY 10023 (SAN 201-0003) Tel 212-373-8931.
Arden Lib, *(Arden Library; 0-8495),* Mill & Main Sts., Darby, PA 19023 (SAN 207-477X) Tel 215-726-5505.
Ardis Pubs, *(Ardis Pubs.; 0-88233; 0-87501),* 2901 Heatherway, Ann Arbor, MI 48104 (SAN 201-1492) Tel 313-971-2367.
ARE Pr, *(A.R.E. Pr.; 0-87604),* 215 67th St., Virginia Beach, VA 23451 (SAN 201-1484) Tel 804-428-3588; Toll free: 800-368-2727; P.O. Box 595, Virginia Beach, VA 23451 (SAN 692-8234).
Arena Lettres, *(Arena Lettres; 0-88479),* Div. of John Taylor, Inc., 8 Lincoln Pl., Waldwick, NJ 07463 (SAN 206-3247) Tel 201-445-7154.
Ares, *(Ares Pubs., Inc.; 0-89005),* 7020 N. Western Ave., Chicago, IL 60645-3416 (SAN 205-6011) Tel 312-743-1405.
Argo Bks, *(Argo Bks.; 0-912148),* Main St., Norwich, VT 05055 (SAN 203-4867) Tel 802-649-1000.
Argus Comm, *(Argus Communications; 0-89505; 0-913592),* Div. of DLM, Inc., 1 DLM Park, P.O. Box 8000, Allen, TX 75002 (SAN 201-1476) Tel 214-727-3346; Toll free: 800-527-4748.
Ariadne Bks *Imprint of* **Beacon Pr**
Arica Inst Pr, *(Arica Institute Pr.; 0-916554),* 150 Fifth Ave., Suite 912, New York, NY 10011 (SAN 208-5321) Tel 212-807-9600.
Ariel OH, *(Ariel Pr.; 0-89804),* Subs. of Light, P.O. Box 30975, Columbus, OH 43230 (SAN 219-8460) Tel 614-471-1163; Toll free: 800-336-7769; Toll free: 800-336-7768 (in Ohio).
Ariel Pr CA, *(Ariel Pr.; 0-914863),* 1541 Pkwy. Loop, Suite D, P.O. Box 3723, Tustin, CA 92680 (SAN 289-0534) Tel 714-259-4800.
Ark Comm Inst, *(Ark Communications Institute; 0-934325),* 250 Lafayeete Cir., No. 10, Lafayette, CA 94549 (SAN 693-0905) Tel 415-283-7920; Orders to: P.O. Box 3245, Ogden, UT 84409-9951 (SAN 200-2132); Dist. by: St. Martin's Pr., Inc., 175 Fifth Ave., New York, NY 10010 (SAN 665-8814) Tel 212-674-5151.
Ark Paperbks *Imprint of* **Methuen Inc**
Aronson, *(Aronson, Jason, Inc.; 0-87668),* 230 Livingston St., Northvale, NJ 07647 (SAN 201-0127) Tel 201-767-4093; Orders to: 1205 O'Neill Highway, Dunmore, PA 18512 (SAN 665-6536) Tel 717-342-1449. Do not confuse with J. H. Aronson, Highmount, NY.
Art Alliance, *(Art Alliance Pr.; 0-87982),* Dist. by: Associated University Presses, 440 Forsgate Dr., Cranbury, NJ 08512 (SAN 281-2959) Tel 609-665-4770.
Art Inst Chi, *(Art Institute of Chicago; 0-86559),* Michigan Ave. & Adams St., Chicago, IL 60603 (SAN 204-479X) Tel 312-443-3540; Toll free: 800-621-2736.
Arthur Pub, *(Arthur Publishing; 0-934849),* P.O. Box 749, Clayton, CA 94517-0749 (SAN 694-454X) Tel 415-672-4112.
Arthur Pubns, *(Arthur Pubns., Inc.; 0-932782),* P.O. Box 23101, Jacksonville, FL 32241-3101 (SAN 211-8823) Tel 904-241-5575.
Artisan Sales, *(Artisan Sales; 0-934666),* P.O. Box 1497, Thousand Oaks, CA 91360 (SAN 211-8408) Tel 805-482-8076.
Asante Pubns, *(Asante Pubns.; 0-9614210),* P.O. Box 1085, San Diego, CA 92112 (SAN 686-9599) Tel 619-448-6179.
Asbury Theological, *(Asbury Theological Seminary; 0-914368),* Wilmore, KY 40390 (SAN 208-2616).
Asclepiad, *(Asclepiad Pubns.; 0-935718),* 2848 Page, Ann Arbor, MI 48104 (SAN 213-7240).
Ash-Kar Pr, *(Ash-Kar Pr.; 0-9605308),* P.O. Box 14547, San Francisco, CA 94114 (SAN 213-0025) Tel 415-864-2430; Dist. by: Bookpeople, 2929 Fifth St., Berkeley, CA 94710 (SAN 168-9517) Tel 415-549-3030.
Ashley Bks, *(Ashley Bks., Inc.; 0-87949),* 30 Main St., Pt. Washington, NY 11050 (SAN 201-1409) Tel 516-883-2221; Orders to: P.O. Box 768, Pt. Washington, NY 11050 (SAN 201-1417).

ASHMM, *(American Society for Hospital Materials Management),* Div. of American Hospital Assn., 840 N. Lake Shore Dr., Chicago, IL 60611 (SAN 224-3326) Tel 312-280-6137.

ASI Pubs Inc, *(ASI Pubs., Inc.; 0-88231),* 63 W. 38th St., Suite 505, New York, NY 10018 (SAN 201-1395) Tel 212-719-2919.

Asia Bk Corp, *(Asia Bk. Corp. of America; 0-940500),* 94-41 218th St., Queens Village, NY 11426 (SAN 214-493X) Tel 718-740-4612.

Asia Resource, *(Asia Resource Ctr.; 0-9604518),* P.O. Box 15275, Washington, DC 20003 (SAN 207-7647) Tel 202-547-1114.

Asia Soc, *(Asia Society, Inc.; 0-87848),* 725 Park Ave., New York, NY 10021 (SAN 281-2916) Tel 212-288-6400; Dist. by: Charles E. Tuttle, Co., P.O. Box 410, 28 S. Main St., Rutland, VT 05701-0410 (SAN 213-2621) Tel 802-773-8930.

Asian Conserv Lab, *(Asian Conservation Laboratory; 0-940492),* Dist. by: Raiko Corp., P.O. Box 597, New York, NY 10003 (SAN 240-9542) Tel 212-783-2597.

Asian Human Pr, *(Asian Humanities Pr.; 0-89581; 0-87573),* P.O. Box 4177, Santa Clara, CA 95054-0177 (SAN 213-6503) Tel 408-727-3151.

Aspen Pub, *(Aspen Pubs., Inc.; 0-912862; 0-89443; 0-87189; 0-912654),* Affil. of Wolters Samson Group, 1600 Research Blvd., Rockville, MD 20850 (SAN 203-4999) Tel 301-251-5000; Toll free: 800-638-8437.

Assn Arab-Amer U Grads, *(Association of Arab-American University Graduates; 0-937694),* 556 Trapelo Rd., Belmont, MA 02178 (SAN 240-0820) Tel 617-484-5483.

Assn Baptist Profs
See NABPR

Assn Busn Comm, *(Association for Business Communication, The; 0-931874),* 100 English Bldg., 608 S. Wright St., Urbana, IL 61801 (SAN 211-9382) Tel 217-333-1007.

Assn Chr Libs, *(Association of Christian Librarians),* Asbury College, Wilmore, KY 40390 (SAN 217-2267); Orders to: Ruth G. Butler, Houghton College, Buffalo Suburban Campus, West Seneca, NY 14224 (SAN 665-6617) Tel 716-674-6363.

Assn Christian Pub, *(Association of Christian Pubs.; 0-943258),* Sub. of Assemblies of God, 3360 NW 110th St., Miami, FL 33167 (SAN 240-3390) Tel 305-685-6334; Dist. by: Libros Int'l, 7214 SW 41st St.702, Miami, FL 33155 (SAN 200-9501); Dist. by: Spanish Hse., 1360 NW 88th Ave., Miami, FL 33172 (SAN 169-1171); Dist. by: Nueva Vida Dist., 807 N. Piedras, El Paso, TX 79903 (SAN 200-951X) Tel 915-755-2058; Dist. by: Vida Dist., 1362D E. Edinger, Santa Ana, CA 92705 (SAN 200-9528) Tel 714-547-4996.

Assn Public Justice, *(Association for Public Justice Education Fund; 0-936456),* 806 15th St. NW, Suite 218, Washington, DC 20005 (SAN 214-1000) Tel 202-737-2110.

Assn Sexologists, *(Association of Sexologists, The; 0-939902),* 1523 Franklin St., San Francisco, CA 94109 (SAN 216-7867).

Assoc Faculty Pr, *(Associated Faculty Pr.; 0-86733; 0-87198; 0-8046),* Affil. of Kraus Reprint & Periodical, Rte. 100, Millwood, NY 10546 (SAN 217-4979) Tel 914-762-2200; Orders to: 19 W. 36th St., New York, NY 10018 (SAN 694-9495) Tel 212-307-1300. *Imprints:* Natl U (National University Publications).

Assoc Univ Prs, *(Associated University Presses; 0-8453),* 440 Forsgate Dr., Cranbury, NJ 08512 (SAN 281-2959) Tel 609-655-4770. *Imprints:* Cornwall Bks (Cornwall Books).

Assocs Thanatology, *(Associates in Thanatology; 0-9607928),* 115 Blue Rock Rd., South Yarmouth, MA 02664 (SAN 281-2967) Tel 617-394-6520; Dist. by: DeVorrs & Co., P.O. Box 550, Marina del Rey, CA 90294 (SAN 168-9886) Tel 213-870-7487; Dist. by: Inland Bk. Co., P.O. Box 261, East Haven, CT 06512 (SAN 200-4151) Tel 203-467-4257; Dist. by: New Leaf, 1020 White St., Atlanta, GA 30310 (SAN 169-1449) Tel 404-755-2665; Dist. by: Bookpeople, 2929 Fifth St., Berkeley, CA 94710 (SAN 168-9517) Tel 415-549-3030.

Assocs Urbanus, *(Associates of Urbanus; 0-930957),* P.O. Box 457, 36200 Freedom Rd., Farmington, MI 48024 (SAN 678-8750) Tel 313-474-9110.

Assurance Pubs, *(Assurance Pubs.; 0-932940),* 330 Clover Ln., Garland, TX 75043 (SAN 213-005X).

Astara, *(Astara, Inc.; 0-918936),* 800 W. Arrow Hwy., P.O. Box 5003, Upland, CA 91785 (SAN 207-6446) Tel 714-981-4941.

Astor-Honor, *(Astor-Honor, Inc.; 0-8392),* 48 E. 43rd St., New York, NY 10017 (SAN 203-5022) Tel 212-687-6190.

Astro Dynasty Pub Hse, *(Astro Dynasty Publishing Hse.; 0-914725),* 270 N. Canon Dr., No. 1021, Beverly Hills, CA 90210 (SAN 291-8307) Tel 213-274-7249.

ASU Ctr Asian, *(Arizona State Univ. Ctr. for Asian Studies; 0-939252),* Tempe, AZ 85287 (SAN 220-1623) Tel 602-965-7184.

ASU Lat Am St, *(Arizona State Univ., Ctr. for Latin American Studies; 0-87918),* Social Sciences Bldg., Rm. 213, Tempe, AZ 85287 (SAN 201-1336) Tel 602-965-5127.

Atheneum, *(Atheneum Pubs.; 0-689),* Subs. of Scribner Bk. Cos., Inc., 115 Fifth Ave., New York, NY 10003 (SAN 201-0011) Tel 212-614-1300; Toll free: 800-257-5755; Dist. by: Riverside Distribution Ctr., Front & Brown Sts., Riverside, NJ 08075 (SAN 200-5018).

Atlantic Monthly, *(Atlantic Monthly Pr.; 0-87113),* Div. of Navarre Atlantic Co., 420 Lexington Ave., Suite 2304, New York, NY 10170 (SAN 226-4587) Tel 212-557-6030; Dist. by: Little, Brown & Co., 34 Beacon St., Boston, MA 02108 (SAN 200-2205) Tel 617-227-0730.

Atma Bks, *(Atma Bks.; 0-914557),* Box 432, Fallsburg, NY 12733 (SAN 289-1425) Tel 914-434-6707; Dist. by: New Leaf Distributing Co., 1020 White St., SW, Atlanta, GA 30310 (SAN 169-1449) Tel 404-755-2665; Dist. by: Starlite Distributors, P. O. Box 20729, Reno, NV 89515 (SAN 200-7789) Tel 702-359-5676.

Atonement Ent, *(Atonement Enterprises; 0-9616739),* P.O. Box 660460, Sacramento, CA 95866-0460 (SAN 659-7386); 616 25th St., Apt. 1, Sacramento, CA 95816 (SAN 659-7394) Tel 916-443-5540.

Attic Pr, *(Attic Pr.; 0-87921),* Stony Point, Rte. 2, Greenwood, SC 29646 (SAN 201-1328) Tel 803-374-3013.

Auburn Hse, *(Auburn Hse. Publishing Co., Inc.; 0-86569),* Affil. of Affiliated Pubns., 14 Dedham St., Dover, MA 02030-0658 (SAN 220-0341) Tel 617-785-2220; Toll free: 800-223-2665.

Augsburg, *(Augsburg Publishing Hse.; 0-8066),* 6601 220th St., SW, Box 199, Mountain Terrace, WA 98043 (SAN 169-4081) Tel 206-778-1552; Toll free: 800-752-8153, Minnesota only.

August Hse, *(August Hse.; 0-935304; 0-87483),* P.O. Box 3223, Little Rock, AR 72203-3223 (SAN 223-7288) Tel 501-663-7300.

Augustana, *(Augustana Historical Society; 0-910184),* Augustana College Library, Rock Island, IL 61201 (SAN 206-6378) Tel 309-794-7266.

Augustana Coll, *(Augustana College Library; 0-910182),* 35th St. & Seventh Ave., Rock Island, IL 61201 (SAN 203-5073) Tel 309-794-7266.

Augustinian Coll Pr, *(Augustinian College Press; 0-9612336),* 3900 Harewood Rd. NE, Washington, DC 20017 (SAN 289-1174) Tel 202-526-4580.

Aum Pubns, *(Aum Pubns.; 0-88497),* Subs. of Agni Pr., 86-24 Parsons Blvd., Jamaica, NY 11432 (SAN 201-128X) Tel 718-523-3471.

Aura Bks, *(Aura Bks.; 0-937736),* 7911 Willoughby Ave., Los Angeles, CA 90046 (SAN 215-7268) Tel 213-656-9373; Dist. by: Bookpeople, 2929 Fifth St., Berkeley, CA 94710 (SAN 168-9517) Tel 415-549-3030; Dist. by: Samuel Weiser, Inc., P.O. Box 612, York Beach, ME 03910 (SAN 202-9588) Tel 207-363-4393; Dist. by: The Great Tradition, 750 Adrian Way, Suite 111, San Rafael, CA 94903 (SAN 200-5743) Tel 415-492-9382; Dist. by: DeVorss & Co., P.O. Box 550, Marina Del Rey, CA 90291 (SAN 168-9886) Tel 213-870-7478; Dist. by: New Leaf Distributing, 1020 White St., S.W., Atlanta, GA 30310 (SAN 169-1449) Tel 404-755-2665.

Aurea, *(Aurea Pubns.; 0-87174),* P.O. Box 176, Allenhurst, NJ 07711 (SAN 203-5081) Tel 201-531-4535.

Auromere, *(Auromere, Inc.; 0-89744),* 1291 Weber St., Pomona, CA 91768 (SAN 169-0043) Tel 714-629-8255; Toll free: 800-243-0138; Dist. by: Bookpeople, 2929 Fifth St., Berkeley, CA 94710 (SAN 168-9517) Tel 415-549-3030; Dist. by: DeVorss & Co., P.O. Box 550, Marina del Rey, CA 90294 (SAN 168-9886) Tel 213-870-7478; Dist. by: New Leaf Distributing Co., 1020 White St. SW, Atlanta, GA 30310 (SAN 169-1449) Tel 404-755-2665; Dist. by: Samuel Weiser, P.O. Box 612, York Beach, ME 03910 (SAN 202-9588) Tel 207-363-4393; Dist. by: Inland Bk. Co., 22 Hemingway Ave., East Haven, CT 06512 (SAN 200-4151) Tel 203-467-4257; Dist. by: The Distributors, 702 S. Michigan St., South Bend, IN 46618 (SAN 212-0364) Tel 219-232-8500; Dist. by: Starlite Distributors, P.O. Box 20729, Reno, NV 89515 (SAN 131-1921) Tel 702-359-5676.

Aurora Press, *(Aurora Pr.; 0-943358),* 205 Third Ave., Apt 2A, New York, NY 10003 (SAN 240-5881) Tel 212-673-1831; Dist. by: New Leaf Distributing, 1020 White St., SW, Atlanta, GA 30310 (SAN 169-1449) Tel 404-755-2665; Dist. by: Samuel Weiser, Inc., P.O. Box 612, York Beach, ME 03910 (SAN 202-9588) Tel 207-363-4393; Dist. by: Bookpeople, 2929 Fifth St., Berkeley, CA 94710 (SAN 168-9517) Tel 415-549-3030.

Aurora Pubs, *(Aurora Pubs.; 0-87695),* 118 16th Ave., S., Nashville, TN 37203 (SAN 201-1271) Tel 615-254-5842.

Austin Bilingual Lang Ed, *(Austin Bilingual Language Editions; 0-940048),* P.O. Box 3864, Austin, TX 78764 (SAN 220-2069) Tel 512-441-1436.

Authors Unltd, *(Authors Unlimited; 1-55666),* 3330 Barham Blvd., Suite 204, Los Angeles, CA 90068 (SAN 662-8044) Tel 213-874-0902.

Autumngold Pub, *(Autumngold Publishing; 0-931253),* P.O. Box 634, Beverly Hills, CA 90213 (SAN 681-9664) Tel 818-783-2477.

Auxiliary U Pr, *(Auxiliary Univ. Pr.; 0-913034),* Box 772, Barrington, IL 60010 (SAN 202-327X) Tel 312-381-7888.

Avanyu Pub, *(Avanyu Publishing, Inc.; 0-936755),* Adobe Gallery, 413 Romero NW, Albuquerque, NM 87104 (SAN 699-8550) Tel 505-243-8485; P.O. Box 27134, Albuquerque, NM 87125 (SAN 699-8569); Orders to: Avanyu Publishing, P.O. Box 27134, Albuquerque, NM 87125 (SAN 213-9588); Dist. by: Univ. of New Mexico Press, Journalism Bldg., Rm. 220, Albuquerque, NM 87131 (SAN 665-9144) Tel 505-277-2346.

Ave Maria, *(Ave Maria Pr.; 0-87793),* Notre Dame, IN 46556 (SAN 201-1255) Tel 219-287-2831.

Avon, *(Avon Bks.; 0-380),* Div. of Hearst Corp., 105 Madison Ave., New York, NY 10016 (SAN 201-4009) Tel 212-481-5600; Toll free: 800-367-2494; Orders to: ICD, 250 W. 55th St., New York, NY 10019 (SAN 169-5800) Tel 212-262-8652. *Imprints:* Bard (Avon Bard Books); Discus (Avon Discus Books).

Ayer Co Pubs, *(Ayer Co. Pubs., Inc.; 0-88143),* 382 Main St., P.O. Box 958, Salem, NH 03079 (SAN 211-6936) Tel 603-898-1200.

Aza Khana, *(A. Aza Khana-E-Zahra; 0-933543),* 1365 Exeter St., Baldwin, NY 11510 (SAN 691-8492) Tel 516-223-7294.

B & B Pub CA, *(B. & B. Publishing; 0-9607008),* P.O. Box 165, Saugus, CA 91350 (SAN 238-9452) Tel 805-255-3422. Do not confuse with B&B Pub., Inc., Westminster, CO.

B & D Pub, *(B & D Publishing; 0-9613328),* 1915 Solano St., Suite B, Corning, CA 96021 (SAN 289-5854) Tel 916-824-1410.

B & E Pub Co
See Scojtia Renee

B & K Pub Hse, *(B & K Publishing Hse.; 0-940415),* P.O. Box 418, Fremont, WI 54940-0418 (SAN 664-3590) Tel 414-446-3913.

B C Scribe, *(Scribe, B. C., Pubns.; 0-930548),* P.O. Box 2453, Providence, RI 02906-0453 (SAN 212-1727) Tel 401-245-6478.

B Dolphin Pub, *(Blue Dolphin Publishing, Inc.; 0-931892),* P.O. Box 1908, Nevada City, CA 95959 (SAN 223-2480); 12380 Nevada City Hwy., Grass Valley, CA 95945 (SAN 696-009X) Tel 916-265-6923; Dist. by: Baker & Taylor Co., Eastern Div., 50 Kirby Ave., Somerville, NJ 08876 (SAN 169-4901); Dist. by: Baker & Taylor Co., Midwest Div., 501 Gladiola Ave., Momence, IL 60954 (SAN 169-2100); Dist. by: Baker & Taylor Co., Southeast Div., Mt. Olive Rd., Commerce, GA 30529 (SAN 169-1503); Dist. by: Baker & Taylor Co., Western Div., 380 Edison Way, Reno, NV 89564 (SAN 169-4464) Tel 702-786-6700; Dist. by: Bookpeople, 2929 Fifth St., Berkeley, CA 94710 (SAN 168-9517) Tel 415-549-3030; Dist. by: New Leaf Distributing, The, 1020 White St., SW, Atlanta, GA 30310 (SAN 169-1449) Tel 404-755-2665; Dist. by: Pacific PipeLine, Inc., 19215 66th Ave., S., Kent, WA 98032 (SAN 208-2128) Tel 206-872-5523.

B Franklin, *(Franklin, Burt, Pub.; 0-89102),* Affil. of Lenox Hill Publishing & Distributing Corp., 235 E. 44th St., New York, NY 10017 (SAN 282-597X) Tel 212-687-5250; Toll free: 800-223-0766.

B Grimes
See B & D Pub

B J Hebrew Tchrs, *(Beth Jacob Hebrew Teachers College Inc.; 0-934390),* 1213 Elm Ave., Brooklyn, NY 11230 (SAN 222-741X).

B J Phunn
See Phunn Pubs

B M Johnson, *(Johnson, Barbara Mary),* 7381 Webb Rd., Chatsworth, CA 91311 (SAN 263-2381) Tel 818-703-1594.

B of A, *(B of A Communications Co.; 0-911238),* P.O. Box 22252, Louisiana State Univ., Baton Rouge, LA 70893 (SAN 204-6776) Tel 504-272-6600; Pelican Office Ctr., 11628 S. Choctaw Dr., Baton Rouge, LA 70815 (SAN 200-4208); Orders to: P.O. Box 15809, Broadview Sta., Pelican Office Products Ctr., Baton Rouge, LA 70895 (SAN 669-2567).

B R E Pub, *(B.R.E. Pubs.; 0-9611368),* Affil. of Non-Denominational Bible Prophecy Study Assn, 339 E. Laguna Dr., Tempe, AZ 85282 (SAN 265-380X) Tel 602-967-3066.

B W Brace, *(Brace, Beverly W.),* 6352 St. Joseph Ave. NW, Albuquerque, NM 87120 (SAN 210-3435) Tel 505-836-7244.

B Wilson, *(Wilson, Bob; 0-9608192),* 1542 Big Horn Ave., Sheridan, WY 82801 (SAN 240-3021) Tel 307-674-8422.

Back to Eden, *(Back To Eden Bks., Publishing Co.; 0-940676),* P.O. Box 1439, Loma Linda, CA 92354 (SAN 218-5318) Tel 714-796-9615.

Baha'i, *(Baha'i Publishing Trust; 0-87743),* 415 Linden Ave., Wilmette, IL 60091 (SAN 213-7496) Tel 312-251-1854; Toll free: 800-323-1880.

Bahm, *(Bahm, Archie J.; 0-911714),* 1915 Las Lomas Rd., NE, Albuquerque, NM 87106 (SAN 212-5854) Tel 505-242-9983.

Baker Bk, *(Baker Bk. Hse.; 0-8010),* P.O. Box 6287, Grand Rapids, MI 49516-6287 (SAN 201-4041) Tel 616-676-9186.

Bala Bks, *(Bala Bks.; 0-89647),* 268 W. 23rd St., New York, NY 10011 (SAN 284-9747) Tel 212-929-8073.

Balcom, *(Balcom Bks.; 0-9600008),* 320 Bawden St., Apt. 401, Ketchikan, AK 99901 (SAN 202-3725) Tel 907-225-2496.

Ballantine, *(Ballantine Bks., Inc.; 0-345),* Div. of Random Hse., Inc., 201 E. 50th St., New York, NY 10022 (SAN 214-1175) Tel 212-872-8120; Toll free: 800-638-6460; Orders to: 400 Hahn Rd., Westminster, MD 21157 (SAN 214-1183).

Ballena Pr, *(Ballena Pr.; 0-87919),* 823 Valparaiso Ave., Menlo Park, CA 94025 (SAN 201-4076) Tel 415-323-9261; Orders to: P.O. Box 2510, Novato, CA 94948 (SAN 669-0181) Tel 415-883-3530.

Ballinger Pub, *(Ballinger Publishing Co.; 0-88410; 0-88730),* Subs. of Harper & Row, Inc., 54 Church St., Cambridge, MA 02138 (SAN 201-4084) Tel 617-492-0670; Toll free: 800-242-7737.

B&N Bks *Imprint of* **Har-Row**

B&N Imports, *(Barnes & Noble Bks.-Imports; 0-389),* Div. of Littlefield, Adams & Co., 81 Adams Dr., Totowa, NJ 07512 (SAN 206-7803) Tel 201-256-8600.

Banner *Imprint of* **Exposition Pr FL**

Banner of Truth, *(Banner of Truth, The; 0-85151),* P.O. Box 621, Carlisle, PA 17013 (SAN 211-7738) Tel 717-249-5747.

Banner Pr AL, *(Banner Pr., Inc.; 0-87121),* P.O. Box 20180, Birmingham, AL 35216 (SAN 204-5362) Tel 205-822-4783.

Banning Pr, *(Banning, Arthur J., Pr.; 0-938060),* 1312 Foshay Tower, Minneapolis, MN 55402 (SAN 220-0368) Tel 612-788-9248.

Bantam, *(Bantam Bks., Inc.; 0-553),* 666 Fifth Ave., New York, NY 10103 (SAN 201-3975) Tel 212-765-6500; Toll free: 800-323-9872; Orders to: 414 E. Golf Rd., Des Plaines, IL 60016 (SAN 201-3983).

Banyan Bks, *(Banyan Bks.; 0-916224),* P.O. Box 431160, Miami, FL 33243 (SAN 208-340X) Tel 305-665-6011.

Baptist Pub Hse, *(Baptist Publishing Hse.; 0-89114),* Div. of Baptist Missionary Assn. of America, 1319 Magnolia St., Texarkana, TX 75501-4493 (SAN 183-6544) Tel 214-793-6531.

Baraka Bk, *(Baraka Bks.; 0-914829),* Subs. of Movement of Spiritual Inner Awareness, P.O. Box 3935, Los Angeles, CA 90051 (SAN 289-1395); 3500 W. Adams Blvd., Los Angeles, CA 90018 (SAN 289-1409) Tel 213-737-4055.

Barber Pr, *(Barber, Lilian, Pr.; 0-936508),* P.O. Box 232, Grand Central Sta., New York, NY 10163 (SAN 214-1817) Tel 212-874-2678. *Imprints:* Ethnographica (Ethnographica).

Barbour & Co, *(Barbour & Co., Inc.; 0-916441; 1-55748),* Div. of Book Bargains, Inc., 164 Mill St., P.O. Box 1219, Westwood, NJ 07675 (SAN 295-7094) Tel 201-664-0577; Toll free: 800-221-2648; Dist. by: Spring Arbor Distributors, 10885 Textile Rd., Belleville, MI 48111 (SAN 158-9016) Tel 313-481-0900; Dist. by: Ingram Industries, 347 Reedwood Dr., Nashville, TN 37217 (SAN 169-7978) Tel 615-361-5000; Dist. by: Baker & Taylor Cos., The, 1515 Broadway, New York, NY 10036 (SAN 169-5606) Tel 212-730-7650; Dist. by: Riverside Bk. & Bible Hse., Inc., 1500 Riverside Dr., P.O. Box 370, Iowa Falls, IA 50126 (SAN 169-2666) Tel 515-648-4269; Dist. by: Living Bks., Inc., 12155 Magnolia Ave., Bldg. 11-B, Riverside, CA 92503 (SAN 169-006X) Tel 714-354-7330; Dist. by: Cicero Bible Pr., 1901 Airport Rd., Harrison, AR 72601 (SAN 200-7231) Tel 501-741-3400.

Barclay Pr, *(Barclay Pr.; 0-913342),* Div. of Northwest Yearly Meeting of Friends Church, P.O. Box 232, Newberg, OR 97132 (SAN 201-7520) Tel 503-538-7345.

Bard *Imprint of* **Avon**

Bard Games, *(Bard Games/Arcanum, Inc.; 0-9610770),* P.O. Box 7729, Greenwich, CT 06836 (SAN 265-0789) Tel 203-661-4547.

Bardic, *(Bardic Echoes Pubns.; 0-915020),* P.O. Box 5339, Ft. Wayne, IN 46895 (SAN 207-0952) Tel 219-484-3718.

Barniak Pubns, *(Barniak Pubns; 0-9613803),* 424 S. Kentucky Ave., Evansville, IN 47714 (SAN 679-3959) Tel 812-425-1272.

Barron, *(Barron's Educational Series, Inc.; 0-8120),* 113 Crossways Park Dr., Woodbury, NY 11797 (SAN 201-453X) Tel 516-921-8750; Toll free: 800-645-3476. Do not confuse with Barron Enterprises, Santa Barbara, CA.

Bartholomew Bks, *(Bartholomew Bks.; 0-933123),* P.O. Box 634, Inverness, CA 94937 (SAN 689-7363) Tel 415-669-1664.

Basic, *(Basic Bks., Inc.; 0-465),* Subs. of Harper & Row Pubs., Inc., 10 E. 53rd St., New York, NY 10022 (SAN 201-4521) Tel 212-207-7292; Toll free: 800-242-7737.

Basil Blackwell, *(Blackwell, Basil, Inc.; 0-631; 0-85520; 0-423; 0-900186; 0-904679; 0-7456; 0-233),* Subs. of Basil Blackwell, Ltd. (UK), 432 Park Ave., S., Suite 1503, New York, NY 10016 (SAN 680-5035) Tel 212-684-2890; Orders to: (Individuals' orders only), P.O. Box 1655, Hagerstown, MD 21741 (SAN 658-2656) Tel 301-824-7300; Orders to: Harper & Row Pubs., Inc. (Trade orders), Keystone Industrial Pk., Scranton, PA 18512 (SAN 215-3742).

Bat Yaakov Pubns, *(Bat Yaakov Pubns.; 0-9617361),* P.O. Box 20153 Columbus Cir. Sta., New York, NY 10023 (SAN 663-6969) Tel 212-247-8271.

Bauhan, *(Bauhan, William L., Inc.; 0-87233),* Old County Rd., Dublin, NH 03444 (SAN 204-384X) Tel 603-563-8020.

Bay Area CA, *(Bay Area Explorers; 0-9615635),* P.O. Box 519, San Ramon, CA 94583 (SAN 696-0782) Tel 415-828-4957.

Bayberry Pr, *(Bayberry Pr.; 0-916326),* 21 Little Fox Ln., Westport, CT 06880 (SAN 222-562X).

Baylor Univ Pr, *(Baylor Univ. Pr.; 0-918954),* Academic Pubns., CSB 547, Baylor Univ., Waco, TX 76798 (SAN 685-317X) Tel 817-755-3164; Orders to: P.O. Box 6325, Waco, TX 76706 (SAN 204-4404) Tel 817-755-2161.

BC *Imprint of* **Grove**

BCA Pub
See JBR Pub

Bd of Pubn LCA, *(Board of Pubn., LCA; 0-8006),* 2900 Queen Lane, Philadelphia, PA 19129 (SAN 213-1110) Tel 215-848-6800; Toll free: 800-367-8737.

Beachcomber Bks, *(Beachcomber Bks.; 0-913076),* P.O. Box 197, Cortaro, AZ 85652 (SAN 202-3822) Tel 602-744-1619.

Beacon Hill, *(Beacon Hill Pr. of Kansas City; 0-8341),* Subs. of Nazarene Publishing Hse., ; Dist. by: Nazarene Publishing Hse., P.O. Box 419527, Kansas City, MO 64141 (SAN 202-9022) Tel 816-931-1900.

Beacon Hse, *(Beacon Hse., Inc.; 0-87648),* Welsh Rd. & Butler Pk., Ambler, PA 19002 (SAN 202-3830) Tel 215-643-7800.

Beacon Pr, *(Beacon Pr., Inc.; 0-8070),* 25 Beacon St., Boston, MA 02108 (SAN 201-4483) Tel 617-742-2110; Orders to: Harper & Row Pubs., Inc., 10 E. 53rd St., New York, NY 10022 (SAN 200-2086) Tel 212-207-7099. *Imprints:* Ariadne Bks (Ariadne Books).

Bear & Co, *(Bear & Co., Inc.; 0-939680),* P.O. Drawer 2860, Santa Fe, NM 87504-2860 (SAN 216-7174) Tel 505-983-5968; Toll free: 800-932-3277; Dist. by: Bookpeople, 2929 Fifth St., Berkeley, CA 94710 (SAN 168-9517) Tel 415-549-3030; Dist. by: Spring Arbor Distributors, 10885 Textile Rd., Belleville, MI 48111 (SAN 158-9016) Tel 313-481-0900; Dist. by: New Leaf Distributing, 1020 White St., SW, Atlanta, GA 30310 (SAN 169-1449) Tel 404-755-3454; Dist. by: Distributors, The, 702 S. Michigan, South Bend, IN 46618 (SAN 212-0364) Tel 219-232-8500; Dist. by: Inland Bk. Co., 22 Hemingway Ave., East Haven, CT 06512 (SAN 200-4151) Tel 203-467-4257; Dist. by: Quality Bks., 400 Anthony Trail, Northbrook, IL 60062 (SAN 169-2127) Tel 312-498-4000.

Beatty, *(Beatty, R. W.; 0-87948),* P.O. Box 26, Arlington, VA 22210 (SAN 206-7110).

Beaufort Bks NY, *(Beaufort Bks., Pubs.; 0-8253),* 9 E. 40th St., New York, NY 10016 (SAN 215-2304) Tel 212-685-8588; Toll free: 800-526-7626; Dist. by: Kampmann & Co., 9 E. 40th St., New York, NY 10016 (SAN 202-5191) Tel 212-685-2928.

Beautiful Am, *(Beautiful America Publishing Co.; 0-89802; 0-915796),* 9725 SW Commerce Cir., Wilsonville, OR 97070 (SAN 211-4623) Tel 503-682-0173.

Beckwith, *(Beckwith, Burnham Putnam; 0-9603262),* 656 Lytton Ave., (C430), Palo Alto, CA 94301 (SAN 211-884X) Tel 415-324-0342.

Bedrick Blackie *Imprint of* **P Bedrick Bks**

Beecher Found, *(Beecher, Willard & Marguerite, Foundation; 0-942350),* 8400 Westchester, Suite 300, Dallas, TX 75225 (SAN 281-3165); c/o Today's Bks., 3775 Walnut Hill Ln., Dallas, TX 75229-6139 (SAN 281-3173).

Beechwood, *(Beechwood Bks.; 0-912221),* Route 1, Box 870, Leeds, AL 35094 (SAN 265-0797) Tel 205-699-6935.
Beekman Pubs, *(Beekman Pubs., Inc.; 0-8464),* P.O. Box 888, Woodstock, NY 12498 (SAN 201-4467) Tel 914-679-2300.
Behavorial Sys Inc, *(Behavioral Systems, Inc.; 0-9610136),* Rte. 2, P.O. Box 630, Marshall, VA 22115 (SAN 268-2559) Tel 703-435-8181.
Behemoth Pub, *(Behemoth Publishing; 0-9606782),* Star Rte., Oasis, UT 84650 (SAN 217-331X) Tel 801-864-2842; Dist. by: Horizon Books, P.O. Box 490, Bountiful, UT 84010 (SAN 200-9102) Tel 801-295-9451.
Behrman, *(Behrman Hse., Inc.; 0-87441),* 235 Watchung Ave., West Orange, NJ 07052 (SAN 201-4459) Tel 201-669-0447; Toll free: 800-221-2755.
Beil, *(Beil, Frederic C., Pub., Inc.; 0-913720),* 321 E. 43rd St., New York, NY 10017 (SAN 240-9909) Tel 212-682-5519.
Being Bks, *(Being Bks.; 0-938292),* 19834 Gresham St., Northridge, CA 91324 (SAN 215-7292) Tel 818-341-0283.
Bel-Air, *(Bel-Air Publishing Co.),* 249 S. Camden Drive, Beverly Hills, CA 90212 (SAN 263-2454).
Bel Esprit, *(Bel Esprit Press; 0-9607118),* 10 E. 23rd St., New York, NY 10010 (SAN 239-409X).
Believers Bkshelf, *(Believers Bookshelf; 0-941202),* Box 261, Sunbury, PA 17801 (SAN 211-7746) Tel 717-672-2134.
Believers Faith, *(Believers Faith Ctr.; 0-912573),* 148 E. 22nd St., Costa Mesa, CA 92627 (SAN 277-657X) Tel 714-650-0447.
Bell Ent, *(Bell Enterprises, Inc.; 0-918340),* P.O. Box 9054, Pine Bluff, AR 71611 (SAN 209-1895) Tel 501-247-1922.
Bell Gal
See D W Bell Gallery
Bellerophon Bks, *(Bellerophon Bks; 0-88388),* 36 Anacapa St., Santa Barbara, CA 93101 (SAN 202-392X) Tel 805-965-7034.
Benjamins North Am, *(Benjamins, John, North America, Inc.; 90-272; 1-55619; 0-915027),* 1 Buttonwood Sq., Philadelphia, PA 19130 (SAN 219-7677) Tel 215-564-6379.
Benmir Bks, *(Benmir Bks.; 0-917883),* 570 Vistamont Ave., Berkeley, CA 94718 (SAN 656-9641) Tel 415-527-0266.
Bennet Pub, *(Bennet, Rebecca, Pubns., Inc.; 0-910218),* 5409 18th Ave., Brooklyn, NY 11204 (SAN 206-8443) Tel 718-256-1954.
Bennett-Edwards, *(Bennett-Edwards; 0-9617271),* 337 W. 36th St., New York, NY 10018 (SAN 663-4508) Tel 212-279-9586.
Benson Co TN
See Paragon Benson
Benziger Pub Co, *(Benziger Publishing Co.; 0-02; 0-8460),* Div. of Glencoe Publishing Co., ; c/o Macmillan Publishing Co., Inc., 866 Third Ave., New York, NY 10022 (SAN 202-5574) Tel 212-935-2000.
Berg, *(Berg, Norman S. , Pub.; 0-910220),* P.O. Box 15232, Atlanta, GA 30333 (SAN 226-8086).
Bergin & Garvey, *(Bergin & Garvey Pubs., Inc.; 0-89789),* 670 Amherst Rd., South Hadley, MA 01075 (SAN 213-6120) Tel 413-467-3113; Dist. by: Independent Publishers Group, 1 Pleasant Ave., Port Washington, NY 11050 (SAN 287-2544) Tel 516-944-9325.
Berkeley Slavic, *(Berkeley Slavic Specialties; 0-933884),* P.O. Box 3034, Oakland, CA 94609 (SAN 212-7245) Tel 415-653-8048.
Berkley Pub, *(Berkley Publishing Group; 0-425; 0-515),* Affil. of G.P. Putnam's Sons, 200 Madison Ave., New York, NY 10016 (SAN 201-3991) Tel 212-686-9820; Toll free: 800-223-0510; Dist. by: ICD, 250 W. 55th St., New York, NY 10019 (SAN 169-5800) Tel 212-262-7444. *Imprints:* Medallion (Medallion Books).
Berkshire Traveller, *(Berkshire Traveller, Pr.; 0-912944),* Pine St., Stockbridge, MA 01262 (SAN 201-4424) Tel 413-298-3636.
Bern Porter, *(Porter, Bern; 0-911156),* 22 Salmond Rd., Belfast, ME 04915 (SAN 202-0130). Do not confuse with Porter Publishing Co., Center City, MN.
Bernan-Unipub, *(Bernan-Unipub; 0-89059; 0-400; 0-527),* Div. of Kraus-Thomson Organization, Ltd., 4611-F Assembly Dr., Lanham, MD 20706-4391 (SAN 169-3182) Tel 301-459-7666; Toll free: 800-233-0506; Toll free: 800-233-0504. *Imprints:* UNESCO (United Nations Educational, Scientific & Cultural Organization).
Best Bks, *(Best Bks., Inc.; 0-910228),* P.O. Box 2309, Henderson, NV 89015 (SAN 202-4012) Tel 702-565-7182.
Bet Yoatz Lib Serv
See BYLS Pr
Bethany Hse, *(Bethany Hse. Pubs.; 0-87123; 1-55661),* Div. of Bethany Fellowship, Inc., 6820 Auto Club Rd., Minneapolis, MN 55438 (SAN 201-4416) Tel 612-944-2121; Toll free: 800-328-6109.
Bethel Pub, *(Bethel Publishing Co.; 0-934998),* Div. of Missionary Church, Inc., 1819 S. Main St., Elkhart, IN 46516 (SAN 201-7555) Tel 219-293-8585; Toll free: 800-348-7657.
Bethel Pub OR, *(Bethel Pubns.; 0-9600096),* 4803 Kathy, Temple, TX 76502 (SAN 241-273X) Tel 503-859-8365.
Better Am Corp
See J Blalock
Betterway Pubns, *(Betterway Pubns., Inc.; 0-932620),* White Hall, VA 22987 (SAN 215-2975) Tel 804-823-5661.
Beulah, *(Beulah Records & Publishing Co.; 0-911870),* Rte. 1, Crossville, IL 62827 (SAN 202-4047) Tel 618-966-3405.
Beyond Words Pub
See Island Heritage
Bhaktipada Bks, *(Bhaktipada Bks.; 0-932215),* Div. of Palace Press, R.D. 1. Box 331, Moundsville,, VA 26041 (SAN 686-5763) Tel 304-845-3890.
Bhaktivedanta, *(Bhaktivedanta Bk. Trust; 0-912776),* 3764 Watseka Ave., Los Angeles, CA 90034 (SAN 203-8560) Tel 213-559-4455; Toll free: 800-356-3000.
BH&G, *(Better Homes & Gardens Bks.; 0-696),* Div. of Meredith Corp., 1716 Locust St., Des Moines, IA 50336 (SAN 202-4055) Tel 515-284-2371.
Bible Light, *(Bible Light Pubns.; 0-937078),* P.O. Box 168, Jerome Ave. Sta., Bronx, NY 10468 (SAN 214-3445) Tel 212-231-3579.
Bible Memory, *(Bible Memory Assn., Inc.; 0-89323),* P.O. Box 12000, Ringgold, LA 71068 (SAN 214-1019).
Bible-Speak, *(Bible-Speak Enterprises; 0-911423),* 1940 Mount Vernon Ct., No. 4, Mountain View, CA 94040 (SAN 268-2931) Tel 415-965-9020.
Bible Study Pr, *(Bible Study, Pr.; 0-9600154),* 9017 N. 70th St., Milwaukee, WI 53223 (SAN 281-3211) Tel 414-354-3504; Dist. by: Omnibook Co., N. 57 W. 13688 Carmen Ave., Menomonee Falls, WI 53051 (SAN 281-322X) Tel 414-781-2866.
Bible Temple, *(Bible Temple Pubns.; 0-914936),* 7545 NE Glisan St., Portland, OR 97213 (SAN 206-1953) Tel 503-253-9020.
Biblical News Serv, *(Biblical News Service Pubns.; 0-89921),* P.O. Box 10428, Costa Mesa, CA 92627 (SAN 213-2257) Tel 714-850-0527.
Biblical Res Assocs, *(Biblical Research Assocs., Inc.; 0-935106),* College of Wooster, Wooster, OH 44691 (SAN 211-2876) Tel 216-263-2470.
Biblio Dist, *(Biblio Distribution Ctr.),* Div. of Littlefield, Adams & Co., 81 Adams Dr., Totowa, NJ 07512 (SAN 211-724X) Tel 201-256-8600. Do not confuse with Biblio Pr. in Fresh Meadows, NY.
Biblio NY, *(Biblio Pr.; 0-9602036),* P.O. Box 22, Fresh Meadows, NY 11365-0022 (SAN 217-0892); 50-17 40th St., Sunnyside, NY 11104 (SAN 695-4464) Tel 718-361-3141; Dist. by: Inland Bk. Co., P.O. Box 261, 22 Hemingway Ave., East Haven, CT 06512 (SAN 200-4151) Tel 203-467-4257. Do not confuse with Biblio Distribution Centre of Totowa, NJ.
Bibliotheca, *(Bibliotheca Islamica, Inc.; 0-88297),* P.O. Box 14474, University Sta., Minneapolis, MN 55414 (SAN 202-4063) Tel 612-221-9883.
Biblo, *(Biblo & Tannen Booksellers & Pubs., Inc.; 0-8196),* 321 Sandbank Rd., P.O. Box 302, Cheshire, CT 06410 (SAN 202-4071) Tel 203-272-2308.
Big Moose, *(Big Moose Pr.; 0-914692),* P.O. Box 180, Big Moose, NY 13331 (SAN 206-3336) Tel 315-357-2821.
Binford-Metropolitan, *(Binford & Mort Publishing; Metropolitan Pr.; 0-8323),* 1202 NW 17th Ave., Portland, OR 97209 (SAN 201-4386) Tel 503-221-0866.
Birds' Meadow Pub, *(Birds' Meadow Publishing Co., Inc.; 0-9606360),* 1150 N. Olson Rd., Coupeville, WA 98239-9776 (SAN 208-0710).
Birth Day, *(Birth Day Publishing Co.; 0-9600958),* P.O. Box 7722, San Diego, CA 92107 (SAN 208-5542) Tel 619-296-3194.
Bishop Mus, *(Bishop Museum Pr.; 0-910240),* P.O. Box 19000-A, Honolulu, HI 96817-0916 (SAN 202-408X) Tel 808-848-4139.
Bishop Pine, *(Bishop Pine Press; 0-9612760),* P.O. Box 128, Inverness, CA 94937 (SAN 289-7342) Tel 415-663-1744; Dist. by: Nancy Kleban, Box 486, Point Reyes Station, CA 94956 (SAN 200-4283).
Bk Revel
See B R E Pub
Bks Demand UMI, *(Books on Demand; 0-8357),* Div. of University Microfilms, International, 300 N. Zeeb Rd., Ann Arbor, MI 48106 (SAN 212-2464) Tel 313-761-4700; Toll free: 800-521-0600. On-demand reprints of out-of-print books reproduced by xerography & bound in paper covers (cloth covers are available for 6.00 additional). Imprint of University Microfilms International.
Bks Distinction, *(Books of Distinction; 0-915948),* 16 Tahquitz Ct., Camarillo, CA 93010 (SAN 208-9181) Tel 805-987-5760.
Bks Intl DH-TE, *(Books International of DH-TE International, Inc.),* P.O. Box 14487, St. Louis, MO 63178 (SAN 202-4101) Tel 314-721-8787.
Bks of Truth, *(Books of Truth; 0-939399),* P.O. Box 2324, Bath, OH 44210 (SAN 663-1304); 1742 Orchard Dr., Akron, OH 44313 (SAN 663-1312) Tel 216-666-3852.
Bks of Value, *(Books of Value; 0-9603174),* 2458 Chislehurst Dr., Los Angeles, CA 90027 (SAN 210-5896) Tel 213-664-8981.
Black Light Fellow, *(Black Light Fellowship; 0-933176),* P.O. Box 5369, Chicago, IL 60680 (SAN 212-3347); 2859 W. Wilcox, Chicago, IL 60612 (SAN 669-0211) Tel 312-722-1441.
Black Rose Bks, *(Black Rose Bks.; 0-919618; 0-919619; 0-920057),* 340 Nagel Dr., Cheektowaga, NY 14225 (SAN 661-9606) Tel 716-683-4547; Dist. by: Inland Bk. Co., 22 Hemingway Ave., East Haven, CT 06512 (SAN 200-4151) Tel 203-467-4257. U. S. office of Black Rose Bks. Canadian address: 3981 boul. St.-Laurent, Montreal, PQ H2W 1T7. Tel: 514-844-4076.
Black Sparrow, *(Black Sparrow Pr.; 0-87685),* 24 Tenth St., Santa Rosa, CA 95401 (SAN 201-4343) Tel 707-579-4011.
Black Swan CT, *(Black Swan Bks., Ltd.; 0-933806),* P.O. Box 327, Redding Ridge, CT 06876 (SAN 213-4675) Tel 203-938-9548; Dist. by: Consortium Bk. Sales & Distribution, 213 E. Fourth St., St. Paul, MN 55101 (SAN 200-6049) Tel 612-221-9035.
Blagrove Pubns, *(Blagrove Pubns.; 0-9604466; 0-939776),* P.O. Box 584, Manchester, CT 06040 (SAN 215-1316).
Blessitt Pub, *(Blessitt Publishing; 0-934461),* P.O. Box 69544, Hollywood, CA 90069 (SAN 693-7616) Tel 213-654-7871.
Bloch, *(Bloch Publishing Co.; 0-8197),* 37 W. 26th St., New York, NY 10010 (SAN 214-204X) Tel 212-532-3977.
Blue Dragon, *(Blue Dragon Pr.),* 1515 Poplar Ave., Richmond Heights, CA 94805 (SAN 214-3453) Tel 415-235-0361.
Blue Feather, *(Blue Feather Pr.; 0-932482),* P.O. Box 5113, Santa Fe, NM 87502 (SAN 211-9293) Tel 505-983-2776.
Blue Mtn Pr CO, *(Blue Mountain Pr., Inc.; 0-88396),* P.O. Box 1007, Boulder, CO 80306 (SAN 169-0477) Tel 303-449-0536; Toll free: 800-525-0642.
Blue Ridge, *(Blue Ridge Pr. of Boone; 0-938980),* Rte. 2, Vilas, NC 28692 (SAN 216-3373).
BMA Pr
See Bible Memory

BMC Intl Inc, *(BMC International, Inc.; 0-86508),* 237 Fairfield Ave., Upper Darby, PA 19082 (SAN 211-7762) Tel 215-352-7177.

BMB Pub Co, *(BMB Publishing Co.; 0-930924; 0-9600164),* P.O. Box 1622, Boston, MA 02105 (SAN 201-4270) Tel 617-492-5762.

BMH Bks, *(BMH Bks.; 0-88469),* Div. of Brethren Missionary Herald, Inc., P.O. Box 544, Winona Lake, IN 46590 (SAN 201-7571) Tel 219-267-7158; Toll free: 800-348-2756.

B'nai B'rith-Hillel, *(B'nai B'rith Hillel Foundations; 0-9603058),* 1640 Rhode Island Ave., NW, Washington, DC 20036 (SAN 204-4080) Tel 202-857-6556.

Board Jewish Educ, *(Board of Jewish Education of Greater New York; 0-88384),* 426 W. 58th St., New York, NY 10019 (SAN 213-0165) Tel 212-245-8200.

Board Pub Evang, *(Board for Publications of The Evangelical Lutheran Synod; 0-89279),* 734 Marsh St., Mankato, MN 56001 (SAN 262-0030).

Boardman, *(Boardman, Clark, Co., Ltd.; 0-87632),* Subs. of International Thomson Organization, Inc., 435 Hudson St., New York, NY 10014 (SAN 202-4136) Tel 212-929-7500; Toll free: 800-221-9428.

Bob Jones Univ Pr, *(Jones, Bob, Univ. Pr.; 0-89084),* Bob Jones Univ., Greenville, SC 29614 (SAN 223-7512) Tel 803-242-5100; Toll free: 800-845-5731.

Bobbs, *(Bobbs-Merrill Co.; 0-672),* Subs. of Macmillan Publishing Co., Inc., 866 Third Ave., New York, NY 10022 (SAN 201-3959) Tel 212-702-2000.

Bolchazy-Carducci, *(Bolchazy-Carducci Pubs.; 0-86516),* 44 Lake St., Oak Park, IL 60302 (SAN 219-7685) Tel 312-386-8360.

Bond Pub Co, *(Bond Publishing, Co.; 0-939296),* Div. of Progressive Artistic Communications Enterprises, Inc., P.O. Box 1217, Landover, MD 20785 (SAN 220-1488) Tel 301-946-8152.

Book Dept, *(Book Department, The; 0-9606080),* P.O. Box 241, Hartford, CT 06141-0241 (SAN 216-7921) Tel 203-728-3470.

Book Dist Ctr, *(Bk. Distribution Ctr.; 0-941722),* P.O. Box 31669, Houston, TX 77235 (SAN 226-2770) Tel 713-721-1980.

Book Pub Co, *(Book Publishing Co., The; 0-913990),* P.O. Box 99, Summertown, TN 38483 (SAN 202-439X) Tel 615-964-3571.

Book Searchers, *(Bk., Searchers; 0-932484),* 2622 15th Ave., Forest Grove, OR 97116 (SAN 212-0739) Tel 503-357-6948.

Bookcraft Inc, *(Bookcraft, Inc.; 0-88494),* 1848 W. 2300, S., Salt Lake City, UT 84119 (SAN 204-3998) Tel 801-972-6180.

Bookmark CA
See Pasadena Pr

Bookmates Intl, *(Bookmates International, Inc.; 0-933082),* P.O. Box 9883, Fresno, CA 93795 (SAN 212-8799) Tel 209-298-3308; Dist. by: Spring Arbor Distributors, 10885 Textile Rd., Belleville, MI 48111 (SAN 158-9016) Tel 313-481-0900.

Borden, *(Borden Publishing Co.; 0-87505),* 1855 W. Main St., Alhambra, CA 91801 (SAN 201-419X) Tel 213-283-5031.

Borderline NY, *(Borderline Pr.; 0-9614941),* 27 W. 11th St., New York, NY 10011 (SAN 693-6644) Tel 212-989-9248; Dist. by: Samuel Weiser, Inc., P.O. Box 612, York Beach, ME 03910 (SAN 202-9588) Tel 207-363-4393; Dist. by: New Leaf Distributing, The, 1020 White St., SW, Atlanta, GA 30310 (SAN 169-1449) Tel 404-755-2665.

Borgo Pr, *(Borgo Pr.; 0-89370; 0-8095),* P.O. Box 2845, San Bernardino, CA 92406-2845 (SAN 208-9459) Tel 714-884-5813.

Boston Public Lib, *(Boston Public Library; 0-89073),* P.O. Box 286, Boston, MA 02117 (SAN 204-3971) Tel 617-536-5400.

Bowdoin Coll, *(President & Trustees of Bowdoin College; 0-916606),* Bowdoin College, Getchell Hse., Brunswick, ME 04011 (SAN 695-6394) Tel 207-725-8731.

Bowker, *(Bowker, R. R., Co.; 0-8352; 0-911255),* Div. of Reed Publishing USA, 245 W. 17th St., New York, NY 10011 (SAN 214-1191) Tel 212-645-9700; Toll free: 800-521-8110 US; Toll free: 800-537-8416 Canada; Toll free: 800-431-1713 subscriptions to: Publishers Weekly, School Library Journal, Library Journal (in Ohio: 614-383-3141); Toll free: 800-257-7894 subscriptions to: Library Hotline, Reviews-on-Cards (in New Jersey: 609-786-1160). On April 1, 1986, R. R. Bowker Co. became the sole supplier for all Bowker annuals & continuation books. Any orders or standing orders for these titles placed with wholesalers should be changed, & ordered directly from Bowker from the address above. BOWKER NOW OFFERS A 5 PERCENT DISCOUNT FOR ALL STANDING ORDERS. This new policy does not affect subscriptions & non-continuation titles.

Bowling Green Univ, *(Bowling Green Univ. Popular Pr.; 0-87972),* Bowling Green State Univ., Popular Culture Ctr., Bowling Green, OH 43403 (SAN 201-4165) Tel 419-372-7865.

Boxwood, *(Boxwood Pr.; 0-910286; 0-940168),* 183 Ocean View Blvd., Pacific Grove, CA 93950 (SAN 201-4149) Tel 408-375-9110.

Boykin, *(Boykin, James H.; 0-9603342),* 1260 NW 122nd St., Miami, FL 33167 (SAN 215-0603) Tel 305-681-7663.

Boynton Cook Pubs, *(Boynton Cook Pubs., Inc.; 0-86709),* P.O. Box 860, 52 Upper Montclair Plaza, Upper Montclair, NJ 07043 (SAN 216-6186) Tel 201-783-3310.

Bradford & Wilson, *(Bradford & Wilson, Ltd.; 0-915073),* Box 7189 University Sta., Provo, UT 84602 (SAN 289-7466) Tel 801-377-4819.

Bradley Pubns, *(Bradley Pubns.; 0-89748),* 80 Eighth Ave., New York, NY 10011 (SAN 696-2912); Dist. by: Warner Brothers Publications, Incorporated, 265 Secaucus Rd., Secaucus, NJ 07094 (SAN 203-0586) Tel 201-348-0700.

Brandeis-Bardin Inst, *(Brandeis-Bardin Institute Pubns., The; 0-916952),* Brandeis, CA 93064 (SAN 208-5666) Tel 213-348-7201.

Branden Pub Co, *(Branden Publishing Co.; 0-8283),* Box 843, Brookline Village, Boston, MA 02147 (SAN 201-4106) Tel 617-734-2045.

Branford, *(Branford, Charles T., Co.; 0-8231),* P.O. Box 41, Newton Centre, MA 02159 (SAN 201-9302) Tel 617-964-2441.

Braziller, *(Braziller, George, Inc.; 0-8076),* 60 Madison Ave., Suite 1001, New York, NY 10010 (SAN 201-9310) Tel 212-889-0909.

Bread and Butter, *(Bread & Butter, Pr.; 0-912549),* 2582 S. Clayton, Denver, CO 80210 (SAN 223-1700) Tel 303-753-0912.

Breitenbush Bks, *(Breitenbush Bks.; 0-932576),* P.O. Box 02137, Portland, OR 97202 (SAN 219-7707) Tel 503-230-1900.

Brentwood Comm, *(Brentwood Communications Group; 0-916573; 1-55630),* 3914 Cody Rd., Columbus, GA 31907 (SAN 297-1895) Tel 404-561-1772; Toll free: 800-334-8861.

Breslov Res Inst, *(Breslov Research Institute; 0-930213),* 1201 Beach Ninth St., Far Rockaway, NY 11691 (SAN 670-7890); Dist. by: Great Tradition, 750 Adrian Way, Suite 111, San Rafael, CA 94903 (SAN 200-5743) Tel 415-492-9382.

Bret Pubns, *(B'Ret Pubns.; 0-933357),* 1810 Michael Faraday Dr., Suite 101, Reston, VA 22090 (SAN 691-7666) Tel 703-471-7388.

Brethren, *(Brethren Pr.; 0-87178),* Div. of Church of the Brethren, 1451 Dundee Ave., Elgin, IL 60120 (SAN 201-9329) Tel 312-742-5100; Toll free: 800-323-8039. Do not confuse with Brethren Publishing Co., Ashland, Ohio.

Brethren Encyclopedia, *(Brethren Encyclopedia; 0-936693),* 313 Fairview Ave., Ambler, PA 19002 (SAN 291-817X); Orders to: (SAN 685-3803).

Brethren Ohio, *(Brethren Publishing Co.; 0-934970),* 524 College Ave., Ashland, OH 44805 (SAN 201-730X) Tel 419-289-1708. Do not confuse with Brethren Pr., Elgin, Illinois.

Brevet Pr, *(Brevet Pr.; 0-88498),* Box 1404, Sioux Falls, SD 57101 (SAN 201-7563) Tel 605-361-6121.

Brians Pub
See VHI Library

Bridge Pub, *(Bridge Publishing, Inc.; 0-88270),* 2500 Hamilton Blvd., South Plainfield, NJ 07080 (SAN 239-5061) Tel 201-754-0745; Toll free: 800-631-5802. Do not confuse with Bridge Pubns., Los Angeles, CA. *Imprints:* Haven Bks (Haven Books).

Bridge Pubns Inc, *(Bridge Pubns., Inc.; 0-88404),* 1414 N. Catalina St., Los Angeles, CA 90027 (SAN 208-3884) Tel 213-382-0382; Toll free: 800-722-1733; Toll free: 800-843-7389 (in California). Do not confuse with Bridge Publishing, Inc., South Plainfield, NJ.

Brigham, *(Young, Brigham, Univ. Pr.; 0-8425),* P.O. Box 140, Tanner Bldg., Provo, UT 84602 (SAN 201-9337) Tel 801-378-6599; Toll free: 800-453-3235; Orders to: 205 University Press Bldg., Provo, UT 84602 (SAN 201-9345) Tel 801-378-2809.

Bright Mtn Bks, *(Bright Mountain Bks.; 0-914875),* 138 Springside Rd., Asheville, NC 28803 (SAN 289-0674); Dist. by: Bright Horizons, 138 Springside Rd., Asheville, NC 28803 (SAN 200-7193) Tel 704-684-8840.

Bro Life Inc, *(Brotherhood of Life, Inc.; 0-914732),* 110 Dartmouth, SE, Albuquerque, NM 87106 (SAN 202-4233) Tel 505-255-8980.

Broadman, *(Broadman Pr.; 0-8054),* Div. of Sunday School Board of the Southern Baptist Convention, 127 Ninth Ave. N., Nashville, TN 37234 (SAN 201-937X) Tel 615-251-2544; Toll free: 800-251-3225.

Brob Hse Bks, *(Brob Hse. Bks.; 0-938407),* P.O. Box 7829, Atlanta, GA 30309 (SAN 659-9117) Tel 404-876-1311.

Brokering Pr, *(Brokering Pr.; 0-942562),* 11641 Palmer Rd., Bloomington, MN 55437 (SAN 239-622X) Tel 612-888-5281.

Brookings, *(Brookings Institution; 0-8157),* 1775 Massachusetts Ave., NW, Washington, DC 20036-2188 (SAN 201-9396) Tel 202-797-6000.

Brookline Bks, *(Brookline Bks.; 0-914797),* P.O. Box 1046, Cambridge, MA 02238 (SAN 289-0690) Tel 617-868-0360.

Brooklyn Coll Pr, *(Brooklyn College, Pr.; 0-930888),* 2227 Boylan Hall, Society In Change, Brooklyn, NY 11210 (SAN 281-3467); Orders to: 136 S. Broadway, Irvington-on-Hudson, NY 10533 (SAN 281-3475) Tel 914-591-9111.

Broude, *(Broude Brothers Ltd.; 0-8450),* 170 Varick St., New York, NY 10013 (SAN 281-3483) Tel 212-242-7001; Toll free: 800-225-3197 (SAN 281-3491); Orders to: 141 White Oaks Rd., Williamstown, MA 01267 (SAN 666-6493) Tel 413-458-8131.

Brown Bk, *(Brown Bk. Co.; 0-910294),* P.O. Box 69-3883, Miami, FL 33269 (SAN 202-4276).

Brown Rabbit, *(Brown Rabbit Pr.; 0-933988),* Smithdale Ct., No. 3, Houston, TX 77024 (SAN 213-0246) Tel 713-465-1168.

Brownlow Pub Co, *(Brownlow Publishing Co., Inc.; 0-915720),* 6309 Airport Freeway, Fort Worth, TX 76117 (SAN 207-5105) Tel 817-831-3831; Toll free: 800-433-7610.

Bruner, *(Bruner, William T.; 0-9606566),* 3848 Southern Pkwy., Louisville, KY 40214 (SAN 211-2884) Tel 502-367-7089. Moved, left no forwarding address.

Brunner-Mazel, *(Brunner/Mazel, Inc.; 0-87630),* 19 Union Sq., W., New York, NY 10003 (SAN 164-9167) Tel 212-924-3344.

Brunswick Pub, *(Brunswick Publishing Co.; 0-931494; 1-55618),* Rte. 1, Box 1A1, Lawrenceville, VA 23868 (SAN 211-6332) Tel 804-848-3865.

BSA, *(Boy Scouts of America; 0-8395),* 1325 Walnut Hill Ln., Irving, TX 75038-3096 (SAN 284-9798) Tel 214-659-2273; Orders to: Eastern Distribution Ctr., 2109 Westinghouse Blvd., P.O. Box 7143, Charlotte, NC 28217 (SAN 284-9801) Tel 704-588-4260.

Bubbling-Well, *(Bubbling-Well Pr.; 0-938045),* P.O. Box 961, St. Cloud, MN 56302 (SAN 659-9257) Tel 612-253-0426; 37 N. 28th Ave., Rm. 103, St. Cloud, MN 56301 (SAN 659-9265) Tel 612-253-0426.

Buccaneer Bks, *(Buccaneer Bks.; 0-89966),* P.O. Box 168, Cutchogue, NY 11935 (SAN 209-1542).

Buckley Pubns, *(Buckley Pubns., Inc.; 0-915388),* 4848 N. Clark St., Chicago, IL 60640-4711 (SAN 208-1954) Tel 312-271-0202.

Bucknell U Pr, *(Bucknell Univ. Pr.; 0-8387),* Dist. by: Associated University Presses, 440 Forsgate Dr., Cranbury, NJ 08512 (SAN 281-2959) Tel 609-655-4770.
Bucks Co Hist, *(Bucks County Historical Society; 0-910302),* Pine & Ashland Sts., Doylestown, PA 18901 (SAN 203-6835) Tel 215-345-0210.
Buddhist Assn US, *(Buddhist Assn. of the U.S., The; 0-915078),* Dist. by: Institute for Advanced Studies of World Religions, 2150 Center Ave., Fort Lee, NJ 07024 (SAN 265-3885) Tel 516-632-6580.
Buddhist Bks, *(Buddhist Bks. International; 0-914910),* Subs. of Buddhist Bks. International of Japan, 9701 Wilshire Blvd., Suite 850, Beverly Hills, CA 90212 (SAN 281-3548).
Buddhist Study, *(Buddhist Study Ctr. Pr., The; 0-938474),* c/o Ruth M. Tabrah, 1221 Victoria St., No. 2001, Honolulu, HI 96814 (SAN 284-9860) Tel 808-533-7633; Orders to: 1727 Pali Hwy., Honolulu, HI 96813 (SAN 665-6676).
Buddhist Text, *(Buddhist Text Translation Society; 0-917512),* Box 217, City of Ten Thousand Buddhas, Talmage, CA 95481 (SAN 281-3556) Tel 707-462-0939.
Buffalo Acad, *(Buffalo Fine Arts Academy; 0-914782),* Albright-Knox Art Gallery, 1285 Elmwood Ave., Buffalo, NY 14222 (SAN 202-4845) Tel 716-882-8700; Dist. by: Univ. of Washington Pr., P.O. Box C50096, Seattle, WA 98145 (SAN 212-2502) Tel 206-543-4050.
Builders of Adytum, *(Builders of the Adytum, Ltd.; 0-938002),* 5105 N. Figueroa St., Los Angeles, CA 90042 (SAN 202-4853) Tel 213-255-7141; Orders to: P.O. Box 42278, Dept. O, Los Angeles, CA 90042 (SAN 202-4861).
Builders Pub, *(Builders Publishing Co., The; 0-941848),* P.O. Box 2122, Oasis, NV 89835 (SAN 212-8675) Tel 702-478-5131; Dist. by: New Leaf Distributing, The, 1020 White St. SW, Atlanta, GA 30310 (SAN 169-1449) Tel 404-755-2665; Dist. by: Bookpeople, 2929 Fifth St., Berkeley, CA 94710 (SAN 168-9517) Tel 415-549-3030; Dist. by: The Distributors, 702 S. Michigan, South Bend, IN 46618 (SAN 169-2488) Tel 219-232-8500; Dist. by: Devorss & Co., P.O. Box 550, 1046 Princeton Dr., Marina del Rey, CA 90294 (SAN 168-9886) Tel 213-870-7478.
Bull Pub, *(Bull Publishing Co.; 0-915950),* P.O. Box 208, Palo Alto, CA 94302 (SAN 208-5712); 110 Gilbert St., Menlo Park, CA 94025 (SAN 665-6684) Tel 415-322-2855; Dist. by: Publishers Group West, 5855 Beaudry St., Emeryville, CA 94608 (SAN 202-8522) Tel 415-658-3453.
Bur Intl Aff, *(Bureau of International Affairs; 0-938780),* 1613 Chelsea Rd., San Marino, CA 91108 (SAN 201-9442) Tel 818-793-2841; Dist. by: Baker & Taylor Co. Eastern Div., 50 Kirby Ave., Somerville, NJ 08876 (SAN 169-4901); Dist. by: Emery-Pratt Co., 1966 W. Main St., Owasso, MI 48867-1372 (SAN 170-1401) Tel 517-723-5291.
Burkharts, *(Burkhart's; 0-9615199),* 259 Midway Ave., P.O. Box 807, Blandon, PA 19510 (SAN 694-3594) Tel 215-926-2564.
Burn Hart, *(Burn, Hart & Co., Pubs.; 0-918060),* 632 Calle Yucca, Box 1772, Thousand Oaks, CA 91360 (SAN 210-1823) Tel 805-498-3985.
Burtis Ent, *(Burtis Enterprises, Pubs.; 0-939530),* 23651 Gerrad Way, Canoga Park, CA 91307 (SAN 216-6593) Tel 818-346-8534.
Busn *Imprint of* **P-H**
But It Really Works Bks, *(But It Really Works Bks.; 0-9617419),* P.O. Box 634, Millbrook, AL 36054 (SAN 663-9496); 106 Quail Ridge Dr., Elmore, AL 36025 (SAN 663-950X) Tel 205-285-3394.
Button Gwin, *(Gwinnett, Button, Publishers, Inc.; 0-938386),* 125 Scott St., P.O. Box 508, Buford, GA 30518 (SAN 264-0732).
BYLS Pr, *(BYLS Pr.; 0-934402),* 6247 N. Francisco Ave., Chicago, IL 60659 (SAN 212-7253) Tel 312-262-8959.
BYR *Imprint of* **Random**
Byron Daven Pubs, *(Byron-Davenport Pubs.; 0-930895),* P.O. Box 34165, Bethesda, MD 20817 (SAN 679-2022) Tel 301-983-0742.
Byzantine Pr, *(Byzantine Pr.; 0-913168),* 115 N. Seventh St., Las Vegas, NV 89101 (SAN 204-3785) Tel 702-384-4200.
C A Parker Pubns, *(Parker, Clayton A., Pubns.; 0-9606438),* 450 Wendell Dr., Salt Lake City, UT 84115 (SAN 218-5768) Tel 801-266-2292.
C & R Anthony, *(Anthony, C. & R., Inc.; 0-910140),* P.O. Box 1802, Madison Sq. Sta., New York, NY 10159 (SAN 203-4786) Tel 212-986-7693. Do not confuse with Anthony Pub Co., Stow, MA.
C & R Loo, *(Loo, C. & R., Inc.),* 1550 62nd St., P.O. Box 8397, Emeryville, CA 94608 (SAN 211-366X).
C Bissell, *(Bissell, Charles B., III; 0-9612604),* 1911 Flintwood Dr., Richmond, VA 23233 (SAN 289-0631) Tel 804-741-6008.
C C Brown Pub, *(Brown, C. C., Publishing Co.; 0-9600378),* 17425 Burnett Rd., Nine Mile Falls, WA 99026 (SAN 203-6789) Tel 509-244-5807.
C C Fisher, *(Fisher, Clay C.),* 702 Tenth St., NE, Massillon, OH 44646 (SAN 202-4977).
C C Thomas, *(Thomas, Charles C., Pub.; 0-398),* 2600 S. First St., Springfield, IL 62794-9265 (SAN 201-9485) Tel 217-789-8980.
C E Barbour
See Pitts Theolog
C E M Comp, *(C. E. M. Co.; 0-930004),* 3154 Coventry Dr., Bay City, MI 48706 (SAN 209-5378) Tel 517-686-4208.
C E Tuttle, *(Tuttle, Charles E., Co., Inc.; 0-8048),* P.O. Box 410, 28 S. Main St., Rutland, VT 05701-0410 (SAN 213-2621) Tel 802-773-8930.
C Elder, *(Elder, Charles & Randy, Pubs.; 0-918450),* 2115 Elliston Pl., Nashville, TN 37203 (SAN 201-8292) Tel 615-327-1867.
C-Four Res, *(C-4 Resources; 0-914527),* 115 Neil St., Champaign, IL 61820 (SAN 289-1565) Tel 217-395-6242.
C H Kerr, *(Kerr, Charles H., Publishing, Co.; 0-88286),* 1740 W. Greenleaf Ave., Chicago, IL 60626 (SAN 207-7043) Tel 312-465-7774.
C Hallberg, *(Hallberg Publishing Corp.; 0-87319),* P.O. Box 547, Delavan, WI 53115 (SAN 205-3063) Tel 414-728-3173.
C I L Inc, *(C.I.L., Inc., Bks.; 0-9613326),* P.O. Box 27-3855, Boca Raton, FL 33427 (SAN 655-6205) Tel 305-392-3936.
C N Potter Bks *Imprint of* **Crown**
C Redd Ctr, *(Redd, Charles, Ctr. for Western Studies),* Brigham Young Univ., Harold B. Lee Library, Provo, UT 84602 (SAN 287-2900) Tel 801-378-4048; Dist. by: Signature Bks., 3503 Fourth East, Suite G4, Salt Lake City, UT 84111 (SAN 217-4391) Tel 801-531-1483.
C Schneider, *(Schneider, Coleman; 0-9601662),* P.O. Box 762, Tenafly, NJ 07670 (SAN 211-4186) Tel 201-567-9157.
Cadmus Press, *(Cadmus Pr.; 0-930685),* 25 Waterview Dr., Port Jefferson, NY 11777 (SAN 677-1300) Tel 516-928-9896.
Caedmon, *(Caedmon; 0-9601156; 0-89845),* Div. of Raytheon Co., 1995 Broadway, New York, NY 10023 (SAN 206-278X) Tel 212-580-3400; Toll free: 800-223-0420.
Callahan CA, *(Callahan, John D.; 0-9615767),* P.O. Box 1281, LaCanada, CA 91011 (SAN 696-1789); 8601 Sunland Blvd., Suite 44, Sun Valley, CA 91352 (SAN 696-1797) Tel 818-767-5362.
Calvary Miss Pr, *(Calvary Missionary Pr.; 0-912375),* Div. of Calvary Missionary Fellowship, P.O. Box 13532, Tucson, AZ 85732 (SAN 265-2021) Tel 602-745-3822.
Calvary Pr, *(Calvary Pr.; 0-9604138),* 400 S. Bennett St., Southern Pines, NC 28387 (SAN 223-4505).
Cambridge Bk, *(Cambridge Bk. Co.; 0-8428),* Div. of Simon & Schuster, a Gulf & Western Co., 888 Seventh Ave., New York, NY 10106 (SAN 169-5703) Tel 212-957-5300; Toll free: 800-221-4764.
Cambridge U Pr, *(Cambridge Univ. Pr.; 0-521),* 32 E. 57th St., New York, NY 10022 (SAN 200-206X) Tel 212-688-8888; Toll free: 800-221-4512; Orders to: 510 North Ave., New Rochelle, NY 10801 (SAN 281-3769) Tel 914-235-0300.
Camda, *(Camda; 0-9600434),* P.O. Box 2467, Staunton, VA 24401 (SAN 202-5027).
Camden Hse, *(Camden Hse., Inc.; 0-938100),* Drawer 2025, Columbia, SC 29202 (SAN 215-9376) Tel 803-788-8689; Orders to: P.O. Box 4836, Hampden Sta., Baltimore, MD 21211 (SAN 661-9681) Tel 301-338-6950.
Camp Guidepts, *(Camping Guideposts; 0-942684),* Whiteface Woods, Cotton, MN 55724 (SAN 239-6246) Tel 218-482-3446.
Campus, *(Campus Pubs.; 0-87506),* 713 W. Ellsworth Rd., Ann Arbor, MI 48104 (SAN 201-9558) Tel 313-663-4033.
Campus Crusade, *(Campus Crusade for Christ, International; 0-918956),* c/o Heres Life Pub., P.O. Box 1576, San Bernardino, CA 92402 (SAN 212-4254) Tel 714-886-7981.
C&M Bessie Bks *Imprint of* **Har-Row**
Candy Apple Pub, *(Candy Apple Publishing Co.; 0-9616464),* P.O. Box 48421, St. Petersburg, FL 33743-8421 (SAN 659-3178); 6575 Bonnie Bay Cir. N., Pinellas Park, FL 33565 (SAN 659-3186) Tel 813-544-0355.
Canner, *(Canner, J. S., & Co.; 0-910324),* Sub. of Plenum Publishing Corp., 49-65 Lansdowne St., Boston, MA 02215 (SAN 202-5094) Tel 617-437-1923. Microcards; also microfilm of Plenum journals only.
Canon Law Soc, *(Canon Law Society of America; 0-943616),* Catholic Univ., Caldwell Hall, Rm. 431, Washington, DC 20064 (SAN 237-6296) Tel 202-269-3491.
Canon Pr, *(Canon Pr.; 0-939651),* P.O. Box 213, Centerville, UT 84014-0213 (SAN 663-5830) Tel 801-298-8689; 497 E. 400 N., Bountiful, UT 84010 (SAN 663-5849) Tel 801-295-6003; Dist. by: Signature Books, 350 S. 400 E., Salt Lake City, UT 84111 (SAN 217-4391) Tel 801-531-1483 (SAN 200-8971).
Canon Pubns, *(Canon Publications; 0-88181),* P.O. Box 698, Talent, OR 97540 (SAN 264-7206) Tel 503-535-1490.
Capitalist Pr OH, *(Capitalist Pr.; 0-938770),* P.O. Box 2753, North Canton, OH 44720 (SAN 696-9194).
Caratzas, *(Caratzas, Aristide D., Pub.; 0-89241),* Affil. of C.B.P. Publishing & Distributing Co., Inc., 30 Church St., New Rochelle, NY 10801 (SAN 201-3134) Tel 914-632-8487; P.O. Box 210, New Rochelle, NY 10802 (SAN 658-0238).
Caravan Bks, *(Caravan Bks.; 0-88206),* Subs. of Scholar's Facsimiles & Reprints, P.O. Box 344, Delmar, NY 12054 (SAN 206-7323) Tel 518-439-5978.
Carcanet, *(Carcanet Pr.; 0-85635; 0-902145),* Subs. of Carcanet Pr., (UK), 198 Sixth Ave., New York, NY 10013 (SAN 686-192X) Tel 212-334-0988; Dist. by: Harper & Row Pubs., Inc., Keystone Industrial Pk., Scranton, PA 18512 (SAN 215-3742).
Caregiving Resc, *(Caregiving Resources; 0-939273),* 29 Oberlin St., Maplewood, NJ 07040 (SAN 662-8834) Tel 201-761-7188.
Carib Pubns *Imprint of* **Casa Bautista**
Carlton, *(Carlton Pr.; 0-8062),* 11 W. 32nd St., New York, NY 10001 (SAN 201-9655) Tel 212-714-0300.
Carnation, *(Carnation Pr.; 0-87601),* P.O. Box 101, State College, PA 16804 (SAN 203-5103) Tel 814-238-3577; 346 W. Hillcrest Ave., State College, PA 16803 (SAN 661-9703) Tel 814-238-3577.
Carnegie Endow, *(Carnegie Endowment for International Peace; 0-87003),* 11 Dupont Cir., NW, Washington, DC 20036 (SAN 281-3955) Tel 202-797-6424.
Carolina Acad Pr, *(Carolina Academic Pr.; 0-89089),* P.O. Box 8795, Forest Hills Sta., Durham, NC 27707 (SAN 210-7848) Tel 919-489-7486.
Carolina Wren, *(Carolina Wren Pr., The; 0-932112),* Affil. of Durham Arts Council, P.O. Box 277, Carrboro, NC 27510 (SAN 213-0327) Tel 919-376-8152.
Carolrhoda Bks, *(Carolrhoda Bks., Inc.; 0-87614),* 241 First Ave., N., Minneapolis, MN 55401 (SAN 201-9671) Tel 612-332-3344; Toll free: 800-328-4929.
Carothers, *(Carothers Co.; 0-943026),* Box 2518, Escondido, CA 92025 (SAN 240-3536) Tel 619-741-2755.
Carpenter Pr, *(Carpenter Pr.; 0-914140),* Rte. 4, Pomeroy, OH 45769 (SAN 206-4650) Tel 614-992-7520.

Carrol Gate Pr, *(Carrol Gate Press, The; 0-9608714),* 951 W. Liberty Dr., Wheaton, IL 60187 (SAN 238-048X) Tel 312-690-8574.

Carroll Pr, *(Carroll Pr.; 0-910328),* 43 Squantum St., Cranston, RI 02920 (SAN 203-6231) Tel 401-942-1587; P.O. Box 8113, Cranston, RI 02920 (SAN 658-0270).

Carson-Dellos, *(Carson-Dellosa Publishing Co., Inc.; 0-88724),* 207 Creek Ridge, Greensboro, NC 27406 (SAN 287-5896) Tel 919-274-1150; Toll free: 800-321-0943; Orders to: P.O. Drawer 16327, Greensboro, NC 27416 (SAN 665-8296) Tel 919-274-1150.

Casa Bautista, *(Casa Bautista de Publicaciones; 0-311),* Div. of Southern Baptist Convention, P.O. Box 4255, 7000 Alabama St., El Paso, TX 79914 (SAN 220-0139) Tel 915-566-9656; Dist. by: Broadman Pr., 127 Ninth Ave., N., Nashville, TN 37234 (SAN 201-937X) Tel 615-251-2606. *Imprints:* Carib Pubns (Carib Publications); Edit Mundo (Editorial Mundo Hispano).

Cassandra Pr, *(Cassandra Pr.; 0-9615875),* P.O. Box 2044, Boulder, CO 80306 (SAN 697-0389) Tel 303-499-7651; 445 43rd St., Boulder, CO 80306 (SAN 697-0397); Dist. by: Bookpeople, 2929 Fifth St., Berkeley, CA 94710 (SAN 168-9517) Tel 415-549-3030; Dist. by: New Leaf Distributing, The, 1020 White St., SW, Atlanta, GA 30310 (SAN 169-1449) Tel 404-755-2665; Dist. by: Publishers Group West, 5855 Beaudry St., Emeryville, CA 94608 (SAN 202-8522) Tel 415-658-3453; Dist. by: Samuel Weiser, Inc., P.O. Box 612, York Beach, ME 03910 (SAN 202-9588) Tel 415-658-3453; Dist. by: Nutri-Bks., Corp., P.O. Box 5793, Denver, CO 80223 (SAN 295-3404); Dist. by: Starlite, P.O. Box 20729, Reno, NV 89515 (SAN 131-1921) Tel 702-359-5676.

Cassizzi, *(Cassizzi, Vic),* P.O. Box 8788, 710 Town Mtn. Rd., Asheville, NC 28804 (SAN 217-0922) Tel 704-253-5016.

Cath Authors, *(Catholic Authors Pr.; 0-910334),* 1201 S. Kirkwood Rd., Kirkwood, MO 63122 (SAN 203-6274) Tel 314-965-4801.

Cath Free Choice, *(Catholics for a Free Choice; 0-915365),* 2008 17th St. NW, Washington, DC 20009 (SAN 291-1116) Tel 202-638-1706.

Cath Health, *(Catholic Health Assn. of the U.S.; 0-87125),* 4455 Woodson Rd., St. Louis, MO 63134-0889 (SAN 201-968X) Tel 314-427-2500.

Cath Lib Assn, *(Catholic Library Assn.; 0-87507),* 461 W. Lancaster Ave., Haverford, PA 19041 (SAN 203-6282) Tel 215-649-5251.

Cath News Pub Co, *(Catholic News Publishing Co.; 0-910635),* 210 North Ave., New Rochelle, NY 10801 (SAN 268-7240) Tel 914-632-7771; Toll free: 800-433-7771.

Cath Pr Assn, *(Catholic Pr. Assn.),* 119 N. Park Ave., Rockville Centre, NY 11570 (SAN 204-3335) Tel 516-766-3400.

Cath U Pr, *(Catholic Univ. of America Pr.; 0-8132),* 620 Michigan Ave., NE, Washington, DC 20064 (SAN 203-6290) Tel 202-635-5052; Orders to: P.O. Box 4852, Hampden Sta., Baltimore, MD 21211 (SAN 203-6304) Tel 301-338-6953.

Catholic Bibl Assn, *(Catholic Biblical Assn. of America; 0-915170),* Catholic Univ. of America, 620 Michigan Ave., NE, Washington, DC 20064 (SAN 210-7856) Tel 202-635-5519.

Catholic Bk Pub, *(Catholic Bk. Publishing Co.; 0-89942),* 257 W. 17th St., New York, NY 10011 (SAN 204-3432) Tel 212-243-4515.

Catoctin Pr, *(Catoctin Pr.; 0-914385),* 709 E. Main St., Middletown, MD 21769 (SAN 289-6117) Tel 301-371-6293.

Cayuse Pr, *(Cayuse Pr.; 0-933529),* P.O. Box 9086, Berkeley, CA 94709 (SAN 693-8744) Tel 415-525-8515; Dist. by: Bookpeople, 2929 Fifth St., Berkeley, CA 94710 (SAN 168-9517) Tel 415-549-3030; Dist. by: The Distributors, 702 S. Michigan, South Bend, IN 46618 (SAN 169-2488) Tel 219-232-8500.

CBP, *(CBP Pr.; 0-8272),* Div. of Christian Board of Pubn., P.O. Box 179, St. Louis, MO 63166 (SAN 201-4408) Tel 314-231-8500; Toll free: 800-351-2665; Toll free: 800-451-2665 (in Maryland).

CBS Ed
See HR&W

CEF Press, *(Child Evangelism Fellowship Press),* Highway M, Warrenton, MO 63383 (SAN 211-7789) Tel 314-456-4321.

Celestial Arts, *(Celestial Arts Publishing Co.; 0-912310; 0-89087),* Subs. of Ten Speed Pr., P.O. Box 7327, Berkeley, CA 94707 (SAN 159-8333) Tel 415-524-1801; Toll free: 800-841-2665.

Celestial Gems, *(Celestial Gems; 0-914154),* 404 State St., Centralia, WA 98531 (SAN 201-1948) Tel 206-736-5083.

Celestial Pr, *(Celestial Pr.; 0-910340),* 441 NE 24th St., Boca Raton, FL 33432 (SAN 203-6320) Tel 305-368-1309.

Cellar, *(Cellar Bk. Shop),* 18090 Wyoming, Detroit, MI 48221 (SAN 213-4330) Tel 313-861-1776.

Celo Pr, *(Celo Pr.; 0-914064),* 1901 Hannah Branch Rd., Burnsville, NC 28714 (SAN 201-971X) Tel 704-675-4925.

Celt Heritage Pr, *(Celtic Heritage Pr., Inc.; 0-9614753),* 59-10 Queens Blvd., No. 9B, Woodside, NY 11377 (SAN 692-929X) Tel 718-478-8162.

Center Concern, *(Center of Concern; 0-934255),* 3700 13th St., NE, Washington, DC 20017 (SAN 268-8115) Tel 202-635-2757.

Center Pubns, *(Center Pubns.; 0-916820),* Div. of Zen Ctr. of Los Angeles, Inc., 923 S. Normandie Ave., Los Angeles, CA 90006 (SAN 208-9386) Tel 213-387-2351; Dist. by: Bookpeople, 2929 Fifth St., Berkeley, CA 94710 (SAN 168-9517) Tel 415-549-3030.

Center Reform, *(Center for Reformation Research; 0-910345),* 6477 San Bonita Ave., St. Louis, MO 63105 (SAN 241-2845) Tel 314-727-6655.

Centerpoint Pr, *(Centerpoint Pr.; 0-937897),* Div. of Neeld & Neeld, Inc., P.O. Box 4771, Bryan, TX 77805 (SAN 659-4352) Tel 409-775-7887.

Central Conf, *(Central Conference of American Rabbis; 0-916694),* 21 E. 40th St., New York, NY 10016 (SAN 204-3262) Tel 212-684-4990.

Centre Ent, *(Centre Enterprise, The; 0-932876),* Box 640506, Sta. "O", San Francisco, CA 94164-0506 (SAN 212-3401) Tel 415-673-1377.

Century Bookbindery, *(Century Bookbindery; 0-89984),* P.O. Box 6471, Philadelphia, PA 19145 (SAN 209-2441) Tel 215-583-4550.

Ch Brethren Womens Caucus, *(Church of the Brethren, Women's Caucus; 0-9618243),* Rte. 1, Box 215, Mount Solon, VA 22843 (SAN 666-9042) Tel 703-350-2922.

Chadwyck-Healey, *(Chadwyck-Healey, Inc.; 0-914146; 0-89887; 0-85964),* 1021 Prince St., Alexandria, VA 22314 (SAN 282-3306) Tel 203-683-4890.

Challenge Pr, *(Challenge Pr.; 0-89421),* Div. of Economic Research Ctr., Inc., 1107 Lexington Ave., Dayton, OH 45407 (SAN 210-0509) Tel 513-275-8637.

CHAMAH Pubs, *(CHAMAH Pubs.; 0-938666),* 25 Broadway, Suite 1042, New York, NY 10004 (SAN 215-9430).

Chan Shal Imi, *(Chan Shal Imi Society Press; 0-936380),* P.O. Box 1365, Stone Mountain, GA 30086 (SAN 213-2974).

Chandler & Sharp, *(Chandler & Sharp Pubs., Inc.; 0-88316),* 11A Commercial Blvd., Novato, CA 94947 (SAN 205-6127) Tel 415-883-2353.

Chandler Pub
See Har-Row

Character Res, *(Character Research Pr.; 0-915744),* 266 State St., Schenectady, NY 12305 (SAN 209-1240) Tel 518-370-0025.

Chariot Bks *Imprint of* **Cook**

Charisma Pr, *(Charisma Pr.; 0-933402),* P.O. Box 263, Andover, MA 01810 (SAN 212-6478) Tel 617-851-7910.

Charismatic Ren Servs, *(Charismatic Renewal Services; 0-943780),* 237 N. Michigan, South Bend, IN 46601 (SAN 268-8492) Tel 219-234-6021; Toll free: 800-348-2227.

Charles River Bks, *(Charles River Bks.; 0-89182),* 1 Thompson Sq., P.O. Box 65, Boston, MA 02129 (SAN 209-2530) Tel 617-259-8857.

Chatham Comm Inc, *(Chatham Communicators, Inc.; 0-910347),* 3857 N. High St., P.O. Box 14091, Columbus, OH 43214 (SAN 241-2861) Tel 614-268-8989.

Checkerboard Pr *Imprint of* **Macmillan**

Chedney, *(Chedney Pr.; 0-910358),* P.O. Box 1148, Auburn, ME 04210 (SAN 203-6428).

Chelsea Hse, *(Chelsea Hse. Pubs.; 0-87754; 1-55546),* Div. of Chelsea Hse. Educational Communications, Inc., 5014 West Chester Pike, Edgemont, PA 19028 (SAN 206-7609) Tel 215-353-6625; Toll free: 800-523-0458.

Chen Fu, *(Chen Fu Tien),* P.O. Box 1854, Norwalk, CA 90650 (SAN 287-2870).

Cherokee Pubns, *(Cherokee Pubns.; 0-935741),* P.O. Box 256, Cherokee, NC 28719 (SAN 696-2785) Tel 704-488-2988.

Chicago Inst
See Art Inst Chi

Chicago Review, *(Chicago Review Pr., Inc.; 0-914090; 1-55652),* 814 N. Franklin St., Chicago, IL 60610 (SAN 213-5744) Tel 312-337-0747.

Chicago Visual Lib *Imprint of* **U of Chicago Pr**

Chick Pubns, *(Chick Pubns.; 0-937958),* P.O. Box 662, Chino, CA 91710 (SAN 211-7770) Tel 714-987-0771.

Chidvilas Found, *(Chidvilas Foundation, Inc.; 0-88050),* Div. of Chidvilas Inc., P.O. Box 1510, Boulder, CO 80306 (SAN 240-0987) Tel 303-665-6611.

Childrens, *(Children's Pr.; 0-516),* Div. of Regensteiner Publishing Enterprises, Inc., 1224 W. Van Buren St., Chicago, IL 60607 (SAN 201-9264) Tel 312-666-4200; Toll free: 800-621-1115.

Children's Memorial, *(Children's Memorial Hospital, The; 0-9607400),* 2300 Children's Plaza, Chicago, IL 60614 (SAN 239-4189).

Childs World, *(Child's World, Inc., The; 0-89565; 0-913778),* 980 N. McLean Blvd., Elgin, IL 60123 (SAN 211-0032) Tel 312-741-7591; P.O. Box 989, Elgin, IL 60121 (SAN 661-9738); Dist. by: Children's Pr., 1224 W. Van Buren St., Chicago, IL 60607 (SAN 201-9264) Tel 312-666-4200.

Chiltern Yoga, *(Chiltern Yoga Foundation; 0-9612762),* 1029 Hyde St., Suite 6, San Francisco, CA 94109 (SAN 289-8284) Tel 415-776-1158.

Chilton, *(Chilton Bk. Co.; 0-8019),* Subs. of ABC Publishing, Chilton Way, Radnor, PA 19089 (SAN 658-0319) Tel 215-964-4000; Toll free: 800-345-1214; Orders to: School Library Services, Chilton Way, Radnor, PA 19089 (SAN 200-6669) Tel 215-964-4729.

China Bks, *(China Bks. & Periodicals, Inc.; 0-8351),* 2929 24th St., San Francisco, CA 94110 (SAN 145-0557) Tel 415-282-2994.

Chiron Pubns, *(Chiron Pubns.; 0-933029),* 400 Linden Ave., Wilmette, IL 60091 (SAN 689-1659) Tel 312-256-7551; Dist. by: Open Court Publishing Co., P.O. Box 599, Peru, IL 61354 (SAN 202-5876) Tel 815-223-2520.

Chisum Pub, *(Chisum Publishing, Inc.; 0-937689),* 1000 E. 14th St., Suite 388, Plano, TX 75074 (SAN 659-0284) Tel 214-423-2120; 1541 Ave. K, Plano, TX 75074 (SAN 659-0292) Tel 214-422-7066.

Chosen Bks *Imprint of* **Revell**

Chr Acad Success, *(Christian Academy of Success; 0-941280),* 5428 W. Barbara Ave., Glendale, AZ 85302 (SAN 238-924X).

Chr Bksellers, *(Christian Booksellers Assn.),* 2620 Venetucci Blvd., P.O. Box 200, Colorado Springs, CO 80901 (SAN 216-3519) Tel 303-576-7880.

Chr Classics, *(Christian Classics, Inc.; 0-87061),* P.O. Box 30, Westminster, MD 21157 (SAN 203-6525) Tel 301-848-3065.

Chr Coll Pr *Imprint of* **Christendom Pubns**

Chr Concil Serv, *(Christian Conciliation Service),* P.O. Box 2069, Oak Park, IL 60303 (SAN 277-6634).

Chr Educ Res Inst, *(Christian Education Research Institute; 0-943708),* Box 888-747, Atlanta, GA 30356 (SAN 238-0501) Tel 404-972-3888.

Chr Intl Pubs, *(Christian International Pubs.; 0-939868),* Rt. 2 Box 351, Point Washington, FL 32454 (SAN 281-4102).

Chr Lib Pr, *(Christian's Library Pr., Inc.; 0-934874),* P.O. Box 2226, Grand Rapids, MI 49501 (SAN 222-7061).

Chr Lit, *(Christian Literature Crusade, Inc.; 0-87508),* P.O. Box 1449, Fort Washington, PA 19034-8449 (SAN 169-7358) Tel 215-542-1240.
Chr Marriage, *(Christian Marriage Enrichment; 0-938786),* 1913 E. 17th St., Suite 118, Santa Ana, CA 92701 (SAN 216-1141) Tel 714-542-3506.
Chr Overeaters Bks
See VHI Library
Chr Pubns, *(Christian Pubns., Inc.; 0-87509),* 3825 Hartzdale Dr., Camp Hill, PA 17011-8870 (SAN 202-1617) Tel 717-761-7044; Toll free: 800-932-0382.
Chr Restor Assn, *(Christian Restoration Assn.; 0-9614213),* 5664 Cheviot Rd., Cincinnati, OH 45247 (SAN 687-0635) Tel 513-385-0461.
Chr Stud Ctr, *(Christen Studies Ctr.; 0-939200),* P.O. Box 11110, Memphis, TN 38111 (SAN 220-0406) Tel 901-458-0738.
Chr Today, *(Christianity Today, Inc.; 0-917463),* 465 Gundersen Dr., Carol Stream, IL 60188 (SAN 656-884X) Tel 312-260-6200.
Chris Mass, *(Christopher Publishing Hse.; 0-8158),* 106 Longwater Dr., Norwell, MA 02061 (SAN 202-1625) Tel 617-878-9336.
Christ Found, *(Christ Foundation, The; 0-910315),* P.O. Box 10, Port Angeles, WA 98362 (SAN 241-4872) Tel 206-452-5249.
Christ Life Revivals, *(Christ Life Revivals Inc.; 0-930033),* P.O. Box 493, Quitman, TX 75783 (SAN 669-7658) Tel 214-763-4267.
Christ Nations, *(Christ for the Nations, Inc.; 0-89985),* P.O. Box 769000, Dallas, TX 75376-9000 (SAN 211-7800) Tel 214-376-1711.
Christ Serv Ctrs, *(Christian Service Ctrs., Inc.; 0-936801),* 5300 Ulmerton Rd., Clearwater, FL 33520 (SAN 699-8798) Tel 813-535-4532.
Christendom Pubns, *(Christendom Pubns.; 0-931888),* Rte. 3, Box 87, Front Royal, VA 22630 (SAN 214-2570) Tel 703-636-2908. *Imprints:* Chr Coll Pr (Christendom College Press).
Christian Bks, *(Christian Bks. Pub. Hse.; 0-940232),* P.O. Box 959, Gardiner, ME 04345 (SAN 201-8942) Tel 207-737-8267; Toll free: 800-228-2665.
Christian Fellow Pubs, *(Christian Fellowship Pubs., Inc.; 0-935008),* 11515 Allecingie Pkwy., Richmond, VA 23235 (SAN 207-4885) Tel 804-794-5333.
Christian Freedom, *(Christian Freedom Pr., Inc.; 0-9617746),* 518 Lincoln Ave., West Chicago, IL 60185 (SAN 289-7059) Tel 312-231-6792.
Christian Lib
See Barbour & Co
Christian Light, *(Christian Light Pubns., Inc.; 0-87813),* P.O. Box 1126, Harrisonburg, VA 22801 (SAN 206-7315) Tel 703-434-0768.
Christian Mini, *(Christian Ministries Pubns.; 0-911567),* 173 Woodland Ave., Lexington, KY 40502 (SAN 264-2115) Tel 606-254-6003.
Christian Pub, *(Christian Publishing Services, Inc.; 0-88144),* Subs. of Harrison Hse. Pubns., P.O. Box 55388, Tulsa, OK 74155 (SAN 260-0285) Tel 918-584-5535; Toll free: 800-826-5992.
Christian Res Pr, *(Christian Research, Pr., The; 0-915923),* P.O. Box 2013, Des Moines, IA 50310 (SAN 293-4868); 3825 Kingman, Des Moines, IA 50311 (SAN 293-4876) Tel 515-255-8854.
Christianica, *(Christianica Ctr.; 0-911346),* 6 N. Michigan Ave., Chicago, IL 60602 (SAN 204-739X) Tel 312-782-4230.
ChristLife Pubs, *(ChristLife Pubs.; 0-939079),* 1909 Willowbend, Deer Park, TX 77536 (SAN 662-9199) Tel 713-476-9916.
Christmas Star, *(Christmas Star Church; 0-9613670),* P.O. Box 3921, St. Augustine, FL 32085 (SAN 676-2085).
Christs Mission, *(Christ's Mission; 0-935120),* P.O. Box 203, Prospect Heights, IL 60070 (SAN 211-7819) Tel 312-870-3800. Out of business.
Christward, *(Christward Ministry; 0-910378),* 20560 Questhaven Rd., Escondido, CA 92025 (SAN 202-1633) Tel 619-744-1500.
Chrstphrs NY, *(Christophers, The; 0-939055),* 12 E. 48th St., New York, NY 10017 (SAN 226-6679) Tel 212-759-4050.
Church Bytes, *(Church Bytes, Inc.; 0-9615086),* 201 W. Laflin, Waukesha, WI 53186 (SAN 694-3411) Tel 414-542-0905.
Church History, *(Church History Research & Archives; 0-935122),* 220 Graystone Dr., Gallatin, TN 37066 (SAN 211-7827) Tel 615-452-7027.
Church Lib, *(Church Library Council; 0-9603060),* 4748 Eastern Ave., N.E., Washington, DC 20017 (SAN 210-5322) Tel 202-526-0034.
Church Man Pub, *(Church of Man Publishing Co.; 0-936435),* 6112 N. Mesa, Suite 210, El Paso, TX 79912 (SAN 697-8568); Dist. by: Great Tradition, 750 Adrian Way, Suite 111, San Rafael, CA 94903 (SAN 200-5743) Tel 415-492-9382.
Church of Light, *(Church of Light; 0-87887),* Box 76862, Sanford Sta., Los Angeles, CA 90076 (SAN 209-150X) Tel 818-352-9335.
Church of Scient Info, *(Church of Scientology Information Service-Pubns.; 0-915598),* c/o Bridge Pubns., Inc., 1414 N. Catalina, Los Angeles, CA 90029 (SAN 268-9774).
Church Open Door, *(Church of the Open Door; 0-935729),* 701 W. Sierra Madre Ave., Glendora, CA 91740 (SAN 693-9465) Tel 818-914-4646.
Church Scient NY, *(Church of Scientology of New York, The),* 227 W. 46th St., New York, NY 10036 (SAN 211-786X).
Church St. Leo, *(Church of St. Leo the Great Press; 0-9607014),* 227 S. Exeter St., Baltimore, MD 21202 (SAN 238-9630) Tel 301-675-7275. No longer publishing.
Churches Alive, *(Churches Alive, International; 0-934396),* P.O. Box 3800, San Bernardino, CA 92413 (SAN 213-2982) Tel 714-886-5361.
Ciga Pr, *(Ciga Pr.; 0-942574),* Box 654, Fallbrook, CA 92028 (SAN 239-6289) Tel 619-728-9308.
Cistercian Pubns, *(Cistercian Pubns., Inc.; 0-87907),* Western Michigan Univ. Sta., Kalamazoo, MI 49008 (SAN 202-1668) Tel 616-383-4985.
Citadel Pr, *(Citadel Pr.; 0-8065),* Subs. of Lyle Stuart, Inc., 120 Enterprise Ave., Secaucus, NJ 07094 (SAN 202-1676) Tel 201-866-4199; Toll free: 800-572-6657.
City Lights, *(City Lights Bks.; 0-87286),* 261 Columbus Ave., San Francisco, CA 94133 (SAN 202-1684) Tel 415-362-8193; Dist. by: Subterranean Co., 1327 W. Second, P.O. Box 10233, Eugene, OR 97440 (SAN 169-7102) Tel 503-343-6324.
Civilized Pubns, *(Civilized Pubns.; 0-933405),* 2019 S. Seventh St., Philadelphia, PA 19148 (SAN 691-4829) Tel 215-467-0744; Dist. by: New Leaf Distributing, The, 1020 White St., SW, Atlanta, GA 30310 (SAN 169-1449) Tel 404-755-2665; Dist. by: ECA Associates, Cathedral Finance Sta., P. O. Box 20186, New York, NY 10025 (SAN 215-9511) Tel 804-547-5542.
Claitors, *(Claitors Publishing Div.; 0-87511),* 3165 S. Acadian at Interstate 10, Box 3333, Baton Rouge, LA 70821 (SAN 206-8346) Tel 504-344-0476.
Clar Call Bks, *(Clarion Call Bks.; 0-935993),* Subs. of Clarion Call Music, 102 Bluebonnet Tr., Keene, TX 76059 (SAN 696-7140) Tel 817-645-8785; P.O. Box 45, Keene, TX 76059 (SAN 698-214X).
Clarion Class *Imprint of* **Zondervan**
Clarity Pub, *(Clarity Publishing; 0-915488),* 75 Champlain St., Albany, NY 12204 (SAN 211-5093) Tel 518-465-4591.
Clark U Pr, *(Clark Univ. Pr.; 0-914206),* 950 Main St., Worcester, MA 01610 (SAN 205-6135) Tel 617-793-7206.
Classical Folia, *(Classical Folia),* College of the Holy Cross, Worcester, MA 01610 (SAN 207-5369).
Claud Crawford, *(Crawford, Claud C.; 0-933697),* 4627 Martin Mill Pike, Knoxville, TN 37920 (SAN 692-5200) Tel 615-573-7248.
Claymont Comm, *(Claymont Communications; 0-934254),* Box 112, Charles Town, WV 25414 (SAN 211-7010) Tel 304-725-1523.
Clayton Pub Hse, *(Clayton Publishing Hse., Inc.; 0-915644),* 3438 Russell Blvd., Suite 203, St. Louis, MO 63104 (SAN 158-6807) Tel 314-772-5757; Dist. by: People Lovers Bks., 27 N. Gore, Webster Groves, MO 63119 (SAN 200-6138).
Cliffs, *(Cliff's Notes, Inc.; 0-8220),* 1701 P St., Lincoln, NE 68501 (SAN 202-1706) Tel 402-477-6971; Toll free: 800-228-4078.
CO Springs Fine Arts, *(Colorado Springs Fine Arts Ctr.; 0-916537),* 30 W. Dale St., Colorado Springs, CO 80903 (SAN 240-9372) Tel 303-634-5581.
Coach Hse, *(Coach Hse. Pr., Inc.; 0-88020),* P.O. Box 458, Morton Grove, IL 60053 (SAN 201-7709) Tel 312-967-1777.
Coalition Women-Relig, *(Coalition on Women & Religion; 0-9603042),* 4759 15th Ave. NE, Seattle, WA 98105 (SAN 210-7880) Tel 206-525-1213.
Coastlight Pr, *(Coastlight Pr.; 0-9606288),* 210 A California Ave., Palo Alto, CA 94306 (SAN 223-2146) Tel 415-325-9088; Dist. by: Bookpeople, 2929 Fifth St., Berkeley, CA 94710 (SAN 168-9517) Tel 415-549-3030.
Cole-Outreach, *(Cole, David M./Outreach Bks.),* P.O. Box 425, Corona, CA 91718 (SAN 214-2589).
Coleman Pub, *(Coleman Publishing, Inc.; 0-942494; 0-87418),* 99 Milbar Blvd., Farmingdale, NY 11735 (SAN 238-1508) Tel 516-293-0383; Toll free: 800-227-3489.
Coll & U Pr
See New Coll U Pr
Collage Inc, *(Collage, Inc.; 0-938728),* Subs. of Whitehall Co., 1200 S. Willis Ave., Wheeling, IL 60090 (SAN 205-5244) Tel 312-541-9290.
Colleasius Pr, *(Colleasius Pr.; 0-941036),* P.O. Box 1198, Ava, MO 65608 (SAN 212-1522) Tel 417-683-3465.
Collector Bks, *(Collector Bks.; 0-89145),* Div. of Schroeder Publishing Co., Inc., 5801 Kentucky Dam Rd., Paducah, KY 42001 (SAN 157-5368) Tel 502-898-6211; Toll free: 800-626-5420; P.O. Box 3009, Paducah, KY 42001 (SAN 200-7479).
College Pr Pub, *(College Pr. Publishing Co., Inc.; 0-89900),* Box 1132, 205 N. Main, Joplin, MO 64802 (SAN 211-9951) Tel 417-623-6280; Toll free: 800-641-7148.
Collier *Imprint of* **Macmillan**
Colo Assoc, *(Colorado Associated Univ. Pr.; 0-87081),* Univ. of Colorado, P.O. Box 480, Boulder, CO 80309 (SAN 202-1749); Univ. of Colorado, 1344 Grandview Ave., Boulder, CO 80309 (SAN 658-0343) Tel 303-492-7191.
Colonial Soc MA *Imprint of* **U Pr of Va**
Colourpicture, *(Colourpicture Pubs., Inc.; 0-938440),* 76 Atherton St., Boston, MA 02130 (SAN 216-2318); Dist. by: Smith Novelty Co., 460 Ninth St., San Francisco, CA 94103 (SAN 216-2326) Tel 415-861-4900.
Columbia U Pr, *(Columbia Univ. Pr.; 0-231),* 562 W. 113th St., New York, NY 10025 (SAN 212-2472) Tel 212-316-7100; Orders to: 136 S. Broadway, Irvington-on-Hudson, NY 10533 (SAN 212-2480) Tel 914-591-9111. *Imprints:* King's Crown Paperbacks (King's Crown Paperbacks).
Columbine Pr, *(Columbine Press; 0-9609108),* Box 845, Aspen, CO 81612 (SAN 241-483X) Tel 303-925-6025.
Comm & Learning, *(Communication & Learning Innovators Ltd.; 0-932361),* 4906 Painters St., New Orleans, LA 70122 (SAN 687-3723) Tel 504-282-1174.
Comm Chapel Pubns, *(Community Chapel Pubns.; 0-934287),* 18635 Eighth Ave. S., Seattle, WA 98148 (SAN 693-2851) Tel 206-431-3140.
Comm Res, *(Communications Research; 0-9611910),* 12267 Natural Bridge Rd., Bridgeton, MO 63044 (SAN 286-0813) Tel 314-739-1742.
Comment Pr, *(Commentary Pr.; 0-914675),* P.O. Box 43532, Atlanta, GA 30336 (SAN 289-7040) Tel 404-949-4947.
Commonwealth Pr, *(Commonwealth Pr., Inc.; 0-89227),* 415 First St., Radford, VA 24141 (SAN 281-515X) Tel 703-639-2475.
Communication Arts *Imprint of* **Hastings**
Concerned Pubns, *(Concerned Pubns., Inc.; 0-939286),* P.O. Box 1024, Clermont, FL 32711 (SAN 220-1496) Tel 904-429-3022.
Conch Mag, *(Conch Magazine, Ltd. Pubs.; 0-914970),* Div. of Conch Communications Co., P.O. Box 777, Buffalo, NY 14213 (SAN 206-4855) Tel 716-885-3686.
Concord Bks, *(Concord Bks.),* P.O. Box 3380, Kailua-Kona, HI 96740 (SAN 158-0337) Tel 808-326-2514.

Concord Grove, *(Concord Grove Pr.; 0-88695),* Subs. of Institute of World Culture, Concord Hse., 1407 Chapala St., Santa Barbara, CA 93101 (SAN 283-0388) Tel 805-966-3941.
Concord Pr, *(Concord Pr.),* P.O. Box 2686, Seal Beach, CA 90740 (SAN 206-4669) Tel 213-431-5711.
Concordant, *(Concordant Publishing Concern; 0-910424),* 15570 Knochaven Rd., Canyon Country, CA 91351 (SAN 203-5790) Tel 805-252-2112.
Concordia, *(Concordia Publishing Hse.; 0-570),* 3558 S. Jefferson Ave., St. Louis, MO 63118 (SAN 202-1781) Tel 314-664-7000; Toll free: 800-325-3040.
Concordia Hist, *(Concordia Historical Institute),* 801 DeMun Ave., St. Louis, MO 63105 (SAN 225-459X) Tel 314-721-5934.
Concordia Schl Grad Studies, *(Concordia Seminary, Schl. for Graduate Studies; 0-911770),* 801 DeMun Ave., St. Louis, MO 63105 (SAN 204-3165) Tel 314-721-5934.
Concordia Theo Sem, *(Concordia Theological Seminary; 0-9615927),* 6600 N. Clinton St., Ft. Wayne, IN 46825 (SAN 696-9216) Tel 219-482-9611.
Conn Hist Soc, *(Connecticut Historical Society Pr., The; 0-940748),* 1 Elizabeth St., Hartford, CT 06105 (SAN 204-2843) Tel 203-236-5621.
Conococheague Assoc
See Anima Pubns
Constellation Pr, *(Constellation Pr., Inc.; 0-9616620),* Box 1271, Manhattan Beach, CA 90266 (SAN 661-0404); 1817 Agnes Rd., Manhattan Beach, CA 90266 (SAN 661-0412) Tel 213-545-2284.
Context Pubns, *(Context Pubns.; 0-932654),* P.O. Box 2909, Rohnert Park, CA 94928-6506 (SAN 212-8977) Tel 707-584-4423; Dist. by: Bookpeople, 2929 Fifth St., Berkeley, CA 94710 (SAN 168-9517) Tel 415-549-3030; Dist. by: Publishers Group West, 5855 Beaudry St., Emeryville, CA 94608 (SAN 202-8522) Tel 415-658-3453; Dist. by: DeVorss & Co., P.O. Box 550, Marina del Rey, CA 90291 (SAN 168-9886) Tel 213-870-7478.
Continent Assn Funeral, *(Continental Assn. of Funeral & Memorial Societies, Inc.),* 2001 S St. NW, Suite 530, Washington, DC 20009 (SAN 202-6201) Tel 202-745-0634.
Continuum, *(Continuum Publishing Co.; 0-8264),* 370 Lexington Ave., New York, NY 10017 (SAN 213-8220) Tel 212-532-3650; Dist. by: Harper & Row, Keystone Industrial Pk., Scranton, PA 18512 (SAN 215-3742).
Cook, *(Cook, David C., Publishing Co.; 0-89191; 0-912692; 1-55513),* 850 N. Grove Ave., Elgin, IL 60120 (SAN 206-0981) Tel 312-741-2400; Toll free: 800-323-7543. *Imprints:* Chariot Bks (Chariot Books).
Coole
See M Akers
Cooling Spring, *(Cooling Spring Pr., The; 0-935883),* Div. of Challenge Hse., 405 Jefferson St., Saluda, SC 29138 (SAN 696-3412) Tel 704-669-2782.
Cooper & Cooper Pub, *(Cooper & Cooper Pub.; 0-931429),* P.O. Box 1516, Palo Alto, CA 94302 (SAN 683-2121) Tel 415-327-6472.
Cooper Sq, *(Cooper Sq. Pubs., Inc.; 0-8154),* Div. of Littlefield, Adams & Co., 81 Adams Dr., Totowa, NJ 07512 (SAN 281-5621) Tel 201-256-8600.
Copley Bks, *(Copley Bks.; 0-913938),* Subs. of Copley Pr., Inc., P.O. Box 957, La Jolla, CA 92038 (SAN 202-1846); 7776 Ivanhoe Ave., La Jolla, CA 92037 (SAN 662-720X) Tel 619-454-1842.
Copper Canyon, *(Copper Canyon Pr.; 0-914742; 1-55659),* P.O. Box 271, Port Townsend, WA 98368 (SAN 206-488X) Tel 206-385-4925; Dist. by: Consortium Bk. Sales & Distribution, 213 E. Fourth St., St. Paul, MN 55101 (SAN 200-6049) Tel 612-221-9035.
Cormac Inc, *(Cormac, Inc.; 0-9617749),* P.O. Box 62808, Washington, DC 20019 (SAN 665-0317) Tel 202-396-0375; 3016 P St., SE, Washington, DC 20020 (SAN 665-0325) Tel 202-583-1748.
Cornell Mod Indo, *(Cornell Modern Indonesia Project; 0-87763),* Affil. of Cornell Univ. Southeast Asia Program, 102 West Ave., Ithaca, NY 14850 (SAN 203-591X) Tel 607-255-4359.
Cornell SE Asia, *(Cornell Univ., Southeast Asia Program; 0-87727),* 102 West Ave., Ithaca, NY 14850 (SAN 206-6416) Tel 607-255-4359.
Cornell U Pr, *(Cornell Univ. Pr.; 0-8014),* 124 Roberts Pl., P.O. Box 250, Ithaca, NY 14851 (SAN 202-1862) Tel 607-257-7000; Orders to: 740 Cascadilla St., Ithaca, NY 14851 (SAN 281-5680) Tel 607-277-2211.
Corner Hse, *(Corner Hse. Pubs.; 0-87928),* 1321 Green River Rd., Williamstown, MA 01267 (SAN 203-5936) Tel 413-458-8561.
Cornerstone, *(Cornerstone Library, Inc.; 0-346),* Div. of Simon & Schuster, Inc., ; Orders to: Simon & Schuster, Inc., 1230 Ave. of the Americas, New York, NY 10020 (SAN 200-2450) Tel 212-698-7000.
Cornwall Bks *Imprint of* **Assoc Univ Prs**
Coronado Pr, *(Coronado Pr., Inc.; 0-87291),* P.O. Box 3232, Lawrence, KS 66044 (SAN 201-7776) Tel 913-843-5988.
Coronet Bks, *(Coronet Bks.; 0-89563),* 311 Bainbridge St., Philadelphia, PA 19147 (SAN 210-6043) Tel 215-925-2762.
Cos Sci Orange, *(Cosmic Science Pub.; 0-9615973),* 12932 Malma Dr., Santa Ana, CA 92705 (SAN 696-785X) Tel 714-771-0448. Do not confuse with Cosmic Science Pub. of Louisville, KY.
Cosmic Comm, *(Cosmic Communication Co.; 0-912038),* 100 Elm Ct., Decorah, IA 52101 (SAN 201-9043) Tel 319-382-8350.
Cosmic Pr Chico, *(Cosmic Pr. of Chico, California; 0-941227),* 1159 Lawton Dr., Chico, CA 95926 (SAN 665-472X) Tel 916-895-6323.
Coun India Ed, *(Council for Indian Education; 0-89992),* 517 Rimrock Rd., Billings, MT 59102 (SAN 202-2117) Tel 406-252-1800; Orders to: Box 31215, Billings, MT 59107 (SAN 689-836X) Tel 406-252-1800.
Counsel & Stress, *(Counseling & Stress Research Ctr.; 0-912561),* 21 Montauk Ave., New London, CT 06320 (SAN 283-9466) Tel 203-447-9935.
Country Bazaar, *(Country Bazaar Publishing & Distributing; 0-936744),* Honey, Inc. Bldg., Rte. 2, Box 190, Berryville, AR 72616 (SAN 215-1669) Tel 501-423-3131; Dist. by: Nutri Bks., P.O. Box 5793, Denver, CO 80223 (SAN 295-3404) Tel 303-778-8383.
Countryman, *(Countryman Pr., Inc.; 0-914378; 0-88150),* P.O. Box 175, Woodstock, VT 05091-0175 (SAN 206-4901) Tel 802-457-1049; Toll free: 800-635-5009.
Covenant, *(Covenant Pr.; 0-910452),* 3200 W. Foster Ave., Chicago, IL 60625 (SAN 203-6029) Tel 312-478-4676; Toll free: 800-621-1290.
Coward *Imprint of* **Putnam Pub Group**
Cowley Pubns, *(Cowley Pubns.; 0-936384),* Div. of Society of St. John the Evangelist, 980 Memorial Dr., Cambridge, MA 02138 (SAN 213-9987) Tel 617-876-3507.
CPL Biblios, *(CPL Bibliographies),* 1313 E. 60th St., Merriam Ctr., Chicago, IL 60637-2897 (SAN 210-3516) Tel 312-947-2007.
Crane Pubns CA, *(Crane Pubns.; 0-915561),* Box 90155, San Diego, CA 92109 (SAN 292-3297) Tel 619-273-7018.
CRC Pubns, *(CRC Pubns.; 0-933140; 0-930265),* 2850 Kalamazoo Ave. SE, Grand Rapids, MI 49560 (SAN 212-727X) Tel 616-246-0752.
CRCS Pubns NV, *(CRCS Pubns.; 0-916360),* P.O. Box 20850, Reno, NV 89515 (SAN 200-626X) Tel 702-358-2850. Do not confuse with CRC Pr., Boca Raton, FL.
Creat Arts Dev, *(Creative Arts Development; 0-912801),* P.O. Box 1240, Soquel, CA 95073 (SAN 277-6693) Tel 408-475-2396.
Creat Gospel Prod, *(Creative Gospel Productions, Inc.; 0-931965),* 23381 L'Enfant Plaza, SW, Washington, DC 20026 (SAN 686-0753) Tel 202-563-6319.
Creat Pubns B P C M, *(Creative Pubns B P C M; 0-914569),* 1431 St. James Pkwy., Concord, CA 94521 (SAN 289-1921) Tel 415-687-6401.
Creation Hse, *(Creation Hse.; 0-88419),* 396 E. St. Charles Rd., Wheaton, IL 60188 (SAN 202-2001) Tel 312-653-1472.
Creation Research, *(Creation Research Society Bks.; 0-940384),* Div. of Creation Research Society, 5093 Williamsport Dr., Norcross, GA 30092 (SAN 216-2873) Tel 404-449-4758.
Creative Arts Bk, *(Creative Arts Bk. Co.; 0-88739; 0-916870),* 833 Bancroft Way, Berkeley, CA 94710 (SAN 208-4880) Tel 415-848-4777.
Creative Ed, *(Creative Education, Inc.; 0-87191; 0-88682),* 123 S. Broad St., P.O. Box 227, Mankato, MN 56001 (SAN 202-201X) Tel 507-388-6273.
Cricketfield Pr, *(Cricketfield Pr.; 0-9614281),* 39 Meguntícook St., Camden, ME 04843 (SAN 687-4401) Tel 207-236-3083.
Crises Res Pr, *(Crises Research Pr.; 0-86627),* 301 W. 45th St., New York, NY 10036 (SAN 238-9274).
Criterion Pubns, *(Criterion Pubns.; 0-937969),* 209 N. Beckley, De Soto, TX 75115 (SAN 659-5006) Tel 214-223-9348; Orders to: P.O. Box 214749, Dallas, TX 75221-4749 (SAN 662-426X).
Crofton Pub, *(Crofton Publishing Corp.; 0-89020),* 21 Wilson Ave., Belmont, MA 02178 (SAN 206-7560) Tel 617-489-2149.
Cross Cult, *(Cross-Cultural Communications; 0-89304),* 239 Wynsum Ave., Merrick, NY 11566 (SAN 208-6212) Tel 516-868-5635.
Cross Cultural Pubns, *(Cross Cultural Pubns., Inc.; 0-940121),* P.O. Box 506, Notre Dame, IN 46556 (SAN 664-2551) Tel 219-272-3321.
Crossing Pr, *(Crossing Pr., The; 0-89594; 0-912278),* 22-D Roache Rd., P.O. Box 207, Freedom, CA 95019 (SAN 202-2060) Tel 408-772-0711.
Crossroad NY, *(Crossroad Pub. Co.; 0-8245),* 370 Lexington Ave., New York, NY 10017 (SAN 287-0118) Tel 212-532-3650; Dist. by: Harper & Row Pubs., Inc., Keystone Industrial Pk., Scranton, PA 08075 (SAN 215-3742).
Crossway Bks *Imprint of* **Good News**
Crown, *(Crown Pubs., Inc.; 0-517),* 225 Park Ave., S., New York, NY 10003 (SAN 200-2639) Tel 212-254-1600; Toll free: 800-526-4264. *Imprints:* C N Potter Bks (Potter, Clarkson N., Books); Harmony (Harmony Books); Julian Pr. (Julian Press).
Crown Min, *(Crown Ministries International; 0-935779),* P.O. Box 49, Euclid, MN 56722 (SAN 696-7108) Tel 218-745-5826.
CRPS, *(Center for Research on Population & Security; 0-937307),* 322 Azalea Dr., Chapel Hill, NC 27514 (SAN 658-7712) Tel 919-933-7491; P.O. Box 13067, Research Triangle Park, NC 27709 (SAN 658-7720).
Crusade Pubs, *(Crusade Pubns),* 11326 Ranchito St., El Monte, CA 91732 (SAN 203-8595). Religious Publications Only.
Crystal MI, *(Crystal Pr.; 0-930402),* 1909 Proctor St., Flint, MI 48504 (SAN 220-522X) Tel 313-239-8281.
CSA Pr, *(CSA Pr.; 0-87707),* Lake Ravun Rd., Lakemont, GA 30552 (SAN 207-7329) Tel 404-782-4723; P.O. Box 7, Lakemont, GA 30552 (SAN 658-0408).
CSI Studies, *(Georgetown Univ., Ctr. for Strategic & International Studies; 0-89206),* 1800 K St. NW, Suite 400, Washington, DC 20006 (SAN 281-4021) Tel 202-775-3119.
CSLA, *(Church & Synagogue Library Assn.; 0-915324),* P.O. Box 1130, Bryn Mawr, PA 19010 (SAN 210-7872) Tel 215-853-2870.
CSS of Ohio, *(C.S.S. of Ohio; 0-89536; 1-55673),* 628 S. Main St., Lima, OH 45804 (SAN 207-0707) Tel 419-227-1818; Toll free: 800-537-1030.
CSU Fullerton, *(California State Univ., Fullerton),* California State Univ. at Fullerton, Philosophy Dept., Fullerton, CA 92634 (SAN 215-1952); Dist. by: Hackett Publishing Co., Inc., P.O. Box 44937, 832 Pierson St., Indianapolis, IN 46204 (SAN 201-6044) Tel 317-635-9250.
Ctr Judaic-Christ Studies, *(Center for Judaic-Christian Studies; 0-918873),* P.O. Box 202707, Austin, TX 78720 (SAN 669-9979) Tel 512-343-3101.
Ctr Migration, *(Center for Migration Studies; 0-913256; 0-934733),* 209 Flagg Pl., Staten Island, NY 10304-1148 (SAN 281-4013) Tel 718-351-8800.
Ctr Res Soc Chg, *(Center for Research in Social Change; 0-89937),* Emory Univ., Fred Roberts Crawford Witness to the Holocaust Project, Atlanta, GA 30322 (SAN 211-5247) Tel 404-727-7525. Out of business.

Ctr S&SE Asian, *(Univ. of Michigan, Ctr. for South & Southeast Asian Studies; 0-89148),* 130 Lane Hall, Ann Arbor, MI 48109 (SAN 206-491X) Tel 313-763-5790.
Ctr Sci Study, *(Center for the Scientific Study of Religion; 0-913348),* 5757 University Ave., Chicago, IL 60637 (SAN 203-8749) Tel 312-752-5757.
Ctr Sutton Movement, *(Center for Sutton Movement Writing, Inc., The; 0-914336),* P.O. Box 7344, Newport Beach, CA 92658-7344 (SAN 203-154X) Tel 714-644-8342.
Ctr Thanatology, *(Center for Thanatology Research & Education, Inc.; 0-930194),* 391 Atlantic Ave., Brooklyn, NY 11217-1701 (SAN 210-7414) Tel 718-858-3026; Orders to: P.O. Box 989, Brooklyn, NY 11202-1202 (SAN 215-0425).
Ctr Trad Orthodox, *(Center for Traditionalist Orthodox Studies; 0-911165),* St. Gregory Palamas Monastery, P.O. Box 398, Etna, CA 96027 (SAN 287-0029) Tel 916-467-3228.
Ctr Western Studies, *(Center for Western Studies; 0-931170),* Augustana College, Box 727, Sioux Falls, SD 57197 (SAN 211-4844) Tel 605-336-4007.
Cumberland Pr, *(Cumberland Pr.; 0-87027),* 136 Main St., Freeport, ME 04032 (SAN 203-2090) Tel 207-865-6045.
Cunningham Pr, *(Cunningham Press),* 3063 W. Main, Alhambra, CA 91801 (SAN 203-8773) Tel 818-283-8838; Dist. by: Theosophy Co., 245 W. 33rd St., Los Angeles, CA 90007 (SAN 295-3560) Tel 213-748-7244.
Curtis Pub Co, *(Curtis Publishing Co., The; 0-89387),* Div. of Saturday Evening Post, 1100 Waterway Blvd., Indianapolis, IN 46206 (SAN 216-3624) Tel 317-634-1100.
Cyclopedia, *(Cyclopedia Publishing Co.; 0-914226),* 6 Freedom Rd., Pleasant Valley, NY 12569 (SAN 206-6327).
D Bosco Pubns *Imprint of* **Don Bosco Multimedia**
D C Brown, *(Brown, David C.; 0-9613415),* 931 N. Negley Ave., Pittsburgh, PA 15206 (SAN 656-9730) Tel 412-363-2390; Dist. by: Bruce Shatswell, 10 Phillips Ave., Apt. 2, Lynn, MA 01902 (SAN 200-6103) Tel 617-595-8511.
D Crank Pubns, *(Crank, David, Pubns.; 0-936437),* 1416 Larkin Williams Rd., Fenton, MO 63026 (SAN 697-8266) Tel 314-343-4359.
D Enyi, *(Enyi, Donatus O.; 0-937171),* Div. of World Trend, USA, 1514 First St., NW, Washington, DC 20001 (SAN 658-5264) Tel 202-387-2019; Dist. by: World Trend USA, P.O. Box 1886, Washington, DC 20013 (SAN 200-6820) Tel 202-387-2619.
D H Shubin, *(Shubin, Daniel H.),* 5865 Crown Dr., Mira Loma, CA 91752 (SAN 659-4026).
D I Fine, *(Fine, Donald I.; 0-917657; 1-55611),* 128 E. 36th St., New York, NY 10016 (SAN 656-9749) Tel 212-696-1838; Orders to: Haddon Craftsmen, Inc., 1205K O'Neill Hwy., Dunmore, PA 18512 (SAN 662-7625) Tel 717-348-9292.
D I Weiss, *(Weiss, David I.; 0-9618049),* P.O. Box 1705, Brookline, MA 02146 (SAN 666-2552); 17 Parkman St., Brookline, MA 02146 (SAN 666-2560) Tel 617-277-1704.
D Landman
See Dennis-Landman
D McCalden
See Truth Missions
D Moriarty, *(Moriarty, Dan, Assocs.; 0-933968),* 1410 Second Ave., Newport, MN 55055 (SAN 211-6448) Tel 612-459-1857.
D O A C, *(Diocese of Armenian Church; 0-934728),* 630 Second Ave., New York, NY 10016 (SAN 216-0625).
D R Bell, *(Bell, D. Rayford, Bishop; 0-9604820; 0-938195),* 1225 McDaniel Ave., Evanston, IL 60202 (SAN 215-8388) Tel 618-869-1907.
D R Benbow, *(Benbow, D. R.; 0-931611),* 441 Clairmont Ave., Apt. 1014, Decatur, GA 30030 (SAN 206-7293) Tel 404-378-7028.
D R Gilmore, *(Gilmore, Donald R.; 0-9617810),* P.O. Box 44, Portage, IN 46368 (SAN 665-2832); 2874 Monnier St., Minneapolis, MN 55959 (SAN 665-2840) Tel 219-762-3958.
D W Bell Gallery, *(Brown Univ., David Winton Bell Gallery; 0-933519),* 64 College St., Providence, RI 02912 (SAN 278-2758) Tel 401-863-2421.
D W Hemingway, *(Hemingway, Donald W.),* 309 S. Tenth W., Salt Lake City, UT 84104 (SAN 220-2506); Dist. by: George Mc. Co. Inc., P.O. Box 15671, Salt Lake City, UT 84115 (SAN 220-2514).
Da Capo, *(Da Capo Pr., Inc.; 0-306),* Subs. of Plenum Publishing Corp., 233 Spring St., New York, NY 10013 (SAN 201-2944) Tel 212-620-8000; Toll free: 800-221-9369.
Dabbs, *(Dabbs, Jack A.; 0-911494),* 2806 Cherry Ln., Austin, TX 78703 (SAN 205-4248) Tel 512-472-7463.
Dada Ctr, *(Dada Ctr. Pubns.; 0-930608),* 2319 W. Dry Creek Rd., Healdsburg, CA 95448 (SAN 211-1225) Tel 707-433-1237.
Dahlin Family Pr, *(Dahlin Family Pr.; 0-940291),* 5339 Prospect Rd., No. 300, San Jose, CA 95129 (SAN 664-2454).
Damon Pub, *(Damon Publishing; 0-9617788),* 741 E. Montana, St. Paul, MN 55106 (SAN 664-7480) Tel 612-731-4110.
DaNa Pubns, *(DaNa Pubns.; 0-937103),* 1050 Austin Ave., Idaho Falls, ID 83401 (SAN 658-568X) Tel 208-524-1067.
DanBury Hse Bks, *(Danbury Hse., Bks.; 0-935207),* P.O. Box 253, Oakland, ME 04963 (SAN 669-6724) Tel 207-465-2610.
Dandelion Hse, *(Dandelion Hse., The; 0-89693),* Div. of Child's World, Inc., P.O. Box 989, Elgin, IL 60121 (SAN 240-8910) Tel 312-741-7591; Dist. by: Scripture Pr., 1825 College Ave., Wheaton, IL 60187 (SAN 222-9471) Tel 312-668-6000.
Dandelion Pr, *(Dandelion Pr.; 0-89799),* 184 Fifth Ave., New York, NY 10010 (SAN 212-0836) Tel 212-929-0090.
Dane Bks, *(Dane Books; 0-917655),* 15 St. Regis Circle, Salinas, CA 93905 (SAN 657-1336) Tel 415-956-5966.
Darby Bks, *(Darby Bks.; 0-89987),* P.O. Box 148, Darby, PA 19023 (SAN 204-2371) Tel 215-583-4550.
Daring Bks, *(Daring Bks.; 0-938936),* Div. of Daring Publishing Group, 2020 Ninth St., SW, Canton, OH 44706 (SAN 216-0293) Tel 216-454-7519; Orders to: P.O. Box 526, Canton, OH 47701 (SAN 685-3242).
Darwin Pr, *(Darwin Pr., Inc.; 0-87850),* P.O. Box 2202, Princeton, NJ 08540 (SAN 201-2987) Tel 609-737-1349.
Data & Res Tech, *(Data & Research Technology Corp.; 0-935025),* 1102 McNeilly Ave., Pittsburgh, PA 15216 (SAN 694-5503) Tel 412-563-2212.
Davey, *(Davey, Daniel, & Co., Inc., Pubs.; 0-8088),* P.O. Box 6088, Hartford, CT 06106 (SAN 203-882X) Tel 203-525-4334.
David & Charles, *(David & Charles, Inc.; 0-7153),* P.O. Box 257, North Pomfret, VT 05053 (SAN 213-8859) Tel 802-457-1911; Toll free: 800-423-4525.
David Pub MN, *(David Publishing; 0-9616767),* Box 7, St. Bonifacius, MN 55375-0007 (SAN 661-0935); 6425 County Rd. 30, St. Bonifacius, MN 55375 (SAN 661-0943) Tel 612-472-7126.
Davis Pub, *(Davis Publishing Co.; 0-9615877),* 4112 Hart Rd., Richfield, OH 44286 (SAN 697-0591) Tel 216-659-4449.
Dawn Horse Pr, *(Dawn Horse Pr.; 0-913922; 0-918801),* Div. of The Free Daist Communion, 750 Adrian Way, San Rafael, CA 94903 (SAN 201-3029) Tel 415-492-0922; Toll free: 800-521-4785; Dist. by: The Great Tradition, 750 Adrian Way, Suite 111, San Rafael, CA 94903 (SAN 200-5743) Tel 415-492-9382.
Dawn Ministries, *(Dawn Ministries; 0-9605892),* 2789 Mendel Way, Sacramento, CA 95833 (SAN 216-5937).
Dawn Pr, *(Dawn Pr.; 0-933704),* 1011 Jeffrey Rd., Wilmington, DE 19810 (SAN 221-2269).
Dawn Pubns CA, *(Dawn Pubns.; 0-916124),* 14618 Tyler Foote Rd., Nevada City, CA 95959 (SAN 201-1778) Tel 916-292-3482.
Dawn Valley, *(Dawn Valley, Pr.; 0-936014),* P.O. Box 58, New Wilmington, PA 16142 (SAN 208-9734) Tel 412-946-2948.
Dawnfire, *(Dawnfire Bks.; 0-942058),* 2218 24th St., No. B, Santa Monica, CA 90405 (SAN 239-4332) Tel 213-450-2911; Dist. by: Bookpeople, 2929 Fifth St., Berkeley, CA 94710 (SAN 663-6381) Tel 415-549-3030.
Dawsons, *(Dawson's Bk. Shop; 0-87093),* 535 N. Larchmont Blvd., Los Angeles, CA 90004 (SAN 201-3045) Tel 213-469-2186.
Day Bk Co, *(Day Bk. Co.; 0-9611310),* 3641 N. Maple Ave., Fresno, CA 93726 (SAN 277-6723). Out of business.
Day Star, *(Day Star Pubs.; 0-932994),* 1550 View Dr., San Leandro, CA 94577 (SAN 212-4130).
Daystar Co Carson, *(Daystar Publishing Co.; 0-933650),* 21405 Lostime Ave., Carson, CA 90745 (SAN 221-2277).
Daystar Comm, *(Daystar Communications; 0-930037),* P.O. Box 748, Millville, NJ 08332 (SAN 669-7798) Tel 609-327-1231.
Dayton Labs, *(Dayton Laboratories; 0-916750),* 3235 Dayton Ave., Lorain, OH 44055 (SAN 208-1946) Tel 216-246-1397.
De Gruyter, *(De Gruyter, Walter, Inc.; 3-11; 0-89925),* Div. of Walter de Gruyter & Co., 200 Saw Mill River Rd., Hawthorne, NY 10532 (SAN 201-3088) Tel 914-747-0110.
De Gruyter Aldine, *(De Gruyter/Aldine; 0-202),* Div. of Walter De Gruyter, Inc., 200 Saw Mill River Rd., Hawthorne, NY 10532 (SAN 212-4726) Tel 914-747-0110.
De Vorss, *(De Vorss & Co.; 0-87516),* P.O. Box 550, Marina del Rey, CA 90292 (SAN 168-9886) Tel 213-870-7478; Toll free: 800-843-5743; Toll free: 800-331-4719.
De Young Pr, *(De Young Pr.; 0-936128),* P.O. Box 7252, Spencer, IA 51301-7252 (SAN 212-7652).
Dearen Pub, *(Dearen, Leah, Publishing; 0-938575),* P.O. Box 162, Alpine, CA 92001 (SAN 661-1036); 3330 Zumbrota Rd., Alpine, CA 92001 (SAN 661-1044) Tel 619-445-9611.
Decatur Hse, *(Decatur House Press, Ltd; 0-916276),* 2122 Decatur Pl., NW, Washington, DC 20008 (SAN 208-1539) Tel 202-387-3913.
Decker Pr Inc, *(Decker Pr., Inc.; 0-933724),* P.O. Box 3838, Grand Junction, CO 81502 (SAN 216-115X) Tel 303-241-6193; Toll free: 800-525-3454.
Dekker, *(Dekker, Marcel, Inc.; 0-8247),* 270 Madison Ave., New York, NY 10016 (SAN 201-3118) Tel 212-696-9000; Toll free: 800-228-1160.
Dekotek Inc
See Bowker
Del Mar Pr, *(Del Mar Pr.; 0-9611124),* P.O. Box 2508, Del Mar, CA 92014 (SAN 283-2682) Tel 619-481-1808.
Delacorte, *(Delacorte Pr.; 0-87459),* 1 Dag Hammarskjold Plaza, New York, NY 10017 (SAN 201-0097) Tel 212-605-3000; Toll free: 800-221-4676. *Imprints:* Sey Lawr (Lawrence, Seymour).
Delair
See World Bible
Dell, *(Dell Publishing Co., Inc.; 0-440),* Subs. of Doubleday & Co., Inc., 1 Dag Hammarskjold Plaza, 245 E. 47th St., New York, NY 10017 (SAN 201-0097) Tel 212-605-3000. *Imprints:* Delta (Delta Books); LE (Laurel Editions); LFL (Laurel Leaf Library).
Delta *Imprint of* **Dell**
Dembner Bks, *(Dembner Bks.; 0-934878; 0-942637),* Div. of Red Dembner Enterprises Corp., 80 Eighth Ave., New York, NY 10011 (SAN 211-5573) Tel 212-924-2525; Dist. by: W. W. Norton & Co., Inc., 500 Fifth Ave., New York, NY 10110 (SAN 202-5795) Tel 212-354-5500.
Dennis & Co Inc
See W S Hein
Dennis-Landman, *(Dennis-Landman Pubs.; 0-930422),* 1150 18th St., Santa Monica, CA 90403 (SAN 210-9352) Tel 213-453-4643.
Dentan Pr, *(Dentan Pr.; 0-9610080),* 1404 Buchanan St.,P.O. Box 1745, Novato, CA 94948 (SAN 269-6738) Tel 415-897-1483.
Derek Prince, *(Prince, Derek, Ministries Pubns.; 0-934920),* P.O. Box 300, Fort Lauderdale, FL 33302 (SAN 211-822X) Tel 305-763-5202.
Deseret Bk, *(Deseret Bk. Co.; 0-87747; 0-87579),* Div. of Deseret Management Corp., P.O. Box 30178, Salt Lake City, UT 84130 (SAN 201-3185) Tel 801-534-1515; Toll free: 800-453-3876.
Deseret News, *(Deseret News Publishing Co.; 0-910901),* 30 E. First South St., P.O. Box 1257, Salt Lake City, UT 84110 (SAN 269-6835) Tel 801-237-2137.

Desert Min, *(Desert Ministries, Inc.; 0-914733),* P.O. Box 13235, Pittsburgh, PA 15243 (SAN 657-6036) Tel 412-854-3311.
Desserco Pub, *(Desserco Publishing; 0-916698),* Div. of Design Services Co., P.O. Box 2433, Culver City, CA 90230 (SAN 208-3914) Tel 213-618-2030.
Destiny, *(Destiny Pubs.; 0-910500),* 43 Grove St., Merrimac, MA 01860 (SAN 203-8889) Tel 617-346-9311.
Destiny Bks *Imprint of* **Inner Tradit**
Devin, *(Devin-Adair Pubs., Inc.; 0-8159),* 6 N. Water St., Greenwich, CT 06830 (SAN 213-750X) Tel 203-531-7755.
Devon Pub, *(Devon Publishing Co., Inc., The; 0-941402),* 2700 Virginia Ave., NW, Washington, DC 20037 (SAN 238-9703) Tel 202-337-5197; Dist. by: Baker & Taylor Co., Eastern Div., 50 Kirby Ave., Somerville, NJ 08876 (SAN 169-4901).
Dghtrs St Paul, *(Daughters of St. Paul; 0-8198),* 50 St. Paul's Ave., Boston, MA 02130 (SAN 203-8900) Tel 617-522-8911.
Dharma Drum Pubs, *(Dharma Drum Pubns.; 0-9609854),* 90-31 Corona Ave., Elmhurst, NY 11373 (SAN 269-6967) Tel 718-592-6593.
Dharma Pub, *(Dharma Publishing; 0-913546; 0-89800),* 2425 Hillside Ave., Berkeley, CA 94704 (SAN 201-2723) Tel 415-548-5407.
Di-Tri Bks, *(Di-Tri Bks.; 0-9603374),* 261 Waubesa St., Madison, WI 53704 (SAN 209-1712).
Dial *Imprint of* **Doubleday**
Dial Bks Young, *(Dial Bks. for Young Readers),* Div. of E. P. Dutton, 2 Park Ave., New York, NY 10016 (SAN 264-0058) Tel 212-725-1818; Toll free: 800-526-0275; Orders to: New American Library, P.O. Box 120, Bergenfield, NJ 07261 (SAN 200-6758) Tel 201-387-0600.
Dialog, *(Dialog Pr.; 0-914153),* Subs. of Feature Group, Inc., Dept. 856, P.O. Box 59072, Chicago, IL 60659 (SAN 669-3474).
Dialogue Hse, *(Dialogue Hse. Library; 0-87941),* 80 E. 11th St., New York, NY 10003 (SAN 201-8195) Tel 212-673-5880; Toll free: 800-221-5844.
Diane Bks, *(Diane Bks. Publishing, Inc.; 0-88264),* 2807 Oregon Ct., No. E3, Torrance, CA 90503 (SAN 201-2731) Tel 213-320-2591; Orders to: P.O. Box 2948, Torrance, CA 90509 (SAN 693-4862) Tel 213-533-5872.
Dietz, *(Dietz Pr.; 0-87517),* 109 E. Cary, Richmond, VA 23219 (SAN 201-3258) Tel 804-648-0195.
Dignity Inc, *(Dignity, Inc.; 0-940680),* 1500 Massachusetts Ave., NW, No. 11, Washington, DC 20005 (SAN 223-7431) Tel 202-861-0017.
Dildo Pr
See Mho & Mho
Dillon, *(Dillon Pr., Inc.; 0-87518),* 242 Portland Ave., S., Minneapolis, MN 55415 (SAN 201-3266) Tel 612-333-2691; Toll free: 800-328-8322 ext. 687.
Dillon-Liederbach, *(Dillon/Liederbach, Inc.; 0-913228),* 4953 Stonington Rd., Winston-Salem, NC 27103 (SAN 201-3274) Tel 919-768-7014.
Dilman Pr, *(Dilman Pr.; 0-9615301),* 773 Cole, No. 8, San Francisco, CA 94117 (SAN 694-4639) Tel 415-386-6072; Dist. by: Bookpeople, 2929 Fifth St., Berkeley, CA 94710 (SAN 168-9517) Tel 415-549-3030.
Dimension Bks, *(Dimension Bks.; 0-87193),* P.O. Box 811, Denville, NJ 07834 (SAN 211-7916) Tel 201-627-4334.
Dimona Pr, *(Dimona Pr.; 0-940733),* P.O. Box 1516, Miami, FL 33160 (SAN 665-0295).
Directed Media, *(Directed Media Inc.; 0-939688),* P.O. Box 3005, Wenatchee, WA 98801 (SAN 216-7263) Tel 509-662-7693.
Directions Pr, *(Directions Pr.; 0-940564),* 523 Gainsborough, No. 101, Thousand Oaks, CA 91360 (SAN 215-6350).
Discipleship Res, *(Discipleship Resources; 0-88177),* Subs. of Board of Discipleship of the United Methodist Church, P.O. Box 840, 1908 Grand Ave., Nashville, TN 37202 (SAN 264-0074) Tel 615-340-7068; Orders to: P.O. Box 189, Nashville, TN 37202 (SAN 661-9932) Tel 615-340-7285.
Discovery Bks, *(Discovery Bks.; 0-913976),* Star Rte., Mountain View, Owls Heads, NY 12969 (SAN 206-9512) Tel 518-483-0079.
Discus *Imprint of* **Avon**
Diversity Okla, *(Diversity Pr.; 0-936715),* P.O. Box 25, Idabel, OK 74745 (SAN 699-9131) Tel 405-286-3148. Do not confuse with Diversity Pr., Chicago, IL.
Divine Love Pub, *(Divine Love Publishing Co.; 0-9617038),* P.O. Box 1844, Soquel, CA 95073 (SAN 662-8230); 4631 Soquel Dr., Soquel, CA 95073 (SAN 662-8249) Tel 408-462-6282.
Divine Sci Fed, *(Divine Science Federation International),* 1819 E. 14th Ave., Denver, CO 80218 (SAN 204-1103) Tel 303-322-7730.
Divry, *(Divry, D. C., Inc.; 0-910516),* 148 W. 24th St., New York, NY 10011 (SAN 201-3320) Tel 212-255-2153.
DMS Publishing Co, *(DMS Publishing Co.; 0-914731),* 28311 S. Ridge Haven Ct., Rancho Palos Verdes, CA 90274 (SAN 291-8188) Tel 213-541-9441; Orders to: Holy Shroud Shrine, c/o Marcia Mascia, Corpus Christi Church, 136 S. Regent St., Port Chester, NY 10573 (SAN 662-2232) Tel 914-939-2553.
Doctrine Christ, *(Doctrine of Christ Pubns.; 0-940068),* 2215 Bourbon St., Beaumont, TX 77705 (SAN 220-2131).
Documentary Pubns, *(Documentary Pubns.; 0-89712),* 106 Kenan St., Chapel Hill, NC 27514 (SAN 211-559X) Tel 919-929-1833.
Dodd, *(Dodd, Mead & Co.; 0-396; 0-89696),* 71 Fifth Ave., New York, NY 10003 (SAN 201-3339) Tel 212-627-8444; Orders to: 6 Ram Ridge Rd., Spring Valley, NY 10977 (SAN 665-6862) Tel 914-352-3900.
DOK Pubs, *(DOK Pubs., Inc.; 0-914634),* Div. of United Educational Services, Inc., Box 605, East Aurora, NY 14052 (SAN 201-3347) Tel 716-652-9131; Toll free: 800-458-7900.
Dolores Pr, *(Dolores Pr.; 0-934117),* 69 Rensselaer Dr., Commack, NY 11725 (SAN 693-2916) Tel 516-499-4281.
Dolp *Imprint of* **Doubleday**
Dominion Pr, *(Dominion Pr.; 0-912132),* Div. of Invisible Ministry, P.O. Box 37, San Marcos, CA 92069-0025 (SAN 203-8935) Tel 619-746-9430.
Don Bosco Multimedia, *(Don Bosco Multimedia; 0-89944),* Div. of Salesian Society, Inc., 475 North Ave., Box T, New Rochelle, NY 10802 (SAN 213-2613) Tel 914-576-0122. *Imprints:* D Bosco Pubns (Don Bosco Publications).
Donahoe Pubs, *(Donahoe, Edward D., Pubs.; 0-938400),* P.O. Box 22011, Louisville, KY 40222 (SAN 217-0973) Tel 502-423-9638.
Donning Co, *(Donning Co. Pubs.; 0-915442; 0-89865),* Subs. of Walsworth Publishing Co., 5659 Virginia Beach Blvd., Norfolk, VA 23502 (SAN 211-6316) Tel 804-461-8090; Toll free: 800-446-8572; Warehouse: 801 S. Missouri Ave., Marceline, MO 64658 (SAN 661-9940). *Imprints:* Unilaw (Unilaw).
Dordt Coll Pr, *(Dordt College Pr.; 0-932914),* Affil. of Dordt College, 498 Fourth Ave., NE, Sioux Center, IA 51250 (SAN 221-2110) Tel 712-722-6002.
Dorrance, *(Dorrance & Co.; 0-8059),* 828 Lancaster Ave., Bryn Mawr, PA 19010 (SAN 201-3363) Tel 215-527-7880.
Dorsey, *(Dorsey Pr., The; 0-256),* Div. of Richard D. Irwin, Inc., 224 S. Michigan Ave., Chicago, IL 60604 (SAN 203-8943) Tel 312-322-8400; Orders to: Richard D. Irwin, Inc., 1818 Ridge Rd., Homewood, IL 60430 (SAN 661-9959) Tel 312-798-6000.
Double M Pr, *(Double M Pr.; 0-916634),* 16455 Tuba St., Sepulveda, CA 91343 (SAN 213-9510) Tel 818-360-3166.
Doubleday, *(Doubleday & Co., Inc.; 0-385),* Subs. of Bertelsman, Inc., 245 Park Ave., New York, NY 10017 (SAN 201-0089) Tel 212-984-7561; Toll free: 800-645-6156; Toll free: 800-457-7605 (Sales service); Orders to: 501 Franklin Ave., Garden City, NY 11530 (SAN 281-6083) Tel 516-873-4561. *Imprints:* Anch (Anchor Books); Anchor Pr (Anchor Press); Dial (Dial Press); Dolp (Dolphin Books); Galilee (Galilee); Zephyr (Zephyr).
Doulos Pubs, *(Doulos Pubs.; 0-9617379),* P.O. Box 66, Elkton, MD 21921 (SAN 663-8791); 3228 Old Elk Neck Rd., Elkton, MD 21921 (SAN 663-8805) Tel 301-398-6667.
Dovehaven Pr Ltd, *(Dovehaven Pr., Ltd.; 0-942345),* Box HH, Jackson, WY 83001 (SAN 693-2231); 1040 Smith Ave., Suite 43, Jackson, WY 83001 (SAN 666-7023) Tel 307-733-8050.
Dover, *(Dover Pubns., Inc.; 0-486),* 180 Varick St., New York, NY 10014; Toll free: 800-223-3130; Orders to: 31 E. Second St., Mineola, NY 11501 (SAN 201-338X) Tel 516-294-7000.
Doxology Lane, *(Doxology Lane Pr.; 0-9617890),* 3813 Fields S. Ct., Champaign, IL 61821 (SAN 665-5459) Tel 217-356-7238.
Draco Prod Pubns, *(Draco Productions & Pubns.; 0-936121),* 2036 Pauoa Rd., Honolulu, HI 96813 (SAN 697-0664) Tel 808-523-1752; P.O. Box 27373, Honolulu, HI 96827 (SAN 697-0672).
Drain Enterprise, *(Drain Enterprise, The; 0-930419),* 309 First St., Drain, OR 97435 (SAN 240-902X).
Drame Pr, *(Drame Pr.; 0-9617190),* Box 6276, Phoenix, AZ 85009 (SAN 663-2599); 2928 W. Washington, Phoenix, AZ 85009 (SAN 664-6433).
Dream Garden, *(Dream Garden Pr.; 0-9604402; 0-942688),* P.O. Box 27076, Salt Lake City, UT 84127 (SAN 217-1007); 1042 S. Seventh W., Salt Lake City, UT 84104 (SAN 696-5547) Tel 801-972-0663.
Dropsie Coll, *(Dropsie College; 0-9602686; 0-935135),* 250 N. Highland, Merion, PA 19066 (SAN 223-4602); Dist. by: Eisenbrauns, P.O. Box 275, Winona Lake, IN 46590-0278 (SAN 200-7835) Tel 219-269-2011.
Druid Heights, *(Druid Heights Books; 0-9606568),* 685 Camino del Canyon, Muir Woods, Mill Valley, CA 94941 (SAN 206-4693) Tel 415-388-2111.
Dryden Pr, *(Dryden Pr.; 0-8498),* Div. of Holt, Rinehart & Winston, Inc., 901 N. Elm, Hinsdale, IL 60521 (SAN 281-613X) Tel 312-325-2985; Toll free: 800-323-7437; 1 Salt Creek Ln., Hinsdale, IL 60521 (SAN 658-0483); Orders to: CBS College Publishing, 383 Madison Ave., New York, NY 10017 (SAN 281-6148) Tel 212-872-2219.
Duane Shinn, *(Shinn, Duane, Pubns.; 0-912732),* Box 700, Medford, OR 97501 (SAN 204-5931) Tel 503-664-2317.
Dufour, *(Dufour Editions, Inc.; 0-8023),* Box 449, Chester Springs, PA 19425-0449 (SAN 201-341X) Tel 215-458-5005.
Duir Press, *(Duir Pr.; 0-9602912),* 919 Sutter St., Apt. 9, San Francisco, CA 94109 (SAN 223-5722).
Duke, *(Duke Univ. Pr.; 0-8223),* Box 6697 College Sta., Durham, NC 27708 (SAN 201-3436) Tel 919-684-2173.
Dumbarton Oaks, *(Dumbarton Oaks; 0-88402),* 1703 32nd St., NW, Washington, DC 20007 (SAN 293-2547) Tel 202-342-3259; Orders to: P.O. Box 4866, Hampden Sta., Baltimore, MD 21211 (SAN 665-6870) Tel 301-338-6954.
Dunstan Pr, *(Dunstan Pr.; 0-930995),* 30 Linden St., Rockland, ME 04841 (SAN 678-8920) Tel 207-596-0064.
Duquesne, *(Duquesne Univ. Pr.; 0-8207),* 600 Forbes Ave., Pittsburgh, PA 15282 (SAN 658-0491) Tel 412-434-6610; Toll free: 800-221-3845; Dist. by: Humanities Pr. International, Inc., 171 First Ave., Atlantic Highlands, NJ 07716-1289 (SAN 201-9272) Tel 201-872-1441.
Dutton, *(Dutton, E. P.; 0-525),* Div. of NAL/Penguin, Inc., 2 Park Ave., New York, NY 10016 (SAN 201-0070) Tel 212-725-1818; Orders to: New American Library, P.O. Box 120, Bergenfield, NJ 07621 (SAN 665-6889).
Dynamic Reflections, *(Dynamic Reflections; 0-9616971),* P.O. Box 881, East Brunswick, NJ 08816 (SAN 661-8219); 24 Colonial Dr., New Brunswick, NJ 08816 (SAN 661-8227) Tel 201-254-0415.
Dynamics Chr Liv, *(Dynamics of Christian Living Inc.; 0-940386),* Box 1053, Akron, OH 44309 (SAN 219-7839).
E A Martin, *(Martin, Edward A.),* 550 North Ave., Grand Junction, CO 81501 (SAN 210-6108) Tel 303-243-1538.
E A Seemann, *(Seemann, E. A., Publishing, Inc.; 0-912458; 0-89530),* 14701 SW 84 Ct., Miami, FL 33158-1921 (SAN 201-3495) Tel 305-233-5852.

E Arnold, *(Arnold, Edward, Pubs., Ltd.; 0-7131),* 3 E. Read St., Baltimore, MD 21202 (SAN 263-9203) Tel 301-539-1529; Toll free: 800-638-7511; York County Industrial Pk., Connolly Rd., Emigsville, PA 17318 (SAN 200-6367).
E B Grandin, *(Grandin, E. B., Bk. Co., Inc.; 0-910523),* 148 N. 100 W., Provo, UT 84601 (SAN 260-1931) Tel 801-224-6706.
E Fudge, *(Fudge, Edward, Publishing),* P.O. Box 218026, Houston, TX 77218 (SAN 211-7975) Tel 713-578-7837.
E G Busch, *(Busch, Ernestine G.; 0-9614750),* 8717 Echo St., El Paso, TX 79904 (SAN 692-9257) Tel 915-755-5991.
E Katz, *(Ernst Katz; 0-9613745),* Sub. of Rudolf Steiner Institute of the Great Lakes Area, 1923 Geddes Ave., Ann Arbor, MI 48104 (SAN 677-6272) Tel 313-662-9355.
E Mellen, *(Mellen, Edwin, Pr.; 0-88946),* P.O. Box 450, Lewiston, NY 14092 (SAN 207-110X); 450 Ridge St., Lewiston, NY 14092 (SAN 658-1218) Tel 716-754-2266.
E Mennonite Bd, *(Eastern Mennonite Board of Missions & Charities; 0-9613368),* Oak Ln. & Brandt Blvd., Salunga, PA 17538-0628 (SAN 657-1360) Tel 717-898-2251.
E P Press, *(E.P. Pr., Inc.),* P.O. Box 1172, Gastonia, NC 28052 (SAN 297-1771).
E R Lindemann, *(Lindemann, Emil R.; 0-9612192),* P.O. Box 399, Deshler, NE 68340 (SAN 289-6001).
E Sifton Bks *Imprint of* **Viking**
E T Church, *(Church, Elmer Tuttle),* P.O. Box 42, Yukon, WV 24899 (SAN 665-2352).
E Torres & Sons, *(Torres, Eliseo, & Sons; 0-88303),* Box 2, Eastchester, NY 10709 (SAN 207-0235).
E W Beitzell, *(Beitzell, Edwin W.; 0-9604502),* P.O. Box 107, Abell, MD 20606 (SAN 204-4374) Tel 301-769-3279; Dist. by: St. Mary's County Historical Society, P.O. Box 212, Leonardtown, MD 20650 (SAN 200-545X) Tel 301-475-2467.
E-W Cultural Ctr, *(East-West Cultural Ctr.; 0-930736),* 2865 W. Ninth St., Los Angeles, CA 90006 (SAN 211-0121) Tel 213-480-8325.
E Y Anderson, *(Anderson, Elizabeth Y.; 0-9614002),* 8302 Stevens Rd., Thurmont, MD 21788 (SAN 694-5333).
Eakin Pr, *(Eakin Pr.; 0-89015),* P.O. Box 23069, Austin, TX 78735 (SAN 207-3633) Tel 512-288-1771.
Eakin Pubns
See Eakin Pr
Earth-Song, *(Earth-Song Pr.; 0-9605170),* 202 Hartnell Pl., Sacramento, CA 95825 (SAN 220-0473) Tel 916-927-6863.
East Eur Quarterly, *(East European Quarterly; 0-914710; 0-88033),* Univ. of Colorado, Boulder, CO 80309-0029 (SAN 661-9983); Dist. by: Columbia Univ. Pr., 136 S. Broadway, Irvington-on-Hudson, NY 10533 (SAN 212-2472) Tel 914-591-9111.
East Ridge Pr, *(East Ridge Pr.; 0-914896),* 126 Ridge Rd., Hankins, NY 12741 (SAN 201-2871) Tel 914-887-5161; Dist. by: Ridge Bk. Service, 161 Ridge Rd., Hankins, NY 12741 (SAN 282-6453).
East School Pr, *(Eastern Schl. Pr.; 0-912181),* P.O. Box 684, Talent, OR 97540 (SAN 264-7362) Tel 503-535-1490.
East Woods
See Globe Pequot
Eastern Orthodox, *(Eastern Orthodox Bks.; 0-89981),* P.O. Box 302, Willits, CA 95490 (SAN 201-355X).
Eastern Pr, *(Eastern Pr.; 0-939758),* 426 E. Sixth St., Bloomington, IN 47401 (SAN 216-3713) Tel 812-336-5865; Orders to: P.O. Box 881, Bloomington, IN 47402 (SAN 661-9991).
Eastview, *(Eastview Editions, Inc.; 0-89860),* P.O. Box 783, Westfield, NJ 07091 (SAN 169-4952) Tel 201-964-9485.
ECA Assoc, *(ECA Assocs.; 0-938818),* P.O. Box 15004, Great Bridge Sta., Chesapeake, VA 23320 (SAN 215-9503) Tel 804-547-5542; P.O. Box 20186, Cathedral Finance Sta., New York, NY 10025 (SAN 215-9511) Tel 212-866-8694.
Ecclesia *Imprint of* **William Carey Lib**
Ecumenical Phila, *(Ecumenical Pr.; 0-931214),* Affil. of Journal of Ecumenical Studies, Temple Univ., 022-38, Philadelphia, PA 19122 (SAN 222-8211) Tel 215-787-7714; Dist. by: Hippocrene Bks., 171 Madison Ave., New York, NY 10016 (SAN 213-2060) Tel 718-454-2366.
Ed Ministries, *(Educational Ministries, Inc.; 0-940754),* 2861-C Saturn St., Brea, CA 92621 (SAN 219-7316) Tel 714-961-0622; Toll free: 800-221-0910.
Ed Tecnicos
See French & Eur
EDC, *(EDC Publishing; 0-88110),* Div. of Educational Development Corp., 10302 E. 55th Pl., Tulsa, OK 74146 (SAN 226-2134) Tel 918-622-4522; Toll free: 800-331-4418; P.O. Box 470663, Tulsa, OK 74147 (SAN 658-0505); P.O. Box 702253, Tulsa, OK 74170 (SAN 658-0513). *Imprints:* Usborne-Hayes (Usborne-Hayes).
Eden Co
See A Cohen
Eden Hill Pub *Imprint of* **Signature Bks**
Eden Pr, *(Eden Pr.; 0-920792; 0-88831),* Dist. by: Univ. of Toronto Pr., 33 E. Tupper St., Buffalo, NY 14203 (SAN 214-2651) Tel 716-852-0342.
Eden Valley, *(Eden Valley Press),* P.O. Box 238, Loveland, CO 80537 (SAN 215-6393); Dist. by: David M. Cole/Outreach Books, P.O. Box 425, Corona, CA 91718 (SAN 214-2589) Tel 213-926-9381.
Edenite, *(Edenite Society, Inc.; 0-938520),* Rte. 526, Imlaystown, NJ 08526 (SAN 239-9040) Tel 609-259-7517.
Eden's Work, *(Eden's Work; 0-937226),* RFD 1, Box 540A, Franklin, ME 04634 (SAN 219-998X) Tel 207-565-3533.
Edenwood Hse, *(Edenwood Hse.),* P.O. Box 607, Garner, NC 27529 (SAN 263-2179) Tel 919-772-0107.
Ediciones, *(Ediciones Universal; 0-89729),* 3090 SW Eighth St., Miami, FL 33135 (SAN 207-2203) Tel 305-642-3355; P.O. Box 450353, Shenandoah Sta., Miami, FL 33145 (SAN 658-0548).
Ediciones Huracan, *(Ediciones Huracan, Inc.; 0-940238),* Avenida Gonzalez 1002, Rio Piedras, PR 00925 (SAN 217-5134) Tel 809-763-7407.
Edit Betania, *(Editorial Betania; 0-88113),* Div. of Bethany Fellowship, Inc., 5541 NW 82nd Ave., Miami, FL 33166 (SAN 240-6349) Tel 305-592-5121.
Edit Caribe, *(Editorial Caribe; 0-89922),* 3934 SW Eighth St., Suite 303, Miami, FL 33134 (SAN 215-1421) Tel 305-445-0564; Toll free: 800-222-5342; 4243 NW 37th Ct., Miami, FL 33134 (SAN 658-0556).
Edit Mundo *Imprint of* **Casa Bautista**
Editions Ltd, *(Editions Ltd.; 0-9607938),* 1123 Kapahulu Ave., Honolulu, HI 96816-5811 (SAN 691-9510) Tel 808-735-7644; Dist. by: Pacific Trade Group, P.O. Box 668, Pearl City, HI 96782-0668 (SAN 169-1635).
Editorial Justa, *(Editorial Justa Pubns. Inc.; 0-915808),* 2831 Seventh St., Berkeley, CA 94710 (SAN 208-1962) Tel 415-848-3628; Orders to: P.O. Box 2131-C, Berkeley, CA 94702 (SAN 208-1970).
Educator Pubns, *(Educator Pubns.; 0-913558),* 1110 S. Pomona Ave., Fullerton, CA 92632 (SAN 201-3746) Tel 714-871-2950; P.O. Box 333, Fullerton, CA 92632 (SAN 201-3754).
Eerdmans, *(Eerdmans, William B., Publishing Co.; 0-8028),* 255 Jefferson Ave., SE, Grand Rapids, MI 49503 (SAN 220-0058) Tel 616-459-4591; Toll free: 800-253-7521.
Effect Pub, *(Effect Publishing, Inc.; 0-911971),* 501 Fifth Ave., Suite 1612, New York, NY 10017 (SAN 264-665X) Tel 212-557-1321; 50 Eastbourne Dr., Chestnut Ridge, NY 10977 (SAN 665-8180) Tel 914-356-6626.
Effective Learn, *(Effective Learning, Inc.; 0-915474),* 7 N. MacQuesten Pkwy., P.O. Box 2212, Mount Vernon, NY 10550 (SAN 208-4791) Tel 914-664-7944; 25 N. MacQuesten Pkwy., Mount Vernon, NY 10550 (SAN 658-0572).
EHM Pub, *(EHM Publishing; 0-9609828),* Box 3173, Tallahassee, FL 32315 (SAN 262-0170) Tel 904-539-9767.
Eisenbrauns, *(Eisenbrauns; 0-931464),* P.O. Box 275, Winona Lake, IN 46590-0278 (SAN 200-7835) Tel 219-269-2011.
EKS Pub Co, *(EKS Publishing, Co.; 0-939144),* 5336 College Ave., Oakland, CA 94618 (SAN 216-1281) Tel 415-653-5183.
El-Shabazz Pr, *(El-Hajj Malik El-Shabazz Pr.; 0-913358),* P.O. Box 1115, Washington, DC 20013 (SAN 201-2340).
Eleventh Hour, *(11th Hour Gospel; 0-9608662),* Box 190, Prosser, WA 99350 (SAN 240-6365) Tel 509-786-4230.
Elijah-John, *(Elijah-John Pubns.; 0-9614311),* 103 Russell, Apt. 6, Saline, MI 48176 (SAN 687-5106) Tel 313-429-5717.
Eliopoulos, *(Eliopoulos, Nicholas C, Publishing; 0-9605396),* P.O. Box 65, Oak Park, IL 60303 (SAN 220-0856); 5711 W. School St., Chicago, IL 60634 (SAN 662-0027) Tel 312-725-1960.
Elite Pubs, *(Elite Publishers; 0-941813),* P.O. Box 17961, Anaheim, CA 92807 (SAN 666-3931); 100 Avenida Palmera, Anaheim, CA 92807 (SAN 666-394X) Tel 714-974-4297.
Elliots Bks, *(Elliot's Bks.; 0-911830),* P.O. Box 6, Northford, CT 06472 (SAN 204-1529) Tel 203-484-2184.
Elsevier, *(Elsevier Science Publishing Co., Inc.; 0-444; 0-7204),* Subs. of Elsevier NDU NV, 52 Vanderbilt Ave., New York, NY 10017 (SAN 200-2051) Tel 212-370-5520. *Imprints:* North Holland (North-Holland).
Embee Pr, *(Embee Pr.; 0-89816),* 82 Pine Grove, Kingston, NY 12401 (SAN 212-1603).
Embroidy Bk
See C Schneider
Emerald Hse, *(Emerald Hse.; 0-936958),* P.O. Box 1769, Sandpoint, ID 83864 (SAN 214-3682) Tel 208-263-1071; Dist. by: DeVorss & Co., P.O. Box 550, 1046 Princeton Dr., Marina del Rey, CA 90294 (SAN 168-9886); Dist. by: Angel Bk. Distribution Ctr., 561 Tyler St., Monterey, CA 93940 (SAN 200-5042); Dist. by: New Pathways, 103 Goldencrest Ave., Waltham, MA 02154 (SAN 200-5050).
Emerson, *(Emerson Bks., Inc.; 0-87523),* 121 N. Hampton Dr., White Plains, NY 10603 (SAN 201-3819) Tel 914-739-3506; Madelyn Ave., Verplanck, NY 10596 (SAN 658-0580).
Eminent Pubns, *(Eminent Pubns. Enterprises; 0-936955),* P.O. Box 1026, Jeffersonville, IN 47131 (SAN 658-6589) Tel 812-282-8338.
Emissaries Divine, *(Emissaries of Divine Light; 0-932869),* 5569 N. County Rd., Loveland, CO 80537 (SAN 688-9875) Tel 303-667-4675.
Emmanuel Christian, *(Emmanuel Christian Ministries; 0-9615955),* 1050 Barberry Rd., Yorktown Heights, NY 10598 (SAN 697-3299) Tel 914-245-5635.
Emmett, *(Emmett Pub. Co.; 0-934682),* 2861 Burnham Blvd., Minneapolis, MN 55416 (SAN 210-556X).
Emmons-Fairfied Pub, *(Emmons-Fairfied Publishing Co.; 0-9607956),* 18674 Fairfield, Detroit, MI 48221 (SAN 240-0707) Tel 313-284-0180.
ENR Word, *(ENR Wordsmiths; 0-911511),* P.O. Box 160081, Miami, FL 33116 (SAN 264-2468) Tel 305-596-4523.
Enrich Enter, *(Enrichment Enterprises; 0-9609612),* 1424 Hacienda Pl., Pomona, CA 91768 (SAN 264-0260) Tel 714-622-4887.
Ensign Pub, *(Ensign Publishing Co.; 0-910558),* P.O. Box 298, Riverton, UT 84065 (SAN 686-287X).
Enslow Pubs, *(Enslow Pubs., Inc.; 0-89490),* Bloy St. & Ramsey Ave., Box 777, Hillside, NJ 07205 (SAN 213-7518) Tel 201-964-4116.
Entropy Ltd, *(Entropy, Ltd.; 0-938876),* S. Great Rd., Lincoln, MA 01773 (SAN 215-6423) Tel 617-259-8901.
EO Pr, *(EO Pr.; 0-935830),* RR 1, Box 353-A Minuet Ln., Kingston, NY 12401 (SAN 221-1858) Tel 914-336-8797.
Episcopal Ctr, *(Episcopal Ctr. for Evangelism; 0-918903),* P.O. Box 920, Live Oak, FL 32060 (SAN 208-1598) Tel 904-963-2199.
Epistemics, *(Epistemics Institute Pr.; 0-930371),* Subs. of Institute for Applied Epistemics, 8620 Wilshire Blvd., Suite 104, Beverly Hills, CA 90211 (SAN 670-7637) Tel 213-659-4541; Orders to: P.O. Box 18672, Los Angeles, CA 90007 (SAN 662-247X) Tel 213-389-0307.

EPM Pubns, *(EPM Pubns.; 0-914440; 0-939009),* 1003 Turkey Run Rd., McLean, VA 22101 (SAN 206-7498) Tel 703-442-7810; Orders to: P.O. Box 490, McLean, VA 22101 (SAN 206-7501).
Eriksson, *(Eriksson, Paul S., Pub.; 0-8397),* 208 Battell Bldg., Middlebury, VT 05753 (SAN 201-6702) Tel 802-388-7303; Dist. by: Independent Publishers Group, 1 Pleasant Ave., Pt. Washington, NY 11050 (SAN 287-2544) Tel 516-944-9325.
ESPress, *(ESPress; 0-917200),* 5605 16th St., NW, Washington, DC 20011 (SAN 206-748X) Tel 202-723-4578.
Essex Inst, *(Essex Institute; 0-88389),* 132 Essex St., Salem, MA 01970 (SAN 203-8447) Tel 617-744-3390.
Esther McBride, *(McBride, Esther; 0-9613017),* 1460 Bramble Ct., Rio Rancho, NM 87124 (SAN 293-8928) Tel 505-892-6277.
ETC Pubns, *(ETC Pubns.; 0-88280),* 700 E. Vereda del Sur, Palm Springs, CA 92262 (SAN 201-4637) Tel 619-325-5352; Orders to: Box ETC, Palm Springs, CA 92263-1608 (SAN 201-4645).
Etheridge Minist, *(Etheridge, G. & M., Ministries, Inc.; 0-937417),* P.O. Box 564, Sikeston, MO 63801 (SAN 658-8581); 415 Louise Ave., Sikeston, MO 63801 (SAN 658-859X) Tel 314-471-9344.
Ethics & Public Policy, *(Ethics & Public Policy Ctr., Inc.; 0-89633),* 1030 15th St., NW, Suite 300, Washington, DC 20005 (SAN 216-132X) Tel 202-682-1200.
Ethnographica *Imprint of* **Barber Pr**
Eustace CSB, *(Eustace, Herbert W., C.S.B.),* P.O. Box 7328, Berkeley, CA 94707 (SAN 276-9743) Tel 415-524-0846.
Eva Hruska, *(Hruska, Eva J. Cummings; 0-9614616),* Rte. 2, Schuyler, NE 68661 (SAN 691-6805) Tel 402-352-3645.
Evanescent Pr, *(Evanescent Pr., The),* P.O. Box 968, Bell Springs Rd., Laytonville, CA 95454 (SAN 663-0871) Tel 707-984-6208.
Evang & Ref, *(Evangelical & Reformed Historical Society; 0-910564),* 555 W. James St., Lancaster, PA 17603 (SAN 281-6849).
Evang Sisterhood Mary, *(Evangelical Sisterhood of Mary),* 9849 N. 40th St., Phoenix, AZ 85028 (SAN 211-8335) Tel 602-996-4040.
Evang Tchr, *(Evangelical Teacher Training Assn.; 0-910566),* 110 Bridge St., P.O. Box 327, Wheaton, IL 60189-0327 (SAN 203-8471) Tel 312-668-6400.
Evangel Indiana, *(Evangel Pr.; 0-916035),* Div. of Brethren in Christ Church, 301 N. Elm, Nappanee, IN 46550-0189 (SAN 211-7940) Tel 219-773-3164.
Evangelical Lit, *(Evangelical Literature League, The; 0-939125),* P.O. Box 6219, Grand Rapids, MI 49516-6219 (SAN 662-4812); 941 Wealthy, SE, Grand Rapids, MI 49516-6219 (SAN 662-4820) Tel 616-454-3196.
Evans Pubns, *(Evans Pubns.; 0-934188),* P.O. Box 520, Perkins, OK 74059 (SAN 212-9019) Tel 405-547-2411.
Ever *Imprint of* **Grove**
Evergreen Dist, *(Evergreen Bk. Distributors; 0-903729),* 6513 Lankershim Blvd., Suite 37, N. Hollywood, CA 91606 (SAN 223-1522) Tel 818-986-9689.
Everson Mus, *(Everson Museum of Art; 0-914407),* 401 Harrison St., Syracuse, NY 13202 (SAN 278-7458) Tel 315-474-6064.
Everyday Ser, *(Everyday Series; 0-915517),* 13 Riverview Terrace, Rensselaer, NY 12144 (SAN 291-154X) Tel 518-449-8737.
Exhorters, *(Exhorters, Inc., The; 0-9609260),* P.O. Box 492, Vienna, VA 22180 (SAN 241-3825) Tel 703-698-6880.
Exile Pr, *(Exile Pr.; 0-933515),* P.O. Box 1768, Novato, CA 94948 (SAN 297-1747) Tel 415-883-2132.
Existential Bks, *(Existential Bks.; 0-89231),* 1816 Stevens Ave. S., Suite 25, Minneapolis, MN 55403 (SAN 208-1547) Tel 612-871-7275.
Exploration Pr, *(Exploration Pr.; 0-913552),* Div. of Chicago Theological Seminary, Chicago Theological Seminary, 5757 S. University Ave., Chicago, IL 60637 (SAN 203-851X) Tel 312-752-5757.
Exposition Pr FL, *(Exposition Pr. of Florida, Inc.; 0-682),* 1701 Blount Rd., Suite C, Pompano Beach, FL 33069 (SAN 207-0642) Tel 305-979-3200. *Imprints:* Banner (Banner); Lochinvar (Lochinvar); Testament (Testament); University (University).
F A Bowen, *(Bowen, F A., Reports, Inc.; 0-9602830),* P.O. Box 213, Janesville, WI 53547 (SAN 212-8810) Tel 608-752-6333.
F B Foster Pubns, *(Foster, Fred B., Pubns.; 0-9613762),* 5200 Stockton Blvd., No. 155-21, Sacramento, CA 95820 (SAN 682-269X) Tel 916-383-8579.
F Elmo
See Action Life Pubns
F M Crawford, *(Crawford, F. Marion, Memorial Society),* Saracinesca House 3610 Meadowbrook Ave., Nashville, TN 37205 (SAN 225-2821) Tel 615-292-9695.
F Roberts Crawford
See Ctr Res Soc Chg
Faber & Faber, *(Faber & Faber, Inc.; 0-571; 0-905209),* Affil. of Faber & Faber, Ltd., London, 50 Cross St., Winchester, MA 01890 (SAN 218-7256) Tel 617-721-1427; Dist. by: Harper & Row Pubs., Inc., Keystone Industrial Pk., Scranton, PA 18512 (SAN 215-3742) Tel 717-343-4761.
Facts on File, *(Facts on File, Inc.; 0-87196; 0-8160),* Subs. of Commerce Clearing Hse., 460 Park Ave. S., New York, NY 10016 (SAN 201-4696) Tel 212-683-2244; Toll free: 800-322-8755.
Fag Rag, *(Fag Rag Bks.; 0-915480),* P.O. Box 331, Kenmore Sta., Boston, MA 02215 (SAN 207-3498).
Fairleigh Dickinson, *(Fairleigh Dickinson Univ. Pr.; 0-8386),* Dist. by: Associated University Presses, 440 Forsgate Dr., Cranbury, NJ 08512 (SAN 281-2959) Tel 609-655-4770.
Faith & Life, *(Faith & Life Pr.; 0-87303),* 718 Main St., Newton, KS 67114-0347 (SAN 201-4726) Tel 316-283-5100; Box 347, Newton, KS 67114-0347 (SAN 658-0637).
Faith Messenger, *(Faith Messenger Pubns.; 0-938544),* P.O. Box 641, Upland, CA 91785 (SAN 281-7020) Tel 714-946-3134.
Faith Print, *(Faith Printing Co.; 0-939241),* Rte. 2, Hwy. 290, Taylors, SC 29687 (SAN 694-5341) Tel 803-895-3822.
Faith Pub Hse, *(Faith Publishing Hse.),* P.O. Box 518, Guthrie, OK 73044 (SAN 204-1243); 920 W. Mansur, Guthrie, OK 73044 (SAN 658-0645) Tel 405-282-1479.
Falcon Pr Az, *(Falcon Pr.; 0-941404),* 3660 N. Third St., Phoenix, AZ 85012 (SAN 262-0243) Tel 602-246-3546; Dist. by: Inland Bk. Co., P.O. Box 261, 22 Hemingway Ave., East Haven, CT 06512 (SAN 200-4151) Tel 203-467-4257; Dist. by: Samuel Weiser, Inc., P.O. Box 612, York Beach, ME 03910 (SAN 202-9588) Tel 207-363-4393; Dist. by: Baker & Taylor Co., Western Div., 380 Edison Way, Reno, NV 89564 (SAN 169-4464) Tel 702-786-6700; Dist. by: Bookpeople, 2929 Fifth St., Berkeley, CA 94710 (SAN 168-9517); Dist. by: Great Tradition, The, 750 Adrian Way, Suite 111, San Rafael, CA 94903 (SAN 200-5743) Tel 415-492-9382; Dist. by: Nascorp, Inc., 528 E. Lorain St., Oberlin, OH 44074 (SAN 169-6823) Tel 216-775-8048.
Falcon Pr MT, *(Falcon Pr. Publishing Co., Inc.; 0-934318; 0-937959),* P.O. Box 731, Helena, MT 59624 (SAN 221-1726); 27 Neill Ave., Helena, MT 59624 (SAN 658-0653) Tel 406-442-6597; Orders to: P.O. Box 279, Billings, MT 59103 (SAN 281-7047).
Falkynor Bks, *(G-Jo Institute/Falkynor Bks., The; 0-916878),* 4950 SW 70th Ave., Davie, FL 33314 (SAN 208-645X) Tel 305-791-1562; Dist. by: The Great Tradition, 750 Adrian Way, Suite 111, San Rafael, CA 94903 (SAN 200-5743) Tel 415-492-9382; Dist. by: Samuel Weiser, P.O. Box 612, York Beach, ME 03910 (SAN 202-9588) Tel 207-363-4393; Dist. by: The Distributors, 702 S. Michigan, South Bend, IN 46618 (SAN 169-2488) Tel 219-232-8500.
Falls Tar, *(Falls of the Tar Pubns.; 0-938828),* P.O. Box 4194, Rocky Mount, NC 27801 (SAN 240-0189) Tel 919-442-7423.
Falmer Pr *Imprint of* **Taylor & Francis**
Family Circle Bks, *(Family Circle Bks.; 0-933585),* Subs. of Family Circle, Inc., 488 Madison Ave., New York, NY 10022 (SAN 692-2120) Tel 212-593-8419; Toll free: 800-247-2904; Orders to: P.O. Box 10814, Des Moines, IA 50381 (SAN 662-2976).
Far Eastern Pubns, *(Yale Univ., Far Eastern Pubns; 0-88710),* 340 Edwards St., New Haven, CT 06520 (SAN 219-0710) Tel 203-432-3109.
Far West Edns, *(Far West Editions; 0-914480),* P.O. Box 549, San Francisco, CA 94101 (SAN 207-0456) Tel 415-587-4951.
Faraday, *(Faraday Press; 0-939762),* P.O. Box 4098, Mountain View, CA 94040 (SAN 216-731X). Out of business.
FARMS, *(F.A.R.M.S.; 0-934893),* P.O. Box 7113, Univ. Sta., Provo, UT 84602 (SAN 694-4469) Tel 801-378-3295.
FBF Pubns, *(FBF Pubns.; 0-9616026),* P.O. Box 3296, San Bernardino, CA 92413 (SAN 698-1518) Tel 714-864-0865; 5695 McKinley Ave., San Bernardino, CA 92413 (SAN 698-1526) Tel 714-820-2280.
Fed Jewish Mens Clubs, *(Federation of Jewish Men's Clubs; 0-935665),* 475 Riverside Dr., Suite 244, New York, NY 10115 (SAN 273-4230) Tel 212-749-8100.
Feldheim, *(Feldheim, Philipp, Inc.; 0-87306),* 200 Airport Executive Pk., Spring Valley, NY 10977 (SAN 164-9671) Tel 914-356-2282; Toll free: 800-237-7149.
Fell, *(Fell, Frederick, Pubs., Inc.; 0-8119),* 2131 Hollywood Blvd., Suite 204, Hollywood, FL 33020 (SAN 208-2365) Tel 305-925-5242; Toll free: 800-526-7626; Dist. by: Kampmann & Co., 9 E. 40th St., New York, NY 10016 (SAN 202-5191) Tel 212-685-2928.
Fellowship Crown, *(Fellowship of the Crown),* P.O. Box 3743, Carmel, CA 93921 (SAN 206-4103) Tel 408-624-5600.
Fellowship Pr PA, *(Fellowship Pr.; 0-914390; 0-87728),* 5820 Overbrook Ave., Philadelphia, PA 19131 (SAN 201-6117) Tel 215-879-8604.
Fellowship Spirit, *(Fellowship for Spiritual Understanding; 0-940581),* P.O. Box 816, Palos Verdes Estates, CA 90274 (SAN 270-1227); 2550 Via Tejon, Malaga Cove Plaza, Palos Verdes Estates, CA 90274 (SAN 663-639X) Tel 213-373-2669; Dist. by: DeVorss & Co., P.O. Box 550, Marina del Rey, CA 90294 (SAN 282-6151) Tel 213-870-7478.
Feminist Pr, *(Feminist Pr. at the City Univ. of New York, The; 0-912670; 0-935312),* 311 E. 94th St., New York, NY 10128 (SAN 213-6813) Tel 212-360-5790; Dist. by: Harper & Row, Pubs., Inc., Keystone Industrial Pk., Scranton, PA 18512 (SAN 215-3742); Dist. by: Bookpeople, 2929 Fifth St., Berkeley, CA 94710 (SAN 168-9517) Tel 415-549-3030; Dist. by: Inland Bk. Co., 22 Hemingway Ave., East Haven, CT 06512 (SAN 200-4151) Tel 203-467-4257.
Fenton Valley Pr, *(Fenton Valley Pr.; 0-9615149),* 657 Chaffeeville Rd., Storrs, CT 06268 (SAN 694-3683) Tel 203-429-0710; Dist. by: DeVorss & Co., P.O. Box 550, 1046 Princeton Dr., Marina del Rey, CA 90294 (SAN 168-9886); Dist. by: Inland Bk. Co., P.O. Box 261, 22 Hemingway Ave., East Haven, CT 06512 (SAN 200-4151) Tel 203-467-4257; Dist. by: New Leaf Distributing Co., 1020 White St. SW, Atlanta, GA 30310 (SAN 169-1449) Tel 404-755-2665; Dist. by: Baker & Taylor, Eastern Div., 50 Kirby Ave., Somerville, NJ 08876 (SAN 169-4901).
Ferndale Hse, *(Ferndale Hse.; 0-931637),* P.O. Box 1029, Ferndale, CA 95536 (SAN 683-7735) Tel 707-786-9332; Dist. by: Spring Arbor Distributors, 10885 Textile Rd., Belleville, MI 48111 (SAN 158-9016) Tel 313-481-0900.
Fertig, *(Fertig, Howard, Inc.; 0-86527),* 80 E. 11th St., New York, NY 10003 (SAN 201-4777) Tel 212-982-7922.
Festival *Imprint of* **Abingdon**
Field Ent
See World Bk

Fiery Water, *(Fiery Water Pr.; 0-9613401),* 1202 Loma Dr., No. 129, Ojai, CA 93023 (SAN 656-9854) Tel 805-646-1671; Dist. by: DeVorss & Co., P.O. Box 550, 1046 Princeton Dr., Marina del Rey, CA 90294 (SAN 168-9886) Tel 213-870-7478; Dist. by: Valley Lights Pubns., P.O. Box 1537, Ojai, CA 93023 (SAN 219-8320) Tel 805-646-9888.

Fifth Wave Pr, *(Fifth Wave Pr.; 0-911761),* P.O. Box 9355, San Rafael, CA 94912 (SAN 264-0368) Tel 415-472-4649.

Fig Leaf Pr, *(Fig Leaf Pr.; 0-912235),* 5791 E. Shields Ave., Fresno, CA 93727 (SAN 264-0376) Tel 209-292-4222. Moved, left no forwarding address.

Fill the Gap, *(Fill the Gap Pubns.; 0-89858),* P.O. Box 30760, Lafayette, LA 70503 (SAN 211-9978) Tel 318-984-2004.

Finan Pub, *(Financial Publishing Co.; 0-87600),* 82 Brookline Ave., Boston, MA 02215 (SAN 205-5805) Tel 617-262-4040.

Financial, *(Financial Partners Publishing; 0-9607644),* 4929 S. 121st St., Omaha, NE 68137 (SAN 679-1530) Tel 402-895-0346.

Fireside *Imprint of* **S&S**

Fireside Bks, *(Fireside Bks.; 0-87527),* Div. of Warren H. Green, Inc., 8356 Olive Blvd., St. Louis, MO 63132 (SAN 201-8500) Tel 314-991-1335; Toll free: 800-223-2336.

Firm Foun Pub, *(Firm Foundation Publishing Hse.; 0-88027),* P.O. Box 17200, Pensacola, FL 32522 (SAN 201-4858) Tel 904-433-4258.

First Amend Pubs, *(First Amendment Pubs.; 0-9617573),* P.O. Box 5216, Hercules, CA 94547-5216 (SAN 664-3558); 985 Baypoint Way, Rodeo, CA 94572 (SAN 664-3566) Tel 415-222-1812.

First Bapt AL, *(First Baptist Church AL; 0-9616158),* P.O. Box 400, Jacksonville, AL 36265 (SAN 699-9557) Tel 205-435-7263; 231 E. Seventh St., Jacksonville, AL 36265 (SAN 699-9565).

First Baptist, *(First Baptist Church of Steinhatchee),* P.O. Box 113, Steinhatchee, FL 32359 (SAN 240-1754) Tel 904-498-3242.

First Church, *(First Church of Christ Scientist; 0-87952),* 1 Norway St., Boston, MA 02115 (SAN 206-6467) Tel 617-450-2000.

First Divine Sci Ch Denver, *(First Divine Science Church of Denver, Colorado; 0-9617598),* 1400 Williams St., Denver, CO 80218 (SAN 664-5003) Tel 303-322-7738; Dist. by: Divine Science Federation International, 1819 E. 14th, Denver, CO 80218 (SAN 204-1103) Tel 303-322-7730.

First Love Min, *(First Love Ministries; 0-9614947),* 420 Laurita St., Linden, NJ 07036 (SAN 693-6482) Tel 201-862-7172.

First Mntn Foun, *(First Mountain Foundation, The; 0-916834),* Montclair State College, Upper Montclair, NJ 07043 (SAN 281-7144) Tel 201-893-7174; IAPC, Alderdice Hse., 14 Normal Ave., Upper Montclair, NJ 07043 (SAN 665-696X) Tel 201-893-4277; Orders to: P.O. Box 196, Montclair, NJ 07042 (SAN 281-7152).

Fischer Inc NY, *(Fischer, Carl, Inc.; 0-8258),* 62 Cooper Sq., New York, NY 10003 (SAN 215-1979) Tel 212-772-0900; Toll free: 847-4260.

FitzSimons, *(FitzSimons, H.T., Co., Inc.; 0-912222),* 211 S. Park Rd., La Grange, IL 60525-2126 (SAN 206-4200).

Flame Intl, *(Flame International Inc.; 0-933184),* P.O. Box 305, Quantico, VA 22134 (SAN 215-3114).

Fleet, *(Fleet Pr. Corp.; 0-8303),* Subs. of Fleet Academic Editions, Inc., 160 Fifth Ave., New York, NY 10010 (SAN 201-4874) Tel 212-243-6100.

Folcroft, *(Folcroft Library Editions; 0-8414; 0-88305; 0-8482),* P.O. Box 182, Folcroft, PA 19032 (SAN 206-8362) Tel 215-583-4550.

Folger Bks, *(Folger Bks.; 0-918016; 0-942321),* Dist. by: Associated University Presses, 440 Forsgate Dr., Cranbury, NJ 08512 (SAN 281-2959) Tel 609-655-4770.

Fontana
See J M Fontana

Fordham, *(Fordham Univ. Pr.; 0-8232),* University Box L, Bronx, NY 10458 (SAN 201-6516) Tel 212-579-2320.

Foreign Policy, *(Foreign Policy Assn.; 0-87124),* 205 Lexington Ave., New York, NY 10016 (SAN 212-9426) Tel 212-481-8450.

Forest Peace, *(Forest of Peace Bks., Inc.; 0-939516),* Rte. One, Box 247, Easton, KS 66020 (SAN 216-6739) Tel 913-773-8255.

Fortress, *(Fortress Pr.; 0-8006),* 2900 Queen Ln., Philadelphia, PA 19129 (SAN 220-0074); Toll free: 800-367-8737.

Forum Pr IL, *(Forum Pr., Inc.; 0-88273),* Subs. of Harlan Davidson Inc., 3110 N. Arlington Heights Rd., Arlington Heights, IL 60004 (SAN 201-2375) Tel 312-253-9720.

Forum Script, *(Forum for Scriptural Christianity, Inc.; 0-917851),* P.O. Box 150, Wilmore, KY 40390 (SAN 225-4638) Tel 606-858-4661 (SAN 200-6863).

Forward Movement, *(Forward Movement Pubns.; 0-88028),* Publishing agency of the Episcopal Church, 412 Sycamore St., Cincinnati, OH 45202-4195 (SAN 208-3841) Tel 513-721-6659; Toll free: 800-543-1813.

Foun Bks, *(Foundation Bks.; 0-934988),* P.O. Box 29229, Lincoln, NE 68529 (SAN 201-6567) Tel 402-466-4988.

Foun Chr Self Govt
See Mayflower Inst

Foun Christ Serv, *(Foundation for Christian Services Inc.),* P.O. Box 1555, Altamonte Springs, FL 32715 (SAN 264-0457) Tel 305-830-7424.

Foun Church New Birth
See New Age Min Spiritualist

Foun Human Under, *(Foundation of Human Understanding, The; 0-933900),* P.O. Box 811, 111 NE Evelyn St., Grants Pass, OR 97526-9997 (SAN 213-9545) Tel 503-479-0549; 8780 Venice Blvd., P.O. Box 34036, Los Angeles, CA 90034 (SAN 680-0327) Tel 213-559-3711.

Foun Miracles, *(Foundation for "A Course In Miracles"; 0-933291),* P.O. Box 783, Crompond, NY 10517 (SAN 692-2902) Tel 914-528-0101.

Found Am Christ, *(Foundation for American Christian Education; 0-912498),* 2946 25th Ave., San Francisco, CA 94132 (SAN 205-5856) Tel 415-661-1775.

Found Class Reprints, *(Foundation for Classical Reprints, The; 0-89901),* 607 McKnight St. NW, Albuquerque, NM 87102 (SAN 212-9051) Tel 505-843-7749.

Found Inner Peace, *(Foundation for Inner Peace; 0-9606388),* P.O. Box 635, Tiburon, CA 94920 (SAN 212-422X) Tel 415-435-2255.

Found Life Act
See Life Action Pr

Foundation Ctr, *(Foundation Ctr., The; 0-87954),* 79 Fifth Ave., New York, NY 10003 (SAN 207-5687) Tel 212-620-4230; Toll free: 800-424-9836.

Fountain Pr, *(Fountain Pr., Inc.; 0-89350),* Dist. by: Inspirational Marketing Inc., Box 301, Indianola, IA 50125 (SAN 208-6557).

Fountain Publications Oregon, *(Fountain Pubns.; 0-911376),* 3728 NW Thurman St., Portland, OR 97210 (SAN 205-5880) Tel 503-223-2232.

Four Seasons Foun, *(Four Seasons Foundation; 0-87704),* P.O. Box 31190, San Francisco, CA 94131 (SAN 201-6591) Tel 415-824-5774; Dist. by: Subterranean Co., 1327 W. Second, P.O. Box 10233, Eugene, OR 97440 (SAN 169-7102) Tel 503-343-6324.

Fox Head, *(D Fox Head Press; 0-910521),* 28 Vandeventer Ave., Princeton, NJ 08540 (SAN 260-1893) Tel 609-924-9316.

Foxhound Ent, *(Foxhound Enterprises; 0-940502),* 6577 Sand Wedge Ct., Alexandria, VA 22312 (SAN 223-1034) Tel 703-750-3439; Dist. by: M. E. Repass, Box 68, Louisa, KY 41230 (SAN 223-1042).

Franciscan Herald, *(Franciscan Herald Pr.; 0-8199),* Subs. of Sacred Heart Province of Order of Friais Minor, 1434 W. 51st St., Chicago, IL 60609 (SAN 201-6621) Tel 312-254-4462.

Franciscan Inst, *(Franciscan Institute Pubns.),* Drawer F, St. Bonaventure Univ., St. Bonaventure, NY 14778 (SAN 201-8543) Tel 716-375-2105.

Franciscan U Pr, *(Franciscan Univ. Pr.; 0-940535),* Div. of Franciscan Univ. of Steubenville, Franciscan Way, Steubenville, OH 43952 (SAN 664-953X) Tel 614-283-3771.

Franklin & Marshall, *(Franklin & Marshall College; 0-910626),* P.O. Box 3003, Lancaster, PA 17604-3003 (SAN 226-3408) Tel 717-291-3981.

Free Church Pubns, *(Free Church Pubns.; 0-911802),* Div. of Evangelical Free Church of America, 1515 E. 66th St., Minneapolis, MN 55423 (SAN 206-4146) Tel 612-866-3343.

Free Pr, *(Free Pr.; 0-02),* Div. of Macmillan Publishing Co., Inc., 866 Third Ave., New York, NY 10022 (SAN 201-6656) Tel 212-702-2004; Toll free: 800-257-5755; Dist. by: Macmillan Pub. Co., Front & Brown Sts., Riverside, NJ 08370 (SAN 202-5582) Tel 609-461-6500.

Freedeeds Bks *Imprint of* **Garber Comm**

Freedom Hse, *(Freedom Hse.; 0-932088),* 48 E. 21st St., New York, NY 10010 (SAN 211-7339) Tel 212-473-9691.

Freedom Pr, *(Freedom Pr.; 0-941630),* P.O. Box 5503, Scottsdale, AZ 85261 (SAN 239-2100) Tel 607-991-5414.

Freedom Rel Found, *(Freedom from Religion Foundation),* P.O. Box 750, Madison, WI 53701 (SAN 276-9484) Tel 608-256-8900.

Freedom Univ-FSP, *(Freedom Univ./Seminary Pr.),* 5927 Windhover Dr., Orlando, FL 32819 (SAN 209-505X) Tel 305-351-0898.

Freelandia, *(Freelandia Institute; 0-914674),* Star Rte., Cassville, MO 65625 (SAN 205-6216).

French & Eur, *(French & European Pubns., Inc.; 0-8288),* 115 Fifth Ave., New York, NY 10003 (SAN 206-8109) Tel 212-673-7400.

French Lit
See Summa Pubns

Friedman, *(Friedman, Ira J.; 0-87198),* Div. of Associated Faculty Pr., Inc., Rte. 100, Millwood, NY 10546 (SAN 217-4979) Tel 914-767-2200.

Friend Pr, *(Friendship Pr.; 0-377),* Subs. of National Council of the Churches of Christ USA, 475 Riverside Dr., Rm. 772, New York, NY 10027 (SAN 201-5773) Tel 212-870-2495; Orders to: P.O. Box 37844, Cincinnati, OH 45222-0844 (SAN 201-5781) Tel 513-761-2100.

Friendly Pr NY, *(Friendly Pr., Inc.; 0-914919),* 401 Park Ave., S, New York, NY 10016 (SAN 207-9496) Tel 212-684-4255.

Friends Fla St, *(Friends of Florida State Univ. Library),* Florida State Univ., Tallahassee, FL 32306 (SAN 205-5937).

Friends Israel-Spearhead Pr, *(Friends of Israel-Spearhead Pr., The),* P.O. Box 908, Bellmawr, NJ 08031 (SAN 212-5056) Tel 609-853-5590; Toll free: 257-7843.

Friends Truth, *(Friends of Truth; 0-930682),* 16 Huber St., Glenside, PA 19038 (SAN 211-0423) Tel 215-576-1450.

Friends United, *(Friends United Pr.; 0-913408),* 101 Quaker Hill Dr., Richmond, IN 47374 (SAN 201-5803) Tel 317-962-7573.

Frnds Israel, *(Friends of Israel Gospel Ministry, Inc., The; 0-915540),* P.O. Box 908, Bellmawr, NJ 08031 (SAN 225-445X) Tel 609-853-5590; Toll free: 800-257-7843.

From Here, *(From Here Pr.; 0-89120),* P.O. Box 219, Fanwood, NJ 07023 (SAN 209-746X) Tel 201-889-7886.

Fruitlands Mus, *(Fruitlands Museums, Inc.; 0-941632),* 102 Prospect Hill Rd., Harvard, MA 01451 (SAN 239-2119) Tel 617-456-3924.

FS&G, *(Farrar, Straus & Giroux, Inc.; 0-374),* 19 Union Sq., W., New York, NY 10003 (SAN 206-782X) Tel 212-741-6900; Toll free: 800-242-7737.

Full Gospel, *(Full Gospel Business Men's Fellowship International; 0-86595),* P.O. Box 5050, 3150 Bear St., Costa Mesa, CA 92626 (SAN 220-2476) Tel 714-754-1400.

Fuller Theol Soc, *(Fuller Theological Seminary; 0-9602638),* 84 N. Los Robles, Pasadena, CA 91101 (SAN 221-8259).

Fulness Hse, *(Fulness Hse., Inc.; 0-937778),* P.O. Box 79350, Ft. Worth, TX 76179 (SAN 215-9961) Tel 817-232-9171.

Fun Pub OH, *(Fun Publishing Co.; 0-938293),* 5860 Miami Rd., Cincinnati, OH 45243 (SAN 661-1761) Tel 513-272-3672. Do not confuse with Fun Publishing Co., Scottsdale, AZ.

Future Pr, *(Future Pr.; 0-918406),* P.O. Box 73, Canal St. Sta., New York, NY 10013 (SAN 210-0886).

G Brummel Pub, *(Brummel Publishing Company; 0-9613041),* P.O. Box 198, Richmond Hill, NY 11419 (SAN 295-3765); 116-10 103rd Ave., Richmond Hill, NY 11419 (SAN 295-3773) Tel 718-835-1155.
G Gannett, *(Gannett Bks.; 0-930096),* Subs. of Guy Gannett Publishing Co., P.O. Box 1460B, Portland, ME 04101 (SAN 210-7295) Tel 207-775-5811; Toll free: 800-442-6036.
G Hein, *(Hein, G.; 0-9614649),* 141 N. 11th St., Lehighton, PA 18235 (SAN 691-862X) Tel 215-377-3595.
G K Hall, *(Hall, G. K., & Co.; 0-8161),* Div. of Macmillian Publishing Co., 70 Lincoln St., Boston, MA 02111 (SAN 206-8427); Toll free: 800-343-2806. *Imprints:* Hall Library (Hall Library Catalogs); Hall Reference (Hall Reference Books); Large Print Bks (Large Print Books).
G K Westgard, *(Westgard, Gilbert K., II; 0-916061),* 1001 SW Fifth Ct., Boynton Beach, FL 33435 (SAN 240-5032) Tel 305-736-2340.
G L Tucker, *(Tucker, Grayson L.; 0-9610706),* 2310 Tyler Ln., Louisville, KY 40205 (SAN 264-8024) Tel 502-458-2234.
G Lutheran Foun, *(Grace Lutheran Foundation of Boulder Colorado, Inc.; 0-9606516),* 1001 13th St., Boulder, CO 80302 (SAN 217-1783) Tel 303-442-1883.
G McBride, *(McBride, Gisela; 0-9613270),* 1443 Court St., Allentown, PA 18101 (SAN 297-0252) Tel 215-776-1824.
G Ronald Pub, *(Ronald, George, Pub., Ltd.; 0-85398),* P.O. Box 447, St. Louis, MO 63166 (SAN 679-1859).
G W Ferguson
See B Franklin
G Whitefield Pub, *(Whitefield, George, Publishing Co.; 0-9614323),* P.O. Box 243, Gladstone, OR 97027 (SAN 687-5343) Tel 503-653-2249.
Gabriel Pr CA, *(Gabriel Pr., Inc.; 0-934469),* P.O. Box 5100, Ventura, CA 93003 (SAN 693-7659).
Gabriel's Horn, *(Gabriel's Horn Publishing Co.; 0-911861),* P.O. Box 141, Bowling Green, OH 43402 (SAN 283-4219) Tel 419-352-1338.
Galahand Pr, *(Galahand Pr., The; 0-940578),* 1001 W. 34th St., Austin, TX 78705 (SAN 223-7687) Tel 512-459-9384.
Gale, *(Gale Research Co.; 0-8103),* Subs. of International Thomson Information, Inc., Book Tower, Detroit, MI 48226 (SAN 213-4373) Tel 313-961-2242; Toll free: 800-521-0707.
Galilee *Imprint of* **Doubleday**
Gallimaufry, *(Gallimaufry; 0-916300),* Dist. by: Apple-Wood Pr., P.O. Box 2870, Cambridge, MA 02139 (SAN 210-3419) Tel 617-964-5150.
Gallopade Pub Group, *(Gallopade: Publishing Group; 0-935326; 1-55609),* Main St., Bath, NC 27808 (SAN 213-8441) Tel 919-923-4291.
G&D *Imprint of* **Putnam Pub Group**
Gannon, *(Gannon, William; 0-88307),* 205 E. Palace Ave., Santa Fe, NM 87501 (SAN 201-5889) Tel 505-983-1579.
Garber Comm, *(Garber Communications, Inc.; 0-89345; 0-8334),* 5 Garber Hill Rd., Blauvelt, NY 10913 (SAN 226-2789) Tel 914-359-9292. *Imprints:* Freedeeds Bks (Freedeeds Books); Spiritual Sci Lib (Spiritual Science Library); Steinerbks (Steinerbooks).
Garden Creek Pubns, *(Garden Creek Pubns.; 0-9617522),* P.O. Box 612, San Luis Obispo, CA 93406 (SAN 664-3450).
Garland Pub, *(Garland Publishing, Inc.; 0-8240),* 136 Madison Ave., New York, NY 10016 (SAN 201-5897) Tel 212-686-7492.
Garrard, *(Garrard Pub. Co.; 0-8116),* 29 Goldsborough St., Easton, MD 21601 (SAN 201-5900); Orders to: 1607 N. Market St., Champaign, IL 61820 (SAN 201-5919) Tel 217-352-7685.
Garric Pr, *(Garric Pr.; 0-9609922),* P.O. Box 517, Glen Ellen, CA 95442 (SAN 270-4404) Tel 415-547-2630.
Gary Guthrie, *(Guthrie, Gary; 0-9612980),* 977 Myra Ave., Chula Vista, CA 92011 (SAN 292-515X) Tel 619-427-8098.
Gateways Bks & Tapes, *(Gateways Bks. & Tapes; 0-89556),* Div. of Institute for the Development of the Harmonious Human Being, Inc., P.O. Box 370, Nevada City, CA 95959 (SAN 211-3635) Tel 916-786-7313.
Gaus, *(Gaus, Theo, Ltd.; 0-912444),* P.O. Box 1168, Brooklyn, NY 11202 (SAN 203-4174) Tel 718-625-4651.
Gazelle Pubns, *(Gazelle Pubns.; 0-930192),* 5580 Stanley Dr., Auburn, CA 95603 (SAN 209-5610) Tel 916-878-1223.
GBM Bks, *(GBM Bks.; 0-912695),* Div. of God's Broadcaster Ministries, Inc., P.O. Box 4895, 4850 Whisett Ave., North Hollywood, CA 91607 (SAN 277-6820) Tel 818-763-0942.
Genealog Pub, *(Genealogical Publishing Co., Inc.; 0-8063),* 1001 N. Calvert St., Baltimore, MD 21202 (SAN 206-8370) Tel 301-837-8271.
General Board, *(General Board of Church & Society of the United Methodist Church; 0-9613222),* 100 Maryland Ave., NE, Washington, DC 20002 (SAN 295-1266) Tel 202-488-5631.
Genesis Two, *(Genesis II; 0-9615649),* 99 Bishop Allen Dr., Cambridge, MA 02139 (SAN 696-3994) Tel 617-576-1801.
Geneva Divinity
See Geneva Ministr
Geneva Ministr, *(Geneva Ministries; 0-939404),* 708 Hamvassy Rd., Tyler, TX 75701 (SAN 216-5759) Tel 214-592-0620.
Geneva Pr, *(Geneva Pr., The; 0-664),* Div. of The Westminster Pr., 925 Chestnut St., Philadelphia, PA 19107 (SAN 215-076X) Tel 215-928-2700; Toll free: 800-523-1631; Toll free: 800-462-0405 (in PA); Orders to: William Penn Annex, P.O. Box 718, Philadelphia, PA 19105 (SAN 665-701X).
Georgetown U Pr, *(Georgetown Univ. Pr.; 0-87840),* Intercultural Ctr., Rm. 111, Washington, DC 20057 (SAN 203-4247) Tel 202-625-8041.
Ghosh A, *(Ghosh, A.; 0-9611614),* 5720 W. Little York, Suite 216, Houston, TX 77091 (SAN 285-2780) Tel 713-445-5526.
Ghost Pony Pr, *(Ghost Pony Pr.; 0-941160),* 2518 Gregory St., Madison, WI 53711 (SAN 237-9546) Tel 608-238-0175; Dist. by: Small Pr. Distribution, Inc., 1816 San Pablo Ave., Berkeley, CA 94702 (SAN 204-5826) Tel 415-549-3336.
Gibson, *(Gibson, C. R., Co.; 0-8378; 0-937970),* 32 Knight St., Norwalk, CT 06856 (SAN 201-5765) Tel 203-847-4543; Toll free: 800-243-6004; Orders to: C. R. Gibson, Distribution Ctr., Beacon Falls, CT 06403 (SAN 665-7028).
Gick, *(Gick Publishing Inc.; 0-918170),* 9 Studebaker Dr., Irvine, CA 92718 (SAN 209-6641) Tel 714-581-5830.
Gift Pubns, *(Gift Pubns.; 0-86595),* 3150 Bear St., Costa Mesa, CA 92626 (SAN 216-387X).
Gilgal Pubns, *(Gilgal Pubns.; 0-916895),* P.O. Box 3386, Sunriver, OR 97707 (SAN 655-8801) Tel 503-593-8639.
Gita-Nagari, *(Gita-Nagari Pr.; 0-911233),* 10310 Oaklyn Rd., Potomac, MD 20854 (SAN 262-8759) Tel 301-983-3386.
Glenmary Res Ctr, *(Glenmary Research Ctr.; 0-914422),* 750 Piedmont Ave., NE, Atlanta, GA 30308 (SAN 201-6443) Tel 404-876-6518.
Global Church
See Overseas Crusade
Global Comm, *(Global Communications; 0-938294),* GPO Box 1994, New York, NY 10001 (SAN 216-3896) Tel 212-685-4080; Orders to: Box 753, New Brunswick, NJ 08903 (SAN 662-0191).
Global TN, *(Global Pubs.; 0-937931),* P.O. Box 21788, Chattanooga, TN 37421-0788 (SAN 659-5065) Tel 615-899-9148.
Globe Pequot, *(Globe Pequot Pr.; 0-87106; 0-914788; 0-88742),* Subs. of Boston Globe, Old Chester Rd., Chester, CT 06412 (SAN 201-9892) Tel 203-526-9571; Toll free: 800-243-0495; Toll free: 800-962-0973 (in Connecticut).
Gloria Pubs, *(Gloria Pubs.; 0-9604080),* 2489 East Lake Rd., Livonia, NY 14487 (SAN 221-6132).
Gloucester Art, *(Gloucester Art Pr.; 0-930582; 0-86650),* P.O. Box 4526, Albuquerque, NM 87196 (SAN 205-2865); 607 McKnight St., NW, Albuquerque, NM 87102 (SAN 662-0205) Tel 505-843-7749.
Glyndwr Resc, *(Glyndwr Resources; 0-937505),* 43779 Valley Rd., Decatur, MI 49045 (SAN 658-8832) Tel 616-423-8639.
GMI Pubns Inc, *(GMI Pubns., Inc.; 0-937408),* P.O. Box 16824, Jacksonville, FL 32216 (SAN 215-2479) Tel 904-359-2427.
Godine, *(Godine, David R., Pub., Inc.; 0-87923),* 300 Massachusetts Ave., Horticultural Hall, Boston, MA 02115 (SAN 213-4381) Tel 617-536-0761; Dist. by: Harper & Row Pubs., Inc., Keystone Industrial Pk., Scranton, PA 18512 (SAN 215-3742).
Gods Universe, *(Gods of the Universe; 0-9607228),* P.O. Box 1543, Highland, IN 46322 (SAN 239-0957) Tel 219-924-8200.
Gold Penny, *(Gold Penny Pr. The; 0-87786),* Box 2177, Canoga Park, CA 91306 (SAN 281-7470) Tel 213-368-1417; Orders to: Associated Booksellers, 147 McKinley Ave., Bridgeport, CT 06606 (SAN 281-7489) Tel 203-366-5494.
Golden Key, *(Golden Key Pubns.; 0-9602166),* P.O. Box 1463, Mesa, AZ 85201-0270 (SAN 212-3576) Tel 602-834-7000; Dist. by: DeVorss & Co., P.O. Box 550, Marina del Rey, CA 90291 (SAN 168-9886) Tel 213-870-7478; Dist. by: Baker & Taylor Co., Western Div., 380 Edison Way, Reno, NV 89564 (SAN 169-4464) Tel 702-786-6700.
Golden Mean, *(Golden Mean Pubs., The; 0-937698),* 271 Beach St., Ashland, OR 97520 (SAN 216-2490) Tel 503-482-9771.
Golden Phoenix, *(Golden Phoenix Pr.; 0-910727),* 1300 LaPlaya No. 1, San Francisco, CA 94122 (SAN 262-6772) Tel 415-681-1563.
Golden Pr *Imprint of* **Western Pub**
Golden Quill, *(Golden Quill Pr., The; 0-8233),* Subs. of Audio Amateur Pubns., Avery Rd., Francestown, NH 03043 (SAN 201-6419) Tel 603-547-6622.
Golden Seal, *(Golden Seal Research Headquarters; 0-912368),* P.O. Box 27821, Hollywood, CA 90027 (SAN 201-8365).
Gonzaga U Pr, *(Gonzaga Univ. Pr.),* Spokane, WA 99202 (SAN 206-4480).
Good Apple, *(Good Apple, Inc.; 0-916456; 0-86653),* P.O. Box 299, Carthage, IL 62321-0299 (SAN 208-6646) Tel 217-357-3981; Toll free: 800-435-7234.
Good Bks PA, *(Good Bks.; 0-934672),* Subs. of Good Enterprises, Ltd., Main St., Intercourse, PA 17534 (SAN 693-9597) Tel 717-768-7171; Toll free: 800-762-7171.
Good Life, *(Good Life Pr.; 0-89074),* Div. of Charing Cross Publishing Co., 658 S. Bonnie Brae St., Los Angeles, CA 90057 (SAN 206-4944) Tel 213-483-5832.
Good News, *(Good News Pubs.; 0-89107),* 9825 W. Roosevelt Rd., Westchester, IL 60153 (SAN 211-7991) Tel 312-345-7474; Toll free: 800-323-3890 (sales only). *Imprints:* Crossway Bks (Crossway Books).
Good News KY, *(Good News: A Forum For Scriptual Christianity, Inc.),* P. O. Box 150, Wilmore, KY 40390 (SAN 657-1441) Tel 606-858-4661.
Gordian, *(Gordian Pr., Inc.; 0-87752),* P.O. Box 304, Staten Island, NY 10304 (SAN 201-6389) Tel 718-273-4700.
Gordon & Breach, *(Gordon & Breach Science Pubs., Inc.; 0-677),* P.O. Box 786, Cooper Sta., New York, NY 10276 (SAN 201-6370) Tel 212-206-8900.
Gordon Pr, *(Gordon Pr. Pubs.; 0-87968; 0-8490),* P.O. Box 459, Bowling Green Sta., New York, NY 10004 (SAN 201-6362) Tel 212-628-4390.
Gospel Advocate, *(Gospel Advocate Co., Inc.; 0-89225),* P.O. Box 150, Nashville, TN 37202 (SAN 205-2792); Toll free: 800-251-8446; 1006 Elm Hill Pike, Nashville, TN 37210 (SAN 662-0213); Toll free: 800-242-8006 in Tennesee; Dist. by: Christian Communications, P.O. Box 150, Nashville, TN 37202 (SAN 200-7207).
Gospel Place, *(Gospel Place, The),* P.O. Box 110304, Nashville, TN 37211 (SAN 277-6847) Tel 615-377-3910.

Gospel Pub, *(Gospel Publishing Hse.; 0-88243),* Div. of General Council of the Assemblies of God, 1445 Boonville Ave., Springfield, MO 65802 (SAN 206-8826) Tel 417-862-2781; Toll free: 800-641-4310; Toll free: 800-492-7625 in Missouri.
Gospel Pubns FL
See GMI Pubns Inc
Gospel Themes Pr, *(Gospel Themes Pr.; 0-938855),* P.O. Box 69097, Seattle, WA 98168 (SAN 662-5797) Tel 206-824-3159.
Gotham, *(Gotham Bk. Mart; 0-910664),* 41 W. 47th St., New York, NY 10036 (SAN 203-4417) Tel 212-719-4448.
Gower Pub Co, *(Gower Publishing Co.; 0-566),* Div. of Gower Publishing Co., Ltd. (UK), Old Post Rd., Brookfield, VT 05036 (SAN 262-0308) Tel 802-276-3162.
Grace Pub Co, *(Grace Publishing Co.),* P.O. Box 23385, Tampa, FL 33622 (SAN 211-8017) Tel 813-884-8003.
Grace World Outreach, *(Grace World Outreach Ctr.; 0-933643),* 2695 Creve Coeur Mill Rd., Maryland Heights, MO 63043 (SAN 692-6495) Tel 314-291-6647.
Graded Pr, *(Graded Pr.; 0-939697),* Div. of United Methodist Publishing Hse., P.O. Box 801, Nashville, TN 37202 (SAN 201-839X); 201 Eighth Ave. S., Nashville, TN 37201 (SAN 663-2920) Tel 615-749-6269.
Graham & Trotman, *(Graham & Trotman, Inc.; 0-86010),* Subs. of Graham & Trotman Ltd., 13 Park Ave., Gaithersburg, MD 20877 (SAN 699-5284) Tel 301-670-1767.
Graphic Pub, *(Graphic Publishing Co., Inc.; 0-89279),* 204 N. Second Ave., W., Lake Mills, IA 50450 (SAN 202-4306) Tel 515-592-2000.
Great Comm Pubns, *(Great Commission Pubns.; 0-934688),* 7401 Old York Rd., Philadelphia, PA 19126 (SAN 215-1502) Tel 215-635-6510.
Great Plains Emporium
See Grt Plains Emporium
Great Traditions, *(Great Traditions),* P.O. Box 3680, Clearlake, CA 95422 (SAN 679-1301). *Imprints:* Wisdom Pubns (Wisdom Publications).
Green, *(Green, Warren H., Inc.; 0-87527),* 8356 Olive Blvd., St. Louis, MO 63132 (SAN 201-4939) Tel 314-991-1335.
Green Leaf CA, *(Green Leaf Pr.; 0-938462),* P.O. Box 6880, Alhambra, CA 91802 (SAN 239-3646); 20 W. Commonwealth Ave., Alhambra, CA 91801 (SAN 239-3654) Tel 818-281-6809.
Greene, *(Greene, Stephen, Pr.; 0-8289; 0-86616),* Div. of Viking Penguin, Inc., 15 Muzzey St., Lexington, MA 02173 (SAN 201-6222) Tel 617-861-0170; Dist. by: Viking Penguin, Inc., 299 Murray Hill Pkwy., East Rutherford, NJ 07073 (SAN 282-5074) Tel 201-933-1460.
Greenhaven, *(Greenhaven Pr.; 0-912616; 0-89908),* 577 Shoreview Park Rd., St. Paul, MN 55126 (SAN 201-6214) Tel 612-482-1582; Toll free: 800-231-5163.
Greenlawn Pr, *(Greenlawn Pr.; 0-937779),* Div. of LaSalle Co., 237 S. Greenlawn Ave., South Bend, IN 46601 (SAN 659-2309) Tel 219-234-5088; Dist. by: CRS/Communication Ctr., 107 N. Michigan, South Bend, IN 46606 (SAN 200-6421).
Greenlf Bks, *(Greenleaf Bks.; 0-934676),* Canton, ME 04221 (SAN 203-4514) Tel 207-843-5789.
Greenwillow, *(Greenwillow Bks.; 0-688),* Div. of William Morrow & Co., Inc., 105 Madison Ave., New York, NY 10016 (SAN 202-5760) Tel 212-889-3050; Toll free: 800-631-1199; Orders to: William Morrow & Co., Inc., 39 Plymouth St., P.O. Box 1219, Fairfield, NJ 07007 (SAN 202-5779).
Greenwood, *(Greenwood Pr.; 0-8371; 0-313; 0-89930),* 88 Post Rd., W., Box 5007, Westport, CT 06881 (SAN 213-2028) Tel 203-226-3571.
Greenwood Hse, *(Greenwood Hse.; 0-9601982),* 1655 Flatbush Ave., Apt. B1902, Brooklyn, NY 11210-3270 (SAN 212-3584) Tel 718-253-9299.
Gregg Intl, *(Gregg International; 0-576),* Old Post Rd., Brookfield, VT 05036 (SAN 695-2046) Tel 802-276-3162.
Gregory Pub, *(Gregory Publishing Co.; 0-911541),* 806 N. Maple St., Itasca, IL 60143 (SAN 211-5646).
Grey Fox, *(Grey Fox Pr.; 0-912516),* Box 31190, San Francisco, CA 94131 (SAN 201-6176); Dist. by: Subterranean Co., 1327 W. Second, P.O. Box 10233, Eugene, OR 97440 (SAN 169-7102) Tel 503-343-6324.
Griffon Hse, *(Griffon Hse. Pubns./Bagehot Council; 0-918680),* P.O. Box 81, Whitestone, NY 11357 (SAN 211-6685) Tel 718-767-8380.
Group Bks, *(Group Bks.; 0-936664; 0-931529),* P.O. Box 481, Loveland, CO 80539 (SAN 214-4689); 2890 N. Monroe, Loveland, CO 80539 (SAN 662-1376) Tel 303-669-3836.
Grove, *(Grove Pr.; 0-8021; 0-394),* 920 Broadway, New York, NY 10010 (SAN 201-4890) Tel 212-529-3600; Toll free: 800-638-6460; Orders to: Grove Pr., Sales Dept., 10 East 53rd St., 14th Flr., New York, NY 10022 Tel 212-207-6900; Dist. by: Random Hse., Inc., 400 Hahn Rd., Westminster, MD 21157 (SAN 202-5515) Tel 301-848-1900. *Imprints:* BC (Black Cat Books); Ever (Evergreen Books).
Growth Assoc, *(Growth Assocs.; 0-918834),* P.O. Box 18429, Rochester, NY 14618-0429 (SAN 210-430X) Tel 716-244-1225.
Growth Pub, *(Growth Publishing; 0-931225),* P.O. Box 661, Herndon, VA 22070 (SAN 682-9112) Tel 703-471-1160.
Grt Plains Emporium, *(Great Plains Emporium; 0-9616365),* P.O. Box 416, Schaller, IA 51053 (SAN 658-9448) Tel 712-275-4542; 303 Berwick, Schaller, IA 51053 (SAN 658-9456).
Grune, *(Grune & Stratton, Inc.; 0-8089),* Subs. of Harcourt Brace Jovanovich, Inc., ; c/o Promotion Dept., Orlando, FL 32887-0018 (SAN 206-8990) Tel 305-345-4212.
Guardian Devot Pr, *(Guardian of Devotion Pr.; 0-940431),* 62 S. 13th St., San Jose, CA 95112 (SAN 664-404X) Tel 408-971-7171.
Guild Bks, *(Guild Bks., Catholic Polls, Inc.; 0-912080),* 86 Riverside Dr., New York, NY 10024 (SAN 203-4646) Tel 212-799-2600.
Guild Psy, *(Guild for Psychological Studies Publishing Hse.; 0-917479),* 2230 Divisadero St., San Francisco, CA 94115 (SAN 656-0687) Tel 415-931-0668.
Guildhall Pubs, *(Guildhall Pubs., Ltd.; 0-940518),* P.O. Box 325, Peoria, IL 61651 (SAN 219-838X); 231 E. Oak Cliff Ct., No. 4, Peoria, IL 61614 (SAN 662-0256) Tel 309-688-5985.
Guilford Pr, *(Guilford Pr., The; 0-89862),* Div. of Guilford Pubns., Inc., 200 Park Ave., S., New York, NY 10003 (SAN 212-9442) Tel 212-674-1900; Toll free: 800-221-3966.
Gulf Pub, *(Gulf Publishing Co.; 0-87201; 0-88415),* P.O. Box 2608, Houston, TX 77252 (SAN 201-6125) Tel 713-529-4301.
Gusto Pr, *(Gusto Pr.; 0-933906),* 2960 Philip Ave., Bronx, NY 10465 (SAN 212-9450) Tel 212-931-8964.
Gutenberg, *(Gutenberg Pr., The; 0-9603872),* P.O. Box 26345, San Francisco, CA 94126 (SAN 213-9278) Tel 415-548-3776; Orders to: The Gutenberg Press, P.O. Box 9875, Berkeley, CA 94209 (SAN 665-7044) Tel 415-548-3776.
Guthrie Gary
See Gary Guthrie
H E Ferguson, *(Ferguson, Howard E.; 0-9611180),* 22445 Lorain Rd., Fairview Park, OH 44126 (SAN 277-6863) Tel 216-734-3233.
H F Snow, *(Snow, Helen F.; 0-911392),* 148 Mungertown Rd., Madison, CT 06443 (SAN 206-3131) Tel 203-245-9714.
H Holt & Co, *(Holt, Henry, & Co.; 0-8050),* 521 Fifth Ave., New York, NY 10175 (SAN 200-6472) Tel 212-599-7600. Former trade-book arm of Holt, Rinehart & Winston. Acquired in 1985 by Verlagsgruppe Georg von Holtzbrinck, from CBS. *Imprints:* North South Bks (North-South Books).
H J Kramer Inc, *(Kramer, H. J., Inc.; 0-915811),* P.O. Box 1082, Tiburon, CA 94920 (SAN 294-0833); Orders to: 1474 West Ave. No. 43, Los Angeles, CA 90065 (SAN 662-2259); Dist. by: Publishers Group West, 5855 Beaudry St., Emeryville, CA 94608 (SAN 202-8522); Dist. by: Bookpeople, 2929 Fifth St., Berkeley, CA 94710 (SAN 168-9517).
H J Schneider
See World Wide OR
H L Levin, *(Levin, Hugh Lauter, Assocs.; 0-88363),* 236 W. 26th St., Suite 5NE, New York, NY 10001 (SAN 201-6109) Tel 212-242-1405; Dist. by: Macmillan Publishing Co., Front & Brown Sts., Riverside, NJ 08370 (SAN 202-5582).
H Leonard Pub Corp, *(Leonard, Hal, Publishing Corp.; 0-9607350; 0-88188),* 8112 W. Bluemound Rd., P.O. Box 13819, Milwaukee, WI 53213 (SAN 239-250X) Tel 414-774-3630; Toll free: 800-642-6692.
H M Taylor, *(Taylor, Horace M.; 0-9617424),* 1629 Robin Rd., Lebanon, PA 17042 (SAN 663-9453) Tel 717-273-4645.
H R Gale, *(Gale, Hoyt Rodney),* 669 Sturtevant Dr., Sierra Madre, CA 91024 (SAN 212-8209) Tel 818-355-2988.
H Reichner, *(Reichner, Herbert; 0-9601520),* Shaker Hill, Enfield, NH 03748 (SAN 205-2210) Tel 603-632-7725.
H. H. Wait
See N S Wait
Haas Ent NH, *(Haas Enterprises; 0-9605552),* 7 N. Main, Box 218, Ashland, NH 03217 (SAN 216-034X) Tel 603-968-7177.
Hacker, *(Hacker Art Bks.; 0-87817),* 54 W. 57th St., New York, NY 10019 (SAN 201-6052) Tel 212-757-1450.
Hackett Pub, *(Hackett Publishing Co., Inc.; 0-915144; 0-915145; 0-87220),* P.O. Box 7, Cambridge, MA 02139 (SAN 201-6044) Tel 617-354-1318; Orders to: 832 Pierson St., Indianapolis, IN 46204 (SAN 665-7052) Tel 315-635-9250.
Hafner, *(Hafner Pr.; 0-02),* Div. of Macmillan Publishing Co., Inc., 866 Third Ave., New York, NY 10022 (SAN 201-6001) Tel 212-702-2000; Toll free: 800-257-5755; Dist. by: Collier-Macmillan Distribution Ctr., Front & Brown Sts., Riverside, NJ 08075 (SAN 202-5582).
Hagin Ministries, *(Hagin, Kenneth, Ministries, Inc.; 0-89276),* P.O. Box 50126, Tulsa, OK 74150-0126 (SAN 208-2578) Tel 918-258-1588.
Haimowoods, *(Haimowoods Pr.; 0-917790),* 1101 Forest Ave., Evanston, IL 60202 (SAN 210-296X) Tel 312-864-7209.
Halcyon Bk, *(Halcyon Bk. Concern/The Temple of the People; 0-933797),* P.O. Box 7095, Halcyon, CA 93420 (SAN 692-8773) Tel 805-489-2822; Dist. by: DeVorss & Co., P.O. Box 550, 1046 Princeton Dr., Marina del Rey, CA 90294-0550 (SAN 168-9886); Dist. by: The Philosophical Research Society, 3910 Los Feliz Blvd., Los Angeles, CA 90027 (SAN 205-3829); Dist. by: Starlite Distributors, P.O. Box 20729, Reno, NV 89515 (SAN 200-7789) Tel 702-359-5676.
Hall Library *Imprint of* **G K Hall**
Hall Reference *Imprint of* **G K Hall**
Halsted Pr, *(Halsted Pr.; 0-470),* Div. of John Wiley & Sons, Inc., 605 Third Ave., New York, NY 10158 (SAN 202-2680) Tel 212-850-6465; Toll free: 800-526-5368.
Hambledon Press, *(Hambledon Pr., The; 0-907628),* 309 Greenbrier Ave., Ronceverte, WV 24970 (SAN 677-4946) Tel 304-645-1058.
Hammond Inc, *(Hammond Inc.; 0-8437),* 515 Valley St., Maplewood, NJ 07040 (SAN 202-2702) Tel 201-763-6000; Toll free: 800-526-4953.
Hamoroh Pr, *(Hamoroh Pr.; 0-9604754),* P.O. Box 48862, Los Angeles, CA 90048 (SAN 215-6512).
Hanging Loose, *(Hanging Loose Pr.; 0-914610),* 231 Wyckoff St., Brooklyn, NY 11217 (SAN 206-4960) Tel 718-643-9559; Dist. by: Inland Bk. Co., P.O. Box 261, 22 Hemingway Ave., East Haven, CT 06512 (SAN 200-4151) Tel 203-467-4257; Dist. by: Bookslinger, 213 E. Fourth St., St. Paul, MN 55101 (SAN 169-4154) Tel 612-221-0429; Dist. by: Small Pr. Distributors, Inc., 1814 San Pablo Ave., Berkeley, CA 94702 (SAN 204-5826) Tel 415-549-3336.
Hansa Pub, *(Hansa Publishing; 0-933593),* 2124 Kittredge St., No. 76, Berkeley, CA 94704 (SAN 692-2147) Tel 415-528-6377; Dist. by: Bookpeople, 2929 Fifth St., Berkeley, CA 94710 (SAN 168-9517) Tel 415-549-3030.
Hansi, *(Hansi Ministries, Inc.; 0-932878),* P.O. Box 3009, Fallbrook, CA 92028-0945 (SAN 213-5086) Tel 619-728-7847.

Hapi Pr, *(Hapi Pr.; 0-913244),* 512 SW Maplecrest Dr., Portland, OR 97219 (SAN 699-5292) Tel 503-246-9632.

Happiness Pr, *(Happiness Pr.; 0-916508),* 14351 Wycliff, Postal Drawer DD, Magalia, CA 95954 (SAN 208-6719) Tel 916-873-0294; Orders to: P.O. Box B-DD, Magalia, CA 95954 (SAN 662-0329).

Har-Row, *(Harper & Row Pubs., Inc.; 0-06),* 10 E. 53rd St., New York, NY 10022 (SAN 200-2086) Tel 212-207-7146; Toll free: 800-242-7737; Icehouse 1-401, 151 Union St., San Francisco, CA 94111 (SAN 215-3734) Tel 415-477-4400; Dist. by: Harper & Row Pubs. Inc., Keystone Industrial Pk., Scranton, PA 18512 (SAN 215-3742). *Imprints:* B&N Bks (Barnes & Noble Books); C&M Bessie Bks (Cornelia & Michael Bessie Books); HarpC (Harper's College Division); HarpR (Harper Religious Books); HarpT (Harper Trade Books); PL (Perennial Library); Torch (Torchbooks).

HarBraceJ, *(Harcourt Brace Jovanovich, Inc.; 0-15),* 1250 Sixth Ave., San Diego, CA 92101 (SAN 200-2736) Tel 619-699-6335; Toll free: 800-543-1918; Harcourt Brace Jovanovich Bldg., Orlando, FL 32887 (SAN 200-2299) Tel 305-345-2000; 555 Academic Ct., San Antonio, TX 78204 (SAN 200-2833); 1627 Woodland Ave., Austin, TX 78741 (SAN 200-2841); 7555 Caldwell Ave., Chicago, IL 60648 (SAN 200-285X); P.O. Box 819077, Dallas, TX 75381-9077 (SAN 200-2868); 3800 Lakeville Hwy., Petaluma, CA 94952 (SAN 200-2876); Saddle Brook Industrial Pk., Saddle Brook, NJ 07662 (SAN 200-2884); 7401 Dowden Rd., Orlando, FL 32812 (SAN 200-2906); 465 S. Lincoln Dr., Troy, MO 63379 (SAN 200-2914). *Imprints:* Harv (Harvest Books); HC (Harcourt Brace Jovanovich, Inc., College Dept.); HJ (HarBraceJ Juvenile Books).

Harlan Davidson, *(Davidson, Harlan, Inc.; 0-88295),* 3110 N. Arlington Heights Rd., Arlington Heights, IL 60004 (SAN 201-2375) Tel 312-253-9720.

Harlo Pr, *(Harlo Pr.; 0-8187),* 50 Victor Ave., Detroit, MI 48203 (SAN 202-2745) Tel 313-883-3600.

Harmonious Pr, *(Harmonious Circle Pr.; 0-9610544),* 15 Ozone Ave., Apt. 2, Venice, CA 90291 (SAN 264-0813).

Harmony *Imprint of* **Crown**

Harmony Pr, *(Harmony Pr., Inc.; 0-941600),* P.O. Box 122, North Granby, CT 06060 (SAN 238-8790) Tel 203-653-2722.

HarpC *Imprint of* **Har-Row**

HarpJ, *(Harper & Row Junior Bks. Group; 0-06),* Div. of Harper & Row Pubs., Inc., 10 E. 53rd St., New York, NY 10022 (SAN 200-2086) Tel 212-207-7000; Orders to: Keystone Industrial Pk., Scranton, PA 18512 (SAN 215-3742).

HarpR *Imprint of* **Har-Row**

Harpswell Pr, *(Harpswell Pr.; 0-88448),* 132 Water St., Gardiner, ME 04345 (SAN 208-1199) Tel 207-582-1899.

HarpT *Imprint of* **Har-Row**

Harrington Pk, *(Harrington Park Pr., Inc.; 0-918393),* Subs. of Haworth Pr., 12 W. 32nd St., New York, NY 10001 (SAN 657-3487) Tel 212-279-1200.

Harrison Co GA, *(Harrison Co.; 0-910694),* 3110 Crossing Pk., Norcross, GA 30071 (SAN 205-0536) Tel 404-447-9150; Toll free: 800-241-3561; Toll free: 800-282-9867 (In Georgia).

Harrison Hse, *(Harrison Hse., Inc.; 0-89274),* P.O. Box 35035, Tulsa, OK 74153 (SAN 208-676X) Tel 918-582-2126; Toll free: 800-331-3647.

Hart Eden Pr, *(Hart-Eden Pr.; 0-937497),* Div. of Center for Zen Sensualism, 6114 LaSalle, Suite 283, Oakland, CA 94611 (SAN 658-9626) Tel 415-339-1753.

Hartmore, *(Hartmore Hse.; 0-87677),* Subs. of Media Judaica, Inc., 304 E. 49th St., New York, NY 10017 (SAN 293-2717) Tel 212-319-6666; Orders to: Media Judaica, Inc., 1363 Fairfield Ave., Bridgeport, CT 06605 (SAN 207-0022) Tel 203-384-2284.

Harv *Imprint of* **HarBraceJ**

Harvard Common Pr, *(Harvard Common Pr.; 0-916782; 0-87645),* 535 Albany St., Boston, MA 02118 (SAN 208-6778) Tel 617-423-5803; Dist. by: Kampmann & Co., 9 E. 40th St., New York, NY 10016 (SAN 202-5191) Tel 212-685-2928.

Harvard Educ Rev, *(Harvard Educational Review; 0-916690),* 13 Appian Way, Cambridge, MA 02138 (SAN 208-3426) Tel 617-495-3432.

Harvard U Ctr Jewish, *(Harvard Univ. Ctr. for Jewish Studies),* Dist. by: Harvard Univ. Pr., 79 Garden St., Cambridge, MA 02138 (SAN 200-2043) Tel 617-495-2600.

Harvard U Pr, *(Harvard Univ. Pr.; 0-674),* 79 Garden St., Cambridge, MA 02138 (SAN 200-2043) Tel 617-495-2600.

Harvest Hse, *(Harvest Hse. Pubs., Inc.; 0-89081),* 1075 Arrowsmith, Eugene, OR 97402 (SAN 207-4745) Tel 503-343-0123; Toll free: 800-547-8979.

Harvest IL, *(Harvest Pubns.; 0-935797),* Div. of Baptist General Conference, 2002 S. Arlington Heights Rd., Arlington Heights, IL 60005 (SAN 696-8023) Tel 312-228-0200.

Harvey J M, *(Harvey, James M.; 0-933799),* 825 N-Lamb Blvd., Las Vegas, NV 89110 (SAN 692-8943) Tel 702-452-1217.

Harwood Academic, *(Harwood Academic Pubs.; 3-7186),* P.O. Box 786, Cooper Sta., New York, NY 10276 (SAN 213-9294) Tel 212-206-8900.

Haskell, *(Haskell Booksellers, Inc.; 0-8383),* P.O. Box 420, Blythebourne Sta., Brooklyn, NY 11219 (SAN 202-2818) Tel 718-435-7878.

Haskett Spec, *(Haskett Specialties; 0-9609724),* 26 E. Harrison St., Mooresville, IN 46158 (SAN 270-6946) Tel 317-831-1668.

Hastings, *(Hastings Hse. Pubs.; 0-8038),* c/o Kampmann & Co, Inc., 9 E. 40 St., New York, NY 10016 (SAN 202-5191) Tel 212-685-2928. *Imprints:* Communication Arts (Communication Arts Books).

Hastings Ctr, *(Hastings Ctr.; 0-916558),* 360 Broadway, Hastings-on-Hudson, NY 10706 (SAN 208-6980) Tel 914-478-0500.

Haunted Bk Shop, *(Haunted Bookshop, The; 0-940882),* 214 St. Francis St., Mobile, AL 36602 (SAN 223-1344) Tel 205-432-6606.

Haven Bks *Imprint of* **Bridge Pub**

Havertown Bks, *(Havertown Books),* P.O. Box 711, Havertown, PA 19083 (SAN 208-4384).

Hawkes Pub Inc, *(Hawkes Publishing Inc.; 0-89036),* Box 15711, Salt Lake City, UT 84115 (SAN 205-6232) Tel 801-262-5555.

Haworth Pr, *(Haworth Pr., Inc., The; 0-917724; 0-86656),* 12 W. 32nd St., New York, NY 10001 (SAN 211-0156) Tel 212-279-1200; Toll free: 800-342-9678.

Hay House, *(Hay Hse.; 0-937611),* 3029 Wilshire Blvd., Suite 206, Santa Monica, CA 90404 (SAN 658-9618) Tel 213-828-3666; Toll free: 800-654-5126.

Hayes, *(Hayes Publishing Co., Inc.; 0-910728),* 6304 Hamilton Ave., Cincinnati, OH 45224 (SAN 277-6154) Tel 513-681-7559.

Haymark, *(Haymark Pubns.; 0-933910),* P.O. Box 243, Fredericksburg, VA 22401 (SAN 213-2508) Tel 703-373-5780.

Hazelden, *(Hazelden Foundation; 0-89486),* Box 176, Center City, MN 55012 (SAN 209-4010) Tel 612-257-4010; Toll free: 800-328-9000.

HBC, *(H. B. C.; 0-9601276),* Box 626, Lansing, IL 60438 (SAN 210-4318) Tel 312-474-7999.

HC *Imprint of* **HarBraceJ**

HDL Pubs, *(HDL Publishing Co.; 0-937359),* Div. of HDL Communications, 599 Adamsdale Rd., North Attleboro, MA 02760 (SAN 659-0403) Tel 617-761-7721; 650 Town Center Dr., Costa Mesa, CA 92626 (SAN 665-9195) Tel 714-540-8945.

Heal Tao Bks, *(Healing Tao Bks.; 0-935621),* 2 Creskill Pl., Huntington, NY 11743 (SAN 695-9318) Tel 516-549-9452; Dist. by: The Talman Co., 150 Fifth Ave., Rm. 514, New York, NY 10011 (SAN 200-5204) Tel 212-620-3182.

Health Admin Pr, *(Health Administration Pr.; 0-914904; 0-910701),* Div. of Foundation of the American College of Healthcare Executives, 1021 E. Huron St., Ann Arbor, MI 48104-9990 (SAN 207-0464) Tel 313-764-1380.

Health Comm, *(Health Communications, Inc.; 0-932194),* 1721 Blount Rd., Suite 1, Pompano Beach, FL 33069 (SAN 212-100X) Tel 305-979-6776; Toll free: 800-851-9100.

Health Ed & Life Exp Res, *(Health Education & Life Expansion Research; 0-9607142),* Box 70027, Los Angeles, CA 90309 (SAN 238-9878) Tel 213-738-9940.

Hearst Bks, *(Hearst Bks.; 0-910992; 0-87851; 0-910990; 0-688),* Div. of William Morrow & Co., Inc., 105 Madison Ave., New York, NY 10016 (SAN 202-2842) Tel 212-889-3050.

Heath, *(Heath, D. C., Co.; 0-669; 0-278; 0-88408),* 125 Spring St., Lexington, MA 02173 (SAN 213-7526) Tel 617-862-6650; Toll free: 800-334-3284; Orders to: D. C. Heath & Co. Distribution Ctr., 2700 Richardt Ave., Indianapolis, IN 46219 (SAN 202-2885) Tel 317-359-5585.

Heatherdown Pr, *(Heatherdown Pr.; 0-9610038),* 3450 Brantford Rd., Toledo, OH 43606 (SAN 270-7284) Tel 419-877-0073.

Hebraeus Pr, *(Hebraeus Press; 0-910511),* Box 32 HBLL Brigham Young Univ., Provo, UT 84603 (SAN 260-0692) Tel 801-347-8839.

Hebrew Pub, *(Hebrew Publishing Co.; 0-88482),* P.O. Box 875, 100 Water St., Brooklyn, NY 11202-0875 (SAN 201-5404) Tel 718-858-6928.

Hebrew Union Coll Pr, *(Hebrew Union College Press; 0-87820),* 3101 Clifton Ave., Cincinnati, OH 45220 (SAN 220-6358) Tel 513-221-1875; Dist. by: Ktav Publishing Hse., Inc., 900 Jefferson St., Hoboken, NJ 07030-7205 (SAN 200-8866) Tel 201-963-9524.

Heian Intl, *(Heian International Publishing, Inc.; 0-89346),* P.O. Box 1013, Union City, CA 94587 (SAN 213-2036) Tel 415-471-8440.

Heineman, *(Heineman, James H., Inc., Pub.; 0-87008),* 475 Park Ave., New York, NY 10022 (SAN 204-0409) Tel 212-688-2028.

Heinemann Ed, *(Heinemann Educational Bks., Inc.; 0-435),* 70 Court St., Portsmouth, NH 03801 (SAN 210-5829) Tel 603-431-7894; Dist. by: CSSC, 300 Raritan Ctr., Edison, NJ 08818 (SAN 200-9404) Tel 201-225-5555.

Heinman, *(Heinman, W. S., Imported Bks.; 0-88431),* 225 W. 57th St., Rm. 404, New York, NY 10019 (SAN 121-6201) Tel 212-757-7628; P.O. Box 926, New York, NY 10023 (SAN 660-935X) (SAN 200-8483).

Heldon Pr, *(Heldon Pr.; 0-933169),* 9146 Arrington Ave., Downey, CA 90240 (SAN 692-3127) Tel 213-869-5741.

Hellenic Coll Pr, *(Hellenic College Pr.; 0-917653),* Div. of Holy Cross Orthodox Pr., 50 Goddard Ave., Brookline, MA 02146 (SAN 213-6694) Tel 617-731-3500.

Helpful Beginnings, *(Helpful Beginnings; 0-938783),* P.O. Box 1684, Clovis, CA 93613-1684 (SAN 661-5465); 1502 Celeste, Clovis, CA 93612 (SAN 661-5473) Tel 209-299-1876.

Hemisphere Pub, *(Hemisphere Publishing Corp.; 0-89116),* Subs. of Harper & Row Pubs., 79 Madison Ave., Suite 1110, New York, NY 10016 (SAN 207-4001) Tel 212-725-1999; Toll free: 800-242-7737.

Hemlock Soc, *(Hemlock Society; 0-9606030),* P.O. Box 66218, Los Angeles, CA 90066 (SAN 293-275X) Tel 213-391-1871; Dist. by: Grove Pr., 196 W. Houston St., New York, NY 10014 (SAN 201-4890) Tel 212-242-4900.

Henceforth, *(Henceforth Pubns.; 0-913437; 0-913439),* c/o Berkshire Christian College, Lenox, MA 01240 (SAN 285-1628) Tel 413-637-0030.

Hendrickson MA, *(Hendrickson Pubs., Inc.; 0-913573),* P.O. Box 3473, Peabody, MA 01961-3473 (SAN 285-2772); 137 Summit St., Peabody, MA 01961-3473 (SAN 663-6594) Tel 617-532-6546.

Hennessey, *(Hennessey & Ingalls, Inc.; 0-912158),* 1254 Third St. Mall, Santa Monica, CA 90401 (SAN 293-2776) Tel 213-458-9074; Orders to: 8321 Campion Dr., Los Angeles, CA 90045 (SAN 293-2784).

Heptangle, *(Heptangle Bks.; 0-935214),* P.O. Box 283, Berkeley Heights, NJ 07922 (SAN 210-6329) Tel 201-647-4449.

Herald Hse, *(Herald Hse.; 0-8309),* P.O. Box HH, Independence, MO 64055 (SAN 202-2907) Tel 816-252-5010; Toll free: 800-821-7550.

Herald Pr, *(Herald Pr.; 0-8361),* Div. of Mennonite Publishing Hse., Inc., 616 Walnut Ave., Scottdale, PA 15683 (SAN 202-2915) Tel 412-887-8500; Toll free: 800-245-7894.

Heres Life, *(Here's Life Pubs., Inc.; 0-89840),* P.O. Box 1576, San Bernardino, CA 92402 (SAN 212-4254) Tel 714-886-7981.

Heridonius, *(Heridonius Foundation; 0-940539),* 606 N. Wrightwood Dr., Orange, CA 92669 (SAN 664-8150) Tel 714-532-2680.

Heritage Res Hse, *(Heritage Research Hse., Inc.; 0-912617),* Box 64003, Virginia Beach, VA 23464 (SAN 282-7956) Tel 804-467-4777.

Hermitage, *(Hermitage; 0-938920; 1-55779),* P.O. Box 410, Tenafly, NJ 07670 (SAN 239-4413) Tel 201-894-8247; 27 Cambridge Ave., Englewood, NJ 07631.

Hermon, *(Sepher-Hermon Pr., Inc.; 0-87203),* 1265 46th St., Brooklyn, NY 11219 (SAN 169-5959) Tel 718-972-9010.

Herzl Pr, *(Herzl Pr.; 0-930832),* Subs. of World Zionist Organization, 515 Park Ave., New York, NY 10022 (SAN 201-5374) Tel 212-752-0600.

Hi-Time Pub, *(Hi-Time Publishing Corp.; 0-937997),* P.O. Box 13337, Milwaukee, WI 53213 (SAN 661-2520); Toll free: 800-558-2292; 12040F W. Feerick St., Wauwatosa, WI 53222 (SAN 661-2539) Tel 414-466-2420.

Hiawatha Bondurant, *(Hiawatha Bk. Co.),* 7567 NE 102nd Ave., Bondurant, IA 50035 (SAN 162-8348) Tel 515-967-4025.

Hid Valley MD, *(Hidden Valley Pr.; 0-935710),* P.O. Box 606, 7051 Poole Jones Rd., Frederick, MD 21701 (SAN 213-5094) Tel 301-662-6745.

Hieroglyphics, *(Hieroglyphics Pr.; 0-916395),* P.O. Box 906, Maggie Valley, NC 28751 (SAN 295-8309) Tel 704-926-3245.

High Country Bks, *(High Country Bks.; 0-932773),* P.O. Box 45060, Boise, ID 83711-5060 (SAN 688-4830) Tel 208-322-3925.

High Mesa Pr, *(High Mesa Pr.; 0-9614010),* P.O. Box 2267, Taos, NM 87571 (SAN 693-3815) Tel 505-758-8769.

High-Scope, *(High-Scope Educational Research Foundation; 0-931114),* Div. of High-Scope Pr., 600 N. River St., Ypsilanti, MI 48198 (SAN 211-9617) Tel 313-485-2000.

Highland, *(Highland Pr.; 0-914335),* 321 Bello Rio, Sacramento, CA 95831 (SAN 287-5462) Tel 415-421-6509.

Highland CA
See Highland

Highland Pr, *(Highland Pr.; 0-910722),* Rte. 3, Box 3125, Boerne, TX 78006 (SAN 204-0522).

Highlands Pub, *(Highlands Publishing Co.; 0-943328),* 424 NW Lakeview Dr., Sebring, FL 33870 (SAN 240-4826).

Highlights, *(Highlights for Children, Inc.; 0-87534; 0-87534),* 2300 W. Fifth Ave., P.O. Box 269, Columbus, OH 43272-0002 (SAN 281-7810) Tel 614-486-0631; 803 Church Ave., Honesdale, PA 18431 (SAN 281-7802) Tel 717-253-1080.

Highly Specialized
See Ctr Thanatology

Highreach Colorado, *(Highreach Pr.; 0-938380),* 315 Harvard Ln., Boulder, CO 80303 (SAN 220-1259) Tel 303-494-7577; Dist. by: Bookpeople, 2929 Fifth St., Berkeley, CA 94710 (SAN 168-9517) Tel 415-549-3030; Dist. by: DeVorss & Co., P.O. Box 550, 1046 Princeton Dr., Marina del Rey, CA 90291 (SAN 168-9886) Tel 213-870-7478.

Higley, *(Higley Publishing Corp.; 0-9614116),* P.O. Box 2470, Jacksonville, FL 32203 (SAN 211-8041) Tel 904-396-1918; Dist. by: Appalachian Bible Co. & Christian Bks., 604 Rolling Hills Dr., Johnson City, TN 37601 (SAN 169-7889) Tel 615-926-0128; Dist. by: Spring Arbor, 10885 Textile Rd., Belleville, MI 48111 (SAN 158-9016) Tel 313-481-0900.

Hill & Wang, *(Hill & Wang, Inc.; 0-8090),* Div. of Farrar, Straus & Giroux, Inc., 19 Union Sq., W., New York, NY 10003 (SAN 201-9299) Tel 212-741-6900; Toll free: 800-242-7737.

Hill Monastic, *(Hill Monastic Manuscript Library; 0-940250),* Bush Ctr., St. John's Univ., Collegeville, MN 56321 (SAN 238-8839).

Hillside Bks, *(Hillside Bks.; 0-9611350),* P.O. Box 601, Lynnfield, MA 01940 (SAN 283-2364) Tel 617-581-2961 Tel 617-581-2961.

Hilltop Hse, *(Hilltop Hse.; 0-9613717),* 13423 Olive Tree Ln., Poway, CA 92064-4921 (SAN 676-2948) Tel 619-566-2675.

Himalayan Pubs, *(Himalayan Pubs.; 0-89389),* Div. of Himalayan International Institute of Yoga Science & Philosophy, RR 1, Box 405, Honesdale, PA 18431 (SAN 207-5067) Tel 717-253-3022; Toll free: 800-433-5472.

Hippocrene Bks, *(Hippocrene Bks., Inc.; 0-87052; 0-88254),* 171 Madison Ave., New York, NY 10016 (SAN 213-2060) Tel 718-454-2366.

Hispanic Seminary, *(Hispanic Seminary of Medieval Studies; 0-942260; 0-940639),* 3734 Ross St., Madison, WI 53705 (SAN 207-9836) Tel 608-262-2529.

Hispanic Soc, *(Hispanic Society of America, The; 0-87535),* 613 W. 155th St., New York, NY 10032 (SAN 204-0573) Tel 212-926-2234.

Hist Comm S Baptist, *(Historical Commission of the Southern Baptist Convention; 0-939804),* 901 Commerce St., Suite 400, Nashville, TN 37203-3620 (SAN 216-7352) Tel 615-244-0344.

Hist Soc West Pa, *(Historical Society of Western Pennsylvania; 0-936340),* 4338 Bigelow Blvd., Pittsburgh, PA 15213 (SAN 214-0276) Tel 412-681-5537.

Hist Soc Wisconsin
See State Hist Soc Wis

Historical Times, *(Historical Times, Inc.; 0-918678),* 2245 Kohn Rd., Box 8200, Harrisburg, PA 17105 (SAN 685-320X) Tel 717-657-9555.

HJ *Imprint of* **HarBraceJ**

HM, *(Houghton Mifflin Co.; 0-395; 0-87466),* 1 Beacon St., Boston, MA 02108 (SAN 200-2388) Tel 617-725-5000; Toll free: 800-225-3362; Orders to: Wayside Rd., Burlington, MA 01803 (SAN 215-3793) Tel 617-272-1500. *Imprints:* RivEd (Riverside Editions).

Hobby Hse, *(Hobby Hse. Pr.; 0-87588),* 900 Frederick St., Cumberland, MD 21502 (SAN 204-059X) Tel 301-759-3770.

Hogrefe Intl, *(Hogrefe International; 0-88937),* Affil. of C. J. Hogrefe, P.O. Box 51, Lewiston, NY 14092 (SAN 293-2792) Tel 716-754-8145.

Holiday, *(Holiday Hse., Inc.; 0-8234),* 18 E. 53rd St., New York, NY 10022 (SAN 202-3008) Tel 212-688-0085.

Holland Pub Hse, *(Holland Publishing Hse.; 0-9616660),* 2100 Tiebout Ave., Bronx, NY 10457 (SAN 661-3470) Tel 212-584-0229.

Hollybridge Pubns, *(Hollybridge Pubns.; 0-9617668),* P.O. Box 1707, Midlothian, VA 23113 (SAN 664-3884); 2914 Wood Bridge Crossing Dr., Midlothian, VA 23113 (SAN 664-645X) Tel 805-744-6503.

HollyDay, *(HollyDay Bks.; 0-943786),* 130 Ashley Rd., Hopkins, MN 55343 (SAN 241-0281) Tel 612-935-4562; Dist. by: Publishers Group West, 5855 Beaudry St., Emeryville, CA 94608 (SAN 202-8522) Tel 415-658-3453.

Hollym Intl, *(Hollym International Corp.; 0-930878),* 18 Donald Pl., Elizabeth, NJ 07208 (SAN 211-0172) Tel 201-353-1655.

Holman Bible Pub, *(Holman Bible Pub.; 0-87981),* Div. of Baptist Sunday Schl. Bd., 127 Ninth Ave., N., Nashville, TN 37234 (SAN 202-3016) Tel 615-251-2520; Toll free: 800-251-3225.

Holmes, *(Holmes Book Co.; 0-910740),* 274 14th St., Oakland, CA 94612 (SAN 204-0654) Tel 415-893-6860.

Holmes & Meier, *(Holmes & Meier Pubs., Inc.; 0-8419),* Div. of IUB, Inc., IUB Bldg., 30 Irving Pl., New York, NY 10003 (SAN 201-9280) Tel 212-254-4100. *Imprints:* Africana (Africana Pub.).

Holmes Pub, *(Holmes Publishing Group; 0-916411),* P.O. Box 623, Edmonds, WA 98020-0623 (SAN 655-8321) Tel 206-771-2701. *Imprints:* Near Eastern (Near Eastern Press); Oriental Classics (Oriental Classics).

Holocaust Pubns, *(Holocaust Pubns., Inc.; 0-89604),* 216 W. 18th St., New York, NY 10011 (SAN 215-0808); Dist. by: Schocken Bks., 62 Cooper Sq., New York, NY 10003 (SAN 213-7585) Tel 212-475-4900.

Holt
See HR&W

HoltC *Imprint of* **HR&W**

Holy Cow, *(Holy Cow! Pr.; 0-930100),* 5435 Old Hwy. 18, Stevens Point, WI 54481 (SAN 685-3315) Tel 715-345-0888.

Holy Cross Orthodox, *(Holy Cross Orthodox Pr.; 0-917651),* 50 Goddard Ave., Brookline, MA 02146 (SAN 208-6840) Tel 617-731-3500.

Holy Episcopal, *(Holy Trinity Episcopal Church; 0-9615284),* 95 Folly Rd., Charleston, SC 29407 (SAN 694-552X) Tel 803-556-2560.

Holy Transfiguration *Imprint of* **St Nectarios**

Holy Trinity, *(Holy Trinity Monastery; 0-88465),* Jordanville, NY 13361 (SAN 207-3501) Tel 315-858-0940.

Homana Pubns, *(Homana Pubns.; 0-915563),* 3430 E. Tropicana, Suite 44, Las Vegas, NV 89121 (SAN 292-5354) Tel 702-435-8673.

Home Mission, *(Home Mission Board of the Southern Baptist Convention; 0-937170),* 1350 Spring St., NW, Atlanta, GA 30367 (SAN 207-5318) Tel 404-873-4041.

Home Sweet Home, *(Home Sweet Home Pubns.; 0-9616817),* Div. of LCS Music Group, P.O. Box 202406, Dallas, TX 75220 (SAN 661-1370); 6126 Meadow Rd., Dallas, TX 75230 (SAN 661-1389) Tel 214-869-2773.

Honor Bks, *(Honor Bks.; 0-931446),* P.O. Box 641, Rapid City, SD 57709 (SAN 208-0877).

Hoover Inst Pr, *(Hoover Institution Pr.; 0-8179),* Affil. of Hoover Institution, Stanford Univ., Stanford, CA 94305-6010 (SAN 202-3024) Tel 415-723-3373.

Hope Farm, *(Hope Farm Press & Bookshop; 0-910746),* Strong Rd., Cornwallville, NY 12418 (SAN 204-0697) Tel 518-239-4745.

Hope Pub, *(Hope Publishing Co.; 0-916642),* 380 S. Main Pl., Carol Stream, IL 60188 (SAN 208-3361) Tel 312-665-3200; Toll free: 800-323-1049.

Hope Pub Hse, *(Hope Publishing Hse.; 0-932727),* Subs. of Southern California Ecumenical Council, P.O. Box 60008, Pasadena, CA 91106 (SAN 688-4849) Tel 818-792-2121; Dist. by: Meyer, Stone & Assocs., 1821 W. Third St., Bloomington, IN 47401 (SAN 200-8696) Tel 812-333-0313.

Horizon, *(Horizon Pr.; 0-8180),* P.O. Box 402, New York, NY 10108 (SAN 202-3040) Tel 212-757-4420.

Horizon Utah, *(Horizon Pubs. & Distributors, Inc.; 0-88290),* P.O. Box 490, 50 S. 500 West, Bountiful, UT 84010 (SAN 159-4885) Tel 801-295-9451; Toll free: 800-453-0812.

Hover, *(Hover Co., The; 0-934414),* 14713 La Mesa Dr., La Mirada, CA 90638 (SAN 213-747X) Tel 714-521-3046.

Howard U Pr, *(Howard Univ. Pr.; 0-88258),* 2900 Van Ness St. NW, Washington, DC 20008 (SAN 202-3067) Tel 202-686-6696.

Howe Brothers, *(Howe Brothers; 0-935704),* Box 6394, Salt Lake City, UT 84106 (SAN 222-0318) Tel 801-485-7409; 1127 Wilmington Ave., Salt Lake City, UT 84106 (SAN 658-2214).

Howell North, *(Howell-North Bks., Inc.; 0-8310),* Div. of Howell North-Darwin-Superior, 850 N. Hollywood Way, Burbank, CA 91505 (SAN 202-3083) Tel 818-848-0944.

HRAFP, *(Human Relations Area Files Pr., Inc.; 0-87536),* Affil. of Yale Univ., P.O. Box 2015, Yale Sta., New Haven, CT 06520 (SAN 200-4348); 755 Prospect St., New Haven, CT 06520 (SAN 669-0971) Tel 203-777-2334.

HR&W, *(Holt, Rinehart & Winston, Inc.; 0-03),* Div. of CBS College Publishing, 383 Madison Ave., New York, NY 10017 (SAN 200-2108) Tel 212-750-1330. *Imprints:* HoltC (Holt College Department).

HSA Pubns, *(HSA Pubns.; 0-910621),* 4 W. 43rd St., New York, NY 10036 (SAN 270-6490) Tel 212-997-0050.

Hse Better Sales, *(House of Better Sales; 0-9617290),* P.O. Box 2163, Ocala, FL 32678-2163 (SAN 663-5954); 818 SW Fort King St., Ocala, FL 32674 (SAN 663-5962).

Hse of Affirmation
See Affirmation

HUC Pr *Imprint of* **Ktav**

Hudson Hills, *(Hudson Hills Pr., Inc.; 0-933920),* 230 Fifth Ave., Suite 1308, New York, NY 10001-7704 (SAN 213-0815) Tel 212-889-3090; Dist. by: Rizzoli International Pubns., Inc., 597 Fifth Ave., New York, NY 10017 (SAN 207-7000) Tel 212-223-0100.

Hughley Pubns, *(Hughley Pubns.; 0-9605150),* P.O. Box 261, Springfield Gardens, NY 11413 (SAN 215-8078) Tel 718-712-5892.

Human Kinetics, *(Human Kinetics Pubs.; 0-931250; 0-87322),* P.O. Box 5076, Champaign, IL 61820 (SAN 211-7088) Tel 217-351-5076; 1607 N. Market St., Champaign, IL 61820 (SAN 658-0866) Tel 217-351-5076. *Imprints:* YMCA USA (Y M C A of the U S A).

Human Res Dev Pr, *(Human Resource Development Pr.; 0-914234; 0-87425),* 22 Amherst Rd., Amherst, MA 01002 (SAN 201-9213) Tel 413-253-3488; Toll free: 800-822-2801.

Human Sci Pr, *(Human Sciences Pr., Inc.; 0-87705; 0-89885),* 72 Fifth Ave., New York, NY 10011 (SAN 200-2159) Tel 212-243-6000; Dist. by: Independent Pubs. Group, 1 Pleasant Ave., Port Washington, NY 11050 (SAN 287-2544).

Humana, *(Humana Pr., The; 0-89603),* P. O. Box 2148, Clifton, NJ 07015 (SAN 212-3606) Tel 201-773-4389.

Humanics Ltd, *(Humanics, Ltd.; 0-89334),* P.O. Box 7447, Atlanta, GA 30309 (SAN 208-3833); Toll free: 800-874-8844; 1389 Peachtree St. NE, Suite 370, Atlanta, GA 30309 (SAN 658-0882) Tel 404-874-2176.

Humanist Pr, *(Humanist Pr.; 0-931779),* Subs. of American Humanist Assn., 7 Harwood Dr., P.O. Box 146, Amherst, NY 14226-0146 (SAN 684-8702) Tel 716-839-5080.

Humanities, *(Humanities Pr., International, Inc.; 0-391),* 171 First Ave., Atlantic Highlands, NJ 07716-1289 (SAN 201-9272) Tel 201-872-1441; Toll free: 800-221-3845 (orders).

Humble Pub Co, *(Humble Publishing Co.; 0-9611756),* 33 Ivy Trail , NE, Atlanta, GA 30342 (SAN 285-2950) Tel 404-261-3243.

Hummingbird, *(Hummingbird Pr.; 0-912998),* 2400 Hannett, NE, Albuquerque, NM 87106 (SAN 204-0794) Tel 505-268-6277.

Hunter Bks, *(Hunter Bks.; 0-917726),* 201 McClellan Rd., Kingwood, TX 77339-2815 (SAN 209-2611) Tel 713-358-7575; Toll free: 800-231-3024.

Hunter Hse, *(Hunter Hse., Inc.; 0-89793),* Box 1302, Claremont, CA 91711 (SAN 281-7969) Tel 714-624-2277; Dist. by: Publisher's Services, Box 2510, Novato, CA 94948 (SAN 281-7977) Tel 415-883-3140; Dist. by: Bookpeople, 2929 Fifth St., Berkeley, CA 94710 (SAN 169-2488) Tel 415-549-3030; Dist. by: Publishers Group West, 5855 Beaudry St., Emeryville, CA 94608 (SAN 202-8522) Tel 415-658-3453; Dist. by: Distributors, The, 702 S. Michigan, South Bend, IN 46618 (SAN 212-0364) Tel 219-232-8500; Dist. by: New Leaf Distributors, The, 1020 White St., SW, Atlanta, GA 30310 (SAN 169-1449) Tel 404-755-2665; Dist. by: Quality Bks., Inc., 918 Sherwood Dr., Lake Bluff, IL 60044-2204 (SAN 169-2127) Tel 312-295-2010; Dist. by: DeVorss & Co., P.O. Box 550, Marina del Rey, CA 90294 (SAN 168-9886) Tel 213-870-7478; Dist. by: Inland Bk. Co., P.O. Box 261, 22 Hemingway Ave., East Haven, CT 06512 (SAN 200-4151) Tel 203-467-4257; Dist. by: Great Tradition, The, 750 Adrian Way, Suite 111, San Rafael, CA 94903 (SAN 200-5743) Tel 415-492-9382.

Hunter Pub NY, *(Hunter Publishing, Inc.; 0-935161; 1-55650),* 155 Riverside Dr., New York, NY 10024 (SAN 695-3425) Tel 212-595-8933; Orders to: 300 Raritan Center Pkwy., CN 94, Edison, NJ 08818 (SAN 200-4089) Tel 201-225-1900.

Hunterdon Hse, *(Hunterdon Hse.; 0-912606),* 38 Swan St., Lambertville, NJ 08530 (SAN 204-0824) Tel 609-397-2523.

Huntington Hse Inc, *(Huntington Hse., Inc.; 0-910311),* P.O. Box 53788, Lafayette, LA 70505 (SAN 241-5208); Toll free: 800-572-8213.

Huntington Lib, *(Huntington Library Pubns.; 0-87328),* Div. of Huntington Library, Art Collections, & Botantical Gardens, 1151 Oxford Rd., San Marino, CA 91108 (SAN 202-313X) Tel 818-405-2172.

Hymnary Pr, *(Hymnary Pr., The; 0-942466),* P.O. Box 5782, Missoula, MT 59806-5782 (SAN 239-6564) Tel 406-721-4943.

Hyperion Conn, *(Hyperion Pr., Inc.; 0-88355; 0-8305),* 47 Riverside Ave., Westport, CT 06880 (SAN 202-3148) Tel 203-226-1091; P.O. Box 591, Westport, CT 06880 (SAN 658-0890).

I Chalmers, *(Chalmers, Irena, Cookbooks, Inc.; 0-941034),* 23 E. 92nd St., New York, NY 10128 (SAN 217-3425) Tel 212-289-3105; Toll free: 800-334-8128; Orders to: P.O. Box 988, Denton, NC 27239 (SAN 661-972X).

I Tompkins, *(Tompkins, Iverna, Ministry; 0-9611260),* 7036 E. Thunderbird Rd., Scottsdale, AZ 85254 (SAN 283-2240) Tel 602-991-8803.

IA Conf Com Arch, *(Iowa Conference Commission on Archives & History; 0-9616298),* 1019 Chestnut St., Des Moines, IA 50309 (SAN 658-5450) Tel 712-275-4247; Orders to: Rev. Lyle Johnston, Box 416, Schaller, IA 51053 (SAN 662-412X) Tel 712-275-4247.

Ibis Pub VA, *(Ibis Publishing; 0-935005),* Div. of Teleprint Publishing, Inc., 7 Elliewood Ave., Charlottesville, VA 22903 (SAN 661-6658) Tel 804-979-3420; Toll free: 800-582-0026.

IBS Intl, *(I.B.S. Internacional; 0-89564),* 3144 Dove St., San Diego, CA 92103 (SAN 210-3001) Tel 619-298-5061.

Ichthys Bks, *(Ichthys Bks.; 0-930711),* 916 Red Mountain Dr., Glenwood Springs, CO 81601 (SAN 677-2390) Tel 303-945-7052.

ICPSR, *(Inter-University Consortium for Political & Social Research; 0-89138),* Affil. of Univ. of Michigan Institute for Social Research, P.O. Box 1248, Ann Arbor, MI 48106 (SAN 207-7450) Tel 313-763-5010.

ICR, *(Institute for Cross-Cultural Research; 0-911976),* 4000 Albermarle St., NW, Washington, DC 20016 (SAN 206-6505).

ICS Pubns, *(ICS Pubns., Institute of Carmelite Studies; 0-9600876; 0-935216),* 2131 Lincoln Rd., NE, Washington, DC 20002 (SAN 201-5285) Tel 202-832-6622.

Ide Hse, *(Ide Hse., Inc.; 0-86663),* 4631 Harvey Dr., Mesquite, TX 75150-1609 (SAN 216-146X) Tel 214-686-5332; Dist. by: Liberal Pr., P.O. Box 160361, Las Colinas, TX 75016-9998 (SAN 200-5360) Tel 817-572-7409.

Ideals, *(Ideals Publishing Corp.; 0-89542; 0-8249),* Subs. of Thomas Nelson, Inc., Nelson Pl. at Elm Hill Pike, Nashville, TN 37214 (SAN 213-4403) Tel 615-889-9000; Toll free: 800-558-0740.

IDHHB
See Gateways Bks & Tapes

IEAS, *(Univ. of Califorma, Institute of East Asian Studies; 0-912966; 1-55729),* Pubns. Office, 2223 Fulton St., 6th Flr., Berkeley, CA 94720 (SAN 203-8730) Tel 415-643-6325.

Ignatius Pr, *(Ignatius Pr.; 0-89870),* Div. of Guadalupe Assocs., Inc., 2515 McAllister St., San Francisco, CA 94118 (SAN 214-3887) Tel 415-387-2324; Orders to: Ignatius Pr. Distribution Ctr., 15 Oakland Ave., Harrison, NY 10528 (SAN 289-0127) Tel 914-835-4216.

Igram Pr, *(Ingram Pr.; 0-911119),* 2020 16th Ave. SW, Cedar Rapids, IA 52404 (SAN 263-1709) Tel 319-366-5335.

IJP, *(Index to Jewish Periodicals; 0-939698),* P.O. Box 18570, Cleveland Heights, OH 44118 (SAN 204-8566) Tel 216-321-7296.

Illum Pr, *(Illuminations Pr.; 0-937088),* P.O. Box 126, St. Helena, CA 94574 (SAN 241-5445) Tel 707-963-9342.

Illum Way Pr
See IWP Pub

Impact Bks MO, *(Impact Bks., Inc.; 0-89228),* 137 W. Jefferson, Kirkwood, MO 63122 (SAN 214-0330) Tel 314-833-3309.

Impact Pr IL, *(Impact Press; 0-936872),* 6702 N. Sheridan Rd., Chicago, IL 60626 (SAN 213-9782) Tel 312-761-0682.

Imported Pubns, *(Imported Pubns., Inc.; 0-8285),* 320 W. Ohio St., Chicago, IL 60610 (SAN 169-1805) Tel 312-787-9017; Toll free: 800-345-2665.

Impresora Sahuaro, *(Impresora Sahuaro),* 7575 Sendero De Juana, Tucson, AZ 85718 (SAN 218-7760) Tel 602-297-3089.

Ind Christ Pubns, *(Independent Christian Pubns.; 0-915059),* P.O. Box 1970, Dunnellon, FL 32630 (SAN 289-9493) Tel 904-489-1982.

Ind Pubns, *(Independent Pubns.; 0-914937),* P.O. Box 162 Park Sta., Paterson, NJ 07543 (SAN 289-2464) Tel 201-943-7299.

Ind Sch Pr, *(Independent School Pr.; 0-88334),* 51 River St., Wellesley Hills, MA 02181 (SAN 203-8013) Tel 617-237-2591.

Ind U Mus
See W H Mathers Mus

Ind U Pr, *(Indiana Univ. Pr.; 0-253),* Tenth & Morton Sts., Bloomington, IN 47405 (SAN 202-5647) Tel 812-335-7681.

Ind U Res Ctr
See Res Ctr Lang Semiotic

Ind U Res Inst, *(Indiana Univ. Research Institute for Inner Asian Studies; 0-933070),* Goodbody Hall 344, Bloomington, IN 47405 (SAN 215-1553) Tel 812-335-1605.

Ind-US Inc, *(Ind-US, Inc.; 0-86578),* Box 56, East Glastonbury, CT 06025 (SAN 213-5809) Tel 203-663-0045.

Indian U Pr OK, *(Indian Univ. Pr.; 0-940392),* Div. of Bacone College, Bacone College, Muskogee, OK 74403 (SAN 217-1821) Tel 918-683-4581. Do not confuse with Ind U Pr Indiana.

Indiana Africa, *(Indian Univ., African Studies Program; 0-941934),* 221 Woodburn Hall Indiana University, Bloomington, IN 47405 (SAN 238-6135) Tel 812-335-8284.

Info Coord, *(Information Coord., Inc.; 0-911772; 0-89990),* 1435-37 Randolph St., Detroit, MI 48226 (SAN 206-7641) Tel 313-962-9720.

Information Coordinators
See Info Coord

Inner Tradit, *(Inner Traditions International, Ltd.; 0-89281),* 1 Park St., Rochester, VT 05767 (SAN 208-6948) Tel 802-767-3174; Orders to: Harper & Row Pubs., Inc., Keystone Industrial Pk., Scranton, PA 18512 (SAN 215-3742). *Imprints:* Destiny Bks (Destiny Books); Lindisfarne Pr (Lindisfarne Press).

InnerVision, *(InnerVision Publishing Co.; 0-917483),* 1218 Eaglewood Dr., Virginia Beach, VA 23454 (SAN 656-0709) Tel 804-425-2245.

Inquiry Pr, *(Inquiry Pr.; 0-918112),* 1880 N. Eastman, Midland, MI 48640 (SAN 208-1164) Tel 517-631-0009.

Ins Study Human, *(Institute for the Study of Human Knowledge),* P.O. Box 1062, Cambridge, MA 02238 (SAN 226-4536) Tel 617-497-4124; Toll free: 800-222-4745.
Insight Pr, *(Insight Pr., Inc.; 0-914520),* P.O. Box 8369, New Orleans, LA 70182 (SAN 202-6988).
Inspiration Conn, *(Inspiration House Pubs.; 0-918114),* P.O. Box 1, South Windsor, CT 06074 (SAN 206-1066) Tel 203-289-7363.
Inspiration MI, *(Inspiration Co.; 0-934804),* P. O. Box 17, Birmingham, MI 48012 (SAN 221-0738) Tel 313-642-4848.
Inst Adv Stud Wld, *(Institute for Advanced Studies of World Religions, The; 0-915078),* State University of New York, 5th Fl. Library, Stony Brook, NY 11794 (SAN 265-3885) Tel 516-632-6580.
Inst Am Music, *(Institute for Studies in American Music; 0-914678),* Brooklyn College, Conservatory of Music, Brooklyn, NY 11210 (SAN 202-6996) Tel 718-780-5655.
Inst Analysis, *(Institute for the Analysis, Evaluation & Design of Human Action; 0-938526),* 44 Clifford Ave., Pelham, NY 10803 (SAN 215-8752).
Inst Basic Youth, *(Institute in Basic Youth Conflicts; 0-916888),* P.O. Box 1, Oak Brook, IL 60521 (SAN 208-6972) Tel 312-323-9800.
Inst Biblical, *(Institute of Biblical Studies; 0-934743),* P.O. Box 34098, San Diego, CA 92103 (SAN 694-1672) Tel 619-291-7438.
Inst Byzantine, *(Institute for Byzantine & Modern Greek Studies, Inc.; 0-914744),* 115 Gilbert Rd., Belmont, MA 02178 (SAN 201-5110) Tel 617-484-6595.
Inst Christian, *(Institute for Christian Economics; 0-930464),* Affil. of American Bureau of Economic Research, P.O. Box 8000, Tyler, TX 75711 (SAN 297-1828) Tel 214-593-8919.
Inst Econ Finan, *(Institute for Economic & Financial Research; 0-86654; 0-918968),* Subs. of American Classical College, 607 McKnight St., NW, Albuquerque, NM 87102 (SAN 662-0450); Dist. by: American Classical College Pr., P.O. Box 4526, Albuquerque, NM 87196 (SAN 201-2618) Tel 505-843-7749.
Inst Econ Pol, *(Institute for Economic & Political World Strategic Studies; 0-930008; 0-86722),* Affil. of American Classical College, P.O. Box 4526, Sta. A, Albuquerque, NM 87106 (SAN 210-4431); 607 McKnight St., Albuquerque, NM 87102 (SAN 662-0469) Tel 505-843-7749.
Inst Evolutionary, *(Institute for Evolutionary Research; 0-938710),* 200 Park Ave., Suite 303 East, New York, NY 10166 (SAN 215-8760) Tel 212-687-0281; Orders to: P.O. Box 7404, Charlottesville, VA 22906 (SAN 662-0477) Tel 804-979-1270; Dist. by: DeVorss & Co., 1046 Princeton Dr., P.O. Box 550, Marina del Rey, CA 90294 (SAN 168-9886) Tel 213-870-7478; Dist. by: Samuel Weiser, Inc., P.O. Box 612, York Beach, ME 03910 (SAN 202-9588) Tel 207-363-4393.
Inst for the arts, *(Rice Univ., Institute for the Arts Catalogues; 0-914412),* Menil Foundation, 1511 Branard, Houston, TX 77006 (SAN 218-933X) Tel 713-525-9405.
Inst Hist Rev, *(Institute for Historical Review; 0-939484),* P.O. Box 1306, Torrance, CA 90505 (SAN 220-1275) Tel 213-533-8108.
Inst Human Growth, *(Institute for Human Growth & Awareness, The; 0-87852),* P.O. Box 6695, San Jose, CA 95150 (SAN 202-3636) Tel 408-275-1911.
Inst Jesuit, *(Institute of Jesuit Sources, The; 0-912422),* Fusz Memorial, Saint Louis Univ., 3700 W. Pine Blvd., Saint Louis, MO 63108 (SAN 202-7038) Tel 314-652-5737.
Inst Logo, *(Institute of Logotherapy Pr.; 0-917867),* Div. of Institute of Logotherapy, P.O. Box 156, Berkeley, CA 94704 (SAN 657-095X) Tel 415-845-2522; Orders to: P.O. Box 2852, Saratoga, CA 95070 (SAN 665-8466) Tel 408-292-4248.
Inst Mediaeval Mus, *(Institute of Mediaeval Music; 0-912024; 0-931902),* P.O. Box 295, Henryville, PA 18332 (SAN 658-0955) Tel 717-629-1278.
Inst Mennonite, *(Institute of Mennonite Studies; 0-936273),* 3003 Benham Ave., Elkhart, IN 46517 (SAN 697-8835) Tel 219-295-3726.
Inst Palestine, *(Institute for Palestine Studies; 0-88728),* P.O. Box 25697, Georgetown Sta., Washington, DC 20007 (SAN 207-611X) Tel 202-342-3990; Toll free: 800-874-3614.
Inst People's Church, *(Institute for a People's Church; 0-9612114),* 1051 N. Rademacher, Detroit, MI 48209 (SAN 287-7414) Tel 313-841-5885.
Inst Polynesian, *(Institute for Polynesian Studies, The; 0-939154),* Brigham Young Univ., Hawaii Campus, Laie, HI 96762 (SAN 219-1911) Tel 508-293-3667; Dist. by: Univ. of Hawaii Pr., 2840 Kolowalu St., Honolulu, HI 96822 (SAN 202-5353) Tel 808-948-8697.
Inst Rational-Emotive, *(Institute for Rational-Emotive Therapy; 0-917476),* 45 E. 65th St., New York, NY 10021 (SAN 210-3079) Tel 212-535-0822.
Inst Res Hist, *(Institute for Research in History, The; 0-913865),* 1133 Broadway, Rm. 923, New York, NY 10010 (SAN 286-780X) Tel 212-691-7316.
Inst Self Dev
See Mindbody Inc
Inst Soc Ethics
See Hastings Ctr
Inst Study Hum Aware, *(Institute for the Study of Human Awareness; 0-937067),* P.O. Box 11068, Minneapolis, MN 55411 (SAN 658-6112) Tel 612-522-1585; 3931 Sheridan Ave., N, Minneapolis, MN 55412 (SAN 658-6120). Do not confuse with Institute for the Study of Human Knowledge, Cambridge, MA, nor with Institute for the Study of Human Issues, Philadelphia, PA.
Inst Study Man, *(Institute for the Study of Man. Inc.),* 1133 13th St., NW, Suite Comm. 2, Washington, DC 20005 (SAN 213-523X) Tel 202-789-0231.
Inst Study Psych
See Inst Rational-Emotive
Inst Univ, *(Institute of Universal Faith; 0-916801),* P.O. Box 3732 Rd.3, Grove City, PA 16127 (SAN 654-5432) Tel 814-786-9085.
Integ Pr, *(Integration Pr.; 0-9609928),* 180 N. Oakland, Pasadena, CA 91101 (SAN 665-715X) Tel 818-584-5528.
Integral Pub, *(Integral Publishing; 0-941255),* P.O. Box 1030, Lower Lake, CA 95457 (SAN 665-5173); 12748 Perini Rd., Middletown, CA 95461 (SAN 665-5181) Tel 707-928-5751.
Integral Yoga Pubns, *(Integral Yoga Pubns.; 0-932040),* Satchidananda Ashram-Yogaville, Rte. 1, Box 172, Buckingham, VA 23921 (SAN 285-0338) Tel 804-969-4801.
Inter Print Pubs, *(Interstate Printers & Pubs., Inc.; 0-8134),* P.O. Box 50, Danville, IL 61834-0050 (SAN 658-0998) Tel 217-446-0500.
Inter-Religious Task, *(Inter-Religious Task Force for Social Analysis; 0-936476),* 361 Athol Ave., Oakland, CA 94606 (SAN 216-2563).
Inter-Varsity, *(Inter-Varsity Pr.; 0-87784; 0-8308),* Div. of Inter-Varsity Christian Fellowship of the USA, P.O. Box 1400, Downers Grove, IL 60515 (SAN 202-7089) Tel 312-964-5700; Toll free: 800-843-7225.
Interbk Inc, *(Interbook, Inc.; 0-913456; 0-89192),* 131 Varick St., 2nd Flr., New York, NY 10013 (SAN 202-7070) Tel 212-691-7248.
Interspace Bks, *(Interspace Bks.; 0-930061),* 4500 Chesapeake St., NW, Washington, DC 20016 (SAN 669-8913) Tel 202-363-9082.
Intersystems Pubns, *(Intersystems Pubns; 0-914105),* 401 Victor Way, No. 3, Salinas, CA 93907 (SAN 237-9619).
Intl Bk Ctr, *(International Bk. Ctr.; 0-917062; 0-86685),* 2007 Laurel Dr., P.O. Box 295, Troy, MI 48099 (SAN 169-4014) Tel 313-879-8436.
Intl Bk Dist, *(International Bk. Distributors; 0-86732),* P.O. Box 180, Murray Hill Sta., New York, NY 10016 (SAN 210-6337) Tel 212-683-3411.
Intl Comm Christ, *(International Community of Christ; 0-936202),* Pub. Dept. Chancellery, 643 Ralston St., Reno, NV 89503 (SAN 214-0373) Tel 702-786-7827.
Intl Ctr Arid & Semi-Arid, *(Texas Tech Univ., International Ctr. for Arid & Semi-Arid Land Studies),* P.O. Box 4620, Lubbock, TX 79409 (SAN 224-1609) Tel 806-742-2218.
Intl Evang, *(International Evangelism Crusade, Inc.; 0-933470),* 14617 Victory Blvd., Suite 4, Van Nuys, CA 91411 (SAN 203-8153) Tel 818-989-5942; Orders to: P.O. Box 73, Van Nuys, CA 91408 (SAN 688-3966).
Intl Imports, *(International Imports; 0-943832),* 8050 Webb Ave., North Hollywood, CA 91605-1504 (SAN 209-8202) Tel 818-768-0069.
Intl Learn Syst, *(International Learning Systems, Inc.),* 1715 Connecticut Ave., NW, Washington, DC 20009 (SAN 209-1615) Tel 202-232-4111.
Intl Liaison, *(International Liaison of Lay Volunteers in Mission, U. S. Catholic Network of Lay Mission Programs),* 810 Rhode Island Ave., NE, Washington, DC 20018 (SAN 234-7407) Tel 202-529-1100 (SAN 669-1226); 2451 Ridge Rd., Berkeley, CA 94709 (SAN 669-1234); Orders to: Int'l Liaison Business Office, 225 S. Euclid St., St. Louis, MO 63110 (SAN 663-6438) Tel 314-361-6124.
Intl Life Mess, *(International Life Message Inc.; 0-916075),* Nine Ruth Dr., New City, NY 10956 (SAN 294-846X) Tel 914-634-8980.
Intl Marriage, *(International Marriage Encounter, Inc.; 0-936098),* 955 Lake Dr., St. Paul, MN 55120 (SAN 215-6830).
Intl Pubs Co, *(International Pubs. Co.; 0-7178),* 381 Park Ave. S., Suite 1301, New York, NY 10016 (SAN 202-5655) Tel 212-685-2864.
Intl Rel Found
See Paragon Hse
Intl Schol Bk Serv
See Intl Spec Bk
Intl Spec Bk, *(International Specialized Bk. Services; 0-89955),* 5602 NE Hassalo St., Portland, OR 97213-3640 (SAN 169-7129) Tel 503-287-3093; Toll free: 800-547-7734.
Intl Univ Pr, *(International Univ. Pr.; 0-89697),* 1301 S. Noland Rd., Independence, MO 64055 (SAN 271-6291) Tel 816-461-3633.
Intl Univs Pr, *(International Univs. Pr., Inc.; 0-8236),* 59 Boston Post Rd., P.O. Box 1524, Madison, CT 06443-1524 (SAN 202-7186) Tel 203-245-4000.
Intl Yoga Soc
See Yoga Res Foun
Iona Pr, *(Iona Pr. Co., The; 0-910789),* P.O. Box C-3181, Wooster, OH 44691 (SAN 271-6666) Tel 216-262-8361.
Iowa St U Pr, *(Iowa State Univ. Pr.; 0-8138),* 2121 S. State Ave., Ames, IA 50010 (SAN 202-7194) Tel 515-292-0140.
Ipswich Pr, *(Ipswich Pr., The; 0-938864),* P.O. Box 291, Ipswich, MA 01938 (SAN 218-4826) Tel 617-426-3900.
Irish Am Cult, *(Irish American Cultural Institute, The; 0-9614900),* 683 Osceola, St. Paul, MN 55105 (SAN 225-3240) Tel 612-647-5678.
Irish Bk Ctr, *(Irish Bk. Ctr.),* 245 W. 104th St., New York, NY 10025 (SAN 209-1089) Tel 212-866-0309.
Irish Bks Media, *(Irish Bks. & Media; 0-937702),* 2115 Summit Ave. Box 5026, St. Paul, MN 55105 (SAN 215-1987) Tel 612-647-5545.
Irvington, *(Irvington Pubs.; 0-89197; 0-8290; 0-8422),* 740 Broadway, Suite 905, New York, NY 10003 (SAN 207-2408) Tel 212-777-4100.
ISHI PA, *(Institute for the Study of Human Issues; 0-89727; 0-915980),* 210 S. 13th St., Philadelphia, PA 19107 (SAN 207-6608) Tel 215-732-9729.
Islamic Ctr, *(Islamic Ctr. of America, the; 0-942778),* 15571 Joy Rd., Detroit, MI 48228 (SAN 240-2335) Tel 313-582-7442.
Islamic Prods, *(Islamic Productions International; 0-934894),* 739 E. Sixth St., Tucson, AZ 85719 (SAN 203-8625) Tel 602-791-3989.
Islamic Seminary, *(Islamic Seminary, The; 0-941724),* 50-11 Queens Blvd., Woodside, NY 11377 (SAN 239-2372) Tel 718-458-0924.
Island Heritage, *(Island Heritage; 0-89610),* 1819 Kahai St., Honolulu, HI 96819-3136 (SAN 211-1403) Tel 808-847-5566.
Ithaca Pr MA, *(Ithaca Pr.; 0-915940),* P.O. Box 853, Lowell, MA 01853 (SAN 208-709X) Tel 617-453-2177; Dist. by: Bookpeople, 2929 Fifth ST., Berkeley, CA 94710 (SAN 168-9517) Tel 415-549-3030.

IWP Pub, *(IWP Publishing; 0-914766; 0-88155),* Div. of Eckankar, P.O. Box 27200, Minneapolis, MN 55427 (SAN 203-798X).

J Blalock, *(Blalock, Jack; 0-9605156),* P.O. Box 8746, Pembroke Pines, FL 33084-0746 (SAN 215-8396).

J C Brown, *(Brown, John Carter, Library; 0-916617),* P.O. Box 1894, Providence, RI 02912 (SAN 203-6797) Tel 401-863-2725.

J C Print, *(J. C. Printing Co.),* Dawnsonville, GA 30534-0579 (SAN 211-0245) Tel 404-265-2036.

J C Tatham, *(Tatham, Julie Campbell; 0-9617543),* 1202 S. Washington St., Apt. 814, Alexandria, VA 22314 (SAN 664-4252) Tel 703-548-7825.

J Cordner, *(Cordner, John; 0-9617224),* 3712 35th Ave. SW, Seattle, WA 98126 (SAN 663-365X) Tel 206-935-8403.

J Countryman Pubs, *(Countryman, J., Pubs.; 0-937347),* 4420 FM 1960 W., Suite 120, Houston, TX 77068 (SAN 659-1523) Tel 214-630-4300.

J F Wine, *(Wine, J. F.; 0-9604350),* 924 Woodland Ave., Winchester, VA 22601 (SAN 206-0221) Tel 703-662-5735.

J Fankhauser, *(Fankhauser, Jerry; 0-9617006),* 2650 Fountainview, Suite 208, Houston, TX 77057 (SAN 662-5517) Tel 713-783-7264; Dist. by: DeVorss & Co., P.O. Box 550, 1046 Princeton Dr., Marina del Rey, CA 90294 (SAN 168-9886) Tel 213-870-7478; Dist. by: Miracle Pub. Co., 18 Charleston N., Sugar Land, TX 77478 (SAN 272-4618) Tel 713-242-4352.

J Freedman Liturgy, *(Freedman, Jacob, Liturgy Research Foundation),* P.O. Box 317, Forest Park Sta., Springfield, MA 01108 (SAN 207-7582).

J G Anderson
See Anderson Publ

J H Rose, *(Rose, Jack H.; 0-9617430),* 9218 Erie St., Apt. 3D, Highland, IN 46322 (SAN 663-9100) Tel 219-924-3639; Orders to: P.O. Box 9221, Highland, IN 46322 (SAN 665-9519).

J J Augustin, *(Augustin, J. J., Inc., Pub.; 0-87439),* 123 Buckram Rd., Locust Valley, NY 11560 (SAN 204-5451) Tel 516-676-1510.

J J Binns, *(Binns, Joseph J.; 0-89674),* 6919 Radnor Rd., Bethesda, MD 20817 (SAN 213-2095) Tel 301-320-3327; Toll free: 800-243-2790; Dist. by: Robert B. Luce, Inc., 540 Barnum Ave., Bridgeport, CT 06608 (SAN 201-1077) Tel 203-366-1900.

J L Pollnow, *(Pollnow, James L.; 0-9603708),* 1310 Aldersgate Rd., Little Rock, AR 72205 (SAN 213-8670).

J M Fontana, *(Fontana, John M., Pub.; 0-9600034),* 4 Walnut Pl., Huntington, NY 11743 (SAN 206-4235) Tel 516-549-0892.

J M Prods, *(JM Productions; 0-939298),* Box 1911, Brentwood, TN 37027 (SAN 216-4019) Tel 615-373-4814; Toll free: 800-528-8433; Dist. by: Spring Arbor Distributors, 10885 Textile Rd., Belleville, MI 48111 (SAN 158-9016) Tel 313-481-0900; Dist. by: Quality Bks., 918 Sherwood Dr., Lake Bluff, IL 60044-2204 (SAN 169-2127) Tel 312-295-2010; Dist. by: East Coast Christian Distributors, 35 Readington Rd., P.O. Box 4200, Somerville, NJ 08876 (SAN 169-491X) Tel 201-722-5050.

J Norton Pubs, *(Norton, Jeffrey, Pubs., Inc.; 0-88432),* On-the-Green, Guilford, CT 06437 (SAN 213-957X) Tel 203-453-9794; Toll free: 800-243-1234.

J P Tarcher, *(Tarcher, Jeremy P., Inc; 0-87477),* 9110 Sunset Blvd., Suite 250, Los Angeles, CA 90069 (SAN 202-0424) Tel 213-273-3274; Toll free: 800-225-3362; Dist. by: St. Martin's Pr., 175 Fifth Ave., New York, NY 10010 (SAN 200-2132) Tel 212-674-5151.

J Pohl Assocs, *(Pohl, J., Assocs.; 0-939332),* 461 Spring Run Rd., Coraopolis, PA 15108 (SAN 220-181X) Tel 412-457-6300.

J R Berry, *(Berry, John R., Evangelistic Assn.; 0-9616900),* P.O. Box 8252, Philadelphia, PA 19101 (SAN 661-4949); 5622 Florence Ave., Philadelphia, PA 19143 (SAN 661-4957) Tel 215-727-4325.

J R Simon, *(Simon, Jeffrey R., Publishing Co.; 0-916343),* P.O. Box 13390, Pittsburgh, PA 15243 (SAN 295-9801) Tel 412-279-6525.

J Simon, *(Simon, Joseph; 0-934710),* Div. of Pangloss Pr., Box 4071, Malibu, CA 90265 (SAN 213-9669); 29500 Heathercliff Rd., No. 161, Malibu, CA 90265 (SAN 662-1457) Tel 213-457-3293.

J Van Impe, *(Van Impe, Jack, Ministries; 0-934803),* 800 N. Crooks, Clawson, MI 48017 (SAN 697-3620).

Jacbar Pubns, *(Jacbar Pubns.; 0-9606154),* Box 103, Randolph, OH 44265 (SAN 217-1120).

Jacobs Ladder Pubns, *(Jacobs Ladder Pubns.; 0-933647),* 5003 Cascade Ct., Culver City, CA 90230 (SAN 692-6517) Tel 213-558-1166.

Jakubowsky, *(Jakubowsky; 0-932588),* 1565 Madison St., Oakland, CA 94612 (SAN 212-1034) Tel 415-763-4324.

Jalmar Pr, *(Jalmar Pr.; 0-915190; 0-9602214),* Subs. of B. L. Winch & Assocs., 45 Hitching Post Dr., Bldg. 2, Rolling Hills Estate, CA 90274-4297 (SAN 281-8302) Tel 213-539-6430; Toll free: 800-662-9662.

James Pr Inc, *(James Pr., Inc.; 0-9617280),* 4915 11th Ave., Brooklyn, NY 11219 (SAN 663-5229) Tel 718-853-3863; Orders to: Bookazine Co., 303 W. Tenth St., New York, NY 10014 (SAN 665-9462); Dist. by: Baker & Taylor, Eastern Div., 50 Kirby Ave, Somerville, NJ 08876 (SAN 665-9470) Tel 201-526-8000.

Jan Van Pubns, *(Jan Van Pubns.; 0-9616989),* 2101 Geer Rd., Suite 105A, Turlock, CA 95380 (SAN 661-731X) Tel 209-537-2447.

Japan Pubns USA, *(Japan Pubns. (USA), Inc.; 0-87040),* 45 Hawthorn Pl., Briarcliff Manor, NY 10510 (SAN 680-0513).

Jargon Soc, *(Jargon Society, Inc., The; 0-912330),* Highlands, NC 28741 (SAN 662-0515); Toll free: 800-243-0138; 1000 W. Fifth St., Winston-Salem, NC 28741 (SAN 662-0523); Dist. by: Inland Bk. Co., P.O. Box 261, 22 Hemingway Ave., East Haven, CT 06512 (SAN 200-4151) Tel 203-467-4257.

Jarrett, *(Jarrett, Richard Buhler; 0-9606884),* P.O. Box 6007, Suite 250, Redding, CA 96099 (SAN 217-3840).

JBR Pub, *(JBR Publishing Corp.; 0-931564),* P.O. Box 848, Park Forest, IL 60666 (SAN 211-7215) Tel 312-747-6311.

JCL Hse, *(JCL Hse.; 0-9610274),* P.O. Box 1821, East Lansing, MI 48823 (SAN 264-1305) Tel 616-385-2870.

JCMC Louisiana, *(JCMC; 0-940517),* Div. of Jewish Council Millennium Covenant, 1812 N. Hwy. 171 N., DeRidder, LA 70634 (SAN 664-5070) Tel 318-463-9594.

JCP Corp VA, *(JCP Corp. of Virginia; 0-938694),* P.O. Box 814, Virginia Beach, VA 23451 (SAN 220-1313) Tel 804-422-5426.

Jelm Mtn, *(Jelm Mountain Pubns.; 0-936204),* c/o Green Mountain Bk. Co., P.O. Box 338, Markleeville, CA 96120 (SAN 216-1419) Tel 916-694-2141.

Jenkins, *(Jenkins Publishing Co.; 0-8363),* Affil. of Chamber of Commerce, P.O. Box 2085, Austin, TX 78768 (SAN 202-7321) Tel 512-444-6616.

Jenna Pr, *(Jenna Pr.; 0-941752),* 37 W. Eighth St., New York, NY 10011 (SAN 293-2881) Tel 212-477-4471; R.D. 1, Box 227, Petersburg, NY 12138 (SAN 293-289X).

Jesuit Bks, *(Jesuit Bks.; 0-913452),* 2300 S. Washington St., Tacoma, WA 98405 (SAN 201-0232) Tel 206-752-3594; Dist. by: Baker & Taylor, Western Div., 380 Edison Way, Reno, NV 89564 (SAN 169-4464) Tel 702-786-6700; Dist. by: Baker & Taylor, Midwest Div., 501 Gladiola, Momence, IL 60954 (SAN 169-2127); Dist. by: Quality Bks., Inc., 918 Sherwood Dr., Lake Bluff, IL 60044-2204 (SAN 666-6620) Tel 312-295-2010

Jesuit Hist, *(Loyola Univ. Pr., Jesuit Historical Institute),* 3441 N. Ashland Ave., Chicago, IL 60657 (SAN 662-0531) Tel 312-281-1818; Toll free: 800-621-1008 (SAN 211-6537).

Jesuits Holy Cross, *(Jesuits of Holy Cross College, Inc.; 0-9606294),* College of the Holy Cross, Worcester, MA 01610 (SAN 210-1211) Tel 617-793-2011.

Jesus-First, *(Jesus-First Pubs., Inc.; 0-9602440),* 1116-4th St., NW, Ruskin, FL 33570 (SAN 212-3630) Tel 813-645-5726.

Jewel Pr, *(Jewel Pr.; 0-937093),* Div. of Jewel Communications International, P.O. Box 1833, Fort Collins, CO 80522 (SAN 658-6139) Tel 303-226-5914; Orders to: P.O. Box 904, Fort Collins, CO 80522 (SAN 662-4146).

Jewel Pub Hse, *(Jewel Publishing Hse.; 0-9607000),* P.O. Box 146, New York, NY 10002 (SAN 241-5879).

Jewel Pubns, *(Jewel Pubns.; 0-917728),* 2417 Hazelwood Ave., Fort Wayne, IN 46805 (SAN 209-3049) Tel 219-483-6625.

Jewish Bd Family, *(Jewish Board of Family & Children's Services, Library Inc.),* c/o Central Library, 120 W. 57th St., New York, NY 10019 (SAN 211-9080) Tel 212-582-9100.

Jewish Bk Council
See JWB

Jewish Com Pub, *(Jewish Combatants Pubs. House, Inc.; 0-9613219),* P.O. Box 323, Brooklyn, NY 11236 (SAN 295-8821) Tel 718-763-7551.

Jewish Comm Ctr, *(Jewish Community Ctr. of Greater Boston; 0-9605624),* 333 Nahanton St., Newton, MA 02159 (SAN 218-4842).

Jewish Hist, *(Jewish Historical Society of New York, Inc.; 0-916790),* 8 W. 70th St., New York, NY 10023 (SAN 208-7146) Tel 212-873-0300.

Jewish Mens Clubs
See Fed Jewish Mens Clubs

Jewish Pubns, *(Jewish Pubns. Society of America; 0-8276),* 1930 Chestnut St., Philadelphia, PA 19103 (SAN 201-0240) Tel 215-564-5925.

Jewish Sem, *(Jewish Theological Seminary of America; 0-87334),* 3080 Broadway, New York, NY 10027 (SAN 204-9902) Tel 212-678-8000; Dist. by: KTAV Publishing Co., 900 Jefferson St., Box 6249, Hoboken, NJ 07030-7205 (SAN 200-8866) Tel 201-963-9524.

JFJ Pub, *(JFJ Publishing; 0-9616148),* Div. of Jews for Jesus, 60 Haight St., San Francisco, CA 94102 (SAN 699-8240); Toll free: 800-227-3190.

JLJ Pubs, *(JLJ Pubs.; 0-937172),* P.O. Box 1345, Springfield, OH 45501-1345 (SAN 215-322X) Tel 513-322-4454.

John Alden Bks, *(Alden, John, Bks.; 0-9605818),* 187 Barmont Dr., P.O. Box 26668, Rochester, NY 14626 (SAN 216-5678) Tel 716-225-8534.

John Knox, *(Knox, John, Pr.; 0-8042),* Div. of Presbyterian Publishing Hse., 341 Ponce de Leon Ave., NE, Rm. 416, Atlanta, GA 30365 (SAN 201-0275) Tel 404-873-1549; Orders to: P.O. Box 54658, Atlanta, GA 30308 (SAN 662-0566).

Johns Hopkins, *(Johns Hopkins Univ. Pr.; 0-8018),* 701 W. 40th St., Suite 275, Baltimore, MD 21211 (SAN 202-7348) Tel 301-338-6956.

Johnson Chi, *(Johnson Publishing Co., Inc.; 0-87485),* 820 S. Michigan Ave., Chicago, IL 60605 (SAN 201-0305) Tel 312-322-9248.

Johnson NC, *(Johnson Publishing Co.; 0-930230),* P. O. Box 217, Murfreesboro, NC 27855 (SAN 201-0291).

Johnson Repr, *(Johnson Reprint Corp.; 0-384),* Subs. of Harcourt, Brace, Jovanovich, Inc., 111 Fifth Ave., New York, NY 10003 (SAN 285-0362) Tel 212-614-3150.

Johnston Pub, *(Johnston Publishing, Inc.; 0-942934),* Box 96, Afton, MN 55001 (SAN 240-3900) Tel 612-436-7344.

Joi Prod Enter, *(Joi Production Enterprises; 0-9616294),* 9111 Third Ave., Inglewood, CA 90305 (SAN 658-5590) Tel 213-753-1222.

Jonathan David, *(Jonathan David Pubs., Inc.; 0-8246),* 68-22 Eliot Ave., Middle Village, NY 11379 (SAN 169-5274) Tel 718-456-8611.

Jonathan Pubns, *(Jonathan Pubns.; 0-9603348),* 660 Prospect Ave., Hartford, CT 06105 (SAN 213-330X) Tel 203-523-7587.

Jordan & Co
See JCP Corp VA

Joseph Pub Co, *(Joseph Publishing Co.; 0-915878),* P.O. Box 770, San Mateo, CA 94401 (SAN 207-8538) Tel 415-345-4100.

Joshua I Minist, *(Joshua I Ministries, Inc.; 0-939313),* 50 Coe Rd., Suite 223, Belleair, FL 33516 (SAN 663-1398) Tel 813-442-5535.

Jossey Bass, *(Jossey-Bass, Inc., Pubs.; 0-87589; 1-55542),* 433 California St., San Francisco, CA 94104 (SAN 201-033X) Tel 415-433-1740.
Journal Printing, *(Journal Printing Co.; 0-9613631),* 709 N. Davis St., Kirksville, MO 63501 (SAN 670-8838) Tel 816-665-4082; Dist. by: First United Methodist Church, 300 E. Washington St., Kirksville, MO 63501 (SAN 200-7460) Tel 816-665-7712.
Journey Pubns, *(Journey Pubns.; 0-918038),* P.O. Box 423, Woodstock, NY 12498 (SAN 209-570X) Tel 914-657-8434.
Jove Pubns, *(Jove Pubns., Inc.; 0-515),* Div. of Berkley/Jove Pub. Group, 200 Madison Ave., New York, NY 10016 (SAN 215-8817) Tel 212-686-9820; Toll free: 800-223-0510; Dist. by: Kable News Co., Inc., 777 Third Ave., New York, NY 10017 (SAN 169-5835) Tel 212-371-5321.
Joyce Media, *(Joyce Media Inc.; 0-917002),* P.O. Box 57, Action, CA 93510 (SAN 208-7197) Tel 805-269-1169.
Joyce Motion Pict
See Joyce Media
Joyful Woman, *(Joyful Woman, The; 0-912623),* Div. of Joyful Christian Ministries, P.O. Box 90028, Chatanooga, TN 37412 (SAN 282-8073).
Jubilee Pr, *(Jubilee Pr., Inc.; 0-9609674),* 7906 Hillside Ave., Los Angeles, CA 90046 (SAN 262-7663) Tel 213-851-5893; Dist. by: Bookslinger, 213 E. Fourth St., Saint Paul, MN 55101 (SAN 169-4154) Tel 612-221-0429; Dist. by: New Leaf Distributing, 1020 White St., SW, Atlanta, GA 30310 (SAN 169-1449) Tel 404-755-2665; Dist. by: DeVorss & Co., P.O. Box 550, Marina del Rey, CA 90291 (SAN 168-9886) Tel 213-870-7478; Dist. by: Book Dynamics, 836 Broadway, New York, NY 10003 (SAN 169-5649) Tel 212-254-7798.
Judaica Pr, *(Judaica Pr., Inc.; 0-910818),* 521 Fifth Ave., New York, NY 10175 (SAN 204-9856) Tel 212-260-0520.
Judson, *(Judson Pr.; 0-8170),* Div. of American Baptist Churches, U.S.A., P.O. Box 851, Valley Forge, PA 19482-0851 (SAN 201-0348) Tel 215-768-2119; Toll free: 800-331-1053.
Julian Pr. *Imprint of* **Crown**
JWB, *(JWB; 0-914820),* 15 E. 26th St., New York, NY 10010 (SAN 203-9060) Tel 212-532-4949.
JWB Jewish Bk Coun
See JWB
K & S, *(Kapilla, Cleo, & Eleanor Simons; 0-9611466),* P.O. Box 4995, Ocala, FL 32678 (SAN 277-6928) Tel 904-622-4914.
K-Dimension, *(K-Dimension Pubs.; 0-917595),* Div. of Chapel Hill Horvester Church, P.O. Box 371289, Decatur, GA 30037 (SAN 657-1484) Tel 404-241-1565; Toll free: 800-241-4702.
K G Saur, *(Saur, K. G., Inc.; 0-89664; 0-86291; 3-598; 3-7940),* Subs. of K. G. Saur Verlag, 175 Fifth Ave., New York, NY 10010 (SAN 214-1264) Tel 212-982-1302.
K G Wilks, *(Wilks, Karl Glyn; 0-9616912),* 528 N. Main St., McGregor, TX 76657 (SAN 661-521X) Tel 817-840-4503.
K Q Assocs, *(K-Q Assocs., Inc.; 0-941988),* P.O. Box 2132, Cedar Rapids, IA 52406 (SAN 238-4655).
Kaaikaula, *(Kaaikaula, Hale Pa'I O; 0-914599),* P.O. Box 26448, Honolulu, HI 96825-0078 (SAN 289-3207) Tel 808-373-4430.
Kahn & Kahan, *(Kahn & Kahan Publishing Co., Inc.; 0-9604286),* 31 South St., P.O. Box 661, Morristown, NJ 07960 (SAN 214-2597).
Kaihong, *(Kaihong; 0-940446),* P.O. Box 1706, MPK, Los Angeles, CA 91754-1706 (SAN 218-4850).
Kalimat, *(Kalimat Pr.; 0-933770),* 1600 Sawtelle Blvd., Suite 34, Los Angeles, CA 90025 (SAN 213-7666) Tel 213-479-5668.
Kansas St Hist, *(Kansas State Historical Society; 0-87726),* Center for Historical Research, 120 W. Tenth St., Topeka, KS 66612 (SAN 207-0014) Tel 913-296-4784.
Kappeler Inst Pub, *(Kappeler Institute Publishing; 0-942958),* Div. of Kappeler Institute for the Science of Being, 2019 Delaware Ave., Wilmington, DE 19806 (SAN 240-1185) Tel 302-571-9570; Dist. by: Rare Bk. Co., P.O. Box 957, Freehold, NJ 07728 (SAN 205-0978) Tel 201-780-1393.
Kar Ben, *(Kar-Ben Copies, Inc.; 0-930494),* 6800 Tildenwood Ln., Rockville, MD 20852 (SAN 210-7511) Tel 301-984-8733; Toll free: 800-452-7236.
Karma Pub, *(Karma Publishing Co.; 0-9604568),* 4404 Pennsylvania Ave., Pittsburgh, PA 15224 (SAN 238-888X).
Karoma, *(Karoma Pubs., Inc.; 0-89720),* 3400 Daleview Dr., Ann Arbor, MI 48105 (SAN 213-8131) Tel 313-665-3331; Toll free: 800-521-0334.
Kavanagh, *(Kavanagh, Peter, Hand Pr.; 0-914612),* 250 E. 30th St., New York, NY 10016 (SAN 205-6291) Tel 212-686-5099.
Kazi Pubns, *(Kazi Pubns.; 0-935782; 0-933511),* 3023 W. Belmont Ave., Chicago, IL 60618 (SAN 162-3397) Tel 312-267-7001.
KC Pubns, *(KC Pubns.; 0-916122; 0-88714),* P.O. Box 14883, Las Vegas, NV 89114 (SAN 201-0364); Toll free: 800-626-9673; 2901 Industrial Rd., Las Vegas, NV 89109 (SAN 658-103X) Tel 702-731-3123.
KDK Pubns, *(KDK Pubns.; 0-910165),* 1892 Fell St., San Francisco, CA 94117 (SAN 241-2144) Tel 415-386-9656; 4905 Nectar Way, Eugene, OR 97405 (SAN 663-6462) Tel 503-345-0293; Dist. by: Bookpeople, 2929 Fifth St., Berkeley, CA 94710 (SAN 168-9517) Tel 415-599-3030; Dist. by: Great Tradition, 750 Adrian Way, Suite 111, San Rafael, CA 94903 (SAN 200-5743); Dist. by: Snow Lion Pubns., P.O. Box 6483, Ithaca, NY 14851 (SAN 281-7292).
Keats, *(Keats Publishing, Inc.; 0-87983),* P. O. Box 876, New Canaan, CT 06840 (SAN 201-0410) Tel 203-966-8721.
Keeble Pr, *(Keeble Pr., The; 0-933144),* 3634 Winchell Rd., Shaker Heights, OH 44122 (SAN 214-249X) Tel 216-283-8245.
Kelley, *(Kelley, Augustus M., Pubs.; 0-678),* 1140 Broadway, Rm. 901, New York, NY 10001 (SAN 206-975X) Tel 212-685-7202; Orders to: 300 Fairfield Rd., P.O. Box 1308, Fairfield, NJ 07006-0008 (SAN 206-9768). *Imprints:* Reference Bk Pubs (Reference Book Publishers).
Kendall-Hunt, *(Kendall/Hunt Publishing Co.; 0-8403),* Subs. of Wm. C. Brown Co., Pubs., 2460 Kerper Blvd., Dubuque, IA 52001 (SAN 203-9184) Tel 319-589-2833.
Kennikat Pr
See Assoc Faculty Pr
Kent Pubns, *(Kent Pubns.; 0-917458),* 18301 Halstead St., Northridge, CA 91325 (SAN 209-0597) Tel 818-349-2080.
Kent St U Pr, *(Kent State Univ. Pr.; 0-87338),* Kent, OH 44242 (SAN 201-0437) Tel 216-672-7913; Toll free: 800-872-5368; Toll free: 800-367-5368 (in OH); Orders to: 101 Franklin Hall, Kent, OH (SAN 215-3742); Dist. by: Harper & Row, Inc., Keystone Industrial Pk., Scranton, PA 18512 (SAN 282-3993).
Kenyon, *(Kenyon Pubns.; 0-934286),* 361 Pin Oak Ln., Westbury, NY 11590 (SAN 201-5072) Tel 516-333-3236; Dist. by: Hal Leonard Publshing Corp., 8112 W. Bluemound Rd., Box 13819, Milwaukee, WI 53213 (SAN 239-250X) Tel 414-774-3630.
Kesher, *(Kesher Pr.; 0-9602394),* 1817 21st Ave., S., Nashville, TN 37212 (SAN 212-6761).
Key of David, *(Key of David Pubns.; 0-943374),* 222 N. 17th, Philadelphia, PA 19103 (SAN 239-4480) Tel 215-664-4673.
Khaneghah & Maktab, *(Khaneghah & Maktab of Maleknia Naseralishah; 0-917220),* P.O. Box 665, Palisades, NY 10964 (SAN 208-5046) Tel 914-359-7547.
KhaniQahi-Nimatullahi-Sufi, *(KhaniQahi-Nimatullahi, Sufi Order; 0-933546),* 306 W. 11th St., New York, NY 10014 (SAN 212-3673) Tel 212-924-7739; Dist. by: Samuel Weiser, Inc., P.O. Box 612, York Beach, ME 03910 (SAN 202-9588) Tel 207-363-4393; Dist. by: The New Leaf Distributing, 1020 White St., SW, Atlanta, GA 30310 (SAN 169-1449) Tel 404-755-2665.
Kimbell Art, *(Kimbell Art Museum; 0-912804),* 3333 Camp Bowie Blvd., P.O. Box 9440, Ft. Worth, TX 76107 (SAN 208-0516) Tel 817-332-8451; Dist. by: Univ. of Washington Pr., P.O. Box C-50096, Seattle, WA 98145-5096 (SAN 212-2502) Tel 206-543-8870; Dist. by: Harry N. Abrams, Inc., 100 Fifth Ave., New York, NY 10011 (SAN 200-2434) Tel 212-206-7715.
Kindred Pr, *(Kindred Pr.; 0-9606436),* Box L, Hillsboro, KS 67063 (SAN 205-8634) Tel 316-947-3151; Orders to: 616 Walnut Ave., Scottdale, PA 15683 (SAN 202-2915) Tel 412-887-8500. Publishing arm of Pacific District Mennonite Brethren Churches, Family Commission.
Kingdom, *(Kingdom Pr.; 0-910840),* 105 Chestnut Hill Rd., Amherst, NH 03031 (SAN 201-0461) Tel 603-673-3208.
Kingdom Bks, *(Kingdom Bks.; 0-9613181),* 18548 Arminta St., Reseda, CA 91335 (SAN 295-902X) Tel 818-342-8740.
Kingdom God, *(Kingdom of God; 0-9607702),* P.O. Box 7123, Minneapolis, MN 55407 (SAN 238-6704) Tel 612-823-1783.
King's Crown Paperbacks *Imprint of* **Columbia U Pr**
Kings Farspan, *(King's Farspan, Inc.; 0-932814),* 1473 S. La Luna Ave., Ojai, CA 93023 (SAN 211-8084) Tel 805-646-2928; Dist. by: Spring Arbor Distributors, 10885 Textile Rd., Bellville, MI 48111 (SAN 158-9016) Tel 313-481-0900; Dist. by: Living Bks., Inc., 12155 Magnolia Ave., Bldg 11-B, Riverside, CA 92503 (SAN 169-006X) Tel 714-354-7330.
King's Hse Pub, *(King's Hse. Publishing Co.; 0-916333),* 3000 Fairfield at Kings Hwy., Shreveport, LA 71104 (SAN 295-9046) Tel 318-222-1995.
Kingston Pr, *(Kingston Pr., Inc., The; 0-940670),* P.O. Box 1456, Princeton, NJ 08542 (SAN 226-7950) Tel 609-921-0609.
Kirban, *(Kirban, Salem, Inc.; 0-912582),* 2117 Kent Rd., Huntingdon Valley, PA 19006 (SAN 201-047X) Tel 215-947-4894; Dist. by: AMG Pubs., 6815 Shallowford Rd., Chattanooga, TN 37422 (SAN 211-3074) Tel 615-894-6062.
Kitchen Sink, *(Kitchen Sink Pr.; 0-87816),* 2 Swamp Rd., Princeton, WI 54968 (SAN 212-7784) Tel 414-295-6922.
Kjos, *(Kjos, Neil A., Music Co.; 0-910842; 0-8497),* 4380 Jutland Dr., San Diego, CA 92117-0894 (SAN 201-0488) Tel 619-270-9800; Toll free: 800-854-1592.
Klock & Klock, *(Klock & Klock Christian Pubs.; 0-86524),* 2527 Girard Ave. N., Minneapolis, MN 55411 (SAN 212-0003) Tel 612-522-2244.
Kluwer Academic, *(Kluwer Academic Pubs.; 0-89838),* Subs. of Kluwer NV, 101 Philip Dr., Assinippi Pk., Norwell, MA 02061 (SAN 211-481X) Tel 617-871-6600; Orders to: P.O. Box 358, Accord Sta., Hingham, MA 02018-9990 (SAN 662-0647).
Kluwer-Nijhoff, *(Kluwer-Nijhoff Publishing; 0-89838; 90-247),* Div. of Kluwer Academic Pubs., 101 Philip Dr., Assinipi Pk., Norwell, MA 02061 (SAN 211-481X) Tel 617-871-6600; Orders to: P.O. Box 358, Accord Sta., Hingham, MA 02018-0358 (SAN 662-0655).
Knight Media, *(Knight Media; 0-933545),* 60 Benzing Rd., Antioch, TN 37013 (SAN 691-8689) Tel 615-833-1909; Dist. by: JM Pubns., P.O. Box 837, Brentwood, TN 37027 (SAN 200-7975).
Knopf, *(Knopf, Alfred A., Inc.; 0-394),* Subs. of Random Hse., Inc., 201 E. 50th St., New York, NY 10022 (SAN 202-5825) Tel 212-751-2600; Toll free: 800-638-6460; Orders to: 400 Hahn Rd., Westminster, MD 21157 (SAN 202-5833).
Know Him Pr, *(Know Himm Pr.; 0-9614014),* 13425 Valna Dr., Whittier, CA 90602 (SAN 683-6542) Tel 213-693-9118; Orders to: P.O. Box 4002, Whittier, CA 90607 (SAN 662-2615) Tel 213-693-7412; Dist. by: Living Bks., Inc., 12155 Magnolia Ave., Bldg 11-B, Riverside, CA 92503 (SAN 169-006X) Tel 714-354-7330.
Kober Pr, *(Kober Press, The; 0-915034),* P.O. Box 2194, San Francisco, CA 94126 (SAN 207-0758) Tel 415-540-7309.

Kodansha, *(Kodansha International USA, Ltd.; 0-87011),* Subs. of Kodansha, Ltd. (Japan), c/o Harper & Row Pubs., 10 E. 53rd St., New York, NY 10022 (SAN 201-0526) Tel 212-207-7050; Toll free: 800-242-7737; Dist. by: Harper & Row Pubs., Inc., Keystone Industrial Pk., Scranton, PA 18512 (SAN 215-3742); Orders to: Mail Order Dept., P.O. Box 1531, Hagerstown, MD 21741 (SAN 662-0671).
Kosciuszko, *(Kosciuszko Foundation; 0-917004),* 15 E. 65th St., New York, NY 10021 (SAN 208-7251) Tel 212-734-2130.
Kosovo Pub Co, *(Kosovo Publishing Co.; 0-915887),* 1404 Norma Rd., Columbus, OH 43229 (SAN 294-0531) Tel 614-885-5977; 604 S. Hanover St., Nanticoko, PA 18634 (SAN 294-054X).
Kraus Intl, *(Kraus International Pubns.; 0-527),* Div. of Kraus-Thomson Organization, Ltd., 1 Water St., White Plains, NY 10601 (SAN 210-7562) Tel 914-761-9600.
Kraus Repr, *(Kraus Reprint & Periodicals; 0-527; 3-601; 3-262; 0-8115),* Rte. 100, Millwood, NY 10546 (SAN 201-0542) Tel 914-762-2200.
Kregel, *(Kregel Pubns.; 0-8254),* Div. of Kregel, Inc., P.O. Box 2607, Grand Rapids, MI 49501-2607 (SAN 206-9792) Tel 616-451-4775; Toll free: 800-253-5465.
Krieger, *(Krieger, Robert E., Publishing Co., Inc.; 0-88275; 0-89874; 0-89464),* P.O. Box 9542, Melbourne, FL 32902-9542 (SAN 202-6562) Tel 305-724-9542.
Kripalu Pubns, *(Kripalu Pubns.; 0-940258),* Div. of Kripalu Ctr. for Yoga & Health, Rte. 183, Box 793, Lenox, MA 01240 (SAN 217-5320) Tel 413-637-3280; Dist. by: Samuel Weiser, P.O. Box 612, York Beach, ME 03910 (SAN 202-9588) Tel 207-363-4393; Dist. by: The New Leaf Distributing, 1020 White St., SW, Atlanta, GA 30310 (SAN 169-1449) Tel 404-755-2665.
Krishna Pr, *(Krishna Pr.),* Div. of Gordon Press, P.O. Box 459, Bowling Green Sta., New York, NY 10004 (SAN 202-6570).
KSU, *(Kansas State Univ.),* Kansas State Univ. Libraries, Manhattan, KS 66506 (SAN 665-7265) Tel 913-532-6516; Orders to: Library Pubns., Kansas State Univ. Library, Manhattan, KS 66506 (SAN 210-1483).
Ktav, *(Ktav Publishing Hse., Inc.; 0-87068; 0-88125),* Box 6249, Hoboken, NJ 07030 (SAN 201-0038); 900 Jefferson St., Hoboken, NJ 07030 (SAN 200-8866) Tel 201-963-9524. *Imprints:* HUC Pr (Hebrew Union College Press).
Kudzu, *(Kudzu & Co.; 0-9615015),* Box 415, Walls, MS 38680 (SAN 693-823X) Tel 601-781-0267.
Kumarian Pr, *(Kumarian Pr.; 0-931816),* 630 Oakwood Ave., Suite 119, West Hartford, CT 06110 (SAN 212-5978) Tel 203-524-0214.
Kurios Found, *(Kurios Foundation; 0-932210),* P.O. Box 946, Bryn Mawr, PA 19010 (SAN 213-1005) Tel 215-527-4635.
L Amiel Pub, *(Amiel, Leon, Pub.; 0-8148),* 31 W. 46th St., New York, NY 10036 (SAN 207-0766) Tel 212-575-0010; Orders to: 225 Secaucus Rd., Secaucus, NJ 07094 (SAN 665-6501) Tel 201-865-9200.
L De Waters, *(DeWaters, Lillian, Pubns.),* Old Greenwich, CT 06870 (SAN 203-8633) Tel 203-637-0658.
L Erlbaum Assocs, *(Erlbaum, Lawrence, Assocs., Inc.; 0-89859; 0-8058),* 365 Broadway, Hillsdale, NJ 07642 (SAN 213-960X) Tel 201-666-4110.
L Imperio, *(Imperio, Leroy; 0-9609302),* Rte. 1, Box 222-C, Burlington, WV 26241 (SAN 241-5224) Tel 304-636-3434.
L Kempfer, *(Kempfer, Lester L.),* P.O. Box 317, Marysville, OH 43040 (SAN 201-0569).
L M Campbell, *(Campbell, Lucile M.; 0-9607114),* c/o Mrs. Joe Richardson, 615 Sixth Ave. SW, Decatur, AL 35601 (SAN 238-9592) Tel 205-355-8895.
L Orr, *(Orr, Leonard),* Orders to: Inspiration Univ., P.O. Box 234, Sierraville, CA 96126 (SAN 207-2505) Tel 916-994-8984.
L P Pubns, *(L P Pubns.; 0-916192),* Div. of Love Project, P.O. Box 7601, San Diego, CA 92107-0601 (SAN 207-2513); 4470 Orchard Ave., San Diego, CA 92107 (SAN 650-0390) Tel 619-225-0133.
L Victor Pr, *(Leo Victor Press; 0-9606562),* 2203 Brandenburg Way, King of Prussia, PA 19406 (SAN 213-3970).
LA Co Art Mus, *(Los Angeles County Museum of Art; 0-87587),* 5905 Wilshire Blvd., Los Angeles, CA 90036 (SAN 201-0577) Tel 213-857-6044.
La Mariposa, *(La Mariposa Pr.; 0-9613714),* P.O. Box 6117, Mesa, AZ 85206 (SAN 676-2670) Tel 602-981-8747.
La Siesta, *(La Siesta Pr.; 0-910856),* P.O. Box 406, Glendale, CA 91209 (SAN 201-0607) Tel 818-244-9305.
La State U Pr, *(Louisiana State Univ. Pr.; 0-8071),* Highland Rd., Baton Rouge, LA 70893 (SAN 202-6597) Tel 504-388-6666.
Labyrinth Pr, *(Labyrinth Pr., Inc., The; 0-939464),* P.O. Box 2124, Durham, NC 27702-2124 (SAN 216-6011); 2814 Chapel Hill Rd., Durham, NC 27707 (SAN 281-8620) Tel 919-493-5051.
Labyrinthos, *(Labyrinthos; 0-911437),* 6355 Green Valley Cir., Suite 213, Culver City, CA 90230 (SAN 217-3182) Tel 213-649-2612.
Lacon Pubs, *(Lacon Pubs.; 0-930344),* Rte. 1, Box 15, Harrison, ID 83833 (SAN 204-9597) Tel 208-689-3467.
Lambert Bk, *(Lambert Bk. Hse., Inc.; 0-89315),* 133 Kings Hwy., Shreveport, LA 71104 (SAN 208-7278) Tel 318-861-3140; Box 4007, Shreveport, LA 71104 (SAN 658-1064).
Lambeth Pr, *(Lambeth Pr.; 0-931186),* 143 E. 37th St., New York, NY 10016 (SAN 240-0421) Tel 212-679-0163.
Lampus Pr, *(Lampus Pr.; 0-9609002),* P.O. Box 541, Cape May, NJ 08204 (SAN 240-8643) Tel 609-884-4906.
Land & Land, *(Land & Land Publishing Div.; 0-935545),* 196 S. 14th St., Baton Rouge, LA 70802 (SAN 696-2386) Tel 504-344-1059; P.O. Box 1921, Baton Rouge, LA 70821 (SAN 696-964X).
Landmark Pr GA, *(Landmark Pr.; 0-9617493),* Affil. of Landmark Church, P.O. Box 364, Alpharetta, GA 30201 (SAN 664-1814) Rte. 4, Liberty Grove Rd., Alpharetta, GA 30201 (SAN 664-1822) Tel 404-475-4977. Do not confuse with Landmark Pr. in St. Louis, MO, Austin, TX, St. Ann, MO.
Landsberry Pr, *(Landsberry Pr.; 0-9616788),* 709 Massachusetts Ave., NE, Washington, DC 20002 (SAN 661-3128) Tel 202-387-3826.
Lane
See Sunset-Lane
Langdon Pubns, *(Langdon, Larry, Pubns.; 0-943726),* 34735 Perkins Creek Rd., Cottage Grove, OR 97424-9450 (SAN 241-0427).
Langenscheidt, *(Langenscheidt Pubs., Inc.; 0-88729; 3-468),* Subs. of Langenscheidt KG, 46-35 54th Rd., Maspeth, NY 11378 (SAN 276-9441) Tel 718-784-0055.
Langtry Pubns, *(Langtry Pubns.; 0-915369),* 7838 Burnet Ave., Van Nuys, CA 91405-1051 (SAN 291-2473) Tel 818-781-9144.
Large Print Bks *Imprint of* **G K Hall**
Larksdale, *(Larksdale; 0-89896),* 1706 Seamist, No. 575, Houston, TX 77008 (SAN 220-0643) Tel 713-869-9092. *Imprints:* Linolean Pr (Linolean Press).
Larlin Corp, *(Larlin Corp.; 0-89783; 0-87797; 0-87419),* P.O. Box 1523, Marietta, GA 30061 (SAN 201-4432) Tel 404-424-6210. *Imprints:* U Pr of Wash (University Press of Washington, DC).
Larson Pubns Inc, *(Larson Pubns., Inc.; 0-943914),* 4936 Rte. 414, Burdett, NY 14818 (SAN 241-130X) Tel 607-546-9342; Dist. by: Kampmann & Co., 9 E. 40th St., New York, NY 10016 (SAN 202-5191) Tel 212-685-2928; Dist. by: Samuel Weiser Inc., P.O. Box 612, York Beach, ME 03910 (SAN 202-9588) Tel 207-363-4393; Dist. by: New Leaf Distributing, The, 1020 White St., SW, Atlanta, GA 30310 (SAN 169-1449) Tel 404-755-2665; Dist. by: Bookpeople, 2929 Fifth St., Berkeley, CA 94710 (SAN 168-9517) Tel 415-549-3030.
Last Things, *(Last Things Pr.; 0-9616435),* P.O. Box 22642, Alexandria, VA 22304 (SAN 658-9235) Tel 202-274-6867; 5340 Holmes Run, No. 212, Alexandria, VA 22304 (SAN 658-9243).
Lat Am Jewish Studies, *(Latin American Jewish Studies Assn.; 0-916921),* 2104 Georgetown Blvd., Ann Arbor, MI 48105 (SAN 670-7300).
Laughing B P, *(Laughing Buddha Pr., The; 0-910913),* Sarah Lawrence College, Bronxville, NY 10708 (SAN 271-9665) Tel 914-337-0700.
Lawrence Hill, *(Hill, Lawrence, & Co., Inc.; 0-88208),* 520 Riverside Ave., Westport, CT 06880 (SAN 214-1221) Tel 203-226-5980; Dist. by: Independent Publishers Group, 1 Pleasant Ave., Port Washington, NY 11050 (SAN 287-2544) Tel 516-944-9325.
Lay Leadership, *(Lay Leadership Institute, Inc.; 0-88151),* 1267 Hicks Blvd., Fairfield, OH 45014 (SAN 271-9797).
LE *Imprint of* **Dell**
Learned Pubns, *(Learned Pubns., Inc.; 0-912116),* 83-53 Manton St., Jamaica, NY 11435 (SAN 201-0755) Tel 718-441-8084.
Learning Wks, *(Learning Works, Inc., The; 0-88160),* P.O. Box 6187, Santa Barbara, CA 93160 (SAN 272-0078) Tel 805-964-4220; Toll free: 800-235-5767.
Left Bank, *(Left Bank Bks.; 0-939306),* 92 Pike St., Box B, Seattle, WA 98101 . (SAN 216-5368) Tel 206-622-0195.
Legacy Bks, *(Legacy Bks.; 0-913714),* Box 494, Hatboro, PA 19040 (SAN 202-2389) Tel 215-675-6762; 12 Meetinghouse Rd., Hatboro, PA 19040 (SAN 658-1129).
Lerner Pubns, *(Lerner Pubns. Co.; 0-8225),* 241 First Ave. N., Minneapolis, MN 55401 (SAN 201-0828) Tel 612-332-3344; Toll free: 800-328-4929.
LeTourneau Pr, *(LeTourneau Pr.; 0-935899),* 8 Stonegate Dr., Longview, TX 75601 (SAN 696-611X) Tel 214-753-9545.
Levada, *(Levada Services; 0-9605014),* P.O. Box 686, 11300 Eastside Rd., Ft. Jones, CA 96032 (SAN 215-9597) Tel 916-468-5395.
Lewis-Roth, *(Lewis & Roth Pubs.; 0-936083),* Subs. of Church Reform & Revitalization, Inc., P.O. Box 569, Littleton, CO 80160-0569 (SAN 696-6454) Tel 303-794-3239.
Lexik Hse, *(Lexik House Pubs.; 0-936368),* 75 Main St., P.O. Box 247, Cold Spring, NY 10516 (SAN 214-3984) Tel 914-265-2822.
Lexington Bks, *(Lexington Bks.; 0-669),* Div. of D. C. Heath & Co., 125 Spring St., Lexington, MA 02173 (SAN 666-6647) Tel 617-862-6650; Toll free: 800-235-3565; Dist. by: D. C. Heath & Co., 2700 N. Richardt Ave., Indianapolis, IN 46219 (SAN 202-2885) Tel 317-359-5585.
LFL *Imprint of* **Dell**
Lib Arts Pr, *(Liberal Arts Pr.; 0-935175),* 4800 Kelly Elliot Rd., No. 46, Arlington, TX 76017 (SAN 695-4707) Tel 817-572-7409.
Lib Congress, *(Library of Congress; 0-8444),* Washington, DC 20540 (SAN 205-6593) Tel 202-287-5093.
Lib Res, *(Library Research Assocs., Inc.; 0-912526),* Subs. of Empire State Fiction, Dunderberg Rd., RD 5, Box 41, Monroe, NY 10950 (SAN 201-0887) Tel 914-783-1144.
Lib Serv Inc, *(Library Services Inc.),* Box 711, Havertown, PA 19083 (SAN 210-5381).
Liberal Pr, *(Liberal Pr., The; 0-934659),* P.O. Box 160361, Las Colinas, TX 75016 (SAN 200-5360).
Liberation Pubns, *(Liberation Pubns., Inc.; 0-917076),* P.O. Box 4371, Los Angeles, CA 90078 (SAN 208-7367) Tel 213-871-1225.
Liberty Bell Pr, *(Liberty Bell Pr.; 0-914053),* P.O. Box 32, Florissant, MO 63033 (SAN 202-2435) Tel 314-837-5343.
Liberty Clas *Imprint of* **Liberty Fund**
Liberty Fund, *(Liberty Fund, Inc.; 0-913966; 0-86597),* 7440 N. Shadeland Ave., Indianapolis, IN 46250 (SAN 202-6740) Tel 317-842-0880. *Imprints:* Liberty Clas (Liberty Classics).
Libr Commns Servs, *(Library Communications Services; 0-941237),* 13 Norwood St., Albany, NY 12203 (SAN 665-3685) Tel 518-438-0617.
Libra, *(Libra Pubs., Inc.; 0-87212),* 3089C Clairemont Dr., Suite 383, San Diego, CA 92117 (SAN 201-0909) Tel 619-581-9449.

Library of America, *(Library of America, The; 0-940450),* 14 E. 60th St., New York, NY 10022 (SAN 286-9918) Tel 212-308-3360; Toll free: 800-631-3577; Dist. by: Viking Penguin, Inc., 40 W. 23rd St., New York, NY 10010 (SAN 200-2442) Tel 212-337-5200.
Library Pr *Imprint of* **Open Court**
Libs Unl, *(Libraries Unlimited, Inc.; 0-87287),* P.O. Box 263, Littleton, CO 80160-0263 (SAN 202-6767) Tel 303-770-1220; Toll free: 800-237-6124.
Life Action Pr, *(Life Action Pr.; 1-55531),* Div. of For Life Action, 902 S. Burnside Ave., Los Angeles, CA 90036 (SAN 696-4532) Tel 213-933-5591; Toll free: 800-732-5489 (In California); Orders to: P.O. Box 36456, Los Angeles, CA 90036 (SAN 662-3751) Tel 213-933-5591.
Life Arts, *(Life Arts Publishing; 0-937894),* 116 Curryer S., Santa Maria, CA 93454 (SAN 220-0686).
Life Enrich, *(Life Enrichment Pubs.; 0-938736),* Div. of Daring Publishing Group, Box 526, Canton, OH 44701 (SAN 215-9600).
Life in Christ
See ACTA Found
Life Lines, *(Life Lines; 0-932943),* Div. of Leadership Enrichment Ministries, P.O. Box 745, Rimrock, AZ 86335 (SAN 689-1624) Tel 602-567-5864.
Life Pubs Intl, *(Life Pubs. International; 0-8297),* 3360 NW 110th St., Miami, FL 33167 (SAN 213-5817) Tel 305-685-6334.
Life Science, *(Life Science Institute; 0-9609802; 1-88697),* P.O. Box 1057, Ft. Pierce, FL 33454 (SAN 263-1830) Tel 305-466-1271.
Life Skills, *(Life Skills Training Assocs.; 0-9604510; 0-932723),* P.O. Box 48133, Chicago, IL 60648 (SAN 220-0694) Tel 312-986-0070.
Life Values Pr, *(Life Values Pr.; 0-915761),* 820 F Ave., Coronado, CA 92118 (SAN 293-8847) Tel 619-435-3851.
Light & Life, *(Light & Life Pr.; 0-89367),* 999 College Ave., Winona Lake, IN 46590 (SAN 206-8419) Tel 219-267-7161; Toll free: 800-348-2513.
Light Hearted Pub Co, *(Light Hearted Publishing Co.; 0-916043),* Div. of Montgomery's Music, P.O. Box 150246, Nashville, TN 37215 (SAN 294-8648) Tel 615-776-5678.
Light&Life Pub Co MN, *(Light & Life Pub. Co.; 0-937032),* 4836 Park Glen Rd., Minneapolis, MN 55416 (SAN 213-8565) Tel 612-925-3888.
Lightning Tree, *(Lightning Tree; 0-89016),* P.O. Box 1837, Santa Fe, NM 87504 (SAN 206-555X) Tel 505-983-7434.
Lighton Pubns, *(Lighton Pubns.; 0-910892),* 73223 Sunnyvale Dr., Twentynine Palms, CA 92277 (SAN 201-0917) Tel 619-367-7386.
Lightwave Inc
See Starseed Pubns
Liguori Pubns, *(Liguori Pubns.; 0-89243),* 1 Liguori Dr., Liguori, MO 63057 (SAN 202-6783) Tel 314-464-2500; Toll free: 800-325-9521 (Orders).
Limelight Edns, *(Limelight Editions; 0-87910),* Div. of Proscenium Pubs., 118 E. 30th St., New York, NY 10016 (SAN 290-0068) Tel 212-532-5525; Toll free: 800-242-7737; Dist. by: Harper & Row Pubs., Inc., Keystone Industrial Pk., Scranton, PA 18512 (SAN 215-3742).
Limitless Light, *(Limitless Light Publishing Co.; 0-917913),* 8115-1 N. 35th Ave., Phoenix, AZ 85051 (SAN 657-0518).
Linden Pr *Imprint of* **S&S**
Lindisfarne Pr *Imprint of* **Inner Tradit**
Linolean Pr *Imprint of* **Larksdale**
Lion Bks, *(Lion Bks.; 0-87460),* Dist. by: Sayre Publishing, Inc., P.O. Box 1337, Scarsdale, NY 10583 (SAN 201-0925) Tel 914-725-2280.
Lion USA, *(Lion Publishing; 0-7459; 0-85648),* Subs. of Lion Publishing, UK, 1705 Hubbard Ave., Batavia, IL 60510 (SAN 663-611X).
Lions Head Pr, *(Lions Head Pr.; 0-934661),* P.O. Box 5202, Klamath Falls, OR 97601 (SAN 694-0447) Tel 503-883-2101.
Little, *(Little, Brown & Co.; 0-316),* Div. of Time, Inc., 34 Beacon St., Boston, MA 02108 (SAN 200-2205) Tel 617-227-0730; Toll free: 800-343-9204; Orders to: 200 West St., Waltham, MA 02254 (SAN 281-8892).
Little People, *(Little People Productions; 0-910219),* Kennedy Design Ctr., 111 S. Lincoln St., Warsaw, IN 46580 (SAN 241-3930) Tel 219-269-3823.
Little Red Hen, *(Little Red Hen, Inc.; 0-933046),* P.O. Box 4260, Pocatello, ID 83201 (SAN 212-7571) Tel 208-232-1847.
Littlebird, *(Littlebird Pubns.; 0-937896),* 126 Fifth Ave., New York, NY 10011 (SAN 215-7853).
Littlefield, *(Littlefield, Adams & Co.; 0-8226),* 81 Adams Dr., Totowa, NJ 07512 (SAN 202-6791) Tel 201-256-8600.
Liturgical Conf, *(Liturgical Conference, The; 0-918208),* 806 Rhode Island Ave. NE., Washington, DC 20018 (SAN 205-6488) Tel 202-529-7400.
Liturgical Pr, *(Liturgical Pr. The; 0-8146),* Div. of Order of St. Benedict, Inc., St. John's Abbey, Collegeville, MN 56321 (SAN 202-2494) Tel 612-363-2213.
Liturgy & Art
See Monks of New Skete
Liveright, *(Liveright Publishing Corp.; 0-87140),* Subs. of W. W. Norton Co., Inc., 500 Fifth Ave., New York, NY 10110 (SAN 201-0976) Tel 212-354-5500; Toll free: 800-233-4830.
Livia Pr, *(Livia Pr.; 0-933949),* 967 Neilson St., Albany, CA 94706 (SAN 692-6770) Tel 415-526-3281.
Living Flame Pr, *(Living Flame Pr.; 0-914544),* 325 Rabro Dr., Hauppauge, NY 11788 (SAN 202-6805) Tel 516-348-5252.
Living Love, *(Living Love Pubns.; 0-9600688; 0-915972),* 700 Commercial Ave., Coos Bay, OR 97420 (SAN 281-9082) Tel 503-267-4232; Dist. by: DeVorss & Co., P.O. Box 550, Marina del Rey, CA 90291 (SAN 168-9886) Tel 213-870-7478; Dist. by: Bookpeople, 2929 Fifth St., Berkeley, CA 94710 (SAN 168-9517) Tel 415-549-3030; Dist. by: Inland Bk. Co., P.O. Box 261, East Haven, CT 06512 (SAN 200-4151) Tel 203-467-4257; Dist. by: New Leaf Distributing Co., 1020 White St., SW, Atlanta, GA 30316 (SAN 169-1449); Dist. by: Publishers Group West, 5855 Beaudry, Emeryville, CA 94608 (SAN 202-8522) Tel 415-658-3453; Dist. by: Whole Health Bk. Co., 4735 Wunder Ave, Trevose, PA 19047 (SAN 200-6073) Tel 215-322-2880; Dist. by: Distributors, 702 S. Michigan, South Bend, IN 46618 (SAN 169-2488) Tel 219-232-8500; Dist. by: Starlite Distributors, P.O. Box 20729, Sparks, NV 89515 (SAN 131-1921) Tel 702-359-5676.
Living Spring Pubns, *(Living Spring Pubns.; 0-941598),* 389 N. Los Robles, No. 2, Pasadena, CA 91101 (SAN 239-1112) Tel 818-795-2407; 790 Metro Dr., Monterey Park, CA 91754 (SAN 699-5403) Tel 818-572-9468.
Living Stone Pubs, *(Living Stone Pubs.; 0-936637),* 15851 Eighth, NE, Seattle, WA 98155 (SAN 699-6817); P.O. Box 55324, Seattle, WA 98155 (SAN 699-6825).
Living Way, *(Living Way Ministries; 0-916847),* c/o The Church on the Way, 14300 Sherman Way, Van Nuys, CA 91405-2499 (SAN 653-7820) Tel 818-786-7090.
LL Co, *(LL Co.; 0-937892),* 1647 Manning Ave., Los Angeles, CA 90024 (SAN 203-0314) Tel 213-475-3664.
Llewellyn Pubns, *(Llewellyn Pubns.; 0-87542),* Div. of Chester-Kent, Inc., P.O. Box 64383, St. Paul, MN 55164-0383 (SAN 201-100X) Tel 612-291-1970; Toll free: 800-843-6666; Dist. by: Bookslinger, 213 E. Fourth St., St. Paul, MN 55101 (SAN 169-4154) Tel 612-221-0429.
Lochinvar *Imprint of* **Exposition Pr FL**
Locust Hill Pr, *(Locust Hill Pr.; 0-933951),* P.O. Box 260, West Cornwall, CT 06796 (SAN 693-0646) Tel 203-672-0060.
Lodestar Bks, *(Lodestar Bks.; 0-525),* Div. of E. P. Dutton, 2 Park Ave., New York, NY 10016 (SAN 212-5013) Tel 212-725-1818; Toll free: 800-526-0275; Dist. by: New American Library, P.O. Box 999, Bergenfield, NJ 07621 (SAN 206-8079) Tel 201-387-0600.
Loeffler
See Prod Hse
Loizeaux, *(Loizeaux Brothers, Inc.; 0-87213),* P.O. Box 277, Neptune, NJ 07754-0277 (SAN 202-6848); 1238 Corlies Ave., Neptune, NJ 07754-0277 (SAN 699-5411) Tel 201-774-8144; Toll free: 800-526-2796.
Long Beach Pubns, *(Long Beach Pubns.; 0-941910),* P.O. Box 14807, Long Beach, CA 90803 (SAN 239-782X) Tel 213-439-8962.
Long Hse, *(Long House, Inc.; 0-912806),* P.O. Box 3, New Canaan, CT 06840-2931 (SAN 201-4947) Tel 203-966-2931.
Longman, *(Longman, Inc.; 0-582; 0-8013),* Subs. of Longman Group USA, 95 Church St., White Plains, NY 10601 (SAN 202-6856) Tel 914-993-5000.
Longshanks Bk, *(Longshanks Bk.; 0-9601000),* 30 Church St., Mystic, CT 06355 (SAN 208-7391) Tel 203-536-8656.
Longwood Pub Group, *(Longwood Publishing Group, Inc.; 0-89341),* 27 S. Main St, Wolfeboro, NH 03894-2069 (SAN 209-3170) Tel 603-569-4576; Toll free: 800-343-9444.
Lords Line, *(Lord's Line; 0-915952),* 1734 Armour Ln., Redondo Beach, CA 90278 (SAN 207-7086) Tel 213-542-5575.
Lorenz Pr, *(Lorenz Pr., Inc.; 0-89328),* Div. of Lorenz Industries, Subs. of International Entertainment Corp., 501 E. Third St., Dayton, OH 45401 (SAN 208-7413) Tel 513-228-6118; Dist. by: Independent Pubs. Group, 1 Pleasant Ave., Port Washington, NY 11050 (SAN 208-7421).
Lorian Pr, *(Lorian Pr.; 0-936878),* P.O. Box 663, Issaquah, WA 98027 (SAN 214-4042) Tel 206-392-3982; 4440 190th Ave., SE, Issaquah, WA 98027 (SAN 666-6663) Tel 206-641-5679; Dist. by: Bookpeople, 2929 Fifth St., Berkeley, CA 94710 (SAN 168-9517) Tel 415-549-3030; Dist. by: DeVorss & Co., P.O. Box 550, Marina del Rey, CA 90291 (SAN 168-9886) Tel 213-870-7478; Dist. by: Inland Bk. Co., 22 Hemingway Ave., East Haven, CT 06512 (SAN 200-4151) Tel 203-467-4257
Lorien Hse, *(Lorien Hse.; 0-934852),* P.O. Box 1112, Black Mountain, NC 28711 (SAN 209-2999) Tel 704-669-6211.
Los Arboles Pub, *(Los Arboles; 0-941992),* 820 Calle de Arboles, Redondo Beach, CA 90277 (SAN 238-020X) Tel 213-375-0759; Orders to: P.O. Box 7000-54, Redondo Beach, CA 90277 (SAN 662-0752).
Lothrop, *(Lothrop, Lee & Shepard Bks.; 0-688),* Div. of William Morrow & Co., Inc., 105 Madison Ave., New York, NY 10016 (SAN 201-1034) Tel 212-889-3050; Toll free: 800-631-1199; Orders to: William Morrow & Co., Inc., 39 Plymouth St., P.O. Box 1219, Fairfield, NJ 07007 (SAN 202-5779).
Lotsawa, *(Lotsawa, Inc.; 0-932156),* 140 E. 92nd St., New York, NY 10028 (SAN 213-893X) Tel 212-534-3384; Dist. by: Book Dynamics, 836 Broadway, New York, NY 10003 (SAN 169-5649) Tel 212-254-7798; Dist. by: Bookpeople, 2929 Fifth St., Berkeley, CA 94710 (SAN 168-9517); Dist. by: DeVorss & Co., P.O. Box 550, 1046 Princeton Dr., Marina del Rey, CA 90294 (SAN 168-9886).
Lotus, *(Lotus Pr., Inc.; 0-916418),* P.O. Box 21607, Detroit, MI 48221 (SAN 213-8867) Tel 313-861-1280.
Lotus Light, *(Lotus Light Pubns.; 0-941524),* Affil. of Specialized Software, P.O. Box 2, Wilmot, WI 53192 (SAN 239-1120) Tel 414-862-2395.
Louis Found
See Touch Heart
Love Agape Min, *(Love Agape Ministries Pr.; 0-914605),* Subs. of Love Ministries, Inc., P.O. Box 69, Worthville, KY 41098 (SAN 290-7054); 467 Sandalwood Dr., Lexington, KY 40505 (SAN 290-7062) Tel 502-732-6728.
Love Pub Co, *(Love Publishing Co.; 0-89108),* 1777 S. Bellaire St., Denver, CO 80222 (SAN 205-2482) Tel 303-757-2579.

Love Song Mess Assn, *(Love Song to The Messiah Assn., Inc.; 0-915775),* 1609 N. Atlantic Blvd., Ft. Lauderdale, FL 33305 (SAN 293-8871) Tel 305-563-0697; Dist. by: Spring Arbor Distributors, 10885 Textile Rd., Belleville, MI 48111 (SAN 158-9016) Tel 313-481-0900; Dist. by: Living Bks., 12155 Magnolia Ave., Bldg., 11-B, Riverside, CA 92503 (SAN 169-006X) Tel 714-354-7630.

Lovejoy Pr, *(Lovejoy Pr.; 0-9614264),* 501 E. Main Box 36, Wellington, IL 60973 (SAN 687-1429) Tel 815-984-3996.

Loving Pubs, *(Loving Pubs.; 0-938134),* 4576 Alla Rd., Los Angeles, CA 90066 (SAN 215-6768).

Lowell Pr, *(Lowell Pr.; 0-913504; 0-932845),* 115 E. 31st St., Box 411877, Kansas City, MO 64141 (SAN 207-0774) Tel 816-753-4545.

Loyola, *(Loyola Univ. Pr.; 0-8294),* 3441 N. Ashland Ave., Chicago, IL 60657 (SAN 211-6537) Tel 312-281-1818; Toll free: 800-621-1008.

Lubavitch Women, *(Lubavitch Women's Organization; 0-930178),* 770 Eastern Pkwy., Brooklyn, NY 11213 (SAN 210-6345) Tel 718-604-2785.

Lubrecht & Cramer, *(Lubrecht & Cramer, Ltd.; 0-934454),* RD 1, Box 244 Rte. 42 Forestburgh Rd., Forestburgh, NY 12777 (SAN 214-1256) Tel 914-794-8539.

Lucis, *(Lucis Publishing Co.; 0-85330),* Div. of Lucis Trust, 113 University Pl., 11th Flr., New York, NY 10003 (SAN 201-1085) Tel 212-982-8770.

Lucy Mary Bks, *(Lucy Mary Bks.; 0-913829),* P.O. Box 2381, Grand Junction, CO 81502 (SAN 286-1712) Tel 303-243-3231.

Lumeli Pr, *(Lumeli Pr.; 0-930592),* P.O. Box 555, Gonzales, CA 93926 (SAN 211-0326).

Lumen Christi, *(Lumen Christi Pr.; 0-912414),* P.O. Box 13176, Houston, TX 77019 (SAN 201-1093) Tel 713-827-0181.

LuraMedia, *(LuraMedia; 0-931055),* P.O. Box 261668, San Diego, CA 92126 (SAN 678-9234); Toll free: 800-367-5872; 10227 Autumnview Ln., San Diego, CA 92126 (SAN 662-2542) Tel 619-578-1948; Toll free: 800-367-5872.

Luth Acad, *(Lutheran Academy for Scholarship; 0-913160),* c/o Richard Jungkuntz, 6310 Hillcrest Dr., SW, Tacoma, WA 98499 (SAN 285-0451). Out of business.

Luth Bd of Pubn
See Bd of Pubn LCA

Luth Coun IL, *(Lutheran Council in the U.S.A., Div. of Campus Ministries; 0-9609438),* Div. of Lutheran Council in the U.S.A., 35 E. Wacker Dr., Suite 1847, Chicago, IL 60601 (SAN 272-135X) Tel 312-332-1387.

Lutheran Womens, *(Lutheran Women's Missionary League; 0-9614955),* 3558 S. Jefferson Ave., St. Louis, MO 63118 (SAN 693-7454) Tel 314-664-7000.

Lyle Stuart, *(Stuart, Lyle, Inc.; 0-8184),* Div. of Citadel, 120 Enterprise Ave., Secaucus, NJ 07094 (SAN 201-1131) Tel 201-866-0490; Toll free: 800-572-6657.

M A Little, *(Little, Mark A.; 0-9613783),* 8842 N. Winding Way, Fair Oaks, CA 95628 (SAN 678-9838) Tel 916-965-0952.

M A Seguin, *(Seguin, Mary A.; 0-9616951),* 145 S. First Ave., Alpena, MI 49707 (SAN 661-7336) Tel 517-356-1481.

M Akers, *(Akers, Mona J. Coole; 0-912706),* 219 S. Williams St., Denver, CO 80209 (SAN 206-9075) Tel 303-722-1892.

M & L Sales, *(M & L Sales),* P.O. Box 467702, Atlanta, GA 30346 (SAN 693-0409) Tel 404-394-5506.

M B Hall
See Veritat Found

M Boyars Pubs, *(Boyars, Marion, Pubs., Inc.; 0-7145; 0-905223; 0-906890),* 26 E. 23rd St., New York, NY 10036 (SAN 284-981X) Tel 212-213-0167; Dist. by: Kampmann & Co., Inc., 9 E. 40th St., New York, NY 10016 (SAN 201-002X) Tel 212-685-2928.

M Buber Pr, *(Buber, Martin, Press),* G.P.O. Box 2009, Brooklyn, NY 11202 (SAN 212-7318).

M E Sharpe, *(Sharpe, M. E., Inc.; 0-87332),* 80 Business Pk. Dr., Armonk, NY 10504 (SAN 202-7100) Tel 914-273-1800.

M Evans, *(Evans, M., & Co., Inc.; 0-87131),* 216 E. 49th St., New York, NY 10017 (SAN 203-4050) Tel 212-688-2810; Toll free: 800-526-0275; Dist. by: Henry Holt & Co., 521 Fifth Ave., New York, NY 10175 (SAN 200-6472) Tel 212-599-7600.

M F Turner Pub, *(Turner, M. F., Publishing; 0-9616007),* 2963 N. 52nd Pkwy., Phoenix, AZ 85031 (SAN 697-9734) Tel 602-247-5322.

M Glazier, *(Glazier, Michael, Inc.; 0-89453),* 1935 W. Fourth St., Wilmington, DE 19805 (SAN 210-2056) Tel 302-654-1635.

M Jones, *(Jones, Marshall, Co.; 0-8338),* Div. of Golden Quill Pr., Avery Rd, Francestown, NH 03043 (SAN 206-8834) Tel 603-547-6622.

M L Burman, *(Burman, M. L.),* Box 72, Pineland, FL 33945 (SAN 655-3834) Tel 813-283-0777.

M Loke, *(Mele Loke Publishing Co.; 0-930932),* P.O. Box 7142, Honolulu, HI 96821 (SAN 211-1330) Tel 808-734-8611; Dist. by: Pacific Trade Group, P.O. Box 668, Pearl City, HI 96782-0668 (SAN 169-1635) Tel 808-261-6954.

M R Winkler, *(Winkler, Marion R.; 0-9610344),* 5225 N. 20th St., Phoenix, AZ 85016 (SAN 264-4991) Tel 602-957-2922.

M Regehr, *(Regehr, Margaret; 0-9614486),* HCR 85, Box 64, Bonners Ferry, ID 83805 (SAN 689-3929) Tel 208-267-2801.

M S Rosenberg, *(Rosenberg, Mary S., Inc.; 0-917324),* 17 W. 60th St., New York, NY 10023 (SAN 205-2296) Tel 212-362-4873.

M T O Shahmag, *(M.T.O. Shahmaghsoudi; 0-910735),* P.O. Box 1135, San Rafael, CA 94915 (SAN 271-6852) Tel 415-454-1555.

M Wyatt, *(Wyatt, Margert; 0-9616117),* 1127 St. Mary, Casper, WY 82601 (SAN 699-721X) Tel 307-237-7531.

Maat Pub, *(Maat Publishing Co.; 0-917650),* P.O. Box 281, Bronx, NY 10462 (SAN 209-2239).

Mac Col MN, *(Macalester College; 0-9606844),* Weyerhaeuser Library, St. Paul, MN 55105 (SAN 213-2567) Tel 612-696-6345.

Macalester, *(Macalester Park Bookstore; 0-910924),* 1571 Grand Ave., St. Paul, MN 55105 (SAN 110-8077) Tel 612-698-8877.

Maccabee Pub, *(Maccabee Publishing Co., Inc.; 0-942500),* 14 W. Forest Ave., Englewood, NJ 07631 (SAN 226-207X) Tel 201-569-8700.

McClain, *(McClain Printing Co.; 0-87012; 0-9613967),* 212 Main St., Parsons, WV 26287 (SAN 203-9478) Tel 304-478-2881.

McDougal-Littell, *(McDougal, Littell & Co.; 0-88343; 0-8123),* P.O. Box 1667, Evanston, IL 60204 (SAN 202-2532) Tel 312-869-2300.

McFarland & Co, *(McFarland & Co., Inc., Pubs.; 0-89950),* Box 611, Jefferson, NC 28640 (SAN 215-093X) Tel 919-246-4460.

McGill-Queens U Pr, *(McGill-Queens Univ. Pr.; 0-7735),* Dist. by: Univ. of Toronto Pr., 340 Nagel Dr., Cheektowage, NY 14225 (SAN 214-2651) Tel 716-683-4547.

McGraw, *(McGraw-Hill Bk. Co.; 0-07),* Div. of McGraw-Hill, Inc., 1221 Ave. of the Americas, New York, NY 10020 (SAN 200-2248) Tel 212-512-2000; Orders to: Princeton Rd., Hightstown, NJ 08520 (SAN 200-254X) Tel 609-426-5254; Orders to: 8171 Redwood Hwy., Novato, CA 94947 (SAN 200-2566) Tel 415-898-5598; Orders to: 13955 Manchester Rd., Manchester, MO 63011 (SAN 200-2558) Tel 314-256-2300.

McKay, *(McKay, David, Co., Inc.; 0-679),* Subs. of Random Hse., Inc., 201 E. 50th St., New York, NY 10022 (SAN 200-240X) Tel 212-751-2600; Orders to: Random Hse., Inc., 400 Hahn Rd., Westminster, MD 21157 (SAN 202-5515) Tel 301-848-1900.

Mackinac Island, *(Mackinac Island State Park Commission; 0-911872),* P.O. Box 370, Mackinac Island, MI 49757 (SAN 202-5981) Tel 906-847-3328.

Macmillan, *(Macmillan Publishing Co., Inc.; 0-02),* 866 Third Ave., New York, NY 10022 (SAN 202-5574) Tel 212-702-2000; Toll free: 800-257-5755; Orders to: Front & Brown Sts., Riverside, NJ 08370 (SAN 202-5582). Do not confuse with McMillan Pubns., Woodridge, IL. *Imprints:* Aladdin Bks (Aladdin Books); Checkerboard Pr (Checkerboard Press); Collier (Collier Books).

McNally & Loftin, *(McNally & Loftin, Pubs.; 0-87461),* P.O. Box 1316, Santa Barbara, CA 93102 (SAN 202-5973) Tel 805-964-5117; Orders to: 5390 Overpass Rd., Santa Barbara, CA 93111 (SAN 281-9651).

Macoy Pub, *(Macoy Publishing & Masonic Supply Co., Inc.; 0-910928; 0-88053),* P.O. Box 9759, Richmond, VA 23228-0759 (SAN 202-2265) Tel 804-262-6551.

Madison Polk, *(Madison & Polk; 0-910915),* P.O. Box 8447, Asheville, NC 28814 (SAN 272-1708).

Madrona Pubs, *(Madrona Pubs., Inc.; 0-914842; 0-88089),* P.O. Box 22667, Seattle, WA 98122 (SAN 212-0283); 113 Madrona Pl., E., Seattle, WA 98112 (SAN 281-9678) Tel 206-325-3973; Dist. by: Slawson Communications, Inc., 3719 Sixth Ave., San Diego, CA 92103-4316 (SAN 200-6901) Tel 619-291-9126.

Magi Bks, *(Magi Bks., Inc.; 0-87343),* 33 Buckingham Dr., Albany, NY 12208 (SAN 202-6023) Tel 518-482-7781.

Magian Pr, *(Magian Pr., The; 0-917023),* P.O. Box 117, Penn Laird, VA 22846 (SAN 655-2684) Tel 703-289-5596.

Magickal Childe, *(Magickal Childe Inc.; 0-939708),* 35 W. 19th St., New York, NY 10011 (SAN 216-4124) Tel 212-242-7182.

Magnes Mus, *(Magnes, Judah L., Museum; 0-943376),* 2911 Russell St., Berkeley, CA 94705 (SAN 214-2511) Tel 415-849-2710.

Magnolia Bks, *(Magnolia Bks., Inc.; 0-9612000),* 450 17th Ave., San Francisco, CA 94121 (SAN 286-8121) Tel 415-221-3519.

Magnolia Pr, *(Magnolia Pr.; 0-916369),* P.O. Box 3, Swainsboro, GA 30401 (SAN 295-6233) Tel 912-237-8740.

Mah-Tov Pubns, *(Mah-Tov Pubns.; 0-917274),* 1680 45th St., Brooklyn, NY 11204 (SAN 208-7502) Tel 718-871-5337.

Mahayana, *(Mahayana Sutra & Tantra Pr.; 0-918753),* Subs. of Mahayana Sutra & Tantra Center, 216A W. Second St., Howell, NJ 07731 (SAN 657-6532) Tel 609-261-3458.

Mailbox, *(Mailbox Club, The; 0-9603752),* 404 Eager Rd., Valdosta, GA 31602 (SAN 281-9686) Tel 912-244-6812.

Maimes, *(Maimes, S. L.; 0-917246),* 59 Franklin St., Rochester, NH 03867 (SAN 208-1830).

Main Street, *(Main Street Pr., The; 0-915590; 1-55562),* William Case Hse., Pittstown, NJ 08867 (SAN 207-4443) Tel 201-735-9424.

Makepeace Colony, *(Makepeace Colony Press, The; 0-87741),* P.O. Box 111, Stevens Point, WI 54481 (SAN 203-9575) Tel 715-344-2636.

Malcolm Hse, *(Malcolm Hse.),* 805 Malcolm Dr., Silver Spring, MD 20901 (SAN 209-0368) Tel 301-439-4358.

Maledicta, *(Maledicta Pr.; 0-916500),* 331 S. Greenfield Ave., Waukesha, WI 53186-6492 (SAN 208-1083) Tel 414-542-5853.

Man-Root, *(Man-Root),* P.O. Box 982, South San Francisco, CA 94083 (SAN 207-8635); P.O. Box 762, Boyes Hot Springs, CA 95416 (SAN 693-4943).

Manchurch, *(Manchurch; 0-935251),* P.O. Box 4114, Albany, NY 12204 (SAN 695-5037) Tel 518-434-8727; 435 Loudon Rd., Loudonville, NY 12211 (SAN 695-5045).

Mandala
See Irvington

Mandala Holistic, *(Mandala Holistic Health; 0-939410),* P.O. Box 1233, Del Mar, CA 92014 (SAN 216-5783) Tel 619-481-7751.

Mangan Bks, *(Mangan Bks.; 0-930208),* 6245 Snowheights Ct., El Paso, TX 79912 (SAN 209-3804) Tel 915-584-1662.

Manhattan Ltd NC, *(Manhattan, Ltd., Pubs.; 0-932046),* P.O. Box 18865, Raleigh, NC 27619 (SAN 211-8114) Tel 919-833-2121.

Manifestation, *(Manifestation, Inc.; 0-932947),* 708 Eighth Ave. S., Box 991, North Myrtle Beach, SC 29582 (SAN 689-0571) Tel 803-272-8183; Dist. by: Sheriar Pr., 1414 Madison St., North Myrtle Beach, SC 29582 (SAN 203-2457).

Manor of Grace, *(Manor of Grace; 0-9616513),* 3816 Fannin, Houston, TX 77004 (SAN 659-5154) Tel 713-523-6277.

Mansell, *(Mansell; 0-7201),* 950 University Ave., Bronx, NY 10452 (SAN 209-5807) Tel 212-685-8149; Toll free: 800-367-6770.

Maranatha Baptist, *(Maranatha Baptist Pr.; 0-937136),* Maranatha Baptist Bible College, 745 W. Main St., Watertown, WI 53094 (SAN 220-2581) Tel 414-261-9300.
Marco & Johnson
See Paul R Johnson
Marianist Com Ctr, *(Marianist Communication Ctr.; 0-9608124),* 1223 Maryhurst Dr., St. Louis, MO 63122 (SAN 240-2483) Tel 314-965-5634.
Mariological Soc, *(Mariological Society of America),* Marian Library, Univ. of Dayton, Dayton, OH 45469-0001 (SAN 225-4255) Tel 513-229-4214.
Mark-Age, *(Mark-Age Inc.; 0-912322),* P.O. Box 290368, Fort Lauderdale, FL 33329 (SAN 202-6090) Tel 305-587-5555.
Marquette, *(Marquette Univ. Pr.; 0-87462),* 1324 W. Wisconsin Ave., Rm. 409, Milwaukee, WI 53233 (SAN 203-9702) Tel 414-224-1564.
Marriage
See Abbey
Martin-Marrero, *(Martin-Marrero Productions; 0-9613430),* P.O. Box 30081, Indianapolis, IN 46230 (SAN 657-0526) Tel 317-251-4212.
Martin Pr CA, *(Martin Pr., The; 0-941018),* 20600 Grammercy Pl., Suite 205, Torrance, CA 90501 (SAN 217-4014); Toll free: 800-421-1212. No longer publishing.
Marxist-Leninist, *(Marxist-Leninist Pubns.; 0-86714),* Orders to: P.O. Box 11972, Ontario St. Sta., Chicago, IL 60611 (SAN 295-3382).
Maryatta Co, *(Maryatta Co.; 0-9617372),* P.O. Box 68076, Oakgrove, OR 98076 (SAN 663-8724); 17125 SE 82nd Dr., Clackamas, OR 97015 (SAN 663-8732) Tel 503-656-8740.
Maryben Bks, *(Maryben Bks.; 0-913184),* 619 Warfield Dr., Rockville, MD 20850 (SAN 205-6313) Tel 301-762-5291.
Master Bks, *(Master Bk. Pubs.; 0-89051),* Subs. of Creation-Life Pubs., Inc., P.O. Box 1606, El Cajon, CA 92022 (SAN 205-6119) Tel 619-448-1121; Toll free: 800-621-0852 ext. 134.
Masterpiece Pub, *(Masterpiece Publishing Co.; 0-935699),* Subs. of Masterpiece Productions Inc., 14505 NE 29th Pl., Bellevue, WA 98007 (SAN 696-2599) Tel 206-883-4483.
MasterSon Pub, *(MasterSon Publishing; 0-9608418),* 4025 N. Harmon Ave., Peoria, IL 61614 (SAN 240-7175) Tel 309-682-9222.
Matagiri, *(Matagiri Sri Aurobindo Ctr., Inc.; 0-89071),* P.O. Box 372, High Falls, NY 12440 (SAN 214-2058) Tel 914-687-9222.
Mater Dei Provincialate, *(Mater Dei Provincialate; 0-9605784),* 9400 New Harmony Rd., Evansville, IN 47712 (SAN 216-2679).
Maverick Prints, *(Maverick Prints; 0-9612932),* 5890 E. Sedgwick Ct., Jackson, MS 39211 (SAN 292-580X) Tel 601-956-2286.
Max Mus, *(University of New Mexico, Maxwell Museum of Anthropology; 0-912535),* Corner of University & Roma, NE, Albuquerque, NM 87131 (SAN 279-5256) Tel 505-277-4404.
Mayfield Pub, *(Mayfield Publishing Co.; 0-87484),* 1240 Villa St., Mountain View, CA 94041 (SAN 202-8972) Tel 415-960-3222.
Mayflower Bks *Imprint of* **Smith Pubs**
Mayflower Inst, *(Mayflower Institute; 0-941370),* P.O. Box 50218, Santa Barbara, CA 93150 (SAN 238-9800) Tel 805-565-1474.
Mazda Pubs, *(Mazda Pubs.; 0-939214),* P.O. Box 2603, Costa Mesa, CA 92626 (SAN 285-0524); 2991 Grace Ln., Costa Mesa, CA 92626 (SAN 658-120X) Tel 714-751-5252.
Maznaim, *(Maznaim Publishing Corp.; 0-940118),* 4304 12th Ave., Brooklyn, NY 11219 (SAN 214-4123) Tel 718-438-7680.
MD Hist, *(Maryland Historical Society; 0-938420),* 201 W. Monument St., Baltimore, MD 21201 (SAN 203-9788).
Meadow Lane, *(Meadow Lane Pubns.; 0-934826),* 211 N. Citrus Ave., Unit 277, Escondido, CA 92027 (SAN 213-5361) Tel 619-747-0258. Out of business.
Meckler Pub, *(Meckler Publishing Corp.; 0-930466; 0-88736; 0-913672),* 11 Ferry Ln. W., Westport, CT 06880 (SAN 211-0334) Tel 203-226-6967.
Medallion *Imprint of* **Berkley Pub**
Media Inst, *(Media Institute, The; 0-937790),* 3017 M St., NW, Washington, DC 20007 (SAN 215-966X) Tel 202-298-7512.
Medieval, *(Medieval & Renaissance Society; 0-913904),* P.O. Box 13348, N. Texas State Univ., Denton, TX 76203 (SAN 202-2257) Tel 817-565-2101.
Medieval Acad, *(Medieval Academy of America; 0-910956),* 1430 Massachusetts Ave., Cambridge, MA 02138 (SAN 203-9826) Tel 617-491-1622.
Medieval & Renaissance NY, *(Medieval & Renaissance Texts & Studies; 0-86698),* State Univ. of New York at Binghamton, Binghamton, NY 13901 (SAN 216-6119) Tel 607-777-6758.
Medieval Inst, *(Medieval Institute Pubns.; 0-918720),* Western Michigan Univ., Kalamazoo, MI 49008 (SAN 212-2928) Tel 616-383-6096.
Meher Baba Info, *(Meher Baba Information; 0-940700),* Box 1101, Berkeley, CA 94701 (SAN 202-618X) Tel 415-562-1101; Dist. by: Bookpeople, 2929 Fifth St., Berkeley, CA 94710 (SAN 168-9517).
Membrane Pr, *(Membrane Pr.; 0-87924),* P.O. Box 11601, Shorewood, Milwaukee, WI 53211 (SAN 202-621X).
Memory Bks, *(Memory Bks.),* P.O. Box 85, New York, NY 10113 (SAN 699-783X).
Memphis Musicraft, *(Memphis Musicraft Pubns.; 0-934017),* 3149 Southern Ave., Memphis, TN 38111 (SAN 692-7696) Tel 901-452-5265.
Mennonite Church, *(Mennonite Church of Normal; 0-9617978),* 805 S. Cottage, Normal, IL 61761 (SAN 666-0576) Tel 309-452-6622.
Menorah Pub, *(Menorah Publishing Co., Inc.; 0-932232),* 15 W. 84th St., New York, NY 10024 (SAN 212-1158) Tel 212-787-2248.
Ment *Imprint of* **NAL**
Mer *Imprint of* **NAL**
Mercer Univ Pr, *(Mercer Univ. Pr.; 0-86554),* Macon, GA 31207 (SAN 220-0716) Tel 912-744-2880; Toll free: 800-637-2378 (orders only); Toll free: 800-342-0841 (order in GA only).
Mercury Pr, *(Mercury Pr.; 0-912393),* P.O. Box 8884, Munger Sta., Witchita, KS 67208 (SAN 264-2069).
Mercy & Truth, *(Mercy & Truth Pubs.; 0-9615494),* Rte 1, P.O. Box 503, Osceola, WI 54020 (SAN 696-379X) Tel 715-294-2052.
Meridian Pub, *(Meridian Publishing; 0-86610),* 2643 Edgewood Rd., Utica, NY 13501 (SAN 215-2568).
Merit Bks, *(Merit Bks.; 0-915929),* Div. of Merit Media Intl., P.O. Box 3319, Laguna Hills, CA 92654 (SAN 294-0620) Tel 714-768-5777. Moved, left no forwarding address.
Meriwether Pub, *(Meriwether Publishing, Ltd.; 0-916260),* Box 7710, Colorado Springs, CO 80933 (SAN 208-4716); 885 Elkton Dr., Colorado Springs, CO 80907 (SAN 658-2877) Tel 303-594-4422.
Merrill, *(Merrill Publishing Co.; 0-675),* Div. of Bell & Howell Co., 1300 Alum Creek Dr., Columbus, OH 43216 (SAN 200-2116) Tel 614-258-8441; Toll free: 800-848-1567.
Merrimack Pub Cir
See Salem Hse Pubs
Mesorah Pubns, *(Mesorah Pubns., Ltd.; 0-89906),* 1969 Coney Island Ave., Brooklyn, NY 11223 (SAN 213-1269) Tel 718-339-1700; Toll free: 800-Mesorah.
Messenger Comm, *(Messenger Communications; 0-939336),* 18706 25th Ave. SE, Bothell, WA 98011 (SAN 216-5392) Tel 206-481-9399. Moved, left no forwarding address.
Messing Pub, *(Messing, Simon D., Pub.; 0-9615946),* 58 Shepard's Knoll Dr., Hamden, CT 06514 (SAN 696-8171) Tel 203-397-4477.
Messner, *(Messner, Julian; 0-671),* A Simon & Schuster Co., Div. of Gulf & Western Corp., 1230 Ave. of the Americas, New York, NY 10020 (SAN 202-6260) Tel 212-245-6400; Toll free: 800-223-2336.
Metamorphous Pr, *(Metamorphous Pr.; 0-943920; 1-55552),* Subs. of Metamorphosis, Inc., P.O. Box 1712, Lake Oswego, OR 97035 (SAN 264-2077) Tel 503-635-6709.
Metascience, *(Metascience Foun.; 0-935436),* Box 747, Franklin, NC 28734 (SAN 213-4179) Tel 704-524-5103.
Methuen Inc, *(Methuen, Inc.; 0-416; 0-7100),* 29 W. 35th St., New York, NY 10001 (SAN 213-196X) Tel 212-244-3336. Do not confuse Tavistock Pubns. (UK), an imprint of Methuen, Inc., with Tavistock Poetry Pr., San Diego, CA. Acquired U. S. branch of Routledge & Kegan Paul, ltd. in 1986. *Imprints:* Ark Paperbks (Ark Paperbacks).
Metro Bks, *(Metro Books, Inc.; 0-8411),* 3110 N. Arlington Heights Rd., Arlington Heights, IL 60004 (SAN 203-9893) Tel 312-253-9720.
Metro Mus Art, *(Metropolitan Museum of Art; 0-87099),* Fifth Ave. & 82nd St., New York, NY 10028 (SAN 202-6279) Tel 212-879-5500; Dist. by: Univ. of Chicago Pr., 5801 Ellis Ave. S., 3rd Flr., Chicago, IL 60637 (SAN 202-5280) Tel 312-962-7693.
Metron Pubns, *(Metron Pubns.; 0-940268),* P.O. Box 1213, Princeton, NJ 08542 (SAN 217-5401) Tel 609-396-7947.
Meyer Stone Bks, *(Meyer-Stone Bks.; 0-940989),* 714 S. Humphrey, Oak Park, IL 60304 (SAN 664-7618) Tel 312-524-0842.
Mgmt Info Serv
See Scholarly
Mho & Mho, *(Mho & Mho Works; 0-917320),* 1259 El Camino Real, Suite 108, Menlo Park, CA 94025 (SAN 238-7999) Tel 415-327-6121; Orders to: Inland Bk. Co., 22 Hemingway Ave., East Haven, CT 06512 (SAN 200-4151) Tel 203-467-4257; Orders to: Bookpeople, 2929 Fifth Ave., Berkeley, CA 94710 (SAN 168-9517); Dist. by: New Leaf Distributing Co., 1020 White St. SW, Atlanta, GA 30310 (SAN 169-1449) Tel 404-755-2665.
Micah Pubns, *(Micah Pubns.; 2-916288),* 255 Humphrey St., Marblehead, MA 01945 (SAN 209-1577) Tel 617-631-7601.
Mich Slavic Pubns, *(Michigan Slavic Pubns.; 0-930042),* Dept. of Slavic Languages & Literatures, Univ. of Michigan, Ann Arbor, MI 48109-1275 (SAN 210-4636) Tel 313-763-4496.
Mich St U Pr, *(Michigan State Univ. Pr.; 0-87013),* 1405 S. Harrison Rd., 25 Manly Miles Bldg., East Lansing, MI 48824 (SAN 202-6295) Tel 517-355-9543; Dist. by: Wayne State Univ. Pr., Leonard N. Simons Bldg., 5959 Woodward Ave., Detroit, MI 48202 (SAN 202-5221) Tel 313-577-4601.
Mickler Hse, *(Mickler Hse. Pubs., The; 0-913122),* P.O. Box 38, Chuluota, FL 32766 (SAN 206-6874) Tel 305-365-3636.
Microfilming Corp, *(Microfilming Corp. of America; 0-88455; 0-667),* 200 Park Ave., New York, NY 10166 (SAN 202-6325) Tel 212-972-1070. Microforms of newspapers, periodicals, books, curriculum materials, documents & archival materials for research.
Microform Rev
See Meckler Pub
Mid Atl Reg Pr, *(Middle Atlantic Regional Pr. of the Apostolic Faith Churches of God; 0-9616056),* Div. of Apostolic Faith Churches of God, 1619 13th St., NW, Washington, DC 20009 (SAN 698-0635) Tel 202-265-7609; Orders to: P.O. Box 6021, Washington, DC 20005 (SAN 662-3972).
Mid East Inst, *(Middle East Institute; 0-916808),* 1761 N St., NW, Washington, DC 20036 (SAN 202-2168) Tel 202-785-1141.
Middle East Edit, *(Middle East Editorial Assocs.; 0-918992),* 1100 17th St., NW, Suite 300, Washington, DC 20036 (SAN 210-4644) Tel 202-785-0022.
Midnight Call, *(Midnight Call; 0-937422),* P.O. Box 4389, West Columbia, SC 29171 (SAN 211-8130).
Midway Reprint *Imprint of* **U of Chicago Pr**
Milford Hse, *(Milford House; 0-87821),* Div. of Longwood Pub. Group, 51 Washington St., Dover, NH 03820 (SAN 202-6368); Toll free: 800-343-9444. Moved, left no forwarding address.
Mill Bks, *(Mill Books),* Mill & Main St., Darby, PA 19023 (SAN 210-6140).
Miller Bks, *(Miller Bks.; 0-912472),* 2908 W. Valley Blvd., Alhambra, CA 91803 (SAN 203-9931) Tel 818-284-7607.

Mills Pub Co, *(Mills Publishing Co.; 0-935356),* King Sta., P.O. Box 6158, Santa Ana, CA 92706 (SAN 272-4464) Tel 714-541-5750.
Mimir, *(Mimir Pubs., Inc.; 0-912084),* P.O. Box 5011, Madison, WI 53705 (SAN 202-6376) Tel 608-231-1667.
Mindbody Inc, *(Mindbody, Inc.),* 50 Maple Pl., Manhasset, NY 11030 (SAN 214-0365) Tel 516-365-7722.
Mindlifter Pr, *(Mindlifter Pr.; 0-931959),* P.O. Box 571, Boston, MA 02215 (SAN 686-0087) Tel 617-236-1758.
Ministries, *(Ministries, Inc.; 0-9607986),* P.O. Box 4038, 319 Fleming, Montgomery, AL 36105 (SAN 238-5449) Tel 205-284-5645.
Ministry Pubns, *(Ministry Pubns.; 0-938234),* P.O. Box 276, Redlands, CA 92373 (SAN 215-787X).
Minn Inst Phil
See De Young Pr
Mission Dolores
See Theoscience Found
Mission Proj Serv, *(Mission Project Service; 0-913671),* 1 Haven Plaza, Apt. 25A, New York, NY 10009 (SAN 286-1461) Tel 212-533-6286.
Missionary Intern, *(Missionary Internship; 0-942726),* 36200 Freedom Rd., P.O. Box 457, Farmington, MI 48024 (SAN 240-253X) Tel 313-474-9110.
Missions Adv Res Com Ctr, *(Missions Advanced Research & Communication Ctr.; 0-912552),* Div. of World Vision International, 919 W. Huntington Dr., Monrovia, CA 91016 (SAN 240-0529) Tel 818-303-8811.
MIT Pr, *(MIT Pr.; 0-262),* 55 Hayward St., Cambridge, MA 02142 (SAN 202-6414) Tel 617-253-2884.
Mizan Pr, *(Mizan Pr.; 0-933782),* P.O. Box 4065, Berkeley, CA 94704 (SAN 213-117X) Tel 415-549-1634.
MMB Music, *(MMB Music, Inc.; 0-918812),* 10370 Page Industrial Blvd., St. Louis, MO 63132 (SAN 210-4601) Tel 314-427-5660.
MMI Pr, *(Mountain Missionary Pr.; 0-912145),* Div. of Mountain Missionary Institute, Inc., Aldworth Rd., P.O. Box 279, Harrisville, NH 03450 (SAN 264-7664) Tel 603-827-3361; Toll free: 800-367-1888.
Mntn Brook Pubns, *(Mountain Brook Pubns.; 0-938747),* P.O. Box 7474, Mountain Brook, AL 35253 (SAN 661-7549); 2652 Alta Glen Dr., Birmingham, AL 35243 (SAN 661-7557) Tel 205-967-6517.
Modern Lang, *(Modern Language Assn. of America; 0-87352),* 10 Astor Pl., New York, NY 10003 (SAN 202-6422) Tel 212-475-9500.
Modern Lib, *(Modern Library, Inc.; 0-394),* 201 E. 50th St., New York, NY 10022 (SAN 204-5605) Tel 212-751-2600; Orders to: Order Dept., 400 Hahn Rd., Westminster, MD 21157 (SAN 204-5613).
Mojave Bks, *(Mojave Bks.; 0-87881),* 7118 Canby Ave., Reseda, CA 91335 (SAN 202-6430) Tel 818-342-3403.
Momos, *(Momo's Pr.; 0-917672),* 45 Sheridan St., San Francisco, CA 94103 (SAN 206-1619) Tel 415-863-3009.
Monarch Pr, *(Monarch Pr.; 0-671),* Div. of Simon & Schuster, Inc., 1 Gulf & Western Bldg., Gulf & Western Plaza, 16th Flr., New York, NY 10023 (SAN 204-5621) Tel 212-373-8208.
Mongolia, *(Mongolia Society, Inc., The; 0-910980),* Indiana Univ. 321-322, Goodbody Hall, Bloomington, IN 47405 (SAN 204-000X) Tel 812-335-4078.
Monks of New Skete, *(Monks of New Skete; 0-9607924; 0-935129),* New Skete Rd. P.O. Box 128, Cambridge, NY 12816 (SAN 240-0553) Tel 518-677-3928.
Monocacy, *(Monocacy Bk. Co.; 0-913186),* P.O. Box 765, Redwood City, CA 94064 (SAN 202-6473) Tel 415-369-8934.
Montfort Pubns, *(Montfort Pubns.; 0-910984),* Div. of Montfort Missionaries, 26 S. Saxon Ave., Bay Shore, NY 11706 (SAN 169-5053) Tel 516-665-0726.
Monthly Rev, *(Monthly Review Pr.; 0-85345),* Div. of Monthly Review Foundation, Inc., 155 W. 23rd St., New York, NY 10011 (SAN 202-6481) Tel 212-691-2555.
Monument Pr, *(Monument Pr.; 0-930383),* P.O. Box 160361, Las Colinas, TX 75016 (SAN 670-7742) Tel 214-948-7001.
Moody, *(Moody Pr.; 0-8024),* Div. of Moody Bible Institute, 820 N. LaSalle Dr., Chicago, IL 60610 (SAN 202-5604) Tel 312-508-6882; Toll free: 800-621-5111; Toll free: 800-621-4323 (In Illinois).
Mooney, *(Mooney, Tom; 0-9601240),* 3410 Balt-Som Rd., Millersport, OH 43046 (SAN 210-1270) Tel 614-862-8159.
Moonlight FL, *(Moonlight Pr.; 0-913545),* 3407 Crystal Lake Dr., Orlando, FL 32806 (SAN 293-3063) Tel 305-857-1113.
Moore-Taylor-Moore
See MTM Pub Co
Mor-Mac, *(Mor-Mac Publishing Co.; 0-912178),* P.O. Box 985, Daytona Beach, FL 32015 (SAN 204-0042) Tel 904-255-4427.
Moravian Music, *(Moravian Music Foundation; 0-8078),* 20 Cascade Ave., Winston-Salem, NC 27107 (SAN 225-3569) Tel 919-725-0651.
Morehouse, *(Morehouse-Barlow Co.; 0-8192),* 78 Danbury Rd., Wilton, CT 06897 (SAN 202-6511) Tel 203-762-0721.
Morningland, *(Morningland Pubns., Inc.; 0-935146),* 2600 E. Seventh St., Long Beach, CA 90804 (SAN 213-6368) Tel 213-433-9906.
Morningstar
See Transform Inc
Morrow, *(Morrow, William, & Co., Inc.; 0-688),* Subs. of Hearst Corp., 105 Madison Ave., New York, NY 10016 (SAN 202-5760) Tel 212-889-3050; Toll free: 800-631-1199; Orders to: Wilmor Warehouse, 39 Plymouth St., Fairfield, NJ 07006 (SAN 202-5779) Tel 201-227-7200. *Imprints:* Quill (Quill Paperbacks).
Morse Pr, *(Morse Pr., Inc.; 0-933350),* Div. of Cone-Heiden, 3441 Thorndyke Ave. W., Seattle, WA 98119 (SAN 211-8165) Tel 206-282-9988; Orders to: P.O. Box 24947, Seattle, WA 98124 (SAN 665-7427).
Mosadot Pubns, *(Mosadot Pubns., Inc.; 0-913185),* 71 Broadway, New York, NY 10006 (SAN 290-6961) Tel 212-425-3466.
Mosaic Pr OH, *(Mosaic Pr.; 0-88014),* 358 Oliver Rd., Cincinnati, OH 45215 (SAN 219-6077) Tel 513-761-5977.
Mosdos Pubs, *(Mosdos Pubs.; 0-939833),* 6504 Greenspring Ave., Baltimore, MD 21209 (SAN 663-8406) Tel 301-484-4943.
Moth Hse, *(Moth House Pubns.; 0-936718),* 3967 S. 2200 W., Salt Lake City, UT 84119 (SAN 222-6375).
Mott Media, *(Mott Media; 0-915134; 0-88062),* 1000 E. Huron, Milford, MI 48042 (SAN 207-1460) Tel 313-685-8773.
Mountain Movers, *(Mountain Movers Ministry; 0-9616309),* Affil. of Mountain Movers Pubs., 1231 Dewey, Wauwatosa, WI 53213 (SAN 658-7453) Tel 414-257-1259.
Mouton, *(Mouton De Gruyter; 90-279),* Div. of Walter De Gruyter, Inc., 200 Saw Mill River Rd., Hawthorne, NY 10532 (SAN 210-9239) Tel 914-747-0110.
Move Short Soc
See Ctr Sutton Movement
Moyer Bell Limited, *(Moyer Bell, Ltd.; 0-918825),* Colonial Hill, Mt. Kisco, NY 10549 (SAN 669-6961) Tel 914-666-0084; Dist. by: Kampmann & Co., 9 E. 40th St., New York, NY 10016 (SAN 202-5191) Tel 212-685-2928.
MSA Inc, *(MSA, Inc.; 0-9616897),* P.O. Box 2289, Provo, UT 84603 (SAN 661-6038); 342 Wymount Terr., No. 6A, Provo, UT 84604 (SAN 661-6046) Tel 801-377-0642.
Mt Coun Indian
See Coun India Ed
MTM Pub Co, *(M/T/M Publishing Co.; 0-938758),* P.O. Box 245, Washougal, WA 98671 (SAN 206-1627).
Multnomah, *(Multnomah Pr.; 0-930014; 0-88070),* Div. of Multnomah Schl. of the Bible, 10209 SE Division St., Portland, OR 97266 (SAN 210-4679) Tel 503-257-0526; Toll free: 800-547-5890.
Mus Am Ind, *(Museum of the American Indian; 0-934490),* Broadway at 155th St., New York, NY 10032-1596 (SAN 204-0085) Tel 212-283-2420.
Mus Northern Ariz, *(Museum of Northern Arizona Pr.; 0-89734),* Rte. 4, Box 720, Flagstaff, AZ 86001 (SAN 204-0093) Tel 602-774-5211.
Museum NM Pr, *(Museum of New Mexico Pr.; 0-89013),* P.O. Box 2087, Santa Fe, NM 87504 (SAN 202-2575) Tel 505-827-6455; Dist. by: William Gannon, 205 E. Palace Ave, Santa Fe, NM 87501 (SAN 201-5889) Tel 505-983-1579.
Music Sales, *(Music Sales Corp.; 0-8256),* 24 E. 22nd St., New York, NY 10010 (SAN 282-0277) Tel 212-254-2100; Orders to: Music Sales Distribution Ctr., 5 Bellvale Rd., P.O. Box 572, Chester, NY 10918 (SAN 662-0876) Tel 914-469-2271.
Musicdata, *(Musicdata, Inc.; 0-88478),* P.O. Box 48010, Philadelphia, PA 19144-8010 (SAN 203-1566) Tel 215-842-0555.
Mustardseed, *(Mustardseed Pr.; 0-917920),* Subs. of Interuniverse, 707 N. Carolina Ave., Cocoa, FL 32922 (SAN 209-9659) Tel 305-632-2769.
MVR Bks, *(MVR Bks.),* 3020 E Ave., Berwyn, IL 60402 (SAN 210-4709) Tel 312-749-7697.
Mystic Jhamom, *(Mystic Jhamom Pubs.; 0-933961),* 1650 Rocky Pl., Arroyo Grande, CA 93420 (SAN 693-0689) Tel 805-922-8802; P.O. Box 904, Santa Maria, CA 93456 (SAN 694-972X).
N American Assn, *(North American Association of Christians in Social Work),* P.O. Box 90, Saint Davids, PA 19087 (SAN 225-994X) Tel 215-687-5777.
N Burleson, *(Norm Burleson, Bookseller; 0-930577),* 104 First Ave., P.O. Box 15007, Spartanburg, SC 29302 (SAN 677-587X) Tel 803-583-8845.
N Foster Baptist, *(North Foster Baptist Church),* R.R. 1 Box 282 E. Killingly Rd., Foster, RI 02825 (SAN 282-0595) Tel 401-647-5805; Dist. by: Rhode Island Pubns. Society, 189 Wickenden St., Providence, RI 02903 (SAN 219-9696) Tel 401-272-1776.
N Geller Pub, *(Geller, Norman, Pubs.; 0-915753),* P.O. Box 3217, Auburn, ME 04210 (SAN 293-9681) Tel 207-783-2400.
N Ill U Pr, *(Northern Illinois Univ. Pr.; 0-87580),* Williston, 320A, DeKalb, IL 60115 (SAN 202-8875) Tel 815-753-1826.
N Kolko
See S G Phillips
N Point Pr, *(North Point Pr.; 0-86547),* 850 Talbot Ave., Berkeley, CA 94706 (SAN 220-133X) Tel 415-527-6260; Dist. by: Farrar Straus Giroux, Inc, 19 Union Sq., W., New York, NY 10003 (SAN 206-782X) Tel 212-741-6900.
N S Wait, *(Wait, N. S.; 0-911588),* Box 407, Valparaiso, IN 46384 (SAN 206-6491). Formerly H. H. Wait Pub.
N Watson
See Watson Pub Intl
NABPR, *(National Assn. of Baptist Professors of Religion; 0-932180; 0-86554),* Mercer Univ., Macon, GA 31207 (SAN 211-2175) Tel 912-744-2880; Toll free: 1-800-637-2378; Dist. by: Mercer Univ. Pr., Macon, GA 31207 (SAN 220-0716).
NACM, *(National Assn. of Credit Management; 0-934914),* 520 Eighth Ave., New York, NY 10018-6571 (SAN 205-7573) Tel 212-947-5070.
Naiad Pr, *(Naiad Pr.; 0-930044; 0-941483),* P.O. Box 10543, Tallahassee, FL 32302 (SAN 206-801X) Tel 904-539-9322.
NAL, *(NAL Penguin, Inc.; 0-451; 0-452; 0-453),* Subs. of Pearson, Inc., 1633 Broadway, New York, NY 10019 (SAN 206-8079) Tel 212-397-8000; Orders to: 120 Woodine St., Bergenfield, NJ 07621 (SAN 206-8087) Tel 201-387-0600. *Imprints:* Ment (Mentor Books); Mer (Meridian Books); Plume (Plume Books); Sig (Signet Books); Sig Classics (Signet Classics).
Namuk Intl Inc, *(Namuk International, Inc.; 0-933057),* P.O. Box 4543, Silver Spring, MD 20904 (SAN 689-7738); 1011 Brantford Ave., Silver Spring, MD 20904 Tel 301-622-4744.
NAPSAC Reprods, *(NAPSAC Reproductions; 0-934426),* Rte. 1, Box 646, Marble Hill, MO 63764 (SAN 222-4607) Tel 314-238-4273.
Natl Acad Pr, *(National Academy Pr.; 0-309),* Div. of National Academy of Sciences, 2101 Constitution Ave., NW, Washington, DC 20418 (SAN 202-8891) Tel 202-334-3313.
Natl Academy Songwriters, *(National Academy of Songwriters; 0-916641),* P.O. Box 421411, San Francisco, CA 94142 (SAN 200-4526).

Natl Assn Child Ed, *(National Assn. for the Education of Young Children; 0-912674; 0-935989),* 1834 Connecticut Ave., NW, Washington, DC 20009-5786 (SAN 202-8905) Tel 202-232-8777; Toll free: 800-424-2460.
Natl Assn Chr Soc Wk *See* N American Assn
Natl Cath Educ, *(National Catholic Educational Assn.),* 1077 30th St. NW, Suite 100, Washington, DC 20007-3852 (SAN 676-8636) Tel 202-337-6232.
Natl Cath Pharm, *(National Catholic Pharmacists Guild of the United States),* 1012 Surrey Hills Dr., St. Louis, MO 63117 (SAN 224-4209) Tel 314-645-0085.
Natl Cath Reporter *See* Sheed & Ward MO
Natl Christian Pr, *(National Christian Pr., Inc.; 0-934916),* P.O. Box 937, Seagoville, TX 75159 (SAN 212-1182) Tel 214-287-7179; P.O. Box 1001, Jonesboro, AR 72401 (SAN 693-496X); Orders to: P.O. Box 6709, Moore, OK 73153 Tel 405-794-8298.
Natl Coun Crime, *(National Council on Crime & Delinquency),* 77 Maiden Ln., 4th Flr., San Francisco, CA 94108 (SAN 236-9095) Tel 415-956-5651.
Natl Ctr Diaconate, *(National Ctr. for the Diaconate; 0-9605798),* 14 Beacon St., Rm. 103, Boston, MA 02108 (SAN 220-1763) Tel 617-742-1460.
Natl Gallery Art, *(National Gallery of Art; 0-89468),* Fourth St. & Constitution Ave., NW, Washington, DC 20565 (SAN 203-5545) Tel 202-842-6207; Dist. by: Univ. of Chicago Pr., 5801 Ellis Ave., 3rd Flr., S., Chicago, IL 60637 (SAN 202-5280) Tel 312-962-7693; Dist. by: Univ. Pr. of New England, 3 Lebanon St., Hanover, NH 03755 (SAN 203-3283) Tel 603-646-3349; Dist. by: Univ. of Wash. Pr., P.O. Box C50096, Seattle, WA 98145 (SAN 212-2502) Tel 206-543-8870.
Natl Inst Phil, *(National Institute of Philanthropy; 0-9614316),* 1092 E. Mendocino St., Altadena, CA 91001 (SAN 687-522X) Tel 818-797-5606.
Natl Learning, *(National Learning Corp.; 0-8373; 0-8293),* 212 Michael Dr., Syosset, NY 11791 (SAN 206-8869) Tel 516-921-8888; Toll free: 800-645-6337. Educational, commercial, industrial and government sales.
Natl Marriage *See* Intl Marriage
Natl Parks & Cons, *(National Parks & Conservation Assn.; 0-940091),* 1015 31st St., NW, Washington, DC 20007 (SAN 225-1124) Tel 202-944-8530.
Natl Poet Foun, *(National Poetry Foundation; 0-915032),* Univ. of Maine, 305 Neville Hall, Orono, ME 04469 (SAN 206-5088) Tel 207-581-3814.
Natl Pr Inc, *(National Pr., Inc.; 0-915765),* 7508 Wisconsin Ave., Bethesda, MD 20814 (SAN 293-8839) Tel 301-657-1616; Toll free: 800-NA-Books.
Natl Textbk, *(National Textbook Co.; 0-8442; 0-8325),* 4255 W. Touhy Ave., Lincolnwood, IL 60646 (SAN 169-2208) Tel 312-679-5500; Toll free: 800-323-4900. *Imprints:* Passport Bks (Passport Books).
Natl U *Imprint of* **Assoc Faculty Pr**
Natl Wildlife, *(National Wildlife Federation, Div. of Bks. & Special Pubns.; 0-912186),* 8925 Leesburg Pike, Vienna, VA 22180 (SAN 202-8980) Tel 703-790-4227.
Naturegraph, *(Naturegraph Pubs., Inc.; 0-911010; 0-87961),* P.O. Box 1075, Happy Camp, CA 96039 (SAN 202-8999) Tel 916-493-5353.
Navajo Coll Pr, *(Navajo Community College Pr.; 0-912586),* Navajo Community College, Tsaile, AZ 86556 (SAN 201-9582).
Navajo Curr, *(Navajo Curriculum Ctr. Pr.; 0-936008),* Rough Rock Demonstration Schl., Star Rte. 1, Rough Rock, AZ 86503 (SAN 203-1604) Tel 602-728-3311.
NavPress, *(Navpress, A Ministry of The Navigators; 0-89109),* P.O. Box 6000, Colorado Springs, CO 80934 (SAN 211-5352) Tel 303-598-1212; Toll free: 800-525-7151.
Nazareth Pubns *See* Yuganta Pr
NC Archives, *(North Carolina Div. of Archives & History; 0-86526),* Historical Pubns. Section, 109 E. Jones St., Raleigh, NC 27611 (SAN 203-7246) Tel 919-733-7442.
NCJW, *(NCJW, Inc.; 0-941840),* 15 E. 26th St., New York, NY 10010 (SAN 239-2658) Tel 212-532-1740.
NCMA, *(North Carolina Museum of Art; 0-88259),* 2110 Blue Ridge Blvd., Raleigh, NC 27607 (SAN 202-9030) Tel 919-833-1935.
NE Bks, *(Northeast Bks.; 0-937374),* Div. of Cultural Society of Northeastern Pennsylvania, 401 Clark St., Clarks Green, PA 18411 (SAN 215-2665) Tel 717-586-0077.
NE U Pr, *(Northeastern Univ. Pr.; 0-930350; 1-55553),* 360 Huntington Ave., Huntington Plaza, Suite 272, Boston, MA 02115 (SAN 205-3764) Tel 617-437-5473; Orders to: P.O. Box 250, Ithaca, NY 14851 (SAN 282-0668) Tel 607-277-2211.
Neal-Schuman, *(Neal-Schuman Pubs., Inc.; 0-918212; 1-55570),* 23 Leonard St., New York, NY 10013 (SAN 210-2455) Tel 212-925-8650.
Near Eastern *Imprint of* **Holmes Pub**
Nelson, *(Nelson, Thomas, Pubs.; 0-8407),* P.O. Box 141000, Nelson Pl. at Elm Hill Pike, Nashville, TN 37214 (SAN 209-3820) Tel 615-889-9000; Toll free: 800-251-4000.
Nelson-Hall, *(Nelson-Hall, Inc.; 0-911012; 0-88229; 0-8304),* 111 N. Canal St., Chicago, IL 60606 (SAN 202-9065) Tel 312-930-9446.
Nembutsu Pr, *(Nembutsu Pr.; 0-912624),* 6257 Golden West Ave., Temple City, CA 91780 (SAN 208-0060).
Neo-Am Church, *(Original Kleptonian Neo-American Church, The),* Box 97, Bethel, VT 05032 (SAN 266-0008) Tel 802-234-5846.
Neolog, *(Neolog Publishing; 0-9613477),* 422 High St., No. 17, Medford, MA 02156 (SAN 657-3673) Tel 617-391-7894.
Net Pr, *(NET Pr.; 0-937462),* 5001 Ave. N, Lubbock, TX 79412 (SAN 291-8005) Tel 806-762-8094; Toll free: 800-632-4769; Toll free: 800-892-4769 (in TX).
Nevada Pubns, *(Nevada Pubns.; 0-913814),* 4135 Badger Cir., Reno, NV 89509 (SAN 203-7319) Tel 702-747-0800.
New Age, *(New Age Pr., Inc.; 0-87613),* 105 WNC Mall Hwy. 70, Black Mountain, NC 28711 (SAN 203-7327) Tel 704-669-6214.
New Age Bible, *(New Age Bible & Philosophy Ctr.; 0-933963),* 1139 Lincoln Blvd., Santa Monica, CA 90403 (SAN 693-0697) Tel 213-395-4346; Dist. by: DeVorss & Co., P.O. Box, 1046 Princeton Dr., Marina del Rey, CA 90294 (SAN 168-9886) Tel 213-870-7478; Dist. by: Rosicrucian Fellowship, 2222 Mission Ave., Oceanside, CA 92054 (SAN 203-0756) Tel 619-757-6600.
New Age Min Spiritualist, *(New Age Ministries Spiritualist Church in Christ on Earth),* P.O. Box 129, Lake Helen, FL 32744 (SAN 211-7967).
New Begin Co, *(New Beginnings Co.; 0-932489),* 711 E. Walnut St. Suite 401, Pasadena, CA 91101 (SAN 687-4304) Tel 818-793-3612.
New Capernaum, *(New Capernaum Works; 0-938792),* Div. of Universal Spiritual Action, 4615 NE Emerson St., Portland, OR 97218 (SAN 215-8922) Tel 503-284-1339.
New Century, *(New Century Pubs., Inc.; 0-8329),* Div. of New Century Education Corp., 220 Old New Brunswick Rd., Piscataway, NJ 08854 (SAN 217-1201) Tel 201-981-0820.
New City, *(New City Pr.; 0-911782),* Div. of Iocolare Movement, 206 Skillman Ave., Brooklyn, NY 11211 (SAN 203-7335) Tel 718-782-2844.
New Coll U Pr, *(New College & Univ. Pr., The; 0-8084),* P.O. Box 1392, Schenectady, NY 12301 (SAN 203-6223) Tel 518-346-2649. *Imprints:* Twayne (Twayne's U. S. Author Series).
New Collage, *(New Collage Pr.; 0-936814),* 5700 N. Tamiami Trail, Sarasota, FL 33580 (SAN 210-6159) Tel 813-355-7671; Dist. by: Faxon Co., The, 15 SW Park, Westwood, MA 02090 (SAN 159-8619) Tel 617-329-3350.
New Directions, *(New Directions Publishing Corp.; 0-8112),* 80 Eighth Ave., New York, NY 10011 (SAN 202-9081) Tel 212-255-0230; Dist. by: W. W. Norton Co., 500 Fifth Ave., New York, NY 10110 (SAN 202-5795) Tel 212-354-5500.
New Eng Pr VT, *(New England Pr., Inc., The; 0-933050),* P.O. Box 575, Shelburne, VT 05482 (SAN 213-6376) Tel 802-863-2520.
New Eng SF Assoc, *(New England Science Fiction Assn.; 0-915368),* Box G, MIT Branch P.O., Cambridge, MA 02139 (SAN 223-8187).
New Era Pubns MI, *(New Era Pubns., Inc.; 0-939830),* P.O. Box 8139, Ann Arbor, MI 48107 (SAN 220-1941) Tel 313-663-1929.
New Hope Bks *Imprint of* **Revell**
New Horizon NJ, *(New Horizon Pr. Pubs., Inc.; 0-88282),* P.O. Box 669, Far Hills, NJ 07931 (SAN 677-119X) Tel 201-234-9546; Toll free: 800-257-5755; Orders to: Charles Scribner & Sons, Front & Brown Sts., Riverside, NJ 08075 (SAN 663-3099).
New Horizons, *(New Horizons Pr.; 0-914914),* P.O. Box 1758, Chico, CA 95927 (SAN 206-7927) Tel 916-895-6227.
New Leaf, *(New Leaf Pr.; 0-89221),* P.O. Box 311, Green Forest, AR 72638 (SAN 207-9518) Tel 501-438-5288; Toll free: 800-643-9535.
New Life Faith, *(New Life Thru Faith Pubns.; 0-934285),* P.O. Box 598, Mesa, AZ 85201 (SAN 693-3173) Tel 602-986-1000.
New Mind Prod, *(New Mind Prods.; 0-933821),* P.O. Box 5185, Jersey City, NJ 07305 (SAN 200-5565) Tel 201-434-1939.
New Puritan, *(New Puritan Library, Inc.; 0-932050),* 91 Lytle Rd., Fletcher, NC 28732 (SAN 213-4217).
New Research, *(New Research Pubns.; 0-910891),* P.O. Box 231, Greenvale, NY 11548 (SAN 274-0389) Tel 516-293-1171.
New Soc Pubs, *(New Society Pubs.; 0-86571),* Div. of New Society Education Foundation, Inc., 4722 Baltimore Ave., Philadelphia, PA 19143 (SAN 213-540X) Tel 215-726-6543.
New Testament Christ Pr, *(New Testament Christian Pr.; 0-931247),* P.O. Box 1694, Media, PA 19063 (SAN 682-0050) Tel 215-544-2871.
New Univ Pr, *(New Univ. Pr.; 0-89044),* 737 N. LaSalle St., Chicago, IL 60610 (SAN 680-0661) Tel 312-944-2525; Orders to: Daphnean Pr., 737 N. LaSalle St., Chicago, IL 60610 (SAN 657-1344) Tel 312-944-2525.
New Ways Min, *(New Ways Ministry; 0-935877),* 4012 29th St., Mount Rainier, MD 20712 (SAN 695-877X) Tel 301-277-5674.
New World Press NY, *(New World Pr.; 0-911026),* P.O. Box 416, New York, NY 10017 (SAN 203-736X) Tel 212-972-0460.
New Worlds, *(New Worlds Unlimited; 0-917398),* 3-42 26th St., Fair Lawn, NJ 07410 (SAN 207-267X); Orders to: P.O. Box 556, Saddle Brook, NJ 07662 (SAN 207-2688).
Newberry, *(Newberry Library; 0-911028),* 60 W. Walton St., Chicago, IL 60610 (SAN 203-7378) Tel 312-943-9090; Toll free: 800-621-2736.
Newbury Bks, *(Newbury Bks.; 0-912728; 0-912729),* P.O. Box 29, Topsfield, MA 01983-0029 (SAN 203-7386) Tel 617-887-5082.
Newcastle Pub, *(Newcastle Publishing Co., Inc.; 0-87877),* 13419 Saticoy St., North Hollywood, CA 91605 (SAN 202-9154) Tel 213-873-3191; Orders to: P.O. Box 7589, Van Nuys, CA 91409 (SAN 202-9162).
NFCLC, *(National Federation of Christian Life Communities; 0-913605),* 3721 Westminster Pl., St. Louis, MO 63108 (SAN 276-4555) Tel 314-533-3185.
Nicolas-Hays, *(Nicolas-Hays, Inc.; 0-89254),* P.O. Box 612, York Beach, ME 03910 (SAN 662-0949) Tel 207-363-4393; Toll free: 800-423-7079 (For orders only); Dist. by: Samuel Weiser, Inc., P.O. Box 612, York Beach, ME 03910 (SAN 202-9588) Tel 207-363-4393.
Nilgiri Pr, *(Nilgiri Pr.; 0-915132),* P.O. Box 477, Petaluma, CA 94953 (SAN 207-6853) Tel 707-878-2369.
Ninth Hse Pr *See* ENR Word
NOK Pubs, *(NOK Pubs., Intl.; 0-88357),* 155 W. 88th St., No. 3R, New York, NY 10024-2428 (SAN 205-7522) Tel 212-675-5785.

NOLPE, *(National Organization on Legal Problems of Education),* 3601 SW 29th St., Suite 223, Topeka, KS 66614 (SAN 226-6105) Tel 913-273-3550.
Noodle-Doosey, *(Noodle-Doosey Pr.; 0-913281),* P.O. Box 716, Manchester, MD 21102 (SAN 285-8258) Tel 301-374-2605.
Noontide, *(Noontide Pr., The; 0-911038; 0-939482),* P.O. Box 1248, Torrance, CA 90505 (SAN 213-1307).
NORC, *(NORC, Social Science Research Ctr.; 0-932132),* Affil. of Univ. of Chicago, 1155 E. 60th St., Chicago, IL 60637 (SAN 205-7735) Tel 312-702-1213.
North American Inc, *(North American, Inc.; 0-930244),* P.O. Box 65, New Brunswick, NJ 08903 (SAN 210-6469) Tel 201-246-8546.
North Atlantic, *(North Atlantic Bks.; 0-938190; 0-913028; 1-55643),* Div. of Society of the Study of Native Arts & Science, 2320 Blake St., Berkeley, CA 94704 (SAN 203-1655) Tel 415-540-7934.
North Central, *(North Central Publishing Co.; 0-935476),* Riverview Industrial Park, 274 Fillmore Ave. East, St. Paul, MN 55107 (SAN 203-7459) Tel 612-224-5455.
North Holland *Imprint of* **Elsevier**
North South Bks *Imprint of* **H Holt & Co**
Northeast A S, *(Northeast Academic Services, Inc.; 0-913811),* 10 Lydia Dr., Wappingers, NY 12590 (SAN 286-1372) Tel 914-297-6389.
Northland, *(Northland Pr.; 0-87358),* Div. of Justin Industries, P.O. Box N, Flagstaff, AZ 86002 (SAN 202-9251) Tel 602-774-5251; Toll free: 800-346-3257; Toll free: 800-462-6657 (in AZ).
Northwest Pub, *(Northwestern Publishing Hse.; 0-8100),* 1250 N. 113th St., Milwaukee, WI 53226-0975 (SAN 206-7943) Tel 414-442-1810; P.O. Box 26975, Milwaukee, WI 53226-0975 (SAN 665-7494).
Northwestern U Pr, *(Northwestern Univ. Pr.; 0-8101),* 1735 Benson Ave., Evanston, IL 60201 (SAN 202-5787) Tel 312-491-5313.
Norton, *(Norton, W. W., & Co., Inc.; 0-393),* 500 Fifth Ave., New York, NY 10110 (SAN 202-5795) Tel 212-354-5500; Toll free: 800-223-2584. *Imprints:* NortonC (Norton College Division).
NortonC *Imprint of* **Norton**
Norwegian-Am Hist Assn, *(Norwegian-American Historical Assn.; 0-87732),* St. Olaf College, Northfield, MN 55057 (SAN 203-1086) Tel 507-663-3221.
Norwood Edns, *(Norwood Editions; 0-88305; 0-8482),* P.O. Box 38, Norwood, PA 19074 (SAN 206-8613) Tel 215-583-4550.
Now Comns, *(Now Communications Co.; 0-940175),* P.O. Box 5668, Austin, TX 78763 (SAN 664-3019); 2511 Hartford Rd., Austin, TX 78703 (SAN 664-3027) Tel 512-478-7109.
Numard Bks, *(Numard Bks.; 0-9612266),* 3231 Beneva Rd., No. 102, Sarasota, FL 33582 (SAN 289-4807) Tel 813-924-5162.
Numismatic Fine Arts, *(Numismatic Fine Arts, Inc.),* Member of Association internationale des Numismatistes professionels, 10100 Santa Monica Blvd., 6th Flr., Los Angeles, CA 90067 (SAN 205-9029) Tel 213-278-1535.
Nur Pubns, *(Nur-I-Alam Pubns.; 0-9608440),* 2331 N. Dunn St., Bloomington, IN 47401 (SAN 663-2963) Tel 812-339-5615; Dist. by: Worldwide Evangelization Crusade, 709 Pennsylvania Ave., Fort Washington, PA 19034 (SAN 276-8577) Tel 215-646-2322.
NW Christian Pubns, *(Northwest Christian Pubns., Inc.; 0-914271),* P.O. Box 31133, Seattle, WA 98103 (SAN 287-5926) Tel 206-523-9911.
NY Acad Sci, *(New York Academy of Sciences; 0-89072; 0-89766),* Pubns. Dept., 2 E. 63rd St., New York, NY 10021 (SAN 203-753X) Tel 212-838-0230; Toll free: 800-843-6927.
NY Circus Pubns, *(New York Circus Pubns., Inc.),* P.O. Box 37, Times Sq. Sta., New York, NY 10108 (SAN 661-440X).
NY Labor News, *(New York Labor News; 0-935534),* 914 Industrial Ave., Palo Alto, CA 94303 (SAN 202-0947) Tel 415-494-1532.
NY Pub Lib, *(New York Public Library; 0-87104),* Pubns. Office, Fifth Ave. & 42nd St., New York, NY 10018 (SAN 202-926X) Tel 212-512-0203; Orders to: Publishing Ctr. for Cultural Resources, 625 Broadway, New York, NY 10012 (SAN 209-9926) Tel 212-260-2010; Orders to: New York Public Library, Branch Libraries, 455 Fifth Ave., New York, NY 10016 (SAN 695-6254) Tel 212-340-0897.
NYGS, *(New York Graphic Society Bks.; 0-8212),* Div. of Little, Brown & Co., 34 Beacon St., Boston, MA 02106 (SAN 202-5841) Tel 617-227-0730; Toll free: 800-343-9204; Dist. by: Little, Brown & Co., 200 West St., Waltham, MA 02254 (SAN 281-8892).
NYU Pr, *(New York Univ. Pr.; 0-8147),* 70 Washington Sq., S., New York, NY 10012 (SAN 658-1293) Tel 212-598-2886; Dist. by: Columbia Univ. Pr., 136 S. Broadway, Irvington-on-Hudson, NY 10533 (SAN 212-2480) Tel 914-591-9111.
O L Holmes, *(Holmes, Opal Laurel, Pub.; 0-918522),* P.O. Box 2535, Boise, ID 83701 (SAN 210-1017) Tel 208-344-4517; Dist. by: Baker & Taylor Co., Midwest Div., 501 Gladiola Ave., Momence, IL 60954 (SAN 169-2100).
O R Miller, *(Miller, Oscar R.; 0-9600552),* P.O. Box 229, Berlin, OH 44610 (SAN 203-7556) Tel 216-893-2870.
O T O, *(OTO (Society Ordo Templi Orientis in America); 0-913735),* P.O. Box 90144, Nashville, TN 37209 (SAN 219-9610); Dist. by: The Distributors, 702 S. Michigan, South Bend, IN 46618 (SAN 169-2488) Tel 219-232-8500. Moved, left no fowarding address.
Oak Tree Pubns, *(Oak Tree Pubns., Inc.; 0-916392; 0-86679),* Div. of Vizcom, Inc., 9601 Aero Dr., Suite 202, San Diego, CA 92123 (SAN 211-4828) Tel 619-560-5163.
OAS, *(Organization of American States; 0-8270),* 17th St. & Constitution Ave., NW, Washington, DC 20006 (SAN 206-8877) Tel 202-789-3533.
Oasis Bks, *(Oasis Bks.; 0-939213),* P.O. Box 37021, Denver, CO 80237 (SAN 662-6092); 7564 E. Hinsdale Ave., Englewood, CO 80112 (SAN 662-6106) Tel 303-694-2710.
Oblate, *(Oblate Fathers),* P.O. Box 96, San Antonio, TX 78291 (SAN 209-5890) Tel 512-736-1685.
O'Brien, *(O'Brien, F. M., Bookseller),* 34 & 36 High St., Portland, ME 04101 (SAN 203-7580).
Occidental, *(Occidental Pr.; 0-911050),* P.O. Box 1005, Washington, DC 20013 (SAN 203-7599).
Ocean Tree Bks, *(Ocean Tree Bks.; 0-943734),* P.O. Box 1295, Santa Fe, NM 87504 (SAN 241-0478) Tel 505-983-1412; Dist. by: Bookpeople, 2929 Fifth St., Berkeley, CA 94710 (SAN 168-9517); Dist. by: DeVorss & Co., P.O. Box 550, 1046 Princeton Dr., Marina del Rey, CA 90294 (SAN 168-9886) Tel 213-870-7478; Dist. by: New Leaf Distributors, 1020 White St., SW, Atlanta, GA 30310 (SAN 169-1449) Tel 404-755-2665; Dist. by: Starlite Distributors, P.O. Box 20729, Reno, NV 89515 (SAN 131-1921) Tel 702-359-5676; Dist. by: Distributors, The, 702 S. Michigan, South Bend, IN 46618 (SAN 169-2488) Tel 219-232-8500.
Oceana, *(Oceana Pubns., Inc.; 0-379),* 75 Main St., Dobbs Ferry, NY 10522 (SAN 202-5744) Tel 914-693-1733.
Ocelot Pr, *(Ocelot Pr.; 0-912434),* P.O. Box 504, Claremont, CA 91711 (SAN 203-7602) Tel 714-621-2200.
October, *(October Hse.; 0-8079),* P.O. Box 454, Stonington, CT 06378 (SAN 203-7610) Tel 203-535-3725.
Oddo, *(Oddo Publishing, Inc.; 0-87783),* Storybook Acres, Box 68, Fayetteville, GA 30214 (SAN 282-0757) Tel 404-461-7627.
Oelgeschlager, *(Oelgeschlager, Gunn & Hain, Inc.; 0-89946),* 131 Clarendon St., Boston, MA 02116 (SAN 213-6937) Tel 617-437-9620.
Off Christian Fellowship, *(Officers Christian Fellowship),* P.O. Box 36200, Denver, CO 80236 (SAN 291-8439).
O'Hara, *(O'Hara, J. Philip, Inc., Pubs.; 0-87955),* c/o Scroll Pr., Inc., 2858 Valerie Ct., Merrick, NY 11566 (SAN 202-5868) Tel 516-379-4283. Do no confuse with Betsy O'Hara in San Francisco, CA.
Ohara Pubns, *(Ohara Pubns., Inc.; 0-89750),* 1813 Victory Pl., Burbank, CA 91504 (SAN 205-3632) Tel 818-843-4444; Toll free: 800-423-2874; P.O. Box 7728, Burbank, CA 91510 (SAN 658-1315). Do not confuse with Betsy O'Hara, San Francisco, CA.
Ohio Hist Soc, *(Ohio Historical Society; 0-87758),* Ohio Historical Ctr., 1985 Velma Ave., Columbus, OH 43211 (SAN 202-1331) Tel 614-297-2300.
Ohio St U Pr, *(Ohio State Univ. Pr.; 0-8142),* 1050 Carmack Rd., Columbus, OH 43210-1002 (SAN 202-8158) Tel 614-292-6930.
Ohio U Pr, *(Ohio Univ. Pr.; 0-8214),* Scott Quadrangle, Rm. 223, Athens, OH 45701 (SAN 282-0773) Tel 614-593-1155; Toll free: 800-242-7737; Orders to: Harper & Row Pubs., Inc., Keystone Industrial Pk., Scranton, PA 18512 (SAN 282-0781).
Okefenokee Pr, *(Okefenokee Press; 0-9601606),* Rte. 3, Box 142-C, Folkston, GA 31537 (SAN 208-3752) Tel 912-496-7401.
Oliver-Nelson, *(Oliver-Nelson; 0-8407),* Div. of Thomas Nelson Pubs., Nelson Pl. at Elm Hill Pike, Nashville, TN 37214 (SAN 689-1470); Toll free: 800-251-4000.
OLW Editions, *(OLW Editions; 0-934995),* Sub. of Servants of Our Lady, Rte. 4, Box 9375, Barre, VT 05641 (SAN 694-6585) Tel 802-476-4618; Dist. by: Ravengate Pr., The, P.O. Box 49, Still River, MA 01467 (SAN 203-090X) Tel 617-456-8181.
Olympus Pub Co, *(Olympus Publishing Co.; 0-913420),* 1670 E. 13th, S., Salt Lake City, UT 84105 (SAN 202-8204) Tel 801-583-3666.
Omaha Sec Nat, *(National Council Of Jewish Women, Omaha Section; 0-9612406),* 1720 S. 86th Ave., Omaha, NE 68124 (SAN 283-3484).
Omega LA, *(Omega Books; 0-9613094),* 5648 Heatherdale Dr., Los Angeles, CA 90043 (SAN 294-6386) Tel 213-293-9608.
Omega Pr NM, *(Omega Pr.; 0-930872),* Div. of Sufi Order in the West, P.O. Box 574, Lebanon Springs, NY 12114 (SAN 214-1493) Tel 518-794-8181; Dist. by: New Leaf Distributing, 1020 White St., SW, Atlanta, GA 30310 (SAN 169-1449) Tel 404-755-2665.
Omega Pubns OR, *(Omega Pubns.; 0-86694),* Div. of Omega Corp., P.O. Box 4130, Medford, OR 97501 (SAN 220-1534) Tel 503-826-1030.
Omenana, *(Omenana; 0-943324),* 116 Howland St., Roxbury, MA 02121 (SAN 240-5571) Tel 617-445-0161.
OMF Bks, *(OMF Bks.; 0-85363),* Div. of Overseas Missionary Fellowship, 404 S. Church St., Robesonia, PA 19551 (SAN 211-8351) Tel 215-693-5881.
Ontario Rev NJ, *(Ontario Review Pr.; 0-86538),* 9 Honey Brook Dr., Princeton, NJ 08540 (SAN 658-134X); Dist. by: Persea Bks., Inc., 225 Lafayette St., New York, NY 10012 (SAN 212-8233) Tel 212-431-5270.
Open Bible, *(Open Bible Pubs.; 0-9608160),* Affil. of Open Bible Standard Churches, 2020 Bell Ave., Des Moines, IA 50315-1096 (SAN 238-8545) Tel 515-288-6761.
Open Court, *(Open Court Publishing Co.; 0-912050; 0-89688; 0-8126; 0-87548),* Div. of Carus Corp., 315 Fifth St., Peru, IL 61354 (SAN 202-5876) Tel 815-223-2520; Toll free: 800-435-6850; Toll free: 800-892-6831. *Imprints:* Library Pr (Library Press).
Open Door Inc, *(Open Door, Inc., The; 0-940136),* P.O. Box 855, Charlottesville, VA 22902 (SAN 217-0795) Tel 804-293-5068; Dist. by: Spring Arbor Distributors, 10885 Textile Rd., Belleville, MI 48111 (SAN 158-9016) Tel 313-481-0900.
Open Path, *(Open Path, The; 0-9602722),* 703 N. 18th St., Boise, ID 83702 (SAN 215-9759) Tel 208-342-0208.
Open Univ Pr *Imprint of* **Taylor & Francis**
Options, *(Options Publishing Co.; 0-917400),* P.O. Box 311, Wayne, NJ 07470 (SAN 208-9629) Tel 201-694-2327.

OR Pub, *(O R Publishing; 0-9614162),* 1481 Lafayette Rd., Claremont, CA 91711 (SAN 686-5518) Tel 714-624-1792; Dist. by: The Huntley Bookstore, 8th at Darthmouth, Claremont, CA 91711 (SAN 200-9447) Tel 714-621-8168.
Oracle Pr LA, *(Oracle Pr.; 0-88127),* 5323 Heatherstone Dr., Baton Rouge, LA 70820 (SAN 241-3434) Tel 504-766-5577.
Orange County Genealog, *(Orange County Genealogical Society; 0-9604116),* 101 Main St., Goshen, NY 10924-1917 (SAN 220-021X).
Orbis Bks, *(Orbis Bks.; 0-88344),* Maryknoll, NY 10545 (SAN 202-828X) Tel 914-941-7590; Toll free: 800-258-5838.
Oreg St U Pr, *(Oregon State Univ. Pr.; 0-87071),* Oregon State Univ., 101 Waldo Hall, Corvallis, OR 97331 (SAN 202-8328) Tel 503-754-3166.
Oregon Hist, *(Oregon Historical Society Pr.; 0-87595),* 1230 SW Park Ave., Portland, OR 97205-2483 (SAN 202-8301) Tel 503-222-1741.
Org Resources Pr, *(Organization Resources Pr., Ltd.; 0-938180),* P.O. Box 977, Indianapolis, IN 46206 (SAN 692-7467).
Orient Bk Dist, *(Orient Bk. Distributors; 0-89684),* P.O. Box 100, Livingston, NJ 07039 (SAN 211-819X) Tel 201-992-6992.
Oriental Bk Store, *(Oriental Bk. Store, The),* P.O. Box 177, South Pasadena, CA 91030-0177 (SAN 285-0818) Tel 818-577-2413; 630 E. Colorado Blvd., Pasadena, CA 91101 (SAN 285-0826) Tel 213-577-2413.
Oriental Classics *Imprint of* **Holmes Pub**
Oriental Inst, *(Univ. of Chicago, Oriental Institute; 0-918986),* 1155 E. 58th St., Chicago, IL 60637 (SAN 276-430X) Tel 312-702-9508.
Orientalia, *(Orientalia Art, Ltd.; 0-87902),* P.O. Box 597, New York, NY 10003 (SAN 282-0919); 61 Fourth Ave., New York, NY 10003 (SAN 282-0927).
Original Pubns, *(Original Pubns.; 0-942272),* Subs. of Jamil Prods. Corp., 2486 Webster Ave., Bronx, NY 10458 (SAN 238-1001) Tel 212-367-9589.
Orion *Imprint of* **Signature Bks**
Orovan Bks, *(Orovan Bks.; 0-913748),* Div. of Orovan Assocs., P.O. Box 6082, Honolulu, HI 96818 (SAN 203-7793) Tel 808-841-7992.
Orthodox Chr, *(Orthodox Christian Educational Society; 0-938366),* 1916 W. Warner Ave., Chicago, IL 60613 (SAN 215-1642) Tel 312-549-0584.
Oryx Pr, *(Oryx Pr.; 0-912700; 0-89774),* 2214 N. Central Ave., Phoenix, AZ 85004-1483 (SAN 220-0201) Tel 602-254-6156; Toll free: 800-457-6799.
Our Baby's
See Gibson
Our Sunday Visitor, *(Our Sunday Visitor, Publishing Div.; 0-87973),* 200 Noll Plaza, Huntington, IN 46750 (SAN 202-8344) Tel 219-356-8400; Toll free: 800-348-2440 except Indiana.
Outdoor Pict, *(Outdoor Pictures; 0-911080),* P.O. Box 277, Anacortes, WA 98221 (SAN 203-7815) Tel 206-293-3200.
Outlet Bk Co, *(Outlet Bk. Co.; 0-87000),* Affil. of Crowns Pubs., Inc., 225 Park Ave., S., New York, NY 10003 (SAN 200-2620) Tel 212-254-1600; Toll free: 800-526-4264. Promotional books of all kinds; remainders, reprints, imports, original publications.
Outlook, *(Outlook Bk. Service, Inc.; 0-911082),* 512 E. Main St., Richmond, VA 23219 (SAN 206-684X).
Overcomer Pr, *(Overcomer Pr., Inc.; 0-942504),* 7300 SW Ninth Ct., P.O. Box 14363, Ft. Lauderdale, FL 33302 (SAN 238-1834) Tel 305-797-8989.
Overlook Pr, *(Overlook Pr.; 0-87951),* 12 W. 21st St., 12th Flr., New York, NY 10010 (SAN 202-8360) Tel 212-337-5472; Orders to: RR 1 Box 496, Woodstock, NY 12498 (SAN 663-6527); Dist. by: Viking Penguin, Inc., 40 W. 23rd St., New York, NY 10010 (SAN 200-2442) Tel 212-337-5200.
Overmountain Pr, *(Overmountain Pr.; 0-932807),* P.O. Box 1261, Johnson City, TN 37605 (SAN 687-6641) Tel 615-926-2691.
Overseas Crusade, *(Overseas Crudades, Inc.),* Div. of Global Church Growth, 25 Corning Ave., Milpitas, CA 95035 (SAN 223-7822) Tel 408-263-1101.
Oxford U Pr, *(Oxford Univ. Pr., Inc.; 0-19),* 200 Madison Ave., New York, NY 10016 (SAN 202-5884) Tel 212-679-7300; Orders to: 16-00 Pollitt Dr., Fair Lawn, NJ 07410 (SAN 202-5892) Tel 201-796-8000.
Oxmoor Hse, *(Oxmoor Hse., Inc.; 0-8487),* P.O. Box 2262, Birmingham, AL 35201 (SAN 205-3462) Tel 205-877-6534; Toll free: 800-242-7737; Dist. by: Little, Brown, 200 West St., Waltham, MA 02254 (SAN 215-3742).
Ozer, *(Ozer, Jerome S., Pub., Inc.; 0-89198),* 340 Tenafly Rd., Englewood, NJ 07631 (SAN 202-8395) Tel 201-567-7040.
P Bedrick Bks, *(Bedrick, Peter, Bks.; 0-911745; 0-87226),* 125 E. 23rd St., New York, NY 10010 (SAN 263-9335) Tel 212-777-1187; Dist. by: Harper & Row Pubs., Inc., Keystone Industrial Pk., Scranton, PA 18512 (SAN 215-3742). *Imprints:* Bedrick Blackie (Bedrick/Blackie).
P C Stauter, *(Stauter, Patrick C.; 0-9617847),* 999 Fortino Blvd., No. 58, Pueblo, CO 81008 (SAN 665-3006) Tel 303-545-6228.
P-H, *(Prentice-Hall; 0-13),* Rte. 9W, Englewood Cliffs, NJ 07632 (SAN 200-2175) Tel 201-592-2000; Orders to: 200 Old Tappan Rd., Old Tappan, NJ 07675 (SAN 215-3939) Tel 201-767-5049. *Imprints:* Busn (Business & Professional Division); Parker Publishing Co (Parker Publishing Company); Reward (Reward Books).
P H Perkins Jr, *(Perkins, Percy H.; 0-9603090),* 1300 Shawnee Dr., Waycross, GA 31501 (SAN 212-2987) Tel 912-283-2803; Dist. by: Lapidary Journal, P.O. Box 80937, San Diego, CA 92138 (SAN 204-9503) Tel 619-297-4841.
P J Willcox, *(Willcox, P. J.; 0-9608436),* P.O. Box 39, Huntington, IN 46750 (SAN 240-8066).
P Lang Pubs, *(Lang, Peter, Publishing, Inc.; 0-8204),* Subs. of Verlag Peter Lang AG (Switzerland), 62 W. 45th St., New York, NY 10036-4202 (SAN 241-5534) Tel 212-302-6740.
P R Odens, *(Odens, Peter R.; 0-9609484),* P.O. Box 222,, El Centro, CA 92244 (SAN 274-2438) Tel 619-356-1243; Orders to: Imperial Arts, P.O. Box 3907, El Centro, CA 92244-3910 (SAN 665-7516).
P Sherrod, *(Sherrod, Paul),* 4410 Olsen, Amarillo, TX 79106 (SAN 212-1395).
P Walsh Pr, *(Walsh, Patrick, Pr.; 0-86700),* 2017 S. Ventura, Tempe, AZ 85282 (SAN 216-6135) Tel 602-968-1549.
Pa Hist & Mus, *(Pennsylvania Historical & Museum Commission; 0-911124; 0-89271),* Box 1026, Harrisburg, PA 17108-1026 (SAN 282-1532) Tel 717-783-1991; Orders to: Pubn. Sales Program, Dept. PL, P.O. Box 11466, Harrisburg, 17108-1466 Tel 717-787-2407.
Pa St U Pr, *(Pennsylvania State Univ. Pr.; 0-271),* 215 Wagner Bldg., University Park, PA 16802 (SAN 213-5760) Tel 814-865-1327.
Pace Educ Systems, *(Pace Educational Systems, Inc.; 0-935385),* 61 Kingsley Rd., Box 113, Kendall Park, NJ 08824 (SAN 695-8915) Tel 201-297-9101.
Pachart Pub Hse, *(Pachart Publishing Hse.; 0-88126; 0-912918),* Div. of Pachart Foundation, P.O. Box 35549, Tucson, AZ 85740 (SAN 204-9139) Tel 602-297-4797; 1130 San Lucas Cir., Tucson, AZ 85704 (SAN 662-1058) Tel 602-297-6760.
Pacif NW Natl Pks, *(Pacific Northwest National Parks & Forests Assn.; 0-914019),* 83 S. King St., Suite 212, Seattle, WA 98104 (SAN 286-8504) Tel 206-442-7958.
Pacific Bks, *(Pacific Bks., Pubs.; 0-87015),* P.O. Box 558, Palo Alto, CA 94302-0558 (SAN 202-8468) Tel 415-856-0550.
Pacific Dist Mennonite
See Kindred Pr
Pacific Inst, *(Pacific Institute; 0-9609174),* P.O. Box 33111, San Diego, CA 92103 (SAN 241-4236) Tel 619-279-9682.
Pacific Mer, *(Pacific Meridian Publishing Co.; 0-911092),* 13540 Lake City Way, NE, Seattle, WA 98125 (SAN 206-832X) Tel 206-362-0900.
Pacific Pr Pub Assn, *(Pacific Pr. Publishing Assn.; 0-8163),* P.O. Box 7000, Boise, ID 83707-1000 (SAN 202-8409) Tel 208-465-2500; Toll free: 800-447-7377.
PAGL Pr, *(PAGL Pr.; 0-913105),* 2854 N. Santiago Blvd., No. 100, Orange, CA 92667 (SAN 283-2372) Tel 714-974-9471.
PAL Pr, *(P.A.L. Pr.; 0-938034),* P.O. Box 487, San Anselmo, CA 94960 (SAN 220-0791) Tel 415-453-8547.
Paladin Pr, *(Paladin Pr.; 0-87364),* P.O. Box 1307, Boulder, CO 80306 (SAN 212-0305); Toll free: 800-824-7888; 2523 Broadway Ave., Boulder, CO 80302 (SAN 662-1066) Tel 303-443-7250.
Palestine Focus, *(Palestine Focus Pubns.; 0-935177),* 1885 Mission St., San Francisco, CA 94103-3584 (SAN 695-460X) Tel 415-861-1552.
Palm Pub Co, *(Palm Publishing Co.; 0-936187),* P.O. Box 8091, Laguna Hills, CA 92654-8091 (SAN 696-8902) Tel 714-458-5708; 25181 Woolwich, Laguna Hills, CA 92653 (SAN 696-8910).
Palos Verdes, *(Palos Verdes Bk. Co.; 0-936848),* P.O. Box 456, Lomita, CA 90717 (SAN 218-4532) Tel 904-383-8727.
Pan-Am Publishing Co, *(Pan-American Publishing Co.; 0-932906),* P.O. Box 1505, Las Vegas, NM 87701 (SAN 212-5366).
Pan Ishtar, *(Pan/Ishtar Unlimited; 0-941698),* P.O. Box 216, Edgewood, TX 75117 (SAN 239-2747) Tel 214-896-1700.
Panjandrum, *(Panjandrum Bks.; 0-915572),* 11321 Iowa Ave., Suite 1, Los Angeles, CA 90025 (SAN 282-1257) Tel 213-477-8771; Dist. by: Baker & Taylor (Western Div.), 380 Edison Way, Reno, NV 89564 (SAN 169-4464) Tel 702-786-6700; Dist. by: Talman Co., Inc., 150 Fifth Ave., Rm. 514, New York, NY 10011 (SAN 200-5204) Tel 212-620-3182; Dist. by: Blackwell North America, 6024 SW Jean Rd., Bldg. G, Lake Oswego, OR 97034 (SAN 656-4917) Tel 503-684-1140; Dist. by: Bookpeople, 2929 Fifth St., Berkeley, CA 94710 (SAN 168-9517); Dist. by: Shakti Distributors, Inc., 1020 White St, SW, Atlanta, GA 30310 (SAN 200-7258); Dist. by: Coutts Library Services, 736-738 Cayuga St., Lewiston, NY 14092 (SAN 169-5401).
Panorama West, *(Panorama West Bks.; 0-914330),* 2002 N. Gateway Suite 102, Fresno, CA 93727 (SAN 216-0501) Tel 209-251-7801.
Pantheon, *(Pantheon Bks.; 0-394),* Div. of Random Hse., Inc., 201 E. 50th St., New York, NY 10022 (SAN 202-862X) Tel 212-751-2600; Orders to: Random Hse., Inc., 400 Hahn Rd., Westminster, MD 21157 (SAN 202-5515).
Para Res, *(Para Research, Inc.; 0-914918),* 1104 Washington St., P.O. Box 61, Gloucester, MA 01930 (SAN 213-4438) Tel 617-283-6297.
Parable, *(Parable),* 38 N. Austin Blvd., Oak Park, IL 60302 (SAN 283-9792) Tel 312-848-0025.
Parables, *(Parables; 0-9614960),* Subs. of Bentley Enterprises, P.O. Box 73, Ludlow, MA 01056 (SAN 693-7535) Tel 413-543-5809.
Paraclete Pr, *(Paraclete Pr.; 0-941478; 1-55725),* Subs. of Creative Joys, Inc., Box 1568, Orleans, MA 02653 (SAN 282-1508); Toll free: 800-451-5006; Rte. 6A, Hilltop Plaza, Orleans, MA 02653 (SAN 664-6239) Tel 617-255-4685.
Paradigm ID, *(Paradigm Co.; 0-941995),* 4650 Seymour Dr., Boise, ID 83704 (SAN 682-8019) Tel 208-322-4440.
Paragon Benson, *(Paragon Assocs./Benson Co., Inc.; 0-89477),* 365 Great Circle Road, Nashville, TN 37228 (SAN 209-9780) Tel 615-259-9111; Dist. by: Alexandria Hse., P.O. Box 23618, Alexandria, IN 46001 (SAN 209-9799).
Paragon-Dynapress, *(Paragon Pr./Dynapress; 0-942910),* P.O. Box 866, Fern Park, FL 32730 (SAN 240-3234) Tel 305-331-5550.
Paragon Hse, *(Paragon Hse. Pubs.; 0-913729; 0-88702; 0-913757),* 2 Hammarskjold Plaza, New York, NY 10017 (SAN 286-1704) Tel 212-223-6433.
Parallax Pr, *(Parallax Pr.; 0-938077),* P.O. Box 7355, Berkeley, CA 94707 (SAN 663-4494) Tel 415-525-0101. Do not confuse with Parallax Pr., Middletown, CT.

Paramount TX, *(Paramount Publishing; 0-942376),* P.O. Box 3730, Amarillo, TX 79116-3730 (SAN 238-1028) Tel 806-355-1040.
Parchment Pr, *(Parchment Pr.; 0-88428),* 1136 Lipscomb Dr., Nashville, TN 37204 (SAN 202-8670) Tel 615-292-6335.
Parent Scene, *(Parent Scene; 0-910529),* P.O. Box 2222, 1280 E. San Bernardino Ave., Redlands, CA 92373 (SAN 260-244X) Tel 714-792-2412.
Park View, *(Park View Pr., Inc.; 0-87813),* 1066 Chicago Ave., Harrisonburg, VA 22801 (SAN 204-9279) Tel 703-434-0765.
Parker Publishing Co *Imprint of* **P-H**
Parkwest Pubns, *(Parkwest Pubns.; 0-88186),* P.O. Caller Box A-10, Cathedral Sta., New York, NY 10025 (SAN 264-6846) Tel 212-222-6100.
Parnassus Imprints, *(Parnassus Imprints; 0-940160),* Box 335, Orleans, MA 02653 (SAN 217-0809); 21 Canal Rd., Orleans, MA 02653 (SAN 658-1366) Tel 617-225-2932.
Partnership Foundation, *(Partnership Foundation, the; 0-934538),* C/O Capon Springs & Farms, Capon Springs, WV 26823 (SAN 220-9918).
Partridge Pair, *(Partridge Pair, Inc., The; 0-9606440),* P.O. Box 61, Sandy Springs, SC 29677 (SAN 218-5776) Tel 803-261-8430.
Pasadena Pr, *(Pasadena Pr.; 0-930227),* 267 S. Madison, No. 204, Pasadena, CA 91106 (SAN 694-6410) Tel 818-796-3840; P.O. Box 60184, Pasadena, CA 91106 (SAN 699-6035).
Pascal Pubs, *(Pascal Pubs.; 0-938836),* 21 Sunnyside Ave., Wellesley, MA 02181 (SAN 215-3319).
Passport Bks *Imprint of* **Natl Textbk**
Past & Mat Rene Ctr, *(Pastoral & Matrimonial Renewal Center; 0-911905),* 67 Prince St., Elizabeth, NJ 07208 (SAN 264-6854) Tel 201-353-8640.
Pastoral Pr, *(Pastoral Pr.; 0-9602378; 0-912405),* Div. of National Assn. of Pastoral Musicians, 225 Sheridan St. NW, Washington, DC 20011 (SAN 272-8966) Tel 202-723-1254.
Pat G Johnson, *(Johnson, Patricia Givens; 0-9614765),* Rte. 2, Box 50, Christiansburg, VA 24073 (SAN 692-915X) Tel 703-382-1251.
Patch As Patch, *(Patch As Patch Can; 0-9601896),* P.O. Box 843, Port Washington, NY 11050 (SAN 239-8575) Tel 516-671-7342.
Path Pr NY, *(Pathfinder Pr.; 0-87348),* 410 West St., New York, NY 10014 (SAN 202-5906) Tel 212-741-0690.
Pathway Pr, *(Pathway Pr.; 0-87148),* Div. of Church of God Publishing Hse., 1080 Montgomery Ave., Cleveland, TN 37311 (SAN 202-8727) Tel 615-476-4512; Toll free: 800-251-7216; Orders to: P.O. Box 2250, Cleveland, TN 37311 (SAN 665-7567).
Pathway Pubns, *(Pathway Pubns., Inc.; 0-9606442),* 1632 Seventh Ave. W., Birmingham, AL 35208 (SAN 218-5784) Tel 205-785-9584.
Pathwork Pr, *(Pathwork Pr.; 0-9614777),* Box 66, Phoenicia, NY 12464 (SAN 692-7009) Tel 914-688-2211; Orders to: Stillpoint Publishing, Box 640, Meeting House Rd., Walpole, NH 03608 (SAN 662-3026) Tel 603-756-3508.
Patmos Pr, *(Patmos Pr.; 0-915762),* P.O. Box V, Shepherdstown, WV 25443 (SAN 207-4192) Tel 304-876-2086.
Patrice Pr, *(Patrice Pr.; 0-935284),* 1701 S. Eighth St., St. Louis, MO 63104 (SAN 203-1019) Tel 314-436-3242.
Patterson Smith, *(Smith, Patterson, Publishing Corp.; 0-87585),* 23 Prospect Terr., Montclair, NJ 07042 (SAN 202-8735) Tel 201-744-3291
Paul R Johnson, *(Johnson, Paul R.; 0-910097),* P.O. Box 2972, Pomona, CA 91769 (SAN 241-3973) Tel 818-338-7245.
Paulist Pr, *(Paulist Pr.; 0-8091),* 997 MacArthur Blvd., Mahwah, NJ 07430 (SAN 202-5159) Tel 201-825-7300.
PAX Tapes, *(PAX Tapes, Inc.),* 611 Rosetta, Florissant, MO 63031 (SAN 265-3923).
PB, *(Pocket Bks., Inc.; 0-671),* Div. of Simon & Schuster, Inc., 1230 Ave. of the Americas, New York, NY 10020 (SAN 202-5922) Tel 212-698-7406; Toll free: 800-223-2336; Orders to: 200 Old Tappan Rd., Old Tappan, NJ 07675 (SAN 662-1147) Tel 201-767-5000.
PBBC Pr, *(Pillsbury Baptist Bible College Pr.; 0-9606952),* 315 S. Grove St., Owatonna, MN 55060 (SAN 207-2734) Tel 507-451-2710.
Peabody Harvard, *(Peabody Museum of Archaeology & Ethnology, Harvard Univ., Pubns. Dept.; 0-87365),* 11 Divinity Ave., Cambridge, MA 02138 (SAN 203-1426) Tel 617-495-3938; Dist. by: Harvard Univ. Pr., 79 Garden St., Cambridge, MA 02138 (SAN 200-2043) Tel 617-495-2600.
Peachtree Pubs, *(Peachtree Pubs., Ltd.; 0-931948),* 494 Armour Cir., NE, Atlanta, GA 30324 (SAN 212-1999) Tel 404-876-8761; Toll free: 800-241-0113; Toll free: 800-282-0225 (In Georgia).
Peacock Ent LA, *(Peacock Enterprises; 0-937673),* P.O. Box 4825, Los Angeles, CA 90051-2825 (SAN 659-2694) Tel 213-722-4669.
Pelican, *(Pelican Publishing Co., Inc.; 0-911116; 0-88289),* 1101 Monroe St., Gretna, LA 70053 (SAN 212-0623) Tel 504-368-1175; Toll free: 800-843-1724; P.O. Box 189, Gretna, LA 70053 (SAN 658-1374); Toll free: 800-843-4558 (in Louisiana).
Pelican Bks *Imprint of* **Penguin**
Pendle Hill, *(Pendle Hill Pubns.; 0-87574),* Pendle Hill, 338 Plush Mill Rd., Wallingford, PA 19086 (SAN 202-8794) Tel 215-566-4514.
Pendragon NY, *(Pendragon Pr.; 0-918728),* Subs. of Camelot Publishing Co., Inc., R.R. 1, Box 159, Stuyvesant, NY 12173-9720 (SAN 213-1463) Tel 518-828-3008.
Pendulum Pr, *(Pendulum Pr., Inc.; 0-88301),* Academic Bldg., Saw Mill Rd., West Haven, CT 06516 (SAN 202-8808) Tel 203-933-2551.
Penfield, *(Penfield Pr.; 0-9603858; 0-941016),* 215 Brown St., Iowa City, IA 52240 (SAN 221-6671) Tel 319-337-9998; Toll free: 800-255-2255 Ext. 9998; Dist. by: Quality Bks., Inc., 918 Sherwood Dr., Lake Bluff, IL 80044-2204 (SAN 169-2127) Tel 312-295-2910.
Penguin, *(Penguin Bks., Inc.; 0-14),* 40 W. 23rd St., New York, NY 10010 (SAN 202-5914) Tel 212-337-5200; Toll free: 800-631-3577. *Imprints:* Pelican Bks (Pelican Books); Puffin Bks (Puffin Books).
Penkevill, *(Penkevill Publishing Co., The; 0-913283),* P.O. Box 212, Greenwood, FL 32443 (SAN 285-8304).
Penn German Soc, *(Pennsylvania German Society; 0-911122),* 55 Kohler School Rd., New Oxford, PA 17350 (SAN 205-1958) Tel 717-624-4106; Orders to: P.O. Box 397, Birdsboro, PA 19508 (SAN 205-1966) Tel 215-582-1441.
Penn Stats Mus
See Univ Mus of U PA
Penn-Yale Expedit, *(Publications of the Pennsylvania-Yale Expedition to Egypt),* Yale Univ., 102 Hall of Graduate Studies, New Haven, CT 06520 (SAN 662-118X) Tel 203-432-2951; c/o Peabody Museum of Natural History, Pubns. Office, 170 Whitney Ave., P.O. Box 6666, New Haven, CT 06511 (SAN 205-177X) Tel 203-432-3786.
Penseur Pr, *(Penseur Pr.; 0-9604044),* P.O. Box 659, El Cerrito, CA 94530 (SAN 214-0764).
Penso Pubns, *(Penso Pubns., Inc.; 0-943796),* 4815 Apollo Dr., Houston, TX 77018 (SAN 241-0656) Tel 713-861-9785.
Pepperdine U Pr, *(Pepperdine Univ. Pr.; 0-932612),* c/o Pepperdine Univ. Bookstore, 1121 W. 79th St., Los Angeles, CA 90044 (SAN 295-3439) Tel 213-971-1884.
Pere Marquette, *(Pere Marquette Pr.; 0-934640),* P.O. Box 495, Alton, IL 62002 (SAN 206-3042) Tel 618-462-5415.
Perf Pr, *(Performance Pr.; 0-9613575),* P.O. Box 7307, Everett, WA 98201 (SAN 670-1523) Tel 206-252-7660.
Pergamon, *(Pergamon Pr., Inc.; 0-08),* Maxwell Hse., Fairview Pk., Elmsford, NY 10523 (SAN 213-9022) Tel 914-592-7700.
Perigee Bks *Imprint of* **Putnam Pub Group**
Perry Enterprises, *(Perry Enterprises; 0-941518),* 2666 N. 650 E, Provo, UT 84604 (SAN 239-0175) Tel 801-375-9529.
Persea Bks, *(Persea Bks., Inc.; 0-89255),* 225 Lafayette St., New York, NY 10012 (SAN 212-8233) Tel 212-431-5270.
Personal Christianity, *(Personal Christianity; 0-938148),* Box 549, Baldwin Park, CA 91706 (SAN 211-8211) Tel 818-338-7333.
Personal Dev Ctr, *(Personal Development Ctr.; 0-917828),* P.O. Box 251, Windham Center, CT 06280 (SAN 209-164X) Tel 203-423-4785.
Perspective Chicago, *(Perspective Pr.; 0-9603382),* 629 Deming Pl., Rm. 401, Chicago, IL 60614 (SAN 208-3191) Tel 312-871-4820.
Peter Li, *(Li, Peter, Inc.; 0-89837),* 2451 E. River Rd., Dayton, OH 45439 (SAN 238-7980) Tel 513-299-8777; Toll free: 800-531-3456.
Peter Pauper, *(Peter Pauper Pr., Inc.; 0-88088),* 202 Mamaroneck Ave., White Plains, NY 10601 (SAN 204-9449) Tel 914-681-0144. Do not confuse with Pauper Pr., Inc., Two Rivers, WI.
Peter Smith, *(Smith, Peter, Pub., Inc.; 0-8446),* 6 Lexington Ave., Magnolia, MA 01930 (SAN 206-8885) Tel 617-525-3562.
Petereins Pr, *(Petereins Pr., The; 0-9606102),* P.O. Box 10446, Glendale, CA 91209 (SAN 215-9007).
Peters Corp NM, *(Peters Corp.; 0-935037),* P.O. Box 2524, Santa Fe, NM 87504-2524 (SAN 697-2462) Tel 505-988-8961; Toll free: 800-621-5884.
Petrocelli, *(Petrocelli Bks.; 0-89433),* Research Pk., 251 Wall St., Princeton, NJ 08540 (SAN 211-3848) Tel 609-924-5851; Dist. by: TAB Bks., P.O. Box 40, Blue Ridge Summit, PA 17214 (SAN 202-568X) Tel 717-794-2191.
Petroglyph, *(Petroglyph Pr., Ltd.; 0-912180),* 201 Kinoole St., Hilo, HI 96720 (SAN 204-9457) Tel 808-935-6006; Dist. by: Pacific Trade Group, P.O. Box 668, Pearl City, HI 96782 (SAN 169-1635) Tel 808-671-6735; Dist. by: Mid-Pacific Book Distributors, 150 Haili St., Hilo, HI 96720 (SAN 169-1597) Tel 808-935-5622.
Pflaum Pr
See Peter Li
Phaeton, *(Phaeton Pr., Inc.; 0-87753),* Orders to: Gordian Press, 85 Tompkins St., P.O. Box 304, Staten Island, NY 10304 (SAN 201-6389) Tel 212-273-4700.
Phanes Pr, *(Phanes Pr.; 0-933999),* P.O. Box 6114, Grand Rapids, MI 49516 (SAN 692-879X) Tel 616-949-2318.
Phi Delta Kappa, *(Phi Delta Kappa Educational Foundation; 0-87367),* Eighth & Union, Box 789, Bloomington, IN 47402 (SAN 289-1859) Tel 812-339-1156.
Phila Free Lib, *(Free Library of Philadelphia; 0-911132),* Rare Book Dept., Logan Square, Philadelphia, PA 19103 (SAN 205-3837) Tel 215-686-5416.
Phila Mus Art, *(Philadelphia Museum of Art; 0-87633),* 26th & Pkwy. P.O. Box 7646, Philadelphia, PA 19101 (SAN 203-0969) Tel 215-763-8100; Dist. by: Univ. of Pennsyvania Pr., 418 Service Dr., Blockley Hall, 13th Flr., Philadelphia, PA 19104 (SAN 202-5345) Tel 215-898-6261.
Phila Patristic, *(Philadelphia Patristic Foundation, Ltd.; 0-915646),* 99 Brattle St., Cambridge, MA 02138 (SAN 208-3507) Tel 617-868-3450.
Phillips Exeter Academy, *(Phillips Exeter Academy Pr., The; 0-939618),* Exeter, NH 03833 (SAN 216-4353); Orders to: Exeter Bookstore, 13 Spring St., Exeter, NH 03833 (SAN 662-1139).
Philomel Bks *Imprint of* **Putnam Pub Group**
Philos Lib, *(Philosophical Library, Inc.; 0-8022),* 200 W. 57th St., Suite 510, New York, NY 10019 (SAN 201-999X) Tel 212-265-6050; Dist. by: Alpha Bk. Distributors (Div. of Bookazine), 303 W. Tenth St., New York, NY 10014 (SAN 200-8440) Tel 212-675-8877.
Philos Pub, *(Philosophical Publishing Co.; 0-932785),* RD 3, Clymeir Rd., Quakertown, PA 18951 (SAN 295-8430) Tel 215-536-5168.

Philos Res, *(Philosophical Research Society, Inc.; 0-89314),* 3910 Los Feliz Blvd., Los Angeles, CA 90027 (SAN 205-3829) Tel 213-663-2167.
Phoenix Pub, *(Phoenix Publishing; 0-914016; 0-914659),* Canaan, NH 03741 (SAN 201-8810) Tel 603-523-9901; Sugar Hill, NH 03585 (SAN 691-4209).
Pholiota, *(Pholiota Pr., Inc.; 0-910231),* 6421 Antrim Cir., Huntington Beach, CA 92647 (SAN 240-8783) Tel 714-898-4129.
Phunn Pubs, *(Phunn Pubs.; 0-931762),* P.O. Box 201, Wild Rose, WI 54984 (SAN 212-128X) Tel 414-622-3251.
Phystiklakis & Eliopoulos
See Eliopoulos
Pi Pr, *(Pi Pr., Inc.; 0-931420),* Box 23371, Honolulu, HI 96822 (SAN 669-2400); 3169-A Alika Ave., Honolulu, HI 96817 Tel 808-595-3426.
Piarist Father, *(Piarist Fathers, Inc.; 0-9614908),* 512 Ave. 20, S., Los Angeles, CA 90031 (SAN 693-5362) Tel 213-223-4153.
Pica Pr *Imprint of* **Universe**
Pickwick, *(Pickwick Pubns.; 0-915138; 1-55635),* 4137 Timberlane Dr., Allison Park, PA 15101 (SAN 210-1319) Tel 412-487-2159.
Picture Bk Studio USA, *(Picture Bk. Studio, USA; 0-88708; 0-907234),* 60 N. Main St., Natick, MA 01760 (SAN 293-8227) Tel 617-655-9696: Toll free: 800-462-1252; Dist. by: Alphabet Pr., 60 N. Main St., Natick, MA 01760 (SAN 217-1449).
Piedmont, *(Piedmont Pr., Inc.; 0-912680),* P.O. Box 3605, Georgetown, Washington, DC 20007 (SAN 205-3861) Tel 703-549-3980.
Pierian, *(Pierian Pr.; 0-87650),* P.O. Box 1808, Ann Arbor, MI 48106 (SAN 204-8949) Tel 313-434-5530.
Pilgrim Hse, *(Pilgrim Hse.; 0-932131),* 1637 Westhaven Ave. NW, Salem, OR 97304 (SAN 686-2195) Tel 503-362-4030.
Pilgrim NY, *(Pilgrim Pr., The United Church Pr.; 0-8298),* Div. of United Church Board for Homeland Ministries, 132 W. 31st St., New York, NY 10001 (SAN 212-601X) Tel 212-239-8700; Dist. by: Publishers Distribution Ctr., 25 Branca Rd., Rutherford, NJ 07073 (SAN 200-5018) Tel 201-939-6064.
Pilgrim Pr, *(Pilgrim Pr., The; 0-933476),* 39 University Pl., Princeton, NJ 08540 (SAN 211-2647) Tel 609-924-9095.
Pilgrim Pubns, *(Pilgrim Pubns.),* P.O. Box 66, Pasadena, TX 77501 (SAN 206-3069) Tel 713-477-2329.
Pilgrim Soc, *(Pilgrim Society; 0-940628),* 75 Court St., Plymouth, MA 02360 (SAN 280-1221) Tel 617-746-1620.
Pine Row, *(Pine Row Pubns.; 0-935238),* P.O. Box 428, Washington Crossing, PA 18977 (SAN 214-0810) Tel 215-493-4259.
Pioneer Vent, *(Pioneer Ventures, Inc.; 0-915321),* 4027 Lanark, Houston, TX 77025 (SAN 290-0351) Tel 713-666-0051; Toll free: 800-521-3690; Toll free: 800-482-3653 (In Michigan); Dist. by: Spring Arbor Distributors, 10885 Textile Rd., Belleville, MI 48111 (SAN 158-9016) Tel 313-481-0900.
Pitts Theolog, *(Pittsburgh Theological Seminary, Clifford E. Barbour Library; 0-931222),* 616 N. Highland Ave., Pittsburgh, PA 15206 (SAN 240-981X) Tel 412-362-5610.
PL *Imprint of* **Har-Row**
Planning Forum, *(Planning Forum, The; 0-912841),* P.O. Box 70, Oxford, OH 45056 (SAN 230-8673); 5500 College Corner Pike, Oxford, OH 45056 (SAN 669-2435) Tel 513-523-4185.
Plantation, *(Plantation Pr.; 0-911150),* 9140 Davies Plantation Rd., Brunswick, Memphis, TN 38134 (SAN 205-1273) Tel 901-386-2015.
Plenum Pr *Imprint of* **Plenum Pub**
Plenum Pub, *(Plenum Publishing Corp.; 0-306),* 233 Spring St., New York, NY 10013-1578 (SAN 201-9248) Tel 212-620-8047; Toll free: 800-221-9369. *Imprints:* Plenum Pr (Plenum Press).
Plough, *(Plough Publishing Hse., The; 0-87486),* Subs. of Woodcrest Service Committee, Hutterian Brethren, Rte. 213, Rifton, NY 12471 (SAN 202-0092) Tel 914-658-3141.
Plume *Imprint of* **NAL**
Plus Seven Bks, *(Plus Seven Bks.; 0-943416),* SR Box 13, Brandy Station, VA 22714 (SAN 240-7469) Tel 703-825-9163.
Plycon Pr, *(Plycon Pr.; 0-916434),* Div. of Plycon Industries, P.O. Box 220, Redondo Beach, CA 90277 (SAN 201-8829) Tel 213-379-9725; Orders to: 10612 Collett, Granada Hills, CA 91344 (SAN 693-9716).
Plymouth Col, *(Plymouth Colony Research Group),* 128 Massasoit Dr., Warwick, RI 02888-6307 (SAN 241-4376) Tel 401-781-6759.
Plymouth Rock Found, *(Plymouth Rock Foundation; 0-942516),* 14 McKinley Cir., Marlborough, NH 03455 (SAN 239-8583) Tel 603-876-4658.
PMS Indus, *(PMS Industries; 0-931463),* Div. of Proto Systems of Atlanta, 1790 Hembree Rd., Alpharetta, GA 30201 (SAN 683-1486) Tel 404-475-1818.
Pneuma Pub, *(Pneuma Publishing; 0-9617733),* Star Rte., Box 180, Bridgeville, CA 95526 (SAN 664-810X); Van Duzen River Rd., Bridgeville, CA 95526 (SAN 664-8118) Tel 707-574-6494.
Pocahontas Pr, *(Pocahontas Pr., Inc.; 0-936015),* 2805 Wellesley Ct., Blacksburg, VA 24060 (SAN 696-6195) Tel 703-951-0467.
Pohl Assoc
See J Pohl Assocs
Point *Imprint of* **Scholastic Inc**
Point Loma Pub, *(Point Loma Pubns., Inc.; 0-913004),* P.O. Box 6507, San Diego, CA 92106 (SAN 204-9023); 3727 Charles St., San Diego, CA 92106 (SAN 662-1155) Tel 619-222-3291.
Polanie, *(Polanie Publishing Co.; 0-911154),* 643 Madison St., N.E., Minneapolis, MN 55413 (SAN 204-9031) Tel 612-379-9134.
Polish Inst Art & Sci, *(Polish Institute of Arts & Sciences of America, Inc.),* 208 E. 30th St., New York, NY 10016 (SAN 225-3747) Tel 212-686-4164.
Pope John Ctr, *(Pope John Ctr.; 0-935372),* 186 Forbes Rd., Braintree, MA 02184 (SAN 282-1729) Tel 617-848-6965.
Popular Pubns, *(Popular Pubns.; 0-9615362),* P.O. Box 1558, Oroville, WA 98844-1558 (SAN 694-4108).
Population Coun, *(Population Council Office of Communications; 0-87834),* 1 Dag Hammarskjold Plaza, New York, NY 10017 (SAN 225-1582) Tel 212-644-1300.
Porcupine Pr, *(Porcupine Pr., Inc.; 0-87991),* 310 S. Juniper St., Philadelphia, PA 19107 (SAN 202-0122) Tel 215-735-0101.
Port Love Intl, *(Port Love International Publishing Co.),* P.O. Box 423, Amazonia, MO 64421 (SAN 686-2764).
Portals Pr, *(Portals Pr.; 0-916620),* P.O. Box 1048, Tuscaloosa, AL 35403 (SAN 208-8126) Tel 205-758-1874.
Porter
See Bern Porter
Porter Pub Co, *(Porter Publishing Co.; 0-933565),* P.O. Box 134, Center City, MN 55012 (SAN 691-9006) Tel 612-257-5232. Do not confuse with Bern Porter, Belfast, ME.
Positive Images, *(Positive Images, Inc.; 0-9615271),* 1203 Carver St., P.O. Box 483, Myrtle Beach, SC 29578-0483 (SAN 695-2682) Tel 803-448-5361.
Post Horn Pr, *(Post Horn Pr., Inc.; 0-935311),* 1288 Lenox Cir., NE, Atlanta, GA 30306 (SAN 695-5525) Tel 404-876-0518.
Potala, *(Potala Corp.; 0-9611474),* 107 E. 31st St., Fourth flr., New York, NY 10016 (SAN 283-1570) Tel 212-213-5011.
Potentials Development, *(Potentials Development, Inc.; 0-932910),* 775 Main St., Suite 321, Buffalo, NY 14203 (SAN 239-5916) Tel 716-842-2658.
Power Bks *Imprint of* **Revell**
Power Word Pubns, *(Power of the Word Pubns.; 0-940853),* P.O. Box 607, Litchfield Park, AZ 85340-0607 (SAN 665-1992); 3606 Zuni, Glendale, AZ 85307 (SAN 665-200X) Tel 602-935-3628.
Powner, *(Powner, Charles T., Co., Inc.; 0-911164),* 7056 W. Higgins Rd., Chicago, IL 60656 (SAN 204-9082) Tel 312-939-7360.
Pr Arden Park, *(Press of Arden Park; 0-936300),* 861 Los Molinos Way, Sacramento, CA 95864 (SAN 209-8644) Tel 916-481-7881.
Pr Pacifica, *(Press Pacifica; 0-916630),* P.O. Box 47, Kailua, HI 96734 (SAN 169-1635) Tel 808-261-6594.
Praeger, *(Praeger Pubs.; 0-275),* Div. of Greenwood Pr., Inc., 521 Fifth Ave., New York, NY 10175 (SAN 202-022X) Tel 212-599-8400.
Prayer Bk, *(Prayer Bk. Pr., Inc.; 0-87677),* Subs. of Media Judaica, Inc., 304 E. 49th St., New York, NY 10017 (SAN 282-1788) Tel 212-319-6666; Orders to: Media Judaica, Inc., 1363 Fairfield Ave., Bridgeport, CT 06605 (SAN 207-0022) Tel 203-384-2284.
Precedent Pub, *(Precedent Publishing, Inc.; 0-913750),* 737 N. LaSalle St., Chicago, IL 60610 (SAN 205-1583) Tel 312-944-2525; Toll free: 800-392-5448.
Precious Res, *(Precious Resources; 0-937836),* Box 14463, Parkville, MO 64152 (SAN 213-3512) Tel 816-386-2946.
Preferred Pr, *(Preferred Press; 0-914759),* 5702 Research Dr., Huntington Beach, CA 92649 (SAN 291-8463) Tel 714-895-1083; Toll free: 800-762-6937.
Prema Bks, *(Prema Bks.; 0-941122),* 310 West End Ave., New York, NY 10023 (SAN 217-4170) Tel 212-874-7692.
Presby & Reformed, *(Presbyterian & Reformed Publishing Co.; 0-87552),* P.O. Box 817, Phillipsburg, NJ 08865 (SAN 205-3918); Toll free: 800-631-0094; Marble Hill Rd., Phillipsburg, NJ 08865 (SAN 658-1463) Tel 201-454-0505. Do not confuse with Presbyterian Renewal Pubns., Oklahoma City, OK.
Presby Hist, *(Presbyterian Historical Society; 0-912686),* 425 Lombard St., Philadelphia, PA 19147 (SAN 205-1575) Tel 215-627-1852.
Presby Renewal Pubns, *(Presbyterian Renewal Pubns.; 0-934421),* Subs. of Presbyterian & Reformed Renewal Ministries, International, 2245 NW 39th St., Oklahoma City, OK 73112-8886 (SAN 274-7804) Tel 405-525-2552. Do not confuse with Presbyterian & Reformed Publishing Co., Phillipsburg, NJ.
Presence Inc, *(Presence, Inc.; 0-937296),* P.O. Box 1867, Easley, SC 29641 (SAN 240-8813) Tel 803-878-7239.
Press Alley, *(Press of Appletree Alley, The; 0-916375),* P.O. Box 608, 138 S. Third St., Lewisburg, PA 17837 (SAN 295-9747) Tel 717-524-7064.
Pressworks, *(Pressworks Publishing, Inc.; 0-939722),* P.O. Box 12606, Dallas, TX 75225 (SAN 216-7581); 6140 Deloache St., Dallas, TX 75225 (SAN 658-1471) Tel 214-369-3113.
Prestige Pubns, *(Prestige Pubns.; 0-911009),* P.O. Box 2157, Princeton, NJ 08540 (SAN 274-791X); 100 Hamilton Ave., Princeton, NJ 08540 (SAN 662-7366) Tel 609-921-7403.
Pretty Good TX, *(Pretty Good Publishing; 0-9130020),* P.O. Box 40, Lindale, TX 75771-0040 (SAN 663-1940).
Price Stern, *(Price, Stern, Sloan, Pubs., Inc.; 0-8431),* 410 N. La Cienega Blvd., Los Angeles, CA 90048 (SAN 202-0246) Tel 213-657-6100; Toll free: 800-421-0892; 1900 Sacramento St., Los Angeles, CA 90021 (SAN 658-148X); Toll free: 800-227-8801 (In California).
Pride Prods, *(Pride Products Co., Inc.; 0-934383),* P.O. Box 1639, Sun City, AZ 85372 (SAN 693-8051) Tel 602-972-4925:
Prince Peace Pub, *(Prince of Peace Publishing Inc.; 0-933173),* 13801 Fairview Dr., Burnsville, MN 55337 (SAN 692-3305) Tel 612-435-8102.
Princeton Bk Co, *(Princeton Bk. Co.; 0-916622; 0-903102; 0-87127; 0-932582),* P.O. Box 109, Princeton, NJ 08542 (SAN 208-404X); 12 W. Delaware Ave., Pennington, NJ 08534 (SAN 658-1498) Tel 609-737-8177.
Princeton Lib, *(Princeton Univ. Library; 0-87811),* P.O. Box 190, Princeton, NJ 08544 (SAN 205-3950) Tel 609-452-3184.
Princeton U Pr, *(Princeton Univ. Pr.; 0-691),* 41 William St., Princeton, NJ 08540 (SAN 202-0254) Tel 609-452-4900; Orders to: 3175 Princeton Pike, Lawrenceville, NJ 08648 (SAN 662-1171) Tel 609-896-1344.
Prinit Pr, *(Prinit Pr.; 0-932970),* Box 65, Dublin, IN 47335 (SAN 212-680X).
Prod Hse, *(Production Hse. Corp.; 0-932638),* P.O. Box 8408, La Jolla, CA 92038 (SAN 201-1018) Tel 619-287-2560.

Prog Bapt Pub, *(Progressive Baptist Publishing Hse.; 0-89191),* 850 N. Grove Ave., Elgin, IL 60120 (SAN 277-7010).
Progresiv Pub, *(Progresiv Publishr; 0-89670),* 401 E. 32nd St., No. 1002, Chicago, IL 60616 (SAN 212-6818) Tel 312-225-9181.
Prometheus Bks, *(Prometheus Bks.; 0-87975),* 700 E. Amherst St., Buffalo, NY 14215 (SAN 202-0289) Tel 716-837-2475; Toll free: 800-421-0351.
Promised Land, *(Promised Land Pubns., Inc.; 0-911712),* Div. of Eagle Systems International, 5600 N. University Ave., Provo, UT 84601 (SAN 204-3130) Tel 801-225-2293.
Prophecy Pressworks *Imprint of* **Sufi Islamia-Prophecy**
Prosperity & Profits, *(Prosperity & Profits Unlimited, Distribution Services),* Box 570213, Houston, TX 77257-0213 (SAN 200-4682).
Prosveta USA, *(Prosveta, USA; 0-911857),* Affil. of Prosveta S. A. France, P.O. Box 49614, Los Angeles, CA 90049-0614 (SAN 264-3235) Tel 213-474-7477.
Providential Pr, *(Providential Press),* P.O. Box 218026, Houston, TX 77218 (SAN 276-9794) Tel 713-578-7837.
Prow Bks-Franciscan, *(Prow Bks./Franciscan Marytown Pr.; 0-913382),* 1600 W. Park Ave., Libertyville, IL 60048 (SAN 205-1060).
Pruett, *(Pruett Publishing Co.; 0-87108),* 2928 Pearl St., Boulder, CO 80301 (SAN 205-4035) Tel 303-449-4919.
Pryor Pettengill, *(Pettengill, Pryor; 0-933462),* Box 7074, Ann Arbor, MI 48107 (SAN 213-8697).
PSG Pub Co, *(PSG Publishing Co., Inc.; 0-88416; 0-7236; 0-931890),* P.O. Box 6, Littleton, MA 01460 (SAN 201-8934); Toll free: 800-225-5020; 545 Great Rd., Littleton, MA 01460 (SAN 658-2230) Tel 617-486-8971.
Psych & Consul Assocs, *(Psychology & Consulting Assocs. Pr.; 0-930626),* P.O. Box 1837, La Jolla, CA 92038 (SAN 211-3856) Tel 619-457-3900.
Psych Dimensions, *(Psychological Dimensions, Inc.; 0-88437),* 10 W. 66th St., Suite 4H, New York, NY 10023 (SAN 204-3866) Tel 212-877-2313.
Psych Genocide Res, *(Psychiatric Genocide Research Institute; 0-9614961),* P.O. Box 80071, Springfield, MA 01108 (SAN 693-7527) Tel 413-788-9523.
Psychegenics, *(Psychegenics Pr.; 0-931865),* Subs. of MCM Inc., P.O. Box 332, Gaithersburg, MD 20877 (SAN 686-0567) Tel 301-948-1122.
Psychic Bks, *(Psychic Bks.; 0-930984),* 440 Avalon Pl., Oxnard, CA 93033 (SAN 219-2586) Tel 805-488-8670.
PTL Enterprises, *(PTL Enterprises, Inc.; 0-912275),* Charlotte, NC 28279 (SAN 283-3085) Tel 704-542-6000.
PTL Repro, *(PTL Reproductions; 0-910709),* 115 S. First St., Broken Arrow, OK 74012 (SAN 260-2423) Tel 918-251-3787.
Pub Aff Pr, *(Public Affairs Pr.; 0-8183),* 419 New Jersey Ave., Washington, DC 20003 (SAN 202-1471) Tel 202-544-3024.
Pub Ctr Cult Res, *(Publishing Ctr. for Cultural Resources, Inc.),* 625 Broadway, New York, NY 10012 (SAN 274-9025) Tel 212-260-2010.
Publishers Guild, *(Publishers Guild),* P.O. Box 754, Palatine, IL 60067 (SAN 212-7180) Tel 312-991-0255.
Publius Pub, *(Publius Publishing; 0-937947),* P.O. Box 411, Pacific Palisades, CA 90272 (SAN 659-7580); 16015 Northfield, Pacific Palisades, CA 90272 (SAN 659-7599) Tel 714-851-9411.
Pubs of Truth
See Friends Truth
Pubs Pr UT, *(Publishers Pr.; 0-916095),* 1900 W. 2300 S., Salt Lake City, UT 84119 (SAN 219-3884) Tel 801-972-6600.
Puckerbrush, *(Puckerbrush Pr.; 0-913006),* 76 Main St., Orono, ME 04473 (SAN 202-0327) Tel 207-581-3832; Dist. by: Inland Bk. Co., P.O. Box 261, 22 Hemingway Ave., East Haven, CT 06512 (SAN 200-4151) Tel 203-467-4257; Dist. by: Maine Writers & Pubs., Alliance, 19D Mason St., Brunswick, ME 04011 (SAN 224-2303) Tel 207-775-6260.
Pueblo Pub Co, *(Pueblo Publishing Co., Inc.; 0-916134),* 100 W. 32nd St., New York, NY 10001-3210 (SAN 211-7606) Tel 212-695-4282.
Pueblo Pub Pr, *(Pueblo Publishing Pr.; 0-942316),* 401 Vandament Ave., Yukon, OK 73099 (SAN 239-5940) Tel 405-354-7825; Dist. by: ARA Services, 909 W. 23rd St., Tulsa, OK 74107 (SAN 169-7013); Dist. by: Baker & Taylor Co., 1515 Broadway, New York, NY 10036 (SAN 169-5606) Tel 212-730-7650.
Puffin Bks *Imprint of* **Penguin**
Puissance Pubns, *(Puissance Pubns., Inc.; 0-940634),* 2802 N. Patton St., Arlington Heights, IL 60004 (SAN 218-5229) Tel 314-870-1840.
Pullen Mem Baptist, *(Pullen Memorial Baptist Church; 0-9614485),* 1801 Hillsborough St., Raleigh, NC 27605 (SAN 689-4216) Tel 919-828-0897.
Purcell Pub, *(Purcell, Royal, Pub.; 0-933189),* 806 W. Second St., Bloomington, IN 47401 (SAN 691-7224) Tel 812-336-4195.
Purcells, *(Purcells, Inc.; 0-931068),* 305 S. 10th, Box 190, Broken Bow, NE 68822 (SAN 211-1357) Tel 308-872-2471.
Purdue U Pr, *(Purdue Univ. Pr.; 0-911198; 1-55753),* South Campus Cts., Bldg. D, West Lafayette, IN 47907 (SAN 203-4026) Tel 317-494-2035; Dist. by: Indiana Univ. Pr. (Regional titles only), Tenth & Morton Sts., Bloomington, IN 47405 (SAN 202-5647) Tel 812-335-7681; Dist. by: Feffer & Simon, Inc., 100 Park Ave., New York, NY 10017 (SAN 200-6804) Tel 212-686-0888. Do not confuse with Purdue U Pubns, same address. Use ISBN to determine publisher.
Putnam *Imprint of* **Putnam Pub Group**
Putnam Pub Group, *(Putnam Publishing Group, The; 0-399),* 200 Madison Ave., New York, NY 10016 (SAN 202-5531) Tel 212-576-8900; Toll free: 800-631-8571. *Imprints:* Coward (Coward, McCann & Geoghegan); G&D (Grossett & Dunlap, Inc.); Perigee Bks (Perigee Books); Philomel Bks (Philomel Books); Putnam (Putnam's, G. P., Sons); Wideview (Wideview).
Pyquag, *(Pyquag Bks. Pubs.; 0-912492),* P.O. Box 328, Wethersfield, CT 06109 (SAN 205-4086).
Pyramid Designs Pr, *(Pyramid Designs Pr.; 0-937071),* Div. of Pyramid Designs, Ltd., Investment Bldg., Suite 1017, Pittsburgh, PA 15222 (SAN 658-4314) Tel 412-642-6698; Seventh & Grant St., Pittsburgh, PA 15230 (SAN 658-4322); Dist. by: The Distributors, 702 S. Michigan, South Bend, IN 46618 (SAN 169-2488) Tel 219-232-8500; Dist. by: Central Wholesale, Inc., 143 S. 25th St., Pittsburgh, PA 15203 (SAN 200-6987) Tel 412-988-2800.
Quaker City, *(Quaker City Books; 0-917931),* Mill & Main Sts., Darby, PA 19023 (SAN 209-1178) Tel 215-583-4550.
Quality Lib, *(Quality Library Editions),* P.O. Box 148, Darby, PA 19023 (SAN 209-1186).
Quality Pubns, *(Quality Pubns.; 0-89137),* Div. of Quality Printing Co., Inc., P.O. Box 1060, Abilene, TX 79604 (SAN 203-0071) Tel 915-677-6262.
Quantal, *(Quantal Publishing Co.; 0-936596),* Div. of Quetzal Investment, Inc., P.O. Box 1598, Goleta, CA 93116 (SAN 215-1014) Tel 805-964-7293; Dist. by: Samuel Weiser, Inc., Box 612, York Beach, ME 03910 (SAN 202-9588) Tel 207-363-4393; Dist. by: Bookpeople, 2929 Fifth St., Berkeley, CA 94710 (SAN 168-9517) Tel 415-549-3030.
Quartus Bks, *(Quartus Bks.; 0-942082),* Div. of Quartus Foundation, P.O. Box 27230, Austin, TX 78755-1230 (SAN 238-0080) Tel 512-335-8346; Dist. by: Bookpeople, 2929 Fifth St., Berkeley, CA 94710 (SAN 168-9517) Tel 415-549-3030; Dist. by: New Leaf Distributing Co., 1020 White St., SW, Atlanta, GA 30310 (SAN 169-1449) Tel 404-755-2665.
Quasem, *(Quasem, M. Adul),* Dist. by: Habibur Rahman, 502 N. Elm St., Centralia, IL 62801 (SAN 209-5939).
Queen Anne Pr, *(Queen Anne Press, The; 0-937692),* Div. of Wye Institute, Inc., Cheston-on-Wye, Queenstown, MD 21658 (SAN 215-272X) Tel 301-827-7401; Orders to: P.O. Box 50, Queenstown, MD 21658 (SAN 215-2738).
Quest *Imprint of* **Theos Pub Hse**
Questpr, *(Questpress; 0-914631),* 103 Briar Rd., Oak Ridge, TN 37830 (SAN 289-5625) Tel 615-483-1183; Orders to: The Fayette Fellowship, 101 Carriage Ln., Peachtree City, GA 30269 (SAN 662-2186) Tel 404-487-5683.
Quill *Imprint of* **Morrow**
Quinlan Pr, *(Quinlan Pr.; 0-9611268; 0-933341; 1-55770),* Affil. of AC Getchell, 131 Beverly St., Boston, MA 02114 (SAN 226-4641) Tel 617-227-4870; Toll free: 800-551-2500.
R & E Pubs, *(R & E Pubs.; 0-88247),* P.O. Box 2008, Saratoga, CA 95070-2008 (SAN 293-3195) Tel 408-866-6303.
R Collier, *(Collier, Robert, Pub., Inc.; 0-912576),* P.O. Box 3684, Indialantic, FL 32903 (SAN 204-2908) Tel 305-723-3228.
R E F Typesetting Pub, *(R.E.F. Typesetting & Publishing, Inc.; 0-9612862),* 9400 Fairview Ave., Manassas, VA 22110 (SAN 291-3976) Tel 703-631-1115.
R E Todd, *(Todd, Richard E.; 0-9605324),* 8055 N. Marion Dr., Clovis, CA 93612 (SAN 215-9805).
R J Liederbach, *(Liederbach, Robert J., Co.; 0-934906),* 4953 Stonington Rd., Winston-Salem, NC 27103 (SAN 213-1080) Tel 919-768-7014.
R Kurz, *(Kurz, Ron; 0-939829),* P.O. Box 28544, Las Vegas, NV 89126-2549 (SAN 663-8333); 6408 Penrose Ln., Las Vegas, NV 89107 (SAN 663-8341) Tel 702-870-5968.
R L Hawkins, *(Hawkins, Robert L.; 0-9607764),* 990 Naranca Ave., El Cajon, CA 92021-5614 (SAN 212-6648) Tel 619-440-7597.
R O Roberts, *(Roberts, Richard Owen, Pubs.; 0-940033),* 5N740 Dunham Rd., St. Charles, IL 60174 (SAN 239-4847) Tel 312-584-8069; Orders to: P.O. Box 21, Wheaton, IL 60189 (SAN 665-7702).
R S Barnes, *(Barnes, Richard S., & Co. Bks.; 0-942448),* 821 Foster St., Evanston, IL 60201 (SAN 209-2395) Tel 312-869-2272.
R S Hoehler, *(Hoehler, Richard S.; 0-930590),* P.O. Box 240, Conifer, CO 80433 (SAN 204-6628) Tel 303-838-4046.
R Schalkenbach Foun
See Schalkenbach
R Seaver Bks
See Seaver Bks
R Tanner Assocs Inc, *(Tanner, Ralph, Assocs., Inc.; 0-942078),* 122 N. Cortez St., Suite 102, Prescott, AZ 86301 (SAN 239-9857) Tel 602-778-4162.
R West, *(West, Richard; 0-8492; 0-8274),* Box 6404, Philadelphia, PA 19145 (SAN 206-8907).
R Woodrow, *(Woodrow, Ralph, Evangelistic Assn., Inc.; 0-916938),* P.O. Box 124, Riverside, CA 92502 (SAN 206-3700) Tel 714-686-5467.
Raccoon Memphis, *(Raccoon Bks., Inc.; 0-938507),* Div. of Ion Bks., Inc., 3387 Poplar Ave., Suite 205, Memphis, TN 38111 (SAN 659-6142).
Radix Bks, *(Radix Bks., Inc.),* 11 Knickerbocker Ln., Orinda, CA 94563 (SAN 209-1364) Tel 415-254-3039.
Ragusan Pr, *(Ragusan Pr.; 0-918660),* 2527 San Carlos Ave., San Carlos, CA 94070 (SAN 212-0445) Tel 415-592-1190.
Rainbow Bks, *(Rainbow Books, Inc.; 0-89508),* 725 Dell Rd., Carlstadt, NJ 07072 (SAN 209-9918) Tel 201-935-3369.
Raintree Pubs, *(Raintree Pubs., Inc.; 0-8172; 0-8393; 0-940742; 0-86514),* 310 W. Wisconsin Ave., Mezzanine Level, Milwaukee, WI 53203 (SAN 207-9607) Tel 414-273-0873; Toll free: 800-558-7264.
Rajneesh Neo-Sannyas Intl, *(Rajneesh Neo-Sannyas International Commune; 0-918963),* P.O. Box 1, Rajneeshpuram, OR 97741 (SAN 669-8786) Tel 503-489-3411; Dist. by: Rajneesh Pubns., Inc., P.O. Box 1510, Boulder, CO 80306 (SAN 240-0987) Tel 303-665-6611.
Rajneesh Pubns
See Chidvilas Found

Rakhamim Pubns, *(Rakhamin Pubns.; 0-9612500),* P.O. Box 3094, Oakland, CA 94609 (SAN 291-848X); Dist. by: Bookpeople, 2929 Fifth St., Berkeley, CA 94710 (SAN 168-9517); Dist. by: Inland Bk. Co., 22 Hemingway Ave., P.O. Box 261, East Haven, CT 06512 (SAN 669-3571) Tel 203-467-4257.

Ralston-Pilot, *(Ralston-Pilot, Inc., Pubs.; 0-931116),* P.O. Box 1357, Cedar City, UT 84720 (SAN 282-2067) Tel 801-586-7395.

Rama Pub Co, *(Rama Publishing Co.; 0-913071),* P.O. Box 793, Carthage, MO 64836 (SAN 283-3875) Tel 417-358-1093.

Ramakrishna, *(Ramakrishna-Vivekananda Ctr.; 0-911206),* 17 E. 94th St., New York, NY 10128 (SAN 204-6687) Tel 212-534-9445.

RanC *Imprint of* **Random**

Randall Bk Co, *(Randall Bk. Co.; 0-934126; 1-55517),* 1181 N. Industrial Park Dr., Oremy, UT 84057 (SAN 214-1329) Tel 801-226-4004; Toll free: 800-453-1356.

Randall Hse, *(Randall Hse. Pubns.; 0-89265),* 114 Bush Rd., P.O. Box 17306, Nashville, TN 37217 (SAN 207-5040) Tel 615-361-1221; Toll free: 800-251-5762; Toll free: 800-624-6538 (in Tennessee).

Random, *(Random Hse., Inc.; 0-394; 0-676),* Random Hse. Publicity, (11-6), 201 E. 50th St., New York, NY 10022 (SAN 202-5507) Tel 212-572-8030; Toll free: 800-638-6460; Orders to: 400 Hahn Rd., Westminster, MD 21157 (SAN 202-5515) Tel 301-848-1900. Do not confuse Random House's imprint 'Vintage' with any other company with a similar name, particularly Vintage Pr., East Hanover, NJ. *Imprints:* BYR (Books for Young Readers); RanC (Random House College Division); Vin (Vintage Trade Books).

Ranney Pubns, *(Ranney Pubns.),* 5395 Industrial Dr., Unit C,, Huntington Beach, CA 92649 (SAN 211-867X) Tel 714-891-2145.

Rapids Christian, *(Rapids Christian Pr., Inc.; 0-915374),* P.O. Box 487, 810 4th Ave. N., Wisconsin Rapids, WI 54494 (SAN 205-0986) Tel 715-423-4670.

Rational Isl, *(Rational Island Pubs.; 0-911214; 0-913937),* P.O. Box 2081, Main Office Sta., Seattle, WA 98111 (SAN 204-6725); 719 Second Ave. N., Seattle, WA 98109 (SAN 662-1201) Tel 206-284-0311.

Ravengate Pr, *(Ravengate Pr.; 0-911218),* P.O. Box 49, Still River, MA 01467 (SAN 203-090X) Tel 617-456-8181.

Rawson Assocs, *(Rawson Assocs.; 0-89256),* Div. of Scribner Bk. Co., Inc, 115 Fifth Ave., New York, NY 10003 (SAN 209-3154) Tel 212-614-1300; Toll free: 800-257-5755; Dist. by: Scribner Bk. Co. Inc., Front & Brown Sts., Riverside, NJ 08075 (SAN 209-3162).

Raymont Pubs
See Randall Bk Co

RBR, *(RBR (Religious Bks. for Russia); 0-934927),* P.O. Box 631, Lenox Hill Sta., New York, NY 10021 (SAN 695-0167) Tel 914-478-2151; Dist. by: MCA Pr., 575 Scarsdale Rd., Crestwood, NY 10707 (SAN 200-5514).

RD Assn, *(Reader's Digest Assn., Inc.; 0-89577),* 750 Third Ave., New York, NY 10017-2797 (SAN 240-9720) Tel 212-850-7007; Toll free: 800-431-1726; Orders to: Customer Service, Pleasantville, NY 10570 (SAN 282-2091) Tel 914-769-7000; Dist. by: Random Hse., Inc., 400 Hahn Rd., Westminster, MD 21157 (SAN 202-5515). Publisher. Not a true association.

Reading Hse, *(Reading Hse., The; 0-9604388),* 1330 Oakmont Rd., Apt. 144-E, Seal Beach, CA 90740 (SAN 282-2105) Tel 213-598-2289; Orders to: Box 2748, Mission Viejo, CA 92692 (SAN 168-9886) Tel 714-770-1511; Dist. by: DeVorss & Co., P.O. Box 550, Marina del Rey, CA 90294 (SAN 168-9886).

Real People, *(Real People Pr.; 0-911226),* P.O. Box F, Moab, UT 84532 (SAN 203-3879) Tel 801-259-7578.

Reality Pr
See Diversity Okla

Rebound Pubns, *(Rebound Pubns.; 0-9615024),* Box 21866, Waco, TX 76750 (SAN 694-0560) Tel 314-546-2773.

Reconstructionist Pr, *(Reconstructionist Pr.; 0-935457),* Div. of Federation of Reconstructionist Congregations & Havurot, 270 W. 89th St., New York, NY 10024 (SAN 695-8745) Tel 212-496-2960; Dist. by: Hebrew Publishing Co., 100 Water St., Brooklyn, NY 11201 (SAN 200-6774).

Rector Pub, *(Rector, L. T., Publishing; 0-9606170),* 310 E. 25th St., Minneapolis, MN 55404 (SAN 223-0704).

Red Alder, *(Red Alder Bks.; 0-914906),* P.O. Box 2992, Santa Cruz, CA 95063 (SAN 206-6181) Tel 408-426-7082.

Red Rose Pr, *(Red Rose Pr.; 0-9609888),* P.O. Box 24, Encino, CA 91426 (SAN 282-2121) Tel 818-981-7638; Dist. by: Bookpeople, 2929 Fifth St., Berkeley, CA 94710 (SAN 168-9517); Dist. by: Moving Bks., 1214 Tenth Ave., Seattle, WA 98122 (SAN 200-6286) Tel 206-325-9077; Orders to: DeVorss & Co., 1046 Princeton Dr., P.O. Box 550, Marina del Rey, CA 90294 (SAN 168-9886); Dist. by: Baker & Taylor, Midwest Div., 501 Gladiola Ave., Momence, IL 60954 (SAN 169-2100); Dist. by: Inland Bk. Co., 22 Hemingway Ave., P.O. Box 261, East Haven, CT 06512 (SAN 200-4151) Tel 203-467-4257; Dist. by: New Leaf Distributing Co., 1020 White St. SW, Atlanta, GA 30310 (SAN 169-1449) Tel 404-755-2665; Dist. by: Starlight Distributors, 395 Freeport Blvd., Sparks, NV 89431 (SAN 200-6502) Tel 702-359-5676; Dist. by: Ingram Distribution Group, Inc., 347 Reedwood Dr., Nashville, TN 37217 (SAN 285-760X) Tel 615-360-2819.

Redencion Viva, *(Redencion Viva; 0-9607576),* Box 141167, Dallas, TX 75214 (SAN 239-6017) Tel 214-821-5357; Orders to: Box 141167, Dallas, TX 75214 (SAN 669-2559) Tel 214-821-5357.

Reed & Cannon, *(Reed & Cannon Co.; 0-918408),* 1446 Sixth St., Suite D, Berkeley, CA 94710 (SAN 282-2393) Tel 415-527-1586; Dist. by: Bookpeople, 2929 Fifth St., Berkeley, CA 94710 (SAN 168-9517); Dist. by: Bookslinger, 213 E. Fourth St., St. Paul, MN 55101 (SAN 169-4154) Tel 612-221-0429; Dist. by: Inland Bk. Co., P.O. Box 261, 22 Hemingway Ave., East Haven, CT 06512 (SAN 200-4151) Tel 203-467-4257; Dist. by: Small Pr. Distribution, 1814 San Pablo Ave., Berkeley, CA 94702 (SAN 204-5826) Tel 415-549-3336.

Ref Guide Bks, *(Reference & Guide Books Pub. Co.; 0-9607942),* 4963 Elmhurst, Box 3581, Ventura, CA 93006 (SAN 240-0650) Tel 805-644-8672.

Ref Presby Theo, *(Reformed Presbyterian Theological Seminary; 0-9616417),* 7418 Penn Ave., Pittsburgh, PA 15208 (SAN 659-1159) Tel 412-731-8690; Dist. by: Crown & Covenant Pubns., 7418 Penn Ave., Pittsburgh, PA 15208 (SAN 200-6766) Tel 412-241-0436.

Reference Bk Pubs *Imprint of* **Kelley**

Reflex Bks, *(Reflex Bks.; 0-9616430),* 2050 Grape St., Denver, CO 80207 (SAN 659-1132) Tel 303-393-0446.

Reformation Res, *(Reformation Research Pr., Inc.; 0-936592),* P.O. Box 1886, Decatur, GA 30031-1886 (SAN 214-1981).

Reformed Church, *(Reformed Church Press, Reformed Church in America; 0-916466),* 475 Riverside Dr., 18th Fl., New York, NY 10027 (SAN 207-4508) Tel 212-870-3020.

Reg Baptist, *(Regular Baptist Pr.; 0-87227),* Div. of General Assn. of Regular Baptist Churches, 1300 N. Meacham Rd., Schaumburg, IL 60173 (SAN 205-2229) Tel 312-843-1600.

Regal, *(Regal Bks.; 0-8307),* Div. of Gospel Light Pubns., 2300 Knoll Dr., Ventura, CA 93003 (SAN 203-3852) Tel 805-644-6869; Toll free: 800-235-3415; Box 3875, Ventura, CA 93006 (SAN 658-1528).

Regenbogen-Verlag, *(Regenbogen-Verlag; 0-940816),* Box 6214, Silver Spring, MD 20906 (SAN 216-0072) Tel 301-933-8521.

Regency *Imprint of* **Scholarly**

Regent Graphic Serv, *(Regent Graphic Services; 0-912710),* P.O. Box 8372, Swissvale, PA 15218 (SAN 204-6768) Tel 412-371-7128

Regents Pub, *(Regents Publishing Co., Inc.; 0-88345),* Subs. of Hachette, 2 Park Ave., New York, NY 10016 (SAN 203-3844) Tel 212-889-2780; Toll free: 800-822-8202

Regional, *(Regional Publishing Co.; 0-8063),* Subs. of Genealogical Publishing Co., 1001 N. Calvert St., Baltimore, MD 21202 (SAN 206-8842) Tel 301-837-8271.

Regnery Bks
See Regnery Gateway

Regnery Gateway, *(Regnery Gateway, Inc.; 0-89526),* 1130 17th St., NW, Washington, DC 20036 (SAN 210-5578); Dist. by: Kampmann & Co., 9 E. 40th St., New York, NY 10016 (SAN 202-5191) Tel 212-685-2928.

REI
See Religion & Ethics

Reiman Assocs, *(Reiman Assocs.; 0-89821),* 5400 S. 60th St., Greendale, WI 53129 (SAN 208-4368) Tel 414-423-0100; Orders to: Country Store, P.O. Box 572, Milwaukee, WI 53201 (SAN 208-4376).

Reiner, *(Reiner Pubns.; 0-87377),* Box 25, Sterling, VA 22170 (SAN 204-6784) Tel 703-430-2813.

Reinhold
See Van Nos Reinhold

Religion & ethics, *(Religion & Ethics Institute; 0-914384),* P.O. Box 664, Evanston, IL 60204 (SAN 202-9731) Tel 312-328-4049.

Religious Activ, *(Religious Activities Pr.),* 413 S. Main St., Goodlettsville, TN 37072 (SAN 212-7911) Tel 615-859-5519.

Religious Educ, *(Religious Education Pr., Inc.; 0-89135),* 1531 Wellington Rd., Birmingham, AL 35209 (SAN 207-3951) Tel 205-879-4040. *Imprints:* REP Bks (REP Books).

Religious Soc Friends, *(Philadelphia Yearly Meeting, Religious Society of Friends, Book Services; 0-941308),* 1515 Cherry St., Philadelphia, PA 19102 (SAN 239-3778).

Renfro Studios, *(Renfro, Nancy, Studios; 0-931044),* 1117 W. Ninth St., Austin, TX 78703 (SAN 211-9730) Tel 512-472-2140.

REP Bks *Imprint of* **Religious Educ**

Reprint, *(Reprint Co.; 0-87152),* P.O. Box 5401, 601 Hillcrest Offices, Spartanburg, SC 29304 (SAN 203-3828) Tel 803-582-0732.

Res Ctr Kabbalah, *(Research Centre of Kabbalah; 0-943688),* 83-15 124th Pl., Kew Gardens, NY 11415 (SAN 210-9484) Tel 718-805-9122.

Res Ctr Lang Semiotic, *(Research Ctr. for Language & Semiotic Studies; 0-87750),* Dist. by: Humanities Pr. International, Inc., 171 First Ave., Atlantic Highlands, NJ 07716 (SAN 201-9272) Tel 201-872-1441.

Res Discover Pubns, *(Research & Discovery Pubns.; 0-940519),* 6554 Winchester Rd., Suite 173, Memphis, TN 38115 (SAN 664-5232).

Res Publs, *(Research Pubs.; 0-911252),* 108 S. Patton, Arlington Heights, IL 60005 (SAN 206-6645) Tel 312-255-1961.

Res Pubns AZ, *(Research Pubns.; 0-914981),* 11855 N. 19th Ave., Phoenix, AZ 85029 (SAN 289-3894) Tel 602-252-4477; Toll free: 800-528-0559.

Res Pubns CT, *(Research Pubns., Inc.; 0-89235),* Subs. of International Thomson Organization, Inc., 12 Lunar Dr., Drawer AB, Woodbridge, CT 06525 (SAN 238-2717) Tel 203-397-2600; Toll free: 800-732-2477.

Resource Pubns, *(Resource Pubns., Inc.; 0-89390),* 160 E. Virginia St., No. 290, San Jose, CA 95112 (SAN 209-3081) Tel 408-286-8505.

Reston, *(Reston; 0-87909; 0-8359),* A Prentice-Hall Co., Englewood Cliffs, NJ 07632 (SAN 699-556X) Tel 201-592-2427; Orders to: P.O. Box 500, Englewood Cliffs, NJ 07632 (SAN 215-3939) Tel 201-767-5049.

Restoration Re, *(Restoration Research; 0-942284),* P.O. Box 547, Bountiful, UT 84010 (SAN 238-1133) Tel 801-298-4058.

Retirement Res, *(Retirement Research; 0-9602938),* Box 401, Appleton, WI 54912 (SAN 204-6849) Tel 414-734-6610.

Reunion Pr, *(Reunion Pr.; 0-935616),* P.O. Box 669, Twain Harte, CA 95383 (SAN 657-7148) Tel 209-928-4800; Dist. by: The Talman Co., 150 5th Ave., New York, NY 10011 (SAN 200-5204) Tel 212-620-3182.

Revelation Hse, *(Revelation Hse. Pubs., Inc.; 0-9604852),* P.O. Box 73175, Metairie, LA 70033 (SAN 217-1295) Tel 504-454-3141.
Revell, *(Revell, Fleming H., Co.; 0-8007),* Subs. of Zondervan Corp., 184 Central Ave., Old Tappan, NJ 07675 (SAN 203-3801) Tel 201-768-8060; Toll free: 800-631-1970. *Imprints:* Chosen Bks (Chosen Books); New Hope Bks (New Hope Books); Power Bks (Power Books); Spire Bks (Spire Books).
Review & Herald, *(Review & Herald Pub. Assn.; 0-8280),* 55 W. Oak Ridge Dr., Hagerstown, MD 21740 (SAN 203-3798) Tel 301-791-7000; Toll free: 800-582-5600.
Revisionist Pr, *(Revisionist Pr.; 0-87700),* P.O. Box 2009, Brooklyn, NY 11202 (SAN 203-378X).
Revival Press, *(Revival Pr., Inc.; 0-938612),* P.O. Box 130, Bedford, TX 76021 (SAN 240-8228) Tel 817-283-2873.
Revival Teach, *(Revival Teaching; 0-9616360),* 21 County Rd., Chatham, IL 62629 (SAN 659-1205) Tel 217-483-4109.
Reward *Imprint of* **P-H**
RI Genealogical, *(Rhode Island Genealogical Society; 0-9604144),* 128 Massasoit Dr., Warwick, RI 02888 (SAN 216-4450) Tel 401-781-6759.
RI Pubns Soc, *(Rhode Island Pubns. Society; 0-917012),* 189 Wickenden St., Providence, RI 02903 (SAN 219-9696) Tel 401-272-1776.
Rice Univ, *(Rice Univ. Pr.; 0-89263; 0-911216),* Rice Univ. P.O. Box 1892, Houston, TX 77251 (SAN 204-689X) Tel 713-527-6035; Dist. by: Texas A & M Univ. Pr., Drawer C, College Station, TX 77843 (SAN 207-5237) Tel 409-845-1436.
Richardson & Steirman, *(Richardson & Steirman; 0-931933),* 246 Fifth Ave., New York, NY 10001 (SAN 685-9852) Tel 212-213-1203; Dist. by: Kampmann & Co., 9 E. 40th St., New York, NY 10016 (SAN 666-7007) Tel 212-685-2928.
Richelieu Court, *(Richelieu Court Pubns., Inc.; 0-911519),* P.O. Box 388 Aspen Heights, Slingerlands, NY 12159 (SAN 264-3480) Tel 518-439-7942; Dist. by: Baker & Taylor, 50 Kirby Ave., Somerville, NJ 08876 (SAN 169-4901).
Richwood Pub, *(Richwood Pub., Co.; 0-915172),* P.O. Box 381, Scarsdale, NY 10583 (SAN 207-3250) Tel 914-723-1286.
Ridge Row, *(Ridge Row Pr.; 0-940866),* Univ. of Scranton, Dept. of Theology & Religious Studies, Scranton, PA 18510 (SAN 688-4067) Tel 717-961-7449; Dist. by: Montrose Publishing Co., 10-20 S. Main St., Montrose, PA 18801 (SAN 200-6898) Tel 717-278-1141.
Ridgeway Bks, *(Ridgeway Bks.),* P.O. Box 6431, Philadelphia, PA 19145 (SAN 207-7485).
RivEd *Imprint of* **HM**
River City MO, *(River City Pubs., Ltd.; 0-933150),* P.O. Box 28665, St. Louis, MO 63141 (SAN 222-982X) Tel 314-724-7160.
Riverdale Co, *(Riverdale Co., Inc., The; 0-913215),* 5506 Kenilworth Ave., No. 102, Riverdale, MD 20737 (SAN 283-3905) Tel 301-864-2029.
Riverrun NY, *(Riverrun Pr.; 0-7145; 0-86676),* Affil. of John Calder Pubs. (London, UK), 1170 Broadway, Rm. 807, New York, NY 10001 (SAN 240-9917) Tel 212-889-6850; Dist. by: Kampmann & Co., Inc., 9 E. 40th St., New York, NY 10016 (SAN 202-5191) Tel 212-685-2928.
Rizzoli Intl, *(Rizzoli International Pubns., Inc.; 0-8478),* 597 Fifth Ave., New York, NY 10017 (SAN 207-7000) Tel 212-223-0100; Toll free: 800-433-1238.
Rob Briggs, *(Briggs, Roberts, Assocs.; 0-9609850; 0-931191),* Box 9, Mill Valley, CA 94942 (SAN 268-4632) Tel 415-461-7051; Dist. by: Publishers Services, 11A Commercial Blvd., Novato, CA 94947 (SAN 200-7223) Tel 415-883-3140.
Robinson Pr, *(Robinson Pr., Inc.; 0-913730),* 1137 Riverside Dr., Fort Collins, CO 80524 (SAN 205-2369) Tel 303-482-5393.
Rock Harbor, *(Rock Harbor Press; 0-932260),* P.O. Box 1206, Hyannis, MA 02601 (SAN 214-199X).
Rock Point, *(Rock Point Community School; 0-910675),* Chinle, AZ 86503 (SAN 262-8910) Tel 602-659-4246.
Rockdale Ridge, *(Rockdale Ridge Pr.; 0-9602338),* 8501 Ridge Rd., Cincinnati, OH 45236 (SAN 212-4459) Tel 513-891-9900; Dist. by: Ingram Bk. Co., P.O. Box 17266, Nashville, TN 37217 (SAN 665-7710) Tel 615-251-5000.
Rocky Mtn Bks, *(Rocky Mountain Bks.; 0-9605648),* P.O. Box 10663, Denver, CO 80210 (SAN 215-7047).
Rod & Staff, *(Rod & Staff Pubs., Inc.),* Hwy. 172, Crockett, KY 41413 (SAN 206-7633) Tel 606-522-4348.
Rodale Pr Inc, *(Rodale Pr., Inc.; 0-87857),* 33 E. Minor St., Emmaus, PA 18098 (SAN 200-2477) Tel 215-967-5171; Toll free: 800-527-8200.
Romance, *(Romance Monographs, Inc.),* P.O. Box 7553, University, MS 38677 (SAN 209-4878) Tel 601-234-0001.
Rorge Pub Co, *(Rorge Publishing Co.; 0-914920),* 824 Laramie Ave., Alliance, NE 69301 (SAN 202-9715).
Rose Pub MI, *(Rose Publishing Co.; 0-937320),* 4676 Morningside Dr., SE, Grand Rapids, MI 49508 (SAN 211-8378) Tel 616-698-8282.
Rose Sharon Pr, *(Rose of Sharon Pr., Inc.; 0-932502),* G.P.O. Box 2432, New York, NY 10116 (SAN 212-3207) Tel 914-736-2521.
Rosejoy Pubns, *(Rosejoy Pubns.; 0-933453),* P.O. Box 668, Kalamazoo, MI 49005-0668 (SAN 691-828X) Tel 616-344-4016; Orders to: Spring Arbor Distributors, 10885 Textile Rd., Belleveille, MI 48111-2398 (SAN 693-5222) Tel 313-483-8462.
Ross Bks, *(Ross Bks.; 0-89496; 0-931272),* P.O. Box 4340, Berkeley, CA 94704 (SAN 209-5912) Tel 415-841-2474.
Ross-Erikson, *(Ross-Erikson, Inc.; 0-915520),* 223 Via Sevilla, Santa Barbara, CA 93105 (SAN 208-0494) Tel 805-965-5367.
Rossel Bks, *(Rossel Bks.; 0-940646),* Div. of Seymour Rossel Co., Inc., 15512 Golden Creek, Dallas, TX 75248 (SAN 213-6414) Tel 214-458-1004; Dist. by: Behrman Hse., Inc., 235 Watchung Ave., West Orange, NJ 07052 (SAN 201-4459) Tel 201-669-0447.
Rossi Pubns, *(Rossi Pubns.; 0-935618),* P.O. Box 2001, Beverly Hills, CA 90213 (SAN 213-6414) Tel 213-556-0337.
Rostrum Bks, *(Rostrum Bks.),* P.O. Box 1191, Miami, FL 33101 (SAN 205-227X) Tel 305-573-5900.
Rosycross Pr, *(Rosycross Pr.; 90-70196),* Affil. of Spiritual Schl. of Golden Rosycross: Lectorium Rosicrucianum, 709 A St., C-21, Bakersfield, CA 93304-1917 (SAN 659-2104) Tel 805-328-0707; Orders to: Lectorium Rosicrucianum, Bk. Sales, P.O. Box 9246, Bakersfield, CA 93389-9246 (SAN 662-4235) Tel 805-327-2827.
Roth Pub, *(Roth Publishing; 0-87957),* 125 Mineola Ave., Roslyn Hts., NY 11577 (SAN 203-0810) Tel 516-621-7242.
Roth Pub Inc, *(Roth Publishing, Inc.; 0-89609; 0-8486),* 185 Great Neck Rd., Great Neck, NY 11021 (SAN 210-9735) Tel 516-466-3676; Toll free: 800-327-0295 (orders).
Rothman, *(Rothman, Fred B., & Co.; 0-8377),* 10368 W. Centennial Rd., Littleton, CO 80127 (SAN 159-9437) Tel 303-979-5657; Toll free: 800-457-1986. Acquired Rothman Reprints.
Round River Pub, *(Round River Publishing Co.; 0-933437),* P.O. Box 3324, Madison, WI 53704 (SAN 691-5116) Tel 608-241-4289.
Roundtable Pr, *(Roundtable Pr.; 0-934512),* 4 Linden Sq., Wellesley, MA 02181-4709 (SAN 282-2628) Tel 617-235-5320. Do not confuse with Roundtable Pub., Santa Monica, CA.
Rowan Tree, *(Rowan Tree Pr., Ltd.; 0-937672),* 124 Chestnut St., Boston, MA 02108 (SAN 214-4638) Tel 617-523-7627; Dist. by: Bookslinger, 213 E. Fourth St., St. Paul, MN 55101 (SAN 169-4154) Tel 612-221-0429; Dist. by: Small Pr. Distribution, 1814 San Pablo Ave., Berkeley, CA 94702 (SAN 204-5826) Tel 415-549-3336; Dist. by: Bookpeople, 2929 Fifth St., Berkeley, CA 94710 (SAN 168-9517); Dist. by: Inland Bk. Co., P.O. Box 261, 22 Hemingway Ave., East Haven, CT 06512 (SAN 200-4151) Tel 203-467-4257.
Rowman, *(Rowman & Littlefield, Pubs.; 0-87471; 0-8476),* Div. of Littlefield, Adams, & Co., 81 Adams Dr., Totowa, NJ 07512 (SAN 203-3704) Tel 201-256-8600. *Imprints:* Rowman & Allanheld (Rowman & Allanheld).
Rowman & Allanheld *Imprint of* **Rowman**
Royalty Pub, *(Royalty Publishing Co.; 0-910487),* P.O. Box 2016, Manassas, VA 22110 (SAN 260-1265) Tel 703-368-9878; Dist. by: Spring Arbor Distributors, 10885 Textile Rd., Belleville, MI 48111 (SAN 158-9016) Tel 313-481-0900; Dist. by: Whitaker Hse., Pittsburgh & Colfax Sts., Springdale, PA 15144 (SAN 203-2104) Tel 412-274-4440.
Rudra Pr, *(Rudra Pr.; 0-915801),* P.O. Box 1973, Cambridge, MA 02238 (SAN 294-1260) Tel 617-576-3394.
Rumbleseat, *(Rumbleseat Pr., Inc.; 0-913444),* Affil. of Green Valley World, Inc., 41 S. Ocean Blvd., Cayucos, CA 93430 (SAN 205-6437) Tel 805-995-1378.
Running Pr, *(Running Pr. Bk. Pubs.; 0-89471),* 125 S. 22nd St., Philadelphia, PA 19103 (SAN 204-5702) Tel 215-567-5080; Toll free: 800-428-1111.
Rural America, *(Rural America),* 1312 18th St. NW, Washington, DC 20036 (SAN 225-946X) Tel 202-659-2800.
Russell, *(Russell & Russell Pubs.; 0-8462),* Div. of Atheneum Pubs., 115 Fifth Ave., New York, NY 10003 (SAN 282-2644) Tel 212-614-1315; Orders to: Scribner Bk. Co., Front & Brown Sts., Riverside, NJ 08075 (SAN 201-002X).
Russell Pr, *(Russell Pr.; 0-918377),* P.O. Box 67, Sharon Hill, PA 19079 (SAN 657-3762) Tel 215-583-4550.
Rutgers U Pr, *(Rutgers Univ. Pr.; 0-8135),* 109 Church St., New Brunswick, NJ 08901 (SAN 203-364X) Tel 201-932-7762; Orders to: R.U.P. Distribution Ctr., P.O. Box 4869, Baltimore, MD 21211 (SAN 662-1325) Tel 301-338-6947.
Rutledge Pr *Imprint of* **Smith Pubs**
RWS Bks, *(RWS Bks.; 0-939400),* 4296 Mulholland St., Salt Lake City, UT 84124 (SAN 220-1593) Tel 801-272-7835.
Rydal, *(Rydal Pr., The; 0-911292),* Div. of Great Southwest Bks., The, 960 Camino Santander, Santa Fe, NM 87501 (SAN 204-7098) Tel 505-983-1680.
Rye Hist Soc, *(Rye Historical Society; 0-9615327),* 1 Purchase St., Rye, NY 10580 (SAN 695-0663) Tel 914-967-7588.
S & F Clark Art, *(Clark, Sterling & Francine, Art Institute; 0-931102),* P.O. Box 8, Williamstown, MA 01267 (SAN 222-8491) Tel 413-458-9545.
S Cudinach
See Piarist Father
S F Vanni, *(Vanni, S. F.; 0-913298),* 30 W. 12th St., New York, NY 10011 (SAN 220-0031) Tel 212-675-6336.
S G Phillips, *(Phillips, S. G., Inc.; 0-87599),* P.O. Box 83, Chatham, NY 12037 (SAN 293-3152) Tel 518-392-3068; c/o M & B Fulfillment Service, Inc., 540 Barnum Ave., Bridgeport, CT 06608 (SAN 293-3160) Tel 203-366-1900.
S Ill U Pr, *(Southern Illinois Univ. Pr.; 0-8093),* P.O. Box 3697, Carbondale, IL 62902-3697 (SAN 203-3623) Tel 618-453-2281.
S J Durst, *(Durst, Sanford J.; 0-915262; 0-942666),* 29-28 41st Ave., Long Island City, NY 11101 (SAN 211-6987) Tel 718-706-0303.
S R Abbott Mini, *(Abbott, Stanley R.; 0-915545),* Div. of Word International, P.O. Box 54975, Tulsa, OK 74155 (SAN 291-0586) Tel 918-252-1036.
S S Hykes, *(Hykes, Susan S.; 0-9608894),* P.O. Box 713, Kilauea, HI 96754 (SAN 241-1202) Tel 808-828-1619.
S Yonay, *(Yonay, Shahar; 0-9616783),* 126 Dover St., Brooklyn, NY 11235 (SAN 661-0544) Tel 718-615-0027.
Sadlier, *(Sadlier, William H., Inc.; 0-8215),* 11 Park Pl., New York, NY 10007 (SAN 204-0948) Tel 212-227-2120; Toll free: 800-221-5175.
Saeta, *(Saeta Ediciones; 0-917049),* 7642 SW 96th Ct., Miami, FL 33173 (SAN 655-2226) Tel 305-596-4097; Orders to: P.O. Box 440156, Miami, FL 33144-0156 (SAN 662-2305) Tel 305-596-4097.

Sagamore Bks MI, *(Sagamore Bks., Inc.; 0-937021),* P.O. Box 195, Grand Rapids, MI 49588 (SAN 699-8038); 2130 Enterprise SE, Kentwood, 49508 Tel 616-455-8530 (SAN 665-9136).
Sage, *(Sage Pubns., Inc.; 0-8039),* 2111 W. Hillcrest Dr., Newbury Park, CA 91320 (SAN 204-7217) Tel 805-499-0721.
Saifer, *(Saifer, Albert, Pub.; 0-87556),* P.O. Box 239 W.O.B., West Orange, NJ 07052 (SAN 204-7225) Tel 201-731-5701.
Salem Hse Pubs, *(Salem Hse. Pubs.; 0-941938),* 462 Boston St., Topsfield, MA 01983 (SAN 212-193X) Tel 617-887-2440. Do not confuse with Merrimack Publishing Corp., Bridgeport, CT.
Salem Pr, *(Salem Pr., Inc.; 0-89356),* P.O. Box 1097, Englewood Cliffs, NJ 07632 (SAN 208-838X) Tel 201-871-3700; Toll free: 800-221-1592.
Salv Army Suppl South, *(Salvation Army Supplies, Southern; 0-86544),* 1424 NE Expressway, Atlanta, GA 30329 (SAN 211-9765) Tel 404-728-1300.
Salvation Army, *(Salvation Army; 0-89216),* 120 W. 14th St., New York, NY 10011 (SAN 237-2649) Tel 212-337-7435; Orders to: 145 W. 15th St., New York, NY 10011 (SAN 662-1341).
SamHar Pr, *(SamHar Pr.; 0-85157),* Div. of Story Hse. Corp., Bindery Ln., Charlotteville, NY 12036 (SAN 203-3585) Tel 607-397-8725.
Samizdat, *(Samizdat; 0-9613814),* 700 New Hampshire Ave., NW, Suite 701, Washington, DC 20037 (SAN 682-0298) Tel 202-338-8424.
Sanatana, *(Sanatana Publishing Society; 0-933116),* 503 Pope St., Menlo Park, CA 94025 (SAN 212-7946) Tel 415-326-4232.
Sandbird Pub, *(Sandbird Publishing Group, The; 0-9615111),* P.O. Box 1257, Shalimar, FL 32579 (SAN 694-1540) Tel 904-862-3746.
S&F Clark Art
See S & F Clark Art
Sandollar Pr, *(Sandollar Pr.),* P.O. Box 4157, Santa Barbara, CA 93140-4157 (SAN 202-9952) Tel 805-963-7077.
Sandpiper CA, *(Sandpiper Pr.; 0-940356),* P.O.Box 128, Solana Beach, CA 92075 (SAN 217-5657) Tel 619-481-5259.
S&S, *(Simon & Schuster, Inc.; 0-671),* Div. of Gulf & Western, 1230 Ave. of the Americas, New York, NY 10020 (SAN 200-2450) Tel 212-698-7000; Toll free: 800-223-2336. *Imprints:* Fireside (Fireside Paperbacks); Linden Pr (Linden Press); Touchstone Bks (Touchstone Books); Wallaby (Wallaby).
Sansper, *(Sansper; 0-916865),* 134 Broadway, Costa Mesa, CA 92627 (SAN 654-5297) Tel 714-631-7273.
Sant Bani Ash, *(Sant Bani Ashram, Inc.; 0-89142),* Franklin, NH 03235 (SAN 209-5114) Tel 603-934-2948.
Santa Barb Mus Art, *(Santa Barbara Museum of Art; 0-89951),* 1130 State St., Santa Barbara, CA 93101 (SAN 130-8165) Tel 805-963-4364; Dist. by: Univ. of Wash. Pr., P.O. Box C50096, Seattle, WA 98145 (SAN 212-2502) Tel 206-543-8870.
Santa Barb Pr, *(Santa Barbara Pr.; 0-915643),* 1129 State St., Suite H, Santa Barbara, CA 93101 (SAN 292-6431) Tel 805-966-2060; Dist. by: Publishers Group West, 5855 Beaudry St., Emeryville, CA 94608 (SAN 202-8522) Tel 415-658-3453.
Santa Barbara Pr
See Santa Barb Pr
Santarasa Pubns, *(Santarasa Pubns.; 0-935548),* P.O. Box 825, Manford, OK 74044 (SAN 213-7925).
Sarasota Sci, *(Sarasota Scientific Pr.; 0-9614464),* P.O. Box 25604, Sarasota, FL 34277 (SAN 689-433X) Tel 813-922-0604.
Sat Eve Post
See Curtis Pub Co
Satori Resources, *(Satori Resources, Inc.; 0-937277),* 732 Hamlin Way, San Leandro, CA 94578 (SAN 659-140X) Tel 415-895-8614; Dist. by: New Leaf Distributing, The, 1020 White St., SW, Atlanta, GA 30310 (SAN 169-1449); Dist. by: Bookpeople, 2929 Fifth St., Berkeley, CA 94710 (SAN 168-9517).
Saturscent Pubns, *(Saturscent Pubns.; 0-934703),* Box 358, South Wellfleet, MA 02663 (SAN 694-2687) Tel 617-349-2921.
Savage
See Hughley Pubns
Sawan Kirpal Pubns, *(Sawan Kirpal Pubns.; 0-918224),* 1195 Mango Dr., West Palm Beach, FL 33415 (SAN 211-0571) Tel 804-633-5789; Orders to: Rte. 1, Box 24, Bowling Green, VA 22427 (SAN 211-058X).
SBA Coven, *(Coven, Susan B. Anthony; 0-937081),* P.O. Box 11363, Oakland, CA 94611 (SAN 658-4551) Tel 415-444-7724; 2927 Harrison St., Oakland, CA 94611 (SAN 658-456X); Dist. by: Bookpeople, 2929 Fifth St., Berkeley, CA 94710 (SAN 168-9517) Tel 415-549-3030.
SBS Pub, *(SBS Publishing, Inc.; 0-89961),* 50 Railroad Ave., Closter, NJ 07624 (SAN 213-3695) Tel 201-767-9450; Toll free: 800-631-2564.
SC Ed Comm Inc, *(South Carolina Educational Communications, Inc.; 0-943274),* 19 Springdale Ln., Spartanburg, SC 29302 (SAN 293-2601); Dist. by: South Carolina ETV, P.O. Drawer L, Columbia, SC 29250 (SAN 293-261X) Tel 803-758-7284.
Scala Books, *(Scala Bks.; 0-935748),* 1035 Fifth Ave., New York, NY 10028 (SAN 282-2784) Tel 212-737-0242; Toll free: 800-242-7737; Orders to: Harper & Row Pubs., Inc., Keystone Industrial Pk., Scranton, PA 18512 (SAN 215-3742).
Scandia Pubs, *(Scandia Pubs.; 0-937242),* 5921 Niwot Rd., Longmont, CO 80501 (SAN 282-2806) Tel 303-530-0824.
Scarecrow, *(Scarecrow Pr., Inc.; 0-8108),* Subs. of Grolier Educational Corp., 52 Liberty St., Box 4167, Metuchen, NJ 08840 (SAN 203-2651) Tel 201-548-8600.
Scarf Pr, *(Scarf Press; 0-934386),* 58 E. 83rd St., New York, NY 10028 (SAN 212-9698) Tel 212-744-3901.
Scepter Pubs, *(Scepter Pubs.; 0-933932),* 30 Church St., New Rochelle, NY 10801 (SAN 207-2858) Tel 914-636-3377.
Sch Zone Pub Co, *(School Zone Publishing Co.; 0-938256; 0-88743),* 1819 Industrial Dr., P.O. Box 703, Grand Haven, MI 49417 (SAN 289-8314) Tel 616-846-5030; Toll free: 800-253-0564.
Schalkenbach, *(Schalkenbach, Robert, Foundation; 0-911312),* 5 E. 44th St., New York, NY 10017 (SAN 206-1317) Tel 212-986-8684.
Schenkman Bks Inc, *(Schenkman Bks., Inc.; 0-87073; 0-87047),* 190 Concord Ave., Cambridge, MA 02138 (SAN 203-2643) Tel 617-492-4952; Orders to: P.O. Box 1570, Cambridge, MA 02138 (SAN 662-1368).
Schiffer, *(Schiffer Publishing, Ltd.; 0-916838; 0-88740),* 1469 Morstein Rd., West Chester, PA 19380 (SAN 208-8428) Tel 215-696-1001.
Schmul Pub Co, *(Schmul Publishing Co. Inc.; 0-88019),* P.O. Box 4068, Salem, OH 44460 (SAN 211-8246) Tel 216-222-2249.
Schocken, *(Schocken Bks., Inc.; 0-8052),* 62 Cooper Sq., New York, NY 10003 (SAN 213-7585) Tel 212-475-4900.
Schol Facsimiles, *(Scholars' Facsimiles & Reprints; 0-8201),* P.O. Box 344, Delmar, NY 12054 (SAN 203-2627) Tel 518-439-5978.
Schola Pr TX, *(Schola Pr.; 0-931016),* P.O. Box 294, Lorena, TX 76655 (SAN 216-4469) Tel 817-857-3566.
Scholarly, *(Scholarly Pr., Inc.; 0-403),* P.O. Box 160, St. Clair Shores, MI 48080 (SAN 209-0473). *Imprints:* Regency (Regency Press).
Scholarly Pubns, *(Scholarly Pubns.; 0-88065; 1-55528),* 7310 El Cresta Dr., Houston, TX 77083 (SAN 650-0587) Tel 713-879-8319.
Scholarly Res Inc, *(Scholarly Resources, Inc.; 0-8420),* 104 Greenhill Ave., Wilmington, DE 19805 (SAN 203-2619) Tel 302-654-7713; Toll free: 800-772-8937. Source materials on 35mm microfilm, monographs, reference books & microfiche. Subjects: ethnic studies, genealogy, history, law, military studies & political science. Government documents, journals, manuscript collections & newspapers.
Scholars Bks, *(Scholars Bks.; 0-938659),* P.O. Box 160361, Irving, TX 75016 (SAN 661-1346) Tel 214-686-5332.
Scholars Pr GA, *(Scholars Pr.; 0-89130; 1-55540),* P.O. Box 1608, Decatur, GA 30031-1608 (SAN 293-3896) Tel 404-636-4757; Dist. by: Scholars Pr. Customer Services, P.O. Box 4869, Hampden Sta., Baltimore, MD 21211 (SAN 293-3896) Tel 301-338-6946.
Scholars Ref Lib, *(Scholar's Reference Library),* P.O. Box 148, Darby, PA 19023 (SAN 205-1400).
Scholars Studies, *(Scholars Studies Press; 0-89177),* 109 E. Ninth St., New York, NY 10003 (SAN 208-3795) Tel 212-674-5296.
Scholastic Inc, *(Scholastic, Inc.; 0-590),* 730 Broadway, New York, NY 10003 (SAN 202-5442) Tel 212-505-3000; Toll free: 800-392-2179; Orders to: P.O. Box 7502, 2931 E. McCarty St., Jefferson City, MO 65102 (SAN 202-5450). *Imprints:* Point (Point).
Schumacher Pubns, *(Schumacher Pubns.; 0-917378),* 28 Holly Ln., Zenith Terr., Proctor, MN 55810 (SAN 208-8436) Tel 218-624-7728.
Schwenkfelder Lib, *(Schwenkfelder Library; 0-935980),* 1 Seminary St., Pennsburg, PA 18073 (SAN 213-795X) Tel 215-679-3103.
Sci of Mind, *(Science of Mind Pubns.; 0-917849; 0-911336),* Div. of United Church of Religious Science, P.O. Box 75127, Los Angeles, CA 90075 (SAN 203-2570) Tel 213-388-2181; Dist. by: Devorss & Co., P.O. Box 550, 1046 Princeton Dr., Marina del Rey, CA 90294 (SAN 168-9886); Dist. by: New Leaf Distributors, The, 1020 White St., SW, Altanta, GA 30310 (SAN 169-1449) Tel 404-755-2665.
Science Identity, *(Science of Identity Foundation; 0-88187),* P.O. Box 27450, Honolulu, HI 96827 (SAN 264-6900) Tel 808-488-4798.
Scojtia Renee, *(Scotjia Renee Publishing Co.; 0-9615560),* P.O. Box 38002, Los Angeles, CA 90038 (SAN 696-480X); 6457 Wilcox St., Los Angeles, CA 90038 (SAN 663-6713).
Scott F, *(Scott, Foresman & Co.; 0-673),* Subs. of Time, Inc., 1900 E. Lake Ave., Glenview, IL 60025 (SAN 200-2140) Tel 312-729-3000.
Scott Pubns CA
See A & S Pr
Scribner, *(Scribner's, Charles, Sons; 0-684),* Div. of Macmillan Publishing Co., 115 Fifth Ave., New York, NY 10003 (SAN 200-2191) Tel 212-614-1300; Toll free: 800-257-5755; Orders to: Order Dept., Front & Brown Sts., Riverside, NJ 08075 (SAN 202-5582).
Scripta, *(Scripta Humanistica; 0-916379),* 1383 Kersey Lane, Potomac, MD 20854 (SAN 295-8562) Tel 301-340-1095.
SDSU Press, *(San Diego State Univ., Pr.; 0-916304),* 5189 College Ave., San Diego, CA 92182 (SAN 202-0637) Tel 619-265-6220.
SE Asia Res Ctr
See Asia Resource
Sea Horse, *(Sea Horse Pr., Ltd., The; 0-933322),* 307 W. 11th St., New York, NY 10014 (SAN 212-4505) Tel 212-691-9066.
SeaHorse Pr
See Sea Horse
Seaver Bks, *(Seaver Bks.; 0-394),* 333 Central Park W., New York, NY 10025 (SAN 214-4719) Tel 212-866-9278; Orders to: Henry Holt & Co., 521 Fifth Ave., New York, NY 10175 (SAN 665-7788) Tel 212-599-7491.
Sebastian LI, *(Sebastian Publishing Co.; 0-9616731),* P.O. Box 471, Port Jefferson Station, NY 11776 (SAN 659-865X); Dark Hollow Rd., Port Jefferson, NY 11777 (SAN 659-8668) Tel 516-928-6745.
SEBT, *(Shrine of the Eternal Breath of Tao, The; 0-937064),* 117 Stonehaven Way, Los Angeles, CA 90049 (SAN 217-2704).
Second Coming, *(Second Coming, Inc.; 0-915016),* P.O. Box 31249, San Francisco, CA 94131 (SAN 206-376X) Tel 415-647-3679. Formerly known as Second Coming Pr.
Second Hand, *(Second Hand, The; 0-9605858),* P.O. Box 204, Plymouth, WI 53073 (SAN 220-1879) Tel 414-893-5226.
Second Soc Foun, *(Second Society Foundation),* 333 N. Michigan Ave., Suite 707, Chicago, IL 60601 (SAN 203-204X) Tel 312-263-1607.

Seed Center, *(Seed Ctr.; 0-916108),* Box 1700, Redway, CA 95560 (SAN 203-2554) Tel 707-923-2524.
Seed Life Pubns, *(Seed of Life Pubns.; 0-930875),* P.O. Box 33961, Phoenix, AZ 85067 (SAN 677-7945) Tel 602-842-9102.
Selbstverlag, *(Selbstverlag Pr.; 0-911706),* P.O. Drawer 606, Bloomington, IN 47402-0606 (SAN 204-5761) Tel 812-334-2166.
Selene Bks, *(Selene Bks.; 0-9609866),* P.O. Box 548, Lawrence, KS 66044-0548 (SAN 275-276X).
Self Realization, *(Self Realization Fellowship; 0-87612),* 3880 San Rafael Ave., Los Angeles, CA 90065 (SAN 204-5788) Tel 213-225-2471.
Seminary Co-Op, *(Seminary Co-Operative Bookstore, Inc.; 0-912182),* 5757 S. University Ave., Chicago, IL 60637 (SAN 204-5818) Tel 312-752-4381.
Seminary Pr, *(Seminary Pr.; 0-912832),* P.O. Box 2218, Univ. Sta., Enid, OK 73702 (SAN 203-2546) Tel 405-237-4433.
Senda Nueva, *(Senda Nueva de Ediciones, Inc.; 0-918454),* 640 W. 231st St., Apt. 3B, Mail Box 139, Bronx, NY 10463 (SAN 210-0061) Tel 212-548-5288; Orders to: P.O. Box 488, Montclair, NJ 07042 (SAN 662-1392).
Seneca Bks, *(Seneca Bks., Inc.; 0-89092),* Rte. 6, Box 81-B, Morgantown, WV 26505 (SAN 213-4322) Tel 304-594-1324.
Sentinel Pub, *(Sentinel Publishing Co.; 0-931097),* 4845 50th St., Lubbock, TX 79414 (SAN 678-9447) Tel 806-792-3801; Toll free: 800-858-4602.
Serendipity Pr
See Price Stern
Serenity Hse, *(Serenity Hse. Publishing; 0-914789),* P.O. Box 462, Port Washington, NY 11050 (SAN 670-6983) Tel 516-883-7198.
Servant, *(Servant Pubns.; 0-89283),* 840 Airport Blvd., Ann Arbor, MI 48107 (SAN 208-9238) Tel 313-761-8505; Orders to: Customer Service Dept., Box 8617, Ann Arbor, MI 48107 (SAN 208-9246) Tel 313-761-8505; Dist. by: Spring Arbor Distributors, 10885 Textile Rd., Belleville, MI 48111 (SAN 662-1406) Tel 313-481-0900; Dist. by: East Coast Christian Distributors, P.O. Box 4200, 35 Readington Rd., Somerville, NJ 08876 (SAN 169-491X).
SES Development, *(SES Development Corp.; 0-943982),* Dist. by: The Book Carrier, Inc., 9121 Industrial Court, Gaithersburg, MD 20877 (SAN 200-4046) Tel 301-258-1177.
Seven Hills Bks, *(Seven Hills Bks.; 0-911403),* Div. of Books for the Decorative Arts, Inc., 49 Central Ave., Cincinnati, OH 45202 (SAN 169-6629) Tel 513-381-3881.
Sey Lawr *Imprint of* **Delacorte**
SF Study Ctr, *(San Francisco Study Ctr.; 0-936434),* P.O. Box 5646, San Francisco, CA 94101 (SAN 214-4654) Tel 415-626-1650.
Shadwold, *(Shadwold Pr.; 0-9603024),* P.O. Box 706, Kennebunkport, ME 04046 (SAN 212-5587) Tel 207-967-4400.
Shaker Her Soc, *(Shaker Heritage Society; 0-89062),* Albany Shaker Rd., Albany, NY 12211 (SAN 289-0410) Tel 518-456-7890.
Shaker Mus, *(Shaker Museum Foundation Inc.; 0-937942),* Shaker Museum Rd., Old Chatham, NY 12136 (SAN 206-7684) Tel 518-794-9100.
Shaker Pr ME, *(Shaker Pr., The; 0-915836),* Sabbathday Lake, Poland Spring, ME 04274 (SAN 214-1388) Tel 207-926-4597.
Shalom, *(Shalom, P., Pubns., Inc.; 0-87559),* 5409 18th Ave., Brooklyn, NY 11204 (SAN 204-5893) Tel 718-256-1954.
Shamar Bk, *(Shamer Bk.; 0-9607058),* 9215 N. Concho Lane, Phoenix, AZ 85028 (SAN 239-3840).
Shambhala Pubns, *(Shambhala Pubns., Inc.; 0-87773; 0-394),* 314 Dartmouth St., Boston, MA 02116 (SAN 203-2481); Toll free: 800-638-6460; Dist. by: Random Hse., Inc., 400 Hahn Rd., Westminster, MD 21157 (SAN 202-5515).
Shapolsky Pubs, *(Shapolsky Pubs., Inc.; 0-933503),* 56 E. 11th St., New York, NY 10003 (SAN 200-8068) Tel 212-505-2505.
Sharing Co, *(Sharing Co., The; 0-941500),* P.O. Box 2224, Austin, TX 78768-2224 (SAN 211-0563) Tel 512-452-4366.
Sharon Hill, *(Sharon Hill Bks.; 0-932062),* P.O. Box 67, Sharon Hill, PA 19079 (SAN 210-5632).
Shasta Abbey, *(Shasta Abbey Pr.; 0-930066),* P.O. Box 199, Mt. Shasta, CA 96067 (SAN 210-6655) Tel 916-926-4208; Dist. by: Bookpeople, 2929 Fifth St., Berkeley, CA 94710 (SAN 168-9517).
Shaw Pubs, *(Shaw, Harold, Pubs.; 0-87788),* P.O. Box 567, 388 Gundersen Dr., Wheaton, IL 60189 (SAN 203-2473) Tel 312-665-6700; Toll free: 800-742-9782.
Shearwater, *(Shearwater Pr.; 0-938050),* Box 417, Wellfleet, MA 02667 (SAN 216-1923).
Sheed & Ward MO, *(Sheed & Ward; 0-934134; 1-55612),* Div. of National Catholic Reporter Publishing Co., Inc., P.O. Box 414292, Kansas City, MO 64141-0281 (SAN 207-7396); Toll free: 800-821-7926; 115 E. Armour Blvd., Kansas City, MO 61414-0281 (SAN 658-1269) Tel 816-531-0538; Toll free: 800-821-7296.
Sheffield Wisc, *(Sheffield Publishing Co.; 0-917974; 0-88133),* Subs. of Waveland Pr., P.O. Box 359, Salem, WI 53168 (SAN 658-4519); 9009 Antioch Rd., Salem, WI 53168 (SAN 658-4527) Tel 414-843-2281.
Shenandoah Hist, *(Shenandoah History; 0-917968),* P.O. Box 98, Edinburg, VA 22824 (SAN 210-0118) Tel 703-459-4598.
Shengold, *(Shengold Pubs., Inc.; 0-88400),* 23 W. 45th St., New York, NY 10036 (SAN 203-2465) Tel 212-944-2555.
Shepherd Bks, *(Shepherd Bks., Inc.; 0-940183),* P.O. Box 663, Redmond, WA 98052 (SAN 664-3108); 17714 NE 26th, Redmond, WA 98052 (SAN 664-3116) Tel 206-885-0463.
Sheriar Pr, *(Sheriar Pr., Inc.; 0-913078),* 1414 Madison St., S., North Myrtle Beach, SC 29582 (SAN 203-2457) Tel 803-272-5333.
Sheridan, *(Sheridan Hse., Inc.; 0-911378),* 145 Palisade St., Dobbs Ferry, NY 10522 (SAN 204-5915) Tel 914-693-2410.
Sheridan Square Pubns, *(Sheridan Square Pubns., Inc.),* P.O. Box 677, New York, NY 10013 (SAN 678-903X) Tel 212-254-1061.
Shilo Pub Hse, *(Shilo Publishing House, Inc.; 0-88328),* 73 Canal St., New York, NY 10002 (SAN 205-9894) Tel 212-925-3468.
Shinn Music
See Duane Shinn
Shoe String, *(Shoe String Pr., Inc.; 0-208),* P.O. Box 4327, Hamden, CT 06514 (SAN 213-2079); 925 Sherman Ave., Hamden, CT 06514 (SAN 696-9410) Tel 203-248-6307. *Imprints:* Archon Bks (Archon Books).
Shorey, *(Shorey Pubns.; 0-8466),* 110 Union St., Seattle, WA 98101 (SAN 204-5958) Tel 206-624-0221.
Shroud of Turin, *(Shroud of Turin Research Project, Inc.; 0-9605516),* P.O. Box 7, Amston, CT 06231 (SAN 216-1834).
Shulsinger Sales, *(Shulsinger Sales, Inc.; 0-914080),* 50 Washington St., Brooklyn, NY 11201 (SAN 205-9851) Tel 718-852-0042.
Shutts Minist, *(Shutts Ministries; 0-9614077),* P.O. Box 28, Marysville, OH 43040 (SAN 686-0648) Tel 513-644-9785.
Siamese Imports, *(Siamese Imports Co., Inc.; 0-940202),* 148 Plandome Rd., Manhasset, NY 11030 (SAN 220-3545) Tel 516-365-8867.
Sig *Imprint of* **NAL**
Sig Classics *Imprint of* **NAL**
Signal Bks, *(Signal Bks.; 0-930095),* Subs. Of Compute Textual Services, 201-C E. Main St., Carrboro, NC 27510 (SAN 670-1795) Tel 919-929-5985.
Signature Bks, *(Signature Bks., Inc.; 0-941214),* 350 S. 400 E., Salt Lake City, UT 84111 (SAN 217-4391) Tel 801-298-0966; Dist. by: Publishers Bk. Sales, 960 W. 850 S., Woods Cross, UT 84087 (SAN 200-8688); Dist. by: Ingram Bk. Co., 347 Reedwood Dr., Nashville, TN 37217 (SAN 169-7978). *Imprints:* Eden Hill Pub (Eden Hill Publishing); Orion (Orion).
Sigo Pr, *(Sigo Pr.; 0-938434),* 77 N. Washington St., No. 201, Boston, MA 02114 (SAN 216-3020) Tel 617-523-2321.
Silo Pubs, *(Silo Pubs., The; 0-937109),* P.O. Box 3662, Hesperia, CA 92345 (SAN 658-439X); 18019 Danbury Ave., Hesperia, CA 92345 (SAN 658-4403) Tel 619-244-1674.
Silver, *(Silver Burdett Pr.; 0-382),* Subs. of Simon & Schuster, A Gulf & Western Co., 250 James St., Morristown, NJ 07960-1918 (SAN 204-5982) Tel 201-285-7700; Toll free: 800-631-8081.
Silver App Pr, *(Silver Apples Pr.; 0-943710),* P.O. Box 292, Hainesport, NJ 08036 (SAN 238-3721).
Simile II, *(Simile II),* 218 12th St., P.O. Box 910, Del Mar, CA 92014 (SAN 208-8525) Tel 619-755-0272.
Single Vision, *(Single Vision Pubns.; 0-9608960),* Box No. 804, Lebanon, OR 97355 (SAN 241-2519) Tel 503-258-5888.
Sirius Bks, *(Sirius Bks.; 0-917108),* 4745 Anderson Ln., Eureka, CA 95501 (SAN 275-3766) Tel 707-442-8481.
Sisters Christ Charity, *(Sisters of Christian Charity; 0-9616887),* 1041 Ridge Rd., Wilmette, IL 60091-1560 (SAN 661-6402) Tel 312-256-1060.
Sixteenth Cent, *(Sixteenth Century Journal Pubs., Inc.; 0-940474),* Northeast Missouri State Univ., Laughlin Bldg., No. 115, Kirksville, MO 63501 (SAN 223-159X) Tel 816-785-4665.
Skinner Hse Bks *Imprint of* **Unitarian Univ**
Skoglie Storevik Pubs, *(Skoglie & Storevik Pubs.; 0-9617564),* P.O. Box 3403, Costa Mesa, CA 92628 (SAN 664-4740); 2191 Harbor Blvd., No. 6, Costa Mesa, CA 92627 (SAN 664-4759) Tel 714-642-4224.
Skribent, *(Skribent Pr.; 0-9609374),* 9700 SW Lakeside Dr., Tigard, OR 97223 (SAN 283-2542) Tel 503-620-0471; Dist. by: Pacific Pipeline, 19215 66th Ave., S, Kent, WA 98032 (SAN 208-2128) Tel 206-872-5523.
Slavica, *(Slavica Pubs., Inc.; 0-89357),* P.O. Box 14388, Columbus, OH 43214 (SAN 208-8576) Tel 614-268-4002.
Slawson Comm, *(Slawson Communications, Inc.; 0-915391),* 3719 Sixth Ave., San Diego, CA 92103-4316 (SAN 200-6901) Tel 619-291-9126.
Sleepy Hollow, *(Sleepy Hollow Pr.; 0-912882),* Div. of Sleepy Hollow Restorations, 150 White Plains Rd., Tarrytown, NY 10591 (SAN 202-0750) Tel 914-631-8200; Dist. by: Independent Pubs. Group, 1 Pleasant Ave., Pt. Washington, NY 11050 (SAN 202-0769).
Small Pr Dist, *(Small Pr. Distribution, Inc.; 0-914068),* 1814 San Pablo Ave., Berkeley, CA 94702 (SAN 204-5826) Tel 415-549-3336.
Smith Pubs, *(Smith, W. H., Pubs., Inc.; 0-8317),* Subs. of W. H. Smith & Son, Ltd., 112 Madison Ave., New York, NY 10016 (SAN 216-3241) Tel 212-532-6600; Toll free: 800-932-0070; 80 Distribution Blvd., Edison, NJ 08817 (SAN 658-1625) Tel 201-287-3550. *Imprints:* Mayflower Bks (Mayflower Books); Rutledge Pr (Rutledge Press).
Smithsonian, *(Smithsonian Institution Pr.; 0-87474),* 955 L'Enfant Plaza, Suite 2100, Washington, DC 20560 (SAN 206-8044) Tel 202-287-3765; Orders to: Customer Services, P.O. Box 4866, Hampden Sta., Baltimore, MD 21211 (SAN 206-8052) Tel 301-338-6963.
Smoloskyp, *(Smoloskyp Pubs., Inc.; 0-914834),* P.O. Box 561, Ellicott City, MD 21043 (SAN 206-1260) Tel 301-461-1764.
SMU Press, *(Southern Methodist Univ. Pr.; 0-87074),* P.O. Box 415, Dallas, TX 75275 (SAN 203-3615); 6410 Airline Dr., Dallas, TX 75205 (SAN 658-1641) Tel 214-739-5959; Dist. by: Texas A & M Univ. Pr., Drawer C, College Station, TX 77843 (SAN 207-5237) Tel 409-845-1436.
Smyres Pubns, *(Smyres Pubns.; 0-9616952),* P.O. Box 4796, Ithaca, NY 14852 (SAN 661-7565); 818 Hanshaw Rd., Ithaca, NY 14850 (SAN 661-7573) Tel 607-257-7517.

Snow Lion, *(Snow Lion Pubns.; 0-937938),* P.O. Box 6483, Ithaca, NY 14851 (SAN 281-7292) Tel 607-273-8506; Dist. by: Bookpeople, 2929 Fifth St., Berkeley, CA 94710 (SAN 168-9517) Tel 415-549-3030; Dist. by: Inland Bk. Co., Inc., P.O. Box 261, 22 Hemingway Ave., East Haven, CT 06512 (SAN 200-4151) Tel 203-467-4257; Dist. by: Samuel Weiser, Inc., P.O. Box 612, York Beach, ME 03910 (SAN 202-9588) Tel 207-363-4393; Dist. by: The Great Tradition, 750 Adrian Way, Suite 111, San Rafael, CA 94903 (SAN 200-5743) Tel 415-492-9382; Dist. by: New Leaf Distributors, The, 1020 White St. SW, Atlanta, GA 30310 (SAN 169-1449) Tel 404-755-2665; Dist. by: Starlite Distributors, P.O. Box 20729, Reno, NV 89515 (SAN 131-1921) Tel 702-359-5676; Dist. by: Distributors, The, 702 S. Michigan, South Bend, IN 46618 (SAN 169-2488) Tel 219-232-8500.

Soc Am Archivists, *(Society of American Archivists; 0-931828),* 600 S. Federal, Suite 504, Chicago, IL 60605 (SAN 211-7614) Tel 312-922-0140.

Soc for Visual, *(Society for Visual Education, Inc.; 0-89290),* 1345 Diversey Pkwy., Chicago, IL 60614 (SAN 208-3930) Tel 312-525-1500; Toll free: 800-621-1900.

Soc Humanistic, *(Society for Humanistic Judaism; 0-912645),* 28611 W. Twelve Mile Rd., Farmington Hills, MI 48018 (SAN 275-4576) Tel 313-478-7610.

Soc Issues, *(Social Issues Resources Series, Inc.; 0-89777),* P.O. Box 2507, Boca Raton, FL 33427 (SAN 222-8920) Tel 305-994-0079; Toll free: 800-327-0513.

Soc New Lang Study, *(Society for New Language Study, Inc.; 0-9502699; 0-936072),* P.O. Box 10596, Denver, CO 80210 (SAN 203-2368) Tel 303-777-6115.

Soc Phil Pol, *(Bowling Green State Univ., Social Philosophy & Policy Ctr.; 0-912051),* Social Philosophy & Policy Ctr., Bowling Green, OH 43403 (SAN 264-6048) Tel 419-372-2536.

Soc Right to Die, *(Society for the Right to Die, Inc.; 0-9613825),* 250 W. 57th St., New York, NY 10107 (SAN 225-9354) Tel 212-246-6973.

Soc Sci Stud Rel, *(Society for the Scientific Study of Religion; 0-932566),* Catholic Univ. of America, Marist Hall, Rm. 108, Storrs, CT 06268 (SAN 212-1670).

Somerset Pub, *(Somerset Pubs.),* 200 Park Ave., Suite 303 E., New York, NY 10017 (SAN 204-6105) Tel 313-884-0400.

Son-Rise Pubns, *(Son-Rise Pubns.; 0-936369),* Rte. 3, Box 202, New Wilmington, PA 16142 (SAN 698-0031) Tel 412-946-8334; Dist. by: Spring Arbor, 10885 Textile, Belleville, MI 48111 (SAN 158-9016) Tel 313-481-0900; Dist. by: Whitaker Hse., Pittsburgh & Colfax Sts., Springdale, PA 15144 (SAN 203-2104) Tel 412-274-4440.

Soncino Pr, *(Soncino Pr.),* 5 Essex St., New York, NY 10002 (SAN 681-2740) Tel 212-505-8900.

Sonflower Bks *Imprint of* **SP Pubns**

Sons Lib, *(Sons of Liberty; 0-89562),* Div. of New Christian Crusade Church, Box 214, Metairie, LA 70004 (SAN 210-6663) Tel 504-887-3217.

Sooty-Face, *(Sooty-Face Publishing Hse.; 0-9602366),* P.O. Box 26, Clairton, PA 15025 (SAN 212-5633) Tel 412-233-6141.

Sophia Inst Pr, *(Sophia Institute Pr.; 0-918477),* P.O. Box 5284, Manchester, NH 03108 (SAN 657-7172) Tel 603-669-1103.

SOS Minist Pr, *(SOS Ministries Pr.; 0-938573),* Div. of Shama Sound Ministries, P.O. Box 27054, San Francisco, CA 94127 (SAN 661-4701); 78 Sycamore St., San Francisco, CA 94110 (SAN 661-471X) Tel 415-552-2300.

SOS Pub OR, *(SOS Publishing; 0-931689),* P.O. Box 68290, Oak Grove, OR 97268 (SAN 686-1814) Tel 503-654-9123.

Sotheby Pubns, *(Sotheby Pubns.),* 1035 Fifth Ave., New York, NY 10028 (SAN 678-9188) Tel 212-737-0242; Orders to: Scala Bks., Keystone Industrial Pk., Scranton, PA 18512 (SAN 215-3742).

SOTOA
See O T O

South Asia Bks, *(South Asia Bks.; 0-88386; 0-8364),* P.O. Box 502, Columbia, MO 65205 (SAN 207-4044) Tel 314-449-1359.

South Carolina
See SC Ed Comm Inc

South End Pr, *(South End Pr.; 0-89608),* 116 St. Botolph St., Boston, MA 02115 (SAN 211-979X) Tel 617-266-0629; Orders to: 300 Raritan Ctr. Pkwy., CN-3137, Edison, NJ 08818 (SAN 695-4502) Tel 201-225-1900.

South Oregon, *(Southern Oregon Historical Society; 0-943388),* P.O. Box 480, 206 N. Fifth St., Jacksonville, OR 97530 (SAN 240-7779) Tel 503-899-1847.

Southern Hist Pr, *(Southern Historical Pr., Inc.; 0-89308),* P.O. Box 738, Easley, SC 29641-0738 (SAN 208-8657) Tel 803-859-2346.

Southwest Mus, *(Southwest Museum; 0-916561),* P.O. Box 128, Highland Park Sta., Los Angeles, CA 90042 (SAN 203-0683) Tel 213-221-2164.

Sovereign Pr, *(Sovereign Pr.; 0-914752),* 326 Harris Rd., Rochester, WA 98579 (SAN 206-1279) Tel 206-273-5109.

Sovereignty, *(Sovereignty, Inc.; 0-932201),* P.O. Box 909, Eastsound, WA 98245-0483 (SAN 686-5968) Tel 206-376-2177; Toll free: 800-654-1407.

SP Pubns, *(Scripture Pr. Pubs., Inc.; 0-88207; 0-89693),* 1825 College Ave., Wheaton, IL 60187 (SAN 222-9471) Tel 312-668-6000; Toll free: 800-323-9409. *Imprints:* Sonflower Bks (Sonflower Books).

Sparrow Pr CA, *(Sparrow Pr. of California; 0-917143),* Subs. of Sparrow Corporation, 9255 Deering Ave., Chatsworth, CA 91311 (SAN 655-8844) Tel 818-703-6599.

Spears, *(Spears, W. H., Jr.; 0-9600106),* 426 N. Kennicott, Arlington Heights, IL 60004 (SAN 204-6180).

Spell Assoc, *(Spell, Leonard, & Assocs.; 0-9615439),* 723 S. Mansfield Ave., Los Angeles, CA 90036 (SAN 696-1118) Tel 213-935-2186.

Speller, *(Speller, Robert, & Sons, Pubs., Inc.; 0-8315),* 30 E. 23rd St., New York, NY 10010 (SAN 203-2295) Tel 212-477-5524; Orders to: P.O. Box 461, Times Sq. Sta., New York, NY 10108 (SAN 203-2309).

Spencer Inst
See Spencer Pr

Spencer Pr, *(Spencer Pr., The; 0-932270),* 8 Burnside Rd., Newton, MA 02161 (SAN 205-5651) Tel 617-965-8388.

Spire Bks *Imprint of* **Revell**

Spirit Christ, *(Spirit of Christ Ministries; 0-9615536),* Box 10952, Suite 194, Houston, TX 77292 (SAN 696-1002) Tel 713-223-0411.

Spirit Faith, *(Spirit of Faith Ministries; 0-936371),* 7040 SW 47th St., Miami, FL 33155 (SAN 698-0147) Tel 305-662-5778.

Spirit Front Fellow, *(Spiritual Frontiers Fellowship; 0-914071),* 3310 Baring St., Philadelphia, PA 19104 (SAN 287-0282) Tel 215-222-0619; 10819 Winner Rd., Independence, MO 64052 (SAN 287-0290); Dist. by: Samuel Weiser, Inc., P.O. Box 612, York Beach, ME 03910 (SAN 202-9588) Tel 207-363-4393.

Spirit Prophecy, *(Spirit of Prophecy Ministries; 0-930351),* 1350 E. Flamingo, Las Vegas, NV 89132 (SAN 670-7661) Tel 702-737-0040; P.O. Box 19020-277, Las Vegas, NV 89132 (SAN 658-2591).

Spiritual, *(Spiritual Union; 0-9614275),* 237 Rivoli St., San Francisco, CA 94117 (SAN 687-407X) Tel 415-564-1826; Dist. by: Bookpeople, 2929 Fifth St., Berkeley, CA 94710 (SAN 168-9517) Tel 415-549-3030.

Spiritual Advisory
See TMH Pub

Spiritual Comm
See Arcline Pubns

Spiritual Growth, *(Spiritual Growth Resources; 0-938180),* Div. of Organization Resoures Pr., Ltd., P.O. Box 977, Indianapolis, IN 46206 (SAN 692-8951).

Spiritual Renaissance
See Highreach Colorado

Spiritual Sci Lib *Imprint of* **Garber Comm**

Spiritual Warfare, *(Spiritual Warfare Ministries; 0-9615445),* P.O. Box 6515, Lakeland, FL 33807 (SAN 695-7064); Toll free: 800-282-8490; 730 Creative Dr., No. 1, Lakeland, FL 33803 (SAN 699-6094) Tel 813-644-7506; Dist. by: Spring Arbor, 10885 Textile Rd., Belleville, MI 48111 (SAN 158-9016) Tel 313-481-0900; Orders to: Whitaker Hse., Pittsburg & Colfax Sts., Springdale, PA 15144 (SAN 662-3549) Tel 412-274-4440.

Spiritwarrior Pub, *(Spiritwarrior Publishing Co.; 0-940298),* 306 Cecil St., Waynoka, OK 73880 (SAN 217-5851).

Spizzirri, *(Spizzirri Pub. Co., Inc.; 0-86545),* P.O. Box 664, Medinah, IL 60157 (SAN 215-2851) Tel 312-529-1181; Toll free: 800-325-9819.

Spoken Lang Serv, *(Spoken Language Services, Inc.; 0-87950),* P.O. Box 783, Ithaca, NY 14851 (SAN 203-2279) Tel 607-257-0500.

Spring Pubns, *(Spring Pubns., Inc.; 0-88214),* P.O. Box 222069, Dallas, TX 75222 (SAN 203-2244); 408 N. Bishop, Suite 108, Dallas, TX 75208 (SAN 658-1692) Tel 214-943-4093.

Springer Pub, *(Springer Publishing Co., Inc.; 0-8261),* 536 Broadway, New York, NY 10012 (SAN 203-2236) Tel 212-431-4370.

Springer-Verlag, *(Springer-Verlag New York, Inc.; 0-387),* Subs. of Springer-Verlag GmbH & Co. KG, 175 Fifth Ave., New York, NY 10010 (SAN 203-2228) Tel 212-460-1500; Toll free: 800-526-7254; Orders to: 44 Hartz Way, Secaucus, NJ 07094 (SAN 665-7842) Tel 201-348-4033.

Squantum Pr, *(Squantum Pr.; 0-9607532),* 92 Old Colony Ave., Quincy, MA 02170 (SAN 238-4817) Tel 617-471-8380.

Sri Aurobindo, *(Sri Aurobindo Universal; 0-935075),* 331 E. 14th St., Apt 6C, New York, NY 10003 (SAN 695-0000) Tel 212-254-3321.

Sri Rama, *(Sri Rama Publishing; 0-918100),* 161 Robles Dr., Santa Cruz, CA 95060 (SAN 282-3578) Tel 408-426-5098; Orders to: P.O. Box 2550, Santa Cruz, CA 95063 (SAN 282-3586).

Sri Shirdi Sai, *(Sri Shirdi Sai Pubns.; 0-938924),* Affil. of Sri Shirdi Sai Baba Priest Services, 251 Wilbur Ave., Pittsburgh, PA 15145 (SAN 220-2751) Tel 412-823-1296.

St Alban Pr, *(St. Alban Pr.; 0-918980),* Div. of The Liberal Catholic Church Province of the United States of America, 10606 Parrot Ave. Apt. A., Downey, CA 90241 (SAN 210-492X) Tel 213-861-7569; Orders to: Gene Smith, P.O. Box 598, Ojai, CA 93023 (SAN 210-4938) Tel 805-646-6790.

St Alban Pr CA, *(St. Alban Pr., San Diego; 0-935461),* Subs. of Liberal Catholic Church, 741 Cerro Gordo Ave., San Diego, CA 92102 (SAN 695-8664) Tel 619-239-0637.

St Andrew Pr, *(St. Andrew Pr.; 0-939485),* Rt. 1, Box 283, Big Island, VA 24526 (SAN 663-3951) Tel 804-299-5956. Do not confuse with St. Andrews Press in Laurinburg, NC or in New York, NY.

St Anthony Mess Pr, *(St. Anthony Messenger Pr.; 0-912228; 0-86716),* Subs. of Franciscan Friars (St. John Baptist Province), 1615 Republic St., Cincinnati, OH 45210 (SAN 204-6237) Tel 513-241-5616; Toll free: 800-325-9521.

St Anthony Orthodox, *(Saint Anthony Orthodox Pubns.; 0-936649),* Div. of Kellion of St. Anthony the Great, P.O. Box 1432, Alamogordo, NM 88311-1432 (SAN 699-7031).

St Bedes Pubns, *(St. Bede's Pubns.; 0-932506),* P.O. Box 545, Petersham, MA 01366-0545 (SAN 222-9692) Tel 617-724-3407.

St George Bk Serv, *(St. George Bk. Service, Inc.; 0-916786),* P.O. Box 225, Spring Valley, NY 10977 (SAN 208-8371) Tel 914-623-7852.

St George Pr, *(St. George Pr.; 0-932104),* 3500 N. Coltrane Rd., Oklahoma City, OK 73121 (SAN 209-6773) Tel 405-427-5005.

St Georges Episcopal, *(St. George's Episcopal Church; 0-9613533),* 8250 Hwy. 72, P.O. Box 38447, Germantown, TN 38138-0447 (SAN 657-3819) Tel 901-525-2494.

St Herman AK, *(St. Herman of Alaska Brotherhood; 0-938635),* P.O. Box 70, Platina, CA 96076 (SAN 661-583X); Beegum Gorge Rd., Platina, CA 96076 (SAN 661-5848).

St John Evang, *(St. John the Evangelist Church; 0-9616134),* 126 W. Georgia St., Indianapolis, IN 46225 (SAN 699-959X) Tel 317-635-2021.
St Johns Univ Christ Hum, *(St. John's Univ., Christian Humanism Project; 0-9613867),* P.O. Box 5766, Collegeville, MN 56321 (SAN 685-2246) Tel 612-363-2417.
St Luke TN, *(St. Luke's Pr.; 0-918518),* Mid-Memphis Tower, 1407 Union Ave., Suite 401, Memphis, TN 38104 (SAN 210-0029) Tel 901-357-5441; Toll free: 800-524-5554 (dial 4617, orders).
St Mark Coptic Orthodox, *(St. Mark Coptic Orthodox Church),* P.O. Box 692, Troy, MI 48094 (SAN 240-1533) Tel 313-764-0350.
St Martin, *(St. Martin's Pr., Inc.; 0-312; 0-9603648),* Subs. of Macmillan Pubs., 175 Fifth Ave., New York, NY 10010 (SAN 200-2132) Tel 212-674-5151; Toll free: 800-221-7945; 165 Marlborough St., Boston, MA 02116 (SAN 650-0560).
St Mary's, *(St. Mary's Pr.; 0-88489),* Subs. of Christian Brothers of Minnesota, Terrace Heights, Winona, MN 55987 (SAN 203-073X) Tel 507-452-9090; Toll free: 800-533-8095.
St Matthew's, *(Saint Matthew's Episcopal Church),* 1401 W. Broad St., Savannah, GA 31401 (SAN 219-0966).
St Michaels, *(St. Michaels Historical Museum),* St. Michaels Mission, Drawer D, St. Michaels, AZ 86511 (SAN 239-5290) Tel 602-871-4172.
St Nectarios, *(St. Nectarios Pr.; 0-913026),* 10300 Ashworth Ave. N., Seattle, WA 98133-9410 (SAN 203-3542) Tel 206-522-4471. *Imprints:* Holy Transfiguration (Holy Transfiguration Monastery).
St Paul the Apostle, *(Saint Paul the Apostle Church; 0-9602352),* 202 E. Washington St., Greencastle, IN 46135 (SAN 212-6206).
St Sophia Religious, *(St. Sophia Religious Assn. of Ukrainian Catholics),* 7911 Whitewood Rd., Philadelphia, PA 19117 (SAN 204-949X) Tel 215-635-1555.
St Thomas, *(St. Thomas Pr.; 0-940648),* P.O. Box 1036 SMS, Fairfield, CT 06430 (SAN 204-6288) Tel 713-666-3111.
St Thomas Pub, *(St. Thomas Pubs.; 0-9615048),* 4831 SE Powell Blvd., Suite 1043, Portland, OR 97206 (SAN 693-8612) Tel 503-231-9080.
St Thomas Seminary
See Vincentian
St Vartan
See D O A C
St Vladimirs, *(St. Vladimir's Seminary Pr.; 0-913836; 0-88141),* 575 Scarsdale Rd., Crestwood, NY 10707 (SAN 204-6296) Tel 914-961-8313.
Standard Pub, *(Standard Publishing Co.; 0-87239; 0-87403),* Div. of Standex International, 8121 Hamilton Ave., Cincinnati, OH 45231 (SAN 220-0147) Tel 513-931-4050; Toll free: 800-543-1301; Toll free: 800-582-1385 in Ohio.
Stanford U Pr, *(Stanford Univ. Pr.; 0-8047),* Stanford, CA 94305 (SAN 203-3526) Tel 415-723-9434.
Star Bks Inc, *(Star Bks., Inc.; 0-915541),* 408 Pearson St., Wilson, NC 27893 (SAN 291-4468) Tel 919-237-1591.
Starseed Pubns, *(Starseed Pubns., Inc.; 0-915763),* P.O. Box 2258, Gearhart, OR 97138 (SAN 293-8863) Tel 503-738-3659.
State Hist Soc Wis, *(State Historical Society of Wisconsin; 0-87020),* 816 State St., Madison, WI 53706 (SAN 203-350X) Tel 608-262-1368.
State Mutual Bk, *(State Mutual Bk. & Periodical Service, Ltd. ; 0-89771),* 521 Fifth Ave., 17th Flr., New York, NY 10017 (SAN 212-5862) Tel 212-682-5844.
State of the Art Ltd, *(State of the Art, Ltd.; 0-930161),* 1625 S. Broadway, Denver, CO 80210 (SAN 669-7089) Tel 303-722-7177; Dist. by: Gordon's Bk., Inc., 2323 Delgany St., Denver, CO 80216 (SAN 169-0531) Tel 303-296-1830.
State U NY Pr, *(State Univ. of New York Pr.; 0-87395; 0-88706),* State Univ. Plaza, Albany, NY 12246 (SAN 658-1730) Tel 518-472-5000; Orders to: P.O. Box 6525, Ithaca, NY 14850 (SAN 203-3496) Tel 607-277-2211.
Station Hill Pr, *(Station Hill Pr.; 0-930794; 0-88268),* Station Hill Rd., Barrytown, NY 12507 (SAN 214-1485) Tel 914-758-5840; Dist. by: Small Pr. Dist., 1814 San Pablo Ave., Berkeley, CA 94702 (SAN 204-5826) Tel 415-549-3336; Dist. by: Inland Bk. Co., P.O. Box 261, 22 Hemingway St., East Haven, CT 06512 (SAN 200-4151) Tel 203-467-4257; Dist. by: Writers & Bks., 740 University Ave., Rochester, NY 14607 (SAN 156-9678) Tel 716-473-2590; Dist. by: Bookpeople, 2929 Fifth St., Berkeley, CA 94710 (SAN 168-9517) Tel 415-549-3030; Dist. by: Talman Co., 150 Fifth Ave., Rm. 514, New York, NY 10011 (SAN 200-5204) Tel 212-620-3182.
Steam Pr MA, *(Steam Pr.; 0-942820),* 15 Warwick Rd., Watertown, MA 02172 (SAN 238-8642) Tel 617-923-1046; Dist. by: Kampmann & Co., 9 E. 40th St., New York, NY 10016 (SAN 202-5191) Tel 212-685-2928.
Steimatzky Pub
See Shapolsky Pubs
Stein & Day, *(Stein & Day; 0-8128),* Scarborough Hse., Briarcliff Manor, NY 10510 (SAN 203-3461) Tel 914-762-2151; Dist. by: Henry Holt & Co., Inc., 521 Fifth Ave., New York, NY 10175 (SAN 200-6472) Tel 212-599-7600.
Steinerbks *Imprint of* **Garber Comm**
Stella Maris Bks, *(Stella Maris Bks.; 0-912103),* P.O. Box 11483, Ft. Worth, TX 76110 (SAN 264-7613) Tel 817-924-7221.
Stelle, *(Stelle Group; 0-9600308),* P.O. Box 75, Quinlan, TX 75474 (SAN 204-6385) Tel 214-864-0799.
Stemmer Hse, *(Stemmer Hse. Pub., Inc.; 0-916144; 0-88045),* 2627 Caves Rd., Owings Mills, MD 21117 (SAN 207-9623) Tel 301-363-3690.
Sterling, *(Sterling Publishing Co., Inc.; 0-8069),* 2 Park Ave., New York, NY 10016 (SAN 211-6324) Tel 212-532-7160; Warehouse: 900 Magnolia Ave., Elizabeth, NJ 07201 (SAN 658-1773) Tel 201-354-1804.
Stevens Bk Pr, *(Stevens Bk. Pr.; 0-913029),* Div. of Stevens Bk. Shop, P.O. Box 71, Wake Forest, NC 27587 (SAN 159-1126) Tel 919-556-3830.
Stewardship Enters, *(Stewardship Enterprises; 0-9611282),* P.O. Box 29403, Richmond, VA 23229 (SAN 283-3468) Tel 804-740-2608.
Stewart Tabori & Chang, *(Stewart, Tabori & Chang, Inc.; 0-941434; 1-55670),* 740 Broadway, New York, NY 10003 (SAN 293-4000) Tel 212-460-5000; Dist. by: Workman Publishing Co., Inc., 1 W. 39th St., New York, NY 10018 (SAN 203-2821) Tel 212-398-9160; Dist. by: Random Hse., Inc., 201 E. 50th St., New York, NY 10022 (SAN 202-5507) Tel 212-572-8030.
Stillpoint, *(Stillpoint Publishing; 0-913299),* Div. of Stillpoint International, P.O. Box 640, Walpole, NH 03608 (SAN 285-8630) Tel 603-756-3508; Toll free: 800-847-4014; Orders to: Dutton-NAL, 34 Engelhard Dr., Cranbury, NJ 08512 (SAN 694-9622); Dist. by: New American Library, P.O. Box 999, Bergenfield, NJ 07621 (SAN 206-8087) Tel 201-387-0600.
Stipes, *(Stipes Publishing Co.; 0-87563),* P.O. Box 526, 10-12 Chester St., Champaign, IL 61820 (SAN 206-8664) Tel 217-356-8391.
Stirrup Assoc, *(Stirrup Assocs., Inc.; 0-937420),* Div. of David C. Cook, 850 N. Grove Ave., Elgin, IL 60120 (SAN 215-1863) Tel 312-741-2400.
STL Intl, *(STL International Inc.; 0-936215),* 12101 E. 51st St., No. 107, Tulsa, OK 74146 (SAN 696-8783) Tel 918-250-1488; Dist. by: International Cassette Corp., P.O. Box 1928, Greenville, TX 75401 (SAN 200-5824).
Stone Canyon Pr, *(Stone Canyon Pr.; 0-937641),* P.O. Box 12866, Dallas, TX 75225 (SAN 659-1884) Tel 214-360-9848.
Stone St Pr, *(Stone St. Pr., The; 0-943984),* 1 Stone St., Staten Island, NY 10304 (SAN 219-8185) Tel 718-447-1436.
Strang Comms Co, *(Strang Communications Co.; 0-930525),* 190 N. Westmonte Dr., Altamonte Springs, FL 32714 (SAN 677-5640) Tel 305-869-5005.
Stravon, *(Stravon Educational Pr.; 0-87396),* Subs. of Stravon Pubs., Inc., 845 Third Ave., New York, NY 10022 (SAN 202-7402) Tel 212-371-2880.
Strawberry Hill, *(Strawberry Hill Pr.; 0-89407),* 2594 15th Ave., San Francisco, CA 94127 (SAN 238-8103) Tel 415-664-8112.
Student Assn, *(Student Assn. Pr.; 0-931118),* 1000 Chervy Rd., Memphis, TN 38117 (SAN 212-5676) Tel 901-761-1353.
Studia Slovenica, *(Studia Slovenica, Inc.; 0-938616),* P.O. Box 232, New York, NY 10032 (SAN 213-6996).
Studio J Pub, *(Studio J Publishing, Inc.; 0-940002),* 274 North St., Ridgefield, CT 06877 (SAN 216-7808) Tel 203-438-7826.
Substance Faith, *(Substance of Faith Ministries; 0-937357),* 221 W. North Ave., Flora, IL 62839 (SAN 659-1892) Tel 618-662-7711.
Sufi Islamia-Prophecy, *(Sufi Islamia/Prophecy Pubns.; 0-915424),* 65 Norwich St., San Francisco, CA 94110 (SAN 282-3748) Tel 415-285-0562. *Imprints:* Prophecy Pressworks (Prophecy Pressworks).
Sufi Order Pubns
See Omega Pr NM
Sugar Marbel Pr, *(Sugar Marbel Pr.; 0-9608320),* 1547 Shenandoah Ave., Cincinnati, OH 45237 (SAN 240-1002) Tel 513-761-8000.
Sugarfree, *(Sugarfree Ctr., Inc.),* 13715 Burbank Blvd., P.O. Box 114, Van Nuys, CA 91408 (SAN 241-5836) Tel 818-994-1093.
Sugden, *(Sugden, Sherwood, & Co.; 0-89385),* 1117 Eighth St., La Salle, IL 61301 (SAN 210-5659) Tel 815-223-1231; Dist. by: Open Court Publishing Co., 315 Fifth St., Box 599, Peru, IL 61354 (SAN 202-5876) Tel 815-223-2520.
Summa Pubns, *(Summa Pubns.; 0-917786),* 3601 Westbury Rd., Birmingham, AL 35223 (SAN 212-0925) Tel 205-967-5724; Orders to: P.O. Box 20725, Birmingham, AL 35216 (SAN 662-0124) Tel 205-822-0463.
Summer Inst Ling, *(Summer Institute of Linguistics, Academic Pubns.; 0-88312; 1-55671),* 7500 W. Camp Wisdom Rd., Dallas, TX 75236 (SAN 204-6466) Tel 214-298-4203.
Summertown, *(Summertown Texts; 0-9614303),* Subs. of Summertown Co., Inc., P.O. Box 453, Signal Mountain, TN 37377-0453 (SAN 687-4908) Tel 615-886-1660.
Summit Bks, *(Summit Bks.; 0-671),* Subs. of Simon & Schuster, 1230 Ave. of the Americas, New York, NY 10020 (SAN 206-1244) Tel 212-698-7501; Toll free: 800-223-2336.
Summit Pub Co
See Gold Penny
Summit Univ, *(Summit Univ. Pr.; 0-916766),* Div. of Summit Univ., Box A, Livingston, MT 59047 (SAN 208-4120) Tel 406-222-8300.
Sun Pr FL, *(Sun Pr. of Florida; 0-937039),* 35 Trotters Cir., Kissimmee, FL 32743 (SAN 658-702X) Tel 305-933-1586.
Sun Pub, *(Sun Publishing Co.; 0-914172; 0-89540),* P.O. Box 5588, Santa Fe, NM 87502-5588 (SAN 206-1325) Tel 505-988-2033.
Sun Pub Chico
See Cosmic Pr Chico
Sun-Scape Pubns, *(Sun-Scape Pubns.; 0-919842),* P.O. Box 42725, Tucson, AZ 85733 (SAN 211-870X) Tel 602-623-2452.
Sunburst Pr, *(Sunburst Pr.; 0-934648),* P.O. Box 14205, Portland, OR 97214 (SAN 206-3840).
Sunday Paper, *(Sunday Paper, The; 0-9614022),* 188 Willow St., New Haven, CT 06511 (SAN 683-6259) Tel 203-624-2520.
Sunday Pubns, *(Sunday Pubns., Inc.; 0-941850),* Div. of Liturgical Pubns., Inc., 1937 Tenth Ave. N., Lake Worth, FL 33461 (SAN 239-3220) Tel 305-533-0990.
Sunday School, *(Sunday Schl. Publishing Board; 0-910683),* 330 Charlotte Ave., Nashville, TN 37201 (SAN 275-8598) Tel 615-256-0856.
Sunnycrest Pub, *(Sunnycrest Publishing; 0-9610012),* Rte. 1, Box 1, Clements, MN 56224 (SAN 264-424X) Tel 507-692-2246.
Sunrise Bks, *(Sunrise Bks.; 0-940652),* 1707 "E" St., Eureka, CA 95501 (SAN 665-7893) Tel 707-442-4004 (SAN 211-8254).
Sunrise Paper
See Sunrise Bks

Sunset-Lane, *(Sunset Bks./Lane Publishing Co.; 0-376),* 80 Willow Rd., Menlo Park, CA 94025 (SAN 201-0658) Tel 415-321-3600; Toll free: 800-227-7346; 1320 Willow Rd., Menlo Park, CA 94025 (SAN 658-182X).
Sunshine Pr, *(Sunshine Pr.; 0-936223),* 3830 N. Oakland St., Arlington, VA 22207 (SAN 696-8252) Tel 703-243-8768.
Sunstone Found, *(Sunstone Foundation; 0-9606760),* 59 West First South, Salt Lake City, UT 84101 (SAN 213-9693) Tel 801-355-5926.
Sunstone Pr, *(Sunstone Pr., The; 0-913270; 0-86534),* Subs. of Sunstone Corp., P.O. Box 2321, Santa Fe, NM 87504-2321 (SAN 214-2090) Tel 505-988-4418.
Sunstone Pubns, *(Sunstone Pubns.; 0-913319),* Div. of Sunstone, Inc., R.D. 3, Box 100A, Cooperstown, NY 13326 (SAN 283-4227) Tel 607-547-8207.
Sunwise Turn, *(Sunwise Turn, Ltd.; 0-88004),* P.O. Box 117, New York, NY 10003 (SAN 222-9838) Tel 718-230-8479.
Suratao, *(Suratao, Inc.; 0-932286),* 4763 W. 12th St., Los Angeles, CA 90019 (SAN 212-1441) Tel 213-931-0371.
Sure Fire, *(Sure Fire Pr.; 0-916411),* Subs. of Holmes Publishing Group, P.O. Box 623, Edmonds, WA 98020 (SAN 656-9102) Tel 206-771-2701.
Susan Hunter, *(Hunter, Susan, Publishing; 0-932419),* 1447 Peachtree St., NE, No. 807, Atlanta, GA 30309 (SAN 200-8653) Tel 404-874-5473.
Susquehanna U Pr, *(Susquehanna Univ. Pr.; 0-941664),* Dist. by: Associated University Presses, 440 Forsgate Dr., Cranbury, NJ 08512 (SAN 281-2959) Tel 609-655-4770.
Sutter House, *(Sutter Hse.; 0-915010),* 77 Main St., P.O. Box 212, Lititz, PA 17543 (SAN 207-1207) Tel 717-626-0800.
SW Mission, *(Southwestern Mission Research Ctr.; 0-915076),* Arizona State Museum, Tucson, AZ 85721 (SAN 215-8167) Tel 602-621-4898.
SW Pks Mnmts, *(Southwest Parks & Monuments Assn.; 0-911408),* 221 North Ct. Ave., Tucson, AZ 85701 (SAN 202-750X) Tel 602-622-1999.
Swedenborg, *(Swedenborg Foundation, Inc.; 0-87785),* 139 E. 23rd St., New York, NY 10010 (SAN 202-7526) Tel 212-673-7310.
Swedenborg Sci Assn, *(Swedenborg Scientific Assn.; 0-915221),* 654 Dale Rd., P.O. Box 11, Bryn Athyn, PA 19009 (SAN 289-8454) Tel 215-947-4200.
Sweet, *(Sweet Publishing; 0-8344),* 3934 Sandshell, Ft. Worth, TX 76137 (SAN 206-8958) Tel 817-232-5661; Toll free: 800-531-5220; Toll free: 800-252-9213 (in Texas).
Sweeter Than Honey, *(Sweeter Than Honey; 0-934244),* P.O. Box 7110, Tyler, TX 75711 (SAN 685-3625) Tel 214-561-6415.
Sweetlight, *(Sweetlight Bks.; 0-9604462),* P.O. Box 307, Arcata, CA 95521 (SAN 215-1154) Tel 707-786-9328; Dist. by: Bookpeople, 2929 Fifth St., Berkeley, CA 94710 (SAN 168-9517) Tel 415-549-3030; Dist. by: Naturegraph Publishers, P.O. Box 1075, Happy Camp, CA 96039 (SAN 202-8999) Tel 916-493-5353.
Sword of Lord, *(Sword of the Lord Pubs.; 0-87398),* P.O. Box 1099, 224 Bridge Ave., Murfreesboro, TN 37130 (SAN 203-5642) Tel 615-893-6700.
SYDA Found, *(SYDA Foundation; 0-914602),* Div. of Sushila Blackman, P.O. Box 600, South Fallsburg, NY 12779 (SAN 206-5649) Tel 914-434-2000; Dist. by: Bookpeople, 2929 Fifth St., Berkeley, CA 94710 (SAN 168-9517) Tel 415-549-3030; Dist. by: New Leaf Distributing, The, 1020 White St. SW, Atlanta, GA 30310 (SAN 169-1449) Tel 404-755-2665.
Sym & Sign, *(Symbols & Signs; 0-912504),* P.O. Box 4536, North Hollywood, CA 91607 (SAN 205-4094).
Synaxis Pr, *(Synaxis Pr.; 0-911523),* P.O. Box 689, Lynden, WA 98264 (SAN 685-4338).
Synod NC Church, *(Synod of North Carolina, Presbyterian Church (U.S.A.)),* 1015 Wade Ave. P.O. Box 10785, Raleigh, NC 27605 (SAN 206-2356) Tel 919-834-4379.
Syracuse U Cont Ed, *(Syracuse Univ. Pubns. in Continuing Education; 0-87060),* Syracuse, NY 13210 (SAN 202-7577) Tel 315-423-3421.
Syracuse U Foreign Comp, *(Syracuse Univ., Foreign & Comparative Studies Program; 0-915984),* 724 Comstock Ave., Syracuse, NY 13244 (SAN 220-0082) Tel 315-423-2552.
Syracuse U Pr, *(Syracuse Univ. Pr.; 0-8156),* 1600 Jamesville Ave., Syracuse, NY 13244-5160 (SAN 206-9776) Tel 315-423-2596.
T Adams, *(Adams, Thomas Dean; 0-9609242),* 2817 Darrow Ave., Klamath, OR 97603 (SAN 241-2624) Tel 213-271-0938.
T Black, *(Black, Tzvi; 0-9609752),* 125 Carey Street, Lakewood, NJ 08701 (SAN 283-2968) Tel 201-363-2127.
T E Lowe, *(Lowe, Thomas E., Ltd.; 0-913926),* 2 Penn Plaza, Suite 1500, New York, NY 10121 (SAN 206-5592) Tel 212-865-3269.
T H Peters, *(Peters, Ted H.; 0-9601466),* Box 1299, Greenville, TX 75401 (SAN 222-1144) Tel 214-455-1240.
T Voigt, *(Voigt, Tracy),* P.O. Box 76382, Los Angeles, CA 90076 (SAN 239-5746) Tel 714-983-5772.
T Y Crowell, *(Crowell, Thomas Y., Co.; 0-690),* 10 E. 53rd St., New York, NY 10022 (SAN 210-5918) Tel 212-593-3900; Toll free: 800-242-7737; Dist. by: Harper & Row Pubs., Keystone Industrial Pk., Scranton, PA 18512 (SAN 215-3742).
Tabor Sarah Bks, *(Tabor Sarah Bks.; 0-935079),* 2419 Jefferson Ave., Berkeley, CA 94703 (SAN 695-0353) Tel 415-845-2540.
Tahrike Tarsile Quran, *(Tahrike Tarsile Quran; 0-940368),* P.O. Box 1115, Elmhurst, NY 11373 (SAN 217-1341); 80-10 51 Ave., Elmhurst, NY 11373 (SAN 658-1870) Tel 718-779-6505.
TAN Bks Pubs, *(TAN Bks. & Pubs., Inc.; 0-89555),* 2135 N. Central Ave., Rockford, IL 61103 (SAN 282-390X) Tel 815-962-2662; Orders to: P.O. Box 424, Rockford, IL 61105 (SAN 282-3918).
Tangelwuld, *(Tangelwuld Pr.; 0-934667),* P.O. Box 160361, Las Colinas, TX 75016 (SAN 695-8982) Tel 817-572-7409.
Tao of Wing, *(Tao of Wing Chun Do; 0-918642),* 11023 NE. 131st, Kirkland, WA 98034 (SAN 211-9854) Tel 206-821-1487; Dist. by: Unique Pubns., 4201 W. Vanowen Pl., Burbank, CA 91505 (SAN 214-3313) Tel 818-845-2656.
Tao Pub, *(Tao Publishing; 0-942196),* 2700 Ocean Ave., San Francisco, CA 94132 (SAN 239-9865) Tel 415-892-0802.
Taoist Pubs, *(Taoist Pubs.; 0-9608030),* Dist. by: EDT, Inc., P.O. Box 979, Royal Oak, MI 48068 (SAN 239-4928) Tel 313-399-4926; Dist. by: New Leaf Distributing Co., 1020 White St., SW, Atlanta, GA 30310 (SAN 169-1449) Tel 404-755-2665.
Taplinger, *(Taplinger Publishing Co., Inc.; 0-8008),* 132 W. 22nd St., New York, NY 10011 (SAN 213-6821) Tel 212-741-0801.
Tara Ctr, *(Tara Ctr., The; 0-936604),* Subs. of Share International Magazine (Amsterdam, Netherlands), P.O. Box 6001, North Hollywood, CA 91603 (SAN 282-3950) Tel 818-785-6300; Dist. by: DeVorss & Co., P.O. Box 550, 1046 Princeton Dr., Marina del Rey, CA 90294 (SAN 168-9886).
Taran House Pub, *(Taran Hse. Publishing; 0-933315),* 3703 E. Cornell Woods Dr., Suite C, Dayton, OH 45406 (SAN 692-3704) Tel 513-274-2942.
TAU Pr, *(TAU Pr.; 0-916453),* P.O. Box 2283, Rolling Hills, CA 90274 (SAN 209-3022).
Taylor & Francis, *(Taylor & Francis, Inc.; 0-85066; 0-905273; 1-85000; 0-335; 0-86353; 0-903796),* 242 Cherry St., Philadelphia, PA 19106-1906 (SAN 286-2182) Tel 215-238-0939; Toll free: 800-821-8312. *Imprints:* Falmer Pr (Falmer Press); Open Univ Pr (Open University Press).
Taylor Museum
See CO Springs Fine Arts
Tayu Pr, *(Tayu Pr.; 0-934350),* Div. of Tayu Ctr. for Gay Spirituality, P.O. Box 11554, Santa Rosa, CA 95406 (SAN 213-1773) Tel 707-887-2490.
Tchrs Coll, *(Columbia Univ., Teachers College, Teachers College Pr.; 0-8077),* 1234 Amsterdam Ave., New York, NY 10027 (SAN 282-3985) Tel 212-678-3929; Orders to: Harper & Row, Keystone Industrial Pk., Scranton, PA 18512 (SAN 282-3993).
Tech Data, *(Tech Data Pubns.; 0-937816),* 6324 W. Fond Du Lac Ave., Milwaukee, WI 53218 (SAN 216-0129).
Tech Group, *(Technology Group, The; 0-939856),* P.O. Box 93124, Pasadena, CA 91109 (SAN 220-195X) Tel 818-794-6013.
Technomic, *(Technomic Publishing Co.; 0-87762),* 851 New Holland Ave., Box 3535, Lancaster, PA 17604 (SAN 202-764X) Tel 717-291-5609; Toll free: 800-233-9936.
Telegraph Bks, *(Telegraph Bks.; 0-89760),* Box 38, Norwood, PA 19074 (SAN 213-8042) Tel 215-583-4550.
Temple Kriya Yoga, *(Temple of Kriya Yoga, The; 0-9613099),* 2414 N. Kedzie Ave., Chicago, IL 60647 (SAN 240-9348) Tel 312-795-0031.
Temple Pubns, *(Temple Pubns., Inc.; 0-918341),* 3327 SW Dosch Rd., Portland, OR 97201 (SAN 657-3045) Tel 503-223-8863; Dist. by: New Leaf Distributing Co., 1020 White St., SW, Atlanta, GA 30310 (SAN 169-1449) Tel 404-755-2665.
Temple U Pr, *(Temple Univ. Pr.; 0-87722),* Broad & Oxford Sts., University Services Bldg., Rm. 305, Philadelphia, PA 19122 (SAN 202-7666) Tel 215-787-8787.
Templegate, *(Templegate Pubs.; 0-87243),* 302 E. Adams St., P.O. Box 5152, Springfield, IL 62705 (SAN 213-1994) Tel 217-522-3361.
Tent Meeting, *(Tent of Meeting, The; 0-9615531),* P.O. Box 8518, Santa Fe, NM 87504 (SAN 696-1479) Tel 505-988-8084.
Terhell Bks, *(Terhell Bks.; 0-9614165),* 5302 Kenwood Ave., Baltimore, MD 21206 (SAN 686-6670) Tel 301-668-0174.
Testament *Imprint of* **Exposition Pr FL**
Tex A&M Univ Pr, *(Texas A & M Univ. Pr.; 0-89096),* Drawer "C", College Station, TX 77843 (SAN 207-5237) Tel 409-845-1436; Lewis St., Univ. Campus, College Station, TX 77843 (SAN 658-1919).
Tex Christian, *(Texas Christian Univ. Pr.; 0-912646; 0-87565),* Box 30783, Fort Worth, TX 76129 (SAN 202-7690) Tel 817-921-7822; Dist. by: Texas A & M Univ. Pr., Drawer C, College Station, TX 77843 (SAN 207-5237) Tel 409-845-1436.
Tex-Mex, *(Tex-Mex Books Publishers International Texas; 0-918268),* Box 186, 820 San Antonio Ave., San Juan, TX 78589 (SAN 208-0079) Tel 512-781-2186.
Tex Tech Univ Pr, *(Texas Tech Univ. Pr.; 0-89672),* Affil. of Texas Tech Univ., P.O. Box 4139, Lubbock, TX 79409 (SAN 218-5989) Tel 806-742-2468.
Tex Western, *(Texas Western Pr.; 0-87404),* Div. of Univ. of Texas at El Paso, Univ. of Texas at El Paso, El Paso, TX 79968 (SAN 202-7712) Tel 915-747-5688.
Texas Month Pr, *(Texas Monthly Pr.; 0-932012; 0-87719),* Subs. of Mediatex Communication Corp., P.O. Box 1569, Austin, TX 78767 (SAN 200-2531); Toll free: 800-252-4437 (Texas only).
Texian, *(Texian Pr.; 0-87244),* P.O. Box 1684, Waco, TX 76703 (SAN 205-4256) Tel 817-754-5636.
Thames Hudson, *(Thames & Hudson; 0-500),* Dist. by: W. W. Norton & Co., Inc., 500 Fifth Ave., New York, NY 10110 (SAN 202-5795) Tel 212-354-5500.
That Patchwork, *(That Patchwork Place, Inc.; 0-943574),* 18800 142nd Ave., NE, Bldg. 2A, Woodinville, WA 98072 (SAN 240-7876) Tel 206-483-3313; Orders to: P.O. Box 118, Bothell, WA 98041 (SAN 665-7923)
Thayer-Jacoby, *(Thayer-Jacoby; 0-9606472),* 1432 E. Ninth St., Brooklyn, NY 11230 (SAN 213-9685) Tel 718-339-3278.
The Smith, *(Smith, The; 0-912292),* Subs. of The Generalist Assoc., Inc., 5 Beekman St., New York, NY 10038 (SAN 202-7747) Tel 212-732-4821.
Theatre Arts, *(Theatre Arts Bks.; 0-87830),* Div. of Methuen, 29 West 35th St., New York, NY 10001 (SAN 202-7763) Tel 212-244-3336.
Theos Pub Hse, *(Theosophical Publishing Hse.; 0-8356),* Div. of Theosophical Society in America., 306 W. Geneva Rd., Wheaton, IL 60187-0270 (SAN 202-5698) Tel 312-665-0123; Toll free: 800-654-9430; P.O. Box 270, Wheaton, IL 60189-0270 (SAN 699-5667). *Imprints:* Quest (Quest Books).

Theos U Pr, *(Theosophical Univ. Pr.; 0-911500; 1-55700),* P.O. Bin C, Pasadena, CA 91109 (SAN 205-4299) Tel 818-798-3378

Theoscience Found, *(Theoscience Foundation Pub.; 0-917802),* 193 Los Robles Dr., Burlingame, CA 94010 (SAN 209-0260).

Theosophy, *(Theosophy Co.; 0-938998),* 245 W. 33rd St., Los Angeles, CA 90007 (SAN 295-3560) Tel 213-748-7244; 347 E. 72nd St., New York, NY 10021 (SAN 295-3579).

Theotes, *(Theotes-Logos Research, Inc.; 0-911806),* 4318 York Ave. S., Minneapolis, MN 55410 (SAN 205-4310) Tel 612-922-3202.

Thirteen Colonies Pr, *(Thirteen Colonies Pr.; 0-934943),* 710 S. Henry St., Williamsburg, VA 23185-4113 (SAN 695-0361) Tel 804-229-1775.

Thoburn Pr, *(Thoburn Pr.; 0-932029),* P.O. Box 6941, Tyler, TX 75711 (SAN 686-0818) Tel 214-581-0677.

Thomas More, *(More, Thomas, Pr.; 0-88347),* Subs. of Thomas More Assn., 223 W. Erie St., Chicago, IL 60610 (SAN 203-0675) Tel 312-951-2100; Toll free: 800-835-8965.

Thor, *(Thor Publishing Co.; 0-87407),* P.O. Box 1782, Ventura, CA 93002 (SAN 202-7801) Tel 805-648-4560.

Thoreau Found, *(Thoreau Foundation, Inc.; 0-912130),* Subs. of Thoreau Society, Inc., 156 Belknap St., Concord, MA 01742 (SAN 205-4353) Tel 617-369-5912.

Thorsons Pubs, *(Thorsons Pubs., Inc.; 0-7225),* Subs. of Thorsons Publishing Group (Great Britain), 1 Park St., Rochester, VT 05767 (SAN 277-7398) Tel 802-767-3174; Dist. by: Inner Traditions, Park St., Rochester, VT 05767 (SAN 208-6948); Orders to: Harper & Row Pubs., Inc., Keystone Industrial Pk., Scranton, PA 18512 (SAN 215-3742).

Thoughts by Bonnie, *(Thoughts by Bonnie; 0-9616611),* Rte. 2, Oslo, MN 56744 (SAN 659-7963) Tel 218-695-5111.

Three Continents, *(Three Continents Pr.; 0-89410; 0-914478),* 1636 Connecticut Ave., NW, Suite 501, Washington, DC 20009 (SAN 212-0070) Tel 202-332-3885.

Three D Pubs, *(3-D Pubs.; 0-9600500),* P.O. Box 428, Edgerton, OH 43517 (SAN 205-4361).

Three Dimensional, *(Three Dimensional Thinking; 0-9613613),* 1420 Iroquois Ave., Long Beach, CA 90815 (SAN 669-8212) Tel 213-423-1441.

Threshold VT, *(Threshold Bks.; 0-939660),* RFD 3, Box 1350, Putney, VT 05346 (SAN 216-6496) Tel 802-254-8300; Dist. by: Great Tradition, The, 750 Adrian Way, Suite 111, San Rafael, CA 94903 (SAN 200-5743) Tel 415-492-9382; Dist. by: Bookpeople, 2929 Fifth St., Berkeley, CA 94710 (SAN 168-9517) Tel 415-549-3030.

Thursday Pubs, *(Thursday Pubs.; 0-934502),* 1846N Pine Bluff Rd., Stevens Point, WI 54481-8905 (SAN 212-9779) Tel 715-344-6441.

Ticknor & Fields, *(Ticknor & Fields; 0-89919),* Affil. of Houghton Mifflin Co., 52 Vanderbilt Ave., New York, NY 10017 (SAN 282-4043) Tel 212-687-8996; Toll free: 800-225-3362; Dist. by: Houghton Mifflin Co., 1 Beacon St., Boston, MA 02108 (SAN 200-2388) Tel 617-725-5000.

Tidal Pr, *(Tidal Pr., The; 0-930954),* P.O. Box 150, Portsmouth, NH 03801 (SAN 211-3783) Tel 603-430-9475.

Timber, *(Timber Pr.; 0-917304; 0-88192),* 9999 SW Wilshire, Portland, OR 97225 (SAN 216-082X) Tel 503-292-0745.

Time-Life, *(Time-Life Bks.; 0-8094),* Div. of Time, Inc., 777 Duke St., Alexandria, VA 22314 (SAN 202-7836) Tel 703-838-7198; Toll free: 800-621-7026; 4200 N. Industrial Blvd., Indianapolis, IN 46254 (SAN 658-1951); Toll free: 800-631-8081; Toll free: 800-343-9204; Dist. by: Little, Brown & Co., 34 Beacon St., Boston, MA 02106 (SAN 281-8892) Tel 617-227-0730; Dist. by: Morgan & Morgan Co., 145 Palisades St., Dobbs Ferry, NY 10522 (SAN 202-5620); Orders to: Silver Burdett Co., 250 James St., Morristown, NJ 07960 (SAN 204-5982). Lib. & School Orders to: Silver Burdett Co.

Timeless Bks, *(Timeless Bks.; 0-931454),* Div. of Association for the Development of Human Potential, P.O. Box 160, Porthill, ID 83853 (SAN 211-6502) Tel 604-227-9224.

Times Bks, *(Times Bks.; 0-8129),* Subs. of Random Hse., Inc., 201 E. 50th St., New York, NY 10022 (SAN 202-5558) Tel 212-751-2600; Toll free: 800-242-7737; Orders to: Random Hse., 400 Hahn Rd., Westminster, MD 21157 (SAN 200-2086).

Times Change, *(Times Change Pr.; 0-87810),* Box 187, Albion, CA 95410-0187 (SAN 202-7860) Tel 707-937-1113; Orders to: Box 2510, Novato, CA 94948-2510 (SAN 665-7958) Tel 415-883-3530.

TMH Pub, *(TMH Publishing, Ltd.; 0-939386),* P.O. Box 6344, Santa Barbara, CA 93160-6344 (SAN 216-3047).

Today Bible, *(Today in Bible Prophecy, Inc.; 0-937682),* 113 S. Delano St. No. 1, Anaheim, CA 92804 (SAN 293-4566) Tel 714-995-1869; Orders to: P.O. Box 5700, Huntington Beach, CA 92615 (SAN 293-4574) Tel 714-963-7766.

Todd & Honeywell, *(Todd & Honeywell, Inc.; 0-89962),* 10 Cuttermill Rd., Great Neck, NY 11021 (SAN 213-179X) Tel 516-487-9777; Toll free: 800-233-3361.

Tolle Pubns, *(Tolle Pubns.; 0-915378),* P.O. Box 6243, Beaumont, TX 77705 (SAN 211-0970) Tel 713-860-5628; 7920 Wilcox Lane, Beaumont, TX 77706 (SAN 211-0989).

Tom Weisser, *(Weisser, Thomas; 0-9610710),* Box 53, Monmouth, OR 97361 (SAN 264-8105) Tel 503-838-6051.

Tools for Inner, *(Tools for Inner Growth; 0-914073),* P.O. Box 520, Chiloquin, OR 97624 (SAN 287-5829).

Top Mtn Pub, *(Top of the Mountain Publishing; 0-914295),* 2980 E. Bay Dr., Largo, FL 33541 (SAN 287-590X) Tel 813-531-1670.

Topgallant, *(Topgallant Publishing Co., Ltd.; 0-914916),* 547 Halekauwila St., Suite 101, Honolulu, HI 96813 (SAN 209-4932) Tel 808-524-0884.

Torah Aura, *(Torah Aura Productions; 0-933873),* 4423 Fruitland Ave., Los Angeles, CA 90058 (SAN 692-7025) Tel 213-585-7312; Toll free: 800-238-6724.

Torah Umesorah, *(Torah Umesorah Pubns.; 0-914131),* 160 Broadway, New York, NY 10003 (SAN 218-9992) Tel 212-227-1000.

Torch *Imprint of* **Har-Row**

Tosefos, *(Tosefos Media, Inc.; 0-936617),* 824 Eastern Pkwy., Brooklyn, NY 11213 (SAN 696-7167) Tel 718-756-1498.

Total Comm Ministries, *(Total Commitment Ministries),* Box 242, Harrisburg, OR 97446 (SAN 689-6499).

Touch Heart, *(Touch the Heart Pr.; 0-9605492),* Div. of Louis Foundation Pubs., Box 210, Eastsound, WA 98245 (SAN 216-1575) Tel 206-376-2250.

Touchstone Bks *Imprint of* **S&S**

TP Assocs, *(TP Assocs./TP Pr.; 0-913939),* P.O. Box 3226, Newport Beach, CA 92663 (SAN 286-8962) Tel 714-963-4482; 22181 Wood Island Ln., Huntington Beach, CA 92646 (SAN 286-8970) Tel 714-963-4482.

Traditional Pr, *(Traditional Pr., Inc.; 0-933711),* 1022 51st St., Brooklyn, NY 11219 (SAN 692-4980).

Trado-Medic, *(Trado-Medic Bks.; 0-932426),* Div. of Conch Magazine, Ltd., Pubs., Box 777, Buffalo, NY 14213 (SAN 212-5722).

Transaction Bks, *(Transaction Bks.; 0-87855; 0-88738),* Rutgers Univ., New Brunswick, NJ 08903 (SAN 202-7941) Tel 201-932-2280.

Transatl Arts, *(Transatlantic Arts, Inc.; 0-693),* P.O. Box 6086, Albuquerque, NM 87197 (SAN 202-7968) Tel 505-898-2289. Do not confuse with Trans-Atlantic Pubns., Inc., Philadelphia, PA.

Transbooks
See Interbk Inc

Transform Inc, *(Transformations, Inc.; 0-9604856),* 2728 N. Prospect Ave., Milwaukee, WI 53211 (SAN 215-8906) Tel 414-962-0213; Orders to: 4200 W. Good Hope Rd., Milwaukee, WI 53209 (SAN 662-085X) Tel 414-351-5770.

Triang Pr, *(Triang Pr., The; 0-931513),* 5850 Hubbard Dr., Rockville, MD 20852 (SAN 682-3149) Tel 301-984-5730; Dist. by: W. W. Norton Co., Inc., 500 Fifth Ave,, New York, NY 10110 (SAN 202-5795) Tel 212-354-5500.

Trillium Pr, *(Trillium Pr.; 0-89824),* P.O. Box 921, New York, NY 10159 (SAN 212-4637) Tel 212-684-7399; Orders to: P.O. Box 209, Monroe, NY 10950 (SAN 662-1627) Tel 914-783-2999.

Trinity Found, *(Trinity Foundation, The; 0-940931),* P.O. Box 169, Jefferson, MD 21755 (SAN 664-6743); 3606 Coolcrest Dr., Jefferson, MD 21755 (SAN 664-6751) Tel 301-371-7155.

Trinity House, *(Trinity Hse., Inc.; 0-913309),* P.O. Box 104, Crestwood, KY 40014 (SAN 283-3182) Tel 502-241-1492.

Trinity Pub Hse, *(Trinity Publishing Hse, Inc.; 0-933656),* 107 Lafayette, Winona, MN 55987 (SAN 215-1189).

Trinity U Pr, *(Trinity Univ. Pr.; 0-911536; 0-939980),* 715 Stadium Dr., San Antonio, TX 78284 (SAN 205-4590) Tel 512-736-7619.

Triple Seven, *(Triple Seven International; 0-9614870),* R2, Box 221, Gaston, IN 47342 (SAN 693-2134) Tel 317-358-3713.

Triumph Pr, *(Triumph Pr., Inc.; 0-931515),* 1062 Edison NW, Grand Rapids, MI 49504 (SAN 682-3157) Tel 616-453-6891.

Triumph Pub, *(Triumph Publishing Co.; 0-917182),* P.O. Box 292, Altadena, CA 91001 (SAN 207-3927).

Troll Assocs, *(Troll Assocs.; 0-89375; 0-8167),* Subs. of Educational Reading Services, 100 Corporate Dr., Mahwah, NJ 07430 (SAN 169-4758) Tel 201-529-4000; Toll free: 800-526-5289.

Tru-Faith, *(Tru-Faith Publishing Co.; 0-937498),* P.O. Box 2283, Gainesville, GA 30503 (SAN 216-3101).

True Life Found, *(True Life Foundation, The; 0-912753),* 14510 Cordary Ave., Hawthorne, CA 90250 (SAN 283-3557) Tel 213-676-7567.

Truth CA, *(Truth Pubs., Inc.; 0-913621),* 146 S. Trevor Ave., Anaheim, CA 92806 (SAN 285-3841) Tel 714-632-9554; Dist. by: Living Bks., 12155 Magnolia Ave., Bldg. 11-B, Riverside, CA 92503 (SAN 669-330X) Tel 714-354-7330.

Truth Consciousness, *(Truth Consciousness; 0-933572),* 10668 Gold Hill Rd., Boulder, CO 80302 (SAN 212-7083) Tel 303-447-1637.

Truth Missions, *(Truth Missions; 0-910607),* P.O. Box 3849, Manhattan Beach, CA 90266 (SAN 264-1909) Tel 213-640-2663.

Truth Seeker, *(Truth Seeker Co., Inc.; 0-939040),* P.O. Box 2832, San Diego, CA 92112 (SAN 226-3645) Tel 619-574-7600.

Tucker Pubns, *(Tucker Pubns.),* 409 Hill St., Fayetteville, TN 37334 (SAN 213-6031).

Tudor Pubs, *(Tudor Pubs., Inc.; 0-936389),* P.O. Box 3443, Greensboro, NC 27402 (SAN 697-3035); 3712 Old Battleground Rd., Greensboro, NC 27410 (SAN 697-3043) Tel 919-282-5907.

Tulane U Ctr Lat, *(Center for Latin American Studies & Howard-Tilton Memorial Library; 0-9603212),* Tulane Univ., New Orleans, LA 70118 (SAN 287-7732) Tel 504-865-5681.

Tundra Bks, *(Tundra Bks. of Northern New York; 0-912766; 0-88776),* Affil. of Tundra Bks. (Canada), P.O. Box 1030, Plattsburgh, NY 12901 (SAN 202-8085) Tel 514-932-5434; Dist. by: Univ. of Toronto Pr., 340 Nagel Dr., Cheektowaga, NY 14225 (SAN 214-2651) Tel 716-683-4547.

Turtle Isl Foun, *(Turtle Island Foundation, Netzahaulcoyotl Historical Society; 0-913666),* 2845 Buena Vista Way, Berkeley, CA 94708 (SAN 205-4639) Tel 415-654-7020.

Turtles Quill, *(Turtles Quill Scriptorium; 0-937686),* P.O. Box 643, Mendocino, CA 95460 (SAN 206-8966) Tel 707-937-4328.

Tusayan Gospel, *(Tusayan Gospel Ministries, Inc.; 0-9601124),* P.O. Box 9861, Phoenix, AZ 85068 (SAN 209-3391) Tel 602-979-2319; Dist. by: Living Bks., Inc., 12155 Magnolia Ave. 11-B, Riverside, CA 92503 (SAN 169-006X) Tel 714-354-7330.

Twayne *Imprint of* **New Coll U Pr**

Twenty-Third, *(Twenty-Third Pubns.; 0-89622),* P.O. Box 180, Mystic, CT 06355 (SAN 210-9204); Toll free: 800-321-0411; 185 Willow St., Mystic, CT 06355 (SAN 658-2052).

Twin Pines Pr, *(Twin Pines Press; 0-9609840),* 851 Rivervale Rd., River Vale, NJ 07675 (SAN 264-4428) Tel 201-391-6860.

Two Rivers, *(Two Rivers Pr.; 0-89756),* 28070 S. Meridan Rd., Aurora, OR 97002 (SAN 211-6510).

Two Trees Pub, *(Two Trees Publishing; 0-938183),* 1272 Bear Mountain Ct., Boulder, CO 80303 (SAN 659-7262) Tel 303-494-5192.

Tyndale, *(Tyndale Hse. Pubs.; 0-8423),* 336 Gundersen Dr., P.O. Box 80, Wheaton, IL 60189 (SAN 206-7749) Tel 312-668-8300; Toll free: 800-323-9400.

U & K Pub, *(U & K Publishing Co.; 0-9616357),* 806 Carter Rd., Rockville, MD 20852 (SAN 659-090X) Tel 301-762-8980.

U Chi Dept Anthro, *(Univ. of Chicago, Dept. of Anthropology; 0-916256),* 1126 E. 59th St., Chicago, IL 60637 (SAN 208-0583) Tel 312-962-7314.

U Chicago Dept Geog, *(Univ. of Chicago, Dept. of Geography, Research Papers; 0-89065),* 5828 S. University Ave., Chicago, IL 60637-1583 (SAN 203-3003) Tel 312-702-8304.

U Delaware Pr, *(Univ. of Delaware Pr.; 0-87413),* c/o Associated Univ. Presses, Inc., 440 Forsgate Dr., Cranbury, NJ 08512 (SAN 203-4476) Tel 609-655-4770.

U Field Staff Intl, *(Universities Field Staff International, Inc.; 0-910116; 0-88333),* 620 Union Dr., Indianapolis, IN 46202-2897 (SAN 202-4764).

U Maine Orono, *(Univ. of Maine, at Orono Pr.; 0-89101),* PICS Bldg., Univ. of Maine at Orono, Orono, ME 04469 (SAN 207-2971) Tel 207-581-1700.

U MI Japan, *(Univ. of Michigan, Ctr. for Japanese Studies; 0-939512),* 108 Lane Hall, Ann Arbor, MI 48109-1290 (SAN 216-7018) Tel 313-763-7265.

U Miami N-S Ctr, *(Univ. of Miami North/South Ctr., Graduate Schl. of International Studies; 0-935501),* P.O. Box 248123, Coral Gables, FL 33124 (SAN 695-8834) Tel 305-284-4303.

U Mich Mus Anthro, *(Univ. of Michigan, Museum of Anthropology, Pubns. Dept.; 0-932206),* 4009 Museums Bldg., 1109 Geddes, Ann Arbor, MI 48109 (SAN 203-0489) Tel 313-764-0465.

U MS Bus Econ, *(Univ. of Mississippi, Bureau of Business & Economic Research; 0-938004),* 300 LaBauve A, University, MS 38677 (SAN 206-0841) Tel 601-232-7481.

U of Ala Pr, *(Univ. of Alabama Pr.; 0-8173),* Univ. of Alabama, Box 2877, Tuscaloosa, AL 35487 (SAN 202-5272) Tel 205-348-5180.

U of Ariz Pr, *(Univ. of Arizona Pr.; 0-8165),* 1615 E. Speedway, Tucson, AZ 85719 (SAN 205-468X) Tel 602-621-1441.

U of Ark Pr, *(Univ. of Arkansas Pr.; 0-938626; 1-55728),* Univ. of Arkansas, McIlroy Hse., 201 Ozark St., Fayetteville, AR 72701 (SAN 239-3972) Tel 501-575-3246; Toll free: 800-242-7737.

U of Cal Intl St, *(Univ. of California, Institute of International Studies; 0-87725),* 215 Moses Hall, Berkeley, CA 94720 (SAN 203-3038) Tel 415-642-7189.

U of Cal Pr, *(Univ. of California Pr.; 0-520),* 2120 Berkeley Way, Berkeley, CA 94720 (SAN 203-3046) Tel 415-642-6683; Toll free: 800-822-6657; 1095 Essex St., Richmond, CA 94801 (SAN 658-2133). Do not confuse U of Cal Pr, Berkeley, CA, with the Univ. of Calgary Pr., Calgary, AB, Canada.

U of Chicago Pr, *(Univ. of Chicago Pr.; 0-226),* Div. of Univ. of Chicago, 5801 Ellis Ave., 3rd Flr., S., Chicago, IL 60637 (SAN 202-5280) Tel 312-702-7693; Toll free: 800-621-2736; Orders to: 11030 S. Langley Ave., Chicago, IL 60628 (SAN 202-5299) Tel 312-568-1550. *Imprints:* Chicago Visual Lib (Chicago Visual Library); Midway Reprint (Midway Reprint).

U of Ga Pr, *(Univ. of Georgia Pr.; 0-8203),* Terrell Hall, Athens, GA 30602 (SAN 203-3054) Tel 404-542-2830.

U of Healing, *(Univ. of Healing Pr.; 0-940480),* 1101 Far Valley Rd., Campo, CA 92006 (SAN 211-7983) Tel 619-478-5111.

U of Idaho Pr, *(Univ. of Idaho Pr.; 0-89301),* Div. of Idaho Research Foundation, Inc., University Sta., Box 3368, Moscow, ID 83843 (SAN 208-905X) Tel 208-885-6245.

U of Ill Pr, *(Univ. of Illinois Pr.; 0-252),* 54 E. Gregory Dr., Champaign, IL 61820 (SAN 202-5310) Tel 217-333-0950; Toll free: 800-242-7737; Orders to: Harper & Row, Inc., Keystone Industrial Pk., Scranton, PA 18512 (SAN 215-3742); Orders to: Univ. of Illinois Pr., P.O. Box 1650, Hagerstown, MD 21741.

U of Iowa Pr, *(Univ. of Iowa Pr.; 0-87745),* Univ. of Iowa, Iowa City, IA 52242 (SAN 282-4868) Tel 319-335-7194; Orders to: Pubns. Order Dept., Graphic Services Bldg., Iowa City, IA 52242 (SAN 282-4876) Tel 319-335-8777.

U of Mass Pr, *(Univ. of Massachusetts Pr.; 0-87023),* P.O. Box 429, Amherst, MA 01004 (SAN 203-3089) Tel 413-545-2217.

U of Miami Pr, *(Univ. of Miami Pr.; 0-87024),* P.O. Box 4836, Hampden Sta., Baltimore, MD 21211 (SAN 203-3119) Tel 301-338-6952.

U of Mich Ctr Chinese, *(Univ. of Michigan, Ctr. for Chinese Studies; 0-89264),* 104 Lane Hall, Ann Arbor, MI 48109 (SAN 208-2772) Tel 313-763-7181.

U of Mich Pr, *(Univ. of Michigan Pr.; 0-472),* P.O. Box 1104, Ann Arbor, MI 48106 (SAN 282-4884) Tel 313-764-4330; Orders to: 839 Greene St., Ann Arbor, MI 48106 (SAN 282-4892) Tel 313-764-4392.

U of Minn Pr, *(Univ. of Minnesota Pr.; 0-8166),* Affil. of Univ. of Minnesota, 2037 University Ave., SE, Minneapolis, MN 55414 (SAN 213-2648) Tel 612-624-0005.

U of Mo Pr, *(Univ. of Missouri Pr.; 0-8262),* 200 Lewis, Columbia, MO 65211 (SAN 203-3143) Tel 314-882-7641; Toll free: 800-242-7737; Dist. by: Harper & Row Pubs., Inc., 10 E. 53rd St., New York, NY 10022 (SAN 215-3742) Tel 212-207-7099.

U of NC Pr, *(Univ. of North Carolina Pr.; 0-8078),* P.O. Box 2288, Chapel Hill, NC 27514 (SAN 203-3151) Tel 919-966-3561.

U of Nebr Pr, *(Univ. of Nebraska Pr.; 0-8032),* 901 N. 17th St., Lincoln, NE 68588-0520 (SAN 202-5337) Tel 402-472-3581.

U of Nev Pr, *(Univ. of Nevada Pr.; 0-87417),* Reno, NV 89557 (SAN 203-316X) Tel 702-784-6573.

U of NM Pr, *(Univ. of New Mexico Pr.; 0-8263),* Journalism Bldg., Rm. 220, Albuquerque, NM 87131 (SAN 213-9588) Tel 505-277-2346.

U of Notre Dame Pr, *(Univ. of Notre Dame Pr.; 0-268),* P.O. Box L, Notre Dame, IN 46556 (SAN 203-3178) Tel 219-239-6346; Toll free: 800-242-7737; Dist. by: Harper & Row Pubs., Keystone Industrial Pk., Scranton, PA 18512 (SAN 215-3742).

U of Okla Pr, *(Univ. of Oklahoma Pr.; 0-8061),* 1005 Asp Ave., Norman, OK 73019 (SAN 203-3194) Tel 405-325-5111; Dist. by: Harper & Row, Inc., Keystone Industrial Pk., Scranton, PA 18512 (SAN 215-3742); Orders to: Univ. of Oklahoma Pr., P.O. Box 1657, Hagerstown, MD 21741 (SAN 203-3194).

U of Pa Pr, *(Univ. of Pennsylvania Pr.; 0-8122),* 418 Service Dr., Blockley Hall, 13th Flr., Philadelphia, PA 19104 (SAN 202-5345) Tel 215-898-6261.

U of Pittsburgh Pr, *(Univ. of Pittsburgh Pr.; 0-8229),* 127 N. Bellefield Ave., Pittsburgh, PA 15260 (SAN 203-3216) Tel 412-624-4110; Toll free: 800-242-7737; Dist. by: Harper & Row Pubs., Inc., Keystone Industrial Pk., Scranton, PA 18512 (SAN 215-3742).

U of PR Pr, *(Univ. of Puerto Rico Pr.; 0-8477),* P.O. Box X, U.P.R. Sta., Rio Piedras, PR 00931 (SAN 208-1245) Tel 809-763-0812.

U of Queensland Pr, *(Univ. of Queensland Pr.; 0-7022),* P.O. Box 1365, New York, NY 10023 (SAN 206-8540) Tel 212-799-3854; Orders to: Publishers Distribution Services, Inc., 250 Commercial St., Manchester, NH 03101 (SAN 206-8559) Tel 603-623-4567.

U of S Cal Pr, *(Univ. of Southern California Pr.; 0-88474),* Univ. of Southern California, Student Union 400, Los Angeles, CA 90007 (SAN 203-1892).

U of SC Pr, *(Univ. of South Carolina Pr.; 0-87249),* Columbia, SC 29208 (SAN 203-3224) Tel 803-777-5243.

U of SW LA Ctr LA Studies, *(Univ. of Southwestern Louisiana, Ctr. for Louisiana Studies; 0-940984),* P.O. Box 40831, USL, Lafayette, LA 70504 (SAN 217-4502) Tel 318-231-6027.

U of Tenn Geo, *(Univ. of Tennessee, Dept. of Geological Sciences; 0-910249),* Div. of Univ. of Tennessee, Knoxville, Geography & Geology Bldg, Rm. 306, Knoxville, TN 37996-1410 (SAN 241-4694) Tel 615-974-2366.

U of Tenn Pr, *(Univ. of Tennessee Pr.; 0-87049),* Div. of Univ. of Tennessee & Member of Assn. of American Univ. Presses, 293 Communications Bldg., Knoxville, TN 37996-0325 (SAN 212-9930) Tel 615-974-3321; Orders to: P.O. Box 6525, Ithaca, NY 14850 (SAN 662-1740) Tel 607-277-2211.

U of Tex H Ransom Ctr, *(Univ. of Texas, Harry Ransom Humanities Research Ctr.; 0-87959),* Div. of Univ. of Texas at Austin, P.O. Box 7219, Austin, TX 78713 (SAN 203-1906) Tel 512-471-9113.

U of Tex Pr, *(Univ. of Texas Pr.; 0-292),* P.O. Box 7819, Austin, TX 78713-7819 (SAN 212-9876) Tel 512-471-7233; Toll free: 800-252-3206.

U of Toronto Pr, *(Univ. of Toronto Pr.; 0-8020),* 340 Nagel Dr., Cheektowaga, NY 14225 (SAN 214-2651) Tel 716-683-4547.

U of Utah Pr, *(Univ. of Utah Pr.; 0-87480),* Div. of Univ. of Utah, 101 University Services Bldg., Salt Lake City, UT 84112 (SAN 220-0023) Tel 801-581-6771; Toll free: 800-662-0062, Ext. 6771.

U of Wash Pr, *(Univ. of Washington Pr.; 0-295),* P.O. Box 50096, Seattle, WA 98145-5096 (SAN 212-2502) Tel 206-543-4050; Toll free: 800-441-4115.

U of Wis Ctr Arch-Urban, *(Univ. of Wisconsin-Milwaukee, Ctr. for Architecture & Urban Planning Research; 0-938744),* Univ. of Wisconsin-Milwaukee, Schl. of Architure & Urban Planning, P.O. Box 413, Milwaukee, WI 53201 (SAN 211-9900) Tel 414-963-4014.

U of Wis Pr, *(Univ. of Wisconsin Pr.; 0-299),* 114 N. Murray St., Madison, WI 53715 (SAN 203-3259) Tel 608-262-8782.

U Pr of Amer, *(University Pr. of America; 0-8191),* 4720 Boston Way, Lanham, MD 20706 (SAN 200-2256) Tel 301-459-3366.

U Pr of KS, *(Univ. Pr. of Kansas; 0-7006),* 329 Carruth, Lawrence, KS 66045 (SAN 203-3267) Tel 913-864-4154.

U Pr of Ky, *(Univ. Pr. of Kentucky; 0-8131),* Univ. of Kentucky, 102 Lafferty Hall, Lexington, KY 40506-0024 (SAN 203-3275) Tel 606-257-2951; Dist. by: Harper & Row Pubs., Inc., Keystone Industrial Pk., Scranton, PA 18512 (SAN 215-3742); Orders to: Harper & Row Pubs., Inc., P.O. Box 1660, Hagerstown, MD 21761 (SAN 665-8059).

U Pr of Miss, *(Univ. Pr. of Mississippi; 0-87805),* 3825 Ridgewood Rd., Jackson, MS 39211 (SAN 203-1914) Tel 601-982-6205.

U Pr of New Eng, *(Univ. Pr. of New England; 0-87451),* 3 Lebanon St., Hanover, NH 03755 (SAN 203-3283) Tel 603-646-3349.

U Pr of Va, *(Univ. Pr. of Virginia; 0-8139),* P.O. Box 3608, Univ. Sta., Charlottesville, VA 22903 (SAN 202-5361) Tel 804-924-3468. *Imprints:* Colonial Soc MA (Colonial Society of Massachusetts).

U Pr of Wash *Imprint of* **Larlin Corp**

U Presses Fla, *(Univ. Presses of Florida; 0-8130),* 15 NW 15th St., Gainesville, FL 32603 (SAN 207-9275) Tel 904-392-1351.

U Pubns Amer, *(University Pubns. of America, Inc.; 0-89093; 1-55655),* 44 N. Market St., Frederick, MD 21701 (SAN 210-5802) Tel 301-694-0100; Toll free: 800-692-6300.

UAHC, *(UAHC Pr.; 0-8074),* 838 Fifth Ave., New York, NY 10021 (SAN 203-3291) Tel 212-249-0100.

UCC UCC
See Union Cong Church

Uchill, *(Uchill, Ida Libert; 0-9604468),* 795 S. Jersey St., Denver, CO 80224 (SAN 214-3305) Tel 303-355-9829; Dist. by: L & B Enterprises, 1205 S. Ivy Way, Denver, CO 80224 (SAN 200-7681) Tel 303-756-4563.

UCLA Arch, *(Univ. of California, Los Angeles, Institute of Archaeology; 0-917956),* 405 Hilgard Ave., Los Angeles, CA 90024 (SAN 210-3281) Tel 213-825-7411.

UCLA Lat Am Ctr, *(Univ. of California, Latin American Ctr.; 0-87903),* 405 Hilgard Ave., Los Angeles, CA 90024 (SAN 201-0704) Tel 213-825-6634.

UH Pr, *(Univ. of Hawaii Pr., The; 0-8248),* 2840 Kolowalu St., Honolulu, HI 96822 (SAN 202-5353) Tel 808-948-8697; 1330 Lower Campus Rd., Honolulu, HI 96822 (SAN 658-215X).

Ukrainian Cult Inst, *(Ukrainian Cultural Institute),* Dickinson State College, Dickinson, ND 58601 (SAN 287-2366).

UMI Res Pr, *(UMI Research Pr.; 0-8357),* Div. of University Microfilms, International, 300 N. Zeeb Rd., Ann Arbor, MI 48106 (SAN 212-2464) Tel 313-761-4700; Toll free: 800-521-0600; Orders to: University Microfilms, Inc., P.O. Box 1307, Ann Arbor, MI 48106 (SAN 665-8458). Do not confuse with UMI Publns., Inc., Charlotte, NC.

UN, *(United Nations; 0-680),* Sales Section, Publishing Div., Rm. DC2-853, New York, NY 10017 (SAN 206-6718).

UNA-USA, *(United Nations Assn. of the United States of America, Inc.; 0-934654),* 300 E. 42nd St, New York, NY 10017 (SAN 204-8892) Tel 212-697-3232.

Unarius Pubns, *(Unarius Pubns.; 0-932642; 0-935097),* 145 S. Magnolia Ave., El Cajon, CA 92020 (SAN 168-9614) Tel 619-447-4170.

Undena Pubns, *(Undena Pubns.; 0-89003),* P.O. Box 97, Malibu, CA 90265 (SAN 293-406X) Tel 213-649-2612; Dist. by: Eisenbrauns, P.O. Box 275, Winona Lake, IN 46590-0278 (SAN 293-4078) Tel 219-269-2011.

UNESCO *Imprint of* **Bernan-Unipub**

Ungar, *(Ungar Publishing Co.; 0-8044),* 370 Lexington Ave., New York, NY 10017 (SAN 202-5256) Tel 212-532-3650; Orders to: Harper & Row, Keystone Industrial Pk., Scranton, PA 18512 (SAN 662-1635).

Uni-Sun, *(UNI-SUN; 0-912949),* 8180 NW Kirkwood Dr., Kansas City, MO 64151 (SAN 283-4332) Tel 816-587-7709.

Unicorn Pub, *(Unicorn Publishing Hse., Inc., The; 0-88101),* 1148 Parsippany Blvd., Parsippany, NJ 07054 (SAN 240-4567) Tel 201-334-0353; Orders to: Courier Systems, Inc., 123 Pennsylvania Ave., Kearny, NJ 07032 (SAN 666-6787).

Unif Theol Seminary, *(Unification Theological Seminary; 0-932894),* G.P.O. Box 2432, New York, NY 10116 (SAN 212-3193) Tel 914-758-6881; Dist. by: Rose of Sharon Pr., Inc., G.P.O. Box 2432, New York, NY 10116 (SAN 212-3207).

Unification Church, *(Unification Church Pubns.),* 4 W. 43rd St., New York, NY 10036 (SAN 211-8270).

Unilaw *Imprint of* **Donning Co**

Union Cong Church, *(Union Congregational Church; 0-9610366),* 176 Cooper Ave., Upper Montclair, NJ 07043 (SAN 264-4509).

Union Messianic Jew Pub, *(Union of Messianic Jewish Congregations Publishing; 0-9614555),* 9057B Gaither Rd., Gaitherburg, MD 20877 (SAN 691-8123) Tel 301-926-8652.

Unitarian Univ, *(Unitarian Universalist Assn.; 0-933840),* 25 Beacon St., Boston, MA 02108 (SAN 225-4840) Tel 617-742-2100. *Imprints:* Skinner Hse Bks (Skinner House Books).

United Bible, *(United Bible Societies; 0-8267),* 1865 Broadway, New York, NY 10023 (SAN 204-8787) Tel 212-581-7400; Orders to: American Bible Society, P.O. Box 5656, Grand Central Station, New York, NY 10163 (SAN 662-1643) Tel 212-581-7400.

United Meth Archives, *(United Methodist Church, Commission on Archives & History; 0-915466),* P.O. Box 127, Madison, NJ 07940 (SAN 203-0578) Tel 201-822-2787.

United Meth Educ, *(United Methodist Board of Higher Education & Ministry; 0-938162),* Office of Interpretation, Box 871, Nashville, TN 37202-0871 (SAN 216-3136) Tel 615-340-7383.

United Syn Bk, *(United Synagogue Bk. Service; 0-8381),* Subs. of United Synagogue of America, 155 Fifth Ave., New York, NY 10010 (SAN 203-0551) Tel 212-533-7800.

United Synagogue, *(United Synagogue Commission on Jewish Education; 0-8381),* 155 Fifth Ave., New York, NY 10010 (SAN 236-4174).

Unity Church Denver, *(Unity Church of Denver; 0-942482),* 3021 S. University, Denver, CO 80210 (SAN 161-4541) Tel 303-758-5664.

Unity Pr, *(Unity Pr.; 0-9615041),* P.O. Box 5500 Jasmine Ct., Castro Valley, CA 94552 (SAN 693-8302) Tel 415-538-5291.

Unity School, *(Unity Schl. of Christianity; 0-87159),* Unity Village, MO 64065 (SAN 204-8817) Tel 816-524-3550.

Univ Bks, *(University Bks., Inc.; 0-8216),* Div. of Lyle Stuart, Inc., 120 Enterprise Ave., Secaucus, NJ 07094 (SAN 203-3348) Tel 201-866-0490; Toll free: 800-572-6657.

Univ Book Hse, *(University Bk. Hse.; 0-936461),* 112 Russell Woods Dr., Lynchburg, VA 24502 (SAN 697-9742) Tel 804-237-1486.

Univ Life Sci
See Top Mtn Pub

Univ Microfilms, *(University Microfilms, Inc.; 0-8357),* Div. of Bell & Howell, 300 N. Zeeb Rd., Ann Arbor, MI 48106 (SAN 212-2464) Tel 313-761-4700; Toll free: 800-521-0600; Toll free: 800-343-5299 (Canada). Serials and newspapers in microform, reprints of articles and issues, dissertations published and available on demand. Imprints: Books on Demand, reprinting of out-of-print books, and UMI Research Pr. scholarly and professional book publishing.

Univ Mus of U PA, *(Univ. of Pennsylvania, Univ. Museum; 0-934718),* 33rd & Spruce Sts., Philadelphia, PA 19104 (SAN 207-9283) Tel 215-898-4090.

Univ of Trees, *(Univ. of the Trees Pr.; 0-916438),* P.O. Box 66, Boulder Creek, CA 95006 (SAN 212-9965); 13165 Pine St., Boulder Creek, CA 95006 (SAN 658-2176) Tel 408-338-2161.

Univ Place, *(University Place Bk. Shop; 0-911556),* 821 Broadway, New York, NY 10003 (SAN 204-8841) Tel 212-254-5998.

Univ Pubns, *(Universal Pubns.; 0-941116),* P.O. Box 117, Fawnskin, CA 92333 (SAN 217-4480) Tel 714-585-9636.

Univ Servs Inc, *(University Services; 0-913535),* 1159 Second Ave., Salt Lake City, UT 84103 (SAN 285-2012).

Univ South, *(Univ. of the South, The; 0-918769),* SPO 1145, Sewanee, TN 37375 (SAN 287-2676).

Universe, *(Universe Bks., Inc.; 0-87663; 1-55550),* Div. of South Park Pr., 381 Park Ave. S., New York, NY 10016 (SAN 202-537X) Tel 212-685-7400; Dist. by: St. Martin's Pr., 175 Fifth Ave, New York, NY 10010 (SAN 200-2132) Tel 212-674-5151. *Imprints:* Pica Pr (Pica Press).

University *Imprint of* **Exposition Pr FL**

Uplift Bks, *(Uplift Bks.; 0-88005),* 760C N. Golden Springs Dr., Diamond Bar, CA 91765 (SAN 219-8312) Tel 714-595-8409.

Upper Rm Pub, *(Upper Room Publishing Co.; 0-938645),* P.O. Box 629, Alamo, GA 30411 (SAN 661-633X); Pine St., Alamo, GA 30311 (SAN 661-6348) Tel 912-568-7249.

Upper Room, *(Upper Room, The; 0-8358; 0-941478),* 1908 Grand Ave., P.O. Box 189, Nashville, TN 37202 (SAN 203-3364) Tel 615-340-7000; Dist. by: Abingdon Pr., 201 Eighth Ave., S., Nashville, TN 37202 (SAN 201-0054) Tel 615-749-6290.

Uptown Bks, *(Uptown Bks.),* Box 11146, Glendale, CA 91206 (SAN 240-9828).

Urban Inst, *(Urban Institute Pr.; 0-87766),* 2100 M St., NW, Washington, DC 20037 (SAN 203-3380) Tel 202-857-8724; Orders to: P.O. Box 19958, Hampden Sta., Baltimore, MD 21211 (SAN 685-3676) Tel 301-338-6951.

Urban Ministries, *(Urban Ministries, Inc.; 0-940955),* 1439 W. 103rd St., Chicago, IL 60643 (SAN 665-2247) Tel 312-233-4499.

US Cath Hist, *(U. S. Catholic Historical Society; 0-930060),* P.O. Box 97, Eltingville Sta., Staten Island, NY 10312 (SAN 210-5470) Tel 718-624-8022.

US Catholic, *(U. S. Catholic Conference; 1-55586),* Affil. of National Conference of Catholic Bishops, Pubns. Office, 1312 Massachusetts Ave., NW, Washington, DC 20005 (SAN 207-5350) Tel 202-659-6860; Toll free: 800-235-8722.

US Games Syst, *(U. S. Games Systems, Inc.; 0-913866; 0-88079),* 38 E. 32nd St., New York, NY 10016 (SAN 158-6483) Tel 212-685-4300.

Usborne-Hayes *Imprint of* **EDC**

Utah St U Pr, *(Utah State Univ. Pr.; 0-87421),* Logan, UT 84322-9515 (SAN 202-9294) Tel 801-750-1362.

Utama Pubns Inc, *(Utama Pubns., Inc.; 0-911527),* 2101 N. Soldier Trail, Tucson, AZ 85749 (SAN 282-4779) Tel 602-749-2122.

V Amati, *(Venti Amati; 0-9614119),* 202 Park, Marshall, MN 56258 (SAN 656-9072) Tel 507-532-3647.

V E Wysinger
See Wysinger Pub

V H Ho, *(Ho, Van H., Assocs.; 0-9602904),* P.O. Box 130, Harbor City, CA 90710 (SAN 213-5124).

V I Pr, *(V.I. Pr., Inc.; 0-916945),* P.O. Box 1403, Pompano Beach, FL 33061 (SAN 655-7813) Tel 305-785-5588.

V Lockman, *(Lockman, Vic; 0-936175),* P.O. Box 1916, Ramona, CA 92065 (SAN 697-2063) Tel 619-789-9572.

VA Bk, *(Virginia Bk. Co.; 0-911578),* Box 431, Berryville, VA 22611 (SAN 206-7773) Tel 703-955-1428.

VA State Lib, *(Virginia State Library; 0-88490),* 11th St. at Capitol Sq., Richmond, VA 23219 (SAN 203-0543) Tel 804-786-2312.

VA Tech Educ Found, *(Virginia Tech Educational Foundation; 0-9617635),* Newman Library, Blacksburg, VA 24061 (SAN 665-147X).

Valiant Pubns, *(Valiant Pubns.; 0-9608244),* 1200 Beneficial Life Tower, Salt Lake City, UT 84111 (SAN 240-4656) Tel 801-538-2000.

Valkyrie Pub Hse, *(Valkyrie Publishing Hse.; 0-912760; 0-934616; 0-912589),* Subs. of Freedom Pr., 8245 26th Ave. N., St. Petersburg, FL 33710 (SAN 203-1671) Tel 813-345-8864.

Valley Calif *Imprint of* **Western Tanager**

Valley Lights, *(Valley Lights Pubns.; 0-9606482),* Div. of Valley Light Ctr., P.O. Box 1537, Ojai, CA 93023 (SAN 219-8320) Tel 805-646-9888.

Valley Sun, *(Valley of the Sun Publishing Co.; 0-911842; 0-87554),* Div. of Sutphen Corp., P.O. Box 38, Malibu, CA 90265 (SAN 206-8974) Tel 818-889-1575; Toll free: 800-421-6603; Toll free: 800-225-4717 (in California); Dist. by: Pocket Bks., 1230 Ave. of the Americas, New York, NY 10020 (SAN 202-5922) Tel 212-246-2121; Orders to: Box 3004, Agoura Hills, CA 91301.

Value Comm, *(Value Communications; 0-916392),* Subs. of Oak Tree Pubns., Inc., 9601 Aero Dr., San Diego, CA 92123 (SAN 208-0990) Tel 619-560-5163.

Van der Marck, *(Van der Marck, Alfred, Editions; 0-912383),* 1133 Broadway, Suite 1301, New York, NY 10010 (SAN 265-2919) Tel 212-645-5150; Orders to: Harper & Row Pubs., Inc., Keystone Industrial Park, Scranton, PA 18512 (SAN 693-9821); Dist. by: Harper & Row Pubs., Inc., 10 E. 53rd St., New York, NY 10022 (SAN 200-2086) Tel 212-207-7099.

Van Nos Reinhold, *(Van Nostrand Reinhold Co., Inc.; 0-442; 0-8436),* Div. of International Thomson Organisation, Inc., 115 Fifth Ave., New York, NY 10003 (SAN 202-5183) Tel 212-254-3232; Orders to: VNR Order Processing, 7625 Empire Dr., Florence, KY 41042 (SAN 202-5191) Tel 606-525-6600.

Van Siclen Bks, *(Van Siclen Bks.; 0-933175),* 111 Winnetka Rd., San Antonio, TX 78229 (SAN 692-3399) Tel 512-749-2913.

Vance Biblios, *(Vance Bibliographies; 0-88066; 0-89028; 1-55590),* P.O. Box 229, 112 N. Charter St., Monticello, IL 61856 (SAN 212-6273) Tel 217-762-3831.

Vancento Pub, *(Vancento Pub. Co.; 0-934142),* 62 Court St., Reno, NV 89501 (SAN 238-7697).
Vanderbilt U Pr, *(Vanderbilt Univ. Pr.; 0-8265),* 1211 18th Ave. S., Nashville, TN 37212 (SAN 202-9308) Tel 615-322-3585; Dist. by: Univ. of Illinois Pr., c/o Harper & Row Pubs., Inc., Keystone Industrial Pk., Scranton, PA 18512 (SAN 202-5310) Tel 217-333-0950; Orders to: Univ. of Illinois Pr., P.O. Box 1650, Hagerstown, MD 21741.
Vanguard, *(Vanguard Pr., Inc.; 0-8149),* 424 Madison Ave., New York, NY 10017 (SAN 202-9316) Tel 212-753-3906.
Vanous, *(Vanous, Arthur, Co.; 0-89918),* P.O. Box 650279, Vero Beach, FL 32965 (SAN 169-4871) Tel 305-562-9186.
Vantage, *(Vantage Pr., Inc.; 0-533),* 516 W. 34th St., New York, NY 10001 (SAN 206-8893) Tel 212-736-1767.
Vaughn Pub KY, *(Vaughn Pubs.),* P.O. Box 97, London, KY 40741 (SAN 693-1006).
Vector Assocs, *(Vector Assocs.; 0-930808),* P.O. Box 6215, Bellevue, WA 98007 (SAN 211-1039) Tel 206-747-5881.
Vedanta Ctr, *(Vedanta Centre Pubs.; 0-911564),* Div. of Vedanta Centre, Inc., 130 Beechwood St., Cohasset, MA 02025 (SAN 206-7781) Tel 617-383-0940.
Vedanta Pr, *(Vedanta Pr.; 0-87481),* Div. of Vedanta Society, 1946 Vedanta Pl., Hollywood, CA 90068-3996 (SAN 202-9340) Tel 213-465-7114.
Vedanta Soc St Louis, *(Vedanta Society of St. Louis; 0-916356),* 205 S. Skinker Blvd., St. Louis, MO 63105 (SAN 208-1180) Tel 314-721-5118.
Vehicle Edns, *(Vehicle Editions; 0-931428),* 238 Mott St., New York, NY 10012 (SAN 212-5773) Tel 212-226-1769; Dist. by: Talman Co., The, 150 Fifth Ave., Rm. 514, New York, NY 10011 (SAN 200-5204) Tel 212-620-3182.
Vendome, *(Vendome Pr., The; 0-86565),* 515 Madison Ave., Suite 1906, New York, NY 10022 (SAN 215-2347) Tel 212-838-8991; Dist. by: Rizzoli International Pubns., 597 Fifth Ave., New York, NY 10017 (SAN 207-7000) Tel 212-223-0100.
Ventnor, *(Ventnor Pubs.; 0-911566),* P.O. Drawer G, Ventnor, NJ 08406-0078 (SAN 205-4760).
Veritat Found, *(Veritat Foundation, Inc.; 0-938760),* 3910 Los Feliz Blvd., Los Angeles, CA 90027 (SAN 205-6348).
Vernal Equinox, *(Vernal Equinox Pr.; 0-942380),* P.O. Box 581, San Anselmo, CA 94960 (SAN 240-1762).
Verry, *(Verry, Lawrence, Inc.; 0-8426),* P.O. Box 215, Mystic, CT 06355 (SAN 202-5205) Tel 203-536-3104.
VHI Library, *(Visually Handicapped Inspiration Library; 0-9608650; 0-914009; 1-55677),* 8010 Petaluma Hill Rd., Penngrove, CA 94951 (SAN 213-3679) Tel 707-795-4875.
Vichitra Pr, *(Vichitra Pr.; 0-941582),* 10582 Cheviot Dr., Los Angeles, CA 90064 (SAN 239-3387) Tel 213-839-8547; Dist. by: Asian Humanities Pr., 3204 Adeline St., P.O. Box 3056, Berkeley, CA 94703 (SAN 213-6503).
Victor Bks, *(Victor Bks.; 0-88207; 0-89693),* Div. of Scripture Pr. Pubns., Inc., P.O. Box 1825, Wheaton, IL 60187 (SAN 207-7302); Toll free: 800-323-9409; Orders to: 1825 College Ave., Wheaton, IL 60187 (SAN 207-7310) Tel 312-668-6000.
Victorious Ministry, *(Victorious Ministry Through Christ, Inc.; 0-9605178),* P.O. Box 1804, Winter Park, FL 32790 (SAN 215-823X); Dist. by: Impact Bks., 137 W. Jefferson, Kirkwood, MO 63122 (SAN 214-0330) Tel 314-833-3309.
Victory Hse, *(Victory Hse., Inc.; 0-932081),* P.O. Box 700238, Tulsa, OK 74170 (SAN 686-2667) Tel 918-747-5009; Dist. by: Spring Arbor Distributors, 10885 Textile Rd., Belleville, MI 48111 (SAN 158-9016) Tel 313-481-0900; Dist. by: Inspirational Marketing, P.O. Box 301, Indianola, IA 50125 (SAN 208-6557).
Vida Pubs
See Life Pubs Intl
Viking, *(Viking Penguin Inc.; 0-670),* 40 W. 23rd St., New York, NY 10010 (SAN 200-2442) Tel 212-337-5327; Toll free: 800-631-3577; Orders to: 299 Murray Hill Pkwy., East Rutherford, NJ 07073 (SAN 282-5074) Tel 201-933-1460. *Imprints:* E Sifton Bks (Elisabeth Sifton Books); Viking Kestrel (Viking Kestrel).
Viking Kestrel *Imprint of* **Viking**
Vin *Imprint of* **Random**
Vincentian, *(Vincentian Evangelization; 0-9608630),* 1302 Kipling St., Houston, TX 77006 (SAN 219-0974) Tel 713-529-7550.
Vishwa, *(Vishwa Dharma Pubns.; 0-942508),* 174 Santa Clara Ave., Oakland, CA 94610 (SAN 238-2075) Tel 415-654-4683.
Vision Hse, *(Vision Hse.; 0-88449),* 2300 Knoll Dr., Ventura, CA 93003 (SAN 282-5155) Tel 805-644-9721; Orders to: Gospel Light Pubns., P.O. Box 6309, Oxnard, CA 93031 (SAN 282-5163).
Vistara Pubns, *(Vistara Pubns.; 0-930551; 0-935384),* P.O. Box 24532, Denver, CO 80224 (SAN 677-4180) Tel 303-292-8423.
Visual Evangels, *(Visual Evangels Publishing Co.; 0-915398),* 1401 Ohio St., Michigan City, IN 46360 (SAN 212-002X) Tel 219-874-3902.
Vivekananda, *(Vivekananda Vedanta Society; 0-9600826),* 5423 S. Hyde Park Blvd., Chicago, IL 60615 (SAN 222-190X).
Volcano Pr, *(Volcano Pr., Inc.; 0-912078),* 330 Ellis St., San Francisco, CA 94102 (SAN 220-0015) Tel 415-664-5600.
W A Benjamin
See Addison-Wesley
W F Cox, *(Cox, Willis F.; 0-9610758),* Box 47, James Store, VA 23080 (SAN 264-7060) Tel 804-693-4533.
W H Freeman, *(Freeman, W. H., & Co.; 0-7167),* Subs. of Scientific American, Inc., 41 Madison Ave., 37th Flr., New York, NY 10010 (SAN 290-6864) Tel 212-532-7660; Orders to: 4419 W. 1980, S, Salt Lake City, UT 84104 (SAN 290-6872) Tel 801-973-4660.
W H Mathers Mus, *(William Hammond Mathers Museum; 0-9605982),* 601 E. Eighth St., Indiana University, Bloomington, IN 47405 (SAN 216-7379) Tel 812-335-6873.
W P Brownell, *(Brownell, W. P., Assocs., Inc.),* 3675 Clark Rd., Sarasota, FL 33583 (SAN 295-0499).
W R Inman, *(Inman, W. Richard),* 996-C Ponderoso Ave., Sunnyvale, CA 94086 (SAN 208-4198).
W S Hein, *(Hein, William S., & Co., Inc.; 0-89941; 0-930342),* Hein Bldg., 1285 Main St., Buffalo, NY 14209 (SAN 210-9212) Tel 716-882-2600; Toll free: 800-828-7571.
W Va U Ctr Exten, *(West Virginia University, Center for Extension & Continuing Education),* 308 Knapp Hall, Morgantown, WV 26506 (SAN 213-4039).
Wadsworth Pub, *(Wadsworth Publishing Co.; 0-534; 0-927794; 0-7150),* Subs. of International Thomson Organization, Ltd., 10 Davis Dr., Belmont, CA 94002 (SAN 200-2213) Tel 415-595-2350; Toll free: 800-354-9706.
Waggener Publ Co, *(Waggener Publishing Co.; 0-9617339),* 255 Massachusetts Ave., Boston, MA 02115 (SAN 663-866X) Tel 617-536-2560.
Wahr, *(Wahr, George, Publishing Co.; 0-911586),* 304 1/2 S. State St., Ann Arbor, MI 48104 (SAN 205-5015) Tel 313-668-6097.
Wake-Brook, *(Wake-Brook Hse.; 0-87482),* 2609 NE 29th Ct., Ft. Lauderdale, FL 33306 (SAN 205-5023) Tel 305-563-9301.
Wake Forest Law, *(Wake Forest Univ., Schl. of Law, Continuing Legal Education; 0-942225),* P.O. Box 7206, Reynolda Sta., Winston-Salem, NC 27109 (SAN 237-9074) Tel 919-761-5432.
Walker & Co, *(Walker & Co.; 0-8027),* Div. of Walker Publishing Co., Inc., 720 Fifth Ave., New York, NY 10019 (SAN 202-5213) Tel 212-265-3632.
Wallaby *Imprint of* **S&S**
Walnut Knoll Assocs, *(Walnut Knoll Assocs.; 0-940045),* P.O. Box 479, Etna, NY 13062 (SAN 663-9577); 39 Sunset West Cir., Ithaca, NY 14850 (SAN 663-9585) Tel 607-347-6604.
Walrus Pr, *(Walrus Pr.; 0-932033),* 102 Preston Forest Dr., Blacksburg, VA 24060 (SAN 686-0796) Tel 703-552-0876.
Walter J Johnson, *(Johnson, Walter J., Inc.; 0-8472),* 355 Chestnut St., Norwood, NJ 07648 (SAN 209-1828) Tel 201-767-1303.
Walterick Pubs, *(Walterick Pubs., Inc.; 0-937396),* Box 2216, Kansas City, KS 66110-0216 (SAN 211-9366) Tel 913-371-3273; Toll free: 800-255-4097.
Walters Art, *(Walters Art Gallery; 0-911886),* 600 N. Charles St., Baltimore, MD 21201 (SAN 202-9448) Tel 301-547-9000.
Wanderer Bks, *(Wanderer Bks.; 0-671),* Div. of Simon & Schuster, 1230 Ave. of the Americas, New York, NY 10020 (SAN 212-5803) Tel 212-245-6400; Toll free: 800-223-2336.
Wanderer Pr, *(Wanderer Pr., The; 0-915245),* Subs. of Wanderer Printing Co., 201 Ohio St., St. Paul, MN 55107-9984 (SAN 240-8961) Tel 612-224-5733.
Wandering You Pr, *(Wandering You Pr.; 0-9617104),* Subs. of Creative Resources, Inc., P.O. Box 20, Lodi, NJ 07644-0020 (SAN 662-5142); 70 Outwater Ln., Garfield, NJ 07026 (SAN 662-5150) Tel 201-772-1052.
Warner Bks, *(Warner Bks., Inc.; 0-446),* Div. of Warner Communications, 666 Fifth Ave., New York, NY 10103 (SAN 282-5368) Tel 212-484-2900; Toll free: 800-638-6460; Dist. by: Ballantine Bks., Inc., 201 E. 50th St., New York, NY 10022 (SAN 214-1183) Tel 212-751-2600.
Warner Pr, *(Warner Pr. Pubs.; 0-87162),* 1200 E. Fifth St., Anderson, IN 46012 (SAN 202-9472) Tel 317-644-7721; Toll free: 800-428-6409; Orders to: P.O. Box 2499, Anderson, IN 46018 (SAN 691-4241).
Warren Pub Hse, *(Warren Publishing Hse., Inc.; 0-911019),* P.O. Box 2255, Everett, WA 98203; 1004 Harborview Ln., Everett, WA 98203 (SAN 660-9465) Tel 206-252-3546; Dist. by: Gryphon Hse., Inc. (Wholesale only), P.O. Box 275, 3706 Otis St., Mt. Rainier, MD 20712 (SAN 169-3190) Tel 301-779-6200
Warthog Pr, *(Warthog Pr.; 0-942292),* 29 S. Valley Rd., West Orange, NJ 07052 (SAN 219-5399) Tel 201-731-9269.
Wash St U Pr, *(Washington State Univ. Pr.; 0-87422),* Pubns. Bldg., Rm. 40, Pullman, WA 99164-5910 (SAN 206-6688) Tel 509-335-3518.
Watercress Pr, *(Watercress Pr.; 0-934955),* Subs. of Evett & Assocs., 111 Grotto, San Antonio, TX 78216 (SAN 694-4116) Tel 512-344-5338.
Watson Pub Intl, *(Watson, Neale, Academic Pubns.; 0-88202),* P.O. Box 493, Canton, MA 02021 (SAN 689-8386) Tel 617-828-8450.
Watts, *(Watts, Franklin, Inc.; 0-531),* Subs. of Grolier, Inc., 387 Park Ave., S., New York, NY 10016 (SAN 285-1156) Tel 212-686-7070; Toll free: 800-672-6672.
Waveland Pr, *(Waveland Pr., Inc.; 0-917974; 0-88133),* P.O. Box 400, Prospect Heights, IL 60070 (SAN 209-0961) Tel 312-634-0081.
Way
See Am Christian
Wayne St U Pr, *(Wayne State Univ. Pr.; 0-8143),* Leonard N. Simons Bldg., 5959 Woodward Ave., Detroit, MI 48202 (SAN 202-5221) Tel 313-577-4603.
WCP Pubns, *(WCP Pubns.; 0-937365),* 9528 Miramar Rd., Suite 106, San Diego, CA 92126 (SAN 659-1043) Tel 619-271-9445; 8767 Covina St., San Diego, CA 92126 (SAN 659-1051).
WCTU, *(National Woman's Christian Temperance Union),* 1730 Chicago Ave., Evanston, IL 60201 (SAN 225-8935).
Weatherhill, *(Weatherhill, John, Inc.; 0-8348),* 157 E. 69th St., New York, NY 10021 (SAN 202-9529) Tel 212-629-6564; Dist. by: Charles E. Tuttle, Co., Inc., 28 S. Main St., P.O. Box 410, Rutland, VT 05701-0410 (SAN 213-2621) Tel 802-773-8930.
Wedge Pub, *(Wedge Publishing),* c/o Radix Bks., Inc., 11 Knickerbocker Ln., Orinda, CA 94563 (SAN 209-1364) Tel 415-254-3039.
Wehman, *(Wehman Brothers, Inc.; 0-911604),* Ridgedale Ave., Morris County Mall, Cedar Knolls, NJ 07927 (SAN 206-779X) Tel 201-539-6300.

Weidenfeld, *(Weidenfeld & Nicolson; 1-55584),* 10 E. 53rd St., 14th Flr., New York, NY 10022 (SAN 658-4497) Tel 212-207-6900.

Weills
See Berkley Pub

Weiser, *(Weiser, Samuel, Inc.; 0-87728),* P.O. Box 612, York Beach, ME 03910 (SAN 202-9588) Tel 207-363-4393; Toll free: 800-423-7087 (Orders only); Dist. by: Bookpeople, 2929 Fifth St., Berkeley, CA 94710 (SAN 168-9517) Tel 415-549-3030; Dist. by: DeVorss & Co., P.O. Box 550, Marina del Rey, CA 90294 (SAN 168-9886) Tel 213-870-7478; Dist. by: Inland Bk. Co., P.O. Box 261, 22 Hemingway St., East Haven, CT 06512 (SAN 200-4151); Dist. by: New Leaf Distributing, 1020 White St., SW, Atlanta, GA 30310 (SAN 169-1449) Tel 404-755-2665.

Wellbeing Bks, *(Wellbeing Bks., Tapes, Seminars; 0-943450),* Div. of Open Marketing Group, P.O. Box 396, 17 Omar Tr., Newtonville, MA 02160 (SAN 240-4680) Tel 617-332-7845.

WELS Board, *(WELS Board for Parish Education; 0-938272),* 2929 N. Mayfair Rd., Milwaukee, WI 53222 (SAN 216-3160) Tel 414-771-9357.

Welstar Pubns, *(Welstar Pubns.; 0-938503),* Div. of Occupational Hygiene Ctr. of New York, Inc., 20 Colonel Robert Magaw Pl., New York, NY 10033 (SAN 660-9791) Tel 212-928-7528.

Wesley Found, *(Wesley Foundation, The; 0-9606652),* 211 N. School St., Normal, IL 61761 (SAN 219-6557) Tel 309-452-1435.

Wesleyan U Pr, *(Wesleyan Univ. Pr.; 0-8195),* 110 Mt. Vernon St., Middletown, CT 06457 (SAN 282-5414) Tel 203-344-7918; Toll free: 800-242-7737; Orders to: Harper & Row Pubs., Inc., Keystone Industrial Pk., Scranton, PA 18512 (SAN 215-3742) Tel 717-343-4761.

West Indies Pub, *(West Indies Publishing Co.),* Div. of Elan Bks., 9228 Kleinman Rd., Highland, IN 46322 (SAN 665-2360).

West Pub, *(West Publishing Co., College Dept.; 0-8299; 0-314),* P.O. Box 64779, 58 W. Kellogg Blvd., St. Paul, MN 55164-0779 (SAN 202-9618) Tel 612-228-2385; Toll free: 800-328-9352.

Westburg, *(Westburg Assocs., Pubs.; 0-87423),* 1745 Madison St., Fennimore, WI 53809 (SAN 205-5171) Tel 608-822-6237.

Westcliff Pubns, *(Westcliff Pubns.; 0-932896),* 1441 Avocado, No. 408, Newport Beach, CA 92660 (SAN 212-2448).

Westcott, *(Westcott Pubs.; 0-911620),* P.O. Box 803, Springfield, MO 65801 (SAN 205-518X) Tel 417-466-7455.

Western Bk Journ, *(Western Bk. Journal Pr.; 0-936029),* 1470 Woodberry Ave., San Mateo, CA 94403 (SAN 206-2305) Tel 415-573-8877.

Western Epics, *(Western Epics Publishing Co.; 0-914740),* 254 S. Main St., Salt Lake City, UT 84101 (SAN 206-1384) Tel 801-328-2586.

Western Islands, *(Western Islands; 0-88279),* 395 Concord Ave., Belmont, MA 02178 (SAN 206-8435) Tel 617-489-0606.

Western NC Pr
See Bks Distinction

Western Pub, *(Western Publishing Co., Inc.; 0-307),* Subs. of Western Publishing Group, Inc., 850 Third Ave., New York, NY 10022 (SAN 202-523X) Tel 212-753-8500; 1220 Mound Ave., Racine, WI 53401 (SAN 669-2982) Tel 414-633-2431; Orders to: Dept. M, P.O. Box 700, Racine, WI 53401; Dist. by: Children's Pr., 1224 W. Van Buren St., Chicago, IL 60607 (SAN 201-9264) Tel 312-666-4200. Do not confuse with Western Pub., Lake Worth, FL. *Imprints:* Golden Pr (Golden Press).

Western Son Acad, *(Western Son Academy; 0-938647),* P.O. Box 4080, Irvine, CA 92716 (SAN 661-6119); 2 Hopkins, Irvine, CA 92715 (SAN 661-6127) Tel 714-786-9585.

Western Sun Pubns, *(Western Sun Pubns.; 0-9608146),* P.O. Box 1470, Yuma, AZ 85364 (SAN 240-5067) Tel 602-726-6239. Out of business.

Western Tanager, *(Western Tanager Pr.; 0-934136),* 1111 Pacific Ave., Santa Cruz, CA 95060 (SAN 220-0155) Tel 408-425-1111. *Imprints:* Valley Calif (Valley Publishers).

Westernlore, *(Westernlore Pubns.; 0-87026),* 609 N. Fourth Ave., Tucson, AZ 85705 (SAN 202-9642) Tel 602-297-5491; Orders to: P.O. Box 35305, Tucson, AZ 85740 (SAN 202-9650).

Westgate Hse, *(Westgate Hse.; 0-9607320),* 56 Westgate Dr., San Francisco, CA 94127 (SAN 239-5819) Tel 415-584-8338.

Westgate Pr, *(Westgate Pr.),* Div. of Westgate Group, Ltd., 8 Bernstein Blvd., Center Moriches, NY 11934 (SAN 687-6579) Tel 516-878-2901.

Westland Pubns, *(Westland Pubns.; 0-915162),* P.O. Box 117, McNeal, AZ 85617-0117 (SAN 207-1169) Tel 602-642-3500.

Westminster, *(Westminster Pr.; 0-664),* 925 Chestnut St., Philadelphia, PA 19107 (SAN 202-9669) Tel 215-928-2734; Toll free: 800-523-1631; Toll free: 800-462-0405 (in Pennsylvania); Orders to: P.O. Box 718, William Penn Annex, Philadelphia, PA 19105 (SAN 202-9677) Tel 215-928-2745.

Westview, *(Westview Pr.; 0-89158; 0-86531; 0-8133),* 5500 Central Ave., Boulder, CO 80301 (SAN 219-970X) Tel 303-444-3541; P.O. Box 20336, Cathedral Finance Sta., New York, NY 10025 (SAN 666-6841) Tel 212-749-4684.

Westwood Pub Co, *(Westwood Publishing Co.; 0-930298),* 312 Riverdale Dr., Glendale, CA 91204 (SAN 211-8769) Tel 818-242-3497.

WFS, *(Women for Sobriety, Inc.),* P.O. Box 618, Quakertown, PA 18951 (SAN 216-4779) Tel 215-536-8026.

What Is Pr, *(What-Is-Pr., The; 0-9617483),* P.O. Box 37, Woodstock, NY 12498 (SAN 664-080X); 113 Tinkler St., Woodstock, NY 12498 (SAN 664-0818) Tel 914-679-8107; Dist. by: DeVorss & Co., P.O. Box 550, Marina del Rey, CA 90294 (SAN 168-9886) Tel 213-870-7478; Dist. by: New Leaf Distributing, 1020 White St., S W, Atlanta, GA 30310 (SAN 169-1449) Tel 404-755-2665.

Whatever Pub, *(Whatever Publishing, Inc.; 0-931432),* 58 Paul Dr., San Rafael, CA 94103 (SAN 211-8777) Tel 415-472-2100; Toll free: 800-227-3900 (Retail orders only); P.O. Box 13257, San Rafael, CA 94103 (SAN 665-8091); Dist. by: Publishers Group West, 5855 Beaudry, Emeryville, CA 94608 (SAN 202-8522) Tel 415-658-3453; Dist. by: Bookpeople, 2929 Fifth St., Berkeley, CA 94710 (SAN 168-9517) Tel 415-549-3030.

Wheat Forders, *(Wheat Forder's Pr.; 0-917888),* P.O. Box 6317, Washington, DC 20015 (SAN 209-9187) Tel 202-362-1588.

Wheelwright Pr, *(Wheelwright Press; 0-935706),* 300 Page St., San Francisco, CA 94102 (SAN 222-0326) Tel 415-863-3136.

Whitaker Hse, *(Whitaker Hse.; 0-88368),* Pittsburgh & Colfax Sts., Springdale, PA 15144 (SAN 203-2104) Tel 412-274-4440; Toll free: 800-245-2422.

White Eagle Pub, *(White Eagle Pub., The; 0-941804),* P.O. Box 1332, Dept. BP-0111, Lowell, MA 01853 (SAN 239-3441); Dist. by: Baker & Taylor Co., Eastern Div., 50 Kirby Ave., Somerville, NJ 08876 (SAN 169-4901).

White Pine, *(White Pine Pr.; 0-934834),* 76 Center St., Fredonia, NY 14063 (SAN 209-8067) Tel 716-672-5743.

White Wing Pub, *(White Wing Publishing Hse. & Pr.; 0-934942),* P.O. Box 3000, Cleveland, TN 37311 (SAN 203-2198) Tel 615-476-8536.

Whitston Pub, *(Whitston Pub. Co., Inc.; 0-87875),* P.O. Box 958, Troy, NY 12181 (SAN 203-2120) Tel 518-283-4363.

Wide World-Tetra, *(Wide World Publishing/Tetra; 0-933174),* P.O. Box 476, San Carlos, CA 94070 (SAN 211-1462) Tel 415-593-2839; Dist. by: Bookpeople, 2929 Fifth St., Berkeley, CA 94710 (SAN 168-9517) Tel 415-549-3030; Dist. by: Publishers Group West, 5855 Beaudry St., Emeryville, CA 94608 (SAN 202-8522) Tel 415-658-3453; Dist. by: Quality Bks., Inc., 918 Sherwood Dr., Lake Bluff, IL 60044-2204 (SAN 169-2127).

Wideview *Imprint of* **Putnam Pub Group**

Wiener Pub Inc, *(Wiener, Markus, Publishing, Inc.; 0-910129),* 2901 Broadway, Suite 107, New York, NY 10025 (SAN 282-5465) Tel 212-678-7138; Dist. by: Schocken Bks. (Masterworks of Jewish Writing Ser. only), 62 Cooper Sq., New York, NY 10003 (SAN 213-7585) Tel 212-475-4900; Dist. by: M & B Fulfillment Services, 540 Barnum Ave., Bridgeport, CT 06608 (SAN 282-6062) Tel 203-366-1900.

Wieser & Wieser, *(Wieser & Wieser, Inc.; 0-914373),* 118 E. 25th St., New York, NY 10010 (SAN 289-6958) Tel 212-260-0860.

Wiley, *(Wiley, John, & Sons, Inc.; 0-471; 0-8260),* 605 Third Ave., New York, NY 10158 (SAN 200-2272) Tel 212-850-6418.

William & Rich, *(William & Richards, Pubs.; 0-9600202),* P.O. Box 2546, San Francisco, CA 94126 (SAN 282-5481) Tel 415-461-2835.

William Carey Lib, *(Carey, William, Library Pubs.; 0-87808),* 1705 N. Sierra Bonita Ave., P.O. Box 40129, Pasadena, CA 91104 (SAN 208-2101) Tel 818-798-0819. *Imprints:* Ecclesia (Ecclesia Pubns.).

William Tyndale Col Pr, *(Tyndale, William, College Pr.; 0-912407),* 35700 W. 12 Mile Rd., Farmington Hills, MI 48018 (SAN 265-3702) Tel 313-553-7200.

Williams & Wilkins, *(Williams & Wilkins Co.; 0-683),* Div. of Waverly Pr., Inc., 428 E. Preston St., Baltimore, MD 21202 (SAN 202-5175) Tel 301-528-4000; Toll free: 800-638-0673; Orders to: P.O. Box 1496, Baltimore, MD 21203 (SAN 665-8105).

Williamsburg, *(Colonial Williamsburg Foundation; 0-910412; 0-87935),* Pubns. Dept., P.O. Box C, Williamsburg, VA 23187 (SAN 203-297X) Tel 804-229-1000; Dist. by: Henry Holt & Co., 521 Fifth Ave., New York, NY (SAN 200-6472) Tel 212-599-7600; Dist. by: Univ. Pr. of Virginia, P.O. Box 3608, University Sta., (SAN 202-5361).

Willyshe Pub, *(Willyshe Publishing Co., Inc.; 0-936112),* 112 Mountain Rd., Linthicum Heights, MD 21090 (SAN 213-9499) Tel 301-789-0241.

Wilshire, *(Wilshire Bk. Co.; 0-87980),* 12015 Sherman Rd., North Hollywood, CA 91605-3781 (SAN 205-5368) Tel 213-875-1711.

Wilson, *(Wilson, H. W.; 0-8242),* 950 University Ave., Bronx, NY 10452 (SAN 203-2961) Tel 212-588-8400; Toll free: 800-367-6770.

Wilton, *(Wilton Enterprises, Bk. Div.; 0-912696),* 1603 S. Michigan Ave., Chicago, IL 60616 (SAN 206-0248) Tel 312-663-5096; Toll free: 800-772-711.

Wimmer Bks, *(Wimmer Brothers Bks.),* 4210 BF Goodrich Blvd., Memphis, TN 38118 (SAN 209-6544) Tel 901-362-8900.

Winds World Pr, *(Winds of the World Pr.; 0-938338),* 35 Whittemore Rd., Framingham, MA 01701 (SAN 215-8310) Tel 617-872-0871.

Wings ME, *(Wings Pr.; 0-939736),* R.F.D 1, Box 390, Warren, ME 04864 (SAN 216-7689) Tel 207-785-4355.

Winston-Derek, *(Winston-Derek Pubs.,Inc.; 0-938232; 1-55523),* P.O. Box 90883, Nashville, TN 37209 (SAN 216-4760) Tel 615-321-0535; Toll free: 800-826-1888; Dist. by: Baker & Taylor Co., Midwest Div., 5 Gladiola Ave., Momence, IL 60954 (SAN 169-2100).

Wisdom Garden, *(Wisdom Garden Bks.; 0-914794),* P.O. Box 29448, Los Angeles, CA 90029 (SAN 206-5584) Tel 213-380-1968.

Wisdom House, *(Wisdom Hse. Pr.; 0-932560),* Div. of Wisdom Hse., Inc., 43222 SE Tapp Rd., Sandy, OR 97055 (SAN 212-2022) Tel 503-668-3119.

Wisdom Pubns *Imprint of* **Great Traditions**

Witness Holocaust, *(Witness to the Holocaust Project; 0-912313),* Div. of Emory Univ., Emory Univ., Atlanta, GA 30322 (SAN 264-5025) Tel 404-329-6428.

Wizards, *(Wizards Bookshelf; 0-913510),* P.O. Box 6600, San Diego, CA 92106 (SAN 203-2872) Tel 619-235-0340; Dist. by: DeVorss & Co., P.O. Box 550, 1046 Princeton Dr., Marina del Rey, CA 90291 (SAN 282-6151); Dist. by: New Leaf Distributing, 1020 White St., SW, Atlanta, GA 30310 (SAN 294-1449).

WLCJ, *(Women's League for Conservative Judaism; 0-936293),* 48 E. 74th St., New York, NY 10021 (SAN 697-9661) Tel 212-628-1600.

Wm C Brown, *(Brown, William C., Pubs.; 0-697),* 2460 Kerper Blvd., Dubuque, IA 52001 (SAN 203-2864) Tel 319-588-1451.

Womans Inst-Cont Jewish Ed, *(Woman's Institute for Continuing Jewish Education; 0-9608054),* 4079 54th St., San Diego, CA 92105 (SAN 240-1061).

Woman's Pr, *(Woman's Pr., The; 0-9614878),* 245 W. 107th St., Apt. 12B, New York, NY 10029 (SAN 659-3631) Tel 212-427-1816; Orders to: P. B. S., P.O. Box 643, Cambridge, MA 02139 (SAN 662-4243) Tel 617-491-6562. Moved, left no forwarding address.

Wood Lake Pr, *(Wood Lake Pr.; 0-919599),* Dist. by: Friendship Pr., 475 Riverside Dr., Rm. 772, New York, NY 10027 (SAN 682-2754) Tel 212-870-2497.

Woodbridge Pr, *(Woodbridge Pr. Publishing Co.; 0-912800; 0-88007),* P.O. Box 6189, Santa Barbara, CA 93160 (SAN 212-9892) Tel 805-965-7039.

Woodland, *(Woodland Publishing Co., Inc.; 0-934104),* 230 Manitoba Ave., Wayzata, MN 55391 (SAN 213-1900) Tel 612-473-2725.

Woods Books & Music Publishing
See Woods Mus Bks Pub

Woods Mus Bks Pub, *(Woods Music & Bks. Publishing; 0-9602990; 0-936661),* P.O. Box 29521, Los Angeles, CA 90029 (SAN 213-1919) Tel 818-247-4177.

Woodsong Graph, *(Woodsong Graphics, Inc.; 0-912661),* P.O. Box 238, New Hope, PA 18938-0238 (SAN 282-8235) Tel 215-794-8321; Orders to: PMG International, 1104 Summit Ave., 100B, Plano, TX 75074 (SAN 662-202X) Tel 214-423-0312.

Word Aflame, *(Word Aflame Pr.; 0-912315; 0-932581),* Subs. of Pentecostal Publishing Hse., 8855 Dunn Rd., Hazelwood, MO 63042 (SAN 212-0046) Tel 314-837-7300.

Word Among Us, *(Word Among Us Pr.; 0-932085),* P.O. Box 3646, Washington, DC 20007 (SAN 686-4651) Tel 301-977-2500; Toll free: 800-638-8539; Dist. by: Spring Arbor Distributors, 10885 Textile Rd., Belleville, MI 48111 (SAN 158-9016) Tel 313-481-0900.

Word Bks, *(Word, Inc.; 0-87680; 0-8499),* Subs. of Capital Cities/American Broadcasting Co., 4800 W. Waco Dr., Waco, TX 76796 (SAN 203-283X) Tel 817-772-7650; Toll free: 800-433-3340; Toll free: 800-792-3270 (in Texas); Orders to: P.O. Box 1790, Waco, TX 76796.

Word Doctor, *(Word Doctor Pubns.; 0-918248),* P.O. Box 9761, 6516 Ben Ave., North Hollywood, CA 91609 (SAN 207-5865) Tel 818-980-3576.

Word Faith, *(Word of Faith; 0-914307),* P.O. Box 819000, Dallas, TX 75381 (SAN 287-6272) Tel 214-620-1586; Dist. by: Harrison Hse. Pubs., Inc., P.O. Box 35035, Tulsa, OK 74135 (SAN 663-6616) Tel 918-582-2126.

Word for Today, *(Word for Today, The; 0-936728),* P.O. Box 8000, Costa Mesa, CA 92628 (SAN 214-2260) Tel 714-979-0706; Dist. by: Living Bks., 12155 Magnolia Ave., Bldg. 11-B, Riverside, CA 92503 (SAN 169-006X) Tel 714-354-7330.

Word Foun, *(Word Foundation, Inc., The; 0-911650),* P. O. Box 18235, Dallas, TX 75218 (SAN 205-549X) Tel 214-348-5006.

Word Ministries Inc, *(Word Ministries Inc.; 0-9613051),* P.O. Box 145, Greenville, SC 29602 (SAN 294-295X) Tel 912-746-3223; Dist. by: First Presbyterian Church, 682 Mulberry St., Macon, GA 31201 (SAN 200-4550).

Word Serv, *(Word Services & Pied Pubns. Publishing Co.; 0-918626),* 1927 S. 26th St., Lincoln, NE 68502 (SAN 210-5519). Out of Business.

Word Works, *(Word Works, Inc.; 0-915380),* P.O. Box 42164, Washington, DC 20015 (SAN 293-4426) Tel 202-554-3014.

Words Living Minis, *(Words for Living Ministries Inc.; 0-934527),* 102 W. Carlisle St., Marion, KY 42064 (SAN 693-8477) Tel 502-965-5060.

Wordscope Inc, *(Wordscope, Inc.; 0-930121),* 8040 Floral Ave., Suite 304, Skokie, IL 60077 (SAN 670-3194) Tel 312-677-0506; Orders to: P.O Box 1594, Skokie, IL 60077 (SAN 662-2445); Dist. by: Bloch Pub. Co., 19 W. 21st St., New York, NY 10010 (SAN 214-204X) Tel 212-989-9104; Dist. by: Jonathan David Co., 68-22 Eliot Ave., Middle Village, NY 11379 (SAN 169-5274) Tel 718-456-8611.

Working Peoples Art, *(Working Peoples Artists),* P.O. Box 2307, Berkeley, CA 94702 (SAN 209-0023).

Workmen's Circle, *(Workmen's Circle Education Dept.),* 45 E. 33rd St., New York, NY 10016 (SAN 216-2075).

World Bible, *(World Bible Pubs., Inc.; 0-529; 0-8326),* Subs. of Riverside Bk. & Bible, 795 Sharon Dr., Westlake, OH 44145 (SAN 215-2789) Tel 216-835-1155; Orders to: P.O. Box 370, Iowa Falls, IA 50126 (SAN 215-2797).

World Bk, *(World Bk., Inc.; 0-7166),* A Scott Fetzer Co., Merchandise Mart Plaza, Rm. 510, Chicago, IL 60654 (SAN 201-4815) Tel 312-245-3456; Toll free: 800-621-8202.

World Confer Rel & Peace, *(World Conference on Religion & Peace; 0-932934),* 777 United Nations Plaza, New York, NY 10017 (SAN 213-8840) Tel 212-687-2163.

World Evang Fellow, *(World Evangelical Fellowship; 0-936444),* P.O. Box WEF, Wheaton, IL 60189 (SAN 214-1760) Tel 312-668-0440.

World Light, *(World Light Pubns.; 0-916940),* 1518 Poplar Level Rd., Louisville, KY 40217 (SAN 208-9300) Tel 502-634-4185.

World Outreach, *(World Outreach; 0-9617623),* P.O. Box 950, Novato, CA 94948 (SAN 664-9033); 1370 S. Novato Blvd., Novato, CA 94948 (SAN 664-9041) Tel 415-892-0714.

World Peace Univ, *(World Peace Univ.; 0-939169),* 35 SE 60th Ave., Portland, OR 97215 (SAN 662-8567) Tel 503-231-3771.

World Prayer, *(World Prayer Band Ministries; 0-933495),* 3939 E. Admiral Pl., Tulsa, OK 74115-8305 (SAN 692-753X) Tel 918-836-6644.

World Pubns
See Anderson World

World Relief, *(World Relief Network, The; 0-9617410),* P.O. Box 15082, Detroit, MI 48215-0082 (SAN 663-9747) Tel 313-331-3190.

World Tribune Pr, *(World Tribune Pr.; 0-915678),* 525 Wilshire Blvd., Santa Monica, CA 90406 (SAN 683-230X).

World Univ Amer, *(World Univ. of America; 0-939375),* 107 N. Ventura St., Ojai, CA 93023 (SAN 662-8907) Tel 805-646-1444.

World Univ AZ, *(World Univ.; 0-941902),* P.O. Box 2470, Benson, AZ 85602 (SAN 239-7943) Tel 602-586-2985.

World Vision Intl, *(World Vision International; 0-918261),* 919 W. Huntington Dr., Monrovia, CA 91016 (SAN 225-4719) Tel 818-303-8811.

World Wide Mini, *(World Wide Ministry of Deliverance, Inc.; 0-9612676),* 104 S. Main, Hersey, MI 49639 (SAN 289-4769) Tel 616-796-5958.

World Wide OR, *(World Wide Publishing Corp.; 0-930294),* P.O. Box 105, Ashland, OR 97520 (SAN 207-4818) Tel 503-482-3800.

World Wide Pubs, *(World Wide Pubns.; 0-89066),* 1303 Hennepin Ave., Minneapolis, MN 55403 (SAN 203-185X) Tel 612-333-0940.

World Without War Pubns, *(World Without War Council; 0-912018),* 421 S. Wabash, Chicago, IL 60605 (SAN 203-2805) Tel 312-663-4250.

Wormhoudt, *(Wormhoudt, Arthur; 0-916358; 0-940307),* 1818 Kemble Dr., Oskaloosa, IA 52577 (SAN 207-5547) Tel 515-673-3091.

WOS, *(Wells of Salvation),* 6821 SR 366, Huntsville, OH 43324 (SAN 217-1414).

Wright Pub Co, *(Wright Publishing Co., Inc.; 0-935087),* 1422 W. Peachtree St., Atlanta, GA 30309 (SAN 695-0507) Tel 404-876-1900.

Writers & Readers, *(Writers & Readers Publishing, Inc.),* 1 W. 125th St., Suite 206, New York, NY 10027 (SAN 665-813X) Tel 212-860-4040; c/o W.W. Norton Co., 500 Fifth Ave., New York, NY 10110 (SAN 216-4795) Tel 212-354-5500.

Wrld Coun Churches, *(World Council of Churches),* 475 Riverside Dr., Rm. 1062, New York, NY 10115 (SAN 234-3207) Tel 212-870-2533.

Wrld Wisdom Bks, *(World Wisdom Bks.; 0-941532),* P.O. Box 2682, Bloomington, IN 47402-2682 (SAN 239-1406) Tel 812-332-1663; Dist. by: Bookpeople, 2929 Fifth St., Berkeley, CA 94710 (SAN 168-9517) Tel 415-549-3030; Dist. by: New Leaf Distributing, 1020 White St., SW, Atlanta, GA 30310 (SAN 169-1449) Tel 404-755-2665; Dist. by: Great Tradition, The, 750 Adrian Way, Suite 111, San Rafael, CA 94903 (SAN 200-5743) Tel 415-492-9382.

WSP, *(Washington Square Pr., Inc.; 0-671),* Div. of Simon & Schuster, Inc., 1230 Ave. of the Americas, New York, NY 10020 (SAN 206-9784) Tel 212-698-7000; Toll free: 800-223-2336; Orders to: 200 Old Tappan Rd., Old Tappan, NJ 07675 (SAN 662-1821) Tel 201-767-5000.

WWUCEAS, *(Western Washington Univ., Ctr. for East Asian Studies; 0-914584),* Bellingham, WA 98225 (SAN 203-218X) Tel 206-676-3041.

Wycliffe Bible, *(Wycliffe Bible Translators; 0-938978),* Huntington Beach, CA 92648 (SAN 211-5484).

Wyndham Hall, *(Wyndham Hall Pr.; 0-932269; 1-55605),* P.O. Box 877, 52857 C.R. 21, Bristol, IN 46507 (SAN 686-6743) Tel 219-848-7920.

Wysinger Pub, *(Wysinger Publishing Co. The),* P.O. Box 158, Berkeley, CA 94704 (SAN 203-1140) Tel 415-655-1742.

Xavier Pr, *(Xavier Pr.; 0-912977),* 3122 Jerome, Dallas, TX 75223 (SAN 283-4057) Tel 214-826-5835.

Yale Russian, *(Yale Russian & East European Pubns.; 0-936586),* P.O. Box 13A, 85 Trumbull St., New Haven, CT 06520 (SAN 283-9806) Tel 203-432-3423; Dist. by: Slavica Pubs., Inc., P.O. Box 14388, Columbus, OH 43214 (SAN 208-8576) Tel 614-268-4002.

Yale U Pr, *(Yale Univ. Pr.; 0-300),* 302 Temple St., New Haven, CT 06520 (SAN 203-2740) Tel 203-432-0960; Orders to: 92A Yale Sta., New Haven, CT 06520 (SAN 203-2759) Tel 203-436-7582.

Yale U SE Asia, *(Yale Univ. Southeast Asia Studies; 0-938692),* Div. of Yale Ctr. for International & Asia Studies, Yale Univ., Box 13A, New Haven, CT 06520 (SAN 206-0027) Tel 203-432-3431.

Yankee Bks, *(Yankee Bks.; 0-911658; 0-89909),* Div. of Yankee Publishing, Inc., Main St., Dublin, NH 03444 (SAN 293-4434) Tel 603-563-8111; Toll free: 800-258-5327.

Ye Galleon, *(Ye Galleon Pr.; 0-87770),* P.O. Box 287, Fairfield, WA 99012 (SAN 205-5597) Tel 509-283-2422.

Yellow Jacket, *(Yellow Jacket Pr.; 0-915626),* 1101 N. Lewis, Stillwater, OK 74075 (SAN 207-3048) Tel 405-743-2566.

Yes Intl, *(Yes International; 0-936663),* 449 Portland Ave., St. Paul, MN 55102 (SAN 699-6787) Tel 612-224-4480; Dist. by: Bookpeople, 2929 Fifth St., Berkeley, CA 94710 (SAN 168-9517) Tel 415-549-3030; Dist. by: New Leaf Dist., 1020 White St., S W, Atlanta, GA 30310 (SAN 169-1449) Tel 404-755-2665; Dist. by: DeVorss & Co., P.O. Box 550, Marina del Rey, CA 90294 (SAN 168-9886) Tel 213-870-7478; Dist. by: The Distributors, 702 S. Michigan, South Bend, IN 46618 (SAN 169-2488) Tel 219-232-8500; Dist. by: Starlite Distributors, P.O. Box 20729, Reno, NV 89515 (SAN 200-7789) Tel 702-359-5676.

Yesod Pubs, *(Yesod Pubs.),* 75 Prospect Park W., Brooklyn, NY 11215 (SAN 211-8300) Tel 718-768-5591.

Yivo Inst, *(Yivo Institute for Jewish Research; 0-914512),* 1048 Fifth Ave., New York, NY 10028 (SAN 207-1614) Tel 212-535-6700.

YMCA USA *Imprint of* **Human Kinetics**
Yoder, *(Ida, Yoder; 0-9614083),* 180 Hall Drive, Wadsworth, OH 44281 (SAN 685-9291) Tel 216-336-0261.
Yoga, *(Yoga Pubn. Society; 0-911662),* P.O. Box 1268, Homewood, IL 60430 (SAN 203-2724); Dist. by: DeVorss & Co., P.O. Box 550, Marina del Rey, CA 90294 (SAN 168-9886) Tel 213-870-7478.
Yoga Res Foun, *(Yoga Research Foundation; 0-934664),* 6111 SW 74th Ave., Miami, FL 33143 (SAN 209-0279) Tel 305-666-2006.
Yogi Gupta, *(Yogi Gupta New York Center; 0-911664),* 90-16 51st Ave., Elmhurst, NY 11373 (SAN 205-5619) Tel 718-592-3217.
Yokefellow Pr, *(Yokefellow Pr.; 0-932970; 0-914005),* 230 College Ave., Richmond, IN 47374 (SAN 276-9336) Tel 317-962-6810.
York Hse, *(York Hse.; 0-9615389),* 148 York Ave., Kensington, CA 94708 (SAN 276-9468) Tel 415-525-7167.
Young Life, *(Young Life National Services; 0-932856),* Box 520, Colorado Springs, CO 80901 (SAN 211-8319) Tel 303-473-4262.
Your New Beginning, *(Your New Beginning; 0-9616892),* 10312 E. Freer St., Temple City, CA 91780 (SAN 661-6461) Tel 818-443-2637.
Youth Special, *(Youth Specialties; 0-910125),* 1224 Greenfield Dr., El Cajon, CA 92021 (SAN 211-8327) Tel 619-440-2333; Dist. by: Zondervan Pub. Hse., 1415 Lake Dr., SE, Grand Rapids, MI 49506 (SAN 203-2694) Tel 616-698-6900.
Yuganta Pr, *(Yuganta Pr.; 0-938999),* 6 Rushmore Cir., Stamford, CT 06905 (SAN 662-541X) Tel 203-323-7160.
Zarathustrotemo Pr, *(Zarathustrotemo Pr., The; 0-937581),* 601-2 Harwood Rd., Suite 172, Bedford, TX 76021 (SAN 658-8301) Tel 817-831-2586; 2900 Haltom Rd., Ft. Worth, TX 76117 (SAN 658-831X).
Zartscorp, *(Zartscorp, Inc. Bks.; 0-9605610),* 333 West End Ave., New York, NY 10023 (SAN 209-5017) Tel 212-724-5071.
Zebra, *(Zebra Bks.; 0-89083; 0-8217),* 475 Park Ave. S., New York, NY 10016 (SAN 207-9860) Tel 212-889-2299; Toll free: 800-221-2649; Dist. by: Simon & Schuster Mass Merchandise Sales Co., 1230 Ave. of the Americas, New York, NY 10020 (SAN 169-5835) Tel 212-245-6400.
Zen Ctr, *(Zen Ctr., The; 0-940306),* 7 Arnold Park, Rochester, NY 14607 (SAN 217-569X) Tel 216-473-9180.
Zen Ctr LA
See Center Pubns
Zenger Pub, *(Zenger Publishing Co., Inc.; 0-89201),* P.O. Box 42026, Washington, DC 20015 (SAN 208-0427) Tel 301-881-1470.
Zephyr *Imprint of* **Doubleday**
Zeppelin, *(Zeppelin Pub. Co.; 0-915628),* P.O. Box 22252, Louisiana State Univ. Sta., Baton Rouge, LA 70893 (SAN 204-6776); Pelican Office Ctr., 11628 S. Choctaw Dr., Baton Rouge, LA 70815 (SAN 200-4208) Tel 504-272-6600.
Zoe Pubns, *(Zoe Pubns.; 0-89841),* P.O. Box 1361, Clemmons, NC 27012 (SAN 212-7148) Tel 919-945-9797.
Zolanka Pubns *See* Spencer Pr
Zondervan, *(Zondervan Publishing Hse.; 0-310),* Div. of Zondervan Corp., 1415 Lake Dr. SE, Grand Rapids, MI 49506 (SAN 203-2694) Tel 616-698-6900; Toll free: 800-253-1309 (wholesale orders, bookstores); Toll free: 800-253-4475 (retail orders). *Imprints:* Clarion Class (Clarion Classics).
Zubal Inc, *(Zubal, John T., Inc.; 0-939738),* 2969 W. 25th St., Cleveland, OH 44113 (SAN 165-5841) Tel 216-241-7640.
Zytech Western Pub, *(Zytech Western Publishing; 0-936749),* 716 E. Valley Pkwy., Escondido, CA 92025 (SAN 699-9867) Tel 619-789-8822.